2025
LexisNexis® Corporate Affiliations™

Content Operations:
Director-News & Business Content Operations & Metadata: Tammy Bair
Manager-Corporate Affiliations & Entity Management: Elizabeth A. Powers
Lead Content Analysts: Eric Eelman, Kevin Gaven

Production:
Senior Production Specialist: Joseph C. Stewart

Reed Elsevier Philippines-Corporate Affiliations Iloilo Team:
Operations Manager: Timothy J. Vilches
Operations Supervisor: Kristel Faye B. De la Cruz
Product Lead: Raquel G. Gajardo

2025

LexisNexis® Corporate Affiliations™

Master Index

U.S. PUBLIC • U.S. PRIVATE • INTERNATIONAL

Volume II

QUESTIONS ABOUT THIS PUBLICATION?

For CONTENT questions concerning this publication, please call:
Content Operations Department at (800) 340-3244
FAX (908) 790-5405

For CUSTOMER SERVICE ASSISTANCE concerning shipments, billing or other matters, please call:
Customer Service at (800) 340-3244, press 3

For SALES ASSISTANCE, please call:
The Sales Department at (800) 340-3244, press 2

No part of this publication may be reproduced or transmitted in any form or by any means sorted in any information storage and retrieval system without prior written permission of LexisNexis, Content Operations, 9443 Springboro Pike, Miamisburg, OH 45342.

Library of Congress Catalog Card Number: 67-22770

Master Index Volume 2, ISBN: 979-8-3417-0460-2

Corporate Affiliations 8-Volume Library, ISBN: 979-8-3417-0458-9

©2025 LexisNexis Group.

All Rights Reserved

LexisNexis, the knowledge burst logo and Corporate Affiliations are trademarks of Reed Elsevier Properties Inc., used under license.

The LexisNexis Group has used its best efforts in collecting and preparing material for inclusion in *Corporate Affiliations*™ but does not assume, and hereby disclaims, any liability to any person for any loss or damage caused by errors or omissions in *Corporate Affiliations* whether such errors or omissions result from negligence, accident or any other cause.

Corporate Affiliations

Content Operations
9443 Springboro Pike
Miamisburg, OH 45342

www.lexisnexis.com

ISBN 979-8-3417-0460-2

9 798341 704602

CONTENTS

Preface vii
How To Use *Corporate Affiliations* ix
Alphabetical Compendium of N.A.I.C.S. Codes 3079
Numerical Compendium of N.A.I.C.S. Codes 3089
Master N.A.I.C.S. Index 3099

CONTENTS

Preface vii
How To Use Corporate Affiliations ix
Alphabetical Compendium of N.A.I.C.S. Codes 3079
Numerical Compendium of N.A.I.C.S. Codes 3089
Master N.A.I.C.S. Index 3099

PREFACE

CORPORATE AFFILIATIONS

Corporate Affiliations is a logically organized business reference tool that covers major public and private businesses in the United States and throughout the world. The principle of organization for the set is geographical (by parent company) and hierarchical (by company reportage). Subsidiaries of a parent company, no matter where they are located, will be found in the same volume as the ultimate parent.

Entry criteria for the set are flexible. Generally speaking, domestic companies must demonstrate revenue in excess of $10 million, a work force in excess of 100 persons, or be traded on a major stock exchange. Non-U.S. based companies must demonstrate revenues in excess of $10 million.

SET ORGANIZATION AND CONTENT

A brief outline of the volumes and their components follows. Please note that every volume in the set, including this one, has a customized 'How-to-Use' guide for the benefit of the researcher. These include extensive listing and referencing examples that go into great detail.

Master Index, Volume I
Company Name Index

Master Index, Volume II
N.A.I.C.S. Index

U.S. Public Companies A-Z, Volume III
Public Company Listings

U.S. Private Companies A-J, Volume IV
Private Company Listings

U.S. Private Companies K-Z, Volume V
Private Company Listings

International Public and Private Companies A-F, Volume VI
International Company Listings

International Public and Private Companies G-O, Volume VII
International Company Listings

International Public and Private Companies P-Z, Volume VIII
International Company Listings

CUMULATIVE ENTRY STATISTICS FOR THIS EDITION

These statistics show the sum of entry listings across all the volumes. Individual statistics are provided in each volume.

Ultimate parent companies 133,466
U.S. located sub companies 186,355
Non-U.S. located sub companies 180,962
Total entry units listed **500,783**

Outside service firms: 70,337

COMPILATION

Corporate Affiliations is compiled and updated from information supplied by the companies themselves, business publications, internet research and annual reports.

RELATED SERVICES

For information on the corporateaffiliations.com web site, please call (800) 340-3244.

Mailing lists compiled from information contained in *Corporate Affiliations* may be ordered from:
R. Michael Patterson, Inside Sales Representative
DM2 Decision Maker
2000 Clearwater Drive, Oak Brook, IL
Tel: (630) 288-8348
E-mail: robert.patterson@dm2decisionmaker.com

Electronic database tapes of the directory in raw data format are available for licensing. For electronic database tapes or alliance opportunities, please contact:
LexisNexis, Corporate Affiliations
9443 Springboro Pike, Miamisburg, OH 45342
Tel: (800) 285-3947
E-mail: information@lexisnexis.com

Companies who wish to add or correct their listings can send information to:
LexisNexis, Corporate Affiliations Content Operations
9443 Springboro Pike
Miamisburg, OH 45342
Tel: (937) 865-6800

In addition to keeping the information in our directories as up to date as possible, we are constantly trying to improve their design and add useful new features. Any comments or suggestions in this regard can be directed to the Managers of Operations at the above address.

HOW TO USE
CORPORATE AFFILIATIONS

Corporate Affiliations contains useful information about firms whose ultimate parent companies, both public and private, are located in the United States and abroad. Entries include information on financials, personnel, outside service firms, and subsidiaries with an emphasis on hierarchy and reportage.

This user guide is divided into three parts:

Part A, 'How to Locate a Company' gives referencing instructions and samples of indexes. It demonstrates many useful methods for getting the information you need from this volume and from the *Corporate Affiliations* set at large.

Part B, 'Sample Entries' shows the various data elements and listing style of companies in *Corporate Affiliations*.

Part C, 'Understanding Levels of Reportage' demonstrates how company reportage structures are simply and clearly presented throughout *Corporate Affiliations*.

PART A: HOW TO LOCATE A COMPANY

1. **If you know the name of the company, but do not know its nationality or ownership status:**

    Look in the 'Master Index of Company Names' located in volume I. This index will direct you to the correct volume of the set (i.e. Public, Private or International) and the correct page listing therein.

    ALLING AND CORY COMPANY; *U.S. Private*, pg. 37
    ALLING-LANDER—See Regal-Beloit Corporation; *U.S. Public*, pg. 1429
    ALLINSURE—See GIB Group; *Int'l*, pg. 511
    ALLIS-CHALMERS CORPORATION; *U.S. Public*, pg. 58

2. **If you do know a parent company's nationality and ownership status:**

    You can turn directly to the company listings in the appropriate volume, all of which are alphabetized by the name of the parent company.

3. **If you know the name of a subsidiary or division**:

    You can turn to the 'Master Index of Company Names' located in volume I. The subsidiary entry will also show you the name of its ultimate parent and the volume and page of its listing.

    JHK & ASSOCIATES, INC.—See Science Applications
        International Corp.; *U.S. Private*, pg. 986
    JIB GROUP PLC—See Jardine Matheson Holdings Limited; *Int'l*, pg. 711

JII/SALES PROMOTION ASSOCIATES, INC.—See Jordan
Industries, Inc.; *U.S. Private*, pg. 604
JIT-STAL AB—See Rautaruukki Oy; *Int'l*, pg. 1036
JJC SPECIALIST CORP.—See The Quick & Reilly Group
Inc.; *U.S. Public*, pg. 1397

4. **If you cannot find the company's name in the indexes:**

   It may mean that the company has been acquired or changed its name. To confirm this, try looking in the 'Mergers and Acquisitions' section at the front of the appropriate volume.

   Sample of Mergers Section

   Friendly Ice Cream Corp.—acquired by Hershey Foods Corp.
   Frigitronics, Inc.—acquired by Revlon, Inc.
   Frontier Oil Corporation—acquired by Wainoco Oil Corporation
   Furr Cafeterias, Inc.—acquired by K Mart Corp.
   GAC Corp.—name changed to Avatar Holdings, Inc.

5. **To locate companies in a given line of business:**

   Use the 'N.A.I.C.S. (North American Industrial Classification System) Master Index' located in volume II. This index interfiles data from all six volumes of Corporate Affiliations, arranging companies by particular products and services according to their primary N.A.I.C.S. code. The index is preceded by two helpful compendia: one sorts the codes alphabetically by the name of the product or service, the other numerically by the code itself.

   Sample of Alpha Compendium of N.A.I.C.S. Codes

Description	N.A.I.C.S.
Administration of Conservation Programs	924120
Administration of Education Programs	923110

   Sample of Numeric Compendium of N.A.I.C.S. Codes

Code	Description
111150	Corn Farming
111160	Rice Farming
111191	Oilseed and Grain Combination Farming

x

Both parent and sub companies are covered in this index; parent companies are printed in bold type, sub companies in regular typeface, followed by the name of its ultimate parent. A samples of the N.A.I.C.S. Master Index is shown here:

337211 — WOOD OFFICE FURNITURE MANUFACTURING

ABCO—Jami, Inc.; *Int'l*, pg. 586
ANDERSON HICKEY, INC.—Haworth, Inc.; *U.S. Public*, pg. 516
BELVEDERE COMPANY—Smith Investment Company; *Int'l*, pg. 1019
BRAYTON INTERNATIONAL INC.—Steelcase Inc.; *U.S. Public*, pg. 1048
BRODART COMPANY; *U.S. Private*, pg. 172
COMMUNITY—Jasper Seating Co., Inc.; *U.S. Private*, pg. 589
CRAMER INC.; *U.S. Public*, pg. 288
EAC CORPORATION; *Int'l*, pg. 357

PART B: BASIC COMPONENTS OF A PUBLIC COMPANY LISTING

Following is an example of a typical parent company listing with tags to some of its basic components.

STANDARD MEDICAL GROUP	Company Name
560 River Rd	Company Address
Richmond, VA 23219	
Tel: 804-223-3289 DE	Telecommunications Data & State of Incorporation
Fax: 804-555-8334	
Web Site: www.smg.com	Electronic Address
Year Founded: 1967	
SMG—(NYSE)	Ticker Symbol & Stock Exchange Data
Rev.: $32,000,000	Financial Data
Assets: $48,000,000	
Liabilities: $32,000,000	
Net Worth: $16,000,000	
Earnings: ($4,500,000)	
Emp: 620	Number of Employees, Including Subsidiaries
Fiscal Year End: 12/31/24	
Research Technology;	Business Description
Medical Products Mfr	
N.A.I.C.S.: 325411	North American Industry Classification Code
John R. Callahan (*Chm*)	Key Personnel
Cynthia I. Jenkins (*Pres & CEO*)	
William E. Kirkpatrick (*Exec VP*)	
Albert N. Hackett (*VP-Res & Dev*)	
Lawrence Woods (*VP-Sls*)	

Following each parent company listing are the entries for each of that company's divisions, subsidiaries, affiliates, joint ventures, units etc. Though companies vary widely in their usage of these terms, some of the more common company designations can be defined as follows:

Affiliate   A chartered business owned by the company at less than 50%.
Division   An internal unit of a company, not incorporated.
Joint Venture   A business in which two or more companies share responsibility and ownership.
Subsidiary   A chartered business owned by the company at 50% or more.

PART C: UNDERSTANDING LEVELS OF REPORTAGE

Each sub-unit of the company will have a number in parentheses to the right of the company name. This number represents the level of reportage for that particular company. Any company with a level (1) reports directly to the parent company. Level (2) companies report to the level (1) company immediately above them. Level (3) companies report to the level (2) company immediately above them, etc.

Subsidiaries:

Brock Corporation   (1) ———— **Reports to the Parent Company**
6060 Wall St   **(Standard Medical Group from**
Hartford, CT 06103   **previous example)**
Tel: 203-251-6526   (100%) ———— **Percentage of Ownership**
Sales Range: $25-49.9 Million
Emp: 98
Pharmaceuticals Mfr
N.A.I.C.S.: 325412
J.M. McAleer *(Pres)*

Subsidiary:

Clark Technology   (2) ———— **Reports to Level 1 Company Above**
601 Pulaski St   **(Brock Corporation)**
Jackson, MS 39215
Tel: 601-848-4626   (100%)
CT—(NYSE)
Sutures Mfr & Other Surgical Products
N.A.I.C.S.: 339113
Steven Colaccino *(Pres)*

Branch:

Clark Technology   (3) ———— **Reports to Level 2 Company Above**
52 Main St   **(Clark Technology)**
Wayne, NJ 07435
Tel: 201-662-7654
Sutures Mfr
N.A.I.C.S.: 339113

Non-U.S. Subsidiary:

Merieux Pharmaceuticals   (1) ———— **Subsidiary Not Located in the U.S.**
1421 rue Gourbet, 75755   **Reports to the Parent Company**
Paris, Cedex 15, France   **(Standard Medical Group)**
Tel: 42 73 10 08
Rev.: $1,500,000   (100%)
Emp: 118
Pharmaceuticals Mfr
N.A.I.C.S.: 325412
G. Bidaud *(Pres)*

Request For Additional Companies Not Now Listed

Corporate Affiliations
The LexisNexis Publishing Group
9443 Springboro Pike, Miamisburg, OH 45342
Tel: 937-865-6800

AS A CURRENT SUBSCRIBER to *Corporate Affiliations*, are there companies not currently listed in the directory that you would like to see included? If so, please fill out the following and return to the above address via mail or fax.

Please type or print all information and return completed form.

_____
Company or Institution Name

_____
Address

_____ _____ _____
City   State/ Country   Zip/ Postal Code

_____ _____
Phone   Fax

_____
Company or Institution Name

_____
Address

_____ _____ _____
City   State/ Country   Zip/ Postal Code

_____ _____
Phone   Fax

ALPHABETICAL COMPENDIUM OF N.A.I.C.S. CODES

North American Industry Classification System Manual, 2022, U.S. Government Office of Management and Budget; All codes for manufacturing unless otherwise stated.

N.A.I.C.S.	Description
A	
Abrasive Product Manufacturing	327910
Adhesive Manufacturing	325520
Administration of Air and Water Resource and Solid Waste Management Programs	924110
Administration of Conservation Programs	924120
Administration of Education Programs	923110
Administration of General Economic Programs	926110
Administration of Housing Programs	925110
Administration of Human Resource Programs (except Education, Public Health, and Veterans' Affairs Programs)	923130
Administration of Public Health Programs	923120
Administration of Urban Planning and Community and Rural Development	925120
Administration of Veterans' Affairs	923140
Administrative Management and General Management Consulting Services	541611
Advertising Agencies	541810
Advertising Material Distribution Services	541870
Agents and Managers for Artists, Athletes, Entertainers, and Other Public Figures	711410
Air and Gas Compressor Manufacturing	333912
Air Purification Equipment Manufacturing	333411
Air Traffic Control	488111
Air-Conditioning and Warm Air Heating Equipment and Commercial and Industrial Refrigeration Equipment Manufacturing	333415
Aircraft Engine and Engine Parts Manufacturing	336412
Aircraft Manufacturing	336411
Alkalies and Chlorine Manufacturing	325181
All Other Amusement and Recreation Industries	713990
All Other Animal Production	112990
All Other Automotive Repair and Maintenance	811198
All Other Basic Inorganic Chemical Manufacturing	325188
All Other Basic Organic Chemical Manufacturing	325199
All Other Business Support Services	561499
All Other Consumer Goods Rental	532299
All Other Converted Paper Product Manufacturing	322299
All Other Cut and Sew Apparel Manufacturing	315299
All Other General Merchandise Stores	452990
All Other Grain Farming	111199
All Other Health and Personal Care Stores	446199
All Other Home Furnishings Stores	442299
All Other Industrial Machinery Manufacturing	333298
All Other Information Services	519190
All Other Insurance Related Activities	524298
All Other Leather Good Manufacturing	316999
All Other Legal Services	541199
All Other Metal Ore Mining	212299
All Other Miscellaneous Ambulatory Health Care Services	621999
All Other Miscellaneous Chemical Product and Preparation Manufacturing	325998
All Other Miscellaneous Crop Farming	111998
All Other Miscellaneous Electrical Equipment and Component Manufacturing	335999
All Other Miscellaneous Fabricated Metal Product Manufacturing	332999
All Other Miscellaneous Food Manufacturing	311999
All Other Miscellaneous General Purpose Machinery Manufacturing	333999
All Other Miscellaneous Manufacturing	339999
All Other Miscellaneous Nonmetallic Mineral Product Manufacturing	327999
All Other Miscellaneous Schools and Instruction	611699
All Other Miscellaneous Store Retailers (except Tobacco Stores)	453998
All Other Miscellaneous Textile Product Mills	314999
All Other Miscellaneous Waste Management Services	562998
All Other Miscellaneous Wood Product Manufacturing	321999
All Other Motor Vehicle Dealers	441229
All Other Motor Vehicle Parts Manufacturing	336399
All Other Nondepository Credit Intermediation	522298
All Other Nonmetallic Mineral Mining	212399
All Other Outpatient Care Centers	621498
All Other Personal Services	812990
All Other Petroleum and Coal Products Manufacturing	324199
All Other Pipeline Transportation	486990
All Other Plastics Product Manufacturing	326199
All Other Professional, Scientific, and Technical Services	541990
All Other Publishers	511199
All Other Rubber Product Manufacturing	326299
All Other Special Trade Contractors	235990
All Other Specialty Food Stores	445299
All Other Specialty Trade Contractors	238990
All Other Support Activities for Transportation	488999

N.A.I.C.S.	Description
All Other Support Services	561990
All Other Transit and Ground Passenger Transportation	485999
All Other Transportation Equipment Manufacturing	336999
All Other Travel Arrangement and Reservation Services	561599
All Other Traveler Accommodation	721199
Alumina Refining	331311
Aluminum Die-Casting Foundries	331521
Aluminum Extruded Product Manufacturing	331316
Aluminum Foundries (except Die-Casting)	331524
Aluminum Sheet, Plate, and Foil Manufacturing	331315
Ambulance Services	621910
American Indian and Alaska Native Tribal Governments	921150
Ammunition (except Small Arms) Manufacturing	332993
Amusement and Theme Parks	713110
Amusement Arcades	713120
Analytical Laboratory Instrument Manufacturing	334516
Animal (except Poultry) Slaughtering	311611
Anthracite Mining	212113
Apiculture	112910
Apple Orchards	111331
Appliance Repair and Maintenance	811412
Apprenticeship Training	611513
Architectural Services	541310
Armored Car Services	561613
Art Dealers	453920
Asphalt Paving Mixture and Block Manufacturing	324121
Asphalt Shingle and Coating Materials Manufacturing	324122
Audio and Video Equipment Manufacturing	334310
Automatic Environmental Control Manufacturing for Residential, Commercial, and Appliance Use	334512
Automatic Vending Machine Manufacturing	333311
Automobile and Other Motor Vehicle Merchant Wholesalers	423110
Automobile and Other Motor Vehicle Wholesalers	421110
Automobile Driving Schools	611692
Automobile Manufacturing	336111
Automotive Body, Paint, and Interior Repair and Maintenance	811121
Automotive Exhaust System Repair	811112
Automotive Glass Replacement Shops	811122
Automotive Oil Change and Lubrication Shops	811191
Automotive Parts and Accessories Stores	441310
Automotive Transmission Repair	811113
B	
Baked Goods Stores	445291
Ball and Roller Bearing Manufacturing	332991
Barber Shops	812111
Bare Printed Circuit Board Manufacturing	334412
Beauty Salons	812112
Bed-and-Breakfast Inns	721191
Beef Cattle Ranching and Farming	112111
Beer and Ale Merchant Wholesalers	424810
Beer and Ale Wholesalers	422810
Beer, Wine, and Liquor Stores	445310
Beet Sugar Manufacturing	311313
Berry (except Strawberry) Farming	111334
Biological Product (except Diagnostic) Manufacturing	325414
Bituminous Coal and Lignite Surface Mining	212111
Bituminous Coal Underground Mining	212112
Blankbook, Looseleaf Binders, and Devices Manufacturing	323118
Blind and Shade Manufacturing	337920
Blood and Organ Banks	621991
Boat Building	336612
Boat Dealers	441222
Bolt, Nut, Screw, Rivet, and Washer Manufacturing	332722
Book Publishers	511130
Book Stores	451211
Book, Periodical, and Newspaper Merchant Wholesalers	424920
Book, Periodical, and Newspaper Wholesalers	422920
Books Printing	323117
Bottled Water Manufacturing	312112
Bowling Centers	713950
Breakfast Cereal Manufacturing	311230
Breweries	312120
Brick and Structural Clay Tile Manufacturing	327121
Brick, Stone, and Related Construction Material Merchant Wholesalers	423320
Brick, Stone, and Related Construction Material Wholesalers	421320
Bridge and Tunnel Construction	234120
Broadwoven Fabric Finishing Mills	313311
Broadwoven Fabric Mills	313210
Broilers and Other Meat Type Chicken Production	112320

Alphabetical N.A.I.C.S. Compendium-continued

Description	N.A.I.C.S.
Broom, Brush, and Mop Manufacturing	339994
Building Equipment and Other Machinery Installation Contractors	235950
Building Inspection Services	541350
Burial Casket Manufacturing	339995
Bus and Other Motor Vehicle Transit Systems	485113
Business and Secretarial Schools	611410
Business Associations	813910
Business to Business Electronic Markets	425110

C

Description	N.A.I.C.S.
Cable and Other Program Distribution	517510
Cable and Other Subscription Programming	515210
Cable Networks	513210
Cafeterias	722212
Camera and Photographic Supplies Stores	443130
Cane Sugar Refining	311312
Canvas and Related Product Mills	314912
Car Washes	811192
Carbon and Graphite Product Manufacturing	335991
Carbon Black Manufacturing	325182
Carbon Paper and Inked Ribbon Manufacturing	339944
Carburetor, Piston, Piston Ring, and Valve Manufacturing	336311
Carpentry Contractors	235510
Carpet and Rug Mills	314110
Carpet and Upholstery Cleaning Services	561740
Casino Hotels	721120
Casinos (except Casino Hotels)	713210
Caterers	722320
Cattle Feedlots	112112
Cellular and Other Wireless Telecommunications	513322
Cellulosic Organic Fiber Manufacturing	325221
Cement Manufacturing	327310
Cemeteries and Crematories	812220
Ceramic Wall and Floor Tile Manufacturing	327122
Charter Bus Industry	485510
Cheese Manufacturing	311513
Chicken Egg Production	112310
Child and Youth Services	624110
Child Day Care Services	624410
Children's and Infants' Clothing Stores	448130
Chocolate and Confectionery Manufacturing from Cacao Beans	311320
Cigarette Manufacturing	312221
Citrus (except Orange) Groves	111320
Civic and Social Organizations	813410
Claims Adjusting	524291
Clay and Ceramic and Refractory Minerals Mining	212325
Clay Refractory Manufacturing	327124
Clothing Accessories Stores	448150
Coal and Other Mineral and Ore Merchant Wholesalers	423520
Coal and Other Mineral and Ore Wholesalers	421520
Coastal and Great Lakes Freight Transportation	483113
Coastal and Great Lakes Passenger Transportation	483114
Coated and Laminated Packaging Paper and Plastics Film Manufacturing	322221
Coated and Laminated Paper Manufacturing	322222
Coffee and Tea Manufacturing	311920
Coin-Operated Laundries and Drycleaners	812310
Collection Agencies	561440
Colleges, Universities, and Professional Schools	611310
Commercial Air, Rail, and Water Transportation Equipment Rental and Leasing	532411
Commercial and Industrial Machinery and Equipment (except Automotive and Electronic) Repair and Maintenance	811310
Commercial and Institutional Building Construction	236220
Commercial Bakeries	311812
Commercial Banking	522110
Commercial Flexographic Printing	323112
Commercial Gravure Printing	323111
Commercial Laundry, Drycleaning, and Pressing Machine Manufacturing	333312
Commercial Lithographic Printing	323110
Commercial Photography	541922
Commercial Screen Printing	323113
Commercial, Industrial, and Institutional Electric Lighting Fixture Manufacturing	335122
Commodity Contracts Brokerage	523140
Commodity Contracts Dealing	523130
Communication Equipment Repair and Maintenance	811213
Community Food Services	624210
Commuter Rail Systems	485112
Computer and Computer Peripheral Equipment and Software Merchant Wholesalers	423430
Computer and Computer Peripheral Equipment and Software Wholesalers	421430
Computer and Office Machine Repair and Maintenance	811212
Computer and Software Stores	443120
Computer Facilities Management Services	541513
Computer Storage Device Manufacturing	334112
Computer Systems Design Services	541512
Computer Terminal Manufacturing	334113
Computer Training	611420
Concrete Block and Brick Manufacturing	327331
Concrete Contractors	235710
Concrete Pipe Manufacturing	327332
Confectionery and Nut Stores	445292
Confectionery Manufacturing from Purchased Chocolate	311330
Confectionery Merchant Wholesalers	424450
Confectionery Wholesalers	422450
Construction and Mining (except Oil Well) Machinery and Equipment Merchant Wholesalers	423810
Construction and Mining (except Oil Well) Machinery and Equipment Wholesalers	421810
Construction Machinery Manufacturing	333120
Construction Sand and Gravel Mining	212321
Construction, Mining, and Forestry Machinery and Equipment Rental and Leasing	532412
Consumer Electronics and Appliances Rental	532210
Consumer Electronics Repair and Maintenance	811211
Consumer Lending	522291
Continuing Care Retirement Communities	623311
Convenience Stores	445120
Convention and Trade Show Organizers	561920
Convention and Visitors Bureaus	561591
Conveyor and Conveying Equipment Manufacturing	333922
Cookie and Cracker Manufacturing	311821
Copper Foundries (except Die-Casting)	331525
Copper Ore and Nickel Ore Mining	212234
Copper Rolling, Drawing, and Extruding	331421
Copper Wire (except Mechanical) Drawing	331422
Corn Farming	111150
Corporate, Subsidiary, and Regional Managing Offices	551114
Correctional Institutions	922140
Corrugated and Solid Fiber Box Manufacturing	322211
Cosmetics, Beauty Supplies, and Perfume Stores	446120
Cosmetology and Barber Schools	611511
Costume Jewelry and Novelty Manufacturing	339914
Cotton Farming	111920
Cotton Ginning	115111
Couriers	492110
Court Reporting and Stenotype Services	561492
Courts	922110
Creamery Butter Manufacturing	311512
Credit Bureaus	561450
Credit Card Issuing	522210
Credit Unions	522130
Crop Harvesting, Primarily by Machine	115113
Crown and Closure Manufacturing	332115
Crude Petroleum and Natural Gas Extraction	211111
Crushed and Broken Granite Mining and Quarrying	212313
Crushed and Broken Limestone Mining and Quarrying	212312
Current-Carrying Wiring Device Manufacturing	335931
Curtain and Drapery Mills	314121
Custom Architectural Woodwork and Millwork Manufacturing	337212
Custom Compounding of Purchased Resins	325991
Custom Computer Programming Services	541511
Custom Roll Forming	332114
Cut Stock, Resawing Lumber, and Planing	321912
Cut Stone and Stone Product Manufacturing	327991
Cutlery and Flatware (except Precious) Manufacturing	332211
Cutting Tool and Machine Tool Accessory Manufacturing	333515
Cyclic Crude and Intermediate Manufacturing	325192

D

Description	N.A.I.C.S.
Dairy Cattle and Milk Production	112120
Dairy Product (except Dried or Canned) Merchant Wholesalers	424430
Dairy Product (except Dried or Canned) Wholesalers	422430
Dance Companies	711120
Data Processing Services	514210
Data Processing, Hosting, and Related Services	518210
Database and Directory Publishers	511140
Deep Sea Freight Transportation	483111
Deep Sea Passenger Transportation	483112
Dental Equipment and Supplies Manufacturing	339114

Alphabetical N.A.I.C.S. Compendium-continued

Description	N.A.I.C.S.
Dental Laboratories	339116
Department Stores	452110
Department Stores (except Discount Department Stores)	452111
Diagnostic Imaging Centers	621512
Die-Cut Paper and Paperboard Office Supplies Manufacturing	322231
Diet and Weight Reducing Centers	812191
Digital Printing	323115
Dimension Stone Mining and Quarrying	212311
Direct Health and Medical Insurance Carriers	524114
Direct Life Insurance Carriers	524113
Direct Mail Advertising	541860
Direct Property and Casualty Insurance Carriers	524126
Direct Title Insurance Carriers	524127
Discount Department Stores	452112
Display Advertising	541850
Distilleries	312140
Document Preparation Services	561410
Dog and Cat Food Manufacturing	311111
Doll and Stuffed Toy Manufacturing	339931
Drafting Services	541340
Dried and Dehydrated Food Manufacturing	311423
Drilling Oil and Gas Wells	213111
Drinking Places (Alcoholic Beverages)	722410
Drive-In Motion Picture Theaters	512132
Drugs and Druggists' Sundries Wholesalers	422210
Drugs and Druggists' Sundries Merchant Wholesalers	424210
Dry Pasta Manufacturing	311823
Dry Pea and Bean Farming	111130
Dry, Condensed, and Evaporated Dairy Product Manufacturing	311514
Drycleaning and Laundry Services (except Coin-Operated)	812320
Drywall and Insulation Contractors	238310
Drywall, Plastering, Acoustical, and Insulation Contractors	235420
Dual Purpose Cattle Ranching and Farming	112130

E

Description	N.A.I.C.S.
Educational Support Services	611710
Electric Bulk Power Transmission and Control	221121
Electric Housewares and Household Fan Manufacturing	335211
Electric Lamp Bulb and Part Manufacturing	335110
Electric Power Distribution	221122
Electrical and Electronic Appliance, Television, and Radio Set Merchant Wholesalers	423620
Electrical Apparatus and Equipment, Wiring Supplies, and Construction Material Wholesalers	421610
Electrical Apparatus and Equipment, Wiring Supplies, and Related Equipment Merchant Wholesalers	423610
Electrical Appliance, Television, and Radio Set Wholesalers	421620
Electrical Contractors	238210
Electromedical and Electrotherapeutic Apparatus Manufacturing	334510
Electrometallurgical Ferroalloy Product Manufacturing	331110
Electron Tube Manufacturing	334411
Electronic Auctions	454112
Electronic Capacitor Manufacturing	334414
Electronic Coil, Transformer, and Other Inductor Manufacturing	334416
Electronic Computer Manufacturing	334111
Electronic Connector Manufacturing	334417
Electronic Resistor Manufacturing	334415
Electronic Shopping	454111
Electronic Shopping and Mail-Order Houses	454110
Electroplating, Plating, Polishing, Anodizing, and Coloring	332813
Elementary and Secondary Schools	611110
Elevator and Moving Stairway Manufacturing	333921
Emergency and Other Relief Services	624230
Employee Leasing Services	561330
Employment Placement Agencies	561310
Enameled Iron and Metal Sanitary Ware Manufacturing	332998
Engineered Wood Member (except Truss) Manufacturing	321213
Engineering Services	541330
Envelope Manufacturing	322232
Environment, Conservation and Wildlife Organizations	813312
Environmental Consulting Services	541620
Ethyl Alcohol Manufacturing	325193
Exam Preparation and Tutoring	611691
Excavation Contractors	235930
Executive and Legislative Offices, Combined	921140
Executive Offices	921110
Explosives Manufacturing	325920
Exterminating and Pest Control Services	561710

F

Description	N.A.I.C.S.
Fabric Coating Mills	313320
Fabricated Pipe and Pipe Fitting Manufacturing	332996
Fabricated Structural Metal Manufacturing	332312
Facilities Support Services	561210
Family Clothing Stores	448140
Family Planning Centers	621410
Farm and Garden Machinery and Equipment Merchant Wholesalers	423820
Farm and Garden Machinery and Equipment Wholesalers	421820
Farm Labor Contractors and Crew Leaders	115115
Farm Machinery and Equipment Manufacturing	333111
Farm Management Services	115116
Farm Product Warehousing and Storage	493130
Farm Supplies Merchant Wholesalers	424910
Farm Supplies Wholesalers	422910
Fast Food Restaurants	722211
Fastener, Button, Needle, and Pin Manufacturing	339993
Fats and Oils Refining and Blending	311225
Fertilizer (Mixing Only) Manufacturing	325314
Fiber Can, Tube, Drum, and Similar Products Manufacturing	322214
Fiber Optic Cable Manufacturing	335921
Financial Transactions Processing, Reserve, and Clearinghouse Activities	522320
Fine Arts Schools	611610
Finfish Farming and Fish Hatcheries	112511
Finfish Fishing	114111
Finish Carpentry Contractors	238350
Fire Protection	922160
Fish and Seafood Markets	445220
Fish and Seafood Merchant Wholesalers	424460
Fish and Seafood Wholesalers	422460
Fitness and Recreational Sports Centers	713940
Flat Glass Manufacturing	327211
Flavoring Syrup and Concentrate Manufacturing	311930
Flight Training	611512
Floor Covering Stores	442210
Floor Laying and Other Floor Contractors	235520
Flooring Contractors	238330
Floriculture Production	111422
Florists	453110
Flour Milling	311211
Flour Mixes and Dough Manufacturing from Purchased Flour	311822
Flower, Nursery Stock, and Florists' Supplies Wholesalers	422930
Flower, Nursery Stock, and Florists' Supplies Merchant Wholesalers	424930
Fluid Milk Manufacturing	311511
Fluid Power Cylinder and Actuator Manufacturing	333995
Fluid Power Pump and Motor Manufacturing	333996
Fluid Power Valve and Hose Fitting Manufacturing	332912
Folding Paperboard Box Manufacturing	322212
Food (Health) Supplement Stores	446191
Food Product Machinery Manufacturing	333294
Food Service Contractors	722310
Footwear and Leather Goods Repair	811430
Footwear Merchant Wholesalers	424340
Footwear Wholesalers	422340
Forest Nurseries and Gathering of Forest Products	113210
Formal Wear and Costume Rental	532220
Fossil Fuel Electric Power Generation	221112
Framing Contractors	238130
Freestanding Ambulatory Surgical and Emergency Centers	621493
Freight Transportation Arrangement	488510
Fresh and Frozen Seafood Processing	311712
Fresh Fruit and Vegetable Merchant Wholesalers	424480
Fresh Fruit and Vegetable Wholesalers	422480
Frozen Cakes, Pies, and Other Pastries Manufacturing	311813
Frozen Fruit, Juice, and Vegetable Manufacturing	311411
Frozen Specialty Food Manufacturing	311412
Fruit and Tree Nut Combination Farming	111336
Fruit and Vegetable Canning	311421
Fruit and Vegetable Markets	445230
Full-Service Restaurants	722110
Funeral Homes and Funeral Services	812210
Fur and Leather Apparel Manufacturing	315292
Fur-Bearing Animal and Rabbit Production	112930
Furniture Merchant Wholesalers	423210
Furniture Stores	442110
Furniture Wholesalers	421210

Alphabetical N.A.I.C.S. Compendium-continued

Description	N.A.I.C.S.
G	
Game, Toy, and Children's Vehicle Manufacturing	339932
Gasket, Packing, and Sealing Device Manufacturing	339991
Gasoline Engine and Engine Parts Manufacturing	336312
Gasoline Stations with Convenience Stores	447110
General Automotive Repair	811111
General Freight Trucking, Local	484110
General Freight Trucking, Long-Distance, Less Than Truckload	484122
General Freight Trucking, Long-Distance, Truckload	484121
General Line Grocery Merchant Wholesalers	424410
General Line Grocery Wholesalers	422410
General Medical and Surgical Hospitals	622110
General Rental Centers	532310
General Warehousing and Storage	493110
Geophysical Surveying and Mapping Services	541360
Gift, Novelty, and Souvenir Stores	453220
Glass and Glazing Contractors	238150
Glass Container Manufacturing	327213
Glass Product Manufacturing Made of Purchased Glass	327215
Glove and Mitten Manufacturing	315992
Goat Farming	112420
Gold Ore Mining	212221
Golf Courses and Country Clubs	713910
Grain and Field Bean Merchant Wholesalers	424510
Grain and Field Bean Wholesalers	422510
Grantmaking Foundations	813211
Grape Vineyards	111332
Graphic Design Services	541430
Greeting Card Publishers	511191
Ground or Treated Mineral and Earth Manufacturing	327992
Guided Missile and Space Vehicle Manufacturing	336414
Guided Missile and Space Vehicle Propulsion Unit and Propulsion Unit Parts Manufacturing	336415
Gum and Wood Chemical Manufacturing	325191
Gypsum Product Manufacturing	327420
H	
Hand and Edge Tool Manufacturing	332212
Hardware Manufacturing	332510
Hardware Merchant Wholesalers	423710
Hardware Stores	444130
Hardware Wholesalers	421710
Hardwood Veneer and Plywood Manufacturing	321211
Hat, Cap, and Millinery Manufacturing	315991
Hay Farming	111940
Hazardous Waste Collection	562112
Hazardous Waste Treatment and Disposal	562211
Health and Welfare Funds	525120
Heating Equipment (except Warm Air Furnaces) Manufacturing	333414
Heating Oil Dealers	454311
Heavy Duty Truck Manufacturing	336120
Highway and Street Construction	234110
Highway, Street, and Bridge Construction	237310
Historical Sites	712120
HMO Medical Centers	621491
Hobby, Toy, and Game Stores	451120
Hog and Pig Farming	112210
Home and Garden Equipment Repair and Maintenance	811411
Home Centers	444110
Home Furnishing Merchant Wholesalers	423220
Home Furnishing Wholesalers	421220
Home Health Care Services	621610
Home Health Equipment Rental	532291
Homes for the Elderly	623312
Horse and Other Equine Production	112920
Hotels (except Casino Hotels) and Motels	721110
House Slipper Manufacturing	316212
Household Appliance Stores	443111
Household Cooking Appliance Manufacturing	335221
Household Furniture (except Wood and Metal) Manufacturing	337125
Household Laundry Equipment Manufacturing	335224
Household Refrigerator and Home Freezer Manufacturing	335222
Household Vacuum Cleaner Manufacturing	335212
Human Resources and Executive Search Consulting Services	541612
Human Rights Organizations	813311
Hunting and Trapping	114210
Hydroelectric Power Generation	221111
I	
Ice Cream and Frozen Dessert Manufacturing	311520
Ice Manufacturing	312113
Independent Artists, Writers, and Performers	711510
Industrial and Commercial Fan and Blower Manufacturing	333412
Industrial and Personal Service Paper Merchant Wholesalers	424130
Industrial and Personal Service Paper Wholesalers	422130
Industrial Building Construction	236210
Industrial Design Services	541420
Industrial Gas Manufacturing	325120
Industrial Launderers	812332
Industrial Machinery and Equipment Merchant Wholesalers	423830
Industrial Machinery and Equipment Wholesalers	421830
Industrial Mold Manufacturing	333511
Industrial Nonbuilding Structure Construction	234930
Industrial Pattern Manufacturing	332997
Industrial Process Furnace and Oven Manufacturing	333994
Industrial Sand Mining	212322
Industrial Supplies Merchant Wholesalers	423840
Industrial Supplies Wholesalers	421840
Industrial Truck, Tractor, Trailer, and Stacker Machinery Manufacturing	333924
Industrial Valve Manufacturing	332911
Infants' Cut and Sew Apparel Manufacturing	315291
Inland Water Freight Transportation	483111
Inland Water Passenger Transportation	483212
Inorganic Dye and Pigment Manufacturing	325131
Institutional Furniture Manufacturing	337127
Instrument Manufacturing for Measuring and Testing Electricity and Electrical Signals	334515
Instruments and Related Products Manufacturing for Measuring, Displaying, and Controlling Industrial Process Variables	334513
Insurance Agencies and Brokerages	524210
Integrated Record Production/Distribution	512220
Interior Design Services	541410
International Affairs	928120
International Trade Financing	522293
Internet Publishing and Broadcasting	516110
Internet Service Providers	518111
Interurban and Rural Bus Transportation	485210
Investigation Services	561611
Investment Advice	523930
Investment Banking and Securities Dealing	523110
In-Vitro Diagnostic Substance Manufacturing	325413
Iron and Steel Forging	332111
Iron and Steel Mills	331111
Iron and Steel Pipe and Tube Manufacturing from Purchased Steel	331210
Iron Foundries	331511
Iron Ore Mining	212210
Irradiation Apparatus Manufacturing	334517
J	
Janitorial Services	561720
Jewelers' Material and Lapidary Work Manufacturing	339913
Jewelry (except Costume) Manufacturing	339911
Jewelry Stores	448310
Jewelry, Watch, Precious Stone, and Precious Metal Merchant Wholesalers	423940
Jewelry, Watch, Precious Stone, and Precious Metal Wholesalers	421940
Junior Colleges	611210
K	
Kaolin and Ball Clay Mining	212324
Kidney Dialysis Centers	621492
Kitchen Utensil, Pot, and Pan Manufacturing	332214
L	
Labor Unions and Similar Labor Organizations	813930
Laboratory Apparatus and Furniture Manufacturing	339111
Laminated Aluminum Foil Manufacturing for Flexible Packaging Uses	322225
Laminated Plastics Plate, Sheet, and Shape Manufacturing	326130
Land Subdivision	237210
Landscape Architectural Services	541320
Landscaping Services	561730
Language Schools	611630
Lawn and Garden Tractor and Home Lawn and Garden Equipment Manufacturing	333112
Lead Ore and Zinc Ore Mining	212231
Lead Pencil and Art Good Manufacturing	339942
Leather and Hide Tanning and Finishing	316110

Alphabetical N.A.I.C.S. Compendium-continued

Description	N.A.I.C.S.
Legal Counsel and Prosecution	922130
Legislative Bodies	921120
Lessors of Miniwarehouses and Self-Storage Units	531130
Lessors of Nonfinancial Intangible Assets (except Copyrighted Works)	533110
Lessors of Nonresidential Buildings (except Miniwarehouses)	531120
Lessors of Other Real Estate Property	531190
Lessors of Residential Buildings and Dwellings	531110
Libraries and Archives	519120
Light Truck and Utility Vehicle Manufacturing	336112
Lime Manufacturing	327410
Limousine Service	485320
Line-Haul Railroads	482111
Linen Supply	812331
Liquefied Petroleum Gas (Bottled Gas) Dealers	454312
Livestock Merchant Wholesalers	424520
Livestock Wholesalers	422520
Local Messengers and Local Delivery	492210
Locksmiths	561622
Logging	113310
Luggage and Leather Goods Stores	448320
Luggage Manufacturing	316991
Lumber, Plywood, Millwork, and Wood Panel Merchant Wholesalers	423310
Lumber, Plywood, Millwork, and Wood Panel Wholesalers	421310

M

Description	N.A.I.C.S.
Machine Shops	332710
Machine Tool (Metal Cutting Types) Manufacturing	333512
Machine Tool (Metal Forming Types) Manufacturing	333513
Magnetic and Optical Recording Media Manufacturing	334613
Mail-Order Houses	454113
Malt Manufacturing	311213
Manifold Business Forms Printing	323116
Manufactured (Mobile) Home Dealers	453930
Manufactured Home (Mobile Home) Manufacturing	321991
Manufacturing and Industrial Building Construction	233310
Marinas	713930
Marine Cargo Handling	488320
Marketing Consulting Services	541613
Marketing Research and Public Opinion Polling	541910
Marking Device Manufacturing	339943
Masonry and Stone Contractors	235410
Masonry Contractors	238140
Materials Recovery Facilities	562920
Mattress Manufacturing	337910
Mayonnaise, Dressing, and Other Prepared Sauce Manufacturing	311941
Measuring and Dispensing Pump Manufacturing	333913
Meat and Meat Product Merchant Wholesalers	424470
Meat and Meat Product Wholesalers	422470
Meat Markets	445210
Meat Processed from Carcasses	311612
Mechanical Power Transmission Equipment Manufacturing	333613
Media Buying Agencies	541830
Media Representatives	541840
Medical Laboratories	621511
Medical, Dental, and Hospital Equipment and Supplies Merchant Wholesalers	423450
Medical, Dental, and Hospital Equipment and Supplies Wholesalers	421450
Medicinal and Botanical Manufacturing	325411
Men's and Boys' Clothing and Furnishings Merchant Wholesalers	424320
Men's and Boys' Clothing and Furnishings Wholesalers	422320
Men's and Boys' Cut and Sew Apparel Contractors	315211
Men's and Boys' Cut and Sew Other Outerwear Manufacturing	315228
Men's and Boys' Cut and Sew Shirt (except Work Shirt) Manufacturing	315223
Men's and Boys' Cut and Sew Suit, Coat, and Overcoat Manufacturing	315222
Men's and Boys' Cut and Sew Trouser, Slack, and Jean Manufacturing	315224
Men's and Boys' Cut and Sew Underwear and Nightwear Manufacturing	315221
Men's and Boys' Cut and Sew Work Clothing Manufacturing	315225
Men's and Boys' Neckwear Manufacturing	315993
Men's Clothing Stores	448110
Men's Footwear (except Athletic) Manufacturing	316213
Metal Can Manufacturing	332431
Metal Coating, Engraving (except Jewelry and Silverware), and Allied Services to Manufacturers	332812
Metal Heat Treating	332811
Metal Household Furniture Manufacturing	337124
Metal Service Centers and Offices	421510
Metal Service Centers and Other Metal Merchant Wholesalers	423510
Metal Stamping	332116
Metal Tank (Heavy Gauge) Manufacturing	332420
Metal Window and Door Manufacturing	332321

Description	N.A.I.C.S.
Military Armored Vehicle, Tank, and Tank Component Manufacturing	336992
Mineral Wool Manufacturing	327993
Mining Machinery and Equipment Manufacturing	333131
Miscellaneous Financial Investment Activities	523999
Miscellaneous Intermediation	523910
Mixed Mode Transit Systems	485111
Mobile Food Services	722330
Monetary Authorities - Central Bank	521110
Mortgage and Nonmortgage Loan Brokers	522310
Motion Picture and Video Distribution	512120
Motion Picture and Video Production	512110
Motion Picture Theaters (except Drive-Ins)	512131
Motor and Generator Manufacturing	335312
Motor Home Manufacturing	336213
Motor Vehicle Air-Conditioning Manufacturing	336391
Motor Vehicle Body Manufacturing	336211
Motor Vehicle Brake System Manufacturing	336340
Motor Vehicle Metal Stamping	336370
Motor Vehicle Parts (Used) Merchant Wholesalers	423140
Motor Vehicle Parts (Used) Wholesalers	421140
Motor Vehicle Seating and Interior Trim Manufacturing	336360
Motor Vehicle Steering and Suspension Components (except Spring) Manufacturing	336330
Motor Vehicle Supplies and New Parts Merchant Wholesalers	423120
Motor Vehicle Supplies and New Parts Wholesalers	421120
Motor Vehicle Towing	488410
Motor Vehicle Transmission and Power Train Parts Manufacturing	336350
Motorcycle Dealers	441221
Motorcycle, Bicycle, and Parts Manufacturing	336991
Multifamily Housing Construction	233220
Museums	712110
Mushroom Production	111411
Music Publishers	512230
Musical Groups and Artists	711130
Musical Instrument and Supplies Stores	451140
Musical Instrument Manufacturing	339992

N

Description	N.A.I.C.S.
Nail Salons	812113
Narrow Fabric Mills	313221
National Security	928110
Natural Gas Distribution	221210
Natural Gas Liquid Extraction	211112
Nature Parks and Other Similar Institutions	712190
Navigational Services to Shipping	488330
New Car Dealers	441110
New Housing Operative Builders	236117
New Multifamily Housing Construction (except Operative Builders)	236116
New Single-Family Housing Construction (except Operative Builders)	236115
News Dealers and Newsstands	451212
News Syndicates	519110
Newspaper Publishers	511110
Newsprint Mills	322122
Nitrogenous Fertilizer Manufacturing	325311
Noncellulosic Organic Fiber Manufacturing	325222
Nonchocolate Confectionery Manufacturing	311340
Nonclay Refractory Manufacturing	327125
Noncurrent-Carrying Wiring Device Manufacturing	335932
Nonferrous (except Aluminum) Die-Casting Foundries	331522
Nonferrous Forging	332112
Nonferrous Metal (except Copper and Aluminum) Rolling, Drawing, and Extruding	331491
Nonfolding Sanitary Food Container Manufacturing	322215
Nonresidential Property Managers	531312
Nonscheduled Chartered Freight Air Transportation	481212
Nonscheduled Chartered Passenger Air Transportation	481211
Nonupholstered Wood Household Furniture Manufacturing	337122
Nonwoven Fabric Mills	313230
Nuclear Electric Power Generation	221113
Nursery and Garden Centers	444220
Nursery and Tree Production	111421
Nursing Care Facilities	623110

O

Description	N.A.I.C.S.
Office Administrative Services	561110
Office Equipment Merchant Wholesalers	423420
Office Equipment Wholesalers	421420
Office Furniture (except Wood) Manufacturing	337214
Office Machinery and Equipment Rental and Leasing	532420
Office Machinery Manufacturing	333313

3083

Alphabetical N.A.I.C.S. Compendium-continued

Description	N.A.I.C.S.
Office Supplies and Stationery Stores	453210
Offices of All Other Miscellaneous Health Practitioners	621399
Offices of Bank Holding Companies	551111
Offices of Certified Public Accountants	541211
Offices of Chiropractors	621310
Offices of Dentists	621210
Offices of Lawyers	541110
Offices of Mental Health Practitioners (except Physicians)	621330
Offices of Notaries	541120
Offices of Optometrists	621320
Offices of Other Holding Companies	551112
Offices of Physical, Occupational and Speech Therapists, and Audiologists	621340
Offices of Physicians (except Mental Health Specialists)	621111
Offices of Physicians, Mental Health Specialists	621112
Offices of Podiatrists	621391
Offices of Real Estate Agents and Brokers	531210
Offices of Real Estate Appraisers	531320
Oil and Gas Field Machinery and Equipment Manufacturing	333132
Oil and Gas Pipeline and Related Structures Construction	237120
Oilseed (except Soybean) Farming	111120
Oilseed and Grain Combination Farming	111191
One-Hour Photofinishing	812922
On-Line Information Services	514191
Open-End Investment Funds	525910
Ophthalmic Goods Manufacturing	339115
Ophthalmic Goods Merchant Wholesalers	423460
Ophthalmic Goods Wholesalers	421460
Optical Goods Stores	446130
Optical Instrument and Lens Manufacturing	333314
Other Fabricated Wire Product Manufacturing	332618
Other Farm Product Raw Material Merchant Wholesalers	424590
Other Farm Product Raw Material Wholesalers	422590
Other Financial Vehicles	525990
Other Food Crops Grown Under Cover	111419
Other Footwear Manufacturing	316219
Other Foundation, Structure, and Building Exterior Contractors	238190
Other Fuel Dealers	454319
Other Gambling Industries	713290
Other Gasoline Stations	447190
Other General Government Support	921190
Other Grantmaking and Giving Services	813290
Other Grocery and Related Products Merchant Wholesalers	424490
Other Grocery and Related Products Wholesalers	422490
Other Guided Missile and Space Vehicle Parts and Auxiliary Equipment Manufacturing	336419
Other Heavy and Civil Engineering Construction	237990
Other Hosiery and Sock Mills	315119
Other Household Textile Product Mills	314129
Other Individual and Family Services	624190
Other Insurance Funds	525190
Other Justice, Public Order, and Safety Activities	922190
Other Knit Fabric and Lace Mills	313249
Other Lighting Equipment Manufacturing	335129
Other Major Household Appliance Manufacturing	335228
Other Management Consulting Services	541618
Other Marine Fishing	114119
Other Measuring and Controlling Device Manufacturing	334519
Other Metal Container Manufacturing	332439
Other Metal Valve and Pipe Fitting Manufacturing	332919
Other Metalworking Machinery Manufacturing	333518
Other Millwork (including Flooring)	321918
Other Miscellaneous Durable Goods Merchant Wholesalers	423990
Other Miscellaneous Durable Goods Wholesalers	421990
Other Miscellaneous Nondurable Goods Wholesalers	422990
Other Motion Picture and Video Industries	512199
Other Motor Vehicle Electrical and Electronic Equipment Manufacturing	336322
Other Noncitrus Fruit Farming	111339
Other Nonferrous Foundries (except Die-Casting)	331528
Other Nonhazardous Waste Treatment and Disposal	562219
Other Nonscheduled Air Transportation	481219
Other Oilseed Processing	311223
Other Ordnance and Accessories Manufacturing	332995
Other Performing Arts Companies	711190
Other Personal and Household Goods Repair and Maintenance	811490
Other Personal Care Services	812199
Other Poultry Production	112390
Other Pressed and Blown Glass and Glassware Manufacturing	327212
Other Professional Equipment and Supplies Merchant Wholesalers	423490
Other Professional Equipment and Supplies Wholesalers	421490
Other Residential Care Facilities	623990
Other Scientific and Technical Consulting Services	541690
Other Services Related to Advertising	541890
Other Services to Buildings and Dwellings	561790
Other Similar Organizations (except Business, Professional, Labor, and Political Organizations)	813990
Other Snack Food Manufacturing	311919
Other Social Advocacy Organizations	813319
Other Sound Recording Industries	512290
Other Specialized Design Services	541490
Other Spectator Sports	711219
Other Structural Clay Product Manufacturing	327123
Other Support Activities for Air Transportation	488190
Other Support Activities for Road Transportation	488490
Other Support Activities for Water Transportation	488390
Other Technical and Trade Schools	611519
Other Telecommunications	517910
Other Tobacco Product Manufacturing	312229
Other Urban Transit Systems	485119
Other Vegetable (except Potato) and Melon Farming	111219
Other Warehousing and Storage	493190
Other Waste Collection	562119
Outdoor Power Equipment Stores	444210
Outerwear Knitting Mills	315191
Outpatient Mental Health and Substance Abuse Centers	621420
Overhead Traveling Crane, Hoist, and Monorail System Manufacturing	333923

P

Description	N.A.I.C.S.
Packaged Frozen Food Merchant Wholesalers	424420
Packaged Frozen Food Wholesalers	422420
Packaging and Labeling Services	561910
Packaging Machinery Manufacturing	333993
Packing and Crating	488991
Paging	517211
Paint and Coating Manufacturing	325510
Paint and Wallpaper Stores	444120
Paint, Varnish, and Supplies Merchant Wholesalers	424950
Paint, Varnish, and Supplies Wholesalers	422950
Painting and Wall Covering Contractors	238320
Paper (except Newsprint) Mills	322121
Paper Industry Machinery Manufacturing	333291
Paperboard Mills	322130
Parking Lots and Garages	812930
Parole Offices and Probation Offices	922150
Passenger Car Leasing	532112
Passenger Car Rental	532111
Payroll Services	541214
Peanut Farming	111992
Pen and Mechanical Pencil Manufacturing	339941
Pension Funds	525110
Periodical Publishers	511120
Perishable Prepared Food Manufacturing	311991
Personal Leather Good (except Women's Handbag and Purse) Manufacturing	316993
Pesticide and Other Agricultural Chemical Manufacturing	325320
Pet and Pet Supplies Stores	453910
Pet Care (except Veterinary) Services	812910
Petrochemical Manufacturing	325110
Petroleum and Petroleum Products Merchant Wholesalers (except Bulk Stations and Terminals)	424720
Petroleum and Petroleum Products Wholesalers (except Bulk Stations and Terminals)	422720
Petroleum Bulk Stations and Terminals	424710
Petroleum Lubricating Oil and Grease Manufacturing	324191
Petroleum Refineries	324110
Pharmaceutical Preparation Manufacturing	325412
Pharmacies and Drug Stores	446110
Phosphate Rock Mining	212392
Phosphatic Fertilizer Manufacturing	325312
Photofinishing Laboratories (except One-Hour)	812921
Photographic and Photocopying Equipment Manufacturing	333315
Photographic Equipment and Supplies Merchant Wholesalers	423410
Photographic Equipment and Supplies Wholesalers	421410
Photographic Film, Paper, Plate, and Chemical Manufacturing	325992
Photography Studios, Portrait	541921
Piece Goods, Notions, and Other Dry Goods Merchant Wholesalers	424310
Piece Goods, Notions, and Other Dry Goods Wholesalers	422310
Pipeline Transportation of Crude Oil	486110
Pipeline Transportation of Natural Gas	486210
Pipeline Transportation of Refined Petroleum Products	486910

Alphabetical N.A.I.C.S. Compendium-continued

Description	N.A.I.C.S.
Plastics and Rubber Industry Machinery Manufacturing	333220
Plastics Bottle Manufacturing	326160
Plastics Material and Resin Manufacturing	325211
Plastics Materials and Basic Forms and Shapes Merchant Wholesalers	424610
Plastics Materials and Basic Forms and Shapes Wholesalers	422610
Plastics Pipe and Pipe Fitting Manufacturing	326122
Plastics Plumbing Fixture Manufacturing	326191
Plastics, Foil, and Coated Paper Bag Manufacturing	322223
Plate Work Manufacturing	332313
Plumbing and Heating Equipment and Supplies (Hydronics) Merchant Wholesalers	423720
Plumbing and Heating Equipment and Supplies (Hydronics) Wholesalers	421720
Plumbing Fixture Fitting and Trim Manufacturing	332913
Plumbing, Heating, and Air-Conditioning Contractors	235110
Police Protection	922120
Polish and Other Sanitation Good Manufacturing	325612
Political Organizations	813940
Polystyrene Foam Product Manufacturing	326140
Porcelain Electrical Supply Manufacturing	327113
Port and Harbor Operations	488310
Portfolio Management	523920
Postal Service	491110
Postharvest Crop Activities (except Cotton Ginning)	115114
Potash, Soda, and Borate Mineral Mining	212391
Potato Farming	111211
Poultry and Poultry Product Merchant Wholesalers	424440
Poultry and Poultry Product Wholesalers	422440
Poultry Hatcheries	112340
Poultry Processing	311615
Poured Concrete Foundation and Structure Contractors	238110
Powder Metallurgy Part Manufacturing	332117
Power and Communication Line and Related Structures Construction	237130
Power and Communication Transmission Line Construction	234920
Power Boiler and Heat Exchanger Manufacturing	332410
Power, Distribution, and Specialty Transformer Manufacturing	335311
Power-Driven Handtool Manufacturing	333991
Precision Turned Product Manufacturing	332721
Prefabricated Metal Building and Component Manufacturing	332311
Prefabricated Wood Building Manufacturing	321992
Prepress Services	323122
Prerecorded Compact Disc (except Software), Tape, and Record Reproducing	334612
Prerecorded Tape, Compact Disc, and Record Stores	451220
Primary Aluminum Production	331312
Primary Battery Manufacturing	335912
Primary Smelting and Refining of Copper	331411
Primary Smelting and Refining of Nonferrous Metal (except Copper and Aluminum)	331419
Printed Circuit Assembly (Electronic Assembly) Manufacturing	334418
Printing and Writing Paper Merchant Wholesalers	424110
Printing and Writing Paper Wholesalers	422110
Printing Ink Manufacturing	325910
Printing Machinery and Equipment Manufacturing	333293
Private Households	814110
Private Mail Centers	561431
Process, Physical Distribution, and Logistics Consulting Services	541614
Professional and Management Development Training	611430
Professional Organizations	813920
Promoters of Performing Arts, Sports, and Similar Events with Facilities	711310
Promoters of Performing Arts, Sports, and Similar Events without Facilities	711320
Psychiatric and Substance Abuse Hospitals	622210
Public Finance Activities	921130
Public Relations Agencies	541820
Pulp Mills	322110
Pump and Pumping Equipment Manufacturing	333911

Q

Description	N.A.I.C.S.
Quick Printing	323114

R

Description	N.A.I.C.S.
Racetracks	711212
Radio and Television Broadcasting and Wireless Communications Equipment Manufacturing	334220
Radio Networks	515111
Radio Stations	515112
Radio, Television, and Other Electronics Stores	443112
Railroad Rolling Stock Manufacturing	336510
Ready-Mix Concrete Manufacturing	327320
Real Estate Credit	522292
Real Estate Investment Trusts	525930
Reconstituted Wood Product Manufacturing	321219
Record Production	512210
Recreational and Vacation Camps (except Campgrounds)	721214
Recreational Goods Rental	532292
Recreational Vehicle Dealers	441210
Recyclable Material Merchant Wholesalers	423930
Recyclable Material Wholesalers	421930
Refrigerated Warehousing and Storage	493120
Refrigeration Equipment and Supplies Merchant Wholesalers	423740
Refrigeration Equipment and Supplies Wholesalers	421740
Regulation and Administration of Communications, Electric, Gas, and Other Utilities	926130
Regulation and Administration of Transportation Programs	926120
Regulation of Agricultural Marketing and Commodities	926140
Regulation, Licensing, and Inspection of Miscellaneous Commercial Sectors	926150
Reinsurance Carriers	524130
Relay and Industrial Control Manufacturing	335314
Religious Organizations	813110
Remediation Services	562910
Rendering and Meat Byproduct Processing	311613
Repossession Services	561450
Research and Development in the Physical, Engineering, and Life Sciences	541710
Research and Development in the Social Sciences and Humanities	541720
Residential Electric Lighting Fixture Manufacturing	335121
Residential Mental Health and Substance Abuse Facilities	623220
Residential Mental Retardation Facilities	623210
Residential Property Managers	531311
Residential Remodelers	236118
Resilient Floor Covering Manufacturing	326192
Retail Bakeries	311811
Reupholstery and Furniture Repair	811420
Rice Farming	111160
Rice Milling	311212
Roasted Nuts and Peanut Butter Manufacturing	311911
Rolled Steel Shape Manufacturing	331221
Rolling Mill Machinery and Equipment Manufacturing	333516
Roofing Contractors	238160
Roofing, Siding, and Insulation Material Merchant Wholesalers	423330
Roofing, Siding, and Insulation Material Wholesalers	421330
Roofing, Siding, and Sheet Metal Contractors	235610
Rooming and Boarding Houses	721310
Rope, Cordage, and Twine Mills	314991
Rubber and Plastics Footwear Manufacturing	316211
Rubber and Plastics Hoses and Belting Manufacturing	326220
Rubber Product Manufacturing for Mechanical Use	326291
RV (Recreational Vehicle) Parks and Campgrounds	721211

S

Description	N.A.I.C.S.
Sales Financing	522220
Sanitary Paper Product Manufacturing	322291
Satellite Telecommunications	517410
Savings Institutions	522120
Saw Blade and Handsaw Manufacturing	332213
Sawmill and Woodworking Machinery Manufacturing	333210
Sawmills	321113
Scale and Balance (except Laboratory) Manufacturing	333997
Scenic and Sightseeing Transportation, Land	487110
Scenic and Sightseeing Transportation, Other	487990
Scenic and Sightseeing Transportation, Water	487210
Scheduled Freight Air Transportation	481112
Scheduled Passenger Air Transportation	481111
Schiffli Machine Embroidery	313222
School and Employee Bus Transportation	485410
Seafood Canning	311711
Search, Detection, Navigation, Guidance, Aeronautical, and Nautical System and Instrument Manufacturing	334511
Secondary Market Financing	522294
Secondary Smelting and Alloying of Aluminum	331314
Secondary Smelting, Refining, and Alloying of Copper	331423
Secondary Smelting, Refining, and Alloying of Nonferrous Metal (except Copper and Aluminum)	331492
Securities and Commodity Exchanges	523210
Securities Brokerage	523120
Security Guards and Patrol Services	561612
Security Systems Services (except Locksmiths)	561621
Semiconductor and Related Device Manufacturing	334413
Semiconductor Machinery Manufacturing	333295

3085

Alphabetical N.A.I.C.S. Compendium-continued

Description	N.A.I.C.S.
Septic Tank and Related Services	562991
Service Establishment Equipment and Supplies Merchant Wholesalers	423850
Service Establishment Equipment and Supplies Wholesalers	421850
Services for the Elderly and Persons with Disabilities	624120
Setup Paperboard Box Manufacturing	322213
Sewage Treatment Facilities	221320
Sewing, Needlework, and Piece Goods Stores	451130
Sheep Farming	112410
Sheer Hosiery Mills	315111
Sheet Metal Work Manufacturing	332322
Shellfish Farming	112512
Shellfish Fishing	114112
Ship Building and Repairing	336611
Shoe Stores	448210
Short Line Railroads	482112
Showcase, Partition, Shelving, and Locker Manufacturing	337215
Siding Contractors	238170
Sign Manufacturing	339950
Silver Ore Mining	212222
Silverware and Holloware Manufacturing	339912
Single Family Housing Construction	233210
Site Preparation Contractors	238910
Skiing Facilities	713920
Small Arms Ammunition Manufacturing	332992
Small Arms Manufacturing	332994
Snack and Nonalcoholic Beverage Bars	722213
Soap and Other Detergent Manufacturing	325611
Soft Drink Manufacturing	312111
Software Publishers	511210
Software Reproducing	334611
Softwood Veneer and Plywood Manufacturing	321212
Soil Preparation, Planting, and Cultivating	115112
Solid Waste Collection	562111
Solid Waste Combustors and Incinerators	562213
Solid Waste Landfill	562212
Sound Recording Studios	512240
Soybean Farming	111110
Soybean Processing	311222
Space Research and Technology	927110
Special Die and Tool, Die Set, Jig, and Fixture Manufacturing	333514
Special Needs Transportation	485991
Specialized Freight (except Used Goods) Trucking, Local	484220
Specialized Freight (except Used Goods) Trucking, Long-Distance	484230
Specialty (except Psychiatric and Substance Abuse) Hospitals	622310
Specialty Canning	311422
Speed Changer, Industrial High-Speed Drive, and Gear Manufacturing	333612
Spice and Extract Manufacturing	311942
Sporting and Athletic Goods Manufacturing	339920
Sporting and Recreational Goods and Supplies Merchant Wholesalers	423910
Sporting and Recreational Goods and Supplies Wholesalers	421910
Sporting Goods Stores	451110
Sports and Recreation Instruction	611620
Sports Teams and Clubs	711211
Spring (Heavy Gauge) Manufacturing	332611
Spring (Light Gauge) Manufacturing	332612
Stationery and Office Supplies Merchant Wholesalers	424120
Stationery and Office Supplies Wholesalers	422120
Stationery, Tablet, and Related Product Manufacturing	322233
Steam and Air-Conditioning Supply	221330
Steel Foundries (except Investment)	331513
Steel Investment Foundries	331512
Steel Wire Drawing	331222
Storage Battery Manufacturing	335911
Strawberry Farming	111333
Structural Steel and Precast Concrete Contractors	238120
Structural Steel Erection Contractors	235910
Sugar Beet Farming	111991
Sugarcane Farming	111930
Sugarcane Mills	311311
Supermarkets and Other Grocery (except Convenience) Stores	445110
Support Activities for Animal Production	115210
Support Activities for Coal Mining	213113
Support Activities for Forestry	115310
Support Activities for Metal Mining	213114
Support Activities for Nonmetallic Minerals (except Fuels)	213115
Support Activities for Oil and Gas Operations	213112
Support Activities for Rail Transportation	488210
Surface Active Agent Manufacturing	325613
Surface-Coated Paperboard Manufacturing	322226
Surgical and Medical Instrument Manufacturing	339112
Surgical Appliance and Supplies Manufacturing	339113
Surveying and Mapping (except Geophysical) Services	541370
Switchgear and Switchboard Apparatus Manufacturing	335313
Synthetic Organic Dye and Pigment Manufacturing	325132
Synthetic Rubber Manufacturing	325212

T

Description	N.A.I.C.S.
Tax Preparation Services	541213
Taxi Service	485310
Telecommunications Resellers	517310
Telemarketing Bureaus	561422
Telephone Answering Services	561421
Telephone Apparatus Manufacturing	334210
Teleproduction and Other Postproduction Services	512191
Television Broadcasting	515120
Temporary Help Services	561320
Temporary Shelters	624221
Testing Laboratories	541380
Textile and Fabric Finishing (except Broadwoven Fabric) Mills	313312
Textile Bag Mills	314911
Textile Machinery Manufacturing	333292
Theater Companies and Dinner Theaters	711110
Third Party Administration of Insurance and Pension Funds	524292
Thread Mills	313113
Tile and Terrazzo Contractors	238340
Tile, Marble, Terrazzo, and Mosaic Contractors	235430
Timber Tract Operations	113110
Tire and Tube Merchant Wholesalers	423130
Tire and Tube Wholesalers	421130
Tire Cord and Tire Fabric Mills	314992
Tire Dealers	441320
Tire Manufacturing (except Retreading)	326211
Tire Retreading	326212
Title Abstract and Settlement Offices	541191
Tobacco and Tobacco Product Merchant Wholesalers	424940
Tobacco and Tobacco Product Wholesalers	422940
Tobacco Farming	111910
Tobacco Stemming and Redrying	312210
Tobacco Stores	453991
Toilet Preparation Manufacturing	325620
Tortilla Manufacturing	311830
Totalizing Fluid Meter and Counting Device Manufacturing	334514
Tour Operators	561520
Toy and Hobby Goods and Supplies Merchant Wholesalers	423920
Toy and Hobby Goods and Supplies Wholesalers	421920
Tradebinding and Related Work	323121
Translation and Interpretation Services	541930
Transportation Equipment and Supplies (except Motor Vehicle) Merchant Wholesalers	423860
Transportation Equipment and Supplies (except Motor Vehicle) Wholesalers	421860
Travel Agencies	561510
Travel Trailer and Camper Manufacturing	336214
Tree Nut Farming	111335
Truck Trailer Manufacturing	336212
Truck, Utility Trailer, and RV (Recreational Vehicle) Rental and Leasing	532120
Truss Manufacturing	321214
Trust, Fiduciary, and Custody Activities	523991
Trusts, Estates, and Agency Accounts	525920
Turbine and Turbine Generator Set Units Manufacturing	333611
Turkey Production	112330

U

Description	N.A.I.C.S.
Unclassified Establishments	999990
Uncoated Paper and Multiwall Bag Manufacturing	322224
Underwear and Nightwear Knitting Mills	315192
Unsupported Plastics Bag Manufacturing	326111
Unsupported Plastics Film and Sheet (except Packaging) Manufacturing	326113
Unsupported Plastics Packaging Film and Sheet Manufacturing	326112
Unsupported Plastics Profile Shape Manufacturing	326121
Upholstered Household Furniture Manufacturing	337121
Uranium-Radium-Vanadium Ore Mining	212291
Urethane and Other Foam Product (except Polystyrene) Manufacturing	326150
Used Car Dealers	441120
Used Household and Office Goods Moving	484210
Used Merchandise Stores	453310

V

Description	N.A.I.C.S.
Vehicular Lighting Equipment Manufacturing	336321

Alphabetical N.A.I.C.S. Compendium-continued

Description	N.A.I.C.S.
Vending Machine Operators	454210
Veterinary Services	541940
Video Tape and Disc Rental	532230
Vitreous China Plumbing Fixture and China and Earthenware Bathroom Accessories Manufacturing	327111
Vitreous China, Fine Earthenware, and Other Pottery Product Manufacturing	327112
Vocational Rehabilitation Services	624310
Voluntary Health Organizations	813212

W

Description	N.A.I.C.S.
Warehouse Clubs and Superstores	452910
Warm Air Heating and Air-Conditioning Equipment and Supplies Merchant Wholesalers	423730
Warm Air Heating and Air-Conditioning Equipment and Supplies Wholesalers	421730
Watch, Clock, and Part Manufacturing	334518
Water and Sewer Line and Related Structures Construction	237110
Water Supply and Irrigation Systems	221310
Water Well Drilling Contractors	235810
Water, Sewer, and Pipeline Construction	234910
Web Search Portals	518112
Weft Knit Fabric Mills	313241
Welding and Soldering Equipment Manufacturing	333992
Wet Corn Milling	311221
Wheat Farming	111140
Wholesale Trade Agents and Brokers	425120
Window Treatment Stores	442291
Wine and Distilled Alcoholic Beverage Merchant Wholesalers	424820
Wine and Distilled Alcoholic Beverage Wholesalers	422820
Wineries	312130
Wired Telecommunications Carriers	517110
Women's, Children's, and Infants' Clothing and Accessories Merchant Wholesalers	424330
Women's and Girls' Cut and Sew Blouse and Shirt Manufacturing	315232
Women's and Girls' Cut and Sew Dress Manufacturing	315233
Women's and Girls' Cut and Sew Lingerie, Loungewear, and Nightwear Manufacturing	315231
Women's and Girls' Cut and Sew Other Outerwear Manufacturing	315239
Women's and Girls' Cut and Sew Suit, Coat, Tailored Jacket, and Skirt Manufacturing	315234
Women's Clothing Stores	448120
Women's Footwear (except Athletic) Manufacturing	316214
Women's Handbag and Purse Manufacturing	316992
Women's, Children's, and Infants' Clothing and Accessories Wholesalers	422330
Women's, Girls', and Infants' Cut and Sew Apparel Contractors	315212
Wood Container and Pallet Manufacturing	321920
Wood Kitchen Cabinet and Countertop Manufacturing	337110
Wood Office Furniture Manufacturing	337211
Wood Preservation	321114
Wood Television, Radio, and Sewing Machine Cabinet Manufacturing	337129
Wood Window and Door Manufacturing	321911
Wrecking and Demolition Contractors	235940

Y

Description	N.A.I.C.S.
Yarn Spinning Mills	313111
Yarn Texturizing, Throwing, and Twisting Mills	313112

Z

Description	N.A.I.C.S.
Zoos and Botanical Gardens	712130

Alphabetical N.A.I.C.S. Compendium—continued

Description	N.A.I.C.S
Vending Machine Operators	454210
Veterinary Services	541940
Video Tape and Disc Rental	532230
Vitreous China Plumbing Fixture and China and Earthenware Bathroom Accessories Manufacturing	327111
Vitreous China, Fine Earthenware, and Other Pottery Product Manufacturing	327112
Vocational Rehabilitation Services	624310
Voluntary Health Organizations	813212

W

Warehouse Clubs and Superstores	452910
Warm Air Heating and Air-Conditioning Equipment and Supplies Merchant Wholesalers	423730
Warm Air Heating and Air-Conditioning Equipment and Supplies Wholesalers	421730
Watch, Clock, and Part Manufacturing	334518
Water and Sewer Line and Related Structures Construction	237110
Water Supply and Irrigation Systems	221310
Water Well Drilling Contractors	023810
Water, Sewer, and Pipeline Construction	234910
Web Search Portals	518112
Weft Knit Fabric Mills	313241
Welding and Soldering Equipment Manufacturing	333992
Wet Corn Milling	311221
Wheat Farming	111140
Wholesale Trade Agents and Brokers	425120
Window Treatment Stores	442291
Wine and Distilled Alcoholic Beverage Merchant Wholesalers	424820
Wine and Distilled Alcoholic Beverage Wholesalers	422820

Description	N.A.I.C.S
Winches	333130
Wired Telecommunications Carriers	517110
Women's, Children's, and Infants' Clothing and Accessories Merchant Wholesalers	424330
Women's and Girls' Cut and Sew Blouse and Shirt Manufacturing	315232
Women's and Girls' Cut and Sew Dress Manufacturing	315233
Women's and Girls' Cut and Sew Lingerie, Loungewear, and Nightwear Manufacturing	315231
Women's and Girls' Cut and Sew Other Outerwear Manufacturing	315239
Women's and Girls' Cut and Sew Suit, Coat, Tailored Jacket, and Skirt Manufacturing	315234
Women's Clothing Stores	448120
Women's Footwear (except Athletic) Manufacturing	316214
Women's Handbag and Purse Manufacturing	316992
Women's, Children's, and Infants' Clothing and Accessories Wholesalers	422330
Women's, Girls', and Infants' Cut and Sew Apparel Contractors	315212
Wood Container and Pallet Manufacturing	321920
Wood Kitchen Cabinet and Countertop Manufacturing	337110
Wood Office Furniture Manufacturing	337211
Wood Preservation	321114
Wood Television, Radio and Sewing Machine Cabinet Manufacturing	337129
Wood Window and Door Manufacturing	321911
Wrecking and Demolition Contractors	235940

Y

| Yarn Spinning Mills | 313111 |
| Yarn Texturizing, Throwing, and Twisting Mills | 313112 |

Z

| Zoos and Botanical Gardens | 712130 |

NUMERICAL COMPENDIUM OF N.A.I.C.S. CODES

North American Industry Classification System Manual, 2022, U.S. Government Office of Management and Budget; All codes for manufacturing unless otherwise stated.

N.A.I.C.S.	Description
111120	Oilseed (except Soybean) Farming
111130	Dry Pea and Bean Farming
111110	Soybean Farming
111140	Wheat Farming
111150	Corn Farming
111160	Rice Farming
111191	Oilseed and Grain Combination Farming
111199	All Other Grain Farming
111211	Potato Farming
111219	Other Vegetable (except Potato) and Melon Farming
111310	Orange Groves
111320	Citrus (except Orange) Groves
111331	Apple Orchards
111332	Grape Vineyards
111333	Strawberry Farming
111334	Berry (except Strawberry) Farming
111335	Tree Nut Farming
111336	Fruit and Tree Nut Combination Farming
111339	Other Noncitrus Fruit Farming
111411	Mushroom Production
111419	Other Food Crops Grown Under Cover
111421	Nursery and Tree Production
111422	Floriculture Production
111910	Tobacco Farming
111920	Cotton Farming
111930	Sugarcane Farming
111940	Hay Farming
111991	Sugar Beet Farming
111992	Peanut Farming
111998	All Other Miscellaneous Crop Farming
112111	Beef Cattle Ranching and Farming
112112	Cattle Feedlots
112120	Dairy Cattle and Milk Production
112130	Dual Purpose Cattle Ranching and Farming
112210	Hog and Pig Farming
112310	Chicken Egg Production
112320	Broilers and Other Meat Type Chicken Production
112330	Turkey Production
112390	Other Poultry Production
112420	Goat Farming
112512	Shellfish Farming
112519	Other Animal Aquaculture
112930	Fur-Bearing Animal and Rabbit Production
112990	All Other Animal Production
113210	Forest Nurseries and Gathering of Forest Products
113310	Logging
114112	Shellfish Fishing
114210	Hunting and Trapping
115112	Soil Preparation, Planting, and Cultivating
115114	Postharvest Crop Activities (except Cotton Ginning)
115115	Farm Labor Contractors and Crew Leaders
115210	Support Activities for Animal Production
211111	Crude Petroleum and Natural Gas Extraction
211112	Natural Gas Liquid Extraction
212112	Bituminous Coal Underground Mining
212113	Anthracite Mining
212221	Gold Ore Mining
212231	Lead Ore and Zinc Ore Mining
212291	Uranium-Radium-Vanadium Ore Mining
212299	All Other Metal Ore Mining
212312	Crushed and Broken Limestone Mining and Quarrying
212313	Crushed and Broken Granite Mining and Quarrying
212321	Construction Sand and Gravel Mining
212322	Industrial Sand Mining
212324	Kaolin and Ball Clay Mining
212391	Potash, Soda, and Borate Mineral Mining
212392	Phosphate Rock Mining
212393	Other Chemical and Fertilizer Mineral Mining
213111	Drilling Oil and Gas Wells
213112	Support Activities for Oil and Gas Operations
213114	Support Activities for Metal Mining
213115	Support Activities for Nonmetallic Minerals (except Fuels)
221112	Fossil Fuel Electric Power Generation
221113	Nuclear Electric Power Generation
221121	Electric Bulk Power Transmission and Control
221122	Electric Power Distribution
221310	Water Supply and Irrigation Systems
221330	Steam and Air-Conditioning Supply
233210	Single Family Housing Construction
233220	Multifamily Housing Construction

N.A.I.C.S.	Description
233310	Manufacturing and Industrial Building Construction
234110	Highway and Street Construction
234120	Bridge and Tunnel Construction
234910	Water, Sewer, and Pipeline Construction
234920	Power and Communication Transmission Line Construction
234930	Industrial Nonbuilding Structure Construction
235110	Plumbing, Heating, and Air-Conditioning Contractors
235410	Masonry and Stone Contractors
235420	Drywall, Plastering, Acoustical, and Insulation Contractors
235430	Tile, Marble, Terrazzo, and Mosaic Contractors
235510	Carpentry Contractors
235520	Floor Laying and Other Floor Contractors
235610	Roofing, Siding, and Sheet Metal Contractors
235710	Concrete Contractors
235810	Water Well Drilling Contractors
235910	Structural Steel Erection Contractors
235930	Excavation Contractors
235940	Wrecking and Demolition Contractors
235950	Building Equipment and Other Machinery Installation Contractors
235990	All Other Special Trade Contractors
311111	Dog and Cat Food Manufacturing
311119	Other Animal Food Manufacturing
311211	Flour Milling
311212	Rice Milling
311213	Malt Manufacturing
311221	Wet Corn Milling
311222	Soybean Processing
311223	Other Oilseed Processing
311225	Fats and Oils Refining and Blending
311230	Breakfast Cereal Manufacturing
311311	Sugarcane Mills
311312	Cane Sugar Refining
311320	Chocolate and Confectionery Manufacturing from Cacao Beans
311340	Nonchocolate Confectionery Manufacturing
311411	Frozen Fruit, Juice, and Vegetable Manufacturing
311412	Frozen Specialty Food Manufacturing
311422	Specialty Canning
311423	Dried and Dehydrated Food Manufacturing
311512	Creamery Butter Manufacturing
311514	Dry, Condensed, and Evaporated Dairy Product Manufacturing
311611	Animal (except Poultry) Slaughtering
311612	Meat Processed from Carcasses
311613	Rendering and Meat Byproduct Processing
311711	Seafood Canning
311811	Retail Bakeries
311812	Commercial Bakeries
311821	Cookie and Cracker Manufacturing
311822	Flour Mixes and Dough Manufacturing from Purchased Flour
311823	Dry Pasta Manufacturing
311911	Roasted Nuts and Peanut Butter Manufacturing
311920	Coffee and Tea Manufacturing
311930	Flavoring Syrup and Concentrate Manufacturing
311942	Spice and Extract Manufacturing
311991	Perishable Prepared Food Manufacturing
311999	All Other Miscellaneous Food Manufacturing
312111	Soft Drink Manufacturing
312112	Bottled Water Manufacturing
312120	Breweries
312210	Tobacco Stemming and Redrying
312229	Other Tobacco Product Manufacturing
313112	Yarn Texturizing, Throwing, and Twisting Mills
313210	Broadwoven Fabric Mills
313222	Schiffli Machine Embroidery
313241	Weft Knit Fabric Mills
313311	Broadwoven Fabric Finishing Mills
313312	Textile and Fabric Finishing (except Broadwoven Fabric) Mills
314110	Carpet and Rug Mills
314129	Other Household Textile Product Mills
314911	Textile Bag Mills
314991	Rope, Cordage, and Twine Mills
314992	Tire Cord and Tire Fabric Mills
315111	Sheer Hosiery Mills
315119	Other Hosiery and Sock Mills
315192	Underwear and Nightwear Knitting Mills
315211	Men's and Boys' Cut and Sew Apparel Contractors
315221	Men's and Boys' Cut and Sew Underwear and Nightwear Manufacturing
315222	Men's and Boys' Cut and Sew Suit, Coat, and Overcoat Manufacturing
315223	Men's and Boys' Cut and Sew Shirt (except Work Shirt)

3089

Numerical N.A.I.C.S. Compendium-continued

N.A.I.C.S.	Description
	Manufacturing
315225	Men's and Boys' Cut and Sew Work Clothing Manufacturing
315228	Men's and Boys' Cut and Sew Other Outerwear Manufacturing
315231	Women's and Girls' Cut and Sew Lingerie, Loungewear, and Nightwear Manufacturing
315232	Women's and Girls' Cut and Sew Blouse and Shirt Manufacturing
315234	Women's and Girls' Cut and Sew Suit, Coat, Tailored Jacket, and Skirt Manufacturing
315239	Women's and Girls' Cut and Sew Other Outerwear Manufacturing
315291	Infants' Cut and Sew Apparel Manufacturing
315299	All Other Cut and Sew Apparel Manufacturing
315991	Hat, Cap, and Millinery Manufacturing
315993	Men's and Boys' Neckwear Manufacturing
315999	Other Apparel Accessories and Other Apparel Manufacturing
316211	Rubber and Plastics Footwear Manufacturing
316212	House Slipper Manufacturing
316214	Women's Footwear (except Athletic) Manufacturing
316219	Other Footwear Manufacturing
316991	Luggage Manufacturing
316993	Personal Leather Good (except Women's Handbag and Purse) Manufacturing
316999	All Other Leather Good Manufacturing
321114	Wood Preservation
321212	Softwood Veneer and Plywood Manufacturing
321213	Engineered Wood Member (except Truss) Manufacturing
321219	Reconstituted Wood Product Manufacturing
321912	Cut Stock, Resawing Lumber, and Planing
321918	Other Millwork (including Flooring)
321991	Manufactured Home (Mobile Home) Manufacturing
321992	Prefabricated Wood Building Manufacturing
321999	All Other Miscellaneous Wood Product Manufacturing
322122	Newsprint Mills
322130	Paperboard Mills
322212	Folding Paperboard Box Manufacturing
322213	Setup Paperboard Box Manufacturing
322214	Fiber Can, Tube, Drum, and Similar Products Manufacturing
322221	Coated and Laminated Packaging Paper and Plastics Film Manufacturing
322222	Coated and Laminated Paper Manufacturing
322224	Uncoated Paper and Multiwall Bag Manufacturing
322225	Laminated Aluminum Foil Manufacturing for Flexible Packaging Uses
322226	Surface-Coated Paperboard Manufacturing
322232	Envelope Manufacturing
322233	Stationery, Tablet, and Related Product Manufacturing
322291	Sanitary Paper Product Manufacturing
322299	All Other Converted Paper Product Manufacturing
323111	Commercial Gravure Printing
323112	Commercial Flexographic Printing
323114	Quick Printing
323116	Manifold Business Forms Printing
323118	Blankbook, Looseleaf Binders, and Devices Manufacturing
323121	Tradebinding and Related Work
324110	Petroleum Refineries
324121	Asphalt Shingle and Coating Materials Manufacturing
324191	Petroleum Lubricating Oil and Grease Manufacturing
324199	All Other Petroleum and Coal Products Manufacturing
325120	Industrial Gas Manufacturing
325131	Inorganic Dye and Pigment Manufacturing
325181	Alkalies and Chlorine Manufacturing
325182	Carbon Black Manufacturing
325188	All Other Basic Inorganic Chemical Manufacturing
325192	Cyclic Crude and Intermediate Manufacturing
325193	Ethyl Alcohol Manufacturing
325211	Plastics Material and Resin Manufacturing
325212	Synthetic Rubber Manufacturing
325222	Noncellulosic Organic Fiber Manufacturing
325311	Nitrogenous Fertilizer Manufacturing
325312	Phosphatic Fertilizer Manufacturing
325320	Pesticide and Other Agricultural Chemical Manufacturing
325411	Medicinal and Botanical Manufacturing
325413	In-Vitro Diagnostic Substance Manufacturing
325414	Biological Product (except Diagnostic) Manufacturing
325520	Adhesive Manufacturing
325611	Soap and Other Detergent Manufacturing
325613	Surface Active Agent Manufacturing
325620	Toilet Preparation Manufacturing
325910	Printing Ink Manufacturing
325991	Custom Compounding of Purchased Resins
325998	All Other Miscellaneous Chemical Product and Preparation Manufacturing
326111	Unsupported Plastics Bag Manufacturing
326112	Unsupported Plastics Packaging Film and Sheet Manufacturing
326113	Unsupported Plastics Film and Sheet (except Packaging) Manufacturing
326122	Plastics Pipe and Pipe Fitting Manufacturing
326130	Laminated Plastics Plate, Sheet, and Shape Manufacturing
326150	Urethane and Other Foam Product (except Polystyrene) Manufacturing
326160	Plastics Bottle Manufacturing
326191	Plastics Plumbing Fixture Manufacturing
326199	All Other Plastics Product Manufacturing
326211	Tire Manufacturing (except Retreading)
326220	Rubber and Plastics Hoses and Belting Manufacturing
326299	All Other Rubber Product Manufacturing
327111	Vitreous China Plumbing Fixture and China and Earthenware Bathroom Accessories Manufacturing
327112	Vitreous China, Fine Earthenware, and Other Pottery Product Manufacturing
327113	Porcelain Electrical Supply Manufacturing
327121	Brick and Structural Clay Tile Manufacturing
327122	Ceramic Wall and Floor Tile Manufacturing
327123	Other Structural Clay Product Manufacturing
327124	Clay Refractory Manufacturing
327125	Nonclay Refractory Manufacturing
327211	Flat Glass Manufacturing
327212	Other Pressed and Blown Glass and Glassware Manufacturing
327213	Glass Container Manufacturing
327215	Glass Product Manufacturing Made of Purchased Glass
327310	Cement Manufacturing
327320	Ready-Mix Concrete Manufacturing
327331	Concrete Block and Brick Manufacturing
327332	Concrete Pipe Manufacturing
327390	Other Concrete Product Manufacturing
327410	Lime Manufacturing
327420	Gypsum Product Manufacturing
327910	Abrasive Product Manufacturing
327991	Cut Stone and Stone Product Manufacturing
327992	Ground or Treated Mineral and Earth Manufacturing
327993	Mineral Wool Manufacturing
327999	All Other Miscellaneous Nonmetallic Mineral Product Manufacturing
331111	Iron and Steel Mills
331112	Electrometallurgical Ferroalloy Product Manufacturing
331210	Iron and Steel Pipe and Tube Manufacturing from Purchased Steel
331221	Rolled Steel Shape Manufacturing
331222	Steel Wire Drawing
331311	Alumina Refining
331312	Primary Aluminum Production
331314	Secondary Smelting and Alloying of Aluminum
331315	Aluminum Sheet, Plate, and Foil Manufacturing
331316	Aluminum Extruded Product Manufacturing
331319	Other Aluminum Rolling and Drawing
331411	Primary Smelting and Refining of Copper
331419	Primary Smelting and Refining of Nonferrous Metal (except Copper and Aluminum)
331421	Copper Rolling, Drawing, and Extruding
331422	Copper Wire (except Mechanical) Drawing
331423	Secondary Smelting, Refining, and Alloying of Copper
331491	Nonferrous Metal (except Copper and Aluminum) Rolling, Drawing, and Extruding
331492	Secondary Smelting, Refining, and Alloying of Nonferrous Metal (except Copper and Aluminum)
331511	Iron Foundries
331512	Steel Investment Foundries
331513	Steel Foundries (except Investment)
331521	Aluminum Die-Casting Foundries
331522	Nonferrous (except Aluminum) Die-Casting Foundries
331524	Aluminum Foundries (except Die-Casting)
331528	Other Nonferrous Foundries (except Die-Casting)
332111	Iron and Steel Forging
332114	Custom Roll Forming
332116	Metal Stamping
332117	Powder Metallurgy Part Manufacturing
332212	Hand and Edge Tool Manufacturing
332213	Saw Blade and Handsaw Manufacturing
332214	Kitchen Utensil, Pot, and Pan Manufacturing
332312	Fabricated Structural Metal Manufacturing
332313	Plate Work Manufacturing
332321	Metal Window and Door Manufacturing
332323	Ornamental and Architectural Metal Work Manufacturing
332410	Power Boiler and Heat Exchanger Manufacturing

Numerical N.A.I.C.S. Compendium-continued

N.A.I.C.S.	Description
332431	Metal Can Manufacturing
332439	Other Metal Container Manufacturing
332510	Hardware Manufacturing
332612	Spring (Light Gauge) Manufacturing
332618	Other Fabricated Wire Product Manufacturing
332721	Precision Turned Product Manufacturing
332811	Metal Heat Treating
332812	Metal Coating, Engraving (except Jewelry and Silverware), and Allied Services to Manufacturers
332813	Electroplating, Plating, Polishing, Anodizing, and Coloring
332912	Fluid Power Valve and Hose Fitting Manufacturing
332913	Plumbing Fixture Fitting and Trim Manufacturing
332991	Ball and Roller Bearing Manufacturing
332992	Small Arms Ammunition Manufacturing
332993	Ammunition (except Small Arms) Manufacturing
332995	Other Ordnance and Accessories Manufacturing
332997	Industrial Pattern Manufacturing
332998	Enameled Iron and Metal Sanitary Ware Manufacturing
332999	All Other Miscellaneous Fabricated Metal Product Manufacturing
333112	Lawn and Garden Tractor and Home Lawn and Garden Equipment Manufacturing
333120	Construction Machinery Manufacturing
333132	Oil and Gas Field Machinery and Equipment Manufacturing
333210	Sawmill and Woodworking Machinery Manufacturing
333220	Plastics and Rubber Industry Machinery Manufacturing
333292	Textile Machinery Manufacturing
333293	Printing Machinery and Equipment Manufacturing
333295	Semiconductor Machinery Manufacturing
333298	All Other Industrial Machinery Manufacturing
333312	Commercial Laundry, Drycleaning, and Pressing Machine Manufacturing
333313	Office Machinery Manufacturing
333315	Photographic and Photocopying Equipment Manufacturing
333319	Other Commercial and Service Industry Machinery Manufacturing
333411	Air Purification Equipment Manufacturing
333414	Heating Equipment (except Warm Air Furnaces) Manufacturing
333415	Air-Conditioning and Warm Air Heating Equipment and Commercial and Industrial Refrigeration Equipment Manufacturing
333511	Industrial Mold Manufacturing
333513	Machine Tool (Metal Forming Types) Manufacturing
333514	Special Die and Tool, Die Set, Jig, and Fixture Manufacturing
333515	Cutting Tool and Machine Tool Accessory Manufacturing
333518	Other Metalworking Machinery Manufacturing
333611	Turbine and Turbine Generator Set Units Manufacturing
333612	Speed Changer, Industrial High-Speed Drive, and Gear Manufacturing
333618	Other Engine Equipment Manufacturing
333911	Pump and Pumping Equipment Manufacturing
333912	Air and Gas Compressor Manufacturing
333921	Elevator and Moving Stairway Manufacturing
333922	Conveyor and Conveying Equipment Manufacturing
333924	Industrial Truck, Tractor, Trailer, and Stacker Machinery Manufacturing
333991	Power-Driven Handtool Manufacturing
333992	Welding and Soldering Equipment Manufacturing
333993	Packaging Machinery Manufacturing
333995	Fluid Power Cylinder and Actuator Manufacturing
333996	Fluid Power Pump and Motor Manufacturing
333997	Scale and Balance (except Laboratory) Manufacturing
334111	Electronic Computer Manufacturing
334112	Computer Storage Device Manufacturing
334113	Computer Terminal Manufacturing
334119	Other Computer Peripheral Equipment Manufacturing
334220	Radio and Television Broadcasting and Wireless Communications Equipment Manufacturing
334290	Other Communications Equipment Manufacturing
334411	Electron Tube Manufacturing
334412	Bare Printed Circuit Board Manufacturing
334414	Electronic Capacitor Manufacturing
334415	Electronic Resistor Manufacturing
334416	Electronic Coil, Transformer, and Other Inductor Manufacturing
334418	Printed Circuit Assembly (Electronic Assembly) Manufacturing
334419	Other Electronic Component Manufacturing
334511	Search, Detection, Navigation, Guidance, Aeronautical, and Nautical System and Instrument Manufacturing
334512	Automatic Environmental Control Manufacturing for Residential, Commercial, and Appliance Use
334513	Instruments and Related Products Manufacturing for Measuring, Displaying, and Controlling Industrial Process Variables
334515	Instrument Manufacturing for Measuring and Testing Electricity and Electrical Signals
334516	Analytical Laboratory Instrument Manufacturing
334517	Irradiation Apparatus Manufacturing
334518	Watch, Clock, and Part Manufacturing
334611	Software Reproducing
334612	Prerecorded Compact Disc (except Software), Tape, and Record Reproducing
334613	Magnetic and Optical Recording Media Manufacturing
335121	Residential Electric Lighting Fixture Manufacturing
335122	Commercial, Industrial, and Institutional Electric Lighting Fixture Manufacturing
335211	Electric Housewares and Household Fan Manufacturing
335212	Household Vacuum Cleaner Manufacturing
335222	Household Refrigerator and Home Freezer Manufacturing
335224	Household Laundry Equipment Manufacturing
335228	Other Major Household Appliance Manufacturing
335312	Motor and Generator Manufacturing
335313	Switchgear and Switchboard Apparatus Manufacturing
335314	Relay and Industrial Control Manufacturing
335912	Primary Battery Manufacturing
335921	Fiber Optic Cable Manufacturing
335931	Current-Carrying Wiring Device Manufacturing
335932	Noncurrent-Carrying Wiring Device Manufacturing
335991	Carbon and Graphite Product Manufacturing
336111	Automobile Manufacturing
336112	Light Truck and Utility Vehicle Manufacturing
336120	Heavy Duty Truck Manufacturing
336211	Motor Vehicle Body Manufacturing
336213	Motor Home Manufacturing
336214	Travel Trailer and Camper Manufacturing
336312	Gasoline Engine and Engine Parts Manufacturing
336321	Vehicular Lighting Equipment Manufacturing
336322	Other Motor Vehicle Electrical and Electronic Equipment Manufacturing
336330	Motor Vehicle Steering and Suspension Components (except Spring) Manufacturing
336350	Motor Vehicle Transmission and Power Train Parts Manufacturing
336360	Motor Vehicle Seating and Interior Trim Manufacturing
336391	Motor Vehicle Air-Conditioning Manufacturing
336399	All Other Motor Vehicle Parts Manufacturing
336411	Aircraft Manufacturing
336413	Other Aircraft Parts and Auxiliary Equipment Manufacturing
336414	Guided Missile and Space Vehicle Manufacturing
336415	Guided Missile and Space Vehicle Propulsion Unit and Propulsion Unit Parts Manufacturing
336510	Railroad Rolling Stock Manufacturing
336611	Ship Building and Repairing
336612	Boat Building
336991	Motorcycle, Bicycle, and Parts Manufacturing
336992	Military Armored Vehicle, Tank, and Tank Component Manufacturing
337110	Wood Kitchen Cabinet and Countertop Manufacturing
337121	Upholstered Household Furniture Manufacturing
337124	Metal Household Furniture Manufacturing
337125	Household Furniture (except Wood and Metal) Manufacturing
337127	Institutional Furniture Manufacturing
337129	Wood Television, Radio, and Sewing Machine Cabinet Manufacturing
337212	Custom Architectural Woodwork and Millwork Manufacturing
337214	Office Furniture (except Wood) Manufacturing
337910	Mattress Manufacturing
337920	Blind and Shade Manufacturing
339111	Laboratory Apparatus and Furniture Manufacturing
339113	Surgical Appliance and Supplies Manufacturing
339114	Dental Equipment and Supplies Manufacturing
339115	Ophthalmic Goods Manufacturing
339911	Jewelry (except Costume) Manufacturing
339913	Jewelers' Material and Lapidary Work Manufacturing
339914	Costume Jewelry and Novelty Manufacturing
339931	Doll and Stuffed Toy Manufacturing
339932	Game, Toy, and Children's Vehicle Manufacturing
339942	Lead Pencil and Art Good Manufacturing
339943	Marking Device Manufacturing
339944	Carbon Paper and Inked Ribbon Manufacturing
339991	Gasket, Packing, and Sealing Device Manufacturing
339993	Fastener, Button, Needle, and Pin Manufacturing
339994	Broom, Brush, and Mop Manufacturing
339999	All Other Miscellaneous Manufacturing
421110	Automobile and Other Motor Vehicle Wholesalers
421120	Motor Vehicle Supplies and New Parts Wholesalers
421130	Tire and Tube Wholesalers
421140	Motor Vehicle Parts (Used) Wholesalers

3091

Numerical N.A.I.C.S. Compendium-continued

N.A.I.C.S.	Description
421210	Furniture Wholesalers
421220	Home Furnishing Wholesalers
421310	Lumber, Plywood, Millwork, and Wood Panel Wholesalers
421320	Brick, Stone, and Related Construction Material Wholesalers
421330	Roofing, Siding, and Insulation Material Wholesalers
421390	Other Construction Material Wholesalers
421410	Photographic Equipment and Supplies Wholesalers
421420	Office Equipment Wholesalers
421430	Computer and Computer Peripheral Equipment and Software Wholesalers
421440	Other Commercial Equipment Wholesalers
421450	Medical, Dental, and Hospital Equipment and Supplies Wholesalers
421460	Ophthalmic Goods Wholesalers
421490	Other Professional Equipment and Supplies Wholesalers
421510	Metal Service Centers and Offices
421520	Coal and Other Mineral and Ore Wholesalers
421610	Electrical Apparatus and Equipment, Wiring Supplies, and Construction Material Wholesalers
421620	Electrical Appliance, Television, and Radio Set Wholesalers
421690	Other Electronic Parts and Equipment Wholesalers
421710	Hardware Wholesalers
421720	Plumbing and Heating Equipment and Supplies (Hydronics) Wholesalers
421730	Warm Air Heating and Air-Conditioning Equipment and Supplies Wholesalers
421740	Refrigeration Equipment and Supplies Wholesalers
421810	Construction and Mining (except Oil Well) Machinery and Equipment Wholesalers
421820	Farm and Garden Machinery and Equipment Wholesalers
421830	Industrial Machinery and Equipment Wholesalers
421840	Industrial Supplies Wholesalers
421850	Service Establishment Equipment and Supplies Wholesalers
421860	Transportation Equipment and Supplies (except Motor Vehicle) Wholesalers
421910	Sporting and Recreational Goods and Supplies Wholesalers
421920	Toy and Hobby Goods and Supplies Wholesalers
421930	Recyclable Material Wholesalers
421940	Jewelry, Watch, Precious Stone, and Precious Metal Wholesalers
421990	Other Miscellaneous Durable Goods Wholesalers
422110	Printing and Writing Paper Wholesalers
422120	Stationery and Office Supplies Wholesalers
422130	Industrial and Personal Service Paper Wholesalers
422210	Drugs and Druggists' Sundries Wholesalers
422310	Piece Goods, Notions, and Other Dry Goods Wholesalers
422320	Men's and Boys' Clothing and Furnishings Wholesalers
422330	Women's, Children's, and Infants' Clothing and Accessories Wholesalers
422340	Footwear Wholesalers
422410	General Line Grocery Wholesalers
422420	Packaged Frozen Food Wholesalers
422430	Dairy Product (except Dried or Canned) Wholesalers
422440	Poultry and Poultry Product Wholesalers
422450	Confectionery Wholesalers
422460	Fish and Seafood Wholesalers
422470	Meat and Meat Product Wholesalers
422480	Fresh Fruit and Vegetable Wholesalers
422490	Other Grocery and Related Products Wholesalers
422510	Grain and Field Bean Wholesalers
422520	Livestock Wholesalers
422590	Other Farm Product Raw Material Wholesalers
422610	Plastics Materials and Basic Forms and Shapes Wholesalers
422720	Petroleum and Petroleum Products Wholesalers (except Bulk Stations and Terminals)
422810	Beer and Ale Wholesalers
422820	Wine and Distilled Alcoholic Beverage Wholesalers
422910	Farm Supplies Wholesalers
422920	Book, Periodical, and Newspaper Wholesalers
422930	Flower, Nursery Stock, and Florists' Supplies Wholesalers
422940	Tobacco and Tobacco Product Wholesalers
422950	Paint, Varnish, and Supplies Wholesalers
422990	Other Miscellaneous Nondurable Goods Wholesalers
441110	New Car Dealers
441120	Used Car Dealers
441221	Motorcycle Dealers
441222	Boat Dealers
441310	Automotive Parts and Accessories Stores
441320	Tire Dealers
442210	Floor Covering Stores
442299	All Other Home Furnishings Stores
443112	Radio, Television, and Other Electronics Stores
443120	Computer and Software Stores
444110	Home Centers
444120	Paint and Wallpaper Stores
444190	Other Building Material Dealers
444220	Nursery and Garden Centers
445110	Supermarkets and Other Grocery (except Convenience) Stores
445210	Meat Markets
445230	Fruit and Vegetable Markets
445292	Confectionery and Nut Stores
445310	Beer, Wine, and Liquor Stores
446110	Pharmacies and Drug Stores
446130	Optical Goods Stores
446191	Food (Health) Supplement Stores
446199	All Other Health and Personal Care Stores
447190	Other Gasoline Stations
448110	Men's Clothing Stores
448130	Children's and Infants' Clothing Stores
448150	Clothing Accessories Stores
448190	Other Clothing Stores
448320	Luggage and Leather Goods Stores
451120	Hobby, Toy, and Game Stores
451140	Musical Instrument and Supplies Stores
451211	Book Stores
451212	News Dealers and Newsstands
452110	Department Stores
452910	Warehouse Clubs and Superstores
452990	All Other General Merchandise Stores
453110	Florists
453220	Gift, Novelty, and Souvenir Stores
453310	Used Merchandise Stores
453920	Art Dealers
453930	Manufactured (Mobile) Home Dealers
454110	Electronic Shopping and Mail-Order Houses
454210	Vending Machine Operators
454311	Heating Oil Dealers
454312	Liquefied Petroleum Gas (Bottled Gas) Dealers
454319	Other Fuel Dealers
481111	Scheduled Passenger Air Transportation
481112	Scheduled Freight Air Transportation
481212	Nonscheduled Chartered Freight Air Transportation
481219	Other Nonscheduled Air Transportation
482111	Line-Haul Railroads
483111	Deep Sea Freight Transportation
483113	Coastal and Great Lakes Freight Transportation
483114	Coastal and Great Lakes Passenger Transportation
483212	Inland Water Passenger Transportation
484110	General Freight Trucking, Local
484122	General Freight Trucking, Long-Distance, Less Than Truckload
484210	Used Household and Office Goods Moving
484220	Specialized Freight (except Used Goods) Trucking, Local
485111	Mixed Mode Transit Systems
485112	Commuter Rail Systems
485113	Bus and Other Motor Vehicle Transit Systems
485119	Other Urban Transit Systems
485310	Taxi Service
485320	Limousine Service
485510	Charter Bus Industry
485999	All Other Transit and Ground Passenger Transportation
486110	Pipeline Transportation of Crude Oil
486210	Pipeline Transportation of Natural Gas
486910	Pipeline Transportation of Refined Petroleum Products
487110	Scenic and Sightseeing Transportation, Land
487210	Scenic and Sightseeing Transportation, Water
488111	Air Traffic Control
488119	Other Airport Operations
488210	Support Activities for Rail Transportation
488310	Port and Harbor Operations
488320	Marine Cargo Handling
488390	Other Support Activities for Water Transportation
488410	Motor Vehicle Towing
488510	Freight Transportation Arrangement
488991	Packing and Crating
488999	All Other Support Activities for Transportation
492110	Couriers
493110	General Warehousing and Storage
493120	Refrigerated Warehousing and Storage
493190	Other Warehousing and Storage
511110	Newspaper Publishers
511130	Book Publishers
511191	Greeting Card Publishers

Numerical N.A.I.C.S. Compendium-continued

N.A.I.C.S.	Description
511199	All Other Publishers
512110	Motion Picture and Video Production
512120	Motion Picture and Video Distribution
512132	Drive-In Motion Picture Theaters
512191	Teleproduction and Other Postproduction Services
512199	Other Motion Picture and Video Industries
512220	Integrated Record Production/Distribution
512240	Sound Recording Studios
513210	Cable Networks
513322	Cellular and Other Wireless Telecommunications
514191	On-Line Information Services
514210	Data Processing Services
521110	Monetary Authorities - Central Bank
522110	Commercial Banking
522130	Credit Unions
522210	Credit Card Issuing
522220	Sales Financing
522292	Real Estate Credit
522294	Secondary Market Financing
522298	All Other Nondepository Credit Intermediation
522320	Financial Transactions Processing, Reserve, and Clearinghouse Activities
522390	Other Activities Related to Credit Intermediation
523120	Securities Brokerage
523130	Commodity Contracts Dealing
523210	Securities and Commodity Exchanges
523910	Miscellaneous Intermediation
523930	Investment Advice
523999	Miscellaneous Financial Investment Activities
524113	Direct Life Insurance Carriers
524126	Direct Property and Casualty Insurance Carriers
524127	Direct Title Insurance Carriers
524128	Other Direct Insurance (except Life, Health, and Medical) Carriers
524210	Insurance Agencies and Brokerages
524292	Third Party Administration of Insurance and Pension Funds
525110	Pension Funds
525120	Health and Welfare Funds
525910	Open-End Investment Funds
525920	Trusts, Estates, and Agency Accounts
525990	Other Financial Vehicles
531120	Lessors of Nonresidential Buildings (except Miniwarehouses)
531130	Lessors of Miniwarehouses and Self-Storage Units
531190	Lessors of Other Real Estate Property
531311	Residential Property Managers
531312	Nonresidential Property Managers
531390	Other Activities Related to Real Estate
532110	Passenger Car Rental
532120	Truck, Utility Trailer, and RV (Recreational Vehicle) Rental and Leasing
532210	Consumer Electronics and Appliances Rental
532230	Video Tape and Disc Rental
532292	Recreational Goods Rental
532299	All Other Consumer Goods Rental
532310	General Rental Centers
532412	Construction, Mining, and Forestry Machinery and Equipment Rental and Leasing
532420	Office Machinery and Equipment Rental and Leasing
532490	Other Commercial and Industrial Machinery and Equipment Rental and Leasing
533110	Lessors of Nonfinancial Intangible Assets (except Copyrighted Works)
541110	Offices of Lawyers
541120	Offices of Notaries
541191	Title Abstract and Settlement Offices
541199	All Other Legal Services
541211	Offices of Certified Public Accountants
541213	Tax Preparation Services
541214	Payroll Services
541219	Other Accounting Services
541310	Architectural Services
541320	Landscape Architectural Services
541330	Engineering Services
541340	Drafting Services
541350	Building Inspection Services
541360	Geophysical Surveying and Mapping Services
541370	Surveying and Mapping (except Geophysical) Services
541380	Testing Laboratories
541410	Interior Design Services
541420	Industrial Design Services
541430	Graphic Design Services

N.A.I.C.S.	Description
541490	Other Specialized Design Services
541511	Custom Computer Programming Services
541512	Computer Systems Design Services
541513	Computer Facilities Management Services
541519	Other Computer Related Services
541611	Administrative Management and General Management Consulting Services
541612	Human Resources and Executive Search Consulting Services
541613	Marketing Consulting Services
541614	Process, Physical Distribution, and Logistics Consulting Services
541618	Other Management Consulting Services
541620	Environmental Consulting Services
541690	Other Scientific and Technical Consulting Services
541710	Research and Development in the Physical, Engineering, and Life Sciences
541720	Research and Development in the Social Sciences and Humanities
541810	Advertising Agencies
541820	Public Relations Agencies
541830	Media Buying Agencies
541840	Media Representatives
541850	Display Advertising
541860	Direct Mail Advertising
541870	Advertising Material Distribution Services
541890	Other Services Related to Advertising
541910	Marketing Research and Public Opinion Polling
541921	Photography Studios, Portrait
541922	Commercial Photography
541930	Translation and Interpretation Services
541940	Veterinary Services
551111	Offices of Bank Holding Companies
551112	Offices of Other Holding Companies
551114	Corporate, Subsidiary, and Regional Managing Offices
561210	Facilities Support Services
561310	Employment Placement Agencies
561330	Employee Leasing Services
561421	Telephone Answering Services
561422	Telemarketing Bureaus
561439	Other Business Service Centers (including Copy Shops)
561450	Credit Bureaus
561492	Court Reporting and Stenotype Services
561510	Travel Agencies
561520	Tour Operators
561599	All Other Travel Arrangement and Reservation Services
561611	Investigation Services
561612	Security Guards and Patrol Services
561613	Armored Car Services
561621	Security Systems Services (except Locksmiths)
561622	Locksmiths
561710	Exterminating and Pest Control Services
561720	Janitorial Services
561730	Landscaping Services
561740	Carpet and Upholstery Cleaning Services
561790	Other Services to Buildings and Dwellings
561910	Packaging and Labeling Services
561920	Convention and Trade Show Organizers
561990	All Other Support Services
562111	Solid Waste Collection
562112	Hazardous Waste Collection
562119	Other Waste Collection
562211	Hazardous Waste Treatment and Disposal
562212	Solid Waste Landfill
562213	Solid Waste Combustors and Incinerators
562219	Other Nonhazardous Waste Treatment and Disposal
562910	Remediation Services
562920	Materials Recovery Facilities
562991	Septic Tank and Related Services
562998	All Other Miscellaneous Waste Management Services
611110	Elementary and Secondary Schools
611210	Junior Colleges
611310	Colleges, Universities, and Professional Schools
611410	Business and Secretarial Schools
611420	Computer Training
611430	Professional and Management Development Training
611511	Cosmetology and Barber Schools
611512	Flight Training
611513	Apprenticeship Training
611519	Other Technical and Trade Schools
611610	Fine Arts Schools
611620	Sports and Recreation Instruction
611630	Language Schools

3093

Numerical N.A.I.C.S. Compendium-continued

N.A.I.C.S.	Description
611691	Exam Preparation and Tutoring
611692	Automobile Driving Schools
611699	All Other Miscellaneous Schools and Instruction
611710	Educational Support Services
621111	Offices of Physicians (except Mental Health Specialists)
621210	Offices of Dentists
621310	Offices of Chiropractors
621320	Offices of Optometrists
621340	Offices of Physical, Occupational and Speech Therapists, and Audiologists
621391	Offices of Podiatrists
621399	Offices of All Other Miscellaneous Health Practitioners
621420	Outpatient Mental Health and Substance Abuse Centers
621492	Kidney Dialysis Centers
621498	All Other Outpatient Care Centers
621511	Medical Laboratories
621512	Diagnostic Imaging Centers
621610	Home Health Care Services
621910	Ambulance Services
621991	Blood and Organ Banks
621999	All Other Miscellaneous Ambulatory Health Care Services
622110	General Medical and Surgical Hospitals
622210	Psychiatric and Substance Abuse Hospitals
622310	Specialty (except Psychiatric and Substance Abuse) Hospitals
623110	Nursing Care Facilities
623210	Residential Mental Retardation Facilities
623220	Residential Mental Health and Substance Abuse Facilities
623311	Continuing Care Retirement Communities
623312	Homes for the Elderly
623990	Other Residential Care Facilities
624110	Child and Youth Services
624120	Services for the Elderly and Persons with Disabilities
624190	Other Individual and Family Services
624210	Community Food Services
624221	Temporary Shelters
624229	Other Community Housing Services
624230	Emergency and Other Relief Services
624310	Vocational Rehabilitation Services
624410	Child Day Care Services
711110	Theater Companies and Dinner Theaters
711120	Dance Companies
711130	Musical Groups and Artists
711190	Other Performing Arts Companies
711211	Sports Teams and Clubs
711212	Racetracks
711219	Other Spectator Sports
711310	Promoters of Performing Arts, Sports, and Similar Events with Facilities
711320	Promoters of Performing Arts, Sports, and Similar Events without Facilities
711410	Agents and Managers for Artists, Athletes, Entertainers, and Other Public Figures
711510	Independent Artists, Writers, and Performers
712110	Museums
712120	Historical Sites
712130	Zoos and Botanical Gardens
712190	Nature Parks and Other Similar Institutions
713110	Amusement and Theme Parks
713120	Amusement Arcades
713210	Casinos (except Casino Hotels)
713290	Other Gambling Industries
713910	Golf Courses and Country Clubs
713920	Skiing Facilities
713930	Marinas
713940	Fitness and Recreational Sports Centers
713950	Bowling Centers
713990	All Other Amusement and Recreation Industries
721110	Hotels (except Casino Hotels) and Motels
721120	Casino Hotels
721191	Bed-and-Breakfast Inns
721199	All Other Traveler Accommodation
721211	RV (Recreational Vehicle) Parks and Campgrounds
721214	Recreational and Vacation Camps (except Campgrounds)
721310	Rooming and Boarding Houses
722110	Full-Service Restaurants
722211	Fast Food Restaurants
722212	Cafeterias
722213	Snack and Nonalcoholic Beverage Bars
722310	Food Service Contractors
722320	Caterers
722330	Mobile Food Services
722410	Drinking Places (Alcoholic Beverages)
811111	General Automotive Repair
811112	Automotive Exhaust System Repair
811113	Automotive Transmission Repair
811118	Other Automotive Mechanical and Electrical Repair and Maintenance
811121	Automotive Body, Paint, and Interior Repair and Maintenance
811122	Automotive Glass Replacement Shops
811191	Automotive Oil Change and Lubrication Shops
811192	Car Washes
811198	All Other Automotive Repair and Maintenance
811211	Consumer Electronics Repair and Maintenance
811212	Computer and Office Machine Repair and Maintenance
811213	Communication Equipment Repair and Maintenance
811219	Other Electronic and Precision Equipment Repair and Maintenance
811310	Commercial and Industrial Machinery and Equipment (except Automotive and Electronic) Repair and Maintenance
811411	Home and Garden Equipment Repair and Maintenance
811412	Appliance Repair and Maintenance
811420	Reupholstery and Furniture Repair
811430	Footwear and Leather Goods Repair
811490	Other Personal and Household Goods Repair and Maintenance
812111	Barber Shops
812112	Beauty Salons
812113	Nail Salons
812191	Diet and Weight Reducing Centers
812199	Other Personal Care Services
812210	Funeral Homes and Funeral Services
812220	Cemeteries and Crematories
812310	Coin-Operated Laundries and Drycleaners
812320	Drycleaning and Laundry Services (except Coin-Operated)
812331	Linen Supply
812332	Industrial Launderers
812910	Pet Care (except Veterinary) Services
812921	Photofinishing Laboratories (except One-Hour)
812922	One-Hour Photofinishing
812930	Parking Lots and Garages
812990	All Other Personal Services
813110	Religious Organizations
813211	Grantmaking Foundations
813212	Voluntary Health Organizations
813219	Other Grantmaking and Giving Services
813311	Human Rights Organizations
813312	Environment, Conservation and Wildlife Organizations
813319	Other Social Advocacy Organizations
813410	Civic and Social Organizations
813910	Business Associations
813920	Professional Organizations
813930	Labor Unions and Similar Labor Organizations
813940	Political Organizations
813990	Other Similar Organizations (except Business, Professional, Labor, and Political Organizations)
814110	Private Households
921110	Executive Offices
921120	Legislative Bodies
921130	Public Finance Activities
921140	Executive and Legislative Offices, Combined
921150	American Indian and Alaska Native Tribal Governments
921190	Other General Government Support
922110	Courts
922120	Police Protection
922130	Legal Counsel and Prosecution
922140	Correctional Institutions
922150	Parole Offices and Probation Offices
922160	Fire Protection
922190	Other Justice, Public Order, and Safety Activities
923110	Administration of Education Programs
923120	Administration of Public Health Programs
923130	Administration of Human Resource Programs (except Education, Public Health, and Veterans' Affairs Programs)
923140	Administration of Veterans' Affairs
924110	Administration of Air and Water Resource and Solid Waste Management Programs
924120	Administration of Conservation Programs
925110	Administration of Housing Programs
925120	Administration of Urban Planning and Community and Rural Development
926110	Administration of General Economic Programs
926120	Regulation and Administration of Transportation Programs
926130	Regulation and Administration of Communications, Electric, Gas, and

Numerical N.A.I.C.S. Compendium-continued

N.A.I.C.S.	Description
	Other Utilities
926140	Regulation of Agricultural Marketing and Commodities
926150	Regulation, Licensing, and Inspection of Miscellaneous Commercial Sectors
927110	Space Research and Technology
928110	National Security
928120	International Affairs
999990	Unclassified Establishments
238910	Site Preparation Contractors
236115	New Single-Family Housing Construction (except Operative Builders)
236220	Commercial and Institutional Building Construction
236116	New Multifamily Housing Construction (except Operative Builders)
236117	New Housing Operative Builders
236210	Industrial Building Construction
237310	Highway, Street, and Bridge Construction
237990	Other Heavy and Civil Engineering Construction
237130	Power and Communication Line and Related Structures Construction
237110	Water and Sewer Line and Related Structures Construction
238210	Electrical Contractors
238320	Painting and Wall Covering Contractors
238310	Drywall and Insulation Contractors
238340	Tile and Terrazzo Contractors
238130	Framing Contractors
238330	Flooring Contractors
238390	Other Building Finishing Contractors
238160	Roofing Contractors
238990	All Other Specialty Trade Contractors
238110	Poured Concrete Foundation and Structure Contractors
238140	Masonry Contractors
238120	Structural Steel and Precast Concrete Contractors
238190	Other Foundation, Structure, and Building Exterior Contractors
238290	Other Building Equipment Contractors
517310	Telecommunications Resellers
517110	Wired Telecommunications Carriers
515112	Radio Stations
515111	Radio Networks
515120	Television Broadcasting
515210	Cable and Other Subscription Programming
425120	Wholesale Trade Agents and Brokers
423100	Automobile and Other Motor Vehicle Merchant Wholesalers
425110	Business to Business Electronic Markets
423410	Photographic Equipment and Supplies Merchant Wholesalers
423440	Other Commercial Equipment Merchant Wholesalers
423460	Ophthalmic Goods Merchant Wholesalers
423520	Coal and Other Mineral and Ore Merchant Wholesalers
423730	Warm Air Heating and Air-Conditioning Equipment and Supplies Merchant Wholesalers
423740	Refrigeration Equipment and Supplies Merchant Wholesalers
423810	Construction and Mining (except Oil Well) Machinery and Equipment Merchant Wholesalers
423830	Industrial Machinery and Equipment Merchant Wholesalers
423840	Industrial Supplies Merchant Wholesalers
423860	Transportation Equipment and Supplies (except Motor Vehicle) Merchant Wholesalers
424130	Industrial and Personal Service Paper Merchant Wholesalers
424420	Packaged Frozen Food Merchant Wholesalers
424520	Livestock Merchant Wholesalers
424690	Other Chemical and Allied Products Merchant Wholesalers
424720	Petroleum and Petroleum Products Merchant Wholesalers (except Bulk Stations and Terminals)
424950	Paint, Varnish, and Supplies Merchant Wholesalers
452112	Discount Department Stores
452111	Department Stores (except Discount Department Stores)
454111	Electronic Shopping
454113	Mail-Order Houses
237210	Land Subdivision
518210	Data Processing, Hosting, and Related Services
518111	Internet Service Providers
519120	Libraries and Archives
541990	All Other Professional, Scientific, and Technical Services
561110	Office Administrative Services
561320	Temporary Help Services
561410	Document Preparation Services
561431	Private Mail Centers
561440	Collection Agencies
561491	Repossession Services
561499	All Other Business Support Services
561591	Convention and Visitors Bureaus
621112	Offices of Physicians, Mental Health Specialists
621330	Offices of Mental Health Practitioners (except Physicians)

N.A.I.C.S.	Description
621410	Family Planning Centers
621491	HMO Medical Centers
621493	Freestanding Ambulatory Surgical and Emergency Centers
485991	Special Needs Transportation
486990	All Other Pipeline Transportation
487990	Scenic and Sightseeing Transportation, Other
488190	Other Support Activities for Air Transportation
488330	Navigational Services to Shipping
488490	Other Support Activities for Road Transportation
491110	Postal Service
492210	Local Messengers and Local Delivery
493130	Farm Product Warehousing and Storage
511120	Periodical Publishers
511140	Database and Directory Publishers
511210	Software Publishers
512131	Motion Picture Theaters (except Drive-Ins)
512210	Record Production
512230	Music Publishers
512290	Other Sound Recording Industries
517211	Paging
517510	Cable and Other Program Distribution
522120	Savings Institutions
522190	Other Depository Credit Intermediation
522291	Consumer Lending
522293	International Trade Financing
522310	Mortgage and Nonmortgage Loan Brokers
523110	Investment Banking and Securities Dealing
523140	Commodity Contracts Brokerage
523920	Portfolio Management
523991	Trust, Fiduciary, and Custody Activities
524114	Direct Health and Medical Insurance Carriers
524130	Reinsurance Carriers
524291	Claims Adjusting
524298	All Other Insurance Related Activities
525190	Other Insurance Funds
525930	Real Estate Investment Trusts
531110	Lessors of Residential Buildings and Dwellings
531210	Offices of Real Estate Agents and Brokers
531320	Offices of Real Estate Appraisers
532112	Passenger Car Leasing
532220	Formal Wear and Costume Rental
532291	Home Health Equipment Rental
532411	Commercial Air, Rail, and Water Transportation Equipment Rental and Leasing
424610	Plastics Materials and Basic Forms and Shapes Merchant Wholesalers
441210	Recreational Vehicle Dealers
441229	All Other Motor Vehicle Dealers
442110	Furniture Stores
442291	Window Treatment Stores
443111	Household Appliance Stores
443130	Camera and Photographic Supplies Stores
444110	Hardware Stores
444210	Outdoor Power Equipment Stores
445120	Convenience Stores
445220	Fish and Seafood Markets
445291	Baked Goods Stores
445299	All Other Specialty Food Stores
446120	Cosmetics, Beauty Supplies, and Perfume Stores
447110	Gasoline Stations with Convenience Stores
448120	Women's Clothing Stores
448140	Family Clothing Stores
448210	Shoe Stores
448310	Jewelry Stores
451110	Sporting Goods Stores
451130	Sewing, Needlework, and Piece Goods Stores
451220	Prerecorded Tape, Compact Disc, and Record Stores
453210	Office Supplies and Stationery Stores
453910	Pet and Pet Supplies Stores
453991	Tobacco Stores
453998	All Other Miscellaneous Store Retailers (except Tobacco Stores)
454112	Electronic Auctions
454390	Other Direct Selling Establishments
481211	Nonscheduled Chartered Passenger Air Transportation
482112	Short Line Railroads
483112	Deep Sea Passenger Transportation
483211	Inland Water Freight Transportation
484121	General Freight Trucking, Long-Distance, Truckload
484230	Specialized Freight (except Used Goods) Trucking, Long-Distance
485210	Interurban and Rural Bus Transportation

3095

Numerical N.A.I.C.S. Compendium-continued

N.A.I.C.S.	Description
485410	School and Employee Bus Transportation
238350	Finish Carpentry Contractors
112340	Poultry Hatcheries
112410	Sheep Farming
112511	Finfish Farming and Fish Hatcheries
112910	Apiculture
112920	Horse and Other Equine Production
113110	Timber Tract Operations
114111	Finfish Fishing
114119	Other Marine Fishing
115111	Cotton Ginning
115113	Crop Harvesting, Primarily by Machine
115116	Farm Management Services
115310	Support Activities for Forestry
212111	Bituminous Coal and Lignite Surface Mining
212210	Iron Ore Mining
212222	Silver Ore Mining
212234	Copper Ore and Nickel Ore Mining
212311	Dimension Stone Mining and Quarrying
212319	Other Crushed and Broken Stone Mining and Quarrying
212325	Clay and Ceramic and Refractory Minerals Mining
212399	All Other Nonmetallic Mineral Mining
213113	Support Activities for Coal Mining
221111	Hydroelectric Power Generation
221119	Other Electric Power Generation
221210	Natural Gas Distribution
221320	Sewage Treatment Facilities
236118	Residential Remodelers
237120	Oil and Gas Pipeline and Related Structures Construction
238170	Siding Contractors
311313	Beet Sugar Manufacturing
311330	Confectionery Manufacturing from Purchased Chocolate
311421	Fruit and Vegetable Canning
311511	Fluid Milk Manufacturing
311513	Cheese Manufacturing
311520	Ice Cream and Frozen Dessert Manufacturing
311615	Poultry Processing
311712	Fresh and Frozen Seafood Processing
311813	Frozen Cakes, Pies, and Other Pastries Manufacturing
311830	Tortilla Manufacturing
311919	Other Snack Food Manufacturing
311941	Mayonnaise, Dressing, and Other Prepared Sauce Manufacturing
312113	Ice Manufacturing
312130	Wineries
312140	Distilleries
312221	Cigarette Manufacturing
313111	Yarn Spinning Mills
313113	Thread Mills
313221	Narrow Fabric Mills
313230	Nonwoven Fabric Mills
313249	Other Knit Fabric and Lace Mills
313320	Fabric Coating Mills
314121	Curtain and Drapery Mills
314912	Canvas and Related Product Mills
314999	All Other Miscellaneous Textile Product Mills
315191	Outerwear Knitting Mills
315212	Women's, Girls', and Infants' Cut and Sew Apparel Contractors
315224	Men's and Boys' Cut and Sew Trouser, Slack, and Jean Manufacturing
315233	Women's and Girls' Cut and Sew Dress Manufacturing
315292	Fur and Leather Apparel Manufacturing
315992	Glove and Mitten Manufacturing
316110	Leather and Hide Tanning and Finishing
316213	Men's Footwear (except Athletic) Manufacturing
316992	Women's Handbag and Purse Manufacturing
321113	Sawmills
321211	Hardwood Veneer and Plywood Manufacturing
321214	Truss Manufacturing
321911	Wood Window and Door Manufacturing
321920	Wood Container and Pallet Manufacturing
322110	Pulp Mills
322121	Paper (except Newsprint) Mills
322211	Corrugated and Solid Fiber Box Manufacturing
322215	Nonfolding Sanitary Food Container Manufacturing
322223	Plastics, Foil, and Coated Paper Bag Manufacturing
322231	Die-Cut Paper and Paperboard Office Supplies Manufacturing
323110	Commercial Lithographic Printing
323113	Commercial Screen Printing
323115	Digital Printing
323117	Books Printing

N.A.I.C.S.	Description
323119	Other Commercial Printing
323122	Prepress Services
324121	Asphalt Paving Mixture and Block Manufacturing
325110	Petrochemical Manufacturing
325132	Synthetic Organic Dye and Pigment Manufacturing
325191	Gum and Wood Chemical Manufacturing
325199	All Other Basic Organic Chemical Manufacturing
325221	Cellulosic Organic Fiber Manufacturing
325314	Fertilizer (Mixing Only) Manufacturing
325412	Pharmaceutical Preparation Manufacturing
325510	Paint and Coating Manufacturing
325612	Polish and Other Sanitation Good Manufacturing
325920	Explosives Manufacturing
325992	Photographic Film, Paper, Plate, and Chemical Manufacturing
326121	Unsupported Plastics Profile Shape Manufacturing
326140	Polystyrene Foam Product Manufacturing
326192	Resilient Floor Covering Manufacturing
326212	Tire Retreading
326291	Rubber Product Manufacturing for Mechanical Use
331525	Copper Foundries (except Die-Casting)
332112	Nonferrous Forging
332115	Crown and Closure Manufacturing
332211	Cutlery and Flatware (except Precious) Manufacturing
332311	Prefabricated Metal Building and Component Manufacturing
332322	Sheet Metal Work Manufacturing
332420	Metal Tank (Heavy Gauge) Manufacturing
332611	Spring (Heavy Gauge) Manufacturing
332710	Machine Shops
332722	Bolt, Nut, Screw, Rivet, and Washer Manufacturing
332911	Industrial Valve Manufacturing
332919	Other Metal Valve and Pipe Fitting Manufacturing
332994	Small Arms Manufacturing
332996	Fabricated Pipe and Pipe Fitting Manufacturing
333111	Farm Machinery and Equipment Manufacturing
333131	Mining Machinery and Equipment Manufacturing
333291	Paper Industry Machinery Manufacturing
333294	Food Product Machinery Manufacturing
333311	Automatic Vending Machine Manufacturing
333314	Optical Instrument and Lens Manufacturing
333412	Industrial and Commercial Fan and Blower Manufacturing
333512	Machine Tool (Metal Cutting Types) Manufacturing
333516	Rolling Mill Machinery and Equipment Manufacturing
333613	Mechanical Power Transmission Equipment Manufacturing
333913	Measuring and Dispensing Pump Manufacturing
333923	Overhead Traveling Crane, Hoist, and Monorail System Manufacturing
333994	Industrial Process Furnace and Oven Manufacturing
333999	All Other Miscellaneous General Purpose Machinery Manufacturing
334210	Telephone Apparatus Manufacturing
334310	Audio and Video Equipment Manufacturing
334413	Semiconductor and Related Device Manufacturing
334417	Electronic Connector Manufacturing
334510	Electromedical and Electrotherapeutic Apparatus Manufacturing
334514	Totalizing Fluid Meter and Counting Device Manufacturing
334519	Other Measuring and Controlling Device Manufacturing
335110	Electric Lamp Bulb and Part Manufacturing
335129	Other Lighting Equipment Manufacturing
335221	Household Cooking Appliance Manufacturing
335311	Power, Distribution, and Specialty Transformer Manufacturing
335911	Storage Battery Manufacturing
335929	Other Communication and Energy Wire Manufacturing
335999	All Other Miscellaneous Electrical Equipment and Component Manufacturing
336212	Truck Trailer Manufacturing
336311	Carburetor, Piston, Piston Ring, and Valve Manufacturing
336340	Motor Vehicle Brake System Manufacturing
336370	Motor Vehicle Metal Stamping
336412	Aircraft Engine and Engine Parts Manufacturing
336419	Other Guided Missile and Space Vehicle Parts and Auxiliary Equipment Manufacturing
336999	All Other Transportation Equipment Manufacturing
337122	Nonupholstered Wood Household Furniture Manufacturing
337211	Wood Office Furniture Manufacturing
337215	Showcase, Partition, Shelving, and Locker Manufacturing
339112	Surgical and Medical Instrument Manufacturing
339116	Dental Laboratories
339912	Silverware and Hollowware Manufacturing
339920	Sporting and Athletic Goods Manufacturing
339941	Pen and Mechanical Pencil Manufacturing
339950	Sign Manufacturing

Numerical N.A.I.C.S. Compendium-continued

N.A.I.C.S.	Description
339992	Musical Instrument Manufacturing
339995	Burial Casket Manufacturing
423510	Metal Service Centers and Other Metal Merchant Wholesalers
423930	Recyclable Material Merchant Wholesalers
516110	Internet Publishing and Broadcasting
517410	Satellite Telecommunications
517910	Other Telecommunications
518112	Web Search Portals
519110	News Syndicates
519190	All Other Information Services
424330	Women's, Children's, and Infants' Clothing and Accessories Merchant Wholesalers
424340	Footwear Merchant Wholesalers
424410	General Line Grocery Merchant Wholesalers
424430	Dairy Product (except Dried or Canned) Merchant Wholesalers
424440	Poultry and Poultry Product Merchant Wholesalers
424450	Confectionery Merchant Wholesalers
424460	Fish and Seafood Merchant Wholesalers
424470	Meat and Meat Product Merchant Wholesalers
424480	Fresh Fruit and Vegetable Merchant Wholesalers
424490	Other Grocery and Related Products Merchant Wholesalers
424510	Grain and Field Bean Merchant Wholesalers
424590	Other Farm Product Raw Material Merchant Wholesalers
424710	Petroleum Bulk Stations and Terminals
424810	Beer and Ale Merchant Wholesalers
424820	Wine and Distilled Alcoholic Beverage Merchant Wholesalers
424910	Farm Supplies Merchant Wholesalers
424920	Book, Periodical, and Newspaper Merchant Wholesalers
424930	Flower, Nursery Stock, and Florists' Supplies Merchant Wholesalers
424940	Tobacco and Tobacco Product Merchant Wholesalers
238150	Glass and Glazing Contractors
423120	Motor Vehicle Supplies and New Parts Merchant Wholesalers
423130	Tire and Tube Merchant Wholesalers
423140	Motor Vehicle Parts (Used) Merchant Wholesalers
423210	Furniture Merchant Wholesalers
423220	Home Furnishing Merchant Wholesalers
423310	Lumber, Plywood, Millwork, and Wood Panel Merchant Wholesalers
423320	Brick, Stone, and Related Construction Material Merchant Wholesalers
423330	Roofing, Siding, and Insulation Material Merchant Wholesalers
423390	Other Construction Material Merchant Wholesalers
423420	Office Equipment Merchant Wholesalers
423430	Computer and Computer Peripheral Equipment and Software Merchant Wholesalers
423450	Medical, Dental, and Hospital Equipment and Supplies Merchant Wholesalers
423490	Other Professional Equipment and Supplies Merchant Wholesalers
423610	Electrical Apparatus and Equipment, Wiring Supplies, and Related Equipment Merchant Wholesalers
423620	Electrical and Electronic Appliance, Television, and Radio Set Merchant Wholesalers
423690	Other Electronic Parts and Equipment Merchant Wholesalers
423710	Hardware Merchant Wholesalers
423720	Plumbing and Heating Equipment and Supplies (Hydronics) Merchant Wholesalers
423820	Farm and Garden Machinery and Equipment Merchant Wholesalers
423850	Service Establishment Equipment and Supplies Merchant Wholesalers
423910	Sporting and Recreational Goods and Supplies Merchant Wholesalers
423920	Toy and Hobby Goods and Supplies Merchant Wholesalers
423940	Jewelry, Watch, Precious Stone, and Precious Metal Merchant Wholesalers
423990	Other Miscellaneous Durable Goods Merchant Wholesalers
424110	Printing and Writing Paper Merchant Wholesalers
424120	Stationery and Office Supplies Merchant Wholesalers
424210	Drugs and Druggists' Sundries Merchant Wholesalers
424310	Piece Goods, Notions, and Other Dry Goods Merchant Wholesalers
424320	Men's and Boys' Clothing and Furnishings Merchant Wholesalers

Numerical N.A.I.C.S. Compendium—continued

NAICS	Description
339992	Musical Instrument Manufacturing
339995	Burial Casket Manufacturing
423510	Metal Service Centers and Other Metal Merchant Wholesalers
423930	Recyclable Material Merchant Wholesalers
516110	Internet Publishing and Broadcasting
517410	Satellite Telecommunications
517910	Other Telecommunications
518112	Web Search Portals
519110	News Syndicates
519190	All Other Information Services
424330	Women's, Children's, and Infants' Clothing and Accessories Merchant Wholesalers
424340	Footwear Merchant Wholesalers
424410	General Line Grocery Merchant Wholesalers
424430	Dairy Product (except Dried or Canned) Merchant Wholesalers
424440	Poultry and Poultry Product Merchant Wholesalers
424450	Confectionery Merchant Wholesalers
424460	Fish and Seafood Merchant Wholesalers
424470	Meat and Meat Product Merchant Wholesalers
424480	Fresh Fruit and Vegetable Merchant Wholesalers
424490	Other Grocery and Related Products Merchant Wholesalers
424510	Grain and Field Bean Merchant Wholesalers
424590	Other Farm Product Raw Material Merchant Wholesalers
424710	Petroleum Bulk Stations and Terminals
424810	Beer and Ale Merchant Wholesalers
424820	Wine and Distilled Alcoholic Beverage Merchant Wholesalers
424910	Farm Supplies Merchant Wholesalers
424920	Book, Periodical, and Newspaper Merchant Wholesalers
424930	Flower, Nursery Stock, and Florists' Supplies Merchant Wholesalers
424940	Tobacco and Tobacco Product Merchant Wholesalers
238150	Glass and Glazing Contractors
423120	Motor Vehicle Supplies and New Parts Merchant Wholesalers
423130	Tire and Tube Merchant Wholesalers
423140	Motor Vehicle Parts (Used) Merchant Wholesalers
423210	Furniture Merchant Wholesalers
423220	Home Furnishing Merchant Wholesalers
423310	Lumber, Plywood, Millwork, and Wood Panel Merchant Wholesalers
423320	Brick, Stone, and Related Construction Material Merchant Wholesalers
423330	Roofing, Siding, and Insulation Material Merchant Wholesalers
423390	Other Construction Material Merchant Wholesalers
423420	Office Equipment Merchant Wholesalers
423430	Computer and Computer Peripheral Equipment and Software Merchant Wholesalers
423450	Medical, Dental and Hospital Equipment and Supplies Merchant Wholesalers
423460	Other Professional Equipment and Supplies Merchant Wholesalers
423610	Electrical Apparatus and Equipment, Wiring Supplies, and Related Equipment Merchant Wholesalers
423620	Electrical and Electronic Appliances, Television, and Radio Set Merchant Wholesalers
423690	Other Electronic Parts and Equipment Merchant Wholesalers
423710	Hardware Merchant Wholesalers
423720	Plumbing and Heating Equipment and Supplies (Hydronics) Merchant Wholesalers
423820	Farm and Garden Machinery and Equipment Merchant Wholesalers
423850	Service Establishment Equipment and Supplies Merchant Wholesalers
423910	Sporting and Recreational Goods and Supplies Merchant Wholesalers
423920	Toy and Hobby Goods and Supplies Merchant Wholesalers
423940	Jewelry, Watch, Precious Stone, and Precious Metal Merchant Wholesalers
423990	Other Miscellaneous Durable Goods Merchant Wholesalers
424110	Printing and Writing Paper Merchant Wholesalers
424120	Stationery and Office Supplies Merchant Wholesalers
424210	Drugs and Druggists' Sundries Merchant Wholesalers
424310	Piece Goods, Notions, and Other Dry Goods Merchant Wholesalers
424320	Men's and Boys' Clothing and Furnishings Merchant Wholesalers

N.A.I.C.S. INDEX

111110 — SOYBEAN FARMING

FERONIA INC.; *Int'l,* pg. 2639
GRUPO DON MARIO; *Int'l,* pg. 3126
HARMONY AGRICULTURAL PRODUCTS IN OHIO, LLC—See Honda Motor Co., Ltd.; *Int'l,* pg. 3462
NUTECH SEED LLC—See Corteva, Inc.; *U.S. Public,* pg. 584
SEABEE CORPORATION FOUNDRY—See Ligon Industries LLC; *U.S. Private,* pg. 2455
SOLBAR INDUSTRIES LTD.—See CHS INC.; *U.S. Public,* pg. 493

111120 — OILSEED (EXCEPT SOYBEAN) FARMING

AGRICOLA NACIONAL S.A.C.I.; *Int'l,* pg. 216
AGRI-TECH (INDIA) LIMITED; *Int'l,* pg. 216
ANGLO EASTERN PLANTATIONS PLC; *Int'l,* pg. 462
BUMITAMA AGRI LTD.; *Int'l,* pg. 1215
CAPITAL METALS PLC; *Int'l,* pg. 1312
CARGILL BULGARIA EOOD—See Cargill, Inc.; *U.S. Private,* pg. 755
GOPENG BERHAD; *Int'l,* pg. 3042
GREENSTAR PLANT PRODUCTS INC.—See Hydrofarm Holdings Group, Inc.; *U.S. Public,* pg. 1079
HENRY LAMOTTE SERVICES GMBH—See Henry Lamotte GmbH; *Int'l,* pg. 3355
LLC ZHERDEVSKY ELEVATOR—See Gruppa Kompaniy Rusagro OOO; *Int'l,* pg. 3140
MASKIMI POLYOL SDN. BHD.—See Bina Puri Holdings Bhd; *Int'l,* pg. 1032
MINERVA S.A. EDIBLE OILS & FOOD ENTERPRISES—See DECA Investments AIFM; *Int'l,* pg. 1999
MONSANTO HELLAS, E.P.E.—See Bayer Aktiengesellschaft; *Int'l,* pg. 909
PGG WRIGHTSON SEEDS (AUSTRALIA) PTY LIMITED—See Agria Corporation; *Int'l,* pg. 216
PT SINAR KENCANA INTI PERKASA—See Golden Agri-Resources Ltd.; *Int'l,* pg. 3028

111130 — DRY PEA AND BEAN FARMING

JACK'S BEAN COMPANY, LLC; *U.S. Private,* pg. 2175
LATHAM HI-TECH HYBRIDS, INC.; *U.S. Private,* pg. 2396
LIMAGRAIN ARGENTINA S.A.—See Groupe Limagrain Holding SA; *Int'l,* pg. 3107
LIMAGRAIN BELGIUM NV—See Groupe Limagrain Holding SA; *Int'l,* pg. 3107
LIMAGRAIN BULGARIA LTD—See Groupe Limagrain Holding SA; *Int'l,* pg. 3107
LIMAGRAIN CENTRAL EUROPE CEREALS, S.R.O.—See Groupe Limagrain Holding SA; *Int'l,* pg. 3107
LIMAGRAIN CENTRAL EUROPE S.E.—See Groupe Limagrain Holding SA; *Int'l,* pg. 3107
LIMAGRAIN CEREAL SEEDS LLC—See Groupe Limagrain Holding SA; *Int'l,* pg. 3107
LIMAGRAIN CESKA REPUBLIKA, S.R.O.—See Groupe Limagrain Holding SA; *Int'l,* pg. 3107
LIMAGRAIN IBERICA S.A.—See Groupe Limagrain Holding SA; *Int'l,* pg. 3107
LIMAGRAIN MAGYARORSZAG KFT.—See Groupe Limagrain Holding SA; *Int'l,* pg. 3107
LIMAGRAIN MOLDOVA SRL—See Groupe Limagrain Holding SA; *Int'l,* pg. 3107
LIMAGRAIN POLSKA SP. Z O.O.—See Groupe Limagrain Holding SA; *Int'l,* pg. 3107
LIMAGRAIN SLOVENSKO, S.R.O.—See Groupe Limagrain Holding SA; *Int'l,* pg. 3107
LIMAGRAIN UK LTD—See Groupe Limagrain Holding SA; *Int'l,* pg. 3107
LIMAGRAIN UKRAINE LLC—See Groupe Limagrain Holding SA; *Int'l,* pg. 3107
SPOKANE SEED COMPANY; *U.S. Private,* pg. 3760
SUNRISE LAND COMPANY, LLC—See HALLADOR ENERGY COMPANY; *U.S. Public,* pg. 980

111140 — WHEAT FARMING

7. JULI A.D.; *Int'l,* pg. 14
ADVANTAGE WHEATS PTY LTD—See Corteva, Inc.; *U.S. Public,* pg. 584
AGRICOLA SAN GIORGIO S.P.A.—See Assicurazioni Generali S.p.A.; *Int'l,* pg. 643
BACKA A.D.; *Int'l,* pg. 795
CARGILL AGRICULTURA SRL—See Cargill, Inc.; *U.S. Private,* pg. 755
CHAMTOR - LEGAL—See Archer-Daniels-Midland Company; *U.S. Public,* pg. 184
ECO FRIENDLY FOOD PROCESSING PARK LTD.; *Int'l,* pg. 2292
FORAKER ELEVATOR—See The Mennel Milling Company; *U.S. Private,* pg. 4077
GALACTIC INC—See Finasucre S.A.; *Int'l,* pg. 2670
GRANICAR A.D.; *Int'l,* pg. 3058
KRISTERA AD—See Agria Group Holding JSC; *Int'l,* pg. 216
KRISTERA-AGRO EOOD—See Agria Group Holding JSC; *Int'l,* pg. 216
LLC SAARE FARMER—See Agromino A/S; *Int'l,* pg. 220
THE MENNEL MILLING COMPANY - VALLEY GRAIN DIVISION—See The Mennel Milling Company; *U.S. Private,* pg. 4077
S&W SEED COMPANY AUSTRALIA PTY LTD—See S&W Seed Co.; *U.S. Public,* pg. 1832
S&W SEED CO.; *U.S. Public,* pg. 1832
TC FARMING UKRAINE LTD.—See Agromino A/S; *Int'l,* pg. 220
TROY ELEVATOR, INC.—See The Mennel Milling Company; *U.S. Private,* pg. 4078
WILLIAM CHARLES LTD—See William Charles, Ltd.; *U.S. Private,* pg. 4522

111150 — CORN FARMING

DON AGRO INTERNATIONAL LIMITED; *Int'l,* pg. 2162
EGREEN CO., LTD.; *Int'l,* pg. 2326
FUJI OIL (SINGAPORE) PTE. LTD.—See Fuji Oil Holdings Inc.; *Int'l,* pg. 2815
GOLDEN GROWERS COOPERATIVE; *U.S. Public,* pg. 950
HARTUNG BROTHERS INC.; *U.S. Private,* pg. 1874
LIMAGRAIN EUROPE—See Groupe Limagrain Holding SA; *Int'l,* pg. 3107
MAICENTRE—See Groupe Limagrain Holding SA; *Int'l,* pg. 3107
MOEWS SEED CO., INC.; *U.S. Private,* pg. 2764
PFISTER SEEDS LLC—See Corteva, Inc.; *U.S. Public,* pg. 584
VALGRAIN—See Groupe Limagrain Holding SA; *Int'l,* pg. 3108
WYFFEL'S HYBRIDS, INC.; *U.S. Private,* pg. 4576

111160 — RICE FARMING

AN GIANG IMPORT-EXPORT COMPANY; *Int'l,* pg. 443
GARBER FARMS; *U.S. Private,* pg. 1642
GRM OVERSEAS LIMITED; *Int'l,* pg. 3087
HAINAN SHENNONG SEED TECHNOLOGY CO., LTD.; *Int'l,* pg. 3212

111191 — OILSEED AND GRAIN COMBINATION FARMING

AFGRI LIMITED; *Int'l,* pg. 188
AGRIA CORPORATION; *Int'l,* pg. 216
AGRICULTURAL ENGINEERING COMPANY FOR INVESTMENTS; *Int'l,* pg. 217
AGROTON PUBLIC LTD; *Int'l,* pg. 221
THE ANDERSONS INCORPORATED; *U.S. Public,* pg. 2034
AVENA NORDIC GRAIN OY—See Apetit Plc; *Int'l,* pg. 509
AYER HOLDINGS BERHAD; *Int'l,* pg. 775
BEIJING DABEINONG TECHNOLOGY GROUP CO., LTD.; *Int'l,* pg. 948
BUUDAIN TSATSAL JOINT STOCK COMPANY; *Int'l,* pg. 1229
CARGILL S.A.C.I.—See Cargill, Inc.; *U.S. Private,* pg. 758
CHAPLYZHENKY ELEVATOR—See Gruppa Kompaniy Rusagro OOO; *Int'l,* pg. 3140
CONTINENTAL SEEDS & CHEMICALS LIMITED; *Int'l,* pg. 1784
DAIRYLAND SEED CO. INC.; *U.S. Private,* pg. 1146
DARKHAN GURIL TEJEEL JOINT STOCK COMPANY; *Int'l,* pg. 1973
DESA TALISAI SDN BHD—See IJM Corporation Berhad; *Int'l,* pg. 3608
GL MANAGEMENT, INC.—See Golden Leaf Holdings Ltd.; *Int'l,* pg. 3030
GLOBAL CLEAN ENERGY HOLDINGS, INC.; *U.S. Public,* pg. 941
GOLDEN LAND BERHAD; *Int'l,* pg. 3030
INDOFOOD AGRI RESOURCES LTD.—See First Pacific Company Limited; *Int'l,* pg. 2686
INDUSTRIAS DE ACEITE S.A.—See Grupo Romero; *Int'l,* pg. 3134
MILDOLA OY—See Apetit Plc; *Int'l,* pg. 509
TIERRA SEED SCIENCE PRIVATE LIMITED—See Grandeur Products Limited; *Int'l,* pg. 3058
UAB AVENA NORDIC GRAIN—See Apetit Plc; *Int'l,* pg. 509

111199 — ALL OTHER GRAIN FARMING

AGRIA CORPORATION—See Agria Corporation; *Int'l,* pg. 216
AGT FOOD AND INGREDIENTS INC.; *Int'l,* pg. 221
ASH-SHARQIYAH DEVELOPMENT COMPANY; *Int'l,* pg. 606
ATAMEKEN-AGRO JSC; *Int'l,* pg. 666
AXEREAL UNION DE COOPERATIVES AGRICOLES; *Int'l,* pg. 767
BARENBRUG BELGIUM NV/SA—See Barenbrug Holding B.V.; *Int'l,* pg. 864
BARENBRUG CHINA R.O.—See Barenbrug Holding B.V.; *Int'l,* pg. 864
BARENBRUG FRANCE S.A.—See Barenbrug Holding B.V.; *Int'l,* pg. 864
BARENBRUG HOLDING B.V.; *Int'l,* pg. 864
BARENBRUG HOLLAND B.V.—See Barenbrug Holding B.V.; *Int'l,* pg. 864
BARENBRUG LUXEMBOURG S.A.—See Barenbrug Holding B.V.; *Int'l,* pg. 864
BARENBRUG POLSKA SP. Z.O.O.—See Barenbrug Holding B.V.; *Int'l,* pg. 864
BARENBRUG U.K. LTD.—See Barenbrug Holding B.V.; *Int'l,* pg. 864
BAYER CROPSCIENCE LIMITED—See Bayer Aktiengesellschaft; *Int'l,* pg. 903

111199 — ALL OTHER GRAIN FAR...

BIOSEED RESEARCH PHILIPPINES INC—See DCM Shriram Limited; *Int'l*, pg. 1992
CEREAL PLANET PLC; *Int'l*, pg. 1421
CONTINENTAL FARMERS GROUP PLC—See Almarai Company Ltd.; *Int'l*, pg. 363
COOPERATIVE LIMAGRAIN—See Groupe Limagrain Holding SA; *Int'l*, pg. 3107
DLF AMBA; *Int'l*, pg. 2140
EATMORE SPROUTS AND GREENS LTD.; *Int'l*, pg. 2277
EMMSONS ASIA PTE. LTD.—See Emmsons International Limited; *Int'l*, pg. 2385
EURALIS SEMENCES SAS—See Euralis Coop; *Int'l*, pg. 2527
EURALIS SEMILLAS, S.A.—See Euralis Coop; *Int'l*, pg. 2527
FORRATEC ARGENTINA S.A.—See Corteva, Inc.; *U.S. Public*, pg. 582
GRO ALLIANCE; *U.S. Private*, pg. 1791
HARINERA DE MAIZ DE JALISCO, S.A. DE C.V.—See Gruma, S.A.B. de C.V.; *Int'l*, pg. 3114
HEILONGJIANG AGRICLTURE COMPANY LIMITED; *Int'l*, pg. 3323
HERITAGE SEEDS PTY. LTD.—See Barenbrug Holding B.V.; *Int'l*, pg. 864
HPC BIOSCIENCES LIMITED; *Int'l*, pg. 3500
INCOTEC AMERICA DO SUL TECNOLOGIA EM SEMENTES LTDA.—See Croda International plc; *Int'l*, pg. 1853
INCOTEC ARGENTINA S.A—See Croda International plc; *Int'l*, pg. 1853
IPM HOLLAND B.V.—See Donegal Investment Group Plc; *Int'l*, pg. 2163
LIMAGRAIN A/S—See Groupe Limagrain Holding SA; *Int'l*, pg. 3107
LIMAGRAIN RU LLC—See Groupe Limagrain Holding SA; *Int'l*, pg. 3107
MONSANTO KOREA LTD.—See Bayer Aktiengesellschaft; *Int'l*, pg. 909
NEW ZEALAND AGRISEEDS LTD.—See Barenbrug Holding B.V.; *Int'l*, pg. 864
NEZHEGOL-AGRO—See Gruppa Kompaniy Rusagro OOO; *Int'l*, pg. 3140
NIKIFOROVSKY ELEVATOR—See Gruppa Kompaniy Rusagro OOO; *Int'l*, pg. 3140
PALAVERSICH Y CIA S.A.—See Barenbrug Holding B.V.; *Int'l*, pg. 864
PARRISH & HEIMBECKER, LIMITED—See Exceldor Cooperative Avicole; *Int'l*, pg. 2577
PGG WRIGHTSON SEEDS LIMITED—See DLF Seeds A/S; *Int'l*, pg. 2141
QUAD COUNTY CORN PROCESSORS COOPERATIVE; *U.S. Private*, pg. 1744
RINDES Y CULTIVOS DAS S.A.—See Corteva, Inc.; *U.S. Public*, pg. 582
SAXON AGRICULTURE, LTD.—See GrainCorp Limited; *Int'l*, pg. 3052
SEED VISION (PTY) LTD.—See S&W Seed Co.; *U.S. Public*, pg. 1832
SORGHUM SOLUTIONS SOUTH AFRICA (PTY) LTD.—See S&W Seed Co.; *U.S. Public*, pg. 1832
THOMPSONS USA LIMITED—See The Andersons Incorporated; *U.S. Public*, pg. 2035
WESTERN FOODS LLC—See Western Milling, LLC; *U.S. Private*, pg. 4494
WRIGHTSON PAS S.A. LIMITED—See Agria Corporation; *Int'l*, pg. 216

111211 — POTATO FARMING

AV THOMAS PRODUCE; *U.S. Private*, pg. 402
BC INSTITUT D.D. ZAGREB; *Int'l*, pg. 921
CECE'S VEGGIE CO.; *U.S. Private*, pg. 804
CEVIAGRO SPA—See Cevital S.p.A.; *Int'l*, pg. 1425
EMSLAND-STARKE GMBH; *Int'l*, pg. 2394
GERMICOPA S.A.; *Int'l*, pg. 2943
HZPC FRANCE SAS—See HZPC Holland B.V.; *Int'l*, pg. 3561
HZPC HOLLAND B.V.; *Int'l*, pg. 3561
HZPC PATATAS ESPANA S.L.—See HZPC Holland B.V.; *Int'l*, pg. 3561
IPM POTATO GROUP LIMITED—See Donegal Investment Group Plc; *Int'l*, pg. 2163
JAPAN POTATO CORPORATION—See Hob Co., Ltd.; *Int'l*, pg. 3436
MOUNTAIN VALLEY PRODUCE, LLC.; *U.S. Private*, pg. 2800
MPG CROP SERVICES, LLC.—See Maine Potato Growers, Inc.; *U.S. Private*, pg. 2552
OCHOA AG UNLIMITED FOODS, INC.; *U.S. Private*, pg. 2992
PINELAND FARMS POTATO COMPANY, INC.—See Post Holdings, Inc.; *U.S. Public*, pg. 1704
PROGRESSIVE FARMS—See Arable Capital Partners LLC; *U.S. Private*, pg. 307
QUAIL H FARMS, LLC.; *U.S. Private*, pg. 3316
SOUTHERN PRODUCE DISTRIBUTORS, INC.; *U.S. Private*, pg. 3734

STET HOLLAND B.V.—See HZPC Holland B.V.; *Int'l*, pg. 3561

111219 — OTHER VEGETABLE (EXCEPT POTATO) AND MELON FARMING

ABUNDANT PRODUCE LIMITED; *Int'l*, pg. 74
APPHARVEST, INC.; *U.S. Public*, pg. 168
ARIAKE FARM CO., LTD.—See ARIAKE JAPAN Co., Ltd.; *Int'l*, pg. 563
BEJO ANDES LTDA.—See Bejo Zaden B.V.; *Int'l*, pg. 962
BEJO BOHEMIA, S.R.O.—See Bejo Zaden B.V.; *Int'l*, pg. 962
BEJO GRAINES FRANCE S.A.R.L.—See Bejo Zaden B.V.; *Int'l*, pg. 962
BEJO IBERICA, S.L.—See Bejo Zaden B.V.; *Int'l*, pg. 962
BEJO ITALIA S.R.L.—See Bejo Zaden B.V.; *Int'l*, pg. 962
BEJO ROMANIA SRL—See Bejo Zaden B.V.; *Int'l*, pg. 962
BEJO SAMEN GMBH—See Bejo Zaden B.V.; *Int'l*, pg. 962
BEJO, S.A.—See Bejo Zaden B.V.; *Int'l*, pg. 962
BEJO SEEDS PTY LTD—See Bejo Zaden B.V.; *Int'l*, pg. 962
BEJO SEMENTES DO BRASIL LTDA—See Bejo Zaden B.V.; *Int'l*, pg. 962
BEJO SEMILLAS ARGENTINA S.A.—See Bejo Zaden B.V.; *Int'l*, pg. 962
BEJO ZADEN BELGIUM B.V.B.A.—See Bejo Zaden B.V.; *Int'l*, pg. 962
BEJO ZADEN D.O.O.—See Bejo Zaden B.V.; *Int'l*, pg. 962
BEJO ZADEN POLAND SP. Z O.O.—See Bejo Zaden B.V.; *Int'l*, pg. 962
BIOCERES S.A.; *Int'l*, pg. 1036
BOLTHOUSE FARMS JAPAN YK—See Campbell Soup Company; *U.S. Public*, pg. 426
BORD NA MONA HORTICULTURE LIMITED—See Bord na Mona Plc; *Int'l*, pg. 1113
BOSKOVICH FARMS INC.; *U.S. Private*, pg. 620
BUURMA FARMS INC.; *U.S. Private*, pg. 698
CHALKIS HEALTH INDUSTRY CO., LTD.; *Int'l*, pg. 1437
CHIMAC S.A—See Element Solutions Inc.; *U.S. Public*, pg. 725
CNOS VILMORIN POLSKA SP ZOO—See Groupe Limagrain Holding SA; *Int'l*, pg. 3107
CPM INTERNACIONAL D.O.O.—See Assicurazioni Generali S.p.A.; *Int'l*, pg. 648
D'ARRIGO BROS. COMPANY; *U.S. Private*, pg. 1139
DGM GROWERS LTD—See Fresca Group Limited; *Int'l*, pg. 2774
EARTHBOUND FARM, LLC—See Danone; *Int'l*, pg. 1967
FARM-OP, INC.—See Lipman & Lipman, Inc.; *U.S. Private*, pg. 2465
FRUTICOLA VICONTO S.A.; *Int'l*, pg. 2797
FRUTTAGEL SCRL - LARINO PLANT—See Fruttagel S.C.p.A.; *Int'l*, pg. 2797
GIGANTE VERDE S. DE R.L. DE C.V.—See General Mills, Inc.; *U.S. Public*, pg. 921
GREEN VALLEY ONION COMPANY; *U.S. Private*, pg. 1774
GRIMMWAY ENTERPRISES INC.; *U.S. Private*, pg. 1790
GROWERS EXPRESS LLC; *U.S. Private*, pg. 1795
HARTUNG BROTHERS INC. - BOWLING GREEN CUCUMBER PLANT—See Hartung Brothers Inc.; *U.S. Private*, pg. 1874
HARTUNG BROTHERS INC. - MADISON SEED PLANT—See Hartung Brothers Inc.; *U.S. Private*, pg. 1874
HARTUNG BROTHERS INC. - MUNCIE ILLINOIS SEED PRODUCTION AND DISTRIBUTION PLANT—See Hartung Brothers Inc.; *U.S. Private*, pg. 1874
HARTUNG BROTHERS, INC.-UVALDE CUCUMBER OPERATIONS—See Hartung Brothers Inc.; *U.S. Private*, pg. 1874
HEARTLAND FARMS INC.; *U.S. Private*, pg. 1900
HORWATH & CO., INC.—See S&H Packing & Sales Co. Inc.; *U.S. Private*, pg. 3513
J&D PRODUCE, INC.; *U.S. Private*, pg. 2154
J&J AG PRODUCTS, INC.; *U.S. Private*, pg. 2154
JV SMITH COMPANIES; *U.S. Private*, pg. 2246
KUZZEN'S, INC.—See Lipman & Lipman, Inc.; *U.S. Private*, pg. 2465
LYNN-ETTE & SONS, INC.; *U.S. Private*, pg. 2522
MCCLURE PROPERTIES LTD.; *U.S. Private*, pg. 2629
NICKERSON ZWAAN GMBH—See Groupe Limagrain Holding SA; *Int'l*, pg. 3108
NICKERSON ZWAAN LTD.—See Groupe Limagrain Holding SA; *Int'l*, pg. 3108
OCEANVIEW PRODUCE COMPANY—See Dole plc; *Int'l*, pg. 2157
PACIFIC TOMATO GROWERS LTD.; *U.S. Private*, pg. 3071
ROCKHEDGE HERB FARMS; *U.S. Private*, pg. 3466
ROYAL PACKING COMPANY—See Dole plc; *Int'l*, pg. 2157
ROYAL PRODUCE SALES INC.—See S&H Packing & Sales Co. Inc.; *U.S. Private*, pg. 3513
SHARYLAND LP; *U.S. Private*, pg. 3627
S&H PACKING & SALES CO. INC.; *U.S. Private*, pg. 3513
SOAVE HYDROPONICS COMPANY - GREAT NORTHERN SEEDLINGS DIVISION—See Soave Enterprises, LLC; *U.S. Private*, pg. 3702
SPEEDLING, INCORPORATED-SAN JUAN BAUTISTA NURSERY—See Speedling Incorporated; *U.S. Private*, pg. 3753
TANIMURA & ANTLE INC.; *U.S. Private*, pg. 3931
TEIXEIRA FARMS INC.; *U.S. Private*, pg. 3958
VILMORIN ANADOLU TOHUMCULUK—See Groupe Limagrain Holding SA; *Int'l*, pg. 3108
VILMORIN JARDIN SA—See Groupe Limagrain Holding SA; *Int'l*, pg. 3108
WORLD AGRICULTURE, INC.—See Lipman & Lipman, Inc.; *U.S. Private*, pg. 2465

111310 — ORANGE GROVES

ASIAN CITRUS (H.K.) COMPANY LIMITED—See Asian Citrus Holdings Limited; *Int'l*, pg. 617
ASIAN CITRUS HOLDINGS LIMITED; *Int'l*, pg. 617
FLORIDA CITRUS MUTUAL, INC.; *U.S. Private*, pg. 1547
GREENWOOD MUSHROOMS—See AGF Management Limited; *Int'l*, pg. 207
HELLER BROS. PACKING CORP.; *U.S. Private*, pg. 1906
LUCKY TEAM BIOTECH DEVELOPMENT (HEPU) LIMITED—See Asian Citrus Holdings Limited; *Int'l*, pg. 617
LYKES BROTHERS INC. - LYKES CITRUS DIVISION—See Lykes Brothers Inc.; *U.S. Private*, pg. 2519
WONDERFUL CITRUS LLC—See The Wonderful Company LLC; *U.S. Private*, pg. 4138

111320 — CITRUS (EXCEPT ORANGE) GROVES

AFRICAN REALTY TRUST (PTY) LTD.—See Hanover Acceptances Limited; *Int'l*, pg. 3258
ALICO FRUIT COMPANY, LLC—See Continental Grain Company; *U.S. Private*, pg. 1029
BEN HILL GRIFFIN INC.; *U.S. Private*, pg. 522
EVANS PROPERTIES INC.; *U.S. Private*, pg. 1435
OAKLEY GROVES INC.; *U.S. Private*, pg. 2985
PEACE RIVER CITRUS PRODUCTS INC.; *U.S. Private*, pg. 3122
SUN-AG INC.; *U.S. Private*, pg. 3864

111331 — APPLE ORCHARDS

AUVIL FRUIT COMPANY, INC.; *U.S. Private*, pg. 402
BROETJE ORCHARDS; *U.S. Private*, pg. 661
CALIFORNIA CIDER CO., INC.—See Vintage Wine Estates, Inc.; *U.S. Public*, pg. 2298
DOLE EUROPE SAS—See Dole plc; *Int'l*, pg. 2157
EVANS FRUIT COMPANY; *U.S. Private*, pg. 1435
KNOUSE FOODS COOPERATIVE INC.; *U.S. Private*, pg. 2323
ONEONTA-STARR RANCH GROWERS LLC—See Oneonta Trading Corporation; *U.S. Private*, pg. 3025
SABA TRADING AB—See Dole plc; *Int'l*, pg. 2157
VALLEY ROZ ORCHARDS INC.; *U.S. Private*, pg. 4335

111332 — GRAPE VINEYARDS

ANTHONY VINEYARDS; *U.S. Private*, pg. 288
BALCOM & MOE INC.; *U.S. Private*, pg. 458
CALLAWAY VINEYARD & WINERY—See Callaway Temecula Limited Partnership; *U.S. Private*, pg. 722
DELICATO VINEYARDS; *U.S. Private*, pg. 1197
DON SEBASTIANI & SONS; *U.S. Private*, pg. 1258
EASTERN PRODUCE CAPE (PTY) LIMITED—See Camellia Plc; *Int'l*, pg. 1271
FAR NIENTE WINERY—See GI Manager L.P.; *U.S. Private*, pg. 1692
FERRARA WINERY; *U.S. Private*, pg. 1498
F. KORBEL BROS. INC.; *U.S. Private*, pg. 1455
GD-TIKVES AD; *Int'l*, pg. 2895
GIUMARRA VINEYARDS CORPORATION; *U.S. Private*, pg. 1703
JASMINE VINEYARDS, INC.; *U.S. Private*, pg. 2189
JEFFERSON VINEYARDS; *U.S. Private*, pg. 2198
JONES PRODUCE, INC.; *U.S. Private*, pg. 2234
KIRRIBILLY VITICULTURE PTY LIMITED—See Cheviot Bridge Limited; *Int'l*, pg. 1474
KLEIN FOODS INC.; *U.S. Private*, pg. 2318
KLINGSHIRN WINERY; *U.S. Private*, pg. 2320
LEONETTI CELLAR; *U.S. Private*, pg. 2430
MERRITT ESTATE WINERY; *U.S. Private*, pg. 2676
OSPREY'S DOMINION VINEYARDS LTD.; *U.S. Private*, pg. 3048
PACHECO RANCH WINERY; *U.S. Private*, pg. 3065
PRESTON VINEYARDS, INC.; *U.S. Private*, pg. 3257
SAN ANTONIO WINERY & MADDALENA RESTAURANT; *U.S. Private*, pg. 3539
SAN BERNABE VINEYARDS—See Delicato Vineyards; *U.S. Private*, pg. 1197
SCHEID VINEYARDS INC.; *U.S. Public*, pg. 1843
SONOMA-CUTRER VINEYARDS, INC.—See The Duckhorn Portfolio, Inc.; *U.S. Public*, pg. 2067

N.A.I.C.S. INDEX

111421 — NURSERY AND TREE PR...

STAGECOACH VINEYARD—See E. & J. Gallo Winery; *U.S. Private*, pg. 1303
SUN WORLD INTERNATIONAL LLC—See Renewable Resources Group Inc.; *U.S. Private*, pg. 3398
SUN WORLD INTERNATIONAL LLC—See Vision Ridge Partners, LLC; *U.S. Private*, pg. 4391
TUDOR RANCH, INC.; *U.S. Private*, pg. 4257
WILLAKENZIE VINEYARDS, INC.—See Jackson Family Wines, Inc.; *U.S. Private*, pg. 2176

111333 — STRAWBERRY FARMING

DOLE BERRY COMPANY—See Dole plc; *Int'l*, pg. 2157
DRISCOLL'S, INC; *U.S. Private*, pg. 1277
HOB CO., LTD.; *Int'l*, pg. 3436
RUTHERFORD FARM, LLC—See The Southern Company; *U.S. Public*, pg. 2131
WALLINGS NURSERY LTD—See Fresca Group Limited; *Int'l*, pg. 2774
WILLAMETTE VALLEY FRUIT COMPANY—See Oregon Potato Company; *U.S. Private*, pg. 3040
WISHNATZKI, INC.; *U.S. Private*, pg. 4550

111334 — BERRY (EXCEPT STRAWBERRY) FARMING

BRADY FARMS INC.; *U.S. Private*, pg. 633
ISLAND GROVE AG PRODUCTS; *U.S. Private*, pg. 2145
PETERSON FARMS, INC.; *U.S. Private*, pg. 3160
RADER FARMS, INC.—See Oregon Potato Company; *U.S. Private*, pg. 3040
ROBERT ROTHSCHILD FARM LLC—See Glencoe Capital LLC; *U.S. Private*, pg. 1709
WYCKOFF FARMS, INCORPORATED; *U.S. Private*, pg. 4575

111335 — TREE NUT FARMING

BLACKWELL LAND, LLC; *U.S. Private*, pg. 577
BLUE DIAMOND GROWERS; *U.S. Private*, pg. 588
BUDERIM MACADAMIAS PTY LTD—See Health and Plant Protein Group Limited; *Int'l*, pg. 3303
CARRIERE FAMILY FARMS, INC.; *U.S. Private*, pg. 772
C. BREWER & CO. LTD.; *U.S. Private*, pg. 704
CONSERVATION SERVICES, INC.—See Waste Management, Inc.; *U.S. Public*, pg. 2330
HAWAIIAN MACADAMIA NUT ORCHARDS, L.P.; *U.S. Private*, pg. 1882
MACFARMS, LLC—See Health and Plant Protein Group Limited; *Int'l*, pg. 3303
MARIANI NUT COMPANY; *U.S. Private*, pg. 2574
MAUNA LOA MACADAMIA NUT CORPORATION—See Hawaiian Host Inc.; *U.S. Private*, pg. 1882
TEJON AGRICULTURAL CORP.—See Tejon Ranch Company; *U.S. Public*, pg. 1991
WAILUKU AGRIBUSINESS CO., INC.—See C. Brewer & Co. Ltd.; *U.S. Private*, pg. 705
WONDERFUL PISTACHIOS & ALMONDS LLC—See The Wonderful Company LLC; *U.S. Private*, pg. 4139
YOUNG PECAN, INC.—See King Ranch, Inc.; *U.S. Private*, pg. 2310

111336 — FRUIT AND TREE NUT COMBINATION FARMING

AGRANA SALES & MARKETING GMBH—See AGRANA Beteiligungs-AG; *Int'l*, pg. 213
ASSOCIATED CITRUS PACKERS, INC.—See Limoneira Company; *U.S. Public*, pg. 1316
BAYING ECOLOGICAL HOLDING GROUP, INC.; *U.S. Public*, pg. 284
C.G. HACKING & SONS LIMITED; *Int'l*, pg. 1240
GREGORIO, NUMO Y NOEL WERTHEIN S.A. - FRUIT DIVISION—See Gregorio, Numo y Noel Werthein S.A.; *Int'l*, pg. 3078
HELIO S.A.; *Int'l*, pg. 3330
HHLP COCONUT GROVE ASSOCIATES, LLC—See KSL Capital Partners, LLC; *U.S. Private*, pg. 2355
SUNKIST GROWERS, INC.-CENTRAL DIVISION—See Sunkist Growers, Inc.; *U.S. Private*, pg. 3867

111339 — OTHER NONCITRUS FRUIT FARMING

BENGUET MANAGEMENT CORPORATION Soo Benguet Corporation; *Int'l*, pg. 974
BOUNDARY BEND LIMITED; *Int'l*, pg. 1119
CALAVO FOODS, INC.—See Calavo Growers, Inc.; *U.S. Public*, pg. 422
CHIQUITA BANANA COMPANY BV—See Banco Safra S.A.; *Int'l*, pg. 824
CHIQUITA BRANDS LLC—See Banco Safra S.A.; *Int'l*, pg. 824

DULCINEA FARMS, LLC—See Arable Capital Partners LLC; *U.S. Private*, pg. 307
DUNDEE CITRUS GROWERS ASSOCIATION; *U.S. Private*, pg. 1288
EASTPACK AVOCADO COMPANY LIMITED—See Eastpack Limited; *Int'l*, pg. 2274
GROWERS REFRIGERATING COMPANY, INC.—See Naumes Inc.; *U.S. Private*, pg. 2868
HENRY AVOCADO CORP.; *U.S. Private*, pg. 1917
NATURIPE BERRY GROWERS INC.; *U.S. Private*, pg. 2868
NAUMES INC.; *U.S. Private*, pg. 2868
POINSETTIA GROVES INC.; *U.S. Private*, pg. 3221
POME ON THE RANGE, LLC—See Louisburg Cider Mill, Inc.; *U.S. Private*, pg. 2499
SACRAMENTO PACKING, INC.; *U.S. Private*, pg. 3522
SAN JOAQUIN FIGS, INC.; *U.S. Private*, pg. 3541
SHORELINE FRUIT, LLC.; *U.S. Private*, pg. 3641

111411 — MUSHROOM PRODUCTION

ALOHA MEDICINALS, INC.—See American Botanicals, LLC; *U.S. Private*, pg. 225
BALTIC CHAMPS, UAB—See AUGA group, AB; *Int'l*, pg. 703
THE CALIFORNIA MUSHROOM FARM, INC.—See Modern Mushroom Farms, Inc.; *U.S. Private*, pg. 2761
CHINA LIAONING DINGXU ECOLOGICAL AGRICULTURE DEVELOPMENT, INC.; *U.S. Public*, pg. 489
CONTINENTAL MUSHROOM CORP.; *Int'l*, pg. 1784
DENNY MUSHROOMS (PTY) LIMITED—See FirstRand Limited; *Int'l*, pg. 2690
FARMMI, INC.; *Int'l*, pg. 2620
FUJIAN WANCHEN BIOTECHNOLOGY GROUP CO., LTD.; *Int'l*, pg. 2820
GULF MUSHROOM PRODUCTS CO. SAOG; *Int'l*, pg. 3181
HOKTO KINOKO COMPANY—See Hokuto Corporation; *Int'l*, pg. 3445
HOKUTO CORPORATION; *Int'l*, pg. 3445
MODERN MUSHROOM FARMS, INC.; *U.S. Private*, pg. 2761
MODERN MUSHROOM SALES—See Modern Mushroom Farms, Inc.; *U.S. Private*, pg. 2761
MONTEREY MUSHROOMS, INC.; *U.S. Private*, pg. 2776
PHILLIPS MUSHROOM FARMS; *U.S. Private*, pg. 3171
PREMIER MUSHROOMS LP; *U.S. Private*, pg. 3250
SOUTH MILL MUSHROOMS SALES, INC.; *U.S. Private*, pg. 3723
SYLVAN INC.—See The Snyder Group, Inc.; *U.S. Private*, pg. 4119
WINDMILL FARMS—See AGF Management Limited; *Int'l*, pg. 207

111419 — OTHER FOOD CROPS GROWN UNDER COVER

BAY BRIDGE FOOD AND PRODUCE COMPANY; *U.S. Private*, pg. 492
BLISSCO CANNABIS CORP.—See Canopy Growth Corporation; *Int'l*, pg. 1298
BUDERIM GINGER AMERICA, INC.—See Health and Plant Protein Group Limited; *Int'l*, pg. 3303
BUDERIM GINGER (OVERSEAS) HOLDINGS PTY LTD—See Health and Plant Protein Group Limited; *Int'l*, pg. 3303
C21 INVESTMENTS INC.; *Int'l*, pg. 1244
CHAODA VEGETABLE & FRUITS LIMITED—See Chaoda Modern Agriculture Holdings Limited; *Int'l*, pg. 1447
CHINA POLYPEPTIDE GROUP, INC.; *Int'l*, pg. 1541
CLS LABS, INC.—See CLS Holdings USA, Inc.; *U.S. Public*, pg. 515
CRITICALITY LLC—See Pyxus International, Inc.; *U.S. Public*, pg. 1740
FOOD MARKET MANAGEMENT, INC.; *U.S. Private*, pg. 1561
FRANCISCO INDUSTRIES, INC.; *U.S. Public*, pg. 877
FRESPAC GINGER (FIJI) LTD—See Health and Plant Protein Group Limited; *Int'l*, pg. 3303
GLM TRADING LTD.—See Health and Plant Protein Group Limited; *Int'l*, pg. 3303
GOODNESS GREENESS; *U.S. Private*, pg. 1740
HARVEST HEALTH & RECREATION INC.—See Trulieve Cannabis Corp.; *U.S. Public*, pg. 2201
HEADSTART NURSERY INC.; *U.S. Private*, pg. 1891
HEMPTOWN ORGANICS CORP.; *U.S. Private*, pg. 3341
MARIJUANA COMPANY OF AMERICA, INC.; *U.S. Public*, pg. 1365
SOCAL HARVEST, INC.; *U.S. Private*, pg. 3702
SPEEDLING INCORPORATED-ALAMO TRANSPLANTS DIVISION—See Speedling Incorporated; *U.S. Private*, pg. 3753
SPEEDLING INCORPORATED-BUSHNELL DIVISION—See Speedling Incorporated; *U.S. Private*, pg. 3753
SPEEDLING, INCORPORATED—See Speedling Incorporated; *U.S. Private*, pg. 3753
STATUS PRODUCE LIMITED—See BayWa AG; *Int'l*, pg. 919

THINKING GREEN; *U.S. Private*, pg. 4144
YAMHILL COUNTY MUSHROOMS, INC.; *U.S. Private*, pg. 4585

111421 — NURSERY AND TREE PRODUCTION

AGRECOL, LLC; *U.S. Private*, pg. 129
AGROBACKA A.D.; *Int'l*, pg. 218
AGROVET A.D.; *Int'l*, pg. 221
A PLUS TREE, LLC; *U.S. Private*, pg. 19
ARIS HORTICULTURE, INC.; *U.S. Private*, pg. 323
ASIAN BAMBOO AG; *Int'l*, pg. 617
ATLANTIC TREE NURSERY, INC.—See The Robert Baker Companies; *U.S. Private*, pg. 4111
BAILEY NURSERIES-SHERMAN DIVISION—See Bailey Nurseries Inc.; *U.S. Private*, pg. 426
BARCELO ENTERPRISES, INC.; *U.S. Private*, pg. 473
BATTLEFIELD FARMS INC.—See Costa Farms, LLC; *U.S. Private*, pg. 1062
BAY BREEZE FARMS, INC.—See Agro-Iron, Inc.; *U.S. Private*, pg. 130
BECKER TREE FARM & NURSERY, INC.—See Becker Holding Corporation; *U.S. Private*, pg. 511
BONNIE PLANT FARM—See Alabama Farmers Cooperative, Inc.; *U.S. Private*, pg. 148
BORDIER'S NURSERY INC; *U.S. Private*, pg. 618
COLOR SPOT NURSERY, INC. - CARSON FACILITY—See Color Spot Nursery, Inc.; *U.S. Private*, pg. 973
COLOR SPOT NURSERY, INC. - CHINO VALLEY FACILITY—See Color Spot Nursery, Inc.; *U.S. Private*, pg. 973
COLOR SPOT NURSERY, INC. - HUNTSVILLE FACILITY—See Color Spot Nursery, Inc.; *U.S. Private*, pg. 973
COLOR SPOT NURSERY, INC. - KATY FACILITY—See Color Spot Nursery, Inc.; *U.S. Private*, pg. 973
COLOR SPOT NURSERY, INC. - LODI FACILITY—See Color Spot Nursery, Inc.; *U.S. Private*, pg. 973
COLOR SPOT NURSERY, INC. - SALINAS FACILITY—See Color Spot Nursery, Inc.; *U.S. Private*, pg. 973
COLOR SPOT NURSERY, INC. - SAN ANTONIO FACILITY—See Color Spot Nursery, Inc.; *U.S. Private*, pg. 973
COLOR SPOT NURSERY, INC. - SAN JUAN CAPISTRANO FACILITY—See Color Spot Nursery, Inc.; *U.S. Private*, pg. 973
COLOR SPOT NURSERY, INC. - TROUP FACILITY—See Color Spot Nursery, Inc.; *U.S. Private*, pg. 973
COLOR SPOT NURSERY, INC. - WACO FACILITY—See Color Spot Nursery, Inc.; *U.S. Private*, pg. 973
COLOR SPOT NURSERY, INC. - WALNUT SPRINGS FACILITY—See Color Spot Nursery, Inc.; *U.S. Private*, pg. 973
COOLEY'S GARDENS INC.; *U.S. Private*, pg. 1040
DAVE WILSON NURSERY, INC.; *U.S. Private*, pg. 1168
DOLOVO U RESTRUKTURIRANJU A.D.; *Int'l*, pg. 2159
DUDA RANCHES - DUDA SOD DIVISION—See A. Duda & Sons Inc.; *U.S. Private*, pg. 23
DUTCH HERITAGE GARDENS; *U.S. Private*, pg. 1294
DUTCHMASTER NURSERIES LTD.; *Int'l*, pg. 2235
EVERGREEN SC, LLC; *U.S. Private*, pg. 1440
FUTURE FORESTS FIJI LTD.; *Int'l*, pg. 2856
GREENLEAF NURSERY CO. INC.; *U.S. Private*, pg. 1778
G.R. KIRK COMPANY; *U.S. Private*, pg. 1631
HERMANN ENGELMANN GREENHOUSES INC.; *U.S. Private*, pg. 1925
HIDAYAT YAKIN SDN. BHD.; *Int'l*, pg. 3384
HINDUSTAN AGRIGENETICS LIMITED; *Int'l*, pg. 3399
INTER-STATE NURSERIES, INC.—See Plantron, Inc.; *U.S. Private*, pg. 3198
KUBE PAK CORP.; *U.S. Private*, pg. 2355
MARGO CARIBE, INC.; *U.S. Public*, pg. 1365
MARGO GARDEN PRODUCTS, INC.—See Margo Caribe, Inc.; *U.S. Public*, pg. 1365
MARGO NURSERY FARMS, INC.—See Margo Caribe, Inc.; *U.S. Public*, pg. 1365
MILLICAN NURSERIES, INC.—See SiteOne Landscape Supply, Inc.; *U.S. Public*, pg. 1889
MONROVIA GROWERS COMPANY; *U.S. Private*, pg. 2774
MONROVIA GROWERS-OREGON—See Monrovia Growers Company; *U.S. Private*, pg. 2774
MUSSER FORESTS, INC.; *U.S. Private*, pg. 2818
NORMAN'S NURSERY; *U.S. Private*, pg. 2938
PATTEN SEED COMPANY INC. - SUPER-SOD DIVISION—See Patten Seed Company Inc.; *U.S. Private*, pg. 3111
PATTEN SEED COMPANY INC. - SUPER-SOD TREES DIVISION—See Patten Seed Company Inc.; *U.S. Private*, pg. 3111
RAYONIER TRS FOREST OPERATIONS, LLC—See Rayonier Inc.; *U.S. Public*, pg. 1765
RUPPERT NURSERIES, INC.; *U.S. Private*, pg. 3504
SAN FELASCO NURSERIES, INC.—See Trulieve Cannabis Corp.; *U.S. Public*, pg. 2201
SHANGHAI GUANGZHAO FORESTRY DEVELOPMENT CO., LTD—See Guangzhao Industrial Forest Biotechnology Group Limited; *Int'l*, pg. 3164

111421 — NURSERY AND TREE PR...

SMITH GARDENS, INC.; *U.S. Private*, pg. 3695
SMITH'S GREENHOUSES, INC.; *U.S. Private*, pg. 3696
SOUTHEASTERN HAY & NURSERY, LLC—See National Association for Stock Car Auto Racing, Inc.; *U.S. Private*, pg. 2846
SPEEDLING, INCORPORATED-SUN CITY NURSERY DIVISION—See Speedling Incorporated; *U.S. Private*, pg. 3754
STARK BROTHERS NURSERIES & ORCHARDS CO.; *U.S. Private*, pg. 3786
SUBURBAN LAWN & GARDEN INC.; *U.S. Private*, pg. 3848
SYNGENTA SEEDS B.V.—See China National Chemical Corporation; *Int'l*, pg. 1530
TREE MEDIC, LLC; *U.S. Private*, pg. 4216
TREESAP FARMS, LLC; *U.S. Private*, pg. 4217
VIVEIROS DO FURADOURO UNIPESSOAL, LDA.—See Altri, SGPS, S.A.; *Int'l*, pg. 398
WAYNESBORO NURSERIES, INC.; *U.S. Private*, pg. 4460

111422 — FLORICULTURE PRODUCTION

A-1 FLORIDA SOD, INC.; *U.S. Private*, pg. 21
AGRIBIO HOLDING B.V.—See H2 Equity Partners B.V.; *Int'l*, pg. 3199
BALL COLOMBIA LTDA.—See Ball Horticultural Company; *U.S. Private*, pg. 459
BALL DO BRASIL—See Ball Horticultural Company; *U.S. Private*, pg. 460
BALL FLORAPLANT—See Ball Horticultural Company; *U.S. Private*, pg. 459
BALL HORTICULTURAL COMPANY - AUSTRALIA—See Ball Horticultural Company; *U.S. Private*, pg. 460
BALL HORTICULTURAL COMPANY; *U.S. Private*, pg. 459
BALL SEED CO.—See Ball Horticultural Company; *U.S. Private*, pg. 460
BALL STRAATHOF (PTY) LTD.—See Ball Horticultural Company; *U.S. Private*, pg. 460
BARBERET & BLANC S.A.—See H2 Equity Partners B.V.; *Int'l*, pg. 3199
BARENBRUG RESEARCH WOLFHEZE—See Barenbrug Holding B.V.; *Int'l*, pg. 864
BORDON HILL NURSERIES LTD.—See Ball Horticultural Company; *U.S. Private*, pg. 460
BRADFORD GREENHOUSES LTD.; *Int'l*, pg. 1134
COLOR SPOT NURSERY, INC.; *U.S. Private*, pg. 973
THE CONARD-PYLE COMPANY—See Ball Horticultural Company; *U.S. Private*, pg. 460
CULLUM SEEDS LLC; *U.S. Private*, pg. 1121
FIDES HOLDING B.V.—See H2 Equity Partners B.V.; *Int'l*, pg. 3199
FLORAL PLANT GROWERS LLC—See Sentinel Capital Partners, L.L.C.; *U.S. Private*, pg. 3609
GROUPE LIMAGRAIN HOLDING SA; *Int'l*, pg. 3107
HARRIS MORAN SEED CO.—See Groupe Limagrain Holding SA; *Int'l*, pg. 3108
HASTINGS NATURE & GARDEN CENTER—See H.G. Hastings Co.; *U.S. Private*, pg. 1826
HENRY F. MICHELL COMPANY INC.; *U.S. Private*, pg. 1918
HRB FLORICULTURE LIMITED; *Int'l*, pg. 3501
JAPAN AGRIBIO CO., LTD.—See H2 Equity Partners B.V.; *Int'l*, pg. 3199
KINDERGARDEN PLANTS LTD—See Ball Horticultural Company; *U.S. Private*, pg. 460
KURT WEISS GREENHOUSES INC.; *U.S. Private*, pg. 2358
KURT WEISS GREENHOUSES OF CONNECTICUT INC.—See Kurt Weiss Greenhouses Inc.; *U.S. Private*, pg. 2358
KURT WEISS OF NJ, INC.—See Kurt Weiss Greenhouses Inc.; *U.S. Private*, pg. 2358
KURT WEISS OF PENNSYLVANIA, INC.—See Kurt Weiss Greenhouses Inc.; *U.S. Private*, pg. 2358
LINDA VISTA S.A.—See Ball Horticultural Company; *U.S. Private*, pg. 460
LUCKY LANDSCAPE SUPPLY LLC—See SiteOne Landscape Supply, Inc.; *U.S. Private*, pg. 1889
MERSCHMAN SEEDS INC.; *U.S. Private*, pg. 2677
MICHIGAN WEST SHORE NURSERY, LLC.; *U.S. Private*, pg. 2701
MONSANTO CO. - ILLIOPOLIS—See Bayer Aktiengesellschaft; *Int'l*, pg. 908
PANAMERICAN SEED CO.—See Ball Horticultural Company; *U.S. Private*, pg. 460
PATTEN SEED COMPANY INC.; *U.S. Private*, pg. 3111
PAUL ECKE RANCH; *U.S. Private*, pg. 3112
PENNINGTON SEED INC.—See Central Garden & Pet Company; *U.S. Public*, pg. 473
SHAMROCK SEED COMPANY INC.—See Groupe Limagrain Holding SA; *Int'l*, pg. 3108
SHARP BROTHERS SEED COMPANY; *U.S. Private*, pg. 3626
SIEGERS SEED COMPANY INC.; *U.S. Private*, pg. 3646
SPEEDLING INCORPORATED; *U.S. Private*, pg. 3753
SUTTON FERNERIES INC.; *U.S. Private*, pg. 3887
TEUFEL HOLLY FARMS, INC.—See Teufel Landscape, Inc.; *U.S. Private*, pg. 3974
VILMORIN INC.—See Groupe Limagrain Holding SA; *Int'l*, pg. 3108
W. ATLEE BURPEE & CO.; *U.S. Private*, pg. 4417
WELBY GARDENS, CO.; *U.S. Private*, pg. 4473
WOERNER HOLDINGS INC.; *U.S. Private*, pg. 4553
WOERNER SOUTH INC.—See Woerner Holdings Inc.; *U.S. Private*, pg. 4553
WOERNER TURF GROUP INC.—See Woerner Holdings Inc.; *U.S. Private*, pg. 4553

111910 — TOBACCO FARMING

B.V. DELI-HTL TABAK MAATSCHAPPIJ—See Blackstone Inc.; *U.S. Public*, pg. 356
F.W. RICKARD SEEDS, INC.—See Altria Group, Inc.; *U.S. Public*, pg. 89
NATIONAL CIGAR CORPORATION; *U.S. Private*, pg. 2850
PHILIP MORRIS SABANCI SIGARA VE TUTUNCULUK A.S.—See Philip Morris International Inc.; *U.S. Public*, pg. 1687

111920 — COTTON FARMING

AUSTRALIAN FOOD & FIBRE LTD.; *Int'l*, pg. 721
CLARK COTTON—See AFGRI Limited; *Int'l*, pg. 188
INDUSTRIA TEXTIL PIURA S.A.—See Axxion Asset Management SAC; *Int'l*, pg. 773
J.G. BOSWELL CO., INC.; *U.S. Private*, pg. 2165
PARKDALE, INC.; *U.S. Private*, pg. 3097
THE SCOTTS COMPANY—See The Scotts Miracle-Gro Company; *U.S. Public*, pg. 2127
WHITE GOLD COTTON MARKETING, LLC.; *U.S. Private*, pg. 4509

111930 — SUGARCANE FARMING

AGRICOLA PONTE ALTA S.A.—See Cosan S.A.; *Int'l*, pg. 1809
AL-ABBAS SUGAR MILLS LIMITED; *Int'l*, pg. 283
ALEXANDER & BALDWIN SUGAR MUSEUM—See Alexander & Baldwin, Inc.; *U.S. Public*, pg. 75
ALTEO LIMITED; *Int'l*, pg. 391
CLEWISTON SUGAR HOUSE—See United States Sugar Corporation; *U.S. Private*, pg. 4300
CROOKES BROTHERS LIMITED; *Int'l*, pg. 1855
CROOKES PLANTATIONS LTD—See CROOKES BROTHERS LIMITED; *Int'l*, pg. 1855
FLORIDA CRYSTALS CORPORATION; *U.S. Private*, pg. 1548
NEW HOPE SOUTH INC.—See Florida Crystals Corporation; *U.S. Private*, pg. 1548
UNITED STATES SUGAR CORPORATION; *U.S. Private*, pg. 4300
UNITED SUGAR COMPANY—See A.K. Al-Muhaidib & Sons Group of Companies; *Int'l*, pg. 24

111991 — SUGAR BEET FARMING

ASTARTA HOLDING N.V.; *Int'l*, pg. 651
BANNARI AMMAN SUGARS LTD.; *Int'l*, pg. 850
HOLLY SEED, LLC.—See Southern Minnesota Beet Sugar Cooperative; *U.S. Private*, pg. 3733
MARIBO SEED INTERNATIONAL APS—See China National Chemical Corporation; *Int'l*, pg. 1529

111992 — PEANUT FARMING

GOLDEN GRASS, INC.; *Int'l*, pg. 3029
GOLDEN PEANUT COMPANY, LLC—See Archer-Daniels-Midland Company; *U.S. Public*, pg. 185

111998 — ALL OTHER MISCELLANEOUS CROP FARMING

AAP, INC.; *Int'l*, pg. 36
ABBA MEDIX CORP.—See Canada House Wellness Group Inc.; *Int'l*, pg. 1278
ACHIT ALKABY JOINT STOCK COMPANY; *Int'l*, pg. 103
ADECOAGRO S.A.; *Int'l*, pg. 141
ADM AGRI-INDUSTRIES COMPANY—See Archer-Daniels-Midland Company; *U.S. Public*, pg. 184
AGDATA, LP—See Levine Leichtman Capital Partners, LLC; *U.S. Private*, pg. 2435
AGNOVA TECHNOLOGIES PTY LTD—See American Vanguard Corporation; *U.S. Public*, pg. 111
AGRARIUS AG; *Int'l*, pg. 214
AGRELIANT GENETICS LLC—See Groupe Limagrain Holding SA; *Int'l*, pg. 3108
AGRICOLA CERRO PRIETO S.A.; *Int'l*, pg. 216
AGRINOS DO BRAZIL FERTILIZANTES BIOLOGICOS LTDA—See American Vanguard Corporation; *U.S. Public*, pg. 111
AGRINOS INDIA PRIVATE LIMITED—See American Vanguard Corporation; *U.S. Public*, pg. 111
AGRINOS UKRAINE LLC—See American Vanguard Corporation; *U.S. Public*, pg. 111
AGRITERRA LTD.; *Int'l*, pg. 218
AGRO100—See Aqua Capital; *Int'l*, pg. 527
AGROHERCEGOVINA A.D.; *Int'l*, pg. 219
AGRO PUCALA S.A.A.; *Int'l*, pg. 218
AGROS A.D.; *Int'l*, pg. 220
ALEKSA SANTIC U RESTRUKTURIRANJU A.D.; *Int'l*, pg. 306
AL-JOUF AGRICULTURAL DEVELOPMENT COMPANY; *Int'l*, pg. 286
ALLC SHIYKIVSKE—See Agroton Public Ltd; *Int'l*, pg. 221
ALSUWAIKET AGRICULTURE DIVISION—See AlSuwaiket Trading & Contracting Co.; *Int'l*, pg. 383
AMANA FARMS, INC.—See Amana Society, Inc.; *U.S. Private*, pg. 216
AMANA SOCIETY, INC.; *U.S. Private*, pg. 216
ASIA CASSAVA RESOURCES HOLDINGS LIMITED; *Int'l*, pg. 610
ATLAS FOR LAND RECLAMATION & AGRICULTURAL PROCESSING; *Int'l*, pg. 685
AUGA GRUDUVA, UAB—See AUGA group, AB; *Int'l*, pg. 702
AUGA JURBARKAI, ZUB—See AUGA group, AB; *Int'l*, pg. 702
AUGA LANKESA, ZUB—See AUGA group, AB; *Int'l*, pg. 702
AUGA MANTVILISKIS, ZUB—See AUGA group, AB; *Int'l*, pg. 702
AUGA NAUSODE, ZUB—See AUGA group, AB; *Int'l*, pg. 702
AUGA SKEMIAI, ZUB—See AUGA group, AB; *Int'l*, pg. 702
AUGA SMILGIAI, ZUB—See AUGA group, AB; *Int'l*, pg. 702
AUGA SPINDULYS, ZUB—See AUGA group, AB; *Int'l*, pg. 703
AUGA ZELSVELE, ZUB—See AUGA group, AB; *Int'l*, pg. 703
AUVERGNE CREATIONS—See Groupe Limagrain Holding SA; *Int'l*, pg. 3107
BAJINOVAC A.D.; *Int'l*, pg. 804
BALAXI PHARMACEUTICALS LIMITED; *Int'l*, pg. 807
BANATSKI DESPOTOVAC A.D.; *Int'l*, pg. 814
BANSIONS TEA INDUSTRIES LIMITED; *Int'l*, pg. 854
BASF ARGENTINA S.A.—See BASF SE; *Int'l*, pg. 872
BAYER BIOSCIENCE GMBH—See Bayer Aktiengesellschaft; *Int'l*, pg. 904
BAYER CROPSCIENCE HOLDING INC.—See Bayer Aktiengesellschaft; *Int'l*, pg. 903
BAYER CROPSCIENCE HOLDINGS INC.—See Bayer Aktiengesellschaft; *Int'l*, pg. 903
BAYER CROPSCIENCE INC.—See Bayer Aktiengesellschaft; *Int'l*, pg. 903
BAYER CROPSCIENCE (PRIVATE) LIMITED—See Bayer Aktiengesellschaft; *Int'l*, pg. 903
BAYER S.A.—See Bayer Aktiengesellschaft; *Int'l*, pg. 906
BEEYU OVERSEAS LIMITED; *Int'l*, pg. 939
BEJO ZADEN B.V.; *Int'l*, pg. 962
BEZDAN POLJOPRIVREDNO PREDUZECE A.D.; *Int'l*, pg. 1006
BORAC A.D.; *Int'l*, pg. 1112
BRASILAGRO - COMPANHIA BRASILEIRA DE PROPRIEDADES AGRICOLAS; *Int'l*, pg. 1140
BUDUCNOST A.D.; *Int'l*, pg. 1211
BUDUCNOST A.D.; *Int'l*, pg. 1211
BZAM LTD.; *Int'l*, pg. 1237
CANADA WEST HARVEST CENTRE INC.—See Claas KGaA mbH; *Int'l*, pg. 1640
CARGILL LIMITED—See Cargill, Inc.; *U.S. Private*, pg. 757
CHAODA MODERN AGRICULTURE HOLDINGS LIMITED; *Int'l*, pg. 1447
CHARLESTON TEA PLANTATION—See R.C. Bigelow, Inc.; *U.S. Private*, pg. 3334
CH BIOTECH R&D CO., LTD.; *Int'l*, pg. 1435
CJSC AGROTON—See Agroton Public Ltd; *Int'l*, pg. 221
COFCO (NEW YORK) CO., LTD.—See COFCO Limited; *Int'l*, pg. 1691
COMPASS MINERALS MANITOBA INC.—See Compass Minerals International, Inc.; *U.S. Public*, pg. 560
COMPASS MINERALS WYNYARD INC.—See Compass Minerals International, Inc.; *U.S. Public*, pg. 560
COUNTY SUPER SPUDS, INC.; *U.S. Private*, pg. 1068
CUBICFARM SYSTEMS CORP.; *Int'l*, pg. 1875
CURLEW VALLEY FARMS, LLC—See Compass Minerals International, Inc.; *U.S. Public*, pg. 560
DAE YU CO., LTD.; *Int'l*, pg. 1905
DANISH AGRO AMBA; *Int'l*, pg. 1963
DLF SEEDS A/S; *Int'l*, pg. 2141
DRAGESHOLM AB—See Carl Bennet AB; *Int'l*, pg. 1331
DUVAN A.D.; *Int'l*, pg. 2236
EL NASR FOR MANUFACTURING AGRICULTURAL CROPS S.A.E.; *Int'l*, pg. 2341
ENL LAND LTD—See ENL Limited; *Int'l*, pg. 2441
EURALIS SAATEN GMBH—See Euralis Coop; *Int'l*, pg. 2527
FARMCARE LIMITED—See Co-operative Group Limited; *Int'l*, pg. 1679
FARMERS ALLIANCE—See CHS INC.; *U.S. Public*, pg. 492
FARM LANDS OF AFRICA, INC.; *Int'l*, pg. 2619
FRESH ORIGINS, LLC—See Sun Capital Partners, Inc.; *U.S. Private*, pg. 3859
GANSU DUNHUANG SEED GROUP CO., LTD.; *Int'l*, pg. 2881

N.A.I.C.S. INDEX

GANSU JOY AGRICULTURAL TECHNOLOGY CO., LTD.; *Int'l*, pg. 2881
GROWGENIX SOLUTIONS LLC—See Nu Skin Enterprises, Inc.; *U.S. Public*, pg. 1551
HAIL AGRICULTURAL DEVELOPMENT COMPANY—See Almarai Company Ltd.; *Int'l*, pg. 363
HAJDUCICA A.D.; *Int'l*, pg. 3219
HAYLEYS AGRO FARMS (PVT) LTD.—See Hayleys PLC; *Int'l*, pg. 3292
HENSALL DISTRICT CO-OPERATIVE, INC.; *Int'l*, pg. 3355
HERCEGOVINA A.D.; *Int'l*, pg. 3360
HITCH ENTERPRISES INC.; *U.S. Private*, pg. 1952
HOVID BERHAD; *Int'l*, pg. 3492
THE HUMPHREY COMPANY—See b.a. Sweetie Candy Company; *U.S. Private*, pg. 420
JENBROOK PTY LTD—See EVE Health Group Limited; *Int'l*, pg. 2561
KALERA PUBLIC LIMITED COMPANY; *U.S. Public*, pg. 1213
KWS ARGENTINA S.A.—See Grupo Don Mario; *Int'l*, pg. 3126
LANCE FUNK FARMS; *U.S. Private*, pg. 2382
LG SEEDS—See Groupe Limagrain Holding SA; *Int'l*, pg. 3108
LIMONEIRA COMPANY; *U.S. Public*, pg. 1316
LINN COOPERATIVE OIL COMPANY; *U.S. Private*, pg. 2462
MADAH PERKASA SDN BHD—See Far East Holdings Berhad; *Int'l*, pg. 2616
MANATI INDUSTRIES, INC.; *U.S. Public*, pg. 1356
MATERRA, LLC.; *U.S. Private*, pg. 2610
MCCORMICK POLSKA S.A.—See McCormick & Company, Incorporated; *U.S. Public*, pg. 1404
MFA OIL BIOMASS LLC—See MFA Oil Company; *U.S. Private*, pg. 2693
MIDWESTERN BIOAG, INC.; *U.S. Private*, pg. 2724
MILK INDUSTRY MANAGEMENT CORP.; *U.S. Private*, pg. 2729
MILLHAVEN COMPANY INC.—See Shivers Trading & Operating Company; *U.S. Private*, pg. 3638
MORRISON ENTERPRISES; *U.S. Private*, pg. 2789
NMG SAN DIEGO, LLC—See Body and Mind Inc.; *Int'l*, pg. 1097
THE NORTON COMPANY; *U.S. Private*, pg. 4085
NUNHEMS HUNGARY KFT.—See Bayer Aktiengesellschaft; *Int'l*, pg. 903
OOO OKA MOLOKO—See Ekosem-Agrar GmbH; *Int'l*, pg. 2339
OSEVA, A.S.—See Agrofert Holding, a.s.; *Int'l*, pg. 219
OSTER COMMUNICATIONS INC.; *U.S. Private*, pg. 3048
PACIFIC FOODS OF OREGON, INC.—See Campbell Soup Company; *U.S. Public*, pg. 427
PACIFIC TRELLIS FRUIT LLC—See Arable Capital Partners LLC; *U.S. Private*, pg. 307
PIONEER HI-BRED INTERNATIONAL—See Corteva, Inc.; *U.S. Public*, pg. 583
PIONEER HI-BRED INTERNATIONAL—See Corteva, Inc.; *U.S. Public*, pg. 583
PIONEER HI-BRED INTERNATIONAL—See Corteva, Inc.; *U.S. Public*, pg. 583
PIONEER HI-BRED INTERNATIONAL—See Corteva, Inc.; *U.S. Public*, pg. 583
PIONEER HI-BRED INTERNATIONAL—See Corteva, Inc.; *U.S. Public*, pg. 583
PIONEER HI-BRED INTERNATIONAL—See Corteva, Inc.; *U.S. Public*, pg. 583
PIONEER HI-BRED INTERNATIONAL—See Corteva, Inc.; *U.S. Public*, pg. 583
PIONEER HI-BRED PUERTO RICO—See Corteva, Inc.; *U.S. Public*, pg. 583
PLUM GROVE PTY LTD—See Seaboard Corporation; *U.S. Public*, pg. 1850
PRT GROWING SERVICES LTD.—See Mill Road Capital Management LLC; *U.S. Private*, pg. 2730
SEED CO. LIMITED—See Cottco Holdings Limited; *Int'l*, pg. 1817
SENECA FOOD CORP.—See General Mills, Inc.; *U.S. Public*, pg. 922
SH MARKETS, INC.—See Sprouts Farmers Markets, Inc.; *U.S. Public*, pg. 1920
THE SOUTH AFRICAN BREWERIES HOP FARMS (PTY) LTD—See Anheuser-Busch InBev SA/NV; *Int'l*, pg. 464
STOLLER MEXICO S.A. DE C.V—See Corteva, Inc.; *U.S. Public*, pg. 584
STWC HOLDINGS, INC.; *U.S. Public*, pg. 1958
SWEETWATER ORGANIC COMMUNITY FARM, INC.; *U.S. Private*, pg. 3892
TURF MERCHANTS, INC.; *U.S. Private*, pg. 4259
UNITED GREENERIES LTD.—See Hygrovest Limited; *Int'l*, pg. 3549
US SEEDS LLC—See Bayer Aktiengesellschaft; *Int'l*, pg. 903
VILMORIN & CIE SA—See Groupe Limagrain Holding SA; *Int'l*, pg. 3108
WINDFALL INVESTORS, LLC—See Limoneira Company; *U.S. Public*, pg. 1316

112111 — BEEF CATTLE RANCHING AND FARMING

ADAMS RANCH INC.; *U.S. Private*, pg. 75
AGROCULTIVO—See HORIBA Ltd; *Int'l*, pg. 3474
ASOCIACION DE COOPERATIVAS ARGENTINAS C.L.; *Int'l*, pg. 628
AUSTRALIAN AGRICULTURAL COMPANY LIMITED; *Int'l*, pg. 720
CARGILL MEAT SOLUTIONS—See Cargill, Inc.; *U.S. Private*, pg. 758
COLORADO CATTLEMEN'S ASSOCIATION; *U.S. Private*, pg. 973
DESERET RANCHES OF FLORIDA; *U.S. Private*, pg. 1212
DOUGLAS LAKE CATTLE CO.; *U.S. Private*, pg. 2181
GRANDS ELEVAGES DE KATONGOLA—See George Forrest International S.A.; *Int'l*, pg. 2938
HEARST RANCH—See The Hearst Corporation; *U.S. Private*, pg. 4048
HOODOO LAND AND CATTLE COMPANY—See Hunt Consolidated, Inc.; *U.S. Private*, pg. 2008
J.G. BOSWELL CO., INC.—See J.G. Boswell Co., Inc.; *U.S. Private*, pg. 2165
KAGOSHIMA SUNRISE FARM K.K.—See AEON Co., Ltd.; *Int'l*, pg. 177
LYKES BROTHERS INC.; *U.S. Private*, pg. 2519
NIMAN RANCH, INC.—See Perdue Farms Incorporated; *U.S. Private*, pg. 3147
STRICKLAND RANCH AND EXPORTS, INC.; *U.S. Private*, pg. 3840
TRUE RANCHES—See True Companies; *U.S. Private*, pg. 4247
ZEMSPOL, S.R.O.—See CPI Property Group, S.A.; *Int'l*, pg. 1825

112112 — CATTLE FEEDLOTS

ADAMS LAND & CATTLE CO.; *U.S. Private*, pg. 74
AGRI BEEF CO., INC.; *U.S. Private*, pg. 129
AGVENTURE FEEDS & SEED INC.; *U.S. Private*, pg. 130
AZTX CATTLE CO., LTD.; *U.S. Private*, pg. 416
BARTLETT CATTLE COMPANY, L.P.—See Bartlett & Company; *U.S. Private*, pg. 483
BRANDT CO., INC.; *U.S. Private*, pg. 638
CACTUS FEEDERS, INC.; *U.S. Private*, pg. 712
CARGILL MEAT SOLUTIONS, CAPROCK CATTLE FEEDERS—See Cargill, Inc.; *U.S. Private*, pg. 758
CATTLELAND FEEDYARDS LTD.; *Int'l*, pg. 1361
FARMSCO.; *Int'l*, pg. 2620
FIVE RIVERS CATTLE FEEDING, LLC—See Pinnacle Asset Management, L.P.; *U.S. Private*, pg. 3184
FORD COUNTY FEED YARD INC.—See Ford Holding Company; *U.S. Private*, pg. 1564
FRIONA FEED YARD—See Friona Industries, LP; *U.S. Private*, pg. 1612
HARRIS FEEDING CO.—See Central Valley Meat Holding Company; *U.S. Private*, pg. 826
HITCH FEEDERS INC.—See Hitch Enterprises Inc.; *U.S. Private*, pg. 1952
INTERSTATE FEEDERS, LLC—See Pinnacle Asset Management, L.P.; *U.S. Private*, pg. 3184
J.R. SIMPLOT COMPANY - LAND & LIVESTOCK—See J.R. Simplot Company; *U.S. Private*, pg. 2170
KILLARA FEEDLOT PTY. LTD.—See Elders Limited; *Int'l*, pg. 2346
LITTLEFIELD FEED YARD—See Friona Industries, LP; *U.S. Private*, pg. 1612
MID-AMERICA FEED YARD; *U.S. Private*, pg. 2707
NEW HORIZON FARM LLP—See Hord Livestock Company, Inc.; *U.S. Private*, pg. 1980
PERRYTON FEEDERS INC.; *U.S. Private*, pg. 3154
P&H MILLING GROUP—See Exceldor Cooperative Avicole; *Int'l*, pg. 2578
RANDALL COUNTY FEED YARD—See Friona Industries, LP; *U.S. Private*, pg. 1612
SCHAAKE CORPORATION; *U.S. Private*, pg. 3562
SETLIFF BROTHERS, INC.; *U.S. Private*, pg. 3617
SUBLETTE ENTERPRISES INC.; *U.S. Private*, pg. 3847
SWISHER COUNTY CATTLE CO.—See Friona Industries, LP; *U.S. Private*, pg. 1612
T & E CATTLE COMPANY; *U.S. Private*, pg. 3908
TEXAS BEEF LTD.; *U.S. Private*, pg. 3974
WHEELER BROTHERS GRAIN CO.; *U.S. Private*, pg. 4505

112120 — DAIRY CATTLE AND MILK PRODUCTION

AGROPRODUKT A.D.; *Int'l*, pg. 220
ALAN RITCHEY INC.; *U.S. Private*, pg. 150
ALBALACT S.A.—See Groupe Lactalis SA; *Int'l*, pg. 3105
AL SAFI DANONE CO.—See Al Faisaliah Group; *Int'l*, pg. 277
AL SAFI DANONE CO.—See Danone; *Int'l*, pg. 1965
ARLA FOODS AB—See Arla Foods amba; *Int'l*, pg. 572
AUSTRALIAN DAIRY NUTRITIONALS GROUP; *Int'l*, pg. 721

112120 — DAIRY CATTLE AND MI...

BD AGRO AD; *Int'l*, pg. 929
CAPITOL DAIRY SOLUTIONS—See AptarGroup, Inc.; *U.S. Public*, pg. 174
CHINA HUISHAN DAIRY HOLDINGS COMPANY LIMITED; *Int'l*, pg. 1509
CHINA MODERN AGRICULTURAL INFORMATION, INC.; *Int'l*, pg. 1524
CHINA MODERN DAIRY HOLDINGS LTD.—See China Mengniu Dairy Company Limited; *Int'l*, pg. 1520
CHINA SHENGMU ORGANIC MILK LIMITED; *Int'l*, pg. 1551
CJSC RUSAGRO-AYDAR—See Gruppa Kompaniy Rusagro OOO; *Int'l*, pg. 3140
DAKIN DAIRY FARMS, INC.; *U.S. Private*, pg. 1147
DARIGOLD, INC.—See Northwest Dairy Association; *U.S. Private*, pg. 2959
DELAVAL SIA—See Alfa Laval AB; *Int'l*, pg. 311
DODLA DAIRY LIMITED; *Int'l*, pg. 2153
THE DOLSEN COMPANIES, INC.; *U.S. Private*, pg. 4022
DONAGHYS LIMITED - DUNEDIN FACTORY—See Donaghys Limited; *Int'l*, pg. 2163
DUKAT MLIJECNA INDUSTRIJA D.D.—See Groupe Lactalis SA; *Int'l*, pg. 3105
EMMI AG; *Int'l*, pg. 2384
FARMLAND A.D.; *Int'l*, pg. 2620
FAUJI FOODS LIMITED; *Int'l*, pg. 2623
FGV AGRO FRESH TECHNOLOGY SDN. BHD.—See FGV Holdings Bhd; *Int'l*, pg. 2649
FGV DAIRY FARM SDN. BHD.—See FGV Holdings Bhd; *Int'l*, pg. 2649
FIRSTFARMS AGRA M. S.R.O.—See FirstFarms A/S; *Int'l*, pg. 2688
FIRSTFARMS SLOVAKIET APS—See FirstFarms A/S; *Int'l*, pg. 2688
FONTERRA BRANDS (MIDDLE EAST) LLC—See Fonterra Co-Operative Group Ltd.; *Int'l*, pg. 2726
FOREMOST FARMS USA COOPERATIVE; *U.S. Private*, pg. 1565
GAY LEA FOODS CO-OPERATIVE LTD.; *Int'l*, pg. 2891
GLANBIA CONSUMER FOODS LIMITED—See Glanbia Co-Operative Society Limited; *Int'l*, pg. 2988
GLANBIA FOOD INGREDIENTS—See Glanbia Co-Operative Society Limited; *Int'l*, pg. 2988
GLANBIA INGREDIENTS IRELAND—See Glanbia Co-Operative Society Limited; *Int'l*, pg. 2988
GRASSLAND DAIRY PRODUCTS, INC.; *U.S. Private*, pg. 1758
HANOIMILK JSC; *Int'l*, pg. 3258
HENAN KEDI DAIRY INDUSTRY CO., LTD.; *Int'l*, pg. 3342
HOLLANDIA DAIRY, INC.; *U.S. Private*, pg. 1964
IMC; *Int'l*, pg. 3620
KAROUN DAIRIES, LLC—See Groupe Lactalis SA; *Int'l*, pg. 3106
LAND O'LAKES ANIMAL MILK PRODUCTS COMPANY - BLACK RIVER FALLS PLANT—See Land O'Lakes, Inc.; *U.S. Private*, pg. 2383
LAND O'LAKES ANIMAL MILK PRODUCTS COMPANY—See Land O'Lakes, Inc.; *U.S. Private*, pg. 2383
LARSON DAIRY INC.; *U.S. Private*, pg. 2393
LIFEWAY FOODS, INC.; *U.S. Public*, pg. 1313
LION DAIRY & DRINKS PTY. LTD. - CHELSEA HEIGHTS PLANT—See Bega Cheese Ltd.; *Int'l*, pg. 940
LION DAIRY & DRINKS PTY. LTD. - PENRITH PLANT—See Bega Cheese Ltd.; *Int'l*, pg. 940
LION DAIRY & DRINKS PTY. LTD. - SALISBURY PLANT—See Bega Cheese Ltd.; *Int'l*, pg. 940
MAYBROOK DAIRY LIMITED—See Donegal Investment Group Plc; *Int'l*, pg. 2163
M&B OF TAMPA INC.—See M&B Products Inc.; *U.S. Private*, pg. 2524
MCARTHUR DAIRY, LLC—See Dean Foods Company; *U.S. Private*, pg. 1183
MCARTHUR FARMS, INC.; *U.S. Private*, pg. 2625
MCCORMICK FARMS, LLC—See WesBanco, Inc.; *U.S. Public*, pg. 2349
MENGNIU DAIRY (DENGKOU BAYAN GAOLE) CO., LTD.—See China Mengniu Dairy Company Limited; *Int'l*, pg. 1520
NATIONAL DAIRY AND FOOD COMPANY LTD.—See Hayel Saeed Anam Group of Companies; *Int'l*, pg. 3291
NORTHWEST DAIRY ASSOCIATION; *U.S. Private*, pg. 2959
OOO AGROFIRMA MEZHDURECHYE—See Ekosem-Agrar GmbH; *Int'l*, pg. 2339
OOO EKONIVAAGRO—See Ekosem-Agrar GmbH; *Int'l*, pg. 2339
OOO SIBIRSKAYA NIVA—See Ekosem-Agrar GmbH; *Int'l*, pg. 2339
OOO STUPINSKAYA NIVA—See Ekosem-Agrar GmbH; *Int'l*, pg. 2339
OOO ZASCHITNOE—See Ekosem-Agrar GmbH; *Int'l*, pg. 2339
POLKA DOT DAIRY; *U.S. Private*, pg. 3224
PURITY DAIRIES, LLC—See Dean Foods Company; *U.S. Private*, pg. 1184
QUALITY CHEKD DAIRIES, INC.; *U.S. Private*, pg. 3318
SHAMROCK FOODS COMPANY; *U.S. Private*, pg. 3624

112120 — DAIRY CATTLE AND MI...

SOUTHEAST MILK, INC.; *U.S. Private*, pg. 3726
TNUVA FOOD INDUSTRIES LTD.—See Bright Food (Group) Co., Ltd.; *Int'l*, pg. 1161
TOFT DAIRY, INC.; *U.S. Private*, pg. 4181
VIGOR ALIMENTOS S.A.—See Grupo LALA S.A. de C.V.; *Int'l*, pg. 3131

112130 — DUAL-PURPOSE CATTLE RANCHING AND FARMING

KING RANCH, INC.; *U.S. Private*, pg. 2310

112210 — HOG AND PIG FARMING

AD DRAGAN MARKOVIC; *Int'l*, pg. 122
AGROCERES PIC—See Genus Plc; *Int'l*, pg. 2930
ATAHUAMPA PIC S.A.—See Genus Plc; *Int'l*, pg. 2931
BELGORODSKY BACON—See Gruppa Kompaniy Rusagro OOO; *Int'l*, pg. 3140
CARRS BILLINGTON AGRICULTURE (SALES), ANNAN—See Carr's Group PLC; *Int'l*, pg. 1343
CESKA PIC S.R.O.—See Genus Plc; *Int'l*, pg. 2931
CHINA PUTIAN FOOD HOLDING LIMITED; *Int'l*, pg. 1542
CHRISTENSEN FARMS MIDWEST, LLC; *U.S. Private*, pg. 890
CHUYING AGRO-PASTORAL GROUP CO., LTD.; *Int'l*, pg. 1600
CLEMENS FAMILY CORPORATION; *U.S. Private*, pg. 940
DOZA DERD A.D.; *Int'l*, pg. 2187
HOG SLAT INC.; *U.S. Private*, pg. 1961
HORD FAMILY FARMS LLC—See Hord Livestock Company, Inc.; *U.S. Private*, pg. 1980
HORD LIVESTOCK COMPANY, INC.; *U.S. Private*, pg. 1980
HUISHENG INTERNATIONAL HOLDINGS LIMITED; *Int'l*, pg. 3527
HUNAN NEW WELLFUL CO., LTD.; *Int'l*, pg. 3533
IAN MOSEY LTD; *Int'l*, pg. 3569
IOWA SELECT FARMS, L.L.P.; *U.S. Private*, pg. 2135
IWATANI CAMBOROUGH CO. LTD.—See Genus Plc; *Int'l*, pg. 2931
KANHYM ESTATES PIC SOUTH AFRICA—See Genus Plc; *Int'l*, pg. 2931
KARRO FOOD GROUP LIMITED—See CapVest Limited; *Int'l*, pg. 1318
MAXWELL FOODS, LLC; *U.S. Private*, pg. 2619
MOUNTAIN PRAIRIE, LLC—See Hormel Foods Corporation; *U.S. Public*, pg. 1054
PENNFIELD CORPORATION; *U.S. Private*, pg. 3136
PIC ARGENTINA—See Genus Plc; *Int'l*, pg. 2931
PIC AUSTRALIA—See Genus Plc; *Int'l*, pg. 2931
PIC BENELUX BV—See Genus Plc; *Int'l*, pg. 2931
PIC CANADA LTD.—See Genus Plc; *Int'l*, pg. 2931
PIC COLOMBIA S.A.—See Genus Plc; *Int'l*, pg. 2931
PIC DENMARK A/S—See Genus Plc; *Int'l*, pg. 2931
PIC DEUTSCHLAND GMBH—See Genus Plc; *Int'l*, pg. 2931
PIC ESPANA—See Genus Plc; *Int'l*, pg. 2931
PIC FRANCE—See Genus Plc; *Int'l*, pg. 2931
PIC GENETICS LLC—See Genus Plc; *Int'l*, pg. 2930
PIC IRELAND GTC—See Genus Plc; *Int'l*, pg. 2931
PIC ITALIA S.P.A.—See Genus Plc; *Int'l*, pg. 2931
PIC KOREA INC.—See Genus Plc; *Int'l*, pg. 2931
PIC MEXICO—See Genus Plc; *Int'l*, pg. 2931
PIC NEW ZEALAND—See Genus Plc; *Int'l*, pg. 2931
PIC PHILIPPINES INC.—See Genus Plc; *Int'l*, pg. 2931
PIC POLSKA SP. Z.O.O.—See Genus Plc; *Int'l*, pg. 2931
PIC PORTUGAL—See Genus Plc; *Int'l*, pg. 2931
PIC SIAM CO., LTD.—See Genus Plc; *Int'l*, pg. 2931
PIC UK—See Genus Plc; *Int'l*, pg. 2930
PIC USA, INC.—See Genus Plc; *Int'l*, pg. 2931
SEABOARD FARMS OF OKLAHOMA INC.—See Seaboard Corporation; *U.S. Public*, pg. 1851
SEABOARD FOODS SERVICES INC.—See Seaboard Corporation; *U.S. Public*, pg. 1851
SWINE GRAPHICS ENTERPRISES LP; *U.S. Private*, pg. 3893
TAMBOVSKY BACON—See Gruppa Kompaniy Rusagro OOO; *Int'l*, pg. 3140

112310 — CHICKEN EGG PRODUCTION

AD VETPRODUKT; *Int'l*, pg. 122
ATLANTIC POULTRY INC. - EGG DIVISION—See Atlantic Poultry Inc.; *Int'l*, pg. 675
ATLANTIC POULTRY INC.; *Int'l*, pg. 675
AVANGARDCO INVESTMENTS PUBLIC LIMITED; *Int'l*, pg. 734
BRASWELL FOODS—See Braswell Milling Company; *U.S. Private*, pg. 640
CAL-MAINE FOODS, INC.; *U.S. Public*, pg. 421
CREIGHTON BROTHERS L.L.C.; *U.S. Private*, pg. 1092
CREIGHTON BROTHERS—See Creighton Brothers L.L.C.; *U.S. Private*, pg. 1092
DELTA EGG FARM, LLC—See Cal-Maine Foods, Inc.; *U.S. Public*, pg. 421
EGGLAND'S BEST, INC.; *U.S. Private*, pg. 1344
FASSIO EGG FARMS, INC.—See Cal-Maine Foods, Inc.; *U.S. Public*, pg. 421
FEATHERLAND EGG FARMS, INC.—See Cal-Maine Foods, Inc.; *U.S. Public*, pg. 421
GLENWOOD FOODS, L.L.C.—See Braswell Milling Company; *U.S. Private*, pg. 640
HLRB PROCESSING SDN. BHD.—See Huat Lai Resources Berhad; *Int'l*, pg. 3514
HOKURYO CO., LTD.; *Int'l*, pg. 3445
IFUJI SANGYO CO., LTD.; *Int'l*, pg. 3600
INVESTMENT AND DEVELOPMENT BREED PROCESSING COMPANY LIMITED—See DABACO Group Joint Stock Company; *Int'l*, pg. 1902
MAHARD EGG FARM, INC.—See Cal-Maine Foods, Inc.; *U.S. Public*, pg. 421
MCNALLY ENTERPRISES, INC—See Moark Productions Inc.; *U.S. Private*, pg. 2756
NOAH W. KREIDER & SON; *U.S. Private*, pg. 2932
OVOPRO—See FPS Food Processing Systems B.V.; *Int'l*, pg. 2757
RITEWOOD, INC.; *U.S. Private*, pg. 3442
SPARBOE FARMS; *U.S. Private*, pg. 3745
TEO SENG FARMING SDN BHD—See Emerging Glory Sdn Bhd; *Int'l*, pg. 2379
TYSON CHICKEN, INC.—See Tyson Foods, Inc.; *U.S. Public*, pg. 2210
VITAL FARMS, INC; *U.S. Public*, pg. 2306
WILLAMETTE EGG FARMS LLC—See Post Holdings, Inc.; *U.S. Public*, pg. 1703

112320 — BROILERS AND OTHER MEAT TYPE CHICKEN PRODUCTION

3-STJERNET A/S—See Atria Plc; *Int'l*, pg. 693
AGRICULTURAL DEVELOPMENT COMPANY LTD.—See Dabbagh Group Holding Company Ltd.; *Int'l*, pg. 1902
AGROSUPER SA; *Int'l*, pg. 220
AKIKAWA FOODS & FARMS CO., LTD.; *Int'l*, pg. 263
ASTRAL OPERATIONS LIMITED - EARLYBIRD FARM DIVISION—See Astral Foods Limited; *Int'l*, pg. 658
ASTRAL OPERATIONS LIMITED—See Astral Foods Limited; *Int'l*, pg. 658
AVICOLA MOLISANA SRL—See Arena Holding S.p.A.; *Int'l*, pg. 558
BANVIT BANDIRMA VITAMINLI YEM SANAYII ANONIM SIRKETI; *Int'l*, pg. 855
COUNTY FAIR FOODS (PTY) LTD—See Astral Foods Limited; *Int'l*, pg. 658
DONGWOO FARM TO TABLE CO., LTD.; *Int'l*, pg. 2171
GEORGE'S FARMS INC.—See George's Inc.; *U.S. Private*, pg. 1683
GFPT PUBLIC COMPANY LIMITED - GFPT PLANT—See GFPT Public Company Limited; *Int'l*, pg. 2957
GOLDEN ROD BROILERS INC.; *U.S. Private*, pg. 1732
GRAND RIVER FOODS; *Int'l*, pg. 3056
GUANGDONG JIALONG FOOD CO., LTD.; *Int'l*, pg. 3156
HORMEL FOODS CORP. - GROCERY PRODUCTS DIVISION—See Hormel Foods Corporation; *U.S. Public*, pg. 1054
HYDINA ZK AS—See Agrofert Holding, a.s.; *Int'l*, pg. 219
OISTINS (PTY) LIMITED—See Country Bird Holdings Limited; *Int'l*, pg. 1818
PECO FARMS INC.—See Peco Foods Inc.; *U.S. Private*, pg. 3127
TEGEL FOODS LIMITED—See Affinity Equity Partners (HK) Ltd.; *Int'l*, pg. 186

112330 — TURKEY PRODUCTION

AVIAGEN INC.—See EW GROUP GmbH; *Int'l*, pg. 2575
BUTTERBALL, LLC—See Maxwell Foods, LLC; *U.S. Private*, pg. 2619
BUTTERBALL, LLC—See Maxwell Foods, LLC; *U.S. Private*, pg. 2619
BUTTERBALL, LLC—See Maxwell Foods, LLC; *U.S. Private*, pg. 2619
BUTTERBALL, LLC—See Seaboard Corporation; *U.S. Public*, pg. 1850
BUTTERBALL, LLC—See Seaboard Corporation; *U.S. Public*, pg. 1850
BUTTERBALL, LLC—See Seaboard Corporation; *U.S. Public*, pg. 1850
CARGILL TURKEY PRODUCTS—See Cargill, Inc.; *U.S. Private*, pg. 759
CARGILL TURKEY PRODUCTS—See Cargill, Inc.; *U.S. Private*, pg. 759
DAKOTA LAYERS, LLP.; *U.S. Private*, pg. 1147
HOF HAUS; *U.S. Private*, pg. 1959
JAINDL FAMILY FARMS LLC; *U.S. Private*, pg. 2182
KAUFFMAN POULTRY FARMS, INC.; *U.S. Private*, pg. 2265
NATURE PURE LLC.; *U.S. Private*, pg. 2867
WEST LIBERTY FOODS, LLC—See Iowa Turkey Growers Cooperative; *U.S. Private*, pg. 2136
WILLMAR POULTRY COMPANY INC.; *U.S. Private*, pg. 4528

ZACKY FARMS, INC.; *U.S. Private*, pg. 4597

112340 — POULTRY HATCHERIES

ABO FARM S.A.; *Int'l*, pg. 65
AMICK PROCESSING INC.; *U.S. Private*, pg. 263
ATLANTIC POULTRY INC. - HATCHERY DIVISION—See Atlantic Poultry Inc.; *Int'l*, pg. 675
AVICOLA BRASOV S.A.; *Int'l*, pg. 743
AVICOLA SLOBOZIA SA; *Int'l*, pg. 743
BAIRAHA FARMS PLC; *Int'l*, pg. 803
BIMAN POULTRY COMPLEX LTD—See Biman Bangladesh Airlines; *Int'l*, pg. 1032
CAIRO THREE A GROUP; *Int'l*, pg. 1253
CCK CONSOLIDATED HOLDINGS BERHAD; *Int'l*, pg. 1367
EW GROUP GMBH; *Int'l*, pg. 2575
FARMACOOP A.D.; *Int'l*, pg. 2619
FOSTER FARMS LLC—See Atlas Holdings, LLC; *U.S. Private*, pg. 376
HARRISON POULTRY INC.; *U.S. Private*, pg. 1870
HLRB BROILER FARM SDN. BHD.—See Huat Lai Resources Berhad; *Int'l*, pg. 3514
HY-LINE INTERNATIONAL; *U.S. Private*, pg. 2015
JFC LLC—See Maschhoff Family Foods, LLC; *U.S. Private*, pg. 2601
MAR-JAC POULTRY, INC.—See Mar-Jac Holdings Inc.; *U.S. Private*, pg. 2569
NATIONAL CHICK LIMITED—See Astral Foods Limited; *Int'l*, pg. 658
PALESTINE POULTRY CO. LTD.—See Arab Supply & Trading Co.; *Int'l*, pg. 532
PECO FOODS INC.; *U.S. Private*, pg. 3127
PECO FOODS INC.—See Peco Foods Inc.; *U.S. Private*, pg. 3127
PERDUE FARMS HATCHERY, INC.—See Perdue Farms Incorporated; *U.S. Private*, pg. 3147
SUCCESS CENTURY SDN BHD—See Emerging Glory Sdn Bhd; *Int'l*, pg. 2379
SUPREME POULTRY (PTY) LIMITED—See Country Bird Holdings Limited; *Int'l*, pg. 1818
TOMASSEN DUCK-TO B.V.—See Bangkok Ranch Public Company Limited; *Int'l*, pg. 835
TYSON BREEDERS, INC.—See Tyson Foods, Inc.; *U.S. Public*, pg. 2210
TYSON FOODS, INC. - ALBERTVILLE—See Tyson Foods, Inc.; *U.S. Public*, pg. 2210

112390 — OTHER POULTRY PRODUCTION

A'SAFFA FOODS S.A.O.G; *Int'l*, pg. 19
AVIAGEN INCORPORATED—See EW GROUP GmbH; *Int'l*, pg. 2575
AVIAGEN LIMITED—See EW GROUP GmbH; *Int'l*, pg. 2575
BANGKOK RANCH PUBLIC COMPANY LIMITED; *Int'l*, pg. 835
CARDINAL FOODS AS—See CapVest Limited; *Int'l*, pg. 1318
CHERRY VALLEY FARMS LTD.—See Beijing Capital Agribusiness Group Co., Ltd.; *Int'l*, pg. 947
CHERRY VALLEY FARMS LTD.—See CITIC Group Corporation; *Int'l*, pg. 1620
CWT FARMS INTERNATIONAL, INC.—See EW GROUP GmbH; *Int'l*, pg. 2575
EARLYBIRD FARM (PTY) LTD.—See Astral Foods Limited; *Int'l*, pg. 658
MAPLE LEAF FARMS INC.; *U.S. Private*, pg. 2568
ROSS POULTRY BREEDERS (PTY) LTD.—See Astral Foods Limited; *Int'l*, pg. 658
THREE ACRE FARMS PLC—See Ceylon Grain Elevators PLC; *Int'l*, pg. 1426

112410 — SHEEP FARMING

ALLIANCE GROUP LIMITED; *Int'l*, pg. 339
AUSTRALIAN WOOL INNOVATION LIMITED (AWI); *Int'l*, pg. 723
CIA DE TIERRAS SUD ARGENTINO S.A.—See Edizione S.r.l.; *Int'l*, pg. 2312

112420 — GOAT FARMING

HAYSTACK MOUNTAIN GOAT DAIRY, INC.—See The Stage Fund, LLC; *U.S. Private*, pg. 4120

112511 — FINFISH FARMING AND FISH HATCHERIES

AGRIMARINE INDUSTRIES INC.—See Dundee Corporation; *Int'l*, pg. 2225
ALABAMA FARMERS CO-OP - SOUTHFRESH FARMS DIVISION—See Alabama Farmers Cooperative, Inc.; *U.S. Private*, pg. 148
AL-AHLYIA FOR AGRICULTURAL PRODUCTION; *Int'l*, pg. 284

N.A.I.C.S. INDEX

113310 — LOGGING

ANVIFISH JOINT-STOCK COMPANY; *Int'l*, pg. 486
ASTERIAS S.A.—See Hellenic Fishfarming S.A.; *Int'l*, pg. 3333
ATLANTIC LUMPUS AS; *Int'l*, pg. 675
BAIYANG INVESTMENT GROUP, INC.; *Int'l*, pg. 803
BERN AQUA—See Archer-Daniels-Midland Company; *U.S. Public*, pg. 184
BLUE ISLAND PLC; *Int'l*, pg. 1068
CLEAR SPRINGS FOODS, INC.—See Riverence Holdings LLC; *U.S. Private*, pg. 3444
COOKE AQUACULTURE INC.—See Cooke, Inc.; *Int'l*, pg. 1788
CUULONG FISH JOINT STOCK COMPANY; *Int'l*, pg. 1881
DAHU AQUACULTURE COMPANY LIMITED; *Int'l*, pg. 1913
EGERSUND GROUP AS; *Int'l*, pg. 2323
ELLAH LAKES PLC.; *Int'l*, pg. 2364
EMPRESAS AQUACHILE SA—See Agrosuper SA; *Int'l*, pg. 221
EUROPACIFICO ALIMENTOS DEL MAR SL—See Friosur Pesquera SA; *Int'l*, pg. 2793
GRAAL S.A.; *Int'l*, pg. 3048
GRIEG SEAFOOD CANADA AS—See Grieg Seafood ASA; *Int'l*, pg. 3083
GRIEG SEAFOOD ROGALAND AS—See Grieg Seafood ASA; *Int'l*, pg. 3083
HELLENIC FISHFARMING S.A.; *Int'l*, pg. 3333
ICE FISH FARM AS; *Int'l*, pg. 3579
ILKNAK SU URUNLERI SAN VE TIC A.S.—See AMERRA Capital Management LLC; *Int'l*, pg. 424
JONES FISH HATCHERIES & DISTRIBUTORS, LLC—See Fort Point Capital, LLC; *U.S. Private*, pg. 1574
KALLONI S.A.—See Hellenic Fishfarming S.A.; *Int'l*, pg. 3333
KEGO AGRI S.A—See AMERRA Capital Management LLC; *Int'l*, pg. 424
KELLY COVE SALMON LTD.—See Cooke, Inc.; *Int'l*, pg. 1788
KIRFIS S.A.—See GALAXIDI MARINE FARM S.A.; *Int'l*, pg. 2871
LANDCATCH NATURAL SELECTION LIMITED—See Hendrix Genetics B.V.; *Int'l*, pg. 3345
NIREUS S.A.—See AMERRA Capital Management LLC; *Int'l*, pg. 424
OPRESA D.D.—See British American Tobacco plc; *Int'l*, pg. 1168
OY BIOMAR AB—See Aktieselskabet Schouw & Co.; *Int'l*, pg. 265
PURE FISHING DEUTSCHLAND GMBH—See Sycamore Partners Management, LP; *U.S. Private*, pg. 3896
RANGEN AQUACULTURE RESEARCH—See Wilbur-Ellis Company; *U.S. Private*, pg. 4518
SALMONES CAMANCHACA S.A.—See Camanchaca S.A.; *Int'l*, pg. 1267
SEGREST FARMS, INC.; *U.S. Private*, pg. 3598
SJOTROLL HAVBRUK AS—See Austevoll Seafood ASA; *Int'l*, pg. 718
SOUTHFRESH FARMS - INDIANOLA PROCESSING PLANT—See Alabama Farmers Cooperative, Inc.; *U.S. Private*, pg. 148
TROUTLODGE, INC.; *U.S. Private*, pg. 4243

112512 — SHELLFISH FARMING

52 WEEKS ENTERTAINMENT LIMITED; *Int'l*, pg. 12
APEX FROZEN FOODS LIMITED; *Int'l*, pg. 509
ASIA AQUACULTURE (M) SDN. BHD.—See Charoen Pokphand Foods Public Company Limited; *Int'l*, pg. 1451
CHAROEN POKPHAND FOODS PHILIPPINES CORPORATION—See Charoen Pokphand Foods Public Company Limited; *Int'l*, pg. 1452
C.P. AQUACULTURE (DONGFANG) CO., LTD.—See Charoen Pokphand Foods Public Company Limited; *Int'l*, pg. 1451
DATIWARE MARITIME INFRA LTD.; *Int'l*, pg. 1952
FLORIDA ORGANIC AQUACULTURE, LLC; *U.S. Private*, pg. 1550
KLANG CO., LTD.—See Charoen Pokphand Foods Public Company Limited; *Int'l*, pg. 1453
PACIFIC ALASKA SHELLFISH CO—See Dulcich, Inc.; *U.S. Private*, pg. 1286
SEAFOODS ENTERPRISE CO., LTD—See Charoen Pokphand Foods Public Company Limited; *Int'l*, pg. 1453
VIKING AQUACULTURE (PTY) LTD.—See Brimstone Investment Corporation Ltd.; *Int'l*, pg. 1164

112519 — OTHER AQUACULTURE

BAHVEST RESOURCES BERHAD; *Int'l*, pg. 801
CALIBRE NATURE (M) SDN. BHD.—See Charoen Pokphand Foods Public Company Limited; *Int'l*, pg. 1452
GENESEAS AQUACULTURA LTDA.; *Int'l*, pg. 2921
GOOD EARTH, INC.; *U.S. Private*, pg. 1737
MARS FISHCARE, INC.—See Mars, Incorporated; *U.S. Private*, pg. 2589
OM3 FISH (ASIA) SDN BHD—See IGB Berhad; *Int'l*, pg. 3601

PACIFIC AQUACULTURE, INC.—See Dulcich, Inc.; *U.S. Private*, pg. 1286
PARABEL INC.; *U.S. Private*, pg. 3089
SEKUNJALO AQUACULTURE (PTY) LTD—See African Equity Empowerment Investmts Limited; *Int'l*, pg. 191
UNITED FISH INDUSTRIES (UK) LIMITED—See Austevoll Seafood ASA; *Int'l*, pg. 718

112910 — APICULTURE

CHARLES RIVER GERMANY GMBH & CO. KG—See Charles River Laboratories International, Inc.; *U.S. Public*, pg. 479
REALLY RAW HONEY; *U.S. Private*, pg. 3368

112920 — HORSES AND OTHER EQUINE PRODUCTION

HARBOUR RACING LIMITED—See Harbour Equine Holdings Limited; *Int'l*, pg. 3272
LOUISIANA QUARTER HORSE BREEDERS ASSOCIATION; *U.S. Private*, pg. 2500
SOB STABLES, INC.; *U.S. Private*, pg. 3702
THREE CHIMNEYS FARM; *U.S. Private*, pg. 4163

112930 — FUR-BEARING ANIMAL AND RABBIT PRODUCTION

AMERICAN LEGEND COOPERATIVE; *U.S. Private*, pg. 239
DONNA SAYLERS' FABULOUS-FURS; *U.S. Private*, pg. 1260

112990 — ALL OTHER ANIMAL PRODUCTION

ABS MEXICO S.A. DE C.V.—See Genus Plc; *Int'l*, pg. 2930
AGROVRSAC A.D.; *Int'l*, pg. 221
ANIMAL REPRODUCTION SYSTEMS—See Dupree, Inc.; *U.S. Private*, pg. 1291
BOEHRINGER INGELHEIM VETMEDICA KOREA LTD.—See C.H. Boehringer Sohn AG & Co. KG; *Int'l*, pg. 1242
BOVEC SAS—See Genus Plc; *Int'l*, pg. 2930
C.P. BANGLADESH CO., LTD.—See Charoen Pokphand Group Co., Ltd.; *Int'l*, pg. 1453
CP VIETNAM CORPORATION—See Charoen Pokphand Group Co., Ltd.; *Int'l*, pg. 1453
EXETARE PARTNERSHIP, L.L.P.—See Christensen Farms Midwest, LLC; *U.S. Private*, pg. 890
GEA FARM TECHNOLOGIES FRANCE SAS—See GEA Group Aktiengesellschaft; *Int'l*, pg. 2898
GEA FARM TECHNOLOGIES SERBIA D.O.O.—See GEA Group Aktiengesellschaft; *Int'l*, pg. 2899
GEA (SHANGHAI) FARM TECHNOLOGIES COMPANY LTD.—See GEA Group Aktiengesellschaft; *Int'l*, pg. 2898
GEA WESTFALIASURGE UKRAINE GMBH—See GEA Group Aktiengesellschaft; *Int'l*, pg. 2904
GENSTAR DEVELOPMENT COMPANY; *U.S. Private*, pg. 1679
THE HANOR COMPANY, INC.; *U.S. Private*, pg. 4043
HARLAN SPRAGUE DAWLEY INC.; *U.S. Private*, pg. 1865
HAZELDENE'S CHICKEN FARM PTY LTD; *Int'l*, pg. 3295
HITCH PORK PRODUCERS, INC.—See Hitch Enterprises Inc.; *U.S. Private*, pg. 1952
I4C INNOVATIONS INC.—See General Catalyst Partners; *U.S. Private*, pg. 1664
I4C INNOVATIONS INC.—See iSubscribed Inc.; *U.S. Private*, pg. 2147
I4C INNOVATIONS INC—See WndrCo Holdings, LLC; *U.S. Private*, pg. 4552
INTERNATIONAL FUND FOR ANIMAL WELFARE; *U.S. Private*, pg. 2117
MUNSTER CATTLE BREEDING GROUP LIMITED—See Dairygold Co-Operative Society Ltd; *Int'l*, pg. 1940
MYANMAR C.P LIVESTOCK CO., LTD—See Charoen Pokphand Group Co., Ltd.; *Int'l*, pg. 1453
RAINBOW CORAL CORP.; *U.S. Private*, pg. 3347
SOUTH EASTERN CATTLE BREEDING SOCIETY LIMITED—See Glanbia Co-Operative Society Limited; *Int'l*, pg. 2988
TACONIC EUROPE A/S—See Taconic Farms, Inc.; *U.S. Private*, pg. 3921
TACONIC FARMS, INC.; *U.S. Private*, pg. 3921
VENTURE CAR WASH—See Car Wash Partners, Inc.; *U.S. Private*, pg. 748

113110 — TIMBER TRACT OPERATIONS

ACADIAN TIMBER CORP.; *Int'l*, pg. 77
AIKBEE TIMBERS (SABAH) SDN. BHD.—See Aikbee Resources Berhad; *Int'l*, pg. 232
ANDERSON-TULLY CO.; *U.S. Private*, pg. 278
ANTHONY TIMBERLANDS, INC.; *U.S. Private*, pg. 288
AS HOLMEN METS—See Holmen AB; *Int'l*, pg. 3452

CAMPBELL GLOBAL, LLC—See JPMorgan Chase & Co.; *U.S. Public*, pg. 1208
CANADIAN FOREST PRODUCTS - CHETWYND—See Canfor Corporation; *Int'l*, pg. 1290
CANADIAN FOREST PRODUCTS - CLEAR LAKE—See Canfor Corporation; *Int'l*, pg. 1290
CANADIAN FOREST PRODUCTS - GRANDE PRAIRIE—See Canfor Corporation; *Int'l*, pg. 1290
CANADIAN FOREST PRODUCTS - ISLE PIERRE—See Canfor Corporation; *Int'l*, pg. 1290
CITIC NEW ZEALAND LTD.—See CITIC Group Corporation; *Int'l*, pg. 1620
COMPTOIR DES BOIS DE BRIVE SAS—See International Paper Company; *U.S. Public*, pg. 1155
DANZER FORESTACION S.A.—See Danzer AG; *Int'l*, pg. 1970
DANZER FORESTLAND, INC.—See Danzer AG; *Int'l*, pg. 1970
ESS ENN TIMBER AB; *Int'l*, pg. 2508
FRIASKOG AB; *Int'l*, pg. 2791
F&W FORESTRY SERVICES INC.; *U.S. Private*, pg. 1455
GREEN DIAMOND RESOURCE COMPANY; *U.S. Private*, pg. 1772
IBERPAPEL ARGENTINA, S.A.—See Iberpapel Gestion SA; *Int'l*, pg. 3574
ILIM TIMBER INDASTRI OOO; *Int'l*, pg. 3614
MATARIKI FORESTS—See Rayonier Inc.; *U.S. Public*, pg. 1765
MAXXAM PROPERTY COMPANY—See Maxxam, Inc.; *U.S. Private*, pg. 2620
MENDOCINO REDWOOD COMPANY, LLC; *U.S. Private*, pg. 2666
POPE RESOURCES LIMITED PARTNERSHIP—See Rayonier Inc.; *U.S. Public*, pg. 1765
RAYONIER NEW ZEALAND LTD.—See Rayonier Inc.; *U.S. Public*, pg. 1765
ROSEBURG RESOURCES CO.—See Roseburg Forest Products; *U.S. Private*, pg. 3482
ROY O. MARTIN LUMBER COMPANY, LLC; *U.S. Private*, pg. 3491
SHAJING GEM HIGH-TECH CO., LTD.—See GEM Co., Ltd.; *Int'l*, pg. 2914
SOTERRA LLC—See Greif Inc.; *U.S. Public*, pg. 968
WEYERHAEUSER COLUMBIA TIMBERLANDS LLC—See Weyerhaeuser Company; *U.S. Public*, pg. 2365

113210 — FOREST NURSERIES AND GATHERING OF FOREST PRODUCTS

ARBORGEN INC.—See ArborGen Holdings Limited; *Int'l*, pg. 538
AURORA PEAT PRODUCTS ULC—See Hydrofarm Holdings Group, Inc.; *U.S. Public*, pg. 1079
BERG EARTH CO., LTD.; *Int'l*, pg. 979
CANADIAN FOREST PRODUCTS LTD.—See Canfor Corporation; *Int'l*, pg. 1290
ENCE ENERGIA Y CELULOSA, S.A.; *Int'l*, pg. 2401
EUFORES, S.A.—See AntarChile S.A.; *Int'l*, pg. 481
FERNLEA FLOWERS LTD.; *Int'l*, pg. 2639
FORESTAL TORNAGALEONES S.A.—See GrupoNueva S.A.; *Int'l*, pg. 3139
HUBER ENGINEERED WOODS LLC—See J.M. Huber Corporation; *U.S. Private*, pg. 2168
IBERFLORESTAL - COMERCIO E SERVICOS FLORESTAIS, S A—See ENCE Energia y Celulosa, S.A.; *Int'l*, pg. 2401
INTERNATIONAL PAPER CO. - WOOD PRODUCTS—See International Paper Company; *U.S. Public*, pg. 1156
INTERNATIONAL PAPER REALTY CORP. - SAVANNAH OFFICE—See International Paper Company; *U.S. Public*, pg. 1155
KELANI VALLEY PLANTATIONS LIMITED—See Hayleys PLC; *Int'l*, pg. 3291
KUMPULAN PENGURUSAN KAYU KAYAN TERENGGANU SDN BHD—See Golden Pharos Berhad; *Int'l*, pg. 3081
TRIMBLE FORESTRY CORPORATION—See Trimble, Inc.; *U.S. Public*, pg. 2192

113310 — LOGGING

1260261 ONTARIO INC; *Int'l*, pg. 2
ANDERSON & MIDDLETON COMPANY; *U.S. Private*, pg. 275
BIG RIVER GROUP PTY. LTD.—See Anacacia Capital Pty Ltd; *Int'l*, pg. 445
BILLERUD SKOG AB—See Billerud AB; *Int'l*, pg. 1030
B&S LOGGING INC.; *U.S. Private*, pg. 419
CANADIAN AIR-CRANE LTD—See Erickson Incorporated; *U.S. Private*, pg. 1419
CANADIAN FOREST PRODUCTS - ENGLEWOOD LOGGING—See Canfor Corporation; *Int'l*, pg. 1290
CHARLES DONALD PULPWOOD, INC.; *U.S. Private*, pg. 852
CITIC RESOURCES HOLDINGS LIMITED—See CITIC Group Corporation; *Int'l*, pg. 1620
COLUMBIA HELICOPTERS, INC.—See AE Industrial Part-

113310 — LOGGING

ners, LP; *U.S. Private*, pg. 112
COLUMBIA WEST VIRGINIA CORPORATION—See Columbia Forest Products Inc.; *U.S. Private*, pg. 976
CROMAN CORPORATION; *U.S. Private*, pg. 1103
F&P ENTERPRISES INC.; *U.S. Private*, pg. 1455
HERBERT C. HAYNES INC.; *U.S. Private*, pg. 1920
HOLMEN AB; *Int'l*, pg. 3452
MILLER SHINGLE COMPANY INC.; *U.S. Private*, pg. 2735
PROBYN LOG, LTD.—See E.R. Probyn Ltd.; *Int'l*, pg. 2260
ROBINSON ENTERPRISES INC.; *U.S. Private*, pg. 3461
SCOTT TIMBER CO.—See Roseburg Forest Products; *U.S. Private*, pg. 3482
STALLWORTH & JOHNSON INC.; *U.S. Private*, pg. 3776
STEVE HENDERSON LOGGING INC.; *U.S. Private*, pg. 3808
SUMTER TIMBER COMPANY, LLC—See McElroy Truck Lines Inc.; *U.S. Private*, pg. 2633
SURCO LOG, INC.; *U.S. Private*, pg. 3883
TIMBERLAND HARVESTERS INC.; *U.S. Private*, pg. 4171
TIMBERWEST FOREST CORP.—See British Columbia Investment Management Corp.; *Int'l*, pg. 1170
T.R. DILLON LOGGING INC.; *U.S. Private*, pg. 3912
WHITFIELD TIMBER INC.; *U.S. Private*, pg. 4512

114111 — FINFISH FISHING

AUSTRAL GROUP S.A.A.—See Austevoll Seafood ASA; *Int'l*, pg. 717
CAMANCHACA S.A.; *Int'l*, pg. 1267
CROMARIS D.D.—See Adris Grupa d.d.; *Int'l*, pg. 153
DARDANEL ONENTAS GIDA SANAYI AS; *Int'l*, pg. 1972
DONG WON FISHERIES CO., LTD.; *Int'l*, pg. 2164
FLORA CORPORATION LIMITED; *Int'l*, pg. 2707
FOODCORP S.A.—See Austevoll Seafood ASA; *Int'l*, pg. 717
GRIEG SEAFOOD FINNMARK AS—See Grieg Seafood ASA; *Int'l*, pg. 3083
HAVFISK ASA—See Austevoll Seafood ASA; *Int'l*, pg. 717
NORFOLK MARINE COMPANY—See OneWater Marine Inc.; *U.S. Public*, pg. 1604
PT INTERNATIONAL ALLIANCE FOOD INDONESIA—See Alliance Select Foods International, Inc.; *Int'l*, pg. 341
TALHADO FISHING ENTERPRISES PROPRIETARY LIMITED—See African Equity Empowerment Investmts Limited; *Int'l*, pg. 191
TRI-STAR MARINE INTERNATIONAL, INC.; *U.S. Private*, pg. 4223
UNITED STATES SEAFOODS, LLC; *U.S. Private*, pg. 4299

114112 — SHELLFISH FISHING

BLUE HARVEST FISHERIES, LLC—See COFRA Holding AG; *Int'l*, pg. 1694
BLUE HARVEST FOODS, LLC - FLEET DIVISION—See COFRA Holding AG; *Int'l*, pg. 1694
BON SECOUR BOATS INC.—See Bon Secour Fisheries Inc.; *U.S. Private*, pg. 612
DANAH AL SAFAT FOODSTUFF COMPANY K.S.C.—See Al-Safwa Group Holding Co, K.P.S.C.; *Int'l*, pg. 288
THE FIRST REPUBLIC BUILDING CORP.—See The First Republic Corporation of America; *U.S. Public*, pg. 2074
FIRST REPUBLIC CORP., REAL ESTATE DIV.—See The First Republic Corporation of America; *U.S. Public*, pg. 2074
PACIFIC OYSTER CO., INC.—See Dulcich, Inc.; *U.S. Private*, pg. 1286
P.T. BONANZA PRATAMA ABADI—See CCK Consolidated Holdings Berhad; *Int'l*, pg. 1367

114119 — OTHER MARINE FISHING

ATLANTIC FISHING ENTERPRISES (PTY) LTD—See African Equity Empowerment Investmts Limited; *Int'l*, pg. 191
AUSTEVOLL SEAFOOD ASA; *Int'l*, pg. 717
BAINE JOHNSTON CORPORATION; *Int'l*, pg. 803
BIOMAR CHILE SA—See Aktieselskabet Schouw & Co.; *Int'l*, pg. 265
BIOMAR GROUP A/S—See Aktieselskabet Schouw & Co.; *Int'l*, pg. 265
CONSOLIDATED FISHERIES LTD.; *Int'l*, pg. 1770
DONGWON INDUSTRIES CO., LTD.—See Dongwon Enterprise Co., Ltd.; *Int'l*, pg. 2171
DUNCAN FOX S.A.; *Int'l*, pg. 2225
GARWARE MARINE INDUSTRIES LTD.; *Int'l*, pg. 2886
HMS GLOBAL MARITIME, INC.; *U.S. Private*, pg. 1955
MAINSTREAM OUTFITTERS—See Dave's Sports Center, Inc.; *U.S. Private*, pg. 1168
PESQUERA IQUIQUE-GUANAYE S.A.—See AntarChile S.A.; *Int'l*, pg. 482
PURE FISHING ASIA CO., LTD.—See Sycamore Partners Management, LP; *U.S. Private*, pg. 3896
PURE FISHING EUROPE S.A.S.—See Sycamore Partners Management, LP; *U.S. Private*, pg. 3896
PURE FISHING MALAYSIA SDN. BHD.—See Sycamore Partners Management, LP; *U.S. Private*, pg. 3896
PURE FISHING NETHERLANDS B.V.—See Sycamore Partners Management, LP; *U.S. Private*, pg. 3896
PURE FISHING (UK) LTD.—See Sycamore Partners Management, LP; *U.S. Private*, pg. 3896

114210 — HUNTING AND TRAPPING

ATLAS PEARLS LTD.; *Int'l*, pg. 686
DUCKS UNLIMITED, INC.; *U.S. Private*, pg. 1284

115111 — COTTON GINNING

ARAB COTTON GINNING COMPANY; *Int'l*, pg. 530
AUSCOTT LIMITED—See Australian Food & Fibre Ltd.; *Int'l*, pg. 721
CARGILL ZIMBABWE (PVT) LIMITED—See Cargill, Inc.; *U.S. Private*, pg. 759
CHONBANG CO., LTD. - GWANGJU FACTORY—See Chonbang Co., Ltd.; *Int'l*, pg. 1578
CURRIE GIN—See Alabama Farmers Cooperative, Inc.; *U.S. Private*, pg. 148
FASO COTON SA—See Aga Khan Development Network; *Int'l*, pg. 199
IVOIRE COTON S.A.—See Aga Khan Development Network; *Int'l*, pg. 199
OLTON CO-OP GIN—See Ag Producers Co-op; *U.S. Private*, pg. 125
THESSALY COTTON GINNING S.A—See Hellenic Fabrics S.A.; *Int'l*, pg. 3333

115112 — SOIL PREPARATION, PLANTING, AND CULTIVATING

ABENGOA BIOENERGY INC.—See Abengoa S.A.; *Int'l*, pg. 59
ADM AGRI-INDUSTRIES COMPANY—See Archer-Daniels-Midland Company; *U.S. Public*, pg. 184
ADM AGRI-INDUSTRIES COMPANY—See Archer-Daniels-Midland Company; *U.S. Public*, pg. 184
ADM AGRI-INDUSTRIES COMPANY—See Archer-Daniels-Midland Company; *U.S. Public*, pg. 184
AEON AGRI CREATE CO., LTD—See AEON Co., Ltd.; *Int'l*, pg. 176
AGRILAND FS, INC.; *U.S. Private*, pg. 129
AG SOLUTIONS L.L.C.; *U.S. Private*, pg. 125
AMANA AGRICULTURAL & INDUSTRIAL INVESTMENT CO.; *Int'l*, pg. 409
AMERICAN SOIL TECHNOLOGIES, INC.; *U.S. Private*, pg. 254
ANCOM NYLEX BERHAD; *Int'l*, pg. 449
AQUATIC VEGETATION CONTROL INC.; *U.S. Private*, pg. 303
AQUA YIELD OPERATIONS, LLC; *U.S. Private*, pg. 303
ASAHI BIOCYCLE CO. LTD.—See Asahi Group Holdings Ltd.; *Int'l*, pg. 593
BALL COLEGRAVE LTD—See Ball Horticultural Company; *U.S. Private*, pg. 459
BALL HORTICULTURAL (KUNMING) CO., LTD.—See Ball Horticultural Company; *U.S. Private*, pg. 460
BAYER CROPSCIENCE, S.L.—See Bayer Aktiengesellschaft; *Int'l*, pg. 903
BECKER HOLDING CORPORATION; *U.S. Private*, pg. 511
BENEFICIADORA DE CEREAIS MANI LTDA—See General Mills, Inc.; *U.S. Public*, pg. 921
BIO SOIL ENHANCERS, INC.; *U.S. Private*, pg. 561
BLD PLANTATION BHD; *Int'l*, pg. 1063
BLUE GOOSE GROWERS, LLC.; *U.S. Private*, pg. 589
BRAXIA SCIENTIFIC CORP.; *Int'l*, pg. 1142
BRAZIL IOWA FARMS, LLC—See BXR Group B.V.; *Int'l*, pg. 1233
B.S. OIL PALM PLANTATIONS SDN BHD—See Far East Holdings Berhad; *Int'l*, pg. 2616
BUCKEYE RESOURCES, INC.—See CRH plc; *Int'l*, pg. 1845
BUXTON OIL CO. INC.; *U.S. Private*, pg. 698
CALLIVOIRE SGFD SA—See Element Solutions Inc.; *U.S. Public*, pg. 725
CHEM GRO OF HOUGHTON INC.; *U.S. Public*, pg. 870
CHS INC.-FAULKTON—See CHS INC.; *U.S. Public*, pg. 491
CHUDENKO WORLD FARM CO., LTD.—See Chudenko Corporation; *Int'l*, pg. 1594
CNH AMERICA - GOODFIELD—See CNH Industrial N.V.; *Int'l*, pg. 1674
COLLIER ARBOR CARE INC.—See The F.A. Bartlett Tree Expert Company; *U.S. Private*, pg. 4027
CORTEVA AGRISCIENCE DE COLOMBIA S.A.S.—See Corteva, Inc.; *U.S. Public*, pg. 581
DELEGAT LIMITED—See Delegat's Group Limited; *Int'l*, pg. 2011
DELLOYD PLANTATION SDN. BHD.—See Delloyd Ventures Sdn Bhd; *Int'l*, pg. 2014
DOW AGROSCIENCES AUSTRALIA LIMITED—See Corteva, Inc.; *U.S. Public*, pg. 582
DOW AGROSCIENCES DE MEXICO S.A. DE C.V.—See Corteva, Inc.; *U.S. Public*, pg. 582
DOW AGROSCIENCES INDUSTRIAL LTDA.—See Corteva, Inc.; *U.S. Public*, pg. 582
DOW AGROSCIENCES PACIFIC LIMITED—See Corteva, Inc.; *U.S. Public*, pg. 582
DOW AGROSCIENCES SWITZERLAND S.A.—See Corteva, Inc.; *U.S. Public*, pg. 582
EARTH MECHANICS, INC.; *U.S. Private*, pg. 1314
EMPRESAS CABO DE HORNOS S.A.; *Int'l*, pg. 2389
ENCAP, LLC; *U.S. Private*, pg. 1390
ENSSOLUTIONS GROUP INC.; *Int'l*, pg. 2448
EVOGENE LTD.—See Compugen Ltd.; *Int'l*, pg. 1755
FAR EAST DELIMA PLANTATIONS SDN BHD—See Far East Holdings Berhad; *Int'l*, pg. 2616
FAR EAST HOLDINGS BERHAD; *Int'l*, pg. 2616
FARMERS' AERIAL APPLICATORS INC.—See Farmer's Supply Cooperative Inc.; *U.S. Private*, pg. 1475
FARMERS COOPERATIVE ASSOCIATION OF RAVENNA; *U.S. Private*, pg. 1477
FARMERS COOPERATIVE CO.; *U.S. Private*, pg. 1477
FOOD PROTECTION SERVICES, L.L.C.—See Ecolab Inc.; *U.S. Public*, pg. 714
GB SCIENCES, INC.; *U.S. Public*, pg. 908
GENERA AGRI CORP LIMITED; *Int'l*, pg. 2917
GRONDRECYCLAGE CENTRUM KALLO N.V.—See Ackermans & van Haaren NV; *Int'l*, pg. 105
GUANGDONG INSTITUTE OF WORLD SOIL RESOURCES—See Hongda Xingye Co., Ltd.; *Int'l*, pg. 3470
GUARDIAN PEST CONTROL LIMITED—See Rollins, Inc.; *U.S. Public*, pg. 1809
GUH PLANTATIONS SDN. BHD.—See GUH Holdings Berhad; *Int'l*, pg. 3173
HAGL RUBBER JSC—See Hoang Anh Gia Lai Joint Stock Company; *Int'l*, pg. 3436
HARDI INTERNATIONAL AS—See Exel Industries SA; *Int'l*, pg. 2582
HONGKANG (JIUJIANG) AGRICULTURAL DEVELOPMENT CO., LTD.—See Heng Tai Consumables Group Limited; *Int'l*, pg. 3345
JACK NEAL & SON, INC.; *U.S. Private*, pg. 2174
JAY MAR INC.; *U.S. Private*, pg. 2192
JIMTEN S.A.—See Aliaxis S.A./N.V.; *Int'l*, pg. 325
KUBAN AGROHOLDING—See Basic Element Company; *Int'l*, pg. 886
LAPARANZA, S.A.—See Banco Santander, S.A.; *Int'l*, pg. 826
MALI PROTECTION DES CULTURES (MPC) SA—See Element Solutions Inc.; *U.S. Public*, pg. 728
MTHAYIZA FARMING (PTY) LTD—See CROOKES BROTHERS LIMITED; *Int'l*, pg. 1855
MULLER-ELEKTRONIK GMBH & CO. KG—See Trimble, Inc.; *U.S. Public*, pg. 2190
O.O.O. SYNGENTA—See China National Chemical Corporation; *Int'l*, pg. 1529
ORGANICS BY GOSH—See QSAM Biosciences, Inc.; *U.S. Public*, pg. 1744
ORGANIX SOLUTIONS, LLC—See Republic Services, Inc.; *U.S. Public*, pg. 1786
PATTEN SEED COMPANY INC. - SOIL3 DIVISION—See Patten Seed Company Inc.; *U.S. Private*, pg. 3111
PT AGRO INDOMAS—See Carson Cumberbatch PLC; *Int'l*, pg. 1347
PT BERKALA MAJU BERSAMA—See CB Industrial Product Holding Berhad; *Int'l*, pg. 1364
PT MURINIWOOD INDAH INDUSTRY—See First Resources Limited; *Int'l*, pg. 2687
PT SURYA INTISARI RAYA—See First Resources Limited; *Int'l*, pg. 2687
QINGDAO RUNDE BIOTECHNOLOGY COMPANY LIMITED—See GLG LIFE TECH CORPORATION; *Int'l*, pg. 2992
QSAM BIOSCIENCES, INC.; *U.S. Public*, pg. 1744
SAATZUCHT EDELHOF GMBH—See BayWa AG; *Int'l*, pg. 919
SEEDLINGS INDIA PRIVATE LIMITED—See Best Agrolife Ltd.; *Int'l*, pg. 998
SEMINIS S DE RL DE CV—See Bayer Aktiengesellschaft; *Int'l*, pg. 910
SHANNON & WILSON, INC.—See Shannon & Wilson, Inc.; *U.S. Private*, pg. 3625
SOUTHEAST SPREADING COMPANY; *U.S. Private*, pg. 3726
SOUTHERN NURSERIES, INC.—See Boyne Capital Management, LLC; *U.S. Private*, pg. 629
SYNGENTA CROP PROTECTION B.V.—See China National Chemical Corporation; *Int'l*, pg. 1530
SYNGENTA LTD.—See China National Chemical Corporation; *Int'l*, pg. 1530
SYNGENTA SEEDCO (PTY) LIMITED—See China National Chemical Corporation; *Int'l*, pg. 1530
SYNGENTA SEEDS GMBH—See China National Chemical Corporation; *Int'l*, pg. 1530
UNITED FARM INDUSTRIES INCORPORATED; *U.S. Private*, pg. 4292
UNITED ROYALE HOLDINGS CORP.—See Cybernorth Ventures Inc.; *Int'l*, pg. 1893
WEBER BASIN WATER CONSERVANCY DISTRICT; *U.S. Private*, pg. 4465

N.A.I.C.S. INDEX

WECARE DENALI, LLC—See Denali Water Solutions LLC; *U.S. Private*, pg. 1204
WILBUR-ELLIS COMPANY - WILBUR-ELLIS AGRIBUSINESS DIVISION—See Wilbur-Ellis Company; *U.S. Private*, pg. 4517

115113 — CROP HARVESTING, PRIMARILY BY MACHINE

ESCORTS CROP SOLUTION LIMITED—See Escorts Kubota Limited; *Int'l*, pg. 2502
HUGHSON NUT, INCORPORATED; *U.S. Private*, pg. 2004
SYNAGRI LP—See Cargill, Inc.; *U.S. Private*, pg. 758

115114 — POSTHARVEST CROP ACTIVITIES (EXCEPT COTTON GINNING)

ADM EDIBLE BEAN SPECIALTIES, INC.—See Archer-Daniels-Midland Company; *U.S. Public*, pg. 181
ADM GRAIN RIVER SYSTEM, INC.—See Archer-Daniels-Midland Company; *U.S. Public*, pg. 182
ADM MILLING CO.—See Archer-Daniels-Midland Company; *U.S. Public*, pg. 182
ADM STANLEY—See Archer-Daniels-Midland Company; *U.S. Public*, pg. 182
AGROFRESH COMERCIAL PERU S.A.C.—See Paine Schwartz Partners, LLC; *U.S. Private*, pg. 3075
AGROMEC SA; *Int'l*, pg. 220
AGROSEME PANONIJA A.D.; *Int'l*, pg. 220
ALLIANCE PULSE PROCESSORS INC.—See AGT Food and Ingredients Inc.; *Int'l*, pg. 221
ARCHER DANIELS MIDLAND CO.—See Archer-Daniels-Midland Company; *U.S. Public*, pg. 183
ARCHER DANIELS MIDLAND CO.—See Archer-Daniels-Midland Company; *U.S. Public*, pg. 183
BAYER CROPSCIENCE PTY LIMITED—See Bayer Aktiengesellschaft; *Int'l*, pg. 903
CARGILL FOODS INC.—See Cargill, Inc.; *U.S. Private*, pg. 756
CARGILL INC.—See Cargill, Inc.; *U.S. Private*, pg. 757
CARGILL INC.—See Cargill, Inc.; *U.S. Private*, pg. 757
COOPERATIVE ELEVATOR CO., INC.; *U.S. Private*, pg. 1042
THE COTTON COMPANY OF ZIMBABWE LIMITED—See Cottco Holdings Limited; *Int'l*, pg. 1817
COUNTRY FRESH PACKAGING—See Dominion Holding Corporation; *Int'l*, pg. 2161
CRUNCH PAK; *U.S. Private*, pg. 1114
CURATION FOODS, INC.—See Lifecore Biomedical, Inc.; *U.S. Public*, pg. 1312
CUSTOM PINE STRAW, INC.; *U.S. Private*, pg. 1129
DIAMOND FRUIT GROWERS INC.; *U.S. Private*, pg. 1223
DOLE DECIDUOUS—See Dole plc; *Int'l*, pg. 2157
DOLE FRESH VEGETABLES, INC.—See Dole plc; *Int'l*, pg. 2157
DURHAM PECAN COMPANY, INC.; *U.S. Private*, pg. 1293
FORD'S PRODUCE CO., INC.; *U.S. Private*, pg. 1565
GEORGE F. BROCKE & SONS, INC.; *U.S. Private*, pg. 1681
GERAWAN FARMING SERVICES, INC.—See Paine Schwartz Partners, LLC; *U.S. Private*, pg. 3076
GOLDEN WEST NUTS INC.; *U.S. Private*, pg. 1734
GOLDRIVER ORCHARDS; *U.S. Private*, pg. 1735
GREEN PRODUCTS CO. INC.; *U.S. Private*, pg. 1773
HAMMONS PRODUCTS CO. - ARKANSAS—See Hammons Products Company; *U.S. Private*, pg. 1851
HESS BROTHER'S FRUIT COMPANY; *U.S. Private*, pg. 1927
LANE SOUTHERN ORCHARDS; *U.S. Private*, pg. 2388
L. H. HAYWARD & CO., LLC; *U.S. Private*, pg. 2364
LIPMAN-PORTLAND, LLC—See Lipman & Lipman, Inc.; *U.S. Private*, pg. 2465
MINN-DAK GROWERS, LTD.; *U.S. Private*, pg. 2742
NASH PRODUCE, LLC; *U.S. Private*, pg. 2836
NORSUN FOOD GROUP LLC—See Sentinel Capital Partners, L.L.C.; *U.S. Private*, pg. 3609
NORTHERN FRUIT COMPANY, INC.; *U.S. Private*, pg. 2953
OCEAN MIST FARMS CORP.; *U.S. Private*, pg. 2989
OREGON CHERRY GROWERS INC.; *U.S. Private*, pg. 3040
PACIFIC AG, LLC; *U.S. Private*, pg. 3065
PARIS FOODS CORPORATION; *U.S. Private*, pg. 3095
PETERSON FARMS FRESH, INC.—See Peterson Farms, Inc.; *U.S. Private*, pg. 3160
PRODUCTION SEEDS PLUS, INC.—See S&W Seed Co.; *U.S. Public*, pg. 1832
QUARTERWAY GIN, INC.; *U.S. Private*, pg. 3324
REDFIELD ENERGY, LLC; *U.S. Private*, pg. 3378
REYNOLDS PACKING CO. INC.; *U.S. Private*, pg. 3418
ROYAL MOONLIGHT CORPORATION—See Moonlight Packing Corporation; *U.S. Private*, pg. 2779
ROYAL RIDGE FRUIT & COLD STORAGE, LLC—See Arable Capital Partners LLC; *U.S. Private*, pg. 307
SEED DYNAMICS, INC.; *U.S. Private*, pg. 3597
SOUTHERN GARDEN CITRUS—See United States Sugar Corporation; *U.S. Public*, pg. 4300
STEMILT GROWERS INC.; *U.S. Private*, pg. 3801
TAYLOR FARMS CALIFORNIA INC.—See Taylor Fresh Foods Inc.; *U.S. Private*, pg. 3940
TAYLOR FRESH FOODS INC.; *U.S. Private*, pg. 3940
THE THOMAS COLACE COMPANY, LLC—See Lipman & Lipman, Inc.; *U.S. Private*, pg. 2465
TROUT-BLUE CHELAN, INC.; *U.S. Private*, pg. 4243
VALLEY FIG GROWERS, INC.; *U.S. Private*, pg. 4333
WASHINGTON QUALITY FOODS—See Wilkins-Rogers, Inc.; *U.S. Private*, pg. 4520
WESTERN REPACKING, LLLP—See Lipman & Lipman, Inc.; *U.S. Private*, pg. 2465
WEST PAK AVOCADO, INC.; *U.S. Private*, pg. 4486
WOODSIDE ELECTRONICS CORPORATION—See Warburg Pincus LLC; *U.S. Private*, pg. 4438
ZEST LABS, INC—See RiskOn International, Inc.; *U.S. Public*, pg. 1799

115115 — FARM LABOR CONTRACTORS AND CREW LEADERS

CHIN TECK PLANTATIONS BERHAD; *Int'l*, pg. 1480
QUELL INDUSTRIAL SERVICES; *U.S. Private*, pg. 3325

115116 — FARM MANAGEMENT SERVICES

ADM AGRICULTURE LIMITED—See Archer-Daniels-Midland Company; *U.S. Public*, pg. 181
AG RESERVES INC; *U.S. Private*, pg. 125
AGRESERVES, INC.—See Ag Reserves Inc; *U.S. Private*, pg. 125
AGRIPLAST TECH INDIA PRIVATE LIMITED—See Ginegar Plastic Products Ltd.; *Int'l*, pg. 2976
ALICO, INC.—See Continental Grain Company; *U.S. Private*, pg. 1029
AMS AMEROPA MARKETING & SALES AG—See Ameropa AG; *Int'l*, pg. 423
ASIA ENERGY LOGISTICS GROUP LIMITED; *Int'l*, pg. 611
BAYWA AGRARHANDEL GMBH—See BayWa AG; *Int'l*, pg. 916
BAYWA AGRO POLSKA SP. Z O.O.—See BayWa AG; *Int'l*, pg. 916
BIOCORE B.V.—See BayWa AG; *Int'l*, pg. 917
BMC BOLSA MERCANTIL DE COLOMBIA SA; *Int'l*, pg. 1076
BRITTANY FARMING CO.—See Smith Frozen Foods, Inc.; *U.S. Private*, pg. 3694
CARLOS CASADO SA; *Int'l*, pg. 1339
CHERRYBRO CO., LTD.; *Int'l*, pg. 1472
CHS BULGARIA LTD.—See CHS INC.; *U.S. Public*, pg. 491
CHS PRIMELAND - WALLA WALLA—See CHS INC.; *U.S. Public*, pg. 491
CORTEVA AGRISCIENCE AUSTRALIA PTY LTD.—See Corteva, Inc.; *U.S. Public*, pg. 581
CORTEVA AGRISCIENCE BULGARIA EOOD—See Corteva, Inc.; *U.S. Public*, pg. 581
CORTEVA AGRISCIENCE CZECH S.R.O.—See Corteva, Inc.; *U.S. Public*, pg. 581
CORTEVA AGRISCIENCE EGYPT LLC—See Corteva, Inc.; *U.S. Public*, pg. 581
CORTEVA AGRISCIENCE HELLAS S.A.—See Corteva, Inc.; *U.S. Public*, pg. 581
CORTEVA AGRISCIENCE KENYA LIMITED—See Corteva, Inc.; *U.S. Public*, pg. 581
CORTEVA AGRISCIENCE KOREA LTD.—See Corteva, Inc.; *U.S. Public*, pg. 581
CORTEVA AGRISCIENCE LITHUANIA UAB—See Corteva, Inc.; *U.S. Public*, pg. 581
CORTEVA AGRISCIENCE NETHERLANDS B.V.—See Corteva, Inc.; *U.S. Public*, pg. 581
CORTEVA AGRISCIENCE NEW ZEALAND LTD.—See Corteva, Inc.; *U.S. Public*, pg. 581
CORTEVA AGRISCIENCE PAKISTAN LIMITED—See Corteva, Inc.; *U.S. Public*, pg. 581
CORTEVA AGRISCIENCE PHILIPPINES, INC.—See Corteva, Inc.; *U.S. Public*, pg. 581
CORTEVA AGRISCIENCE POLAND SP. Z O.O.—See Corteva, Inc.; *U.S. Public*, pg. 581
CORTEVA AGRISCIENCE (THAILAND) CO., LTD.—See Corteva, Inc.; *U.S. Public*, pg. 581
CORTEVA AGRISCIENCE URUGUAY S.A.—See Corteva, Inc.; *U.S. Public*, pg. 581
CORTEVA AGRISCIENCE ZAMBIA LIMITED—See Corteva, Inc.; *U.S. Public*, pg. 581
CORTEVA CROP SOLUTIONS HUN KFT.—See Corteva, Inc.; *U.S. Public*, pg. 581
DARONG AGRICULTURAL & DEVELOPMENT CORPORATION—See Ayala Corporation; *Int'l*, pg. 774
DUPONT MAGYARORSZAG KFT—See Corteva, Inc.; *U.S. Public*, pg. 582
EKOSEM AGRARPROJEKTE GMBH—See Ekosem-Agrar GmbH; *Int'l*, pg. 2339
ELTAC XXI S.L.—See Hydrofarm Holdings Group, Inc.; *U.S. Public*, pg. 1079
EMAK FRANCE SAS—See Emak S.p.A.; *Int'l*, pg. 2373
E. RITTER FARM MANAGEMENT, INC.—See E. Ritter & Company; *U.S. Private*, pg. 1304
E. RITTER FARM MANAGEMENT, INC.—See Grain Management, LLC; *U.S. Private*, pg. 1751
ESTEEM BIO ORGANIC FOOD PROCESSING LTD; *Int'l*, pg. 2517
FARMERS NATIONAL COMPANY; *U.S. Private*, pg. 1478
FARMFACTS GMBH—See BayWa AG; *Int'l*, pg. 917
FARMFACTS HUNGARY KFT—See BayWa AG; *Int'l*, pg. 917
FILTREXX INTERNATIONAL, LLC—See Mativ Holdings, Inc.; *U.S. Public*, pg. 1396
FOUR SEASONS PRODUCE, INC.; *U.S. Private*, pg. 1582
GOLDEN FURROW FERTILIZER INC.; *U.S. Private*, pg. 1730
HAYCHEM (BANGLADESH) LTD.—See Hayleys PLC; *Int'l*, pg. 3291
HYDROGREEN INC.—See CubicFarm Systems Corp.; *Int'l*, pg. 1875
HYUNDAI FARM LAND & DEVELOPMENT COMPANY—See Hyundai Motor Company; *Int'l*, pg. 3559
INTEGRATED CANNABIS SOLUTIONS, INC.; *U.S. Public*, pg. 1136
INTERNATIONAL FOOD NETWORK LTD.—See Laboratory Corporation of America Holdings; *U.S. Public*, pg. 1286
JACK M. BERRY INC.; *U.S. Private*, pg. 2174
JANNAFARM SDN. BHD.—See Berjaya Corporation Berhad; *Int'l*, pg. 984
JATROSOLUTIONS GMBH—See EnBW Energie Baden-Wurttemberg AG; *Int'l*, pg. 2399
KAANAPALI LAND MANAGEMENT CORPORATION—See Kaanapali Land, LLC; *U.S. Public*, pg. 1211
KAMAPIM LTD.—See Floridienne SA; *Int'l*, pg. 2708
KANZEN MANAGEMENT SDN. BHD.—See FACB Industries Incorporated Berhad; *Int'l*, pg. 2600
LAGERHAUS E-SERVICE GMBH—See BayWa AG; *Int'l*, pg. 918
MCBRYDE RESOURCES, INC.—See Alexander & Baldwin, Inc.; *U.S. Public*, pg. 75
MENKE AGRAR POLSKA SP. Z O.O.—See AGRAVIS Raiffeisen AG; *Int'l*, pg. 215
MESA VINEYARD MANAGEMENT, INC.; *U.S. Private*, pg. 2678
MIDWEST FARM MANAGEMENT, INC.; *U.S. Private*, pg. 2721
ORBIA ARGENTINA S.A.U.—See Bayer Aktiengesellschaft; *Int'l*, pg. 909
PHYTOCHEM TECHNOLOGIES, INC.—See Nutralife Biosciences, Inc.; *U.S. Public*, pg. 1556
PIONEER HI-BRED R.S.A. (PTY) LTD.—See Corteva, Inc.; *U.S. Public*, pg. 584
PIVOTRAC—See Valmont Industries, Inc.; *U.S. Public*, pg. 2274
PT BINTAN RESORT CAKRAWALA—See Gallant Venture Ltd.; *Int'l*, pg. 2874
RWA HRVATSKA D.O.O.—See BayWa AG; *Int'l*, pg. 918
SAND MARK CORPORATION—See Berg Equipment Corporation; *U.S. Private*, pg. 530
SPEKTRA AGRI SRL—See Trimble, Inc.; *U.S. Public*, pg. 2191
SPRING MOUNTAIN VINEYARDS, INC.—See MGG Investment Group, LP; *U.S. Private*, pg. 2694
STALLMASTAREN AB—See Merck & Co., Inc.; *U.S. Public*, pg. 1421
SUNBLASTER HOLDINGS ULC—See Hydrofarm Holdings Group, Inc.; *U.S. Public*, pg. 1079
SUN PACIFIC FARMING CO., INC.; *U.S. Private*, pg. 3863
TCI HOLDING COMPANY; *U.S. Private*, pg. 3942
TOWN & COUNTRY CO-OP; *U.S. Private*, pg. 4196
VISTA GEOWISSENSCHAFTLICHE FERNERKUNDUNG GMBH—See BayWa AG; *Int'l*, pg. 919
VR AGRAR CENTER WITTELSBACHER LAND GMBH—See AGRAVIS Raiffeisen AG; *Int'l*, pg. 216
WESTERNGHATS AGRO GROWERS COMPANY LIMITED—See 63 moons technologies limited; *Int'l*, pg. 14
WINTERSHALL LIBYEN OIL & GAS GMBH—See BASF SE; *Int'l*, pg. 886
WINTERSHALL NORGE AS—See BASF SE; *Int'l*, pg. 886

115210 — SUPPORT ACTIVITIES FOR ANIMAL PRODUCTION

3D CORPORATE SOLUTIONS, LLC; *U.S. Private*, pg. 9
ABS GLOBAL—See Genus Plc; *Int'l*, pg. 2930
ACCELERATED GENETICS—See Select Sires Inc.; *U.S. Private*, pg. 3601
AGSOURCE COOPERATIVE SERVICES—See Cooperative Resources International Inc.; *U.S. Private*, pg. 1043
ALL WEST/ SELECT SIRES, INC.—See Select Sires Inc.; *U.S. Private*, pg. 3601
ANIMALCO A.S.—See Agrofert Holding, a.s.; *Int'l*, pg. 218
APIAM ANIMAL HEALTH LIMITED; *Int'l*, pg. 515
ARENA HOLDING S.P.A. - GARBINI PLANT—See Arena Holding S.p.A.; *Int'l*, pg. 558
ARENA HOLDING S.P.A. - NATURICCHI PLANT—See Arena Holding S.p.A.; *Int'l*, pg. 558

115210 — SUPPORT ACTIVITIES ...

COBA / SELECT SIRES INC.—See Select Sires Inc.; *U.S. Private*, pg. 3601
COBB-VANTRESS, INC.—See Tyson Foods, Inc.; *U.S. Public*, pg. 2209
COOPERATIVE RESOURCES INTERNATIONAL INC.; *U.S. Private*, pg. 1043
C.P. LAOS CO., LTD.—See Charoen Pokphand Foods Public Company Limited; *Int'l*, pg. 1452
CREEKSTONE FARMS, INC.—See Triad Foods Group; *U.S. Private*, pg. 4225
DAIRY ONE COOPERATIVE INC.; *U.S. Private*, pg. 1146
DATAMARS, INC.—See Datamars SA; *Int'l*, pg. 1978
DATAMARS SA; *Int'l*, pg. 1978
DNA LANDMARKS INC.—See BASF SE; *Int'l*, pg. 877
EAST CENTRAL/SELECT SIRES—See Select Sires Inc.; *U.S. Private*, pg. 3601
ECO ANIMAL HEALTH GROUP PLC; *Int'l*, pg. 2292
FRIONA INDUSTRIES, LP; *U.S. Private*, pg. 1612
GENEX CANADA—See Cooperative Resources International Inc.; *U.S. Private*, pg. 1043
GENEX INC.—See Cooperative Resources International Inc.; *U.S. Private*, pg. 1043
GENUS AUSTRALIA PTY LTD—See Genus Plc; *Int'l*, pg. 2930
GENUS BREEDING INDIA PRIVATE LIMITED—See Genus Plc; *Int'l*, pg. 2930
GENUS BREEDING LTD—See Genus Plc; *Int'l*, pg. 2930
GENUS PLC; *Int'l*, pg. 2930
GENUS UKRAINE LLC—See Genus Plc; *Int'l*, pg. 2930
THE HAMBLETONIAN SOCIETY, INC.; *U.S. Private*, pg. 4042
HENDRIX GENETICS B.V.; *Int'l*, pg. 3345
INTERVET SOUTH AFRICA (PROPRIETARY) LIMITED—See Merck & Co., Inc.; *U.S. Public*, pg. 1417
MERRICK ANIMAL NUTRITION, INC.; *U.S. Private*, pg. 2675
MIDWEST SUPPLY & DISTRIBUTING—See Animart Inc.; *U.S. Private*, pg. 283
MINNESOTA/SELECT SIRES CO-OP INC.—See Select Sires Inc.; *U.S. Private*, pg. 3601
MSD ANIMAL HEALTH NORGE AS—See Merck & Co., Inc.; *U.S. Public*, pg. 1418
MSD MAGYARORSZAG KERESKEDELMI ES SZOLGALTATO KORLATOLT FELELOSSEGU TARSASAG—See Merck & Co., Inc.; *U.S. Public*, pg. 1418
NEVADA CLASSIC THOROUGHBREDS, INC.; *U.S. Private*, pg. 2891
NEW HOPE RANCH LLC—See Discovery Behavioral Health, Inc; *U.S. Private*, pg. 1237
NEWSHAM CHOICE GENETICS—See Groupe Grimaud La Corbiere SA; *Int'l*, pg. 3103
NORTHSTAR COOPERATIVE INC.; *U.S. Private*, pg. 2957
PIC ANDINA S.A.—See Genus Plc; *Int'l*, pg. 2931
PIG IMPROVEMENT COMPANY DEUTSCHLAND GMBH—See Genus Plc; *Int'l*, pg. 2931
PIG IMPROVEMENT COMPANY UK LIMITED—See Genus Plc; *Int'l*, pg. 2931
PRAIRIE STATE/SELECT SIRES—See Select Sires Inc.; *U.S. Private*, pg. 3601
PRIMA ANJUNG SDN. BHD.—See Emivest Berhad; *Int'l*, pg. 2383
ROSS BREEDERS (BOTSWANA) (PTY) LIMITED—See Country Bird Holdings Limited; *Int'l*, pg. 1818
SALIX ANIMAL HEALTH, LLC—See Spectrum Brands Holdings, Inc.; *U.S. Public*, pg. 1915
SB&B FOODS INC.; *U.S. Private*, pg. 3559
SELECT SIRES INC.; *U.S. Private*, pg. 3601
SELECT SIRES MIDAMERICA, INC.—See Select Sires Inc.; *U.S. Private*, pg. 3601
SELIA—See Groupe Limagrain Holding SA; *Int'l*, pg. 3108
SOUTHEAST SELECT SIRES INC.—See Select Sires Inc.; *U.S. Private*, pg. 3601
ST JACOBS ANIMAL BREEDING CORP.—See Genus Plc; *Int'l*, pg. 2931
VALLEY CO-OPS INC.; *U.S. Private*, pg. 4333
VETERINARIAN'S OUTLET INCORPORATED; *U.S. Private*, pg. 4374
WORLD WIDE SIRES, LTD.; *U.S. Private*, pg. 4567

115310 — SUPPORT ACTIVITIES FOR FORESTRY

AARDWOLF PESTKARE (SINGAPORE) PTE. LTD.—See Rollins, Inc.; *U.S. Public*, pg. 1808
ACCIONA MEDIO AMBIENTE—See Acciona, S.A.; *Int'l*, pg. 90
AMAZONAS FLORESTAL LTD; *U.S. Public*, pg. 91
APEX REFORESTATION LTD; *Int'l*, pg. 512
BID GROUP LTD; *Int'l*, pg. 1019
BILLERUDKORSNAS LATVIA SIA—See Billerud AB; *Int'l*, pg. 1030
CENTRAL SECURITY GROUP, INC.—See Summit Partners, L.P.; *U.S. Private*, pg. 3855
CHINA SANDI HOLDINGS LIMITED; *Int'l*, pg. 1549
COILLTE LTD.; *Int'l*, pg. 1696
CONAIR GROUP INC.; *Int'l*, pg. 1763
COOPERATIVE FORESTIERE BOURGOGNE LIMOUSIN (CFBL); *Int'l*, pg. 1792
ECOWISE AUSTRALIA PTY LTD—See ALS Limited; *Int'l*, pg. 378
FEA PLANTATIONS LIMITED—See Forest Enterprises Australia Limited; *Int'l*, pg. 2732
FORESTAL MININCO S.A.—See Empresas CMPC S.A.; *Int'l*, pg. 2390
FOREST ENTERPRISES AUSTRALIA LIMITED; *Int'l*, pg. 2732
FOREST MANAGEMENT SERVICES (NZ) LIMITED—See Greenheart Group Limited; *Int'l*, pg. 3075
FORSTVERWALTUNG BRANNENBURG GMBH & CO. OHG—See Henkel AG & Co. KGaA; *Int'l*, pg. 3348
FUJIAN JINSEN FORESTRY CO., LTD.; *Int'l*, pg. 2818
THE GLATFELTER PULP WOOD COMPANY—See Glatfelter Corporation; *U.S. Public*, pg. 939
GOLDEN FOREST, S.A.; *Int'l*, pg. 3029
GREENHEART GROUP LIMITED; *Int'l*, pg. 3074
GUANGZHAO INDUSTRIAL FOREST BIOTECHNOLOGY GROUP LIMITED; *Int'l*, pg. 3164
HUBER RESOURCES CORPORATION—See J.M. Huber Corporation; *U.S. Private*, pg. 2168
IBERSILVA, S.A.U.—See ENCE Energia y Celulosa, S.A.; *Int'l*, pg. 2401
IISAAK FOREST RESOURCE LTD.—See Weyerhaeuser Company; *U.S. Public*, pg. 2365
INLAND FOREST MANAGEMENT, INC.—See F&W Forestry Services Inc.; *U.S. Private*, pg. 1455
KEWEENAW LAND ASSOCIATION, LTD.; *U.S. Public*, pg. 1225
LYKES BROS. INC. - RANCH DIVISION—See Lykes Brothers Inc.; *U.S. Private*, pg. 2519
MASISA CHILE S.A.—See GrupoNueva S.A.; *Int'l*, pg. 3139
MATARIKI FORESTRY GROUP—See Rayonier Inc.; *U.S. Public*, pg. 1765
NORTHLAND FOREST MANAGERS (1995) LIMITED—See Greenheart Group Limited; *Int'l*, pg. 3075
RAINFOREST RESOURCES, INC.; *U.S. Public*, pg. 1761
RAYONIER MISSISSIPPI TIMBERLANDS COMPANY—See Rayonier Inc.; *U.S. Public*, pg. 1765
RAYONIER TIMBERLANDS, L.P.—See Rayonier Inc.; *U.S. Public*, pg. 1765
REFORESTATION SERVICES, INC.—See Sterling Partners; *U.S. Private*, pg. 3806
SCIENTIFIC PEST MANAGEMENT (AUSTRALIA/PACIFIC) PTY. LTD.—See Rollins, Inc.; *U.S. Public*, pg. 1809
SEALASKA TIMBER CORPORATION—See Sealaska Corporation; *U.S. Private*, pg. 3585
SINO-PANEL (GUANGXI) LIMITED—See Emerald Plantation Holdings Limited; *Int'l*, pg. 2378
SINO-PANEL (GUANGZHOU) LIMITED—See Emerald Plantation Holdings Limited; *Int'l*, pg. 2378
SINOWOOD LIMITED—See Emerald Plantation Holdings Limited; *Int'l*, pg. 2378
SOUTHEASTERN FOREST MANAGEMENT, LLC—See Windrock Land Company; *U.S. Public*, pg. 2372
SUMMITT FORESTS INC.; *U.S. Private*, pg. 3857
TACOBA CONSULTANT FORESTRY N.V—See China International Marine Containers (Group) Co., Ltd.; *Int'l*, pg. 1512
TENON USA, INC—See Hardwoods Distribution Inc.; *Int'l*, pg. 3273
TRIMBLE FORESTRY LTDA.—See Trimble, Inc.; *U.S. Public*, pg. 2192
UNILES, A.S.—See Agrofert Holding, a.s.; *Int'l*, pg. 219

211120 — CRUDE PETROLEUM EXTRACTION

1ST NRG CORP.; *U.S. Public*, pg. 2
3D ENERGI LIMITED; *Int'l*, pg. 7
3 SIXTY SECURE CORP.; *Int'l*, pg. 5
88 ENERGY LIMITED; *Int'l*, pg. 15
ABILENE OIL & GAS LIMITED; *Int'l*, pg. 61
ABINGTON RESOURCES LTD.; *Int'l*, pg. 61
ABRAXAS PETROLEUM CORPORATION; *U.S. Public*, pg. 26
ABU DHABI COMPANY ONSHORE OIL OPERATIONS—See Abu Dhabi National Oil Company; *Int'l*, pg. 72
ABU DHABI NATIONAL OIL COMPANY; *Int'l*, pg. 72
ACADIAN ENERGY, LLC; *U.S. Private*, pg. 47
ACCESS US OIL AND GAS INC.; *U.S. Private*, pg. 53
ADINO ENERGY CORPORATION; *U.S. Private*, pg. 79
ADIRA ENERGY CORP.—See Empower Clinics Inc.; *Int'l*, pg. 2388
ADVANTAGE ENERGY LTD.; *Int'l*, pg. 164
ADVANTAGEWON OIL CORP.; *Int'l*, pg. 164
ADX ENERGY LIMITED; *Int'l*, pg. 169
AERA ENERGY LLC—See Aera Energy LLC; *U.S. Private*, pg. 117
AFRICA ENERGY CORP.; *Int'l*, pg. 189
AFRICA OIL CORPORATION; *Int'l*, pg. 190
AFRICA OIL TURKANA B.V.—See Africa Oil Corporation; *Int'l*, pg. 191
AFRIQUE ENERGIE CORP.; *Int'l*, pg. 193
AGIP CASPIAN SEA BV—See Eni S.p.A.; *Int'l*, pg. 2436

CORPORATE AFFILIATIONS

AKER BP ASA; *Int'l*, pg. 262
AKER SUBSEA AS—See Aker Solutions ASA; *Int'l*, pg. 262
ALAMO ENERGY CORP.; *U.S. Private*, pg. 149
ALEATOR ENERGY LIMITED; *Int'l*, pg. 305
ALLIANCE OIL COMPANY LTD.; *Int'l*, pg. 340
ALON REFINING KROTZ SPRINGS, INC.—See Delek Group Ltd.; *Int'l*, pg. 2011
ALPHA HUNTER DRILLING, LLC—See Expand Energy Corporation; *U.S. Public*, pg. 808
ALPINE SUMMIT ENERGY PARTNERS, INC.; *U.S. Public*, pg. 85
ALTAGAS OPERATING PARTNERSHIP—See AltaGas Ltd.; *Int'l*, pg. 384
ALTA MESA HOLDINGS, L.P.—See Alta Mesa Resources, Inc.; *U.S. Private*, pg. 203
ALTIMA RESOURCES LTD.; *Int'l*, pg. 393
ALTUS RENEWABLES LIMITED; *Int'l*, pg. 399
ALVOPETRO ENERGY LTD.; *Int'l*, pg. 402
AMERICAN ENERGY PRODUCTION, INC.; *U.S. Private*, pg. 231
AMERICAN PATRIOT OIL & GAS LIMITED; *Int'l*, pg. 422
AMERICAN SHALE OIL, LLC—See Genie Energy Ltd.; *U.S. Public*, pg. 930
AMERITRUST CORPORATION; *U.S. Public*, pg. 115
AMINEX PETROLEUM SERVICES LIMITED—See Aminex PLC; *Int'l*, pg. 428
AMINEX PLC; *Int'l*, pg. 428
AMOCO ARGENTINA OIL CO.—See BP plc; *Int'l*, pg. 1126
AMOSSCO LIMITED—See Aminex PLC; *Int'l*, pg. 428
AMPLIFY ENERGY CORP.; *U.S. Public*, pg. 133
AMROSE OIL COMPANY; *U.S. Private*, pg. 266
ANADARKO ALGERIA COMPANY, LLC—See Occidental Petroleum Corporation; *U.S. Public*, pg. 1561
ANADARKO PETROLEUM CORPORATION—See Occidental Petroleum Corporation; *U.S. Public*, pg. 1561
ANADARKO US OFFSHORE CORPORATION—See Occidental Petroleum Corporation; *U.S. Public*, pg. 1561
ANAM INC.; *U.S. Private*, pg. 271
THE ANDERSONS MARATHON ETHANOL LLC—See The Andersons Incorporated; *U.S. Public*, pg. 2035
ANGLO PHILIPPINE HOLDINGS CORPORATION; *Int'l*, pg. 463
ANNONA ENERGY INC.; *Int'l*, pg. 474
ANSON PARTNERS LLC; *U.S. Private*, pg. 286
ANTRIM ENERGY INC.; *Int'l*, pg. 485
APACHE EGYPT COMPANIES—See APA Corporation; *U.S. Public*, pg. 143
APACHE NORTH SEA LIMITED—See APA Corporation; *U.S. Public*, pg. 143
APC GROUP, INC.; *Int'l*, pg. 507
APPROACH RESOURCES INC.; *U.S. Private*, pg. 300
ARABELLA EXPLORATION, INC.; *U.S. Private*, pg. 307
ARABIAN OIL COMPANY, LTD.—See Fuji Oil Company, Ltd.; *Int'l*, pg. 2815
ARC RESOURCES LTD.; *Int'l*, pg. 539
ARKANOVA ENERGY CORPORATION; *U.S. Public*, pg. 193
ARKOSE ENERGY CORP.; *U.S. Public*, pg. 193
ARMOUR ENERGY LIMITED; *Int'l*, pg. 575
ARROW EXPLORATION CORP.; *Int'l*, pg. 579
ARROWHEAD PIPE & SUPPLY CO—See Mack Energy Corporation; *U.S. Private*, pg. 2536
ARTEX S.A.—See Weatherford International plc; *U.S. Public*, pg. 2339
ASCENT RESOURCES PLC; *Int'l*, pg. 602
ASIA EURO OIL PLC; *Int'l*, pg. 612
ASKARII RESOURCES, LLC—See Petrolia Energy Corporation; *U.S. Public*, pg. 1678
ASPENLEAF ENERGY LIMITED; *Int'l*, pg. 629
ATHABASCA OIL CORP.; *Int'l*, pg. 669
ATTIS OIL AND GAS LIMITED—See Helium One Global Ltd.; *Int'l*, pg. 3331
AVANTI HELIUM CORP.; *Int'l*, pg. 736
AXIOM OIL AND GAS CORP.; *U.S. Public*, pg. 413
AXP ENERGY LIMITED; *Int'l*, pg. 771
AZABACHE ENERGY INC.; *Int'l*, pg. 776
BANDELIER PIPELINE HOLDING, LLC—See Callon Petroleum Company; *U.S. Public*, pg. 424
BANGCHAK CORPORATION PUBLIC COMPANY LIMITED; *Int'l*, pg. 832
BANKERS PETROLEUM LTD.—See Geo-Jade Petroleum Corporation; *Int'l*, pg. 2932
BARNWELL INDUSTRIES, INC.; *U.S. Public*, pg. 278
BARNWELL KONA CORPORATION—See Barnwell Industries, Inc.; *U.S. Public*, pg. 278
BARNWELL OF CANADA LIMITED—See Barnwell Industries, Inc.; *U.S. Public*, pg. 278
BARON ENERGY, INC.; *U.S. Public*, pg. 278
BARREL ENERGY, INC.; *U.S. Public*, pg. 278
BARRYROE OFFSHORE ENERGY PLC; *Int'l*, pg. 870
BASA RESOURCES INC.; *U.S. Private*, pg. 484
BASIC PETROLEUM SERVICES, INC.—See Permian Resources Corp; *U.S. Public*, pg. 1677
BASS OIL LIMITED; *Int'l*, pg. 887
BATTALION OIL CORP.; *U.S. Public*, pg. 279
BAYOU CITY EXPLORATION, INC.; *U.S. Private*, pg. 496
BAYOU STATE OIL CORPORATION; *U.S. Private*, pg. 496

N.A.I.C.S. INDEX

211120 — CRUDE PETROLEUM EXT...

BAYPORT INTERNATIONAL HOLDINGS, INC.; *U.S. Public*, pg. 284
BAYTEX ENERGY CORP.; *Int'l*, pg. 915
BEACH ENERGY LIMITED; *Int'l*, pg. 932
BEACON ENERGY PLC; *Int'l*, pg. 932
BELLELI ENERGY F.Z.E.—See Enerflex Ltd.; *Int'l*, pg. 2418
BELORUSNEFT REPUBLICAN UNITARY ENTERPRISE—See Concern Belneftekhim; *Int'l*, pg. 1764
BERCO RESOURCES LLC; *U.S. Public*, pg. 529
BEREXCO INC.; *U.S. Private*, pg. 530
BERKLEY RENEWABLES INC.; *Int'l*, pg. 985
BERRY CORPORATION (BRY); *U.S. Public*, pg. 320
BERRY PETROLEUM COMPANY, LLC—See Berry Corporation (Bry); *U.S. Public*, pg. 320
BHP GROUP PLC—See BHP Group Limited; *Int'l*, pg. 1015
BISON ENERGY SERVICES PLC; *Int'l*, pg. 1049
BJ SERVICES COMPANY—See Baker Hughes Company; *U.S. Public*, pg. 264
BLACKBRUSH OIL & GAS, L.P.—See Ares Management Corporation; *U.S. Public*, pg. 188
BLACKSANDS PETROLEUM, INC.; *U.S. Private*, pg. 576
BLACK STALLION OIL AND GAS, INC.; *U.S. Public*, pg. 341
BLACK STAR PETROLEUM LIMITED; *Int'l*, pg. 1060
BLACKSTEEL ENERGY INC.; *Int'l*, pg. 1062
BLACK STONE ENERGY COMPANY, LLC—See Black Stone Minerals, L.P.; *U.S. Public*, pg. 341
BLACK WARRIOR METHANE CORP.—See Atlas Energy Group, LLC; *U.S. Public*, pg. 223
BLACK WARRIOR METHANE CORP.—See Warrior Met Coal, Inc; *U.S. Public*, pg. 2329
BLOCKCHAINK2 CORP.; *Int'l*, pg. 1064
BLUE DOLPHIN ENERGY COMPANY; *U.S. Public*, pg. 364
BLUE DOLPHIN PETROLEUM COMPANY—See Blue Dolphin Energy Company; *U.S. Public*, pg. 364
BLUE ENERGY LIMITED; *Int'l*, pg. 1068
BLUE ENSIGN TECHNOLOGIES LIMITED; *Int'l*, pg. 1068
BLUENORD ASA; *Int'l*, pg. 1072
BNK PETROLEUM INC.; *Int'l*, pg. 366
BONANZA CREEK ENERGY OPERATING COMPANY LLC—See Civitas Resources, Inc.; *U.S. Public*, pg. 507
BONANZA CREEK ENERGY RESOURCES, LLC—See Civitas Resources, Inc.; *U.S. Public*, pg. 507
BONANZA OIL AND GAS, INC.; *U.S. Private*, pg. 613
BONTERRA ENERGY CORP.; *Int'l*, pg. 1109
BORDER PETROLEUM LIMITED; *Int'l*, pg. 1113
BOSS ENERGY LIMITED; *Int'l*, pg. 1117
BOULDER ENERGY LTD.—See Highwood Asset Management Ltd.; *Int'l*, pg. 3389
BOUNTY HOLDINGS INC—See Anam Inc.; *U.S. Private*, pg. 271
BOUNTY OIL & GAS NL; *Int'l*, pg. 1119
BP AMERICA, INC.—See BP plc; *Int'l*, pg. 1126
BP AMERICA PRODUCTION CO.—See BP plc; *Int'l*, pg. 1126
BP AMERICA PRODUCTION CO.—See BP plc; *Int'l*, pg. 1126
BP AMERICA PRODUCTION CO.—See BP plc; *Int'l*, pg. 1126
BP AMERICA PRODUCTION CO.—See BP plc; *Int'l*, pg. 1126
BP AMERICA PRODUCTION CO.—See BP plc; *Int'l*, pg. 1126
BP AMERICA PRODUCTION CO.—See BP plc; *Int'l*, pg. 1126
BP ANGOLA—See BP plc; *Int'l*, pg. 1128
BP AZERBAIJAN—See BP plc; *Int'l*, pg. 1128
BP BRASIL LTDA—See BP plc; *Int'l*, pg. 1128
BP CANADA ENERGY COMPANY—See BP plc; *Int'l*, pg. 1126
BP CARSON REFINERY—See BP plc; *Int'l*, pg. 1126
BP EGYPT—See BP plc; *Int'l*, pg. 1128
BP ENERGY COMPANY-TRINIDAD & TOBAGO—See BP plc; *Int'l*, pg. 1128
BP ESPANA S.A.U.—See BP plc; *Int'l*, pg. 1128
BP EXPLORATION (ALASKA) INC.—See BP plc; *Int'l*, pg. 1127
BP EXPLORATION (ALPHA) LIMITED—See BP plc; *Int'l*, pg. 1128
BP EXPLORATION AND PRODUCTION EGYPT LLC—See BP plc; *Int'l*, pg. 1128
BP EXPLORATION COMPANY LIMITED—See BP plc; *Int'l*, pg. 1129
BP EXPLORATION (FAROES) LIMITED—See BP plc; *Int'l*, pg. 1129
BP INTERNATIONAL LTD.—See BP plc; *Int'l*, pg. 1129
BP OIL THAILAND—See BP plc; *Int'l*, pg. 1129
BP PETROLLERI A.S.—See BP plc; *Int'l*, pg. 1129
BP—See BP plc; *Int'l*, pg. 1128
BP SOUTHEAST ASIA LTD.—See BP plc; *Int'l*, pg. 1129
BP WEST COAST PRODUCTS LLC—See BP plc; *Int'l*, pg. 1126
BRAZOS VALLEY LONGHORN, L.L.C.—See Expand Energy Corporation; *U.S. Public*, pg. 808
BRECK OPERATING CORP.—See States Unlimited; *U.S. Private*, pg. 3793
BREITBURN FLORIDA LLC—See Maverick Natural Resources, LLC; *U.S. Private*, pg. 2616
BREITBURN MANAGEMENT COMPANY, LLC—See Maverick Natural Resources, LLC; *U.S. Private*, pg. 2616
BREITBURN OPERATING L.P.—See Maverick Natural Resources, LLC; *U.S. Private*, pg. 2616
BREITLING ENERGY CORPORATION; *U.S. Private*, pg. 644
BRG PETROLEUM CORPORATION; *U.S. Private*, pg. 647
BTA OIL PRODUCERS INC.; *U.S. Private*, pg. 675
BUCKHORN ENERGY SERVICES, LLC—See Blackstone Inc.; *U.S. Public*, pg. 359
BURGUNDY DIAMOND MINES LIMITED; *Int'l*, pg. 1224
BURK ROYALTY CO.; *U.S. Private*, pg. 687
BURU ENERGY LIMITED; *Int'l*, pg. 1227
BUTTE ENERGY INC.; *Int'l*, pg. 1229
BYRON ENERGY LIMITED; *Int'l*, pg. 1235
CABOT ENERGY PLC; *Int'l*, pg. 1246
CABRAL GOLD INC.; *Int'l*, pg. 1246
CADOGAN ENERGY SOLUTIONS PLC; *Int'l*, pg. 1248
CAIRN ENERGY HYDROCARBONS LIMITED—See Capricorn Energy PLC; *Int'l*, pg. 1316
CALIFORNIA RESOURCES CORPORATION; *U.S. Public*, pg. 423
CALIMA ENERGY LIMITED; *Int'l*, pg. 1264
CALLON OFFSHORE PRODUCTION—See Callon Petroleum Company; *U.S. Public*, pg. 424
CALLON PETROLEUM COMPANY; *U.S. Public*, pg. 424
CALMENA ENERGY SERVICES INC.; *Int'l*, pg. 1265
CALVALLEY PETROLEUM (CYPRUS) LTD.—See Calvalley Energy Ltd.; *Int'l*, pg. 1266
CAMAC INTERNATIONAL CORPORATION; *U.S. Private*, pg. 725
CAMBER ENERGY, INC.; *U.S. Public*, pg. 425
CANACOL ENERGY LTD.; *Int'l*, pg. 1277
CANADA RENEWABLE BIOENERGY CORP.; *Int'l*, pg. 1282
CANADIAN NATURAL RESOURCES LTD.; *Int'l*, pg. 1284
CANADIAN OIL RECOVERY & REMEDIATION ENTERPRISES LIMITED; *Int'l*, pg. 1285
CANADIAN SPIRIT RESOURCES INC.; *Int'l*, pg. 1286
CANARGO GEORGIA LTD—See CanArgo Energy Corporation; *Int'l*, pg. 1288
CANARGO LIMITED—See CanArgo Energy Corporation; *Int'l*, pg. 1288
CANNAWAKE CORPORATION—See American Green, Inc.; *U.S. Public*, pg. 103
CAP ENERGY PLC; *Int'l*, pg. 1300
CAPRICORN ENERGY PLC; *Int'l*, pg. 1316
CARCETTI CAPITAL CORP.; *Int'l*, pg. 1321
CARDINAL ENERGY GROUP, INC.; *U.S. Private*, pg. 750
CARDINAL ENERGY LTD.; *Int'l*, pg. 1321
CARNARVON ENERGY LIMITED; *Int'l*, pg. 1342
CARRIZO OIL & GAS, INC.—See Callon Petroleum Company; *U.S. Public*, pg. 424
CASPIAN SUNRISE PLC; *Int'l*, pg. 1354
CASTROL BP PETCO CO., LTD.—See BP plc; *Int'l*, pg. 1131
CENOVUS ENERGY INC.; *Int'l*, pg. 1401
CENTENNIAL RESOURCE PRODUCTION, LLC—See Permian Resources Corp; *U.S. Public*, pg. 1677
CENTRAL PETROLEUM LIMITED; *Int'l*, pg. 1409
CENTURION ENERGY INTERNATIONAL INC.—See Dana Gas PJSC; *Int'l*, pg. 1957
CENTURION PETROLEUM CORPORATION—See Dana Gas PJSC; *Int'l*, pg. 1957
CEP MID-CONTINENT LLC—See Evolve Transition Infrastructure LP; *U.S. Public*, pg. 804
CEQUENCE ENERGY LTD.; *Int'l*, pg. 1420
CF ENERGY CORP.; *Int'l*, pg. 1429
CGX ENERGY INC.; *Int'l*, pg. 1435
CHALKER ENERGY PARTNERS III, LLC—See Quantum Energy Partners, LLC; *U.S. Private*, pg. 3323
CHALLENGER GOLD LIMITED; *Int'l*, pg. 1438
CHAPARRAL ENERGY, INC.; *U.S. Private*, pg. 849
CHARIOT LIMITED; *Int'l*, pg. 1450
CHESAPEAKE MID-CONTINENT CORP.—See Expand Energy Corporation; *U.S. Public*, pg. 808
CHESAPEAKE OPERATING, LLC—See Expand Energy Corporation; *U.S. Public*, pg. 808
CHEVRON EXPLORATION & PRODUCTION INC.—See Chevron Corporation; *U.S. Public*, pg. 486
CHEVRON NORTH SEA LIMITED—See Delek Group Ltd.; *Int'l*, pg. 2012
CHEVRON ORONITE PTE. LTD.—See Chevron Corporation; *U.S. Public*, pg. 486
CHEVRON PHILIPPINES INC.—See Chevron Corporation; *U.S. Public*, pg. 486
CHEVRON THAILAND EXPLORATION & PRODUCTION, LTD.—See Chevron Corporation; *U.S. Public*, pg. 486
CHINA INTEGRATED ENERGY, INC.; *Int'l*, pg. 1510
CHINA NATIONAL OFFSHORE OIL CORP.; *Int'l*, pg. 1532
CHORD ENERGY CORPORATION; *U.S. Public*, pg. 490
CIMAREX ENERGY, INC.—See Coterra Energy Inc.; *U.S. Public*, pg. 587
CIMAREX RESOLUTE LLC—See Coterra Energy Inc.; *U.S. Public*, pg. 587
CINCO RESOURCES, INC.—See Riley Exploration Group, LLC; *U.S. Private*, pg. 3437
CIRCLE STAR ENERGY CORP.; *U.S. Private*, pg. 900
CITADEL EXPLORATION, INC.; *U.S. Public*, pg. 501
CITATION OIL & GAS CORP.; *U.S. Private*, pg. 901
CITIZENS GAS FUEL COMPANY—See DTE Energy Company; *U.S. Public*, pg. 689
CIVITAS RESOURCES, INC.; *U.S. Public*, pg. 507
CLAREN ENERGY CORP.; *Int'l*, pg. 1642
CLONTARF ENERGY PLC; *Int'l*, pg. 1661
CLYDE NETHERLANDS BV—See BASF SE; *Int'l*, pg. 885
CNOOC LIMITED—See China National Offshore Oil Corp.; *Int'l*, pg. 1532
CNOOC UGANDA LTD—See China National Offshore Oil Corp.; *Int'l*, pg. 1532
CNR (ECHO) RESOURCES INC.—See Canadian Natural Resources Ltd.; *Int'l*, pg. 1284
CNR INTERNATIONAL (ANGOLA) LIMITED—See Canadian Natural Resources Ltd.; *Int'l*, pg. 1284
CNR INTERNATIONAL—See Canadian Natural Resources Ltd.; *Int'l*, pg. 1284
CNR INTERNATIONAL UK LIMITED—See Canadian Natural Resources Ltd.; *Int'l*, pg. 1284
COBALT INTERNATIONAL ENERGY, INC.; *U.S. Private*, pg. 957
COJAX OIL AND GAS CORPORATION; *U.S. Public*, pg. 530
COLD LAKE PIPELINE LIMITED PARTNERSHIP—See Brookfield Infrastructure Partners L.P.; *Int'l*, pg. 1193
COLUMBINE VALLEY RESOURCES, INC.; *U.S. Public*, pg. 535
COLUMBUS ENERGY LIMITED; *Int'l*, pg. 1706
COLUMBUS ENERGY, LLC—See Amplify Energy Corp.; *U.S. Public*, pg. 133
COLUMBUS ENERGY RESOURCES PLC—See Challenger Energy Group PLC; *Int'l*, pg. 1438
COMET RIDGE LIMITED; *Int'l*, pg. 1711
COMMERCIAL ENERGY LLC; *U.S. Private*, pg. 983
COMPASS PRODUCTION PARTNERS, LP—See Spectrum Brands Holdings, Inc.; *U.S. Public*, pg. 1915
COMSTOCK RESOURCES, INC.; *U.S. Public*, pg. 562
CONCHO RESOURCES, INC.—See ConocoPhillips; *U.S. Public*, pg. 568
CONDOR PETROLEUM INC.; *Int'l*, pg. 1766
CONNACHER OIL & GAS LIMITED; *Int'l*, pg. 1768
CONOCOPHILLIPS AUSTRALIA PTY LTD—See ConocoPhillips; *U.S. Public*, pg. 568
CONOCOPHILLIPS CANADA—See ConocoPhillips; *U.S. Public*, pg. 568
CONOCOPHILLIPS CANADA—See ConocoPhillips; *U.S. Public*, pg. 568
CONOCOPHILLIPS CHINA INC—See ConocoPhillips; *U.S. Public*, pg. 568
CONOCOPHILLIPS RUSSIA, INC.—See ConocoPhillips; *U.S. Public*, pg. 568
CONOCOPHILLIPS SKANDINAVIA AS—See ConocoPhillips; *U.S. Public*, pg. 568
CONTINENTAL ENERGY CORPORATION; *Int'l*, pg. 1783
CONTINENTAL RESOURCES ILLINOIS, INC.—See Continental Resources, Inc.; *U.S. Private*, pg. 1031
CONTINENTAL RESOURCES, INC.; *U.S. Private*, pg. 1031
CONTINUOUS TUBING—See Ensign Energy Services Inc.; *Int'l*, pg. 2446
COOPER ENERGY LIMITED; *Int'l*, pg. 1791
COSCO CAPITAL, INC.; *Int'l*, pg. 1809
COSMO MATSUYAMA OIL CO., LTD.—See Cosmo Energy Holdings Co., Ltd.; *Int'l*, pg. 1812
COUNTRYMARK REFINING AND LOGISTICS, LLC—See Countrymark Cooperative, Inc.; *U.S. Private*, pg. 1067
COVE PETROLEUM—See Anchor Gasoline Corporation; *U.S. Private*, pg. 273
CRANBERRY PIPELINE CORPORATION—See Coterra Energy Inc.; *U.S. Public*, pg. 587
CRIMSON RESOURCE MANAGEMENT; *U.S. Private*, pg. 1101
CROWN POINT ENERGY INC.; *Int'l*, pg. 1858
CRUDECORP ASA; *Int'l*, pg. 1859
CUBIC ENERGY, LLC; *U.S. Private*, pg. 1120
CYCLIQ GROUP LIMITED; *Int'l*, pg. 1894
CYPRESS HILLS RESOURCE CORP.; *Int'l*, pg. 1897
DAN A. HUGHES COMPANY; *U.S. Private*, pg. 1151
DATALOG DE VENEZUELA SA—See Weatherford International plc; *U.S. Public*, pg. 2339
DAVOIL INC.; *U.S. Private*, pg. 1175
DEA DEUTSCHE ERDOEL AG—See BASF SE; *Int'l*, pg. 885
DEEP ENERGY RESOURCES LTD.; *Int'l*, pg. 2002
DEJOUR ENERGY USA, INC.—See DXI Capital Corp.; *Int'l*, pg. 2237
DELEUM BERHAD; *Int'l*, pg. 2012
DELTA OIL & GAS, INC.; *Int'l*, pg. 2019
DENBURY GREEN PIPELINE - TEXAS, LLC—See Exxon Mobil Corporation; *U.S. Public*, pg. 813
DENBURY OPERATING COMPANY—See Exxon Mobil Corporation; *U.S. Public*, pg. 814
DEVON CANADA CORPORATION—See Canadian Natural Resources Ltd.; *Int'l*, pg. 1284
DEVON CANADA—See Canadian Natural Resources Ltd.; *Int'l*, pg. 1284
DEVON ENERGY CORPORATION; *U.S. Public*, pg. 657
DEVON ENERGY PRODUCTION COMPANY, L.P.—See Devon Energy Corporation; *U.S. Public*, pg. 657

211120 — CRUDE PETROLEUM EXT...

DH ENCHANTMENT, INC.; *U.S. Public,* pg. 657
DIAMONDBACK ENERGY, INC.; *U.S. Public,* pg. 658
DIAMONDBACK E&P LLC—See Diamondback Energy, Inc.; *U.S. Public,* pg. 658
DINOCO OIL, INC.; *U.S. Private,* pg. 1233
DISCOVERY ENERGY CORP.; *U.S. Public,* pg. 668
DISCOVERY RIDGE RESOURCES, INC.; *Int'l,* pg. 2134
DISTRICT MINES LTD.; *Int'l,* pg. 2137
DNO ASA; *Int'l,* pg. 2148
DNO YEMEN AS—See DNO ASA; *Int'l,* pg. 2148
DORADO OIL COMPANY; *U.S. Private,* pg. 1262
DORCHESTER MINERALS, L.P.; *U.S. Public,* pg. 677
DUBAI PETROLEUM COMPANY—See ConocoPhillips; *U.S. Public,* pg. 568
DUGAN PRODUCTION CORP.; *U.S. Private,* pg. 1285
DUNDEE ENERGY LIMITED—See Dundee Corporation; *Int'l,* pg. 2225
DXI CAPITAL CORP.; *Int'l,* pg. 2237
DYNAMIC HYDROCARBONS LTD.; *U.S. Private,* pg. 1298
EAGLE ENERGY INC.; *Int'l,* pg. 2264
EARTHSTONE ENERGY, LLC—See Permian Resources Corp; *U.S. Public,* pg. 1677
E&B NATURAL RESOURCES; *U.S. Private,* pg. 1301
EBN B.V.; *Int'l,* pg. 2285
ECHO ENERGY PLC; *Int'l,* pg. 2289
ECNG ENERGY LIMITED PARTNERSHIP—See AltaGas Ltd.; *Int'l,* pg. 384
EDISON RENEWABLE ENERGY, INC.—See Edison International; *U.S. Public,* pg. 719
EESTI POLEVKIVI AS—See Eesti Energia AS; *Int'l,* pg. 2317
ELATE HOLDINGS LIMITED; *Int'l,* pg. 2343
ELECTROMAGNETIC GEOSERVICES ASA; *Int'l,* pg. 2353
ELIXIR ENERGY LIMITED; *Int'l,* pg. 2363
ELK PETROLEUM INC—See ELK Petroleum Limited; *Int'l,* pg. 2363
ELK PETROLEUM LIMITED; *Int'l,* pg. 2363
ELLORA ENERGY INC.—See Exxon Mobil Corporation; *U.S. Public,* pg. 814
EMAS OFFSHORE LIMITED—See Ezra Holdings Ltd.; *Int'l,* pg. 2594
EMERALD OIL, INC.; *U.S. Private,* pg. 1379
EMERALD RESOURCES NL; *Int'l,* pg. 2378
EMERALD WB LLC—See Emerald Oil, Inc.; *U.S. Private,* pg. 1379
EMO OIL LIMITED—See DCC plc; *Int'l,* pg. 1990
EMPEROR OIL LTD.; *Int'l,* pg. 2386
EMPIRE ENERGY CORPORATION INTERNATIONAL; *U.S. Private,* pg. 1384
EMPIRE ENERGY GROUP LIMITED; *Int'l,* pg. 2387
EMPIRE PETROLEUM PARTNERS, LLC—See Haymaker Acquisition Corp.; *U.S. Private,* pg. 1885
EMPOWER CLINICS INC.; *Int'l,* pg. 2387
EMPRESA PETROLERA CHACO S.A.—See BP plc; *Int'l,* pg. 1131
EMPRESA PETROLERA CHACO S.A.—See Bridas Corporation; *Int'l,* pg. 1152
EMPRESAS PETROLEO IPIRANGA; *Int'l,* pg. 2391
ENABLE MIDSTREAM PARTNERS, LP—See Energy Transfer LP; *U.S. Public,* pg. 763
ENAP REFINERIAS SA—See Empresa Nacional del Petroleo; *Int'l,* pg. 2388
ENCANA CORPORATION - EASTERN CANADA OFFICE—See Ovintiv Inc.; *U.S. Public,* pg. 1625
ENCANA CORPORATION—See Ovintiv Inc.; *U.S. Public,* pg. 1625
ENCANA OIL & GAS (USA) INC.—See Ovintiv Inc.; *U.S. Public,* pg. 1625
ENCORE ENERGY PARTNERS LP—See Grizzly Energy, LLC; *U.S. Public,* pg. 970
ENDEAVOR ENERGY RESOURCES LP; *U.S. Private,* pg. 1391
ENDEAVOR PIPELINE, INC.—See GMX Resources Inc.; *U.S. Private,* pg. 1723
ENECO ENERGY LIMITED; *Int'l,* pg. 2411
ENERFLEX LTD.; *Int'l,* pg. 2418
ENERGEN RESOURCES CORPORATION—See Diamondback Energy, Inc.; *U.S. Public,* pg. 658
ENERGOBALTIC SP. Z O.O.—See Grupa LOTOS S.A.; *Int'l,* pg. 3117
ENERGY 11, L.P.; *U.S. Private,* pg. 1393
ENERGY CORPORATION OF AMERICA; *U.S. Private,* pg. 1394
ENERGY CORPORATION OF AMERICA—See Energy Corporation of America; *U.S. Private,* pg. 1395
ENERGY DEVELOPMENT CORPORATION (CHINA), INC.—See Chevron Corporation; *U.S. Public,* pg. 487
ENERGY & EXPLORATION PARTNERS, LLC—See Energy & Exploration Partners, Inc.; *U.S. Private,* pg. 1393
ENERGY HOLDINGS INTERNATIONAL, INC.; *U.S. Private,* pg. 1395
ENERGY ONE LLC—See U.S. Energy Corp.; *U.S. Public,* pg. 2213
ENERGY PRODUCTION CORPORATION; *U.S. Private,* pg. 1395
ENERGY WORLD CORPORATION LTD; *Int'l,* pg. 2423
ENERPLUS CORPORATION; *Int'l,* pg. 2424
ENERPLUS RESOURCES (USA) CORPORATION—See Enerplus Corporation; *Int'l,* pg. 2424

ENERTOPIA CORPORATION; *Int'l,* pg. 2424
ENERVEST OPERATING, LLC—See EnerVest, Ltd.; *U.S. Private,* pg. 1397
ENGINEERING & MARINE SERVICES (PTE) LTD—See EMS Energy Limited; *Int'l,* pg. 2392
ENI CESKA REPUBLIKA, S.R.O.—See Eni S.p.A.; *Int'l,* pg. 2437
ENI INDONESIA LTD.—See Eni S.p.A.; *Int'l,* pg. 2437
ENI MAGYARORSZAGON—See Eni S.p.A.; *Int'l,* pg. 2437
ENI S.P.A. - REFINING & MARKETING DIVISION—See Eni S.p.A.; *Int'l,* pg. 2437
ENI S.P.A.; *Int'l,* pg. 2436
ENI US OPERATING CO INC—See Eni S.p.A.; *Int'l,* pg. 2438
ENI VENEZUELA—See Eni S.p.A.; *Int'l,* pg. 2438
ENLINK MIDSTREAM PARTNERS, LP—See EnLink Midstream, LLC; *U.S. Public,* pg. 768
ENQUEST PLC; *Int'l,* pg. 2445
ENSERVCO CORPORATION; *U.S. Public,* pg. 775
ENSO OIL & GAS LTD.—See Enso Group; *Int'l,* pg. 2448
ENTEQ TECHNOLOGIES PLC; *Int'l,* pg. 2450
ENVIROGOLD GLOBAL LIMITED; *Int'l,* pg. 2454
ENWELL ENERGY PLC; *Int'l,* pg. 2456
EOG ARGENTINA S.R.L.—See EOG Resources, Inc.; *U.S. Public,* pg. 782
EOG RESOURCES CANADA, INC.—See EOG Resources, Inc.; *U.S. Public,* pg. 782
EOG RESOURCES, INC; *U.S. Public,* pg. 782
EON NRG LIMITED; *Int'l,* pg. 2458
EOS PETRO, INC.; *U.S. Private,* pg. 1411
EP ENERGY LLC—See Access Industries, Inc.; *U.S. Private,* pg. 51
EP ENERGY LLC—See Apollo Global Management, Inc.; *U.S. Public,* pg. 151
EP ENERGY LLC—See Riverstone Holdings LLC; *U.S. Private,* pg. 3447
EPSILON ENERGY LTD.; *U.S. Public,* pg. 784
EPSILON ENERGY USA INC—See Epsilon Energy Ltd.; *U.S. Public,* pg. 784
EQM MIDSTREAM PARTNERS, LP—See EQT Corporation; *U.S. Public,* pg. 785
EQT PRODUCTION COMPANY—See EQT Corporation; *U.S. Public,* pg. 784
EQUINOR AZERBAIJAN AS—See Equinor ASA; *Int'l,* pg. 2484
EQUINOR ENERGY DO BRASIL LTDA—See Equinor ASA; *Int'l,* pg. 2484
EQUINOR E&P AMERICAS LP—See Equinor ASA; *Int'l,* pg. 2485
EQUINOR NIGERIA ENERGY COMPANY LIMITED—See Chappal Energies Mauritius Limited; *Int'l,* pg. 1448
EQUINOR UK LIMITED—See Equinor ASA; *Int'l,* pg. 2485
EQUION ENERGIA LTD.—See Ecopetrol S.A.; *Int'l,* pg. 2298
ERHC ENERGY, INC.; *U.S. Public,* pg. 792
ESSAR POWER LTD.—See Essar Global Limited; *Int'l,* pg. 2508
ESSO NORGE A.S.—See Exxon Mobil Corporation; *U.S. Public,* pg. 814
ESSO (THAILAND) PUBLIC COMPANY LIMITED—See Bangchak Corporation Public Company Limited; *Int'l,* pg. 832
ETC HYDROCARBONS, LLC—See Energy Transfer LP; *U.S. Public,* pg. 763
EUROGAS INTERNATIONAL INC.; *Int'l,* pg. 2552
EUROPEAN ENERGY LIMITED; *Int'l,* pg. 2556
EVERFLOW EASTERN PARTNERS L.P.; *U.S. Private,* pg. 1438
EXCO RESOURCES, INC.; *U.S. Public,* pg. 805
EXILLON ENERGY PLC; *Int'l,* pg. 2585
EXMAR ENERGY PARTNERS LP—See Exmar N.V.; *Int'l,* pg. 2585
EXOIL LIMITED; *Int'l,* pg. 2586
EXOMA ENERGY LIMITED; *Int'l,* pg. 2586
EXPAND ENERGY CORPORATION; *U.S. Public,* pg. 808
EXPLORATION & PRODUCTION BUSINESS DIVISION—See CPC Corporation; *Int'l,* pg. 1823
EXTRACTION OIL & GAS, INC.—See Civitas Resources, Inc.; *U.S. Public,* pg. 507
EXXONMOBIL CHEMICAL COMPANY INC.—See Exxon Mobil Corporation; *U.S. Public,* pg. 814
EXXON MOBIL CORP. - DOWNSTREAM OPERATIONS—See Exxon Mobil Corporation; *U.S. Public,* pg. 814
EXXONMOBIL CORPORATION—See Exxon Mobil Corporation; *U.S. Public,* pg. 815
EXXONMOBIL CORPORATION—See Exxon Mobil Corporation; *U.S. Public,* pg. 815
EXXONMOBIL CORPORATION—See Exxon Mobil Corporation; *U.S. Public,* pg. 815
EXXONMOBIL CORPORATION—See Exxon Mobil Corporation; *U.S. Public,* pg. 815
EXXONMOBIL CORPORATION—See Exxon Mobil Corporation; *U.S. Public,* pg. 815
EXXON MOBIL EXPLORATION & PRODUCTION MALAYSIA INC.—See Exxon Mobil Corporation; *U.S. Public,* pg. 814
EXXONMOBIL EXPLORATION—See Exxon Mobil Corporation; *U.S. Public,* pg. 815

CORPORATE AFFILIATIONS

EXXON MOBIL GLOBAL SERVICES—See Exxon Mobil Corporation; *U.S. Public,* pg. 814
EXXONMOBIL INTERNATIONAL LIMITED—See Exxon Mobil Corporation; *U.S. Public,* pg. 815
EXXONMOBIL OIL INDONESIA, INC.—See Exxon Mobil Corporation; *U.S. Public,* pg. 815
EXXONMOBIL RESEARCH & ENGINEERING—See Exxon Mobil Corporation; *U.S. Public,* pg. 816
FAIRSTAR RESOURCES LTD.; *Int'l,* pg. 2609
FALCON OIL & GAS LTD.—See Condor Petroleum Inc.; *Int'l,* pg. 1766
FAR LIMITED; *Int'l,* pg. 2617
FIELDWOOD ENERGY LLC; *U.S. Public,* pg. 833
FLOGAS UK LIMITED—See DCC plc; *Int'l,* pg. 1990
FORBES ENERGY SERVICES LTD.; *U.S. Public,* pg. 864
FORCE MINERALS CORP.; *U.S. Private,* pg. 1563
FORESTAR PETROLEUM CORPORATION—See Forestar Group Inc.; *U.S. Public,* pg. 867
FOROYAR KOLVETNI P/F—See DNO North Sea Plc; *Int'l,* pg. 2148
FORTUM MARKETS OY—See Fortum Oyj; *Int'l,* pg. 2741
FORTUM O&M (UK) LTD—See Fortum Oyj; *Int'l,* pg. 2741
FORTUM OY—See Fortum Oyj; *Int'l,* pg. 2741
FORTUM PETROLEUM A/S—See Fortum Oyj; *Int'l,* pg. 2741
FORTUM POLSKA SP. Z.O.O.—See Fortum Oyj; *Int'l,* pg. 2741
FORTUM POWER & HEAT AB—See Fortum Oyj; *Int'l,* pg. 2741
FORTUM SERVICE OY—See Fortum Oyj; *Int'l,* pg. 2741
FORZA PETROLEUM LIMITED; *Int'l,* pg. 2747
FOX PETROLEUM INC.; *U.S. Private,* pg. 1584
FREEHOLD ROYALTIES LTD.; *Int'l,* pg. 2769
FREEPORT-MCMORAN OIL & GAS INC.—See Freeport-McMoRan Inc.; *U.S. Public,* pg. 884
FRONTERA ENERGY CORPORATION; *Int'l,* pg. 2794
FRONTIER OIL CORPORATION; *Int'l,* pg. 2795
FRONTLINE MANAGEMENT (BERMUDA) LTD.—See Frontline plc; *Int'l,* pg. 2796
FUELS, INC.; *U.S. Public,* pg. 1619
FUGRO HOLDING BELGIUM N.V.—See Fugro N.V.; *Int'l,* pg. 2806
FUGRO JACQUES GEOSURVEYS, INC.—See Fugro N.V.; *Int'l,* pg. 2806
FUGRO OFFSHORE SURVEY (SHENZHEN) CO. LTD.—See Fugro N.V.; *Int'l,* pg. 2807
FUGRO SURVEY LTD.—See Fugro N.V.; *Int'l,* pg. 2808
FUJI OIL COMPANY, LTD.; *Int'l,* pg. 2814
GALT PETROLEUM, INC.; *U.S. Private,* pg. 1640
GASAG AG—See ENGIE SA; *Int'l,* pg. 2429
GASAG AG—See E.ON SE; *Int'l,* pg. 2257
GASCO ENERGY, INC.; *U.S. Private,* pg. 1648
GASCO PRODUCTION COMPANY—See Gasco Energy, Inc.; *U.S. Private,* pg. 1648
GBK CORP.; *U.S. Private,* pg. 1653
GDF SUEZ E&P DEUTSCHLAND GMBH—See ENGIE SA; *Int'l,* pg. 2431
GEAR ENERGY LTD.; *Int'l,* pg. 2904
GENEL ENERGY PLC; *Int'l,* pg. 2917
GENIE ENERGY LTD.; *U.S. Public,* pg. 930
GENOIL INC.; *U.S. Public,* pg. 931
GEO-JADE PETROLEUM CORPORATION; *Int'l,* pg. 2932
GEOPARK LIMITED; *Int'l,* pg. 2934
GEOPETRO ALASKA LLC—See GeoPetro Resources Company; *U.S. Private,* pg. 1681
GEORGE R. BROWN PARTNERSHIP; *U.S. Private,* pg. 1683
GEOTHERMAL EXPLORATION CO., INC.—See Barnwell Industries, Inc.; *U.S. Public,* pg. 278
GIBSON ENERGY INC.; *Int'l,* pg. 2963
GIVOT OLAM OIL EXPLORATION LIMITED PARTNERSHIP (1993); *Int'l,* pg. 2982
GLENCOE RESOURCES LTD.; *Int'l,* pg. 2990
GLOBAL ENVIRONMENTAL ENERGY CORP.; *Int'l,* pg. 2995
GLOBAL PETROLEUM LIMITED; *Int'l,* pg. 3000
GLOBAL WHOLEHEALTH PARTNERS CORPORATION; *U.S. Public,* pg. 945
GLORI ENERGY INC.; *U.S. Public,* pg. 947
GMX RESOURCES INC.; *U.S. Private,* pg. 1723
GOLDEN COAST ENERGY CORP.; *Int'l,* pg. 3028
GOLDHILLS HOLDING LTD.; *Int'l,* pg. 3033
GORDON CREEK ENERGY INC.; *Int'l,* pg. 3042
GRAND ENERGY, INC.; *U.S. Private,* pg. 1752
GRAN TIERRA ENERGY COLOMBIA, LTD.—See Gran Tierra Energy Inc.; *Int'l,* pg. 3053
GRAN TIERRA ENERGY INC.; *Int'l,* pg. 3053
GRAN TIERRA EXCHANGECO INC.—See Gran Tierra Energy Inc.; *Int'l,* pg. 3053
GRAVIS ENERGY CORP.; *Int'l,* pg. 3061
GREAT ATLANTIC RESOURCES CORP.; *Int'l,* pg. 3063
GREAT DIVIDE PIPELINE LIMITED—See Connacher Oil & Gas Limited; *Int'l,* pg. 1768
GREENFIELDS PETROLEUM CORPORATION; *U.S. Private,* pg. 1778
GREENFIRE RESOURCES INC.—See Greenfire Resources Ltd.; *Int'l,* pg. 3074
GREENFIRE RESOURCES LTD.; *Int'l,* pg. 3074

211120 — CRUDE PETROLEUM EXT...

GREENFIRE RESOURCES OPERATING CORPORATION—See Greenfire Resources Ltd.; *Int'l*, pg. 3074
GREENVALE ENERGY LTD; *Int'l*, pg. 3077
GREKA ENERGY CORPORATION; *U.S. Private*, pg. 1783
GSPC PIPAVAV POWER COMPANY LIMITED—See Gujarat State Petroleum Corporation Limited; *Int'l*, pg. 3177
GUANAJUATO SILVER COMPANY LTD.; *Int'l*, pg. 3152
GULF KEYSTONE PETROLEUM LIMITED; *Int'l*, pg. 3181
GULFPORT ENERGY CORPORATION; *U.S. Public*, pg. 975
GULFSANDS PETROLEUM PLC; *Int'l*, pg. 3182
GULFSLOPE ENERGY, INC.; *U.S. Public*, pg. 975
HAGUE AND LONDON OIL PLC; *Int'l*, pg. 3207
HARRISON INTERESTS LTD.; *U.S. Private*, pg. 1870
HARTSHEAD RESOURCES NL; *Int'l*, pg. 3280
HARVEST VINCCLER, S.C.A.; *Int'l*, pg. 3281
HAWKER ENERGY, INC.; *U.S. Private*, pg. 1882
HCG ENERGY CORPORATION; *U.S. Public*, pg. 1888
HEADWATER EXPLORATION INC.; *Int'l*, pg. 3301
HELIX ENERGY SOLUTIONS GROUP, INC.; *U.S. Public*, pg. 1024
HELLENIC PETROLEUM INTERNATIONAL AG—See HELLENiQ ENERGY Holdings S.A.; *Int'l*, pg. 3334
HELLENiQ ENERGY HOLDINGS S.A.; *Int'l*, pg. 3334
HELLIX VENTURES INC.; *Int'l*, pg. 3334
HENTY OIL LIMITED—See World Kinect Corporation; *U.S. Public*, pg. 2380
HERITAGE OIL CORPORATION—See Heritage Oil Plc; *Int'l*, pg. 3362
HERITAGE OIL & GAS LIMITED—See Heritage Oil Plc; *Int'l*, pg. 3362
HERITAGE OIL PLC; *Int'l*, pg. 3362
HERO TECHNOLOGIES INC.; *U.S. Public*, pg. 1029
HESS BAKKEN INVESTMENTS II L.L.C.—See Hess Corporation; *U.S. Public*, pg. 1030
HESS CORP. - HOUSTON REGIONAL OFFICE—See Hess Corporation; *U.S. Public*, pg. 1030
HESS LTD.—See Hess Corporation; *U.S. Public*, pg. 1030
HESS MALAYSIA SDN. BHD.—See Hess Corporation; *U.S. Public*, pg. 1030
HESS MIDSTREAM PARTNERS LP—See Hess Corporation; *U.S. Public*, pg. 1030
HIBISCUS PETROLEUM BERHAD; *Int'l*, pg. 3383
HICKSGAS, LLC—See DCC plc; *Int'l*, pg. 1989
HIGHLAND TEXAS ENERGY CO; *U.S. Private*, pg. 1939
HILCORP ALASKA LLC; *U.S. Private*, pg. 1944
HILCORP ENERGY CO.; *U.S. Private*, pg. 1944
HILLCREST ENERGY TECHNOLOGIES LTD.; *Int'l*, pg. 3392
HINTO ENERGY, INC.; *U.S. Private*, pg. 1950
HIROSHIMA GAS CO., LTD. - BINGO PLANT—See Hiroshima Gas Co., Ltd.; *Int'l*, pg. 3405
HKN, INC.; *U.S. Public*, pg. 1042
HORIZON PETROLEUM LTD.; *Int'l*, pg. 3479
HOUSTON AMERICAN ENERGY CORPORATION; *U.S. Public*, pg. 1056
HOWDEN THOMASSEN MIDDLE EAST FZCO—See Chart Industries, Inc.; *U.S. Public*, pg. 482
HUNTER TECHNOLOGY CORP.; *Int'l*, pg. 3536
HUNTING ENERGY SERVICES (CANADA) LIMITED—See Hunting Plc; *Int'l*, pg. 3536
HUNT OIL COMPANY—See Hunt Consolidated, Inc.; *U.S. Private*, pg. 2008
HUNT OVERSEAS OIL COMPANY—See Hunt Consolidated, Inc.; *U.S. Private*, pg. 2008
HYDROCARBON DYNAMICS LIMITED; *Int'l*, pg. 3547
HYPERION ENERGY LP; *U.S. Private*, pg. 2019
IDEMITSU PETROLEUM NORGE AS—See Idemitsu Kosan Co., Ltd.; *Int'l*, pg. 3591
IMPERIAL RESOURCES, LLC—See Empire Energy Group Limited; *Int'l*, pg. 2387
INSIGNIA ENERGY LTD.—See Brookfield Corporation; *Int'l*, pg 1189
INTERNATIONAL PAPER COMPANY—See International Paper Company; *U.S. Public*, pg. 1157
ISRAMCO, INC.—See Equital Ltd.; *Int'l*, pg. 2487
IVO ENERGI AB—See Fortum Oyj; *Int'l*, pg. 2741
JAPAN ENERGY E&P AUSTRALIA PTY. LTD.—See ENEOS Holdings, Inc.; *Int'l*, pg. 2417
JAPAN VIETNAM PETROLEUM CO., LTD.—See ENEOS Holdings, Inc.; *Int'l*, pg. 2417
JAY PETROLEUM LLC—See Equital Ltd.; *Int'l*, pg. 2487
J.D. MURCHISON INTERESTS INC.; *U.S. Private*, pg. 2161
JM COX RESOURCES LP; *U.S. Private*, pg. 2213
JOHTOTEC OY—See Fortum Oyj; *Int'l*, pg. 2741
JONES ENERGY, INC.; *U.S. Private*, pg. 2233
JP OIL COMPANY INC.; *U.S. Private*, pg. 2239
JW OPERATING COMPANY; *U.S. Private*, pg. 2246
JX NIPPON EXPLORATION & PRODUCTION (U.K.) LIMITED—See HitecVision AS; *Int'l*, pg. 3426
JX NIPPON OIL EXPLORATION (U.S.A.) LIMITED—See ENEOS Holdings, Inc.; *Int'l*, pg. 2417
JX NIPPON OIL & GAS EXPLORATION (MALAYSIA), LTD.—See ENEOS Holdings, Inc.; *Int'l*, pg. 2416
KAISER-FRANCIS OIL COMPANY; *U.S. Private*, pg. 2256
KENTUCKY OIL GATHERING, LLC—See EnLink Midstream, LLC; *U.S. Public*, pg. 768

KEY PRODUCTION COMPANY, INC.—See Coterra Energy Inc.; *U.S. Public*, pg. 587
KIMBELL ROYALTY PARTNERS, LP; *U.S. Public*, pg. 1228
KLABZUBA OIL & GAS; *U.S. Private*, pg. 2317
KOSMOS ENERGY GHANA HC—See Kosmos Energy Ltd.; *U.S. Public*, pg. 1275
KOSMOS ENERGY, LLC—See Kosmos Energy Ltd.; *U.S. Public*, pg. 1275
KOSMOS ENERGY LTD.; *U.S. Public*, pg. 1275
KOSMOS ENERGY OFFSHORE MOROCCO HC—See Kosmos Energy Ltd.; *U.S. Public*, pg. 1275
LAREDO OIL, INC.; *U.S. Public*, pg. 1293
LARIO OIL & GAS COMPANY—See O's Companies Inc.; *U.S. Private*, pg. 2980
LAZARUS REFINING & MARKETING, LLC—See Blue Dolphin Energy Company; *U.S. Public*, pg. 364
LEGACY RESERVES, INC.; *U.S. Private*, pg. 2417
LEGEND OIL AND GAS, LTD.; *U.S. Public*, pg. 1301
LEWIS ENERGY GROUP LTD; *U.S. Private*, pg. 2438
LIBERTY ENERGY CORP.; *U.S. Private*, pg. 2444
LINJEBYGG OFFSHORE AS—See Fortum Oyj; *Int'l*, pg. 2742
LOTOS PETROBALTIC S.A.—See Grupa LOTOS S.A.; *Int'l*, pg. 3117
LRR ENERGY, L.P.—See Grizzly Energy, LLC; *U.S. Public*, pg. 970
LUBRICANTS BUSINESS DIVISION—See CPC Corporation; *Int'l*, pg. 1824
MACK ENERGY CORPORATION; *U.S. Private*, pg. 2536
MADALENA ENERGY S.A.—See Centaurus Energy Inc.; *Int'l*, pg. 1402
MAECENAS MINERALS LLP—See Dorchester Minerals, L.P.; *U.S. Public*, pg. 677
MAERSK DRILLING SERVICES A/S—See A.P. Moller-Maersk A/S; *Int'l*, pg. 26
MAGNOLIA PETROLEUM PLC; *U.S. Private*, pg. 2548
MAGUIRE OIL COMPANY INC.; *U.S. Private*, pg. 2550
MAGUIRE RESOURCES COMPANY INC.; *U.S. Private*, pg. 2550
MAMMOTH ENERGY PARTNERS LP—See Wexford Capital Limited Partnership; *U.S. Private*, pg. 4502
MAMMOTH ENERGY SERVICES, INC.—See Wexford Capital Limited Partnership; *U.S. Private*, pg. 4502
MANSAROVAR ENERGY COLOMBIA LTD.—See China Petrochemical Corporation; *Int'l*, pg. 1540
MARATHON INTERNATIONAL OIL COMPANY—See ConocoPhillips; *U.S. Public*, pg. 569
MARATHON INTERNATIONAL PETROLEUM INDONESIA LIMITED—See ConocoPhillips; *U.S. Public*, pg. 569
MARATHON OIL SUPPLY COMPANY (U.S.) LIMITED—See ConocoPhillips; *U.S. Public*, pg. 569
MARATHON PETROLEUM INVESTMENT, LTD.—See ConocoPhillips; *U.S. Public*, pg. 569
MARATHON SERVICE (G.B.) LIMITED—See ConocoPhillips; *U.S. Public*, pg. 569
MARBOB ENERGY CORP.—See ConocoPhillips; *U.S. Public*, pg. 568
MARSA TURKEY B.V.—See Condor Petroleum Inc.; *Int'l*, pg. 1766
MARSHALL & WINSTON INC.; *U.S. Private*, pg. 2592
MATADOR RESOURCES COMPANY; *U.S. Public*, pg. 1395
MATRIX OIL CORP.—See Royale Energy, Inc.; *U.S. Public*, pg. 1816
MAVERICK NATURAL RESOURCES, LLC; *U.S. Private*, pg. 2616
MAYNARD OIL CO.—See Plantation Petroleum Holdings IV, LLC (PPH); *U.S. Public*, pg. 3197
MCBEE OPERATING COMPANY LLC; *U.S. Private*, pg. 2625
MCELVAIN OIL & GAS PROPERTIES INC; *U.S. Private*, pg. 2633
MCGOWAN WORKING PARTNERS INC.; *U.S. Private*, pg. 2635
MCMORAN EXPLORATION CO.—See Freeport-McMoRan Inc.; *U.S. Public*, pg. 884
MCMORAN OIL & GAS LLC—See Freeport-McMoRan Inc.; *U.S. Public*, pg. 884
MEWBOURNE HOLDINGS INC.; *U.S. Private*, pg. 2691
MEWBOURNE OIL CO. INC.—See Mewbourne Holdings Inc.; *U.S. Private*, pg. 2691
MEXCO ENERGY CORPORATION; *U.S. Public*, pg. 1433
MID-CON ENERGY PARTNERS, LP—See KKR & Co. Inc.; *U.S. Public*, pg. 1244
MILAGRO EXPLORATION, LLC; *U.S. Private*, pg. 2726
MILLENNIUM ENERGY CORPORATION; *U.S. Public*, pg. 1446
MODERN EXPLORATION INC.; *U.S. Private*, pg. 2760
MOGUL ENERGY INTERNATIONAL, INC.; *U.S. Public*, pg. 1456
MOHAMMAD SAAD ALDREES & SONS COMPANY LIMITED—See Aldrees Petroleum & Transport Services Company; *Int'l*, pg. 305
MONTAGE RESOURCES CORP.—See Expand Energy Corporation; *U.S. Public*, pg. 808
MONTAUK ENERGY CAPITAL LLC—See Hosken Consolidated Investments Limited; *Int'l*, pg. 3485
MONTIVO KFT—See Fortum Oyj; *Int'l*, pg. 2741
MOSBACHER ENERGY COMPANY; *U.S. Private*, pg. 2792

MURPHY OIL CO., LTD.—See Murphy Oil Corporation; *U.S. Public*, pg. 1487
MURPHY PETROLEUM LTD.—See Murphy Oil Corporation; *U.S. Public*, pg. 1487
MUSTANG FUEL CORPORATION; *U.S. Private*, pg. 2819
MUSTANG GAS PRODUCTS—See Mustang Gas Products LLC; *U.S. Private*, pg. 2819
NADEL & GUSSMAN LLC; *U.S. Private*, pg. 2830
NAPS NORWAY A/S—See Fortum Oyj; *Int'l*, pg. 2742
NAPS UNITED KINGDOM—See Fortum Oyj; *Int'l*, pg. 2742
NATIONAL REFINERY LIMITED—See Attock Refinery Ltd; *Int'l*, pg. 697
NAUTILUS MARINE SERVICES PLC—See HKN, Inc.; *U.S. Public*, pg. 1042
NCT MIDDLE EAST—See Fortum Oyj; *Int'l*, pg. 2742
NDOVU RESOURCES LIMITED—See Aminex PLC; *Int'l*, pg. 428
NEW CONCEPT ENERGY, INC.; *U.S. Public*, pg. 1511
NEW FRONTIER ENERGY, INC.; *U.S. Public*, pg. 1511
NEW SOURCE ENERGY CORPORATION; *U.S. Private*, pg. 2906
NEW WESTERN ENERGY CORPORATION; *U.S. Private*, pg. 2908
NFINITI INC.; *U.S. Public*, pg. 1527
NOBLE ENERGY - ARDMORE—See Chevron Corporation; *U.S. Public*, pg. 487
NOBLE ENERGY, INC.—See Chevron Corporation; *U.S. Public*, pg. 487
NORRIS INDUSTRIES, INC.; *U.S. Public*, pg. 1536
NORRIS PRODUCTION SOLUTIONS COLOMBIA SAS—See Dover Corporation; *U.S. Public*, pg. 682
NORSTRA ENERGY INC.; *U.S. Public*, pg. 2939
NORTH AMERICAN OIL & GAS CORP.; *U.S. Private*, pg. 2941
NORTHERN OIL & GAS, INC.; *U.S. Public*, pg. 1537
NUSTAR MARKETING LLC—See Sunoco LP; *U.S. Public*, pg. 1964
OASIS PETROLEUM LLC—See Chord Energy Corporation; *U.S. Public*, pg. 490
OASIS PETROLEUM NORTH AMERICA LLC—See Chord Energy Corporation; *U.S. Public*, pg. 490
OCCIDENTAL DE COLOMBIA, INC.—See Occidental Petroleum Corporation; *U.S. Public*, pg. 1562
OCCIDENTAL OIL & GAS CORPORATION—See Occidental Petroleum Corporation; *U.S. Public*, pg. 1561
OCCIDENTAL PETROLEUM CORPORATION; *U.S. Public*, pg. 1560
OCEANIC EXPLORATION COMPANY; *U.S. Private*, pg. 2990
OCEAN RIG ASA—See DryShips Inc.; *Int'l*, pg. 2207
OCTAGON RESOURCES INC.; *U.S. Private*, pg. 2992
OFFSHORE PETROLEUM CORP.; *U.S. Private*, pg. 3003
OMIMEX RESOURCES, INC.; *U.S. Private*, pg. 3016
OMNI VALVE COMPANY, LLC; *U.S. Private*, pg. 3016
OOGC AMERICA LLC—See China National Offshore Oil Corp.; *Int'l*, pg. 1532
OP HAWLER KURDISTAN LIMITED—See Forza Petroleum Limited; *Int'l*, pg. 2748
OPICOIL AMERICA, INC.—See CPC Corporation; *Int'l*, pg. 1824
OPICOIL HOUSTON, INC.—See CPC Corporation; *Int'l*, pg. 1824
ORIGINCLEAR, INC.; *U.S. Public*, pg. 1617
ORYX PETROLEUM SERVICES SA—See Forza Petroleum Limited; *Int'l*, pg. 2748
O'S COMPANIES INC.; *U.S. Private*, pg. 2980
OVERSEAS PETROLEUM AND INVESTMENT CORPORATION—See CPC Corporation; *Int'l*, pg. 1824
PACIFIC COAST ENERGY COMPANY LP; *U.S. Private*, pg. 3066
PALEO RESOURCES, INC.; *U.S. Public*, pg. 1634
PAN AMERICAN ENERGY LLC—See BP plc; *Int'l*, pg. 1131
PAN AMERICAN ENERGY LLC—See Bridas Corporation; *Int'l*, pg. 1152
PAN ORIENT ENERGY CORP.—See Dialog Group Berhad; *Int'l*, pg. 2104
PAR PICEANCE ENERGY EQUITY, LLC—See Par Pacific Holdings, Inc.; *U.S. Public*, pg. 1636
PEDEVCO CORP.; *U.S. Public*, pg. 1660
PEGASI ENERGY RESOURCES CORPORATION; *U.S. Private*, pg. 3129
PENNACO ENERGY, INC.—See ConocoPhillips; *U.S. Public*, pg. 569
PENNSYLVANIA GENERAL ENERGY; *U.S. Private*, pg. 3136
PENN VIRGINIA MC ENERGY LLC—See Baytex Energy Corp.; *Int'l*, pg. 915
PENN VIRGINIA OIL & GAS, L.P.—See Baytex Energy Corp.; *Int'l*, pg. 915
PERDANA PETROLEUM BERHAD—See Dayang Enterprise Holdings Berhad; *Int'l*, pg. 1985
PERKINS OIL & GAS, INC.; *U.S. Public*, pg. 3152
PETROBRAS ARGENTINA S.A.—See Grupo EMES S.A.; *Int'l*, pg. 3126
PETROCHINA INTERNATIONAL (AMERICA) INC.—See China National Petroleum Corporation; *Int'l*, pg. 1533
PETROCHINA INTERNATIONAL CO. LTD.—See China National Petroleum Corporation; *Int'l*, pg. 1533

N.A.I.C.S. Index

211120 — CRUDE PETROLEUM EXT... CORPORATE AFFILIATIONS

PETROCHINA INTERNATIONAL (INDONESIA)—See China National Petroleum Corporation; *Int'l*, pg. 1533
PETROCHINA INTERNATIONAL (JAPAN) CO., LTD.—See China National Petroleum Corporation; *Int'l*, pg. 1533
PETROCHINA INTERNATIONAL (MIDDLE EAST) COMPANY LIMITED—See China National Petroleum Corporation; *Int'l*, pg. 1533
PETROCHINA INTERNATIONAL (RUS) CO., LTD—See China National Petroleum Corporation; *Int'l*, pg. 1533
PETROFLOW ENERGY CORPORATION; *U.S. Private*, pg. 3162
PETROGLYPH ENERGY, INC.—See Intermountain Industries, Inc.; *U.S. Private*, pg. 2113
PETROGULF CORPORATION; *U.S. Private*, pg. 3162
PETROKAZAKHSTAN INC.—See China National Petroleum Corporation; *Int'l*, pg. 1533
PETROLEOS DEL NORTE S.A.—See Gran Tierra Energy Inc.; *Int'l*, pg. 3053
PETROLEUM AGENCY SA—See CEF (SOC) Limited; *Int'l*, pg. 1389
PETROLEUM INC.; *U.S. Private*, pg. 3162
THE PETROLEUM OIL & GAS CORPORATION OF SOUTH AFRICA (SOC) LIMITED—See CEF (SOC) Limited; *Int'l*, pg. 1389
PETROLIA ENERGY CORPORATION; *U.S. Public*, pg. 1678
PETROMINERALS CORPORATION; *U.S. Private*, pg. 3163
PETROQUEST ENERGY, INC.; *U.S. Private*, pg. 3163
PETROQUEST ENERGY, L.L.C.—See PetroQuest Energy, Inc.; *U.S. Private*, pg. 3163
PETRO RIVER OIL CORP.; *U.S. Public*, pg. 1678
PETROSA EUROPE BV—See CEF (SOC) Limited; *Int'l*, pg. 1389
PETROSANTANDER - COLUMBIA INC.—See Petrosantander Inc.; *U.S. Private*, pg. 3163
PETROSANTANDER INC.; *U.S. Private*, pg. 3163
PETROSANTANDER USA INC.—See Petrosantander Inc.; *U.S. Private*, pg. 3163
PETROSUN, INC.; *U.S. Public*, pg. 1678
PETROTAL PERU S.R.L.—See PetroTal Corp.; *U.S. Public*, pg. 1678
PETROTEQ ENERGY INC.; *U.S. Public*, pg. 1678
PHX MINERALS INC.; *U.S. Public*, pg. 1690
PIONEER EXPLORATION COMPANY; *U.S. Private*, pg. 3187
PIONEER PE HOLDING LLC—See Pioneer Natural Resources Company; *U.S. Public*, pg. 1693
PLAINS ALL AMERICAN, INC.—See Plains All American Pipeline, L.P.; *U.S. Public*, pg. 1696
PLATINUM ENERGY RESOURCES, INC.; *U.S. Private*, pg. 3200
PORTO ENERGY CORP.; *U.S. Private*, pg. 3233
PRECISION OILFIELD SERVICES, LLP—See Weatherford International plc; *U.S. Public*, pg. 2339
PREMIER ENERGY CORP.; *U.S. Private*, pg. 3250
PREMIER OIL EXPLORATION LTD—See Harbour Energy plc; *Int'l*, pg. 3271
PREMIER OIL FAR EAST LIMITED—See Harbour Energy plc; *Int'l*, pg. 3271
PRIMEENERGY RESOURCES CORPORATION; *U.S. Public*, pg. 1717
PRIME OFFSHORE L.L.C.—See PrimeEnergy Resources Corporation; *U.S. Public*, pg. 1717
PRODUCTION MANAGEMENT INDUSTRIES, INC.—See Superior Energy Services, Inc.; *U.S. Private*, pg. 3877
PSEG POWER FOSSIL LLC—See Public Service Enterprise Group Incorporated; *U.S. Public*, pg. 1736
PT CHEVRON PACIFIC INDONESIA—See Chevron Corporation; *U.S. Public*, pg. 487
PT GEO LINK NUSANTARA—See Federal International (2000) Ltd; *Int'l*, pg. 2630
PUISSANT INDUSTRIES, INC.; *U.S. Public*, pg. 1736
PURSUE ENERGY—See Petro-Hunt, L.L.C.; *U.S. Private*, pg. 3162
QEP RESOURCES, INC.—See Diamondback Energy, Inc.; *U.S. Public*, pg. 658
QUATRO RESOURCES INC.—See NGP Energy Capital Management, LLC; *U.S. Private*, pg. 2924
RALLY ENERGY LIMITED—See Citadel Capital S.A.E.; *Int'l*, pg. 1619
RANGEFORD RESOURCES, INC.; *U.S. Private*, pg. 3354
RANGE RESOURCES-APPALACHIA, LLC—See Range Resources Corporation; *U.S. Public*, pg. 1762
RANGE RESOURCES CORPORATION; *U.S. Public*, pg. 1762
RANGER OIL CORPORATION—See Baytex Energy Corp.; *Int'l*, pg. 915
RED RIVER TERMINALS, L.L.C.—See Genesis Energy, L.P.; *U.S. Public*, pg. 930
REGAL GROUP SERVICES LIMITED—See Enwell Energy plc; *Int'l*, pg. 2456
REGENT TECHNOLOGIES, INC.; *U.S. Private*, pg. 3387
RENEWABLE ENERGY GROUP, INC.—See Chevron Corporation; *U.S. Public*, pg. 487
THE RESERVE PETROLEUM COMPANY; *U.S. Public*, pg. 2125
RICELAND PETROLEUM COMPANY; *U.S. Private*, pg. 3425
RILEY EXPLORATION PERMIAN, INC.; *U.S. Public*, pg. 1798
RIM OPERATING, INC.; *U.S. Private*, pg. 3437
RING ENERGY, INC.; *U.S. Public*, pg. 1799
RIO BRAVO OIL, INC.; *U.S. Private*, pg. 3438
ROBINSON'S BEND OPERATING II, LLC—See Castleton Commodities International LLC; *U.S. Private*, pg. 785
ROCKFORD OIL CORP.; *U.S. Private*, pg. 3466
ROC OIL (BOHAI) COMPANY—See Fosun International Limited; *Int'l*, pg. 2752
ROC OIL COMPANY LIMITED—See Fosun International Limited; *Int'l*, pg. 2752
ROC OIL MALAYSIA (HOLDING) SDN BHD—See Fosun International Limited; *Int'l*, pg. 2752
ROC OIL (WA) PTY LIMITED—See Fosun International Limited; *Int'l*, pg. 2752
ROHOL-AUFSUCHUNGS AKTIENGESELLSCHAFT—See EVN AG; *Int'l*, pg. 2571
ROSEHILL RESOURCES INC.; *U.S. Private*, pg. 3482
ROSE ROCK MIDSTREAM, L.P.—See Energy Transfer LP; *U.S. Public*, pg. 764
ROXI PETROLEUM KAZAKHSTAN LLP—See Caspian Sunrise Plc; *Int'l*, pg. 1354
ROYALE ENERGY, INC.; *U.S. Public*, pg. 1816
ROYAL ENERGY RESOURCES, INC.; *U.S. Public*, pg. 1815
SABLE ENVIRONMENTAL, LLC—See Ferrellgas Partners, L.P.; *U.S. Public*, pg. 829
SABLE NATURAL RESOURCES CORPORATION; *U.S. Private*, pg. 3521
SAGA ENERGY, INC.; *U.S. Private*, pg. 3525
SALINS RESIDUOS AUTOMOCION, S.L.—See ACS, Actividades de Construccion y Servicios, S.A.; *Int'l*, pg. 116
SAMSON ENERGY COMPANY, LLC; *U.S. Private*, pg. 3538
SANCHEZ ENERGY CORPORATION; *U.S. Private*, pg. 3542
SANDRIDGE ENERGY, INC.; *U.S. Public*, pg. 1839
SANDRIDGE EXPLORATION AND PRODUCTION, LLC—See SandRidge Energy, Inc.; *U.S. Public*, pg. 1839
SANDRIDGE MIDSTREAM, INC.—See SandRidge Energy, Inc.; *U.S. Public*, pg. 1839
SAN PEDRO BAY PIPELINE COMPANY—See Amplify Energy Corp.; *U.S. Public*, pg. 133
SANTA FE PETROLEUM, INC.; *U.S. Private*, pg. 3547
SARAS S.P.A.—See Angelo Moratti S.A.P.A.; *Int'l*, pg. 460
SARATOGA RESOURCES, INC.; *U.S. Private*, pg. 3550
S.C. FOSERCO S.A.—See Weatherford International plc; *U.S. Public*, pg. 2339
SCHLUMBERGER OILFIELD SERVICES—See Schlumberger Limited; *U.S. Public*, pg. 1845
SENTRY PETROLEUM LTD.; *U.S. Public*, pg. 1868
SEVEN GENERATIONS ENERGY LTD—See ARC Resources Ltd.; *Int'l*, pg. 539
SIERRA INTERNATIONAL GROUP, INC.; *U.S. Private*, pg. 3647
SIF GROUP BV.—See Egeria Capital Management B.V.; *Int'l*, pg. 2323
SILVERBOW RESOURCES, INC.—See KKR & Co. Inc.; *U.S. Public*, pg. 1244
SINGAPORE PETROLEUM COMPANY LIMITED—See China National Petroleum Corporation; *Int'l*, pg. 1533
SINO AMERICAN OIL COMPANY; *U.S. Public*, pg. 1888
SINOPEC DAYLIGHT ENERGY LTD.—See China Petrochemical Corporation; *Int'l*, pg. 1540
SINVEST AS—See Aban Offshore Limited; *Int'l*, pg. 48
SM ENERGY COMPANY; *U.S. Public*, pg. 1895
SNYDER BROTHERS, INC.—See The Snyder Group, Inc.; *U.S. Private*, pg. 4119
SOFIDSIM S.P.A.—See Eni S.p.A.; *Int'l*, pg. 2438
SOUTHCROSS ENERGY PARTNERS,LLC—See Charlesbank Capital Partners, LLC; *U.S. Private*, pg. 856
SOUTHCROSS ENERGY PARTNERS,LLC—See EIG Global Energy Partners, LLC; *U.S. Private*, pg. 1347
SOUTHCROSS ENERGY PARTNERS,LLC—See Tailwater Capital LLC; *U.S. Private*, pg. 3923
SOW GOOD INC.; *U.S. Public*, pg. 1914
SPINDLETOP OIL & GAS CO.; *U.S. Public*, pg. 1918
STANDARD ENERGY CORP.; *U.S. Public*, pg. 1929
STARLIGHT ENERGY CORP.; *U.S. Public*, pg. 1939
STAR PETROLEUM REFINING PUBLIC CO., LTD.—See Chevron Corporation; *U.S. Public*, pg. 488
STARVIN MARVIN, INC.—See Marathon Petroleum Corporation; *U.S. Public*, pg. 1364
STATES UNLIMITED; *U.S. Private*, pg. 3793
STATEX PETROLEUM I, L.P.; *U.S. Private*, pg. 3793
STERLING ENERGY (UK) LIMITED—See Afentra plc; *Int'l*, pg. 185
ST. MARY LAND & EXPLORATION CO. SHREVEPORT—See SM Energy Company; *U.S. Public*, pg. 1895
STONEHOUSE NOV DOWNHOLE EURASIA LIMITED—See NOV, Inc.; *U.S. Public*, pg. 1546
STRIKER OIL & GAS, INC.; *U.S. Private*, pg. 3840
SUMMIT MIDSTREAM PARTNERS, LP; *U.S. Public*, pg. 1960
SUNDANCE ENERGY AUSTRALIA LIMITED; *U.S. Public*, pg. 1964
SUNOCO LOGISTICS PARTNERS GP LLC—See Energy Transfer LP; *U.S. Public*, pg. 764
SUN PIPE LINE COMPANY OF DELAWARE LLC—See Energy Transfer LP; *U.S. Public*, pg. 764
SUPERIOR PROCESSING SERVICE CORPORATION—See Superior Natural Gas Corp.; *U.S. Private*, pg. 3879
SUPERNOVA ENERGY, INC.; *U.S. Private*, pg. 3881
SURGE GLOBAL ENERGY, INC.; *U.S. Private*, pg. 3884
SYDNEY METROPOLITAN PIPELINE PTY LTD—See Ampol Limited; *Int'l*, pg. 437
SYLIOS CORP.; *U.S. Public*, pg. 1969
SYNDIAL SERVIZI AMBIENTALI S.P.A.—See Eni S.p.A.; *Int'l*, pg. 2438
TANZOIL NL—See Aminex PLC; *Int'l*, pg. 428
TAPSTONE ENERGY INC.; *U.S. Private*, pg. 3932
TAYLOR ENERGY COMPANY; *U.S. Private*, pg. 3939
TENKAY RESOURCES INC.—See Hunting Plc; *Int'l*, pg. 3537
TERRA ENERGY PARTNERS LLC—See Kayne Anderson Capital Advisors, L.P.; *U.S. Private*, pg. 2267
TERRA ENERGY PARTNERS LLC—See Warburg Pincus LLC; *U.S. Private*, pg. 4440
TESORO COMPANIES, INC.—See Marathon Petroleum Corporation; *U.S. Public*, pg. 1363
TESORO REFINING & MARKETING COMPANY LLC—See Marathon Petroleum Corporation; *U.S. Public*, pg. 1363
TEXAS AMERICAN RESOURCES OPERATING COMPANY—See Venado Oil & Gas, LLC; *U.S. Private*, pg. 4355
TGH (AP) PTE. LTD.—See Forum Energy Technologies, Inc.; *U.S. Public*, pg. 874
TG HOLDINGS YEMEN INC.—See VAALCO Energy, Inc.; *U.S. Public*, pg. 2270
THC THERAPEUTICS, INC.; *U.S. Public*, pg. 2030
THOMPSON PETROLEUM CORP.; *U.S. Private*, pg. 4160
TIDE PETROLEUM CORP.; *U.S. Private*, pg. 4167
TIGER OIL AND ENERGY, INC.; *U.S. Public*, pg. 2158
TITAN OIL & GAS, INC.; *U.S. Private*, pg. 4177
TN-K ENERGY GROUP INC.; *U.S. Private*, pg. 4180
TOPAZ RESOURCES, INC.; *U.S. Public*, pg. 2163
TRAMMO LTD.—See Trammo, Inc.; *U.S. Private*, pg. 4204
TRANSACT ENERGY CORP.; *U.S. Public*, pg. 2179
TRANS-ASIA PETROLEUM CORPORATION—See Ayala Corporation; *Int'l*, pg. 773
TRANSATLANTIC PETROLEUM LTD.; *U.S. Public*, pg. 2179
TRANSATLANTIC PETROLEUM (USA) CORP.—See Transatlantic Petroleum Ltd.; *U.S. Public*, pg. 2179
TRANSGLOBE PETROLEUM EGYPT INC.—See VAALCO Energy, Inc.; *U.S. Public*, pg. 2270
TRANSGLOBE PETROLEUM INTERNATIONAL INC.—See VAALCO Energy, Inc.; *U.S. Public*, pg. 2270
TRIANGLE PETROLEUM CORPORATION; *U.S. Public*, pg. 2189
TRIANGLE USA PETROLEUM CORPORATION—See Triangle Petroleum Corporation; *U.S. Public*, pg. 2189
TRILINK ENERGY, INC.; *U.S. Private*, pg. 4231
TRINIDAD DRILLING LIMITED PARTNERSHIP—See Ensign Energy Services Inc.; *Int'l*, pg. 2447
TRIUMPH RESOURCES INC—See Chaparral Energy, Inc.; *U.S. Private*, pg. 849
TRUE NORTH ENERGY CORPORATION; *U.S. Public*, pg. 2198
TRUE OIL CO.—See True Companies; *U.S. Private*, pg. 4247
TRULEUM, INC.; *U.S. Public*, pg. 2201
TUBOSCOPE VETCO DE ARGENTINA S.A.—See NOV, Inc.; *U.S. Public*, pg. 1547
TX RAIL PRODUCTS, INC.; *U.S. Public*, pg. 2208
UAB NESTE LIETUVA—See Fortum Oyj; *Int'l*, pg. 2742
ULTRA PETROLEUM CORP.; *U.S. Public*, pg. 2223
UNIT CORPORATION; *U.S. Public*, pg. 2228
UNITED AMERICAN PETROLEUM CORP.; *U.S. Private*, pg. 4287
UNITED OIL CORPORATION—See Forestar Group Inc.; *U.S. Public*, pg. 867
UNIT PETROLEUM COMPANY—See Unit Corporation; *U.S. Public*, pg. 2228
U.S. COMPANIES, INC.; *U.S. Private*, pg. 4270
VAALCO ANGOLA (KWANZA), INC.—See VAALCO Energy, Inc.; *U.S. Public*, pg. 2270
VAALCO ENERGY, INC.; *U.S. Public*, pg. 2270
VAALCO ENERGY (USA), INC.—See VAALCO Energy, Inc.; *U.S. Public*, pg. 2270
VAALCO GABON (ETAME), INC.—See VAALCO Energy, Inc.; *U.S. Public*, pg. 2270
VAALCO INTERNATIONAL, INC.—See VAALCO Energy, Inc.; *U.S. Public*, pg. 2270
VAALCO PRODUCTION (GABON) INC.—See VAALCO Energy, Inc.; *U.S. Public*, pg. 2270
VALERO ENERGY PARTNERS LP—See Valero Energy Corporation; *U.S. Public*, pg. 2272
VENADO OIL & GAS, LLC; *U.S. Private*, pg. 4355
VERNON E. FAULCONER INC.; *U.S. Private*, pg. 4368
VESTBASE AS—See Eidesvik Holding A/S; *Int'l*, pg. 2329
VIPER ENERGY, INC.—See Diamondback Energy, Inc.; *U.S. Public*, pg. 659
VITAL ENERGY, INC.; *U.S. Public*, pg. 2306
WACO OIL & GAS CO., INC.; *U.S. Private*, pg. 4424

N.A.I.C.S. INDEX

WALDEN ENERGY, LLC.; *U.S. Private*, pg. 4427
WALSH & WATTS INC.; *U.S. Private*, pg. 4432
WARREN RESOURCES, INC.; *U.S. Private*, pg. 4444
WESTCHESTER GAS COMPANY; *U.S. Public*, pg. 4489
WEST TEXAS RESOURCES, INC.; *U.S. Public*, pg. 2353
WEXPRO COMPANY—See Enbridge Inc.; *Int'l*, pg. 2397
WGR ASSET HOLDING COMPANY LLC—See Occidental Petroleum Corporation; *U.S. Public*, pg. 1561
WILLBROS GROUP, INC.—See Primoris Services Corporation; *U.S. Public*, pg. 1719
WILLIAMS FIELD SERVICES COMPANY—See The Williams Companies, Inc.; *U.S. Public*, pg. 2142
WINDSOR ENERGY RESOURCES, INC.; *U.S. Private*, pg. 4539
WM KS ENERGY RESOURCES, LLC—See Waste Management, Inc.; *U.S. Public*, pg. 2333
WPX ENERGY APPALACHIA, LLC—See Devon Energy Corporation; *U.S. Public*, pg. 657
WPX ENERGY, INC.—See Devon Energy Corporation; *U.S. Public*, pg. 657
WPX ENERGY WILLISTON, LLC—See Devon Energy Corporation; *U.S. Public*, pg. 657
XCD ENERGY PTY LTD—See 88 Energy Limited; *Int'l*, pg. 15
XTO ENERGY INC.—See Exxon Mobil Corporation; *U.S. Public*, pg. 817
YEMEN HUNT OIL COMPANY, INC.—See Hunt Consolidated, Inc.; *U.S. Private*, pg. 2009
ZAKUM DEVELOPMENT COMPANY—See Abu Dhabi National Oil Company; *Int'l*, pg. 73
ZAZA ENERGY CORPORATION; *U.S. Public*, pg. 2401
ZION OIL & GAS, INC.; *U.S. Public*, pg. 2408
ZWEITE ENVITEC BETEILIGUNGS GMBH & CO. KG—See EnviTec Biogas AG; *Int'l*, pg. 2456

211130 — NATURAL GAS EXTRACTION

ABU DHABI GAS DEVELOPMENT CO. LTD.—See Abu Dhabi National Oil Company; *Int'l*, pg. 72
ABU DHABI GAS LIQUEFACTION LIMITED—See Abu Dhabi National Oil Company; *Int'l*, pg. 72
ACCESS MLP OPERATING, L.L.C.—See The Williams Companies, Inc.; *U.S. Public*, pg. 2143
ACCORD ENERGY LTD.—See Centrica plc; *Int'l*, pg. 1413
ACTBLUE CO., LTD.; *Int'l*, pg. 117
ADMIS HONG KONG LIMITED—See Archer-Daniels-Midland Company; *U.S. Public*, pg. 182
ALENCO INC.—See Ovintiv Inc.; *U.S. Public*, pg. 1625
ALTINEX OIL DENMARK A/S—See BlueNord ASA; *Int'l*, pg. 1072
ALVOPETRO S. A. EXTRACAO DE PETROLEO GAS NATURAL—See Alvopetro Energy Ltd.; *Int'l*, pg. 402
AMANGELDY GAS LLP; *Int'l*, pg. 410
AMERIGAS EAGLE PROPANE, INC.—See UGI Corporation; *U.S. Public*, pg. 2221
ANNOVA LNG, LLC—See Constellation Energy Corporation; *U.S. Public*, pg. 571
AN PHA PETROLEUM GROUP JOINT STOCK COMPANY; *Int'l*, pg. 443
ANTERO MIDSTREAM LLC—See Antero Resources Corporation; *U.S. Public*, pg. 140
APACHE CORPORATION—See APA Corporation; *U.S. Public*, pg. 143
APACHE LOUISIANA MINERALS LLC—See APA Corporation; *U.S. Public*, pg. 143
APACHE SURINAME 58 HOLDINGS CORPORATION LDC—See APA Corporation; *U.S. Public*, pg. 143
APA GROUP; *Int'l*, pg. 499
ARROW ENERGY PTY. LTD.—See China National Petroleum Corporation; *Int'l*, pg. 1533
AUSTRALIS TMS INC.—See Australis Oil & Gas Limited; *Int'l*, pg. 723
AUX SABLE LIQUID PRODUCTS LP; *U.S. Private*, pg. 402
AUX SABLE MIDSTREAM LLC—See The Williams Companies, Inc.; *U.S. Public*, pg. 2143
BIOERDGAS HALLERTAU GMBH—See E.ON SE; *Int'l*, pg. 2251
BIOFUELS ENERGY, LLC; *U.S. Private*, pg. 561
BLUESTEM GAS SERVICES, L.L.C.—See The Williams Companies, Inc.; *U.S. Public*, pg. 2143
BOTALA ENERGY LIMITED; *Int'l*, pg. 1118
BP PLC; *Int'l*, pg. 1131
CAELUS ENERGY ALASKA LLC—See Caelus Energy LLC; *U.S. Private*, pg. 714
CALIFORNIA RESOURCES LONG BEACH, INC.—See California Resources Corporation; *U.S. Public*, pg. 423
CALIFORNIA RESOURCES PRODUCTION CORPORATION—See California Resources Corporation; *U.S. Public*, pg. 423
CARBON MINERALS LIMITED; *Int'l*, pg. 1320
C.C. FORBES, LLC—See Forbes Energy Services Ltd.; *U.S. Public*, pg. 864
THE CENTRICA GAS PRODUCTION LP—See Centrica plc; *Int'l*, pg. 1413
C E READY MIX—See Cable Enterprises Inc.; *U.S. Private*, pg. 711

CGX RESOURCES INC.—See CGX Energy Inc.; *Int'l*, pg. 1435
CHEETAH CANYON RESOURCES CORP.; *Int'l*, pg. 1459
CHINA BLUECHEMICAL LTD.; *Int'l*, pg. 1487
CHINESE PEOPLE HOLDINGS COMPANY LIMITED; *Int'l*, pg. 1569
CHOCTAW GAS GENERATION LLC—See ENGIE SA; *Int'l*, pg. 2433
CHRYSAOR E&P LIMITED—See Harbour Energy plc; *Int'l*, pg. 3271
CIMAREX ENERGY CO. OF COLORADO—See Coterra Energy Inc.; *U.S. Public*, pg. 587
CITEC NORWAY AS—See Cyient Limited; *Int'l*, pg. 1895
CLOVER CORPORATION LIMITED; *Int'l*, pg. 1663
CNGC ENERGY CORP.—See MDU Resources Group, Inc.; *U.S. Public*, pg. 1409
CONOCOPHILLIPS AUSTRALIA GAS HOLDINGS PTY LTD—See ConocoPhillips; *U.S. Public*, pg. 568
CONOCOPHILLIPS (BROWSE BASIN) PTY LTD—See ConocoPhillips; *U.S. Public*, pg. 568
CONRAD ASIA ENERGY LTD.; *Int'l*, pg. 1769
COTERRA ENERGY INC.; *U.S. Public*, pg. 587
CREST RESOURCES, INC.; *Int'l*, pg. 1841
CROWN POINT ENERGIA S.A.—See Crown Point Energy Inc.; *Int'l*, pg. 1858
DELOREAN CORPORATION LIMITED; *Int'l*, pg. 2015
DELTIC ENERGY PLC; *Int'l*, pg. 2021
DIRECT ENERGY RESOURCES PARTNERSHIP—See NRG Energy, Inc.; *U.S. Public*, pg. 1549
DIRECT PETROLEUM BULGARIA EOOD—See TransAtlantic Petroleum Ltd.; *U.S. Public*, pg. 2179
DOMINION ENERGY MIDSTREAM PARTNERS, LP—See Dominion Energy, Inc.; *U.S. Public*, pg. 674
ECLIPSE ENERGY INC.—See Gateway Energy Company, LLC; *U.S. Private*, pg. 1650
EDDA WIND ASA; *Int'l*, pg. 2304
ELKHORN OPERATING CO. INC.; *U.S. Private*, pg. 1363
ENERGY FINDERS, INC.; *U.S. Public*, pg. 762
ENERVEST MONROE GATHERING, LTD.—See EnerVest, Ltd.; *U.S. Private*, pg. 1397
ENTREC CRANES & HEAVY HAUL (WESTERN) LTD.—See Berkshire Hathaway Inc.; *U.S. Public*, pg. 309
ENVEN ENERGY CORPORATION—See Talos Energy Inc.; *U.S. Public*, pg. 1980
EOG RESOURCES TRINIDAD LIMITED—See EOG Resources, Inc.; *U.S. Public*, pg. 782
EOG Y RESOURCES, INC.—See EOG Resources, Inc.; *U.S. Public*, pg. 782
E.ON E&P—See E.ON SE; *Int'l*, pg. 2255
EQUITABLE MINERAL & DEVELOPMENT INC.; *U.S. Private*, pg. 1416
EUROPA OIL & GAS (HOLDINGS) PLC; *Int'l*, pg. 2555
EXXONMOBIL CORPORATION—See Exxon Mobil Corporation; *U.S. Public*, pg. 815
EXXONMOBIL CORPORATION—See Exxon Mobil Corporation; *U.S. Public*, pg. 815
EXXONMOBIL CORPORATION—See Exxon Mobil Corporation; *U.S. Public*, pg. 815
FCX OIL & GAS INC.—See Freeport-McMoRan Inc.; *U.S. Public*, pg. 884
FLAGA SUISSE GMBH—See UGI Corporation; *U.S. Public*, pg. 2222
FRIENDLY ENERGY EXPLORATION; *U.S. Private*, pg. 1611
FUEL PERFORMANCE SOLUTIONS, INC.; *U.S. Private*, pg. 1619
G2 ENERGY CORP.; *Int'l*, pg. 2866
GAIL GAS LIMITED—See GAIL (India) Limited; *Int'l*, pg. 2869
GAS NEA SA; *Int'l*, pg. 2887
GASOL PLC; *Int'l*, pg. 2888
GAS PLUS INTERNATIONAL B.V.—See Gas Plus S.p.A.; *Int'l*, pg. 2887
GAS PLUS S.P.A.; *Int'l*, pg. 2887
GAS PLUS VENDITE S.R.L.—See Gas Plus S.p.A.; *Int'l*, pg. 2887
GAS SUPPLY RESOURCES LLC—See NGL Energy Partners LP; *U.S. Public*, pg. 1527
GAS TO LIQUID JSC; *Int'l*, pg. 2887
GASUM ENERGIAPALVELUT OY—See Gasum Oy; *Int'l*, pg. 2888
GDF BRITAIN LTD.—See ENGIE SA; *Int'l*, pg. 2432
GLACIER DRILLING COMPANY—See ConocoPhillips; *U.S. Public*, pg. 569
GOLAR MANAGEMENT LTD.—See Golar LNG Limited; *Int'l*, pg. 3023
GOLDEN ENERGY OFFSHORE SERVICES AS; *Int'l*, pg. 3029
GREAT NORTHERN MINERALS LIMITED; *Int'l*, pg. 3065
GRUPA LOTOS S.A.; *Int'l*, pg. 3117
GS ENERGY CORPORATION—See GS Holdings Corp.; *Int'l*, pg. 3141
GUARDIAN EXPLORATION INC.; *Int'l*, pg. 3170
GULFSTREAM NATURAL GAS SYSTEM, L.L.C.—See The Williams Companies, Inc.; *U.S. Public*, pg. 2143
GULLEWA LIMITED; *Int'l*, pg. 3182
HALCON ENERGY PROPERTIES, INC.—See Battalion Oil Corp.; *U.S. Public*, pg. 279

211130 — NATURAL GAS EXTRACT...

HERA TRADING S.R.L.—See Hera S.p.A.; *Int'l*, pg. 3356
HIGHPEAK ENERGY ACQUISITION CORP.—See HighPeak Energy, Inc.; *U.S. Public*, pg. 1035
HIGHPEAK ENERGY, INC.; *U.S. Public*, pg. 1035
HORIZON OIL LIMITED; *Int'l*, pg. 3479
HOWARD MIDSTREAM PARTNERS, LP; *U.S. Private*, pg. 1995
HOYER ITALIA S.R.L.—See Hoyer GmbH; *Int'l*, pg. 3499
HSIN TAI GAS CO., LTD.; *Int'l*, pg. 3507
J-W ENERGY COMPANY; *U.S. Private*, pg. 2155
KIMMERIDGE TEXAS GAS, LLC—See Kimmeridge Energy Management Company, LLC; *U.S. Private*, pg. 2305
KUNLUN ENERGY CO. LTD.—See China National Petroleum Corporation; *Int'l*, pg. 1533
LOTOS UPSTREAM SP. Z O.O.—See Grupa LOTOS S.A.; *Int'l*, pg. 3117
MACH NATURAL RESOURCES LP; *U.S. Public*, pg. 1352
MAGNOLIA MIDSTREAM GAS SERVICES, L.L.C.—See The Williams Companies, Inc.; *U.S. Public*, pg. 2143
MARKWEST ENERGY PARTNERS, L.P.—See Marathon Petroleum Corporation; *U.S. Public*, pg. 1364
MARKWEST PINNACLE LP; *U.S. Private*, pg. 2582
MARKWEST POWER TEX, L.L.C.—See Marathon Petroleum Corporation; *U.S. Public*, pg. 1364
MARTIN MIDSTREAM FINANCE CORP—See Martin Midstream Partners LP; *U.S. Public*, pg. 1389
MARYSVILLE HYDROCARBONS LLC—See Phillips 66 Company; *U.S. Public*, pg. 1688
MIDCOAST ENERGY PARTNERS, L.P.—See ArcLight Capital Holdings, LLC; *U.S. Private*, pg. 312
NEPTUNE ENERGY NORGE AS—See Eni S.p.A.; *Int'l*, pg. 2438
NEW ENGLAND UTILITY CONSTRUCTORS, INC.—See Southwest Gas Holdings, Inc.; *U.S. Public*, pg. 1913
NYTIS EXPLORATION COMPANY LLC—See Carbon Energy Corporation; *U.S. Public*, pg. 432
NYTIS EXPLORATION (USA) INC.—See Carbon Energy Corporation; *U.S. Public*, pg. 432
OIL STATES INTERNATIONAL, INC.; *U.S. Public*, pg. 1565
OKMIN RESOURCES, INC.; *U.S. Public*, pg. 1566
OMDA OIL & GAS, INC.; *U.S. Private*, pg. 3015
ONEOK, INC.; *U.S. Public*, pg. 1602
OSTERMAN PROPANE, LLC—See NGL Energy Partners LP; *U.S. Public*, pg. 1527
PARDEE RESOURCES COMPANY; *U.S. Public*, pg. 1637
PECAN PIPELINE (NORTH DAKOTA), INC.—See EOG Resources, Inc.; *U.S. Public*, pg. 782
PIEDMONT INTERSTATE PIPELINE COMPANY—See Duke Energy Corporation; *U.S. Public*, pg. 691
PIONEER NATURAL RESOURCES COMPANY; *U.S. Public*, pg. 1693
PIONEER NATURAL RESOURCES TUNISIA LTD.—See Pioneer Natural Resources Company; *U.S. Public*, pg. 1693
P.J. SERVICES PTE LTD—See Annica Holdings Limited; *Int'l*, pg. 474
PLAINS GAS SOLUTIONS, LLC—See Plains GP Holdings, L.P.; *U.S. Public*, pg. 1697
PORT EVERGLADES ENVIRONMENTAL CORP.—See Marathon Petroleum Corporation; *U.S. Public*, pg. 1364
PRISM GAS SYSTEMS I, LP; *U.S. Public*, pg. 3267
PT. PANAH JAYA SEJAHTERA—See Annica Holdings Limited; *Int'l*, pg. 474
PUBLIC SERVICE COMPANY OF NORTH CAROLINA, INCORPORATED—See Dominion Energy, Inc.; *U.S. Public*, pg. 674
PYPHA ENERGY, LLC.; *U.S. Private*, pg. 3309
QS ENERGY, INC.; *U.S. Public*, pg. 1744
RATTLER MIDSTREAM LP—See Diamondback Energy, Inc.; *U.S. Public*, pg. 658
RESOLUTE NATURAL RESOURCES COMPANY, LLC—See Coterra Energy Inc.; *U.S. Public*, pg. 587
RHONE GAZ—See UGI Corporation; *U.S. Public*, pg. 2222
SABINE PASS LNG, L.P.—See Cheniere Energy, Inc.; *U.S. Public*, pg. 485
SINO GAS & ENERGY LIMITED—See Lone Star Global Acquisitions, LLC; *U.S. Private*, pg. 2489
SOHAR GASES COMPANY L.L.C.—See Global Financial Investments Holding SAOG; *Int'l*, pg. 2996
SOUTHERN REALTY CO.; *U.S. Public*, pg. 1912
SOUTHWESTERN ENERGY COMPANY—See Expand Energy Corporation; *U.S. Public*, pg. 808
STABILIS ENERGY, LLC—See STABILIS SOLUTIONS, INC.; *U.S. Public*, pg. 1924
SUPERIOR MIDSTREAM, LLC; *U.S. Private*, pg. 3879
SUPERIOR TUBING TESTERS, LLC—See Forbes Energy Services Ltd.; *U.S. Public*, pg. 864
SUSTAINABLE PROJECTS GROUP INC.; *U.S. Public*, pg. 1968
TAMAULIGAS S.A. DE C.V.—See ENGIE SA; *Int'l*, pg. 2434
THIRD COAST MIDSTREAM, LLC—See ArcLight Capital Holdings, LLC; *U.S. Private*, pg. 312
TRANSGLOBE ENERGY CORPORATION—See VAALCO Energy, Inc.; *U.S. Public*, pg. 2270
TX ENERGY SERVICES, LLC—See Forbes Energy Services Ltd.; *U.S. Public*, pg. 864
TXO PARTNERS, L.P.; *U.S. Public*, pg. 2208
UNITED GAS TRANSMISSIONS COMPANY LIMITED—See

211130 — NATURAL GAS EXTRACT...

Dana Gas PJSC; *Int'l*, pg. 1957
UNNA ENERGIA S.A.—See Aenza S.A.A.; *Int'l*, pg. 176
UTICA EAST OHIO MIDSTREAM LLC—See The Williams Companies, Inc.; *U.S. Public*, pg. 2143
VITESSE ENERGY, INC.; *U.S. Public*, pg. 2307
WARREN RESOURCES OF CALIFORNIA, INC.—See Warren Resources, Inc.; *U.S. Private*, pg. 4444
WESTCOAST ENERGY, INC.—See Enbridge Inc.; *Int'l*, pg. 2397
WILLIAMS OHIO VALLEY MIDSTREAM LLC—See The Williams Companies, Inc.; *U.S. Public*, pg. 2144
WTG EXPLORATION, INC.—See J.L. Davis Companies; *U.S. Private*, pg. 2167

212114 — SURFACE COAL MINING

A&G COAL CORPORATION—See Southern Coal Corporation; *U.S. Private*, pg. 3730
ALEX ENERGY, INC.—See Alpha Natural Resources, Inc.; *U.S. Private*, pg. 199
ALLIANCE RESOURCE PARTNERS, L.P.—See Alliance Holdings GP, L.P.; *U.S. Private*, pg. 183
ALPHA NATURAL RESOURCES, INC.; *U.S. Private*, pg. 198
AMERIKOHL MINING INC.; *U.S. Private*, pg. 260
ANTELOPE COAL LLC—See Cloud Peak Energy Inc.; *U.S. Private*, pg. 946
ANYUAN COAL INDUSTRY GROUP CO., LTD.; *Int'l*, pg. 487
ARACOMA COAL COMPANY, INC.—See Alpha Natural Resources, Inc.; *U.S. Private*, pg. 198
ARCH COAL TERMINAL, INC.—See Arch Resources, Inc.; *U.S. Public*, pg. 180
ARCH OF WYOMING, LLC—See Arch Resources, Inc.; *U.S. Public*, pg. 180
ARCH RESOURCES, INC.; *U.S. Public*, pg. 180
ASPIRE MINING LIMITED; *Int'l*, pg. 631
A.T. MASSEY COAL COMPANY, INC.—See Alpha Natural Resources, Inc.; *U.S. Private*, pg. 198
BANDMILL COAL CORPORATION—See Alpha Natural Resources, Inc.; *U.S. Private*, pg. 198
BEAR CREEK MINING INC.—See Bear Creek Mining Corporation; *Int'l*, pg. 933
BERWIND NATURAL RESOURCES CORPORATION—See Berwind Corporation; *U.S. Private*, pg. 540
BLASTING & EXCAVATING (PTY) LIMITED—See Basil Read Holdings Limited; *Int'l*, pg. 887
BLEDSOE COAL CORPORATION—See James River Coal Company; *U.S. Private*, pg. 2185
BOGGABRI COAL PTY LIMITED—See Idemitsu Kosan Co., Ltd.; *Int'l*, pg. 3590
BRIDGER COAL COMPANY; *U.S. Private*, pg. 649
BUCKINGHAM COAL COMPANY, LLC—See Westmoreland Coal Company; *U.S. Private*, pg. 4499
BUCKSKIN MINING COMPANY—See Peter Kiewit Sons', Inc.; *U.S. Private*, pg. 3158
BUFFALO COAL CORP.; *Int'l*, pg. 1211
BURTON COAL PTY LTD—See Peabody Energy Corporation; *U.S. Public*, pg. 1659
CADDO CREEK RESOURCES CO., LLC—See NACCO Industries, Inc.; *U.S. Public*, pg. 1490
CAMBRIAN COAL CORPORATION—See Wright Management Company, LLC; *U.S. Private*, pg. 4573
CAMINO REAL FUELS, LLC—See NACCO Industries, Inc.; *U.S. Public*, pg. 1490
CELSIUS RESOURCES LIMITED; *Int'l*, pg. 1395
CHINA COAL ENERGY COMPANY LIMITED; *Int'l*, pg. 1489
CHINA COAL XINJI ENERGY CO., LTD.; *Int'l*, pg. 1490
C&K COAL COMPANY—See GRE Ventures, Inc.; *U.S. Private*, pg. 1761
COAL-MAC, INC.—See Arch Resources, Inc.; *U.S. Public*, pg. 180
COALSPUR MINES LIMITED; *Int'l*, pg. 1680
CONESVILLE COAL PREPARATION CO.—See American Electric Power Company, Inc.; *U.S. Public*, pg. 99
COONEY BROTHERS COAL CO.; *U.S. Private*, pg. 1040
CORONADO COAL LLC; *U.S. Private*, pg. 1053
THE COTEAU PROPERTIES CO.—See NACCO Industries, Inc.; *U.S. Public*, pg. 1490
DAKOTA WESTMORELAND CORPORATION—See Westmoreland Coal Company; *U.S. Private*, pg. 4499
DALRYMPLE BAY COAL TERMINAL PTY LTD—See Peabody Energy Corporation; *U.S. Public*, pg. 1659
DECKER COAL COMPANY; *U.S. Private*, pg. 1187
DEMERY RESOURCES COMPANY, LLC—See NACCO Industries, Inc.; *U.S. Public*, pg. 1489
DOLET HILLS LIGNITE COMPANY—See American Electric Power Company, Inc.; *U.S. Public*, pg. 100
ELK RUN COAL COMPANY, INC.—See Alpha Natural Resources, Inc.; *U.S. Private*, pg. 198
FREEDOM ENERGY INC.; *Int'l*, pg. 2769
GALA-MIBRAG-SERVICE GMBH—See Energeticky a Prumyslovy Holding, a.s.; *Int'l*, pg. 2420
GHGS COAL MINE METHANE, LLC—See The AES Corporation; *U.S. Public*, pg. 2031
GIBSON COUNTY COAL, LLC—See Alliance Holdings GP, L.P.; *U.S. Private*, pg. 183

GREEN VALLEY COAL COMPANY—See Alpha Natural Resources, Inc.; *U.S. Private*, pg. 199
GUIZHOU PANJIANG REFINED COAL CO., LTD.; *Int'l*, pg. 3174
HALF-TIDE MARINE PTY LTD—See Peabody Energy Corporation; *U.S. Public*, pg. 1659
HARTCHROM SCHOCH GMBH.—See Arbonia AG; *Int'l*, pg. 538
HELMSTEDTER REVIER GMBH—See Energeticky a Prumyslovy Holding, a.s.; *Int'l*, pg. 2420
HOMER CITY COAL PROCESSING CO.—See CLI Corporation; *U.S. Private*, pg. 942
HUAIBEI MINING HOLDINGS CO., LTD.; *Int'l*, pg. 3512
HUDSON RESOURCES LIMITED; *Int'l*, pg. 3522
HUSCOKE INTERNATIONAL GROUP LIMITED—See Huscoke Holdings Limited; *Int'l*, pg. 3538
INTEGRITY COAL SALES INTERNATIONAL, INC.—See Integrity Coal Sales Inc.; *U.S. Private*, pg. 2102
JAMES RIVER COAL COMPANY; *U.S. Private*, pg. 2185
JEWELL SMOKELESS COAL CORPORATION—See Sun-Coke Energy, Inc.; *U.S. Public*, pg. 1964
KOPPER GLO FUEL, INC.—See Quintana Capital Group, L.P.; *U.S. Private*, pg. 3328
LEE RANCH COAL COMPANY—See Peabody Energy Corporation; *U.S. Public*, pg. 1659
LOCUST GROVE INC.; *U.S. Private*, pg. 2479
LOGAN COUNTY MINE SERVICES, INC.—See Alpha Natural Resources, Inc.; *U.S. Private*, pg. 199
LONG FORK COAL COMPANY—See Alpha Natural Resources, Inc.; *U.S. Private*, pg. 198
MARFORK COAL COMPANY, INC.—See Alpha Natural Resources, Inc.; *U.S. Private*, pg. 198
MARIETTA COAL CO.; *U.S. Private*, pg. 2574
MARTIN COUNTY COAL CORPORATION—See Alpha Natural Resources, Inc.; *U.S. Private*, pg. 198
MISSISSIPPI LIGNITE MINING COMPANY—See NACCO Industries, Inc.; *U.S. Public*, pg. 1490
MITTELDEUTSCHE BRAUNKOHLENGESELLSCHAFT MBH—See CEZ, a.s.; *Int'l*, pg. 1428
MITTELDEUTSCHE BRAUNKOHLENGESELLSCHAFT MBH—See Energeticky a Prumyslovy Holding, a.s.; *Int'l*, pg. 2420
MOORVALE COAL PTY LTD—See Peabody Energy Corporation; *U.S. Public*, pg. 1659
MUSWELLBROOK COAL COMPANY LIMITED—See Idemitsu Kosan Co., Ltd.; *Int'l*, pg. 3590
THE NORTH AMERICAN COAL CORPORATION—See NACCO Industries, Inc.; *U.S. Public*, pg. 1490
NORTH AMERICAN COAL ROYALTY COMPANY—See NACCO Industries, Inc.; *U.S. Public*, pg. 1489
NORTH CAMBRIA FUEL CO.; *U.S. Private*, pg. 2942
NRP (OPERATING) LLC—See Natural Resource Partners L.P.; *U.S. Public*, pg. 1499
NSL MINING RESOURCES INDIA (PVT) LTD—See Elmore Ltd.; *Int'l*, pg. 2368
OMAR MINING COMPANY—See Alpha Natural Resources, Inc.; *U.S. Private*, pg. 198
OTTER CREEK COAL, LLC—See Arch Resources, Inc.; *U.S. Public*, pg. 180
OXFORD MINING COMPANY, LLC; *U.S. Private*, pg. 3057
PATRIOT MINING COMPANY INC.—See Arch Resources, Inc.; *U.S. Public*, pg. 180
PBS COALS, INC.—See Quintana Capital Group, L.P.; *U.S. Private*, pg. 3328
PEABODY COALTRADE ASIA PRIVATE LTD.—See Peabody Energy Corporation; *U.S. Public*, pg. 1659
PEABODY COPPABELLA PTY LTD—See Peabody Energy Corporation; *U.S. Public*, pg. 1659
PEABODY ENERGY CORPORATION; *U.S. Public*, pg. 1658
PEABODY ENERGY MIDWEST GROUP—See Peabody Energy Corporation; *U.S. Public*, pg. 1659
PEABODY MIDWEST MINING, LLC—See Peabody Energy Corporation; *U.S. Public*, pg. 1659
PEABODY (WILKIE CREEK) PTY LTD.—See Peabody Energy Corporation; *U.S. Public*, pg. 1659
PEABODY-WINSWAY RESOURCES BV—See Peabody Energy Corporation; *U.S. Public*, pg. 1659
PENN-OHIO COAL CO.—See Kimble Companies Inc.; *U.S. Private*, pg. 2305
PERFORMANCE COAL COMPANY—See Alpha Natural Resources, Inc.; *U.S. Private*, pg. 199
PINE BRANCH COAL SALES INC.; *U.S. Private*, pg. 3182
P&N COAL CO. INC.; *U.S. Private*, pg. 3059
PROBIGALP - LIGANTES BETUMINOSOS, S.A.—See Galp Energia SGPS, S.A.; *Int'l*, pg. 2875
PRZEDSIEBIORSTWO GORNICZE SILESIA SP. Z O.O.—See Energeticky a Prumyslovy Holding, a.s.; *Int'l*, pg. 2420
QUALITY AGGREGATES INC.; *U.S. Private*, pg. 3317
RAWL SALES & PROCESSING CO.—See Alpha Natural Resources, Inc.; *U.S. Private*, pg. 199
RFC CORPORATE FINANCE, INC.—See Peabody Energy Corporation; *U.S. Public*, pg. 1659
RIGGS OIL COMPANY INC.; *U.S. Private*, pg. 3435
RIVER HILL COAL COMPANY INC.; *U.S. Private*, pg. 3444
RIVERVIEW TERMINAL COMPANY—See Peabody Energy Corporation; *U.S. Public*, pg. 1659

SAHARA ENTERPRISES INC.; *U.S. Private*, pg. 3528
SEMIRARA MINING AND POWER CORPORATION—See DMCI Holdings, Inc.; *Int'l*, pg. 2143
SEQUATCHIE VALLEY COAL CORPORATION—See Cloud Peak Energy Inc.; *U.S. Private*, pg. 946
SEVEROCESKE DOLY A.S.—See CEZ, a.s.; *Int'l*, pg. 1428
SILESIAN COAL INTERNATIONAL GROUP OF COMPANIES S.A.—See HMS Bergbau AG; *Int'l*, pg. 3432
SOLAR SOURCES, INC.; *U.S. Private*, pg. 3707
SOUTHERN COAL CORPORATION; *U.S. Private*, pg. 3730
SPRAY PAVE (PTY) LIMITED—See AECI Limited; *Int'l*, pg. 171
SPRING CREEK COAL LLC—See Cloud Peak Energy Inc.; *U.S. Private*, pg. 946
STIRRAT COAL COMPANY—See Alpha Natural Resources, Inc.; *U.S. Private*, pg. 198
SUNRISE COAL LLC—See HALLADOR ENERGY COMPANY; *U.S. Public*, pg. 980
TARONG COAL LTD—See ACS, Actividades de Construccion y Servicios, S.A.; *Int'l*, pg. 113
TARONG COAL LTD—See Elliott Management Corporation; *U.S. Private*, pg. 1365
TECO DIVERSIFIED, INC.—See Emera, Inc.; *Int'l*, pg. 2377
TEXAS WESTMORELAND COAL COMPANY—See Westmoreland Coal Company; *U.S. Private*, pg. 4499
TRIAD MINING INC.—See James River Coal Company; *U.S. Private*, pg. 2185
TRIAD UNDERGROUND MINING, LLC—See James River Coal Company; *U.S. Private*, pg. 2185
UNITED MINERALS COMPANY, LLC—See Peabody Energy Corporation; *U.S. Public*, pg. 1659
UPSHUR PROPERTY LLC—See Arch Resources, Inc.; *U.S. Public*, pg. 180
USIBELLI COAL MINE, INC.; *U.S. Private*, pg. 4323
VALLEY MINING, INC.; *U.S. Private*, pg. 4334
WAMBO COAL TERMINAL PTY LTD—See Peabody Energy Corporation; *U.S. Public*, pg. 1659
WEBSTER COUNTY COAL, LLC—See Alliance Holdings GP, L.P.; *U.S. Private*, pg. 183
WESTERN ENERGY COMPANY—See Westmoreland Coal Company; *U.S. Private*, pg. 4500
WESTMORELAND KEMMERER, INC.—See Westmoreland Coal Company; *U.S. Private*, pg. 4500
WESTMORELAND RESOURCES, INC.—See Westmoreland Coal Company; *U.S. Private*, pg. 4500
WESTMORELAND SAVAGE CORPORATION—See Westmoreland Coal Company; *U.S. Private*, pg. 4500
WHITE COUNTY COAL, LLC—See Alliance Holdings GP, L.P.; *U.S. Private*, pg. 183

212115 — UNDERGROUND COAL MINING

ABSALOKA COAL, LLC—See Westmoreland Coal Company; *U.S. Private*, pg. 4500
AK COAL RESOURCES, INC.—See Cleveland-Cliffs, Inc.; *U.S. Public*, pg. 513
ALLEGIANCE COAL LIMITED; *Int'l*, pg. 334
ANHUI HENGYUAN COAL INDUSTRY & ELECTRICITY POWER CO., LTD.; *Int'l*, pg. 468
ATRUM COAL LIMITED; *Int'l*, pg. 694
AUS ASIA MINERALS LIMITED; *Int'l*, pg. 715
AUSTCHINA HOLDINGS LTD; *Int'l*, pg. 716
AUSTRALIAN PACIFIC COAL LTD.; *Int'l*, pg. 722
BAC GIANG EXPLOITABLE MINERAL JOINT STOCK COMPANY; *Int'l*, pg. 793
BANPU PUBLIC COMPANY LIMITED; *Int'l*, pg. 851
BARAKAT ASSOCIATES, LTD—See Reading Anthracite Company; *U.S. Private*, pg. 3366
BAUER RESOURCES CANADA LTD.—See BAUER Aktiengesellschaft; *Int'l*, pg. 892
BEIJING HAOHUA ENERGY RESOURCE CO., LTD.; *Int'l*, pg. 951
BELL COUNTY COAL CORPORATION—See James River Coal Company; *U.S. Private*, pg. 2185
BHP COAL PTY. LTD.—See BHP Group Limited; *Int'l*, pg. 1016
BISICHI PLC; *Int'l*, pg. 1049
BLACKGOLD NATURAL RESOURCES LTD.; *Int'l*, pg. 1061
BLACKHAWK MINING, LLC—See JMP Coal Holdings, LLC; *U.S. Private*, pg. 2216
BLASCHAK ANTHRACITE CORPORATION; *U.S. Private*, pg. 579
BOWIE RESOURCES LLC; *U.S. Private*, pg. 625
CANAM COAL CORP.; *Int'l*, pg. 1287
CANYON FUEL COMPANY, LLC—See Bowie Resources LLC; *U.S. Private*, pg. 625
CENTENNIAL ANGUS PLACE PTY LIMITED—See Banpu Public Company Limited; *Int'l*, pg. 852
CENTENNIAL COAL COMPANY LIMITED—See Banpu Public Company Limited; *Int'l*, pg. 852
C.H. SNYDER COMPANY—See The Snyder Group, Inc.; *U.S. Private*, pg. 4119
COAL ASIA HOLDINGS INC.; *Int'l*, pg. 1680
COAL ENERGY S.A.; *Int'l*, pg. 1680
COALSPUR MINES (OPERATIONS) LTD.—See Coalspur Mines Limited; *Int'l*, pg. 1680

N.A.I.C.S. INDEX

212220 — GOLD ORE AND SILVER...

COKAL LIMITED; *Int'l*, pg. 1696
COUNTY INTERNATIONAL LIMITED; *Int'l*, pg. 1819
CUESTA COAL LIMITED; *Int'l*, pg. 1876
DATONG COAL INDUSTRY CO., LTD.; *Int'l*, pg. 1982
DATONG COAL INDUSTRY JINYU KAOLIN CHEMICAL CO., LTD.—See Datong Coal Mine Group Co., Ltd.; *Int'l*, pg. 1982
DOMINION COAL CORPORATION—See SunCoke Energy, Inc.; *U.S. Public*, pg. 1963
EAST ENERGY RESOURCES LIMITED; *Int'l*, pg. 2270
ECORA RESOURCES PLC; *Int'l*, pg. 2299
EXXARO COAL (PTY) LIMITED—See Exxaro Resources Ltd.; *Int'l*, pg. 2592
EXXARO RESOURCES LTD.; *Int'l*, pg. 2592
FEISHANG ANTHRACITE RESOURCES LIMITED; *Int'l*, pg. 2632
FORBES COAL (PTY) LTD.—See Buffalo Coal Corp.; *Int'l*, pg. 1211
FOREIGN TRADE & ECONOMIC COOPERATION CO., LTD.—See Datong Coal Mine Group Co., Ltd.; *Int'l*, pg. 1982
FORTUNE COAL LIMITED—See Fortune Minerals Limited; *Int'l*, pg. 2743
GANSU JINGYUAN COAL INDUSTRY & ELECTRICITY POWER CO., LTD.; *Int'l*, pg. 2881
GEO ENERGY RESOURCES LIMITED; *Int'l*, pg. 2931
GILBERTON COAL COMPANY—See Reading Anthracite Company; *U.S. Private*, pg. 3366
GLENCORE COAL PTY. LTD.—See Glencore plc; *Int'l*, pg. 2990
GLENCORE COAL QUEENSLAND PTY. LIMITED—See Glencore plc; *Int'l*, pg. 2990
GRANDE CACHE COAL CORPORATION—See CST Canada Coal Limited; *Int'l*, pg. 1868
GREAT EASTERN ENERGY CORPORATION LTD.; *Int'l*, pg. 3064
GREENX METALS LIMITED; *Int'l*, pg. 3077
GUANGDONG GUANGSHENG POWER FUEL CO. LTD.—See Guangdong Rising Assets Management Co., Ltd.; *Int'l*, pg. 3159
HALLADOR ENERGY COMPANY; *U.S. Public*, pg. 980
HARLAN-CUMBERLAND COAL COMPANY; *U.S. Private*, pg. 1865
HIDILI INDUSTRY INTERNATIONAL DEVELOPMENT LIMITED; *Int'l*, pg. 3384
HULLERA VASCO LEONESA S.A.; *Int'l*, pg. 3528
HUNNU COAL LIMITED—See Banpu Public Company Limited; *Int'l*, pg. 852
IDEMITSU AUSTRALIA RESOURCES PTY. LTD.—See Idemitsu Kosan Co., Ltd.; *Int'l*, pg. 3590
INDEPENDENCE COAL COMPANY, INC.—See Alpha Natural Resources, Inc.; *U.S. Private*, pg. 198
INYANDA COAL (PTY) LIMITED—See Exxaro Resources Ltd.; *Int'l*, pg. 2592
JAMES RIVER COAL SERVICE CO.—See James River Coal Company; *U.S. Private*, pg. 2185
JEDDO-HIGHLAND COAL CO. INC.—See Pagnotti Enterprises Inc.; *U.S. Private*, pg. 3075
JERICOL MINING INC.; *U.S. Private*, pg. 2201
J-POWER RESOURCES CO., LTD.—See Electric Power Development Co., Ltd.; *Int'l*, pg. 2349
KNOX CREEK COAL CORPORATION—See Alpha Natural Resources, Inc.; *U.S. Private*, pg. 198
KOPPER GLO MINING, LLC; *U.S. Private*, pg. 2343
LIPARI ENERGY, INC.; *U.S. Private*, pg. 2464
LITTLE EAGLE COAL COMPANY, LLC—See CONSOL Energy Inc.; *U.S. Public*, pg. 569
L & L ENERGY, INC.; *U.S. Private*, pg. 2361
MANGOOLA COAL OPERATIONS PTY. LIMITED—See Glencore plc; *Int'l*, pg. 2990
MCCOY ELKHORN COAL CORPORATION—See James River Coal Company; *U.S. Private*, pg. 2185
MMEX RESOURCES CORPORATION; *U.S. Public*, pg. 1453
NORTH STAR CONTRACTORS INC.; *U.S. Private*, pg. 2947
OXBOW MINING, LLC—See Oxbow Corporation; *U.S. Private*, pg. 3056
PEABODY (BOWEN) PTY LTD.—See Peabody Energy Corporation; *U.S. Public*, pg. 1659
PEABODY DEVELOPMENT COMPANY, LLC—See Peabody Energy Corporation; *U.S. Public*, pg. 1659
PEABODY ENERGY AUSTRALIA PCI LIMITED—See Peabody Energy Corporation; *U.S. Public*, pg. 1659
PITTSTON COAL COMPANY—See The Brink's Company; *U.S. Public*, pg. 2043
RAPOCA ENERGY CO. LP; *U.S. Private*, pg. 3356
READING ANTHRACITE COMPANY; *U.S. Private*, pg. 3366
RHINO RESOURCE PARTNERS LP—See Royal Energy Resources, Inc.; *U.S. Public*, pg. 1815
ROSEBUD MINING COMPANY; *U.S. Private*, pg. 3482
ROXCOAL, INC.—See Quintana Capital Group, L.P.; *U.S. Private*, pg. 3328
SHANXI POLY XINGCHEN COKING CO., LTD.—See China Poly Group Corporation; *Int'l*, pg. 1541
SHARPE RESOURCES CORPORATION; *U.S. Private*, pg. 3627
SIDNEY COAL COMPANY, INC.—See Alpha Natural Resources, Inc.; *U.S. Private*, pg. 199
SOCIEDAD MINERA ISLA RIESCO S.A.—See AntarChile S.A.; *Int'l*, pg. 482
SOUTHERN COAL (PROPRIETARY) LIMITED—See Canaf Investments Inc.; *Int'l*, pg. 1287
STRONGHOLD DIGITAL MINING, INC.; *U.S. Public*, pg. 1955
SUQUASH COAL LTD.—See Electra Stone Ltd.; *Int'l*, pg. 2348
TAHMOOR COAL PTY. LIMITED—See GFG Alliance Limited; *Int'l*, pg. 2956
UK COAL MINING LIMITED—See Harworth Group plc; *Int'l*, pg. 3282
U.S. CHINA MINING GROUP, INC.; *U.S. Private*, pg. 4270
THE VRYHEID (NATAL) RAILWAY COAL AND IRON COMPANY LIMITED—See Exxaro Resources Ltd.; *Int'l*, pg. 2592
WARRIOR MET COAL, INC; *U.S. Public*, pg. 2329

212210 — IRON ORE MINING

37 CAPITAL INC.; *Int'l*, pg. 7
ABTERRA MACAO COMMERCIAL OFFSHORE LIMITED—See Abterra Ltd.; *Int'l*, pg. 70
ADAMANT DRI PROCESSING & MINERALS GROUP; *Int'l*, pg. 123
ADVANCED INVESTMENTS GROUP; *Int'l*, pg. 160
AKORA RESOURCES LIMITED; *Int'l*, pg. 264
ALDERON IRON ORE CORP.; *Int'l*, pg. 304
ALLIED AMERICAN STEEL CORPORATION; *U.S. Private*, pg. 185
ANGLO AMERICAN SOUTH AFRICA LIMITED—See Anglo American PLC; *Int'l*, pg. 461
ANGLO FERROUS BRAZIL S.A.—See Anglo American PLC; *Int'l*, pg. 461
AOWEI HOLDING LIMITED; *Int'l*, pg. 498
AQUILA RESOURCES PTY LIMITED—See China Baowu Steel Group Corp., Ltd.; *Int'l*, pg. 1485
ARCELORMITTAL HAMBURG GMBH—See ArcelorMittal S.A.; *Int'l*, pg. 544
ARCELORMITTAL LOGISTICS BELGIUM—See ArcelorMittal S.A.; *Int'l*, pg. 544
ARCELORMITTAL POINT LISAS LTD—See ArcelorMittal S.A.; *Int'l*, pg. 545
ARCELORMITTAL RUHRORT GMBH—See ArcelorMittal S.A.; *Int'l*, pg. 545
ARCELORMITTAL SSC UK LTD—See ArcelorMittal S.A.; *Int'l*, pg. 545
ARGENTINA LITHIUM & ENERGY CORP.; *Int'l*, pg. 561
ARGOSY MINERALS LIMITED; *Int'l*, pg. 563
ATLANTIC LITHIUM LIMITED; *Int'l*, pg. 675
ATLAS IRON LIMITED; *Int'l*, pg. 686
AUTECO MINERALS LTD.; *Int'l*, pg. 724
BAFFINLAND IRON MINES CORPORATION—See ArcelorMittal S.A.; *Int'l*, pg. 545
BASE RESOURCES LIMITED—See Energy Fuels Inc.; *U.S. Public*, pg. 762
BCI MINERALS LIMITED; *Int'l*, pg. 928
BELLZONE MINING PLC; *Int'l*, pg. 968
BHP BILLITON (BOLIVIA), INC.—See BHP Group Limited; *Int'l*, pg. 1015
BHP BILLITON CHINA—See BHP Group Limited; *Int'l*, pg. 1015
BHP BILLITON IRON ORE PTY. LTD.—See BHP Group Limited; *Int'l*, pg. 1016
BHP BILLITON PETROLEUM LTD—See BHP Group Limited; *Int'l*, pg. 1015
BHP MINERALS—See BHP Group Limited; *Int'l*, pg. 1016
BHP NEW ZEALAND STEEL LTD.—See BlueScope Steel Limited; *Int'l*, pg. 1073
BHP TITANIUM MINERALS—See BHP Group Limited; *Int'l*, pg. 1016
BLACK IRON INC.; *Int'l*, pg. 1059
BLUESCOPE STEEL—See BlueScope Steel Limited; *Int'l*, pg. 1073
BREMER GALVANISIERUNGS GMBH—See ArcelorMittal S.A.; *Int'l*, pg. 543
BRITANNIA MINING INC.; *U.S. Public*, pg. 388
BROCKMAN IRON PTY. LTD.—See Brockman Mining Limited; *Int'l*, pg. 1173
CANADA IRON INC.; *Int'l*, pg. 1278
CAPROCK MINING CORP.; *Int'l*, pg. 1317
CARTIER SILVER CORPORATION; *Int'l*, pg. 1348
CASTINGS PLC; *Int'l*, pg. 1357
CENTRAL IRON ORE LIMITED; *Int'l*, pg. 1408
CENTREX LIMITED; *Int'l*, pg. 1412
CHADORMALU MINING & INDUSTRIAL COMPANY; *Int'l*, pg. 1436
CHICHESTER METALS PTY LIMITED—See Fortescue Ltd; *Int'l*, pg. 2738
CHINA HANKING HOLDINGS LIMITED; *Int'l*, pg. 1506
CHINA VANADIUM TITANO-MAGNETITE MINING COMPANY LIMITED; *Int'l*, pg. 1561
CLEVELAND-CLIFFS, INC.; *U.S. Public*, pg. 513
CLEVELAND-CLIFFS MINORCA MINE INC.—See Cleveland-Cliffs, Inc.; *U.S. Public*, pg. 514
COMPANIA MINERA CERRO COLORADO LIMITADA—See BHP Group Limited; *Int'l*, pg. 1016
COMPANIA MINERA DEL PACIFICO S.A.—See CAP S.A.; *Int'l*, pg. 1300
CRYSTAL LAKE MINING CORPORATION; *Int'l*, pg. 1860
DCM AUSTRIA—See DCM DECOmetal GmbH; *Int'l*, pg. 1992
DELTA END AUSTRALIA PTY. LTD.—See BHP Group Limited; *Int'l*, pg. 1016
DYNASTY RESOURCES LIMITED; *Int'l*, pg. 2242
EASTERN RESOURCES LIMITED; *Int'l*, pg. 2273
EQUATORIAL RESOURCES LIMITED; *Int'l*, pg. 2484
ERP IRON ORE, LLC; *U.S. Private*, pg. 1423
EUROPA METALS LIMITED; *Int'l*, pg. 2555
FENIX RESOURCES LIMITED; *Int'l*, pg. 2634
FERREXPO AG—See Ferrexpo plc; *Int'l*, pg. 2641
FERREXPO BELANOVO MINING LLC—See Ferrexpo plc; *Int'l*, pg. 2641
FERREXPO MIDDLE EAST FZE—See Ferrexpo plc; *Int'l*, pg. 2641
FERREXPO PLC; *Int'l*, pg. 2641
FERREXPO SINGAPORE PTE LTD—See Ferrexpo plc; *Int'l*, pg. 2641
FLINDERS MINES LIMITED; *Int'l*, pg. 2706
FOREMOST CLEAN ENERGY LTD.; *Int'l*, pg. 2731
FORTRESS MINERALS LIMITED; *Int'l*, pg. 2740
FRANKLIN MINING, INC.; *U.S. Public*, pg. 1597
GALTEC N.V.—See ArcelorMittal S.A.; *Int'l*, pg. 545
GENMINI LIMITED; *Int'l*, pg. 2924
GEO JS TECH GROUP CORP.; *U.S. Public*, pg. 934
GINDALBIE METALS LTD—See Anshan Iron & Steel Group Corporation; *Int'l*, pg. 479
GLOBAL SURFACES FZE—See Global Surfaces Limited; *Int'l*, pg. 3001
GOLD VALLEY PTY. LTD.; *Int'l*, pg. 3026
GOLGOHAR MINING & INDUSTRIAL CO.; *Int'l*, pg. 3036
GRACE LIFE-TECH HOLDINGS LIMITED; *Int'l*, pg. 3048
GRANGE RESOURCES LIMITED; *Int'l*, pg. 3058
GRANGE RESOURCES (TASMANIA) PTY. LTD.—See Grange Resources Limited; *Int'l*, pg. 3058
GRUPO ACERERO DEL NORTE S.A. DE C.V.; *Int'l*, pg. 3118
GUANGDONG GUANGSHENG METALLURGY CO., LTD.—See Guangdong Rising Assets Management Co., Ltd.; *Int'l*, pg. 3159
HAINAN MINING CO., LTD.—See Fosun International Limited; *Int'l*, pg. 2751
HANCOCK PROSPECTING PTY. LTD.; *Int'l*, pg. 3242
HARANGA RESOURCES LIMITED; *Int'l*, pg. 3270
HELIX RESOURCES LIMITED; *Int'l*, pg. 3331
IAMGOLD ESSAKANE S.A.—See IAMGOLD Corporation; *Int'l*, pg. 3568
IMOPAC LTDA.—See CAP S.A.; *Int'l*, pg. 1300
JDVC RESOURCES CORPORATION—See Apollo Global Capital, Inc.; *Int'l*, pg. 517
KARARA MINING LTD.—See Anshan Iron & Steel Group Corporation; *Int'l*, pg. 479
KUMBA IRON ORE LTD.—See Anglo American PLC; *Int'l*, pg. 462
MAGNETATION, INC.—See ERP Iron Ore, LLC; *U.S. Private*, pg. 1423
MESABI TRUST; *U.S. Public*, pg. 1426
MINERA HIERRO ATACAMA S.A.—See CAP S.A.; *Int'l*, pg. 1300
MINERAL TECHNOLOGIES, INC.—See Downer EDI Limited; *Int'l*, pg. 2186
MINERAL TECHNOLOGIES PTY. LTD.—See Downer EDI Limited; *Int'l*, pg. 2186
MMX MINERACAO E METALICOS S.A.—See EBX Group Ltd.; *Int'l*, pg. 2287
THE PILBARA INFRASTRUCTURE PTY LIMITED—See Fortescue Ltd; *Int'l*, pg. 2738
POLY METAL AND MINERALS LIMITED—See GT Group Holdings Limited; *Int'l*, pg. 3151
P.T. BHP INDONESIA—See BHP Group Limited; *Int'l*, pg. 1016
QUEBEC CARTIER MINING CO.—See ArcelorMittal S.A.; *Int'l*, pg. 544
ROCHE BAY PLC—See Borealis Exploration Limited; *Int'l*, pg. 1113
SOUTHERN EXPLORATION PTY LIMITED—See Apollo Minerals Limited; *Int'l*, pg. 518
TILDEN MINING COMPANY LC—See Cleveland-Cliffs, Inc.; *U.S. Public*, pg. 514
TOACHI MINING INC.—See Atico Mining Corporation; *Int'l*, pg. 670
TRANSNATIONAL GROUP, INC.; *U.S. Public*, pg. 2183
TURK MAADIN SIRKETI A.S.—See Afarak Group SE; *Int'l*, pg. 185
UNITED STATES STEEL INTERNATIONAL, INC.—See United States Steel Corporation; *U.S. Public*, pg. 2237
UNITED TACONITE, LLC—See Cleveland-Cliffs, Inc.; *U.S. Public*, pg. 514

212220 — GOLD ORE AND SILVER ORE MINING

1911 GOLD CORPORATION; *Int'l*, pg. 3

212220 — GOLD ORE AND SILVER...

55 NORTH MINING INC.; *Int'l*, pg. 13
ABZU GOLD LTD.; *Int'l*, pg. 74
ACACIA MINING PLC—See Barrick Gold Corporation; *Int'l*, pg. 869
ACCENT RESOURCES N.L.; *Int'l*, pg. 81
ACCREDITED SOLUTIONS, INC.; *U.S. Public*, pg. 33
ACROW LIMITED; *Int'l*, pg. 109
ADELONG GOLD LIMITED; *Int'l*, pg. 142
ADVANCE GOLD LIMITED; *Int'l*, pg. 156
ADVANTEGO CORPORATION; *U.S. Private*, pg. 95
AFFINITY GOLD CORP.; *U.S. Private*, pg. 123
AFFINITY METALS CORP.; *Int'l*, pg. 186
AFRICAN EAGLE RESOURCES PLC; *Int'l*, pg. 191
AFRICAN GOLD B.V.—See Conquest Resources Limited; *Int'l*, pg. 1769
AFRIKA GOLD AG; *Int'l*, pg. 192
AFTERMATH SILVER LTD.; *Int'l*, pg. 196
AGNEW GOLD MINING COMPANY (PTY) LIMITED—See Gold Fields Limited; *Int'l*, pg. 3024
AGNICO-EAGLE FINLAND OY—See Agnico Eagle Mines Limited; *Int'l*, pg. 212
AGNICO EAGLE MEXICO S.A. DE C.V.—See Agnico Eagle Mines Limited; *Int'l*, pg. 211
AGNICO-EAGLE MINES LIMITED-EXPLORATION DIVISION—See Agnico Eagle Mines Limited; *Int'l*, pg. 211
AGNICO-EAGLE MINES LIMITED-LARONDE DIVISION—See Agnico Eagle Mines Limited; *Int'l*, pg. 212
AGNICO EAGLE MINES LIMITED; *Int'l*, pg. 211
AGNICO-EAGLE (USA) LIMITED—See Agnico Eagle Mines Limited; *Int'l*, pg. 211
AI KARAAUYL JSC; *Int'l*, pg. 227
AIML RESOURCES INC.; *Int'l*, pg. 234
AIRTRONA INTERNATIONAL, INC.; *Int'l*, pg. 250
A.I.S. RESOURCES LIMITED; *Int'l*, pg. 24
AK ALTYNALMAS JSC; *Int'l*, pg. 259
AKOBO MINERALS AB; *Int'l*, pg. 264
ALAMOS GOLD INC.; *Int'l*, pg. 290
ALCHEMY RESOURCES LIMITED; *Int'l*, pg. 300
ALECTO MINERALS PLC; *Int'l*, pg. 305
ALHAMBRA RESOURCES LTD; *Int'l*, pg. 319
ALICANTO MINERALS LIMITED; *Int'l*, pg. 326
ALIEN METALS LTD.; *Int'l*, pg. 327
ALIO GOLD INC.—See Argonaut Gold Inc.; *U.S. Public*, pg. 191
ALL AMERICAN GLAMOUR CORP.; *U.S. Private*, pg. 169
ALLEGIANT GOLD (U.S.) LTD.—See Allegiant Gold Ltd.; *Int'l*, pg. 334
ALLIED GOLD CORPORATION; *Int'l*, pg. 357
ALMADEX MINERALS LIMITED—See Abacus Mining & Exploration Corporation; *Int'l*, pg. 47
AL MASANE AL KOBRA MINING COMPANY; *Int'l*, pg. 281
ALTALEY MINING CORPORATION; *Int'l*, pg. 384
ALTAMIRA GOLD CORP.; *Int'l*, pg. 385
ALTAN NEVADA MINERALS LIMITED; *Int'l*, pg. 385
ALTYNGOLD PLC; *Int'l*, pg. 399
ALTYNTAU KOKSHETAU JSC—See Glencore plc; *Int'l*, pg. 2991
AMANI GOLD LIMITED; *Int'l*, pg. 410
AMAROQ MINERALS LTD.; *Int'l*, pg. 412
AMAZONIA MINERACAO LTDA; *Int'l*, pg. 413
AMERICAN CREEK RESOURCES LTD.; *Int'l*, pg. 422
AMERICAN PACIFIC MINING CORP.; *Int'l*, pg. 422
AMERICAN SILVER MINING CO.; *U.S. Public*, pg. 109
AMERICAS GOLD AND SILVER CORPORATION; *Int'l*, pg. 423
AMERISUR RESOURCES PLC—See GeoPark Limited; *Int'l*, pg. 2934
AMEX EXPLORATION INC.; *Int'l*, pg. 424
AMILOT CAPITAL INC.; *Int'l*, pg. 427
ANDES GOLD CORP.; *U.S. Public*, pg. 136
ANGEL GOLD CORP.; *Int'l*, pg. 459
ANGKOR RESOURCES CORP.; *Int'l*, pg. 460
ANGLO ASIAN MINING PLC; *Int'l*, pg. 462
ANGLOGOLD ASHANTI PLC; *Int'l*, pg. 463
ANGUS GOLD, INC.; *Int'l*, pg. 463
ANTIOQUIA GOLD INC.; *Int'l*, pg. 483
ANTIPA MINERALS LTD.; *Int'l*, pg. 483
ANTLER GOLD, INC.; *Int'l*, pg. 483
APEX MINING CO., INC.; *Int'l*, pg. 512
APOLLO CONSOLIDATED LIMITED; *Int'l*, pg. 517
APT GOLDFIELDS PTY. LTD.—See APA Group; *Int'l*, pg. 500
ARCHEAN STAR RESOURCES INC.; *Int'l*, pg. 547
ARC MINERALS LTD; *Int'l*, pg. 539
ARCO-IRIS GOLD CORPORATION; *Int'l*, pg. 550
ARCTIC MINERALS AB; *Int'l*, pg. 551
ARDEA RESOURCES LIMITED; *Int'l*, pg. 554
ARGO BLOCKCHAIN PLC; *Int'l*, pg. 561
ARGONAUT GOLD INC.; *U.S. Public*, pg. 191
ARIANA RESOURCES PLC; *Int'l*, pg. 564
ARK MINES LTD; *Int'l*, pg. 568
ARMGOLD/HARMONY FREEGOLD JOINT VENTURE COMPANY (PROPRIETARY) LIMITED—See Harmony Gold Mining Company Limited; *Int'l*, pg. 3278
ARUMA RESOURCES LIMITED; *Int'l*, pg. 586
ARX GOLD CORPORATION; *Int'l*, pg. 588

ASAHI REFINING CANADA LTD.—See ARE Holdings, Inc.; *Int'l*, pg. 557
ASAHI REFINING USA INC.—See ARE Holdings, Inc.; *Int'l*, pg. 557
ASANTE GOLD CORPORATION; *Int'l*, pg. 599
ASHANTI GOLD CORP.—See Desert Gold Ventures Inc.; *Int'l*, pg. 2044
ASHANTI SANKOFA INC.; *Int'l*, pg. 606
ASPIRE MINERALS PTY LTD—See Apollo Consolidated Limited; *Int'l*, pg. 517
ASTRAL RESOURCES NL; *Int'l*, pg. 658
ASTRO RESOURCES N.L.; *Int'l*, pg. 662
ATALAYA MINING PLC; *Int'l*, pg. 665
ATEX RESOURCES, INC.; *Int'l*, pg. 669
ATHENA GOLD CORPORATION; *U.S. Public*, pg. 221
ATLANTA GOLD INC.; *Int'l*, pg. 674
ATLANTA GOLD INC.—See Atlanta Gold Inc.; *Int'l*, pg. 674
ATLAS LITHIUM CORPORATION; *Int'l*, pg. 686
ATNA RESOURCES LTD.; *U.S. Public*, pg. 381
AUGUSTA GOLD CORP.; *Int'l*, pg. 703
AU MIN AFRICA PTY LTD; *Int'l*, pg. 697
AUPLATA SAS; *Int'l*, pg. 706
AURANIA RESOURCES LTD.; *Int'l*, pg. 707
AU-REKA GOLD CORPORATION—See Equinox Gold Corp.; *Int'l*, pg. 2485
AURELIA METALS LTD; *Int'l*, pg. 707
AURELIO RESOURCE CORPORATION; *U.S. Private*, pg. 393
AURIC RESOURCES INTERNATIONAL, INC.; *U.S. Private*, pg. 393
AURIS AG; *Int'l*, pg. 711
AURIS MINERALS LIMITED; *Int'l*, pg. 711
AURWEST RESOURCES CORPORATION; *Int'l*, pg. 715
AURYN MINING CORPORATION; *U.S. Public*, pg. 228
AUSGOLD LIMITED; *Int'l*, pg. 715
AUSTRAL GOLD LIMITED; *Int'l*, pg. 719
AUSTRALIAN POTASH LIMITED; *Int'l*, pg. 722
AUSTRALIA UNITED MINING LIMITED; *Int'l*, pg. 720
AUX MINERACAO DE OURO—See EBX Group Ltd.; *Int'l*, pg. 2287
AVESORO JERSEY LIMITED—See Avesoro Holdings Limited; *Int'l*, pg. 740
AVESORO RESOURCES INC.—See Avesoro Holdings Limited; *Int'l*, pg. 740
AVIDIAN GOLD CORP.; *Int'l*, pg. 743
AVINO SILVER & GOLD MINES LTD.; *Int'l*, pg. 744
AVIRA RESOURCES LTD.; *Int'l*, pg. 744
AVOCET GOLD LIMITED—See Avocet Mining PLC; *Int'l*, pg. 749
AVOCET MINING PLC; *Int'l*, pg. 749
AXMIN, INC.; *Int'l*, pg. 770
AYA GOLD & SILVER INC.; *Int'l*, pg. 773
AZERBAIJAN INTERNATIONAL MINING COMPANY LIMITED—See Anglo Asian Mining plc; *Int'l*, pg. 462
AZUMAH RESOURCES LIMITED; *Int'l*, pg. 782
B2GOLD CORP.; *Int'l*, pg. 790
BAKKEN ENERGY, LLC; *Int'l*, pg. 806
BANRO CORPORATION; *Int'l*, pg. 854
BANYAN GOLD CORP.; *Int'l*, pg. 855
BAROYECA GOLD & SILVER INC.; *Int'l*, pg. 867
BARRICK CHILE LTDA.—See Barrick Gold Corporation; *Int'l*, pg. 869
BARRICK CORTEZ INC.—See Barrick Gold Corporation; *Int'l*, pg. 869
BARRICK GOLD AUSTRALIA LIMITED—See Barrick Gold Corporation; *Int'l*, pg. 869
BARRICK GOLD CORP. - DOYON MINE—See Barrick Gold Corporation; *Int'l*, pg. 869
BARRICK GOLD CORPORATION; *Int'l*, pg. 869
BARRICK GOLD EXPLORATION INC.—See Barrick Gold Corporation; *Int'l*, pg. 869
BARRICK GOLDSTRIKE MINES, INC.—See Barrick Gold Corporation; *Int'l*, pg. 869
BARRICK GOLD U.S. INC.—See Barrick Gold Corporation; *Int'l*, pg. 869
BARRICK (GSM) LTD.—See Barrick Gold Corporation; *Int'l*, pg. 869
BARRICK MINING COMPANY (AUSTRALIA) LIMITED—See Barrick Gold Corporation; *Int'l*, pg. 869
BARRICK (NIUGINI) LIMITED—See Barrick Gold Corporation; *Int'l*, pg. 869
BARRICK (PD) AUSTRALIA LIMITED—See Barrick Gold Corporation; *Int'l*, pg. 869
BARRICK (PLUTONIC) LIMITED—See Barrick Gold Corporation; *Int'l*, pg. 869
BARU GOLD CORP.; *Int'l*, pg. 870
BASSARI RESOURCES LIMITED; *Int'l*, pg. 888
BATTLE NORTH GOLD CORPORATION—See Evolution Mining Limited; *Int'l*, pg. 2572
BAY AREA GOLD GROUP LIMITED; *Int'l*, pg. 900
BAYHORSE SILVER INC.; *Int'l*, pg. 914
BEADELL RESOURCES LIMITED—See Great Panther Mining Limited; *Int'l*, pg. 3065
BEAUCE GOLD FIELDS, INC.; *Int'l*, pg. 934
BELLEVUE GOLD LIMITED; *Int'l*, pg. 967
BENDITO RESOURCES INC.; *U.S. Private*, pg. 524
BENGUET CORPORATION; *Int'l*, pg. 974
BENKALA MINING COMPANY JSC; *Int'l*, pg. 974

BESRA GOLD INC.; *Int'l*, pg. 998
BEYOND LITHIUM INC.; *Int'l*, pg. 1005
BHANG INC.; *Int'l*, pg. 1010
BIG GOLD INC.; *Int'l*, pg. 1021
BIG RIDGE GOLD CORP.; *Int'l*, pg. 1021
BIG ROCK RESOURCES INC.; *Int'l*, pg. 1021
BIRD RIVER RESOURCES INC.; *Int'l*, pg. 1047
BLACK DRAGON GOLD CORP.; *Int'l*, pg. 1059
BLACK MAMMOTH METALS CORPORATION; *Int'l*, pg. 1059
BMEX GOLD, INC.; *Int'l*, pg. 1076
BOADICEA RESOURCES LIMITED; *Int'l*, pg. 1094
BORA BORA RESOURCES LIMITED; *Int'l*, pg. 1112
BOUNDARY GOLD AND COPPER MINING LTD.; *Int'l*, pg. 1119
BRAVADA GOLD CORPORATION; *Int'l*, pg. 1141
BRAVEHEART RESOURCES INC.; *Int'l*, pg. 1141
BRAXTON RESOURCES INC.; *U.S. Private*, pg. 641
BRAZAURO RECURSOS MINERAIS SA—See Eldorado Gold Corporation; *Int'l*, pg. 2347
BREAKER RESOURCES NL; *Int'l*, pg. 1144
BRIGHTON MINING GROUP LIMITED; *Int'l*, pg. 1163
BRIGHTROCK GOLD CORP.; *U.S. Private*, pg. 652
BRIGHTSTAR RESOURCES LIMITED; *Int'l*, pg. 1163
BUCCANEER GOLD CORP.; *Int'l*, pg. 1206
BULLETIN RESOURCES LIMITED; *Int'l*, pg. 1214
BUNKER HILL MINING CORP.; *Int'l*, pg. 1216
BURKE TRADING, INC.—See Hecla Mining Company; *U.S. Public*, pg. 1019
BUSCANDO RESOURCES CORP.; *Int'l*, pg. 1227
C2C METALS CORP.; *Int'l*, pg. 1245
CADIA HOLDINGS PTY LTD—See Newmont Corporation; *U.S. Public*, pg. 1517
CADIA MINES PTY LTD—See Newmont Corporation; *U.S. Public*, pg. 1517
CADILLAC VENTURES INC.; *Int'l*, pg. 1248
CALEDONIA HOLDINGS ZIMBABWE (PRIVATE) LIMITED—See Caledonia Mining Corporation Plc; *Int'l*, pg. 1262
CALEDONIA MINING CORPORATION PLC; *Int'l*, pg. 1262
CALIBRE MINING CORP.; *Int'l*, pg. 1264
CAMBRIDGE CAPITAL HOLDINGS, INC.; *U.S. Public*, pg. 426
CANADA ONE MINING CORP.; *Int'l*, pg. 1278
CANADA SILVER COBALT WORKS INC.; *Int'l*, pg. 1282
CANADIAN MALARTIC PARTNERSHIP—See Agnico Eagle Mines Limited; *Int'l*, pg. 212
CANADIAN METALS INC.; *Int'l*, pg. 1284
CANADIAN PREMIUM SAND INC.; *Int'l*, pg. 1285
CANADIAN SILVER HUNTER INC.; *Int'l*, pg. 1285
CANAGOLD RESOURCES LTD.; *Int'l*, pg. 1287
CANAMEX GOLD CORP.; *Int'l*, pg. 1287
CANARC RESOURCES CORP.; *Int'l*, pg. 1287
CANASIL RESOURCES INC.; *Int'l*, pg. 1288
CANTERBURY RESOURCES LTD.; *Int'l*, pg. 1299
CANUC RESOURCES CORPORATION; *Int'l*, pg. 1300
CANYON RESOURCES LTD.; *Int'l*, pg. 1300
CAPRICORN METALS LTD.; *Int'l*, pgs. 1316
CARACAL GOLD PLC; *Int'l*, pg. 1319
CARAVEL MINERALS LIMITED; *Int'l*, pg. 1320
CARBINE RESOURCES LIMITED; *Int'l*, pg. 1320
CARLIE MINING LTD.—See Castle Minerals Limited; *Int'l*, pg. 1357
CARLIN GOLD CORPORATION; *Int'l*, pg. 1338
CARSON RIVER VENTURES CORP.; *Int'l*, pg. 1347
CASABLANCA MINING LTD.; *U.S. Private*, pg. 778
CASTILLIAN METAIS LTDA.; *Int'l*, pg. 1356
CASTLE MINERALS LIMITED; *Int'l*, pg. 1357
CASTLE PEAK MINING LTD.; *Int'l*, pg. 1357
CAT STRATEGIC METALS CORPORATION; *Int'l*, pg. 1358
CAYENNE GOLD MINES LTD.; *Int'l*, pg. 1363
CELTIC MINERALS LTD.; *Int'l*, pg. 1396
CENTENNIAL MINING LIMITED; *Int'l*, pg. 1402
CENTERRA GOLD INC.; *Int'l*, pg. 1403
CHAARAT GOLD HOLDINGS LIMITED; *Int'l*, pg. 1436
CHAARAT OPERATING COMPANY GMBH—See Chaarat Gold Holdings Limited; *Int'l*, pg. 1436
CHAARAT ZAAV CJSC—See Chaarat Gold Holdings Limited; *Int'l*, pg. 1436
CHAI CHA NA MINING INC.; *Int'l*, pg. 1436
CHANNEL HOLDINGS INC.; *Int'l*, pg. 1446
CHARTERS TOWERS GOLD PTY LTD—See Citigold Corporation Limited; *Int'l*, pg. 1622
CHESAPEAKE GOLD CORPORATION; *Int'l*, pg. 1472
CHIFENG JILONG GOLD MINING CO., LTD.; *Int'l*, pg. 1478
CHINA GOLD INTERNATIONAL RESOURCES CORP. LTD.; *Int'l*, pg. 1505
CHINA SHOUGUAN INVESTMENT HOLDING GROUP CORPORATION; *Int'l*, pg. 1551
CHUGAI MINING CO. LTD. - TOKYO PLANT—See Chugai Mining Co. Ltd.; *Int'l*, pg. 1594
CIBOLAN GOLD CORPORATION; *U.S. Private*, pg. 896
CITIGOLD CORPORATION LIMITED; *Int'l*, pg. 1622
CITY VIEW GREEN HOLDINGS INC.; *Int'l*, pg. 1628
CLEVELAND MINING COMPANY LIMITED; *Int'l*, pg. 1658
CMNM MINING GROUP SDN. BHD.—See CNMC Goldmine Holdings Limited; *Int'l*, pg. 1677
CMX GOLD & SILVER CORP.; *Int'l*, pg. 1672

N.A.I.C.S. INDEX

212220 — GOLD ORE AND SILVER...

CNMC GOLDMINE HOLDINGS LIMITED; *Int'l*, pg. 1677
COEUR CAPITAL, INC.—See Coeur Mining, Inc.; *U.S. Public*, pg. 522
COEUR ROCHESTER, INC.—See Coeur Mining, Inc.; *U.S. Public*, pg. 522
COHIBA MINERALS LIMITED; *Int'l*, pg. 1695
COLORADO GOLDFIELDS INC.; *U.S. Private*, pg. 974
COLT RESOURCES INC.; *Int'l*, pg. 1705
COMMANDER RESOURCES LTD.; *Int'l*, pg. 1714
COMMERCE/SANSEB JOINT VENTURE—See Commerce Group Corp.; *U.S. Public*, pg. 545
COMPANIA MINERA ARES S.A.C.—See Hochschild Mining plc; *Int'l*, pg. 3438
COMPANIA MINERA CASALE LIMITADA—See Barrick Gold Corporation; *Int'l*, pg. 869
COMPANIA MINERA CERROS DEL SUR, S.A. DE C.V.—See Inception Mining, Inc.; *U.S. Public*, pg. 1114
COMPANIA MINERA MALKU KHOTA S.A.—See Gold Springs Resource Corp.; *Int'l*, pg. 3026
COMPANIA MINERA ZALDIVAR S.A.—See Antofagasta plc; *Int'l*, pg. 484
COMPANIA MINERA ZALDIVAR S.A.—See Barrick Gold Corporation; *Int'l*, pg. 869
COMSTOCK INC.; *U.S. Public*, pg. 562
CONROY GOLD & NATURAL RESOURCES PLC; *Int'l*, pg. 1769
CONSTELLATION RESOURCES LIMITED; *Int'l*, pg. 1772
CONTANGO ORE, INC.; *U.S. Public*, pg. 573
CONTINENTAL CATALINA, INC.—See Bee Street Holdings LLC; *U.S. Private*, pg. 513
CORDOBA MINERALS CORP.; *Int'l*, pg. 1796
CORVUS GOLD INC.—See AngloGold Ashanti plc; *Int'l*, pg. 463
COSA RESOURCES CORP.; *Int'l*, pg. 1809
COSIGO RESOURCES LTD.; *Int'l*, pg. 1810
COSMO GOLD PTY LTD—See Adelong Gold Limited; *Int'l*, pg. 142
CRATER GOLD MINING LIMITED; *Int'l*, pg. 1828
CR BRIGGS CORPORATION—See ATNA RESOURCES LTD.; *U.S. Private*, pg. 381
CRESCENT GOLD LIMITED—See Focus Minerals Limited; *Int'l*, pg. 2719
CRESCO LABS, INC.; *U.S. Public*, pg. 594
CRIPPLE CREEK & VICTOR GOLD MINING COMPANY LLC—See Newmont Corporation; *U.S. Public*, pg. 1516
CR KENDALL CORPORATION—See ATNA RESOURCES LTD.; *U.S. Private*, pg. 381
CUFE LTD; *Int'l*, pg. 1876
CURRIE ROSE RESOURCES INC.; *Int'l*, pg. 1879
CYBIN INC.; *Int'l*, pg. 1894
CYCLONE METALS LIMITED; *Int'l*, pg. 1894
CYPRESS DEVELOPMENT CORP.; *Int'l*, pg. 1897
CYPRIUM METALS LIMITED; *Int'l*, pg. 1897
DACIAN GOLD LIMITED—See Genesis Minerals Limited; *Int'l*, pg. 2921
DAKOTA GOLD CORP.; *U.S. Public*, pg. 620
DAMARA GOLD CORP.; *Int'l*, pg. 1955
DANE EXPLORATION INC.; *U.S. Private*, pg. 1153
DART MINING NL; *Int'l*, pg. 1973
DATELINE RESOURCES LTD.; *Int'l*, pg. 1981
DECCAN GOLD MINES LTD.; *Int'l*, pg. 1999
DECLAN RESOURCES INC.; *Int'l*, pg. 2001
DEFIANCE SILVER CORP.; *Int'l*, pg. 2004
DEJIN RESOURCES GROUP COMPANY LIMITED; *Int'l*, pg. 2005
DELTA RESOURCES LIMITED; *Int'l*, pg. 2020
DESERT HAWK GOLD CORP.; *U.S. Private*, pg. 1212
DEVA GOLD SA—See Eldorado Gold Corporation; *Int'l*, pg. 2347
DEVELOP GLOBAL LTD.; *Int'l*, pg. 2087
DEVERON CORP.—See Greencastle Resources Ltd.; *Int'l*, pg. 3073
DGO GOLD LIMITED—See Gold Road Resources Limited; *Int'l*, pg. 3026
DGR GLOBAL LIMITED; *Int'l*, pg. 2097
DOLLY VARDEN SILVER CORPORATION; *Int'l*, pg. 2159
DOME GOLD MINES LIMITED; *Int'l*, pg. 2159
DOUBLE CROWN RESOURCES INC.; *U.S. Private*, pg. 1265
DRAGON MINING; *Int'l*, pg. 2199
DRAGON MINING (SWEDEN) AB—See Dragon Mining; *Int'l*, pg. 2199
DRAGON MOUNTAIN GOLD LIMITED; *Int'l*, pg. 2199
DRDGOLD LIMITED; *Int'l*, pg. 2202
DREADNOUGHT RESOURCES LTD.; *Int'l*, pg. 2202
DUNDEE PRECIOUS METALS INC.; *Int'l*, pg. 2226
DUNDEE PRECIOUS METALS - SOFIA—See Dundee Precious Metals Inc.; *Int'l*, pg. 2226
DUNDEE RESOURCES LTD.—See Dundee Corporation; *Int'l*, pg. 2226
DYNACOR GROUP INC.; *Int'l*, pg. 2239
EAGLE MOUNTAIN MINING LIMITED; *Int'l*, pg. 2266
EASTERN EXPLORATION PTY LTD—See DGR Global Limited; *Int'l*, pg. 2097
EASTERN GOLDFIELDS, INC.; *U.S. Public*, pg. 704
EASTERN MEDITERRANEAN RESOURCES (SLOVAKIA) SRO—See Atalaya Mining plc; *Int'l*, pg. 665
EASTERN RESOURCES, INC.—See Black Diamond Financial Group, LLC; *U.S. Private*, pg. 571
EASTMAIN RESOURCES INC.—See Fury Gold Mines Limited; *Int'l*, pg. 2848
EAST STAR RESOURCES PLC; *Int'l*, pg. 2270
ECHOIQ LIMITED; *Int'l*, pg. 2289
EDGEMONT GOLD CORP.; *Int'l*, pg. 2309
EDGEWATER EXPLORATION LTD.; *Int'l*, pg. 2309
EGR EXPLORATION LTD.; *Int'l*, pg. 2326
ELDORADO GOLD CORPORATION; *Int'l*, pg. 2346
ELECTRA STONE LTD.; *Int'l*, pg. 2348
ELEMENT79 GOLD CORP.; *Int'l*, pg. 2358
ELEVATE URANIUM LTD.; *Int'l*, pg. 2359
ELY GOLD ROYALTIES INC.—See Gold Royalty Corp.; *Int'l*, pg. 3026
EMERGENT METALS CORP.; *Int'l*, pg. 2378
EMERITA RESOURCES CORP.; *Int'l*, pg. 2379
ENDEAVOUR MINING PLC.; *Int'l*, pg. 2402
ENDEAVOUR SILVER CORP.; *Int'l*, pg. 2402
ENDOMINES AB; *Int'l*, pg. 2405
ENDOMINES OY—See Endomines AB; *Int'l*, pg. 2405
ENGINEER GOLD MINES LTD.; *Int'l*, pg. 2435
ENRG ELEMENTS LIMITED; *Int'l*, pg. 2445
ENSURGE, INC.; *U.S. Public*, pg. 775
ENTREE RESOURCES LTD.; *Int'l*, pg. 2452
ESTRELLA RESOURCES (CHILE) SPA—See Estrella Resources Limited; *Int'l*, pg. 2519
ESTRELLA RESOURCES LIMITED; *Int'l*, pg. 2519
EURASIA MINING PLC; *Int'l*, pg. 2527
EUROMAX RESOURCES LTD.; *Int'l*, pg. 2553
EUROPACIFIC METALS INC.; *Int'l*, pg. 2555
EURO RESSOURCES S.A.—See IAMGOLD Corporation; *Int'l*, pg. 3568
EVERTON RESOURCES INC.; *Int'l*, pg. 2569
EVOLUTION MINING LIMITED; *Int'l*, pg. 2572
EVOLVING GOLD CORP.; *Int'l*, pg. 2573
EXCELLON RESOURCES INC.; *Int'l*, pg. 2578
EXMCEUTICALS INC.; *Int'l*, pg. 2585
FELIX GOLD LIMITED; *Int'l*, pg. 2633
FIN RESOURCES LIMITED; *Int'l*, pg. 2664
FIORE GOLD LTD.; *Int'l*, pg. 2678
FIREFINCH LIMITED; *Int'l*, pg. 2679
FIRE RIVER GOLD CORP.; *Int'l*, pg. 2678
FIRST AMERICAN URANIUM INC.; *Int'l*, pg. 2681
FIRST MAJESTIC SILVER CORP.; *Int'l*, pg. 2685
FLEXWORK PROPERTIES LTD.; *Int'l*, pg. 2705
FLOWERY GOLD MINES COMPANY OF NEVADA; *U.S. Public*, pg. 855
FLYNN GOLD LIMITED; *Int'l*, pg. 2716
FOCUS MINERALS LIMITED; *Int'l*, pg. 2719
FOKUS MINING CORPORATION; *Int'l*, pg. 2721
FORAN MINING CORPORATION; *Int'l*, pg. 2728
FORCE COMMODITIES LIMITED; *Int'l*, pg. 2730
FORTE MINERALS CORP.; *Int'l*, pg. 2737
FORTITUDE GOLD CORPORATION; *U.S. Public*, pg. 869
FORTUNA MINING CORP.; *Int'l*, pg. 2742
FOSTERVILLE GOLD MINE PTY. LTD.—See Agnico Eagle Mines Limited; *Int'l*, pg. 212
FRANCO-NEVADA AUSTRALIA PTY. LTD.—See Franco-Nevada Corporation; *Int'l*, pg. 2760
FRANCO-NEVADA CORPORATION; *Int'l*, pg. 2760
FRANCO-NEVADA U.S. CORPORATION—See Franco-Nevada Corporation; *Int'l*, pg. 2760
FREEGOLD VENTURES LIMITED; *Int'l*, pg. 2769
FRESNILLO PLC; *Int'l*, pg. 2782
FRONTIER MINING LTD.; *Int'l*, pg. 2795
FUTURE BATTERY MINERALS LIMITED; *Int'l*, pg. 2852
FUTURIS COMPANY; *U.S. Public*, pg. 893
G2 GOLDFIELDS INC.; *Int'l*, pg. 2866
GABRIEL RESOURCES LTD.; *Int'l*, pg. 2867
GALANE GOLD LTD.; *Int'l*, pg. 2870
GALANTAS GOLD CORPORATION; *Int'l*, pg. 2870
GALATA MADENCILIK SAN. VE TIC. LTD.—See Ariana Resources plc; *Int'l*, pg. 564
GALIANO GOLD INC.; *Int'l*, pg. 2872
GALLERY GOLD PTY LTD.—See Galane Gold Ltd.; *Int'l*, pg. 2870
GALORE RESOURCES INC.; *Int'l*, pg. 2875
GAMA EXPLORATIONS INC.; *Int'l*, pg. 2876
GANDER GOLD CORP.; *Int'l*, pg. 2879
GANSU RONGHUA INDUSTRY GROUP CO., LTD.; *Int'l*, pg 2881
GARIBALDI RESOURCES CORP.; *Int'l*, pg. 2884
GASCOYNE RESOURCES LIMITED; *Int'l*, pg. 2888
GATEWAY MINING LIMITED; *Int'l*, pg. 2889
GATOS SILVER CANADA CORPORATION—See Gatos Silver, Inc.; *U.S. Public*, pg. 907
GBM GOLD LIMITED; *Int'l*, pg. 2893
GENERIC GOLD CORP.; *Int'l*, pg. 2920
GENTOR RESOURCES, INC.; *Int'l*, pg. 2929
GFL MINING SERVICES LIMITED—See Gold Fields Limited; *Int'l*, pg. 3024
GGX GOLD CORP.; *Int'l*, pg. 2958
GLOBAL BATTERY METALS LTD.; *Int'l*, pg. 2993
GLOBAL GOLD CORPORATION; *U.S. Public*, pg. 942
GMV MINERALS INC.; *Int'l*, pg. 3015
GOLD 50 LIMITED; *Int'l*, pg. 3023
GOLD AND GEMSTONE MINING INC.; *U.S. Public*, pg. 949
GOLD CAP RESOURCES INC.; *Int'l*, pg. 3023
GOLDCLIFF RESOURCE CORPORATION; *Int'l*, pg. 3027
GOLDCORP INC.—See Newmont Corporation; *U.S. Public*, pg. 1516
GOLDCORP INC. - TORONTO OFFICE—See Newmont Corporation; *U.S. Public*, pg. 1516
GOLDCORP S.A. DE C.V.—See Newmont Corporation; *U.S. Public*, pg. 1516
GOLD DRAGON ENTERPRISES INC.; *Int'l*, pg. 3024
GOLDEN ARROW RESOURCES CORPORATION - EXPLORATION SERVICES—See Golden Arrow Resources Corporation; *Int'l*, pg. 3028
GOLDEN GLOBAL CORP.; *U.S. Private*, pg. 1732
GOLDEN GOLIATH RESOURCES LTD.; *Int'l*, pg. 3029
GOLDEN HARP RESOURCES INC.; *Int'l*, pg. 3029
GOLDEN MINERALS COMPANY; *U.S. Public*, pg. 950
GOLDEN PHOENIX MINERALS, INC.; *U.S. Private*, pg. 1732
GOLDEN RIVER RESOURCES CORPORATION; *Int'l*, pg. 3031
GOLDEN SAINT AUSTRALIA LIMITED—See Golden Saint Resources Limited; *Int'l*, pg. 3031
GOLDEN SAINT RESOURCES LIMITED; *Int'l*, pg. 3031
GOLDEN STAR RESOURCES LTD.; *Int'l*, pg. 3032
GOLDEX RESOURCES CORPORATION; *Int'l*, pg. 3033
GOLD FIELDS AUSTRALIA PTY LTD—See Gold Fields Limited; *Int'l*, pg. 3024
GOLD FIELDS GHANA LIMITED—See Gold Fields Limited; *Int'l*, pg. 3024
GOLD FIELDS GROUP SERVICES LIMITED—See Gold Fields Limited; *Int'l*, pg. 3024
GOLDFIELDS INTERNATIONAL INC.; *U.S. Private*, pg. 1735
GOLD FIELDS LIMITED; *Int'l*, pg. 3024
GOLD FIELDS NETHERLANDS SERVICES B.V.—See Gold Fields Limited; *Int'l*, pg. 3024
GOLDFLARE EXPLORATION INC.; *Int'l*, pg. 3033
GOLD HILL RESOURCES, INC.; *U.S. Private*, pg. 1728
GOLD HYDROGEN LIMITED; *Int'l*, pg. 3024
GOLD LAKES CORP.; *U.S. Public*, pg. 949
GOLD LINE RESOURCES LTD.—See Barsele Minerals Corp.; *Int'l*, pg. 870
GOLD MOUNTAIN LIMITED; *Int'l*, pg. 3025
GOLD ONE AFRICA LIMITED—See Baiyin Nonferrous Metal (Group) Co., Ltd.; *Int'l*, pg. 803
GOLDON RESOURCES LTD.; *Int'l*, pg. 3034
GOLDPLAT PLC; *Int'l*, pg. 3034
GOLDPLAT RECOVERY (PTY) LTD.—See Goldplat Plc; *Int'l*, pg. 3034
GOLD PORT CORPORATION; *Int'l*, pg. 3026
GOLDQUEST MINING CORP.; *Int'l*, pg. 3034
GOLD RESERVE INC.; *U.S. Public*, pg. 949
GOLD RESOURCE CORPORATION; *U.S. Public*, pg. 949
GOLDRICH MINING COMPANY; *U.S. Public*, pg. 951
GOLD ROAD RESOURCES LIMITED; *Int'l*, pg. 3026
GOLDSHORE RESOURCES INC.; *Int'l*, pg. 3034
GOLD SPRINGS RESOURCE CORP.; *Int'l*, pg. 3026
GOLDSTAR MINERALS INC.; *Int'l*, pg. 3034
GOLDSTAR NORTHAMERICAN MINING INC.; *U.S. Private*, pg. 1735
GOLDSTONE RESOURCES LTD.; *Int'l*, pg. 3034
GOLD TORRENT, INC.; *U.S. Private*, pg. 1728
GOLD TREE RESOURCES LTD.; *Int'l*, pg. 3026
GRAN COLOMBIA GOLD CORP.; *Int'l*, pg. 3053
GRANT HARTFORD CORPORATION; *U.S. Private*, pg. 1756
GREAT BOULDER RESOURCES LIMITED; *Int'l*, pg. 3063
GREAT PANTHER MINING LIMITED; *Int'l*, pg. 3065
GREAT WESTERN MINING CORPORATION PLC; *Int'l*, pg. 3066
GREENCASTLE RESOURCES LTD.; *Int'l*, pg. 3073
GREEN LEADER HOLDINGS GROUP LIMITED; *Int'l*, pg. 3071
GRIFFIN MINING LIMITED; *Int'l*, pg. 3083
GROOVY COMPANY, INC.—See ASAMA; *Int'l*, pg. 599
GR SILVER MINING LTD.; *Int'l*, pg. 3047
GRUPO MINEROS DEL CARIBE, S. A. S.—See City View Green Holdings Inc.; *Int'l*, pg. 1628
GTA FINANCECORP, INC.; *Int'l*, pg. 3151
GT GOLD CORP.—See Newmont Corporation; *U.S. Public*, pg. 1516
GUERRERO EXPLORATION INC.; *Int'l*, pg. 3172
GUNGNIR RESOURCES INC.; *Int'l*, pg. 3183
GUYANA GOLD CORP.; *U.S. Public*, pg. 975
GUYANA GOLDSTRIKE INC.; *Int'l*, pg. 3189
HAMELIN GOLD LIMITED; *Int'l*, pg. 3237
HAMMER METALS LIMITED; *Int'l*, pg. 3238
HANDENI GOLD INC.; *Int'l*, pg. 3243
HAOMA MINING NL; *Int'l*, pg. 3268
HARFANG EXPLORATION INC.; *Int'l*, pg. 3274
HARMONY GOLD MINES—See Harmony Gold Mining Company Limited; *Int'l*, pg. 3278
HARMONY GOLD MINING COMPANY LIMITED; *Int'l*, pg. 3278
HARMONY GOLD (PNG SERVICES) (PROPRIETARY) LIMITED—See Harmony Gold Mining Company Limited; *Int'l*, pg. 3278
HARTE GOLD CORP.; *Int'l*, pg. 3280
HARTSHORNE MINING GROUP, LLC—See Paringa Re-

212220 — GOLD ORE AND SILVER...

sources Limited; *U.S. Private*, pg. 3094
HAVILAH RESOURCES LIMITED; *Int'l*, pg. 3287
HECLA CANADA LTD.—See Hecla Mining Company; *U.S. Public*, pg. 1019
HECLA LIMITED - LUCKY FRIDAY MINE—See Hecla Mining Company; *U.S. Public*, pg. 1019
HECLA MINING COMPANY; *U.S. Public*, pg. 1018
HELLAS GOLD SA—See Eldorado Gold Corporation; *Int'l*, pg. 2347
HENGXING GOLD HOLDING COMPANY LIMITED; *Int'l*, pg. 3347
HIGHGOLD MINING, INC.; *Int'l*, pg. 3387
HIGHLAND GOLD MINING LIMITED—See Fortiana Holdings Ltd; *Int'l*, pg. 2738
HIGHVISTA GOLD INC.; *Int'l*, pg. 3389
HILLGROVE RESOURCES LIMITED; *Int'l*, pg. 3392
HI-VIEW RESOURCES INC.; *Int'l*, pg. 3382
HOCHSCHILD MINING—See Hochschild Mining plc; *Int'l*, pg. 3438
HOPE BAY MINING LTD.—See Newmont Corporation; *U.S. Public*, pg. 1516
HORIZON MINERALS CORP.; *U.S. Public*, pg. 1053
HORIZONTE MINERALS PLC; *Int'l*, pg. 3479
HPQ-SILICON RESOURCES INC.; *Int'l*, pg. 3501
HUMMINGBIRD RESOURCES PLC; *Int'l*, pg. 3531
HYCROFT MINING CORPORATION—See Hycroft Mining Holding Corporation; *U.S. Public*, pg. 1079
HYCROFT MINING HOLDING CORPORATION; *U.S. Public*, pg. 1078
HYCROFT RESOURCES & DEVELOPMENT, INC.—See Hycroft Mining Holding Corporation; *U.S. Public*, pg. 1079
I-80 GOLD CORP.; *U.S. Public*, pg. 1080
IAMGOLD CORPORATION; *Int'l*, pg. 3568
ICENI GOLD LIMITED; *Int'l*, pg. 3579
ICONIC MINERALS LTD.; *Int'l*, pg. 3586
IDAHO-MARYLAND MINING CORPORATION—See Emergent Metals Corp.; *Int'l*, pg. 2378
IDAHO STRATEGIC RESOURCES, INC.; *U.S. Public*, pg. 1088
INCEPTION MINING, INC.; *U.S. Public*, pg. 1114
INDUSTRIAS PENOLES, S.A. DE C.V.—See Grupo BAL; *Int'l*, pg. 3121
INFRASTRUCTURE MATERIALS CORP.; *U.S. Public*, pg. 1118
INTERNATIONAL ROYALTY CORPORATION—See Royal Gold, Inc.; *U.S. Public*, pg. 1815
INTERNATIONAL SILVER, INC.; *U.S. Public*, pg. 1158
INV METALS INC.—See Dundee Precious Metals Inc.; *Int'l*, pg. 2226
IRELAND INC.; *U.S. Public*, pg. 1171
JUPITER GOLD CORPORATION—See ATLAS LITHIUM CORPORATION; *Int'l*, pg. 686
KALAHARI GOLDRIDGE MINING CO LTD—See Harmony Gold Mining Company Limited; *Int'l*, pg. 3278
KINGWEST RESOURCES LIMITED—See Brightstar Resources Limited; *Int'l*, pg. 1163
KRYSO RESOURCES LIMITED—See China Nonferrous Gold Limited; *Int'l*, pg. 1535
KULA GOLD LIMITED—See Geopacific Resources Limited; *Int'l*, pg. 2934
KUMTOR GOLD COMPANY—See Centerra Gold Inc.; *Int'l*, pg. 1403
LGL RESOURCES CI SA—See Newmont Corporation; *U.S. Public*, pg. 1517
LKA GOLD, INC.; *U.S. Public*, pg. 1333
LLC PAKRUT—See China Nonferrous Gold Limited; *Int'l*, pg. 1535
LODE-STAR MINING INC.; *U.S. Public*, pg. 1339
MAGELLAN GOLD CORPORATION; *U.S. Public*, pg. 1354
MANITOU GOLD INC.—See Alamos Gold Inc.; *Int'l*, pg. 290
MARATHON GOLD CORPORATION—See Calibre Mining Corp.; *Int'l*, pg. 1264
MARVION INC.; *U.S. Public*, pg. 1389
MATMOWN, INC.; *U.S. Public*, pg. 1397
MDW GOLD ROCK LLP—See Midway Gold Corp.; *U.S. Private*, pg. 2718
MERIDIAN GOLD HOLDINGS MEXICO S.A DE C.V.—See Equinox Gold Corp.; *Int'l*, pg. 2485
MEXUS GOLD US; *U.S. Public*, pg. 1433
MIDAS GOLD, INC.—See Perpetua Resources Corp.; *U.S. Public*, pg. 1677
MIDWAY GOLD CORP.; *U.S. Private*, pg. 2718
MILLROCK EXPLORATION CORP.—See Alaska Energy Metals Corporation; *Int'l*, pg. 291
MINERA BARRICK MISQUICHILCA S.A.—See Barrick Gold Corporation; *Int'l*, pg. 869
MINERA DYNACOR DEL PERU, S.A.C.—See Dynacor Group Inc.; *Int'l*, pg. 2239
MINERA ESPERANZA LTDA.—See Antofagasta plc; *Int'l*, pg. 484
MINERA GOLD FIELDS PERU SA—See Gold Fields Limited; *Int'l*, pg. 3024
MINERA HOCHSCHILD MEXICO, S.A. DE C.V.—See Hochschild Mining plc; *Int'l*, pg. 3438
MINERA LA ZANJA S.R.L.—See Compania de Minas Buenaventura SAA; *Int'l*, pg. 1748
MINERALES EL PRADO S.A. DE C.V.—See Chesapeake Gold Corporation; *Int'l*, pg. 1472
MINERAL SAN SEBASTIAN, S.A. DE C.V.—See Commerce Group Corp.; *U.S. Public*, pg. 545
MINERA MINASNIOC S.A.C.—See Hochschild Mining plc; *Int'l*, pg. 3438
MINERA PENASQUITO S.A. DE C.V.—See Newmont Corporation; *U.S. Public*, pg. 1516
MINERA PENDER S.A DE C.V.—See Garibaldi Resources Corp.; *Int'l*, pg. 2884
MINERA SANTA CRUZ S.A.—See Hochschild Mining plc; *Int'l*, pg. 3438
MINERA SANTA CRUZ Y GARIBALDI SA DE CV—See Endeavour Silver Corp.; *Int'l*, pg. 2403
MINERA SANTA RITA, S. DE R.L. DE C.V.—See Alamos Gold Inc.; *Int'l*, pg. 290
MINERA SOLITARIO PERU, S.A.—See Solitario Zinc Corp.; *U.S. Public*, pg. 1901
MONTANORE MINERALS CORP.—See Hecla Mining Company; *U.S. Public*, pg. 1019
MPM TECHNOLOGIES, INC.; *U.S. Public*, pg. 1480
MT. HAMILTON, LLC—See Bendito Resources Inc.; *U.S. Private*, pg. 524
N.A. DEGERSTROM INC.; *U.S. Private*, pg. 2827
NEWCREST EXPLORATION HOLDINGS PTY LTD—See Newmont Corporation; *U.S. Public*, pg. 1517
NEWCREST INTERNATIONAL PTY LTD—See Newmont Corporation; *U.S. Public*, pg. 1517
NEWCREST MINING LIMITED—See Newmont Corporation; *U.S. Public*, pg. 1517
NEWCREST OPERATIONS LIMITED—See Newmont Corporation; *U.S. Public*, pg. 1517
NEWCREST SERVICES PTY LTD—See Newmont Corporation; *U.S. Public*, pg. 1517
NEW GOLD DISCOVERIES, INC.; *U.S. Private*, pg. 2896
NEW KLEINFONTEIN GOLDMINE (PROPRIETARY) LIMITED—See Baiyin Nonferrous Metal (Group) Co. Ltd.; *Int'l*, pg. 803
NEWMONT AUSTRALIA PTY LIMITED—See Newmont Corporation; *U.S. Public*, pg. 1517
NEWMONT CORPORATION; *U.S. Public*, pg. 1516
NEWMONT GOLD COMPANY—See Newmont Corporation; *U.S. Public*, pg. 1517
NEWMONT MINING CORPORATION OF CANADA LIMITED—See Newmont Corporation; *U.S. Public*, pg. 1517
NEWMONT NUSA TENGGARA HOLDINGS B.V.—See Newmont Corporation; *U.S. Public*, pg. 1517
NEWORIGIN GOLD CORP.—See Harfang Exploration Inc.; *Int'l*, pg. 3274
NEW PLACER DOME GOLD CORP.—See CopAur Minerals Inc.; *Int'l*, pg. 1793
NEW WORLD GOLD CORP.; *U.S. Public*, pg. 1512
NORTH BAY RESOURCES INC.; *U.S. Private*, pg. 2942
NORWEST MINERALS LIMITED—See Australian Mines Limited; *Int'l*, pg. 722
NOVAGOLD RESOURCES INC.; *U.S. Public*, pg. 1547
NUNZIA PHARMACEUTICAL CORPORATION; *U.S. Public*, pg. 1555
OKSUT MADENCILIK A.S.—See Centerra Gold Inc.; *Int'l*, pg. 1403
OMAGH MINERALS LIMITED—See Galantas Gold Corporation; *Int'l*, pg. 2870
OMAI GOLD MINES LIMITED—See IAMGOLD Corporation; *Int'l*, pg. 3568
ORIGINAL SIXTEEN TO ONE MINE, INC.; *U.S. Public*, pg. 1617
ORO EAST MINING, INC.; *U.S. Public*, pg. 1618
OSCEOLA GOLD, INC.; *U.S. Public*, pg. 1619
OTIS GOLD CORP.—See Excellon Resources Inc.; *Int'l*, pg. 2578
OURAY SILVER MINES, INC.—See Aurcana Silver Corporation; *Int'l*, pg. 707
OZ MINERALS INSURANCE PTE. LTD.—See BHP Group Limited; *Int'l*, pg. 1016
OZ MINERALS PROMINENT HILL PTY LTD—See BHP Group Limited; *Int'l*, pg. 1016
PALAYAN RESOURCES, INC.; *U.S. Public*, pg. 1634
PARINGA RESOURCES LIMITED; *U.S. Private*, pg. 3094
PATRIOT GOLD CORP.; *U.S. Public*, pg. 1653
PERPETUA RESOURCES CORP.; *U.S. Public*, pg. 1677
PHU BIA MINING LIMITED—See Guangdong Rising Assets Management Co., Ltd.; *Int'l*, pg. 3159
PMX COMMUNITIES, INC.; *U.S. Private*, pg. 3219
POLAR MINING OY—See Dragon Mining; *Int'l*, pg. 2199
PREMIER GOLD MINES LIMITED—See Equinox Gold Corp.; *Int'l*, pg. 2485
PRETIUM RESOURCES INC.—See Newmont Corporation; *U.S. Public*, pg. 1517
PT INDO MURO KENCANA—See Aeris Resources Limited; *Int'l*, pg. 180
PT INDONUSA MINING SERVICES—See Cyprium Metals Limited; *Int'l*, pg. 1897
PT KILLARA RESOURCES—See Eco Systems Ltd.; *Int'l*, pg. 2292
PT NATARANG MINING—See ElringKlinger AG; *Int'l*, pg. 2370
PT NUSA HALMAHERA MINERALS—See Newmont Corporation; *U.S. Public*, pg. 1517
Q-GOLD RESOURCES LTD.; *U.S. Public*, pg. 1741
QMX GOLD CORPORATION—See Eldorado Gold Corporation; *Int'l*, pg. 2347
RANDFONTEIN ESTATES LIMITED—See Harmony Gold Mining Company Limited; *Int'l*, pg. 3278
RANDGOLD RESOURCES BURKINA FASO SARL—See Barrick Gold Corporation; *Int'l*, pg. 869
RANDGOLD RESOURCES (COTE D'IVOIRE) LTD.—See Barrick Gold Corporation; *Int'l*, pg. 869
RANDGOLD RESOURCES COTE D'IVOIRE SARL—See Barrick Gold Corporation; *Int'l*, pg. 869
RANDGOLD RESOURCES LIMITED—See Barrick Gold Corporation; *Int'l*, pg. 869
RANDGOLD RESOURCES (MALI) LTD—See Barrick Gold Corporation; *Int'l*, pg. 869
RANDGOLD RESOURCES MALI SARL—See Barrick Gold Corporation; *Int'l*, pg. 869
RANDGOLD RESOURCES (SENEGAL) LTD—See Barrick Gold Corporation; *Int'l*, pg. 869
RANDGOLD RESOURCES TANZANIA LTD—See Barrick Gold Corporation; *Int'l*, pg. 870
RANDGOLD RESOURCES (UK) LTD—See Barrick Gold Corporation; *Int'l*, pg. 870
RC RESOURCES, INC.—See Hecla Mining Company; *U.S. Public*, pg. 1019
RECURSOS MILLROCK S DE R.L. DE C.V.—See Grupo Mexico, S.A.B. de C.V.; *Int'l*, pg. 3132
REUNION GOLD CORPORATION—See G Mining Ventures Corp.; *Int'l*, pg. 2861
REVETT SILVER COMPANY—See Hecla Mining Company; *U.S. Public*, pg. 1019
RIDDARHYTTAN RESOURCES AB—See Agnico Eagle Mines Limited; *Int'l*, pg. 212
RIO GRANDE SILVER, INC.—See Hecla Mining Company; *U.S. Public*, pg. 1019
RIO NARCEA GOLD MINES S.L—See Edgewater Exploration Ltd.; *Int'l*, pg. 2309
ROSEBEL GOLD MINES N.V.—See IAMGOLD Corporation; *Int'l*, pg. 3568
ROSIA MONTANA GOLD CORPORATION S.A.—See Gabriel Resources Ltd.; *Int'l*, pg. 2867
ROUND MOUNTAIN GOLD CORPORATION—See Barrick Gold Corporation; *Int'l*, pg. 869
ROXGOLD INC.—See Fortuna Mining Corp.; *Int'l*, pg. 2743
RUBY GOLD, INC.—See NORTH BAY RESOURCES INC.; *U.S. Private*, pg. 2942
RUBY HILL MINE—See Barrick Gold Corporation; *Int'l*, pg. 869
RYE PATCH GOLD US INC.—See Argonaut Gold Inc.; *U.S. Public*, pg. 191
SABINA GOLD & SILVER CORPORATION—See B2Gold Corp.; *Int'l*, pg. 790
SALTA EXPLORACIONES S.A.—See Cascadero Copper Corporation; *Int'l*, pg. 1349
SAN SEBASTIAN GOLD MINES, INC.—See Commerce Group Corp.; *U.S. Public*, pg. 545
SANTA FE GOLD CORP.; *U.S. Public*, pg. 1841
SAO BENTO MINERACAO SA—See Eldorado Gold Corporation; *Int'l*, pg. 2347
SCANDIUM INTERNATIONAL MINING CORP; *U.S. Public*, pg. 1843
SEMAFO INC.—See Endeavour Mining plc.; *Int'l*, pg. 2402
SHOSHONE SILVER/GOLD MINING COMPANY; *U.S. Private*, pg. 3643
SIERRA NEVADA GOLD INC.; *U.S. Public*, pg. 1877
SILVER BUCKLE MINES, INC.; *U.S. Public*, pg. 1880
SILVER FALCON MINING, INC.; *U.S. Public*, pg. 3653
SOCIEDAD MINERA CAMBIOR PERU SA—See IAMGOLD Corporation; *Int'l*, pg. 3568
SOLITARIO ZINC CORP.; *U.S. Public*, pg. 1901
SOLORO GOLD; *U.S. Private*, pg. 3710
SPARTAN GOLD LTD.; *U.S. Private*, pg. 3746
SPECTRAL CAPITAL CORPORATION; *U.S. Public*, pg. 1915
ST. IVES GOLD MINING COMPANY PTY LIMITED—See Gold Fields Limited; *Int'l*, pg. 3024
STRATAGOLD GUYANA INC.—See Alicanto Minerals Limited; *Int'l*, pg. 327
SUKARI GOLD MINES—See Centamin plc; *Int'l*, pg. 1402
SUNSHINE SILVER MINES CORPORATION; *U.S. Private*, pg. 3872
SURINAME GOLD COMPANY, LLC—See Newmont Corporation; *U.S. Public*, pg. 1517
SUTTER GOLD MINING, INC.; *U.S. Public*, pg. 1968
TANETY ZINA SARL—See Brainchip Holdings Ltd.; *Int'l*, pg. 1137
TERANGA GOLD CORPORATION—See Endeavour Mining plc.; *Int'l*, pg. 2402
THRACEAN GOLD MINING SA—See Eldorado Gold Corporation; *Int'l*, pg. 2347
THRACE MINERALS SA—See Eldorado Gold Corporation; *Int'l*, pg. 2347
THUNDER MOUNTAIN GOLD, INC.; *U.S. Public*, pg. 2157
TIMMINS GOLD CORP MEXICO S.A DE C.V—See Argonaut Gold Inc.; *U.S. Public*, pg. 191
TOLIMA GOLD S.A.—See Amilot Capital Inc.; *Int'l*, pg. 427
TONOGOLD RESOURCES, INC.; *U.S. Public*, pg. 2162
TONOPAH DIVIDE MINING CO.; *U.S. Public*, pg. 2162

N.A.I.C.S. INDEX

212230 — COPPER, NICKEL, LEA...

TRANS-SIBERIAN GOLD MANAGEMENT, LLC—See Horvik Limited; *Int'l*, pg. 3482
TRANS-SIBERIAN GOLD PLC—See Horvik Limited; *Int'l*, pg. 3482
TRIMETALS MINING INC. - CHILE OFFICE—See Gold Springs Resource Corp.; *Int'l*, pg. 3026
TRISTAR GOLD INC.; *U.S. Public*, pg. 2196
TUNDRA GOLD CORP.; *U.S. Public*, pg. 2204
TUPRAG METAL MADENCILIK SANAYI VE TICARET LIMITED SIRKETI—See Eldorado Gold Corporation; *Int'l*, pg. 2347
UNAMGEN MINERACAO E METALURGIA S/A—See Eldorado Gold Corporation; *Int'l*, pg. 2347
U.S. ENERGY CORP.; *U.S. Public*, pg. 2213
U.S. SILVER IDAHO, INC.—See Americas Gold and Silver Corporation; *Int'l*, pg. 423
VANGO MINING LIMITED—See Catalyst Metals Limited; *Int'l*, pg. 1358
VISTA GOLD CORP.; *U.S. Public*, pg. 2304
WALKER LANE EXPLORATION, INC.; *U.S. Public*, pg. 2324
WEGA MINING MALI S.A.—See Avocet Mining PLC; *Int'l*, pg. 749
WHARF RESOURCES (USA) INC.—See Coeur Mining, Inc.; *U.S. Public*, pg. 522
WITS BASIN PRECIOUS MINERALS, INC.; *U.S. Private*, pg. 4551
XTREME FIGHTING CHAMPIONSHIPS, INC.; *U.S. Public*, pg. 2393
ZOLOTO RESOURCES LTD.; *U.S. Private*, pg. 4607

212230 — COPPER, NICKEL, LEAD, AND ZINC MINING

ACMDC VENTURES, INC. (AVI)—See Atlas Consolidated Mining & Development Corporation; *Int'l*, pg. 676
AEON METALS LIMITED; *Int'l*, pg. 178
AERIS RESOURCES LIMITED; *Int'l*, pg. 180
AFFINAGE CHAMPAGNE ARDENNES; *Int'l*, pg. 186
AMERIGO RESOURCES LTD.; *Int'l*, pg. 423
ANGLESEY MINING PLC; *Int'l*, pg. 461
ANGLO AMERICAN BRASIL LIMITADA—See Anglo American PLC; *Int'l*, pg. 461
ANGLO AMERICAN CHILE—See Anglo American PLC; *Int'l*, pg. 461
ANTOFAGASTA MINERALS S.A.—See Antofagasta plc; *Int'l*, pg. 484
AQUILA RESOURCES INC.—See Gold Resource Corporation; *U.S. Public*, pg. 949
ARCHER MATERIALS LIMITED; *Int'l*, pg. 548
ARKLE RESOURCES PLC; *Int'l*, pg. 571
ARMOR MINERALS INC.; *Int'l*, pg. 574
AR ZINC S.A.—See Glencore plc; *Int'l*, pg. 2990
ASARCO INCORPORATED—See Grupo Mexico, S.A.B. de C.V.; *Int'l*, pg. 3132
ASCENDANT RESOURCES INC.; *Int'l*, pg. 601
ASIABASEMETALS INC.; *Int'l*, pg. 616
ASIAMET RESOURCES LIMITED; *Int'l*, pg. 617
ASTON BAY HOLDINGS LTD.; *Int'l*, pg. 655
ATALAYA FINANCING LIMITED—See Atalaya Mining plc; *Int'l*, pg. 665
ATICO MINING CORPORATION COLOMBIA SAS—See Atico Mining Corporation; *Int'l*, pg. 670
ATICO MINING CORPORATION; *Int'l*, pg. 670
ATLAS CONSOLIDATED MINING & DEVELOPMENT CORPORATION; *Int'l*, pg. 676
AUDALIA RESOURCES LIMITED; *Int'l*, pg. 700
AUKING MINING LIMITED; *Int'l*, pg. 704
AUSTRALIAN MINES LIMITED; *Int'l*, pg. 721
AYA GOLD & SILVER MAROC S.A.—See Aya Gold & Silver Inc.; *Int'l*, pg. 773
BALAMARA RESOURCES LIMITED; *Int'l*, pg. 806
BAMA COMPANY; *Int'l*, pg. 813
BEACON MINERALS LTD.; *Int'l*, pg. 932
BEKEM METALS, INC.; *Int'l*, pg. 962
BELL COPPER CORPORATION; *Int'l*, pg. 965
BELVEDERE MINING OY—See GlobalBlock Digital Asset Trading Limited; *Int'l*, pg. 3003
BENGUETCORP NICKEL MINES, INC.—See Benguet Corporation; *Int'l*, pg. 974
BHAGYANAGAR INDIA LIMITED; *Int'l*, pg. 1010
BHP BILLITON NICKEL WEST PTY. LTD.—See BHP Group Limited; *Int'l*, pg. 1016
BLUEJAY MINING PLC; *Int'l*, pg. 1071
BLUE RIVER RESOURCES LTD.; *Int'l*, pg. 1069
BLUE ZEN MEMORIAL PARKS INC.; *Int'l*, pg. 1070
BOBIJA A.D.; *Int'l*, pg. 1095
BOLIDEN AB; *Int'l*, pg. 1102
BOLIDEN TARA MINES LIMITED—See Boliden AB; *Int'l*, pg. 1102
BROKEN HILL OPERATIONS PTY LTD; *Int'l*, pg. 1173
BUENAVISTA DEL COBRE, S.A DE C.V.—See Grupo Mexico, S.A.B. de C.V.; *Int'l*, pg. 3133
CALISSIO RESOURCES GROUP INC.; *U.S. Public*, pg. 424
CAMROVA RESOURCES INC.; *Int'l*, pg. 1275
CANARIACO COPPER PERU S.A.—See Candente Copper Corp.; *Int'l*, pg. 1289

CANICKEL MINING LIMITED; *Int'l*, pg. 1291
CANYON SILVER MINES, INC.; *U.S. Public*, pg. 431
CAPSTONE COPPER CORP.; *Int'l*, pg. 1317
CARNAVALE RESOURCES LIMITED; *Int'l*, pg. 1342
CASSIAR GOLD CORP.; *Int'l*, pg. 1355
CASTILLO COPPER LIMITED; *Int'l*, pg. 1357
CAYELI BAKIR ISLETMELERI A.S—See First Quantum Minerals Ltd.; *Int'l*, pg. 2687
CENTRAL ASIA METALS PLC; *Int'l*, pg. 1404
CGM (WEST YILGARN) PTY. LTD.—See Chalice Mining Limited; *Int'l*, pg. 1437
CHELYABINSK ZINC PLANT JSC; *Int'l*, pg. 1460
CHENGTUN MINING GROUP CO., LTD.; *Int'l*, pg. 1470
CHESSER ARAMA VE MADENCILIK LIMITED SIRKETI—See Fortuna Mining Corp.; *Int'l*, pg. 2743
CHILEAN COBALT CORP.; *U.S. Public*, pg. 488
CHILE MINING TECHNOLOGIES INC.; *Int'l*, pg. 1478
CHINA NONFERROUS MINING CORPORATION LIMITED—See China Nonferrous Metal Mining (Group) Co., Ltd.; *Int'l*, pg. 1535
CK METALL AGENTUR GMBH—See Corporacion Nacional del Cobre de Chile; *Int'l*, pg. 1804
CLARA RESOURCES AUSTRALIA LTD—See DGR Global Limited; *Int'l*, pg. 2097
CLYDESDALE RESOURCES, INC.; *Int'l*, pg. 1665
CODELCO ANDINA DIVISION—See Corporacion Nacional del Cobre de Chile; *Int'l*, pg. 1804
CODELCO-ASIA—See Corporacion Nacional del Cobre de Chile; *Int'l*, pg. 1804
CODELCO CHUQUICAMATA DIVISION—See Corporacion Nacional del Cobre de Chile; *Int'l*, pg. 1804
CODELCO EL TENIENTE DIVISION—See Corporacion Nacional del Cobre de Chile; *Int'l*, pg. 1804
CODELCO-KUPFERHANDEL GMBH—See Corporacion Nacional del Cobre de Chile; *Int'l*, pg. 1805
CODELCO SALVADOR DIVISION—See Corporacion Nacional del Cobre de Chile; *Int'l*, pg. 1804
CODELCO TALLERES DIVISION—See Corporacion Nacional del Cobre de Chile; *Int'l*, pg. 1804
COMET RESOURCES LIMITED; *Int'l*, pg. 1711
COMPANIA MINERA ANTAMINA S.A.; *Int'l*, pg. 1749
COMPANIA MINERA ANTAPACCAY S.A.—See Glencore plc; *Int'l*, pg. 2990
COMPANIA MINERA DONA INES DE COLLAHUASI SCM—See Anglo American PLC; *Int'l*, pg. 461
COMPANIA MINERA DONA INES DE COLLAHUASI SCM—See Glencore plc; *Int'l*, pg. 2991
COMPANIA MINERA LOS TOLMOS S.A.—See Grupo Mexico, S.A.B. de C.V.; *Int'l*, pg. 3132
COMPANIA MINERA QUECHUA S.A.—See ENEOS Holdings, Inc.; *Int'l*, pg. 2415
CONTINENTAL COPPER, INC.—See Bee Street Holdings LLC; *U.S. Private*, pg. 513
COPPER FOX METALS INC.; *Int'l*, pg. 1793
COPPERMOL S.A.—See Corporacion Nacional del Cobre de Chile; *Int'l*, pg. 1805
COPPERMOLY LIMITED; *Int'l*, pg. 1794
COPPER MOUNTAIN MINING CORPORATION—See HudBay Minerals Inc.; *Int'l*, pg. 3521
COPPER NORTH MINING CORP.; *Int'l*, pg. 1793
COPPER QUEST PNG LTD—See Coppermoly Limited; *Int'l*, pg. 1794
CORCEL PLC; *Int'l*, pg. 1795
CORE LITHIUM LTD; *Int'l*, pg. 1798
CORE NICKEL CORP.; *Int'l*, pg. 1798
CORPORACION NACIONAL DEL COBRE DE CHILE; *Int'l*, pg. 1804
CORRIENTE RESOURCES, INC.—See China Railway Construction Corporation Limited; *Int'l*, pg. 1543
CST MINERALS LADY ANNIE PTY LIMITED—See CST Group Limited; *Int'l*, pg. 1868
DIRECT NICKEL LIMITED; *Int'l*, pg. 2130
THE DOE RUN COMPANY—See The Renco Group Inc.; *U.S. Private*, pg. 4104
DOMINION MINERALS CORP.; *U.S. Private*, pg. 1256
ECOGRAF LIMITED; *Int'l*, pg. 2295
EMED TARTESSUS S.L.U.—See Atalaya Mining plc; *Int'l*, pg. 665
ENK PLC—See DMCI Holdings, Inc.; *Int'l*, pg. 2142
EQUUS MINING LIMITED; *Int'l*, pg. 2488
ERAMET NICKFI—See Eramet SA; *Int'l*, pg. 2489
ERA RESOURCES INC.; *Int'l*, pg. 2488
ERNEST HENRY MINING PTY. LTD.—See Evolution Mining Limited; *Int'l*, pg. 2572
ESSENTIAL METALS LIMITED; *Int'l*, pg. 2510
EXCELSIOR MINING CORP.; *Int'l*, pg. 2579
FALCONBRIDGE DOMINICANA S.A.—See Glencore plc; *Int'l*, pg. 2990
FIFTH ELEMENT RESOURCES LIMITED; *Int'l*, pg. 2660
FINDERS RESOURCES LIMITED; *Int'l*, pg. 2672
FIRST QUANTUM MINERALS (AUSTRALIA) PTY LIMITED—See First Quantum Minerals Ltd.; *Int'l*, pg. 2687
FIRST QUANTUM (UK) LTD.—See First Quantum Minerals Ltd.; *Int'l*, pg. 2687
FORT ST. JAMES NICKEL CORP.; *Int'l*, pg. 2737
FORTUNE ASIA GROUP LTD; *Int'l*, pg. 2743
FQM AUSTRALIA HOLDINGS PTY LTD—See First Quantum Minerals Ltd.; *Int'l*, pg. 2687

FQM AUSTRALIA NICKEL PTY LTD—See First Quantum Minerals Ltd.; *Int'l*, pg. 2687
FREEDOM ALLOYS, INC.—See IBC Advanced Alloys Corp.; *U.S. Public*, pg. 1083
FREEPORT-MCMORAN INC. - BAGDAD—See Freeport-McMoRan Inc.; *U.S. Public*, pg. 884
FREEPORT-MCMORAN INC. - EL PASO—See Freeport-McMoRan Inc.; *U.S. Public*, pg. 884
FREEPORT-MCMORAN INC. - MORENCI—See Freeport-McMoRan Inc.; *U.S. Public*, pg. 884
FREEPORT-MCMORAN INC. - SAFFORD—See Freeport-McMoRan Inc.; *U.S. Public*, pg. 884
FREEPORT-MCMORAN INC. - SIERRITA—See Freeport-McMoRan Inc.; *U.S. Public*, pg. 884
FREEPORT-MCMORAN INC.; *U.S. Public*, pg. 884
FREEPORT-MCMORAN MORENCI INC.—See Freeport-McMoRan Inc.; *U.S. Public*, pg. 884
FREEPORT MINERALS CORPORATION—See Freeport-McMoRan Inc.; *U.S. Public*, pg. 884
FRONTIER ENERGY LIMITED; *Int'l*, pg. 2795
GALLEON GOLD CORP.; *Int'l*, pg. 2874
GETTY COPPER INC.; *Int'l*, pg. 2953
GIGA METALS CORPORATION; *Int'l*, pg. 2971
GK RESOURCES LTD.; *Int'l*, pg. 2982
GLADSTONE PACIFIC NICKEL LIMITED; *Int'l*, pg. 2987
GLENCORE NICKEL - SUDBURY—See Glencore plc; *Int'l*, pg. 2991
GLOBAL FERRONICKEL HOLDINGS, INC.; *Int'l*, pg. 2996
GLOBAL HUNTER CORPORATION; *Int'l*, pg. 2997
GREENS CREEK MINING CO.—See Hecla Mining Company; *U.S. Public*, pg. 1019
GUANGDONG DABAOSHAN MINE CO., LTD.—See Guangdong Rising Assets Management Co., Ltd.; *Int'l*, pg. 3159
GUANGDONG RISING MINING INVESTMENT DEVELOPMENT CO., LTD.—See Guangdong Rising Assets Management Co., Ltd.; *Int'l*, pg. 3159
HANDA MINING CORPORATION; *Int'l*, pg. 3243
HECATE EXPLORATION; *U.S. Private*, pg. 1903
HIGHLAND COPPER COMPANY INC.; *Int'l*, pg. 3387
HINDUSTAN COPPER LIMITED; *Int'l*, pg. 3399
HOMERUN RESOURCES INC.; *Int'l*, pg. 3455
HORSESHOE METALS LIMITED; *Int'l*, pg. 3482
HUDBAY PERU S.A.C.—See HudBay Minerals Inc.; *Int'l*, pg. 3521
HUTCHISON MINERALS COMPANY LTD.; *Int'l*, pg. 3540
HUTTENBAU GESELLSCHAFT PEUTE MBH—See Aurubis AG; *Int'l*, pg. 715
INTERNATIONAL CUMO MINING CORPORATION—See Idaho Copper Corporation; *U.S. Public*, pg. 1088
JPX GLOBAL INC.; *U.S. Public*, pg. 1210
KAMOTO COPPER COMPANY SA—See Glencore plc; *Int'l*, pg. 2991
KATANGA MINING LIMITED—See Glencore plc; *Int'l*, pg. 2991
KAZZINC LTD.—See Glencore plc; *Int'l*, pg. 2991
KOPPARBERG MINING EXPLORATION AB—See Copperstone Resources AB; *Int'l*, pg. 1794
KUMARINA RESOURCES LIMITED—See ICM Limited; *Int'l*, pg. 3582
KUPFERBERGBAU STADTBERGE ZU NIEDERMARSBERG GMBH—See GEA Group Aktiengesellschaft; *Int'l*, pg. 2903
KUPFEREXPLORATIONSGESELLSCHAFT MBH—See GEA Group Aktiengesellschaft; *Int'l*, pg. 2903
LUSTROS, INC.; *U.S. Private*, pg. 2516
MANGANESE METAL CO. (PTY.) LTD.—See Valmont Industries, Inc.; *U.S. Public*, pg. 2273
MCARTHUR RIVER MINING PTY. LTD.—See Glencore plc; *Int'l*, pg. 2991
METAUX BILLITON CANADA INCORPORATED—See BHP Group Limited; *Int'l*, pg. 1016
MEXICANA DE COBRE, S.A. DE C V.—See Grupo Mexico, S.A.B. de C.V.; *Int'l*, pg. 3133
MINARA RESOURCES LIMITED—See Glencore plc; *Int'l*, pg. 2991
MINERA ALUMBRERA LIMITED—See Glencore plc; *Int'l*, pg. 2991
MINERA FRESNILLO, S.A. DE C.V.—See Fresnillo PLC; *Int'l*, pg. 2702
MINERA LOMA DE NIQUEL, CA—See Anglo American PLC; *Int'l*, pg. 462
MINERA LOS PELAMBRES LTDA.—See Antofagasta plc; *Int'l*, pg. 484
MINERA PANAMA S.A.—See First Quantum Minerals Ltd.; *Int'l*, pg. 2687
MINERA QUELLAVECO S.A.—See Anglo American PLC; *Int'l*, pg. 462
MINERA TIZAPA, S.A. DE C.V.—See Dowa Holdings Co. Ltd.; *Int'l*, pg. 2184
MINERA VALLE CENTRAL S.A—See Amerigo Resources Ltd.; *Int'l*, pg. 423
MMG AUSTRALIA LIMITED—See China Rare Earth Resources And Technology Co., Ltd.; *Int'l*, pg. 1545
MONTANA RESOURCES—See Washington Corporations; *U.S. Private*, pg. 4446

212230 — COPPER, NICKEL, LEA...

MOUNT ISA MINES LIMITED—See Glencore plc; *Int'l*, pg. 2991
NZURI COPPER LIMITED—See Chengtun Mining Group Co., Ltd.; *Int'l*, pg. 1470
OK TEDI MINING LIMITED—See First Quantum Minerals Ltd.; *Int'l*, pg. 2687
OLYMPIC DAM CORPORATION PTY LTD.—See BHP Group Limited; *Int'l*, pg. 1016
OZ MINERALS LIMITED—See BHP Group Limited; *Int'l*, pg. 1016
PALABORA MINING CO. LTD.—See General Nice Development Limited; *Int'l*, pg. 2919
PALABORA MINING CO. LTD.—See HBIS Group Co., Ltd.; *Int'l*, pg. 3296
PANAUST LIMITED—See Guangdong Rising Assets Management Co., Ltd.; *Int'l*, pg. 3159
PAN PACIFIC COPPER CO., LTD.—See ENEOS Holdings, Inc.; *Int'l*, pg. 2416
PT DIRECT NICKEL PTE—See Direct Nickel Limited; *Int'l*, pg. 2130
PT WEDA BAY NICKEL—See Eramet SA; *Int'l*, pg. 2489
RAVENSTHORPE NICKEL OPERATIONS PTY. LTD.—See First Quantum Minerals Ltd.; *Int'l*, pg. 2687
RINCON RESOURCES LIMITED—See Gunsynd plc; *Int'l*, pg. 3185
ROYALCO RESOURCES LIMITED—See Fitzroy River Corporation Ltd; *Int'l*, pg. 2695
SNC-LAVALIN PANAMA, S.A.—See AtkinsRealis Group Inc.; *Int'l*, pg. 673
SOCIEDAD MINERA EL BROCAL S.A.A.—See Compania de Minas Buenaventura SAA; *Int'l*, pg. 1748
SOUTH CROFTY LIMITED—See Cornish Metals Inc.; *Int'l*, pg. 1801
SOUTHERN COPPER CORPORATION—See Grupo Mexico, S.A.B. de C.V.; *Int'l*, pg. 3132
SOUTHERN COPPER CORPORATION—See Grupo Mexico, S.A.B. de C.V.; *Int'l*, pg. 3133
STRAITS MINING PTY LTD—See Aeris Resources Limited; *Int'l*, pg. 180
TATI NICKEL MINING COMPANY (PTY) LTD.—See BCL Limited; *Int'l*, pg. 928
THOMPSON CREEK MINING CO.—See Centerra Gold Inc.; *Int'l*, pg. 1403
TOLEDO MINING CORPORATION PLC—See DMCI Holdings, Inc.; *Int'l*, pg. 2143
TWIN METALS MINNESOTA LLC—See Antofagasta plc; *Int'l*, pg. 484
WESTERN AREAS LIMITED—See IGO Limited; *Int'l*, pg. 3603
WUHU FEISHANG MINING DEVELOPMENT CO., LTD.—See China Natural Resources, Inc.; *Int'l*, pg. 1534
XSTRATA COPPER CHILE S.A.—See Glencore plc; *Int'l*, pg. 2991
XSTRATA LAS BAMBAS S.A.—See China Rare Earth Resources And Technology Co., Ltd.; *Int'l*, pg. 1545

212290 — OTHER METAL ORE MINING

1844 RESOURCES INC.; *Int'l*, pg. 3
92 ENERGY LIMITED—See ATHA Energy Corp.; *Int'l*, pg. 669
ABERDEEN INTERNATIONAL INC.; *Int'l*, pg. 60
ABITIBI ROYALTIES INC.—See Gold Royalty Inc.; *Int'l*, pg. 3026
ABRA MINING & INDUSTRIAL CORPORATION; *Int'l*, pg. 67
ABX GROUP LIMITED; *Int'l*, pg. 74
ADAMANT HOLDING INC.; *Int'l*, pg. 123
ADEX MINING INC.; *Int'l*, pg. 145
AFARAK GROUP SE; *Int'l*, pg. 185
AFRICAN ENERGY METALS INC.; *Int'l*, pg. 191
AFRICAN INVESTMENT GROUP S.A.—See Grupa Azoty S.A.; *Int'l*, pg. 3116
AFRICAN RAINBOW MINERALS LIMITED; *Int'l*, pg. 192
AGD DIAMONDS JSC—See Central Bank of the Russian Federation; *Int'l*, pg. 1405
AGUIA RESOURCES LIMITED; *Int'l*, pg. 222
AIM EXPLORATION INC.; *U.S. Public*, pg. 63
AKDENIZ MINERAL KAYNAKLARI A.S—See Grecian Magnesite S.A; *Int'l*, pg. 3068
ALASKA ENERGY METALS CORPORATION; *Int'l*, pg. 291
ALBUM TRADING COMPANY LIMITED—See China Rare Earth Resources And Technology Co., Ltd.; *Int'l*, pg. 1545
ALDEBARAN ARGENTINA S.A.—See Aldebaran Resources, Inc.; *Int'l*, pg. 304
ALEXCO RESOURCE CORP.—See Hecla Mining Company; *U.S. Public*, pg. 1018
ALEX MACINTYRE & ASSOCIATES LTD.; *Int'l*, pg. 306
ALICE QUEEN LIMITED; *Int'l*, pg. 327
ALLIANCE MINING CORP.; *Int'l*, pg. 340
ALLIED CRITICAL METALS CORP.; *Int'l*, pg. 357
ALLIGATOR ENERGY LIMITED; *Int'l*, pg. 359
ALLOYCORP MINING INC.—See RCF Management LLC; *U.S. Private*, pg. 3362
ALL THINGS MOBILE ANALYTIC, INC.; *U.S. Public*, pg. 78
ALMADEN MINERALS LTD.; *Int'l*, pg. 363
ALMONTY INDUSTRIES INC.; *Int'l*, pg. 364

ALORO MINING CORP.; *Int'l*, pg. 365
ALRO SPECIALTY METALS, MELROSE PARK—See Alro Steel Corporation; *U.S. Private*, pg. 202
ALTAMIN LIMITED; *Int'l*, pg. 384
ALTIPLANO METALS INC.; *Int'l*, pg. 393
ALTO METALS LIMITED; *Int'l*, pg. 394
ALTONA RESOURCES, INC.; *U.S. Private*, pg. 210
ALTOVIDA, INC.; *U.S. Private*, pg. 210
ALX RESOURCES CORP.; *Int'l*, pg. 402
AMERICAN BATTERY TECHNOLOGY COMPANY; *U.S. Public*, pg. 97
AMERICAN CLEAN RESOURCES GROUP, INC.; *U.S. Public*, pg. 98
AMERICAN CRITICAL ELEMENTS INC.; *Int'l*, pg. 422
AMERICAN LITHIUM MINERALS, INC.; *U.S. Private*, pg. 240
AMERICAN RARE EARTHS & MATERIALS, CORP.; *Int'l*, pg. 423
AMERIWEST LITHIUM INC.; *Int'l*, pg. 423
AMG CRITICAL MATERIALS N.V.; *Int'l*, pg. 425
AMSECO EXPLORATION LTD.; *Int'l*, pg. 441
ANAX METALS LIMITED; *Int'l*, pg. 447
ANDEAN SILVER LIMITED; *Int'l*, pg. 449
ANDRADA MINING LIMITED; *Int'l*, pg. 451
ANFIELD ENERGY INC.; *Int'l*, pg. 459
ANGLO AMERICAN PLATINUM LIMITED—See Anglo American PLC; *Int'l*, pg. 461
ANGLO FERROUS MINAS RIO MINERACAO SA—See Anglo American PLC; *Int'l*, pg. 461
ANSON RESOURCES LIMITED; *Int'l*, pg. 479
ANTLER HILL MINING LTD.; *Int'l*, pg. 484
APPIA RARE EARTHS & URANIUM CORP.; *Int'l*, pg. 520
AQUIRIAN LIMITED; *Int'l*, pg. 528
ARBOR METALS CORP.; *Int'l*, pg. 538
ARCONIC FASTENERS SAS - US OPERATIONS—See Howmet Aerospace Inc.; *U.S. Public*, pg. 1061
ARDIDEN LIMITED; *Int'l*, pg. 556
ARGEX TITANIUM INC.; *Int'l*, pg. 561
ARGO GOLD INC.; *Int'l*, pg. 562
ARTANES MINING GROUP AD; *Int'l*, pg. 581
ASA RESOURCE GROUP PLC.; *Int'l*, pg. 592
ASEC COMPANY FOR MINING; *Int'l*, pg. 605
ASRA MINERALS LIMITED; *Int'l*, pg. 632
ASTON MINERALS LIMITED; *Int'l*, pg. 655
ATERIAN PLC; *Int'l*, pg. 668
ATLATSA RESOURCES CORPORATION; *Int'l*, pg. 686
AUCTUS MINERALS PTY. LTD.—See Denham Capital Management LP; *U.S. Private*, pg. 1205
AU MINERA CORP; *Int'l*, pg. 697
AURA ENERGY LIMITED; *Int'l*, pg. 706
AURCANA SILVER CORPORATION; *Int'l*, pg. 707
AURIC MINING LIMITED; *Int'l*, pg. 710
AURORA ROYALTIES INC.; *Int'l*, pg. 714
AUSMON RESOURCES LIMITED; *Int'l*, pg. 716
AUSTRALIAN URANIUM LTD—See Australian Vanadium Limited; *Int'l*, pg. 723
AUSTRALIAN VANADIUM LIMITED; *Int'l*, pg. 723
AVALON ADVANCED MATERIALS INC.; *Int'l*, pg. 734
AVALON MINERALS VISCARIA AB—See Copperstone Resources AB; *Int'l*, pg. 1794
AVANTI GOLD CORPORATION; *Int'l*, pg. 736
AVARONE METALS INC.; *Int'l*, pg. 737
AVISA DIAGNOSTICS INC.; *Int'l*, pg. 744
AXIOM MINING LIMITED; *Int'l*, pg. 769
AZARGA METALS CORP.; *Int'l*, pg. 776
AZCO-MICA INC.—See Santa Fe Gold Corp.; *U.S. Public*, pg. 1841
AZINCOURT ENERGY CORP.; *Int'l*, pg. 780
AZZ SURFACE TECHNOLOGIES - TERRELL LLC—See AZZ, Inc.; *U.S. Public*, pg. 259
BAFGH MINING COMPANY; *Int'l*, pg. 799
BALLYMORE RESOURCES LIMITED; *Int'l*, pg. 809
BALTO RESOURCES LTD.; *Int'l*, pg. 812
BANNERMAN ENERGY LTD; *Int'l*, pg. 851
BANNY COSMIC INTERNATIONAL HOLDINGS, INC.; *Int'l*, pg. 851
BASE TITANIUM LTD.—See Energy Fuels Inc.; *U.S. Public*, pg. 762
BEARCLAW CAPITAL CORP.; *Int'l*, pg. 933
BEARING LITHIUM CORP.—See Corporacion Nacional del Cobre de Chile; *Int'l*, pg. 1805
BE RESOURCES INC.; *Int'l*, pg. 931
BERKELEY ENERGIA LIMITED; *Int'l*, pg. 985
BERKELEY MINERA ESPANA, S.A.—See Berkeley Energia Limited; *Int'l*, pg. 985
BHAGWATI SYNDICATE PVT. LTD.; *Int'l*, pg. 1010
BIOELIFE INC.; *U.S. Public*, pg. 335
BLACK ISLE RESOURCES CORP.; *Int'l*, pg. 1059
BLACK MOUNTAIN RESOURCES LIMITED; *Int'l*, pg. 1059
BLACK ROCK MINING LIMITED; *Int'l*, pg. 1060
BLAST RESOURCES INC.; *Int'l*, pg. 1063
BLENDE SILVER CORP.; *Int'l*, pg. 1063
BLUE EAGLE LITHIUM INC.; *U.S. Private*, pg. 1066
BLUE LAGOON RESOURCES, INC.; *Int'l*, pg. 1068
BLUE MOON METALS INC.; *Int'l*, pg. 1069
BLUE SKY URANIUM CORP.; *Int'l*, pg. 1069
BMG RESOURCES LIMITED; *Int'l*, pg. 1076
BOAB METALS LIMITED; *Int'l*, pg. 1094

BOKSIT A.D.; *Int'l*, pg. 1102
BOLIVAR MINING CORP.; *U.S. Private*, pg. 610
BONTERRA RESOURCES INC.; *Int'l*, pg. 1109
BREXIA GOLDPLATA PERU S.A.C.—See Auplata SAS; *Int'l*, pg. 706
BRIDGESTONE MINING SOLUTIONS AUSTRALIA PTY. LTD.—See Bridgestone Corporation; *Int'l*, pg. 1159
BRUNSWICK EXPLORATION INC.; *Int'l*, pg. 1200
BRUNSWICK RESOURCES INC.; *Int'l*, pg. 1201
BWR EXPLORATION, INC.; *Int'l*, pg. 1232
C3 METALS INC.; *Int'l*, pg. 1245
CALEDONIA HOLDINGS ZIMBABWE (LIMITED)—See Caledonia Mining Corporation Plc; *Int'l*, pg. 1262
CALLINEX MINES INC.; *Int'l*, pg. 1265
CAMECO AUSTRALIA PTY. LTD.—See Cameco Corporation; *Int'l*, pg. 1270
CAMECO CORPORATION; *Int'l*, pg. 1270
CAMINO MINERALS CORPORATION; *Int'l*, pg. 1273
CANADA CARBON INC.; *Int'l*, pg. 1277
CANADA NICKEL COMPANY, INC.; *Int'l*, pg. 1278
CANADA RARE EARTH CORP.; *Int'l*, pg. 1282
CANALASKA URANIUM LTD.; *Int'l*, pg. 1287
CAN-CAL RESOURCES LTD.; *Int'l*, pg. 1276
CANNINDAH RESOURCES LIMITED; *Int'l*, pg. 1292
CANSO ENTERPRISES LTD.; *Int'l*, pg. 1298
CAROLYN RIVER PROJECTS LTD.; *Int'l*, pg. 1342
CARRIE ARRAN RESOURCES INC.; *Int'l*, pg. 1346
CASSINI RESOURCES LIMITED—See BHP Group Limited; *Int'l*, pg. 1016
CATALINA RESOURCES LTD; *Int'l*, pg. 1358
CAULDRON ENERGY LIMITED; *Int'l*, pg. 1361
CBLT INC.; *Int'l*, pg. 1366
CENTOR ENERGY, INC.; *U.S. Private*, pg. 818
CENTR BRANDS CORP.; *Int'l*, pg. 1403
CENTURY PEAK HOLDINGS CORP.; *Int'l*, pg. 1419
CERRO DE PASCO RESOURCES INC.; *Int'l*, pg. 1422
CERRO LA MINA S.A.—See Armor Minerals Inc.; *Int'l*, pg. 575
CERRO VANGUARDIA S.A.—See AngloGold Ashanti plc; *Int'l*, pg. 463
CHAKANA COPPER CORP.; *Int'l*, pg. 1437
CHANGMING INDUSTRIAL MANAGEMENT GROUP HOLDING; *Int'l*, pg. 1444
CHIBOUGAMAU INDEPENDENT MINES INC.; *Int'l*, pg. 1476
CHIEFTAIN METALS INC.; *Int'l*, pg. 1476
CHINA MAGNESIUM CORPORATION LIMITED; *Int'l*, pg. 1516
CHINA NATIONAL METALS & MINERALS IMPORT & EXPORT CORPORATION—See China Rare Earth Resources And Technology Co., Ltd.; *Int'l*, pg. 1545
CHINA NONFERROUS METAL MINING (GROUP) CO., LTD.; *Int'l*, pg. 1535
CHINA NORTHERN RARE-EARTH GROUP HIGHI-TECH COMPANY LIMITED—See Baotou Iron & Steel (Group) Company Limited; *Int'l*, pg. 856
CHONGYI ZHANGYUAN TUNGSTEN CO., LTD.; *Int'l*, pg. 1582
CHROMETCO LIMITED; *Int'l*, pg. 1588
CHUM MINING GROUP INC.; *Int'l*, pg. 1596
CHUN CAN CAPITAL GROUP; *Int'l*, pg. 1596
CITIC METAL CO., LTD.—See CITIC Group Corporation; *Int'l*, pg. 1620
CLARITY GOLD CORP.; *Int'l*, pg. 1649
CLASSIC MINERALS LIMITED; *Int'l*, pg. 1653
CLEAN AIR METALS, INC.; *Int'l*, pg. 1654
CLIFFS NETHERLANDS B.V.—See Cleveland-Cliffs, Inc.; *U.S. Public*, pg. 514
CLIFTON MINING COMPANY; *U.S. Public*, pg. 514
CLIMAX MOLYBDENUM U.K. LIMITED—See Freeport-McMoRan Inc.; *U.S. Public*, pg. 884
CMC EUROPE GMBH—See Commercial Metals Company; *U.S. Public*, pg. 545
CMC GH SISAK D.O.O.—See Commercial Metals Company; *U.S. Public*, pg. 545
CNC METAL PRODUCTS; *U.S. Private*, pg. 952
CNMC (GUANGXI) PINGGUI PGMA CO., LTD.—See China Nonferrous Metal Mining (Group) Co., Ltd.; *Int'l*, pg. 1535
COEUR MINING, INC.; *U.S. Public*, pg. 522
COKE RESOURCES LIMITED; *Int'l*, pg. 1696
COMET INDUSTRIES LTD.; *Int'l*, pg. 1711
COMPAGNIE DES BAUXITES DE GUINEE SA—See Alcoa Corporation; *U.S. Public*, pg. 74
COMPANIA DE MINAS BUENAVENTURA SAA; *Int'l*, pg. 1748
COMPANIA MINERA NEVADA SPA.—See Barrick Gold Corporation; *Int'l*, pg. 869
COMSTOCK METALS LTD.; *Int'l*, pg. 1761
CONICO LIMITED; *Int'l*, pg. 1768
CONSOLIDATED TIN MINES LIMITED; *Int'l*, pg. 1771
COPPER LAKE RESOURCES LTD.; *Int'l*, pg. 1793
COPPERSTONE RESOURCES AB; *Int'l*, pg. 1794
COTTER CORPORATION—See General Atomics; *U.S. Private*, pg. 1663
CRADLE RESOURCES LIMITED; *Int'l*, pg. 1827
CRISTAL.US, INC.—See One Rock Capital Partners, LLC; *U.S. Private*, pg. 3023

N.A.I.C.S. INDEX

212290 — OTHER METAL ORE MIN...

CRONIMET CENTRAL AFRICA AG—See CRONIMET Holding GmbH; *Int'l*, pg. 1854
CRONIMET MINING AG—See CRONIMET Holding GmbH; *Int'l*, pg. 1854
CROSSLAND STRATEGIC METALS LIMITED; *Int'l*, pg. 1856
CROWN EQUITIES, INC.; *Int'l*, pg. 1857
CVW CLEANTECH INC.; *Int'l*, pg. 1890
CYCLONE URANIUM CORPORATION; *U.S. Private*, pg. 1134
CYPRUS AMAX MINERALS COMPANY—See Freeport-McMoRan Inc.; *U.S. Public*, pg. 884
CYPRUS THOMPSON CREEK MINING COMPANY—See Centerra Gold Inc.; *Int'l*, pg. 1403
DAKOTA MINERALS LIMITED; *Int'l*, pg. 1950
DAMAVAND MINING COMPANY; *Int'l*, pg. 1956
DCM DECOMETAL GMBH; *Int'l*, pg. 1992
DELF SILICA COASTAL—See Afrimat Limited; *Int'l*, pg. 193
DENISON MINES CORP.; *Int'l*, pg. 2026
DENISON MINES CORP. - VANCOUVER OFFICE—See Denison Mines Corp.; *Int'l*, pg. 2026
DEUTSCHE ROHSTOFF AG; *Int'l*, pg. 2083
DING HE MINING HOLDINGS LIMITED; *Int'l*, pg. 2127
DISCOVERY METALS CORP.; *Int'l*, pg. 2134
DOE RUN PERU S.R.L.—See The Renco Group Inc.; *U.S. Private*, pg. 4104
DOT RESOURCES LTD.; *Int'l*, pg. 2180
DRAGADOS OFFSHORE DE MEJICO KU-A2, S.A DE C.V.—See ACS, Actividades de Construccion y Servicios, S.A.; *Int'l*, pg. 111
DST CO., LTD.; *Int'l*, pg. 2210
DUKETON MINING LIMITED; *Int'l*, pg. 2224
DUONG HIEU TRADING & MINING JSC; *Int'l*, pg. 2227
DURANGO RESOURCES INC.; *Int'l*, pg. 2228
DYNARESOURCE, INC.; *U.S. Public*, pg. 699
EAGLE GRAPHITE INCORPORATED; *Int'l*, pg. 2264
EASTERN PLATINUM LIMITED; *Int'l*, pg. 2273
EAUKER MINERALS CORP.; *U.S. Private*, pg. 1323
ECLIPSE METALS LTD.; *Int'l*, pg. 2291
ECO-SYSTEM SANYO CO., LTD.—See Dowa Holdings Co., Ltd.; *Int'l*, pg. 2184
EDISON LITHIUM CORP.; *Int'l*, pg. 2310
EENERGY GROUP PLC; *Int'l*, pg. 2317
ELEMENT LIFESTYLE RETIREMENT INC.; *Int'l*, pg. 2358
ELEMENTOS LIMITED; *Int'l*, pg. 2359
ELK CREEK RESOURCES CORP.—See NioCorp Developments Ltd.; *U.S. Public*, pg. 1530
ELSMORE RESOURCES LIMITED; *Int'l*, pg. 2370
EMERALD ISLE EXPLORATIONS LTD.; *U.S. Private*, pg. 1379
EMINENT GOLD CORP.; *Int'l*, pg. 2380
EMPRESS MINING INC.; *Int'l*, pg. 2392
ENCOUNTER RESOURCES LIMITED; *Int'l*, pg. 2402
ENERGY FUELS INC.; *U.S. Public*, pg. 762
ENERGY METALS LIMITED; *Int'l*, pg. 2422
ENERGY TRANSITION MINERALS LTD; *Int'l*, pg. 2423
ENFIELD EXPLORATION CORP.; *Int'l*, pg. 2425
ENTREPRISE GENERALE MALTA FORREST S.A.—See George Forrest International S.A.; *Int'l*, pg. 2938
EQUAMINERAL SA—See European Metals Holdings Limited; *Int'l*, pg. 2557
ERDENE RESOURCE DEVELOPMENT CORP.; *Int'l*, pg. 2490
ERDENET MINING CORPORATION; *Int'l*, pg. 2490
ETRUSCUS RESOURCES CORP.; *Int'l*, pg. 2524
EUROPEAN FERRO METALS LTD.; *Int'l*, pg. 2556
EUROPEAN METALS CORP.; *Int'l*, pg. 2557
EUROPEAN METALS HOLDINGS LIMITED; *Int'l*, pg. 2557
EUROPEAN METALS UK LIMITED—See European Metals Holdings Limited; *Int'l*, pg. 2557
EUROTIN INC.; *Int'l*, pg. 2558
EXXARO BASE METALS AND INDUSTRIAL MINERALS HOLDINGS (PTY) LIMITED—See Exxaro Resources Ltd.; *Int'l*, pg. 2592
EXXARO BASE METALS (PTY) LIMITED—See Exxaro Resources Ltd.; *Int'l*, pg. 2592
F3 URANIUM CORP.; *Int'l*, pg. 2598
FALCO RESOURCES LTD.; *Int'l*, pg. 2610
FAR CITY MINING LIMITED; *Int'l*, pg. 2615
FE BATTERY METALS CORP.; *Int'l*, pg. 2629
FERNHILL CORP.; *U.S. Public*, pg. 829
FIORE EXPLORATION LTD.; *Int'l*, pg. 2677
FIRST ATLANTIC NICKEL CORP; *Int'l*, pg. 2682
FIRST COLOMBIA GOLD CORP.; *U.S. Private*, pg. 1516
FIRST GRAPHENE LIMITED; *Int'l*, pg. 2684
FIRST QUANTUM MINERALS LTD.; *Int'l*, pg. 2687
FIRST TIN PLC; *Int'l*, pg. 2688
FISSION URANIUM CORP.; *Int'l*, pg. 2695
FLOW METALS CORP.; *Int'l*, pg. 2709
FOCUS GRAPHITE INC.; *Int'l*, pg. 2719
FORSYS METALS CORP.; *Int'l*, pg. 2737
FORTESCUE LTD; *Int'l*, pg. 2738
FORTIFY RESOURCES INC.; *Int'l*, pg. 2739
FORTUNE GRAPHITE INC.; *Int'l*, pg. 2743
FORTUNE MINERALS LIMITED; *Int'l*, pg. 2743
FORUM ENERGY METALS CORP.; *Int'l*, pg. 2744
FRANCO-NEVADA (BARBADOS) CORPORATION—See Franco-Nevada Corporation; *Int'l*, pg. 2760
FREMONT GOLD LTD.; *Int'l*, pg. 2772
FRONTIER RARE EARTHS LIMITED; *Int'l*, pg. 2795
FYI RESOURCES LIMITED; *Int'l*, pg. 2860
GALILEO RESOURCES PLC; *Int'l*, pg. 2873
GALLERY RESOURCES LIMITED; *Int'l*, pg. 2874
GALORE CREEK MINING CORPORATION—See Newmont Corporation; *U.S. Public*, pg. 1516
GALWAY METALS INC.; *Int'l*, pg. 2876
GANZHOU ACHTECK TOOL TECHNOLOGY CO., LTD.—See Chongyi Zhangyuan Tungsten Co., Ltd.; *Int'l*, pg. 1582
GANZHOU GANNAN TUNGSTEN CO., LTD.—See China Rare Earth Resources And Technology Co., Ltd.; *Int'l*, pg. 1545
GEM DIAMOND TECHNICAL SERVICES (PROPRIETARY) LIMITED—See Gem Diamonds Limited; *Int'l*, pg. 2914
GENERAL MOLY, INC.; *U.S. Private*, pg. 1666
GENESIS RESOURCES LTD.; *Int'l*, pg. 2922
GEODRILL COTE D'IVOIRE SARL—See Geodrill Limited; *Int'l*, pg. 2933
GEODRILL ZAMBIA LIMITED—See Geodrill Limited; *Int'l*, pg. 2933
GEOMEGA RESOURCES INC.; *Int'l*, pg. 2933
GEOVIC MINING CORP.; *U.S. Private*, pg. 1685
GETCHELL GOLD CORP.; *Int'l*, pg. 2947
G.E.T.T. GOLD INC.; *Int'l*, pg. 2865
GFG RESOURCES INC.; *Int'l*, pg. 2956
GFM RESOURCES LIMITED—See Grupo Ferrominero, S.A. de C.V.; *Int'l*, pg. 3129
GLACIER LAKE RESOURCES, INC.; *Int'l*, pg. 2987
GLOBAL ADVANCED METALS K. K.—See Global Advanced Metals Pty. Ltd.; *Int'l*, pg. 2993
GLOBAL ADVANCED METALS PTY. LTD.; *Int'l*, pg. 2993
GLOBAL ADVANCED METALS USA, INC. - GLOBAL ADVANCED METALS—See Global Advanced Metals Pty. Ltd.; *Int'l*, pg. 2993
GMCI CORP.; *Int'l*, pg. 3012
GOLD DYNAMICS CORP.; *U.S. Private*, pg. 1727
GOLDEN SECRET VENTURES LTD.; *Int'l*, pg. 3031
GOLDEN STAR RESOURCE CORP.; *U.S. Public*, pg. 951
GOLDEN VALLEY MINES LTD.; *Int'l*, pg. 3032
GOLD RIDGE EXPLORATION CORP.; *Int'l*, pg. 3026
GOLDSTREAM MINERALS INC.; *Int'l*, pg. 3034
GOLIK HOLDINGS LIMITED; *Int'l*, pg. 3036
GOVIEX URANIUM INC.; *Int'l*, pg. 3044
GPM METALS INC.; *Int'l*, pg. 3046
GRAPHITE ONE INC.; *Int'l*, pg. 3061
GRATOMIC INC.; *Int'l*, pg. 3061
GREAT SOUTHERN MINING LIMITED; *Int'l*, pg. 3065
GREAT WESTERN MINERALS GROUP LTD.; *Int'l*, pg. 3066
GRECIAN MAGNESITE S.A; *Int'l*, pg. 3068
GREEN ARROW RESOURCES INC.; *Int'l*, pg. 3069
GREEN IMPACT PARTNERS INC.; *Int'l*, pg. 3071
GREEN SHIFT COMMODITIES LTD.; *Int'l*, pg. 3072
GREEN STANDARD VANADIUM RESOURCES CORP.; *Int'l*, pg. 3072
GREENSTONE MANAGEMENT SERVICES (PTY) LTD.—See Caledonia Mining Corporation Plc; *Int'l*, pg. 1263
GRID BATTERY METALS INC; *Int'l*, pg. 3082
GRIZZLY DISCOVERIES INC.; *Int'l*, pg. 3087
GROUP 6 METALS LIMITED; *Int'l*, pg. 3088
GRUPO MEXICO, S.A.B. DE C.V.; *Int'l*, pg. 3132
GUANGXI START MANGANESE MATERIALS CO., LTD.—See CITIC Group Corporation; *Int'l*, pg. 1621
GULF MANGANESE CORPORATION LIMITED; *Int'l*, pg. 3181
GWR GROUP LIMITED; *Int'l*, pg. 3190
HANNA CAPITAL CORP; *Int'l*, pg. 3257
HASTINGS TECHNOLOGY METALS LIMITED; *Int'l*, pg. 3284
HEATHGATE RESOURCES PTY, LTD.—See General Atomics; *U.S. Private*, pg. 1663
HEAVY RARE EARTHS LIMITED; *Int'l*, pg. 3305
HELIOS ENERGY LTD.; *Int'l*, pg. 3330
HENAN ARMCO & METAWISE TRADING CO., LTD.—See Armco Metals Holdings, Inc.; *U.S. Private*, pg. 330
HERAEUS DRIJFHOUT BV—See Heraeus Holding GmbH; *Int'l*, pg. 3357
HERAEUS MEDICAL AUSTRALIA PTY LIMITED—See Heraeus Holding GmbH; *Int'l*, pg. 3358
HERAEUS ZHAOYUAN PRECIOUS METAL MATERIALS CO. LTD.—See Heraeus Holding GmbH; *Int'l*, pg. 3358
HEZHOU PINGGUI PGMA CEMENT CO. LTD—See China Nonferrous Metal Mining (Group) Co., Ltd.; *Int'l*, pg. 1535
HIGHBANK RESOURCES LTD.; *Int'l*, pg. 3386
HOCHSCHILD MINING ARES (UK) LTD.—See Hochschild Mining plc; *Int'l*, pg. 3438
HOT CHILI LIMITED, *Int'l*, pg. 3407
HUAYOU COBALT CO., LTD.; *Int'l*, pg. 3516
HUDBAY MINERALS INC.; *Int'l*, pg. 3521
HUNTMOUNTAIN RESOURCES LTD.; *U.S. Private*, pg. 2010
HUNTSMAN EXPLORATION INC.; *Int'l*, pg. 3537
HYLANDS INTERNATIONAL HOLDINGS INC.; *Int'l*, pg. 3549
IDEMITSU CANADA RESOURCES LTD.—See Idemitsu Kosan Co., Ltd.; *Int'l*, pg. 3590
IGO LIMITED; *Int'l*, pg. 3603
IHLAS GAYRIMENKUL PROJE GELISTIRME VE TICARET A.S.—See Ihlas Holding A.S.; *Int'l*, pg. 3606
ILUKA RESOURCES LIMITED; *Int'l*, pg. 3616
IPC (USA) INC.—See Truman Arnold Companies; *U.S. Private*, pg. 4250
LABMAG SERVICES INC.—See Abaxx Technologies Inc.; *Int'l*, pg. 48
LANGER HEINRICH URANIUM (PTY) LTD.—See China National Nuclear Corporation; *Int'l*, pg. 1532
LA PAZ MINING CORP.; *U.S. Private*, pg. 2369
LESS COMMON METALS LIMITED—See Great Western Minerals Group Ltd.; *Int'l*, pg. 3066
LIBERTY STAR URANIUM & METALS CORP.; *U.S. Public*, pg. 1311
LITHIUM CORPORATION; *U.S. Public*, pg. 1326
LITHIUM EXPLORATION GROUP, INC.; *U.S. Private*, pg. 2467
LOST SANDS PTY LTD—See Diatreme Resources Limited; *Int'l*, pg. 2107
LOWELL FARMS INC.; *U.S. Public*, pg. 1343
MAANSHAN IRON AND STEEL (AUSTRALIA) PROPRIETARY LIMITED—See China Baowu Steel Group Corp., Ltd.; *Int'l*, pg. 1486
MANSFIELD MINERA S.A.—See Fortuna Mining Corp.; *Int'l*, pg. 2743
MARMOTA LTD.—See Auteco Minerals Ltd.; *Int'l*, pg. 724
MATERION BREWSTER LLC—See Materion Corporation; *U.S. Public*, pg. 1395
MATERION PRECISION OPTICS (SHANGHAI) LIMITED—See Materion Corporation; *U.S. Public*, pg. 1395
MATERION PRECISION OPTICS (U.K.) LIMITED—See Materion Corporation; *U.S. Public*, pg. 1395
MAXWELL RESOURCES, INC.; *U.S. Private*, pg. 2619
METALINE CONTACT MINES CO.; *U.S. Public*, pg. 1427
METALLICA MINERALS LIMITED—See Diatreme Resources Limited; *Int'l*, pg. 2107
MINAS SANTA MARIA DE MORIS, S.A. DE C.V.—See Hochschild Mining plc; *Int'l*, pg. 3438
MINERA ALTA VISTA S.A. DE C.V.—See Global UAV Technologies Ltd.; *Int'l*, pg. 3002
MINERA DE RIO ALAGON, S.L.—See Berkeley Energia Limited; *Int'l*, pg. 985
MINERALS GANZHOU RARE EARTH CO., LTD—See China Rare Earth Resources And Technology Co., Ltd.; *Int'l*, pg. 1546
MINERA MEXICO S.A. DE C.V.—See Grupo Mexico, S.A.B. de C.V.; *Int'l*, pg. 3133
MINMETALS ENGINEERING CO. LTD.—See China Rare Earth Resources And Technology Co., Ltd.; *Int'l*, pg. 1546
MINMETALS ENVIRONMENTAL TECHNOLOGY CO., LTD—See China Rare Earth Resources And Technology Co., Ltd.; *Int'l*, pg. 1546
MINMETALS (GUIZHOU) FERRO-ALLOYS CO. LTD.—See China Rare Earth Resources And Technology Co., Ltd.; *Int'l*, pg. 1546
MINMETALS (HUNAN) FERROALLOYS CO. LTD.—See China Rare Earth Resources And Technology Co., Ltd.; *Int'l*, pg. 1546
MINMETALS ZHENJIANG IMPORT AND EXPORT TRADING CO., LTD.—See China Rare Earth Resources And Technology Co., Ltd.; *Int'l*, pg. 1546
MOGALE ALLOYS (PTY) LTD—See Afarak Group SE; *Int'l*, pg. 185
MONTE RESOURCES INC.; *U.S. Private*, pg. 2775
MURRIN MURRIN INVESTMENTS PTY LTD—See Glencore plc; *Int'l*, pg. 2991
NEXT GRAPHITE, INC.; *U.S. Public*, pg. 1525
NIOCORP DEVELOPMENTS LTD.; *U.S. Public*, pg. 1529
NORRA METALS CORP.—See EMX Royalty Corporation; *Int'l*, pg. 2395
NORTH AMERICAN GOLD & MINERALS FUND; *U.S. Private*, pg. 2940
NORTH AMERICAN TUNGSTEN CORPORATION LTD.—See Alvarez & Marsal, Inc.; *U.S. Private*, pg 213
NORTHCLIFF RESOURCES LTD.—See Hunter Dickinson Inc.; *Int'l*, pg. 3536
NUCLEAR FUELS CORPORATION—See General Atomics; *U.S. Private*, pg. 1663
OKLO RESOURCES LIMITED—See B2Gold Corp.; *Int'l*, pg. 790
ONCOLOGY PHARMA, INC.; *U.S. Public*, pg. 1601
OREGON METALLURGICAL, LLC—See ATI Inc.; *U.S. Public*, pg. 222
THE O.T. MINING CORPORATION; *U.S. Public*, pg. 2117
PELAWAN INVESTMENTS (PROPRIETARY) LIMITED—See Atlatsa Resources Corporation; *Int'l*, pg. 687
PERSHIMEX RESOURCES CORPORATION—See Abcourt Mines Inc.; *Int'l*, pg. 58
PERSHING RESOURCES COMPANY, INC.; *U.S. Public*, pg. 1677
PLATEAU ENERGY METALS INC.—See American Lithium Corp.; *Int'l*, pg. 422
PLATEAU RESOURCES (PROPRIETARY) LIMITED—See Atlatsa Resources Corporation; *Int'l*, pg. 687

212290 — OTHER METAL ORE MIN...

PT FREEPORT INDONESIA—See Freeport-McMoRan Inc.; U.S. Public, pg. 884
RANCHO SANTA FE MINING, INC.; U.S. Private, pg. 3352
REPTILE URANIUM NAMIBIA (PTY.) LTD.—See Deep Yellow Limited; Int'l, pg. 2002
ROSSING URANIUM LTD.—See China National Nuclear Corporation; Int'l, pg. 1532
ROXGOLD SANGO S.A.—See Fortuna Mining Corp.; Int'l, pg. 2743
ROYAL MINES & MINERALS CORP.; U.S. Public, pg. 1816
RW SILICIUM GMBH—See AMG Critical Materials N.V.; Int'l, pg. 426
SEAVIEW RESOURCES INC.; U.S. Private, pg. 3592
SIDNEY RESOURCES CORP.; U.S. Public, pg. 1876
SIERRA RUTILE LIMITED—See Iluka Resources Limited; Int'l, pg. 3616
SILVERTON ENERGY, INC.; U.S. Private, pg. 3664
SOCIEDAD CONTRACTUAL MINERA EL ABRA—See Corporacion Nacional del Cobre de Chile; Int'l, pg. 1805
SOCIEDAD CONTRACTUAL MINERA PUREN—See Corporacion Nacional del Cobre de Chile; Int'l, pg. 1805
SOUTH MANGANESE INVESTMENT LIMITED—See CITIC Group Corporation; Int'l, pg. 1621
STAR MOUNTAIN RESOURCES, INC.; U.S. Public, pg. 1938
STRIKEFORCE MINING & RESOURCES LTD—See En+ Group Ltd.; Int'l, pg. 2395
SUPERIOR URANIUM PTY. LTD.—See Deep Yellow Limited; Int'l, pg. 2002
SURINAME ALUMINUM COMPANY, L.L.C.—See Alcoa Corporation; U.S. Public, pg. 74
TALISON LITHIUM PTY. LTD.—See Albemarle Corporation; U.S. Public, pg. 73
TALISON LITHIUM PTY, LTD.—See Chengdu Tianqi Industry (Group) Co., Ltd.; Int'l, pg. 1469
TANGERINE HOLDINGS, INC.; U.S. Private, pg. 3930
TASMANIAN ELECTRO METALLURGICAL COMPANY PTY. LTD.—See GFG Alliance Limited; Int'l, pg. 2956
TECHNOLOGY METALS AUSTRALIA LIMITED—See Australian Vanadium Limited; Int'l, pg. 723
THOMPSON CREEK METALS COMPANY INC.—See Centerra Gold Inc.; Int'l, pg. 1403
THOMPSON CREEK METALS COMPANY USA—See Centerra Gold Inc.; Int'l, pg. 1403
TMAC RESOURCES, INC.—See Agnico Eagle Mines Limited; Int'l, pg. 212
TOMBSTONE EXPLORATION CORPORATION; U.S. Public, pg. 2162
TRITTON RESOURCES LIMITED—See Aeris Resources Limited; Int'l, pg. 180
TWO RIVERS PLATINUM (PROPRIETARY) LIMITED—See African Rainbow Minerals Limited; Int'l, pg. 192
UNITED RESOURCE HOLDINGS GROUP, INC.; U.S. Public, pg. 2235
URANIUM TRADING CORPORATION; U.S. Private, pg. 4313
UR-ENERGY INC.; U.S. Public, pg. 2264
UR-ENERGY USA INC.—See Ur-Energy Inc.; U.S. Public, pg. 2264
USMETALS, INC.; U.S. Private, pg. 4323
U.S. RARE EARTHS, INC.; U.S. Private, pg. 4272
VANSTAR MINING RESOURCES INC.—See IAMGOLD Corporation; Int'l, pg. 3569
VERDANT MINERALS LTD.—See CD Capital Asset Management Ltd; Int'l, pg. 1370
VIMY RESOURCES LIMITED—See Deep Yellow Limited; Int'l, pg. 2002
VNUE, INC.; U.S. Public, pg. 2308
VOYAGER METALS INC.—See Cerrado Gold Inc.; Int'l, pg. 1422
WD HALL EXPLORATION COMPANY; U.S. Private, pg. 4462
WESTWATER RESOURCES, INC.; U.S. Public, pg. 2363
WILDROSE MINING, INC.; U.S. Private, pg. 4519
YT PARKSONG AUSTRALIA HOLDING PTY LIMITED—See Greentech Technology International Limited; Int'l, pg. 3076
ZANGEZUR COPPER & MOLYBDENUM COMBINE CJSC—See CRONIMET Holding GmbH; Int'l, pg. 1855

212311 — DIMENSION STONE MINING AND QUARRYING

AFRIMAT CONCRETE PRODUCTS—See Afrimat Limited; Int'l, pg. 192
AGREPOR AGREGADOS - EXTRACCAO DE INERTES S.A.—See Camargo Correa S.A.; Int'l, pg. 1267
AMERICAN ROCK SALT COMPANY LLC; U.S. Private, pg. 246
ARIDOS SANZ S.L.U.—See Heidelberg Materials AG; Int'l, pg. 3308
ASI INDUSTRIES LIMITED; Int'l, pg. 609
AUSTRALIAN SANDSTONE INDUSTRIES PTY. LTD.—See ChongHerr Investments Ltd.; Int'l, pg. 1578
AUSTRALIA SANDSTONE MERCHANTS PTY. LTD.—See Int'l, pg. 720
BLUEROCK DIAMONDS PLC; Int'l, pg. 1072
BOTSWANA DIAMONDS PLC; Int'l, pg. 1118
CANADIAN ELECTROLYTIC ZINC LIMITED—See Glencore plc; Int'l, pg. 2990
CANTERAS MECANICAS CARCABA, S.A.U.—See Heidelberg Materials AG; Int'l, pg. 3309
CIMBAR PERFORMANCE MINERALS, INC.; U.S. Private, pg. 897
COLD SPRING GRANITE (CANADA) LTD.—See Cold Spring Granite Company; U.S. Private, pg. 965
CONSTRUCTION MATERIALS INDUSTRIES & CONTRACTING CO. SAOG; Int'l, pg. 1778
DENVER QUARRIES (PTY) LIMITED—See Afrimat Limited; Int'l, pg. 192
DIAMCOR MINING INC.; Int'l, pg. 2104
EDEN STONE CO. INC.; U.S. Private, pg. 1333
EL PACHON S.A.—See Glencore plc; Int'l, pg. 2990
EMU NL; Int'l, pg. 2394
ENERGOLD DRILLING CORP.; Int'l, pg. 2421
FAIRFAX MATERIALS INC.—See Fairfax Holding Company Inc.; U.S. Private, pg. 1463
FECON CORPORATION; Int'l, pg. 2629
FLINDERS EXPLORATION LIMITED; Int'l, pg. 2706
FUTURE BRIGHT MINING HOLDINGS LIMITED; Int'l, pg. 2852
GEMFIELDS LIMITED—See Gemfields Group Limited; Int'l, pg. 2916
GILLIS QUARRIES LTD.; Int'l, pg. 2976
GRANIT-BRONZ, INC.—See Cold Spring Granite Company; U.S. Private, pg. 966
GRANIT D.D. JABLANICA; Int'l, pg. 3059
GRANITE MOUNTAIN STONE DESIGN—See Cold Spring Granite Company; U.S. Private, pg. 966
GULFSTREAM CAPITAL CORPORATION; Int'l, pg. 3182
HANSON AGGREGATES SOUTH WALES HOLDINGS LIMITED—See Heidelberg Materials AG; Int'l, pg. 3311
HANSON QUARRY PRODUCTS (KUANTAN) SDN BHD—See Heidelberg Materials AG; Int'l, pg. 3312
HOCK HENG GRANITE SDN. BHD—See DFCITY Group Berhad; Int'l, pg. 2094
ILSHIN STONE CO., LTD; Int'l, pg. 3616
KIESWERK MAAS-ROELOFFS GMBH & CO. KG—See Heidelberg Materials AG; Int'l, pg. 3317
LAFARGE DUNDAS QUARRY—See Holcim Ltd.; Int'l, pg. 3449
LUHR BROS., INC.; U.S. Private, pg. 2512
MARITZBURG QUARRIES (PTY) LIMITED—See Afrimat Limited; Int'l, pg. 193
MINERA DEL NORTE—See Grupo Acerero del Norte S.A. de C.V.; Int'l, pg. 3118
OKLAHOMASTONE.COM INC.; U.S. Private, pg. 3007
PAKISTAN TOBACCO CO. LTD.—See British American Tobacco plc; Int'l, pg. 1168
TRG TRADING (PTY) LIMITED—See Basil Read Holdings Limited; Int'l, pg. 887
ZPW TRZUSKAWICA S.A.—See CRH plc; Int'l, pg. 1849

212312 — CRUSHED AND BROKEN LIMESTONE MINING AND QUARRYING

ALLEGHENY MINERAL CORPORATION—See The Snyder Group, Inc.; U.S. Private, pg. 4119
ALLIED CONSTRUCTION CO. INC.; U.S. Private, pg. 185
ANCHOR STONE COMPANY; U.S. Private, pg. 273
ARCELORMITTAL BERYSLAV—See ArcelorMittal S.A.; Int'l, pg. 543
ARKANSAS LIME COMPANY—See United States Lime & Minerals, Inc.; U.S. Public, pg. 2236
ARTGO HOLDINGS LIMITED; Int'l, pg. 583
ASCOM CARBONATE & CHEMICAL MANUFACTURING COMPANY—See ASEC Company for Mining; Int'l, pg. 605
ASH GROVE AGGREGATES, INC.—See CRH plc; Int'l, pg. 1842
ASH GROVE AGGREGATES—See CRH plc; Int'l, pg. 1842
ASH GROVE CEMENT COMPANY—See CRH plc; Int'l, pg. 1842
ASIA MINERAL JOINT STOCK COMPANY; Int'l, pg. 613
BAUVAL INC. - BAUVAL SAINTE-SOPHIE DIVISION—See BAUVAL inc.; Int'l, pg. 898
BAUVAL INC. - CARRIERE L'ANGE-GARDIEN DIVISION—See BAUVAL inc.; Int'l, pg. 898
BAUVAL INC. - LES CARRIERES REGIONALES DIVISION—See BAUVAL inc.; Int'l, pg. 898
BAUVAL INC. - SABLES L.G. DIVISION—See BAUVAL inc.; Int'l, pg. 899
BUSSEN QUARRIES, INC. - JEFFERSON BARRACKS QUARRY—See Bussen Quarries, Inc.; U.S. Private, pg. 696
BUSSEN QUARRIES, INC.; U.S. Private, pg. 696
BUSSEN QUARRIES, INC. - TRAUTMAN QUARRY—See Bussen Quarries, Inc.; U.S. Private, pg. 696
BUZZI UNICEM USA INC.—See Buzzi SpA; Int'l, pg. 1230
CANTERAS PREBETONG, S.L.—See Camargo Correa S.A.; Int'l, pg. 1267
CARMEUSE LIME INC.—See Carmeuse Holding SA; Int'l, pg. 1341
CARMEUSE LIME & STONE, INC.—See Carmeuse Holding SA; Int'l, pg. 1341
CARMEUSE LIME & STONE—See Carmeuse Holding SA; Int'l, pg. 1341
CARMEUSE LIME & STONE—See Carmeuse Holding SA; Int'l, pg. 1341
CARMEUSE LIME & STONE—See Carmeuse Holding SA; Int'l, pg. 1341
CARMEUSE LIME & STONE—See Carmeuse Holding SA; Int'l, pg. 1341
CENTRAL STONE CO.—See RiverStone Group, Inc.; U.S. Private, pg. 3446
CIMBENIN S.A.—See Heidelberg Materials AG; Int'l, pg. 3315
CMISTONE VIET NAM JOINT STOCK COMPANY; Int'l, pg. 1670
COBLESKILL STONE PRODUCTS INC.; U.S. Private, pg. 958
COLORADO LIME COMPANY—See United States Lime & Minerals, Inc.; U.S. Public, pg. 2236
CONMAT—See The Helm Group; U.S. Private, pg. 4051
CS MUNDY QUARRIES INC.—See Eagle Corporation; U.S. Private, pg. 1309
D.M. STOLTZFUS & SON INC.; U.S. Private, pg. 1142
EMX (USA) SERVICES CORP.—See EMX Royalty Corporation; Int'l, pg. 2395
FUJAIRAH NATIONAL QUARRY—See Fujairah Building Industries Company P.S.C.; Int'l, pg. 2808
GHACEM LTD.—See Heidelberg Materials AG; Int'l, pg. 3315
HALQUIST STONE COMPANY, INC.; U.S. Private, pg. 1846
HAMMERSTONE CORPORATION—See Brookfield Corporation; Int'l, pg. 1187
HAMM, INC.—See Summit Materials, Inc.; U.S. Public, pg. 1960
HANSON AGGREGATES MIDWEST LLC—See Heidelberg Materials AG; Int'l, pg. 3313
HANSON AGGREGATES WRP, INC.—See Heidelberg Materials AG; Int'l, pg. 3313
HANSON QUARRY PRODUCTS (ISRAEL) LTD—See Heidelberg Materials AG; Int'l, pg. 3312
H.B. MELLOTT ESTATE, INC.; U.S. Private, pg. 1825
HUBER ENGINEERED MATERIALS, LLC - QUINCY—See J.M. Huber Corporation; U.S. Private, pg. 2168
J.A.JACK & SONS, INC.—See Arcosa, Inc.; U.S. Public, pg. 186
KERFORD LIMESTONE CO. INC.—See Constructors Inc.; U.S. Private, pg. 1025
KNOX COUNTY STONE CO. INC.—See RiverStone Group, Inc.; U.S. Private, pg. 3446
KOTOUC STRAMBERK SPOL, S.R.O.—See CEZ, a.s.; Int'l, pg. 1428
LAUREL AGGREGATES LLC—See Sun Capital Partners, Inc.; U.S. Private, pg. 3861
LEO JOURNAGAN CONSTRUCTION CO.; U.S. Private, pg. 2422
LINWOOD MINING & MINERALS CORP.—See McCarthy Bush Corporation; U.S. Private, pg. 2626
LITERS QUARRY INC.; U.S. Private, pg. 2467
LOMY MORINA SPOL, S.R.O.—See CEZ, a.s.; Int'l, pg. 1428
MCDONALD'S LIME - OTOROHANGA PLANT—See Graymont Limited; Int'l, pg. 3063
MECKLEYS LIMESTONE PRODUCTS; U.S. Private, pg. 2649
MONTANA LIMESTONE COMPANY—See Basin Electric Power Cooperative; U.S. Private, pg. 485
MULZER CRUSHED STONE INC.—See CRH plc; Int'l, pg. 1845
NALLY & GIBSON GEORGETOWN, LLC—See Summit Materials, Inc.; U.S. Public, pg. 1960
NEW ENTERPRISE STONE & LIME CO., INC.; U.S. Private, pg. 2895
NEW POINT STONE CO.; U.S. Private, pg. 2905
NORTH FLORIDA ROCK, LTD.—See Arcosa, Inc.; U.S. Public, pg. 186
OMI MINING CO., LTD.—See Aichi Steel Corporation; Int'l, pg. 392
READY MIX USA - EAST TENNESSEE—See CEMEX, S.A.B. de C.V.; Int'l, pg. 1399
REAGENT AND TECHNOLOGY SERVICES—See HBM Holdings Company; U.S. Private, pg. 1887
RIVER PRODUCTS COMPANY, INC.; U.S. Private, pg. 3444
ROGERS GROUP INC.; U.S. Private, pg. 3472
ROHRERS QUARRY INC.; U.S. Private, pg. 3473
SELLERSBURG STONE COMPANY, INC.—See Gohmann Asphalt & Construction Co.; U.S. Private, pg. 1726
SHELLY MATERIALS, INC.—See CRH plc; Int'l, pg. 1847
SPECIALTY SAND CO.—See MineralTech Gulf Coast Abrasives, LLC; U.S. Private, pg. 2742
STONEPOINT MATERIALS, LLC—See Sun Capital Partners, Inc.; U.S. Private, pg. 3861
STONE & SOIL DEPOT INC.—See SiteOne Landscape Supply, Inc.; U.S. Public, pg. 1889
STUART M. PERRY INC.; U.S. Private, pg. 3843
TEXAS CRUSHED STONE CO.; U.S. Private, pg. 3975
TEXAS LIME COMPANY—See United States Lime & Miner-

N.A.I.C.S. INDEX

212321 — CONSTRUCTION SAND A...

als, Inc.; *U.S. Public*, pg. 2236
TOWER ROCK STONE COMPANY INC.; *U.S. Private*, pg. 4194
UNITED STATES LIME & MINERALS, INC., *U.S. Public*, pg. 2236
U.S. AGGREGATES INC. - LAFAYETTE PLANT—See Heritage Group; *U.S. Public*, pg. 1923
U.S. AGGREGATES INC.—See Heritage Group; *U.S. Private*, pg. 1923
U.S. LIME COMPANY - SHREVEPORT—See United States Lime & Minerals, Inc.; *U.S. Public*, pg. 2236
U.S. LIME COMPANY—See United States Lime & Minerals, Inc.; *U.S. Public*, pg. 2236
U.S. LIME COMPANY - ST. CLAIR—See United States Lime & Minerals, Inc.; *U.S. Public*, pg. 2236
VANTACORE PARTNERS LP—See Sun Capital Partners, Inc.; *U.S. Private*, pg. 3861
WEST VIRGINIA PAVING INC; *U.S. Private*, pg. 4487

212313 — CRUSHED AND BROKEN GRANITE MINING AND QUARRYING

BITUMIX GRANITE SDN BHD—See Heidelberg Materials AG; *Int'l*, pg. 3309
COLD SPRING GRANITE CO.—See Cold Spring Granite Company; *U.S. Private*, pg. 965
DAMANSARA ROCK PRODUCTS SDN BHD—See IJM Corporation Berhad; *Int'l*, pg. 3608
ECKA GRANULES GERMANY GMBH—See Palladium Equity Partners, LLC; *U.S. Private*, pg. 3078
FHL I. KIRIAKIDIS MARBLE - GRANITE SA; *Int'l*, pg. 2650
GUERNSEY STONE COMPANY—See Martin Marietta Materials, Inc.; *U.S. Public*, pg. 1389
IMERYS MINERALI S.P.A.—See Groupe Bruxelles Lambert SA; *Int'l*, pg. 3100
KUANG ROCK PRODUCTS SDN BHD—See IJM Corporation Berhad; *Int'l*, pg. 3609
LUCK STONE CORPORATION; *U.S. Private*, pg. 2511
MARMI BIANCHI SRL—See FHL I. KIRIAKIDIS MARBLE - GRANITE SA; *Int'l*, pg. 2650
MARTIN MARIETTA AGGREGATES—See Martin Marietta Materials, Inc.; *U.S. Public*, pg. 1389
MCGEORGE CONTRACTING CO., INC.; *U.S. Private*, pg. 2634
RINKER MATERIALS-TWIN MOUNTAIN—See CEMEX, S.A.B. de C.V.; *Int'l*, pg. 1399
ROYAL MELROSE GRANITES—See Cold Spring Granite Company; *U.S. Private*, pg. 966
SALEM STONE CORPORATION; *U.S. Private*, pg. 3531
SUNGAI LONG INDUSTRIES SDN BHD—See Bina Puri Holdings Bhd; *Int'l*, pg. 1032
WAKE STONE CORPORATION; *U.S. Private*, pg. 4427

212319 — OTHER CRUSHED AND BROKEN STONE MINING AND QUARRYING

APAC-TENNESSEE, INC.—See CRH plc; *Int'l*, pg. 1846
AZAM EKUITI SDN BHD—See IJM Corporation Berhad; *Int'l*, pg. 3608
BLUEGRASS MATERIALS COMPANY, LLC—See Martin Marietta Materials, Inc.; *U.S. Public*, pg. 1389
BREEDON AGGREGATES ENGLAND LIMITED—See Breedon Group plc; *Int'l*, pg. 1144
BREEDON AGGREGATES SCOTLAND LIMITED—See Breedon Group plc; *Int'l*, pg. 1144
BUECHEL STONE CORPORATION; *U.S. Private*, pg. 680
CENTRAL DIVISION LOGISTICS, LLC—See Vulcan Materials Company; *U.S. Public*, pg. 2313
CHONGHERR INVESTMENTS LTD.; *Int'l*, pg. 1578
CONNOLLY-PACIFIC CO.—See MDU Resources Group, Inc.; *U.S. Public*, pg. 1410
CORNEJO & SONS, LLC—See Summit Materials, Inc.; *U.S. Public*, pg. 1960
DEATLEY CRUSHING COMPANY; *U.S. Private*, pg. 1185
DE BEERS CONSOLIDATED MINES LIMITED—See Anglo American PLC; *Int'l*, pg. 462
THE DETROIT SALT COMPANY—See Stone Canyon Industries, LLC; *U.S. Private*, pg. 3818
DFR GOLD INC.; *Int'l*, pg. 2096
DIAMOND FIELDS NAMIBIA (PTY) LTD.—See DFR Gold Inc.; *Int'l*, pg. 2096
ELKEM TANA—See China National Chemical Corporation; *Int'l*, pg. 1527
EUCON CORPORATION; *U.S. Private*, pg. 1433
FOX MARBLE HOLDINGS PLC; *Int'l*, pg. 2756
GCCP RESOURCES LIMITED; *Int'l*, pg. 2895
GRAYMONT MATERIALS (NY) INC.—See Barrett Industries, Inc.; *U.S. Private*, pg. 480
HANSON AGGREGATES LIMITED—See Heidelberg Materials AG; *Int'l*, pg. 3312
HANSON AGGREGATES UK - SOUTH WEST—See Heidelberg Materials AG; *Int'l*, pg. 3312
HANSON MATERIAL SERVICE—See Heidelberg Materials AG; *Int'l*, pg. 3313
HANSON QUARRY PRODUCTS EUROPE LTD.—See Heidelberg Materials AG; *Int'l*, pg. 3312

HANSON QUARRY PRODUCTS SDN. BHD.—See Heidelberg Materials AG; *Int'l*, pg. 3313
INFRASORS HOLDINGS LIMITED—See Afrimat Limited; *Int'l*, pg. 192
JAMAICA GYPSUM & QUARRIES LIMITED—See CEMEX, S.A.B. de C.V.; *Int'l*, pg. 1400
KNIFE RIVER-MEDFORD—See MDU Resources Group, Inc.; *U.S. Public*, pg. 1410
LAUREL AGGREGATES OF DELAWARE, LLC—See Natural Resource Partners L.P.; *U.S. Public*, pg. 1499
L.G. EVERIST INC.; *U.S. Private*, pg. 2365
MAINE DRILLING & BLASTING INC. - CENTRAL DIVISION—See Maine Drilling & Blasting Inc.; *U.S. Private*, pg. 2552
MAINE DRILLING & BLASTING INC. - EASTERN DIVISION—See Maine Drilling & Blasting Inc.; *U.S. Private*, pg. 2552
MAINE DRILLING & BLASTING INC. - MID-ATLANTIC DIVISION—See Maine Drilling & Blasting Inc.; *U.S. Private*, pg. 2552
MAINE DRILLING & BLASTING INC. - NORTH DIVISION—See Maine Drilling & Blasting Inc.; *U.S. Private*, pg. 2552
MAINE DRILLING & BLASTING INC. - SOUTH DIVISION—See Maine Drilling & Blasting Inc.; *U.S. Private*, pg. 2552
MAINE DRILLING & BLASTING INC. - WESTERN DIVISION—See Maine Drilling & Blasting Inc.; *U.S. Private*, pg. 2552
MASTEN ENTERPRISES LLC; *U.S. Private*, pg. 2607
MCASPHALT, LLC—See Natural Resource Partners L.P.; *U.S. Public*, pg. 1499
MCINTOSH CONSTRUCTION COMPANY, LLC—See Natural Resource Partners L.P.; *U.S. Public*, pg. 1499
METROMIX PTY. LTD.—See Heidelberg Materials AG; *Int'l*, pg. 3311
METROMIX PTY. LTD.—See Holcim Ltd.; *Int'l*, pg. 3446
MIDLAND QUARRY PRODUCTS LTD.—See Anglo American PLC; *Int'l*, pg. 462
MIDLAND QUARRY PRODUCTS LTD.—See Heidelberg Materials AG; *Int'l*, pg. 3314
MINERAL DEPOSITS LIMITED—See Eramet SA; *Int'l*, pg. 2489
MOUNTAIN WEST, LLC; *U.S. Private*, pg. 2800
MOUNTAIN WEST LOGISTICS, LLC—See Vulcan Materials Company; *U.S. Public*, pg. 2313
NIPPON PGM AMERICA INC.—See Dowa Holdings Co., Ltd.; *Int'l*, pg. 2184
NOTTINGHAM COATED STONE—See CEMEX, S.A.B. de C.V.; *Int'l*, pg. 1399
OSSIPEE AGGREGATES CORP—See Boston Sand & Gravel Company; *U.S. Public*, pg. 373
PYHASALMI MINE OY—See First Quantum Minerals Ltd.; *Int'l*, pg. 2687
THE QUAPAW COMPANY—See Dolese Bros. Co.; *U.S. Private*, pg. 1254
SAN RAFAEL ROCK QUARRY INC.—See The Dutra Group Inc.; *U.S. Private*, pg. 4024
SHEFFIELD COATED STONE—See CEMEX, S.A.B. de C.V.; *Int'l*, pg. 1399
SHOWA KAIHATSU KOGYO CO., LTD.—See Dowa Holdings Co., Ltd.; *Int'l*, pg. 2184
SOUTHEAST DIVISION LOGISTICS, LLC—See Vulcan Materials Company; *U.S. Public*, pg. 2313
SOUTHERN AGGREGATES, LLC—See Natural Resource Partners L.P.; *U.S. Public*, pg. 1499
SOUTHERN QUARRIES PTY LTD—See CRH plc; *Int'l*, pg. 1842
SPENCER QUARRIES, INC.; *U.S. Private*, pg. 3755
U.S. AGGREGATES INC. - STONE QUARRY - COLUMBUS PLANT—See Heritage Group; *U.S. Public*, pg. 1923
U.S. AGGREGATES INC. - STONE QUARRY - DELPHI PLANT—See Heritage Group; *U.S. Public*, pg. 1923
U.S. AGGREGATES INC. - STONE QUARRY - LINN GROVE PLANT—See Heritage Group; *U.S. Public*, pg. 1923
U.S. AGGREGATES INC. - STONE QUARRY - PLEASANT MILLS PLANT—See Heritage Group; *U.S. Public*, pg. 1923
U.S. AGGREGATES INC. - STONE QUARRY - PORTLAND PLANT—See Heritage Group; *U.S. Public*, pg. 1923
U.S. AGGREGATES INC. - STONE QUARRY - RIDGEVILLE PLANT—See Heritage Group; *U.S. Public*, pg. 1923
VGCM, LLC—See Vulcan Materials Company; *U.S. Public*, pg. 2314
VULCAN MATERIALS COMPANY; *U.S. Public*, pg. 2313
WINN MATERIALS, LLC—See Natural Resource Partners L.P.; *U.S. Public*, pg. 1499
WINN MATERIALS OF KENTUCKY, LLC—See Natural Resource Partners L.P.; *U.S. Public*, pg. 1499

212321 — CONSTRUCTION SAND AND GRAVEL MINING

ACME MATERIALS COMPANY—See WG Block Co.; *U.S. Private*, pg. 4503

ALBERT FREI & SONS INC.—See Martin Marietta Materials, Inc.; *U.S. Public*, pg. 1389
AMERICAN MATERIALS COMPANY, LLC—See Summit Materials, Inc.; *U.S. Public*, pg. 1960
APAC MID-SOUTH, INC.—See CRH plc; *Int'l*, pg. 1846
BERGERON PROPERTIES & INVESTMENT CORP.; *U.S. Private*, pg. 530
B. GRIMM TRADING COMPANY—See B. Grimm Group; *Int'l*, pg. 788
BULLSEYE MINING LIMITED—See Emerald Resources NL; *Int'l*, pg. 2378
CADMAN (ROCK), INC.—See Heidelberg Materials AG; *Int'l*, pg. 3309
CARLISLE CONSTRUCTION MATERIALS GMBH—See Carlisle Companies Incorporated; *U.S. Public*, pg. 436
CASTLE CONCRETE COMPANY—See Bee Street Holdings LLC; *U.S. Private*, pg. 513
CGS SERVICES, INC.—See Waste Management, Inc.; *U.S. Public*, pg. 2330
CJ MABARDY INC.; *U.S. Private*, pg. 908
DCON PRODUCTS PUBLIC COMPANY LIMITED; *Int'l*, pg. 1992
DEMIX AGREGATS - LAVAL—See CRH plc; *Int'l*, pg. 1843
DENNIS M. MCCOY & SONS; *U.S. Private*, pg. 1205
DERRYARKIN SAND AND GRAVEL LIMITED—See Bord na Mona Plc; *Int'l*, pg. 1113
DIPLOMA GROUP LIMITED; *Int'l*, pg. 2128
D&J CONSTRUCTION COMPANY INC.; *U.S. Private*, pg. 1137
DKLS QUARRY & PREMIX SDN. BHD.—See DKLS Industries Berhad; *Int'l*, pg. 2139
DOLKAM SUJA A.S.; *Int'l*, pg. 2158
DUFFERIN AGGREGATES BUTLER PIT—See CRH plc; *Int'l*, pg. 1843
DURANCE GRANULATS; *Int'l*, pg. 2228
ELMHURST-CHICAGO STONE CO; *U.S. Private*, pg. 1376
E.R. JAHNA INDUSTRIES INC.; *U.S. Private*, pg. 1306
EUGENE SAND & GRAVEL, INC.—See CRH plc; *Int'l*, pg. 1847
EXAKT KIESAUFBEREITUNG-GESELLSCHAFT MIT BESCHRANKTER HAFTUNG & CO KOMMANDITGESELLSCHAFT—See Heidelberg Materials AG; *Int'l*, pg. 3310
EXXARO HOLDINGS SANDS (PTY) LIMITED—See Exxaro Resources Ltd.; *Int'l*, pg. 2592
FAIRMOUNT SANTROL HOLDINGS INC.—See Covia Holdings Corporation; *U.S. Public*, pg. 1072
FISHER INDUSTRIES; *U.S. Private*, pg. 1534
FISHER SAND & GRAVEL CO. INC.—See Fisher Industries; *U.S. Private*, pg. 1534
GRANITE ROCK COMPANY; *U.S. Private*, pg. 1756
GREEN DIAMOND SAND PRODUCTS INC.—See AAVIN, LLC; *U.S. Private*, pg. 33
GREEN DIAMOND SAND PRODUCTS INC.—See MSI Capital Partners LLC; *U.S. Private*, pg. 2807
GRUPA AZOTY KOPALNIE I ZAKIADY CHEMICZNE SIARKI SIARKOPOL S. A.—See Grupa Azoty S.A.; *Int'l*, pg. 3115
HANSON AGGREGATES PENNSYLVANIA LLC—See Heidelberg Materials AG; *Int'l*, pg. 3313
HANSON MARINE LIMITED—See Heidelberg Materials AG; *Int'l*, pg. 3312
HANSON QUARRY PRODUCTS (BATU PAHAT) SDN BHD—See Heidelberg Materials AG; *Int'l*, pg. 3312
HANSON QUARRY PRODUCTS (KULAI) SDN BHD—See Heidelberg Materials AG; *Int'l*, pg. 3312
HANSON QUARRY PRODUCTS (RAWANG) SDN BHD—See Heidelberg Materials AG; *Int'l*, pg. 3312
HANSON QUARRY PRODUCTS (TERENGGANU) SDN BHD—See Heidelberg Materials AG; *Int'l*, pg. 3312
HEDRICK INDUSTRIES INC.; *U.S. Private*, pg. 1903
HEIDELBERGER SAND UND KIES HANDEL & LOGISTIK GMBH—See Heidelberg Materials AG; *Int'l*, pg. 3316
HELENA SAND & GRAVEL, INC.—See CRH plc; *Int'l*, pg. 1847
HI-CRUSH CHAMBERS LLC—See Atlas Energy Solutions Inc.; *U.S. Public*, pg. 224
HI-CRUSH OPERATING LLC—See Atlas Energy Solutions Inc.; *U.S. Public*, pg. 224
HILLTOP BASIC RESOURCES, INC.; *U.S. Private*, pg. 1947
HLB GLOBAL CO LTD; *Int'l*, pg. 3430
HOA AN JOINT STOCK COMPANY; *Int'l*, pg. 3435
THE HOLMS SAND & GRAVEL COMPANY (1985)—See Heidelberg Materials AG; *Int'l*, pg. 3320
HOPKINS HILL SAND & STONE, LLC—See Cardi Corporation; *U.S. Private*, pg. 749
IHC MERWEDE HOLDING B.V.; *Int'l*, pg. 3603
INGRAM MATERIALS CO.—See Ingram Industries, Inc.; *U.S. Private*, pg. 2077
ISLAND AGGREGATES LIMITED—See CEMEX, S.A.B. de C.V.; *Int'l*, pg. 1399
JIANGSU ZHONGKE INTELLIGENT SYSTEM CO., LTD.—See China Security Co., Ltd.; *Int'l*, pg. 1550
KAMENIVO SLOVAKIA A.S.—See Heidelberg Materials AG; *Int'l*, pg. 3317
KIESWERKE ANDRESEN GMBH—See Heidelberg Materials AG; *Int'l*, pg. 3317

212321 — CONSTRUCTION SAND A...

KNIFE RIVER CORPORATION—See MDU Resources Group, Inc.; *U.S. Public*, pg. 1409
KOENIG SAND & GRAVEL LLC—See Koenig Company Inc.; *U.S. Private*, pg. 2336
KUDSK & DAHL A/S—See Cementir Holding N.V.; *Int'l*, pg. 1397
LLANELLI SAND DREDGING LTD.—See HAL Trust N.V.; *Int'l*, pg. 3225
LLOYD ENTERPRISES INC.; *U.S. Private*, pg. 2475
LYMAN-RICHEY CORPORATION; *U.S. Private*, pg. 2520
MICHIGAN MATERIALS & AGGREGATES COMPANY—See CRH plc; *Int'l*, pg. 1847
NORRKOPINGS SAND AB—See Heidelberg Materials AG; *Int'l*, pg. 3315
NUGENT SAND COMPANY; *U.S. Private*, pg. 2972
NX GOLD S.A.—See Ero Copper Corp.; *Int'l*, pg. 2496
ORCA SAND & GRAVEL LTD.—See Vulcan Materials Company; *U.S. Public*, pg. 2314
PINNACLE MATERIALS, INC.; *U.S. Private*, pg. 3185
PIONEER LANDSCAPING MATERIALS; *U.S. Private*, pg. 3187
POPEJOY CONSTRUCTION COMPANY INC.; *U.S. Private*, pg. 3228
RGE STORM LAKE—See Reding Gravel & Excavating Co., Inc.; *U.S. Private*, pg. 3379
RHEINISCHE BAUSTOFFWERKE GMBH & CO. KG—See ACS, Actividades de Construccion y Servicios, S.A.; *Int'l*, pg. 114
SAINT-GOBAIN DISTRIBUTION BATIMENT—See Compagnie de Saint-Gobain SA; *Int'l*, pg. 1732
SEVEROCESKE PISKOVNY A STERKOVNY S.R.O.—See Heidelberg Materials AG; *Int'l*, pg. 3319
SKANE GRUS AB—See Cementir Holding N.V.; *Int'l*, pg. 1397
SP BOHEMIA, K.S.—See Heidelberg Materials AG; *Int'l*, pg. 3319
STAKER & PARSON COMPANIES INC.—See CRH plc; *Int'l*, pg. 1847
SUPERSTITION CRUSHING LLC; *U.S. Private*, pg. 3881
SWEETMAN CONSTRUCTION CO.—See MDU Resources Group, Inc.; *U.S. Public*, pg. 1411
TANAH MERAH QUARRY SDN BHD—See Heidelberg Materials AG; *Int'l*, pg. 3320
TARMAC AGGREGATES LIMITED—See CRH plc; *Int'l*, pg. 1848
THELEN SAND & GRAVEL INC.; *U.S. Private*, pg. 4141
TILLER CORP.—See Martin Marietta Materials, Inc.; *U.S. Public*, pg. 1389
TRIANGLE AGGREGATES LLC.; *U.S. Private*, pg. 4254
TUCKAHOE SAND & GRAVEL CO., INC.—See Johnston Enterprises Inc.; *U.S. Private*, pg. 2230
U.S. AGGREGATES INC. - FRANCESVILLE PLANT—See Heritage Group; *U.S. Private*, pg. 1923
U.S. AGGREGATES INC. - LOWELL PLANT—See Heritage Group; *U.S. Private*, pg. 1923
U.S. AGGREGATES INC. - MONON PLANT—See Heritage Group; *U.S. Private*, pg. 1923
U.S. AGGREGATES INC. - SAND & GRAVEL - CRAWFORDSVILLE PLANT—See Heritage Group; *U.S. Private*, pg. 1923
U.S. AGGREGATES INC. - SAND & GRAVEL - PERKINSVILLE PLANT—See Heritage Group; *U.S. Private*, pg. 1923
U.S. AGGREGATES INC. - SAND & GRAVEL - RICHMOND PLANT—See Heritage Group; *U.S. Private*, pg. 1923
U.S. AGGREGATES INC. - SAND & GRAVEL - THORNTOWN PLANT—See Heritage Group; *U.S. Private*, pg. 1923
VALLEY QUARRIES INC. - MT. CYDONIA PLANT II—See New Enterprise Stone & Lime Co., Inc.; *U.S. Private*, pg. 2895
VALLEY QUARRIES INC. - MT. CYDONIA PLANT I—See New Enterprise Stone & Lime Co., Inc.; *U.S. Private*, pg. 2895
WASHINGTON BUILDERS SUPPLY CO.—See GMS Inc.; *U.S. Public*, pg. 948
WATERFALL QUARRIES PTY LIMITED—See Heidelberg Materials AG; *Int'l*, pg. 3320
WATSON GRAVEL, INC.; *U.S. Private*, pg. 4455
WHIBCO, INC. - PORT ELIZABETH PLANT—See Whibco, Inc.; *U.S. Private*, pg. 4506
WINDSOR ROCK PRODUCTS, INC.—See GMS Inc.; *U.S. Public*, pg. 948
YAGER MATERIALS LLC—See Carmeuse Holding SA; *Int'l*, pg. 1341

212322 — INDUSTRIAL SAND MINING

AECON MINING INC.—See Aecon Group Inc.; *Int'l*, pg. 172
AGC MINERAL CO., LTD.—See AGC Inc.; *Int'l*, pg. 202
ALLUP SILICA LIMITED; *Int'l*, pg. 361
BADGER MINING CORPORATION; *U.S. Private*, pg. 424
BASE TOLIARA SARL—See Energy Fuels Inc.; *U.S. Public*, pg. 762
BEST SAND CORPORATION—See Covia Holdings Corporation; *U.S. Private*, pg. 1072
CADRE PROPPANTS - VOCA PLANT—See Apollo Global Management, Inc.; *U.S. Public*, pg. 164
CHONGQING CHANGJIANG RIVER MOULDING MATERIAL (GROUP) CO., LTD.; *Int'l*, pg. 1579
COATED SAND SOLUTIONS, LLC—See Apollo Global Management, Inc.; *U.S. Public*, pg. 164
COLOMBIA MINERALES INDUSTRIALES S.A.—See Gruppo Minerali Maffei S.p.A.; *Int'l*, pg. 3140
COVIA HOLDINGS CORPORATION; *U.S. Private*, pg. 1072
CRS PROPPANTS LLC—See Eagle Materials Inc.; *U.S. Public*, pg. 702
FAIRMOUNT SANTROL INC.—See Covia Holdings Corporation; *U.S. Private*, pg. 1072
HOURGLASS ACQUISITION I, LLC—See Apollo Global Management, Inc.; *U.S. Public*, pg. 165
INDUSTRIAL SANDS & GRAVELS PTY. LTD.—See GBM Gold Limited; *Int'l*, pg. 2893
PENNSYLVANIA GLASS SAND CORPORATION—See Apollo Global Management, Inc.; *U.S. Public*, pg. 165
PREFERRED SANDS, INC.; *U.S. Private*, pg. 3248
TECHNISAND, INC.—See Covia Holdings Corporation; *U.S. Private*, pg. 1072
UNIMIN CORPORATION—See Covia Holdings Corporation; *U.S. Private*, pg. 1072
U.S. SILICA COMPANY—See Apollo Global Management, Inc.; *U.S. Public*, pg. 165
WEDRON SILICA COMPANY—See Covia Holdings Corporation; *U.S. Private*, pg. 1072
WHIBCO, INC.; *U.S. Private*, pg. 4506
WISCONSIN INDUSTRIAL SAND COMPANY, LLC—See Covia Holdings Corporation; *U.S. Private*, pg. 1072

212323 — KAOLIN, CLAY, AND CERAMIC AND REFRACTORY MINERALS MINING

20 MICRONS NANO MINERALS LTD—See 20 Microns Limited; *Int'l*, pg. 4
AGS SA—See Groupe Bruxelles Lambert SA; *Int'l*, pg. 3099
AMCOL AUSTRALIA PTY LTD—See Minerals Technologies, Inc.; *U.S. Public*, pg. 1448
AMCOL INTERNATIONAL CORPORATION—See Minerals Technologies, Inc.; *U.S. Public*, pg. 1448
AMCOL MINERALS EUROPE LIMITED—See Minerals Technologies, Inc.; *U.S. Public*, pg. 1448
ASSOCIATED KAOLIN INDUSTRIES SDN. BHD.—See Doka Wawasan TKH Holdings Berhad; *Int'l*, pg. 2156
AYERS EXPLORATION INC.; *Int'l*, pg. 775
BENTONIT A.D.; *Int'l*, pg. 977
BINH DINH MINERALS JOINT STOCK COMPANY; *Int'l*, pg. 1034
BLACK HILLS BENTONITE LLP; *U.S. Private*, pg. 572
CADAM S.A.—See IMin Partners, L.P.; *U.S. Private*, pg. 2047
CERAMIKA NOWA GALA S.A.; *Int'l*, pg. 1421
CERCO LLC - CESCO PLANT—See CerCo LLC; *U.S. Private*, pg. 840
CETCO (EUROPE) LTD.—See Minerals Technologies, Inc.; *U.S. Public*, pg. 1448
COLLOID ENVIRONMENTAL TECHNOLOGIES COMPANY (CETCO)—See Minerals Technologies, Inc.; *U.S. Public*, pg. 1448
COMPANIA MINERA PITALLA, S.A. DE C.V.—See Argonaut Gold Inc.; *U.S. Public*, pg. 191
DOKA WAWASAN TKH HOLDINGS BERHAD; *Int'l*, pg. 2156
DONGKUK REFRACTORIES & STEEL CO., LTD.; *Int'l*, pg. 2168
EICL LIMITED; *Int'l*, pg. 2328
GLOBAL ROYALTY CORP.—See Coeur Mining, Inc.; *U.S. Public*, pg. 522
GOLD STAR POWDERS PRIVATE LIMITED—See Goodwin PLC; *Int'l*, pg. 3042
HAICHENG LINLI MINING CO., LTD.; *Int'l*, pg. 3209
HOBEN INTERNATIONAL LTD.—See Goodwin PLC; *Int'l*, pg. 3041
IMERYS MINERAUX BELGIQUE S.A./NV—See Groupe Bruxelles Lambert SA; *Int'l*, pg. 3100
IMERYS TILES MINERALS ITALIA SRL—See Groupe Bruxelles Lambert SA; *Int'l*, pg. 3100
KAMIN LLC—See IMin Partners, L.P.; *U.S. Private*, pg. 2047
KENTUCKY-TENNESSEE CLAY COMPANY; *U.S. Private*, pg. 2289
KYANITE MINING CORPORATION; *U.S. Private*, pg. 2360
MAGNA REFRACTARIOS MEXICO SA DE CV—See Grecian Magnesite S.A.; *Int'l*, pg. 3068
MAGNA REFRACTORIES INC.—See Grecian Magnesite S.A.; *Int'l*, pg. 3068
MAGNESITAS NAVARRAS S.A.—See Grecian Magnesite S.A.; *Int'l*, pg. 3068
NIZEROLLES S.A.—See Groupe Bruxelles Lambert SA; *Int'l*, pg. 3100
NORLITE CORPORATION—See Grupo Tradebe Medioambiente S.L.; *Int'l*, pg. 3138
PRINCE MINERALS, LTD.—See American Securities LLC; *U.S. Private*, pg. 253
PST PRESS + SINTERTECHNIK SP.Z.O.O.—See BC Partners LLP; *Int'l*, pg. 923
ROMIN SLOVAKIA, SPOL. S.R.O.—See Minerals Technologies, Inc.; *U.S. Public*, pg. 1449
SAINT-GOBAIN CERAMIC MATERIALS CANADA INC.—See Compagnie de Saint-Gobain SA; *Int'l*, pg. 1731
SEG—See Groupe Bruxelles Lambert SA; *Int'l*, pg. 3100
SIAM CASTING POWDERS LTD.—See Goodwin PLC; *Int'l*, pg. 3042
SVENSKA KAOLIN AB—See Barclays PLC; *Int'l*, pg. 863
THIELE KAOLIN COMPANY; *U.S. Private*, pg. 4144
ZIRCOSIL (USA) INC.—See American Securities LLC; *U.S. Private*, pg. 251

212390 — OTHER NONMETALLIC MINERAL MINING AND QUARRYING

1 DIAMOND, LLC—See Quanta Services, Inc.; *U.S. Public*, pg. 1750
ADEX MINERALS CORP.—See Adex Mining Inc.; *Int'l*, pg. 145
ADMIRALTY RESOURCES NL; *Int'l*, pg. 152
AFRICAN EXPLOSIVES HOLDINGS (PTY) LIMITED—See AECI Limited; *Int'l*, pg. 171
AFRICAN GOLD LTD.; *Int'l*, pg. 191
AGC SODA CORP.—See AGC Inc.; *Int'l*, pg. 203
AGRIMINCO CORP.; *Int'l*, pg. 217
AGRIMIN LIMITED; *Int'l*, pg. 217
AKZO NOBEL SALT A/S—See GIC Pte. Ltd.; *Int'l*, pg. 2968
AKZO NOBEL SALT A/S—See The Carlyle Group Inc.; *U.S. Public*, pg. 2051
ALLKEM LIMITED; *Int'l*, pg. 359
ALROSA CO. LTD.; *Int'l*, pg. 377
ALVO MINERALS LIMITED; *Int'l*, pg. 402
AMANTA LAO CO., LTD.—See Amanta Resources Ltd.; *Int'l*, pg. 411
AMARILLO MINERACAO DO BRASIL LIMITADA—See Hochschild Mining plc; *Int'l*, pg. 3438
AMERICAN BORATE CORPORATION; *U.S. Private*, pg. 225
AMERICAN GILSONITE CO.-BONANZA MINE—See Palladium Equity Partners, LLC; *U.S. Private*, pg. 3077
AMERICAN GILSONITE CO.—See Palladium Equity Partners, LLC; *U.S. Private*, pg. 3077
AMERICAN POTASH CORP.; *Int'l*, pg. 422
AMERICAS POTASH PERU S.A.—See Coloured Ties Capital Inc.; *Int'l*, pg. 1704
ARCADIA MINERALS LIMITED; *Int'l*, pg. 540
ARCHON MINERALS LIMITED; *Int'l*, pg. 549
ARCLAND RESOURCES, INC.; *Int'l*, pg. 549
ARCTIC CANADIAN DIAMOND COMPANY LTD.—See Burgundy Diamond Mines Limited; *Int'l*, pg. 1224
ARCTIC STAR EXPLORATION CORP.; *Int'l*, pg. 552
ARIANNE PHOSPHATE INC.; *Int'l*, pg. 564
ART WILSON COMPANY—See Arcosa, Inc.; *U.S. Public*, pg. 186
ASAM RESOURCES SA (PROPRIETARY) LIMITED—See Firestone Diamonds plc; *Int'l*, pg. 2679
ASBURY CARBONS INC.—See Great Mill Rock LLC; *U.S. Private*, pg. 1765
ASHAPURA MINECHEM LIMITED; *Int'l*, pg. 606
ASIAPHOS LIMITED; *Int'l*, pg. 620
ASSORE LIMITED; *Int'l*, pg. 649
AS TARTU JOUJAAM—See Fortum Oyj; *Int'l*, pg. 2740
ATHA ENERGY CORP.; *Int'l*, pg. 669
AURUMIN LIMITED; *Int'l*, pg. 715
AUSTRALIAN GOLDFIELDS LIMITED; *Int'l*, pg. 721
AUSTRALIAN RARE EARTHS LIMITED; *Int'l*, pg. 722
AUSTRAL RESOURCES AUSTRALIA LTD.; *Int'l*, pg. 719
AVENIRA LIMITED; *Int'l*, pg. 738
B&A FERTILIZERS LIMITED—See AGN Agroindustrial, Projetos e Participacoes Ltda.; *Int'l*, pg. 211
B&A FERTILIZERS LIMITED—See BTG Pactual Holding S.A.; *Int'l*, pg. 1204
BALKAN MINING & MINERALS LIMITED; *Int'l*, pg. 808
BANNERMAN MINING RESOURCES (NAMIBIA) (PTY.) LTD.—See Bannerman Energy Ltd; *Int'l*, pg. 851
BARTON MINES COMPANY LLC; *U.S. Private*, pg. 483
BASIN ENERGY LIMITED; *Int'l*, pg. 887
BASTION MINERALS LIMITED; *Int'l*, pg. 888
BAST JSC; *Int'l*, pg. 888
BATLA MINERALS SA; *Int'l*, pg. 890
BATTERY MINERALS LIMITED; *Int'l*, pg. 890
BAYRIDGE RESOURCES CORP.; *Int'l*, pg. 915
BELARAROX LIMITED; *Int'l*, pg. 963
BELGRAVIA HARTFORD CAPITAL INC.; *Int'l*, pg. 963
BELLAVISTA RESOURCES LTD.; *Int'l*, pg. 966
BELO SUN MINING (BARBADOS) CORP—See Belo Sun Mining Corp.; *Int'l*, pg. 968
BENCHMARK METALS INC.; *Int'l*, pg. 970
BERKH UUL JOINT STOCK COMPANY; *Int'l*, pg. 985
BESSOR MINERALS INC.; *Int'l*, pg. 998
BLACK CANYON LIMITED; *Int'l*, pg. 1059
BLI ZAMBIA LTD—See Boart Longyear Ltd.; *Int'l*, pg. 1094
BLUE STAR GOLD CORP.; *Int'l*, pg. 1069
BML HOLDINGS PTY. LTD.—See Grange Resources Limited; *Int'l*, pg. 3058
BOART LONGYEAR ALBERTA LIMITED—See Boart Longyear Ltd.; *Int'l*, pg. 1094

N.A.I.C.S. INDEX

212390 — OTHER NONMETALLIC M...

BORAX ARGENTINA S.A.; *Int'l*, pg. 1112
BORAX MORARJI LIMITED; *Int'l*, pg. 1112
BPM MINERALS LIMITED; *Int'l*, pg. 1133
BRADDA HEAD LITHIUM LIMITED; *Int'l*, pg. 1134
BUBALUS RESOURCES LIMITED; *Int'l*, pg. 1206
BURLEY MINERALS LTD.; *Int'l*, pg. 1226
CALDERYS BELGIUM SA/NV—See Groupe Bruxelles Lambert SA; *Int'l*, pg. 3099
CALDERYS NORDIC AB—See Groupe Bruxelles Lambert SA; *Int'l*, pg. 3099
CALDERYS SOUTH AFRICA PTY LTD—See Groupe Bruxelles Lambert SA; *Int'l*, pg. 3099
CALIFORNIA-ENGELS MINING CO; *U.S. Public*, pg. 424
CALIX LIMITED; *Int'l*, pg. 1265
CAMINO ROJO S.A. DE C.V.—See Newmont Corporation; *U.S. Public*, pg. 1516
CANN GLOBAL LIMITED; *Int'l*, pg. 1291
CANTERRA MINERALS CORPORATION; *Int'l*, pg. 1299
CANXGOLD MINING CORP.; *Int'l*, pg. 1300
CAPITOL W.B.C. D.O.O.—See Capitol W.B.C. PLC; *Int'l*, pg. 1314
CARGILL DEICING TECHNOLOGIES—See Cargill, Inc.; *U.S. Private*, pg. 756
CARGILL DEICING TECHNOLOGIES—See Cargill, Inc.; *U.S. Private*, pg. 756
CARGILL DEICING TECHNOLOGIES—See Cargill, Inc.; *U.S. Private*, pg. 756
CARLYLE COMMODITIES CORP.; *Int'l*, pg. 1341
CARMEUSE LIME & STONE—See Carmeuse Holding SA; *Int'l*, pg. 1341
CCM CHEMICALS SDN. BHD.—See Batu Kawan Berhad; *Int'l*, pg. 890
CELITE CORPORATION—See Groupe Bruxelles Lambert SA; *Int'l*, pg. 3100
CENTAURUS DIAMOND TECHNOLOGIES, INC.; *U.S. Public*, pg. 467
CENTURY COBALT CORP.; *U.S. Public*, pg. 474
CEYLON GRAPHITE CORP.; *Int'l*, pg. 1426
CFS GROUP, INC.; *Int'l*, pg. 1430
CHARGES MINERALES DU PERIGORD—See Groupe Bruxelles Lambert SA; *Int'l*, pg. 3100
CHATHAM ROCK PHOSPHATE LIMITED; *Int'l*, pg. 1457
CHEMICAL COMPANY OF MALAYSIA BERHAD—See Batu Kawan Berhad; *Int'l*, pg. 890
CHINA KINGS RESOURCES GROUP CO., LTD.; *Int'l*, pg. 1514
CHINA KINGSTONE MINING HOLDINGS LIMITED; *Int'l*, pg. 1514
CINIS FERTILIZER AB; *Int'l*, pg. 1611
CI RESOURCES LIMITED; *Int'l*, pg. 1601
CLEANTECH LITHIUM PLC; *Int'l*, pg. 1655
CLOUDBREAK DISCOVERY PLC; *Int'l*, pg. 1662
CMOC MINING SERVICES PTY LTD—See Evolution Mining Limited; *Int'l*, pg. 2572
CMP MINING INC.; *Int'l*, pg. 1672
CN RESOURCES INC.; *Int'l*, pg. 1673
COBRE LIMITED; *Int'l*, pg. 1683
CODA MINERALS LTD.; *Int'l*, pg. 1687
COMPANHIA INDUSTRIAL FLUMINENSE MINERACAO S.A.—See AMG Critical Materials N.V.; *Int'l*, pg. 426
COMPANIA MINERA MOLINETES SAC—See eEnergy Group Plc; *Int'l*, pg. 2317
COMPASS MINERALS AMERICA INC.—See Compass Minerals International, Inc.; *U.S. Public*, pg. 560
COMPASS MINERALS INTERNATIONAL, INC.; *U.S. Public*, pg. 560
COMPASS MINERALS LOUISIANA INC.—See Compass Minerals International, Inc.; *U.S. Public*, pg. 560
COMPASS MINERALS ODGEN INC.—See Compass Minerals International, Inc.; *U.S. Public*, pg. 560
COMPASS MINERALS STORAGE & ARCHIVES LIMITED—See Compass Minerals International, Inc.; *U.S. Public*, pg. 560
COMPASS MINERALS (UK) LIMITED—See Compass Minerals International, Inc.; *U.S. Public*, pg. 560
COMPASS MINERALS USA INC.—See Compass Minerals International, Inc.; *U.S. Public*, pg. 560
CONDOR EXPLORATION PERU S.A.C.—See Condor Resources Inc.; *Int'l*, pg. 1766
CONTACTO CORREDORES DE SEGUROS S.A.—See Compania de Minas Buenaventura SAA; *Int'l*, pg. 1748
COPPER SEARCH LIMITED; *Int'l*, pg. 1794
CORSA COAL CORP.—See Quintana Capital Group, L.P.; *U.S. Private*, pg. 3328
COSMOS EXPLORATION LIMITED; *Int'l*, pg. 1813
CPG RESOURCES - MINERAL TECHNOLOGIES (PROPRIETARY) LTD—See Downer EDI Limited; *Int'l*, pg. 2185
CPG RESOURCES - QCC PTY LTD—See Downer EDI Limited; *Int'l*, pg. 2185
CRITICAL METALS CORP.—See European Lithium Limited; *Int'l*, pg. 2556
CRITICAL MINERALS GROUP LIMITED; *Int'l*, pg. 1851
CULLEN RESOURCES LIMITED; *Int'l*, pg. 1876
CULPEO MINERALS LIMITED; *Int'l*, pg. 1877
DANAKALI LIMITED; *Int'l*, pg. 1958
DE BEERS AUCTION SALES BELGIUM N.V.—See Anglo American PLC; *Int'l*, pg. 462

DE BEERS AUCTION SALES HONG KONG LIMITED—See Anglo American PLC; *Int'l*, pg. 462
DE BEERS AUCTION SALES ISRAEL LTD—See Anglo American PLC; *Int'l*, pg. 462
DE BEERS AUCTION SALES SINGAPORE PTE LTD—See Anglo American PLC; *Int'l*, pg. 462
DE BEERS CANADA—See Anglo American PLC; *Int'l*, pg. 462
DE BEERS INDIA PVT. LTD—See Anglo American PLC; *Int'l*, pg. 462
DE BEERS SOCIETE ANONYME—See Anglo American PLC; *Int'l*, pg. 462
DEBSWANA DIAMOND COMPANY (PTY) LTD—See Anglo American PLC; *Int'l*, pg. 462
DEBUT DIAMONDS INC.; *Int'l*, pg. 1999
DEYANG HAOHUA QINGPING LINKUANG CO., LTD.—See China National Chemical Corporation; *Int'l*, pg. 1527
DIAMOND GYPSUM, LLC—See Arcosa, Inc.; *U.S. Public*, pg. 186
DICALITE CORPORATION—See RGP Holding, Inc.; *U.S. Private*, pg. 3420
DISCOVERY ALASKA LIMITED; *Int'l*, pg. 2134
DONALD MINERAL SANDS PTY. LTD.—See Astron Corporation Limited; *Int'l*, pg. 662
DUNDAS MINERALS LIMITED; *Int'l*, pg. 2225
DUNDEE PRECIOUS METALS KRUMOVGRAD EAD—See Dundee Precious Metals Inc.; *Int'l*, pg. 2226
ECR MINERALS PLC; *Int'l*, pg. 2301
EKATI DIAMOND MINE—See Burgundy Diamond Mines Limited; *Int'l*, pg. 1224
ELEMENT 21 GOLF CANADA INC—See American Rare Earths & Materials, Corp.; *Int'l*, pg. 423
ENCANTO POTASH CORP.; *Int'l*, pg. 2401
ENCANTO RESOURCES LTD—See Encanto Potash Corp.; *Int'l*, pg. 2401
ENERGOLD DE MEXICO S.A. DE C.V.—See Energold Drilling Corp.; *Int'l*, pg. 2421
ENGELHARD PERU S.A.—See BASF SE; *Int'l*, pg. 883
ENK PLC AUSTRALIAN REGIONAL OFFICE—See DMCI Holdings, Inc.; *Int'l*, pg. 2143
ENTREE LLC—See Entree Resources Ltd.; *Int'l*, pg. 2452
ENTREPRISE MINIERE ET CHIMIQUE SA; *Int'l*, pg. 2453
EP MINERALS, LLC—See Apollo Global Management, Inc.; *U.S. Public*, pg. 165
E-POWER RESOURCES INC.; *Int'l*, pg. 2249
EUROPEAN ENERGY METALS CORP.; *Int'l*, pg. 2556
EUROPEAN LITHIUM LIMITED; *Int'l*, pg. 2556
EVOLUTION ENERGY MINERALS LIMITED; *Int'l*, pg. 2572
EXCALIBAR MINERALS LLC—See Cimbar Performance Minerals, Inc.; *U.S. Private*, pg. 897
EXPLOREX RESOURCES INC.; *Int'l*, pg. 2588
FERRO-ALLOY RESOURCES LIMITED; *Int'l*, pg. 2642
FIRERING STRATEGIC MINERALS PLC; *Int'l*, pg. 2679
FIRESTONE DIAMONDS PLC; *Int'l*, pg. 2679
FIRST IDAHO RESOURCES INC.; *Int'l*, pg. 2684
FLSMIDTH (PTY.) LTD.—See FLSmidth & Co. A/S; *Int'l*, pg. 2711
FMC CORP. - LITHIUM DIVISION, BESSEMER PLANT—See FMC Corporation; *U.S. Public*, pg. 862
FMC CORP. - SPECIALTY CHEMICALS GROUP, LITHIUM DIVISION—See FMC Corporation; *U.S. Public*, pg. 862
FOCUS OPERATIONS PTY LTD—See Focus Minerals Limited; *Int'l*, pg. 2719
FORACO INTERNATIONAL S.A.; *Int'l*, pg. 2728
FORTUNE MINERALS NWT INC.—See Fortune Minerals Limited; *Int'l*, pg. 2743
FRONTIER LITHIUM INC.; *Int'l*, pg. 2795
FUCHS LUBRICANTES S.A.—See FUCHS SE; *Int'l*, pg. 2802
FUCHS LUBRICANTS (HONG KONG) LTD.—See FUCHS SE; *Int'l*, pg. 2803
GALAN LITHIUM LIMITED; *Int'l*, pg. 2870
GALAXY RESOURCES LIMITED—See Allkem Limited; *Int'l*, pg. 359
GEM DIAMONDS LIMITED; *Int'l*, pg. 2914
GEMXX CORPORATION; *U.S. Public*, pg. 910
GENERAL MINING; *Int'l*, pg. 2919
GENSOURCE POTASH CORPORATION; *Int'l*, pg. 2928
GEOALCALI SLU—See Highfield Resources Limited; *Int'l*, pg. 3387
GEOGRACE RESOURCES PHILIPPINES, INC.; *Int'l*, pg. 2933
GEOMET S.R.O.—See CEZ, a.s.; *Int'l*, pg. 1428
GIBB RIVER DIAMONDS LIMITED; *Int'l*, pg. 2962
GK GRAPHIT KROPFMUHL GMBH—See AMG Critical Materials N.V.; *Int'l*, pg. 426
GOLDEN AGE EXPLORATION LTD.; *Int'l*, pg. 3027
GOLDSANDS DEVELOPMENT COMPANY; *Int'l*, pg. 3034
GRAPHITE TYN SPOL. S R.O.—See AMG Critical Materials N.V.; *Int'l*, pg. 426
GREAT QUEST GOLD LTD.; *Int'l*, pg. 3065
GREEN RIVER GOLD CORP.; *Int'l*, pg. 3072
GREENROC STRATEGIC MATERIALS PLC; *Int'l*, pg. 3076
GREFCO, INC.—See RGP Holding, Inc.; *U.S. Private*, pg. 3420
GROWMAX AGRI CORP.—See Coloured Ties Capital Inc.; *Int'l*, pg. 1704
GRUPA AZOTY KOPALNIE I ZAKLADY CHEMICZNE SIARKI "SIARKOPOL" S.A.—See Grupa Azoty S.A.; *Int'l*, pg. 3115

GRUPEX D.D; *Int'l*, pg. 3118
GRUPO INDUSTRIAL MINERA MEXICO, S.A. DE C.V.—See Grupo Mexico, S.A.B. de C.V.; *Int'l*, pg. 3132
GT ADVANCED SAPPHIRE SYSTEMS GROUP LLC—See GT Advanced Technologies Inc.; *U.S. Private*, pg. 1801
HA GIANG MINERAL MECHANICS JOINT STOCK COMPANY; *Int'l*, pg. 3201
HARRISON GYPSUM, LLC—See Arcosa, Inc.; *U.S. Public*, pg. 186
HARVEST MINERALS LIMITED; *Int'l*, pg. 3280
HAWTHORNE COAL COMPANY, INC.—See Arch Resources, Inc.; *U.S. Public*, pg. 180
HAWTHORN RESOURCES CORP.; *Int'l*, pg. 3289
HEAVY MINERALS LIMITED; *Int'l*, pg. 3305
HEXAGON ENERGY MATERIALS LIMITED; *Int'l*, pg. 3370
HI-CRUSH INC.—See Atlas Energy Solutions Inc.; *U.S. Public*, pg. 223
HIGHFIELD RESOURCES LIMITED; *Int'l*, pg. 3387
HYPONEX CORPORATION—See The Scotts Miracle-Gro Company; *U.S. Public*, pg. 2127
ILSE BERGBAU-GMBH—See E.ON SE; *Int'l*, pg. 2258
IMAGE INTERNATIONAL GROUP, INC.; *U.S. Public*, pg. 1112
IMERYS MINERAUX FRANCE SA—See Groupe Bruxelles Lambert SA; *Int'l*, pg. 3100
IMERYS SERVICES SAS—See Groupe Bruxelles Lambert SA; *Int'l*, pg. 3100
I M QUARRIES LIMITED; *Int'l*, pg. 3562
INTERGEMAS MINERACAO E INDUSTRIALIZACAO LTDA—See Belo Sun Mining Corp.; *Int'l*, pg. 968
INTREPID POTASH-NEW MEXICO, LLC—See Intrepid Potash, Inc.; *U.S. Public*, pg. 1159
KAREEVLEI MINING PROPRIETORY LIMITED—See BlueRock Diamonds plc; *Int'l*, pg. 1072
KOCH AGRONOMIC SERVICES, LLC—See Koch Industries, Inc.; *U.S. Private*, pg. 2333
KRONOS B.V.—See Contran Corporation; *U.S. Private*, pg. 1033
LAFARGE GYPSUM (PTY) LTD.—See Holcim Ltd.; *Int'l*, pg. 3448
LEVON RESOURCES LTD.—See Discovery Metals Corp.; *Int'l*, pg. 2134
LIQHOBONG MINING DEVELOPMENT CO.(PROPRIETARY) LIMITED—See Firestone Diamonds plc; *Int'l*, pg. 2679
LITHIUM POWER INTERNATIONAL LIMITED—See Corporacion Nacional del Cobre de Chile; *Int'l*, pg. 1805
LOTOS ASFALT SP. Z O.O.—See Grupa LOTOS S.A.; *Int'l*, pg. 3117
MAFFEI SARDA SILICATI S.P.A.—See Gruppo Minerali Maffei S.p.A.; *Int'l*, pg. 3140
MANA MINERAL S.A.—See Endeavour Mining plc.; *Int'l*, pg. 2402
MEXICHEM FLUOR, S.A. DE C.V.—See Grupo Empresarial Kaluz S.A. de C.V.; *Int'l*, pg. 3127
MICRO-LITE, LLC—See Clarkson Construction Company; *U.S. Private*, pg. 915
MINEMAKERS AUSTRALIA PTY LTD—See Avenira Limited; *Int'l*, pg. 738
MINERA CUORO S.A.S.—See Eat Well Investment Group Inc.; *Int'l*, pg. 2277
MINERA JULCANI S.A.DE C.V.—See Compania de Minas Buenaventura SAA; *Int'l*, pg. 1748
MINERALI INDUSTRIALI S.P.A.—See Gruppo Minerali Maffei S.p.A.; *Int'l*, pg. 3140
MINING REMEDIAL RECOVERY COMPANY—See Mueller Industries, Inc.; *U.S. Public*, pg. 1484
MOSAIC CANADA ULC—See The Mosaic Company; *U.S. Public*, pg. 2116
MOSAIC POTASH COLONSAY ULC—See The Mosaic Company; *U.S. Public*, pg. 2116
MOSAIC POTASH ESTERHAZY LIMITED PARTNERSHIP—See The Mosaic Company; *U.S. Public*, pg. 2116
MP MINERAL LTD.—See Access Industries, Inc.; *U.S. Private*, pg. 51
MULTIBOND, INC.—See CFS Group, Inc.; *Int'l*, pg. 1430
MULTIBOND, INC.—See CFS Group, Inc.; *Int'l*, pg. 1430
MY CITY BUILDERS, INC.; *U.S. Public*, pg. 1487
NEVADA CANYON GOLD CORP.; *U.S. Public*, pg. 1510
NYCO MINERALS, INC.—See RCF Management LLC; *U.S. Private*, pg. 3362
O.K.S.M. SP. Z O.O.—See CRH plc; *Int'l*, pg. 1845
OROPLATA S.A.—See Newmont Corporation; *U.S. Public*, pg. 1516
PELE DIAMOND CORPORATION—See Bhang Inc.; *Int'l*, pg. 1010
PHOSPHATE RESOURCES LIMITED—See CI Resources Limited; *Int'l*, pg. 1601
PRIDE CHEM INDUSTRIES SDN BHD—See Coogee Chemicals Pty Ltd.; *Int'l*, pg. 1788
PROSPECT GLOBAL RESOURCES INC.; *U.S. Private*, pg. 3287
PROYESO, S.A. DE C.V.—See Grupo Lamosa S.A. de C.V.; *Int'l*, pg. 3132

212390 — OTHER NONMETALLIC M...

QUEENSLAND POTASH PTY LIMITED—See Anglo American PLC; *Int'l*, pg. 461
QUIMICA DEL REY S.A. DE C.V.—See Grupo BAL; *Int'l*, pg. 3121
RARE ELEMENT RESOURCES LTD.; *U.S. Public*, pg. 1763
RECON DRILLING S.A.C.—See Geodrill Limited; *Int'l*, pg. 2933
ROCKFORT MINERAL BATH COMPLEX LIMITED—See CEMEX, S.A.B. de C.V.; *Int'l*, pg. 1400
SACHTLEBEN BERGBAU VERWALTUNGSGESELLSCHAFT MIT BESCHRANKTER HAFTUNG—See GEA Group Aktiengesellschaft; *Int'l*, pg. 2903
SALT OF THE EARTH LTD.—See Fortissimo Capital Management Ltd.; *Int'l*, pg. 2740
SALT UNION LIMITED—See Compass Minerals International, Inc.; *U.S. Public*, pg. 560
SAMA S.A.—See Eternit S.A.; *Int'l*, pg. 2521
SAMIN S.A.—See Compagnie de Saint-Gobain SA; *Int'l*, pg. 1733
SAMREC PTY LTD—See Groupe Bruxelles Lambert SA; *Int'l*, pg. 3100
SARDES NIKEL MADENCILIK A.S—See DMCI Holdings, Inc.; *Int'l*, pg. 2143
THE SCOTTS COMPANY—See The Scotts Miracle-Gro Company; *U.S. Public*, pg. 2127
SEA-3 INC.—See Trammo, Inc.; *U.S. Private*, pg. 4204
SIFTO CANADA, INC.—See Compass Minerals International, Inc.; *U.S. Public*, pg. 561
SIMILCO MINES LTD—See HudBay Minerals Inc.; *Int'l*, pg. 3521
SIRIUS MINERALS (AUSTRALIA) PTY LIMITED—See Anglo American PLC; *Int'l*, pg. 461
SMART SAND, INC.; *U.S. Public*, pg. 1895
SNC-LAVALIN PERU S.A.—See AtkinsRealis Group Inc.; *Int'l*, pg. 673
SNC-LAVALIN (PTY) LTD—See AtkinsRealis Group Inc.; *Int'l*, pg. 672
SOHAR ASHAPURA CHEMICALS LLC—See Ashapura Minechem Limited; *Int'l*, pg. 606
SPECIALTY MINERALS, INC.—See Minerals Technologies, Inc.; *U.S. Public*, pg. 1449
SPICA SRL—See Groupe Bruxelles Lambert SA; *Int'l*, pg. 3100
SUNERGY, INC.; *U.S. Private*, pg. 3867
SUZORITE MICA PRODUCTS, INC.—See Cementos Pacasmayo S.A.A.; *Int'l*, pg. 1398
TOR MINERALS INTERNATIONAL INC.; *U.S. Public*, pg. 2164
UNION MINERA DEL SUR, S.A. DE C.V.—See Grupo Empresarial Kaluz S.A. de C.V.; *Int'l*, pg. 3128
UNITED HELIUM, INCORPORATED; *U.S. Private*, pg. 4293
UNITED SALT CORPORATION; *U.S. Private*, pg. 4296
UNIVERSAL POTASH CORPORATION; *U.S. Private*, pg. 4306
URI, INC.—See Westwater Resources, Inc.; *U.S. Public*, pg. 2363
WILSON CREEK ENERGY, LLC—See Quintana Capital Group, L.P.; *U.S. Private*, pg. 3328
WINECO PRODUCTIONS, INC.; *U.S. Public*, pg. 2374
WORLD MINERALS FRANCE—See Groupe Bruxelles Lambert SA; *Int'l*, pg. 3100
WORLD MINERALS, INC.—See Groupe Bruxelles Lambert SA; *Int'l*, pg. 3100
WORLD MINERALS ITALIA SRL—See Groupe Bruxelles Lambert SA; *Int'l*, pg. 3100
YAMANASHI ASAHI DIAMOND INDUSTRIAL CO., LTD.—See Asahi Diamond Industrial Co. Ltd.; *Int'l*, pg. 593
YINGKOU ASTRON MINERAL RESOURCES CO., LTD.—See Astron Corporation Limited; *Int'l*, pg. 662
YOLANI MINERALS (PROPRIETARY) LTD.—See Frontier Rare Earths Limited; *Int'l*, pg. 2795
YORK POTASH LIMITED—See Anglo American PLC; *Int'l*, pg. 461
ZONED PROPERTIES, INC.; *U.S. Public*, pg. 2411

213111 — DRILLING OIL AND GAS WELLS

ABAN OFFSHORE LIMITED; *Int'l*, pg. 48
ABAN SINGAPORE PTE. LTD.—See Aban Offshore Limited; *Int'l*, pg. 48
ABU DHABI OIL CO., LTD.—See ENEOS Holdings, Inc.; *Int'l*, pg. 2415
ADES INTERNATIONAL HOLDING PLC; *Int'l*, pg. 144
ADNOC DRILLING COMPANY PJSC—See Abu Dhabi National Oil Company; *Int'l*, pg. 72
AERA ENERGY LLC; *U.S. Private*, pg. 117
AES DRILLING FLUIDS, LLC—See CES Energy Solutions Corp.; *Int'l*, pg. 1423
AGUA LIBRE MIDSTREAM LLC—See Basic Energy Services Inc.; *U.S. Public*, pg. 279
AJ LUCAS COAL TECHNOLOGIES PTY LIMITED—See A.J. Lucas Group Limited; *Int'l*, pg. 24
AKER FLOATING PRODUCTION ASA—See KKR & Co. Inc.; *U.S. Public*, pg. 1262
AKITA DRILLING LTD.; *Int'l*, pg. 263
AL GHURAIR ENERGY TRADING DMCC—See Al Ghurair Investment LLC; *Int'l*, pg. 278
ALTAIR WATER & DRILLING SERVICES INC.—See Callidus Capital Corporation; *Int'l*, pg. 1265
AMERICAN NOBLE GAS, INC.; *U.S. Public*, pg. 108
ANCHOR KING LTD.—See Clean Harbors, Inc.; *U.S. Public*, pg. 510
ANGUS ENERGY PLC; *Int'l*, pg. 463
ANTON OILFIELD SERVICES GROUP LIMITED; *Int'l*, pg. 484
AQUAMARINE SUBSEA HOUSTON, INC.—See HitecVision AS; *Int'l*, pg. 3426
ARCHER (UK) LIMITED—See Archer Limited; *Int'l*, pg. 547
ARCHER WELL COMPANY (AUSTRALIA) PTY LTD.—See Archer Limited; *Int'l*, pg. 548
ASPAC LUBRICANTS (MALAYSIA) SDN. BHD.—See BP plc; *Int'l*, pg. 1126
ATLAS PETROLEUM EXPLORATION WORLDWIDE, LTD.—See Corcel plc; *Int'l*, pg. 1795
AURORA WELL SERVICE, LLC—See Aurora Power Resources Inc.; *U.S. Private*, pg. 395
AWILCO DRILLING PLC; *Int'l*, pg. 753
AXXIS DRILLING INC.—See Ensign Energy Services Inc.; *Int'l*, pg. 2447
AZTEC WELL SERVICING CO. INC.; *U.S. Private*, pg. 416
BADGER INFRASTRUCTURE SOLUTIONS LTD.; *Int'l*, pg. 796
BARNWELL GEOTHERMAL CORPORATION—See Barnwell Industries, Inc.; *U.S. Public*, pg. 278
BARNWELL OVERSEAS, INC.—See Barnwell Industries, Inc.; *U.S. Public*, pg. 278
BARNWELL SHALLOW OIL, INC.—See Barnwell Industries, Inc.; *U.S. Public*, pg. 278
BCM ENERGY PARTNERS, INC.; *U.S. Private*, pg. 499
BENGAL ENERGY LTD.; *Int'l*, pg. 973
BIG E DRILLING CO.—See Eastham Enterprises Inc.; *U.S. Private*, pg. 1321
BKE SHELF LTD.—See Eurasia Drilling Company Limited; *Int'l*, pg. 2527
BLACKBOX TECHNOLOGIES INTERNATIONAL LLC—See Quanta Services, Inc.; *U.S. Public*, pg. 1750
BLACK DIAMOND ENERGY, INC.; *U.S. Private*, pg. 571
BLAKE INTERNATIONAL USA RIGS, LLC; *U.S. Private*, pg. 578
BLOCK ENERGY PLC; *Int'l*, pg. 1064
BLUE DOLPHIN EXPLORATION COMPANY—See Blue Dolphin Energy Company; *U.S. Public*, pg. 364
BLUE RIDGE GROUP INC.; *U.S. Private*, pg. 591
BOART LONGYEAR DRILLING SERVICES—See Boart Longyear Ltd.; *Int'l*, pg. 1095
BORR DRILLING MANAGEMENT DMCC—See Borr Drilling Limited; *Int'l*, pg. 1114
BOTTOM LINE SERVICES, LLC—See MasTec, Inc.; *U.S. Public*, pg. 1393
BRUNEL ENERGY PTY LTD—See Brunel International N.V.; *Int'l*, pg. 1199
BURGAN COMPANY FOR WELL DRILLING, TRADING & MAINTENANCE KSCC; *Int'l*, pg. 1223
CABO DRILLING (ATLANTIC) CORP—See Cabo Drilling Corp.; *Int'l*, pg. 1246
CABO DRILLING CORP.; *Int'l*, pg. 1246
CABO DRILLING (ONTARIO) CORP.—See Cabo Drilling Corp.; *Int'l*, pg. 1246
CABO DRILLING (PACIFIC) CORP.—See Cabo Drilling Corp.; *Int'l*, pg. 1246
CABO DRILLING (PANAMA) CORP.—See Cabo Drilling Corp.; *Int'l*, pg. 1246
CADOGAN PETROLEUM HOLDINGS LTD—See Cadogan Energy Solutions plc; *Int'l*, pg. 1248
CALFRAC WELL SERVICES CORP.—See Calfrac Well Services Ltd.; *Int'l*, pg. 1263
CANELSON DRILLING (US), INC.—See Ensign Energy Services Inc.; *Int'l*, pg. 2447
CANYON OFFSHORE, INC.—See Helix Energy Solutions Group, Inc.; *U.S. Public*, pg. 1024
CANYON OFFSHORE LIMITED—See Helix Energy Solutions Group, Inc.; *U.S. Public*, pg. 1024
CASTOR DRILLING SOLUTION AS—See Cassa Depositi e Prestiti S.p.A.; *Int'l*, pg. 1355
CATHEDRAL ENERGY SERVICES INC.—See Cathedral Energy Services Ltd.; *Int'l*, pg. 1361
CATHEDRAL ENERGY SERVICES LTD.; *Int'l*, pg. 1361
CENTURION PIPELINE L.P.—See Occidental Petroleum Corporation; *U.S. Public*, pg. 1561
CHAMPION DRILLING, INC.—See Ensign Energy Services Inc.; *Int'l*, pg. 2446
CHESAPEAKE OILFIELD SERVICES, INC.—See Expand Energy Corporation; *U.S. Public*, pg. 808
CHEVRON CANADA LIMITED—See Chevron Corporation; *U.S. Public*, pg. 486
CHEVRON TRINIDAD, INC.—See Chevron Corporation; *U.S. Public*, pg. 487
CHINA OFFSHORE OIL (SINGAPORE) INTERNATIONAL PTE. LTD.—See China National Offshore Oil Corp.; *Int'l*, pg. 1532
C&J WELL SERVICES, INC.—See Basic Energy Services Inc.; *U.S. Public*, pg. 279
CLEAN HARBORS EXPLORATION SERVICES LTD. -
SEISMIC SERVICES—See Clean Harbors, Inc.; *U.S. Public*, pg. 509
COE DRILLING PTY LTD.—See Quanta Services, Inc.; *U.S. Public*, pg. 1750
COMET RIDGE RESOURCES, LLC—See Comet Ridge Limited; *Int'l*, pg. 1711
COMET RIDGE RESOURCES, LLC—See Pine Brook Partners, LLC; *U.S. Private*, pg. 3182
COMET RIDGE USA, INC.—See Comet Ridge Limited; *Int'l*, pg. 1711
COMPASS DIRECTIONAL SERVICES LTD—See Cathedral Energy Services Ltd.; *Int'l*, pg. 1361
COMPLETE ENERGY SERVICES, INC.—See Superior Energy Services, Inc.; *U.S. Private*, pg. 3877
CORE LABORATORIES CANADA LTD.—See Core Laboratories N.V.; *Int'l*, pg. 1798
CORO ENERGY PLC; *Int'l*, pg. 1801
CQSL (AUSTRALIA) PTY LTD.—See China National Offshore Oil Corp.; *Int'l*, pg. 1532
COSL CHEMICALS (TIANJIN), LTD.—See China National Offshore Oil Corp.; *Int'l*, pg. 1532
COSL DRILLING PAN-PACIFIC LTD.—See China National Offshore Oil Corp.; *Int'l*, pg. 1532
COSL MEXICO S.A.DE C.V—See China National Offshore Oil Corp.; *Int'l*, pg. 1532
COSL (MIDDLE EAST) FZE—See China National Offshore Oil Corp.; *Int'l*, pg. 1532
CP ENERGY SERVICES, INC.—See Prospect Capital Corporation; *U.S. Public*, pg. 1728
CYCLONE DRILLING, INC.; *U.S. Private*, pg. 1134
DALDRUP & SOHNE AG; *Int'l*, pg. 1950
DEEP SEA MOORING AS—See Delmar Systems, Inc.; *U.S. Private*, pg. 1197
DIAMOND OFFSHORE DEVELOPMENT COMPANY—See Loews Corporation; *U.S. Public*, pg. 1340
DIAMOND OFFSHORE DRILLING, INC.; *U.S. Public*, pg. 658
DIVERSIFIED ENERGY HOLDINGS, INC.; *U.S. Public*, pg. 670
DLS ARGENTINA LIMITED—See Archer Limited; *Int'l*, pg. 548
DOUBLE STAR DRILLING (1998) LTD; *Int'l*, pg. 2181
DOWNER EDI MINING - MINERALS EXPLORATION PTY LTD—See Downer EDI Limited; *Int'l*, pg. 2185
EASTERN SHORE NATURAL GAS COMPANY—See Chesapeake Utilities Corporation; *U.S. Public*, pg. 485
EASTERNWELL GROUP PTY LIMITED—See Apollo Global Management, Inc.; *U.S. Public*, pg. 166
EASTERNWELL WA PTY LIMITED—See Apollo Global Management, Inc.; *U.S. Public*, pg. 166
E GLOBAL DRILLING CORP—See Energold Drilling Corp.; *Int'l*, pg. 2421
E.G.L. RESOURCES, INC.—See PBEX, LLC; *U.S. Private*, pg. 3118
EMKEY ENERGY, LLC; *U.S. Private*, pg. 1383
ENERGY DRILLING COMPANY; *U.S. Private*, pg. 1395
ENERGY NORTH INCORPORATED; *U.S. Private*, pg. 1395
ENERGY WEST RESOURCES, INC.—See First Reserve Management, L.P.; *U.S. Private*, pg. 1525
ENHANCED PETROLEUM SERVICES PARTNERSHIP—See Ensign Energy Services Inc.; *Int'l*, pg. 2446
ENHANCED WELL TECHNOLOGIES AS—See EV Private Equity; *Int'l*, pg. 2560
ENSIGN ARGENTINA S.A.—See Ensign Energy Services Inc.; *Int'l*, pg. 2446
ENSIGN AUSTRALIA PTY LIMITED—See Ensign Energy Services Inc.; *Int'l*, pg. 2446
ENSIGN DE VENEZUELA C.A.—See Ensign Energy Services Inc.; *Int'l*, pg. 2447
ENSIGN DRILLING, INC.-NISKU OPERATIONS CENTRE—See Ensign Energy Services Inc.; *Int'l*, pg. 2446
ENSIGN DRILLING, INC.—See Ensign Energy Services Inc.; *Int'l*, pg. 2446
ENSIGN DRILLING PARTNERSHIP - ENCORE CORING & DRILLING DIVISION—See Ensign Energy Services Inc.; *Int'l*, pg. 2446
ENSIGN DRILLING PARTNERSHIP - ENSIGN ATLANTIC DIRECTIONAL SERVICES DIVISION—See Ensign Energy Services Inc.; *Int'l*, pg. 2446
ENSIGN DRILLING PARTNERSHIP - ENSIGN CANADIAN DRILLING DIVISION—See Ensign Energy Services Inc.; *Int'l*, pg. 2446
ENSIGN DRILLING PARTNERSHIP - ENSIGN DIRECTIONAL SERVICES DIVISION—See Ensign Energy Services Inc.; *Int'l*, pg. 2446
ENSIGN ENERGY SERVICES INC.; *Int'l*, pg. 2446
ENSIGN INTERNATIONAL ENERGY SERVICES INC. - LATIN AMERICA DIVISION—See Ensign Energy Services Inc.; *Int'l*, pg. 2446
ENSIGN INTERNATIONAL ENERGY SERVICES INC.—See Ensign Energy Services Inc.; *Int'l*, pg. 2446
ENSIGN INTERNATIONAL ENERGY SERVICES—See Ensign Energy Services Inc.; *Int'l*, pg. 2446
ENSIGN ROCKWELL SERVICES—See Ensign Energy Services Inc.; *Int'l*, pg. 2447
ENSIGN UNITED STATES DRILLING (CALIFORNIA) INC. -

N.A.I.C.S. INDEX

213111 — DRILLING OIL AND GA...

ENSIGN CALIFORNIA WELL SERVICES DIVISION—See Ensign Energy Services Inc.; *Int'l*, pg. 2447
ENSIGN UNITED STATES DRILLING (CALIFORNIA) INC. - WEST COAST OILFIELD RENTALS DIVISON—See Ensign Energy Services Inc.; *Int'l*, pg. 2447
ENSIGN UNITED STATES DRILLING-CALIFORNIA—See Ensign Energy Services Inc.; *Int'l*, pg. 2447
ENSIGN UNITED STATES DRILLING INC. - ENSIGN DIRECTIONAL DRILLING SERVICES DIVISION—See Ensign Energy Services Inc.; *Int'l*, pg. 2447
ENSIGN UNITED STATES DRILLING INC. - ENSIGN WELL SERVICES DIVISION—See Ensign Energy Services Inc.; *Int'l*, pg. 2447
ENSIGN UNITED STATES DRILLING INC. - ROCKY MOUNTAIN OILFIELD RENTALS DIVISION—See Ensign Energy Services Inc.; *Int'l*, pg. 2447
ENSIGN UNITED STATES DRILLING, INC.—See Ensign Energy Services Inc.; *Int'l*, pg. 2447
ENSIGN US SOUTHERN DRILLING LLC—See Ensign Energy Services Inc.; *Int'l*, pg. 2447
EXCO RESOURCES-RAVENSWOOD—See EXCO Resources, Inc.; *U.S. Public*, pg. 805
EXXONMOBIL CANADA PROPERTIES—See Exxon Mobil Corporation; *U.S. Public*, pg. 814
FALCON SEABOARD OIL & GAS COMPANY—See Falcon Seaboard Holdings LP; *U.S. Private*, pg. 1466
FEDERAL INTERNATIONAL (2000) LTD; *Int'l*, pg. 2630
FINCANTIERI OIL & GAS S.P.A—See Fincantieri S.p.A.; *Int'l*, pg. 2671
FORAJ SONDE CRAIOVA; *Int'l*, pg. 2728
FORZA PETROLEUM SERVICES S.A.—See Forza Petroleum Limited; *Int'l*, pg. 2748
FRONTERA RESOURCES CORP.; *U.S. Public*, pg. 887
FRONTICA ENGINEERING AS—See Akastor ASA; *Int'l*, pg. 260
GAS2GRID LIMITED; *Int'l*, pg. 2887
GASSEARCH DRILLING SERVICES CORPORATION—See Coterra Energy Inc.; *U.S. Public*, pg. 587
GEODYNAMICS (U.K.) LIMITED—See Oil States International, Inc.; *U.S. Public*, pg. 1565
GREAT WHITE ENERGY SERVICES, INC.—See Archer Limited; *Int'l*, pg. 548
GREAT WHITE PRESSURE CONTROL LLC—See Archer Limited; *Int'l*, pg. 548
GULF DRILLING INTERNATIONAL LIMITED Q.S.C.—See Gulf International Services QSC; *Int'l*, pg. 3181
HALLIBURTON COMPANY GERMANY GMBH—See Halliburton Company; *U.S. Public*, pg. 980
HALLIBURTON DRILLING & EVALUATION—See Halliburton Company; *U.S. Public*, pg. 980
H.B. RENTALS, L.C.—See Superior Energy Services, Inc.; *U.S. Private*, pg. 3877
HELMERICH AND PAYNE MEXICO DRILLING, S. DE R.L. DE C.V.—See Helmerich & Payne, Inc.; *U.S. Public*, pg. 1024
HELMERICH & PAYNE (COLOMBIA) DRILLING CO.—See Helmerich & Payne, Inc.; *U.S. Public*, pg. 1024
HELMERICH & PAYNE DEL ECUADOR, INC.—See Helmerich & Payne, Inc.; *U.S. Public*, pg. 1024
HELMERICH & PAYNE DE VENEZUELA C.A.—See Helmerich & Payne, Inc.; *U.S. Public*, pg. 1024
HELMERICH & PAYNE, INC.; *U.S. Public*, pg. 1024
HELMERICH & PAYNE INC—See Helmerich & Payne, Inc.; *U.S. Public*, pg. 1024
HELMERICH & PAYNE INTERNATIONAL DRILLING CO.—See Helmerich & Payne, Inc.; *U.S. Public*, pg. 1024
HELMERICH & PAYNE PROPERTIES, INC.—See Helmerich & Payne, Inc.; *U.S. Public*, pg. 1024
HELMERICH & PAYNE RASCO, INC.—See Helmerich & Payne, Inc.; *U.S. Public*, pg. 1024
HERCULES DRILLING COMPANY, LLC—See Hercules Offshore, Inc.; *U.S. Private*, pg. 1921
HERCULES OFFSHORE, INC.; *U.S. Private*, pg. 1921
HERCULES OFFSHORE LABUAN CORPORATION—See Hercules Offshore, Inc.; *U.S. Private*, pg. 1921
HERCULES OFFSHORE UK LIMITED—See Hercules Offshore, Inc.; *U.S. Private*, pg. 1921
HESS EQUATORIAL GUINEA INC.—See Kosmos Energy Ltd.; *U.S. Public*, pg. 1275
HESS EQUATORIAL GUINEA INC.—See Warburg Pincus LLC; *U.S. Private*, pg. 4440
HESS TRADING CORPORATION—See Hess Corporation; *U.S. Public*, pg. 1030
HIGH ARCTIC ENERGY SERVICES INC.; *Int'l*, pg. 3385
HIGH ARCTIC ENERGY SERVICES LP—See High Arctic Energy Services Inc.; *Int'l*, pg. 3385
HIGH PLAINS DRILLING, INC.—See Terracon Consultants, Inc.; *U.S. Private*, pg. 3971
HIGHPOINT RESOURCES CORPORATION—See Civitas Resources, Inc.; *U.S. Public*, pg. 507
HILONG (COLOMBIA) OIL SERVICE & ENGINEERING CO., LTD.—See Hilong Holding Limited; *Int'l*, pg. 3393
HILONG MARINE ENGINEERING (HONG KONG) LIMITED—See Hilong Holding Limited; *Int'l*, pg. 3393
HILONG OIL SERVICE & ENGINEERING CO., LTD.—See Hilong Holding Limited; *Int'l*, pg. 3393
HILONG OIL SERVICE & ENGINEERING ECUADOR CIA. LTDA.—See Hilong Holding Limited; *Int'l*, pg. 3393
HILONG OIL SERVICE & ENGINEERING NIGERIA LTD.—See Hilong Holding Limited; *Int'l*, pg. 3393
HILONG OIL SERVICE & ENGINEERING PAKISTAN (PRIVATE) LIMITED—See Hilong Holding Limited; *Int'l*, pg. 3393
HMS BERGBAU AG OIL & GAS DIVISION—See HMS Bergbau AG; *Int'l*, pg. 3432
HUNTING ENERGY SERVICES (DRILLING TOOLS) LIMITED—See Hunting Plc; *Int'l*, pg. 3536
HUNTING ENERGY SERVICES (WELL INTERVENTION) LIMITED—See Hunting Plc; *Int'l*, pg. 3536
HUNTING WELLTONIC LLC—See Hunting Plc; *Int'l*, pg. 3537
HUNTING WELLTONIC LTD.—See Hunting Plc; *Int'l*, pg. 3537
I3 ENERGY PLC; *Int'l*, pg. 3566
IMDEX LIMITED; *Int'l*, pg. 3623
INDEPENDENCE CONTRACT DRILLING, INC.; *U.S. Public*, pg. 1115
INFINITY OIL AND GAS OF TEXAS, INC.—See American Noble Gas, Inc.; *U.S. Public*, pg. 108
INTERNATIONAL DRILLING FLUIDS AND ENGINEERING SERVICES (IDEC) LTD—See Palladium Equity Partners, LLC; *U.S. Private*, pg. 3078
ITHACA ENERGY INC.—See Delek Group Ltd.; *Int'l*, pg. 2012
ITS NETHERLANDS B.V.—See Parker Wellbore Company; *U.S. Public*, pg. 1650
JANNAH HUNT OIL INC.—See Hunt Consolidated, Inc.; *U.S. Private*, pg. 2009
JOHNSON SCREENS (INDIA) PRIVATE LIMITED—See Brookfield Corporation; *Int'l*, pg. 1182
JUSTISS OIL COMPANY, INC.; *U.S. Private*, pg. 2246
JX NIPPON DRILLING CO., LTD.—See ENEOS Holdings, Inc.; *Int'l*, pg. 2416
KENAI DRILLING LIMITED; *U.S. Private*, pg. 2283
KEY ENERGY SERVICES, INC.-APPALACHIAN DIVISION—See Key Energy Services, Inc.; *U.S. Public*, pg. 1225
KEY ENERGY SERVICES, INC.-CALIFORNIA DIVISION—See Key Energy Services, Inc.; *U.S. Public*, pg. 1225
KEY ENERGY SERVICES, INC.-PERMIAN BASIN NORTH DIVISION—See Key Energy Services, Inc.; *U.S. Public*, pg. 1225
KEY ENERGY SERVICES, INC.-ROCKY MOUNTAIN DIVISION—See Key Energy Services, Inc.; *U.S. Public*, pg. 1225
KEY ENERGY SERVICES, INC.; *U.S. Public*, pg. 1225
LARAMIE ENERGY, LLC—See Par Pacific Holdings, Inc.; *U.S. Private*, pg. 1636
LARIAT SERVICES, INC.—See SandRidge Energy, Inc.; *U.S. Private*, pg. 1839
LATSHAW DRILLING AND EXPLORATION COMPANY; *U.S. Private*, pg. 2397
LITTLE RED SERVICES, INC.; *U.S. Private*, pg. 2469
MAERSK DRILLING A/S—See A.P. Moller-Maersk A/S; *Int'l*, pg. 26
MAERSK DRILLING HOLDINGS SINGAPORE PTE. LTD.—See A.P. Moller-Maersk A/S; *Int'l*, pg. 26
MAERSK DRILLING NORGE AS—See A.P. Moller-Maersk A/S; *Int'l*, pg. 26
MAERSK DRILLING USA INC.—See A.P. Moller-Maersk A/S; *Int'l*, pg. 26
MINARD RUN OIL COMPANY; *U.S. Private*, pg. 2740
MONUMENT PRODUCTION, INC.—See Occidental Petroleum Corporation; *U.S. Public*, pg. 1561
MOTIVE DRILLING TECHNOLOGIES, INC.—See Helmerich & Payne, Inc.; *U.S. Public*, pg. 1024
MS DIRECTIONAL, LLC—See Patterson-UTI Energy, Inc.; *U.S. Public*, pg. 1654
MULTI-SHOT, LLC—See Patterson-UTI Energy, Inc.; *U.S. Public*, pg. 1654
MURFIN DRILLING COMPANY INC.; *U.S. Private*, pg. 2815
NASSAU HOLDING CORP.; *U.S. Private*, pg. 2837
NEWPARK AUSTRALIA PTY LTD.—See Newpark Resources, Inc.; *U.S. Public*, pg. 1517
NEWPARK DRILLING FLUIDS ASIA PACIFIC LLC—See Newpark Resources, Inc.; *U.S. Public*, pg. 1517
NEWPARK DRILLING FLUIDS LLC—See SCF Partners Ltd.; *U.S. Private*, pg. 3562
NEXTIER OILFIELD SOLUTIONS INC.—See Patterson-UTI Energy, Inc.; *U.S. Public*, pg. 1654
NIZHNEVARTOVSKBURNEFT, CJSC—See Weatherford International plc; *U.S. Public*, pg. 2339
NORTH COAST ENERGY, INC,—See EXCO Resources, Inc.; *U.S. Public*, pg. 805
NOV DOWNHOLE ITALIA S.R.L.—See NOV, Inc.; *U.S. Public*, pg. 1545
OCCIDENTAL CHEMICAL FAR EAST LIMITED—See Occidental Petroleum Corporation; *U.S. Public*, pg. 1561
OCEAN RIG—See DryShips Inc.; *Int'l*, pg. 2207
OMNI DIRECTIONA BORING LP—See Sage Park, Inc.; *U.S. Private*, pg. 3526
OMNI DIRECTIONAL BORING LP—See Sage Park, Inc.; *U.S. Private*, pg. 3526
ONEOK ENERGY RESOURCES COMPANY—See ONEOK, Inc.; *U.S. Public*, pg. 1603
OXYCHEM DO BRASIL LTDA.—See Occidental Petroleum Corporation; *U.S. Public*, pg. 1562
OXY USA INC.—See Occidental Petroleum Corporation; *U.S. Public*, pg. 1561
PARAFIN CORP.; *U.S. Public*, pg. 1636
PARKER DRILLING ARCTIC OPERATING INC.—See Parker Wellbore Company; *U.S. Public*, pg. 1650
PARKER DRILLING CANADA COMPANY—See Parker Wellbore Company; *U.S. Public*, pg. 1650
PARKER DRILLING COMPANY INTERNATIONAL LIMITED—See Parker Wellbore Company; *U.S. Public*, pg. 1650
PARKER DRILLING COMPANY—See Parker Wellbore Company; *U.S. Public*, pg. 1650
PARKER USA DRILLING COMPANY—See Parker Wellbore Company; *U.S. Public*, pg. 1650
PARRATT-WOLFF, INC.; *U.S. Private*, pg. 3099
PARSLEY ENERGY, LLC—See Pioneer Natural Resources Company; *U.S. Public*, pg. 1693
PARTICLE DRILLING TECHNOLOGIES, LLC; *U.S. Private*, pg. 3101
PATTERSON-UTI DRILLING CANADA LIMITED—See Patterson-UTI Energy, Inc.; *U.S. Public*, pg. 1654
PATTERSON-UTI DRILLING COMPANY, LLC—See Patterson-UTI Energy, Inc.; *U.S. Public*, pg. 1654
PATTERSON-UTI ENERGY, INC.; *U.S. Public*, pg. 1654
PAULSBORO NATURAL GAS PIPELINE COMPANY LLC—See PBF Energy Inc.; *U.S. Public*, pg. 1657
PAYZONE DIRECTIONAL SERVICES; *U.S. Private*, pg. 3118
PBEX, LLC; *U.S. Private*, pg. 3118
PBEX RESOURCES, LLC—See PBEX, LLC; *U.S. Private*, pg. 3118
PD MEXICANA, S. DE R.L. DE C.V.—See Weatherford International plc; *U.S. Public*, pg. 2339
PEAK ENERGY SERVICES LTD.—See Clean Harbors, Inc.; *U.S. Public*, pg. 510
PHELPS DRILLING CO.—See Patterson-UTI Energy, Inc.; *U.S. Public*, pg. 1654
PIONEER ENERGY SERVICES CORP.—See Patterson-UTI Energy, Inc.; *U.S. Public*, pg. 1654
PIONEER WIRELINE SERVICES, L.L.C.—See Patterson-UTI Energy, Inc.; *U.S. Public*, pg. 1654
PLATINUM PRESSURE SERVICES, INC.—See Basic Energy Services Inc.; *U.S. Public*, pg. 279
PRODUCTIONQUEST—See Baker Hughes Company; *U.S. Public*, pg. 265
PROPETRO SERVICES, INC.; *U.S. Private*, pg. 3285
PROTEXA S.A. DE C.V.—See Grupo Protexa S.A. de C.V.; *Int'l*, pg. 3134
PROVIDENCE RESOURCES, INC.; *U.S. Public*, pg. 1730
P.T. BOART LONGYEAR—See Boart Longyear Ltd.; *Int'l*, pg. 1095
PT. COSL INDO—See China National Offshore Oil Corp.; *Int'l*, pg. 1533
PYRAMID DRILLING S.A.E.—See Gulf Petroleum Investment Co. S.A.K.C.; *Int'l*, pg. 3182
QUAIL TOOLS—See Parker Wellbore Company; *U.S. Public*, pg. 1650
QUEST CORING INC.—See ALS Limited; *Int'l*, pg. 378
RADIAL DRILLING SERVICES INC.; *U.S. Private*, pg. 3342
RHEOCHEM INDIA PVT.—See Newpark Resources, Inc.; *U.S. Public*, pg. 1518
RIVAL DOWNHOLE TOOLS LC; *U.S. Private*, pg. 3442
ROCK FALL COMPANY LTD.—See HAL Trust N.V.; *Int'l*, pg. 3225
ROCKWELL SERVICE—See Ensign Energy Services Inc.; *Int'l*, pg. 2447
ROCKWELL SERVICING, INC.—See Ensign Energy Services Inc.; *Int'l*, pg. 2447
SAXON ENERGY SERVICES DEL ECUADOR S.A.—See Schlumberger Limited; *U.S. Public*, pg. 1844
SAXON ENERGY SERVICES INC.—See Schlumberger Limited; *U.S. Public*, pg. 1844
SCANDRILL, INC.; *U.S. Private*, pg. 3561
SCHLUMBERGER B.V.—See Schlumberger Limited; *U.S. Public*, pg. 1844
SCHLUMBERGER CANADA LIMITED—See Schlumberger Limited; *U.S. Public*, pg. 1844
SCHLUMBERGER INDUSTRIES—See Schlumberger Limited; *U.S. Public*, pg. 1846
SCHLUMBERGER INTERNATIONAL—See Schlumberger Limited; *U.S. Public*, pg. 1845
SCIENTIFIC DRILLING INTERNATIONAL INC.; *U.S. Private*, pg. 3574
SCIENTIFIC DRILLING—See Applied Technologies Associates; *U.S. Private*, pg. 299
SEAGAS PIPELINE COMPANY—See Phillips 66 Company; *U.S. Public*, pg. 1688
SERVICES PETROLIERS SCHLUMBERGER S.A.—See Schlumberger Limited; *U.S. Public*, pg. 1846
SERVICIOS HALLIBURTON DE VENEZUELA S.A.—See KBR, Inc.; *U.S. Public*, pg. 1216
SILVER CITY DRILLING (QLD) PTY LIMITED—See Apollo

3127

213111 — DRILLING OIL AND GA...

Global Management, Inc.; *U.S. Public*, pg. 167
SINOR ENGINE COMPANY, INC.—See Arcline Investment Management LP; *U.S. Private*, pg. 313
SOLAR PETROLEUM CORP.—See United Salt Corporation; *U.S. Private*, pg. 4297
SPN WELL SERVICES, INC.—See Superior Energy Services, Inc.; *U.S. Public*, pg. 3877
SST ENERGY CORPORATION; *U.S. Private*, pg. 3770
STALLION OILFIELD SERVICES, LTD.; *U.S. Private*, pg. 3776
STEIER OIL FIELD SERVICE INC.—See Apollo Global Management, Inc.; *U.S. Public*, pg. 167
SUNOCO INC. (R&M)—See Energy Transfer LP; *U.S. Public*, pg. 764
SUPERIOR ENERGY SERVICES DO BRASIL—See Superior Energy Services, Inc.; *U.S. Public*, pg. 3877
SUPERIOR ENERGY SERVICES (SPN) B.V.—See Superior Energy Services, Inc.; *U.S. Public*, pg. 3877
SWN WELL SERVICES, LLC—See Expand Energy Corporation; *U.S. Public*, pg. 809
TALON/LPE; *U.S. Private*, pg. 3927
TAQA ENERGY B.V.—See Abu Dhabi Water & Electricity Authority; *Int'l*, pg. 73
TERRAVICI DRILLING SOLUTIONS, INC.—See Helmerich & Payne, Inc.; *U.S. Public*, pg. 1024
TEXAS KEYSTONE INC.; *U.S. Private*, pg. 3976
TRINIDAD COLOMBIA SAS—See Ensign Energy Services Inc.; *Int'l*, pg. 2447
TRINIDAD DRILLING LTD.—See Ensign Energy Services Inc.; *Int'l*, pg. 2447
TRUE DRILLING CO.—See True Companies; *U.S. Private*, pg. 4247
TWOADAY OIL, INC.; *U.S. Private*, pg. 4267
UAH LIMITED—See Capricorn Energy PLC; *Int'l*, pg. 1316
UNIT DRILLING COMPANY—See Unit Corporation; *U.S. Public*, pg. 2228
UNITED HELICHARTERS PRIVATE LIMITED—See Exhicon Events Media Solutions Ltd.; *Int'l*, pg. 2584
UNITED PETROLEUM DEVELOPMENT CO., LTD.—See ENEOS Holdings, Inc.; *Int'l*, pg. 2418
UNITED PRECISION DRILLING COMPANY W.L.L.—See Weatherford International plc; *U.S. Public*, pg. 2339
U.S. ENERGY DEVELOPMENT CORPORATION; *U.S. Private*, pg. 4270
VANTAGE DRILLING INTERNATIONAL; *U.S. Public*, pg. 2275
VANTAGE ENERGY SERVICES, INC.—See Vantage Drilling Company; *U.S. Public*, pg. 2275
VANTAGE INTERNATIONAL MANAGEMENT COMPANY PTE LTD—See Vantage Drilling Company; *U.S. Public*, pg. 2275
VIBRATION TECHNOLOGY, INC.—See Granite Construction Incorporated; *U.S. Public*, pg. 958
WEATHERFORD CANADA PARTNERSHIP (ADMINISTRATION CENTER)—See Weatherford International plc; *U.S. Public*, pg. 2340
WEATHERFORD CSG DRILLING PTY LTD—See Weatherford International plc; *U.S. Public*, pg. 2340
WEATHERFORD DANMARK AS—See Weatherford International plc; *U.S. Public*, pg. 2340
WEATHERFORD EAST EUROPE SERVICE GMBH—See Weatherford International plc; *U.S. Public*, pg. 2340
WEATHERFORD INTERNATIONAL EASTERN EUROPE SRL—See Weatherford International plc; *U.S. Public*, pg. 2340
WELL ENHANCEMENT SERVICES LLC—See AusTex Oil Limited; *Int'l*, pg. 718
WESTERN WELL PRODUCTION SERVICES LTD.; *U.S. Private*, pg. 4498
ZION OIL & GAS - ISRAEL—See Zion Oil & Gas, Inc.; *U.S. Public*, pg. 2408

213112 — SUPPORT ACTIVITIES FOR OIL AND GAS OPERATIONS

3A-BESTGROUP JSC; *Int'l*, pg. 7
49 NORTH RESOURCES INC.; *Int'l*, pg. 11
5J OILFIELD SERVICES, LLC—See SMG Industries Inc.; *U.S. Public*, pg. 1896
AAKASH EXPLORATION SERVICES LIMITED; *Int'l*, pg. 32
AARON OIL COMPANY, LLC—See Grupo Tradebe Medioambiente S.L.; *Int'l*, pg. 3138
A&A TANK TRUCK, INC.—See Gibson Energy Inc.; *Int'l*, pg. 2963
ABRASILVER RESOURCE CORP.; *Int'l*, pg. 67
ACCELERATED PRODUCTION SYSTEMS, INC.—See Dover Corporation; *U.S. Public*, pg. 678
ACEN CORPORATION—See Ayala Corporation; *Int'l*, pg. 773
ACE SOLAR LLC—See ALLETE, Inc.; *U.S. Public*, pg. 79
ACOMA ENERGY, LLC; *U.S. Private*, pg. 62
ACTEON GROUP LTD.—See Buckthorn Partners LLP; *Int'l*, pg. 1210
ACTEON GROUP LTD.—See OEP Capital Advisors, L.P.; *U.S. Private*, pg. 2997
ACTIVA RESOURCES, LLC—See Activa Resources AG; *Int'l*, pg. 119

ACTIVA RESOURCES, LLC—See CIC Partners, L.P.; *U.S. Private*, pg. 896
ADANI GLOBAL LTD.—See Adani Enterprises Limited; *Int'l*, pg. 125
ADANI WELSPUN EXPLORATION LIMITED—See Adani Enterprises Limited; *Int'l*, pg. 125
ADIRA ENERGY ISRAEL LTD.—See Empower Clinics Inc.; *Int'l*, pg. 2388
ADLER & ALLAN LIMITED—See Sun Capital Partners, Inc.; *U.S. Private*, pg. 3861
ADVANCED DEPOSITION TECHNOLOGIES, INC.; *U.S. Public*, pg. 46
ADVANCED PRODUCTION & LOADING INC.—See NOV, Inc.; *U.S. Public*, pg. 1543
ADVANCED STIMULATION TECHNOLOGIES INC.; *U.S. Private*, pg. 92
ADVANCE HYDROCARBON CORPORATION—See COFRA Holding AG; *Int'l*, pg. 1694
ADX ENERGY PANONIA SRL—See ADX Energy Limited; *Int'l*, pg. 169
ADX VIE GMBH—See ADX Energy Limited; *Int'l*, pg. 169
AFENTRA PLC; *Int'l*, pg. 185
AFFCO LLC; *U.S. Private*, pg. 121
AFRICA OIL ETHIOPIA B.V.—See Africa Oil Corporation; *Int'l*, pg. 190
AFRICA OIL KENYA B.V.—See Africa Oil Corporation; *Int'l*, pg. 190
AFRICA OIL UK LIMITED—See Africa Oil Corporation; *Int'l*, pg. 191
AGR ENERGY SERVICES AS—See Akastor ASA; *Int'l*, pg. 260
AGR GROUP ASA—See Altor Equity Partners AB; *Int'l*, pg. 394
AIBEL AS—See Ferd AS; *Int'l*, pg. 2635
AIBEL AS—See Herkules Capital AS; *Int'l*, pg. 3362
AIDALA MUNAI JSC; *Int'l*, pg. 231
AKITA DRILLING USA CORP.—See Akita Drilling Ltd.; *Int'l*, pg. 263
AKRAB PERKASA SDN BHD—See IJM Corporation Berhad; *Int'l*, pg. 3608
ALCORN PETROLEUM & MINERALS CORPORATION—See Cosco Capital, Inc.; *Int'l*, pg. 1809
AL-DORRA PETROLEUM SERVICES KSCC; *Int'l*, pg. 285
ALFRED FUELING SYSTEMS INC.—See Dover Corporation; *U.S. Public*, pg. 678
AL-HAJ ENTERPRISES (PRIVATE) LIMITED—See Al-Haj Group of Companies; *Int'l*, pg. 285
ALKANE ENERGY LIMITED—See 3i Group plc; *Int'l*, pg. 8
ALL COAST, LLC; *U.S. Private*, pg. 170
ALLIED ENERGY INVESTMENT PTY. LTD.—See CAMAC International Corporation; *U.S. Private*, pg. 725
ALLIED ENERGY PLC.—See CAMAC International Corporation; *U.S. Private*, pg. 725
ALLIED RESOURCES INC.; *U.S. Public*, pg. 80
ALLSTAR ENERGY LIMITED—See 49 North Resources Inc.; *Int'l*, pg. 11
AL MASAOOD OIL INDUSTRY SUPPLIES & SERVICES CO.; *Int'l*, pg. 281
AL-MUNTASER TRADING & CONTRACTING CO. W.L.L.; *Int'l*, pg. 287
ALS COAL - COLLIE—See ALS Limited; *Int'l*, pg. 378
ALSTAR OILFIELD CONTRACTORS LTD.; *Int'l*, pg. 379
ALTO ENERGY LIMITED—See Grand Gulf Energy Limited; *Int'l*, pg. 3054
AL YUSR INDUSTRIAL CONTRACTING COMPANY WLL; *Int'l*, pg. 283
AMEREN MICHIGAN GAS STORAGE, LLC—See Ameren Corporation; *U.S. Public*, pg. 94
AMERICAN BIOFUELS INC.; *Int'l*, pg. 422
THE AMERICAN ENERGY GROUP, LTD.; *U.S. Public*, pg. 2034
AMERICAN ENERGY TRANSPORT, LLC—See AET Holdings, LLC; *U.S. Private*, pg. 120
AMERICAN NATURAL ENERGY CORPORATION; *U.S. Private*, pg. 241
AMERICAN OIL RECOVERY, LLC—See Waste Management, Inc.; *U.S. Public*, pg. 2330
AMERICAN PETRO-HUNTER INC.; *U.S. Public*, pg. 243
AMERICAN SANDS ENERGY CORP.; *U.S. Private*, pg. 246
AMOCO TRINIDAD GAS B.V.—See BP plc; *Int'l*, pg. 1126
AMODAIMI OIL COMPANY, LTD.—See China Petrochemical Corporation; *Int'l*, pg. 1539
ANCHOR DRILLING FLUIDS USA, LLC—See Palladium Equity Partners, LLC; *U.S. Private*, pg. 3078
THE ANDERSONS CLYMERS ETHANOL LLC—See The Andersons Incorporated; *U.S. Public*, pg. 2034
ANDREWS OIL BUYERS, INC.—See NGL Energy Partners LP; *U.S. Public*, pg. 1527
ANGLO AFRICAN OIL & GAS PLC; *Int'l*, pg. 461
ANKOR ENERGY, LLC; *U.S. Private*, pg. 284
ANOTECH DO BRASIL LTDA—See Alten S.A.; *Int'l*, pg. 390
ANOTECH ENERGY DOHA LLC—See Alten S.A.; *Int'l*, pg. 390
ANOTECH ENERGY NIGERIA LIMITED—See Alten S.A.; *Int'l*, pg. 390
ANOTECH ENERGY SA—See Alten S.A.; *Int'l*, pg. 389

ANOTECH ENERGY SINGAPORE PTE. LTD.—See Alten S.A.; *Int'l*, pg. 390
ANOTECH ENERGY USA INC.—See Alten S.A.; *Int'l*, pg. 390
ANTERO RESOURCES CORPORATION; *U.S. Public*, pg. 140
ANTHONY VEDER GROUP N.V.—See HAL Trust N.V.; *Int'l*, pg. 3223
AOC EGYPT PETROLEUM COMPANY, LTD—See Fuji Oil Company, Ltd.; *Int'l*, pg. 2815
APACHE FINANCE CANADA CORPORATION—See APA Corporation; *U.S. Public*, pg. 143
APACHE INTERNATIONAL, INC.—See APA Corporation; *U.S. Public*, pg. 143
APACHE NORTH SEA INVESTMENT—See APA Corporation; *U.S. Public*, pg. 143
APPLIED PETROLEUM TECHNOLOGY A.S.—See Weatherford International plc; *U.S. Public*, pg. 2339
APPLIED PETROLEUM TECHNOLOGY (UK) LIMITED—See Weatherford International plc; *U.S. Public*, pg. 2339
APPLY ASA; *Int'l*, pg. 521
APPROACH OIL & GAS INC.—See Approach Resources Inc.; *U.S. Public*, pg. 300
AQUATIC ENGINEERING & CONSTRUCTION LIMITED—See H2 Equity Partners B.V.; *Int'l*, pg. 3199
ARABIAN DARB GENERAL TRADING & CONTRACTING COMPANY—See Endress+Hauser (International) Holding AG; *Int'l*, pg. 2405
ARCHER LIMITED; *Int'l*, pg. 547
ARCHER OIL TOOLS AS—See Archer Limited; *Int'l*, pg. 547
ARCHER PRESSURE PUMPING LLC—See Archer Limited; *Int'l*, pg. 547
ARCTIC PIPE ENGINEERING, INC.—See Arctic Slope Regional Corporation; *U.S. Public*, pg. 316
ARCTIC PIPE INSPECTION, INC.—See Arctic Slope Regional Corporation; *U.S. Public*, pg. 316
ARGENTA ENERGIA S.A.—See Azabache Energy Inc.; *Int'l*, pg. 776
ARGENTA OIL AND GAS T&T LIMITED—See Azabache Energy Inc.; *Int'l*, pg. 776
AROWAY ENERGY INC.; *Int'l*, pg. 578
ARROWHEAD RESOURCES (U.S.A.) LTD.—See Bucking Horse Energy Inc.; *Int'l*, pg. 1210
ASCO GROUP LIMITED—See Endless LLP; *Int'l*, pg. 2403
ASKER MUNAI EXPLORATION JSC; *Int'l*, pg. 621
ASPECT HOLDINGS, LLC; *U.S. Private*, pg. 351
ASPEN GROUP RESOURCES CORP.; *Int'l*, pg. 629
ASSOCIATED RESOURCES, INC.—See Avisto Capital Partners, LLC; *U.S. Private*, pg. 409
ASTANAGAS KMG JSC; *Int'l*, pg. 651
ATCHAFALAYA MEASUREMENT, INC.—See Sentinel Capital Partners, L.L.C.; *U.S. Private*, pg. 3609
ATINUM E&P, INC.—See Atinum Investment Co., Ltd; *Int'l*, pg. 670
ATLAS ENERGY SOLUTIONS INC.; *U.S. Public*, pg. 223
ATLAS PIPELINE MID-CONTINENT WESTTEX, LLC—See Targa Resources Corp.; *U.S. Public*, pg. 1982
AUDAX ENERGY GMBH—See ADX Energy Limited; *Int'l*, pg. 169
AUDAX ENERGY SRL—See ADX Energy Limited; *Int'l*, pg. 169
AURORA GAS LLC—See Aurora Power Resources Inc.; *U.S. Private*, pg. 395
AUSTEX OIL LIMITED; *Int'l*, pg. 718
AUSTRALIAN OIL & GAS CORP.; *Int'l*, pg. 722
AUSTRALIS OIL & GAS LIMITED; *Int'l*, pg. 723
AUTOSEIS, INC.—See Global Geophysical Services, Inc.; *U.S. Private*, pg. 1714
AUXILLIUM ENERGY, INC.; *U.S. Private*, pg. 402
AVA AFRICA S.A.R.L.—See Newpark Resources, Inc.; *U.S. Public*, pg. 1517
AVA EASTERN EUROPE D.F.& S., S.R.L.—See Newpark Resources, Inc.; *U.S. Public*, pg. 1517
AVA, S.P.A.—See Newpark Resources, Inc.; *U.S. Public*, pg. 1517
A&W WATER SERVICE, INC.—See Superior Energy Services, Inc.; *U.S. Private*, pg. 3877
AXIS EXPLORATION, LLC—See Civitas Resources, Inc.; *U.S. Public*, pg. 507
AZINCOURT ENERGY CORP.; *Int'l*, pg. 780
BABCOCK EAGLETON INC.—See Babcock International Group PLC; *Int'l*, pg. 792
BADLANDS LEASING, LLC—See Select Water Solutions, Inc.; *U.S. Public*, pg. 1862
BADLANDS POWER FUELS, LLC—See Select Water Solutions, Inc.; *U.S. Public*, pg. 1862
BAKER ATLAS - DENVER—See Baker Hughes Company; *U.S. Public*, pg. 264
BAKER ATLAS - PEARLAND—See Baker Hughes Company; *U.S. Public*, pg. 264
BAKER HUGHES AUSTRALIA - CANNING VALE—See Baker Hughes Company; *U.S. Public*, pg. 264
BAKER HUGHES CANADA COMPANY—See Baker Hughes Company; *U.S. Public*, pg. 264
BAKER HUGHES DRILLING FLUIDS—See Baker Hughes Company; *U.S. Public*, pg. 265

N.A.I.C.S. INDEX

213112 — SUPPORT ACTIVITIES ...

BAKER HUGHES INTEQ GMBH—See Baker Hughes Company; *U.S. Public*, pg. 264
BAKER HUGHES ITALIANA SRL—See Baker Hughes Company; *U.S. Public*, pg. 265
BAKER HUGHES SINGAPORE PVT—See Baker Hughes Company; *U.S. Public*, pg. 265
BAKER HUGHES SRL—See Baker Hughes Company; *U.S. Public*, pg. 265
BAKER OIL TOOLS GMBH—See Baker Hughes Company; *U.S. Public*, pg. 264
BAKER PETROLITE IBERICA, S.A.—See Baker Hughes Company; *U.S. Public*, pg. 265
BAKER PETROLITE (MALAYSIA) SDN. BHD.—See Baker Hughes Company; *U.S. Public*, pg. 265
BAKER PETROLITE NORGE—See Baker Hughes Company; *U.S. Public*, pg. 265
BAKER PETROLITE SAUDI ARABIA LTD—See Baker Hughes Company; *U.S. Public*, pg. 265
BAKER PETROLITE—See Baker Hughes Company; *U.S. Public*, pg. 265
BAKER PETROLITE—See Baker Hughes Company; *U.S. Public*, pg. 265
BAKKEN HUNTER, LLC—See Expand Energy Corporation; *U.S. Public*, pg. 808
BALLARD EXPLORATION COMPANY INC; *U.S. Private*, pg. 460
BASF SONATRACH PROPANCHEM S.A.—See BASF SE; *Int'l*, pg. 878
BASIC ENERGY CORPORATION; *Int'l*, pg. 886
BASIN WELL LOGGING WIRELINE SERVICES, INC.—See Steel Partners Holdings L.P.; *U.S. Public*, pg. 1943
BAYWA INTEROIL MINERALOLHANDELSGESELLSCHAFT MBH—See BayWa AG; *Int'l*, pg. 916
BDI - BIOENERGY INTERNATIONAL AG; *Int'l*, pg. 929
BECKMAN PRODUCTION SERVICES, INC.—See Rock Hill Capital Group, LLC; *U.S. Private*, pg. 3464
BEERENBERG CORP.—See Altrad Investment Authority SAS; *Int'l*, pg. 398
BEG LIQUID MUD SERVICES CORP.—See Gibson Energy Inc.; *Int'l*, pg. 2963
BERGESEN WORLDWIDE MEXICO, S.A. DE CV—See BW Offshore Limited; *Int'l*, pg. 1232
BEST WELL SERVICES, LLC (BWS); *U.S. Private*, pg. 544
BETA SA BUZAU; *Int'l*, pg. 1001
BHP BILLITON PETROLEUM (AMERICAS) INC.—See BHP Group Limited; *Int'l*, pg. 1015
BIBBY OFFSHORE AS—See HAL Trust N.V.; *Int'l*, pg. 3226
BIG LAKE SERVICES LLC—See Rock Hill Capital Group, LLC; *U.S. Private*, pg. 3464
BILOXI MARSH LANDS CORP.; *U.S. Public*, pg. 331
BINZAGR FACTORY FOR INSULATION MATERIALS LTD.—See Binzagr Company; *Int'l*, pg. 1035
BIOCNG, LLC—See Tetra Tech, Inc.; *U.S. Public*, pg. 2022
BIO-EN HOLDINGS CORP.; *U.S. Public*, pg. 332
BIRCHCLIFF ENERGY LTD; *Int'l*, pg. 1046
BJ PROCESS & PIPELINE SERVICES CO.—See Baker Hughes Company; *U.S. Public*, pg. 264
BLACK DRAGON RESOURCE COMPANIES, INC.; *U.S. Public*, pg. 340
BLACK ELK ENERGY OFFSHORE OPERATIONS, LLC; *U.S. Private*, pg. 572
BLACK ELK ENERGY; *U.S. Private*, pg. 572
BLACKHAWK GROWTH CORP.; *Int'l*, pg. 1061
BLACK HILLS EXPLORATION & PRODUCTION, INC.—See Black Hills Corporation; *U.S. Public*, pg. 340
BLACKMER PUMP—See Dover Corporation; *U.S. Public*, pg. 679
BLACKROCK OIL CORPORATION; *Int'l*, pg. 1062
BLACK SABLE ENERGY, LLC—See Pass Creek Resources LLC; *U.S. Private*, pg. 3104
BLACK STONE MINERALS, L.P.; *U.S. Public*, pg. 341
BLENCOWE RESOURCES PLC; *Int'l*, pg. 1063
BLUE DOLPHIN SERVICES CO.—See Blue Dolphin Energy Company; *U.S. Public*, pg. 364
BLUE MOUNTAIN MIDSTREAM LLC—See Citizen Energy Operating LLC; *U.S. Private*, pg. 902
BLUE SKY ENERGY INC.; *Int'l*, pg. 1069
BLUE SPHERE CORPORATION; *U.S. Public*, pg. 365
BLUE STAR HELIUM LTD.; *Int'l*, pg. 1070
BLUE WATER PETROLEUM CORP.; *U.S. Private*, pg. 594
BOARDWALK ACQUISITION COMPANY, LLC—See Loews Corporation; *U.S. Public*, pg. 1339
BOARDWALK OPERATING GP, LLC—See Loews Corporation; *U.S. Public*, pg. 1339
BOARDWALK STORAGE COMPANY, LLC—See Loews Corporation; *U.S. Public*, pg. 1339
BOOT CREEK ROYALTY LTD.; *U.S. Private*, pg. 616
B.O.P. PRODUCTS, LLC.; *U.S. Private*, pg. 421
BORDERS & SOUTHERN PETROLEUM PLC; *Int'l*, pg. 1113
BORR COMPANY; *Int'l*, pg. 1114
BORR DRILLING MANAGEMENT (UK) LTD.—See Borr Drilling Limited; *Int'l*, pg. 1114
BOSKALIS OFFSHORE B.V.—See HAL Trust N.V.; *Int'l*, pg. 3225
BOURBON; *Int'l*, pg. 1120
BOWLEVEN PLC; *Int'l*, pg. 1124
BP BERAU LTD.—See BP plc; *Int'l*, pg. 1128

BP EUROPA SE ZWEIGNIEDERLASSUNG BP GAS AUSTRIA—See BP plc; *Int'l*, pg. 1128
BP EXPLORATION (CASPIAN SEA) LTD—See BP plc; *Int'l*, pg. 1128
BP EXPLORATION OPERATING CO LTD—See BP plc; *Int'l*, pg. 1128
BP GAS ESPANA S.A.—See BP plc; *Int'l*, pg. 1128
BP INDIA SERVICES PVT. LTD—See BP plc; *Int'l*, pg. 1129
BP TRINIDAD AND TOBAGO LLC—See BP plc; *Int'l*, pg. 1130
BPX ENERGY INC.—See BP plc; *Int'l*, pg. 1130
BRAMMER ENGINEERING INC.; *U.S. Private*, pg. 635
BRANDT OILFIELD SERVICES—See NOV, Inc.; *U.S. Public*, pg. 1544
BRIGHAM RESOURCES LLC—See Sitio Royalties Corp.; *U.S. Public*, pg. 1889
BRINX RESOURCES LTD.; *U.S. Private*, pg. 655
BROADLAND RADIATORS AND HEAT EXCHANGERS LIMITED—See Caterpillar, Inc.; *U.S. Public*, pg. 449
BRS RESOURCES LTD.; *Int'l*, pg. 1199
BRUNEL ENERGY L.L.C.—See Brunel International N.V.; *Int'l*, pg. 1199
BRUNEL ENERGY QATAR W.L.L.—See Brunel International N.V.; *Int'l*, pg. 1199
BUCKING HORSE ENERGY INC.; *Int'l*, pg. 1209
BURU FITZROY PTY LIMITED—See Buru Energy Limited; *Int'l*, pg. 1227
BW ENERGY GABON SA—See BW Offshore Limited; *Int'l*, pg. 1231
BW EPIC KOSAN LTD.; *Int'l*, pg. 1231
BW LPG LIMITED—See BW Group Ltd.; *Int'l*, pg. 1231
BW OFFSHORE CHINA LTD.—See BW Offshore Limited; *Int'l*, pg. 1231
BW OFFSHORE CYPRUS LTD—See BW Offshore Limited; *Int'l*, pg. 1231
BW OFFSHORE DO BRASIL LTDA—See BW Offshore Limited; *Int'l*, pg. 1232
BW OFFSHORE LIMITED; *Int'l*, pg. 1231
BW OFFSHORE MANAGEMENT B.V.—See BW Offshore Limited; *Int'l*, pg. 1231
BW OFFSHORE NIGERIA LTD.—See BW Offshore Limited; *Int'l*, pg. 1231
BW OFFSHORE NORWAY AS—See BW Offshore Limited; *Int'l*, pg. 1231
BW OFFSHORE SHIPHOLDING CYPRUS LIMITED—See BW Offshore Limited; *Int'l*, pg. 1231
BW OFFSHORE SINGAPORE PTE. LTD.—See BW Offshore Limited; *Int'l*, pg. 1232
BW OFFSHORE (UK) LIMITED—See BW Offshore Limited; *Int'l*, pg. 1231
BW OFFSHORE USA, LLC—See BW Offshore Limited; *Int'l*, pg. 1232
BW OFFSHORE USA MANAGEMENT, INC.—See BW Offshore Limited; *Int'l*, pg. 1232
CADOGAN BITLYANSKE BV—See Cadogan Energy Solutions plc; *Int'l*, pg. 1248
CADOGAN PETROLEUM HOLDINGS BV—See Cadogan Energy Solutions plc; *Int'l*, pg. 1248
CADRE SERVICES INC.—See Apollo Global Management, Inc.; *U.S. Public*, pg. 164
CAIN'S PIPELINE & INDUSTRIAL SERVICES, LLC.; *U.S. Private*, pg. 714
CAIRN ENERGY LUMBINI LIMITED—See Capricorn Energy PLC; *Int'l*, pg. 1316
CALFRAC WELL SERVICES CORP.—See Calfrac Well Services Ltd.; *Int'l*, pg. 1263
CALFRAC WELL SERVICES LTD.; *Int'l*, pg. 1263
CALIMA ENERGY INC.—See Calima Energy Limited; *Int'l*, pg. 1264
CALLON PETROLEUM OPERATING COMPANY—See Callon Petroleum Company; *U.S. Public*, pg. 424
CALTEX LUBRICATING OIL REFINERY PTY LTD.—See Ampol Limited; *Int'l*, pg. 436
CAMAC DEVELOPMENT SERVICES PTY. LTD.—See CAMAC International Corporation; *U.S. Private*, pg. 725
CAMAC INTERNATIONAL LIMITED—See CAMAC International Corporation; *U.S. Private*, pg. 725
CAMAC INTERNATIONAL (UK) LTD.—See CAMAC International Corporation; *U.S. Private*, pg. 725
CAMAC NIGERIA LIMITED—See CAMAC International Corporation; *U.S. Private*, pg. 725
CAMAC TRADING, LLC—See CAMAC International Corporation; *U.S. Private*, pg. 725
CAMERON SYSTEMS LIMITED—See Schlumberger Limited; *U.S. Public*, pg. 1843
CAMERON WEST COAST INC.—See Schlumberger Limited; *U.S. Public*, pg. 1844
CAMINO AGAVE INC.; *U.S. Private*, pg. 729
CAMTERRA RESOURCES PARTNERS; *U.S. Private*, pg. 732
CANADA ENERGY PARTNERS INC.; *Int'l*, pg. 1278
CANADIAN OVERSEAS PETROLEUM LIMITED; *Int'l*, pg. 1285
CANAMAX ENERGY LTD.—See Edge Natural Resources LLC; *U.S. Private*, pg. 1334
CANARY RESOURCES, INC.; *U.S. Private*, pg. 733
CANNING BASIN OIL LIMITED—See Emperor Energy Limited; *Int'l*, pg. 2386

CAPITAL CITY ENERGY GROUP, INC.; *U.S. Private*, pg. 739
CAPITAN CORPORATION—See Duke Energy Corporation; *U.S. Public*, pg. 690
CAPRICORN AMERICAS MEXICO S. DE R.L. DE C.V.—See Capricorn Energy PLC; *Int'l*, pg. 1316
CARBOLIM B.V.—See Air Products & Chemicals, Inc.; *U.S. Public*, pg. 66
CARIBBEAN UTILITIES COMPANY, LTD.—See Fortis Inc.; *U.S. Public*, pg. 2739
CARIMIN PETROLEUM BERHAD; *Int'l*, pg. 1331
CASPIAN ENERGY INC.; *Int'l*, pg. 1354
CASPIAN SERVICES, INC.; *U.S. Public*, pg. 446
CASTROL PAKISTAN PVT. LTD.—See BP plc; *Int'l*, pg. 1130
CAVERTON HELICOPTERS LIMITED—See Caverton Offshore Support Group PLC; *Int'l*, pg. 1362
CAVERTON OFFSHORE SUPPORT GROUP PLC; *Int'l*, pg. 1362
CB&I EUROPE B.V.—See McDermott International, Inc.; *U.S. Public*, pg. 1405
CB&I OIL & GAS EUROPE B.V.—See McDermott International, Inc.; *U.S. Public*, pg. 1405
CDK PERFORATING HOLDINGS, INC.—See Nine Energy Service, Inc.; *U.S. Public*, pg. 1529
CDM RESOURCE MANAGEMENT LLC—See Riverstone Holdings LLC; *U.S. Private*, pg. 3447
C&D PRODUCTION SPECIALISTS CO., INC.; *U.S. Private*, pg. 702
CENTAURUS ENERGY INC.; *Int'l*, pg. 1402
CENTENNIAL GAS LIQUIDS, ULC—See NGL Energy Partners LP; *U.S. Public*, pg. 1527
CENTRAL ENERGY AUSTRALIA PTY LTD—See Energy World Corporation Ltd; *Int'l*, pg. 2423
CENTRAL NATURAL RESOURCES, INC.; *U.S. Public*, pg. 473
CENTRICA STORAGE LIMITED—See Centrica plc; *Int'l*, pg. 1413
CES ENERGY SOLUTIONS CORP.; *Int'l*, pg. 1423
CGG MARINE (AUSTRALIA) PTY. LTD.—See CGG; *Int'l*, pg. 1431
CGG MARINE (NORWAY) AS—See CGG; *Int'l*, pg. 1431
CGG MARINE USA—See CGG; *Int'l*, pg. 1431
CGG SERVICES S.A.—See CGG; *Int'l*, pg. 1431
CGG SERVICES (SINGAPORE) PTE. LTD.—See CGG; *Int'l*, pg. 1431
CGG SERVICES (U.S.) INC.—See CGG; *Int'l*, pg. 1432
CH4 OPERATIONS PTY LTD—See China National Petroleum Corporation; *Int'l*, pg. 1533
CHAGALA COOPERATIEF U.A.—See Chagala Group Limited; *Int'l*, pg. 1436
CHALLENGER ENERGY GROUP PLC; *Int'l*, pg. 1438
CHAPPAL ENERGIES MAURITIUS LIMITED; *Int'l*, pg. 1448
CHARIOT BRASIL PETROLEO E GAS LTDA.—See Chariot Limited; *Int'l*, pg. 1450
CHARIOT OIL & GAS STATISTICS LIMITED—See Chariot Limited; *Int'l*, pg. 1450
CHARTWELL ENERGY LIMITED—See Comet Ridge Limited; *Int'l*, pg. 1711
CHEETAH OIL & GAS LTD.; *Int'l*, pg. 1459
CHELSEA OIL AND GAS LTD.; *Int'l*, pg. 1460
CHEM-GROW PTE. LTD.—See Heatec JieTong Holdings Ltd; *Int'l*, pg. 3305
CHEMINEER, INC.—See NOV, Inc.; *U.S. Public*, pg. 1544
CHEMISOL ITALIA S.R.L.; *Int'l*, pg. 1462
CHENIERE ENERGY, INC.; *U.S. Public*, pg. 485
CHENIERE ENERGY PARTNERS, L.P.—See Cheniere Energy, Inc.; *U.S. Public*, pg. 485
CHESAPEAKE APPALACHIA, LLC—See Expand Energy Corporation; *U.S. Public*, pg. 808
CHESAPEAKE GRANITE WASH TRUST; *U.S. Public*, pg. 485
CHEVRON ARGENTINA S.R.L.—See Chevron Corporation; *U.S. Public*, pg. 486
CHEVRON AUSTRALIA PTY LTD—See Chevron Corporation; *U.S. Public*, pg. 486
CHEVRON CANADA RESOURCES—See Chevron Corporation; *U.S. Public*, pg. 486
CHEVRON FUNDING CORPORATION—See Chevron Corporation; *U.S. Public*, pg. 486
CHEVRON GLOBAL ENERGY INC.—See Chevron Corporation; *U.S. Public*, pg. 486
CHEVRON NIGERIA LIMITED—See Chevron Corporation; *U.S. Public*, pg. 486
CHEVRON U.S.A. INC.—See Chevron Corporation; *U.S. Public*, pg. 487
CHINA ENERGY DEVELOPMENT HOLDINGS LIMITED; *Int'l*, pg. 1500
CHINA OIL & GAS GROUP LIMITED; *Int'l*, pg. 1538
CHIYODA DO BRASIL REPRESENTACOES LTDA.—See Chiyoda Corporation; *Int'l*, pg. 1575
CHIYODA KEISO CO., LTD.—See Chiyoda Corporation; *Int'l*, pg. 1574
CH OFFSHORE LTD—See Baker Technology Limited; *Int'l*, pg. 805
CHOYA OPERATING, LLC—See NGL Energy Partners LP; *U.S. Public*, pg. 1527
CHRISTIE CORROSION CONTROL LTD.—See Corrosion & Abrasion Solutions Ltd.; *Int'l*, pg. 1806

213112 — SUPPORT ACTIVITIES ...

CIMAREX ENERGY CO.—See Coterra Energy Inc.; *U.S. Public*, pg. 587
CIMC RAFFLES OFFSHORE (SINGAPORE) LIMITED—See China International Marine Containers (Group) Co., Ltd.; *Int'l*, pg. 1511
CIRCLE OIL OMAN LIMITED—See Circle Oil PLC; *Int'l*, pg. 1617
CIRCLE OIL PLC; *Int'l*, pg. 1617
CIRMAC INTERNATIONAL B.V.—See Atlas Copco AB; *Int'l*, pg. 679
CKX LANDS, INC.; *U.S. Public*, pg. 507
CLARKSON NORWAY AS—See Clarkson PLC; *Int'l*, pg. 1650
CLAXTON ENGINEERING SERVICES LTD—See Buckthorn Partners LLP; *Int'l*, pg. 1210
CLAXTON ENGINEERING SERVICES LTD—See OEP Capital Advisors, L.P.; *U.S. Private*, pg. 2997
CLAYTON CONSTRUCTION CO. LTD.; *Int'l*, pg. 1653
CLEANCOR ENERGY SOLUTIONS LLC—See AIP, LLC; *U.S. Private*, pg. 136
CLEAN HARBORS SURFACE RENTALS USA, INC.—See Clean Harbors, Inc.; *U.S. Public*, pg. 509
CLEANTEK INDUSTRIES INC.; *Int'l*, pg. 1655
CLEAR CREEK HUNTING PRESERVE, INC.—See APA Corporation; *U.S. Public*, pg. 143
CLEARFORK MIDSTREAM LLC; *U.S. Private*, pg. 932
CLYDE UNION SOUTH EAST ASIA PTE. LTD.—See Lone Star Funds; *U.S. Private*, pg. 2485
CM AROMATICS CO LTD—See Cosmo Energy Holdings Co., Ltd.; *Int'l*, pg. 1811
CNPC — AMG JSC—See China National Petroleum Corporation; *Int'l*, pg. 1533
CNR INTERNATIONAL (COTE D'IVOIRE) S A R L—See Canadian Natural Resources Ltd.; *Int'l*, pg. 1284
CNR INTERNATIONAL (GABON) LIMITED—See Canadian Natural Resources Ltd.; *Int'l*, pg. 1284
CNR INTERNATIONAL (SOUTH AFRICA) LIMITED—See Canadian Natural Resources Ltd.; *Int'l*, pg. 1284
COASTAL CARRIBEAN OIL & MINERALS LTD.; *Int'l*, pg. 1681
COBALT INTERNATIONAL ENERGY, L.P.—See Cobalt International Energy, Inc.; *U.S. Public*, pg. 957
COBRA VENTURE CORPORATION; *Int'l*, pg. 1683
C.O. CYPRUS OPPORTUNITY ENERGY PUBLIC LIMITED; *Int'l*, pg. 1243
COHEN DEVELOPMENT GAS & OIL LTD—See Delek Group Ltd.; *Int'l*, pg. 2011
COLOURED TIES CAPITAL INC.; *U.S. Public*, pg. 1704
COLUMBIA RETAIL SERVICES—See NiSource Inc.; *U.S. Public*, pg. 1530
COMBINED GENERAL FOR GENERAL TRADING & CONTRACTING CO. W.L.L.—See Combined Group Contracting Company KSCC; *Int'l*, pg. 1709
COMPANIA DE INVERSIONES DE ENERGIA S.A.—See Grupo EMES S.A.; *Int'l*, pg. 3126
COMPLETE ENERGY, LLC—See Superior Energy Services, Inc.; *U.S. Private*, pg. 3877
COMPRESSCO CANADA, INC.—See EQT AB; *Int'l*, pg. 2478
COMPRESSCO, INC.—See TETRA Technologies, Inc.; *U.S. Public*, pg. 2024
COMPUTER MODELLING GROUP LTD.; *Int'l*, pg. 1759
COMREP SA; *Int'l*, pg. 1761
CONFIPETROL S.A.; *Int'l*, pg. 1768
CONTACT ENERGY LIMITED; *Int'l*, pg. 1778
CONTANGO OIL & GAS COMPANY—See KKR & Co. Inc.; *U.S. Public*, pg. 1243
CONTANGO OPERATORS, INC.—See KKR & Co. Inc.; *U.S. Public*, pg. 1243
COOL SORPTION A/S—See Diamond Key International Pty. Ltd; *Int'l*, pg. 2105
CORE LAB DE MEXICO S.A. DE C.V.—See Core Laboratories N.V.; *Int'l*, pg. 1798
CORE LABORATORIES LP—See Core Laboratories N.V.; *Int'l*, pg. 1798
CORE LABORATORIES N.V.; *Int'l*, pg. 1798
CORE LABORATORIES (U.K.) LIMITED—See Core Laboratories N.V.; *Int'l*, pg. 1798
COREX (UK) LTD—See Premier Oilfield Laboratories LLC; *U.S. Private*, pg. 3250
CORROSION & ABRASION SOLUTIONS LTD.; *Int'l*, pg. 1806
COSMO ABU DHABI ENERGY EXPLORATION & PRODUCTION CO., LTD.—See Cosmo Energy Holdings Co., Ltd.; *Int'l*, pg. 1811
COSMO DELIVERY SERVICE CO., LTD.—See Cosmo Energy Holdings Co., Ltd.; *Int'l*, pg. 1812
COSMO ENERGY EXPLORATION & PRODUCTION CO., LTD.—See Cosmo Energy Holdings Co., Ltd.; *Int'l*, pg. 1811
COSMO OIL ASHMORE, LTD—See Cosmo Energy Holdings Co., Ltd.; *Int'l*, pg. 1812
COSMO OIL INTERNATIONAL PTE LTD—See Cosmo Energy Holdings Co., Ltd.; *Int'l*, pg. 1812
COSMO OIL SALES CO., LTD.—See Cosmo Energy Holdings Co., Ltd.; *Int'l*, pg. 1812
COSMO PETROLEUM GAS CO., LTD.—See Cosmo Energy Holdings Co., Ltd.; *Int'l*, pg. 1812

COSMO REFINERY SUPPORT SAKAI CO., LTD.—See Cosmo Energy Holdings Co., Ltd.; *Int'l*, pg. 1812
COSTAIN OIL, GAS & PROCESS LTD—See Costain Group PLC; *Int'l*, pg. 1815
CPC INTERNATIONAL TRADING PTE LTD—See CPC Corporation; *Int'l*, pg. 1823
CP WELL TESTING LLC—See Prospect Capital Corporation; *U.S. Public*, pg. 1728
CRESCENT ENERGY COMPANY—See KKR & Co. Inc.; *U.S. Public*, pg. 1243
CREST PUMPING TECHNOLOGIES, LLC—See Nine Energy Service, Inc.; *U.S. Public*, pg. 1529
CROSSROAD CARRIERS LP—See Vertex Energy, Inc.; *U.S. Public*, pg. 2287
CROWCON DETECTION INSTRUMENTS LTD.—See Halma plc; *Int'l*, pg. 3231
CSI COMPRESSCO LP—See EQT AB; *Int'l*, pg. 2478
CURCAS OIL N.V.; *Int'l*, pg. 1878
CURZON ENERGY PLC; *Int'l*, pg. 1880
CWA CONSULTORES & SERVICOS DE PETROLEO LTDA.—See Weatherford International plc; *U.S. Public*, pg. 2339
CWC ENERGY SERVICES CORP.—See Brookfield Corporation; *Int'l*, pg. 1175
CYGAM ENERGY INC.; *Int'l*, pg. 1895
CYGNUS OIL & GAS CORPORATION; *U.S. Public*, pg. 617
CYPRESS ENVIRONMENTAL PARTNERS, L.P.; *U.S. Public*, pg. 617
DAFORA S.A.; *Int'l*, pg. 1912
DAK-TANA WIRELINE, LLC—See Nine Energy Service, Inc.; *U.S. Public*, pg. 1529
DANOS & CUROLE MARINE CONTRACTORS INC.; *U.S. Private*, pg. 1157
DATALOG LWT INC.—See Datalog Technology Inc.; *Int'l*, pg. 1978
DATALOG TECHNOLOGY INC.; *Int'l*, pg. 1978
DATALOG TECHNOLOGY INC.—See Datalog Technology Inc.; *Int'l*, pg. 1978
DAVIS GAS PROCESSING, INC.—See J.L. Davis Companies; *U.S. Private*, pg. 2167
DAWSON OPERATING COMPANY—See Wilks Brothers LLC; *U.S. Private*, pg. 4521
DAWSON SEISMIC SERVICES ULC—See Wilks Brothers LLC; *U.S. Private*, pg. 4521
DAYBREAK OIL AND GAS, INC.; *U.S. Public*, pg. 644
DBNGP HOLDINGS PTY LIMITED—See CK Hutchison Holdings Limited; *Int'l*, pg. 1636
DC INTERNATIONAL; *U.S. Private*, pg. 1179
DEA NORGE AS—See BASF SE; *Int'l*, pg. 885
DECKMA HAMBURG GMBH; *Int'l*, pg. 2001
DEEP ENERGY LLC—See Deep Energy Resources Ltd.; *Int'l*, pg. 2002
DEEP NATURAL RESOURCES LIMITED—See Deep Energy Resources Ltd.; *Int'l*, pg. 2002
DEEP WELL OIL & GAS, INC.; *Int'l*, pg. 2002
DELCOM OILFIELD SERVICES SDN. BHD.—See Deleum Berhad; *Int'l*, pg. 2012
DELEK INFRASTRUCTURES LTD.—See Delek Group Ltd.; *Int'l*, pg. 2011
DELEUM TECHNOLOGY SOLUTIONS SDN. BHD.—See Deleum Berhad; *Int'l*, pg. 2012
DELMAR SYSTEMS, INC.; *U.S. Private*, pg. 1197
DELSCO NORTHWEST, INC.—See Savage Services Corporation; *U.S. Private*, pg. 3555
DEMAND BRANDS, INC.; *U.S. Public*, pg. 653
DENVER PARENT CORPORATION; *U.S. Private*, pg. 1207
DESCO ACQUISITION LLC—See Desco Corporation; *U.S. Private*, pg. 1211
DEVON MIDSTREAM PARTNERS, L.P.—See Devon Energy Corporation; *U.S. Public*, pg. 657
DEVON NEC CORPORATION—See Canadian Natural Resources Ltd.; *Int'l*, pg. 1284
DEXTER ATC FIELD SERVICES LLC—See GI Manager L.P.; *U.S. Private*, pg. 1691
DHS OIL INTERNATIONAL PTY LTD—See Lime Rock Partners, LLC; *U.S. Private*, pg. 2456
DIAMOND ALTERNATIVE ENERGY, LLC—See Valero Energy Corporation; *U.S. Public*, pg. 2272
DIETSMANN N.V.; *Int'l*, pg. 2117
DIGITAL LOCATIONS, INC.; *U.S. Public*, pg. 662
DIMENSION ENERGY CO. LLC; *U.S. Private*, pg. 1232
DIRECT ENERGIE SA; *Int'l*, pg. 2129
DISCOVERY ENERGY SA PTY LTD—See Discovery Energy Corp.; *U.S. Public*, pg. 668
DIVERGENT ENERGY SERVICES CORP.; *Int'l*, pg. 2137
DIVERSCO SUPPLY INC.; *Int'l*, pg. 2137
DIVERSIFIED GAS & OIL CORPORATION—See Diversified Energy Company PLC; *U.S. Public*, pg. 670
DIVERSIFIED OIL & GAS HOLDINGS, LTD.; *U.S. Public*, pg. 670
DM PETROLEUM OPERATIONS COMPANY—See Jacobs Engineering Group, Inc.; *U.S. Public*, pg. 1185
DOLPHIN OFFSHORE ENTERPRISES (INDIA) LTD; *Int'l*, pg. 2159
DOW PIPE LINE COMPANY—See Dow Inc.; *U.S. Public*, pg. 684
DOYON, LIMITED; *U.S. Private*, pg. 1270
DRAEGERWERK AG & CO. KGAA; *Int'l*, pg. 2196

DRAGADOS OFFSHORE, S.A.—See ACS, Actividades de Construccion y Servicios, S.A.; *Int'l*, pg. 111
DRAGON OIL PLC—See Emirates National Oil Company Limited; *Int'l*, pg. 2381
DRILLING TOOLS INTERNATIONAL, INC.—See Drilling Tools International Corp.; *U.S. Public*, pg. 688
DRILLSCAN EUROPE SAS—See Helmerich & Payne, Inc.; *U.S. Public*, pg. 1024
DRILLSCAN SAS—See Helmerich & Payne, Inc.; *U.S. Public*, pg. 1024
DRILLSCAN US, INC.—See Helmerich & Payne, Inc.; *U.S. Public*, pg. 1024
DSG ENERGY LIMITED—See DCC plc; *Int'l*, pg. 1990
DTI DIVERSITECH, INC.—See Bureau Veritas S.A.; *Int'l*, pg. 1221
DT MIDSTREAM, INC.; *U.S. Public*, pg. 689
DUKE OFFSHORE LIMITED; *Int'l*, pg. 2224
DUPRE ENERGY SERVICES, LLC; *U.S. Private*, pg. 1291
DYM ENERGY CORPORATION; *U.S. Private*, pg. 1296
DYNAMIC OFFSHORE RESOURCES, LLC—See SandRidge Energy, Inc.; *U.S. Public*, pg. 1839
EAGLE EXPLORATION CO.; *U.S. Public*, pg. 702
EAGLE FORD OIL AND GAS CORP; *U.S. Public*, pg. 702
EASTERN MARINE SERVICES LIMITED—See China National Offshore Oil Corp.; *Int'l*, pg. 1533
EASTERN MARINE SERVICES LIMITED—See Trico Marine Services, Inc.; *U.S. Private*, pg. 4229
EASTERN PIPELINE CORP.—See Energy Corporation of America; *U.S. Private*, pg. 1394
EASTERN SOLDAR ENGINEERING & CONSTRUCTION SDN. BHD.—See Harbour-Link Group Berhad; *Int'l*, pg. 3272
EASTSIBERIAN PLC; *Int'l*, pg. 2275
EASTVIEW FUEL OILS LIMITED—See Valero Energy Corporation; *U.S. Public*, pg. 2272
EAST WEST PETROLEUM CORP.; *Int'l*, pg. 2270
ECLIPSE IOR SERVICES, LLC—See Flotek Industries, Inc.; *U.S. Public*, pg. 853
ECLIPSE RESOURCES - OHIO, LLC—See Expand Energy Corporation; *U.S. Public*, pg. 808
ECO (ATLANTIC) OIL & GAS LTD.; *Int'l*, pg. 2292
ECOEMISSIONS SOLUTIONS, INC.; *U.S. Private*, pg. 1329
ECOPETROL OLEO E GAS DO BRASIL LTDA.—See Ecopetrol S.A.; *Int'l*, pg. 2298
ECOPETROL USA INC.—See Ecopetrol S.A.; *Int'l*, pg. 2298
ECOSPRAY TECHNOLOGIES S.R.L.—See Carnival Corporation; *U.S. Public*, pg. 438
ECO-STIM ENERGY SOLUTIONS, INC.; *U.S. Public*, pg. 712
EDEN INNOVATIONS LTD.; *Int'l*, pg. 2306
ED INA D.O.O.—See Electricite de France S.A.; *Int'l*, pg. 2350
EDINBURGH PETROLEUM EQUIPMENT LIMITED—See Weatherford International plc; *U.S. Public*, pg. 2339
E ENERGY ADAMS, LLC—See NGL Energy Partners LP; *U.S. Public*, pg. 1527
EES LEASING LLC—See Archrock, Inc.; *U.S. Public*, pg. 186
EIKEN INDUSTRIES CO., LTD; *Int'l*, pg. 2332
ELAND ENERGY INC.; *U.S. Private*, pg. 1350
ELEMENT TECHNICAL SERVICES INC.; *Int'l*, pg. 2358
ELEPHANT OIL CORP.; *U.S. Private*, pg. 1358
ELG OIL LLC—See Energy Transfer LP; *U.S. Public*, pg. 763
EMA LUBRICANTS CO. LTD.—See Exxon Mobil Corporation; *U.S. Public*, pg. 814
EMA LUBRICANTS CO. LTD.—See GIBCA Limited; *Int'l*, pg. 2962
EMIRATES NATIONAL OIL COMPANY LIMITED; *Int'l*, pg. 2381
EMPEROR ENERGY LIMITED; *Int'l*, pg. 2386
EMPIRE PETROLEUM CORPORATION; *U.S. Public*, pg. 753
EMPIRE PETROLEUM PARTNERS, LP—See Haymaker Acquisition Corp.; *U.S. Private*, pg. 1885
EMPIRICA LLC—See ALS Limited; *Int'l*, pg. 378
ENAUTA PARTICIPACOES S.A.; *Int'l*, pg. 2396
ENBRIDGE ENERGY MANAGEMENT, LLC—See Enbridge Inc.; *Int'l*, pg. 2397
ENEGEX LIMITED; *Int'l*, pg. 2411
ENERCLEAR SERVICES INC.—See Corrosion & Abrasion Solutions Ltd.; *Int'l*, pg. 1806
ENEREV5 METALS INC.; *Int'l*, pg. 2418
ENERFIN RESOURCES LP; *U.S. Private*, pg. 1393
ENERGEAN ISRAEL FINANCE LTD.—See Energean plc; *Int'l*, pg. 2419
ENERGEAN ISRAEL TRANSMISSION LTD.—See Energean plc; *Int'l*, pg. 2419
ENERGEAN OIL & GAS S.A.—See Energean plc; *Int'l*, pg. 2419
ENERGEAN PLC; *Int'l*, pg. 2419
ENERGULF RESOURCES INC.; *Int'l*, pg. 2422
ENERGY ACTION LIMITED; *Int'l*, pg. 2422
ENERGY ALLOYS, LLC; *U.S. Private*, pg. 1393
ENERGY ASSETS GROUP LIMITED—See Astatine Investment Partners LLC; *U.S. Private*, pg. 360
ENERGY CORP OF AMERICA—See Energy Corporation of America; *U.S. Private*, pg. 1394
ENERGY OPERATORS, L. P.; *U.S. Private*, pg. 1395

N.A.I.C.S. INDEX

213112 — SUPPORT ACTIVITIES ...

ENERGY REVENUE AMERICA, INC.; *U.S. Public*, pg. 762
ENERVEST, LTD.; *U.S. Private*, pg. 1396
ENESA A.S.—See CEZ, a.s.; *Int'l*, pg. 1427
ENHANCED HYDROCARBON RECOVERY INC.—See HTC Purenergy Inc.; *Int'l*, pg. 3508
ENI ANGOLA EXPLORATION—See Eni S.p.A.; *Int'l*, pg. 2437
ENI AUSTRALIA LIMITED—See Eni S.p.A.; *Int'l*, pg. 2437
ENI AUSTRIA GMBH—See Eni S.p.A.; *Int'l*, pg. 2437
ENI BTC LTD—See Eni S.p.A.; *Int'l*, pg. 2437
ENI GAS & POWER BELGIUM SA—See Eni S.p.A.; *Int'l*, pg. 2437
ENI JPDA 06-105 PTY LTD—See Eni S.p.A.; *Int'l*, pg. 2437
ENI PETROLEUM—See Eni S.p.A.; *Int'l*, pg. 2437
ENI SCHMIERTECHNIK GMBH—See Eni S.p.A.; *Int'l*, pg. 2437
ENI SLOVENSKO SPOL SRO—See Eni S.p.A.; *Int'l*, pg. 2437
ENI TUNISIA BV—See Eni S.p.A.; *Int'l*, pg. 2437
ENI ULX LTD—See Eni S.p.A.; *Int'l*, pg. 2438
ENI USA INC—See Eni S.p.A.; *Int'l*, pg. 2438
ENSIGN ENERGY SERVICES INTERNATIONAL LIMITED - EASTERN HEMISPHERE DIVISION—See Ensign Energy Services Inc.; *Int'l*, pg. 2446
ENSIGN ENERGY SERVICES INTERNATIONAL LIMITED—See Ensign Energy Services Inc.; *Int'l*, pg. 2446
ENSIGN EUROPA SP. Z.O.O.—See Ensign Energy Services Inc.; *Int'l*, pg. 2446
ENSIGN OPERATING COMPANY INC.—See Ensign Energy Services Inc.; *Int'l*, pg. 2446
ENTX GROUP LLC; *U.S. Private*, pg. 1406
EOG RESOURCES TRINIDAD NITRO UNLIMITED—See EOG Resources, Inc.; *U.S. Public*, pg. 782
E.ON BIOERDGAS GMBH—See E.ON SE; *Int'l*, pg. 2252
E.ON IS FURSTENWALDE—See E.ON SE; *Int'l*, pg. 2253
E.ON KOZEP-DUNANTULI GAZHALOZATI ZRT.—See E.ON SE; *Int'l*, pg. 2254
E.ON RUHRGAS AUSTRIA GMBH—See E.ON SE; *Int'l*, pg. 2255
E.ON RUHRGAS E & P GMBH—See E.ON SE; *Int'l*, pg. 2255
E.ON RUHRGAS GPA GMBH—See E.ON SE; *Int'l*, pg. 2255
E.ON RUHRGAS PERSONALAGENTUR GMBH—See E.ON SE; *Int'l*, pg. 2255
E.ON RUHRGAS UK E&P LIMITED—See E.ON SE; *Int'l*, pg. 2255
EOWS MIDLAND COMPANY—See PrimeEnergy Resources Corporation; *U.S. Public*, pg. 1717
EPPING TRANSMISSION COMPANY LLC—See Summit Midstream Partners, LP; *U.S. Public*, pg. 1960
EPRODUCTION SOLUTIONS - CALIFORNIA—See Weatherford International plc; *U.S. Public*, pg. 2341
EPRODUCTION SOLUTIONS—See Weatherford International plc; *U.S. Public*, pg. 2341
EQUINOR ALGERIA AS—See Equinor ASA; *Int'l*, pg. 2484
EQUINOR ANGOLA AS—See Equinor ASA; *Int'l*, pg. 2484
EQUINOR APSHERON AS—See Equinor ASA; *Int'l*, pg. 2484
EQUINOR ARGENTINA AS—See Equinor ASA; *Int'l*, pg. 2484
EQUINOR ASSET MANAGEMENT ASA—See Equinor ASA; *Int'l*, pg. 2484
EQUINOR CANADA LTD.—See Equinor ASA; *Int'l*, pg. 2484
EQUINOR CHINA AS—See Equinor ASA; *Int'l*, pg. 2484
EQUINOR ENERGY AS—See Equinor ASA; *Int'l*, pg. 2484
EQUINOR HOLDING NETHERLANDS B.V.—See Equinor ASA; *Int'l*, pg. 2484
EQUION ENERGIA LIMITED—See Ecopetrol S.A.; *Int'l*, pg. 2298
EQUITABLE ENERGY, LLC—See EQT Corporation; *U.S. Public*, pg. 784
ERCL LIMITED—See Getech Group plc; *Int'l*, pg. 2947
ERGON ENERGY PARTNERS, LP—See Ergon, Inc.; *U.S. Private*, pg. 1418
ERIDGE CAPITAL LIMITED; *Int'l*, pg. 2493
ESIR1, INC.; *U.S. Private*, pg. 1426
ESMARK INC.; *U.S. Private*, pg. 1426
ESREY RESOURCES LTD; *Int'l*, pg. 2508
ESSAR EXPLORATION & PRODUCTION LTD.—See Essar Global Limited; *Int'l*, pg. 2508
ESSAR OILFIELDS SERVICES LIMITED—See Essar Global Limited; *Int'l*, pg. 2508
ESSEM CORPORATION SDN BHD—See Daeyang Electric Co., Ltd.; *Int'l*, pg. 1911
ESSENTIAL ENERGY SERVICES LTD.—See Element Technical Services Inc.; *Int'l*, pg. 2358
ESSO AUSTRALIA PTY LTD—See Exxon Mobil Corporation; *U.S. Public*, pg. 814
ESSO DEUTSCHLAND GMBH—See Exxon Mobil Corporation; *U.S. Public*, pg. 814
ESSO ERDGAS BETEILIGUNGSGESELLSCHAFT MBH—See Exxon Mobil Corporation; *U.S. Public*, pg. 814
ESSO EXPLORATION AND PRODUCTION GUYANA LIMITED—See Exxon Mobil Corporation; *U.S. Public*, pg. 814
ESTACADO ENERGY LLC; *U.S. Private*, pg. 1428

EURASIA DRILLING COMPANY LIMITED; *Int'l*, pg. 2527
EURASIA ENERGY LIMITED; *Int'l*, pg. 2527
EUROIL LIMITED—See Bowleven plc; *Int'l*, pg. 1124
EUROPA OIL & GAS LIMITED—See Europa Oil & Gas (Holdings) plc; *Int'l*, pg. 2555
EXGEO CA—See CGG; *Int'l*, pg. 1432
EXH GP LP LLC—See Archrock, Inc.; *U.S. Public*, pg. 186
EXH MLP LP LLC—See Archrock, Inc.; *U.S. Public*, pg. 186
EXSIF WORLDWIDE, INC.—See Berkshire Hathaway Inc.; *U.S. Public*, pg. 311
EXTERRAN CORPORATION—See Enerflex Ltd.; *Int'l*, pg. 2418
EXTERRAN ENERGY CORP.—See Archrock, Inc.; *U.S. Public*, pg. 186
EXTERRAN ENERGY DE MEXICO, S.A. DE C.V.—See Enerflex Ltd.; *Int'l*, pg. 2419
EXTERRANENERGY SOLUTIONS ECUADOR CIA. LTDA.—See Enerflex Ltd.; *Int'l*, pg. 2419
EXTERRAN HL LLC—See Archrock, Inc.; *U.S. Public*, pg. 186
EXTERRAN SERVICOS DE OLEO E GAS LTDA.—See Enerflex Ltd.; *Int'l*, pg. 2419
EXTERRAN (SINGAPORE) PTE. LTD.—See Enerflex Ltd.; *Int'l*, pg. 2418
EXTERRAN WATER SOLUTIONS ULC—See Enerflex Ltd.; *Int'l*, pg. 2419
EXTREME PLASTICS PLUS, LLC—See Blue Wolf Capital Partners LLC; *U.S. Private*, pg. 594
EXXON AZERBAIJAN LIMITED—See Exxon Mobil Corporation; *U.S. Public*, pg. 814
EXXONMOBIL CANADA LTD.—See Exxon Mobil Corporation; *U.S. Public*, pg. 814
EXXONMOBIL (CHINA) INVESTMENT CO., LTD.—See Exxon Mobil Corporation; *U.S. Public*, pg. 814
EXXONMOBIL CORPORATION—See Exxon Mobil Corporation; *U.S. Public*, pg. 815
EXXONMOBIL EXPLORATION AND PRODUCTION NORWAY AS—See Exxon Mobil Corporation; *U.S. Public*, pg. 815
EXXONMOBIL EXPLORATION & PRODUCTION MALAYSIA INC.—See Exxon Mobil Corporation; *U.S. Public*, pg. 815
EXXONMOBIL FINLAND OY A.B.—See Exxon Mobil Corporation; *U.S. Public*, pg. 815
EXXONMOBIL GAS MARKETING DEUTSCHLAND GMBH—See Exxon Mobil Corporation; *U.S. Public*, pg. 815
EXXONMOBIL GAS MARKETING EUROPE LIMITED—See Exxon Mobil Corporation; *U.S. Public*, pg. 815
EXXONMOBIL PNG LIMITED—See Exxon Mobil Corporation; *U.S. Public*, pg. 816
EXXONMOBIL PRODUCING NETHERLANDS B.V.—See Exxon Mobil Corporation; *U.S. Public*, pg. 816
EXXON NEFTEGAS LIMITED—See Exxon Mobil Corporation; *U.S. Public*, pg. 814
EZRA HOLDINGS LTD.; *Int'l*, pg. 2594
FACT-O-RIG—See Dietswell S.A.; *Int'l*, pg. 2117
FAIRFIELD INDUSTRIES INC.—See Fairfield Maxwell Ltd.; *U.S. Private*, pg. 1463
FALCAN CHAAL PETROLEUM, LTD—See Candax Energy Inc.; *Int'l*, pg. 1289
FALCON ENERGY GROUP LIMITED; *Int'l*, pg. 2610
FALCON OIL & GAS LTD.; *Int'l*, pg. 2611
FAROE PETROLEUM NORGE AS—See DNO North Sea Plc; *Int'l*, pg. 2148
FAROE PETROLEUM (UK) LIMITED—See DNO North Sea Plc; *Int'l*, pg. 2148
FJORDS PROCESSING LIMITED—See NOV, Inc.; *U.S. Public*, pg. 1544
FLOW ENERGY LIMITED—See FAR Limited; *Int'l*, pg. 2617
FLSMIDTH AIRTECH—See FLSmidth & Co. A/S; *Int'l*, pg. 2710
FLUITEC INTERNATIONAL CHINA—See Fluitec International LLC; *U.S. Private*, pg. 1552
FLUKE ENGENHARIA LTDA—See Buckthorn Partners LLP; *Int'l*, pg. 1210
FLUKE ENGENHARIA LTDA.—See OEP Capital Advisors, L.P.; *U.S. Private*, pg. 2997
FLYING A PETROLEUM LTD.; *Int'l*, pg. 2716
FOLEY INSPECTION SERVICES, ULC—See Cypress Environmental Partners, L.P.; *U.S. Public*, pg. 618
FOOTHILLS EXPLORATION, INC.; *U.S. Public*, pg. 864
FORMCAP CORP.; *U.S. Public*, pg. 868
FORTIS ENERGY SERVICES, INC.; *U.S. Private*, pg. 1576
FORTUNE OIL LIMITED; *Int'l*, pg. 2744
FORWARD TRANSPORT—See Forward Corporation; *U.S. Private*, pg. 1577
FOUNDERS OIL & GAS, LLC—See D.R. Horton, Inc.; *U.S. Public*, pg. 620
FRANKLIN MOUNTAIN ENERGY, LLC; *U.S. Private*, pg. 1597
FRANK'S CASING CREW & RENTAL TOOLS, INC.; *U.S. Private*, pg. 1596
FRANK'S TONG SERVICE INC.—See Frank's Casing Crew & Rental Tools, Inc.; *U.S. Private*, pg. 1596
FREESTONE RESOURCES, INC.; *U.S. Private*, pg. 1607
FT. WORTH PIPE SERVICES, LP—See Savage Services Corporation; *U.S. Private*, pg. 3555

FUGRO BRASIL LTDA.—See Fugro N.V.; *Int'l*, pg. 2805
FUGRO CAMEROUN SA—See Fugro N.V.; *Int'l*, pg. 2805
FUGRO GABON SARL—See Fugro N.V.; *Int'l*, pg. 2806
FUGRO GEODETIC LTD.—See Fugro N.V.; *Int'l*, pg. 2806
FUGRO GEOID S.A.S.—See Fugro N.V.; *Int'l*, pg. 2806
FUGRO OCEANSISMICA S.P.A.—See Fugro N.V.; *Int'l*, pg. 2807
FUGRO (USA), INC.—See Fugro N.V.; *Int'l*, pg. 2805
FUTURE METALS NL; *Int'l*, pg. 2856
GAIL GLOBAL (USA) INC.—See GAIL (India) Limited; *Int'l*, pg. 2869
GARY-WILLIAMS PRODUCTION CO.—See Gary Community Investment Company; *U.S. Private*, pg. 1646
GAS CONNECT AUSTRIA GMBH—See Allianz SE; *Int'l*, pg. 344
GAS CONNECT AUSTRIA GMBH—See Eni S.p.A.; *Int'l*, pg. 2438
GAS DIRECT LIMITED—See Air Products & Chemicals, Inc.; *U.S. Public*, pg. 66
GAS RECOVERY SYSTEMS INC.; *U.S. Private*, pg. 1647
GASSECURE AS—See Draegerwerk AG & Co. KGaA; *Int'l*, pg. 2198
GASTAR EXPLORATION LLC—See Ares Management Corporation; *U.S. Public*, pg. 189
GATEWAY GATHERING & MARKETING CO.—See Rosemore, Inc.; *U.S. Private*, pg. 3483
GAZPROM GAZORASP ROSTOV AO; *Int'l*, pg. 2891
GDF SUEZ E&P NEDERLAND B.V.—See ENGIE SA; *Int'l*, pg. 2433
GDF SUEZ E&P NORGE AS—See ENGIE SA; *Int'l*, pg. 2433
GDF SUEZ E&P UK LTD—See ENGIE SA; *Int'l*, pg. 2433
GDS INTERNATIONAL, LLC—See Premium Oilfield Technologies LLC; *U.S. Private*, pg. 3252
GEA BISCHOFF OY—See GEA Group Aktiengesellschaft; *Int'l*, pg. 2898
GENCO ENERGY SERVICES, INC.; *U.S. Private*, pg. 1660
GENEL ENERGY YONETIM HIZMETLERI ANONIM SIRKETI—See Genel Energy plc; *Int'l*, pg. 2917
GENERATION CAPITAL LTD.; *Int'l*, pg. 2920
GENERATION DEVELOPMENT COMPANY, LLC—See Black Hills Corporation; *U.S. Public*, pg. 341
GENTING BIO-OIL SDN BHD—See Genting Berhad; *Int'l*, pg. 2928
GENTING OIL & GAS LIMITED—See Genting Berhad; *Int'l*, pg. 2928
GEOFOR GABON SA—See Fugro N.V.; *Int'l*, pg. 2808
GEO LINK NUSANTARA PTE LTD—See Federal International (2000) Ltd; *Int'l*, pg. 2630
GEOPARK ARGENTINA LIMITED-BERMUDA—See GeoPark Limited; *Int'l*, pg. 2934
GEOPETRO RESOURCES COMPANY; *U.S. Private*, pg. 1681
GEORG PIENING GMBH & CO. KG—See AGRAVIS Raiffeisen AG; *Int'l*, pg. 215
GEOTECH SEISMIC SERVICES PJSC; *Int'l*, pg. 2941
GEOVAULT PTY LIMITED—See Buru Energy Limited; *Int'l*, pg. 1227
GETECH GROUP PLC; *Int'l*, pg. 2947
GIBCA PETROLEUM SERVICES LLC—See GIBCA Limited; *Int'l*, pg. 2962
GLOBAL BIOENERGIES SA; *Int'l*, pg. 2993
GLOBAL CLEAN ENERGY INC.; *U.S. Public*, pg. 941
GLOBAL COMPANIES LLC—See Global Partners LP; *U.S. Public*, pg. 942
GLOBAL DAILY FANTASY SPORTS, INC.; *Int'l*, pg. 2994
GLOBAL ENERGY (HOLDINGS) LTD.; *Int'l*, pg. 2995
GLOBAL GEOPHYSICAL SERVICES, SP. Z.O.O.—See Global Geophysical Services, Inc.; *U.S. Private*, pg. 1714
GLOBAL OFFSHORE SERVICES LTD.; *Int'l*, pg. 2999
GLOBALOGIX, INC.; *U.S. Private*, pg. 1719
GLOBAL PROCESS SYSTEMS LLC—See Al Jaber Group; *Int'l*, pg. 280
GLOBAL PROCESS SYSTEMS PTE LTD—See Al Jaber Group; *Int'l*, pg. 280
GLOBAL PROCESS SYSTEMS SDN BHD—See Al Jaber Group; *Int'l*, pg. 280
GLOBE ENERGY SERVICES, LLC—See Clearlake Capital Group, L.P.; *U.S. Private*, pg. 935
GLOBE EXPLORATION (Y.C.D.) LIMITED PARTNERSHIP; *Int'l*, pg. 3006
GLOBOTEK HOLDINGS INC.; *U.S. Private*, pg. 1720
GM OFFSHORE, INC.—See Tidewater Inc.; *U.S. Public*, pg. 2158
GOAR, ALLISON & ASSOCIATES, LLC—See Fluor Corporation; *U.S. Public*, pg. 859
GOEBEL GATHERING COMPANY, L.L.C.—See The Williams Companies, Inc.; *U.S. Public*, pg. 2142
G.O.I. ENERGY LIMITED; *Int'l*, pg. 2866
GOLAR LNG PARTNERS LP—See New Fortress Energy Inc.; *U.S. Public*, pg. 1511
GOT GERMAN OIL TOOLS GMBH—See NOV, Inc.; *U.S. Public*, pg. 1544
GRAND GULF ENERGY INC.—See Grand Gulf Energy Limited; *Int'l*, pg. 3054
GRAND GULF ENERGY LIMITED; *Int'l*, pg. 3054
GRAND ISLE SHIPYARD INC.—See Nana Regional Corporation, Inc.; *U.S. Private*, pg. 2832
GRAND RIVER GATHERING, LLC—See Summit Midstream

Partners, LP; *U.S. Public*, pg. 1960
GRANITE OPERATING COMPANY—See APA Corporation; *U.S. Public*, pg. 143
GRANITE RIDGE RESOURCES INC.; *U.S. Public*, pg. 958
GRASSLAND WATER SOLUTIONS, LLC—See NGL Energy Partners LP; *U.S. Public*, pg. 1527
GRAYLOC PRODUCTS CANADA LTD.—See Oceaneering International, Inc.; *U.S. Public*, pg. 1562
GREAT WESTERN OIL AND GAS COMPANY—See The Broe Companies, Inc.; *U.S. Private*, pg. 4001
GREENE'S ENERGY CORP.; *U.S. Private*, pg. 1777
GREENHUNTER ENVIRONMENTAL SOLUTIONS, LLC—See GreenHunter Resources, Inc.; *U.S. Private*, pg. 1778
GREEN PLAINS PARTNERS LP—See Green Plains Inc.; *U.S. Public*, pg. 963
GREENS PORT CBR, LLC—See Kinder Morgan, Inc.; *U.S. Public*, pg. 1233
GREKA DRILLING (INDIA) LTD—See Greka Drilling Limited; *Int'l*, pg. 3080
GREKA ENERGY, CHINA—See Greka Energy Corporation; *U.S. Private*, pg. 1783
GREMZ, INC.; *Int'l*, pg. 3080
GROOVE BOTANICALS INC.; *U.S. Public*, pg. 970
GROUNDSTAR RESOURCES LIMITED; *Int'l*, pg. 3088
GRUS, LLC—See Gulfport Energy Corporation; *U.S. Public*, pg. 975
GS CALTEX SINGAPORE PTE., LTD.—See GS Holdings Corp.; *Int'l*, pg. 3142
GS POWER CO.,LTD—See GS Holdings Corp; *Int'l*, pg. 3142
GSV, INC.; *U.S. Public*, pg. 973
GTUIT, LLC—See Caterpillar, Inc.; *U.S. Public*, pg. 452
GUARDIAN GLOBAL SECURITY PLC; *Int'l*, pg. 3170
GUAR GLOBAL LTD.; *U.S. Private*, pg. 1808
GUJARAT ENERGY RESEARCH AND MANAGEMENT INSTITUTE—See Gujarat State Petroleum Corporation Limited; *Int'l*, pg. 3177
GUJARAT NATURAL RESOURCES LIMITED; *Int'l*, pg. 3176
GULF COAST ULTRA DEEP ROYALTY TRUST; *U.S. Public*, pg. 974
GULF ENERGY SAOC—See National Energy Services Reunited Corp.; *U.S. Public*, pg. 1494
GULF KEYSTONE PETROLEUM INTERNATIONAL LTD.—See Gulf Keystone Petroleum Limited; *Int'l*, pg. 3181
GULF KEYSTONE PETROLEUM (UK) LIMITED—See Gulf Keystone Petroleum Limited; *Int'l*, pg. 3181
GULF MARINE SAUDI ARABIA CO. LIMITED—See Gulf Marine Services Plc; *Int'l*, pg. 3181
GULFMARK AMERICAS, INC.—See Tidewater Inc.; *U.S. Public*, pg. 2158
GULFMARK ASIA PTE., LTD.—See Tidewater Inc.; *U.S. Public*, pg. 2158
GULFMARK AS—See Tidewater Inc.; *U.S. Public*, pg. 2158
GULFMARK MANAGEMENT, INC.—See Tidewater Inc.; *U.S. Public*, pg. 2158
GULFMARK OFFSHORE INC.—See Tidewater Inc.; *U.S. Public*, pg. 2158
GULFMARK REDERI AS—See Tidewater Inc.; *U.S. Public*, pg. 2158
GULFMARK U.K. LTD.—See Tidewater Inc.; *U.S. Public*, pg. 2158
GULF PETROLEUM INVESTMENT CO. S.A.K.C.; *Int'l*, pg. 3182
GULF STANDARD ENERGY COMPANY, LLC; *U.S. Private*, pg. 1816
GULLIVER ENERGY LTD.; *Int'l*, pg. 3183
GVS NETZ GMBH—See EnBW Energie Baden-Wurttemberg AG; *Int'l*, pg. 2399
GWE FRANCE S.A.S.—See BAUER Aktiengesellschaft; *Int'l*, pg. 893
GWE PUMPENBOESE GMBH.—See BAUER Aktiengesellschaft; *Int'l*, pg. 893
GX TECHNOLOGY AUSTRALIA PTY LTD.—See ION Geophysical Corporation; *U.S. Public*, pg. 1166
GYRODATA, INC.—See Schlumberger Limited; *U.S. Public*, pg. 1844
GYRO TECHNOLOGIES, INC.—See Lime Rock Partners, LLC; *U.S. Private*, pg. 2456
HAIMO OILFIELD SERVICES CO., LTD.—See Haimo Technologies Group Corp.; *Int'l*, pg. 3211
HALCON FIELD SERVICES, LLC—See Battalion Oil Corp.; *U.S. Public*, pg. 279
THE HALLEN CONSTRUCTION CO. INC.—See Quanta Services, Inc.; *U.S. Public*, pg. 1753
HALLIBURTON ARGENTINA S.A.—See Halliburton Company; *U.S. Public*, pg. 980
HALLIBURTON CANADA CORP.—See Halliburton Company; *U.S. Public*, pg. 980
HALLIBURTON DE MEXICO S.A. DE C.V.—See Halliburton Company; *U.S. Public*, pg. 980
HALLIBURTON ENERGY SERVICES, INC.—See Halliburton Company; *U.S. Public*, pg. 980
HALLIBURTON ENERGY SERVICES, INC.—See Halliburton Company; *U.S. Public*, pg. 980

HALLIBURTON LIMITED—See Halliburton Company; *U.S. Public*, pg. 980
HALLIBURTON NIGERIA LIMITED—See Halliburton Company; *U.S. Public*, pg. 980
HALLIBURTON TRINIDAD LIMITED—See Halliburton Company; *U.S. Public*, pg. 980
HALLIBURTON/WELLDYNAMICS—See Halliburton Company; *U.S. Public*, pg. 981
HALLIN MARINE PTE. LTD.—See Superior Energy Services, Inc.; *U.S. Private*, pg. 3877
HAMMER CONSTRUCTION, INC.; *U.S. Private*, pg. 1849
HARDY OIL AND GAS PLC—See Blake Holdings Limited; *Int'l*, pg. 1062
HARRIET (ONYX) PTY LTD—See APA Corporation; *U.S. Public*, pg. 143
HASCOL PETROLEUM LIMITED; *Int'l*, pg. 3282
HATHAWAY LLC; *U.S. Private*, pg. 1880
HAYNES WIRE ROPE, INC.—See Dot Family Holdings LLC; *U.S. Public*, pg. 1264
HB RENTALS LIMITED—See Superior Energy Services, Inc.; *U.S. Private*, pg. 3877
HEAT WAVES HOT OIL SERVICE, LLC—See Enservco Corporation; *U.S. Public*, pg. 775
HEINRICH HIRDES GMBH—See HAL Trust N.V.; *Int'l*, pg. 3226
HEMISPHERE ENERGY CORPORATION; *Int'l*, pg. 3341
HERA SERVIZI ENERGIA SRL—See Hera S.p.A.; *Int'l*, pg. 3356
HESS CORPORATION; *U.S. Public*, pg. 1030
HESS EXPLORATION AUSTRALIA PTY LIMITED—See Hess Corporation; *U.S. Public*, pg. 1030
HF SINCLAIR CASPER REFINING LLC—See HF Sinclair Corporation; *U.S. Public*, pg. 1033
HF SINCLAIR EL DORADO REFINING LLC—See HF Sinclair Corporation; *U.S. Public*, pg. 1033
HF SINCLAIR PARCO REFINING LLC—See HF Sinclair Corporation; *U.S. Public*, pg. 1033
HF SINCLAIR PUGET SOUND REFINING LLC—See HF Sinclair Corporation; *U.S. Public*, pg. 1033
HIGHLANDER OIL & GAS ASSET LLC—See Magnolia Oil & Gas Corporation; *U.S. Public*, pg. 1354
HIGH SIERRA CRUDE OIL & MARKETING, LLC—See NGL Energy Partners LP; *U.S. Public*, pg. 1527
HILL PETROLEUM—See Hill Petroleum, Inc.; *U.S. Private*, pg. 1945
HILONG PETROLEUM COMPANY LLC—See Hilong Holding Limited; *Int'l*, pg. 3393
HIMALAYA TECHNOLOGIES, INC.; *U.S. Public*, pg. 1041
HINDUSTAN OIL EXPLORATION COMPANY LTD; *Int'l*, pg. 3400
HNZ AUSTRALIA PTY LTD.—See PHI, Inc.; *U.S. Public*, pg. 3168
HNZ NEW ZEALAND LTD.—See PHI, Inc.; *U.S. Public*, pg. 3168
HOEC BARDAHL INDIA LIMITED—See Hindustan Oil Exploration Company Ltd; *Int'l*, pg. 3400
HOLLAND SERVICES, LLC—See H.I.G. Capital, LLC; *U.S. Private*, pg. 1829
HORIZON CONSTRUCTION MANAGEMENT LTD.—See Canadian Natural Resources Ltd.; *Int'l*, pg. 1284
HOUSTON WELL SCREEN COMPANY—See Weatherford International plc; *U.S. Public*, pg. 2339
HOYER MINERALOL LOGISTIK GMBH—See Hoyer GmbH; *Int'l*, pg. 3499
HRC ENERGY RESOURCES (WV), INC.—See Battalion Oil Corp.; *U.S. Public*, pg. 279
HSE INTEGRATED LTD.—See DXP Enterprises, Inc.; *U.S. Public*, pg. 697
H&S PRODUCTIONS, LLC—See CJ Corporation; *Int'l*, pg. 1634
HTC HYDROGEN TECHNOLOGIES CORP.—See HTC Purenergy Inc.; *Int'l*, pg. 3508
HTC PURENERGY INC.; *Int'l*, pg. 3508
HUMBLE ENERGY, INC.; *U.S. Public*, pg. 1071
HUMICLIMA SUR, S.L.—See ACS, Actividades de Construccion y Servicios, S.A.; *Int'l*, pg. 114
HUNTER DISPOSAL, LLC—See GreenHunter Resources, Inc.; *U.S. Private*, pg. 1778
HUNTING COMPANY, US OFFICE—See Hunting Plc; *Int'l*, pg. 3537
HUNTING ENERGY SERVICES (INTERNATIONAL) PTE LIMITED—See Hunting Plc; *Int'l*, pg. 3536
HUNTING ENERGY SERVICES L.P.—See Hunting Plc; *Int'l*, pg. 3537
HUNTINGTON EXPLORATION INC.; *Int'l*, pg. 3537
HYDRODEC DEVELOPMENT CORPORATION PTY LIMITED—See Hydrodec Group plc; *Int'l*, pg. 3547
HYDUKE BUILDING SOLUTIONS—See Hyduke Energy Services Inc.; *Int'l*, pg. 3548
IACX ENERGY LLC—See Glenfarne Group, LLC; *U.S. Private*, pg. 1710
ICON ENERGY LIMITED; *Int'l*, pg. 3583
IDEMITSU OIL & GAS CO., LTD.—See Idemitsu Kosan Co., Ltd.; *Int'l*, pg. 3591
IDEMITSU TANKER CO., LTD.—See Idemitsu Kosan Co., Ltd.; *Int'l*, pg. 3591
IKM CLEANDRILL AS—See EV Private Equity; *Int'l*, pg. 2560
IKM ELEKTRO AS—See IKM Gruppen AS; *Int'l*, pg. 3611

IKM MEASUREMENT SERVICES AUSTRALIA PTY. LTD.—See IKM Gruppen AS; *Int'l*, pg. 3611
IKM MEASUREMENT SERVICES LTD.—See IKM Gruppen AS; *Int'l*, pg. 3611
IKM NORWEGIAN TECHNOLOGY SOLUTIONS AS—See IKM Gruppen AS; *Int'l*, pg. 3611
IKM TESTING ASIA PTE. LTD.—See IKM Gruppen AS; *Int'l*, pg. 3612
IKM TESTING AS—See IKM Gruppen AS; *Int'l*, pg. 3612
IKM TESTING AUSTRALIA PTY. LTD.—See IKM Gruppen AS; *Int'l*, pg. 3612
IKM TESTING BRASIL LTDA—See IKM Gruppen AS; *Int'l*, pg. 3612
IKM TESTING CANADA LTD—See IKM Gruppen AS; *Int'l*, pg. 3612
IKM TESTING KAZAKSTHAN—See IKM Gruppen AS; *Int'l*, pg. 3612
IKM TESTING POLAND SP. Z.O.O—See IKM Gruppen AS; *Int'l*, pg. 3612
IKM TESTING (THAILAND) CO. LTD.—See IKM Gruppen AS; *Int'l*, pg. 3612
IKM TESTING UK LIMITED—See IKM Gruppen AS; *Int'l*, pg. 3612
ILI TECHNOLOGIES (2002) USA CORP.—See Divergent Energy Services Corp.; *Int'l*, pg. 2137
IMPERIAL OIL LIMITED—See Exxon Mobil Corporation; *U.S. Public*, pg. 816
INNOVEX DOWNHOLE SOLUTIONS, INC.—See Intervale Capital, LLC; *U.S. Private*, pg. 2127
INPLAY OIL CORP.—See Freehold Royalties Ltd.; *Int'l*, pg. 2770
INTEGRATED PETROLEUM TECHNOLOGIES, INC.; *U.S. Private*, pg. 2100
INTEGRATED PIPELINE SERVICES, INC.—See Brookfield Corporation; *Int'l*, pg. 1181
INTEGRATED PRODUCTION SERVICES—See Superior Energy Services, Inc.; *U.S. Private*, pg. 3877
INTEGRATED SERVICES (INTL) LIMITED—See Expro Group Holdings N.V.; *Int'l*, pg. 2591
INTERACT PMTI, INC.—See Buckthorn Partners LLP; *Int'l*, pg. 1210
INTERACT PMTI, INC.—See OEP Capital Advisors, L.P.; *U.S. Private*, pg. 2997
INTERMOOR PTE. LTD.—See Buckthorn Partners LLP; *Int'l*, pg. 1210
INTERMOOR PTE. LTD.—See OEP Capital Advisors, L.P.; *U.S. Private*, pg. 2997
INTERMOOR—See Buckthorn Partners LLP; *Int'l*, pg. 1210
INTERMOOR—See OEP Capital Advisors, L.P.; *U.S. Private*, pg. 2997
INTERNATIONAL ENERGY SERVICES, INC.; *U.S. Private*, pg. 2116
INTERNATIONAL ENERGY TRADING LLC—See Osyka Corporation; *U.S. Public*, pg. 1622
INTERNATIONAL LOGGING NETHERLANDS B.V.—See Weatherford International plc; *U.S. Public*, pg. 2339
INTRA OIL SERVICES BERHAD—See Dayang Enterprise Holdings Berhad; *Int'l*, pg. 1985
ION EXPLORATION PRODUCTS (U.S.A.), INC.—See ION Geophysical Corporation; *U.S. Public*, pg. 1166
ISAB S.R.L.—See G.O.I. Energy Limited; *Int'l*, pg. 2866
ITHACA ENERGY (UK) LIMITED—See Delek Group Ltd.; *Int'l*, pg. 2012
JAGGED PEAK ENERGY INC.—See Pioneer Natural Resources Company; *U.S. Public*, pg. 1693
JD FIELD SERVICES, INC.—See National Energy Services, Inc.; *U.S. Private*, pg. 2853
JEBRO INCORPORATED—See MDU Resources Group, Inc.; *U.S. Public*, pg. 1410
JET SPECIALTY, INC.; *U.S. Private*, pg. 2204
JETTA PRODUCTION COMPANY, INC.; *U.S. Private*, pg. 2204
J.O.E.L. JERUSALEM OIL EXPLORATION LTD.—See Equital Ltd.; *Int'l*, pg. 2487
JONES ENERGY FINANCE CORP.—See Jones Energy, Inc.; *U.S. Public*, pg. 2233
J & R WELL SERVICE, LLC—See Rock Hill Capital Group, LLC; *U.S. Private*, pg. 3464
K13 EXTENSIE BEHEER B.V.—See EBN B.V.; *Int'l*, pg. 2285
KEANE FRAC, LP—See Keane Group Holdings, LLC; *U.S. Private*, pg. 2271
KEETON SERVICES, INC.—See Gibson Energy Inc.; *Int'l*, pg. 2963
KERR-MCGEE OIL AND GAS CORPORATION—See Occidental Petroleum Corporation; *U.S. Public*, pg. 1561
KEY ENERGY QTS—See Key Energy Services, Inc.; *U.S. Public*, pg. 1225
KFG RESOURCES LTD.; *U.S. Public*, pg. 1227
KIBO COMPRESSOR CORP.—See Burk Royalty Co.; *U.S. Private*, pg. 687
KILLAM OIL CO. LTD.; *U.S. Private*, pg. 2304
KINDER MORGAN (DELAWARE), INC.—See Kinder Morgan, Inc.; *U.S. Public*, pg. 1233
KIWETINOHK RESOURCES CORP.—See ARC Financial Corp.; *Int'l*, pg. 539
K.K. MARUSHIN—See Idemitsu Kosan Co., Ltd.; *Int'l*, pg. 3591

N.A.I.C.S. INDEX

213112 — SUPPORT ACTIVITIES ...

KLX ENERGY SERVICES—See The Boeing Company; *U.S. Public*, pg. 2040
KOCH HC PARTNERSHIP BV—See Koch Industries, Inc.; *U.S. Private*, pg. 2333
KOIL ENERGY SOLUTIONS, INC.; *U.S. Public*, pg. 1270
KREUZ ENGINEERING LTD.—See Headland Capital Partners Limited; *Int'l*, pg. 3301
LACLEDE ENERGY RESOURCES, INC.—See Spire, Inc; *U.S. Public*, pg. 1918
LAREDO MIDSTREAM SERVICES, LLC—See Vital Energy, Inc.; *U.S. Public*, pg. 2306
LARIO OIL & GAS COMPANY - DENVER DIVISION—See O's Companies Inc.; *U.S. Public*, pg. 2980
LCTI LOW CARBON TECHNOLOGIES INTERNATIONAL INC.; *U.S. Public*, pg. 1296
LEED TOOL CORPORATION—See Superior Energy Services, Inc.; *U.S. Private*, pg. 3877
LEGACY RESERVES SERVICES INC.—See Legacy Reserves, Inc.; *U.S. Private*, pg. 2417
LIBERTY OILFIELD SERVICES LLC—See Liberty Energy Inc.; *U.S. Public*, pg. 1311
LILIS ENERGY, INC.; *U.S. Private*, pg. 2455
LIVECHAIN, INC.; *U.S. Private*, pg. 2473
LIVETOBEHAPPY, INC.; *U.S. Public*, pg. 1333
LLC ASTROINVEST-ENERGY—See Cadogan Energy Solutions plc; *Int'l*, pg. 1248
LLC INDUSTRIAL COMPANY GAZVYDOBUVANNYA—See Cadogan Energy Solutions plc; *Int'l*, pg. 1248
LLOG EXPLORATION OFFSHORE, INC.; *U.S. Private*, pg. 2475
LOGICOM N.G.—See Vontier Corporation; *U.S. Public*, pg. 2309
LONESTAR RESOURCES US INC.—See Baytex Energy Corp.; *Int'l*, pg. 915
LONESTAR WEST INC.—See Clean Harbors, Inc.; *U.S. Public*, pg. 510
LONGWOOD GATHERING & DISPOSAL SYSTEMS, LP—See Matador Resources Company; *U.S. Public*, pg. 1395
LOTOS EXPLORATION AND PRODUCTION NORGE AS—See Grupa LOTOS S.A.; *Int'l*, pg. 3117
LOUISIANA GAS DEVELOPMENT CORP.; *U.S. Private*, pg. 2499
LUCA TECHNOLOGIES INC.; *U.S. Private*, pg. 2510
LUCID ENERGY GROUP II, LLC—See Targa Resources Corp.; *U.S. Public*, pg. 1981
LUCID ENERGY GROUP, LLC—See EnCap Investments L.P.; *U.S. Private*, pg. 1390
LYNX OPERATING COMPANY INCORPORATED; *U.S. Private*, pg. 2522
MACPHERSON ENERGY CORP.—See Berry Corporation (Bry); *U.S. Public*, pg. 320
MAGNEGAS ARC APPLIED SOLUTIONS—See BBHC, Inc.; *U.S. Public*, pg. 284
MARATHON MARTINEZ REFINERY—See Marathon Petroleum Corporation; *U.S. Public*, pg. 1363
MARATHON OIL EXPLORATION (U.K.) LIMITED—See ConocoPhillips; *U.S. Public*, pg. 569
MARTIN OPERATING PARTNERSHIP L.P.—See Martin Midstream Partners LP; *U.S. Public*, pg. 1389
MASTERBLASTERS INDUSTRIAL COATINGS INC.—See Corrosion & Abrasion Solutions Ltd.; *Int'l*, pg. 1806
MATADOR PRODUCTION COMPANY—See Matador Resources Company; *U.S. Public*, pg. 1395
MATRIX SERVICE, INC.—See Matrix Service Company; *U.S. Public*, pg. 1397
MATRIX SERVICE, INC.—See Matrix Service Company; *U.S. Public*, pg. 1397
MATRIX SERVICE, INC.—See Matrix Service Company; *U.S. Public*, pg. 1397
MAVERICK ENERGY GROUP, LTD.; *U.S. Public*, pg. 1402
MCDERMOTT MARINE CONSTRUCTION LIMITED—See McDermott International, Inc.; *U.S. Public*, pg. 1405
MDM PERMIAN, INC.; *U.S. Public*, pg. 1409
MEENAN OIL CO., LP—See Star Group, L.P.; *U.S. Public*, pg. 1937
MERITAGE MIDSTREAM SERVICES II, LLC—See Western Midstream Partners, LP; *U.S. Public*, pg. 2356
MG CLEANERS LLC—See SMG Industries Inc.; *U.S. Public*, pg. 1896
MHR MANAGEMENT, LLC—See Expand Energy Corporation; *U.S. Public*, pg. 808
MIDCON MIDSTREAM, LP—See SandRidge Energy, Inc.; *U.S. Public*, pg. 1839
MIDFLOW SERVICES, LLC—See Profire Energy, Inc.; *U.S. Public*, pg. 1724
MISSION CRITICAL FACILITIES INTERNATIONAL LLC—See Mission Critical Group; *U.S. Private*, pg. 2747
MISSOURI BASIN WELL SERVICE, INC.; *U.S. Private*, pg. 2749
MMI SERVICES, INC.; *U.S. Private*, pg. 2755
MONDIAL VENTURES, INC.; *U.S. Private*, pg. 2769
MOUNTAINVIEW ENERGY LTD.; *U.S. Public*, pg. 1479
MULLER HRM ENGINEERING AB—See ATON GmbH; *Int'l*, pg. 689
MURPHY EXPLORATION & PRODUCTION COMPANY—See Murphy Oil Corporation; *U.S. Public*, pg. 1487

MUSTANG HEAVY HAUL LLC—See Latshaw Drilling and Exploration Company; *U.S. Private*, pg. 2397
NANA REGIONAL CORPORATION, INC.; *U.S. Private*, pg. 2832
NAPHTHA ISRAEL PETROLEUM CORPORATION LTD.—See Equital Ltd.; *Int'l*, pg. 2487
NATIONAL GULF PETROLEUM SERVICES WLL—See National Energy Services Reunited Corp.; *U.S. Public*, pg. 1494
NATIONAL PETROLEUM SERVICES JSC—See National Energy Services Reunited Corp.; *U.S. Public*, pg. 1494
NATIVE AMERICAN ENERGY GROUP, INC.; *U.S. Private*, pg. 2866
NCS MULTISTAGE INC.—See NCS Multistage Holdings, Inc.; *U.S. Public*, pg. 1503
NEPTUNE E&P NORGE—See Eni S.p.A.; *Int'l*, pg. 2438
NEWCASTLE PIPE LINE COMPANY PTY LTD—See Ampol Limited; *Int'l*, pg. 436
NEW FORTRESS ENERGY INC.; *U.S. Public*, pg. 1511
NEWPARK CANADA, INC.—See Newpark Resources, Inc.; *U.S. Public*, pg. 1517
NEWPARK CHILE LIMITADA—See Newpark Resources, Inc.; *U.S. Public*, pg. 1517
NEWPARK DRILLING FLUIDS (AUSTRALIA) LIMITED—See Newpark Resources, Inc.; *U.S. Public*, pg. 1517
NEWPARK DRILLING FLUIDS DO BRASIL TRATAMENTO DE FLUIDOS LTDA.—See Newpark Resources, Inc.; *U.S. Public*, pg. 1517
NEWPARK DRILLING FLUIDS GERMANY GMBH—See Newpark Resources, Inc.; *U.S. Public*, pg. 1517
NEWPARK MATS & INTEGRATED SERVICES LLC—See Newpark Resources, Inc.; *U.S. Public*, pg. 1518
NEWPARK RESOURCES, INC.; *U.S. Public*, pg. 1517
NGL CRUDE TERMINALS, LLC—See NGL Energy Partners LP; *U.S. Public*, pg. 1527
NGL CRUDE TRANSPORTATION, LLC—See NGL Energy Partners LP; *U.S. Public*, pg. 1527
NGL MILAN INVESTMENTS, LLC—See NGL Energy Partners LP; *U.S. Public*, pg. 1527
NGL SOLIDS SOLUTIONS, LLC—See NGL Energy Partners LP; *U.S. Public*, pg. 1527
NIDO PETROLEUM LIMITED—See Bangchak Corporation Public Company Limited; *Int'l*, pg. 832
NINE ENERGY CANADA INC.—See Nine Energy Service, Inc.; *U.S. Public*, pg. 1529
NINE ENERGY SERVICE, INC.; *U.S. Public*, pg. 1529
NIPPON GLOBAL TANKER CO., LTD.—See ENEOS Holdings, Inc.; *Int'l*, pg. 2417
NOBLE ENERGY - DENVER—See Chevron Corporation; *U.S. Public*, pg. 487
NOBLE MIDSTREAM PARTNERS LP—See Chevron Corporation; *U.S. Public*, pg. 487
NORDZUCKER BIOERDGAS VERWALTUNG-GMBH—See E.ON SE; *Int'l*, pg. 2258
NORGAL—See UGI Corporation; *U.S. Public*, pg. 2222
NORRIS PRODUCTION SOLUTIONS MIDDLE EAST LLC—See Dover Corporation; *U.S. Public*, pg. 682
NORSEA AS—See Eidesvik Holding A/S; *Int'l*, pg. 2329
NORSK ANALYSE OY—See Addtech AB; *Int'l*, pg. 134
NORTHAMERICAN ENERGY GROUP CORP.; *U.S. Public*, pg. 1537
NORTHERN ALBERTA OIL LTD.—See Deep Well Oil & Gas, Inc.; *Int'l*, pg. 2002
NORTHERN PETROLEUM (GB) LIMITED—See Cabot Energy Plc; *Int'l*, pg. 1246
NORTHERN PRODUCTION COMPANY, LLC—See Nine Energy Service, Inc.; *U.S. Public*, pg. 1529
NORTHERN STATES COMPLETIONS, INC.—See Nine Energy Service, Inc.; *U.S. Public*, pg. 1529
NORTHWEST OIL & GAS TRADING COMPANY, INC.; *U.S. Private*, pg. 2961
NOVAMEX ENERGY, INC.; *U.S. Private*, pg. 2966
NOV FLUID CONTROL—See NOV, Inc.; *U.S. Public*, pg. 1547
NPS ENERGY INDIA PRIVATE LIMITED—See National Energy Services Reunited Corp.; *U.S. Public*, pg. 1494
OAK VALLEY OPERATING, LLC—See Permian Resources Corp; *U.S. Public*, pg. 1677
OASIS MIDSTREAM PARTNERS LP—See Chord Energy Corporation; *U.S. Public*, pg. 490
OCCIDENTAL ENERGY MARKETING, INC.—See Occidental Petroleum Corporation; *U.S. Public*, pg. 1561
OCCIDENTAL INTERNATIONAL CORPORATION—See Occidental Petroleum Corporation; *U.S. Public*, pg. 1561
OCCIDENTAL PETROLEUM INVESTMENT CO.—See Occidental Petroleum Corporation; *U.S. Public*, pg. 1561
OCEANEERING INTERNATIONAL, INC.; *U.S. Public*, pg. 1562
OCEANEERING INTERNATIONAL PTE. LTD.—See Oceaneering International, Inc.; *U.S. Public*, pg. 1562
OCEANEERING INTERNATIONAL SERVICES, LTD.—See Oceaneering International, Inc.; *U.S. Public*, pg. 1563
OCEAN RIG 1 AS—See DryShips Inc.; *Int'l*, pg. 2207
OCEAN RIG AS—See DryShips Inc.; *Int'l*, pg. 2207
OCEAN RIG NORWAY AS—See DryShips Inc.; *Int'l*, pg. 2207
OCEAN RIG UK LTD.—See DryShips Inc.; *Int'l*, pg. 2207

OCEAN YIELD ASA—See KKR & Co. Inc.; *U.S. Public*, pg. 1262
OFFSHORE ENERGY SERVICES INC.; *U.S. Private*, pg. 3002
OFFSHORE JOINT SERVICES, INC.; *U.S. Private*, pg. 3002
OFS INTERNATIONAL LLC; *U.S. Private*, pg. 3003
OGPC SDN. BHD.—See Dagang NeXchange Berhad; *Int'l*, pg. 1912
OIL AND GAS EXPLORATION AND PRODUCTION PLC—See Chimimport AD; *Int'l*, pg. 1479
OIL SHIPPING (BUNKERING) B.V.—See World Kinect Corporation; *U.S. Public*, pg. 2381
OIL STATES ENERGY SERVICES (CANADA) INC.—See Oil States International, Inc.; *U.S. Public*, pg. 1565
OIL STATES ENERGY SERVICES, INC.—See Oil States International, Inc.; *U.S. Public*, pg. 1565
OIL STATES ENERGY SERVICES, INC.—See Oil States International, Inc.; *U.S. Public*, pg. 1565
OIL STATES ENERGY SERVICES L.L.C.—See Oil States International, Inc.; *U.S. Public*, pg. 1565
OIL STATES INDUSTRIES, INC.—See Oil States International, Inc.; *U.S. Public*, pg. 1565
OIL STATES SKAGIT SMATCO L.L.C.—See Oil States International, Inc.; *U.S. Public*, pg. 1565
OIL WELL SERVICE CO.; *U.S. Private*, pg. 3006
OLYMPIC SEISMIC, LTD.—See ValueAct Capital Management, L.P.; *U.S. Private*, pg. 4338
OMNI ENERGY SERVICES CORP.—See Gibson Energy Inc.; *Int'l*, pg. 2963
ONTRAS GASTRANSPORT GMBH—See EnBW Energie Baden-Wurttemberg AG; *Int'l*, pg. 2400
OPIC AFRICA CORPORATION—See CPC Corporation; *Int'l*, pg. 1824
OSX BRASIL SA—See EBX Group Ltd.; *Int'l*, pg. 2287
OSYKA CORPORATION; *U.S. Public*, pg. 1622
OUTBACK OIL & MINERAL EXPLORATION CORP.; *U.S. Public*, pg. 1624
PAA NATURAL GAS STORAGE, L.P.—See Plains All American Pipeline, L.P.; *U.S. Public*, pg. 1696
PACIFIC RUBIALES ENERGY CORP.—See Frontera Energy Corporation; *Int'l*, pg. 2794
PAINTED PONY ENERGY LTD.—See Canadian Natural Resources Ltd.; *Int'l*, pg. 1284
PALL SAS—See Danaher Corporation; *U.S. Public*, pg. 630
PALOMA RESOURCES, LLC; *U.S. Public*, pg. 1635
PANHANDLE OILFIELD SERVICE COMPANIES, INC.—See Argosy Capital Group, LLC; *U.S. Private*, pg. 321
PARKER DRILLING NETHERLANDS BV—See Parker Wellbore Company; *U.S. Public*, pg. 1650
PARKER WELLBORE COMPANY; *U.S. Public*, pg. 1650
PARK L PROJECTS LTD.—See Tetra Tech, Inc.; *U.S. Public*, pg. 2023
PARSLEY ENERGY OPERATIONS, LLC—See Pioneer Natural Resources Company; *U.S. Public*, pg. 1693
PATHFINDER - A SCHLUMBERGER COMPANY—See Schlumberger Limited; *U.S. Public*, pg. 1844
PATHFINDER ENERGY SERVICES, CANADA LTD.—See Schlumberger Limited; *U.S. Public*, pg. 1844
PATHFINDER—See Schlumberger Limited; *U.S. Public*, pg. 1844
PATTERSON-UTI MANAGEMENT SERVICES, LLC—See Patterson-UTI Energy, Inc.; *U.S. Public*, pg. 1654
PDC ENERGY, INC.—See Chevron Corporation; *U.S. Public*, pg. 487
PEAK OILFIELD SERVICES, LLC—See Select Water Solutions, Inc.; *U.S. Public*, pg. 1862
PENN VIRGINIA OIL & GAS CORP.—See Baytex Energy Corp.; *Int'l*, pg. 915
PENN VIRGINIA OIL & GAS GP LLC—See Baytex Energy Corp.; *Int'l*, pg. 915
PENN VIRGINIA OIL & GAS LP LLC—See Baytex Energy Corp.; *Int'l*, pg. 915
PERCHERON, LLC—See Percheron, LLC; *U.S. Public*, pg. 3146
PERMEX PETROLEUM CORPORATION; *U.S. Public*, pg. 1677
PERMIANVILLE ROYALTY TRUST; *U.S. Public*, pg. 1677
PETCO PETROLEUM CORPORATION; *U.S. Private*, pg. 3156
PETERSON ENERGY—See Integrated Petroleum Technologies, Inc.; *U.S. Public*, pg. 2100
PETREX S.A.—See Eni S.p.A.; *Int'l*, pg. 2438
PETROGAL BRASIL, LDA.—See Galp Energia SGPS, S.A.; *Int'l*, pg. 2875
PETROGAL - COUNSELHO FISCAL—See Galp Energia SGPS, S.A.; *Int'l*, pg. 2875
PETROGAS COMPANY; *U.S. Public*, pg. 1678
PETRO-HUNT, L.L.C.; *U.S. Private*, pg. 3161
PETROLANE, INC.—See UGI Corporation; *U.S. Public*, pg. 2222
PETROLEUM ENGINEERS, INC.—See Harlow Aerostructures, LLC; *U.S. Private*, pg. 1865
PETROLIG SRL—See Eni S.p.A.; *Int'l*, pg. 2438
PETROMAR ENERGY SERVICES LLC—See Daeyang Electric Co., Ltd.; *Int'l*, pg. 1911
PETROMAX OPERATING CO., INC.; *U.S. Private*, pg. 3163
PETROSERVICIOS DE COSTA RICA, S.R.L.—See World

213112 — SUPPORT ACTIVITIES ...   CORPORATE AFFILIATIONS

Kinect Corporation; *U.S. Public*, pg. 2381
PETROSERVICIOS DE MEXICO S.A. DE C.V.—See World Kinect Corporation; *U.S. Public*, pg. 2381
PETROSHALE, INC.; *U.S. Public*, pg. 1678
PETROSHARE CORP.; *U.S. Private*, pg. 3163
PETROTAL CORP.; *U.S. Public*, pg. 1678
PETROTAL LLC—See PetroTal Corp.; *U.S. Public*, pg. 1678
PETRO-VICTORY ENERGY CORP.; *U.S. Public*, pg. 1678
PI 2 PELICAN STATE LLC—See Kinder Morgan, Inc.; *U.S. Public*, pg. 1234
PILGRIM PETROLEUM CORP.; *U.S. Private*, pg. 3180
PINE PRAIRIE ENERGY CENTER, LLC—See Plains All American Pipeline, L.P.; *U.S. Public*, pg. 1696
PING PETROLEUM UK PLC—See Dagang NeXchange Berhad; *Int'l*, pg. 1912
PINNACLE OILFIELD SERVICES, INC.—See J Fitzgibbons LLC; *U.S. Private*, pg. 2153
PIONEER COILED TUBING SERVICES, LLC—See Patterson-UTI Energy, Inc.; *U.S. Public*, pg. 1654
PIONEER ENERGY SERVICES CORP. - COILED TUBING SERVICES—See Patterson-UTI Energy, Inc.; *U.S. Public*, pg. 1654
PIONEER NATURAL RESOURCES USA, INC.—See Pioneer Natural Resources Company; *U.S. Public*, pg. 1693
PIONEER OIL & GAS; *U.S. Public*, pg. 1693
PIPEX LIMITED—See NOV, Inc.; *U.S. Public*, pg. 1546
PIPEX PX (SCOTLAND) LIMITED—See NOV, Inc.; *U.S. Public*, pg. 1546
PLACID REFINING COMPANY LLC—See Placid Holding Company; *U.S. Private*, pg. 3194
PLAINS GAS SOLUTIONS, LLC—See Plains All American Pipeline, L.P.; *U.S. Public*, pg. 1696
PLAINS MARKETING GP INC.—See Plains All American Pipeline, L.P.; *U.S. Public*, pg. 1696
PLAINS MIDSTREAM CANADA ULC—See Plains All American Pipeline, L.P.; *U.S. Public*, pg. 1696
PLATEAU MINERAL DEVELOPMENT, INC.; *U.S. Public*, pg. 1697
PLATFORM CRANE SERVICES MEXICO S. DE R.L.—See Cargotec Corporation; *Int'l*, pg. 1329
POROCEL INDUSTRIES, LLC; *U.S. Private*, pg. 3229
PQTEN & PARTNERS (AUSTRALIA) PTY. LTD.—See BGC Group, Inc.; *U.S. Public*, pg. 330
POTEN & PARTNERS (HELLAS) LTD.—See BGC Group, Inc.; *U.S. Public*, pg. 330
POTEN & PARTNERS PTE. LTD.—See BGC Group, Inc.; *U.S. Public*, pg. 330
POTEN & PARTNERS (UK) LTD.—See BGC Group, Inc.; *U.S. Public*, pg. 330
POWER HOME REMODELING GROUP, INC.; *U.S. Private*, pg. 3238
PRABHA ENERGY PRIVATE LIMITED—See Deep Energy Resources Ltd.; *Int'l*, pg. 2002
PRADON CONSTRUCTION & TRUCKING CO.; *U.S. Private*, pg. 3241
PRAGMATIC DRILLING FLUIDS ADDITIVES LTD—See Newpark Resources, Inc.; *U.S. Public*, pg. 1518
PREHEAT, INC.—See Gibson Energy Inc.; *Int'l*, pg. 2963
PREMIER OILFIELD LABORATORIES LLC; *U.S. Private*, pg. 3250
PREMIER OIL GROUP LTD—See Harbour Energy plc; *Int'l*, pg. 3271
PREMIER OIL NATUNA SEA BV—See Harbour Energy plc; *Int'l*, pg. 3271
PREMIER OIL UK LTD—See Harbour Energy plc; *Int'l*, pg. 3271
PREMIER OIL VIETNAM OFFSHORE BV—See Harbour Energy plc; *Int'l*, pg. 3271
PREMIER PICT PETROLEUM LTD—See Harbour Energy plc; *Int'l*, pg. 3271
PREMIUM OILFIELD TECHNOLOGIES LLC; *U.S. Private*, pg. 3252
PRISM SEISMIC, INC.—See Symphony Technology Group, LLC; *U.S. Private*, pg. 3901
PRODIRECTIONAL; *U.S. Private*, pg. 3272
PROPANE ENERGIES—See UGI Corporation; *U.S. Public*, pg. 2222
PROPETRO HOLDING CORP.; *U.S. Public*, pg. 1727
PROSAFE PRODUCTION NIGERIA LIMITED—See BW Offshore Limited; *Int'l*, pg. 1232
PROVIDENCE RESOURCES UK LIMITED—See Barryroe Offshore Energy plc; *Int'l*, pg. 870
PT ADANI GLOBAL—See Adani Enterprises Limited; *Int'l*, pg. 125
PT ATLAS COPCO FLUIDCON—See Atlas Copco AB; *Int'l*, pg. 684
PT. BAYU MARITIM BERKAH—See Falcon Energy Group Limited; *Int'l*, pg. 2611
PT CORELAB INDONESIA—See Core Laboratories N.V.; *Int'l*, pg. 1798
PT FRANKS INDONESIA—See Expro Group Holdings N.V.; *Int'l*, pg. 2591
PT IKM INDONESIA—See IKM Gruppen AS; *Int'l*, pg. 3612
PT OJS KOMPLEX—See Offshore Joint Services, Inc.; *U.S. Private*, pg. 3003
P.T. PETROLITE INDONESIA PRATAMA—See Baker Hughes Company; *U.S. Public*, pg. 265
P.T. SMB INDUSTRI—See Hunting Plc; *Int'l*, pg. 3537

PT SOUTH SULAWESI LNG—See Energy World Corporation Ltd; *Int'l*, pg. 2423
PT STEP OILTOOLS—See Akastor ASA; *Int'l*, pg. 260
PUMPCO ENERGY SERVICES, INC.—See Superior Energy Services, Inc.; *U.S. Private*, pg. 3877
PXP OFFSHORE LLC—See Freeport-McMoRan Inc.; *U.S. Public*, pg. 884
QATAR PETROLEUM DEVELOPMENT CO., LTD.—See Cosmo Energy Holdings Co., Ltd.; *Int'l*, pg. 1812
QBIG GMBH—See EWE Aktiengesellschaft; *Int'l*, pg. 2576
QINTERRA AS—See EQT AB; *Int'l*, pg. 2479
Q'MAX SOLUTIONS INC.—See Palladium Equity Partners, LLC; *U.S. Private*, pg. 3078
QUALITY WIRELINE & CABLE INC.—See Forum Energy Technologies, Inc.; *U.S. Public*, pg. 874
QUANTUM ENERGY, INC.; *U.S. Private*, pg. 3323
QUEENSLAND SHALE OIL PTY. LTD.—See Blue Ensign Technologies Limited; *Int'l*, pg. 1068
QUEST OIL CORP.; *U.S. Public*, pg. 3326
RADIANT OIL & GAS, INC.; *U.S. Private*, pg. 3343
RED CEDAR GATHERING COMPANY—See Kinder Morgan, Inc.; *U.S. Public*, pg. 1234
REDZONE COIL TUBING, LLC—See Nine Energy Service, Inc.; *U.S. Public*, pg. 1529
REEDHYCALOG, L.P.—See NOV, Inc.; *U.S. Public*, pg. 1546
REEVES OILFIELD SERVICES LTD.—See Weatherford International plc; *U.S. Public*, pg. 2339
REGENCY ENERGY PARTNERS LP—See Energy Transfer LP; *U.S. Public*, pg. 763
REGENCY FIELD SERVICES LLC—See Energy Transfer LP; *U.S. Public*, pg. 763
REGENCY GAS SERVICES LP—See Energy Transfer LP; *U.S. Public*, pg. 763
REOSTAR ENERGY CORPORATION; *U.S. Public*, pg. 1784
RETRAGAS SRL—See A2A S.p.A.; *Int'l*, pg. 29
RIFE ENERGY OPERATING LLC—See East West Energy Ltd.; *U.S. Private*, pg. 1318
RIGO OIL COMPANY TUNISIA LTD—See CYGAM Energy Inc.; *Int'l*, pg. 1895
RILEY EXPLORATION - PERMIAN, LLC—See Riley Exploration Permian, Inc.; *U.S. Public*, pg. 1798
RILEY PERMIAN OPERATING COMPANY, LLC—See Riley Exploration Permian, Inc.; *U.S. Public*, pg. 1798
RIVERDALE OIL & GAS CORP.; *U.S. Public*, pg. 1801
RN INDUSTRIES TRUCKING, INC.; *U.S. Private*, pg. 3452
ROCKGAS LTD.—See Gas Services NZ Ltd.; *Int'l*, pg. 2887
ROCKWATER ENERGY SOLUTIONS, INC. - MIDLAND—See Select Water Solutions, Inc.; *U.S. Public*, pg. 1862
ROCKY MOUNTAIN INFRASTRUCTURE, LLC—See Civitas Resources, Inc.; *U.S. Public*, pg. 507
ROGUE PRESSURE SERVICES LTD.—See Steel Partners Holdings L.P.; *U.S. Public*, pg. 1943
ROOSTER ENERGY LTD.; *U.S. Public*, pg. 1810
ROSEMORE INC.; *U.S. Private*, pg. 3483
ROTOSTAT SERVICES PRIVATE LIMITED—See ManpowerGroup Inc.; *U.S. Public*, pg. 1361
ROYAL HAWAIIAN RESOURCES, INC.—See Hawaiian Macadamia Nut Orchards, L.P.; *U.S. Private*, pg. 1882
ROYAL RESOURCES PARTNERS LP; *U.S. Private*, pg. 3493
ROY E. HANSON JR. MANUFACTURING; *U.S. Private*, pg. 3490
ROYWELL SERVICES, INC.; *U.S. Private*, pg. 3494
RPC, INC.; *U.S. Public*, pg. 1816
R & S WELL SERVICE, INC.—See Rock Hill Capital Group, LLC; *U.S. Private*, pg. 3464
RUBICON OILFIELD INTERNATIONAL LIMITED—See Intervale Capital, LLC; *U.S. Private*, pg. 2127
RUELCO SERVICES INC.; *U.S. Private*, pg. 3502
SABLE OFFSHORE CORP.; *U.S. Public*, pg. 1833
SAIPEM (MALAYSIA) SDN. BHD.—See Eni S.p.A.; *Int'l*, pg. 2438
SANDRIDGE PERMIAN TRUST—See SandRidge Energy, Inc.; *U.S. Public*, pg. 1840
SAVOY ENERGY CORPORATION; *U.S. Public*, pg. 1842
SAYBOLT BELGIUM N.V.—See Core Laboratories N.V.; *Int'l*, pg. 1798
SAYBOLT, LP—See Core Laboratories N.V.; *Int'l*, pg. 1798
SAYBOLT NEDERLAND B.V.—See Core Laboratories N.V.; *Int'l*, pg. 1798
SCHLUMBERGER BARTLESVILLE PRODUCT CENTER—See Schlumberger Limited; *U.S. Public*, pg. 1846
SCHLUMBERGER COMPLETIONS & PRODUCTIVITY—See Schlumberger Limited; *U.S. Public*, pg. 1846
SCHLUMBERGER CONVEYENCE AND DELIVERY TECHNOLOGY CORP.—See Schlumberger Limited; *U.S. Public*, pg. 1844
SCHLUMBERGER DRILLING AND MEASUREMENT—See Schlumberger Limited; *U.S. Public*, pg. 1844
SCHLUMBERGER GMBH & CO. KG—See Schlumberger Limited; *U.S. Public*, pg. 1844
SCHLUMBERGER INTERNATIONAL—See Schlumberger Limited; *U.S. Public*, pg. 1844
SCHLUMBERGER INTERNATIONAL—See Schlumberger

Limited; *U.S. Public*, pg. 1844
SCHLUMBERGER INTERNATIONAL—See Schlumberger Limited; *U.S. Public*, pg. 1844
SCHLUMBERGER INTERNATIONAL—See Schlumberger Limited; *U.S. Public*, pg. 1844
SCHLUMBERGER LIMITED - COILED TUBING SERVICES—See Schlumberger Limited; *U.S. Public*, pg. 1845
SCHLUMBERGER LIMITED—See Schlumberger Limited; *U.S. Public*, pg. 1845
SCHLUMBERGER LIMITED—See Schlumberger Limited; *U.S. Public*, pg. 1845
SCHLUMBERGER LIMITED—See Schlumberger Limited; *U.S. Public*, pg. 1845
SCHLUMBERGER LIMITED—See Schlumberger Limited; *U.S. Public*, pg. 1845
SCHLUMBERGER LIMITED—See Schlumberger Limited; *U.S. Public*, pg. 1845
SCHLUMBERGER LIMITED—See Schlumberger Limited; *U.S. Public*, pg. 1845
SCHLUMBERGER LIMITED—See Schlumberger Limited; *U.S. Public*, pg. 1845
SCHLUMBERGER LIMITED—See Schlumberger Limited; *U.S. Public*, pg. 1845
SCHLUMBERGER NORGE AS—See Schlumberger Limited; *U.S. Public*, pg. 1845
SCHLUMBERGER OILFIELD SERVICES—See Schlumberger Limited; *U.S. Public*, pg. 1845
SCHLUMBERGER OILFIELD UK PLC—See Schlumberger Limited; *U.S. Public*, pg. 1845
SCHLUMBERGER REDA PRODUCTION SYSTEMS—See Schlumberger Limited; *U.S. Public*, pg. 1846
SCHLUMBERGER SA—See Schlumberger Limited; *U.S. Public*, pg. 1845
SCHLUMBERGER—See Schlumberger Limited; *U.S. Public*, pg. 1844
SCHLUMBERGER—See Schlumberger Limited; *U.S. Public*, pg. 1844
SCHLUMBERGER TECHNOLOGY CORPORATION—See Schlumberger Limited; *U.S. Public*, pg. 1845
SCHLUMBERGER TECHNOLOGY CORP.—See Schlumberger Limited; *U.S. Public*, pg. 1845
SCHLUMBERGER TECHNOLOGY CORP.—See Schlumberger Limited; *U.S. Public*, pg. 1845
SCHLUMBERGER TECHNOLOGY CORP.—See Schlumberger Limited; *U.S. Public*, pg. 1845
SCHLUMBERGER TECHNOLOGY CORP.—See Schlumberger Limited; *U.S. Public*, pg. 1845
SCHLUMBERGER TECHNOLOGY CORP.—See Schlumberger Limited; *U.S. Public*, pg. 1845
SCHLUMBERGER TECHNOLOGY CORP.—See Schlumberger Limited; *U.S. Public*, pg. 1845
SCHLUMBERGER TECHNOLOGY CORP.—See Schlumberger Limited; *U.S. Public*, pg. 1845
SCHLUMBERGER TECHNOLOGY CORP.—See Schlumberger Limited; *U.S. Public*, pg. 1845
SCHLUMBERGER TECHNOLOGY CORP.—See Schlumberger Limited; *U.S. Public*, pg. 1845
SCHLUMBERGER TECHNOLOGY CORP.—See Schlumberger Limited; *U.S. Public*, pg. 1845
SCHLUMBERGER TECHNOLOGY CORP.—See Schlumberger Limited; *U.S. Public*, pg. 1845
SCHLUMBERGER TECHNOLOGY CORP.—See Schlumberger Limited; *U.S. Public*, pg. 1845
SCHLUMBERGER TECHNOLOGY CORP.—See Schlumberger Limited; *U.S. Public*, pg. 1845
SCHLUMBERGER TECHNOLOGY CORP.—See Schlumberger Limited; *U.S. Public*, pg. 1845
SCHLUMBERGER TECHNOLOGY CORP.—See Schlumberger Limited; *U.S. Public*, pg. 1845
SCHLUMBERGER TECHNOLOGY CORP.—See Schlumberger Limited; *U.S. Public*, pg. 1845
SCHLUMBERGER TECHNOLOGY CORP.—See Schlumberger Limited; *U.S. Public*, pg. 1845
SCHLUMBERGER TECHNOLOGY CORP.—See Schlumberger Limited; *U.S. Public*, pg. 1845
SCHLUMBERGER TECHNOLOGY CORP.—See Schlumberger Limited; *U.S. Public*, pg. 1845
SCHLUMBERGER TECHNOLOGY CORP.—See Schlumberger Limited; *U.S. Public*, pg. 1845
SCHLUMBERGER TECHNOLOGY CORP.—See Schlumberger Limited; *U.S. Public*, pg. 1845
SCHLUMBERGER TECHNOLOGY CORP.—See Schlumberger Limited; *U.S. Public*, pg. 1846
SCHLUMBERGER TECHNOLOGY CORP.—See Schlumberger Limited; *U.S. Public*, pg. 1846
SCHLUMBERGER TECHNOLOGY CORP.—See Schlumberger Limited; *U.S. Public*, pg. 1846
SCHLUMBERGER TECHNOLOGY CORP.—See Schlumberger Limited; *U.S. Public*, pg. 1846
SCHLUMBERGER TECHNOLOGY CORP.—See Schlumberger Limited; *U.S. Public*, pg. 1846
SCHLUMBERGER TECHNOLOGY CORP.—See Schlumberger Limited; *U.S. Public*, pg. 1846
SCHLUMBERGER TECHNOLOGY CORP.—See Schlumberger Limited; *U.S. Public*, pg. 1846

N.A.I.C.S. INDEX

213112 — SUPPORT ACTIVITIES ...

SCHLUMBERGER TECHNOLOGY CORP.—See Schlumberger Limited; *U.S. Public*, pg. 1846
SCHLUMBERGER TECHNOLOGY CORP.—See Schlumberger Limited; *U.S. Public*, pg. 1846
SCHLUMBERGER TECHNOLOGY CORP.—See Schlumberger Limited; *U.S. Public*, pg. 1846
SCHLUMBERGER TECHNOLOGY CORP.—See Schlumberger Limited; *U.S. Public*, pg. 1846
SCHLUMBERGER TECHNOLOGY CORP.—See Schlumberger Limited; *U.S. Public*, pg. 1846
SCHLUMBERGER TECHNOLOGY CORP.—See Schlumberger Limited; *U.S. Public*, pg. 1846
SCHLUMBERGER WELL COMPLETIONS—See Schlumberger Limited; *U.S. Public*, pg. 1846
SCHLUMBERGER WELL SERVICES—See Schlumberger Limited; *U.S. Public*, pg. 1846
SEA HIBISCUS SDN BHD—See Hibiscus Petroleum Berhad; *Int'l*, pg. 3383
SEAMEC LIMITED—See HAL Offshore Limited; *Int'l*, pg. 3223
SEECO, INC.—See Expand Energy Corporation; *U.S. Public*, pg. 808
SEGEPER, S.A.—See ENCE Energia y Celulosa, S.A.; *Int'l*, pg. 2401
SEISMIC EXCHANGE INC.; *U.S. Private*, pg. 3599
SEISMIC SUPPORT SERVICES—See CGG; *Int'l*, pg. 1432
SEITEL DATA, LTD.—See ValueAct Capital Management, L.P.; *U.S. Private*, pg. 4338
SEITEL SOLUTIONS CANADA, LTD.—See ValueAct Capital Management, L.P.; *U.S. Private*, pg. 4338
SELECT ENERGY SERVICES LLC—See Select Water Solutions, Inc.; *U.S. Public*, pg. 1862
SELECT WATER SOLUTIONS, INC.; *U.S. Public*, pg. 1862
SEMGROUP CORPORATION—See Energy Transfer LP; *U.S. Public*, pg. 764
SENDERO DRILLING COMPANY, LLC—See Pioneer Natural Resources Company; *U.S. Public*, pg. 1693
SENECA RESOURCES CORPORATION—See National Fuel Gas Company; *U.S. Public*, pg. 1494
SERVELEC CONTROLS - ABERDEEN—See CSE Global Ltd.; *Int'l*, pg. 1863
SES NEW ENERGY TECHNOLOGIES, (SHANGHAI) CO., LTD.—See Synthesis Energy Systems, Inc.; *U.S. Public*, pg. 1972
SHANDONG PRECEDE PETROLEUM TECHNOLOGY CO., LTD.—See Anton Oilfield Services Group Limited; *Int'l*, pg. 484
SHEBESTER BECHTEL, INC.; *U.S. Private*, pg. 3629
SHELL OLIE - OG GASUDVINDING DANMARK B.V.—See BlueNord ASA; *Int'l*, pg. 1072
SHELL TECHNOLOGY VENTURES, INC.—See ConocoPhillips; *U.S. Public*, pg. 569
SHOWA SHELL SEMPAKU K.K.—See Idemitsu Kosan Co., Ltd.; *Int'l*, pg. 3592
SIGMA3 INTEGRATED RESERVOIR SOLUTIONS—See Symphony Technology Group, LLC; *U.S. Private*, pg. 3901
SINOPEC OILFIELD SERVICE CORPORATION—See China Petrochemical Corporation; *Int'l*, pg. 1540
SJL WELL SERVICE, LLC—See Nine Energy Service, Inc.; *U.S. Public*, pg. 1529
SMART DRILLING GMBH—See NOV, Inc.; *U.S. Public*, pg. 1546
SMART STABILIZER SYSTEMS LIMITED—See Weatherford International plc; *U.S. Public*, pg. 2339
SM ENERGY COMPANY - HOUSTON—See SM Energy Company; *U.S. Public*, pg. 1895
SNC-LAVALIN INTERNATIONAL MAROC S.A.S.—See AtkinsRealis Group Inc.; *Int'l*, pg. 672
SNC-LAVALIN KUWAIT GENERAL TRADING AND CONTRACTING CO.—See AtkinsRealis Group Inc.; *Int'l*, pg. 672
SNELSON STATIONS & FACILITIES DIVISION—See Primoris Services Corporation; *U.S. Public*, pg. 1719
SONAH & WELL TESTING SERVICES INO.—See United Salt Corporation; *U.S. Private*, pg. 4297
SORGENIA S.P.A—See Asterion Industrial Partners SGEIC SA; *Int'l*, pg. 654
SORGENIA S.P.A—See F2i - Fondi Italiani per le infrastrutture SGR S.p.A.; *Int'l*, pg. 2598
SOUTHCROSS MISSISSIPPI INDUSTRIAL GAS SALES, L.P.—See Charlesbank Capital Partners, LLC; *U.S. Private*, pg. 856
SOUTHCROSS MISSISSIPPI INDUSTRIAL GAS SALES, L.P.—See EIG Global Energy Partners, LLC; *U.S. Private*, pg. 1347
SOUTHCROSS MISSISSIPPI INDUSTRIAL GAS SALES, L.P.—See Tailwater Capital LLC; *U.S. Private*, pg. 3923
SOUTHERN FLOW COMPANIES, INC.—See IGP Industries, LLC; *U.S. Public*, pg. 2040
SOUTHERN STAR ENERGY CORP.; *U.S. Public*, pg. 1912
SOUTHWESTERN ENERGY PRODUCTION CO.—See Expand Energy Corporation; *U.S. Public*, pg. 809
SOUTHWESTERN ENERGY SERVICES COMPANY—See Expand Energy Corporation; *U.S. Public*, pg. 809
SOUTHWEST IOWA RENEWABLE ENERGY, LLC; *U.S. Private*, pg. 3739
SOUTHWEST OILFIELD CONSTRUCTION COMPANY—See PrimeEnergy Resources Corporation; *U.S. Public*, pg. 1717
SPARTAN ENERGY PARTNERS, LP—See Silverhawk Capital Partners, LLC; *U.S. Private*, pg. 3663
SPECTRA SENSORTECH, LTD.—See MKS Instruments, Inc.; *U.S. Public*, pg. 1453
SPINDLETOP DRILLING COMPANY—See SPINDLETOP OIL & GAS CO.; *U.S. Public*, pg. 1918
SPIRIT ENERGY DANMARK APS—See Centrica plc; *Int'l*, pg. 1413
SPIRIT ENERGY LIMITED—See Centrica plc; *Int'l*, pg. 1413
SPIRIT ENERGY NEDERLAND BV—See Centrica plc; *Int'l*, pg. 1413
SPRINT INDUSTRIAL SERVICES, LLC—See Sprint Industrial Holdings LLC; *U.S. Private*, pg. 3765
STABIL DRILL—See Superior Energy Services, Inc.; *U.S. Private*, pg. 3877
STEEL TEST (PROPRIETARY) LTD.—See I Squared Capital Advisors (US) LLC; *U.S. Private*, pg. 2023
STEPHENS PRODUCTION COMPANY—See SF Holding Corp.; *U.S. Private*, pg. 3621
STEP OILTOOLS AS—See Akastor ASA; *Int'l*, pg. 260
STEP OILTOOLS (AUSTRALIA) PTY LTD—See Akastor ASA; *Int'l*, pg. 260
STEP OILTOOLS LLC—See Akastor ASA; *Int'l*, pg. 260
STEP OILTOOLS LLP—See Akastor ASA; *Int'l*, pg. 260
STEP OILTOOLS PTE LTD—See Akastor ASA; *Int'l*, pg. 260
STEP OILTOOLS (THAILAND) LTD.—See Akastor ASA; *Int'l*, pg. 260
STEP OILTOOLS (UK) LTD.—See Akastor ASA; *Int'l*, pg. 260
STERLING ENERGY RESOURCES INC.; *U.S. Public*, pg. 1946
STEWART & STEVENSON POWER PRODUCTS, LLC—See Kirby Corporation; *U.S. Public*, pg. 1236
STIM-LAB, INC.—See Core Laboratories N.V.; *Int'l*, pg. 1798
STINGER WELLHEAD PROTECTION (CANADA) INCORPORATED—See Oil States International, Inc.; *U.S. Public*, pg. 1565
STM LOTTERY SDN. BHD.—See Berjaya Corporation Berhad; *Int'l*, pg. 984
STOKES & SPIEHLER INC.; *U.S. Private*, pg. 3816
STORK TECHNICAL SERVICES LIMITED—See Fluor Corporation; *U.S. Public*, pg. 860
STREAMLINE PRODUCTION SYSTEMS, INC.—See First Reserve Management, L.P.; *U.S. Private*, pg. 1526
STRIC-LAN COMPANIES CORP; *U.S. Private*, pg. 3839
STRIDE WELL SERVICE—See Hamm Management Co.; *U.S. Private*, pg. 1849
STS TRACER SERVICES, LTD.—See NCS Multistage Holdings, Inc.; *U.S. Public*, pg. 1503
SUBURBAN PROPANE, L.P.—See Suburban Propane Partners, L.P.; *U.S. Public*, pg. 1959
SULPHCO, INC.; *U.S. Private*, pg. 3852
SUMMIT MIDSTREAM FINANCE CORP.—See Summit Midstream Partners, LP; *U.S. Public*, pg. 1960
SUNDANCE ENERGY INC.—See KKR & Co. Inc.; *U.S. Public*, pg. 1244
SUPERIOR ENERGY SERVICES, INC.; *U.S. Private*, pg. 3877
SUPERIOR ENERGY SERVICES—See Superior Energy Services, Inc.; *U.S. Private*, pg. 3877
SWAT ENVIRONMENTAL INC.; *U.S. Private*, pg. 3891
SWIFT ENERGY OPERATING, LLC—See KKR & Co. Inc.; *U.S. Public*, pg. 1244
SWN RESOURCES CANADA, INC.—See Expand Energy Corporation; *U.S. Public*, pg. 808
SYNTHESIS ENERGY SYSTEMS, INC. - SHANGHAI—See Synthesis Energy Systems, Inc.; *U.S. Public*, pg. 1972
TALLGRASS ENERGY, LP—See Blackstone Inc.; *U.S. Public*, pg. 359
TALOS ENERGY LLC—See Talos Energy Inc.; *U.S. Public*, pg. 1980
TAMIMI POWER AND INDUSTRIAL GROUP—See Ali Abdullah Al Tamimi Company; *Int'l*, pg. 319
TARGA CANADA LIQUIDS INC.—See Targa Resources Corp.; *U.S. Public*, pg. 1981
TBO OIL & GAS, LLC—See Mexco Energy Corporation; *U.S. Public*, pg. 1433
TB SUPPLY BASE SDN BHD—See Ahmad Zaki Resources Berhad; *Int'l*, pg. 225
TDW SERVICES, INC.—See T.D. Williamson, Inc.; *U.S. Private*, pg. 3911
TEAM ENERGY RESOURCES LTD.—See Buckthorn Partners LLP; *Int'l*, pg. 1210
TEAM ENERGY RESOURCES LTD.—See OEP Capital Advisors, L.P.; *U.S. Private*, pg. 2997
TEAM TRIDENT LP; *U.S. Private*, pg. 3950
TECHINFORMSERVICE, LLC—See Weatherford International plc; *U.S. Public*, pg. 2339
TECO SOLUTIONS, INC.—See Emera, Inc.; *Int'l*, pg. 2377
T. E. C. WELL SERVICE, INC.; *U.S. Private*, pg. 3911
TERAX ENERGY, INC.; *U.S. Public*, pg. 2018
TERESOFT AS—See HitecVision AS; *Int'l*, pg. 3426
TERMINALE GNL ADRIATICO S.R.L—See Exxon Mobil Corporation; *U.S. Public*, pg. 817
TERVITA, LLC—See Republic Services, Inc.; *U.S. Public*, pg. 1787
T.E.S. FILER CITY STATION LIMITED PARTNERSHIP—See CMS Energy Corporation; *U.S. Public*, pg. 519
TEXAS INTERNATIONAL GAS & OIL CO., INC.; *U.S. Private*, pg. 3975
TEXAS OIL & MINERALS, INC.; *U.S. Public*, pg. 2027
TEXAS PETROLEUM INVESTMENT CO.; *U.S. Private*, pg. 3976
TEXAS WEST BOP SALES & SERVICE LLC—See Meyer Service, Inc.; *U.S. Private*, pg. 2692
TEXHOMA ENERGY, INC.; *U.S. Public*, pg. 3978
THREE RIVERS OPERATING COMPANY LLC—See ConocoPhillips; *U.S. Public*, pg. 568
THUNDER CREEK GAS SERVICES, LLC—See Western Midstream Partners, LP; *U.S. Public*, pg. 2356
THUNDER ENERGIES CORPORATION; *U.S. Public*, pg. 2157
TIMKEN BORING SPECIALTIES, LLC—See The Timken Company; *U.S. Public*, pg. 2133
TIORCO LLC—See Ecolab Inc.; *U.S. Public*, pg. 716
TPG OIL & GAS SDN. BHD.—See CB Industrial Product Holding Berhad; *Int'l*, pg. 1364
T-PRODUCTION TESTING LLC—See TETRA Technologies, Inc.; *U.S. Public*, pg. 2024
TRAIL MOUNTAIN INC.—See EOG Resources, Inc.; *U.S. Public*, pg. 782
TRAMP OIL (BRASIL) LIMITADA—See World Kinect Corporation; *U.S. Public*, pg. 2381
TRAMP OIL GERMANY GMBH & CO KG—See World Kinect Corporation; *U.S. Public*, pg. 2381
TRAMP OIL SCHIFFAHRTS-UND HANDELSGESELLSCHAFT GMBH—See World Kinect Corporation; *U.S. Public*, pg. 2381
TRANSCOASTAL CORPORATION OF TEXAS—See Transcoastal Corporation; *U.S. Private*, pg. 4207
TRANSCOASTAL CORPORATION; *U.S. Private*, pg. 4207
TRANSTEX HUNTER, LLC—See Expand Energy Corporation; *U.S. Public*, pg. 808
TREK RESOURCES, INC.; *U.S. Public*, pg. 2188
TRIDENT ENERGY MANAGEMENT LIMITED—See Warburg Pincus LLC; *U.S. Private*, pg. 4440
TRINITY PETROLEUM TRUST; *U.S. Public*, pg. 2194
TROPHY RESOURCES, INC.; *U.S. Public*, pg. 2198
TRU ENERGY SERVICES, LLC—See NACCO Industries, Inc.; *U.S. Public*, pg. 1490
TRUSSCO, INC.—See Gibson Energy Inc.; *Int'l*, pg. 2963
TRUSTAR ENERGY LLC—See Fortistar LLC; *U.S. Private*, pg. 1576
TUBULAR SERVICES LP; *U.S. Private*, pg. 4256
TULSA INSPECTION RESOURCES, LLC—See Cypress Environmental Partners, L.P.; *U.S. Public*, pg. 618
TWIN EAGLE RESOURCE MANAGEMENT, LLC—See Blackstone Inc.; *U.S. Public*, pg. 349
TWIN EAGLE RESOURCE MANAGEMENT, LLC—See Five Point Energy LLC; *U.S. Private*, pg. 1537
ULTRA RESOURCES, INC.—See Ultra Petroleum Corp.; *U.S. Public*, pg. 2223
UNION TECNICO COMERCIAL S.R.L.—See Henkel AG & Co. KGaA; *Int'l*, pg. 3354
UNIPEC ASIA CO. LTD.—See China Petrochemical Corporation; *Int'l*, pg. 1540
UNIPEC UK CO. LTD.—See China Petrochemical Corporation; *Int'l*, pg. 1540
THE UNITED COMPANY; *U.S. Private*, pg. 4129
UNITED ENERGEX LP—See Michelson Energy Company; *U.S. Private*, pg. 2700
UNITED E&P, INC.; *U.S. Public*, pg. 2230
UNITED PRODUCTION & CONSTRUCTION SERVICES; *U.S. Private*, pg. 4296
UNIVERSAL ENERGY CORP.; *U.S. Public*, pg. 2255
UNIVERSAL PRESSURE PUMPING, INC.—See Patterson-UTI Energy, Inc.; *U.S. Public*, pg. 1654
UNIVERSAL WELL SERVICES, INC.—See Patterson-UTI Energy, Inc.; *U.S. Public*, pg. 1654
UPHAM OIL & GAS COMPANY; *U.S. Private*, pg. 4311
UPSTREAM PRODUCTION SOLUTIONS PTY. LTD.—See GR Engineering Services Limited; *Int'l*, pg. 3047
URBAOIL, S.A.—See ACS, Actividades de Construccion y Servicios, S.A.; *Int'l*, pg. 117
USA COMPRESSION PARTNERS, LLC—See Riverstone Holdings LLC; *U.S. Public*, pg. 3448
UTE ENERGY LLC—See Quantum Energy Partners, LLC; *U.S. Private*, pg. 3323
VALERO EQUITY SERVICES LTD—See Valero Energy Corporation; *U.S. Public*, pg. 2272
VALERUS COMPRESSION SERVICES, LP—See TPG Capital, L.P.; *U.S. Public*, pg. 2177
VANGUARD OPERATING, LLC—See Grizzly Energy, LLC; *U.S. Public*, pg. 970
VAR ENERGI AS—See Eni S.p.A.; *Int'l*, pg. 2438
VENICE ENERGY SERVICES COMPANY, L.L.C.—See Targa Resources Corp.; *U.S. Public*, pg. 1982
VENTURE NORTH SEA GAS LIMITED—See Centrica plc; *Int'l*, pg. 1413
VERTEX RECOVERY L.P.—See Vertex Energy, Inc.; *U.S. Public*, pg. 2287
VICTORY OILFIELD TECH, INC.; *U.S. Public*, pg. 2296
VINTAGE PRODUCTION CALIFORNIA LLC—See Occidental Petroleum Corporation; *U.S. Public*, pg. 1562

213112 — SUPPORT ACTIVITIES ...

VISEAN INFORMATION SERVICES PTY LTD—See Weatherford International plc; *U.S. Public*, pg. 2339
VISIBLE ASSETS, INC.—See NOV, Inc.; *U.S. Public*, pg. 1547
VOEST ALPINE TUBULARS GMBH & CO KG—See NOV, Inc.; *U.S. Public*, pg. 1547
VOEST ALPINE TUBULARS GMBH—See NOV, Inc.; *U.S. Public*, pg. 1547
VOLTERRA SA—See Avax S.A.; *Int'l*, pg. 737
WAI ON SERVICE LIMITED—See Digital China Holdings Limited; *Int'l*, pg. 2121
WAKAMATSU GAS K.K.—See Idemitsu Kosan Co., Ltd.; *Int'l*, pg. 3592
WARD WILLISTON OIL COMPANY; *U.S. Private*, pg. 4441
WARREN ENERGY SERVICES, LLC—See Warren Resources, Inc.; *U.S. Private*, pg. 4444
WARRIOR ENERGY SERVICES CORPORATION—See Superior Energy Services, Inc.; *U.S. Private*, pg. 3877
WBI ENERGY MIDSTREAM, LLC—See MDU Resources Group, Inc.; *U.S. Public*, pg. 1411
WEATHERFORD AARBAKKE AS—See Weatherford International plc; *U.S. Public*, pg. 2339
WEATHERFORD ARTIFICIAL LIFT SYSTEMS CANADA LTD.—See Weatherford International plc; *U.S. Public*, pg. 2340
WEATHERFORD AUSTRALIA PTY. LTD.—See Weatherford International plc; *U.S. Public*, pg. 2340
WEATHERFORD (B) SDN. BHD.—See Weatherford International plc; *U.S. Public*, pg. 2339
WEATHERFORD CANADA LIMITED—See Weatherford International plc; *U.S. Public*, pg. 2340
WEATHERFORD ENERGY SERVICES GMBH—See Weatherford International plc; *U.S. Public*, pg. 2340
WEATHERFORD FRANCE, S.A.—See Weatherford International plc; *U.S. Public*, pg. 2340
WEATHERFORD, INC.—See Weatherford International plc; *U.S. Public*, pg. 2341
WEATHERFORD LINERS SYSTEMS LTD.—See Weatherford International plc; *U.S. Public*, pg. 2340
WEATHERFORD (MALAYSIA) SDN. BHD.—See Weatherford International plc; *U.S. Public*, pg. 2339
WEATHERFORD NEW ZEALAND LTD.—See Weatherford International plc; *U.S. Public*, pg. 2340
WEATHERFORD NORGE, A/S—See Weatherford International plc; *U.S. Public*, pg. 2340
WEATHERFORD NORGE A/S—See Weatherford International plc; *U.S. Public*, pg. 2340
WEATHERFORD OIL TOOL GMBH—See Weatherford International plc; *U.S. Public*, pg. 2340
WEATHERFORD OIL TOOL MIDDLE EAST LTD.—See Weatherford International plc; *U.S. Public*, pg. 2340
WEATHERFORD OIL TOOL NEDERLAND B.V.—See Weatherford International plc; *U.S. Public*, pg. 2340
WEATHERFORD POLAND SP.Z.O.O—See Weatherford International plc; *U.S. Public*, pg. 2340
WEATHERFORD SERVICES S.A.—See Weatherford International plc; *U.S. Public*, pg. 2341
WEATHERFORD UK LTD.—See Weatherford International plc; *U.S. Public*, pg. 2341
WELLBORE CAPITAL, LLC—See Morgan Stanley; *U.S. Public*, pg. 1476
WESTERN REFINING LOGISTICS, LP—See Marathon Petroleum Corporation; *U.S. Public*, pg. 1364
WEST INDIAN ENERGY GROUP LTD.—See Challenger Energy Group PLC; *Int'l*, pg. 1438
WILD WELL CONTROL, INC.—See Superior Energy Services, Inc.; *U.S. Private*, pg. 3877
WILLBROS T&D SERVICES, LLC—See Primoris Services Corporation; *U.S. Public*, pg. 1719
WILLIAMS ENERGY CANADA ULC—See The Williams Companies, Inc.; *U.S. Public*, pg. 2142
WILLIAMS MIDSTREAM—See The Williams Companies, Inc.; *U.S. Public*, pg. 2143
WILLIAMS MOBILE BAY PRODUCER SERVICES, L.L.C.—See The Williams Companies, Inc.; *U.S. Public*, pg. 2143
WILLIAMS PARTNERS L.P.—See The Williams Companies, Inc.; *U.S. Public*, pg. 2143
WILLIAMS PRODUCTION APPALACHIA LLC—See The Williams Companies, Inc.; *U.S. Public*, pg. 2144
WILLIAMS PRODUCTION COMPANY, LLC—See The Williams Companies, Inc.; *U.S. Public*, pg. 2144
WILSON'S PIPE FABRICATION PTY. LTD.—See Duratec Limited; *Int'l*, pg. 2228
WINTERSHALL CHILE LDA.—See BASF SE; *Int'l*, pg. 885
WINTERSHALL ERDGAS BETEILIGUNGS GMBH—See BASF SE; *Int'l*, pg. 885
WINTERSHALL ERDGAS HANDELSHAUS GMBH AG—See BASF SE; *Int'l*, pg. 885
WINTERSHALL ERDGAS HANDELSHAUS ZUG AG—See BASF SE; *Int'l*, pg. 885
WINTERSHALL EXPLORATION AND PRODUCTION INTERNATIONAL C.V.—See BASF SE; *Int'l*, pg. 885
WINTERSHALL LIBYA—See BASF SE; *Int'l*, pg. 885
WINTERSHALL MIDDLE EAST GMBH-ABU DHABI—See BASF SE; *Int'l*, pg. 885
WINTERSHALL NEDERLAND B.V.—See BASF SE; *Int'l*, pg. 885
WINTERSHALL NEDERLAND TRANSPORT AND TRADING B.V.—See BASF SE; *Int'l*, pg. 885
WINTERSHALL NOORDZEE B.V.—See BASF SE; *Int'l*, pg. 885
WINTERSHALL NORWEGEN EXPLORATIONS- UND PRODUKTIONS- GMBH—See BASF SE; *Int'l*, pg. 886
WINTERSHALL OIL AG—See BASF SE; *Int'l*, pg. 885
WINTERSHALL PETROLEUM (E&P) B.V.—See BASF SE; *Int'l*, pg. 885
WINTERSHALL PETROLEUM IBERIA S.A.—See BASF SE; *Int'l*, pg. 886
WINTERSHALL SERVICES B.V.—See BASF SE; *Int'l*, pg. 886
WINTERSHALL (UK NORTH SEA) LTD.—See BASF SE; *Int'l*, pg. 885
WINTERSHALL VERMOGENSVERWALTUNGSGESELLSCHAFT MBH—See BASF SE; *Int'l*, pg. 886
WINTERSHALL WOLGA PETROLEUM GMBH—See BASF SE; *Int'l*, pg. 886
WLP ENERGY SERVICES, LLC; *U.S. Private*, pg. 4551
WORLD FUEL SERVICES AVIATION LIMITED—See World Kinect Corporation; *U.S. Public*, pg. 2381
WORLD FUEL SERVICES COMPANY, INC.—See World Kinect Corporation; *U.S. Public*, pg. 2381
WORLD FUEL SERVICES (DENMARK) APS—See World Kinect Corporation; *U.S. Public*, pg. 2381
WORLD FUEL SERVICES EUROPE, LTD.—See World Kinect Corporation; *U.S. Public*, pg. 2381
WORTHINGTON ENERGY, INC.; *U.S. Private*, pg. 4570
W&T OFFSHORE INC.; *U.S. Public*, pg. 2315
WW ENERGY, INC.; *U.S. Private*, pg. 4575
XL SYSTEMS, L.P.—See NOV, Inc.; *U.S. Public*, pg. 1547
YOHO RESOURCES INC.—See One Stone Energy Partners, L.P.; *U.S. Private*, pg. 3023
THE YUMA COMPANIES; *U.S. Private*, pg. 4140
ZEDI INC.—See IGP Industries, LLC; *U.S. Private*, pg. 2040

213113 — SUPPORT ACTIVITIES FOR COAL MINING

ACC MINERAL RESOURCES LIMITED—See ACC Limited; *Int'l*, pg. 79
ADAVALE RESOURCES LIMITED; *Int'l*, pg. 126
AFRICAN EXPLORATION MINING AND FINANCE CORPORATION—See CEF (SOC) Limited; *Int'l*, pg. 1389
AKIRA ENERGY LTD.—See Banpu Public Company Limited; *Int'l*, pg. 851
ALPHA COAL RESOURCES COMPANY, LLC—See Alpha Natural Resources, Inc.; *U.S. Private*, pg. 199
ALPHA COAL WEST, INC.—See Alpha Natural Resources, Inc.; *U.S. Private*, pg. 199
ALPHA METALLURGICAL RESOURCES, INC.; *U.S. Public*, pg. 82
ALPHA MIDWEST HOLDING COMPANY—See Alpha Natural Resources, Inc.; *U.S. Private*, pg. 199
ALPHA NATURAL RESOURCES, LLC—See Alpha Natural Resources, Inc.; *U.S. Private*, pg. 199
ALS USA, INC—See ALS Limited; *Int'l*, pg. 378
ALTONA RARE EARTHS PLC; *Int'l*, pg. 394
AMHERST MADISON, INC.—See Port Amherst, Ltd.; *U.S. Private*, pg. 3229
AN THONG MINING INVESTMENT JSC—See Hoa Phat Group Joint Stock Company; *Int'l*, pg. 3435
ARAH EDAR (M) SDN. BHD.—See Dancomech Holdings Berhad; *Int'l*, pg. 1959
ARCH COAL, INC.—See Arch Resources, Inc.; *U.S. Public*, pg. 180
ASIAN AMERICAN COAL INC.—See Banpu Public Company Limited; *Int'l*, pg. 851
AURASOURCE, INC.; *Int'l*, pg. 227
BANPU AUSTRALIA CO., PTY LTD—See Banpu Public Company Limited; *Int'l*, pg. 852
BANPU ENERGY SERVICES (THAILAND) CO., LTD.—See Banpu Public Company Limited; *Int'l*, pg. 851
BANPU INTERNATIONAL LTD.—See Banpu Public Company Limited; *Int'l*, pg. 852
BANPU INVESTMENT (CHINA) CO., LTD.—See Banpu Public Company Limited; *Int'l*, pg. 852
BANPU MINERALS CO., LTD.—See Banpu Public Company Limited; *Int'l*, pg. 852
BANPU SINGAPORE PTE. LTD.—See Banpu Public Company Limited; *Int'l*, pg. 851
BATHURST RESOURCES LIMITED; *Int'l*, pg. 889
BEL GLOBAL RESOURCES HOLDINGS LIMITED; *Int'l*, pg. 962
BERRIMA COAL PTY LIMITED—See Banpu Public Company Limited; *Int'l*, pg. 852
BHARAT COKING COAL LIMITED—See Coal India Limited; *Int'l*, pg. 1680
BHP BILLITON INTERNATIONAL TRADING (SHANGHAI) CO. LTD.—See BHP Group Limited; *Int'l*, pg. 1015
BLACK MOUNTAIN RESOURCES LLC—See Alpha Natural Resources, Inc.; *U.S. Private*, pg. 199
BLUESTONE INDUSTRIES, INC.—See Mechel Bluestone Inc.; *U.S. Private*, pg. 2649
BORNEO RESOURCE INVESTMENTS LTD.; *Int'l*, pg. 1114
BPP RENEWABLE INVESTMENT (CHINA) CO., LTD.—See Banpu Public Company Limited; *Int'l*, pg. 851
BROOKS RUN MINING COMPANY, LLC—See Alpha Natural Resources, Inc.; *U.S. Private*, pg. 199
BUREAU VERITAS ASSET INTEGRITY & RELIABILITY SERVICES PTY. LTD.—See Bureau Veritas S.A.; *Int'l*, pg. 1221
CALEDON COAL PTY. LTD.—See Guangdong Rising Assets Management Co., Ltd.; *Int'l*, pg. 3159
CAMALCO SA—See Canyon Resources Ltd; *Int'l*, pg. 1300
CANADA COAL INC.; *Int'l*, pg. 1277
CEDAR COAL CO.—See American Electric Power Company, Inc.; *U.S. Public*, pg. 99
CENTENNIAL AIRLY PTY LIMITED—See Banpu Public Company Limited; *Int'l*, pg. 852
CENTENNIAL CLARENCE PTY LIMITED—See Banpu Public Company Limited; *Int'l*, pg. 852
CENTENNIAL MANDALONG PTY LIMITED—See Banpu Public Company Limited; *Int'l*, pg. 852
CENTENNIAL MANNERING PTY LIMITED—See Banpu Public Company Limited; *Int'l*, pg. 852
CENTENNIAL MUNMORAH PTY LIMITED—See Banpu Public Company Limited; *Int'l*, pg. 852
CENTENNIAL MYUNA PTY LIMITED—See Banpu Public Company Limited; *Int'l*, pg. 852
CENTENNIAL NEWSTAN PTY LIMITED—See Banpu Public Company Limited; *Int'l*, pg. 852
CHARBON COAL PTY LIMITED—See Banpu Public Company Limited; *Int'l*, pg. 852
CHINA COAL ENERGY SHANDONG CO., LTD.—See China Coal Energy Company Limited; *Int'l*, pg. 1490
CHINA COAL HANDAN DESIGN ENGINEERING CO.,LTD.—See China Coal Energy Company Limited; *Int'l*, pg. 1490
CHINA LEON INSPECTION HOLDING LIMITED; *Int'l*, pg. 1514
CHINA NATIONAL COAL IMPORT & EXPORT (TIANJIN) CO., LTD.—See China Coal Energy Company Limited; *Int'l*, pg. 1490
CHINA NATIONAL COAL INDUSTRY QINHUANGDAO IMP. & EXP. CO., LTD.—See China Coal Energy Company Limited; *Int'l*, pg. 1490.
CHINA QINFA GROUP LIMITED; *Int'l*, pg. 1542
CHONGQING MAS SCI. & TECH. CO., LTD.; *Int'l*, pg. 1580
CIGENCO SA PROPRIETARY LIMITED—See Consolidated Infrastructure Group Limited; *Int'l*, pg. 1771
CITATION RESOURCES LIMITED; *Int'l*, pg. 1619
CLARENCE COAL PTY LIMITED—See Banpu Public Company Limited; *Int'l*, pg. 852
CLARENCE COLLIERY PTY LIMITED—See Banpu Public Company Limited; *Int'l*, pg. 852
CLIFFS MINING COMPANY—See Cleveland-Cliffs, Inc.; *U.S. Public*, pg. 514
CLOUD PEAK ENERGY SERVICES COMPANY—See Cloud Peak Energy Inc.; *U.S. Private*, pg. 946
COALEX PTY LIMITED—See Banpu Public Company Limited; *Int'l*, pg. 852
COBRA NATURAL RESOURCES, LLC—See Alpha Natural Resources, Inc.; *U.S. Private*, pg. 199
COECLERICI COAL NETWORK, INC.—See Coeclerici S.p.A.; *Int'l*, pg. 1688
COECLERICI S.P.A.; *Int'l*, pg. 1688
CONSOL COAL RESOURCES LP—See CONSOL Energy Inc.; *U.S. Public*, pg. 569
COOK RESOURCES MINING PTY LTD—See Glencore plc; *Int'l*, pg. 2990
CST CANADA COAL LIMITED; *Int'l*, pg. 1868
EASTERN COALFIELDS LIMITED—See Coal India Limited; *Int'l*, pg. 1680
EAST MORGAN HOLDINGS, INC.; *U.S. Public*, pg. 703
EDENVILLE ENERGY PLC; *Int'l*, pg. 2308
ELMORE LTD.; *Int'l*, pg. 2367
ENEX OAKBRIDGE PTY LTD—See Glencore plc; *Int'l*, pg. 2990
E&P GLOBAL HOLDINGS LIMITED; *Int'l*, pg. 2247
FENNER DUNLOP CHILE SPA—See Compagnie Generale des Etablissements Michelin SCA; *Int'l*, pg. 1742
FORESIGHT ENERGY SERVICES LLC—See Foresight Energy LP; *U.S. Public*, pg. 867
FREEPORT MINING, LLC—See Alpha Natural Resources, Inc.; *U.S. Private*, pg. 199
GALILEE RESOURCES LIMITED—See Galilee Energy Limited; *Int'l*, pg. 2873
GCM RESOURCES PLC; *Int'l*, pg. 2895
GEWERKSCHAFT DES KONSOLIDIERTEN STEINKOHLENBERGWERKS BREITENBACH GMBH—See BASF SE; *Int'l*, pg. 883
GOLDEN POGADA LLC—See Green Leader Holdings Group Limited; *Int'l*, pg. 3071
GREKA CHINA LTD—See G3 Exploration Limited; *Int'l*, pg. 2866
HCI KHUSELA COAL (PROPRIETARY) LIMITED—See Hosken Consolidated Investments Limited; *Int'l*, pg. 3485
HOA PHAT MINING JSC—See Hoa Phat Group Joint Stock Company; *Int'l*, pg. 3435
HUDSON INVESTMENT GROUP LIMITED; *Int'l*, pg. 3522
HUILI RESOURCES (GROUP) LIMITED; *Int'l*, pg. 3526

N.A.I.C.S. INDEX

HUNAN SUNDY SCIENCE AND TECHNOLOGY CO.,LTD; *Int'l*, pg. 3533
HWANGE COLLIERY COMPANY LIMITED; *Int'l*, pg. 3542
IDEMITSU CLEAN ENERGY (YANTAI) CO., LTD.—See Idemitsu Kosan Co., Ltd.; *Int'l*, pg. 3590
IDEMITSU ENERGY CONSULTING (BEIJING) CO., LTD.—See Idemitsu Kosan Co., Ltd.; *Int'l*, pg. 3590
IKWEZI MINING LIMITED; *Int'l*, pg. 3612
IMC RESOURCES (AUSTRALIA) PTY LTD—See IMC Pan Asia Alliance Pte. Ltd.; *Int'l*, pg. 3621
IMC RESOURCES (CHINA) LTD—See IMC Pan Asia Alliance Pte. Ltd.; *Int'l*, pg. 3621
INDEPENDENCE MATERIAL HANDLING, LLC—See Peabody Energy Corporation; *U.S. Public*, pg. 1659
INDUSTRIAL RESOURCES, INC.—See Victory of West Virginia, Inc.; *U.S. Private*, pg. 4379
INTERNATIONAL INDUSTRIES, INC.; *U.S. Private*, pg. 2117
INVERSIONES PCS CHILE S.A.—See GraceKennedy Limited; *Int'l*, pg. 3049
IVANHOE COAL PTY LIMITED—See Banpu Public Company Limited; *Int'l*, pg. 852
JACOBS MINERALS CANADA INC.—See Jacobs Engineering Group, Inc.; *U.S. Public*, pg. 1185
JACOBS PERU S.A.—See Jacobs Engineering Group, Inc.; *U.S. Public*, pg. 1185
JESDENE LIMITED—See African Rainbow Minerals Limited; *Int'l*, pg. 192
J-POWER AUSTRALIA PTY. LTD.—See Electric Power Development Co., Ltd.; *Int'l*, pg. 2349
JX NIPPON OIL & ENERGY (AUSTRALIA) PTY. LTD.—See ENEOS Holdings, Inc.; *Int'l*, pg. 2417
KIEWIT MINING GROUP, INC.—See Peter Kiewit Sons', Inc.; *U.S. Private*, pg. 3158
KINGSTON MINING, INC.—See Alpha Natural Resources, Inc.; *U.S. Private*, pg. 199
KINGSTON PROCESSING, INC.—See Alpha Natural Resources, Inc.; *U.S. Private*, pg. 199
KINGWOOD MINING COMPANY, LLC—See Alpha Natural Resources, Inc.; *U.S. Private*, pg. 199
LEON INSPECTION & TESTING INDIA PRIVATE LIMITED—See China Leon Inspection Holding Limited; *Int'l*, pg. 1514
LEON INSPECTION TESTING SERVICES SDN. BHD—See China Leon Inspection Holding Limited; *Int'l*, pg. 1514
LIBERTY FUELS COMPANY, LLC—See NACCO Industries, Inc.; *U.S. Public*, pg. 1490
LUMINANT ENERGY COMPANY, LLC—See Vistra Corp.; *U.S. Public*, pg. 2306
MACOUPIN ENERGY LLC—See Foresight Energy LP; *U.S. Public*, pg. 867
MAHANADI COALFIELDS LIMITED—See Coal India Limited; *Int'l*, pg. 1680
MASSEY COAL SERVICES, INC.—See Alpha Natural Resources, Inc.; *U.S. Private*, pg. 198
MAXXIM REBUILD CO., LLC—See Alpha Natural Resources, Inc.; *U.S. Private*, pg. 199
MIDCO SUPPLY AND EQUIPMENT CORPORATION—See Peabody Energy Corporation; *U.S. Public*, pg. 1659
MIDDLEMOUNT COAL PTY LTD—See Peabody Energy Corporation; *U.S. Public*, pg. 1659
MOOLMAN MINING BOTSWANA (PTY) LIMITED—See Aveng Limited; *Int'l*, pg. 738
MOUNT THORLEY COAL LOADING PTY LTD.—See Peabody Energy Corporation; *U.S. Public*, pg. 1659
NEW MARKET LAND COMPANY—See Alpha Natural Resources, Inc.; *U.S. Private*, pg. 199
NICHOLAS ENERGY COMPANY—See Alpha Natural Resources, Inc.; *U.S. Private*, pg. 199
NORTHERN COALFIELDS LIMITED—See Coal India Limited; *Int'l*, pg. 1680
OAKBRIDGE PTY LIMITED—See Glencore plc; *Int'l*, pg. 2990
OAKY CREEK COAL JOINT VENTURE—See Glencore plc; *Int'l*, pg. 2991
THE OHIO VALLEY COAL COMPANY—See Ohio Valley Resources Inc.; *U.S. Private*, pg. 3005
OHIO VALLEY RESOURCES INC.; *U.S. Private*, pg. 3005
PACIFIC EXPORT RESOURCES, LLC—See Peabody Energy Corporation; *U.S. Public*, pg. 1659
PEABODY AUSTRALIA HOLDCO PTY LTD.—See Peabody Energy Corporation; *U.S. Public*, pg. 1659
PEABODY CAPRICORN PTY LTD—See Peabody Energy Corporation; *U.S. Public*, pg. 1659
PEABODY COALTRADE GMBH—See Peabody Energy Corporation; *U.S. Public*, pg. 1659
PILGRIM MINING COMPANY, INC.—See Alpha Natural Resources, Inc.; *U.S. Private*, pg. 199
POWDER RIVER COAL, LLC—See Peabody Energy Corporation; *U.S. Public*, pg. 1659
POWERCOAL PTY LIMITED—See Banpu Public Company Limited; *Int'l*, pg. 852
PRAIRIE MINES & ROYALTY ULC—See Westmoreland Coal Company; *U.S. Private*, pg. 4499
PRODECO GROUP—See Glencore plc; *Int'l*, pg. 2991
PT COKAL—See Cokal Limited; *Int'l*, pg. 1696
PT. GEO ENERGY COALINDO—See Geo Energy Resources Limited; *Int'l*, pg. 2932
PT. INDOTAMBANGRAYA MEGAH TBK—See Banpu Public Company Limited; *Int'l*, pg. 852
PT. LEON TESTING & CONSULTANCY—See China Leon Inspection Holding Limited; *Int'l*, pg. 1514
RAMACO RESOURCES, INC.; *U.S. Public*, pg. 1762
RAVENSWORTH OPERATIONS PTY LIMITED—See Glencore plc; *Int'l*, pg. 2990
REED MINERALS, INC.—See NACCO Industries, Inc.; *U.S. Public*, pg. 1490
RIO ALGOM INC.—See BHP Group Limited; *Int'l*, pg. 1016
RUM CREEK COAL SALES, INC.—See Alpha Natural Resources, Inc.; *U.S. Private*, pg. 199
THE SABINE MINING COMPANY—See NACCO Industries, Inc.; *U.S. Public*, pg. 1490
SEMAFO GUINEE S.A.—See Endeavour Mining plc.; *Int'l*, pg. 2402
SEMAFO MINERAL S.A.—See Endeavour Mining plc.; *Int'l*, pg. 2402
SHANGHAI CHINACOAL EAST CHINA CO., LTD.—See China Coal Energy Company Limited; *Int'l*, pg. 1490
SITRAN LLC—See Foresight Energy LP; *U.S. Public*, pg. 867
SOUTH EASTERN COALFIELDS LIMITED—See Coal India Limited; *Int'l*, pg. 1680
SPRINGVALE COAL PTY LIMITED—See Banpu Public Company Limited; *Int'l*, pg. 852
SYNTHESIS ENERGY SYSTEMS, INC. ZAOZHUANG—See Synthesis Energy Systems, Inc.; *U.S. Public*, pg. 1972
TAKITIMU COAL LIMITED—See Galilee Energy Limited; *Int'l*, pg. 2873
TEXAS & OKLAHOMA COAL COMPANY LTD—See Advance Metals Limited; *Int'l*, pg. 156
TEXAS & OKLAHOMA COAL COMPANY (USA) LLC—See Advance Metals Limited; *Int'l*, pg. 156
UNITED COLLIERIES PTY LIMITED—See Glencore plc; *Int'l*, pg. 2990
US COAL CORPORATION; *U.S. Private*, pg. 4318
WCC HOLDING B.V.—See Westmoreland Coal Company; *U.S. Private*, pg. 4500
WESTERN COALFIELDS LIMITED—See Coal India Limited; *Int'l*, pg. 1680
WESTMORELAND CANADA HOLDINGS INC.—See Westmoreland Coal Company; *U.S. Private*, pg. 4500
WILLIAMSON ENERGY, LLC—See Foresight Energy LP; *U.S. Public*, pg. 867
WINDROCK LAND COMPANY; *U.S. Public*, pg. 2372
XI AN ENGINEERING DESIGN CO., LTD.—See China Coal Energy Company Limited; *Int'l*, pg. 1490

213114 — SUPPORT ACTIVITIES FOR METAL MINING

29METALS LIMITED; *Int'l*, pg. 4
55 NORTH MINING, INC.; *Int'l*, pg. 13
5E ADVANCED MATERIALS, INC.; *U.S. Public*, pg. 9
ABACUS MINING & EXPLORATION CORPORATION; *Int'l*, pg. 47
ABCOURT MINES INC.; *Int'l*, pg. 57
ABEN MINERALS LTD; *Int'l*, pg. 59
ABITIBI MINING CORP.; *Int'l*, pg. 62
ABRA MINING LIMITED—See Hunan Nonferrous Metals Corporation Ltd.; *Int'l*, pg. 3533
ACCELERATE RESOURCES LIMITED; *Int'l*, pg. 80
ACDC METALS LTD.; *Int'l*, pg. 94
ADAMERA MINERALS CORP.; *Int'l*, pg. 124
ADISHAKTI LOHA & ISPAT LIMITED; *Int'l*, pg. 149
ADRIATIC METALS PLC; *Int'l*, pg. 153
AFRI-CAN MARINE MINERALS CORPORATION; *Int'l*, pg. 189
AFR NUVENTURE RESOURCES INC.; *Int'l*, pg. 189
AGRI-DYNAMICS, INC.; *U.S. Public*, pg. 63
AGUILA COPPER CORP.; *Int'l*, pg. 222
AIC MINES LIMITED; *Int'l*, pg. 228
AIC RESOURCES LIMITED—See AIC Mines Limited; *Int'l*, pg. 228
ALARA RESOURCES LIMITED; *Int'l*, pg. 291
ALBION RESOURCES LIMITED; *Int'l*, pg. 299
ALDEBARAN RESOURCES, INC.; *Int'l*, pg. 304
ALDERAN RESOURCES LIMITED; *Int'l*, pg. 304
ALDORO RESOURCES LIMITED; *Int'l*, pg. 305
ALDRIDGE MINERALS INC.; *Int'l*, pg. 305
ALGOLD RESOURCES LTD.—See Aya Gold & Silver Inc.; *Int'l*, pg. 773
ALITA RESOURCES LIMITED; *Int'l*, pg. 329
ALLEGIANT GOLD LTD.; *Int'l*, pg. 334
ALPHA EXPLORATION ERITREA LIMITED—See Alpha Exploration Limited; *Int'l*, pg. 368
ALPHAMIN RESOURCES CORP.; *Int'l*, pg. 370
ALTAIR RESOURCES INC.; *Int'l*, pg. 384
ALTIUS MINERALS CORPORATION; *Int'l*, pg. 394
ALTIUS RESOURCES, INC.—See Altius Minerals Corporation; *Int'l*, pg. 394
ALTURAS MINERALS CORP.; *Int'l*, pg. 399
ALTUS STRATEGIES PLC—See Elemental Altus Royalties Corp.; *Int'l*, pg. 2358
ALTYNEX COMPANY JSC; *Int'l*, pg. 399
AMANTA RESOURCES LTD.; *Int'l*, pg. 411
AMARILLO GOLD CORPORATION—See Hochschild Mining plc; *Int'l*, pg. 3437
A.M. CASTLE & CO. (CANADA) INC.—See A. M. Castle & Co.; *U.S. Public*, pg. 11
A.M. CASTLE METALS UK LIMITED—See A. M. Castle & Co.; *U.S. Public*, pg. 11
AMCOL MINERAL MADENCILIK SANAYI VE TICARET A.S.—See Minerals Technologies, Inc.; *U.S. Public*, pg. 1448
AMERICAN BATTERY METALS CORP.; *U.S. Public*, pg. 97
AMERICAN LITHIUM CORP.; *Int'l*, pg. 422
AMERICAN WEST METALS LIMITED; *Int'l*, pg. 423
AMG MINERACAO S.A.—See AMG Critical Materials N.V.; *Int'l*, pg. 425
AM RESOURCES CORP.; *Int'l*, pg. 402
ANGANG GROUP HONG KONG CO. LTD.—See Anshan Iron & Steel Group Corporation; *Int'l*, pg. 479
ANGLO AMERICAN MINERIO DE FERRO BRASIL S.A.—See Anglo American PLC; *Int'l*, pg. 461
ANGLO AMERICAN NIQUEL BRASIL LTDA.—See Anglo American PLC; *Int'l*, pg. 461
ANGLO AMERICAN PERU S.A.—See Anglo American PLC; *Int'l*, pg. 461
ANGLO AMERICAN PROJECTS (UK) LTD.—See Anglo American PLC; *Int'l*, pg. 461
ANGLO-BOMARC MINES LTD.; *Int'l*, pg. 463
APEX RESOURCES INC.; *Int'l*, pg. 512
APOLLO SILVER CORP.; *Int'l*, pg. 518
ARCUS DEVELOPMENT GROUP INC.; *Int'l*, pg. 552
ARGENTUM SILVER CORP.; *Int'l*, pg. 561
ARGONAUT EXPLORATION INC.; *Int'l*, pg. 563
ARMADA METALS LIMITED; *Int'l*, pg. 573
ARROW MINERALS LTD; *Int'l*, pg. 579
ASCOM PRECIOUS METALS MINING SAE—See ASEC Company for Mining; *Int'l*, pg. 605
ASCOT RESOURCES LTD.; *Int'l*, pg. 604
ASKARI METALS LIMITED; *Int'l*, pg. 621
ASPEN INTERNATIONAL HOLDINGS, INC.; *U.S. Public*, pg. 213
ATAC RESOURCES LTD.—See Hecla Mining Company; *U.S. Public*, pg. 1018
ATHABASCA MINERALS INC.; *Int'l*, pg. 669
ATOMIC MINERALS CORPORATION; *Int'l*, pg. 687
ATON RESOURCES INC.; *Int'l*, pg. 690
AUMEGA METALS LTD.; *Int'l*, pg. 705
AUQ GOLD MINING INC.; *Int'l*, pg. 706
AURELIUS MINERALS LIMITED; *Int'l*, pg. 710
AURIANT MINING AB; *Int'l*, pg. 710
AURION RESOURCES AB—See Aurion Resources Ltd.; *Int'l*, pg. 711
AURION RESOURCES LTD.; *Int'l*, pg. 711
AUROVALLIS SARL—See Aurania Resources Ltd.; *Int'l*, pg. 707
AURUM RESOURCES LIMITED; *Int'l*, pg. 715
AUSTIN GOLD CORP.; *Int'l*, pg. 718
AUSTRALASIAN METALS LIMITED; *Int'l*, pg. 719
AUSTRALIAN GOLD & COPPER LIMITED; *Int'l*, pg. 721
AUSTRALIAN STRATEGIC MATERIALS LIMITED; *Int'l*, pg. 722
AVRUPA MINERALS LTD.; *Int'l*, pg. 750
AWALE RESOURCES LTD.; *Int'l*, pg. 751
AZARGA URANIUM CORP.; *Int'l*, pg. 776
AZTEC MINERALS CORP.; *Int'l*, pg. 781
BACANORA LITHIUM LTD.; *Int'l*, pg. 793
BAL SEAL ENGINEERING, INC.—See Arcline Investment Management LP; *U.S. Private*, pg. 314
BARKER MINERALS LTD.; *Int'l*, pg. 865
BARRACK MINES PTY. LTD.—See Grange Resources Limited; *Int'l*, pg. 3058
BARRICK INTERNATIONAL (BARBADOS) CORP.—See Barrick Gold Corporation; *Int'l*, pg. 869
BARSELE MINERALS CORP.; *Int'l*, pg. 870
BATERO GOLD CORP.; *Int'l*, pg. 889
BATHURST METALS CORP.; *Int'l*, pg. 889
BC MOLY LTD.; *Int'l*, pg. 922
BCM RESOURCES CORP.; *Int'l*, pg. 928
BEAR CREEK MINING CORPORATION; *Int'l*, pg. 933
BEAR CREEK MINING S.A.C.—See Bear Creek Mining Corporation; *Int'l*, pg. 933
BEDFORD METALS CORP.; *Int'l*, pg. 938
BELMONT RESOURCES INC.; *Int'l*, pg. 968
BELO SUN MINING CORP.; *Int'l*, pg. 968
BENTON RESOURCES INC.; *Int'l*, pg. 977
BERING STRAITS NATIVE CORPORATION; *U.S. Private*, pg. 532
BERKELEY EXPLORATION ESPANA S.L.U.—See Berkeley Energia Limited; *Int'l*, pg. 985
BHP SHARED SERVICES MALAYSIA SDN. BHD.—See BHP Group Limited; *Int'l*, pg. 1016
BHP SHARED SERVICES PHILIPPINES INC.—See BHP Group Limited; *Int'l*, pg. 1016
BIG TREE CARBON INC.; *Int'l*, pg. 1021
BINDI METALS LIMITED; *Int'l*, pg. 1033
BITTERROOT RESOURCES LTD.; *Int'l*, pg. 1050
BLACK CAT SYNDICATE LIMITED; *Int'l*, pg. 1059
BLACKROCK SILVER CORP.; *Int'l*, pg. 1062
BLACKSTONE MINERALS LIMITED; *Int'l*, pg. 1062

213114 — SUPPORT ACTIVITIES ...

BLACKSTONE RESOURCES MANAGEMENT AG—See Blackstone Resources AG; *Int'l*, pg. 1062
BLACK TUSK RESOURCES, INC.; *Int'l*, pg. 1060
BLOX, INC.; *U.S. Public*, pg. 363
BLUESTONE RESOURCES INC.; *Int'l*, pg. 1075
BOTNIA EXPLORATION HOLDINGS AB; *Int'l*, pg. 1118
BRIXTON METALS CORPORATION; *Int'l*, pg. 1171
BRONCO CREEK EXPLORATION, INC.—See EMX Royalty Corporation; *Int'l*, pg. 2395
BRYAH RESOURCES LIMITED; *Int'l*, pg. 1201
BTQ TECHNOLOGIES CORP; *Int'l*, pg. 1205
BULLION GOLD RESOURCES CORP.; *Int'l*, pg. 1214
BUNTING MAGNETICS CO.—See Bunting Magnetics Co.; *U.S. Private*, pg. 686
C29 METALS LIMITED; *Int'l*, pg. 1245
CABO DRILLING (INTERNATIONAL) INC.—See Cabo Drilling Corp.; *Int'l*, pg. 1246
CALDAS GOLD CORP.; *Int'l*, pg. 1262
CANADA FLUORSPAR INC.—See African Minerals Exploration & Development SICAR SCA; *Int'l*, pg. 192
CANADIAN MALARTIC CORPORATION—See Agnico Eagle Mines Limited; *Int'l*, pg. 212
CANADIAN NEXUS TEAM VENTURES CORP.; *Int'l*, pg. 1285
CANAF INVESTMENTS INC.; *Int'l*, pg. 1287
CANDENTE COPPER CORP.; *Int'l*, pg. 1289
CANEX METALS INC.; *Int'l*, pg. 1290
CANOE MINING VENTURES CORP.—See Giyani Metals Corp.; *Int'l*, pg. 2982
CANSTAR RESOURCES INC.; *Int'l*, pg. 1299
CANTEX MINE DEVELOPMENT CORP.; *Int'l*, pg. 1299
CAPE LIME PROPRIETARY LIMITED—See Afrimat Limited; *Int'l*, pg. 192
CAPELLA MINERALS LIMITED; *Int'l*, pg. 1303
CAPITAN SILVER CORP.; *Int'l*, pg. 1314
CAPRICE RESOURCES LIMITED; *Int'l*, pg. 1316
CARIBBEAN RESOURCES CORPORATION; *Int'l*, pg. 1330
CARIBOO ROSE RESOURCES LTD.; *Int'l*, pg. 1330
CARTIER RESOURCES INC.; *Int'l*, pg. 1348
CASCADE DRILLING, L.P.—See TruArc Partners, L.P.; *U.S. Private*, pg. 4245
CASCADE COPPER CORPORATION; *Int'l*, pg. 1349
CASCADERO MINERALS S.A.—See Cascadero Copper Corporation; *Int'l*, pg. 1349
CASSIDY GOLD CORP.; *Int'l*, pg. 1355
CASTLE METALS DE MEXICALI, S.A. DE C.V.—See A. M. Castle & Co.; *U.S. Public*, pg. 11
CASTLE METALS FRANCE—See A. M. Castle & Co.; *U.S. Public*, pg. 11
CDN MAVERICK CAPITAL CORP.; *Int'l*, pg. 1371
CELIK HALAT VE TEL SANAYII AS—See Adil Bey Holding A.S.; *Int'l*, pg. 148
CELLCUBE ENERGY STORAGE SYSTEMS INC.; *Int'l*, pg. 1392
CENTAMIN GROUP SERVICES UK LIMITED—See Centamin plc; *Int'l*, pg. 1402
CENTAURUS METALS LIMITED; *Int'l*, pg. 1402
CENTURION MINERALS LTD.; *Int'l*, pg. 1417
CERITECH AG—See Deutsche Rohstoff AG; *Int'l*, pg. 2083
CERRO MINING CORP.; *Int'l*, pg. 1423
CEVITAL MINERALS, SPA—See Cevital S.p.A.; *Int'l*, pg. 1425
CHAMPION BEAR RESOURCES LTD.; *Int'l*, pg. 1440
CHAMPION ELECTRIC METALS INC.; *Int'l*, pg. 1440
CHAMPION IRON LIMITED; *Int'l*, pg. 1440
CHARGER METALS NL; *Int'l*, pg. 1448
CHESTER MINING CO; *U.S. Public*, pg. 486
CHINA ANTIMONY TECHNOLOGY CO., LTD.—See China Rare Earth Resources And Technology Co., Ltd.; *Int'l*, pg. 1545
CHINA MINMETALS HAINAN TRADING DEVELOPMENT CORP.—See China Rare Earth Resources And Technology Co., Ltd.; *Int'l*, pg. 1545
CHINA MINMETALS NZ LTD.—See China Rare Earth Resources And Technology Co., Ltd.; *Int'l*, pg. 1545
CHINA RARE EARTH RESOURCES AND TECHNOLOGY CO., LTD.; *Int'l*, pg. 1545
CHINA ZHONG QI HOLDINGS LIMITED; *Int'l*, pg. 1567
CIC MINING RESOURCES LIMITED; *Int'l*, pg. 1602
CINDISUE MINING CORP.; *U.S. Private*, pg. 898
CITA MINERAL INVESTINDO TBK; *Int'l*, pg. 1618
CMC METALS LTD.; *Int'l*, pg. 1669
COAST RESOURCES LIMITED—See Astron Corporation Limited; *Int'l*, pg. 662
COEUR EXPLORATIONS, INC.—See Coeur Mining, Inc.; *U.S. Public*, pg. 522
COEUR MINING, INC.; *U.S. Private*, pg. 960
COFFEY MINING PTY. LTD.—See Tetra Tech, Inc.; *U.S. Public*, pg. 2022
COFFEY MINING (SOUTH AFRICA) PTY. LTD.—See Tetra Tech, Inc.; *U.S. Public*, pg. 2022
COLDSTREAM MINERAL VENTURES CORP.—See Giyani Metals Corp.; *Int'l*, pg. 2982
COLIBRI RESOURCE CORPORATION; *Int'l*, pg. 1698
COMMERCE RESOURCES CORP.; *Int'l*, pg. 1714
COMPASS GOLD CORPORATION; *Int'l*, pg. 1750
CONDOR RESOURCES INC.; *Int'l*, pg. 1766
CONNELL MINING PRODUCTS, LLC.—See The Connell Company; *U.S. Private*, pg. 4014
CONQUEST RESOURCES LIMITED; *Int'l*, pg. 1769
CONSTANTINE METAL RESOURCES LTD.—See American Pacific Mining Corp.; *Int'l*, pg. 422
CONSTANTINE NORTH INC.—See American Pacific Mining Corp.; *Int'l*, pg. 422
COOLABAH METALS LIMITED; *Int'l*, pg. 1789
COOPER METALS LIMITED; *Int'l*, pg. 1791
COPAUR MINERALS INC.; *Int'l*, pg. 1793
CORAZON MINING LIMITED; *Int'l*, pg. 1795
CORESCAN PTY. LTD.—See Epiroc AB; *Int'l*, pg. 2461
CORESCAN S.A.C.—See Epiroc AB; *Int'l*, pg. 2461
CORESCAN S.A. DE C.V.—See Epiroc AB; *Int'l*, pg. 2461
CORESCAN SPA—See Epiroc AB; *Int'l*, pg. 2461
CORNISH METALS INC.; *Int'l*, pg. 1801
COSMO METALS LIMITED; *Int'l*, pg. 1813
COTEC HOLDINGS CORP.; *Int'l*, pg. 1815
CRITICAL ELEMENTS LITHIUM CORPORATION; *Int'l*, pg. 1851
CSC SONOMA PTY. LTD.—See China Steel Corporation; *Int'l*, pg. 1555
CULLINAN METALS CORP.; *Int'l*, pg. 1877
CYGNUS METALS LIMITED; *Int'l*, pg. 1895
CZR RESOURCES LIMITED; *Int'l*, pg. 1898
DALAROO METAL LIMITED; *Int'l*, pg. 1950
DALRADIAN GOLD LIMITED—See Orion Resource Partners (USA) LP; *U.S. Private*, pg. 3043
DANSK AFGRATNINGSTEKNIK A/S—See Aktieselskabet Schouw & Co.; *Int'l*, pg. 265
DARGUES GOLD MINES PTY. LTD.—See Aurelia Metals Ltd; *Int'l*, pg. 707
DE BEERS NAMIBIA HOLDINGS (PTY) LTD.—See Anglo American PLC; *Int'l*, pg. 462
DECADE RESOURCES LTD.; *Int'l*, pg. 1999
DECKLAR RESOURCES INC.; *Int'l*, pg. 2001
DEEPROCK MINERALS, INC.; *Int'l*, pg. 2003
DEEP-SOUTH RESOURCES INC.; *Int'l*, pg. 2002
DEEP YELLOW LIMITED; *Int'l*, pg. 2002
DEFENSE METALS CORP.; *Int'l*, pg. 2004
DESERT GOLD VENTURES INC.; *Int'l*, pg. 2044
DESERT METALS LIMITED; *Int'l*, pg. 2044
DESERT MOUNTAIN ENERGY CORP.; *Int'l*, pg. 2045
DESERT PEAK MINERALS INC.; *U.S. Private*, pg. 1213
DIOS EXPLORATION INC.; *Int'l*, pg. 2128
DISCOVERY-CORP ENTERPRISES INC.; *Int'l*, pg. 2134
DISCOVERY MINERALS LTD.; *U.S. Public*, pg. 668
DISTRICT COPPER CORP.; *Int'l*, pg. 2137
DNI METALS INC.; *Int'l*, pg. 2148
DON BOURGEOIS & FILS CONTRACTEUR INC—See EBC Inc.; *Int'l*, pg. 2284
DRAKE RESOURCES LIMITED; *Int'l*, pg. 2200
DY6 METALS LTD.; *Int'l*, pg. 2237
DYNAMIC METALS LIMITED; *Int'l*, pg. 2240
DYNASTY GOLD CORP.; *Int'l*, pg. 2242
EAGLE PLAINS RESOURCES LTD.; *Int'l*, pg. 2266
EARTHLABS INC.; *Int'l*, pg. 2268
EAST AFRICA METALS INC.; *Int'l*, pg. 2269
EASTERN METALS LIMITED; *Int'l*, pg. 2273
EASTFIELD RESOURCES LTD.; *Int'l*, pg. 2274
ECO ORO MINERALS CORP.; *Int'l*, pg. 2292
E-ENERGY VENTURES INC.; *Int'l*, pg. 2247
E.HARDING & SONS LIMITED—See A. M. Castle & Co.; *U.S. Public*, pg. 11
EL CAPITAN PRECIOUS METALS INC.; *U.S. Public*, pg. 722
ELECTRA BATTERY MATERIALS CORPORATION; *Int'l*, pg. 2348
ELEMENT 25 LIMITED; *Int'l*, pg. 2357
ELORO RESOURCES LTD.; *Int'l*, pg. 2369
EMP METALS CORP.; *Int'l*, pg. 2385
EMPRESS RESOURCES CORP.—See Big Ridge Gold Corp.; *Int'l*, pg. 1021
EMX ROYALTY CORPORATION; *Int'l*, pg. 2395
ENCORE ENERGY CORP.; *Int'l*, pg. 2402
ENDURANCE GOLD CORPORATION; *Int'l*, pg. 2410
ENERGIA MINERALS (ITALIA) S.R.L—See Altamin Limited; *Int'l*, pg. 385
ENGOLD MINES LTD.; *Int'l*, pg. 2435
ENTREE GOLD (US) INC.—See Entree Resources Ltd.; *Int'l*, pg. 2452
EPOWER METALS INC.; *Int'l*, pg. 2463
EQUINOX GOLD CORP.; *Int'l*, pg. 2485
EQUITY METALS CORPORATION; *Int'l*, pg. 2488
ERAMET MARIETTA INC.—See Eramet SA; *Int'l*, pg. 2489
ERDENE MONGOL LLC—See Erdene Resource Development Corp.; *Int'l*, pg. 2490
ERIN VENTURES INC.; *Int'l*, pg. 2493
ERO COPPER CORP.; *Int'l*, pg. 2496
EROS RESOURCES CORP.; *Int'l*, pg. 2497
ESGOLD CORP.; *Int'l*, pg. 2503
ESKAY MINING CORPORATION; *Int'l*, pg. 2503
EURO MANGANESE, INC.; *Int'l*, pg. 2531
EUROPEAN ELECTRIC METALS INC.; *Int'l*, pg. 2556
EVION GROUP NL; *Int'l*, pg. 2570
EXGEN RESOURCES INC.; *Int'l*, pg. 2584
FALCON GOLD CORP.; *Int'l*, pg. 2611
FALCON METALS LIMITED; *Int'l*, pg. 2611
FANCAMP EXPLORATION LTD.; *Int'l*, pg. 2612

CORPORATE AFFILIATIONS

FARADAY COPPER CORP.; *Int'l*, pg. 2617
FCM CO., LTD.—See Aspirant Group, Inc.; *Int'l*, pg. 630
FIDELITY MINERALS CORP.; *Int'l*, pg. 2654
FILO CORP.; *Int'l*, pg. 2663
FINLAY MINERALS LTD.; *Int'l*, pg. 2675
FIREBIRD METALS LIMITED; *Int'l*, pg. 2678
FIREFLY RESOURCES LIMITED—See Gascoyne Resources Limited; *Int'l*, pg. 2888
FIREFOX GOLD CORP.; *Int'l*, pg. 2679
FIRESTONE VENTURES INC.; *Int'l*, pg. 2679
FIREWEED ZINC LTD.; *Int'l*, pg. 2679
FIRST BAUXITE CORPORATION—See RCF Management LLC; *U.S. Private*, pg. 3362
FIRST TELLURIUM CORP.; *Int'l*, pg. 2688
FJORDLAND EXPLORATION INC.; *Int'l*, pg. 2697
FLOW-CHEM TECHNOLOGIES, LLC—See Dorf-Ketal Chemicals India Pvt. Ltd.; *Int'l*, pg. 2176
FLUIDOIL LIMITED; *Int'l*, pg. 2713
FOSFATOS DEL PACIFICO SA; *Int'l*, pg. 2748
FPX NICKEL CORP.; *Int'l*, pg. 2758
FQML SCANDINAVIA INC.—See First Quantum Minerals Ltd.; *Int'l*, pg. 2687
FREEHILL MINING LTD.; *Int'l*, pg. 2769
FREEPORT RESOURCES INC.; *Int'l*, pg. 2771
FRONTIER DIAMONDS LTD.; *Int'l*, pg. 2795
FULL METAL MINERALS LTD.; *Int'l*, pg. 2842
FURY GOLD MINES LIMITED; *Int'l*, pg. 2848
FUSE GROUP HOLDING INC.; *U.S. Public*, pg. 893
GALILEO MINING LTD.; *Int'l*, pg. 2873
GATOS SILVER, INC.; *U.S. Public*, pg. 907
GBM RESOURCES LTD; *Int'l*, pg. 2893
GENERATION MINING LTD.—See Herkules S.A.; *Int'l*, pg. 3362
GEOPACIFIC RESOURCES LIMITED; *Int'l*, pg. 2933
GGL RESOURCES CORP.; *Int'l*, pg. 2957
GITENNES EXPLORATION INC.; *Int'l*, pg. 2979
GIYANI METALS CORP.; *Int'l*, pg. 2982
GLEN EAGLE RESOURCES INC.; *Int'l*, pg. 2990
GLOBALBLOCK DIGITAL ASSET TRADING LIMITED; *Int'l*, pg. 3003
GLOBAL ENERGY METALS CORPORATION; *Int'l*, pg. 2995
GLOBAL HEALTH CLINICS LTD.; *Int'l*, pg. 2997
GLOBAL UAV TECHNOLOGIES LTD.; *Int'l*, pg. 3002
GLOBE METALS & MINING LIMITED; *Int'l*, pg. 3006
GOGOLD RESOURCES INC.; *Int'l*, pg. 3022
GOLD79 MINES LTD.; *Int'l*, pg. 3026
GOLDBANK MINING CORPORATION; *Int'l*, pg. 3026
GOLD BULL RESOURCES CORP.; *Int'l*, pg. 3023
GOLDEN ARROW RESOURCES CORPORATION; *Int'l*, pg. 3028
GOLDEN CROSS OPERATIONS PTY. LTD.—See Golden Cross Resources Limited; *Int'l*, pg. 3029
GOLDEN MILE RESOURCES LTD.; *Int'l*, pg. 3030
GOLDEN PURSUIT RESOURCES LTD.; *Int'l*, pg. 3031
GOLDEN RIDGE RESOURCES LTD.; *Int'l*, pg. 3031
GOLDEN SHARE RESOURCES CORPORATION; *Int'l*, pg. 3031
GOLDEN STATE MINING LIMITED; *Int'l*, pg. 3032
GOLDEN TAG MEXICO SA DE CV—See Golden Tag Resources Ltd.; *Int'l*, pg. 3032
GOLDEN TAG RESOURCES LTD.; *Int'l*, pg. 3032
GOLDMINING INC.; *Int'l*, pg. 3034
GOLDREA RESOURCES CORP.; *Int'l*, pg. 3034
GOLD RUSH CARIBOO CORP.; *Int'l*, pg. 3026
GOLDSTRIKE RESOURCES LTD.; *Int'l*, pg. 3034
GOLD TERRA RESOURCE CORP.; *Int'l*, pg. 3026
GOLD X MINING CORP.—See Gran Colombia Gold Corp.; *Int'l*, pg. 3053
GO METALS CORP.; *Int'l*, pg. 3017
GOPE EXPLORATION COMPANY (PROPRIETARY) LIMITED—See Gem Diamonds Limited; *Int'l*, pg. 2915
GOSSAN RESOURCES LIMITED; *Int'l*, pg. 3043
GOWEST GOLD LTD.; *Int'l*, pg. 3044
GRAFINTEC OY—See Beowulf Mining plc; *Int'l*, pg. 978
GRANADA GOLD MINE INC.; *Int'l*, pg. 3053
GRANDE PORTAGE RESOURCES LTD.; *Int'l*, pg. 3057
GREAT BASIN ENERGIES, INC.; *U.S. Public*, pg. 961
GREAT LAKES GRAPHITE INC.; *Int'l*, pg. 3065
GREAT WESTERN EXPLORATION LIMITED; *Int'l*, pg. 3066
GREEN BATTERY MINERALS INC.; *Int'l*, pg. 3069
GREEN CRITICAL MINERALS LIMITED; *Int'l*, pg. 3070
GREEN ENERGY INC.—See CDN Maverick Capital Corp.; *Int'l*, pg. 1371
GREEN MOUNTAIN MERGER, INC.; *U.S. Public*, pg. 963
GREENTECH METALS LIMITED; *Int'l*, pg. 3076
GREEN TECHNOLOGY METALS LIMITED; *Int'l*, pg. 3073
GREEN TECHNOLOGY SOLUTIONS, INC.; *U.S. Private*, pg. 1774
GRID METALS CORP.; *Int'l*, pg. 3082
GROSVENOR RESOURCE CORPORATION; *Int'l*, pg. 3088
GSP RESOURCE CORP.; *Int'l*, pg. 3150
GUANACO COMPANIA MINERA SPA—See Austral Gold Limited; *Int'l*, pg. 719
GUIDELINE GEO AMERICAS, INC.—See Guideline Geo AB; *Int'l*, pg. 3173
GUNPOINT EXPLORATION LTD.; *Int'l*, pg. 3185
GUSKIN GOLD CORP.; *U.S. Public*, pg. 975

N.A.I.C.S. INDEX

213115 — SUPPORT ACTIVITIES ...

GUYANA FRONTIER MINING CORP.; *Int'l*, pg. 3189
HAMMER METALS AUSTRALIA PTY. LTD.—See Hammer Metals Limited; *Int'l*, pg. 3238
HAMPTON HILL MINING NL; *Int'l*, pg. 3239
HANNAN METALS LTD.; *Int'l*, pg. 3257
HANNANS LIMITED; *Int'l*, pg. 3257
HANWHA INTERNACIONAL DO BRASIL LTDA.—See Hanwha Group; *Int'l*, pg. 3265
HANXING METALLURGICAL MINE ADMINISTRATION—See China Rare Earth Resources And Technology Co., Ltd.; *Int'l*, pg. 1545
HAPPY CREEK MINERALS LTD.; *Int'l*, pg. 3269
HAWKEYE GOLD & DIAMOND INC.; *Int'l*, pg. 3289
HAWTHORN RESOURCES LIMITED; *Int'l*, pg. 3289
HELIOSTAR METALS LTD.; *Int'l*, pg. 3330
HELLYER MILL OPERATIONS PTY LTD; *Int'l*, pg. 3337
HERITAGE MINING LTD.; *Int'l*, pg. 3362
HERON RESOURCES LIMITED; *Int'l*, pg. 3364
HIGHLAND SURPRISE CONSOLIDATED MINING CO.; *U.S. Public*, pg. 1035
HIGH-TECH METALS LIMITED; *Int'l*, pg. 3386
HIGHWAY 50 GOLD CORP.; *Int'l*, pg. 3389
HOMESTEAD GOLD & SILVER LTD.; *U.S. Public*, pg. 1046
HONEY BADGER SILVER INC.; *Int'l*, pg. 3465
HONSEN ENERGY & RESOURCES INTERNATIONAL LTD.; *Int'l*, pg. 3472
HORIZON MINERALS LIMITED; *Int'l*, pg. 3479
HORNBY BAY MINERAL EXPLORATION LTD.; *Int'l*, pg. 3482
HUAKAN INTERNATIONAL MINING INC.; *Int'l*, pg. 3512
HUDSON RESOURCES INC.; *Int'l*, pg. 3522
HUNTER CREEK MINING CO.; *U.S. Public*, pg. 1071
HUNTER DICKINSON INC.; *Int'l*, pg. 3536
I3 INTERACTIVE, INC.; *Int'l*, pg. 3566
IDAHO NORTH RESOURCES CORP.; *U.S. Private*, pg. 2035
IMAGINE LITHIUM INC.; *Int'l*, pg. 3619
INDOPHIL RESOURCES NL—See Alcantara Group; *Int'l*, pg. 300
INSPIRATION LEAD CO., INC.; *U.S. Public*, pg. 1131
INTEX RESOURCES PHILIPPINES, INC.—See DLT ASA; *Int'l*, pg. 2142
KEWEENAW COPPER CO.—See Highland Copper Company Inc.; *Int'l*, pg. 3387
KODI KLIP CORPORATION—See Dayton Superior Corporation; *U.S. Private*, pg. 1178
KUMBA SINGAPORE PTE. LTD.—See Anglo American PLC; *Int'l*, pg. 462
LABRADOR URANIUM INC.—See ATHA Energy Corp.; *Int'l*, pg. 669
LUCKY FRIDAY EXTENSION MINING CO.; *U.S. Public*, pg. 1345
LYNX RESOURCES (US) INC.—See BHP Group Limited; *Int'l*, pg. 1016
MARINDI METALS PTY. LTD.—See Gascoyne Resources Limited; *Int'l*, pg. 2888
MARKRAY CORP.; *U.S. Public*, pg. 1370
MCC CONTRACTS (PTY) LIMITED—See eXtract Group Limited; *Int'l*, pg. 2592
MEDINAH MINERALS, INC.; *U.S. Public*, pg. 1413
MINERA BATEAS S.A.C.—See Fortuna Mining Corp.; *Int'l*, pg. 2743
MINERA COSALA S.A. DE C.V.—See Americas Gold and Silver Corporation; *Int'l*, pg. 423
MINERA DELTA S.A. DE C.V.—See Golden Goliath Resources Ltd.; *Int'l*, pg. 3029
MINERA MARIANA ARGENTINA S.A.—See Capella Minerals Limited; *Int'l*, pg. 1303
MINERA MH CHILE LTDA.—See Hochschild Mining plc; *Int'l*, pg. 3438
MINING TAG S.A.—See Epiroc AB; *Int'l*, pg. 2463
MINNAT RESOURCES PTE. LTD.—See China Rare Earth Resources And Technology Co., Ltd.; *Int'l*, pg. 1546
MINOTAUR EXPLORATION LTD.—See Andromeda Metals Limited; *Int'l*, pg. 457
MMG CANADA—See China Rare Earth Resources And Technology Co., Ltd.; *Int'l*, pg. 1545
NATIONAL GRAPHITE CORP.; *U.S. Public*, pg. 1494
NEBTA FOR GEOLOGY & MINING LTD.—See ASEC Company for Mining; *Int'l*, pg. 605
NEO OIL PTY LTD—See Havilah Resources Limited; *Int'l*, pg. 3287
NEW CONCEPT MINING CHILE SPA—See Epiroc AB; *Int'l*, pg. 2463
NEW ENGLAND TRADING GLOBAL, INC.; *U.S. Private*, pg. 2894
NEWMONT NORTH AMERICA EXPLORATION LIMITED—See Newmont Corporation; *U.S. Public*, pg. 1517
NEW SLEEPER GOLD, LLC—See Paramount Gold Nevada Corp.; *U.S. Public*, pg. 1637
NEXGEN MINING, INC.; *U.S. Public*, pg. 1522
NORTH AMERICAN EXPLORATION CORP.; *U.S. Public*, pg. 1536
NORTHERN MINERALS & EXPLORATION LTD.; *U.S. Public*, pg. 1537
NORZINC LTD.—See RCF Management LLC; *U.S. Private*, pg. 3362

OSISKO MINING INC.—See Gold Fields Limited; *Int'l*, pg. 3024
OY FENNOSCANDIAN RESOURCES AB—See Beowulf Mining plc; *Int'l*, pg. 978
PANTERRA GOLD (PERU) S.A.—See Antilles Gold Limited; *Int'l*, pg. 483
PARAMOUNT GOLD NEVADA CORP.; *U.S. Public*, pg. 1637
PEABODY INVESTMENT & DEVELOPMENT BUSINESS SERVICES BEIJING CO. LTD.—See Peabody Energy Corporation; *U.S. Public*, pg. 1659
PECK TECH CONSULTING LTD.—See Caterpillar, Inc.; *U.S. Public*, pg. 453
PGI ACQUISITION LIMITED—See Berry Global Group, Inc; *U.S. Public*, pg. 322
PGI COLUMBIA LTDA—See Berry Global Group, Inc; *U.S. Public*, pg. 322
PGI NONWOVENS B.V.—See Berry Global Group, Inc; *U.S. Public*, pg. 322
PHILIPPINE ASSOCIATED SMELTING & REFINING CORPORATION—See Glencore plc; *Int'l*, pg. 2991
PIT N PORTAL MINING SERVICES PTY LTD—See Emeco Holdings Limited; *Int'l*, pg. 2376
PLATINUM BLASTING SERVICES PTY. LIMITED—See Deepak Fertilisers & Petrochemicals Corporation Limited; *Int'l*, pg. 2003
POLARIS INTERNATIONAL HOLDINGS, INC.; *U.S. Public*, pg. 1700
POLYMET MINING CORP.—See Glencore plc; *Int'l*, pg. 2991
POLYMET MINING, INC.—See Glencore plc; *Int'l*, pg. 2991
POWERTECH (USA) INC.—See Azarga Uranium Corp.; *Int'l*, pg. 776
PROLER STEEL INTERNATIONAL, LLC; *U.S. Private*, pg. 3282
PT ASHAPURA RESOURCES—See Ashapura Minechem Limited; *Int'l*, pg. 606
P.T. BATUTUA TEMBAGA RAYA—See Finders Resources Limited; *Int'l*, pg. 2672
PT. HANWHA MINING SERVICES—See Hanwha Group; *Int'l*, pg. 3266
PUERTO LAS LOSAS S.A.—See CAP S.A.; *Int'l*, pg. 1301
QUANTUM EXPLOSIVES—See ACS, Actividades de Construccion y Servicios, S.A.; *Int'l*, pg. 113
QUANTUM EXPLOSIVES—See Elliott Management Corporation; *U.S. Private*, pg. 1365
RADIUM RESOURCES CORP.; *U.S. Public*, pg. 1760
RANGER GOLD CORP.; *U.S. Private*, pg. 3354
RARE ELEMENT RESOURCES, INC.—See Rare Element Resources Ltd.; *U.S. Public*, pg. 1763
RCT GLOBAL SPA—See Epiroc AB; *Int'l*, pg. 2463
REARDEN MINERALS, LLC—See Sitio Royalties Corp.; *U.S. Public*, pg. 1890
RED CHRIS DEVELOPMENT COMPANY LTD.—See Newmont Corporation; *U.S. Public*, pg. 1517
REDCLIFFE PROJECT PTY LTD—See Genesis Minerals Limited; *Int'l*, pg. 2921
REDPATH MINING INC.—See ATON GmbH; *Int'l*, pg. 689
REDSTAR GOLD USA INC.—See Heliostar Metals Ltd.; *Int'l*, pg. 3331
REMOTE CONTROL TECHNOLOGIES PTY LTD.—See Epiroc AB; *Int'l*, pg. 2463
REVELO RESOURCES CORP.—See Austral Gold Limited; *Int'l*, pg. 719
RIO TINTO EXPLORATION CANADA INC.—See Benton Resources Inc.; *Int'l*, pg. 977
ROCKCLIFF METALS CORPORATION—See HudBay Minerals Inc.; *Int'l*, pg. 3521
RUNNING FOX RESOURCE CORP.; *U.S. Public*, pg. 1826
SALVA RESOURCES PTY LTD—See HDR, Inc.; *U.S. Private*, pg. 1890
SALVA RESOURCES PVT LTD—See HDR, Inc.; *U.S. Private*, pg. 1890
SGL SPEZIAL- UND BERGBAU-SERVICEGESELLSCHAFT LAUCHHAMMER MBH—See General Atomics; *U.S. Private*, pg. 1664
SILVER VERDE MAY MINING CO.; *U.S. Public*, pg. 1880
SMALL MINE DEVELOPMENT LLC; *U.S. Private*, pg. 3690
SOCIEDAD MINERA QUINCHIA S.A.S.—See Batero Gold Corp.; *Int'l*, pg. 889
SOCIETE LE NICKEL—See Eramet SA; *Int'l*, pg. 2489
SOUTH AMERICAN GOLD CORP.; *U.S. Public*, pg. 1910
SPECTREM AIR PTY LTD—See Anglo American PLC; *Int'l*, pg. 462
STAR GOLD CORP.; *U.S. Public*, pg. 1937
SUPERIOR GOLD, INC.—See Catalyst Metals Limited; *Int'l*, pg. 1358
TELKWA COAL LIMITED—See Allegiance Coal Limited; *Int'l*, pg. 334
TIGER INTERNATIONAL RESOURCES INC.; *U.S. Public*, pg. 2158
TIZIR LTD.—See Eramet SA; *Int'l*, pg. 2489
TIZIR TITANIUM & IRON A/S—See Eramet SA; *Int'l*, pg. 2489
TORRENS MINING LTD.—See Coda Minerals Ltd.; *Int'l*, pg. 1687
TRAYLOR MINING, LLC—See Traylor Brothers, Inc.; *U.S. Private*, pg. 4215

TRIUMPH PROCESSING, INC.—See ATL Partners, LLC; *U.S. Private*, pg. 369
TRIUMPH PROCESSING, INC.—See British Columbia Investment Management Corp.; *Int'l*, pg. 1170
TUBE CITY IMS CANADA LIMITED—See The Pritzker Organization, LLC; *U.S. Private*, pg. 4100
UNITED BULLION EXCHANGE, INC.; *U.S. Public*, pg. 2229
U.S. GOLD CORP.; *U.S. Public*, pg. 2213
U.S. GOLDMINING INC.—See GoldMining Inc.; *Int'l*, pg. 3034
WONDERSTONE LIMITED—See Assore Limited; *Int'l*, pg. 649

213115 — SUPPORT ACTIVITIES FOR NONMETALLIC MINERALS (EXCEPT FUELS) MINING

79 RESOURCES LTD.; *Int'l*, pg. 15
ACLARA RESOURCES INC.; *Int'l*, pg. 107
ACTIVEX LIMITED; *Int'l*, pg. 120
AFRICO RESOURCES (B.C.) LTD.—See Eurasian Natural Resources Corporation Limited; *Int'l*, pg. 2527
AGNICO-EAGLE MINES MEXICO COOPERATIE U.A.—See Agnico Eagle Mines Limited; *Int'l*, pg. 212
AGNICO-EAGLE MINES SWEDEN COOPERATIE U.A.—See Agnico Eagle Mines Limited; *Int'l*, pg. 212
ALBA MINERAL RESOURCES PLC; *Int'l*, pg. 292
ALERIO GOLD CORP.; *Int'l*, pg. 306
ALEXCO KENO HILL MINING CORP.—See Hecla Mining Company; *U.S. Public*, pg. 1018
ALEXCO RESOURCE US CORP—See Hecla Mining Company; *U.S. Public*, pg. 1019
ALKANE RESOURCES LIMITED; *Int'l*, pg. 330
ALLIANCE MAGNESIUM INC.; *Int'l*, pg. 340
ALLIANCE NICKEL LIMITED; *Int'l*, pg. 340
ALLIANCE RESOURCES LIMITED; *Int'l*, pg. 340
ALLIANCE (SA) PTY. LTD.—See Alliance Resources Limited; *Int'l*, pg. 341
ALPHA COPPER CORP.; *Int'l*, pg. 367
ALPHA RESOURCES LIMITED; *Int'l*, pg. 368
ALPHA HPA LIMITED; *Int'l*, pg. 368
ALS METALLURGY HOLDINGS PTY. LTD.—See ALS Limited; *Int'l*, pg. 378
ALTAI RESOURCES INC.; *Int'l*, pg. 384
AMARC RESOURCES LTD.—See Hunter Dickinson Inc.; *Int'l*, pg. 3536
AMED MANAGEMENT SERVICES LTD—See African Minerals Exploration & Development SICAR SCA; *Int'l*, pg. 192
AMERICAN COPPER DEVELOPMENT CORPORATION; *Int'l*, pg. 422
AMUR MINERALS CORPORATION; *Int'l*, pg. 442
AMV CAPITAL CORPORATION; *Int'l*, pg. 442
ANCHOR RESOURCES LIMITED; *Int'l*, pg. 448
ANDROMEDA METALS LIMITED; *Int'l*, pg. 457
ANGLO AMERICAN WOODSMITH LIMITED—See Anglo American PLC; *Int'l*, pg. 461
ANTOFAGASTA PLC; *Int'l*, pg. 484
APOLLO MINERALS LIMITED; *Int'l*, pg. 518
ARAFURA RARE EARTHS LIMITED; *Int'l*, pg. 534
ARANJIN RESOURCES LIMITED; *Int'l*, pg. 536
ARCHER EXPLORATION CORP.; *Int'l*, pg. 547
ARCOS LIMITED—See ALROSA Co. Ltd.; *Int'l*, pg. 377
ARCTIC FOX LITHIUM CORP.; *Int'l*, pg. 551
ARGENT MINERALS LIMITED; *Int'l*, pg. 561
ARGO EXPLORATION LIMITED; *Int'l*, pg. 561
ARIZONA SONORAN COPPER COMPANY INC.; *Int'l*, pg. 567
AROS MINERAL AB—See Barolays PLC; *Int'l*, pg. 859
ARTEMIS GOLD, INC.; *Int'l*, pg. 581
ASTRA EXPLORATION INC.; *Int'l*, pg. 657
ATCO MINING INC.; *Int'l*, pg. 667
ATHENA MINES LIMITED—See Argo Exploration Limited; *Int'l*, pg. 561
ATHENA RESOURCES LIMITED; *Int'l*, pg. 669
AUSQUEST LIMITED; *Int'l*, pg. 716
AUSTAR GOLD LIMITED; *Int'l*, pg. 716
AUSTPAC RESOURCES NL - NEWCASTLE DEMONSTRATION PLANT—See Austpac Resources N.L.; *Int'l*, pg. 719
AUSTPAC RESOURCES N.L.; *Int'l*, pg. 719
AUXICO RESOURCES CANADA, INC.; *Int'l*, pg. 732
AVT-URAL LLC—See Evraz plc; *Int'l*, pg. 2573
AZIMUT EXPLORATION INC.; *Int'l*, pg. 779
AZURE MINERALS LIMITED—See Hancock Prospecting Pty. Ltd.; *Int'l*, pg. 3242
BAJA INTERNATIONAL S.A R.L.—See Camrova Resources Inc.; *Int'l*, pg. 1275
BARKSDALE RESOURCES CORP.; *Int'l*, pg. 865
BASELODE ENERGY CORP.; *Int'l*, pg. 871
BASIN URANIUM CORP.; *Int'l*, pg. 887
BATTERY X METALS INC.; *Int'l*, pg. 890
BAUER TECHNOLOGIES SOUTH AFRICA (PTY) LTD.—See BAUER Aktiengesellschaft; *Int'l*, pg. 892
BBX MINERALS LIMITED; *Int'l*, pg. 921
BEOWULF MINING PLC; *Int'l*, pg. 978
BEREC LAND RESOURCES LNC.—See Benguet Corporation; *Int'l*, pg. 974

213115 — SUPPORT ACTIVITIES ...

BEZANT RESOURCES PLC; *Int'l*, pg. 1006
BIG RED MINING CORPORATION; *Int'l*, pg. 1021
BINH DUONG MINERAL & CONSTRUCTION JSC; *Int'l*, pg. 1034
BIS INDUSTRIER DANMARK A/S—See Bilfinger SE; *Int'l*, pg. 1025
BLAZE MINERALS LIMITED; *Int'l*, pg. 1063
BLUELAKE MINERAL AB; *Int'l*, pg. 1072
BLUE THUNDER MINING, INC.; *Int'l*, pg. 1070
BOART LONGYEAR AUSTRALIA PTY LTD—See Boart Longyear Ltd.; *Int'l*, pg. 1094
BOART LONGYEAR BV—See Boart Longyear Ltd.; *Int'l*, pg. 1094
BOART LONGYEAR COMPANY INC.—See Boart Longyear Ltd.; *Int'l*, pg. 1095
BOART LONGYEAR DRILLING PRODUCTS COMPANY (WUXI) LTD—See Boart Longyear Ltd.; *Int'l*, pg. 1095
BOART LONGYEAR EMEA COOPERATIEF U.A—See Boart Longyear Ltd.; *Int'l*, pg. 1094
BOART LONGYEAR GMBH & CO. KG—See Boart Longyear Ltd.; *Int'l*, pg. 1094
BOART LONGYEAR INTERNATIONAL BV—See Boart Longyear Ltd.; *Int'l*, pg. 1094
BOART LONGYEAR INTERNATIONAL HOLDINGS INC.—See Boart Longyear Ltd.; *Int'l*, pg. 1094
BOART LONGYEAR INVESTMENTS PTY LTD—See Boart Longyear Ltd.; *Int'l*, pg. 1095
BOART LONGYEAR LIMITED—See Boart Longyear Ltd.; *Int'l*, pg. 1095
BOART LONGYEAR MANAGEMENT PTY LTD—See Boart Longyear Ltd.; *Int'l*, pg. 1095
BOART LONGYEAR NETHERLANDS BV—See Boart Longyear Ltd.; *Int'l*, pg. 1095
BOART LONGYEAR SAC - LIMA, PERU—See Boart Longyear Ltd.; *Int'l*, pg. 1095
BOLT METALS CORP.; *Int'l*, pg. 1103
BOND RESOURCES, INC.; *Int'l*, pg. 1105
BRIGHAM MINERALS, INC.—See Sitio Royalties Corp.; *U.S. Public*, pg. 1889
BUXTON RESOURCES LIMITED; *Int'l*, pg. 1230
CALDERYS AUSTRIA GMBH—See Groupe Bruxelles Lambert SA; *Int'l*, pg. 3099
CALDERYS MAGYARORSZAG KFT—See Groupe Bruxelles Lambert SA; *Int'l*, pg. 3099
CANADIAN GOLDCAMPS CORP.; *Int'l*, pg. 1283
CANADIAN MANGANESE COMPANY INC.; *Int'l*, pg. 1284
CANADIAN NORTH RESOURCES INC.; *Int'l*, pg. 1285
CANADIAN PALLADIUM RESOURCES, INC.; *Int'l*, pg. 1285
CANAMERA ENERGY METALS CORP.; *Int'l*, pg. 1287
CAPITAL DRILLING CHILE S.A.—See Capital Limited; *Int'l*, pg. 1311
CAPITAL DRILLING EGYPT (LIMITED LIABILITY COMPANY)—See Capital Limited; *Int'l*, pg. 1311
CAPITAL DRILLING MOZAMBIQUE LIMITADA—See Capital Limited; *Int'l*, pg. 1311
CAPITAL DRILLING (SINGAPORE) PTE. LTD.—See Capital Limited; *Int'l*, pg. 1311
CAPITAL DRILLING ZAMBIA LIMITED—See Capital Limited; *Int'l*, pg. 1311
CAPITAL LIMITED; *Int'l*, pg. 1311
CAPITAL MINING LIMITED; *Int'l*, pg. 1312
CARAVAN ENERGY CORPORATION; *Int'l*, pg. 1320
CARNABY RESOURCES LIMITED; *Int'l*, pg. 1342
CASPIN RESOURCES LIMITED; *Int'l*, pg. 1354
CASSIUS MINING LIMITED; *Int'l*, pg. 1355
CATALYST METALS LIMITED; *Int'l*, pg. 1358
CAVALIER RESOURCES LIMITED; *Int'l*, pg. 1361
CAZALY RESOURCES LIMITED; *Int'l*, pg. 1364
CERRO GRANDE MINING CORPORATION; *Int'l*, pg. 1423
CERRO GRANDE MINING CORPORATION—See Cerro Grande Mining Corporation; *Int'l*, pg. 1423
CHALICE MINING LIMITED; *Int'l*, pg. 1437
CHESSER RESOURCES LIMITED—See Fortuna Mining Corp.; *Int'l*, pg. 2742
CHESTERFIELD RESOURCES PLC; *Int'l*, pg. 1473
CHINA NONFERROUS GOLD LIMITED; *Int'l*, pg. 1535
CLASS 1 NICKEL & TECHNOLOGIES LIMITED; *Int'l*, pg. 1652
CLEARMIND MEDICINE INC.; *Int'l*, pg. 1657
CLIFFMONT RESOURCES LTD.; *Int'l*, pg. 1659
CMOC GROUP LIMITED; *Int'l*, pg. 1671
COGENT DEVELOPMENT GROUP LIMITED; *Int'l*, pg. 1694
COLLECTIVE METALS INC.; *Int'l*, pg. 1699
COMJOYFUL INTERNATIONAL COMPANY; *Int'l*, pg. 1714
COMPANIA MINERA CUZCATLAN S.A.—See Fortuna Mining Corp.; *Int'l*, pg. 2743
COMPANIA MINERA MENA RESOURCES (CHILE) LIMITADA—See Austral Gold Limited; *Int'l*, pg. 719
CONSOLIDATED GENERAL MINERALS PLC; *Int'l*, pg. 1770
COPPERCORP RESOURCES INC.; *Int'l*, pg. 1794
COPPERHEAD RESOURCES INC.; *Int'l*, pg. 1794
COPPER STRIKE LIMITED; *Int'l*, pg. 1794
CORE ASSETS CORP.; *Int'l*, pg. 1797
COUGAR METALS NL; *Int'l*, pg. 1817
CPG RESOURCES - MINERAL TECHNOLOGIES PTY LTD—See Downer EDI Limited; *Int'l*, pg. 2185
CRESTVIEW EXPLORATION, INC.; *Int'l*, pg. 1841
CRITICAL MINERAL RESOURCES PLC; *Int'l*, pg. 1851
CROSS RIVER VENTURES CORP.; *Int'l*, pg. 1856
CULLEN EXPLORATION PTY LTD—See Cullen Resources Limited; *Int'l*, pg. 1877
CYPHERPUNK HOLDINGS INC.; *Int'l*, pg. 1897
D2 LITHIUM CORP.; *Int'l*, pg. 1901
DARK STAR MINERALS, INC.; *Int'l*, pg. 1973
DE GREY MINING LIMITED; *Int'l*, pg. 1995
DEMESNE RESOURCES LTD.; *Int'l*, pg. 2025
DESOTO RESOURCES LIMITED; *Int'l*, pg. 2045
DEVEX RESOURCES LIMITED; *Int'l*, pg. 2088
DIABLO RESOURCES LIMITED; *Int'l*, pg. 2101
DIAMOND DISCOVERIES INTERNATIONAL CORP.; *U.S. Public*, pg. 658
DIATREME RESOURCES LIMITED; *Int'l*, pg. 2106
DISCOVERY MINING SERVICES LTD.—See Clairvest Group Inc.; *Int'l*, pg. 1641
DISCOVEX RESOURCES LIMITED; *Int'l*, pg. 2134
DORE COPPER MINING CORPORATION; *Int'l*, pg. 2175
E3 LITHIUM LTD.; *Int'l*, pg. 2261
EAGLE BAY RESOURCES CORP.; *Int'l*, pg. 2264
EARTHWISE MINERALS CORP.; *Int'l*, pg. 2268
EASTERN MINING D.O.O—See Adriatic Metals plc; *Int'l*, pg. 153
ELCORA ADVANCED MATERIALS CORP.; *Int'l*, pg. 2346
ELEMENT 29 RESOURCES INC.; *Int'l*, pg. 2357
EMMERSON RESOURCES LIMITED; *Int'l*, pg. 2384
EMPEROR METALS INC.; *Int'l*, pg. 2386
EMPIRE METALS CORP.; *Int'l*, pg. 2387
EMPIRE METALS LIMITED; *Int'l*, pg. 2387
EMPIRE RESOURCES LIMITED; *Int'l*, pg. 2387
EMPRESS ROYALTY CORP.; *Int'l*, pg. 2392
ENK PLC PHILIPPINES REGIONAL OFFICE—See DMCI Holdings, Inc.; *Int'l*, pg. 2143
ENTOURAGE MINING LTD.; *Int'l*, pg. 2452
EQ RESOURCES LIMITED; *Int'l*, pg. 2466
EQUINOX RESOURCES LIMITED; *Int'l*, pg. 2485
ERG EXPLORATION JSC; *Int'l*, pg. 2490
ERRAWARRA RESOURCES LTD.; *Int'l*, pg. 2497
ESSEX MINERALS, INC.; *Int'l*, pg. 2512
EUREKA LITHIUM CORP.; *Int'l*, pg. 2530
EUROBATTERY MINERALS AB; *Int'l*, pg. 2533
EVERGOLD CORP.; *Int'l*, pg. 2565
EVERGREEN LITHIUM LIMITED; *Int'l*, pg. 2566
EV NICKEL INC.; *Int'l*, pg. 2560
EV RESOURCES LIMITED; *Int'l*, pg. 2560
EXPLOITS DISCOVERY CORP.; *Int'l*, pg. 2588
FABLED COPPER CORP.; *Int'l*, pg. 2599
FAIRMILE GOLDTECH INC.; *Int'l*, pg. 2609
FATHOM NICKEL INC.; *Int'l*, pg. 2623
FIRETAIL RESOURCES LIMITED; *Int'l*, pg. 2679
FIRST CLASS METALS PLC; *Int'l*, pg. 2683
FIRST HELIUM INC.; *Int'l*, pg. 2684
FIRST LITHIUM MINERALS CORP.; *Int'l*, pg. 2685
FORACO ARGENTINA SA—See Foraco International S.A.; *Int'l*, pg. 2728
FORACO BURKINA FASO SA—See Foraco International S.A.; *Int'l*, pg. 2728
FORACO CANADA LTD.—See Foraco International S.A.; *Int'l*, pg. 2728
FORACO CHILE SA—See Foraco International S.A.; *Int'l*, pg. 2728
FORACO CI S.A.—See Foraco International S.A.; *Int'l*, pg. 2728
FORACO GHANA LTD.—See Foraco International S.A.; *Int'l*, pg. 2728
FORACO GUINEE SARL—See Foraco International S.A.; *Int'l*, pg. 2728
FORACO NIGER S.A.—See Foraco International S.A.; *Int'l*, pg. 2728
FORACO PACIFIQUE SASU—See Foraco International S.A.; *Int'l*, pg. 2728
FORACO SAHEL SARL—See Foraco International S.A.; *Int'l*, pg. 2728
FORACO SINGAPORE PTE. LTD.—See Foraco International S.A.; *Int'l*, pg. 2728
FORAFRIC GLOBAL PLC; *Int'l*, pg. 2728
FORMATION CAPITAL CORPORATION, U.S.—See Sunshine Silver Mines Corporation; *U.S. Public*, pg. 3872
FORRESTANIA RESOURCES LIMITED; *Int'l*, pg. 2737
FORTIS MINERALS, LLC; *U.S. Private*, pg. 1576
FORZA LITHIUM CORP.; *Int'l*, pg. 2747
FOSTERVILLE SOUTH EXPLORATION LTD.; *Int'l*, pg. 2750
FOUR NINES GOLD INC/CA; *Int'l*, pg. 2755
FOX RIVER RESOURCES CORPORATION; *Int'l*, pg. 2756
FREEMAN GOLD CORP.; *Int'l*, pg. 2770
FURA GEMS INC.; *Int'l*, pg. 2846
FUSE BATTERY METALS INC.; *Int'l*, pg. 2848
GAINEY RESOURCES LTD.; *Int'l*, pg. 2869
GALENA MINING LIMITED; *Int'l*, pg. 2872
GENESIS MINERALS LIMITED; *Int'l*, pg. 2921
GENIUS METALS, INC; *Int'l*, pg. 2924
GEOLGICA RESOURCE CORP.; *Int'l*, pg. 2983
GLADIATOR RESOURCES LIMITED; *Int'l*, pg. 2987
GLOBAL ECOLOGY CORPORATION; *U.S. Public*, pg. 942
GLOBAL HELIUM CORP.; *Int'l*, pg. 2997
GLOBAL LITHIUM RESOURCES LIMITED; *Int'l*, pg. 2998
GLOBEX MINING ENTERPRISES INC.; *Int'l*, pg. 3007
G MINING VENTURES CORP.; *Int'l*, pg. 2861
GODOLPHIN RESOURCES LIMITED; *Int'l*, pg. 3020
GOLCAP RESOURCES CORP.; *Int'l*, pg. 3023
GOLD BASIN RESOURCES CORPORATION; *Int'l*, pg. 3023
GOLDBELT EMPIRES LIMITED; *Int'l*, pg. 3027
GOLDBLOCK CAPITAL, INC.; *Int'l*, pg. 3027
GOLD BULL RESOURCES CORP.; *Int'l*, pg. 3023
GOLDEN CROSS RESOURCES LIMITED; *Int'l*, pg. 3029
GOLDEN DEEPS LIMITED; *Int'l*, pg. 3029
GOLDEN LAKE EXPLORATION, INC.; *Int'l*, pg. 3030
GOLDEN RIM RESOURCES LTD; *Int'l*, pg. 3031
GOLDEN SKY MINERALS CORP.; *Int'l*, pg. 3031
GOLDEN SPIKE RESOURCES CORP.; *Int'l*, pg. 3032
GOLDEN VALLEY DEVELOPMENT, INC.; *U.S. Public*, pg. 951
GOLDHAVEN RESOURCES CORP.; *Int'l*, pg. 3033
GOLD LION RESOURCES, INC.; *Int'l*, pg. 3024
GOLDSEEK RESOURCES, INC.; *Int'l*, pg. 3034
GOLIATH RESOURCES LIMITED; *Int'l*, pg. 3036
GRAYCLIFF EXPLORATION LIMITED; *Int'l*, pg. 3062
GREATLAND GOLD PLC; *Int'l*, pg. 3067
GREAT SOUTHERN COPPER PLC; *Int'l*, pg. 3065
GREENLAND RESOURCES INC.; *Int'l*, pg. 3075
GREEN MINERALS AS; *Int'l*, pg. 3071
GREENWING RESOURCES LTD.; *Int'l*, pg. 3077
GROUP ELEVEN RESOURCES CORP.; *Int'l*, pg. 3088
GT GROUP HOLDINGS LIMITED; *Int'l*, pg. 3151
GUJARAT MINERAL DEVELOPMENT CORPORATION LIMITED; *Int'l*, pg. 3176
HAMAK GOLD LIMITED; *Int'l*, pg. 3235
HANSTONE GOLD CORP.; *Int'l*, pg. 3261
HARDCORE DISCOVERIES LTD.; *Int'l*, pg. 3272
HAWSONS IRON LIMITED; *Int'l*, pg. 3272
THE HEALING COMPANY INC.; *U.S. Public*, pg. 2088
HERENCIA RESOURCES PLC; *Int'l*, pg. 3361
HIGH DESERT HOLDING CORP.; *U.S. Private*, pg. 1935
HIGHLANDER SILVER CORP.; *Int'l*, pg. 3387
HIGHROCK RESOURCES LTD.; *Int'l*, pg. 3388
HORIZON GOLD LIMITED—See ICM Limited; *Int'l*, pg. 3582
IMAGE RESOURCES NL; *Int'l*, pg. 3617
INTERNATIONAL DIRECTIONAL SERVICES OF CANADA, LTD.—See Granite Construction Incorporated; *U.S. Public*, pg. 957
KING OF PINE CREEK MINING LTD.; *U.S. Public*, pg. 1234
LASALLE EXPLORATION CORP.—See Harfang Exploration Inc.; *Int'l*, pg. 3274
LONGYEAR SOUTH AFRICA (PTY) LTD—See Boart Longyear Ltd.; *Int'l*, pg. 1095
MANSFIELD-MARTIN EXPLORATION MINING, INC.; *U.S. Private*, pg. 2566
MARMOSA PTY LTD—See Auteco Minerals Ltd.; *Int'l*, pg. 724
MINERA CANASIL, S.A. DE C.V.—See Canasil Resources Inc.; *Int'l*, pg. 1288
MINERA PIEDRA AZUL, S.A. DE C.V.—See Hancock Prospecting Pty. Ltd.; *Int'l*, pg. 3242
MINERA ROCA RODANDO S. DE R.L. DE C.V.—See RCF Management LLC; *U.S. Private*, pg. 3362
MINERA TERRANOVA, S.A. DE C.V.—See Sunshine Silver Mines Corporation; *U.S. Public*, pg. 3872
MINOPEX—See DRA Group Holdings Proprietary Limited; *Int'l*, pg. 2196
ONASSIS HOLDINGS CORP.; *U.S. Public*, pg. 1601
PATERSON RESOURCES LIMITED—See Carling Capital Partners Pty Ltd.; *Int'l*, pg. 1338
PYBAR MINING SERVICES PTY. LTD.—See ACS, Actividades de Construccion y Servicios, S.A.; *Int'l*, pg. 113
PYBAR MINING SERVICES PTY. LTD.—See Elliott Management Corporation; *U.S. Public*, pg. 1365
QCI BRITANNIC—See ROW Inc.; *U.S. Private*, pg. 3490
QUAD M SOLUTIONS, INC.; *U.S. Public*, pg. 1744
REGIONAL EXPLORATION MANAGEMENT PTY LTD—See Diatreme Resources Limited; *Int'l*, pg. 2107
RHINO MINERALS PTY LTD—See Groupe Bruxelles Lambert SA; *Int'l*, pg. 3100
ROW INC.; *U.S. Private*, pg. 3490
SALORO S.L.U.—See EQ Resources Limited; *Int'l*, pg. 2466
SCARBOROUGH MINERALS INTERNATIONAL BV—See Cyclone Metals Limited; *Int'l*, pg. 1894
SEARCHLIGHT MINERALS CORP.; *U.S. Public*, pg. 1855
SILVER SCOTT MINES, INC.; *U.S. Public*, pg. 1880
SONORO ENERGY IRAQ B.V.—See Blue Sky Energy; *U.S. Private*, pg. 593
SOUTHERN ENERGY CORPORATION PTY LTD—See Agrimin Limited; *Int'l*, pg. 217
SPECIALTY GRANULES INC.; *U.S. Private*, pg. 3749
TENEDORA AGNICO EAGLE MEXICO S.A. DE C.V.—See Agnico Eagle Mines Limited; *Int'l*, pg. 212
TEXAS MINERAL RESOURCES CORP.; *U.S. Public*, pg. 2026
THRACE INVESTMENTS BV—See Cyclone Metals Limited; *Int'l*, pg. 1894
TROY GOLD & MINERAL CORP.; *U.S. Public*, pg. 2198
TWIGG GOLD LIMITED—See African Eagle Resources PLC; *Int'l*, pg. 191

N.A.I.C.S. INDEX

221111 — HYDROELECTRIC POWER...

TWIGG RESOURCES LIMITED—See African Eagle Resources PLC; *Int'l*, pg. 191
UGL OPERATIONS AND MAINTENANCE PTY LTD—See ACS, Actividades de Construccion y Servicios, S.A.; *Int'l*, pg. 113
VIRTUAL INTERACTIVE TECHNOLOGIES CORP.; *U.S. Public*, pg. 2300
WHITE OAK RESOURCES LLC—See Alliance Holdings GP, L.P.; *U.S. Private*, pg. 183
WITLAB (PROPRIETARY) LTD—See ALS Limited; *Int'l*, pg. 378
WORLD WIDE MINERALS LTD.—See Dundee Corporation; *Int'l*, pg. 2226

221111 — HYDROELECTRIC POWER GENERATION

ABOITIZ POWER CORPORATION—See Aboitiz Equity Ventures, Inc.; *Int'l*, pg. 66
AEP GENERATING COMPANY—See American Electric Power Company, Inc.; *U.S. Public*, pg. 99
AES ANDES SA—See The AES Corporation; *U.S. Public*, pg. 2030
THE AES CORPORATION; *U.S. Public*, pg. 2030
AES TEG OPERATIONS, S. DE R.L. DE C.V.—See The AES Corporation; *U.S. Public*, pg. 2031
AES URUGUAIANA EMPREENDIMENTOS S.A.—See The AES Corporation; *U.S. Public*, pg. 2031
AET ITALIA SPA—See Azienda Elettrica Ticinese; *Int'l*, pg. 778
AHOCHN AG—See BKW AG; *Int'l*, pg. 1054
AKENERJI ELEKTRIK URETIM A.S.; *Int'l*, pg. 262
ALASKA HYDRO CORPORATION; *Int'l*, pg. 291
ALECTRA UTILITIES CORPORATION—See Hydro One Limited; *Int'l*, pg. 3546
ALPIQ ECOPOWER LTD.—See Alpiq Holding AG; *Int'l*, pg. 372
ALPIQ ECOPOWER SCANDINAVIA AS—See Alpiq Holding AG; *Int'l*, pg. 373
ALPIQ ECOPOWER SWITZERLAND LTD.—See Alpiq Holding AG; *Int'l*, pg. 372
ALPIQ HYDRO AARE AG—See Alpiq Holding AG; *Int'l*, pg. 373
ALPIQ SUISSE SA—See Alpiq Holding AG; *Int'l*, pg. 373
ALSTOM HYDRO—See Alstom S.A.; *Int'l*, pg. 380
ALSTOM VANNKRAFT AS—See Alstom S.A.; *Int'l*, pg. 381
AMERICAN ELECTRIC POWER COMPANY, INC.; *U.S. Public*, pg. 99
ANDRITZ HYDRO, INC.—See ANDRITZ AG; *Int'l*, pg. 453
ANDRITZ HYDRO S.A.S.—See ANDRITZ AG; *Int'l*, pg. 453
ANDRITZ INDIA PRIVATE LIMITED—See ANDRITZ AG; *Int'l*, pg. 454
ANINO INTERNATIONAL PLC; *Int'l*, pg. 471
ANKHU KHOLA HYDROPOWER COMPANY LTD; *Int'l*, pg. 472
AOYAMA-KOGEN WIND FARM CO., LTD.—See Chubu Electric Power Co., Inc.; *Int'l*, pg. 1593
API POWER COMPANY LIMITED; *Int'l*, pg. 514
ARUN VALLEY HYDROPOWER DEVELOPMENT CO. LTD.; *Int'l*, pg. 586
ATCO ENERGY LTD.—See ATCO Ltd.; *Int'l*, pg. 666
AXPO D.O.O.—See Axpo Holding AG; *Int'l*, pg. 771
AXPO SINGAPORE PTE. LTD.—See Axpo Holding AG; *Int'l*, pg. 771
AXPO SLOVENSKO, S.R.O.—See Axpo Holding AG; *Int'l*, pg. 771
AXPO TURKEY ENERJI A.S.—See Axpo Holding AG; *Int'l*, pg. 771
AXPO UKRAINE LLC—See Axpo Holding AG; *Int'l*, pg. 771
AXPO U.S. LLC—See Axpo Holding AG; *Int'l*, pg. 771
BAC-MAN GEOTHERMAL INC.—See First Gen Corporation; *Int'l*, pg. 2684
BAHIA LAS MINAS CORP.; *Int'l*, pg. 800
BARO LAGERHAUS GMBH & CO. KG—See AGRAVIS Raiffeisen AG; *Int'l*, pg. 215
BKW AG; *Int'l*, pg. 1054
BKW ENERGIE AG—See BKW AG; *Int'l*, pg. 1054
BOOTT HYDROPOWER INC.—See Enel S.p.A.; *Int'l*, pg. 2411
BORALEX INC.; *Int'l*, pg. 1112
BURGO ENERGIA SRL—See Burgo Group S.p.A.; *Int'l*, pg. 1223
BUTWAL POWER COMPANY LIMITED; *Int'l*, pg. 1229
CADRE AS; *Int'l*, pg. 1248
CALANCASCA AG—See Axpo Holding AG; *Int'l*, pg. 771
CALORE SA—See Azienda Elettrica Ticinese; *Int'l*, pg. 778
CAN DON HYDRO POWER JOINT STOCK COMPANY; *Int'l*, pg. 1276
CASCADE CREEK LLC—See Alaska Hydro Corporation; *Int'l*, pg. 291
CENTRAIR ENERGY SUPPLY CO., LTD.—See Chubu Electric Power Co., Inc.; *Int'l*, pg. 1593
CENTRAIS ELETRICAS DO NORTE DO BRASIL SA—See Centrais Eletricas Brasileiras S.A.; *Int'l*, pg. 1403
CENTRAL ASIAN ELECTRIC POWER CORPORATION JSC—See Central-Asian Power Energy Company JSC; *Int'l*, pg. 1410

CENTRAL HYDROPOWER JOINT STOCK COMPANY; *Int'l*, pg. 1407
CENTRAL PUERTO S.A.; *Int'l*, pg. 1409
CEPO HANDA BIOMASS POWER GENERATION CO., INC.—See Chubu Electric Power Co., Inc.; *Int'l*, pg. 1593
CHILIME ENGINEERING & SERVICES COMPANY LIMITED—See Chilime Hydropower Company Limited; *Int'l*, pg. 1478
CHILIME HYDROPOWER COMPANY LIMITED; *Int'l*, pg. 1478
CHINA POWER INTERNATIONAL DEVELOPMENT LIMITED; *Int'l*, pg. 1542
CHINA THREE GORGES CORPORATION; *Int'l*, pg. 1558
CHINA YANGTZE POWER CO., LTD.—See China Three Gorges Corporation; *Int'l*, pg. 1558
CHINA YANGTZE POWER INTERNATIONAL (HONG KONG) CO., LTD.—See China Three Gorges Corporation; *Int'l*, pg. 1558
CHONGQING THREE GORGES WATER CONSERVANCY AND ELECTRIC POWER CO., LTD.; *Int'l*, pg. 1581
CHURCH & SCHOOL FINANCING—See The Ziegler Companies, Inc.; *U.S. Private*, pg. 4140
CLEAR PEAK ENERGY, INC.; *U.S. Public*, pg. 512
CMS GENERATION SAN NICOLAS COMPANY—See The AES Corporation; *U.S. Public*, pg. 2031
COMMONWEALTH EDISON COMPANY—See Exelon Corporation; *U.S. Public*, pg. 806
COMPANHIA BRASILIANA DE ENERGIA—See The AES Corporation; *U.S. Public*, pg. 2031
COMPANIA DE TRANSPORTE DE ENERGIA ELECTRICA EN ALTA TENSION TRANSENER S.A.—See Grupo EMES S.A.; *Int'l*, pg. 3126
CONSOLIDATED HYDRO NEW YORK INC—See Enel S.p.A.; *Int'l*, pg. 2411
CONSOLIDATED HYDRO SOUTHEAST INC.—See Enel S.p.A.; *Int'l*, pg. 2411
CRYSTAL MANAGEMENT JSC; *Int'l*, pg. 1860
CURTIS/PALMER HYDROELECTRIC COMPANY LP—See I Squared Capital Advisors (US) LLC; *U.S. Private*, pg. 2025
DALCOM ENGINEERING GMBH—See Dalekovod d.d.; *Int'l*, pg. 1951
DALEKOVOD AG—See Dalekovod d.d.; *Int'l*, pg. 1951
DALEKOVOD D.O.O., LJUBLJANA—See Dalekovod d.d.; *Int'l*, pg. 1951
DALEKOVOD KAZAKHSTAN—See Dalekovod d.d.; *Int'l*, pg. 1951
DALEKOVOD SKOPJE—See Dalekovod d.d.; *Int'l*, pg. 1951
DKLS ENERGY SDN. BHD.—See DKLS Industries Berhad; *Int'l*, pg. 2139
DONBASENERGO PJSC; *Int'l*, pg. 2163
E3 HLK AG—See BKW AG; *Int'l*, pg. 1055
ECOSESTO SPA—See Falck S.p.A.; *Int'l*, pg. 2610
EDC WIND ENERGY HOLDINGS, INC.—See First Gen Corporation; *Int'l*, pg. 2684
EDF LUMINUS NV—See Electricite de France S.A.; *Int'l*, pg. 2350
EDISON INTERNATIONAL; *U.S. Public*, pg. 719
EFD INDUCTION GROUP AS—See Arendals Fossekompani ASA; *Int'l*, pg. 559
EFFICIENTIA S.A.—See Companhia Energetica de Minas Gerais - CEMIG; *Int'l*, pg. 1747
ELEKTRIZITATSWERK AACH EG.—See EnBW Energie Baden-Wurttemberg AG; *Int'l*, pg. 2398
EMAE - EMPRESA METROPOLITANA DE AGUAS E ENERGIA S.A.; *Int'l*, pg. 2373
EMPRESA DE GENERACION ELECTRICA SAN GABAN S.A.; *Int'l*, pg. 2388
EMPRESA ELECTRICA PILMAIQUEN S.A.; *Int'l*, pg. 2388
EMPRESA ELECTRICIDAD DEL PERU-ELECTROPERU SA; *Int'l*, pg. 2388
ENBW BALTIC 1 VERWALTUNGS GESELLSCHAFT MBH—See EnBW Energie Baden-Wurttemberg AG; *Int'l*, pg. 2398
ENBW HOLDING A.S.—See EnBW Energie Baden-Wurttemberg AG; *Int'l*, pg. 2398
ENEFI VAGYONKEZELO NYRT; *Int'l*, pg. 2411
ENEL COVE FORT LLC—See Enel S.p.A.; *Int'l*, pg. 2412
ENEL GREEN POWER ROMANIA SRL—See Enel S.p.A.; *Int'l*, pg. 2413
ENEL GREEN POWER S.p.A.—See Enel S.p.A.; *Int'l*, pg. 2413
ENEL GUATEMALA SA—See Enel S.p.A.; *Int'l*, pg. 2413
ENEL STILLWATER LLC—See Enel S.p.A.; *Int'l*, pg. 2413
ENERGIAS DE GRAUS SL—See Enel S.p.A.; *Int'l*, pg. 2413
ENERGIEDIENST AG—See EnBW Energie Baden-Wurttemberg AG; *Int'l*, pg. 2398
ENERGIE ELECTRIQUE DU SIMPLON SA—See Alpiq Holding AG; *Int'l*, pg. 373
ENERGOAQUA A.S.; *Int'l*, pg. 2421
ENERGONOVA D.D.; *Int'l*, pg. 2421
ENERGO-PRO BULGARIA EAD—See ENERGO-PRO a.s.; *Int'l*, pg. 2420
ENERGO-PRO CAUCASUS LLC—See ENERGO-PRO a.s.; *Int'l*, pg. 2420
ENERGO-PRO CZECH S.R.O.—See ENERGO-PRO a.s.; *Int'l*, pg. 2420

ENERGO-PRO GEORGIA JSC—See ENERGO-PRO a.s.; *Int'l*, pg. 2420
ENERGO-PRO GUNEY ELEKTRIK URETIM SAN. VE TIC. A.S.—See ENERGO-PRO a.s.; *Int'l*, pg. 2420
ENERGY DEVELOPMENT COMPANY LIMITED; *Int'l*, pg. 2422
ENERGY DEVELOPMENT CORPORATION; *Int'l*, pg. 2422
ENERGY MANAGEMENT SERVICES INTERNATIONAL LLC—See Al Hassan Ghazi Ibrahim Shaker; *Int'l*, pg. 279
ENERGY OTTAWA INC.—See Hydro Ottawa Holding Inc.; *Int'l*, pg. 3546
ENGIE ENERGIE NEDERLAND N.V.—See ENGIE SA; *Int'l*, pg. 2428
ENGRO POWERGEN QADIRPUR LIMITED—See Engro Corporation Limited; *Int'l*, pg. 2435
ENSYNC, INC.; *U.S. Public*, pg. 775
ENTEGRA WASSERKRAFT AG—See Alpiq Holding AG; *Int'l*, pg. 373
EQUINOR SOUTH KOREA CO., LTD.—See Equinor ASA; *Int'l*, pg. 2484
EUROSIBENERGO PLC—See En+ Group Ltd.; *Int'l*, pg. 2395
EVN NATURKRAFT ERZEUGUNGSGESELLSCHAFT M.B.H.—See EVN AG; *Int'l*, pg. 2571
FASTNED B.V.; *Int'l*, pg. 2622
FDC UTILITIES, INC.—See Filinvest Development Corporation; *Int'l*, pg. 2663
FERREIRA GOMES ENERGIA S.A.—See Alupar Investimento S.A.; *Int'l*, pg. 401
FG BUKIDNON POWER CORPORATION - BUKIDNON PLANT—See First Gen Corporation; *Int'l*, pg. 2684
FIRST GAS POWER CORPORATION - BATANGAS PLANT—See First Gen Corporation; *Int'l*, pg. 2684
FIRST GEN HYDRO POWER CORPORATION - PANTABANGAN PLANT—See First Gen Corporation; *Int'l*, pg. 2684
FLORIDA POWER & LIGHT COMPANY—See NextEra Energy, Inc.; *U.S. Public*, pg. 1526
FLORIDA PUBLIC UTILITIES COMPANY—See Chesapeake Utilities Corporation; *U.S. Public*, pg. 485
FORTISONTARIO INC—See Fortis Inc.; *Int'l*, pg. 2739
FORTUM FRANCE S.N.C—See Fortum Oyj; *Int'l*, pg. 2741
FRENDY ENERGY S.P.A.; *Int'l*, pg. 2773
FUJIAN DONGSHAN AOZISHAN WIND POWER DEVELOPMENT CO., LTD.—See China Guodian Corporation; *Int'l*, pg. 1506
FUJIAN MINDONG ELECTRIC POWER CO., LTD.; *Int'l*, pg. 2818
FURNAS CENTRAIS ELETRICAS S.A.—See Centrais Eletricas Brasileiras S.A.; *Int'l*, pg. 1403
GENERTECH PAKISTAN LIMITED; *Int'l*, pg. 2921
GENON AMERICAS GENERATION, LLC—See NRG Energy, Inc.; *U.S. Public*, pg. 1550
GENON ENERGY, INC.—See NRG Energy, Inc.; *U.S. Public*, pg. 1550
GENON MID-ATLANTIC, LLC—See NRG Energy, Inc.; *U.S. Public*, pg. 1550
GEOCOMPLEX AS; *Int'l*, pg. 2932
GEPIC ENERGY DEVELOPMENT CO., LTD.; *Int'l*, pg. 2942
GE POWER SWEDEN AB—See General Electric Company; *U.S. Public*, pg. 917
GREEN VENTURES LIMITED; *Int'l*, pg. 3073
GRUPPO GREEN POWER S.P.A.—See Alperia SpA; *Int'l*, pg. 366
GUANGDONG MEIYAN JIXIANG HYDROPOWER CO., LTD.; *Int'l*, pg. 3158
GUANGXI GUIDONG ELECTRIC POWER CO., LTD.; *Int'l*, pg. 3163
GUIZHOU QIANYUAN POWER CO., LTD.; *Int'l*, pg. 3174
GUODIAN CHONGQING HENGTAI POWER GENERATION CO., LTD.—See China Guodian Corporation; *Int'l*, pg. 1506
GUODIAN JINGMEN JIANGSHAN POWER GENERATION CO., LTD.—See China Guodian Corporation; *Int'l*, pg. 1506
GUODIAN YUYUAN POWER GENERATION CO., LTD.—See China Guodian Corporation; *Int'l*, pg. 1506
HAITIAN ENERGY INTERNATIONAL LIMITED; *Int'l*, pg. 3217
HEP-PROIZVODNJA D.O.O.—See Hrvatska elektroprivreda d.d.; *Int'l*, pg. 3502
HIDIV ELEKTRIK ENERJISI TOPTAN SATIS A.S—See EnBW Energie Baden-Wurttemberg AG; *Int'l*, pg. 2399
HIDROECOLOGICA DEL TERIBE S.A.—See Empresas Publicas de Medellin ESP; *Int'l*, pg. 2392
HIDROELEKTRANE NA DRINI A.D.; *Int'l*, pg. 3384
HIDROELEKTRANE NA VRBASU A.D; *Int'l*, pg. 3384
HRVATSKA ELEKTROPRIVREDA D.D.; *Int'l*, pg. 3502
HUBEI ENERGY GROUP CO., LTD.; *Int'l*, pg. 3517
HUSCOKE HOLDINGS LIMITED; *Int'l*, pg. 3538
HYDROELECTRICITY INVESTMENT & DEVELOPMENT COMPANY LTD.; *Int'l*, pg. 3547
HYDRO EXPLOITATION SA; *Int'l*, pg. 3546
HYDROGEN PARK MARGHERA PER L'IDROGENO SCRL—See Enel S.p.A.; *Int'l*, pg. 2414
HYDROGENPRO A.S.; *Int'l*, pg. 3547
HYDRO POWER JOINT STOCK COMPANY; *Int'l*, pg. 3547
HYDRO-QUEBEC; *Int'l*, pg. 3547

221111 — HYDROELECTRIC POWER...

HYDRO-SOLAR ENERGIE AG—See Alpiq Holding AG; *Int'l*, pg. 373
IBERDROLA ENERGIA DO BRASIL, LTDA.—See Iberdrola, S.A.; *Int'l*, pg. 3572
ICEMENERG SA—See CNTEE TRANSELECTRICA SA; *Int'l*, pg. 1678
INTEPE ELEKTRIK URETIM VE TIC. A.S—See EnBW Energie Baden-Wurttemberg AG; *Int'l*, pg. 2399
ISAGEN S.A. E.S.P.—See Brookfield Corporation; *Int'l*, pg. 1186
KENTUCKY UTILITIES COMPANY—See PPL Corporation; *U.S. Public*, pg. 1711
KERNKRAFTWERK OBRIGHEIM GMBH—See EnBW Energie Baden-Wurttemberg AG; *Int'l*, pg. 2399
KNG KRAFTWERKS- UND NETZGESELLSCHAFT MBH—See EnBW Energie Baden-Wurttemberg AG; *Int'l*, pg. 2399
LUCENDRO SA—See Azienda Elettrica Ticinese; *Int'l*, pg. 778
MADHYA BHOTEKOSHI JALAVIDHYUT COMPANY LIMITED—See Chilime Hydropower Company Limited; *Int'l*, pg. 1478
MAYA ENERJI YATIRIMLARI A.S.—See EnBW Energie Baden-Wurttemberg AG; *Int'l*, pg. 2399
MITSUBISHI HITACHI POWER SYSTEMS AFRICA (PTY) LTD.—See Hitachi, Ltd.; *Int'l*, pg. 3423
MONONGAHELA POWER COMPANY—See FirstEnergy Corp.; *U.S. Public*, pg. 849
MONTEVUE LANE SOLAR LLC—See Ameresco, Inc.; *U.S. Public*, pg. 95
NATURLICHENERGIE EMH GMBH—See EnBW Energie Baden-Wurttemberg AG; *Int'l*, pg. 2399
NECEC TRANSMISSION, LLC—See Iberdrola, S.A.; *Int'l*, pg. 3573
NEVO ENERGY, INC.; *U.S. Private*, pg. 2891
NORD POOL FINLAND OY—See Euronext N.V.; *Int'l*, pg. 2554
NORD POOL HOLDING AS—See Euronext N.V.; *Int'l*, pg. 2554
NORTHERN INDIANA PUBLIC SERVICE COMPANY LLC—See NiSource Inc.; *U.S. Public*, pg. 1530
NORTHWESTERN CORPORATION; *U.S. Public*, pg. 1542
NYADI HYDROPOWER LIMITED—See Butwal Power Company Limited; *Int'l*, pg. 1229
OCEAN POWER TECHNOLOGIES, LTD.—See Ocean Power Technologies, Inc.; *U.S. Public*, pg. 1562
OGLETHORPE POWER CORPORATION; *U.S. Private*, pg. 3003
OLD DOMINION ELECTRIC COOPERATIVE; *U.S. Private*, pg. 3008
ORAZUL ENERGY EGENOR S. EN C. POR A.—See I Squared Capital Advisors (US) LLC; *U.S. Private*, pg. 2026
ORAZUL ENERGY GENERATING S.A.—See I Squared Capital Advisors (US) LLC; *U.S. Private*, pg. 2026
ORAZUL ENERGY INTERNATIONAL CHILE C.P.A.—See I Squared Capital Advisors (US) LLC; *U.S. Private*, pg. 2026
PACIFICORP—See Berkshire Hathaway Inc.; *U.S. Public*, pg. 301
PHI SERVICE COMPANY—See Exelon Corporation; *U.S. Public*, pg. 807
PILOT POWER GROUP, INC.—See Boyne Capital Management, LLC; *U.S. Private*, pg. 629
THE POTOMAC EDISON COMPANY—See FirstEnergy Corp.; *U.S. Public*, pg. 849
PROGRESS ENERGY, INC.—See Duke Energy Corporation; *U.S. Public*, pg. 691
PSEG ENERGY HOLDINGS LLC—See Public Service Enterprise Group Incorporated; *U.S. Public*, pg. 1735
PSEG RESOURCES LLC—See Public Service Enterprise Group Incorporated; *U.S. Public*, pg. 1736
RASUWAGADHI HYDROPOWER COMPANY LIMITED—See Chilime Hydropower Company Limited; *Int'l*, pg. 1478
REGIONAL POWER, INC.—See Connor, Clark & Lunn Financial Group; *Int'l*, pg. 1769
RETIRO BAIXO ENERGETICA S.A.—See Centrais Eletricas Brasileiras S.A.; *Int'l*, pg. 1403
RHEINKRAFTWERK IFFEZHEIM GMBH—See EnBW Energie Baden-Wurttemberg AG; *Int'l*, pg. 2399
RHEIN-MAIN-DONAU AG—See Fortum Oyj; *Int'l*, pg. 2742
RIO PARANAPANEMA ENERGIA S.A.—See China Three Gorges Corporation; *Int'l*, pg. 1558
SAFE HARBOR WATER POWER CORPORATION—See Constellation Energy Corporation; *U.S. Public*, pg. 572
SAFE HARBOR WATER POWER CORPORATION—See LS Power Development, LLC; *U.S. Private*, pg. 2508
SANJEN JALAVIDHYUT COMPANY LIMITED—See Chilime Hydropower Company Limited; *Int'l*, pg. 1478
SCANA CORPORATION—See Dominion Energy, Inc.; *U.S. Public*, pg. 674
SHANDONG RIZHAO POWER COMPANY LIMITED—See China Huaneng Group Co., Ltd.; *Int'l*, pg. 1509
SHANXI DATANG INTERNATIONAL SHENTOU POWER GENERATION COMPANY LIMITED—See China Datang Corporation; *Int'l*, pg. 1497
SMART WIRES INC.; *U.S. Private*, pg. 3691

SNC-LAVALIN INC. - HYDRO DIVISION—See AtkinsRealis Group Inc.; *Int'l*, pg. 671
SNC-LAVALIN TRANSMISSION & DISTRIBUTION—See AtkinsRealis Group Inc.; *Int'l*, pg. 673
SOCIETA ELETTRICA SOPRACENERINA SA—See Azienda Elettrica Ticinese; *Int'l*, pg. 779
SOCIETE HYDROELECTRIQUE DU MIDI—See ENGIE SA; *Int'l*, pg. 2435
SOUTHEAST ASIA ENERGY LIMITED—See CH. Karnchang Public Company Limited; *Int'l*, pg. 1435
SOUTHERN PHILIPPINES POWER CORPORATION—See Alcantara Group; *Int'l*, pg. 300
ST. LEON WIND ENERGY LP—See Algonquin Power & Utilities Corp.; *Int'l*, pg. 319
SYSTEM ENERGY RESOURCES, INC.—See Entergy Corporation; *U.S. Public*, pg. 777
TENNESSEE VALLEY AUTHORITY; *U.S. Public*, pg. 2016
TERMOPERNAMBUCO S.A.—See Iberdrola, S.A.; *Int'l*, pg. 3573
TRACTEBEL ENERGIA S.A. - HPP CANA BRAVA - UHCB PLANT—See ENGIE SA; *Int'l*, pg. 2432
TRACTEBEL ENERGIA S.A. - HPP MACHADINHO - UHMA PLANT—See ENGIE SA; *Int'l*, pg. 2432
TRACTEBEL ENERGIA S.A. - HPP PONTE DE PEDRA - UHPP PLANT—See ENGIE SA; *Int'l*, pg. 2432
TRACTEBEL ENERGIA S.A. - HPP SALTO OSORIO - UHSO PLANT—See ENGIE SA; *Int'l*, pg. 2432
TRACTEBEL ENERGIA S.A. - HPP SALTO SANTIAGO - UHSS PLANT—See ENGIE SA; *Int'l*, pg. 2432
TRACTEBEL ENERGIA S.A. - HPP SAO SALVADOR - UHSA PLANT—See ENGIE SA; *Int'l*, pg. 2432
VERDANT ENVIRONMENTAL TECHNOLOGIES INC.—See Emerson Electric Co.; *U.S. Public*, pg. 752
VOLUE AG—See Arendals Fossekompani ASA; *Int'l*, pg. 559
WYSOKA WIND FARM SP. Z.O.O.—See Falck S.p.A.; *Int'l*, pg. 2610
XINJIANG TIANFENG POWER GENERATION CO., LTD—See China Guodian Corporation; *Int'l*, pg. 1506
YICHUN XINGANLING WIND POWER CO., LTD.—See China Guodian Corporation; *Int'l*, pg. 1506
YOKKAICHI KASUMI POWER CO., LTD.—See Cosmo Energy Holdings Co., Ltd.; *Int'l*, pg. 1812
YONAGO BIOMASS POWER GENERATION LLC—See Chubu Electric Power Co., Inc.; *Int'l*, pg. 1593
ZAO MAREM—See En+ Group Ltd.; *Int'l*, pg. 2395

221112 — FOSSIL FUEL ELECTRIC POWER GENERATION

ACWA POWER BARKA S.A.O.G.—See The AES Corporation; *U.S. Public*, pg. 2030
ADHUNIK POWER & NATURAL RESOURCES LTD.—See GFG Alliance Limited; *Int'l*, pg. 2956
AES ELSTA BV—See The AES Corporation; *U.S. Public*, pg. 2030
AES (IRELAND) LIMITED—See Bord na Mona Plc; *Int'l*, pg. 1113
AES KILROOT POWER LIMITED—See The AES Corporation; *U.S. Public*, pg. 2031
AES LAL PIR (PVT) LTD.—See The AES Corporation; *U.S. Public*, pg. 2031
AES PANAMA S.A.—See The AES Corporation; *U.S. Public*, pg. 2031
AES SONEL S.A.—See General Atlantic Service Company, L.P.; *U.S. Private*, pg. 1661
AES-TISZA EROMU KFT—See The AES Corporation; *U.S. Public*, pg. 2031
AGL MACQUARIE—See AGL Energy Limited; *Int'l*, pg. 211
AKSA ENERJI URETIM A.S.; *Int'l*, pg. 264
ALLIANCE ENERGY GROUP, LLC; *U.S. Private*, pg. 182
AMATA B.GRIMM POWER 2 LTD.—See B. Grimm Group; *Int'l*, pg. 788
AMATA B.GRIMM POWER (RAYONG) 1 LTD.—See B. Grimm Group; *Int'l*, pg. 788
AMITE BIOENERGY LLC—See Drax Group plc; *Int'l*, pg. 2200
APPALACHIAN POWER COMPANY—See American Electric Power Company, Inc.; *U.S. Public*, pg. 99
ASTORIA ENERGY LLC—See APG Asset Management NV; *Int'l*, pg. 512
ASTORIA ENERGY LLC—See IDB Development Corporation Ltd.; *Int'l*, pg. 3588
BABCOCK & WILCOX POWER GENERATION GROUP, INC.—See Babcock & Wilcox Enterprises, Inc.; *U.S. Public*, pg. 262
BAHIA DE BIZKAIA ELECTRICIDAD S.L.—See BP plc; *Int'l*, pg. 1130
BAHIA DE BIZKAIA ELECTRICIDAD S.L.—See Ente Vasco de la Energia; *Int'l*, pg. 2450
BAINOUNAH POWER COMPANY—See Abu Dhabi Water & Electricity Authority; *Int'l*, pg. 73
BALTIMORE GAS AND ELECTRIC COMPANY—See Exelon Corporation; *U.S. Public*, pg. 806
BLACKWELL 3D CONSTRUCTION CORP; *U.S. Public*, pg. 361
BLUEFIRE RENEWABLES, INC.; *U.S. Public*, pg. 365

BLUE TOWER GMBH—See Concord Blue Engineering GmbH; *Int'l*, pg. 1764
BNI ENERGY, INC.—See ALLETE, Inc.; *U.S. Public*, pg. 79
BORD NA MONA PLC; *Int'l*, pg. 1113
BOUYGUES E&S INTEC AG—See Bouygues S.A.; *Int'l*, pg. 1123
C2E ENERGY, INC.; *U.S. Public*, pg. 415
CANDAX ENERGY INC.; *Int'l*, pg. 1289
CANDAX MADAGASCAR LTD.—See Candax Energy Inc.; *Int'l*, pg. 1289
CHEMOIL ENERGY LIMITED—See Glencore plc; *Int'l*, pg. 2990
CHIAHUI POWER CORP.—See Asia Cement Corporation; *Int'l*, pg. 611
CHOW INTERNATIONAL CO., LTD.—See Chow Steel Industries Public Company Limited; *Int'l*, pg. 1584
CLP POWER INDIA PVT. LTD.—See CLP Holdings Limited; *Int'l*, pg. 1663
COLBUN S.A.; *Int'l*, pg. 1697
COLUMBUS SOUTHERN POWER COMPANY—See American Electric Power Company, Inc.; *U.S. Public*, pg. 99
CONSUMERS ENERGY COMPANY—See CMS Energy Corporation; *U.S. Public*, pg. 518
COOPERHEAT OF AFRICA PTY. LTD.—See Stanley Black & Decker, Inc.; *U.S. Public*, pg. 1932
DEESIDE POWER (UK) LIMITED—See ENGIE SA; *Int'l*, pg. 2432
DRAX GROUP PLC; *Int'l*, pg. 2200
DRAX POWER LIMITED—See Drax Group plc; *Int'l*, pg. 2200
EGGBOROUGH POWER LTD—See Energeticky a Prumyslovy Holding, a.s.; *Int'l*, pg. 2420
ELQ S.A.; *Int'l*, pg. 2369
EMIRATES CMS POWER COMPANY—See Abu Dhabi Water & Electricity Authority; *Int'l*, pg. 73
ENEL WASHINGTON DC LTD.—See Enel S.p.A.; *Int'l*, pg. 2413
ENERGIEUNION GMBH—See EnBW Energie Baden-Wurttemberg AG; *Int'l*, pg. 2400
ENEVA S.A.; *Int'l*, pg. 2425
E.ON ITALIA S.P.A.—See F2i - Fondi Italiani per le infrastrutture SGR S.p.A.; *Int'l*, pg. 2597
E.ON KRAFTWERKE GMBH—See E.ON SE; *Int'l*, pg. 2253
E.ON UK PLC—See E.ON SE; *Int'l*, pg. 2256
FUEL CARD SERVICES LIMITED—See DCC plc; *Int'l*, pg. 1990
GBR GEMEINSCHAFTSKRAFTWERK WEST—See Asterion Industrial Partners SGEIC SA; *Int'l*, pg. 654
GCL TECHNOLOGY HOLDINGS LIMITED—See Golden Concord Holdings Limited; *Int'l*, pg. 3029
GEMEINSCHAFTSKRAFTWERK BREMEN GMBH & CO. KG—See EWE Aktiengesellschaft; *Int'l*, pg. 2575
GOLDGAS GMBH—See EnBW Energie Baden-Wurttemberg AG; *Int'l*, pg. 2400
GOLDGAS GMBH—See EnBW Energie Baden-Wurttemberg AG; *Int'l*, pg. 2400
GRUPO ENERGIA BOGOTA S.A. E.S.P.; *Int'l*, pg. 3128
HANDEN SP. Z O.O.—See EnBW Energie Baden-Wurttemberg AG; *Int'l*, pg. 2400
HARBIN HATOU INVESTMENT CO., LTD.; *Int'l*, pg. 3270
HIDD POWER COMPANY BSC—See ENGIE SA; *Int'l*, pg. 2432
HUANENG POWER INTERNATIONAL, INC.—See China Huaneng Group Co., Ltd.; *Int'l*, pg. 1509
HYBRID ENERGY HOLDINGS, INC.; *U.S. Public*, pg. 1078
IBERDROLA, S.A.; *Int'l*, pg. 3570
INDIANAPOLIS POWER & LIGHT COMPANY—See The AES Corporation; *U.S. Public*, pg. 2031
INDIAN QUEENS POWER LTD.—See ENGIE SA; *Int'l*, pg. 2433
J-POWER USA DEVELOPMENT CO., LTD.—See Electric Power Development Co., Ltd.; *Int'l*, pg. 2349
KEDCO POWER LIMITED—See EQTEC plc; *Int'l*, pg. 2483
KENTUCKY POWER COMPANY—See American Electric Power Company, Inc.; *U.S. Public*, pg. 100
KORINTHOS POWER S.A.—See Iberdrola, S.A.; *Int'l*, pg. 3573
NEW YORK STATE ELECTRIC & GAS CORP.—See Iberdrola, S.A.; *Int'l*, pg. 3571
NOBLE ENERGY NEW VENTURES, LLC—See Chevron Corporation; *U.S. Public*, pg. 487
NORTH AMERICAN NATURAL RESOURCES, LLC—See Kinder Morgan, Inc.; *U.S. Public*, pg. 1234
OILDALE ENERGY, LLC—See Enpower Corp.; *U.S. Private*, pg. 1401
ORAZUL ENERGY EL SALVADOR, S. EN C. DE C.V.—See I Squared Capital Advisors (US) LLC; *U.S. Private*, pg. 2026
PEOPLES ENERGY, LLC—See WEC Energy Group, Inc.; *U.S. Public*, pg. 2342
POET, LLC; *U.S. Private*, pg. 3220
PUBLIC SERVICE ELECTRIC & GAS COMPANY—See Public Service Enterprise Group Incorporated; *U.S. Public*, pg. 1736
SKODA POWER PRIVATE LTD.—See Doosan Corporation; *Int'l*, pg. 2174
STEAG GMBH—See Asterion Industrial Partners SGEIC SA; *Int'l*, pg. 654

N.A.I.C.S. INDEX

STEAG POWER SAAR GMBH—See Asterion Industrial Partners SGEIC SA; *Int'l*, pg. 654
SYNATOM SA—See ENGIE SA; *Int'l*, pg. 2435
TAWEELAH ASIA POWER COMPANY—See Abu Dhabi Water & Electricity Authority; *Int'l*, pg. 73
UIL HOLDINGS CORPORATION—See Iberdrola, S.A.; *Int'l*, pg. 3571
WEC INVESTMENTS, LLC—See WEC Energy Group, Inc.; *U.S. Public*, pg. 2342
WESTMORELAND PARTNERS—See Westmoreland Coal Company; *U.S. Private*, pg. 4500
WORLD ENERGY BUSINESS S.A.—See Grupo EMES S.A.; *Int'l*, pg. 3126
YUNNAN SHENYU NEW ENERGY COMPANY LIMITED—See China Sandi Holdings Limited; *Int'l*, pg. 1549

221113 — NUCLEAR ELECTRIC POWER GENERATION

ALLIED HOME WARRANTY GP LLC—See NRG Energy, Inc.; *U.S. Public*, pg. 1549
ALSTOM TAIWAN LTD—See Alstom S.A.; *Int'l*, pg. 381
BABCOCK & WILCOX INVESTMENT COMPANY—See BWX Technologies, Inc.; *U.S. Public*, pg. 413
CANDU-ARGENTINA—See AtkinsRealis Group Inc.; *Int'l*, pg. 671
CANDU-CHINA—See AtkinsRealis Group Inc.; *Int'l*, pg. 671
CENTRAL NUCLEAR DE TRILLO—See Iberdrola, S.A.; *Int'l*, pg. 3571
CHINA NUCLEAR POWER CO., LTD.; *Int'l*, pg. 1536
COFELY ENERGY SOLUTIONS BV—See ENGIE SA; *Int'l*, pg. 2430
DAYA BAY NUCLEAR POWER OPERATIONS AND MANAGEMENT CO., LTD.—See CGN Power Co., Ltd.; *Int'l*, pg. 1435
DUKE ENERGY AMERICAS, LLC—See Duke Energy Corporation; *U.S. Public*, pg. 690
DUKE ENERGY CAROLINAS, LLC—See Duke Energy Corporation; *U.S. Public*, pg. 690
DUKE ENERGY INTERNATIONAL, LLC—See Duke Energy Corporation; *U.S. Public*, pg. 690
DUKE ENERGY NORTH AMERICA, LLC—See Duke Energy Corporation; *U.S. Public*, pg. 690
ELETROBRAS TERMONUCLEAR SA—See Centrais Eletricas Brasileiras S.A.; *Int'l*, pg. 1403
ENTERGY NUCLEAR GENERATION COMPANY—See Entergy Corporation; *U.S. Public*, pg. 777
ENTERGY NUCLEAR VERMONT YANKEE, LLC—See J.F. Lehman & Company, Inc.; *U.S. Private*, pg. 2164
ENTERGY WHOLESALE COMMODITIES—See Entergy Corporation; *U.S. Public*, pg. 777
FORTUM NUCLEAR SERVICES OY—See Fortum Oyj; *Int'l*, pg. 2741
FORTUM OSLO VARME AS—See Fortum Oyj; *Int'l*, pg. 2741
FORTUM OYJ; *Int'l*, pg. 2740
FRAMATOME SPAIN SLU—See Electricite de France S.A.; *Int'l*, pg. 2351
GE ENERGY - SAN JOSE—See General Electric Company; *U.S. Public*, pg. 917
GUJARAT PAGUTHAN ENERGY CORPORATION PRIVATE LIMITED—See CLP Holdings Limited; *Int'l*, pg. 1663
HIGHLANDER SOLAR 1, LLC—See Duke Energy Corporation; *U.S. Public*, pg. 691
HOKKAIDO ELECTRIC POWER CO., INC.; *Int'l*, pg. 3442
HONG KONG NUCLEAR INVESTMENT COMPANY LIMITED—See CLP Holdings Limited; *Int'l*, pg. 1663
HORIZON NUCLEAR POWER LIMITED—See Hitachi, Ltd.; *Int'l*, pg. 3420
KERNKRAFTWERKE ISAR VERWALTUNGS GMBH—See E.ON SE; *Int'l*, pg. 2258
KERNKRAFTWERK GOSGEN-DANIKEN AG—See Axpo Holding AG; *Int'l*, pg. 771
KERNKRAFTWERK STADE GMBH & CO. OHG—See E.ON SE; *Int'l*, pg. 2258
KKK GMBH & CO OHV—See E.ON SE; *Int'l*, pg. 2254
LIGHTBRIDGE CORPORATION; *U.S. Public*, pg. 1315
MISSISSIPPI POWER COMPANY—See The Southern Company; *U.S. Public*, pg. 2131
NANJING XINSU THERMOELECTRICITY CO., LTD.—See CGN Power Co., Ltd.; *Int'l*, pg. 1435
NEWPORT NEWS NUCLEAR BWXT-LOS ALAMOS, LLC—See Huntington Ingalls Industries, Inc.; *U.S. Public*, pg. 1072
NORTHEAST NUCLEAR ENERGY COMPANY—See Eversource Energy; *U.S. Public*, pg. 801
OCHRANA A BEZPECNOST SE AS—See Enel S.p.A.; *Int'l*, pg. 2412
OCOTILLO WINDPOWER, LP—See Duke Energy Corporation; *U.S. Public*, pg. 691
ORAZUL ENERGY INTERNATIONAL SOUTHERN CONE S.R.L.—See I Squared Capital Advisors (US) LLC; *U.S. Private*, pg. 2026
PARAGON ENERGY SOLUTIONS, LLC; *U.S. Private*, pg. 3091
PHOENIX LLC—See SHINE Medical Technologies, LLC; *U.S. Private*, pg. 3637
PPL SUSQUEHANNA LLC—See PPL Corporation; *U.S. Public*, pg. 1712
R.E. GINNA NUCLEAR POWER PLANT, LLC—See Constellation Energy Corporation; *U.S. Public*, pg. 571
ROUSCH (PAKISTAN) POWER LIMITED—See Crescent Steel and Allied Products Limited; *Int'l*, pg. 1839
SAN DIEGO GAS & ELECTRIC COMPANY—See Sempra; *U.S. Public*, pg. 1863
SHIRLEY WIND, LLC—See Duke Energy Corporation; *U.S. Public*, pg. 691
SLOVENSKE ELEKTRARNE AS—See Enel S.p.A.; *Int'l*, pg. 2412
SOCIEDAD ELECTRICA SANTIAGO S.A.—See The AES Corporation; *U.S. Public*, pg. 2032
SOUTHERN NUCLEAR OPERATING COMPANY, INC.—See The Southern Company; *U.S. Public*, pg. 2131
STEAG KETEK IT GMBH—See Asterion Industrial Partners SGEIC SA; *Int'l*, pg. 654
SYDKRAFT NUCLEAR POWER AB—See Fortum Oyj; *Int'l*, pg. 2742
TALEN NUCLEAR DEVELOPMENT, LLC—See Riverstone Holdings LLC; *U.S. Private*, pg. 3447
USTAV JADERNEHO VYZKUMU REZ, A.S.—See CEZ, a.s.; *Int'l*, pg. 1429
WOLF CREEK NUCLEAR OPERATING CORPORATION—See Evergy, Inc.; *U.S. Public*, pg. 801

221114 — SOLAR ELECTRIC POWER GENERATION

3D SOLAR LLC; *U.S. Private*, pg. 9
808 RENEWABLE ENERGY CORP.; *U.S. Public*, pg. 9
ABOUND SOLAR, INC.—See United Power Inc.; *U.S. Private*, pg. 4295
ADVAIT INFRATECH LIMITED; *Int'l*, pg. 155
ADVANCED SOLTECH SWEDEN AB; *Int'l*, pg. 162
AEG SOLAR INDIA PVT. LTD.—See Armstrong Energy Global Limited; *Int'l*, pg. 575
AES SOUTHLAND, LLC—See The AES Corporation; *U.S. Public*, pg. 2031
AFRY MALAYSIA SDN. BHD.—See AFRY AB; *Int'l*, pg. 194
AFRY (PERU) S.A.C.—See AFRY AB; *Int'l*, pg. 194
AFRY SOUTH-EAST ASIA LTD.—See AFRY AB; *Int'l*, pg. 194
AFRY (THAILAND) LTD.—See AFRY AB; *Int'l*, pg. 194
ALLIED ENERGY, INC.; *U.S. Public*, pg. 80
ALLIUM RENEWABLE ENERGY, LLC—See Lotus Infrastructure Partners LLC; *U.S. Private*, pg. 2497
ALTERNUS CLEAN ENERGY INC.; *U.S. Public*, pg. 87
ALTERNUS ENERGY, INC.; *U.S. Public*, pg. 87
AMERESCO, INC.; *U.S. Public*, pg. 95
AMERESCO SOLAR - SOLUTIONS INC.—See Ameresco, Inc.; *U.S. Public*, pg. 95
AMERGY MEXICANA, S.A. DE C.V.—See Iberdrola, S.A.; *Int'l*, pg. 3571
AMIA ENERGY GMBH; *Int'l*, pg. 426
AMPYR GLOBAL ENERGY HOLDINGS PTE. LTD.; *Int'l*, pg. 437
ANDES SOLAR SPA—See The AES Corporation; *U.S. Public*, pg. 2031
AS FORTUM TARTU—See Fortum Oyj; *Int'l*, pg. 2740
AZURE POWER GLOBAL LIMITED; *Int'l*, pg. 782
BAKER ELECTRIC SOLAR; *U.S. Private*, pg. 456
BANPU INFINERGY CO., LTD.—See Banpu Public Company Limited; *Int'l*, pg. 851
BANPU POWER (JAPAN) CO., LTD.—See Banpu Power PCL; *Int'l*, pg. 851
BAYWA R.E. ASSET MANAGEMENT GMBH—See BayWa AG; *Int'l*, pg. 916
BAYWA R.E. ENERGY VENTURES GMBH—See BayWa AG; *Int'l*, pg. 916
BAYWA R.E. HELLAS MEPE—See BayWa AG; *Int'l*, pg. 916
BAYWA R.E. ITALIA S.R.L.—See BayWa AG; *Int'l*, pg. 916
BAYWA RE (MALAYSIA) SDN. BHD.—See BayWa AG; *Int'l*, pg. 917
BAYWA R.E. NORDIC AB—See BayWa AG; *Int'l*, pg. 916
BAYWA R.E. OFFSHORE WIND GMBH—See BayWa AG; *Int'l*, pg. 916
BAYWA R.E. OPERATION SERVICES S.R.L.—See BayWa AG; *Int'l*, pg. 916
BAYWA R.E. POLSKA SP. Z O.O.—See BayWa AG; *Int'l*, pg. 916
BAYWA R.E. PROGETTI S.R.L.—See BayWa AG; *Int'l*, pg. 916
BAYWA R.E. RENEWABLE ENERGY GMBH—See BayWa AG; *Int'l*, pg. 917
BAYWA R.E. ROMANIA S.R.L.—See BayWa AG; *Int'l*, pg. 916
BAYWA R.E. SOLAR PTE. LTD.—See BayWa AG; *Int'l*, pg. 916
BAYWA R.E. SOLAR SYSTEMS S.A R.L.—See BayWa AG; *Int'l*, pg. 916
BAYWA R.E. SOLAR SYSTEMS SAS—See BayWa AG; *Int'l*, pg. 916
BAYWA R.E. SOLAR SYSTEMS S. DE R.L DE C.V.—See BayWa AG; *Int'l*, pg. 916
BAYWA R.E. SOLAR SYSTEMS S.R.L.—See BayWa AG; *Int'l*, pg. 916
BAYWA R.E. WIND LLC—See BayWa AG; *Int'l*, pg. 917
BIOFUELS POWER CORP.; *U.S. Private*, pg. 561
BKW ITALIA S.P.A.—See BKW AG; *Int'l*, pg. 1054
BLUE RAVEN SOLAR, LLC—See SunPower Corporation; *U.S. Public*, pg. 1965
BLUSOLAR PTY LTD—See BluGlass Limited; *Int'l*, pg. 1075
BRIGHT SOLAR LTD.; *Int'l*, pg. 1162
BSL ECO ENERGY SDN. BHD.—See BSL Corporation Berhad; *Int'l*, pg. 1202
CANADIAN SOLAR CONSTRUCTION S.R.L.—See Canadian Solar Inc.; *Int'l*, pg. 1286
CENTRICA BUSINESS SOLUTIONS BV—See Centrica plc; *Int'l*, pg. 1413
CENTRICA BUSINESS SOLUTIONS ITALIA S.R.L.—See Centrica plc; *Int'l*, pg. 1413
CHAILEASE ENERGY INTEGRATION CO., LTD.—See Chailease Holding Company Limited; *Int'l*, pg. 1436
CHINA NATIONAL NUCLEAR POWER CO LTD.—See China National Nuclear Corporation; *Int'l*, pg. 1532
CHOW SHINING ENERGY COMPANY LIMITED—See Chow Steel Industries Public Company Limited; *Int'l*, pg. 1584
COMPLETE SOLARIA, INC.; *U.S. Public*, pg. 561
COMPLINA GMBH—See DZ BANK AG Deutsche Zentral-Genossenschaftsbank; *Int'l*, pg. 2243
CONERGY ASIA & ME PTE LTD—See Kawa Capital Management, Inc.; *U.S. Private*, pg. 2266
CONSTELLATION SOLAR MARYLAND MC, LLC—See Constellation Energy Corporation; *U.S. Public*, pg. 572
COVANTA DURHAN YORK RENEWABLE ENERGY LIMITED PARTNERSHIP—See EQT AB; *Int'l*, pg. 2473
CRITICAL POWER SOLUTIONS PTE. LTD.—See Air Water Inc.; *Int'l*, pg. 240
CSC SOLAR CORPORATION—See China Steel Corporation; *Int'l*, pg. 1555
CYPRESS CREEK RENEWABLES, LLC; *U.S. Private*, pg. 1134
DAIPUR WIND FARM PTY. LTD.—See BayWa AG; *Int'l*, pg. 917
DE VRIJE ENERGIE PRODUCENT B.V.—See UGI Corporation; *U.S. Public*, pg. 2222
DIGITAL CHARGING SOLUTION CORP.—See Bayerische Motoren Werke Aktiengesellschaft; *Int'l*, pg. 912
DJK SOLAR SOLUTION CO., LTD.—See Daiichi Jitsugyo Co. Ltd.; *Int'l*, pg. 1927
DUKE ENERGY RENEWABLE SERVICES, LLC—See Duke Energy Corporation; *U.S. Public*, pg. 691
E3 CO., LTD.—See Envipro Holdings Inc.; *Int'l*, pg. 2454
ECO DEPOT, INC.; *U.S. Private*, pg. 711
EDISUN POWER SWITZERLAND LTD.—See Edisun Power Europe AG; *Int'l*, pg. 2311
EIGENSONNE GMBH—See Amia Energy GmbH; *Int'l*, pg. 426
EKO ENERGETIKA DOO—See ERA d.o.o.; *Int'l*, pg. 2488
EK POWER SOLUTIONS AB—See Addtech AB; *Int'l*, pg. 133
ELECTROHOLD BULGARIA EOOD—See Eurohold Bulgaria AD; *Int'l*, pg. 2553
ELECTROHOLD TRADE EAD—See Eurohold Bulgaria AD; *Int'l*, pg. 2553
EMERGENT ENERGY PROPRIETARY LIMITED—See African Equity Empowerment Investmts Limited; *Int'l*, pg. 191
ENBW SVERIGE AB—See EnBW Energie Baden-Wurttemberg AG; *Int'l*, pg. 2398
ENEL DISTRIBUCION CHILE SA—See Enel S.p.A.; *Int'l*, pg. 2412
ENEL DISTRIBUCION PERU SAA—See Enel S.p.A.; *Int'l*, pg. 2412
ENEL F2I SOLARE ITALIA S.P.A.—See F2i - Fondi Italiani per le infrastrutture SGR S.p.A.; *Int'l*, pg. 2597
ENEL X BRASIL SA—See Enel S.p.A.; *Int'l*, pg. 2414
ENEL X KOREA LIMITED—See Enel S.p.A.; *Int'l*, pg. 2414
ENERGEIA A.S.; *Int'l*, pg. 2419
ENERGIEKONTOR UK LTD.—See Energiekontor AG; *Int'l*, pg. 2420
ENERGIEKONTOR US INC.—See Energiekontor AG; *Int'l*, pg. 2420
ENERGIEVERSUM GMBH & CO. KG—See EnBW Energie Baden-Wurttemberg AG; *Int'l*, pg. 2398
ENERZEA POWER SOLUTION PRIVATE LIMITED—See 2G Energy AG; *Int'l*, pg. 5
ENLIGHT RENEWABLE ENERGY LTD.; *Int'l*, pg. 2442
E.ON ENERGY INFRASTRUCTURE SOLUTIONS D.O.O.—See E.ON SE; *Int'l*, pg. 2254
EQUAL EARTH CORP.; *U.S. Private*, pg. 1415
E.S.CO. COMUNI SRL—See Enel S.p.A.; *Int'l*, pg. 2411
ESDEC USA—See Esdec BV; *Int'l*, pg. 2502
ESSEL INFRAPROJECTS LIMITED—See Essel Corporate Resources Pvt. Ltd.; *Int'l*, pg. 2509
ETERBRIGHT SOLAR CORPORATION—See Hiwin Technologies Corp.; *Int'l*, pg. 3427
EWE ERNEUERBARE ENERGIEN GMBH—See EWE Aktiengesellschaft; *Int'l*, pg. 2575

221114 — SOLAR ELECTRIC POWE...

EXRO TECHNOLOGIES, INC.; *Int'l*, pg. 2591
FERGUSON WIND FARM PTY. LTD.—See BayWa AG; *Int'l*, pg. 917
FILOTIPO, LDA—See 2G Energy AG; *Int'l*, pg. 5
FIRESTONE ENERGY SOLUTIONS—See Bridgestone Corporation; *Int'l*, pg. 1157
FIRST SOLAR ASSET MANAGEMENT, LLC—See First Solar, Inc.; *U.S. Public*, pg. 847
FIRST SOLAR (AUSTRALIA) PTY LTD—See First Solar, Inc.; *U.S. Public*, pg. 847
FIRST SOLAR ELECTRICO (CHILE) SPA—See First Solar, Inc.; *U.S. Public*, pg. 847
FIRST SOLAR POWER INDIA PVT LTD—See First Solar, Inc.; *U.S. Public*, pg. 847
FORTUM MARKETS AS—See Fortum Oyj; *Int'l*, pg. 2741
FREEDOM FOREVER LLC; *U.S. Private*, pg. 1603
FRESH AIR ENERGY X, LLC—See Duke Energy Corporation; *U.S. Public*, pg. 691
GENCAN CAPITAL, INC.; *Int'l*, pg. 2917
GIGAWATTS, LLC—See APPLIED DIGITAL CORPORATION; *U.S. Public*, pg. 170
GOAL ZERO LLC—See NRG Energy, Inc.; *U.S. Public*, pg. 1550
GOH CLEAN ENERGY LLC—See Elixir Energy Limited; *Int'l*, pg. 2363
GRAZIELLA GREEN POWER S.P.A; *Int'l*, pg. 3063
GREEN RAIN SOLAR, INC.—See The Now Corporation; *U.S. Public*, pg. 2117
GREEN STREET POWER PARTNERS LLC; *U.S. Private*, pg. 1774
GREMZ SOLAR, INC.—See gremz, Inc.; *Int'l*, pg. 3080
GROENLEVEN B.V.—See BayWa AG; *Int'l*, pg. 918
GSG SOLAR BERLIN GMBH—See CPI Property Group, S.A.; *Int'l*, pg. 1825
HANWHA SOLUTIONS CORP.—See Hanwha Group; *Int'l*, pg. 3266
HAWAII ENERGY CONNECTION—See Hercules Capital, Inc.; *U.S. Public*, pg. 1028
HAWAII ENERGY CONNECTION—See Northern Pacific Group; *U.S. Private*, pg. 2954
HECATE ENERGY, LLC; *U.S. Private*, pg. 1903
HELIOS ENERGY USA LTD.—See Helios Energy Ltd.; *Int'l*, pg. 3330
HIGH NOON SOLAR PROJECT LLC—See Enel S.p.A.; *Int'l*, pg. 2414
HOLU ENERGY LLC—See EnSync, Inc.; *U.S. Public*, pg. 776
IBERDROLA ENERGIE FRANCE, S.A.S.—See Iberdrola, S.A.; *Int'l*, pg. 3572
IES RENEWABLE ENERGY, LLC—See IES Holdings, Inc.; *U.S. Public*, pg. 1094
KSM METALS CO., LTD.—See Australian Strategic Materials Limited; *Int'l*, pg. 722
LE VAL ENERGIE SARL—See EnBW Energie Baden-Wurttemberg AG; *Int'l*, pg. 2399
LINEA GREEN S.P.A.—See A2A S.p.A.; *Int'l*, pg. 29
MERLIN SOLAR TECHNOLOGIES, INC.—See Ayala Corporation; *Int'l*, pg. 774
MIASOLE, INC.—See Hanergy Holding Group Limited; *Int'l*, pg. 3244
NEW ENERGY EQUITY LLC—See ALLETE, Inc.; *U.S. Public*, pg. 79
NEWPORT SOLAR, LLC—See CMS Energy Corporation; *U.S. Public*, pg. 518
ORBITAL RENEWABLES, LLC—See Orbital Infrastructure Group, Inc.; *U.S. Public*, pg. 1615
ORBITAL SOLAR SERVICES, LLC—See Orbital Infrastructure Group, Inc.; *U.S. Public*, pg. 1615
PHOTON POWER PLC—See Borealis Exploration Limited; *Int'l*, pg. 1113
PINEAPPLE ENERGY INC.; *U.S. Public*, pg. 1691
PLANET SOLAR INC.; *U.S. Private*, pg. 3196
PRINCIPAL SOLAR, INC.; *U.S. Public*, pg. 1722
PRISMATIC LTD.—See BAE Systems plc; *Int'l*, pg. 798
PROLECTRIC SERVICES LIMITED—See Hill & Smith PLC; *Int'l*, pg. 3392
P.T. AFRY INDONESIA—See AFRY AB; *Int'l*, pg. 194
PVBJ INC.—See VISION ENERGY CORPORATION; *U.S. Public*, pg. 2304
Q-CELLS NORTH AMERICA; *U.S. Private*, pg. 3312
REC SOLAR COMMERCIAL CORPORATION—See Duke Energy Corporation; *U.S. Public*, pg. 691
RENEWABLE ENERGY SOLUTION SYSTEMS, INC.; *U.S. Public*, pg. 1783
RENT-A-PORT GREEN ENERGY N.V.—See Ackermans & van Haaren NV; *Int'l*, pg. 106
SANEI ECOHOME INC.—See Daiki Axis Co., Ltd.; *Int'l*, pg. 1932
SAVON AURINKOENERGIA OY—See Bravida Holding AB; *Int'l*, pg. 1142
SCHOTT SOLAR S.L.—See Carl-Zeiss-Stiftung; *Int'l*, pg. 1337
SEABOARD SOLAR LLC—See Duke Energy Corporation; *U.S. Public*, pg. 691
SEABOARD SOLAR OPERATIONS, LLC—See Seaboard Solar Holdings, LLC; *U.S. Private*, pg. 3583
SEMPRA RENEWABLES, LLC—See American Electric Power Company, Inc.; *U.S. Public*, pg. 100

SIMPLERAY, LLC; *U.S. Private*, pg. 3667
SOLAR LIBERTY; *U.S. Private*, pg. 3707
SOLAR-LOG GMBH—See BKW AG; *Int'l*, pg. 1056
SOLAR ONE ENERGY PRIVATE LIMITED—See Fortum Oyj; *Int'l*, pg. 2742
SOLAR SPECTRUM LLC—See Hercules Capital, Inc.; *U.S. Public*, pg. 1028
SOLAR SPECTRUM LLC—See Northern Pacific Group; *U.S. Private*, pg. 2954
SOLBRIGHT RENEWABLE ENERGY, LLC—See Iota Communications, Inc.; *U.S. Public*, pg. 1167
SOLKRAFT EMK AB—See Bravida Holding AB; *Int'l*, pg. 1142
SPECIALIZED TECHNOLOGY RESOURCES (CONNECTICUT), LLC—See STR Holdings, Inc.; *U.S. Public*, pg. 1953
SPECIALIZED TECHNOLOGY RESOURCES ESPANA S.A.—See STR Holdings, Inc.; *U.S. Public*, pg. 1953
SPECIALIZED TECHNOLOGY RESOURCES (MALAYSIA) SDN. BHD.—See STR Holdings, Inc.; *U.S. Public*, pg. 1953
SPECIALIZED TECHNOLOGY RESOURCES SOLAR (SUZHOU) CO. LIMITED—See STR Holdings, Inc.; *U.S. Public*, pg. 1953
SPECTACULAR SOLAR, INC.; *U.S. Public*, pg. 1915
S.R.G.A. COMPANY LIMITED—See Chow Steel Industries Public Company Limited; *Int'l*, pg. 1584
STEAG SOLAR ENERGY SOLUTIONS GMBH—See Asterion Industrial Partners SGEIC SA; *Int'l*, pg. 654
STROMNETZGESELLSCHAFT HERRENBERG MBH & CO. KG—See EnBW Energie Baden-Wurttemberg AG; *Int'l*, pg. 2400
SUGAR MAPLE SOLAR, LLC—See The AES Corporation; *U.S. Public*, pg. 2032
SUNCITY ENERGY S.R.L.—See A2A S.p.A.; *Int'l*, pg. 29
SUNEDISON ENERGY INDIA PVT. LTD.—See SunEdison, Inc.; *U.S. Private*, pg. 3867
SUNGEVITY, INC.—See Hercules Capital, Inc.; *U.S. Public*, pg. 1028
SUNGEVITY, INC.—See Northern Pacific Group; *U.S. Private*, pg. 2954
SURACHAI (1997) CO., LTD.—See Energy Absolute Public Company Limited; *Int'l*, pg. 2422
TECO PARTNERS, INC.—See Emera, Inc.; *Int'l*, pg. 2377
TIRRENO SOLAR S.R.L.—See ENGIE SA; *Int'l*, pg. 2434
TRAILAR LIMITED—See Deutsche Post AG; *Int'l*, pg. 2082
TRITEC AG—See EnBW Energie Baden-Wurttemberg AG; *Int'l*, pg. 2400
VENTURE SOLAR, LLC; *U.S. Private*, pg. 4358
VERENGO INC.—See Crius Energy, LLC; *U.S. Private*, pg. 1102
VIETNAM SUNERGY JOINT STOCK COMPANY—See Abalance Corporation Ltd.; *Int'l*, pg. 48
VOLTH2 OPERATING BV—See VISION ENERGY CORPORATION; *U.S. Public*, pg. 2304
WINSUN AG—See EnBW Energie Baden-Wurttemberg AG; *Int'l*, pg. 2400
WOLLAR SOLAR HOLDING PTY LTD—See Beijing Energy International Holding Co., Ltd.; *Int'l*, pg. 949
WOODWARD IDS SWITZERLAND GMBH—See Woodward, Inc.; *U.S. Public*, pg. 2378

221115 — WIND ELECTRIC POWER GENERATION

3U ENERGY AG—See 3U Holding AG; *Int'l*, pg. 10
3U ENERGY PE GMBH—See 3U Holding AG; *Int'l*, pg. 10
ABAN ENERGIES LIMITED—See Aban Offshore Limited; *Int'l*, pg. 48
ABO WIND BELGIUM SPRL—See ABO Wind AG; *Int'l*, pg. 65
ABO WIND BETRIEBS GMBH—See ABO Wind AG; *Int'l*, pg. 65
ABO WIND BULGARIA EOOD—See ABO Wind AG; *Int'l*, pg. 65
ABO WIND ENERGIAS RENOVABLES S.A.—See ABO Wind AG; *Int'l*, pg. 66
ABO WIND ESPANA S.A.U.—See ABO Wind AG; *Int'l*, pg. 66
ABO WIND IRELAND LTD.—See ABO Wind AG; *Int'l*, pg. 66
ABO WIND MEZZANINE GMBH & CO. KG—See ABO Wind AG; *Int'l*, pg. 66
ABO WIND OY—See ABO Wind AG; *Int'l*, pg. 66
ABO WIND SARL—See ABO Wind AG; *Int'l*, pg. 66
ABO WIND UK LTD.—See ABO Wind AG; *Int'l*, pg. 66
ADVANCE METERING TECHNOLOGY LIMITED; *Int'l*, pg. 156
AEP ENERGY PARTNERS, INC.—See American Electric Power Company, Inc.; *U.S. Public*, pg. 99
AILES MARINE, S.A.S.—See Iberdrola, S.A.; *Int'l*, pg. 3570
ALLETE CLEAN ENERGY, INC.—See ALLETE, Inc.; *U.S. Public*, pg. 79
ATLANTIC ENERGIAS RENOVAVEIS S/A—See General Atlantic Service Company, L.P.; *U.S. Private*, pg. 1661
ATLANTIC WIND & SOLAR, INC.; *U.S. Public*, pg. 675
ATLANTIS S.A.; *Int'l*, pg. 676

BORAX MORARJI (EUROPE) GMBH—See Borax Morarji Limited; *Int'l*, pg. 1112
BP WIND ENERGY NORTH AMERICA INC.—See BP plc; *Int'l*, pg. 1126
CARROLL AREA WIND FARM, LLC—See New Jersey Resources Corporation; *U.S. Public*, pg. 1511
CECEP WIND-POWER CORPORATION CO., LTD.; *Int'l*, pg. 1373
CHESTNUT FLATS WIND, LLC—See MetLife, Inc.; *U.S. Public*, pg. 1430
CHINA HUADIAN CORPORATION LTD.; *Int'l*, pg. 1508
CHINA LONGYUAN POWER GROUP CORP LTD.; *Int'l*, pg. 1515
CHINA RENEWABLE ENERGY INVESTMENT LTD.; *Int'l*, pg. 1547
CHINA RUIFENG RENEWABLE ENERGY HOLDINGS LIMITED; *Int'l*, pg. 1549
CHINA STEEL POWER CORPORATION—See China Steel Corporation; *Int'l*, pg. 1555
CHINA THREE GORGES RENEWABLES (GROUP) CO., LTD.—See China Three Gorges Corporation; *Int'l*, pg. 1558
CLEARVISE AG; *Int'l*, pg. 1657
COMERTON CORP.; *U.S. Public*, pg. 542
COMPETITIVE POWER VENTURES HOLDINGS, LLC—See BlackRock, Inc.; *U.S. Public*, pg. 345
CONNECTED WIND SERVICES DANMARK A/S—See EnBW Energie Baden-Wurttemberg AG; *Int'l*, pg. 2398
CONNECTED WIND SERVICES DEUTSCHLAND GMBH—See EnBW Energie Baden-Wurttemberg AG; *Int'l*, pg. 2398
COSMO ECO POWER CO., LTD.—See Cosmo Energy Holdings Co., Ltd.; *Int'l*, pg. 1811
ECO POWER CO., LTD.—See Cosmo Energy Holdings Co., Ltd.; *Int'l*, pg. 1812
ECOWIND D.O.O.—See BayWa AG; *Int'l*, pg. 917
ECOWIND HANDELS- & WARTUNGS-GMBH—See BayWa AG; *Int'l*, pg. 917
EGMF KENYA—See George Forrest International S.A.; *Int'l*, pg. 2938
ENBW ASIA PACIFIC LTD.—See EnBW Energie Baden-Wurttemberg AG; *Int'l*, pg. 2398
ENBW NORTH AMERICA INC.—See EnBW Energie Baden-Wurttemberg AG; *Int'l*, pg. 2398
ENCAVIS ASSET MANAGEMENT AG—See Encavis AG; *Int'l*, pg. 2401
ENVISION ENERGY USA LIMITED—See Envision Group; *Int'l*, pg. 2455
ENVISION GROUP; *Int'l*, pg. 2455
EOLE GENERATION SAS—See ENGIE SA; *Int'l*, pg. 2429
EOLUS VIND AB; *Int'l*, pg. 2457
EPURON S.A.S.—See ERG S.p.A.; *Int'l*, pg. 2491
ERG EOLICA ITALIA SRL—See ERG S.p.A.; *Int'l*, pg. 2491
ERG WIND 6 S.R.L.—See ERG S.p.A.; *Int'l*, pg. 2491
ERG WIND SICILIA 3 S.R.L.—See ERG S.p.A.; *Int'l*, pg. 2491
FAR EAST WIND POWER CORP.; *Int'l*, pg. 2617
FINTEL ENERGIJA A.D—See Fintel Energia Group S.p.A.; *Int'l*, pg. 2677
GAENSEL ENERGY GROUP, INC.; *U.S. Public*, pg. 894
GALA S.P.A.; *Int'l*, pg. 2870
GE DISTRIBUTED POWER, INC.—See General Electric Company; *U.S. Public*, pg. 916
GE ENERGY POWER CONVERSION GMBH—See General Electric Company; *U.S. Public*, pg. 916
GE ENERGY POWER CONVERSION UK HOLDINGS LIMITED—See General Electric Company; *U.S. Public*, pg. 916
GE ENERGY POWER CONVERSION USA INC.—See General Electric Company; *U.S. Public*, pg. 916
GE ENERGY SWITZERLAND GMBH—See General Electric Company; *U.S. Public*, pg. 916
GENERAL ELECTRIC AUSTRIA GMBH—See General Electric Company; *U.S. Public*, pg. 918
GODAWARI ENERGY LIMITED—See Godawari Power & Ispat Ltd.; *Int'l*, pg. 3018
GODAWARI GREEN ENERGY LIMITED—See KKR & Co. Inc.; *U.S. Public*, pg. 1266
GUANGDONG BAOLIHUA NEW ENERGY STOCK CO., LTD.; *Int'l*, pg. 3153
GUODIAN UNITED POWER TECHNOLOGY (BAODING) CO., LTD.—See Guodian Technology & Environment Group Corporation Limited; *Int'l*, pg. 3186
GWYNT Y MOR OFTO PLC—See Balfour Beatty plc; *Int'l*, pg. 808
HATCHET RIDGE WIND, LLC—See Canada Pension Plan Investment Board; *Int'l*, pg. 1281
HEBEI HONGSONG WIND POWER CO., LTD.—See China Ruifeng Renewable Energy Holdings Limited; *Int'l*, pg. 1549
HERO ASIA INVESTMENT LIMITED—See China Longyuan Power Group Corp Ltd.; *Int'l*, pg. 1515
HIRA ENERGY LIMITED—See Godawari Power & Ispat Ltd.; *Int'l*, pg. 3018
HYDROGRAPH CLEAN POWER INC.; *Int'l*, pg. 3547
IBERDROLA CLIENTI ITALIA, S.R.L.—See Iberdrola, S.A.; *Int'l*, pg. 3572

N.A.I.C.S. INDEX

221118 — OTHER ELECTRIC POWE...

IBERDROLA ESPANA, S.A.U.—See Iberdrola, S.A.; *Int'l*, pg. 3572

IBERDROLA RENEWABLES ROMANIA, S.R.L.—See Iberdrola, S.A.; *Int'l*, pg. 3572

IBERDROLA RENOVABLES FRANCE, S.A.S.—See Iberdrola, S.A.; *Int'l*, pg. 3572

IBERDROLA RENOVABLES MAGYARORSZAG, KFT.—See Iberdrola, S.A.; *Int'l*, pg. 3572

JIANGSU LONGYUAN WIND POWER GENERATION CO., LTD.—See China Longyuan Power Group Corp Ltd.; *Int'l*, pg. 1515

LA COMPAGNIE DU VENT SAS—See ENGIE SA; *Int'l*, pg. 2434

LONGBURN WIND FARM LTD.—See ERG S.p.A.; *Int'l*, pg. 2491

LUZY ENERGIA RENOVABLE, S.L.U.—See Elecnor, S.A.; *Int'l*, pg. 2347

NATURENER ENERGY CANADA INC.—See Morgan Stanley; *U.S. Public*, pg. 1475

NATURENER USA, LLC—See Morgan Stanley; *U.S. Public*, pg. 1475

NRG SYSTEMS, INC.—See ESCO Technologies, Inc.; *U.S. Public*, pg. 794

OWNENERGY, INC.—See Electricite de France S.A.; *Int'l*, pg. 2350

PATTERN ENERGY GROUP LP—See Canada Pension Plan Investment Board; *Int'l*, pg. 1281

RENERCO PLAN CONSULT GMBH—See BayWa AG; *Int'l*, pg. 918

RENERGY ELECTRIC TIANJIN LTD.—See China Ming Yang Wind Power Group Limited; *Int'l*, pg. 1524

SACHAL ENERGY DEVELOPMENT (PRIVATE) LIMITED—See Arif Habib Corporation Limited; *Int'l*, pg. 564

SAUER ENERGY, INC.—See Better For You Wellness, Inc.; *U.S. Public*, pg. 326

SC PUTEREA VERDE S.R.L.—See BayWa AG; *Int'l*, pg. 919

SHINAN WIND POWER GENERATION CO—See Dongkuk S&C Co., Ltd.; *Int'l*, pg. 2169

SHINFOX CO., LTD.—See Cheng Eui Precision Industry Co., Ltd.; *Int'l*, pg. 1465

SING DA MARINE STRUCTURE CORPORATION—See China Steel Corporation; *Int'l*, pg. 1556

SOLAR WIND ENERGY, INC.; *U.S. Private*, pg. 3707

TPI INTERNATIONAL, INC.; *U.S. Public*, pg. 2178

U.S. WIND FARMING, INC.; *U.S. Public*, pg. 2217

VIATRON S.A.—See Herkules S.A.; *Int'l*, pg. 3362

WIND COMPOSITE SERVICE GROUP, LLC; *U.S. Private*, pg. 4533

WINDPARK BERSCHWEILER GMBH & CO. KG—See BayWa AG; *Int'l*, pg. 919

WINDPARK KREEKRAKSLUIS B.V.—See Delta N.V.; *Int'l*, pg. 2019

WINDPARK LANGENDORF GMBH & CO. KG—See 3U Holding AG; *Int'l*, pg. 10

WWH, LLC—See The Southern Company; *U.S. Public*, pg. 2131

YAPISAN ELEKTRIK URETIM AS—See Bilgin Enerji Yatirim Holding A.S.; *Int'l*, pg. 1029

221116 — GEOTHERMAL ELECTRIC POWER GENERATION

A2A ENERGIEFUTURE S.P.A.—See A2A S.p.A.; *Int'l*, pg. 29

A2A GENCOGAS S.P.A.—See A2A S.p.A.; *Int'l*, pg. 29

ALTERN ENERGY LIMITED; *Int'l*, pg. 391

BEIJING JINGNENG POWER CO., LTD.; *Int'l*, pg. 953

BEIJING KINGFORE HV & ENERGY CONSERVATION TECHNOLOGY CO., LTD.; *Int'l*, pg. 954

BRENMILLER ENERGY LTD.; *Int'l*, pg. 1145

CAELUM CO., LTD.; *Int'l*, pg. 1249

CLINTON WIND, LLC—See E.ON SE; *Int'l*, pg. 2251

CYRQ ENERGY, INC.; *U.S. Private*, pg. 1135

DALIAN THERMAL POWER CO., LTD.; *Int'l*, pg. 1952

E.DISNATUR ERNEUERBARE ENERGIEN GMBH—See E.ON SE; *Int'l*, pg. 2260

EMERSON NETWORK POWER GMBH—See Vertiv Holdings Co; *U.S. Public*, pg. 2288

ENDESA GENERACION PORTUGAL, S.A.—See Enel S.p.A.; *Int'l*, pg. 2412

ENEL PRODUZIONE S.P.A.—See Enel S.p.A.; *Int'l*, pg. 2412

ENERJISA ENERJI URETIM A.S. - CANAKKALE POWER PLANT—See E.ON SE; *Int'l*, pg. 2257

ENERJISA ENERJI URETIM A.S. - CANAKKALE POWER PLANT—See Haci Omer Sabanci Holding A.S.; *Int'l*, pg. 3204

ENERJISA ENERJI URETIM A.S. - KENTSA POWER PLANT—See E.ON SE; *Int'l*, pg. 2257

ENERJISA ENERJI URETIM A.S. - KENTSA POWER PLANT—See Haci Omer Sabanci Holding A.S.; *Int'l*, pg. 3204

ENERJISA ENERJI URETIM A.S. - MERSIN POWER PLANT—See E.ON SE; *Int'l*, pg. 2257

ENERJISA ENERJI URETIM A.S. - MERSIN POWER PLANT—See Haci Omer Sabanci Holding A.S.; *Int'l*, pg. 3204

GROUNDHEAT ENERGY SOLAR WIND CORP.; *Int'l*, pg. 3088

GUANGDONG SHAONENG GROUP CO., LTD.; *Int'l*, pg. 3160

HRL HOLDINGS LIMITED; *Int'l*, pg. 3501

MAGMA ENERGY ITALIA S.R.L.—See Graziella Green Power S.p.A.; *Int'l*, pg. 3063

PARQUE EOLICO PAMPA SA—See Enel S.p.A.; *Int'l*, pg. 2414

PLZENSKA ENERGETIKA A.S.—See Energeticky a Prumyslovy Holding, a.s.; *Int'l*, pg. 2420

PRVNI MOSTECKA A.S.—See Energeticky a Prumyslovy Holding, a.s.; *Int'l*, pg. 2420

TERRA ENERGIA—See Grupo Terra S.A. de C.V.; *Int'l*, pg. 3137

TRACTEBEL ENERGIA S.A. - TPP CHARQUEADAS - UTCH PLANT—See ENGIE SA; *Int'l*, pg. 2432

UNITED ENERGY A.S.—See Energeticky a Prumyslovy Holding, a.s.; *Int'l*, pg. 2420

221117 — BIOMASS ELECTRIC POWER GENERATION

2G ENERGIE SAS—See 2G Energy AG; *Int'l*, pg. 5

2G STATION FOR AFRICA GMBH—See 2G Energy AG; *Int'l*, pg. 5

2G STATION LLC—See 2G Energy AG; *Int'l*, pg. 5

ALBIOMA SA—See KKR & Co. Inc.; *U.S. Public*, pg. 1239

AMERICAN ENVIRONMENTAL ENERGY, INC.; *U.S. Public*, pg. 100

AMG BIOENERGY RESOURCES HOLDINGS LTD.; *Int'l*, pg. 425

BEBAG BIOENERGIE BATTERKINDEN AG—See BKW AG; *Int'l*, pg. 1054

BIOLECTRIC NV—See Ackermans & van Haaren NV; *Int'l*, pg. 104

COMPANHIA ENERGETICA DE PERNAMBUCO - CELPE—See Iberdrola, S.A.; *Int'l*, pg. 3573

COX RECOVERY SERVICES, LLC—See Koppers Holdings Inc.; *U.S. Public*, pg. 1271

DANSKE COMMODITIES UK LIMITED—See Equinor ASA; *Int'l*, pg. 2484

DOMINION ENERGY QUESTAR PIPELINE, LLC—See Southwest Gas Holdings, Inc.; *U.S. Public*, pg. 1913

EEW ENERGY FROM WASTE DELFZIJL B.V.—See Beijing Enterprises Holdings Limited; *Int'l*, pg. 950

EEW ENERGY FROM WASTE GOPPINGEN GMBH—See Beijing Enterprises Holdings Limited; *Int'l*, pg. 950

EEW ENERGY FROM WASTE GROSSRASCHEN GMBH—See Beijing Enterprises Holdings Limited; *Int'l*, pg. 950

EEW ENERGY FROM WASTE HANNOVER GMBH—See Beijing Enterprises Holdings Limited; *Int'l*, pg. 950

EEW ENERGY FROM WASTE HELMSTEDT GMBH—See Beijing Enterprises Holdings Limited; *Int'l*, pg. 950

EEW ENERGY FROM WASTE HERINGEN GMBH—See Beijing Enterprises Holdings Limited; *Int'l*, pg. 950

EEW ENERGY FROM WASTE PREMNITZ GMBH—See Beijing Enterprises Holdings Limited; *Int'l*, pg. 950

EEW ENERGY FROM WASTE SAARBRUCKEN GMBH—See Beijing Enterprises Holdings Limited; *Int'l*, pg. 950

EEW ENERGY FROM WASTE STAPELFELD GMBH—See Beijing Enterprises Holdings Limited; *Int'l*, pg. 950

ENBW BIOMASSE GMBH—See EnBW Energie Baden-Wurttemberg AG; *Int'l*, pg. 2398

FORTISTAR LLC; *U.S. Private*, pg. 1576

GLORYWIN ENTERTAINMENT GROUP, INC.; *U.S. Public*, pg. 947

GRANBIO INVESTIMENTOS SA—See GranInvestimentos SA; *Int'l*, pg. 3059

GREEN CIRCLE BIO ENERGY INC.; *U.S. Private*, pg. 1772

GREEN FOR ENERGY, INC.; *U.S. Public*, pg. 963

GREENPRINT HOLDINGS, INC.—See TA Associates, Inc.; *U.S. Private*, pg. 3917

HEDESELSKABET SP. Z.O.O.—See Det Danske Hedeselskab; *Int'l*, pg. 2047

HITACHI ZOSEN INOVA BIOMETHAN FRANCE S.A.R.L.—See Hitachi Zosen Corporation; *Int'l*, pg. 3411

HITACHI ZOSEN INOVA BIOMETHAN GMBH—See Hitachi Zosen Corporation; *Int'l*, pg. 3411

HITACHI ZOSEN INOVA DEUTSCHLAND GMBH—See Hitachi Zosen Corporation; *Int'l*, pg. 3411

KAWASAKI BIOMASS POWER GENERATION CO., LTD.—See Fuluhashi EPO Corporation; *Int'l*, pg. 2844

NATURAL ENERGY JAPAN CORPORATION—See Hitachi Zosen Corporation; *Int'l*, pg. 3411

NATURE ENERGY BIOGAS A/S—See Davidson Kempner Capital Management LP; *U.S. Private*, pg. 1172

NATURE ENERGY CONSTRUCTION A/S—See Davidson Kempner Capital Management LP; *U.S. Private*, pg. 1172

TERRAVIS GMBH—See AGRAVIS Raiffeisen AG; *Int'l*, pg. 215

TILBURY GREEN POWER LIMITED—See KKR & Co. Inc.; *U.S. Public*, pg. 1252

UTILIWORKS CONSULTING, LLC—See Align Capital Partners, LLC; *U.S. Private*, pg. 167

WHITECOURT POWER LIMITED PARTNERSHIP—See iCON Infrastructure LLP; *Int'l*, pg. 3583

221118 — OTHER ELECTRIC POWER GENERATION

2G ENERGY CORP.—See 2G Energy AG; *Int'l*, pg. 5

2G RENTAL GMBH—See 2G Energy AG; *Int'l*, pg. 5

2G STATION TUNISIE SARL—See 2G Energy AG; *Int'l*, pg. 5

2H RESOURCES PTY LIMITED—See Buru Energy Limited; *Int'l*, pg. 1227

2VALORISE N.V.; *Int'l*, pg. 5

9REN GROUP—See First Reserve Management, L.P.; *U.S. Private*, pg. 1525

A2A ENERGIA S.P.A.—See A2A S.p.A.; *Int'l*, pg. 29

A2A MONTENEGRO D.O.O.—See A2A S.p.A.; *Int'l*, pg. 29

A2Z POWERCOM LIMITED—See A2Z Infra Engineering Limited; *Int'l*, pg. 30

AAGES DEVCO SERVICES S.A.—See Abengoa S.A.; *Int'l*, pg. 59

AAGES DEVCO SERVICES S.A.—See Algonquin Power & Utilities Corp.; *Int'l*, pg. 319

ABB AG—See ABB Ltd.; *Int'l*, pg. 50

ABB ENTRELEC SP. Z.O.O.—See ABB Ltd.; *Int'l*, pg. 55

ABB LTD.—See ABB Ltd.; *Int'l*, pg. 55

ABB MALAYSIA SDN BHD.—See ABB Ltd.; *Int'l*, pg. 53

ABBNG LIMITED—See ABB Ltd.; *Int'l*, pg. 53

ABEKA EL & KRAFTANLAGGNINGAR AB—See Bravida Holding AB; *Int'l*, pg. 1142

ABERGELLI POWER LIMITED—See Drax Group plc; *Int'l*, pg. 2200

AB FORTUM VARME SAMAGT MED STOCKHOLMS STAD—See Fortum Oyj; *Int'l*, pg. 2741

ABM ENERGIE CONSEIL SAS—See ENGIE SA; *Int'l*, pg. 2428

ABO WIND AG; *Int'l*, pg. 65

ABRUZZOENERGIA S.P.A.—See A2A S.p.A.; *Int'l*, pg. 29

ACCIONA DO BRASIL, LTDA—See Acciona, S.A.; *Int'l*, pg. 90

ACCIONA ENERGIA, S.A.—See Acciona, S.A.; *Int'l*, pg. 90

ACCIONA ENERGY GLOBAL POLAND SP. Z.O.O.—See Acciona, S.A.; *Int'l*, pg. 90

ACCIONA ENERGY USA GLOBAL LLC—See Acciona, S.A.; *Int'l*, pg. 90

ACCIONA FACILITY SERVICES SUR, S.A.—See Acciona, S.A.; *Int'l*, pg. 90

ACCIONA SOLAR, S.A.—See Acciona, S.A.; *Int'l*, pg. 90

AC ENERGY, INC.—See Ayala Corporation; *Int'l*, pg. 773

ACE SOLAR CO., LTD.—See Absolute Clean Energy Public Company Limited; *Int'l*, pg. 70

ADAMS-COLUMBIA ELECTRIC COOPERATIVE; *U.S. Private*, pg. 76

ADAMS ELECTRIC COOPERATIVE; *U.S. Private*, pg. 74

AECON ATLANTIC INDUSTRIAL INC.—See Aecon Group Inc.; *Int'l*, pg. 172

AEG POWER SOLUTIONS (FRANCE) S.A.S—See 3W Power S.A.; *Int'l*, pg. 10

AEG POWER SOLUTIONS S.A.S—See 3W Power S.A.; *Int'l*, pg. 10

AEG POWER SOLUTIONS SDN BHD—See 3W Power S.A.; *Int'l*, pg. 10

AEL TEXTILES LIMITED—See Dar Al-Maal Al-Islami Trust; *Int'l*, pg. 1971

AEOLIKI KANDILIOU SA—See ELLAKTOR S.A.; *Int'l*, pg. 2364

AES BALLYLUMFORD—See The AES Corporation; *U.S. Public*, pg. 2030

AES BRASIL ENERGIA SA; *Int'l*, pg. 182

AES RED OAK, L.L.C.—See The AES Corporation; *U.S. Public*, pg. 2031

AES SHADY POINT LLC—See OGE Energy Corp.; *U.S. Public*, pg. 1564

AES SOLAR ALCUDIA, S.L.—See The AES Corporation; *U.S. Public*, pg. 2031

AES WARRIOR RUN, INC.—See The AES Corporation; *U.S. Public*, pg. 2031

AFKEM AG; *Int'l*, pg. 189

AFLUENTE GERACAO DE ENERGIA ELETRICA SA—See ContourGlobal Limited; *Int'l*, pg. 1785

AGENA S.A.—See Deutsche Bank Aktiengesellschaft; *Int'l*, pg. 2055

AGGREGATED MICRO POWER HOLDINGS PLC; *Int'l*, pg. 209

AGL ACT RETAIL INVESTMENTS PTY LIMITED—See AGL Energy Limited; *Int'l*, pg. 211

AGL CORPORATE SERVICES PTY LIMITED—See AGL Energy Limited; *Int'l*, pg. 211

AGL ENERGY LIMITED; *Int'l*, pg. 210

AGL POWER GENERATION PTY LIMITED—See AGL Energy Limited; *Int'l*, pg. 211

AGL SA GENERATION PTY LIMITED—See AGL Energy Limited; *Int'l*, pg. 211

AGL SOUTHERN HYDRO (NSW) PTY LIMITED—See AGL Energy Limited; *Int'l*, pg. 211

AGL SOUTHERN HYDRO PTY LIMITED—See AGL Energy Limited; *Int'l*, pg. 211

221118 — OTHER ELECTRIC POWE... CORPORATE AFFILIATIONS

AGL TORRENS ISLAND HOLDINGS PTY LIMITED—See AGL Energy Limited; *Int'l*, pg. 211
AGL TORRENS ISLAND PTY LIMITED—See AGL Energy Limited; *Int'l*, pg. 211
AGRO ENERGY CO., LTD—See Electricity Generating Public Co., Ltd.; *Int'l*, pg. 2352
AGRUPACION EOLICA, S.L.U.—See EDP - Energias de Portugal, S.A.; *Int'l*, pg. 2314
AIKEN ELECTRIC COOPERATIVE INC.; *U.S. Private*, pg. 132
AJD FOREST PRODUCTS LIMITED PARTNERSHIP—See CMS Energy Corporation; *U.S. Public*, pg. 518
AKSU ENERJI VE TICARET A.S.; *Int'l*, pg. 265
AKZO NOBEL ENERGY B.V.—See Akzo Nobel N.V.; *Int'l*, pg. 271
ALASKA ELECTRIC LIGHT & POWER COMPANY; *U.S. Private*, pg. 150
ALATAU ZHARYK COMPANY JSC; *Int'l*, pg. 291
AL BATINAH POWER CO SAOG; *Int'l*, pg. 276
ALEA HEAT & POWER S.R.L.—See CogenInfra SpA; *Int'l*, pg. 1694
ALERION CLEAN POWER S.P.A.; *Int'l*, pg. 306
ALETSCH AG—See EnBW Energie Baden-Wurttemberg AG; *Int'l*, pg. 2398
ALLIANZ RENEWABLE ENERGY MANAGEMENT GMBH—See Allianz SE; *Int'l*, pg. 349
ALLTECK LIMITED PARTNERSHIP—See Quanta Services, Inc.; *U.S. Public*, pg. 1750
ALMATINSKIE ELEKTRICHESKIE SETI JSC; *Int'l*, pg. 363
AL MIRFA POWER COMPANY—See Abu Dhabi Water & Electricity Authority; *Int'l*, pg. 73
ALPHA GREEN ENERGY LIMITED; *U.S. Private*, pg. 197
ALPIQ CSEPELI EROMU KFT—See Alpiq Holding AG; *Int'l*, pg. 372
ALPIQ CSEPELI SZOLGALTATO KFT.—See Alpiq Holding AG; *Int'l*, pg. 372
ALPIQ DEUTSCHLAND GMBH—See Alpiq Holding AG; *Int'l*, pg. 372
ALPIQ ENERGIA BULGARIA EOOD—See Alpiq Holding AG; *Int'l*, pg. 373
ALPIQ ENERGIA ESPANA S.A.U.—See Alpiq Holding AG; *Int'l*, pg. 372
ALPIQ ENERGIE DEUTSCHLAND GMBH—See Alpiq Holding AG; *Int'l*, pg. 373
ALPIQ ENERGIJA SKOPJE DOOEL—See Alpiq Holding AG; *Int'l*, pg. 373
ALPIQ ENERGY SE—See Alpiq Holding AG; *Int'l*, pg. 373
ALPIQ ENERGY UKRAINE LLC—See Alpiq Holding AG; *Int'l*, pg. 373
ALPIQ ITALIA S.R.L.—See Alpiq Holding AG; *Int'l*, pg. 373
ALPIQ NARZOLE S.R.L.—See Alpiq Holding AG; *Int'l*, pg. 373
ALPIQ ROMINDUSTRIES SRL—See Alpiq Holding AG; *Int'l*, pg. 373
ALSTOM AUSTRIA GMBH—See Alstom S.A.; *Int'l*, pg. 380
ALSTOM CARBON CAPTURE GMBH—See Alstom S.A.; *Int'l*, pg. 380
ALSTOM FINLAND OY—See Alstom S.A.; *Int'l*, pg. 380
ALSTOM HONG KONG LTD.—See Alstom S.A.; *Int'l*, pg. 380
ALSTOM KONSTAL S.A.—See Alstom S.A.; *Int'l*, pg. 380
ALSTOM LLC—See Alstom S.A.; *Int'l*, pg. 380
ALSTOM NORWAY AS—See Alstom S.A.; *Int'l*, pg. 381
ALSTOM S&E AFRICA (PTY) LTD—See Alstom S.A.; *Int'l*, pg. 381
ALSTOM SLOVAKIA, S.R.O.—See Alstom S.A.; *Int'l*, pg. 381
ALSTOM S.R.O.—See Alstom S.A.; *Int'l*, pg. 381
ALSTOM VIETNAM LTD.—See Alstom S.A.; *Int'l*, pg. 381
AL SUWADI POWER COMPANY SAOG; *Int'l*, pg. 283
ALTERNATIVE EARTH RESOURCES INC.; *Int'l*, pg. 391
ALTERNUS ENERGY GROUP PLC—See Alternus Clean Energy Inc.; *U.S. Public*, pg. 87
ALUPAR INVESTIMENTO S.A.; *Int'l*, pg. 401
AMATA B. GRIMM POWER 1 LIMITED—See Amata Corporation Public Company Limited; *Int'l*, pg. 412
AMATA B. GRIMM POWER 1 LIMITED—See EGAT Public Company Limited; *Int'l*, pg. 2322
AMATA B.GRIMM POWER 3 LTD.—See B. Grimm Group; *Int'l*, pg. 788
AMATA B.GRIMM POWER LTD.—See B. Grimm Group; *Int'l*, pg. 788
AMEREN ENERGY FUELS & SERVICES CO.—See Ameren Corporation; *U.S. Public*, pg. 94
AMERENIP—See Ameren Corporation; *U.S. Public*, pg. 94
AMERICAN ELECTRIC POWER SERVICE CORPORATION—See American Electric Power Company, Inc.; *U.S. Public*, pg. 99
AMERICAN MUNICIPAL POWER-OHIO, INC.; *U.S. Private*, pg. 241
AMERICAN SOLAR ELECTRIC, INC.; *U.S. Private*, pg. 254
AMMEGA—See Advent International Corporation; *U.S. Private*, pg. 98
AMRUMBANK-WEST GMBH—See E.ON SE; *Int'l*, pg. 2252
ANACACHO WIND FARM, LLC—See E.ON SE; *Int'l*, pg. 2251
ANDRADE GUTIERREZ CONCESSOES S.A.; *Int'l*, pg. 451
ANDRITZ POWER SDN. BHD.—See ANDRITZ AG; *Int'l*, pg. 454

ANP BLACKSTONE ENERGY COMPANY, LLC—See ENGIE SA; *Int'l*, pg. 2433
ANSALDO ENERGIA SWITZERLAND AG—See Cassa Depositi e Prestiti S.p.A.; *Int'l*, pg. 1354
ANSALDO RUSSIA LLC—See Cassa Depositi e Prestiti S.p.A.; *Int'l*, pg. 1354
APRAAVA ENERGY PRIVATE LIMITED—See CLP Holdings Limited; *Int'l*, pg. 1663
AP RENEWABLES LTD.—See Ardova Plc.; *Int'l*, pg. 557
AQUA POWER SYSTEMS INC.; *Int'l*, pg. 527
ARCKARINGA ENERGY PTY LTD—See Altona Rare Earths PLC; *Int'l*, pg. 394
ARISE AB; *Int'l*, pg. 566
ARISE SERVICE & PROJEKTERING AB—See Arise AB; *Int'l*, pg. 566
ARISE WIND FARM 3 AB—See Arise AB; *Int'l*, pg. 566
ARISE WIND FARM 4 AB—See Arise AB; *Int'l*, pg. 566
ARIZONA ELECTRIC POWER COOPERATIVE INC.; *U.S. Private*, pg. 324
ARKANSAS ELECTRIC COOPERATIVES, INC.; *U.S. Private*, pg. 325
ARKANSAS VALLEY ELECTRIC COOPERATIVE CORPORATION; *U.S. Private*, pg. 326
ARMAEC ENERGY GROUP PLC; *Int'l*, pg. 574
ASCO EG S.P.A.—See Ascopiave S.p.A.; *Int'l*, pg. 603
ATCO POWER AUSTRALIA PTY LTD—See ATCO Ltd.; *Int'l*, pg. 666
ATHENA INVESTMENTS A/S; *Int'l*, pg. 669
ATLANTICA SUSTAINABLE INFRASTRUCTURE PLC; *Int'l*, pg. 676
ATLAS POWER LIMITED—See Atlas Group of Companies; *Int'l*, pg. 685
AT SYSTEMATIZATION BERHAD; *Int'l*, pg. 664
AUFWIND SCHMACK ELSO BIOGAZ SZOLGALTATO KFT.—See BayWa AG; *Int'l*, pg. 915
AUTENSYS GMBH—See EnBW Energie Baden-Wurttemberg AG; *Int'l*, pg. 2398
AVANGRID RENEWABLES, LLC—See Iberdrola, S.A.; *Int'l*, pg. 3570
AVANTHA POWER & INFRASTRUCTURE LIMITED—See Avantha Group; *Int'l*, pg. 735
AVISTA UTILITIES—See Avista Corporation; *U.S. Public*, pg. 249
AXA POWER APS—See Illinois Tool Works Inc.; *U.S. Public*, pg. 1103
AXPO ALBANIA SH.A.—See Axpo Holding AG; *Int'l*, pg. 771
AXPO IBERIA S.L.—See Axpo Holding AG; *Int'l*, pg. 771
AXPO KOMPOGAS AG—See Axpo Holding AG; *Int'l*, pg. 771
AXPO NORDIC AS—See Axpo Holding AG; *Int'l*, pg. 771
AXPO TEGRA AG—See Axpo Holding AG; *Int'l*, pg. 771
BABCOCK BORSIG SERVICE ARABIA LTD.—See Bilfinger SE; *Int'l*, pg. 1024
BABCOCK KRAFTWERKSERVICE GMBH—See Bilfinger SE; *Int'l*, pg. 1024
BABCOCK POWER RENEWABLES LLC—See Babcock Power, Inc.; *U.S. Private*, pg. 422
BALTIC GREEN CONSTRUCTION SP. Z O.O.—See CEZ, a.s.; *Int'l*, pg. 1426
BANDERA ELECTRIC COOPERATIVE, INC.; *U.S. Private*, pg. 465
BANGKOK COGENERATION COMPANY LIMITED—See Air Products & Chemicals, Inc.; *U.S. Public*, pg. 66
BANGPA-IN COGENERATION LIMITED—See CH. Karnchang Public Company Limited; *Int'l*, pg. 1435
BANGPA-IN COGENERATION LIMITED—See CK Power Public Company Limited; *Int'l*, pg. 1638
BANPONG UTILITIES CO., LTD.—See Electricity Generating Public Co., Ltd.; *Int'l*, pg. 2352
BANPU COAL POWER LTD.—See Banpu Public Company Limited; *Int'l*, pg. 851
BANPU POWER INTERNATIONAL LTD.—See Banpu Public Company Limited; *Int'l*, pg. 852
BANPU POWER INVESTMENT (CHINA) LTD.—See Banpu Public Company Limited; *Int'l*, pg. 852
BANPU POWER PCL; *Int'l*, pg. 851
BARAKA PATENGA POWER LIMITED—See Baraka Power Limited; *Int'l*, pg. 858
BARAKA POWER LIMITED; *Int'l*, pg. 858
BARTON COUNTY ELECTRIC COOPERATIVE INC.; *U.S. Private*, pg. 483
BASIN ELECTRIC POWER COOPERATIVE; *U.S. Private*, pg. 485
BATYS TRANSIT JSC; *Int'l*, pg. 891
BAYWA R.E. ASSET HOLDING GMBH—See BayWa AG; *Int'l*, pg. 916
BAYWA R.E. BIOENERGY GMBH—See BayWa AG; *Int'l*, pg. 916
BAYWA R.E. CLEAN ENERGY SOURCING GMBH—See BayWa AG; *Int'l*, pg. 916
BAYWA R.E. CLEAN ENERGY S.R.L.—See BayWa AG; *Int'l*, pg. 916
BAYWA R.E. ESPANA S.L.U.—See BayWa AG; *Int'l*, pg. 916
BAYWA R.E. FRANCE SAS—See BayWa AG; *Int'l*, pg. 916
BAYWA R.E. GREEN ENERGY PRODUCTS GMBH—See BayWa AG; *Int'l*, pg. 916
BAYWA R.E. JAPAN K.K.—See BayWa AG; *Int'l*, pg. 916

BAYWA R.E. OPERATION SERVICES GMBH—See BayWa AG; *Int'l*, pg. 916
BAYWA R.E. OPERATION SERVICES LIMITED—See BayWa AG; *Int'l*, pg. 916
BAYWA R.E. ROTOR SERVICE GMBH—See BayWa AG; *Int'l*, pg. 916
BAYWA R.E. SCANDINAVIA AB—See BayWa AG; *Int'l*, pg. 916
BAYWA R.E. SOLAR ENERGY SYSTEMS GMBH—See BayWa AG; *Int'l*, pg. 916
BAYWA R.E. SOLAR PROJECTS GMBH—See BayWa AG; *Int'l*, pg. 916
BAYWA R.E. SOLAR PROJECTS LLC—See BayWa AG; *Int'l*, pg. 916
BAYWA R.E. SOLAR SYSTEMS CO., LTD.—See BayWa AG; *Int'l*, pg. 916
BAYWA R.E. SOLAR SYSTEMS LLC—See BayWa AG; *Int'l*, pg. 916
BAYWA R.E. SOLAR SYSTEMS PTY. LTD.—See BayWa AG; *Int'l*, pg. 916
BAYWA R.E. (THAILAND) CO., LTD.—See BayWa AG; *Int'l*, pg. 916
BAYWA R.E. UK LIMITED—See BayWa AG; *Int'l*, pg. 917
BAYWA R.E. WIND GMBH—See BayWa AG; *Int'l*, pg. 917
BELTRAMI ELECTRIC COOPERATIVE, INC.; *U.S. Private*, pg. 521
BF UTILITIES LTD.; *Int'l*, pg. 1006
BHE RENEWABLES, LLC—See Berkshire Hathaway Inc.; *U.S. Public*, pg. 300
BIDELEK SAREAK, A.I.E.—See Iberdrola, S.A.; *Int'l*, pg. 3571
BIG RIVERS ELECTRIC CORPORATION; *U.S. Private*, pg. 554
BIG SANDY RECC; *U.S. Private*, pg. 554
BIG TOP, LLC—See Constellation Energy Corporation; *U.S. Public*, pg. 571
BIOGAS ENERGY SOLUTIONS, LLC; *U.S. Private*, pg. 561
BIOGAS NEU KOSENOW GMBH & CO KG—See Alpiq Holding AG; *Int'l*, pg. 372
BIOGEN LIMITED; *Int'l*, pg. 1038
BIRS WASSERKRAFT AG—See Alpiq Holding AG; *Int'l*, pg. 373
BISHOP & BROGDON, INC.; *U.S. Private*, pg. 565
BLACK HILLS POWER, INC.—See Black Hills Corporation; *U.S. Public*, pg. 340
BLACK RIVER ELECTRIC CO-OP; *U.S. Private*, pg. 572
BLCP POWER LTD.—See Banpu Public Company Limited; *Int'l*, pg. 851
BLCP POWER LTD.—See Electricity Generating Public Co., Ltd.; *Int'l*, pg. 2352
BLUE CREEK WIND FARM, LLC—See Iberdrola, S.A.; *Int'l*, pg. 3570
BLUE EARTH-NICOLLET COOPERATIVE ELECTRIC ASSOCIATION; *U.S. Private*, pg. 588
BLUE-GRASS ENERGY COOPERATIVE; *U.S. Private*, pg. 596
BLUE RIDGE ELECTRIC COOPERATIVE INC.; *U.S. Private*, pg. 591
BLYTHE ENERGY, LLC—See AltaGas Ltd.; *Int'l*, pg. 384
BOCO ROCK WIND FARM PTY. LTD.—See Electricity Generating Public Co., Ltd.; *Int'l*, pg. 2352
BON VENT DE L EBRE, S.L.—See EDP - Energias de Portugal, S.A.; *Int'l*, pg. 2314
BORALEX S.A.S.—See Boralex Inc.; *Int'l*, pg. 1112
BORD GAIS ENERGY LIMITED—See Centrica plc; *Int'l*, pg. 1413
BORD NA MONA ENERGY TECH/ADMIN—See Bord na Mona Plc; *Int'l*, pg. 1113
BOT ELEKTROWINA TUROW SA—See Elektrownia Belchatow S.A.; *Int'l*, pg. 2357
BOTTLE ROCK POWER, LLC—See AltaRock Energy Inc.; *U.S. Private*, pg. 206
BP ALTERNATIVE ENERGY INTERNATIONAL LTD.—See BP plc; *Int'l*, pg. 1126
BRAZOS ELECTRIC POWER COOPERATIVE, INC.; *U.S. Private*, pg. 642
BRIGHTSOURCE ENERGY, INC.; *U.S. Private*, pg. 652
BROKEN BOW WIND, LLC—See NRG Energy, Inc.; *U.S. Public*, pg. 1549
BROOKFIDELD RENEWABLE POWER PREFERRED EQUALITY INC.—See Brookfield Renewable Corporation; *U.S. Public*, pg. 395
BROWNSVILLE PUBLIC UTILITIES BOARD; *U.S. Private*, pg. 670
BUDAPESTI EROMU ZRT—See Energeticky a Prumyslovy Holding, a.s.; *Int'l*, pg. 2419
BURLINGTON VERMONT CITY ELECTRIC; *U.S. Private*, pg. 689
BUSHVELD ENERGY COMPANY (PTY) LIMITED—See Bushveld Minerals Limited; *Int'l*, pg. 1228
CADILLAC RENEWABLE ENERGY LLC—See I Squared Capital Advisors (US) LLC; *U.S. Private*, pg. 2025
CAELUS ENERGY LLC; *U.S. Private*, pg. 713
CAITHNESS ENERGY, LLC; *U.S. Private*, pg. 714
CALENIA ENERGIA S.P.A.—See Axpo Holding AG; *Int'l*, pg. 771
CALIFORNIA PV ENERGY, LLC—See Constellation Energy Corporation; *U.S. Public*, pg. 571

N.A.I.C.S. INDEX

221118 — OTHER ELECTRIC POWE...

CALLIANCE GESTION—See ENGIE SA; *Int'l*, pg. 2428
CALPINE BOSQUE ENERGY CENTER, LLC—See Energy Capital Partners Management, LP; *U.S. Private*, pg. 1394
CALPINE CORPORATION - DUBLIN—See Energy Capital Partners Management, LP; *U.S. Private*, pg. 1394
CALPINE CORPORATION—See Energy Capital Partners Management, LP; *U.S. Private*, pg. 1394
CALPINE GUADALUPE GP, LLC—See Energy Capital Partners Management, LP; *U.S. Private*, pg. 1394
CALPINE HIDALGO ENERGY CENTER, L.P.—See Energy Capital Partners Management, LP; *U.S. Private*, pg. 1394
CALPINE TURBINE MAINTENANCE GROUP—See Energy Capital Partners Management, LP; *U.S. Private*, pg. 1394
CAMBRIAN WIND ENERGY LTD—See Falck S.p.A.; *Int'l*, pg. 2610
CAMDEN RESOURCE RECOVERY FACILITY—See EQT AB; *Int'l*, pg. 2473
CANEY FORK ELECTRIC COOP; *U.S. Private*, pg. 734
CANNONAU CORP.; *U.S. Public*, pg. 430
CANTON CROSSING DISTRICT ENERGY LLC—See Constellation Energy Corporation; *U.S. Public*, pg. 571
CAPITAL POWER CORPORATION; *Int'l*, pg. 1312
CARBONBW (THAILAND) LTD.—See EnBW Energie Baden-Wurttemberg AG; *Int'l*, pg. 2398
CARBON POWER & LIGHT, INC.; *U.S. Private*, pg. 748
CARBOPEGO - ABASTECIMENTO DE COMBUSTIVEIS, S.A.—See ENGIE SA; *Int'l*, pg. 2431
CARDINAL POWER OF CANADA, L.P.—See iCON Infrastructure LLP; *Int'l*, pg. 3583
THE CARROLL ELECTRIC MEMBERSHIP CORPORATION; *U.S. Private*, pg. 4005
CASA RAMPART LP—See Edison International; *U.S. Public*, pg. 719
CASC EU S.A.—See Enovos International S.A.; *Int'l*, pg. 2444
CASTELNOU ENERGIA S.L—See ENGIE SA; *Int'l*, pg. 2431
CELULOSA ENERGIA, S.L.—See ENCE Energia y Celulosa, S.A.; *Int'l*, pg. 2401
CEMIG GERACAO E TRANSMISSAO S.A.—See Companhia Energetica de Minas Gerais - CEMIG; *Int'l*, pg. 1747
CENTENNIAL POWER, INC.—See Beowulf Energy LLC; *U.S. Private*, pg. 529
CENTENNIAL POWER, INC.—See NGP Energy Capital Management, LLC; *U.S. Private*, pg. 2924
CENTRAL DOCK SUD SA—See Enel S.p.A.; *Int'l*, pg. 2411
CENTRALE EOLIENNE DE FONDS DE FRESNES—See Electricite de France S.A.; *Int'l*, pg. 2350
CENTRAL GERADORA TERMELETRICA FORTALEZA SA—See Enel S.p.A.; *Int'l*, pg. 2412
CENTRAL MAINE POWER COMPANY—See Iberdrola, S.A.; *Int'l*, pg. 3570
CENTRAL NEBRASKA PUBLIC POWER & IRRIGATION DISTRICT, INC.; *U.S. Private*, pg. 823
CENTRAL VIRGINIA ELECTRIC COOPERATIVE INC.; *U.S. Private*, pg. 826
CENTRICA BRIGG LIMITED—See Centrica plc; *Int'l*, pg. 1413
CENTRICA ENERGY LIMITED—See Centrica plc; *Int'l*, pg. 1413
CEP RESERVES, INC.—See PPL Corporation; *U.S. Public*, pg. 1711
CER-COLORADO BEND ENERGY PARTNERS LP—See Constellation Energy Corporation; *U.S. Public*, pg. 571
CER-QUAIL RUN ENERGY PARTNERS LP—See Constellation Energy Corporation; *U.S. Public*, pg. 571
CESP - COMPANHIA ENERGETICA DE SAO PAULO; *Int'l*, pg. 1424
CEU PARADIGM, LLC—See Constellation Energy Corporation; *U.S. Public*, pg. 571
CEZ, A.S. - DUKOVANY NUCLEAR POWER STATION—See CEZ, a.s.; *Int'l*, pg. 1427
CEZ, A.S. - HODONIN POWER PLANT—See CEZ, a.s.; *Int'l*, pg. 1427
CEZ, A.S. - HYDRO POWER STATIONS—See CEZ, a.s.; *Int'l*, pg. 1427
CEZ, A.S. - LEDVICE POWER STATION—See CEZ, a.s.; *Int'l*, pg. 1427
CEZ, A.S. - MELNIK POWER STATION—See CEZ, a.s.; *Int'l*, pg. 1427
CEZ, A.S. - PORICI POWER STATIONS—See CEZ, a.s.; *Int'l*, pg. 1427
CEZ, A.S. - PRUNEROV POWER STATIONS—See CEZ, a.s.; *Int'l*, pg. 1427
CEZ, A.S. - TEMELIN NUCLEAR POWER STATION—See CEZ, a.s.; *Int'l*, pg. 1427
CEZ, A.S. - TISOVA POWER PLANT—See CEZ, a.s.; *Int'l*, pg. 1427
CEZ, A.S. - TUSIMICE POWER STATIONS—See CEZ, a.s.; *Int'l*, pg. 1427
CEZ BOHUNICE A S—See CEZ, a.s.; *Int'l*, pg. 1426
CEZ BULGARIA EAD—See CEZ, a.s.; *Int'l*, pg. 1426
CEZ CHORZOW S.A.—See CEZ, a.s.; *Int'l*, pg. 1427
CEZ DEUTSCHLAND GMBH—See CEZ, a.s.; *Int'l*, pg. 1426
CEZ ENERGETICKE PRODUKTY, S.R.O.—See CEZ, a.s.; *Int'l*, pg. 1426
CEZ ENERGETICKE SLUZBY, S.R.O.—See CEZ, a.s.; *Int'l*, pg. 1426
CEZ ESCO, A.S.—See CEZ, a.s.; *Int'l*, pg. 1426
CEZ ESCO POLSKA SP. Z O.O.—See CEZ, a.s.; *Int'l*, pg. 1426
CEZ PRODUKTY ENERGETYCZNE POLSKA SP. Z.O.O.—See CEZ, a.s.; *Int'l*, pg. 1427
CEZ TRADE ALBANIA SH.P.K.—See CEZ, a.s.; *Int'l*, pg. 1427
CEZ TRADE POLSKA SP. Z O.O.—See CEZ, a.s.; *Int'l*, pg. 1427
CGN NEW ENERGY HOLDINGS CO., LTD.; *Int'l*, pg. 1435
CHAMPION WIND FARM, LLC—See E.ON SE; *Int'l*, pg. 2251
CHAPADA DO PIAUI II HOLDING S.A.—See ContourGlobal Limited; *Int'l*, pg. 1785
CHERKASYOBLENERGO PJSC; *Int'l*, pg. 1471
CHERNIGIVOBLENERGO PJSC; *Int'l*, pg. 1471
CHINA DATANG CORPORATION RENEWABLE POWER CO., LIMITED—See China Datang Corporation; *Int'l*, pg. 1496
CHINA NUCLEAR POWER ENGINEERING CO., LTD.—See CGN Power Co., Ltd.; *Int'l*, pg. 1435
CHINA SOLAR & CLEAN ENERGY SOLUTIONS, INC.; *Int'l*, pg. 1552
CHINA WIND POWER INTERNATIONAL CORP.; *Int'l*, pg. 1563
CHI WEST INC.—See Enel S.p.A.; *Int'l*, pg. 2411
CHOWTAW GENERATION LIMITED PARTNERSHIP—See ENGIE SA; *Int'l*, pg. 2431
CHUBU ELECTRIC POWER COMPANY U.S.A. INC.—See Chubu Electric Power Co., Inc.; *Int'l*, pg. 1593
CHUGACH ELECTRIC ASSOCIATION, INC.; *U.S. Private*, pg. 894
CIA ESTADUAL GER.TRANS.ENER.ELET-CEEE-GT; *Int'l*, pg. 1602
CIE DUPAQUIER SARL—See ENGIE SA; *Int'l*, pg. 2428
CIRQUE ENERGY, INC.; *U.S. Private*, pg. 900
CITIGEN (LONDON) LIMITED—See E.ON SE; *Int'l*, pg. 2256
CITY WATER & LIGHT; *U.S. Private*, pg. 907
CLEAN ENERGY SOLUTIONS, LLC—See Orion Energy Systems, Inc.; *U.S. Public*, pg. 1618
CLEANLIGHT ENERGY, LLC—See New Jersey Resources Corporation; *U.S. Public*, pg. 1511
CLEARVUE TECHNOLOGIES LIMITED; *Int'l*, pg. 1657
CLEARWAY ENERGY, INC.—See BlackRock, Inc.; *U.S. Public*, pg. 345
C&L ELECTRIC CO-OPERATIVE; *U.S. Private*, pg. 703
CLENERGEN CORPORATION LIMITED—See HNO International, Inc.; *U.S. Public*, pg. 1044
CLENERGEN GHANA LIMITED—See HNO International, Inc.; *U.S. Public*, pg. 1044
CLENERGEN PHILIPPINES CORPORATION—See HNO International, Inc.; *U.S. Public*, pg. 1044
CLEVELAND UTILITIES; *U.S. Private*, pg. 941
CLPE HOLDINGS LIMITED—See CLP Holdings Limited; *Int'l*, pg. 1663
CLP INDIA PRIVATE LIMITED—See CLP Holdings Limited; *Int'l*, pg. 1663
CMS LAND COMPANY—See CMS Energy Corporation; *U.S. Public*, pg. 518
COALINGA COGENERATION COMPANY—See Chevron Corporation; *U.S. Public*, pg. 487
COBRA LA RIOJA SUR SA—See ACS, Actividades de Construccion y Servicios, S.A.; *Int'l*, pg. 110
COBRA TERMOSOLAR USA, S.L.—See ACS, Actividades de Construccion y Servicios, S.A.; *Int'l*, pg. 110
COBRE LAS CRUCES S.A.—See First Quantum Minerals Ltd.; *Int'l*, pg. 2687
COFELY DISTRICT ENERGY LTD—See ENGIE SA; *Int'l*, pg. 2429
COFELY ENDEL—See ENGIE SA; *Int'l*, pg. 2429
COFELY MOROCCO—See ENGIE SA; *Int'l*, pg. 2430
COFELY NOORD BV—See ENGIE SA; *Int'l*, pg. 2430
COFELY PACIFIC—See ENGIE SA; *Int'l*, pg. 2430
COFELY PORTUGAL—See ENGIE SA; *Int'l*, pg. 2430
COFELY SERVICES—See ENGIE SA; *Int'l*, pg. 2430
COFELY VANUATU—See ENGIE SA; *Int'l*, pg. 2430
COFELY WEST INDUSTRIE BV—See ENGIE SA; *Int'l*, pg. 2430
COFELY WEST NEDERLAND BV—See ENGIE SA; *Int'l*, pg. 2430
COFELY ZUID NEDERLAND BV—See ENGIE SA; *Int'l*, pg. 2430
COGENEX CORPORATION—See Constellation Energy Corporation; *U.S. Public*, pg. 571
COLETO CREEK POWER, LP—See ENGIE SA; *Int'l*, pg. 2433
COLMAC ENERGY, INC.—See Denham Capital Management LP; *U.S. Private*, pg. 1205
COLORADO ENERGY MANAGEMENT, LLC—See Beowulf Energy LLC; *U.S. Private*, pg. 529
COLORADO ENERGY MANAGEMENT, LLC—See NGP Energy Capital Management, LLC; *U.S. Private*, pg. 2924
COLORADO ENERGY NATIONS COMPANY, LLLP—See ENGIE SA; *Int'l*, pg. 2433
COLORADO SPRINGS UTILITIES, INC.; *U.S. Private*, pg. 974
COLOWYO COAL COMPANY L.P.—See Tri-State Generation and Transmission Association, Inc.; *U.S. Private*, pg. 4224
COLUMBUS LIFE AND WATER; *U.S. Private*, pg. 979
CO-MO ELECTRIC COOPERATIVE; *U.S. Private*, pg. 953
COMPANHIA DE GERACAO TERMICA DE ENERGIA ELETRICA—See Centrais Eletricas Brasileiras S.A.; *Int'l*, pg. 1403
COMPANHIA ENERGETICA DE RORAIMA—See Centrais Eletricas Brasileiras S.A.; *Int'l*, pg. 1403
COMPANHIA ENERGETICA DO RIO GRANDE DO NORTE - COSERN—See Iberdrola, S.A.; *Int'l*, pg. 3573
COMPANHIA HIDRELETRICA DO SAO FRANCISCO—See Centrais Eletricas Brasileiras S.A.; *Int'l*, pg. 1403
COMPANIA ELECTRICA TARAPACA SA—See Enel S.p.A.; *Int'l*, pg. 2412
COMPANIA EOLICA TIERRAS ALTAS SA—See Enel S.p.A.; *Int'l*, pg. 2413
COMPHANIA ENERGETICA SAO SALVADOR S.A.—See ENGIE SA; *Int'l*, pg. 2433
CONCERT SRL—See Accenture plc; *Int'l*, pg. 86
CONEMAUGH STATION; *U.S. Private*, pg. 1012
CONSOLIDATED EDISON COMPANY OF NEW YORK, INC.—See Consolidated Edison, Inc.; *U.S. Public*, pg. 570
CONSOLIDATED POWER MAINTENANCE (PTY) LIMITED—See Consolidated Infrastructure Group Limited; *Int'l*, pg. 1771
CONSTELLATION ENERGY CONTROL AND DISPATCH, LLC—See Constellation Energy Corporation; *U.S. Public*, pg. 572
CONSTELLATION ENERGY PROJECTS & SERVICES GROUP ADVISORS, LLC—See Constellation Energy Corporation; *U.S. Public*, pg. 572
CONSTELLATION MYSTIC POWER, LLC—See Constellation Energy Corporation; *U.S. Public*, pg. 572
CONSTELLATION OPERATING SERVICES—See Constellation Energy Corporation; *U.S. Public*, pg. 572
CONTOUR GLOBAL DO BRASIL PARTICIPACOES LTDA—See ContourGlobal Limited; *Int'l*, pg. 1785
CONTOURGLOBAL HYDRO CASCADE CJSC—See ContourGlobal Limited; *Int'l*, pg. 1785
CONTOUR GLOBAL MANAGEMENT, INC.—See ContourGlobal Limited; *Int'l*, pg. 1785
CONTOURGLOBAL MANAGEMENT SOFIA EOOD—See ContourGlobal Limited; *Int'l*, pg. 1785
CONTOURGLOBAL MARITSA EAST 3 AD—See ContourGlobal Limited; *Int'l*, pg. 1785
CONWAY CORPORATION; *U.S. Private*, pg. 1036
COPPER CROSSING SOLAR, LLC—See Iberdrola, S.A.; *Int'l*, pg. 3570
COPPER VALLEY ELECTRIC ASSOCIATION; *U.S. Private*, pg. 1045
CORN BELT POWER COOPERATIVE; *U.S. Private*, pg. 1050
COSO OPERATING COMPANY, LLC—See ArcLight Capital Holdings, LLC; *U.S. Private*, pg. 312
COVANTA BURNABY RENEWABLE ENERGY, INC.—See EQT AB; *Int'l*, pg. 2473
COVANTA DADE RENEWABLE ENERGY, LLC—See EQT AB; *Int'l*, pg. 2473
COVANTA PLYMOUTH RENEWABLE ENERGY LP—See EQT AB; *Int'l*, pg. 2474
CPS ENERGY; *U.S. Private*, pg. 1081
CQ ENERGY PTY. LTD.—See Energy One Limited; *Int'l*, pg. 2423
CRAWFORDSVILLE ELECTRIC LIGHT & POWER; *U.S. Private*, pg. 1086
CRESTCHIC (MIDDLE EAST) FZE—See Crestchic PLC; *Int'l*, pg. 1841
CREST OPERATIONS LLC—See Crest Industries, LLC; *U.S. Private*, pg. 1096
CRISP COUNTY POWER COMMISSION INC.; *U.S. Private*, pg. 1101
C. ROKAS INDUSTRIAL COMMERCIAL COMPANY, S.A.—See Iberdrola, S.A.; *Int'l*, pg. 3573
CTEEP - COMPANHIA DE TRANSMISSAO DE ENERGIA ELETRICA PAULISTA—See Ecopetrol S.A.; *Int'l*, pg. 2299
CWP GMBH—See Electricite de France S.A.; *Int'l*, pg. 2350
DAIRYLAND POWER COOPERATIVE; *U.S. Private*, pg. 1146
DEARBORN INDUSTRIAL GENERATION, L.L.C.—See CMS Energy Corporation; *U.S. Public*, pg. 518
DEBRECENI KOMBINALT CIKLUSU EROMU KFT.—See E.ON SE; *Int'l*, pg. 2251
DELMARVA POWER & LIGHT COMPANY—See Exelon Corporation; *U.S. Public*, pg. 807
DELTA ELECTRONICS INT'L (SINGAPORE) PTE LTD—See Delta Electronics, Inc.; *Int'l*, pg. 2018
DELTA ENERGY B.V.—See Delta N.V.; *Int'l*, pg. 2019
DESERET GENERATION & TRANSMISSION COOPERATIVE, INC.; *U.S. Private*, pg. 1212
DF-AP#1, LLC—See Dean Foods Company; *U.S. Private*, pg. 1183
DISTRIBUTIE ENERGIE OLTENIA S.A.—See CEZ, a.s.; *Int'l*, pg. 1427
DMCI POWER CORPORATION—See DMCI Holdings, Inc.; *Int'l*, pg. 2143

221118 — OTHER ELECTRIC POWE... — CORPORATE AFFILIATIONS

DOHOME ENERGY COMPANY LIMITED—See DoHome Public Company Limited; *Int'l*, pg. 2156
DONAU-WASSERKRAFT AKTIENGESELLSCHAFT—See E.ON SE; *Int'l*, pg. 2252
DONGKUK S&C CO., LTD. - DK WIND POWER PLANT—See Dongkuk S&C Co., Ltd.; *Int'l*, pg. 2169
DORAL GROUP RENEWABLE ENERGY RSRCS LTD.; *Int'l*, pg. 2175
DREAM-UP TOMAMAE CO., LTD.—See Electric Power Development Co., Ltd.; *Int'l*, pg. 2349
DRY LAKE WIND POWER II, LLC—See Iberdrola, S.A.; *Int'l*, pg. 3570
DUKE ENERGY BUSINESS SERVICES LLC—See Duke Energy Corporation; *U.S. Public*, pg. 690
DUKE ENERGY CORP. - SENECA—See Duke Energy Corporation; *U.S. Public*, pg. 690
DUKE ENERGY FLORIDA, LLC—See Duke Energy Corporation; *U.S. Public*, pg. 690
DUKE ENERGY GENERATION SERVICES—See Duke Energy Corporation; *U.S. Public*, pg. 690
DUKE ENERGY KENTUCKY, INC.—See Duke Energy Corporation; *U.S. Public*, pg. 690
DUKE ENERGY PROGRESS, LLC—See Duke Energy Corporation; *U.S. Public*, pg. 691
DUNKIRK POWER LLC—See NRG Energy, Inc.; *U.S. Public*, pg. 1550
DU PONT APOLLO (SHENZHEN) LIMITED—See DuPont de Nemours, Inc.; *U.S. Public*, pg. 692
DURO DAKOVIC TERMOENERGETSKA POSTROJENJA D.O.O.; *Int'l*, pg. 2228
DYERSBURG ELECTRIC SYSTEM; *U.S. Private*, pg. 1296
DYNEGY MIDWEST GENERATION, LLC—See Vistra Corp.; *U.S. Public*, pg. 2306
DYNEGY NORTH AMERICA, INC.—See Energy Capital Partners Management, LP; *U.S. Private*, pg. 1394
E2S CO., LTD.; *Int'l*, pg. 2261
E4U A.S.; *Int'l*, pg. 2261
EAM SOLAR ASA; *Int'l*, pg. 2267
EASLEY COMBINED UTILITY SYSTEM; *U.S. Private*, pg. 1315
EAST KENTUCKY POWER COOPERATIVE; *U.S. Private*, pg. 1316
EASUN REYROLLE LTD; *Int'l*, pg. 2275
E-BEN GMBH & CO. KG—See HEAG Sudhessische Energie AG; *Int'l*, pg. 3302
EBENSBURG POWER CO.—See Babcock & Wilcox Enterprises, Inc.; *U.S. Public*, pg. 263
ECOBIO HOLDINGS CO., LTD.; *Int'l*, pg. 2294
ECOLOCAP SOLUTIONS INC.; *U.S. Public*, pg. 717
ECONERGY RENEWABLE ENERGY LTD.; *Int'l*, pg. 2296
ECOPLUS, INC.; *U.S. Public*, pg. 717
ECOVAL TECHNOLOGY SAS—See Electricite de France S.A.; *Int'l*, pg. 2350
ECO WAVE POWER GLOBAL AB; *Int'l*, pg. 2292
EC&R NA SOLAR PV, LLC—See E.ON SE; *Int'l*, pg. 2256
EC&R PANTHER CREEK WIND FARM III, LLC—See E.ON SE; *Int'l*, pg. 2256
EC&R PANTHER CREEK WIND FARM I&II, LLC—See E.ON SE; *Int'l*, pg. 2256
EC&R PAPALOTE CREEK II, LLC—See E.ON SE; *Int'l*, pg. 2256
EC&R PAPALOTE CREEK I, LLC—See E.ON SE; *Int'l*, pg. 2256
EC&R QSE, LLC—See E.ON SE; *Int'l*, pg. 2256
EC&R SERVICES, LLC—See E.ON SE; *Int'l*, pg. 2256
EDENDERRY POWER LIMITED—See Bord na Mona Plc; *Int'l*, pg. 1113
EDF BELGIUM SA—See Electricite de France S.A.; *Int'l*, pg. 2350
EDF ENERGIES NOUVELLES S.A.—See Electricite de France S.A.; *Int'l*, pg. 2350
EDF ENERGY PLC—See Electricite de France S.A.; *Int'l*, pg. 2350
EDF ENERGY UK LTD—See Electricite de France S.A.; *Int'l*, pg. 2350
EDF POLSKA SP. Z O.O.—See Electricite de France S.A.; *Int'l*, pg. 2350
EDF PRODUCTION UK LTD—See Electricite de France S.A.; *Int'l*, pg. 2350
EDISUN POWER EUROPE AG; *Int'l*, pg. 2311
E-DOME A. S.—See CEZ, a.s.; *Int'l*, pg. 1429
EDP - GESTAO DA PRODUCAO DE ENERGIA, S.A.—See EDP - Energias de Portugal, S.A.; *Int'l*, pg. 2314
EDP - PROJECTOS S.G.P.S., S.A.—See EDP - Energias de Portugal, S.A.; *Int'l*, pg. 2314
EDP RENEWABLES CANADA, LTD—See EDP - Energias de Portugal, S.A.; *Int'l*, pg. 2314
EDP RENEWABLES POLSKA, SP. Z O.O.—See EDP - Energias de Portugal, S.A.; *Int'l*, pg. 2314
EDP RENOVAVEIS S.A.—See EDP - Energias de Portugal, S.A.; *Int'l*, pg. 2314
EF OXNARD LLC—See I Squared Capital Advisors (US) LLC; *U.S. Private*, pg. 2025
EGCO GREEN ENERGY CO., LTD—See Electricity Generating Public Co., Ltd.; *Int'l*, pg. 2352
EGS HOLDINGS, LLC—See Entergy Corporation; *U.S. Public*, pg. 777

EIF KC LANDFILL GAS, LLC—See Enpower Corp.; *U.S. Private*, pg. 1401
ELANGO INDUSTRIES LIMITED; *Int'l*, pg. 2343
ELECTRABEL GREEN PROJECTS FLANDERS SCRL—See ENGIE SA; *Int'l*, pg. 2432
ELECTRICA DE LA RIBERA DEL EBRO, S.A.—See EDP - Energias de Portugal, S.A.; *Int'l*, pg. 2314
ELECTRICA PUNTILLA SA; *Int'l*, pg. 2349
ELECTRIC ENERGY, INC.—See Ameren Corporation; *U.S. Public*, pg. 94
ELECTRICIDAD DE LA PAZ, S.A.—See Iberdrola, S.A.; *Int'l*, pg. 3571
ELECTRICITY GENERATING PUBLIC CO., LTD.; *Int'l*, pg. 2352
ELECTROQUIL, S.A.—See I Squared Capital Advisors (US) LLC; *U.S. Private*, pg. 2025
ELECTROTHERM INDIA LTD - ELECTROTHERM RENEWABLES—See Electrotherm India Ltd; *Int'l*, pg. 2354
ELEJOR - CENTRAIS ELETRICAS DO RIO JORDAO S.A.—See Companhia Paranaense de Energia; *Int'l*, pg. 1748
ELEKTRARNA POCERADY, A.S.—See CEZ, a.s.; *Int'l*, pg. 1427
ELEKTRO REDES S.A.—See Iberdrola, S.A.; *Int'l*, pg. 3572
ELEKTROWNIA SKAWINA S.A.—See CEZ, a.s.; *Int'l*, pg. 1427
ELEKTROWNIE WIATROWE LUBIECHOVO SP. Z.O.O.—See CEZ, a.s.; *Int'l*, pg. 1427
ELEKTROWNIE WODNE SP. Z O.O.—See ENEA S.A.; *Int'l*, pg. 2410
ELETROBRAS ELETRONORTE—See Centrais Eletricas Brasileiras S.A.; *Int'l*, pg. 1403
ELETTRONICA SANTERNO S.P.A.—See Enertronica Santerno S.p.A.; *Int'l*, pg. 2425
ELK RIVER WIND FARM, LLC.—See Iberdrola, S.A.; *Int'l*, pg. 3570
ELM CREEK WIND II, LLC—See Iberdrola, S.A.; *Int'l*, pg. 3570
EL SEGUNDO POWER II LLC—See NRG Energy, Inc.; *U.S. Public*, pg. 1550
EMERSON NETWORK POWER GUC SISTEMLERI LIMITED SIRKETI—See Emerson Electric Co.; *U.S. Public*, pg. 745
EMPOWER ENERGIES, INC.—See General Motors Company; *U.S. Public*, pg. 924
EMPRESA AMAZONENSE DE TRANSMISSAO DE ENERGIA S.A.—See Alupar Investimento S.A.; *Int'l*, pg. 401
EMPRESA CATARINENSE DE TRANSMISSAO DE ENERGIA S.A.—See Alupar Investimento S.A.; *Int'l*, pg. 401
EMPRESA DE GENERACION ELECTRICA DEL SUR SA; *Int'l*, pg. 2388
EMPRESA DE LUZ Y FUERZA ELECTRICA DE ORURO, S.A.—See Iberdrola, S.A.; *Int'l*, pg. 3571
EMPRESA DE SERVICOS E COMERCIALIZACAO DE ENERGIA ELETRICA S.A.—See Companhia Energetica de Minas Gerais - CEMIG; *Int'l*, pg. 1747
EMPRESA ELECTRICA SANTIAGO SPA—See The AES Corporation; *U.S. Public*, pg. 2031
EMPRESA NACIONAL DEL PETROLEO; *Int'l*, pg. 2388
ENBW BALTIC 1 GMBH & CO. KG—See EnBW Energie Baden-Wurttemberg AG; *Int'l*, pg. 2398
ENBW OMEGA DREIUNDZWANZIGSTE VERWALTUNGSGESELLSCHAFT MBH—See EnBW Energie Baden-Wurttemberg AG; *Int'l*, pg. 2398
ENBW OMEGA ELFTE VERWALTUNGSGESELLSCHAFT MBH—See EnBW Energie Baden-Wurttemberg AG; *Int'l*, pg. 2398
ENDESA ARGENTINA SA—See Enel S.p.A.; *Int'l*, pg. 2413
ENDESA DESARROLLO SL—See Enel S.p.A.; *Int'l*, pg. 2412
ENDESA ECO SA—See Enel S.p.A.; *Int'l*, pg. 2413
ENDESA GENERACION, S.A.—See Enel S.p.A.; *Int'l*, pg. 2412
ENDESA INGENIERIA SLU—See Enel S.p.A.; *Int'l*, pg. 2412
ENEA BIOENERGIA SP. Z O.O.—See ENEA S.A.; *Int'l*, pg. 2410
ENEA CIEPLO SERWIS SP. Z O.O.—See ENEA S.A.; *Int'l*, pg. 2410
ENEA CIEPLO SP. Z O.O.—See ENEA S.A.; *Int'l*, pg. 2410
ENEA ELEKTROWNIA POLANIEC S.A.—See ENEA S.A.; *Int'l*, pg. 2410
ENEA OSWIETLENIE SP. Z O.O.—See ENEA S.A.; *Int'l*, pg. 2410
ENEA POLANIEC SERWIS SP. Z O.O.—See ENEA S.A.; *Int'l*, pg. 2410
ENEFIT OUTOTEC TECHNOLOGY OU—See Eesti Energia AS; *Int'l*, pg. 2317
ENEFIT SIA—See Eesti Energia AS; *Int'l*, pg. 2317
ENEL BRASIL PARTICIPACOES LTDA—See Enel S.p.A.; *Int'l*, pg. 2413
ENEL DE COSTA RICA SA—See Enel S.p.A.; *Int'l*, pg. 2414
ENEL GREEN POWER CANADA, INC.—See Enel S.p.A.; *Int'l*, pg. 2413
ENEL GREEN POWER CHILE LTDA.—See Enel S.p.A.; *Int'l*, pg. 2413
ENEL GREEN POWER COSTA RICA SA—See Enel S.p.A.; *Int'l*, pg. 2413

ENEL GREEN POWER ESPANA SL—See Enel S.p.A.; *Int'l*, pg. 2413
ENEL GREEN POWER FRANCE SAS—See Enel S.p.A.; *Int'l*, pg. 2413
ENEL GREEN POWER GUATEMALA SA—See Enel S.p.A.; *Int'l*, pg. 2413
ENEL GREEN POWER HELLAS SA—See Enel S.p.A.; *Int'l*, pg. 2413
ENEL GREEN POWER MEXICO S DE RL DE CV—See Enel S.p.A.; *Int'l*, pg. 2413
ENEL GREEN POWER NORTH AMERICA, INC.—See Enel S.p.A.; *Int'l*, pg. 2413
ENEL GREEN POWER PANAMA SA—See Enel S.p.A.; *Int'l*, pg. 2413
ENEL GREEN POWER PERU SA—See Enel S.p.A.; *Int'l*, pg. 2413
ENEL GREEN POWER ROME VILLORESI SRL—See Enel S.p.A.; *Int'l*, pg. 2413
ENEL LATIN AMERICA (CHILE) LTDA.—See Enel S.p.A.; *Int'l*, pg. 2414
ENEL M@P SRL—See Enel S.p.A.; *Int'l*, pg. 2413
ENEL PANAMA SA—See Enel S.p.A.; *Int'l*, pg. 2413
ENEL X ARGENTINA SAU—See Enel S.p.A.; *Int'l*, pg. 2413
ENEL X AUSTRALIA (PTY) LTD.—See Enel S.p.A.; *Int'l*, pg. 2414
ENEL X JAPAN KK—See Enel S.p.A.; *Int'l*, pg. 2414
ENERGETICKE CENTRUM S.R.O.—See CEZ, a.s.; *Int'l*, pg. 1427
ENERGETIKA SERVIS S.R.O.—See E.ON SE; *Int'l*, pg. 2256
ENERGIA ALTERNATIVA SRL.—See Athena Investments A/S; *Int'l*, pg. 669
ENERGIA E INDUSTRIA DE TOLEDO, S.A.—See EDP - Energias de Portugal, S.A.; *Int'l*, pg. 2314
ENERGIA LATINA SA; *Int'l*, pg. 2420
ENERGIA NUEVA ENERGIA LIMPIA MEXICO SRL DE CV—See Enel S.p.A.; *Int'l*, pg. 2413
ENERGIAS AMBIENTALES, S.A.—See ACS, Actividades de Construccion y Servicios, S.A.; *Int'l*, pg. 112
ENERGIA, SAS—See ENGIE SA; *Int'l*, pg. 2428
ENERGIA VERDE SRL.—See Athena Investments A/S; *Int'l*, pg. 669
ENERGIEPARK TRELDER BERG GMBH—See Enovos International S.A.; *Int'l*, pg. 2444
ENERGIE SAARLORLUX AG—See ENGIE SA; *Int'l*, pg. 2432
ENERGIEVERSORGUNG GERA GMBH—See ENGIE SA; *Int'l*, pg. 2431
ENERGIX RENEWABLE ENERGIES LTD.; *Int'l*, pg. 2420
ENERGOPARTNER SP. Z O.O.—See ENEA S.A.; *Int'l*, pg. 2410
ENERGY ACTION (AUSTRALIA) PTY LIMITED—See Energy Action Limited; *Int'l*, pg. 2422
ENERGYAUSTRALIA YALLOURN PTY. LTD.—See CLP Holdings Limited; *Int'l*, pg. 1663
ENERGY CENTER MINNEAPOLIS LLC—See BlackRock, Inc.; *U.S. Public*, pg. 345
ENERGY CENTER PHOENIX LL—See BlackRock, Inc.; *U.S. Public*, pg. 345
ENERGY CENTER PITTSBURGH LLC—See BlackRock, Inc.; *U.S. Public*, pg. 345
ENERGY CONVERSION SERVICES, INC.; *U.S. Private*, pg. 1394
ENERGY DEVELOPMENTS, INC.—See CK Hutchison Holdings Limited; *Int'l*, pg. 1637
ENERGY DEVELOPMENTS LIMITED—See CK Hutchison Holdings Limited; *Int'l*, pg. 1636
ENERGY DEVELOPMENTS (UK) LIMITED—See CK Hutchison Holdings Limited; *Int'l*, pg. 1637
ENERGYNET (PVT) LTD.—See Hayleys PLC; *Int'l*, pg. 3291
ENERGY NORTHWEST; *U.S. Private*, pg. 1395
ENERGY SOLUTION MANAGEMENT CO., LTD.—See Energy Absolute Public Company Limited; *Int'l*, pg. 2422
ENERGYST B.V.—See Caterpillar, Inc.; *U.S. Public*, pg. 452
ENERGY TRANSFER GROUP, LLC—See Energy Transfer LP; *U.S. Public*, pg. 763
ENERGY VENTURES, LLC—See Enterprise Products Partners L.P.; *U.S. Public*, pg. 778
ENERGYWORKS ARANDA, S.L.—See Iberdrola, S.A.; *Int'l*, pg. 3571
ENERGYWORKS CARBALLO, S.L.—See Iberdrola, S.A.; *Int'l*, pg. 3571
ENERGYWORKS FONZ, S.L.—See Iberdrola, S.A.; *Int'l*, pg. 3571
ENERGYWORKS MONZON, S.L.—See Iberdrola, S.A.; *Int'l*, pg. 3571
ENERGYWORKS SAN MILLAN, S.L.—See Iberdrola, S.A.; *Int'l*, pg. 3571
ENERGYWORKS VENEZUELA, S.A.—See Iberdrola, S.A.; *Int'l*, pg. 3571
ENERGYWORKS VILLARROBLEDO, S.L.—See Iberdrola, S.A.; *Int'l*, pg. 3571
ENERJISA ENERJI URETIM A.S.—See E.ON SE; *Int'l*, pg. 2257
ENERJISA ENERJI URETIM A.S.—See Haci Omer Sabanci Holding A.S.; *Int'l*, pg. 3204
ENERMON S.A. DE C.V.—See Iberdrola, S.A.; *Int'l*, pg. 3571
ENEX ENERGY CORP; *Int'l*, pg. 2425

221118 — OTHER ELECTRIC POWE...

ENGIE ENERGIA PERU S.A.—See ENGIE SA; *Int'l*, pg. 2428
ENGRO ENERGY LIMITED—See Engro Corporation Limited; *Int'l*, pg. 2435
ENGYCO PLC; *Int'l*, pg. 2436
ENIPOWER MANTOVA SPA—See Eni S.p.A., *Int'l*, pg. 2438
ENIPOWER SPA—See Eni S.p.A., *Int'l*, pg. 2438
ENMAX GREEN POWER INC.—See ENMAX Corporation; *Int'l*, pg. 2442
ENNIS POWER COMPANY LLC—See ENGIE SA; *Int'l*, pg. 2433
ENTEGRA LIMITED; *Int'l*, pg. 2450
ENTERGY POWER VENTURES, LLC—See Entergy Corporation; *U.S. Public*, pg. 777
ENTERGY TEXAS, INC.—See Entergy Corporation; *U.S. Public*, pg. 777
EOLFLOR - PRODUCAO DE ENERGIA EO LICA LDA—See Enel S.p.A.; *Int'l*, pg. 2414
EOLICA ARLANZON, S.A.—See EDP - Energias de Portugal, S.A.; *Int'l*, pg. 2314
EOLICA DOBROGEA (SCHWEIZ) I, GMBH.—See Iberdrola, S.A.; *Int'l*, pg. 3571
EOLICA EL PEDREGOSO, S.L.—See AUDAX RENOVABLES, S.A.; *Int'l*, pg. 700
EOLICA GUADALTEBA, S.L.—See EDP - Energias de Portugal, S.A.; *Int'l*, pg. 2314
EOLICA POLCZYNO SP. Z O.O.—See Athena Investments A/S; *Int'l*, pg. 669
EOLIKI ZARAKA METAMORFOSSIS SA—See ELLAKTOR S.A.; *Int'l*, pg. 2365
E.ON CLIMATE & RENEWABLES GMBH—See E.ON SE; *Int'l*, pg. 2252
E.ON CLIMATE & RENEWABLES ITALIA S.R.L.—See F2i - Fondi Italiani per le infrastrutture SGR S.p.A.; *Int'l*, pg. 2597
E.ON CLIMATE & RENEWABLES NORTH AMERICA LLC—See E.ON SE; *Int'l*, pg. 2252
E.ON CLIMATE & RENEWABLES UK BIOMASS LIMITED—See E.ON SE; *Int'l*, pg. 2256
E.ON CLIMATE & RENEWABLES UK OFFSHORE WIND LIMITED—See E.ON SE; *Int'l*, pg. 2256
E.ON CLIMATE & RENEWABLES UK WIND LIMITED—See E.ON SE; *Int'l*, pg. 2256
E.ON DRIVE GMBH—See E.ON SE; *Int'l*, pg. 2252
E.ON ELEKTRARNE S.R.O.—See E.ON SE; *Int'l*, pg. 2252
E.ON EUROPA, S.L.—See E.ON SE; *Int'l*, pg. 2254
E.ON FRANCE MANAGEMENT S.A.S.—See E.ON SE; *Int'l*, pg. 2254
E.ON KARNKRAFT SVERIGE AB—See E.ON SE; *Int'l*, pg. 2255
E.ON MYENERGY KFT.—See E.ON SE; *Int'l*, pg. 2254
E.ON PRODUKTION DANMARK A/S—See E.ON SE; *Int'l*, pg. 2254
E.ON PRODUZIONE CENTRALE LIVORNO FERRARIS S.P.A.—See E.ON SE; *Int'l*, pg. 2255
E.ON REGENERABILE ROMANIA S.R.L—See E.ON SE; *Int'l*, pg. 2255
E.ON RENOVABLES, S.L.—See E.ON SE; *Int'l*, pg. 2252
E.ON RENOVAVEIS PORTUGAL, SGPS S.A.—See E.ON SE; *Int'l*, pg. 2255
E.ON RUHRGAS E & P AGYPTEN GMBH—See E.ON SE; *Int'l*, pg. 2255
E.ON RUSSIA HOLDING GMBH—See E.ON SE; *Int'l*, pg. 2255
E.ON TREND S.R.O.—See E.ON SE; *Int'l*, pg. 2256
E.ON UK CHP LIMITED—See E.ON SE; *Int'l*, pg. 2256
E.ON UK ENERGY SERVICES LIMITED—See E.ON SE; *Int'l*, pg. 2256
E.ON UK POWER TECHNOLOGY LIMITED—See E.ON SE; *Int'l*, pg. 2256
E.ON VIND SVERIGE AB—See E.ON SE; *Int'l*, pg. 2255
EPURON SARL—See Kawa Capital Management, Inc.; *U.S. Private*, pg. 2266
EQTEC PLC; *Int'l*, pg. 2483
EQUATORIAL ENERGIA ALAGOAS—See Equatorial Energia SA; *Int'l*, pg. 2484
EQUATORIAL PARA—See Equatorial Energia SA; *Int'l*, pg. 2484
EQUINOR ENERGY BELGIUM NV - MECHELEN OFFICE—See Equinor ASA; *Int'l*, pg. 2484
ERG DEVELOPPEMENT FRANCE S.A.S.—See ERG S.p.A.; *Int'l*, pg. 2491
ESOLAR, INC.—See Idealab Holdings, LLC; *U.S. Private*, pg. 2037
ETRION CORPORATION; *Int'l*, pg. 2524
ETRION SERVICES JAPAN KK—See Etrion Corporation; *Int'l*, pg. 2524
EVERGREEN ENERGY INC.; *U.S. Private*, pg. 1439
EVGO SERVICES LLC—See LS Power Development, LLC; *U.S. Private*, pg. 2508
EVN KRAFTWERKS- UND BETEILIGUNGSGESELLSCHAFT MBH—See EVN AG; *Int'l*, pg. 2571
EVN MACEDONIA ELEKTRANI DOOEL—See EVN AG; *Int'l*, pg. 2571
EVN NATURKRAFT BETEILIGUNGS- UND BETRIEBS- GMBH—See EVN AG; *Int'l*, pg. 2571
EVN PROJEKTMANAGEMENT GMBH—See EVN AG; *Int'l*, pg. 2571

EVN WARME GMBH—See EVN AG; *Int'l*, pg. 2571
EWE BIOGAS GMBH & CO. KG—See EWE Aktiengesellschaft; *Int'l*, pg. 2575
EXERGY FUEL CELLS S.R.L.—See Amasten Fastighets AB; *Int'l*, pg. 412
FALCK RENEWABLES S.P.A.—See Falck S.p.A.; *Int'l*, pg. 2610
FALCON SEABOARD HOLDINGS LP; *U.S. Private*, pg. 1466
FARMERS' ELECTRIC COOPERATIVE INC. OF NEW MEXICO; *U.S. Private*, pg. 1480
FARMERS ELECTRIC CO-OPERATIVE; *U.S. Private*, pg. 1477
FAUJI KABIRWALA POWER COMPANY LIMITED—See Fauji Foundation; *Int'l*, pg. 2623
FB GENERATION SERVICES B.V.—See Fortum Oyj; *Int'l*, pg. 2740
FERCOM EOLICA, S.L.—See AUDAX RENOVABLES, S.A.; *Int'l*, pg. 700
FERMICAISE SA DE CV—See Enel S.p.A.; *Int'l*, pg. 2414
FIBREGEN PLC; *Int'l*, pg. 2653
FINETEX ENE, INC. - HWASUNG PLANT—See Finetex EnE, Inc.; *Int'l*, pg. 2674
FIRST CHOICE POWER, L.P.—See NRG Energy, Inc.; *U.S. Public*, pg. 1549
FIRSTENERGY FOUNDATION—See FirstEnergy Corp.; *U.S. Public*, pg. 849
FIRSTENERGY NUCLEAR OPERATING CO.—See FirstEnergy Corp.; *U.S. Public*, pg. 849
FIRSTENERGY SOLUTIONS CORP.—See FirstEnergy Corp.; *U.S. Public*, pg. 849
FIRST HYDRO HOLDINGS COMPANY—See ENGIE SA; *Int'l*, pg. 2429
FIRST NATIONAL ENERGY CORPORATION; *Int'l*, pg. 2686
FIRST SOLAR GMBH—See First Solar, Inc.; *U.S. Public*, pg. 847
FLORIDA MUNICIPAL POWER AGENCY; *U.S. Private*, pg. 1550
FLORIDA PROGRESS CORPORATION—See Duke Energy Corporation; *U.S. Public*, pg. 691
FON SE; *Int'l*, pg. 2724
FOREST CREEK WF HOLDCO, LLC—See E.ON SE; *Int'l*, pg. 2257
FORTISTAR NORTH TONAWANDA, INC.—See Fortistar LLC; *U.S. Private*, pg. 1576
FORT PIERCE UTILITIES AUTHORITY; *U.S. Private*, pg. 1574
FORTUM 1 AB—See Fortum Oyj; *Int'l*, pg. 2741
FORTUM AMCO AB—See Fortum Oyj; *Int'l*, pg. 2741
FORTUM EESTI AS—See Fortum Oyj; *Int'l*, pg. 2740
FORTUM GENERATION AB—See Fortum Oyj; *Int'l*, pg. 2741
FORTUM HEAT NAANTALI OY—See Fortum Oyj; *Int'l*, pg. 2741
FORTUM METER LEASE SNC—See Fortum Oyj; *Int'l*, pg. 2741
FORTUM NORDIC AB—See Fortum Oyj; *Int'l*, pg. 2741
FORTUM PRODUKTIONSNAT AB—See Fortum Oyj; *Int'l*, pg. 2741
FORTUM ZABRZE SA—See Fortum Oyj; *Int'l*, pg. 2741
FORTUNE ELECTRIC AMERICA INC.—See Fortune Electric Co., Ltd.; *Int'l*, pg. 2743
FRANKENLUK AG—See Alpiq Holding AG; *Int'l*, pg. 372
FREDERICKSON POWER, LP—See Capital Power Corporation; *Int'l*, pg. 1312
FRED. OLSEN RENEWABLES AS—See Fred. Olsen & Co.; *Int'l*, pg. 2768
FRED. OLSEN RENEWABLES LTD.—See Fred. Olsen & Co.; *Int'l*, pg. 2768
FRENCH BROAD ELECTRIC MEMBERSHIP CORPORATION; *U.S. Private*, pg. 1608
FRONTERA GENERATION LP—See NRG Energy, Inc.; *U.S. Public*, pg. 1549
FSP (GB) LTD.—See FSP Technology Inc.; *Int'l*, pg. 2800
FUJIAN OPCON ENERGY TECHNOLOGY CO., LTD.—See Fujian Snowman Co., Ltd.; *Int'l*, pg. 2819
GAINESVILLE REGIONAL UTILITIES INC.; *U.S. Private*, pg. 1635
GALHEIROS GERACAO DE ENERGIA ELETRICA S.A.—See ContourGlobal Limited; *Int'l*, pg. 1785
GASAG CONTRACTING GMBH—See ENGIE SA; *Int'l*, pg. 2429
GASAG CONTRACTING GMBH—See E.ON SE; *Int'l*, pg. 2257
GAS Y ELECTRICIDAD GENERACION SAU—See Enel S.p.A.; *Int'l*, pg. 2414
GAZ ELECTRICITE DE GRENOBLE SE—See ENGIE SA; *Int'l*, pg. 2434
GDF SUEZ BIOENERGIA SP. Z O.O.—See ENGIE SA; *Int'l*, pg. 2433
GDF SUEZ ENERGIA ESPANA SLU—See ENGIE SA; *Int'l*, pg. 2433
GDF SUEZ ENERGIA POLSKA SA—See ENGIE SA; *Int'l*, pg. 2433
GDF SUEZ ENERGY UK LIMITED—See ENGIE SA; *Int'l*, pg. 2432
GDF SUEZ TEESSIDE LTD—See ENGIE SA; *Int'l*, pg. 2432

GEHLENBERG APS—See Athena Investments A/S; *Int'l*, pg. 669
GEMEINSCHAFTSKERNKRAFTWERK GROHNDE MANAGEMENT GMBH—See E.ON SE; *Int'l*, pg. 2257
GEMEINSCHAFTSKERNKRAFTWERK ISAR 2 GMBH—See E.ON SE; *Int'l*, pg. 2257
GEMEINSCHAFTSKRAFTWERK IRSCHING GMBH—See Fortum Oyj; *Int'l*, pg. 2742
GEMEINSCHAFTSKRAFTWERK VELTHEIM GESELLSCHAFT MIT BESCHRANKTER HAFTUNG—See E.ON SE; *Int'l*, pg. 2258
GEM MATTHEWS INTERNATIONAL S.R.L.—See Matthews International Corporation; *U.S. Public*, pg. 1400
GENALTA POWER INC.—See Enbridge Inc.; *Int'l*, pg. 2397
GENERADORA DE OCCIDENTE LTDA—See Enel S.p.A.; *Int'l*, pg. 2413
GENERSOL, S.A.—See Ecoener, S.A.; *Int'l*, pg. 2295
GENESEE POWER STATION LIMITED PARTNERSHIP—See CMS Energy Corporation; *U.S. Public*, pg. 519
GENESIS ENERGY LIMITED; *Int'l*, pg. 2921
GENEX CO., LTD.—See Idemitsu Kosan Co., Ltd.; *Int'l*, pg. 3590
GENEX POWER LIMITED; *Int'l*, pg. 2923
GENTING SANYEN POWER SDN BHD—See Genting Berhad; *Int'l*, pg. 2929
GEORGIA TRANSMISSION CORPORATION; *U.S. Private*, pg. 1684
GEP ENERGIES SA—See Global EcoPower SA; *Int'l*, pg. 2995
GE POWER AG—See General Electric Company; *U.S. Public*, pg. 917
GE POWER—See General Electric Company; *U.S. Public*, pg. 917
GHD E.ON BAYERN AG & CO. KG—See E.ON SE; *Int'l*, pg. 2257
GIA LAI ELECTRICITY JOINT STOCK COMPANY; *Int'l*, pg. 2960
GILBERTON POWER COMPANY—See Reading Anthracite Company; *U.S. Private*, pg. 3366
GILROY ENERGY CENTER, LLC—See Energy Capital Partners Management, LP; *U.S. Private*, pg. 1394
GK TNS ENERGO PAO; *Int'l*, pg. 2982
GLOBAL ATREO S.L.—See The AES Corporation; *U.S. Public*, pg. 2031
GLOBAL ECOPOWER SA; *Int'l*, pg. 2995
GLOBAL POWER SUPPLY, LLC; *U.S. Private*, pg. 1716
GLOBAL SOLAR ENERGY DEUTSCHLAND GMBH—See Global Solar Energy, Inc.; *U.S. Private*, pg. 1717
GLOBAL SOLAR ENERGY, INC.; *U.S. Private*, pg. 1717
GLOBAL WEDGE, INC.; *U.S. Private*, pg. 1719
GLOBELEQ GENERATION LIMITED—See General Atlantic Service Company, L.P.; *U.S. Private*, pg. 1661
GLOBUS POWER GENERATION LIMITED; *Int'l*, pg. 3008
GLOW SPP 1 COMPANY LIMITED—See B. Grimm Group; *Int'l*, pg. 788
GNPOWER KAUSWAGAN CO., LTD.—See Ayala Corporation; *Int'l*, pg. 774
GOLDEN VALLEY ELECTRIC ASSOCIATION; *U.S. Private*, pg. 1734
G.P. GLOBAL POWERM LTD.; *Int'l*, pg. 2866
GRANDE DIXENCE SA—See Alpiq Holding AG; *Int'l*, pg. 373
GRANDE PRAIRIE GENERATION, INC.—See Exelon Corporation; *U.S. Public*, pg. 807
GRANITE RIDGE ENERGY, LLC—See Energy Capital Partners Management, LP; *U.S. Private*, pg. 1394
GREAT RIVER ENERGY; *U.S. Private*, pg. 1767
GREENALIA SA; *Int'l*, pg. 3073
GREENBACKER RENEWABLE ENERGY CORPORATION; *U.S. Private*, pg. 1774
GREENIDGE GENERATION LLC—See Greenidge Generation Holdings Inc.; *U.S. Public*, pg. 964
GREENLEAF POWER, LLC—See Denham Capital Management LP; *U.S. Private*, pg. 1205
GREENLOGIC ENERGY; *U.S. Private*, pg. 1779
GREEN MOUNTAIN AS—See Azrieli Group Ltd.; *Int'l*, pg. 781
GREEN POWER KUZUMAKI CO., LTD.—See Electric Power Development Co., Ltd.; *Int'l*, pg. 2349
GREENWIND, S.A.—See EDP - Energias de Portugal, S.A.; *Int'l*, pg. 2314
GRENERGY ERNEUERBARE ENERGIEN GMBH—See Grenergy Renovables SA; *Int'l*, pg. 3080
GRENERGY POLSKA SP. Z O.O.—See Grenergy Renovables SA; *Int'l*, pg. 3080
GRENERGY RENEWABLES UK LIMITED—See Grenergy Renovables SA; *Int'l*, pg. 3080
GRESGYING DIGITAL TECHNOLOGY CO., LTD.; *Int'l*, pg. 3082
GREXEL SYSTEMS OY—See Deutsche Borse AG; *Int'l*, pg. 2064
GREYSTONE POWER CORPORATION; *U.S. Private*, pg. 1786
GRIFFITH ENERGY, LLC—See ArcLight Capital Holdings, LLC; *U.S. Private*, pg. 312
GROTON WIND, LLC—See Iberdrola, S.A.; *Int'l*, pg. 3570

221118 — OTHER ELECTRIC POWE...   CORPORATE AFFILIATIONS

GRUPO IBERDROLA MEXICO, S.A. DE C.V.—See Iberdrola, S.A.; *Int'l*, pg. 3571
GUADALUPE POWER PARTNERS, LP—See Energy Capital Partners Management, LP; *U.S. Private*, pg. 1394
GUANGXI GUIGUAN ELECTRIC POWER CO., LTD.—See China Datang Corporation; *Int'l*, pg. 1497
GUANGZHOU DEVELOPMENT GROUP INCORPORATED; *Int'l*, pg. 3164
GULF COAST ELECTRIC COOPERATIVE INC.; *U.S. Private*, pg. 1815
GULF ELECTRIC PUBLIC CO. LTD—See EGAT Public Company Limited; *Int'l*, pg. 2322
GULF ENERGY DEVELOPMENT PUBLIC COMPANY LIMITED; *Int'l*, pg. 3180
HAFSLUND PRODUKSJON AS—See Hafslund ASA; *Int'l*, pg. 3206
HALLYEO ENERGY RESOURCE—See Dongkuk S&C Co., Ltd.; *Int'l*, pg. 2169
HANCOCK-WOOD ELECTRIC COOP INC.; *U.S. Private*, pg. 1852
HANERGY AMERICA SOLAR SOLUTIONS—See Hanergy Holding Group Limited; *Int'l*, pg. 3244
HANERGY SOLAR POWER (EUROPE) B. V.—See Hanergy Holding Group Limited; *Int'l*, pg. 3244
HANERGY SOLAR POWER (ITALY) S.R.L.—See Hanergy Holding Group Limited; *Int'l*, pg. 3244
HANGZHOU HUADIAN BANSHAN POWER GENERATION COMPANY LIMITED—See Huadian Power International Corporation Limited; *Int'l*, pg. 3511
HARDSCRABBLE WIND POWER, LLC—See Iberdrola, S.A.; *Int'l*, pg. 3570
HAVEN POWER LIMITED—See Drax Group plc; *Int'l*, pg. 2200
HAWAII ELECTRIC LIGHT COMPANY, INC.—See Hawaiian Electric Industries, Inc.; *U.S. Public*, pg. 989
HAY CANYON WIND, LLC—See Iberdrola, S.A.; *Int'l*, pg. 3570
HAYLEYS INDUSTRIAL SOLUTIONS LIMITED—See Hayleys PLC; *Int'l*, pg. 3292
HAYS ENERGY LIMITED PARTNERSHIP—See ENGIE SA; *Int'l*, pg. 2433
HAYWOOD ELECTRIC MEMBERSHIP CORPORATION; *U.S. Private*, pg. 1886
HAZELWOOD POWER PARTNERSHIP—See ENGIE SA; *Int'l*, pg. 2432
HEARTLAND RURAL ELECTRIC COOPERATIVE, INC.; *U.S. Private*, pg. 1900
HEBEI HUADIAN SHIJIAZHUANG THERMAL POWER COMPANY LIMITED—See Huadian Power International Corporation Limited; *Int'l*, pg. 3511
HELBIO S.A.—See Amasten Fastighets AB; *Int'l*, pg. 412
HELECTOR SA—See ELLAKTOR S.A.; *Int'l*, pg. 2365
HEMAS POWER LIMITED—See Hemas Holdings PLC; *Int'l*, pg. 3340
HERA COMM S.P.A.—See Hera S.p.A.; *Int'l*, pg. 3356
HEV HOHENLOHER ENERGIE VERSORGUNG GMBH—See EnBW Energie Baden-Wurttemberg AG; *Int'l*, pg. 2399
HIDROCANTABRICO COGENERACION, S.L.—See EDP - Energias de Portugal, S.A.; *Int'l*, pg. 2314
HIDROELECTRICA IBERICA, S.L.—See Iberdrola, S.A.; *Int'l*, pg. 3572
HIDROELECTRICIDAD DEL PACIFICO SRL DE CV—See Enel S.p.A.; *Int'l*, pg. 2414
HINDUJA NATIONAL POWER CORPORATION LTD.—See Hinduja Group Ltd.; *Int'l*, pg. 3399
HOBART GROUND POWER—See Illinois Tool Works Inc.; *U.S. Public*, pg. 1103
HOKKAIDO POWER ENGINEERING CO., INC.—See Hokkaido Electric Power Co., Inc.; *Int'l*, pg. 3443
HOLMEN ENERGI AB—See Holmen AB; *Int'l*, pg. 3452
HOOSIER ENERGY RURAL ELECTRIC COOPERATIVE INC.; *U.S. Private*, pg. 1978
HOPEWELL COGENERATION LP—See ENGIE SA; *Int'l*, pg. 2433
HORIZONTES ENERGIA S.A.—See Companhia Energetica de Minas Gerais - CEMIG; *Int'l*, pg. 1747
HOT SPRING POWER COMPANY, LLC—See ENGIE SA; *Int'l*, pg. 2433
HQ ENERGY SERVICES (U.S.) INC.—See Hydro-Quebec; *Int'l*, pg. 3547
HUADIAN ENERGY COMPANY LIMITED—See China Huadian Corporation Ltd.; *Int'l*, pg. 1508
HUADIAN FUXIN ENERGY CORPORATION LIMITED—See China Huadian Corporation Ltd.; *Int'l*, pg. 1508
HUADIAN LIAONING ENERGY DEVELOPMENT CO., LTD.; *Int'l*, pg. 3511
HUANENG LANCANG RIVER HYDROPOWER CO., LTD.—See China Huaneng Group Co., Ltd.; *Int'l*, pg. 1509
HUANENG RENEWABLES CORPORATION LIMITED—See China Huaneng Group Co., Ltd.; *Int'l*, pg. 1509
HULISANI LTD.; *Int'l*, pg. 3528
HUNAN CHENDIAN INTERNATIONAL DEVELOPMENT CO., LTD.; *Int'l*, pg. 3531
HUNTLEY POWER LLC—See NRG Energy, Inc.; *U.S. Public*, pg. 1550

HYDRO DEVELOPMENT GROUP INC.—See Enel S.p.A.; *Int'l*, pg. 2411
HYDROGEN FUTURE CORPORATION; *U.S. Private*, pg. 2017
HYDROPOWER EVOLUTIONS GMBH—See Fortum Oyj; *Int'l*, pg. 2742
IBERDROLA CANADA ENERGY SERVICES, LTD.—See Iberdrola, S.A.; *Int'l*, pg. 3573
IBERDROLA COGENERACION, S.L.U.—See Iberdrola, S.A.; *Int'l*, pg. 3572
IBERDROLA CONSULTORIA E SERVICOS DO BRASIL, LTD.—See Iberdrola, S.A.; *Int'l*, pg. 3572
IBERDROLA ENERGIA ALTAMIRA DE SERVICIOS, S.A. DE C.V.—See Iberdrola, S.A.; *Int'l*, pg. 3571
IBERDROLA ENERGIA ALTAMIRA, S.A. DE C.V.—See Iberdrola, S.A.; *Int'l*, pg. 3571
IBERDROLA ENERGIA DEL GOLFO, S.A. DE C.V.—See Iberdrola, S.A.; *Int'l*, pg. 3572
IBERDROLA ENERGIA LA LAGUNA, S.A. DE C.V.—See Iberdrola, S.A.; *Int'l*, pg. 3571
IBERDROLA ENERGIA MONTERREY, S.A. DE C.V.—See Iberdrola, S.A.; *Int'l*, pg. 3571
IBERDROLA ENERGIA SOLAR PUERTOLLANO, S.A.—See Iberdrola, S.A.; *Int'l*, pg. 3572
IBERDROLA ENERGIAS RENOVAVEIS DO BRASIL, S.A.—See Iberdrola, S.A.; *Int'l*, pg. 3572
IBERDROLA ENERGIAS RENOVAVEIS S.A.—See Iberdrola, S.A.; *Int'l*, pg. 3572
IBERDROLA ENERGY SERVICE, LLC—See Iberdrola, S.A.; *Int'l*, pg. 3570
IBERDROLA INGENIERIA DE EXPLOTACION, S.A.U.—See Iberdrola, S.A.; *Int'l*, pg. 3572
IBERDROLA INGENIERIA Y CONSTRUCCION MEXICO, S.A. DE C.V.—See Iberdrola, S.A.; *Int'l*, pg. 3572
IBERDROLA INTERNATIONAL, B.V.—See Iberdrola, S.A.; *Int'l*, pg. 3572
IBERDROLA MAGYARORSZAG MERNOKI ES EPITO KORLATOLF—See Iberdrola, S.A.; *Int'l*, pg. 3572
IBERDROLA MEXICO, S.A. DE C.V.—See Iberdrola, S.A.; *Int'l*, pg. 3571
IBERDROLA RENOVABLES ANDALUCIA, S.A.U.—See Iberdrola, S.A.; *Int'l*, pg. 3572
IBERDROLA RENOVABLES ARAGON, S.A.U.—See Iberdrola, S.A.; *Int'l*, pg. 3572
IBERDROLA RENOVABLES CASTILLA LA MANCHA, S.A.U.—See Iberdrola, S.A.; *Int'l*, pg. 3572
IBERDROLA RENOVABLES CASTILLA Y LEON, S.A.—See Iberdrola, S.A.; *Int'l*, pg. 3572
IBERDROLA RENOVABLES DE VALENCIA, S.A.U.—See Iberdrola, S.A.; *Int'l*, pg. 3572
IBERDROLA RENOVABLES LA RIOJA, S.A.—See Iberdrola, S.A.; *Int'l*, pg. 3572
IBERDROLA RENOVABLES MAGYARORSZAG MEGUJULO—See Iberdrola, S.A.; *Int'l*, pg. 3572
IBERDROLA SERVICIOS ENERGETICOS, S.A.U.—See Iberdrola, S.A.; *Int'l*, pg. 3573
IBERDROLA USA, INC.—See Iberdrola, S.A.; *Int'l*, pg. 3570
IBERDROLA USA, INC.—See Iberdrola, S.A.; *Int'l*, pg. 3570
IBERDROLA USA, INC.—See Iberdrola, S.A.; *Int'l*, pg. 3570
IBERDROLA USA, INC.—See Iberdrola, S.A.; *Int'l*, pg. 3570
IBERDROLA USA, INC.—See Iberdrola, S.A.; *Int'l*, pg. 3570
ICAD, INC.—See iCad, Inc.; *U.S. Public*, pg. 1083
ICSA (INGENIERIA Y COMPUTACION, S.A.)—See Hexagon AB; *Int'l*, pg. 3369
IDROVALSESIA S.R.L.—See Alpiq Holding AG; *Int'l*, pg. 373
INADALE WF HOLDCO, LLC—See E.ON SE; *Int'l*, pg. 2258
INADALE WIND FARM, LLC—See E.ON SE; *Int'l*, pg. 2258
INDECK-CORINTH LIMITED PARTNERSHIP—See Indeck Power Equipment Company; *U.S. Private*, pg. 2055
INDECK ENERGY SERVICES OF ILION INC.—See Indeck Power Equipment Company; *U.S. Private*, pg. 2055
INDECK ENERGY SERVICES OF OLEAN INC.—See Indeck Power Equipment Company; *U.S. Private*, pg. 2055
INDECK-YERKES ENERGY SERVICES INC.—See Indeck Power Equipment Company; *U.S. Private*, pg. 2055
INDO ASIAN FUSEGEAR LTD - HARIDWAR LIGHTING PLANT—See EON Electric Ltd.; *Int'l*, pg. 2457
INDO ASIAN FUSEGEAR LTD - INDO SIMON PLANT HARIDWAR—See EON Electric Ltd.; *Int'l*, pg. 2458
INDO ASIAN FUSEGEAR LTD - JALANDHAR SWITCHGEAR PLANT—See EON Electric Ltd.; *Int'l*, pg. 2458
INDO ASIAN FUSEGEAR LTD - NOIDA LIGHTING PLANT—See EON Electric Ltd.; *Int'l*, pg. 2458
INDUBODEN GMBH & CO. INDUSTRIEWERTE OHG—See E.ON SE; *Int'l*, pg. 2258
INFINIS LIMITED—See 3i Group plc; *Int'l*, pg. 8
INFORUM NORGE AS—See Hafslund ASA; *Int'l*, pg. 3206
INFRAESTRUCTURAS ENERGETICAS CASTELLANAS, S.L.—See ACS, Actividades de Construccion y Servicios, S.A.; *Int'l*, pg. 114
INTERCOUNTY ELECTRIC COOPERATIVE; *U.S. Private*, pg. 2110
INTERLIGACAO ELETRICA GARANHUNS S.A.—See Cia de Transmissao de Energia Eletrica Paulista; *Int'l*, pg. 1601
INTERMOUNTAIN RURAL ELECTRIC ASSOCIATION; *U.S. Private*, pg. 2113

INTER-POWER /AHLCON PARTNERS LP; *U.S. Private*, pg. 2107
IOWA LAKES ELECTRIC COOPERATIVE; *U.S. Private*, pg. 2134
IPM ENERGY TRADING LIMITED—See ENGIE SA; *Int'l*, pg. 2432
IPR - GDF SUEZ AUSTRALIA PTY LTD - KWINANA COGENERATION PLANT—See ENGIE SA; *Int'l*, pg. 2432
IPR - GDF SUEZ AUSTRALIA PTY LTD—See ENGIE SA; *Int'l*, pg. 2432
IPR - GDF SUEZ LATIN AMERICA—See ENGIE SA; *Int'l*, pg. 2432
IPR - GDF SUEZ MIDDLE EAST, TURKEY & AFRICA—See ENGIE SA; *Int'l*, pg. 2433
IPR - GDF SUEZ NORTH AFRICA—See ENGIE SA; *Int'l*, pg. 2433
IPR - GDF SUEZ NORTH AMERICA—See ENGIE SA; *Int'l*, pg. 2433
IRU ELEKTRIJAAM OU—See Eesti Energia AS; *Int'l*, pg. 2317
ISA BOLIVIA S.A.—See Ecopetrol S.A.; *Int'l*, pg. 2299
ITW GSE INC.—See Illinois Tool Works Inc.; *U.S. Public*, pg. 1103
IZMIR ELEKTRIK URETIM LIMITED SIRKETI—See Enka Insaat ve Sanayi A.S.; *Int'l*, pg. 2440
JACKSON ELECTRIC CO-OPERATIVE CORPORATION; *U.S. Private*, pg. 2176
JACKSON ENERGY AUTHORITY; *U.S. Private*, pg. 2176
JAZ TECHNOLOGY DEVELOPMENT (SHENZHEN) CO., LTD—See Asia Power Corporation Limited; *Int'l*, pg. 615
JBSOLAR MALAGON, S.L.—See The AES Corporation; *U.S. Public*, pg. 2032
KARLSHAMN KRAFT AB—See E.ON SE; *Int'l*, pg. 2255
KASHIMA SOUTH JOINT POWER CORP.—See AGC Inc.; *Int'l*, pg. 204
KGEN POWER CORPORATION; *U.S. Private*, pg. 2301
KGW-KRAFTWERK GRENZACH-WYHLEN GMBH—See E.ON SE; *Int'l*, pg. 2253
KHANOM ELECTRICITY GENERATING CO. LTD.—See EGAT Public Company Limited; *Int'l*, pg. 2322
KHANOM ELECTRICITY GENERATING CO., LTD.—See Electricity Generating Public Co., Ltd.; *Int'l*, pg. 2352
KINDER MORGAN SERVICES LLC—See Kinder Morgan, Inc.; *U.S. Public*, pg. 1233
KINGSPORT POWER COMPANY—See American Electric Power Company, Inc.; *U.S. Public*, pg. 100
KLAMATH ENERGY, LLC—See Iberdrola, S.A.; *Int'l*, pg. 3570
KLONGLUANG UTILITIES CO., LTD.—See Electricity Generating Public Co., Ltd.; *Int'l*, pg. 2352
KORBA WEST POWER COMPANY LIMITED—See Avantha Group; *Int'l*, pg. 735
KRAFTWERK SCHWEDT GMBH & CO. KG—See Beijing Enterprises Holdings Limited; *Int'l*, pg. 950
LAKE PARK MUNICIPAL UTILITIES; *U.S. Private*, pg. 2375
LANDE GMBH—See E.ON SE; *Int'l*, pg. 2258
LEE COUNTY ELECTRIC COOPERATIVE, INC.; *U.S. Private*, pg. 2411
LEVANTO GSEF (LUX) S.A.R.L.—See ENGIE SA; *Int'l*, pg. 2433
LIAONING GAOKE ENERGY GROUP COMPANY LIMITED—See A-Power Energy Generation Systems, Ltd.; *Int'l*, pg. 20
LIMON GMBH—See EWE Aktiengesellschaft; *Int'l*, pg. 2575
LINCOLN ELECTRIC SYSTEM; *U.S. Private*, pg. 2457
LIQVIS GMBH—See Fortum Oyj; *Int'l*, pg. 2742
LL PLANT ENGINEERING AG—See GEA Group Aktiengesellschaft; *Int'l*, pg. 2903
THE LOS ANGELES DEPARTMENT OF WATER & POWER; *U.S. Private*, pg. 4072
LOS MEDANOS ENERGY CENTER LLC—See Energy Capital Partners Management, LP; *U.S. Private*, pg. 1394
LOUP RIVER PUBLIC POWER DISTRICT; *U.S. Private*, pg. 2500
LUMO ENERGIA OYJ—See Genie Energy Ltd.; *U.S. Public*, pg. 931
MACTAN ENERZONE CORPORATION—See Aboitiz Equity Ventures, Inc.; *Int'l*, pg. 67
MAESSA TELECOMUNICACIONES, INGENIERIA, INSTALACIONES Y SERVICIOS, S.A.—See ACS, Actividades de Construccion y Servicios, S.A.; *Int'l*, pg. 115
MAESSA TELECOMUNICACIONES, S.A.—See ACS, Actividades de Construccion y Servicios, S.A.; *Int'l*, pg. 115
MAESTRALE GREEN ENERGY SRL—See Electricite de France S.A.; *Int'l*, pg. 2350
MAGIC VALLEY ELECTRIC COOPERATIVE; *U.S. Private*, pg. 2546
MAGNETEK MATERIAL HANDLING—See Columbus McKinnon Corporation; *U.S. Public*, pg. 536
MAINE ELECTRIC POWER CO., INC.—See Iberdrola, S.A.; *Int'l*, pg. 3570
MAINKRAFTWERK SCHWEINFURT GESELLSCHAFT MIT BESCHRANKTER HAFTUNG—See E.ON SE; *Int'l*, pg. 2258
MALANPUR CAPTIVE POWER LIMITED—See Avantha Group; *Int'l*, pg. 735
MAMMOTH PACIFIC LP—See Ormat Technologies, Inc.; *U.S. Public*, pg. 1618

N.A.I.C.S. INDEX

221118 — OTHER ELECTRIC POWE...

MANCHASOL 1 CENTRAL TERMOSOLAR UNO, S.L.—See ACS, Actividades de Construccion y Servicios, S.A.; *Int'l*, pg. 115

MANITOWOC PUBLIC UTILITIES; *U.S. Private*, pg. 2564

MANTYNUMMEN LAMPO OY—See Fortum Oyj; *Int'l*, pg. 2742

MAQUOKETA VALLEY ELECTRIC COOP; *U.S. Private*, pg. 2569

MARBLE RIVER, L.L.C.—See EDP - Energias de Portugal, S.A.; *Int'l*, pg. 2314

MARTE ENGENHARIA LTDA—See AtkinsRealis Group Inc.; *Int'l*, pg. 671

MASON COUNTY PUBLIC UTILITY DISTRICT 3; *U.S. Private*, pg. 2602

MASSACHUSETTS MUNICIPAL WHOLESALE ELECTRIC CO.; *U.S. Private*, pg. 2604

MASS MEGAWATTS WIND POWER, INC; *U.S. Public*, pg. 1392

MEADE COUNTY RURAL ELECTRIC COOP; *U.S. Private*, pg. 2646

MEADOW LAKE WIND FARM IV, L.L.C.—See EDP - Energias de Portugal, S.A.; *Int'l*, pg. 2314

MEADOW LAKE WIND FARM, L.L.C.—See EDP - Energias de Portugal, S.A.; *Int'l*, pg. 2314

MECKLENBURG COMMUNICATIONS SERVICES, INC.—See Mecklenburg Electric Cooperative; *U.S. Private*, pg. 2649

MECKLENBURG ELECTRIC COOPERATIVE; *U.S. Private*, pg. 2649

MEDICAL AREA TOTAL ENERGY PLANT, LLC—See Morgan Stanley; *U.S. Public*, pg. 1474

MEDINA ELECTRIC CO-OPERATIVE; *U.S. Private*, pg. 2657

MEGATRON HOLDINGS (PTY) LTD.—See Ellies Holdings Limited; *Int'l*, pg. 2366

MELINK CORPORATION; *U.S. Private*, pg. 2662

MEMPHIS LIGHT, GAS & WATER; *U.S. Private*, pg. 2664

MENASHA ELECTRIC & WATER UTILITIES; *U.S. Private*, pg. 2666

MERCED IRRIGATION DISTRICT; *U.S. Private*, pg. 2668

MGE ENERGY, INC.; *U.S. Public*, pg. 1434

MGE POWER LLC—See MGE Energy, Inc.; *U.S. Public*, pg. 1434

MHKW ROTHENSEE GMBH—See Beijing Enterprises Holdings Limited; *Int'l*, pg. 950

MIDLANDS POWER (UK) LIMITED—See E.ON SE; *Int'l*, pg. 2256

MIDLOTHIAN ENERGY LIMITED PARTNERSHIP—See ENGIE SA; *Int'l*, pg. 2433

MIDWEST ENERGY INC.; *U.S. Private*, pg. 2721

MIDWEST GENERATION EME, LLC—See NRG Energy, Inc.; *U.S. Public*, pg. 1550

MIDWEST GENERATION, LLC—See NRG Energy, Inc.; *U.S. Public*, pg. 1550

MILLBROOK POWER LIMITED—See Drax Group plc; *Int'l*, pg. 2200

MINAS GARGALLO SL—See Enel S.p.A.; *Int'l*, pg. 2414

MINICENTRALES DEL TAJO, S.A.—See Iberdrola, S.A.; *Int'l*, pg. 3573

MITTLERE DONAU KRAFTWERKE AKTIENGESELLSCHAFT—See Fortum Oyj; *Int'l*, pg. 2742

MODESTO IRRIGATION DISTRICT INC.; *U.S. Private*, pg. 2763

MORRISTOWN UTILITY COMMISSION; *U.S. Private*, pg. 2790

MORROW-MEADOWS CORPORATION - ALTERNATIVE ENERGY DIVISION—See Morrow-Meadows Corporation; *U.S. Private*, pg. 2790

MORROW-MEADOWS CORPORATION - CHERRY CITY ELECTRIC DIVISION—See Morrow-Meadows Corporation; *U.S. Private*, pg. 2790

MOUNT CARMEL PUBLIC UTILITY CO.; *U.S. Public*, pg. 1479

MSR PUBLIC POWER AGENCY; *U.S. Private*, pg. 2808

MT. TOM GENERATING COMPANY LLC—See ENGIE SA; *Int'l*, pg. 2433

MUNNSVILLE INVESTCO, LLC—See E.ON SE; *Int'l*, pg. 2258

MUSCATINE POWER & WATER; *U.S. Private*, pg. 2817

NALANDA POWER COMPANY LIMITED—See CESC Limited; *Int'l*, pg. 1424

NANT DE DRANCE SA—See Alpiq Holding AG; *Int'l*, pg. 373

NAPS SYSTEMS OY—See Fortum Oyj; *Int'l*, pg. 2742

NASSAU ENERGY CORP.—See ENGIE SA; *Int'l*, pg. 2429

NATCHEZ TRACE ELECTRIC POWER ASSOCIATION; *U.S. Private*, pg. 2838

NATURAL ENERGY DEVELOPMENT CO., LTD.—See Electricity Generating Public Co., Ltd.; *Int'l*, pg. 2352

NATURGAS ENERGIA SERVICIOS COMUNES, S.A.—See Enagas, S.A.; *Int'l*, pg. 2396

NATURPUR ENERGIE AG—See HEAG Sudhessische Energie AG; *Int'l*, pg. 3302

NAVAJO TRIBAL UTILITY AUTHORITY; *U.S. Private*, pg. 2872

NEBRASKA PUBLIC POWER DISTRICT; *U.S. Private*, pg. 2879

NEOENERGIA S.A.—See Iberdrola, S.A.; *Int'l*, pg. 3573

NET ZERO TEESSIDE POWER LIMITED—See BP plc; *Int'l*, pg. 1131

NETZGESELLSCHAFT HERRENWALD VERWALTUNG GMBH—See E.ON SE; *Int'l*, pg. 2258

NEVADA SOLAR SOLUTIONS, LLC—See MDU Resources Group, Inc.; *U.S. Public*, pg. 1411

NEW HARVEST WIND PROJECT, LLC—See Iberdrola, S.A.; *Int'l*, pg. 3571

NEWIND GROUP INC.—See Enel S.p.A.; *Int'l*, pg. 2413

NEWPORT UTILITIES BOARD INC.; *U.S. Private*, pg. 2916

NEW YORK STATE ELECTRIC & GAS CORP.—See Iberdrola, S.A.; *Int'l*, pg. 3571

NIHON KENGYO K.K.—See Alstom S.A.; *Int'l*, pg. 380

NISOURCE ENERGY TECHNOLOGIES, INC.—See NiSource Inc.; *U.S. Public*, pg. 1530

NOBLE ENVIRONMENTAL POWER LLC—See CCMP Capital Advisors, LP; *U.S. Private*, pg. 800

NODAL CLEAR, LLC—See Deutsche Borse AG; *Int'l*, pg. 2064

NORRIS ELECTRIC COOPERATIVE; *U.S. Private*, pg. 2939

NORTH ARKANSAS ELECTRIC COOPERATIVE, INC.; *U.S. Private*, pg. 2942

NORTHEAST ENERGY ASSOCIATES, A LIMITED PARTNERSHIP—See NextEra Energy, Inc.; *U.S. Public*, pg. 1526

NORTHEAST GENERATION SERVICES COMPANY—See Eversource Energy; *U.S. Public*, pg. 801

NORTHERN LIGHTS INC.; *U.S. Private*, pg. 2953

NORTHERN RELIABILITY INC.—See KORE Power, Inc.; *U.S. Private*, pg. 2343

NORTHERN STATES POWER COMPANY—See Xcel Energy Inc.; *U.S. Public*, pg. 2385

NORTHWESTERN NETWORKS, INC.—See NorthWestern Corporation; *U.S. Public*, pg. 1543

NORTHWEST HYDRO INC.—See Enel S.p.A.; *Int'l*, pg. 2414

NORTH WEST RURAL ELECTRIC COOPERATIVE; *U.S. Private*, pg. 2948

NPG ENERGY NV—See Enovos International S.A.; *Int'l*, pg. 2444

NRG DEVON OPERATIONS INC.—See NRG Energy, Inc.; *U.S. Public*, pg. 1550

NRG ENERGY CENTER DOVER LLC—See BlackRock, Inc.; *U.S. Public*, pg. 345

NRG FLORIDA, LP—See NRG Energy, Inc.; *U.S. Public*, pg. 1550

NRG GLADSTONE OPERATING SERVICES PTY LTD—See NRG Energy, Inc.; *U.S. Public*, pg. 1550

NRG HOMER CITY SERVICES LLC—See NRG Energy, Inc.; *U.S. Public*, pg. 1550

NRG HUNTLEY OPERATIONS INC.—See NRG Energy, Inc.; *U.S. Public*, pg. 1550

NRG MIDDLETOWN OPERATIONS INC.—See NRG Energy, Inc.; *U.S. Public*, pg. 1550

NRG MONTVILLE OPERATIONS INC.—See NRG Energy, Inc.; *U.S. Public*, pg. 1550

NRG RENEW LLC—See NRG Energy, Inc.; *U.S. Public*, pg. 1550

NRG THERMAL LLC—See BlackRock, Inc.; *U.S. Public*, pg. 345

NU ENTERPRISES, INC.—See Eversource Energy; *U.S. Public*, pg. 801

NUPOWER, LLC; *U.S. Private*, pg. 2973

OAO SHATURSKAYA UPRAVLYAYUSHCHAYA KOMPANIYA—See E.ON SE; *Int'l*, pg. 2258

OBERE DONAU KRAFTWERKE AKTIENGESELLSCHAFT—See E.ON SE; *Int'l*, pg. 2258

OCEAN STATE POWER—See LS Power Development, LLC; *U.S. Private*, pg. 2508

OFFSHORE WINDPARK RIFFGAT GMBH & CO. KG—See EWE Aktiengesellschaft; *Int'l*, pg. 2576

OHB CHILE SPA—See Hiscox Ltd.; *Int'l*, pg. 3407

OHIO EDISON COMPANY—See FirstEnergy Corp.; *U.S. Public*, pg. 849

OHIO VALLEY ELECTRIC CORPORATION; *U.S. Private*, pg. 3005

OKG AB—See E.ON SE; *Int'l*, pg. 2258

O&M SERVICOS - OPERACAO E MANUTENCAO INDUSTRIAL, S.A.—See EDP - Energias de Portugal, S.A.; *Int'l*, pg. 2314

OMV SAMSUN ELEKTRIK URETIM SANAYI VE TICARET A.S.—See Bilgin Enerji Yatirim Holding A.S.; *Int'l*, pg. 1029

ONCOR ELECTRIC DELIVERY COMPANY LLC—See Sempra; *U.S. Public*, pg. 1863

ONFORCE SOLAR, INC.—See Hanwha Group; *Int'l*, pg. 3264

ORAZUL ENERGY CERROS COLORADOS, S.A.—See I Squared Capital Advisors (US) LLC; *U.S. Private*, pg. 2026

ORAZUL ENERGY GUATEMALA Y COMPANIA SOCIEDAD EN COMANDITA POR ACCIONES—See I Squared Capital Advisors (US) LLC; *U.S. Private*, pg. 2026

ORLANDO UTILITIES COMMISSION; *U.S. Private*, pg. 3044

OSWEGO HARBOR POWER LLC—See NRG Energy, Inc.; *U.S. Public*, pg. 1550

OTERO COUNTY ELECTRIC COOP; *U.S. Private*, pg. 3049

OTTAUQUECHEE HYDRO COMPANY INC.—See Enel S.p.A.; *Int'l*, pg. 2414

PACIFICLIGHT POWER PTE. LTD.—See First Pacific Company Limited; *Int'l*, pg. 2686

PAMPA ENERGIA S.A.—See Grupo EMES S.A.; *Int'l*, pg. 3126

PARQUES EOLICOS DEL CANTABRICO S.A.—See EDP - Energias de Portugal, S.A.; *Int'l*, pg. 2315

PAULDING WIND FARM II, L.L.C.—See EDP - Energias de Portugal, S.A.; *Int'l*, pg. 2314

PAVANA POWER CORPORATION—See First National Energy Corporation; *Int'l*, pg. 2686

PEBBLE SPRINGS WIND LLC—See Iberdrola, S.A.; *Int'l*, pg. 3571

PEDERNALES ELECTRIC COOPERATIVE INC.; *U.S. Private*, pg. 3127

PEGOP - ENERGIA ELECTRICA, S.A.—See ENGIE SA; *Int'l*, pg. 2434

PEISSENBERGER KRAFTWERKSGESELLSCHAFT MIT BESCHRANKTER HAFTUNG—See E.ON SE; *Int'l*, pg. 2258

PELEGOL LTD.—See Golan Plastic Products Ltd.; *Int'l*, pg. 3023

PETROBRAS ENERGIA INTERNACIONAL S.A.—See Grupo EMES S.A.; *Int'l*, pg. 3126

PG&E GENERATING COMPANY—See PG&E Corporation; *U.S. Public*, pg. 1684

PIKES PEAK SOLAR GARDEN I LLC—See BlackRock, Inc.; *U.S. Public*, pg. 345

PINE GATE RENEWABLES LLC; *U.S. Private*, pg. 3182

PLACER COUNTY WATER AGENCY; *U.S. Private*, pg. 3194

PLANTA EOLICA EUROPEA SA—See Enel S.p.A.; *Int'l*, pg. 2414

PLANTERS ELECTRIC MEMBERSHIP CORP; *U.S. Private*, pg. 3197

PNE BIOGAS OHRETAL GMBH—See Enovos International S.A.; *Int'l*, pg. 2444

PORTSIDE ENERGY CORP.—See EPCOR Utilities, Inc.; *Int'l*, pg. 2459

POWERFILM, INC.; *U.S. Private*, pg. 3239

POWERGEN UK LIMITED—See E.ON SE; *Int'l*, pg. 2258

POWERSECURE, INC.—See The Southern Company; *U.S. Public*, pg. 2131

POWER TECHNOLOGY LIMITED—See E.ON SE; *Int'l*, pg. 2256

POYRY EROTERV ZRT.—See AFRY AB; *Int'l*, pg. 195

PPC RENEWABLES ROKAS, S.A.—See Iberdrola, S.A.; *Int'l*, pg. 3573

PPL GENERATION, LLC—See PPL Corporation; *U.S. Public*, pg. 1711

PPL MONTANA, LLC—See PPL Corporation; *U.S. Public*, pg. 1712

PPL MONTOUR, LLC—See PPL Corporation; *U.S. Public*, pg. 1712

PREMIER POWER RENEWABLE ENERGY, INC.; *U.S. Public*, pg. 1715

PROPANE PLUS INC.—See Southwestern Electric Co-Operative Inc.; *U.S. Private*, pg. 3741

PROVIDER POWER LLC—See Via Renewables, Inc.; *U.S. Public*, pg. 2290

PROYECTOS EOLICOS VALENCIANOS SA—See Enel S.p.A.; *Int'l*, pg. 2414

PRZEDSIEBIORSTWO ENERGETYKI CIEPLNEJ W BARLINKU SP. Z O.O.—See E.ON SE; *Int'l*, pg. 2259

PT PAITON ENERGY—See ENGIE SA; *Int'l*, pg. 2434

PUBLIC SERVICE COMPANY OF NEW HAMPSHIRE—See Eversource Energy; *U.S. Public*, pg. 802

PUBLIC UTILITY DISTRICT 1 LEWIS COUNTY; *U.S. Private*, pg. 3300

PUBLIC UTILITY DISTRICT NO. 1 CHELAN COUNTY; *U.S. Private*, pg. 3300

PUBLIC UTILITY DISTRICT NO. 1 OF PEND OREILLE COUNTY; *U.S. Private*, pg. 3300

PUBLIC WORKS COMMISSION; *U.S. Private*, pg. 3300

PURE ENERGIES GROUP INC.—See NRG Energy, Inc.; *U.S. Public*, pg. 1550

PURTHANOL RESOURCES LIMITED; *U.S. Public*, pg. 1738

PYRON WIND FARM, LLC—See E.ON SE; *Int'l*, pg. 2259

Q-ENERGIE B.V.—See E.ON SE; *Int'l*, pg. 2259

QINGDAO DONGJIANG ENVIRONMENTAL RECYCLED POWER LIMITED—See Dongjiang Environmental Company Limited; *Int'l*, pg. 2168

RAYONG ELECTRICITY GENERATING CO., LTD.—See Electricity Generating Public Co., Ltd.; *Int'l*, pg. 2352

REA ENERGY CO-OPERATIVE CORP.; *U.S. Private*, pg. 3365

RECURRENT ENERGY, LLC—See Canadian Solar Inc.; *Int'l*, pg. 1286

REDEN SOLAR SAS—See British Columbia Investment Management Corp.; *Int'l*, pg. 1169

REDEN SRL—See CogenInfra SpA; *Int'l*, pg. 1694

RED TOP WIND POWER, LLC—See ACS, Actividades de Construccion y Servicios, S.A.; *Int'l*, pg. 115

RELIANT ENERGY RETAIL SERVICES, LLC—See NRG Energy, Inc.; *U.S. Public*, pg. 1551

221118 — OTHER ELECTRIC POWE...

RENEGY, LLC—See Renegy Holdings, Inc.; *U.S. Private*, pg. 3397
RENERCO RENEWABLE ENERGY CONCEPTS AG—See BayWa AG; *Int'l*, pg. 918
RENOVALIA ENERGY, S.A.—See F2i - Fondi Italiani per le infrastrutture SGR S.p.A.; *Int'l*, pg. 2598
RIO PCH I S.A.—See ContourGlobal Limited; *Int'l*, pg. 1785
RISING SUN SOLAR & ELECTRIC; *U.S. Private*, pg. 3440
RIZZICONI ENERGIA SPA—See Axpo Holding AG; *Int'l*, pg. 771
RMD-CONSULT GMBH WASSERBAU UND ENERGIE—See E.ON SE; *Int'l*, pg. 2259
ROCHESTER GAS & ELECTRIC CORPORATION—See Iberdrola, S.A.; *Int'l*, pg. 3571
ROCKY MOUNTAIN POWER—See Berkshire Hathaway Inc.; *U.S. Public*, pg. 301
ROKAS AEOLIKI EVIA, S.A.—See Iberdrola, S.A.; *Int'l*, pg. 3573
ROKAS AEOLIKI KOMITO, S.A.—See Iberdrola, S.A.; *Int'l*, pg. 3573
ROKAS AEOLIKI KRITI, S.A.—See Iberdrola, S.A.; *Int'l*, pg. 3573
ROKAS AEOLIKI, S.A.—See Iberdrola, S.A.; *Int'l*, pg. 3573
ROKAS AEOLIKI THRAKI III, S.A.—See Iberdrola, S.A.; *Int'l*, pg. 3573
ROKAS AEOLIKI THRAKI II, S.A.—See Iberdrola, S.A.; *Int'l*, pg. 3573
ROKAS AEOLIKI THRAKI, S.A.—See Iberdrola, S.A.; *Int'l*, pg. 3573
ROKAS AEOLIKI ZARAKES, S.A.—See Iberdrola, S.A.; *Int'l*, pg. 3573
ROLLCAST ENERGY, INC.—See I Squared Capital Advisors (US) LLC; *U.S. Private*, pg. 2025
ROSCOE WIND FARM, LLC—See E.ON SE; *Int'l*, pg. 2259
ROSIGNANO ENERGIA SPA—See ENGIE SA; *Int'l*, pg. 2434
ROUMANIE SRL—See ENGIE SA; *Int'l*, pg. 2434
RRI ENERGY SERVICES, INC.—See NRG Energy, Inc.; *U.S. Public*, pg. 1550
SAGUARO POWER COMPANY, A LIMITED PARTNERSHIP—See NRG Energy, Inc.; *U.S. Public*, pg. 1551
SALINCO V.O.F.—See Akzo Nobel N.V.; *Int'l*, pg. 275
SALTEND COGENERATION COMPANY LIMITED—See ENGIE SA; *Int'l*, pg. 2433
SALTEND—See ENGIE SA; *Int'l*, pg. 2434
SALT RIVER PROJECT; *U.S. Private*, pg. 3534
SAM HOUSTON ELECTRIC CO-OPERATIVE INC.; *U.S. Private*, pg. 3535
SAN FERNANDO ELECTRIC LIGHT & POWER CO., INC.—See Aboitiz Equity Ventures, Inc.; *Int'l*, pg. 67
SAN JOAQUIN ENERGY, LLC—See NRG Energy, Inc.; *U.S. Public*, pg. 1551
SANTA MARIA ENERGIAS RENOVAVEIS S.A.—See Companhia Paranaense de Energia; *Int'l*, pg. 1748
SANTA ROSA ENERGY CENTER, LLC—See LS Power Development, LLC; *U.S. Private*, pg. 1502
SARLUX S.R.L.—See Angelo Moratti S.A.P.A.; *Int'l*, pg. 460
SASKPOWER INTERNATIONAL—See Crown Investments Corporation of Saskatchewan; *Int'l*, pg. 1857
SCHNEIDER POWER INC.—See Quantum Fuel Systems Technologies Worldwide, Inc.; *U.S. Public*, pg. 1754
SCHUYLKILL ENERGY RESOURCES INC.; *U.S. Private*, pg. 3571
SCITUATE SOLAR I, LLC—See The AES Corporation; *U.S. Public*, pg. 2032
SCOTTISHPOWER ENERGY MANAGEMENT, LTD.—See Iberdrola, S.A.; *Int'l*, pg. 3573
SCOTTISHPOWER NA 1, LTD.—See Iberdrola, S.A.; *Int'l*, pg. 3574
SCOTTISH POWER RENEWABLE ENERGY, LTD.—See Iberdrola, S.A.; *Int'l*, pg. 3573
SCOTTISH POWER RENEWABLE UK, LTD.—See Iberdrola, S.A.; *Int'l*, pg. 3573
SCOTTISH POWER UK GROUP, LTD.—See Iberdrola, S.A.; *Int'l*, pg. 3573
SEABOARD ENERGY, LLC—See Seaboard Corporation; *U.S. Public*, pg. 1851
SEALVE - SOCIEDADE ELECTRICA DE ALVAIAZERE SA—See Enel S.p.A.; *Int'l*, pg. 2414
SEC ENERGIA SP. Z O.O.—See E.ON SE; *Int'l*, pg. 2259
SEC LOBEZ SP. Z O.O.—See E.ON SE; *Int'l*, pg. 2259
SEE-SUL ENERGIA EOLICA, LDA—See E.ON SE; *Int'l*, pg. 2259
SEM-CALACA POWER CORPORATION—See DMCI Holdings, Inc.; *Int'l*, pg. 2143
SENOKO ENERGY PTE LTD.—See ENGIE SA; *Int'l*, pg. 2434
SETTLERS TRAIL WIND FARM, LLC—See E.ON SE; *Int'l*, pg. 2259
SHANGHAI G&W ELECTRIC LTD.—See G&W Electric Company; *U.S. Private*, pg. 1629
SHENANDOAH VALLEY ELECTRIC COOPERATIVE; *U.S. Private*, pg. 3632
SHIJIAZHUANG CHENGFENG COGEN CO., LTD.—See Banpu Public Company Limited; *Int'l*, pg. 852
SHOOTING STAR WIND PROJECT, LLC—See Constellation Energy Corporation; *U.S. Public*, pg. 572

SIA FORTUM JELGAVA—See Fortum Oyj; *Int'l*, pg. 2742
SIERRA PACIFIC POWER COMPANY—See Berkshire Hathaway Inc.; *U.S. Public*, pg. 301
SISTEMAS ENERGETICOS LA GOMERA, S.A.U—See Iberdrola, S.A.; *Int'l*, pg. 3574
SISTEMAS ENERGETICOS LOS LIRIOS, S.A.U.—See Iberdrola, S.A.; *Int'l*, pg. 3574
SISTEMAS ENERGETICOS MAS GARULLO, S.A.—See Iberdrola, S.A.; *Int'l*, pg. 3574
SMOKY HILLS WIND FARM LLC—See Enel S.p.A.; *Int'l*, pg. 2414
SMOKY HILLS WIND PROJECT II LLC—See Enel S.p.A.; *Int'l*, pg. 2414
SMW, LTD.—See Iberdrola, S.A.; *Int'l*, pg. 3573
SNC-LAVALIN POLSKA SP. Z O.O.—See AtkinsRealis Group Inc.; *Int'l*, pg. 673
SNOHOMISH COUNTY PUBLIC UTILITY DISTRICT; *U.S. Private*, pg. 3700
SNYDER WIND FARM LLC—See Enel S.p.A.; *Int'l*, pg. 2414
SOCIEDAD DE GENERACION EOLICA MANCHEGA, S.L.—See ACS, Actividades de Construccion y Servicios, S.A.; *Int'l*, pg. 116
SOCIEDAD GESTORA PARQUES EOLICOS ANDALUCIA, S.A.—See Iberdrola, S.A.; *Int'l*, pg. 3574
SOCIEDAD INVERSORA DOCK SUD SA—See Enel S.p.A.; *Int'l*, pg. 2412
SOLARKRAFTWERK MERZIG GMBH & CO. KG—See Electricite de France S.A.; *Int'l*, pg. 2350
SOLARMARKT GMBH—See BayWa AG; *Int'l*, pg. 919
SOLARPACK CORP TECNOLOGICA SA—See EQT AB; *Int'l*, pg. 2483
SOLARWINDOW TECHNOLOGIES, INC.; *U.S. Public*, pg. 1900
SOLIGENT HOLDINGS INC.; *U.S. Private*, pg. 3709
SOL SYSTEMS; *U.S. Private*, pg. 3706
SO.MET. ENERGIA S.R.L.—See F2i - Fondi Italiani per le infrastrutture SGR S.p.A.; *Int'l*, pg. 2597
SOUTH EASTERN ELECTRIC DEVELOPMENT CORPORATION—See Morgan Stanley; *U.S. Public*, pg. 1475
SOUTHERN CONE POWER ARGENTINA SA—See Enel S.p.A.; *Int'l*, pg. 2413
SOUTHERN ILLINOIS POWER COOP; *U.S. Private*, pg. 3732
SOUTHERN PUBLIC POWER DISTRICT; *U.S. Private*, pg. 3734
SOUTH FEATHER WATER & POWER AGENCY; *U.S. Private*, pg. 3722
SOUTH KENTUCKY RURAL ELECTRIC CO-OPERATIVE CORPORATION; *U.S. Private*, pg. 3723
SOUTH MISSISSIPPI ELECTRIC & POWER ASSOCIATION; *U.S. Private*, pg. 3723
SOUTHSIDE ELECTRIC COOPERATIVE INC.; *U.S. Private*, pg. 3737
SOUTHWESTERN ELECTRIC POWER COMPANY—See American Electric Power Company, Inc.; *U.S. Public*, pg. 100
SOUTHWEST PUBLIC POWER DISTRICT; *U.S. Private*, pg. 3740
SPRINGFIELD UTILITY BOARD INC.; *U.S. Private*, pg. 3764
SQUARE BUTTE ELECTRIC COOPERATIVE—See Minnkota Power Cooperative, Inc.; *U.S. Private*, pg. 2744
S.R. BRAY LLC; *U.S. Private*, pg. 3518
SSE CONTRACTING LTD.—See Aurelius Equity Opportunities SE & Co. KGaA; *Int'l*, pg. 709
STANDARD SOLAR, INC.—See Brookfield Corporation; *Int'l*, pg. 1186
STAND ENERGY CORPORATION; *U.S. Private*, pg. 3777
STATCO SIX LIMITED—See E.ON SE; *Int'l*, pg. 2256
STEINMULLER AFRICA (PTY) LTD.—See Bilfinger SE; *Int'l*, pg. 1027
STERLING ENERGY LLC—See Commerzbank AG; *Int'l*, pg. 1719
STONY CREEK WF HOLDCO, LLC—See E.ON SE; *Int'l*, pg. 2259
STONY CREEK WIND FARM, LLC—See E.ON SE; *Int'l*, pg. 2259
STORMGEO DENMARK A/S—See Alfa Laval AB; *Int'l*, pg. 312
STREAM ENERGY MARYLAND, LLC—See NRG Energy, Inc.; *U.S. Public*, pg. 1551
STREAM ENERGY NEW JERSEY, LLC—See NRG Energy, Inc.; *U.S. Public*, pg. 1551
STREAM ENERGY NEW YORK, LLC—See NRG Energy, Inc.; *U.S. Public*, pg. 1551
SUMMIT ENERGY LLC; *U.S. Private*, pg. 3854
SUMMIT FARMS SOLAR, LLC—See Dominion Energy, Inc.; *U.S. Public*, pg. 674
SUNEDISON LLC—See SunEdison, Inc.; *U.S. Private*, pg. 3867
SUNFLOWER ELECTRIC POWER CORPORATION; *U.S. Private*, pg. 3867
SUNPOWER CORPORATION-EAST COAST REGIONAL OFFICE—See SunPower Corporation; *U.S. Public*, pg. 1965
SUNPOWER CORPORATION; *U.S. Public*, pg. 1965
SUNPOWER CORPORATION, SYSTEMS—See SunPower Corporation; *U.S. Public*, pg. 1965

SUNPOWER ENERGY SYSTEMS-KOREA—See SunPower Corporation; *U.S. Public*, pg. 1965
SUNPOWER ENERGY SYSTEMS SPAIN, S.L.—See SunPower Corporation; *U.S. Public*, pg. 1965
SUNPOWER SYSTEMS SARL—See SunPower Corporation; *U.S. Public*, pg. 1965
SUNRISE ENERGY, LLC—See HALLADOR ENERGY COMPANY; *U.S. Public*, pg. 980
SUNTECHNICS FABRISOLAR AG—See Elektrizitatswerk der Stadt Zurich; *Int'l*, pg. 2356
SUPERIOR WATER, LIGHT & POWER COMPANY—See ALLETE, Inc.; *U.S. Public*, pg. 79
SURSCHISTE, S.A.—See E.ON SE; *Int'l*, pg. 2259
SWB ERZEUGUNG GMBH & CO. KG—See EWE Aktiengesellschaft; *Int'l*, pg. 2576
SYCARPHA BOLTON, LLC—See The AES Corporation; *U.S. Public*, pg. 2032
SYDKRAFT AB—See Fortum Oyj; *Int'l*, pg. 2742
SYDKRAFT HYDROPOWER AB—See Fortum Oyj; *Int'l*, pg. 2742
SYDKRAFT THERMAL POWER AB—See Fortum Oyj; *Int'l*, pg. 2742
SYDKRAFT ZLOTOW SP. Z O.O.—See E.ON SE; *Int'l*, pg. 2259
TACOMA PUBLIC UTILITIES; *U.S. Private*, pg. 3921
TAHLEQUAH PUBLIC WORKS AUTHORITY; *U.S. Private*, pg. 3923
TALQUIN ELECTRIC COOPERATIVE, INC.; *U.S. Private*, pg. 3927
TAUNTON MUNICIPAL LIGHTING PLANT INC.; *U.S. Private*, pg. 3936
T'DASH G.K.—See eREX Co., Ltd.; *Int'l*, pg. 2490
TECMO ARABIA LTD—See A.H. Algosaibi & Bros.; *Int'l*, pg. 24
TECNEIRA, S.A.—See ACS, Actividades de Construccion y Servicios, S.A.; *Int'l*, pg. 116
TEPLARNA KYJOV, A.S.—See E.ON SE; *Int'l*, pg. 2259
TEPLARNA LIBEREC A.S.—See Groupe BPCE; *Int'l*, pg. 3094
TEPLARNA OTROKOVICE A.S.—See E.ON SE; *Int'l*, pg. 2256
TEPLARNA TABOR, A.S.—See Carpaterra Capital Partners sro; *Int'l*, pg. 1343
TEPLARNA TRMICE, A.S.—See CEZ, a.s.; *Int'l*, pg. 1428
TERMINUS ENERGY, INC.; *U.S. Public*, pg. 2020
TERMOSOLAR ALVARADO, S.L.—See ContourGlobal Limited; *Int'l*, pg. 1785
TERMOSOLAR MAJADAS, S.L.—See ContourGlobal Limited; *Int'l*, pg. 1785
TERMOSOLAR PALMA SAETILLA, S.L.—See ContourGlobal Limited; *Int'l*, pg. 1785
TERNA ENERGY SA—See Gek Terna Societe Anonyme Holdings Real Estate Constructions; *Int'l*, pg. 2913
TERRAFORM GLOBAL, INC.—See Brookfield Corporation; *Int'l*, pg. 1189
TERRA-GEN OPERATING CO., LLC—See ArcLight Capital Holdings, LLC; *U.S. Private*, pg. 312
TERRA-GEN OPERATING COMPANY, LLC—See ArcLight Capital Holdings, LLC; *U.S. Private*, pg. 312
TERRANAVIGATOR, LLC—See Ameresco, Inc.; *U.S. Public*, pg. 95
TEXAS MUNICIPAL POWER AGENCY; *U.S. Private*, pg. 3976
TEXAS-NEW MEXICO POWER COMPANY—See TXNM Energy, Inc.; *U.S. Public*, pg. 2208
THAI NATIONAL POWER CO., LTD.—See ENGIE SA; *Int'l*, pg. 2433
THINKAES, INC.—See The AES Corporation; *U.S. Public*, pg. 2032
THIRD PLANET WINDPOWER, LLC—See Morgan Stanley; *U.S. Public*, pg. 1475
THOMASSEN AMCOT INTERNATIONAL, LLC.; *U.S. Private*, pg. 4158
TIDAL POWER SERVICES, LLC.; *U.S. Private*, pg. 4167
TIRRENO POWER SPA—See ENGIE SA; *Int'l*, pg. 2434
TMG ENERGY CORP.; *U.S. Private*, pg. 4179
TNP ENTERPRISES, INC.—See TXNM Energy, Inc.; *U.S. Public*, pg. 2208
TOTAL ENERGI AS—See Hafslund ASA; *Int'l*, pg. 3206
THE TOWNSEND CORPORATION; *U.S. Private*, pg. 4127
TRACTEBEL ENERGIA COMERCIALIZADORA LIMITADA—See ENGIE SA; *Int'l*, pg. 2433
TRACTEBEL ENERGIA S.A. - JORGE LACERDA THERMO-ELECTRIC COMPLEX - CJL PLANT—See ENGIE SA; *Int'l*, pg. 2432
TRACTEBEL ENERGIA S.A. - LAGES COGENERATION UNIT - UCLA PLANT—See ENGIE SA; *Int'l*, pg. 2432
TRACTEBEL ENERGIA S.A. - TPP ALEGRETE - UTAL PLANT—See ENGIE SA; *Int'l*, pg. 2432
TRACTEBEL ENERGIA S.A. - TPP WILLIAM ARJONA - UTWA PLANT—See ENGIE SA; *Int'l*, pg. 2432
TRANSTECH INDUSTRIES, INC.; *U.S. Public*, pg. 2184
TRINITY VALLEY ELECTRIC COOP. (ATHENS OFFICE)—See Trinity Valley Electric Coop; *U.S. Private*, pg. 4236
TRI-STATE GENERATION AND TRANSMISSION ASSOCIATION, INC.; *U.S. Private*, pg. 4224

N.A.I.C.S. INDEX

221121 — ELECTRIC BULK POWER...

TSAVO POWER COMPANY LTD—See Aga Khan Development Network; *Int'l*, pg. 199
TSF ENGINEERING PTY LTD—See EVZ Limited; *Int'l*, pg. 2574
TULE WIND LLC—See Iberdrola, S.A.; *Int'l*, pg. 3571
TURLOCK IRRIGATION DISTRICT; *U.S. Private*, pg. 4259
TWIN BUTTES WIND, LLC—See Iberdrola, S.A.; *Int'l*, pg. 3571
TWO DOT WIND FARM, LLC—See New Jersey Resources Corporation; *U.S. Public*, pg. 1512
TYNAGH ENERGY LTD.—See Energeticky a Prumyslovy Holding, a.s.; *Int'l*, pg. 2420
UEGA - USINA ELETRICA A GAS DE ARAUCARIA LTDA.—See Companhia Paranaense de Energia; *Int'l*, pg. 1748
UGI DEVELOPMENT COMPANY—See UGI Corporation; *U.S. Public*, pg. 2223
UNION ELECTRICA DE CANARIAS GENERACION SAU—See Enel S.p.A.; *Int'l*, pg. 2415
UNIPER ANLAGENSERVICE GMBH—See Fortum Oyj; *Int'l*, pg. 2742
UNIPER BELGIUM N.V.—See Fortum Oyj; *Int'l*, pg. 2742
UNIPER BENELUX N.V.—See Fortum Oyj; *Int'l*, pg. 2742
UNIPER ENERGY SOUTHERN AFRICA (PTY) LTD.—See Fortum Oyj; *Int'l*, pg. 2742
UNIPRO PJSC—See Fortum Oyj; *Int'l*, pg. 2742
UNITED COGEN, INC.—See United Airlines Holdings, Inc.; *U.S. Public*, pg. 2229
UNITIL ENERGY SYSTEMS, INC.—See Unitil Corporation; *U.S. Public*, pg. 2253
UNITIL POWER CORPORATION—See Unitil Corporation; *U.S. Public*, pg. 2253
UNITIL RESOURCES, INC.—See Unitil Corporation; *U.S. Public*, pg. 2253
URBAENERGIA, S.L.—See ACS, Actividades de Construccion y Servicios, S.A.; *Int'l*, pg. 117
UTAH ASSOCIATED MUNICIPLE POWER SYSTEMS; *U.S. Private*, pg. 4324
UTAH MUNICIPAL POWER AGENCY INC.; *U.S. Private*, pg. 4324
UTILITIES BOARD OF THE CITY OF FOLEY ALABAMA; *U.S. Private*, pg. 4326
VALENER INC.—See Caisse de Depot et Placement du Quebec; *Int'l*, pg. 1256
VBC ENERGIA S.A.—See Camargo Correa S.A.; *Int'l*, pg. 1268
VCE ELEKTRARNY, S.R.O.—See CEZ, a.s.; *Int'l*, pg. 1429
VENADO WIND FARM, LLC—See E.ON SE; *Int'l*, pg. 2260
VERDE ENERGY USA, INC.—See Via Renewables, Inc.; *U.S. Public*, pg. 2290
VERIZON WIRELESS – CHAPMANVILLE—See Verizon Communications Inc.; *U.S. Public*, pg. 2284
VERSORGUNGSBETRIEBE HELGOLAND GMBH—See E.ON SE; *Int'l*, pg. 2260
VESZPREM-KOGENERACIO ENERGIATERMELO ZRT.—See E.ON SE; *Int'l*, pg. 2260
VIOTIKOS ANEMOS SA—See ELLAKTOR S.A.; *Int'l*, pg. 2365
VIRGIN ISLAND WATER & POWER AUTHORITY; *U.S. Private*, pg. 4387
VJP CO., LTD.—See ASIA PILE HOLDINGS CORPORATION; *Int'l*, pg. 614
VORTEX BRANDS CO.; *U.S. Public*, pg. 2310
WADHAM ENERGY LIMITED PARTNERSHIP—See Enpower Corp.; *U.S. Public*, pg. 1401
WASHINGTON GAS ENERGY SYSTEMS, INC.—See AltaGas Ltd.; *Int'l*, pg. 384
WATERBURY GENERATION LLC—See Hull Street Energy, LLC; *U.S. Public*, pg. 2005
WATER GAS & LIGHT COMMISSION; *U.S. Private*, pg. 4451
WEISSMAINKRAFTWERK ROHRENHOF AKTIENGESELLSCHAFT—See E.ON SE; *Int'l*, pg. 2260
WESERNETZ BREMERHAVEN GMBH—See EWE Aktiengesellschaft; *Int'l*, pg. 2576
WESTBROOK ENERGY CENTER, LLC—See Energy Capital Partners Management, LP; *U.S. Public*, pg. 1394
WESTERN FARMERS ELECTRIC COOPERATIVE, INC.; *U.S. Private*, pg. 4493
WESTERN SIERRA ENERGY, LLC—See NRG Energy, Inc.; *U.S. Public*, pg. 1551
WHITBY COGENERATION LIMITED PARTNERSHIP—See Energy Capital Partners Management, LP; *U.S. Public*, pg. 1394
WHITE RIVER VALLEY ELECTRIC COOP; *U.S. Private*, pg. 4509
WIATROPOL SMOLECIN SP. Z O.O.—See Athena Investments A/S; *Int'l*, pg. 669
WIATROPOL USTKA SP. Z O.O.—See Athena Investments A/S; *Int'l*, pg. 669
WINDPARK EMMENDORF GMBH & CO.KG—See Allianz SE; *Int'l*, pg. 356
WINDPARK MUTZSCHEN OHG—See E.ON SE; *Int'l*, pg. 2260
WINDPARK NAUNDORF OHG—See E.ON SE; *Int'l*, pg. 2260
WINDPARK QUITZOW GMBH & CO. KG—See Allianz SE; *Int'l*, pg. 356

WINDPARK REDEKIN GMBH & CO KG—See Allianz SE; *Int'l*, pg. 356
WINDPARK WERDER ZINNDORF GMBH & CO. KG—See Allianz SE; *Int'l*, pg. 356
WINDSTREAM TECHNOLOGIES, INC.; *U.S. Private*, pg. 4539
WISCONSIN RIVER POWER COMPANY—See Alliant Energy Corporation; *U.S. Public*, pg. 79
WISCONSIN RIVER POWER COMPANY—See WEC Energy Group, Inc.; *U.S. Public*, pg. 2342
WOLF HOLLOW I, LP—See Constellation Energy Corporation; *U.S. Public*, pg. 572
WOLVERINE POWER SUPPLY COOPERATIVE INC.; *U.S. Private*, pg. 4555
WP GROSS WARNOW GMBH & CO. KG—See Electricite de France S.A.; *Int'l*, pg. 2350
WU LING POWER CORPORATION—See China Power International Development Limited; *Int'l*, pg. 1542
XCEL ENERGY SERVICES INCORPORATED—See Xcel Energy Inc.; *U.S. Public*, pg. 2385
YAMPA VALLEY ELECTRIC ASSOCIATION; *U.S. Private*, pg. 4585
YELLOWSTONE ENERGY LP; *U.S. Private*, pg. 4588
YUBA COUNTY WATER AGENCY; *U.S. Private*, pg. 4595
ZASOBOVANI TEPLEM VSETIN A.S.—See Groupe BPCE; *Int'l*, pg. 3094
ZION ENERGY LLC—See Energy Capital Partners Management, LP; *U.S. Public*, pg. 1394
ZOUPING PEAK CHP CO., LTD.—See Banpu Public Company Limited; *Int'l*, pg. 852
ZOUPING PEAK PTE. LTD.—See Banpu Public Company Limited; *Int'l*, pg. 852

221121 — ELECTRIC BULK POWER TRANSMISSION AND CONTROL

1414 DEGREES LIMITED; *Int'l*, pg. 2
50HERTZ TRANSMISSION GMBH—See Elia Group SA; *Int'l*, pg. 2360
ABU DHABI TRANSMISSION & DESPATCH COMPANY—See Abu Dhabi Water & Electricity Authority; *Int'l*, pg. 73
ADANI INFRASTRUCTURE PRIVATE LIMITED—See Adani Enterprises Limited; *Int'l*, pg. 125
AEP TRANSMISSION COMPANY, LLC—See American Electric Power Company, Inc.; *U.S. Public*, pg. 99
ALABAMA POWER COMPANY—See The Southern Company; *U.S. Public*, pg. 2130
ALAMEDA MUNICIPAL POWER; *U.S. Private*, pg. 149
AL-BABTAIN POWER & TELECOMMUNICATION COMPANY; *Int'l*, pg. 284
ALLIANDER N.V.; *Int'l*, pg. 341
ALPIQ ENERGY SE—See Alpiq Holding AG; *Int'l*, pg. 373
ALPIQ ENERTRANS AG—See Alpiq Holding AG; *Int'l*, pg. 372
ALPIQ RESEAU SA LAUSANNE—See Alpiq Holding AG; *Int'l*, pg. 373
ALTALINK INVESTMENTS, L.P.—See Berkshire Hathaway Inc.; *U.S. Public*, pg. 299
APR ENERGY, LLC—See ACON Investments, LLC; *U.S. Private*, pg. 62
APR ENERGY, LLC—See Fairfax Financial Holdings Limited; *Int'l*, pg. 2605
BANGOR HYDRO-ELECTRIC COMPANY-HANCOCK COUNTY DIVISION—See Emera, Inc.; *Int'l*, pg. 2377
BANGOR HYDRO-ELECTRIC COMPANY-NORTHERN DIVISION—See Emera, Inc.; *Int'l*, pg. 2377
BANGOR HYDRO-ELECTRIC COMPANY—See Emera, Inc.; *Int'l*, pg. 2377
B. GRIMM & CO., R.O.P.—See Electricity Generating Public Co., Ltd.; *Int'l*, pg. 2352
BLEDSOE COAL LEASING COMPANY—See James River Coal Company; *U.S. Public*, pg. 2185
CASTLE PEAK POWER COMPANY LIMITED—See Exxon Mobil Corporation; *U.S. Public*, pg. 813
CATXERE TRANSMISSORA DE ENERGIA, S.A.—See ACS, Actividades de Construccion y Servicios, S.A.; *Int'l*, pg. 110
CD ENERGY DIRECT CO., LTD.—See Chubu Electric Power Co., Inc.; *Int'l*, pg. 1593
CENERGY HOLDINGS SA; *Int'l*, pg. 1401
CENTRAL ELECTRIC POWER ASSOCIATION; *U.S. Private*, pg. 820
CENTRAL LINCOLN PEOPLE'S UTILITY DISTRICT; *U.S. Private*, pg. 822
CENTRICA SHB LIMITED—See Centrica plc; *Int'l*, pg. 1413
CHERYONG INDUSTRIAL CO LTD; *Int'l*, pg. 1472
CHUDEN WING CO., LTD.—See Chubu Electric Power Co., Inc.; *Int'l*, pg. 1593
COMANCHE ELECTRIC COOP ASSOCIATION; *U.S. Private*, pg. 980
CONDUCTIX-WAMPFLER PTE LTD—See CVC Capital Partners SICAV-FIS S.A.; *Int'l*, pg. 1887
CONDUCTIX-WAMPFLER SDN BHD—See CVC Capital Partners SICAV-FIS S.A.; *Int'l*, pg. 1887
CONSUMER POWER INC.; *U.S. Private*, pg. 1025

COUNT + CARE GMBH—See HEAG Sudhessische Energie AG; *Int'l*, pg. 3302
DAVIS JEFFERSON ELECTRIC COOP; *U.S. Private*, pg. 1173
DENSO POWERTRAIN TECHNOLOGIES CORPORATION—See Denso Corporation; *Int'l*, pg. 2032
EGCO ENGINEERING & SERVICE CO., LTD—See Electricity Generating Public Co., Ltd.; *Int'l*, pg. 2352
ELES-GEN, D.O.O.—See Elektro Slovenia d.o.o.; *Int'l*, pg. 2357
ELETROSUL CENTRAIS ELETRICAS S.A.—See Centrais Eletricas Brasileiras S.A.; *Int'l*, pg. 1403
EMC LIMITED; *Int'l*, pg. 2376
EMERA MAINE—See ENMAX Corporation; *Int'l*, pg. 2442
ENERTEK, S.A. DE C.V.—See Iberdrola, S.A.; *Int'l*, pg. 3571
ENMAX COMMERCIAL ENERGY MARKETING INC.—See ENMAX Corporation; *Int'l*, pg. 2442
ENMAX ENERGY MARKETING INC.—See ENMAX Corporation; *Int'l*, pg. 2442
ENTE VASCO DE LA ENERGIA; *Int'l*, pg. 2450
EOS ENERGY STORAGE LLC—See B. Riley Financial, Inc.; *U.S. Public*, pg. 261
EPCOR WATER ARIZONA INC.—See EPCOR Utilities, Inc.; *Int'l*, pg. 2459
EVERSOURCE ENERGY; *U.S. Public*, pg. 801
FANDSTAN ELECTRIC SYSTEMS, LTD.—See Westinghouse Air Brake Technologies Corporation; *U.S. Public*, pg. 2358
FCC INMOBILIEN HOLDING GMBH—See Fomento de Construcciones y Contratas, S.A.; *Int'l*, pg. 2723
GAMMON INDIA LIMITED (T&D BUSINESS)—See Gammon India Limited; *Int'l*, pg. 2879
GE ENERGY EUROPE BV—See General Electric Company; *U.S. Public*, pg. 917
GREEN POWER EMC; *U.S. Private*, pg. 1773
GUANGZHOU POWER SUPPLY CO., LTD—See China Southern Power Grid Co., Ltd.; *Int'l*, pg. 1553
HEP-OPERATOR DISTRIBUCIJSKOG SUSTAVA D.O.O.—See Hrvatska elektroprivreda d.d.; *Int'l*, pg. 3502
HIDROCANTABRICO ENERGIA, S.A.U.—See EDP - Energias de Portugal, S.A.; *Int'l*, pg. 2314
HIGH PLAINS POWER INC.; *U.S. Private*, pg. 1936
IBERDROLA SERVICIOS MONTERREY, S.A. DE C.V.—See Iberdrola, S.A.; *Int'l*, pg. 3572
INDEPENDENT POWER TRANSMISSION OPERATOR S.A.—See Holding Co ADMIE (IPTO) SA; *Int'l*, pg. 3450
INTERNATIONAL TRANSMISSION COMPANY—See Fortis Inc.; *Int'l*, pg. 2739
ISA CAPITAL DO BRASIL S.A.—See Ecopetrol S.A.; *Int'l*, pg. 2299
ITC GRID DEVELOPMENT, LLC—See Fortis Inc.; *Int'l*, pg. 2739
ITC MIDWEST LLC—See Fortis Inc.; *Int'l*, pg. 2740
KAMO ELECTRIC COOPERATIVE; *U.S. Private*, pg. 2258
KODIAK ELECTRIC ASSOCIATION, INC.; *U.S. Private*, pg. 2336
LA FORET ENGINEERING CO., LTD.—See AGC Inc.; *Int'l*, pg. 204
MATANUSKA ELECTRIC ASSOCIATION, INC.; *U.S. Private*, pg. 2608
MEDISWITCH NAMIBIA PROPRIETARY LIMITED—See Altron Limited; *Int'l*, pg. 399
MICHIGAN ELECTRIC TRANSMISSION COMPANY, LLC—See Fortis Inc.; *Int'l*, pg. 2740
MORGAN COUNTY RURAL ELECTRIC ASSOCIATION; *U.S. Private*, pg. 2783
NACAP AUSTRALIA PTY LTD.—See Quanta Services, Inc.; *U.S. Public*, pg. 1752
NAGOYA CITY ENERGY CO., LTD.—See Chubu Electric Power Co., Inc.; *Int'l*, pg. 1593
NORRIS PUBLIC POWER DISTRICT; *U.S. Private*, pg. 2939
NORTHERN CALIFORNIA POWER AGENCY; *U.S. Private*, pg. 2952
NORTHWEST IOWA POWER COOPERATIVE; *U.S. Private*, pg. 2960
OKLAHOMA GAS & ELECTRIC COMPANY—See OGE Energy Corp.; *U.S. Public*, pg. 1564
OPTIM ENERGY ALTURA COGEN LLC—See BlackRock, Inc.; *U.S. Public*, pg. 346
PORTO VELHO TRANSMISSORA DE ENERGIA S.A.—See Centrais Eletricas Brasileiras S.A.; *Int'l*, pg. 1403
PREFORMED LINE PRODUCTS (MALAYSIA) SDN. BHD—See Preformed Line Products Company; *U.S. Public*, pg. 1714
QUANTA TECHNOLOGY, LLC—See Quanta Services, Inc.; *U.S. Public*, pg. 1752
SNC-LAVALIN CONSTRUCTORS INC.—See AtkinsRealis Group Inc.; *Int'l*, pg. 672
SOUTHERN MARYLAND ELECTRIC COOPERATIVE INC.; *U.S. Private*, pg. 3733
STEMMANN TECHNIK FRANCE SAS—See Westinghouse Air Brake Technologies Corporation; *U.S. Public*, pg. 2359
STEMMANN TECHNIK POLSKA SP ZOO—See Westing-

221121 — ELECTRIC BULK POWER...

house Air Brake Technologies Corporation; *U.S. Public*, pg. 2359
SUMMIT LINE CONSTRUCTION, INC.—See Quanta Services, Inc.; *U.S. Public*, pg. 1753
SUMTER ELECTRIC MEMBERSHIP CORPORATION; *U.S. Private*, pg. 3858
TEN THURINGER ENERGIENETZE GMBH—See E.ON SE; *Int'l*, pg. 2259
TEX-LA ELECTRIC COOPERATIVE OF TEXAS INC; *U.S. Private*, pg. 3974
THUNDER MOUNTAIN WATER COMPANY—See EPCOR Utilities, Inc.; *Int'l*, pg. 2459
TRANSNETBW GMBH—See EnBW Energie Baden-Wurttemberg AG; *Int'l*, pg. 2400
TRELEC, S. A.—See Empresas Publicas de Medellin ESP; *Int'l*, pg. 2392
TRES AMIGAS, LLC—See American Superconductor Corporation; *U.S. Public*, pg. 110
VACON AT ANTRIEBSSYSTEME GMBH—See Danfoss A/S; *Int'l*, pg. 1961
VALARD GEOMATICS LTD.—See Quanta Services, Inc.; *U.S. Public*, pg. 1753
VALLEY RURAL ELECTRIC COOPERATIVE, INC.; *U.S. Private*, pg. 4335
VERMONT ELECTRIC POWER COMPANY, INC.—See Caisse de Depot et Placement du Quebec; *Int'l*, pg. 1256
WEST OREGON ELECTRIC COOPERATIVE, INC.; *U.S. Private*, pg. 4486
WITHLACOOCHEE RIVER ELECTRIC COOPERATIVE, INC.; *U.S. Private*, pg. 4550
XCEL ENERGY INC.; *U.S. Public*, pg. 2385

221122 — ELECTRIC POWER DISTRIBUTION

174 POWER GLOBAL CORPORATION—See Hanwha Group; *Int'l*, pg. 3264
24/7 TECHNOLOGY INC.—See Incline MGMT Corp.; *U.S. Private*, pg. 2054
A2A S.P.A.; *Int'l*, pg. 29
A2A TRADING S.R.L.—See A2A S.p.A.; *Int'l*, pg. 29
AARE ENERGIE AG—See Alpiq Holding AG; *Int'l*, pg. 372
ABB AS—See ABB Ltd.; *Int'l*, pg. 50
ABB SWITZERLAND LTD - NORMELEC—See ABB Ltd.; *Int'l*, pg. 54
ABH STROMSCHIENEN GMBH—See Addtech AB; *Int'l*, pg. 131
ABSOLUTE CLEAN ENERGY PUBLIC COMPANY LIMITED; *Int'l*, pg. 70
ABU DHABI DISTRIBUTION COMPANY—See Abu Dhabi Water & Electricity Authority; *Int'l*, pg. 73
ACEGAS-APS SPA; *Int'l*, pg. 95
ACWA POWER COMPANY; *Int'l*, pg. 122
ADAMS RURAL ELECTRIC COOPERATIVE INC.; *U.S. Private*, pg. 75
ADANI ELECTRICITY MUMBAI LIMITED—See Adani Energy Solutions Limited; *Int'l*, pg. 124
ADANI ENERGY SOLUTIONS LIMITED; *Int'l*, pg. 124
ADANI POWER LIMITED—See Adani Enterprises Limited; *Int'l*, pg. 125
AEK PELLET AG—See BKW AG; *Int'l*, pg. 1054
AEP ENERGY, INC.—See American Electric Power Company, Inc.; *U.S. Public*, pg. 99
AEP TEXAS INC.—See American Electric Power Company, Inc.; *U.S. Public*, pg. 99
AES ANDES, INC.—See The AES Corporation; *U.S. Public*, pg. 2030
AES BALLYLUMFORD LIMITED—See The AES Corporation; *U.S. Public*, pg. 2030
AES CHENGDU—See The AES Corporation; *U.S. Public*, pg. 2030
AES CHIVOR & CIA S.C.A. E.S.P.—See The AES Corporation; *U.S. Public*, pg. 2030
AES ENERJI LIMITED SIRKETI—See The AES Corporation; *U.S. Public*, pg. 2030
AES HAMES LLC—See The AES Corporation; *U.S. Public*, pg. 2030
AES HUNTINGTON BEACH, L.L.C.—See The AES Corporation; *U.S. Public*, pg. 2031
AES MERIDA MANAGEMENT SERVICES, S. DE R.L. DE C.V.—See The AES Corporation; *U.S. Public*, pg. 2031
AES PACIFIC OCEAN HOLDINGS B.V.—See The AES Corporation; *U.S. Public*, pg. 2031
AES PANAMA, S.R.L.—See The AES Corporation; *U.S. Public*, pg. 2031
AES POLAND WIND SP.Z O.O.—See The AES Corporation; *U.S. Public*, pg. 2031
AES PUERTO RICO, L.P.—See The AES Corporation; *U.S. Public*, pg. 2031
AES SERVICES, INC.—See The AES Corporation; *U.S. Public*, pg. 2031
AFLUENTE TRANSMISSAO DE ENERGIA ELETRICA S.A.—See Iberdrola, S.A.; *Int'l*, pg. 3573
AGDER ENERGI AS; *Int'l*, pg. 204
AGL ELECTRICITY (VIC) PTY LIMITED—See AGL Energy Limited; *Int'l*, pg. 211
AGL HYDRO PARTNERSHIP—See AGL Energy Limited; *Int'l*, pg. 211

AGL LOY YANG PTY LTD—See AGL Energy Limited; *Int'l*, pg. 211
AGL SALES (QUEENSLAND ELECTRICITY) PTY LIMITED—See AGL Energy Limited; *Int'l*, pg. 211
AL AIN DISTRIBUTION COMPANY—See Abu Dhabi Water & Electricity Authority; *Int'l*, pg. 73
ALASKA VILLAGE ELECTRIC COOPERATIVE, INC.; *U.S. Private*, pg. 151
ALECTRA INC.—See Hydro One Limited; *Int'l*, pg. 3546
ALFEN N.V.; *Int'l*, pg. 315
ALGOMA POWER INC.—See Fortis Inc.; *Int'l*, pg. 2739
ALLAN BRITEWAY ELECTRICAL CONTRACTORS, INC.; *U.S. Private*, pg. 174
ALLEGHENY ELECTRIC COOPERATIVE; *U.S. Private*, pg. 176
ALLETE ENTERPRISES, INC.—See ALLETE, Inc.; *U.S. Public*, pg. 79
ALLIANDER AG—See Alliander N.V.; *Int'l*, pg. 341
ALPERIA SPA; *Int'l*, pg. 366
ALPIQ CENTRAL EUROPE AG—See Alpiq Holding AG; *Int'l*, pg. 372
ALPIQ ENERGIE FRANCE S.A.S.—See Alpiq Holding AG; *Int'l*, pg. 372
ALPIQ ENERGIJA BH D.O.O.—See Alpiq Holding AG; *Int'l*, pg. 372
ALPIQ ENERGIJA HRVATSKA D.O.O.—See Alpiq Holding AG; *Int'l*, pg. 372
ALPIQ ENERGY HELLAS S.A.—See Alpiq Holding AG; *Int'l*, pg. 373
ALPIQ ENERGY ITALY S.P.A.—See Alpiq Holding AG; *Int'l*, pg. 373
ALPIQ GRID LTD.—See Alpiq Holding AG; *Int'l*, pg. 373
ALPIQ TRADING LTD.—See Alpiq Holding AG; *Int'l*, pg. 373
ALPIQ ZLIN S.R.O.—See Alpiq Holding AG; *Int'l*, pg. 373
ALSTOM CHILE S.A.—See Alstom S.A.; *Int'l*, pg. 380
ALTALINK L.P.—See Berkshire Hathaway Inc.; *U.S. Public*, pg. 300
ALTAMAHA ELECTRIC MEMBERSHIP CORPORATION; *U.S. Private*, pg. 204
ALTEK ALARKO ELEKTRIK SANT. TES. ISL. VE TIC. A.S.—See Alarko Holding A.S.; *Int'l*, pg. 291
AMALGAMATED ELECTRICITY CO., LTD.; *Int'l*, pg. 408
AMANA SOCIETY SERVICE CO.—See Amana Society, Inc.; *U.S. Private*, pg. 216
AMATA B. GRIMM POWER LTD.—See B. Grimm Group; *Int'l*, pg. 788
AMEREN ILLINOIS COMPANY—See Ameren Corporation; *U.S. Public*, pg. 94
AMERESCO SELECT, INC.—See Ameresco, Inc.; *U.S. Public*, pg. 95
AMERESCO SOUTHWEST, INC.—See Ameresco, Inc.; *U.S. Public*, pg. 95
AMERICAN DG ENERGY INC.—See Tecogen Inc.; *U.S. Public*, pg. 1989
AMF GROUP JSC; *Int'l*, pg. 424
AMICALOLA ELECTRIC MEMBERSHIP CORPORATION; *U.S. Private*, pg. 263
AMPLA ENERGIA E SERVICOS, S.A.—See Enel S.p.A.; *Int'l*, pg. 2412
AMPRION GMBH; *Int'l*, pg. 437
ANHUI TONGYUAN ENVIRONMENT ENERGY SAVING CO., LTD.; *Int'l*, pg. 470
AN HUI WENERGY CO., LTD.; *Int'l*, pg. 443
ANSALDO ENERGIA S.P.A.—See Cassa Depositi e Prestiti S.p.A.; *Int'l*, pg. 1354
ANSELMO LEON DISTRIBUCION, S.L.—See Iberdrola, S.A.; *Int'l*, pg. 3570
ANTHRACITE POWER AND LIGHT—See Reading Anthracite Company; *U.S. Private*, pg. 3366
APAMAN ENERGY CO., LTD.—See Apaman Co., Ltd.; *Int'l*, pg. 500
APOLLO DEVELOPMENT ASSOCIATES LP—See Edison International; *U.S. Public*, pg. 719
APPLIED ENERGY LLC—See I Squared Capital Advisors (US) LLC; *U.S. Public*, pg. 2025
ARENDALS FOSSEKOMPANI ASA; *Int'l*, pg. 558
ARETI SPA—See ACEA S.p.A.; *Int'l*, pg. 95
ARGENCOBRA, S.A.—See ACS, Actividades de Construccion y Servicios, S.A.; *Int'l*, pg. 110
AS ANNE SOOJUS—See Fortum Oyj; *Int'l*, pg. 2740
ASEFA PUBLIC COMPANY LIMITED; *Int'l*, pg. 605
AS FORTUM POWER & HEAT—See Fortum Oyj; *Int'l*, pg. 2741
ASMEA S.R.L.—See A2A S.p.A.; *Int'l*, pg. 29
ASM ENERGIA E AMBIENTE S.R.L.—See A2A S.p.A.; *Int'l*, pg. 29
ASM ENERGY SRL—See A2A S.p.A.; *Int'l*, pg. 29
ASPEM S.P.A.—See A2A S.p.A.; *Int'l*, pg. 29
ASSOCIATED ELECTRIC COOPERATIVE INC.; *U.S. Private*, pg. 355
ASTMAX ENERGY, INC.—See ASTMAX Trading, Inc.; *Int'l*, pg. 655
ATCO ELECTRIC LTD.—See ATCO Ltd.; *Int'l*, pg. 667
ATCO LTD.; *Int'l*, pg. 666
ATEL HELLAS S.A.—See Alpiq Holding AG; *Int'l*, pg. 373
ATLANTIC CITY ELECTRIC COMPANY—See Exelon Corporation; *U.S. Public*, pg. 807
ATLANTIC RENEWABLE ENERGY CORPORATION—See

CORPORATE AFFILIATIONS

Iberdrola, S.A.; *Int'l*, pg. 3570
AUSTIN ENERGY; *U.S. Private*, pg. 395
AVANGRID, INC.—See Iberdrola, S.A.; *Int'l*, pg. 3570
AVENIS SA—See Alpiq Holding AG; *Int'l*, pg. 373
AVISTA CORPORATION; *U.S. Public*, pg. 249
AXPO AUSTRIA GMBH—See Axpo Holding AG; *Int'l*, pg. 771
AXPO BENELUX S.A.—See Axpo Holding AG; *Int'l*, pg. 771
AXPO BH DOO—See Axpo Holding AG; *Int'l*, pg. 771
AXPO BULGARIA EAD—See Axpo Holding AG; *Int'l*, pg. 771
AXPO DEUTSCHLAND GMBH—See Axpo Holding AG; *Int'l*, pg. 771
AXPO D.O.O. BEOGRAD—See Axpo Holding AG; *Int'l*, pg. 771
AXPO DOOEL MK—See Axpo Holding AG; *Int'l*, pg. 771
AXPO ENERGY ROMANIA S.A.—See Axpo Holding AG; *Int'l*, pg. 771
AXPO FINLAND OY—See Axpo Holding AG; *Int'l*, pg. 771
AXPO FRANCE S.A.S.—See Axpo Holding AG; *Int'l*, pg. 771
AXPO GAS SERVICE ITALIA SPA—See Axpo Holding AG; *Int'l*, pg. 771
AXPO INTERNATIONAL S.A.—See Axpo Holding AG; *Int'l*, pg. 771
AXPO ITALIA S.P.A.—See Axpo Holding AG; *Int'l*, pg. 771
AXPO POLSKA SP.Z.O.O.—See Axpo Holding AG; *Int'l*, pg. 771
AXPO SVERIGE AB—See Axpo Holding AG; *Int'l*, pg. 771
AXPO TRGOVINA D.O.O.—See Axpo Holding AG; *Int'l*, pg. 771
AXPO UK LTD.—See Axpo Holding AG; *Int'l*, pg. 771
AYDEM YENILENEBILIR ENERJI A.S.; *Int'l*, pg. 774
AYEN ELECTRIC TRADING INC.—See Ayen Enerji AS; *Int'l*, pg. 774
AYEN ENERGIJA D.O.O—See Ayen Enerji AS; *Int'l*, pg. 774
AYEN ENERGY TRADING D.O.O.—See Ayen Enerji AS; *Int'l*, pg. 775
AYEN ENERGY TRADING SHA—See Ayen Enerji AS; *Int'l*, pg. 775
AYEN ENERJI AS; *Int'l*, pg. 774
AZIENDA ELETTRICA TICINESE; *Int'l*, pg. 778
BACKNANGSTROM GMBH & CO. KG—See EnBW Energie Baden-Wurttemberg AG; *Int'l*, pg. 2401
BALDWIN EMC; *U.S. Private*, pg. 458
BANDEIRANTE ENERGIA SA—See EDP - Energias de Portugal, S.A.; *Int'l*, pg. 2314
BANPU JAPAN K.K.—See Banpu Power PCL; *Int'l*, pg. 851
THE BARBADOS LIGHT & POWER COMPANY LIMITED—See Emera, Inc.; *Int'l*, pg. 2377
BARC ELECTRIC COOPERATIVE; *U.S. Private*, pg. 472
BARRY DANMARK APS—See Fortum Oyj; *Int'l*, pg. 2740
BARRY ELECTRIC COOPERATIVE; *U.S. Private*, pg. 481
BARTHOLOMEW COUNTY RURAL ELECTRIC MEMBERSHIP CORPORATION; *U.S. Private*, pg. 482
BAYERNWERK AG—See E.ON SE; *Int'l*, pg. 2252
BAYMINA ENERJI AS—See ENGIE SA; *Int'l*, pg. 2432
BCPG PUBLIC COMPANY LIMITED—See Bangchak Corporation Public Company Limited; *Int'l*, pg. 832
BEAR VALLEY ELECTRIC SERVICE, INC.—See American States Water Company; *U.S. Public*, pg. 110
BEAUREGARD ELECTRIC COOPERATIVE, INC.; *U.S. Private*, pg. 508
BEIJING JINGNENG CLEAN ENERGY CO., LTD.; *Int'l*, pg. 953
BELIZE ELECTRIC COMPANY LIMITED—See Fortis Inc.; *Int'l*, pg. 2739
BENTON RURAL ELECTRIC ASSOCIATION; *U.S. Private*, pg. 529
BERKELEY ELECTRIC COOPERATIVE INC.; *U.S. Private*, pg. 532
BERMUDA ELECTRIC LIGHT COMPANY LIMITED—See Abengoa S.A.; *Int'l*, pg. 59
BERMUDA ELECTRIC LIGHT COMPANY LIMITED—See Algonquin Power & Utilities Corp.; *Int'l*, pg. 319
BGE HOME PRODUCTS & SERVICES, LLC—See Constellation Energy Corporation; *U.S. Public*, pg. 571
B.GRIMM POWER (LAEM CHABANG) 1 LIMITED—See B. Grimm Group; *Int'l*, pg. 788
BICENT POWER LLC—See Beowulf Energy LLC; *U.S. Private*, pg. 529
BICENT POWER LLC—See NGP Energy Capital Management, LLC; *U.S. Private*, pg. 2923
BIG BEND ELECTRIC COOPERATIVE, INC.; *U.S. Private*, pg. 552
BIG COUNTRY ELECTRIC COOP; *U.S. Private*, pg. 552
BIOMASS SECURE POWER INC.; *Int'l*, pg. 1039
BKW FMB ENERGIE AG—See E.ON SE; *Int'l*, pg. 2251
BLACHLY-LANE COUNTY COOPERATIVE ELECTRIC ASSOCIATION; *U.S. Private*, pg. 569
BLACK HILLS/COLORADO ELECTRIC UTILITY COMPANY, LP—See Black Hills Corporation; *U.S. Public*, pg. 340
BLACK HILLS CORPORATION; *U.S. Public*, pg. 340
BLACK HILLS ELECTRIC GENERATION, LLC—See Black Hills Corporation; *U.S. Public*, pg. 340
BLACK RIVER ELECTRIC CO-OP., INC.; *U.S. Private*, pg. 572
BLOOM ENERGY (INDIA) PVT. LTD.—See Bloom Energy Corporation; *U.S. Public*, pg. 362

N.A.I.C.S. INDEX

221122 — ELECTRIC POWER DIST...

BLUEBONNET ELECTRIC CO-OP, INC.; *U.S. Private*, pg. 596
BLUE RIDGE ELECTRIC MEMBERSHIP CORPORATION; *U.S. Private*, pg. 591
BLUEROCK ENERGY, INC.; *U.S. Private*, pg. 597
B&M INDUSTRIAL, INC.; *U.S. Private*, pg. 419
BORALEX POWER INC.—See Boralex Inc.; *Int'l*, pg. 1112
BORYEONG LNG TERMINAL CO., LTD.—See GS Holdings Corp.; *Int'l*, pg. 3141
BOUNCE ENERGY, INC.—See NRG Energy, Inc.; *U.S. Public*, pg. 1549
BP ENERGY COMPANY—See BP plc; *Int'l*, pg. 1127
BRAINTREE ELECTRIC LIGHT DEPARTMENT; *U.S. Private*, pg. 634
BRIDGER VALLEY ELECTRIC ASSOCIATION, INC.; *U.S. Private*, pg. 649
BRILLIANT LIGHT POWER, INC.—See Exelon Corporation; *U.S. Public*, pg. 807
BROOKFIELD RENEWABLE PARTNERS L.P.—See Brookfield Corporation; *Int'l*, pg. 1186
BRUNSWICK ELECTRIC MEMBERSHIP CORPORATION; *U.S. Private*, pg. 672
BULLER ELECTRICITY LTD.; *Int'l*, pg. 1214
CADDO ELECTRIC COOPERATIVE; *U.S. Private*, pg. 712
CALIFORNIA INDEPENDENT SYSTEMS OPERATOR; *U.S. Private*, pg. 719
CALLAWAY ELECTRIC COOPERATIVE; *U.S. Private*, pg. 722
CALPINE CORPORATION - MIDDLETOWN—See Energy Capital Partners Management, LP; *U.S. Private*, pg. 1394
CALPINE ENERGY SERVICES—See Energy Capital Partners Management, LP; *U.S. Private*, pg. 1394
CALPINE MERCHANT SERVICES COMPANY—See Energy Capital Partners Management, LP; *U.S. Private*, pg. 1394
CAMUNA ENERGIA S.R.L.—See A2A S.p.A.; *Int'l*, pg. 29
CANADIAN NIAGARA POWER INC. - EASTERN ONTARIO POWER DIVISION—See Fortis Inc.; *Int'l*, pg. 2739
CANADIAN NIAGARA POWER INC.—See Fortis Inc.; *Int'l*, pg. 2739
CANADIAN VALLEY ELECTRIC CO-OP; *U.S. Private*, pg. 732
CANOOCHEE ELECTRIC MEMBERSHIP CORPORATION; *U.S. Private*, pg. 735
CAPITAL ELECTRIC COOPERATIVE, INC.; *U.S. Private*, pg. 740
CAROHOME, LLC—See Duke Energy Corporation; *U.S. Public*, pg. 690
CARROLL ELECTRIC COOPERATIVE CORP.; *U.S. Private*, pg. 773
CARTERET-CRAVEN ELECTRIC COOPERATIVE; *U.S. Private*, pg. 776
CASS COUNTY ELECTRIC COOPERATIVE, INC.; *U.S. Private*, pg. 783
CC ENERGIE SA—See BKW AG; *Int'l*, pg. 1055
CELSIA SA ESP—See Grupo Argos S.A.; *Int'l*, pg. 3120
CELSIA S.A.—See Grupo Argos S.A.; *Int'l*, pg. 3120
CEMAR - COMPANHIA ENERGETICA DO MARANHAO—See Equatorial Energia SA; *Int'l*, pg. 2484
CEMIG DISTRIBUICAO S.A.—See Companhia Energetica de Minas Gerais - CEMIG; *Int'l*, pg. 1747
CEMIG TRADING S.A.—See Companhia Energetica de Minas Gerais - CEMIG; *Int'l*, pg. 1747
CENTERPOINT ENERGY, INC.; *U.S. Public*, pg. 471
CENTRAL ALABAMA ELECTRIC COOPERATIVE; *U.S. Private*, pg. 818
CENTRAL ELECTRIC COOPERATIVE INC.; *U.S. Private*, pg. 820
CENTRAL ELECTRICITY SUPPLY COMPANY OF ORISSA LIMITED—See The AES Corporation; *U.S. Public*, pg. 2031
CENTRAL ELECTRIC POWER COOPERATIVE INC.; *U.S. Private*, pg. 820
CENTRAL ELECTRIC POWER COOPERATIVE, INC.; *U.S. Private*, pg. 820
CENTRAL FLORIDA ELECTRIC COOPERATIVE INC.; *U.S. Private*, pg. 820
CENTRAL GEORGIA EMC FOUNDATION, INC.; *U.S. Private*, pg. 821
CENTRAL HUDSON GAS & ELECTRIC CORPORATION—See Fortis Inc.; *Int'l*, pg. 2739
CENTRAL IOWA POWER COOPERATIVE; *U.S. Private*, pg. 821
CENTRAL MAINE POWER COMPANY—See Iberdrola, S.A.; *Int'l*, pg. 3570
CENTRAL MAINE POWER COMPANY—See Iberdrola, S.A.; *Int'l*, pg. 3570
CENTRAL RURAL ELECTRIC COOPERATIVE; *U.S. Private*, pg. 824
CENTRALSCHWEIZERISCHE KRAFTWERKE AG—See Axpo Holding AG; *Int'l*, pg. 771
CENTRAL TERMELETRICA DE COGERACAO S.A.—See Companhia Energetica de Minas Gerais - CEMIG; *Int'l*, pg. 1747
CENTRICA RPS LIMITED—See Centrica plc; *Int'l*, pg. 1413
CEOLPAR - CENTRAIS EOLICAS DO PARANA LTDA.—See Companhia Paranaense de Energia; *Int'l*, pg. 1747

CESC LIMITED; *Int'l*, pg. 1424
CES POWER LLC; *U.S. Private*, pg. 842
CEZ, A.S.; *Int'l*, pg. 1426
CEZ CHORZOW B.V.—See CEZ, a.s.; *Int'l*, pg. 1426
CEZ DISTRIBUCE, A. S.—See CEZ, a.s.; *Int'l*, pg. 1426
CEZ DISTRIBUCNE SUSTAVY A.S.—See CEZ, a.s.; *Int'l*, pg. 1426
CEZ ELEKTRO BULGARIA AD—See CEZ, a.s.; *Int'l*, pg. 1426
CEZ HUNGARY LTD.—See CEZ, a.s.; *Int'l*, pg. 1426
CEZ MH B.V.—See CEZ, a.s.; *Int'l*, pg. 1426
CEZ POLAND DISTRIBUTION B.V.—See CEZ, a.s.; *Int'l*, pg. 1427
CEZ POLSKA SP. Z.O.O.—See CEZ, a.s.; *Int'l*, pg. 1427
CEZ RAZPREDELENIE BULGARIA AD—See Eurohold Bulgaria Ad; *Int'l*, pg. 2553
CEZ SHPERNDARJE SH.A.—See CEZ, a.s.; *Int'l*, pg. 1427
CEZ SRBIJA D.O.O.—See CEZ, a.s.; *Int'l*, pg. 1427
CHAMPION ENERGY SERVICES, LLC—See Energy Capital Partners Management, LP; *U.S. Private*, pg. 1394
CHANGCHUN ZHIYUAN NEW ENERGY EQUIPMENT CO., LTD.; *Int'l*, pg. 1443
CHEROKEE COUNTY ELECTRIC COOPERATIVE ASSOCIATION; *U.S. Private*, pg. 873
CHERRYLAND ELECTRIC COOPERATIVE; *U.S. Private*, pg. 874
CHEYENNE LIGHT, FUEL & POWER CO.—See Black Hills Corporation; *U.S. Public*, pg. 341
CHINA DATANG CORPORATION; *Int'l*, pg. 1496
CHINA SOUTHERN POWER GRID ENERGY EFFICIENCY & CLEAN ENERGY CO., LTD.; *Int'l*, pg. 1553
CHI OPERATIONS INC.—See Enel S.p.A.; *Int'l*, pg. 2411
CHN ENERGY CHANGYUAN ELECTRIC POWER CO., LTD.; *Int'l*, pg. 1576
CHOCTAW ELECTRIC COOPERATIVE, INC.; *U.S. Private*, pg. 888
CHOCTAWHATCHEE ELECTRIC COOPERATIVE INC.; *U.S. Private*, pg. 888
CHONGQING FULING ELECTRIC POWER INDUSTRIAL CO., LTD.; *Int'l*, pg. 1579
CHOPTANK ELECTRIC COOPERATIVE, INC.; *U.S. Private*, pg. 888
CHUBU ELECTRIC POWER CO., INC.; *Int'l*, pg. 1593
CHUBU ELECTRIC POWER CO., INC. - UK OFFICE—See Chubu Electric Power Co., Inc.; *Int'l*, pg. 1593
CIA DE TRANSMISSAO DE ENERGIA ELETRICA PAULISTA; *Int'l*, pg. 1601
CIA ELECTRICA DEL LITORAL SA; *Int'l*, pg. 1602
CIA ENERGETICA DE PERNAMBUCO - CELPE; *Int'l*, pg. 1602
CIA PAULISTA DE FORCA E LUZ LTDA—See Bradespar S.A.; *Int'l*, pg. 1134
CIA PIRATININGA DE FORCA E LUZ LTDA—See Bradespar S.A.; *Int'l*, pg. 1134
CITIGROUP ENERGY INC.—See Citigroup Inc.; *U.S. Public*, pg. 503
CITIPOWER—See CK Hutchison Holdings Limited; *Int'l*, pg. 1636
CITIZENS ELECTRIC CORPORATION; *U.S. Private*, pg. 903
CK POWER PUBLIC COMPANY LIMITED; *Int'l*, pg. 1638
CLAIBORNE ELECTRIC CO-OP INC.; *U.S. Private*, pg. 910
CLAL ENERGY—See Access Industries, Inc.; *U.S. Private*, pg. 51
CLALLAM COUNTY PUBLIC UTILITY DISTRICT; *U.S. Private*, pg. 910
CLARKE ELECTRIC COOPERATIVE, INC.; *U.S. Private*, pg. 914
CLARK ELECTRIC COOPERATIVE; *U.S. Private*, pg. 912
CLARK PUBLIC UTILITIES; *U.S. Private*, pg. 913
CLAVERACK RURAL ELECTRIC COOPERATIVE; *U.S. Private*, pg. 917
CLAY COUNTY ELECTRIC COOPERATIVE CORPORATION; *U.S. Private*, pg. 917
CLAY ELECTRIC COOPERATIVE INC.; *U.S. Private*, pg. 917
CLEAN ENERGY SOURCING AG—See BayWa AG; *Int'l*, pg. 917
CLEARVIEW ELECTRIC, INC.; *U.S. Private*, pg. 939
CLEARWATER POWER COMPANY; *U.S. Private*, pg. 939
CLECO CORPORATE HOLDINGS LLC; *U.S. Private*, pg. 939
THE CLEVELAND ELECTRIC ILLUMINATING COMPANY—See FirstEnergy Corp.; *U.S. Public*, pg. 849
CLINTON COUNTY ELECTRIC COOPERATIVE, INC.; *U.S. Private*, pg. 944
CLP POWER HONG KONG LIMITED—See CLP Holdings Limited; *Int'l*, pg. 1663
CLP RESEARCH INSTITUTE LIMITED—See CLP Holdings Limited; *Int'l*, pg. 1663
CLT ENERGY SERVICES GROUP, L.L.C.—See Constellation Energy Corporation; *U.S. Public*, pg. 571
COFELY A.S.—See ENGIE SA; *Int'l*, pg. 2431
COFELY ITALIA S.P.A.—See ENGIE SA; *Int'l*, pg. 2430
COFELY LIMITED—See ENGIE SA; *Int'l*, pg. 2430
COGAS ENERGIE B.V.—See ENGIE SA; *Int'l*, pg. 2431
COLA RESOURCES LLC—See Constellation Energy Corporation; *U.S. Public*, pg. 571

COLES-MOULTRIE ELECTRIC COOPERATIVE; *U.S. Private*, pg. 967
COLQUITT ELECTRIC MEMBERSHIP CORPORATION; *U.S. Private*, pg. 975
COMANCHE COUNTY ELECTRIC COOPERATIVE ASSOCIATION; *U.S. Private*, pg. 980
COMEGSA—See Empresas Publicas de Medellin ESP; *Int'l*, pg. 2391
COMISION FEDERAL DE ELECTRICIDAD; *Int'l*, pg. 1714
COMPAGNIE PARISIENNE DE CHAUFFAGE URBAIN—See ENGIE SA; *Int'l*, pg. 2431
COMPANHIA DE ELETRICIDADE DO ESTADO DA BAHIA—See Iberdrola, S.A.; *Int'l*, pg. 3573
COMPANHIA ESTADUAL DE DISTRIBUICAO DE ENERGIA ELETRICA—See Equatorial Energia SA; *Int'l*, pg. 2484
COMPANHIA HIDRO ELETRICA DO SAO FRANCISCO SA—See Centrais Eletricas Brasileiras S.A.; *Int'l*, pg. 1403
COMPANHIA PARANAENSE DE ENERGIA; *Int'l*, pg. 1747
COMSTOCK OIL AND GAS—See Comstock Resources, Inc.; *U.S. Public*, pg. 562
CONCORDIA ELECTRIC COOPERATIVE, INC.; *U.S. Private*, pg. 1010
CONLOG (PTY) LTD—See Consolidated Infrastructure Group Limited; *Int'l*, pg. 1771
THE CONNECTICUT LIGHT AND POWER COMPANY—See Eversource Energy; *U.S. Public*, pg. 802
CONNEXUS ENERGY; *U.S. Private*, pg. 1018
CONSOLIDATED ELECTRIC COOPERATIVE; *U.S. Private*, pg. 1020
CONSOLIDATED POWER PROJECTS (PTY) LIMITED—See Consolidated Infrastructure Group Limited; *Int'l*, pg. 1771
CONSORCIO ENERGETICO DE HUANCAVELICA S.A.—See Compania de Minas Buenaventura SAA; *Int'l*, pg. 1748
CONSTELLATION ENERGY CORPORATION; *U.S. Public*, pg. 571
CONSTELLATION ENERGY GENERATION, LLC—See Constellation Energy Corporation; *U.S. Public*, pg. 571
CONSTELLATION ENERGY RESOURCES, LLC—See Constellation Energy Corporation; *U.S. Public*, pg. 571
CONSTELLATION ENERGY SERVICES, INC.—See Constellation Energy Corporation; *U.S. Public*, pg. 572
CONTINENTAL DIVIDE ELECTRIC COOPERATIVE INC; *U.S. Private*, pg. 1028
COOKSON HILLS ELECTRIC COOP; *U.S. Private*, pg. 1039
COOLIDGE STATION APARTMENTS LLC—See Edison International; *U.S. Public*, pg. 719
COPEL DISTRIBUICAO SA—See Companhia Paranaense de Energia; *Int'l*, pg. 1748
CORE UTILITY SOLUTIONS LTD—See Iberdrola, S.A.; *Int'l*, pg. 3573
CORNWALL ELECTRIC INC.—See Fortis Inc.; *Int'l*, pg. 2739
COSTA OESTE TRANSMISSORA DE ENERGIA S.A.—See Companhia Paranaense de Energia; *Int'l*, pg. 1748
COTTON ELECTRIC COOPERATIVE, INC.; *U.S. Private*, pg. 1064
COVANTA MENDOTA, L.P.—See EQT AB; *Int'l*, pg. 2474
COVINGTON ELECTRIC COOPERATIVE; *U.S. Private*, pg. 1073
COWETA-FAYETTE ELECTRIC MEMBERSHIP CORPORATION; *U.S. Private*, pg. 1073
COWET-FYTTE ELECTRIC MEMBERSHIP CORP.; *U.S. Private*, pg. 1073
COWLITZ COUNTY PUBLIC UTILITY DISTRICT; *U.S. Private*, pg. 1074
CRAIG ELECTRIC CORPORATION; *U.S. Private*, pg. 1082
CRE ENERGY LTD—See Iberdrola, S.A.; *Int'l*, pg. 3573
CRIUS ENERGY, LLC; *U.S. Private*, pg. 1102
CROW WING COOPERATIVE POWER & LIGHT COMPANY; *U.S. Private*, pg. 1109
CSG SMART ELECTRIC TECHNOLOGY CO., LTD.—See CSG Smart Science & Technology Co., Ltd.; *Int'l*, pg. 1864
CST LIMITED, LLC—See Duke Energy Corporation; *U.S. Public*, pg. 690
CUIVRE RIVER ELECTRIC CO-OPERATIVE INC.; *U.S. Private*, pg. 1120
CULLMAN ELECTRIC CO-OPERATIVE INC.; *U.S. Private*, pg. 1121
CUMBERLAND ELECTRIC MEMBERSHIP CORPORATION; *U.S. Private*, pg. 1122
CVA EOS S.R.L.—See CVA S.p.A. a s.u.; *Int'l*, pg. 1881
DAGESTAN ENERGOSBYT COMPANY; *Int'l*, pg. 1912
DAKOTA COAL COMPANY—See Basin Electric Power Cooperative; *U.S. Private*, pg. 485
DAKOTA ELECTRIC ASSOCIATION; *U.S. Private*, pg. 1147
DAKOTA GASIFICATION COMPANY—See Basin Electric Power Cooperative; *U.S. Private*, pg. 485
DAKOTA VALLEY ELECTRIC COORPERATIVE INC.; *U.S. Private*, pg. 1148
DALKIA NV-SA—See Electricite de France S.A.; *Int'l*, pg. 2350

221122 — ELECTRIC POWER DIST...   CORPORATE AFFILIATIONS

DATANG HUAYIN ELECTRIC POWER CO., LTD.; *Int'l*, pg. 1979
DAVIESS-MARTIN COUNTY RURAL ELECTRIC MEMBERSHIP CORPORATION; *U.S. Private*, pg. 1172
DAWSON COUNTY PUBLIC POWER DISTRICT; *U.S. Private*, pg. 1176
THE DAYTON POWER AND LIGHT COMPANY—See The AES Corporation; *U.S. Public*, pg. 2031
DBT; *Int'l*, pg. 1989
DC GROUP, INC.; *U.S. Private*, pg. 1179
DEEP EAST TEXAS ELECTRIC COOPERATIVE, INC.; *U.S. Private*, pg. 1189
DEE PEE ELECTRIC MEMBERSHIP; *U.S. Private*, pg. 1189
DELAWARE ELECTRIC COOPERATIVE; *U.S. Private*, pg. 1194
DELTA ELECTRIC POWER ASSOCIATION; *U.S. Private*, pg. 1200
DELTA ELECTRONICS (THAILAND) PUBLIC COMPANY LIMITED—See Delta Electronics, Inc.; *Int'l*, pg. 2018
DELTA-MONTROSE ELECTRIC ASSOCIATION; *U.S. Private*, pg. 1202
DELTA NETWERKBEDRIJF B.V.—See Delta N.V.; *Int'l*, pg. 2019
DELTA N.V.; *Int'l*, pg. 2019
DEMASZ PRIMAVILL HALOZATSZERELO IPARI KFT—See Electricite de France S.A.; *Int'l*, pg. 2350
DEVAL SPA—See Enel S.p.A.; *Int'l*, pg. 2411
DHAKA ELECTRIC SUPPLY COMPANY LIMITED; *Int'l*, pg. 2097
DIAMOND POWER CORPORATION—See Chubu Electric Power Co., Inc.; *Int'l*, pg. 1593
DIRECT ENERGY BUSINESS, LLC—See NRG Energy, Inc.; *U.S. Public*, pg. 1549
DISTRIBUIDORA DE ENERGIA ELECTRICA DEL BAGES SA—See Enel S.p.A.; *Int'l*, pg. 2412
DIVERSIFIED CONTROLS & SYSTEMS, INC.; *U.S. Private*, pg. 1241
DIXIE ELECTRIC COOPERATIVE; *U.S. Private*, pg. 1245
DIXIE ELECTRIC MEMBERSHIP CORP.; *U.S. Private*, pg. 1245
DIXIE ELECTRIC POWER ASSOCIATION; *U.S. Private*, pg. 1245
DIXIE ESCALANTE RURAL ELECTRIC ASSOCIATION, INC.; *U.S. Private*, pg. 1245
DOGAN SIRKETLER GRUBU HOLDING A.S.—See Adil Bey Holding A.S.; *Int'l*, pg. 148
DOMINICA ELECTRICITY SERVICES LTD.—See Emera, Inc.; *Int'l*, pg. 2377
DOMINION CLEARINGHOUSE—See Dominion Energy, Inc.; *U.S. Public*, pg. 674
DOMINION ENERGY, INC.—See Dominion Energy, Inc.; *U.S. Public*, pg. 674
DOMINION ENERGY KEWAUNEE, INC.—See Dominion Energy, Inc.; *U.S. Public*, pg. 674
DOMINION ENERGY SOUTH CAROLINA, INC.—See Dominion Energy, Inc.; *U.S. Public*, pg. 674
DOMINION GENERATION CORPORATION—See Dominion Energy, Inc.; *U.S. Public*, pg. 674
DOMINION INVESTMENTS, INC.—See Dominion Energy, Inc.; *U.S. Public*, pg. 674
DOREEN POWER GENERATIONS & SYSTEMS LIMITED; *Int'l*, pg. 2175
DOUGLAS ELECTRIC COOPERATIVE, INC.; *U.S. Private*, pg. 1267
DPL ENERGY RESOURCES, INC.—See Interstate Gas Supply Inc.; *U.S. Private*, pg. 2124
DPL INC.—See The AES Corporation; *U.S. Public*, pg. 2031
DTE ELECTRIC COMPANY—See DTE Energy Company; *U.S. Public*, pg. 689
DTE ENERGY TRADING, INC.—See DTE Energy Company; *U.S. Public*, pg. 689
DUCK RIVER ELECTRIC MEMBERSHIP CORPORATION; *U.S. Private*, pg. 1284
DUISBURGER VERSORGUNGS- UND VERKEHRSGESELLSCHAFT MBH; *Int'l*, pg. 2224
DUKE ENERGY CAROLINAS, LLC—See Duke Energy Corporation; *U.S. Public*, pg. 690
DUKE ENERGY CORPORATION; *U.S. Public*, pg. 690
DUKE ENERGY INDIANA, LLC—See Duke Energy Corporation; *U.S. Public*, pg. 690
DUKE ENERGY OHIO, INC.—See Duke Energy Corporation; *U.S. Public*, pg. 690
DUKE ENERGY OHIO, INC—See Duke Energy Corporation; *U.S. Public*, pg. 690
DURO DAKOVIC ELEKTROMONT D.D.—See Duro Dakovic Holding d.d.; *Int'l*, pg. 2228
DURO DAKOVIC ENERGETIKA I INFRASTRUKTURA D.O.O.—See Duro Dakovic Holding d.d.; *Int'l*, pg. 2228
DYNEGY, INC.—See Vistra Corp.; *U.S. Public*, pg. 2306
DYNEGY MARKETING AND TRADE, LLC—See Vistra Corp.; *U.S. Public*, pg. 2306
EARTH TECH ENVIRONMENT PUBLIC COMPANY LIMITED—See Better World Green Public Company Limited; *Int'l*, pg. 1003
EAST CENTRAL ENERGY; *U.S. Private*, pg. 1315
EAST CENTRAL OKLAHOMA ELECTRIC COOPERATIVE, INC.; *U.S. Private*, pg. 1316

EASTERN ILLINI ELECTRIC COOPERATIVE; *U.S. Private*, pg. 1319
EASTERN IOWA LIGHT & POWER COOPERATIVE INC.; *U.S. Private*, pg. 1320
EAST MISSISSIPPI ELECTRIC POWER ASSOCIATION; *U.S. Private*, pg. 1316
EAST RIVER ELECTRIC POWER COOPERATIVE; *U.S. Private*, pg. 1317
EAST TEXAS ELECTRIC COOPERATIVE, INC.; *U.S. Private*, pg. 1318
E.CL S.A.—See ENGIE SA; *Int'l*, pg. 2434
ECOTRICITY GROUP LTD.; *Int'l*, pg. 2300
ECS - ENERGY CONSULTING SERVICES—See ENGIE SA; *Int'l*, pg. 2434
ECURV INC.—See Exelon Corporation; *U.S. Public*, pg. 807
EDF DEMASZ PARTNER KFT—See Electricite de France S.A.; *Int'l*, pg. 2350
EDF HOLDING SAS—See Electricite de France S.A.; *Int'l*, pg. 2350
EDF RENEWABLES, INC.—See Electricite de France S.A.; *Int'l*, pg. 2350
EDISON S.P.A.—See Electricite de France S.A.; *Int'l*, pg. 2350
E.DISTHERM ENERGIELOSUNGEN GMBH—See E.ON SE; *Int'l*, pg. 2260
E.DISTHERM WARMEDIENSTLEISTUNGEN GMBH—See E.ON SE; *Int'l*, pg. 2260
EDISTO ELECTRIC COOPERATIVE; *U.S. Private*, pg. 1337
EDISTRIBUCION REDES DIGITALES SL—See Enel S.p.A.; *Int'l*, pg. 2411
ED NETZE GMBH—See EnBW Energie Baden-Wurttemberg AG; *Int'l*, pg. 2398
EDP DISTRIBUICAO DE ENERGIA, S.A.—See EDP - Energias de Portugal, S.A.; *Int'l*, pg. 2314
EDP DISTRIBUICAO—See EDP - Energias de Portugal, S.A.; *Int'l*, pg. 2314
EDP - ENERGIAS DE PORTUGAL, S.A.; *Int'l*, pg. 2314
EDP ESCELSA - ESPIRITO SANTO CENTRAIS ELETRICAS, S.A.—See EDP - Energias de Portugal, S.A.; *Int'l*, pg. 2314
EF KENILWORTH LLC—See I Squared Capital Advisors (US) LLC; *U.S. Private*, pg. 2025
EGW UTILITIES, INC.; *U.S. Private*, pg. 1346
ELBIS SP. Z O.O.—See Elektrownia Belchatow S.A.; *Int'l*, pg. 2357
ELCOTHERM AG—See Ariston Thermo S.p.A.; *Int'l*, pg. 567
ELECTRABEL CUSTOMER SOLUTIONS N.V./S.A.—See ENGIE SA; *Int'l*, pg. 2431
ELECTRABEL FRANCE S.A.—See ENGIE SA; *Int'l*, pg. 2431
ELECTRABEL NEDERLAND RETAIL N.V.—See ENGIE SA; *Int'l*, pg. 2431
ELECTRABEL S.A.—See ENGIE SA; *Int'l*, pg. 2431
ELECTRATHERM, INC.—See BITZER SE; *Int'l*, pg. 1052
ELECTRICA CONQUENSE, S.A.—See Iberdrola, S.A.; *Int'l*, pg. 3571
ELECTRICITE DE FRANCE S.A.; *Int'l*, pg. 2350
ELECTRICITE DE STRASBOURG; *Int'l*, pg. 2352
ELECTRICITE DE TAHITI—See ENGIE SA; *Int'l*, pg. 2431
ELECTRIC POWER DEVELOPMENT CO., LTD.; *Int'l*, pg. 2349
ELECTRO PUNO SAA; *Int'l*, pg. 2353
ELECTRO SUR ESTE SAA; *Int'l*, pg. 2353
ELEKTRILEVI OU—See Eesti Energia AS; *Int'l*, pg. 2317
ELEKTRIZITAETSWERK MINDEN-RAVENSBERG—See E.ON SE; *Int'l*, pg. 2253
ELEKTRIZITATSWERK DER STADT ZURICH; *Int'l*, pg. 2356
ELEKTRIZITATSWERK WEISSENHORN AG—See EnBW Energie Baden-Wurttemberg AG; *Int'l*, pg. 2398
ELEKTRODISTRIBUCIJA DOOEL—See EVN AG; *Int'l*, pg. 2571
ELEKTRO ELECTRICIDADE E SERVICOS, S.A.—See Iberdrola, S.A.; *Int'l*, pg. 3571
ELEKTROKRAJINA A.D. BANJA LUKA; *Int'l*, pg. 2357
ELEKTRO MACK GMBH; *Int'l*, pg. 2357
ELEKTRORAZPREDELENIE YUG EAD—See EVN AG; *Int'l*, pg. 2571
ELEKTRO SLOVENIA D.O.O.; *Int'l*, pg. 2357
ELEKTROWNIA BELCHATOW S.A.; *Int'l*, pg. 2357
ELEKTROWNIA KOZIENICE S.A.—See ENEA S.A.; *Int'l*, pg. 2410
ELETROPAULO METROPOLITANA ELETRICIDADE DE SAO PAULO S.A.—See Enel S.p.A.; *Int'l*, pg. 2412
ELETTRA INVESTIMENTI SPA—See CogenInfra SpA; *Int'l*, pg. 1694
ELIA GROUP SA; *Int'l*, pg. 2360
ELKHORN RURAL PUBLIC POWER DISTRICT; *U.S. Private*, pg. 1363
EL PASO ELECTRIC COMPANY—See JPMorgan Chase & Co.; *U.S. Public*, pg. 1206
ELSTA BV & CO. CV—See The AES Corporation; *U.S. Public*, pg. 2031
EMASZ; *Int'l*, pg. 2374
EMERA (CARIBBEAN) INCORPORATED—See Emera, Inc.; *Int'l*, pg. 2377
EMERSON D.O.O.—See Emerson Electric Co.; *U.S. Public*, pg. 749

THE EMPIRE DISTRICT ELECTRIC COMPANY—See Algonquin Power & Utilities Corp.; *Int'l*, pg. 319
EMPIRE ELECTRIC ASSOCIATION, INC.; *U.S. Private*, pg. 1384
EMPOWER LIMITED—See Contact Energy Limited; *Int'l*, pg. 1778
EMPRESA DE ALUMBRADO ELECTRICO DE CEUTA SA—See Enel S.p.A.; *Int'l*, pg. 2412
EMPRESA DE DISTRIBUCION ELECTRICA DE LIMA NORTE S.A.A.—See Enel S.p.A.; *Int'l*, pg. 2412
EMPRESA DISTRIBUIDORA SUR S.A.—See Enel S.p.A.; *Int'l*, pg. 2412
EMPRESA DISTRIBUIDORA Y COMERCIALIZADORA NORTE S.A.—See Grupo EMES S.A.; *Int'l*, pg. 3126
EMPRESA ELECTRICA CAMPICHE S.A.—See The AES Corporation; *U.S. Public*, pg. 2031
EMPRESA ELECTRICA DE ORIENTE, S.A. DE C.V.—See The AES Corporation; *U.S. Public*, pg. 2031
EMPRESA ELECTRICA PEHUENCHE, S.A.—See Enel S.p.A.; *Int'l*, pg. 2413
EMPRESA ENERGETICA DO MATO GROSSO DO SUL S.A.—See EDP - Energias de Portugal, S.A.; *Int'l*, pg. 2314
ENALPIN AG—See EnBW Energie Baden-Wurttemberg AG; *Int'l*, pg. 2398
ENBW ENERGY FACTORY GMBH—See EnBW Energie Baden-Wurttemberg AG; *Int'l*, pg. 2398
ENBW ENERGYWATCHERS GMBH—See EnBW Energie Baden-Wurttemberg AG; *Int'l*, pg. 2398
ENBW KERNKRAFT GMBH—See EnBW Energie Baden-Wurttemberg AG; *Int'l*, pg. 2398
ENBW KOMMUNALE BETEILIGUNGEN GMBH—See EnBW Energie Baden-Wurttemberg AG; *Int'l*, pg. 2398
ENBW KRAFTWERKE AG—See EnBW Energie Baden-Wurttemberg AG; *Int'l*, pg. 2398
ENBW OSTWURTTEMBERG DONAURIES AG—See EnBW Energie Baden-Wurttemberg AG; *Int'l*, pg. 2398
ENBW VERTRIEB GMBH—See EnBW Energie Baden-Wurttemberg AG; *Int'l*, pg. 2398
ENDESA CEMSA SA—See Enel S.p.A.; *Int'l*, pg. 2413
ENDESA NETWORK FACTORY SL—See Enel S.p.A.; *Int'l*, pg. 2412
ENDESA RED SA—See Enel S.p.A.; *Int'l*, pg. 2412
ENDESA, S.A.—See Enel S.p.A.; *Int'l*, pg. 2412
ENDINET B.V.—See Alliander N.V.; *Int'l*, pg. 341
ENEA INNOWACJE SP. Z O.O.—See ENEA S.A.; *Int'l*, pg. 2410
ENEA LOGISTYKA SP. Z O.O.—See ENEA S.A.; *Int'l*, pg. 2410
ENEA OPERATOR SP. Z O.O.—See ENEA S.A.; *Int'l*, pg. 2410
ENEA S.A.; *Int'l*, pg. 2410
ENEA SERWIS SP. Z O.O.—See ENEA S.A.; *Int'l*, pg. 2410
ENEA TRADING SP. Z O.O.—See ENEA S.A.; *Int'l*, pg. 2410
ENECO BELGIUM N.V.—See Eneco Holding N.V.; *Int'l*, pg. 2411
ENECO ZUID NEDERLAND B.V.—See Eneco Holding N.V.; *Int'l*, pg. 2411
ENEL AMERICAS S.A.—See Enel S.p.A.; *Int'l*, pg. 2412
ENEL CHILE S.A.—See Enel S.p.A.; *Int'l*, pg. 2412
ENEL DISTRIBUCION CEAR S.A.—See Enel S.p.A.; *Int'l*, pg. 2412
ENEL DISTRIBUCION CHILE SA—See Enel S.p.A.; *Int'l*, pg. 2412
ENEL DISTRIBUZIONE S.P.A.—See Enel S.p.A.; *Int'l*, pg. 2412
ENEL ENERGIA S.P.A.—See Enel S.p.A.; *Int'l*, pg. 2412
ENEL GENERACION CHILE S.A.—See Enel S.p.A.; *Int'l*, pg. 2413
ENEL SERVIZIO ELETTRICO SPA—See Enel S.p.A.; *Int'l*, pg. 2412
ENERGETIKA CHROPYNE, A.S.—See Agrofert Holding, a.s.; *Int'l*, pg. 219
ENERGETIKA MALENOVICE, A.S.—See E.ON SE; *Int'l*, pg. 2257
ENERGETIKA VITKOVICE, A.S.—See CEZ, a.s.; *Int'l*, pg. 1428
ENERGIA CEUTA XXI COMERCIALIZADORA DE REFERENCIA SA—See Enel S.p.A.; *Int'l*, pg. 2414
ENERGIA DEL SUR S.A.—See ENGIE SA; *Int'l*, pg. 2434
ENERGIAOK SP. Z O.O.—See City Service SE; *Int'l*, pg. 1627
ENERGIE AG; *Int'l*, pg. 2420
ENERGIE ELECTRIQUE DE TAHADDART SA—See Enel S.p.A.; *Int'l*, pg. 2414
ENERGIEOBJEKTGESELLSCHAFT MBH-EOG—See E.ON SE; *Int'l*, pg. 2253
ENERGIEVERSORGUNG GAILDORF OHG DER ENBW KOMMUNALE BETEILIGUNGEN GMBH—See EnBW Energie Baden-Wurttemberg AG; *Int'l*, pg. 2398
ENERGIEVERSORGUNGSBETRIEB GERRY WEBER GMBH—See GERRY WEBER International AG; *Int'l*, pg. 2944
ENERGIEWERKE ROSTOCK AG—See E.ON SE; *Int'l*, pg. 2253
ENERGIPARTNER AS—See Alpiq Holding AG; *Int'l*, pg. 373
ENERGISMART NORGE AS—See Elmera Group ASA; *Int'l*, pg. 2367

N.A.I.C.S. INDEX 221122 — ELECTRIC POWER DIST...

ENERGIT S.P.A.—See Alpiq Holding AG; *Int'l*, pg. 373
ENERGOMIAR SP. Z O.O.—See ENEA S.A.; *Int'l*, pg. 2410
ENERGO-PRO A.S.; *Int'l*, pg. 2420
ENERGO-PRO EAD—See ENERGO-PRO a.s.; *Int'l*, pg. 2420
ENERGO-PRO GRID AD—See E.ON SE; *Int'l*, pg. 2256
ENERGOS DEUTSCHLAND GMBH—See E.ON SE; *Int'l*, pg. 2257
ENERGY AIR GMBH—See Fraport AG; *Int'l*, pg. 2764
ENERGY DEVELOPMENT CORPORATION PERU S.A.C.—See First Gen Corporation; *Int'l*, pg. 2684
ENERGY POWER SYSTEMS PNG LIMITED—See Energy Power Systems Australia Pty. Ltd.; *Int'l*, pg. 2423
ENERGY UNITED ELECTRIC MEMBERSHIP CORPORATION; *U.S. Private*, pg. 1396
ENERGZET, A.S.—See Energeticky a Prumyslovy Holding, a.s.; *Int'l*, pg. 2419
ENERJISA BASKENT ELEKTRIK DAGITIM A.S.—See E.ON SE; *Int'l*, pg. 2257
ENERJISA BASKENT ELEKTRIK DAGITIM A.S.—See Haci Omer Sabanci Holding A.S.; *Int'l*, pg. 3204
ENERJISA ELEKTRIK ENERJISI TOPTAN SATIS A.S.—See E.ON SE; *Int'l*, pg. 2257
ENERJISA ELEKTRIK ENERJISI TOPTAN SATIS A.S.—See Haci Omer Sabanci Holding A.S.; *Int'l*, pg. 3204
ENERSOURCE TECHNOLOGIES—See Hydro One Limited; *Int'l*, pg. 3546
ENERTRADE—See EDP - Energias de Portugal, S.A.; *Int'l*, pg. 2314
ENGIE BRASIL ENERGIA SA—See ENGIE SA; *Int'l*, pg. 2432
ENGIE RESOURCES LLC—See ENGIE SA; *Int'l*, pg. 2428
ENGIE ROMANIA SA—See ENGIE SA; *Int'l*, pg. 2429
ENMAX COMMERCIAL SERVICES INC.—See ENMAX Corporation; *Int'l*, pg. 2442
ENMAX ENERGY CORPORATION—See ENMAX Corporation; *Int'l*, pg. 2442
ENOVOS DEUTSCHLAND SE—See Enovos International S.A.; *Int'l*, pg. 2444
ENOVOS LUXEMBOURG S.A.—See Enovos International S.A.; *Int'l*, pg. 2444
ENRO ENERGIE SE; *Int'l*, pg. 2445
ENRO LUDWIGSFELDE ENERGIE GMBH—See EWE Aktiengesellschaft; *Int'l*, pg. 2575
ENTERGY ARKANSAS, LLC—See Entergy Corporation; *U.S. Public*, pg. 777
ENTERGY CORPORATION; *U.S. Public*, pg. 777
ENTERGY LOUISIANA, LLC—See Entergy Corporation; *U.S. Public*, pg. 777
ENTERGY MISSISSIPPI, LLC—See Entergy Corporation; *U.S. Public*, pg. 777
ENTERGY NEW ORLEANS, LLC—See Entergy Corporation; *U.S. Public*, pg. 777
E.ON AUSTRIA GMBH—See E.ON SE; *Int'l*, pg. 2252
E.ON AVACON AG—See E.ON SE; *Int'l*, pg. 2252
E.ON AVACON VERTRIEB GMBH—See E.ON SE; *Int'l*, pg. 2252
E.ON BAYERN VERTRIEB GMBH—See E.ON SE; *Int'l*, pg. 2252
E.ON BAYERN WARME GMBH—See E.ON SE; *Int'l*, pg. 2252
E.ON BELGIUM N.V.—See E.ON SE; *Int'l*, pg. 2252
E.ON BENELUX CCS PROJECT B.V.—See E.ON SE; *Int'l*, pg. 2252
E.ON CESKA REPUBLIKA, S.R.O.—See E.ON SE; *Int'l*, pg. 2252
E.ON CLIMATE & RENEWABLES UK LONDON ARRAY LIMITED—See E.ON SE; *Int'l*, pg. 2256
E.ON CLIMATE & RENEWABLES UK ROBIN RIGG WEST LIMITED—See E.ON SE; *Int'l*, pg. 2256
E.ON COMERCIALIZADORA DE ULTIMO RECURSO S.L.—See E.ON SE; *Int'l*, pg. 2252
E.ON DANMARK A/S—See E.ON SE; *Int'l*, pg. 2252
E.ON DEL-DUNANTULI ARAMSZOLGALTATO ZRT.—See E.ON SE; *Int'l*, pg. 2253
E.ON DIREKT GMBH—See E.ON SE; *Int'l*, pg. 2252
E.ON DISTRIBUCE, A.S.—See E.ON SE; *Int'l*, pg. 2252
E.ON EDIS AG—See E.ON SE; *Int'l*, pg. 2256
E.ON EDIS CONTRACTING GMBH—See E.ON SE; *Int'l*, pg. 2256
E.ON ELNAT STOCKHOLM AB—See E.ON SE; *Int'l*, pg. 2255
E.ON ELNAT SVERIGE AB—See E.ON SE; *Int'l*, pg. 2255
E.ON ENERGIAKERESKEDO KFT.—See E.ON SE; *Int'l*, pg. 2253
E.ON ENERGIA S.P.A.—See F2i - Fondi Italiani per le infrastrutture SGR S.p.A.; *Int'l*, pg. 2597
E.ON ENERGIATERMELO KFT.—See E.ON SE; *Int'l*, pg. 2262
E.ON ENERGIE AG—See E.ON SE; *Int'l*, pg. 2252
E.ON ENERGIE, A.S.—See E.ON SE; *Int'l*, pg. 2252
E.ON ENERGIE ODNAWIALNE SP. Z O.O.—See E.ON SE; *Int'l*, pg. 2254
E.ON ENERGIE ROMANIA S.A.—See E.ON SE; *Int'l*, pg. 2254
E.ON ENERGY PROJECTS GMBH—See E.ON SE; *Int'l*, pg. 2253

E.ON ENERGY SALES GMBH—See E.ON SE; *Int'l*, pg. 2253
E.ON ENERGY TRADING BULGARIEN EOOD—See E.ON SE; *Int'l*, pg. 2254
E.ON ENERGY TRADING NL STAFF COMPANY B.V.—See E.ON SE; *Int'l*, pg. 2254
E.ON ENERGY UK LIMITED—See E.ON SE; *Int'l*, pg. 2256
E.ON EROMUVEK TERMELO ES UZEMELTETO KFT—See E.ON SE; *Int'l*, pg. 2254
E.ON ESZAK-DUNANTULI ARAMSZOLGALTATO ZRT.—See E.ON SE; *Int'l*, pg. 2253
E.ON FORSALJNING SVERIGE AB—See E.ON SE; *Int'l*, pg. 2255
E.ON FRANCE S.A.S.—See E.ON SE; *Int'l*, pg. 2254
E.ON HANSE VERTRIEB GMBH—See E.ON SE; *Int'l*, pg. 2254
E.ON HUNGARIA ZRT.—See E.ON SE; *Int'l*, pg. 2253
E.ON KAINUU OY—See E.ON SE; *Int'l*, pg. 2254
E.ON KUNDENSERVICE GMBH—See E.ON SE; *Int'l*, pg. 2254
E.ON METERING GMBH—See E.ON SE; *Int'l*, pg. 2253
E.ON MITTE WARME GMBH—See E.ON SE; *Int'l*, pg. 2254
E.ON MOLDOVA-FURNIZARE—See E.ON SE; *Int'l*, pg. 2253
E.ON NETZ GMBH—See E.ON SE; *Int'l*, pg. 2253
E.ON SERVISNI, S.R.O.—See E.ON SE; *Int'l*, pg. 2255
E.ON SUOMI OY—See E.ON SE; *Int'l*, pg. 2255
E.ON SVERIGE AB—See E.ON SE; *Int'l*, pg. 2255
E.ON TISZANTULI ARAMSZOLGALTATO RT.—See E.ON SE; *Int'l*, pg. 2253
E.ON VARME DANMARK APS—See E.ON SE; *Int'l*, pg. 2252
E.ON VERTRIEB DEUTSCHLAND GMBH—See E.ON SE; *Int'l*, pg. 2256
E.ON WASSERKRAFT GMBH—See E.ON SE; *Int'l*, pg. 2253
E.ON WESTFALEN WESER AG—See E.ON SE; *Int'l*, pg. 2253
E.ON WESTFALEN WESER VERTRIEB GMBH—See E.ON SE; *Int'l*, pg. 2253
EPB; *U.S. Private*, pg. 1411
EPCOR ENERGY—See EPCOR Utilities, Inc.; *Int'l*, pg. 2459
EPCOR MERCHANT & CAPITAL, L.P.—See EPCOR Utilities, Inc.; *Int'l*, pg. 2459
EPCOR UTILITIES, INC.; *Int'l*, pg. 2459
EP ENERGY TRADING, A.S.—See Energeticky a Prumyslovy Holding, a.s.; *Int'l*, pg. 2420
EP POWER EUROPE, A.S.—See Energeticky a Prumyslovy Holding, a.s.; *Int'l*, pg. 2420
EPS POLSKA SP. Z O.O.—See E.ON SE; *Int'l*, pg. 2256
EQUATORIAL ENERGIA SA; *Int'l*, pg. 2483
ERAG ELEKTRIZITATSWERK RHEINAU AG—See EnBW Energie Baden-Wurttemberg AG; *Int'l*, pg. 2398
ERDGAS-BETEILIGUNGSGESELLSCHAFT SUD MBH—See EnBW Energie Baden-Wurttemberg AG; *Int'l*, pg. 2399
EREX CO., LTD.; *Int'l*, pg. 2490
ERGON ENERGY CORPORATION LIMITED; *Int'l*, pg. 2491
ERGYTECH INC.—See Iberdrola, S.A.; *Int'l*, pg. 3570
ESENBOGA ELEKTRIK URETIM A.S.; *Int'l*, pg. 2502
ESKOM HOLDINGS SOC LIMITED; *Int'l*, pg. 2503
E-SQUARE CO., LTD.—See Ebara Corporation; *Int'l*, pg. 2282
ESSEL VIDYUT VITARAN (GWALIOR) PVT. LTD.—See Essel Corporate Resources Pvt. Ltd.; *Int'l*, pg. 2509
ESSEL VIDYUT VITARAN (MUZAFFARPUR) LIMITED—See Essel Corporate Resources Pvt. Ltd.; *Int'l*, pg. 2509
ESSEL VIDYUT VITARAN (SAGAR) PRIVATE LIMITED—See Essel Corporate Resources Pvt. Ltd.; *Int'l*, pg. 2509
ESSEL VIDYUT VITARAN (UJJAIN) PVT. LTD.—See Essel Corporate Resources Pvt. Ltd.; *Int'l*, pg. 2509
ESSENT N.V.—See E.ON SE; *Int'l*, pg. 2257
ESTONIA AS FORTUM—See Fortum Oyj; *Int'l*, pg. 2740
ETA ELECTRIC INDUSTRY CO., LTD.; *Int'l*, pg. 2519
EUROCOMPONENTES, S.A.—See Arrow Electronics, Inc.; *U.S. Public*, pg. 199
EUROSITE POWER INC.—See Tecogen Inc.; *U.S. Public*, pg. 1989
EVERGY KANSAS CENTRAL, INC.—See Evergy, Inc.; *U.S. Public*, pg. 800
EVERSOURCEENERGY—See Eversource Energy; *U.S. Public*, pg. 801
EVERYTHING ENERGY LLC—See NRG Energy, Inc.; *U.S. Public*, pg. 1550
EVIVA-LEBORK SP.Z O.O.—See The AES Corporation; *U.S. Public*, pg. 2031
EVN AG; *Int'l*, pg. 2570
EVN BULGARIA ELEKTRORAZPREDELENIE AD—See EVN AG; *Int'l*, pg. 2570
EVN BULGARIA ELEKTROSNABDIAVANE AD—See EVN AG; *Int'l*, pg. 2571
EVN MACEDONIA AD—See EVN AG; *Int'l*, pg. 2571
EVN MACEDONIA ELEKTROSNABDUVANJE DOOEL—See EVN AG; *Int'l*, pg. 2571
EVN TRADING D.O.O. BEOGRAD—See EVN AG; *Int'l*, pg. 2571

EVN TRADING SOUTH EAST EUROPE EAD—See EVN AG; *Int'l*, pg. 2571
EWE AKTIENGESELLSCHAFT; *Int'l*, pg. 2575
EWE TRADING GMBH—See EWE Aktiengesellschaft; *Int'l*, pg. 2575
EWE VERTRIEB GMBH—See EWE Aktiengesellschaft; *Int'l*, pg. 2575
E WIE EINFACH STROM & GAS GMBH—See E.ON SE; *Int'l*, pg. 2252
EXCELSIOR ELECTRIC MEMBERSHIP CORPORATION; *U.S. Private*, pg. 1446
EXELON ENERGY DELIVERY COMPANY, LLC—See Exelon Corporation; *U.S. Public*, pg. 806
EXELON NUCLEAR PARTNERS, LLC—See Constellation Energy Corporation; *U.S. Public*, pg. 572
EXELON POWERLABS, LLC—See Constellation Energy Corporation; *U.S. Public*, pg. 572
EXELON TRANSMISSION COMPANY, LLC—See Exelon Corporation; *U.S. Public*, pg. 807
FAHRENHEIT—See Electricite de France S.A.; *Int'l*, pg. 2351
FAIRFIELD ELECTRIC COOPERATIVE; *U.S. Private*, pg. 1463
FALL RIVER RURAL ELECTRIC COOPERATIVE, INC.; *U.S. Private*, pg. 1467
FARASIS ENERGY (GANZHOU) CO., LTD.; *Int'l*, pg. 2618
FARMERS ELECTRIC COOPERATIVE CORPORATION; *U.S. Private*, pg. 1477
FARMERS RURAL ELECTRIC COOP CORP.; *U.S. Private*, pg. 1479
THE FARMINGTON RIVER POWER COMPANY—See Stanley Black & Decker, Inc.; *U.S. Public*, pg. 1936
FAYETTEVILLE ELECTRIC SYSTEM, INC.; *U.S. Private*, pg. 1484
FEDERAL ENERGI PTE LTD—See Federal International (2000) Ltd; *Int'l*, pg. 2630
FEM ELECTRIC ASSOCIATION, INC.; *U.S. Private*, pg. 1494
FINA ENERJI HOLDING A.S.—See Fiba Holding A.S.; *Int'l*, pg. 2651
FINTEL ENERGIA GROUP S.P.A.; *Int'l*, pg. 2677
FIRELANDS ELECTRIC COOPERATIVE, INC.; *U.S. Private*, pg. 1512
FIRST ELECTRIC COOPERATIVE CORP.; *U.S. Private*, pg. 1517
FIRSTENERGY SERVICE COMPANY—See FirstEnergy Corp.; *U.S. Public*, pg. 849
FIRST GEN CORPORATION; *Int'l*, pg. 2683
FLATHEAD ELECTRIC COOPERATIVE, INC.; *U.S. Private*, pg. 1541
FLINT ELECTRIC MEMBERSHIP CORPORATION; *U.S. Private*, pg. 1545
FLINT HILLS RURAL ELECTRIC COOP; *U.S. Private*, pg. 1545
FLORIDA KEYS ELECTRIC COOPERATIVE ASSOCIATION, INC.; *U.S. Private*, pg. 1549
FLORIDA POWER & LIGHT COMPANY—See NextEra Energy, Inc.; *U.S. Public*, pg. 1526
FORCEFIELD ENERGY INC.; *U.S. Public*, pg. 1563
FORT BELKNAP ELECTRIC COOP; *U.S. Private*, pg. 1574
FORTISALBERTA INC.—See Fortis Inc.; *Int'l*, pg. 2739
FORTISBC INC.—See Fortis Inc.; *Int'l*, pg. 2739
FORTISTCI LIMITED—See Fortis Inc.; *Int'l*, pg. 2739
FORT LOUDOUN ELECTRIC COOPERATIVE; *U.S. Private*, pg. 1574
FORTUM BCS OY—See Fortum Oyj; *Int'l*, pg. 2740
FORTUM DISTRIBUTION AB—See Folksam omsesidig sakforsakring; *Int'l*, pg. 2721
FORTUM DISTRIBUTION AS—See Hafslund ASA; *Int'l*, pg. 3206
FORTUM FNW OY—See Fortum Oyj; *Int'l*, pg. 2741
FORTUM INDIA PRIVATE LIMITED—See Fortum Oyj; *Int'l*, pg. 2741
FORTUM LATVIA SIA—See Fortum Oyj; *Int'l*, pg. 2741
FORTUM MARKETING & SALES POLSKA S.A.—See Fortum Oyj; *Int'l*, pg. 2741
FORTUM MARKETS AB—See Fortum Oyj; *Int'l*, pg. 2741
FORTUM NETWORK WROCLAW SP. Z O.O.—See Fortum Oyj; *Int'l*, pg. 2741
FORTUM POWER AND HEAT OY—See Fortum Oyj; *Int'l*, pg. 2741
FORTUM SERVICE DEUTSCHLAND GMBH—See Fortum Oyj; *Int'l*, pg. 2741
FORTUM SVERIGE AB—See Fortum Oyj; *Int'l*, pg. 2741
FORTUM SWEDEN AB—See Fortum Oyj; *Int'l*, pg. 2741
FORTUM WASTE SOLUTIONS NORWAY AS—See Fortum Oyj; *Int'l*, pg. 2741
FORTUM WASTE SOLUTIONS OY—See Fortum Oyj; *Int'l*, pg. 2741
FOUR COUNTY ELECTRIC MEMBERSHIP CORPORATION; *U.S. Private*, pg. 1582
FOUR COUNTY ELECTRIC POWER ASSOCIATION; *U.S. Private*, pg. 1582
FOURMILE WIND ENERGY, LLC—See Constellation Energy Corporation; *U.S. Public*, pg. 572
FRANKLIN COUNTY PUD INC.; *U.S. Private*, pg. 1597
FRANZ LOHR GMBH—See Alpiq Holding AG; *Int'l*, pg. 372
FREENET ENERGY GMBH—See freenet AG; *Int'l*, pg. 2770

221122 — ELECTRIC POWER DIST...   CORPORATE AFFILIATIONS

FULTON COUNTY RURAL ELECTRIC MEMBERSHIP CORPORATION; *U.S. Private*, pg. 1621
FUTUREN SA—See Electricite de France S.A.; *Int'l*, pg. 2350
GAH PENSIONS GMBH—See Alpiq Holding AG; *Int'l*, pg. 372
GALATA WIND ENERJI A.S.; *Int'l*, pg. 2871
GARKANE ENERGY COOPERATIVE, INC.; *U.S. Private*, pg. 1644
GASCOSAGE ELECTRIC COOPERATIVE; *U.S. Private*, pg. 1648
GAYLOR INC. - UTILITY DIVISION—See Gaylor Inc.; *U.S. Private*, pg. 1652
GBB POWER LTD.; *Int'l*, pg. 2893
GDF SUEZ ENERGIE SERVICES SA—See ENGIE SA; *Int'l*, pg. 2429
GDF SUEZ ENERGY ANDINO S.A.—See ENGIE SA; *Int'l*, pg. 2434
GDF SUEZ ENERGY ARGENTINA—See ENGIE SA; *Int'l*, pg. 2434
GDF SUEZ ENERGY ASIA—See ENGIE SA; *Int'l*, pg. 2433
GDF SUEZ ENERGY BRASIL—See ENGIE SA; *Int'l*, pg. 2434
GDF SUEZ ENERGY LATIN AMERICA—See ENGIE SA; *Int'l*, pg. 2433
GDF SUEZ ENERGY PERU—See ENGIE SA; *Int'l*, pg. 2434
GDF SUEZ ENERGY UK RETAIL—See ENGIE SA; *Int'l*, pg. 2433
GDF SUEZ SHOTTON LIMITED—See ENGIE SA; *Int'l*, pg. 2432
GDF SUEZ SOLUTIONS LIMITED—See ENGIE SA; *Int'l*, pg. 2432
GEDIA S.A.; *Int'l*, pg. 2910
GE ENERGY—See General Electric Company; *U.S. Public*, pg. 917
GE GRID SOLUTIONS LLC—See Alstom S.A.; *Int'l*, pg. 381
GE GRID SOLUTIONS LLC—See General Electric Company; *U.S. Public*, pg. 917
GEORGIA ENERGY COOPERATIVE; *U.S. Private*, pg. 1684
GEORGIA POWER COMPANY—See The Southern Company; *U.S. Public*, pg. 2130
GETEC ENERGIE AG—See BP plc; *Int'l*, pg. 1131
GE VERNOVA INC.; *U.S. Public*, pg. 909
GIBSON ELECTRIC MEMBERSHIP CORP.; *U.S. Private*, pg. 1696
GITA RENEWABLE ENERGY LIMITED; *Int'l*, pg. 2979
GLADES ELECTRIC COOPERATIVE; *U.S. Private*, pg. 1704
GNPOWER MARIVELES ENERGY CENTER LTD. CO.—See Aboitiz Equity Ventures, Inc.; *Int'l*, pg. 66
GOTA ENERGI AB—See Fortum Oyj; *Int'l*, pg. 2741
GRADY ELECTRIC MEMBERSHIP CORPORATION; *U.S. Private*, pg. 1750
GRAHAM COUNTY ELECTRIC COOPERATIVE, INC.; *U.S. Private*, pg. 1751
GRAND BAHAMA POWER COMPANY LIMITED—See Emera, Inc.; *Int'l*, pg. 2377
GRANITE STATE ELECTRIC COMPANY—See Algonquin Power & Utilities Corp.; *Int'l*, pg. 319
GRAYBAR ENERGY LIMITED—See Graybar Electric Company, Inc.; *U.S. Private*, pg. 1760
GRAYS HARBOR PUD NO. 1; *U.S. Private*, pg. 1761
GRAYSON-COLLIN ELECTRIC COOPERATIVE, INC.; *U.S. Private*, pg. 1761
GREAT BAY POWER MARKETING, INC.—See Tavistock Group, Inc.; *U.S. Private*, pg. 3937
GREAT LAKES ENERGY COOPERATIVE; *U.S. Private*, pg. 1764
GREEN ENERGY SOLUTION INDUSTRIES, INC.; *Int'l*, pg. 3071
GREENEVILLE LIGHT & POWER SYSTEM; *U.S. Private*, pg. 1777
GREENHUNTER RESOURCES, INC.; *U.S. Private*, pg. 1778
GREEN MOUNTAIN ENERGY COMPANY—See NRG Energy, Inc.; *U.S. Public*, pg. 1550
GREEN MOUNTAIN POWER CORPORATION—See Caisse de Depot et Placement du Quebec; *Int'l*, pg. 1256
GREENPOWER GROUP PTY. LTD.—See Great Northern Minerals Limited; *Int'l*, pg. 3065
GREENSBURG WIND FARM, LLC—See Constellation Energy Corporation; *U.S. Public*, pg. 572
GREMZ POWER, INC.—See gremz, Inc.; *Int'l*, pg. 3080
GRENADA ELECTRICITY SERVICES LIMITED; *Int'l*, pg. 3080
GRUNDY ELECTRIC COOPERATIVE, INC.; *U.S. Private*, pg. 1797
GS E&C CORP.—See GS Holdings Corp.; *Int'l*, pg. 3141
GS EPS CO., LTD.—See GS Holdings Corp.; *Int'l*, pg. 3141
GUADALUPE VALLEY ELECTRIC COOP; *U.S. Private*, pg. 1808
GUJARAT INDUSTRIES POWER COMPANY LIMITED; *Int'l*, pg. 3176
GULF TOTAL TRACTEBEL POWER COMPANY; *Int'l*, pg. 3182
HAFSLUND ASA; *Int'l*, pg. 3206

HAFSLUND EIENDOM AS—See Hafslund ASA; *Int'l*, pg. 3206
HAFSLUND ENERGI AB—See Fortum Oyj; *Int'l*, pg. 2742
HAFSLUND ENERGY TRADING AS—See Hafslund ASA; *Int'l*, pg. 3206
HAFSLUND FJERNVARME AS—See Hafslund ASA; *Int'l*, pg. 3206
HAFSLUND HEDGING AS—See Hafslund ASA; *Int'l*, pg. 3206
HAFSLUND NETT AS—See Hafslund ASA; *Int'l*, pg. 3206
HAFSLUND STROM AS—See Hafslund ASA; *Int'l*, pg. 3206
HAINAN POWER GRID COMPANY—See China Southern Power Grid Co., Ltd.; *Int'l*, pg. 1553
HALIFAX ELECTRIC MEMBERSHIP CORP.; *U.S. Private*, pg. 1842
HALLINGKRAFT AS—See Hafslund ASA; *Int'l*, pg. 3206
HALTON HILLS HYDRO INC.; *Int'l*, pg. 3234
HAMILTON COUNTY ELECTRIC COOPERATIVE; *U.S. Private*, pg. 1847
HANJUNG POWER CO., LTD.—See Doosan Corporation; *Int'l*, pg. 2174
HANSEWERK AG—See E.ON SE; *Int'l*, pg. 2253
HANWHA ENERGY CORP.—See Hanwha Group; *Int'l*, pg. 3265
HARBOR ELECTRIC ENERGY COMPANY—See Eversource Energy; *U.S. Public*, pg. 801
HART ELECTRIC MEMBERSHIP CORPORATION; *U.S. Private*, pg. 1872
HAWAIIAN ELECTRIC COMPANY, INC.—See Hawaiian Electric Industries, Inc.; *U.S. Public*, pg. 989
HBIS GROUP ELECTRICITY SALES CO., LTD.—See HBIS Group Co., Ltd.; *Int'l*, pg. 3296
HEART OF TEXAS ELECTRIC COOPERATIVE INC.; *U.S. Private*, pg. 1899
HEATH FARM ENERGY LIMITED—See Aviva plc; *Int'l*, pg. 746
HENAN BCCY ENVIRONMENTAL ENERGY CO., LTD.; *Int'l*, pg. 3342
HEP ENERGIJA D.O.O.—See Hrvatska elektroprivreda d.d.; *Int'l*, pg. 3502
HEP ESCO D.O.O.—See Hrvatska elektroprivreda d.d.; *Int'l*, pg. 3502
HEP-ODMOR I REKREACIJA D.O.O.—See Hrvatska elektroprivreda d.d.; *Int'l*, pg. 3502
HEP-OPERATOR PRIJENOSNOG SUSTAVA D.O.O.—See Hrvatska elektroprivreda d.d.; *Int'l*, pg. 3502
HEP OPSKRBA D.O.O.—See Hrvatska elektroprivreda d.d.; *Int'l*, pg. 3502
HEP-TELEKOMUNIKACIJE D.O.O.—See Hrvatska elektroprivreda d.d.; *Int'l*, pg. 3502
HEP-TRGOVINA D.O.O.—See Hrvatska elektroprivreda d.d.; *Int'l*, pg. 3502
HEP-UPRAVLJANJE IMOVINOM D.O.O.—See Hrvatska elektroprivreda d.d.; *Int'l*, pg. 3502
HIDROELECTRICA DEL CANTABRICO, S.A.—See EDP - Energias de Portugal, S.A.; *Int'l*, pg. 2314
HIGH ENERGY INC.; *U.S. Public*, pg. 1935
HIGHLINE ELECTRIC ASSOCIATION; *U.S. Private*, pg. 1940
HIGH WEST ENERGY, INC.; *U.S. Private*, pg. 1937
HILCO ELECTRIC COOPERATIVE; *U.S. Private*, pg. 1943
H.I.S. SUPER POWER CO., LTD.—See H.I.S. Co., Ltd.; *Int'l*, pg. 3195
HOA PHAT ENERGY JSC—See Hoa Phat Group Joint Stock Company; *Int'l*, pg. 3435
HOKUDEN ECO-ENERGY CO., LTD.—See Hokkaido Electric Power Co., Inc.; *Int'l*, pg. 3443
HOKURIKU ELECTRIC POWER CO.; *Int'l*, pg. 3445
HOLSTON ELECTRIC COOPERATIVE INC.; *U.S. Private*, pg. 1968
HOLY CROSS ENERGY; *U.S. Private*, pg. 1969
HORIZON ENERGY DISTRIBUTION LIMITED—See Eastern Bay Energy Trust; *Int'l*, pg. 2271
HORIZON POWER, INC.—See National Fuel Gas Company; *U.S. Public*, pg. 1494
HORRY ELECTRIC COOPERATIVE INC.; *U.S. Private*, pg. 1984
HOWELL-OREGON ELECTRIC COOPERATIVE, INC.; *U.S. Private*, pg. 1996
HTB ENERGY CO., LTD.—See H.I.S. Co., Ltd.; *Int'l*, pg. 3195
HUADIAN POWER INTERNATIONAL CORPORATION LIMITED; *Int'l*, pg. 3511
HUNAN YUSSEN ENERGY TECHNOLOGY CO., LTD.; *Int'l*, pg. 3534
HYDRO ENERGIES CORPORATION—See Enel S.p.A.; *Int'l*, pg. 2414
HYDRO ONE INC.—See Hydro One Limited; *Int'l*, pg. 3546
HYDRO ONE NETWORKS, INC.—See Hydro One Limited; *Int'l*, pg. 3546
HYDRO OTTAWA LIMITED—See Hydro Ottawa Holding Inc.; *Int'l*, pg. 3546
IAHL CORP.; *U.S. Public*, pg. 1083
IBERDROLA CLIENTES PORTUGAL, UNIPESSOAL—See Iberdrola, S.A.; *Int'l*, pg. 3572
IBERDROLA DISTRIBUCION DE GAS, S.A.U.—See Iberdrola, S.A.; *Int'l*, pg. 3572
IBERDROLA DISTRIBUCION ELECTRICA, S.A.U.—See Iberdrola, S.A.; *Int'l*, pg. 3572

IBERDROLA ENERGIAS RENOVABLES, S.A.U.—See Iberdrola, S.A.; *Int'l*, pg. 3572
IBERDROLA GENERACION, S.A.U.—See Iberdrola, S.A.; *Int'l*, pg. 3572
IBERDROLA IRELAND, LTD.—See Iberdrola, S.A.; *Int'l*, pg. 3572
IBERDROLA REDES, S.A.U.—See Iberdrola, S.A.; *Int'l*, pg. 3572
IBERDROLA USA, INC.—See Iberdrola, S.A.; *Int'l*, pg. 3570
ICAP ENERGY AS—See CME Group, Inc.; *U.S. Public*, pg. 516
IC ICTAS ELEKTRIK URETIM A.S.—See The AES Corporation; *U.S. Public*, pg. 2031
IDAHO ENERGY RESOURCES COMPANY—See IDACORP, Inc.; *U.S. Public*, pg. 1088
IDAHO POWER COMPANY—See IDACORP, Inc.; *U.S. Public*, pg. 1088
IDA-WEST ENERGY COMPANY—See IDACORP, Inc.; *U.S. Public*, pg. 1088
IETV ELEKTROTEKNIK AB—See Addtech AB; *Int'l*, pg. 133
ILLINOIS RURAL ELECTRIC COOPERATIVE; *U.S. Private*, pg. 2042
INCHEON TOTAL ENERGY COMPANY—See GS Holdings Corp.; *Int'l*, pg. 3142
INDECK ENERGY SERVICES, INC.—See Indeck Power Equipment Company; *U.S. Private*, pg. 2055
INDECK ENERGY SERVICES OF OSWEGO INC.—See Indeck Power Equipment Company; *U.S. Private*, pg. 2055
INDEPENDENCE ENERGY GROUP LLC—See NRG Energy, Inc.; *U.S. Public*, pg. 1550
INDIANA MICHIGAN POWER COMPANY—See American Electric Power Company, Inc.; *U.S. Public*, pg. 99
INDIANA MUNICIPAL POWER AGENCY; *U.S. Private*, pg. 2062
INDIAN ELECTRIC COOPERATIVE; *U.S. Private*, pg. 2061
INFINITE ENERGY INC.; *U.S. Private*, pg. 2071
INFRAESTRUCTURA ENERGETICA NOVA, S.A.B. DE C.V.—See Sempra; *U.S. Public*, pg. 1863
INLAND POWER & LIGHT COMPANY INC.; *U.S. Private*, pg. 2079
INTERCONEXION ELECTRICA ISA PERU S.A.—See Ecopetrol S.A.; *Int'l*, pg. 2299
INTERCONEXION ELECTRICA S.A. E.S.P.—See Ecopetrol S.A.; *Int'l*, pg. 2299
INTER-COUNTY ELECTRIC COOP ASSOCIATION; *U.S. Private*, pg. 2107
INTER-COUNTY ENERGY COOP CORP.; *U.S. Private*, pg. 2107
INTERNATIONAL POWER AMERICA, INC.—See ENGIE SA; *Int'l*, pg. 2433
INTERNATIONAL POWER AUSTRALIA PTY LTD.—See ENGIE SA; *Int'l*, pg. 2433
IRIDIUM SERVICES DEUTSCHLAND GMBH—See E.ON SE; *Int'l*, pg. 2260
JACKSON COUNTY RURAL ELECTRIC MEMBERSHIP CORPORATION; *U.S. Private*, pg. 2176
JACKSON ELECTRIC MEMBERSHIP CORP.; *U.S. Private*, pg. 2176
JACKSON ENERGY COOPERATIVE; *U.S. Private*, pg. 2176
JEA; *U.S. Private*, pg. 2196
JEFFERSON ENERGY COOPERATIVE; *U.S. Private*, pg. 2197
JEMEZ MOUNTAIN ELECTRIC CO-OP; *U.S. Private*, pg. 2199
JERSEY CENTRAL POWER & LIGHT COMPANY—See FirstEnergy Corp.; *U.S. Public*, pg. 849
JEXEL NUCLEAR COMPANY—See Exelon Corporation; *U.S. Public*, pg. 807
JOE WHEELER ELECTRIC MEMBERSHIP; *U.S. Private*, pg. 2219
JUICE TECHNOLOGIES, LLC; *U.S. Private*, pg. 2243
KC ELECTRIC ASSOCIATION; *U.S. Private*, pg. 2269
KCP&L GREATER MISSOURI OPERATIONS COMPANY—See Evergy, Inc.; *U.S. Public*, pg. 801
K-ELECTRIC LIMITED—See Abraaj Capital Limited; *Int'l*, pg. 67
KENERGY CORP.; *U.S. Private*, pg. 2283
KINCAID GENERATION, L.L.C.—See Dominion Energy, Inc.; *U.S. Public*, pg. 674
KISSIMMEE UTILITY AUTHORITY; *U.S. Private*, pg. 2315
KLONDYKE CONSTRUCTION LLC—See Goldberg Lindsay & Co., LLC; *U.S. Private*, pg. 1729
KOMMENERGIE GMBH—See E.ON SE; *Int'l*, pg. 2258
KOTA ELECTRICITY DISTRIBUTION LIMITED—See CESC Limited; *Int'l*, pg. 1424
KOTIMAAN ENERGIA OY—See Fortum Oyj; *Int'l*, pg. 2742
KOZIENICE II SP. Z O.O.—See ENEA S.A.; *Int'l*, pg. 2410
KRAFTANLAGEN HAMBURG GMBH—See Alpiq Holding AG; *Int'l*, pg. 372
KRAFTANLAGEN HEIDELBERG GMBH—See Alpiq Holding AG; *Int'l*, pg. 372
KRAFTPOWER KFT.—See Alpiq Holding AG; *Int'l*, pg. 373
KRAFTWERK MEHRUM GMBH—See Energeticky a Prumyslovy Holding, a.s.; *Int'l*, pg. 2420

3158

N.A.I.C.S. INDEX

221122 — ELECTRIC POWER DIST...

LACLEDE ELECTRIC COOPERATIVE INC.; *U.S. Private*, pg. 2371
LAKE COUNTRY POWER; *U.S. Private*, pg. 2374
LAKELAND ELECTRIC; *U.S. Private*, pg. 2376
LAKE REGION ELECTRIC COOP; *U.S. Private*, pg. 2375
LAMB COUNTY ELECTRIC COOPERATIVE, INC.; *U.S. Private*, pg. 2379
LA PLATA ELECTRIC ASSOCIATION; *U.S. Private*, pg. 2369
LATROBE POWER PARTNERSHIP—See ENGIE SA; *Int'l*, pg. 2432
LAURENS ELECTRIC COOPERATIVE; *U.S. Private*, pg. 2399
LEA COUNTY ELECTRIC COOP; *U.S. Private*, pg. 2405
LENOIR CITY UTILITIES BOARD INC.; *U.S. Private*, pg. 2422
LG&E AND KU ENERGY LLC—See PPL Corporation; *U.S. Public*, pg. 1711
LIBERTY POWER CORP. LLC; *U.S. Private*, pg. 2447
LIBERTY UTILITIES (CANADA) CORP.—See Algonquin Power & Utilities Corp.; *Int'l*, pg. 319
LIBERTY UTILITIES WEST—See Algonquin Power & Utilities Corp.; *Int'l*, pg. 319
LINN COUNTY RURAL ELECTRIC COOPERATIVE ASSOCIATION; *U.S. Private*, pg. 2462
LITTLE OCMULGEE ELECTRIC CORPORATION; *U.S. Private*, pg. 2469
LOGAN COUNTY ELECTRIC COOPERATIVE; *U.S. Private*, pg. 2480
LONG ISLAND POWER AUTHORITY; *U.S. Private*, pg. 2490
L & O POWER COOPERATIVE; *U.S. Private*, pg. 2361
LORAIN-MEDINA RURAL ELECTRONIC COOPERATIVE, INC.; *U.S. Private*, pg. 2494
LOUISIANA ENERGY & POWER AUTHORITY; *U.S. Private*, pg. 2499
LOUISVILLE GAS AND ELECTRIC COMPANY—See PPL Corporation; *U.S. Public*, pg. 1711
LOWER COLORADO RIVER AUTHORITY; *U.S. Private*, pg. 2505
LOWER VALLEY ENERGY INC.; *U.S. Private*, pg. 2506
LSW LANDE-STADTWERKE WOLFSBURG GMBH & CO. KG—See E.ON SE; *Int'l*, pg. 2254
LUFKIN INDUSTRIES LLC—See KPS Capital Partners, LP; *U.S. Private*, pg. 2347
LUMBEE RIVER ELECTRIC MEMBERSHIP CORP.; *U.S. Private*, pg. 2513
LUMENERGIA S.P.A.—See A2A S.p.A.; *Int'l*, pg. 29
LUZ DEL SUR S.A.A—See Sempra; *U.S. Public*, pg. 1863
LYON-COFFEY ELECTRIC COOPERATIVE, INC.; *U.S. Private*, pg. 2522
MADISON GAS & ELECTRIC COMPANY—See MGE Energy, Inc.; *U.S. Public*, pg. 1434
M & A ELECTRIC POWER COOPERATIVE; *U.S. Private*, pg. 2522
MAI-LIAO POWER CORPORATION—See Formosa Plastics Corporation; *Int'l*, pg. 2736
MANAUS ENERGIA S/A—See Centrais Eletricas Brasileiras S.A.; *Int'l*, pg. 1403
MARITIME ELECTRIC COMPANY LIMITED—See Fortis Inc.; *Int'l*, pg. 2740
MARKEDSKRAFT ASA—See Agder Energi AS; *Int'l*, pg. 204
MARKEDSKRAFT ASA—See Arendals Fossekompani ASA; *Int'l*, pg. 559
MAUI ELECTRIC COMPANY, LIMITED—See Hawaiian Electric Industries, Inc.; *U.S. Public*, pg. 989
MCKENZIE ELECTRIC COOPERATIVE, INC.; *U.S. Private*, pg. 2638
MC SQUARED ENERGY SERVICES, LLC; *U.S. Private*, pg. 2625
THE MEDICAL CENTER COMPANY; *U.S. Private*, pg. 4077
MEKONG ENERGY COMPANY LTD.—See Electricite de France S.A.; *Int'l*, pg. 2352
MENARD ELECTRIC COOPERATIVE; *U.S. Private*, pg. 2665
MERIWETHER LEWIS ELECTRIC COOPERATIVE; *U.S. Private*, pg. 2675
METROPOLITAN EDISON COMPANY—See FirstEnergy Corp.; *U.S. Public*, pg. 849
MIAMI VALLEY LIGHTING, LLC—See The AES Corporation; *U.S. Public*, pg. 2031
MIDAMERICAN ENERGY COMPANY—See Berkshire Hathaway Inc.; *U.S. Public*, pg. 300
MID-CAROLINA ELECTRIC COOPERATIVE, INC.; *U.S. Private*, pg. 2707
MIDCONTINENT INDEPENDENT SYSTEM OPERATOR, INC.; *U.S. Private*, pg. 2710
MIDDLE TENNESSEE ELECTRIC MEMBERSHIP CORPORATION; *U.S. Private*, pg. 2711
MID-SOUTH SYNERGY; *U.S. Private*, pg. 2709
MIDSTATE ELECTRIC COOPERATIVE, INC.; *U.S. Private*, pg. 2718
MIDWAY-SUNSET COGENERATION COMPANY—See Edison International; *U.S. Public*, pg. 719
MIDWEST CONNECTIONS, INC.—See Midwest Energy Cooperative Inc.; *U.S. Private*, pg. 2721
MIDWEST ELECTRIC COOP CORP.; *U.S. Private*, pg. 2721

MIDWEST ENERGY COOPERATIVE INC.; *U.S. Private*, pg. 2721
MINNKOTA POWER COOPERATIVE, INC.; *U.S. Private*, pg. 2744
MISSOULA ELECTRIC CO-OP INC.; *U.S. Private*, pg. 2749
MITCHELL ELECTRIC MEMBERSHIP CORPORATION; *U.S. Private*, pg. 2750
MJM ELECTRIC COOPERATIVE, INC.; *U.S. Private*, pg. 2753
MOHAVE ELECTRIC COOP INC.; *U.S. Private*, pg. 2765
MONTAGUE SOLAR, LLC—See Iberdrola, S.A.; *Int'l*, pg. 3573
MOON LAKE ELECTRIC ASSOCIATION INC.; *U.S. Private*, pg. 2778
MORA-SAN MIGUEL ELECTRIC COOPERATIVE, INC.; *U.S. Private*, pg. 2781
MOUNTAIN ELECTRIC COOPERATIVE INC.; *U.S. Private*, pg. 2799
MOUNT WHEELER POWER INC.; *U.S. Private*, pg. 2798
MULBERRY FARM, LLC—See Dominion Energy, Inc.; *U.S. Public*, pg. 674
MUSTEQ HYDRO SDN. BHD.—See Eden Inc. Berhad; *Int'l*, pg. 2306
MYR TRANSMISSION SERVICES CANADA, LTD.—See MYR Group Inc.; *U.S. Public*, pg. 1489
NARVA SOOJUSVORK AS—See Eesti Energia AS; *Int'l*, pg. 2318
NASHVILLE ELECTRIC SERVICE; *U.S. Private*, pg. 2836
NATENCO WINDPARK 1 MANAGEMENT GMBH—See Electricite de France S.A.; *Int'l*, pg. 2350
NATIONAL FUEL RESOURCES, INC.—See National Fuel Gas Company; *U.S. Public*, pg. 1494
NATIONAL RURAL ELECTRIC COOPERATIVE ASSOCIATION—See Touchstone Energy Cooperative, Inc.; *U.S. Private*, pg. 4192
NATURWATT GMBH—See EWE Aktiengesellschaft; *Int'l*, pg. 2575
NAVARRO COUNTY ELECTRIC COOPERATIVE, INC.; *U.S. Private*, pg. 2872
NAVASOTA VALLEY ELECTRIC COOPERATIVE; *U.S. Private*, pg. 2872
NAVOPACHE ELECTRIC COOPERATIVE INC.; *U.S. Private*, pg. 2873
NEBRASKA ELECTRIC GENERATION & TRANSMISSION COOPERATIVE, INC.; *U.S. Private*, pg. 2878
NECKS ELECTRIC AB—See Addtech AB; *Int'l*, pg. 134
NETZE BW GMBH—See EnBW Energie Baden-Wurttemberg AG; *Int'l*, pg. 2399
NETZE BW WASSER GMBH—See EnBW Energie Baden-Wurttemberg AG; *Int'l*, pg. 2399
NETZGESELLSCHAFT DUSSELDORF MBH—See EnBW Energie Baden-Wurttemberg AG; *Int'l*, pg. 2399
NETZGESELLSCHAFT ELZ-NECKAR GMBH & CO. KG—See EnBW Energie Baden-Wurttemberg AG; *Int'l*, pg. 2399
NETZGESELLSCHAFT OSTWURTTEMBERG DONAU-RIES GMBH—See EnBW Energie Baden-Wurttemberg AG; *Int'l*, pg. 2399
NETZGESELLSCHAFT STEINHEIM GMBH & CO. KG—See EnBW Energie Baden-Wurttemberg AG; *Int'l*, pg. 2399
NETZGESELLSCHAFT STEINHEIM VERWALTUNGSGE-SELLSCHAFT MBH.—See EnBW Energie Baden-Wurttemberg AG; *Int'l*, pg. 2399
NETZ NIEDEROSTERREICH GMBH—See EVN AG; *Int'l*, pg. 2571
NETZ VELTHEIM GMBH—See E.ON SE; *Int'l*, pg. 2258
NEVADA POWER COMPANY—See Berkshire Hathaway Inc.; *U.S. Public*, pg. 300
NEW BRAUNFELS UTILITIES; *U.S. Private*, pg. 2892
NEWFOUNDLAND POWER INC.—See Fortis Inc.; *Int'l*, pg. 2740
NEW HAMPSHIRE ELECTRIC COOPERATIVE INC.; *U.S. Private*, pg. 2896
NEW LEAF ENERGY, INC.—See Energy Capital Partners Management, LP; *U.S. Public*, pg. 1394
NEW MAC ELECTRIC COOPERATIVE; *U.S. Private*, pg. 2898
NEW YORK STATE ELECTRIC & GAS CORP.—See Iberdrola, S.A.; *Int'l*, pg. 3571
NEW YORK STATE ELECTRIC & GAS CORP.—See Iberdrola, S.A.; *Int'l*, pg. 3571
NEW YORK STATE ELECTRIC & GAS CORP.—See Iberdrola, S.A.; *Int'l*, pg. 3571
NEW YORK STATE ELECTRIC & GAS CORP.—See Iberdrola, S.A.; *Int'l*, pg. 3571
NEXTERA ENERGY PARTNERS, LP—See NextEra Energy, Inc.; *U.S. Public*, pg. 1526
NHF NETZGESELLSCHAFT HEILBRONN-FRANKEN MBH—See EnBW Energie Baden-Wurttemberg AG; *Int'l*, pg. 2399
NHL NETZGESELLSCHAFT HEILBRONNER LAND GMBH & CO. KG—See EnBW Energie Baden-Wurttemberg AG; *Int'l*, pg. 2399
NINNESCAH RURAL ELECTRIC COOPERATIVE ASSOCIATION, INC.; *U.S. Private*, pg. 2928
NOBLES COOPERATIVE ELECTRIC; *U.S. Private*, pg. 2933

NODAK ELECTRIC COOPERATIVE, INC.; *U.S. Private*, pg. 2933
NOLIN RURAL ELECTRIC COOPERATIVE CORPORATION; *U.S. Private*, pg. 2934
NORDIC ENERGY SERVICES, LLC; *U.S. Private*, pg. 2936
NORENERGI A/S—See World Kinect Corporation; *U.S. Public*, pg. 2381
NORGESENERGI AS—See Hafslund ASA; *Int'l*, pg. 3206
NORTH CAROLINA ELECTRIC MEMBERSHIP CORPORATION; *U.S. Private*, pg. 2943
NORTHCENTRAL MISSISSIPPI ELECTRIC POWER ASSOCIATION; *U.S. Private*, pg. 2948
NORTH CENTRAL MISSOURI ELECTRIC COOPERATIVE, INC.; *U.S. Private*, pg. 2944
NORTHEASTERN RURAL ELECTRIC MEMBERSHIP CORPORATION; *U.S. Private*, pg. 2951
NORTHEAST LOUISIANA POWER COOP; *U.S. Private*, pg. 2950
NORTH EAST MISSISSIPPI ELECTRIC POWER ASSOCIATION; *U.S. Private*, pg. 2945
NORTHEAST OKLAHOMA ELECTRIC COOPERATIVE INC.; *U.S. Private*, pg. 2950
NORTHERN ELECTRIC PLC—See Berkshire Hathaway Inc.; *U.S. Public*, pg. 313
NORTHERN PLAINS ELECTRIC COOPERATIVE; *U.S. Private*, pg. 2954
NORTHERN POWERGRID LIMITED—See Berkshire Hathaway Inc.; *U.S. Public*, pg. 313
NORTHERN POWERGRID U.K. HOLDINGS—See Berkshire Hathaway Inc.; *U.S. Public*, pg. 313
NORTHERN TRANSMISSION SERVICES, LTD.—See MYR Group Inc.; *U.S. Public*, pg. 1489
NORTHERN VIRGINIA ELECTRIC COOPERATIVE INC.; *U.S. Private*, pg. 2954
NORTH GEORGIA ELECTRIC MEMBERSHIP CORPORATION; *U.S. Private*, pg. 2945
NORTH-KAZAKHSTAN REGIONAL ELECTRIC DISTRIBUTION COMPANY JSC—See Central-Asian Power Energy Company JSC; *Int'l*, pg. 1410
NORTHSTAR CLEAN ENERGY—See CMS Energy Corporation; *U.S. Public*, pg. 518
NORTHWESTERN ELECTRIC COOPERATIVE, INC.; *U.S. Private*, pg. 2962
NORTHWESTERN WISCONSIN ELECTRIC CO.; *U.S. Private*, pg. 2963
NOVA SCOTIA POWER INC.—See Emera, Inc.; *Int'l*, pg. 2377
NRG CANAL 3 DEVELOPMENT LLC—See NRG Energy, Inc.; *U.S. Public*, pg. 1550
NRG DUNKIRK OPERATIONS INC.—See NRG Energy, Inc.; *U.S. Public*, pg. 1550
NRG EL SEGUNDO OPERATIONS INC.—See NRG Energy, Inc.; *U.S. Public*, pg. 1550
NRG ENERGY CENTER SAN FRANCISCO LLC—See BlackRock, Inc.; *U.S. Public*, pg. 345
NRG ENERGY, INC.; *U.S. Public*, pg. 1549
NRG EV SERVICES LLC—See Vision Ridge Partners, LLC; *U.S. Public*, pg. 4391
NRG TEXAS, LLC—See NRG Energy, Inc.; *U.S. Public*, pg. 1550
NSTAR ELECTRIC & GAS CORPORATION—See Eversource Energy; *U.S. Public*, pg. 801
NTPC GE POWER SERVICES PRIVATE LIMITED—See General Electric Company; *U.S. Public*, pg. 917
OASIS POWER, LLC—See Via Renewables, Inc.; *U.S. Public*, pg. 2290
OCEANE RE SA—See Electricite de France S.A.; *Int'l*, pg. 2352
OCMULGEE ELECTRIC MEMBERSHIP CORPORATION; *U.S. Private*, pg. 2992
OCONEE ELECTRIC MEMBERSHIP; *U.S. Private*, pg. 2992
OCONTO ELECTRIC COOPERATIVE; *U.S. Private*, pg. 2992
OHIO POWER COMPANY—See American Electric Power Company, Inc.; *U.S. Public*, pg. 100
OKEFENOKE RURAL ELECTRIC MEMBERSHIP CORPORATION; *U.S. Private*, pg. 3007
OKLAHOMA MUNICIPAL POWER AUTHORITY; *U.S. Private*, pg. 3007
OMAHA PUBLIC POWER DISTRICT; *U.S. Private*, pg. 3014
ON-DEMAND ENERGY, L.P—See World Kinect Corporation; *U.S. Public*, pg. 2381
ORANGE COUNTY REMC; *U.S. Private*, pg. 3037
ORANGE & ROCKLAND UTILITIES, INC.—See Consolidated Edison, Inc.; *U.S. Public*, pg. 570
ORBITAL POWER, INC.—See Orbital Infrastructure Group, Inc.; *U.S. Public*, pg. 1615
ORCAS POWER & LIGHT COOP; *U.S. Private*, pg. 3039
ORION NEW ZEALAND LTD—See Christchurch City Holdings Ltd.; *Int'l*, pg. 1586
ORISSA POWER GENERATION CORPORATION LIMITED—See The AES Corporation; *U.S. Public*, pg. 2032
ORMAT TECHNOLOGIES, INC.; *U.S. Public*, pg. 1618
OSAGE VALLEY ELECTRIC COOP ASSOCIATION; *U.S. Private*, pg. 3046
OTTER TAIL CORPORATION; *U.S. Public*, pg. 1624

221122 — ELECTRIC POWER DIST...

OTTER TAIL POWER COMPANY—See Otter Tail Corporation; *U.S. Public*, pg. 1624
OUTBACK SOLAR, LLC—See Constellation Energy Corporation; *U.S. Public*, pg. 572
OVERTON POWER DISTRICT NO 5; *U.S. Private*, pg. 3054
OWEN ELECTRIC COOPERATIVE INC.; *U.S. Private*, pg. 3054
OZARK BORDER ELECTRIC COOP ASSOCIATION; *U.S. Private*, pg. 3057
OZARKS ELECTRIC COOPERATIVE CORPORATION; *U.S. Private*, pg. 3058
PACIFIC GAS & ELECTRIC COMPANY—See PG&E Corporation; *U.S. Public*, pg. 1684
PALMETTO ELECTRIC COOPERATIVE; *U.S. Private*, pg. 3081
PANDA POWER CORP.—See Panda Energy International Inc.; *U.S. Private*, pg. 3085
PAO FORTUM—See Fortum Oyj; *Int'l*, pg. 2742
P.A.P A/S—See AFRY AB; *Int'l*, pg. 194
PASCO COGEN, LTD.—See Quantum Energy Partners, LLC; *U.S. Private*, pg. 3323
PAVLODAR HEATING NETWORKS LLP—See Central-Asian Power Energy Company JSC; *Int'l*, pg. 1410
PEACE RIVER ELECTRIC COOPERATIVE, INC.; *U.S. Private*, pg. 3122
PEARL RIVER VALLEY ELECTRIC POWER ASSOCIATION; *U.S. Private*, pg. 3125
PECO ENERGY COMPANY—See Exelon Corporation; *U.S. Public*, pg. 807
PEE DEE ELECTRIC COOPERATIVE INC.; *U.S. Private*, pg. 3128
PENINSULA GENERATION COOPERATIVE; *U.S. Private*, pg. 3133
PENINSULA LIGHT COMPANY; *U.S. Private*, pg. 3133
PENNSYLVANIA ELECTRIC COMPANY—See FirstEnergy Corp.; *U.S. Public*, pg. 849
PENNYRILE RURAL ELECTRIC COOPERATIVE CORPORATION; *U.S. Private*, pg. 3138
PEOPLES ELECTRIC COOPERATIVE; *U.S. Private*, pg. 3142
PERMASCAND TOP HOLDING AB—See Altor Equity Partners AB; *Int'l*, pg. 395
PERTH ENERGY PTY. LIMITED—See AGL Energy Limited; *Int'l*, pg. 211
PETIT JEAN ELECTRIC COOPERATIVE; *U.S. Private*, pg. 3161
PG&E CORPORATION; *U.S. Public*, pg. 1683
PICKWICK ELECTRIC COOPERATIVE; *U.S. Private*, pg. 3176
PIEDMONT ELECTRIC MEMBERSHIP CORP.; *U.S. Private*, pg. 3177
PIKE COUNTY LIGHT & POWER COMPANY—See Argo Infrastructure Partners LLC; *U.S. Public*, pg. 320
PIONEER ELECTRIC COOPERATIVE; *U.S. Private*, pg. 3186
PIONEER RURAL ELECTRIC COOPERATIVE INC.; *U.S. Private*, pg. 3188
PLATEAU ELECTRIC COOPERATIVE; *U.S. Private*, pg. 3200
PLATTE-CLAY ELECTRIC COOP; *U.S. Private*, pg. 3212
PLATTE RIVER POWER AUTHORITY; *U.S. Private*, pg. 3211
PLOMIN HOLDING D.O.O.—See Hrvatska elektroprivreda d.d.; *Int'l*, pg. 3502
PLUG POWER INC.; *U.S. Public*, pg. 1699
POLICOM AB—See Hafslund ASA; *Int'l*, pg. 3206
POLK-BURNETT ELECTRIC COOPERATIVE; *U.S. Private*, pg. 3224
PONTOTOC ELECTRIC POWER ASSOCIATION; *U.S. Private*, pg. 3227
PORTLAND GENERAL ELECTRIC COMPANY; *U.S. Public*, pg. 1702
POTOMAC ELECTRIC POWER COMPANY—See Exelon Corporation; *U.S. Public*, pg. 807
POWDER RIVER ENERGY CORPORATION; *U.S. Private*, pg. 3236
POWELL INDUSTRIES, INC.; *U.S. Public*, pg. 1705
POWELL VALLEY ELECTRIC COOPERATIVE; *U.S. Private*, pg. 3237
POWERCOR AUSTRALIA LIMITED—See CK Hutchison Holdings Limited; *Int'l*, pg. 1637
POWERDIRECT PTY LTD—See AGL Energy Limited; *Int'l*, pg. 211
POWER-EQUIP SALES REPS, LTD.—See Emek Elektrik Endustrisi A.S.; *Int'l*, pg. 2377
POWEREX CORP.—See B.C. Hydro; *Int'l*, pg. 789
POWERGEN LIMITED—See E.ON SE; *Int'l*, pg. 2258
POWERSOUTH ENERGY COOPERATIVE; *U.S. Private*, pg. 3240
PPL ELECTRIC UTILITIES CORPORATION—See PPL Corporation; *U.S. Public*, pg. 1711
PPL MONTANA HOLDINGS, LLC—See PPL Corporation; *U.S. Public*, pg. 1712
PRAIRIE POWER, INC.; *U.S. Private*, pg. 3243
PREDISTRIBUCE A.S.—See EnBW Energie Baden-Wurttemberg AG; *Int'l*, pg. 2399
PREFORMED LINE PRODUCTS (VIETNAM) LTD.—See Preformed Line Products Company; *U.S. Public*, pg. 1714
PREMERENI A.S.—See EnBW Energie Baden-Wurttemberg AG; *Int'l*, pg. 2399
PRESQUE ISLE ELECTRIC & GAS CO-OP; *U.S. Private*, pg. 3255
PSEG POWER LLC—See Public Service Enterprise Group Incorporated; *U.S. Public*, pg. 1736
PT HITACHI ASIA INDONESIA—See Hitachi, Ltd.; *Int'l*, pg. 3423
PT. MEGA FEDERAL ENERGY—See Federal International (2000) Ltd; *Int'l*, pg. 2630
PUBLIC SERVICE COMPANY OF NEW MEXICO—See TXNM Energy, Inc.; *U.S. Public*, pg. 2208
PUBLIC SERVICE COMPANY OF OKLAHOMA—See American Electric Power Company, Inc.; *U.S. Public*, pg. 100
PUBLIC UTILITY DISTRICT 1 OF BENTON COUNTY; *U.S. Private*, pg. 3300
PUBLIC UTILITY DISTRICT 1 OF DOUGLAS COUNTY; *U.S. Private*, pg. 3300
PUBLIC UTILITY DISTRICT 1 OKANOGAN; *U.S. Private*, pg. 3300
PUBLIC UTILITY DISTRICT 2 PACIFIC COUNTY; *U.S. Private*, pg. 3300
PUBLIC UTILITY DISTRICT KLICKITAT COUNTY; *U.S. Private*, pg. 3300
PUBLIC UTILITY DISTRICT NO. 2 OF GRANT COUNTY; *U.S. Private*, pg. 3300
PUERTO RICO ELECTRIC POWER AUTHORITY; *U.S. Private*, pg. 3302
PUGET SOUND ENERGY, INC.—See Alberta Investment Management Corporation; *Int'l*, pg. 298
PUGET SOUND ENERGY, INC.—See British Columbia Investment Management Corporation; *Int'l*, pg. 1169
PUGET SOUND ENERGY, INC.—See Canada Pension Plan Investment Board; *Int'l*, pg. 1281
PULASKI ELECTRIC SYSTEM, INC. (PES); *U.S. Public*, pg. 3303
PULSE ENERGY LIMITED—See Buller Electricity Ltd.; *Int'l*, pg. 1214
PWRCOR, INC.; *U.S. Public*, pg. 1739
QUEZON POWER (PHILIPPINES) LIMITED CO.—See Electricity Generating Public Co., Ltd.; *Int'l*, pg. 2352
RAFT RIVER RURAL ELECTRIC COOPERATIVE, INC.; *U.S. Private*, pg. 3345
RANDOLPH ELECTRIC MEMBERSHIP CORPORATION; *U.S. Private*, pg. 3354
RAPPAHANNOCK ELECTRIC COOP; *U.S. Private*, pg. 3356
RAYLE ELECTRIC MEMBERSHIP; *U.S. Private*, pg. 3359
RDE REGIONALE DIENSTLEISTUNGEN ENERGIE GMBH & CO. KG—See E.ON SE; *Int'l*, pg. 2259
RED RIVER VALLEY RURAL ELECTRIC ASSOCIATION; *U.S. Private*, pg. 3375
RELIANT ENERGY RETAIL HOLDINGS, LLC—See NRG Energy, Inc.; *U.S. Public*, pg. 1551
RIEGER BETEILIGUNGS-GMBH—See EnBW Energie Baden-Wurttemberg AG; *Int'l*, pg. 2400
RIO GRANDE ELECTRIC COOP; *U.S. Private*, pg. 3438
RITA BLANCA ELECTRIC COOPERATIVE, INC.; *U.S. Private*, pg. 3441
RKN RHEINKRAFTWERK NEUHAUSEN AG—See EnBW Energie Baden-Wurttemberg AG; *Int'l*, pg. 2398
ROANOKE ELECTRIC MEMBERSHIP; *U.S. Private*, pg. 3453
ROCKLAND ELECTRIC COMPANY—See Consolidated Edison, Inc.; *U.S. Public*, pg. 570
ROGERSON AIRCRAFT SYSTEMS—See Rogerson Aircraft Corporation; *U.S. Private*, pg. 3472
ROOSEVELT COUNTY ELECTRIC COOPERATIVE, INC.; *U.S. Private*, pg. 3479
ROTEK ENGINEERING (PTY) LTD.—See Eskom Holdings SOC Limited; *Int'l*, pg. 2504
ROUGHRIDER ELECTRIC COOPERATIVE, INC.; *U.S. Private*, pg. 3488
RSB BONDCO LLC—See Exelon Corporation; *U.S. Public*, pg. 807
RUGELEY POWER LTD—See ENGIE SA; *Int'l*, pg. 2433
RUNESTONE ELECTRIC ASSOCIATION; *U.S. Private*, pg. 3504
RURAL ELECTRIC COOPERATIVE, INC.; *U.S. Private*, pg. 3504
RUSHMORE ELECTRIC POWER COOPERATIVE INC.; *U.S. Private*, pg. 3505
RUSK COUNTY ELECTRIC COOP; *U.S. Private*, pg. 3505
RUTHERFORD ELECTRIC MEMBERSHIP; *U.S. Private*, pg. 3507
SALT RIVER ELECTRIC COOP CORP.; *U.S. Private*, pg. 3533
SAN BERNARD ELECTRIC COOP; *U.S. Private*, pg. 3539
SANGRE DE CRISTO ELECTRIC ASSOCIATION, INC.; *U.S. Private*, pg. 3546
SAN ISABEL ELECTRIC ASSOCIATION INC; *U.S. Private*, pg. 3542
SAN LUIS VALLEY RURAL ELECTRIC COOPERATIVE, INC.; *U.S. Private*, pg. 3541
SAN MIGUEL POWER ASSOCIATION; *U.S. Private*, pg. 3542
SAN PATRICIO ELECTRIC COOPERATIVE, INC.; *U.S. Private*, pg. 3542
SA POWER NETWORKS—See CK Hutchison Holdings Limited; *Int'l*, pg. 1637
SASKATCHEWAN POWER CORPORATION—See Crown Investments Corporation of Saskatchewan; *Int'l*, pg. 1857
SATILLA RURAL ELECTRIC MEMBERSHIP CORPORATION; *U.S. Private*, pg. 3553
SAWNEE ELECTRIC MEMBERSHIP CORPORATION; *U.S. Private*, pg. 3558
SC CASA DE COMPENSARE BUCURESTI SA—See Daimyo AS; *Int'l*, pg. 1938
SCENIC RIVERS ENERGY COOP; *U.S. Private*, pg. 3562
SCHLESWIG-HOLSTEIN NETZ VERWALTUNGS-GMBH—See E.ON SE; *Int'l*, pg. 2259
SCOTTISHPOWER ENERGY RETAIL LTD—See Iberdrola, S.A.; *Int'l*, pg. 3573
SCOTTISH POWER PLC—See Iberdrola, S.A.; *Int'l*, pg. 3573
SEATTLE CITY LIGHT; *U.S. Private*, pg. 3591
SEAWEST PROPERTIES, LLC—See The AES Corporation; *U.S. Public*, pg. 2032
SELEN ELEKTRIK URETIM A.S.—See The AES Corporation; *U.S. Public*, pg. 2032
SEMINOLE ELECTRIC COOPERATIVE, INC.; *U.S. Private*, pg. 3604
SEMO ELECTRICAL COOPERATIVE; *U.S. Private*, pg. 3605
SEMPRA ENERGY TRADING CORP.—See Sempra; *U.S. Public*, pg. 1863
SEQUACHEE VALLEY ELECTRIC CO-OPERATIVE INC.; *U.S. Private*, pg. 3612
SERVICIOS OPERACION EOLOELECTRICA DE MEXICO, S.A. DE C.V.—See Iberdrola, S.A.; *Int'l*, pg. 3572
SERVIZI AEREI SPA—See Eni S.p.A.; *Int'l*, pg. 2438
SEVEROMORAVSKA ENERGETIKA, A.S.—See CEZ, a.s.; *Int'l*, pg. 1428
SHALEPRO ENERGY SERVICES, LLC; *U.S. Private*, pg. 3623
SHARYLAND UTILITIES LP—See Hunt Consolidated, Inc.; *U.S. Private*, pg. 2009
SHELBYVILLE POWER, WATER, & SEWAGE SYSTEM; *U.S. Private*, pg. 3630
SHO-ME POWER ELECTRIC COOPERATIVE INC.; *U.S. Private*, pg. 3639
SINGING RIVER ELECTRIC POWER ASSOCIATION; *U.S. Private*, pg. 3670
SIOUX VALLEY ENERGY; *U.S. Private*, pg. 3671
SIOUX VALLEY RURAL TELEVISION—See Sioux Valley Energy; *U.S. Private*, pg. 3671
SIOUX VALLEY-SOUTHWESTERN ELECTRIC COOPERATIVE, INC.; *U.S. Private*, pg. 3671
SISTEMAS ENERGETICOS CHANDREXA, S.A.—See Iberdrola, S.A.; *Int'l*, pg. 3574
SLASH PINE ELECTRIC MEMBERSHIP CORPORATION; *U.S. Private*, pg. 3687
SNAPPING SHOALS ELECTRIC MEMBERSHIP CORP.; *U.S. Private*, pg. 3700
SND LIMITED—See Essel Corporate Resources Pvt. Ltd.; *Int'l*, pg. 2509
SOAVE HYDROPONICS COMPANY—See Soave Enterprises, LLC; *U.S. Private*, pg. 3702
SOCIEDAD ESPANOLA DE MONTAJES INDUSTRIALES S.A.—See ACS, Actividades de Construccion y Servicios, S.A.; *Int'l*, pg. 116
SOCIETE HYDRO-ELECTRIQUE DU MIDI—See ENGIE SA; *Int'l*, pg. 2434
SOCORRO ELECTRIC COOPERATIVE; *U.S. Private*, pg. 3704
SOHAR POWER COMPANY—See ENGIE SA; *Int'l*, pg. 2433
SOL DISTRIBUTION PTY. LIMITED—See AGL Energy Limited; *Int'l*, pg. 211
SOLIDUS OY—See Eesti Energia AS; *Int'l*, pg. 2318
SOUTH ALABAMA ELECTRIC COOPERATIVE; *U.S. Private*, pg. 3719
SOUTH CENTRAL ARKANSAS ELECTRIC COOPERATIVE, INC.; *U.S. Private*, pg. 3720
SOUTH CENTRAL POWER COMPANY INC.; *U.S. Private*, pg. 3721
SOUTHEAST COLORADO POWER ASSOCIATION; *U.S. Private*, pg. 3725
SOUTHEASTERN ILLINOIS ELECTRIC CO-OPERATIVE INC.; *U.S. Private*, pg. 3728
SOUTHERN CALIFORNIA EDISON COMPANY—See Edison International; *U.S. Public*, pg. 719
SOUTHERN FEDERAL POWER, LLC—See Genie Energy Ltd.; *U.S. Public*, pg. 931
SOUTHERN PINE ELECTRIC CO-OPERATIVE INC.; *U.S. Private*, pg. 3734
SOUTHERN POWER COMPANY—See The Southern Company; *U.S. Public*, pg. 2131
SOUTH PLAINS ELECTRIC COOPERATIVE; *U.S. Private*, pg. 3723
SOUTH RIVER ELECTRIC MEMBERSHIP CORPORATION; *U.S. Private*, pg. 3723

N.A.I.C.S. INDEX
221122 — ELECTRIC POWER DIST...

SOUTH TEXAS ELECTRIC COOPERATIVE, INC.; *U.S. Private*, pg. 3724
SOUTHWEST ARKANSAS ELECTRIC COOPERATIVE CORPORATION; *U.S. Private*, pg. 3738
SOUTHWEST ELECTRIC COOPERATIVE, INC.; *U.S. Private*, pg. 3739
SOUTHWEST ENERGY SOLUTIONS, INC.—See Fortis Inc.; *Int'l*, pg. 2740
SOUTHWESTERN ELECTRIC CO-OPERATIVE INC.; *U.S. Private*, pg. 3741
SOUTHWEST LOUISIANA ELECTRIC MEMBERSHIP CORPORATION; *U.S. Private*, pg. 3739
SOUTHWEST MISSISSIPPI ELECTRIC POWER ASSOCIATION; *U.S. Private*, pg. 3740
SOUTHWEST TENNESSEE ELECTRIC MEMBERSHIP CORP.; *U.S. Private*, pg. 3741
SOUTHWEST TEXAS ELECTRIC CO-OP; *U.S. Private*, pg. 3741
SP DISTRIBUTION, LTD.—See Iberdrola, S.A.; *Int'l*, pg. 3573
STADTWERKE DUSSELDORF NETZ GMBH—See EnBW Energie Baden-Wurttemberg AG; *Int'l*, pg. 2400
STADTWERKE SINSHEIM VERWALTUNGS GMBH—See EnBW Energie Baden-Wurttemberg AG; *Int'l*, pg. 2400
STAM HEERHUGOWAARD HOLDING B.V—See Alliander N.V.; *Int'l*, pg. 341
STAR ELECTRICITY, INC.—See Constellation Energy Corporation; *U.S. Public*, pg. 572
STARS ALLIANCE, LLC—See Ameren Corporation; *U.S. Public*, pg. 94
STATION A LLC—See NRG Energy, Inc.; *U.S. Public*, pg. 1551
STEARNS ELECTRIC ASSOCIATION; *U.S. Private*, pg. 3795
STRATAVEST SDN. BHD.—See Eden Inc. Berhad; *Int'l*, pg. 2306
STREAM ENERGY ILLINOIS, LLC—See NRG Energy, Inc.; *U.S. Public*, pg. 1551
STREDOCESKA ENERGETICKA, A.S.—See CEZ, a.s.; *Int'l*, pg. 1428
STROM GERMERING GMBH—See E.ON SE; *Int'l*, pg. 2259
STROMNETZ HAMBURG GMBH—See HGV Hamburger Gesellschaft fur Vermogens- und Beteiligungsmanagement mbH; *Int'l*, pg. 3378
STROMVERSORGUNG AHRENSBURG GMBH—See E.ON SE; *Int'l*, pg. 2259
STROMVERSORGUNG RUHPOLDING GESELLSCHAFT MIT BESCHRANKTER HAFTUNG—See E.ON SE; *Int'l*, pg. 2259
STROTOG GMBH—See E.ON SE; *Int'l*, pg. 2259
SULPHUR SPRINGS VALLEY ELECTRIC COOPERATIVE INC.; *U.S. Private*, pg. 3852
SUMINISTRO DE LUZ Y FUERZA SL—See Enel S.p.A.; *Int'l*, pg. 2414
SUMMER ENERGY HOLDINGS, INC.; *U.S. Public*, pg. 1959
SUMNER-COWLEY ELECTRIC COOPERATIVE, INC.; *U.S. Private*, pg. 3857
SUMTER ELECTRIC COOPERATIVE INC.; *U.S. Private*, pg. 3857
SUNFLOWER ELECTRIC POWER HOLCOMB STATION—See Sunflower Electric Power Corporation; *U.S. Private*, pg. 3867
SUSSEX RURAL ELECTRIC COOPERATIVE; *U.S. Private*, pg. 3886
SUWANNEE VALLEY ELECTRIC COOPERATIVE, INC.; *U.S. Private*, pg. 3887
SVO VERTRIEB GMBH—See E.ON SE; *Int'l*, pg. 2259
SWB VERTRIEB BREMEN GMBH—See EWE Aktiengesellschaft; *Int'l*, pg. 2576
SWB VERTRIEB BREMERHAVEN GMBH & CO. KG—See EWE Aktiengesellschaft; *Int'l*, pg. 2576
SWISHER ELECTRIC COOPERATIVE, INC.; *U.S. Private*, pg. 3894
SWITCH NORDIC GREEN AB—See Elmera Group ASA; *Int'l*, pg. 2367
SYDKRAFT EC SLUPSK SP. Z O.O.—See E.ON SE; *Int'l*, pg. 2259
SYDKRAFT POLEN AB—See E.ON SE; *Int'l*, pg. 2259
SYRACUSE ENERGY CORPORATION—See ENGIE SA; *Int'l*, pg. 2433
SZCZECINSKA ENERGETYKA CIEPLNA SP. Z O.O.—See E.ON SE; *Int'l*, pg. 2259
TALEN ENERGY MARKETING, LLC—See Riverstone Holdings LLC; *U.S. Private*, pg. 3447
TALEN ENERGY SUPPLY, LLC—See Riverstone Holdings LLC; *U.S. Private*, pg. 3447
TALLAHATCHIE VALLEY ELECTRIC POWER ASSOCIATION; *U.S. Private*, pg. 3927
TALLAPOOSA RIVER ELECTRIC CO-OP; *U.S. Private*, pg. 3927
TAMPA ELECTRIC COMPANY—See Emera, Inc.; *Int'l*, pg. 2377
TAYLOR ELECTRIC CO-OPERATIVE; *U.S. Private*, pg. 3939
TECO ENERGY, INC.—See Emera, Inc.; *Int'l*, pg. 2377
TECO GUATEMALA, INC.—See Emera, Inc.; *Int'l*, pg. 2377
TENASKA POWER SERVICES CO.—See Tenaska, Inc.; *U.S. Private*, pg. 3965

TENNESSEE VALLEY ELECTRIC COOPERATIVE; *U.S. Private*, pg. 3968
THEOLIA NATURENERGIEN GMBH—See Electricite de France S.A.; *Int'l*, pg. 2350
THERMAL TECHNOLOGY DISTRIBUTION SOLUTIONS—See Gryphon Investors, LLC; *U.S. Private*, pg. 1799
THERMA MOBILE, INC.—See Aboitiz Equity Ventures, Inc.; *Int'l*, pg. 67
THERMA SOUTH, INC.—See Aboitiz Equity Ventures, Inc.; *Int'l*, pg. 67
THIRO LTEE.—See Brookfield Corporation; *Int'l*, pg. 1181
THREE NOTCH ELECTRIC MEMBERSHIP CORP.; *U.S. Private*, pg. 4164
THREE RIVERS ELECTRIC COOP; *U.S. Private*, pg. 4164
THUMB ELECTRIC COOP OF MICHIGAN; *U.S. Private*, pg. 4165
THURINGER ENERGIE NETZSERVICE GMBH—See E.ON SE; *Int'l*, pg. 2259
TIDELAND ELECTRIC MEMBERSHIP CORPORATION; *U.S. Private*, pg. 4168
TIPMONT RURAL ELECTRIC MEMBERSHIP CORPORATION; *U.S. Private*, pg. 4175
TKO POWER INC.—See Enel S.p.A.; *Int'l*, pg. 2411
TNS ENERGO KARELIA JSC—See GK TNS Energo PAO; *Int'l*, pg. 2983
TNS ENERGO NN PJSC—See GK TNS Energo PAO; *Int'l*, pg. 2983
TNS ENERGO PENZA LLC—See GK TNS Energo PAO; *Int'l*, pg. 2983
TNS ENERGO TULA JSC—See GK TNS Energo PAO; *Int'l*, pg. 2983
TNS ENERGO VELIKIY NOVGOROD LLC—See GK TNS Energo PAO; *Int'l*, pg. 2983
TOGO ELECTRICITE—See ENGIE SA; *Int'l*, pg. 2431
THE TOLEDO EDISON COMPANY—See FirstEnergy Corp.; *U.S. Public*, pg. 849
TOMBIGBEE ELECTRIC POWER ASSOCIATION; *U.S. Private*, pg. 4183
TRACTEBEL S.A.—See ENGIE SA; *Int'l*, pg. 2432
TRANSALTA POWER, L.P.—See CK Hutchison Holdings Limited; *Int'l*, pg. 1637
TRANSPORTADORA DE ENERGIA DE CENTROAMERICA S.A.—See Grupo Energia Bogota S.A. E.S.P.; *Int'l*, pg. 3128
TRICO ELECTRIC CO-OP; *U.S. Private*, pg. 4229
TRI-COUNTY ELECTRIC COOPERATIVE, INC.; *U.S. Private*, pg. 4222
TRI-COUNTY ELECTRIC COOPERATIVE INC.; *U.S. Private*, pg. 4222
TRI-COUNTY ELECTRIC COOP; *U.S. Private*, pg. 4222
TRI-COUNTY ELECTRIC COOP; *U.S. Private*, pg. 4222
TRI-COUNTY ELECTRIC COOP; *U.S. Private*, pg. 4222
TRI-COUNTY ELECTRIC COOP; *U.S. Private*, pg. 4222
TRI-COUNTY ELECTRIC MEMBERSHIP CORP.; *U.S. Private*, pg. 4222
TRI-COUNTY ELECTRIC MEMBERSHIP CORP; *U.S. Private*, pg. 4222
TRI-COUNTY RURAL ELECTRIC CO; *U.S. Private*, pg. 4222
TRIEAGLE ENERGY LP—See Vistra Corp.; *U.S. Public*, pg. 2306
TRINITY VALLEY ELECTRIC COOP; *U.S. Private*, pg. 4236
TUCSON ELECTRIC POWER COMPANY—See Fortis Inc.; *Int'l*, pg. 2740
TWIN COUNTY ELECTRIC POWER ASSOCIATION; *U.S. Private*, pg. 4265
TXU ENERGY RETAIL COMPANY LLC—See Vistra Corp.; *U.S. Public*, pg. 2306
UAB JONISKIO ENERGIJA—See Fortum Oyj; *Int'l*, pg. 2742
UCH POWER LIMITED—See ENGIE SA; *Int'l*, pg. 2435
UEBERLANDWERK LEINETAL GMBH—See E.ON SE; *Int'l*, pg. 2254
UMATILLA ELECTRIC COOPERATIVE INC.; *U.S. Private*, pg. 4278
UNARETI S.P.A.—See A2A S.p.A.; *Int'l*, pg. 29
UNION ELECTRIC COMPANY—See Ameren Corporation; *U.S. Public*, pg. 94
UNION POWER COOPERATIVE; *U.S. Private*, pg. 4285
UNIPER SE—See Fortum Oyj; *Int'l*, pg. 2742
UNIPER TECHNOLOGIES B.V.—See Fortum Oyj; *Int'l*, pg. 2742
UNIPER TECHNOLOGIES GMBH—See Fortum Oyj; *Int'l*, pg. 2742
UNIPER TECHNOLOGIES LIMITED—See Fortum Oyj; *Int'l*, pg. 2742
UNISOURCE ENERGY SERVICES, INC.—See Fortis Inc.; *Int'l*, pg. 2740
UNITED COOPERATIVE SERVICES; *U.S. Private*, pg. 4290
UNITED ELECTRIC COOPERATIVE, INC.; *U.S. Private*, pg. 4291
UNITED ENERGY DISTRIBUTION PTY LIMITED—See CK Hutchison Holdings Limited; *Int'l*, pg. 1637
THE UNITED ILLUMINATING COMPANY—See Iberdrola, S.A.; *Int'l*, pg. 3571
UNITED POWER INC.; *U.S. Private*, pg. 4295
UNS ELECTRIC, INC.—See Fortis Inc.; *Int'l*, pg. 2740
UPPER CUMBERLAND ELECTRIC MEMBERSHIP CORPORATION; *U.S. Private*, pg. 4312

UPPER PENINSULA POWER COMPANY—See Colliers International Group Inc.; *Int'l*, pg. 1700
UPSHUR RURAL ELECTRIC COOPERATIVE CORPORATION; *U.S. Private*, pg. 4312
UPSON ELECTRIC MEMBERSHIP CORPORATION; *U.S. Private*, pg. 4312
US POWER GENERATING COMPANY—See Tenaska, Inc.; *U.S. Private*, pg. 3965
US RETAILERS LLC—See NRG Energy, Inc.; *U.S. Public*, pg. 1551
UTE NORTE FLUMINENSE S.A.—See Electricite de France S.A.; *Int'l*, pg. 2352
UTILITIES DISTRICT OF WESTERN INDIANA REMC; *U.S. Private*, pg. 4326
VARESE RISORSE S.P.A.—See A2A S.p.A.; *Int'l*, pg. 29
VEBACOM GMBH—See E.ON SE; *Int'l*, pg. 2260
VERDE ENERGY USA TEXAS, LLC—See Via Renewables, Inc.; *U.S. Public*, pg. 2290
VERDIGRIS VALLEY ELECTRIC COOPERATIVE; *U.S. Private*, pg. 4359
VERENDRYE ELECTRIC COOPERATIVE; *U.S. Private*, pg. 4359
VERMONT ELECTRIC COOPERATIVE; *U.S. Private*, pg. 4367
VERMONT YANKEE NUCLEAR POWER CORPORATION—See Caisse de Depot et Placement du Quebec; *Int'l*, pg. 1256
VIA RENEWABLES, INC.; *U.S. Public*, pg. 2290
VIRGINIA ELECTRIC AND POWER COMPANY—See Dominion Energy, Inc.; *U.S. Public*, pg. 674
VIRIDIAN ENERGY, LLC—See Vistra Corp.; *U.S. Public*, pg. 2306
VIRIDIAN GROUP LTD.—See I Squared Capital Advisors (US) LLC; *U.S. Private*, pg. 2026
VISTRA CORP.; *U.S. Public*, pg. 2306
VOLTCOM SPOL. S R.O.—See EnBW Energie Baden-Wurttemberg AG; *Int'l*, pg. 2400
VOLUNTEER ENERGY COOPERATIVE, INC.; *U.S. Private*, pg. 4411
VYCHODOCESKA ENERGETIKA, A.S.—See CEZ, a.s.; *Int'l*, pg. 1429
WAKEFELD MUNICIPAL GAS LIGHT DEPARTMENT; *U.S. Private*, pg. 4427
WALTON ELECTRIC MEMBERSHIP CORP.; *U.S. Private*, pg. 4434
WARMEVERSORGUNGSGESELLSCHAFT KONIGS WUSTERHAUSEN MBH—See E.ON SE; *Int'l*, pg. 2260
WARREN RURAL ELECTRIC COOPERATIVE CORP.; *U.S. Private*, pg. 4444
WASHINGTON ELECTRIC COOPERATIVE, INC.; *U.S. Private*, pg. 4447
WASHINGTON ELECTRIC MEMBERSHIP CORPORATION; *U.S. Private*, pg. 4447
WASHINGTON GAS ENERGY SERVICES, INC.—See AltaGas Ltd.; *Int'l*, pg. 384
WASHINGTON-SAINT TAMMANY ELECTRIC COOPERATIVE INC.; *U.S. Private*, pg. 4449
WEAKLEY COUNTY MUNICIPAL ELECTRIC SYSTEM; *U.S. Private*, pg. 4462
WELLS RURAL ELECTRIC COMPANY; *U.S. Private*, pg. 4476
WEST CENTRAL ELECTRIC COOPERATIVE; *U.S. Private*, pg. 4483
WESTERN COOPERATIVE ELECTRIC ASSOCIATION, INC.; *U.S. Private*, pg. 4492
WEST FLORIDA ELECTRICAL COOPERATIVE ASSOCIATION; *U.S. Private*, pg. 4485
WEST KENTUCKY RURAL ELECTRIC COOPERATIVE CORP., INC.; *U.S. Private*, pg. 4485
WEST RIVER ELECTRIC ASSOCIATION; *U.S. Private*, pg. 4487
WEVG SALZGITTER GMBH & CO. KG—See E.ON SE; *Int'l*, pg. 2260
WEVG VERWALTUNGS GMBH—See E.ON SE; *Int'l*, pg. 2260
WHEATLAND ELECTRIC COOPERATIVE; *U.S. Private*, pg. 4504
WILD RICE ELECTRIC COOPERATIVE INC.; *U.S. Private*, pg. 4518
WIN ENERGY REMC; *U.S. Private*, pg. 4532
WIREGRASS ELECTRIC COOPERATIVE, INC.; *U.S. Private*, pg. 4546
WIREGRASS ELECTRIC COOPERATIVE; *U.S. Private*, pg. 4546
WISCONSIN ELECTRIC POWER COMPANY—See WEC Energy Group, Inc.; *U.S. Public*, pg. 2342
WISCONSIN POWER AND LIGHT COMPANY—See Alliant Energy Corporation; *U.S. Public*, pg. 79
WISCONSIN PUBLIC SERVICE CORPORATION—See WEC Energy Group, Inc.; *U.S. Public*, pg. 2342
WISE ELECTRIC COOPERATIVE, INC.; *U.S. Private*, pg. 4550
WOODRUFF ELECTRIC COOPERATIVE CORPORATION; *U.S. Private*, pg. 4560
WP HECKELBERG-BREYDIN GMBH & CO. KG—See Electricite de France S.A.; *Int'l*, pg. 2350
WRIGHT-HENNEPIN COOPERATIVE ELECTRIC ASSO-

221122 — ELECTRIC POWER DIST...

CIATION; *U.S. Private*, pg. 4573
WTU RETAIL ENERGY LP—See NRG Energy, Inc.; *U.S. Public*, pg. 1550
XM COMPANIA DE EXPERTOS EN MERCADOS SA ESP—See Ecopetrol S.A.; *Int'l*, pg. 2299
YELLO STROM GMBH—See EnBW Energie Baden-Wurttemberg AG; *Int'l*, pg. 2400
YELLO STROM VERWALTUNGSGESELLSCHAFT MBH—See EnBW Energie Baden-Wurttemberg AG; *Int'l*, pg. 2400
YORK ELECTRIC COOPERATIVE INC.; *U.S. Private*, pg. 4590
THE YUKON ELECTRICAL CO. LTD.—See ATCO Ltd.; *Int'l*, pg. 667
Y-W ELECTRIC ASSOCIATION INC; *U.S. Private*, pg. 4584
ZAPADOSLOVENSKA ENERGETIKA, A.S.—See E.ON SE; *Int'l*, pg. 2254
ZEAG ENERGIE AG—See EnBW Energie Baden-Wurttemberg AG; *Int'l*, pg. 2400
ZEAG ENERGIE AG—See EnBW Energie Baden-Wurttemberg AG; *Int'l*, pg. 2401
ZEO ENERGY CORP.; *U.S. Public*, pg. 2402

221210 — NATURAL GAS DISTRIBUTION

A2A RETI GAS S.P.A.—See A2A S.p.A.; *Int'l*, pg. 29
AB AMBER GRID; *Int'l*, pg. 39
ACCENT ENERGY GROUP, LLC—See ACI Capital Co. LLC; *U.S. Private*, pg. 59
ACSM-AGAM S.P.A.; *Int'l*, pg. 117
ADANI GAS LTD—See Adani Enterprises Limited; *Int'l*, pg. 124
ADRIAPLIN PODJETJE ZA DISTRIBUCIJO ZEMELJSKEGA PLINA D.O.O.—See Eni S.p.A.; *Int'l*, pg. 2436
ADVANCE POWER & TRADING GMBH—See Advance Metering Technology Limited; *Int'l*, pg. 156
AGWAY ENERGY SERVICES, LLC—See Suburban Propane Partners, L.P.; *U.S. Public*, pg. 1958
AIR LIQUIDE WELDING POLSKA SPOLKA ZOGRANICZONA ODPOWIEDZIALNOSCIA—See Lincoln Electric Holdings, Inc.; *U.S. Public*, pg. 1317
AIR PRODUCTS IBERICA, S.L.—See Air Products & Chemicals, Inc.; *U.S. Public*, pg. 65
AIR PRODUCTS INTERNATIONAL CORPORATION—See Air Products & Chemicals, Inc.; *U.S. Public*, pg. 65
AIR PRODUCTS INVESTMENTS ESPANA, S.L.—See Air Products & Chemicals, Inc.; *U.S. Public*, pg. 65
AIR PRODUCTS JAPAN K.K.—See Air Products & Chemicals, Inc.; *U.S. Public*, pg. 65
AIR PRODUCTS MANAGEMENT S.A.—See Air Products & Chemicals, Inc.; *U.S. Public*, pg. 65
AIR PRODUCTS O.O.O.—See Air Products & Chemicals, Inc.; *U.S. Public*, pg. 65
AIR PRODUCTS PERFORMANCE MANUFACTURING, INC.—See Air Products & Chemicals, Inc.; *U.S. Public*, pg. 65
AIR PRODUCTS SERVICES EUROPE, S.A.—See Air Products & Chemicals, Inc.; *U.S. Public*, pg. 65
AIR WATER ASIA PTE. LTD.—See Air Water Inc.; *Int'l*, pg. 239
AIR WATER INDIA PRIVATE LIMITED—See Air Water Inc.; *Int'l*, pg. 239
AIR WATER PHILIPPINES, INC.—See Air Water Inc.; *Int'l*, pg. 239
AIR WATER PLANT & ENGINEERING, INC.—See Air Water Inc.; *Int'l*, pg. 239
AIR WATER SPECIAL GAS CO., LTD.—See Air Water Inc.; *Int'l*, pg. 239
AIR WATER VIETNAM CO., LTD.—See Air Water Inc.; *Int'l*, pg. 239
ALGONQUIN POWER & UTILITIES CORP.; *Int'l*, pg. 318
ALTAGAS LTD.; *Int'l*, pg. 384
ALTAGAS UTILITY GROUP INC.—See AltaGas Ltd.; *Int'l*, pg. 384
ALTEA GREEN POWER S.P.A.; *Int'l*, pg. 388
AMATA NATURAL GAS DISTRIBUTION CO. LTD.—See Amata Corporation Public Company Limited; *Int'l*, pg. 412
AMERICAN NATURAL GAS, LLC—See INNOVATE Corp.; *U.S. Public*, pg. 1125
AMERIGAS POLSKA SP. Z.O.O.—See UGI Corporation; *U.S. Public*, pg. 2221
AMGAS BLU S.R.L.—See Ascopiave S.p.A.; *Int'l*, pg. 603
AM NGV (S) PTE. LTD.—See Asian Micro Holdings Ltd.; *Int'l*, pg. 618
AM NGV (T) CO., LTD.—See Asian Micro Holdings Ltd.; *Int'l*, pg. 618
AMSA SPA—See A2A S.p.A.; *Int'l*, pg. 29
ANADARKO UINTAH MIDSTREAM, LLC—See Occidental Petroleum Corporation; *U.S. Public*, pg. 1561
ANADARKO WATTENBERG COMPANY, LLC—See Western Midstream Partners, LP; *U.S. Public*, pg. 2356
ANTARGAZ BELGIUM N.V.—See UGI Corporation; *U.S. Public*, pg. 2222
ANTARGAZ LUXEMBOURG S.A.—See UGI Corporation; *U.S. Public*, pg. 2222

ANTERO MIDSTREAM CORPORATION; *U.S. Public*, pg. 139
AOG CORPORATION—See Summit Utilities Inc.; *U.S. Private*, pg. 3857
AP RETI GAS NORD EST S.R.L.—See Ascopiave S.p.A.; *Int'l*, pg. 603
AP RETI GAS ROVIGO S.R.L.—See Ascopiave S.p.A.; *Int'l*, pg. 603
AP RETI GAS S.P.A.—See Ascopiave S.p.A.; *Int'l*, pg. 603
AQUITAINE RHONE GAZ—See UGI Corporation; *U.S. Public*, pg. 2222
ARABI COMPANY W.L.L.—See Arabi Holding Group Company K.S.C.C.; *Int'l*, pg. 532
ARESGAS EAD—See Hera S.p.A.; *Int'l*, pg. 3356
ASCOPIAVE ENERGIE S.P.A.—See Ascopiave S.p.A.; *Int'l*, pg. 603
ASCOPIAVE S.P.A.; *Int'l*, pg. 603
AS EESTI GAAS—See AS Infortar; *Int'l*, pg. 590
ASPIRE ENERGY OF OHIO, LLC—See Chesapeake Utilities Corporation; *U.S. Public*, pg. 485
ATCO BLUE FLAME KITCHEN—See ATCO Ltd.; *Int'l*, pg. 666
ATCO GAS—See ATCO Ltd.; *Int'l*, pg. 667
ATCO MIDSTREAM NWT LTD.—See ATCO Ltd.; *Int'l*, pg. 666
ATHENS UTILITY BOARD; *U.S. Private*, pg. 368
ATLANTA GAS LIGHT COMPANY—See The Southern Company; *U.S. Public*, pg. 2131
ATMOS ENERGY CORPORATION; *U.S. Public*, pg. 224
ATMOS ENERGY HOLDINGS, INC.—See Atmos Energy Corporation; *U.S. Public*, pg. 224
ATMOS ENERGY SERVICES, LLC—See Atmos Energy Corporation; *U.S. Public*, pg. 224
ATMOS GATHERING COMPANY, LLC—See Atmos Energy Corporation; *U.S. Public*, pg. 224
ATMOS PIPELINE AND STORAGE, LLC—See Atmos Energy Corporation; *U.S. Public*, pg. 224
ATMOS POWER SYSTEMS, INC.—See Atmos Energy Corporation; *U.S. Public*, pg. 224
ATOME ENERGY PLC; *Int'l*, pg. 687
AURORA POWER RESOURCES INC.; *U.S. Private*, pg. 395
AUSNET SERVICES LTD.—See Brookfield Corporation; *Int'l*, pg. 1175
AUSTELL NATURAL GAS SYSTEM; *U.S. Private*, pg. 395
THE AUSTRALIAN GAS LIGHT COMPANY—See AGL Energy Limited; *Int'l*, pg. 211
AUSTRALIAN GAS NETWORKS LIMITED; *Int'l*, pg. 721
BAHIA DE BIZKAIA GAS, S.L.—See Enagas, S.A.; *Int'l*, pg. 2396
BAHIA DE BIZKAIA GAS, S.L.—See Ente Vasco de la Energia; *Int'l*, pg. 2450
BALANCE ERNEUERBARE ENERGIEN GMBH—See EnBW Energie Baden-Wurttemberg AG; *Int'l*, pg. 2400
BALGAS—See UGI Corporation; *U.S. Public*, pg. 2221
BANGOR GAS COMPANY—See First Reserve Management, L.P.; *U.S. Private*, pg. 1525
BARNES KOREA LTD.—See Barnes Group Inc.; *U.S. Public*, pg. 277
BAS OMNISERVIZI SRL—See A2A S.p.A.; *Int'l*, pg. 29
BAY STATE GAS COMPANY—See Eversource Energy; *U.S. Public*, pg. 801
BEIJING GAS BLUE SKY HOLDINGS LIMITED; *Int'l*, pg. 950
BEIRAGAS - COMPANHIA DE GAS DAS BEIRAS, S.A.—See Galp Energia SGPS, S.A.; *Int'l*, pg. 2875
BENEGAS B.V.—See DCC plc; *Int'l*, pg. 1990
BENGAL GAS COMPANY LIMITED—See GAIL (India) Limited; *Int'l*, pg. 2869
BENOIT OILFIELD CONSTRUCTION (1997) LTD.; *Int'l*, pg. 975
THE BERKSHIRE GAS COMPANY—See Iberdrola, S.A.; *Int'l*, pg. 3571
BHARAT PETRO RESOURCES LTD.—See Bharat Petroleum Corporation Limited; *Int'l*, pg. 1011
BIOENERGIE MERZIG GMBH—See E.ON SE; *Int'l*, pg. 2251
BIOGAS DUCHEROW GMBH—See E.ON SE; *Int'l*, pg. 2251
BIOGAS FRIEDLAND GMBH & CO. KG—See EnviTec Biogas AG; *Int'l*, pg. 2455
BISHOP ENERGY SERVICES, L.L.C.; *U.S. Private*, pg. 565
BLACK HILLS/COLORADO UTILITY COMPANY, LLC—See Black Hills Corporation; *U.S. Public*, pg. 340
BLACK HILLS ENERGY SERVICES COMPANY—See Black Hills Corporation; *U.S. Public*, pg. 340
BLACK HILLS GAS, LLC—See Black Hills Corporation; *U.S. Public*, pg. 340
BLACK HILLS/IOWA GAS UTILITY COMPANY, LLC—See Black Hills Corporation; *U.S. Public*, pg. 340
BLACK HILLS/KANSAS GAS UTILITY COMPANY, LLC—See Black Hills Corporation; *U.S. Public*, pg. 340
BLACK HILLS/NEBRASKA GAS UTILITY COMPANY, LLC—See Black Hills Corporation; *U.S. Public*, pg. 341
BLACK MARLIN PIPELINE LLC—See The Williams Companies, Inc.; *U.S. Public*, pg. 2142
BLACK STONE MINERALS COMPANY, L.P.—See Black Stone Minerals, L.P.; *U.S. Public*, pg. 341

BLUEKNIGHT ENERGY PARTNERS, L.P.—See Ergon, Inc.; *U.S. Private*, pg. 1418
BLUE META S.P.A.—See Ascopiave S.p.A.; *Int'l*, pg. 603
BMP GREENGAS GMBH—See EnBW Energie Baden-Wurttemberg AG; *Int'l*, pg. 2401
BP ENERGY CO.—See BP plc; *Int'l*, pg. 1127
BP PRODUCTS NORTH AMERICA INC.—See BP plc; *Int'l*, pg. 1127
BREITBURN TRANSPETCO LP LLC—See Maverick Natural Resources, LLC; *U.S. Private*, pg. 2616
BRITISH GAS SERVICES LIMITED—See Centrica plc; *Int'l*, pg. 1413
BURSAGAZ BURSA SEHIRICI DOGALGAZ DAGITIM TICARET VE TAAHHUT A.S.—See EWE Aktiengesellschaft; *Int'l*, pg. 2575
CABOT PETROLEUM NORTH SEA LIMITED—See Coterra Energy Inc.; *U.S. Public*, pg. 587
CAMUZZI GAS PAMPEANA S.A.; *Int'l*, pg. 1275
CANADIAN ENTERPRISE GAS PRODUCTS, LTD.—See Enterprise Products Partners L.P.; *U.S. Public*, pg. 778
CASCADE NATURAL GAS CORPORATION—See MDU Resources Group, Inc.; *U.S. Public*, pg. 1409
CENSTAR ENERGY CORP.—See Via Renewables, Inc.; *U.S. Public*, pg. 2290
CENSTAR OPERATING COMPANY, LLC—See Via Renewables, Inc.; *U.S. Public*, pg. 2290
CENTERPOINT ENERGY MISSISSIPPI RIVER TRANSMISSION CORPORATION—See CenterPoint Energy, Inc.; *U.S. Public*, pg. 471
CENTERPOINT ENERGY SERVICES, INC.—See CenterPoint Energy, Inc.; *U.S. Public*, pg. 471
CENTERPOINT ENERGY—See CenterPoint Energy, Inc.; *U.S. Public*, pg. 471
CENTERPOINT ENERGY—See CenterPoint Energy, Inc.; *U.S. Public*, pg. 471
CESAP VENDITA GAS S.R.L.—See ACEA S.p.A.; *Int'l*, pg. 95
CEZ ICT SERVICES, A. S.—See CEZ, a.s.; *Int'l*, pg. 1426
CEZ OBNOVITELNE ZDROJE, S.R.O.—See CEZ, a.s.; *Int'l*, pg. 1426
CEZ TRADE BULGARIA EAD—See CEZ, a.s.; *Int'l*, pg. 1427
CEZ VANZARE S.A.—See CEZ, a.s.; *Int'l*, pg. 1427
CGE GAS NATURAL SA; *Int'l*, pg. 1430
CHANGZHOU XINAO GAS ENGINEERING COMPANY LIMITED—See ENN Energy Holdings Limited; *Int'l*, pg. 2442
CHART ASIA, INC.—See Chart Industries, Inc.; *U.S. Public*, pg. 481
CHATTANOOGA GAS COMPANY—See The Southern Company; *U.S. Public*, pg. 2131
CHENGDU GAS GROUP CO., LTD.; *Int'l*, pg. 1467
CHESAPEAKE UTILITIES CORPORATION; *U.S. Public*, pg. 485
CHESTER COUNTY NATURAL GAS AUTHORITY; *U.S. Private*, pg. 875
CHINA PROSPEROUS CLEAN ENERGY CORPORATION; *Int'l*, pg. 1542
CHINA SUNTIEN GREEN ENERGY CORPORATION LTD.; *Int'l*, pg. 1556
CHONGQING GAS GROUP CORPORATION LTD.; *Int'l*, pg. 1579
CIA DE GAS DE SAO PAULO - COMGAS ON—See Cosan S.A.; *Int'l*, pg. 1809
CIA DISTRIB DE GAS DO RIO DE JANEIRO - CEG; *Int'l*, pg. 1601
CIRCA GROUP AS; *Int'l*, pg. 1617
CITIZENS ENERGY GROUP - CITIZENS GAS DIVISION—See Citizens Energy Group; *U.S. Private*, pg. 903
CITIZENS ENERGY GROUP - CITIZENS RESOURCES DIVISION—See Citizens Energy Group; *U.S. Private*, pg. 903
CITIZENS ENERGY GROUP; *U.S. Private*, pg. 903
CITIZENS GAS UTILITY DISTRICT; *U.S. Private*, pg. 903
CITY MOV S.A R.L.—See Enovos International S.A.; *Int'l*, pg. 2444
CLARKE-MOBILE COUNTIES GAS DISTRICT; *U.S. Private*, pg. 914
CLARK FORK AND BLACKFOOT, L.L.C.—See NorthWestern Corporation; *U.S. Public*, pg. 1543
CLARK MOBILE COUNTIES GAS DISTRICT; *U.S. Private*, pg. 913
CLEAN ENERGY-DALLAS—See Clean Energy Fuels Corp.; *U.S. Public*, pg. 508
CLEAN ENERGY-DENVER—See Clean Energy Fuels Corp.; *U.S. Public*, pg. 508
CLEAN ENERGY-EAST COAST—See Clean Energy Fuels Corp.; *U.S. Public*, pg. 508
CLEAN ENERGY FUELS CORP.; *U.S. Public*, pg. 508
CLEAN POWER HYDROGEN PLC; *Int'l*, pg. 1654
CLEANTECH POWER CORP.; *Int'l*, pg. 1655
CLOUDBERRY CLEAN ENERGY ASA; *Int'l*, pg. 1662
CNE ENERGY SERVICES GROUP, LLC—See Iberdrola, S.A.; *Int'l*, pg. 3570
CNG VIETNAM JOINT STOCK COMPANY; *Int'l*, pg. 1674
COKINOS ENERGY CORPORATION; *U.S. Public*, pg. 965
COKINOS NATURAL GAS COMPANY—See Cokinos Energy Corporation; *U.S. Private*, pg. 965

N.A.I.C.S. INDEX

221210 — NATURAL GAS DISTRIB...

COLONIAL ENERGY, INC.—See Colonial Group, Inc.; *U.S. Private*, pg. 971
COLORADO NATURAL GAS, INC.—See Summit Utilities Inc.; *U.S. Private*, pg. 3857
COLUMBIA GAS OF KENTUCKY, INC.—See NiSource Inc.; *U.S. Public*, pg. 1530
COLUMBIA GAS OF MARYLAND, INC.—See NiSource Inc.; *U.S. Public*, pg. 1530
COLUMBIA GAS OF OHIO, INC.—See NiSource Inc.; *U.S. Public*, pg. 1530
COLUMBIA GAS OF PENNSYLVANIA, INC.—See NiSource Inc.; *U.S. Public*, pg. 1530
COLUMBIA GAS OF VIRGINIA, INC.—See NiSource Inc.; *U.S. Public*, pg. 1530
COLUMBUS ENERGY SA; *Int'l*, pg. 1706
COMPAGAS - CIA. PARANAENSE DE GAS—See Companhia Paranaense de Energia; *Int'l*, pg. 1747
COMPAGNIA NAPOLETANA DI ILLUMINAZIONE E SCALDAMENTO COL GAS SPA—See Eni S.p.A.; *Int'l*, pg. 2437
COMPANHIA DE GAS DE SAO PAULO - COMGAS—See Cosan S.A.; *Int'l*, pg. 1809
COMPASS GAS & ENERGIA SA—See Cosan S.A.; *Int'l*, pg. 1809
CONSTELLATION NEWENERGY-GAS DIVISION, LLC—See Constellation Energy Corporation; *U.S. Public*, pg. 572
CONTINENTAL PRODUCT ENGINEERING LIMITED—See Ferguson plc; *Int'l*, pg. 2637
COOL COMPANY LTD.; *Int'l*, pg. 1789
CORNING NATURAL GAS CORPORATION—See Argo Infrastructure Partners LLC; *U.S. Private*, pg. 320
CORPORACION ACCIONA ENERGIAS RENOVABLES S.A.; *Int'l*, pg. 1802
CORRE ENERGY B.V.; *Int'l*, pg. 1806
CORTUS ENERGY AB; *Int'l*, pg. 1808
CREOS DEUTSCHLAND GMBH—See Enovos International S.A.; *Int'l*, pg. 2444
CRITICAL SYSTEMS SERVICES PTE. LTD.—See Air Water Inc.; *Int'l*, pg. 240
CRODUX PLIN D.O.O.; *Int'l*, pg. 1853
CRYOSERVICE LIMITED—See Air Products & Chemicals, Inc.; *U.S. Public*, pg. 66
CULLMAN JEFFERSON COUNTIES GAS DISTRIBUTION; *U.S. Private*, pg. 1121
CUT BANK GAS COMPANY—See First Reserve Management, L.P.; *U.S. Private*, pg. 1525
DAESUNG ENERGY CO., LTD.—See Daesung Holdings Co., Ltd.; *Int'l*, pg. 1909
DCP MICHIGAN PIPELINE & PROCESSING, LLC—See Phillips 66 Company; *U.S. Public*, pg. 1688
DCP MIDSTREAM, LP—See Phillips 66 Company; *U.S. Public*, pg. 1688
DEKALB CHEROKEE COUNTIES GAS DISTRIBUTORS; *U.S. Private*, pg. 1192
DELGASCO, LLC—See Essential Utilities Inc.; *U.S. Public*, pg. 795
DELGAZ GRID S.A.—See E.ON SE; *Int'l*, pg. 2252
DELTA NATURAL GAS COMPANY, INC.—See Essential Utilities Inc.; *U.S. Public*, pg. 795
DELTA RESOURCES, LLC—See Essential Utilities Inc.; *U.S. Public*, pg. 795
DE RAJ GROUP AG; *Int'l*, pg. 1996
DEVON OEI OPERATING, INC—See Devon Energy Corporation; *U.S. Public*, pg. 657
DIAMOND KEY INTERNATIONAL PTY. LTD; *Int'l*, pg. 2105
DIANAGAS - SOC. DISTRIB. DE GAS NATURAL DE EVORA, S.A.—See Galp Energia SGPS, S.A.; *Int'l*, pg. 2875
DIRECT ENERGY BUSINESS MARKETING, LLC—See NRG Energy, Inc.; *U.S. Public*, pg. 1549
DIRECT ENERGY BUSINESS MARKETING, LLC - SOUTHEAST REGION—See NRG Energy, Inc.; *U.S. Public*, pg. 1549
DIRECT ENERGY NEW YORK CORPORATION—See NRG Energy, Inc.; *U.S. Public*, pg. 1549
DISTRIBUIDORA DE GAS DEL CENTRO S.A.; *Int'l*, pg. 2136
DISTRIGAS OF MASSACHUSETTS LLC—See ENGIE SA; *Int'l*, pg. 2428
DOMINION EAST OHIO ENERGY—See Dominion Energy, Inc.; *U.S. Public*, pg. 673
DOMINION HOPE GAS—See Dominion Energy, Inc.; *U.S. Public*, pg. 674
DOMINION TRANSMISSION, INC.—See Dominion Energy, Inc.; *U.S. Public*, pg. 674
DTE GAS COMPANY—See DTE Energy Company; *U.S. Public*, pg. 689
DUET GROUP—See CK Hutchison Holdings Limited; *Int'l*, pg 1636
DURIENSEGAS - SOC. DISTRIB. DE GAS NATURAL DO DOURO, S.A.—See Galp Energia SGPS, S.A.; *Int'l*, pg. 2875
DYNASTAR HOLDINGS, INC.; *U.S. Public*, pg. 699
EAGLE GAS MARKETING COMPANY—See Mustang Fuel Corporation; *U.S. Private*, pg. 2819
EAM GMBH & CO. KG; *Int'l*, pg. 2267
EASTERN GASES LIMITED; *Int'l*, pg. 2272

EASTERN PROPANE GAS, INC.—See Eastern Propane Gas, Inc.; *U.S. Private*, pg. 1321
THE EAST OHIO GAS COMPANY—See Enbridge Inc.; *Int'l*, pg. 2397
EAST TENNESSEE NATURAL GAS, LLC—See Enbridge Inc.; *Int'l*, pg. 2397
E&D ENERGIE- UND DIENSTLEISTUNGS GMBH & CO. KG—See EWE Aktiengesellschaft; *Int'l*, pg. 2575
ED IMMOBILIEN GMBH & CO. KG—See EnBW Energie Baden-Wurttemberg AG; *Int'l*, pg. 2398
EDP ESPIRITO SANTO DISTRIBUICAO DE ENERGIA S.A.—See EDP - Energias de Portugal, S.A.; *Int'l*, pg. 2314
EDP GAS.COM - COMERCIO DE GAS NATURAL, S.A.—See EDP - Energias de Portugal, S.A.; *Int'l*, pg. 2314
EDP GAS SERVICO UNIVERSAL, S.A.—See EDP - Energias de Portugal, S.A.; *Int'l*, pg. 2314
EFFICIENCY FOR LNG APPLICATIONS, S.L.—See Enagas, S.A.; *Int'l*, pg. 2396
EGAZ-DEGAZ FOLDGAZELOSZTO ZRT.—See ENGIE SA; *Int'l*, pg. 2431
EGCO COGENERATION CO., LTD.—See Electricity Generating Public Co., Ltd.; *Int'l*, pg. 2352
ELBENERGIE GMBH—See E.ON SE; *Int'l*, pg. 2257
ELITE COMPRESSION SERVICES, LLC—See Archrock, Inc.; *U.S. Public*, pg. 186
ELIZABETHTOWN GAS COMPANY—See JPMorgan Chase & Co.; *U.S. Public*, pg. 1210
ELK RIVER PUBLIC UTILITY DISTRICT; *U.S. Private*, pg. 1363
ELKTON GAS COMPANY—See Chesapeake Utilities Corporation; *U.S. Public*, pg. 485
EL PASO NATURAL GAS COMPANY, LLC—See Kinder Morgan, Inc.; *U.S. Public*, pg. 1232
EMBER RESOURCES INC.—See ARC Financial Corp.; *Int'l*, pg. 539
EMBER RESOURCES INC.—See Brookfield Corporation; *Int'l*, pg. 1187
EMIRATES GAS LLC—See Emirates National Oil Company Limited; *Int'l*, pg. 2381
EMPIRE NATURAL GAS CORPORATION; *U.S. Private*, pg. 1385
EMPRESAS PUBLICAS DE MEDELLIN ESP; *Int'l*, pg. 2391
ENABLE GAS GATHERING, LLC—See Energy Transfer LP; *U.S. Public*, pg. 763
ENABLE GAS TRANSMISSION, LLC—See Energy Transfer LP; *U.S. Public*, pg. 763
ENABLE GATHERING AND PROCESSING, LLC—See Energy Transfer LP; *U.S. Public*, pg. 763
ENABLE OKLAHOMA INTRASTATE TRANSMISSION, LLC—See Energy Transfer LP; *U.S. Public*, pg. 763
ENABLE PRODUCTS, LLC—See Energy Transfer LP; *U.S. Public*, pg. 763
ENBRIDGE ENERGY COMPANY, INC.—See Enbridge Inc.; *Int'l*, pg. 2397
ENBRIDGE GAS INC.—See Enbridge Inc.; *Int'l*, pg. 2397
ENBRIDGE GAS NEW BRUNSWICK INC.—See Algonquin Power & Utilities Corp.; *Int'l*, pg. 319
ENBRIDGE PIPELINE CORPORATION—See Enbridge Inc.; *Int'l*, pg. 2397
ENBW GASNETZ GMBH—See EnBW Energie Baden-Wurttemberg AG; *Int'l*, pg. 2398
ENCANA MARKETING (USA) INC.—See Ovintiv Inc.; *U.S. Public*, pg. 1625
ENDESA ENERGIA SA—See Enel S.p.A.; *Int'l*, pg. 2412
ENDESA X SERVICIOS SLU—See Enel S.p.A.; *Int'l*, pg. 2412
ENEFIT GREEN AS; *Int'l*, pg. 2411
ENEOS TRADING COMPANY LIMITED—See ENEOS Holdings, Inc.; *Int'l*, pg. 2415
ENERGAS CORP.; *U.S. Private*, pg. 1393
ENERGEN CORPORATION—See Diamondback Energy, Inc.; *U.S. Public*, pg. 658
ENERGIE DE SION REGION SA—See EnBW Energie Baden-Wurttemberg AG; *Int'l*, pg. 2398
ENERGIENETZE BAYERN GMBH—See E.ON SE; *Int'l*, pg. 2257
ENERGIENETZE SCHAAFHEIM GMBH—See E.ON SE; *Int'l*, pg. 2257
ENERGIESUDWEST NETZ GMBH—See Enovos International S.A.; *Int'l*, pg. 2444
ENERGIEVERSORGUNG ALZENAU GMBH—See E.ON SE; *Int'l*, pg. 2257
ENERGOTRANS, A.S.—See CEZ, a.s.; *Int'l*, pg. 1427
ENERGYAUSTRALIA—See CLP Holdings Limited; *Int'l*, pg. 1663
ENERGY CORPORATION OF AMERICA—See Energy Corporation of America; *U.S. Private*, pg. 1395
ENERGY SOURCE NATURAL GAS SERVICES INC.; *Int'l*, pg. 2423
ENERGY TRANSFER PARTNERS, L.L.C.—See Energy Transfer LP; *U.S. Public*, pg. 763
ENERGY WEST MONTANA, INC.—See First Reserve Management, L.P.; *U.S. Private*, pg. 1525
ENERGYWORKS CARTAGENA, S.L.—See Iberdrola, S.A.; *Int'l*, pg. 3571
ENGIE DEUTSCHLAND AG—See ENGIE SA; *Int'l*, pg. 2431

ENGIE GAS & LNG LLC—See ENGIE SA; *Int'l*, pg. 2428
EN+ GROUP INTERNATIONAL PJSC; *Int'l*, pg. 2395
ENI ARGENTINA EXPLORACION Y EXPLOTACION SA—See Eni S.p.A.; *Int'l*, pg. 2437
ENI AUSTRIA TANKSTELLENBETRIEB GMBH—See Eni S.p.A.; *Int'l*, pg. 2437
ENI FRANCE SARL—See Eni S.p.A.; *Int'l*, pg. 2437
ENIPROGETTI SPA—See Eni S.p.A.; *Int'l*, pg. 2438
ENI S.P.A. - GAS & POWER DIVISION—See Eni S.p.A.; *Int'l*, pg. 2437
ENKSZ ELSO NEMZETI KOZMUSZOLGALTATO ZRT.; *Int'l*, pg. 2440
ENN ENERGY HOLDINGS LIMITED; *Int'l*, pg. 2442
ENOVOS BALANCE DEUTSCHLAND GMBH—See Enovos International S.A.; *Int'l*, pg. 2444
ENPRO, LLC—See Essential Utilities Inc.; *U.S. Public*, pg. 795
ENSTAR NATURAL GAS COMPANY—See AltaGas Ltd.; *Int'l*, pg. 384
ENSTOR WAHA STORAGE AND TRANSPORTATION L.P.—See Iberdrola, S.A.; *Int'l*, pg. 3570
E.ON DEL-DUNANTULI GAZSZOLGALTATO ZRT.—See E.ON SE; *Int'l*, pg. 2253
E.ON ENERGIHANDEL NORDIC AB—See E.ON SE; *Int'l*, pg. 2254
E.ON GASHANDEL SVERIGE AB—See E.ON SE; *Int'l*, pg. 2255
E.ON GAZ DISTRIBUTIE S.A.—See E.ON SE; *Int'l*, pg. 2254
E.ON ROMANIA S.R.L.—See E.ON SE; *Int'l*, pg. 2255
E.ON RUHRGAS AG—See E.ON SE; *Int'l*, pg. 2255
E.ON RUHRGAS BBL B.V.—See E.ON SE; *Int'l*, pg. 2255
E.ON RUHRGAS GGH GMBH—See E.ON SE; *Int'l*, pg. 2255
E.ON RUHRGAS INTERNATIONAL AG—See E.ON SE; *Int'l*, pg. 2255
E.O. RESOURCES, LLC—See Iberdrola, S.A.; *Int'l*, pg. 3570
EQT CORPORATION; *U.S. Public*, pg. 784
EQT ENERGY, LLC—See EQT Corporation; *U.S. Public*, pg. 784
EQUINOR ENERGY BELGIUM NV—See Equinor ASA; *Int'l*, pg. 2484
EQUINOR NORSK LNG AS—See Equinor ASA; *Int'l*, pg. 2484
ERDGAS SUDWEST GMBH—See EnBW Energie Baden-Wurttemberg AG; *Int'l*, pg. 2399
ESSENT BELGIUM N.V.—See E.ON SE; *Int'l*, pg. 2257
ESSENT RETAIL ENERGIE B.V.—See E.ON SE; *Int'l*, pg. 2257
ETRA ENERGIA S.R.L.—See Ascopiave S.p.A.; *Int'l*, pg. 603
EVN CROATIA PLIN D.O.O—See EVN AG; *Int'l*, pg. 2571
EVO CNG, LLC—See EVO Transportation & Energy Services, Inc.; *U.S. Public*, pg. 804
EVOLUTION PETROLEUM CORPORATION; *U.S. Public*, pg. 804
EWE ENERGIA SP. Z O. O.—See EWE Aktiengesellschaft; *Int'l*, pg. 2575
EWE ENERJI AS—See EWE Aktiengesellschaft; *Int'l*, pg. 2575
EWE IMMOBILIEN GMBH—See EWE Aktiengesellschaft; *Int'l*, pg. 2575
EWE POLSKA SP. Z O.O.—See EWE Aktiengesellschaft; *Int'l*, pg. 2575
EXETER ENERGY LIMITED PARTNERSHIP—See CMS Energy Corporation; *U.S. Public*, pg. 518
EXXONMOBIL CORPORATION—See Exxon Mobil Corporation; *U.S. Public*, pg. 815
EXXONMOBIL OIL CORPORATION—See Exxon Mobil Corporation; *U.S. Public*, pg. 815
FACTOR GAS LIQUIDS INC.; *Int'l*, pg. 2601
FERNGAS NETZGESELLSCHAFT MBH—See Commonwealth Bank of Australia; *Int'l*, pg. 1720
FERNGAS NORDBAYERN GMBH—See E.ON SE; *Int'l*, pg. 2255
FIRMUS ENERGY LTD—See iCON Infrastructure LLP; *Int'l*, pg. 3583
FLAGA GAZ MAGYARORSZAG KFT.—See UGI Corporation; *U.S. Public*, pg. 2222
FLAGA GMBH—See UGI Corporation; *U.S. Public*, pg. 2222
FLAGA GPL ROMANIA S.R.L.—See UGI Corporation; *U.S. Public*, pg. 2222
FLAGA SPOL S.R.O.—See UGI Corporation; *U.S. Public*, pg. 2222
FLAGA S.R.O.—See UGI Corporation; *U.S. Public*, pg. 2222
FLINT ENERGY SERVICES INC.—See AECOM; *U.S. Public*, pg. 51
FLOGAS NORGE AS—See DCC plc; *Int'l*, pg. 1990
FLOGAS SVERIGE AB—See DCC plc; *Int'l*, pg. 1990
FOGAZ ZRT.—See ENKSZ Elso Nemzeti Kozmuszolgaltato Zrt.; *Int'l*, pg. 2440
FORMOSA PETROCHEMICAL CORPORATION; *Int'l*, pg. 2735
FORT HILL NATURAL GAS AUTHORITY INC.; *U.S. Private*, pg. 1574
FORTISBC ENERGY INC.—See Fortis Inc.; *Int'l*, pg. 2739
FORTUM MARKETS POLSKA S.A.—See Fortum Oyj; *Int'l*, pg. 2741
FORT UNION GAS GATHERING, LLC—See Kinder Morgan, Inc.; *U.S. Public*, pg. 1233

221210 — NATURAL GAS DISTRIB...

FOSMAX LNG SAS—See ENGIE SA; *Int'l*, pg. 2429
FRAMES HOLDING BV—See Plug Power Inc.; *U.S. Public*, pg. 1699
FREE RUNNING BUILDINGS LTD.; *Int'l*, pg. 2769
FREUDENBERG FILTRATION TECHNOLOGIES INC.—See Freudenberg SE; *Int'l*, pg. 2786
FRIO PIPE LINE COMPANY INC.—See George R. Brown Partnership; *U.S. Private*, pg. 1683
GAIL (INDIA) LIMITED; *Int'l*, pg. 2869
GAON GROUP LTD; *Int'l*, pg. 2882
GAS & ALLOY SUPPLY COMPANY, INC.—See CI Capital Partners LLC; *U.S. Private*, pg. 895
GASCADE GASTRANSPORT GMBH—See BASF SE; *Int'l*, pg. 883
GASCO ENERGY SUPPLY, LLC—See Ferrellgas Partners, L.P.; *U.S. Public*, pg. 829
GASES DEL PACIFICO S.A.C.—See Grupo Aval Acciones y Valores S.A.; *Int'l*, pg. 3121
GAS MALAYSIA BERHAD; *Int'l*, pg. 2887
GAS MALAYSIA VIRTUAL PIPELINE SDN. BHD.—See Gas Malaysia Berhad; *Int'l*, pg. 2887
GAS NATURAL DE LIMA Y CALLAO S.A.—See Ashmore Group plc; *Int'l*, pg. 608
GASODUCTO ATACAMA ARGENTINA SA—See Enel S.p.A.; *Int'l*, pg. 2413
GASPAL KYUSHU CORPORATION—See Daito Trust Construction Co., Ltd.; *Int'l*, pg. 1943
GAS PURIFICATION ENGINEERING CORPORATION; *U.S. Private*, pg. 1647
GAS SERVICES NZ LTD.; *Int'l*, pg. 2887
GAS SUPPLY COMPANY THESSALONIKI - THESSALIA SA—See Eni S.p.A.; *Int'l*, pg. 2438
GASTERRA B.V.; *Int'l*, pg. 2888
GASUM OY; *Int'l*, pg. 2888
GAS-UNION GMBH—See E.ON SE; *Int'l*, pg. 2255
GASVERSORGUNG HUNXE GMBH—See Gelsenwasser AG; *Int'l*, pg. 2914
GASVERSORGUNG IM LANDKREIS GIFHORN GMBH—See E.ON SE; *Int'l*, pg. 2257
GASVERSORGUNG SUDDEUTSCHLAND GMBH—See EnBW Energie Baden-Wurttemberg AG; *Int'l*, pg. 2399
GASVERSORGUNG UNTERLAND GMBH—See EnBW Energie Baden-Wurttemberg AG; *Int'l*, pg. 2399
GATEWAY ENERGY SERVICES CORPORATION—See NRG Energy, Inc.; *U.S. Public*, pg. 1549
GATEWAY PIPELINE COMPANY—See Gateway Energy Company, LLC; *U.S. Private*, pg. 1650
GAZ DE PARIS SAS—See DCC plc; *Int'l*, pg. 1990
GAZIFERE INC.—See Enbridge Inc.; *Int'l*, pg. 2397
GAZ METRO LIMITED PARTNERSHIP—See Caisse de Depot et Placement du Quebec; *Int'l*, pg. 1255
GAZNAT SA—See EnBW Energie Baden-Wurttemberg AG; *Int'l*, pg. 2398
GDF SUEZ CC SCRL—See ENGIE SA; *Int'l*, pg. 2433
GDF SUEZ GAS ENERGY SALES GMBH—See ENGIE SA; *Int'l*, pg. 2431
GDF SUEZ GAS SUPPLY & SALES NEDERLAND BV—See ENGIE SA; *Int'l*, pg. 2434
GDF SUEZ GLOBAL GAS & LNG—See ENGIE SA; *Int'l*, pg. 2434
GDF SUEZ INFRASTRUCTURES—See ENGIE SA; *Int'l*, pg. 2434
GDF SUEZ SALES LTD—See ENGIE SA; *Int'l*, pg. 2432
GDF SUEZ SERVICES LIMITED—See ENGIE SA; *Int'l*, pg. 2432
GELSENWASSER ENERGIENETZE GMBH—See Gelsenwasser AG; *Int'l*, pg. 2913
G.EN. GAZ ENERGIA SP. Z O.O.—See EnBW Energie Baden-Wurttemberg AG; *Int'l*, pg. 2400
G ENONE ENERGY CO., LTD.; *Int'l*, pg. 2861
GEORGIA NATURAL GAS COMPANY—See The Southern Company; *U.S. Public*, pg. 2131
GESA GAS SAU—See Enel S.p.A.; *Int'l*, pg. 2414
GEXA ENERGY, L.P.—See NextEra Energy, Inc.; *U.S. Public*, pg. 1526
GLG NETZ GMBH—See E.ON SE; *Int'l*, pg. 2257
GLOBAL ENERGY MARKETING II LLC—See Global Partners LP; *U.S. Public*, pg. 942
GRANDBLUE ENVIRONMENT CO., LTD.; *Int'l*, pg. 3057
GRAYLING GENERATING STATION LIMITED PARTNERSHIP—See CMS Energy Corporation; *U.S. Public*, pg. 518
GRDF—See ENGIE SA; *Int'l*, pg. 2434
GREATER DICKSON GAS AUTHORITY; *U.S. Private*, pg. 1769
GREEN EARTH INSTITUTE CO., LTD.; *Int'l*, pg. 3070
GREENLANE RENEWABLES; *U.S. Public*, pg. 3075
GREENVOLT - ENERGIAS RENOVAVEIS, S.A.—See KKR & Co. Inc.; *U.S. Public*, pg. 1252
GRTGAZ SA—See ENGIE SA; *Int'l*, pg. 2434
GSPC LNG LIMITED—See Gujarat State Petroleum Corporation Limited; *Int'l*, pg. 3177
GUANGDONG HUATE GAS CO., LTD.; *Int'l*, pg. 3156
GUARDIAN PIPELINE, L.L.C.—See ONEOK, Inc.; *U.S. Public*, pg. 1603
GUJARAT GAS LIMITED—See Gujarat State Petroleum Corporation Limited; *Int'l*, pg. 3177
HAFFNER ENERGY SA; *Int'l*, pg. 3206

HAIDKOPF GMBH—See BASF SE; *Int'l*, pg. 885
HANJIN CITY GAS—See HJ Shipbuilding & Construction Company, Ltd.; *Int'l*, pg. 3428
HAWKINS COUNTY GAS UTILITY DISTRICT; *U.S. Private*, pg. 1883
HC NATURGAS COMERCIALIZADORA DE ULTIMO RECURSO, S.A.—See EDP - Energias de Portugal, S.A.; *Int'l*, pg. 2314
HENAN LANTIAN GAS CO., LTD.; *Int'l*, pg. 3342
HEP-PLIN D.O.O.—See Hrvatska elektroprivreda d.d.; *Int'l*, pg. 3502
HERA S.P.A.; *Int'l*, pg. 3356
HEXICON AB; *Int'l*, pg. 3371
HIGHWOOD ASSET MANAGEMENT LTD.; *Int'l*, pg. 3389
HIKO ENERGY, LLC—See Via Renewables, Inc.; *U.S. Public*, pg. 2290
HIROSHIMA GAS CO., LTD.; *Int'l*, pg. 3405
HITACHI ZOSEN INOVA ETOGAS GMBH—See Hitachi Zosen Corporation; *Int'l*, pg. 3411
HITEC HOLDING B.V.—See Air Water Inc.; *Int'l*, pg. 240
HITEC POWER PROTECTION (BEIJING) CO., LTD.—See Air Water Inc.; *Int'l*, pg. 240
HITEC POWER PROTECTION IBERICA S.L.—See Air Water Inc.; *Int'l*, pg. 240
HITEC POWER PROTECTION LTD.—See Air Water Inc.; *Int'l*, pg. 240
HITEC POWER PROTECTION (MALAYSIA) SDN. BHD.—See Air Water Inc.; *Int'l*, pg. 240
HITEC POWER PROTECTION TAIWAN LTD.—See Air Water Inc.; *Int'l*, pg. 240
HOKKAIDO GAS CO LTD; *Int'l*, pg. 3443
HOLALUZ-CLIDOM SA; *Int'l*, pg. 3445
HOLYOKE GAS & ELECTRIC DEPARTMENT; *U.S. Private*, pg. 1969
HONG KONG & CHINA GAS COMPANY LIMITED—See Henderson Land Development Co. Ltd.; *Int'l*, pg. 3344
HOPE GAS, INC.—See Ullico Inc.; *U.S. Private*, pg. 4276
HOPE UTILITIES—See Ullico Inc.; *U.S. Private*, pg. 4276
HSIN KAO GAS CO., LTD.; *Int'l*, pg. 3507
HUBEI HEYUAN GAS CO., LTD.; *Int'l*, pg. 3517
HUNT OIL COMPANY OF CANADA, INC.—See Hunt Consolidated, Inc.; *U.S. Private*, pg. 2008
HYDROGENE DE FRANCE SA; *Int'l*, pg. 3547
IBERDROLA USA ENTERPRISES, INC.—See Iberdrola, S.A.; *Int'l*, pg. 3570
IDEON S.A.; *Int'l*, pg. 3592
ILLINOIS GAS CO.; *U.S. Private*, pg. 2042
INDIANA NATURAL GAS CORP.—See Midwest Natural Gas Corp.; *U.S. Private*, pg. 2722
INFRACON INFRASTRUKTUR SERVICE GMBH & CO. KG—See EnBW Energie Baden-Wurttemberg AG; *Int'l*, pg. 2400
INOUEKI SINGAPORE PTE. LTD.—See Air Water Inc.; *Int'l*, pg. 240
INTERCONN RESOURCES, LLC; *U.S. Private*, pg. 2109
INTERMOUNTAIN GAS COMPANY—See MDU Resources Group, Inc.; *U.S. Public*, pg. 1411
INTERSTATE GAS SUPPLY INC; *U.S. Private*, pg. 2124
ISLANDMAGEE ENERGY LIMITED—See Harland & Wolff Group Holdings plc; *Int'l*, pg. 3277
JEFFERSON-COCKE COUNTY UTILITY DISTRICT; *U.S. Private*, pg. 2198
JSC GASO—See AS Infortar; *Int'l*, pg. 590
KAASUPORSSI OY—See Gasum Oy; *Int'l*, pg. 2888
KANSAS GAS SERVICE COMPANY—See ONEOK, Inc.; *U.S. Public*, pg. 1603
KAWASAKI NATURAL GAS POWER GENERATION CO., LTD.—See ENEOS Holdings, Inc.; *Int'l*, pg. 2417
KAYSERIGAZ KAYSERI DOGALGAZ DAGITIM PAZARLAMA VE TICARET A.S.—See EWE Aktiengesellschaft; *Int'l*, pg. 2575
KEEP ENTERPRISES, INC.; *U.S. Private*, pg. 2272
KINDER MORGAN ALTAMONT LLC—See Kinder Morgan, Inc.; *U.S. Public*, pg. 1233
KINDER MORGAN, INC.; *U.S. Public*, pg. 1232
K N GAS GATHERING, INC.—See Kinder Morgan, Inc.; *U.S. Public*, pg. 1233
KNOX ENERGY COOPERATIVE ASSOCIATION INC.; *U.S. Private*, pg. 2324
KOGAZ RT.—See E.ON SE; *Int'l*, pg. 2253
KONKAN LNG LIMITED—See GAIL (India) Limited; *Int'l*, pg. 2869
KOSAN GAS FINLAND OY—See UGI Corporation; *U.S. Public*, pg. 2222
KOSAN GAS NORGE A/S—See UGI Corporation; *U.S. Public*, pg. 2222
KOSAN GAS SVERIGE AB—See UGI Corporation; *U.S. Public*, pg. 2222
LACLEDE VENTURE CORP.—See Spire, Inc; *U.S. Public*, pg. 1918
LAURENS COMMISSION OF PUBLIC WORKS; *U.S. Private*, pg. 2399
LAVACA PIPE LINE COMPANY—See Formosa Plastics Corporation; *Int'l*, pg. 2736
LD RETI S.R.L.—See A2A S.p.A.; *Int'l*, pg. 29
LEO S.A.—See Enovos International S.A.; *Int'l*, pg. 2444
LGP OPERATIONS LLC—See CrossAmerica Partners LP; *U.S. Public*, pg. 596

LIBERTY UTILITIES CO.—See Algonquin Power & Utilities Corp.; *Int'l*, pg. 319
LIMAGAS NATURAL PERU S.A.—See Empresas Lipigas SA; *Int'l*, pg. 2391
LISBOAGAS GDL - SOCIEDADE DISTRIBUIDORA DE GAS NATURAL DE LISBOA, S.A.—See Galp Energia SGPS, S.A.; *Int'l*, pg. 2875
LITORAL GAS SA—See ENGIE SA; *Int'l*, pg. 2434
LNG HRVATSKA D.O.O.—See Hrvatska elektroprivreda d.d.; *Int'l*, pg. 3502
LOI THERMPROCESS GMBH—See E.ON SE; *Int'l*, pg. 2255
LUSITANIAGAS COMERCIALIZACAO, S.A.—See Galp Energia SGPS, S.A.; *Int'l*, pg. 2875
MAINE NATURAL GAS—See Iberdrola, S.A.; *Int'l*, pg. 3570
MARITIMES & NORTHEAST PIPELINE LIMITED PARTNERSHIP—See Enbridge Inc.; *Int'l*, pg. 2397
MAXIMA AIR SEPARATION CENTER LTD.—See IDB Development Corporation Ltd.; *Int'l*, pg. 3588
MEDA PHARMA S.R.O.—See Viatris Inc.; *U.S. Public*, pg. 2293
METHA-METHANHANDEL GMBH—See E.ON SE; *Int'l*, pg. 2258
METROPOLITAN UTILITIES DISTRICT; *U.S. Private*, pg. 2689
MICHCON PIPELINE COMPANY—See DTE Energy Company; *U.S. Public*, pg. 689
MICHELSON ENERGY COMPANY; *U.S. Private*, pg. 2700
MICHIGAN GAS UTILITIES CORPORATION—See WEC Energy Group, Inc.; *U.S. Public*, pg. 2342
MID AMERICAN NATURAL RESOURCES, LLC—See Emkey Energy, LLC; *U.S. Private*, pg. 1383
MIDCONTINENT EXPRESS PIPELINE LLC—See Energy Transfer LP; *U.S. Public*, pg. 764
MIDDLE TENNESSEE NATURAL GAS UTILITY DISTRICT INC.; *U.S. Private*, pg. 2711
MIDWEST ENERGY RESOURCES COMPANY—See DTE Energy Company; *U.S. Public*, pg. 689
MIDWESTERN GAS TRANSMISSION COMPANY—See ONEOK, Inc.; *U.S. Public*, pg. 1603
MIDWEST NATURAL GAS CORP; *U.S. Private*, pg. 2722
MILES ENTERPRISES, INC.; *U.S. Private*, pg. 2727
MILLER PIPELINE, LLC—See CenterPoint Energy, Inc.; *U.S. Public*, pg. 472
MINNESOTA ENERGY RESOURCES CORPORATION—See WEC Energy Group, Inc.; *U.S. Public*, pg. 2342
MISSOURI GAS ENERGY EMPLOYEES' ASSOCIATION—See Energy Transfer LP; *U.S. Public*, pg. 763
MISSOURI GAS ENERGY INC.—See Spire, Inc; *U.S. Public*, pg. 1918
MN8 ENERGY, INC.; *U.S. Public*, pg. 1453
MOBILE GAS SERVICE CORPORATION—See Sempra; *U.S. Public*, pg. 1863
MONTANA-DAKOTA UTILITIES CO.—See MDU Resources Group, Inc.; *U.S. Public*, pg. 1411
MONTANA TECHNOLOGIES CORPORATION; *U.S. Public*, pg. 1465
MORNINGSTAR OPERATING LLC—See TXO Partners, L.P.; *U.S. Public*, pg. 2208
MOSS MARITIME A/S—See Eni S.p.A.; *Int'l*, pg. 2438
MOUNTAINEER GAS COMPANY—See UGI Corporation; *U.S. Public*, pg. 2222
MOVIATEC GMBH—See EnBW Energie Baden-Wurttemberg AG; *Int'l*, pg. 2400
MUSTANG GAS PRODUCTS LTD.; *U.S. Private*, pg. 2819
N2 SOLUTIONS LLC; *U.S. Private*, pg. 2829
NATIONAL FUEL GAS COMPANY; *U.S. Public*, pg. 1494
NATIONAL FUEL GAS DISTRIBUTION CORPORATION—See National Fuel Gas Company; *U.S. Public*, pg. 1494
NATURAL GAS PROCESSING COMPANY; *U.S. Private*, pg. 2867
NATURELGAZ SANAYI VE TICARET A.S.—See Global Yatirim Holding A.S.; *Int'l*, pg. 3003
NATURGAS ENERGIA COMERCIALIZADORAS ULTIMO RECURSO, S.A.—See EDP - Energias de Portugal, S.A.; *Int'l*, pg. 2314
NATURGAS ENERGIA GRUPO, S.A.—See EDP - Energias de Portugal, S.A.; *Int'l*, pg. 2314
NBB NETZ GESELLSCHAFT BERLIN-BRANDENBURG MBH—See ENGIE SA; *Int'l*, pg. 2429
NBB NETZ GESELLSCHAFT BERLIN-BRANDENBURG MBH—See E.ON SE; *Int'l*, pg. 2257
NED ESPANA DISTRIBUCION GAS, S.A.U.—See Covalis Capital LP; *Int'l*, pg. 1820
NED ESPANA DISTRIBUCION GAS, S.A.U.—See JPMorgan Chase & Co.; *U.S. Public*, pg. 1209
NEPTUNE LNG LLC—See ENGIE SA; *Int'l*, pg. 2428
NET POWER INC.; *U.S. Public*, pg. 1506
NETZE-GESELLSCHAFT SUDWEST MBH—See EnBW Energie Baden-Wurttemberg AG; *Int'l*, pg. 2399
NEW HAMPSHIRE GAS CORPORATION—See Iberdrola, S.A.; *Int'l*, pg. 3570
NEW JERSEY NATURAL GAS COMPANY—See New Jersey Resources Corporation; *U.S. Public*, pg. 1512
NEW JERSEY NATURAL RESOURCES COMPANY—See

221210 — NATURAL GAS DISTRIB...

New Jersey Resources Corporation; *U.S. Public*, pg. 1512
NEW MEXICO GAS COMPANY, INC.—See Emera, Inc.; *Int'l*, pg. 2377
NEW RIVER ENERGY CORPORATION—See Alpha Natural Resources, Inc.; *U.S. Private*, pg. 198
NEXTDECADE CORPORATION; *U.S. Public*, pg. 1526
NGT NEUE GEBAUDETECHNIK GMBH—See E.ON SE; *Int'l*, pg. 2255
NIEDERRHEINISCHE GAS- UND WASSERWERKE GMBH—See Gelsenwasser AG; *Int'l*, pg. 2914
NIPPON HELIUM INC.—See Air Water Inc.; *Int'l*, pg. 240
NISOURCE INC.; *U.S. Public*, pg. 1530
NJR CAPITAL SERVICES CORPORATION—See New Jersey Resources Corporation; *U.S. Public*, pg. 1511
NJR CLEAN ENERGY VENTURES—See New Jersey Resources Corporation; *U.S. Public*, pg. 1512
NJR ENERGY CORP—See New Jersey Resources Corporation; *U.S. Public*, pg. 1512
NJR ENERGY SERVICES COMPANY—See New Jersey Resources Corporation; *U.S. Public*, pg. 1512
NJR RETAIL HOLDINGS CORPORATION—See New Jersey Resources Corporation; *U.S. Public*, pg. 1512
NJR SERVICE CORPORATION—See New Jersey Resources Corporation; *U.S. Public*, pg. 1512
NOBLE ENERGY MEXICO, S. DE R.L. DE C.V.—See Chevron Corporation; *U.S. Public*, pg. 487
NORSK ANALYSE AS—See Addtech AB; *Int'l*, pg. 134
NORSK ANALYSE A/S—See Addtech AB; *Int'l*, pg. 134
NORTEGAS ENERGIA DISTRIBUCION, S.A.U.—See Covalis Capital LP; *Int'l*, pg. 1820
NORTEGAS ENERGIA DISTRIBUCION, S.A.U.—See JPMorgan Chase & Co.; *U.S. Public*, pg. 1209
NORTH AMERICAN POWER AND GAS, LLC—See Energy Capital Partners Management, LP; *U.S. Private*, pg. 1394
NORTH EAST HEAT & LIGHT CO.; *U.S. Private*, pg. 2945
NORTHEAST OHIO NATURAL GAS CORP.—See First Reserve Management, L.P.; *U.S. Private*, pg. 1525
NORTHEAST OKLAHOMA PUBLIC FACILTIES AUTHORITY; *U.S. Private*, pg. 2951
NORTHERN ILLINOIS GAS COMPANY—See The Southern Company; *U.S. Public*, pg. 2131
NORTHERN NEW ENGLAND ENERGY CORPORATION—See Caisse de Depot et Placement du Quebec; *Int'l*, pg. 1256
NORTHLAND UTILITIES ENTERPRISES LTD.—See ATCO Ltd.; *Int'l*, pg. 667
NORTHLAND UTILITIES (NWT) LIMITED—See ATCO Ltd.; *Int'l*, pg. 667
NORTHLAND UTILITIES (YELLOWKNIFE) LIMITED—See ATCO Ltd.; *Int'l*, pg. 667
NORTHVILLE NATURAL GAS, LLC—See NIC Holding Corporation; *U.S. Private*, pg. 2925
NORTHWEST ALABAMA GAS DISTRICT; *U.S. Private*, pg. 2958
NORTHWEST NATURAL GAS COMPANY—See Northwest Natural Holding Company; *U.S. Public*, pg. 1542
NORTHWEST PIPELINE CORPORATION—See The Williams Companies, Inc.; *U.S. Public*, pg. 2144
NORTHWEST PIPELINE CORPORATION—See The Williams Companies, Inc.; *U.S. Public*, pg. 2144
NPL CANADA LTD.—See Southwest Gas Holdings, Inc.; *U.S. Public*, pg. 1913
NSCC AIR WATER, INC.—See Air Water Inc.; *Int'l*, pg. 240
NSTAR GAS COMPANY—See Eversource Energy; *U.S. Public*, pg. 801
N.T. GAS PTY. LTD.—See APA Group; *Int'l*, pg. 500
NUTECH ENERGY RESOURCES, INC.; *U.S. Private*, pg. 1555
OAK RIDGE UTILITY DISTRICT; *U.S. Private*, pg. 2984
OCCIDENTAL OF ELK HILLS, INC.—See Occidental Petroleum Corporation; *U.S. Public*, pg. 1562
OCCIDENTAL POWER MARKETING, L.P.—See Occidental Petroleum Corporation; *U.S. Public*, pg. 1561
ODOR-TECH LLC—See Arkema S.A.; *Int'l*, pg. 569
OHIO GAS COMPANY; *U.S. Public*, pg. 3004
OKALOOSA GAS DISTRICT; *U.S. Private*, pg. 3006
OKLAHOMA NATURAL GAS COMPANY—See ONEOK, Inc.; *U.S. Public*, pg. 1603
ONE GAS, INC.; *U.S. Public*, pg. 1602
ONEOK ENERGY MARKETING & TRADING COMPANY, II—See ONEOK, Inc.; *U.S. Public*, pg. 1603
ONEOK FIELD SERVICES COMPANY, L.L.C.—See ONEOK, Inc.; *U.S. Public*, pg. 1603
ONEOK HYDROCARBON, L.L.C.—See ONEOK, Inc.; *U.S. Public*, pg. 1603
ON SITE GAS SYSTEMS, INC.; *U.S. Private*, pg. 3018
OOO ENI ENERGHIA—See Eni S.p.A.; *Int'l*, pg. 2438
OPAL FUELS INC.; *U.S. Public*, pg. 1606
PACIFIC NORTHERN GAS LTD—See AltaGas Ltd.; *Int'l*, pg. 384
PACIFIC PETRO IMPORT & EXPORT TRADING JOINT STOCK COMPANY—See Air Water Inc.; *Int'l*, pg. 240
PAIUTE PIPELINE COMPANY—See Southwest Gas Holdings, Inc.; *U.S. Public*, pg. 1913
PAX DISTRIBUTION, LLC—See World Kinect Corporation; *U.S. Public*, pg. 2381
PENINSULA ENERGY SERVICES COMPANY, INC.—See Chesapeake Utilities Corporation; *U.S. Public*, pg. 486
PENN ENERGY RESOURCES, LLC; *U.S. Private*, pg. 3134
THE PEOPLES GAS LIGHT AND COKE COMPANY—See WEC Energy Group, Inc.; *U.S. Public*, pg. 2342
PEOPLES NATURAL GAS CO. LLC—See Essential Utilities Inc.; *U.S. Public*, pg. 795
PEOPLES NATURAL GAS COMPANY, LLC—See SteelRiver Infrastructure Partners LP; *U.S. Private*, pg. 3797
PEOPLES TWP LLC—See SteelRiver Infrastructure Partners LP; *U.S. Private*, pg. 3797
PETROCHINA COMPANY LIMITED—See China National Petroleum Corporation; *Int'l*, pg. 1533
PETROCHINA INTERNATIONAL (LONDON) CO., LIMITED—See China National Petroleum Corporation; *Int'l*, pg. 1533
PETROGAS ENERGY CORPORATION—See AltaGas Ltd.; *Int'l*, pg. 384
THE PETROLEUM ALLIANCE OF OKLAHOMA; *U.S. Private*, pg. 4094
PIEDMONT NATURAL GAS COMPANY, INC.—See Duke Energy Corporation; *U.S. Public*, pg. 691
PINNACLE GAS TREATING LLC—See Western Midstream Partners, LP; *U.S. Public*, pg. 2356
PLE PIPELINE ENGINEERING GMBH—See E.ON SE; *Int'l*, pg. 2255
POLIMERI EUROPA UK LTD—See Eni S.p.A.; *Int'l*, pg. 2438
PORTGAS-SOCIEDADE DE PRODUCAO E DISTRIBUICAO DE GAS SA—See EDP - Energias de Portugal, S.A.; *Int'l*, pg. 2315
PORTGAS—See ENGIE SA; *Int'l*, pg. 2434
POWELL CLINCH GAS UTILITY DISTRIBUTION; *U.S. Private*, pg. 3236
PRAZSKA PLYNARENSKA DISTRIBUCE, A.S.—See E.ON SE; *Int'l*, pg. 2258
PRAZSKA PLYNARENSKA SERVIS DISTRIBUCE, A.S.—See E.ON SE; *Int'l*, pg. 2259
PRESSBURG, LLC—See Citizen Energy Operating LLC; *U.S. Private*, pg. 902
PRIMAGAS AD—See Hera S.p.A.; *Int'l*, pg. 3356
PRIMAX S.A.—See Grupo Romero; *Int'l*, pg. 3135
PRODAIR ET CIE S.C.S.—See Air Products & Chemicals, Inc.; *U.S. Public*, pg. 67
PRODUCERS GAS SALES, INC.—See The Energy Cooperative, Inc.; *U.S. Private*, pg. 4026
PROMORIENTE S.A. E.S.P—See Grupo Aval Acciones y Valores S.A.; *Int'l*, pg. 3121
PT. INDONESIA AIR WATER—See Air Water Inc.; *Int'l*, pg. 240
PTT NATURAL GAS DISTRIBUTION CO., LTD.—See ENGIE SA; *Int'l*, pg. 2433
PUBLIC SERVICE CO OF NEW MEXICO; *U.S. Public*, pg. 1735
PUBLIC SERVICE ENTERPRISE GROUP INCORPORATED; *U.S. Public*, pg. 1735
QUESTAR GAS COMPANY—See Enbridge Inc.; *Int'l*, pg. 2397
QWINT B.V.—See UGI Corporation; *U.S. Public*, pg. 2222
RABASKA INC.—See Enbridge Inc.; *Int'l*, pg. 2397
RAG AUSTRIA AG—See EVN AG; *Int'l*, pg. 2571
RAGER MOUNTAIN STORAGE COMPANY, LLC—See EQT Corporation; *U.S. Public*, pg. 764
REGENCY DESOTO-HESCO SERVICES LLC—See Energy Transfer LP; *U.S. Public*, pg. 764
REGENCY PIPELINE LLC—See Energy Transfer LP; *U.S. Public*, pg. 764
REGENCY UTICA GAS GATHERING LLC—See Energy Transfer LP; *U.S. Public*, pg. 764
RETE GAS FIDENZA S.R.L.—See Gas Plus S.p.A.; *Int'l*, pg. 2887
RILEY NATURAL GAS COMPANY—See Chevron Corporation; *U.S. Public*, pg. 487
ROANOKE GAS COMPANY—See RGC Resources, Inc.; *U.S. Public*, pg. 1796
ROCKY MOUNTAIN NATURAL GAS LLC—See Black Hills Corporation; *U.S. Public*, pg. 340
ROMEO GAS S.P.A.—See Ascopiave S.p.A.; *Int'l*, pg. 603
SASKENERGY INC.—See Crown Investments Corporation of Saskatchewan; *Int'l*, pg. 1857
SCALE GAS SOLUTIONS, S.L.—See Enagas, S.A.; *Int'l*, pg. 2396
SCANA ENERGY MARKETING INC. (SEMI)—See Dominion Energy, Inc.; *U.S. Public*, pg. 674
SCANA ENERGY—See Dominion Energy, Inc.; *U.S. Public*, pg. 674
SC CARPATGAS S.R.L.—See UGI Corporation; *U.S. Public*, pg. 2222
SC GDF SUEZ ENERGY ROMANIA SA—See ENGIE SA; *Int'l*, pg. 2434
SEMCAMS ULC—See Energy Transfer LP; *U.S. Public*, pg. 764
SEMCO ENERGY, INC.—See AltaGas Ltd.; *Int'l*, pg. 384
SEMINOLE PIPELINE COMPANY LLC—See Enterprise Products Partners L.P.; *U.S. Public*, pg. 779
SEQUENT ENERGY MANAGEMENT, L.P.—See The Williams Companies, Inc.; *U.S. Public*, pg. 2142
SETGAS - SOCIEDADE DE PRODUCAO E DISTRIBUICAO DE GAS, S.A.—See Galp Energia SGPS, S.A.; *Int'l*, pg. 2875

SHANGHAI AIR WATER MEDICAL GAS CO., LTD.—See Air Water Inc.; *Int'l*, pg. 240
SIENERGY, L.P.—See Ridgewood Infrastructure LLC; *U.S. Private*, pg. 3434
SJ ENERTRADE, INC.—See JPMorgan Chase & Co.; *U.S. Public*, pg. 1210
SKANGAS AS—See Gasum Oy; *Int'l*, pg. 2888
SNELSON COMPANIES INC. GAS DISTRIBUTION DIVISION—See Primoris Services Corporation; *U.S. Public*, pg. 1719
SOCIEDAD PORTUARIA EL CAYAO S.A. E.S.P.—See Grupo Aval Acciones y Valores S.A.; *Int'l*, pg. 3121
SOCIETA ITALIANA PER IL GAS—See Eni S.p.A.; *Int'l*, pg. 2437
SOCIETE DE SERVICE DU GAZODUC TRANSTUNISIEN SA - SERGAZ SA—See Eni S.p.A.; *Int'l*, pg. 2438
SOLGAS S.A.—See ENGIE SA; *Int'l*, pg. 2434
SOUTH ALABAMA GAS; *U.S. Private*, pg. 3719
SOUTHCROSS ENERGY OPERATING, LLC—See Targa Resources Corp.; *U.S. Public*, pg. 1981
SOUTHEAST ALABAMA GAS DISTRICT; *U.S. Private*, pg. 3724
SOUTHERN CALIFORNIA GAS COMPANY—See Sempra; *U.S. Public*, pg. 1863
SOUTHERN COMPANY GAS—See The Southern Company; *U.S. Public*, pg. 2131
THE SOUTHERN CONNECTICUT GAS COMPANY—See Iberdrola, S.A.; *Int'l*, pg. 3571
SOUTHERN PUBLIC SERVICE CO, INC.—See Ullico Inc.; *U.S. Private*, pg. 4276
SOUTHERN STAR CENTRAL GAS PIPELINE, INC.—See The Williams Companies, Inc.; *U.S. Public*, pg. 2143
SOUTH JERSEY ENERGY COMPANY—See JPMorgan Chase & Co.; *U.S. Public*, pg. 1210
SOUTH JERSEY GAS CO. - GLASSBORO DIVISION—See JPMorgan Chase & Co.; *U.S. Public*, pg. 1210
SOUTH JERSEY GAS COMPANY—See JPMorgan Chase & Co.; *U.S. Public*, pg. 1210
SOUTHSTAR ENERGY SERVICES LLC—See The Southern Company; *U.S. Public*, pg. 2131
SOUTHWESTERN MIDSTREAM SERVICES COMPANY—See Expand Energy Corporation; *U.S. Public*, pg. 809
SOUTHWEST GAS CORPORATION—See Southwest Gas Holdings, Inc.; *U.S. Public*, pg. 1913
SOUTHWEST GAS CORPORATION—See Southwest Gas Holdings, Inc.; *U.S. Public*, pg. 1913
SOUTHWEST GAS TRANSMISSION COMPANY—See Southwest Gas Holdings, Inc.; *U.S. Public*, pg. 1913
SPARK ENERGY GAS, LLC—See Via Renewables, Inc.; *U.S. Public*, pg. 2290
SPIGAS S.R.L.—See EnBW Energie Baden-Wurttemberg AG; *Int'l*, pg. 2400
SPIRE ALABAMA INC.—See Spire, Inc; *U.S. Public*, pg. 1918
SPIRE MISSOURI INC.—See Spire, Inc; *U.S. Public*, pg. 1919
SPIRIT ENERGY NORGE AS—See Centrica plc; *Int'l*, pg. 1413
SPRAGUE ENERGY SOLUTIONS INC.—See Brookfield Corporation; *U.S. Public*, pg. 1182
SPREEGAS GESELLSCHAFT FUR GASVERSORGUNG UND ENERGIEDIENSTLEISTUNG MBH—See ENGIE SA; *Int'l*, pg. 2429
SPREEGAS GESELLSCHAFT FUR GASVERSORGUNG UND ENERGIEDIENSTLEISTUNG MBH—See E.ON SE; *Int'l*, pg. 2257
STEREO SDN BHD—See Balchem Corporation; *U.S. Public*, pg. 266
STOCCAGGI GAS ITALIA S.P.A.—See Eni S.p.A.; *Int'l*, pg. 2438
STOCKHOLM GAS AB—See Fortum Oyj; *Int'l*, pg. 2741
STONE HORN RIDGE, LLC—See Cook Inlet Region, Inc.; *U.S. Private*, pg. 1038
SUBURBAN FRANCHISING, LLC—See Suburban Propane Partners, L.P.; *U.S. Public*, pg. 1958
SUBURBAN NATURAL GAS COMPANY; *U.S. Private*, pg. 3848
SUMMIT NATURAL GAS OF MAINE, INC.—See Summit Utilities Inc.; *U.S. Private*, pg. 3857
SUMMIT NATURAL GAS OF MISSOURI, INC.—See Summit Utilities Inc.; *U.S. Private*, pg. 3857
SUNOCO LOGISTIC PARTNERS L.P.—See Energy Transfer LP; *U.S. Public*, pg. 764
SUPERGAS ISRAEL GAS DISTRIBUTION CO. LTD—See Azrieli Group Ltd.; *Int'l*, pg. 781
SURTIGAS S.A. E.S.P.—See Grupo Aval Acciones y Valores S.A.; *Int'l*, pg. 3121
SUSSER ENERGY SERVICES LLC—See Energy Transfer LP; *U.S. Public*, pg. 764
SUZHOU AIR WATER TRADING CO., LTD.—See Air Water Inc.; *Int'l*, pg. 240
SWB GASUMSTELLUNG GMBH—See EWE Aktiengesellschaft; *Int'l*, pg. 2576
TAIWAN AIR WATER MACH TECH. CO., LTD.—See Air Water Inc.; *Int'l*, pg. 241
TARGA ENERGY LP—See Targa Resources Corp.; *U.S. Public*, pg. 1981

221210 — NATURAL GAS DISTRIB...

TATEHO CHEMICAL DALIAN CO., LTD.—See Air Water Inc.; *Int'l*, pg. 241
TECHNISCHE GASE UND GASETECHNIK GMBH—See DCC plc; *Int'l*, pg. 1991
TECO PEOPLES GAS—See Emera, Inc.; *Int'l*, pg. 2377
TELDIG SYSTEMS, INC.—See Caisse de Depot et Placement du Quebec; *Int'l*, pg. 1256
TENASKA, INC.; *U.S. Private*, pg. 3964
TENASKA MARKETING CANADA—See Tenaska, Inc.; *U.S. Private*, pg. 3965
TENASKA MARKETING VENTURES—See Tenaska, Inc.; *U.S. Private*, pg. 3965
TEN TRANSMISSION COMPANY—See Iberdrola, S.A.; *Int'l*, pg. 3571
TERRANETS BW GMBH—See EnBW Energie Baden-Wurttemberg AG; *Int'l*, pg. 2401
TEXAS GAS SERVICE CO.—See ONEOK, Inc.; *U.S. Public*, pg. 1603
TEXAS LPG STORAGE CO. INC.; *U.S. Private*, pg. 3976
TIANJIN VIAM AUTOMOTIVE PRODUCTS CO., LTD.—See Freudenberg SE; *Int'l*, pg. 2790
TIDAL ENERGY MARKETING INC.—See Enbridge Inc.; *Int'l*, pg. 2397
TIGER NATURAL GAS, INC.; *U.S. Private*, pg. 4170
TION RENEWABLES AG—See EQT AB; *Int'l*, pg. 2481
TND BEVERAGE, LLC—See Energy Transfer LP; *U.S. Public*, pg. 764
TPL ARKOMA MIDSTREAM LLC—See Targa Resources Corp.; *U.S. Public*, pg. 1981
TRANSCO GAS PIPE LINE CORP.—See The Williams Companies, Inc.; *U.S. Public*, pg. 2143
TRANSCO GAS PIPE LINE CORP.—See The Williams Companies, Inc.; *U.S. Public*, pg. 2143
TRANSCO GAS PIPE LINE CORP.—See The Williams Companies, Inc.; *U.S. Public*, pg. 2143
TRANSCONTINENTAL GAS PIPE LINE COMPANY, LLC—See The Williams Companies, Inc.; *U.S. Public*, pg. 2143
TRANSCONTINENTAL GAS PIPE LINE CORP.—See The Williams Companies, Inc.; *U.S. Public*, pg. 2143
TRANSCONTINENTAL GAS PIPE LINE CORP.—See The Williams Companies, Inc.; *U.S. Public*, pg. 2143
TRANSGAS ARMAZENAGEM - SOC. PORTUGUESA DE ARMAZENAGEM DE GAS NATURAL, S.A.—See Galp Energia SGPS, S.A.; *Int'l*, pg. 2876
TRANSMETANO E.S.P. S.A.—See Grupo Aval Acciones y Valores S.A.; *Int'l*, pg. 3121
TRANSPORTADORA DE GAS DEL SUR S.A.—See Grupo EMES S.A.; *Int'l*, pg. 3126
TRUSSVILLE GAS & WATER DEPARTMENTS; *U.S. Private*, pg. 4250
UGI CENTRAL PENN GAS, INC.—See UGI Corporation; *U.S. Public*, pg. 2223
UGI ENERGY SERVICES, INC.—See UGI Corporation; *U.S. Public*, pg. 2223
UGI ENERGY SERVICES, LLC—See UGI Corporation; *U.S. Public*, pg. 2222
UGI PENN NATURAL GAS, INC.—See UGI Corporation; *U.S. Public*, pg. 2223
UGI STORAGE COMPANY—See UGI Corporation; *U.S. Public*, pg. 2223
UGI UTILITIES, INC.—See UGI Corporation; *U.S. Public*, pg. 2223
UK ENERGY SYSTEMS, LTD.—See Biogas Energy Solutions, LLC; *U.S. Private*, pg. 562
UNARETI SERVIZI METRICI S.R.L.—See A2A S.p.A.; *Int'l*, pg. 29
UNIPER WARME GMBH—See Fortum Oyj; *Int'l*, pg. 2742
UNITED HYDROGEN GROUP, INC.—See Plug Power Inc.; *U.S. Public*, pg. 1699
UNITIL—See Unitil Corporation; *U.S. Public*, pg. 2253
UNS GAS, INC.—See Fortis Inc.; *Int'l*, pg. 2740
U.S. GAS & ELECTRIC, INC.—See Crius Energy, LLC; *U.S. Private*, pg. 1102
UTILITIES BOARD OF TRUSSVILLE; *U.S. Private*, pg. 4326
VALLEY ENERGY CORP.; *U.S. Private*, pg. 4333
VALNOR AS—See Addtech AB; *Int'l*, pg. 135
VANTI SA., ESP—See Brookfield Corporation; *Int'l*, pg. 1189
VECTREN ENTERPRISES, INC.—See CenterPoint Energy, Inc.; *U.S. Public*, pg. 472
VENEZIANA GAS S.P.A.—See Eni S.p.A.; *Int'l*, pg. 2437
VERMONT GAS SYSTEMS, INC.—See Caisse de Depot et Placement du Quebec; *Int'l*, pg. 1256
VERSALIS PACIFIC TRADING (SHANGHAI) CO. LTD.—See Eni S.p.A.; *Int'l*, pg. 2438
VIRGINIA NATURAL GAS, INC.—See The Southern Company; *U.S. Public*, pg. 2131
VIRGINIA POWER ENERGY MARKETING, INC.—See Dominion Energy, Inc.; *U.S. Public*, pg. 674
VNG AG—See EnBW Energie Baden-Wurttemberg AG; *Int'l*, pg. 2400
VNG AUSTRIA GMBH—See EnBW Energie Baden-Wurttemberg AG; *Int'l*, pg. 2400
VNG ENERGIE CZECH S.R.O.—See EnBW Energie Baden-Wurttemberg AG; *Int'l*, pg. 2400
VNG GASSPEICHER GMBH—See EnBW Energie Baden-Wurttemberg AG; *Int'l*, pg. 2400

VNG HANDEL & VERTRIEB GMBH—See EnBW Energie Baden-Wurttemberg AG; *Int'l*, pg. 2400
WARD PETROLEUM CORPORATION; *U.S. Private*, pg. 4441
WASHINGTON GAS LIGHT COMPANY—See AltaGas Ltd.; *Int'l*, pg. 384
WESERNETZ BREMEN GMBH—See EWE Aktiengesellschaft; *Int'l*, pg. 2576
WESTFALICA—See Gelsenwasser AG; *Int'l*, pg. 2914
WEST TEXAS GAS, INC.—See J.L. Davis Companies; *U.S. Private*, pg. 2167
THE WILLIAMS COMPANIES, INC. - NESHANIC STATION—See The Williams Companies, Inc.; *U.S. Public*, pg. 2142
WILLIAMS FIELD SERVICES GROUP, LLC—See The Williams Companies, Inc.; *U.S. Public*, pg. 2143
WILLIAMS FIELD SERVICES—See The Williams Companies, Inc.; *U.S. Public*, pg. 2142
WILLIAMS GAS PIPELINE CORP.—See The Williams Companies, Inc.; *U.S. Public*, pg. 2144
WILLIAMS GAS PIPELINE CORP.—See The Williams Companies, Inc.; *U.S. Public*, pg. 2144
WILLIAMS GAS PIPELINES CENTRAL—See The Williams Companies, Inc.; *U.S. Public*, pg. 2144
WILLIAMS GAS PIPELINE—See The Williams Companies, Inc.; *U.S. Public*, pg. 2143
WILLIAMS GAS PIPELINE—See The Williams Companies, Inc.; *U.S. Public*, pg. 2143
WILLIAMS GAS PIPELINE—See The Williams Companies, Inc.; *U.S. Public*, pg. 2143
WILLIAMS GAS PIPELINE—See The Williams Companies, Inc.; *U.S. Public*, pg. 2144
WILLIAMS GAS PIPELINE TRANSCO—See The Williams Companies, Inc.; *U.S. Public*, pg. 2144
WILLMUT GAS & OIL COMPANY—See Sempra; *U.S. Public*, pg. 1864
WINGAS BELGIUM S.P.R.L./B.V.B.A.—See BASF SE; *Int'l*, pg. 885
WINGAS GMBH—See BASF SE; *Int'l*, pg. 885
WINGAS UK LTD.—See BASF SE; *Int'l*, pg. 885
WISCONSIN GAS LLC—See WEC Energy Group, Inc.; *U.S. Public*, pg. 2342
WISCONSIN VALLEY IMPROVEMENT COMPANY—See WEC Energy Group, Inc.; *U.S. Public*, pg. 2342
WISE GAS, INC.; *U.S. Private*, pg. 4550
WORLD FUEL SERVICES TRADING DMCC—See World Kinect Corporation; *U.S. Public*, pg. 2381
WUHAN NATURAL GAS COMPANY LIMITED—See Henderson Land Development Co. Ltd.; *Int'l*, pg. 3344
XOOM ENERGY, LLC—See NRG Energy, Inc.; *U.S. Public*, pg. 1551
XOOM ENERGY, LLC.—See NRG Energy, Inc.; *U.S. Public*, pg. 1551
XOOM ENERGY ONT, ULC—See NRG Energy, Inc.; *U.S. Public*, pg. 1551
YANKEE GAS SERVICES COMPANY—See Eversource Energy; *U.S. Public*, pg. 802
YOKOHAMA LIQUIFIED GAS TERMINAL CO., LTD.—See Azuma Shipping Co., Ltd.; *Int'l*, pg. 782

221310 — WATER SUPPLY AND IRRIGATION SYSTEMS

4G ENTERPRISES, INC.; *U.S. Private*, pg. 15
A2A CICLO IDRICO S.P.A.—See A2A S.p.A.; *Int'l*, pg. 29
ABENAKI WATER COMPANY—See New England Services Company; *U.S. Public*, pg. 1511
ABRIMIX (PTY) LTD.—See LifeQuest World Corp.; *U.S. Public*, pg. 1313
ABWASSERGESELLSCHAFT GELSENKIRCHEN MBH—See Gelsenwasser AG; *Int'l*, pg. 2913
ACEA ATO 2 S.P.A.—See ACEA S.p.A.; *Int'l*, pg. 95
ACEA DOMINICANA S.A.—See ACEA S.p.A.; *Int'l*, pg. 95
ACEA MOLISE SRL—See ACEA S.p.A.; *Int'l*, pg. 95
ACEARIETI S.R.L.—See ACEA S.p.A.; *Int'l*, pg. 95
ACEA S.P.A.; *Int'l*, pg. 95
ACQUEDOTTO DI DOMODOSSOLA S.P.A.—See Eni S.p.A.; *Int'l*, pg. 2437
ACQUEDOTTO DI SAVONA S.P.A.—See Eni S.p.A.; *Int'l*, pg. 2437
ADECOM QUIMICA LTDA—See Ecolab Inc.; *U.S. Public*, pg. 712
ADRITEC DE LAS AMERICAS S. DE R.L. DE C.V—See Adritec Group International, E.C.; *Int'l*, pg. 153
ADRITEC EUROPE—See Adritec Group International, E.C.; *Int'l*, pg. 153
ADRITEC JORDAN—See Adritec Group International, E.C.; *Int'l*, pg. 153
ADRITEC MAROC—See Adritec Group International, E.C.; *Int'l*, pg. 153
ADRITEC TRADING & SERVICES COMPANY—See Adritec Group International, E.C.; *Int'l*, pg. 153
ADRITEC TUNIS—See Adritec Group International, E.C.; *Int'l*, pg. 153
ADRITEC TURKEY—See Adritec Group International, E.C.; *Int'l*, pg. 153
AGUA DE ORO VENTURES CORPORATION—See Ben-

CORPORATE AFFILIATIONS

guet Corporation; *Int'l*, pg. 974
AGUASIN SPA—See Danaher Corporation; *U.S. Public*, pg. 624
AGUAS Y SERVICIOS DE LA COSTA TROPICAL DE GRANADA, A.I.E.—See Fomento de Construcciones y Contratas, S.A.; *Int'l*, pg. 2722
AGUA Y SANEAMIENTOS ARGENTINOS, S.A.; *Int'l*, pg. 222
AIGUES DE VALLIRANA, S.A.—See Fomento de Construcciones y Contratas, S.A.; *Int'l*, pg. 2722
AKWA-WORX PTY. LTD.—See De.mem Limited; *Int'l*, pg. 1997
ALAMEDA COUNTY WATER DISTRICT; *U.S. Private*, pg. 149
ALDERWOOD WATER & WASTE WATER DISTRICT; *U.S. Private*, pg. 159
ALIAXIS NEDERLAND B.V.—See Aliaxis S.A./N.V.; *Int'l*, pg. 323
ALIAXIS UTILITIES & INDUSTRY AG—See Aliaxis S.A./N.V.; *Int'l*, pg. 323
ALIRAN IHSAN RESOURCES BERHAD; *Int'l*, pg. 329
ALPIQ CSEPEL KFT.—See Alpiq Holding AG; *Int'l*, pg. 372
ALTOONA WATER AUTHORITY; *U.S. Private*, pg. 210
ALULA WATER PTY LTD; *Int'l*, pg. 400
AMBIENTE H2O INC.; *U.S. Private*, pg. 217
AMBIENT WATER CORPORATION; *U.S. Private*, pg. 217
AMERICAN ENERGY PARTNERS, INC.; *U.S. Public*, pg. 100
AMERICAN STATES WATER COMPANY; *U.S. Public*, pg. 109
AMERICAN WATER WORKS COMPANY, INC.; *U.S. Public*, pg. 112
AMIAD WATER SYSTEMS SAS—See Amiad Water Systems Ltd.; *Int'l*, pg. 427
ANGLIAN WATER SERVICES LIMITED—See Canada Pension Plan Investment Board; *Int'l*, pg. 1278
ANGLIAN WATER SERVICES LIMITED—See Commonwealth Bank of Australia; *Int'l*, pg. 1720
ANTELOPE VALLEY EAST KERN WATER AGENCY; *U.S. Private*, pg. 287
APCOA PARKING ITALIA S.P.A.—See Centerbridge Partners, L.P.; *U.S. Private*, pg. 812
AQUA-CHEM, INC.—See Crimson Investment; *U.S. Private*, pg. 1100
AQUAFUNDALIA - AGUA DO FUNDAO, S.A.—See Fomento de Construcciones y Contratas, S.A.; *Int'l*, pg. 2722
AQUAGIB LIMITED—See CK Hutchison Holdings Limited; *Int'l*, pg. 1637
AQUA ILLINOIS, INC.—See Essential Utilities Inc.; *U.S. Public*, pg. 795
AQUA ILLINOIS—See Essential Utilities Inc.; *U.S. Public*, pg. 795
AQUA INDIANA, INC.—See Essential Utilities Inc.; *U.S. Public*, pg. 795
AQUALIA CZECH, S.L.—See Fomento de Construcciones y Contratas, S.A.; *Int'l*, pg. 2722
AQUALIA INFRAESTRUCTURAS D.O.O.—See Fomento de Construcciones y Contratas, S.A.; *Int'l*, pg. 2722
AQUALIA INFRAESTRUCTURAS D.O.O.—See Fomento de Construcciones y Contratas, S.A.; *Int'l*, pg. 2722
AQUALIA INFRAESTRUCTURAS MONTENEGRO (AIM) D.O.O.—See Fomento de Construcciones y Contratas, S.A.; *Int'l*, pg. 2722
AQUALIA MEXICO, S.A. DE C.V.—See Fomento de Construcciones y Contratas, S.A.; *Int'l*, pg. 2722
AQUAMAIOR - AGUAS DE CAMPO MAIOR, S.A.—See Fomento de Construcciones y Contratas, S.A.; *Int'l*, pg. 2722
AQUA NEW JERSEY, INC.—See Essential Utilities Inc.; *U.S. Public*, pg. 795
AQUA NEW JERSEY—See Essential Utilities Inc.; *U.S. Public*, pg. 795
AQUA NEW YORK, INC.—See American Water Works Company, Inc.; *U.S. Public*, pg. 112
AQUA OHIO, INC.—See Essential Utilities Inc.; *U.S. Public*, pg. 795
AQUA OHIO, INC.—See Essential Utilities Inc.; *U.S. Public*, pg. 795
AQUA OHIO - LAKE SHORE DIVISION—See Essential Utilities Inc.; *U.S. Public*, pg. 795
AQUA OHIO - MARION DIVISION—See Essential Utilities Inc.; *U.S. Public*, pg. 795
AQUA PENNSYLVANIA, INC.—See Essential Utilities Inc.; *U.S. Public*, pg. 795
AQUA PENNSYLVANIA - ROARING CREEK DIVISION—See Essential Utilities Inc.; *U.S. Public*, pg. 795
AQUA PENNSYLVANIA - SHENANGO VALLEY DIVISION—See Essential Utilities Inc.; *U.S. Public*, pg. 795
AQUAPORIN ASIA PTE. LTD.—See Aquaporin A/S; *Int'l*, pg. 528
AQUAPORIN A/S; *Int'l*, pg. 527
AQUARION WATER COMPANY OF MASSACHUSETTS, INC.—See Eversource Energy; *U.S. Public*, pg. 801
AQUARION WATER COMPANY OF NEW HAMPSHIRE, INC.—See Eversource Energy; *U.S. Public*, pg. 801

N.A.I.C.S. INDEX

221310 — WATER SUPPLY AND IR...

AQUARION WATER COMPANY—See Eversource Energy; *U.S. Public*, pg. 801
AQUA TEXAS, INC.—See Essential Utilities Inc.; *U.S. Public*, pg. 795
AQUATROL—See Momar, Inc.; *U.S. Private*, pg. 2767
ARAB DRIP IRRIGATION TECHNOLOGY COMPANY LTD.—See Adritec Group International, E.C.; *Int'l*, pg. 153
ARIDTEC PTE LTD.—See Eneco Refresh Limited; *Int'l*, pg. 2411
ARIZONA-AMERICAN WATER COMPANY—See EPCOR Utilities, Inc.; *Int'l*, pg. 2459
ARIZONA WATER COMPANY—See Fontana Water Company; *U.S. Private*, pg. 1560
ARMADA WATER ASSETS, INC.; *U.S. Private*, pg. 329
ARTESIAN RESOURCES CORPORATION; *U.S. Public*, pg. 201
ARTESIAN WASTEWATER MANAGEMENT, INC.—See Artesian Resources Corporation; *U.S. Public*, pg. 201
ARTESIAN WATER COMPANY, INC.—See Artesian Resources Corporation; *U.S. Public*, pg. 202
ARTESIAN WATER MARYLAND, INC.—See Artesian Resources Corporation; *U.S. Public*, pg. 202
ARTESIAN WATER PENNSYLVANIA, INC.—See Artesian Resources Corporation; *U.S. Public*, pg. 202
ARVIN-EDISON WATER STORAGE DISTRICT; *U.S. Private*, pg. 345
ASCENSION WATER CO.—See Baton Rouge Water Works Company; *U.S. Private*, pg. 487
AS TALLINNA VESI; *Int'l*, pg. 591
ATCO WATER, LTD.—See ATCO Ltd.; *Int'l*, pg. 666
ATHENS WATER SUPPLY & SEWERAGE S.A.; *Int'l*, pg. 670
ATLANTIC CITY MUNICIPAL UTILITIES AUTHORITY; *U.S. Private*, pg. 372
BARR + WRAY FZE—See Barr + Wray Limited; *Int'l*, pg. 867
BARR + WRAY (H.K.) LIMITED—See Barr + Wray Limited; *Int'l*, pg. 867
BARR + WRAY LIMITED; *Int'l*, pg. 867
BASIC WATER COMPANY—See Contran Corporation; *U.S. Private*, pg. 1033
BATON ROUGE WATER WORKS COMPANY; *U.S. Private*, pg. 487
BAYSAVER TECHNOLOGIES, LLC—See Advanced Drainage Systems, Inc.; *U.S. Public*, pg. 46
BCR ENVIRONMENTAL CORPORATION; *U.S. Private*, pg. 499
BEAUFORT-JASPER WATER & SEWER AUTHORITY; *U.S. Private*, pg. 508
BECMAR SPRINKLER SYSTEMS, INC.; *U.S. Private*, pg. 512
BEIJING ENTERPRISES WATER GROUP LIMITED; *Int'l*, pg. 950
BENISAF WATER COMPANY, SPA—See ACS, Actividades de Construccion y Servicios, S.A.; *Int'l*, pg. 110
BERKELEY COUNTY WATER & SANITATION AUTHORITY; *U.S. Private*, pg. 532
BERRENDA MESA WATER DISTRICT; *U.S. Private*, pg. 538
BEST WATER TECHNOLOGY (IRELAND) LTD.—See BWT Aktiengesellschaft; *Int'l*, pg. 1233
BE WATER S.A.—See Beijing Enterprises Water Group Limited; *Int'l*, pg. 950
BGR ENERGY SYSTEMS LIMITED - ENVIRONMENT ENGINEERING DIVISION—See BGR Energy Systems Limited; *Int'l*, pg. 1008
BGT GROUP CO., LTD.; *Int'l*, pg. 1009
BINH DUONG WATER ENVIRONMENT JSC; *Int'l*, pg. 1034
BIOLAB ARABIA LTD. - JUBAIL FACTORY—See Al-Hejailan Group; *Int'l*, pg. 286
BIOLAB ARABIA LTD.—See Al-Hejailan Group; *Int'l*, pg. 286
BIOTEQ ARIZONA, INC.—See BQE Water Inc.; *Int'l*, pg. 1133
BI PURE WATER INC.; *Int'l*, pg. 1016
BIWATER AEWT, INC.—See Biwater Holdings Limited; *Int'l*, pg. 1052
BIWATER HOLDINGS LIMITED; *Int'l*, pg. 1052
BIWATER INTERNATIONAL LIMITED (PANAMA)—See Biwater Holdings Limited; *Int'l*, pg. 1052
BIWATER (PTY) LIMITED—See Biwater Holdings Limited; *Int'l*, pg. 1052
BIWATER S.A.—See Biwater Holdings Limited; *Int'l*, pg. 1052
BLUE PRINT TECHNOLOGIES (PTY) LTD.—See Current Water Technologies Inc.; *Int'l*, pg. 1879
BLUE RIDGE ATLANTIC, INC.—See Watts Water Technologies, Inc.; *U.S. Public*, pg. 2337
BOHAI WATER INDUSTRY CO., LTD.; *Int'l*, pg. 1100
BONITA SPRINGS UTILITIES INC.; *U.S. Private*, pg. 614
BUCKS COUNTY WATER & SEWER AUTHORITY; *U.S. Private*, pg. 678
BWT AUSTRIA GMBH—See BWT Aktiengesellschaft; *Int'l*, pg. 1232
BWT FRANCE SAS—See BWT Aktiengesellschaft; *Int'l*, pg. 1232
BWT INTERNATIONAL TRADING LTD—See BWT Aktiengesellschaft; *Int'l*, pg. 1232

BWT NEDERLAND BV—See BWT Aktiengesellschaft; *Int'l*, pg. 1232
BWT PHARMA & BIOTECH LTD.—See BWT Aktiengesellschaft; *Int'l*, pg. 1232
BWT POLSKA SP. Z.O.O.—See BWT Aktiengesellschaft; *Int'l*, pg. 1232
BWT UK LIMITED—See BWT Aktiengesellschaft; *Int'l*, pg. 1233
BWT UKRAINE LTD.—See BWT Aktiengesellschaft; *Int'l*, pg. 1232
BWT WATER AND MORE IBERICA S.L.—See BWT Aktiengesellschaft; *Int'l*, pg. 1232
BWT WATER+MORE DEUTSCHLAND GMBH—See BWT Aktiengesellschaft; *Int'l*, pg. 1232
BWT WATER + MORE GMBH—See BWT Aktiengesellschaft; *Int'l*, pg. 1233
BWT WATER+MORE ITALIA SRL—See BWT Aktiengesellschaft; *Int'l*, pg. 1232
BWT WATER TECHNOLOGY (SHANGHAI) CO. LTD.—See BWT Aktiengesellschaft; *Int'l*, pg. 1233
BW WATER PTE. LTD.—See BW Group Ltd.; *Int'l*, pg. 1231
CADIZ INC.; *U.S. Public*, pg. 419
CALIFORNIA CITIES WATER COMPANY, INC.—See American States Water Company; *U.S. Public*, pg. 110
CALIFORNIA WATER SERVICE COMPANY—See California Water Service Group; *U.S. Public*, pg. 423
CALIFORNIA WATER SERVICE COMPANY—See California Water Service Group; *U.S. Public*, pg. 423
CALIFORNIA WATER SERVICE COMPANY—See California Water Service Group; *U.S. Public*, pg. 423
CALIFORNIA WATER SERVICE COMPANY—See California Water Service Group; *U.S. Public*, pg. 423
CALIFORNIA WATER SERVICE COMPANY—See California Water Service Group; *U.S. Public*, pg. 423
CALIFORNIA WATER SERVICE COMPANY—See California Water Service Group; *U.S. Public*, pg. 424
CALIFORNIA WATER SERVICE COMPANY—See California Water Service Group; *U.S. Public*, pg. 424
CALIFORNIA WATER SERVICE COMPANY—See California Water Service Group; *U.S. Public*, pg. 424
CALIFORNIA WATER SERVICE COMPANY—See California Water Service Group; *U.S. Public*, pg. 424
CALIFORNIA WATER SERVICE COMPANY—See California Water Service Group; *U.S. Public*, pg. 424
CALIFORNIA WATER SERVICE COMPANY—See California Water Service Group; *U.S. Public*, pg. 424
CAMBRIDGE WATER PLC—See Arjun Infrastructure Partners Limited; *Int'l*, pg. 568
CANADIAN RIVER MUNICIPAL WATER AUTHORITY; *U.S. Private*, pg. 732
CANATURE HEALTH TECHNOLOGY GROUP CO., LTD.; *Int'l*, pg. 1288
CART ACQUA S.R.L.—See Ascopiave S.p.A.; *Int'l*, pg. 603
CARTHAGE WATER & ELECTRIC PLANT; *U.S. Private*, pg. 776
CASCADIA WATER, LLC—See Northwest Natural Holding Company; *U.S. Public*, pg. 1542
CAYMAN WATER COMPANY LIMITED—See Consolidated Water Co. Ltd.; *Int'l*, pg. 1771
CEC ENVIRONMENTAL PROTECTION CO., LTD.; *Int'l*, pg. 1372
CHARITY GLOBAL, INC.; *U.S. Private*, pg. 851
CHARLESTON COMMISSIONERS OF PUBLIC WORKS; *U.S. Private*, pg. 856
CHEM-AQUA, INC.,—See NCH Corporation; *U.S. Private*, pg. 2876
CHENGDU XINGRONG ENVIRONMENT CO., LTD.; *Int'l*, pg. 1469
CHEROKEE COUNTY WATER SEWAGE AUTHORITY; *U.S. Private*, pg. 873
CHESTER WATER AUTHORITY; *U.S. Private*, pg. 875
CHINA TIANYF HOLDINGS GROUP LIMITED; *Int'l*, pg. 1559
CHINA WATER AFFAIRS GROUP LTD; *Int'l*, pg. 1563
CHOCOLATE BAYOU WATER COMPANY—See International Paper Company; *U.S. Public*, pg. 1155
CHONGQING WATER GROUP CO., LTD.; *Int'l*, pg. 1581
CILIT SA—See BWT Aktiengesellschaft; *Int'l*, pg. 1233
CILLICHEMIE ITALIANA SRL—See BWT Aktiengesellschaft; *Int'l*, pg. 1233
CIRCULAR WATERS SOLUTIONS S.R.L.; *Int'l*, pg. 1618
CITIZENS ENERGY GROUP - CITIZENS THERMAL DIVISION—See Citizens Energy Group; *U.S. Private*, pg. 903
CITIZENS ENERGY GROUP - CITIZENS WATER DIVISION—See Citizens Energy Group; *U.S. Private*, pg. 903
CLEANWATER1, INC.—See Baird Financial Group, Inc.; *U.S. Private*, pg. 453
CLEARFORD - KOESTER CANADA, INC.—See Clearford Water Systems Inc.; *Int'l*, pg. 1657
CLEARWATER ENVIRO TECHNOLOGIES, INC.; *U.S. Private*, pg. 939
COACHELLA VALLEY WATER DISTRICT; *U.S. Private*, pg. 953
COLONIAL WATER COMPANY—See New England Services Company; *U.S. Public*, pg. 1511
COLUMBIA POWER & WATER SYSTEMS; *U.S. Private*, pg. 977
COLUMBUS WATER WORKS; *U.S. Private*, pg. 979
COMPANHIA DE SANEAMENTO BASICO DO ESTADO DE SAO PAULO - SABESP; *Int'l*, pg. 1747

COMPANHIA DE SANEAMENTO DO PARANA SANEPAR; *Int'l*, pg. 1747
THE CONNECTICUT WATER COMPANY—See SJW Group; *U.S. Public*, pg. 1891
CONSOLIDATED UTILITY DISTRICT; *U.S. Private*, pg. 1022
CONSOLIDATED WATER CO. LTD.; *Int'l*, pg. 1771
CONSOLIDATED WATER WORKS DISTRICT 1; *U.S. Private*, pg. 1022
CONSORCIO AGUA AZUL S.A.—See ACEA S.p.A.; *Int'l*, pg. 95
CONTRA COSTA WATER DISTRICT INC.; *U.S. Private*, pg. 1031
CORE LABORATORIES INTERNATIONAL B.V.—See Core Laboratories N.V.; *Int'l*, pg. 1798
CORE LABORATORIES MALAYSIA SDN BHD—See Core Laboratories N.V.; *Int'l*, pg. 1798
CPS DISTRIBUTORS, INC.; *U.S. Private*, pg. 1080
CSA COSMIC CO., LTD.; *Int'l*, pg. 1861
CSE-HANKIN INC—See CSE Global Ltd.; *Int'l*, pg. 1863
CT ENVIRONMENTAL GROUP LIMITED; *Int'l*, pg. 1868
CUCAMONGA VALLEY WATER DISTRICT; *U.S. Private*, pg. 1120
CULLIGAN WATER CONDITIONING SERVICE; *U.S. Private*, pg. 1121
DAIKI AXIS CO., LTD.; *Int'l*, pg. 1932
DAIPOLY SYSTEM CORPORATION—See CREATE CORPORATION; *Int'l*, pg. 1832
DAITEC CO., LTD.—See Daiki Axis Co., Ltd.; *Int'l*, pg. 1932
DALPEX S.P.A.—See Aliaxis S.A./N.V.; *Int'l*, pg. 323
DARCO-ENVIDAN SDN BHD—See Darco Water Technologies Limited; *Int'l*, pg. 1972
DAVIDSON WATER INC.; *U.S. Private*, pg. 1172
DAYU IRRIGATION GROUP CO., LTD.; *Int'l*, pg. 1985
DEL-CO. WATER CO. INC.; *U.S. Private*, pg. 1193
DELTA PURE FILTRATION CORPORATION; *U.S. Private*, pg. 1201
DESALCO (BARBADOS) LTD—See Consolidated Water Co. Ltd.; *Int'l*, pg. 1771
DESALCO LIMITED—See Consolidated Water Co. Ltd.; *Int'l*, pg. 1771
DES EAUX DE DOUAI SA; *Int'l*, pg. 2043
DES MOINES WATER WORKS; *U.S. Private*, pg. 1210
DODSON ENGINEERED PRODUCTS, INC.—See Core & Main, Inc.; *U.S. Public*, pg. 576
DUBLIN SAN RAMON SERVICES DISTRICT; *U.S. Private*, pg. 1283
DUOYUAN GLOBAL WATER INC.—See Duoyuan Investments Limited; *Int'l*, pg. 2227
EAST BAY MUNICIPAL UTILITY DISTRICT; *U.S. Private*, pg. 1315
EASTERN MUNICIPAL WATER DISTRICT INC.; *U.S. Private*, pg. 1320
EASTERN WATER RESOURCES DEVELOPMENT & MANAGEMENT PUBLIC COMPANY LIMITED; *Int'l*, pg. 2274
EAST OF HUDSON WATERSHED CORPORATION; *U.S. Private*, pg. 1317
EAST PASADENA WATER CO.—See American Water Works Company, Inc.; *U.S. Public*, pg. 112
ECOCITYSERVICE CORPORATION—See Bain Capital, LP; *U.S. Public*, pg. 434
ECOLAB EAST AFRICA (KENYA) LIMITED—See Ecolab Inc.; *U.S. Public*, pg. 713
ECOLAB HISPANO-PORTUGUESA S.L.—See Ecolab Inc.; *U.S. Public*, pg. 713
ECOLAB LTD.—See Ecolab Inc.; *U.S. Public*, pg. 713
ECOLAB MAROC S.A.—See Ecolab Inc.; *U.S. Public*, pg. 713
ECOLAB NL 10 B.V.—See Ecolab Inc.; *U.S. Public*, pg. 713
ECOLAB, S. DE R.L. DE C.V.—See Ecolab Inc.; *U.S. Public*, pg. 714
ECOLAB SDN BHD—See Ecolab Inc.; *U.S. Public*, pg. 714
ECOLAB SERVICES POLAND SP. Z O O—See Ecolab Inc.; *U.S. Public*, pg. 714
ECOLAB S.H.U.—See Ecolab Inc.; *U.S. Public*, pg. 714
ECOLAB Y COMPANIA COLECTIVA DE RESPONSABILIDAD LIMITADA—See Ecolab Inc.; *U.S. Public*, pg. 714
ECO SAFE SYSTEMS USA, INC.; *U.S. Public*, pg. 712
ECOWATER CANADA LTD.—See Berkshire Hathaway Inc.; *U.S. Public*, pg. 311
ECOWATER SYSTEMS LLC—See Berkshire Hathaway Inc.; *U.S. Public*, pg. 311
EGCOM TARA CO. LTD.—See Eastern Water Resources Development & Management Public Company Limited; *Int'l*, pg. 2274
EKOPAK NV; *Int'l*, pg. 2339
EL DORADO UTILITIES, INC.—See AMREP Corporation; *U.S. Public*, pg. 133
ELGO IRRIGATION LTD.—See Trans-Resources, Inc.; *U.S. Private*, pg. 4206
ELSINORE VALLEY MUNICIPAL WATER DISTRICT; *U.S. Private*, pg. 1377
EL TORO WATER DISTRICT; *U.S. Private*, pg. 1349
EMEFCY LTD.—See Fluence Corporation Limited; *U.S. Public*, pg. 857
EMERALD COAST UTILITY SERVICES, INC.—See American States Water Company; *U.S. Public*, pg. 110

221310 — WATER SUPPLY AND IR...

EMPRESA DE SERVICIOS SANITARIOS DE LOS LAGOS SA; *Int'l*, pg. 2388
ENERGY AND WATER DEVELOPMENT CORP.; *U.S. Public*, pg. 762
ENEX-DYNAMIC SDN. BHD.—See Fiamma Holdings Berhad; *Int'l*, pg. 2650
ENVIROFLO ENGINEERING LIMITED—See Ecolab Inc.; *U.S. Public*, pg. 714
EPCOR USA INC.—See EPCOR Utilities, Inc.; *Int'l*, pg. 2459
ERIE COUNTY WATER AUTHORITY; *U.S. Private*, pg. 1420
ESSBIO SA; *Int'l*, pg. 2509
ESSEL UTILITIES DISTRIBUTION COMPANY LTD—See Essel Corporate Resources Pvt. Ltd.; *Int'l*, pg. 2509
ESSENTIAL UTILITIES INC.; *U.S. Public*, pg. 795
ESSEX & SUFFOLK WATER LTD—See CK Hutchison Holdings Limited; *Int'l*, pg. 1637
EUROFINS HYDROLOGIE FRANCE SAS—See Eurofins Scientific S.E.; *Int'l*, pg. 2542
EUROFINS IPL EST SAS—See Eurofins Scientific S.E.; *Int'l*, pg. 2542
EVESHAM MUNICIPAL UTILITIES AUTHORITY; *U.S. Private*, pg. 1441
EVN WASSER GMBH—See EVN AG; *Int'l*, pg. 2571
EVOQUA WATER TECHNOLOGIES—See Xylem Inc.; *U.S. Public*, pg. 2394
FAIRFAX COUNTY WATER AUTHORITY INC.; *U.S. Private*, pg. 1462
FALLBROOK PUBLIC UTILITY DISTRICT; *U.S. Private*, pg. 1467
FALLS WATER CO., INC.—See Northwest Natural Holding Company; *U.S. Public*, pg. 1542
FEDERAL IESE ENVIRONMENTAL TECHNOLOGY (SHANGHAI) CO., LTD.—See Federal International (2000) Ltd; *Int'l*, pg. 2630
FILTER VISION PUBLIC COMPANY LIMITED; *Int'l*, pg. 2663
FLOCON TECHNOLOGIES OY—See Axolot Solutions Holding AB; *Int'l*, pg. 770
FLORIDA IRRIGATION SUPPLY INC.—See Leonard Green & Partners, L.P.; *U.S. Private*, pg. 2429
FLORIDA KEYS AQUEDUCT AUTHORITY; *U.S. Private*, pg. 1549
FLUENCE CORPORATION LIMITED; *U.S. Public*, pg. 857
FLUIDRA SA; *Int'l*, pg. 2713
FONTAINE EUROPE SAS—See Zurn Elkay Water Solutions Corporation; *U.S. Public*, pg. 2412
FONTAINE INDUSTRIES LTD.—See Zurn Elkay Water Solutions Corporation; *U.S. Public*, pg. 2412
FONTANA UNION WATER COMPANY—See Cucamonga Valley Water District; *U.S. Private*, pg. 1120
FONTANA WATER COMPANY; *U.S. Private*, pg. 1560
FOREST WATER ENVIRONMENTAL ENGINEERING CO., LTD.; *Int'l*, pg. 2732
FORT RILEY UTILITY SERVICES, INC.—See American States Water Company; *U.S. Public*, pg. 110
FRANKE WATER SYSTEMS AG—See Artemis Holding AG; *Int'l*, pg. 582
FRESH WATER MIIKE CO., LTD.—See Electric Power Development Co., Ltd.; *Int'l*, pg. 2349
FRUITRIDGE VISTA WATER CO.—See American Water Works Company, Inc.; *U.S. Public*, pg. 112
FUTURAQUA MINERAL WATER PRODUCTION AND ASSET MANAGEMENT PUBLIC LIMITED COMPANY; *Int'l*, pg. 2852
GAMUDA WATER SDN. BHD.—See Gamuda Berhad; *Int'l*, pg. 2879
GELSENWASSER AG; *Int'l*, pg. 2913
GELSENWASSER PROJEKTGESELLSCHAFT MBH—See Gelsenwasser AG; *Int'l*, pg. 2913
GENERAL ECOLOGY, INC.—See Loar Group, Inc.; *U.S. Private*, pg. 2477
GEORGE KENT (MALAYSIA) BERHAD; *Int'l*, pg. 2938
GEORGIAN WATER AND POWER, LLC—See Georgia Capital PLC; *Int'l*, pg. 2939
GLOBAL ENVIRONMENTAL SOLUTIONS LTD.—See Azrieli Group Ltd.; *Int'l*, pg. 781
GLOBAL WATER ASSET CORPORATION; *Int'l*, pg. 3002
GLOBAL WATER MANAGEMENT, INC.—See Global Water Resources, Inc.; *U.S. Public*, pg. 945
GME INNOTAINMENT, INC.; *Int'l*, pg. 3012
GOLDEN STATE WATER COMPANY—See American States Water Company; *U.S. Public*, pg. 110
GOLETA WATER DISTRICT; *U.S. Private*, pg. 1735
GREYTER WATER SYSTEMS; *Int'l*, pg. 3082
GUANGDONG GOLDEN DRAGON DEVELOPMENT INC.; *Int'l*, pg. 3154
GUANGDONG SHUNKONG DEVELOPMENT CO., LTD.; *Int'l*, pg. 3160
GULF UTILITY SERVICE INC.—See Ember Infrastructure Management, LP; *U.S. Private*, pg. 1378
H2O NATIONWIDE LIMITED—See Cap10 Partners LLP; *Int'l*, pg. 1301
H2O INC.; *U.S. Private*, pg. 1837
H2O INNOVATION INC.—See Ember Infrastructure Management, LP; *U.S. Private*, pg. 1378
H2O INNOVATION INC.—See Ember Infrastructure Management, LP; *U.S. Private*, pg. 1378

HACH LANGE APS—See Danaher Corporation; *U.S. Public*, pg. 627
HAITIAN WATER GROUP CO., LTD.; *Int'l*, pg. 3217
HARBOUR WATER CORPORATION—See Veolia Water Indianapolis, LLC; *U.S. Private*, pg. 4358
HAWAII WATER SERVICE COMPANY—See California Water Service Group; *U.S. Public*, pg. 424
HEADWATER COMPANIES, LLC—See Franklin Electric Co., Inc.; *U.S. Public*, pg. 878
HEC INFRA PROJECTS LTD.; *Int'l*, pg. 3306
HELIX WATER DISTRICT; *U.S. Private*, pg. 1906
HERAMBIENTE SPA—See Hera S.p.A.; *Int'l*, pg. 3356
HITACHI AQUA-TECH ENGINEERING PTE. LTD.—See Hitachi, Ltd.; *Int'l*, pg. 3414
HOH BIRGER CHRISTENSEN AS—See BWT Aktiengesellschaft; *Int'l*, pg. 1233
HYDRO INTERNATIONAL LIMITED—See CRH plc; *Int'l*, pg. 1846
HYDRO-QUEBEC INTERNATIONAL—See Hydro-Quebec; *Int'l*, pg. 3547
HYDRO-SCAPE PRODUCTS, INC.—See SiteOne Landscape Supply, Inc.; *U.S. Public*, pg. 1889
HYNAR WATER GROUP CO., LTD.; *Int'l*, pg. 3550
I2O WATER LTD.—See Mueller Water Products, Inc.; *U.S. Public*, pg. 1486
ILLINOIS AMERICAN WATER—See American Water Works Company, Inc.; *U.S. Public*, pg. 112
INDIANA AMERICAN WATER—See American Water Works Company, Inc.; *U.S. Public*, pg. 112
INLAND EMPIRE UTILITIES AGENCY; *U.S. Private*, pg. 2078
INNOVATIVE WATER CARE, LLC—See Platinum Equity, LLC; *U.S. Private*, pg. 3204
INTEGRATED WATER SERVICES LTD.—See Arjun Infrastructure Partners Limited; *Int'l*, pg. 568
INVENIO SYSTEMS LIMITED—See Halma plc; *Int'l*, pg. 3232
IOWA REGIONAL UTILITIES ASSOCIATION; *U.S. Private*, pg. 2135
IRVINE RANCH WATER DISTRICT INC.; *U.S. Private*, pg. 2141
IRZ CONSULTING LLC—See Lindsay Corporation; *U.S. Public*, pg. 1319
ISP MICROCAPS (U.K.) LIMITED—See Ashland Inc.; *U.S. Public*, pg. 213
JARDINIER ALTERNATIVE IRRIGATION SYSTEMS, INC.; *U.S. Private*, pg. 2188
JURUPA COMMUNITY SERVICES DISTRICT; *U.S. Private*, pg. 2245
KALSEP UK LTD.—See RLR, Inc.; *U.S. Private*, pg. 3451
KENTUCKY AMERICAN WATER—See American Water Works Company, Inc.; *U.S. Public*, pg. 112
KLC LAND COMPANY—See Walton Street Capital, LLC; *U.S. Private*, pg. 4435
KOMPOGAS SLO LLC—See Hitachi Zosen Corporation; *Int'l*, pg. 3411
KROFTA TECHNOLOGIES, LLC—See Ecolab Inc.; *U.S. Public*, pg. 714
LAS VEGAS VALLEY WATER DISTRICT; *U.S. Private*, pg. 2394
LAUREL MANAGEMENT COMPANY—See Laurel Holdings Inc.; *U.S. Private*, pg. 2399
LIBERTY UTILITIES APPLE VALLEY—See Algonquin Power & Utilities Corp.; *Int'l*, pg. 319
LIBERTY UTILITIES (PINE BLUFF WATER) INC.—See Algonquin Power & Utilities Corp.; *Int'l*, pg. 319
LINDSAY AMERICA DO SUL LTDA.—See Lindsay Corporation; *U.S. Public*, pg. 1319
LINDSAY EUROPE SA—See Lindsay Corporation; *U.S. Public*, pg. 1319
LINDSAY MANUFACTURING AFRICA PTY. LTD.—See Lindsay Corporation; *U.S. Public*, pg. 1319
LONESTAR ECOLOGY, LLC—See EQT AB; *Int'l*, pg. 2473
LOUDOUN COUNTY SANITATION AUTHORITY; *U.S. Private*, pg. 2498
LOUISIANA WATER COMPANY—See Utility Holdings Inc.; *U.S. Private*, pg. 4326
MACON WATER AUTHORITY; *U.S. Private*, pg. 2538
THE MAINE WATER CO. - BIDDEFORD & SACO—See SJW Group; *U.S. Public*, pg. 1891
THE MAINE WATER CO. - BUCKSPORT—See SJW Group; *U.S. Public*, pg. 1891
THE MAINE WATER CO. - GREENVILLE—See SJW Group; *U.S. Public*, pg. 1891
THE MAINE WATER CO. - KEZAR FALLS—See SJW Group; *U.S. Public*, pg. 1891
THE MAINE WATER CO. - MILLINOCKET—See SJW Group; *U.S. Public*, pg. 1891
THE MAINE WATER COMPANY—See SJW Group; *U.S. Public*, pg. 1891
THE MAINE WATER CO. - SKOWHEGAN—See SJW Group; *U.S. Public*, pg. 1891
MANCHAUG POND FOUNDATION; *U.S. Private*, pg. 2562
MANN WASTE MANAGEMENT PTY LTD—See Cleanaway Waste Management Limited; *Int'l*, pg. 1655
MARIN MUNICIPAL WATER DISTRICT; *U.S. Private*, pg. 2574
MARYLAND-AMERICAN WATER COMPANY—See American Water Works Company, Inc.; *U.S. Public*, pg. 112

MECO INC.; *U.S. Private*, pg. 2649
MEGOLA INC.—See Acordy Invest S.A.; *Int'l*, pg. 108
METAWATER SERVICE CO., LTD.—See Fuji Electric Co., Ltd.; *Int'l*, pg. 2812
THE METROPOLITAN DISTRICT; *U.S. Private*, pg. 4078
THE METROPOLITAN WATER DISTRICT OF SOUTHERN CALIFORNIA INC.; *U.S. Public*, pg. 4078
MICHIGAN-AMERICAN WATER COMPANY—See American Water Works Company, Inc.; *U.S. Public*, pg. 112
MIDDLESEX WATER COMPANY; *U.S. Public*, pg. 1445
MISSOURI-AMERICAN WATER COMPANY—See American Water Works Company, Inc.; *U.S. Public*, pg. 112
MIYA LUXEMBURG HOLDINGS S.A.R.L.—See Bridgepoint Group Plc; *Int'l*, pg. 1155
MOBOTEC EUROPE AB—See Ecolab Inc.; *U.S. Public*, pg. 715
MONEGROS DEPURA, S.A.—See ACS, Actividades de Construccion y Servicios, S.A.; *Int'l*, pg. 115
MONROE COUNTY WATER AUTHORITY; *U.S. Private*, pg. 2773
MONTGOMERY WATER WORKS & SANITARY SEWER BOARD; *U.S. Private*, pg. 2777
MORRIS COUNTY MUNICIPAL UTILITIES AUTHORITY; *U.S. Private*, pg. 2787
MOULTON-NIGUEL WATER DISTRICT; *U.S. Private*, pg. 2797
MOUNTAIN WATER SYSTEMS, INC.—See New England Services Company; *U.S. Public*, pg. 1511
MUNICIPAL AUTHORITY OF WESTMORELAND COUNTY; *U.S. Private*, pg. 2813
NAKORNSAWAN WATER SUPPLY COMPANY LIMITED—See Eastern Water Resources Development & Management Public Company Limited; *Int'l*, pg. 2274
NALCO AB—See Ecolab Inc.; *U.S. Public*, pg. 715
NALCO AFRICA (PTY.) LTD.—See Ecolab Inc.; *U.S. Public*, pg. 715
NALCO ANADOLU KIMYA SANAYI VE TICARET LIMITED SIRKETI—See Ecolab Inc.; *U.S. Public*, pg. 715
NALCO BELGIUM BVBA—See Ecolab Inc.; *U.S. Public*, pg. 715
NALCO (CHINA) ENVIRONMENTAL SOLUTION CO. LTD.—See Ecolab Inc.; *U.S. Public*, pg. 715
NALCO COMPANY OOO—See Ecolab Inc.; *U.S. Public*, pg. 715
NALCO CZECHIA S.R.O.—See Ecolab Inc.; *U.S. Public*, pg. 715
NALCO DELAWARE COMPANY—See Ecolab Inc.; *U.S. Public*, pg. 715
NALCO DE MEXICO, S. DE R. L. DE C.V.—See Ecolab Inc.; *U.S. Public*, pg. 715
NALCO DEUTSCHLAND GMBH—See Ecolab Inc.; *U.S. Public*, pg. 715
NALCO EGYPT, LTD.—See Ecolab Inc.; *U.S. Public*, pg. 715
NALCO ENERGY SERVICES LIMITED—See Ecolab Inc.; *U.S. Public*, pg. 715
NALCO ENVIRONMENTAL SOLUTIONS LLC—See Ecolab Inc.; *U.S. Public*, pg. 715
NALCO ESPANOLA MANUFACTURING, S.L.U.—See Ecolab Inc.; *U.S. Public*, pg. 715
NALCO ESPANOLA, S.L.—See Ecolab Inc.; *U.S. Public*, pg. 715
NALCO FRANCE—See Ecolab Inc.; *U.S. Public*, pg. 715
NALCO HELLAS S.A.—See Ecolab Inc.; *U.S. Public*, pg. 715
NALCO INDUSTRIAL SERVICES CHILE LIMITADA—See Ecolab Inc.; *U.S. Public*, pg. 716
NALCO INDUSTRIAL SERVICES MALAYSIA SDN. BHD—See Ecolab Inc.; *U.S. Public*, pg. 716
NALCO INDUSTRIAL SERVICES (SUZHOU) CO., LTD.—See Ecolab Inc.; *U.S. Public*, pg. 716
NALCO ISRAEL INDUSTRIAL SERVICES LTD.—See Ecolab Inc.; *U.S. Public*, pg. 716
NALCO ITALIANA SRL—See Ecolab Inc.; *U.S. Public*, pg. 716
NALCO KOREA LIMITED—See Ecolab Inc.; *U.S. Public*, pg. 716
NALCO LIMITED—See Ecolab Inc.; *U.S. Public*, pg. 716
NALCO NETHERLANDS BV—See Ecolab Inc.; *U.S. Public*, pg. 716
NALCO NORGE AS—See Ecolab Inc.; *U.S. Public*, pg. 716
NALCO OSTERREICH GES M.B.H.—See Ecolab Inc.; *U.S. Public*, pg. 716
NALCO PAKISTAN (PRIVATE) LIMITED—See Ecolab Inc.; *U.S. Public*, pg. 716
NALCO POLSKA SP. Z O. O.—See Ecolab Inc.; *U.S. Public*, pg. 716
NALCO PORTUGUESA (QUIMICA INDUSTRIAL) LTD.—See Ecolab Inc.; *U.S. Public*, pg. 716
NALCO SCHWEIZ GMBH—See Ecolab Inc.; *U.S. Public*, pg. 716
NALCO TAIWAN CO., LTD.—See Ecolab Inc.; *U.S. Public*, pg. 716
NALCO VENEZUELA S. C. A.—See Ecolab Inc.; *U.S. Public*, pg. 716
NEVADA IRRIGATION DISTRICT; *U.S. Private*, pg. 2891
THE NEWELL COMPANY—See The Homer Laughlin China Company; *U.S. Private*, pg. 4054

N.A.I.C.S. INDEX

221310 — WATER SUPPLY AND IR...

NEW ENGLAND SERVICES COMPANY; *U.S. Public*, pg. 1511

NEW ENGLAND WATER UTILITY SERVICES, INC.—See SJW Group; *U.S. Public*, pg. 1891

NEW JERSEY AMERICAN WATER—See American Water Works Company, Inc.; *U.S. Public*, pg. 112

NEW MEXICO AMERICAN WATER—See EPCOR Utilities, Inc.; *Int'l*, pg. 2459

NEW MEXICO WATER SERVICE COMPANY—See California Water Service Group; *U.S. Public*, pg. 424

NLC PROCESS & WATER SERVICES SARL—See Ecolab Inc.; *U.S. Public*, pg. 715

NOBLE WATER TECHNOLOGIES, INC.—See Xylem Inc.; *U.S. Public*, pg. 2394

NOGGERATH FRANCE EURL—See Bilfinger SE; *Int'l*, pg. 1028

NOP-NASS WLL—See Abdulla Ahmed Nass Group WLL; *Int'l*, pg. 58

NORTHERN KENTUCKY WATER DISTRICT; *U.S. Private*, pg. 2953

NORTH PENN WATER AUTHORITY; *U.S. Private*, pg. 2946

NORTHSHORE UTILITY DISTRICT; *U.S. Private*, pg. 2957

NORTH TEXAS MUNICIPAL WATER DISTRICT; *U.S. Private*, pg. 2948

NORTHUMBRIAN SERVICES LIMITED—See CK Hutchison Holdings Limited; *Int'l*, pg. 1637

NORTHUMBRIAN WATER LIMITED—See CK Hutchison Holdings Limited; *Int'l*, pg. 1637

OCEAN CONVERSION (CAYMAN) LIMITED—See Consolidated Water Co. Ltd.; *Int'l*, pg. 1771

OLD BRIDGE MUNICIPAL UTILITY AUTHORITY; *U.S. Private*, pg. 3008

ONDEO NALCO ENERGY SERVICES—See Ecolab Inc.; *U.S. Public*, pg. 716

ONONDAGA COUNTY WATER AUTHORITY; *U.S. Private*, pg. 3027

OOO BWT—See BWT Aktiengesellschaft; *Int'l*, pg. 1233

ORANGE COUNTY WATER DISTRICT; *U.S. Private*, pg. 3037

ORANGE WATER & SEWER AUTHORITY; *U.S. Private*, pg. 3037

OREGE SA - SCIENTIFIC DIVISION—See Eren Groupe SA; *Int'l*, pg. 2490

OREGE SA—See Eren Groupe SA; *Int'l*, pg. 2490

OSMOFLO ENGINEERING SERVICES PVT. LTD.—See Hitachi Zosen Corporation; *Int'l*, pg. 3412

OSMOFLO HOLDINGS PTY LTD—See Hitachi Zosen Corporation; *Int'l*, pg. 3412

OSMOFLO INTERNATIONAL FZE—See Hitachi Zosen Corporation; *Int'l*, pg. 3412

OWT OIL-WATER TREATMENT SERVICES B.V.—See Ecolab Inc.; *U.S. Public*, pg. 716

PARISH WATER COMPANY, INC.—See Baton Rouge Water Works Company; *U.S. Private*, pg. 487

PARKWOOD GROUP LIMITED—See KKR & Co. Inc.; *U.S. Public*, pg. 1266

PASCOAG UTILITY DISTRICT; *U.S. Private*, pg. 3104

PASSAIC VALLEY WATER COMMISSION; *U.S. Private*, pg. 3104

PASSAVANT ENERGY & ENVIRONMENT GMBH—See Drake & Scull International PJSC; *Int'l*, pg. 2200

PENNICHUCK CORPORATION; *U.S. Private*, pg. 3136

PENNICHUCK EAST UTILITY, INC.—See Pennichuck Corporation; *U.S. Private*, pg. 3136

PENNICHUCK WATER SERVICE CORP.—See Pennichuck Corporation; *U.S. Private*, pg. 3136

PENNICHUCK WATER WORKS, INC.—See Pennichuck Corporation; *U.S. Private*, pg. 3136

PENNSYLVANIA AMERICAN WATER—See American Water Works Company, Inc.; *U.S. Public*, pg. 112

PEOPLES WATER SERVICE COMPANY; *U.S. Private*, pg. 3142

PESA ENGINEERING, S.A.—See BAUER Aktiengesellschaft; *Int'l*, pg. 893

PHOENIX PROCESS EQUIPMENT; *U.S. Private*, pg. 3173

PINELANDS WATER COMPANY—See Middlesex Water Company; *U.S. Public*, pg. 1445

PITTSBURGH WATER & SEWER AUTHORITY; *U.S. Private*, pg. 3191

PITTSFIELD AQUEDUCT COMPANY INC.—See Pennichuck Corporation; *U.S. Private*, pg. 3136

P & LS BETEILIGUNGS GMBH—See BWT Aktiengesellschaft; *Int'l*, pg. 1233

PROGRESSIVE WATER TREATMENT, INC.—See OriginClear, Inc.; *U.S. Public*, pg. 1617

PURE CYCLE CORPORATION; *U.S. Public*, pg. 1738

PURENA GMBH—See E.ON SE; *Int'l*, pg. 2259

QVS HOLDING INC.; *U.S. Private*, pg. 3331

RAINIER VIEW WATER CO, INC.—See California Water Service Group; *U.S. Public*, pg 424

RAIN MASTER IRRIGATION SYSTEMS, INC.—See The Toro Company; *U.S. Public*, pg. 2135

RAMONA MUNICIPAL WATER DISTRICT; *U.S. Private*, pg. 3351

RANCHO CADIZ MUTUAL WATER COMPANY—See Cadiz Inc.; *U.S. Public*, pg. 419

RATHBUN REGIONAL WATER ASSOCIATION, INC.; *U.S. Private*, pg. 3357

REAL HUOT INC.—See Groupe Deschenes Inc.; *Int'l*, pg. 3102

RECUPERACION DE RODAS E MADEIRA, S.L.—See ACS, Actividades de Construccion y Servicios, S.A.; *Int'l*, pg. 115

RESOURCE CONSERVATION SYSTEMS, LLC—See Bonita Bay Properties, Inc.; *U.S. Public*, pg. 614

RODI SYSTEMS CORPORATION; *U.S. Private*, pg. 3470

ROSE VALLEY WATER COMPANY, INC.—See Northwest Natural Holding Company; *U.S. Public*, pg. 1542

SABINE RIVER AUTHORITY OF TEXAS; *U.S. Private*, pg. 3521

SABINE RIVER AUTHORITY, STATE OF LOUISIANA; *U.S. Private*, pg. 3521

SAFBON WATER TECHNOLOGY, INC.—See BW Group Ltd.; *Int'l*, pg. 1231

SAN BERNARDINO MUNICIPAL WATER DEPARTMENT; *U.S. Private*, pg. 3539

SAN GABRIEL VALLEY WATER CO—See Fontana Water Company; *U.S. Private*, pg. 1560

SAN JOSE WATER COMPANY—See SJW Group; *U.S. Public*, pg. 1891

SEMITROPIC WATER STORAGE DISTRICT; *U.S. Private*, pg. 3605

SENNINGER IRRIGATION, INC.—See Hunter Industries Incorporated; *U.S. Private*, pg. 2010

SEPROTECH—See BluMetric Environmental Inc.; *Int'l*, pg. 1075

SERVICE LINE WARRANTIES OF AMERICA, INC.—See Brookfield Corporation; *Int'l*, pg. 1188

SEVEN SEAS WATER CORPORATION—See Morgan Stanley; *U.S. Public*, pg. 1472

SEVEN SEAS WATER CORPORATION—See Morgan Stanley; *U.S. Public*, pg. 1472

SEYCHELLE ENVIRONMENTAL TECHNOLOGIES, INC.; *U.S. Public*, pg. 1873

SHANGHAI DARCO ENGINEERING CO. LTD—See Darco Water Technologies Limited; *Int'l*, pg. 1972

SIONIX CORPORATION; *U.S. Private*, pg. 3670

SJW LAND COMPANY—See SJW Group; *U.S. Public*, pg. 1891

SMARTWATER MEMPHIS, INC.—See Perpetual Capital, LLC; *U.S. Private*, pg. 3153

SMITH & LOVELESS GEORGIA INC.—See RLR, Inc.; *U.S. Private*, pg. 3451

SMITH & LOVELESS, INC.—See RLR, Inc.; *U.S. Private*, pg. 3451

SMITH & LOVELESS NEW ZEALAND LIMITED—See RLR, Inc.; *U.S. Private*, pg. 3451

SOCIETE ITALIANA PER CONDOTTE D'ACQUA S.P.A.—See Ferfina S.p.A.; *Int'l*, pg. 2637

SOUTH CENTRAL CONNECTICUT REGIONAL WATER AUTHORITY INC.; *U.S. Private*, pg. 3721

SOUTH COAST WATER DISTRICT; *U.S. Private*, pg. 3721

SOUTH STAFFORDSHIRE WATER PLC—See Arjun Infrastructure Partners Limited; *Int'l*, pg. 568

SOUTHWEST WATER COMPANY—See JPMorgan Chase & Co.; *U.S. Public*, pg. 1207

SOUTHWEST WATER COMPANY—See Water Asset Management, LLC; *U.S. Private*, pg. 4451

SPARTANBURG WATER SYSTEM; *U.S. Private*, pg. 3747

SPRINGFIELD WATER & SEWER COMMISSION; *U.S. Private*, pg. 3764

STORITVENO PODJETJE LASKO D.O.O.—See EVN AG; *Int'l*, pg. 2571

SUBIC WATER & SEWERAGE COMPANY INC.—See DMCI Holdings, Inc.; *Int'l*, pg. 2143

SUBURBAN WATER SYSTEMS—See JPMorgan Chase & Co.; *U.S. Public*, pg. 1207

SUBURBAN WATER SYSTEMS—See Water Asset Management, LLC; *U.S. Private*, pg. 4451

SUDWASSER GMBH—See E.ON SE; *Int'l*, pg. 2259

SUNCADIA WATER COMPANY, LLC—See Northwest Natural Holding Company; *U.S. Public*, pg. 1542

SUNRIVER ENVIRONMENTAL LLC—See Northwest Natural Holding Company; *U.S. Public*, pg. 1542

SUNRIVER UTILITIES COMPANY INC.—See Sunriver Resort Limited Partnership; *U.S. Public*, pg. 3870

SWISSINSO HOLDING INC.; *U.S. Private*, pg. 3894

SWWC UTILITIES, INC.,—See JPMorgan Chase & Co.; *U.S. Public*, pg. 1207

SWWC UTILITIES, INC.,—See Water Asset Management, LLC; *U.S. Private*, pg. 4451

TAMPA BAY WATER-REGIONAL WATER SUPPLY AUTHORITY; *U.S. Private*, pg. 3929

TEAM AQUATIC INC.—See Clearford Water Systems Inc.; *Int'l*, pg. 1657

TECHNICAL ASSOCIATES SERVICES P. LTD.—See Endress+Hauser (International) Holding AG; *Int'l*, pg. 2409

TECHNICAL SERVICES BUREAU CO.—See Endress+Hauser (International) Holding AG; *Int'l*, pg. 2409

TENNESSEE AMERICAN WATER—See American Water Works Company, Inc.; *U.S. Public*, pg. 112

TEXARKANA WATER UTILITIES; *U.S. Private*, pg. 3974

TIDEWATER UTILITIES, INC.—See Middlesex Water Company; *U.S. Public*, pg. 1445

TOHOPEKALIGA WATER AUTHORITY; *U.S. Private*, pg. 4181

TOLEDO BEND PROJECT JOINT OPERATIONS—See Sabine River Authority of Texas; *U.S. Private*, pg. 3521

TOLEDO BEND PROJECT JOINT OPERATIONS—See Sabine River Authority, State of Louisiana; *U.S. Private*, pg. 3521

THE TORO COMPANY IRRIGATION PRODUCTS—See The Toro Company; *U.S. Public*, pg. 2135

TORRINGTON WATER COMPANY—See Eversource Energy; *U.S. Public*, pg. 802

TRENTON WATER WORKS; *U.S. Private*, pg. 4218

TRI-DAM PROJECT; *U.S. Private*, pg. 4222

TWO RIVERS WATER & FARMING COMPANY; *U.S. Private*, pg. 4266

T & W WATER SERVICE COMPANY—See Northwest Natural Holding Company; *U.S. Public*, pg. 1542

UAB WTE BALTIC—See EVN AG; *Int'l*, pg. 2571

UGL (SINGAPORE) PTE LTD—See ACS, Actividades de Construccion y Servicios, S.A.; *Int'l*, pg. 113

ULTRA PURE WATER TECHNOLOGIES, LLC; *U.S. Public*, pg. 2223

UMBRA ACQUE S.P.A.—See ACEA S.p.A.; *Int'l*, pg. 95

UNITED FLOW TECHNOLOGIES—See H.I.G. Capital, LLC; *U.S. Private*, pg. 1834

UNITED WATER INTERNATIONAL—See KBR, Inc.; *U.S. Public*, pg. 1216

UNIVERSAL UTILITIES PUBLIC COMPANY LIMITED—See Eastern Water Resources Development & Management Public Company Limited; *Int'l*, pg. 2274

UPPER TRINITY REGIONAL WATER DISTRICT; *U.S. Private*, pg. 4312

UTILITIES, INC.; *U.S. Private*, pg. 4326

UTILITY HOLDINGS INC.; *U.S. Private*, pg. 4326

UTILITY SERVICE AFFILIATES, INC.—See Middlesex Water Company; *U.S. Public*, pg. 1445

UTILITY SERVICE AFFILIATES (PERTH AMBOY) INC.—See Middlesex Water Company; *U.S. Public*, pg. 1445

UV PURE TECHNOLOGIES INC.—See Clearford Water Systems Inc.; *Int'l*, pg. 1657

VAG ARMATURA POLSKA SP.Z.O.O.—See Zurn Elkay Water Solutions Corporation; *U.S. Public*, pg. 2414

VAG ARMATUREN GMBH—See Zurn Elkay Water Solutions Corporation; *U.S. Public*, pg. 2414

VAG-VALVES INDIA (PRIVATE) LIMITED—See Zurn Elkay Water Solutions Corporation; *U.S. Public*, pg. 2414

VAG WATER SYSTEMS (TAICANG) CO., LTD.—See Zurn Elkay Water Solutions Corporation; *U.S. Public*, pg. 2414

VALLECITOS WATER DISTRICT; *U.S. Private*, pg. 4332

VALLEY WATER SYSTEMS, INC.—See New England Services Company; *U.S. Private*, pg. 1511

VALVULAS VAG DE MEXICO, S.A. DE C.V.—See Zurn Elkay Water Solutions Corporation; *U.S. Public*, pg. 2414

VARISCO WELLPOINT SRL—See Atlas Copco AB; *Int'l*, pg. 684

VEOLIA WATER INDIANAPOLIS, LLC; *U.S. Public*, pg. 4358

VEREINIGTE GAS- UND WASSERVERSORGUNG GMBH—See Gelsenwasser AG; *Int'l*, pg. 2914

VERSATECH LIMITED—See ENL Limited; *Int'l*, pg. 2441

VIQUA—See Danaher Corporation; *U.S. Public*, pg. 632

VIRGINIA AMERICAN WATER CO.—See American Water Works Company, Inc.; *U.S. Public*, pg. 112

VIRIDOR WASTE EXETER LIMITED—See KKR & Co. Inc.; *U.S. Public*, pg. 1266

VIRIDOR WASTE (SOMERSET) LIMITED—See KKR & Co. Inc.; *U.S. Public*, pg. 1266

VIRIDOR WASTE (SUFFOLK) LIMITED—See KKR & Co. Inc.; *U.S. Public*, pg. 1266

VIRIDOR WASTE (THAMES) LIMITED—See KKR & Co. Inc.; *U.S. Public*, pg. 1266

VODOTECH, SPOL. S.R.O.—See Fomento de Construcciones y Contratas, S.A.; *Int'l*, pg. 2723

WABAG WATER SERVICES SHL—See Circular Waters Solutions S.R.L; *Int'l*, pg. 1618

WARREN COUNTY WATER DISTRICT; *U.S. Private*, pg. 4443

WASHINGTON SUBURBAN SANITARY COMMISSION; *U.S. Private*, pg. 4449

WASHINGTON WATER SERVICE COMPANY—See California Water Service Group; *U.S. Public*, pg. 424

WATERBRIDGE RESOURCES LLC—See Five Point Energy LLC; *U.S. Public*, pg. 1537

WATERFIELD COMPANY LIMITED—See Consolidated Water Co. Ltd.; *Int'l*, pg. 1771

WATER INTELLIGENCE PLC; *U.S. Public*, pg. 2334

WATERMARK RESTORATION INC.—See FirstService Corporation; *Int'l*, pg. 2691

WATER REDEVELOPMENT COMPANY—See Two Rivers Water & Farming Company; *U.S. Private*, pg. 4266

WATER REMEDIATION TECHNOLOGY LLC; *U.S. Private*, pg. 4451

WATER-RIGHT, INC.—See A. O. Smith Corporation; *U.S. Public*, pg. 12

WATER SOLUTIONS HOLDINGS LLC—See American Water Works Company, Inc.; *U.S. Public*, pg. 112

221310 — WATER SUPPLY AND IR...

WATERSOURCE PTY LTD—See Hitachi Zosen Corporation; *Int'l*, pg. 3412
WATER STANDARD MANAGEMENT; *U.S. Private*, pg. 4451
WATER TECHNOLOGIES INTERNATIONAL, INC.; *U.S. Public*, pg. 2334
WATER TREATMENT SOLUTION LTD.—See BRENNTAG SE; *Int'l*, pg. 1150
WATER WORKS & SANITARY SEWER; *U.S. Private*, pg. 4452
WEIMAR WATER CO.—See Placer County Water Agency; *U.S. Private*, pg. 3194
WEST KNOX UTILITY DISTRICT; *U.S. Private*, pg. 4486
WESTLANDS WATER DISTRICT INC.; *U.S. Private*, pg. 4499
WEST VIRGINIA AMERICAN WATER COMPANY; *U.S. Public*, pg. 2354
WILKINSBERG-PENN JOINT WATER AUTHORITY; *U.S. Private*, pg. 4520
WILSON IRRIGATION & ORCHARD SUPPLY, INC.—See Clearview Capital, LLC; *U.S. Private*, pg. 939
WINDERMERE UTILITY COMPANY—See JPMorgan Chase & Co.; *U.S. Public*, pg. 1207
WINDERMERE UTILITY COMPANY—See Water Asset Management, LLC; *U.S. Private*, pg. 4451
WOLF CREEK COMPANY INC.—See Leonard Green & Partners, L.P.; *U.S. Private*, pg. 2429
WORLD WATER WORKS, INC.; *U.S. Private*, pg. 4567
WTA - WASSERTECHNISCHER ANLAGENBAU PLAUEN GMBH—See BWT Aktiengesellschaft; *Int'l*, pg. 1233
WTE BETRIEBSGESELLSCHAFT MBH—See EVN AG; *Int'l*, pg. 2571
WTE PROJEKTGESELLSCHAFT SUD-WEST WASSER MBH—See EVN AG; *Int'l*, pg. 2571
WTE PROJEKTNA DRUZBA BLED D.O.O.—See EVN AG; *Int'l*, pg. 2571
WTE PROJEKTNA DRUZBA KRANJSKA GORA D.O.O.—See EVN AG; *Int'l*, pg. 2571
WTE WASSERTECHNIK GMBH—See EVN AG; *Int'l*, pg. 2571
WTE WASSERTECHNIK (POLSKA) SP. Z O.O—See EVN AG; *Int'l*, pg. 2571
XYLEM WATER SOLUTIONS BELGIUM BVBA—See Xylem Inc.; *U.S. Public*, pg. 2396
XYLEM WATER SOLUTIONS CANADA—See Xylem Inc.; *U.S. Public*, pg. 2397
XYLEM WATER SOLUTIONS CANADA—See Xylem Inc.; *U.S. Public*, pg. 2397
XYLEM WATER SOLUTIONS NEDERLAND B.V.—See Xylem Inc.; *U.S. Public*, pg. 2397
THE YORK WATER COMPANY; *U.S. Public*, pg. 2144
ZIONSVILLE WATER CORPORATION—See Veolia Water Indianapolis, LLC; *U.S. Private*, pg. 4358

221320 — SEWAGE TREATMENT FACILITIES

AGUAS DE ANTOFAGASTA S.A.—See Empresas Publicas de Medellin ESP; *Int'l*, pg. 2391
AKATHERM FIP GMBH—See Aliaxis S.A./N.V.; *Int'l*, pg. 323
AKATHERM INTERNATIONAL B.V.—See Aliaxis S.A./N.V.; *Int'l*, pg. 323
AKVA-TEK SDN. BHD.—See Brite-Tech Berhad; *Int'l*, pg. 1165
AMERICAN WATER ACCIONA AGUA LLC—See American Water Works Company, Inc.; *U.S. Public*, pg. 112
ANHUI ZHONGHUAN ENVIRONMENTAL PROTECTION TECHNOLOGY CO., LTD.; *Int'l*, pg. 471
AQUABIO LTD.—See Freudenberg SE; *Int'l*, pg. 2782
ARNOMIJ B.V.—See Aliaxis S.A./N.V.; *Int'l*, pg. 323
ARVIND ENVISOL LIMITED—See Arvind Fashions Ltd.; *Int'l*, pg. 587
ASCENSION WASTEWATER TREATMENT—See Bernhard Capital Partners Management, LP; *U.S. Private*, pg. 536
ATLANTIC COUNTY UTILITIES AUTHORITY; *U.S. Private*, pg. 372
AWP GMBH—See E.ON SE; *Int'l*, pg. 2251
AWS GMBH—See Gelsenwasser AG; *Int'l*, pg. 2913
BEIJING NEW BIOLINK TECHNOLOGY DEVELOPMENT CO., LTD.—See Focused Photonics (Hangzhou), Inc.; *Int'l*, pg. 2720
BEIJING ORIGIN WATER TECHNOLOGY CO., LTD.; *Int'l*, pg. 955
BIWATER ALGERIE SPA—See Biwater Holdings Limited; *Int'l*, pg. 1052
BIWATER CONSTRUCTION LIMITED—See Biwater Holdings Limited; *Int'l*, pg. 1052
BIWATER CONTRACTING B.V.—See Biwater Holdings Limited; *Int'l*, pg. 1052
BIWATER INTERNATIONAL LIMITED—See Biwater Holdings Limited; *Int'l*, pg. 1052
BIWATER INTERNATIONAL LIMITED—See Biwater Holdings Limited; *Int'l*, pg. 1052
BIWATER INTERNATIONAL LIMITED—See Biwater Holdings Limited; *Int'l*, pg. 1052
BIWATER LEISURE PLC—See Biwater Holdings Limited; *Int'l*, pg. 1052
BIWATER (MALAYSIA) SDN BHD—See Biwater Holdings Limited; *Int'l*, pg. 1052
BIWATER MAROC SA—See Biwater Holdings Limited; *Int'l*, pg. 1052
BIWATER (NIGERIA) LIMITED—See Biwater Holdings Limited; *Int'l*, pg. 1052
BIWATER PHILIPPINES INC.—See Biwater Holdings Limited; *Int'l*, pg. 1052
BLUE WHALE WATER TECHNOLOGIES CORPORATION—See Continental Holdings Corp.; *Int'l*, pg. 1784
BRITE-TECH BERHAD; *Int'l*, pg. 1165
BWT CESKA REPUBLIKA S.R.O.—See BWT Aktiengesellschaft; *Int'l*, pg. 1232
CANADIAN CONSULTING GROUP LIMITED—See Bird Construction Inc.; *Int'l*, pg. 1046
CECEP GUOZHEN ENVIRONMENTAL PROTECTION TECHNOLOGY CO., LTD.; *Int'l*, pg. 1372
CENTRAL CONTRA COSTA SANITARY DISTRICT; *U.S. Private*, pg. 820
CENTRAL PLAINS ENVIRONMENT PROTECTION CO., LTD.; *Int'l*, pg. 1409
CHARLESTON SANITARY BOARD; *U.S. Private*, pg. 857
CHINA ENVIRONMENTAL TECHNOLOGY HOLDINGS LIMITED; *Int'l*, pg. 1500
CHINA WATER INDUSTRY GROUP LIMITED; *Int'l*, pg. 1563
CLARK COUNTY WATER RECLAMATION DISTRICT; *U.S. Private*, pg. 912
COMPANHIA DE SANEAMENTO DE MINAS GERAIS COPASA MG; *Int'l*, pg. 1747
CONPOREC S.A.S.—See Conporec Inc.; *Int'l*, pg. 1769
CONSTANTINE ENGINEERING, INC.—See Littlejohn & Co., LLC; *U.S. Private*, pg. 2469
CSD WATER SERVICE CO., LTD.; *Int'l*, pg. 1863
CYGNUS INTERNATIONAL CO., LTD.—See Catcher Technology Co., Ltd.; *Int'l*, pg. 1359
DAISEKI CO. LTD. - HOKURIKU UNIT—See Daiseki Co. Ltd.; *Int'l*, pg. 1941
DAISEKI CO. LTD. - KANSAI UNIT—See Daiseki Co. Ltd.; *Int'l*, pg. 1941
DAISEKI CO. LTD. - NAGOYA UNIT—See Daiseki Co. Ltd.; *Int'l*, pg. 1941
DALIAN LIPP ENVIRONMENTAL ENERGY ENGINEERING & TECHNOLOGY CO., LTD—See China Industrial Waste Management, Inc.; *Int'l*, pg. 1510
DAPHNE UTILITY DEPT; *U.S. Private*, pg. 1158
DELAWARE COUNTY REGIONAL WATER QUALITY CONTROL AUTHORITY; *U.S. Private*, pg. 1194
DELTA TREATMENT SYSTEMS, LLC—See Advanced Drainage Systems, Inc.; *U.S. Public*, pg. 46
DE.MEM LIMITED; *Int'l*, pg. 1997
DERICHEBOURG AQUA SAS—See Derichebourg S.A.; *Int'l*, pg. 2041
DRACE INFRAESTRUCTURAS, S.A.—See ACS, Actividades de Construccion y Servicios, S.A.; *Int'l*, pg. 111
DRYDON EQUIPMENT, INC.—See DXP Enterprises, Inc.; *U.S. Public*, pg. 697
DUCKETT CREEK SEWER DISTRICT; *U.S. Private*, pg. 1284
ENJAZ ENERGY & PROJECTS CO.—See Al-Hejailan Group; *Int'l*, pg. 286
ENVIRONMENTAL MANAGEMENT CORPORATION—See American Water Works Company, Inc.; *U.S. Public*, pg. 112
ENVIROSUITE TAIWAN LTD.—See EnviroSuite Limited; *Int'l*, pg. 2455
EVOQUA WATER TECHNOLOGIES CORP.—See Xylem Inc.; *U.S. Public*, pg. 2393
EVOQUA WATER TECHNOLOGIES INDIA PRIVATE LIMITED—See Xylem Inc.; *U.S. Public*, pg. 2393
EVOQUA WATER TECHNOLOGIES PTY. LTD.—See Xylem Inc.; *U.S. Public*, pg. 2394
EVOQUA WATER TECHNOLOGIES (SHANGHAI) CO., LTD.—See Xylem Inc.; *U.S. Public*, pg. 2393
EWE WASSER GMBH—See EWE Aktiengesellschaft; *Int'l*, pg. 2575
FELIX INDUSTRIES LIMITED; *Int'l*, pg. 2633
FINNCHAIN OY—See Addtech AB; *Int'l*, pg. 133
FOX RIVER WATER RECLAMATION DISTRICT; *U.S. Private*, pg. 1584
FUJIAN HAIXIA ENVIRONMENTAL PROTECTION GROUP CO., LTD.; *Int'l*, pg. 2818
GAMUDA LAND (HCMC) JOINT STOCK COMPANY—See Gamuda Berhad; *Int'l*, pg. 2879
GAMUDA LAND VIETNAM LIMITED LIABILITY COMPANY—See Gamuda Berhad; *Int'l*, pg. 2879
GEM STATE WATER COMPANY, LLC—See Northwest Natural Holding Company; *U.S. Public*, pg. 1542
GLOBAL ENVIRONMENTAL MANAGEMENT SERVICES, LLC; *Int'l*, pg. 2996
GREEN & SMART HOLDINGS PLC; *Int'l*, pg. 3069
GUANGDONG LIANTAI ENVIRONMENTAL PROTECTION CO., LTD.; *Int'l*, pg. 3158
GUANGXI BOSSCO ENVIRONMENTAL PROTECTION TECHNOLOGY CO., LTD.; *Int'l*, pg. 3162
GUANGXI NANNING WATERWORKS CO., LTD.; *Int'l*, pg. 3163
GULF CITY CLEANING COMPANY—See Abdulla Ahmed Nass Group WLL; *Int'l*, pg. 58
H2O INNOVATION OPERATION & MAINTENANCE, LLC—See Ember Infrastructure Management, LP; *U.S. Private*, pg. 1378
HEILONGJIANG INTERCHINA WATER TREATMENT CO., LTD.; *Int'l*, pg. 3323
HIDROGESTION, S.A.—See ACS, Actividades de Construccion y Servicios, S.A.; *Int'l*, pg. 114
HITACHI ZOSEN INOVA RUS LLC—See Hitachi Zosen Corporation; *Int'l*, pg. 3412
HITACHI ZOSEN SUS ENVIRONMENT TECHNOLOGY CO., LTD.—See Hitachi Zosen Corporation; *Int'l*, pg. 3412
HOUSTON NATURAL RESOURCES CORP.; *U.S. Public*, pg. 1056
HUNTINGTON SANITARY BOARD; *U.S. Private*, pg. 2010
IGUA SANEAMENTO SA; *Int'l*, pg. 3603
INDIANA-AMERICAN WATER COMPANY, INC.—See American Water Works Company, Inc.; *U.S. Public*, pg. 112
INFILTRATOR WATER TECHNOLOGIES, LLC—See Advanced Drainage Systems, Inc.; *U.S. Public*, pg. 46
JOHNSON COUNTY WASTEWATER; *U.S. Private*, pg. 2227
JOHNSON SCREENS, INC.—See Brookfield Corporation; *Int'l*, pg. 1182
JOHNSON UTILITIES, LLC—See EPCOR Utilities, Inc.; *Int'l*, pg. 2459
LIFEQUEST WORLD CORP.; *U.S. Public*, pg. 1813
LITTLE ROCK WASTE WATER UTILITY; *U.S. Private*, pg. 2469
LOUISVILLE & JEFFERSON COUNTY METROPOLITAN SEWER DISTRICT; *U.S. Private*, pg. 2500
MANASQUAN RIVER REGIONAL SEWERAGE AUTHORITY; *U.S. Private*, pg. 2561
METRO WASTEWATER RECLAMATION DISTRICT; *U.S. Private*, pg. 2687
MICROMIDAS, INC.—See Origin Materials, Inc.; *U.S. Public*, pg. 1617
MIDDLESEX COUNTY UTILITIES AUTHORITY; *U.S. Private*, pg. 2714
MILWAUKEE METROPOLITAN SEWERAGE DISTRICT; *U.S. Private*, pg. 2739
MOBILE AREA WATER & SEWER SYSTEM; *U.S. Private*, pg. 2756
MONTEREY REGIONAL WATER POLLUTION CONTROL; *U.S. Private*, pg. 2776
MPR SERVICES, INC.—See ORG CHEM Group, LLC; *U.S. Private*, pg. 3041
NEW JERSEY-AMERICAN WATER COMPANY, INC.—See American Water Works Company, Inc.; *U.S. Public*, pg. 112
NEW YORK AMERICAN WATER COMPANY, INC.—See Algonquin Power & Utilities Corp.; *Int'l*, pg. 319
NICOLL E.P.E.—See Aliaxis S.A./N.V.; *Int'l*, pg. 325
NORTH CHARLESTON SEWER DISTRICT; *U.S. Private*, pg. 2944
NORTHEAST OHIO REGIONAL SEWER DISTRICT - EASTERLY WASTEWATER TREATMENT PLANT—See Northeast Ohio Regional Sewer District; *U.S. Private*, pg. 2950
NORTHEAST OHIO REGIONAL SEWER DISTRICT - SOUTHERLY WASTEWATER TREATMENT PLANT—See Northeast Ohio Regional Sewer District; *U.S. Private*, pg. 2950
NORTHEAST OHIO REGIONAL SEWER DISTRICT - WESTERLY WASTEWATER TREATMENT PLANT—See Northeast Ohio Regional Sewer District; *U.S. Private*, pg. 2950
NORTH SHORE SANITARY DISTRICT; *U.S. Private*, pg. 2947
OBSED A.S.—See Fomento de Construcciones y Contratas, S.A.; *Int'l*, pg. 2723
OCEAN COUNTY UTILITIES AUTHORITY; *U.S. Private*, pg. 2989
OPERATIONS MANAGEMENT INTERNATIONAL, INC.—See Jacobs Engineering Group, Inc.; *U.S. Public*, pg. 1184
PORTLAND WATER DISTRICT; *U.S. Private*, pg. 3233
PRESBY ENVIRONMENTAL, INC.—See Advanced Drainage Systems, Inc.; *U.S. Public*, pg. 46
PURITAS (PVT) LTD.—See Hayleys PLC; *Int'l*, pg. 3292
QUAIL RUN SERVICES, LLC—See Republic Services, Inc.; *U.S. Public*, pg. 1788
RAULAND-BORG CORPORATION OF FLORIDA—See AMETEK, Inc.; *U.S. Public*, pg. 119
REI-BIWATER CONSORTIUM SDN BHD—See Biwater Holdings Limited; *Int'l*, pg. 1052
RENEWABLE WATER RESOURCES; *U.S. Private*, pg. 3398
RIUVERT S.A.—See Aliaxis S.A./N.V.; *Int'l*, pg. 325
SALMON VALLEY WATER COMPANY—See Northwest Natural Holding Company; *U.S. Public*, pg. 1542
SASKATCHEWAN WATER CORPORATION—See Crown Investments Corporation of Saskatchewan; *Int'l*, pg. 1857
SERVICES MATREC INC.—See BC Partners LLP; *Int'l*, pg. 924

N.A.I.C.S. INDEX

SOUTH TAHOE PUBLIC UTILITY DISTRICT; *U.S. Private*, pg. 3724
STREAM ENVIRONMENT SDN. BHD.—See AWC Berhad; *Int'l*, pg. 752
SUNRIVER WATER LLC—See Northwest Natural Holding Company; *U.S. Public*, pg. 1542
TED BERRY COMPANY LLC—See Vortex Company, LLC; *U.S. Private*, pg. 4413
TEKNOSERV ENGINEERING SDN. BHD.—See GUH Holdings Berhad; *Int'l*, pg. 3173
TETRA TECH, INC. - LEXINGTON—See Tetra Tech, Inc.; *U.S. Public*, pg. 2024
TMC SERVICES, INC.; *U.S. Private*, pg. 4179
TRACTAMENT METROPOLITA DE FANGS, S.L.—See GS Holdings Corp.; *Int'l*, pg. 3142
TROJAN TECHNOLOGIES GROUP ULC—See Danaher Corporation; *U.S. Public*, pg. 631
UNION SANITARY DISTRICT; *U.S. Private*, pg. 4285
UNITED WATER SERVICES; *U.S. Private*, pg. 4301
VIGOTECAKATHERM N.V.—See Aliaxis S.A./N.V.; *Int'l*, pg. 323
WATER & INDUSTRIAL SERVICES COMPANY SPA—See Enel S.p.A.; *Int'l*, pg. 2415
WUXI QIANHUI SEWAGE TREATMENT CO., LTD.—See Build King Holdings Limited; *Int'l*, pg. 1212

221330 — STEAM AND AIR-CONDITIONING SUPPLY

ADVEN EESTI AS—See AMP Limited; *Int'l*, pg. 432
ADVEN OY—See AMP Limited; *Int'l*, pg. 432
BAYWA R.E. AG—See BayWa AG; *Int'l*, pg. 916
BEIJING JINGNENG THERMAL CO., LTD; *Int'l*, pg. 953
BIOMASSEHEIZKRAFTWERK EMDEN GMBH—See E.ON SE; *Int'l*, pg. 2251
CESKOLIPSKE TEPLO A.S.—See Groupe BPCE; *Int'l*, pg. 3094
CLIMATISATION ET CHAUFFAGE URBAINS DE MONTREAL (CCUM)—See Caisse de Depot et Placement du Quebec; *Int'l*, pg. 1256
ENERGIE HOLDING A.S.—See Groupe BPCE; *Int'l*, pg. 3094
ENERGY CENTER HARRISBURG LLC—See BlackRock, Inc.; *U.S. Public*, pg. 345
ENERGY CENTER PAXTON LLC—See BlackRock, Inc.; *U.S. Public*, pg. 345
EVN BULGARIA TOPLOFIKATSIA EAD—See EVN AG; *Int'l*, pg. 2571
FORTUM BYTOM SA—See Fortum Oyj; *Int'l*, pg. 2741
FORTUM CORPORATION—See Fortum Oyj; *Int'l*, pg. 2740
FORTUM ENERGY LLC—See Fortum Oyj; *Int'l*, pg. 2740
FORTUM FORVALTNING AS—See Fortum Oyj; *Int'l*, pg. 2741
FORTUM PLOCK SP. Z.O.O.—See Fortum Oyj; *Int'l*, pg. 2741
FORTUM POWER AND HEAT POLSKA SP. Z.O.O—See Fortum Oyj; *Int'l*, pg. 2741
HALOPOLYMER KIROVO-CHEPETSK LLC; *Int'l*, pg. 3233
HALOPOLYMER PERM, OJSC; *Int'l*, pg. 3233
THE HARTFORD STEAM COMPANY—See Iberdrola, S.A.; *Int'l*, pg. 3571
HEP-TOPLINARSTVO D.O.O.—See Hrvatska elektroprivreda d.d.; *Int'l*, pg. 3502
IROMEZ S.R.O.—See Groupe BPCE; *Int'l*, pg. 3094
JABLONECKA TEPLARENSKA A REALITNI A.S.—See Groupe BPCE; *Int'l*, pg. 3094
MIEJSKA ENERGETYKA CIEPLNA SP. Z O.O.—See ENEA S.A.; *Int'l*, pg. 2410
OPATHERM A.S.—See Groupe BPCE; *Int'l*, pg. 3094
OSLOFJORD VARME AS—See Groupe BPCE; *Int'l*, pg. 3096
PRZEDSIEBIORSTWO ENERGETYKI CIEPLNEJ - GOZDNICA SP. Z O.O.—See ENEA S.A.; *Int'l*, pg. 2410
PUNA GEOTHERMAL VENTURE L.P.—See Ormat Technologies, Inc.; *U.S. Public*, pg. 1618
SOLAR-PLANIT SOFTWARE GMBH—See BayWa AG; *Int'l*, pg. 919
STEAG FERNWARME GMBH—See Asterion Industrial Partners SGEIC SA; *Int'l*, pg. 654
SYDKRAFT TERM SP. Z O.O.—See E.ON SE; *Int'l*, pg. 2259
TARRAGONA POWER, S.L.—See Iberdrola, S.A.; *Int'l*, pg. 3574
TOTAL COMFORT SOLUTIONS LLC; *U.S. Private*, pg. 4190
UAB FORTUM HEAT LIETUVA—See Fortum Oyj; *Int'l*, pg. 2742
UAB FORTUM KLAIPEDA—See Fortum Oyj; *Int'l*, pg. 2742
WESTCODE INC. - BINGHAMTON PLANT—See Westcode Inc.; *U.S. Private*, pg. 4489
XOOM ENERGY GEORGIA, LLC—See NRG Energy, Inc.; *U.S. Public*, pg. 1551
XOOM ENERGY MICHIGAN, LLC—See NRG Energy, Inc.; *U.S. Public*, pg. 1551

236115 — NEW SINGLE-FAMILY HOUSING CONSTRUCTION (EXCEPT FOR-SALE BUILDERS)

4 CORNERS CUSTOM HOMES; *U.S. Private*, pg. 14
ABBEY DEVELOPMENTS LIMITED—See Gallagher Holdings Ltd.; *Int'l*, pg. 2873
ACHEN-GARDNER INC. - GDC HOMES—See Achen-Gardner Construction, LLC; *U.S. Private*, pg. 58
ADAMS HOMES OF NORTHWEST FLORIDA INC.; *U.S. Private*, pg. 74
A.F. STERLING HOME BUILDERS LTD. INC.; *U.S. Private*, pg. 25
AGESON BERHAD; *Int'l*, pg. 206
AGRATIO URBAN DESIGN, INC.; *Int'l*, pg. 214
AHMAD ZAKI RESOURCES BERHAD; *Int'l*, pg. 225
ALL STATE HOMES, INC.; *U.S. Private*, pg. 172
ALTURA HOMES DFW, LP.; *U.S. Private*, pg. 211
ALVAREZ HOMES, INC.; *U.S. Private*, pg. 214
AMERICAN HOUSING CORPORATION; *U.S. Private*, pg. 237
AMERICAN SOUTHERN HOMES, LLC; *U.S. Private*, pg. 254
AMERICA'S HOME PLACE INC.; *U.S. Private*, pg. 221
AMPERSAND CONSTRUCTION, LLC; *U.S. Private*, pg. 265
AMVERTON BERHAD; *Int'l*, pg. 442
ANSCA HOMES; *U.S. Private*, pg. 285
AONE PLUS CO., LTD.—See Iida Group Holdings Co., Ltd.; *Int'l*, pg. 3607
APEX CONTRACTING & RESTORATION, INC.; *U.S. Private*, pg. 292
APS BUILDING SERVICES, INC.; *U.S. Private*, pg. 302
ARAMARK WORKPLACE SOLUTIONS YONETIM HIZMETLERI LIMITED SIRKETI—See Aramark; *U.S. Public*, pg. 177
ARBOR HOMES, LLC—See Berkshire Hathaway Inc.; *U.S. Public*, pg. 304
ARCADIA DEVELOPMENT PTE. LTD.—See Allgreen Properties Ltd.; *Int'l*, pg. 338
ARCS INVESTMENTS, LLC; *U.S. Private*, pg. 315
ARTHUR RUTENBERG HOMES INC.; *U.S. Private*, pg. 342
ASHTON ATLANTA RESIDENTIAL LLC; *U.S. Private*, pg. 350
ASHTON WOODS HOMES; *U.S. Private*, pg. 350
AUBUCHON HOMES, INC.; *U.S. Private*, pg. 385
AVALON AT INVERNESS, LLC—See Century Communities, Inc.; *U.S. Public*, pg. 475
AVANTIA CO., LTD.; *Int'l*, pg. 736
AVTEC HOMES; *U.S. Private*, pg. 410
BALFOUR BEATTY HOMES LTD.—See Balfour Beatty plc; *Int'l*, pg. 808
BALL HOMES INC.; *U.S. Private*, pg. 459
BANDAR RAYA DEVELOPMENTS BERHAD; *Int'l*, pg. 829
BASS PROPERTIES, INC.; *U.S. Private*, pg. 486
BATIVAL; *Int'l*, pg. 890
BAYFAIR QUALITY BUILDERS, LLC; *U.S. Private*, pg. 496
B & B GERIG, INC.; *U.S. Private*, pg. 416
BCB HOMES INC.; *U.S. Private*, pg. 498
BD&A REALTY & CONSTRUCTION; *U.S. Private*, pg. 500
BEACH TO BAY CONSTRUCTION INC.; *U.S. Private*, pg. 503
BEAR CONSTRUCTION CO., INC.; *U.S. Private*, pg. 506
BEATTIE HOMES LTD; *Int'l*, pg. 933
BEAZER HOMES USA, INC.; *U.S. Public*, pg. 287
BELLA VISTA GROUP, INC.; *U.S. Private*, pg. 519
BELLEMEAD DEVELOPMENT CORPORATION—See Chubb Limited; *Int'l*, pg. 1590
BERMAX CONSTRUCTION; *Int'l*, pg. 986
BEST BUILT INC.—See VHC Inc.; *U.S. Private*, pg. 4375
BETSILL BROTHERS CONSTRUCTION, INC.; *U.S. Private*, pg. 546
BILL CLARK HOMES LLC; *U.S. Private*, pg. 556
BING CONSTRUCTION COMPANY INC.; *U.S. Private*, pg. 560
BLACK DIAMOND LIMITED PARTNERSHIP—See Black Diamond Group Limited; *Int'l*, pg. 1059
BLUERIDGE GROUP—See Blue Ridge Group Inc.; *U.S. Private*, pg. 591
BLUESTONE PARTNERS LLC; *U.S. Private*, pg. 598
BOB SCHMITT HOMES INC.; *U.S. Private*, pg. 605
BONNAVILLA—See Chief Industries, Inc.; *U.S. Private*, pg. 881
BOXX MODULAR INC.—See Black Diamond Group Limited; *Int'l*, pg. 1059
THE BOZZUTO GROUP; *U.S. Private*, pg. 3999
BOZZUTO HOMES—See The Bozzuto Group; *U.S. Private*, pg. 3999
BRAEBURY HOMES; *Int'l*, pg. 1135
BRANDON CONSTRUCTION COMPANY, INC.; *U.S. Private*, pg. 638
BRASELTON HOMES, INC.—See D.R. Horton, Inc.; *U.S. Public*, pg. 619
BRIGHTON HOMES LTD.; *U.S. Private*, pg. 652
BROCCOLINI CONSTRUCTION INC.; *Int'l*, pg. 1172
THE BROHN GROUP LLC—See Berkshire Hathaway Inc.; *U.S. Public*, pg. 304
BROOKMAN-FELS ASSOCIATES INCORPORATED; *U.S. Private*, pg. 664
BRUCE WILLIAMS HOMES, INC.; *U.S. Private*, pg. 671
BUBNY DEVELOPMENT S.R.O.; *Int'l*, pg. 1206
BUDLEX SP ZOO; *Int'l*, pg. 1211
BUDUCNOST NOVI SAD A.D.; *Int'l*, pg. 1211
BUESCHER INTERESTS LP; *U.S. Private*, pg. 680
BUKIT SELIM SDN. BHD.—See Hua Yang Berhad; *Int'l*, pg. 3510
BUNTING CONSTRUCTION CORPORATION; *U.S. Private*, pg. 686
BURBANK AUSTRALIA PTY LTD; *Int'l*, pg. 1220
BURNSTEAD CONSTRUCTION COMPANY; *U.S. Private*, pg. 691
BURSA ARES CEVRE VE ENERJI TEKNOLOJILERI SANAYI VE TICARET A.S.—See Bursa Cimento Fabrikasi A.S.; *Int'l*, pg. 1226
CALATLANTIC HOMES OF TEXAS, INC.—See Lennar Corporation; *U.S. Public*, pg. 1305
CALGRO M3 HOLDINGS LIMITED; *Int'l*, pg. 1263
CANADAY & COMPANY; *U.S. Private*, pg. 732
CARGILL INC.—See Cargill, Inc.; *U.S. Private*, pg. 756
CARLETON CONSTRUCTION LTD.; *U.S. Private*, pg. 763
CASAS BETA DEL CENTRO, S DE R L DE C V—See Desarrolladora Homex, S.A. de C.V.; *Int'l*, pg. 2044
CASAS BETA DEL NOROESTE, S.A. DE C.V.—See Desarrolladora Homex, S.A. de C.V.; *Int'l*, pg. 2044
CASAS BETA DEL NORTE, S.A. DE C.V.—See Desarrolladora Homex, S.A. de C.V.; *Int'l*, pg. 2044
THE CASSIDY ORGANIZATION, INC.; *U.S. Private*, pg. 4005
CB JENI MANAGEMENT, LLC—See Green Brick Partners, Inc.; *U.S. Public*, pg. 962
CDK BUILDERS INC.; *U.S. Private*, pg. 802
CEMENTIR DELTA S.P.A.—See Cementir Holding N.V.; *Int'l*, pg. 1397
CENTRE LIVING HOMES, LLC—See Green Brick Partners, Inc.; *U.S. Public*, pg. 962
CENTREX HOMES—See Apex Limited Partnership; *Int'l*, pg. 511
CENTURY COMMUNITIES, INC.; *U.S. Public*, pg. 474
CHAMPION HOMES OF TENNESSEE—See Champion Homes, Inc.; *U.S. Public*, pg. 477
CHARTERED DEVELOPMENT CORP.—See Chartered Homes; *U.S. Private*, pg. 859
CHARTERED HOMES; *U.S. Private*, pg. 858
CHRISTOPHERSON HOMES INC.; *U.S. Private*, pg. 892
CITRUS HILLS CONSTRUCTION COMPANY LLC; *U.S. Private*, pg. 904
CITY VENTURES, INC.; *U.S. Private*, pg. 907
CLARENCE W GOSNELL INC; *U.S. Private*, pg. 911
CLASSIC BUILDERS, INC.—See D.R. Horton, Inc.; *U.S. Public*, pg. 619
CMI INDUSTRY AMERICAS INC.—See Euremis Holding SA; *Int'l*, pg. 2530
C&N GROUP INC.; *U.S. Private*, pg. 703
COASTAL CONSTRUCTION GROUP OF SOUTH FLORIDA INC.; *U.S. Private*, pg. 955
COLLEGE CITY HOMES INC.; *U.S. Private*, pg. 968
COLONIAL COMPANY; *U.S. Private*, pg. 970
COLONIAL HOMES INC.; *U.S. Private*, pg. 971
COLSON & COLSON GENERAL CONTRACTORS; *U.S. Private*, pg. 975
COLUMBIA PROPERTY MAINTENANCE—See Columbia Sweeping Services Inc.; *U.S. Private*, pg. 978
COMMERCIAL CONTRACTORS GROUP INC.; *U.S. Private*, pg. 983
COMMONWEALTH DESIGNS, INC.; *U.S. Private*, pg. 986
COMMUNITY HOUSING PARTNERS CORPORATION; *U.S. Private*, pg. 995
CONNAUGHTON CONSTRUCTION CORP; *U.S. Private*, pg. 1014
CONSORCIO HOGAR, S.A.B. DE C.V.; *Int'l*, pg. 1772
CONSTRUCTION-CAD SOLUTIONS, INC.; *U.S. Private*, pg. 1024
CONTINENTAL HOMES OF AUSTIN, L.P.—See D.R. Horton, Inc.; *U.S. Public*, pg. 619
COOPER REALTY INVESTMENT INC.—See Cooper Communities, Inc.; *U.S. Private*, pg. 1041
CORE CONSTRUCTION SERVICES OF FLORIDA, LLC—See Core Construction; *U.S. Private*, pg. 1048
CORONADO CORPORATION—See LTC Properties, Inc.; *U.S. Public*, pg. 1344
COUNTRY LIFE HOMES INC.; *U.S. Private*, pg. 1067
COURTLAND HOMES INC.; *U.S. Private*, pg. 1070
CPH HOLDING, LLC; *U.S. Private*, pg. 1080
CRAFTMARK HOMES INC.; *U.S. Private*, pg. 1082
CRESLEIGH HOMES ARIZONA INC—See Harbor View Holdings Inc.; *U.S. Private*, pg. 1859
CREST HOMES CORPORATION—See Berkshire Hathaway Inc.; *U.S. Public*, pg. 304
CROCKETT HOMES, INC.; *U.S. Private*, pg. 1103
CROWELL & COMPANY INC.; *U.S. Private*, pg. 1109
C.S. BACHLY BUILDERS LTD.; *Int'l*, pg. 1244
CUSTOM DESIGN & CONSTRUCTION; *U.S. Private*, pg. 1128
DA CIN CONSTRUCTION CO., LTD.; *Int'l*, pg. 1901
DAHUA INC.; *Int'l*, pg. 1913

236115 — NEW SINGLE-FAMILY H...

DAIBES BROTHERS INC.; *U.S. Private*, pg. 1145
DANCENTER A/S—See Axel Springer SE; *Int'l*, pg. 766
DANIS BUILDERS, LLC—See Danis Building Construction Company Inc.; *U.S. Private*, pg. 1156
DANRIC HOMES; *U.S. Private*, pg. 1157
DAN RYAN BUILDERS, INC.; *U.S. Private*, pg. 1151
DARLING HOMES; *U.S. Private*, pg. 1159
DARLING INTERESTS, INC.—See Darling Homes; *U.S. Private*, pg. 1159
DASIGN SOURCE & CO. INC.; *U.S. Private*, pg. 1162
DAVE BREWER INC.; *U.S. Private*, pg. 1168
DAVID WEEKLEY HOMES, LP; *U.S. Private*, pg. 1171
DEANGELIS DIAMOND CONSTRUCTION, INC.; *U.S. Private*, pg. 1185
DE LUCA ENTERPRISES INC.; *U.S. Private*, pg. 1181
DEL WEBB TEXAS LIMITED PARTNERSHIP—See Pulte-Group, Inc.; *U.S. Public*, pg. 1737
DESARROLLADORA HOMEX, S.A. DE C.V.; *Int'l*, pg. 2043
DESIGN+BUILD GROUP; *U.S. Private*, pg. 1214
D H GRIFFIN CONSTRUCTION CO. LLC—See D.H. Griffin Wrecking Co. Inc.; *U.S. Private*, pg. 1142
DHIC - PIONEER HILL, LLC—See D.R. Horton, Inc.; *U.S. Public*, pg. 619
DHIC - RIDGEWOOD, LLC—See D.R. Horton, Inc.; *U.S. Public*, pg. 619
DHIR - AMBER CREEK, LLC—See D.R. Horton, Inc.; *U.S. Public*, pg. 619
DHIR - ARABELLA, LLC—See D.R. Horton, Inc.; *U.S. Public*, pg. 619
DHIR - BRIDGE HARBOR, LLC—See D.R. Horton, Inc.; *U.S. Public*, pg. 619
DHIR - BROOKSIDE AT PLEASANT VALLEY, LLC—See D.R. Horton, Inc.; *U.S. Public*, pg. 619
DHIR - CEDAR STATION, LLC—See D.R. Horton, Inc.; *U.S. Public*, pg. 620
DHIR - CYPRESS BAY, LLC—See D.R. Horton, Inc.; *U.S. Public*, pg. 620
DHIR - FOUNTAIN PARK, LLC—See D.R. Horton, Inc.; *U.S. Public*, pg. 620
DHIR - LAKESHORE VILLAGES, LLC—See D.R. Horton, Inc.; *U.S. Public*, pg. 620
DHIR - MILLBROOK PARK, LLC—See D.R. Horton, Inc.; *U.S. Public*, pg. 620
DHIR - RIVERSTONE AT WESTPOINTE, LLC—See D.R. Horton, Inc.; *U.S. Public*, pg. 620
DHI TITLE OF WASHINGTON, INC.—See D.R. Horton, Inc.; *U.S. Public*, pg. 619
DI CANIO ORGANIZATION INC.; *U.S. Private*, pg. 1221
DI CANIO RESIDENTIAL COMMUNITIES INC—See Di Canio Organization Inc.; *U.S. Private*, pg. 1221
DIVCO CONSTRUCTION CORP.; *U.S. Private*, pg. 1240
DLP BUILDERS—See Don Wenner Home Selling, Inc.; *U.S. Private*, pg. 1259
DOING STEEL, INC.; *U.S. Private*, pg. 1254
DOLOMITE CORPORATION BERHAD; *Int'l*, pg. 2159
DORN HOMES, INC.—See American Southern Homes, LLC; *U.S. Private*, pg. 255
DREAM FINDERS HOMES LLC; *U.S. Private*, pg. 1275
DREAM HOMES & DEVELOPMENT CORP.; *U.S. Public*, pg. 687
THE DREES COMPANY, INC.; *U.S. Private*, pg. 4023
DREES HOMES—See The Drees Company, Inc.; *U.S. Private*, pg. 4023
DREES PREFERRED COLLECTION, INC.—See The Drees Company, Inc.; *U.S. Private*, pg. 4023
DRH CAMBRIDGE HOMES, INC.—See D.R. Horton, Inc.; *U.S. Public*, pg. 620
D.R. HORTON, INC. - CONROE OFFICE—See D.R. Horton, Inc.; *U.S. Public*, pg. 619
D.R. HORTON, INC. - DFW EAST DIVISION OFFICE—See D.R. Horton, Inc.; *U.S. Public*, pg. 619
D.R. HORTON, INC. - SAN ANTONIO OFFICE—See D.R. Horton, Inc.; *U.S. Public*, pg. 619
D.R. HORTON, INC. - SEATTLE OFFICE—See D.R. Horton, Inc.; *U.S. Public*, pg. 619
D.R. HORTON—See D.R. Horton, Inc.; *U.S. Public*, pg. 619
DRH TUCSON CONSTRUCTION, INC.—See D.R. Horton, Inc.; *U.S. Public*, pg. 619
THE DUGGAN RHODES GROUP; *U.S. Private*, pg. 4023
DVELE, INC.; *U.S. Private*, pg. 1295
EASTBROOK HOMES INC.; *U.S. Private*, pg. 1319
EASTERN MANAGEMENT COMPANY; *U.S. Private*, pg. 1320
EASTWOOD HOMES; *U.S. Private*, pg. 1322
ECOFIRST CONSOLIDATED BHD; *Int'l*, pg. 2295
EDIL.GI SRL; *Int'l*, pg. 2309
EDILIZIACROBATICA S.P.A.; *Int'l*, pg. 2309
ELITE HOMES—See Berkshire Hathaway Inc.; *U.S. Public*, pg. 304
ELITE PROPERTIES OF AMERICA, INC.; *U.S. Private*, pg. 1361
EMERCON CONSTRUCTION INC.; *U.S. Private*, pg. 1380
EMMY BUILDING CO. INC.; *U.S. Private*, pg. 1383
ENGEL GENERAL DEVELOPERS LTD.—See Engel Construction & Development Group; *Int'l*, pg. 2426
ENKA TEKNIK A.S.—See Enka Insaat ve Sanayi A.S.; *Int'l*, pg. 2440
THE ESTRIDGE GROUP INC.; *U.S. Private*, pg. 4027

EXCEL HOMES LP—See Apex Limited Partnership; *Int'l*, pg. 511
FAXONGILLIS HOMES INC.; *U.S. Private*, pg. 1484
FIMARO INVEST SA; *Int'l*, pg. 2664
FIRST DAKOTA ENTERPRISES INCORPORATED; *U.S. Private*, pg. 1516
FIRST HOME BUILDERS OF FLORIDA; *U.S. Private*, pg. 1520
FIRST JUKEN CO., LTD.; *Int'l*, pg. 2685
FIRST TEXAS HOMES INC.; *U.S. Private*, pg. 1530
FIRST WOOD CO., LTD.—See Iida Group Holdings Co., Ltd.; *Int'l*, pg. 3607
FISH CONSTRUCTION COMPANY; *U.S. Private*, pg. 1533
FISKARHEDENVILLAN AB; *Int'l*, pg. 2693
FLORIDA COASTAL HOMES INC.—See The Goldfield Corporation; *U.S. Public*, pg. 2075
FLORIDA HOME PARTNERSHIP, INC.; *U.S. Private*, pg. 1549
FLORIDA LIFESTYLE HOMES OF FORT MYERS, INC.; *U.S. Private*, pg. 1549
FOREST CONSTRUCTION COMPANY; *U.S. Private*, pg. 1566
FORM700 PTY. LTD.; *Int'l*, pg. 2733
FORMATION GROUP PLC; *Int'l*, pg. 2733
FORT HILL CONSTRUCTION INC.; *U.S. Private*, pg. 1574
FOWLER CONSTRUCTION & DEVELOPMENT, INC.; *U.S. Private*, pg. 1583
FOX RIDGE HOMES—See NVR Incorporated; *U.S. Public*, pg. 1558
FRALIN AND WALDRON, INC.; *U.S. Private*, pg. 1586
FREESTONE COMPANIES; *U.S. Private*, pg. 1607
FRONTIER COMMUNITY BUILDERS; *U.S. Private*, pg. 1615
FUJI CORPORATION LIMITED; *Int'l*, pg. 2810
FULFORD CONSTRUCTION INC.; *U.S. Private*, pg. 1620
GAFISA S.A.; *Int'l*, pg. 2868
GALLAGHER & HENRY, INC.; *U.S. Private*, pg. 1638
GANESH HOUSING CORPORATION LTD; *Int'l*, pg. 2880
GATEWAY HOMES LTD; *U.S. Private*, pg. 1650
GEMCRAFT HOMES INC.; *U.S. Private*, pg. 1657
GENTOO GROUP LTD.; *Int'l*, pg. 2929
GENTRY HOMES LTD; *U.S. Private*, pg. 1680
GEONERCO INC.; *U.S. Private*, pg. 1681
GERSTAD BUILDERS INC.; *U.S. Private*, pg. 1688
GHI HOLDINGS INC.; *U.S. Private*, pg. 1690
GILC INCORPORATED—See Granite Construction Incorporated; *U.S. Public*, pg. 957
GKN AUTOMOTIVE, INC - ALAMANCE FACILITY—See GKN plc; *Int'l*, pg. 2984
GLASS CONSTRUCTION; *U.S. Private*, pg. 1706
GL HOMES OF FLORIDA CORP.; *U.S. Private*, pg. 1704
GLOMAC BERHAD; *Int'l*, pg. 3008
GOLDEN BAY REALTY (PRIVATE) LIMITED—See Hiap Hoe Limited; *Int'l*, pg. 3382
GOOD COM CO., LTD.—See Good Com Asset Co., Ltd.; *Int'l*, pg. 3038
GOODMAN FAMILY OF BUILDERS; *U.S. Private*, pg. 1739
GRACE HOMES COLORADO; *U.S. Private*, pg. 1749
GRAFTON MERCHANTING GB LIMITED—See Grafton Group plc; *Int'l*, pg. 3050
GRANITE CONSTRUCTION CO. - BAY AREA BRANCH—See Granite Construction Incorporated; *U.S. Public*, pg. 957
GRANT CONSTRUCTION, INC.; *U.S. Private*, pg. 1756
GREGAN CONSTRUCTION CORP.; *U.S. Private*, pg. 1782
GREG WEBER, INC.; *U.S. Private*, pg. 1782
GRUPE HOLDING COMPANY; *U.S. Private*, pg. 1797
HALLE ENTERPRISES INC.; *U.S. Private*, pg. 1844
HAMPTON HOMES, LLC.; *U.S. Private*, pg. 1851
HANKIN GROUP; *U.S. Private*, pg. 1853
HANS HAGEN HOMES INC.; *U.S. Private*, pg. 1855
HARBOUR HOMES LLC; *U.S. Private*, pg. 1861
HARTZ CONSTRUCTION CO. INC.; *U.S. Private*, pg. 1874
HEARTHSIDE HOMES, INC.—See California Coastal Communities, Inc.; *U.S. Private*, pg. 718
HEAVENSTONE CORP.; *U.S. Private*, pg. 1902
HELMA EIGENHEIMBAU AG; *Int'l*, pg. 3338
HELMES INC.; *U.S. Private*, pg. 1912
HERITAGE HOMES INC.; *U.S. Private*, pg. 1924
HIGHLAND HOLDINGS, INC.—See Berkshire Hathaway Inc.; *U.S. Public*, pg. 304
HIGHLAND HOMES LTD.; *U.S. Private*, pg. 1938
HOBBS INCORPORATED; *U.S. Private*, pg. 1958
HOFFMAN CONSTRUCTION COMPANY OF WASHINGTON—See Hoffman Corporation; *U.S. Private*, pg. 1960
HOGAN HOMES INC; *U.S. Private*, pg. 1961
HOLIDAY BUILDERS INC.; *U.S. Private*, pg. 1962
HOLMES & ASSOCIATES LLC; *U.S. Private*, pg. 1967
HOLT CONSTRUCTION CORP.; *U.S. Private*, pg. 1968
HOMES BY AVI INC.; *Int'l*, pg. 3455
HOMES BY DAVID POWERS; *U.S. Private*, pg. 1973
HOMES BY JOHN C. FOWKE, INC.; *U.S. Private*, pg. 1974
HOMES BY WESTBAY, LLC; *U.S. Private*, pg. 1974
HOMES BY WHITTAKER; *U.S. Private*, pg. 1974
HOME TRADE CENTER CO., LTD.—See Iida Group Holdings Co., Ltd.; *Int'l*, pg. 3607
HONG LAI HUAT CONSTRUCTION PTE LTD—See Hong Lai Huat Group Limited; *Int'l*, pg. 3467
HONKARAKENNE OYJ; *Int'l*, pg. 3471
HOUSING DEVELOPMENT & INFRASTRUCTURE LIMITED; *Int'l*, pg. 3491
HRH CONSTRUCTION LLC; *U.S. Private*, pg. 1998
HUNT CONSTRUCTION GROUP, INC. - SOUTH DIVISION—See AECOM; *U.S. Public*, pg. 51
IIDA SANGYO CO., LTD.—See Iida Group Holdings Co., Ltd.; *Int'l*, pg. 3607
IJM BUILDING SYSTEMS SDN BHD—See IJM Corporation Berhad; *Int'l*, pg. 3608
INLAND COMPANIES, INC.; *U.S. Private*, pg. 2078
INNOVATIVE CONSTRUCTION SERVICES—See P.J. Dick Incorporated; *U.S. Private*, pg. 3060
INSURANCE RESTORATION SPECIALISTS, INC.—See FirstService Corporation; *Int'l*, pg. 2691
IVORY HOMES; *U.S. Private*, pg. 2151
J.A.M SHELL BUILDERS, INC.; *U.S. Private*, pg. 2158
JAVIC PROPERTY LLC; *U.S. Private*, pg. 2191
JCH CONSTRUCTION, LLC—See Brookfield Corporation; *Int'l*, pg. 1183
J.D. SMITH CUSTOM HOMES, LLC; *U.S. Private*, pg. 2161
J.F. SHEA CO., INC.; *U.S. Private*, pg. 2164
JHC STRUCTURES CORPORATION; *U.S. Private*, pg. 2207
J. MCGARVEY CONSTRUCTION COMPANY, INC.; *U.S. Private*, pg. 2156
JOE KOCH CONSTRUCTION, INC.; *U.S. Private*, pg. 2218
JOHN CANNON HOMES INC.; *U.S. Private*, pg. 2220
JOHN FOGARTY CUSTOM BUILT HOMES; *U.S. Private*, pg. 2221
JOHN MOURIER CONSTRUCTION, INC.; *U.S. Private*, pg. 2223
JOHN NEAL HOMES, INC.—See Estuary Investment Corp.; *U.S. Private*, pg. 1429
JPR HOMES; *U.S. Private*, pg. 2239
JTS COMMUNITIES, INC.; *U.S. Private*, pg. 2242
JUNIPER ROCK CORPORATION—See Primoris Services Corporation; *U.S. Public*, pg. 1718
JUTAKUJOHOKAN CO., LTD.—See Iida Group Holdings Co., Ltd.; *Int'l*, pg. 3607
JUTAKUJOHOKAN FINANCIAL SERVICE CO., LTD.—See Iida Group Holdings Co., Ltd.; *Int'l*, pg. 3607
JWC CONSTRUCTION INC.; *U.S. Private*, pg. 2246
K1 INVESTMENT MANAGEMENT, LLC; *U.S. Private*, pg. 2252
KAEREK HOMES, INC.; *U.S. Private*, pg. 2253
KALIAN CORPORATION; *U.S. Private*, pg. 2257
KB HOME COLORADO, INC.—See KB Home; *U.S. Public*, pg. 1215
KB HOME GREATER LOS ANGELES, INC.—See KB Home; *U.S. Public*, pg. 1215
KB HOME JACKSONVILLE LLC—See KB Home; *U.S. Public*, pg. 1215
KB HOME MORTGAGE COMPANY—See KB Home; *U.S. Public*, pg. 1215
KB HOME NEVADA INC.—See KB Home; *U.S. Public*, pg. 1215
KB HOME NORTHERN CALIFORNIA—See KB Home; *U.S. Public*, pg. 1215
KB HOME—See KB Home; *U.S. Public*, pg. 1215
KB HOME TAMPA LLC—See KB Home; *U.S. Public*, pg. 1215
KEIM CORP.; *U.S. Private*, pg. 2273
KELLER HOMES, INC.—See Toll Brothers, Inc.; *U.S. Public*, pg. 2162
KELLEY HOLDINGS INC.; *U.S. Private*, pg. 2276
KEYSTONE BUILDERS RESOURCE GROUP, INC.; *U.S. Private*, pg. 2295
K. HOVNANIAN ASPIRE AT AULD FARMS, LLC—See Hovnanian Enterprises, Inc.; *U.S. Public*, pg. 1056
K. HOVNANIAN ASPIRE AT CALITERRA RANCH, LLC—See Hovnanian Enterprises, Inc.; *U.S. Public*, pg. 1056
K. HOVNANIAN ASPIRE AT SOLAIRE, LLC—See Hovnanian Enterprises, Inc.; *U.S. Public*, pg. 1056
K. HOVNANIAN AT ALAMEDA POINT, LLC—See Hovnanian Enterprises, Inc.; *U.S. Public*, pg. 1058
K. HOVNANIAN AT BOOTH FARM, LLC—See Hovnanian Enterprises, Inc.; *U.S. Public*, pg. 1058
K. HOVNANIAN AT COUNTRY VIEW ESTATES, LLC—See Hovnanian Enterprises, Inc.; *U.S. Public*, pg. 1058
K. HOVNANIAN AT HAMPSHIRE FARMS, LLC—See Hovnanian Enterprises, Inc.; *U.S. Public*, pg. 1059
K. HOVNANIAN AT HARVEST MEADOWS, LLC—See Hovnanian Enterprises, Inc.; *U.S. Public*, pg. 1059
K. HOVNANIAN AT MARLBORO GROVE, LLC—See Hovnanian Enterprises, Inc.; *U.S. Public*, pg. 1059
K. HOVNANIAN AT NEW POST, LLC—See Hovnanian Enterprises, Inc.; *U.S. Public*, pg. 1059
K. HOVNANIAN AT NORTH RIDGE, LLC—See Hovnanian Enterprises, Inc.; *U.S. Public*, pg. 1059
K. HOVNANIAN AT OYSTER COVE, LLC—See Hovnanian Enterprises, Inc.; *U.S. Public*, pg. 1059
K. HOVNANIAN AT RANCHO EL DORADO, LLC—See Hovnanian Enterprises, Inc.; *U.S. Public*, pg. 1059
K. HOVNANIAN AT SAGE II HARVEST AT LIMONEIRA,

N.A.I.C.S. INDEX

236115 — NEW SINGLE-FAMILY H...

LLC—See Hovnanian Enterprises, Inc.; *U.S. Public*, pg. 1059
K. HOVNANIAN AT SANDPIPER PLACE, LLC—See Hovnanian Enterprises, Inc.; *U.S. Public*, pg. 1059
K. HOVNANIAN AT SUMMIT CROSSING ESTATES, LLC—See Hovnanian Enterprises, Inc.; *U.S. Public*, pg. 1059
K. HOVNANIAN AT TORTOSA SOUTH, LLC—See Hovnanian Enterprises, Inc.; *U.S. Public*, pg. 1060
K. HOVNANIAN CAMBRIDGE HOMES, LLC—See Hovnanian Enterprises, Inc.; *U.S. Public*, pg. 1056
K. HOVNANIAN COMPANIES NORTHEAST, INC.—See Hovnanian Enterprises, Inc.; *U.S. Public*, pg. 1056
K. HOVNANIAN DFW SAPPHIRE BAY, LLC—See Hovnanian Enterprises, Inc.; *U.S. Public*, pg. 1057
K. HOVNANIAN FOUR SEASONS AT HOMESTEAD, LLC—See Hovnanian Enterprises, Inc.; *U.S. Public*, pg. 1057
K. HOVNANIAN HOMES OF MARYLAND, LLC—See Hovnanian Enterprises, Inc.; *U.S. Public*, pg. 1057
K. HOVNANIAN T&C HOMES AT ILLINOIS, L.L.C.—See Hovnanian Enterprises, Inc.; *U.S. Public*, pg. 1058
K. HOVNANIAN WINDWARD HOMES, LLC—See Hovnanian Enterprises, Inc.; *U.S. Public*, pg. 1058
KILLEARN CONSTRUCTION, INC.—See Killearn Properties, Inc.; *U.S. Private*, pg. 2304
KINGSCROFT DEVELOPMENTS LIMITED—See Gallagher Holdings Ltd.; *Int'l*, pg. 2873
KINGS WAY HOMES INC.; *U.S. Private*, pg. 2311
KIRLIN CUSTOM HOMES INC.; *U.S. Private*, pg. 2315
KLM BUILDERS INC.; *U.S. Private*, pg. 2320
KLUTTS PROPERTY MANAGEMENT, INC.; *U.S. Private*, pg. 2321
KOLTER HOMES, LLC—See The Kolter Group LLC; *U.S. Private*, pg. 4065
KREISLER BORG FLORMAN GENERAL CONSTRUCTION COMPANY INC.; *U.S. Private*, pg. 2350
KUSHNER COMPANIES; *U.S. Private*, pg. 2358
LANDMARK HOMES OF TENNESSEE, INC.—See Century Communities, Inc.; *U.S. Public*, pg. 475
LANDSTAR DEVELOPMENT CORPORATION; *U.S. Private*, pg. 2387
LAROSA BUILDING GROUP LLC; *U.S. Private*, pg. 2392
LEGEND CLASSIC HOMES LTD.; *U.S. Private*, pg. 2418
LENNAR CHICAGO, INC.—See Lennar Corporation; *U.S. Public*, pg. 1306
LENNAR CORPORATION; *U.S. Public*, pg. 1305
LENNAR DESIGN STUDIO HOME—See Lennar Corporation; *U.S. Public*, pg. 1306
LENNAR HOMES, COLORADO DIV—See Lennar Corporation; *U.S. Public*, pg. 1306
LENNAR HOMES, INC. - ORLANDO—See Lennar Corporation; *U.S. Public*, pg. 1306
LENNAR HOMES, INC.—See Lennar Corporation; *U.S. Public*, pg. 1306
LENNAR HOMES, INC.—See Lennar Corporation; *U.S. Public*, pg. 1306
LENNAR HOMES, INC.—See Lennar Corporation; *U.S. Public*, pg. 1306
LENNAR HOMES, INC.—See Lennar Corporation; *U.S. Public*, pg. 1306
LENNAR HOMES, INC.—See Lennar Corporation; *U.S. Public*, pg. 1306
LENNAR HOMES OF TENNESSEE, LLC—See Lennar Corporation; *U.S. Public*, pg. 1306
LENNAR SACRAMENTO, INC.—See Lennar Corporation; *U.S. Public*, pg. 1306
LENNAR—See Lennar Corporation; *U.S. Public*, pg. 1306
LENNAR US HOMES—See Lennar Corporation; *U.S. Public*, pg. 1306
LEVITT HOMES CORPORATION; *U.S. Private*, pg. 2437
LGI HOMES AVONDALE, LLC—See LGI Homes, Inc.; *U.S. Public*, pg. 1310
LGI HOMES AZ SALES, LLC—See LGI Homes, Inc.; *U.S. Public*, pg. 1310
LGI HOMES, INC.; *U.S. Public*, pg. 1309
LGI HOMES - MAPLE PARK, LLC—See LGI Homes, Inc.; *U.S. Public*, pg. 1310
LGI HOMES REALTY LLC—See LGI Homes, Inc.; *U.S. Public*, pg. 1310
LGI HOMES - SC, LLC—See LGI Homes, Inc.; *U.S. Public*, pg. 1310
LGI HOMES - STERLING LAKES PARTNERS, LLC—See LGI Homes, Inc.; *U.S. Public*, pg. 1310
LINBECK CONSTRUCTION CORPORATION-FT. WORTH—See Linbeck Group LLC; *U.S. Private*, pg. 2456
LINTHICUM CUSTOM BUILDERS, LLC—See Linthicum Corporation; *U.S. Private*, pg. 2463
LITHIUM DEVELOPMENT PTE LTD—See Hong Lai Huat Group Limited; *Int'l*, pg. 3467
LIVING CORPORATION, INC.—See Iida Group Holdings Co., Ltd.; *Int'l*, pg. 3607
LMI CONTRACTORS, LLC—See Lennar Corporation; *U.S. Public*, pg. 1306
THE LONGFORD GROUP, INC.; *U.S. Private*, pg. 4072
LOWDER NEW HOMES—See Colonial Company; *U.S. Private*, pg. 970

MAJESTIC WOODS, LLC—See Lennar Corporation; *U.S. Public*, pg. 1306
MARC RUTENBERG HOMES INC.; *U.S. Private*, pg. 2571
MARSHA LYNN BUILDING CORP.; *U.S. Private*, pg. 2592
MARVIN DEVELOPMENT CORP.; *U.S. Private*, pg. 2597
MB HAYNES CORPORATION; *U.S. Private*, pg. 2623
MCGEE-HUNTLEY CONSTRUCTION CO. INC.—See McGee Brothers Co. Inc.; *U.S. Private*, pg. 2634
MCGUYER HOMEBUILDERS INC.; *U.S. Private*, pg. 2636
MCKELVEY HOMES, LLC.; *U.S. Private*, pg. 2638
MCNEIL COMPANY, INC.; *U.S. Private*, pg. 2643
MCSTAIN ENTERPRISES; *U.S. Private*, pg. 2644
MEDALLION HOMES GULF COAST, INC.; *U.S. Private*, pg. 2650
MERCEDES HOMES INC.; *U.S. Private*, pg. 2668
MERCEDES HOMES OF TEXAS LTD.—See Mercedes Homes Inc.; *U.S. Private*, pg. 2668
MERITAGE HOMES OF ARIZONA, INC.—See Meritage Homes Corporation; *U.S. Public*, pg. 1425
MHI PARTNERSHIP LTD.; *U.S. Private*, pg. 2695
M/I HOMES OF CHARLOTTE, LLC—See M/I Homes, Inc.; *U.S. Public*, pg. 1351
M/I HOMES OF INDIANA, L.P.—See M/I Homes, Inc.; *U.S. Public*, pg. 1351
M/I HOMES OF RALEIGH, LLC—See M/I Homes, Inc.; *U.S. Public*, pg. 1351
MIKEN BUILDERS, INC.; *U.S. Private*, pg. 2726
MILENDER WHITE CONSTRUCTION CO.; *U.S. Private*, pg. 2727
MILLARD BOWEN COMMUNITIES, LLC; *U.S. Private*, pg. 2730
THE MILLER GROUP LTD.—See Bridgepoint Group Plc; *Int'l*, pg. 1154
MILLER & RAVED INC.; *U.S. Private*, pg. 2732
MILLER & SMITH CO.—See Miller & Smith Holding Company Inc.; *U.S. Private*, pg. 2732
MILLER & SMITH HOLDING COMPANY INC.; *U.S. Private*, pg. 2732
M/I PROPERTIES, LLC—See M/I Homes, Inc.; *U.S. Public*, pg. 1351
M/I TITLE AGENCY LTD.—See M/I Homes, Inc.; *U.S. Public*, pg. 1351
MIZNER COUNTRY CLUB, INC.; *U.S. Private*, pg. 2752
M. LUIS CONSTRUCTION CO., INC.; *U.S. Private*, pg. 2527
MOBLEY HOMES OF FLORIDA INC.; *U.S. Private*, pg. 2758
MOREY DEVELOPMENT CO. INC.—See Morey's Piers Incorporated; *U.S. Private*, pg. 2782
M.R. TANNER DEVELOPMENT & CONSTRUCTION; *U.S. Private*, pg. 2529
M TAMPA CORP.—See Mobley Homes of Florida Inc.; *U.S. Private*, pg. 2758
THE MUNGO COMPANY, INC.—See Berkshire Hathaway Inc.; *U.S. Public*, pg. 304
MUNGO HOMES OF GEORGIA LLC—See Berkshire Hathaway Inc.; *U.S. Public*, pg. 304
MUNGO HOMES OF NORTH CAROLINA, INC.—See Berkshire Hathaway Inc.; *U.S. Public*, pg. 304
MUNGO HOMES—See Berkshire Hathaway Inc.; *U.S. Public*, pg. 304
MURCHISON PROPERTIES INC.—See J.D. Murchison Interests Inc.; *U.S. Private*, pg. 2161
NAPLES REDEVELOPMENT INC.; *U.S. Private*, pg. 2834
NASSA LLC—See Lennar Corporation; *U.S. Public*, pg. 1306
NATIONSBUILDERS INSURANCE SERVICES, INC.—See Align Financial Group, LLC; *U.S. Private*, pg. 168
NEIGHBORS CONSTRUCTION CO. INC.; *U.S. Private*, pg. 2881
NELSON HOMES, INC.; *U.S. Private*, pg. 2883
NEWCASTLE CONSTRUCTION, INC.; *U.S. Private*, pg. 2914
NEW DIMENSIONS INC.; *U.S. Private*, pg. 2893
THE NEW HOME COMPANY INC.—See Apollo Global Management, Inc.; *U.S. Public*, pg. 164
THE NEW HOME COMPANY NORTHERN CALIFORNIA LLC—See Apollo Global Management, Inc.; *U.S. Public*, pg. 164
NEW URBAN WEST INC.; *U.S. Private*, pg. 2907
NIBLOCK DEVELOPMENT CORP.; *U.S. Private*, pg. 2924
NILSON AND COMPANY INC.; *U.S. Private*, pg. 2927
NORMANDY HOMES CYPRESS MEADOWS, LLC—See Green Brick Partners, Inc.; *U.S. Public*, pg. 962
NORMANDY HOMES LAKESIDE, LLC—See Green Brick Partners, Inc.; *U.S. Public*, pg. 962
NORPAC CONSTRUCTION, LLC—See UFP Industries, Inc.; *U.S. Public*, pg. 2219
NORTH AMERICAN NATIONAL TITLE SOLUTIONS, LLC—See Lennar Corporation; *U.S. Public*, pg. 1307
NRP CONTRACTORS LLC—See The NRP Group, LLC; *U.S. Private*, pg. 4085
THE NRP GROUP, LLC; *U.S. Private*, pg. 4085
NUTTER CUSTOM CONSTRUCTION, LLC; *U.S. Private*, pg. 2974
OAKBROOK HOMES INC.; *U.S. Private*, pg. 2984
OAK RIDGE, INC.; *U.S. Private*, pg. 2984
ODC CONSTRUCTION, LLC—See Asahi Kasei Corporation; *Int'l*, pg. 595
OLE SOUTH PROPERTIES INC.; *U.S. Private*, pg. 3010

THE OLSON COMPANY; *U.S. Private*, pg. 4088
OLYMPUS HOMES INC.; *U.S. Private*, pg. 3013
ON SITE MANAGEMENT INC.; *U.S. Private*, pg. 3018
ORENCO STATION SALES LLC—See RAK Development Company; *U.S. Private*, pg. 3349
PANHANDLE BUILDERS & EXCAVATING INC.; *U.S. Private*, pg. 3086
PARAMOUNT HOMES LLC; *U.S. Private*, pg. 3093
PARDEE HOMES—See Tri Pointe Homes, Inc.; *U.S. Public*, pg. 2188
PARKSIDE TOWNHOMES, LLC—See Goff Capital, Inc.; *U.S. Private*, pg. 1726
PARK SQUARE ENTERPRISES INC.; *U.S. Private*, pg. 3097
PBS CONSTRUCTION INC.; *U.S. Private*, pg. 3119
PEACHTREE COMMUNITIES, LLC—See Century Communities, Inc.; *U.S. Public*, pg. 475
PENNSYLVANIA RESOURCES CORP.; *U.S. Private*, pg. 3137
PENNYWORTH HOMES INCORPORATED; *U.S. Private*, pg. 3138
PERRY HOMES INC.; *U.S. Private*, pg. 3154
PIERSON-GIBBS HOMES INC.; *U.S. Private*, pg. 3179
PINNACLE MOUNTAIN HOMES, INC.; *U.S. Private*, pg. 3185
PINN BROTHERS CONSTRUCTION; *U.S. Private*, pg. 3184
PIONEER HOMES, INC.; *U.S. Private*, pg. 3187
PLANNED COMMUNITY DEVELOPERS LTD; *U.S. Private*, pg. 3196
PN HOFFMAN INC.; *U.S. Private*, pg. 3219
PNW CASCADIAN COMPANY, L.L.C.—See Brookfield Corporation; *Int'l*, pg. 1183
POINTE GROUP LTD.; *U.S. Private*, pg. 3222
PONDS & SONS CONSTRUCTION COMPANY, INC.; *U.S. Private*, pg. 3227
PORTSIDE BUILDERS, INC.; *U.S. Private*, pg. 3233
PRATT CONSTRUCTION INCORPORATED; *U.S. Private*, pg. 3243
PREMIER DESIGN HOMES INC.; *U.S. Private*, pg. 3250
PROMOTORA Y DESARROLLADORA DE CENTROS COMERCIALES, S. A. DE C. V.—See Consorcio ARA, S.A.B. de C.V.; *Int'l*, pg. 1771
THE PROVIDENCE GROUP OF GEORGIA, L.L.C.—See Green Brick Partners, Inc.; *U.S. Public*, pg. 963
PROVIDENCE LUXURY HOMES, L.L.C.—See Green Brick Partners, Inc.; *U.S. Public*, pg. 963
PSI PROFESSIONAL SERVICE INDUSTRIES INC; *U.S. Private*, pg. 3297
PULTE HOME COMPANY, LLC—See PulteGroup, Inc.; *U.S. Public*, pg. 1737
PULTE HOMES - CARY—See PulteGroup, Inc.; *U.S. Public*, pg. 1737
PULTE HOMES OF MICHIGAN, LLC—See PulteGroup, Inc.; *U.S. Public*, pg. 1737
PULTE HOMES OF PA, LIMITED PARTNERSHIP—See PulteGroup, Inc.; *U.S. Public*, pg. 1737
PULTE HOMES - SOUTHWEST FLORIDA—See PulteGroup, Inc.; *U.S. Public*, pg. 1737
PULTE HOMES - ST. LOUIS—See PulteGroup, Inc.; *U.S. Public*, pg. 1737
PULTE HOMES - TAMPA—See PulteGroup, Inc.; *U.S. Public*, pg. 1737
PULTE HOMES - WASHINGTON, DC—See PulteGroup, Inc.; *U.S. Public*, pg. 1737
PURCELL CO., INC.; *U.S. Private*, pg. 3304
PWI CONSTRUCTION INC.; *U.S. Private*, pg. 3308
QUALITY ADVANTAGE HOME PRODUCTS, INC.—See West Shore Window & Door, Inc.; *U.S. Private*, pg. 4487
RAINBOW DESIGN BUILDERS, INC.; *U.S. Private*, pg. 3347
RAK DEVELOPMENT COMPANY; *U.S. Private*, pg. 3349
RAMSEY & WALKER, LLC; *U.S. Private*, pg. 3352
RAN-MAR INC.; *U.S. Private*, pg. 3352
RAY M. WRIGHT INC.; *U.S. Private*, pg. 3358
RENTENBACH CONSTRUCTORS INC.—See The Christman Company Inc.; *U.S. Private*, pg. 4009
REPCONSTRICKLAND, INC.—See EMCOR Group, Inc.; *U.S. Public*, pg. 738
RICHARD SMYKAL INCORPORATED; *U.S. Private*, pg. 3428
RICHARDSON HOUSING GROUP INC.; *U.S. Private*, pg. 3429
RICK BURNSTEAD CONSTRUCTION LLC—See Burnstead Construction Company; *U.S. Private*, pg. 691
RINGLAND CONSTRUCTION INC.; *U.S. Private*, pg. 3438
RJM BUILDERS INCORPORATED; *U.S. Private*, pg. 3449
ROBUCK HOMES; *U.S. Private*, pg. 3463
ROHE & WRIGHT BUILDERS, INC.; *U.S. Private*, pg. 3472
ROYAL AMERICAN CONSTRUCTION—See Peoples First Properties Inc.; *U.S. Private*, pg. 3142
ROYAL CORINTHIAN HOMES INC.; *U.S. Private*, pg. 3492
RPM DEVELOPMENT GROUP; *U.S. Private*, pg. 3495
THE RYLAND CORPORATION—See Lennar Corporation; *U.S. Public*, pg. 1306
S&A CUSTOM BUILT HOMES INC.; *U.S. Private*, pg. 3512
SAM RODGERS PROPERTIES, INC.; *U.S. Private*, pg. 3536
SANDERS & ASSOCIATES CUSTOM BUILDERS

INC.—See Highland Homes Ltd.; *U.S. Private*, pg. 1938
SASA BROTHERS, INC.; *U.S. Private*, pg. 3552
SCOTT FELDER HOMES, LLC—See BR Homebuilding Group, L.P.; *U.S. Private*, pg. 630
SCROGGS & GRIZZEL CONTRACTING, INC.; *U.S. Private*, pg. 3580
SEATTLE CEDAR HOMES—See Lindal Cedar Homes, Inc.; *U.S. Private*, pg. 2459
SEDA CONSTRUCTION COMPANY INC.; *U.S. Private*, pg. 3597
SEH DESIGN BUILD INC.—See Short Elliott Hendrickson Inc.; *U.S. Private*, pg. 3642
SELECTBUILD CONSTRUCTION, INC.—See Builders FirstSource, Inc.; *U.S. Public*, pg. 410
SHARBELL DEVELOPMENT CORP.; *U.S. Private*, pg. 3625
SHARP RESIDENTIAL, LLC—See Toll Brothers, Inc.; *U.S. Public*, pg. 2162
SHEA HOMES LIMITED PARTNERSHIP—See J.F. Shea Co., Inc.; *U.S. Private*, pg. 2164
SHUGART ENTERPRISES LLC; *U.S. Private*, pg. 3644
SKOGMAN CONSTRUCTION COMPANY OF IOWA INC.; *U.S. Private*, pg. 3683
S & L CONTRACTING INC.—See Strait & Lamp Lumber Co. Inc.; *U.S. Private*, pg. 3833
SNAVELY DEVELOPMENT COMPANY; *U.S. Private*, pg. 3700
SOUERS CONSTRUCTION INC.; *U.S. Private*, pg. 3716
SOUTHERN CRAFTED HOMES, INC.; *U.S. Private*, pg. 3730
SOUTHGATE HOMES - SUBURBAN LIVING, LLC—See Green Brick Partners, Inc.; *U.S. Public*, pg. 963
SOVEREIGN HOMES, LLC—See Berkshire Hathaway Inc.; *U.S. Public*, pg. 304
SPANISH TRAILS ASSOCIATES LP; *U.S. Private*, pg. 3745
SPROUT TINY HOMES, INC.; *U.S. Public*, pg. 1920
SPRUCE CREEK DEVELOPMENT CO. OF OCALA; *U.S. Private*, pg. 3765
STANDARD PACIFIC OF THE CAROLINAS, LLC—See Lennar Corporation; *U.S. Public*, pg. 1305
STANLEY MARTIN COMPANIES INC.; *U.S. Private*, pg. 3783
STANLEY MARTIN HOLDINGS, LLC—See Daiwa House Industry Co., Ltd.; *Int'l*, pg. 1947
S.T. BUNN CONSTRUCTION COMPANY; *U.S. Private*, pg. 3519
ST. LAWRENCE HOMES INC.; *U.S. Private*, pg. 3772
STOCK CONSTRUCTION—See Stock Development, LLC; *U.S. Private*, pg. 3814
STRATUS BUILDING SOLUTIONS; *U.S. Private*, pg. 3837
STREETMAN HOMES CORP.—See Lennar Corporation; *U.S. Public*, pg. 1305
STRUCTURA INC.; *U.S. Private*, pg. 3841
STRUEVER BROS. ECCLES & ROUSE INC.; *U.S. Private*, pg. 3842
SUMMIT CONSTRUCTION CORP.; *U.S. Private*, pg. 3854
SUN PLAZA HOME CO., LTD.—See Iida Group Holdings Co., Ltd.; *Int'l*, pg. 3607
SUNRISE CONSTRUCTION INC.; *U.S. Private*, pg. 3869
SUNRISE HOMES; *U.S. Private*, pg. 3870
SUPERFLOORS INC.; *U.S. Private*, pg. 3875
TAMPA LENNAR DIVISION—See Lennar Corporation; *U.S. Public*, pg. 1306
TANGLIN PLACE DEVELOPMENT PTE LTD—See Allgreen Properties Ltd.; *Int'l*, pg. 338
TAYLOR MORRISON, INC.—See Brookfield Corporation; *Int'l*, pg. 1183
TAYLOR MORRISON OF CALIFORNIA, LLC—See Brookfield Corporation; *Int'l*, pg. 1183
TCS CONTRACTING CORPORATION; *U.S. Private*, pg. 3943
TDG INC.; *U.S. Private*, pg. 3944
TENDON SYSTEMS, LLC—See Commercial Metals Company; *U.S. Public*, pg. 547
TERRAMOR HOMES, INC.—See D.R. Horton, Inc.; *U.S. Public*, pg. 620
TETON HERITAGE BUILDERS INC.; *U.S. Private*, pg. 3973
THOMPSON REALTY CORPORATION—See The Thompson Company; *U.S. Private*, pg. 4126
TIMOTHY F. PASCH INC.; *U.S. Private*, pg. 4173
TIVOLI HOMES OF SARASOTA; *U.S. Private*, pg. 4177
T. JERULLE CONSTRUCTION, LLC; *U.S. Private*, pg. 3911
T.K. CONSTRUCTORS INC.; *U.S. Private*, pg. 3912
TOUEI FUJIYOSHI CONSTRUCTION CORPORATION—See Iida Group Holdings Co., Ltd.; *Int'l*, pg. 3607
TOUEI HOME SERVICE CORPORATION—See Iida Group Holdings Co., Ltd.; *Int'l*, pg. 3607
TRADE MARK CONSTRUCTION, INC.—See Chastain Construction Inc.; *U.S. Private*, pg. 860
TREMONT HOMES INC.; *U.S. Private*, pg. 4218
TRENDMAKER HOMES, INC.—See Tri Pointe Homes, Inc.; *U.S. Public*, pg. 2188
TRI POINTE HOMES, INC.; *U.S. Public*, pg. 2188
T.W. LEWIS COMPANY INC.; *U.S. Private*, pg. 3912
TYROC CONSTRUCTION, LLC—See Blunt Enterprises LLC; *U.S. Private*, pg. 600
UNIFIED HOUSING FOUNDATION, INC.; *U.S. Private*, pg. 4282

UNITED BILT HOMES INCORPORATED; *U.S. Private*, pg. 4288
U.S. HOME OF ARIZONA CONSTRUCTION CO.—See Lennar Corporation; *U.S. Public*, pg. 1307
VALENCIA AT DORAL, LLC—See Lennar Corporation; *U.S. Public*, pg. 1307
VAN'S LUMBER & CUSTOM BUILDERS; *U.S. Private*, pg. 4341
THE VESTCOR COMPANIES; *U.S. Private*, pg. 4130
VICTORY HOUSING, INC.; *U.S. Private*, pg. 4378
VILLAGE HOMES OF COLORADO, INC.—See Brookfield Corporation; *Int'l*, pg. 1183
VINEYARDS DEVELOPMENT CORP.; *U.S. Private*, pg. 4385
VOLK CONSTRUCTION COMPANY—See Kennedy Associates/Architects, Inc.; *U.S. Private*, pg. 2284
WATERMARKE HOMES LLC; *U.S. Private*, pg. 4454
WATERSIDE BUILDERS INC.; *U.S. Private*, pg. 4454
W.C. & A.N. MILLER COMPANIES; *U.S. Private*, pg. 4419
WCI COMMUNITIES, INC.—See Lennar Corporation; *U.S. Public*, pg. 1307
WEB CONSTRUCTION CO.; *U.S. Private*, pg. 4463
WESSELN CONSTRUCTION CO., INC.; *U.S. Private*, pg. 4483
WESTWATER CONSTRUCTION, INC.; *U.S. Private*, pg. 4501
WEXFORD HOMES INC.—See The Longford Group, Inc.; *U.S. Private*, pg. 4072
WHITE DEVELOPMENT CORP.—See R.H. White Companies Inc.; *U.S. Private*, pg. 3336
WILLIAM RYAN HOMES, INC.; *U.S. Private*, pg. 4525
WILLIAMS SCOTSMAN MEXICO S. DE R. L. DE C.V.—See WillScot Mobile Mini Holdings Corp.; *U.S. Public*, pg. 2372
WINCHESTER HOMES, INC.—See Tri Pointe Homes, Inc.; *U.S. Public*, pg. 2188
WINDWARD BUILDERS INC.; *U.S. Private*, pg. 4539
WINMARK HOMES INC.—See D.G. Jenkins Development Corp.; *U.S. Private*, pg. 1142
WINSTON-JAMES DEVELOPMENT, INC.; *U.S. Private*, pg. 4544
WM GREEN SQUAD, LLC—See Waste Management, Inc.; *U.S. Public*, pg. 2333
WOOLDRIDGE CONSTRUCTION OF PENNSYLVANIA INC.—See Wooldridge Construction Co., Inc.; *U.S. Private*, pg. 4562
WORTHGROUP MASTERBUILDERS, INC.; *U.S. Private*, pg. 4570
YINGST HOMES INC.; *U.S. Private*, pg. 4589
ZETA COMMUNITIES; *U.S. Private*, pg. 4602
ZONKO BUILDERS INC.; *U.S. Private*, pg. 4608

236116 — NEW MULTIFAMILY HOUSING CONSTRUCTION (EXCEPT FOR-SALE BUILDERS)

8990 HOUSING DEVELOPMENT CORP.—See 8990 Holdings, Inc.; *Int'l*, pg. 15
908 DEVELOPMENT GROUP; *U.S. Private*, pg. 17
AB BUILDERS GROUP LTD.; *Int'l*, pg. 39
A.G. SPANOS COMPANIES; *U.S. Private*, pg. 25
A.G. SPANOS CONSTRUCTION—See A.G. Spanos Companies; *U.S. Private*, pg. 25
AHC LIMITED; *Int'l*, pg. 222
ALAN HICKINBOTHAM PTY. LTD.; *Int'l*, pg. 290
AL JABER BUILDING L.L.C.—See Al Jaber Group; *Int'l*, pg. 279
ALMIRA DEVELOPMENT PTE LTD—See Hong Lai Huat Group Limited; *Int'l*, pg. 3467
ALTMAN CONTRACTORS, INC.—See Hilton Grand Vacations Inc.; *U.S. Public*, pg. 1040
ALTMAN DEVELOPMENT CORPORATION—See Hilton Grand Vacations Inc.; *U.S. Public*, pg. 1040
ANANDA DEVELOPMENT PUBLIC COMPANY LIMITED; *Int'l*, pg. 447
ANTRIM CONSTRUCTION COMPANY LTD; *Int'l*, pg. 485
APARTAMENTUL SA; *Int'l*, pg. 501
AQRS THE BUILDING COMPANY SDN. BHD.—See Gabungan AQRS Berhad; *Int'l*, pg. 2868
ARC OVERLAND PARK LLC—See Welltower Inc.; *U.S. Public*, pg. 2347
ARX SA—See Becton, Dickinson & Company; *U.S. Public*, pg. 288
ARX SAS—See Becton, Dickinson & Company; *U.S. Public*, pg. 288
ASCOT CORP.; *Int'l*, pg. 603
ASHCO EXTERIORS INC.; *U.S. Private*, pg. 349
ASPEN GROUP LTD.; *Int'l*, pg. 629
ASPIRE DEFENCE CAPITAL WORKS JV—See KBR, Inc.; *U.S. Public*, pg. 1215
ATHENA CONSTRUCTIONS LIMITED; *Int'l*, pg. 669
AVALON PARK—See Avalon Park Group Management, Inc.; *U.S. Public*, pg. 403
AVENIDA NAPERVILLE PARTNERS LLC—See Safehold Inc.; *U.S. Public*, pg. 1834
BANCROFT CONSTRUCTION COMPANY; *U.S. Private*, pg. 464

BDB LAND SDN. BHD.—See Bina Darulaman Berhad; *Int'l*, pg. 1032
BEACON COMMUNITIES LLC; *U.S. Private*, pg. 504
BEAVER BUILDERS, INC.; *U.S. Public*, pg. 509
BEAZER-INSPIRADA LLC—See Beazer Homes USA, Inc.; *U.S. Public*, pg. 288
BEE LINE CONSTRUCTION L.L.C.—See Bee Line, Inc.; *U.S. Public*, pg. 512
BENCHMARK CONTRACTORS, INC.—See Morley Builders; *Int'l*, pg. 2785
BGC (AUSTRALIA) PTY. LTD.; *Int'l*, pg. 1007
BH CAPITAL PARTNERS, LLC; *U.S. Private*, pg. 549
BIEN-ZENKER GMBH—See Equistone Partners Europe Limited; *Int'l*, pg. 2486
BINA DARULAMAN BERHAD; *Int'l*, pg. 1032
BINA PURI (B) SDN BHD—See Bina Puri Holdings Bhd; *Int'l*, pg. 1032
BINA PURI CONSTRUCTION SDN BHD—See Bina Puri Holdings Bhd; *Int'l*, pg. 1032
BINA PURI SDN BHD—See Bina Puri Holdings Bhd; *Int'l*, pg. 1032
BITUMINOUS ROADWAYS, INC. - INVER GROVE HEIGHTS PLANT—See Bituminous Roadways, Inc.; *U.S. Private*, pg. 567
BITUMINOUS ROADWAYS, INC. - MINNEAPOLIS PLANT—See Bituminous Roadways, Inc.; *U.S. Private*, pg. 567
BITUMINOUS ROADWAYS, INC. - SHAKOPEE PLANT—See Bituminous Roadways, Inc.; *U.S. Private*, pg. 567
BONEI HATICHON CIVIL ENGINEERING & INFRASTRUCTURES LTD.; *Int'l*, pg. 1106
BORAN CRAIG BARBER ENGEL CONSTRUCTION CO., INC.; *U.S. Private*, pg. 617
BOXABL INC.; *U.S. Private*, pg. 626
BOZZUTO CONSTRUCTION COMPANY—See The Bozzuto Group; *U.S. Private*, pg. 3999
BRVENIK A.D.; *Int'l*, pg. 1201
CALHOUN BUILDERS INC.; *U.S. Private*, pg. 717
CALIFORNIA PACIFIC HOMES INC.; *U.S. Private*, pg. 720
CAPELLI SA; *Int'l*, pg. 1303
CB JENI APPLES CROSSING, LLC—See Green Brick Partners, Inc.; *U.S. Public*, pg. 962
CB JENI IRON HORSE, LLC—See Green Brick Partners, Inc.; *U.S. Public*, pg. 962
CB JENI RIDGE VIEW VILLAS, LLC—See Green Brick Partners, Inc.; *U.S. Public*, pg. 962
CB JENI TERRACES AT LAS COLINAS, LLC—See Green Brick Partners, Inc.; *U.S. Public*, pg. 962
CB JENI VISTA DEL LAGO, LLC—See Green Brick Partners, Inc.; *U.S. Public*, pg. 962
CEL DEVELOPMENT PTE. LTD.—See Chip Eng Seng Corporation Ltd.; *Int'l*, pg. 1572
CES ENGINEERING & CONSTRUCTION PTE. LTD—See Chip Eng Seng Corporation Ltd.; *Int'l*, pg. 1572
C.F. JORDAN RESIDENTIAL INCORPORATED—See C.F. Jordan L.P.; *U.S. Private*, pg. 707
CHINA RAILWAY REAL ESTATE GROUP CO LTD—See China Railway Group Limited; *Int'l*, pg. 1543
CLARIDGE HOMES INC.; *Int'l*, pg. 1648
CLARK REALTY BUILDERS LLC; *U.S. Private*, pg. 913
COLE CAPITAL CORPORATION—See Realty Income Corporation; *U.S. Public*, pg. 1768
COMINCO S.A.; *Int'l*, pg. 1713
COMMERCIAL CONSTRUCTION SERVICES, INC.; *U.S. Private*, pg. 983
CONCAS SA; *Int'l*, pg. 1763
CONCIVIA SA; *Int'l*, pg. 1764
CONDOR TCM SA; *Int'l*, pg. 1766
CONLOC S.A.; *Int'l*, pg. 1768
CONSTREXIM NO. 8 INVESTMENT & CONSTRUCTION JSC; *Int'l*, pg. 1776
CONSTRUCTII BIHOR SA; *Int'l*, pg. 1777
CONSTRUTORA TENDA S.A.; *Int'l*, pg. 1778
CORNERSTONE DEVELOPERS, INC.; *U.S. Private*, pg. 1052
CPI BAUTRAGER UND IMMOBILIENVERWALTUNG GMBH—See CPI Immobilien AG; *Int'l*, pg. 1825
CP OF BOZEMAN, INC.; *U.S. Private*, pg. 1079
DAIDO LIFE SERVICE CO., LTD.—See Daido Steel Co., Ltd.; *Int'l*, pg. 1922
DAITO CONSTRUCTION CO., LTD.—See Daito Trust Construction Co., Ltd.; *Int'l*, pg. 1943
DALE ALCOCK HOMES PTY. LTD.; *Int'l*, pg. 1950
DA-LI DEVELOPMENT CO., LTD.; *Int'l*, pg. 1902
DANYA CEBUS LTD.—See Africa Israel Investments Ltd.; *Int'l*, pg. 190
DAVIS DEVELOPMENT, INC.; *U.S. Private*, pg. 1173
D&B CONSTRUCTION GROUP; *U.S. Private*, pg. 1136
DIPLOMA PROPERTIES PTY. LTD.—See Diploma Group Limited; *Int'l*, pg. 2128
DIRHAM CONSTRUCTION LTD; *Int'l*, pg. 2130
DKLS DEVELOPMENT SDN. BHD.—See DKLS Industries Berhad; *Int'l*, pg. 2139
DLF HOME DEVELOPERS LIMITED—See DLF Limited; *Int'l*, pg. 2141
D.R. HORTON, INC. - FRESNO—See D.R. Horton, Inc.; *U.S. Public*, pg. 619

N.A.I.C.S. INDEX

236117 — NEW HOUSING FOR-SAL...

DUPLEX SA; *Int'l*, pg. 2227
E-CITY BIOSCOPE ENTERTAINMENT PVT LTD—See Essel Corporate Resources Pvt. Ltd.; *Int'l*, pg. 2509
ECO WORLD-BALLYMORE EMBASSY GARDENS COMPANY LIMITED—See Eco World International Berhad; *Int'l*, pg. 2293
ECO WORLD-BALLYMORE LONDON CITY ISLAND COMPANY LIMITED—See Eco World International Berhad; *Int'l*, pg. 2293
EDEN HOUSING, INC.; *U.S. Private*, pg. 1333
EDGEWATER COMMERCIAL CONSTRUCTION, INC.; *U.S. Private*, pg. 1335
ELPRO ESTATES LIMITED—See Elpro International Ltd.; *Int'l*, pg. 2369
EMAAR LEBANON S.A.—See Emaar Properties PJSC; *Int'l*, pg. 2372
EMICO DEVELOPMENT SDN. BHD.—See Emico Holdings Berhad; *Int'l*, pg. 2380
ENVIRONMENTAL DESIGN & CONSTRUCTION, LLC; *U.S. Private*, pg. 1407
EPOCH PROPERTIES INC.; *U.S. Private*, pg. 1414
THE EPSTEN GROUP, INC.; *U.S. Private*, pg. 4026
ERC PROPERTIES INC.; *U.S. Private*, pg. 1417
ERICKSON BUILDERS & CO.; *U.S. Private*, pg. 1419
EWE URBANISATION DIENSTLEISTUNGS GMBH—See EWE Aktiengesellschaft; *Int'l*, pg. 2575
FC CONSTRUCTION SERVICES; *U.S. Private*, pg. 1485
FERNBROOK HOMES; *Int'l*, pg. 2639
FINCANTIERI INFRASTRUCTURE OPERE MARITTIME S.P.A.—See Cassa Depositi e Prestiti S.p.A.; *Int'l*, pg. 1355
FIREWATCH CONTRACTING OF FLORIDA LLC; *U.S. Private*, pg. 1512
FIRST-CORPORATION INC.; *Int'l*, pg. 2688
FIRST FLORIDA BUILDING CORP.; *U.S. Private*, pg. 1519
FIT CO., LTD.; *Int'l*, pg. 2695
FLUOR-SKM IRON ORE JOINT VENTURE—See Fluor Corporation; *U.S. Public*, pg. 858
FOUNDING CONSTRUCTION DEVELOPMENT CO., LTD.; *Int'l*, pg. 2753
FOWLER CUSTOM HOMES; *U.S. Private*, pg. 1583
GABUNGAN STRATEGIK SDN. BHD.—See Gabungan AQRS Berhad; *Int'l*, pg. 2868
GALLOPS ENTERPRISE LIMITED; *Int'l*, pg. 2875
GARANTI KOZA CONSTRUCTION INDUSTRY AND COMMERCE CO. INC.—See Garanti Koza Insaat Sanayi ve Ticaret A.S.; *Int'l*, pg. 2883
GIKEN AMERICA CORPORATION—See GIKEN Ltd.; *Int'l*, pg. 2972
GIKEN SEKO CO., LTD.—See GIKEN Ltd.; *Int'l*, pg. 2972
GOSNELL BUILDERS—See Pointe Group Ltd.; *U.S. Private*, pg. 3222
GPS GMBH & CO KG—See Aliaxis S.A./N.V.; *Int'l*, pg. 324
GRADNJA GP A.D.; *Int'l*, pg. 3050
GRANDES INC.; *Int'l*, pg. 3057
GRANIT AD; *Int'l*, pg. 3059
GREEN BUILDERS, INC.; *U.S. Private*, pg. 1772
GROUP FIVE HOUSING (PROPRIETARY) LIMITED—See Group Five Limited; *Int'l*, pg. 3089
GROUP FIVE LIMITED; *Int'l*, pg. 3088
GUANGDONG GIANT LEAP CONSTRUCTION CO., LTD.—See Country Garden Holdings Company Limited; *Int'l*, pg. 1818
GUANGDONG HUAJIAN ENTERPRISE GROUP CO., LTD.—See Guangdong Rising Assets Management Co., Ltd.; *Int'l*, pg. 3159
GZP DOM A.D.; *Int'l*, pg. 3191
HARBOR CUSTOM DEVELOPMENT, INC.; *U.S. Public*, pg. 984
HARKINS BUILDERS, INC.—See Harkins Builders, Inc.; *U.S. Private*, pg. 1864
HARMONY DEVELOPMENT CO., LLC; *U.S. Private*, pg. 1866
HATHAWAY CONSTRUCTION COMPANY, INC.; *U.S. Private*, pg. 1879
HEIJMANS BURGH HAAMSTEDE B.V.—See Heijmans N.V.; *Int'l*, pg. 3322
HEIJMANS BURGH HAAMSTEDE B.V.—See Heijmans N.V.; *Int'l*, pg. 3323
HEIJMANS WONINGBOUW B.V.—See Heijmans N.V.; *Int'l*, pg. 3322
HEIJMANS WONINGBOUW B.V.—See Heijmans N.V.; *Int'l*, pg. 3322
HEIJMANS WONINGBOUW B.V.—See Heijmans N.V.; *Int'l*, pg. 3323
HELICAL BAR (WALES) LTD—See Helical Plc; *Int'l*, pg. 3330
HERITAGE CONSTRUCTION CO. INC.; *U.S. Private*, pg. 1922
HM INWEST S.A.; *Int'l*, pg. 3431
HONG PHAT CONSTRUCTION INVESTMENT JSC; *Int'l*, pg. 3469
HOTONDO BUILDING PTY. LTD.; *Int'l*, pg. 3489
HUACHENG REAL ESTATE SA; *Int'l*, pg. 3511
HUNT BUILDING COMPANY, LTD.—See Hunt Companies, Inc.; *U.S. Private*, pg. 2008

HUNZA PARADE DEVELOPMENT SDN. BHD.—See Hunza Properties Berhad; *Int'l*, pg. 3537
IBI GROUP HOLDINGS LIMITED; *Int'l*, pg. 3574
I&MJ GROSS COMPANY; *U.S. Private*, pg. 2026
INGENIEROS CIVILES ASOCIADOS MEXICO, S.A.—See Empresas ICA S.A.B. de C.V.; *Int'l*, pg. 2391
INTERSTATE CONSTRUCTION CO.; *U.S. Private*, pg. 2124
IRET - ASHLAND APARTMENTS, LLC—See Centerspace; *U.S. Public*, pg. 472
IRET - PARK MEADOWS, LLC—See Centerspace; *U.S. Public*, pg. 472
IRET - WHISPERING RIDGE APARTMENTS, LLC—See Centerspace; *U.S. Public*, pg. 472
THE JACK PARKER CORPORATION; *U.S. Private*, pg. 4058
JERRY'S HOMES INC.; *U.S. Private*, pg. 2202
JIWA REALTY SDN. BHD.—See DutaLand Berhad; *Int'l*, pg. 2235
JONES HOMES (NORTHERN) LIMITED—See Emerson Developments (Holdings) Limited; *Int'l*, pg. 2379
JONES HOMES (SOUTHERN) LIMITED—See Emerson Developments (Holdings) Limited; *Int'l*, pg. 2380
JPI NATIONAL CONSTRUCTION INC.; *U.S. Private*, pg. 2239
KB HOME NEVADA INC.—See KB Home; *U.S. Public*, pg. 1215
KH LAND SDN. BHD.—See DutaLand Berhad; *Int'l*, pg. 2235
K. HOVNANIAN AT ASPIRE AT APRICOT GROVE PH2, LLC—See Hovnanian Enterprises, Inc.; *U.S. Public*, pg. 1058
K. HOVNANIAN GREAT WESTERN HOMES, LLC—See Hovnanian Enterprises, Inc.; *U.S. Public*, pg. 1056
K. HOVNANIAN'S COVE AT ASBURY PARK URBAN RENEWAL, LLC—See Hovnanian Enterprises, Inc.; *U.S. Public*, pg. 1060
K. HOVNANIAN'S FOUR SEASONS AT LAKES OF CANE BAY LLC—See Hovnanian Enterprises, Inc.; *U.S. Public*, pg. 1060
LAKE GEORGE VENTURES INC.—See Galesi Group; *U.S. Private*, pg. 1637
LANCASTER COUNTY TIMBER FRAMES, INC.; *U.S. Private*, pg. 2381
LAUREL RIDGE—See Reading Anthracite Company; *U.S. Private*, pg. 3366
LAVASA CORPORATION LIMITED—See Hindustan Construction Co. Ltd; *Int'l*, pg. 3399
LENNAR HOMES OF UTAH, INC.—See Lennar Corporation; *U.S. Public*, pg. 1305
LENNAR MULTIFAMILY COMMUNITIES, LLC—See Lennar Corporation; *U.S. Public*, pg. 1306
LGI HOMES - WINDMILL FARMS, LLC—See LGI Homes, Inc.; *U.S. Public*, pg. 1310
MELCARA CORP.—See Property Resources Corp.; *U.S. Private*, pg. 3285
MHT HOUSING, INC.; *U.S. Private*, pg. 2695
MICHAELS GROUP, LLC; *U.S. Private*, pg. 2699
MI HOMES OF MICHIGAN, LLC—See M/I Homes, Inc.; *U.S. Public*, pg. 1351
MI HOMES OF MINNEAPOLISST. PAUL, LLC—See M/I Homes, Inc.; *U.S. Public*, pg. 1351
MUSS DEVELOPMENT CO; *U.S. Private*, pg. 2818
NORMANDY HOMES APPLES CROSSING, LLC—See Green Brick Partners, Inc.; *U.S. Public*, pg. 962
NORMANDY HOMES EDGEWOOD, LLC—See Green Brick Partners, Inc.; *U.S. Public*, pg. 962
NORMANDY HOMES LIBERTY HILLS, LLC—See Green Brick Partners, Inc.; *U.S. Public*, pg. 962
NORTH ATLANTIC STATES REGIONAL COUNCIL OF CARPENTERS; *U.S. Private*, pg. 2942
OEVERMANN HOCHBAU GMBH—See Heijmans N.V.; *Int'l*, pg. 3323
OMNIBUILD CONSTRUCTION INC.; *U.S. Private*, pg. 3017
ONE UP CO., LTD.—See Areeya Property Public Company Limited; *Int'l*, pg. 557
OXFORD PROPERTIES, LLC; *U.S. Private*, pg. 3057
PEMBINAAN HUA YANG SDN. BHD.—See Hua Yang Berhad; *Int'l*, pg. 3510
PHILLIPS DEVELOPMENT CORP.; *U.S. Private*, pg. 3170
PHILLIPS DEVELOPMENT & REALTY, LLC; *U.S. Private*, pg. 3170
POWERS CONSTRUCTION CO., INC.; *U.S. Private*, pg. 3240
PRISKE JONES SOUTHEAST—See Priske-Jones Company; *U.S. Private*, pg. 3267
PULTE.COM, INC.—See PulteGroup, Inc.; *U.S. Public*, pg. 1738
RAKYAT HOLDINGS SDN BHD—See Bank Kerjasama Rakyat Malaysia Berhad; *Int'l*, pg. 838
REALTEX CONSTRUCTION, LLC—See Realtex Development Corporation; *U.S. Private*, pg. 3369
RENEWABLE HOLDING MANAGEMENT S.A.—See ELECTROARGES SA; *Int'l*, pg. 2353
RIACON SDN. BHD.—See Eupe Corporation Berhad; *Int'l*, pg. 2526
RIVER PARK WEST APARTMENTS OWNER, LLC—See RAIT Financial Trust; *U.S. Public*, pg. 3349
ROSSMOYNE, INC.; *U.S. Private*, pg. 3486
SCHEAR CORPORATION; *U.S. Private*, pg. 3563

SCHNEIDER HOMES INC.; *U.S. Private*, pg. 3566
SHENZHEN CHANGCHENG HUIHUA GROUP CO., LTD—See Guangdong Rising Assets Management Co., Ltd.; *Int'l*, pg. 3159
SINGH DEVELOPMENT CO. LTD.; *U.S. Private*, pg. 3670
SPLENDID PAVILION SDN BHD—See Gadang Holdings Berhad; *Int'l*, pg. 2868
STONEBROOKE ENGINEERING, INC.; *U.S. Private*, pg. 3827
T2 CONSTRUCTION, LLC—See Lennar Corporation; *U.S. Public*, pg. 1305
TAT HONG EQUIPMENT SERVICE CO., LTD.—See Affirma Capital Limited; *Int'l*, pg. 187
TAYLOR COMMERCIAL, INC.; *U.S. Private*, pg. 3937
T.H. MARSH CONSTRUCTION COMPANY; *U.S. Private*, pg. 3912
TRIMBLE DBO INFORMATION TECHNOLOGY (SHANGHAI) CO. LTD.—See Trimble, Inc.; *U.S. Public*, pg. 2192
TRIMBLE SOLUTIONS FRANCE SARL—See Trimble, Inc.; *U.S. Public*, pg. 2192
TROPHY SIGNATURE HOMES, LLC—See Green Brick Partners, Inc.; *U.S. Public*, pg. 963
TULIPA ROKYTKA S.R.O.—See Africa Israel Investments Ltd.; *Int'l*, pg. 190
TULIPA VOKOVICE S.R.O.—See Africa Israel Investments Ltd.; *Int'l*, pg. 190
TYCORE BUILT LLC.; *U.S. Public*, pg. 4267
U. DORI CONSTRUCTION LTD.—See Amos Luzon Development and Energy Group Ltd.; *Int'l*, pg. 430
WALSH CONSTRUCTION CO.; *U.S. Private*, pg. 4432
WEAVER COOKE CONSTRUCTION, LLC; *U.S. Private*, pg. 4463
WEGENBOUWMAATSCHAPPIJ J. HEIJMANS B.V.—See Heijmans N.V.; *Int'l*, pg. 3323
WEINTRAUB CONSTRUCTION CO. INC.; *U.S. Private*, pg. 4472
WESTGATE MANAGEMENT CO. INC.; *U.S. Private*, pg. 4498
WESTPORT HOMES, INC.—See D.R. Horton, Inc.; *U.S. Public*, pg. 620
WINDHAM & MCDONALD CONSTRUCTION., INC.; *U.S. Private*, pg. 4537
WODA GROUP INC.; *U.S. Private*, pg. 4553
WORTHINGTON CONSTRUCTION GROUP, INC.—See Worthington Industries, Inc.; *U.S. Public*, pg. 2382
ZMG CONSTRUCTION, INC.; *U.S. Private*, pg. 4606
ZOM FLORIDA, INC.—See ZOM Holding, Inc.; *U.S. Private*, pg. 4607

236117 — NEW HOUSING FOR-SALE BUILDERS

ABBEY PLC—See Gallagher Holdings Ltd.; *Int'l*, pg. 2873
ADMIRALS COVE ASSOCIATES LTD.; *U.S. Private*, pg. 81
AD NOBI CO., LTD.—See AISIN Corporation; *Int'l*, pg. 251
ADVANCE SYNERGY BERHAD; *Int'l*, pg. 156
A.G. SPANOS REALTY—See A.G. Spanos Companies; *U.S. Private*, pg. 26
A.G. SPANOS SECURITIES—See A.G. Spanos Companies; *U.S. Private*, pg. 26
AL JABER DELTA ENERGY SERVICES & GENERAL CONSTRUCTION—See Al Jaber Group; *Int'l*, pg. 279
AMRAPALI GROUP; *Int'l*, pg. 437
ANCHOR LAND HOLDINGS, INC.; *Int'l*, pg. 448
ANSAL HOUSING LTD; *Int'l*, pg. 477
AQUA SUN PROPERTIES; *U.S. Private*, pg. 303
ARAGON LLC.; *U.S. Private*, pg. 307
ARDEN PARK VENTURES, LLC—See Beazer Homes USA, Inc.; *U.S. Public*, pg. 287
AREEYA PROPERTY PUBLIC COMPANY LIMITED; *Int'l*, pg. 557
ATLANTIC HOUSING PARTNERS, LLLP; *U.S. Private*, pg. 373
AUSTRALIAN PORTABLE BUILDINGS PTY LIMITED—See Black Diamond Group Limited; *Int'l*, pg. 1059
AVESTA HOUSING DEVELOPMENT CORP.; *U.S. Private*, pg. 406
AVIDE DEVELOPMENTS INC.—See Co-op Atlantic; *Int'l*, pg. 1679
BAMCO CONSTRUCTION, INC.; *U.S. Private*, pg. 463
BARRATT SOUTHERN COUNTIES LIMITED—See Barratt Developments PLC; *Int'l*, pg. 868
BARRATT SOUTH WEST LIMITED—See Barratt Developments PLC; *Int'l*, pg. 868
BARRATT WEST SCOTLAND LIMITED—See Barratt Developments PLC; *Int'l*, pg. 868
BARRIER ISLAND STATION INC.; *U.S. Private*, pg. 480
BASSAC; *Int'l*, pg. 888
BDW TRADING LIMITED—See Barratt Developments PLC; *Int'l*, pg. 867
BEAZER HOMES CORP.—See Beazer Homes USA, Inc.; *U.S. Public*, pg. 287
BEAZER HOMES INDIANA, LLP—See Beazer Homes USA, Inc.; *U.S. Public*, pg. 287
BEAZER HOMES INVESTMENTS, LLC—See Beazer Homes USA, Inc.; *U.S. Public*, pg. 287

236117 — NEW HOUSING FOR-SAL...   CORPORATE AFFILIATIONS

BEAZER HOMES TEXAS, LP—See Beazer Homes USA, Inc.; *U.S. Public*, pg. 288
BEAZER SPE, LLC—See Beazer Homes USA, Inc.; *U.S. Public*, pg. 288
BELLWAY HOMES LIMITED EAST MIDLANDS—See Bellway plc; *Int'l*, pg. 967
BELLWAY HOMES LIMITED ESSEX—See Bellway plc; *Int'l*, pg. 967
BELLWAY HOMES LIMITED MANCHESTER—See Bellway plc; *Int'l*, pg. 967
BELLWAY HOMES LIMITED NORTH EAST—See Bellway plc; *Int'l*, pg. 967
BELLWAY HOMES LIMITED NORTHERN HOME COUNTIES—See Bellway plc; *Int'l*, pg. 968
BELLWAY HOMES LIMITED NORTH LONDON—See Bellway plc; *Int'l*, pg. 968
BELLWAY HOMES LIMITED NORTH WEST—See Bellway plc; *Int'l*, pg. 968
BELLWAY HOMES LIMITED SCOTLAND—See Bellway plc; *Int'l*, pg. 968
BELLWAY HOMES LIMITED SOUTH EAST—See Bellway plc; *Int'l*, pg. 968
BELLWAY HOMES LIMITED THAMES GATEWAY—See Bellway plc; *Int'l*, pg. 968
BELLWAY HOMES LIMITED WALES—See Bellway plc; *Int'l*, pg. 968
BELLWAY HOMES LIMITED WESSEX—See Bellway plc; *Int'l*, pg. 968
BELLWAY HOMES LIMITED WEST MIDLANDS—See Bellway plc; *Int'l*, pg. 968
BELLWAY HOMES LIMITED YORKSHIRE—See Bellway plc; *Int'l*, pg. 968
BELLWAY PLC; *Int'l*, pg. 967
BENKO CONSTRUCTION CO., INC.—See Zilber Ltd.; *U.S. Private*, pg. 4604
BERKS HOME DESIGN BUILD; *U.S. Private*, pg. 533
BERTRAM ASSOCIATES; *U.S. Private*, pg. 539
BIGELOW HOMES, LLC.; *U.S. Private*, pg. 555
BMCH TENNESSEE, LLC—See Century Communities, Inc.; *U.S. Public*, pg. 475
BOLOGNESI EMPREENDIMENTOS LTDA.; *Int'l*, pg. 1103
BONTERRA BUILDERS, LLC—See Brookfield Corporation; *Int'l*, pg. 1183
BOUYGUES BATIMENT ILE-DE-FRANCE—See Bouygues S.A.; *Int'l*, pg. 1121
BOYD MANAGEMENT; *U.S. Private*, pg. 627
BPTP LIMITED; *Int'l*, pg. 1133
BRIGHTON HOMES; *U.S. Private*, pg. 652
BROAD OAK HOMES LIMITED—See Barratt Developments PLC; *Int'l*, pg. 868
BROMPTON HOMES LIMITED—See Co-operative Group Limited; *Int'l*, pg. 1679
BURLAGE HOTEL ASSOCIATES LLC; *U.S. Private*, pg. 688
THE BUSH COMPANY; *U.S. Private*, pg. 4003
CABINETWERKS DESIGN STUDIO, LLC.; *U.S. Private*, pg. 711
CA IMMO GALLERIA LIEGENSCHAFTSVERWALTUNG GMBH—See Starwood Capital Group Global I, LLC; *U.S. Private*, pg. 3789
CAPE ASSOCIATES, INC.; *U.S. Private*, pg. 737
CAREAGE INC.; *U.S. Private*, pg. 752
CATSKILL-VALLEY HOMES, LLC—See Cavco Industries, Inc.; *U.S. Public*, pg. 455
CB JENI MAJESTIC GARDENS, LLC—See Green Brick Partners, Inc.; *U.S. Public*, pg. 962
CB JENI MERIDIAN AT SOUTHGATE, LLC—See Green Brick Partners, Inc.; *U.S. Public*, pg. 962
CB JENI PECAN SQUARE, LLC—See Green Brick Partners, Inc.; *U.S. Public*, pg. 962
CB JENI RIVERSET, LLC—See Green Brick Partners, Inc.; *U.S. Public*, pg. 962
CB JENI TROPHY CLUB, LLC—See Green Brick Partners, Inc.; *U.S. Public*, pg. 962
CB JENI TWIN CREEKS, LLC—See Green Brick Partners, Inc.; *U.S. Public*, pg. 962
CEDAR WOODS PROPERTIES LIMITED; *Int'l*, pg. 1388
CENTERLINE HOMES, INC.; *U.S. Private*, pg. 816
CHATEAU PROPERTIES—See Carpionato Group LLC; *U.S. Private*, pg. 771
COLEMAN-TOLL LIMITED PARTNERSHIP—See Toll Brothers, Inc.; *U.S. Public*, pg. 2161
CONCORD MILLS LP—See Simon Property Group, Inc.; *U.S. Public*, pg. 1882
CONNOR & GASKINS UNLIMITED LLC; *U.S. Private*, pg. 1018
CONSORCIO ARA, S.A.B. DE C.V.; *Int'l*, pg. 1771
COSMOS MORE CO., LTD.—See Daiwa House Industry Co., Ltd.; *Int'l*, pg. 1945
CPD S.A.; *Int'l*, pg. 1824
CREST NICHOLSON (CHILTERN) LTD.—See Crest Nicholson PLC; *Int'l*, pg. 1840
CREST NICHOLSON (EASTERN) LTD.—See Crest Nicholson PLC; *Int'l*, pg. 1840
CREST NICHOLSON PLC; *Int'l*, pg. 1840
CREST NICHOLSON (SOUTH) LTD.—See Crest Nicholson PLC; *Int'l*, pg. 1840
CREST NICHOLSON (SOUTH WEST) LTD.—See Crest Nicholson PLC; *Int'l*, pg. 1840
CREST PARTNERSHIP HOMES LTD.—See Crest Nicholson PLC; *Int'l*, pg. 1841
CRESTVIEW BUILDERS, INC.; *U.S. Private*, pg. 1097
CROWN COMMUNITIES, INC.—See D.R. Horton, Inc.; *U.S. Public*, pg. 619
DAHN CORPORATION; *U.S. Private*, pg. 1144
DAVID WILSON HOMES (NORTH MIDLANDS) LIMITED—See Barratt Developments PLC; *Int'l*, pg. 868
DAVID WILSON HOMES (SOUTHERN) LIMITED—See Barratt Developments PLC; *Int'l*, pg. 868
DAVID WILSON HOMES (SOUTH MIDLANDS) LIMITED—See Barratt Developments PLC; *Int'l*, pg. 868
DAVID WILSON HOMES YORKSHIRE LIMITED—See Barratt Developments PLC; *Int'l*, pg. 868
DAVIS & SONS CONSTRUCTION CO. LLC; *U.S. Private*, pg. 1172
DAYTONA HOMES; *Int'l*, pg. 1985
DDR BUILDERS, LLC; *U.S. Private*, pg. 1181
DELANT CONSTRUCTION CO.; *U.S. Private*, pg. 1193
DELTONA MARKETING CORP.—See The Deltona Corporation; *U.S. Private*, pg. 4020
DEL WEBB CORPORATION—See PulteGroup, Inc.; *U.S. Public*, pg. 1737
DEVINE LIMITED—See ACS, Actividades de Construccion y Servicios, S.A.; *Int'l*, pg. 113
DHI COMMUNITIES, INC.—See D.R. Horton, Inc.; *U.S. Public*, pg. 619
DHI TITLE OF NEVADA, INC.—See D.R. Horton, Inc.; *U.S. Public*, pg. 619
DHI TITLE OF OHIO, LLC—See D.R. Horton, Inc.; *U.S. Public*, pg. 619
DINE S.A.B. DE C.V.; *Int'l*, pg. 2127
DISCOVERY HOMES; *U.S. Private*, pg. 1238
D. L. FALK CONSTRUCTION INC.; *U.S. Private*, pg. 1140
DNT CONSTRUCTION, LLC.; *U.S. Private*, pg. 1249
DRH CONSTRUCTION, INC.—See D.R. Horton, Inc.; *U.S. Public*, pg. 620
D.R. HORTON, INC.; *U.S. Public*, pg. 619
D.R. HORTON, INC—See D.R. Horton, Inc.; *U.S. Public*, pg. 619
D.R. HORTON - IOWA, LLC—See D.R. Horton, Inc.; *U.S. Public*, pg. 619
DUNHILL HOMES, LLC; *U.S. Private*, pg. 1289
EASTWARD COMPANIES, INC.; *U.S. Private*, pg. 1322
ECOGROUP INC.; *U.S. Private*, pg. 1329
EDGEWATER BEACH RESORT MANAGEMENT, INC.; *U.S. Private*, pg. 1334
EDL PROPERTIES LIMITED—See Empee Distilleries Limited; *Int'l*, pg. 2385
EDWARD ROSE BUILDING COMPANY—See Edward Rose Company; *U.S. Private*, pg. 1341
EJM DEVELOPMENT CO.; *U.S. Private*, pg. 1348
ELLIOTT HOMES INC.; *U.S. Private*, pg. 1364
ENCLAVE AT PINE GROVE, LLC—See Century Communities, Inc.; *U.S. Public*, pg. 475
ESSEX BUILDERS CORP.; *U.S. Private*, pg. 1427
ESTEEM GLORY SDN. BHD.—See Eupe Corporation Berhad; *Int'l*, pg. 2526
FLETCHER RESIDENTIAL LIMITED—See Fletcher Building Limited; *Int'l*, pg. 2700
FOREST CITY RESIDENTIAL DEVELOPMENT INC.—See Brookfield Corporation; *Int'l*, pg. 1187
FORTUNE HOMES OF TALLAHASSEE INC.; *U.S. Private*, pg. 1577
FRED TEITELBAUM CONSTRUCTION CO. INC.; *U.S. Private*, pg. 1601
GADANG ENGINEERING (M) SDN BHD.—See Gadang Holdings Berhad; *Int'l*, pg. 2868
GLADEDALE HOLDINGS PLC; *Int'l*, pg. 2987
GLENN C BARBER & ASOC.; *U.S. Private*, pg. 1710
GLOBAL LINKS CORP.; *U.S. Public*, pg. 942
GLORIOUS PROPERTY HOLDINGS LTD.; *Int'l*, pg. 3008
GOLDEN ISLES CUSTOM HOMES LLC; *U.S. Private*, pg. 1732
GOODALL HOMES & COMMUNITIES—See Berkshire Hathaway Inc.; *U.S. Public*, pg. 304
GOODLAND GROUP LIMITED; *Int'l*, pg. 3040
GOOD TIME LIVING CO. LTD.—See Daiwa Securities Group Inc.; *Int'l*, pg. 1949
GOUGH INC.; *U.S. Private*, pg. 1745
GPG CONSTRUCTION & MODULAR HOMES, LLC.; *U.S. Private*, pg. 1748
THE GRAHAM COMPANIES INC.; *U.S. Private*, pg. 4035
GREYSTAR DEVELOPMENT & CONSTRUCTION, L.P.—See Greystar Real Estate Partners, LLC; *U.S. Private*, pg. 1785
GT CONTRACTING CORP; *U.S. Private*, pg. 1801
HAJIME CONSTRUCTION CO., LTD.—See Iida Group Holdings Co., Ltd.; *Int'l*, pg. 3607
HARKINS BUILDERS, INC.; *U.S. Private*, pg. 1864
HARKINS BUILDERS, INC. VIRGINIA—See Harkins Builders, Inc.; *U.S. Private*, pg. 1864
HATHAWAY DEVELOPMENT CORP.; *U.S. Private*, pg. 1879
HILLS; *U.S. Private*, pg. 1946
HIMALAYA HOMES INC.; *U.S. Private*, pg. 1948
HOLLADAY CORPORATION; *U.S. Private*, pg. 1963
HOMES BY TOWNE, A ZILBER COMPANY, LLC—See Zilber Ltd.; *U.S. Private*, pg. 4604
HOMEWOOD CORPORATION; *U.S. Private*, pg. 1975
INSPIRE HOME LOANS, INC.—See Century Communities, Inc.; *U.S. Public*, pg. 475
JACKSONVILLE TBI REALTY, LLC—See Toll Brothers, Inc.; *U.S. Public*, pg. 2162
JAMES F. KNOTT REALITY GROUP; *U.S. Private*, pg. 2183
JOHN F BUCHAN HOMES; *U.S. Private*, pg. 2221
JOHN WIELAND HOMES & NEIGHBORHOODS, INC.—See PulteGroup, Inc.; *U.S. Public*, pg. 1737
KB HOME CALIFORNIA LLC—See KB Home; *U.S. Public*, pg. 1215
KB HOME PHOENIX INC.—See KB Home; *U.S. Public*, pg. 1215
KB HOME RALEIGH-DURHAM INC.—See KB Home; *U.S. Public*, pg. 1215
KB HOME SACRAMENTO INC.—See KB Home; *U.S. Public*, pg. 1215
KB HOME SACRAMENTO INC.—See KB Home; *U.S. Public*, pg. 1215
KB HOME; *U.S. Public*, pg. 1215
KB HOME—See KB Home; *U.S. Public*, pg. 1215
KB HOME SOUTH BAY INC.—See KB Home; *U.S. Public*, pg. 1215
KEN KOJAIAN HOMES, INC.; *U.S. Private*, pg. 2282
K. HOVNANIAN ASPIRE AT HAWKS RIDGE, LLC—See Hovnanian Enterprises, Inc.; *U.S. Public*, pg. 1056
K. HOVNANIAN AT 240 MISSOURI, LLC—See Hovnanian Enterprises, Inc.; *U.S. Public*, pg. 1058
K. HOVNANIAN AT BEACON PARK AREA 129, LLC—See Hovnanian Enterprises, Inc.; *U.S. Public*, pg. 1058
K. HOVNANIAN AT CHRISTINA COURT, LLC—See Hovnanian Enterprises, Inc.; *U.S. Public*, pg. 1058
K. HOVNANIAN AT HAMPTON COVE, LLC—See Hovnanian Enterprises, Inc.; *U.S. Public*, pg. 1059
K. HOVNANIAN AT LAKE LECLARE, LLC—See Hovnanian Enterprises, Inc.; *U.S. Public*, pg. 1059
K. HOVNANIAN AT REDTAIL, LLC—See Hovnanian Enterprises, Inc.; *U.S. Public*, pg. 1059
K. HOVNANIAN AT SAGEBROOK, LLC—See Hovnanian Enterprises, Inc.; *U.S. Public*, pg. 1059
K. HOVNANIAN AT SOMERSET, LLC—See Hovnanian Enterprises, Inc.; *U.S. Public*, pg. 1059
K. HOVNANIAN AT SUMMERLAKE, LLC—See Hovnanian Enterprises, Inc.; *U.S. Public*, pg. 1059
K. HOVNANIAN DFW MIDTOWN PARK, LLC—See Hovnanian Enterprises, Inc.; *U.S. Public*, pg. 1057
K. HOVNANIAN DFW VILLAS AT MUSTANG PARK, LLC—See Hovnanian Enterprises, Inc.; *U.S. Public*, pg. 1057
K. HOVNANIAN DFW WILDRIDGE, LLC—See Hovnanian Enterprises, Inc.; *U.S. Public*, pg. 1057
K. HOVNANIAN LEGACY AT VIA BELLA, LLC—See Hovnanian Enterprises, Inc.; *U.S. Public*, pg. 1057
K. HOVNANIAN SERENO, LLC—See Hovnanian Enterprises, Inc.; *U.S. Public*, pg. 1058
K. HOVNANIAN'S FOUR SEASONS AT THE MANOR, LLC—See Hovnanian Enterprises, Inc.; *U.S. Public*, pg. 1060
KIPER DEVELOPMENT, INC.; *U.S. Private*, pg. 2314
L'AMBIANCE BEACHES LTD.; *U.S. Private*, pg. 2363
LANDSTED, LLC.; *U.S. Private*, pg. 2387
LARRY PEEL & CO., INC.; *U.S. Private*, pg. 2393
LECESSE DEVELOPMENT CORPORATION; *U.S. Private*, pg. 2409
LEE WETHERINGTON HOMES INC.; *U.S. Private*, pg. 2414
LEGEND HOME CORP.; *U.S. Private*, pg. 2418
LEWIS PROPERTIES INC.; *U.S. Private*, pg. 2439
LONDON GROUP, INC.; *U.S. Private*, pg. 2483
MACNAUGHTON BLAIR LIMITED—See Grafton Group plc; *Int'l*, pg. 3051
MAJESTIC CONSTRUCTION LLC; *U.S. Private*, pg. 2554
MARK JACOBSON & ASSOCIATES; *U.S. Private*, pg. 2577
MARK SCOTT CONSTRUCTION, INC.; *U.S. Private*, pg. 2578
MAVERICK FRAMING, INC.; *U.S. Private*, pg. 2616
MAYFAIR CONSTRUCTION GROUP, LLC.; *U.S. Private*, pg. 2621
MD CARLISLE CONSTRUCTION CORP; *U.S. Private*, pg. 2646
MILESTONE COMMUNITY BUILDERS LLC.; *U.S. Private*, pg. 2728
THE MITCHELL COMPANY, INC.; *U.S. Private*, pg. 4080
MOZEL DEVELOPMENT CORP.; *U.S. Private*, pg. 2802
M.S.G. ASSOCIATES INC.; *U.S. Private*, pg. 2529
NORMANDY HOMES ESSEX PARK, LLC—See Green Brick Partners, Inc.; *U.S. Public*, pg. 962
NORMANDY HOMES FRISCO SPRINGS, LLC—See Green Brick Partners, Inc.; *U.S. Public*, pg. 962
NORMANDY HOMES LEGENDS AT TWIN CREEKS, LLC—See Green Brick Partners, Inc.; *U.S. Public*, pg. 962
NORSOUTH CONSTRUCTS; *U.S. Private*, pg. 2939
NORTH AMERICAN COMPANY; *U.S. Private*, pg. 2940
NORTHVIEW ENTERPRISES; *U.S. Private*, pg. 2958
OAKWOOD HOMES LLC—See Berkshire Hathaway Inc.; *U.S. Public*, pg. 304

N.A.I.C.S. INDEX

236118 — RESIDENTIAL REMODEL...

ON TOP OF THE WORLD INC.; *U.S. Private*, pg. 3018
OOT BROS. INC.; *U.S. Private*, pg. 3028
ORLEANS CORPORATION—See Orleans Homebuilders, Inc.; *U.S. Private*, pg. 3044
ORLEANS RH PA-IL, LP—See Orleans Homebuilders, Inc.; *U.S. Private*, pg. 3044
OVERTON MOORE PROPERTIES; *U.S. Private*, pg. 3054
PARAGON CERTIFIED RESTORATION; *U.S. Private*, pg. 3090
PARK AVENUE SERVICE CORPORATION—See Great American Bancorp, Inc.; *U.S. Public*, pg. 961
PARKER & ORLEANS HOMEBUILDERS, INC.—See Orleans Homebuilders, Inc.; *U.S. Private*, pg. 3044
PAVARINI CONSTRUCTION CO. INC.—See STO Building Group Inc.; *U.S. Private*, pg. 3813
P & D BUILDERS, LTD.; *U.S. Private*, pg. 3058
PIT ANTWERPEN NV—See Eiffage S.A.; *Int'l*, pg. 2330
PMC HOMES CORPORATION; *U.S. Private*, pg. 3218
POHJOLAN DESIGN-TALO OY—See Afarak Group SE; *Int'l*, pg. 185
PRECISION STRUCTURES INC.—See Precision Structures Incorporated (PSI); *U.S. Private*, pg. 3247
PULTE ARIZONA SERVICES, INC.—See PulteGroup, Inc.; *U.S. Public*, pg. 1737
PULTE HOMES OF TEXAS, L.P. - DALLAS—See Pulte-Group, Inc.; *U.S. Public*, pg. 1737
PULTE INTERNATIONAL CORPORATION—See Pulte-Group, Inc.; *U.S. Public*, pg. 1737
QM CORPORATION; *U.S. Private*, pg. 3313
QUAYSIDE ASSOCIATES LTD.; *U.S. Private*, pg. 3325
REDROW HOMES (EASTERN) LIMITED—See Barratt Developments PLC; *Int'l*, pg. 868
REDROW HOMES (LANCASHIRE) LIMITED—See Barratt Developments PLC; *Int'l*, pg. 868
REDROW HOMES (MIDLANDS) LIMITED—See Barratt Developments PLC; *Int'l*, pg. 868
REDROW HOMES (NORTHWEST) LTD.—See Barratt Developments PLC; *Int'l*, pg. 868
REDROW HOMES (SOUTHERN) LIMITED—See Barratt Developments PLC; *Int'l*, pg. 868
REDROW HOMES SOUTH WEST LTD—See Barratt Developments PLC; *Int'l*, pg. 868
REDROW HOMES (YORKSHIRE) LIMITED—See Barratt Developments PLC; *Int'l*, pg. 868
REDROW PLC—See Barratt Developments PLC; *Int'l*, pg. 868
REGENCY AT DOMINION VALLEY LLC—See Apollo Global Management, Inc.; *U.S. Public*, pg. 150
THE RETREAT AT RIDGEGATE, LLC—See Century Communities, Inc.; *U.S. Public*, pg. 475
RICHPORT PROPERTIES INC.; *U.S. Private*, pg. 3430
ROBERTS, J. R. CORP.; *U.S. Private*, pg. 3460
ROBERTS PROPERTIES CONSTRUCTION, INC.—See Roberts Properties, Inc.; *U.S. Private*, pg. 3460
ROERSMA & WURN BUILDERS; *U.S. Private*, pg. 3470
ROYAL OAK HOMES, LLC—See Brookfield Corporation; *Int'l*, pg. 1183
RYLAND HOMES OF CALIFORNIA, INC.—See Lennar Corporation; *U.S. Public*, pg. 1305
SABAL HOMES, LLC—See Toll Brothers, Inc.; *U.S. Public*, pg. 2162
SAUSSY BURBANK, LLC.; *U.S. Private*, pg. 3555
SCHUMACHER HOMES, INC.; *U.S. Private*, pg. 3571
SEBASTIAN & ASSOCIATES, INC.; *U.S. Private*, pg. 3593
S. F. BALLOU, INC.; *U.S. Private*, pg. 3515
SHEA HOMES ARIZONA—See J.F. Shea Co., Inc.; *U.S. Private*, pg. 2164
SHEA HOMES-COLORADO—See J.F. Shea Co., Inc.; *U.S. Private*, pg. 2165
SHEA HOMES, LLC.; *U.S. Private*, pg. 3629
SHEA HOMES NORTHERN CALIFORNIA—See J.F. Shea Co., Inc.; *U.S. Private*, pg. 2164
SHEA HOMES SAN DIEGO—See J.F. Shea Co., Inc.; *U.S. Private*, pg. 2164
SHEA HOMES SOUTHERN CALIFORNIA—See J.F. Shea Co., Inc.; *U.S. Private*, pg. 2164
SHO-DEEN CONSTRUCTION, LLC—See Sho-Deen Inc.; *U.S. Private*, pg. 3639
SHOEMAKER CAPITAL PARTNERS LLC.; *U.S. Private*, pg. 3639
SIMONINI BUILDERS; *U.S. Private*, pg. 3666
SITTERLE HOMES; *U.S. Private*, pg. 3677
S&K ROOFING, SIDING & WINDOWS, INC.; *U.S. Private*, pg. 3513
SMEE BUILDERS INC.; *U.S. Private*, pg. 3693
SNOWBIRD CORPORATION; *U.S. Private*, pg. 3701
SOLIDONE CO., LTD.—See Iida Group Holdings Co., Ltd.; *Int'l*, pg. 3607
THE SPANOS CORPORATION—See A.G. Spanos Companies; *U.S. Private*, pg. 26
SPECTRUM BUILDING SYSTEMS, INC.—See Black Diamond Group Limited; *Int'l*, pg. 1059
STANDARD PACIFIC OF COLORADO, INC.—See Lennar Corporation; *U.S. Public*, pg. 1305
STRUCTURE WORKS, INC.—See Wind Point Advisors LLC; *U.S. Private*, pg. 4535
TAYLOR MORRISON OF TEXAS, INC. - HOUSTON DIVISION—See Brookfield Corporation; *Int'l*, pg. 1183

TEITELBAUM CONCRETE—See Fred Teitelbaum Construction Co. Inc.; *U.S. Private*, pg. 1601
THOMPSON TURNER CONSTRUCTION—See Thompson Industrial Services, LLC; *U.S. Private*, pg. 4160
THOMSON HOMES INC—See Thomson Properties Inc.; *U.S. Private*, pg. 4162
TIM O'BRIEN HOMES, INC.; *U.S. Private*, pg. 4171
TOLL BROOKLYN L.P.—See Toll Brothers, Inc.; *U.S. Public*, pg. 2162
TOUEI HOUSING CORPORATION—See Iida Group Holdings Co., Ltd.; *Int'l*, pg. 3607
TOWN MANAGEMENT CORP; *U.S. Private*, pg. 4197
TRI POINTE HOMES, INC.—See Tri Pointe Homes, Inc.; *U.S. Public*, pg. 2188
TURNBERRY HOMES; *U.S. Private*, pg. 4260
UNITED, INC.—See Anthem Works Ltd.; *Int'l*, pg. 483
VANJIA CORPORATION; *U.S. Public*, pg. 2275
VAN'S REALTY & CONSTRUCTION; *U.S. Private*, pg. 4341
VANTEM GLOBAL, INC.; *U.S. Private*, pg. 4345
VILLA WORLD (VIC) PTY LTD—See AVID Property Group; *Int'l*, pg. 743
VINTAGE HOUSING HOLDINGS, LLC—See Kennedy-Wilson Holdings, Inc.; *U.S. Public*, pg. 1223
VISNIC HOMES, INC.; *U.S. Private*, pg. 4393
WEIS BUILDERS INC.; *U.S. Private*, pg. 4472
WESTERN NATIONAL GROUP; *U.S. Private*, pg. 4494
WESTFIELD HOMES USA, INC.—See Lennar Corporation; *U.S. Public*, pg. 1306
WILLIAM R. BEACH GENERAL CONTRACTOR, INC.; *U.S. Private*, pg. 4524
WPC III, INC.; *U.S. Private*, pg. 4571
YIKED-DXN STARGATE SDN. BHD.—See DXN Holdings Bhd.; *Int'l*, pg. 2237

236118 — RESIDENTIAL REMODELERS

123 EXTERIORS, INC.; *U.S. Private*, pg. 2
ABCO BUILDING CORPORATION—See Selzer-Ornst Construction Company LLC; *U.S. Private*, pg. 3603
ACR FAMILY CONSTRUCTION, INC—See Builders FirstSource, Inc.; *U.S. Public*, pg. 409
AGBAYANI CONSTRUCTION CORP.; *U.S. Private*, pg. 126
AGMS INC.—See Bausch Health Companies Inc.; *Int'l*, pg. 895
A & I CORPORATION; *U.S. Private*, pg. 18
AIROOM INCORPORATED; *U.S. Private*, pg. 142
ALGIERE CONSTRUCTION SERVICES, INC.; *U.S. Private*, pg. 166
ALL AROUND PROPERTY PRESERVATION, LLC.; *U.S. Private*, pg. 170
ALLEN ASSOCIATES; *U.S. Private*, pg. 178
AMBLING COMPANIES, INC.; *U.S. Private*, pg. 218
AMERICAN DREAM HOME IMPROVEMENT, INC.; *U.S. Private*, pg. 230
AMERICLEAN TILE & GROUT, LLC—See Midwest Remediation Inc.; *U.S. Private*, pg. 2723
AMORE CONSTRUCTION CO.; *U.S. Private*, pg. 264
ANDREW CONSTRUCTION CO II, INC.; *U.S. Private*, pg. 279
ASAHI INFRASTRUCTURE & PROJECTS LIMITED; *Int'l*, pg. 594
ASAHI KASEI REFORM CO., LTD.—See Asahi Kasei Corporation; *Int'l*, pg. 596
ASANTE INCORPORATED; *Int'l*, pg. 599
ASAS DUNIA BERHAD; *Int'l*, pg. 599
THE BAKER COMPANIES; *U.S. Private*, pg. 3991
BARRATT BRISTOL LIMITED—See Barratt Developments PLC; *Int'l*, pg. 868
BARRATT CENTRAL LIMITED—See Barratt Developments PLC; *Int'l*, pg. 867
BARRATT CHESTER LIMITED—See Barratt Developments PLC; *Int'l*, pg. 867
BARRATT COMMERCIAL LTD.—See Barratt Developments PLC; *Int'l*, pg. 867
BARRATT CONSTRUCTION LTD.—See Barratt Developments PLC; *Int'l*, pg. 867
BARRATT EASTERN COUNTIES LIMITED—See Barratt Developments PLC; *Int'l*, pg. 867
BARRATT EAST MIDLANDS LIMITED—See Barratt Developments PLC; *Int'l*, pg. 867
BARRATT EAST SCOTLAND LIMITED—See Barratt Developments PLC; *Int'l*, pg. 867
BARRATT EXETER—See Barratt Developments PLC; *Int'l*, pg. 868
BARRATT HOMES MERCIA—See Barratt Developments PLC; *Int'l*, pg. 867
BARRATT MANCHESTER LIMITED—See Barratt Developments PLC; *Int'l*, pg. 867
BARRATT NORTHAMPTON LIMITED—See Barratt Developments PLC; *Int'l*, pg. 868
BARRATT NORTHERN LIMITED—See Barratt Developments PLC; *Int'l*, pg. 868
BARRATT SHEFFIELD—See Barratt Developments PLC; *Int'l*, pg. 867
BARRATT SOUTHAMPTON—See Barratt Developments PLC; *Int'l*, pg. 868

BARRATT SOUTHERN LIMITED—See Barratt Developments PLC; *Int'l*, pg. 868
BARRATT SOUTH WALES LIMITED—See Barratt Developments PLC; *Int'l*, pg. 868
BARRATT WEST MIDLANDS LIMITED—See Barratt Developments PLC; *Int'l*, pg. 867
BARRATT WEST—See Barratt Developments PLC; *Int'l*, pg. 868
BARRATT YORK LIMITED—See Barratt Developments PLC; *Int'l*, pg. 868
BARRON BUILDERS & MANAGEMENT COMPANY INC.; *U.S. Private*, pg. 480
BASSI CONSTRUCTION LP—See Fairfax Financial Holdings Limited; *Int'l*, pg. 2607
BATH SAVER INC.; *U.S. Private*, pg. 487
BCI CONSTRUCTION INC.—See The Pike Company Inc.; *U.S. Private*, pg. 4095
BELLWAY FINANCIAL SERVICES LIMITED—See Bellway plc; *Int'l*, pg. 967
BLACK FOREST BUILDING COMPANY; *U.S. Private*, pg. 572
BLUE RIVER GROUP, LLC.; *U.S. Private*, pg. 592
BMS CAT, INC.; *U.S. Private*, pg. 601
BONEL BUILDING CORPORATION INC.; *U.S. Private*, pg. 614
BX YUTORI FORM CO., LTD.—See Bunka Shutter Co., Ltd.; *Int'l*, pg. 1216
CANYON CONSTRUCTION; *U.S. Private*, pg. 736
CAPRI ATLANTIQUE—See Caisse des Depots et Consignations; *Int'l*, pg. 1258
CAPRI LYON MEDITERRANEE—See Caisse des Depots et Consignations; *Int'l*, pg. 1258
CARY RECONSTRUCTION INC.; *U.S. Private*, pg. 777
CASE DESIGN/REMODELING, INC.; *U.S. Private*, pg. 781
CAVALRY CONSTRUCTION COMPANY INC.; *U.S. Private*, pg. 795
C & B DEVELOPMENT, INC.; *U.S. Private*, pg. 701
CEDAR VALLEY EXTERIORS, INC.; *U.S. Private*, pg. 805
CELERITY VENTURES LLC; *U.S. Private*, pg. 806
CEMCARE, INC.—See Service Corporation International; *U.S. Public*, pg. 1869
CERTIFIED RESTORATION DRYCLEANING NETWORK, LLC; *U.S. Private*, pg. 842
CHASTAIN CONSTRUCTION INC.; *U.S. Private*, pg. 860
CHING LEE HOLDINGS LIMITED; *Int'l*, pg. 1570
CLARK WAYLAND BUILDERS L.C.; *U.S. Private*, pg. 914
CLAYTON WATKINS CONSTRUCTION COMPANY, INC.; *U.S. Private*, pg. 918
COOLPOINT INNONISM HOLDING LIMITED; *Int'l*, pg. 1789
DAIWA HOUSE CHINTAI REFORM CO., LTD.—See Daiwa House Industry Co., Ltd.; *Int'l*, pg. 1945
DAIWA HOUSE PROPERTY MANAGEMENT CO., LTD.—See Daiwa House Industry Co., Ltd.; *Int'l*, pg. 1945
DAIWA HOUSE REFORM CO., LTD.—See Daiwa House REIT Investment Corporation; *Int'l*, pg. 1947
DAIWA HOUSE RENEW CO., LTD.—See Daiwa House Industry Co., Ltd.; *Int'l*, pg. 1945
DAIWA LIVING CO., LTD.—See Daiwa House Industry Co., Ltd.; *Int'l*, pg. 1946
DB DIENSTLEISTUNGEN GMBH—See Deutsche Bahn AG; *Int'l*, pg. 2050
DELTA DISASTER SERVICES LLC—See Baird Financial Group, Inc.; *U.S. Private*, pg. 453
DE TOEKOMST VZW—See Ackermans & van Haaren NV; *Int'l*, pg. 105
DIGNEY YORK ASSOCIATES LLC—See Zurn Elkay Water Solutions Corporation; *U.S. Public*, pg. 2412
DISABATINO CONSTRUCTION COMPANY INC.; *U.S. Private*, pg. 1237
DISASTER RESTORATION SERVICES; *U.S. Private*, pg. 1237
DOM AG SICHERHEITSTECHNIK—See Groupe SFPI SA; *Int'l*, pg. 3111
DOM S.A.R.L.—See Groupe SFPI SA; *Int'l*, pg. 3111
DOM SICHERHEITSTECHNIK GMBH & CO. KG—See Groupe SFPI SA; *Int'l*, pg. 3111
DRAEGER CONSTRUCTION INC.; *U.S. Private*, pg. 1271
DRAHOTA CONSTRUCTION CO—See Federal Contracting Inc; *U.S. Private*, pg. 1487
DRC INC.; *U.S. Private*, pg. 1272
DREAMSTYLE REMODELING, INC.; *U.S. Private*, pg. 1275
DRI-EAZ PRODUCTS LIMITED—See RPM International Inc.; *U.S. Public*, pg. 1816
DRYMASTER RESTORATION—See BMS CAT, Inc.; *U.S. Private*, pg. 601
DYKSTRA CONSTRUCTION, INC.—See MidOcean Partners, LLP; *U.S. Private*, pg. 2716
EDION HOUSE SYSTEM CORPORATION—See EDION Corporation; *Int'l*, pg. 2310
E'GRAND CO., LTD.; *Int'l*, pg. 2247
EMERGENCY RESTORATION EXPERTS, LLC; *U.S. Private*, pg. 1380
EMERSON PROCESS MANAGEMENT—See Emerson Electric Co.; *U.S. Public*, pg. 747
EMPIRE EAST LAND HOLDINGS, INC.—See Alliance Global Group, Inc.; *Int'l*, pg. 339
ETABLISSEMENTS CAMILLE HOLTZ ET CIE S.A.—See

236118 — RESIDENTIAL REMODEL...

Hornbach Holding AG & Co. KGaA; *Int'l*, pg. 3481
EXTENDED HOME LIVING SERVICES, INC.—See Rockwood Equity Partners, LLC; *U.S. Private*, pg. 3468
FFI CONTRACTING SERVICES; *U.S. Private*, pg. 1500
FIBRWRAP CONSTRUCTION, INC.; *U.S. Private*, pg. 1502
FLORIDA RESTORATION OF TAMPA BAY LLC; *U.S. Private*, pg. 1550
FP PROPERTY RESTORATION OF NORTH FLORIDA, LLC; *U.S. Private*, pg. 1585
FRSTEAM, INC.—See MidOcean Partners, LLP; *U.S. Private*, pg. 2717
FULL CIRCLE RESTORATION & CONSTRUCTION SERVICES, INC.—See Cotton Holdings, Inc.; *U.S. Private*, pg. 1064
GEORG PIENING HAUSTECHNIK UND ENERGIESERVICE GMBH—See AGRAVIS Raiffeisen AG; *Int'l*, pg. 215
GERALD WOOD HOMES LIMITED—See Galliford Try Holdings plc; *Int'l*, pg. 2874
GERLOFF COMPANY INC.; *U.S. Private*, pg. 1686
GIBRALTAR CONSTRUCTION CO. INC.; *U.S. Private*, pg. 1695
GIERTSEN COMPANY; *U.S. Private*, pg. 1697
GREEN STAR EXTERIORS, LLC; *U.S. Private*, pg. 1774
GULF COAST INSULATION LLC—See Installed Building Products, Inc.; *U.S. Public*, pg. 1132
HANSON CONSTRUCTION CO, INC.; *U.S. Private*, pg. 1856
HARTZ CONSTRUCTION CORP.—See Scott and Murphy, Inc.; *U.S. Private*, pg. 3576
HASEKO INTECH, INC.—See Haseko Corporation; *Int'l*, pg. 3283
HASEKO REFORM INC.—See Haseko Corporation; *Int'l*, pg. 3283
H-DO (THAILAND) LIMITED; *Int'l*, pg. 3194
HD SUPPLY CANADA INC.—See Clayton, Dubilier & Rice, LLC; *U.S. Private*, pg. 930
HJM ENTERPRISES, INC.—See BMS CAT, Inc.; *U.S. Private*, pg. 601
HOFFMAN WEBER CONSTRUCTION; *U.S. Private*, pg. 1960
HOMEFIX CORPORATION; *U.S. Private*, pg. 1973
HOWELL & HOWELL CONTRACTORS, INC.; *U.S. Private*, pg. 1996
ICADE CAPRI S.A.—See Caisse des Depots et Consignations; *Int'l*, pg. 1258
ICYNENE LAPOLLA FRANCE SAS—See Huntsman Corporation; *U.S. Public*, pg. 1075
IMPROVEIT; *U.S. Private*, pg. 2051
INFINITY HOME SERVICES; *U.S. Private*, pg. 2071
INGLE-BARR INC.; *U.S. Private*, pg. 2075
INSURCOMM CONSTRUCTION, INC.; *U.S. Private*, pg. 2095
INTEGRATED PROPERTY SYSTEMS; *U.S. Private*, pg. 2101
IRWIN CONTRACTING INC.; *U.S. Private*, pg. 2142
ISPIRI; *U.S. Private*, pg. 2146
JACKSON DESIGN & REMODELING, INC.; *U.S. Private*, pg. 2176
J.A. MOORE & SONS INC.; *U.S. Private*, pg. 2157
JARVIS PAINTING, INC.—See BMS CAT, Inc.; *U.S. Private*, pg. 601
J & R CONTRACTING CO. INC.—See Kohlberg & Company, LLC; *U.S. Private*, pg. 2337
JUDSON ENTERPRISES, LLC—See Great Day Improvements LLC; *U.S. Private*, pg. 1762
KB HOME GREATER LOS ANGELES INC.—See KB Home; *U.S. Public*, pg. 1215
KIER CONSTRUCTION CORPORATION; *U.S. Private*, pg. 2303
KINGSOAK HOMES LTD.—See Barratt Developments PLC; *Int'l*, pg. 868
THE KITCHEN GUILD; *U.S. Private*, pg. 4065
LAURENS RESTORATION, INC.; *U.S. Private*, pg. 2399
LEGACY CUSTOM BUILDING & REMODELING, INC.—See Dreamstyle Remodeling, Inc.; *U.S. Private*, pg. 1275
LINK CONSTRUCTION GROUP, INC.; *U.S. Private*, pg. 2461
LINN-MATHES INC.—See The Linn Contracting Companies Inc.; *U.S. Private*, pg. 4070
LMC LIVING, LLC—See Lennar Corporation; *U.S. Public*, pg. 1306
MAXHOME, LLC—See York Capital Management Global Advisors, LLC; *U.S. Private*, pg. 4590
MCCARTY CORPORATION; *U.S. Private*, pg. 2628
MERCER FRASER COMPANY; *U.S. Private*, pg. 2669
MERITAGE HOMES CORPORATION; *U.S. Public*, pg. 1425
MONMOUTH CUSTOM BUILDERS; *U.S. Private*, pg. 2771
MOORE RESTORATION, INC.—See FirstService Corporation; *Int'l*, pg. 2691
MR. HANDYMAN INTERNATIONAL, LLC—See Harvest Partners L.P.; *U.S. Private*, pg. 1877
MR. ROOF HOLDING COMPANY LLC; *U.S. Private*, pg. 2805
MYHOME LLC; *U.S. Private*, pg. 2825
MY SIGNATURE LIVING, LLC; *U.S. Private*, pg. 2823
NDC CONSTRUCTION COMPANY; *U.S. Private*, pg. 2876
NEIL KELLY CO. INC.; *U.S. Private*, pg. 2882
NEW BARON LEVEQUE INTERNATIONAL AFRIQUE—See George Forrest International S.A.; *Int'l*, pg. 2938
NEWBURY BUILDERS, LLC; *U.S. Private*, pg. 2914
NIBBI BROTHERS; *U.S. Private*, pg. 2924
NORDIC CONTRACTING COMPANY, INCORPORATED; *U.S. Private*, pg. 2936
NORMANDY CONSTRUCTION CO. INC.; *U.S. Private*, pg. 2938
NORTHSTAR RESTORATION SERVICES, LLC; *U.S. Private*, pg. 2958
NTH DEGREE INC.—See Shamrock Capital Advisors, LLC; *U.S. Private*, pg. 3624
NVR INCORPORATED; *U.S. Public*, pg. 1558
OLNEYA RESTORATION GROUP; *U.S. Private*, pg. 3011
ONDRA-HUYETT ASSOCIATES, INC.; *U.S. Private*, pg. 3020
PACIFIC SALES KITCHEN AND BATH CENTERS, LLC—See Best Buy Co., Inc.; *U.S. Public*, pg. 326
PARADISE HOME IMPROVEMENT LLC—See York Capital Management Global Advisors, LLC; *U.S. Private*, pg. 4590
PARAMOUNT WINDOWS, INC.—See Altamont Capital Partners; *U.S. Private*, pg. 205
PLN CONTRACTING INC.; *U.S. Private*, pg. 3214
PROCON AND ASSOCIATES, INC; *U.S. Private*, pg. 3272
PROMOMIDI—See Caisse des Depots et Consignations; *Int'l*, pg. 1258
PRUESLER & ASSOCIATES INC.; *U.S. Private*, pg. 3296
PULTE HOMES TENNESSEE, INC.—See PulteGroup, Inc.; *U.S. Public*, pg. 1737
THE QUADRANT CORPORATION—See Tri Pointe Homes, Inc.; *U.S. Public*, pg. 2188
REDROW HOMES (SOUTH MIDLANDS) LIMITED—See Barratt Developments PLC; *Int'l*, pg. 868
THE REMODELING COMPANY; *U.S. Private*, pg. 4104
RENEWAL BY ANDERSEN CORPORATION—See Andersen Corporation; *U.S. Private*, pg. 275
RENOVO HOME PARTNERS—See Audax Group, Limited Partnership; *U.S. Private*, pg. 389
RESTORE FORCE INC.—See FOODFEST INTERNATIONAL 2000 INC.; *U.S. Public*, pg. 863
ROBISON-NIERI-WHITE CONSTRUCTION; *U.S. Private*, pg. 3462
ROCK SOLID CONSTRUCTION GROUP, INC.; *U.S. Private*, pg. 3465
ROLYN CONSTRUCTION CORPORATION; *U.S. Private*, pg. 3475
RO RESTORATION SPECIALISTS—See Rogers-O'Brien Construction Company Inc.; *U.S. Private*, pg. 3472
RUVAL SA—See Barclays PLC; *Int'l*, pg. 863
SANJOSE CONCESIONES Y SERVICIOS, S.A.U—See Grupo Empresarial San Jose, S.A.; *Int'l*, pg. 3128
SCHMID CONSTRUCTION INC.; *U.S. Private*, pg. 3565
SCOTBILT HOMES, INC.—See Champion Homes, Inc.; *U.S. Public*, pg. 477
SECURE FOUNDATION SYSTEMS, INC; *U.S. Private*, pg. 3593
SELA ROOFING & REMODELING; *U.S. Private*, pg. 3600
SELZER-ORNST CONSTRUCTION COMPANY LLC; *U.S. Private*, pg. 3603
SENIOR CRAFTSMAN INC.; *U.S. Private*, pg. 3606
SERVICE.COM LLC; *U.S. Private*, pg. 3616
SG RESIDENTIAL, INC.—See Safe & Green Holdings Corp.; *U.S. Public*, pg. 1834
SHELCIDY CUSTOM REMODELING, INC.; *U.S. Private*, pg. 3630
SIA LATVIJAS NAMSAIMNIEKS—See City Service SE; *Int'l*, pg. 1627
SIA NAMU SERVISS APSE—See City Service SE; *Int'l*, pg. 1628
SILVERLINING INTERIORS, INC.; *U.S. Private*, pg. 3663
SIMPSON HOUSING SOLUTIONS, LLC; *U.S. Private*, pg. 3668
SOCIETE DELTA BATIMENT—See Delta Plus Group; *Int'l*, pg. 2020
SOUTHEAST RESTORATION GROUP; *U.S. Private*, pg. 3726
SOUTHERN RESIDENTIAL INSTALLATIONS LLC; *U.S. Private*, pg. 3735
SPECIALTY RESTORATION OF TEXAS; *U.S. Private*, pg. 3750
SPRINT SANIERUNG GMBH—See DZ BANK AG Deutsche Zentral-Genossenschaftsbank; *Int'l*, pg. 2244
SRI-CUTTER'S INSULATION INC.—See Southern Residential Installations LLC; *U.S. Private*, pg. 3735
STARMAX ASSETS LIMITED—See Henderson Land Development Co. Ltd.; *Int'l*, pg. 3344
STATEWIDE REMODELING, INC.—See Florida Home Improvement Associates Inc.; *U.S. Private*, pg. 1549
STICKLER CONSTRUCTION LLC; *U.S. Private*, pg. 3812
SUNDQUIST HOMES LLC—See Century Communities, Inc.; *U.S. Public*, pg. 475
TECHNOLOGIE & ART PTE. LTD.—See New Mountain Capital, LLC; *U.S. Private*, pg. 2900
THOMAS CONSTRUCTION INC.—See True Home Value, Inc.; *U.S. Private*, pg. 4247
THORNTON FLATS JV, LLC—See Bluerock Residential Growth REIT, Inc.; *U.S. Public*, pg. 366
TIGER HOME SERVICES, INC.—See Universal Insurance Holdings, Inc.; *U.S. Public*, pg. 2261
TITAN HOME IMPROVEMENT INC.—See York Capital Management Global Advisors, LLC; *U.S. Private*, pg. 4590
TORBA INSAAT VE TURISTIK A.S—See Global Yatirim Holding A.S.; *Int'l*, pg. 3003
TR KENZAI CO., LTD.—See Bunka Shutter Co., Ltd.; *Int'l*, pg. 1216
TRNLWB, LLC—See Trinity Industries, Inc.; *U.S. Public*, pg. 2193
TURNER INDUSTRIES GROUP L.L.C.—See Turner Industries Group, L.L.C.; *U.S. Private*, pg. 4261
UAB MANO BUSTAS ALYTUS—See City Service SE; *Int'l*, pg. 1628
UAB MANO BUSTAS KAUNAS—See City Service SE; *Int'l*, pg. 1628
UAB MANO BUSTAS KLAIPEDA—See City Service SE; *Int'l*, pg. 1628
UAB MANO BUSTAS SIAULIAI—See City Service SE; *Int'l*, pg. 1628
UAB MANO BUSTAS—See City Service SE; *Int'l*, pg. 1628
UAB MANO BUSTAS VILNIUS—See City Service SE; *Int'l*, pg. 1628
ULRICH HUBER AG—See Burkhalter Holding AG; *Int'l*, pg. 1226
UTAH DISASTER KLEENUP; *U.S. Private*, pg. 4324
VVV CORPORATION; *U.S. Private*, pg. 4416
WATT COMMUNITIES—See Watt Companies, Inc.; *U.S. Private*, pg. 4456
WERMERS CORPORATION; *U.S. Private*, pg. 4481
WESTERN GRADE, LLC; *U.S. Private*, pg. 4493
WESTON AMERICAN, INC.—See Kohlberg & Company, LLC; *U.S. Private*, pg. 2337
WEWORK COMPANIES INC.—See WeWork Inc.; *U.S. Public*, pg. 2364
WG YATES & SONS CONSTRUCTION COMPANY, JACKSON—See W.G. Yates & Sons Construction Company; *U.S. Private*, pg. 4420
WILKINSON CONSTRUCTION INC—See Wilkinson Real Estate Advisors Inc; *U.S. Private*, pg. 4521
WINDOW NATION, LLC—See AEA Investors LP; *U.S. Private*, pg. 116
WINDOW WORLD OF UPSTATE—See Window World Inc.; *U.S. Private*, pg. 4538
WINN DESIGN, LLC; *U.S. Private*, pg. 4542
WODA MANAGEMENT & REAL ESTATE, LLC; *U.S. Private*, pg. 4553
W.S. CUMBY, INC.; *U.S. Private*, pg. 4422
YOUR HOME IMPROVEMENT, CO.—See Great Day Improvements LLC; *U.S. Private*, pg. 1762
YUTORI FORM CO., LTD.—See Bunka Shutter Co., Ltd.; *Int'l*, pg. 1216

236210 — INDUSTRIAL BUILDING CONSTRUCTION

3-D ENVIRONMENTAL SERVICES CORP.; *U.S. Private*, pg. 7
723926 ONTARIO LIMITED; *Int'l*, pg. 14
ABEL CONSTRUCTION COMPANY; *U.S. Private*, pg. 37
ABI COMPANIES, INC.; *U.S. Private*, pg. 38
ABINGTON GROUP INC.; *U.S. Private*, pg. 38
ACC CONSTRUCTION COMPANY, INC.; *U.S. Private*, pg. 47
ACCIONA AGUA, S.A.—See Acciona, S.A.; *Int'l*, pg. 90
ACC LIMITED - TIKARIA CEMENT GRINDING AND PACKING PLANT—See ACC Limited; *Int'l*, pg. 79
ACCRUIT HOLDINGS LLC—See ABRY Partners, LLC; *U.S. Private*, pg. 42
ACTIVIDADES DE SERVICIOS E INSTALACIONES COBRA, S.A.—See ACS, Actividades de Construccion y Servicios, S.A.; *Int'l*, pg. 110
ADVANCED AMERICAN CONSTRUCTION, INC.; *U.S. Private*, pg. 87
AECON INDUSTRIAL—See Aecon Group Inc.; *Int'l*, pg. 172
AECON INFRASTRUCTURE—See Aecon Group Inc.; *Int'l*, pg. 172
AEON TOWN CO., LTD.—See AEON Co., Ltd.; *Int'l*, pg. 177
AF INTERNATIONAL CORPORATION; *U.S. Private*, pg. 121
AFRIMAT LIMITED; *Int'l*, pg. 192
AHERN & ASSOCIATES INC.; *U.S. Private*, pg. 130
AHTNA INCORPORATED; *U.S. Private*, pg. 131
AIC INGENIEURGESELLSCHAFT FUER BAUPLANUNG CHEMNITZ GMBH—See Hormann Holding GmbH & Co. KG; *Int'l*, pg. 3479
AIR FORCE ONE; *U.S. Private*, pg. 138
AJ LUCAS OPERATIONS PTY LIMITED—See A.J. Lucas Group Limited; *Int'l*, pg. 24
ALASKA MECHANICAL INC.; *U.S. Private*, pg. 151
ALGEMENE AANNEMINGEN VAN LAERE NV—See Ackermans & van Haaren NV; *Int'l*, pg. 104
AL HAMAD INDUSTRIAL COMPANY LLC—See Al Hamad Contracting Company LLC; *Int'l*, pg. 278
ALLAN MYERS, INC.; *U.S. Private*, pg. 174
ALLIANZ HANDWERKER SERVICES GMBH—See Allianz SE; *Int'l*, pg. 350

N.A.I.C.S. INDEX

236210 — INDUSTRIAL BUILDING...

ALTER DESIGN BUILDERS LLC—See The Alter Group Ltd.; *U.S. Private*, pg. 3985
AMAN BUILDERS INC.; *Int'l*, pg. 409
AMATA CORPORATION PUBLIC COMPANY LIMITED; *Int'l*, pg. 412
AMATA (VIETNAM) JOINT STOCK COMPANY—See Amata Corporation Public Company Limited; *Int'l*, pg. 412
ANCON CONSTRUCTION COMPANY; *U.S. Private*, pg. 274
ANDERSON BAUMAN TOURTELLOT VOS & CO.—See B. Riley Financial, Inc.; *U.S. Public*, pg. 260
A.O. HARDEE & SON, INC.; *U.S. Private*, pg. 27
ARENT, INC.; *Int'l*, pg. 559
ARGAN SA; *Int'l*, pg. 560
ARIES BUILDING SYSTEMS, LLC—See Reliant Asset Management LLC; *U.S. Private*, pg. 3395
ARMADA MATERIALS, LLC; *U.S. Private*, pg. 329
ARROW BUILDING CENTER - POST FRAME DIVISION—See Consolidated Lumber Co.; *U.S. Private*, pg. 1021
ARROWSTREAM, INC.—See Buyers Edge Platform LLC; *U.S. Private*, pg. 699
A SERVIDONE INC; *U.S. Private*, pg. 19
ASPEN GROUP LIMITED; *Int'l*, pg. 628
ATKINSON CONSTRUCTION—See Clark Enterprises, Inc.; *U.S. Private*, pg. 912
AUDUBON MATERIALS LLC—See Eagle Materials Inc.; *U.S. Public*, pg. 702
AUDUBON READYMIX LLC—See Eagle Materials Inc.; *U.S. Public*, pg. 702
AUSGROUP LIMITED; *Int'l*, pg. 715
AVCO DISPOSAL INC.—See Burrtec Waste Industries, Inc.; *U.S. Private*, pg. 692
BALDWIN & SHELL CONSTRUCTION CO. INC. - NORTH-EAST ARKANSAS DIVISION—See Baldwin & Shell Construction Co. Inc.; *U.S. Private*, pg. 458
BALDWIN & SHELL CONSTRUCTION CO. INC. - NORTH-WEST ARKANSAS DIVISION—See Baldwin & Shell Construction Co. Inc.; *U.S. Private*, pg. 458
BALFOUR BEATTY CONSTRUCTION LLC—See Balfour Beatty plc; *Int'l*, pg. 807
BALZER'S CANADA INC.; *Int'l*, pg. 813
BAMBOO CAPITAL JSC; *Int'l*, pg. 813
BANTREL CONSTRUCTORS CO.—See Bantrel Co.; *Int'l*, pg. 855
BARLOWORLD SIYAKHULA (PTY) LIMITED—See Barloworld Ltd.; *Int'l*, pg. 866
BATES ENGINEERS/CONTRACTORS INC.; *U.S. Private*, pg. 486
BAUER HOLZBAU GMBH; *Int'l*, pg. 894
BAY INTERNATIONAL CANADA, ULC—See Berry Contracting L.P.; *U.S. Private*, pg. 538
BAY TANK & VESSEL CANADA, LTD.—See Berry Contracting L.P.; *U.S. Private*, pg. 538
BCM CONSTRUCTION COMPANY INC.; *U.S. Private*, pg. 499
BEAZER HOMES INDIANA HOLDINGS CORP.—See Beazer Homes USA, Inc.; *U.S. Public*, pg. 287
BECHO INC.—See Tutor Perini Corporation; *U.S. Public*, pg. 2205
BELLINGHAM MARINE INDUSTRIES INC.—See Bellwether Financial Group, Inc.; *U.S. Private*, pg. 520
BEMAC CONSTRUCTION CORP.—See Bantrel Co.; *Int'l*, pg. 855
BERGERON LAND DEVELOPMENT INC.—See Bergeron Properties & Investment Corp.; *U.S. Private*, pg. 530
BERNARDS BROTHERS, INC.; *U.S. Private*, pg. 536
BERRY CONTRACTING L.P. - BELLE CHASSE FACILITY—See Berry Contracting L.P.; *U.S. Private*, pg. 538
BERRY CONTRACTING L.P. - COLOMBIA FACILITY—See Berry Contracting L.P.; *U.S. Private*, pg. 538
BERRY CONTRACTING L.P. - HOUSTON FACILITY—See Berry Contracting L.P.; *U.S. Private*, pg. 538
BERRY CONTRACTING L.P. - MEXICO FACILITY—See Berry Contracting L.P.; *U.S. Private*, pg. 538
BERRY CONTRACTING L.P. - MONTANA FACILITY—See Berry Contracting L.P.; *U.S. Private*, pg. 538
BERRY CONTRACTING L.P. - MORGAN CITY FACILITY—See Berry Contracting L.P.; *U.S. Private*, pg. 538
BERRY CONTRACTING L.P. - REDFISH BAY TERMINAL FACILITY—See Berry Contracting L.P.; *U.S. Private*, pg. 538
BERTUCCI CONTRACTING CORPORATION; *U.S. Private*, pg. 540
BETONUT CONSTRUCTII S.R.L.—See Betonut Szolgaltato es Epito Rt.; *Int'l*, pg. 1003
BEXIMCO ENGINEERING LTD.—See Bangladesh Export Import Co. Ltd.; *Int'l*, pg. 835
BIG-D CONSTRUCTION CORPORATION; *U.S. Private*, pg. 555
BIJELJINA PUT AD—See Grupa Fortis d.o.o. Banja Luka; *Int'l*, pg. 3116
BILFINGER BERGER EMIRATES CONSTRUCTION B.V.—See Bilfinger SE; *Int'l*, pg. 1025
BILFINGER BERGER INDUSTRIAL SERVICES GMBH—See Bilfinger SE; *Int'l*, pg. 1025
BINA PURI PAKISTAN (PRIVATE) LTD.—See Bina Puri Holdings Bhd; *Int'l*, pg. 1032
BIS FRUCON INDUSTRIAL SERVICES INC.—See Bilfinger SE; *Int'l*, pg. 1026
BIS INTERNATIONAL CONSTRUCTION AND TRADING N.V.—See Bilfinger SE; *Int'l*, pg. 1025
BIS MAINTENANCE SUDWEST GMBH—See Bilfinger SE; *Int'l*, pg. 1025
BIS VAM ANLAGENTECHNIK GMBH—See Bilfinger SE; *Int'l*, pg. 1026
BITUMINA INDUSTRIES LTD.; *Int'l*, pg. 1050
BLACH CONSTRUCTION; *U.S. Private*, pg. 569
BLACK & MCDONALD BERMUDA LIMITED—See Black & McDonald Limited; *Int'l*, pg. 1056
BLATT WELDING AND FABRICATION, INC.—See Blatt Group; *U.S. Private*, pg. 580
BLUNDEN CONSTRUCTION LTD.; *Int'l*, pg. 1075
BODELL CONSTRUCTION COMPANY INC. - HAWAII DIVISION—See Bodell Construction Company Inc.; *U.S. Private*, pg. 608
THE BOLDT COMPANY—See The Boldt Group Inc.; *U.S. Private*, pg. 3996
BONNETTE PAGE & STONE CORP.; *U.S. Private*, pg. 614
BOOTH INDUSTRIES LTD.—See Avingtrans plc; *Int'l*, pg. 743
BOSTON COMMON ASSET MANAGEMENT, LLC; *U.S. Private*, pg. 621
BOUWBORG B.V.—See Friso Bouwgroep B.V.; *Int'l*, pg. 2793
BRAD COLE CONSTRUCTION COMPANY, INCORPORATED—See Arctic Slope Regional Corporation; *U.S. Private*, pg. 316
BRAHMA GROUP, INC.—See Terra Millenium Corporation; *U.S. Private*, pg. 3970
BRAND ENERGY & INFRASTRUCTURE SERVICES NV/SA—See Brand Industrial Services, Inc.; *U.S. Private*, pg. 636
BRANDPOINT SERVICES, INC.; *U.S. Private*, pg. 638
BREIHOLZ CONSTRUCTION CO; *U.S. Private*, pg. 644
BREZILLON SA—See Bouygues S.A.; *Int'l*, pg. 1122
B-RIGHT REAL ESTATE LIMITED; *Int'l*, pg. 785
BRISTOL GENERAL CONTRACTORS, LLC—See Bristol Bay Native Corporation; *U.S. Private*, pg. 656
BROCK CANADA INC.—See AIP, LLC; *U.S. Private*, pg. 134
BSI CONSTRUCTORS, INC.; *U.S. Private*, pg. 675
BUILD GROUP, INC.; *U.S. Private*, pg. 681
BUILDING TEMPERATURE SOLUTIONS, LLC—See Comfort Systems USA, Inc.; *U.S. Public*, pg. 543
BURKEY CONSTRUCTION INC.; *U.S. Private*, pg. 688
BYGGPARTNER GRUPPEN AB; *Int'l*, pg. 1235
CAMPBELL CONSTRUCTION INC.; *U.S. Private*, pg. 730
CAPE FEAR CONSTRUCTION CO. INC.; *U.S. Private*, pg. 737
CARIMALO; *Int'l*, pg. 1331
CARL BOLANDER & SONS CO., INC.; *U.S. Private*, pg. 762
CARL E. WOODWARD LLC; *U.S. Private*, pg. 762
CAS CONSTRUCTORS, LLC—See Alberici Corporation; *U.S. Private*, pg. 152
CASEY INDUSTRIAL INC.; *U.S. Private*, pg. 782
CAZ (THAILAND) PUBLIC COMPANY LIMITED; *Int'l*, pg. 1364
CBI SERVICES, INC. (NEW CASTLE)—See McDermott International, Inc.; *U.S. Public*, pg. 1405
CCB INC.; *U.S. Private*, pg. 799
CCC GROUP INC.; *U.S. Private*, pg. 799
CCI SOLUTIONS, LLC—See Bristol Bay Native Corporation; *U.S. Private*, pg. 656
CD DEUTSCHE EIGENHEIM AG; *Int'l*, pg. 1370
CDI, INC.; *U.S. Private*, pg. 802
CECCON FRERES SA; *Int'l*, pg. 1372
CEI BOSTON LLC; *U.S. Private*, pg. 805
CENTRAL PATTANA PUBLIC COMPANY LIMITED; *Int'l*, pg. 1409
CENTURY CONTRACTORS, INC.; *U.S. Private*, pg. 832
CERIC TECHNOLOGIES; *Int'l*, pg. 1422
CERTIFIED TECHNICAL SERVICES, L.P.—See Forum Energy Technologies, Inc.; *U.S. Public*, pg. 873
CHERNE CONTRACTING CORPORATION; *U.S. Private*, pg. 873
CHICAGO HEIGHTS CONSTRUCTION CO.; *U.S. Private*, pg. 877
CHIEF CONSTRUCTION COMPANY—See Chief Industries, Inc.; *U.S. Private*, pg. 881
CHILDS MANAGEMENT INC.; *U.S. Private*, pg. 885
CHINA CONSTRUCTION AMERICAN CO.—See China State Construction Engineering Corporation Limited; *Int'l*, pg. 1554
CHINA CONSTRUCTION FIRST BUILDING (GROUP) CORPORATION LTD.—See China State Construction Engineering Corporation Limited; *Int'l*, pg. 1554
CHINA CONSTRUCTION (SOUTH PACIFIC) DEVELOPMENT CO. PTE. LTD.—See China State Construction Engineering Corporation Limited; *Int'l*, pg. 1554
CHINA OVERSEAS HOLDING LTD.—See China State Construction Engineering Corporation Limited; *Int'l*, pg. 1554
CHINA OVERSEAS HOLDING LTD.—See China State Construction Engineering Corporation Limited; *Int'l*, pg. 1554
CHINA POWER CLEAN ENERGY DEVELOPMENT COMPANY LIMITED; *Int'l*, pg. 1542
CHINA STATE CONSTRUCTION ENGINEERING CORPORATION LIMITED; *Int'l*, pg. 1554
CHINA STATE CONSTRUCTION INTERNATIONAL CO.—See China State Construction Engineering Corporation Limited; *Int'l*, pg. 1554
CHINA VAST INDUSTRIAL URBAN DEVELOPMENT COMPANY LIMITED; *Int'l*, pg. 1562
CHINA ZHONGHUA GEOTECHNICAL ENGINEERING CO., LTD.; *Int'l*, pg. 1567
CHIYODA CORPORATION; *Int'l*, pg. 1574
CHIYODA INTERNATIONAL CORPORATION—See Chiyoda Corporation; *Int'l*, pg. 1574
CHIYODA & PUBLIC WORKS CO., LTD.—See Chiyoda Corporation; *Int'l*, pg. 1574
CHIYODA SINGAPORE (PTE) LIMITED—See Chiyoda Corporation; *Int'l*, pg. 1574
CHRISTIANI & NIELSEN (THAI) PUBLIC COMPANY LIMITED; *Int'l*, pg. 1586
CHRISTY-FOLTZ INCORPORATED; *U.S. Private*, pg. 892
CIANBRO CORPORATION; *U.S. Private*, pg. 896
CIVIL MECHANICAL INC.—See Wolfenson Electric, Inc.; *U.S. Private*, pg. 4554
CLANCY & THEYS CONSTRUCTION COMPANY - NEWPORT NEWS—See Clancy & Theys Construction Company; *U.S. Private*, pg. 910
CLANCY & THEYS CONSTRUCTION COMPANY - ORLANDO—See Clancy & Theys Construction Company; *U.S. Private*, pg. 910
CLANCY & THEYS CONSTRUCTION COMPANY; *U.S. Private*, pg. 910
CLANCY & THEYS CONSTRUCTION COMPANY—See Clancy & Theys Construction Company; *U.S. Private*, pg. 910
CLARK & SULLIVAN CONSTRUCTION, INC.; *U.S. Private*, pg. 912
CLAYCO CONSTRUCTION COMPANY INC.; *U.S. Private*, pg. 918
CLC CONSTRUCTION GROUP INC.; *U.S. Private*, pg. 930
CLEANAIR SOLUTIONS, INC.; *U.S. Private*, pg. 931
CLEARSTREAM CONTRACTING LP—See FLINT Corp.; *Int'l*, pg. 2706
CLEARSTREAM WEAR TECHNOLOGIES LP—See FLINT Corp.; *Int'l*, pg. 2706
CLEARWATER ENERGY SERVICES LP—See FLINT Corp.; *Int'l*, pg. 2706
CLESTRA CLEANROOM SA—See Clestra Hauserman S.A.; *Int'l*, pg. 1658
CMM INFRAPROJECTS LIMITED; *Int'l*, pg. 1671
CONS CONSTRUCT SRL—See Bog'Art S.R.L.; *Int'l*, pg. 1100
CONSIGLI CONSTRUCTION CO., INC.; *U.S. Private*, pg. 1019
CONSORCIO ARISTOS, S.A.B. DE C.V.; *Int'l*, pg. 1771
CONSTRUEXPORT, S.A. DE C.V.—See Empresas ICA S.A.B. de C.V.; *Int'l*, pg. 2390
CONTEXTURE, INC; *U.S. Private*, pg. 1028
CONTINENTAL CONSTRUCTION CO.; *U.S. Private*, pg. 1028
COTECCONS CONSTRUCTION JOINT STOCK COMPANY; *Int'l*, pg. 1815
COTTER CONSULTING, INC.; *U.S. Private*, pg. 1063
COTTRELL CONTRACTING CORP; *U.S. Private*, pg. 1064
C. OVERAA & CO.; *U.S. Private*, pg. 705
COWEN CONSTRUCTION INC.; *U.S. Private*, pg. 1073
COWIN & COMPANY, INC.; *U.S. Private*, pg. 1073
C.R. BUILDING COMPANY—See Klewin Construction Inc.; *U.S. Private*, pg. 2319
CR CONSTRUCTION COMPANY—See Columbia National Group Inc; *U.S. Private*, pg. 977
CREATIVE CONTRACTORS INC.; *U.S. Private*, pg. 1088
C.R. KLEWIN SOUTHEAST—See Klewin Construction Inc.; *U.S. Private*, pg. 2319
CROWN CASTLE OPERATING COMPANY—See Crown Castle Inc.; *U.S. Public*, pg. 596
CSC & EC (PTY) LTD.—See China State Construction Engineering Corporation Limited; *Int'l*, pg. 1554
CTCI-HDEC (CHUNGLI) CORP.—See CTCI Corporation; *Int'l*, pg. 1870
CURTIS-LAYER CONSTRUCTION CO.; *U.S. Private*, pg. 1127
CW ROEN CONSTRUCTION CO.; *U.S. Private*, pg. 1132
DAELIM-DAR CO., LTD.—See Daelim Industrial Co., Ltd.; *Int'l*, pg. 1908
DAELIM (NANJING) CONSTRUCTION PROJECT MANAGEMENT CO., LTD.—See Daelim Industrial Co., Ltd.; *Int'l*, pg. 1908
DAELIM PHILIPPINES INC.—See Daelim Industrial Co., Ltd.; *Int'l*, pg. 1908
DANIEL J. KEATING CONSTRUCTION COMPANY, LLC; *U.S. Private*, pg. 1155
DANIEL O'CONNELL'S SONS INC.—See The O'Connell Companies, Incorporated; *U.S. Private*, pg. 4087
DARK HORSE ENTERPRISE, LLC—See Owl Services, Inc.; *U.S. Private*, pg. 3055
DAVID A. BRAMBLE, INC.; *U.S. Private*, pg. 1169
DAVID BOLAND, INC.; *U.S. Private*, pg. 1169

3179

DAYTNER CONSTRUCTION GROUP; *U.S. Private*, pg. 1177
DEIG BROS. LUMBER & CONSTRUCTION CO. INC.; *U.S. Private*, pg. 1191
DEJEAN CONSTRUCTION COMPANY, INC.; *U.S. Private*, pg. 1192
DELTA RAILROAD CONSTRUCTION; *U.S. Private*, pg. 1201
DEMPSEY CONSTRUCTION, INC.; *U.S. Private*, pg. 1204
DESCCO DESIGN & CONSTRUCTION; *U.S. Private*, pg. 1211
DEVERE CONSTRUCTION COMPANY INC.; *U.S. Private*, pg. 1218
DIAMOND SERVICES CORPORATION; *U.S. Private*, pg. 1224
DISTECH CONTROLS INC.—See Acuity Brands, Inc.; *U.S. Public*, pg. 37
DONDLINGER & SONS CONSTRUCTION CO. INC.; *U.S. Private*, pg. 1260
DONDLINGER & SONS CONSTRUCTION CO. INC.- TEXAS—See Dondlinger & Sons Construction Co. Inc.; *U.S. Private*, pg. 1260
DOOSAN INDUSTRIAL DEVELOPMENT CO., LTD.—See Doosan Corporation; *Int'l*, pg. 2173
DOWNER EDI LIMITED; *Int'l*, pg. 2185
DRAFT INC.; *Int'l*, pg. 2199
DRAGADOS S.A.—See ACS, Actividades de Construccion y Servicios, S.A.; *Int'l*, pg. 111
DRA TAGGART, LLC—See DRA Group Holdings Proprietary Limited; *Int'l*, pg. 2196
DTB-DEUTSCHE BIOGAS AG; *Int'l*, pg. 2216
DUGAN & MEYERS CONSTRUCTION SERVICES, LTD.—See Baker Concrete Construction, Inc.; *U.S. Private*, pg. 456
DUGAN & MEYERS LLC—See Baker Concrete Construction, Inc.; *U.S. Private*, pg. 455
DUROCHER MARINE—See Kokosing Construction Company, Inc.; *U.S. Private*, pg. 2340
THE DUTRA GROUP INC.; *U.S. Private*, pg. 4024
DYNAMIC BUILDERS INC.; *U.S. Private*, pg. 1297
EASTERN OMNI CONSTRUCTORS INC.; *U.S. Private*, pg. 1320
EBY CORPORATION; *U.S. Private*, pg. 1326
ECO ENERGY COMPANY LIMITED—See Henderson Land Development Co. Ltd.; *Int'l*, pg. 3344
EDGE DEVELOPMENT, INC.; *U.S. Private*, pg. 1334
EDWARD LESKE CO.; *U.S. Private*, pg. 1341
EDWARDS CONSTRUCTION SERVICES INC.—See REX Engineering Group, Inc.; *U.S. Private*, pg. 3417
E.E. AUSTIN & SON INC.; *U.S. Private*, pg. 1305
EIFFAGE ENERGIE S.A.S.—See Eiffage S.A.; *Int'l*, pg. 2330
EKOSTAV A.S; *Int'l*, pg. 2339
ELLSWORTH PAULSEN CONSTRUCTION CO.—See ACS, Actividades de Construccion y Servicios, S.A.; *Int'l*, pg. 113
EMERICK CONSTRUCTION CO. INC.; *U.S. Private*, pg. 1381
ENOMOTO PRECISION ENGINEERING (S) PTE.LTD—See Enomoto Co., Ltd.; *Int'l*, pg. 2444
ENVIRONMENTAL CONTAINMENT CORPORATION; *U.S. Private*, pg. 1407
EP INDUSTRIJA A.D.—See Energoprojekt Holding a.d.; *Int'l*, pg. 2421
EPM CHILE S.A.—See Empresas Publicas de Medellin ESP; *Int'l*, pg. 2392
EVERGREEN MEDICAL SERVICES, INC; *U.S. Private*, pg. 1439
FARGLORY LAND DEVELOPMENT CO., LTD.; *Int'l*, pg. 2618
FAST TRACK MANAGEMENT SERVICES (LONDON) LIMITED—See Empresaria Group Plc; *Int'l*, pg. 2388
FAST TRACK MANAGEMENT SERVICES (MIDLANDS) LIMITED—See Empresaria Group Plc; *Int'l*, pg. 2389
FAULCONER CONSTRUCTION CO. INC.; *U.S. Private*, pg. 1483
F.A. WILHELM CONSTRUCTION CO., INC.; *U.S. Private*, pg. 1455
FCL BUILDERS INC.; *U.S. Private*, pg. 1486
FERGUSON CONSTRUCTION COMPANY INC.; *U.S. Private*, pg. 1496
FLORIDA FLOATS INC.—See Bellwether Financial Group, Inc.; *U.S. Private*, pg. 520
FLUOR DANIEL, INC.—See Fluor Corporation; *U.S. Public*, pg. 858
FOCAL AIMS LAND SDN. BHD.—See Eco World Development Group Berhad; *Int'l*, pg. 2293
FOCAL AIMS SDN. BHD.—See Eco World Development Group Berhad; *Int'l*, pg. 2293
FOLCRA BEACH INDUSTRIAL COMPANY LLC—See Dubai Investments PJSC; *Int'l*, pg. 2219
FORD CONSTRUCTION COMPANY INC.; *U.S. Private*, pg. 1564
FOUNDATION CONSTRUCTORS INC.; *U.S. Private*, pg. 1579
FOUNTAIN CONSTRUCTION COMPANY, INC.; *U.S. Private*, pg. 1581
FRANK MERCEDE & SONS INC.; *U.S. Private*, pg. 1595
FRISO BOUWGROEP B.V.; *Int'l*, pg. 2793

FUJITA ENGINEERING CO., LTD.; *Int'l*, pg. 2831
FUJITA PHILIPPINES INC.—See Daiwa House Industry Co., Ltd.; *Int'l*, pg. 1946
FULLMER CONSTRUCTION INC.; *U.S. Private*, pg. 1621
GAMMA-CIVIC LTD; *Int'l*, pg. 2878
GAMMA CONSTRUCTION LTD—See Gamma-Civic Ltd; *Int'l*, pg. 2878
GANNETT FLEMING PROJECT DEVELOPMENT CORP.—See OceanSound Partners, LP; *U.S. Private*, pg. 2991
GARRETT CONSTRUCTION COMPANY; *U.S. Private*, pg. 1645
G.A. WEST & COMPANY INC.; *U.S. Private*, pg. 1630
GDB HOLDINGS BERHAD; *Int'l*, pg. 2895
GEMMA POWER SYSTEMS, LLC—See Argan, Inc.; *U.S. Public*, pg. 191
GENESIS BUILDERS GROUP INC—See Genesis Land Development Corp.; *Int'l*, pg. 2921
GEOMETRICA, INC.; *U.S. Private*, pg. 1680
GEORGE C. HOPKINS CONSTRUCTION COMPANY, INC.; *U.S. Private*, pg. 1681
GERACE CONSTRUCTION COMPANY INC.; *U.S. Private*, pg. 1685
GETHMANN CONSTRUCTION COMPANY; *U.S. Private*, pg. 1688
GFC CONSTRUCTION SA—See Bouygues S.A.; *Int'l*, pg. 1122
GHILOTTI CONSTRUCTION COMPANY INC.; *U.S. Private*, pg. 1690
GILBANE, INC.; *U.S. Private*, pg. 1698
GISBORNE HOLDINGS LTD.; *Int'l*, pg. 2979
GLENN & WRIGHT, INC.; *U.S. Private*, pg. 1710
GLENROY CONSTRUCTION CO. INC.; *U.S. Private*, pg. 1711
G.L. WILSON BUILDING COMPANY; *U.S. Private*, pg. 1631
GOLDEN METROPOLIS INTERNATIONAL LIMITED; *Int'l*, pg. 3030
GP KRAJINA A.D.; *Int'l*, pg. 3046
GRADIP A.D. PRNJAVOR; *Int'l*, pg. 3049
GRANITE CONSTRUCTION CO. - ARIZONA—See Granite Construction Incorporated; *U.S. Public*, pg. 957
GRANITE CONSTRUCTION CO. - SACRAMENTO VALLEY BRANCH—See Granite Construction Incorporated; *U.S. Public*, pg. 957
GRANITE CONSTRUCTION NORTHEAST, INC.—See Granite Construction Incorporated; *U.S. Public*, pg. 957
GRAYCOR INTERNATIONAL INC.—See Graycor Inc.; *U.S. Private*, pg. 1761
GREEN BAY REMODELING, INC.; *U.S. Private*, pg. 1771
GROUPE BRIAND SAS; *Int'l*, pg. 3099
GROUP PSAGOT FOR FINANCE AND INVESTMENTS LTD.; *Int'l*, pg. 3089
GS ENGINEERING & CONSTRUCTION CORPORATION—See GS Holdings Corp.; *Int'l*, pg. 3142
GULF EXTRUSIONS CO. (LLC)—See Al Ghurair Group; *Int'l*, pg. 277
GUNDLACH CHAMPION, INC.—See Champion, Inc.; *U.S. Private*, pg. 847
GUNTHER NASH INCORPORATED—See Alberici Corporation; *U.S. Private*, pg. 152
GUY F. ATKINSON CONSTRUCTION, LLC - NORTHWEST DIVISION—See Clark Enterprises, Inc.; *U.S. Private*, pg. 913
HAAS-ANDERSON CONSTRUCTION; *U.S. Private*, pg. 1837
HALLSTROM CONSTRUCTION INC.; *U.S. Private*, pg. 1845
HARMONY LLC—See Turner Industries Group, L.L.C.; *U.S. Private*, pg. 4260
HARSCO INFRASTRUCTURE CONSTRUCTION SERVICES B.V.—See Brand Industrial Services, Inc.; *U.S. Private*, pg. 636
HARTY TRACTOR SERVICES, INC.; *U.S. Private*, pg. 1874
HASKELL DE MEXICO, S.A. DE C.V.—See The Haskell Company; *U.S. Private*, pg. 4043
HEALEY RAILROAD CORPORATION; *U.S. Private*, pg. 1891
HEATHERWOOD CONSTRUCTION COMPANY; *U.S. Private*, pg. 1902
H&E EQUIPMENT SERVICES, INC.; *U.S. Public*, pg. 976
HEFAL SERWIS S.A.; *Int'l*, pg. 3307
H.E. HUNEWILL CONSTRUCTION CO.; *U.S. Private*, pg. 1826
HEIJMANS NEDERLAND B.V.—See Heijmans N.V.; *Int'l*, pg. 3322
HEIJMANS N.V.; *Int'l*, pg. 3322
HENRY BOOT CONSTRUCTION (UK) LIMITED—See Henry Boot PLC; *Int'l*, pg. 3355
HENRY F. TEICHMANN INCORPORATED; *U.S. Private*, pg. 1918
HENSEL PHELPS INTERNATIONAL LLC—See Hensel Phelps Construction Co.; *U.S. Private*, pg. 1920
HERZOG CONTRACTING CORP.; *U.S. Private*, pg. 1927
THE HESSE COMPANIES; *U.S. Private*, pg. 4052
H&H ENGINEERING CONSTRUCTION—See Wind Point Advisors LLC; *U.S. Private*, pg. 4535
H+H UK LIMITED—See H+H International A/S; *Int'l*, pg. 3194

HICKINGBOTHAM INVESTMENTS, INC.; *U.S. Private*, pg. 1933
HIGGERSON-BUCHANAN INC.; *U.S. Private*, pg. 1934
HILL & COX CORPORATION; *U.S. Private*, pg. 1944
HINDUSTAN CONSTRUCTION CO. LTD; *Int'l*, pg. 3399
HITACHI ZOSEN INOVA AG—See Hitachi Zosen Corporation; *Int'l*, pg. 3411
HI-TECH CONSTRUCTION COMPANY; *U.S. Private*, pg. 1932
HITIT CONSTRUCTION COMPANY—See Hitit Holding A.S.; *Int'l*, pg. 3427
HOA BINH CONSTRUCTION GROUP JSC; *Int'l*, pg. 3435
HOLLENBACH CONSTRUCTION, INC.; *U.S. Private*, pg. 1964
HOME PRODUCT CENTER PUBLIC COMPANY LIMITED; *Int'l*, pg. 3455
HOPEWELL CONSTRUCTION COMPANY LIMITED—See Hopewell Holdings Limited; *Int'l*, pg. 3473
HOPEWELL PROPERTY MANAGEMENT COMPANY LIMITED—See Hopewell Holdings Limited; *Int'l*, pg. 3473
HUAKU DEVELOPMENT CO., LTD.; *Int'l*, pg. 3512
HUNTER CONTRACTING COMPANY; *U.S. Private*, pg. 2009
IBEROAMERICANA DE HIDROCARBUROS, S.A. DE C.V.—See ACS, Actividades de Construccion y Servicios, S.A.; *Int'l*, pg. 114
IDEALBASE SDN. BHD.—See Gromutual Berhad; *Int'l*, pg. 3087
IDT AUSTRALIA LIMITED; *Int'l*, pg. 3596
IJM LAND BERHAD—See IJM Corporation Berhad; *Int'l*, pg. 3608
INDUSTRIAL TURNAROUND CORPORATION; *U.S. Private*, pg. 2069
INNOVATIVE MODULAR SOLUTIONS, INC.—See McGrath RentCorp.; *U.S. Public*, pg. 1407
INSULATION HOLDINGS LNC.—See Bird Construction Inc.; *Int'l*, pg. 1047
IRMSCHER INC.; *U.S. Private*, pg. 2139
ISEMOTO CONTRACTING CO. LTD.; *U.S. Private*, pg. 2143
IVEYS CONSTRUCTION INC.; *U.S. Private*, pg. 2151
J2 ENGINEERING, INC.; *U.S. Private*, pg. 2172
J2 SOLUTIONS, INC.; *U.S. Private*, pg. 2172
JACKSON BUILDERS, INC.; *U.S. Private*, pg. 2175
JACOBS CONSULTANCY SPOL S.R.O—See Jacobs Engineering Group, Inc.; *U.S. Public*, pg. 1184
JACOBS ENGINEERING SA INTERNATIONAL—See Jacobs Engineering Group, Inc.; *U.S. Public*, pg. 1184
JAMCO INC.; *U.S. Private*, pg. 2182
JAMES A. JENNINGS CO. INC.; *U.S. Private*, pg. 2183
JAMES & LUTHER, INC.; *U.S. Private*, pg. 2183
JARVIS DOWNING & EMCH INC.; *U.S. Private*, pg. 2188
JAY CASHMAN INC.; *U.S. Private*, pg. 2191
J.D. DIFFENBAUGH, INC.; *U.S. Private*, pg. 2160
JESCO CONSTRUCTION CORPORATION; *U.S. Private*, pg. 2203
J.F. BRENNAN CO., INC.; *U.S. Private*, pg. 2162
JMJ ENVIRONMENTAL INC.—See M.A. Bongiovanni Inc.; *U.S. Private*, pg. 2527
JMJ ORGANICS, LTD.—See SiteOne Landscape Supply, Inc.; *U.S. Public*, pg. 1888
J.O. DELOTTO AND SONS, INC.; *U.S. Private*, pg. 2169
JOHN COLEMAN HAYES CONSTRUCTION CO.; *U.S. Private*, pg. 2221
JOHNSON BROS. CORPORATION; *U.S. Private*, pg. 2226
JOHNSON CONTRACTORS INC.; *U.S. Private*, pg. 2227
J.R. KELLY COMPANY INC.; *U.S. Private*, pg. 2170
JRM CONSTRUCTION MANAGEMENT, LLC; *U.S. Private*, pg. 2240
J&S CONSTRUCTION COMPANY INC; *U.S. Private*, pg. 2155
JT CONSTRUCTION CO. INC.; *U.S. Private*, pg. 2241
J.W. GRAND INC.; *U.S. Private*, pg. 2172
KBR CONSTRUCTION COMPANY, LLC—See KBR, Inc.; *U.S. Public*, pg. 1216
KELLER HCW GMBH—See Groupe Legris Industries; *Int'l*, pg. 3106
KIDD CONSTRUCTION CO., INC.; *U.S. Private*, pg. 2302
KILGORE INDUSTRIES; *U.S. Private*, pg. 2304
KINSLEY CONSTRUCTION INC.; *U.S. Private*, pg. 2313
KIRCO; *U.S. Private*, pg. 2314
KISAQ, LLC—See Nana Regional Corporation, Inc.; *U.S. Private*, pg. 2832
KJELLSTROM & LEE, INC.; *U.S. Private*, pg. 2317
KLEWIN CONSTRUCTION INC.; *U.S. Private*, pg. 2319
KNUTSON CONSTRUCTION SERVICES, INC.—See Knutson Construction Services; *U.S. Private*, pg. 2325
KNUTSON CONSTRUCTION SERVICES; *U.S. Private*, pg. 2325
KOSTMAYER CONSTRUCTION INC.; *U.S. Private*, pg. 2345
KOTIVIEP 'B KFT.—See Betonut Szolgaltato es Epito Rt.; *Int'l*, pg. 1003
KRAUS-ANDERSON CONSTRUCTION COMPANY, INC.—See Kraus-Anderson Incorporated; *U.S. Private*, pg. 2349
KUHLKE CONSTRUCTION & ASSOCIATES, INC.; *U.S. Private*, pg. 2356

N.A.I.C.S. INDEX

236210 — INDUSTRIAL BUILDING...

K.W. REESE INC.; *U.S. Private*, pg. 2252
LAKEHEAD CONSTRUCTORS, INC.—See Lakehead Holding Corp.; *U.S. Private*, pg. 2376
LAKEHEAD HOLDING CORP.; *U.S. Private*, pg. 2376
LANDSCAPES UNLIMITED LLC; *U.S. Private*, pg. 2387
LARSON CONTRACTING CENTRAL, LLC; *U.S. Private*, pg. 2393
LAYTON CONSTRUCTION COMPANY, LLC—See STO Building Group Inc.; *U.S. Private*, pg. 3813
LEMARTEC ENGINEERING & CONSTRUCTION CORPORATION; *U.S. Private*, pg. 2420
THE LIBERTY BLUE GROUP LLC; *U.S. Private*, pg. 4069
LYDALL FILTRATION, INC.—See Lydall, Inc.; *U.S. Public*, pg. 1349
MADISON INDUSTRIES INC. OF GEORGIA—See John S. Frey Enterprises; *U.S. Private*, pg. 2224
MAFI SRL—See Clariane SE; *Int'l*, pg. 1643
MAINE DRILLING & BLASTING INC.; *U.S. Private*, pg. 2552
MANSON CONSTRUCTION CO., INC.; *U.S. Private*, pg. 2566
MARATHON CONSTRUCTION CORP.; *U.S. Private*, pg. 2570
MARINO/WARE—See Ware Industries; *U.S. Private*, pg. 4441
MARTEL CONSTRUCTION, INC.; *U.S. Private*, pg. 2593
MATRIX NORTH AMERICAN CONSTRUCTION, INC.—See Matrix Service Company; *U.S. Private*, pg. 1397
MATTHEWS CONSTRUCTION CO., INC.; *U.S. Private*, pg. 2613
MAY CONSTRUCTION CO.; *U.S. Private*, pg. 2620
MCCONNELL DOWELL SOUTH EAST ASIA PRIVATE LIMITED—See Aveng Limited; *Int'l*, pg. 738
MC INDUSTRIAL, INC.—See McCarthy Holdings, Inc.; *U.S. Private*, pg. 2627
MCM CORP.; *U.S. Private*, pg. 2642
M.D. DESCANT, INC.; *U.S. Private*, pg. 2528
MDI GROUP, INC.—See Littlejohn & Co., LLC; *U.S. Private*, pg. 2471
MEDCO CONSTRUCTION, LLC—See The Christman Company Inc.; *U.S. Private*, pg. 4009
MID STATES CONSTRUCTION INC.; *U.S. Private*, pg. 2706
MIDWEST FORESTREE LLC.; *U.S. Private*, pg. 2721
MIDWEST FOUNDATION CORPORATION—See Midco Construction Corporation; *U.S. Private*, pg. 2710
MILCO NATIONAL CONSTRUCTORS, INC.—See INNOVATE Corp.; *U.S. Public*, pg. 1126
MILEPOST INDUSTRIES; *U.S. Private*, pg. 2727
MILTON J. WOOD COMPANY; *U.S. Private*, pg. 2738
MIWEL CONSTRUCTION LIMITED—See Aecon Group Inc.; *Int'l*, pg. 172
M&J GENERAL CONTRACTORS INC.; *U.S. Private*, pg. 2524
MONTEREY MECHANICAL COMPANY; *U.S. Private*, pg. 2776
MORA ENGINEERING CONTRACTORS, INC.; *U.S. Private*, pg. 2781
MORRIS-SHEA BRIDGE COMPANY, INC.; *U.S. Private*, pg. 2788
MRM CONSTRUCTION SERVICES, INC.; *U.S. Private*, pg. 2805
MSI GENERAL CORPORATION; *U.S. Private*, pg. 2807
MULLANEY CORPORATION; *U.S. Private*, pg. 2811
MYGREENBUILDINGS, LLC; *U.S. Private*, pg. 2825
NAGELBUSH MECHANICAL, INC.—See Tutor Perini Corporation; *U.S. Public*, pg. 2206
NASA MULTIPLEX LLC—See Brookfield Corporation; *Int'l*, pg. 1185
NICHOLS TEAM, INC.; *U.S. Private*, pg. 2925
NORDIC INDUSTRIES INC.; *U.S. Private*, pg. 2937
NORFOLK DREDGING COMPANY; *U.S. Private*, pg. 2937
NORTH STAR CONSTRUCTION MANAGEMENT; *U.S. Private*, pg. 2947
NORTON CONSTRUCTION CO.; *U.S. Private*, pg. 2963
OCCI INC.; *U.S. Private*, pg. 2988
O'HARROW CONSTRUCTION COMPANY; *U.S. Private*, pg. 2978
OLTMANS CONSTRUCTION COMPANY; *U.S. Private*, pg. 3012
OPTIMAL OUTCOMES, LLC; *U.S. Private*, pg. 3034
OPTIMUM BARRIERS—See Hill & Smith PLC; *Int'l*, pg. 3392
ORION CONSTRUCTION LP—See Orion Group Holdings, Inc.; *U.S. Public*, pg. 1618
OSPREY MANAGEMENT, LLC; *U.S. Private*, pg. 3048
OVERLAND CONTRACTING INC.—See Black & Veatch Holding Company; *U.S. Private*, pg. 569
PALA INTERSTATE, LLC—See Pala Group, Inc.; *U.S. Private*, pg. 3076
PARADISE EXTERIORS LLC; *U.S. Private*, pg. 3090
PARK WEST LANDSCAPE—See Tracy Industries Inc.; *U.S. Private*, pg. 4201
PARSONS CONSTRUCTION GROUP INC.—See Parsons Corporation; *U.S. Public*, pg. 1651
PEARSON HOLDING COMPANY INC.; *U.S. Private*, pg. 3126
PERFORMANCE CONTRACTORS INC.; *U.S. Private*, pg. 3149
PERINI BUILDING COMPANY, INC.—See Tutor Perini Corporation; *U.S. Public*, pg. 2206
PERINI MANAGEMENT SERVICES, INC.—See Tutor Perini Corporation; *U.S. Public*, pg. 2206
PERLO MCCORMACK PACIFIC—See W.L. McCormack & Co. Inc.; *U.S. Private*, pg. 4421
PERRY CONSTRUCTION GROUP INC.; *U.S. Private*, pg. 3153
PETRA INCORPORATED; *U.S. Private*, pg. 3161
PETRO ENVIRONMENTAL TECHNOLOGIES INC.; *U.S. Private*, pg. 3161
PHILLIPS & JORDAN INCORPORATED; *U.S. Private*, pg. 3170
PINE BLUFF SAND AND GRAVEL CO; *U.S. Private*, pg. 3182
PITAGORA SRL—See Acciona, S.A.; *Int'l*, pg. 90
PLURIBUS INTERNATIONAL CORPORATION—See Amentum Services, Inc.; *U.S. Private*, pg. 219
PORTICO SERVICES, LLC—See Nana Regional Corporation, Inc.; *U.S. Private*, pg. 2832
POWERPLANT MAINTENANCE SPECIALISTS INC.; *U.S. Private*, pg. 3239
PPM—See EMCOR Group, Inc.; *U.S. Public*, pg. 738
PRINCIPLE CONSTRUCTION CORP.; *U.S. Private*, pg. 3265
PROMINENT CONSTRUCTION, LLC; *U.S. Private*, pg. 3283
PYRAMID PROJECT MANAGEMENT—See Pyramid Advisors LLC; *U.S. Private*, pg. 3310
QSS INTERNATIONAL INC.; *U.S. Private*, pg. 3314
QUALITY PROJECT MANAGEMENT LLC; *U.S. Private*, pg. 3321
RACO GENERAL CONTRACTORS INC.; *U.S. Private*, pg. 3342
RAGNAR BENSON, INC.—See MasTec, Inc.; *U.S. Public*, pg. 1393
RC STEVENS CONSTRUCTION COMPANY—See Cianbro Corporation; *U.S. Private*, pg. 896
R&D MAINTENANCE SERVICES, INC.; *U.S. Private*, pg. 3332
REFLEX HR LIMITED—See Empresaria Group Plc; *Int'l*, pg. 2389
R.E. MONKS CONSTRUCTION COMPANY LLC; *U.S. Private*, pg. 3335
RE MONKS CONSTRUCTION COMPANY; *U.S. Private*, pg. 3364
RENEWAL DESIGN-BUILD INC.; *U.S. Private*, pg. 3398
RENTENBACH CONSTRUCTORS INCORPORATED—See The Christman Company Inc.; *U.S. Private*, pg. 4009
RENTENBACH ENGINEERING COMPANY—See The Christman Company Inc.; *U.S. Private*, pg. 4009
RESTORATION BUILDERS INC.; *U.S. Private*, pg. 3409
REVCON CONSTRUCTION CORP.; *U.S. Private*, pg. 3413
R.J. CORMAN RAILROAD GROUP LLC; *U.S. Private*, pg. 3337
ROB'T J. BAGGETT INC.; *U.S. Private*, pg. 3456
ROGERS-O'BRIEN CONSTRUCTION COMPANY INC.; *U.S. Private*, pg. 3472
ROOSEVELT ASSOCIATES—See Republic Services, Inc.; *U.S. Public*, pg. 1787
ROSS BROTHERS CONSTRUCTION CO; *U.S. Private*, pg. 3485
RUNNEBOHM CONSTRUCTION COMPANY INC.; *U.S. Private*, pg. 3504
RUSCILLI CONSTRUCTION CO. INC.; *U.S. Private*, pg. 3505
RYAN INCORPORATED CENTRAL; *U.S. Private*, pg. 3510
RYAN SALES & SERVICE, INC.—See The Ryan Companies, LLC; *U.S. Private*, pg. 4113
SAMPSON CONSTRUCTION CO. INC.; *U.S. Private*, pg. 3537
S.C.BOG'ART VEST S.R.L.—See Bog'Art S.R.L.; *Int'l*, pg. 1100
SCELERIN HEATERS LLC—See Primoris Services Corporation; *U.S. Public*, pg. 1719
SCHIAVONE CONSTRUCTION CO. LLC—See ACS, Actividades de Construccion y Servicios, S.A.; *Int'l*, pg. 111
SCHMUESER & ASSOCIATES INC.; *U.S. Private*, pg. 3566
SCHMUESER & ASSOCIATES INC.—See Schmueser & Associates Inc.; *U.S. Private*, pg. 3566
SCOTT AND MURPHY, INC.; *U.S. Private*, pg. 3576
SCOTTYS CONTRACTING & STONE LLC; *U.S. Private*, pg. 3578
SCRUFARI CONSTRUCTION CO. INC.; *U.S. Private*, pg. 3580
THE SELMER COMPANY—See AF International Corporation; *U.S. Private*, pg. 121
SES CONSTRUCTION AND FUEL SERVICES LLC—See Bristol Bay Native Corporation; *U.S. Private*, pg. 656
SHAYCORE ENTERPRISES INC.; *U.S. Private*, pg. 3628
SHELCO, LLC; *U.S. Private*, pg. 3631
SHERIDAN CONSTRUCTION CORP—See Sheri-Key; *U.S. Private*, pg. 3633
SHERI-KEY; *U.S. Private*, pg. 3633
SHOEMAKER CONSTRUCTION CO.—See Butz Enterprises, Inc.; *U.S. Private*, pg. 698
SHOOK NORTHERN OHIO DIVISION—See Shook National Corporation; *U.S. Private*, pg. 3640
THE SHURTLEFF & ANDREWS CORP.; *U.S. Private*, pg. 4117
SICHUAN DEVELOPMENT GUORUN WATER SUPPLY INVESTMENT CO LTD—See Beijing SPC Environment Protection Tech Co., Ltd.; *Int'l*, pg. 957
SIERRA INDUSTRIES INC.; *U.S. Private*, pg. 3647
SKINNER & COOK, INC.—See Borgman Capital LLC; *U.S. Private*, pg. 618
SMART CITY DEVELOPMENT HOLDINGS LIMITED—See Deson Development International Holdings Ltd; *Int'l*, pg. 2045
SMITH & COMPANY INC.; *U.S. Private*, pg. 3693
SMITH DOUGLAS HOMES CORP.; *U.S. Public*, pg. 1896
SNC-LAVALIN EUROPE S.A.S.—See AtkinsRealis Group Inc.; *Int'l*, pg. 672
SNELSON COMPANIES INC.—See Primoris Services Corporation; *U.S. Public*, pg. 1719
SOUTH CONSTRUCTION COMPANY, INC.—See Duke Energy Corporation; *U.S. Public*, pg. 691
SOUTHEASTERN PUBLIC SERVICE AUTHORITY; *U.S. Private*, pg. 3728
SOUTHWEST ROCK PRODUCTS, LLC—See Arcosa, Inc.; *U.S. Public*, pg. 186
SPIRIT CONSTRUCTION SERVICES INC.—See VHC Inc.; *U.S. Private*, pg. 4375
SRS, INC.; *U.S. Private*, pg. 3768
SSP RECLAMATION CO.—See Radius Recycling, Inc.; *U.S. Public*, pg. 1760
STANMAR INC.; *U.S. Private*, pg. 3783
STATE SERVICE CO. INC.; *U.S. Private*, pg. 3792
S&TECHS (JAPAN) LIMITED—See STO Building Group Inc.; *U.S. Private*, pg. 3814
S&TECHS (TAIWAN) LIMITED—See STO Building Group Inc.; *U.S. Private*, pg. 3814
STELLAR DEVELOPMENT, INC.; *U.S. Private*, pg. 3799
STENSTROM COMPANIES LTD.; *U.S. Private*, pg. 3801
STEVENS ENGINEERS & CONSTRUCTORS; *U.S. Private*, pg. 3809
STEWART SENTER INC.; *U.S. Private*, pg. 3811
STILES CORPORATION; *U.S. Private*, pg. 3812
STRAMIT INDUSTRIES LTD.—See Eleco Plc; *Int'l*, pg. 2348
STRUCTURE TONE, INC.—See STO Building Group Inc.; *U.S. Private*, pg. 3814
STRUCTURE VENTURES LLC; *U.S. Private*, pg. 3842
STRUKTON GROEP N.V.—See Centric Holding B.V.; *Int'l*, pg. 1412
STV INC.—See STV Group, Inc.; *U.S. Private*, pg. 3845
SULLIVAN AND MERRITT INC.; *U.S. Private*, pg. 3851
SUMMIT CONTRACTING LLC—See Irex Corporation; *U.S. Private*, pg. 2138
SUVIC OY—See Dovre Group Plc; *Int'l*, pg. 2182
SWINDELL DRESSLER INTERNATIONAL CO.; *U.S. Private*, pg. 3893
TARLTON CORPORATION; *U.S. Private*, pg. 3934
TEAMWORK SAUDI ARABIA LTD.—See Ali Zaid Al-Quraishi & Brothers Co.; *Int'l*, pg. 323
TECHNOLOGIA INTERCONTINENETAL S.A. DE C.V.—See Empresas Publicas de Medellin ESP; *Int'l*, pg. 2391
TERNA S.A.—See Gek Terna Societe Anonyme Holdings Real Estate Constructions; *Int'l*, pg. 2913
TETON BUILDINGS LLC; *U.S. Private*, pg. 3973
TETRA TECH TESORO, INC.—See Tetra Tech, Inc.; *U.S. Public*, pg. 4154
THOMAS & MARKER CONSTRUCTION COMPANY; *U.S. Private*, pg. 4154
THOMPSON CONSTRUCTION GROUP—See Thompson Industrial Services, LLC; *U.S. Private*, pg. 4159
THOMPSON TURNER CONSTRUCTION—See Thompson Industrial Services, LLC; *U.S. Private*, pg. 4160
TIC ENERGY & CHEMICAL—See Peter Kiewit Sons', Inc.; *U.S. Private*, pg. 3158
TIC HOLDINGS INC.—See Peter Kiewit Sons', Inc.; *U.S. Private*, pg. 3158
TIFFANY CONSTRUCTION COMPANY; *U.S. Private*, pg. 4169
TIMBERLINE LAND CO. INC.; *U.S. Private*, pg. 4172
TOKAI KOGYO CO., LTD.—See AGC Inc.; *Int'l*, pg. 204
TORRENT RESOURSES INC; *U.S. Private*, pg. 4189
TRAC-WORK INC.; *U.S. Private*, pg. 4200
TRILLACORPE CONSTRUCTION; *U.S. Private*, pg. 4231
TRIMBLE SOLUTIONS SANDVIKA AS—See Trimble, Inc.; *U.S. Public*, pg. 2193
TRITON MARINE CONSTRUCTION; *U.S. Private*, pg. 4239
TULSA CEMEMT LLC—See Eagle Materials Inc.; *U.S. Public*, pg. 702
TURNER INDUSTRIES GROUP, L.L.C. - HOUSTON FACILITY—See Turner Industries Group, L.L.C.; *U.S. Private*, pg. 4261
TURNER INDUSTRIES—See Turner Industries Group, L.L.C.; *U.S. Private*, pg. 4261
TUTOR PERINI BUILDING CORP.—See Tutor Perini Corporation; *U.S. Public*, pg. 2206
TYLER 2 CONSTRUCTION, INC.; *U.S. Private*, pg. 4267
TYSAN HOLDINGS LIMITED—See Blackstone Inc.; *U.S. Public*, pg. 351
UDELHOVEN OILFIELD SYSTEMS SERVICES INC.—See Harding Holdings Inc.; *U.S. Private*, pg. 1863

236210 — INDUSTRIAL BUILDING...

UNDERWATER CONSTRUCTION CORP.; *U.S. Private*, pg. 4279
UNIFIED DOOR & HARDWARE GROUP, LLC—See American Securities LLC; *U.S. Private*, pg. 249
UNITED CONSTRUCTION CO. INC.; *U.S. Private*, pg. 4290
VALHALLA BUILDERS & DEVELOPERS INC.; *U.S. Private*, pg. 4331
VENEGAS CONSTRUCTION CORP.; *U.S. Private*, pg. 4356
VJ USINA CONTRACTING, INC.; *U.S. Private*, pg. 4407
VOLKMANN RAILROAD BUILDERS; *U.S. Private*, pg. 4410
VORTEX MARINE CONSTRUCTION; *U.S. Private*, pg. 4413
WAKELEE ASSOCIATES LLC—See Kelso & Company, L.P.; *U.S. Private*, pg. 2278
W.A. KLINGER, LLC.; *U.S. Private*, pg. 4418
WALSH CONSTRUCTION CO. OF ILLINOIS—See The Walsh Group; *U.S. Private*, pg. 4133
WALTON CONSTRUCTION-A CORE COMPANY, LLC—See Otto Baum Company, Inc.; *U.S. Private*, pg. 3050
WANZEK CONSTRUCTION INC.—See MasTec, Inc.; *U.S. Public*, pg. 1393
WARE INDUSTRIES; *U.S. Private*, pg. 4441
THE WARRIOR GROUP, INC.; *U.S. Private*, pg. 4133
WBW GMBH—See Clariane SE; *Int'l*, pg. 1645
WEBER MARINE INCORPORATED; *U.S. Private*, pg. 4465
WEEKS MARINE, INC.—See Kiewit Corp.; *U.S. Private*, pg. 2304
WEISS CONSTRUCTION COMPANY LLC; *U.S. Private*, pg. 4472
WELTY BUILDING COMPANY, LTD.; *U.S. Private*, pg. 4480
W.E. O'NEIL CONSTRUCTION—See O'Neil Industries Inc.; *U.S. Private*, pg. 2979
WILLIAMS COMPANY INC.; *U.S. Private*, pg. 4525
WIZE SOLUTIONS INC.—See Argosy Capital Group, LLC; *U.S. Private*, pg. 322
WOODWARD DESIGN+BUILD; *U.S. Private*, pg. 4561
WWPS, LLC.—See Alberici Corporation; *U.S. Private*, pg. 152
YORK BRIDGE CONCEPTS; *U.S. Private*, pg. 4590
ZIBO SHUANGFENG SHANSHUI CEMENT CO., LTD.—See China Shanshui Cement Group Ltd.; *Int'l*, pg. 1550

236220 — COMMERCIAL AND INSTITUTIONAL BUILDING CONSTRUCTION

1369 CONSTRUCTION JOINT STOCK COMPANY; *Int'l*, pg. 2
142258 CANADA INC; *Int'l*, pg. 2
1ST CHOICE FACILITIES SERVICES CORP.; *U.S. Private*, pg. 4
2700 EMPIRE, LLC—See Hovnanian Enterprises, Inc.; *U.S. Public*, pg. 1056
2825 FOUR MILE ROAD LLC—See WEC Energy Group, Inc.; *U.S. Public*, pg. 2342
360 RESIDENCES, L.P.—See Essex Property Trust, Inc.; *U.S. Public*, pg. 795
3 BOYS ENTERPRISES LLC.; *U.S. Private*, pg. 7
5B INVESTMENTS, INC.; *U.S. Private*, pg. 16
ABCO BUILDERS, INC.—See C.P. Richards Construction Co., Inc.; *U.S. Private*, pg. 708
ABDULLAH ABDUL MOHSIN AL-KHODARI SONS COMPANY; *Int'l*, pg. 59
ABHE & SVOBODA, INC.; *U.S. Private*, pg. 38
ABILIA D.O.O.—See Adris Grupa d.d.; *Int'l*, pg. 153
A B INFRABUILD LIMITED; *Int'l*, pg. 17
ABSHER CONSTRUCTION COMPANY; *U.S. Private*, pg. 44
ACCESS AUSTRALASIA SDN. BHD.—See AusGroup Limited; *Int'l*, pg. 716
ACCESS CONSTRUCTIONS PTY LTD—See Charter Hall Limited; *Int'l*, pg. 1454
ACCESS SERVICES (HK) LIMITED—See Hargreaves Services plc; *Int'l*, pg. 3275
ACCESS SYSTEMS INC.—See Computer Sites Inc.; *U.S. Private*, pg. 1005
ACS INFRASTRUCTURE CANADA, INC.—See ACS, Actividades de Construccion y Servicios, S.A.; *Int'l*, pg. 109
ACS, SERVICIOS COMUNICACIONES Y ENERGA, S.L.—See ACS, Actividades de Construccion y Servicios, S.A.; *Int'l*, pg. 109
ADDNODE BALKAN D.O.O.—See Addnode Group AB; *Int'l*, pg. 130
ADLER GROUP, INC.; *U.S. Private*, pg. 80
A.D. MORGAN CORPORATION; *U.S. Private*, pg. 25
ADOLFSON & PETERSON, ARIZONA—See Adolfson & Peterson, Inc.; *U.S. Private*, pg. 81
ADOLFSON & PETERSON, COLORADO—See Adolfson & Peterson, Inc.; *U.S. Private*, pg. 81
ADOLFSON & PETERSON, INC.; *U.S. Private*, pg. 81
ADOLFSON & PETERSON, TEXAS—See Adolfson & Peterson, Inc.; *U.S. Private*, pg. 81
ADONIS CONSTRUCTION LTD; *Int'l*, pg. 152
ADR INFRASTRUTTURE S.P.A—See Edizione S.r.l.; *Int'l*, pg. 2311

ADVANCED ARCHITECTURAL PRODUCTS, LLC; *U.S. Private*, pg. 87
AECON BUILDINGS—See Aecon Group Inc.; *Int'l*, pg. 172
AECON BUILDINGS—See Aecon Group Inc.; *Int'l*, pg. 172
AECON GROUP INC.; *Int'l*, pg. 172
AEK BUILD TEC AG—See BKW AG; *Int'l*, pg. 1054
AEK ELEKTRO AG—See BKW AG; *Int'l*, pg. 1054
A.E. NEW, JR., INC.; *U.S. Private*, pg. 25
AEON TOWN CO., LTD.—See AEON Co., Ltd.; *Int'l*, pg. 177
AESO HOLDING LIMITED; *Int'l*, pg. 182
AETNA CONSTRUCTION, INC.—See Oxford Holdings Inc.; *U.S. Private*, pg. 3057
AF AERONMOLLIER AS—See AF Gruppen ASA; *Int'l*, pg. 184
AF BYGG GOTEBORG AB—See AF Gruppen ASA; *Int'l*, pg. 184
AF BYGG SYD AB—See AF Gruppen ASA; *Int'l*, pg. 184
AF DECOM AS—See AF Gruppen ASA; *Int'l*, pg. 184
AF ENERGI & MILJOTEKNIKK AS—See AF Gruppen ASA; *Int'l*, pg. 184
AF ENERGI OG MILJO AS—See AF Gruppen ASA; *Int'l*, pg. 184
AFFINITY BUILDING SYSTEMS, LLC—See Vantem Global, Inc.; *U.S. Private*, pg. 4345
AFFORDABLE CONCEPTS, INC.; *U.S. Private*, pg. 123
AFI PALACE COTROCENI—See Africa Israel Investments Ltd.; *Int'l*, pg. 190
AGDER OPS VEGSELSKAP AS—See BBGI Global Infrastructure S.A; *Int'l*, pg. 920
AGI INFRA LTD.; *Int'l*, pg. 209
AGRICO SALES INC.; *U.S. Private*, pg. 129
AGRI-SYSTEMS; *U.S. Private*, pg. 129
AGSTEN CONSTRUCTION COMPANY; *U.S. Private*, pg. 130
AHMED MANSOOR AL-A'ALI CO.; *Int'l*, pg. 225
AHTNA ENTERPRISES CORPORATION—See Ahtna Incorporated; *U.S. Private*, pg. 131
AICHER, DE MARTIN, ZWENG AG—See BKW AG; *Int'l*, pg. 1054
AIRPORT CITY BELGRADE D.O.O.—See Africa Israel Investments Ltd.; *Int'l*, pg. 190
AJAX BUILDING CORPORATION; *U.S. Private*, pg. 143
AJAX CONSTRUCTION CO., INC.; *U.S. Private*, pg. 143
AJ DIANI CONSTRUCTION CO; *U.S. Private*, pg. 143
AKASH INFRA PROJECTS LTD.; *Int'l*, pg. 260
AKELIUS LAGENHETER AB—See Akelius Residential AB; *Int'l*, pg. 262
AKIMA CONSTRUCTION SERVICES, LLC—See Nana Regional Corporation, Inc.; *U.S. Private*, pg. 2832
AKM LLC; *U.S. Private*, pg. 145
AKTIVE ENERGI ANLAEG A/S—See 2G Energy AG; *Int'l*, pg. 5
AKTOR BULGARIA SA—See ELLAKTOR S.A.; *Int'l*, pg. 2364
ALAN SHINTANI INC.; *U.S. Private*, pg. 150
ALBERICI CONSTRUCCIONES S.A. DE C.V.—See Alberici Corporation; *U.S. Private*, pg. 152
ALBERICI CONSTRUCTORS, LTD.—See Alberici Corporation; *U.S. Private*, pg. 152
ALBERICI CORPORATION; *U.S. Private*, pg. 152
ALBERICI HEALTHCARE, LLC—See Alberici Corporation; *U.S. Private*, pg. 152
ALBERT C. KOBAYASHI INC.; *U.S. Private*, pg. 152
ALBERT M. HIGLEY COMPANY; *U.S. Private*, pg. 153
ALBU & ASSOCIATES, INC.; *U.S. Private*, pg. 153
ALDERMAN BUILDING COMPANY, INC.; *U.S. Private*, pg. 159
ALEXANDER BUILDING CONSTRUCTION, CO.; *U.S. Private*, pg. 163
ALEXANDER BUILDING CONSTRUCTION LLC—See Butz Enterprises, Inc.; *U.S. Private*, pg. 698
AL HABTOOR GROUP LLC; *Int'l*, pg. 278
AL HABTOOR LEIGHTON GROUP—See Al Habtoor Group LLC; *Int'l*, pg. 278
AL HAMAD CONTRACTING COMPANY LLC; *Int'l*, pg. 278
AL JABER CATERING SERVICES L.L.C—See Al Jaber Group; *Int'l*, pg. 279
AL JABER CONTRACTING LTD.—See Al Jaber Group; *Int'l*, pg. 279
AL JABER LANDSCAPE LLC—See Al Jaber Group; *Int'l*, pg. 279
AL JABER LEASING SERVICES L.L.C.—See Al Jaber Group; *Int'l*, pg. 279
AL JABER & PARTNERS - CONSTRUCTION & ENERGY PROJECTS W.L.L.—See Al Jaber Group; *Int'l*, pg. 279
AL J. MUELLER CONSTRUCTION COMPANY; *U.S. Private*, pg. 147
ALLEN-KEITH CONSTRUCTION CO., INC.; *U.S. Private*, pg. 180
ALLEN L. BENDER, INC.; *U.S. Private*, pg. 179
ALLIANCE CONSTRUCTION SOLUTIONS LLC; *U.S. Private*, pg. 181
ALLIED BUILDING CORP.; *U.S. Private*, pg. 185
ALLOS SA; *Int'l*, pg. 359
ALLSTATE CONSTRUCTION INC.; *U.S. Private*, pg. 193
ALL TRI-R INC.; *U.S. Private*, pg. 173
AL-OSAIS CONTRACTING CO.—See Al-Osais International Holding Company; *Int'l*, pg. 287

ALPS CONSTRUCTION INC.; *U.S. Private*, pg. 202
AL SABAH TRADING & CONTRACTING INC.—See Ali Zaid Al-Quraishi & Brothers Co.; *Int'l*, pg. 323
AL-SAWAM GENERAL CONTRACTING COMPANY LTD.—See Eng. Shabah Al-Shammery & Partners Co.; *Int'l*, pg. 2426
AL SHANKLE CONSTRUCTION COMPANY; *U.S. Private*, pg. 147
ALTAIR-STRICKLAND INCORPORATED; *U.S. Private*, pg. 204
ALTAPEX CORPORATION; *Int'l*, pg. 385
AL TATWEER CONTRACTING L.L.C—See Belhasa Group of Companies; *Int'l*, pg. 963
AL TAYER STOCKS LLC—See Al Tayer Group LLC; *Int'l*, pg. 283
ALTMAN-CHARTER COMPANY; *U.S. Private*, pg. 210
ALTRAD COLLECTIVITES SA—See Altrad Investment Authority SAS; *Int'l*, pg. 397
ALTRAD FAMEA ECA S.A.S.—See Altrad Investment Authority SAS; *Int'l*, pg. 397
ALTRAD SAINT DENIS S.A.—See Altrad Investment Authority SAS; *Int'l*, pg. 397
AL TUWAIRQI TRADING & CONTRACTING—See Al-Tuwairqi Group; *Int'l*, pg. 289
ALVARADO CONSTRUCTION, INC.; *U.S. Private*, pg. 211
ALV INFRASTRUCTURE DEVELOPMENT INVESTMENT JSC; *Int'l*, pg. 401
AM CONTRACTING LLC; *U.S. Private*, pg. 214
AME ELITE CONSORTIUM BERHAD; *Int'l*, pg. 420
AME INCORPORATED; *U.S. Private*, pg. 218
AMERICAN CONSTRUCTORS LP; *U.S. Private*, pg. 228
AMERICAN INTERNATIONAL CONTRACTORS INC.; *U.S. Private*, pg. 238
AMERICAN WINDOW FILM INC—See Solar Art Window Film, Inc.; *U.S. Private*, pg. 3707
AMERIDIAN SPECIALTY SERVICES INC.; *U.S. Private*, pg. 259
AMG & ASSOCIATES, INC.; *U.S. Private*, pg. 262
AM&G WATERPROOFING, LLC; *U.S. Private*, pg. 215
AMHULT 2 AB; *Int'l*, pg. 426
AMOS LUZON DEVELOPMENT AND ENERGY GROUP LTD.; *Int'l*, pg. 430
AMSDELL COMPANIES; *U.S. Private*, pg. 267
ANCHOR FIRE PROTECTION CO.—See The Carlyle Group Inc.; *U.S. Public*, pg. 2053
ANCHOR TAMPA, INC.; *U.S. Private*, pg. 273
ANDERSON CONSTRUCTION COMPANY OF FORT GAINES; *U.S. Private*, pg. 276
ANDERSON GROUP LIMITED; *Int'l*, pg. 450
ANDREW R. MANCINI ASSOCIATES, INC.; *U.S. Private*, pg. 279
ANHUI GOURGEN TRAFFIC CONSTRUCTION CO., LTD.; *Int'l*, pg. 467
ANSAL IT CITY & PARKS LTD.—See Ansal Properties & Infrastructure Limited; *Int'l*, pg. 478
A.O. CONSTRUCTION COMPANY, INC.; *U.S. Private*, pg. 27
APODACA WALL SYSTEMS, INC.; *U.S. Private*, pg. 294
APOLLO, INC.; *U.S. Private*, pg. 295
APPARATEBAU GAUTING GESELLSCHAFT MIT BESCHRANKTER HAFTUNG—See Diehl Stiftung & Co. KG; *Int'l*, pg. 2114
APPRO DEVELOPMENT, INC.; *U.S. Private*, pg. 300
AP (THAILAND) PUBLIC COMPANY LIMITED; *Int'l*, pg. 499
APTIM GOVERNMENT SOLUTIONS, LLC—See McDermott International, Inc.; *U.S. Public*, pg. 1405
ARAB TOWER CONTRACTING COMPANY LTD.—See Enjaz for Development & Multi Projects Company P.L.C.; *Int'l*, pg. 2439
ARAMARK CHUGACH ALASKA SERVICES, LLC—See Aramark; *U.S. Public*, pg. 177
ARBEN GROUP LLC.; *U.S. Private*, pg. 308
ARBEN GROUP; *U.S. Private*, pg. 308
ARB, INC.—See Primoris Services Corporation; *U.S. Public*, pg. 1718
ARCHER WESTERN CONTRACTORS—See The Walsh Group; *U.S. Private*, pg. 4133
ARCHITECTURAL DOORS & WINDOWS; *U.S. Private*, pg. 311
ARCHITECTURAL GLASS & GLAZING—See Aluma-Glass Industries, Inc.; *U.S. Private*, pg. 211
ARCON CONSTRUCTION & MANAGEMENT SERVICES, INC.; *U.S. Private*, pg. 315
ARCO (QLD) PTY LTD—See Bunka Shutter Co., Ltd.; *Int'l*, pg. 1216
ARDENT SERVICES, LLC - KENNER—See EMCOR Group, Inc.; *U.S. Public*, pg. 736
ARIES BUILDING SYSTEMS, LLC - PNW MAJOR PROJECTS—See Reliant Asset Management LLC; *U.S. Private*, pg. 3395
ARIZONA TRENCH COMPANY, LLC—See Quanta Services, Inc.; *U.S. Public*, pg. 1750
ARIZON COMPANIES; *U.S. Private*, pg. 323
A.R.K. CONTRACTING SERVICES LLC.; *U.S. Private*, pg. 27
ARKEL CONSTRUCTORS, INC.; *U.S. Private*, pg. 326
ARKEL INTERNATIONAL INC.; *U.S. Private*, pg. 326
ARMSTRONG STEEL; *U.S. Private*, pg. 332

N.A.I.C.S. INDEX

236220 — COMMERCIAL AND INST...

ARNELL-WEST INC.; *U.S. Private*, pg. 332
ARNEXX S.A.—See Echeverria Izquierdo S.A.; *Int'l*, pg. 2289
AROK INC.; *U.S. Private*, pg. 334
ARPA-SEVAN OJSC; *Int'l*, pg. 578
ARPE AG—See BKW AG; *Int'l*, pg. 1054
ARRIYADH DEVELOPMENT COMPANY; *Int'l*, pg. 579
ARTEC CONSTRUCTION LTD.; *Int'l*, pg. 581
ART FORCE JAPAN CO., LTD.; *Int'l*, pg. 580
ART NIRMAN LTD.; *Int'l*, pg. 580
ASANE BYGGMESTERFORRETNING AS—See AF Gruppen ASA; *Int'l*, pg. 184
ASANUMA CORPORATION; *Int'l*, pg. 599
ASBI JOINT STOCK COMPANY; *Int'l*, pg. 600
ASH & LACY BUILDING SYSTEMS LTD; *Int'l*, pg. 606
ASHTROM GROUP LTD.; *Int'l*, pg. 609
ASHTROM PROPERTIES LTD.; *Int'l*, pg. 609
ASPEN EXTERIORS, INC.; *U.S. Private*, pg. 351
ASRC SKW ESKIMOS, INC.—See Arctic Slope Regional Corporation; *U.S. Private*, pg. 316
ASSOCIATED BRIGHAM CONTRACTORS; *U.S. Private*, pg. 354
ATHLETICA SPORT SYSTEMS INC—See Fulcrum Capital Partners Inc.; *Int'l*, pg. 2841
ATLANTA LIMITED; *Int'l*, pg. 674
ATLAS PROFESSIONALS B.V.—See HAL Trust N.V.; *Int'l*, pg. 3223
ATLAS PUMPING SERVICE—See Audax Group, Limited Partnership; *U.S. Private*, pg. 388
ATTI-KAT SA; *Int'l*, pg. 696
AUGERE CONSTRUCTION; *U.S. Private*, pg. 392
AUI CONTRACTORS, LLC.; *U.S. Private*, pg. 392
AUKETT FITZROY ROBINSON LIMITED—See Aukett Swanke Group Plc; *Int'l*, pg. 704
AUSGROUP CORPORATION CO., LTD.—See AusGroup Limited; *Int'l*, pg. 716
AUSTIN COMMERCIAL, INC.—See Austin Industries, Inc.; *U.S. Private*, pg. 395
AUSTIN INDUSTRIES, INC.; *U.S. Private*, pg. 395
AV BUILDER CORP.; *U.S. Private*, pg. 402
AVENG LIMITED; *Int'l*, pg. 738
AVICOR CONSTRUCTION; *Int'l*, pg. 743
AVIENT ARGENTINA S.A.—See Avient Corporation; *U.S. Public*, pg. 246
AVIENT CHILE S.P.A.—See Avient Corporation; *U.S. Public*, pg. 246
AVILA CONSTRUCTION COMPANY INC; *U.S. Private*, pg. 407
A. WATTS, INC.; *U.S. Private*, pg. 24
AYARS & AYARS INCORPORATED; *U.S. Private*, pg. 414
AYUDA MANAGEMENT CORPORATION; *U.S. Private*, pg. 415
AZBIL CONTROL INSTRUMENT TRADING (DALIAN) CO., LTD.—See Azbil Corporation; *Int'l*, pg. 777
A/Z CORPORATION—See Cianbro Corporation; *U.S. Private*, pg. 896
THE AZTECA-OMEGA GROUP; *U.S. Private*, pg. 3990
BABCO CONSTRUCTION INC.; *U.S. Private*, pg. 421
BAILEY-HARRIS CONSTRUCTION, INC.; *U.S. Private*, pg. 426
BALDWIN & SHELL CONSTRUCTION CO. INC.; *U.S. Private*, pg. 458
BALFOUR BEATTY CONSTRUCTION LIMITED—See Balfour Beatty plc; *Int'l*, pg. 807
BALFOUR BEATTY CONSTRUCTION LLC—See Balfour Beatty plc; *Int'l*, pg. 807
BALFOUR BEATTY CONSTRUCTION NORTHERN LIMITED—See Balfour Beatty plc; *Int'l*, pg. 807
BALFOUR BEATTY CONSTRUCTION - SCOTTISH & SOUTHERN LIMITED—See Balfour Beatty plc; *Int'l*, pg. 807
BALFOUR BEATTY CONSTRUCTION SERVICES UK—See Balfour Beatty plc; *Int'l*, pg. 807
BALFOUR BEATTY-CONSTRUCTION SERVICES UK—See Balfour Beatty plc; *Int'l*, pg. 808
BALLARENA CONSTRUCTION; *U.S. Private*, pg. 461
BAMBECK & VEST ASSOCIATES INC.; *U.S. Private*, pg. 463
BAMCO INC.; *U.S. Private*, pg. 463
BAMPTON (REDBRIDGE) LIMITED—See Centremanor Ltd.; *Int'l*, pg. 1411
BANCROFT CONTRACTING CORP.; *U.S. Private*, pg. 464
BANDES CONSTRUCTION COMPANY INC; *U.S. Private*, pg. 465
BANES GENERAL CONTRACTORS, INC.; *U.S. Private*, pg. 465
BANGKOK METRO PUBLIC COMPANY LIMITED—See CH. Karnchang Public Company Limited; *Int'l*, pg. 1435
BANTON CONSTRUCTION COMPANY; *U.S. Private*, pg. 470
BAOYE GROUP COMPANY LIMITED; *Int'l*, pg. 857
BAQUS GROUP LIMITED; *Int'l*, pg. 857
BARCOM COMMERCIAL INC.; *U.S. Private*, pg. 473
BAREFOOT & COMPANY, LLC—See Builders FirstSource, Inc.; *U.S. Public*, pg. 410
BARILGA CORPORATION JOINT STOCK COMPANY; *Int'l*, pg. 864
BARLOVENTO, LLC; *U.S. Private*, pg. 476

BARNHART-REESE CONSTRUCTION INC.; *U.S. Private*, pg. 478
BARON + DOWDLE CONSTRUCTION, LLC.; *U.S. Private*, pg. 478
BARR & BARR, INC.; *U.S. Private*, pg. 479
BARRY, BETTE & LED DUKE, INC.; *U.S. Private*, pg. 481
BARRY SWENSON BUILDER; *U.S. Private*, pg. 481
BARTLETT BRAINARD EACOTT, INC.; *U.S. Private*, pg. 483
BARTLETT COCKE, LP; *U.S. Private*, pg. 483
BARTON MALOW COMPANY—See Barton Malow Enterprises, Inc.; *U.S. Private*, pg. 483
BARTON MALOW COMPANY—See Barton Malow Enterprises, Inc.; *U.S. Private*, pg. 483
BARTON MALOW COMPANY—See Barton Malow Enterprises, Inc.; *U.S. Private*, pg. 483
BARTON MALOW ENTERPRISES, INC.; *U.S. Private*, pg. 483
BASF WEST AFRICA LTD.—See BASF SE; *Int'l*, pg. 882
BASIL READ (PTY) LIMITED—See Basil Read Holdings Limited; *Int'l*, pg. 886
B&A TELECOM—See Bulley & Andrews, LLC; *U.S. Private*, pg. 685
BATEMAN-HALL INC; *U.S. Private*, pg. 486
BATZER CONSTRUCTION, INC.; *U.S. Private*, pg. 490
BAUMELER LEITUNGSBAU AG—See BKW AG; *Int'l*, pg. 1055
BAUVAL INC.; *Int'l*, pg. 898
BAYALAG NALAIKH JOINT STOCK COMPANY; *Int'l*, pg. 901
BAY AREA BUILDING SOLUTIONS, INC.; *U.S. Private*, pg. 491
BAY AREA HIGH REACH, INC.; *U.S. Private*, pg. 491
BAYBUTT CONSTRUCTION CORP.; *U.S. Private*, pg. 495
BAYERN CORPORATE SERVICES GMBH—See BayernLB Holding AG; *Int'l*, pg. 913
BAYLAND BUILDINGS, INC.; *U.S. Private*, pg. 496
BAYLEY CONSTRUCTION INC.; *U.S. Private*, pg. 496
BAYPORT MORTGAGE - SACRAMENTO—See The Warmington Group; *U.S. Private*, pg. 4133
BAY TO BAY PROPERTIES, LLC; *U.S. Private*, pg. 495
BAY VISTA AT MEADOW PARK, L.P.—See PulteGroup, Inc.; *U.S. Private*, pg. 1737
BB&B CONSTRUCTION SERVICES OF FLORIDA, INC.; *U.S. Private*, pg. 497
B&B CONSTRUCTION CO. OF OHIO—See B&B Contractors & Developers; *U.S. Private*, pg. 417
B&B CONTRACTORS & DEVELOPERS; *U.S. Private*, pg. 417
BCCI CONSTRUCTION COMPANY; *U.S. Private*, pg. 499
BEAM CONSTRUCTION CO. INC.; *U.S. Private*, pg. 506
BECHTEL CONSTRUCTION COMPANY, INC.—See Bechtel Group, Inc.; *U.S. Private*, pg. 510
BECKER ARENA PRODUCTS INC.—See Fulcrum Capital Partners Inc.; *Int'l*, pg. 2841
THE BECK GROUP; *U.S. Private*, pg. 3992
BECK & HOFER CONSTRUCTION, INC.; *U.S. Private*, pg. 510
BEC SOUTHWEST, INC.—See Johnson Carlier Inc.; *U.S. Private*, pg. 2227
BEIJING HILL CONSTRUCTION CONSULTING CO., LTD.—See Global Infrastructure Solutions, Inc.; *U.S. Private*, pg. 1715
BEIJING-SHANGHAI HIGH SPEED RAILWAY CO., LTD.; *Int'l*, pg. 961
BEITZEL CORPORATION; *U.S. Private*, pg. 516
BE&K BUILDING GROUP, LLC - CHARLOTTE—See Pernix Group, Inc.; *U.S. Public*, pg. 1677
BE&K BUILDING GROUP, LLC—See Pernix Group, Inc.; *U.S. Public*, pg. 1677
BELAIR BUILDERS INC.; *U.S. Private*, pg. 516
BELHASA PROJECTS LLC—See Belhasa Group of Companies; *Int'l*, pg. 964
BELHASA SIX CONSTRUCTION COMPANY—See Belhasa Group of Companies; *Int'l*, pg. 964
BELL & ASSOCIATES CONSTRUCTION, LP.; *U.S. Private*, pg. 518
BELL CONSTRUCTORS INC.—See Bell Corp. of Rochester; *U.S. Private*, pg. 518
BELL CORP. OF ROCHESTER; *U.S. Private*, pg. 518
BELLEVUE HOLDING COMPANY INC.; *U.S. Private*, pg. 520
BEMPFINGER LEBENSMITTEL GMBH—See Hero AG; *Int'l*, pg. 3363
BENAKA, INC.; *U.S. Private*, pg. 523
BENCHMARK CONSTRUCTION COMPANY, INC.; *U.S. Private*, pg. 523
BENNING CONSTRUCTION COMPANY INC.; *U.S. Private*, pg. 528
BFRGBOLAGET I GOTALAND AB—See AF Gruppen ASA; *Int'l*, pg. 184
BERGER BAU GMBH—See BERGER Holding GmbH; *Int'l*, pg. 979
BERGLUND CONSTRUCTION COMPANY; *U.S. Private*, pg. 531
BERKIM CONSTRUCTION INC.; *Int'l*, pg. 985
BERNDORF BADERBAU SCHWEIZ AG—See Berndorf AG; *Int'l*, pg. 986

BERSCHAUER PHILLIPS CONSTRUCTION CO; *U.S. Private*, pg. 539
BESSETTE DEVELOPMENT CORPORATION; *U.S. Private*, pg. 542
BETHLEHEM CONSTRUCTION INC.; *U.S. Private*, pg. 546
BETON A.D.; *Int'l*, pg. 1002
BETONMAST AS—See AF Gruppen ASA; *Int'l*, pg. 184
BETONMAST BUSKERUD-VESTFOLD AS—See AF Gruppen ASA; *Int'l*, pg. 184
BETONMAST INNLANDET AS—See AF Gruppen ASA; *Int'l*, pg. 184
BETONMAST OSTFOLD AS—See AF Gruppen ASA; *Int'l*, pg. 184
BETONMAST RINGERIKE AS—See AF Gruppen ASA; *Int'l*, pg. 184
BETONMAST ROMERIKE AS—See AF Gruppen ASA; *Int'l*, pg. 184
BETONMAST ROSAND AS—See AF Gruppen ASA; *Int'l*, pg. 184
BETONMAST TELEMARK AS—See AF Gruppen ASA; *Int'l*, pg. 184
BETONMAST TRONDELAG AS—See AF Gruppen ASA; *Int'l*, pg. 184
BETTE & CRING, LLC; *U.S. Private*, pg. 546
BEYER CONSTRUCTION LTD.; *U.S. Private*, pg. 548
BEYON3D LTD.; *Int'l*, pg. 1005
BGMC INTERNATIONAL LIMITED; *Int'l*, pg. 1008
BHCC CONSTRUCTION PTE. LTD.—See BHCC Holding Limited; *Int'l*, pg. 1014
BHCC HOLDING LIMITED; *Int'l*, pg. 1014
B. H. CRAIG CONSTRUCTION COMPANY; *U.S. Private*, pg. 419
BILFINGER BERGER AG-HOCHBAU—See Bilfinger SE; *Int'l*, pg. 1024
BILFINGER BERGER PROJECT INVESTMENTS GMBH—See Bilfinger SE; *Int'l*, pg. 1026
BILFINGER BERGER PROJECT INVESTMENTS INC.—See Bilfinger SE; *Int'l*, pg. 1026
BILFINGER BERGER PROJECTS S.A.R.L.—See Bilfinger SE; *Int'l*, pg. 1026
BIL-RAY HOME IMPROVEMENTS—See Bil-Ray Group; *U.S. Private*, pg. 556
BILTMORE CONSTRUCTION CO. INC.; *U.S. Private*, pg. 559
BIRD CONSTRUCTION COMPANY, INC.; *U.S. Private*, pg. 564
BIRD CONSTRUCTION INC.; *Int'l*, pg. 1046
BIRLA ESTATES PRIVATE LIMITED—See Century Textiles and Industries Limited; *Int'l*, pg. 1419
BISCAYNE CONTRACTORS INCORPORATED; *U.S. Private*, pg. 565
BITROS CONSTRUCTION S.A.—See Bitros Holding S.A.; *Int'l*, pg. 1050
BLACK CONSTRUCTION CORPORATION—See Tutor Perini Corporation; *U.S. Public*, pg. 2206
BLACK & DEW; *U.S. Private*, pg. 569
BLAINE CONSTRUCTION CORPORATION—See W.G. Yates & Sons Construction Company; *U.S. Private*, pg. 4420
BLAIR CONSTRUCTION INC.; *U.S. Private*, pg. 578
BLATT CONSTRUCTION INC.—See Blatt Group; *U.S. Private*, pg. 580
BLATTNER ENERGY, LLC—See Quanta Services, Inc.; *U.S. Public*, pg. 1750
B.L. HARBERT INTERNATIONAL, LLC; *U.S. Private*, pg. 420
B.L. SPILLE CONSTRUCTION, INC.; *U.S. Private*, pg. 421
BLUE & ASSOCIATES, INC.; *U.S. Private*, pg. 585
BLUESCOPE LYSAGHT (SINGAPORE) PTE. LTD.—See BlueScope Steel Limited; *Int'l*, pg. 1073
BLUESCOPE PROPERTIES GROUP LLC—See BlueScope Steel Limited; *Int'l*, pg. 1073
BLUNT ENTERPRISES LLC; *U.S. Private*, pg. 599
BLUSKY RESTORATION CONTRACTORS, LLC—See Kohlberg & Company, LLC; *U.S. Private*, pg. 2337
BMWC CONSTRUCTORS, INC. - SEATTLE—See BMWC Group Inc.; *U.S. Private*, pg. 601
BNBUILDERS, INC.; *U.S. Private*, pg. 601
BOATNER CONSTRUCTION CO INC.; *U.S. Private*, pg. 603
BOB PARRETT CONSTRUCTION INC.; *U.S. Private*, pg. 605
BOCKSTAEL CONSTRUCTION LIMITED; *Int'l*, pg. 1097
BODELL CONSTRUCTION COMPANY INC.; *U.S. Private*, pg. 608
BOGNER CONSTRUCTION COMPANY; *U.S. Private*, pg. 609
BOLDT CONSULTING SERVICES—See The Boldt Group Inc.; *U.S. Private*, pg. 3995
BOLLER CONSTRUCTION COMPANY, INC.; *U.S. Private*, pg. 610
BOMEL CONSTRUCTION CO. INC.; *U.S. Private*, pg. 612
BONAVENTURA SERVICES GMBH—See Groupe Egis S.A.; *Int'l*, pg. 3102
BONDFIELD CONSTRUCTION COMPANY LIMITED; *Int'l*, pg. 1105
BORO CONSTRUCTION; *U.S. Private*, pg. 619
BORTON, LC.; *U.S. Private*, pg. 619

236220 — COMMERCIAL AND INST...

BOSA PROPERTIES INC.; *Int'l*, pg. 1116
BOSSE MATTINGLY CONSTRUCTORS, INC.; *U.S. Private*, pg. 620
BOSTLEMAN CORP.; *U.S. Private*, pg. 621
BOSWORTH STEEL ERECTORS, INC.; *U.S. Private*, pg. 622
BOUSTEAD PROJECTS LTD.—See Boustead Singapore Limited; *Int'l*, pg. 1120
BOUYGUES BATIMENT INTERNATIONAL—See Bouygues S.A.; *Int'l*, pg. 1122
BOUYGUES IMMOBILIER—See Bouygues S.A.; *Int'l*, 1122
BOUYGUES (UK) LTD.—See Bouygues S.A.; *Int'l*, pg. 1121
BOWMAN CONSTRUCTORS, INC.; *U.S. Private*, pg. 626
BOYLE CONSTRUCTION INC.; *U.S. Private*, pg. 628
BOYLE INVESTMENT COMPANY; *U.S. Private*, pg. 628
BOYUAN CONSTRUCTION GROUP, INC.; *Int'l*, pg. 1125
BRADBURY STAMM CONSTRUCTION, INC.; *U.S. Private*, pg. 631
BRAE BURN CONSTRUCTION, CO.—See Welty Building Company, Ltd.; *U.S. Private*, pg. 4480
BRANAGH INC.; *U.S. Private*, pg. 635
BRANCH & ASSOCIATES, INC.—See The Branch Group, Inc.; *U.S. Private*, pg. 3999
THE BRANCH GROUP, INC.; *U.S. Private*, pg. 3999
BRANDED GROUP, INC.; *U.S. Private*, pg. 637
BRANDENBURG INDUSTRIAL SERVICE COMPANY INC.; *U.S. Private*, pg. 637
BRANDWELLS CONSTRUCTION; *Int'l*, pg. 1140
BRASFIELD & GORRIE, LLC; *U.S. Private*, pg. 640
BRAUN & BUTLER CONSTRUCTION, INC.; *U.S. Private*, pg. 641
BRICE BUILDING COMPANY, INC.—See Tutor Perini Corporation; *U.S. Public*, pg. 2206
BRIDGEPOINT, LLC—See Bridgepoint Group Plc; *Int'l*, pg. 1155
BRIDGES & COMPANY, INC.; *U.S. Private*, pg. 649
BRINDLEY CONSTRUCTION, LLC; *U.S. Private*, pg. 654
BRISTILE LTD.—See Brickworks Limited; *Int'l*, pg. 1152
BROAD CONSTRUCTION SERVICES PTY LTD—See ACS, Actividades de Construccion y Servicios, S.A.; *Int'l*, pg. 110
BROOKS & FREUND, LLC; *U.S. Private*, pg. 664
BROWN BUILDERS INC.; *U.S. Private*, pg. 667
BRUNO'S CONTRACTING (THUNDER BAY) LTD.; *Int'l*, pg. 1200
BRYAN BUSH CONSTRUCTION COMPANY, INC.; *U.S. Private*, pg. 673
BRYAN CONSTRUCTION COMPANY; *U.S. Private*, pg. 673
BRYCON CORP; *U.S. Private*, pg. 674
BSE INDUSTRIAL CONTRACTORS; *U.S. Private*, pg. 674
B+S ELEKTRO TELEMATIK AG—See BKW AG; *Int'l*, pg. 1056
BUILDING EQUITY SOONER FOR TOMORROW; *U.S. Private*, pg. 682
BUILDING ERECTION SERVICES CO.; *U.S. Private*, pg. 682
BUILDINGPOINT DEUTSCHLAND NORD GMBH—See Trimble, Inc.; *U.S. Public*, pg. 2190
BULILD SJC—See Build Group, Inc.; *U.S. Private*, pg. 681
BULLARD CONSTRUCTION INC.; *U.S. Private*, pg. 684
BULLEY & ANDREWS, LLC; *U.S. Private*, pg. 685
BUNKA SHUTTER SERVICE CO., LTD.—See Bunka Shutter Co., Ltd.; *Int'l*, pg. 1216
BUNKOFF GENERAL CONTRACTORS; *U.S. Private*, pg. 685
BUQUET & LE BLANC INC.; *U.S. Private*, pg. 686
BURTON BROTHERS GENERAL CONTRACTORS LC; *U.S. Private*, pg. 693
BURTON F CLARK INC.; *U.S. Private*, pg. 693
BUSH CONSTRUCTION COMPANY, INC.—See McCarthy Bush Corporation; *U.S. Private*, pg. 2626
BUTZ ENTERPRISES, INC.; *U.S. Private*, pg. 698
BUZICK CONSTRUCTION INC.; *U.S. Private*, pg. 699
BVB GENERAL CONTRACTORS, LLC; *U.S. Private*, pg. 700
BX AIWA INSURANCE SERVICE CO., LTD.—See Bunka Shutter Co., Ltd.; *Int'l*, pg. 1216
BX ASAHI KENZAI CO., LTD.—See Bunka Shutter Co., Ltd.; *Int'l*, pg. 1216
BX BUNKA AUSTRALIA PTY LTD—See Bunka Shutter Co., Ltd.; *Int'l*, pg. 1216
BX BUNKA KOUGEI CO., LTD.—See Bunka Shutter Co., Ltd.; *Int'l*, pg. 1216
BX BUNKA PANEL CO., LTD.—See Bunka Shutter Co., Ltd.; *Int'l*, pg. 1216
BX KANESHIN CO., LTD.—See Bunka Shutter Co., Ltd.; *Int'l*, pg. 1216
BX KENSEI CO., LTD.—See Bunka Shutter Co., Ltd.; *Int'l*, pg. 1216
BX NISHIYAMA TETSUMOU CO., LTD.—See Bunka Shutter Co., Ltd.; *Int'l*, pg. 1216
BX ROOTES CO., LTD.—See Bunka Shutter Co., Ltd.; *Int'l*, pg. 1216
BX TETSUYA CO., LTD.—See Bunka Shutter Co., Ltd.; *Int'l*, pg. 1216
BX TOHOKU TETSUYA CO., LTD.—See Bunka Shutter Co., Ltd.; *Int'l*, pg. 1216

BX TOSHO CO., LTD.—See Bunka Shutter Co., Ltd.; *Int'l*, pg. 1216
BX TR CO., LTD.—See Bunka Shutter Co., Ltd.; *Int'l*, pg. 1216
CADDELL CONSTRUCTION CO., INC.; *U.S. Private*, pg. 712
CADENCE MCSHANE CORPORATION; *U.S. Private*, pg. 713
CAESARS GENERAL TRADING AND CONTRACTING COMPANY W.L.L.—See Caesars Group; *Int'l*, pg. 1249
CALCON CONSTRUCTORS, INC.; *U.S. Private*, pg. 716
CAL DEVELOPMENT INC.; *U.S. Private*, pg. 715
CALIFORNIA COASTAL COMMUNITIES, INC.; *U.S. Private*, pg. 718
C.A. LINDMAN INC.; *U.S. Private*, pg. 705
CALLAHAN INC.; *U.S. Private*, pg. 722
CALVIN L. WADSWORTH CONSTRUCTION CO.; *U.S. Private*, pg. 724
CAM CONSULTANTS, INC.; *U.S. Private*, pg. 725
CAMDON CONSTRUCTION LTD; *Int'l*, pg. 1270
CAMFAUD CONCRETE PUMPS LIMITED—See Concrete Pumping Holdings, Inc.; *U.S. Public*, pg. 566
CAMOSY CONSTRUCTION; *U.S. Private*, pg. 729
CAMOSY, INC.; *U.S. Private*, pg. 729
CAMROST-FELCORP INC.; *Int'l*, pg. 1275
CANACRE LTD.—See Quanta Services, Inc.; *U.S. Public*, pg. 1750
CANCO GENERAL CONTRACTORS INC.; *U.S. Private*, pg. 733
CAN-DER CONSTRUCTION LTD; *Int'l*, pg. 1276
CANINE FENCE COS., INC.—See Radio Systems Corporation; *U.S. Private*, pg. 3344
CANNON ENTERPRISES INC.; *U.S. Private*, pg. 735
CANPRO CONSTRUCTION LTD.; *Int'l*, pg. 1298
CAPITAL PUMPING, LP—See Concrete Pumping Holdings, Inc.; *U.S. Public*, pg. 566
CAPITAL RECONSTRUCTION, INC.; *U.S. Private*, pg. 741
CAPITOL CONTRACTORS INC.; *U.S. Private*, pg. 743
THE CAPSTONE CONTRACTING COMPANY—See Hourigan Construction Corp.; *U.S. Private*, pg. 1991
CARDINAL CONSTRUCTION INC.; *U.S. Private*, pg. 750
CARDINAL CONTRACTORS, INC.—See Primoris Services Corporation; *U.S. Public*, pg. 1718
CAREY GROUP PLC; *Int'l*, pg. 1325
CAREY GROUP PLC—See Carey Group PLC; *Int'l*, pg. 1325
CARIGE REOCO SPA—See Banca Carige S.p.A.; *Int'l*, pg. 814
CARILLION DEFENCE—See Carillion plc; *Int'l*, pg. 1330
CARL BELT INC.; *U.S. Private*, pg. 762
CARLTON, INC.—See Barry, Bette & Led Duke, Inc.; *U.S. Private*, pg. 481
CAROMA CONSTRUCTION CO.; *U.S. Private*, pg. 769
CARREFOUR PROPERTY ESPANA, SLU—See Carrefour SA; *Int'l*, pg. 1345
CARREFOUR PROPERTY FRANCE SAS—See Carrefour SA; *Int'l*, pg. 1345
CARREFOUR PROPERTY ITALIA SRL—See Carrefour SA; *Int'l*, pg. 1345
CARROLL DANIEL CONSTRUCTION COMPANY; *U.S. Private*, pg. 773
CARSO INFRAESTRUCTURA Y CONSTRUCCION, S.A.B. DE C.V.—See Grupo Carso, S.A.B. de C.V.; *Int'l*, pg. 3123
CARSON & ASSOCIATES, INC.; *U.S. Private*, pg. 774
CARTUJA INMOBILIARIA, S.A.U.—See Grupo Empresarial San Jose, S.A.; *Int'l*, pg. 3128
CARVER CONSTRUCTION COMPANY; *U.S. Private*, pg. 777
CASBY BROS, INC.; *U.S. Private*, pg. 778
CASE CONTRACTING COMPANY; *U.S. Private*, pg. 781
CASTO; *U.S. Private*, pg. 785
CATALYST CONSTRUCTION; *U.S. Private*, pg. 786
CATAMOUNT CONSTRUCTORS, INC.; *U.S. Private*, pg. 787
CB CENTRAL BUILDERS INCORPORATED; *U.S. Private*, pg. 796
CBS CONSTRUCTION LTD.; *Int'l*, pg. 1366
C.C. BORDEN CONSTRUCTION, INC.; *U.S. Private*, pg. 706
CCCL INFRASTRUCTURE LTD.—See Consolidated Construction Consortium Ltd; *Int'l*, pg. 1770
CDI CONTRACTORS, LLC—See Dillard's Inc.; *U.S. Public*, pg. 666
CDS, LLC.; *U.S. Private*, pg. 803
C.D. SMITH CONSTRUCTION INC.; *U.S. Private*, pg. 706
CEC INTERNATIONAL CORPORATION (INDIA) PRIVATE LIMITED—See Continental Holdings Corp.; *Int'l*, pg. 1784
CEM ENTERPRISES INC.; *U.S. Private*, pg. 808
CENERGY, LLC.; *U.S. Private*, pg. 809
CENTENNIAL AMERICAN PROPERTIES, LLC; *U.S. Private*, pg. 809
CENTEX HOUSE LEVELING; *U.S. Private*, pg. 817
CENTURY CITY INTERNATIONAL HOLDINGS LTD; *Int'l*, pg. 1417
CENTURY CONSTRUCTION, INC.; *U.S. Private*, pg. 832
CEO CONSTRUCTION JOINT STOCK COMPANY—See C.E.O Group Joint Stock Company; *Int'l*, pg. 1240

C. ERICKSON & SONS INC.; *U.S. Private*, pg. 705
CES BUILDING AND CONSTRUCTION PTE LTD—See Chip Eng Seng Corporation Ltd.; *Int'l*, pg. 1572
CES LAND PTE. LTD.—See Chip Eng Seng Corporation Ltd.; *Int'l*, pg. 1572
C.F. HAGLIN & SONS, INC.; *U.S. Private*, pg. 707
C.F. JORDAN L.P.; *U.S. Private*, pg. 707
CFPS ENGENHARIA E PROJETOS, S.A.—See Fluor Corporation; *U.S. Public*, pg. 858
C&G BEAULIEU GROUP INC.; *Int'l*, pg. 1238
CGL MANAGEMENT GROUP, LLC—See Hunt Companies, Inc.; *U.S. Private*, pg. 2008
C.G. SCHMIDT INC.; *U.S. Private*, pg. 707
CH2M HILL ARGENTINA S.A—See Jacobs Engineering Group, Inc.; *U.S. Public*, pg. 1183
CH2M HILL DO BRASIL ENGENHARIA LTDA.—See Jacobs Engineering Group, Inc.; *U.S. Public*, pg. 1184
CHAMPION CONSTRUCTION CORPORATION; *U.S. Private*, pg. 846
CHANEN CONSTRUCTION CO, INC—See Chanen Corporation; *U.S. Private*, pg. 848
CHANEN CORPORATION; *U.S. Private*, pg. 848
CHANGSHENG CHINA PROPERTY COMPANY LIMITED; *Int'l*, pg. 1444
CHANNELL CONSULTING COMPANY; *U.S. Private*, pg. 848
CHARLES BLANCHARD CONSTRUCTION CORPORATION; *U.S. Private*, pg. 851
CHARLES DEWEESE CONSTRUCTION, INC.; *U.S. Private*, pg. 852
CHARLES H. WILSON CONSTRUCTION COMPANY; *U.S. Private*, pg. 852
CHARLES N. WHITE CONSTRUCTION CO. INC.; *U.S. Private*, pg. 853
CHARLES PANKOW BUILDERS, LTD.; *U.S. Private*, pg. 853
CHARLES PERRY PARTNERS, INC.; *U.S. Private*, pg. 853
CHARLES & VINZANT CONSTRUCTION CO. LLC; *U.S. Private*, pg. 851
CHARTER SOUTH INC.; *U.S. Private*, pg. 858
CHASCO CONSTRUCTORS, LTD., LLP.; *U.S. Private*, pg. 859
CHENGDU SHUODE PHARMACEUTICAL CO., LTD.—See Chengdu Easton Biopharmaceuticals Co., Ltd.; *Int'l*, pg. 1467
CHERRY COMPANIES MANAGEMENT, INC.—See Arcosa, Inc.; *U.S. Public*, pg. 186
CHESTER INC.; *U.S. Private*, pg. 875
CHIANGMAI RIMDOI PCL; *Int'l*, pg. 1476
CHIBA GRANDY HOUSE CO., LTD.—See Grandy House Corporation; *Int'l*, pg. 3058
CHIEN KUO CONSTRUCTION CO., LTD.; *Int'l*, pg. 1476
CHI HO DEVELOPMENT HOLDINGS LIMITED; *Int'l*, pg. 1475
CHINA MERCHANTS EXPRESSWAY NETWORK & TECHNOLOGY HOLDINGS CO., LTD.—See China Merchants Group Limited; *Int'l*, pg. 1520
CHINA RAILWAY ELECTRIFICATION BUREAU (GROUP) CO., LTD.—See China Railway Construction Corporation Limited; *Int'l*, pg. 1543
CHINA RAILWAY GUANGZHOU ENGINEERING GROUP CO. LTD.—See China Railway Group Limited; *Int'l*, pg. 1543
CHINA RAILWAY NO 8 ENGINEERING GROUP CO., LTD.—See China Railway Group Limited; *Int'l*, pg. 1543
CHINA-SINGAPORE SUZHOU INDUSTRIAL PARK DEVELOPMENT GROUP CO., LTD.; *Int'l*, pg. 1568
CHINA SOUTH CITY HOLDINGS LIMITED; *Int'l*, pg. 1552
CHIP ENG SENG CONTRACTORS (1988) PTE LTD.—See Chip Eng Seng Corporation Ltd.; *Int'l*, pg. 1572
CHIP ENG SENG CORPORATION LTD.; *Int'l*, pg. 1572
CH. KARNCHANG PUBLIC COMPANY LIMITED; *Int'l*, pg. 1435
CHOATE CONSTRUCTION COMPANY; *U.S. Private*, pg. 887
CHRIS ALBRITTON CONSTRUCTION COMPANY, INC.; *U.S. Private*, pg. 889
CHRISTA CONSTRUCTION LLC; *U.S. Private*, pg. 890
CHRISTOFFERSON COMMERCIAL BUILDERS; *U.S. Private*, pg. 891
CHUAN HOLDINGS LIMITED; *Int'l*, pg. 1589
CHUN WO BUILDING CONSTRUCTION LIMITED—See Asia Allied Infrastructure Holdings Limited; *Int'l*, pg. 610
CHUN WO (CHINA) LIMITED—See Asia Allied Infrastructure Holdings Limited; *Int'l*, pg. 610
CHUN WO CONSTRUCTION AND ENGINEERING COMPANY LIMITED—See Asia Allied Infrastructure Holdings Limited; *Int'l*, pg. 610
CHUN WO CONTRACTORS LIMITED—See Asia Allied Infrastructure Holdings Limited; *Int'l*, pg. 610
CHUN YUAN CONSTRUCTION CO., LTD.—See Chun Yuan Steel Industry Co., Ltd.; *Int'l*, pg. 1596
CIATTO CONSTRUCTION CO.; *U.S. Private*, pg. 896
C.I. CONSTRUCTION, LLC; *U.S. Private*, pg. 707
CITRON EXPORT INC.—See Hero AG; *Int'l*, pg. 3363
CITY CARE LTD—See Christchurch City Holdings Ltd.; *Int'l*, pg. 1586

N.A.I.C.S. INDEX

236220 — COMMERCIAL AND INST...

CITYCON DEVELOPMENT AB—See Citycon Oyj; *Int'l*, pg. 1629
CITY WINDOW & CONSTRUCTION COMPANY; *U.S. Private*, pg. 907
C J O'SHEA GROUP LTD; *Int'l*, pg. 1238
CLAGGETT & SONS, INC.; *U.S. Private*, pg. 909
CLARION CONSTRUCTION INC.; *U.S. Private*, pg. 911
CLARK BUILDERS LIMITED—See ACS, Actividades de Construccion y Servicios, S.A.; *Int'l*, pg. 113
CLARK CONSTRUCTION GROUP - CALIFORNIA, LP—See Clark Enterprises, Inc.; *U.S. Private*, pg. 912
CLARK CONSTRUCTION GROUP - CHICAGO, LLC—See Clark Enterprises, Inc.; *U.S. Private*, pg. 912
CLARK CONSTRUCTION GROUP, LLC—See Clark Enterprises, Inc.; *U.S. Private*, pg. 912
CLARK CONTRACTS LTD; *Int'l*, pg. 1650
CLARK & SULLIVAN CONSTRUCTORS INC.—See C.S. General Inc.; *U.S. Private*, pg. 709
CLASS LEASING, LLC—See Reliant Asset Management LLC; *U.S. Private*, pg. 3395
CLAYTON & LAMBERT MANUFACTURING CO.; *U.S. Public*, pg. 508
CLEAN MODULES LTD—See Atlas Clean Air Ltd.; *Int'l*, pg. 676
CLEARY BUILDING CORP.; *U.S. Private*, pg. 939
CLEMENS CONSTRUCTION CO. INC.; *U.S. Private*, pg. 940
CLEMENS CONSTRUCTION CO. INC—See Clemens Construction Co. Inc.; *U.S. Private*, pg. 940
CLEMENT CONTRACTING GROUP INC.; *U.S. Private*, pg. 940
CLERHP ESTRUCTURAS SA; *Int'l*, pg. 1658
CLEVELAND CONSTRUCTION INC.; *U.S. Private*, pg. 941
C. MARTIN COMPANY, INC.; *U.S. Private*, pg. 705
CM COMPANY INC.; *U.S. Private*, pg. 949
CME CORPORATION; *U.S. Private*, pg. 950
COAKLEY & WILLIAMS CONSTRUCTION INC.; *U.S. Private*, pg. 953
CODDING CONSTRUCTION CO—See Codding Enterprises; *U.S. Private*, pg. 960
COGIR LIMITEE—See ENL Limited; *Int'l*, pg. 2441
COGUN INC.; *U.S. Private*, pg. 962
COIL CONSTRUCTION INC.; *U.S. Private*, pg. 964
COLDWELL BANKER MARYL REALTY, INC.—See Maryl Group, Inc.; *U.S. Private*, pg. 2600
COLEMAN-ADAMS CONSTRUCTION, INC.; *U.S. Private*, pg. 967
COLORADO STRUCTURES INC.; *U.S. Private*, pg. 974
COLUMBIA DEVELOPMENT COMPANIES; *U.S. Private*, pg. 976
COMMERCIAL CONTRACTORS, INC.; *U.S. Private*, pg. 983
COMMERCIAL INSTALLATION & CONSTRUCTION COMPANY—See Color Art Office Interiors Inc.; *U.S. Private*, pg. 972
COMMERCIAL STOREFRONT SERVICES, INC.; *U.S. Private*, pg. 984
COMMODORE BUILDERS; *U.S. Private*, pg. 985
COMPAGNIE D'ENTERPRISES CFE SA—See Ackermans & van Haaren NV; *Int'l*, pg. 104
COMPANIA HIDROELECTRICA LA YESCA, S.A. DE C.V.—See Empresas ICA S.A.B. de C.V.; *Int'l*, pg. 2390
COMPANIA LEVANTINA DE EDIFICACION Y OBRAS PUBLICAS SA; *Int'l*, pg. 1749
COMPLETE PROPERTY SERVICES, INC.; *U.S. Private*, pg. 1001
COMPOSITE LIMITED; *Int'l*, pg. 1754
COMPREMUM S.A.; *Int'l*, pg. 1754
COMPUTER POWER SYSTEMS INC.—See Incline MGMT Corp.; *U.S. Private*, pg. 2054
COMPUTER SITES INC.; *U.S. Private*, pg. 1005
COMQI INC.—See AUO Corporation; *Int'l*, pg. 706
COMTURE NETWORK CORPORATION—See Comture Corporation; *Int'l*, pg. 1763
CON-AGG COMPANIES, LLC—See Summit Materials, Inc.; *U.S. Public*, pg. 1959
CONART ENGINEERS LIMITED; *Int'l*, pg. 1763
CONATSER SITE SERVICES TX, L.P.; *U.S. Private*, pg. 1008
CONCORD COMPANIES INCORPORATED; *U.S. Private*, pg. 1009
CONGAREE CONSTRUCTION CO., INC.; *U.S. Private*, pg. 1013
THE CONLAN COMPANY; *U.S. Private*, pg. 4014
CONLON CONSTRUCTION CO. INC.; *U.S. Private*, pg. 1014
CONNOLY-PACIFIC COMPANY—See MDU Resources Group, Inc.; *U.S. Public*, pg. 1410
CONRAD SCHMITT STUDIOS, INC.; *U.S. Private*, pg. 1019
CONROY & CONROY CONTRACTORS, INC.; *U.S. Private*, pg. 1019
CONSOLIDATED CONTRACTING SERVICE; *U.S. Private*, pg. 1020
CONSOLIDATED CONTRACTORS COMPANY (KUWAIT) W.L.L.—See Consolidated Contractors International Company S.A.L.; *Int'l*, pg. 1770
CONSOLIDATED CONTRACTORS COMPANY LTD.—See Consolidated Contractors International Company S.A.L.; *Int'l*, pg. 1770
CONSOLIDATED CONTRACTORS INTERNATIONAL (UK) LTD.—See Consolidated Contractors International Company S.A.L.; *Int'l*, pg. 1770
CONSOLVO AS—See AF Gruppen ASA; *Int'l*, pg. 184
CONSTANTINOU BROS DEVELOPERS PLC; *Int'l*, pg. 1772
CONSTANTINOU BROS PROPERTIES PLC; *Int'l*, pg. 1772
CONSTRUCTION ALBERT JEAN LTD.; *Int'l*, pg. 1777
CONSTRUCTION AND SERVICE SOLUTIONS CORP.; *U.S. Private*, pg. 1023
CONSTRUCTION JOINT STOCK COMPANY NO 5; *Int'l*, pg. 1777
CONSTRUCTIONS DE LA COTE D'EMERAUDE; *Int'l*, pg. 1778
CONSTRUCTION SERVICES BRANFORD LLC; *U.S. Private*, pg. 1024
CONSTRUCTION SOCAM LTEE; *Int'l*, pg. 1778
CONSTRUCTION TECHNOLOGY GROUP; *U.S. Private*, pg. 1024
CONSTRUCTORA DE PROYECTOS HIDROELECTRICOS, S.A. DE C.V.—See Empresas ICA S.A.B. de C.V.; *Int'l*, pg. 2390
CONSTRUCTORA EL CAJON, S.A. DE C.V.—See Empresas ICA S.A.B. de C.V.; *Int'l*, pg. 2390
CONSTRUCTORA SAN JOSE ARGENTINA, S.A.—See Grupo Empresarial San Jose, S.A.; *Int'l*, pg. 3128
CONSTRUCTORA SAN JOSE CABO VERDE, S.A.—See Grupo Empresarial San Jose, S.A.; *Int'l*, pg. 3128
CONSTRUCTORA UDRA LIMITADA—See Grupo Empresarial San Jose, S.A.; *Int'l*, pg. 3128
CONSTRUCT TWO GROUP; *U.S. Private*, pg. 1023
CONSTRUSOFT GROEP BV—See Trimble, Inc.; *U.S. Public*, pg. 2190
CONSTRUTORA BETER S.A.; *Int'l*, pg. 1778
CONSULTANTS & BUILDERS, INC.; *U.S. Private*, pg. 1025
CONTINENTAL DEVELOPMENT CORP.; *U.S. Private*, pg. 1028
CONTINENTAL REAL ESTATE COMPANIES INC.; *U.S. Private*, pg. 1030
CONTRACK INTERNATIONAL INC.; *U.S. Private*, pg. 1032
CONTRACTORS NORTHWEST INC.; *U.S. Private*, pg. 1032
CONTROLADORA DE EMPRESAS DE VIVIENDA, S. A. DE C. V.—See Empresas ICA S.A.B. de C.V.; *Int'l*, pg. 2390
COOLING TOWER TECHNOLOGIES—See Crown Enterprises Inc.; *U.S. Private*, pg. 1111
COONROD & ASSOCIATES CONSTRUCTION CO., INC.; *U.S. Private*, pg. 1040
COOPERS PARK CORPORATION; *Int'l*, pg. 1792
COPRO VIETNAM CO., LTD.—See Copro Holdings Co., Ltd.; *Int'l*, pg. 1794
CORE CONSTRUCTION; *U.S. Private*, pg. 1048
CORNELL & COMPANY, INC.; *U.S. Private*, pg. 1051
CORNERSTONE BUILDING SOLUTIONS, INC.—See Simplex Industries Inc; *U.S. Private*, pg. 3667
CORNERSTONE GROUP DEVELOPMENT CORPORATION; *U.S. Private*, pg. 1052
CORNWALL GRAVEL CO. LTD; *Int'l*, pg. 1801
CORPORATE CONSTRUCTION LTD; *U.S. Private*, pg. 1054
CORTE CONSTRUCTION CO. INC.; *U.S. Private*, pg. 1060
COSTAIN CONSTRUCTION LIMITED—See Costain Group PLC; *Int'l*, pg. 1815
COTABIG JOINT STOCK COMPANY—See Cotana Group Joint Stock Company; *Int'l*, pg. 1815
COTANA CAPITAL HOUSING INVESTMENT & DEVELOPMENT JOINT STOCK COMPANY—See Cotana Group Joint Stock Company; *Int'l*, pg. 1815
COTANA GREEN LANDSCAPE ARCHITECTURE JOINT STOCK COMPANY—See Cotana Group Joint Stock Company; *Int'l*, pg. 1815
COTANA GROUP JOINT STOCK COMPANY; *Int'l*, pg. 1815
COTANA INFRASTRUCTURE CONSTRUCTION JOINT STOCK COMPANY—See Cotana Group Joint Stock Company; *Int'l*, pg. 1815
COWLIN TIMBER FRAME—See Balfour Beatty plc; *Int'l*, pg. 808
CPB CONTRACTORS PTY LIMITED—See ACS, Actividades de Construccion y Servicios, S.A.; *Int'l*, pg. 110
CPC CONSTRUCTION HONG KONG LIMITED—See Chevalier International Holdings Limited; *Int'l*, pg. 1473
C.P. RICHARDS CONSTRUCTION CO., INC.; *U.S. Private*, pg. 708
CRAFTCORPS INC.; *U.S. Private*, pg. 1082
CRANE CONSTRUCTION CO.; *U.S. Private*, pg. 1085
CRANSHAW CONSTRUCTION—See National Development; *U.S. Private*, pg. 2852
CRAWFORD RENOVATION; *U.S. Private*, pg. 1086
C.R. CALDERON CONSTRUCTION, INC.; *U.S. Private*, pg. 708
CR DEVELOPPEMENT SAS—See AmRest Holdings SE; *Int'l*, pg. 437
CREATIVE BUSINESS INTERIORS; *U.S. Private*, pg. 1088
CREEKSIDE CUSTOM HOMES LLC—See United Homes Group, Inc; *U.S. Public*, pg. 2231
CRE HOLDINGS LLC—See First Citizens BancShares, Inc.; *U.S. Public*, pg. 841
CRESSWELL BROTHERS GENERAL CONTRACTORS, INC.; *U.S. Private*, pg. 1095
CRISAK INC.; *U.S. Private*, pg. 1101
C.R. MEYER & SONS COMPANY INC.; *U.S. Private*, pg. 708
CROSSLAND CONSTRUCTION CO. INC.; *U.S. Private*, pg. 1106
CROSSLANDS CONSTRUCTION CO., INC.; *U.S. Private*, pg. 1106
CROWELL DEVELOPMENT CORP.; *Int'l*, pg. 1857
CROWN ENTERPRISES INC.; *U.S. Private*, pg. 1111
C&S CONTRACTORS INC.; *U.S. Private*, pg. 703
CSF GROUP PLC; *Int'l*, pg. 1864
CSP BUILDING & SERVICE INC.—See Central Security Patrols Co., Ltd.; *Int'l*, pg. 1409
CTD NETWORKS CO., LTD.—See Central Security Patrols Co., Ltd.; *Int'l*, pg. 1410
CT VISION (INTERNATIONAL) HOLDINGS LIMITED—See CT Vision Investment Ltd; *Int'l*, pg. 1868
CULP CONSTRUCTION CO.; *U.S. Private*, pg. 1121
CULP EUROPE—See Culp, Inc.; *U.S. Public*, pg. 604
CUMBRA PERU S.A.—See Aenza S.A.A.; *Int'l*, pg. 176
CUMMING CONSTRUCTION MANAGEMENT, INC.; *U.S. Private*, pg. 1123
CUNNINGHAM-LIMP COMPANY; *U.S. Private*, pg. 1123
CUREA ELEKTRO AG—See BKW AG; *Int'l*, pg. 1055
CURRENT BUILDERS OF FLORIDA INC.; *U.S. Private*, pg. 1125
CUTLER ASSOCIATES INC.; *U.S. Private*, pg. 1131
CUTTING EDGE PROPERTY MAINTENANCE, INC.—See BrightView Holdings, Inc.; *U.S. Public*, pg. 384
C.W. BROWN, INC.—See LeChase Construction Services, LLC; *U.S. Private*, pg. 2410
C. W. DRIVER, INC.; *U.S. Private*, pg. 705
CW HAYES CONSTRUCTION COMPANY; *U.S. Private*, pg. 1132
CWR CONSTRUCTION, INC.; *U.S. Private*, pg. 1132
CYPRUS LIMNI RESORTS & GOLFCOURSES PLC; *Int'l*, pg. 1897
DACON CORPORATION—See Quanta Services, Inc.; *U.S. Public*, pg. 1751
DADABHAI GROUP; *Int'l*, pg. 1904
DAEJEON RIVERSIDE EXPRESSWAY CO., LTD.—See Groupe Egis S.A.; *Int'l*, pg. 3102
DAEWON CO., LTD.; *Int'l*, pg. 1910
D.A.G. CONSTRUCTION CO., INC.; *U.S. Private*, pg. 1141
DAGIT GROUP; *U.S. Private*, pg. 1144
DAIICHI PROJECT SERVICE CO., LTD.—See Daiichi Jitsugyo Co. Ltd.; *Int'l*, pg. 1927
DAIKEN CORPORATION; *Int'l*, pg. 1931
DAIWA HOUSE CONSTRUCTION MANAGEMENT INC.—See Daiwa House Industry Co., Ltd.; *Int'l*, pg. 1945
DAIWA HOUSE MALAYSIA SDN. BHD.—See Daiwa House Industry Co., Ltd.; *Int'l*, pg. 1945
DAIWA HOUSE REAL ASSET MANAGEMENT VIETNAM, CO., LTD.—See Daiwa House Industry Co., Ltd.; *Int'l*, pg. 1945
DAIWASYSTEM CO., LTD.; *Int'l*, pg. 1950
DALAT REAL ESTATE JOINT STOCK COMPANY; *Int'l*, pg. 1950
DALEKOVOD UKRAJINA D.O.O.—See Dalekovod d.d.; *Int'l*, pg. 1951
DALIAN WANDA COMMERCIAL PROPERTIES CO., LTD.—See Dalian Wanda Group Corporation Ltd.; *Int'l*, pg. 1953
DALMAC CONSTRUCTION PARTNERS LTD.; *U.S. Private*, pg. 1150
DALMAC DEVELOPMENT CORP.—See DalMac Construction Partners Ltd.; *U.S. Private*, pg. 1150
DAMON G. DOUGLAS COMPANY INC.—See The Greenleaf Company Inc.; *U.S. Private*, pg. 4039
DANA B. KENYON COMPANY, INC.; *U.S. Private*, pg. 1152
DANIELS BUILDING & CONSTRUCTION, INC.; *U.S. Private*, pg. 1156
DANIS BUILDING CONSTRUCTION COMPANY INC.; *U.S. Private*, pg. 1156
DANIS CONSTRUCTION COMPANY LLC—See Danis Building Construction Company Inc.; *U.S. Private*, pg. 1156
DANLEY LUMBER CO. INC.; *U.S. Private*, pg. 1157
DARLAND PROPERTIES; *U.S. Private*, pg. 1159
DARLIND; *U.S. Private*, pg. 1159
DARLING DEVELOPMENT INC.—See Chanen Corporation; *U.S. Private*, pg. 848
DAVID E. HARVEY BUILDERS INC.; *U.S. Private*, pg. 1170
DAVID MONTOYA CONSTRUCTION, INC.; *U.S. Private*, pg. 1171
DAVIS & ASSOCIATES, INC.; *U.S. Private*, pg. 1172
DAVIS CONSTRUCTION, INC.; *U.S. Private*, pg. 1173
THE DAVIS GROUP INC.; *U.S. Private*, pg. 4018
DAWSON BUILDING CONTRACTORS, INC.; *U.S. Private*, pg. 1175
DAWSON CONSTRUCTION INC.; *U.S. Private*, pg. 1175
DAYSPRING RESTORATION, LLC—See Trinity Hunt Management, L.P.; *U.S. Private*, pg. 4234
DBM VIRCON SERVICES (CANADA) LTD.—See INNO-

VATE Corp.; *U.S. Public*, pg. 1126
DBS CORPORATION; *U.S. Private*, pg. 1179
DC BUILDING GROUP LLC; *U.S. Private*, pg. 1179
DCI CONSTRUCTION, LLC.; *U.S. Private*, pg. 1180
DCK INTERNATIONAL, LLC—See Dck Worldwide, LLC; *U.S. Private*, pg. 1180
DCK-TTEC LLC—See Tetra Tech, Inc.; *U.S. Public*, pg. 2023
DCK WORLDWIDE, LLC; *U.S. Private*, pg. 1180
THE DDS COMPANIES—See Feeney Brothers Excavation LLC; *U.S. Private*, pg. 1493
DD TECHNICHE SDN. BHD.—See AWC Berhad; *Int'l*, pg. 752
DEAN KURTZ CONSTRUCTION; *U.S. Private*, pg. 1184
DEAN SNYDER CONSTRUCTION COMPANY; *U.S. Private*, pg. 1184
DEB CONSTRUCTION; *U.S. Private*, pg. 1186
DE CONSTRUCTII NAPOCA S.A.; *Int'l*, pg. 1995
DEEB CONSTRUCTION & DEVELOPMENT CO.; *U.S. Private*, pg. 1189
DEERFIELD CONSTRUCTION CO., INC.; *U.S. Private*, pg. 1190
DE JAGER CONSTRUCTION, INC.; *U.S. Private*, pg. 1181
DEKPOL S.A.; *Int'l*, pg. 2006
DELESLINE CONSTRUCTION, INC.; *U.S. Private*, pg. 1196
DELNOR CONSTRUCTION 2012 LTD.—See Delnor Construction Ltd.; *Int'l*, pg. 2014
DELNOR CONSTRUCTION LTD.; *Int'l*, pg. 2014
DELPHA CONSTRUCTION CO., LTD.; *Int'l*, pg. 2015
DEMARIA BUILDING COMPANY INC.; *U.S. Private*, pg. 1203
DEMAR LTD—See Burrow Global, LLC; *U.S. Private*, pg. 692
DEMATTIA GROUP; *U.S. Private*, pg. 1203
THE DEMOSS COMPANY; *U.S. Private*, pg. 4020
DENARK CONSTRUCTION, INC.; *U.S. Private*, pg. 1204
DENHOLTZ MANAGEMENT CORP.; *U.S. Private*, pg. 1205
DENTON-RENFROE, INC.; *U.S. Private*, pg. 1206
DESARROLLOS METROPOLITANOS, LLC.; *U.S. Private*, pg. 1211
DESBUILD INCORPORATED; *U.S. Private*, pg. 1211
DESIGN-BUILD SOLUTIONS, INC.—See Garland Industries Inc.; *U.S. Private*, pg. 1644
DESIGNED MOBILE SYSTEMS INDUSTRIES, INC.; *U.S. Private*, pg. 1214
DETCON, INC.—See Battery Ventures, L.P.; *U.S. Private*, pg. 488
DEUTSCHE EUROSHOP AG; *Int'l*, pg. 2065
DEVCON CONSTRUCTION INCORPORATED; *U.S. Private*, pg. 1217
DEVELOPMENT INVESTMENT CONSTRUCTION JSC; *Int'l*, pg. 2088
DEVOTED CONSTRUCTION LTD; *Int'l*, pg. 2090
DEWITT & ASSOCIATES, INC.—See South Barnes Development Co.; *U.S. Private*, pg. 3719
DEXION ASIA LIMITED—See Amotiv Limited; *Int'l*, pg. 431
D.F. CHASE INC.; *U.S. Private*, pg. 1142
D.F. PRAY INC.; *U.S. Private*, pg. 1142
D.G.S. CONSTRUCTION COMPANY LTD.; *Int'l*, pg. 1900
DH LOGISTIC PROPERTY VIETNAM CO., LTD.—See Daiwa House Industry Co., Ltd.; *Int'l*, pg. 1945
D. HONORE CONSTRUCTION, INC.; *U.S. Private*, pg. 1140
DHRUV CONSULTANCY SERVICES LIMITED; *Int'l*, pg. 2100
DIANI CONSTRUCTION; *U.S. Private*, pg. 1224
DIAZ FRITZ ISABEL GENERAL CONTRACTORS; *U.S. Private*, pg. 1225
DICK ANDERSON CONSTRUCTION; *U.S. Private*, pg. 1225
DICKINSON CAMERON CONSTRUCTION COMPANY, INC.; *U.S. Private*, pg. 1227
DIMENSION CONSTRUCTION, INC.; *U.S. Private*, pg. 1232
DIMEO CONSTRUCTION COMPANY; *U.S. Private*, pg. 1233
DIMMI LIFE HOLDINGS LIMITED; *Int'l*, pg. 2126
DINEEN CONSTRUCTION CORPORATION; *Int'l*, pg. 2127
DING-YUE DEVELOPMENT CO., LTD.—See China Petrochemical Development Corp.; *Int'l*, pg. 1540
DISCOVERY DOOR, INC.—See Platinum Equity, LLC; *U.S. Private*, pg. 3208
D'LAURO & RODGERS, INC.; *U.S. Private*, pg. 1139
DL CONSTRUCTION CO., LTD.; *Int'l*, pg. 2140
DL E&C CO., LTD.—See Daelim Industrial Co., Ltd.; *Int'l*, pg. 1908
DLF AKRUTI INFO PARKS (PUNE) LIMITED—See DLF Limited; *Int'l*, pg. 2141
D.L. PORTER CONSTRUCTORS INC.; *U.S. Private*, pg. 1142
D&M GENERAL CONTRACTING, INC.; *U.S. Private*, pg. 1138
DM WENCESLAO & ASSOCIATES, INC.; *Int'l*, pg. 2142
DOLAN CONSTRUCTION INC.; *U.S. Private*, pg. 1254
DOME CORPORATION NORTH AMERICA; *U.S. Private*, pg. 1255
DOMINION HOMES, INC.; *U.S. Private*, pg. 1256
DON C. MUSICK CONSTRUCTION CO., INC.; *U.S. Private*, pg. 1257
DONG-AH GEOLOGICAL ENGINEERING COMPANY LIMITED—See DongAh Geological Engineering Co., Ltd.; *Int'l*, pg. 2165
DONGYANG ENGINEERING & CONSTRUCTION CORP.; *Int'l*, pg. 2171
DON KRUEGER CONSTRUCTION CO.; *U.S. Private*, pg. 1258
THE DONOHOE COMPANIES, INC.; *U.S. Private*, pg. 4022
DOOLEYMACK CONSTRUCTORS INC.; *U.S. Private*, pg. 1261
DORA CONSTRUCTION LIMITED; *Int'l*, pg. 2175
DOSTER CONSTRUCTION COMPANY INC.; *U.S. Private*, pg. 1264
DOUBLE AA BUILDERS, LTD.; *U.S. Private*, pg. 1265
DOUG HOLLYHAND CONSTRUCTION CO.; *U.S. Private*, pg. 1266
THE DOUGLAS COMPANY, INC.; *U.S. Private*, pg. 4023
DOUGLAS EMMETT BUILDERS—See Douglas Emmett, Inc.; *U.S. Public*, pg. 678
DOVE CONTRACTING, INC.; *U.S. Private*, pg. 1268
DOWNING CONSTRUCTION, INC.; *U.S. Private*, pg. 1269
DOWNS CONSTRUCTION LTD.; *Int'l*, pg. 2187
DPR CONSTRUCTION, INC.; *U.S. Private*, pg. 1270
DPR HARDIN CONSTRUCTION COMPANY, LLC—See DPR Construction, Inc.; *U.S. Private*, pg. 1270
DRAGADOS CANADA, INC.—See ACS, Actividades de Construccion y Servicios, S.A.; *Int'l*, pg. 111
DRAGADOS UK LIMITED—See ACS, Actividades de Construccion y Servicios, S.A.; *Int'l*, pg. 111
DRAHOTA COMMERCIAL LLC.; *U.S. Private*, pg. 1272
DRC ENGINEERING PTE. LTD.—See Grandshores Technology Group Limited; *Int'l*, pg. 3058
DREES & SOMMER SE; *Int'l*, pg. 2203
D & R GENERAL CONTRACTING & DESIGN, INC.; *U.S. Private*, pg. 1136
D.R. HORTON HOMES—See D.R. Horton, Inc.; *U.S. Public*, pg. 619
DRYMALLA CONSTRUCTION COMPANY; *U.S. Private*, pg. 1281
DSP BUILDERS INC.; *U.S. Private*, pg. 1281
DUBLIN CONSTRUCTION COMPANY, INC.; *U.S. Private*, pg. 1283
DUGAN & MEYERS LLC—See Baker Concrete Construction, Inc.; *U.S. Private*, pg. 456
DUGGAN CONTRACTING CORPORATION; *U.S. Private*, pg. 1285
DUMAS CONCEPTS IN BUILDING; *U.S. Private*, pg. 1287
DUNLAP & CO., INC.; *U.S. Private*, pg. 1289
DUO-FAST LLC—See Illinois Tool Works Inc.; *U.S. Public*, pg. 1102
DUPHIL INC.; *U.S. Private*, pg. 1291
DUQUETTE CONSTRUCTION; *U.S. Private*, pg. 2227
DURAND BUILDERS SERVICE INC.; *U.S. Private*, pg. 1292
DUROTECH, INC.; *U.S. Private*, pg. 1294
DURWEST CONSTRUCTION MANAGEMENT; *Int'l*, pg. 2234
DUTCO MCCONNELL DOWELL QATAR LLC—See Aveng Limited; *Int'l*, pg. 738
DYCASA S.A.—See ACS, Actividades de Construccion y Servicios, S.A.; *Int'l*, pg. 111
DYNAMIC BUILDING CORP.; *U.S. Private*, pg. 1297
E1 CONTAINER TERMINAL CORP.—See E1 Corporation; *Int'l*, pg. 2260
EAGLE COMMERCIAL CONSTRUCTION, LLC—See Markel Group Inc.; *U.S. Public*, pg. 1367
EARTHWORKS PACIFIC INC.; *U.S. Private*, pg. 1315
EASTERN CONSTRUCTION COMPANY LIMITED; *Int'l*, pg. 2272
EASTERN REFRIGERATION, CO.—See Ares Management Corporation; *U.S. Public*, pg. 189
EBC INC.; *Int'l*, pg. 2284
EBCO GENERAL CONTRACTORS; *U.S. Private*, pg. 1324
EBL PARTNERS LLC; *U.S. Private*, pg. 1324
E. BOWMAN & SONS LTD; *Int'l*, pg. 2250
ECHO MAINTENANCE, LLC; *U.S. Private*, pg. 1327
ECKMAN CONSTRUCTION COMPANY, INC.; *U.S. Private*, pg. 1328
ECONOLODGE CO., LTD.—See Heeton Holdings Limited; *Int'l*, pg. 3307
E CONSTRUCTION GROUP INC.; *U.S. Private*, pg. 1300
E CONTRACTORS USA, LLC; *U.S. Private*, pg. 1300
ECOWOOD CO. LTD.—See Bunka Shutter Co., Ltd.; *Int'l*, pg. 1216
ECS ENGINEERING & CONSTRUCTION LIMITED; *Int'l*, pg. 2301
ED A. WILSON INC.—See Tenir Investments Inc.; *U.S. Private*, pg. 3967
EDGEWATER CONSTRUCTION SERVICES,LLC; *U.S. Private*, pg. 1335
EDIFICE, INC.; *U.S. Private*, pg. 1336
EDILIZIACROBATICA FRANCE SAS—See EdiliziAcrobatica S.p.A.; *Int'l*, pg. 2309
EDILIZIACROBATICA IBERICA S.L.—See EdiliziAcrobatica S.p.A.; *Int'l*, pg. 2310
EDIS COMPANY; *U.S. Private*, pg. 1336
E! DISTRIBUTION, L.L.C.—See Comcast Corporation; *U.S. Public*, pg. 538
ED SEIFRIED CONSTRUCTION, INC.; *U.S. Private*, pg. 1331
ED TAYLOR CONSTRUCTION INC.; *U.S. Private*, pg. 1332
E.E. BLACK, LTD.—See Tutor Perini Corporation; *U.S. Public*, pg. 2206
EECON CONSTRUCTION SERVICES; *U.S. Private*, pg. 1343
EEI-CONSTRUCTION DIVISION—See EEI Corporation; *Int'l*, pg. 2317
E.E. REED CONSTRUCTION, L.P.; *U.S. Private*, pg. 1305
EGIS D.O.O. BEOGRAD—See Groupe Egis S.A.; *Int'l*, pg. 3102
EGIS EMIRATES LLC—See Groupe Egis S.A.; *Int'l*, pg. 3102
EGIS LAGAN SERVICES LTD.—See Groupe Egis S.A.; *Int'l*, pg. 3102
EGISMEX, S. DE R.L. DE C.V.—See Groupe Egis S.A.; *Int'l*, pg. 3102
EGIS RAIL KSA—See Groupe Egis S.A.; *Int'l*, pg. 3102
EGIS ROAD OPERATION M40 LTD.—See Groupe Egis S.A.; *Int'l*, pg. 3102
EGIS ROAD & TUNNEL OPERATION IRELAND LIMITED—See Groupe Egis S.A.; *Int'l*, pg. 3102
EGIS ROMANIA SA—See Groupe Egis S.A.; *Int'l*, pg. 3102
EGIS TUNEL ISLETMECILIGI A.S.—See Groupe Egis S.A.; *Int'l*, pg. 3102
EG PENNER BUILDING CENTRES; *Int'l*, pg. 2322
EG SIERRA L.L.C.; *U.S. Private*, pg. 1344
EHC INC.; *U.S. Private*, pg. 1346
EH CONSTRUCTION LLC; *U.S. Private*, pg. 1346
E HOLDINGS, LLC—See Comcast Corporation; *U.S. Public*, pg. 538
EIFFAGE CONSTRUCTION—See Eiffage S.A.; *Int'l*, pg. 2329
EIFFAGE S.A.; *Int'l*, pg. 2329
EIQON AS—See AF Gruppen ASA; *Int'l*, pg. 184
E.K. BAILEY CONSTRUCTION, INC.; *U.S. Private*, pg. 1306
EKLUNDS INC.; *U.S. Private*, pg. 1348
EKONO HOMES LTD.—See Alam Group of Companies; *Int'l*, pg. 289
ELAN CONSTRUCTION LIMITED; *Int'l*, pg. 2342
ELDER-JONES, INC.; *U.S. Private*, pg. 1351
ELECTRONIC TRAFFIC, S.A.—See ACS, Actividades de Construccion y Servicios, S.A.; *Int'l*, pg. 112
ELEKTRO NAEGELIN AG—See BKW AG; *Int'l*, pg. 1055
ELEKTRO WINTER AG—See BKW AG; *Int'l*, pg. 1055
E.L. HAMM & ASSOCIATES INC.; *U.S. Private*, pg. 1306
ELIN TECHNICAL SA—See ELINOIL S.A.; *Int'l*, pg. 2361
ELITE RETAILS SERVICES INC.; *U.S. Private*, pg. 1361
ELKINS CONSTRUCTORS, INC.; *U.S. Private*, pg. 1363
ELLISDON CONSTRUCTION INC.—See EllisDon Corporation; *Int'l*, pg. 2366
ELLISDON CONSTRUCTION INC.—See EllisDon Corporation; *Int'l*, pg. 2366
ELLISDON CONSTRUCTION SERVICES INC.—See EllisDon Corporation; *Int'l*, pg. 2366
ELLISDON CORPORATION; *Int'l*, pg. 2366
ELLISDON CORPORATION—See EllisDon Corporation; *Int'l*, pg. 2366
ELLISDON CORPORATION—See EllisDon Corporation; *Int'l*, pg. 2366
ELLISDON CORPORATION—See EllisDon Corporation; *Int'l*, pg. 2367
ELLISDON CORPORATION—See EllisDon Corporation; *Int'l*, pg. 2367
ELLISDON CORPORATION—See EllisDon Corporation; *Int'l*, pg. 2367
ELLIS STONE CONSTRUCTION COMPANY; *U.S. Private*, pg. 1374
ELZINGA & VOLKERS, INC.; *U.S. Private*, pg. 1377
ELZINGA & VOLKERS PROFESSIONAL SERVICES INC.—See Elzinga & Volkers, Inc.; *U.S. Private*, pg. 1377
EMAAR HOSPITALITY GROUP LLC—See Emaar Properties PJSC; *Int'l*, pg. 2372
EMAAR MALLS GROUP LLC—See Emaar Properties PJSC; *Int'l*, pg. 2372
EMAAR RETAIL LLC—See Emaar Properties PJSC; *Int'l*, pg. 2372
EMCO TECH CONSTRUCTION CORP.; *U.S. Private*, pg. 1379
EMERALD CONSTRUCTION MANAGEMENT, INC.—See urban-gro, Inc.; *U.S. Public*, pg. 2266
EMJ CORPORATION; *U.S. Private*, pg. 1382
ENERGOPROJEKT ENTEL COMPANY—See Energoprojekt Holding a.d.; *Int'l*, pg. 2421
ENERGOPROJEKT ENTEL L.L.C.—See Energoprojekt Holding a.d.; *Int'l*, pg. 2421
ENERGOPROJEKT ENTEL LTD.—See Energoprojekt Holding a.d.; *Int'l*, pg. 2421
ENERGOPROJEKT HOLDING GUINEE S.A.—See Energoprojekt Holding a.d.; *Int'l*, pg. 2422
ENERGOPROJEKT-KRAKOW S.A.—See Eltel AB; *Int'l*, pg. 2371
ENERGY SPECIALTY CONTRACTING, INC.—See The CapStreet Group LLC; *U.S. Private*, pg. 4005
ENGELBERTH CONSTRUCTION INC.; *U.S. Private*, pg. 1397
ENGEL CONSTRUCTION & DEVELOPMENT GROUP; *Int'l*, pg. 2426
ENGLISH AMERICAN CONSTRUCTORS INC.—See Benning Construction Company Inc.; *U.S. Private*, pg. 528

N.A.I.C.S. INDEX

236220 — COMMERCIAL AND INST...

ENKA INSAAT VE SANAYI A.S.; *Int'l*, pg. 2439
ENSIGNIA CONSTRUCTION SDN. BHD.—See IGB Berhad; *Int'l*, pg. 3601
ENTREPRISE BOYER—See Ardian SAS; *Int'l*, pg. 555
ENTREPRISE GUILLERM; *Int'l*, pg. 2453
ENVIRONAMICS INC.; *U.S. Private*, pg. 1407
ENVIROSTRUCT, LLC; *U.S. Private*, pg. 1409
ENVIRO TECH—See Dome Corporation North America; *U.S. Private*, pg. 1255
EOMJIHOUSE CO., LTD.; *Int'l*, pg. 2457
EPSOM PROPERTIES LIMITED; *Int'l*, pg. 2466
EPSTEIN CONSTRUCTION INC.—See A. Epstein & Sons International, Inc.; *U.S. Private*, pg. 23
EQUITY, INC.; *U.S. Private*, pg. 1416
ERBACON INVESTMENT HOLDINGS LIMITED; *Int'l*, pg. 2489
ERBUD S.A.; *Int'l*, pg. 2489
ERDMAN HOLDINGS, INC.; *U.S. Private*, pg. 1417
ERFATOR PROJEKTLEDNING AB—See Bravida Holding AB; *Int'l*, pg. 1142
ERKA-AS—See Eroglu Holding AS; *Int'l*, pg. 2496
E.R. STUEBNER CONSTRUCTION INC.; *U.S. Private*, pg. 1306
ERYAP CONSTRUCTION AND TRADE INC.—See Eroglu Holding AS; *Int'l*, pg. 2496
ESE CONSULTANTS, INC.—See Toll Brothers, Inc.; *U.S. Public*, pg. 2161
ESI GROUP USA; *U.S. Private*, pg. 1426
ESSEX CONSTRUCTION, LLC—See Blunt Enterprises LLC; *U.S. Private*, pg. 600
ETABLISSEMENTS GASCHEAU; *Int'l*, pg. 2519
EUROWINDOW., JSC—See Bunka Shutter Co., Ltd.; *Int'l*, pg. 1216
EVANS GRADING CO.; *U.S. Private*, pg. 1435
EVERDIGM MONGOLIA LLC—See Hyundai Everdigm Corp; *Int'l*, pg. 3556
EVEREST INDUSTRIES LTD; *Int'l*, pg. 2564
EVRARD-STRANG CONSTRUCTION, INC.; *U.S. Private*, pg. 1444
EWI CONSTRUCTION, LLC; *U.S. Private*, pg. 1444
EWING CONSTRUCTION CO., INC.; *U.S. Private*, pg. 1444
EXCEL ARCADE PRIVATE LTD.—See Housing Development & Infrastructure Limited; *Int'l*, pg. 3491
EXCELLENCE REAL ESTATE GROUP LIMITED; *Int'l*, pg. 2578
EXEO TECH CORPORATION—See EXEO Group Inc.; *Int'l*, pg. 2583
EXTENSA GROUP SA—See Ackermans & van Haaren NV; *Int'l*, pg. 105
EXXEL PACIFIC, INC.; *U.S. Private*, pg. 1453
FACILITY SUPPORT SERVICES, LLC—See Gold Belt Incorporated; *U.S. Private*, pg. 1727
FAGEN INC.; *U.S. Private*, pg. 1461
FAGER-MCGEE COMMERCIAL CONSTRUCTION INC.; *U.S. Private*, pg. 1461
FARMER CONSTRUCTION LTD.; *Int'l*, pg. 2619
FAULK & MEEK GENERAL CONTRACTORS, LLC.; *U.S. Private*, pg. 1483
FAULKNERUSA; *U.S. Private*, pg. 1483
FAYOLLE CANADA INC.—See Fayolle et Fils; *Int'l*, pg. 2626
FAYOLLE ET FILS; *Int'l*, pg. 2626
FBI BUILDINGS, INC.; *U.S. Private*, pg. 1485
FCC CONSTRUCCION CHILE, SPA—See Fomento de Construcciones y Contratas, S.A.; *Int'l*, pg. 2722
FCC CONSTRUCCION COSTA RICA, S.A.—See Fomento de Construcciones y Contratas, S.A.; *Int'l*, pg. 2722
FCC CONSTRUCCION PERU, S.A.C.—See Fomento de Construcciones y Contratas, S.A.; *Int'l*, pg. 2722
FCC CONSTRUCCION INC.—See Fomento de Construcciones y Contratas, S.A.; *Int'l*, pg. 2722
FCC CONSTRUCTION IRELAND DAC—See Fomento de Construcciones y Contratas, S.A.; *Int'l*, pg. 2722
FCC CONSTRUGOES DO BRASIL LTDA.—See Fomento de Construcciones y Contratas, S.A.; *Int'l*, pg. 2722
FCI CONSTRUCTORS INC.; *U.S. Private*, pg. 1486
THE FCM GROUP, INC.; *U.S. Private*, pg. 4028
FELMLEY-DICKERSON CO.; *U.S. Private*, pg. 1494
FENIX CONSTRUCTORS INC.; *U.S. Private*, pg. 1495
FENNICK/MCCREDIE ARCHITECTURE LTD.; *U.S. Private*, pg. 1495
FERGUSON CONSTRUCTION; *U.S. Private*, pg. 1496
FERNWARMEVERSORGUNG HERNE GMBH—See E.ON SE; *Int'l*, pg. 2253
FGI GROUP INC.; *U.S. Private*, pg. 1501
FHC CONTRACTING, INC.; *U.S. Private*, pg. 1501
F.H. CHASE, INC.; *U.S. Private*, pg. 1456
F&H CONSTRUCTION; *U.S. Private*, pg. 1454
F.H. PASCHEN, S.N. NIELSEN, INC.; *U.S. Private*, pg. 1456
FIBERTEL, LLC—See Quanta Services, Inc.; *U.S. Public*, pg. 1751
FIGTREE HOLDINGS LIMITED; *Int'l*, pg. 2661
FIGTREE PROJECTS (SHANGHAI) CO., LTD.—See Figtree Holdings Limited; *Int'l*, pg. 2661
FINDREWNO SP. Z O.O.—See Honkarakenne Oyj; *Int'l*, pg. 3471
FINGER LAKES CONSTRUCTION COMPANY; *U.S. Private*, pg. 1510

FIP CONSTRUCTION INC.—See The FIP Corporation; *U.S. Private*, pg. 4029
FIRST CONSTRUCTION GROUP; *U.S. Private*, pg. 1516
FIRST MUTUAL PROPERTIES LIMITED; *Int'l*, pg. 2686
FISHER DEVELOPMENT INC.; *U.S. Private*, pg. 1534
FITE BUILDING COMPANY, INC.; *U.S. Private*, pg. 1535
F.J. SCIAME CONSTRUCTION CO. INC.; *U.S. Private*, pg. 1456
FJW CONSTRUCTION, LLC—See Broaddus & Associates, Inc.; *U.S. Private*, pg. 659
FKP COMMERCIAL DEVELOPMENTS PTY. LTD.—See Brookfield Corporation; *Int'l*, pg. 1186
FKP POLAND SP. Z O. O.—See CTS Eventim AG & Co. KGAA; *Int'l*, pg. 1873
FLARE CONSTRUCTION, LLC—See Quanta Services, Inc.; *U.S. Public*, pg. 1751
FLETCHER CONSTRUCTION BUILDINGS LIMITED—See Fletcher Building Limited; *Int'l*, pg. 2700
FLETCHER CONSTRUCTION (SOLOMON ISLANDS) LIMITED—See Fletcher Building Limited; *Int'l*, pg. 2700
FLINT INDUSTRIES, INC.; *U.S. Private*, pg. 1545
FLUOR AUSTRALIA PTY. LTD.—See Fluor Corporation; *U.S. Public*, pg. 858
FLUOR BV—See Fluor Corporation; *U.S. Public*, pg. 858
FLUOR CANADA LTD.—See Fluor Corporation; *U.S. Public*, pg. 858
FLUOR CONSTRUCTORS INTERNATIONAL, INC.—See Fluor Corporation; *U.S. Public*, pg. 858
FLUOR CONSULTANTS BV—See Fluor Corporation; *U.S. Public*, pg. 858
FLUOR DANIEL BRASIL, LTDA.—See Fluor Corporation; *U.S. Public*, pg. 858
FLUOR DANIEL CHILE, S.A.—See Fluor Corporation; *U.S. Public*, pg. 858
FLUOR DANIEL (JAPAN), INC.—See Fluor Corporation; *U.S. Public*, pg. 858
FLUOR DANIEL PACIFIC, INC.—See Fluor Corporation; *U.S. Public*, pg. 858
FLUOR ENTERPRISES, INC.—See Fluor Corporation; *U.S. Public*, pg. 858
FLUOR GLOBAL SERVICES AUSTRALIA PTY. LTD.—See Fluor Corporation; *U.S. Public*, pg. 858
FLUOR INFRASTRUCTURE BV—See Fluor Corporation; *U.S. Public*, pg. 858
FLUOR LIMITED—See Fluor Corporation; *U.S. Public*, pg. 859
FLUOR MAINTENANCE SERVICES, INC.—See Fluor Corporation; *U.S. Public*, pg. 859
FLUOR S.A.—See Fluor Corporation; *U.S. Public*, pg. 859
F&M CONSTRUCTION CO.; *U.S. Private*, pg. 1455
FOMENTO DE CONSTRUCCIONES Y CONTRATAS CANADA LTD.—See Fomento de Construcciones y Contratas, S.A.; *Int'l*, pg. 2723
FORCLUM ALSACE FRANCHE COMTE SAS—See Eiffage S.A.; *Int'l*, pg. 2330
FORD DEVELOPMENT CORPORATION; *U.S. Private*, pg. 1564
FORECON OY—See Byggfakta Group Nordic HoldCo AB; *Int'l*, pg. 1234
FORINO CO., L.P.; *U.S. Private*, pg. 1569
FORISH CONSTRUCTION COMPANY, INC.; *U.S. Private*, pg. 1569
FORTIS CONSTRUCTION, INC.; *U.S. Private*, pg. 1576
FORTNEY & WEYGANDT, INC.; *U.S. Private*, pg. 1576
FOULGER-PRATT CONTRACTING LLC; *U.S. Private*, pg. 1579
FOUSHEE & ASSOCIATES CO., INC.; *U.S. Private*, pg. 1583
FOWLER GENERAL CONSTRUCTION, INC.; *U.S. Private*, pg. 1583
FRANK L. BLUM CONSTRUCTION COMPANY; *U.S. Private*, pg. 1595
FRANK M. BOOTH INC.; *U.S. Private*, pg. 1595
FRANK REWOLD & SON, INC.; *U.S. Private*, pg. 1595
FRAZEE INC.; *U.S. Private*, pg. 1599
FRED BERGLUND & SONS INC.; *U.S. Private*, pg. 1600
FRED GROENESTEGE CONSTRUCTION LIMITED; *Int'l*, pg. 2767
FRED M. STARLING, INC.; *U.S. Private*, pg. 1601
FRED OLIVIERI CONSTRUCTION CO.; *U.S. Private*, pg. 1601
FREESE JOHNSON, LLC; *U.S. Private*, pg. 1607
FREESIA HOUSE CO., LTD.—See Freesia Macross Corporation; *Int'l*, pg. 2771
FRIEDLER CONSTRUCTION COMPANY; *U.S. Private*, pg. 1610
FRIZZELL CONSTRUCTION CO. INC.; *U.S. Private*, pg. 1613
FROEHLICH BAU AG; *Int'l*, pg. 2794
FRONTIER-KEMPER CONSTRUCTORS, INC.—See Tutor Perini Corporation; *U.S. Public*, pg. 2206
FRYE BUILDERS & ASSOCIATES, INC.; *U.S. Private*, pg. 1618
FUJI AMENITY SERVICE CO., LTD.—See Fuji Corporation Limited; *Int'l*, pg. 2810
FUJITA AMERICAS, INC.—See Daiwa House Industry Co., Ltd.; *Int'l*, pg. 1946
FUJITA (CHINA) CONSTRUCTION CO., LTD.—See Daiwa House Industry Co., Ltd.; *Int'l*, pg. 1946

FUJITA CORPORATION (M) SDN. BHD.—See Daiwa House Industry Co., Ltd.; *Int'l*, pg. 1946
FUJITA CORPORATION SINGAPORE PTE. LTD.—See Daiwa House Industry Co., Ltd.; *Int'l*, pg. 1946
FUJITA CORPORATION (THAILAND) LTD.—See Daiwa House Industry Co., Ltd.; *Int'l*, pg. 1946
FUJITA CORPORATION VIETNAM CO., LTD.—See Daiwa House Industry Co., Ltd.; *Int'l*, pg. 1946
FUJITA ENGINEERING INDIA PVT., LTD.—See Daiwa House Industry Co., Ltd.; *Int'l*, pg. 1946
FUJITA INTEGRAL MEXICO S.A. DE C.V.—See Daiwa House Industry Co., Ltd.; *Int'l*, pg. 1946
FUJITA PHILIPPINES CONSTRUCTION & DEVELOPMENT, INC.—See Daiwa House Industry Co., Ltd.; *Int'l*, pg. 1946
FULCRUM LLC—See Wind Point Advisors LLC; *U.S. Private*, pg. 4536
FULL WANG INTERNATIONAL DEVELOPMENT CO., LTD.; *Int'l*, pg. 2842
FULTON HOGAN EGIS O&M PTY LTD.—See Groupe Egis S.A.; *Int'l*, pg. 3102
FUNDAMENTERING AS—See AF Gruppen ASA; *Int'l*, pg. 184
FURINO & SONS INC.; *U.S. Private*, pg. 1623
FURST CONSTRUCTION CO. INC.—See Furst Enterprises Inc.; *U.S. Private*, pg. 1624
FURST ENTERPRISES INC.; *U.S. Private*, pg. 1624
THE FUSCO CORPORATION; *U.S. Private*, pg. 4031
FUSION GEOPHYSICAL LLC—See Symphony Technology Group, LLC; *U.S. Private*, pg. 3901
FUTURE CAPITAL HOLDING CORPORATION; *U.S. Private*, pg. 1626
FUTURENET GROUP, INC.; *U.S. Private*, pg. 1627
FU YU PROPERTY CO., LTD.; *Int'l*, pg. 2801
F. W. OWENS COMPANY, INC.; *U.S. Private*, pg. 1455
G2 BUILDERS, LLC.; *U.S. Private*, pg. 1632
G2, INC.; *U.S. Private*, pg. 1632
G5 ENTERPRISES, INC.—See Quad-C Management, Inc.; *U.S. Private*, pg. 3315
GAGASAN NADI CERGAS BHD; *Int'l*, pg. 2868
GAIN PLUS HOLDINGS LIMITED; *Int'l*, pg. 2869
GALLAGHER CONSTRUCTION SERVICES—See Arthur J. Gallagher & Co.; *U.S. Public*, pg. 205
GALLIFORD TRY HOLDINGS PLC; *Int'l*, pg. 2874
GAMMA CONSTRUCTION COMPANY INC.; *U.S. Private*, pg. 1640
GAMMON CONSTRUCTION LTD.—See Balfour Beatty plc; *Int'l*, pg. 807
GAMUDA NAIM ENGINEERING & CONSTRUCTION (GNEC) SDN. BHD.—See Gamuda Berhad; *Int'l*, pg. 2879
GARCO CONSTRUCTION, INC.; *U.S. Private*, pg. 1642
GARLING CONSTRUCTION INC.; *U.S. Private*, pg. 1644
GATEWAY WAREHOUSE INC.; *U.S. Private*, pg. 1651
GCG CONSTRUCTION INC.; *U.S. Private*, pg. 1653
GCM CONTRACTING SOLUTIONS, INC.; *U.S. Private*, pg. 1654
GDC CONSTRUCTION INC.; *U.S. Private*, pg. 1654
GDC PROPERTIES, LLC; *U.S. Private*, pg. 1654
GEA MTS FLOWTEC AG—See GEA Group Aktiengesellschaft; *Int'l*, pg. 2901
GEBERIT CERAMICA S.P.A.—See Geberit AG; *Int'l*, pg. 2904
GEBERIT NIGERIA LTD.—See Geberit AG; *Int'l*, pg. 2904
GEBERIT RUS LLC—See Geberit AG; *Int'l*, pg. 2905
GEBERIT S.A.U.—See Geberit AG; *Int'l*, pg. 2905
G.E. JOHNSON CONSTRUCTION COMPANY, INC.; *U.S. Private*, pg. 1630
GENCO HOLDINGS LIMITED—See Genco Shipping & Trading Limited; *U.S. Public*, pg. 911
GENERAL SHOPPING E OUTLETS DO BRASIL S.A.; *Int'l*, pg. 2919
GEORGE A. GRANT, INC.; *U.S. Private*, pg. 1681
GEORGE SOLLITT CONSTRUCTION; *U.S. Private*, pg. 1683
GEORGIA/ATLANTIC CONTRACTORS, INC; *U.S. Private*, pg. 1685
GEORGIOU GROUP PTY. LTD.; *Int'l*, pg. 2939
GEOSONDA-FUNDIRANJE A.D.; *Int'l*, pg. 2941
GERALD H. PHIPPS, INC.; *U.S. Private*, pg. 1685
GERAMA; *Int'l*, pg. 2942
GERARDI CONSTRUCTION, INC.; *U.S. Private*, pg. 1686
GHT GESELLSCHAFT FUR PROJEKTMANAGEMENT HESSEN-THURINGEN MBH—See Helaba Landesbank Hessen-Thuringen; *Int'l*, pg. 3327
GIBRALTAR CONSTRUCTION, CORP.; *U.S. Private*, pg. 1696
GIEAS IMMOBILIEN AG; *Int'l*, pg. 2968
GIGA TECH CO., LTD.—See FreeBit Co., Ltd.; *Int'l*, pg. 2769
GILBANE BUILDING COMPANY—See Gilbane, Inc.; *U.S. Private*, pg. 1698
GILBANE, INC.—See Gilbane, Inc.; *U.S. Private*, pg. 1698
GILFORD CORPORATION; *U.S. Private*, pg. 1699
GIL HAUGAN CONSTRUCTION, INC.; *U.S. Private*, pg. 1698
GIL HAUGAN CONSTRUCTION—See Gil Haugan Construction, Inc.; *U.S. Private*, pg. 1698

GILLANDERS CONSTRUCTION INC.; *Int'l*, pg. 2976
GILLIS GILKERSON INC.; *U.S. Private*, pg. 1700
GIORDANO CONSTRUCTION CO., INC.; *U.S. Private*, pg. 1702
GLEN BUILDERS INC.; *U.S. Private*, pg. 1709
GLENN H. JOHNSON CONSTRUCTION; *U.S. Private*, pg. 1710
G L MORRIS GENERAL BUILDING CONTRACTORS; *U.S. Private*, pg. 1628
GLOBAL CONSTRUCTORS LLC.; *U.S. Private*, pg. 1713
GLOBALWIDE INTERNATIONAL PTE. LTD.—See Air Water Inc.; *Int'l*, pg. 240
GLOHAB, INC.; *U.S. Private*, pg. 1720
GLOMAC BINA SDN. BHD.—See GLOMAC Berhad; *Int'l*, pg. 3008
GLOVER MAINTENANCE; *U.S. Private*, pg. 1720
GLY CONSTRUCTION INC.; *U.S. Private*, pg. 1721
G.M. CRISALLI ASSOCIATES, INC.; *U.S. Private*, pg. 1631
G.M. MCCROSSIN INC.; *U.S. Private*, pg. 1631
G.M. NORTHRUP CORPORATION; *U.S. Private*, pg. 1631
GMR AIRPORTS INFRASTRUCTURE LIMITED; *Int'l*, pg. 3015
GODREJ PROPERTIES LIMITED—See Godrej & Boyce Mfg. Co. Ltd.; *Int'l*, pg. 3021
GODSELL CONSTRUCTION CORP.; *U.S. Private*, pg. 1724
GODSIL CONSTRUCTION, INC.; *U.S. Private*, pg. 1725
GO ENERGISTICS LLC; *U.S. Private*, pg. 1723
GOLDEN ENERGY AND RESOURCES LIMITED; *Int'l*, pg. 3029
GOLDEN PONDER HOLDINGS LIMITED; *Int'l*, pg. 3031
GOLF CORPORATION; *U.S. Private*, pg. 1735
GOMEZ CONSTRUCTION COMPANY; *U.S. Private*, pg. 1737
GONSALVES & SANTUCCI INC.; *U.S. Private*, pg. 1737
GOTENEHUS GROUP AB; *Int'l*, pg. 3043
GP GUNTER PAPENBURG AG; *Int'l*, pg. 3045
G-PILE SISTEM SDN. BHD.—See CSC Holdings Limited; *Int'l*, pg. 1862
GPM BUILDERS PTE. LTD.—See Goodland Group Limited; *Int'l*, pg. 3040
GP PLANUM AD BEOGRAD; *Int'l*, pg. 3046
GRADEVINAR A.D.; *Int'l*, pg. 3049
GRADITELJ A.D.; *Int'l*, pg. 3049
GRADNJA A.D.; *Int'l*, pg. 3050
GRAE-CON CONSTRUCTION, INC.; *U.S. Private*, pg. 1750
GRAHAM CONSTRUCTION & MANAGEMENT, INC.—See Graham Group Ltd.; *Int'l*, pg. 3051
GRAHAM CONSTRUCTION - OMAHA—See Graham Group Ltd.; *Int'l*, pg. 3051
GRAHAM CONSTRUCTION SERVICES, INC.—See Graham Group Ltd.; *Int'l*, pg. 3051
GRAHAM CONTRACTING LTD.—See Graham Group Ltd.; *Int'l*, pg. 3051
GRAHAM GROUP LTD. - DELTA—See Graham Group Ltd.; *Int'l*, pg. 3051
GRAHAM GROUP LTD. - EDMONTON—See Graham Group Ltd.; *Int'l*, pg. 3051
GRAHAM GROUP LTD. - KELOWNA—See Graham Group Ltd.; *Int'l*, pg. 3051
GRAHAM GROUP LTD. - MISSISSAUGA—See Graham Group Ltd.; *Int'l*, pg. 3051
GRAHAM GROUP LTD. - REGINA—See Graham Group Ltd.; *Int'l*, pg. 3051
GRAHAM GROUP LTD. - SASKATOON—See Graham Group Ltd.; *Int'l*, pg. 3051
GRAHAM GROUP LTD.; *Int'l*, pg. 3051
GRANDALL SOLUTIONS INC.; *Int'l*, pg. 3057
GRAND CONSTRUCTION LTD.; *Int'l*, pg. 3054
GRAND MING GROUP HOLDINGS LIMITED; *Int'l*, pg. 3055
GRANDSHORES TECHNOLOGY GROUP LIMITED; *Int'l*, pg. 3058
GRANDY REFORM CO., LTD.—See Grandy House Corporation; *Int'l*, pg. 3058
GRANGER CONSTRUCTION COMPANY; *U.S. Private*, pg. 1754
GRANI INSTALLATION INC.; *U.S. Private*, pg. 1755
GRAVES & GRAVES CONSTRUCTION CO., INC.; *U.S. Private*, pg. 1758
GRAYBACH, LLC; *U.S. Private*, pg. 1759
GRAY CONSTRUCTION, INC.—See Gray Inc.; *U.S. Private*, pg. 1759
GRAYCOR INDUSTRIAL CONSTRUCTORS INC.—See Graycor Inc.; *U.S. Private*, pg. 1761
GRAY-I.C.E. BUILDERS—See Gray Inc.; *U.S. Private*, pg. 1759
GRAYWOLF INDUSTRIAL, INC.—See INNOVATE Corp.; *U.S. Public*, pg. 1126
GREAT PORTLAND ESTATES PLC; *Int'l*, pg. 3065
GREENHUT CONSTRUCTION COMPANY, INC.; *U.S. Private*, pg. 1778
GREENLAM INDUSTRIES LIMITED; *Int'l*, pg. 3075
THE GREENLEAF COMPANY INC.; *U.S. Private*, pg. 4039
GREENWAY ENTERPRISES INCORPORATED; *U.S. Private*, pg. 1781
GREENWOOD INC.; *U.S. Private*, pg. 1782
GREGORY CONSTRUCTION INC.—See Pumford Construction Inc.; *U.S. Private*, pg. 3303

GREYSTONE CONSTRUCTION COMPANY; *U.S. Private*, pg. 1786
GRINAKER-LTA CONSTRUCTION AND DEVELOPMENT LIMITED; *Int'l*, pg. 3086
GRINDER HAIZLIP CONSTRUCTION CO., INC.; *U.S. Private*, pg. 1790
GROCON GROUP HOLDINGS PTY. LTD.; *Int'l*, pg. 3087
GROUPE CEGERCO INC.; *Int'l*, pg. 3101
GROUPE PLOMBACTION INC; *Int'l*, pg. 3109
GROUP FIVE DESIGN AND PROJECT MANAGEMENT (PROPRIETARY) LIMITED—See Group Five Limited; *Int'l*, pg. 3089
GROUP FIVE ENERGY (PROPRIETARY) LIMITED—See Group Five Limited; *Int'l*, pg. 3089
GROUP FIVE INFRASTRUCTURE DEVELOPMENTS (PROPRIETARY) LIMITED—See Group Five Limited; *Int'l*, pg. 3089
GROUP FIVE LIMITED - BUILDING WESTERN CAPE BUSINESS UNIT—See Group Five Limited; *Int'l*, pg. 3089
GROUP FIVE PROJECTS (PROPRIETARY) LIMITED—See Group Five Limited; *Int'l*, pg. 3089
GROUP FIVE WESTERN CAPE (PROPRIETARY) LIMITED—See Group Five Limited; *Int'l*, pg. 3089
GROUP SIX CORPORATION; *U.S. Private*, pg. 1794
THE GROUT MEDIC LLC—See Susquehanna International Group, LLP; *U.S. Private*, pg. 3885
GRUNLEY CONSTRUCTION CO. INC.; *U.S. Private*, pg. 1797
GRUNWELL-CASHERO CO. INC.; *U.S. Private*, pg. 1797
GRUPA AZOTY AUTOMATYKA SP. Z O.O.—See Grupa Azoty S.A.; *Int'l*, pg. 3115
GRUPA AZOTY POLICE SERWIS SP. Z O.O.—See Grupa Azoty S.A.; *Int'l*, pg. 3116
THE GRUPE COMPANY—See Grupe Holding Company; *U.S. Private*, pg. 1797
GSJ SOLUTIONS, S.L.U.—See Grupo Empresarial San Jose, S.A.; *Int'l*, pg. 3128
GT (SCOTLAND) CONSTRUCTION LIMITED—See Galliford Try Holdings plc; *Int'l*, pg. 2874
GUANGDONG HAIKONG SPECIAL GLASS TECHNOLOGY CO., LTD.—See Hainan Development Holdings Nanhai Co., Ltd.; *Int'l*, pg. 3211
GUANGDONG HONG KONG GREATER BAY AREA HOLDINGS LTD.; *Int'l*, pg. 3155
GUANGDONG HUIYUN TITANIUM INDUSTRY CO., LTD.; *Int'l*, pg. 3156
GUARDIAN FUELING TECHNOLOGIES; *U.S. Private*, pg. 1810
GUIDO & COMPANIES; *U.S. Private*, pg. 1814
GULF BAY HOTELS INC.; *U.S. Private*, pg. 1814
GULF BUILDING CORP.; *U.S. Private*, pg. 1815
GULF EQUIPMENT CORPORATION; *U.S. Private*, pg. 1816
GULF & PACIFIC EQUITIES CORP.; *Int'l*, pg. 3178
GUNMA GRANDY HOUSE CO., LTD.—See Grandy House Corporation; *Int'l*, pg. 3058
GUTHRIE CONSTRUCTION & RETROFITTING (S) PTE LTD—See Guthrie GTS Limited; *Int'l*, pg. 3188
GUTKNECHT CONSTRUCTION COMPANY; *U.S. Private*, pg. 1820
GUY HOPKINS CONSTRUCTION CO., INC.; *U.S. Private*, pg. 1820
GWB IMMOBILIEN AG; *Int'l*, pg. 3190
GWI BAUUNTERNEHMUNG GMBH—See Erbud S.A.; *Int'l*, pg. 2489
H2I GROUP, INC.; *U.S. Private*, pg. 1836
HABAU HOCH- UND TIEFBAUGESELLSCHAFT M.B.H.; *Int'l*, pg. 3202
HAGA & BERG ENTREPRENOR AS—See AF Gruppen ASA; *Int'l*, pg. 184
HAGERMAN CONSTRUCTION CORPORATION; *U.S. Private*, pg. 1839
HAHNER FOREMAN & HARNESS INC.; *U.S. Private*, pg. 1840
HALEY CONSTRUCTION INC.; *U.S. Private*, pg. 1842
HALFACRE CONSTRUCTION COMPANY; *U.S. Private*, pg. 1842
HALLMARK VENTURE GROUP, INC.; *U.S. Public*, pg. 981
HALSE MARTIN CONSTRUCTION CO LTD; *Int'l*, pg. 3233
HALTEC HALE SP. Z O.O.—See HALTEC Hallensysteme GmbH; *Int'l*, pg. 3233
HALTEC HALLENSYSTEME AG—See HALTEC Hallensysteme GmbH; *Int'l*, pg. 3233
HALTEC HALLENSYSTEME GMBH; *Int'l*, pg. 3233
HALTEC HALLENSYSTEME GMBH—See HALTEC Hallensysteme GmbH; *Int'l*, pg. 3234
HALTEC NEDERLAND B.V.—See HALTEC Hallensysteme GmbH; *Int'l*, pg. 3234
HALTEC SAS—See HALTEC Hallensysteme GmbH; *Int'l*, pg. 3234
HAMEL BUILDERS; *U.S. Private*, pg. 1847
HAMMER COMMERCIAL; *U.S. Private*, pg. 1849
HAMSTRA GROUP, INC.; *U.S. Private*, pg. 1851
HAND CONSTRUCTION, LLC; *U.S. Private*, pg. 1852
HANISON CONSTRUCTION HOLDINGS LIMITED; *Int'l*, pg. 3252
HANMIGLOBAL CONSTRUCTION CONSULTING (SHANG-

HAI) CO., LTD.—See HanmiGlobal Co., LTD.; *Int'l*, pg. 3257
HANMIGLOBAL INDIA PRIVATE LTD.—See HanmiGlobal Co., LTD.; *Int'l*, pg. 3257
HANMIGLOBAL UK LIMITED—See HanmiGlobal Co., LTD.; *Int'l*, pg. 3257
HANNIG CONSTRUCTION, INC.—See Central State Construction, Corporation; *U.S. Private*, pg. 825
HANSEN COMPANY INC.; *U.S. Private*, pg. 1856
HANSEN YUNCKEN PTY LTD; *Int'l*, pg. 3260
HANSON CONSTRUCTION MATERIALS PTY LTD.—See Heidelberg Materials AG; *Int'l*, pg. 3311
HAOERSAI TECHNOLOGY GROUP CORP., LTD.; *Int'l*, pg. 3268
HARBOR VIEW HOLDINGS INC.; *U.S. Private*, pg. 1859
HARBRIDGE + CROSS LIMITED; *Int'l*, pg. 3272
HARDAWAY CONSTRUCTION CORP.—See Hardaway Group, Inc.; *U.S. Private*, pg. 1862
HARDISON/DOWNEY CONSTRUCTION INC.; *U.S. Private*, pg. 1863
HARDISON/DOWNEY, INC.—See Kitchell Corporation; *U.S. Private*, pg. 2316
HARGREAVES INDUSTRIAL SERVICES (HK) LIMITED—See Hargreaves Services plc; *Int'l*, pg. 3275
HARPER CONSTRUCTION COMPANY; *U.S. Private*, pg. 1867
THE HARPER CORPORATION; *U.S. Private*, pg. 4043
HARRISON WALKER & HARPER LP; *U.S. Private*, pg. 1870
HARVEY-CLEARY BUILDERS—See David E. Harvey Builders Inc.; *U.S. Private*, pg. 1170
HARVEY-CLEARY BUILDERS—See David E. Harvey Builders Inc.; *U.S. Private*, pg. 1170
HASELDEN CONSTRUCTION LLC; *U.S. Private*, pg. 1878
THE HASKELL COMPANY; *U.S. Private*, pg. 4043
HASKELL CORPORATION; *U.S. Private*, pg. 1878
HASSINGER COMPANIES; *U.S. Private*, pg. 1879
HASSLEN CONSTRUCTION COMPANY; *U.S. Private*, pg. 1879
HATCHER CONSTRUCTION SERVICES LLC; *U.S. Private*, pg. 1879
HATHAWAY DINWIDDIE CONSTRUCTION COMPANY; *U.S. Private*, pg. 1880
HAWKINS CONSTRUCTION COMPANY; *U.S. Private*, pg. 1883
HAWKINS CONSTRUCTION, INC.; *U.S. Private*, pg. 1883
HAYDON BUILDING CORP.; *U.S. Private*, pg. 1884
HAYNES-EAGLIN-WATERS, LLP; *U.S. Private*, pg. 1885
HAZAMA ANDO THAILAND CO., LTD.—See Hazama Ando Corporation; *Int'l*, pg. 3294
HAZ HOLDINGS, INC.; *U.S. Public*, pg. 990
HBD CONSTRUCTION, INC.; *U.S. Private*, pg. 1887
HEAD FAME COMPANY LIMITED—See Golden Ponder Holdings Limited; *Int'l*, pg. 3031
HEBERT STEEL CO. INC.; *U.S. Private*, pg. 1903
H.E. CALLAHAN CONSTRUCTION CO.; *U.S. Private*, pg. 1826
HEDRICK BROTHERS CONSTRUCTION CO., INC.; *U.S. Private*, pg. 1903
HEETON SG50 LIMITED—See Heeton Holdings Limited; *Int'l*, pg. 3307
HEISEY MECHANICAL, LTD.—See Cemtrex, Inc.; *U.S. Public*, pg. 466
HELGESEN TEKNISKE BYGG AS—See AF Gruppen ASA; *Int'l*, pg. 184
HELIX CO., LTD.—See Ananda Development Public Company Limited; *Int'l*, pg. 447
HELPFUL ALLIANCE COMPANY; *U.S. Private*, pg. 1912
HELP PHILADELPHIA—See Help USA Inc.; *U.S. Private*, pg. 1912
THE HENDERSON CORPORATION; *U.S. Private*, pg. 4051
HENKEL CONSTRUCTION COMPANY; *U.S. Private*, pg. 1916
HENNESSY CONSTRUCTION SERVICES CORP.; *U.S. Private*, pg. 1916
HENNING CONSTRUCTION COMPANY LLC; *U.S. Private*, pg. 1917
HENRY CARLSON COMPANY; *U.S. Private*, pg. 1917
HENRY HEYINK CONSTRUCTION LTD.; *Int'l*, pg. 3355
HENRY H. LEWIS CONTRACTORS LLC—See Stewart & Tate, Inc.; *U.S. Private*, pg. 3811
HENSEL PHELPS CONSTRUCTION CO.; *U.S. Private*, pg. 1919
HERCULES SITE SERVICES PLC; *Int'l*, pg. 3361
HERMAN CONSTRUCTION GROUP, INC.—See Bristol Bay Native Corporation; *U.S. Private*, pg. 656
HERMAN CONSTRUCTION SERVICES,INC.; *U.S. Private*, pg. 1925
HERM HUGHES & SONS, INC.; *U.S. Private*, pg. 1925
H.E. WHITLOCK INC.; *U.S. Private*, pg. 1826
HEYMANN CONSTRUCTION COMPANY; *U.S. Private*, pg. 1928
H.G. INFRA ENGINEERING LTD.; *Int'l*, pg. 3195
H.G. REYNOLDS CO. INC.; *U.S. Private*, pg. 1826
HHS CONSTRUCTION, INC.—See Crestview Partners, L.P.; *U.S. Private*, pg. 1098
H&H SYSTEMS AND DESIGN INC.; *U.S. Private*, pg. 1823
HHT CONSTRUCTION CO., LTD.—See BTS Group Hold-

N.A.I.C.S. INDEX

236220 — COMMERCIAL AND INST...

ings Public Company Limited; *Int'l*, pg. 1205
HICKORY CONSTRUCTION COMPANY; *U.S. Private*, pg. 1933
HILL CONSTRUCTION CORPORATION; *U.S. Private*, pg. 1945
HILLCREST DEVELOPMENT INC.; *U.S. Private*, pg. 1946
HILL INTERNATIONAL (HONG KONG) LTD.—See Global Infrastructure Solutions, Inc.; *U.S. Private*, pg. 1715
HINDMAN MANUFACTURING CO.; *U.S. Private*, pg. 1948
HISTORIC CONSTRUCTION INC.—See Historic Restoration, Inc.; *U.S. Private*, pg. 1952
HITT CONTRACTING, INC.; *U.S. Private*, pg. 1953
H.J. KALIKOW & CO. LLC; *U.S. Private*, pg. 1834
H.J. RUSSELL & COMPANY; *U.S. Private*, pg. 1834
HJ SHIPBUILDING & CONSTRUCTION COMPANY, LTD.; *Int'l*, pg. 3428
HKC (HOLDINGS) LIMITED; *Int'l*, pg. 3428
HLHI (CAMBODIA) CO., LTD.—See Hong Lai Huat Group Limited; *Int'l*, pg. 3467
HMB CONSTRUCTION AB—See AF Gruppen ASA; *Int'l*, pg. 184
HMB CONSTRUCTION OREBRO AB—See AF Gruppen ASA; *Int'l*, pg. 184
H&M COMPANY INC.; *U.S. Private*, pg. 1823
H & M CONSTRUCTORS CO.; *U.S. Private*, pg. 1822
HOA BINH INFRASTRUCTURE INVESTMENT & CONSTRUCTION JSC—See Hoa Binh Construction Group JSC; *Int'l*, pg. 3435
HOA BINH RENEWABLE ENERGY & INVESTMENT JOINT STOCK COMPANY—See Hoa Binh Construction Group JSC; *Int'l*, pg. 3435
HOAR CONSTRUCTION LLC; *U.S. Private*, pg. 1957
HOCHTIEF INFRASTRUCTURE GMBH—See ACS, Actividades de Construccion y Servicios, S.A.; *Int'l*, pg. 114
HODESS CLEANROOM CONSTRUCTION, LLC; *U.S. Private*, pg. 1959
HODGEN CONSTRUCTION & DEVELOPMENT GROUP INC.; *U.S. Private*, pg. 1959
HOFFMAN CORPORATION; *U.S. Private*, pg. 1960
HOFFMAN PLANNING, DESIGN & CONSTRUCTION, INC.; *U.S. Private*, pg. 1960
HOGG CONSTRUCTION INC.; *U.S. Private*, pg. 1961
HOHL INDUSTRIAL SERVICES CO.; *U.S. Private*, pg. 1961
HOLBAT SAS—See GCC SAS; *Int'l*, pg. 2894
HOLDER CONSTRUCTION COMPANY; *U.S. Private*, pg. 1962
HOLLAND CONSTRUCTION COMPANY, INC.; *U.S. Private*, pg. 1964
HOLOBUILDER, INC.—See FARO Technologies, Inc.; *U.S. Public*, pg. 823
HOLYOKE FINE HOMES—See Lease Crutcher Lewis; *U.S. Private*, pg. 2408
HOMES & SON CONTRACTORS, INC.; *U.S. Private*, pg. 1973
HON CORPORATION LTD.; *Int'l*, pg. 3456
HONKA FINLAND HOUSES EOOD—See Honkarakenne Oyj; *Int'l*, pg. 3471
HONKA LOG HOME LLC—See Honkarakenne Oyj; *Int'l*, pg. 3471
HONORS CONTRACTORS, INC.; *U.S. Private*, pg. 1977
HORAN CONSTRUCTION; *U.S. Private*, pg. 1980
HORIZON DEVELOPMENT GROUP, INC.; *U.S. Private*, pg. 1980
HOR KEW CORPORATION LIMITED; *Int'l*, pg. 3474
HOR KEW PRIVATE LIMITED—See Hor Kew Corporation Limited; *Int'l*, pg. 3474
HORNE BROTHERS CONSTRUCTION INC—See Pine Gate Renewables LLC; *U.S. Private*, pg. 3182
HORST CONSTRUCTION COMPANY INC.—See The Horst Group Inc.; *U.S. Private*, pg. 4054
THE HORST GROUP INC.; *U.S. Private*, pg. 4054
HOSPITAL DESIGNERS, INC.—See HBE Corporation; *U.S. Private*, pg. 1887
HOURIGAN CONSTRUCTION CORP.; *U.S. Private*, pg. 1991
HPC HOLDINGS LIMITED; *Int'l*, pg. 3500
H.P. CUMMINGS CONSTRUCTION COMPANY INC.; *U.S. Private*, pg. 1835
HRW LLC—See Majestic Construction LLC; *U.S. Private*, pg. 2554
HSIN DAR ENVIRONMENT CORPORATION—See Continental Holdings Corp.; *Int'l*, pg. 1784
HSU DEVELOPMENT; *U.S. Private*, pg. 1999
HUANG HSIANG CONSTRUCTION CORPORATION; *Int'l*, pg. 3513
HUBERT CONSTRUCTION; *U.S. Private*, pg. 2001
HUDSON CONSTRUCTION COMPANY; *U.S. Private*, pg. 2001
HUMBLE CONSTRUCTION CO.; *U.S. Private*, pg. 2007
HUMPHRIES & COMPANY, LLC; *U.S. Private*, pg. 2007
HUNG THINH INCONS JSC; *Int'l*, pg. 3535
HUNT CONSTRUCTION GROUP, INC. - EAST DIVISION—See AECOM; *U.S. Public*, pg. 51
HUNT CONSTRUCTION GROUP, INC. - ORLANDO—See AECOM; *U.S. Public*, pg. 51
HUNT CONSTRUCTION GROUP, INC.—See AECOM; *U.S. Public*, pg. 51
HUNT CONSTRUCTION GROUP, INC. - WEST DIVISION—See AECOM; *U.S. Public*, pg. 51
THE HUNT PAVING COMPANY, INC.—See AECOM; *U.S. Public*, pg. 51
HUNZINGER CONSTRUCTION COMPANY; *U.S. Private*, pg. 2011
HUTTON CONSTRUCTION CORP.; *U.S. Private*, pg. 2015
H.W. LOCHNER, INC.; *U.S. Private*, pg. 1836
HXMTD, S.A. DE C.V.—See Desarrolladora Homex, S.A. de C.V.; *Int'l*, pg. 2044
HYOSUNG CONSTRUCTION PERFORMANCE UNIT—See Hyosung Corporation; *Int'l*, pg. 3550
HY-VEE CONSTRUCTION LLC—See Hy-Vee, Inc.; *U.S. Private*, pg. 2016
IBARAKI GRANDY HOUSE CO., LTD.—See Grandy House Corporation; *Int'l*, pg. 3058
IBEX CONSTRUCTION COMPANY, LLC; *U.S. Private*, pg. 2028
IBI MACAU LIMITED—See IBI Group Holdings Limited; *Int'l*, pg. 3574
ICA CONSTRUCCION CIVIL, S.A. DE C.V.—See Empresas ICA S.A.B. de C.V.; *Int'l*, pg. 2390
ICA FLUOR—See Fluor Corporation; *U.S. Public*, pg. 859
ICA INFRAESTRUCTURA, S.A. DE C.V.—See Empresas ICA S.A.B. de C.V.; *Int'l*, pg. 2391
ICA INGENIERIA, S.A. DE C.V.—See Empresas ICA S.A.B. de C.V.; *Int'l*, pg. 2391
ICAPITAL, S.A. DE C.V.—See Empresas ICA S.A.B. de C.V.; *Int'l*, pg. 2391
ICC BIG CONSTRUCTION INVESTMENT JOINT STOCK COMPANY; *Int'l*, pg. 3578
ICI CONSTRUCTION INC.; *U.S. Private*, pg. 2031
ICONSTRUCTORS, LLC; *U.S. Private*, pg. 2033
ICP CONSTRUCTION, INC.—See Audax Group, Limited Partnership; *U.S. Public*, pg. 388
ICS BUILDERS INC.; *U.S. Private*, pg. 2033
ICSH S.A; *Int'l*, pg. 3586
ICS, INC.; *U.S. Private*, pg. 2033
THE IDEAL COMPANY INC.; *U.S. Private*, pg. 4055
IDEAL CONTRACTING L.L.C.—See The Ideal Group, Inc.; *U.S. Private*, pg. 4055
IDH DEVELOPMENT SA; *Int'l*, pg. 3594
IGUATEMI EMPRESA DE SHOPPING CENTERS S.A.—See Iguatemi S.A.; *Int'l*, pg. 3603
IJM CORPORATION BERHAD; *Int'l*, pg. 3608
I L LONG CONSTRUCTION COMPANY, INC.; *U.S. Private*, pg. 2020
IMC INC.—See International Management Consultants Inc.; *U.S. Private*, pg. 2118
INDUSTRIAL CONSTRUCTION COMPANY, INC.; *U.S. Private*, pg. 2065
INDUSTRIAL CONSTRUCTORS/MANAGERS, INC.; *U.S. Private*, pg. 2065
INFANTE ASSOCIATES INC.; *U.S. Private*, pg. 2070
INFRA SILESIA S.A.—See Deutsche Bahn AG; *Int'l*, pg. 2051
INFRASTRUCTURE DEVELOPMENTS CORP.; *U.S. Public*, pg. 1118
INGRAIN CONSTRUCTION, LLC; *U.S. Private*, pg. 2076
INLAND CONSTRUCTION COMPANY; *U.S. Private*, pg. 2078
INNOVATIVE CONSTRUCTION GROUP, LLC—See PulteGroup, Inc.; *U.S. Public*, pg. 1737
INTEGRATED CONSTRUCTION, LLC; *U.S. Private*, pg. 2099
INTERNATIONAL CERAMIC CONSTRUCTION, LLC; *U.S. Private*, pg. 2115
INTERNATIONAL MANAGEMENT CONSULTANTS INC.; *U.S. Private*, pg. 2118
INTERSTEEL INC.; *U.S. Private*, pg. 2126
INTERTEX GENERAL CONTRACTORS, INC.; *U.S. Private*, pg. 2127
INTERWEST CONSTRUCTION COMPANY, INC.—See Interwest Corporation; *U.S. Private*, pg. 2128
IOLKOS S.A.—See Gek Terna Societe Anonyme Holdings Real Estate Constructions; *Int'l*, pg. 2913
ISIS BELGIQUE SPRL—See Groupe Egis S.A.; *Int'l*, pg. 3102
IZUMO TEC CO., LTD.—See Hanwa Co., Ltd.; *Int'l*, pg. 3263
JA CARPENTRY, INC.; *U.S. Private*, pg. 2172
JACK B. HENDERSON CONSTRUCTION CO. INC.; *U.S. Private*, pg. 2173
JACK JENNINGS & SONS, INC.; *U.S. Private*, pg. 2174
JACKSON & ASSOCIATES GENERAL CONTRACTORS, INC.; *U.S. Private*, pg. 2175
JACKSON PROPERTIES INC.; *U.S. Private*, pg. 2178
JACOBSEN CONSTRUCTION COMPANY, INC.; *U.S. Private*, pg. 2180
JAG CONSTRUCTION CO.; *U.S. Private*, pg. 2181
JALMAT ACTIVITES INTERNATIONALES, SA—See Altrad Investment Authority SAS; *Int'l*, pg. 398
JALMAT OUEST ATLANTIQUE, SA—See Altrad Investment Authority SAS; *Int'l*, pg. 398
JAMERSON-LEWIS CONSTRUCTION INC.; *U.S. Private*, pg. 2182
JAMES A. CUMMINGS, INC.—See Tutor Perini Corporation; *U.S. Public*, pg. 2206
JAMES G. DAVIS CONSTRUCTION CORPORATION; *U.S. Private*, pg. 2184
JAMES J. WELCH & CO., INC.; *U.S. Private*, pg. 2184
JAMES MCHUGH CONSTRUCTION CO.—See McHugh Enterprises Inc.; *U.S. Private*, pg. 2636
JAMES R. THOMPSON INC.; *U.S. Private*, pg. 2185
JAMES R. VANNOY & SONS CONSTRUCTION COMPANY INC.; *U.S. Private*, pg. 2185
J. A. MOSS CONSTRUCTION CO. INC.; *U.S. Private*, pg. 2155
JANOTTA & HERNER, INC.; *U.S. Private*, pg. 2187
THE JANSEN GROUP INC.; *U.S. Private*, pg. 4058
JAPAN PILE CORPORATION—See ASIA PILE HOLDINGS CORPORATION; *Int'l*, pg. 614
J.A. STREET & ASSOCIATES, INC.; *U.S. Private*, pg. 2158
J. A. TIBERTI CONSTRUCTION CO., INC.—See Tiberti Organization; *U.S. Private*, pg. 4167
JAY KADOWAKI INC.; *U.S. Private*, pg. 2192
JAYNES CORPORATION; *U.S. Private*, pg. 2192
J. CALNAN & ASSOCIATES, INC.; *U.S. Private*, pg. 2155
JCAT GENERAL CONTRACTORS & MAINTENANCE; *U.S. Private*, pg. 2194
J. CHRISTY CONSTRUCTION CO., INC.—See Delek Group Ltd.; *Int'l*, pg. 2012
JD2 INC. - SAN DIEGO—See JD2 Inc.; *U.S. Private*, pg. 2195
JD2 INC.; *U.S. Private*, pg. 2195
J.E. CHARLOTTE CONSTRUCTION CORP.; *U.S. Private*, pg. 2161
J.E. DUNN CONSTRUCTION CO.—See J.E. Dunn Construction Group, Inc.; *U.S. Private*, pg. 2161
J.E. DUNN CONSTRUCTION CO.—See J.E. Dunn Construction Group, Inc.; *U.S. Private*, pg. 2161
J.E. DUNN CONSTRUCTION CO.—See J.E. Dunn Construction Group, Inc.; *U.S. Private*, pg. 2161
J.E. DUNN CONSTRUCTION CO.—See J.E. Dunn Construction Group, Inc.; *U.S. Private*, pg. 2161
J.E. DUNN CONSTRUCTION GROUP, INC.; *U.S. Private*, pg. 2161
JEFFREY M. BROWN ASSOCIATES; *U.S. Private*, pg. 2198
J.E. KINGHAM CONSTRUCTION CO., INC.; *U.S. Private*, pg. 2162
JENKINS-ESSEX COMPANY; *U.S. Private*, pg. 2199
JENSEN BUILDERS LTD. (INC.)—See Moore Brothers Asphalt Inc.; *U.S. Private*, pg. 2779
JERAL CONSTRUCTION SERVICES; *U.S. Private*, pg. 2201
JESCO, INC.—See W.G. Yates & Sons Construction Company; *U.S. Private*, pg. 4420
J. FLETCHER CREAMER & SON, INC.—See J. Fletcher Creamer & Son Inc.; *U.S. Private*, pg. 2156
J. FLETCHER CREAMER & SON, INC.—See J. Fletcher Creamer & Son Inc.; *U.S. Private*, pg. 2156
J.H. ALLEN INC.; *U.S. Private*, pg. 2165
J.H. FINDORFF & SON, INC.; *U.S. Private*, pg. 2165
J.H. MCCORMICK, INC.; *U.S. Private*, pg. 2166
J.I. GARCIA CONSTRUCTION CO.; *U.S. Private*, pg. 2166
J. KOKOLAKIS CONTRACTING, INC.; *U.S. Private*, pg. 2156
J.L. BURKE CONTRACTING, INC.; *U.S. Private*, pg. 2167
JLMOORE, INC.; *U.S. Private*, pg. 2213
J.L. WALLACE, INC.; *U.S. Private*, pg. 2168
JM WALKER LP; *U.S. Private*, pg. 2214
JOHN HOLLAND CONSTRUCTIONS PTY LTD.—See China Communications Construction Company Limited; *Int'l*, pg. 1491
JOHN HOLLAND GROUP PTY. LTD.—See China Communications Construction Company Limited; *Int'l*, pg. 1491
JOHN MORIARTY & ASSOCIATES INC.; *U.S. Private*, pg. 2223
JOHNNY RIBEIRO BUILDER INC.; *U.S. Private*, pg. 2226
JOHNSON CARLIER INC.; *U.S. Private*, pg. 2227
JOHN W. ROOKER & ASSOCIATES INC.; *U.S. Private*, pg. 2225
JONES & JONES INC.; *U.S. Private*, pg. 2231
JONES PERINI JOINT VENTURE; *U.S. Private*, pg. 2233
JON F. SWIFT INC.; *U.S. Private*, pg. 2231
JONQUIL STEEL & CONSTRUCTION CO.; *U.S. Private*, pg. 2234
JORDAN-WILCOMB CONSTRUCTION, INC.; *U.S. Private*, pg. 2235
JOSEPH A. NATOLI CONSTRUCTION CORP.; *U.S. Private*, pg. 2236
JOSEPH CONSTRUCTION CO. INC.; *U.S. Private*, pg. 2236
JOSEPH HUGHES CONSTRUCTION; *U.S. Private*, pg. 2236
JOURNEYMAN CONSTRUCTION, INC.; *U.S. Private*, pg. 2238
JOYCE & ASSOCIATES CONSTRUCTION, INC.; *U.S. Private*, pg. 2238
JOYSPEED GLOBAL CARGO CHINA LIMITED—See Hon Hai Precision Industry Co., Ltd.; *Int'l*, pg. 3457
J.P. CULLEN & SONS INC.; *U.S. Private*, pg. 2169
J.R. ABBOTT CONSTRUCTION, INC.; *U.S. Private*, pg. 2170
JTF CONSTRUCTION, INC.; *U.S. Private*, pg. 2242
JTO INC.; *U.S. Private*, pg. 2242
J.T. TURNER CONSTRUCTION CO.; *U.S. Private*, pg. 2171

3189

236220 — COMMERCIAL AND INST... CORPORATE AFFILIATIONS

N.A.I.C.S. Index

J.T. VAUGHN CONSTRUCTION COMPANY INCORPORATED; *U.S. Private*, pg. 2171
JUNGCLAUS-CAMPBELL CO. INC.; *U.S. Private*, pg. 2244
J. VINTON SCHAFER & SONS, INC.; *U.S. Private*, pg. 2157
JVK CONSTRUCTORS LLC.; *U.S. Private*, pg. 2246
J.W. BAILEY CONSTRUCTION COMPANY; *U.S. Private*, pg. 2171
J W R CONSTRUCTION SERVICES; *U.S. Private*, pg. 2153
K3 CONSTRUCTION GROUP, INC.; *U.S. Private*, pg. 2253
KANONADEN ENTREPRENAD AB—See AF Gruppen ASA; *Int'l*, pg. 184
KAPLAN CORPORATION; *U.S. Private*, pg. 2261
KAPP CONSTRUCTION COMPANY, INC.; *U.S. Private*, pg. 2262
KAST CONSTRUCTION COMPANY, LLC; *U.S. Private*, pg. 2264
KASTEEL ENTERPRISES, INC.; *U.S. Private*, pg. 2264
KAUFMAN LYNN CONSTRUCTION, INC.; *U.S. Private*, pg. 2265
K.B.C. GROUP INC.; *U.S. Private*, pg. 2251
KBE BUILDING CORPORATION; *U.S. Private*, pg. 2268
KBS BUILDERS, INC.—See Star Equity Holdings, Inc.; *U.S. Public*, pg. 1937
KBS CONSTRUCTION, INC.; *U.S. Private*, pg. 2268
KCC CONTRACTOR INC.; *U.S. Private*, pg. 2269
KCI CONSTRUCTION CO.; *U.S. Private*, pg. 2269
KEATING BUILDING COMPANY—See Tutor Perini Corporation; *U.S. Public*, pg. 2206
KEEFE CONSTRUCTION SERVICES; *U.S. Private*, pg. 2272
KEENAN, HOPKINS, SCHMIDT & STOWELL CONTRACTORS INC.; *U.S. Private*, pg. 2272
KELLER BUILDERS, INC.—See Swinerton Incorporated; *U.S. Private*, pg. 3894
KELLER CONSTRUCTION INC.; *U.S. Private*, pg. 2274
KELLER INC.; *U.S. Private*, pg. 2275
KELLOGG & KIMSEY, INC.; *U.S. Private*, pg. 2276
KELSEY CONSTRUCTION, INC.; *U.S. Private*, pg. 2277
KEN BRATNEY COMPANY—See K.B.C. Group Inc.; *U.S. Private*, pg. 2251
KENNEDY CONTRACTORS, INC.; *U.S. Private*, pg. 2284
KENOSIA CONSTRUCTION INC.; *U.S. Private*, pg. 2287
KESSEL CONSTRUCTION INC.; *U.S. Private*, pg. 2291
KETTELHUT CONSTRUCTION, INC.; *U.S. Private*, pg. 2292
KEY CONSTRUCTION INC.—See Wagman Companies, Inc.; *U.S. Private*, pg. 4426
KEYSTRUCT CONSTRUCTION, INC.; *U.S. Private*, pg. 2300
K & F BUSINESS BROKERS; *U.S. Private*, pg. 2249
K. HOVNANIAN ASPIRE AT RIVER TERRACE, LLC—See Hovnanian Enterprises, Inc.; *U.S. Public*, pg. 1056
K. HOVNANIAN ASPIRE AT WATERSTONE, LLC—See Hovnanian Enterprises, Inc.; *U.S. Public*, pg. 1056
K. HOVNANIAN AT ALEXANDER LAKES, LLC—See Hovnanian Enterprises, Inc.; *U.S. Public*, pg. 1058
K. HOVNANIAN AT ASHLEY POINTE LLC—See Hovnanian Enterprises, Inc.; *U.S. Public*, pg. 1058
K. HOVNANIAN AT AUTUMN RIDGE, LLC—See Hovnanian Enterprises, Inc.; *U.S. Public*, pg. 1058
K. HOVNANIAN AT BENSEN'S MILL ESTATES, LLC—See Hovnanian Enterprises, Inc.; *U.S. Public*, pg. 1058
K. HOVNANIAN AT BOCA DUNES, LLC—See Hovnanian Enterprises, Inc.; *U.S. Public*, pg. 1058
K. HOVNANIAN AT BRITTANY MANOR, LLC—See Hovnanian Enterprises, Inc.; *U.S. Public*, pg. 1058
K. HOVNANIAN AT CADENCE PARK, LLC—See Hovnanian Enterprises, Inc.; *U.S. Public*, pg. 1058
K. HOVNANIAN AT CHURCHILL FARMS LLC—See Hovnanian Enterprises, Inc.; *U.S. Public*, pg. 1058
K. HOVNANIAN AT DEER RIDGE, LLC—See Hovnanian Enterprises, Inc.; *U.S. Public*, pg. 1058
K. HOVNANIAN AT EDEN TERRACE, LLC—See Hovnanian Enterprises, Inc.; *U.S. Public*, pg. 1058
K. HOVNANIAN AT EMBREY MILL VILLAGE, LLC—See Hovnanian Enterprises, Inc.; *U.S. Public*, pg. 1058
K. HOVNANIAN AT ESTATES OF CHANCELLORSVILLE, LLC—See Hovnanian Enterprises, Inc.; *U.S. Public*, pg. 1058
K. HOVNANIAN AT ESTATES OF FOX CHASE, LLC—See Hovnanian Enterprises, Inc.; *U.S. Public*, pg. 1058
K. HOVNANIAN AT GRANDE PARK, LLC—See Hovnanian Enterprises, Inc.; *U.S. Public*, pg. 1058
K. HOVNANIAN AT HAMMOCK BREEZE, LLC—See Hovnanian Enterprises, Inc.; *U.S. Public*, pg. 1059
K. HOVNANIAN AT HIDDEN BROOK, LLC—See Hovnanian Enterprises, Inc.; *U.S. Public*, pg. 1059
K. HOVNANIAN AT JACKS RUN, LLC—See Hovnanian Enterprises, Inc.; *U.S. Public*, pg. 1059
K. HOVNANIAN AT LINK CROSSING, LLC—See Hovnanian Enterprises, Inc.; *U.S. Public*, pg. 1059
K. HOVNANIAN AT LUKE LANDING, LLC—See Hovnanian Enterprises, Inc.; *U.S. Public*, pg. 1059
K. HOVNANIAN AT LUNA VISTA, LLC—See Hovnanian Enterprises, Inc.; *U.S. Public*, pg. 1059
K. HOVNANIAN AT MAPLE HILL LLC—See Hovnanian Enterprises, Inc.; *U.S. Public*, pg. 1059
K. HOVNANIAN AT NORTH GROVE CROSSING, LLC—See Hovnanian Enterprises, Inc.; *U.S. Public*, pg. 1059
K. HOVNANIAN AT NORTH POINTE ESTATES LLC—See Hovnanian Enterprises, Inc.; *U.S. Public*, pg. 1059
K. HOVNANIAN AT PARK PASEO, LLC—See Hovnanian Enterprises, Inc.; *U.S. Public*, pg. 1059
K. HOVNANIAN AT PINCKNEY FARM, LLC—See Hovnanian Enterprises, Inc.; *U.S. Public*, pg. 1059
K. HOVNANIAN AT RETREAT AT MILLSTONE, LLC—See Hovnanian Enterprises, Inc.; *U.S. Public*, pg. 1059
K. HOVNANIAN AT ROCKLAND VILLAGE GREEN, LLC—See Hovnanian Enterprises, Inc.; *U.S. Public*, pg. 1059
K. HOVNANIAN AT SCOTTSDALE HEIGHTS, LLC—See Hovnanian Enterprises, Inc.; *U.S. Public*, pg. 1059
K. HOVNANIAN AT SEABROOK, LLC—See Hovnanian Enterprises, Inc.; *U.S. Public*, pg. 1059
K. HOVNANIAN AT SIERRA VISTA, LLC—See Hovnanian Enterprises, Inc.; *U.S. Public*, pg. 1059
K. HOVNANIAN AT SILVER LEAF, LLC—See Hovnanian Enterprises, Inc.; *U.S. Public*, pg. 1059
K. HOVNANIAN AT TOWNES AT COUNTY CENTER, LLC—See Hovnanian Enterprises, Inc.; *U.S. Public*, pg. 1060
K. HOVNANIAN AT UNION PARK, LLC—See Hovnanian Enterprises, Inc.; *U.S. Public*, pg. 1060
K. HOVNANIAN AT VERRADO MARKETSIDE, LLC—See Hovnanian Enterprises, Inc.; *U.S. Public*, pg. 1060
K. HOVNANIAN AT VILLAGE CENTER, LLC—See Hovnanian Enterprises, Inc.; *U.S. Public*, pg. 1060
K. HOVNANIAN AT WADE'S GRANT, LLC—See Hovnanian Enterprises, Inc.; *U.S. Public*, pg. 1060
K. HOVNANIAN AT WILLOWSFORD GREENS III, LLC—See Hovnanian Enterprises, Inc.; *U.S. Public*, pg. 1060
K. HOVNANIAN BRITTANY MANOR BORROWER, LLC—See Hovnanian Enterprises, Inc.; *U.S. Public*, pg. 1056
K. HOVNANIAN CORNERSTONE FARMS, LLC—See Hovnanian Enterprises, Inc.; *U.S. Public*, pg. 1056
K. HOVNANIAN DFW BAYSIDE, LLC—See Hovnanian Enterprises, Inc.; *U.S. Public*, pg. 1056
K. HOVNANIAN DFW CANYON FALLS, LLC—See Hovnanian Enterprises, Inc.; *U.S. Public*, pg. 1056
K. HOVNANIAN DFW COMMODORE AT PRESTON, LLC—See Hovnanian Enterprises, Inc.; *U.S. Public*, pg. 1056
K. HOVNANIAN DFW DIAMOND CREEK ESTATES, LLC—See Hovnanian Enterprises, Inc.; *U.S. Public*, pg. 1056
K. HOVNANIAN DFW HIGH POINTE, LLC—See Hovnanian Enterprises, Inc.; *U.S. Public*, pg. 1056
K. HOVNANIAN DFW LIBERTY, LLC—See Hovnanian Enterprises, Inc.; *U.S. Public*, pg. 1057
K. HOVNANIAN DFW OAKMONT PARK, LLC—See Hovnanian Enterprises, Inc.; *U.S. Public*, pg. 1057
K. HOVNANIAN DFW SANFORD PARK, LLC—See Hovnanian Enterprises, Inc.; *U.S. Public*, pg. 1057
K. HOVNANIAN DFW TRAILWOOD, LLC—See Hovnanian Enterprises, Inc.; *U.S. Public*, pg. 1057
K. HOVNANIAN DFW WATSON CREEK, LLC—See Hovnanian Enterprises, Inc.; *U.S. Public*, pg. 1057
K. HOVNANIAN DFW WELLINGTON VILLAS, LLC—See Hovnanian Enterprises, Inc.; *U.S. Public*, pg. 1057
K. HOVNANIAN FOUR SEASONS AT CHESTNUT RIDGE, LLC—See Hovnanian Enterprises, Inc.; *U.S. Public*, pg. 1057
K. HOVNANIAN HOMES AT SHENANDOAH SPRINGS, LLC—See Hovnanian Enterprises, Inc.; *U.S. Public*, pg. 1057
K. HOVNANIAN HOUSTON BAYOU OAKS AT WEST OREM, LLC—See Hovnanian Enterprises, Inc.; *U.S. Public*, pg. 1057
K. HOVNANIAN HOUSTON CREEK BEND, LLC—See Hovnanian Enterprises, Inc.; *U.S. Public*, pg. 1057
K. HOVNANIAN HOUSTON DRY CREEK VILLAGE, LLC—See Hovnanian Enterprises, Inc.; *U.S. Public*, pg. 1057
K. HOVNANIAN HOUSTON GREATWOOD LAKE, LLC—See Hovnanian Enterprises, Inc.; *U.S. Public*, pg. 1057
K. HOVNANIAN HOUSTON KATY POINTE, LLC—See Hovnanian Enterprises, Inc.; *U.S. Public*, pg. 1057
K. HOVNANIAN HOUSTON LAUREL GLEN, LLC—See Hovnanian Enterprises, Inc.; *U.S. Public*, pg. 1057
K. HOVNANIAN HOUSTON MIDTOWN PARK I, LLC—See Hovnanian Enterprises, Inc.; *U.S. Public*, pg. 1057
K. HOVNANIAN HOUSTON PARK LAKES EAST, LLC—See Hovnanian Enterprises, Inc.; *U.S. Public*, pg. 1057
K. HOVNANIAN HOUSTON PARKWAY TRAILS, LLC—See Hovnanian Enterprises, Inc.; *U.S. Public*, pg. 1057
K. HOVNANIAN HOUSTON RIVER FARMS, LLC—See Hovnanian Enterprises, Inc.; *U.S. Public*, pg. 1057
K. HOVNANIAN HOUSTON THUNDER BAY SUBDIVISION, LLC—See Hovnanian Enterprises, Inc.; *U.S. Public*, pg. 1057
K. HOVNANIAN HOUSTON TRANQUILITY LAKE ESTATES, LLC—See Hovnanian Enterprises, Inc.; *U.S. Public*, pg. 1057
K. HOVNANIAN LANDINGS 40S, LLC—See Hovnanian Enterprises, Inc.; *U.S. Public*, pg. 1057
K. HOVNANIAN MAGNOLIA AT WESTSIDE, LLC—See Hovnanian Enterprises, Inc.; *U.S. Public*, pg. 1057
K. HOVNANIAN MEADOW LAKES, LLC—See Hovnanian Enterprises, Inc.; *U.S. Public*, pg. 1057
K. HOVNANIAN MEADOW VIEW AT MOUNTAIN HOUSE, LLC—See Hovnanian Enterprises, Inc.; *U.S. Public*, pg. 1058
K. HOVNANIAN NORTON PLACE, LLC—See Hovnanian Enterprises, Inc.; *U.S. Public*, pg. 1058
K. HOVNANIAN OCOEE LANDINGS, LLC—See Hovnanian Enterprises, Inc.; *U.S. Public*, pg. 1058
K. HOVNANIAN REDFERN TRAILS, LLC—See Hovnanian Enterprises, Inc.; *U.S. Public*, pg. 1058
K. HOVNANIAN SAN SEBASTIAN, LLC—See Hovnanian Enterprises, Inc.; *U.S. Public*, pg. 1058
K. HOVNANIAN'S ASPIRE AT UNION VILLAGE, LLC—See Hovnanian Enterprises, Inc.; *U.S. Public*, pg. 1060
K. HOVNANIAN'S FOUR SEASONS AT BAYMONT FARMS LLC—See Hovnanian Enterprises, Inc.; *U.S. Public*, pg. 1060
K. HOVNANIAN'S FOUR SEASONS AT BELLE TERRE, LLC—See Hovnanian Enterprises, Inc.; *U.S. Public*, pg. 1060
K. HOVNANIAN'S FOUR SEASONS AT CAROLINA OAKS, LLC—See Hovnanian Enterprises, Inc.; *U.S. Public*, pg. 1060
K. HOVNANIAN VILLAGE GLEN, LLC—See Hovnanian Enterprises, Inc.; *U.S. Public*, pg. 1058
K. HOVNANIAN VILLAS AT THE COMMONS, LLC—See Hovnanian Enterprises, Inc.; *U.S. Public*, pg. 1058
K. HOVNANIAN WINDING BAY PRESERVE, LLC—See Hovnanian Enterprises, Inc.; *U.S. Public*, pg. 1058
KHS&S CONTRACTORS; *U.S. Private*, pg. 2301
KIEFNER BROTHERS, INC.; *U.S. Private*, pg. 2303
KIENLEN CONSTRUCTORS—See Alberici Corporation; *U.S. Private*, pg. 152
KINCO CONSTRUCTORS LLC; *U.S. Private*, pg. 2306
KIRKESTUEN AS—See AF Gruppen ASA; *Int'l*, pg. 184
KIRTLEY-COLE ASSOCIATES, LLC.; *U.S. Private*, pg. 2315
KITCHELL CONTRACTORS, INC. OF ARIZONA—See Kitchell Corporation; *U.S. Private*, pg. 2316
KITCHELL CORPORATION; *U.S. Private*, pg. 2316
KLASSEN CORPORATION; *U.S. Private*, pg. 2318
KLINGER COMPANIES INCORPORATED; *U.S. Private*, pg. 2320
KMAC, INC.—See KKR & Co. Inc.; *U.S. Public*, pg. 1249
KNESTRICK CONTRACTOR INC.; *U.S. Private*, pg. 2321
KNUTSON CONSTRUCTION SERVICES MIDWEST INC.—See Knutson Construction Services; *U.S. Private*, pg. 2325
KOPLAR PROPERTIES INC—See Koplar Communications International, Inc.; *U.S. Private*, pg. 2343
KORTE CONSTRUCTION COMPANY INC.; *U.S. Private*, pg. 2344
KORTE CONSTRUCTION; *U.S. Private*, pg. 2344
KRAEMER BROTHERS, LLC.; *U.S. Private*, pg. 2348
KRAUS-ANDERSON INCORPORATED; *U.S. Private*, pg. 2349
KRAUS CONSTRUCTION INC.; *U.S. Private*, pg. 2349
KREMPP LUMBER CO.; *U.S. Private*, pg. 2351
KULBACK'S CONSTRUCTION, INC.; *U.S. Private*, pg. 2356
KULLMAN BUILDINGS CORP.; *U.S. Private*, pg. 2357
KYBURZ-CARLSON CONSTRUCTION; *U.S. Private*, pg. 2360
LAB ENTREPRENOR AS—See AF Gruppen ASA; *Int'l*, pg. 184
LAGERHAUS FRANCHISE GMBH—See BayWa AG; *Int'l*, pg. 918
LAGO BUILDERS INC.; *U.S. Private*, pg. 2373
LAKEVIEW CONSTRUCTION INC.; *U.S. Private*, pg. 2378
LAMAR CONSTRUCTION COMPANY; *U.S. Private*, pg. 2379
LANDAU BUILDING COMPANY; *U.S. Private*, pg. 2384
LANDCO CONSTRUCTION; *U.S. Private*, pg. 2384
LANDIS CONSTRUCTION CO., LLC.; *U.S. Private*, pg. 2385
LANDMARK CONSTRUCTION COMPANY, INC.; *U.S. Private*, pg. 2385
LANDMARK RETAIL CORP.; *U.S. Private*, pg. 2385
LAND-RON, INC.; *U.S. Private*, pg. 2384
LAND SOUTH CONSTRUCTION LLC; *U.S. Private*, pg. 2384
LANHAM BROTHERS GENERAL CONTRACTORS; *U.S. Private*, pg. 2390
LANTZ CONSTRUCTION COMPANY; *U.S. Private*, pg. 2391
LARRY'S MINING, INC.; *U.S. Private*, pg. 2393
LARSON-DANIELSON CONSTRUCTION COMPANY, INC.; *U.S. Private*, pg. 2394
LASCO CONSTRUCTION, INC.; *U.S. Private*, pg. 2395
THE LATHROP COMPANY, INC.—See ACS, Actividades de Construccion y Servicios, S.A.; *Int'l*, pg. 113

N.A.I.C.S. INDEX

236220 — COMMERCIAL AND INST...

LAUREN HOLDINGS INC.; *U.S. Private*, pg. 2399
LAUTH GROUP, INC; *U.S. Private*, pg. 2400
LAVERDIERE CONSTRUCTION INC.; *U.S. Private*, pg. 2400
THE LAW COMPANY, INC.; *U.S. Private*, pg. 4068
LBM CONSTRUCTION COMPANY, INC.; *U.S. Private*, pg. 2403
LCS CONSTRUCTORS, INC.; *U.S. Private*, pg. 2403
LCS HOLDINGS INC.; *U.S. Private*, pg. 2403
LEASE CRUTCHER LEWIS; *U.S. Private*, pg. 2408
LEE F. COWPER, INC.; *U.S. Private*, pg. 2413
LEE KENNEDY CO. INC.; *U.S. Private*, pg. 2413
LEE LEWIS CONSTRUCTION, INC.; *U.S. Private*, pg. 2413
LEHR CONSTRUCTION COMPANY; *U.S. Private*, pg. 2419
LEIGHTON CONTRACTORS PTY. LIMITED—See ACS, Actividades de Construccion y Servicios, S.A.; *Int'l*, pg. 113
LEIGHTON CONTRACTORS PTY. LIMITED—See Apollo Global Management, Inc.; *U.S. Public*, pg. 153
LEIGHTON PROPERTIES PTY LIMITED—See ACS, Actividades de Construccion y Servicios, S.A.; *Int'l*, pg. 115
LEISURE CONSTRUCTION LLC—See Leisure Hotel Corporation; *U.S. Private*, pg. 2420
THE LEMOINE COMPANY INCORPORATED; *U.S. Private*, pg. 4069
LENNAR HOMES, INC.—See Lennar Corporation; *U.S. Public*, pg. 1306
LEONARD S. FIORE, INC.; *U.S. Private*, pg. 2430
LEON D. DEMATTEIS CONSTRUCTION; *U.S. Private*, pg. 2422
LEONE & KEEBLE INC.; *U.S. Private*, pg. 2430
LEOPARDO COMPANIES INC.; *U.S. Private*, pg. 2431
LESTER BUILDING SYSTEMS, LLC; *U.S. Private*, pg. 2432
L.E. WENTZ GROUP, INC.; *U.S. Private*, pg. 2365
LEWIS INVESTMENT COMPANIES, LLC—See Lewis Operating Corp.; *U.S. Private*, pg. 2439
L.F. DRISCOLL COMPANY LLC—See STO Building Group Inc.; *U.S. Private*, pg. 3813
LIBRAMIENTO ICA LA PIEDAD, S.A. DE C.V.—See Empresas ICA S.A.B. de C.V.; *Int'l*, pg. 2391
LILJA CORP.; *U.S. Private*, pg. 2455
LIMBACH COMPANY LLC—See Limbach Holdings, Inc.; *U.S. Public*, pg. 1316
LINBECK CONSTRUCTION CORPORATION-HOUSTON—See Linbeck Group LLC; *U.S. Private*, pg. 2456
LINBECK GROUP LLC; *U.S. Private*, pg. 2456
LINBECK—See Linbeck Group LLC; *U.S. Private*, pg. 2456
LINCOLN BUILDERS INC.; *U.S. Private*, pg. 2457
LINCOLN PROPERTY COMPANY COMMERCIAL, INC.—See Lincoln Property Company; *U.S. Private*, pg. 2458
LINDSCHULTE THILLMANN GMBH—See BKW AG; *Int'l*, pg. 1055
LINKOUS CONSTRUCTION COMPANY, INC.; *U.S. Private*, pg. 2462
LLJ INC.; *U.S. Private*, pg. 2475
LLT BUILDING CORPORATION; *U.S. Private*, pg. 2476
LMC CONSTRUCTION, LLC—See Lennar Corporation; *U.S. Public*, pg. 1306
LOCKERBIE & HOLE INC.—See Aecon Group Inc.; *Int'l*, pg. 172
LODGE CONSTRUCTION INC.; *U.S. Private*, pg. 2479
LODGICO LTD.—See Honkarakenne Oyj; *Int'l*, pg. 3471
LOJAC INC.; *U.S. Private*, pg. 2482
THE LOMBARD CO., INC.—See The Lombard Investment Co.; *U.S. Private*, pg. 4072
THE LOMBARD INVESTMENT CO.; *U.S. Private*, pg. 4072
LOTSPEICH CO.; *U.S. Private*, pg. 2497
LOUISIANA-PACIFIC ARGENTINA S.R.L.—See Louisiana-Pacific Corporation; *U.S. Public*, pg. 1342
LOUISIANA-PACIFIC COLOMBIA S.A.S.—See Louisiana-Pacific Corporation; *U.S. Public*, pg. 1342
LOWDER CONSTRUCTION COMPANY, INC.—See Colonial Company; *U.S. Private*, pg. 970
LOXITE GMBH—See Aurelius Equity Opportunities SE & Co. KGaA; *Int'l*, pg. 709
L&R CONSTRUCTION SERVICES, INC.; *U.S. Private*, pg. 2363
L R HEIN CONSTRUCTION CORP.; *U.S. Private*, pg. 2361
LS SYSTEMS, LLC; *U.S. Private*, pg. 2508
LTB LEITUNGSBAU GMBH—See BKW AG; *Int'l*, pg. 1055
LUEDER CONSTRUCTION COMPANY; *U.S. Private*, pg. 2512
LUNDAHL BUILDING SYSTEMS, INC.; *U.S. Private*, pg. 2515
LUNDY CONSTRUCTION CO., INC.; *U.S. Private*, pg. 2515
LUSARDI CONSTRUCTION CO.; *U.S. Private*, pg. 2516
L. WOLF COMPANY; *U.S. Private*, pg. 2364
LYDA SWINERTON BUILDERS, INC.; *U.S. Private*, pg. 2519
LYDIG CONSTRUCTION INC.; *U.S. Private*, pg. 2519
M1-ENERGY LLC—See E1 Corporation; *Int'l*, pg. 2260
M30 STANDS 2003 S.A.—See Espiga Capital Gestion S.G.E.C.R, S.A.; *Int'l*, pg. 2506
M6 TOLNA UZEMELTETO KFT—See Groupe Egis S.A.; *Int'l*, pg. 3102
M.A. ANGELIADES INC.; *U.S. Private*, pg. 2527
MACMILLAN COMPANY INC.; *U.S. Private*, pg. 2538

MAD DOG DESIGN & CONSTRUCTION CO., INC.; *U.S. Private*, pg. 2539
MADISON, INC.—See John S. Frey Enterprises; *U.S. Private*, pg. 2224
MADISON INDUSTRIES INC.—See John S. Frey Enterprises; *U.S. Private*, pg. 2224
MAGCO DRILLING, INC.—See Aldridge Construction, Inc.; *U.S. Private*, pg. 160
MAGIL CONSTRUCTION—See Fayolle et Fils; *Int'l*, pg. 2626
MAGILL CONSTRUCTION COMPANY, INC.; *U.S. Private*, pg. 2546
MAGNITE SINGAPORE PTE. LTD.—See Magnite, Inc.; *U.S. Public*, pg. 1354
MAGNUM BUILDERS OF SARASOTA, INC.; *U.S. Private*, pg. 2548
MAGNUM CONSTRUCTION MANAGEMENT; *U.S. Private*, pg. 2548
MAGNUM ENTERPRISES INC.; *U.S. Private*, pg. 2549
MAINTENANCE ENTERPRISES LLC—See Bernhard Capital Partners Management, LP; *U.S. Private*, pg. 537
MAINTENANCE ENTERPRISES LLC—See KBR, Inc.; *U.S. Public*, pg. 1216
M. ALFIERI CO. INC.; *U.S. Private*, pg. 2526
MALL CRAFT INC.; *U.S. Private*, pg. 2557
MALONEY & BELL GENERAL CONTRACTORS, INC. OF CALIFORNIA; *U.S. Private*, pg. 2558
MALOUF CONSTRUCTION CORP.; *U.S. Private*, pg. 2558
M.A. MORTENSON COMPANY; *U.S. Private*, pg. 2527
MANASOTA COMMERCIAL CONSTRUCTION CO., INC.; *U.S. Private*, pg. 2561
MANHATTAN CONSTRUCTION COMPANY—See Rooney Holdings, Inc.; *U.S. Private*, pg. 3479
MANHATTAN CONSTRUCTION COMPANY—See Rooney Holdings, Inc.; *U.S. Private*, pg. 3479
MANNING-SQUIRES-HENNIG CO. INC.; *U.S. Private*, pg. 2565
MANTENIMIENTO DE INFRAESTRUCTURAS, S.A.—See Fomento de Construcciones y Contratas, S.A.; *Int'l*, pg. 2723
MANTENIMIENTOS, AYUDA A LA EXPLOTACION Y SERVICIOS, S.A.—See ACS, Actividades de Construccion y Servicios, S.A.; *Int'l*, pg. 115
MAPLE-LEAF CONSTRUCTION CO, INC.; *U.S. Private*, pg. 2568
MAPP CONSTRUCTION, LLC; *U.S. Private*, pg. 2569
MARANATHA VOLUNTEERS INTERNATIONAL, INC.; *U.S. Private*, pg. 2569
MARAWOOD CONSTRUCTION SERVICES; *U.S. Private*, pg. 2570
MARCHETTI CONSTRUCTION INC.; *U.S. Private*, pg. 2571
MARCO ENTERPRISES, INC.; *U.S. Private*, pg. 2571
MARK CONSTRUCTION CO. INC.; *U.S. Private*, pg. 2577
MARKET CONTRACTORS LTD.; *U.S. Private*, pg. 2578
MARKET & JOHNSON, INC.; *U.S. Private*, pg. 2578
MARKS-LANDAU CONSTRUCTION, LLC—See Landau Building Company; *U.S. Private*, pg. 2384
MARK WRIGHT CONSTRUCTION INC.; *U.S. Private*, pg. 2578
MARNELL CORRAO ASSOCIATES, INC.; *U.S. Private*, pg. 2586
MARSHALL COMPANY; *U.S. Private*, pg. 2592
MARSH CONSTRUCTION SERVICES, INC.; *U.S. Private*, pg. 2591
MARYL CONSTRUCTION, INC.—See Maryl Group, Inc.; *U.S. Private*, pg. 2600
MASCARO CONSTRUCTION CO. LP; *U.S. Private*, pg. 2600
MASCON INCORPORATED; *U.S. Private*, pg. 2601
MASHBURN CONSTRUCTION COMPANY; *U.S. Private*, pg. 2601
MASSENBERG GMBH—See DPE Deutsche Private Equity GmbH; *Int'l*, pg. 2188
MASTER BUILDERS SOLUTIONS BELGIUM N.V.—See BASF SE; *Int'l*, pg. 884
MASTER BUILDERS SOLUTIONS NEDERLAND B.V.—See BASF SE; *Int'l*, pg. 884
MASTER BUILDERS SOLUTIONS POLSKA SP. Z O.O.—See BASF SE; *Int'l*, pg. 884
MASTER BUILDERS SOLUTIONS YAPI KIMYASALLARI SANAYI VE TICARET LIMITED SIRKETI—See BASF SE; *Int'l*, pg. 884
MATASSA CONSTRUCTION INC.; *U.S. Private*, pg. 2609
MATCON CONSTRUCTION SERVICES, INC.; *U.S. Private*, pg. 2609
MATRIX SERVICE, INC.—See Matrix Service Company; *U.S. Public*, pg. 1397
MATT CONSTRUCTION SERVICES INC.—See Columbia National Group Inc; *U.S. Private*, pg. 977
MATTHEWS GIBRALTAR MAUSOLEUM & CONSTRUCTION COMPANY—See Matthews International Corporation; *U.S. Public*, pg. 1399
MAULDIN-DORFMEIER CONSTRUCTION; *U.S. Private*, pg. 2615
MAVO SYSTEMS, INC.—See Arctic Slope Regional Corporation; *U.S. Private*, pg. 316
M.B. KAHN CONSTRUCTION CO., INC.; *U.S. Private*, pg. 2528

MCBRIDE CONSTRUCTION RESOURCES, INC.; *U.S. Private*, pg. 2625
MCCARTHY BUILDING COMPANIES, INC. - CENTRAL DIVISION—See McCarthy Holdings, Inc.; *U.S. Private*, pg. 2627
MCCARTHY BUILDING COMPANIES, INC. NEVADA/UTAH DIVISION—See McCarthy Holdings, Inc.; *U.S. Private*, pg. 2627
MCCARTHY BUILDING COMPANIES, INC. - NORTHERN PACIFIC DIVISION-SACRAMENTO—See McCarthy Holdings, Inc.; *U.S. Private*, pg. 2627
MCCARTHY BUILDING COMPANIES, INC. - NORTHERN PACIFIC DIVISION—See McCarthy Holdings, Inc.; *U.S. Private*, pg. 2627
MCCARTHY BUILDING COMPANIES, INC.—See McCarthy Holdings, Inc.; *U.S. Private*, pg. 2627
MCCARTHY BUILDING COMPANIES, INC. - SOUTHEAST DIVISION—See McCarthy Holdings, Inc.; *U.S. Private*, pg. 2627
MCCARTHY BUILDING COMPANIES, INC. - SOUTHERN CALIFORNIA DIVISION—See McCarthy Holdings, Inc.; *U.S. Private*, pg. 2627
MCCARTHY BUILDING COMPANIES, INC. - SOUTHWEST DIVISION—See McCarthy Holdings, Inc.; *U.S. Private*, pg. 2627
MCCARTHY BUILDING COMPANIES, INC. - TEXAS DIVISION—See McCarthy Holdings, Inc.; *U.S. Private*, pg. 2627
MCCARTY CONSTRUCTION INC.; *U.S. Private*, pg. 2628
MCCORMACK CONSTRUCTION CO. INC.—See Emerick Construction Co. Inc.; *U.S. Private*, pg. 1381
MCCREE GENERAL CONTRACTORS & ARCHITECTS; *U.S. Private*, pg. 2631
MCCRORY CONSTRUCTION CO., LLC; *U.S. Private*, pg. 2631
MCDONALD YORK BUILDING COMPANY; *U.S. Private*, pg. 2632
MCGOLDRICK CONSTRUCTION SERVICES CORPORATION; *U.S. Private*, pg. 2635
MCGOUGH CONSTRUCTION CO. INC.; *U.S. Private*, pg. 2635
MC GOWAN BUILDERS, INC.; *U.S. Private*, pg. 2625
MCGRAW/KOKOSING, INC.—See Kokosing Construction Company, Inc.; *U.S. Private*, pg. 2341
MC GROUP—See Fayolle et Fils; *Int'l*, pg. 2626
MCHUGH ENTERPRISES INC.; *U.S. Private*, pg. 2636
MCINNIS BUILDERS, LLC.; *U.S. Private*, pg. 2637
MCINTYRE ELWELL & STRAMMER GENERAL CONTRACTORS, INC.; *U.S. Private*, pg. 2637
MCKAY-COCKER CONSTRUCTION LIMITED—See Fayolle et Fils; *Int'l*, pg. 2626
MCK BUILDING ASSOCIATES INC.; *U.S. Private*, pg. 2637
MCL COMPANIES; *U.S. Private*, pg. 2639
MCM PAVING & CONSTUCTION; *U.S. Private*, pg. 2642
MCNEIL HEALTHCARE LLC—See Kenvue Inc.; *U.S. Public*, pg. 1224
MCV COMPANIES INC.; *U.S. Private*, pg. 2645
M. DAVID PAUL & ASSOCIATES; *U.S. Private*, pg. 2526
MEINECKE-JOHNSON COMPANY, INC.; *U.S. Private*, pg. 2660
MEISINGER CONSTRUCTION COMPANY; *U.S. Private*, pg. 2661
MELO CONTRACTORS, INC.; *U.S. Private*, pg. 2662
MENEMSHA; *U.S. Private*, pg. 2666
MERIDIENNE CORPORATION; *U.S. Private*, pg. 2674
MERTES CONTRACTING CORPORATION; *U.S. Private*, pg. 2677
MESSER CONSTRUCTION CO.; *U.S. Private*, pg. 2679
MET-CON CONSTRUCTION INC.; *U.S. Private*, pg. 2679
METRON CONSTRUCTION CO. INC.; *U.S. Private*, pg. 2687
METROPOLITAN ENTERTAINMENT & CONVENTION AUTHORITY; *U.S. Private*, pg. 2688
MEYER & NAJEM INC.; *U.S. Private*, pg. 2692
MIANYANG SCIENCE TECHNOLOGY CITY DEVELOPMENT INVESTMENT (GROUP) CO., LTD.—See China Metal Resources Utilization Ltd.; *Int'l*, pg. 1524
MICCO CONSTRUCTION LLC.—See National Construction Enterprises Inc.; *U.S. Private*, pg. 2851
MICCO LLC—See National Construction Enterprises Inc.; *U.S. Private*, pg. 2851
MICHAEL RAYMOND NIGERIA LTD.—See Haulotte Group SA; *Int'l*, pg. 3285
MICHAEL RIESZ & CO. INC.; *U.S. Private*, pg. 2698
MIC-RON GENERAL CONTRACTORS INC.; *U.S. Private*, pg. 2697
MID AMERICA CONTRACTORS, L.L.C.—See Republic Services, Inc.; *U.S. Public*, pg. 1786
MID ATLANTIC CONSTRUCTION GROUP INC.; *U.S. Private*, pg. 2705
MID-LINK M7/M8 LTD.—See Groupe Egis S.A.; *Int'l*, pg. 3102
MID-SOUTH MAINTENANCE, INC.; *U.S. Private*, pg. 2709
MID-STATES GENERAL & MECHANICAL CONTRACTING; *U.S. Private*, pg. 2709
MID-TEX OF MIDLAND, INC.; *U.S. Private*, pg. 2709
M/I HOMES, INC.; *U.S. Public*, pg. 1351

236220 — COMMERCIAL AND INST...

MIKE CARTER CONSTRUCTION INC.; *U.S. Private*, pg. 2725
MIKELE INTERNATIONAL GROUP, LLC; *U.S. Private*, pg. 2726
MILES-MCCLELLAN CONSTRUCTION COMPANY; *U.S. Private*, pg. 2728
MILESTONE CONSTRUCTION SERVICES, INC.; *U.S. Private*, pg. 2728
MILITARY CONSTRUCTION CORPORATION; *U.S. Private*, pg. 2729
MILLENNIUM BUILDERS, INC.—See Riverstone Holdings LLC; *U.S. Private*, pg. 3447
MILLENNIUM STEEL SERVICE LLC.; *U.S. Private*, pg. 2732
MILLER AND SMITH HOMES, INC.—See Miller & Smith Holding Company Inc.; *U.S. Private*, pg. 2732
MILLER CONSTRUCTION COMPANY; *U.S. Private*, pg. 2733
MILLER, MILLER & MCLACHLAN CONSTRUCTION, INC.; *U.S. Private*, pg. 2736
MILLIE & SEVERSON INC.—See Severson Group Incorporated; *U.S. Private*, pg. 3619
MILNE CONSTRUCTION CO.; *U.S. Private*, pg. 2738
MINARDOS CONSTRUCTION & ASSOCIATES; *U.S. Private*, pg. 2740
MINELLI CONSTRUCTION CO., INC.; *U.S. Private*, pg. 2741
THE MINER-DEDERICK COMPANIES INC.; *U.S. Private*, pg. 4079
MINKOFF COMPANY INC.; *U.S. Private*, pg. 2742
MIRON CONSTRUCTION CO. INC.; *U.S. Private*, pg. 2746
MITCHELL ENTERPRISES INC.; *U.S. Private*, pg. 2750
MIVENT AS—See AF Gruppen ASA; *Int'l*, pg. 184
M & J ENGINEERING, P.C.; *U.S. Private*, pg. 2522
M.J. HARRIS INC.; *U.S. Private*, pg. 2529
MJ HARVEST, INC.; *U.S. Public*, pg. 1452
MJ SIMPSON CORPORATION; *U.S. Private*, pg. 2752
M.L.B. CONSTRUCTION SERVICES, LLC; *U.S. Private*, pg. 2529
MOC HOA BINH MANUFACTURING & DECORATING JSC—See Hoa Binh Construction Group JSC; *Int'l*, pg. 3435
MODERN ACCESS SERVICES SINGAPORE PTE. LTD.—See AusGroup Limited; *Int'l*, pg. 716
MODERNA HOMES PTE. LTD.—See BBR Holdings (S) Ltd.; *Int'l*, pg. 921
MODERN BUILDERS, INC.; *U.S. Private*, pg. 2759
MODERN CONSTRUCTION INC.; *U.S. Private*, pg. 2760
MOEN GUANGZHOU FAUCET CO., LTD.—See Fortune Brands Innovations, Inc.; *U.S. Public*, pg. 873
THE MONAHAN COMPANY; *U.S. Private*, pg. 4080
MONARCH CONSTRUCTION COMPANY; *U.S. Private*, pg. 2768
MONARCH CONSTRUCTION CORP.; *U.S. Private*, pg. 2769
MONTGOMERY MARTIN CONTRACTORS, LLC; *U.S. Private*, pg. 2777
MOOREFIELD CONSTRUCTION INC.; *U.S. Private*, pg. 2780
MORCON CONSTRUCTION INC.; *U.S. Private*, pg. 2782
MORELCO S.A.S.—See Aenza S.A.A.; *Int'l*, pg. 176
MORET CONSTRUCTION; *U.S. Private*, pg. 2782
MORETTE COMPANY, INC.; *U.S. Private*, pg. 2782
MORGANTI FLORIDA INC.—See Morganti Group/SKH Holdings Inc.; *U.S. Private*, pg. 2785
THE MORGANTI GROUP, INC.—See Morganti Group/SKH Holdings Inc.; *U.S. Private*, pg. 2785
MORGANTI TEXAS INC.—See Morganti Group/SKH Holdings Inc.; *U.S. Private*, pg. 2785
MORIZOU CO., LTD.—See Grandes Inc.; *Int'l*, pg. 3057
MORLEY BUILDERS; *U.S. Private*, pg. 2785
MORROW CONSTRUCTION COMPANY; *U.S. Private*, pg. 2790
MOSS & ASSOCIATES, LLC; *U.S. Private*, pg. 2793
MOSSER CONSTRUCTION INC.; *U.S. Private*, pg. 2794
MOSTOSTAL KRAKOW S.A.—See Ferrovial S.A.; *Int'l*, pg. 2644
MPA SYSTEMS, LLC—See Black Diamond Group Limited; *Int'l*, pg. 1059
MRA GMBH—See AGRAVIS Raiffeisen AG; *Int'l*, pg. 215
MSNW GROUP, LLC; *U.S. Private*, pg. 2808
MST CONSTRUCTORS INC.; *U.S. Private*, pg. 2808
MULLIGAN CONSTRUCTORS INC.; *U.S. Private*, pg. 2811
MUNDY INDUSTRIAL CONTRACTORS—See The Mundy Companies; *U.S. Private*, pg. 4081
MURNANE BUILDING CONTRACTORS INC; *U.S. Private*, pg. 2815
MURRAY COMPANY; *U.S. Private*, pg. 2816
MUTUAL CONSTRUCTION COMPANY TRANSVAAL (PTY) LIMITED—See eXtract Group Limited; *Int'l*, pg. 2592
M.W. BUILDERS INC—See MMC Corp.; *U.S. Private*, pg. 2754
MYCON GENERAL CONTRACTORS INC.; *U.S. Private*, pg. 2823
MYLER CHURCH BUILDING SYSTEMS, INC.—See The Myler Company Inc.; *U.S. Private*, pg. 4081
THE MYLER COMPANY INC.; *U.S. Private*, pg. 4081
MYRICK CONSTRUCTION INC.; *U.S. Private*, pg. 2826

MYRICK GUROSKY & ASSOCIATES; *U.S. Private*, pg. 2826
NAB CONSTRUCTION CORP.; *U.S. Private*, pg. 2829
NABHOLZ CONSTRUCTION CORP. - OZARK DIVISION—See Nabholz Construction Corp.; *U.S. Private*, pg. 2829
NABHOLZ CONSTRUCTION CORP.; *U.S. Private*, pg. 2829
NABHOLZ CONSTRUCTION CORP. - TULSA DIVISION—See Nabholz Construction Corp.; *U.S. Private*, pg. 2829
NAN, INC.; *U.S. Private*, pg. 2832
NASON CONSTRUCTION, INC.; *U.S. Private*, pg. 2837
NASTOS CONSTRUCTION INC.; *U.S. Private*, pg. 2837
NATFORM PTY LTD—See Acrow Limited; *Int'l*, pg. 109
NATFORM (QLD) PTY LTD—See Acrow Limited; *Int'l*, pg. 109
NATIONAL CONSTRUCTORS INC.; *U.S. Private*, pg. 2851
NATIONAL ENCLOSURE COMPANY—See National Construction Enterprises Inc.; *U.S. Private*, pg. 2851
NATIONAL INSULATED BLOCKS INDUSTRIES—See Dubai Investments PJSC; *Int'l*, pg. 2219
NATIONAL MAINTENANCE SERVICES, LLC—See National Construction Enterprises Inc.; *U.S. Private*, pg. 2851
NAYLOR & BREEN BUILDERS, INC.; *U.S. Private*, pg. 2874
NAYLOR COMMERCIAL INTERIORS, INC.; *U.S. Private*, pg. 2874
NEENAN COMPANY; *U.S. Private*, pg. 2880
N.E. FINCH CO.; *U.S. Private*, pg. 2827
NESHKIN CONSTRUCTION COMPANY INCORPORATED; *U.S. Private*, pg. 2886
NES MILJOPARK AS—See AF Gruppen ASA; *Int'l*, pg. 184
NEST INTERNATIONAL; *U.S. Private*, pg. 2886
NEUMANN BROTHERS INC.; *U.S. Private*, pg. 2890
NEW ERA BUILDERS; *U.S. Private*, pg. 2895
NEWGROUND CONSULTING—See NewGround Resources; *U.S. Private*, pg. 2915
NEWGROUND RESOURCES; *U.S. Private*, pg. 2915
NEWGROUND RESOURCES—See NewGround Resources; *U.S. Private*, pg. 2915
NEWPORT CONSTRUCTION (PTY) LIMITED—See Basil Read Holdings Limited; *Int'l*, pg. 887
NEXXO S.A.—See Echeverria Izquierdo S.A.; *Int'l*, pg. 2289
NGAI SHUN CONSTRUCTION & DRILLING COMPANY LIMITED—See Boill Healthcare Holdings Limited; *Int'l*, pg. 1101
NICHIMOKU SANGYOU LTD.—See Hitachi, Ltd.; *Int'l*, pg. 3423
NIRAM, INC.; *U.S. Private*, pg. 2928
NOOTER CONSTRUCTION CO.—See CIC Group, Inc.; *U.S. Private*, pg. 896
NORCON INC.; *U.S. Private*, pg. 2936
NORD COMAT SHPK.—See Ading AD; *Int'l*, pg. 149
NORKOTE OF WASHINGTON, LLC—See Installed Building Products, Inc.; *U.S. Public*, pg. 1133
NORTHEAST CONSTRUCTION SERVICES—See LeChase Construction Services, LLC; *U.S. Private*, pg. 2410
NORTHERN INDUSTRIAL INSULATION CONTRACTORS, INC.—See Bird Construction Inc.; *Int'l*, pg. 1047
NORTHLAND BUILDINGS INC.; *U.S. Private*, pg. 2955
NORTH-LINK M1 LTD.—See Groupe Egis S.A.; *Int'l*, pg. 3102
NORTH SHORE CORP.—See Continental Holdings Corp.; *Int'l*, pg. 1784
NORTH WEST MINING & CIVIL PTY LTD—See E&A Limited; *Int'l*, pg. 2247
NORTHWEST PAINTING, INC.—See UFP Industries, Inc.; *U.S. Public*, pg. 2219
THE NORWOOD COMPANY INC.; *U.S. Private*, pg. 4085
NOVA HOTEL RENOVATION & CONSTRUCTION LLC; *U.S. Private*, pg. 2965
N.P. CONSTRUCTION OF NORTH FLORIDA, INC.; *U.S. Private*, pg. 2828
NTC MAZZUCA CONTRACTING; *U.S. Private*, pg. 2970
NUCOR BUILDING SYSTEMS—See Nucor Corporation; *U.S. Public*, pg. 1553
NUDURA INC.—See RPM International Inc.; *U.S. Public*, pg. 1817
NUJAK DEVELOPMENT, INC.; *U.S. Private*, pg. 2973
OAKBROOK PROPERTIES, INC.—See Oakbrook Companies, Inc.; *U.S. Private*, pg. 2984
OAK CONTRACTING, LLC.; *U.S. Private*, pg. 2983
OAKRIDGE BUILDERS INC.; *U.S. Private*, pg. 2985
OAKS CONSTRUCTION INC.; *U.S. Private*, pg. 2985
THE OAKVIEW COMPANIES, INC.; *U.S. Private*, pg. 4087
OAKVIEW CONSTRUCTION, INC.—See The Oakview Companies, Inc.; *U.S. Private*, pg. 4088
OAKWOOD CONSTRUCTION & RESTORATION SERVICES, INC.—See BlackEagle Partners, LLC; *U.S. Private*, pg. 573
OBERLE & ASSOCIATES, INC.; *U.S. Private*, pg. 2987
O'BRIEN & GERE TECHNICAL SERVICES INC.—See The O'Brien & Gere Companies; *U.S. Private*, pg. 4087
OCACSA S.A.—See Groupe Egis S.A.; *Int'l*, pg. 3102
ODINSA—See Grupo Argos S.A.; *Int'l*, pg. 3121
ODOM CONSTRUCTION SERVICES, INC.; *U.S. Private*, pg. 2993

CORPORATE AFFILIATIONS

O'DONNELL METAL DECK, LLC.—See Slate Capital Group LLC; *U.S. Private*, pg. 3687
O&G INDUSTRIES, INC. - HARWINTON CONCRETE PLANT—See O&G Industries, Inc.; *U.S. Private*, pg. 2977
O&G INDUSTRIES, INC.; *U.S. Private*, pg. 2977
OKLAND CONSTRUCTION COMPANY INC.; *U.S. Private*, pg. 3008
OMAGINE, INC.; *U.S. Public*, pg. 1571
OMEGA FLEX, INC.; *U.S. Public*, pg. 1571
OMNI STRUCTURES & MANAGEMENT INC.; *U.S. Private*, pg. 3016
O'NEAL CONSTRUCTION INC.—See O'Neal, Inc.; *U.S. Private*, pg. 2979
O'NEAL, INC.; *U.S. Private*, pg. 2979
O'NEIL INDUSTRIES INC.; *U.S. Private*, pg. 2979
ONESOURCE GENERAL CONTRACTING, INC.; *U.S. Private*, pg. 3025
OOO DBA PROEKT—See DBA Group SRL; *Int'l*, pg. 1986
OPERADORA DE LA AUTOPISTA DEL OCCIDENTE, S.A. DE C.V.—See Empresas ICA S.A.B. de C.V.; *Int'l*, pg. 2391
ORION BUILDING CORPORATION; *U.S. Private*, pg. 3042
ORION MALL MANAGEMENT COMPANY LIMITED—See Brigade Enterprises Ltd.; *Int'l*, pg. 1161
O,R&L CONSTRUCTION CORP.; *U.S. Private*, pg. 2981
OSBORNE CONSTRUCTION COMPANY; *U.S. Private*, pg. 3046
OSCAR J. BOLDT CONSTRUCTION CO. INC.—See The Boldt Group Inc.; *U.S. Private*, pg. 3996
OSCAR ORDUNO, INC.; *U.S. Private*, pg. 3046
OSLO BRANNSIKRING AS—See AF Gruppen ASA; *Int'l*, pg. 184
OSLO PROSJEKTBYGG AS—See AF Gruppen ASA; *Int'l*, pg. 184
OTAK JAPAN INC.—See HanmiGlobal Co., LTD.; *Int'l*, pg. 3257
OUTSIDE THE LINES, INC; *U.S. Private*, pg. 3051
OWEN-AMES-KIMBALL COMPANY; *U.S. Private*, pg. 3054
OWEN-AMES-KIMBALL COMPANY—See Owen-Ames-Kimball Company; *U.S. Private*, pg. 3054
OWENS CORNING CANADA GP INC.—See Owens Corning; *U.S. Public*, pg. 1628
OXFORD HOLDINGS INC.; *U.S. Private*, pg. 3057
OZANNE CONSTRUCTION COMPANY; *U.S. Private*, pg. 3057
PACIFIC BUILDING GROUP; *U.S. Private*, pg. 3065
PACIFIC NATIONAL GROUP; *U.S. Private*, pg. 3069
P. AGNES INC.; *U.S. Private*, pg. 3059
PALATIA INGENIEUR- UND STADTEBAU GMBH—See BKW AG; *Int'l*, pg. 1055
PALIBURG HOLDINGS LIMITED—See Century City International Holdings Ltd; *Int'l*, pg. 1417
PANATTONI CONSTRUCTION, INC.—See Panattoni Development Company; *U.S. Private*, pg. 3085
PARAMOUNT CONTRACTING, INC.; *U.S. Private*, pg. 3092
PARAMOUNT INSURANCE REPAIR SERVICE; *U.S. Private*, pg. 3093
THE PARENT COMPANY, INC.; *U.S. Private*, pg. 4090
PARIC CORP.; *U.S. Private*, pg. 3094
THE PARK AT ONE RIVERFRONT, LLC—See Goff Capital, Inc.; *U.S. Private*, pg. 1726
PARK LANE CONSTRUCTION INC.; *U.S. Private*, pg. 3096
PARKWAY CONSTRUCTION & ASSOCIATES LP; *U.S. Private*, pg. 3098
PARRISH-MCCALL CONSTRUCTORS, INC.; *U.S. Private*, pg. 3100
PAT COOK CONSTRUCTION, INC.; *U.S. Private*, pg. 3105
PAUL RISK ASSOCIATES, INC.; *U.S. Private*, pg. 3113
PAVARINI CONSTRUCTION CO. INC.-STAMFORD—See STO Building Group Inc.; *U.S. Private*, pg. 3814
PAVARINI MCGOVERN LLC—See STO Building Group Inc.; *U.S. Private*, pg. 3814
PAYTON CONSTRUCTION CORP.; *U.S. Private*, pg. 3118
PBG BUILDERS, INC.; *U.S. Private*, pg. 3118
PC CONSTRUCTION COMPANY; *U.S. Private*, pg. 3119
PCI MILLWORK; *U.S. Private*, pg. 3120
PDC FACILITIES INC.; *U.S. Private*, pg. 3121
PEAK CONSTRUCTION, INC.—See The Ensign Group, Inc.; *U.S. Public*, pg. 2072
PEAK PROFESSIONAL CONTRACTORS INC.—See CUSiTech, LLC; *U.S. Private*, pg. 1127
PEARSON CONSTRUCTION COMPANY, INC.; *U.S. Private*, pg. 3126
PECO CONSTRUCTION COMPANY; *U.S. Private*, pg. 3127
THE PEEBLES CORPORATION; *U.S. Private*, pg. 4092
PEG INFRASTRUKTUR AG—See E.ON SE; *Int'l*, pg. 2258
PEO CONSTRUCTION MACHINERY OPERATORS TRAINING CENTER CO., LTD.—See Bain Capital, LP; *U.S. Private*, pg. 435
PEPPER CONSTRUCTION COMPANY OF OHIO—See Pepper Construction Group, LLC; *U.S. Private*, pg. 3144
PEPPER CONSTRUCTION CO. OF INDIANA, LLC—See Pepper Construction Group, LLC; *U.S. Private*, pg. 3144
PEPPER CONSTRUCTION CO.—See Pepper Construction Group, LLC; *U.S. Private*, pg. 3144

N.A.I.C.S. INDEX
236220 — COMMERCIAL AND INST...

PERFORM'HABITAT SAS—See AST GROUPE SA; *Int'l*, pg. 651
PERIS COMPANIES INC.; *U.S. Private*, pg. 3151
PERMASTEELISA CLADDING TECHNOLOGIES—See Atlas Holdings, LLC; *U.S. Private*, pg. 377
PERMASTEELISA CLADDING TECH—See Atlas Holdings, LLC; *U.S. Private*, pg. 377
PERRY MCCALL CONSTRUCTION INC.; *U.S. Private*, pg. 3154
PERSAUD COMPANIES INC.; *U.S. Private*, pg. 3154
PETERS CONSTRUCTION CORPORATION; *U.S. Private*, pg. 3159
PETRA ROOFING COMPANY, LLC; *U.S. Private*, pg. 3161
P. GEROLEMOU CONSTRUCTION (PTY) LIMITED—See Basil Read Holdings Limited; *Int'l*, pg. 887
PGMB BUDOPOL S.A.—See Herkules S.A.; *Int'l*, pg. 3362
P-H INVESTMENTS INC.; *U.S. Private*, pg. 3059
PHOENIX ASSOCIATES OF SOUTH FLORIDA, INC.; *U.S. Private*, pg. 3172
PICERNE CONSTRUCTION CORP.—See Picerne Real Estate Group; *U.S. Private*, pg. 3176
PIEDMONT CONSTRUCTION GROUP LLC; *U.S. Private*, pg. 3177
THE PIKE COMPANY INC.; *U.S. Private*, pg. 4095
PILOTES TERRATEST PERU S.A.C.—See Echeverria Izquierdo S.A.; *Int'l*, pg. 2289
PILOTES TERRATEST S.A.—See Echeverria Izquierdo S.A.; *Int'l*, pg. 2289
PINKARD CONSTRUCTION COMPANY; *U.S. Private*, pg. 3184
PINKERTON & LAWS INC.; *U.S. Private*, pg. 3184
PINNACLE CONSTRUCTION GROUP; *U.S. Private*, pg. 3185
PISGAH INSULATION AND FIREPLACES OF NC, LLC—See Installed Building Products, Inc.; *U.S. Public*, pg. 1133
PITLIK & WICK, INC.; *U.S. Private*, pg. 3190
P.J. DICK INCORPORATED; *U.S. Private*, pg. 3060
P.J. DICK-TRUMBULL-LINDY - HOMER CITY PLANT—See P.J. Dick Incorporated; *U.S. Private*, pg. 3060
P.J. DICK-TRUMBULL-LINDY - KOPPEL PLANT—See P.J. Dick Incorporated; *U.S. Private*, pg. 3060
P.J. DICK-TRUMBULL-LINDY - NEVILLE ISLAND PLANT—See P.J. Dick Incorporated; *U.S. Private*, pg. 3060
P.J. DICK-TRUMBULL-LINDY - NEW KENSINGTON PLANT—See P.J. Dick Incorporated; *U.S. Private*, pg. 3060
P.J. DICK-TRUMBULL-LINDY - SECOND AVENUE PLANT—See P.J. Dick Incorporated; *U.S. Private*, pg. 3060
P.J. HAYES, INC.; *U.S. Private*, pg. 3060
P.J. HOERR, INC.; *U.S. Private*, pg. 3060
PKC CONSTRUCTION; *U.S. Private*, pg. 3193
PLANT PROCESS EQUIPMENT INC.; *U.S. Private*, pg. 3197
PLANUM CYPRUS LIMITED—See GP PLANUM AD; *Int'l*, pg. 3046
PLATT CONSTRUCTION, INC.; *U.S. Private*, pg. 3210
PLUMB HOUSE INC.; *U.S. Private*, pg. 3214
PM CONSTRUCTION CO. INC.; *U.S. Private*, pg. 3216
PM MACKAY GROUP; *U.S. Private*, pg. 3216
POINT BUILDERS, LLC; *U.S. Private*, pg. 3221
POSBAU S.A.—See CVC Capital Partners SICAV-FIS S.A.; *Int'l*, pg. 1881
POTTS COMPANY INC.; *U.S. Private*, pg. 3235
POWELL COMPANIES INC.; *U.S. Private*, pg. 3236
POWER CONSTRUCTION COMPANY; *U.S. Private*, pg. 3237
POWERS & SONS CONSTRUCTION CO., INC.; *U.S. Private*, pg. 3239
PPF PARAMOUNT ONE MARKET PLAZA OWNER, L.P.—See Paramount Group Inc.; *U.S. Public*, pg. 1637
PRAIRIE CONTRACTORS, INC.; *U.S. Private*, pg. 3242
PRECISE CONSTRUCTION INC.; *U.S. Private*, pg. 3244
PRECISION CONSTRUCTION COMPANY—See Hoffman Corporation; *U.S. Private*, pg. 1960
PREFABRICADOS Y TRANSPORTES, S.A. DE C.V.—See Empresas ICA S.A.B. de C.V.; *Int'l*, pg. 2391
PREMIER CONCRETE PUMPING LIMITED—See Concrete Pumping Holdings, Inc.; *U.S. Public*, pg. 566
PREMIER MODULAR LIMITED—See Cabot Square Capital LLP; *Int'l*, pg. 1246
PRESTIGE BUILDING COMPANY—See The Michael's Development Company Inc.; *U.S. Private*, pg. 4079
PRIME CONTRACTORS INC.; *U.S. Private*, pg. 3261
PRITCHARD INDUSTRIES, INC. - VIENNA OFFICE—See Littlejohn & Co., LLC; *U.S. Private*, pg. 2471
PROCONSTRUCTION LLC—See FirstService Corporation; *Int'l*, pg. 2691
PROCTOR CONSTRUCTION COMPANY INC.; *U.S. Private*, pg. 3272
PRODUCT VENTURES, LTD; *U.S. Private*, pg. 3273
PROFESSIONAL CONSTRUCTION STRATEGIES GROUP LIMITED—See Bentley Systems, Inc.; *U.S. Public*, pg. 297
PROGNOSCENTRET AB—See Byggfakta Group Nordic HoldCo AB; *Int'l*, pg. 1235

PROGNOSESENTERET AS—See Byggfakta Group Nordic HoldCo AB; *Int'l*, pg. 1235
PROGRESSIVE CONTRACTING CO; *U.S. Private*, pg. 3278
PROIZVODNJA MK D.O.O.—See Dalekovod d.d.; *Int'l*, pg. 1951
PROJECT DEVELOPMENT SERVICES, INC.; *U.S. Private*, pg. 3280
PROMAC, INC.; *U.S. Private*, pg. 3282
PROPERTY MASTERS INC.; *U.S. Private*, pg. 3285
PROST BUILDERS INC.; *U.S. Private*, pg. 3289
PRO TECH CONSTRUCTION, INC.—See Enterprise Group, Inc.; *U.S. Private*, pg. 2014
PROXIMA SCANDINAVIA AS—See BKW AG; *Int'l*, pg. 1056
PT. HAZAMA ANDO MURINDA—See Hazama Ando Corporation; *Int'l*, pg. 3295
PT. HITACHI PLANT TECHNOLOGIES INDONESIA—See Hitachi, Ltd.; *Int'l*, pg. 3424
PT. NAS FITNESS INDONESIA—See Daiwa House Industry Co., Ltd.; *Int'l*, pg. 1947
PULTE HOMES OF NEW ENGLAND LLC—See PulteGroup, Inc.; *U.S. Public*, pg. 1737
PULTE PAYROLL CORPORATION—See PulteGroup, Inc.; *U.S. Public*, pg. 1738
PUMFORD CONSTRUCTION INC.; *U.S. Private*, pg. 3303
PURCELL CONSTRUCTION CORP; *U.S. Private*, pg. 3304
PURCELL CONSTRUCTION INC.; *U.S. Private*, pg. 3304
QINGJIAN INTERNATIONAL (SOUTH PACIFIC) GROUP DEVELOPMENT CO., PTE. LTD.—See CNQC International Holdings Ltd.; *Int'l*, pg. 1678
QUALITY CONTRACTORS INCORPORATED; *U.S. Private*, pg. 3318
THE QUANDEL CONSTRUCTION GROUP, INC.—See The Quandel Group Inc.; *U.S. Private*, pg. 4101
THE QUANDEL GROUP INC.; *U.S. Private*, pg. 4101
THE QUANDEL GROUP, MINERSVILLE—See The Quandel Group Inc.; *U.S. Private*, pg. 4101
QUDOTECH SDN. BHD.—See AWC Berhad; *Int'l*, pg. 752
RAMALHO ROSA COBETAR SOCIEDADE DE CONSTRUCOES, S.A.—See Fomento de Construcciones y Contratas, S.A.; *Int'l*, pg. 2723
RAND CONSTRUCTION CORPORATION; *U.S. Private*, pg. 3353
RANGOONERS COMPANY LIMITED—See Endress+Hauser (International) Holding AG; *Int'l*, pg. 2409
RAY ANGELINI, INC.; *U.S. Private*, pg. 3358
RAY BELL CONSTRUCTION COMPANY INC.; *U.S. Private*, pg. 3358
RAY FOGG BUILDING METHODS INC.; *U.S. Private*, pg. 3358
RAYMOND CONSTRUCTION COMPANY INCORPORATED; *U.S. Private*, pg. 3359
RCC ASSOCIATES, INC.; *U.S. Private*, pg. 3361
RCD GENERAL CONTRACTORS; *U.S. Private*, pg. 3361
RC DOLNER LLC; *U.S. Private*, pg. 3361
RD ENGINEERING & CONSTRUCTION INC.; *U.S. Private*, pg. 3362
R.D. OLSON CONSTRUCTION; *U.S. Private*, pg. 3335
R.E. CRAWFORD CONSTRUCTION LLC; *U.S. Private*, pg. 3335
R.E. DAFFAN, INC.—See The Branch Group, Inc.; *U.S. Private*, pg. 3999
REDRA CONSTRUCT GROUP S.A—See Edrasis - C. Psallidas S.A.; *Int'l*, pg. 2315
REECE-CAMPBELL, INC.; *U.S. Private*, pg. 3381
REGENT CONTRACTING CORP.; *U.S. Private*, pg. 3387
REGIONAL CONSTRUCTION CORP.—See National Realty & Development Corp.; *U.S. Private*, pg. 2861
RENO CONTRACTING INC.; *U.S. Private*, pg. 3399
RESTORATION BUILDERS INC.; *U.S. Private*, pg. 3409
RETAIL CONSTRUCTION SERVICES; *U.S. Private*, pg. 3411
R F STEARNS INC; *U.S. Private*, pg. 3331
R&G CONSTRUCTION COMPANY; *U.S. Private*, pg. 3332
R.G. SMITH CO. INC.; *U.S. Private*, pg. 3336
R&H CONSTRUCTION CO. - CENTRAL OREGON—See R&H Construction Co.; *U.S. Private*, pg. 3332
R&H CONSTRUCTION CO.; *U.S. Private*, pg. 3332
RICH DUNCAN CONSTRUCTION INC.; *U.S. Private*, pg. 3426
RICH KRAMER CONSTRUCTION INC.; *U.S. Private*, pg. 3427
RICHTER & RATNER CONTRACTING CORPORATION; *U.S. Private*, pg. 3430
RIGGS INDUSTRIES, INC.; *U.S. Private*, pg. 3435
RILEY CONSTRUCTION COMPANY INC.; *U.S. Private*, pg. 3436
RINGLAND-JOHNSON INC.; *U.S. Private*, pg. 3438
RITCHIE-CURBOW CONSTRUCTION CO.; *U.S. Private*, pg. 3441
RIVAL HOLDINGS, LLC; *U.S. Private*, pg. 3442
RIVER CITY CONSTRUCTION L.L.C.; *U.S. Private*, pg. 3443
RIVER CITY CONSTRUCTION—See River City Construction L.L.C.; *U.S. Private*, pg. 3443
RIVES E. WORRELL COMPANY, INC.; *U.S. Private*, pg. 3448

R.J. DAUM CONSTRUCTION COMPANY; *U.S. Private*, pg. 3337
R.J. MILLER & ASSOCIATES INC.; *U.S. Private*, pg. 3337
RJS CONSTRUCTION GROUP, LLC; *U.S. Private*, pg. 3449
R & L CONSTRUCTION INC.; *U.S. Private*, pg. 3331
RL HAINES CONSTRUCTION, LLC; *U.S. Private*, pg. 3450
RMA LAND CONSTRUCTION, INC.; *U.S. Private*, pg. 3451
R&M KUHLLAGERBAU HOLDING GMBH—See Bilfinger SE; *Int'l*, pg. 1028
RN FIELD CONSTRUCTION INC.; *U.S. Private*, pg. 3452
R.N. ROUSE & CO. INC.—See Danis Building Construction Company Inc.; *U.S. Private*, pg. 1156
ROAD SAFETY OPERATIONS IRELAND LTD.—See Groupe Egis S.A.; *Int'l*, pg. 3102
ROBERT E. LAMB, INC.; *U.S. Private*, pg. 3457
THE ROBINS AND MORTON GROUP; *U.S. Private*, pg. 4111
ROBINSON BROTHERS CONSTRUCTION, LLC—See Quanta Services, Inc.; *U.S. Public*, pg. 1752
ROBINSON GAREISS LC; *U.S. Private*, pg. 3461
ROCHE CONSTRUCTORS INC. - LAS VEGAS—See Roche Constructors, Inc.; *U.S. Private*, pg. 3463
ROCHE CONSTRUCTORS, INC.; *U.S. Private*, pg. 3463
ROCHON CORPORATION; *U.S. Private*, pg. 3464
R&O CONSTRUCTION COMPANY INC.; *U.S. Private*, pg. 3332
RODGERS BUILDERS, INC.; *U.S. Private*, pg. 3470
ROGER B. KENNEDY, INC.; *U.S. Private*, pg. 3471
ROGER & SONS CONSTRUCTION INC.; *U.S. Private*, pg. 3471
ROLLINS-PCI CONSTRUCTION COMPANY; *U.S. Private*, pg. 3475
ROSE CONSTRUCTION CO., INC.—See Rose Design Build, Inc.; *U.S. Private*, pg. 3481
ROSE CONSTRUCTION, INC.; *U.S. Private*, pg. 3481
ROUGH BROTHERS MANUFACTURING, INC.—See Gibraltar Industries, Inc.; *U.S. Public*, pg. 936
ROWE & NEWBERRY INC.; *U.S. Private*, pg. 3490
ROYALS COMMERCIAL SERVICES, INC.—See Installed Building Products, Inc.; *U.S. Public*, pg. 1133
ROYAL SEAL CONSTRUCTION INC.; *U.S. Private*, pg. 3493
ROY ANDERSON CORP - RIDGELAND—See Tutor Perini Corporation; *U.S. Public*, pg. 2206
ROY ANDERSON CORP—See Tutor Perini Corporation; *U.S. Public*, pg. 2206
RP INDUSTRIES INC.; *U.S. Private*, pg. 3495
R.R. SIMMONS CONSTRUCTION CORP.; *U.S. Private*, pg. 3339
RUDOLPH AND SLETTEN, INC.—See Tutor Perini Corporation; *U.S. Public*, pg. 2206
THE RUDOLPH/LIBBE COMPANIES; *U.S. Private*, pg. 4113
RUDOLPH/LIBBE, INC.—See The Rudolph/Libbe Companies; *U.S. Private*, pg. 4113
RUDOLPH & SLETTEN, INC.—See Tutor Perini Corporation; *U.S. Public*, pg. 2206
THE RUHLIN COMPANY; *U.S. Private*, pg. 4113
RUSCON CORPORATION; *U.S. Private*, pg. 3505
RUSSCO INC.; *U.S. Private*, pg. 3506
RYAN COMPANIES US, INC.; *U.S. Private*, pg. 3509
RYAN COMPANIES US, INC.—See Ryan Companies US, Inc.; *U.S. Private*, pg. 3510
RYAN CONSTRUCTION CO. INC—See Boyne Capital Management, LLC; *U.S. Public*, pg. 629
RYCON CONSTRUCTION INC.; *U.S. Private*, pg. 3511
SAIEED CONSTRUCTION SYSTEMS; *U.S. Private*, pg. 3529
SALCE CONTRACTING ASSOCIATES, INC.; *U.S. Private*, pg. 3531
SALIBA CONSTRUCTION CO. INC.; *U.S. Private*, pg. 3532
SALOMONE BROTHERS INC; *U.S. Private*, pg. 3533
SAMBE CONSTRUCTION COMPANY; *U.S. Private*, pg. 3536
SAMET CORPORATION; *U.S. Private*, pg. 3537
SAMUELS GROUP, INC.; *U.S. Private*, pg. 3538
SANJOSE CONTRACTING, L.L.C.—See Grupo Empresarial San Jose, S.A.; *Int'l*, pg. 3128
SANJOSE PANAMA, S.A.—See Grupo Empresarial San Jose, S.A.; *Int'l*, pg. 3128
SAN JUAN CONSTRUCTION INC.; *U.S. Private*, pg. 3541
SANNECT CO., LTD.—See COMSYS Holdings Corporation; *Int'l*, pg. 1762
SANTAPAUL CORP.—See Ares Management Corporation; *U.S. Public*, pg. 189
SANTINI TRANSFER & STORAGE; *U.S. Private*, pg. 3548
SARL COMI SERVICE—See Altrad Investment Authority SAS; *Int'l*, pg. 398
SASAKI—See Sasaki Associates Inc.; *U.S. Private*, pg. 3552
SATTERFIELD & PONTIKES CONSTRUCTION, INC.; *U.S. Private*, pg. 3553
SAVANT CONSTRUCTION, INC.; *U.S. Private*, pg. 3556
S B BALLARD CONSTRUCTION CO.; *U.S. Private*, pg. 3512
SBCC INC; *U.S. Private*, pg. 3559
SCANDIA, INC.; *U.S. Public*, pg. 1842
S. CARPENTER CONSTRUCTION CO.; *U.S. Private*, pg. 3515

236220 — COMMERCIAL AND INST...

SCE ENVIRONMENTAL GROUP INC.; *U.S. Private*, pg. 3562
SCHERER CONSTRUCTION OF WEST FLORIDA, LLC; *U.S. Private*, pg. 3564
SCHIMENTI CONSTRUCTION CO.; *U.S. Private*, pg. 3565
SCHMEECKLE BROS CONSTRUCTION CO.; *U.S. Private*, pg. 3565
SCHROEDER/LEVERINGTON INC.; *U.S. Private*, pg. 3569
SCHUCHART CORPORATION; *U.S. Private*, pg. 3570
THE SCHULTZ ORGANIZATION, LLC; *U.S. Private*, pg. 4115
SCHUMACHER DUGAN CONSTRUCTION, INC.; *U.S. Private*, pg. 3571
SCIAME CONSTRUCTION, LLC—See F.J. Sciame Construction Co. Inc.; *U.S. Private*, pg. 1456
SCIAME DEVELOPMENT, INC.—See F.J. Sciame Construction Co. Inc.; *U.S. Private*, pg. 1456
SCIENCE, ENGINEERING, AND TECHNOLOGY ASSOCIATES CORPORATION—See Leidos Holdings, Inc.; *U.S. Public*, pg. 1304
SCOTT & REID GENERAL CONTRACTORS INC.; *U.S. Private*, pg. 3576
SCRUBADUB AUTO WASH CENTERS; *U.S. Private*, pg. 3580
SCUT SA—See Comcm S.A.; *Int'l*, pg. 1709
S.D. DEACON CORPORATION; *U.S. Private*, pg. 3517
S.D. DEACON CORP.—See S.D. Deacon Corporation; *U.S. Private*, pg. 3517
SD NETWORK CO., LTD.—See Carlit Co., Ltd.; *Int'l*, pg. 1338
SEABAY BUILDING GROUP, LLC; *U.S. Private*, pg. 3583
SEA PAC ENGINEERING, INC.; *U.S. Private*, pg. 3582
SEATER CONSTRUCTION CO. INC.; *U.S. Private*, pg. 3591
SELLEN CONSTRUCTION COMPANY; *U.S. Private*, pg. 3602
THE SEMBLER COMPANY; *U.S. Private*, pg. 4116
SENATE CONSTRUCTION CORP.; *U.S. Private*, pg. 3605
SEPTAGON INDUSTRIES INC.; *U.S. Private*, pg. 3611
SERFASS CONSTRUCTION COMPANY INC.; *U.S. Private*, pg. 3613
SERVEONE CO., LTD.—See Affinity Equity Partners (HK) Ltd.; *Int'l*, pg. 186
SESSLER INC.; *U.S. Private*, pg. 3617
SEVERSON GROUP INCORPORATED; *U.S. Private*, pg. 3619
SGI INC.; *U.S. Private*, pg. 3622
SHANGHAI JOYSPEED GLOBAL CARGO CO., LTD.—See Hon Hai Precision Industry Co., Ltd.; *Int'l*, pg. 3457
SHANGHAI MODERN INTERNATIONAL EXHIBITION CO., LTD.—See DLG Exhibitions & Events Corp Ltd.; *Int'l*, pg. 2141
SHAW - LUNDQUIST ASSOCIATES, INC.; *U.S. Private*, pg. 3627
SHAWMUT WOODWORKING & SUPPLY INC.; *U.S. Private*, pg. 3628
SHAWNEE CONSTRUCTION & ENGINEERING INC.; *U.S. Private*, pg. 3628
SHED BOSS NZ LIMITED—See Fletcher Building Limited; *Int'l*, pg. 2701
SHEEHY CONSTRUCTION COMPANY; *U.S. Private*, pg. 3629
SHEETS CONSTRUCTION INC.; *U.S. Private*, pg. 3630
SHELTAIR AVIATION CENTER, LLC; *U.S. Private*, pg. 3631
SHERIDAN CORPORATION—See Sheri-Key; *U.S. Private*, pg. 3633
SHINGOBEE BUILDERS INC.; *U.S. Private*, pg. 3637
SHOOK, INCORPORATED—See Shook National Corporation; *U.S. Private*, pg. 3640
SHOOK INDIANA DIVISION—See Shook National Corporation; *U.S. Private*, pg. 3640
SHOOK WATER RESOURCES—See Shook National Corporation; *U.S. Private*, pg. 3640
SHRADER & MARTINEZ CONSTRUCTION INC.; *U.S. Private*, pg. 3643
SIERRA BAY CONTRACTORS INC.; *U.S. Private*, pg. 3646
SIERRA CONSTRUCTION COMPANY, INC.—See Sierra Industries Inc.; *U.S. Private*, pg. 3647
SIERRA PACIFIC CONSTRUCTORS; *U.S. Private*, pg. 3647
SIGAL CONSTRUCTION CORPORATION; *U.S. Private*, pg. 3648
SIGNATURE CONTRACTING SERVICES LLC; *U.S. Private*, pg. 3650
SILVERITE CONSTRUCTION CO., INC.; *U.S. Private*, pg. 3663
SILVERTON CONSTRUCTION COMPANY, INC.; *U.S. Private*, pg. 3664
SIMONSON CONSTRUCTION SERVICES, INC.; *U.S. Private*, pg. 3666
SIMPSON CONSTRUCTION SERVICES, INC.; *U.S. Private*, pg. 3668
SIMPSON OF MARYLAND, INC.; *U.S. Private*, pg. 3668
SIOUX FALLS CONSTRUCTION COMPANY; *U.S. Private*, pg. 3671
SITELINES, INC.; *U.S. Private*, pg. 3676
SJ AMOROSO CONSTRUCTION CO.; *U.S. Private*, pg. 3678
SJOSTROM & SONS INC.; *U.S. Private*, pg. 3678
SKENDER CONSTRUCTION; *U.S. Private*, pg. 3681
SKEPTON CONSTRUCTION, INC.; *U.S. Private*, pg. 3681
SKIP CONVERSE, INC.; *U.S. Private*, pg. 3682
SKY BUILDING SERVICE CO., LTD—See ANA Holdings Inc.; *Int'l*, pg. 444
SKY-HI SCAFFOLDING LTD.—See Andover Capital Corporation; *Int'l*, pg. 451
SKYLINE COMMERCIAL INTERIORS; *U.S. Private*, pg. 3685
THE SLANE COMPANY LLC; *U.S. Private*, pg. 4118
SLETTEN CONSTRUCTION BOISE—See Sletten Construction Inc.; *U.S. Private*, pg. 3688
SLETTEN CONSTRUCTION INC.; *U.S. Private*, pg. 3688
SLETTEN CONSTRUCTION OF NEVADA, INC.—See Sletten Construction Inc.; *U.S. Private*, pg. 3688
SLETTEN CONSTRUCTION OF WYOMING, INC.—See Sletten Construction Inc.; *U.S. Private*, pg. 3688
SLETTEN CONSTRUCTION PHOENIX—See Sletten Construction Inc.; *U.S. Private*, pg. 3688
SLI CONSTRUCTION INC.—See SLI Group Inc.; *U.S. Private*, pg. 3688
SLI GROUP INC.; *U.S. Private*, pg. 3688
SLOAN CONSTRUCTION COMPANY, INC.—See Reeves Construction Company; *U.S. Private*, pg. 3384
SLR CONTRACTING & SERVICE COMPANY, INC.; *U.S. Private*, pg. 3689
S&M SAKAMOTO INC.—See S Group Inc.; *U.S. Private*, pg. 3512
SNAP CONTRACTING CORPORATION; *U.S. Private*, pg. 3700
SNYDER, CROMPTON & ASSOCIATES, INC.; *U.S. Private*, pg. 3701
SNYDER LANGSTON LP; *U.S. Private*, pg. 3701
SOBEL CO.; *U.S. Private*, pg. 3702
SO CALIFORNIA VENTURES LTD.; *U.S. Private*, pg. 3701
SOLIDARITY CONTRACTING LLC.; *U.S. Private*, pg. 3709
SOLOMON BUILDERS, INC.; *U.S. Private*, pg. 3709
SOLPAC INC.; *U.S. Private*, pg. 3710
SOLTEK PACIFIC; *U.S. Private*, pg. 3710
SOMAGUE ENGENHARIA, S.A.—See HAL Trust N.V.; *Int'l*, pg. 3227
SOMERSET STEEL ERECTION COMPANY INC—See Riggs Industries, Inc.; *U.S. Private*, pg. 3435
SONAG COMPANY, INC.; *U.S. Private*, pg. 3712
SORDONI CONSTRUCTION CO.—See Sordoni Construction Services, Inc.; *U.S. Private*, pg. 3715
SOUTH COAST CONSTRUCTION SERVICES; *U.S. Private*, pg. 3721
SOUTHEASTERN INDUSTRIAL CONSTRUCTION COMPANY INC.; *U.S. Private*, pg. 3728
SOUTHERN CROSS CONTRACTING, INC.; *U.S. Private*, pg. 3731
SOUTH-LINK N25 LTD.—See Groupe Egis S.A.; *Int'l*, pg. 3102
SOUTH SEAS INSPECTION (S) PTE LTD—See NOV, Inc.; *U.S. Public*, pg. 1546
SOUTHWEST ARCHITECTURAL BUILDERS, INC.; *U.S. Private*, pg. 3738
SPAAN TECH, INC.; *U.S. Private*, pg. 3743
SPACEMAKERS INC.; *U.S. Private*, pg. 3744
SPAN CONSTRUCTION & ENGINEERING INC; *U.S. Private*, pg. 3744
SPAW GLASS CONSTRUCTION CORP.—See Spaw Glass Holding LP; *U.S. Private*, pg. 3747
SPAW GLASS CONTRACTORS INC.—See Spaw Glass Holding LP; *U.S. Private*, pg. 3747
SPAW GLASS HOLDING LP; *U.S. Private*, pg. 3747
SPECIALTY CONSTRUCTION MANAGEMENT, INC.; *U.S. Private*, pg. 3749
SPECIALTY PIPING CORP.; *U.S. Private*, pg. 3750
SPEED FAB-CRETE; *U.S. Private*, pg. 3753
SPERBER LANDSCAPE COS. LLC; *U.S. Private*, pg. 3755
SPIRK BROTHERS INC.; *U.S. Private*, pg. 3758
SPORTS FIELD HOLDINGS, INC.; *U.S. Private*, pg. 3761
SS&C TECHNOLOGIES, INC.—See SS&C Technologies Holdings, Inc.; *U.S. Public*, pg. 1924
SSI INCORPORATED; *U.S. Private*, pg. 3769
SSN GEBAUDETECHNIK GMBH—See Consus Real Estate AG; *Int'l*, pg. 1778
STACEY ENTERPRISES INC.; *U.S. Private*, pg. 3774
STAFFORD CONSTRUCTION COMPANY, L.L.C.; *U.S. Private*, pg. 3775
STANGER INDUSTRIES; *U.S. Private*, pg. 3782
STANLEY MILLER CONSTRUCTION CO.; *U.S. Private*, pg. 3783
STAN'S CONTRACTING INC.; *U.S. Private*, pg. 3777
STAR BUILDING SYSTEMS - MONTICELLO—See Clayton, Dubilier & Rice, LLC; *U.S. Private*, pg. 921
STAR CONSTRUCTION, INC.—See MidOcean Partners, LLP; *U.S. Private*, pg. 2717
STATEWIDE SERVICES, INC.—See Compass Group PLC; *Int'l*, pg. 1752
STEBBINS ENTERPRISES INC.; *U.S. Private*, pg. 3795
S&TECHS (HONG KONG) LIMITED—See STO Building Group Inc.; *U.S. Private*, pg. 3814
STEED CONSTRUCTION, INC.; *U.S. Private*, pg. 3795
STEELARIS PTE. LTD.—See AYS Ventures Berhad; *Int'l*, pg. 776
STEELCELL OF NORTH AMERICA, INC.; *U.S. Private*, pg. 3796
STEEL SYSTEMS INC.—See Clayton, Dubilier & Rice, LLC; *U.S. Private*, pg. 921
THE STELLAR GROUP INC.; *U.S. Private*, pg. 4121
STENSTROM GENERAL CONTRACTOR-DESIGN BUILD GROUP—See Stenstrom Companies Ltd.; *U.S. Private*, pg. 3801
STEPHEN GROSS & SONS INC.; *U.S. Private*, pg. 3802
STEUART-KRET HOMES—See Steuart Investment Company; *U.S. Private*, pg. 3807
STEVENS CONSTRUCTION CORP; *U.S. Private*, pg. 3809
STEVENS CONSTRUCTION, INC.; *U.S. Private*, pg. 3809
STEWARD CONSTRUCTION SERVICES, LLC; *U.S. Private*, pg. 3810
STEWART-RICHEY CONSTRUCTION, INC.—See Houchens Industries, Inc.; *U.S. Private*, pg. 1990
STITZ & ASSOCIATES, INC—See Heffernan Insurance Brokers; *U.S. Private*, pg. 1904
STOCKADE BUILDINGS INC.; *U.S. Private*, pg. 3814
STODOLA-MAAS CONSTRUCTION INC.; *U.S. Private*, pg. 3815
STONEWALL CONTRACTING CORP; *U.S. Private*, pg. 3830
STORY CONSTRUCTION CO; *U.S. Private*, pg. 3832
STRAMIT PTY LIMITED—See Fletcher Building Limited; *Int'l*, pg. 2701
STREETER ASSOCIATES INC.; *U.S. Private*, pg. 3838
STROM GUNDERSEN AS—See AF Gruppen ASA; *Int'l*, pg. 184
STROM GUNDERSEN VESTFOLD AS—See AF Gruppen ASA; *Int'l*, pg. 184
STRUCTURES UNLIMITED, INC.; *U.S. Private*, pg. 3842
STRUCTURE TONE, INC. - BOSTON—See STO Building Group Inc.; *U.S. Private*, pg. 3814
STRUCTURE TONE INC.-HAMILTON—See STO Building Group Inc.; *U.S. Private*, pg. 3814
STRUCTURE TONE INC.-PHILADELPHIA—See STO Building Group Inc.; *U.S. Private*, pg. 3814
STRUCTURE TONE, INC.—See STO Building Group Inc.; *U.S. Private*, pg. 3814
STRUCTURE TONE, INC.—See STO Building Group Inc.; *U.S. Private*, pg. 3814
STRUCTURE TONE LIMITED—See STO Building Group Inc.; *U.S. Private*, pg. 3814
STRUCTURE TONE, LLC—See STO Building Group Inc.; *U.S. Private*, pg. 3814
STRUCTURE TONE SOUTHWEST—See STO Building Group Inc.; *U.S. Private*, pg. 3814
STRUCTURE TONE UK—See STO Building Group Inc.; *U.S. Private*, pg. 3814
STRUKTON BOUW B.V.—See Centric Holding B.V.; *Int'l*, pg. 1412
STUART OLSON DOMINION CONSTRUCTION LTD.—See Bird Construction Inc.; *Int'l*, pg. 1047
STUART OLSON INC.—See Bird Construction Inc.; *Int'l*, pg. 1046
STULTZ, INC.; *U.S. Private*, pg. 3844
SUD-FASSADEN GMBH—See BayernLB Holding AG; *Int'l*, pg. 914
SUFFOLK CONSTRUCTION COMPANY, INC.; *U.S. Private*, pg. 3849
SUFFOLK-ROEL—See Suffolk Construction Company, Inc.; *U.S. Private*, pg. 3849
SULLIVAN & COZART INC.; *U.S. Private*, pg. 3850
SULLIVAN ENGINEERING, LLC—See Rimkus Consulting Group, Inc.; *U.S. Private*, pg. 3437
SUNBELT CONSTRUCTION INC.; *U.S. Private*, pg. 3864
SUNLEY M&E ENGINEERING PTE. LTD.—See CNQC International Holdings Ltd.; *Int'l*, pg. 1678
SUNRIDGE PROPERTIES INC.; *U.S. Private*, pg. 3869
SUNTECH BUILDING SYSTEMS INC.; *U.S. Private*, pg. 3873
SUPER KIAN HOLDINGS SDN. BHD.—See Harvest Miracle Capital Berhad; *Int'l*, pg. 3281
SUPER WASH INC.; *U.S. Private*, pg. 3875
SUREFIRE MANAGEMENT SERVICES LTD.—See Berger Paints India Limited; *Int'l*, pg. 980
SUSTAINABLE COMFORT, INC.; *U.S. Private*, pg. 3886
SWANK ENTERPRISES INC.; *U.S. Private*, pg. 3890
SWINERTON INCORPORATED; *U.S. Private*, pg. 3893
SYSKEN CORPORATION—See COMSYS Holdings Corporation; *Int'l*, pg. 1762
SYSTEMAX PTY LTD—See Carrier Global Corporation; *U.S. Public*, pg. 444
SYSTEM ENGINEERING CO., LTD.—See Densan System Co., Ltd.; *Int'l*, pg. 2028
SYSTEMS ELECTRONICS, INC.—See Wind Point Advisors LLC; *U.S. Private*, pg. 4535
TABER CRANE CONSTRUCTION SERVICES CORP.; *U.S. Private*, pg. 3919
TANGSHAN JIDONG DEVELOPMENT YAN DONG CONSTRUCTION CO., LTD.—See BBMG Corporation; *Int'l*, pg. 921
TARR WHITMAN GROUP, LLC—See HanmiGlobal Co., LTD.; *Int'l*, pg. 3257
TASK CONSTRUCTION MANAGEMENT INC.—See Fayolle et Fils; *Int'l*, pg. 2626

N.A.I.C.S. INDEX

236220 — COMMERCIAL AND INST...

TATA HITACHI CONSTRUCTION MACHINERY COMPANY PRIVATE LIMITED—See Hitachi, Ltd.; *Int'l*, pg. 3424
TATA PROJECTS LIMITED—See Artson Engineering Ltd; *Int'l*, pg. 586
TAYLOR BROS. CONSTRUCTION CO., INC.—See Harmon Group; *U.S. Private*, pg. 1866
TAYLOR-PANSING INC.; *U.S. Private*, pg. 3941
TCI ARCHITECTS ENGINEERS CONTRACTORS INC.; *U.S. Private*, pg. 3942
TDK CONSTRUCTION CO. INC.; *U.S. Private*, pg. 3944
TDS CONSTRUCTION INC.; *U.S. Private*, pg. 3944
TEAL CONSTRUCTION COMPANY; *U.S. Private*, pg. 3948
TECHNO COATINGS INC.; *U.S. Private*, pg. 3954
TECH-STEEL INC.; *U.S. Private*, pg. 3952
TECNOCONSULT S A—See Fluor Corporation; *U.S. Public*, pg. 859
TEEL CONSTRUCTION INC.; *U.S. Private*, pg. 3958
TELAMON CONSTRUCTION INC.—See Mosser Construction Inc.; *U.S. Private*, pg. 2795
TEMPLETON CONSTRUCTION CO.; *U.S. Private*, pg. 3963
TERRABAU GMBH—See CR Capital Real Estate AG; *Int'l*, pg. 1827
TERRAFOUNDATIONS S.A.—See Echeverria Izquierdo S.A.; *Int'l*, pg. 2289
TETRA TECH CONTINGENCY CONSTRUCTORS, LLC—See Tetra Tech, Inc.; *U.S. Public*, pg. 2023
TG CONSTRUCTION INC.; *U.S. Private*, pg. 3979
T&G CORPORATION; *U.S. Private*, pg. 3909
T. GERDING CONSTRUCTION CO. (TGCC); *U.S. Private*, pg. 3911
THAI DAIHO COMPANY LIMITED—See DAIHO CORPORATION; *Int'l*, pg. 1927
THAI NIPPON STEEL ENGINEERING & CONSTRUCTION CORPORATION CO., LTD.—See GJ Steel Public Company Limited; *Int'l*, pg. 2982
THALHIMER COMMERCIAL REAL ESTATE; *U.S. Private*, pg. 3979
THARALDSON DEVELOPMENT CO.; *U.S. Private*, pg. 3980
THOMAS J. O'BEIRNE & CO. INC.; *U.S. Private*, pg. 4156
THOMAS P. CARNEY INC.; *U.S. Private*, pg. 4157
THOMPSON BUILDERS CORPORATION; *U.S. Private*, pg. 4159
THOMPSON CONSTRUCTION GROUP—See Thompson Industrial Services, LLC; *U.S. Private*, pg. 4159
THOMPSON TURNER CONSTRUCTION—See Thompson Industrial Services, LLC; *U.S. Private*, pg. 4159
THORENDAHL AS—See AF Gruppen ASA; *Int'l*, pg. 184
THOS. S. BYRNE, INC.; *U.S. Private*, pg. 4163
THRIVE HOMES LLC—See Toll Brothers, Inc.; *U.S. Public*, pg. 2162
TIMBER & BUILDING SUPPLIES HOLLAND N.V.—See HAL Trust N.V.; *Int'l*, pg. 3227
TIP TOP CONSTRUCTION CORP; *U.S. Private*, pg. 4175
TKC PROSJEKT AS—See AF Gruppen ASA; *Int'l*, pg. 184
T&K MECHANICAL INC.; *U.S. Private*, pg. 3909
TLG IMMOBILIEN AG—See Aroundtown SA; *Int'l*, pg. 578
T.N. WARD COMPANY; *U.S. Private*, pg. 3912
TODD & SARGENT, INC.; *U.S. Private*, pg. 4180
TOMASSO BROTHERS INC.; *U.S. Private*, pg. 4183
TOMKINS BUILDERS, INC.—See ACS, Actividades de Construccion y Servicios, S.A.; *Int'l*, pg. 113
TOM WESSEL CONSTRUCTION CORP.; *U.S. Private*, pg. 4183
TORMEE CONSTRUCTION INC.; *U.S. Private*, pg. 4189
TOWNHOMES AT RIVERFRONT PARK, LLC—See Goff Capital, Inc.; *U.S. Private*, pg. 1726
TRANSCO GAS PIPE LINE CORP.—See The Williams Companies, Inc.; *U.S. Public*, pg. 2143
TRANSYSTEMS LLC—See Transystems LLC; *U.S. Private*, pg. 4212
TREASURE ISLAND COMMUNITY DEVELOPMENT, LLC—See Lennar Corporation; *U.S. Public*, pg. 1307
TREHEL CORPORATION; *U.S. Private*, pg. 4217
TRIBBLE & STEPHENS CONSTRUCTORS LIMITED; *U.S. Private*, pg. 4227
TRIBIA AS—See Addnode Group AB; *Int'l*, pg. 131
TRIMAR CONSTRUCTION, INC.; *U.S. Private*, pg. 4232
TRINITY BUILDING & CONSTRUCTION MANAGEMENT CORP.; *U.S. Private*, pg. 4233
TRI-NORTH BUILDERS INC.; *U.S. Private*, pg. 4223
TRI-STATE INDUSTRIAL GROUP; *U.S. Private*, pg. 4224
TRITEC BUILDING COMPANY INC.; *U.S. Private*, pg. 4238
TRITON PROJECTS—See Jacobs Engineering Group, Inc.; *U.S. Public*, pg. 1185
TROON ENTERPRISES INC.; *U.S. Private*, pg. 4242
TSAY CONSTRUCTION & SERVICES, LLC—See Tsay Corporation; *U.S. Private*, pg. 4252
TUNELES CONCESIONADOS DE ACAPULCO, S.A. DE C.V.—See Empresas ICA S.A.B. de C.V.; *Int'l*, pg. 2391
TURELK INC.; *U.S. Private*, pg. 4259
TURNBULL-WAHLERT CONSTRUCTION, INC.; *U.S. Private*, pg. 4260
TURNER CONSTRUCTION COMPANY—See ACS, Actividades de Construccion y Servicios, S.A.; *Int'l*, pg. 113
TURNER CONSTRUCTION INTERNATIONAL LLC—See ACS, Actividades de Construccion y Servicios, S.A.; *Int'l*, pg. 113
TURNER INDUSTRIES GROUP, L.L.C.; *U.S. Private*, pg. 4260
TURNER INDUSTRIES GROUP L.L.C.—See Turner Industries Group, L.L.C.; *U.S. Private*, pg. 4261
TUTERA GROUP INC.; *U.S. Private*, pg. 4262
TUTOR PERINI CORPORATION; *U.S. Public*, pg. 2205
TUTOR-SALIBA CORPORATION—See Tutor Perini Corporation; *U.S. Public*, pg. 2206
TWO RIVERS DEVELOPMENT LIMITED—See Centum Investment Company Limited; *Int'l*, pg. 1416
TWO-STATE CONSTRUCTION COMPANY, INC.; *U.S. Private*, pg. 4267
UAB PASTATU PRIEZIURA—See City Service SE; *Int'l*, pg. 1628
UDRA MEXICO S.A. DE C.V.—See Grupo Empresarial San Jose, S.A.; *Int'l*, pg. 3128
UHRIG CONSTRUCTION INC.; *U.S. Private*, pg. 4274
UNIVERSAL CONSTRUCTION COMPANY, INC.; *U.S. Private*, pg. 4304
UNLIMITED CONSTRUCTION SERVICES; *U.S. Private*, pg. 4310
URBAN RETAIL PROPERTIES CO. OF FLORIDA—See RAIT Financial Trust; *U.S. Private*, pg. 3349
URBAN RETAIL PROPERTIES CO. OF MASSACHUSETTS—See RAIT Financial Trust; *U.S. Private*, pg. 3349
URBAN TANTRA INTERNATIONAL, INC.; *U.S. Private*, pg. 4315
US DESIGN & CONSTRUCTION CORP.; *U.S. Private*, pg. 4318
UTILITY MANAGEMENT & CONSTRUCTION, LLC—See Renavotio, Inc.; *U.S. Public*, pg. 1783
U.W. MARX CONSTRUCTION COMPANY, INC.; *U.S. Private*, pg. 4272
VALLEY COMMERCIAL CONTRACTORS; *U.S. Private*, pg. 4333
VAMED AG—See Fresenius SE & Co. KGaA; *Int'l*, pg. 2781
VAN BEBBER & ASSOCIATES, INC.; *U.S. Private*, pg. 4338
VANDERVERT CONSTRUCTION INC.; *U.S. Private*, pg. 4343
VAN HOOSE CONSTRUCTION CO.; *U.S. Private*, pg. 4340
VANNMEISLING AS—See AF Gruppen ASA; *Int'l*, pg. 184
VANSON ENTERPRISES, INC.; *U.S. Private*, pg. 4344
VANTAGE CONTRACTORS, LLC; *U.S. Private*, pg. 4344
VENTURE CONSTRUCTION COMPANY INC.; *U.S. Private*, pg. 4357
VEOLIA ENVIRONMENTAL SERVICES EMIRATES LLC—See Al Jaber Group; *Int'l*, pg. 280
VERKLER INC.; *U.S. Private*, pg. 4366
VESTA HOUSING SOLUTIONS LLC—See McGrath RentCorp.; *U.S. Public*, pg. 1407
VIAS Y CONSTRUCCIONES S.A.—See ACS, Actividades de Construccion y Servicios, S.A.; *Int'l*, pg. 117
VIETNAM DEVELOPMENT CONSTRUCTION CO. LTD.—See Hazama Ando Corporation; *Int'l*, pg. 3295
VIEWPOINT CONSTRUCTION SOFTWARE LIMITED—See Trimble, Inc.; *U.S. Public*, pg. 2193
VIGEN CONSTRUCTION INC.; *U.S. Private*, pg. 4381
VIPINGO DEVELOPMENT LIMITED—See Centum Investment Company Limited; *Int'l*, pg. 1416
VIRTEXCO CORPORATION; *U.S. Private*, pg. 4388
VISION CONSTRUCTION SERVICES OF ATLANTA—See James Group, Inc.; *U.S. Private*, pg. 2184
VISION FOUNDATION PTE. LTD.—See Green Economy Development Limited; *Int'l*, pg. 3071
VISSERING CONSTRUCTION CO.; *U.S. Private*, pg. 4393
V.L. RENDINA INC.; *U.S. Private*, pg. 4328
VOGEL BROS BUILDING CO. INC.; *U.S. Private*, pg. 4409
VOLMAR CONSTRUCTION INC.; *U.S. Private*, pg. 4411
VRATSINAS CONSTRUCTION COMPANY, INC.; *U.S. Private*, pg. 4415
VRH CONSTRUCTION CORP.; *U.S. Private*, pg. 4415
WADMAN CORPORATION; *U.S. Private*, pg. 4425
WAGMAN CONSTRUCTION, INC.—See Wagman Companies, Inc.; *U.S. Private*, pg. 4426
WAGNER CONSTRUCTION COMPANY, LLC—See A.O. Construction Company, Inc.; *U.S. Private*, pg. 27
WALBRIDGE ALDINGER LLC; *U.S. Private*, pg. 4427
WALDROP CONSTRUCTION CO. INC.; *U.S. Private*, pg. 4428
WALKER & COMPANY, INC.; *U.S. Private*, pg. 4428
WALSH BROTHERS INC.; *U.S. Private*, pg. 4432
WALZ HARMAN HUFFMAN COMPANIES; *U.S. Private*, pg. 4435
WAN CHUNG CONSTRUCTION (SINGAPORE) PTE. LIMITED—See Green Economy Development Limited; *Int'l*, pg. 3071
WARFEL CONSTRUCTION CO.; *U.S. Private*, pg. 4442
WARWICK CONSTRUCTION, INC.; *U.S. Private*, pg. 4445
W.A. SHEETS & SONS, INC.; *U.S. Private*, pg. 4419
WATT RETAIL DEVELOPMENT—See Watt Companies, Inc.; *U.S. Private*, pg. 4456
WAYNESBORO CONSTRUCTION CO. INC.; *U.S. Private*, pg. 4460
WBB MANAGEMENT COMPANY, INC.—See Thompson Builders Corporation; *U.S. Private*, pg. 4159
WEATHERBY CONSTRUCTION CORP.; *U.S. Private*, pg. 4462
WEATHERSEAL COMPANY, LLC—See Installed Building Products, Inc.; *U.S. Public*, pg. 1134
WEBB AND PARTNERS, INC.; *U.S. Private*, pg. 4464
WEBB & SONS CONSTRUCTION CO. INC; *U.S. Private*, pg. 4464
WECC, INC.—See Werner Enterprises, Inc.; *U.S. Public*, pg. 2349
WEDDLE BROS. CONSTRUCTION CO., INC.; *U.S. Private*, pg. 4468
WEIMAR CONSTRUCTION COMPANY, INC.; *U.S. Private*, pg. 4471
WEISS CONSTRUCTION; *U.S. Private*, pg. 4472
WELBRO BUILDING CORPORATION; *U.S. Private*, pg. 4473
WELFL CONSTRUCTION CORPORATION; *U.S. Private*, pg. 4474
WELLIVER MCGUIRE INC.; *U.S. Private*, pg. 4475
WELLTECH CONSTRUCTION PTE. LTD.—See CNQC International Holdings Ltd.; *Int'l*, pg. 1678
WELSH CONSTRUCTION LLC—See Welsh Companies LLC; *U.S. Private*, pg. 4479
WENCO, INC.; *U.S. Private*, pg. 4480
WENTZ GROUP INC.; *U.S. Private*, pg. 4481
W.E. O'NEIL CONSTRUCTION COMPANY OF ARIZONA—See O'Neil Industries Inc.; *U.S. Private*, pg. 2980
W.E. O'NEIL CONSTRUCTION COMPANY—See O'Neil Industries Inc.; *U.S. Private*, pg. 2980
W.E. O'NEIL CONSTRUCTION CO. OF CALIFORNIA—See O'Neil Industries Inc.; *U.S. Private*, pg. 2979
W.E. O'NEIL CONSTRUCTION CO. OF COLORADO—See O'Neil Industries Inc.; *U.S. Private*, pg. 2980
WESTAR OILFIELD RENTALS, INC.—See Enterprise Group, Inc.; *Int'l*, pg. 2451
WESTCON, INC.—See Bilfinger SE; *Int'l*, pg. 1026
WESTERCHIL CONSTRUCTION CO.; *U.S. Private*, pg. 4490
WESTERN BUILDERS INC.—See The O'Connell Companies, Incorporated; *U.S. Private*, pg. 4087
WESTERN CONSTRUCTION SERVICES, INC.; *U.S. Private*, pg. 4492
WESTERN ENVIRONMENTAL CORP.—See Controlled Environment Systems, LLC; *U.S. Private*, pg. 1034
WESTERN LAND PROPERTIES—See Lewis Operating Corp.; *U.S. Private*, pg. 2439
WESTIN CONSTRUCTION COMPANY INC.; *U.S. Private*, pg. 4498
WEST MAUI CONSTRUCTION, INC.; *U.S. Private*, pg. 4486
WESTPORT CORPORATION; *U.S. Private*, pg. 4500
WESTWOOD CONTRACTORS INC.; *U.S. Private*, pg. 4501
W. GOHMAN CONSTRUCTION CO.; *U.S. Private*, pg. 4418
WG YATES & SONS CONSTRUCTION COMPANY, BILOXI—See W.G. Yates & Sons Construction Company; *U.S. Private*, pg. 4420
WG YATES & SONS CONSTRUCTION COMPANY, DESTIN—See W.G. Yates & Sons Construction Company; *U.S. Private*, pg. 4420
WG YATES & SONS CONSTRUCTION COMPANY - HEAVY DIVISION—See W.G. Yates & Sons Construction Company; *U.S. Private*, pg. 4420
WG YATES & SONS CONSTRUCTION COMPANY, MEMPHIS—See W.G. Yates & Sons Construction Company; *U.S. Private*, pg. 4420
WG YATES & SONS CONSTRUCTION COMPANY, MOBILE—See W.G. Yates & Sons Construction Company; *U.S. Private*, pg. 4420
W.G. YATES & SONS CONSTRUCTION COMPANY; *U.S. Private*, pg. 4420
WHITE CONSTRUCTION COMPANY—See Crestview Partners, L.P.; *U.S. Private*, pg. 1098
WHITE CONTRUCTION, INC.; *U.S. Private*, pg. 4508
WHITERIVER CONSTRUCTION, INC.; *U.S. Private*, pg. 4511
WHITESELL CONSTRUCTION INC.; *U.S. Private*, pg. 4512
THE WHITING-TURNER CONTRACTING COMPANY; *U.S. Private*, pg. 4135
WHITLEY MANUFACTURING COMPANY, INC.; *U.S. Private*, pg. 4512
WHITTENBERG CONSTRUCTION CO.; *U.S. Private*, pg. 4513
WICHMAN CONSTRUCTION; *U.S. Private*, pg. 4515
WILD BUILDING CONTRACTORS INC.; *U.S. Private*, pg. 4518
WILLIAM A. RANDOLPH, INC.; *U.S. Private*, pg. 4522
WILLIAM BRONNER & SON CONTRACTORS INC.; *U.S. Private*, pg. 4522
WILLIAMS BROTHERS CONSTRUCTION INC.; *U.S. Private*, pg. 4525
WILLIAMS & ROWE CO., INC.; *U.S. Private*, pg. 4525
WILLIS A. SMITH CONSTRUCTION, INC.; *U.S. Private*, pg. 4527
WILSON ASSOCIATES; *U.S. Private*, pg. 4530
WILSON BOWDEN DEVELOPMENTS LTD.—See Barratt Developments PLC; *Int'l*, pg. 868
WILSON & COMPANY, INC.; *U.S. Private*, pg. 4529

236220 — COMMERCIAL AND INST...   CORPORATE AFFILIATIONS

WILSON CONSTRUCTION COMPANY INC.; *U.S. Private*, pg. 4530
WILSON CONSTRUCTION COMPANY—See The Wilson Holding Company; *U.S. Private*, pg. 4137
WIMCO CORP.; *U.S. Private*, pg. 4532
WIN-CON ENTERPRISES INC.; *U.S. Private*, pg. 4532
WINSUPPLY, INC.; *U.S. Private*, pg. 4544
WINTER CONSTRUCTION COMPANY; *U.S. Private*, pg. 4545
WISHON & CARTER BUILDERS; *U.S. Private*, pg. 4550
THE WITTERS CONSTRUCTION COMPANY; *U.S. Private*, pg. 4138
W. J. MOUNTFORD CO.; *U.S. Private*, pg. 4418
W.L. BUTLER CONSTRUCTION INC.; *U.S. Private*, pg. 4421
WLH STILLWATER, LLC—See Brookfield Corporation; *Int'l*, pg. 1183
WLH STONEWALL, LLC—See Brookfield Corporation; *Int'l*, pg. 1183
WLH TRAILS AT LEANDER, LLC—See Brookfield Corporation; *Int'l*, pg. 1183
W.L. MCCORMACK & CO. INC.; *U.S. Private*, pg. 4421
WM. BLANCHARD CO.; *U.S. Private*, pg. 4552
W.M. JORDAN COMPANY INC.; *U.S. Private*, pg. 4422
W.M. JORDAN COMPANY—See W.M. Jordan Company Inc.; *U.S. Private*, pg. 4422
W.M. SCHLOSSER CO. INC.; *U.S. Private*, pg. 4422
WOHLSEN CONSTRUCTION COMPANY; *U.S. Private*, pg. 4553
WOHNEN AM LERCHENBERG GMBH & CO. KG—See BayWa AG; *Int'l*, pg. 919
WOHNEN AM LERCHENBERG VERWALTUNGS GMBH—See BayWa AG; *Int'l*, pg. 919
WOJCIK BUILDERS, INC.; *U.S. Private*, pg. 4553
WOLGAST CORPORATION; *U.S. Private*, pg. 4554
WOLMAN CONSTRUCTION—See Waterford Group, LLC; *U.S. Private*, pg. 4453
WOLVERINE BUILDING GROUP; *U.S. Private*, pg. 4554
WOODMAN CONSTRUCTION INC.; *U.S. Private*, pg. 4559
WOODROW WILSON CONSTRUCTION COMPANY, INC.; *U.S. Private*, pg. 4559
WOODRUFF CONSTRUCTION LLC; *U.S. Private*, pg. 4560
WORKMAN COMMERCIAL CONSTRUCTION SERVICES, LTD.; *U.S. Private*, pg. 4564
WRENN CONSTRUCTION; *U.S. Private*, pg. 4572
WRIGHT BROTHERS BUILDING CO.; *U.S. Private*, pg. 4572
WRIGHT CONSTRUCTION GROUP, INC.; *U.S. Private*, pg. 4573
WRIGHT-RYAN CONSTRUCTION INC.; *U.S. Private*, pg. 4573
W.S. BELLOWS CONSTRUCTION CORPORATION; *U.S. Private*, pg. 4422
WURZEL BUILDERS, LTD.; *U.S. Private*, pg. 4575
WYATT MANAGEMENT, INC.; *U.S. Private*, pg. 4575
XPERA, INC.—See Wind Point Advisors LLC; *U.S. Private*, pg. 4536
YEARGIN POTTER SHACKELFORD CONSTRUCTION, INC.; *U.S. Private*, pg. 4587
YI-CHI CONSTRUCTION CORPORATION—See Formosa Petrochemical Corporation; *Int'l*, pg. 2735
ZAREMBA CONTRACTORS, LLC—See Zaremba Group, LLC; *U.S. Private*, pg. 4598
ZARTMAN CONSTRUCTION INC.; *U.S. Private*, pg. 4598
ZIOLKOWSKI CONSTRUCTION INC.; *U.S. Private*, pg. 4605
ZIRKELBACH CONSTRUCTION, INC.; *U.S. Private*, pg. 4606

237110 — WATER AND SEWER LINE AND RELATED STRUCTURES CONSTRUCTION

A-1 EXCAVATING, INC.; *U.S. Private*, pg. 21
A3 WATER SOLUTIONS GMBH—See EnviTec Biogas AG; *Int'l*, pg. 2455
ABEL CONSTRUCTION CO. INC.; *U.S. Private*, pg. 37
ACQUE SERVIZI S.R.L.—See ACEA S.p.A.; *Int'l*, pg. 95
A.C. SCHULTES, INC.; *U.S. Private*, pg. 24
A.C. SCHULTES OF CAROLINA, INC.—See A.C. Schultes, Inc.; *U.S. Private*, pg. 24
A.C. SCHULTES OF DELAWARE, INC.—See A.C. Schultes, Inc.; *U.S. Private*, pg. 24
A.C. SCHULTES OF FLORIDA, INC.—See A.C. Schultes, Inc.; *U.S. Private*, pg. 24
A.C. SCHULTES OF MARYLAND, INC.—See A.C. Schultes, Inc.; *U.S. Private*, pg. 25
ADAMS ROBINSON ENTERPRISES; *U.S. Private*, pg. 75
AEGEK GROUP; *Int'l*, pg. 173
AGUAS DE ANDRADINA S.A.—See Igua Saneamento SA; *Int'l*, pg. 3603
AGUAS DE CASTILHO S.A.—See Igua Saneamento SA; *Int'l*, pg. 3603
AJ LUCAS DRILLING PTY LIMITED—See A.J. Lucas Group Limited; *Int'l*, pg. 24
AJ LUCAS PLANT & EQUIPMENT PTY LIMITED—See A.J. Lucas Group Limited; *Int'l*, pg. 24
A&K EARTH MOVERS INC.; *U.S. Private*, pg. 20
ALASKA ROAD BORING COMPANY; *U.S. Private*, pg. 151
ALEX E. PARIS CONTRACTING CO., INC.; *U.S. Private*, pg. 162
AL JABER TUNNELING & MECHANICAL WORKS EST—See Al Jaber Group; *Int'l*, pg. 280
ALLCO INCORPORATED; *U.S. Private*, pg. 175
ALSAY INCORPORATED—See Venquest Capital Partners LLC; *U.S. Private*, pg. 4356
AMERICAN CONTRACTING & SERVICES INC.—See Hughes Group, Inc.; *U.S. Private*, pg. 2003
AMERICAN STATES UTILITY SERVICES, INC.—See American States Water Company; *U.S. Public*, pg. 110
AMIAD WATER SYSTEMS EUROPE SAS—See Amiad Water Systems Ltd.; *Int'l*, pg. 427
AP CONSTRUCTION INC.; *U.S. Private*, pg. 290
A. P. O'HORO COMPANY; *U.S. Private*, pg. 275
AQSEPTENCE GROUP GMBH—See Brookfield Corporation; *Int'l*, pg. 1181
AQSEPTENCE GROUP - HANAU—See Brookfield Corporation; *Int'l*, pg. 1181
ARGONAUT CONSTRUCTORS, INC.; *U.S. Private*, pg. 321
ARIZONA PIPE LINE COMPANY INC.; *U.S. Private*, pg. 324
ASCORP, INC.; *U.S. Private*, pg. 348
ASTRAMATIC S.A.U.—See Fluidra SA; *Int'l*, pg. 2714
AVENG WATER PTY LTD; *Int'l*, pg. 738
BALKEMA EXCAVATING INC.; *U.S. Private*, pg. 459
BALL WINCH, LLC—See L.B. Foster Company; *U.S. Public*, pg. 1278
BAMAG GMBH—See Allied Resource Corporation; *U.S. Private*, pg. 187
BARBAROSSA AND SONS INC.; *U.S. Private*, pg. 472
BARNARD CONSTRUCTION CO. INC.; *U.S. Private*, pg. 477
BAYER CONSTRUCTION COMPANY, INC.; *U.S. Private*, pg. 496
BEAN HORIZON CORP.—See C.F. Bean, LLC; *U.S. Private*, pg. 707
BECHTEL SERVICES (AUSTRALIA) PTY LTD—See Bechtel Group, Inc.; *U.S. Private*, pg. 510
BEIJING JIUAN CONSTRUCTION INVESTMENT GROUP CO., LTD.—See Beijing Origin Water Technology Co., Ltd.; *Int'l*, pg. 955
BEIJING ORIGINWATER MEMBRANE TECHNOLOGY CO., LTD.—See Beijing Origin Water Technology Co., Ltd.; *Int'l*, pg. 955
BEIJING ORIGINWATER PURETECH CO., LTD.—See Beijing Origin Water Technology Co., Ltd.; *Int'l*, pg. 955
BELIZE WATER SERVICES LIMITED; *Int'l*, pg. 965
BENTON-GEORGIA, INC.; *U.S. Private*, pg. 529
BERWICK ELECTRIC CO.; *U.S. Private*, pg. 540
BETTER ENVIRONMENT CONCEPTS, INC.; *U.S. Public*, pg. 326
B&K CONSTRUCTION CO. INC.; *U.S. Private*, pg. 418
BLEIGH CONSTRUCTION CO. INC.; *U.S. Private*, pg. 580
BLUE MOUNTAIN POWER COMPANY INC.,—See Alternative Earth Resources Inc.; *Int'l*, pg. 391
BOAN CONTRACTING CO. INC.; *U.S. Private*, pg. 602
BORING & TUNNELING CO. OF AMERICA; *U.S. Private*, pg. 618
BOWEN ENGINEERING CORPORATION; *U.S. Private*, pg. 625
BRADSHAW CONSTRUCTION CORP; *U.S. Private*, pg. 633
BRB CONTRACTORS, INC.; *U.S. Private*, pg. 642
BRENT SCARBROUGH & COMPANY, INC.; *U.S. Private*, pg. 645
BREWER ELECTRIC & UTILITIES—See Reilly Electrical Contractors; *U.S. Private*, pg. 3391
BUILDING CRAFTS INC.; *U.S. Private*, pg. 682
BYRON E. TALBOT CONTRACTOR; *U.S. Private*, pg. 701
CAB AGUAS DE PARANAGUA S.A.—See Igua Saneamento SA; *Int'l*, pg. 3603
CAB CANARANA LTDA.—See Igua Saneamento SA; *Int'l*, pg. 3603
CAB COLIDER LTDA.—See Igua Saneamento SA; *Int'l*, pg. 3603
CAB COMODORO LTDA.—See Igua Saneamento SA; *Int'l*, pg. 3603
CAB GUARATINGUETA S.A.—See Igua Saneamento SA; *Int'l*, pg. 3603
CAB MT PARTICIPACOES LTDA.—See Igua Saneamento SA; *Int'l*, pg. 3603
CAB PIQUETE S.A.—See Igua Saneamento SA; *Int'l*, pg. 3603
CAC INDUSTRIES INC.; *U.S. Private*, pg. 711
CADAGUA S.A.—See Ferrovial S.A.; *Int'l*, pg. 2644
CAJUN CONSTRUCTORS INC.; *U.S. Private*, pg. 714
CAMPBELL MANUFACTURING INC.; *U.S. Private*, pg. 730
C.A. MURREN & SONS COMPANY; *U.S. Private*, pg. 706
CARILLION ALAWI LLC—See Carillion plc; *Int'l*, pg. 1330
CARILLION CONSTRUCTION CANADA—See Carillion plc; *Int'l*, pg. 1330
CARILLION CONSTRUCTION (CARIBBEAN) LTD.—See Carillion plc; *Int'l*, pg. 1330
CARLIN CONTRACTING COMPANY, INC.; *U.S. Private*, pg. 763
CASPER COLOSIMO & SON INC.; *U.S. Private*, pg. 783
CBC SERVICES, INC.; *U.S. Private*, pg. 797
CHARLES SARGENT IRRIGATION; *U.S. Private*, pg. 853
CHELCO SERVICES, INC.—See Choctawhatchee Electric Cooperative Inc.; *U.S. Private*, pg. 888
CIMARRON UNDERGROUND SERVICES, LLC; *U.S. Private*, pg. 897
C. J. HUGHES CONSTRUCTION COMPANY, INC.—See Energy Services of America Corporation; *U.S. Public*, pg. 762
CLARK HUNT CONSTRUCTION, INC.; *U.S. Private*, pg. 913
COMPORIUM TELECOM INC.—See Comporium Group; *U.S. Private*, pg. 1002
CONNELL RESOURCES INC.; *U.S. Private*, pg. 1017
CORIX GROUP—See British Columbia Investment Management Corp.; *Int'l*, pg. 1169
CORIX GROUP—See CAI Private Equity; *Int'l*, pg. 1252
CORNERSTONE OF NORTH FLORIDA—See Cornerstone Businesses Inc.; *U.S. Private*, pg. 1051
COSMOSTEEL HOLDINGS LIMITED; *Int'l*, pg. 1814
CRAIG SHEFFIELD & AUSTIN INC.; *U.S. Private*, pg. 1083
C.R. JACKSON INC.; *U.S. Private*, pg. 708
CRUZ CONTRACTORS LLC; *U.S. Private*, pg. 1114
CULLUM CONSTRUCTION COMPANY; *U.S. Private*, pg. 1121
CULY CONTRACTING, LLC—See New Mountain Capital, LLC; *U.S. Private*, pg. 2899
CUSTOM UNDERGROUND INC.; *U.S. Private*, pg. 1129
DALLAS 1 CORP.; *U.S. Private*, pg. 1149
DANELLA CONSTRUCTION CORP. OF NEW YORK—See The Danella Companies Inc.; *U.S. Private*, pg. 4018
DANELLA RENTAL SYSTEMS, INC.—See The Danella Companies Inc.; *U.S. Private*, pg. 4018
D&C CONSTRUCTION CO. INC.; *U.S. Private*, pg. 1137
DELAWARE WATER MANAGEMENT COMPANY, LLC—See Matador Resources Company; *U.S. Public*, pg. 1395
DEME BUILDING MATERIALS N.V.—See Ackermans & van Haaren NV; *Int'l*, pg. 105
DEVINEY CONSTRUCTION CO., INC.; *U.S. Private*, pg. 1218
DIGCO UTILITY CONSTRUCTION, L.P.—See Quanta Services, Inc.; *U.S. Public*, pg. 1751
DIVERSIFIED UTILITY SERVICES, INC.; *U.S. Private*, pg. 1243
DLF UTILITIES LIMITED—See DLF Limited; *Int'l*, pg. 2141
DOG LAKE CONSTRUCTION, INC.; *U.S. Private*, pg. 1253
DOMINION PRIVATIZATION FLORIDA, LLC—See Dominion Energy, Inc.; *U.S. Public*, pg. 674
DOMINION PRIVATIZATION TEXAS, LLC—See Dominion Energy, Inc.; *U.S. Public*, pg. 674
DON M. BARRON CONTRACTORS INC.; *U.S. Private*, pg. 1258
DOUGLAS N. HIGGINS INC.; *U.S. Private*, pg. 1267
DRANCO CONSTRUCTION LIMITED; *Int'l*, pg. 2200
DREDGING INTERNATIONAL NV—See Ackermans & van Haaren NV; *Int'l*, pg. 105
DYKAB I LULEA AB—See Endur ASA; *Int'l*, pg. 2410
DYNAMIX MECHANICAL, LLC; *U.S. Private*, pg. 1299
EATHERLY CONSTRUCTORS INC.; *U.S. Private*, pg. 1323
ECODYNE LIMITED—See Berkshire Hathaway Inc.; *U.S. Public*, pg. 311
EDISON MISSION GROUP INC.—See Edison International; *U.S. Public*, pg. 719
EJM PIPE SERVICES INC.; *U.S. Private*, pg. 1348
ELCON CORPORATION; *U.S. Private*, pg. 1350
EL PASO WATER UTILITIES; *U.S. Private*, pg. 1349
E&M BRUNNENBAU UND BOHRTECHNIK GMBH; *Int'l*, pg. 2247
ENERGOPROJEKT NISKOGRADNJA JOINT STOCK CO.—See Energoprojekt Holding a.d.; *Int'l*, pg. 2422
EN-TECH CORP.; *U.S. Private*, pg. 1389
ENVIRONMENTAL CONSULTANTS, LLC—See Ember Infrastructure Management, LP; *U.S. Private*, pg. 1378
E.ON HALOZATI SZOLGALTATO KFT.—See E.ON SE; *Int'l*, pg. 2254
ESAU & HUEBER GMBH.—See Buhler AG; *Int'l*, pg. 1212
ETABLISSEMENTS R. LEGRAND; *Int'l*, pg. 2519
EVAC NORWAY AS—See Bridgepoint Group Plc; *Int'l*, pg. 1153
EVAC OY—See Bridgepoint Group Plc; *Int'l*, pg. 1153
EVERGREEN UTILITY CONTRACTORS, INC.—See Tetra Tech, Inc.; *U.S. Public*, pg. 2023
EXLINE INC.; *U.S. Private*, pg. 1449
FABRIZI TRUCKING & PAVING CO.; *U.S. Private*, pg. 1459
FER-PAL CONSTRUCTION USA LLC—See Ferpal Infrastructure Ltd.; *Int'l*, pg. 2639
FERPAL INFRASTRUCTURE LTD.; *Int'l*, pg. 2639
FLIPPO CONSTRUCTION CO. INC.; *U.S. Private*, pg. 1546
FLORIDA GULF CONTRACTING, INC.; *U.S. Private*, pg. 1548
FLYNN BROTHERS CONTRACTING INC.; *U.S. Private*, pg. 1553
FLYNN TRUCKING LLC—See Flynn Brothers Contracting Inc.; *U.S. Private*, pg. 1553
FORAGES CABO INC.—See Cabo Drilling Corp.; *Int'l*, pg. 1246
FORSBERG CONSTRUCTION, INC.; *U.S. Private*, pg. 1573
FORT BLISS WATER SERVICES COMPANY—See Ameri-

can States Water Company; *U.S. Public*, pg. 110
FOUTZ & BURSUM CONSTRUCTION CO.; *U.S. Private*, pg. 1583
FRANK COLUCCIO CONSTRUCTION CO.; *U.S. Private*, pg. 1594
GALFAR ENGINEERING & CONTRACTING WLL—See Galfar Engineering & Contracting SAOG; *Int'l*, pg. 2872
GAMUDA BERHAD; *Int'l*, pg. 2879
GARNEY HOLDING COMPANY, INC.; *U.S. Private*, pg. 1645
GENERAL EXCAVATING COMPANY; *U.S. Private*, pg. 1665
GEOENERGIE TAUFKIRCHEN GMBH & CO. KG—See Daldrup & Sohne AG; *Int'l*, pg. 1950
GEORG FISCHER N.V.—See Georg Fischer AG; *Int'l*, pg. 2936
GEORG FISCHER S.P.A.—See Georg Fischer AG; *Int'l*, pg. 2937
GEOTECHNOS CO., LTD.—See Dowa Holdings Co., Ltd.; *Int'l*, pg. 2184
GEOTHERMIE NEURIED VERWALTUNGS GMBH—See Daldrup & Sohne AG; *Int'l*, pg. 1950
GI PROPERTIES INC.; *U.S. Private*, pg. 1694
GLANUA UK LIMITED—See Biomass Heating Solutions Ltd.; *Int'l*, pg. 1039
GLOW SPP 1 CO., LTD. - DEMIN WATER PLANT—See B. Grimm Group; *Int'l*, pg. 788
THE GOLDFIELD CORPORATION; *U.S. Public*, pg. 2075
GRADY CRAWFORD CONSTRUCTION CO., INC. OF BATON ROUGE; *U.S. Private*, pg. 1750
GRANGER COMPOST SERVICES—See Granger Associates, Inc.; *U.S. Private*, pg. 1754
GRANGER CONTAINER SERVICE, INC.—See Granger Associates, Inc.; *U.S. Private*, pg. 1754
GRANGER LAND DEVELOPMENT CO.—See Granger Associates, Inc.; *U.S. Private*, pg. 1754
GRANITE INLINER, LLC—See Granite Construction Incorporated; *U.S. Public*, pg. 957
GRAY SUPPLY CORP.; *U.S. Private*, pg. 1759
GRINER DRILLING SERVICE INC.; *U.S. Private*, pg. 1790
GRUPO ROTOPLAS, S.A.B. DE C.V.; *Int'l*, pg. 3135
G-TEK; *Int'l*, pg. 2863
GUANGDONG O'WATER ENVIRONMENTAL PROTECTIVE TECHNOLOGY CO., LTD.—See Beijing Origin Water Technology Co., Ltd.; *Int'l*, pg. 955
GUARDIAN COMPANIES INC.; *U.S. Private*, pg. 1810
HALL CONTRACTING CORP.; *U.S. Private*, pg. 1843
HALL CONTRACTING OF KENTUCKY; *U.S. Private*, pg. 1843
HALL-IRWIN CORPORATION; *U.S. Private*, pg. 1843
HAMM CONSTRUCTION LTD.; *Int'l*, pg. 3238
HAO BAI INTERNATIONAL (CAYMAN) LIMITED; *Int'l*, pg. 3267
HAREN CONSTRUCTION COMPANY INC; *U.S. Private*, pg. 1864
HDEC CONSTRUCTION CORPORATION—See Continental Holdings Corp.; *Int'l*, pg. 1784
HEITKAMP, INC.—See Michels Corporation; *U.S. Private*, pg. 2700
HSW INC.—See Balfour Beatty plc; *Int'l*, pg. 808
H. WILSON INDUSTRIES LTD; *Int'l*, pg. 3195
HYDROCHEM ENGINEERING (SHANGHAI) CO., LTD.—See Hyflux Ltd; *Int'l*, pg. 3548
HYDROCHEM ENGINEERING (S) PTE LTD—See Hyflux Ltd; *Int'l*, pg. 3548
HYOSUNG EBARA ENGINEERING CO., LTD.—See Hyosung Corporation; *Int'l*, pg. 3551
HYPOWER INC.; *U.S. Private*, pg. 2020
IHC GROUP, INC.; *U.S. Private*, pg. 2040
INGELEC S.A.—See Golden Minerals Company; *U.S. Public*, pg. 950
INLAND PIPE REHABILITATION LLC—See J.F. Lehman & Company, Inc.; *U.S. Private*, pg. 2163
INQUIP ASSOCIATES INCORPORATED—See Forgen, LLC; *U.S. Private*, pg. 1568
INQUIP ASSOCIATES—See Forgen, LLC; *U.S. Private*, pg. 1568
INSITUFORM RIOOLRENOVATIETECHNIEKEN B.V.—See New Mountain Capital, LLC; *U.S. Private*, pg. 2899
INSITUFORM—See New Mountain Capital, LLC; *U.S. Private*, pg. 2900
INSTITUTE ROSTOVSKIY VODOKANALPROEKT JSC—See HMS Hydraulic Machines & Systems Group plc; *Int'l*, pg. 3432
INTERWEST CONSTRUCTION, INC.; *U.S. Private*, pg. 2128
IQGEO AMERICA INC.—See KKR & Co. Inc.; *U.S. Public*, pg. 1253
IQGEO GERMANY GMBH—See KKR & Co. Inc.; *U.S. Public*, pg. 1253
IQGEO JAPAN KK—See KKR & Co. Inc.; *U.S. Public*, pg. 1253
IQGEO UK LIMITED—See KKR & Co. Inc.; *U.S. Public*, pg. 1253

JAFFER WELL DRILLING—See A.C. Schultes, Inc.; *U.S. Private*, pg. 24
J.B. COXWELL CONTRACTING, INC.; *U.S. Private*, pg. 2158
JOHN D STEPHENS INC.; *U.S. Private*, pg. 2221
JOHN P. PICONE INC.—See ACS, Actividades de Construccion y Servicios, S.A.; *Int'l*, pg. 111
JOHN W. DANFORTH CO.; *U.S. Private*, pg. 2225
JOSEPH J. HENDERSON & SON, INC.; *U.S. Private*, pg. 2236
JUDDS BROTHERS CONSTRUCTION COMPANY; *U.S. Private*, pg. 2242
KANA PIPELINE, INC.; *U.S. Private*, pg. 2259
KASTOR S.A.—See ELLAKTOR S.A.; *Int'l*, pg. 2364
KEYSTONE CLEARWATER SOLUTIONS, LLC; *U.S. Private*, pg. 2295
KRAFTWERK SCHKOPAU GMBH—See E.ON SE; *Int'l*, pg. 2253
LANDWEHR WASSERTECHNIK GMBH—See E.ON SE; *Int'l*, pg. 2258
LANZO CONSTRUCTION COMPANY FLORIDA INC.—See Lanzo Construction Company Inc.; *U.S. Private*, pg. 2391
LANZO CONSTRUCTION COMPANY INC.; *U.S. Private*, pg. 2391
LAYNE DRILLING ZAMBIA—See Granite Construction Incorporated; *U.S. Public*, pg. 958
LAYNE ENERGY, INC.—See Granite Construction Incorporated; *U.S. Public*, pg. 958
LAYNE HEAVY CIVIL, INC.—See Reynolds Construction, LLC; *U.S. Private*, pg. 3418
LAYNE SOUTHWEST, INC.—See Reynolds Construction, LLC; *U.S. Private*, pg. 3418
LAYNE TEXAS, INCORPORATED—See Granite Construction Incorporated; *U.S. Public*, pg. 958
LAYNE-WESTERN CO., INC.—See Granite Construction Incorporated; *U.S. Public*, pg. 958
L. D'AGOSTINI & SONS INC.; *U.S. Private*, pg. 2364
LEMNA TECHNOLOGIES, INC.—See The Lemna Corporation; *U.S. Private*, pg. 4069
LEO CONSTRUCTION COMPANY; *U.S. Private*, pg. 2422
LINCOLN CONTRACTING & EQUIPMENT COMPANY, INC.—See Riggs Industries, Inc.; *U.S. Private*, pg. 3435
LLANO UTILITY SERVICES INC.; *U.S. Private*, pg. 2475
L.M. McLAMB & SON CONSTRUCTION CO., INC.; *U.S. Private*, pg. 2366
LONGO-DE PUERTO RICO INC.; *U.S. Private*, pg. 2492
LOWER NECHES VALLEY AUTHORITY; *U.S. Private*, pg. 2506
LOY CLARK PIPELINE CO. INC.; *U.S. Private*, pg. 2506
LOY CLARK PIPELINE CO.—See MDU Resources Group, Inc.; *U.S. Public*, pg. 1410
LYLES DIVERSIFIED INC.; *U.S. Private*, pg. 2520
M.A. BONGIOVANNI INC.; *U.S. Private*, pg. 2527
MABUS BROTHERS CONSTRUCTION COMPANY INC.; *U.S. Private*, pg. 2531
MAC CONSTRUCTION & EXCAVATING, INC.; *U.S. Private*, pg. 2531
MAINLINING SERVICE INC.; *U.S. Private*, pg. 2553
MAN-CON INCORPORATED; *U.S. Private*, pg. 2559
MAX FOOTE CONSTRUCTION COMPANY, INC.; *U.S. Private*, pg. 2617
MCANINCH CORPORATION; *U.S. Private*, pg. 2625
MEADORS CONSTRUCTION CO., INC.—See Reynolds Construction, LLC; *U.S. Private*, pg. 3418
MICHELS CORPORATION; *U.S. Private*, pg. 2700
MIDAS COMPANIES; *U.S. Private*, pg. 2710
MING HING WATERWORKS ENGINEERING (PRC) LIMITED—See China Water Affairs Group Ltd; *Int'l*, pg. 1563
MINGUS CONSTRUCTORS INCORPORATED; *U.S. Private*, pg. 2742
MIRASSOL S/A SANEAMENTO DE MIRASSOL—See Igua Saneamento SA; *Int'l*, pg. 3603
MITCHELL & STARK CONSTRUCTION CO. INC.; *U.S. Private*, pg. 2750
MMC INC.—See New-Com Inc.; *U.S. Private*, pg. 2913
MOBLEY CONTRACTORS INC.; *U.S. Private*, pg. 2758
MODERN WATER INC.—See Deepverge PLC; *Int'l*, pg. 2003
MODERN WATER MONITORING LIMITED—See Deepverge PLC; *Int'l*, pg. 2003
MODERN WATER PLC—See Deepverge PLC; *Int'l*, pg. 2003
MODERN WATER TECHNOLOGY (SHANGHAI) CO., LTD.—See Deepverge PLC; *Int'l*, pg. 2003
MORENO TRENCHING, LTD.; *U.S. Private*, pg. 2782
MURPHY BROTHERS INC.; *U.S. Private*, pg. 2815
NALCO CHEMICALS INDIA LIMITED—See Ecolab Inc.; *U.S. Public*, pg. 715
NALCO INDUSTRIAL SERVICES (THAILAND) CO. LTD.—See Ecolab Inc.; *U.S. Public*, pg. 716
NESS PLUS TRADING SDN. BHD.—See Darco Water Technologies Limited; *Int'l*, pg. 1972
NICHIWA SOUGOU SETSUBI CO., LTD.—See Hitachi, Ltd.; *Int'l*, pg. 3423
NIELS FUGAL SONS COMPANY, LLC—See Dycom Industries, Inc.; *U.S. Public*, pg. 698
NIPPON NO-DIG TECHNOLOGY CO., LTD.—See HIROSE

HOLDINGS & CO.,LTD.; *Int'l*, pg. 3405
NORTH BERGEN MUNICIPAL UTILITY AUTHORITY; *U.S. Private*, pg. 2942
NORTHEAST REMSCO CONSTRUCTION, INC.; *U.S. Private*, pg. 2951
NORTHWEST CASCADE INC.; *U.S. Private*, pg. 2959
NOVA GROUP, INC.—See Quanta Services, Inc.; *U.S. Public*, pg. 1752
NOVO ENVIROTECH (TIANJIN) CO. LTD—See CITIC Group Corporation; *Int'l*, pg. 1620
NOWAK CONSTRUCTION CO. INC.; *U.S. Private*, pg. 2968
O'BRIEN SOUTHERN TRENCHING, INC.; *U.S. Private*, pg. 2977
OLD DOMINION UTILITY SERVICES, INC.—See American States Water Company; *U.S. Public*, pg. 110
OSCAR RENDA CONTRACTING INC.; *U.S. Private*, pg. 3046
PALMETTO STATE UTILITY SERVICES, INC.—See American States Water Company; *U.S. Public*, pg. 110
PARKER DRILLING ALASKA SERVICES, LTD—See Parker Wellbore Company; *U.S. Public*, pg. 1650
PASSAVANT-ROEDIGER GMBH—See Drake & Scull International PJSC; *Int'l*, pg. 2200
PDC DRILLING PTY. LTD.—See Dynamic Group Holdings Limited; *Int'l*, pg. 2240
PEERLESS MIDWEST INC.; *U.S. Private*, pg. 3128
PEMCO, INC.; *U.S. Private*, pg. 3132
PF MOON AND COMPANY INC.; *U.S. Private*, pg. 3164
P. GIOIOSO & SONS, INC.; *U.S. Private*, pg. 3060
PIPELINE INDUSTRIES, INC.—See CIVC Partners LLC; *U.S. Private*, pg. 908
PIPING & EQUIPMENT CO., INC.; *U.S. Private*, pg. 3190
PKF-MARK III, INC.; *U.S. Private*, pg. 3194
PLANNED & ENGINEERED CONSTRUCTION, INC.—See Vortex Company, LLC; *U.S. Private*, pg. 4413
PM CONSTRUCTION—See J.F. Lehman & Company, Inc.; *U.S. Private*, pg. 2163
PORTLAND UTILITIES CONSTRUCTION COMPANY, LLC—See New Mountain Capital, LLC; *U.S. Private*, pg. 2900
PRELOAD CONCRETE STRUCTURES; *U.S. Private*, pg. 3249
PREMIER RESTORATION HAWAII—See Koa Capital Partners LLC; *U.S. Private*, pg. 2325
PROGRESSIVE CONTRACTING INCORPORATED; *U.S. Private*, pg. 3278
PRO-VAC, LLC—See Gallant Capital Partners, LLC; *U.S. Private*, pg. 1639
QHY GROUP; *U.S. Public*, pg. 1742
RANSOM PUMP & SUPPLY INC.—See Bain Capital, LP; *U.S. Private*, pg. 432
REPIPE, INC.—See J.F. Lehman & Company, Inc.; *U.S. Private*, pg. 2163
R.H. WHITE CONSTRUCTION CO.—See R.H. White Companies Inc.; *U.S. Private*, pg. 3336
RICHARDSON-WAYLAND ELECTRIC COMPANY LLC—See Cadent Energy Partners, LLC; *U.S. Private*, pg. 713
RIPA & ASSOCIATES, INC.; *U.S. Private*, pg. 3439
R.J. CARROLL COMPANY INC.; *U.S. Private*, pg. 3337
R.J. GRONDIN & SONS; *U.S. Private*, pg. 3337
ROCKDALE PIPELINE INC.; *U.S. Private*, pg. 3465
ROCKFORD CORPORATION; *U.S. Private*, pg. 3466
ROCKWALL PROPERTY CORPORATION—See Columbia Ventures Corporation; *U.S. Private*, pg. 978
ROYCE TECHNOLOGIES—See Xylem Inc.; *U.S. Public*, pg. 2395
R.S. YOUNG EXCAVATING, INC.; *U.S. Private*, pg. 3339
RUBY COLLINS COMPANY INC.; *U.S. Private*, pg. 3500
SALSNES FILTER AS—See Danaher Corporation; *U.S. Public*, pg. 631
SCHACHTBAU NORDHAUSEN GMBH - ENVIRONMENTAL TECHNOLOGY DIVISION—See BAUER Aktiengesellschaft; *Int'l*, pg. 894
SCHOON CONSTRUCTION INC.; *U.S. Private*, pg. 3568
SEASIDE UTILITIES INC.; *U.S. Private*, pg. 3591
SHOOK NATIONAL CORPORATION; *U.S. Private*, pg. 3640
SIGNAL POINT SYSTEMS INC.—See BAI Communications Pty Ltd; *Int'l*, pg. 801
SJB SERVICES, INC.—See Atlantic Testing Laboratories, Ltd.; *U.S. Private*, pg. 374
S.J. LOUIS CONSTRUCTION INC.; *U.S. Private*, pg. 3517
S&N INC.; *U.S. Private*, pg. 3513
SOCAMEX, S.A.—See ACS, Actividades de Construccion y Servicios, S.A.; *Int'l*, pg. 116
SOUTHEAST UTILITIES OF GEORGIA, LLC—See Crestview Partners, L.P.; *U.S. Private*, pg. 1098
SOUTHWEST CONTRACTORS, INC.; *U.S. Private*, pg. 3738
SOUTHWEST TRANSPORT, CO.—See U.S. Venture, Inc.; *U.S. Private*, pg. 4272
SPECTRASERV INC.; *U.S. Private*, pg. 3751
SPINIELLO COMPANIES; *U.S. Private*, pg. 3757
STAAB CONSTRUCTION CORPORATION; *U.S. Private*, pg. 3774
STATE UTILITY CONTRACTORS INC.; *U.S. Private*, pg. 3793

237110 — WATER AND SEWER LIN...

STENSTROM EXCAVATION & BLACKTOP GROUP—See Stenstrom Companies Ltd.; *U.S. Private*, pg. 3801
STERLING CONSTRUCTION COMPANY; *U.S. Private*, pg. 3805
STILLWELL ENTERPRISES, INC.; *U.S. Private*, pg. 3812
SWALLOW CONSTRUCTION CORPORATION; *U.S. Private*, pg. 3889
SWANBERG CONSTRUCTION, INC., *U.S. Private*, pg. 3889
TAB CONTRACTORS INC.—See New-Com Inc.; *U.S. Private*, pg. 2913
TAY NINH WATER SUPPLY SEWERAGE JOINT STOCK COMPANY—See DongNai Plastic JSC; *Int'l*, pg. 2169
T & C CONTRACTING INC.; *U.S. Private*, pg. 3908
TECNICAS DE DESALINIZACION DE AGUAS, S.A.—See ACS, Actividades de Construccion y Servicios, S.A.; *Int'l*, pg. 116
TEE PEE CONTRACTORS INC.; *U.S. Private*, pg. 3957
TESTAMERICA DRILLING CORP.—See H.I.G. Capital, LLC; *U.S. Private*, pg. 1831
TIANJIN DAGANG NEWSPRING CO., LTD.—See Hyflux Ltd; *Int'l*, pg. 3548
TLC DIVERSIFIED INC.; *U.S. Private*, pg. 4178
TRI DAL LTD.; *U.S. Private*, pg. 4220
UKDN WATERFLOW LIMITED—See Horizon Capital LLP; *Int'l*, pg. 3479
ULLIMAN SCHUTTE CONSTRUCTION LLC; *U.S. Private*, pg. 4276
UNDERGROUND CONSTRUCTION CO., INC.—See Quanta Services, Inc.; *U.S. Public*, pg. 1753
USA TANK SALES & ERECTION CO., INC.—See Cameron Holdings Corporation; *U.S. Private*, pg. 729
U.S. PIPELINE, INC.—See Dearborn Resources, Inc.; *U.S. Private*, pg. 1185
UTILIQUEST, LLC—See Dycom Industries, Inc.; *U.S. Public*, pg. 699
UTILITY CONTRACTORS INC.; *U.S. Private*, pg. 4326
UTILITY LINE SERVICES INC.; *U.S. Private*, pg. 4326
VALARD CONSTRUCTION AUSTRALIA PTY. LTD.—See Quanta Services, Inc.; *U.S. Public*, pg. 1753
VALARD GEOMATICS BC, LTD.—See Quanta Services, Inc.; *U.S. Public*, pg. 1753
VALORGA INTERNATIONAL, S.A.S.—See ACS, Actividades de Construccion y Servicios, S.A.; *Int'l*, pg. 117
VALVERDE CONSTRUCTION INC.; *U.S. Private*, pg. 4338
VIDEO PIPE SERVICES INC.—See Carylon Corporation; *U.S. Private*, pg. 777
VIETNAM DARCO ENVIRONMENT COMPANY LIMITED—See Darco Water Technologies Limited; *Int'l*, pg. 1972
VORTEX COMPANY, LLC; *U.S. Private*, pg. 4413
WATER RESOURCES INTERNATIONAL, INC.—See Barnwell Industries, Inc.; *U.S. Public*, pg. 278
WATKINS CONSTRUCTION CO., INC.; *U.S. Private*, pg. 4455
WAVE DISPERSION TECHNOLOGIES, INC.; *U.S. Private*, pg. 4458
WAVIN FRANCE S.A.S.—See Bharti Enterprises Limited; *Int'l*, pg. 1012
W.B. HOPKE CO.; *U.S. Private*, pg. 4419
WESATECH—See BluMetric Environmental Inc.; *Int'l*, pg. 1075
WESTERN REGIONAL OFF-TRACK BETTING CORPORATION; *U.S. Private*, pg. 4496
WESTERN SUMMIT CONSTRUCTORS, INC.—See Peter Kiewit Sons', Inc.; *U.S. Private*, pg. 3158
WEST VALLEY CONSTRUCTION COMPANY INC.; *U.S. Private*, pg. 4487
WEST VIRGINIA PIPELINE, INC.—See Energy Services of America Corporation; *U.S. Public*, pg. 762
WHARTON-SMITH, INC.; *U.S. Private*, pg. 4504
WHC, INC.; *U.S. Private*, pg. 4504
WILLIAM A. HAZEL INC.; *U.S. Private*, pg. 4522
WILLIAM J. SCHULTZ INC.; *U.S. Private*, pg. 4523
WILLOW PUMPS LIMITED—See Franchise Brands plc; *Int'l*, pg. 2760
W.L. HAILEY & COMPANY, INC.—See Reynolds Construction, LLC; *U.S. Private*, pg. 3418
W.M. LYLES CO. INC.—See Lyles Diversified Inc.; *U.S. Private*, pg. 2520
W & O CONSTRUCTION CO., INC.; *U.S. Private*, pg. 4417
WOODLAWN CONSTRUCTION COMPANY; *U.S. Private*, pg. 4559
WOODRUFF & SONS INC.; *U.S. Private*, pg. 4560
W. R. GRACE (MALAYSIA) SDN. BHD.—See Standard Industries Holdings Inc.; *U.S. Private*, pg. 3780
W. ROGERS COMPANY; *U.S. Private*, pg. 4418
WSI INTERNATIONAL, LLC; *U.S. Private*, pg. 4574
WUHAN KAIDI WATER SERVICES CO., LTD.—See Darco Water Technologies Limited; *Int'l*, pg. 1972
XYLEM WATER SOLUTIONS HERFORD GMBH—See Xylem Inc.; *U.S. Public*, pg. 2397
ZIM INDUSTRIES INC.; *U.S. Private*, pg. 4605

237120 — OIL AND GAS PIPELINE AND RELATED STRUCTURES CONSTRUCTION

2H OFFSHORE ENGINEERING LTD.—See Buckthorn Partners LLP; *Int'l*, pg. 1210
2H OFFSHORE ENGINEERING LTD.—See OEP Capital Advisors, L.P.; *U.S. Private*, pg. 2997
ABDULLA FOUAD CORPORATION LTD.—See Abdulla Fouad Holding Co.; *Int'l*, pg. 58
ADANI GLOBAL FZE—See Adani Enterprises Limited; *Int'l*, pg. 125
ADVANCED ENERGY PROTECTION—See Irex Corporation; *U.S. Private*, pg. 2137
AECON UTILITIES—See Aecon Group Inc.; *Int'l*, pg. 172
AERISON GROUP LIMITED; *Int'l*, pg. 180
AHTNA CONSTRUCTION & PRIMARY PRODUCTS CORPORATION—See Ahtna Incorporated; *U.S. Private*, pg. 131
AIRCRAFT KLIMA-WARME- KALTE -ROHRLEITUNGSBAU GMBH—See E.ON SE; *Int'l*, pg. 2251
ALSUWAIKET TRADING & CONTRACTING CO. - CONSTRUCTION DIVISION—See AlSuwaiket Trading & Contracting Co.; *Int'l*, pg. 383
ALSUWAIKET TRADING & CONTRACTING CO. - TRADING DIVISION—See AlSuwaiket Trading & Contracting Co.; *Int'l*, pg. 383
ANHUI PROVINCE NATURAL GAS DEVELOPMENT CO., LTD.—See Henderson Land Development Co. Ltd.; *Int'l*, pg. 3344
ARABIAN PIPELINE & SERVICES CO. LTD.—See Al-Osais International Holding Company; *Int'l*, pg. 287
ARB STRUCTURES—See Primoris Services Corporation; *U.S. Public*, pg. 1718
ARNETT & BURGESS ENERGY SERVICES LP—See Quanta Services, Inc.; *U.S. Public*, pg. 1750
ASRC ENERGY SERVICES POWER & COMMUNICATIONS, LLC—See Arctic Slope Regional Corporation; *U.S. Private*, pg. 316
ASRC ENERGY SERVICES—See Arctic Slope Regional Corporation; *U.S. Private*, pg. 316
ASSOCIATED PIPE LINE CONTRACTORS, INC.; *U.S. Private*, pg. 356
AUSENCO PSI LLC—See RCF Management LLC; *U.S. Private*, pg. 3362
AVANCE GAS AS—See Avance Gas Holding Ltd.; *Int'l*, pg. 734
BANISTER PIPELINES CONSTRUCTORS CORP.—See Quanta Services, Inc.; *U.S. Public*, pg. 1750
BANQUE ENI SA—See Eni S.p.A.; *Int'l*, pg. 2436
BASIC ENERGY SERVICES INC.; *U.S. Public*, pg. 279
BASIC ENERGY SERVICES, L.P.—See Basic Energy Services Inc.; *U.S. Public*, pg. 279
BENG KUANG MARINE (B&Y) PTE. LTD.—See Beng Kuang Marine Limited; *Int'l*, pg. 973
BERRY CONTRACTING L.P.; *U.S. Private*, pg. 538
B&H MAINTENANCE & CONSTRUCTION INC.; *U.S. Private*, pg. 418
BIG COUNTRY ENERGY SERVICES LLC—See MasTec, Inc.; *U.S. Public*, pg. 1393
BILFINGER LIFE SCIENCE GMBH—See Bilfinger SE; *Int'l*, pg. 1026
BILFINGER ROB N.V.—See Bilfinger SE; *Int'l*, pg. 1027
BINHAI INVESTMENT COMPANY LIMITED; *Int'l*, pg. 1034
BIOENERGIE AHLEN GMBH & CO. KG—See Biogas Nord AG; *Int'l*, pg. 1038
BIOGAS NORD ANLAGENBAU GMBH—See Biogas Nord AG; *Int'l*, pg. 1038
BIOGAS NORD POLSKA SP.Z O.O.—See Biogas Nord AG; *Int'l*, pg. 1038
BIOGAS NORD UK LTD.—See Biogas Nord AG; *Int'l*, pg. 1038
BIO.S BIOGAS VERWALTUNGS GMBH—See Biogas Nord AG; *Int'l*, pg. 1038
BIS ROHRBAU GRENZACH GMBH—See Bilfinger SE; *Int'l*, pg. 1025
BIS ROHRLEITUNGSBAU GMBH—See Bilfinger SE; *Int'l*, pg. 1025
BLUE RACER MIDSTREAM, LLC—See The Williams Companies, Inc.; *U.S. Public*, pg. 2143
B&N CLEARING AND ENVIRONMENTAL, LLC—See Quanta Services, Inc.; *U.S. Public*, pg. 1750
BOOTS SMITH OILFIELD SERVICES, LLC; *U.S. Private*, pg. 617
BRINDERSON L.P.—See New Mountain Capital, LLC; *U.S. Private*, pg. 2899
BRITISH PIPELINE AGENCY LTD.—See BP plc; *Int'l*, pg. 1129
BW ENERGY LIMITED; *Int'l*, pg. 1231
CAJUN INDUSTRIES, L.L.C.; *U.S. Private*, pg. 714
CANYON PIPELINE CONSTRUCTION INC.—See Southwest Gas Holdings, Inc.; *U.S. Public*, pg. 1913
CATALYST CHANGERS INC.—See Quanta Services, Inc.; *U.S. Public*, pg. 1750
CB&I LONDON—See McDermott International, Inc.; *U.S. Public*, pg. 1405
CB&I PADDINGTON LIMITED—See McDermott International, Inc.; *U.S. Public*, pg. 1405
CERMAK A HRACHOVEC A.S.; *Int'l*, pg. 1422
CHALLAND PIPELINE LTD; *Int'l*, pg. 1438
CHARGE SERVICES, LLC—See Charge Enterprises, Inc.; *U.S. Public*, pg. 479

CHASE PROTECTIVE COATINGS LIMITED—See KKR & Co. Inc.; *U.S. Public*, pg. 1242
CHENIERE MARKETING, LTD.—See Cheniere Energy, Inc.; *U.S. Public*, pg. 485
CLIMASOL S.A.—See Bharti Enterprises Limited; *Int'l*, pg. 1012
CONAM CONSTRUCTION; *U.S. Private*, pg. 1008
CONCENTRIC PIPE & TOOL, INC.—See Superior Energy Services, Inc.; *U.S. Private*, pg. 3877
CONDMAG S.A.; *Int'l*, pg. 1766
CONSTITUTION PIPELINE COMPANY, LLC—See The Williams Companies, Inc.; *U.S. Public*, pg. 2143
CORRPRO CANADA INC.—See New Mountain Capital, LLC; *U.S. Public*, pg. 2900
CORRPRO COMPANIES EUROPE LTD.—See New Mountain Capital, LLC; *U.S. Private*, pg. 2900
CORRPRO COMPANIES, INC.—See New Mountain Capital, LLC; *U.S. Private*, pg. 2900
COSTAIN ABU DHABI COMPANY—See Costain Group PLC; *Int'l*, pg. 1814
COSTAIN OIL, GAS & PROCESS LIMITED PIPELINE & OFFSHORE DIVISION—See Costain Group PLC; *Int'l*, pg. 1815
CRAIN BROTHERS INC.; *U.S. Private*, pg. 1083
CRC-EVANS PIH SERVIOS DE TUBULAO DO BRASIL LTDA—See Stanley Black & Decker, Inc.; *U.S. Public*, pg. 1932
CULBERSON CONSTRUCTION, LLC—See Independence Capital Partners, LLC; *U.S. Private*, pg. 2057
DALRYMPLE BAY INFRASTRUCTURE LIMITED; *Int'l*, pg. 1955
DAVID ENERGY SYSTEMS, INC.; *U.S. Private*, pg. 1170
DBNGP (WA) TRANSMISSION PTY LIMITED—See CK Hutchison Holdings Limited; *Int'l*, pg. 1636
DEVON ARL CORPORATION—See Canadian Natural Resources Ltd.; *Int'l*, pg. 1284
DISTRIBUTION CONSTRUCTION, LLC—See Clayton, Dubilier & Rice, LLC; *U.S. Private*, pg. 919
DNR PRESSURE WELDING LTD.—See Quanta Services, Inc.; *U.S. Public*, pg. 1751
DOOSAN ENERBILITY—See Doosan Corporation; *Int'l*, pg. 2173
DRIVER PIPELINE COMPANY INC.; *U.S. Private*, pg. 1278
DYNA-MAC ENGINEERING SERVICES PTE LTD—See Hanwha Group; *Int'l*, pg. 3264
DYNA-MAC ENGINEERING SERVICES PTE LTD—See Hanwha Ocean Co., Ltd.; *Int'l*, pg. 3266
EAGLE INFRASTRUCTURE SERVICES, INC.; *U.S. Private*, pg. 1309
EASTERN OIL WELL SERVICE COMPANY—See PrimeEnergy Resources Corporation; *U.S. Public*, pg. 1717
ED WALTON CONSTRUCTION CO.; *U.S. Private*, pg. 1332
ENERGY 360 PTY. LTD.—See AGL Energy Limited; *Int'l*, pg. 211
ENERGY TRANSFER FUEL, LP—See Energy Transfer LP; *U.S. Public*, pg. 763
ENERGY TRANSFER TECHNOLOGIES, LTD.—See Energy Transfer LP; *U.S. Public*, pg. 763
ENERPIPE LTD.; *U.S. Private*, pg. 1396
ENSCOPE PTY LTD—See Quanta Services, Inc.; *U.S. Public*, pg. 1751
ENTERPRISE FIELD SERVICES, LLC—See Enterprise Products Partners L.P.; *U.S. Public*, pg. 778
ENTERPRISE GROUP, INC.; *Int'l*, pg. 2451
ENVITEC BIOGAS UK LTD.—See EnviTec Biogas AG; *Int'l*, pg. 2455
EOG RESOURCES TRINIDAD LIMITED—See EOG Resources, Inc.; *U.S. Public*, pg. 782
ESORFRANKI PIPELINES (PTY) LIMITED—See Esor Limited; *Int'l*, pg. 2504
ETC FAYETTEVILLE OPERATING COMPANY, LLC—See Energy Transfer LP; *U.S. Public*, pg. 763
ET FUEL PIPELINE, L.P.—See Energy Transfer LP; *U.S. Public*, pg. 763
FABCOR 2001, INC.—See MasTec, Inc.; *U.S. Public*, pg. 1393
FH CONSTRUCTION OF MARION, LLC—See CenterPoint Energy, Inc.; *U.S. Public*, pg. 472
FIBRWRAP CONSTRUCTION (M) SDN BHD—See New Mountain Capital, LLC; *U.S. Public*, pg. 2899
FIBRWRAP CONSTRUCTION PTE LTD—See New Mountain Capital, LLC; *U.S. Private*, pg. 2899
FIBRWRAP CONSTRUCTION SERVICES, INC.—See New Mountain Capital, LLC; *U.S. Private*, pg. 2899
FIBRWRAP CONSTRUCTION SERVICES LTD.—See New Mountain Capital, LLC; *U.S. Private*, pg. 2899
FLINT ENERGY CONSTRUCTION SERVICES INC.; *U.S. Private*, pg. 1545
FLOWMOLE—See Avon Lippiatt Hobbs (Contracting) Limited; *Int'l*, pg. 749
FORAN ENERGY GROUP CO., LTD.; *Int'l*, pg. 2728
FOREMOST PIPELINE CONSTRUCTION—See Sunland Construction Inc.; *U.S. Private*, pg. 3868
FRONT RANGE PIPELINE, LLC—See CHS INC.; *U.S. Public*, pg. 492
FYFE ASIA PTE. LTD.—See New Mountain Capital, LLC; *U.S. Private*, pg. 2899

FYFE BORNEO SDN BHD—See New Mountain Capital, LLC; *U.S. Private*, pg. 2899
FYFE CO. LLC—See New Mountain Capital, LLC; *U.S. Private*, pg. 2899
FYFE (HONG KONG) LIMITED—See New Mountain Capital, LLC; *U.S. Private*, pg. 2899
FYFE JAPAN CO. LTD.—See New Mountain Capital, LLC; *U.S. Private*, pg. 2899
GAASIENERGIA AS—See Gasum Oy; *Int'l*, pg. 2888
GALVANIC APPLIED SCIENCES INC.; *U.S. Private*, pg. 2876
GASODUCTOS Y REDES GISCA, S.A.—See ACS, Actividades de Construccion y Servicios, S.A.; *Int'l*, pg. 112
GE GRID GMBH—See General Electric Company; *U.S. Public*, pg. 918
GENERAL, MECHANICAL & CIVIL CONTRACTORS LTD.; *Int'l*, pg. 2920
GENUSPLUS GROUP LTD.; *Int'l*, pg. 2931
GROUP FIVE OIL & GAS (PROPRIETARY) LIMITED—See Group Five Limited; *Int'l*, pg. 3089
GUANGXHOU GAS GROUP CO., LTD.—See Guangzhou Development Group Incorporated; *Int'l*, pg. 3164
GULF CONSOLIDATED CONTRACTORS CO. LTD.; *Int'l*, pg. 3180
GULF INTERSTATE ENGINEERING COMPANY—See Gulf International Corporation; *Int'l*, pg. 1816
GULF ISLAND FABRICATION, INC.; *U.S. Public*, pg. 975
HALLIBURTON GROUP CANADA INC.—See Halliburton Company; *U.S. Public*, pg. 980
HAMMERHEAD ENERGY INC.; *Int'l*, pg. 3238
HARDING HOLDINGS INC.; *U.S. Private*, pg. 1863
HEATEC VESLINK MARINE SERVICES CORP.—See Heatec JieTong Holdings Ltd; *Int'l*, pg. 3305
HELIUM ONE GLOBAL LTD.; *Int'l*, pg. 3331
HEXAGON-TATSUNO ENGINEERING SDN. BHD.—See Hexagon Holdings Berhad; *Int'l*, pg. 3370
HOCKWAY MIDDLE EAST FZE—See New Mountain Capital, LLC; *U.S. Private*, pg. 2899
HOLLOMAN CORPORATION; *U.S. Private*, pg. 1966
IMW COLOMBIA LTD.—See Clean Energy Fuels Corp.; *U.S. Public*, pg. 508
INLINER TECHNOLOGIES, LLC—See J.F. Lehman & Company, Inc.; *U.S. Private*, pg. 2163
INSITU ENVIROTECH (S.E. ASIA) PTE. LTD.—See New Mountain Capital, LLC; *U.S. Private*, pg. 2899
INSITUFORM ASIA LIMITED—See New Mountain Capital, LLC; *U.S. Private*, pg. 2899
INSITUFORM LININGS LIMITED—See New Mountain Capital, LLC; *U.S. Private*, pg. 2899
INSITUFORM TECHNOLOGIES IBERICA S.A.—See New Mountain Capital, LLC; *U.S. Private*, pg. 2899
INSITUFORM TECHNOLOGIES LIMITED—See New Mountain Capital, LLC; *U.S. Private*, pg. 2900
INSITUFORM TECHNOLOGIES LIMITED—See New Mountain Capital, LLC; *U.S. Private*, pg. 2900
INSITUFORM TECHNOLOGIES USA, INC.—See New Mountain Capital, LLC; *U.S. Private*, pg. 2900
INTEGRATED WATER SERVICES LTD. - PIPELINE SERVICES DIV—See Arjun Infrastructure Partners Limited; *Int'l*, pg. 568
INTERMOOR INC.—See Buckthorn Partners LLP; *Int'l*, pg. 1210
INTERMOOR INC.—See OEP Capital Advisors, L.P.; *U.S. Private*, pg. 2997
ISLANDER EAST PIPELINE COMPANY, L.L.C.—See Enbridge Inc.; *Int'l*, pg. 2397
ISLAND MECHANICAL CORPORATION—See Quanta Services, Inc.; *U.S. Public*, pg. 1751
IVY H. SMITH COMPANY, LLC—See Dycom Industries, Inc.; *U.S. Public*, pg. 698
JOMAX CONSTRUCTION COMPANY; *U.S. Private*, pg. 2231
KELLOGG BROWN & ROOT SERVICES, INC.—See KBR, Inc.; *U.S. Public*, pg. 1216
KIINTEISTO OY PIISPANPIHA 5—See EnviTec Biogas AG; *Int'l*, pg. 2456
KINDER MORGAN CO2 COMPANY, L.P.—See Kinder Morgan, Inc.; *U.S. Public*, pg. 1233
KINDER MORGAN PIPELINES (USA) INC.—See Kinder Morgan, Inc.; *U.S. Public*, pg. 1233
KRAFTANLAGEN MUNCHEN GMBH—See Bouygues S.A.; *Int'l*, pg. 1123
KREUZ HOLDINGS LIMITED—See Headland Capital Partners Limited; *Int'l*, pg. 3301
KREUZ SUBSEA PTE. LTD.—See Headland Capital Partners Limited; *Int'l*, pg. 3301
LATEX CONSTRUCTION COMPANY; *U.S. Private*, pg. 2396
LINESTAR SERVICES, INC.—See First Reserve Management, L.P.; *U.S. Public*, pg. 1526
LONE STAR NGL HATTIESBURG LLC—See Energy Transfer LP; *U.S. Public*, pg. 763
LONE STAR NGL REFINERY SERVICES LLC—See Energy Transfer LP; *U.S. Public*, pg. 763
L.T.M. INDUSTRIE SAS—See Bilfinger SE; *Int'l*, pg. 1028
MACE SAUDI ARABIA CO. LTD.—See Abdullah Abdul Mohsin Al-Khodari Sons Company; *Int'l*, pg. 59
MARTIN BOHSUNG GMBH—See Alpiq Holding AG; *Int'l*, pg. 372

MASTEC CANADA, INC.—See MasTec, Inc.; *U.S. Public*, pg. 1393
MATRIX APPLIED TECHNOLOGIES, LTD.—See Matrix Service Company; *U.S. Public*, pg. 1397
MATRIX APPLIED TECHNOLOGIES, PTY. LTD.—See Matrix Service Company; *U.S. Public*, pg. 1397
MCCONNELL DOWELL CONSTRUCTORS THAI LIMITED—See Aveng Limited; *Int'l*, pg. 738
MEARS INLINE INSPECTION SERVICES—See Quanta Services, Inc.; *U.S. Public*, pg. 1752
MILAM OIL CORPORATION; *U.S. Private*, pg. 2726
MINNESOTA LIMITED, LLC—See CenterPoint Energy, Inc.; *U.S. Public*, pg. 472
MINNESOTA PIPE LINE COMPANY, LLC—See Marathon Petroleum Corporation; *U.S. Public*, pg. 1364
MONTAUK HOLDINGS LIMITED; *U.S. Public*, pg. 1465
MURPHY BUILDING CORPORATION—See Murphy Oil Corporation; *U.S. Public*, pg. 1487
NACAP PTY LTD.—See Quanta Services, Inc.; *U.S. Public*, pg. 1752
NATURAL GAS SERVICES GROUP, INC.; *U.S. Public*, pg. 1499
NEWPORT NEWS INDUSTRIAL CORPORATION—See Huntington Ingalls Industries, Inc.; *U.S. Public*, pg. 1072
NG ADVANTAGE LLC—See Clean Energy Fuels Corp.; *U.S. Public*, pg. 508
NMDC ENERGY—See Abu Dhabi National Oil Company; *Int'l*, pg. 73
NOPETRO, LLC; *U.S. Private*, pg. 2935
NORTH DENTON PIPELINE, L.L.C.—See Kinder Morgan, Inc.; *U.S. Public*, pg. 1234
NORTHERN PIPELINE CONSTRUCTION CO.—See Southwest Gas Holdings, Inc.; *U.S. Public*, pg. 1913
NORTHSTAR ENERGY SERVICES, INC.—See Quanta Services, Inc.; *U.S. Public*, pg. 1752
NPL CONSTRUCTION CO.—See Southwest Gas Holdings, Inc.; *U.S. Public*, pg. 1913
NUSTAR TERMINALS MARINE SERVICES N.V.—See Sunoco LP; *U.S. Public*, pg. 1965
OASIS PIPE LINE COMPANY TEXAS L.P.—See Energy Transfer LP; *U.S. Public*, pg. 763
O.J. INDUSTRIAL MAINTENANCE—See Quanta Services, Inc.; *U.S. Public*, pg. 1752
O.J. PIPELINES CANADA LIMITED PARTNERSHIP—See Quanta Services, Inc.; *U.S. Public*, pg. 1752
THE OMAN CONSTRUCTION COMPANY LLC—See Primoris Services Corporation; *U.S. Public*, pg. 1719
OTIS EASTERN SERVICE, INC.—See Clayton, Dubilier & Rice, LLC; *U.S. Private*, pg. 919
PAN EUROPEAN TERMINALS LIMITED—See Belphar Ltd.; *Int'l*, pg. 968
PANHANDLE EASTERN PIPE LINE COMPANY, LP—See Energy Transfer LP; *U.S. Public*, pg. 763
PARKLAND PIPELINE CONTRACTORS LTD—See Tetra Tech, Inc.; *U.S. Public*, pg. 2023
PIPELINE TECHNIQUE LTD.—See Blue Water Energy LLP; *Int'l*, pg. 1070
PIPELINE TECHNOLOGIES PHILIPPINES CORP.—See Xylem Inc.; *U.S. Public*, pg. 2394
PIPERGY, INC.; *U.S. Private*, pg. 3190
PORTAL SERVICE CO.; *U.S. Private*, pg. 3231
PRECISION PIPELINE LLC—See MasTec, Inc.; *U.S. Public*, pg. 1393
PRECISION PIPELINE SOLUTIONS, LLC.; *U.S. Private*, pg. 3246
PRICE GREGORY INTERNATIONAL, INC.; *U.S. Private*, pg. 3258
PRICE GREGORY INTERNATIONAL, INC.—See Quanta Services, Inc.; *U.S. Public*, pg. 1752
PRIMORIS DISTRIBUTION SERVICES, INC.—See Primoris Services Corporation; *U.S. Public*, pg. 1719
PT BERGER BATAM—See Beng Kuang Marine Limited; *Int'l*, pg. 973
PUMPCO, INC.—See MasTec, Inc.; *U.S. Public*, pg. 1393
PUREHM INC.—See Xylem Inc.; *U.S. Public*, pg. 2394
PUREHM U.S. INC.—See Xylem Inc.; *U.S. Public*, pg. 2394
PURE (SHANGHAI) TECHNOLOGIES CO., LTD.—See Xylem Inc.; *U.S. Public*, pg. 2394
PURE TECHNOLOGIES ABU DHABI—See Xylem Inc.; *U.S. Public*, pg. 2394
PURE TECHNOLOGIES (AUSTRALIA) PTY. LTD.—See Xylem Inc.; *U.S. Public*, pg. 2394
PURE TECHNOLOGIES CANADA LTD.—See Xylem Inc.; *U.S. Public*, pg. 2394
PURE TECHNOLOGIES LTD.—See Xylem Inc.; *U.S. Public*, pg. 2394
PURE TECHNOLOGIES (NANJING) LIMITED—See Xylem Inc.; *U.S. Public*, pg. 2394
QPS ENGINEERING, LLC—See Quanta Services, Inc.; *U.S. Public*, pg. 1752
QPS ENGINEERING LTD.—See Quanta Services, Inc.; *U.S. Public*, pg. 1752
QUEST INSPAR, LLC—See Quest Integrated, LLC; *U.S. Private*, pg. 3325
RANGER ENERGY EQUIPMENT, LLC—See Ranger Energy Services, Inc.; *U.S. Public*, pg. 1762
RANGER ENERGY SERVICES, LLC—See Ranger Energy Services, Inc.; *U.S. Public*, pg. 1762

RAYMOND SAUDI ARABIA LIMITED—See A.H. Algosaibi & Bros.; *Int'l*, pg. 24
ROONEY ENGINEERING, INC.—See Tetra Tech, Inc.; *U.S. Public*, pg. 2023
SAN PATRICIO PIPELINE LLC—See Occidental Petroleum Corporation; *U.S. Public*, pg. 1562
SCHLUMBERGER LIMITED - HOUMA—See Schlumberger Limited; *U.S. Public*, pg. 1845
SCHLUMBERGER TECHNOLOGY CORP.—See Schlumberger Limited; *U.S. Public*, pg. 1845
SCHLUMBERGER TECHNOLOGY CORP.—See Schlumberger Limited; *U.S. Public*, pg. 1845
SCHLUMBERGER TECHNOLOGY CORP.—See Schlumberger Limited; *U.S. Public*, pg. 1846
SCHMACK BIOGAS S.R.L.—See Hitachi Zosen Corporation; *Int'l*, pg. 3411
SCIENTIFIC PRODUCTION SERVICES—See Applied Technologies Associates; *U.S. Private*, pg. 299
SCOGAT SA SOCIETE POUR LA CONSTRUCTION DU GAZODUC TRANST—See Eni S.p.A.; *Int'l*, pg. 2437
SELECTA INFRATECHNIEK B.V.—See Allianz SE; *Int'l*, pg. 355
SERVICIOS PETROTEC DE S.A. DE C.V.—See Superior Energy Services, Inc.; *U.S. Public*, pg. 3877
SNELSON COMPANIES INC. PIPELINE DIVISION—See Primoris Services Corporation; *U.S. Public*, pg. 1719
SONSUB LTD.—See Eni S.p.A.; *Int'l*, pg. 2438
SPECIAL FLEET SERVICE INC.; *U.S. Private*, pg. 3748
SPECIALIZED PIPE SERVICES, INC.—See Berkshire Hathaway Inc.; *U.S. Public*, pg. 315
SU DEVELOPMENT CO., LLC—See Energy Transfer LP; *U.S. Public*, pg. 763
SUDWESTDEUTSCHE ROHRLEITUNGSBAU GMBH—See ACS, Actividades de Construccion y Servicios, S.A.; *Int'l*, pg. 114
SUG ENERGY, LLC—See Energy Transfer LP; *U.S. Public*, pg. 763
SUNLAND CONSTRUCTION INC.; *U.S. Private*, pg. 3868
TAIAN AGS PIPELINE CONSTRUCTION CO., LTD.—See Halcyon Coast Investment (Canada) Ltd.; *Int'l*, pg. 3227
T. G. MERCER CONSULTING SERVICES, INC.—See Quanta Services, Inc.; *U.S. Public*, pg. 1753
T.K. STANLEY, INC.; *U.S. Private*, pg. 3912
TOMSKGAZSTROY PJSC—See HMS Hydraulic Machines & Systems Group plc; *Int'l*, pg. 3432
TRAIN OILFIELD SERVICES LTD.—See APi Group Corporation; *Int'l*, pg. 514
TRANSMONTAIGNE, INC.—See NGL Energy Partners LP; *U.S. Public*, pg. 1527
TRIO PETROLEUM CORP.; *U.S. Public*, pg. 2194
TUCKER CONSTRUCTION CO.—See First Reserve Management, L.P.; *U.S. Public*, pg. 1526
TUCKER MIDSTREAM, INC.—See First Reserve Management, L.P.; *U.S. Public*, pg. 1526
TURBINATE INTERNATIONAL, B.V.—See Team, Inc.; *U.S. Public*, pg. 1988
UNDERGROUND SOLUTIONS, INC.—See New Mountain Capital, LLC; *U.S. Private*, pg. 2900
UNITED PIPELINE SYSTEMS, INC.—See New Mountain Capital, LLC; *U.S. Private*, pg. 2900
UNITED SISTEMA DE TUBERIAS LTDA.—See New Mountain Capital, LLC; *U.S. Private*, pg. 2900
UNITED SPECIAL TECHNICAL SERVICES LLC—See New Mountain Capital, LLC; *U.S. Private*, pg. 2900
VELOSI PROMSERVICE LLC—See I Squared Capital Advisors (US) LLC; *U.S. Public*, pg. 2024
VINYLTECH CORPORATION—See Otter Tail Corporation; *U.S. Public*, pg. 1624
WALKER CRANE & RIGGING CORP.—See US Service Group, LLC; *U.S. Private*, pg. 4320
WEDGE GROUP INC.; *U.S. Private*, pg. 4468
WELDED CONSTRUCTION LP; *U.S. Private*, pg. 4474
WHITAKER CONSTRUCTION COMPANY; *U.S. Private*, pg. 4507
WZS MISI SETIA SDN BHD—See Citaglobal Berhad; *Int'l*, pg. 1619
ZHENHAI PETROCHEMICAL ENGINEERING CO., LTD.—See China Petrochemical Corporation; *Int'l*, pg. 1540

237130 — POWER AND COMMUNICATION LINE AND RELATED STRUCTURES CONSTRUCTION

50HERTZ OFFSHORE GMBH—See Elia Group SA; *Int'l*, pg. 2360
7C SOLARPARKEN BELGIUM B.V.—See 7C Solarparken AG; *Int'l*, pg. 15
A2Z POWERTECH LIMITED—See A2Z Infra Engineering Limited; *Int'l*, pg. 30
ADVANCED NUCLEAR FUELS GMBH—See Electricite de France S.A.; *Int'l*, pg. 2351
AE&E ENERGY & ENVIRONMENT CONSULTING SHANGHAI CO. LTD.—See A-TEC Industries AG; *Int'l*, pg. 21
AGATOS ENERGIA SRL—See Agatos S.p.A.; *Int'l*, pg. 200
AGO ENERGY (PTY) LTD.—See HCS Beteiligungsgesellschaft mbH; *Int'l*, pg. 3299

237130 — POWER AND COMMUNICA...

AIR2, LLC—See Primoris Services Corporation; *U.S. Public,* pg. 1718
ALASKA UNITED FIBER SYSTEM PARTNERSHIP—See Liberty Broadband Corporation; *U.S. Public,* pg. 1310
ALLIED POWER HOLDINGS, LLC—See Bernhard Capital Partners Management, LP; *U.S. Private,* pg. 536
ALPHAMAN E&C JOINT STOCK COMPANY—See Alphanam Joint Stock Company; *Int'l,* pg. 370
ALPIQ ANLAGENTECHNIK GMBH—See Alpiq Holding AG; *Int'l,* pg. 372
ALPIQ VERCELLI S.R.L.—See Alpiq Holding AG; *Int'l,* pg. 373
ALSTOM ASIA PACIFIC SDN. BHD.—See Alstom S.A.; *Int'l,* pg. 380
AMERESCOSOLUTIONS, INC.—See Ameresco, Inc.; *U.S. Public,* pg. 95
AMERICAN CIVIL CONSTRUCTORS WEST COAST LLC—See MasTec, Inc.; *U.S. Public,* pg. 1393
AMERICAN LIGHTING AND SIGNALIZATION, INC.—See Asplundh Tree Expert Co.; *U.S. Private,* pg. 353
AMERICOM TECHNOLOGY, INC.—See Crestone Services Group LLC; *U.S. Private,* pg. 1097
AMSC AUSTRIA GMBH—See American Superconductor Corporation; *U.S. Public,* pg. 110
AMSC INDIA PRIVATE LIMITED—See American Superconductor Corporation; *U.S. Public,* pg. 110
AMTEL RESOURCES SDN. BHD.—See Amtel Holdings Berhad; *Int'l,* pg. 442
ANDALAY SOLAR, INC.; *U.S. Private,* pg. 275
ANDERSON & HOWARD ELECTRIC INC.; *U.S. Private,* pg. 275
ANSCO & ASSOCIATES, LLC—See Dycom Industries, Inc.; *U.S. Public,* pg. 698
ANTERO MIDSTREAM PARTNERS LP—See Antero Midstream Corporation; *U.S. Public,* pg. 140
ARCADIS LOGOS LTDA.—See ARCADIS N.V.; *Int'l,* pg. 540
ARIZONA PUBLIC SERVICE COMPANY—See Pinnacle West Capital Corporation; *U.S. Public,* pg. 1692
ARTEMIS TRANSMISSORA DE ENERGIA, LTDA.—See ACS, Actividades de Construccion y Servicios, S.A.; *Int'l,* pg. 110
ARTSAKHHEK OJSC; *Int'l,* pg. 586
ATOMIC ENERGY OF CANADA LIMITED; *Int'l,* pg. 687
ATREX INC.; *U.S. Private,* pg. 382
AT&T—See Frontier Communications Parent, Inc.; *U.S. Public,* pg. 887
AUDAX RENOVABLES, S.A.; *Int'l,* pg. 700
AUGER SERVICES, INC.—See Primoris Services Corporation; *U.S. Public,* pg. 1718
BABCOCK & WILCOX VOLUND LIMITED—See Babcock & Wilcox Enterprises, Inc.; *U.S. Public,* pg. 262
BARAN TELECOM, INC.—See Baran Group Ltd.; *Int'l,* pg. 858
BAUMINERAL GMBH HERTEN—See E.ON SE; *Int'l,* pg. 2252
BEACON POWER, LLC—See Rockland Capital, LLC; *U.S. Private,* pg. 3467
BEI CONSTRUCTION, INC.; *U.S. Private,* pg. 516
BEIJING SHUZHI TECHNOLOGY CO., LTD.; *Int'l,* pg. 957
BGR ENERGY SYSTEMS LIMITED - CAPTIVE POWER DIVISION—See BGR Energy Systems Limited; *Int'l,* pg. 1008
BGR ENERGY SYSTEMS LIMITED - POWER PROJECTS DIVISION—See BGR Energy Systems Limited; *Int'l,* pg. 1009
BIGHAM CABLE CONSTRUCTION INC.; *U.S. Private,* pg. 555
BIGHAM CABLE CONSTRUCTION, INC.—See Dycom Industries, Inc.; *U.S. Public,* pg. 698
BILFINGER BERGER POWER HOLDINGS (PTY) LTD.—See Bilfinger SE; *Int'l,* pg. 1026
BLUE SKY TOWERS PTY LTD—See American Tower Corporation; *U.S. Public,* pg. 111
BOUYGUES E&S INTEC ITALIA S.P.A.—See Bouygues S.A.; *Int'l,* pg. 1123
BRAVIDA NORGE 4 AS—See Bravida Holding AB; *Int'l,* pg. 1142
BREMAR CONSTRUCTION LTD.—See Aecon Group Inc.; *Int'l,* pg. 172
BS LIMITED; *Int'l,* pg. 1201
C-2 UTILITY CONTRACTORS, LLC—See Dycom Industries, Inc.; *U.S. Public,* pg. 698
CAMDEN COUNTY ENERGY RECOVERY ASSOCIATES, L.P.—See EQT AB; *Int'l,* pg. 2473
CAPITAL ELECTRIC LINE BUILDERS, INC.—See MDU Resources Group, Inc.; *U.S. Public,* pg. 1410
CAVO BROADBAND COMMUNICATIONS, LLC—See Dycom Industries, Inc.; *U.S. Public,* pg. 698
CCI SYSTEMS INC.; *U.S. Private,* pg. 799
C & C POWER LINE, INC.—See The Goldfield Corporation; *U.S. Public,* pg. 2076
C-CUBE CORPORATION—See EXEO Group Inc.; *Int'l,* pg. 2583
C-D UTILITY CONSTRUCTION INC.; *U.S. Private,* pg. 704
CELLXION LLC—See The Jordan Company, L.P.; *U.S. Private,* pg. 4061
CENTERLINE SOLUTIONS LLC; *U.S. Private,* pg. 816

CENTRAL-ASIAN POWER ENERGY COMPANY JSC; *Int'l,* pg. 1410
CENTRICA ENERGY TRADING A/S—See Centrica plc; *Int'l,* pg. 1413
CG POWER SOLUTIONS USA INC.—See Avantha Group; *Int'l,* pg. 735
CHINA EVERBRIGHT GREENTECH LTD.—See China Everbright Group Limited; *Int'l,* pg. 1501
CHINA SOUTHERN POWER GRID CO., LTD.; *Int'l,* pg. 1553
CHIYODA CORPORATION (SHANGHAI)—See Chiyoda Corporation; *Int'l,* pg. 1574
CHIYODA (THAILAND) LIMITED—See Chiyoda Corporation; *Int'l,* pg. 1574
CKS MANAGEMENT INC.—See Microwave Transmission Systems, Inc.; *U.S. Private,* pg. 2704
CNTEE TRANSELECTRICA SA; *Int'l,* pg. 1678
COMLINK CONTRACTORS INC.; *U.S. Private,* pg. 982
COMLINK MIDWEST INC.—See Comlink Contractors Inc.; *U.S. Private,* pg. 982
COMMUNICATIONS CONSTRUCTION GROUP, LLC—See Dycom Industries, Inc.; *U.S. Public,* pg. 698
CONNECTED NATION, INC.; *U.S. Private,* pg. 1015
CORPORATE TECHNOLOGY SOLUTIONS LLC—See P.A.G. Capital Partners, LLC; *U.S. Private,* pg. 3060
COVANTA TULSA RENEWABLE ENERGY LLC—See EQT AB; *Int'l,* pg. 2474
CROWN CASTLE USA INC.—See Crown Castle Inc.; *U.S. Public,* pg. 596
CS WIND CORPORATION; *Int'l,* pg. 1861
CUTIX PLC.; *Int'l,* pg. 1881
C.W. WRIGHT CONSTRUCTION CO., INC.; *U.S. Private,* pg. 709
CYMIMASA BRASIL, LTDA.—See ACS, Actividades de Construccion y Servicios, S.A.; *Int'l,* pg. 111
DALEKOVOD TKS A.D.—See Dalekovod d.d.; *Int'l,* pg. 1951
DALKIA FRANCE S.C.A.—See Electricite de France S.A.; *Int'l,* pg. 2350
THE DANELLA COMPANIES INC.; *U.S. Private,* pg. 4018
DANELLA CONSTRUCTION CORPORATION OF FLORIDA INC.—See The Danella Companies Inc.; *U.S. Private,* pg. 4018
DEERFIELD CONSTRUCTION GROUP INC.; *U.S. Private,* pg. 1190
DENSO FACILITIES CORPORATION—See Denso Corporation; *Int'l,* pg. 2029
DIAMOND ENGINEERING COMPANY; *U.S. Private,* pg. 1223
DIXIE ELECTRIC LLC—See First Reserve Management, L.P.; *U.S. Private,* pg. 1525
DOOSAN BABCOCK ENERGY GERMANY GMBH—See Doosan Corporation; *Int'l,* pg. 2172
DOOSAN POWER SYSTEMS CO., LTD.—See Doosan Corporation; *Int'l,* pg. 2173
DOWNER EDI ENGINEERING TRANSMISSION PTY LTD—See Downer EDI Limited; *Int'l,* pg. 2185
DYNAGRID CONSTRUCTION GROUP, LLC—See Brown Brothers Harriman & Co.; *U.S. Private,* pg. 667
ECLIPSE FOUNDATION GROUP, INC.—See Orbital Infrastructure Group, Inc.; *U.S. Public,* pg. 1615
ECOSITE OY—See Elisa Corporation; *Int'l,* pg. 2361
ECOSUNTEK S.P.A.; *Int'l,* pg. 2300
ECO-WIND CONSTRUCTION S.A.—See CEZ, a.s.; *Int'l,* pg. 1427
ECV—See Eiffage S.A.; *Int'l,* pg. 2329
EDP RENEWABLES NORTH AMERICA, L.L.C.—See EDP - Energias de Portugal, S.A.; *Int'l,* pg. 2314
EKI POWER TRADING PRIVATE LIMITED—See EKI Energy Services Limited; *Int'l,* pg. 2338
ELECTRA LINK INC.; *U.S. Private,* pg. 1352
ELECTRIC CONDUIT CONSTRUCTION CO.; *U.S. Private,* pg. 1352
ELECTROPAR LTD.—See Preformed Line Products Company; *U.S. Public,* pg. 1714
ELEKTROCIEPŁOWNIA CHORZOW ELCHO SP. Z.O.O.—See CEZ, a.s.; *Int'l,* pg. 1426
ELMERA GROUP ASA; *Int'l,* pg. 2367
ELTEL INFRANET GMBH—See Eltel AB; *Int'l,* pg. 2370
ELTEL NETWORKS A/S—See Eltel AB; *Int'l,* pg. 2370
ELTEL NETWORKS AS—See Eltel AB; *Int'l,* pg. 2370
ELTEL NETWORKS INFRANET AB—See Eltel AB; *Int'l,* pg. 2370
ELTEL NETWORKS OY—See Eltel AB; *Int'l,* pg. 2371
ELTEL NETWORKS SIA—See Eltel AB; *Int'l,* pg. 2371
ELTEL NETWORKS TE AB—See Eltel AB; *Int'l,* pg. 2371
ELTEL NETWORKS TELECOM SP. Z O.O.—See Eltel AB; *Int'l,* pg. 2371
ENERGETIKAI ES TAVKOZLESI HALOZATEPITO ES SZERELO KFT.—See E.ON SE; *Int'l,* pg. 2253
ENERGOMONTAJ S.A. - ELECTRICAL, AUTOMATION & TELECOMMUNICATION INSTALLATIONS DIVISION—See Energomontaj S.A.; *Int'l,* pg. 2421
ENERGOSBYT PLUS JSC; *Int'l,* pg. 2422
ENERGY LAB S.P.A.; *Int'l,* pg. 2422
ENERTRONICA SANTERNO S.P.A.; *Int'l,* pg. 2425
ENFINITY CORPORATION—See Enfinity N.V.; *Int'l,* pg. 2425
ENFINITY N.V.; *Int'l,* pg. 2425

CORPORATE AFFILIATIONS

ENRA IOL SDN. BHD.—See ENRA Group Berhad; *Int'l,* pg. 2445
EOLUS NORTH AMERICA INC.—See Eolus Vind AB; *Int'l,* pg. 2457
E.ON FERNWAERME GMBH—See E.ON SE; *Int'l,* pg. 2253
EPURON GMBH—See Kawa Capital Management, Inc.; *U.S. Private,* pg. 2266
EPURON SPAIN SLU—See Kawa Capital Management, Inc.; *U.S. Private,* pg. 2266
ETS HOLDINGS CO., LTD.; *Int'l,* pg. 2524
EVERSENDAI CONSTRUCTION PVT. LTD.—See Eversendai Corporation Berhad; *Int'l,* pg. 2568
EVERSENDAI CONSTRUCTIONS (M) SDN BHD—See Eversendai Corporation Berhad; *Int'l,* pg. 2568
EVERSENDAI CONSTRUCTION (S) PTE. LTD.—See Eversendai Corporation Berhad; *Int'l,* pg. 2568
EVERSENDAI ENGINEERING FZE—See Eversendai Corporation Berhad; *Int'l,* pg. 2568
EVERSENDAI ENGINEERING LLC—See Eversendai Corporation Berhad; *Int'l,* pg. 2568
EVERSENDAI ENGINEERING QATAR WLL—See Eversendai Corporation Berhad; *Int'l,* pg. 2568
EVERSENDAI ENGINEERING SAUDI LLC—See Eversendai Corporation Berhad; *Int'l,* pg. 2568
EVERSENDAI OFFSHORE RMC FZE—See Eversendai Corporation Berhad; *Int'l,* pg. 2568
EVERSENDAI OFFSHORE SDN BHD—See Eversendai Corporation Berhad; *Int'l,* pg. 2568
EVERSENDAI S-CON ENGINEERING CO. LTD. - SANAMCHAIKHED FACTORY—See Eversendai Corporation Berhad; *Int'l,* pg. 2568
EVERSENDAI S-CON ENGINEERING CO. LTD.—See Eversendai Corporation Berhad; *Int'l,* pg. 2568
EWE DIREKT GMBH—See EWE Aktiengesellschaft; *Int'l,* pg. 2575
EWE NETZ GMBH—See EWE Aktiengesellschaft; *Int'l,* pg. 2575
EXTENET SYSTEMS, INC.—See Stonepeak Partners L.P.; *U.S. Private,* pg. 3829
FIBER TECHNOLOGIES SOLUTIONS, LLC—See Dycom Industries, Inc.; *U.S. Public,* pg. 698
FINETEX ENE, INC.; *Int'l,* pg. 2674
THE FISHEL COMPANY INC.; *U.S. Private,* pg. 4029
FLOWGROUP PLC; *Int'l,* pg. 2709
FOREST CONSTRUCTION COMPANY INC.—See Penn Line Corp.; *U.S. Private,* pg. 3134
FRAMATOME CANADA LTD.—See Electricite de France S.A.; *Int'l,* pg. 2351
FRAMATOME GMBH—See Electricite de France S.A.; *Int'l,* pg. 2351
FULLER COMMUNICATIONS INC.; *U.S. Private,* pg. 1621
GA AUSTRIA GMBH—See Alpiq Holding AG; *Int'l,* pg. 373
GA ENERGO TECHNIK S.R.O.—See Alpiq Holding AG; *Int'l,* pg. 373
GA-MAGYARORSZAG KFT.—See Alpiq Holding AG; *Int'l,* pg. 373
GEHRLICHER-IKHWEZI (PTY) LTD—See Gehrlicher Solar AG; *Int'l,* pg. 2912
GEHRLICHER SOLAR AG; *Int'l,* pg. 2912
GEHRLICHER SOLAR ESPANA S.L.—See Gehrlicher Solar AG; *Int'l,* pg. 2912
GEHRLICHER SOLAR FRANCE SAS—See Gehrlicher Solar AG; *Int'l,* pg. 2912
GEOTHERMAL RESOURCES LIMITED—See Havilah Resources Limited; *Int'l,* pg. 3287
GE POWER S.R.O—See General Electric Company; *U.S. Public,* pg. 917
GEUMHWA PSC CO., LTD.; *Int'l,* pg. 2954
GLOBAL MARINE SYSTEMS LIMITED—See J.F. Lehman & Company, Inc.; *U.S. Private,* pg. 2163
GLOBE COMMUNICATIONS, LLC—See Dycom Industries, Inc.; *U.S. Public,* pg. 698
GOFF COMMUNICATIONS INC.; *U.S. Private,* pg. 1726
GRADY CRAWFORD CONSTRUCTION CO.—See Grady Crawford Construction Co., Inc. of Baton Rouge; *U.S. Private,* pg. 1750
GREAT SOUTHWESTERN CONSTRUCTION, INC.—See MYR Group Inc.; *U.S. Public,* pg. 1489
GREENSPRING ENERGY LLC; *U.S. Private,* pg. 1780
GREENTECH ENERGY SYSTEMS POLSKA SP. Z O.O.—See Athena Investments A/S; *Int'l,* pg. 669
GRID SOLUTIONS ENERJI ENDUSTRISI A.S—See General Electric Company; *U.S. Public,* pg. 918
GROUP FIVE BUILDING (PROPRIETARY) LIMITED—See Group Five Limited; *Int'l,* pg. 3089
GRUNWERKE GMBH—See EnBW Energie Baden-Wurttemberg AG; *Int'l,* pg. 2399
GSW INTEGRATED SERVICES, LLC—See MYR Group Inc.; *U.S. Public,* pg. 1489
GUDENKAUF CORPORATION—See Crestview Partners, L.P.; *U.S. Private,* pg. 1098
GVK POWER AND INFRASTRUCTURE LIMITED; *Int'l,* pg. 3189
HANKOOK TECHNOLOGY INC.; *Int'l,* pg. 3253
HARGREAVES POWER SERVICES (HK) LIMITED—See Hargreaves Services plc; *Int'l,* pg. 3275
HARLAN ELECTRIC COMPANY—See MYR Group Inc.; *U.S. Public,* pg. 1489

N.A.I.C.S. INDEX

237130 — POWER AND COMMUNICA...

HAVERFIELD INTERNATIONAL INCORPORATED—See Quanta Services, Inc.; *U.S. Public*, pg. 1751

H.B. WHITE CANADA CORP.—See MasTec, Inc.; *U.S. Public*, pg. 1393

HENKELS & MCCOY, INC.—See MasTec, Inc.; *U.S. Public*, pg. 1393

HERHOF GMBH—See ELLAKTOR S.A.; *Int'l*, pg. 2365

HIGH COUNTRY LINE CONSTRUCTION, INC.—See MYR Group Inc.; *U.S. Public*, pg. 1489

HITACHI PLANT ENGINEERING & CONSTRUCTION (SUZHOU) CO., LTD.—See Hitachi, Ltd.; *Int'l*, pg. 3420

HOLSOTHERM GMBH; *Int'l*, pg. 3453

HOOPER CORPORATION; *U.S. Private*, pg. 1978

INDUS TOWERS LIMITED—See Bharti Enterprises Limited; *Int'l*, pg. 1013

INGENIEURBURO KIEFER & VOSS GMBH—See Alpiq Holding AG; *Int'l*, pg. 372

INITEC ENERGIA, S.A.—See ACS, Actividades de Construccion y Servicios, S.A.; *Int'l*, pg. 114

INTEGRATED TOWER SYSTEMS, INC.—See The Will-Burt Co., Inc.; *U.S. Private*, pg. 4136

INTERFACING COMPANY OF TEXAS, LLC—See I Squared Capital Advisors (US) LLC; *U.S. Private*, pg. 2025

ISBELL CONSTRUCTION CO. LTD; *U.S. Private*, pg. 2143

ISO NEW ENGLAND INC.; *U.S. Private*, pg. 2146

JAMES H. DREW CORPORATION—See Paychex, Inc.; *U.S. Public*, pg. 1655

JP DESIGN CO., LTD.—See Electric Power Development Co., Ltd.; *Int'l*, pg. 2349

JPEC CO., LTD.—See Electric Power Development Co., Ltd.; *Int'l*, pg. 2349

JUHL ENERGY, INC.; *U.S. Private*, pg. 2243

JUNIPER GROUP, INC.; *U.S. Private*, pg. 2244

KEYS ENERGY SERVICES; *U.S. Public*, pg. 2295

KNIGHT ENTERPRISES, INC.—See Guggenheim Partners, LLC; *U.S. Private*, pg. 1812

KOHLER CONSTRUCTION COMPANY INC.—See Dycom Industries, Inc.; *U.S. Public*, pg. 698

KRAFTANLAGEN POWER PLANTS GMBH—See Alpiq Holding AG; *Int'l*, pg. 372

KRAFTANLAGEN ROMANIA S.R.L.—See Alpiq Holding AG; *Int'l*, pg. 372

KRAFTSZER VALLALKOZASI KFT.—See Alpiq Holding AG; *Int'l*, pg. 373

KUWAIT NETWORK ELECTRONIC TECHNOLOGY COMPANY W.L.L—See Fouad Alghanim & Sons Group of Companies; *Int'l*, pg. 2753

LAGLASSE & OMHOVERE—See FAYAT SAS; *Int'l*, pg. 2625

LAMBERT'S CABLE SPLICING COMPANY, LLC—See Dycom Industries, Inc.; *U.S. Public*, pg. 698

LEE ELECTRICAL CONSTRUCTION, LLC—See Quanta Services, Inc.; *U.S. Public*, pg. 1751

THE L.E. MYERS CO.—See MYR Group Inc.; *U.S. Public*, pg. 1489

LEO TIDWELL EXCAVATING CORP; *U.S. Private*, pg. 2422

LIANDER N.V.—See Alliander N.V.; *Int'l*, pg. 341

LIBLA COMMUNICATIONS, INC.; *U.S. Private*, pg. 2447

LINX LLLP; *U.S. Private*, pg. 2463

LOWE-NORTH CONSTRUCTION INC.; *U.S. Private*, pg. 2505

MANAGED ENERGY SYSTEMS LLC; *U.S. Private*, pg. 2559

MASTEC, INC.; *U.S. Public*, pg. 1392

MASTEC NORTH AMERICA, INC.—See MasTec, Inc.; *U.S. Public*, pg. 1393

MAVERICK CONSTRUCTION CORPORATION; *U.S. Private*, pg. 2615

MAXGEN ENERGY SERVICES CORP.—See Willcrest Partners; *U.S. Private*, pg. 4521

MCLEAN CONSTRUCTION LTD.; *U.S. Private*, pg. 2641

MERCURY COMMUNICATIONS, INC.—See Warren Equity Partners, LLC; *U.S. Public*, pg. 4443

MTS QUANTA, LLC—See Quanta Services, Inc.; *U.S. Public*, pg. 1752

MYR TRANSMISSION SERVICES, INC.—See MYR Group Inc.; *U.S. Public*, pg. 1489

NABORS ENERGY TRANSITION CORP.; *U.S. Public*, pg. 1489

NATIONAL POWER CORPORATION—See Valley Ridge Investment Partners; *U.S. Private*, pg. 4335

NATIONAL POWERLINE LLC—See Southwest Gas Holdings, Inc.; *U.S. Public*, pg. 1913

NETEL AB—See IK Investment Partners Limited; *Int'l*, pg. 3609

NETEL AS—See IK Investment Partners Limited; *Int'l*, pg. 3609

NEW ERA TECHNOLOGY; *U.S. Private*, pg. 2896

NEWMARKET INFORMATION (PUBLICATIONS) LIMITED—See Byggfakta Group Nordic HoldCo AD; *Int'l*, pg. 1235

NGP BLUE MOUNTAIN I LLC—See Alternative Earth Resources Inc.; *Int'l*, pg. 391

NICHOLS CONSTRUCTION, LLC—See Dycom Industries, Inc.; *U.S. Public*, pg. 698

NORTHERN POWERLINE CONSTRUCTORS, INC.—See Quanta Services, Inc.; *U.S. Public*, pg. 1752

NORTHERN STATES POWER COMPANY—See Xcel Energy Inc.; *U.S. Public*, pg. 2385

OCEAN THERMAL ENERGY CORPORATION; *U.S. Public*, pg. 1562

OCLARO JAPAN, INC.—See Lumentum Holdings Inc.; *U.S. Public*, pg. 1348

OLD NORTH UTILITY SERVICES, INC.—See American States Water Company; *U.S. Public*, pg. 110

ONESHORE ENERGY GMBH—See BayWa AG; *Int'l*, pg. 918

ORMAT NEVADA INC.—See Ormat Technologies, Inc.; *U.S. Public*, pg. 1618

ORTITLAN LIMITADA—See Ormat Technologies, Inc.; *U.S. Public*, pg. 1618

OSMOSE UTILITIES SERVICES, INC.—See EQT AB; *Int'l*, pg. 2479

OSMOSE UTILITIES SERVICES, INC. - SYRACUSE—See EQT AB; *Int'l*, pg. 2479

OU BALTIC WIND ENERGY—See Eolus Vind AB; *Int'l*, pg. 2457

OVO ENERGY PTY. LIMITED—See AGL Energy Limited; *Int'l*, pg. 211

PAULEY CONSTRUCTION INC.—See Dycom Industries, Inc.; *U.S. Public*, pg. 699

PEARCE SERVICES, LLC—See Willcrest Partners; *U.S. Private*, pg. 4521

PENN LINE CORP.; *U.S. Private*, pg. 3134

PENN LINE SERVICE, INC.—See Penn Line Corp.; *U.S. Private*, pg. 3134

PESADO CONSTRUCTION COMPANY; *U.S. Private*, pg. 3156

PLH GROUP, INC.—See Primoris Services Corporation; *U.S. Public*, pg. 1718

PM CONTROL SYSTEMS (INDIA) PRIVATE LTD.—See Woodward, Inc.; *U.S. Public*, pg. 2377

POWER CORPORATION OF AMERICA—See The Goldfield Corporation; *U.S. Public*, pg. 2075

POWER LINE SERVICES, INC.—See Primoris Services Corporation; *U.S. Public*, pg. 1718

POYRY NORWAY AS—See AFRY AB; *Int'l*, pg. 196

PREFORMED LINE PRODUCTS COMPANY; *U.S. Public*, pg. 1714

PREUSSENELEKTRA GMBH—See E.ON SE; *Int'l*, pg. 2259

PRIMORIS AEVENIA, INC.—See Primoris Services Corporation; *U.S. Public*, pg. 1719

PSOMASFMG, LLC—See Psomas; *U.S. Private*, pg. 3297

PT PREFORMED LINE PRODUCTS INDONESIA—See Preformed Line Products Company; *U.S. Public*, pg. 1714

PURE SOLAR POWER (IP) PTY. LTD.—See EnviroMission Limited; *Int'l*, pg. 2454

PUSH INC.; *U.S. Private*, pg. 3307

QUALITY UPTIME SERVICES, LLC—See ABM Industries, Inc.; *U.S. Public*, pg. 26

RACO INCORPORATED; *U.S. Private*, pg. 3342

R.A.D.I SVERIGE AB/ABVAC—See Borr Company; *Int'l*, pg. 1114

R.B. HINKLE CONSTRUCTION, INC.—See Primoris Services Corporation; *U.S. Public*, pg. 1719

REEL TELECOMMUNICATION SERVICES, LLC—See Guggenheim Partners, LLC; *U.S. Private*, pg. 1812

RENU ENERGY SOLUTIONS LLC—See Swell Energy Inc; *U.S. Private*, pg. 3892

RICHTER & ASSOCIATES INC.—See Bowman Consulting Group Ltd.; *U.S. Private*, pg. 376

ROCKINGHAM CONSTRUCTION CO; *U.S. Private*, pg. 3466

ROCKY MOUNTAIN CONTRACTORS, INC.—See MDU Resources Group, Inc.; *U.S. Public*, pg. 1410

ROCKY MOUNTAIN FIBER PLUS; *U.S. Private*, pg. 3468

R. ROESE CONTRACTING CO., INC.; *U.S. Private*, pg. 3334

RSL FIBER SYSTEMS, LLC.; *U.S. Private*, pg. 3497

THE RYAN COMPANY, INC.—See Quanta Services, Inc.; *U.S. Public*, pg. 1753

SABRE INDUSTRIES, INC.—See The Jordan Company, L.P.; *U.S. Private*, pg. 4061

SABRE TELECOM SERVICES—See The Jordan Company, L.P.; *U.S. Private*, pg. 4061

SAE POWERLINES S.R.L.—See Gammon India Limited; *Int'l*, pg. 2879

SAGE TELECOMMUNICATIONS CORP. OF COLORADO, LLC—See Dycom Industries, Inc.; *U.S. Public*, pg. 699

SANTA QUITERIA ENERGIA, S.L.U.—See EDP - Energias de Portugal, S.A.; *Int'l*, pg. 2315

SATELEC—See FAYAT SAS; *Int'l*, pg. 2626

SATRA SA—See Eiffage S.A.; *Int'l*, pg. 2331

SBA NETWORK SERVICES, INC.—See SBA Communications Corporation; *U.S. Public*, pg. 1842

SEFNCO COMMUNICATIONS, INC.—See MasTec, Inc.; *U.S. Public*, pg. 1393

SERVICE ELECTRIC COMPANY—See Quanta Services, Inc.; *U.S. Public*, pg. 1752

SHENANDOAH TOWER SERVICE LTD.; *U.S. Private*, pg. 3632

SIA EOLUS—See Eolus Vind AB; *Int'l*, pg. 2457

SISTEMAS SEC, S.A.—See ACS, Actividades de Construccion y Servicios, S.A.; *Int'l*, pg. 116

SKODA PRAHA INVEST S.R.O.—See CEZ, a.s.; *Int'l*, pg. 1428

SKY TOWER PUBLIC COMPANY LIMITED—See Capital Engineering Network Public Company Limited; *Int'l*, pg. 1310

SOC. ESPANOLA DE MONTAJES INDUSTRIALES, S.A.—See ACS, Actividades de Construccion y Servicios, S.A.; *Int'l*, pg. 116

SOUTHEAST POWER CORPORATION—See The Goldfield Corporation; *U.S. Public*, pg. 2076

SOUTHWEST FLORIDA CABLE CONSTRUCTION, INC.; *U.S. Private*, pg. 3739

SPECTRUM WIRELESS SOLUTIONS, INC. - EF&I DIVISION—See Dycom Industries, Inc.; *U.S. Public*, pg. 699

SPECTRUM WIRELESS SOLUTIONS, INC.—See Dycom Industries, Inc.; *U.S. Public*, pg. 699

SPIVEY UTILITY CONSTRUCTION CO. INC.; *U.S. Private*, pg. 3758

SPP DG DEVCO 4A, LLC—See NRG Energy, Inc.; *U.S. Public*, pg. 1551

STAR CONSTRUCTION, LLC—See Dycom Industries, Inc.; *U.S. Public*, pg. 699

STERN ENERGY LTD.—See Encavis AG; *Int'l*, pg. 2401

STERN ENERGY S.P.A.—See Encavis AG; *Int'l*, pg. 2401

STEVENS COMMUNICATIONS, LLC—See Dycom Industries, Inc.; *U.S. Public*, pg. 699

ST. PAUL TOWER, L.L.C.—See Northeast Communications of Wisconsin Incorporated; *U.S. Private*, pg. 2949

S.T.S., LLC—See Dycom Industries, Inc.; *U.S. Public*, pg. 699

STURGEON ELECTRIC CALIFORNIA, LLC—See MYR Group Inc.; *U.S. Public*, pg. 1489

STURGEON ELECTRIC COMPANY INC. - OREGON—See MYR Group Inc.; *U.S. Public*, pg. 1489

SUMTER UTILITIES, INC.—See Quanta Services, Inc.; *U.S. Public*, pg. 1753

SUN ELECTRIC SERVICES, INC.—See Primoris Services Corporation; *U.S. Public*, pg. 1719

SWELL ENERGY INC; *U.S. Private*, pg. 3892

TELCOM CONSTRUCTION, INC.—See Dycom Industries, Inc.; *U.S. Public*, pg. 699

TELCO SUPPLY COMPANY—See Chickasaw Holding Company; *U.S. Private*, pg. 880

TELEKOM PROJEKTENTWICKLUNGS GMBH—See America Movil, S.A.B. de C.V.; *Int'l*, pg. 421

TELIDYNE INC.; *U.S. Public*, pg. 1998

TETRA TECH EM INC.—See Tetra Tech, Inc.; *U.S. Public*, pg. 2023

TEXSTAR ENTERPRISES, INC.—See Dycom Industries, Inc.; *U.S. Public*, pg. 699

THAYER POWER & COMMUNICATION LINE CONTRUCTION CO., LLC—See The Anderson Group, LLC; *U.S. Private*, pg. 3986

TJADER & HIGHSTROM UTILITY SERVICES, LLC—See Dycom Industries, Inc.; *U.S. Public*, pg. 699

TOTAL ELECTRICAL SERVICE & SUPPLY CO.—See Primoris Services Corporation; *U.S. Public*, pg. 1719

TOWER VENTURES HOLDINGS LLC—See Blackstone Inc.; *U.S. Public*, pg. 356

TRANSCEND INFRASTRUCTURE LIMITED—See American Tower Corporation; *U.S. Public*, pg. 111

TRANSCEND INFRASTRUCTURE PRIVATE LIMITED—See American Tower Corporation; *U.S. Public*, pg. 111

TRAWICK CONSTRUCTION COMPANY, LLC—See Dycom Industries, Inc.; *U.S. Public*, pg. 699

TRI-WIRE ENGINEERING SOLUTIONS, INC.; *U.S. Private*, pg. 4225

TRUTH HONOUR ELECTRONIC LIMITED—See China Technology Industry Group Limited; *Int'l*, pg. 1557

UBBINK B.V.—See CENTROTEC SE; *Int'l*, pg. 1414

UBBINK FRANCE S.A.S.—See CENTROTEC SE; *Int'l*, pg. 1415

UBBINK NV—See CENTROTEC SE; *Int'l*, pg. 1415

UBBINK (UK) LTD.—See CENTROTEC SE; *Int'l*, pg. 1415

UDUPI POWER CORPORATION LIMITED—See Adani Enterprises Limited; *Int'l*, pg. 125

UIRAPURU TRANSMISSORA DE ENERGIA, LTDA—See Companhia Paranaense de Energia; *Int'l*, pg. 1748

ULTIMA ITALIA S.R.L.—See Bhartiya International Ltd.; *Int'l*, pg. 1013

UNDERGROUND SERVICES AUSTRALIA PTY LTD—See CFC Group Pty. Ltd.; *Int'l*, pg. 1429

UTEC CONSTRUCTORS CORP.; *U.S. Private*, pg. 4325

UTILICON SOLUTIONS, LTD.—See Asplundh Tree Expert Co.; *U.S. Private*, pg. 353

UTILIPATH, LLC—See NewSpring Capital LLC; *U.S. Private*, pg. 2918

UTILITY DYNAMICS CORPORATION; *U.S. Private*, pg. 4326

VALARD POLSKA SP. Z O.O.—See Quanta Services, Inc.; *U.S. Public*, pg. 1753

VANGUARD ENERGY PARTNERS, LLC; *U.S. Private*, pg. 4343

VANTAGE TOWERS AG—See KKR & Co. Inc.; *U.S. Public*, pg. 1266

237130 — POWER AND COMMUNICA...

VERSALIFT NORTHWEST, LLC.—See The Sterling Group, L.P.; *U.S. Private*, pg. 4123
VERTICAL LIMIT CONSTRUCTION, LLC—See QualTek Services Inc.; *U.S. Public*, pg. 1748
W.A. CHESTER, LLC—See Bernhard Capital Partners Management, LP; *U.S. Private*, pg. 537
WESTERN UTILITY CONTRACTORS, INC.—See Hylan Datacom & Electrical, LLC; *U.S. Private*, pg. 2018
WESTOWER COMMUNICATIONS, LLC—See MasTec, Inc.; *U.S. Public*, pg. 1393
WESTTOWER COMMUNICATIONS LTD.—See Exchange Income Corporation; *Int'l*, pg. 2579
WHITE MOUNTAIN CABLE CONSTRUCTION, LLC—See Dycom Industries, Inc.; *U.S. Public*, pg. 699
WILSON CONSTRUCTION CO., INC.; *U.S. Private*, pg. 4530
WINCO, INC.—See Quanta Services, Inc.; *U.S. Public*, pg. 1753
WINDPARK KESFELD HECKHUSCHEID GMBH & CO. KG—See Allianz SE; *Int'l*, pg. 356
WINDPARK KIRF GMBH & CO. KG—See Allianz SE; *Int'l*, pg. 356
WP BULGARIA 12 EOOD—See Enel S.p.A.; *Int'l*, pg. 2415
YEW HOCK MARINE ENGINEERING PTE. LTD.—See Charisma Energy Services Limited; *Int'l*, pg. 1450

237210 — LAND SUBDIVISION

ABBELL ASSOCIATES, LLC; *U.S. Private*, pg. 34
ABBEY ROAD GROUP LAND DEVELOPMENT SERVICES COMPANY—See Abbey Road Group LLC; *U.S. Private*, pg. 34
ACN 108 719 197 PTY LTD—See Insight Venture Management, LLC; *U.S. Private*, pg. 2088
ACN 108 719 197 PTY LTD—See Stone Point Capital LLC; *U.S. Private*, pg. 3822
AFCO GLOBAL PORTS LLC—See Aviation Facilities Company, Inc.; *U.S. Private*, pg. 406
A.G. SPANOS DEVELOPMENT—See A.G. Spanos Companies; *U.S. Private*, pg. 26
A.G. SPANOS ENTERPRISES—See A.G. Spanos Companies; *U.S. Private*, pg. 26
ALM EQUITY AB; *Int'l*, pg. 361
AL NEYER, LLC; *U.S. Private*, pg. 147
THE ALTER GROUP LTD.; *U.S. Private*, pg. 3985
THE ALTMAN COMPANIES, INC.—See Hilton Grand Vacations Inc.; *U.S. Public*, pg. 1040
AMERICAN BEAUTY CORP; *U.S. Private*, pg. 224
AMERICAN COMMUNITY PROPERTIES TRUST—See Federal Capital Partners; *U.S. Private*, pg. 1487
AMERICAN LAND VENTURES, LLC; *U.S. Private*, pg. 239
AMERICAN RESURGENS MANAGEMENT CORPORATION; *U.S. Private*, pg. 246
AMERICAN TRUST SENIOR CARE LLC; *U.S. Private*, pg. 257
AMERICAN WEST HOMES INC.; *U.S. Private*, pg. 258
AMFAC HAWAII LLC—See Walton Street Capital, LLC; *U.S. Private*, pg. 4435
AMREP CORPORATION; *U.S. Public*, pg. 133
AMREP SOUTHWEST, INC.—See AMREP Corporation; *U.S. Public*, pg. 133
ANASTASI CONSTRUCTION COMPANY, L.L.C.; *U.S. Private*, pg. 272
ANASTASI DEVELOPMENT COMPANY, LLC.; *U.S. Private*, pg. 272
ANSAL PROPERTIES & INFRASTRUCTURE LIMITED; *Int'l*, pg. 478
AP JOY LIMITED—See Hang Lung Group Limited; *Int'l*, pg. 3244
APPENINN NYRT.; *Int'l*, pg. 519
AP PROPERTIES LIMITED—See Hang Lung Group Limited; *Int'l*, pg. 3244
AP WIN LIMITED—See Hang Lung Group Limited; *Int'l*, pg. 3244
AP WORLD LIMITED—See Hang Lung Group Limited; *Int'l*, pg. 3244
ARAB COMPANY FOR LAND RECLAMATION S.A.E.; *Int'l*, pg. 530
A.R. LOCKHART DEVELOPMENT CO.; *U.S. Private*, pg. 27
ARRICANO REAL ESTATE PLC; *Int'l*, pg. 579
ARTESIAN DEVELOPMENT CORPORATION—See Artesian Resources Corporation; *U.S. Public*, pg. 201
ASIAN HOTELS & PROPERTIES PLC; *Int'l*, pg. 617
ATKINSON UNDERGROUND GROUP—See Clark Enterprises, Inc.; *U.S. Private*, pg. 913
ATLANTA CAFE HOLDINGS CORP.; *U.S. Private*, pg. 370
ATRIUM DEVELOPMENT INC.; *U.S. Private*, pg. 382
AVALON PARK GROUP MANAGEMENT, INC.; *U.S. Private*, pg. 403
AVEO GROUP LIMITED—See Brookfield Corporation; *Int'l*, pg. 1185
BARNWELL HAWAIIAN PROPERTIES, INC.—See Barnwell Industries, Inc.; *U.S. Public*, pg. 278
BARNWELL MANAGEMENT CO., INC.—See Barnwell Industries, Inc.; *U.S. Public*, pg. 278
BARON SALAZAR & ASSOCIATES—See McCormack Baron Salazar, Inc.; *U.S. Private*, pg. 2630
BARRON COLLIER CORPORATION—See Barron Collier Company, Ltd.; *U.S. Private*, pg. 480
BEACH COMPANY INC.; *U.S. Private*, pg. 503
BELIN & ASSOCIATES, INC.; *U.S. Private*, pg. 518
BELLEAIR DEVELOPMENT GROUP, INC.; *U.S. Private*, pg. 520
BENCHMARK HOMES INC.; *U.S. Private*, pg. 523
BENDERSON DEVELOPMENT COMPANY, LLC; *U.S. Private*, pg. 524
BERKOWITZ DEVELOPMENT GROUP, INC.; *U.S. Private*, pg. 533
BF ENTERPRISES, INC.; *U.S. Private*, pg. 548
BHANDERI INFRACON LIMITED; *Int'l*, pg. 1010
BIGGE DEVELOPMENT CORPORATION—See Bigge Crane & Rigging Company; *U.S. Private*, pg. 555
BLUEGREEN VACATIONS CORPORATION—See Hilton Grand Vacations Inc.; *U.S. Public*, pg. 1039
BNE LAND & DEVELOPMENT CO.—See Boddie-Noell Enterprises, Inc.; *U.S. Private*, pg. 607
BONITA BAY PROPERTIES, INC.; *U.S. Private*, pg. 614
BOONE EAST DEVELOPMENT CO.—See Alpha Natural Resources, Inc.; *U.S. Private*, pg. 198
BORGESTAD ASA; *Int'l*, pg. 1114
BOSC REALTY ADVISORS; *U.S. Private*, pg. 619
BOSWELL PROPERTIES INC.—See J.G. Boswell Co., Inc.; *U.S. Private*, pg. 2165
BOUWFONDS PROPERTY DEVELOPMENT B.V.—See Cooperatieve Centrale Raiffeisen-Boerenleenbank B.A.; *Int'l*, pg. 1791
BOZZUTO DEVELOPMENT CO. INC—See The Bozzuto Group; *U.S. Private*, pg. 3999
BOZZUTO LAND SERVICES—See The Bozzuto Group; *U.S. Private*, pg. 3999
BP REALTY, LLC—See United Natural Foods, Inc.; *U.S. Public*, pg. 2231
BRANDYWINE CONSTRUCTION & MANAGEMENT; *U.S. Private*, pg. 639
BRANDYWINE REAL ESTATE MANAGEMENT SERVICES CORPORATION—See The Brandywine Companies, LLC; *U.S. Private*, pg. 4000
BREEZY POINT INTERNATIONAL, INC.—See Whitebirch Enterprises, Inc.; *U.S. Private*, pg. 4511
BREEZY POINT LP; *U.S. Private*, pg. 644
BRIGHTWORK REAL ESTATE, INC.; *U.S. Private*, pg. 654
THE BROADSTONE GROUP, INC.; *U.S. Private*, pg. 4000
BRONZE INFRA-TECH LIMITED; *Int'l*, pg. 1174
BROOKS RESOURCES SALES CORP.—See Brooks Resources Corporation; *U.S. Private*, pg. 664
BUILDERS DEVELOPMENT INC.—See Builders Inc.; *U.S. Private*, pg. 682
BULGARIAN LAND DEVELOPMENT EAD—See AG Capital; *Int'l*, pg. 197
BULGARIAN LAND DEVELOPMENT EAD—See CLS Holdings plc; *Int'l*, pg. 1663
BURROUGHS & CHAPIN CO. INC.; *U.S. Private*, pg. 692
BUZZ OATES COMPANIES; *U.S. Private*, pg. 699
BVB PROPERTIES; *U.S. Private*, pg. 700
CABI DEVELOPERS, LLC; *U.S. Private*, pg. 710
CAMPBELL-HOGUE & ASSOCIATES; *U.S. Private*, pg. 731
CAMPUS LIVING VILLAGES, CENTURY; *U.S. Private*, pg. 732
CAPE CAVE CORP.—See Rotonda Holdings Inc.; *U.S. Private*, pg. 3487
CAPITALAND MALL ASIA LIMITED—See CapitaLand Investment Limited; *Int'l*, pg. 1313
CAPITAL DEVELOPMENT COMPANY; *U.S. Private*, pg. 739
CAPITAL DEVELOPMENT CO.; *U.S. Private*, pg. 739
CAPITAL & REGIONAL PROPERTY MANAGEMENT LIMITED—See Capital & Regional plc; *Int'l*, pg. 1309
CAPITOL FUNDS INC.; *U.S. Private*, pg. 744
CARPINATO GROUP LLC; *U.S. Private*, pg. 770
CARTER RESOURCES INC.—See Carter Lumber Co.; *U.S. Private*, pg. 776
CASDEN PROPERTIES INC.; *U.S. Private*, pg. 781
CBO TERRITORIA; *Int'l*, pg. 1366
CB RESORT CORPORATION—See Equity LifeStyle Properties, Inc.; *U.S. Public*, pg. 790
CENTERFIRE REAL ESTATE; *U.S. Private*, pg. 816
CENTRAL FLORIDA INVESTMENTS INC.; *U.S. Private*, pg. 820
CENTURY 21 NACHMAN REALTY, L.L.C.; *U.S. Private*, pg. 831
CENTURYTOUCH LTD, INC.; *Int'l*, pg. 1420
THE CHADMAR GROUP; *U.S. Private*, pg. 4007
CHALMERS PROPERTY COMPANY; *U.S. Private*, pg. 845
CHEUK NANG (HOLDINGS) LIMITED; *Int'l*, pg. 1473
CHILDRESS-KLEIN PROPERTIES, INC.; *U.S. Private*, pg. 851
CHINA RAILWAY MAJOR BRIDGE ENGINEERING GROUP CO., LTD.—See China Railway Group Limited; *Int'l*, pg. 1543
CIRI LAND DEVELOPMENT COMPANY—See Cook Inlet Region, Inc.; *U.S. Private*, pg. 1038
CITRUS HILL INVESTMENT PROPERTIES; *U.S. Private*, pg. 904

CITYCHAMP DARTONG CO., LTD.; *Int'l*, pg. 1628
CLERMONT PARTNERS—See Kohlberg & Company, LLC; *U.S. Private*, pg. 2339
COASTAL GREENLAND LIMITED; *Int'l*, pg. 1681
COATES FIELD SERVICE, INC.; *U.S. Private*, pg. 957
COCCA DEVELOPMENT, LTD.; *U.S. Private*, pg. 959
COLLIER LAND DEVELOPMENT, INC.—See Collier Enterprises, Inc.; *U.S. Private*, pg. 969
COLORADO FIRST CONSTRUCTION CO.; *U.S. Private*, pg. 974
COLUMBIA RESIDENTIAL; *U.S. Private*, pg. 977
COMMONBOND COMMUNITIES; *U.S. Private*, pg. 986
COMPREHENSIVE LAND DEVELOPMENT & INVESTMENT PLC; *Int'l*, pg. 1754
CONTINENTAL FINANCIAL LTD; *U.S. Private*, pg. 1029
CONTRACTOR PROPERTY DEVELOPERS CO.—See Scherer Brothers Lumber Company; *U.S. Private*, pg. 3564
CONTRAVEST MANAGEMENT COMPANY; *U.S. Private*, pg. 1034
COOPER COMMUNITIES, INC.; *U.S. Private*, pg. 1041
COOPER LAND DEVELOPMENT, INC.—See Cooper Communities, Inc.; *U.S. Private*, pg. 1041
CORBELIS DEVELOPMENT SWFL, LLC—See Corbelis Management, LLC; *U.S. Private*, pg. 1047
CORBELIS MANAGEMENT, LLC; *U.S. Private*, pg. 1047
THE CORDISH COMPANIES; *U.S. Private*, pg. 4015
CORELOGIC TAX COLLECTION SERVICES, LLC—See Insight Venture Management, LLC; *U.S. Private*, pg. 2089
CORELOGIC TAX COLLECTION SERVICES, LLC—See Stone Point Capital LLC; *U.S. Private*, pg. 3822
CORNERSTONE COMMUNITIES CORPORATION; *U.S. Private*, pg. 1051
CORPORATE DEVELOPMENT SERVICES, LLC—See COPT Defense Properties; *U.S. Public*, pg. 575
COSCAN WATERWAYS INC.; *U.S. Private*, pg. 1061
CRESCENT HEIGHTS OF AMERICA INC.; *U.S. Private*, pg. 1093
CRESLEIGH MANAGEMENT INC—See Harbor View Holdings Inc.; *U.S. Private*, pg. 1859
CRM DEVELOPMENT COMPANY; *U.S. Private*, pg. 1102
CRM PROPERTIES—See Caruso Affiliated; *U.S. Private*, pg. 777
CUMBERLAND AMERICA DEVELOPMENT COMPANY INC.; *U.S. Private*, pg. 1122
CYFIELD DEVELOPMENT CO. LTD.; *Int'l*, pg. 1895
CYMBAL DEVELOPMENT; *U.S. Private*, pg. 1134
DAITO TRUST CONSTRUCTION CO., LTD.; *Int'l*, pg. 1943
DANIEL CORPORATION; *U.S. Private*, pg. 1153
DAVID HOCKER & ASSOCIATES, INC.; *U.S. Private*, pg. 1170
DAVIDON HOMES LTD.; *U.S. Private*, pg. 1171
DAYCO HOLDING CORP.; *U.S. Private*, pg. 1177
DEAN REALTY CO—See Dean Operations, Inc.; *U.S. Private*, pg. 1184
DEER CROSSING, INC.; *U.S. Private*, pg. 1190
THE DELTONA CORPORATION; *U.S. Private*, pg. 4020
DELTONA CORP. REALTY CO.—See The Deltona Corporation; *U.S. Private*, pg. 4020
DENISON PROPERTIES INC.—See Denison Inc.; *U.S. Private*, pg. 1205
DENVER TECHNOLOGICAL CENTER—See Dubai World Corporation; *Int'l*, pg. 2220
DESERT MOUNTAIN PROPERTIES LIMITED PARTNERSHIP; *U.S. Private*, pg. 1213
DESON DEVELOPMENT INTERNATIONAL HOLDINGS LTD; *Int'l*, pg. 2045
D.G. JENKINS DEVELOPMENT CORP.; *U.S. Private*, pg. 1142
DOMINION PROPERTIES INC.; *U.S. Private*, pg. 1256
DOSS, LTD.; *U.S. Private*, pg. 1264
DOUBLE DELAWARE INC.; *U.S. Private*, pg. 1265
DOUBLE DIAMOND COMPANIES—See Double Delaware Inc.; *U.S. Private*, pg. 1265
DOUBLEDRAGON CORPORATION; *Int'l*, pg. 2181
DOUCETTE HOMES, INC.; *U.S. Private*, pg. 1266
DUNDEE REALTY USA INC.—See Dundee Corporation; *Int'l*, pg. 2226
EAGLE CANADA, INC.—See Wilks Brothers LLC; *U.S. Private*, pg. 4521
THE EASTLAKE COMPANY—See J.G. Boswell Co., Inc.; *U.S. Private*, pg. 2165
EAST WEST PARTNERS MANAGEMENT CO.; *U.S. Private*, pg. 1319
E.C. GRIFFITH CO.; *U.S. Private*, pg. 1304
ECHELON REAL ESTATE SERVICES LLC; *U.S. Private*, pg. 1326
ECL DEVELOPMENTS LIMITED—See Empire Company Limited; *Int'l*, pg. 2387
EDGEWOOD PROPERTIES INC.; *U.S. Private*, pg. 1336
E.J. DEL MONTE CORP.; *U.S. Private*, pg. 1305
ELLICOTT DEVELOPMENT CO.; *U.S. Private*, pg. 1363
EMERSON DEVELOPMENTS (HOLDINGS) LIMITED; *Int'l*, pg. 2379
EMERSON INTERNATIONAL, INC.—See Emerson Developments (Holdings) Limited; *Int'l*, pg. 2379

N.A.I.C.S. INDEX

237210 — LAND SUBDIVISION

EMLAK KONUT GAYRIMENKUL YATIRIM ORTAKLIGI AS; *Int'l*, pg. 2384
EMMER DEVELOPMENT CORP.; *U.S. Private*, pg. 1383
EMPEROR INTERNATIONAL HOLDINGS LIMITED; *Int'l*, pg. 2386
EOLO SRL—See ERG S.p.A.; *Int'l*, pg. 2491
ERICKSON LIVING MANAGEMENT, LLC—See Redwood Capital Investments, LLC; *U.S. Private*, pg. 3380
ESPRAL INTERNATIONAL LTD.—See ENL Limited; *Int'l*, pg. 2441
ESPRAL LTD.—See ENL Limited; *Int'l*, pg. 2441
ESSEX CORPORATION; *U.S. Private*, pg. 1427
EUROTUNNEL DEVELOPMENTS LIMITED—See Getlink SE; *Int'l*, pg. 2953
EVERGREEN DEVCO INC.; *U.S. Private*, pg. 1439
FAISON & ASSOCIATES LLC; *U.S. Private*, pg. 1465
FAR EAST CONSORTIUM HOLDINGS (AUSTRALIA) PTY LIMITED—See Far East Consortium International Limited; *Int'l*, pg. 2615
FARNSWORTH DEVELOPMENT COMPANIES; *U.S. Private*, pg. 1480
FAWN CREEK COURT SALES LTD.—See Crown Communities, LLC; *U.S. Private*, pg. 1110
FENTELL CORPORATION; *U.S. Private*, pg. 1495
FICKLING & COMPANY INCORPORATED; *U.S. Private*, pg. 1502
FINANCE REALTY COMPANY LTD.—See Finance Factors, Limited1952; *U.S. Private*, pg. 1506
FINERGY DEVELOPMENT, LLC; *U.S. Private*, pg. 1509
THE FIP CORPORATION; *U.S. Private*, pg. 4028
FLETCHER INDUSTRIES INC.; *U.S. Private*, pg. 1542
FLOURNOY DEVELOPMENT CO. LLC; *U.S. Private*, pg. 1551
FOCUS ENTERPRISES INC.; *U.S. Private*, pg. 1556
FOLMAR & ASSOCIATES LLP; *U.S. Private*, pg. 1559
FOLSOM INVESTMENTS INC.; *U.S. Private*, pg. 1559
FORD LAND—See Ford Motor Company; *U.S. Public*, pg. 865
FORGE INNOVATION DEVELOPMENT CORP.; *U.S. Public*, pg. 867
FORINO DEVELOPERS COMPANY; *U.S. Private*, pg. 1569
FOSTER DEVELOPMENT COMPANY; *U.S. Private*, pg. 1578
FOUR STAR HOLDINGS, INC.; *U.S. Private*, pg. 1582
THE FRANKLIN GROUP, INC.; *U.S. Private*, pg. 4030
FRANKLIN MILLS LLC—See Simon Property Group, Inc.; *U.S. Public*, pg. 1882
FRIENDLY FUELS INC.; *U.S. Private*, pg. 1611
GABRIEL PROPERTIES, LLC.; *U.S. Private*, pg. 1632
GABUNGAN AQRS BERHAD; *Int'l*, pg. 2867
THE GAMBONE GROUP; *U.S. Private*, pg. 4031
GATEHOUSE COMPANIES, INC.; *U.S. Private*, pg. 1649
GATEWAY LIFESTYLE GROUP; *Int'l*, pg. 2889
GC BUILDERS INC; *U.S. Private*, pg. 1653
GENESIS LAND DEVELOPMENT CORP.; *Int'l*, pg. 2921
GENOA CONSTRUCTION SERVICES, INC.; *U.S. Private*, pg. 1672
GENTING PROPERTY SDN. BHD.—See Genting Berhad; *Int'l*, pg. 2929
GENTRY PACIFIC, LTD.; *U.S. Private*, pg. 1680
GERMANN ROAD LAND DEVELOPMENT, LLC—See Brookfield Corporation; *Int'l*, pg. 1174
GIALAMAS COMPANY INCORPORATED; *U.S. Private*, pg. 1694
GINSBURG DEVELOPMENT CORP.; *U.S. Private*, pg. 1702
GIRKIN DEVELOPMENT, LLC; *U.S. Private*, pg. 1702
G & K MANAGEMENT; *U.S. Private*, pg. 1628
GLENN SPRINGS HOLDINGS, INC.—See Occidental Petroleum Corporation; *U.S. Public*, pg. 1561
GOLDRICH & KEST INDUSTRIES LLC—See G&K Management Company; *U.S. Private*, pg. 1629
GOLUB & CO; *U.S. Private*, pg. 1736
THE GOODMAN GROUP, INC.; *U.S. Private*, pg. 4034
THE GOODMAN GROUP UK—See The Goodman Group, Inc.; *U.S. Private*, pg. 4034
GOODMAN UK LTD.—See Goodman Limited; *Int'l*, pg. 3041
GORMAN & COMPANY INC.; *U.S. Private*, pg. 1744
GOTHAM ORGANIZATION INC.; *U.S. Private*, pg. 1745
GRAHAM CONSTRUCTION CORP.—See The Graham Group, Inc.; *U.S. Private*, pg. 4036
GREATER MISSOURI BUILDERS; *U.S. Private*, pg. 1770
GREEN BRICK PARTNERS, INC.; *U.S. Public*, pg. 962
GREENWAY INVESTMENT COMPANY; *U.S. Private*, pg. 1781
GREENWOOD COMMUNITIES & RESORTS, INC.—See GMI Holding, Inc.; *U.S. Private*, pg. 1722
GULF BAY GROUP OF COMPANIES; *U.S. Private*, pg. 1814
THE GUTIERREZ COMPANY; *U.S. Private*, pg. 4040
HALLMARK DEVELOPMENT OF FLORIDA, INC.; *U.S. Private*, pg. 1845
HALLMARK PARTNERS INC.; *U.S. Private*, pg. 1845
HALVORSEN HOLDINGS LLC; *U.S. Private*, pg. 1847
HAMILTON PARTNERS, INC.; *U.S. Private*, pg. 1848
HAMMES PARTNERS WISCONSIN LP; *U.S. Private*, pg. 1849
THE HANOVER COMPANY—See Hanover R.S. Limited Partnership; *U.S. Private*, pg. 1855

HARBOR INN OF CS ASSOCIATES—See MSL Property Management; *U.S. Private*, pg. 2807
HARVARD DEVELOPMENT COMPANY LLC; *U.S. Private*, pg. 1875
HASEKO AMERICA, INC.—See Haseko Corporation; *Int'l*, pg. 3283
HAYDEN HOMES INC.; *U.S. Private*, pg. 1884
THE HEARN COMPANY; *U.S. Private*, pg. 4044
HENDERSON INVESTMENT LIMITED—See Henderson Land Development Co. Ltd.; *Int'l*, pg. 3344
HENRY S. MILLER REALTY SERVICES, LLC—See Henry S. Miller Management Corp.; *U.S. Private*, pg. 1919
HISTORIC RESTORATION, INC.; *U.S. Private*, pg. 1952
HO BEE LAND LTD; *Int'l*, pg. 3434
HOLIDAYS SELECT LIMITED—See Emerson Developments (Holdings) Limited; *Int'l*, pg. 2379
HOMEFED RESOURCES CORPORATION—See Jefferies Financial Group Inc.; *U.S. Public*, pg. 1188
HONG FOK LAND PTE. LTD.—See Hong Fok Corporation Limited; *Int'l*, pg. 3465
HOOSIERS CORPORATION—See Hoosiers Holdings; *Int'l*, pg. 3472
HOPEFLUENT GROUP HOLDINGS LTD; *Int'l*, pg. 3473
HOUSING CAPITAL COMPANY—See U.S. Bancorp; *U.S. Public*, pg. 2212
HOWARD GROUP; *U.S. Private*, pg. 1994
HOWARD HUGHES MANAGEMENT SERVICES COMPANY, LLC—See Howard Hughes Holdings Inc.; *U.S. Public*, pg. 1060
H&R GRUNDSTUCKSVERWALTUNGS-BETEILIGUNGSGESELLSCHAFT MBH—See H&R KGaA; *Int'l*, pg. 3193
H&R GRUNDSTUCKSVERWALTUNGS GMBH—See H&R KGaA; *Int'l*, pg. 3193
HSA COMMERCIAL REAL ESTATE; *U.S. Private*, pg. 1999
HSM DEVELOPMENT, INC.—See Henry S. Miller Management Corp.; *U.S. Private*, pg. 1919
H&S PROPERTIES DEVELOPMENT CORPORATION—See H&S Bakery Inc.; *U.S. Private*, pg. 1823
HUDLAND REAL ESTATE INVESTMENT AND DEVELOPMENT JSC; *Int'l*, pg. 3522
HUNT DEVELOPMENT GROUP, LLC—See Hunt Companies, Inc.; *U.S. Private*, pg. 2008
HUNT MIDWEST ENTERPRISES INC.; *U.S. Private*, pg. 2009
INDIGO DEVELOPMENT INC.—See CTO Realty Growth, Inc.; *U.S. Public*, pg. 602
INDIGO GROUP INC.—See CTO Realty Growth, Inc.; *U.S. Public*, pg. 602
INNVENTURES INC.; *U.S. Private*, pg. 2084
THE INTEGRAL GROUP LLC; *U.S. Private*, pg. 4056
IRVINE COMMUNITY DEVELOPMENT COMPANY—See The Irvine Company Inc.; *U.S. Private*, pg. 4057
THE IRVINE COMPANY INC.; *U.S. Private*, pg. 4057
ITAGROUP, INC.-ATLANTA—See ITAGroup, Inc.; *U.S. Private*, pg. 2148
ITALIA NAVIGANDO S.P.A.—See Agenzia Nazionale per l'Attrazione degli Investimenti e lo Svillupo d'Impresa SpA; *Int'l*, pg. 206
JAMES DORAN COMPANY INC.; *U.S. Private*, pg. 2183
JBG PROPERTIES; *U.S. Private*, pg. 2193
JCP REALTY, INC.—See J.C. Penney Company, Inc.; *U.S. Public*, pg. 2160
JDL DEVELOPMENT CORP.; *U.S. Private*, pg. 2195
JEBCO VENTURES, INC.; *U.S. Private*, pg. 2196
THE JERALD DEVELOPMENT GROUP INC.; *U.S. Private*, pg. 4058
JERRY CHEN; *U.S. Private*, pg. 2202
JERRY ERWIN ASSOCIATES INC.; *U.S. Private*, pg. 2202
JJ DETWEILER ENTERPRISES INC.; *U.S. Private*, pg. 2211
JMC COMMUNITIES, INC.; *U.S. Private*, pg. 2215
THE JOHNSON GROUP, INC.; *U.S. Private*, pg. 4059
JULIUS SCHEPPS COMPANY, INC.; *U.S. Private*, pg. 2243
JUPITER REALTY CORPORATION; *U.S. Private*, pg. 2245
JWM MANAGEMENT, INC.; *U.S. Private*, pg. 2247
KAANAPALI LAND, LLC; *U.S. Public*, pg. 1211
KAI INVESTMENTS, LLC—See Howard Hughes Holdings Inc.; *U.S. Public*, pg. 1060
KANSAS SPEEDWAY DEVELOPMENT CORP.—See National Association for Stock Car Auto Racing, Inc.; *U.S. Private*, pg. 2845
KAPALUA LAND COMPANY, LTD.—See Maui Land & Pineapple Company, Inc.; *U.S. Public*, pg. 1402
KASCO VENTURES INC.—See Kasco Corporation; *U.S. Private*, pg. 2263
KDC REAL ESTATE DEVELOPMENT & INVESTMENTS; *U.S. Private*, pg. 2270
KERRYTOWN SHOPS OF ANN ARBOR INC.—See O'Neal, Inc.; *U.S. Private*, pg. 2979
KEWALO HARBOR, LLC—See Howard Hughes Holdings Inc.; *U.S. Public*, pg. 1060
KEYSTONE CORPORATION; *U.S. Private*, pg. 2296
KIM KING ASSOCIATES, LLC; *U.S. Private*, pg. 2305
KITCHELL DEVELOPMENT COMPANY—See Kitchell Corporation; *U.S. Private*, pg. 2316
KITSON & PARTNERS COMMERCIAL—See Kitson & Part-

ners, LLC; *U.S. Private*, pg. 2316
KITSON & PARTNERS COMMUNITIES—See Kitson & Partners, LLC; *U.S. Private*, pg. 2316
KITSON & PARTNERS, LLC; *U.S. Private*, pg. 2316
KM DEVELOPMENT CORP.—See Zilber Ltd.; *U.S. Private*, pg. 4604
KOLTER COMMERCIAL LLC—See The Kolter Group LLC; *U.S. Private*, pg. 4065
THE KOLTER GROUP LLC; *U.S. Private*, pg. 4065
KOLTER LAND PARTNERS LLC—See The Kolter Group LLC; *U.S. Private*, pg. 4065
KVC DEVELOPMENT, INC.; *U.S. Private*, pg. 2359
KWONG WAN REALTY LIMITED—See Hysan Development Company Limited; *Int'l*, pg. 3554
LAKE ARROWHEAD DIV.—See Purcell Co., Inc.; *U.S. Private*, pg. 3304
LAKE LYNDON B. JOHNSON IMPROVEMENT CORPORATION; *U.S. Private*, pg. 2375
LANDCOM INC.; *U.S. Private*, pg. 2385
LANDMAR GROUP L.L.C.—See Crescent Resources, LLC; *U.S. Private*, pg. 1094
LANDSCAPE PARCSUD SL—See Banco de Sabadell, S.A.; *Int'l*, pg. 821
LAUREN LAND COMPANY—See Alpha Natural Resources, Inc.; *U.S. Private*, pg. 198
LEE NATIONAL CORPORATION; *U.S. Private*, pg. 2413
LEGACY PARTNERS INC.; *U.S. Private*, pg. 2416
LEGEND HOMES CORPORATION; *U.S. Private*, pg. 2418
LEGGAT MCCALL PROPERTIES LLC; *U.S. Private*, pg. 2418
LEGGAT MCCALL PROPERTIES, LLC.; *U.S. Private*, pg. 2418
LENNAR COMMUNITIES, INC.—See Lennar Corporation; *U.S. Public*, pg. 1306
LENNAR WINNCREST, LLC—See Lennar Corporation; *U.S. Public*, pg. 1306
LEON N. WEINER & ASSOCIATES; *U.S. Private*, pg. 2423
LERNER ENTERPRISES; *U.S. Private*, pg. 2431
LE TRIOMPHE PROPERTY GROUP LLC; *U.S. Private*, pg. 2405
LEVINE PROPERTIES, INC.; *U.S. Private*, pg. 2436
LG DEVELOPMENT GROUP, LLC.; *U.S. Private*, pg. 2441
LGI DEVELOPMENT; *U.S. Private*, pg. 2441
LIMITLESS PJSC—See Dubai World Corporation; *Int'l*, pg. 2222
LINCOLN TRIANGLE PARTNERS L.P.—See Millennium Management Inc.; *U.S. Private*, pg. 2731
LINDELL PROPERTIES, INC.; *U.S. Private*, pg. 2459
LINGER LONGER DEVELOPMENT COMPANY; *U.S. Private*, pg. 2461
LIVE OAK GOTTESMAN, LLC.; *U.S. Private*, pg. 2473
LOCKOO LIMITED—See Hang Lung Group Limited; *Int'l*, pg. 3245
THE LOJETA GROUP; *U.S. Private*, pg. 4071
LOOKOUT GROUP INC.; *U.S. Private*, pg. 2493
LOWE DESTINATION DEVELOPMENT DESERT—See Lowe Enterprises, Inc.; *U.S. Private*, pg. 2504
LOWE DESTINATION DEVELOPMENT, INC.—See Lowe Enterprises, Inc.; *U.S. Private*, pg. 2504
LOWE DESTINATION DEVELOPMENT SOUTHEAST—See Lowe Enterprises, Inc.; *U.S. Private*, pg. 2504
LOWE ENTERPRISES INVESTMENT MANAGEMENT INC.—See The Guardian Life Insurance Company of America; *U.S. Private*, pg. 4040
LR DEVELOPMENT COMPANY LLC—See The Related Companies, L.P.; *U.S. Private*, pg. 4103
LUCKY START LTD.; *U.S. Private*, pg. 2511
THE LYND COMPANY; *U.S. Private*, pg. 4073
MAB DEVELOPMENT NEDERLAND B.V.—See Cooperatieve Centrale Raiffeisen-Boerenleenbank B.A.; *Int'l*, pg. 1791
THE MACERICH COMPANY—See The Macerich Company; *U.S. Public*, pg. 2111
MADISON MARQUETTE REALTY SERVICES LLC—See Madison Marquette Development Corporation; *U.S. Private*, pg. 2544
MAINSAIL LODGING & DEVELOPMENT, LLC; *U.S. Private*, pg. 2553
MAMMOTH PROPERTIES, INC.; *U.S. Private*, pg. 2559
MANIFOLD SERVICES INC.; *U.S. Private*, pg. 2564
MANN REALTY COMPANY; *U.S. Private*, pg. 2564
MARONDA INC.; *U.S. Private*, pg. 2586
MARTIN K. EBY CONSTRUCTION COMPANY, INC.—See Eby Corporation; *U.S. Private*, pg. 1326
MARYL GROUP, INC.; *U.S. Private*, pg. 2600
MATRIX DEVELOPMENT GROUP INC.; *U.S. Private*, pg. 2611
MAURIN-OGDEN PROPERTIES; *U.S. Private*, pg. 2615
MCCORMACK BARON SALAZAR, INC.; *U.S. Private*, pg. 2629
MCGARVEY DEVELOPMENT COMPANY; *U.S. Private*, pg. 2634
MCGUIRE DEVELOPMENT COMPANY, LLC; *U.S. Private*, pg. 2636
MCKAY MANAGEMENT CORPORATION—See Associations, Inc.; *U.S. Private*, pg. 359
MCKENZIE PROPERTIES INC.—See Wildish Land Com-

N.A.I.C.S. Index

237210 — LAND SUBDIVISION CORPORATE AFFILIATIONS

pany; *U.S. Private*, pg. 4519
MEDALLIST DEVELOPMENTS INC.—See Great White Shark Enterprises, Inc.; *U.S. Private*, pg. 1768
MEDALLIST DEVELOPMENTS PTY. LIMITED—See Great White Shark Enterprises, Inc.; *U.S. Private*, pg. 1768
MEDICAL ACADEMIC & SCIENTIFIC COMMUNITY ORGANIZATION, INC.; *U.S. Private*, pg. 2654
METRO DEVELOPMENT GROUP, LLC; *U.S. Private*, pg. 2685
MEXICAN TOWN REAL ESTATE CO.—See CenTra, Inc.; *U.S. Private*, pg. 818
MEYER PROPERTIES CORP.; *U.S. Private*, pg. 2692
M.H. PODELL COMPANY; *U.S. Private*, pg. 2529
MICHAEL COLLARD PROPERTIES INC.; *U.S. Private*, pg. 2697
THE MICHAEL'S DEVELOPMENT COMPANY INC.; *U.S. Private*, pg. 4078
MID-ATLANTIC TOWER MANAGEMENT, LLC—See American Tower Corporation; *U.S. Public*, pg. 111
MIDLAND ATLANTIC PROPERTIES, LLC; *U.S. Private*, pg. 2714
MIDLAND ATLANTIC PROPERTIES, LLC—See Midland Atlantic Properties, LLC; *U.S. Private*, pg. 2714
MIDLAND ATLANTIC PROPERTIES, LLC—See Midland Atlantic Properties, LLC; *U.S. Private*, pg. 2714
MILLENNIUM MANAGEMENT INC.; *U.S. Private*, pg. 2731
MILLER DIVERSIFIED INC.; *U.S. Private*, pg. 2733
MIROMAR DEVELOPMENT CORPORATION; *U.S. Private*, pg. 2746
MIROMAR OUTLET EAST, LLC—See Miromar Development Corporation; *U.S. Private*, pg. 2746
MODUS OPERANDI PARTNERS, LLC; *U.S. Private*, pg. 2764
MONDSEE LIMITED—See Hysan Development Company Limited; *Int'l*, pg. 3554
MONTREUX GOLF CLUB LIMITED; *U.S. Private*, pg. 2777
NAPPEN & ASSOCIATES; *U.S. Private*, pg. 2835
NARRAGANSETT IMPROVEMENT CO; *U.S. Private*, pg. 2835
NATERRA LAND; *U.S. Private*, pg. 2838
NATIONAL DEVELOPMENT; *U.S. Private*, pg. 2852
NEAL COMMUNITIES INC.—See Estuary Investment Corp.; *U.S. Private*, pg. 1429
NEHEMIAH CORPORATION OF AMERICA; *U.S. Private*, pg. 2880
NESTUCCA RIDGE STORAGE; *U.S. Private*, pg. 2886
NEW BOSTON FUND, INC.; *U.S. Private*, pg. 2892
NEW BOSTON MANAGEMENT SERVICES INC.—See New Boston Fund, Inc.; *U.S. Private*, pg. 2892
NEWCASTLE ADVISORS LLC—See Newcastle Limited; *U.S. Private*, pg. 2914
NEWCASTLE LIMITED; *U.S. Private*, pg. 2914
NEW ENGLAND DEVELOPMENT CORPORATION; *U.S. Private*, pg. 2894
NEWFIELD CONSTRUCTION LIMITED—See Emerson Developments (Holdings) Limited; *Int'l*, pg. 2380
NEWGARD DEVELOPMENT GROUP INC.; *U.S. Private*, pg. 2915
THE NEWHALL LAND & FARMING COMPANY, INC.—See Lennar Corporation; *U.S. Public*, pg. 1307
NEW HORIZONS INCORPORATED; *U.S. Private*, pg. 2897
NEYER HOLDINGS—See Al Neyer, LLC; *U.S. Private*, pg. 147
N.O. SIMMONS & ASSOCIATES INCORPORATED; *U.S. Private*, pg. 2828
NOVASTAR DEVELOPMENT INC.; *U.S. Private*, pg. 2967
NTS DEVELOPMENT COMPANY—See NTS Corporation; *U.S. Private*, pg. 2971
NTS RESIDENTIAL PROPERTIES, INC.—See NTS Corporation; *U.S. Private*, pg. 2971
OAKBROOK COMPANIES, INC.; *U.S. Private*, pg. 2984
OBERER DEVELOPMENT CO.; *U.S. Private*, pg. 2986
O'BRIEN GROUP; *U.S. Private*, pg. 2977
OCEAN COLONY PARTNERS; *U.S. Private*, pg. 2989
OCMULGEE FIELDS INC.; *U.S. Private*, pg. 2992
O'CONNELL DEVELOPMENT GROUP INC.—See The O'Connell Companies, Incorporated; *U.S. Private*, pg. 4087
O'CONNELL PROPERTIES INC.—See The O'Connell Companies, Incorporated; *U.S. Private*, pg. 4087
ODYSSEY DEVELOPMENT, INC.; *U.S. Private*, pg. 2993
ONE HUGHES LANDING, LLC—See Howard Hughes Holdings Inc.; *U.S. Public*, pg. 1060
O'NEILL PROPERTIES GROUP, LP; *U.S. Private*, pg. 2980
OPUS DEVELOPMENT CORPORATION—See Opus Holding, LLC; *U.S. Private*, pg. 3036
ORBIT DEVELOPMENTS (SOUTHERN) LIMITED—See Emerson Developments (Holdings) Limited; *Int'l*, pg. 2380
OUTDOOR RESORTS OF AMERICA; *U.S. Private*, pg. 3051
OYER INC.; *U.S. Private*, pg. 3057
PALMER RANCH HOLDINGS LTD.; *U.S. Private*, pg. 3081
PARKSIDE MANAGEMENT SERVICES, LLC; *U.S. Private*, pg. 3098
PATHWAY COMMUNITIES INC.; *U.S. Private*, pg. 3106
PATTEN SALES & MARKETING, LLC; *U.S. Private*, pg. 3111
PAYLESS BUILDING CENTER INC.; *U.S. Private*, pg. 3117
PECCOLE NEVADA CORP; *U.S. Private*, pg. 3126
PERTAMA LAND & DEVELOPMENT SDN. BHD.—See DutaLand Berhad; *Int'l*, pg. 2235
PETULA ASSOCIATES, LLC—See Principal Financial Group, Inc.; *U.S. Public*, pg. 1720
PICERNE DEVELOPMENT CORP.—See Picerne Real Estate Group; *U.S. Private*, pg. 3176
PICERNE INVESTMENT CORPORATION; *U.S. Private*, pg. 3176
PICERNE REAL ESTATE GROUP; *U.S. Private*, pg. 3176
PLATINUM PROPERTIES, LLC.; *U.S. Private*, pg. 3210
PLAZA RESORT CLUB INC.—See World Holdings Inc.; *U.S. Private*, pg. 4565
POCAHONTAS DEVELOPMENT CORPORATION—See Norfolk Southern Corporation; *U.S. Public*, pg. 1536
POINDEXTER EXCAVATING, INC.; *U.S. Private*, pg. 3221
POINTE BUILDERS—See Pointe Group Ltd.; *U.S. Private*, pg. 3222
PORT ST. JOE MARINA INC.—See The St. Joe Company; *U.S. Public*, pg. 2131
POWER HOLDING CORPORATION; *U.S. Private*, pg. 3238
PRAIRIE MANAGEMENT & DEVELOPMENT; *U.S. Private*, pg. 3242
PRATT MANAGEMENT COMPANY LLC; *U.S. Private*, pg. 3243
PRISKE-JONES COMPANY; *U.S. Private*, pg. 3267
PUGET WESTERN, INC.—See Alberta Investment Management Corporation; *Int'l*, pg. 298
PUGET WESTERN, INC.—See British Columbia Investment Management Corp.; *Int'l*, pg. 1169
PUGET WESTERN, INC.—See Canada Pension Plan Investment Board; *Int'l*, pg. 1281
PULTE HOMES OF TEXAS, L.P.—See PulteGroup, Inc.; *U.S. Public*, pg. 1737
QUEENS HARBOUR YACHT & COUNTRY CLUB, LTD.—See Apollo Global Management, Inc.; *U.S. Public*, pg. 150
RAM DEVELOPMENT COMPANY, INC.; *U.S. Private*, pg. 3350
RAMPART CAPITAL CORPORATION; *U.S. Private*, pg. 3352
RANCHWOOD HOMES CORPORATION; *U.S. Private*, pg. 3353
RAUL WALTERS PROPERTIES, LLC; *U.S. Private*, pg. 3357
RAY STONE INCORPORATED; *U.S. Private*, pg. 3359
REA GROUP LIMITED—See News Corporation; *U.S. Public*, pg. 1521
REALMARK DEVELOPMENT, LLC; *U.S. Private*, pg. 3368
REAL SUB, LLC—See Publix Super Markets, Inc.; *U.S. Private*, pg. 3301
REALTEX DEVELOPMENT CORPORATION; *U.S. Private*, pg. 3369
REALTY RESOURCES CHARTERED; *U.S. Private*, pg. 3369
RELATED CHINA LIMITED—See The Related Companies, L.P.; *U.S. Private*, pg. 4103
RELATED FLORIDA, INC.; *U.S. Private*, pg. 3392
RELATED RETAIL, L.P.—See The Related Companies, L.P.; *U.S. Private*, pg. 4104
RELATED URBAN DEVELOPMENT, L.P.—See The Related Companies, L.P.; *U.S. Private*, pg. 4104
RENAISSANCE HOTEL GROUP N.V.—See Marriott International, Inc.; *U.S. Public*, pg. 1371
REYNEN & BARDIS COMMUNITIES, INC.; *U.S. Private*, pg. 3418
THE RICHMAN GROUP DEVELOPMENT CORPORATION; *U.S. Private*, pg. 4107
THE RICHMAN GROUP OF FLORIDA, INC.—See The Richman Group Development Corporation; *U.S. Private*, pg. 4107
RILEA GROUP INC.; *U.S. Private*, pg. 3436
RIVIERA POINT HOLDINGS, LLC; *U.S. Private*, pg. 3448
RJB DEVELOPMENT CO. INC.—See World Holdings Inc.; *U.S. Private*, pg. 4565
ROBERT C. RHEIN INTERESTS INC.; *U.S. Private*, pg. 3457
ROBINSON CAPITAL & INVESTMENTS INC.; *U.S. Private*, pg. 3461
ROBSON COMMUNITIES, INC.; *U.S. Private*, pg. 3463
ROCKWELL COMMUNITY DEVELOPMENT, INC.—See Bickerdike Redevelopment Corporation; *U.S. Private*, pg. 550
ROGER ARTZ; *U.S. Private*, pg. 3471
RONNING ENTERPRISES; *U.S. Private*, pg. 3478
RONTO GROUP, INC.; *U.S. Private*, pg. 3478
ROSEWOOD DEVELOPMENT CORPORATION—See Emerson Developments (Holdings) Limited; *Int'l*, pg. 2380
ROTONDA HOLDINGS INC.; *U.S. Private*, pg. 3487
ROYAL IMPERIAL GROUP INC.; *U.S. Private*, pg. 3492
R.T. MILORD CO.; *U.S. Private*, pg. 3339
RUBEN-HOLLAND DEVELOPMENT, LLC; *U.S. Private*, pg. 3499
RUDOLPH/LIBBE PROPERTIES, INC.—See The Rudolph/Libbe Companies; *U.S. Private*, pg. 4113
SANJOSE INMOBILIARIA—See Grupo Empresarial San Jose, S.A.; *Int'l*, pg. 3128
SAWYER DISPOSAL SERVICES, LLC—See Clean Harbors, Inc.; *U.S. Public*, pg. 510
SCARBOROUGH DEVELOPMENT LIMITED—See Far East Consortium International Limited; *Int'l*, pg. 2615
SCHOMAC GROUP INC.; *U.S. Private*, pg. 3568
SCHROEDER-MANATEE RANCH, INC.; *U.S. Private*, pg. 3569
THE SCOTTSDALE CO.; *U.S. Private*, pg. 4115
SEATRAIL GULF RESORT; *U.S. Private*, pg. 3591
SEMLING-MENKE COMPANY INC.; *U.S. Private*, pg. 3605
SEMPER DEVELOPMENT LTD; *U.S. Private*, pg. 3605
SERRANO ASSOCIATES, LLC; *U.S. Private*, pg. 3614
SHADDOCK DEVELOPMENT CO.; *U.S. Private*, pg. 3622
SHERWOOD DEVELOPMENT COMPANY—See Murdock Holdings, LLC; *U.S. Private*, pg. 2815
SIERRA CREST EQUITIES LLC; *U.S. Private*, pg. 3647
SIERRA LAND GROUP INC.; *U.S. Private*, pg. 3647
SIERRA PROPERTIES; *U.S. Private*, pg. 3647
SIGNA DEVELOPMENT SERVICES, INC.—See DLR Holding, LLC; *U.S. Private*, pg. 1247
SIMON KONOVER DEVELOPMENT CORPORATION—See The Simon Konover Company; *U.S. Private*, pg. 4118
SMG ASSOCIATES—See Ginsburg Development Corp.; *U.S. Private*, pg. 1702
SNYDER CORP.; *U.S. Private*, pg. 3701
SOUTH BARNES DEVELOPMENT CO.; *U.S. Private*, pg. 3719
SOUTHERN CALIFORNIA HOUSING DEVELOPMENT CORP.; *U.S. Private*, pg. 3729
SOUTHWESTERN PROPERTY CORP.; *U.S. Private*, pg. 3742
SOUTHWOOD CORPORATION—See Pennichuck Corporation; *U.S. Private*, pg. 3136
SP EAST HIGHLANDS RANCH—See Westbrook Real Estate Partners, LLC; *U.S. Private*, pg. 4488
S.R. WEINER & ASSOCIATES INC.; *U.S. Private*, pg. 3518
STARRETT CORPORATION; *U.S. Private*, pg. 3787
STEVEN WALKER COMMUNITIES, INC; *U.S. Private*, pg. 3809
THE ST. JOE COMPANY; *U.S. Public*, pg. 2131
ST. MODWEN DEVELOPMENTS LIMITED—See Blackstone Inc.; *U.S. Public*, pg. 358
STOCK DEVELOPMENT, LLC; *U.S. Private*, pg. 3814
STOKE-ON-TRENT REGENERATION LIMITED—See Blackstone Inc.; *U.S. Public*, pg. 358
STONEBURNER COMPANIES, LLC; *U.S. Private*, pg. 3827
STORM-WESTERN DEVELOPMENT CORP.—See Storm Industries, Inc.; *U.S. Private*, pg. 3831
STRATUS INVESTMENTS, LLC—See Stratus Properties, Inc.; *U.S. Public*, pg. 1954
STRATUS PROPERTIES, INC.; *U.S. Public*, pg. 1954
THE STRIP DEVELOPMENT, INC.; *U.S. Private*, pg. 4123
SUBURBAN DEVELOPMENTS INC.—See Wimmer Brothers Realty Inc.; *U.S. Private*, pg. 4532
SUMMERLIN DEVELOPMENT, LLC—See Howard Hughes Holdings Inc.; *U.S. Public*, pg. 1060
SUMMERLIN LAS VEGAS BASEBALL CLUB, LLC—See Howard Hughes Holdings Inc.; *U.S. Public*, pg. 1060
SUN LAKES MARKETING LP; *U.S. Private*, pg. 3863
SUNRIVER RESORT LIMITED PARTNERSHIP; *U.S. Private*, pg. 3870
SWERDLOW GROUP; *U.S. Private*, pg. 3892
TAILWINDS DEVELOPMENT, LLC; *U.S. Private*, pg. 3924
TASJA DEVELOPMENT SDN. BHD.—See Astral Asia Berhad; *Int'l*, pg. 658
TECON CORPORATION; *U.S. Private*, pg. 3957
TERRA GROUP; *U.S. Private*, pg. 3970
THOMSON PROPERTIES INC.; *U.S. Private*, pg. 4162
TH PROPERTIES; *U.S. Private*, pg. 3979
T & M ASPHALT PAVING; *U.S. Private*, pg. 3908
TOWNE DEVELOPMENT OF HAWAII, INC.—See Zilber Ltd.; *U.S. Private*, pg. 4604
TOWNHOMES MANAGEMENT, INC.; *U.S. Private*, pg. 4198
TRAMMELL CROW COMPANY, LLC—See CBRE Group, Inc.; *U.S. Public*, pg. 460
TRATON CORP.; *U.S. Private*, pg. 4212
TVO REALTY PARTNERS; *U.S. Private*, pg. 4263
UNICORP NATIONAL DEVELOPMENTS, INC.; *U.S. Private*, pg. 4282
UNIWELL CORPORATION; *U.S. Private*, pg. 4310
USA DEVELOPMENT CORP.; *U.S. Private*, pg. 4321
USA PROPERTIES FUND, INC.; *U.S. Private*, pg. 4321
U.S. ASSETS GROUP; *U.S. Private*, pg. 4270
VAIL RESORTS DEVELOPMENT COMPANY—See Vail Resorts, Inc.; *U.S. Public*, pg. 2272
VELUR LAND INVESTMENTS, INC.; *U.S. Private*, pg. 4355
VENTURE DEVELOPMENT CORP.; *U.S. Private*, pg. 4357
THE VIERA COMPANY—See A. Duda & Sons Inc.; *U.S. Private*, pg. 23
THE VILLAGES, FLORIDA INC.; *U.S. Private*, pg. 4131
VISTANA DEVELOPMENT, INC.—See Marriott International, Inc.; *U.S. Public*, pg. 1372
VOLUMETRIC BUILDING COMPANIES; *U.S. Private*, pg. 4411
WARD VILLAGE PROPERTIES, LLC—See Howard Hughes Holdings Inc.; *U.S. Public*, pg. 1061
THE WARMINGTON GROUP - NORTHERN CALIFORNIA

N.A.I.C.S. INDEX 237310 — HIGHWAY, STREET, AN...

N.A.I.C.S. Index

DIVISION OFFICE—See The Warmington Group; *U.S. Private*, pg. 4133
THE WARMINGTON GROUP; *U.S. Private*, pg. 4133
WC INVESTMENT COMPANY—See William Charles, Ltd.; *U.S. Private*, pg. 4522
WECCR GENERAL PARTNERSHIP—See Howard Hughes Holdings Inc.; *U.S. Public*, pg. 1060
WEEKS ROBINSON PROPERTIES; *U.S. Private*, pg. 4469
WILLIAM LYON HOMES, INC.—See Brookfield Corporation; *Int'l*, pg. 1183
THE WILSON COMPANY; *U.S. Private*, pg. 4136
THE WILSON HOLDING COMPANY; *U.S. Private*, pg. 4136
WINDSOR PROPERTIES INC.; *U.S. Private*, pg. 4539
WINNRESIDENTIAL LIMITED PARTNERSHIP; *U.S. Private*, pg. 4543
WINROCK ENTERPRISES, INC.; *U.S. Private*, pg. 4543
WISPARK LLC—See WEC Energy Group, Inc.; *U.S. Public*, pg. 2342
THE WOODLANDS BEVERAGE, INC.—See Howard Hughes Holdings Inc.; *U.S. Public*, pg. 1060
WOODLANDS OPERATING COMPANY LP; *U.S. Private*, pg. 4559
WOOD PARTNERS, L.L.C. - ORLANDO—See Wood Partners, L.L.C.; *U.S. Private*, pg. 4557
WOOD PARTNERS, L.L.C.; *U.S. Private*, pg. 4557
WOOLDRIDGE CONSTRUCTION CO., INC.; *U.S. Private*, pg. 4561
WOOLDRIDGE CONSTRUCTION CO., INC.—See Wooldridge Construction Co., Inc.; *U.S. Private*, pg. 4562
WORLD HOLDINGS INC.; *U.S. Private*, pg. 4565
WRIGHT RUNSTAD & COMPANY; *U.S. Private*, pg. 4573
WYNDHAM VACATION RESORTS—See Travel & Leisure Co.; *U.S. Public*, pg. 2186
XENTURY CITY DEVELOPMENT COMPANY, L.C.; *U.S. Private*, pg. 4581
YAMADA GROUP USA LTD.; *U.S. Private*, pg. 4585
YAT YUEN HONG CO., LTD.—See Hong Fok Corporation Limited; *Int'l*, pg. 3465
YORK PROPERTIES, INC. OF RALEIGH; *U.S. Private*, pg. 4591
ZAREMBA GROUP, LLC; *U.S. Private*, pg. 4598

237310 — HIGHWAY, STREET, AND BRIDGE CONSTRUCTION

565 CONSTRUCTION JOINT STOCK COMPANY; *Int'l*, pg. 13
AAA VALLEY GRAVEL, LLC—See Ahtna, Inc.; *U.S. Private*, pg. 131
ABC PAVING CO. INC.—See New Enterprise Stone & Lime Co., Inc.; *U.S. Private*, pg. 2895
ABC PAVING COMPANY; *U.S. Private*, pg. 36
ABRAMS INTERNATIONAL LLP; *U.S. Private*, pg. 40
ACCIONA INFRAESTRUCTURAS, S.A.—See Acciona, S.A.; *Int'l*, pg. 90
ACE ASPHALT OF ARIZONA, INC.—See Huron Capital Partners LLC; *U.S. Private*, pg. 2012
ACE ENGINEERING INC.; *U.S. Private*, pg. 56
ACE PAVING CO. INC.; *U.S. Private*, pg. 57
ACHEN-GARDNER CONSTRUCTION, LLC; *U.S. Private*, pg. 58
ACME CONCRETE PAVING INC.; *U.S. Private*, pg. 60
ADAMS CONSTRUCTION COMPANY; *U.S. Private*, pg. 74
ADAMS & SMITH INC.; *U.S. Private*, pg. 73
A-DEL CONSTRUCTION COMPANY, INC.; *U.S. Private*, pg. 22
ADENA CORPORATION; *U.S. Private*, pg. 77
AD PUTEVI UZICE; *Int'l*, pg. 122
ADVANCED ASPHALT COMPANY; *U.S. Private*, pg. 87
ADVANTAGE BARRICADE AND ROADMARKS, LLC—See Kohlberg & Company, LLC; *U.S. Private*, pg. 2337
AECON CONSTRUCTORS—See Aecon Group Inc.; *Int'l*, pg. 172
AECON INDUSTRIAL - WESTERN CANADA—See Aecon Group Inc.; *Int'l*, pg. 172
AECON TRANSPORTATION WEST LTD.—See Aecon Group Inc.; *Int'l*, pg. 172
AETNA BRIDGE COMPANY; *U.S. Private*, pg. 120
AETNA CONSTRUCTION CO. INC.—See Aetna Bridge Company; *U.S. Private*, pg. 120
AGATE CONSTRUCTION COMPANY, INC.—See Johnston Enterprises Inc.; *U.S. Private*, pg. 2230
AGI GENERAL CONTRACTING; *U.S. Private*, pg. 127
AGI TRAFFIC TECHNOLOGY, INC.—See Aecon Group Inc.; *Int'l*, pg. 172
AJAX PAVING INDUSTRIES, INC.; *U.S. Private*, pg. 143
AJAX PAVING INDUSTRIES INC.—See HHJ Holdings Limited; *U.S. Private*, pg. 1931
A.J. JOHNS, INC.; *U.S. Private*, pg. 26
AJR INFRA AND TOLLING LIMITED—See Gammon India Limited; *Int'l*, pg. 2879
AKROTEX WAREHOUSING, INC.—See Akrotex, Inc.; *U.S. Private*, pg. 146
AKTOR KUWAIT WLL—See ELLAKTOR S.A.; *Int'l*, pg. 2364
AKTOR S.A.—See ELLAKTOR S.A.; *Int'l*, pg. 2364
ALBERCO CONSTRUCTION LTD.; *Int'l*, pg. 293
A LIENOR S.A.—See Eiffage S.A.; *Int'l*, pg. 2329
AL JABER BITUMEN LLC—See Al Jaber Group; *Int'l*, pg. 279
AL JABER & PARTNERS L.L.C.—See Al Jaber Group; *Int'l*, pg. 280
AL JABER TRANSPORT & GENERAL CONTRACTING CO.—See Al Jaber Group; *Int'l*, pg. 280
ALL AMERICAN ASPHALT; *U.S. Private*, pg. 169
ALLAN A. MYERS, INC.; *U.S. Private*, pg. 174
ALLCO LTD.; *U.S. Private*, pg. 175
THE ALLEN COMPANY INC.; *U.S. Private*, pg. 3984
ALL STAR STRIPING LLC—See Trilantic Capital Management L.P.; *U.S. Private*, pg. 4231
AL MINNERATH INC.; *U.S. Private*, pg. 147
AL-OSAIS TRANSPORTATION & ROAD CONSTRUCTION CO.—See Al-Osais International Holding Company; *Int'l*, pg. 287
ALPINE BAU DEUTSCHLAND AG—See ALPINE Bau GmbH; *Int'l*, pg. 371
ALVIN J. COLEMAN & SON INC.; *U.S. Private*, pg. 214
A.M. COHRON & SON, INC.; *U.S. Private*, pg. 27
AMERICAN ASPHALT PAVING CO.; *U.S. Private*, pg. 222
AMERICAN ASPHALT REPAIR & RESURFACING; *U.S. Private*, pg. 222
AMERICAN BRIDGE MANUFACTURING COMPANY—See Continental Holdings Corp.; *Int'l*, pg. 1784
AMERICAN CIVIL CONSTRUCTORS HOLDING INC.—See MasTec, Inc.; *U.S. Public*, pg. 1393
AMERICAN PAVING CO. INC.—See Lyles Diversified Inc.; *U.S. Private*, pg. 2520
AMES CONSTRUCTION, INC.; *U.S. Private*, pg. 261
AMICK CONSTRUCTION, INC.; *U.S. Private*, pg. 263
ANCHOR CONSTRUCTION CORPORATION; *U.S. Private*, pg. 273
ANDERSON BROTHERS CONSTRUCTION CO. BRAINERD, INC.; *U.S. Private*, pg. 276
ANDERSON COLUMBIA CO. INC.; *U.S. Private*, pg. 276
ANDRELL INC.; *U.S. Private*, pg. 279
ANGELO IAFRATE CONSTRUCTION COMPANY—See The Angelo Iafrate Companies; *U.S. Private*, pg. 3986
ANHUI EXPRESSWAY COMPANY LIMITED; *Int'l*, pg. 467
APAC-KANSAS - KANSAS CITY DIVISION—See CRH plc; *Int'l*, pg. 1846
APAC-KANSAS - SHEARS DIVISION—See CRH plc; *Int'l*, pg. 1846
APAC-OKLAHOMA, INC.—See CRH plc; *Int'l*, pg. 1846
APAC-SOUTHEAST - SOUTHERN FLORIDA DIVISION—See CRH plc; *Int'l*, pg. 1846
A PANAYIDES CONTRACTING PUBLIC LTD; *Int'l*, pg. 18
A&P CONSULTING TRANSPORTATION ENGINEERS CORP.—See H.I.G. Capital, LLC; *U.S. Private*, pg. 1827
API MOVILIDAD, S.A.—See ACS, Actividades de Construccion y Servicios, S.A.; *Int'l*, pg. 110
APPIA LIANTS EMULSION RHONE ALPES—See Eiffage S.A.; *Int'l*, pg. 2330
APPLE TUCK & ASSOCIATES, INC.—See Sunland Builders; *U.S. Private*, pg. 3868
APPLY-A-LINE, LLC—See The Sterling Group, L.P.; *U.S. Private*, pg. 4121
ARAWAK PAVING CO. INC.; *U.S. Private*, pg. 308
ARCO INCORPORATED; *U.S. Private*, pg. 315
ARCO/MURRAY NATIONAL CONSTRUCTION COMPANY, INC.; *U.S. Private*, pg. 315
AREA SOCIETE DES AUTOROUTES RHONES-ALPES SA—See Eiffage S.A.; *Int'l*, pg. 2331
ARIZONA PAVEMENT PROFILING—See Nesbitt Investment Company; *U.S. Private*, pg. 2886
ARKIL HOLDING A/S; *Int'l*, pg. 571
ARROW ROAD CONSTRUCTION COMPANY; *U.S. Private*, pg. 335
ARSS INFRASTRUCTURE PROJECTS LIMITED; *Int'l*, pg. 580
ARTEFACT INFRASTRUCTURE LTD.—See Artefact Projects Ltd.; *Int'l*, pg. 581
ARTERIS S.A.—See Brookfield Corporation; *Int'l*, pg. 1175
ASHMORE BROS., INC.; *U.S. Private*, pg. 350
ASHOKA BUILDCON LTD.; *Int'l*, pg. 608
ASHOKA CONCESSIONS LIMITED—See Ashoka Buildcon Ltd.; *Int'l*, pg. 608
ASLAN CONSTRUCTION INC.; *U.S. Private*, pg. 351
A&S PAVING, INC.; *U.S. Private*, pg. 21
ASPHALT CONTRACTORS INC.; *U.S. Private*, pg. 352
ASPHALT PAVING COMPANY OF AUSTIN, LLC—See Summit Materials, Inc.; *U.S. Public*, pg. 1960
ASPHALT SURFACING COMPANY—See Henry Carlson Company; *U.S. Private*, pg. 1917
ASTM S.P.A.—See Argo Finanziaria S.p.A.; *Int'l*, pg. 561
A.S.W. SERVICES INC.; *U.S. Private*, pg. 28
ATA HILL & SMITH AB—See Hill & Smith PLC; *Int'l*, pg. 3391
ATA HILL & SMITH AS—See Hill & Smith PLC; *Int'l*, pg. 3391
ATLAS EXCAVATING INC.; *U.S. Private*, pg. 376
ATM CONSTRUCT S.A.; *Int'l*, pg. 687
ATWOOD FENCE COMPANY INC.; *U.S. Private*, pg. 384
AUSTIN BRIDGE & ROAD, INC.—See Austin Industries, Inc.; *U.S. Private*, pg. 395
AUSTIN ENGINEERING CO., INC.; *U.S. Private*, pg. 395
AUTOCAMIONALE DELLA CISA S.P.A.—See Argo Finanziaria S.p.A.; *Int'l*, pg. 562
AUTOPISTAS DEL CAFE S.A.—See Grupo Argos S.A.; *Int'l*, pg. 3120
AUTOPISTAS DE LEON, S.A.C.E.—See ACS, Actividades de Construccion y Servicios, S.A.; *Int'l*, pg. 112
AUTOPISTAS DEL NORDESTE S.A.—See Grupo Argos S.A.; *Int'l*, pg. 3120
AUTOSTRADA ASTI-CUNEO S.P.A.—See Argo Finanziaria S.p.A.; *Int'l*, pg. 562
AUTOSTRADA DEL BRENNERO S.P.A.—See Edizione S.r.l.; *Int'l*, pg. 2311
AUTOSTRADA LIGURE TOSCANA S.P.A.—See Argo Finanziaria S.p.A.; *Int'l*, pg. 562
AUTOSTRADE CONCESSIONI E COSTRUZIONI S.P.A.—See Edizione S.r.l.; *Int'l*, pg. 2311
AUTOSTRADE PER L'ITALIA S.P.A.—See Edizione S.r.l.; *Int'l*, pg. 2312
AUTOVIA DE LA MANCHA, S.A—See ACS, Actividades de Construccion y Servicios, S.A.; *Int'l*, pg. 110
AUTOVIA DEL CAMP DEL TURIA, S.A.—See ACS, Actividades de Construccion y Servicios, S.A.; *Int'l*, pg. 110
AUTOVIA DEL PIRINEO, S.A.—See ACS, Actividades de Construccion y Servicios, S.A.; *Int'l*, pg. 110
AXIMUM—See Bouygues S.A.; *Int'l*, pg. 1122
AYOUBCO GENERAL CONTRACTING; *Int'l*, pg. 775
BAKER ROCK CRUSHING CO.; *U.S. Private*, pg. 456
BALDWIN CONTRACTING COMPANY, INC.—See MDU Resources Group, Inc.; *U.S. Public*, pg. 1410
BALDWIN PAVING COMPANY INC.; *U.S. Private*, pg. 459
BALLENGER PAVING DIVISION—See CRH plc; *Int'l*, pg. 1846
BALLOU CONSTRUCTION COMPANY INCORPORATED; *U.S. Private*, pg. 461
BANGKOK EXPRESSWAY AND METRO PUBLIC COMPANY LIMITED—See CH. Karnchang Public Company Limited; *Int'l*, pg. 1435
BARBER BROTHERS CONTRACTING COMPANY; *U.S. Private*, pg. 472
BARNHILL CONTRACTING COMPANY; *U.S. Private*, pg. 478
BARRIERE CONSTRUCTION CO. LLC; *U.S. Private*, pg. 480
BARTHEL CONTRACTING COMPANY; *U.S. Private*, pg. 482
BASIC CONSTRUCTION COMPANY; *U.S. Private*, pg. 485
BASIC RESOURCES INC.; *U.S. Private*, pg. 485
BASIL READ HOLDINGS LIMITED; *Int'l*, pg. 886
BAST HATFIELD INC.; *U.S. Private*, pg. 486
BATTEN & SHAW, INC.; *U.S. Private*, pg. 488
BAUMEISTER DOO; *Int'l*, pg. 895
BCB BERHAD; *Int'l*, pg. 926
BC CANNON CO. INC.—See Trilantic Capital Management L.P.; *U.S. Private*, pg. 4231
BDB INFRA SDN. BHD.—See Bina Darulaman Berhad; *Int'l*, pg. 1032
BDC VIETNAM INVESTMENT & CONSTRUCTION JSC; *Int'l*, pg. 929
BECCO CONTRACTORS, INC.; *U.S. Private*, pg. 509
BEIJING CHANG CHENG BILFINGER BERGER CONSTRUCTION ENGINEERING CORP. LTD.—See Beijing Construction Engineering (Group) Co., Ltd.; *Int'l*, pg. 948
BENTON & BROWN INC.; *U.S. Private*, pg. 528
BERNARDS BROS, INC.; *U.S. Private*, pg. 536
BERRY CONTRACT INC.; *U.S. Private*, pg. 538
BETON-STIP; *Int'l*, pg. 1003
BETON- UND MONIERBAU GESELLSCHAFT M.B.H.—See ALPINE Bau GmbH; *Int'l*, pg. 371
BETONUT SZOLGALTATO ES EPITO RT.; *Int'l*, pg. 1003
BETTEROADS ASPHALT CORP; *U.S. Private*, pg. 547
BETTER ROADS INC.; *U.S. Private*, pg. 547
BHARAT ROAD NETWORK LTD.; *Int'l*, pg. 1011
BIANCO—See FAYAT SAS; *Int'l*, pg. 2624
BICK CO.; *U.S. Private*, pg. 550
BIG CREEK CONSTRUCTION, LTD.; *U.S. Private*, pg. 553
BILLET SAS; *Int'l*, pg. 1030
BILLS SWEEPING SERVICE, INC.—See Warburg Pincus LLC; *U.S. Private*, pg. 4440
BINA PURI HOLDINGS BHD; *Int'l*, pg. 1032
BIZZACK, INC.—See CRH plc; *Int'l*, pg. 1847
BLACK DIAMOND GROUP, INC.; *U.S. Private*, pg. 571
BLAKEMORE CONSTRUCTION CORP.; *U.S. Private*, pg. 578
BLAKESLEE ARPAIA CHAPMAN INC.; *U.S. Private*, pg. 578
BLANTON CONSTRUCTION; *U.S. Private*, pg. 579
BLOOMING GLEN CONTRACTORS INC.—See Haines & Kibblehouse Inc.; *U.S. Private*, pg. 1840
BLYNCSY, INC.—See Bentley Systems, Inc.; *U.S. Public*, pg. 297
BLYTHE DEVELOPMENT CO.; *U.S. Private*, pg. 600
BMO ENTREPRENOR AS—See Endur ASA; *Int'l*, pg. 2409
BOB PROPHETER CONSTRUCTION LLC; *U.S. Private*, pg. 605
BOH BROS. CONSTRUCTION CO., LLC; *U.S. Private*, pg. 609
BOLLO CONSTRUCTION, INC.; *U.S. Private*, pg. 611
BONDS COMPANY, INC.; *U.S. Private*, pg. 613
BORDER STATES PAVING, INC.; *U.S. Private*, pg. 618

237310 — HIGHWAY, STREET, AN... CORPORATE AFFILIATIONS

BORGHESI BUILDING & ENGINEERING CO., INC.; *U.S. Private*, pg. 618
BOWES CONSTRUCTION, INC.; *U.S. Private*, pg. 625
B.P. SHORT & SON PAVING CO.; *U.S. Private*, pg. 421
BRADENBURG INDUSTRIAL SERVICE COMPANY INC. - BETHLEHEM, PA—See Brandenburg Industrial Service Company Inc.; *U.S. Private*, pg. 637
B.R. AMON & SONS INC.; *U.S. Private*, pg. 421
BRANCH HIGHWAYS, INC.—See The Branch Group, Inc.; *U.S. Private*, pg. 3999
BRANNAN PAVING COMPANY, LTD.; *U.S. Private*, pg. 639
BRANNAN SAND & GRAVEL CO. LLC; *U.S. Private*, pg. 639
BRANSCUM CONSTRUCTION COMPANY, INC.; *U.S. Private*, pg. 640
BRAYMAN CONSTRUCTION CORPORATION; *U.S. Private*, pg. 642
BRISA AUTO-ESTRADAS DE PORTUGAL, S.A.—See APG Asset Management NV; *Int'l*, pg. 512
BRISA NORTH AMERICA, INC—See APG Asset Management NV; *Int'l*, pg. 512
BRISA O&M, S.A.—See APG Asset Management NV; *Int'l*, pg. 512
BRISA UNITED STATES, LLC—See APG Asset Management NV; *Int'l*, pg. 512
BRIX CORPORATION; *U.S. Private*, pg. 657
BROOKS CONSTRUCTION COMPANY; *U.S. Private*, pg. 664
BRUNEL ENGINEERING CONSULTANTS NV—See Brunel International N.V.; *Int'l*, pg. 1199
BRUTOCO ENGINEERING & CONSTRUCTION, INC.; *U.S. Private*, pg. 673
BRYSTAR CONTRACTING, INC.; *U.S. Private*, pg. 674
BUCKLEY & COMPANY INC.; *U.S. Private*, pg. 678
BUQUET & LEBLANC CONTRACTORS, INC.; *U.S. Private*, pg. 686
BURESKI HOLDINGS, INC.—See Advanced Pavement Group Corp.; *U.S. Private*, pg. 91
CAHYA MATA ROADS SDN. BHD.—See Cahya Mata Sarawak Berhad; *Int'l*, pg. 1251
CALHOUN COUNTY ROAD COMMISSION; *U.S. Private*, pg. 717
CALIFORNIA PAVEMENT MAINTENANCE CO., INC.; *U.S. Private*, pg. 720
CAMINOS DE LAS SIERRAS S.A.; *Int'l*, pg. 1273
CANAM-BRIDGE—See AIP, LLC; *U.S. Private*, pg. 134
CAPCO CONTRACTORS, INC.; *U.S. Private*, pg. 737
CAPITAL EXCAVATION COMPANY; *U.S. Private*, pg. 740
CAPITOL PAVING OF D.C., INC.; *U.S. Private*, pg. 744
C.A. RASMUSSEN, INC.; *U.S. Private*, pg. 706
CARDI CORPORATION; *U.S. Private*, pg. 749
CARIBBEAN INDUSTRIAL CONSTRUCTION SE; *U.S. Private*, pg. 760
CARLO LIZZA & SONS PAVING; *U.S. Private*, pg. 764
CARL ROSE & SONS INC; *U.S. Private*, pg. 763
CAROLINA TRAFFIC DEVICES INC.; *U.S. Private*, pg. 769
CCCC FINANCIAL LEASING CO., LTD.—See China Communications Construction Company Limited; *Int'l*, pg. 1490
CCCC FIRST HARBOUR ENGINEERING CO., LTD.—See China Communications Construction Company Limited; *Int'l*, pg. 1490
CCCC FOURTH HARBOUR ENGINEERING CO., LTD.—See China Communications Construction Company Limited; *Int'l*, pg. 1490
CCCC FOURTH HIGHWAY ENGINEERING CO., LTD.—See China Communications Construction Company Limited; *Int'l*, pg. 1490
CCCC HIGHWAY CONSULTANTS CO., LTD.—See China Communications Construction Company Limited; *Int'l*, pg. 1490
CCCC SECOND HARBOUR ENGINEERING CO., LTD.—See China Communications Construction Company Limited; *Int'l*, pg. 1490
CCCC SECOND HIGHWAY CONSULTANTS CO., LTD.—See China Communications Construction Company Limited; *Int'l*, pg. 1490
CCCC SECOND HIGHWAY ENGINEERING CO., LTD.—See China Communications Construction Company Limited; *Int'l*, pg. 1490
CCCC THIRD HARBOUR ENGINEERING CO., LTD.—See China Communications Construction Company Limited; *Int'l*, pg. 1490
C & C CONSTRUCTIONS LIMITED; *Int'l*, pg. 1237
CCL INTERNATIONAL LIMITED; *Int'l*, pg. 1369
C.C. MYERS, INC.; *U.S. Private*, pg. 706
CCR S.A.; *Int'l*, pg. 1369
CENTRAL BLACKTOP CO., INC.; *U.S. Private*, pg. 819
CENTRAL CONTRACTING COMPANY; *U.S. Private*, pg. 820
CENTROVIAS SISTEMAS RODOVIARIOS, S.A.—See Brookfield Corporation; *Int'l*, pg. 1175
CENTURY COMPANIES, INC.; *U.S. Private*, pg. 832
CESSFORD CONSTRUCTION COMPANY—See CRH plc; *Int'l*, pg. 1847
CESTNE SATVBY AS; *Int'l*, pg. 1424
C.G. ENTERPRISES INC.; *U.S. Private*, pg. 707
CHANCELLOR & SON INC.; *U.S. Private*, pg. 847

CHANNEL TUNNEL RAIL LINK—See Getlink SE; *Int'l*, pg. 2952
CHARLES BLALOCK & SONS INC.; *U.S. Private*, pg. 851
CHARLIE'S CONTRACTING, INC.; *U.S. Private*, pg. 857
CHEMCOTE, INC.; *U.S. Private*, pg. 871
CHENGDU EXPRESSWAY CO., LTD.; *Int'l*, pg. 1467
CHENGDU ROAD & BRIDGE ENGINEERING CO., LTD.; *Int'l*, pg. 1468
CHERRY HILL CONSTRUCTION INC.—See Tutor Perini Corporation; *U.S. Public*, pg. 2205
CHINA MERCHANTS HUAJIAN HIGHWAY INVESTMENT CO., LTD.—See China Merchants Group Limited; *Int'l*, pg. 1520
CHINA RAILWAY CONSTRUCTION BRIDGE ENGINEERING BUREAU GROUP CO., LTD.—See China Railway Construction Corporation Limited; *Int'l*, pg. 1543
CHINA RESOURCES AND TRANSPORTATION GROUP LIMITED; *Int'l*, pg. 1548
CHINA ROAD & BRIDGE CORPORATION—See China Communications Construction Company Limited; *Int'l*, pg. 1490
C. H. LANGMAN & SONS INC.; *U.S. Private*, pg. 705
CHONGQING ROAD & BRIDGE CO., LTD.; *Int'l*, pg. 1580
CHUNGKWANG CONSTRUCTION CO., LTD.; *Int'l*, pg. 1598
CII BRIDGES AND ROAD INVESTMENT JOINT STOCK COMPANY; *Int'l*, pg. 1607
CITEPARK—See FAYAT SAS; *Int'l*, pg. 2625
C.J. HESSE, INC.—See The Hesse Companies; *U.S. Private*, pg. 4052
C.J. MILLER LLC; *U.S. Private*, pg. 708
CLARKSON CONSTRUCTION COMPANY; *U.S. Private*, pg. 915
CLARY HOOD, INC.; *U.S. Private*, pg. 915
C & L SERVICES LLC; *U.S. Private*, pg. 701
CLYDE COMPANIES INC.; *U.S. Private*, pg. 949
CMES, INC.; *U.S. Private*, pg. 950
CMS PAVEMENT TECH SDN. BHD.—See Cahya Mata Sarawak Berhad; *Int'l*, pg. 1251
CMS ROADS SDN. BHD.—See Cahya Mata Sarawak Berhad; *Int'l*, pg. 1251
CMS WORKS SDN. BHD.—See Cahya Mata Sarawak Berhad; *Int'l*, pg. 1251
COASTAL BRIDGE COMPANY, LLC - CONVENT ASPHALT PLANT—See Coastal Bridge Company, LLC; *U.S. Private*, pg. 955
COASTAL BRIDGE COMPANY, LLC - PORT ALLEN ASPHALT PLANT—See Coastal Bridge Company, LLC; *U.S. Private*, pg. 955
COASTAL BRIDGE COMPANY, LLC; *U.S. Private*, pg. 955
COLAS BELGIUM SA—See Bouygues S.A.; *Int'l*, pg. 1122
COLAS CANADA INC—See Bouygues S.A.; *Int'l*, pg. 1122
COLAS CZ, A.S.—See Bouygues S.A.; *Int'l*, pg. 1122
COLAS INC.—See Bouygues S.A.; *Int'l*, pg. 1122
COLASKA INC.; *U.S. Private*, pg. 965
COLAS MARTINIQUE—See Bouygues S.A.; *Int'l*, pg. 1123
COLAS POLSKA SP.Z.O.O—See Bouygues S.A.; *Int'l*, pg. 1123
COLAS SA—See Bouygues S.A.; *Int'l*, pg. 1122
COLUMBIA CURB & GUTTER CO.; *U.S. Private*, pg. 976
COMANCHE CONSTRUCTION INC.; *U.S. Private*, pg. 980
COMBINED GROUP FACTORIES COMPANY W.L.L.—See Combined Group Contracting Company KSCC; *Int'l*, pg. 1709
COMBINED GROUP TRADING & CONTRACTING CO. W.L.L.—See Combined Group Contracting Company KSCC; *Int'l*, pg. 1709
COMMUNITY ASPHALT CORP.; *U.S. Private*, pg. 989
COMPAGNIE EIFFAGE DU VIADUC DE MILLAU—See Caisse des Depots et Consignations; *Int'l*, pg. 1257
COMPAGNIE EIFFAGE DU VIADUC DE MILLAU—See Eiffage S.A.; *Int'l*, pg. 2329
COMPANHIA DA METRO DA BAHIA SA—See CCR S.A.; *Int'l*, pg. 1369
COMPLETE GENERAL CONSTRUCTION CO. INC.; *U.S. Private*, pg. 1000
CONALVIAS S.A.; *Int'l*, pg. 1763
CONCESIONARIA PANAMERICANA S.A.S.—See Grupo Aval Acciones y Valores S.A.; *Int'l*, pg. 3121
CONCESIONARIA SAN RAFAEL, S.A.—See ACS, Actividades de Construccion y Servicios, S.A.; *Int'l*, pg. 111
CONCESIONARIA VIAL ANDINA S.A.S.—See Grupo Aval Acciones y Valores S.A.; *Int'l*, pg. 3121
CONCESIONARIA VIAL DEL PACIFICO S.A.S.—See Grupo Aval Acciones y Valores S.A.; *Int'l*, pg. 3121
CONCESION CANCHAQUE S.A.C.—See Aenza S.A.A.; *Int'l*, pg. 176
CONCESIONES CCFC S.A.S.—See Grupo Aval Acciones y Valores S.A.; *Int'l*, pg. 3121
CONCESION LA PINTADA S.A.S.—See Grupo Argos S.A.; *Int'l*, pg. 3121
CONCESION VIAL DE LOS LLANOS S.A.S.—See Grupo Argos S.A.; *Int'l*, pg. 3121
CONCESSIONARIA AUTO RAPOSO TAVARES S.A.; *Int'l*, pg. 1764
CONCESSIONARIA DA RODOVIA DOS LAGOS SA—See CCR S.A.; *Int'l*, pg. 1369
CONCESSIONARIA DA RODOVIA PRESIDENTE DUTRA SA—See CCR S.A.; *Int'l*, pg. 1369
CONCESSIONARIA DE RODOVIAS INTEGRADAS DO OESTE S/A—See CCR S.A.; *Int'l*, pg. 1369
CONCESSIONARIA DO RODOANEL OESTE S.A.—See CCR S.A.; *Int'l*, pg. 1369
CONCESSIONARIA ECOVIAS DOS IMIGRANTES S.A.; *Int'l*, pg. 1764
CONCESSIONARIA RODOVIAS DO TIETE S.A.; *Int'l*, pg. 1764
CONCESSIONARIA ROTA DAS BANDEIRAS S.A.; *Int'l*, pg. 1764
CONCRETE GENERAL, INC.; *U.S. Private*, pg. 1011
CONDOTTE AMERICA INC.—See Ferfina S.p.A.; *Int'l*, pg. 2637
CONE ENGINEERING CONTRACTORS; *U.S. Private*, pg. 1012
CONE & GRAHAM, INC.; *U.S. Private*, pg. 1012
CONNECT ROADS SUNDERLAND LTD—See Balfour Beatty plc; *Int'l*, pg. 807
CONNELLY PAVING; *U.S. Private*, pg. 1017
CONSTRUCOES E COMERCIO CAMARGO CORREA SA—See Camargo Correa S.A.; *Int'l*, pg. 1268
CONSTRUCTII FEROVIARE CRAIOVA SA; *Int'l*, pg. 1777
CONSTRUCTION ARMBRO BFC INC.—See Aecon Group Inc.; *Int'l*, pg. 172
CONSTRUCTORS INC.; *U.S. Private*, pg. 1024
CONTEGRA CONSTRUCTION COMPANY, L.L.C.; *U.S. Private*, pg. 1027
THE CONTI GROUP; *U.S. Private*, pg. 4014
CONTOUR STEEL INC; *U.S. Private*, pg. 1031
COOPER BARNETTE & PAGE; *U.S. Private*, pg. 1040
COP CONSTRUCTION CO.; *U.S. Private*, pg. 1044
CORAL CONSTRUCTION COMPANY; *U.S. Private*, pg. 1046
CORMAN CONSTRUCTION INC.—See C.G. Enterprises Inc.; *U.S. Private*, pg. 707
CORNERSTONE BUSINESSES INC.; *U.S. Private*, pg. 1051
COSTELLO INDUSTRIES INC.; *U.S. Private*, pg. 1063
CPC INGENIERIA Y CONSTRUCCIONES SA; *Int'l*, pg. 1824
CP WARD INC.; *U.S. Private*, pg. 1079
CRAIG PAVING INC.; *U.S. Private*, pg. 1083
CRANFORD CONSTRUCTION CO.—See McGeorge Contracting Co., Inc.; *U.S. Private*, pg. 2634
CROOKER CONSTRUCTION, LLC; *U.S. Private*, pg. 1103
CROWDER CONSTRUCTION COMPANY; *U.S. Private*, pg. 1109
CRT CONSTRUCTION INC.; *Int'l*, pg. 1859
CSA MATERIALS, INC.—See Reece Albert Inc.; *U.S. Private*, pg. 3381
C.S. MCCROSSAN, INC.; *U.S. Private*, pg. 709
CTI MYANMAR CO., LTD.—See CTI Engineering Co., Ltd.; *Int'l*, pg. 1871
THE CUMMINS CONSTRUCTION COMPANY INC.—See RLC Holding Co. Inc.; *U.S. Private*, pg. 3450
CURRAN CONTRACTING COMPANY—See Curran Group, Inc.; *U.S. Private*, pg. 1125
CURRAN CONTRACTING INC—See Curran Group, Inc.; *U.S. Private*, pg. 1125
C. WILLIAM HETZER, INC.; *U.S. Private*, pg. 705
C.W. MATTHEWS CONTRACTING COMPANY, INC.; *U.S. Private*, pg. 709
C.W. ROBERTS CONTRACTING, INC.—See Construction Partners, Inc.; *U.S. Public*, pg. 572
THE D.A. COLLINS CONSTRUCTION CO., INC.; *U.S. Private*, pg. 4017
D'ADDARIO INDUSTRIES INC.; *U.S. Private*, pg. 1138
DALRYMPLE HOLDING CORP.; *U.S. Private*, pg. 1150
DANE CONSTRUCTION INC.; *U.S. Private*, pg. 1153
DAN WILLIAMS COMPANY; *U.S. Private*, pg. 1152
DARRELL DINSMORE GRADING INC.; *U.S. Private*, pg. 1159
DAVID A. BRAMBLE, INC. - MASSEY FACILITY—See David A. Bramble, Inc.; *U.S. Private*, pg. 1169
DCK PACIFIC CONSTRUCTION LLC.; *U.S. Private*, pg. 1180
D. CONSTRUCTION; *U.S. Private*, pg. 1139
D & D BUILDING, INC.; *U.S. Private*, pg. 1136
DD DOBOJPUTEVI; *Int'l*, pg. 1993
DEAN WORD COMPANY LTD.; *U.S. Private*, pg. 1184
DEMENT CONSTRUCTION COMPANY INC.; *U.S. Private*, pg. 1203
DEMIX CONSTRUCTION - LAVAL—See CRH plc; *Int'l*, pg. 1843
DE MOYA GROUP INC.; *U.S. Private*, pg. 1181
DENTON CONCRETE SERVICES INC.—See Denton Enterprises Inc.; *U.S. Private*, pg. 1206
DENTON ENTERPRISES INC.; *U.S. Private*, pg. 1206
DESERT PAVING, INC.; *U.S. Private*, pg. 1213
DESILVA GATES CONSTRUCTION; *U.S. Private*, pg. 1215
DEWEY JORDAN INC.; *U.S. Private*, pg. 1219
D&F CONSTRUCTION, INC.; *U.S. Private*, pg. 1137
D. H. GRIFFIN CO.; *U.S. Private*, pg. 1140
DIAMOND B CONSTRUCTION CO., LLC; *U.S. Private*, pg. 1222
DICKERSON FLORIDA, INC.—See The Dickerson Group, Inc.; *U.S. Private*, pg. 4021

N.A.I.C.S. INDEX

237310 — HIGHWAY, STREET, AN...

DIFIORE GROUP; *U.S. Private*, pg. 1229
D L BECK INC.; *U.S. Private*, pg. 1136
DLB INC.; *U.S. Private*, pg. 1247
DLE SPECIALITES—See Eiffage S.A.; *Int'l*, pg. 2330
DOMINION PAVING & SEALING, INC.—See Shoreline Equity Partners, LLC; *U.S. Private*, pg. 3641
THE DON CHAPIN CO. INC.; *U.S. Private*, pg. 4022
DONEGAL CONSTRUCTION CORPORATION—See SurfaceCycle, Inc.; *U.S. Private*, pg. 3884
DOWNER EDI WORKS PTY LTD.—See Downer EDI Limited; *Int'l*, pg. 2186
DPR CONSTRUCTION; *U.S. Private*, pg. 1270
DRG & ASSOCIATES, INC.; *U.S. Private*, pg. 1277
DROGOMEX SP. Z O.O.—See CRH plc; *Int'l*, pg. 1844
DRYCO CONSTRUCTION, INC.; *U.S. Private*, pg. 1280
DRY CREEK STRUCTURES; *U.S. Private*, pg. 1280
DUBRAC TP; *Int'l*, pg. 2222
DUFFERIN CONSTRUCTION COMPANY—See CRH plc; *Int'l*, pg. 1843
DUININCK COMPANIES LLC; *U.S. Private*, pg. 1285
DUNA ASZFALT ZTR; *Int'l*, pg. 2225
DUNN CONSTRUCTION COMPANY, INC.; *U.S. Private*, pg. 1290
DUNN ROADBUILDERS LLC; *U.S. Private*, pg. 1290
DURACO INDUSTRIES, INC.—See Hines Corporation; *U.S. Private*, pg. 1949
DWC CONSTRUCTION COMPANY, INC.; *U.S. Private*, pg. 1295
EAGLE INDUSTRY HUNGARY KFT.—See Eagle Industry Co., Ltd.; *Int'l*, pg. 2265
ECCO III ENTERPRISES, INC.; *U.S. Private*, pg. 1326
ECO CONSTRUCTION & MAINTENANCE MANAGEMENT, LLC.; *U.S. Private*, pg. 1328
ECONOMY PAVING CO. INC.; *U.S. Private*, pg. 1330
ECO TECH CONTRACTORS INC.; *U.S. Private*, pg. 1328
ED BELL CONSTRUCTION COMPANY INC.—See Ed Bell Investments Company Inc.; *U.S. Private*, pg. 1331
ED BELL INVESTMENTS COMPANY INC.; *U.S. Private*, pg. 1331
EDILE SAN FELICE S.P.A.; *Int'l*, pg. 2309
EDWARD KRAEMER & SONS INC.; *U.S. Private*, pg. 1341
EDWARDS CONTRACTING—See Reding Gravel & Excavating Co., Inc.; *U.S. Private*, pg. 3379
EE CRUZ & COMPANY INC.—See ACS, Actividades de Construccion y Servicios, S.A.; *Int'l*, pg. 113
E E HOOD & SONS CONSTRUCTION; *U.S. Private*, pg. 1300
EIFFAGE ENERGIE TRANSPORT & DISTRIBUTION S.A.S.—See Eiffage S.A.; *Int'l*, pg. 2330
EIFFAGE TRAVAUX PUBLICS EST—See Eiffage S.A.; *Int'l*, pg. 2331
EIFFAGE TRAVAUX PUBLICS NORD S.N.C—See Eiffage S.A.; *Int'l*, pg. 2331
EIFFAGE TRAVAUX PUBLICS SAS—See Eiffage S.A.; *Int'l*, pg. 2330
EIX DIAGONAL CONCESSIONARIA DE LA GENERALITAT DE CATALUNYA, S.A.—See ACS, Actividades de Construccion y Servicios, S.A.; *Int'l*, pg. 111
EJB PAVING & MATERIALS CO.—See New Enterprise Stone & Lime Co., Inc.; *U.S. Private*, pg. 2895
E.J. BRENEMAN, LP; *U.S. Private*, pg. 1305
EKANSH CONCEPTS LIMITED; *Int'l*, pg. 2338
EKVE SDN BHD—See Ahmad Zaki Resources Berhad; *Int'l*, pg. 225
ELAM CONSTRUCTION, INC.—See Summit Materials, Inc.; *U.S. Public*, pg. 1960
ELGIN SWEEPING SERVICES, INC.; *U.S. Private*, pg. 1359
ELLENDALE ELECTRIC COMPANY, INC.; *U.S. Private*, pg. 1363
ELLIS-WALKER BUILDERS, INC.; *U.S. Private*, pg. 1374
ELMO GREER & SONS INC.; *U.S. Private*, pg. 1376
EMERALD ACQUISITION, INC.—See Harbor Beach Capital, LLC; *U.S. Private*, pg. 1858
ENGLISH CONSTRUCTION CO. INC.—See W.C. English Incorporated; *U.S. Private*, pg. 4419
ENOP - ENGENHARIA E OBRAS PUBLICAS, LDA.—See CONDURIL, Engenharia S.A.; *Int'l*, pg. 1767
ENVIRONMENTAL EQUIPMENT & SERVICES; *U.S. Private*, pg. 1407
ERIE MATERIALS INC.; *U.S. Private*, pg. 1420
ER SNELL CONTRACTOR INC.; *U.S. Private*, pg. 1417
ESTES CONSTRUCTION; *U.S. Private*, pg. 1429
E.T. SIMONDS CONSTRUCTION COMPANY; *U.S. Private*, pg. 1307
ET TECHTONICS, INC.—See Hill & Smith PLC; *Int'l*, pg. 3391
ETT LIMITED; *Int'l*, pg. 2524
EUROTUNNEL DEVELOPMENTS S.A.—See Getlink SE; *Int'l*, pg. 2953
EUTAW CONSTRUCTION COMPANY INC.; *U.S. Private*, pg. 1434
EVANS & ASSOCIATES ENTERPRISES; *U.S. Private*, pg. 1434
EVANS CONSTRUCTION COMPANY—See CRH plc; *Int'l*, pg. 1847
EVANS & SONS CONSTRUCTION; *U.S. Private*, pg. 1434
EVERETT DYKE'S GRASSING CO., INC.; *U.S. Private*, pg. 1438

E.V. WILLIAMS, INC.—See The Branch Group, Inc.; *U.S. Private*, pg. 3999
FACCHIANO, MICHAEL CONTRACTING INC.; *U.S. Private*, pg. 1459
FAHRNER ASPHALT SEALERS, L.L.C.; *U.S. Private*, pg. 1461
FALCON CONTRACTING CO., INC.; *U.S. Private*, pg. 1466
FEREBEE CORPORATION—See Construction Partners, Inc.; *U.S. Public*, pg. 572
FERREIRA CONSTRUCTION COMPANY, INC.; *U.S. Private*, pg. 1498
FERROVIAL CONSTRUCCION, S.A.—See Ferrovial S.A.; *Int'l*, pg. 2644
FERROVIAL CONSTRUCTION CANADA INC.—See Ferrovial S.A.; *Int'l*, pg. 2644
FERROVIAL CONSTRUCTION TEXAS, LLC—See Ferrovial S.A.; *Int'l*, pg. 2644
FERROVIAL CORPORACION, S.A.—See Ferrovial S.A.; *Int'l*, pg. 2644
FERROVIAL SERVICIOS CHILE SPA—See Ferrovial S.A.; *Int'l*, pg. 2644
FEUTZ CONTRACTORS, INC.; *U.S. Private*, pg. 1500
FLATIRON CONSTRUCTION CORP. - HEAVY CIVIL DIVISION—See ACS, Actividades de Construccion y Servicios, S.A.; *Int'l*, pg. 113
FLINT CO. INC.; *U.S. Private*, pg. 1545
FLORENCE CEMENT COMPANY; *U.S. Private*, pg. 1546
FNF CONSTRUCTION, INC.—See J.H. Whitney & Co., LLC; *U.S. Private*, pg. 2166
FOGEL ANDERSON CONSTRUCTION; *U.S. Private*, pg. 1557
FORD CONSTRUCTION COMPANY; *U.S. Private*, pg. 1564
FORT DODGE ASPHALT CO. (INC.)—See Moore Brothers Asphalt Inc.; *U.S. Private*, pg. 2779
FOX CONTRACTORS CORP.; *U.S. Private*, pg. 1584
FRANK G. SULLIVAN JR. INC.; *U.S. Private*, pg. 1594
FRANK W. WHITCOMB CONSTRUCTION CORP.; *U.S. Private*, pg. 1596
FREDERICK DERR & COMPANY INCORPORATED; *U.S. Private*, pg. 1602
FRED SMITH COMPANY; *U.S. Private*, pg. 1601
FRED SMITH CONSTRUCTION, INC.—See Construction Partners, Inc.; *U.S. Public*, pg. 572
FREESEN INC.—See United Contractors Midwest, Inc.; *U.S. Private*, pg. 4290
FUJIAN EXPRESSWAY DEVELOPMENT CO., LTD.; *Int'l*, pg. 2817
FUJITA ROAD CONSTRUCTION CO., LTD.—See Daiwa House Industry Co., Ltd.; *Int'l*, pg. 1946
GAC CONTRACTORS; *U.S. Private*, pg. 1633
GADDIE-SHAMROCK LLC; *U.S. Private*, pg. 1633
G.A. & F.C. WAGMAN, INC.—See Wagman Companies, Inc.; *U.S. Private*, pg. 4426
GALFAR PEMBINAAN DAN PERUSAHAAN (B) SDN BHD—See Galfar Engineering & Contracting SAOG; *Int'l*, pg. 2872
GALLAGHER ASPHALT CORPORATION; *U.S. Private*, pg. 1638
GALLAGHER & BURK INC.; *U.S. Private*, pg. 1638
GARRITY ASPHALT RECLAIMING INC.; *U.S. Private*, pg. 1646
GARY MERLINO CONSTRUCTION CO., INC.; *U.S. Private*, pg. 1646
GAYATRI HIGHWAYS LTD.; *Int'l*, pg. 2891
GELDER & ASSOCIATES, INC.—See Construction Partners, Inc.; *U.S. Public*, pg. 572
GEMCO CONSTRUCTION LTD.; *Int'l*, pg. 2915
GEORGE HARMS CONSTRUCTION COMPANY, INC.; *U.S. Private*, pg. 1682
GEORGE & LYNCH, INC.; *U.S. Private*, pg. 1681
GEOTECNIA Y CIMIENTOS, S.A.—See ACS, Actividades de Construccion y Servicios, S.A.; *Int'l*, pg. 112
GERKEN MATERIALS INC.; *U.S. Private*, pg. 1686
GERKEN PAVING INC.—See Gerken Materials Inc.; *U.S. Private*, pg. 1686
GHILOTTI BROS INC.; *U.S. Private*, pg. 1690
GILKYO E&C CO., LTD.; *Int'l*, pg. 2975
GILVIN-TERRILL INC.; *U.S. Private*, pg. 1701
GLENN FUQUA, INC.; *U.S. Private*, pg. 1710
GLENN O. HAWBAKER, INC.; *U.S. Private*, pg. 1710
GLENN THURMAN, INC.; *U.S. Private*, pg. 1711
GLOBAL SPECIALTY CONTRACTORS; *U.S. Private*, pg. 1718
GOHMANN ASPHALT & CONSTRUCTION INC.; *U.S. Private*, pg. 1726
GOLD EXPRESS, LLC; *U.S. Private*, pg. 1728
GOODFELLOW BROS., INC.; *U.S. Private*, pg. 1739
GORAZDE PUTEVI D.D. GORAZDE; *Int'l*, pg. 3042
GORMAN BROTHERS INC.; *U.S. Private*, pg. 1744
GP PUT D.D. SARAJEVO; *Int'l*, pg. 3046
GP ZGP D.D. SARAJEVO; *Int'l*, pg. 3046
GRACE PACIFIC LLC—See Nan, Inc.; *U.S. Private*, pg. 2832
GRADY BROTHER'S, INC.; *U.S. Private*, pg. 1750
GRAHAM BROS. CONSTRUCTION LIMITED; *Int'l*, pg. 3051
GRANDS TRAVAUX OCEAN INDIEN (GTOI) SA—See Bouygues S.A.; *Int'l*, pg. 1123

GRANIT CONSTRUCTION STOCK CO.; *Int'l*, pg. 3059
GRANITE CONSTRUCTION CO. - BAKERSFIELD BRANCH—See Granite Construction Incorporated; *U.S. Public*, pg. 957
GRANITE CONSTRUCTION CO. - CENTRAL VALLEY BRANCH—See Granite Construction Incorporated; *U.S. Public*, pg. 957
GRANITE CONSTRUCTION CO. - MONTEREY BAY BRANCH—See Granite Construction Incorporated; *U.S. Public*, pg. 957
GRANITE CONSTRUCTION CO. - NEVADA—See Granite Construction Incorporated; *U.S. Public*, pg. 957
GRANITE CONSTRUCTION CO. - SANTA BARBARA BRANCH—See Granite Construction Incorporated; *U.S. Public*, pg. 957
GRANITE CONSTRUCTION CO. - SOUTHERN CALIFORNIA BRANCH—See Granite Construction Incorporated; *U.S. Public*, pg. 957
GRANITE CONSTRUCTION CO. - STOCKTON BRANCH—See Granite Construction Incorporated; *U.S. Public*, pg. 957
GRANITE CONSTRUCTION CO. - UTAH—See Granite Construction Incorporated; *U.S. Public*, pg. 957
GRANITE CONSTRUCTION CO. - YAKIMA—See Granite Construction Incorporated; *U.S. Public*, pg. 957
GRANITE CONSTRUCTION - WASHINGTON REGION—See Granite Construction Incorporated; *U.S. Public*, pg. 957
GRANITE CONTRACTING, LLC—See Reeves Construction Company; *U.S. Private*, pg. 3384
THE GREAT LAKES CONSTRUCTION CO.; *U.S. Private*, pg. 4038
GREEN ACRES CONTRACTING CO. INC.; *U.S. Private*, pg. 1771
GREGGO & FERRARA INC.; *U.S. Private*, pg. 1782
GRIFFITH COMPANY; *U.S. Private*, pg. 1789
G R INFRAPROJECTS LIMITED; *Int'l*, pg. 2861
GROOME INDUSTRIAL SERVICE GROUP—See Argosy Capital Group, LLC; *U.S. Private*, pg. 321
GROUP FIVE CONSTRUCTION (PROPRIETARY) LIMITED—See Group Five Limited; *Int'l*, pg. 3089
GROUP FIVE KWAZULU-NATAL (PROPRIETARY) LIMITED—See Group Five Limited; *Int'l*, pg. 3089
GR PHAGWARA EXPRESSWAY LIMITED—See G R Infraprojects Limited; *Int'l*, pg. 2861
GRUPO CONCESIONARIO DEL OESTE, S.A.—See ACS, Actividades de Construccion y Servicios, S.A.; *Int'l*, pg. 112
GRUPO MEXICANO DE DESARROLLO S.A.B. DE C.V.; *Int'l*, pg. 3132
GVK AIRPORT DEVELOPERS PRIVATE LIMITED—See GVK Power and Infrastructure Limited; *Int'l*, pg. 3190
GVK JAIPUR EXPRESSWAY PRIVATE LIMITED—See GVK Power and Infrastructure Limited; *Int'l*, pg. 3190
HAL JONES CONTRACTORS INC.; *U.S. Private*, pg. 1841
HAMILTON CONSTRUCTION CO. OREGON INC.; *U.S. Private*, pg. 1847
HANDFORD GENERAL CONTRACTORS; *U.S. Private*, pg. 1852
HARDAWAY GROUP, INC.; *U.S. Private*, pg. 1862
HARD-CO CONSTRUCTION LTD.; *Int'l*, pg. 3272
HARDRIVES, INC.; *U.S. Private*, pg. 1863
HARDRIVES OF DELRAY, INC.; *U.S. Private*, pg. 1863
THE HARPER COMPANY; *U.S. Private*, pg. 4043
HASKELL LEMON CONSTRUCTION CO.; *U.S. Private*, pg. 1878
H.B.D. CONTRACTING INC.; *U.S. Private*, pg. 1825
HEAVY CONSTRUCTORS INC.; *U.S. Private*, pg. 1902
HEIJMANS TECHNIEK EN MOBILITEIT B.V.—See Heijmans N.V.; *Int'l*, pg. 3322
HEMPT BROTHERS, INC.; *U.S. Private*, pg. 1913
HENAN COMMUNICATIONS PLANNING AND DESIGN INSTITUTE CO., LTD; *Int'l*, pg. 3342
HENDERSON, JOSEPH J. & SONS; *U.S. Private*, pg. 1914
HIGHWAYS, INC.; *U.S. Private*, pg. 1943
HIGHWAY SUPPLY, LLC—See Trilantic Capital Management L.P.; *U.S. Private*, pg. 4231
HILL BROTHERS CONSTRUCTION & ENGINEERING CO.; *U.S. Private*, pg. 1944
HILL & SMITH, INC.—See Hill & Smith PLC; *Int'l*, pg. 3391
H-K CONTRACTORS, INC.; *U.S. Private*, pg. 1824
HOA BINH 479 JOINT STOCK COMPANY—See Hoa Binh Construction Group JSC; *Int'l*, pg. 3435
HOCHTIEF CONSTRUCCIONES S.A.—See ACS, Actividades de Construccion y Servicios, S.A.; *Int'l*, pg. 113
HOCHTIEF-LUXEMBOURG S.A.—See ACS, Actividades de Construccion y Servicios, S.A.; *Int'l*, pg. 114
HOCHTIEF POLSKA SP. Z.O.O.—See ACS, Actividades de Construccion y Servicios, S.A.; *Int'l*, pg. 114
HOCHTIEF (UK) CONSTRUCTION LTD.—See ACS, Actividades de Construccion y Servicios, S.A.; *Int'l*, pg. 114
HOCHTIEF VERKEHRSWEGEBAU GMBH—See ACS, Actividades de Construccion y Servicios, S.A.; *Int'l*, pg. 114
HOJGAARD INDUSTRI A/S—See Hojgaard Holding A/S; *Int'l*, pg. 3442
HOLLAND CORPORATION INC.; *U.S. Private*, pg. 1964
HOLMES CONSTRUCTION CO. LP; *U.S. Private*, pg. 1967

237310 — HIGHWAY, STREET, AN...

HONGRUN CONSTRUCTION GROUP CO., LTD.; *Int'l*, pg. 3471
HOOVER CONSTRUCTION COMPANY; *U.S. Private*, pg. 1978
HOS BROTHERS CONSTRUCTION, INC.; *U.S. Private*, pg. 1984
HOSEA O. WEAVER AND SONS INC.; *U.S. Private*, pg. 1985
HPS PLUMBING SERVICE, INC.; *U.S. Private*, pg. 1997
HUAYU EXPRESSWAY GROUP LIMITED; *Int'l*, pg. 3516
HUBBARD PAVING & GRADING, INC.—See Construction Partners, Inc.; *U.S. Public*, pg. 572
HUEY STOCKSTILL, INC.; *U.S. Private*, pg. 2002
HUFFMAN & WRIGHT LOGGING INC.; *U.S. Private*, pg. 2003
HUNTER INDUSTRIES LTD.; *U.S. Private*, pg. 2010
I 595 EXPRESS, LLC—See ACS, Actividades de Construccion y Servicios, S.A.; *Int'l*, pg. 114
ICA- MIRAMAR CORPORATION—See Empresas ICA S.A.B. de C.V.; *Int'l*, pg. 2391
ICA- MIRAMAR METRO SAN JUAN CORP.—See Empresas ICA S.A.B. de C.V.; *Int'l*, pg. 2391
IDEAL FENCING CORP.; *U.S. Private*, pg. 2036
IHI INFRASTRUCTURE ASIA CO., LTD.—See IHI Corporation; *Int'l*, pg. 3604
ILLINOIS ROAD CONTRACTORS; *U.S. Private*, pg. 2042
IMASA S.A.; *Int'l*, pg. 3620
IMS ENGINEERS, PA—See Integrated Management Services, PA; *U.S. Private*, pg. 2100
INFRARAIL FIRENZE S.R.L.—See Ferrovie dello Stato Italiane S.p.A.; *Int'l*, pg. 2645
INFRASTRUCTURE & ENERGY ALTERNATIVES, LLC—See MasTec, Inc.; *U.S. Public*, pg. 1393
INFRASTRUCTURE SERVICES INC.; *U.S. Private*, pg. 2075
INFRASTRUCTURE SERVICES INC.—See Infrastructure Services Inc.; *U.S. Private*, pg. 2075
INSTITUT DR.-ING. GAUER INGENIEURGESELLSCHAFT MBH—See BKW AG; *Int'l*, pg. 1055
INTEGRATED MANAGEMENT SERVICES, PA; *U.S. Private*, pg. 2100
INTERASPHALT SP. Z O.O.—See Dortmunder Gussasphalt GmbH & Co. KG; *Int'l*, pg. 2180
INTERSTATE HIGHWAY CONSTRUCTION; *U.S. Private*, pg. 2125
INTERSTATE ROCK PRODUCTS INC.; *U.S. Private*, pg. 2126
INTREN, INC.—See MasTec, Inc.; *U.S. Public*, pg. 1393
IOWA BRIDGE & CULVERT LLC; *U.S. Private*, pg. 2134
IROQUOIS PAVING CORPORATION; *U.S. Private*, pg. 2140
JAMES D. MORRISSEY INC.; *U.S. Private*, pg. 2183
JAMES HAMILTON CONSTRUCTION CO.; *U.S. Private*, pg. 2184
JAMES H. MALOY INC.; *U.S. Private*, pg. 2184
JAMES J. ANDERSON CONSTRUCTION CO. INC.; *U.S. Private*, pg. 2184
JAS W. GLOVER LTD. INC.; *U.S. Private*, pg. 2188
JAXON ENTERPRISES; *U.S. Private*, pg. 2191
JAY FULKROAD & SONS INC.; *U.S. Private*, pg. 2191
J.B. BOSTICK COMPANY; *U.S. Private*, pg. 2158
J.B. JAMES CONSTRUCTION, LLC.; *U.S. Private*, pg. 2158
J.D. ABRAMS LP—See Abrams International LLP; *U.S. Private*, pg. 40
JEFFERSON ASPHALT PRODUCTS COMPANY; *U.S. Private*, pg. 2197
JENSEN CONSTRUCTION COMPANY—See Rasmussen Group Inc.; *U.S. Private*, pg. 3357
JENSEN UNDERGROUND UTILITIES, INC.; *U.S. Private*, pg. 2201
JERSEY CONSTRUCTION INCORPORATED; *U.S. Private*, pg. 2202
J. FLETCHER CREAMER & SON INC.; *U.S. Private*, pg. 2156
J.F. WHITE CONTRACTING CO.—See ACS, Actividades de Construccion y Servicios, S.A.; *Int'l*, pg. 111
J.H. BERRA CONSTRUCTION CO., INC.—See J.H. Berra Holding Co., Inc.; *U.S. Private*, pg. 2165
J.H. LYNCH & SONS INC.; *U.S. Private*, pg. 2166
J.H. RUDOLPH & CO. INC.; *U.S. Private*, pg. 2166
JIM GILMAN EXCAVATING INC.; *U.S. Private*, pg. 2209
JIM SMITH CONTRACTING CO. LLC; *U.S. Private*, pg. 2210
J.M. DAVIDSON INC.; *U.S. Private*, pg. 2168
J.M. FAHEY CONSTRUCTION COMPANY; *U.S. Private*, pg. 2168
J. M. MARSCHUETZ CONSTRUCTION, CO.; *U.S. Private*, pg. 2156
JOE BLAND CONSTRUCTION, LP.; *U.S. Private*, pg. 2218
JOE DANIELS CONSTRUCTION COMPANY; *U.S. Private*, pg. 2218
JOKAKE CONSTRUCTION COMPANY; *U.S. Private*, pg. 2230
JONES BROS. DIRT & PAVING CONTRACTORS, INC.; *U.S. Private*, pg. 2231
JOSEPH MCCORMICK CONSTRUCTION CO, INC.; *U.S. Private*, pg. 2237

J. RAYMOND CONSTRUCTION CORPORATION; *U.S. Private*, pg. 2157
JTS CONSTRUCTION; *U.S. Private*, pg. 2242
JULIUS BRANSCOME INC.; *U.S. Private*, pg. 2243
JUNPUZI. CO., LTD.—See Chodai Co., Ltd.; *Int'l*, pg. 1577
KANAWHA STONE COMPANY INC.; *U.S. Private*, pg. 2259
KARSON KONSTRUCTION LIMITED—See Aecon Group Inc.; *Int'l*, pg. 172
KENMORE CONSTRUCTION CO., INC.; *U.S. Private*, pg. 2284
KENNY CONSTRUCTION COMPANY INC.—See Kenny Industries Inc.; *U.S. Private*, pg. 2286
KENNY INDUSTRIES INC.; *U.S. Private*, pg. 2286
KEY CONSTRUCTORS INC.; *U.S. Private*, pg. 2293
KEYSTONE LIME COMPANY; *U.S. Private*, pg. 2300
K-FIVE CONSTRUCTION CORPORATION; *U.S. Private*, pg. 2251
K.F. JACOBSON & CO. INC.—See R.B. Pamplin Corporation; *U.S. Private*, pg. 3334
KIEWIT INFRASTRUCTURE SOUTH CO.; *U.S. Private*, pg. 2304
KIEWIT INFRASTRUCTURE WEST CO. - VANCOUVER—See Peter Kiewit Sons', Inc.; *U.S. Private*, pg. 3158
KING'S CONSTRUCTION CO., INC.; *U.S. Private*, pg. 2310
KINGSLEY CONSTRUCTORS INC.; *U.S. Private*, pg. 2311
KIRBY NAGELHOUT CONSTRUCTION CO.; *U.S. Private*, pg. 2314
KIRILA CONTRACTORS INC.; *U.S. Private*, pg. 2314
KLETT CONSTRUCTION COMPANY; *U.S. Private*, pg. 2319
KLUKWAN INC.; *U.S. Private*, pg. 2320
KNIFE RIVER CORPORATION - SAULK RAPIDS—See MDU Resources Group, Inc.; *U.S. Public*, pg. 1410
KNIFE RIVER MATERIALS—See MDU Resources Group, Inc.; *U.S. Public*, pg. 1410
KNIK CONSTRUCTION CO. INC.—See Lynden Incorporated; *U.S. Private*, pg. 2521
KOGA ENGINEERING & CONSTRUCTION, INC.; *U.S. Private*, pg. 2337
KOKOSING CONSTRUCTION COMPANY, INC. - HIGHWAY DIVISION—See Kokosing Construction Company, Inc.; *U.S. Private*, pg. 2340
KOKOSING CONSTRUCTION COMPANY, INC.; *U.S. Private*, pg. 2340
KOKOSING CONSTRUCTION COMPANY INC—See Kokosing Construction Company, Inc.; *U.S. Private*, pg. 2340
KOMAN INC.; *U.S. Private*, pg. 2341
KPRS CONSTRUCTION SERVICES, INC.; *U.S. Private*, pg. 2346
KRUPP L CONSTRUCTION INC.; *U.S. Private*, pg. 2353
KUBRICKY CONSTRUCTION CORP.—See The D.A. Collins Construction Co., Inc.; *U.S. Private*, pg. 4017
KYLE CONTI CONSTRUCTION, L.L.C.; *U.S. Private*, pg. 2360
L&A CONTRACTING COMPANY INC.; *U.S. Private*, pg. 2362
LAKESIDE INDUSTRIES; *U.S. Private*, pg. 2378
LANIER CONSTRUCTION COMPANY; *U.S. Private*, pg. 2390
LANWEHR BAU GMBH—See Eiffage S.A.; *Int'l*, pg. 2331
LAREDO PAVING INC.; *U.S. Private*, pg. 2392
LAS PIEDRAS CONSTRUCTION CORP.; *U.S. Private*, pg. 2394
LAUX CONSTRUCTION, LLC—See Rival Holdings, LLC.; *U.S. Private*, pg. 3442
LAWRENCE-LYNCH CORPORATION; *U.S. Private*, pg. 2402
L.C. WHITFORD CO. INC.; *U.S. Private*, pg. 2365
LEE CONSTRUCTION CO.—See W.C. English Incorporated; *U.S. Private*, pg. 4419
LEE HY PAVING CORPORATION; *U.S. Private*, pg. 2413
LEHIGH ASPHALT, PAVING & CONSTRUCTION—See Barletta Materials & Construction; *U.S. Private*, pg. 476
LEHMAN-ROBERTS COMPANY; *U.S. Private*, pg. 2419
LEM CONSTRUCTION; *U.S. Private*, pg. 2420
LEON E. WINTERMYER INC.—See L.E.W. Holding Co. Inc.; *U.S. Private*, pg. 2365
LES PAVAGES DORVAL INC.—See BAUVAL inc.; *Int'l*, pg. 899
LEWARE CONSTRUCTION COMPANY OF FLORIDA, INC.; *U.S. Private*, pg. 2437
L.H. LACY COMPANY; *U.S. Private*, pg. 2366
LILLARD & CLARK CONSTRUCTION COMPANY INC.; *U.S. Private*, pg. 2455
LILLARD & CLARK-WYOMING—See Lillard & Clark Construction Company Inc.; *U.S. Private*, pg. 2456
LINDY PAVING, INC.—See P.J. Dick Incorporated; *U.S. Private*, pg. 3060
LIONMARK INC.; *U.S. Private*, pg. 2464
LIPHAM CONSTRUCTION CO. INC.; *U.S. Private*, pg. 2464
LL PELLING COMPANY INC.; *U.S. Private*, pg. 2475
L & N BRIDGE, LLC.; *U.S. Private*, pg. 2361
LOCKERBIE & HOLE CONTRACTING LIMITED—See Aecon Group Inc.; *Int'l*, pg. 172
LOCKERBIE & HOLE CONTRACTING LIMITED—See Aecon Group Inc.; *Int'l*, pg. 172
LOCKERBIE & HOLE CONTRACTING LIMITED—See Aecon Group Inc.; *Int'l*, pg. 172
LOVECE HOLDING INC.; *U.S. Private*, pg. 2501
LOVIN CONSTRUCTION, INC.; *U.S. Private*, pg. 2504
LOWELL WOLF INDUSTRIES INC.; *U.S. Private*, pg. 2505
L.S. LEE INC.—See REH Holdings Inc.; *U.S. Private*, pg. 3389
LUCK BROTHERS INC.; *U.S. Private*, pg. 2511
LUNDA CONSTRUCTION COMPANY—See Tutor Perini Corporation; *U.S. Public*, pg. 2206
MACC OF ILLINOIS INC.; *U.S. Private*, pg. 2535
MACLEOD CONSTRUCTION INC.; *U.S. Private*, pg. 2538
MACRO-Z-TECHNOLOGY COMPANY; *U.S. Private*, pg. 2538
MADDEN CONTRACTING COMPANY INC.; *U.S. Private*, pg. 2539
MANATT'S, INC.; *U.S. Private*, pg. 2561
MANHATTAN ROAD & BRIDGE CO.—See Rooney Holdings, Inc.; *U.S. Private*, pg. 3479
MANHATTAN ROAD & BRIDGE-MUSKOGEE OFFICE—See Rooney Holdings, Inc.; *U.S. Private*, pg. 3479
MARKS BROTHERS, INC.; *U.S. Private*, pg. 2582
MARTAM CONSTRUCTION, INC.; *U.S. Private*, pg. 2593
MARTIN BROTHERS CONSTRUCTION, INC.; *U.S. Private*, pg. 2594
MARTINS CONSTRUCTION CORP.—See Posillico, Inc.; *U.S. Private*, pg. 3233
MASSMAN CONSTRUCTION CO.; *U.S. Private*, pg. 2606
MATHIOWETZ CONSTRUCTION COMPANY; *U.S. Private*, pg. 2611
MATHY CONSTRUCTION CO; *U.S. Private*, pg. 2611
MATICH CORPORATION; *U.S. Private*, pg. 2611
MAUI PAVING, LLC—See Alexander & Baldwin, Inc.; *U.S. Public*, pg. 75
MAX J. KUNEY CONSTRUCTION COMPANY; *U.S. Private*, pg. 2617
MAYER BROTHERS CONSTRUCTION CO.; *U.S. Private*, pg. 2621
MBC HOLDINGS, INC.; *U.S. Private*, pg. 2624
MBD CONSTRUCTION COMPANY, INC.; *U.S. Private*, pg. 2624
MCCARTHY BUSH CORPORATION; *U.S. Private*, pg. 2626
MCCARTHY IMPROVEMENT COMPANY—See McCarthy Bush Corporation; *U.S. Private*, pg. 2626
MCCARTNEY CONSTRUCTION CO. INC.—See Vulcan Materials Company; *U.S. Public*, pg. 2314
MCCORMICK INCORPORATED; *U.S. Private*, pg. 2630
MCCORMICK TAYLOR; *U.S. Private*, pg. 2630
MCCOURT CONSTRUCTION CO. INC.; *U.S. Private*, pg. 2630
MCFADDEN & MILLER CONSTRUCTION; *U.S. Private*, pg. 2633
MCLEAN CONTRACTING COMPANY INC.; *U.S. Private*, pg. 2641
MCMAHON CONTRACTING, L.P.; *U.S. Private*, pg. 2642
MCM CONSTRUCTION, INC.; *U.S. Private*, pg. 2642
MCMINN'S ASPHALT CO., INC.—See CRH plc; *Int'l*, pg. 1847
MCMURRY READY MIX CO.—See MDU Resources Group, Inc.; *U.S. Public*, pg. 1410
MEADOW VALLEY CONTRACTORS INC.—See Insight Equity Holdings LLC; *U.S. Private*, pg. 2086
MEADOW VALLEY CORPORATION—See Insight Equity Holdings LLC; *U.S. Private*, pg. 2086
MECCOR INDUSTRIES, LTD.; *U.S. Private*, pg. 2648
M-E COMPANIES, INC.; *U.S. Private*, pg. 2525
METCON INC.; *U.S. Private*, pg. 2683
METIS ENGENHARIA, LDA.—See CONDURIL, Engenharia S.A.; *Int'l*, pg. 1767
METRO PAVING CORPORATION; *U.S. Private*, pg. 2686
MICA CORPORATION; *U.S. Private*, pg. 2697
MIDCO CONSTRUCTION CORPORATION; *U.S. Private*, pg. 2710
THE MIDDLESEX CORPORATION; *U.S. Private*, pg. 4079
MIDDLESEX LLC.; *U.S. Private*, pg. 2714
MID EASTERN BUILDERS, INC.; *U.S. Private*, pg. 2706
MIDWEST ASPHALT CORP.; *U.S. Private*, pg. 2720
MIKE RYAN TREE SERVICE INC.; *U.S. Private*, pg. 2725
MILESTONE CONTRACTORS, LP; *U.S. Private*, pg. 2728
MILLER BROS. CONSTRUCTION—See MBC Holdings, Inc.; *U.S. Private*, pg. 2624
THE MILLER GROUP, INC. (USA)—See Bouygues S.A.; *Int'l*, pg. 1122
MILLER PAVING LIMITED—See Bouygues S.A.; *Int'l*, pg. 1122
MILLSTONE WEBER, LLC—See Fred Weber, Inc.; *U.S. Private*, pg. 1601
MINE SERVICE INC.; *U.S. Private*, pg. 2741
MOHAWK NORTHEAST, INC.; *U.S. Private*, pg. 2765
MOHR CONSTRUCTION CO. INC.; *U.S. Private*, pg. 2765
MONTGOMERY MARTIN CONTRACTORS, LLC.; *U.S. Private*, pg. 2777
MOORE BROTHERS CONSTRUCTION CO.; *U.S. Private*, pg. 2779
MOORE BROTHERS PAVING INC.—See Moore Brothers Asphalt Inc.; *U.S. Private*, pg. 2779
MORGAN/HARBOUR CONSTRUCTION, LLC.; *U.S. Private*, pg. 2784

N.A.I.C.S. INDEX

237310 — HIGHWAY, STREET, AN...

MOUNTAINEER CONTRACTORS INC.; *U.S. Private*, pg. 2801
MOUNTAIN ENTERPRISES, INC.—See CRH plc; *Int'l*, pg. 1847
MOWAT CONSTRUCTION COMPANY; *U.S. Private*, pg. 2802
MT HOJGAARD A/S—See Hojgaard Holding A/S; *Int'l*, pg. 3442
MURPHREE PAVING LLC—See Harbor Beach Capital, LLC; *U.S. Private*, pg. 1858
MUSSELMAN & HALL CONTRACTORS LLC.; *U.S. Private*, pg. 2818
MUSSON BROS., INC. - BROOKFIELD OFFICE—See Musson Bros., Inc.; *U.S. Private*, pg. 2819
MUSSON BROS., INC.; *U.S. Private*, pg. 2818
MYERS & SONS CONSTRUCTION, LLC—See Sterling Infrastructure, Inc.; *U.S. Public*, pg. 1946
NAGLE PAVING COMPANY; *U.S. Private*, pg. 2830
N.B. WEST CONTRACTING COMPANY; *U.S. Private*, pg. 2827
NEA ODOS SA—See Gek Terna Societe Anonyme Holdings Real Estate Constructions; *Int'l*, pg. 2913
NESBITT CONTRACTING CO INC—See Nesbitt Investment Company; *U.S. Private*, pg. 2886
NEWFIELD CONSTRUCTION, INC.; *U.S. Private*, pg. 2914
NEWMAN & KENG PAVING COMPANY; *U.S. Private*, pg. 2915
NEW YORK PAVING INC.; *U.S. Private*, pg. 2911
NEW YORK SAND & STONE LLC—See Vulcan Materials Company; *U.S. Public*, pg. 2314
N.H. STONE INC.; *U.S. Private*, pg. 2828
NIELSON CONSTRUCTION; *U.S. Private*, pg. 2927
NOGAMA CONSTRUCTION CORP.; *U.S. Private*, pg. 2933
NORRIS AGGREGATE PAVING CO.; *U.S. Private*, pg. 2939
NORWOOD COMMERCIAL CONTRACTORS INC.; *U.S. Private*, pg. 2964
NTE MOBILITY PARTNERS LLC—See Ferrovial S.A.; *Int'l*, pg. 2645
NYLEVE BRIDGE CORP.—See The Schultz Organization, LLC; *U.S. Private*, pg. 4115
NYMAN CONSTRUCTION; *U.S. Private*, pg. 2976
OAKLEY CONSTRUCTION COMPANY, INC.; *U.S. Private*, pg. 2985
O.C. JONES & SONS INC.; *U.S. Private*, pg. 2981
O'DONNELL & SONS CONSTRUCTION CO.—See Clarkson Construction Company; *U.S. Private*, pg. 915
OMNI ENGINEERING INC.—See Omni Holding Company; *U.S. Private*, pg. 3016
OMNI HOLDING COMPANY; *U.S. Private*, pg. 3016
ONDE S.A.—See Erbud S.A.; *Int'l*, pg. 2489
OPP CONSTRUCTION LLC; *U.S. Private*, pg. 3032
ORDERS CONSTRUCTION COMPANY, INC.; *U.S. Private*, pg. 3039
O'STEEN BROTHERS INC.; *U.S. Private*, pg. 2980
OTAK, INC.; *U.S. Private*, pg. 3048
OVERSTREET PAVING COMPANY; *U.S. Private*, pg. 3053
OXFORD CONSTRUCTION COMPANY; *U.S. Private*, pg. 3057
PACE CONSTRUCTION COMPANY INC.—See Lionmark Inc.; *U.S. Private*, pg. 2464
PALA-INTERSTATE, INC.; *U.S. Private*, pg. 3076
P.A. LANDERS INC.; *U.S. Private*, pg. 3060
PALMER PAVING CORP.—See Peckham Industries, Inc.; *U.S. Private*, pg. 3127
PANKOW SPECIAL PROJECTS; *U.S. Private*, pg. 3086
PARAGON SPORTS CONSTRUCTORS LLC.; *U.S. Private*, pg. 3091
PARK CONSTRUCTION COMPANY; *U.S. Private*, pg. 3096
PAULSEN, INC.; *U.S. Private*, pg. 3114
PAVIMENTAL SPA—See Edizione S.r.l.; *Int'l*, pg. 2312
PAYNE & DOLAN, INC.; *U.S. Private*, pg. 3117
PCE CONSTRUCTORS, INC.; *U.S. Private*, pg. 3120
PCI ROADS; *U.S. Private*, pg. 3120
PCL CIVIL CONSTRUCTORS, INC.; *U.S. Private*, pg. 3120
PECKHAM ROAD CORPORATION—See Peckham Industries, Inc.; *U.S. Private*, pg. 3127
PETER BAKER & SON CO. INC.; *U.S. Private*, pg. 3157
PETERSON CONTRACTORS, INC.; *U.S. Private*, pg. 3160
PETRACCA & SONS INC.; *U.S. Private*, pg. 3161
P. FLANIGAN & SONS INC.; *U.S. Private*, pg. 3059
PHEND & BROWN INC.; *U.S. Private*, pg. 3167
PIKE INDUSTRIES, INC.—See CRH plc; *Int'l*, pg. 1847
PIKE INDUSTRIES—See CRH plc; *Int'l*, pg. 1847
PIONEER ROAD SERVICES PTY. LTD.—See Fulton Hogan Limited; *Int'l*, pg. 2843
PITTMAN CONSTRUCTION COMPANY; *U.S. Private*, pg. 3191
POE ASPHALT PAVING INC.; *U.S. Private*, pg. 3220
POSILLICO CIVIL, INC.—See Posillico, Inc.; *U.S. Private*, pg. 3233
PPESW BPSB JV SDN. BHD.—See Cahya Mata Sarawak Berhad; *Int'l*, pg. 1251
PRICE CONSTRUCTION INC.; *U.S. Private*, pg. 3258
PRIJEDORPUTEVI A.D. PRIJEDOR—See Grupa Fortis d.o.o. Banja Luka; *Int'l*, pg. 3116
PROBST ELECTRIC INC.; *U.S. Private*, pg. 3271
PROGRESSIVE CONTRACTORS INC.; *U.S. Private*, pg. 3278

PROVIAS CONSTRUCTION, L.L.C.; *U.S. Private*, pg. 3291
PROYECTOS DE INFRAESTRUCTURA S.A.—See Grupo Aval Acciones y Valores S.A.; *Int'l*, pg. 3121
PULICE CONSTRUCTION, INC.—See ACS, Actividades de Construccion y Servicios, S.A.; *Int'l*, pg. 115
Q & D CONSTRUCTION; *U.S. Private*, pg. 3311
QUADRILATERO MARCHE-UMBRIA S.P.A.—See Ferrovie dello Stato Italiane S.p.A.; *Int'l*, pg. 2645
RACON INC.; *U.S. Private*, pg. 3342
RADMACHER BROTHERS EXCAVATING CO, INC.; *U.S. Private*, pg. 3345
THE RADOS COMPANIES; *U.S. Private*, pg. 4102
RAGLE INC.; *U.S. Private*, pg. 3346
RAILROAD CONSTRUCTION COMPANY, INC.; *U.S. Private*, pg. 3346
RALPH L. WADSWORTH CONSTRUCTION COMPANY, INC.; *U.S. Private*, pg. 3350
RASMUSSEN GROUP INC.; *U.S. Private*, pg. 3356
R.B. BAKER CONSTRUCTION INC.—See Reeves Construction Company; *U.S. Private*, pg. 3384
RB JERGENS CONTRACTORS INC.; *U.S. Private*, pg. 3360
REAMES & SON CONSTRUCTION CO.; *U.S. Private*, pg. 3370
RECON REFRACTORY & CONSTRUCTION INC.; *U.S. Private*, pg. 3371
RED CLAY INDUSTRIES INC.; *U.S. Private*, pg. 3373
REECE ALBERT INC.; *U.S. Private*, pg. 3381
REESMANS EXCAVATING & GRADING, INC.; *U.S. Private*, pg. 3383
R.E. HEIDT CONSTRUCTION CO.; *U.S. Private*, pg. 3335
REH HOLDINGS INC.; *U.S. Private*, pg. 3389
REILLY CONSTRUCTION CO. INC.; *U.S. Private*, pg. 3391
RELIABLE CONTRACTING COMPANY INC.; *U.S. Private*, pg. 3393
REPUBLIC CONTRACTING CORP.; *U.S. Private*, pg. 3401
R.E. PURCELL CONSTRUCTION COMPANY INCORPORATED; *U.S. Private*, pg. 3335
RGW CONSTRUCTION INC.; *U.S. Private*, pg. 3421
R.H.MOORE COMPANY, INC.; *U.S. Private*, pg. 3336
RICE-KILROY CONSTRUCTION COMPANY INC.; *U.S. Private*, pg. 3425
RIETH-RILEY CONSTRUCTION CO., INC. - BIG RAPIDS—See Rieth-Riley Construction Co., Inc.; *U.S. Private*, pg. 3435
RIETH-RILEY CONSTRUCTION CO., INC. - GRAND VALLEY—See Rieth-Riley Construction Co., Inc.; *U.S. Private*, pg. 3435
RIETH-RILEY CONSTRUCTION CO., INC. - LANSING—See Rieth-Riley Construction Co., Inc.; *U.S. Private*, pg. 3435
RIETH-RILEY CONSTRUCTION CO., INC.; *U.S. Private*, pg. 3434
RIFENBURG CONSTRUCTION INC.; *U.S. Private*, pg. 3435
THE RIGHTER COMPANY, INC.; *U.S. Private*, pg. 4107
RILEY PAVING, INC.—See Construction Partners, Inc.; *U.S. Public*, pg. 572
RINGWAY JACOBS LIMITED—See Jacobs Engineering Group, Inc.; *U.S. Public*, pg. 1186
R.J. NOBLE COMPANY; *U.S. Private*, pg. 3337
R.L. BRINK CORP.; *U.S. Private*, pg. 3338
R&L BROSAMER INC.—See The Walsh Group; *U.S. Private*, pg. 4133
RLC HOLDING CO. INC.; *U.S. Private*, pg. 3450
R.L. MCCOY, INC.; *U.S. Private*, pg. 3338
ROAD BUILDERS, LLC—See Sun Capital Partners, Inc.; *U.S. Private*, pg. 3861
ROAD & HIGHWAY BUILDERS LLC—See Sterling Infrastructure, Inc.; *U.S. Public*, pg. 1947
ROADMARK CORPORATION; *U.S. Private*, pg. 3453
ROBERTS CONSTRUCTION COMPANY INC.—See McCormick Incorporated; *U.S. Private*, pg. 2630
ROBERT T. WINZINGER INC.; *U.S. Private*, pg. 3459
ROBINSON INDUSTRIES INC.; *U.S. Private*, pg. 3462
ROBINSON PAVING COMPANY—See Construction Partners, Inc.; *U.S. Public*, pg. 572
ROCK SOLID STABILIZATION & RECLAMATION, INC.; *U.S. Private*, pg. 3465
ROC SERVICE COMPANY; *U.S. Private*, pg. 3463
RODIO CIMENTACIONES ESPECIALES, S.A.—See Empresas ICA S.A.B. de C.V.; *Int'l*, pg. 2391
ROGERS BRIDGE COMPANY, INC—See Shepherd Construction Co., Inc.; *U.S. Private*, pg. 3632
ROGERS CONSTRUCTION INC.; *U.S. Private*, pg. 3471
ROGERS NORTHWEST INC.; *U.S. Private*, pg. 3472
ROMERO GENERAL CONSTRUCTION CORPORATION; *U.S. Private*, pg. 3476
ROSE BROTHERS PAVING, INC.; *U.S. Private*, pg. 3481
ROSIEK CONSTRUCTION CO. INC.; *U.S. Private*, pg. 3484
ROSS BROTHERS CONSTRUCTION INC.; *U.S. Private*, pg. 3485
ROY E. LADD INC.; *U.S. Private*, pg. 3490
RPQ ASPHALT PTY. LTD.—See Downer EDI Limited; *Int'l*, pg. 2186
RPQ MACKAY PTY. LTD.—See Downer EDI Limited; *Int'l*, pg. 2186
RPQ NORTH COAST PTY. LTD.—See Downer EDI Limited; *Int'l*, pg. 2186

RPQ PTY. LTD.—See Downer EDI Limited; *Int'l*, pg. 2186
R.R. DAWSON BRIDGE COMPANY LLC; *U.S. Private*, pg. 3339
RTD CONSTRUCTION, INC.; *U.S. Private*, pg. 3498
RUSSELL STANDARD CORPORATION; *U.S. Private*, pg. 3507
RUSTON PAVING CO. INC.; *U.S. Private*, pg. 3507
RUTAS DEL PACIFICO S.A.—See ACS, Actividades de Construccion y Servicios, S.A.; *Int'l*, pg. 112
S.A. GRAHAM COMPANY INC.; *U.S. Private*, pg. 3515
SAGREX FRANCE S.A.S.—See Heidelberg Materials AG; *Int'l*, pg. 3319
SAIN CONSTRUCTION CO.; *U.S. Private*, pg. 3529
SAN BAR CONSTRUCTION CORP.; *U.S. Private*, pg. 3539
SANDERS BROTHERS CONSTRUCTION CO; *U.S. Private*, pg. 3543
SANDRO CONSTRUCTION, INC.; *U.S. Private*, pg. 3544
SANTARO INDUSTRIES INC.; *U.S. Private*, pg. 3548
SATAP S.P.A.—See Argo Finanziaria S.p.A.; *Int'l*, pg. 562
SAV S.P.A.—See Argo Finanziaria S.p.A.; *Int'l*, pg. 562
SCARSELLA BROS INC.; *U.S. Private*, pg. 3561
SCHACHTBAU NORDHAUSEN GMBH - RECONSTRUCTION DIVISION—See BAUER Aktiengesellschaft; *Int'l*, pg. 894
S.C. INSCUT BUCURESTI S.A.—See ELLAKTOR S.A.; *Int'l*, pg. 2365
SCOTT BRIDGE COMPANY INC.; *U.S. Private*, pg. 3576
SCR CONSTRUCTION CO. INC.; *U.S. Private*, pg. 3579
THE SCRUGGS COMPANY INC.; *U.S. Private*, pg. 4115
SEALAND CONTRACTORS CORP.; *U.S. Private*, pg. 3584
SEVEN K CONSTRUCTION COMPANY INC.—See Kenny Industries Inc.; *U.S. Private*, pg. 2286
SGS, LLC; *U.S. Private*, pg. 3622
SHARPE BROTHERS, INC.—See Vecellio Group, Inc.; *U.S. Private*, pg. 4349
SHELLY & SANDS INC.; *U.S. Private*, pg. 3631
SHEPHERD CONSTRUCTION CO., INC.; *U.S. Private*, pg. 3632
SILLARS (B. & C.E.) LTD—See Downer EDI Limited; *Int'l*, pg. 2186
SIMMONS EROSION CONTROL, INC.; *U.S. Private*, pg. 3665
SIMON CONTRACTORS INC.; *U.S. Private*, pg. 3666
SIMPSON CONSTRUCTION COMPANY, INC.; *U.S. Private*, pg. 3668
SINELEC S.P.A.—See Argo Finanziaria S.p.A.; *Int'l*, pg. 562
S&J CONSTRUCTION CO. INC.; *U.S. Private*, pg. 3513
SLACK & CO. CONTRACTING, INC.; *U.S. Private*, pg. 3686
SLURRY PAVERS INC.; *U.S. Private*, pg. 3690
S.L. WILLIAMSON COMPANY INC.; *U.S. Private*, pg. 3518
SMITH & PICKLE CONSTRUCTION, INC.; *U.S. Private*, pg. 3694
S M WILSON & CO.; *U.S. Private*, pg. 3512
SOCIEDAD CONCESIONARIA AUTOPISTA NORORIENTE SA—See Edizione S.r.l.; *Int'l*, pg. 2312
SOCIEDAD CONCESIONARIA AUTOPISTA NUEVA VESPUCIO SUR SA—See Edizione S.r.l.; *Int'l*, pg. 2312
SOCIEDAD CONCESIONARIA CONSTANERA NORTE SA—See Edizione S.r.l.; *Int'l*, pg. 2312
SOCIEDAD CONCESIONARIA DE LOS LAGOS SA—See Edizione S.r.l.; *Int'l*, pg. 2312
SOCIEDAD CONCESIONARIA RUTA DEL CANAL, S.A.—See Empresas Penta S.A.; *Int'l*, pg. 2391
SOCIETA AUTOSTRADA TIRRENICA P.A.—See Edizione S.r.l.; *Int'l*, pg. 2312
SOCOTHERM LABARGE; *U.S. Private*, pg. 3704
SONDAGENS RODIO LTDA.—See Empresas ICA S.A.B. de C.V.; *Int'l*, pg. 2391
SOUTH ATLANTIC EQUIPMENT COMPANY, INC.—See The Dickerson Group, Inc.; *U.S. Private*, pg. 4021
SOUTHERN CONCRETE CONSTRUCTION CO.; *U.S. Private*, pg. 3730
SOUTHERN MINNESOTA CONSTRUCTION COMPANY—See CRH plc; *Int'l*, pg. 1847
SOUTHERN STRIPING SOLUTIONS, LLC; *U.S. Private*, pg. 3735
SPEA DO BRASIL PROJECTOS E INFRAESTRUTURA LIMITEDA—See Edizione S.r.l.; *Int'l*, pg. 2312
STANDARD CONSTRUCTION COMPANY, INC.; *U.S. Private*, pg. 3778
STARK EXCAVATING INC.; *U.S. Private*, pg. 3787
STAR PAVING CO.; *U.S. Private*, pg. 3785
STAVOLA CONTRACTING CO. INC.; *U.S. Private*, pg. 3794
STEELMAN-DUFF INC.; *U.S. Private*, pg. 3797
STERLING INFRASTRUCTURE, INC.; *U.S. Public*, pg. 1946
STEVENS CREEK QUARRY INC.; *U.S. Private*, pg. 3809
STEVE P. RADOS, INC.—See The Rados Companies; *U.S. Private*, pg. 4102
STEWART BROS INC.; *U.S. Private*, pg. 3811
STEWART & TATE, INC.; *U.S. Private*, pg. 3811
ST. JOSEPH COUNTY HIGHWAY DEPARTMENT; *U.S. Private*, pg. 3772
ST. LOUIS BRIDGE CONSTRUCTION CO.; *U.S. Private*, pg. 3772
STONECREST AT DOUBLE OAK MOUNTAIN; *U.S. Private*, pg. 3828
STRATA CORPORATION; *U.S. Private*, pg. 3833

237310 — HIGHWAY, STREET, AN...

STRAWSER PAVING CO., INC.; *U.S. Private*, pg. 3837
STRONGHOLD ENGINEERING, INC.; *U.S. Private*, pg. 3841
STV INC.—See STV Group, Inc.; *U.S. Private*, pg. 3845
S.T. WOOTEN CORPORATION; *U.S. Private*, pg. 3519
SUKUT CONSTRUCTION INC.; *U.S. Private*, pg. 3850
SUMMERS-TAYLOR INC.; *U.S. Private*, pg. 3853
SUNESIS CONSTRUCTION COMPANY, INC.; *U.S. Private*, pg. 3867
SUNLAND ASPHALT & CONSTRUCTION, LLC—See Huron Capital Partners LLC; *U.S. Private*, pg. 2012
SUPERIOR BOWEN ASPHALT COMPANY—See Clarkson Construction Company; *U.S. Private*, pg. 915
SUPERIOR CONSTRUCTION CO., INC.; *U.S. Private*, pg. 3876
SUPERIOR INDUSTRIAL MAINTENANCE COMPANY, LLC—See Warren Equity Partners, LLC; *U.S. Private*, pg. 4443
SURFACECYCLE, INC.; *U.S. Private*, pg. 3884
SURVIAL S.A.—See Aenza S.A.A.; *Int'l*, pg. 176
SWANK ASSOCIATED COMPANIES INC.; *U.S. Private*, pg. 3890
SYRIAN COMBINED GROUP CONTRACTING CO. W.L.L.—See Combined Group Contracting Company KSCC; *Int'l*, pg. 1709
SZAM-ERT KFT.—See Betonut Szolgaltato es Epito Rt.; *Int'l*, pg. 1003
T.A. LOVING COMPANY; *U.S. Private*, pg. 3911
TAMPA STEEL ERECTING COMPANY; *U.S. Private*, pg. 3930
TANGENZIALE DI NAPOLI SPA—See Edizione S.r.l.; *Int'l*, pg. 2312
TANKNOLOGY CANADA INC.—See Colliers International Group Inc.; *Int'l*, pg. 1701
TAYLOR & MURPHY CONSTRUCTION CO.; *U.S. Private*, pg. 3937
TEALSTONE COMMERCIAL, INC.—See Sterling Infrastructure, Inc.; *U.S. Public*, pg. 1947
TEICHERT, INC.; *U.S. Private*, pg. 3958
TELFER OIL COMPANIES; *U.S. Private*, pg. 3962
TEMPLE & TEMPLE EXCAVATING & PAVING, INC.; *U.S. Private*, pg. 3963
TERRY HUNT CONSTRUCTION; *U.S. Private*, pg. 3972
TESSA CONSTRUCTION & TECH COMPANY LLC.; *U.S. Private*, pg. 3973
TEWE BAUCHEMIEGESELLSCHAFT MBH—See Dortmunder Gussasphalt GmbH & Co. KG; *Int'l*, pg. 2180
TEXAS EXCAVATION SAFETY; *U.S. Private*, pg. 3975
TEZAK HEAVY EQUIPMENT CO., INC.—See Holcim Ltd.; *Int'l*, pg. 3447
TFW INC.; *U.S. Private*, pg. 3979
THALLE CONSTRUCTION CO., INC.; *U.S. Private*, pg. 3980
THIESS PTY. LIMITED—See ACS, Actividades de Construccion y Servicios, S.A.; *Int'l*, pg. 113
THIESS PTY. LIMITED—See Elliott Management Corporation; *U.S. Private*, pg. 1365
TIC WESTERN—See Peter Kiewit Sons', Inc.; *U.S. Private*, pg. 3158
T.J. CAMPBELL CONSTRUCTION CO.; *U.S. Private*, pg. 3912
T.L. EDWARDS INC.; *U.S. Private*, pg. 3912
T&N ASPHALT SERVICES, INC.; *U.S. Private*, pg. 3910
TOPPINO'S INC.; *U.S. Private*, pg. 4187
TOWER ASPHALT INC.—See Hardrives, Inc.; *U.S. Private*, pg. 1863
TPAM SAS—See Eiffage S.A.; *Int'l*, pg. 2331
TRANSROUTE SA—See Eiffage S.A.; *Int'l*, pg. 2331
TRAVAUX PUBLICS ET ASSAINISSEMENT—See Eiffage S.A.; *Int'l*, pg. 2331
TRIANGLE GRADING & PAVING INC.; *U.S. Private*, pg. 4226
TRI CITY PAVING INC.; *U.S. Private*, pg. 4220
TRIERWEILER CONSTRUCTION & SUPPLY CO. INC.; *U.S. Private*, pg. 4230
TRI-STATE CONSTRUCTION, INC.; *U.S. Private*, pg. 4223
TRI-STATE PAVING & SEALCOATING, INC.—See Energy Services of America Corporation; *U.S. Public*, pg. 762
TRUMBALL CORPORATION/P.J. DICK, INC.—See P.J. Dick Incorporated; *U.S. Private*, pg. 3060
TULLY CONSTRUCTION CO., INC.; *U.S. Private*, pg. 4257
TUSCOLA COUNTY ROAD COMMISSION; *U.S. Private*, pg. 4262
TYMCO INTERNATIONAL LTD.; *U.S. Private*, pg. 4268
ULLAND BROTHERS INC.; *U.S. Private*, pg. 4276
UNITED COMPANIES OF MESA COUNTY—See CRH plc; *Int'l*, pg. 1848
UNITED CONTRACTORS INC.; *U.S. Private*, pg. 4290
UNITED CONTRACTORS INC.; *U.S. Private*, pg. 4290
US ASPHALT CO—See Omni Holding Company; *U.S. Private*, pg. 3016
US COATINGS, LLC—See SK Capital Partners, LP; *U.S. Private*, pg. 3679
UTILI-COMM SOUTH, INC.; *U.S. Private*, pg. 4326
VALLEY CONSTRUCTION COMPANY—See The Valley Group, Inc.; *U.S. Private*, pg. 4130
VALLEY PAVING INC.; *U.S. Private*, pg. 4335
VIKING CONSTRUCTION INC.; *U.S. Private*, pg. 4382

V.K. KNOWLTON CONSTRUCTION & UTILITIES, INC.—See TETCO, Inc.; *U.S. Private*, pg. 3973
VOJVODINAPUT BACKAPUT A.D.—See Baumeister doo; *Int'l*, pg. 895
V&S COLUMBUS GALVANIZING LLC—See Hill & Smith PLC; *Int'l*, pg. 3392
V&S MEMPHIS GALVANIZING LLC—See Hill & Smith PLC; *Int'l*, pg. 3392
WALTERS-MORGAN CONSTRUCTION; *U.S. Private*, pg. 4434
WARREN PAVING INC.; *U.S. Private*, pg. 4444
WASHTENAW COUNTY ROAD COMMISSION; *U.S. Private*, pg. 4449
WAYNE ASPHALT & CONSTRUCTION CO.; *U.S. Private*, pg. 4459
WCC CABLE, INC.; *U.S. Private*, pg. 4461
W.C. ENGLISH INCORPORATED; *U.S. Private*, pg. 4419
W. E. BLAIN & SONS, INC.; *U.S. Private*, pg. 4418
WERNER CONSTRUCTION INC.; *U.S. Private*, pg. 4481
WEST CONSTRUCTION COMPANY; *U.S. Private*, pg. 4484
WESTERN ENGINEERING CO. INC.; *U.S. Private*, pg. 4493
WEST VIRGINIA PAVING, INC.—See CRH plc; *Int'l*, pg. 1848
WHITE CONSTRUCTION COMPANY INC.; *U.S. Private*, pg. 4508
WHITE OAK CORPORATION; *U.S. Private*, pg. 4509
WHITE'S SITE DEVELOPMENT, INC.; *U.S. Private*, pg. 4510
WILDISH LAND COMPANY; *U.S. Private*, pg. 4519
WILDISH PAVING CO., INC.—See Wildish Land Company; *U.S. Private*, pg. 4519
WILDISH STANDARD PAVING CO., INC.—See Wildish Land Company; *U.S. Private*, pg. 4519
WILDISH STANDARD PAVING—See Wildish Land Company; *U.S. Private*, pg. 4519
WILLAMETTE CRUSHING CO., INC.—See Wildish Land Company; *U.S. Private*, pg. 4519
WILLARD ASPHALT PAVING, INC.; *U.S. Private*, pg. 4521
WILLIAM CHARLES CONSTRUCTION COMPANY, LLC—See MasTec, Inc.; *U.S. Public*, pg. 1393
WILLIAM CHARLES, LTD.; *U.S. Private*, pg. 4522
WILLIAM MUELLER & SONS INC.; *U.S. Private*, pg. 4524
WINTER PROPERTIES INC.; *U.S. Private*, pg. 4545
WIREGRASS CONSTRUCTION COMPANY; *U.S. Private*, pg. 4546
W-L CONSTRUCTION & PAVING, INC.—See CRH plc; *Int'l*, pg. 1848
W.L. MILLER CO. INC.; *U.S. Private*, pg. 4421
WOLF PAVING CO. INC.—See Lowell Wolf Industries Inc.; *U.S. Private*, pg. 2505
WRIGHT & MORRISSEY, INC.; *U.S. Private*, pg. 4572
WRIGHT PAVING CONTRACTORS INC—See Armada Materials, LLC; *U.S. Private*, pg. 329
YONKERS CONTRACTING COMPANY INC.; *U.S. Private*, pg. 4590
YVAN PAQUE S.A. - VILLEROUX PLANT—See Eiffage S.A.; *Int'l*, pg. 2330
ZACK BURKETT CO.; *U.S. Private*, pg. 4596
ZELLNER CONSTRUCTION COMPANY, INC.; *U.S. Private*, pg. 4600
ZENITH TECH INC.; *U.S. Private*, pg. 4601
ZIGNEGO COMPANY, INCORPORATED; *U.S. Private*, pg. 4604

237990 — OTHER HEAVY AND CIVIL ENGINEERING CONSTRUCTION

2G CENERGY POWER SYSTEMS TECHNOLOGIES INC.—See 2G Energy AG; *Int'l*, pg. 5
2G ENERGY AG; *Int'l*, pg. 4
2G ENERGY LTD.—See 2G Energy AG; *Int'l*, pg. 5
2G ITALIA S.R.L.—See 2G Energy AG; *Int'l*, pg. 5
2G POLSKA SP. Z O.O.—See 2G Energy AG; *Int'l*, pg. 5
2G SOLUTIONS OF COGENERATION, S.L.—See 2G Energy AG; *Int'l*, pg. 5
A2Z INFRA ENGINEERING LIMITED; *Int'l*, pg. 30
ABDULLA AHMED NASS CONTRACTING COMPANY WLL—See Abdulla Ahmed Nass Group WLL; *Int'l*, pg. 58
ABL GROUP ASA; *Int'l*, pg. 62
ACS INFRASTRUCTURE DEVELOPMENT, INC.—See ACS, Actividades de Construccion y Servicios, S.A.; *Int'l*, pg. 109
ADAPAZARI ELEKTRIK URETIM LIMITED SIRKETI—See Enka Insaat ve Sanayi A.S.; *Int'l*, pg. 2440
ADB COMPANIES, INC.—See Warren Equity Partners, LLC; *U.S. Private*, pg. 4443
ADVANCETEK ENTERPRISE CO., LTD.; *Int'l*, pg. 163
AECON CONSTRUCTION MANAGEMENT INC.—See Aecon Group Inc.; *Int'l*, pg. 172
AECON INDUSTRIAL WESTERN INC.—See Aecon Group Inc.; *Int'l*, pg. 172
AF GRUPPEN ASA; *Int'l*, pg. 183
AGLOMERADOS ALBACETE SA—See Eiffage S.A.; *Int'l*, pg. 2330
AGLOMERADOS LOS SERRANOS SA—See Eiffage S.A.; *Int'l*, pg. 2330

AGL SALES PTY LIMITED—See AGL Energy Limited; *Int'l*, pg. 211
AGRUPACION GUINOVART OBRAS Y SERVICIOS HISPANIA, S.A.—See Grupo Villar Mir, S.A.U.; *Int'l*, pg. 3138
AISIN DEVELOPMENT CO., LTD.—See AISIN Corporation; *Int'l*, pg. 252
AKER SOLUTIONS DO BRASIL LTDA.—See Aker Solutions ASA; *Int'l*, pg. 262
ALDRIDGE CONSTRUCTION, INC.; *U.S. Private*, pg. 160
ALFRED BENESCH & COMPANY—See Alfred Benesch & Company; *U.S. Private*, pg. 165
ALFRED BENESCH & COMPANY—See Alfred Benesch & Company; *U.S. Private*, pg. 165
ALFRED BENESCH & COMPANY—See Alfred Benesch & Company; *U.S. Private*, pg. 165
ALFRED BENESCH & COMPANY—See Alfred Benesch & Company; *U.S. Private*, pg. 165
ALFRED BENESCH & COMPANY—See Alfred Benesch & Company; *U.S. Private*, pg. 165
ALFRED BENESCH & COMPANY—See Alfred Benesch & Company; *U.S. Private*, pg. 165
ALFRED BENESCH & COMPANY—See Alfred Benesch & Company; *U.S. Private*, pg. 165
ALFRED BENESCH & COMPANY—See Alfred Benesch & Company; *U.S. Private*, pg. 165
ALFRED BENESCH & COMPANY—See Alfred Benesch & Company; *U.S. Private*, pg. 165
ALFRED BENESCH & COMPANY—See Alfred Benesch & Company; *U.S. Private*, pg. 165
AL FUTTAIM CARILLION—See Carillion plc; *Int'l*, pg. 1330
AL FUTTAIM CARILLION—See KKR & Co. Inc.; *U.S. Public*, pg. 1329
AL GHURAIR CONSTRUCTION - FOUNDATIONS LLC—See Al Ghurair Investment LLC; *Int'l*, pg. 278
AL GHURAIR CONSTRUCTION & FOUNDATIONS SAUDI LLC—See Al Ghurair Investment LLC; *Int'l*, pg. 278
AL GHURAIR CONSTRUCTION LLC—See Al Ghurair Investment LLC; *Int'l*, pg. 278
AL HASSAN ENGINEERING COMPANY S.A.O.G.; *Int'l*, pg. 278
ALLEN & SHARIFF CORPORATION; *U.S. Private*, pg. 178
ALLIANCE INTEGRATED METALIKS LIMITED; *Int'l*, pg. 340
AL MUHAIDIB CONTRACTING CO.—See A.K. Al-Muhaidib & Sons Group of Companies; *Int'l*, pg. 24
ALPINE BAU GMBH; *Int'l*, pg. 371
ALPINE HOUSING DEVELOPMENT CORPORATION LTD.; *Int'l*, pg. 371
ALUSYSTEM SRL—See Bog'Art S.R.L.; *Int'l*, pg. 1100
AMBIENT SERVICOS AMBIENTAIS DE RIBEIRAO PRETO, S.A.—See GS Holdings Corp.; *Int'l*, pg. 3142
AMEREN CORPORATION; *U.S. Public*, pg. 94
AMTRAC OF OHIO, INC.; *U.S. Private*, pg. 268
ANDERSON CONSTRUCTION LTD—See Anderson Group Limited; *Int'l*, pg. 450
ANI JOINT STOCK COMPANY; *Int'l*, pg. 471
ANMECO N.V.—See Ackermans & van Haaren NV; *Int'l*, pg. 104
ANTROPE SNC—See Eiffage S.A.; *Int'l*, pg. 2330
ANTWERPSE BOUWWERKEN NV—See Eiffage S.A.; *Int'l*, pg. 2329
APPIA GRANDS TRAVAUX SNC—See Eiffage S.A.; *Int'l*, pg. 2330
ARBICO PLC.; *Int'l*, pg. 537
ARCADIS - SYDNEY—See ARCADIS N.V.; *Int'l*, pg. 541
ARELLANO CONSTRUCTION COMPANY—See Grupo Villar Mir, S.A.U.; *Int'l*, pg. 3139
ARIA ENERGY LLC—See BP plc; *Int'l*, pg. 1126
ASEA BROWN BOVERI S.A.E.—See ABB Ltd.; *Int'l*, pg. 55
AS GUSTAF—See AS Merko Ehitus; *Int'l*, pg. 590
ASHIANA ISPAT LTD.; *Int'l*, pg. 607
ASHRAM ONLINE.COM LIMITED; *Int'l*, pg. 608
ASHTON COMPANY, INC.; *U.S. Private*, pg. 350
ASIA POWER PROJECTS PRIVATE LTD.—See Cassa Depositi e Prestiti S.p.A.; *Int'l*, pg. 1354
AS MERKO EHITUS EESTI—See AS Merko Ehitus; *Int'l*, pg. 590
AS MERKO INFRA—See AS Merko Ehitus; *Int'l*, pg. 590
AS MERKO TARTU—See AS Merko Ehitus; *Int'l*, pg. 590
ASRC CIVIL CONSTRUCTION, LLC—See Arctic Slope Regional Corporation; *U.S. Private*, pg. 316
ASRC CONSTRUCTION HOLDING COMPANY, LLC—See Arctic Slope Regional Corporation; *U.S. Private*, pg. 316
ATHENA EMIRATES LLC—See ATHENA S.A.; *Int'l*, pg. 670
ATHENA FUJAIRAH LLC—See ATHENA S.A.; *Int'l*, pg. 670
ATHENA S.A.; *Int'l*, pg. 670
AUBREY SILVEY ENTERPRISES INC.; *U.S. Private*, pg. 385
AUTO PARK POZNAN SP. Z O.O.—See Eiffage S.A.; *Int'l*, pg. 2329
BABCOCK WANSON AG—See CNIM Constructions Industrielles de la Mediterranee SA; *Int'l*, pg. 1676
BALFOUR BEATTY GROUP LTD—See Balfour Beatty plc; *Int'l*, pg. 807
BALFOUR BEATTY RAIL—See Balfour Beatty plc; *Int'l*, pg. 807
BALVAC, LTD.—See Balfour Beatty plc; *Int'l*, pg. 807

N.A.I.C.S. INDEX

237990 — OTHER HEAVY AND CIV...

BARBELLA CONSTRUCTION SERVICES, LLC; *U.S. Private*, pg. 472

BASIC CONSTRUCTION COMPANY - NEW KENT FACILITY—See Basic Construction Company; *U.S. Private*, pg. 485

BASIC CONSTRUCTION COMPANY - OYSTER POINT FACILITY—See Basic Construction Company; *U.S. Private*, pg. 485

BAUUNTERNEHMUNG GEBR. ECHTERHOFF GMBH & CO. KG—See Bauunterneham Echterhoff GmbH & Co. KG; *Int'l*, pg. 898

BAYSIDE ENGINEERING, INC.; *U.S. Private*, pg. 497

BBR PILING PTE LTD.—See BBR Holdings (S) Ltd.; *Int'l*, pg. 921

BBV SYSTEMS SP. Z O.O.—See Bilfinger SE; *Int'l*, pg. 1024

BEAN DREDGING, L.L.C.—See C.F. Bean, LLC; *U.S. Private*, pg. 707

BECHTEL CANADA CO.—See Bechtel Group, Inc.; *U.S. Private*, pg. 509

BECHTEL CHILE LTDA.—See Bechtel Group, Inc.; *U.S. Private*, pg. 510

BECHTEL DO BRASIL CONSTRUCOES LTDA.—See Bechtel Group, Inc.; *U.S. Private*, pg. 510

BECHTEL INDIA PRIVATE LIMITED—See Bechtel Group, Inc.; *U.S. Private*, pg. 510

BECHTEL INTERNATIONAL INC.—See Bechtel Group, Inc.; *U.S. Private*, pg. 510

BECHTEL INTERNATIONAL INC.—See Bechtel Group, Inc.; *U.S. Private*, pg. 510

BECHTEL INTERNATIONAL INC.—See Bechtel Group, Inc.; *U.S. Private*, pg. 510

BECHTEL JACOBS COMPANY LLC—See Bechtel Group, Inc.; *U.S. Private*, pg. 510

BECHTEL LTD.—See Bechtel Group, Inc.; *U.S. Private*, pg. 510

BECHTEL MALAYSIA INC.—See Bechtel Group, Inc.; *U.S. Private*, pg. 510

BEIJING AOSAIKANG PHARMACEUTICAL CO., LTD.; *Int'l*, pg. 945

BEIJING CONSTRUCTION ENGINEERING (GROUP) CO., LTD.; *Int'l*, pg. 948

BEIJING URBAN CONSTRUCTION DESIGN & DEVELOPMENT GROUP CO., LTD.; *Int'l*, pg. 959

BEML LIMITED; *Int'l*, pg. 969

BENALEC HOLDINGS BERHAD; *Int'l*, pg. 969

BENTON'S EQUIPMENT & CONSTRUCTION, INC.; *U.S. Private*, pg. 529

BHARAT HEAVY ELECTRICALS LIMITED; *Int'l*, pg. 1011

BH GLOBAL CORPORATION LIMITED; *Int'l*, pg. 1009

BIA-HAZLETON—See Barry Isett & Associates Inc.; *U.S. Private*, pg. 481

BIA-PHOENIXVILLE—See Barry Isett & Associates Inc.; *U.S. Private*, pg. 481

BIBBY OFFSHORE LIMITED—See HAL Trust N.V.; *Int'l*, pg. 3226

BILFINGER BERGER AG-CIVIL—See Bilfinger SE; *Int'l*, pg. 1024

BILFINGER BERGER BAUGESELLSCHAFT MBH—See Bilfinger SE; *Int'l*, pg. 1024

BILFINGER BERGER BELGIUM S.A.—See Bilfinger SE; *Int'l*, pg. 1025

BILFINGER BERGER (CANADA) INC.—See Bilfinger SE; *Int'l*, pg. 1024

BILFINGER BERGER CONSTRUCTION, LLC—See Bilfinger SE; *Int'l*, pg. 1024

BILFINGER BERGER INSTANDSETZUNG GMBH—See Bilfinger SE; *Int'l*, pg. 1024

BILFINGER BERGER STAVEBNI PRAHA, S.R.O.—See Bilfinger SE; *Int'l*, pg. 1027

BILFINGER BERGER (THAI) CONSTRUCTION CO., LTD.—See Bilfinger SE; *Int'l*, pg. 1024

BILFINGER BERGER UK LIMITED—See Bilfinger SE; *Int'l*, pg. 1024

BILFINGER BOHR- UND ROHRTECHNIK GMBH—See Bilfinger SE; *Int'l*, pg. 1027

BILFINGER SE; *Int'l*, pg. 1023

BILFINGER WOLFFERTS GEBAUDETECHNIK GMBH—See Bilfinger SE; *Int'l*, pg. 1028

BILLINGTON HOLDINGS PLC; *Int'l*, pg. 1031

BINNINGTON COPELAND & ASSOCIATES (PTY.) LTD.—See Global Infrastructure Solutions, Inc.; *U.S. Private*, pg. 1715

BIORRECICLAJE DE CADIZ, S.A.—See GS Holdings Corp.; *Int'l*, pg. 3142

BIOTER S.A.; *Int'l*, pg. 1043

BIRSE METRO LIMITED—See Balfour Beatty plc; *Int'l*, pg. 807

BIS TEPSCO INC.—See Bilfinger SE; *Int'l*, pg. 1026

BJC HEAVY INDUSTRIES PUBLIC COMPANY LIMITED; *Int'l*, pg. 1053

BLACK & VEATCH CONSTRUCTION, INC—See Black & Veatch Holding Company; *U.S. Private*, pg. 569

BLACK & VEATCH INTERNATIONAL COMPANY—See Black & Veatch Holding Company; *U.S. Private*, pg. 569

BLAXTAIR INC.—See Arcure; *Int'l*, pg. 552

BLUE-CON CONSTRUCTION; *Int'l*, pg. 1070

BMWC CONSTRUCTORS, INC.—See BMWC Group Inc.; *U.S. Private*, pg. 601

BOKWANG INDUSTRY CO.,LTD; *Int'l*, pg. 1102

BOLSONES VERFT AS—See Havila Holding As; *Int'l*, pg. 3287

BOLSONES VERFT AS—See Vision Ridge Partners, LLC; *U.S. Private*, pg. 4391

BOREK CONSTRUCTION, LTD.; *Int'l*, pg. 1114

BOSKALIS ARGENTINA—See HAL Trust N.V.; *Int'l*, pg. 3224

BOSKALIS DO BRASIL DRAGAGEM E SERVICOS MARITIMOS LTDA.—See HAL Trust N.V.; *Int'l*, pg. 3225

BOSKALIS GUYANA INC.—See HAL Trust N.V.; *Int'l*, pg. 3225

BOSKALIS POLSKA SP. Z O.O.—See HAL Trust N.V.; *Int'l*, pg. 3225

BOSKALIS SWEDEN AB—See HAL Trust N.V.; *Int'l*, pg. 3225

BOSKALIS WESTMINSTER DREDGING LTD.—See HAL Trust N.V.; *Int'l*, pg. 3225

BOSKALIS WESTMINSTER MIDDLE EAST LTD.—See HAL Trust N.V.; *Int'l*, pg. 3225

BOUYGUES CONSTRUCTION—See Bouygues S.A.; *Int'l*, pg. 1121

BOUYGUES ENTREPRISES FRANCE-EUROPE—See Bouygues S.A.; *Int'l*, pg. 1122

BOUYGUES E&S INFRASTRUCTURE UK LIMITED—See Bouygues S.A.; *Int'l*, pg. 1122

BOUYGUES TRAVAUX PUBLICS—See Bouygues S.A.; *Int'l*, pg. 1122

BRAHMAPUTRA INFRASTRUCTURE LIMITED; *Int'l*, pg. 1136

BRECO INTERNATIONAL INC.—See Arcline Investment Management LP; *U.S. Private*, pg. 313

BRODA CONSTRUCTION LNC.—See Bird Construction Inc.; *Int'l*, pg. 1046

BROKEN ARROW COMMUNICATIONS, INC.—See QualTek Services Inc.; *U.S. Public*, pg. 1748

BRYEN & LANGLEY LTD.; *Int'l*, pg. 1201

BUDIMEX S.A.—See Ferrovial S.A.; *Int'l*, pg. 2644

BULLEY & ANDREWS CONCRETE RESTORATION—See Bulley & Andrews, LLC; *U.S. Private*, pg. 685

BURGESS CIVIL, LLC; *U.S. Private*, pg. 687

BURSICH ASSOCIATES, INC.—See Bursich Associates, Inc.; *U.S. Private*, pg. 692

CAGUAS MECHANICAL CONTRACTOR, INC.; *U.S. Private*, pg. 714

CALDWELL MARINE INTERNATIONAL, LLC (CMI)—See Northeast Remsco Construction, Inc.; *U.S. Private*, pg. 2951

CAMBRIDGE BRASS—See A.Y. McDonald Manufacturing Co.; *U.S. Private*, pg. 29

CANADIAN HIGHWAYS INFRASTRUCTURE CORPORATION—See Aecon Group Inc.; *Int'l*, pg. 172

CARDNO VICTORIA PTY. LTD.—See Cardno Limited; *Int'l*, pg. 1322

CARRIERE DE LA ROCHE BLAIN—See Eiffage S.A.; *Int'l*, pg. 2330

CARRIERE DES CHENES S.A.—See Eiffage S.A.; *Int'l*, pg. 2330

CASH CONSTRUCTION COMPANY, INC.—See MasTec, Inc.; *U.S. Public*, pg. 1393

CASTLE CONTRACTING, LLC—See McCarthy Holdings, Inc.; *U.S. Private*, pg. 2627

CATALANA DE TREBALLS PUBLICS, S.A.—See ACS, Actividades de Construccion y Servicios, S.A.; *Int'l*, pg. 110

CAVACHE, INC.—See Ahtna, Inc.; *U.S. Private*, pg. 131

CB&I UK LIMITED—See McDermott International, Inc.; *U.S. Public*, pg. 1405

CCCC DREDGING (GROUP) CO., LTD.—See China Communications Construction Company Limited; *Int'l*, pg. 1490

CCCC GUANGZHOU DREDGING CO., LTD.—See China Communications Construction Company Limited; *Int'l*, pg. 1490

CC NAPRED JSC; *Int'l*, pg. 1366

CCR PLATFORMING CANGREJERA S.A. DE C.V.—See ACS, Actividades de Construccion y Servicios, S.A.; *Int'l*, pg. 110

CDM CONSTRUCTORS INC.—See CDM Smith Inc.; *U.S. Private*, pg. 802

CD-TELEMATIKA A.S.—See Grupo Villar Mir, S.A.U.; *Int'l*, pg. 3139

CEFLA IMPIANTI GROUP—See Cefla S.C.; *Int'l*, pg. 1389

CENTRAL TERMICA DE MEJILLONES, S.A.—See ACS, Actividades de Construccion y Servicios, S.A.; *Int'l*, pg. 110

CENTRUM NOWOCZESNYCH TECHNOLOGII S.A.; *Int'l*, pg. 1416

CERES ENVIRONMENTAL SERVICES, INC.; *U.S. Private*, pg. 840

CESIONARIA VALLES OCCIDENTAL, S.A.—See ACS, Actividades de Construccion y Servicios, S.A.; *Int'l*, pg. 110

CHAN LIAN CONSTRUCTION PTE LTD—See Downer EDI Limited; *Int'l*, pg. 2185

CHAYAH CONSULTING GROUP LLC; *U.S. Private*, pg. 868

CHET MORRISON CONTRACTORS INC.; *U.S. Private*, pg. 875

CHINA COMMUNICATIONS CONSTRUCTION COMPANY LIMITED; *Int'l*, pg. 1490

CHINA EVERBRIGHT ENVIRONMENT GROUP LIMITED—See China Everbright Group Limited; *Int'l*, pg. 1501

CHINA HUARONG ENERGY CO. LTD.; *Int'l*, pg. 1509

CHINA MACHINERY ENGINEERING CORPORATION; *Int'l*, pg. 1515

CHINA NATIONAL COMPLETE PLANT IMPORT & EXPORT CORPORATION; *Int'l*, pg. 1531

CHINA NEW ENERGY LIMITED; *Int'l*, pg. 1534

CHINA POWER CONSTRUCTION ENGINEERING CONSULTING CORPORATION—See China Machinery Engineering Corporation; *Int'l*, pg. 1516

CHINA RAILWAY 12TH BUREAU GROUP CO., LTD.—See China Railway Construction Corporation Limited; *Int'l*, pg. 1543

CHINA RAILWAY 14TH BUREAU GROUP CO., LTD.—See China Railway Construction Corporation Limited; *Int'l*, pg. 1543

CHINA RAILWAY 16TH BUREAU GROUP CO., LTD.—See China Railway Construction Corporation Limited; *Int'l*, pg. 1543

CHINA RAILWAY 17TH BUREAU GROUP CO., LTD.—See China Railway Construction Corporation Limited; *Int'l*, pg. 1543

CHINA RAILWAY 18TH BUREAU GROUP CO., LTD.—See China Railway Construction Corporation Limited; *Int'l*, pg. 1543

CHINA RAILWAY 19TH BUREAU GROUP CO., LTD.—See China Railway Construction Corporation Limited; *Int'l*, pg. 1543

CHINA RAILWAY 20TH BUREAU GROUP CO., LTD.—See China Railway Construction Corporation Limited; *Int'l*, pg. 1543

CHINA RAILWAY 21ST BUREAU GROUP CO., LTD.—See China Railway Construction Corporation Limited; *Int'l*, pg. 1543

CHINA RAILWAY 22ND BUREAU GROUP CO., LTD.—See China Railway Construction Corporation Limited; *Int'l*, pg. 1543

CHINA RAILWAY CONSTRUCTION CORPORATION LIMITED; *Int'l*, pg. 1542

CHINA RAILWAY CONSTRUCTION (HK) LIMITED—See China Railway Construction Corporation Limited; *Int'l*, pg. 1543

CHINA RAILWAY HI-TECH INDUSTRY CORPORATION; *Int'l*, pg. 1543

CHINA STATE CONSTRUCTION DEVELOPMENT HOLDINGS LIMITED—See China State Construction International Holdings Limited; *Int'l*, pg. 1554

CHUBU PLANT SERVICE CO., LTD.—See Chubu Electric Power Co., Inc.; *Int'l*, pg. 1593

CHUN WO FOUNDATIONS LIMITED—See Asia Allied Infrastructure Holdings Limited; *Int'l*, pg. 610

CHUONG DUONG CORPORATION; *Int'l*, pg. 1600

CIMTAS GEMI INSA SANAYI VE TICARET A.S.—See Enka Insaat ve Sanayi A.S.; *Int'l*, pg. 2440

CITADEL REALTY & DEVELOPERS LTD.; *Int'l*, pg. 1619

CITY POINT PARTNERS LLC—See HDR, Inc.; *U.S. Private*, pg. 1890

CIVIL CONSTRUCTION CONTRACTORS INC.; *U.S. Private*, pg. 908

CIVIL CONSTRUCTORS, INC.—See The Helm Group; *U.S. Private*, pg. 4051

CIVILSOURCE, INC.—See NV5 Global, Inc.; *U.S. Public*, pg. 1557

CIVMEC LIMITED; *Int'l*, pg. 1630

CNIM CONSTRUCTIONS INDUSTRIELLES DE LA MEDITERRANEE SA; *Int'l*, pg. 1676

COASTAL AND INLAND MARINE SERVICES INC.—See HAL Trust N.V.; *Int'l*, pg. 3225

COBRA CONCESIONES, S.L.—See ACS, Actividades de Construccion y Servicios, S.A.; *Int'l*, pg. 110

COBRA GESTION DE INFRAESTRUCTURAS, S.L.U—See ACS, Actividades de Construccion y Servicios, S.A.; *Int'l*, pg. 110

COBRA INFRAESTRUCTURAS HIDRAULICAS, S.A.—See ACS, Actividades de Construccion y Servicios, S.A.; *Int'l*, pg. 110

COBRA INSTALACIONES Y SERVICIOS INTERNACIONAL, S.L.—See ACS, Actividades de Construccion y Servicios, S.A.; *Int'l*, pg. 110

CODA OCTOPUS PRODUCTS A/S—See Coda Octopus Group, Inc.; *U.S. Public*, pg. 521

CODA OCTOPUS PRODUCTS, INC.—See Coda Octopus Group, Inc.; *U.S. Public*, pg. 521

CODRAMEX SA DE CV—See HAL Trust N.V.; *Int'l*, pg. 3225

COFELY FM S.R.O.—See ENGIE SA; *Int'l*, pg. 2430

COGEN ENERGIA ESPANA S.L—See Arendals Fossekompani ASA; *Int'l*, pg. 558

COLAS LTD—See Bouygues S.A.; *Int'l*, pg. 1122

COLAS RAIL—See Bouygues S.A.; *Int'l*, pg. 1123

COMER INDUSTRIES INC—See Comer Industries S.p.A.; *Int'l*, pg. 1710

COMMERZ REAL BAUMANAGEMENT GMBH—See Commerzbank AG; *Int'l*, pg. 1716

COMPANHIA DE CONSTRUCAO E ENGENHARIA KIN SUN (MACAU), LIMITADA—See Bilfinger SE; *Int'l*, pg. 1024

3211

237990 — OTHER HEAVY AND CIV...

COMSA EMTE S.L.; *Int'l*, pg. 1761
CONCESIONARIA DE EJES TERRESTRES DE COAHUILA, S.A. DE C.V.—See Empresas ICA S.A.B. de C.V.; *Int'l*, pg. 2390
CONSORCIO TECDRA, S.A.—See ACS, Actividades de Construccion y Servicios, S.A.; *Int'l*, pg. 111
CONSTRUCCIONES ENRIQUE DE LUIS, S.A.—See Grupo Villar Mir, S.A.U.; *Int'l*, pg. 3139
CONSTRUCTII COMPLEXE SA; *Int'l*, pg. 1777
CONSTRUCTII FEROVIARE SA; *Int'l*, pg. 1777
CONSTRUCTII HIDROTEHNICE SA; *Int'l*, pg. 1777
CONSTRUCTION JOINT STOCK COMPANY 47; *Int'l*, pg. 1777
CONSTRUCTION KIEWIT CIE—See Peter Kiewit Sons', Inc.; *U.S. Private*, pg. 3158
CONSTRUCTION & MATERIALS TRADING JOINT STOCK COMPANY; *Int'l*, pg. 1777
CONSTRUCTORA DYCVEN, S.A.—See ACS, Actividades de Construccion y Servicios, S.A.; *Int'l*, pg. 111
CONSTRUCTORA HIDROELECTRICA LA YESCA, S.A. DE C.V.—See Empresas ICA S.A.B. de C.V.; *Int'l*, pg. 2390
CONTECH CONSTRUCTION PRODUCTS INC.—See Apax Partners LLP; *Int'l*, pg. 503
CONTRACTING & MARINE SERVICES CO. (S.A.K.); *Int'l*, pg. 1785
CORMAN MARINE CONSTRUCTION, INC.—See C.G. Enterprises Inc.; *U.S. Private*, pg. 707
COSTAIN BUILDING & CIVIL ENGINEERING LTD.—See Costain Group PLC; *Int'l*, pg. 1815
COSTAIN ENGINEERING & CONSTRUCTION LTD.—See Costain Group PLC; *Int'l*, pg. 1814
CRANE MATERIALS INTERNATIONAL (CMI)—See Crane Group Co.; *U.S. Private*, pg. 1085
CRCC HARBOUR & CHANNEL ENGINEERING BUREAU GROUP CO., LTD.—See China Railway Construction Corporation Limited; *Int'l*, pg. 1542
CRC-EVANS OFFSHORE LIMITED—See Stanley Black & Decker, Inc.; *U.S. Public*, pg. 1932
C.R. FEDRICK, INC.; *U.S. Private*, pg. 708
THE CROM CORPORATION; *U.S. Private*, pg. 4016
CRUZ MARINE LLC—See Cook Inlet Region, Inc.; *U.S. Private*, pg. 1038
CTCI CORPORATION; *Int'l*, pg. 1869
CTCI ENGINEERING & CONSTRUCTION SDN BHD—See CTCI Corporation; *Int'l*, pg. 1870
CTCI (THAILAND) CO., LTD.—See CTCI Corporation; *Int'l*, pg. 1870
CURRIER CONSTRUCTION INC.; *U.S. Private*, pg. 1125
CYMI SEGURIDAD, S.A.—See ACS, Actividades de Construccion y Servicios, S.A.; *Int'l*, pg. 111
DAI-ICHI CUTTER KOGYO K.K.; *Int'l*, pg. 1917
DALA ENERGI AB; *Int'l*, pg. 1950
DANANG HOUSING DEVELOPMENT JOINT STOCK COMPANY; *Int'l*, pg. 1958
DANIEL C. BAKER ASSOCIATES, INC.—See Larson Design Group; *U.S. Private*, pg. 2393
DAZZEL CONFINDIVE LTD.; *Int'l*, pg. 1985
DB ENERGY SA; *Int'l*, pg. 1986
DBSI INCORPORATED; *U.S. Private*, pg. 1179
DE GRAEVE ENTREPRISES GENERALES SA—See Eiffage S.A.; *Int'l*, pg. 2329
DEILMANN-HANIEL SHAFT SINKING GMBH—See ATON GmbH; *Int'l*, pg. 688
DENNIS CORPORATION—See Bowman Consulting Group Ltd.; *U.S. Public*, pg. 376
DENVER TRANSIT PARTNERS, LLC—See Fluor Corporation; *U.S. Public*, pg. 858
D.E. RICE CONSTRUCTION CO., INC.; *U.S. Private*, pg. 1141
DESALARI LTDA.—See GS Holdings Corp.; *Int'l*, pg. 3142
DESARROLLO DE CONCESIONARIAS VIARIAS UNO, S.L.—See ACS, Actividades de Construccion y Servicios, S.A.; *Int'l*, pg. 111
DESARROLLO DE CONCESIONES FERROVIARIAS, S.L.—See ACS, Actividades de Construccion y Servicios, S.A.; *Int'l*, pg. 111
DESQUESNES SNC—See Eiffage S.A.; *Int'l*, pg. 2330
DEVCON (TCI) LTD.; *U.S. Private*, pg. 1217
DEVELOPMENT OF NEW ALIMOS MARINA S.A.—See ELLAKTOR S.A.; *Int'l*, pg. 2365
DIAMANT INFRASTRUCTURE LIMITED; *Int'l*, pg. 2104
DIAMOND LAKE MINERALS, INC.; *U.S. Public*, pg. 658
DIC NO. 4 JOINT STOCK COMPANY—See Development Investment Construction JSC; *Int'l*, pg. 2088
DIETER HAFEMEISTER ERDBAU GMBH & CO.—See ACS, Actividades de Construccion y Servicios, S.A.; *Int'l*, pg. 113
DIETSWELL S.A.; *Int'l*, pg. 2117
DJURO DJAKOVIC MONTAGE GMBH—See Bilfinger SE; *Int'l*, pg. 1028
DLE OUEST—See Eiffage S.A.; *Int'l*, pg. 2330
DLE OUTRE-MER—See Eiffage S.A.; *Int'l*, pg. 2330
DLF GOLF RESORT LIMITED—See DLF Limited; *Int'l*, pg. 2141
DOCKYARD GENERAL ENGINEERING SERVICES (PVT) LTD.—See Colombo Dockyard PLC; *Int'l*, pg. 1702
DOHWA ENGINEERING CO., LTD.; *Int'l*, pg. 2156
DOMIKI KRITIS S.A.; *Int'l*, pg. 2161

DOOSAN ELECTRO-MATERIALS SINGAPORE PTE LTD—See Doosan Corporation; *Int'l*, pg. 2173
DOOSAN LENTJES GMBH—See Doosan Corporation; *Int'l*, pg. 2173
DOPPELMAYR ITALIA SRL—See Doppelmayr Group; *Int'l*, pg. 2174
DOSJAN TEMIR JOLY JSC; *Int'l*, pg. 2180
DOWNER AUSTRALIA PTY LTD—See Downer EDI Limited; *Int'l*, pg. 2185
DOWN UNDER CONSTRUCTION, LLC—See Hylan Datacom & Electrical, LLC; *U.S. Private*, pg. 2018
DRAGADOS GULF CONSTRUCTION, LTDA.—See ACS, Actividades de Construccion y Servicios, S.A.; *Int'l*, pg. 111
DRAGADOS INVERSIONES USA, S.L.—See ACS, Actividades de Construccion y Servicios, S.A.; *Int'l*, pg. 111
DRAGADOS USA INC.—See ACS, Actividades de Construccion y Servicios, S.A.; *Int'l*, pg. 111
DRAGAMEX SA DE CV—See HAL Trust N.V.; *Int'l*, pg. 3226
DRAGAPOR DRAGAGENS DE PORTUGAL S.A.—See HAL Trust N.V.; *Int'l*, pg. 3226
DREDGING CORPORATION OF INDIA LTD; *Int'l*, pg. 2203
DREDGING INTERNATIONAL ASIA PACIFIC (PTE) LTD—See Ackermans & van Haaren NV; *Int'l*, pg. 105
DRIVER PROJECT SERVICES (UAE) LLC—See Diales; *Int'l*, pg. 2104
DUNCAN SEAWALL, DOCK & BOAT LIFT, LLC; *U.S. Private*, pg. 1287
DURHAM PUMP, INC.; *U.S. Private*, pg. 1293
DURO DAKOVIC MONTAZA D.D.—See Bilfinger SE; *Int'l*, pg. 1028
DURST-BAU GMBH—See ACS, Actividades de Construccion y Servicios, S.A.; *Int'l*, pg. 113
DYNA-MAC HOLDINGS LTD.—See Hanwha Group; *Int'l*, pg. 3264
DYNA-MAC HOLDINGS LTD.—See Hanwha Ocean Co., Ltd.; *Int'l*, pg. 3266
EAGLE ENGINEERING, INC.—See Arsenal Capital Management LP; *U.S. Private*, pg. 338
ECOCIVIL ELECTROMUR G.E., S.L.—See ACS, Actividades de Construccion y Servicios, S.A.; *Int'l*, pg. 111
ECOENER, S.A.; *Int'l*, pg. 2295
EDEIS S.A.S.—See Ciclad SA; *Int'l*, pg. 1603
EICKHOFF INDUSTRIE-ANLAGENBAU UDN MONTAGEN GMBH—See Georgsmarienhutte Holding GmbH; *Int'l*, pg. 2940
EIFFAGE CONSTRUCTION BASSE NORMANDIE—See Eiffage S.A.; *Int'l*, pg. 2329
EIFFAGE CONSTRUCTION BOURGOGNE—See Eiffage S.A.; *Int'l*, pg. 2329
EIFFAGE CONSTRUCTION BRETAGNE S.N.C—See Eiffage S.A.; *Int'l*, pg. 2329
EIFFAGE CONSTRUCTION CENTRE—See Eiffage S.A.; *Int'l*, pg. 2329
EIFFAGE CONSTRUCTION CHAMPAGNE—See Eiffage S.A.; *Int'l*, pg. 2329
EIFFAGE CONSTRUCTION COTE D AZUR S.N.C—See Eiffage S.A.; *Int'l*, pg. 2329
EIFFAGE CONSTRUCTION METALLIQUE S.A.—See Eiffage S.A.; *Int'l*, pg. 2329
EIFFAGE CONSTRUCTION SERVICES—See Eiffage S.A.; *Int'l*, pg. 2330
EIFFAGE DEUTSCHLAND BAUHOLDING GMBH—See Eiffage S.A.; *Int'l*, pg. 2330
EIFFAGE GENIE CIVIL—See Eiffage S.A.; *Int'l*, pg. 2330
EIFFAGE INFRAESTRUCTURAS—See Eiffage S.A.; *Int'l*, pg. 2331
EIFFAGE INFRA-NORDWEST GMBH—See Eiffage S.A.; *Int'l*, pg. 2330
EIFFAGE INFRA-WEST GMBH—See Eiffage S.A.; *Int'l*, pg. 2331
EIFFAGE INTERNATIONAL S.A.—See Eiffage S.A.; *Int'l*, pg. 2331
EIFFAGE POLSKA BUDOWNICTWO SA—See Eiffage S.A.; *Int'l*, pg. 2330
EIFFAGE POLSKA KOLEJE SP. Z O.O.—See Eiffage S.A.; *Int'l*, pg. 2330
EIFFAGE TRAVAUX PUBLICS OUEST S.N.C—See Eiffage S.A.; *Int'l*, pg. 2331
EIFFAGE TRAVAUX PUBLICS RESEAUX—See Eiffage S.A.; *Int'l*, pg. 2331
EKTER S.A.; *Int'l*, pg. 2340
ELECNOR HAWKEYE, LLC—See Elecnor, S.A.; *Int'l*, pg. 2347
EMPRESA CONSTRUCTORA BELFI SA; *Int'l*, pg. 2388
EMPRESAS ICA S.A.B. DE C.V.; *Int'l*, pg. 2390
EMS ENERGY LIMITED; *Int'l*, pg. 2392
ENEABBA GAS LIMITED; *Int'l*, pg. 2410
ENERGOINVEST-DALEKOVODIZGRADNJA, D.D.; *Int'l*, pg. 2421
ENERGOMONTAJ S.A.; *Int'l*, pg. 2421
ENERGOMONTAJ S.A. - THERMO DIVISION—See Energomontaj S.A.; *Int'l*, pg. 2421
ENERGY PROCESS TECHNOLOGY INC.; *U.S. Private*, pg. 1395
ENGEMA RAIL—See Ackermans & van Haaren NV; *Int'l*, pg. 105
ENGINEERS INDIA LTD.; *Int'l*, pg. 2435

ENKA TEKNIK GENEL MUTEAHHITLIK BAKIM ISLETME SEVK VE IDARE ANONIM SIRKETI—See Enka Insaat ve Sanayi A.S.; *Int'l*, pg. 2440
ENTECH ENGINEERING INC.—See Entech Engineering Inc.; *U.S. Private*, pg. 1402
E-PANGO SA; *Int'l*, pg. 2249
ERITH GROUP; *Int'l*, pg. 2494
EUGENE RACANELLI INC.; *U.S. Private*, pg. 1433
EXCEL FABRICATION & CONSTRUCTION, INC.—See Excel Group, Inc.; *U.S. Private*, pg. 1445
EXMAR OFFSHORE COMPANY—See Exmar N.V.; *Int'l*, pg. 2585
FACCHINA CONSTRUCTION CO., INC.—See Empresas ICA S.A.B. de C.V.; *Int'l*, pg. 2390
FAJARBARU BUILDER SDN. BHD.—See Fajarbaru Builder Group Bhd.; *Int'l*, pg. 2610
FAMOS GRADNJA D.D.; *Int'l*, pg. 2612
FATA SPA—See Danieli & C. Officine Meccaniche S.p.A.; *Int'l*, pg. 1963
FERROVIAL AGROMAN US CORP.—See Ferrovial S.A.; *Int'l*, pg. 2644
FERROVIAL CONSTRUCTION—See Ferrovial S.A.; *Int'l*, pg. 2644
FIELDS, INC.; *U.S. Private*, pg. 1504
FIGENE CAPITAL SA; *Int'l*, pg. 2661
FIGENE ENERGIA SP. Z O.O.—See Figene Capital SA; *Int'l*, pg. 2661
FINCANTIERI INFRASTRUTTURE SOCIALI S.P.A.—See Fincantieri S.p.A.; *Int'l*, pg. 2671
FINELLI CONSULTING ENGINEERS, INC.—See Finelli Consulting Engineers, Inc.; *U.S. Private*, pg. 1509
FINN POWER ENERGY CORP; *U.S. Private*, pg. 1510
FIRESTONE METAL PRODUCTS COMPANY, LLC - JACKSON MANUFACTURING FACILITY—See Bridgestone Corporation; *Int'l*, pg. 1160
FLATIRON CONSTRUCTION CORP.—See ACS, Actividades de Construccion y Servicios, S.A.; *Int'l*, pg. 113
FLETCHER BUILDING NOMINEES LIMITED—See Fletcher Building Limited; *Int'l*, pg. 2700
THE FLETCHER CONSTRUCTION COMPANY LIMITED—See Fletcher Building Limited; *Int'l*, pg. 2701
FLETCHER MOROBE CONSTRUCTION PTY LIMITED—See Fletcher Building Limited; *Int'l*, pg. 2700
FLUOR CARLSBAD, LLC—See Fluor Corporation; *U.S. Public*, pg. 858
FLUOR (CHINA) ENGINEERING & CONSTRUCTION CO. LTD.—See Fluor Corporation; *U.S. Public*, pg. 858
FLUOR DANIEL, INC. - PHILIPPINES—See Fluor Corporation; *U.S. Public*, pg. 858
FLUOR FEDERAL SERVICES, LLC—See Fluor Corporation; *U.S. Public*, pg. 859
FLUOR IRELAND LIMITED—See Fluor Corporation; *U.S. Public*, pg. 859
FOMENTO DE CONSTRUCCIONES Y CONTRATAS, S.A.; *Int'l*, pg. 2721
FORCLUM RHONE ALPES S.A.S—See Eiffage S.A.; *Int'l*, pg. 2330
FORGEN, LLC; *U.S. Private*, pg. 1568
FRANK LILL & SON INC.; *U.S. Private*, pg. 1595
FRANZ KASSECKER GMBH—See Bilfinger SE; *Int'l*, pg. 1028
FRED WEBER, INC.; *U.S. Private*, pg. 1601
FRITZ PLANUNG GMBH; *Int'l*, pg. 2794
FRONTIER-KEMPER CONSTRUCTORS, INC.—See ATON GmbH; *Int'l*, pg. 688
FSA CONSTRUCTION, LLC—See Fort Sill Apache Tribe of Oklahoma; *U.S. Private*, pg. 1575
F.S. SPERRY CO. INC.; *U.S. Private*, pg. 1457
FUDO CONSTRUCTION INC.—See Fudo Tetra Corporation; *Int'l*, pg. 2804
FUGRO GEOSERVICES LIMITED—See Fugro N.V.; *Int'l*, pg. 2806
FUJITA CORPORATION—See Daiwa House Industry Co., Ltd.; *Int'l*, pg. 1946
FUKUDA CORPORATION; *Int'l*, pg. 2839
FULLER INTERNATIONAL INC.—See FLSmidth & Co. A/S; *Int'l*, pg. 2712
FULTON HOGAN LIMITED; *Int'l*, pg. 2843
GALENFEHA, INC.; *U.S. Private*, pg. 1637
GALLIFORD TRY BUILDING 2014 LIMITED—See Galliford Try Holdings plc; *Int'l*, pg. 2874
GALLIFORD TRY CONSTRUCTION CENTRAL—See Galliford Try Holdings plc; *Int'l*, pg. 2874
GALLIFORD TRY CONSTRUCTION LIMITED—See Galliford Try Holdings plc; *Int'l*, pg. 2874
GALLIFORD TRY CONSTRUCTION SOUTH—See Galliford Try Holdings plc; *Int'l*, pg. 2874
GALLIFORD TRY EMPLOYMENT LIMITED—See Galliford Try Holdings plc; *Int'l*, pg. 2874
GALLIFORD TRY INFRASTRUCTURE LIMITED—See Galliford Try Holdings plc; *Int'l*, pg. 2874
GALLIFORD TRY SERVICES LIMITED—See Galliford Try Holdings plc; *Int'l*, pg. 2874
GAMMON INDIA LIMITED; *Int'l*, pg. 2879
GARANTI KOZA INSAAT SANAYI VE TICARET A.S.; *Int'l*, pg. 2883
G. CAPPA PLC; *Int'l*, pg. 2864
GCC SAS; *Int'l*, pg. 2894

N.A.I.C.S. INDEX

237990 — OTHER HEAVY AND CIV...

GEBZE ELEKTRIK URETIM LIMITED SIRKETI—See Enka Insaat ve Sanayi A.S.; *Int'l*, pg. 2440
GEMAC ENGINEERING MACHINERY CO., LTD.; *Int'l*, pg. 2915
GENERAL ENGINEERING PUBLIC COMPANY LIMITED; *Int'l*, pg. 2918
GENIE CIVIL INDUSTRIEL—See Eiffage S.A.; *Int'l*, pg. 2330
GENTEX—See Lower Colorado River Authority; *U.S. Private*, pg. 2505
GEO-SOLUTIONS INC.; *U.S. Private*, pg. 1680
GEOSONDA KONSOLIDACIJA A.D.; *Int'l*, pg. 2941
GE POWER INDIA LIMITED; *Int'l*, pg. 2897
GESTION DE PARTICIPES DE BIORRECICLAJE, S.A.—See GS Holdings Corp.; *Int'l*, pg. 3142
GILMORE & ASSOCIATES, INC.—See Gilmore & Associates Inc.; *U.S. Private*, pg. 1701
GLADSTONE PRESSURE WELDERS PTY LTD—See Fluor Corporation; *U.S. Public*, pg. 859
GLOBAL MARINE HOLDINGS LIMITED—See J.F. Lehman & Company, Inc.; *U.S. Private*, pg. 2163
GLOBAL MARINE SYSTEMS OIL AND GAS, LTD—See INNOVATE Corp.; *U.S. Public*, pg. 1126
GLOBETEC CONSTRUCTION, LLC—See MasTec, Inc.; *U.S. Public*, pg. 1393
GME GROUP HOLDINGS LIMITED; *Int'l*, pg. 3012
GP 7. JUL A.D.; *Int'l*, pg. 3045
GP PLANUM AD; *Int'l*, pg. 3046
GRADEZEN INSTITUT MAKEDONIJA; *Int'l*, pg. 3049
GRADITELJSKO DIONICKO DRUSTVO VIADUKT; *Int'l*, pg. 3049
GRANITE CONSTRUCTION COMPANY—See Granite Construction Incorporated; *U.S. Public*, pg. 957
GREAT LAKES DREDGE & DOCK COMPANY, LLC—See Great Lakes Dredge & Dock Corporation; *U.S. Public*, pg. 962
GREAT LAKES DREDGE & DOCK CORPORATION; *U.S. Public*, pg. 961
GREAT WESTERN DEVELOPMENT COMPANY—See The Broe Companies, Inc.; *U.S. Private*, pg. 4000
GR ENGINEERING SERVICES LIMITED; *Int'l*, pg. 3047
GRIFOLS ENGINEERING, S.A.—See Grifols, S.A.; *Int'l*, pg. 3084
GROUND INVESTIGATION & PILING LIMITED; *Int'l*, pg. 3088
GS CONSTRUCTION ARABIA CO., LTD.—See GS Holdings Corp.; *Int'l*, pg. 3142
GS E&C INDIA PVT. LTD.—See GS Holdings Corp.; *Int'l*, pg. 3142
GS E&C NANJING CO., LTD.—See GS Holdings Corp.; *Int'l*, pg. 3142
GS E&C THAI CO., LTD.—See GS Holdings Corp.; *Int'l*, pg. 3142
GS INIMA ENVIRONMENT, S.A.—See GS Holdings Corp.; *Int'l*, pg. 3142
GS NHA BE DEVELOPMENT ONE-MEMBER LLC—See GS Holdings Corp.; *Int'l*, pg. 3142
GS PHNOM PENH DEVELOPMENT CO., LTD.—See GS Holdings Corp.; *Int'l*, pg. 3142
GS SAIGON DEVELOPMENT ONE-MEMBER LLC—See GS Holdings Corp.; *Int'l*, pg. 3142
GTV ENGINEERING LTD.; *Int'l*, pg. 3152
GULF DREDGING AND GENERAL CONTRACTING COMPANY KSE—See Heavy Engineering Industries & Shipbuilding Co. K.S.C.; *Int'l*, pg. 3305
GULF ENGINEERING, LLC; *U.S. Private*, pg. 1816
GUY F. ATKINSON CONSTRUCTION, LLC—See Clark Enterprises, Inc.; *U.S. Private*, pg. 912
GVK INDUSTRIES LIMITED—See GVK Power and Infrastructure Limited; *Int'l*, pg. 3190
HAI LECK HOLDINGS LIMITED; *Int'l*, pg. 3208
HALL CONSTRUCTION SERVICES LTD; *Int'l*, pg. 3229
HANJIN HEAVY INDUSTRIES & CONSTRUCTION - CONSTRUCTION DIVISION—See HJ Shipbuilding & Construction Company, Ltd.; *Int'l*, pg. 3428
HANKYU SEKKEI CONSULTANT CO., LTD.—See Hankyu Hanshin Holdings Inc.; *Int'l*, pg. 3255
HANMIGLOBAL CO., LTD.; *Int'l*, pg. 3256
HANSON, WALTER & ASSOCIATES, INC.; *U.S. Private*, pg. 1857
HARRINGTON & CORTELYOU, INC.—See Burns & McDonnell, Inc.; *U.S. Private*, pg. 690
HARROP INDUSTRIES, INC.; *U.S. Private*, pg. 1871
HEIJMANS BETON- EN WATERBOUW B.V.—See Heijmans N.V.; *Int'l*, pg. 3322
HEIWA SERVICE CO., LTD.—See HEIWA REAL ESTATE CO. LTD.; *Int'l*, pg. 3327
HELD ENLOE & ASSOCIATES, LLC—See Lovell Minnick Partners LLC; *U.S. Private*, pg. 2503
HELMKAMP CONSTRUCTION CO.; *U.S. Private*, pg. 1912
HERCEGOVINAPUTEVI A.D.; *Int'l*, pg. 3361
HEXACON CONSTRUCTION PTE LIMITED—See IJM Corporation Berhad; *Int'l*, pg. 3608
HGC, INC.—See Chevron Corporation; *U.S. Public*, pg. 487
HIDROGRADEVINAR A.D.; *Int'l*, pg. 3384
HIDROGRADNJA A.D.; *Int'l*, pg. 3384
HIFAB GROUP AB; *Int'l*, pg. 3385
HIFAB INTERNATIONAL AB—See Hifab Group AB; *Int'l*, pg. 3385

HIFAB OY—See Hifab Group AB; *Int'l*, pg. 3385
HIGGINS GROUP HOLDINGS LIMITED—See Fletcher Building Limited; *Int'l*, pg. 2700
HIGHTEX GMBH; *Int'l*, pg. 3389
HIGHWEALTH CONSTRUCTION CORP.; *Int'l*, pg. 3389
HILL ENGINEERING CONSULTANCY, LLC—See Global Infrastructure Solutions, Inc.; *U.S. Private*, pg. 1715
HILL INTERNATIONAL (NEW ENGLAND) INC.—See Global Infrastructure Solutions, Inc.; *U.S. Private*, pg. 1715
HILL INTERNATIONAL—See Global Infrastructure Solutions, Inc.; *U.S. Private*, pg. 1715
HINKLE CONTRACTING CO., LLC - LEXINGTON—See Summit Materials, Inc.; *U.S. Public*, pg. 1960
HINKLE CONTRACTING COMPANY, LLC—See Summit Materials, Inc.; *U.S. Public*, pg. 1960
HK KOMGRAP AD; *Int'l*, pg. 3428
HL D&I HALLA CORPORATION—See Halla Group; *Int'l*, pg. 3229
HME CONSTRUCTION, INC.—See Ukpeagvik Inupiat Corporation; *U.S. Private*, pg. 4275
HOA PHAT URBAN DEVELOPMENT AND CONSTRUCTION JSC—See Hoa Phat Group Joint Stock Company; *Int'l*, pg. 3435
HOCHTIEF AG—See ACS, Actividades de Construccion y Servicios, S.A.; *Int'l*, pg. 112
HOCHTIEF AKTIENGESELLSCHAFT VORM. GEBR. HELFMAN GES. M.B.H.—See ACS, Actividades de Construccion y Servicios, S.A.; *Int'l*, pg. 113
HOCHTIEF CONSTRUCTION AUSTRIA GMBH & CO KG—See ACS, Actividades de Construccion y Servicios, S.A.; *Int'l*, pg. 114
HOCHTIEF PPP SOLUTIONS GMBH—See ACS, Actividades de Construccion y Servicios, S.A.; *Int'l*, pg. 114
HOCHTIEF PPP SOLUTIONS (UK) LTD.—See ACS, Actividades de Construccion y Servicios, S.A.; *Int'l*, pg. 114
HOKUETSU ENGINEERING CO., LTD.—See Hokuetsu Corporation; *Int'l*, pg. 3443
HOLLISTER CONSTRUCTION SERVICES, LLC; *U.S. Private*, pg. 1965
HONC MARINE CONTRACTING, INC.; *U.S. Private*, pg. 1976
HORMIGONES LOS SERRANOS S.L—See Eiffage S.A.; *Int'l*, pg. 2331
HORMIGONES Y MORTEROS SERRANO SL—See Eiffage S.A.; *Int'l*, pg. 2331
HORTON CBI, LIMITED—See McDermott International, Inc.; *U.S. Public*, pg. 1405
HORTON CBI, LIMITED—See McDermott International, Inc.; *U.S. Public*, pg. 1405
HORTON CBI, LIMITED—See McDermott International, Inc.; *U.S. Public*, pg. 1405
HORTON CBI, LIMITED—See McDermott International, Inc.; *U.S. Public*, pg. 1405
HOSODA CORPORATION—See Haseko Corporation; *Int'l*, pg. 3283
HOSPITAL BUILDING & EQUIPMENT CO.—See HBE Corporation; *U.S. Private*, pg. 1887
HSIN BA BA CORPORATION; *Int'l*, pg. 3507
HUATIONG GLOBAL LIMITED; *Int'l*, pg. 3514
HUENNEBECK DEUTSCHLAND GMBH—See Brand Industrial Services, Inc.; *U.S. Private*, pg. 636
HUY THANG CONSTRUCTION JSC; *Int'l*, pg. 3541
HWANG CHANG GENERAL CONTRACTOR CO., LTD.; *Int'l*, pg. 3542
HYDROBUDOWA-6 S.A.—See Bilfinger SE; *Int'l*, pg. 1026
HYDRO ONE REMOTE COMMUNITIES INC.—See Hydro One Limited; *Int'l*, pg. 3546
HYOSUNG HEAVY INDUSTRIES CORP.; *Int'l*, pg. 3552
HY-VEE CONSTRUCTION, L.C.—See Hy-Vee, Inc.; *U.S. Private*, pg. 2016
IAG INDUSTRIE-ANLAGEN-BAU GEORGSMARIEN-HUETTE GMBH—See Georgsmarienhutte Holding GmbH; *Int'l*, pg. 2940
IBBERSON, INC.—See Peter Kiewit Sons', Inc.; *U.S. Private*, pg. 3158
IBBERSON INTERNATIONAL, INC.—See Peter Kiewit Sons', Inc.; *U.S. Private*, pg. 3158
IBIDEN GREENTEC CO., LTD.—See Ibiden Co., Ltd.; *Int'l*, pg. 3575
ICE ENGINEERING & CONSTRUCTION PTY. LTD.—See E&A Limited; *Int'l*, pg. 2247
IDEMITSU ENGINEERING CO., LTD.—See Idemitsu Kosan Co., Ltd.; *Int'l*, pg. 3590
IL&FS ENGINEERING & CONSTRUCTION COMPANY LTD.; *Int'l*, pg. 3613
IMTC, INC.; *U.S. Private*, pg. 2051
INALIA CAP DJINET, S.L.—See GS Holdings Corp.; *Int'l*, pg. 3142
INCO SERVICES, INC.—See INNOVATE Corp.; *U.S. Public*, pg. 1126
INDUSTRIAL DESIGN & CONSTRUCTION, INC.; *U.S. Private*, pg. 2065
INFRAESTRUCTURES VIARIES DE CATALUNYA, S.A.—See ACS, Actividades de Construccion y Servicios, S.A.; *Int'l*, pg. 112
INFRASOURCE CONSTRUCTION, LLC—See Quanta Services, Inc.; *U.S. Public*, pg. 1751
INGENIERIA DE LOS RECURSOS NATURALES, S.A.—See Grupo Villar Mir, S.A.U.; *Int'l*, pg. 3139
INGENIEROS CIVILES ASOCIADOS, S. A. DE C. V.—See Empresas ICA S.A.B. de C.V.; *Int'l*, pg. 2391
INIMA CHILE LTDA.—See GS Holdings Corp.; *Int'l*, pg. 3142
INIMA CVV, S.A.—See GS Holdings Corp.; *Int'l*, pg. 3142
INLAND MARINE SERVICES, LLC; *U.S. Private*, pg. 2078
INLINE MANAGEMENT, LLC—See Accenture plc; *Int'l*, pg. 86
INNOVATIVE ENERGY SYSTEMS, LLC—See BP plc; *Int'l*, pg. 1126
INSITUFORM OF NEW ENGLAND, INC—See New Mountain Capital, LLC; *U.S. Private*, pg. 2900
INSITUFORM TECH, INC.—See New Mountain Capital, LLC; *U.S. Private*, pg. 2900
INSITUFORM TECHNOLOGIES, LLC—See New Mountain Capital, LLC; *U.S. Private*, pg. 2900
INSTALACIONES Y SERVICIOS CODEVEN, C.A.—See ACS, Actividades de Construccion y Servicios, S.A.; *Int'l*, pg. 115
INTERNATIONAL LINE BUILDERS, INC.—See MDU Resources Group, Inc.; *U.S. Public*, pg. 1410
INTERNATIONAL PROJECT DEVELOPERS INC.—See Dabbagh Group Holding Company Ltd.; *Int'l*, pg. 1902
IONBOND ITALIA SRL—See IHI Corporation; *Int'l*, pg. 3605
IRIDIUM CONCESIONES DE INFRAESTRUCTURAS, S.A.—See ACS, Actividades de Construccion y Servicios, S.A.; *Int'l*, pg. 115
IRISH DREDGING COMPANY LTD.—See HAL Trust N.V.; *Int'l*, pg. 3226
JACOBS ENGINEERING GROUP, INC. - CONSHOHOCKEN, PA—See Jacobs Engineering Group, Inc.; *U.S. Public*, pg. 1184
JACOBS FIELD SERVICES NORTH AMERICA, INC.—See Jacobs Engineering Group, Inc.; *U.S. Public*, pg. 1185
JAMES CONSTRUCTION GROUP LLC—See Primoris Services Corporation; *U.S. Public*, pg. 1718
J. BANICKI CONSTRUCTION, INC.—See Sterling Infrastructure, Inc.; *U.S. Public*, pg. 1946
JC RESTORATION INC.; *U.S. Private*, pg. 2194
J. CROWDER CORPORATION—See Fluor Corporation; *U.S. Public*, pg. 859
JELUTONG DEVELOPMENT SDN BHD—See IJM Corporation Berhad; *Int'l*, pg. 3609
JENSEN CONSTRUCTION MANAGEMENT, INC.—See Ventas, Inc.; *U.S. Public*, pg. 2278
J.F. KIELY CONSTRUCTION CO.; *U.S. Private*, pg. 2162
JIM F WEBB, INC.—See Cadent Energy Partners, LLC; *U.S. Private*, pg. 713
JOHN CARLO, INC.—See Carlo Management Corporation; *U.S. Private*, pg. 764
JPHYTEC CO., LTD.—See Electric Power Development Co., Ltd.; *Int'l*, pg. 2349
JR TOKAI CONSTRUCTION CO., LTD.—See Central Japan Railway Company; *Int'l*, pg. 1408
JUDLAU CONTRACTING, INC.—See Grupo Villar Mir, S.A.U.; *Int'l*, pg. 3139
JUDY CONSTRUCTION COMPANY INC.; *U.S. Private*, pg. 2242
JULIUS BERGER NIGERIA PLC—See Bilfinger SE; *Int'l*, pg. 1028
KABOOM!, INC.; *U.S. Private*, pg. 2253
KAWEAH CONSTRUCTION CO. INC.—See Lyles Diversified Inc.; *U.S. Private*, pg. 2520
KBR INDUSTRIAL CANADA CO.—See KBR, Inc.; *U.S. Public*, pg. 1216
KBR NETHERLANDS INVESTMENTS B.V.—See KBR, Inc.; *U.S. Public*, pg. 1216
KEIKYU CONSTRUCTION CO., LTD.—See Gunze Limited; *Int'l*, pg. 3186
KELLOGG BROWN & ROOT ASIA PACIFIC PTE LTD—See KBR, Inc.; *U.S. Public*, pg. 1216
KELLOGG BROWN & ROOT (CANADA) COMPANY—See KBR, Inc.; *U.S. Public*, pg. 1216
KELLOGG BROWN & ROOT HOLDINGS (U.K.) LIMITED—See KBR, Inc.; *U.S. Public*, pg. 1216
KENDALL CROSS HOLDINGS LIMITED—See Galliford Try Holdings plc; *Int'l*, pg. 2874
KENTZ CORPORATION LIMITED—See AtkinsRealis Group Inc.; *U.S. Public*, pg. 671
KEYSTONE CONSULTING ENGINEERS, INC.—See Keystone Consulting Engineers, Inc.; *U.S. Private*, pg. 2296
K. HOVNANIAN AT NEUSE RIVER, LLC—See Hovnanian Enterprises, Inc.; *U.S. Public*, pg. 1059
K. HOVNANIAN AT PALM VALLEY, L.L.C.—See Hovnanian Enterprises, Inc.; *U.S. Public*, pg. 1059
K. HOVNANIAN AT QUAIL CREEK, L.L.C.—See Hovnanian Enterprises, Inc.; *U.S. Public*, pg. 1059
K. HOVNANIAN AT RANCHO CABRILLO, LLC—See Hovnanian Enterprises, Inc.; *U.S. Public*, pg. 1059
K. HOVNANIAN BUILDING COMPANY, LLC—See Hovnanian Enterprises, Inc.; *U.S. Public*, pg. 1056
K. HOVNANIAN GREAT WESTERN BUILDING COMPANY, LLC—See Hovnanian Enterprises, Inc.; *U.S. Public*, pg. 1056
K. HOVNANIAN'S FOUR SEASONS, LLC—See Hovnanian Enterprises, Inc.; *U.S. Public*, pg. 1060
K. HOVNANIAN SUMMIT HOMES, L.L.C.—See Hovnanian Enterprises, Inc.; *U.S. Public*, pg. 1058

237990 — OTHER HEAVY AND CIV...

KIEWIT CORP.; *U.S. Private*, pg. 2304
KIEWIT MANAGEMENT LTD.—See Peter Kiewit Sons', Inc.; *U.S. Private*, pg. 3158
KINETIC PROCESS SYSTEMS LTD—See Gemini Corporation; *Int'l*, pg. 2916
KISOKOMAKOGEN KANKOKAIHATSU CO., LTD.—See Daido Steel Co., Ltd.; *Int'l*, pg. 1923
KNIFE RIVER CORPORATION - NORTHWEST—See MDU Resources Group, Inc.; *U.S. Public*, pg. 1410
KNIFE RIVER CORPORATION - SOUTH—See MDU Resources Group, Inc.; *U.S. Public*, pg. 1411
KOKANKYO ENGINEERING CORPORATION (EAE)—See Daiwa House Industry Co., Ltd.; *Int'l*, pg. 1946
LANWEHR ASPHALT GMBH—See Eiffage S.A.; *Int'l*, pg. 2331
LARSON DESIGN GROUP - APALACHIN—See Larson Design Group; *U.S. Private*, pg. 2394
LARSON DESIGN GROUP—See Larson Design Group; *U.S. Private*, pg. 2394
LARSON DESIGN GROUP—See Larson Design Group; *U.S. Private*, pg. 2394
LARSON DESIGN GROUP—See Larson Design Group; *U.S. Private*, pg. 2394
LDG SAN ANTONIO—See Larson Design Group; *U.S. Private*, pg. 2394
LECON, INC.—See KKR & Co. Inc.; *U.S. Public*, pg. 1263
LIFECYCLE CONSTRUCTION SERVICES INC.; *U.S. Private*, pg. 2449
LINDE CORPORATION; *U.S. Private*, pg. 2459
LLW REPOSITORY LIMITED—See AECOM; *U.S. Public*, pg. 51
LONDON MARINE CONSULTANTS LIMITED—See Ezra Holdings Ltd.; *Int'l*, pg. 2594
LONE MOUNTAIN EXCAVATION & UTILITIES, LLC—See MDU Resources Group, Inc.; *U.S. Public*, pg. 1411
L&T INFRASTRUCTURE DEVELOPMENT PROJECTS LIMITED—See Edelweiss Financial Services Ltd.; *Int'l*, pg. 2306
LYLES UTILITY CONSTRUCTION, LLC—See Lyles Diversified Inc.; *U.S. Private*, pg. 2520
MASER CONSULTING—See Colliers International Group Inc.; *Int'l*, pg. 1700
MASER CONSULTING—See Colliers International Group Inc.; *Int'l*, pg. 1700
MASER CONSULTING—See Colliers International Group Inc.; *Int'l*, pg. 1700
MASER CONSULTING—See Colliers International Group Inc.; *Int'l*, pg. 1700
MASER CONSULTING—See Colliers International Group Inc.; *Int'l*, pg. 1700
MASER CONSULTING—See Colliers International Group Inc.; *Int'l*, pg. 1700
MASER CONSULTING—See Colliers International Group Inc.; *Int'l*, pg. 1700
MASER CONSULTING—See Colliers International Group Inc.; *Int'l*, pg. 1700
MASER CONSULTING—See Colliers International Group Inc.; *Int'l*, pg. 1700
MASFALT S.A—See Eiffage S.A.; *Int'l*, pg. 2331
MAX ENGINEERING LLC—See AYRO, Inc.; *U.S. Public*, pg. 256
MBR CONSTRUCTION SERVICES INC.—See MBR Construction Services Inc.; *U.S. Private*, pg. 2624
MCABEE CONSTRUCTION, INC.; *U.S. Private*, pg. 2625
MCCONNELL DOWELL CONSTRUCTORS (AUST.) PTY LIMITED—See Aveng Limited; *Int'l*, pg. 738
MCCONNELL DOWELL CORPORATION LIMITED—See Aveng Limited; *Int'l*, pg. 738
MCNALLY INTERNATIONAL INC.—See Kiewit Corp.; *U.S. Private*, pg. 2304
MERIDIAN SYSTEMS—See Trimble, Inc.; *U.S. Public*, pg. 2190
METRA AKDENIZ DIS TICARET A.S.—See Enka Insaat ve Sanayi A.S.; *Int'l*, pg. 2440
MFS CONSULTING ENGINEERS & SURVEYOR CORPORATION; *U.S. Private*, pg. 2693
MID ATLANTIC CONTRACTING INC.; *U.S. Private*, pg. 2705
MIDCOAST MARINE GROUP LLC—See MarineMax, Inc.; *U.S. Public*, pg. 1367
MID COLUMBIA ENGINEERING INC.; *U.S. Private*, pg. 2705
MIDLAND TECHNICAL CRAFTS, INC.—See MDU Resources Group, Inc.; *U.S. Public*, pg. 1411
MISSOURI VALLEY INC.; *U.S. Private*, pg. 2749
MIYAMOTO INTERNATIONAL, INC.; *U.S. Private*, pg. 2752
MODERNBAU GMBH—See Bilfinger SE; *Int'l*, pg. 1024
MOHAWK FIELD SERVICES INC—See Energy Process Technology Inc.; *U.S. Private*, pg. 1395
MOSENKA OAO—See Enka Insaat ve Sanayi A.S.; *Int'l*, pg. 2440
MT HOJGAARD FOROYAR P/F—See Hojgaard Holding A/S; *Int'l*, pg. 3442
MUSHRIF TRADING & CONTRACTING COMPANY K.S.C.P.—See Al-Wazzan Holding Group; *Int'l*, pg. 289
MYERS & SONS CONSTRUCTION, L.P.—See Sterling Infrastructure, Inc.; *U.S. Public*, pg. 1946

NAKHEEL PVT JSC—See Dubai World Corporation; *Int'l*, pg. 2222
NASS CORPORATION B.S.C.—See Abdulla Ahmed Nass Group WLL; *Int'l*, pg. 58
NATIONAL OILWELL VARCO UK LIMITED—See NOV, Inc.; *U.S. Public*, pg. 1546
NICHIYO ENGINEERING CORPORATION—See ENEOS Holdings, Inc.; *Int'l*, pg. 2417
NICHIZO KYUSHU SERVICE CORPORATION—See Hitachi Zosen Corporation; *Int'l*, pg. 3411
NICOLL ETERPLAST S.A.—See Aliaxis S.A./N.V.; *Int'l*, pg. 325
NIGERIAN WESTMINSTER DREDGING & MARINE LTD.—See HAL Trust N.V.; *Int'l*, pg. 3226
NIPPO CORPORATION—See ENEOS Holdings, Inc.; *Int'l*, pg. 2418
NORAIR ENGINEERING CORPORATION; *U.S. Private*, pg. 2935
NORPAC SA—See Bouygues S.A.; *Int'l*, pg. 1123
NORTHSIDE ENGINEERING SERVICES, INC.; *U.S. Private*, pg. 2957
NOVA BOCANA BARCELONA, S.A.—See Grupo Villar Mir, S.A.U.; *Int'l*, pg. 3139
OBRASCON HUARTE LAIN, CONSTRUCCION INTERNACIONAL S.L.—See Grupo Villar Mir, S.A.U.; *Int'l*, pg. 3139
OBRASCON HUARTE LAIN, DESARROLLOS S. L.—See Grupo Villar Mir, S.A.U.; *Int'l*, pg. 3139
OBRASCON HUARTE LAIN, S.A.—See Grupo Villar Mir, S.A.U.; *Int'l*, pg. 3138
OCAENLINE (LABUAN) LTD.—See Benalec Holdings Berhad; *Int'l*, pg. 969
OHL ANDINA, S.A.—See Grupo Villar Mir, S.A.U.; *Int'l*, pg. 3139
OHL CENTRAL EUROPE, A.S.—See Grupo Villar Mir, S.A.U.; *Int'l*, pg. 3139
OHL COLOMBIA, S.A.S.—See Grupo Villar Mir, S.A.U.; *Int'l*, pg. 3139
OHL CONSTRUCCION NACIONAL EDIFICACION—See Grupo Villar Mir, S.A.U.; *Int'l*, pg. 3138
OHL CONSTRUCCION NACIONAL OBRA CIVIL—See Grupo Villar Mir, S.A.U.; *Int'l*, pg. 3139
OHL CONSTRUCTION CANADA, INC.—See Grupo Villar Mir, S.A.U.; *Int'l*, pg. 3139
OHL CONSTRUCTION NATIONAL SERVICES—See Grupo Villar Mir, S.A.U.; *Int'l*, pg. 3139
OHL CONSTRUCTION PACIFIC PTY LTD—See Grupo Villar Mir, S.A.U.; *Int'l*, pg. 3139
OHL INDUSTRIAL, S.L.—See Grupo Villar Mir, S.A.U.; *Int'l*, pg. 3139
OHL URUGUAY, S.A.—See Grupo Villar Mir, S.A.U.; *Int'l*, pg. 3139
OHL USA, INC.—See Grupo Villar Mir, S.A.U.; *Int'l*, pg. 3139
OHL ZS, A.S. - OSTRAVA—See Grupo Villar Mir, S.A.U.; *Int'l*, pg. 3139
OHL ZS, A.S.—See Grupo Villar Mir, S.A.U.; *Int'l*, pg. 3139
ONESUBSEA OPERATIONS LIMITED—See Schlumberger Limited; *U.S. Public*, pg. 1844
ORION GROUP HOLDINGS, INC.; *U.S. Public*, pg. 1618
ORION INDUSTRIAL CONSTRUCTION, LLC—See Orion Group Holdings, Inc.; *U.S. Public*, pg. 1618
ORION MARINE CONSTRUCTION, INC.—See Orion Group Holdings, Inc.; *U.S. Public*, pg. 1618
ORION MARINE CONTRACTORS, INC.—See Orion Group Holdings, Inc.; *U.S. Public*, pg. 1618
OTT CONSULTING INC.; *U.S. Private*, pg. 3049
OU FORT EHITUS—See AS Merko Ehitus; *Int'l*, pg. 590
OU GUSTAF TALLINN—See AS Merko Ehitus; *Int'l*, pg. 590
PACIFIC INTERNATIONAL GROUT COMPANY—See Cematrix Corporation; *Int'l*, pg. 1396
PACIFIC PARTNERSHIPS PTY LTD—See ACS, Actividades de Construccion y Servicios, S.A.; *Int'l*, pg. 115
PACSA, SERVICIOS URBANOS Y DEL MEDIO NATURAL, S.L.—See Grupo Villar Mir, S.A.U.; *Int'l*, pg. 3139
PALA GROUP, INC.; *U.S. Private*, pg. 3076
PARKSIDE UTILITY CONSTRUCTION, LLC—See Dycom Industries, Inc.; *U.S. Public*, pg. 699
PARSONS CORPORATION; *U.S. Public*, pg. 1650
PEASE & SONS INC.; *U.S. Private*, pg. 3126
PEGASUS LINK CONSTRUCTORS, LLC—See Fluor Corporation; *U.S. Public*, pg. 859
PERNIX GROUP, INC.; *U.S. Public*, pg. 1677
PERRARD S.A.—See Eiffage S.A.; *Int'l*, pg. 2330
PERTUY CONSTRUCTION SA—See Bouygues S.A.; *Int'l*, pg. 1123
PETTICOAT-SCHMITT CIVIL CONTRACTORS, INC.; *U.S. Private*, pg. 3163
PIEPS GMBH—See Clarus Corporation; *U.S. Public*, pg. 508
PIONEER HOMES AUSTRALIA PTY LTD—See ACS, Actividades de Construccion y Servicios, S.A.; *Int'l*, pg. 113
PIPE JACKING TRENCHLESS, INC.—See Primoris Services Corporation; *U.S. Public*, pg. 1719
PIPELINE AND DRAINAGE SYSTEMS LIMITED—See RPM International Inc.; *U.S. Public*, pg. 1817
PNR RAILWORKS INC - SIGNALS & COMMUNICATIONS DIVISION—See Wind Point Advisors LLC; *U.S. Private*, pg. 4535

CORPORATE AFFILIATIONS

PNR RAILWORKS INC—See Wind Point Advisors LLC; *U.S. Private*, pg. 4535
POC AUSTRIA—See Clarus Corporation; *U.S. Public*, pg. 508
POC SWEDEN AB—See Clarus Corporation; *U.S. Public*, pg. 508
POC USA LLC—See Clarus Corporation; *U.S. Public*, pg. 508
POLARIS MATERIALS CORPORATION—See Vulcan Materials Company; *U.S. Public*, pg. 2314
POWER GRID ENGINEERING, LLC—See New Mountain Capital, LLC; *U.S. Private*, pg. 2903
POYRY CONSULTING AND ENGINEERING (INDIA) PRIVATE LIMITED—See AFRY AB; *Int'l*, pg. 195
POYRY INFRA DE VENEZUELA S.A.—See AFRY AB; *Int'l*, pg. 195
PPES WORKS (SARAWAK) SDN. BHD.—See Cahya Mata Sarawak Berhad; *Int'l*, pg. 1251
P&P VALLEY VIEW HOLDINGS, INC.—See Pete & Pete Container Service, Inc.; *U.S. Private*, pg. 3157
PRINCE CONTRACTING, LLC—See ACS, Actividades de Construccion y Servicios, S.A.; *Int'l*, pg. 111
PROFESSIONAL CONSTRUCTION SERVICES INC.; *U.S. Private*, pg. 3274
P.T. BILFINGER BERGER INDONESIA—See Bilfinger SE; *Int'l*, pg. 1028
PT HITACHI PLANT TECHNOLOGIES—See Hitachi, Ltd.; *Int'l*, pg. 3423
PT. MCCONNELL DOWELL INDONESIA—See Aveng Limited; *Int'l*, pg. 738
PULLMAN POWER, LLC—See Structural Group, Inc.; *U.S. Private*, pg. 3841
PVPII - FNSS ACQUISITION, INC.; *U.S. Private*, pg. 3308
QSC, INC.; *U.S. Private*, pg. 3314
QUANTA LINES PTY. LTD.—See Quanta Services, Inc.; *U.S. Public*, pg. 1752
QUANTA SUBSURFACE, LLC—See Quanta Services, Inc.; *U.S. Public*, pg. 1752
QUANTUM INTERNATIONAL GROUP, INC.—See Terra Millenium Corporation; *U.S. Private*, pg. 3970
RAIL ENGINEERING SP. Z O.O.—See Alstom S.A.; *Int'l*, pg. 383
RAIL TO ROAD, INC.—See MDU Resources Group, Inc.; *U.S. Public*, pg. 1411
RAILWORKS TRACK SYSTEMS, INC.—See Wind Point Advisors LLC; *U.S. Private*, pg. 4535
RALEIGH MINE & INDUSTRIAL SUPPLY, INC.; *U.S. Private*, pg. 3349
RAZEL-BEC S.A.S.—See FAYAT SAS; *Int'l*, pg. 2626
REF-CHEM, L.P. - BROWNFIELD—See Ref-Chem, L.P.; *U.S. Private*, pg. 3384
REF-CHEM, L.P.; *U.S. Private*, pg. 3384
THE REINFORCED EARTH COMPANY; *U.S. Private*, pg. 4103
REMACOM NV—See Ackermans & van Haaren NV; *Int'l*, pg. 105
REPCON, INC.; *U.S. Private*, pg. 3400
RESOURCES ENGINEERING SERVICES INC.—See CTCI Corporation; *Int'l*, pg. 1870
REVER OFFSHORE UK LIMITED—See HAL Trust N.V.; *Int'l*, pg. 3226
REYNOLDS CONSTRUCTION, LLC; *U.S. Private*, pg. 3418
R.H. WHITE COMPANIES INC.; *U.S. Private*, pg. 3336
RICHARD E. PIERSON CONSTRUCTION COMPANY, INC. - LOGAN PLANT—See Richard E. Pierson Construction Company, Inc.; *U.S. Private*, pg. 3428
RIOVIA S.A.—See HAL Trust N.V.; *Int'l*, pg. 3226
THE ROBERTS COMPANY, INC.—See Argan, Inc.; *U.S. Public*, pg. 191
ROBINSON MECHANICAL CONTRACTORS INC.; *U.S. Private*, pg. 3462
RON WILLIAMS CONSTRUCTION INC.; *U.S. Private*, pg. 3477
R&R ASSOCIATES LLC - HEAVY PRODUCTION DIVISION—See R&R Associates LLC; *U.S. Private*, pg. 3332
RYANGOLF CORPORATION—See The Ryan Companies, LLC; *U.S. Private*, pg. 4113
RYAN INCORPORATED MINING—See The Ryan Companies, LLC; *U.S. Private*, pg. 4113
SA EIFFAGE BENELUX—See Eiffage S.A.; *Int'l*, pg. 2330
SAINT-GOBAIN TRANSFORMADOS S.A.—See Compagnie de Saint-Gobain SA; *Int'l*, pg. 1736
SAKHALINNEFTEGASSERVIS LLC—See Fluor Corporation; *U.S. Public*, pg. 859
SALMANTINA DE SEGURIDAD VIAL, S.A.—See ACS, Actividades de Construccion y Servicios, S.A.; *Int'l*, pg. 116
SARGENT CORPORATION; *U.S. Private*, pg. 3550
S&B ENGINEERS & CONSTRUCTORS, LTD.; *U.S. Private*, pg. 3512
SCHILDBERG CONSTRUCTION CO. INC.; *U.S. Private*, pg. 3565
SEALASKA CONSTRUCTORS, LLC—See Sealaska Corporation; *U.S. Private*, pg. 3585
SEAONICS AS—See Fincantieri S.p.A.; *Int'l*, pg. 2671
SELLAFIELD LIMITED—See AECOM; *U.S. Public*, pg. 51
SHIMMICK CONSTRUCTION COMPANY, INC.—See AECOM; *U.S. Public*, pg. 51

N.A.I.C.S. INDEX

238110 — POURED CONCRETE FOU...

SHOSEKI ENGINEERING & CONSTRUCTION CO., LTD.—See Idemitsu Kosan Co., Ltd.; *Int'l*, pg. 3592
SICE PTY, LTD.—See ACS, Actividades de Construccion y Servicios, S.A.; *Int'l*, pg. 116
SLOVENSKE TUNELY, A.S.—See Grupo Villar Mir, S.A.U.; *Int'l*, pg. 3139
SOCIEDAD ANONIMA TRABAJOS Y OBRAS—See Grupo Villar Mir, S.A.U.; *Int'l*, pg. 3139
SOCIEDAD CONCESIONARIA CENTRO DE JUSTICIA DE SANTIAGO, S.A.—See Grupo Villar Mir, S.A.U.; *Int'l*, pg. 3139
SOCIETE DES CARRIERES DE LA 113—See Eiffage S.A.; *Int'l*, pg. 2331
SODAI ITALIA SPA—See ERG S.p.A.; *Int'l*, pg. 2491
SOUTHEAST CONNECTIONS LLC—See Kelso & Company, L.P.; *U.S. Private*, pg. 2280
SOUTHEASTERN CONSTRUCTION & MAINTENANCE, INC.; *U.S. Private*, pg. 3727
SOUTHERN INDUSTRIAL CONSTRUCTION INC.—See EMCOR Group, Inc.; *U.S. Public*, pg. 739
SOUTHWESTERN POWER GROUP II LLC—See MMR Group Inc.; *U.S. Private*, pg. 2755
SPARTA, INC.—See Parsons Corporation; *U.S. Public*, pg. 1651
SPIDER ACCESS CLADDING WORKS & BUILDING CLEANING LLC—See EdilziAcrobatica S.p.A.; *Int'l*, pg. 2310
STAKE CENTER LOCATING INC.; *U.S. Private*, pg. 3776
STERLING HAWAII ASPHALT, LLC—See Sterling Infrastructure, Inc.; *U.S. Public*, pg. 1947
STRUCTHERM LIMITED—See Heidelberg Materials AG; *Int'l*, pg. 3319
STRUKTON CIVIEL B.V.—See Centric Holding B.V.; *Int'l*, pg. 1412
STV INC.—See STV Group, Inc.; *U.S. Private*, pg. 3845
STV INC.—See STV Group, Inc.; *U.S. Private*, pg. 3845
STV INC.—See STV Group, Inc.; *U.S. Private*, pg. 3845
SUNDT CONSTRUCTION, INC. - IRVINE OFFICE—See The Sundt Companies, Inc.; *U.S. Private*, pg. 4125
SUNDT CONSTRUCTION, INC. - SACRAMENTO OFFICE—See The Sundt Companies, Inc.; *U.S. Private*, pg. 4125
SUNDT CONSTRUCTION, INC. - SAN ANTONIO OFFICE—See The Sundt Companies, Inc.; *U.S. Private*, pg. 4125
SUNDT CONSTRUCTION, INC. - SAN DIEGO OFFICE—See The Sundt Companies, Inc.; *U.S. Private*, pg. 4125
SUNDT CONSTRUCTION, INC.—See The Sundt Companies, Inc.; *U.S. Private*, pg. 4125
SWAGELOK CAPITAL PROJECTS COMPANY—See Swagelok Company; *U.S. Private*, pg. 3889
SWINERTON BUILDERS—See Swinerton Incorporated; *U.S. Private*, pg. 3894
SYNERGY SYSTEMS, INC.—See Sealaska Corporation; *U.S. Private*, pg. 3585
SYSTEMS CONTRACTING CORP; *U.S. Private*, pg. 3907
TANNER SERVICES, LLC; *U.S. Private*, pg. 3932
T.A.S. COMMERCIAL CONCRETE SOLUTIONS, LLC—See Orion Group Holdings, Inc.; *U.S. Public*, pg. 1618
TECON SERVICES INC.; *U.S. Private*, pg. 3957
TECSA EMPRESA CONSTRUCTORA, S.A.—See ACS, Actividades de Construccion y Servicios, S.A.; *Int'l*, pg. 116
TEDAGUA INTERNACIONAL, S.L.—See ACS, Actividades de Construccion y Servicios, S.A.; *Int'l*, pg. 116
T.E. IBBERSON COMPANY—See Peter Kiewit Sons', Inc.; *U.S. Private*, pg. 3158
TELLEPSEN BUILDERS LP; *U.S. Private*, pg. 3962
TERRAMARE OY—See HAL Trust N.V.; *Int'l*, pg. 3227
TERRAM GEOSYNTHETICS PRIVATE LIMITED—See Berry Global Group, Inc; *U.S. Public*, pg. 325
TESCA INGENIERIA DEL ECUADOR, S.A.—See ACS, Actividades de Construccion y Servicios, S.A.; *Int'l*, pg. 116
TEXAS STERLING CONSTRUCTION CO.—See Sterling Infrastructure, Inc.; *U.S. Public*, pg. 1947
TEXEL GEOSOL INC.—See Lydall, Inc.; *U.S. Private*, pg. 1350
THOMPSON THRIFT DEVELOPMENT, INC.; *U.S. Private*, pg. 4162
TIC-THE INDUSTRIAL COMPANY—See Peter Kiewit Sons', Inc.; *U.S. Private*, pg. 3158
TIC-THE INDUSTRIAL COMPANY WYOMING, INC.—See Peter Kiewit Sons', Inc.; *U.S. Private*, pg. 3158
TILLAGE CONSTRUCTION L.L.C.; *U.S. Private*, pg. 4170
TIMEC COMPANY, INC.; *U.S. Private*, pg. 4172
TINEL SA—See Eiffage S.A.; *Int'l*, pg. 2331
TITAN FABRICATORS, INC.—See INNOVATE Corp.; *U.S. Public*, pg. 1126
TITAS TOPRAK INSAAT VE TAAHHUT ANONIM SIRKETI—See Enka Insaat ve Sanayi A.S.; *Int'l*, pg. 2440
T&M ASSOCIATES - COLUMBUS—See T&M Associates; *U.S. Private*, pg. 3910
T&M ASSOCIATES - MOORESTOWN—See T&M Associates; *U.S. Private*, pg. 3910
T&M ASSOCIATES; *U.S. Private*, pg. 3909
T&M ASSOCIATES—See T&M Associates; *U.S. Private*, pg. 3909
T&M ASSOCIATES—See T&M Associates; *U.S. Private*, pg. 3909
T&M ASSOCIATES—See T&M Associates; *U.S. Private*, pg. 3909
T&M ASSOCIATES—See T&M Associates; *U.S. Private*, pg. 3909
T&M ASSOCIATES—See T&M Associates; *U.S. Private*, pg. 3909
T&M ASSOCIATES—See T&M Associates; *U.S. Private*, pg. 3909
T&M ASSOCIATES—See T&M Associates; *U.S. Private*, pg. 3910
T&M ASSOCIATES—See T&M Associates; *U.S. Private*, pg. 3910
TOKUSHIMA TSUSHINKENSETSU CO., LTD.—See COMSYS Holdings Corporation; *Int'l*, pg. 1762
TOMI-REMONT A.S.—See Grupo Villar Mir, S.A.U.; *Int'l*, pg. 3139
TOP GRADE CONSTRUCTION, INC.—See Goodfellow Bros., Inc.; *U.S. Private*, pg. 1739
TOP SHELF DRILLING—See Haines & Kibblehouse Inc.; *U.S. Private*, pg. 1841
TOTAL-WESTERN, INC.; *U.S. Private*, pg. 4192
TRAYLOR BROTHERS, INC.; *U.S. Private*, pg. 4215
TRC ACQUISITION, LLC—See Argan, Inc.; *U.S. Public*, pg. 345
TRI-CONSTRUCTION COMPANY, INC.; *U.S. Private*, pg. 4221
TRUEFORM ENGINEERING LIMITED—See GIL Investments Ltd.; *Int'l*, pg. 2973
TWINING INC.; *U.S. Private*, pg. 4266
UAB MERKO STATYBA—See AS Merko Ehitus; *Int'l*, pg. 590
UGL ENGINEERING PTY LTD—See ACS, Actividades de Construccion y Servicios, S.A.; *Int'l*, pg. 113
UNITED STEEL ENGINEERING & CONSTRUTION CORP.—See China Steel Corporation; *Int'l*, pg. 1556
UNIVERSAL SEALANTS (U.K.) LIMITED—See RPM International Inc.; *U.S. Public*, pg. 1820
UTILITY LINES CONSTRUCTION SERVICES, INC.—See Asplundh Tree Expert Co.; *U.S. Private*, pg. 353
VARD ELECTRICAL INSTALLATION AND ENGINEERING (INDIA) PRIVATE LIMITED—See Fincantieri S.p.A.; *Int'l*, pg. 2672
VARD ELECTRO AS—See Fincantieri S.p.A.; *Int'l*, pg. 2671
VARD ELECTRO BRAILA SRL—See Fincantieri S.p.A.; *Int'l*, pg. 2672
VARD ELECTRO BRAZIL LTDA.—See Fincantieri S.p.A.; *Int'l*, pg. 2672
VARD ELECTRO TULCEA SRL—See Fincantieri S.p.A.; *Int'l*, pg. 2672
VECELLIO & GROGAN, INC.—See Vecellio Group, Inc.; *U.S. Private*, pg. 4349
VENTECH ENGINEERS INC.—See Ventech Inc.; *U.S. Private*, pg. 4357
VETERAN CONSTRUCTORS, INC.; *U.S. Private*, pg. 4373
VIAPOL LTDA.—See RPM International Inc.; *U.S. Public*, pg. 1820
VIASS Y CONSTRUCCIONES S.A.—See ACS, Actividades de Construccion y Servicios, S.A.; *Int'l*, pg. 117
VSL—See Structural Group, Inc.; *U.S. Private*, pg. 3841
WALDROP ENGINEERING, P.A.—See Atwell, LLC; *U.S. Private*, pg. 384
WATERMAN INFRASTRUCTURE & ENVIRONMENT LIMITED—See CTI Engineering Co., Ltd.; *Int'l*, pg. 1871
WEBBER LLC—See Ferrovial S.A.; *Int'l*, pg. 2644
WESERWIND GMBH OFFSHORE CONSTRUCTION GEORGSMARIENHUTTE—See Georgsmarienhutte Holding GmbH; *Int'l*, pg. 2940
WESTINGHOUSE ELECTRIC COMPANY LLC—See Brookfield Corporation; *Int'l*, pg. 1186
WESTINGHOUSE ELECTRIC GERMANY GMBH—See Brookfield Corporation; *Int'l*, pg. 1187
WESTINGHOUSE ENERGY SYSTEMS EUROPE S.A.—See Brookfield Corporation; *Int'l*, pg. 1187
WESTMINSTER GRAVELS LTD.—See HAL Trust N.V.; *Int'l*, pg. 3225
WEST YOST ASSOCIATES, INC.-PLEASANTON—See West Yost Associates, Inc.; *U.S. Private*, pg. 4488
WEST YOST ASSOCIATES, INC.-ROSEVILLE—See West Yost Associates, Inc.; *U.S. Private*, pg. 4488
WHITE CONSTRUCTION INC.—See MasTec, Inc.; *U.S. Public*, pg. 1393
WILDISH BUILDING MATERIAL CO., INC.—See Wildish Land Company; *U.S. Private*, pg. 4519
WILLBROS CONSTRUCTION SERVICES (CANADA) L.P.—See Primoris Services Corporation; *U.S. Public*, pg. 1719
WILLIAM CHARLES WEST INC—See William Charles, Ltd.; *U.S. Private*, pg. 4523
W.S. NICHOLLS CONSTRUCTION INC.—See Southwest Gas Holdings, Inc.; *U.S. Public*, pg. 1913
W.S. NICHOLLS INDUSTRIES INC.—See Southwest Gas Holdings, Inc.; *U.S. Public*, pg. 1914
WUHAN INTERNATIONAL CONTAINER COMPANY LIMITED—See China Infrastructure & Logistics Group Ltd.; *Int'l*, pg. 1510
WYG INTERNATIONAL LIMITED—See Tetra Tech, Inc.; *U.S. Public*, pg. 2024
XORAIL, INC. - SHAWNEE MISSION—See Westinghouse Air Brake Technologies Corporation; *U.S. Public*, pg. 2360
XORAIL, INC.—See Westinghouse Air Brake Technologies Corporation; *U.S. Public*, pg. 2360
YOWA KOUEI CO., LTD.—See Dowa Holdings Co., Ltd.; *Int'l*, pg. 2184
ZACHRY CONSTRUCTION CORPORATION—See Zachry Holdings, Inc.; *U.S. Private*, pg. 4596

238110 — POURED CONCRETE FOUNDATION AND STRUCTURE CONTRACTORS

A-1 STRIPING INC.—See Warburg Pincus LLC; *U.S. Private*, pg. 4439
AALBORG WHITE ITALIA SRL—See Cementir Holding N.V.; *Int'l*, pg. 1397
AARON CONCRETE CONTRACTORS LP—See Heidelberg Materials AG; *Int'l*, pg. 3313
ABSOLUTE CONCRETE, INC.; *U.S. Private*, pg. 44
ADONEL CONCRETE; *U.S. Private*, pg. 82
AFFLUENT FOUNDATION HOLDINGS LIMITED; *Int'l*, pg. 188
A LAMP CONCRETE CONTRACTORS, INC.; *U.S. Private*, pg. 18
ALLIANCE CONSTRUCTION MATERIALS LTD.—See CK Hutchison Holdings Limited; *Int'l*, pg. 1636
ALLIANCE CONSTRUCTION MATERIALS LTD.—See Heidelberg Materials AG; *Int'l*, pg. 3311
ALUMA ENTERPRISES, INC.—See Brand Industrial Services, Inc.; *U.S. Private*, pg. 636
ASPHALT SPECIALTIES CO. INC.; *U.S. Private*, pg. 352
BAKER CONCRETE CONSTRUCTION, INC.; *U.S. Private*, pg. 455
BAKER-HIGHRISE TUNNEL FORM OPERATIONS—See Baker Concrete Construction, Inc.; *U.S. Private*, pg. 455
BARRO GROUP PTY LTD; *Int'l*, pg. 870
BAUER EGYPT S.A.E.—See BAUER Aktiengesellschaft; *Int'l*, pg. 891
BAUER GEOTEKNOLOJI INSAAT ANONIM SIRKETI—See BAUER Aktiengesellschaft; *Int'l*, pg. 893
BELL CONCRETE INCORPORATED; *U.S. Private*, pg. 518
BERKEL & COMPANY CONTRACTORS INC.; *U.S. Private*, pg. 532
BJ SERVICES, INC.; *U.S. Private*, pg. 568
B-K CONCRETE PRODUCTS INC.—See K-Five Construction Corporation; *U.S. Private*, pg. 2251
BRAYMAN FOUNDATIONS LLC—See Brayman Construction Corporation; *U.S. Private*, pg. 642
BRUNDAGE-BONE CONCRETE PUMPING, INC.—See Peninsula Pacific Strategic Partners, LLC; *U.S. Private*, pg. 3133
BUILDERS CONCRETE SERVICES LLC; *U.S. Private*, pg. 682
BUM BETON- UND MONIERBAU GMBH; *Int'l*, pg. 1215
CARSON CONCRETE CORPORATION; *U.S. Private*, pg. 774
CHEMINEES SECURITE INTERNATIONAL LTEE—See Lennox International Inc.; *U.S. Public*, pg. 1307
CHONG KIN GROUP HOLDINGS LIMITED; *Int'l*, pg. 1578
CLEVELAND CEMENT CONTRACTORS INC.; *U.S. Private*, pg. 940
COASTAL CAROLINA PUMPING, INC.—See Concrete Pumping Holdings, Inc.; *U.S. Public*, pg. 566
COASTAL GUNITE CONSTRUCTION CO; *U.S. Private*, pg. 956
COLASANTI SPECIALTY SERVICES; *U.S. Private*, pg. 965
CONCRETE AGGREGATES CORPORATION; *Int'l*, pg. 1765
CONCRETE SOLUTIONS LIMITED—See New Mountain Capital, LLC; *U.S. Private*, pg. 2899
CONSEL, INC.; *U.S. Private*, pg. 1019
COOK PAVING & CONSTRUCTION CO.; *U.S. Private*, pg. 1038
CRC-EVANS WEIGHTING SYSTEMS, INC.—See Stanley Black & Decker, Inc.; *U.S. Public*, pg. 1932
DANIEL G. SCHUSTER INC.; *U.S. Private*, pg. 1154
DAREX UK LIMITED—See Standard Industries Holdings Inc.; *U.S. Private*, pg. 3779
DE NEEF CONSTRUCTION CHEMICALS NV—See Standard Industries Holdings Inc.; *U.S. Private*, pg. 3779
DE NEEF CONSTRUCTION CHEMICALS (US) INC.—See Standard Industries Holdings Inc.; *U.S. Private*, pg. 3779
DE NEEF DEUTSCHLAND GMBH—See Standard Industries Holdings Inc.; *U.S. Private*, pg. 3779
DE NEEF FRANCE S.A.R.L.—See Standard Industries Holdings Inc.; *U.S. Private*, pg. 3779
DE NEEF SCANDANAVIA AB—See Standard Industries Holdings Inc.; *U.S. Private*, pg. 3779
DE NEEF TECHNOLOGIES S.L.—See Standard Industries Holdings Inc.; *U.S. Private*, pg. 3779
DENKA CONSTRUCTION SOLUTIONS MALAYSIA SDN. BHD.—See Denki Company Limited; *U.S. Private*, pg. 2027
DOMOPLAN BAUGESELLSCHAFT MBH—See Bauunternehman Echterhoff GmbH & Co. KG; *Int'l*, pg. 898

238110 — POURED CONCRETE FOU...

DONLEY'S, INC.; *U.S. Private,* pg. 1260
FLETCHER CONCRETE AND INFRASTRUCTURE LIMITED—See Fletcher Building Limited; *Int'l,* pg. 2700
FLOORCON CORPORATION—See Central Concrete Corporation; *U.S. Private,* pg. 819
FLORIDA LEMARK CORPORATION; *U.S. Private,* pg. 1549
GATEWAY CON FORMING SYSTEMS; *U.S. Private,* pg. 1650
GEO-LOGICAL INC.; *U.S. Private,* pg. 1680
GETIAN GENERAL SERVICES LTD—See Charilaos Apostolides Public Ltd.; *Int'l,* pg. 1450
HANSON CONCRETE PRODUCTS—See Heidelberg Materials AG; *Int'l,* pg. 3313
HANSON CONCRETE PRODUCTS—See Heidelberg Materials AG; *Int'l,* pg. 3313
HARCON INC.; *U.S. Private,* pg. 1862
HARRY S. PETERSON COMPANY—See Western Construction Group; *U.S. Private,* pg. 4492
HARTMAN & CO. INC.; *U.S. Private,* pg. 1874
HOFFMAN STRUCTURES, INC.—See Hoffman Corporation; *U.S. Private,* pg. 1960
HOLES, INC.; *U.S. Private,* pg. 1962
ICF SOLUTIONS, LLC—See Ritchie Corporation; *U.S. Private,* pg. 3441
IMAGES FLOORING, INC.—See The Sterling Group, L.P.; *U.S. Private,* pg. 4122
INLAND CONCRETE CONSTRUCTORS—See J.D. Diffenbaugh, Inc.; *U.S. Private,* pg. 2160
JASTICON INC.; *U.S. Private,* pg. 2191
JEZOWSKI & MARKEL CONTRACTORS INC.; *U.S. Private,* pg. 2206
JIM'S CONCRETE OF BREVARD INC.; *U.S. Private,* pg. 2210
JOHN ROHRER CONTRACTING CO.; *U.S. Private,* pg. 2224
J.T. WIMSATT CONTRACTING CO., INC.; *U.S. Private,* pg. 2171
KENT COMPANIES INC.; *U.S. Private,* pg. 2287
LANDAVAZO BROS. INC.; *U.S. Private,* pg. 2384
LARGO CONCRETE INC.; *U.S. Private,* pg. 2392
LARUSSO CONCRETE COMPANY INC.; *U.S. Private,* pg. 2394
LIBCON INC.; *U.S. Private,* pg. 2442
LITHKO CONTRACTING LLC—See The Pritzker Organization, LLC; *U.S. Private,* pg. 4100
LTI DEVELOPMENT CO. INC.; *U.S. Private,* pg. 2509
MANEVAL CONSTRUCTION CO. INC.; *U.S. Private,* pg. 2563
MCCLONE CONSTRUCTION COMPANY, INC.; *U.S. Private,* pg. 2628
MCCLONE CONSTRUCTION COMPANY-NORTHWEST REGIONAL OFFICE—See McClone Construction Company, Inc.; *U.S. Private,* pg. 2628
MCCLONE CONSTRUCTION COMPANY-SOUTHWEST REGIONAL OFFICE—See McClone Construction Company, Inc.; *U.S. Private,* pg. 2628
MCE CORPORATION; *U.S. Private,* pg. 2633
MILLER & LONG COMPANY, INC.; *U.S. Private,* pg. 2732
MIXONSITE USA, INC.—See Cematrix Corporation; *Int'l,* pg. 1396
M&M CONCRETE—See Lycon, Inc.; *U.S. Private,* pg. 2519
MODERN POURED WALLS INC.; *U.S. Private,* pg. 2762
MORLEY CONSTRUCTION CO., INC.—See Morley Builders; *U.S. Private,* pg. 2785
MORTEROS DE GALICIA S.L.—See Camargo Correa S.A.; *Int'l,* pg. 1268
MUELLER CONCRETE CONSTRUCTION COMPANY—See Primoris Services Corporation; *U.S. Public,* pg. 1719
NATIONAL RESTORATION SYSTEMS; *U.S. Private,* pg. 2862
NEW ENGLAND FOUNDATION CO. INC.; *U.S. Private,* pg. 2894
NICOLIA READY-MIX INC.; *U.S. Private,* pg. 2926
NORBETONG PUMPING AS—See Heidelberg Materials AG; *Int'l,* pg. 3318
NORTHERN LAKES CONCRETE, INC.—See Pitlik & Wick, Inc.; *U.S. Private,* pg. 3190
O'BRIEN CONCRETE PUMPING COLORADO, INC.—See Peninsula Pacific Strategic Partners, LLC; *U.S. Private,* pg. 3133
OLSHAN FOUNDATION REPAIR; *U.S. Private,* pg. 3011
PACIFIC PAVINGSTONE, INC.; *U.S. Private,* pg. 3070
PETER A. BASILE SONS, INC.; *U.S. Private,* pg. 3157
PIONEER CONCRETE PUMPING SERVICE; *U.S. Private,* pg. 3186
POTTER CONCRETE LTD; *U.S. Private,* pg. 3235
PRECAST SERVICES INC.; *U.S. Private,* pg. 3243
PREDIANA — SOCIEDADE DE PRE-ESFORCADOS S.A.—See Camargo Correa S.A.; *Int'l,* pg. 1268
PROPERTY PAVING INC.—See Harbor Beach Capital, LLC; *U.S. Private,* pg. 1858
PT ANEKA JARINGAN INDONESIA—See Aneka Jaringan Holdings Berhad; *Int'l,* pg. 457
QUALITY CONCRETE & RENTAL INC.; *U.S. Private,* pg. 3318
RABINE PAVING AMERICA, LLC; *U.S. Private,* pg. 3341

RITCHIE CORPORATION; *U.S. Private,* pg. 3441
R.J.S. & ASSOCIATES INC.; *U.S. Private,* pg. 3338
R&W CONCRETE CONTRACTOR; *U.S. Private,* pg. 3333
R.W. HARRIS INC.; *U.S. Private,* pg. 3340
SCP CONSTRUCTION, LLC; *U.S. Private,* pg. 3579
SERETTA CONSTRUCTION INC.; *U.S. Private,* pg. 3613
SHAW & SONS INC.; *U.S. Private,* pg. 3627
SOUTHERN PAN SERVICES COMPANY; *U.S. Private,* pg. 3734
SPARTAN CONCRETE, INC.—See Advanced Drainage Systems, Inc.; *U.S. Public,* pg. 46
S&S BUILDERS, LLC.; *U.S. Private,* pg. 3514
SSR SCHADSTOFFSANIERUNG ROSTOCK GMBH—See Heidelberg Materials AG; *Int'l,* pg. 3319
STEPHENS & SMITH CONSTRUCTION CO. INC; *U.S. Private,* pg. 3803
STEWART BUILDERS LTD; *U.S. Private,* pg. 3811
STRUCTURAL GROUP, INC.; *U.S. Private,* pg. 3841
STRUCTURAL PRESERVATION SYSTEMS, INC.—See Structural Group, Inc.; *U.S. Private,* pg. 3841
TAS COMMERCIAL CONCRETE CONSTRUCTION, L.P.—See Orion Group Holdings, Inc.; *U.S. Public,* pg. 1618
TAS CONCRETE CONSTRUCTION, LLC—See Orion Group Holdings, Inc.; *U.S. Public,* pg. 1618
TECHNICAL FOUNDATIONS INC.; *U.S. Private,* pg. 3954
TOM GREENAUER DEVELOPMENT, INC.—See Greenauer Holding Inc.; *U.S. Private,* pg. 1774
TOWA CONCRETE PUMPING INC.—See Fujii Sangyo Corporation; *Int'l,* pg. 2826
TRADEMARK CONSTRUCTION, INC.—See HITT Contracting, Inc.; *U.S. Private,* pg. 1953
UNITED FORMING INC.; *U.S. Private,* pg. 4292
URETEK USA INC.; *U.S. Private,* pg. 4315
VAN LAAN CONCRETE CONSTRUCTION, INC.; *U.S. Private,* pg. 4340
WALKER CONTRACTING GROUP INC.; *U.S. Private,* pg. 4429
WELLS LAND DEVELOPMENT, INC.; *U.S. Private,* pg. 4476
WESTCOAST STRUCTURAL CONCRETE & MASONRY, INC.; *U.S. Private,* pg. 4489
ZGURA'S CONCRETE SERVICES INC.; *U.S. Private,* pg. 4603

238120 — STRUCTURAL STEEL AND PRECAST CONCRETE CONTRACTORS

ADF GROUP INC.; *Int'l,* pg. 145
ADVANCE TANK & CONSTRUCTION CO. INC.; *U.S. Private,* pg. 87
ALLENS STEEL PRODUCTS INC.; *U.S. Private,* pg. 180
ALLIED STEEL BUILDINGS, INC.; *U.S. Private,* pg. 188
ALLSTATE STEEL COMPANY INC.; *U.S. Private,* pg. 193
ALL STEEL CONSULTANTS, INC.; *U.S. Private,* pg. 173
AMERICAN BRIDGE COMPANY—See Continental Holdings Corp.; *Int'l,* pg. 1784
AMERICAN FABRICATORS; *U.S. Private,* pg. 232
AMERICAN TANK & VESSEL INC.; *U.S. Private,* pg. 256
ARCELORMITTAL - ARCELORMITTAL AVELLINO MILL—See ArcelorMittal S.A.; *Int'l,* pg. 543
ARCELORMITTAL BISSEN S.A.—See ArcelorMittal S.A.; *Int'l,* pg. 543
AREA ERECTORS INC.; *U.S. Private,* pg. 317
ARMATURES BOIS-FRANCS INC.; *Int'l,* pg. 574
ARNOLD STEEL COMPANY INC.; *U.S. Private,* pg. 333
ASAHI INDUSTRIES CO., LTD.—See Godo Steel, Ltd.; *Int'l,* pg. 3020
ASSOCIATED STEEL WORKERS, LTD.; *U.S. Private,* pg. 357
ATLANTA STEEL ERECTORS, INC.—See Williams Enterprises of Georgia, Inc.; *U.S. Private,* pg. 4525
BAJA CONSTRUCTION CO. INC.; *U.S. Private,* pg. 454
BAMBACIGNO STEEL COMPANY, INC.; *U.S. Private,* pg. 463
BAPKO METAL FABRICATORS INC.; *U.S. Private,* pg. 470
BAY SHIP & YACHT CO; *U.S. Private,* pg. 494
BEN HUR CONSTRUCTION CO. INC.; *U.S. Private,* pg. 522
BILDCO REINFORCING STEEL SERVICES—See Abu Dhabi National Company for Building Material; *Int'l,* pg. 72
BILLINGTON STRUCTURES LIMITED—See Billington Holdings Plc; *Int'l,* pg. 1031
BM CARPENTERIE OIL & GAS S.R.L.; *Int'l,* pg. 1075
BRATTON CORPORATION; *U.S. Private,* pg. 640
CAL-STATE STEEL CORP; *U.S. Private,* pg. 715
CANTERA CONCRETE COMPANY—See Rooney Holdings, Inc.; *U.S. Private,* pg. 3479
CARR CONSTRUCTION, INC.; *U.S. Private,* pg. 771
C A S CORP.—See Jones Sign Co., Inc.; *U.S. Private,* pg. 2234
CB&I INC.—See McDermott International, Inc.; *U.S. Public,* pg. 1405
CENTURY IRON & STEEL INDUSTRIAL CO., LTD.; *Int'l,* pg. 1418
CHATTANOOGA BOILER & TANK CO., INC.—See Williams Enterprises of Georgia, Inc.; *U.S. Private,* pg. 4525

CHINA SAITE GROUP COMPANY LIMITED; *Int'l,* pg. 1549
CLARK STEEL FABRICATORS, INC.; *U.S. Private,* pg. 914
CLAUS QUECK GMBH—See Hutter & Schrantz PMS Ges.m.b.H; *Int'l,* pg. 3540
CMC UK LTD.—See Commercial Metals Company; *U.S. Public,* pg. 545
COMMONWEALTH DYNAMICS, INC.—See Global Dominion Access SA; *Int'l,* pg. 2995
CONCRETE ENGINEERING PRODUCTS BERHAD; *Int'l,* pg. 1765
COOPERS STEEL FABRICATORS INC.; *U.S. Private,* pg. 1043
CORESLAB INTERNATIONAL, INC.; *Int'l,* pg. 1799
CORESLAB STRUCTURES (TEXAS) INC.—See Coreslab International, Inc.; *Int'l,* pg. 1799
CORSETTI STRUCTURAL STEEL INC.; *U.S. Private,* pg. 1059
C & T REINFORCING STEEL CO (1987) LIMITED; *Int'l,* pg. 1237
CUBIC DESIGNS, INC.—See Berkshire Hathaway Inc.; *U.S. Public,* pg. 312
DANNY'S CONSTRUCTION CO., INC.; *U.S. Private,* pg. 1157
DAVIS ERECTION CO. INC.—See Ridgetop Holding Co., Inc.; *U.S. Private,* pg. 3433
DENT STEEL SERVICES LTD; *Int'l,* pg. 2033
DOLPHIN SERVICES, LLC—See Gulf Island Fabrication, Inc.; *U.S. Public,* pg. 975
DURABON SDN BHD—See IJM Corporation Berhad; *Int'l,* pg. 3608
DYMIN STEEL INC.; *Int'l,* pg. 2238
ENDO STAINLESS STEEL (THAILAND) CO. LTD.—See Endo Manufacturing Co., Ltd.; *Int'l,* pg. 2405
E PATTI & SONS INC.; *U.S. Private,* pg. 1301
EVERSENDAI CORPORATION BERHAD; *Int'l,* pg. 2568
FIELDERS AUSTRALIA PTY. LTD.—See BlueScope Steel Limited; *Int'l,* pg. 1073
FOUGHT & COMPANY INC.; *U.S. Private,* pg. 1579
GENERAL ENGINEERING CORP—See TTI Holdings Inc.; *U.S. Private,* pg. 4254
GEORGE THIRD & SON PARTNERSHIP—See Dynamic Technologies Group Inc.; *Int'l,* pg. 2241
GILBERT STEEL LIMITED; *Int'l,* pg. 2973
GREAT WESTERN ERECTORS CO.; *U.S. Private,* pg. 1768
GRUPA KAPITALOWA IMMOBILE S.A.; *Int'l,* pg. 3116
GULF ISLAND, LLC—See Gulf Island Fabrication, Inc.; *U.S. Public,* pg. 975
GULF MARINE FABRICATORS, L.P.—See Gulf Island Fabrication, Inc.; *U.S. Public,* pg. 975
HABIA CABLE SA—See Beijer Alma AB; *Int'l,* pg. 942
HAMMERT'S IRON WORKS, INC.—See Stupp Bros., Inc.; *U.S. Private,* pg. 3844
HARMON STEEL, INC.—See Harmon Group; *U.S. Private,* pg. 1866
HARRIS REBAR—See Nucor Corporation; *U.S. Public,* pg. 1553
HILLSDALE FABRICATORS—See Alberici Corporation; *U.S. Private,* pg. 152
HILLSDALE STRUCTURES, LP.—See Alberici Corporation; *U.S. Private,* pg. 152
HILLSTONE INTERNATIONAL, LLC—See Global Infrastructure Solutions, Inc.; *U.S. Private,* pg. 1715
HOARD-IT LIMITED—See Billington Holdings Plc; *Int'l,* pg. 1031
H & S STAHLBAU AG—See Hutter & Schrantz PMS Ges.m.b.H; *Int'l,* pg. 3540
HUSSOR ERECTA SOC; *Int'l,* pg. 3540
INDUSTRIAL STEEL INC.; *U.S. Private,* pg. 2068
INDUSTRIAL TECHNOLOGIES INC.; *U.S. Private,* pg. 2068
JERDON CONSTRUCTION SERVICES LLC; *U.S. Private,* pg. 2201
J & R SLAW, INC.; *U.S. Private,* pg. 2152
K.D. STEEL, INC.; *U.S. Private,* pg. 2251
KEEL HOLDINGS, LLC—See Arlington Capital Partners LLC; *U.S. Private,* pg. 328
KELLEY STEEL ERECTORS INC.—See Kelley Holdings Inc.; *U.S. Private,* pg. 2276
KERKSTRA PRECAST, INC.—See Solace Capital Partners, LLC; *U.S. Private,* pg. 3706
KINSLEY INDUSTRIAL—See Kinsley Construction Inc.; *U.S. Private,* pg. 2313
KINSLEY MANUFACTURING-STEEL FABRICATION & ERECTION—See Kinsley Construction Inc.; *U.S. Private,* pg. 2313
KOKOSING CONSTRUCTION COMPANY, INC. - HEAVY INDUSTRIAL DIVISION—See Kokosing Construction Company, Inc.; *U.S. Private,* pg. 2340
LAMPROS STEEL, INC.—See Reliance Steel & Aluminum Co.; *U.S. Public,* pg. 1780
LEMASTER STEEL ERECTORS INC.; *U.S. Private,* pg. 2420
LESJOFORS A/S—See Beijer Alma AB; *Int'l,* pg. 943
LICO STEEL, INC.—See Columbus McKinnon Corporation; *U.S. Public,* pg. 536
L.P.R. CONSTRUCTION CO.; *U.S. Private,* pg. 2367
L. R. WILLSON & SONS, INC.; *U.S. Private,* pg. 2364
THE MCINTYRE COMPANY; *U.S. Private,* pg. 4077

N.A.I.C.S. INDEX

238140 — MASONRY CONTRACTORS

MID ATLANTIC STORAGE SYSTEMS; *U.S. Private*, pg. 2705
MIDWEST STEEL INC.; *U.S. Private*, pg. 2723
MOZ DESIGNS, INC.—See Armstrong World Industries, Inc.; *U.S. Public*, pg. 194
MUTUAL WELDING CO., LTD.; *U.S. Private*, pg. 2820
NIAGARA STRUCTURAL STEEL—See Canerector Inc.; *Int'l*, pg. 1290
NORSTEEL LIMITED—See Canerector Inc.; *Int'l*, pg. 1290
NORTHWEST STEEL ERECTION CO.—See Ridgetop Holding Co., Inc.; *U.S. Private*, pg. 3433
O. TREVINO CONSTRUCTION, LLC.; *U.S. Private*, pg. 2981
PANGERE CORPORATION; *U.S. Private*, pg. 3086
PARCELL STEEL CO., INC.; *U.S. Private*, pg. 3094
PETER MARSHALL STEEL STAIRS LIMITED—See Billington Holdings Plc; *Int'l*, pg. 1031
PETERSON BECKNER INDUSTRIES; *U.S. Private*, pg. 3160
PROMOTEC CORPORATION—See Hitachi Zosen Corporation; *Int'l*, pg. 3412
PUK LTD.—See FLSmidth & Co. A/S; *Int'l*, pg. 2711
REX CONTRUCTION SERVICES—See REX Engineering Group, Inc.; *U.S. Private*, pg. 3417
RIGID GLOBAL BUILDINGS, LLC; *U.S. Private*, pg. 3436
ROCKY MOUNTAIN FABRICATION INC.; *U.S. Private*, pg. 3468
SCHUECK STEEL—See Lexicon, Inc.; *U.S. Private*, pg. 2440
SCHUFF STEEL COMPANY—See INNOVATE Corp.; *U.S. Public*, pg. 1125
SCHUFF STEEL-PACIFIC, INC.—See INNOVATE Corp.; *U.S. Public*, pg. 1126
SEMINOLE MACHINE & WELDING, INC.; *U.S. Private*, pg. 3604
SIS NORTHWEST, INC.—See Primoris Services Corporation; *U.S. Public*, pg. 1719
SNODGRASS & SONS CONSTRUCTION CO., INC.; *U.S. Private*, pg. 3700
SOUTHERN ERECTORS INCORPORATED; *U.S. Private*, pg. 3731
SOUTHWEST STEEL, LLC—See SME Industries Inc.; *U.S. Private*, pg. 3693
THE SOWLES COMPANY; *U.S. Private*, pg. 4119
SOWLES COMPANY—See The Sowles Company; *U.S. Private*, pg. 4119
SOWLES COMPANY—See The Sowles Company; *U.S. Private*, pg. 4119
STANLEY BLACK & DECKER, INC.; *U.S. Public*, pg. 1931
STONEBRIDGE INC.—See AIP, Inc.; *U.S. Private*, pg. 134
STRAIGHT LINE METAL BUILDINGS, INC.—See Ambassador Enterprises, LLC; *U.S. Private*, pg. 217
TIW STEEL PLATEWORK INC.—See Canerector Inc.; *Int'l*, pg. 1290
TIW WESTERN, INC.—See Canerector Inc.; *Int'l*, pg. 1290
TOP FLITE CONSTRUCTION INC.; *U.S. Private*, pg. 4186
UNISTRUCTURAL SUPPORT SYSTEMS, LTD.—See Brixey & Meyer, Inc.; *U.S. Private*, pg. 658
VALMONT NEDERLAND B.V.—See Valmont Industries, Inc.; *U.S. Public*, pg. 2274
WILLIAMS ENTERPRISES OF GEORGIA, INC.; *U.S. Private*, pg. 4525
WILLIAMS ERECTION COMPANY INC.—See Williams Enterprises of Georgia, Inc.; *U.S. Private*, pg. 4525
WRIGHT METAL PRODUCTS, INC.—See Trans Machine Technologies; *U.S. Private*, pg. 4205

238130 — FRAMING CONTRACTORS

A&A WINDOW PRODUCTS INC.; *U.S. Private*, pg. 19
ABERDEEN MANUFACTURING CORPORATION—See CHF Industries, Inc.; *U.S. Private*, pg. 876
A&D AUTOMATIC GATE & ACCESS; *U.S. Private*, pg. 20
A-E DOOR SALES AND SERVICE, INC.; *U.S. Private*, pg. 22
ALLISON DOOR SALES, INC.—See On-Point Group, LLC; *U.S. Private*, pg. 3019
ALL PURPOSE, INC.; *U.S. Private*, pg. 171
A&P AG STRUCTURES INC.; *U.S. Private*, pg. 20
AR-BE DOORS INC.; *U.S. Private*, pg. 306
BOB'S OVERHEAD DOOR REPAIR & SERVICE, INC.—See On-Point Group, LLC; *U.S. Private*, pg. 3018
BOSTON KITCHEN DIST. INC; *U.S. Private*, pg. 621
BSC STEEL INC.; *U.S. Private*, pg. 674
CARPENTER COMPONENTS OF ILLINOIS—See R&D Thiel Inc.-Carpenter Contractors of America; *U.S. Private*, pg. 3332
CARPENTER CONTRACTORS OF AMERICA—See R&D Thiel Inc.-Carpenter Contractors of America; *U.S. Private*, pg. 3332
CARPENTER CONTRACTORS OF AMERICA—See R&D Thiel Inc.-Carpenter Contractors of America; *U.S. Private*, pg. 3332
CARPENTER CONTRACTORS OF AMERICA—See R&D Thiel Inc.-Carpenter Contractors of America; *U.S. Private*, pg. 3332
CARPENTER CONTRACTORS OF AMERICA—See R&D Thiel Inc.-Carpenter Contractors of America; *U.S. Private*, pg. 3332
CARPENTER CONTRACTORS OF AMERICA—See R&D Thiel Inc.-Carpenter Contractors of America; *U.S. Private*, pg. 3332
CARPENTRY & HARDWARE SERVICES—See Harkins Builders, Inc.; *U.S. Private*, pg. 1864
CARTER LUMBER CO. - CARTER COMPONENTS PLANT—See Carter Lumber Co.; *U.S. Private*, pg. 775
CARTER LUMBER CO. - CARTER CUSTOM MILLWORK—See Carter Lumber Co.; *U.S. Private*, pg. 775
CARTER LUMBER CO. - GRIGGS LUMBER—See Carter Lumber Co.; *U.S. Private*, pg. 775
CARTER LUMBER CO. - KEMPSVILLE BUILDING MATERIALS DIVISION—See Carter Lumber Co.; *U.S. Private*, pg. 775
CARTER LUMBER CO. - KIGHT HOME CENTER—See Carter Lumber Co.; *U.S. Private*, pg. 775
CBC FRAMING INC.; *U.S. Private*, pg. 797
CHRISTMAN CONSTRUCTORS INC.—See The Christman Company Inc.; *U.S. Private*, pg. 4009
CLOSET WORLD, INC.; *U.S. Private*, pg. 946
COMPONENT ASSEMBLY SYSTEMS, INC.; *U.S. Private*, pg. 1001
CONTRACT LUMBER INC.; *U.S. Private*, pg. 1032
CREATIVE WOOD DESIGNS—See Patrick Industries, Inc.; *U.S. Public*, pg. 1652
D.A. WHITACRE CONSTRUCTION, INC.; *U.S. Private*, pg. 1141
DECORATIVE SPECIALTIES; *U.S. Private*, pg. 1188
DIETRICH INDUSTRIES, INC.—See Worthington Industries, Inc.; *U.S. Public*, pg. 2382
DIETRICH METAL FRAMING CANADA INC—See Worthington Industries, Inc.; *U.S. Public*, pg. 2382
DOOR SYSTEMS INC.—See ASSA ABLOY AB; *Int'l*, pg. 639
ENGINEERED PRODUCTS INC—See Engineered Products, Inc.; *U.S. Private*, pg. 1398
ERICKSON BUILDING COMPONENTS, A CALIFORNIA LIMITED PARTNERSHIP—See Masco Corporation; *U.S. Public*, pg. 1390
ERIE CONSTRUCTION MID-WEST INC.; *U.S. Private*, pg. 1420
FRAMES UNLIMITED INC.—See Zimdar Enterprises; *U.S. Private*, pg. 4605
FUTUROL INDUSTRIE; *Int'l*, pg. 2858
G. BAILEY COMPANY INC.; *U.S. Private*, pg. 1630
GWANAK CONSTRUCTION AND EQUIPMENT SERVICE CO LTD; *Int'l*, pg. 3190
HARDWOOD CREATIONS; *U.S. Private*, pg. 1864
J.B. MATHEWS COMPANY; *U.S. Private*, pg. 2158
KARAS & KARAS GLASS CO. INC.; *U.S. Private*, pg. 2262
MACKENZIE GROUP INC.; *U.S. Private*, pg. 2537
MANDERE CONSTRUCTION, INC.—See Kodiak Building Partners LLC; *U.S. Private*, pg. 2336
MCMURRAY STERN INC.—See Grays Peak Capital LP; *U.S. Private*, pg. 1761
MCMURRAY STERN INC.—See Valore Ventures, Inc.; *U.S. Private*, pg. 4337
METROPOLITAN SIDING & WINDOWS; *U.S. Private*, pg. 2689
MOLDED FIBER GLASS TEXAS—See Molded Fiber Glass Companies; *U.S. Private*, pg. 2766
NICHOLAS HOMES INC.; *U.S. Private*, pg. 2925
OKLAHOMA INSTALLATION COMPANY; *U.S. Private*, pg. 3007
PAULY JAIL BUILDING COMPANY, INC.; *U.S. Private*, pg. 3114
PIONEER WINDOWS INC.—See Pioneer Window Holdings Inc.; *U.S. Private*, pg. 3189
QUILLEN BROTHERS, INC.—See Leaf Home, LLC; *U.S. Private*, pg. 2407
R&D THIEL INC.-CARPENTER CONTRACTORS OF AMERICA; *U.S. Private*, pg. 3332
SHORELINE BUILDERS INC.; *U.S. Private*, pg. 3641
UNIVERSAL WINDOW SOLUTIONS, LLC; *U.S. Private*, pg. 4307
WORTHINGTON MID-RISE CONSTRUCTION, INC.—See Worthington Industries, Inc.; *U.S. Public*, pg. 2382
YOUNGER BROTHERS GROUP INC.; *U.S. Private*, pg. 4593

238140 — MASONRY CONTRACTORS

ADVANCED MASONRY SYSTEMS LLC; *U.S. Private*, pg. 91
APCI, INC.; *U.S. Private*, pg. 290
ARD CONTRACTING, INC.; *U.S. Private*, pg. 317
BLUE ROCK OF MAINE; *U.S. Private*, pg. 592
BRATTON MASONRY INC.; *U.S. Private*, pg. 640
BRODIE CONTRACTORS INC.; *U.S. Private*, pg. 661
BUTCHER & BAECKER CONSTRUCTION CO., INC.; *U.S. Private*, pg. 696
CARETTI, INC.; *U.S. Private*, pg. 754
CEDCO INC.; *U.S. Private*, pg. 805
CITY MASONRY INC.; *U.S. Private*, pg. 906
COSTA BROTHERS MASONRY; *U.S. Private*, pg. 1062
DBM/HATCH INC.—See Dee Brown, Inc.; *U.S. Private*, pg. 1188
DEE BROWN, INC.; *U.S. Private*, pg. 1188
D & H MASONRY, INC.; *U.S. Private*, pg. 1136
EDGAR BOETTCHER MASON CONTRACTORS; *U.S. Private*, pg. 1333
ELITE MASONRY, INC.; *U.S. Private*, pg. 1361
ENTERPRISE MASONRY CORPORATION; *U.S. Private*, pg. 1404
F & M, INC.; *U.S. Private*, pg. 1454
FRANKIPILE INTERNATIONAL PROJECTS LIMITED—See Esor Limited; *Int'l*, pg. 2504
FRANKIPILE MAURITIUS INTERNATIONAL LIMITED—See Esor Limited; *Int'l*, pg. 2504
GALLEGOS CORPORATION; *U.S. Private*, pg. 1639
G-A MASONRY CORP. OF NEW YORK; *U.S. Private*, pg. 1630
GAY & SON MASONRY INC.; *U.S. Private*, pg. 1652
GEO COMPACTION DYNAMICS (PTY) LIMITED—See Esor Limited; *Int'l*, pg. 2504
GLAUSER INTERNATIONAL MM; *Int'l*, pg. 2989
GRACIANO CORPORATION; *U.S. Private*, pg. 1749
GRACOM MASONRY—See Graham Group Ltd.; *Int'l*, pg. 3051
GREATER AUSTIN DEVELOPMENT; *U.S. Private*, pg. 1769
HARD-CO SAND & GRAVEL LTD.—See Hard-Co Construction Ltd.; *Int'l*, pg. 3272
ICC COMMONWEALTH CORPORATION—See Global Dominion Access SA; *Int'l*, pg. 2995
INDIAN COUNTRY BLUESTONE, LLC—See Indian Country Inc.; *U.S. Private*, pg. 2061
INDUSTRIAL FIRST INC.; *U.S. Private*, pg. 2066
INTREPID ENTERPRISES, INC.; *U.S. Private*, pg. 2129
JOHN JACKSON MASONRY; *U.S. Private*, pg. 2222
J&S MASONRY INC.; *U.S. Private*, pg. 2155
J.T. THORPE & SON, INC.—See Terra Millenium Corporation; *U.S. Private*, pg. 3970
L. FERIOZZI CONCRETE COMPANY; *U.S. Private*, pg. 2364
L&M FOUNDATION SPECIALIST PTE. LTD.—See CSC Holdings Limited; *Int'l*, pg. 1862
LUPINI CONSTRUCTION INC.—See Valcourt Building Services LLC; *U.S. Private*, pg. 4330
MANGANARO MIDATLANTIC, LLC; *U.S. Private*, pg. 2563
MASONRY BUILDERS, INC.; *U.S. Private*, pg. 2603
MCGEE BROTHERS CO. INC.; *U.S. Private*, pg. 2634
M & D MASONRY, INC.; *U.S. Private*, pg. 2522
MID-CONTINENTAL RESTORATION CO.; *U.S. Private*, pg. 2708
MIF CONSTRUCTION, INC.; *U.S. Private*, pg. 2724
M. L. SMITH, JR., INC.; *U.S. Private*, pg. 2526
M. T. LANEY COMPANY, INC.; *U.S. Private*, pg. 2527
NER CONSTRUCTION MANAGEMENT, INC.; *U.S. Private*, pg. 2885
OLD VETERAN CONSTRUCTION, INC.; *U.S. Private*, pg. 3009
OTTO BAUM COMPANY, INC.; *U.S. Private*, pg. 3050
P & S MASONRY, INC.; *U.S. Private*, pg. 3058
PYE-BARKER FIRE & SAFETY, LLC; *U.S. Private*, pg. 3308
PYRAMID MASONRY CONTRACTORS; *U.S. Private*, pg. 3310
REINTJES SERVICES INC.—See George P. Reintjes Co., Inc.; *U.S. Private*, pg. 1683
RESTORX OF TEXAS, LTD.—See Interstate Restoration Group, Inc.; *U.S. Private*, pg. 2126
ROSE PAVING CO.; *U.S. Private*, pg. 3481
SAND BUILDING MATERIALS, INC.; *U.S. Private*, pg. 3542
SHANE DEMLER MASONRY, INC; *U.S. Private*, pg. 3625
SHAW & JONES MASONRY, INC.; *U.S. Private*, pg. 3627
SIGNATURE GROUP INC—See The Jansen Group Inc.; *U.S. Private*, pg. 4058
STRUCTURAL MAINTENANCE SYSTEMS, INC.—See Structural Group, Inc.; *U.S. Private*, pg. 3841
SUB-CONTRACTORS INC—See Walz Harman Huffman Companies; *U.S. Private*, pg. 4435
SUN VALLEY MASONRY INC.; *U.S. Private*, pg. 3864
SYSTEM PAVERS INC.; *U.S. Private*, pg. 3907
TAB REFRACTORY CONSTRUCTION & MAINTENANCE CO. LTD.—See Pyrotek Incorporated; *U.S. Private*, pg. 3311
THORPE-SUNBELT, INC.—See The CapStreet Group LLC; *U.S. Private*, pg. 4005
URATA & SONS CEMENT COMPANY; *U.S. Private*, pg. 4313
URBAN CONCRETE CONTRACTORS, LTD.; *U.S. Private*, pg. 4313
VEE-JAY CEMENT CONTRACTING CO., INC.; *U.S. Private*, pg. 4353
VILLA CONSTRUCTION OF CONNECTICUT, INC.; *U.S. Private*, pg. 4383
WALKER & ZANGER STONEWORKS—See Walker & Zanger, Inc.; *U.S. Private*, pg. 4428
THE WALL COMPANY; *U.S. Private*, pg. 4133
WASCO INC.; *U.S. Private*, pg. 4445
WEAVER PRECAST INC.; *U.S. Private*, pg. 4463

238140 — MASONRY CONTRACTORS

WESTERN SPECIALTY CONTRACTORS; *U.S. Private,* pg. 4496
WILKS MASONRY CORPORATION; *U.S. Private,* pg. 4521

238150 — GLASS AND GLAZING CONTRACTORS

AGC GLASS KENZAI CO., LTD.—See AGC Inc.; *Int'l,* pg. 202
AJAY GLASS & MIRROR COMPANY INCORPORATED; *U.S. Private,* pg. 143
ALLGLASS SYSTEMS INC.; *U.S. Private,* pg. 181
APG-EUROPE GMBH—See APG International Inc.; *U.S. Private,* pg. 293
APG EUROPE LTD.—See APG International Inc.; *U.S. Private,* pg. 293
APG FAR EAST LTD.—See APG International Inc.; *U.S. Private,* pg. 293
APG INTERNATIONAL INC.; *U.S. Private,* pg. 293
APG MIDDLE EAST FZC—See APG International Inc.; *U.S. Private,* pg. 293
ARCHITECTURAL GLASS & ALUMINUM CO. INC.; *U.S. Private,* pg. 311
ARROW GLASS & MIRROR, INC.; *U.S. Private,* pg. 335
ASSOCIATED CRAFTS, INC.; *U.S. Private,* pg. 355
ATLANTA COMMERCIAL GLAZING, INC.—See Installed Building Products, Inc.; *U.S. Public,* pg. 1132
B&B GLASS, INC.; *U.S. Private,* pg. 417
BENSON INDUSTRIES, LLC—See Berkshire Hathaway Inc.; *U.S. Public,* pg. 312
THE BROWER GLASS TINTING COMPANY—See Solar Art Window Film, Inc.; *U.S. Private,* pg. 3707
BUTTE GLASS; *U.S. Private,* pg. 698
CAROLINA MANAGEMENT, INC.—See Installed Building Products, Inc.; *U.S. Public,* pg. 1132
CENTRAL GLASS ENGINEERING CO., LTD.—See Central Glass Co., Ltd.; *Int'l,* pg. 1406
C.H. HOLDINGS, USA INC.; *U.S. Private,* pg. 707
CH HOLDINGS USA, INC.; *U.S. Private,* pg. 844
COLORADO WINDOW SYSTEMS, INC.—See Platform Partners LLC; *U.S. Private,* pg. 3200
CONTINENTAL GLASS SYSTEMS LLC—See The Graham Group, Inc.; *U.S. Private,* pg. 4036
CULVER GLASS COMPANY; *U.S. Private,* pg. 1122
CUSTOM GLASS ATLANTA, INC.—See Installed Building Products, Inc.; *U.S. Public,* pg. 1132
CUSTOM GLASS SOLUTIONS, LLC—See Stellex Capital Management LP; *U.S. Private,* pg. 3800
DOTHAN GLASS CO. INC.; *U.S. Private,* pg. 1265
DYNAMIC GLASS, LLC—See Platform Partners LLC; *U.S. Private,* pg. 3200
ENCLOS CORP.—See C.H. Holdings, USA Inc.; *U.S. Private,* pg. 707
ENGINEERED GLASS WALLS; *U.S. Private,* pg. 1398
FAR EAST ALUMINIUM WORKS COMPANY LIMITED—See China State Construction International Holdings Limited; *Int'l,* pg. 1554
FAR EAST FACADE, INC.—See China State Construction International Holdings Limited; *Int'l,* pg. 1554
GAMMA WINDOWS AND WALLS INTERNATIONAL INC.—See China State Construction International Holdings Limited; *Int'l,* pg. 1554
GENERAL PLASTICS GROUP, INC.—See PMC Capital Partners, LLC; *U.S. Private,* pg. 3217
GLASBAU HAHN GMBH; *Int'l,* pg. 2988
GLASS & SASH INC.; *U.S. Private,* pg. 1706
GLAS TROSCH HOLDING AG; *Int'l,* pg. 2988
GLOBAL DISPLAY CO., LTD.; *Int'l,* pg. 2994
G & M HOLDINGS LIMITED; *Int'l,* pg. 2861
GUANGDONG SANSHUI T&H GLAZE CO., LTD.—See China Glaze Co., Ltd.; *Int'l,* pg. 1504
HALEY-GREER INC.; *U.S. Private,* pg. 1842
HARMON, INC.—See Apogee Enterprises, Inc.; *U.S. Public,* pg. 145
HEINZ-GLAS GMBH & CO. KGAA; *Int'l,* pg. 3325
HENTGES GLASS COMPANY INC.—See Brin Northwestern Glass Company Inc.; *U.S. Private,* pg. 654
HERSHOCKS INC.; *U.S. Private,* pg. 1927
HOME FRAGRANCE ITALIA S.R.L.—See Newell Brands Inc.; *U.S. Public,* pg. 1514
HURON VALLEY GLASS COMPANY LLC—See National Construction Enterprises Inc.; *U.S. Private,* pg. 2851
JOHNSON ARCHITECTURAL METAL COMPANY; *U.S. Private,* pg. 2226
KAS INVESTMENT CO. INC.; *U.S. Private,* pg. 2263
KEY GLASS LLC; *U.S. Private,* pg. 2293
LUMI GLASS INDUSTRIES LLC—See Dubai Investments PJSC; *Int'l,* pg. 2219
THE LURIE COMPANIES; *U.S. Private,* pg. 4073
LURIE GLASS COMPANY—See The Lurie Companies; *U.S. Private,* pg. 4073
MASONRYARTS, INC.; *U.S. Private,* pg. 2603
MASSEY'S PLATE GLASS & ALUMINUM, INC.; *U.S. Private,* pg. 2606
MESKO GLASS AND MIRROR CO.; *U.S. Private,* pg. 2679
METRALITE INDUSTRIES INC.; *U.S. Private,* pg. 2684
MEYDA STAINED GLASS STUDIO & LIGHTING CORP.; *U.S. Private,* pg. 2692
MIDWEST GLASS, INC.; *U.S. Private,* pg. 2721
NG&G FACILITY SERVICES INTERNATIONAL; *U.S. Private,* pg. 2923
PILTZ GLASS AND MIRROR, INC.—See Brin Northwestern Glass Company Inc.; *U.S. Private,* pg. 654
PROGRESS GLASS CO. INC.; *U.S. Private,* pg. 3278
PSC FABRICATING, INC—See PMC Capital Partners, LLC; *U.S. Private,* pg. 3218
PSC INDUSTRIES, INC. - GLASRITE DIVISION—See PMC Capital Partners, LLC; *U.S. Private,* pg. 3218
THE R.E. KRUG CORPORATION; *U.S. Private,* pg. 4101
RYANS ALL-GLASS INC.; *U.S. Private,* pg. 3511
SHANDONG T&H GLAZE CO., LTD.—See China Glaze Co., Ltd.; *Int'l,* pg. 1505
SHANGHAI T&H GLAZE CO., LTD.—See China Glaze Co., Ltd.; *Int'l,* pg. 1505
SOUND GLASS SALES, INC.; *U.S. Private,* pg. 3717
ST. CHARLES GLASS & GLAZING, INC.; *U.S. Private,* pg. 3771
ST. GERMAIN'S GLASS CO.—See Brin Northwestern Glass Company Inc.; *U.S. Private,* pg. 654
THAD ZIEGLER GLASS LTD.; *U.S. Private,* pg. 3979
US GLASS & ALUMINUM INC.; *U.S. Private,* pg. 4318
WALKER & LABERGE COMPANY INCORPORATED; *U.S. Private,* pg. 4428
WALTERS & WOLF CONSTRUCTION SPECIALTIES, INC.—See Walters & Wolf; *U.S. Private,* pg. 4434
WALTERS & WOLF INTERIORS—See Walters & Wolf; *U.S. Private,* pg. 4434
WALTERS & WOLF; *U.S. Private,* pg. 4434
WILLET HAUSER ARCHITECTURAL GLASS, INC.—See Associated Crafts, Inc.; *U.S. Private,* pg. 355
ZIBO ASAHI GLASS ALUMINA MATERIALS CO., LTD.—See AGC Inc.; *Int'l,* pg. 204

238160 — ROOFING CONTRACTORS

413554 ONTARIO LIMITED; *Int'l,* pg. 11
5 STAR ROOFING & RESTORATION LLC; *U.S. Private,* pg. 16
AAR OF NORTH CAROLINA INC.; *U.S. Private,* pg. 32
A.C. DELLOVADE INC.; *U.S. Private,* pg. 24
AC HOLDING CO.; *U.S. Private,* pg. 45
ADVANCED ROOFING INC.; *U.S. Private,* pg. 92
AHI ROOFING LIMITED—See Fletcher Building Limited; *Int'l,* pg. 2699
ALDEN ROOFING, INC.—See Restoration Builders Inc.; *U.S. Private,* pg. 3409
ALL AREA ROOFING & WATERPROOFING, INC.; *U.S. Private,* pg. 170
ALLENTECH, INC.—See Matrix Service Company; *U.S. Public,* pg. 1397
ALL-SOUTH SUBCONTRACTORS INC.; *U.S. Private,* pg. 173
ALL-TEX ROOFING INC.; *U.S. Private,* pg. 174
ALPHA ROOFING INDUSTRIES, LLC; *U.S. Private,* pg. 199
AMERICAN ROOFING & METAL CO. INC.; *U.S. Private,* pg. 246
ANTHONY ROOFING LTD.—See Altas Partners LP; *Int'l,* pg. 386
APEXTERIORS INC.; *U.S. Private,* pg. 293
ARC CONTRACTING, INC.; *U.S. Private,* pg. 309
ARDE, INC.—See L3Harris Technologies, Inc.; *U.S. Public,* pg. 1279
ASPENMARK ROOFING SOLUTIONS LLC—See Restoration Builders Inc.; *U.S. Private,* pg. 3410
AVCO ROOFING INC.—See Restoration Builders Inc.; *U.S. Private,* pg. 3409
AVONSIDE GROUP SERVICES LIMITED; *Int'l,* pg. 750
AZZ CANADA LIMITED—See AZZ, Inc.; *U.S. Public,* pg. 258
BAKER ROOFING COMPANY; *U.S. Private,* pg. 456
BARRETT INC.; *U.S. Private,* pg. 479
BELDON ENTERPRISES, INC.; *U.S. Private,* pg. 517
BELDON ROOFING COMPANY—See Beldon Enterprises, Inc.; *U.S. Private,* pg. 517
BENNETT & BROSSEAU ROOFING INC.; *U.S. Private,* pg. 526
BEST CONTRACTING SERVICES INC.; *U.S. Private,* pg. 542
BHW SHEET METAL COMPANY; *U.S. Private,* pg. 549
BLACKMORE & BUCKNER ROOFING, LLC.—See Altas Partners LP; *Int'l,* pg. 386
B&M ROOFING OF COLORADO. INC.; *U.S. Private,* pg. 419
BONITZ INC. - ROOFING SYSTEMS DIVISION—See Bonitz Inc.; *U.S. Private,* pg. 614
BONITZ INSULATION COMPANY, INC.—See Bonitz Inc.; *U.S. Private,* pg. 614
BRACKNELL ROOFING LTD.—See Avonside Group Services Limited; *Int'l,* pg. 750
BRISTILE ROOFING PTY. LTD.—See Brickworks Limited; *Int'l,* pg. 1152
BURKE INDUSTRIES, INC. - BURKELINE ROOFING SYSTEMS DIVISION—See Mannington Mills, Inc.; *U.S. Private,* pg. 2565
BURNS & SCALO NORTH CAROLINA, INC.—See Burns & Scalo Roofing Co., Inc.; *U.S. Private,* pg. 690
BURNS & SCALO OHIO, INC.—See Burns & Scalo Roofing Co., Inc.; *U.S. Private,* pg. 690
BURNS & SCALO ROOFING CO., INC.; *U.S. Private,* pg. 690
CAMBIE ROOFING & DRAINAGE CONTRACTORS LTD.; *Int'l,* pg. 1268
CAPITAL CONSTRUCTION HOLDINGS—See O2 Investment Partners, LLC; *U.S. Private,* pg. 2982
CARPENTERS ROOFING & SHEET METAL, INC.—See Infinity Home Services; *U.S. Private,* pg. 2071
CEI ROOFING COLORADO, LLC—See Altas Partners LP; *Int'l,* pg. 386
CEI ROOFING TEXAS, LLC—See Altas Partners LP; *Int'l,* pg. 386
CEI ROOFING - TEXAS—See Altas Partners LP; *Int'l,* pg. 386
CENTIMARK CORPORATION; *U.S. Private,* pg. 817
CENTIMARK LTD.—See Centimark Corporation; *U.S. Private,* pg. 817
CENTROTEC COMPOSITES GMBH—See CENTROTEC SE; *Int'l,* pg. 1414
CIRSCO, INC.; *U.S. Private,* pg. 900
CLARKS QUALITY ROOFING INC.; *U.S. Private,* pg. 914
CMR CONSTRUCTION COLUMBUS—See CMR Construction & Roofing LLC; *U.S. Private,* pg. 951
CMR CONSTRUCTION KANSAS—See CMR Construction & Roofing LLC; *U.S. Private,* pg. 951
CMR CONSTRUCTION LOUISIANA—See CMR Construction & Roofing LLC; *U.S. Private,* pg. 951
CMR CONSTRUCTION MINNESOTA—See CMR Construction & Roofing LLC; *U.S. Private,* pg. 951
CMR CONSTRUCTION MISSOURI - ST LOUIS—See CMR Construction & Roofing LLC; *U.S. Private,* pg. 951
CMR CONSTRUCTION NORTH DAKOTA—See CMR Construction & Roofing LLC; *U.S. Private,* pg. 951
CMR CONSTRUCTION & ROOFING LLC; *U.S. Private,* pg. 951
CMR CONSTRUCTION & ROOFING OF TEXAS—See CMR Construction & Roofing LLC; *U.S. Private,* pg. 951
COATINGS APPLICATION WATERPROOFING CO., INC.; *U.S. Private,* pg. 957
COMMERCIAL ROOFERS, INC.; *U.S. Private,* pg. 984
COMMERCIAL ROOFING, INC.—See Altas Partners LP; *Int'l,* pg. 386
COMMERCIAL SIDING AND MAINTENANCE CO; *U.S. Private,* pg. 984
CONSTRUCTION METALS, LLC—See Gibraltar Industries, Inc.; *U.S. Public,* pg. 936
CONSTRUCT SOLUTIONS, INC.; *U.S. Private,* pg. 1023
CRAFTS INC.; *U.S. Private,* pg. 1082
CROWN CORR, INC.; *U.S. Private,* pg. 1110
CROWN ROOFING (CENTRES) LIMITED—See Brickability Group plc; *Int'l,* pg. 1151
CROWTHER ROOFING & SHEET METAL OF FLORIDA, INC.—See FirstService Corporation; *Int'l,* pg. 2691
D.C. TAYLOR CO.; *U.S. Private,* pg. 1141
DDP ROOFING SERVICES, INC.; *U.S. Private,* pg. 1181
DEAN ROOFING CO. INC.; *U.S. Private,* pg. 1184
DEER PARK ROOFING, LLC; *U.S. Private,* pg. 1190
DMC CONSTRUCTION, INC.; *U.S. Private,* pg. 1248
DOGWOOD SOLAR, LLC—See Duke Energy Corporation; *U.S. Public,* pg. 690
DOUGLASS COLONY GROUP, INC.; *U.S. Private,* pg. 1267
DRI COMPANIES; *U.S. Private,* pg. 1277
EAGLE CORNICE CO. INC.—See Altas Partners LP; *Int'l,* pg. 386
EARL W. JOHNSTON ROOFING INC.—See Dunes Point Capital, LLC; *U.S. Private,* pg. 1288
E.B. CREASY & COMPANY PLC; *Int'l,* pg. 2251
ELECTRA-FINISH, INC.—See PPG Industries, Inc.; *U.S. Public,* pg. 1707
ELITE CUSTOM BUILDERS LLC; *U.S. Private,* pg. 1360
EMPIRE ROOFING, INC.—See Altas Partners LP; *Int'l,* pg. 386
E.R. BERWALD ROOFING COMPANY; *U.S. Private,* pg. 1306
ESDEC BV; *Int'l,* pg. 2502
ESKOLA LLC—See EMP Management, LLC; *U.S. Private,* pg. 1384
EVANS SERVICE COMPANY INC.; *U.S. Private,* pg. 1435
EXCEL ROOFING SERVICES LIMITED—See Brickability Group plc; *Int'l,* pg. 1151
FIDELITY ROOF COMPANY—See HCI Equity Management, L.P.; *U.S. Private,* pg. 1889
FIRESTONE BUILDING PRODUCTS COMPANY, LLC - TUSCUMBIA MANUFACTURING FACILITY—See Bridgestone Corporation; *Int'l,* pg. 1157
FIRESTONE METAL PRODUCTS COMPANY, LLC - ANOKA MANUFACTURING FACILITY—See Bridgestone Corporation; *Int'l,* pg. 1159
FJA CHRISTIANSEN ROOFING CO., INC.—See Altas Partners LP; *Int'l,* pg. 386
FLORIDA SOUTHERN ROOFING & SHEET METAL, INC.; *U.S. Private,* pg. 1550
FOLCARELLI SHEET METAL INC.; *U.S. Private,* pg. 1557

N.A.I.C.S. INDEX

238190 — OTHER FOUNDATION, S...

FRED CHRISTEN & SONS COMPANY; *U.S. Private*, pg. 1600
FRONT RANGE ROOFING SYSTEMS, LLC—See FirstService Corporation; *Int'l*, pg. 2691
FRYE ROOFING, INC. - BECKLEY—See Frye Roofing, Inc.; *U.S. Private*, pg. 1618
FRYE ROOFING, INC.; *U.S. Private*, pg. 1618
GARCIA ROOFING & SHEET METAL; *U.S. Private*, pg. 1642
GARY W. CURRY, INC.; *U.S. Private*, pg. 1646
GENERAL WORKS, LLC—See Altas Partners LP; *Int'l*, pg. 386
G & F ROOF SUPPLY INC.—See Hendricks Holding Company, Inc.; *U.S. Private*, pg. 1914
GREAT PLAINS ROOFING & SHEET METAL—See Western Construction Group; *U.S. Private*, pg. 4492
GREENBERG ROOFING, INC.—See Altas Partners LP; *Int'l*, pg. 386
GREENBERG ROOFING, INC.—See Altas Partners LP; *Int'l*, pg. 386
GREENWOOD INDUSTRIES; *U.S. Private*, pg. 1782
GRID ALTERNATIVES; *U.S. Private*, pg. 1786
HAAS GROUP, LLC—See Platinum Equity, LLC; *U.S. Private*, pg. 3210
HANOVER IRON WORKS, INC.—See Highland Roofing Co.; *U.S. Private*, pg. 1939
HAYDEN BUILDING MAINTENANCE CORP.; *U.S. Private*, pg. 1884
HIGHLAND COMMERCIAL ROOFING—See HCI Equity Management, L.P.; *U.S. Private*, pg. 1889
HIGHLAND ROOFING CO.; *U.S. Private*, pg. 1939
HORIZON ROOFING; *U.S. Private*, pg. 1982
HRGM CORPORATION; *U.S. Private*, pg. 1998
HUDSON VALLEY ROOFING & SHEETMETAL, INC.—See Greenwood Industries; *U.S. Private*, pg. 1782
ICOPAL ENTREPRENAD AB—See GAF Materials Corporation; *U.S. Private*, pg. 1633
ICOPAL KFT.—See GAF Materials Corporation; *U.S. Private*, pg. 1633
INFINITY ROOFING & SIDING, INC.—See O2 Investment Partners, LLC; *U.S. Private*, pg. 2982
INNOVATIVE CONSTRUCTION & ROOFING; *U.S. Private*, pg. 2082
JASPER CONTRACTORS INC; *U.S. Private*, pg. 2190
JD2 INC. - LOS ANGELES—See JD2 Inc.; *U.S. Private*, pg. 2195
JOHN J. CAMPBELL CO., INC.; *U.S. Private*, pg. 2222
JOTTAN INC.; *U.S. Private*, pg. 2238
J.P. HUNTER ENTERPRISES INC.; *U.S. Private*, pg. 2170
J.P. PATTI TECTA AMERICA, LLC—See Altas Partners LP; *Int'l*, pg. 386
J. REYNOLDS & CO.; *U.S. Private*, pg. 2157
KALKREUTH ROOFING & SHEETMETAL INC.; *U.S. Private*, pg. 2257
KEE SAFETY, INC.; *U.S. Private*, pg. 2271
KIDD ROOFING; *U.S. Private*, pg. 2302
KIRBERG ROOFING INC.; *U.S. Private*, pg. 2314
LEGACY CONTRACTING SOLUTIONS, INC; *U.S. Private*, pg. 2416
L.E. SCHWARTZ & SON INC.; *U.S. Private*, pg. 2365
LYON ROOFING & SUPPLY; *U.S. Private*, pg. 2522
MAHANEY GROUP—See Altas Partners LP; *Int'l*, pg. 386
MARGO, INC.—See Altas Partners LP; *Int'l*, pg. 386
MARLEY CONTRACT SERVICES—See Etex SA/NV; *Int'l*, pg. 2522
MAUI ROOFING—See Petersen-Dean Inc.; *U.S. Private*, pg. 3160
MCCURDY-WALDEN, INC.—See Shoreline Equity Partners, LLC; *U.S. Private*, pg. 3641
MCENANY ROOFING & CONTRACTING INC.; *U.S. Private*, pg. 2633
MCKAY ROOFING COMPANY, INC.—See Solar Integrated Roofing Corporation; *U.S. Public*, pg. 1899
THE MELANSON COMPANY INC—See Altas Partners LP; *Int'l*, pg. 387
MERRICK - KEMPER—See Merrick Industries Incorporated; *U.S. Private*, pg. 2675
MIDLAND ENGINEERING COMPANY; *U.S. Private*, pg. 2715
MOUNTAIN COMPANY INC.; *U.S. Private*, pg. 2799
NATIONAL ROOFING CO. INC.; *U.S. Private*, pg. 2862
NATIONS ROOF EAST—See AEA Investors LP; *U.S. Private*, pg. 115
NATIONS ROOF LLC—See AEA Investors LP; *U.S. Private*, pg. 115
NETH & SON INC.; *U.S. Private*, pg. 2887
NFFS INC.; *U.S. Private*, pg. 2922
NORTH AMERICAN ROOFING SYSTEMS, INC.; *U.S. Private*, pg. 2941
NORTHLAND ASSOCIATES, INC.; *U.S. Private*, pg. 2955
NU-TEC ROOFING CONTRACTORS LLC; *U.S. Private*, pg. 2971
OPSTALAN BV—See Mohawk Industries, Inc.; *U.S. Public*, pg. 1458
ORNDORFF & SPAID, INC.; *U.S. Private*, pg. 3044
OWEN PACIFIC; *U.S. Private*, pg. 3054
PANELIZED STRUCTURES, INC.; *U.S. Private*, pg. 3086

PARSONS ROOFING COMPANY, INC.; *U.S. Private*, pg. 3100
PATUXENT ROOFING & CONTRACTING, LLC—See New State Capital Partners LLC; *U.S. Private*, pg. 2907
PEACH STATE ROOFING INC.; *U.S. Private*, pg. 3123
PENNSYLVANIA INTERACTIVE, LLC—See Tyler Technologies, Inc.; *U.S. Public*, pg. 2209
PEORIA ROOFING AND RESTORATION COMPANY—See Western Construction Group; *U.S. Private*, pg. 4492
PETERSEN-DEAN INC.; *U.S. Private*, pg. 3159
PHOENIX ROOFING, INC.; *U.S. Private*, pg. 3173
PIEROS CONSTRUCTION CO, INC.—See Altas Partners LP; *Int'l*, pg. 386
PINKSTON-HOLLAR CONSTRUCTION SERVICES INC.—See Altas Partners LP; *Int'l*, pg. 386
PIONEER ROOFING, LLC—See Altas Partners LP; *Int'l*, pg. 386
P.I. ROOF MAINTENANCE, INC.; *U.S. Private*, pg. 3060
PORTER ROOFING CONTRACTORS; *U.S. Private*, pg. 3232
PRECISION CONSTRUCTION & ROOFING; *U.S. Private*, pg. 3244
PROFESSIONAL ROOFING & EXTERIORS; *U.S. Private*, pg. 3276
PROGRESSIVE SERVICES INC.; *U.S. Private*, pg. 3279
PRO-TEC ROOFING, INC.—See Altas Partners LP; *Int'l*, pg. 386
QUALITY ROOFING CENTER OF SOUTHEAST MISSOURI; *U.S. Private*, pg. 3321
REMEDY ROOFING, INC.; *U.S. Private*, pg. 3396
RENEWABLE PROPERTIES, INC.—See Eversource Energy; *U.S. Public*, pg. 802
RENOWN CONSTRUCTION OF TEXAS LLC—See Restoration Builders Inc.; *U.S. Private*, pg. 3409
REROOF AMERICA CORPORATION; *U.S. Private*, pg. 3403
R.L. CAMPBELL ROOFING CO. INC.; *U.S. Private*, pg. 3338
ROMAN ROOFING, INC.; *U.S. Private*, pg. 3476
ROOF DIAGNOSTICS SOLAR OF MASS., LLC—See NRG Energy, Inc.; *U.S. Public*, pg. 1551
ROOFED RIGHT AMERICA, LLC; *U.S. Private*, pg. 3478
THE ROOFING CENTRE (TASMANIA) PTY LTD.—See BlueScope Steel Limited; *Int'l*, pg. 1074
ROOFING CORP OF AMERICA, LLC—See FirstService Corporation; *Int'l*, pg. 2691
ROOF SERVICES JGM CORPORATION—See Altas Partners LP; *Int'l*, pg. 386
ROOF SYSTEMS OF MAINE—See Altas Partners LP; *Int'l*, pg. 386
ROOF SYSTEMS OF VA INC.; *U.S. Private*, pg. 3478
SBB ROOFING INC.; *U.S. Private*, pg. 3559
SCHWICKERT'S TECTA AMERICA LLC—See Altas Partners LP; *Int'l*, pg. 386
SCHWICKERT'S TECTA AMERICA LLC - STEWARTVILLE—See Altas Partners LP; *Int'l*, pg. 386
SCHWICKERT'S TECTA AMERICA OF MANKATO LLC—See Altas Partners LP; *Int'l*, pg. 386
SECURE ROOFING & SOLAR, INC.—See Solar Integrated Roofing Corporation; *U.S. Public*, pg. 1900
SHERRIFF-GOSLIN CO.; *U.S. Private*, pg. 3634
SIMON ROOFING AND SHEET METAL CORP.; *U.S. Private*, pg. 3666
SNYDER ROOFING & SHEETMETAL INC.; *U.S. Private*, pg. 3701
SONORAN ROOFING INC.; *U.S. Private*, pg. 3714
SPS CORPORATION, CURTAIN WALL DIVISION—See SPS Corporation; *U.S. Private*, pg. 3765
SPS CORPORATION, RETROFIT DIVISION—See SPS Corporation; *U.S. Private*, pg. 3765
STOCK ROOFING COMPANY, LLC—See Altas Partners LP; *Int'l*, pg. 386
STOUT ROOFING INC.; *U.S. Private*, pg. 3832
SULLIVAN ROOFING, INC.; *U.S. Private*, pg. 3851
SUTTER ROOFING COMPANY OF FLORIDA; *U.S. Private*, pg. 3887
SYFON SYSTEMS PTY LTD—See EVZ Limited; *Int'l*, pg. 2574
TARGET ROOFING INC.—See Altas Partners LP; *Int'l*, pg. 386
TBI INC.; *U.S. Private*, pg. 3911
TECTA AMERICA ARIZONA, LLC—See Altas Partners LP; *Int'l*, pg. 386
TECTA AMERICA CAROLINAS, LLC—See Altas Partners LP; *Int'l*, pg. 386
TECTA AMERICA COLORADO, LLC—See Altas Partners LP; *Int'l*, pg. 386
TECTA AMERICA DAKOTAS, LLC - JAMESTOWN—See Altas Partners LP; *Int'l*, pg. 387
TECTA AMERICA DAKOTAS, LLC—See Altas Partners LP; *Int'l*, pg. 386
TECTA AMERICA EAST LLC - FRUITLAND—See Altas Partners LP; *Int'l*, pg. 387
TECTA AMERICA EAST LLC - GLEN ROCK—See Altas Partners LP; *Int'l*, pg. 387
TECTA AMERICA EAST LLC - JESSUP—See Altas Partners LP; *Int'l*, pg. 387

TECTA AMERICA EAST LLC—See Altas Partners LP; *Int'l*, pg. 387
TECTA AMERICA ILLINOIS ROOFING, LLC—See Altas Partners LP; *Int'l*, pg. 387
TECTA AMERICA METRO NEW YORK, LLC—See Altas Partners LP; *Int'l*, pg. 387
TECTA AMERICA NEW ENGLAND, LLC—See Altas Partners LP; *Int'l*, pg. 387
TECTA AMERICA SACRAMENTO INC.—See Altas Partners LP; *Int'l*, pg. 387
TECTA AMERICA SOUTHERN CALIFORNIA, INC.—See Altas Partners LP; *Int'l*, pg. 387
TECTA AMERICA SOUTH FLORIDA—See Altas Partners LP; *Int'l*, pg. 387
TECTA AMERICA WEST FLORIDA, LLC—See Altas Partners LP; *Int'l*, pg. 387
TECTA AMERICA ZERO COMPANY LLC - COLUMBUS—See Altas Partners LP; *Int'l*, pg. 387
TECTA AMERICA ZERO COMPANY LLC - LOUISVILLE—See Altas Partners LP; *Int'l*, pg. 387
TECTA AMERICA ZERO COMPANY LLC—See Altas Partners LP; *Int'l*, pg. 387
THERMA-SEAL ROOFS INC.; *U.S. Private*, pg. 4142
TITAN ROOFING INC.; *U.S. Private*, pg. 4177
TRIPLE M ROOFING CORP.; *U.S. Private*, pg. 4237
TUSCANO-MAHER ROOFING, INC.—See Altas Partners LP; *Int'l*, pg. 387
UPSTATE ROOFING & PAINTING, INC.—See Roofed Right America, LLC; *U.S. Private*, pg. 3478
VALLEY GUTTER SUPPLY INC.—See TopBuild Corp.; *U.S. Public*, pg. 2163
VIVINT SOLAR OPERATIONS, LLC—See Sunrun Inc.; *U.S. Public*, pg. 1966
WARREN ROOFING & INSULATING CO.—See AC Holding Co.; *U.S. Private*, pg. 45
WEATHERGUARD TECTA AMERICA, LLC—See Altas Partners LP; *Int'l*, pg. 387
WEISS SHEET METAL COMPANY; *U.S. Private*, pg. 4473
WESTERN PACIFIC ROOFING CORPORATION; *U.S. Private*, pg. 4495
WESTERN ROOFING & INSULATION CO.—See Western Construction Group; *U.S. Private*, pg. 4492
WESTERN ROOFING SERVICE, INC.—See Altas Partners LP; *Int'l*, pg. 387
WESTERN ROOFING SERVICE, INC.—See Altas Partners LP; *Int'l*, pg. 387
WESTFALL ROOFING; *U.S. Private*, pg. 4498
WEST ROOFING SYSTEMS, INC.; *U.S. Private*, pg. 4487
THE WILLIAMS COMPANIES, INC. - OKLAHOMA CITY—See The Williams Companies, Inc.; *U.S. Public*, pg. 2142
WNR INC.; *U.S. Private*, pg. 4553
WOLFE ROOFING, A TECTA AMERICA COMPANY, LLC—See Altas Partners LP; *Int'l*, pg. 387

238170 — SIDING CONTRACTORS

ABC INC.; *U.S. Private*, pg. 36
AMERICAN EXTERIORS, LLC; *U.S. Private*, pg. 232
ARCHER EXTERIORS; *U.S. Private*, pg. 310
B&B BUILDERS, INC.; *U.S. Private*, pg. 417
BIL-RAY GROUP; *U.S. Private*, pg. 556
FALLS SIDING, INC.; *U.S. Private*, pg. 1468
JACK'S WHOLESALE WINDOWS AND DESIGN; *U.S. Private*, pg. 2175
SECO ARCHITECTURAL SYSTEM; *U.S. Private*, pg. 3593
SOUTHEND EXTERIORS, INC.—See Professional Builders Supply, LLC; *U.S. Private*, pg. 3274
SOUTHERN SIDING COMPANY INC.; *U.S. Private*, pg. 3735
SPS CORPORATION; *U.S. Private*, pg. 3765
STEELMART, INC.; *U.S. Private*, pg. 3797
THERMAL TECH, INC.—See ABC Supply Co. Inc.; *U.S. Private*, pg. 36
THOMPSON BROOKS, INCORPORATED; *U.S. Private*, pg. 4158
TSI GLOBAL COMPANIES; *U.S. Private*, pg. 4253
US ALUMINUM SERVICES, CORP.; *U.S. Private*, pg. 4317
WEST SHORE WINDOW & DOOR, INC.; *U.S. Private*, pg. 4487

238190 — OTHER FOUNDATION, STRUCTURE, AND BUILDING EXTERIOR CONTRACTORS

AES CLEAN TECHNOLOGY INC.; *U.S. Private*, pg. 120
AUI, INC.; *U.S. Private*, pg. 392
BASF WALL SYSTEMS, INC.—See BASF SE; *Int'l*, pg. 875
BATENBURG TECHNIEK N.V.; *Int'l*, pg. 889
BAUER VIETNAM LTD.—See BAUER Aktiengesellschaft; *Int'l*, pg. 892
BHI ENERGY I SPECIALTY SERVICES LLC—See Bernhard Capital Partners Management, LP; *U.S. Private*, pg. 537
BILFINGER BERGER PARKING GMBH—See Bilfinger SE; *Int'l*, pg. 1024
BRYMOR CONTRACTORS LTD.; *Int'l*, pg. 1201
CHARLES H. HODGES & SON, INC.—See On-Point Group, LLC; *U.S. Private*, pg. 3018

238190 — OTHER FOUNDATION, S...

CMC REBAR—See Commercial Metals Company; *U.S. Public*, pg. 546
COMBINED GROUP CONTRACTING COMPANY KSCC; *Int'l*, pg. 1709
CONDON-JOHNSON & ASSOCIATES INC.; *U.S. Private*, pg. 1012
CONTRACT EXTERIORS LLC; *U.S. Private*, pg. 1032
CORNELL STOREFRONT SYSTEMS, INC.—See Griffon Corporation; *U.S. Public*, pg. 969
DALE INCORPORATED; *U.S. Private*, pg. 1148
DAVIAN CONSTRUCTION LTD.; *Int'l*, pg. 1983
DEEM STEEL; *U.S. Private*, pg. 1189
DIRECT EXTERIORS, INC.; *U.S. Private*, pg. 1235
D. L. KENNEY GENERAL CONTRACTORS INC.; *U.S. Private*, pg. 1140
DOUGLAS STEEL FABRICATING CORPORATION; *U.S. Private*, pg. 1267
DREXEL BUILDING SUPPLY; *U.S. Private*, pg. 1276
ECONPILE HOLDINGS BERHAD; *Int'l*, pg. 2298
ELITE CUSTOM EXTERIORS, INC.; *U.S. Private*, pg. 1360
EMERY & ASSOCIATES; *U.S. Private*, pg. 1382
ENEMAERKE & PETERSEN A/S—See Hojgaard Holding A/S; *Int'l*, pg. 3442
EVANS BROTHERS INC.; *U.S. Private*, pg. 1434
FAB-FORM INDUSTRIES LTD.; *Int'l*, pg. 2598
FIREGUARD LLC—See Align Capital Partners, LLC; *U.S. Private*, pg. 167
GARAGE DOOR STORE—See APi Group Corporation; *Int'l*, pg. 514
GENTEK BUILDING PRODUCTS LTD.; *Int'l*, pg. 2928
GOH KWANG HENG PTE LTD—See Chasen Holdings Limited; *Int'l*, pg. 1457
GOTTLIEB TESCH BAUUNTERNEHMEN GMBH; *Int'l*, pg. 3044
GRIFFIN PAVEMENT STRIPING, INC.—See The Sterling Group, L.P.; *U.S. Private*, pg. 4123
HEATHERBRAE INC; *Int'l*, pg. 3305
HUARONG INVESTMENT STOCK CORPORATION LIMITED—See China CITIC Financial Asset Management Co., Ltd.; *Int'l*, pg. 1489
JD STEEL CO. INC.; *U.S. Private*, pg. 2195
JES CONSTRUCTION, LLC; *U.S. Private*, pg. 2203
J. FLETCHER CREAMER & SON, INC.—See J. Fletcher Creamer & Son Inc.; *U.S. Private*, pg. 2156
LEONG HIN PILING (PTE) LTD—See Enviro-Hub Holdings Ltd.; *Int'l*, pg. 2454
LIGHTNING VENTURES INC.; *U.S. Private*, pg. 2453
MAJOR CLEAN, INC.—See Warburg Pincus LLC; *U.S. Private*, pg. 4440
MARIUS HANSEN FACADER A/S—See Hojgaard Holding A/S; *Int'l*, pg. 3442
MASONPRO, INC.—See The Sterling Group, L.P.; *U.S. Private*, pg. 4122
MCE GMBH—See HABAU Hoch- und Tiefbaugesellschaft m.b.H.; *Int'l*, pg. 3202
NASS SCAFFORM—See Abdulla Ahmed Nass Group WLL; *Int'l*, pg. 58
PARKING STRUCTURES, INC.—See R.W. Sidley, Incorporated; *U.S. Private*, pg. 3340
RAB FOUNDATION REPAIR LLC; *U.S. Private*, pg. 3341
REYTEC CONSTRUCTION RESOURCES, INC.; *U.S. Private*, pg. 3418
RPM STEEL INC.; *U.S. Private*, pg. 3495
SUN MECHANICAL CONTRACTING INC.; *U.S. Private*, pg. 3863
TERRE HILL COMPOSITES, INC.—See Terre Hill Concrete Products, Inc.; *U.S. Private*, pg. 3972
WALTERS & WOLF CURTAIN WALL, LLC—See Walters & Wolf; *U.S. Private*, pg. 4434
WELDING TECHNOLOGIES, INC.—See Babcock Power, Inc.; *U.S. Private*, pg. 422
WILLIAMS STEEL ERECTION CO., INC.—See Williams Industries, Inc.; *U.S. Private*, pg. 4526

238210 — ELECTRICAL CONTRACTORS AND OTHER WIRING INSTALLATION CONTRACTORS

066 059 809 PTY LIMITED—See BSA Limited; *Int'l*, pg. 1201
1901 GROUP, LLC—See Leidos Holdings, Inc.; *U.S. Public*, pg. 1304
4WALL ENTERTAINMENT, INC.; *U.S. Private*, pg. 15
55 WEST 17TH STREET PARTNERS LLC.—See Toll Brothers, Inc.; *U.S. Public*, pg. 2161
A-1 A-LECTRICIAN INC.; *U.S. Private*, pg. 21
ACCELERATE SOLAR LLC; *U.S. Private*, pg. 49
ACCESS CONTROL SYSTEMS, LLC—See Brixey & Meyer, Inc.; *U.S. Private*, pg. 658
A-C ELECTRIC COMPANY; *U.S. Private*, pg. 22
ADCO ELECTRICAL CORP.; *U.S. Private*, pg. 76
ADKINS ELECTRIC, INC.—See White Wolf Capital LLC; *U.S. Private*, pg. 4510
ADMAN ELECTRIC, INC.; *U.S. Private*, pg. 80
ADS SECURITY L.P.—See The Philadelphia Contributionship; *U.S. Private*, pg. 4094
ADVANCED AUTOMATED SYSTEMS, INC.—See Huron Capital Partners LLC; *U.S. Private*, pg. 2011

ADVANCED CABLE CONNECTION, INC.; *U.S. Private*, pg. 88
ADVANCED ELECTRIC SYSTEMS, LLC—See Quanta Services, Inc.; *U.S. Public*, pg. 1750
ADVANCED ELECTRONIC SYSTEMS INTEGRATORS, LLC; *U.S. Private*, pg. 89
ADVANCED POWER CONTROL INCORPORATED; *U.S. Private*, pg. 92
AERIAL LIGHTING & ELECTRIC INC.—See IES Holdings, Inc.; *U.S. Public*, pg. 1094
AERO COMMUNICATIONS, INC.—See Resilience Capital Partners, LLC; *U.S. Private*, pg. 3405
AES BULGARIA TRADING EOOD—See The AES Corporation; *U.S. Public*, pg. 2030
AES ELECTRICAL, INC.; *U.S. Private*, pg. 120
ALABAMA ELECTRIC COMPANY INC. OF DOTHAN; *U.S. Private*, pg. 148
AL-AHLIA INTEGRATED GENERAL TRADING & CONTRACTING CO. W.L.L—See Fouad Alghanim & Sons Group of Companies; *Int'l*, pg. 2753
ALAMON TELCO INCORPORATED; *U.S. Private*, pg. 149
ALBANY SOLAR LLC—See Enel S.p.A.; *Int'l*, pg. 2411
ALBARELL ELECTRIC INC.; *U.S. Private*, pg. 152
ALCAN ELECTRICAL & ENGINEERING; *U.S. Private*, pg. 153
ALDRIDGE ELECTRIC INC.; *U.S. Private*, pg. 160
ALFANAR TRADING CO.; *Int'l*, pg. 315
AL JABER ENERGY SERVICES—See Al Jaber Group; *Int'l*, pg. 279
ALL FLORIDA ELECTRIC COMPANY INC.; *U.S. Private*, pg. 170
ALLIANCE ENERGY LTD. - REGINA OFFICE—See Alliance Energy Ltd.; *Int'l*, pg. 338
ALLIANCE ENERGY LTD.; *Int'l*, pg. 338
ALLIANT INTEGRATORS, INC.—See Apollo Global Management, Inc.; *U.S. Public*, pg. 146
ALLIED COMMUNICATIONS INC—See Bertelsmann SE & Co. KGaA; *Int'l*, pg. 993
ALLIED ELECTRIC INC.; *U.S. Private*, pg. 185
ALLIS ELECTRIC CO., LTD.; *Int'l*, pg. 359
ALL STATE COMMUNICATIONS, INC.—See Arvig Enterprises, Inc.; *U.S. Private*, pg. 344
ALLTECK LINE CONTRACTORS INC.—See Quanta Services, Inc.; *U.S. Public*, pg. 1750
ALMAN ELECTRIC INC.; *U.S. Private*, pg. 195
ALMAN ELECTRIC; *U.S. Private*, pg. 195
ALMUNEEF CO.; *Int'l*, pg. 364
ALPINE POWER SYSTEMS INC.—See TFI Inc.; *U.S. Private*, pg. 3979
ALPIQ INTEC EAST LTD.—See Bouygues S.A.; *Int'l*, pg. 1123
ALTERMAN, INC.; *U.S. Private*, pg. 207
AM ELEKTRISKA AB—See Bravida Holding AB; *Int'l*, pg. 1142
AMERESCO FEDERAL SOLUTIONS, INC.—See Ameresco, Inc.; *U.S. Public*, pg. 95
AMERESCO LIMITED—See Ameresco, Inc.; *U.S. Public*, pg. 95
AMERESCO STAFFORD LLC—See Ameresco, Inc.; *U.S. Public*, pg. 95
AMERICAN ELECTRIC CO. LLC; *U.S. Private*, pg. 231
AMERICAN FIRE PROTECTION GROUP, INC.—See APi Group Corporation; *Int'l*, pg. 513
AMERICAN INTEGRATION CONTRACTORS, LLC; *U.S. Private*, pg. 238
AMERICAN SERVICE COMPANY—See The Riverside Company; *U.S. Private*, pg. 4107
AMF ELECTRICAL CONTRACTORS, INC.; *U.S. Private*, pg. 262
A.M. ORTEGA CONSTRUCTION INC.; *U.S. Private*, pg. 27
AMP ELECTRIC INC.—See Morse Electric Incorporated; *U.S. Private*, pg. 2790
AMPERE LIMITED; *Int'l*, pg. 433
AMPRITE ELECTRIC COMPANY INC.; *U.S. Private*, pg. 266
AMTECK OF KENTUCKY, LLC—See Comfort Systems USA, Inc.; *U.S. Public*, pg. 543
AMTEL HOLDINGS BERHAD; *Int'l*, pg. 442
ANDERSON ELECTRIC, INC.; *U.S. Private*, pg. 276
ANDERSON & HOWARD ELECTRIC, INC.; *U.S. Private*, pg. 275
ANELMARIN GEMI ELK. ELKT. SIS. TIC. VE SAN. A.S.—See Anel Electrical Project Contracting Trade Inc.; *Int'l*, pg. 458
ANS ADVANCED NETWORK SERVICES, LLC—See Charge Enterprises, Inc.; *U.S. Public*, pg. 479
APEX ELECTRIC—See Motor City Electric Co., Inc.; *U.S. Private*, pg. 2796
APG ELECTRIC INC.; *U.S. Private*, pg. 293
API NATIONAL SERVICE GROUP—See APi Group Corporation; *Int'l*, pg. 513
API SYSTEMS GROUP, INC.—See APi Group Corporation; *Int'l*, pg. 513
ARCO ELECTRIC, INC.; *U.S. Private*, pg. 315
ARCON ELECTRIC, LLC—See ARCON Construction & Management Services, Inc.; *U.S. Private*, pg. 315
ARDENT SERVICES, LLC—See EMCOR Group, Inc.; *U.S. Public*, pg. 736

AREA ENERGY AND ELECTRIC INC.; *U.S. Private*, pg. 317
AREA ENERGY & ELECTRIC, INC.; *U.S. Private*, pg. 317
ARROW ELECTRIC CO. INC.; *U.S. Private*, pg. 335
ARROW ELECTRONICS AUSTRALIA PTY LTD.—See Arrow Electronics, Inc.; *U.S. Public*, pg. 196
ASCHINGER ELECTRIC CO.; *U.S. Private*, pg. 348
ASCOM-HG, LLC—See Huizenga Manufacturing Group, Inc.; *U.S. Private*, pg. 2004
ASIAMOST SDN. BHD.—See AME Elite Consortium Berhad; *Int'l*, pg. 420
A.S.R. ELECTRICAL CONTRACTING; *U.S. Private*, pg. 28
ASTRAKHAN POWER SALE COMPANY PAO; *Int'l*, pg. 658
ATCOM, INC.; *U.S. Private*, pg. 365
ATLANTIC ELECTRIC, LLC—See Comfort Systems USA, Inc.; *U.S. Public*, pg. 543
ATLAS ALARM CORPORATION; *U.S. Private*, pg. 375
ATLAS INDUSTRIAL CONTRACTORS, LLC; *U.S. Private*, pg. 378
ATON PROJECTS V.O.F.—See E.ON SE; *Int'l*, pg. 2251
ATS ELECTRIC, INC.; *U.S. Private*, pg. 382
ATS TRAINING, LLC.; *U.S. Private*, pg. 382
AUSTIN TRAFFIC SIGNAL CONSTRUCTION CO., LP; *U.S. Private*, pg. 396
AUTOMATED GATE SERVICES, INC.—See Aurora Capital Group, LLC; *U.S. Private*, pg. 394
AVATEL TECHNOLOGIES, INC.; *U.S. Private*, pg. 404
AVENIR ELECTRIQUE DE LIMOGES; *Int'l*, pg. 738
AVIATION CONSTRUCTORS, INC.—See Cleveland Group, Inc.; *U.S. Private*, pg. 941
AVIO, INC.—See General Electric Company; *U.S. Public*, pg. 916
AWC BERHAD; *Int'l*, pg. 752
AZBIL CONTROL SOLUTIONS (SHANGHAI) CO., LTD.—See Azbil Corporation; *Int'l*, pg. 777
AZBIL PHILIPPINES CORPORATION—See Azbil Corporation; *Int'l*, pg. 777
AZBIL SINGAPORE PTE. LTD.—See Azbil Corporation; *Int'l*, pg. 777
AZTEC COMMUNICATIONS LTD.; *Int'l*, pg. 415
AZTECH ELECTRIC INC.; *U.S. Private*, pg. 416
BAKER INSTALLATIONS INC.; *U.S. Private*, pg. 456
BALLARD COMPANIES, INC.; *U.S. Private*, pg. 460
BARSPLICE PRODUCTS, INC.—See F.C. Industries Inc.; *U.S. Private*, pg. 1456
BAY ELECTRIC COMPANY, INC.; *U.S. Private*, pg. 492
BAY HILL CONTRACTING LTD.; *Int'l*, pg. 901
BAYSWATER DEVELOPMENT CORPORATION—See The Goldfield Corporation; *U.S. Public*, pg. 2075
BAYVIEW ELECTRIC COMPANY, LLC.; *U.S. Private*, pg. 497
BAYWA R.E. SOLAR SYSTEMS GMBH—See BayWa AG; *Int'l*, pg. 916
BEACH ELECTRIC COMPANY INC.—See Railroad Construction Company, Inc.; *U.S. Private*, pg. 3346
BEAVER ELECTRICAL MACHINERY LTD.; *Int'l*, pg. 935
BECKSTROM ELECTRIC; *U.S. Private*, pg. 511
BE.MAINTENANCE—See Ackermans & van Haaren NV; *Int'l*, pg. 105
BENFIELD ELECTRIC COMPANY, INC.; *U.S. Private*, pg. 525
BERG ELECTRIC CORPORATION; *U.S. Private*, pg. 530
BERGSTROM ELECTRIC INC.; *U.S. Private*, pg. 531
BERTKE INVESTMENTS, INC.; *U.S. Private*, pg. 539
BETA ENGINEERING LLC—See Crest Industries, LLC; *U.S. Private*, pg. 1096
BEZAIRE ELECTRIC INC.; *U.S. Private*, pg. 548
B&G ELECTRICAL CONTRACTORS OF NY—See B&G Industries, Ltd.; *U.S. Private*, pg. 418
B&G INDUSTRIES, LTD.; *U.S. Private*, pg. 418
B & I CONTRACTORS, INC.; *U.S. Private*, pg. 417
BIG STATE ELECTRIC LTD.; *U.S. Private*, pg. 554
BILLSAVE UK LIMITED; *Int'l*, pg. 1031
BILLS ELECTRIC, INC.; *U.S. Private*, pg. 559
B.J. BALDWIN ELECTRIC INC.; *U.S. Private*, pg. 420
BLACK BOX AB—See Black Box Limited; *Int'l*, pg. 1056
BLACK BOX NETWORK SERVICES SDN. BHD.—See Black Box Limited; *Int'l*, pg. 1058
BLACK BOX NETWORK SERVICES S.R.L.—See Black Box Limited; *Int'l*, pg. 1058
BLACK BOX SERVICES RESEAUX MEDITERRANEE—See Black Box Limited; *Int'l*, pg. 1058
BLACK ELECTRIC, INC.—See Hull Street Energy, LLC; *U.S. Private*, pg. 2005
BLACKHAWK NEFF INC.; *U.S. Private*, pg. 575
BLACK & MCDONALD LIMITED; *Int'l*, pg. 1056
BLOCK ELECTRIC CO. INC.; *U.S. Private*, pg. 582
BLOOM & WAKE LTD; *Int'l*, pg. 1065
BLUEWATER POWER DISTRIBUTION CORPORATION; *Int'l*, pg. 1075
BLUE WAVE COMMUNICATIONS, LLC—See Dosal Capital, LLC; *U.S. Private*, pg. 1264
BOSH GLOBAL SERVICES, INC.—See MAG DS Corp.; *U.S. Public*, pg. 2545
BOUYGUES E&S INTEC ITALIA SPA—See Bouygues S.A.; *Int'l*, pg. 1123
BOUYGUES E&S INTEC SCHWEIZ AG—See Bouygues S.A.; *Int'l*, pg. 1123

N.A.I.C.S. INDEX

238210 — ELECTRICAL CONTRACT...

BOUYGUES E&S INTEC SCHWEIZ AG—See Bouygues S.A.; *Int'l*, pg. 1123
THE BOWLIN GROUP LLC; *U.S. Private*, pg. 3998
BOYKIN CONTRACTING, INC.; *U.S. Private*, pg. 628
BOZ ELECTRICAL CONTRACTORS, INC.; *U.S. Private*, pg. 629
BRAUN ELECTRIC COMPANY INCORPORATED; *U.S. Private*, pg. 641
BRENNAN ELECTRIC, LLC—See Area Energy & Electric, Inc.; *U.S. Private*, pg. 317
BRENT WOODWARD, INC.—See Quanta Services, Inc.; *U.S. Public*, pg. 1750
BRIGGS ELECTRIC INC.; *U.S. Private*, pg. 651
BRIGHTEK OPTOELECTRONIC CO., LTD.; *Int'l*, pg. 1162
BRINK CONSTRUCTORS, INC.; *U.S. Private*, pg. 654
BRITT RICE ELECTRIC LP.; *U.S. Private*, pg. 657
BROADBAND SPECIALIST; *U.S. Private*, pg. 658
BROADWAY ELECTRIC SERVICE CORPORATION; *U.S. Private*, pg. 660
BROOKS AUTOMATION (GERMANY) GMBH—See Azenta, Inc.; *U.S. Public*, pg. 257
BROOKS AUTOMATION (SINGAPORE), PTE LTD.—See Azenta, Inc.; *U.S. Public*, pg. 257
BROTJE AUTOMATION GMBH—See Claas KGaA mbH; *Int'l*, pg. 1640
BRYANT-DURHAM ELECTRIC CO., INC.; *U.S. Private*, pg. 673
BRYANT-DURHAM SERVICES INC.—See Bryant-Durham Electric Co., Inc.; *U.S. Private*, pg. 674
BUFFALO GAP INSTRUMENTATION & ELECTRICAL CO., INC.—See Sunland Construction Inc.; *U.S. Private*, pg. 3868
BW ELECTRICAL SERVICES LLC—See Charge Enterprises, Inc.; *U.S. Public*, pg. 478
BYTEWISE MEASUREMENT SYSTEMS—See Middle-Ground Management, LP; *U.S. Private*, pg. 2713
C2 BLOCKCHAIN, INC.; *U.S. Public*, pg. 415
C2CE PTY, LTD.—See Westinghouse Air Brake Technologies Corporation; *U.S. Public*, pg. 2357
CABLE CONNECTORS, LLC—See Dycom Industries, Inc.; *U.S. Public*, pg. 698
CABLENET SERVICES UNLIMITED, LLC—See Resilience Capital Partners, LLC; *U.S. Private*, pg. 3405
CACHE VALLEY ELECTRIC COMPANY INC. - AVTEC SYSTEMS INTEGRATOR DIVISION—See Cache Valley Electric Company Inc.; *U.S. Private*, pg. 712
CACHE VALLEY ELECTRIC COMPANY INC.; *U.S. Private*, pg. 712
CACHE VALLEY ELECTRIC COMPANY INC.—See Cache Valley Electric Company Inc.; *U.S. Private*, pg. 712
CAN-AM COMMUNICATIONS, INC.—See Dycom Industries, Inc.; *U.S. Public*, pg. 698
CAN-FER UTILITY SERVICES, LLC—See Quanta Services, Inc.; *U.S. Public*, pg. 1750
CANNON & WENDT ELECTRIC CO.; *U.S. Private*, pg. 734
CANONBIE CONTRACTING LIMITED—See Aecon Group Inc.; *Int'l*, pg. 172
CAPITAL CITY CONTROLS—See Harris Companies; *U.S. Private*, pg. 1869
CAPITAL COMMUNICATION SERVICES, INC.; *U.S. Private*, pg. 739
CAPITAL ELECTRIC CONSTRUCTION COMPANY INC.; *U.S. Private*, pg. 739
CAPITAL ELECTRIC CONSTRUCTION COMPANY, INC.—See MDU Resources Group, Inc.; *U.S. Public*, pg. 1410
CARL T. MADSEN INC.; *U.S. Private*, pg. 763
CAROL ELECTRIC COMPANY INC.; *U.S. Private*, pg. 766
CARR AND DUFF INC.; *U.S. Private*, pg. 771
CASSON-MARK CORP.; *U.S. Private*, pg. 784
CAT SPEC, LTD.—See Quanta Services, Inc.; *U.S. Public*, pg. 1750
CAVANAUGH ELECTRICAL CONTRACTING, INC.; *U.S. Private*, pg. 795
CDL ELECTRIC COMPANY, INC.; *U.S. Private*, pg. 802
CEDAR CREEK ENERGY CORPORATION; *U.S. Private*, pg. 804
CENTER LINE ELECTRIC INC.; *U.S. Private*, pg. 811
CENTRAL MECHANICAL CONSTRUCTION CO., INC.—See EMCOR Group, Inc.; *U.S. Public*, pg. 736
CENTRELEC; *Int'l*, pg. 1411
CF MCDONALD ELECTRIC INC.; *U.S. Private*, pg. 843
CFS SERVICE CORPORATION; *U.S. Private*, pg. 844
CGN POWER CO., LTD.; *Int'l*, pg. 1435
CHEMCO ELECTRICAL CONTRACTORS LTD.; *Int'l*, pg. 1461
CHEWNING & WILMER INCORPORATED; *U.S. Private*, pg. 876
CHICKASAW TELECOM, INC.—See Chickasaw Holding Company; *U.S. Private*, pg. 880
CHN ELECTRICAL SERVICES LIMITED—See E.ON SE; *Int'l*, pg. 2256
CH REYNOLDS, INC.; *U.S. Private*, pg. 844
CHRISTENSON ELECTRIC, INC.; *U.S. Private*, pg. 890
CHUDENKO ELETECH YAMAGUCHI CO., LTD.—See Chudenko Corporation; *Int'l*, pg. 1594
CHULA VISTA ELECTRIC CO.; *U.S. Private*, pg. 894

CHURCH & MURDOCK ELECTRIC, INC.; *U.S. Private*, pg. 894
CITY SECURITY COMPANY LIMITED—See Asia Allied Infrastructure Holdings Limited; *Int'l*, pg. 610
CLAWSON COMMUNICATIONS INC.; *U.S. Private*, pg. 917
CLEVELAND ELECTRIC CO.—See Cleveland Group, Inc.; *U.S. Private*, pg. 941
COAX FIBER SOLUTIONS, LLC—See Orbital Infrastructure Group, Inc.; *U.S. Public*, pg. 1615
COBRA CHILE, S.A.—See ACS, Actividades de Construccion y Servicios, S.A.; *Int'l*, pg. 110
COBRA SERVICIOS AUXILIARES, S.A.—See ACS, Actividades de Construccion y Servicios, S.A.; *Int'l*, pg. 110
COBRA SISTEMAS DE SEGURIDAD, S.A.—See ACS, Actividades de Construccion y Servicios, S.A.; *Int'l*, pg. 110
COBRA SISTEMAS Y REDES, S.A.—See ACS, Actividades de Construccion y Servicios, S.A.; *Int'l*, pg. 110
COCHRAN INC.; *U.S. Private*, pg. 959
C. O. CHRISTIAN & SONS COMPANY, INC.; *U.S. Private*, pg. 705
COFFMAN & COMPANY GROUP—See The SEER Group LLC; *U.S. Private*, pg. 4115
COGHLIN CONSTRUCTION SERVICE; *U.S. Private*, pg. 962
COLLIGNON ENG SA - LIEGE DIVISION—See Eiffage S.A.; *Int'l*, pg. 2329
COLLIGNON ENG SA—See Eiffage S.A.; *Int'l*, pg. 2329
COLLINS ELECTRICAL COMPANY; *U.S. Private*, pg. 969
COLLINS ELECTRIC COMPANY, INC. - BERKSHIRE DIVISION—See Collins Electric Company, Inc.; *U.S. Private*, pg. 969
COLLINS ELECTRIC COMPANY, INC.; *U.S. Private*, pg. 969
COLWILL ENGINEERING, INC.; *U.S. Private*, pg. 980
COMDESIGN INC.; *U.S. Private*, pg. 981
COMINTEL CORPORATION BERHAD; *Int'l*, pg. 1714
COMMONWEALTH ELECTRICAL TECHNOLOGIES, INC.—See Aterian Investment Management, L.P.; *U.S. Private*, pg. 366
COMMONWEALTH ELECTRIC COMPANY OF THE MIDWEST INC.; *U.S. Private*, pg. 986
COMMUNICATION COMPANY OF SOUTH BEND, INC.; *U.S. Private*, pg. 988
COMM-WORKS, LLC - INDIANAPOLIS—See Comm-Works, LLC; *U.S. Private*, pg. 982
COMNET COMMUNICATIONS LLC; *U.S. Private*, pg. 997
COMPUTER CABLE CONNECTION INC.; *U.S. Private*, pg. 1004
COMPUTER PROTECTION TECHNOLOGY, INC.—See Hyosung Heavy Industries Corp.; *Int'l*, pg. 3552
COMSIP AL A'ALI W.L.L.—See Ahmed Mansoor Al-A'ali Co.; *Int'l*, pg. 225
COMSIP AL A'ALI W.L.L.—See Ahmed Mansoor Al-A'ali Co.; *Int'l*, pg. 225
THE COMTRAN GROUP INC; *U.S. Private*, pg. 4013
CONCORD CORPORATION PTE LTD—See Hollysys Automation Technologies Ltd.; *Int'l*, pg. 3452
CONSTRUCTION MANAGEMENT SERVICE; *U.S. Private*, pg. 1023
CONSULTING & BANKING & ADMINISTRATIVE SERVICES, LTD.—See Brithol Michcoma Mozambique Limited; *Int'l*, pg. 1165
CONTECH MSI CO.—See Kelso-Burnett Company; *U.S. Private*, pg. 2281
CONTI ELECTRIC INC.; *U.S. Private*, pg. 1028
CONTINENTAL ELECTRIC CONSTRUCTION COMPANY; *U.S. Private*, pg. 1028
CONTRA COSTA ELECTRIC, INC.—See EMCOR Group, Inc.; *U.S. Public*, pg. 736
CONTRACTING ENTERPRISES, LLC—See Cadent Energy Partners, LLC; *U.S. Private*, pg. 713
CONTROL CONTRACTORS, INC.; *U.S. Private*, pg. 1034
CONTROL INSTALLATIONS OF IOWA, INC.; *U.S. Private*, pg. 1034
CONTROL Y MONTAJES INDUSTRIALES CYMI, S.A.—See ACS, Actividades de Construccion y Servicios, S.A.; *Int'l*, pg. 111
CONUNDRUM TECHNOLOGIES; *U.S. Private*, pg. 1035
COX FIRE PROTECTION, INC.—See Pye-Barker Fire & Safety, LLC; *U.S. Private*, pg. 3309
CRANNEY COMPANIES, INC.—See Koch Industries, Inc.; *U.S. Private*, pg. 2327
CRANNEY COMPANIES, INC.—See The Goldman Sachs Group, Inc.; *U.S. Public*, pg. 2076
CRESTONE SERVICES GROUP LLC; *U.S. Private*, pg. 1097
CROSBY ELECTRIC COMPANY, INC.; *U.S. Private*, pg. 1103
C & R SYSTEMS, INC.; *U.S. Private*, pg. 701
CRUX SUBSURFACE INC.—See Quanta Services, Inc.; *U.S. Public*, pg. 1750
CSE-EIS PTE LTD—See CSE Global Ltd.; *Int'l*, pg. 1863
CSE-GLOBAL (AUSTRALIA) PTY LTD—See CSE Global Ltd.; *Int'l*, pg. 1863
CSE-IAP PTE LTD—See CSE Global Ltd.; *Int'l*, pg. 1863
CSE SYSTEMS & ENGINEERING (INDIA) PVT LIMITED—See CSE Global Ltd.; *Int'l*, pg. 1863

CSE-UNISERVE CORPORATION PTY LTD—See CSE Global Ltd.; *Int'l*, pg. 1863
CSI ELECTRICAL CONTRACTORS, INC.—See MYR Group Inc.; *U.S. Public*, pg. 1488
CSI POWERLINE; *U.S. Private*, pg. 1117
CSRWARE, INC.—See BC Partners LLP; *Int'l*, pg. 925
CUPERTINO ELECTRIC, INC.—See Quanta Services, Inc.; *U.S. Public*, pg. 1750
CUPERTINO ELECTRIC, INC.—See Quanta Services, Inc.; *U.S. Public*, pg. 1751
CUPERTINO ELECTRIC, INC.—See Quanta Services, Inc.; *U.S. Public*, pg. 1751
CURRY CONTROLS COMPANY INC.; *U.S. Private*, pg. 1125
CUSTOM ELECTRIC LTD.; *Int'l*, pg. 1880
DAI-DAN CO LTD; *Int'l*, pg. 1917
DAI-DAN PHILIPPINES, INC.—See DAI-DAN Co Ltd; *Int'l*, pg. 1917
DAIDONE ELECTRICAL INC.; *U.S. Private*, pg. 1145
DAINICHI TSUSHIN CO., LTD.—See COMSYS Holdings Corporation; *Int'l*, pg. 1761
DAIWA DENSETSU CORP.—See EXEO Group Inc.; *Int'l*, pg. 2583
DAKA SERVIS A.D.; *Int'l*, pg. 1950
DALLAS SIGHT AND SOUND, INC.—See Echo Group, Inc.; *U.S. Private*, pg. 1327
DASHIELL CORPORATION—See Quanta Services, Inc.; *U.S. Public*, pg. 1751
DATA SPECIALTIES INC.; *U.S. Private*, pg. 1163
DAUSIN ELECTRIC CO.; *U.S. Private*, pg. 1168
D & D POWER INC.—See Bernhard Capital Partners Management, LP; *U.S. Private*, pg. 537
DEAN JOHNSTON INC.; *U.S. Private*, pg. 1184
DEEP BLUE COMMUNICATIONS, LLC—See Comcast Corporation; *U.S. Public*, pg. 538
DELL-COMM INC.; *U.S. Private*, pg. 1197
DEL MONTE ELECTRIC CO. INC.; *U.S. Private*, pg. 1192
DELTA DIVERSIFIED ENTERPRISES INC.; *U.S. Private*, pg. 1200
DENIER ELECTRIC CO. INC.; *U.S. Private*, pg. 1205
DEPENDABLE HOMETECH—See Creative Vistas Inc.; *Int'l*, pg. 1834
DESERT COMMUNICATIONS, INC.; *U.S. Private*, pg. 1212
DESERT FIRE PROTECTION, INC.—See MDU Resources Group, Inc.; *U.S. Public*, pg. 1410
DESIGN ELECTRIC INC.; *U.S. Private*, pg. 1213
DIAMOND ELECTRONICS LLC—See Pye-Barker Fire & Safety, LLC; *U.S. Private*, pg. 3309
DIAMOND P ENTERPRISES, INC.; *U.S. Private*, pg. 1223
DILLIE & KUHN, INC.—See Crestone Services Group LLC; *U.S. Private*, pg. 1097
DIRECT LINE COMMUNICATIONS; *U.S. Private*, pg. 1235
DIVANE BROS. ELECTRIC COMPANY; *U.S. Private*, pg. 1240
DMW ELECTRICAL INSTRUMENTATION INC.; *Int'l*, pg. 2147
D&N ELECTRIC COMPANY; *U.S. Private*, pg. 1138
DOLEAC ELECTRIC COMPANY INCORPORATED; *U.S. Private*, pg. 1254
DOMINION NUCLEAR CONNECTICUT, INC.—See Dominion Energy, Inc.; *U.S. Public*, pg. 674
DOREY ELECTRIC COMPANY; *U.S. Private*, pg. 1262
DOYLE ELECTRIC SERVICES INC.; *U.S. Private*, pg. 1270
DOYON UTILITIES, LLC.; *U.S. Private*, pg. 1270
DRAKE & SCULL INTERNATIONAL PJSC; *Int'l*, pg. 2200
DSG INTERNATIONAL BELGIUM BVBA—See Currys plc; *Int'l*, pg. 1879
DSP TECHNOLOGY—See Synaptics Incorporated; *U.S. Public*, pg. 1969
DUNN ELECTRIC CO.; *U.S. Private*, pg. 1290
DURO ELECTRIC, LLC—See MDU Resources Group, Inc.; *U.S. Public*, pg. 1410
DURR SYSTEMS GMBH—See Durr AG; *Int'l*, pg. 2231
DYNALECTRIC COMPANY OF COLORADO—See EMCOR Group, Inc.; *U.S. Public*, pg. 736
DYNALECTRIC COMPANY OF NEVADA—See EMCOR Group, Inc.; *U.S. Public*, pg. 736
DYNALECTRIC COMPANY OF OHIO—See EMCOR Group, Inc.; *U.S. Public*, pg. 736
DYNALECTRIC COMPANY—See EMCOR Group, Inc.; *U.S. Public*, pg. 736
DYNALECTRIC - FLORIDA—See EMCOR Group, Inc.; *U.S. Public*, pg. 736
DYNALECTRIC - GEORGIA—See EMCOR Group, Inc.; *U.S. Public*, pg. 736
DYNALECTRIC - LOS ANGELES—See EMCOR Group, Inc.; *U.S. Public*, pg. 736
DYNALECTRIC - OREGON—See EMCOR Group, Inc.; *U.S. Public*, pg. 736
DYNALECTRIC - SAN DIEGO—See EMCOR Group, Inc.; *U.S. Public*, pg. 736
DYNAMIC CONTROLS, INC.—See Daikin Industries, Ltd.; *Int'l*, pg. 1936
DYNA TEN MAINTENANCE SERVICES, LLC—See Comfort Systems USA, Inc.; *U.S. Public*, pg. 544
E-3 ELECTRICAL; *U.S. Private*, pg. 1302
EAB ELEKTROANLAGENBAU GMBH RHEIN/MAIN—See CEZ, a.s.; *Int'l*, pg. 1427

238210 — ELECTRICAL CONTRACT...

EAPEC HIROSHIMA CO., LTD.—See Chudenko Corporation; *Int'l*, pg. 1594
EAST COURT PROPERTIES LLC.; *U.S. Private*, pg. 1316
EASTERN INSTRUMENT LABORATORIES, INC.; *U.S. Private*, pg. 1320
E A TECHNICAL SERVICES, INC.—See Dycom Industries, Inc.; *U.S. Public*, pg. 698
EC COMPANY INC.; *U.S. Private*, pg. 1326
E.C. ERNST, INC.—See The Philadelphia Bourse, Inc.; *U.S. Private*, pg. 4094
E.C. ERNST SOUTH EAST—See The Philadelphia Bourse, Inc.; *U.S. Private*, pg. 4094
ECKARDT ELECTRIC COMPANY, INC.; *U.S. Private*, pg. 1327
ECOMARK ENERGY, INC.; *U.S. Private*, pg. 1329
ECOS HOKUEI CORP.—See EXEO Group Inc.; *Int'l*, pg. 2583
EDD HELMS ELECTRICAL, INC.—See Edd Helms Group, Inc.; *U.S. Public*, pg. 717
EDD HELMS GROUP, INC.; *U.S. Public*, pg. 717
EDUSERVE INTERNATIONAL LIMITED—See i-Control Holdings Limited; *Int'l*, pg. 3563
EDWARDS ELECTRICAL & MECHANICAL, INC.—See Comfort Systems USA, Inc.; *U.S. Public*, pg. 544
EDWARD W. SCOTT ELECTRIC CO.; *U.S. Private*, pg. 1341
EDWIN L. HEIM COMPANY INC.; *U.S. Private*, pg. 1342
EEI HOLDING CORPORATION; *U.S. Private*, pg. 1343
EF&I SERVICES CORP.—See Willcrest Partners; *U.S. Private*, pg. 4521
EGAN AUTOMATION, INC.—See The Egan Companies; *U.S. Private*, pg. 4025
EGAN ELECTRICAL CONTRACTORS—See The Egan Companies; *U.S. Private*, pg. 4025
EGCO ENGINEERING AND SERVICE CO. LTD—See EGAT Public Company Limited; *Int'l*, pg. 2322
EG COMPONETS NORWAY AS—See Amplex AB; *Int'l*, pg. 434
EG ELECTRONICS AB—See Amplex AB; *Int'l*, pg. 434
EGG ELECTRIC INC.; *U.S. Private*, pg. 1344
EGIZII ELECTRIC, INC.—See EEI Holding Corporation; *U.S. Private*, pg. 1343
EHV POWER ULC—See Quanta Services, Inc.; *U.S. Public*, pg. 1751
EIFFAGE ENERGIA S.L.—See Eiffage S.A.; *Int'l*, pg. 2330
EIFFAGE ENERGIE CENTRE-EST—See Eiffage S.A.; *Int'l*, pg. 2330
EIFFAGE ENERGIE ELECTRONIQUE S.A.S.—See Eiffage S.A.; *Int'l*, pg. 2330
EIFFAGE ENERGIE ILE-DE-FRANCE—See Eiffage S.A.; *Int'l*, pg. 2330
EIFFAGE ENERGIE THERMIE S.A.S.—See Eiffage S.A.; *Int'l*, pg. 2330
EII INC.; *U.S. Private*, pg. 1347
EJ ELECTRIC INSTALLATION CO.; *U.S. Private*, pg. 1348
EKB GROEP B.V.—See Eiffage S.A.; *Int'l*, pg. 2329
ELB POWER SYSTEMS LIMITED—See ELB Group Limited; *Int'l*, pg. 2343
ELDECO, INC.—See Comfort Systems USA, Inc.; *U.S. Public*, pg. 544
ELDRIDGE ELECTRIC CO.; *U.S. Private*, pg. 1351
ELECTRICAL CONSTRUCTION & MAINTENANCE AUSTRALIA PTY LTD - FABRICATION FACILITY—See Electrical Construction & Maintenance Australia Pty Ltd; *Int'l*, pg. 2349
ELECTRICAL CONSTRUCTION & MAINTENANCE AUSTRALIA PTY LTD; *Int'l*, pg. 2349
ELECTRICAL CONTRACTORS, INC.; *U.S. Private*, pg. 1352
ELECTRICAL CORP. AMERICA INC.; *U.S. Private*, pg. 1352
ELECTRICAL SYSTEMS AND INSTRUMENTATION, INC.; *U.S. Private*, pg. 1353
ELECTRICAL SYSTEMS INC.—See Monico Inc.; *U.S. Private*, pg. 2770
ELECTRICITE G. BUGNARD SA—See BKW AG; *Int'l*, pg. 1055
ELECTRO-COMMUNICATIONS CO.; *U.S. Private*, pg. 1354
ELECTROCONSTRUCTIA ELCO TIMISOARA S.A.; *Int'l*, pg. 2353
ELECTRO MANAGEMENT CORPORATION; *U.S. Private*, pg. 1353
ELECTROMUR, S.A.—See ACS, Actividades de Construccion y Servicios, S.A.; *Int'l*, pg. 111
ELECTRONIC CONTROL SYSTEMS, INC.—See Huron Capital Partners LLC; *U.S. Private*, pg. 2011
ELECTRONIC MICRO SYSTEMS INC.—See Halma plc; *Int'l*, pg. 3231
ELEKTRIM-MEGADEX S.A.—See Elektrim S.A.; *Int'l*, pg. 2356
ELEKTRIM-VOLT S.A.—See Elektrim S.A.; *Int'l*, pg. 2356
ELEKTRO-DECKER GMBH—See CEZ, a.s.; *Int'l*, pg. 1427
ELEKTRO FEUZ AG—See BKW AG; *Int'l*, pg. 1055
ELEKTRO GRUPA D.D.; *Int'l*, pg. 2356
ELEKTROMONT A.D.; *Int'l*, pg. 2357
ELEKTROTIM S.A.; *Int'l*, pg. 2357
ELETTROPIEMME S.R.L.—See Gefran S.p.A.; *Int'l*, pg. 2912

ELGAR ELECTRIC LTD.; *Int'l*, pg. 2359
ELKOP S.A.; *Int'l*, pg. 2364
ELLIOTT COMPANY; *U.S. Private*, pg. 1364
ELMONT A.D.; *Int'l*, pg. 2367
ELOMECH ELEKTROANLAGEN GMBH—See Eiffage S.A.; *Int'l*, pg. 2331
EL-TEKNIK I GAVLE AB—See Bravida Holding AB; *Int'l*, pg. 1142
EMCOR INTERNATIONAL, INC.—See EMCOR Group, Inc.; *U.S. Public*, pg. 737
EMC PUBLIC COMPANY LIMITED; *Int'l*, pg. 2376
EMERA UTILITY SERVICES INC.—See Emera, Inc.; *Int'l*, pg. 2377
EMORY ELECTRIC INC.; *U.S. Private*, pg. 1383
EMPIRE ELECTRIC MAINTENANCE & SERVICE, INC.—See The Carlyle Group Inc.; *U.S. Public*, pg. 2053
EMPRESA DE ALUMBRADO ELECTRICO DE CEUTA ENERGIA S.L.U.—See Enel S.p.A.; *Int'l*, pg. 2411
ENAP SA—See APS Energia SA; *Int'l*, pg. 522
ENERGIAS AMBIENTALES DE NOVO, S.A.—See ACS, Actividades de Construccion y Servicios, S.A.; *Int'l*, pg. 112
ENERGOAPARATURA S.A.; *Int'l*, pg. 2420
ENERGY ALTERNATIVES, INC.—See Dakota Electric Association; *U.S. Private*, pg. 1147
ENERGY ERECTORS, INC.; *Int'l*, pg. 1395
ENERGY OPTIONS, INC.—See Huron Capital Partners LLC; *U.S. Private*, pg. 2011
ENERGY SOURCE, LLC—See Revolution Lighting Technologies, Inc.; *U.S. Public*, pg. 1793
ENERNOC GMBH—See Enel S.p.A.; *Int'l*, pg. 2413
ENERNOC KOREA LIMITED—See Enel S.p.A.; *Int'l*, pg. 2413
ENERNOC UK LIMITED—See Enel S.p.A.; *Int'l*, pg. 2413
ENE SYSTEMS INC.; *U.S. Private*, pg. 1392
ENGEMA MONTAGE—See Ackermans & van Haaren NV; *Int'l*, pg. 105
ENGEMA SA/NV—See Ackermans & van Haaren NV; *Int'l*, pg. 105
ENGINEERING ASSOCIATES, INC.—See Dycom Industries, Inc.; *U.S. Public*, pg. 698
ENTECH SALES & SERVICE, INC.; *U.S. Private*, pg. 1402
ENTELIOS AG—See Enel S.p.A.; *Int'l*, pg. 2413
ENTERPRISE ELECTRICAL, INC.; *U.S. Private*, pg. 1403
ENVIPROSYSTEMS S.A.—See Edrasis - C. Psallidas S.A.; *Int'l*, pg. 2315
ENVIRONMENTAL CONTROLS CORP.; *U.S. Private*, pg. 1407
EP TECHNOLOGY CORPORATION; *U.S. Private*, pg. 1411
EQUIPOS DE SENALIZACION Y CONTROL, S.A.—See ACS, Actividades de Construccion y Servicios, S.A.; *Int'l*, pg. 112
ERB ELECTRIC CO.; *U.S. Private*, pg. 1417
ERMCO, INC.; *U.S. Private*, pg. 1421
ERVIN CABLE CONSTRUCTION, LLC—See Dycom Industries, Inc.; *U.S. Public*, pg. 698
E.S. BOULOS COMPANY—See MYR Group Inc.; *U.S. Public*, pg. 1489
E.S. BOULOS COMPANY - UTILITIES DIVISION—See MYR Group Inc.; *U.S. Public*, pg. 1489
ESCO ENERGY SERVICES COMPANY—See The Southern Company; *U.S. Public*, pg. 2131
ESCO GROUP; *U.S. Private*, pg. 1425
ESI DAYTON—See MDU Resources Group, Inc.; *U.S. Public*, pg. 1410
ESI, INC.—See MDU Resources Group, Inc.; *U.S. Public*, pg. 1410
ETEC SA—See Ackermans & van Haaren NV; *Int'l*, pg. 105
ETRA INTERANDINA, S.A.—See ACS, Actividades de Construccion y Servicios, S.A.; *Int'l*, pg. 112
ETRALUX, S.A.—See ACS, Actividades de Construccion y Servicios, S.A.; *Int'l*, pg. 112
ETRANORTE, S.A.—See ACS, Actividades de Construccion y Servicios, S.A.; *Int'l*, pg. 112
EUROFINS SEPO SP. Z O.O.—See Eurofins Scientific S.E.; *Int'l*, pg. 2547
EUROKLIMAT SP. Z O.O.—See CEZ, a.s.; *Int'l*, pg. 1427
EURO MECHANICAL & ELECTRICAL CONTRACTORS LTD.; *Int'l*, pg. 2531
EUROPE VISION SYSTEMS S.R.O.—See GeoVision Inc.; *Int'l*, pg. 2942
EUS COMMUNICATION INC.; *U.S. Private*, pg. 1434
EVERWARM LIMITED—See Cap10 Partners LLP; *Int'l*, pg. 1301
E.W. AUDET & SONS, INC.; *U.S. Private*, pg. 1307
EXCELLENCE ENGINEERING, LLC—See Bowman Consulting Group Ltd.; *U.S. Public*, pg. 376
EXEO GROUP INC.; *Int'l*, pg. 2583
EZ ELECTRIC; *U.S. Private*, pg. 1454
FAHNESTOCK PLUMBING, HVAC & ELECTRIC; *U.S. Private*, pg. 1461
FALCON COMMUNICATIONS INC.; *U.S. Private*, pg. 1466
THE FARMERS TELEPHONE COMPANY, LLC—See Telephone & Data Systems, Inc.; *U.S. Public*, pg. 1998
FBS COMMUNICATIONS, L.P.—See Black Box Limited; *Int'l*, pg. 1058
F.D. HAYES ELECTRIC COMPANY; *U.S. Private*, pg. 1456

CORPORATE AFFILIATIONS

FERGUSON ELECTRIC COMPANY INC.; *U.S. Private*, pg. 1496
FERGUSON ELECTRIC CONSTRUCTION CO., INC.—See Ferguson Electric Holdings Corp.; *U.S. Private*, pg. 1497
FERGUSON ELECTRIC SERVICE CO., INC.—See Ferguson Electric Holdings Corp.; *U.S. Private*, pg. 1497
FERNDALE ELECTRIC COMPANY INC.; *U.S. Private*, pg. 1497
FEYEN ZYLSTRA ELECTRIC INC.; *U.S. Private*, pg. 1500
F&H ELECTRICAL CONTRACTORS, INC.; *U.S. Private*, pg. 1454
FIELDWAY GROUP LIMITED; *Int'l*, pg. 2655
FIRST INFRASTRUCTURE CAPITAL ADVISORS, LLC—See Quanta Services, Inc.; *U.S. Public*, pg. 1751
FISK ELECTRIC COMPANY INC.—See Tutor Perini Corporation; *U.S. Public*, pg. 2206
FIVE STAR AIRPORT ALLIANCE, INC.; *U.S. Private*, pg. 1537
FIVE STAR ELECTRIC CORP.—See WDF/Five Star Holding Corporation; *U.S. Private*, pg. 4462
FLEMINGTON INSTRUMENT CO. INC.; *U.S. Private*, pg. 1542
F.LLI FRANCHINI S.R.L.—See Hera S.p.A.; *Int'l*, pg. 3356
FLORENCE ELECTRIC LLC; *U.S. Private*, pg. 1547
FOKKER ELMO B.V.—See GKN plc; *Int'l*, pg. 2983
FORCLUM RESEAUX NORD S.A.S.—See Eiffage S.A.; *Int'l*, pg. 2330
FOREST ELECTRIC CORP.—See EMCOR Group, Inc.; *U.S. Public*, pg. 736
FOX ELECTRIC LTD.; *U.S. Private*, pg. 1584
FOX VALLEY FIRE & SAFETY COMPANY, INC.; *U.S. Private*, pg. 1585
FRANCE SEMI, S.A.—See ACS, Actividades de Construccion y Servicios, S.A.; *Int'l*, pg. 112
FRED GELLER ELECTRICAL, INC.; *U.S. Private*, pg. 1601
FRISCHHERTZ ELECTRIC COMPANY, INC.; *U.S. Private*, pg. 1612
FRONTIER TECHNOLOGIES S.R.O.—See EnBW Energie Baden-Wurttemberg AG; *Int'l*, pg. 2399
FUELLGRAF ELECTRIC CO.; *U.S. Private*, pg. 1619
GALLAHER & ASSOCIATES, INC.; *U.S. Private*, pg. 1639
GARBER ELECTRICAL CONTRACTORS INC.; *U.S. Private*, pg. 1642
GARDNER TELECOMMUNICATIONS, INC.; *U.S. Private*, pg. 1644
THE GARDNER ZEMKE COMPANY; *U.S. Private*, pg. 4032
GARNET ELECTRIC CO., INC.; *U.S. Private*, pg. 1645
GASTON ELECTRICAL CO., LLC—See EMCOR Group, Inc.; *U.S. Public*, pg. 738
GAYLOR INC.; *U.S. Private*, pg. 1652
GDMCOM GMBH—See EnBW Energie Baden-Wurttemberg AG; *Int'l*, pg. 2400
GENTZLER ELECTRIC; *U.S. Private*, pg. 1680
GENUS POWER INFRASTRUCTURES LTD.; *Int'l*, pg. 2931
GEOQUIP LIMITED—See CRH plc; *Int'l*, pg. 1844
GEORGE J. HAYDEN INC.; *U.S. Private*, pg. 1682
GERELCO ELECTRICAL CONTRACTORS; *U.S. Private*, pg. 1686
GETTLE, INC.; *U.S. Private*, pg. 1689
GHL (BEIJING) CO. LTD.—See General Atlantic Service Company, L.P.; *U.S. Private*, pg. 1661
GHL (CHINA) CO. LTD.—See General Atlantic Service Company, L.P.; *U.S. Private*, pg. 1661
GHL (THAILAND) CO. LTD.—See General Atlantic Service Company, L.P.; *U.S. Private*, pg. 1661
GHL TRANSACT SDN. BHD.—See General Atlantic Service Company, L.P.; *U.S. Private*, pg. 1661
GIBSON ELECTRIC & TECHNOLOGY SOLUTIONS—See EMCOR Group, Inc.; *U.S. Public*, pg. 736
GIJIMAAST ELECTRONIC AND SECURITY SYSTEMS (PTY) LIMITED—See Guma Group; *Int'l*, pg. 3183
GILBERT MECHANICAL CONTRACTORS, LLC—See Blackstone Inc.; *U.S. Public*, pg. 361
GILCREST ELECTRIC & SUPPLY CO.; *U.S. Private*, pg. 1699
GILL-SIMPSON INCORPORATED; *U.S. Private*, pg. 1700
G&M ELECTRICAL CONTRACTORS CO. INC.; *U.S. Private*, pg. 1629
GOLDEN BRIDGE ELECTECH INC.; *Int'l*, pg. 3028
GOLDEN FAITH GROUP HOLDINGS LIMITED; *Int'l*, pg. 3029
GOODTECH PROCESS AB—See Goodtech ASA; *Int'l*, pg. 3041
GOODTECH SOLUTIONS INDUSTRIAUTOMATION AB—See Goodtech ASA; *Int'l*, pg. 3041
GOODTECH SOLUTIONS SAFFLE AB—See Goodtech ASA; *Int'l*, pg. 3041
GORDON ELECTRIC; *Int'l*, pg. 3042
GRAND KAHN ELECTRIC, LLC; *U.S. Private*, pg. 1753
GREAT SALT LAKE ELECTRIC INCORPORATED; *U.S. Private*, pg. 1767
GREEN ENERGY MANAGEMENT SERVICES HOLDINGS, INC.; *U.S. Private*, pg. 1772
GREENSPEED ENERGY SOLUTIONS, LLC—See Charge Enterprises, Inc.; *U.S. Public*, pg. 479
GREEN WAVE LLC—See Amaresco, Inc.; *U.S. Public*, pg. 95
GREGORY ELECTRIC CO. INC.; *U.S. Private*, pg. 1783

GROTBERG ELECTRIC, INC.; *U.S. Private*, pg. 1792
GROUPWARE INTERNATIONAL INC.; *U.S. Private*, pg. 1794
GUARANTEE ELECTRICAL COMPANY; *U.S. Private*, pg. 1808
GUILD ELECTRIC LTD.; *Int'l*, pg. 3173
GULFDETECTION LLC—See Bhatia Brothers Group; *Int'l*, pg. 1014
HALCO SERVICE CORP.—See Blue Sea Capital Management LLC; *U.S. Private*, pg. 592
HAMAMATSU NDS CO., LTD.—See COMSYS Holdings Corporation; *Int'l*, pg. 1761
HAMPTON TEDDER ELECTRIC CO.; *U.S. Private*, pg. 1851
HANSON ELECTRIC OF BEMIDJI; *U.S. Private*, pg. 1856
HANSON RESOURCE MANAGEMENT LIMITED—See The Pritzker Organization, LLC; *U.S. Private*, pg. 4100
HARBIN COSLIGHT ELECTRIC AUTOMATION COMPANY LIMITED—See Coslight Technology International Group Limited; *Int'l*, pg. 1810
HARBOR GROUP INC; *U.S. Private*, pg. 1859
HARLAN ELECTRIC COMPANY INC.; *U.S. Private*, pg. 1865
HARRY F. ORTLIP COMPANY INC.; *U.S. Private*, pg. 1871
HART CABLE, INC.—See Lintel Inc.; *U.S. Private*, pg. 2463
HARTMANN ELECTRIC COMPANY INC.; *U.S. Private*, pg. 1874
HASEKE GMBH & CO. KG—See Gesco AG; *Int'l*, pg. 2945
HASKINS ELECTRIC INC.; *U.S. Private*, pg. 1878
HATZEL & BUEHLER, INC.—See Construction Management Service; *U.S. Private*, pg. 1023
HAYES & LUNSFORD ELECTRIC, LLC—See Comfort Systems USA, Inc.; *U.S. Public*, pg. 544
HAYLEYS ELECTRONICS LTD.—See Hayleys PLC; *Int'l*, pg. 3292
H.B. FRAZER COMPANY; *U.S. Private*, pg. 1825
H. BRUCE AND SONS INC.; *U.S. Private*, pg. 1824
HEIJMANS TECHNISCHE INFRA B.V.—See Heijmans N.V.; *Int'l*, pg. 3322
HELIX ELECTRIC INC.; *U.S. Private*, pg. 1906
HENDERSON SERVICES LLC; *U.S. Private*, pg. 1914
HENRIQUEZ ELECTRIC CORP.; *U.S. Private*, pg. 1917
HERA LUCE S.R.L.—See Hera S.p.A.; *Int'l*, pg. 3356
H&H GROUP INC.; *U.S. Private*, pg. 1822
HICKS LIGHTNING PROTECTION, INC.; *U.S. Private*, pg. 1934
HIGGINS ELECTRIC, INC. OF DOTHAN; *U.S. Private*, pg. 1935
HIGH NOON SOLAR, LLC—See Duke Energy Corporation; *U.S. Public*, pg. 691
HIGH POWER TECHNICAL SERVICES; *U.S. Private*, pg. 1936
HIGH-TECH CLIMA S.A.—See CEZ, a.s.; *Int'l*, pg. 1428
HIG SERVICES US INC—See Howden Group Holdings Limited; *Int'l*, pg. 3493
HILSCHER-CLARKE ELECTRIC COMPANY; *U.S. Private*, pg. 1948
HI-TECH ELECTRIC INC.; *U.S. Private*, pg. 1932
HOKKAI ELECTRICAL CONSTRUCTION CO., INC.—See Hokkaido Electric Power Co., Inc.; *Int'l*, pg. 3443
HOKUDEN SERVICE CO., LTD.—See Hokkaido Electric Power Co., Inc.; *Int'l*, pg. 3443
HORIZON SERVICES LIMITED—See Eastern Bay Energy Trust; *Int'l*, pg. 2272
HOTLINE TELECOMMUNICATIONS; *U.S. Private*, pg. 1989
HOULE ELECTRIC LIMITED; *Int'l*, pg. 3490
HOUMA ARMATURE WORKS & SUPPLY, INC.—See Arcline Investment Management LP; *U.S. Private*, pg. 313
HOUSLEY COMMUNICATIONS LIMITED; *U.S. Private*, pg. 1992
HOWE ELECTRIC INC.; *U.S. Private*, pg. 1996
HUDSON ROBOTICS, INC.—See Argosy Capital Group, LLC; *U.S. Private*, pg. 321
HUEN ELECTRIC INC.—See MYR Group Inc.; *U.S. Public*, pg. 1489
HUMBOLDT ELECTRIC LIMITED; *Int'l*, pg. 3530
HUMPHREY & ASSOCIATES INC.; *U.S. Private*, pg. 2007
HURON VALLEY ELECTRIC, INC.—See Motor City Electric Co., Inc.; *U.S. Private*, pg. 2796
HUSTON ELECTRIC INC.; *U.S. Private*, pg. 2014
HYLAN ELECTRICAL CONTRACTING; *U.S. Private*, pg. 2018
HYRE ELECTRIC COMPANY OF INDIANA, INC.—See EMCOR Group, Inc.; *U.S. Public*, pg. 737
HYUNDAI HT CO., LTD; *Int'l*, pg. 3557
IES COMMERCIAL & INDUSTRIAL, LLC - GREENVILLE—See IES Holdings, Inc.; *U.S. Public*, pg. 1094
IES COMMERCIAL & INDUSTRIAL, LLC—See IES Holdings, Inc.; *U.S. Public*, pg. 1094
IES RESIDENTIAL, INC.—See IES Holdings, Inc.; *U.S. Public*, pg. 1094
ILLINOIS J. LIVINGSTON COMPANY; *U.S. Private*, pg. 2042
ILOKA, INC.—See Schurz Communications, Inc.; *U.S. Private*, pg. 3571
IMCORP; *U.S. Private*, pg. 2046
IMESAPI, S.A.—See ACS, Actividades de Construccion y Servicios, S.A.; *Int'l*, pg. 114
IMPACT POWER SOLUTIONS, LLC—See Smartpitch Ventures, LLC; *U.S. Private*, pg. 3692
IMTECH INVIRON LTD.—See Electricite de France S.A.; *Int'l*, pg. 2351
IMTECH PROJECTS N.V.—See Electricite de France S.A.; *Int'l*, pg. 2351
IMTECH TECHNOLOGY SRL—See Electricite de France S.A.; *Int'l*, pg. 2351
INDIANA FIBER NETWORK, LLC—See DigitalBridge Group, Inc.; *U.S. Public*, pg. 665
INDIANA FIBER NETWORK, LLC—See EQT AB; *Int'l*, pg. 2481
INDIANAPOLIS ELECTRIC COMPANY, INC.; *U.S. Private*, pg. 2063
INDUSTRIAL ELECTRIC COMPANY—See The Egan Companies; *U.S. Private*, pg. 4025
INDUSTRIAL POWER & LIGHTING CORP.; *U.S. Private*, pg. 2068
INDUSTRIAL SPECIALITY CONTRACTOR LLC; *U.S. Private*, pg. 2068
INDUSTRIAL SPECIALTY CONTRACTORS INC.—See Industrial Speciality Contractor LLC; *U.S. Private*, pg. 2068
INFRASOURCE INSTALLATION, LLC—See Quanta Services, Inc.; *U.S. Public*, pg. 1751
INGLETT & STUBBS, LLC; *U.S. Private*, pg. 2076
INLITE PTY LIMITED—See Bain Capital, LP; *U.S. Private*, pg. 439
INNOVATIVE ELECTRIC, INC.—See Gryphon Investors, LLC; *U.S. Private*, pg. 1799
INNOVATIVE ENGINEERING, INC.—See OceanSound Partners, LP; *U.S. Private*, pg. 2991
INNOVATIVE POWER SYSTEMS, INC.—See TSS, Inc.; *U.S. Public*, pg. 2202
INSTALACIONES Y MONTAJES DE AIRE CLIMATIZADO, S.L.—See ACS, Actividades de Construccion y Servicios, S.A.; *Int'l*, pg. 114
INTEGRATED ACCESS SOLUTIONS, INC.—See TTEC Holdings, Inc.; *U.S. Public*, pg. 2203
INTEK SP. Z O.O.—See Dekpol S.A.; *Int'l*, pg. 2006
INTERFACE CABLE ASSEMBLIES & SERVICES CORP.; *U.S. Private*, pg. 2110
INTERMOUNTAIN ELECTRIC, INC.; *U.S. Private*, pg. 2113
INTERMOUNTAIN ELECTRIC, INC.—See Quanta Services, Inc.; *U.S. Public*, pg. 1751
INTERMOUNTAIN ELECTRIC SERVICE INC.; *U.S. Private*, pg. 2113
INTERSTATE ELECTRICAL SERVICES CORP.; *U.S. Private*, pg. 2124
INTERSTATES CONSTRUCTION SERVICES INC—See Harbor Group Inc; *U.S. Private*, pg. 1859
INVESTIGACION Y DESARROLLO DE EQUIPOS AVANZADOS, S.A.U.—See Iberdrola, S.A.; *Int'l*, pg. 3573
IOWA CITY ELECTRIC COMPANY—See Motor City Electric Co., Inc.; *U.S. Private*, pg. 2796
IQA OPERATIOS GROUP, LTD.—See Elecnor, S.A.; *Int'l*, pg. 2347
IRBY CONSTRUCTION COMPANY—See Quanta Services, Inc.; *U.S. Public*, pg. 1751
ISC CONSTRUCTORS, LLC.; *U.S. Private*, pg. 2143
ISLA COMMUNICATIONS CO., INC.—See Deutsche Telekom AG; *Int'l*, pg. 2083
ISTIMEWA ELECTROTECHNIEK B.V.—See Fluor Corporation; *U.S. Public*, pg. 859
IWIRED, INC.—See Vangeo Technology Group, LLC; *U.S. Private*, pg. 4343
JACOBS TELECOMMUNICATIONS INC.—See Jacobs Engineering Group, Inc.; *U.S. Public*, pg. 1185
JAMERSON & BAUWENS ELEC CONTRS; *U.S. Private*, pg. 2182
JB CONTRACTING CORPORATION; *U.S. Private*, pg. 2193
JBI ELECTRICAL SYSTEMS INCORPORATED; *U.S. Private*, pg. 2193
JBT ELECTRIC, LLC—See Quanta Services, Inc.; *U.S. Public*, pg. 1751
J.C.R. CONSTRUCTION CO., INC.—See Quanta Services, Inc.; *U.S. Public*, pg. 1751
JELEC, INC.; *U.S. Private*, pg. 2198
JESS HOWARD ELECTRIC COMPANY; *U.S. Private*, pg. 2203
JETTON ELECTRIC INC.; *U.S. Private*, pg. 2204
J.L. MAUPIN ENTERPRISES INC.; *U.S. Private*, pg. 2167
JNS POWER & CONTROL SYSTEMS, INC.—See JNS Holdings Corporation; *U.S. Public*, pg. 1190
JOAO JACINTO TOME, S.A.—See Eiffage S.A.; *Int'l*, pg. 2331
JOE DICKEY ELECTRIC INC.; *U.S. Private*, pg. 2218
JOE SWARTZ ELECTRIC COMPANY; *U.S. Private*, pg. 2210
JOHN A. PENNY CO. INC.; *U.S. Private*, pg. 2220
JOHN E. KELLY & SONS ELECTRICAL CONSTRUCTION, INC.; *U.S. Private*, pg. 2221
JONES & LANIER ELECTRIC INC.; *U.S. Private*, pg. 2231
J. RANCK ELECTRIC INC.; *U.S. Private*, pg. 2157
JS CONSTRUCTION, S.E.; *U.S. Private*, pg. 2240
J.T. LANEHART ELECTRIC CO. INC.; *U.S. Private*, pg. 2171
JTMEC PTY LTD.—See Epiroc AB; *Int'l*, pg. 2463
J.W. KOEHLER ELECTRIC, INC.; *U.S. Private*, pg. 2172
KAMIC INSTALLATION OY—See Amplex AB; *Int'l*, pg. 434
KANAAN COMMUNICATIONS, LLC—See Dycom Industries, Inc.; *U.S. Public*, pg. 698
KANSAI HITACHI CO., LTD.—See Hitachi, Ltd.; *Int'l*, pg. 3423
KASTLE ELECTRIC COMPANY; *U.S. Private*, pg. 2264
KDC SYSTEMS—See EMCOR Group, Inc.; *U.S. Public*, pg. 736
KEARNEY ELECTRIC, INC.; *U.S. Private*, pg. 2271
KELE, INC.—See The Stephens Group, LLC; *U.S. Private*, pg. 4121
KELLEY ELECTRIC COMPANY—See The Townsend Corporation; *U.S. Private*, pg. 4127
KELSO-BURNETT COMPANY; *U.S. Private*, pg. 2281
KENMOR ELECTRIC CO. LP; *U.S. Private*, pg. 2284
KENNY ELECTRIC SERVICE INC.; *U.S. Private*, pg. 2286
KIDWELL INC.; *U.S. Private*, pg. 2303
KINDER ELECTRIC COMPANY INC.; *U.S. Private*, pg. 2306
K&K ELECTRIC, INC.—See Kian Capital Partners, LLC; *U.S. Private*, pg. 2302
K&K ELECTRIC, INC.—See RFE Investment Partners; *U.S. Private*, pg. 3419
KLEINKNECHT ELECTRIC CO. INC.; *U.S. Private*, pg. 2319
KM KELLY, INC.; *U.S. Private*, pg. 2321
KOLB ELEKTRO AG—See Burkhalter Holding AG; *Int'l*, pg. 1225
KRATOS SOUTHWEST, L.P.—See Kratos Defense & Security Solutions, Inc.; *U.S. Public*, pg. 1276
KST ELECTRIC, LTD.—See Rosendin Electric, Inc.; *U.S. Private*, pg. 3483
K-TECH CORP.; *U.S. Private*, pg. 2251
KURE ASSOCIATES LLC—See M&B Corporation; *U.S. Private*, pg. 2524
LAIRD ELECTRIC LNC.—See Bird Construction Inc.; *Int'l*, pg. 1047
LAKE ERIE ELECTRIC INC-HIRSCH DIVISION—See Lake Erie Electric, Inc.; *U.S. Private*, pg. 2375
LAKE ERIE ELECTRIC, INC.; *U.S. Private*, pg. 2375
L.A. LACY, INC.—See The Branch Group, Inc.; *U.S. Private*, pg. 3999
LAND MARK ELECTRIC, INC.; *U.S. Private*, pg. 2382
LANEY'S INC.; *U.S. Private*, pg. 2388
LANGER ELECTRIC COMPANY; *U.S. Private*, pg. 2389
LARRY C. MCCRAE INC.; *U.S. Private*, pg. 2392
LAWSON ELECTRIC COMPANY; *U.S. Private*, pg. 2402
LB&L CABLE INC.; *U.S. Private*, pg. 2403
LCS INC.—See Dunes Point Capital, LLC; *U.S. Private*, pg. 1288
LEESBURG SOUTHERN ELECTRIC INC.; *U.S. Private*, pg. 2415
LEX ENGINEERING LTD.—See Quanta Services, Inc.; *U.S. Public*, pg. 1751
LGCY POWER, LLC; *U.S. Private*, pg. 2441
L&H COMPANY INC.; *U.S. Private*, pg. 2362
LIBRA ELECTRIC COMPANY; *U.S. Private*, pg. 2447
LIGHTING FOR STAFFORDSHIRE LIMITED—See E.ON SE; *Int'l*, pg. 2256
LIGHTING TECHNOLOGY SERVICES, INC.—See Willdan Group, Inc.; *U.S. Public*, pg. 2371
LIGHTWAVE TELECOMMUNICATIONS, INC.; *U.S. Private*, pg. 2454
LIMBACH FACILITY SERVICES LLC—See Limbach Holdings, Inc.; *U.S. Public*, pg. 1316
LINDER & ASSOCIATES, INC.; *U.S. Private*, pg. 2460
LINDSTENS ELEKTRISKA AB—See Bravida Holding AB; *Int'l*, pg. 1142
LIN R. ROGERS ELECTRICAL CONTRACTORS INC.; *U.S. Private*, pg. 2456
L.K. COMSTOCK & COMPANY, INC.—See Wind Point Advisors LLC; *U.S. Private*, pg. 4535
LLOYD ELECTRIC, INC.; *U.S. Private*, pg. 2475
L.L. VANN ELECTRIC INC.; *U.S. Private*, pg. 2366
L & M ELECTRIC, INC.—See Strada Services, LLC; *U.S. Private*, pg. 3832
LOMBARDO & LIPE ELECTRICAL CONTRACTORS INC.; *U.S. Private*, pg. 2483
LONG ELECTRIC COMPANY INC.; *U.S. Private*, pg. 2490
LORD ELECTRIC COMPANY OF PUERTO RICO INC.; *U.S. Private*, pg. 2495
LORELEC SARL—See Alstom S.A.; *Int'l*, pg. 383
LOUDOUN ELECTRIC COMPANY; *U.S. Private*, pg. 2498
LOWRIE ELECTRIC COMPANY, INC.—See EMCOR Group, Inc.; *U.S. Public*, pg. 737
LOW VOLTAGE INTEGRATED SYSTEMS INC.—See The Carlyle Group Inc.; *U.S. Public*, pg. 2053
LOWY & DONNATH, INC.—See EJ Electric Installation Co.; *U.S. Private*, pg. 1348
LPS CORPORATION—See Louisiana-Pacific Corporation; *U.S. Public*, pg. 1342
LUDVIK ELECTRIC CO., INC.; *U.S. Private*, pg. 2512
LUMICAN, S.A.—See ACS, Actividades de Construccion y Servicios, S.A.; *Int'l*, pg. 115
MACDONALD-MILLER FACILITY SOLUTIONS INC.; *U.S. Private*, pg. 2535
MACELROYS INC.; *U.S. Private*, pg. 2535

238210 — ELECTRICAL CONTRACT...

MACLEAN ELECTRICAL INC.—See DNOW Inc.; *U.S. Public*, pg. 671
MACRO INTEGRATION SERVICES INC.—See The Graham Group, Inc.; *U.S. Private*, pg. 4036
MALKO ELECTRIC COMPANY; *U.S. Private*, pg. 2557
MARATHON ELECTRICAL CONTRACTORS, INC.; *U.S. Private*, pg. 2570
MARJAN INDUSTRIAL DEVELOPMENT CO.—See Al Fahim Group; *Int'l*, pg. 277
MARON ELECTRIC COMPANY; *U.S. Private*, pg. 2586
MARRS ELECTRIC INC.; *U.S. Private*, pg. 2588
MARTELL ELECTRIC, LLC; *U.S. Private*, pg. 2593
MASCAL ELECTRIC, INC.; *U.S. Private*, pg. 2600
MASS. ELECTRIC CONSTRUCTION CO., INC.—See Peter Kiewit Sons', Inc.; *U.S. Private*, pg. 3158
MASSEY CONSTRUCTION INC.; *U.S. Private*, pg. 2606
MASTER ELECTRIC CO. INC.; *U.S. Private*, pg. 2607
MATCO ELECTRIC CORPORATION; *U.S. Private*, pg. 2609
MAUL ELECTRIC INC.; *U.S. Private*, pg. 2615
MBR CONSTRUCTION SERVICES INC.; *U.S. Private*, pg. 2624
MCBRIDE ELECTRIC INC.; *U.S. Private*, pg. 2625
MCC ELECTRIC, L.L.C.—See The MCC Group, LLC; *U.S. Private*, pg. 4076
MCCLINTOCK ELECTRIC, INC.; *U.S. Private*, pg. 2628
MCCLURE COMPANY—See Riverstone Holdings LLC; *U.S. Private*, pg. 3447
MC COMMUNICATIONS INC.; *U.S. Private*, pg. 2625
M.C. DEAN, INC.; *U.S. Private*, pg. 2528
MCI WORLDCOM—See Verizon Communications Inc.; *U.S. Public*, pg. 2285
MCMILLAN BROTHERS ELECTRIC SERVICE; *U.S. Private*, pg. 2642
MCWILLIAMS ELECTRIC CO. INC.; *U.S. Private*, pg. 2645
MEADE ELECTRIC COMPANY, INC.—See L&H Company Inc.; *U.S. Private*, pg. 2362
MEARS GROUP INC.—See Quanta Services, Inc.; *U.S. Public*, pg. 1752
MEISNER ELECTRIC, INC.; *U.S. Private*, pg. 2661
MEITEC INC.; *U.S. Private*, pg. 2661
MELVILLE LOGISTICS GMBH—See Viad Corp.; *U.S. Public*, pg. 2291
MERIT ELECTRIC COMPANY, INC.; *U.S. Private*, pg. 2674
MERIT ELECTRIC INC.; *U.S. Private*, pg. 2674
MERIT ELECTRIC OF SPOKANE; *U.S. Private*, pg. 2674
METAL MANUFACTURES PTY LIMITED—See Blackfriars Corp.; *U.S. Private*, pg. 575
METASPACE (BEIJING) AIR DOME CORP.—See Beijing Sports & Entertainment Industry Group Limited; *Int'l*, pg. 957
METHODE ELECTRONICS CONNECTIVITY TECHNOLOGIES, INC.—See Methode Electronics, Inc.; *U.S. Public*, pg. 1428
METRO ELECTRIC INC.; *U.S. Private*, pg. 2685
METROPOWER INC.; *U.S. Private*, pg. 2691
M.G. ABBOTT, INC.; *U.S. Private*, pg. 2529
MG ELECTRIC SERVICE COMPANY; *U.S. Private*, pg. 2694
M&H ELEKTRO AG—See Burkhalter Holding AG; *Int'l*, pg. 1225
MICROWAVE TRANSMISSION SYSTEMS, INC.; *U.S. Private*, pg. 2704
MID SOUTH CONTRACTORS LTD.—See Motor City, Electric Co., Inc.; *U.S. Private*, pg. 2796
MIDTOWN EXPRESS, LLC—See Dycom Industries, Inc.; *U.S. Public*, pg. 698
MIDWEST COOLING TOWER SERVICES INC.—See Hastings Equity Partners, LLC; *U.S. Private*, pg. 1879
MIDWEST ELECTRIC; *U.S. Private*, pg. 2721
MIDWEST ENERGY SERVICES, INC.—See Dakota Electric Association; *U.S. Private*, pg. 1147
MIDWEST UNDERGROUND TECHNOLOGIES, INC.; *U.S. Private*, pg. 2723
MIKE BROWN ELECTRIC CO.; *U.S. Private*, pg. 2724
MILESTONE ELECTRIC & SECURITY; *U.S. Private*, pg. 2728
MILHOLLAND ELECTRIC, INC.—See Solar Integrated Roofing Corporation; *U.S. Public*, pg. 1900
MILLER ADAMS ELECTRIC INC.—See Garber Electrical Contractors Inc.; *U.S. Private*, pg. 1642
MILLER ELECTRIC COMPANY; *U.S. Private*, pg. 2733
MILLER ELECTRIC CONSTRUCTION INC.; *U.S. Private*, pg. 2733
MILLER ELECTRIC CONSTRUCTION—See Miller Electric Construction Inc.; *U.S. Private*, pg. 2734
MILNER ELECTRICAL COMPANY; *U.S. Private*, pg. 2738
MITSUBOSHI TECHNO CO., LTD.—See COMSYS Holdings Corporation; *Int'l*, pg. 1761
M.J. ELECTRIC, LLC—See Quanta Services, Inc.; *U.S. Public*, pg. 1751
MJM ELECTRIC, INC.; *U.S. Private*, pg. 2753
MMR CONSTRUCTORS INC. - CORPUS CHRISTI—See MMR Group Inc.; *U.S. Private*, pg. 2755
MMR CONSTRUCTORS INC.—See MMR Group Inc.; *U.S. Private*, pg. 2755
MMR GROUP INC.; *U.S. Private*, pg. 2755
MOBIX STEVENS—See Ackermans & van Haaren NV; *Int'l*, pg. 105

MODERN BUSINESS MACHINES, INC.—See Xerox Holdings Corporation; *U.S. Public*, pg. 2389
MODERN ELECTRIC CO.; *U.S. Private*, pg. 2760
MONA ELECTRIC GROUP INC.; *U.S. Private*, pg. 2768
MONELEC, S.L.—See ACS, Actividades de Construccion y Servicios, S.A.; *Int'l*, pg. 115
MONTAJES ELECTRICOS ARRANZ, S.L.—See Elecnor, S.A.; *Int'l*, pg. 2347
MOORE COMMUNICATIONS SYSTEMS, INC.—See CloudScale365, Inc.; *U.S. Private*, pg. 947
MOORE'S ELECTRICAL & MECHANICAL CONSTRUCTION, INC.; *U.S. Private*, pg. 2780
MOREFIELD COMMUNICATIONS INC.; *U.S. Private*, pg. 2782
MORROW-MEADOWS CORPORATION; *U.S. Private*, pg. 2790
MORROW-MEADOWS CORP—See Morrow-Meadows Corporation; *U.S. Private*, pg. 2790
MORSE ELECTRIC INCORPORATED; *U.S. Private*, pg. 2790
MOSS TELECOMMUNICATIONS SERVICES; *U.S. Private*, pg. 2794
MOTOR CITY ELECTRIC UTILITIES CO., INC.—See Motor City Electric Co., Inc.; *U.S. Private*, pg. 2796
MURCIANA DE TRAFICO, S.A.—See ACS, Actividades de Construccion y Servicios, S.A.; *Int'l*, pg. 115
MUSKA ELECTRIC COMPANY; *U.S. Private*, pg. 2818
MWMPC CORP.—See Cappadonna Electrical Management Corporation; *U.S. Private*, pg. 745
MYR GROUP INC.; *U.S. Public*, pg. 1488
NABCO ELECTRIC; *U.S. Private*, pg. 2829
NAMASTE SOLAR ELECTRIC, INC.; *U.S. Private*, pg. 2831
NASS ELECTRICAL—See Abdulla Ahmed Nass Group WLL; *Int'l*, pg. 58
NATIONWIDE DISTRIBUTION SERVICES LTD.—See Ferrovial S.A.; *Int'l*, pg. 2645
NEAD ELECTRIC INC—See Nead Organization Inc.; *U.S. Private*, pg. 2877
NEAD ORGANIZATION INC.; *U.S. Private*, pg. 2877
NELSON ELECTRIC CO.; *U.S. Private*, pg. 2883
NET100 LTD.—See Aterian Investment Management, L.P.; *U.S. Private*, pg. 366
NETCOM TECHNOLOGIES, INC.; *U.S. Private*, pg. 2887
NETRONIX INTEGRATION, INC.—See Wind Point Advisors LLC; *U.S. Private*, pg. 4535
NETVERSANT SOLUTIONS LLC—See Patriarch Partners, LLC; *U.S. Private*, pg. 3109
NETWORK9, LLC; *U.S. Private*, pg. 2889
NEWKIRK ELECTRIC ASSOCIATES; *U.S. Private*, pg. 2915
NEW RIVER ELECTRICAL CORPORATION; *U.S. Private*, pg. 2906
THE NEWTRON GROUP INC.; *U.S. Private*, pg. 4083
NEWTRON INC.—See The Newtron Group Inc.; *U.S. Private*, pg. 4084
NEXT ELECTRIC, LLC—See IES Holdings, Inc.; *U.S. Public*, pg. 1094
NEXTRIDGE, INC.—See Charge Enterprises, Inc.; *U.S. Public*, pg. 479
NIETZ ELECTRIC, INC.—See The Egan Companies; *U.S. Private*, pg. 4025
NIHON CEVA K.K.—See CEVA, Inc.; *U.S. Public*, pg. 476
NIKKEL & ASSOCIATES INC.; *U.S. Private*, pg. 2927
NISCAYAH TEKNIK AB—See Stanley Black & Decker, Inc.; *U.S. Public*, pg. 1933
NITRO CONSTRUCTION SERVICES, INC.—See Energy Services of America Corporation; *U.S. Public*, pg. 762
NIZET ENTREPRISE SA—See Ackermans & van Haaren NV; *Int'l*, pg. 105
N.J. CONSTRUCTION PTY LTD—See Quanta Services, Inc.; *U.S. Public*, pg. 1752
NJR HOME SERVICES COMPANY—See New Jersey Resources Corporation; *U.S. Public*, pg. 1512
NOKIA MOBILE PHONES (SEA) PTE LTD.—See Microsoft Corporation; *U.S. Public*, pg. 1441
NORRSTYR AB—See Bravida Holding AB; *Int'l*, pg. 1142
NORTHCENTRAL TELCOM INC.; *U.S. Private*, pg. 2949
NORTHGATE ELECTRIC CORP.; *U.S. Private*, pg. 2955
NORTH HOUSTON POLE LINE, L.P.—See Quanta Services, Inc.; *U.S. Public*, pg. 1752
NORTHSIDE SERVICES, INC.; *U.S. Private*, pg. 2957
NORTH SKY COMMUNICATIONS, INC.—See Dycom Industries, Inc.; *U.S. Public*, pg. 699
NORTHSTAR SHARPS FOUNDATION SPECIALISTS LTD.—See Quanta Services, Inc.; *U.S. Public*, pg. 1752
NU-SONS ELECTRIC INC.; *U.S. Private*, pg. 2971
OBERGS VENT TEKNIK AB—See Bravida Holding AB; *Int'l*, pg. 1142
O'BRYANT ELECTRIC, INC.; *U.S. Private*, pg. 2977
O'CONNELL ELECTRIC COMPANY, INC.; *U.S. Private*, pg. 2977
O'CONNELL ELECTRIC COMPANY, INC.—See O'Connell Electric Company, Inc.; *U.S. Private*, pg. 2977
O'CONNOR TELESERVICES INC.; *U.S. Private*, pg. 2978
OEG, INC.—See MDU Resources Group, Inc.; *U.S. Public*, pg. 1410
OKAY CONSTRUCTION COMPANY—See Quanta Services, Inc.; *U.S. Public*, pg. 1751

OKLAHOMA ELECTRICAL SUPPLY COMPANY, INC.; *U.S. Private*, pg. 3007
OMEGA ELECTRIC CONSTRUCTION CO.; *U.S. Private*, pg. 3015
O'NEILL ELECTRIC INC.; *U.S. Private*, pg. 2980
OPSEC SECURITY GROUP LTD—See Crane NXT, Co.; *U.S. Public*, pg. 592
ORBOTECH PACIFIC LTD.—See KLA Corporation; *U.S. Public*, pg. 1268
ORBOTECH S.A., EUROPE—See KLA Corporation; *U.S. Public*, pg. 1268
OREGON ELECTRIC GROUP; *U.S. Private*, pg. 3040
OSRAM ASIA PACIFIC LTD.—See ams AG; *Int'l*, pg. 438
OSRAM ASIA PACIFIC MANAGEMENT COMPANY LTD.—See ams AG; *Int'l*, pg. 439
OSRAM COMERCIO DE SOLUCOES DE ILUMINACAO LTDA.—See ams AG; *Int'l*, pg. 439
OSRAM KUNSHAN DISPLAY OPTIC CO., LTD.—See ams AG; *Int'l*, pg. 439
OSRAM LIGHTING PRIVATE LIMITED—See ams AG; *Int'l*, pg. 439
OSRAM LIGHTING PTE. LTD.—See ams AG; *Int'l*, pg. 439
OSRAM OPTO SEMICONDUCTORS (CHINA) CO., LTD.—See ams AG; *Int'l*, pg. 439
OSRAM OPTO SEMICONDUCTORS (JAPAN) LTD.—See ams AG; *Int'l*, pg. 439
OSRAM S.A.—See ams AG; *Int'l*, pg. 439
OSRAM (THAILAND) CO., LTD.—See ams AG; *Int'l*, pg. 438
OSTERLINDS EL-AGENTUR AB—See Amplex AB; *Int'l*, pg. 434
OSTROW ELECTRICAL CO. INC.; *U.S. Private*, pg. 3048
OVERCASH ELECTRIC INC.; *U.S. Private*, pg. 3052
OVERHEAD DOOR CO OF NEW ORLEANS, INC.—See DuraServ Corp; *U.S. Private*, pg. 1293
PACIFIC COAST CABLING INC.; *U.S. Private*, pg. 3066
PACIFIC FIRE AND SECURITY, INC.—See Pye-Barker Fire & Safety, LLC; *U.S. Private*, pg. 3309
PACIFIC POWER & SYSTEMS, INC.—See White Wolf Capital LLC; *U.S. Private*, pg. 4510
PALMER ELECTRIC CO.; *U.S. Private*, pg. 3081
PANDA ENERGY INTERNATIONAL INC.; *U.S. Private*, pg. 3085
PARACON HOLDINGS LIMITED—See Adcorp Holdings Limited; *Int'l*, pg. 127
PARADIGM ENERGY, INC.—See Ares Management Corporation; *U.S. Public*, pg. 188
PAR ELECTRICAL CONTRACTORS, INC.—See Quanta Services, Inc.; *U.S. Public*, pg. 1752
PARKSIDE UTILITY CONSTRUCTION CORP.—See Dycom Industries, Inc.; *U.S. Public*, pg. 699
PARKWAY ELECTRIC & COMMUNICATIONS LLC—See Huizenga Manufacturing Group, Inc.; *U.S. Private*, pg. 2004
PARSONS ELECTRIC LLC; *U.S. Private*, pg. 3100
PAUL DINTO ELECTRICAL CONTRS; *U.S. Private*, pg. 3112
PAUL WAGNER ET FILS—See Electricite de France S.A.; *Int'l*, pg. 2352
PEDRO FALCON ELECTRICAL CONTRACTORS INC.; *U.S. Private*, pg. 3128
PEOPLES COMMUNICATIONS SYSTEM—See Peoples Electric Contractor, Inc.; *U.S. Private*, pg. 3141
PEOPLES ELECTRIC CONTRACTOR, INC.; *U.S. Private*, pg. 3141
PERLECTRIC, INC.—See MDU Resources Group, Inc.; *U.S. Public*, pg. 1411
PERRAM ELECTRIC, INC.; *U.S. Private*, pg. 3153
PERRECA ELECTRIC CO. INC.; *U.S. Private*, pg. 3153
PFEIFFER & SON LTD.; *U.S. Private*, pg. 3164
PFMG SOLAR TUSTIN, LLC—See Primoris Services Corporation; *U.S. Public*, pg. 1718
THE PHILADELPHIA BOURSE, INC.; *U.S. Private*, pg. 4094
PHOENIX POWER GROUP, INC.—See Quanta Services, Inc.; *U.S. Public*, pg. 1752
PHPC CO. LTD. INC.—See Hitachi, Ltd.; *Int'l*, pg. 3424
PIEPER ELECTRIC INC.; *U.S. Private*, pg. 3178
PIKE CORPORATION—See Goldberg Lindsay & Co., LLC; *U.S. Private*, pg. 1729
PIKE ELECTRIC, LLC—See Goldberg Lindsay & Co., LLC; *U.S. Private*, pg. 1729
PINNACLE TELECOMMUNICATIONS, INC.; *U.S. Private*, pg. 3185
PLACER ELECTRIC INCORPORATED; *U.S. Private*, pg. 3194
PLAN A SP. Z O.O.—See Agora S.A.; *Int'l*, pg. 212
PLANTRONICS INTERNATIONAL—See HP Inc.; *U.S. Public*, pg. 1064
PLC TRENCHING CO., LLC; *U.S. Private*, pg. 3213
PM & M ELECTRIC, INC.; *U.S. Private*, pg. 3216
POLK MECHANICAL COMPANY, LLC.; *U.S. Private*, pg. 3224
POTELCO, INC.—See Quanta Services, Inc.; *U.S. Public*, pg. 1752
POWERCOM INC.—See SESCO Electrical Services Group; *U.S. Private*, pg. 3617
POWER DESIGN, INC.; *U.S. Private*, pg. 3237
POWER OF CLEAN ENERGY LLC—See Fidelity Engineer-

N.A.I.C.S. INDEX 238210 — ELECTRICAL CONTRACT...

N.A.I.C.S. Index

ing LLC; *U.S. Private*, pg. 1502
POWER PARTNERS MASTEC LLC—See MasTec, Inc.; *U.S. Public*, pg. 1393
POWER SOLUTIONS LLC; *U.S. Private*, pg. 3238
PREFERRED ELECTRIC CO. INC.; *U.S. Private*, pg. 3247
PREMIER ELECTRICAL CORPORATION; *U.S. Private*, pg. 3250
PRESLEY GROUP LTD; *U.S. Private*, pg. 3255
PRIDE ELECTRIC, INC.—See MDU Resources Group, Inc.; *U.S. Public*, pg. 1410
PRIMARY SYSTEMS, INC.; *U.S. Private*, pg. 3261
PRIME ELECTRIC, INC.—See WestView Capital Partners, L.P.; *U.S. Private*, pg. 4501
PRIME SERVICES GROUP INC.; *U.S. Private*, pg. 3262
PRIMETECH COMMUNICATIONS INC.—See Warren Equity Partners, LLC; *U.S. Private*, pg. 4443
PRIMORIS ELECTRIC, INC.—See Primoris Services Corporation; *U.S. Public*, pg. 1719
PRITCHARD ELECTRIC COMPANY, INC.; *U.S. Private*, pg. 3268
PRO SOUND INC.; *U.S. Private*, pg. 3270
P.T. AZBIL BERCA INDONESIA—See Azbil Corporation; *Int'l*, pg. 777
PURDY ELECTRIC, INC.—See Kassel Equity Group, LLC; *U.S. Private*, pg. 2264
PUTNAM MECHANICAL, LLC—See White Wolf Capital LLC; *U.S. Private*, pg. 4510
Q3 CONTRACTING, INC.—See Primoris Services Corporation; *U.S. Public*, pg. 1719
QP ENERGY SERVICES, LLC—See Quanta Services, Inc.; *U.S. Public*, pg. 1752
QUALITY PLUS SERVICES INC.; *U.S. Private*, pg. 3320
QUALITY STANDBY SERVICES, LLC—See High Road Capital Partners, LLC; *U.S. Private*, pg. 1936
QUANTA TELECOM CANADA LTD.—See Quanta Services, Inc.; *U.S. Public*, pg. 1752
QUANTA TELECOMMUNICATION SERVICES, LLC—See Quanta Services, Inc.; *U.S. Public*, pg. 1752
QUANTA UTILITY ENGINEERING SERVICES, INC.—See Quanta Services, Inc.; *U.S. Public*, pg. 1752
QUANTUM RENEWABLE ENERGY SDN. BHD.—See AME Elite Consortium Berhad; *Int'l*, pg. 420
RABALAIS CONSTRUCTORS, LLC—See EMCOR Group, Inc.; *U.S. Public*, pg. 738
RA ELECTRIC, INC.—See Hull Street Energy, LLC; *U.S. Private*, pg. 2005
RATHJE ENTERPRISES INC.; *U.S. Private*, pg. 3357
RAYONG ELECTRICITY GENERATING CO. LTD.—See EGAT Public Company Limited; *Int'l*, pg. 2322
REAL MECHANICAL INC.—See GEMCO Constructors, LLC; *U.S. Private*, pg. 1657
REALTIME UTILITY ENGINEERS, INC.—See Quanta Services, Inc.; *U.S. Public*, pg. 1752
REDFLEX TRAFFIC SYSTEMS (CALIFORNIA) INC.—See Verra Mobility Corporation; *U.S. Public*, pg. 2286
REECES FANTASIES INC.—See Wind Point Advisors LLC; *U.S. Private*, pg. 4535
REGAL BELOIT NEW ZEALAND LTD.—See Regal Rexnord Corporation; *U.S. Public*, pg. 1773
REGAL ELECTRIC, INC.; *U.S. Private*, pg. 3385
REILLY ELECTRICAL CONTRACTORS; *U.S. Private*, pg. 3391
RENEWABLE SOLUTIONS LIGHTING LIMITED—See eEnergy Group Plc; *Int'l*, pg. 2317
RETAIL MAINTENANCE, INC.; *U.S. Private*, pg. 3411
REX MOORE ELECTRICAL CONTRACTORS & ENGINEERS; *U.S. Private*, pg. 3417
R.F. FISHER ELECTRIC CO LLC; *U.S. Private*, pg. 3335
RFI ENTERPRISES INC.—See Wind Point Advisors LLC; *U.S. Private*, pg. 4535
RHODIUS MAGYARORSZAG KFT.—See Equistone Partners Europe Limited; *Int'l*, pg. 2487
RHODIUS SAFETY AND ENVIRONMENTAL SOLUTIONS (KUNSHAN) CO., LTD—See Equistone Partners Europe Limited; *Int'l*, pg. 2487
RHYTHM ENGINEERING; *U.S. Private*, pg. 3424
RIDLEY ELECTRIC CO. INC.; *U.S. Private*, pg. 3434
RIGGS DISTLER & COMPANY INC.; *U.S. Private*, pg. 3435
R.K. ELECTRIC INC.; *U.S. Private*, pg. 3338
RKS ELECTRIC CORP.; *U.S. Private*, pg. 3450
ROBERT FORBIS INC.; *U.S. Private*, pg. 3458
ROBERT WIDMER AG—See Burkhalter Holding AG; *Int'l*, pg. 1225
ROCKWELL AUTOMATION ASIA PACIFIC LIMITED—See Rockwell Automation, Inc.; *U.S. Public*, pg. 1805
ROCKWELL AUTOMATION GESMBH—See Rockwell Automation, Inc.; *U.S. Public*, pg. 1806
ROCKWELL AUTOMATION LIMITED—See Rockwell Automation, Inc.; *U.S. Public*, pg. 1806
ROCKWELL AUTOMATION (MALAYSIA) SDN. BHD.—See Rockwell Automation, Inc.; *U.S. Public*, pg. 1805
ROCKWELL AUTOMATION S.A.—See Rockwell Automation, Inc.; *U.S. Public*, pg. 1806
ROCKWELL AUTOMATION—See Rockwell Automation, Inc.; *U.S. Public*, pg. 1806
ROMAN ELECTRIC COMPANY, INC.; *U.S. Private*, pg. 3475
RONALD THOMPSON LIMITED—See Environ Group (Investments) plc; *Int'l*, pg. 2454
ROSENDIN ELECTRIC, INC.; *U.S. Private*, pg. 3483
ROTOR ELECTRIC LLC.—See Motor City Electric Co., Inc.; *U.S. Private*, pg. 2796
ROYAL PLUS ELECTRIC, INC.; *U.S. Private*, pg. 3493
RUDOLF FRITZ GMBH—See CEZ, a.s.; *Int'l*, pg. 1428
RYDALCH ELECTRIC INC.; *U.S. Private*, pg. 3511
S-1 CORPORATION—See ACI Worldwide, Inc.; *U.S. Public*, pg. 35
SACHS ELECTRIC COMPANY; *U.S. Private*, pg. 3521
SACHS SYSTEMS INC.—See Sachs Electric Company; *U.S. Private*, pg. 3521
SACRED POWER CORP.; *U.S. Private*, pg. 3522
SAIA ELECTRIC, INC.; *U.S. Private*, pg. 3528
SALEM ELECTRIC COMPANY—See Victory of West Virginia, Inc.; *U.S. Private*, pg. 4379
SALUS CONTROLS ROMANIA S.R.L.—See Computime Group Limited; *Int'l*, pg. 1760
SALUS NORDIC A/S—See Computime Group Limited; *Int'l*, pg. 1760
SAN JOAQUIN HELICOPTERS INC.; *U.S. Private*, pg. 3541
SANPULSE TECHNOLOGIES INC.; *U.S. Private*, pg. 3546
SANTSU KENSETSU KOJI CO., LTD.—See COMSYS Holdings Corporation; *Int'l*, pg. 1762
SARGENT ELECTRIC COMPANY; *U.S. Private*, pg. 3550
SASCO ELECTRIC; *U.S. Private*, pg. 3552
SASCO ELECTRIC—See Sasco Electric; *U.S. Private*, pg. 3552
SASCO ELECTRIC—See Sasco Electric; *U.S. Private*, pg. 3552
SAT CORPORATION—See Kratos Defense & Security Solutions, Inc.; *U.S. Public*, pg. 1277
SAULSBURY ELECTRIC CO., INC.—See Saulsbury Industries; *U.S. Private*, pg. 3554
SAULSBURY INDUSTRIES; *U.S. Private*, pg. 3554
SCANDITRON FINLAND OY—See Amplex AB; *Int'l*, pg. 434
SCHACHENMANN & CO. AG—See Burkhalter Holding AG; *Int'l*, pg. 1225
SCHACHENMANN & CO. AG—See Burkhalter Holding AG; *Int'l*, pg. 1225
SCHENECTADY HARDWARE & ELECTRIC CO; *U.S. Private*, pg. 3564
SCHONHOLZER AG—See Burkhalter Holding AG; *Int'l*, pg. 1225
SECCO, INC.; *U.S. Private*, pg. 3593
SECURECOM INC.; *U.S. Private*, pg. 3594
SEDCO LTD.; *U.S. Private*, pg. 3597
SEMI MAROC, S.A.—See ACS, Actividades de Construccion y Servicios, S.A.; *Int'l*, pg. 116
SERGIO LO STANCO ELEKTRO AG—See Burkhalter Holding AG; *Int'l*, pg. 1225
SERVEIS CATALANS, SERVEICA, S.A.—See ACS, Actividades de Construccion y Servicios, S.A.; *Int'l*, pg. 116
SERVICE ELECTRIC CO., INC.; *U.S. Private*, pg. 3615
SETTLE MUTER ELECTRIC; *U.S. Private*, pg. 3618
SEVEN SISTERS INC.—See JH Kelly LLC; *U.S. Private*, pg. 2207
SFS FIRE SERVICES LIMITED—See Carrier Global Corporation; *U.S. Public*, pg. 441
SHAMBAUGH & SON - ED GRACE DIVISION—See EMCOR Group, Inc.; *U.S. Public*, pg. 739
SHAMBAUGH & SON, L.P.—See EMCOR Group, Inc.; *U.S. Public*, pg. 738
SHANAHAN MECHANICAL & ELECTRICAL, INC.—See IES Holdings, Inc.; *U.S. Public*, pg. 1094
SHANGHAI AZBIL AUTOMATION CO., LTD.—See Azbil Corporation; *Int'l*, pg. 777
SHAW ELECTRIC CO.; *U.S. Private*, pg. 3627
SHAW ELECTRIC INC.; *U.S. Private*, pg. 3628
SHAWVER & SON, INC.; *U.S. Private*, pg. 3628
SHELLEY ELECTRIC INC.; *U.S. Private*, pg. 3631
SHEW ELECTRIC, INC.; *U.S. Private*, pg. 3635
SHIZUOKA NDS CO., LTD.—See COMSYS Holdings Corporation; *Int'l*, pg. 1762
SHORT CIRCUIT ELECTRONICS, INC.—See Wind Point Advisors LLC; *U.S. Private*, pg. 4535
SICE ENERGIA, S.L.—See ACS, Actividades de Construccion y Servicios, S.A.; *Int'l*, pg. 116
SICE TECNOLOGIA Y SISTEMAS, S.A.—See ACS, Actividades de Construccion y Servicios, S.A.; *Int'l*, pg. 116
SIDETEL, S.A—See ACS, Actividades de Construccion y Servicios, S.A.; *Int'l*, pg. 116
SIGNAMAX CONNECTIVITY SYSTEMS CANADA, INC.—See AESP, Inc.; *U.S. Private*, pg. 120
SIGORA SOLAR, LLC; *U.S. Private*, pg. 3651
SINTEL S.R.L—See Cellnex Telecom, S.A.; *Int'l*, pg. 1394
SITECO FRANCE S.A.S.—See ams AG; *Int'l*, pg. 440
SITECO GMBH—See ams AG; *Int'l*, pg. 440
SKOGLUND EL & TELE AB—See Bravida Holding AB; *Int'l*, pg. 1142
SMALLS ELECTRICAL CONSTRUCTION, INC.; *U.S. Private*, pg. 3690
SMARTHOUSE INTEGRATION, LLC; *U.S. Private*, pg. 3692
SMITH-GRAY ELECTRIC CO. INC.; *U.S. Private*, pg. 3696
SMITH & KEENE ELECTRIC SERVICE, INC.; *U.S. Private*, pg. 3694
S.N. TANNOR INC.; *U.S. Private*, pg. 3518
SOC IBERICA DE CONSTRUCCIONES ELECTRICAS DE SEGURIDAD, S.L.—See ACS, Actividades de Construccion y Servicios, S.A.; *Int'l*, pg. 116
SOLAR FUNDING SOLUTIONS CORP.; *U.S. Private*, pg. 3707
SOLARINVEST - GREEN ENERGY S.R.O.—See EnBW Energie Baden-Wurttemberg AG; *Int'l*, pg. 2400
SOL IN ONE GMBH—See BayWa AG; *Int'l*, pg. 919
SOREEL—See Kohler Company; *U.S. Private*, pg. 2340
SOREN ANDERSSONS EL I DELSBO AKTIEBOLAG—See Bravida Holding AB; *Int'l*, pg. 1142
SOUND COM CORPORATION—See AMETEK, Inc.; *U.S. Public*, pg. 122
SOUTHEASTERN TELECOM INC.; *U.S. Private*, pg. 3729
SOUTHEASTERN TELECOM OF KNOXVILLE INC.—See Southeastern Telecom Inc.; *U.S. Private*, pg. 3729
SOUTHEASTERN TELECOM—See Southeastern Telecom Inc.; *U.S. Private*, pg. 3729
SOUTHERN CALIFORNIA SOUND IMAGE, INC.; *U.S. Private*, pg. 3730
SOUTHERN DIVERSIFIED TECHNOLOGIES; *U.S. Private*, pg. 3731
SOUTHERN ELECTRIC CORPORATION—See Quanta Services, Inc.; *U.S. Public*, pg. 1753
SOUTHERN POWER & CONTROLS CORP.; *U.S. Private*, pg. 3734
SOUTHERN REWINDING & SALES; *U.S. Private*, pg. 3735
SOUTH JERSEY ENERGY SERVICES PLUS, LLC—See JPMorgan Chase & Co.; *U.S. Public*, pg. 1210
SOUTHLAND INDUSTRIES-MID-ATLANTIC DIVISION—See Southland Industries; *U.S. Private*, pg. 3737
SOUTHWESTERN ELECTRICAL COMPANY INC.; *U.S. Private*, pg. 3741
SPECHT ELECTRIC CO. INC.; *U.S. Private*, pg. 3748
SPENCER TECHNOLOGIES INC.; *U.S. Private*, pg. 3755
SPRIG ELECTRIC CO.; *U.S. Private*, pg. 3763
SRI TELECOM; *U.S. Private*, pg. 3768
S&S ELECTRIC CO., INC.; *U.S. Private*, pg. 3514
STALEY INC.; *U.S. Private*, pg. 3776
STARGATE TELECOM INC.; *U.S. Private*, pg. 3786
STARR ELECTRIC CO. INC.—See Comfort Systems USA, Inc.; *U.S. Public*, pg. 544
STARR ELECTRIC COMPANY—See Comfort Systems USA, Inc.; *U.S. Public*, pg. 544
STEINY & COMPANY, INC.; *U.S. Private*, pg. 3799
STEINY & COMPANY INC.—See Steiny & Company, Inc.; *U.S. Private*, pg. 3799
STELKO ELECTRIC, INC.—See Motor City Electric Co., Inc.; *U.S. Private*, pg. 2797
STOCKTON TELECOMMUNICATIONS; *U.S. Private*, pg. 3815
STONER ELECTRIC INC.; *U.S. Private*, pg. 3830
STROH CORPORATION—See MMC Corp.; *U.S. Private*, pg. 2754
STURGEON ELECTRIC COMPANY—See MYR Group Inc.; *U.S. Public*, pg. 1489
SULLIVAN & MCLAUGHLIN COMPANIES, INC.; *U.S. Private*, pg. 3851
SULLIVAN SOLAR POWER; *U.S. Private*, pg. 3851
SUNETRIC; *U.S. Private*, pg. 3867
SUNPRO, INC.—See Savage Services Corporation; *U.S. Private*, pg. 3555
SUN WEST COMMUNICATIONS, INC.; *U.S. Private*, pg. 3864
SUNWEST ELECTRIC, INC.; *U.S. Private*, pg. 3874
SUPER-ELECTRIC CONSTRUCTION CO.; *U.S. Private*, pg. 3875
SUPERIOR CONTROLS, INC.—See The Graham Group, Inc.; *U.S. Private*, pg. 4036
SUPERIOR GROUP; *U.S. Private*, pg. 3878
SURESERVE FIRE & ELECTRICAL LIMITED—See Cap10 Partners LLP; *Int'l*, pg. 1301
SVAGSTROMSINSTALLATIONER I NORRKOPING AB—See Bravida Holding AB; *Int'l*, pg. 1142
SVENSK INSTALLATIONSPARTNER AB—See BHG Group AB; *Int'l*, pg. 1014
SWAN ELECTRIC COMPANY INC.; *U.S. Private*, pg. 3889
S & W CONTRACTING COMPANY INC.; *U.S. Private*, pg. 3512
SYLVANIA LIGHTING SERVICES—See WESCO International, Inc.; *U.S. Public*, pg. 2352
SYSTEM ELECTRIC CO.; *U.S. Private*, pg. 3906
SYSTEM ONE CONTROL—See Peoples Electric Contractor, Inc.; *U.S. Private*, pg. 3142
SYSTEMS DESIGN GROUP LLC—See Pye-Barker Fire & Safety, LLC; *U.S. Private*, pg. 3309
TAG ELECTRIC COMPANY; *U.S. Private*, pg. 3922
T.A. KAISER HEATING & AIR, INC.—See NRG Energy, Inc.; *U.S. Public*, pg. 1549
TC INFRASTRUCTURE SERVICES LTD.—See Quanta Services, Inc.; *U.S. Public*, pg. 1753
TEAGUE ELECTRIC CONSTRUCTION; *U.S. Private*, pg. 3948
TEC CORP; *U.S. Private*, pg. 3951
TECH ELECTRONICS, INC.—See Tronicom Corp.; *U.S. Private*, pg. 4241
TECH ELECTRONICS OF COLUMBIA, INC.—See Troni-

238210 — ELECTRICAL CONTRACT...

com Corp.; *U.S. Private*, pg. 4242
TECH ELECTRONICS OF ILLINOIS, LLC—See Tronicom Corp.; *U.S. Private*, pg. 4242
TECH ELECTRONICS OF INDIANA, LLC—See Tronicom Corp.; *U.S. Private*, pg. 4242
TECHNICAL SERVICES, INC.—See SkyKnight Capital LLC; *U.S. Private*, pg. 3685
TECHNISONIC SAS—See Gerard Perrier Industrie S.A.; *Int'l*, pg. 2942
TECHNOLOGY RESOURCES INDUSTRIES—See Axiata Group Berhad; *Int'l*, pg. 768
TECHPRO POWER GROUP, INC.; *U.S. Private*, pg. 3956
TECSUR S.A.—See China Three Gorges Corporation; *Int'l*, pg. 1559
TELECLOUD, LLC; *U.S. Private*, pg. 3960
TELECOM TECHNICIANS INC.—See Motor City Electric Co., Inc.; *U.S. Private*, pg. 2797
TELE-OPTICS INC.; *U.S. Private*, pg. 3960
TELSA INSTALACIONES DE TELECOMUNICACIONES Y ELECTRICIDAD, S.A.—See ACS, Actividades de Construccion y Servicios, S.A.; *Int'l*, pg. 116
TELSIS GMBH—See Gamma Communications PLC; *Int'l*, pg. 2878
TERRAFIX GEOSYNTHETICS INC.—See Leggett & Platt, Incorporated; *U.S. Public*, pg. 1303
TERRY'S ELECTRIC INC.; *U.S. Private*, pg. 3972
TEX-CAP ELECTRIC INC.—See McCarty Corporation; *U.S. Private*, pg. 2628
THOMPSON ELECTRIC, INC.; *U.S. Private*, pg. 4159
THOROUGHBRED TECHNOLOGY AND TELECOMMUNICATIONS—See Norfolk Southern Corporation; *U.S. Public*, pg. 1536
THREE PHASE LINE CONSTRUCTION, INC.—See MasTec, Inc.; *U.S. Public*, pg. 1393
TIEPOLO S.R.L.—See Hera S.p.A.; *Int'l*, pg. 3856
TIM RHODES ELECTRIC CO., INC.—See Shoals MPE, LLC; *U.S. Private*, pg. 3639
TOHO KOJI CO., LTD.—See COMSYS Holdings Corporation; *Int'l*, pg. 1762
TOTEM ELECTRIC OF TACOMA INC.; *U.S. Private*, pg. 4192
TOWNSEND SYSTEMS—See MSCO Inc.; *U.S. Private*, pg. 2806
TRAFFIC CONTROL DEVICES INC.; *U.S. Private*, pg. 4203
TRANSCORE MARKETING COMMUNICATIONS—See Roper Technologies, Inc.; *U.S. Public*, pg. 1814
TRANSGLOBAL COMMUNICATIONS INC.; *U.S. Private*, pg. 4208
TRESCH ELECTRICAL COMPANY; *U.S. Private*, pg. 4218
TRIANGLE ELECTRIC COMPANY; *U.S. Private*, pg. 4226
TRI-CITY ELECTRICAL CONTRACTORS, INC.; *U.S. Private*, pg. 4221
TRI-CITY ELECTRICAL CONTRACTORS, INC. - TAMPA DIVISION—See Tri-City Electrical Contractors, Inc.; *U.S. Private*, pg. 4221
TRI-CITY ELECTRIC CO.; *U.S. Private*, pg. 4221
TRI-COUNTY ELECTRIC COMPANY, INC.—See Penn Line Corp.; *U.S. Private*, pg. 3134
TRI GLOBAL ENERGY LLC—See Enbridge Inc.; *Int'l*, pg. 2397
TRIPLE-D COMMUNICATIONS, LLC—See Dycom Industries, Inc.; *U.S. Public*, pg. 699
TRONICOM CORP.; *U.S. Private*, pg. 4241
TROPICAL COMMUNICATIONS, INC.—See High Wire Networks Inc.; *U.S. Public*, pg. 1035
TRUENET COMMUNICATIONS, CORP.—See Fujitsu Limited; *Int'l*, pg. 2833
TRUMBO ELECTRIC, INCORPORATED—See Comfort Systems USA, Inc.; *U.S. Public*, pg. 544
TURBO FILTRATION, LLC—See AIP, LLC; *U.S. Private*, pg. 136
TURNUPSEED ELECTRIC SERVICE, INC.; *U.S. Private*, pg. 4261
UNDERGROUND SPECIALISTS INC.; *U.S. Private*, pg. 4279
UNDERGROUND SPECIALTIES, LLC—See Dycom Industries, Inc.; *U.S. Public*, pg. 699
UNI-DATA SERVICES, LLC—See Unity Electric Co., Inc.; *U.S. Private*, pg. 4302
UNITED ELECTRIC CO. INC.; *U.S. Private*, pg. 4291
UNITED STATES INFO SYSTEMS INC.; *U.S. Private*, pg. 4299
UNITY DATA & ELECTRICAL SERVICES—See Unity Electric Co, Inc.; *U.S. Private*, pg. 4302
UNITY ELECTRIC CO. INC.; *U.S. Private*, pg. 4302
UNITY ELECTRIC LLC—See Unity Electric Co. Inc.; *U.S. Private*, pg. 4302
URBAN CABLE TECHNOLOGY INC.—See QualTek Services Inc.; *U.S. Public*, pg. 1748
UTILITY LINE MANAGEMENT SERVICES, INC.—See Quanta Services, Inc.; *U.S. Public*, pg. 1753
VALARD CONSTRUCTION LP—See Quanta Services, Inc.; *U.S. Public*, pg. 1753
VALLEY ELECTRIC COMPANY OF MOUNT VERNON, INC.; *U.S. Private*, pg. 4333
VALLEY POWER LIMITED PARTNERSHIP—See Algonquin Power & Utilities Corp.; *Int'l*, pg. 319
VANDERHOYDONCKS ELEKTROTECHNIEKEN NV—See Ackermans & van Haaren NV; *Int'l*, pg. 105
VAN ERT ELECTRIC COMPANY INC.; *U.S. Private*, pg. 4340
VARCOMAC LLC—See Blackstone Inc.; *U.S. Public*, pg. 361
VARNEY INC.; *U.S. Private*, pg. 4347
VAUGHN INDUSTRIES, LLC.; *U.S. Private*, pg. 4348
VDH ELECTRIC INC.—See VHC Inc.; *U.S. Private*, pg. 4375
V E C A ELECTRIC COMPANY INC.; *U.S. Private*, pg. 4327
VECTORUSA; *U.S. Private*, pg. 4353
VELPA SOLUCIONES INTEGRALES S.A.—See Emek Elektrik Endustrisi A.S.; *Int'l*, pg. 2377
VERDE ELECTRIC CORP.; *U.S. Private*, pg. 4359
VHC INC.; *U.S. Private*, pg. 4374
VIPOND FIRE PROTECTION, LTD—See APi Group Corporation; *Int'l*, pg. 514
VIPOND, INC.—See APi Group Corporation; *Int'l*, pg. 514
VIVINT, INC.—See NRG Energy, Inc.; *U.S. Public*, pg. 1551
VOS ELECTRIC INC.—See VHC Inc.; *U.S. Private*, pg. 4375
VOZZCOM, INC.; *U.S. Private*, pg. 4414
THE WAGNER SMITH COMPANY; *U.S. Private*, pg. 4132
THE WAGNER-SMITH COMPANY—See MDU Resources Group, Inc.; *U.S. Public*, pg. 1410
WALKER ENGINEERING, INC.; *U.S. Private*, pg. 4429
WALLACE ENGINEERING, INC.—See Comfort Systems USA, Inc.; *U.S. Public*, pg. 543
WARRAN ELECTRIC MANUFACTURING LIMITED—See Allan International Holdings Limited; *Int'l*, pg. 332
WASATCH ELECTRIC—See EMCOR Group, Inc.; *U.S. Public*, pg. 737
WAVEGUIDE, INC.; *U.S. Private*, pg. 4458
WAYNE J. GRIFFIN ELECTRIC INC.; *U.S. Private*, pg. 4459
WAYNE J. GRIFFIN ELECTRIC INC.—See Wayne J. Griffin Electric Inc.; *U.S. Private*, pg. 4460
WAYNE J. GRIFFIN ELECTRIC INC.—See Wayne J. Griffin Electric Inc.; *U.S. Private*, pg. 4460
WAYPOINT SYSTEMS, INC.—See ATS Automation Inc.; *U.S. Private*, pg. 382
WBI ENERGY WIND RIDGE PIPELINE, LLC—See MDU Resources Group, Inc.; *U.S. Public*, pg. 1411
WDF/FIVE STAR HOLDING CORPORATION; *U.S. Private*, pg. 4462
WECKWORTH ELECTRIC COMPANY, INC.; *U.S. Private*, pg. 4468
WEIFIELD GROUP CONTRACTING, LLC; *U.S. Private*, pg. 4470
WELLS & TATE ELECTRIC COMPANY INC.; *U.S. Private*, pg. 4476
WELSBACH ELECTRIC CORP. OF LONG ISLAND—See EMCOR Group, Inc.; *U.S. Public*, pg. 737
WELSBACH ELECTRIC CORP.—See EMCOR Group, Inc.; *U.S. Public*, pg. 737
WESTERN PACIFIC ENTERPRISES LTD.—See MYR Group Inc.; *U.S. Public*, pg. 1489
WESTERN TEL-COM INC.; *U.S. Private*, pg. 4497
WEST-FAIR ELECTRIC CONTRACTORS INC.; *U.S. Private*, pg. 4488
WESTGATE, INC.; *U.S. Private*, pg. 4498
WEST SIDE HAMMER ELECTRIC; *U.S. Private*, pg. 4487
WEST VIRGINIA ELECTRIC CORP.—See Victory of West Virginia, Inc.; *U.S. Private*, pg. 4379
WHITE CREEK WIND PROJECT; *U.S. Private*, pg. 4508
WHITE ELECTRICAL CONSTRUCTION CO.; *U.S. Private*, pg. 4509
WIGDAHL ELECTRIC CO.; *U.S. Private*, pg. 4517
THE WILL GROUP, INC.; *U.S. Private*, pg. 4136
WILLIAM MASTERS INC.; *U.S. Private*, pg. 4523
WILLIAMS ELECTRIC CO. INC.—See Parsons Corporation; *U.S. Public*, pg. 1651
WILSON ELECTRIC SERVICES CORP.; *U.S. Private*, pg. 4530
WINDEMULLER ELECTRIC INC.; *U.S. Private*, pg. 4537
WINDEMULLER TECHNICAL SERVICES, INC.; *U.S. Private*, pg. 4537
WINDY CITY ELECTRIC COMPANY; *U.S. Private*, pg. 4540
WINSTON ELECTRIC; *U.S. Private*, pg. 4544
THE WIRENUT; *U.S. Private*, pg. 4138
W & M SPRINKLER COMPANY, INC.—See APi Group Corporation; *Int'l*, pg. 513
W & M SPRINKLER NYC LLC—See APi Group Corporation; *Int'l*, pg. 513
WOLFENSON ELECTRIC, INC.; *U.S. Private*, pg. 4554
WOLFE & TRAVIS ELECTRIC COMPANY, INC.; *U.S. Private*, pg. 4554
WOLTCOM, INC.; *U.S. Private*, pg. 4554
XTREME COMMUNICATIONS, INC.; *U.S. Private*, pg. 4583
YAMATAKE ENVIRONMENTAL CONTROL TECHNOLOGY (BEIJING) CO., LTD.—See Azbil Corporation; *Int'l*, pg. 777
YMH TORRANCE INC.; *U.S. Private*, pg. 4589
YORK RIVER ELECTRIC, INC.; *U.S. Private*, pg. 4591
YOUNG'S COMMUNICATIONS CO, INC.—See Cotton Creek Capital Management LLC; *U.S. Private*, pg. 1064
YVAN PAQUE S.A.—See Eiffage S.A.; *Int'l*, pg. 2330
ZILLER ELECTRIC INC.; *U.S. Private*, pg. 4604
ZWICKER ELECTRIC CO., INC.; *U.S. Private*, pg. 4610

238220 — PLUMBING, HEATING, AND AIR-CONDITIONING CONTRACTORS

1 PRIORITY ENVIRONMENTAL SERVICES, LLC—See Earth Services & Abatement, Inc.; *U.S. Private*, pg. 1314
2ND WIND HEATING & AIR CONDITIONING, INC.—See NearU Services; *U.S. Private*, pg. 2877
5-STAR REFRIGERATION & AIR CONDITIONING, INC.; *U.S. Private*, pg. 16
7AC TECHNOLOGIES INC.—See Emerson Electric Co.; *U.S. Public*, pg. 740
A-1 HEATING & AIR CONDITIONING, INC.; *U.S. Private*, pg. 21
AA ADVANCE AIR, INC.; *U.S. Private*, pg. 29
AAA REFRIGERATION SERVICE INC; *U.S. Private*, pg. 30
ABACUS PLUMBING COMPANY; *U.S. Private*, pg. 34
ABBAR & ZAINY DAIKIN AIRCONDITIONING COMPANY LTD.—See Daikin Industries, Ltd.; *Int'l*, pg. 1932
ABCO FIRE PROTECTION, INC.; *U.S. Private*, pg. 36
ABC REFRIGERATION & AIR CONDITIONING, INC.—See Ares Management Corporation; *U.S. Public*, pg. 189
AB HANGO ELEKTRISKA - HANGON SAHKO OY—See Bravida Holding AB; *Int'l*, pg. 1142
AB HANGO ELEKTRISKA—See Bravida Holding AB; *Int'l*, pg. 1142
ABM BUILDING SERVICES, LLC—See ABM Industries, Inc.; *U.S. Public*, pg. 25
ABM BUILDING SOLUTIONS, LLC—See ABM Industries, Inc.; *U.S. Public*, pg. 25
ABSOLUTE PROTECTIVE SYSTEMS, INC.—See The Carlyle Group Inc.; *U.S. Public*, pg. 2053
ACCELERATED ARTIFICIAL LIFT SYSTEMS, LLC—See Dover Corporation; *U.S. Public*, pg. 678
ACCELERATED COMPANIES, LLC—See Dover Corporation; *U.S. Public*, pg. 678
ACC INDUSTRIES INCORPORATED; *U.S. Private*, pg. 47
ACCO ENGINEERED SYSTEMS; *U.S. Private*, pg. 53
AC CORPORATION; *U.S. Private*, pg. 45
AC DESIGNS, INC.—See Gemini Investors LLC; *U.S. Private*, pg. 1658
ACI NORTHWEST, INC.; *U.S. Private*, pg. 59
ACORN INDUSTRIAL, INC.—See Comfort Systems USA, Inc.; *U.S. Public*, pg. 543
ACTION AIR SYSTEMS, INC.; *U.S. Private*, pg. 67
ACTION, INC.; *U.S. Private*, pg. 68
ADEEDO! DRAIN, PLUMBING, HEATING, AIR, & ELECTRICAL—See Odyssey Investment Partners, LLC; *U.S. Private*, pg. 2995
ADEKA ENGINEERING & CONSTRUCTION CORP.—See Adeka Corporation; *Int'l*, pg. 141
A+ DERR HEATING & AIR CONDITIONING, LLC; *U.S. Private*, pg. 21
A & D FIRE PROTECTION INC.; *U.S. Private*, pg. 17
ADVANCED FIRE SYSTEMS INC.—See Halma plc; *Int'l*, pg. 3230
ADVANCE MECHANICAL CONTRACTORS; *U.S. Private*, pg. 83
ADVANCE MECHANICAL SYSTEMS, INC.; *U.S. Private*, pg. 83
ADVANTAGE FIRE SPRINKLER CO., INC.—See FirstService Corporation; *Int'l*, pg. 2691
A.D. WINSTON CORPORATION; *U.S. Private*, pg. 25
AEMS SERVICE COMPANY; *U.S. Private*, pg. 117
AESA AIR ENGINEERING SA—See Batliboi Ltd.; *Int'l*, pg. 890
A.E. SMITH SERVICE PTY LTD—See Downer EDI Limited; *Int'l*, pg. 2185
A.E. SMITH & SON PROPRIETARY LIMITED—See Downer EDI Limited; *Int'l*, pg. 2185
AFR LIMITED—See Carillion plc; *Int'l*, pg. 1330
AHERN FIRE PROTECTION—See J.F. Ahern Co.; *U.S. Private*, pg. 2162
AHERN FIRE PROTECTION—See J.F. Ahern Co.; *U.S. Private*, pg. 2162
AHERN FIRE PROTECTION—See J.F. Ahern Co.; *U.S. Private*, pg. 2162
AHERN FIRE PROTECTION—See J.F. Ahern Co.; *U.S. Private*, pg. 2162
AHLSELL DANMARK APS—See Ahlsell AB; *Int'l*, pg. 223
AIRCO MECHANICAL INC.; *U.S. Private*, pg. 140
AIREKO CONSTRUCTION CORP.; *U.S. Private*, pg. 141
AIRE SERV LLC—See Harvest Partners L.P.; *U.S. Private*, pg. 1877
AIR EXPERTS TODAY CORP.; *U.S. Private*, pg. 138
AIR FLOW DESIGNS INC.; *U.S. Private*, pg. 138
AIR GENIE AIR CONDITIONING CO.; *U.S. Private*, pg. 138
AIRITE HEATING, AIR CONDITIONING & SHEET METAL, INC.—See ABM Industries, Inc.; *U.S. Public*, pg. 25
AIR MANAGEMENT SYSTEMS INC.; *U.S. Private*, pg. 139
AIR MASTERS HVAC SERVICES OF NEW ENGLAND, INC.—See Thielsch Engineering, Inc.; *U.S. Private*, pg. 4144
AIR MECHANICAL & SERVICE CORP.; *U.S. Private*, pg. 139
AIRPLUS, SPOL. S R O.—See CEZ, a.s.; *Int'l*, pg. 1426
AIRPRO INC.—See Comfort Services Inc.; *U.S. Private*, pg. 981
AIR PROS USA; *U.S. Private*, pg. 139

N.A.I.C.S. INDEX

238220 — PLUMBING, HEATING, ...

AIR QUALITY CONTROL, INC.; *U.S. Private*, pg. 139
AIR RESCUE AIR CONDITIONING, INC.; *U.S. Private*, pg. 139
AIR-RITE HEATING & COOLING; *U.S. Private*, pg. 140
AIR SYSTEMS ENGINEERING, INC.—See Comfort Systems USA, Inc.; *U.S. Public*, pg. 543
AIR SYSTEMS, INC.—See EMCOR Group, Inc.; *U.S. Public*, pg. 736
AIR SYSTEM TECHNOLOGY (S) PTE LTD—See Acesian Partners Limited; *Int'l*, pg. 102
AIRTEMP, INC.—See Comfort Systems USA, Inc.; *U.S. Public*, pg. 543
AIRTROL, INC.; *U.S. Private*, pg. 142
AIRTRON HOUSTON—See NRG Energy, Inc.; *U.S. Public*, pg. 1549
A.J. DANBOISE SON INC.; *U.S. Private*, pg. 26
AJ DEMOR & SONS INC.; *U.S. Private*, pg. 143
A. J. PERRI, INC.—See Del-Air Heating, Air Conditioning & Refrigeration Corp.; *U.S. Private*, pg. 1193
AK HVAC, INC.—See Marathon HVAC Services, LLC; *U.S. Private*, pg. 2570
ALBERN CO.; *U.S. Private*, pg. 152
ALCON MECHANICAL, INC.; *U.S. Private*, pg. 154
ALDAG-HONOLD MECHANICAL, INC.; *U.S. Private*, pg. 154
ALFA LAVAL AALBORG INDUSTRIA E COMERCIO LTDA.—See Alfa Laval AB; *Int'l*, pg. 308
AL-FUTTAIM ENGINEERING COMPANY LLC—See Al-Futtaim Private Company LLC; *Int'l*, pg. 285
ALL AREA PLUMBING, INC.—See ACCO Engineered Systems; *U.S. Private*, pg. 53
ALLCOOL REFRIGERANT RECLAIM, LLC—See BC Partners LLP; *Int'l*, pg. 923
ALLCOOL REFRIGERANT RECLAIM, LLC—See EQT AB; *Int'l*, pg. 2482
ALLSTAFF AIRCONDITIONING (ACT) PTY LIMITED—See BSA Limited; *Int'l*, pg. 1201
ALLSTAFF AIRCONDITIONING (NSW) PTY LIMITED—See BSA Limited; *Int'l*, pg. 1201
ALLSTAFF AIRCONDITIONING (VIC) PTY LIMITED—See BSA Limited; *Int'l*, pg. 1201
ALMCOE REFRIGERATION CO.—See Wind Point Advisors LLC; *U.S. Private*, pg. 4536
ALTA INTERCONNECTION MANAGEMENT, LLC—See NRG Energy, Inc.; *U.S. Public*, pg. 1549
ALTHOFF INDUSTRIES INC.; *U.S. Private*, pg. 208
AMBASSADOR SERVICES, INC.; *U.S. Private*, pg. 217
AMERICAN AIR & HEAT, INC.—See Catterton Management Company, LLC; *U.S. Private*, pg. 793
AMERICAN AIR SYSTEMS, INC.; *U.S. Private*, pg. 222
AMERICAN FIRE PROTECTION, INC.; *U.S. Private*, pg. 234
AMERICAN REFRACTORIES CO.—See RGP Holding, Inc.; *U.S. Private*, pg. 3420
AMERICAN REFRIGERATION LLC—See EMC Company; *U.S. Private*, pg. 1379
AMERICAN RESIDENTIAL SERVICES LLC—See Del-Air Heating, Air Conditioning & Refrigeration Corp.; *U.S. Private*, pg. 1193
AMOS & ANDREWS INC.—See Andrews Group; *U.S. Private*, pg. 280
AMPAM PARKS MECHANICAL, INC.—See Gemspring Capital Management, LLC; *U.S. Private*, pg. 1658
AMS MECHANICAL SYSTEMS, INC.; *U.S. Private*, pg. 266
ANDERSEN COMMERCIAL PLUMBING, INC.—See Sun Capital Partners, Inc.; *U.S. Private*, pg. 3858
ANDGAR CORPORATION; *U.S. Private*, pg. 278
ANDREWS GROUP; *U.S. Private*, pg. 280
ANDREWS SYKES BVBA—See ANDREWS SYKES GROUP PLC; *Int'l*, pg. 452
ANDREWS SYKES B.V.—See ANDREWS SYKES GROUP PLC; *Int'l*, pg. 452
ANDREWS SYKES LUXEMBOURG SARL—See ANDREWS SYKES GROUP PLC; *Int'l*, pg. 452
ANMAR MECHANICAL AND ELECTRICAL CONTRACTORS LTD.; *Int'l*, pg. 473
ANN ARBOR FIRE PROTECTION INC.; *U.S. Private*, pg. 284
A.O. REED & CO.—See Blackstone Inc.; *U.S. Private*, pg. 355
APEX SERVICE PARTNERS LLC; *U.S. Private*, pg. 293
APOLLO SHEET METAL INC.; *U.S. Private*, pg. 295
APPLEGATE, INC; *U.S. Private*, pg. 297
APPLIED MECHANICAL SYSTEMS, INC.; *U.S. Private*, pg. 299
ARAMENDIA PLUMBING, HEATING & AIR, LTD.—See Brookfield Infrastructure Partners L.P.; *Int'l*, pg. 1190
ARDEN ENGINEERING CONSTRUCTORS LLC; *U.S. Private*, pg. 317
ARISTA AIR CONDITIONING CORPORATION; *U.S. Private*, pg. 323
ARJAE SHEET METAL COMPANY, INC.—See Ares Management Corporation; *U.S. Public*, pg. 189
ARMISTEAD MECHANICAL INC.; *U.S. Private*, pg. 330
ARMSTRONG AIR & HEATING INC.; *U.S. Private*, pg. 331
A & R PLUMBING, INC.; *U.S. Private*, pg. 18
ASAHI ENGINEERING (MALAYSIA) SDN. BHD.—See Asahi Kogyosha Co., Ltd.; *Int'l*, pg. 598

ASAHI KOGYOSHA CO., LTD.; *Int'l*, pg. 598
ASIATIC GROUP (HOLDINGS) LIMITED; *Int'l*, pg. 620
ASIA VITAL COMPONENTS CO., LTD.; *Int'l*, pg. 616
A.S.I. HASTINGS, INC.—See Odyssey Investment Partners, LLC; *U.S. Private*, pg. 2995
ASPEN AIR CONDITIONING, INC.—See Del-Air Heating, Air Conditioning & Refrigeration Corp.; *U.S. Private*, pg. 1193
ATLANTA REFRIGERATION SERVICE COMPANY, INC.; *U.S. Private*, pg. 371
ATLAS BUTLER HEATING & COOLING; *U.S. Private*, pg. 375
ATLAS COMFORT SYSTEMS USA, INC.—See Comfort Systems USA, Inc.; *U.S. Public*, pg. 543
ATLAS TRILLO HEATING & AIR CONDITIONING, INC.—See Del-Air Heating, Air Conditioning & Refrigeration Corp.; *U.S. Private*, pg. 1193
ATOMATIC MECHANICAL SERVICES, INC.; *U.S. Private*, pg. 381
AUGUST WINTER & SONS INC.; *U.S. Private*, pg. 392
AUJARD SAS—See Brookfield Corporation; *Int'l*, pg. 1188
AUSTIN INDUSTRIAL, INC.—See Austin Industries, Inc.; *U.S. Private*, pg. 396
AUTOMATIC FIRE SPRINKLERS, INC.—See Pye-Barker Fire & Safety, LLC; *U.S. Private*, pg. 3309
AVENAL PARK LLC—See BlackRock, Inc.; *U.S. Public*, pg. 345
AVON LIPPIATT HOBBS (CONTRACTING) LIMITED; *Int'l*, pg. 749
AV SOLAR RANCH 1, LLC—See Constellation Energy Corporation; *U.S. Public*, pg. 571
AXBERG HEATING—See Black Diamond Plumbing & Mechanical, Inc.; *U.S. Private*, pg. 571
AZCO INC.—See Burns & McDonnell, Inc.; *U.S. Private*, pg. 690
AZ KLIMA SK, S.R.O.—See CEZ, a.s.; *Int'l*, pg. 1426
AZTEC SOLAR, INC.—See Sigora Solar, LLC; *U.S. Private*, pg. 3651
BAETE FORSETH INC.; *U.S. Private*, pg. 425
BAKER GROUP; *U.S. Private*, pg. 456
BAKER & SONS AIR CONDITIONING, INC.; *U.S. Private*, pg. 455
BANNER FURNACE & FUEL INC.; *U.S. Private*, pg. 469
BARRON HEATING & AIR CONDITIONING INC.; *U.S. Private*, pg. 480
BASEELAH MECHANICAL WORKS—See Al-Osais International Holding Company; *Int'l*, pg. 287
BASS AIR CONDITIONING CO, INC.—See DLVA, Inc.; *U.S. Private*, pg. 1248
BATCHELOR & KIMBALL, INC.—See EMCOR Group, Inc.; *U.S. Public*, pg. 736
BATJER SERVICE; *U.S. Private*, pg. 487
BAY MECHANICAL INC.; *U.S. Private*, pg. 494
BAYONET PLUMBING, HEATING & AIR CONDITIONING, LLC—See IES Holdings, Inc.; *U.S. Public*, pg. 1094
BAYWA ENERGIE DIENSTLEISTUNGS GMBH—See BayWa AG; *Int'l*, pg. 916
B&B TRADE DISTRIBUTION CENTRE; *Int'l*, pg. 783
BCH MECHANICAL LLC—See Comfort Systems USA, Inc.; *U.S. Public*, pg. 543
BCM CONTROLS CORPORATION—See Comfort Systems USA, Inc.; *U.S. Public*, pg. 543
BEAR'S PLUMBING INC.; *U.S. Private*, pg. 506
BEE MINE PRODUCTS INC.; *U.S. Private*, pg. 512
BEIJING FUEL TECH ENVIRONMENTAL TECHNOLOGIES CO., LTD.—See Fuel Tech, Inc.; *U.S. Public*, pg. 891
BELL BCI COMPANY—See Bell Corp. of Rochester; *U.S. Private*, pg. 518
BELLE AIR INC.—See NorthCurrent Partners, LLC; *U.S. Private*, pg. 2949
BELL PRODUCTS, INC.; *U.S. Private*, pg. 519
BENDER & MODLIN FIRE SPRINKLER, INC.—See Pye-Barker Fire & Safety, LLC; *U.S. Private*, pg. 3309
BENEDICT REFRIGERATION SERVICE, INC.; *U.S. Private*, pg. 525
BEN LEWIS PLUMBING, HEATING & AIR CONDITIONING, INC.; *U.S. Private*, pg. 522
BENTZEL MECHANICAL INC.; *U.S. Private*, pg. 529
BERKLEY EAST SOLAR, LLC—See Duke Energy Corporation; *U.S. Public*, pg. 690
BERNHARD BROTHERS MECHANICAL CONTRACTORS, LLC; *U.S. Private*, pg. 536
BETLEM SERVICE CORPORATION—See EMCOR Group, Inc.; *U.S. Public*, pg. 737
BEUTLER HEATING & AIR CONDITIONING INC.; *U.S. Private*, pg. 547
BEYER MECHANICAL, LTD.; *U.S. Private*, pg. 548
B-G MECHANICAL, INC.—See Bouygues S.A.; *Int'l*, pg. 1121
B-G MECHANICAL SERVICE, INC.—See Bouygues S.A.; *Int'l*, pg. 1121
BIG BEAR A/C & HEATING, LLC—See Coltala Holdings, LLC; *U.S. Private*, pg. 976
BIG CHIEF INC.—See Gryphon Investors, LLC; *U.S. Private*, pg. 1799
BIG J ENTERPRISES LLC; *U.S. Private*, pg. 553
BILFINGER ROTRING ENGINEERING GMBH—See Bilfinger SE; *Int'l*, pg. 1027

BIS NYHAMMAR VAST AB—See Bilfinger SE; *Int'l*, pg. 1025
BLACK-HAAK HEATING, INC.; *U.S. Private*, pg. 573
BLOOM ENGINEERING (EUROPA) GMBH—See Caledonia Investments plc; *Int'l*, pg. 1262
BONLAND INDUSTRIES, INC.; *U.S. Private*, pg. 614
BOONE & DARR, INC.; *U.S. Private*, pg. 616
BORRELL ELECTRIC CO INC.; *U.S. Private*, pg. 619
BOWEN INDUSTRIAL CONTRACTORS; *U.S. Private*, pg. 625
BRADBURN PLUMBING CO. INC.—See Bryant-Durham Electric Co., Inc.; *U.S. Private*, pg. 674
BRAGG CRANE & RIGGING; *U.S. Private*, pg. 634
THE BRANDT COMPANIES, LLC—See Southland Industries; *U.S. Private*, pg. 3737
BRAVIDA DANMARK AS—See Bravida Holding AB; *Int'l*, pg. 1142
BRAVIDA FINLAND OY—See Bravida Holding AB; *Int'l*, pg. 1142
BRAVIDA NORGE AS—See Bravida Holding AB; *Int'l*, pg. 1142
BRAVIDA SVERIGE AB—See Bravida Holding AB; *Int'l*, pg. 1142
BREWER & COMPANY OF WEST VIRGINIA, INC.; *U.S. Private*, pg. 647
BREWER-GARRETT CO; *U.S. Private*, pg. 647
BRIGHT SHEET METAL COMPANY, INC.; *U.S. Private*, pg. 651
BRODRENE DAHL A/S—See Compagnie de Saint-Gobain SA; *Int'l*, pg. 1733
BROTHERS AIR & HEAT, INC.—See Del-Air Heating, Air Conditioning & Refrigeration Corp.; *U.S. Private*, pg. 1193
BROWN SPRINKLER CORPORATION; *U.S. Private*, pg. 669
BRUBAKER, INC.; *U.S. Private*, pg. 670
BUCKEYE HEATING AND COOLING SERVICES, INC.—See Leonard Green & Partners, L.P.; *U.S. Private*, pg. 2430
BUILDING AIR SERVICES, INC.—See Ares Management Corporation; *U.S. Public*, pg. 189
BUILDING TECHNOLOGY ENGINEERS, INC.—See EMCOR Group, Inc.; *U.S. Public*, pg. 737
BURDICK PLUMBING & HEATING CO; *U.S. Private*, pg. 686
BURKE AIR PTY LIMITED - KALGOORLIE DIVISION—See BSA Limited; *Int'l*, pg. 1201
BURKE AIR PTY LIMITED—See BSA Limited; *Int'l*, pg. 1201
BURKHOLDER'S HEATING & AIR CONDITIONING, INC.; *U.S. Private*, pg. 688
BURNS BROS. CONTRACTORS, INC.; *U.S. Private*, pg. 690
BURNS MECHANICAL, INC.—See Riverstone Holdings LLC; *U.S. Private*, pg. 3447
BURT-BURNETT, INC.—See Fiat Incorporated; *U.S. Private*, pg. 1501
B & W MECHANICAL CONTRACTORS, INC.; *U.S. Private*, pg. 417
CALDWELL PLUMBING CO., INC.; *U.S. Private*, pg. 716
CALIQUA ANLAGENTECHNIK GMBH—See Alpiq Holding AG; *Int'l*, pg. 372
CANADIAN CHEMICAL CLEANING SERVICES INC.—See AIP, LLC; *U.S. Private*, pg. 135
CANYON STATE AIR CONDITIONING & HEATING, INC.—See Brookfield Corporation; *Int'l*, pg. 1188
THE CAPITAL REFRIGERATION COMPANY—See Comfort Systems USA, Inc.; *U.S. Public*, pg. 544
CARLYSLE ENGINEERING INC.; *U.S. Private*, pg. 765
CAROLINA HEATING SERVICE OF GREENVILLE, INC.—See DLVA, Inc.; *U.S. Private*, pg. 1248
CARRIER INTERAMERICA CORPORATION—See Watsco, Inc.; *U.S. Public*, pg. 2336
CASM, INC.—See CyberAgent, Inc.; *Int'l*, pg. 1892
CATTRELL COMPANIES, INC.; *U.S. Private*, pg. 794
CAYCE COMPANY INC.; *U.S. Private*, pg. 795
C.B. STRAIN & SON INC.; *U.S. Private*, pg. 706
CCI THERMAL TECHNOLOGIES, INC.—See Thermon Group Holdings, Inc.; *U.S. Public*, pg. 2155
C & C SERVICE, LLC.—See Crete Mechanical Group, Inc.; *U.S. Private*, pg. 1099
CELEY'S QUALITY PLUMBING, INC.; *U.S. Private*, pg. 806
CEN-CAL FIRE SYSTEMS INC.—See The Carlyle Group Inc.; *U.S. Public*, pg. 2053
CENERGIST SPAIN SL—See Eneraqua Technologies Plc; *Int'l*, pg. 2418
CENTRAL REFRIGERATION AND AIR CONDITIONING LTD.; *Int'l*, pg. 1409
CENTRAL STATE CONSTRUCTION, CORPORATION; *U.S. Private*, pg. 825
CEZ ESCO BULGARIA EOOD—See CEZ, a.s.; *Int'l*, pg. 1426
CHAMPION INDUSTRIAL CONTRACTORS INC.; *U.S. Private*, pg. 846
CHARLES A. KLEIN AND SONS, INC; *U.S. Private*, pg. 851
CHARLES E. JARRELL CONTRACTING COMPANY, INC.; *U.S. Private*, pg. 852
CHARLES P. BLOUIN, INC.; *U.S. Private*, pg. 853
CHARLESTON HEATING & AIR, LLC; *U.S. Private*, pg. 856

238220 — PLUMBING, HEATING, ...

CHAS ROBERTS AIR CONDITIONING, INC.; *U.S. Private,* pg. 859
CHC MECHANICAL CONTRACTORS; *U.S. Private,* pg. 868
CHEMED CORPORATION; *U.S. Public,* pg. 484
CHEMFAB INDUSTRIES INC.; *Int'l,* pg. 1461
CHEMINVEST AS; *Int'l,* pg. 1462
CHESAPEAKE SPRINKLER COMPANY; *U.S. Private,* pg. 875
CHRONOMITE LABORATORIES, INC.—See Acorn Engineering Company, Inc.; *U.S. Private,* pg. 63
CIEMME S.R.L.—See I.M.A. Industria Macchine Automatiche S.p.A; *Int'l,* pg. 3565
C.J. BETTERS CORPORATION; *U.S. Private,* pg. 708
C.J. ERICKSON PLUMBING CO.; *U.S. Private,* pg. 708
CLEVELAND AIR COMFORT CORP.—See Morgan Stanley; *U.S. Public,* pg. 1474
CLIMAT LOCATION SA—See ANDREWS SYKES GROUP PLC; *Int'l,* pg. 452
CM3 BUILDING SOLUTIONS, INC.—See Daikin Industries, Ltd.; *Int'l,* pg. 1936
CMC REBAR—See Commercial Metals Company; *U.S. Public,* pg. 546
CMH INC.; *U.S. Private,* pg. 951
CNA INTEGRATED TECHNOLOGIES (LLC)—See CNA Group Ltd.; *Int'l,* pg. 1673
CNIM HONG KONG LIMITED—See CNIM Constructions Industrielles de la Mediterranee SA; *Int'l,* pg. 1677
COBB MECHANICAL CONTRACTORS; *U.S. Private,* pg. 957
COGENINFRA SPA; *Int'l,* pg. 1694
COLONIALWEBB CONTRACTORS COMPANY—See Comfort Systems USA, Inc.; *U.S. Public,* pg. 543
COLONY HEATING & AIR CONDITIONING INC.; *U.S. Private,* pg. 972
COLTEC ENGINEERING, INC.; *U.S. Private,* pg. 976
COMBUSTIONEER CORP.—See EMCOR Group, Inc.; *U.S. Public,* pg. 737
COMFORT-AIR ENGINEERING, INC.; *U.S. Private,* pg. 981
COMFORT CONTROL INC.—See Metals Inc.; *U.S. Private,* pg. 2682
COMFORT ENGINEERS, INC.; *U.S. Private,* pg. 981
COMFORT SYSTEMS USA (ARKANSAS), INC.—See Comfort Systems USA, Inc.; *U.S. Public,* pg. 543
COMFORT SYSTEMS USA (BRISTOL), INC.—See Comfort Systems USA, Inc.; *U.S. Public,* pg. 543
COMFORT SYSTEMS USA (CAROLINAS), LLC—See Comfort Systems USA, Inc.; *U.S. Public,* pg. 543
COMFORT SYSTEMS USA ENERGY SERVICES, INC.—See Comfort Systems USA, Inc.; *U.S. Public,* pg. 543
COMFORT SYSTEMS USA, INC.; *U.S. Public,* pg. 542
COMFORT SYSTEMS USA (INTERMOUNTAIN), INC.—See Comfort Systems USA, Inc.; *U.S. Public,* pg. 543
COMFORT SYSTEMS USA (KENTUCKY), INC.—See Comfort Systems USA, Inc.; *U.S. Public,* pg. 543
COMFORT SYSTEMS USA (MIDATLANTIC), LLC—See Comfort Systems USA, Inc.; *U.S. Public,* pg. 543
COMFORT SYSTEMS USA (NORTHWEST), INC.—See Comfort Systems USA, Inc.; *U.S. Public,* pg. 543
COMFORT SYSTEMS USA (OHIO), INC.—See Comfort Systems USA, Inc.; *U.S. Public,* pg. 543
COMFORT SYSTEMS USA (SOUTH CENTRAL), INC.—See Comfort Systems USA, Inc.; *U.S. Public,* pg. 543
COMFORT SYSTEMS USA (SOUTHEAST), INC.—See Comfort Systems USA, Inc.; *U.S. Public,* pg. 543
COMFORT SYSTEMS USA (SOUTHWEST), INC.—See Comfort Systems USA, Inc.; *U.S. Public,* pg. 543
COMFORT SYSTEMS USA (SYRACUSE), INC.—See Comfort Systems USA, Inc.; *U.S. Public,* pg. 543
COMMERCIAL DESIGN ENGINEERING; *U.S. Private,* pg. 983
COMPLETE MECHANICAL SERVICES, LLC.; *U.S. Private,* pg. 1001
COMPLEX AIRCONDITIONING PTY LIMITED—See BSA Limited; *Int'l,* pg. 1201
COMPREHENSIVE ENERGY SERVICES, INC.; *U.S. Private,* pg. 1003
CONDITION-AIRE INC.—See Comfort Services, Inc.; *U.S. Private,* pg. 981
CONDITIONED AIR COMPANY OF NAPLES LLC—See Gemini Investors LLC; *U.S. Private,* pg. 1658
CONDITIONED AIR CORP. OF NAPLES INC.; *U.S. Private,* pg. 1011
CONDITIONED AIR SOLUTIONS, LLC—See Leap Partners; *U.S. Private,* pg. 2407
CONSOLIDATED SUPPLY CO. - WATER WORKS DIVISON—See Consolidated Supply Co.; *U.S. Private,* pg. 1022
CONTI SANITARARMATUREN GMBH—See Aalberts N.V.; *Int'l,* pg. 33
CONTRACT PLUMBING AND SANITATION (PTY) LIMITED—See Basil Read Holdings Limited; *Int'l,* pg. 887
CONTROL AIR CONDITIONING CORPORATION; *U.S. Private,* pg. 1034

CONTROL CONCEPTS, LLC—See Comfort Systems USA, Inc.; *U.S. Public,* pg. 543
CONTROLLED AIR, INC.; *U.S. Private,* pg. 1034
COOLRAY HEATING & AIR CONDITIONING; *U.S. Private,* pg. 1040
COREY DELTA INC.; *U.S. Private,* pg. 1050
CORIANCE SAS—See Commonwealth Bank of Australia; *Int'l,* pg. 1720
CORRIGAN BROS., INC.; *U.S. Private,* pg. 1058
CORRIGAN COMPANY MECHANICAL CONTRACTORS—See Corrigan Bros., Inc.; *U.S. Private,* pg. 1058
CORTEZ HEATING & AIR CONDITIONING, INC.; *U.S. Private,* pg. 1060
CORVAL CONSTRUCTORS, INC.; *U.S. Private,* pg. 1061
COTTAGE SHEET METAL, LLC.; *U.S. Private,* pg. 1063
COX ENGINEERING COMPANY; *U.S. Private,* pg. 1074
CPS HVAC PARTNERS INC—See CPS Capital; *Int'l,* pg. 1826
CRAWFORD COMPANY; *U.S. Private,* pg. 1086
CRAWFORD HEATING & COOLING CO.; *U.S. Private,* pg. 1086
CRAWFORD SERVICES, INC.—See Brookfield Corporation; *Int'l,* pg. 1188
CREEMERS COMPRESSORS B.V.—See Atlas Copco AB; *Int'l,* pg. 679
CRITCHFIELD MECHANICAL INC.; *U.S. Private,* pg. 1101
C & R MECHANICAL CO.; *U.S. Private,* pg. 701
CROCKETT FACILITIES SERVICES, INC.; *U.S. Private,* pg. 1103
CROPP-METCALFE CO.; *U.S. Private,* pg. 1103
CROPP-METCALFE CO.—See Cropp-Metcalfe Co.; *U.S. Private,* pg. 1103
CRR INVESTMENTS, INC.—See CSX Corporation; *U.S. Public,* pg. 602
CRR INVESTMENTS, INC.—See Norfolk Southern Corporation; *U.S. Public,* pg. 1535
CRUDELI SA; *Int'l,* pg. 1859
CULLIGAN WATER COMPANY OF NEW JERSEY, INC.; *U.S. Private,* pg. 1121
CULLUM MECHANICAL CONSTRUCTION, INC.; *U.S. Private,* pg. 1121
CUSTOM AIR, INC.; *U.S. Private,* pg. 1128
C.W. SUTER SERVICES; *U.S. Private,* pg. 709
D.A. DODD, LLC—See Pokagon Band of Potawatomi Indians; *U.S. Private,* pg. 3223
DAIKEN NEW ZELAND LIMITED—See Daiken Corporation; *Int'l,* pg. 1931
DALMATIAN FIRE INC.; *U.S. Private,* pg. 1150
DAVE JONES, INC.; *U.S. Private,* pg. 1168
DAVIS ENERGY GROUP, INC.—See Gas Technology Institute; *U.S. Private,* pg. 1647
DAVIS FIRE PROTECTION CO., INC.—See Joseph Davis, Inc.; *U.S. Private,* pg. 2236
DAVIS-ULMER SPRINKLER CO.—See APi Group Corporation; *Int'l,* pg. 513
DEAD RIVER COMPANY - COUNTRY OIL—See Dead River Company; *U.S. Private,* pg. 1182
DEAD RIVER COMPANY - FLEMING OIL DIVISION—See Dead River Company; *U.S. Private,* pg. 1182
D&E AIR CONDITIONING PTY. LIMITED; *Int'l,* pg. 1899
DEBRA-KUEMPEL—See EMCOR Group, Inc.; *U.S. Public,* pg. 736
DEE CRAMER INC.; *U.S. Private,* pg. 1188
DEERPATH CORPORATION; *U.S. Private,* pg. 1190
DEITER BROTHERS; *U.S. Private,* pg. 1192
DEKALB MECHANICAL, INC.; *U.S. Private,* pg. 1192
DEL-AIR HEATING, AIR CONDITIONING & REFRIGERATION CORP.; *U.S. Private,* pg. 1193
DEL-MONDE INC.; *U.S. Private,* pg. 1193
DELTA FIRE SYSTEMS INC.—See APi Group Corporation; *Int'l,* pg. 514
DELUXE SHEET METAL, INC.—See Alpine 4 Holdings, Inc.; *U.S. Public,* pg. 85
DENRON PLUMBING & HVAC, LLC.; *U.S. Private,* pg. 1205
DENS PARTNERS, INC.; *U.S. Private,* pg. 1206
DESERT FIRE PROTECTION LP; *U.S. Private,* pg. 1212
DESIGN AIR, LTD.—See EMCOR Group, Inc.; *U.S. Public,* pg. 736
DESIGN MECHANICAL INCORPORATED—See Comfort Systems USA, Inc.; *U.S. Public,* pg. 543
DEVEKO KLIMAATBEHEERSING B.V.—See CENTROTEC SE; *Int'l,* pg. 1414
DILLING MECHANICAL CONTRACTORS, INC.; *U.S. Private,* pg. 1231
DIRECT ENERGY MARKETING LTD. - CANADA HOME SERVICES—See NRG Energy, Inc.; *U.S. Public,* pg. 1549
DISTRIGAZ CONFORT SRL—See ENGIE SA; *Int'l,* pg. 2431
DMI CORP.; *U.S. Private,* pg. 1248
DMR MECHANICAL, LLC.; *U.S. Private,* pg. 1249
DONOHUE COMMERCIAL SERVICE INC.—See United Mechanical, Inc.; *U.S. Private,* pg. 4294
DOODY MECHANICAL, INC.—See APi Group Corporation; *Int'l,* pg. 514
DORVIN LEIS COMPANY INC.; *U.S. Private,* pg. 1264

DOWA THT AMERICA, INC.—See Dowa Holdings Co., Ltd.; *Int'l,* pg. 2183
DOWNSVIEW HEATING & AIR CONDITIONING; *Int'l,* pg. 2187
DRING AIR CONDITIONING & HEATING, LP; *U.S. Private,* pg. 1277
DR POWER LLC—See Dead River Company; *U.S. Private,* pg. 1182
DRUART S.A.—See Ackermans & van Haaren NV; *Int'l,* pg. 105
DRYCO LLC—See I Squared Capital Advisors (US) LLC; *U.S. Private,* pg. 2021
DSH FLOORING LIMITED—See Brickability Group plc; *Int'l,* pg. 1151
DUAL TEMP COMPANY, INC.; *U.S. Private,* pg. 1282
DUCTS UNLIMITED MECHANICAL SYSTEMS, INC.; *U.S. Private,* pg. 1284
DUCTTESTERS, INC.—See Gallant Capital Partners, LLC; *U.S. Private,* pg. 1639
DUFFY MECHANICAL CORP.—See EMCOR Group, Inc.; *U.S. Public,* pg. 736
DUPREE PLUMBING COMPANY; *U.S. Private,* pg. 1291
DURR MECHANICAL CONSTRUCTION INC.; *U.S. Private,* pg. 1294
DUTCH ENTERPRISES INC.; *U.S. Private,* pg. 1294
DUTTON PLUMBING, INC.—See Baum Capital Partners Management LLC; *U.S. Private,* pg. 490
D.V. BROWN & ASSOCIATES, INC.; *U.S. Private,* pg. 1143
DYNAMIC MECHANICAL CONTRACTORS INC.; *U.S. Private,* pg. 1298
DYNAMIC SYSTEMS INC.—See FGI Group Inc.; *U.S. Private,* pg. 1501
EAGLE ELEVATOR CO., INC.—See 3Phase Elevator Corp; *U.S. Private,* pg. 13
EAST COAST AIR & HEAT, LLC—See Del-Air Heating, Air Conditioning & Refrigeration Corp.; *U.S. Private,* pg. 1193
EASTERN HEATING & COOLING, INC.—See Comfort Systems USA, Inc.; *U.S. Public,* pg. 544
EAST WEST ENERGY LTD.; *U.S. Private,* pg. 1318
EC SERWIS SP. Z O.O.—See E.ON SE; *Int'l,* pg. 2256
EDD HELMS MCDONALD AIR CONDITIONING, INC.—See Edd Helms Group, Inc.; *U.S. Public,* pg. 717
EDMONSON ELECTRIC, LLC—See IES Holdings, Inc.; *U.S. Public,* pg. 1094
EDWARD B. O'REILLY & ASSOCIATES, INC.; *U.S. Private,* pg. 1340
EDWARDS ENGINEERING, INC.; *U.S. Private,* pg. 1342
E. ESCHER INC.; *U.S. Private,* pg. 1303
THE EGAN COMPANIES; *U.S. Private,* pg. 4025
EGAN MECHANICAL CONTRACTORS INC.—See The Egan Companies; *U.S. Private,* pg. 4025
ELECTRA LTD.—See Elco Limited; *Int'l,* pg. 2345
ELECTRO GAZ SERVICE SA—See Brookfield Corporation; *Int'l,* pg. 1188
EMC COMPANY; *U.S. Private,* pg. 1379
EMCOR SERVICES AIRCOND CORPORATION—See EMCOR Group, Inc.; *U.S. Public,* pg. 737
EMCOR SERVICES ARC—See EMCOR Group, Inc.; *U.S. Public,* pg. 738
EMCOR SERVICES NEW YORK/NEW JERSEY—See EMCOR Group, Inc.; *U.S. Public,* pg. 737
EMCOR SERVICES NORTHEAST, INC.—See EMCOR Group, Inc.; *U.S. Public,* pg. 738
EMCOR SERVICES TEAM MECHANICAL, INC.—See EMCOR Group, Inc.; *U.S. Public,* pg. 738
ENERGIEKONTOR AG; *Int'l,* pg. 2420
ENERGY CONTROL CONSULTANTS, INC.; *U.S. Private,* pg. 1394
ENERGY CONTROL, INC.—See ENGIE SA; *Int'l,* pg. 2428
ENERGY SYSTEMS CO.—See BlackRock, Inc.; *U.S. Public,* pg. 345
ENGIE AXIMA GERMANY GMBH—See ENGIE SA; *Int'l,* pg. 2428
ENGIE MECHANICAL SERVICES AUSTRALIA PTY LIMITED—See ENGIE SA; *Int'l,* pg. 2431
ENGINEERING EXCELLENCE INCORPORATED; *U.S. Private,* pg. 1398
EN.PLUS GMBH—See CEZ, a.s.; *Int'l,* pg. 1427
ENTEGA HAUSTECHNIK GMBH & CO. KG—See HEAG Sudhessische Energie AG; *Int'l,* pg. 3302
ENTREPRISE GUIBAN ANTILLES—See Entreprise Guiban SA; *Int'l,* pg. 2453
ENTREPRISE GUIBAN SA; *Int'l,* pg. 2453
ENVIRONMENTAL AIR SYSTEMS, LLC—See Comfort Systems USA, Inc.; *U.S. Public,* pg. 544
ENVIRONMENTAL FIRE PROTECTION, INC.; *U.S. Private,* pg. 1407
ENVIRONMENTAL SERVICES, INC.—See Terracon Consultants, Inc.; *U.S. Private,* pg. 3971
ENVIRONMENTAL SYSTEMS ASSOCIATES, INC.—See Brookfield Corporation; *Int'l,* pg. 1188
ENVIRONMENTAL TECHNIQUES CORP.; *U.S. Private,* pg. 1409
ENVIROTROL, LLC—See Comfort Systems USA, Inc.; *U.S. Public,* pg. 544
E.ON ENERGY—See E.ON SE; *Int'l,* pg. 2256

N.A.I.C.S. INDEX

238220 — PLUMBING, HEATING, ...

E.ON HANSE WARME GMBH—See E.ON SE; *Int'l*, pg. 2254
E.ON UK TECHNICAL SERVICES LIMITED—See E.ON SE; *Int'l*, pg. 2256
ERICKSON ASSOCIATES, INC.; *U.S. Private*, pg. 1419
ESTES HEATING & AIR CONDITIONING, INC.; *U.S. Private*, pg. 1429
ETUDES INSTALLATIONS ET MAINTENANCE INDUSTRIELLES SAS; *Int'l*, pg. 2525
E.W. TOMPKINS COMPANY INC.; *U.S. Private*, pg. 1307
EXIGENT HOLDCO LLC—See Huron Capital Partners LLC; *U.S. Private*, pg. 2012
THE FAGAN COMPANY—See EMCOR Group, Inc.; *U.S. Public*, pg. 739
FALLS HEATING & COOLING, INC.—See User Friendly Home Services, LLC; *U.S. Private*, pg. 4322
FASZOLD SERVICE COMPANY—See Heartland Home Services, Inc.; *U.S. Private*, pg. 1900
F.E. MORAN—See Armon Inc.; *U.S. Private*, pg. 331
FENHAMS LTD.—See Environ Group (Investments) plc; *Int'l*, pg. 2454
FERRAN SERVICES & CONTRACTING; *U.S. Private*, pg. 1498
FFJMP SDN. BHD.—See Fuji Furukawa Engineering & Construction Co., Ltd.; *Int'l*, pg. 2813
FG HAGGERTY COMPANY, INC.; *U.S. Private*, pg. 1501
F&G MECHANICAL CORPORATION—See EMCOR Group, Inc.; *U.S. Public*, pg. 738
FIAT INCORPORATED; *U.S. Private*, pg. 1501
FIRE AND LIFE SAFETY AMERICA, INC.—See Blue Point Capital Partners, LLC; *U.S. Private*, pg. 590
FIRELINE SPRINKLER CORPORATION; *U.S. Private*, pg. 1512
FIRE SPRINKLER SYSTEMS INC.; *U.S. Private*, pg. 1511
FLAMCO STAG GMBH—See Aalberts N.V.; *Int'l*, pg. 34
FLAME FURNACE CO.; *U.S. Private*, pg. 1540
FLORIDA COOL INC.—See Leonard Green & Partners, L.P.; *U.S. Private*, pg. 2430
FLOW SERVICE PARTNERS—See LP First Capital; *U.S. Private*, pg. 2507
FLOW SERVICE PARTNERS—See The RLJ Companies, LLC; *U.S. Private*, pg. 4111
FM SYLVAN, INC.—See Blue Point Capital Partners, LLC; *U.S. Private*, pg. 590
FOOD SERVICE REFRIGERATION INC.; *U.S. Private*, pg. 1561
FOX SERVICE CO.; *U.S. Private*, pg. 1585
FRANKLIN HOLWERDA COMPANY—See FHC Holding Company; *U.S. Private*, pg. 1501
FRANK MILLARD CO. INC.; *U.S. Private*, pg. 1595
FRED MCGILVRAY INC.; *U.S. Private*, pg. 1601
FRED WILLIAMS, INC.—See ENGIE SA; *Int'l*, pg. 2429
FRESNO PLUMBING & HEATING INC.; *U.S. Private*, pg. 1610
FREUND & COMPANY INC.; *U.S. Private*, pg. 1610
FRN, INC.—See Universal Health Services, Inc.; *U.S. Public*, pg. 2257
FRS MECHANICAL CORP.; *U.S. Private*, pg. 1617
FUEL TECH, INC.; *U.S. Public*, pg. 891
FUEL TECH SRL—See Fuel Tech, Inc.; *U.S. Public*, pg. 891
FUGRO SINGAPORE LAND PTE LTD—See Fugro N.V.; *Int'l*, pg. 2807
FUJI FURMANITE CO., LTD.—See Fuji Electric Co., Ltd.; *Int'l*, pg. 2812
FUJITEC (HK) COMPANY LIMITED—See Fujitec Co., Ltd.; *Int'l*, pg. 2831
GAGNON INCORPORATED; *U.S. Private*, pg. 1635
GALLO CORPORATION; *U.S. Private*, pg. 1639
GALLO MECHANICAL CONTRACTORS—See Gallo Corporation; *U.S. Private*, pg. 1639
GARDEN CITY PLUMBING & HEATING; *U.S. Private*, pg. 1643
GAS CALL SERVICES LIMITED; *Int'l*, pg. 2887
GAS MAINTENANCE AND TRAINING LIMITED—See Booth Securities Ltd.; *Int'l*, pg. 1111
GATOR AIR CONDITIONING; *U.S. Private*, pg. 1651
GEA LYOPHIL (BEIJING) CO. LTD.—See GEA Group Aktiengesellschaft; *Int'l*, pg. 2899
GEA PROCESS ENGINEERING S.A.—See GEA Group Aktiengesellschaft; *Int'l*, pg. 2902
GEA REFRIGERATION NETHERLANDS N.V.—See GEA Group Aktiengesellschaft; *Int'l*, pg. 2902
GEBERIT AS—See Geberit AG; *Int'l*, pg. 2904
GEBERIT TESISAT SISTEMLERI TICARET LTD.—See Geberit AG; *Int'l*, pg. 2905
GEBERIT TRADING LLC—See Geberit AG; *Int'l*, pg. 2905
GEISEL HEATING, AIR CONDITIONING & PLUMBING, INC.—See Brookfield Corporation; *Int'l*, pg. 1188
GEMCO CONSTRUCTORS, LLC; *U.S. Private*, pg. 1657
GEM INDUSTRIAL, INC.—See The Rudolph/Libbe Companies; *U.S. Private*, pg. 4113
GENERAL HEATING & AIR CONDITIONING INC.—See Hooper Corporation; *U.S. Private*, pg. 1978
GENERAL MECHANICAL CONTRACTORS INC; *U.S. Private*, pg. 1666
GEORGE T. WILKINSON, INC.; *U.S. Private*, pg. 1683
GEOSTELLAR, INC.—See NRG Energy, Inc.; *U.S. Public*, pg. 1550

GES MECHANICAL SERVICES, INC.—See Amco Group Inc.; *U.S. Private*, pg. 218
GILLESPIE POWERS REFRIGERATION & ENGINEERING; *U.S. Private*, pg. 1700
GIOVENCO INDUSTRIES (AUST) PTY LIMITED—See Fluor Corporation; *U.S. Public*, pg. 858
G.J. HOPKINS, INC.—See The Branch Group, Inc.; *U.S. Private*, pg. 3999
GODWIN PLUMBING INC.—See Godwin Hardware, Inc.; *U.S. Private*, pg. 1725
GOLD MEDAL PLUMBING HEATING COOLING ELECTRIC, INC.—See New Mountain Capital, LLC; *U.S. Private*, pg. 2902
GOLD MEDAL SERVICE, LLC—See New Mountain Capital, LLC; *U.S. Private*, pg. 2902
GOLU KLIMAATBEHEERSING B.V.—See CENTROTEC SE; *Int'l*, pg. 1414
GORDON BROTHERS INDUSTRIES PTY. LIMITED; *Int'l*, pg. 3042
GOWAN, INC.—See EMCOR Group, Inc.; *U.S. Public*, pg. 737
GOYETTE MECHANICAL; *U.S. Private*, pg. 1747
GRACON CORPORATION; *U.S. Private*, pg. 1749
GRANITE COMFORT, LP—See Tiger Infrastructure Partners LP; *U.S. Private*, pg. 4170
GRANITE STATE PLUMBING & HEATING, LLC—See Comfort Systems USA, Inc.; *U.S. Public*, pg. 544
GRASS-AIR COMPRESSOREN B.V.—See Atlas Copco AB; *Int'l*, pg. 680
GRC HOLDING, INC.—See RGP Holding, Inc.; *U.S. Private*, pg. 3420
GREAT LAKES MECHANICAL CORP.—See Blue Point Capital Partners, LLC; *U.S. Private*, pg. 590
GREAT LAKES PLUMBING & HEATING CO. INC.; *U.S. Private*, pg. 1765
GREEN AIR CARE GROUP INC.—See Tiger Infrastructure Partners LP; *U.S. Private*, pg. 4170
GREENFIELD AG—See Atlas Copco AB; *Int'l*, pg. 677
GREENHILL AIR, INC.; *U.S. Private*, pg. 1778
GREENLEE PLUMBING INC.—See Emerson Electric Co.; *U.S. Public*, pg. 741
GREENLEE PLUMBING INC.—See Emerson Electric Co.; *U.S. Public*, pg. 750
GREGG MECHANICAL CORP.—See Brookfield Corporation; *Int'l*, pg. 1188
GRISWOLD ACQUISITION COMPANY—See Dover Corporation; *U.S. Public*, pg. 681
GRUNAU COMPANY, INC.—See APi Group Corporation; *Int'l*, pg. 514
GSI SYSTEMS INC.—See Gatekeeper Systems Inc.; *Int'l*, pg. 2889
GUARANTEED INDUSTRIES LIMITED; *Int'l*, pg. 3169
GUNTHER KALTETECHNIK GMBH—See DZ BANK AG Deutsche Zentral-Genossenschaftsbank; *Int'l*, pg. 2244
GUYER WARME UND WASSER AG—See Burkhalter Holding AG; *Int'l*, pg. 1225
HADFIELD ELEVATOR—See 3Phase Elevator Corp; *U.S. Private*, pg. 14
HA.EM OSTRAVA S.R.O.—See CEZ, a.s.; *Int'l*, pg. 1428
HALEY MECHANICAL, LLC—See Apex Service Partners LLC; *U.S. Private*, pg. 293
HAMEL & MCALISTER INC.; *U.S. Private*, pg. 1847
THE HANDYMAN VAN LIMITED—See Franchise Brands plc; *Int'l*, pg. 2760
HANNABERY ELECTRIC INC.; *U.S. Private*, pg. 1855
HANSEN MECHANICAL CONTRACTORS, INC.—See EMCOR Group, Inc.; *U.S. Public*, pg. 737
HARDER MECHANICAL CONTRACTORS INC.; *U.S. Private*, pg. 1863
THE HARDY CORPORATION; *U.S. Private*, pg. 4043
HARPER LIMBACH LLC—See Limbach Holdings, Inc.; *U.S. Public*, pg. 1316
HARRIS COMPANIES; *U.S. Private*, pg. 1869
HARRISON-ORR AIR CONDITIONING, INC.; *U.S. Private*, pg. 1871
HARRY GRODSKY & CO., INC.-HARTFORD OFFICE—See Harry Grodsky & Co., Inc.; *U.S. Private*, pg. 1871
HARRY GRODSKY & CO., INC.; *U.S. Private*, pg. 1871
HARSHAW SERVICE INC.; *U.S. Private*, pg. 1872
HAYS COOLING & HEATING LLC—See Brookfield Corporation; *Int'l*, pg. 1188
H.B. MCCLURE COMPANY; *U.S. Private*, pg. 1825
HEARTLAND HOME SERVICES, INC.; *U.S. Private*, pg. 1900
HEATING & PLUMBING ENGINEERS INC.; *U.S. Private*, pg. 1902
HEIDE & COOK, LTD.—See Heide & Cook Mechanical Contractors; *U.S. Private*, pg. 1904
HELP-LINK UK LTD.—See Brookfield Corporation; *Int'l*, pg. 1188
H.E. NEUMANN CO.; *U.S. Private*, pg. 1826
HERA ENERGIE BOLOGNA S.R.L.—See Hera S.p.A.; *Int'l*, pg. 3356
HERITAGE MECHANICAL SERVICES, INC.—See EMCOR Group, Inc.; *U.S. Public*, pg. 738
HERMAN GOLDNER COMPANY INC.; *U.S. Private*, pg. 1925
HERRMAN & COETZ INC.; *U.S. Private*, pg. 1926

H&G INFOTECH OFFICE—See Herrman & Goetz Inc.; *U.S. Private*, pg. 1926
HGP INTERNATIONAL BV—See Eneraqua Technologies Plc; *Int'l*, pg. 2418
HIBIYA ENGINEERING LTD; *Int'l*, pg. 3383
HIDALGO INDUSTRIAL SERVICES, INC.; *U.S. Private*, pg. 1934
HILLER PLUMBING, HEATING & COOLING COMPANY; *U.S. Private*, pg. 1946
THE HILL GROUP; *U.S. Private*, pg. 4052
HILL YORK CORPORATION; *U.S. Private*, pg. 1945
HIMEC INC.; *U.S. Private*, pg. 1948
H & M MECHANICAL, INC.—See Comfort Systems USA, Inc.; *U.S. Public*, pg. 544
HOBSON FABRICATING CORPORATION; *U.S. Private*, pg. 1958
HOLADAY-PARKS FABRICATORS INC.; *U.S. Private*, pg. 1961
HOMESERVE SERVOWARM LIMITED—See Brookfield Corporation; *Int'l*, pg. 1188
HOMESERVE USA ENERGY SERVICES (NEW ENGLAND) LLC—See Brookfield Corporation; *Int'l*, pg. 1188
HOME-TECH CONSOLIDATED, INC.; *U.S. Private*, pg. 1972
HOMETOWN PLUMBING & HEATING CO.; *U.S. Private*, pg. 1975
HOOVER MECHANICAL PLUMBING & HEATING LTD.; *Int'l*, pg. 3472
HORWITZ NS/I INC.; *U.S. Private*, pg. 1984
HOYT BRUMM & LINK, INC.; *U.S. Private*, pg. 1996
HPS MECHANICAL, INC.; *U.S. Private*, pg. 1997
H&S CONSTRUCTORS INC.; *U.S. Private*, pg. 1824
HUBBARD & DRAKE GENERAL CONTRACTOR; *U.S. Private*, pg. 2000
HUMICLIMA CENTRO, S.A.—See ACS, Actividades de Construccion y Servicios, S.A.; *Int'l*, pg. 114
HUMICLIMA EST CATALUNYA, S.L.—See ACS, Actividades de Construccion y Servicios, S.A.; *Int'l*, pg. 114
HUMICLIMA SAC, S.A.—See ACS, Actividades de Construccion y Servicios, S.A.; *Int'l*, pg. 114
HURCKMAN MECHANICAL INDUSTRIES; *U.S. Private*, pg. 2011
HUSSMANN SERVICE DO BRASIL LTDA.—See Ingersoll Rand Inc.; *U.S. Public*, pg. 1120
HUSSUNG MECHANICAL CONTRACTORS, INC.; *U.S. Private*, pg. 2014
HVAC TECHNOLOGIES, INC.; *U.S. Private*, pg. 2015
HVAC TECHNOLOGIES, INC.; *U.S. Private*, pg. 2015
HYDROMAX PLUMBING, INC.—See Gallant Capital Partners, LLC; *U.S. Private*, pg. 1639
IBIDEN ENGINEERING CO., LTD.—See Ibiden Co., Ltd.; *Int'l*, pg. 3575
I.D. GRIFFITH, INC.; *U.S. Private*, pg. 2027
IHP INDUSTRIAL, INC.; *U.S. Private*, pg. 2040
ILLINGWORTH CORPORATION—See EMCOR Group, Inc.; *U.S. Public*, pg. 738
IMC INC.; *U.S. Private*, pg. 2046
IMOCO, INC.; *U.S. Private*, pg. 2047
IMPACT TECHNICAL SERVICES LTD.—See Addtech AB; *Int'l*, pg. 134
IMTECH SPAIN S.L.—See Electricite de France S.A.; *Int'l*, pg. 2351
IMWINKELRIED LUFTUNG UND KLIMA AG—See Burkhalter Holding AG; *Int'l*, pg. 1225
INDUSTRIAL CONTRACTORS, INC.—See APi Group Corporation; *Int'l*, pg. 514
INDUSTRIAL POWER SYSTEMS INCORPORATED; *U.S. Private*, pg. 2068
INDUSTRIAL VENTILATION INC.; *U.S. Private*, pg. 2069
INTERLINE BRANDS, INC.—See The Home Depot, Inc.; *U.S. Public*, pg. 2089
INTERNATIONAL FIRE PROTECTION, INC.—See APi Group Corporation; *Int'l*, pg. 514
INTERSTATE ENGINEERING CORP.; *U.S. Private*, pg. 2124
INTERSTATE MECHANICAL CONTRACTORS, INC.; *U.S. Private*, pg. 2125
IRVINE MECHANICAL, INC.—See Halmos Capital Partners; *U.S. Private*, pg. 1845
IRVINE MECHANICAL, INC.—See Trivest Partners, LP; *U.S. Private*, pg. 4241
ISAAC HEATING & AC; *U.S. Private*, pg. 2142
I-SYS CORPORATION - EL DORADO HILLS—See System Development.Integration LLC; *U.S. Private*, pg. 3906
JACKSON & BLANC; *U.S. Private*, pg. 2175
JACKSON COMFORT SYSTEMS, INC.—See Morgan Stanley; *U.S. Public*, pg. 1474
JACOBS MECHANICAL CO.; *U.S. Private*, pg. 2180
J.A. CROSON, L.L.C.; *U.S. Private*, pg. 2157
THE JAMAR COMPANY—See APi Group Corporation; *Int'l*, pg. 514
JAMES CRAFT AND SON INC.; *U.S. Private*, pg. 2183
JAMES MCCULLAGH CO. INC.; *U.S. Private*, pg. 2184
JARBOE'S PLUMBING, HEATING & COOLING, INC.; *U.S. Private*, pg. 2188
JARRELL CONTRACTING—See Charles E. Jarrell Contracting Company, Inc.; *U.S. Private*, pg. 852

238220 — PLUMBING, HEATING, ...

J. BEESE VVS & BLIK A/S—See Bravida Holding AB; *Int'l*, pg. 1142
J.C. CANNISTRARO, LLC.; *U.S. Private*, pg. 2159
J.E. JOHNSON INC.; *U.S. Private*, pg. 2162
JENNINGS-DILL, INC.; *U.S. Private*, pg. 2200
J.E. SHEKELL INC.; *U.S. Private*, pg. 2162
JETT MECHANICAL INC.; *U.S. Private*, pg. 2204
J.F AHERN CO. - INDUSTRIAL & PROCESS PIPING DIVISION—See J.F. Ahern Co.; *U.S. Private*, pg. 2162
J.F. AHERN CO.; *U.S. Private*, pg. 2162
JH KELLY LLC; *U.S. Private*, pg. 2207
J&K PLUMBING AND HEATING CO.; *U.S. Private*, pg. 2154
J. MOORE & CO. INC.; *U.S. Private*, pg. 2156
JOHN E. GREEN CO.; *U.S. Private*, pg. 2221
JOHN J. KIRLIN INC. CAROLINAS DIV.—See John J. Kirlin Inc.; *U.S. Private*, pg. 2222
JOHN J. KIRLIN INC.; *U.S. Private*, pg. 2222
JOHN W. DANFORTH SERVICE CO.—See JWD Group Inc.; *U.S. Private*, pg. 2247
J.O. MORY INC.; *U.S. Private*, pg. 2169
JOSEPH DAVIS, INC.; *U.S. Private*, pg. 2236
JOSEPH M. ZIMMER INC.; *U.S. Private*, pg. 2237
JPG PLUMBING AND MECHANICAL SERVICES, INC.—See Huron Capital Partners LLC; *U.S. Private*, pg. 2012
J.R. PIERCE PLUMBING CO., INC.; *U.S. Private*, pg. 2170
JUDSON'S INC.; *U.S. Private*, pg. 2242
JWD GROUP INC. - DANFORTH ALBANY FACILITY—See JWD Group Inc.; *U.S. Private*, pg. 2247
JWD GROUP INC. - DANFORTH ROCHESTER FACILITY—See JWD Group Inc.; *U.S. Private*, pg. 2247
JWD GROUP INC.; *U.S. Private*, pg. 2247
KALTE 3000 AG—See Burkhalter Holding AG; *Int'l*, pg. 1225
KAPPE ASSOCIATES, INC.—See DXP Enterprises, Inc.; *U.S. Public*, pg. 697
KAYEMA ENERGY SOLUTIONS (PROPRIETARY) LIMITED—See Group Five Limited; *Int'l*, pg. 3089
KEEN AIR SERVICES, INC.—See Dring Air Conditioning & Heating, LP; *U.S. Private*, pg. 1277
KE GUTRIDGE, LLC—See Kassel Equity Group, LLC; *U.S. Private*, pg. 2264
KEMPAIR KLIMAATBEHEERSING B.V.—See CENTROTEC SE; *Int'l*, pg. 1414
KENT ISLAND MECHANICAL, LLC—See Crawford United Corporation; *U.S. Public*, pg. 592
KENT M. LIM & COMPANY, INC.; *U.S. Private*, pg. 2288
KENTUCKIANA COMFORT CENTER, INC.; *U.S. Private*, pg. 2288
KENUS LLP—See Alfa Laval AB; *Int'l*, pg. 312
KEY MECHANICAL COMPANY; *U.S. Private*, pg. 2293
KHI MECHANICAL SERVICES; *U.S. Private*, pg. 2301
KILGUST MECHANICAL, INC.—See EMCOR Group, Inc.; *U.S. Public*, pg. 738
KINETICS MECHANICAL ENERGY; *U.S. Private*, pg. 2308
KING INDUSTRIES; *U.S. Private*, pg. 2309
KING-LAR COMPANY; *U.S. Private*, pg. 2310
KORTE DOES IT ALL; *U.S. Private*, pg. 2344
KROESCHELL ENGINEERING CO. INC.—See Kroeschell, Inc.; *U.S. Private*, pg. 2352
KROESCHELL ENGINEERING NORTH, INC.—See Kroeschell, Inc.; *U.S. Private*, pg. 2352
KROESCHELL ENGINEERING SERVICE, INC.—See Kroeschell, Inc.; *U.S. Private*, pg. 2352
KROESCHELL, INC.; *U.S. Private*, pg. 2352
KSW MECHANICAL SERVICES, INC.—See The Related Companies, L.P.; *U.S. Private*, pg. 4103
KUHLMAN, INC.; *U.S. Private*, pg. 2356
KUNTSCHAR U. SCHLUTER GMBH—See CENTROTEC SE; *Int'l*, pg. 1414
LABOV MECHANICAL, INC.—See EMCOR Group, Inc.; *U.S. Public*, pg. 738
LAKE MECHANICAL CONTRACTORS; *U.S. Private*, pg. 2375
LAKEWAY MECHANICAL CONTRACTORS; *U.S. Private*, pg. 2378
LAPENSEE PLUMBING INC.; *U.S. Private*, pg. 2391
LAS VEGAS AIR CONDITIONING, INC.—See Baum Capital Partners Management LLC; *U.S. Private*, pg. 490
LAUREL HOLDINGS INC.; *U.S. Private*, pg. 2398
LAWMAN HEATING & COOLING, INC.; *U.S. Private*, pg. 2401
LAWSON MECHANICAL CONTRACTORS; *U.S. Private*, pg. 2402
LEDUC & DEXTER INC.; *U.S. Private*, pg. 2411
LEE COMPANY; *U.S. Private*, pg. 2411
LENNOX NATIONAL ACCOUNT SERVICES INC.—See Lennox International Inc.; *U.S. Public*, pg. 1307
LEN THE PLUMBER, LLC—See Catterton Management Company, LLC; *U.S. Private*, pg. 793
LETSOS COMPANY; *U.S. Private*, pg. 2433
LEWIS CORP.; *U.S. Private*, pg. 2438
LIMPENS SA—See Eiffage S.A.; *Int'l*, pg. 2330
LINACAL S.L.U.—See Brookfield Corporation; *Int'l*, pg. 1188
LINDSTROM AIR CONDITIONING & PLUMBING, INC.; *U.S. Private*, pg. 2460
LOCHRIDGE-PRIEST INC.; *U.S. Private*, pg. 2478
LONG MECHANICAL INC.; *U.S. Private*, pg. 2491

LUCKINBILL INC.; *U.S. Private*, pg. 2511
LUNSETH PLUMBING AND HEATING CO.; *U.S. Private*, pg. 2515
LVI HELIN OY—See Electricite de France S.A.; *Int'l*, pg. 2351
LYLES MECHANICAL CO.—See Lyles Diversified Inc.; *U.S. Private*, pg. 2520
MAINLINE FIRE PROTECTION, LLC.; *U.S. Private*, pg. 2553
MAINLINE PIPELINES LIMITED—See Valero Energy Corporation; *U.S. Public*, pg. 2272
MAJEK FIRE PROTECTION INC.; *U.S. Private*, pg. 2554
MALLORY & EVANS INC.; *U.S. Private*, pg. 2557
MAMPAEY INSTALLATIETECHNIEK B.V.—See E.ON SE; *Int'l*, pg. 2258
MARATHON HVAC SERVICES, LLC; *U.S. Private*, pg. 2570
MARELICH MECHANICAL CO., INC.—See EMCOR Group, Inc.; *U.S. Public*, pg. 737
MARELICH MECHANICAL CO.—See EMCOR Group, Inc.; *U.S. Public*, pg. 737
MARK-AIR INC.—See DLVA, Inc.; *U.S. Private*, pg. 1248
MARK GROUP AUSTRALIA PTY LTD.—See Anchorage Capital Partners Pty. Limited; *Int'l*, pg. 448
MARMION INDUSTRIES CORP.; *U.S. Private*, pg. 2586
MARTIN PETERSEN COMPANY, INC.; *U.S. Private*, pg. 2595
MARTINS CREEK SOLAR NC, LLC—See Duke Energy Corporation; *U.S. Public*, pg. 691
MASTERS, INC.—See NRG Energy, Inc.; *U.S. Public*, pg. 1549
MATRIX SERVICE INDUSTRIAL CONTRACTORS INC.—See Matrix Service Company; *U.S. Public*, pg. 1397
THE MCBURNEY CORPORATION; *U.S. Private*, pg. 4076
MCCARL'S, INC.—See Riverstone Holdings LLC; *U.S. Private*, pg. 3447
THE MCC GROUP, LLC; *U.S. Private*, pg. 4076
MCC MECHANICAL LLC—See The MCC Group, LLC; *U.S. Private*, pg. 4076
MCCREA HEATING AND AIR CONDITIONING; *U.S. Private*, pg. 2631
MCDONOUGH CONTRACTING SERVICES—See Wm. F. McDonough Plumbing, Inc.; *U.S. Private*, pg. 4552
MCDONOUGH PLUMBING SERVICE—See Wm. F. McDonough Plumbing, Inc.; *U.S. Private*, pg. 4552
MCDOWALL COMPANY; *U.S. Private*, pg. 2633
MCELROY'S, INC.; *U.S. Private*, pg. 2633
MCKAMISH CHESAPEAKE INC.; *U.S. Private*, pg. 2637
MCKINSTRY CO., LLC; *U.S. Private*, pg. 2639
MCKINZIE MECHANICAL HEATING & AIR CONDITIONING, L.L.C.—See Hiller Plumbing, Heating & Cooling Company; *U.S. Private*, pg. 1946
MCLAIN PLUMBING & ELECTRIC SERVICE; *U.S. Private*, pg. 2639
M. DAVIS & SONS INC.; *U.S. Private*, pg. 2526
MEASUREMENT & VERIFICATION PTE. LTD.—See Furniweb Holdings Limited; *Int'l*, pg. 2846
MECCON, INC.; *U.S. Private*, pg. 2648
MECCON INDUSTRIES INC.—See Monico Inc.; *U.S. Private*, pg. 2770
MECHANICAL CONSTRUCTION SERVICES; *U.S. Private*, pg. 2648
MECHANICAL, INC.—See The Helm Group; *U.S. Private*, pg. 4051
MECHANICAL MAINTENANCE INCORPORATED; *U.S. Private*, pg. 2648
MECHANICAL SERVICES INC.; *U.S. Private*, pg. 2649
MECHANICAL SERVICES LTD.—See Daikin Industries, Ltd.; *Int'l*, pg. 1936
MECHANICAL SYSTEMS INC.; *U.S. Private*, pg. 2649
MECHANICAL TECHNICAL SERVICES, INC.—See Comfort Systems USA, Inc.; *U.S. Public*, pg. 544
MEG SERVICES PTY LIMITED—See BSA Limited; *Int'l*, pg. 1201
MENDEL PLUMBING & HEATING, INC.; *U.S. Private*, pg. 2666
MERRYMANN-FARR, LLC.; *U.S. Private*, pg. 2676
MESA ENERGY SYSTEMS, INC.—See EMCOR Group, Inc.; *U.S. Public*, pg. 738
METALS INC.; *U.S. Private*, pg. 2682
MICHIGAN PAVING & MATERIALS CO.—See CRH plc; *Int'l*, pg. 1847
MIDDLETON INC.; *U.S. Private*, pg. 2714
MIDLANDS MECHANICAL INC.; *U.S. Private*, pg. 2715
MID-OHIO MECHANICAL, INC. SHEETMETAL DIVISION—See Mid-Ohio Mechanical, Inc.; *U.S. Private*, pg. 2708
MID-OHIO MECHANICAL, INC.; *U.S. Private*, pg. 2708
MID-STATE CONTRACTING LLC; *U.S. Private*, pg. 2709
MIDWEST MECHANICAL CONTRACTORS, INC.—See MMC Corp.; *U.S. Private*, pg. 2754
MIDWEST MECHANICAL CONTRACTORS, INC.—See MMC Corp.; *U.S. Private*, pg. 2754
MIKE PATTERSON PLUMBING INC.—See Lovett Inc.; *U.S. Private*, pg. 2504
MILLER & ANDERSON INC.; *U.S. Private*, pg. 2732
MILLER & ANDERSON—See Miller & Anderson Inc.; *U.S. Private*, pg. 2732

CORPORATE AFFILIATIONS

M.J. DALY LLC—See Arden Engineering Constructors LLC; *U.S. Private*, pg. 317
MJ MECHANICAL SERVICES, INC.—See Comfort Systems USA, Inc.; *U.S. Public*, pg. 544
MMC CONTRACTORS NORTHEAST, INC.—See MMC Corp.; *U.S. Private*, pg. 2754
MMC CONTRACTORS WEST, INC.—See MMC Corp.; *U.S. Private*, pg. 2754
MMC CORP.; *U.S. Private*, pg. 2754
MOCK PLUMBING & MECHANICAL, INC.; *U.S. Private*, pg. 2759
MOLLENBERG-BETZ INC.; *U.S. Private*, pg. 2767
MONARCH WELDING & ENGINEERING; *U.S. Private*, pg. 2769
MONICO INC.; *U.S. Private*, pg. 2770
MONROE PIPING & SHEET METAL LLC; *U.S. Private*, pg. 2773
MONSEN ENGINEERING COMPANY; *U.S. Private*, pg. 2774
MORGAN & THORNBURG, INC.; *U.S. Private*, pg. 2783
MORRISON CONSTRUCTION COMPANY; *U.S. Private*, pg. 2789
MORRIS SHEET METAL CORP.; *U.S. Private*, pg. 2788
MOUNTAIN MECHANICAL CONTRACTORS INC.; *U.S. Private*, pg. 2799
MRC SYSTEMS FZE—See ADDvise Group AB; *Int'l*, pg. 136
MR. ROOTER LLC—See Harvest Partners L.P.; *U.S. Private*, pg. 1877
MSHC, INC.—See Leonard Green & Partners, L.P.; *U.S. Private*, pg. 2426
MULTI MECHANICAL, INC.—See Gemspring Capital Management, LLC; *U.S. Private*, pg. 1658
MURPHY COMPANY MECHANICAL CONTRACTORS & ENGINEERING INC.—See Murphy Company Mechanical Contractors & Engineers Inc.; *U.S. Private*, pg. 2815
MURPHY COMPANY MECHANICAL CONTRACTORS & ENGINEERS INC.; *U.S. Private*, pg. 2815
MURRAY COMPANY; *U.S. Private*, pg. 2816
MVELA PHANDA CONSTRUCTION (PTY) LIMITED—See Basil Read Holdings Limited; *Int'l*, pg. 887
MY PLUMBER INC.; *U.S. Private*, pg. 2823
NAHWARME DUSSELDORF GMBH—See EnBW Energie Baden-Wurttemberg AG; *Int'l*, pg. 2399
NASHVILLE MACHINE COMPANY, INC.; *U.S. Private*, pg. 2836
NATIONAL AIR FILTER SERVICE CO OF NEW JERSEY—See Daikin Industries, Ltd.; *Int'l*, pg. 1936
NATIONAL BOILER SERVICE INC.; *U.S. Private*, pg. 2849
NATIONAL FIRE PROTECTION INC.; *U.S. Private*, pg. 2854
NATIONAL HEATING & AIR CONDITIONING COMPANY—See Heartland Home Services, Inc.; *U.S. Private*, pg. 1900
NATIONAL HEAT & POWER CORP; *U.S. Private*, pg. 2856
NATIONAL HVAC SERVICE LTD.; *U.S. Private*, pg. 2856
NATIONAL MECHANICAL SERVICES, LLC; *U.S. Private*, pg. 2859
NEARU SERVICES; *U.S. Private*, pg. 2877
NELSON AIR DEVICE CORP; *U.S. Private*, pg. 2883
NELSON PIPING COMPANY; *U.S. Private*, pg. 2883
NEW ENGLAND AIR SYSTEMS INC.; *U.S. Private*, pg. 2893
NEW ENGLAND MECHANICAL SERVICES, INC.—See EMCOR Group, Inc.; *U.S. Public*, pg. 738
NILAI CIPTA SDN BHD—See IJM Corporation Berhad; *Int'l*, pg. 3609
NJR ENERGY HOLDINGS CORPORATION—See New Jersey Resources Corporation; *U.S. Public*, pg. 1512
N&M COOL TODAY, INC.; *U.S. Private*, pg. 2847
NOLO CLIMAT S.R.L.—See ANDREWS SYKES GROUP PLC; *Int'l*, pg. 452
NORRIS RODS, INC.—See Dover Corporation; *U.S. Public*, pg. 682
NORTHERN BOILER & MECHANICAL CONTRACTORS; *U.S. Private*, pg. 2952
NORTHSTAR FIRE PROTECTION OF TEXAS, INC.; *U.S. Private*, pg. 2957
NORTHWEST WATER HEATER INC.; *U.S. Private*, pg. 2962
NPI VENTILATION AB—See Bravida Holding AB; *Int'l*, pg. 1142
NRG RESIDENTIAL SOLAR SOLUTIONS LLC—See NRG Energy, Inc.; *U.S. Public*, pg. 1550
N&S SUPPLY LLC—See Watsco, Inc.; *U.S. Public*, pg. 2336
NU FLOW AMERICA INC.; *U.S. Private*, pg. 2971
N.V. HEATHORN INC.; *U.S. Private*, pg. 2828
O'CONNOR CONSTRUCTORS INC.; *U.S. Private*, pg. 2978
OHMSTEDE, LTD.—See EMCOR Group, Inc.; *U.S. Public*, pg. 738
OJS BUILDING SERVICES INC.; *U.S. Private*, pg. 3006
O&M INDUSTRIES INC.; *U.S. Private*, pg. 2977
OMNITEAM INC.; *U.S. Private*, pg. 3017
ONSITE ENERGY, INC.—See NRG Energy, Inc.; *U.S. Public*, pg. 1550
ONTARIO REFRIGERATION SERVICE; *U.S. Private*, pg. 3028
ORANGUTAN HOME SERVICES; *U.S. Private*, pg. 3038
ORAS AS—See Bravida Holding AB; *Int'l*, pg. 1142

N.A.I.C.S. INDEX

238220 — PLUMBING, HEATING, ...

OREGON CASCADE PLUMBING & HEATING, INC.; *U.S. Private*, pg. 3039
OUTDOOR CONSTRUCTION INC.—See Munie Outdoor Services, Inc.; *U.S. Private*, pg. 2814
OWENS COMPANIES, INC.; *U.S. Private*, pg. 3055
P1 GROUP, INC.; *U.S. Private*, pg. 3061
PACE MECHANICAL SERVICES II, INC.—See EMCOR Group, Inc.; *U.S. Public*, pg. 738
PACIFIC PLUMBING CO.—See Jarboe's Plumbing, Heating & Cooling, Inc.; *U.S. Private*, pg. 2188
PALMER AND SICARD INC.; *U.S. Private*, pg. 3080
PARAGON MECHANICAL INC.; *U.S. Private*, pg. 3091
PARMAC AIR CONDITIONING & MECHANICAL SERVICES PTY. LTD.—See BlueNRGY Group Limited; *Int'l*, pg. 1072
PAR PLUMBING CO. INC.; *U.S. Private*, pg. 3089
PASCHAL HOME SERVICES, LLC; *U.S. Private*, pg. 3103
PATRICK MECHANICAL LLC—See The Aleut Corporation; *U.S. Private*, pg. 3984
PATRIOT FIRE PROTECTION INC.; *U.S. Private*, pg. 3110
THE PECK-HANNAFORD & BRIGGS CO. INC.; *U.S. Private*, pg. 4091
PECK-HANNAFORD & BRIGGS SERVICE CORP.—See The Peck-Hannaford & Briggs Co. Inc.; *U.S. Private*, pg. 4092
PENGUIN AIR CONDITIONING CORP.—See EMCOR Group, Inc.; *U.S. Public*, pg. 738
PERFECTION GROUP, INC.; *U.S. Private*, pg. 3148
PERSONALIZED AIR CONDITIONING, INC.—See Air Pros; *U.S. Private*, pg. 139
PETCOSKY & SONS PLUMBING, HEATING & A/C INC.—See Morgan Stanley; *U.S. Public*, pg. 1474
PETERS HEATING & AC; *U.S. Private*, pg. 3159
PETTUS PLUMBING & PIPING INC.; *U.S. Private*, pg. 3163
PIEDMONT AIR CONDITIONING CO.; *U.S. Private*, pg. 3176
PIEDMONT MECHANICAL, INC. - LAGRANGE—See Piedmont Mechanical, Inc.; *U.S. Private*, pg. 3177
PIEDMONT MECHANICAL, INC.; *U.S. Private*, pg. 3177
PIERCE ASSOCIATES INC.; *U.S. Private*, pg. 3178
PIHER INTERNATIONAL LTD.—See Parker Hannifin Corporation; *U.S. Public*, pg. 1643
THE PIPCO COMPANIES LTD.; *U.S. Private*, pg. 4096
PIPE SYSTEMS INC.; *U.S. Private*, pg. 3189
P & J SPRINKLER COMPANY, INC.—See TruArc Partners, L.P.; *U.S. Private*, pg. 4244
PLEUNE SERVICE COMPANY; *U.S. Private*, pg. 3214
PLIBRICO CO. LLC; *U.S. Private*, pg. 3214
PLUMBING N' THINGS, INC.—See Slakey Brothers Inc.; *U.S. Private*, pg. 3687
PLUMB LINE MECHANICAL, INC.; *U.S. Private*, pg. 3214
PNEC CORPORATION; *U.S. Private*, pg. 3219
THE POOLE & KENT COMPANY OF FLORIDA—See EMCOR Group, Inc.; *U.S. Public*, pg. 739
THE POOLE & KENT CORPORATION—See EMCOR Group, Inc.; *U.S. Public*, pg. 739
PORTER COMPANY/MECHANICAL CONTRACTORS; *U.S. Private*, pg. 3231
POSIGEN LLC; *U.S. Private*, pg. 3233
POSTLER & JAECKLE CORP.; *U.S. Private*, pg. 3235
POWER MAINTENANCE & CONSTRUCTORS LLC; *U.S. Private*, pg. 3238
POWER PLUMBING, INC.; *U.S. Private*, pg. 3238
POWER PROCESS PIPING, INC.; *U.S. Private*, pg. 3238
PRAIRIE MECHANICAL CORPORATION; *U.S. Private*, pg. 3243
PRECISION MECHANICAL INC.—See Precision Resources Inc.; *U.S. Private*, pg. 3246
PRECISION PIPING AND MECHANICAL INC.; *U.S. Private*, pg. 3246
PREFERRED HOME SERVICES, LLC; *U.S. Private*, pg. 3248
PRESIDENTIAL HEATING & AIR CONDITIONING, INC.—See Gryphon Investors, LLC; *U.S. Private*, pg. 1799
PRESTON REFRIGERATION COMPANY INC.; *U.S. Private*, pg. 3257
PREVENTIVI SRL—See Brookfield Corporation; *Int'l*, pg. 1188
PROFESSIONAL PLUMBERS GROUP, INC.—See Sterling Infrastructure, Inc.; *U.S. Public*, pg. 1947
PROGRESSIVE PLUMBING INC.; *U.S. Private*, pg. 3279
PRO-MARK, LLC—See Platinum Equity, LLC; *U.S. Private*, pg. 3207
PRO-TECH AIR CONDITIONING & HEATING SERVICE, INC.; *U.S. Private*, pg. 3271
PTAC 4 LESS INC.—See Mollenhour Gross LLC; *U.S. Private*, pg. 2767
PUMPJACK SOLAR I, LLC—See Duke Energy Corporation; *U.S. Public*, pg. 691
QUACKENBUSH CO., INC.; *U.S. Private*, pg. 3314
QUALITY AIR HEATING AND COOLING, INC.—See Comfort Systems USA, Inc.; *U.S. Public*, pg. 544
QUIRKS AUSTRALIA PTY LTD—See COCA-COLA EUROPACIFIC PARTNERS PLC; *Int'l*, pg. 1684
RAM SERVICES INC.—See AEMS Service Company; *U.S. Private*, pg. 117
RAWLINGS MECHANICAL CORP.; *U.S. Private*, pg. 3358

R. BROOKS MECHANICAL, INC.—See LP First Capital; *U.S. Private*, pg. 2507
R. BROOKS MECHANICAL, INC.—See The RLJ Companies, LLC; *U.S. Private*, pg. 4111
RCS COMPANY OF TAMPA; *U.S. Private*, pg. 3362
RECTORSEAL AUSTRALIA PROPRIETARY LIMITED—See CSW Industrials, Inc.; *U.S. Public*, pg. 601
REDDI INDUSTRIES, INC.; *U.S. Private*, pg. 3377
REDDI SERVICES, INC.; *U.S. Private*, pg. 3377
REDMAN EQUIPMENT & MANUFACTURING CO.—See EMCOR Group, Inc.; *U.S. Public*, pg. 738
REDWOOD INDUSTRIES INC.; *U.S. Private*, pg. 3381
REECE-HOPPER SALES, LLC; *U.S. Private*, pg. 3381
R.E. GRIESEMER INC.; *U.S. Private*, pg. 3335
RELIANCE HEATING & AIR CONDITIONING COMPANY; *U.S. Private*, pg. 3394
RELMEC MECHANICAL LLC; *U.S. Private*, pg. 3395
REPIPE SPECIALISTS, INC.; *U.S. Private*, pg. 3400
RGB MECHANICAL CONTRACTORS INC.; *U.S. Private*, pg. 3420
RICHARD MEEK AIR CONDITIONING, INC.—See Wind Point Advisors LLC; *U.S. Private*, pg. 4536
RICHMOND REFRIGERATION SERVICE, INC.—See Ares Management Corporation; *U.S. Public*, pg. 189
RIDDLEBERGER BROS., INC.; *U.S. Private*, pg. 3431
RIGGS DISTLER & COMPANY INC.—See Southwest Gas Holdings, Inc.; *U.S. Public*, pg. 1913
RIGHT TIME GROUP INC.—See Gryphon Investors, LLC; *U.S. Private*, pg. 1799
R.J. KIELTY PLUMBING INC.; *U.S. Private*, pg. 3337
RK MECHANICAL, INC.; *U.S. Private*, pg. 3450
RM MECHANICAL INC.; *U.S. Private*, pg. 3451
ROADRUNNER SUNTOWER, LLC—See NRG Energy, Inc.; *U.S. Public*, pg. 1551
ROBERT GIBB & SONS, INC.; *U.S. Private*, pg. 3458
ROBERT LLOYD SHEET METAL INC.; *U.S. Private*, pg. 3458
ROCK CITY MECHANICAL CO. LLC; *U.S. Private*, pg. 3464
ROCK HILL MECHANICAL CORP; *U.S. Private*, pg. 3464
ROEDIGER GEBAUDETECHNIK GMBH—See Bilfinger SE; *Int'l*, pg. 1028
ROTH-ZACHRY HEATING INC.; *U.S. Private*, pg. 3487
ROTO-ROOTER CANADA, LTD.—See Chemed Corporation; *U.S. Public*, pg. 484
ROTO-ROOTER, CORP.—See Chemed Corporation; *U.S. Public*, pg. 484
ROTO-ROOTER SERVICES CO—See Chemed Corporation; *U.S. Public*, pg. 484
ROYALAIRE MECHANICAL SERVICES, LLC—See Comfort Systems USA, Inc.; *U.S. Public*, pg. 544
R.S. ANDREWS ENTERPRISES INC.; *U.S. Private*, pg. 3339
R.S. HARRITAN & COMPANY, INC.—See EMCOR Group, Inc.; *U.S. Public*, pg. 737
RTH MECHANICAL CONTRACTORS, INC.; *U.S. Private*, pg. 3498
RUTHRAUFF LLC; *U.S. Private*, pg. 3508
RYAN COMPANY INC.—See Quanta Services, Inc.; *U.S. Public*, pg. 1753
RYAN FIREPROTECTION INC.; *U.S. Private*, pg. 3510
SAN MARCOS AIR CONDITIONING, INC.—See Novak Group LLC; *U.S. Private*, pg. 2966
SA NTI—See Hiolle Industries S.A.; *Int'l*, pg. 3401
SARRACCO MECHANICAL SERVICES INC.; *U.S. Private*, pg. 3550
SAVAGE & SON, INC.; *U.S. Private*, pg. 3555
SCHAAL HEATING & COOLING, INC.; *U.S. Private*, pg. 3562
SCHADEGG MECHANICAL INC.; *U.S. Private*, pg. 3563
THE SCHAEFER GROUP, INC.; *U.S. Private*, pg. 4114
SCHAFFER MECHANICAL, INC.; *U.S. Private*, pg. 3563
SCHECK MECHANICAL CORP; *U.S. Private*, pg. 3563
SCHMIDT FIRE PROTECTION COMPANY, INC.; *U.S. Private*, pg. 3566
SCOPE SERVICES INC.; *U.S. Private*, pg. 3575
S&D OSTERFELD MECHANICAL CONTRACTORS—See Unitize Company Inc.; *U.S. Private*, pg. 4302
SEASONAIR, INC.—See Comfort Systems USA, Inc.; *U.S. Public*, pg. 544
SEAWALL SOLAR 9 LLC—See NRG Energy, Inc.; *U.S. Public*, pg. 1551
SECURITY FIRE PROTECTION COMPANY, INC.—See API Group Corporation; *Int'l*, pg. 514
THE SEER GROUP LLC; *U.S. Private*, pg. 4115
SEITER SERVICES, LLC; *U.S. Private*, pg. 3600
SELFIO GMBH—See 3U Holding AG; *Int'l*, pg. 10
SENICA AIR CONDITIONING, INC.; *U.S. Private*, pg. 3606
SENNINGER PLUMBING COMPANY, INC.; *U.S. Private*, pg. 3607
SERVICE CHAMPIONS, INC.—See Odyssey Investment Partners, LLC; *U.S. Private*, pg. 2995
SERVICEMASTER TOTAL RESTORATION SERVICES; *U.S. Private*, pg. 3616
SERVICIOS TECNICOS SATE S.L.—See Brookfield Corporation; *Int'l*, pg. 1189
SERVICIO TECNICO URUENA S.L.—See Brookfield Corporation; *Int'l*, pg. 1189
SHELBY MECHANICAL, INC.; *U.S. Private*, pg. 3630

SHOALS MPE, LLC; *U.S. Private*, pg. 3639
SHOFFNERKALTHOFF MECHANICAL ELECTRICAL SERVICE, LLC—See Comfort Systems USA, Inc.; *U.S. Public*, pg. 544
SIERRA AIR, INC.—See Odyssey Investment Partners, LLC; *U.S. Private*, pg. 2995
SIG AIR HANDLING N.V.—See AIRVANCE GROUP; *Int'l*, pg. 250
S.I. GOLDMAN CO., INC.—See Comfort Systems USA, Inc.; *U.S. Public*, pg. 544
SILA HEATING & AIR CONDITIONING, INC.—See Morgan Stanley; *U.S. Public*, pg. 1474
SILA SERVICES, LLC—See Morgan Stanley; *U.S. Public*, pg. 1474
SIMAKAS COMPANY INC.; *U.S. Private*, pg. 3665
SINAK PLUMBING COMPANY INC.—See CPS Capital; *Int'l*, pg. 1826
SIRINA FIRE PROTECTION CORP.; *U.S. Private*, pg. 3672
SJESP PLUMBING SERVICES LLC—See Brookfield Corporation; *Int'l*, pg. 1188
SKI HI ENTERPRISES LTD.; *U.S. Private*, pg. 3681
SLAYDEN PLUMBING & HEATING, INC.; *U.S. Private*, pg. 3688
SMITH FIRE SYSTEMS INC.; *U.S. Private*, pg. 3694
THE SMITH & OBY COMPANY; *U.S. Private*, pg. 4118
THE SMITH & OBY SERVICE CO.—See The Smith & Oby Company; *U.S. Private*, pg. 4118
S.M. LAWRENCE COMPANY, INC.—See Comfort Systems USA, Inc.; *U.S. Public*, pg. 544
SNELL SERVICES INC.; *U.S. Private*, pg. 3700
SOEHNLEN PIPING COMPANY; *U.S. Private*, pg. 3704
SOLAR SOLUTIONS & DISTRIBUTION, LLC.; *U.S. Private*, pg. 3707
SOLAR UNIVERSE INC.; *U.S. Private*, pg. 3707
SOLAR WATT SOLUTIONS INC.—See CleanSpark, Inc.; *U.S. Public*, pg. 511
SOLO MECHANICAL MAINTENANCE, INC.—See United Mechanical, Inc.; *U.S. Private*, pg. 4294
SOMGAS HOGAR S.L.—See Brookfield Corporation; *Int'l*, pg. 1189
SONORAN AIR INC.; *U.S. Private*, pg. 3714
SOS MECHANICAL LLC—See CPS Capital; *Int'l*, pg. 1826
SOUTHEASTERN AUTOMATIC SPRINKLER CO., INC.—See Comfort Systems USA, Inc.; *U.S. Public*, pg. 543
SOUTHEAST MECHANICAL, LLC—See Palladin Consumer Retail Partners, LLC; *U.S. Private*, pg. 3077
SOUTHERN AIR, INC.; *U.S. Private*, pg. 3729
SOUTHERN EQUIPMENT CORPORATION; *U.S. Private*, pg. 3731
SOUTHERN HOME SERVICES LLC—See Gryphon Investors, LLC; *U.S. Private*, pg. 1799
SOUTHERN PIPING COMPANY; *U.S. Private*, pg. 3734
SOUTHLAND INDUSTRIES-NORTHERN CALIFORNIA DIVISION—See Southland Industries; *U.S. Private*, pg. 3737
SOUTHLAND INDUSTRIES; *U.S. Private*, pg. 3737
SOUTHLAND INDUSTRIES-SOUTHERN CALIFORNIA DIVISION—See Southland Industries; *U.S. Private*, pg. 3737
SOUTHLAND INDUSTRIES-SOUTHWEST DIVISION—See Southland Industries; *U.S. Private*, pg. 3737
SOUTHTOWN HEATING & COOLING, INC.—See Seiter Services, LLC; *U.S. Private*, pg. 3600
SOUTH-TOWN REFRIGERATION INC.—See Haier Smart Home Co., Ltd.; *Int'l*, pg. 3210
SOUTHWEST PLUMBING & WATER HEATERS, INC.—See Koch Industries, Inc.; *U.S. Private*, pg. 2327
SOUTHWEST PLUMBING & WATER HEATERS, INC.—See The Goldman Sachs Group, Inc.; *U.S. Public*, pg. 2077
SPANISH TOWN ESTATE SOLAR 1 LLC—See NRG Energy, Inc.; *U.S. Public*, pg. 1551
SRI FIRE SPRINKLER CORP.; *U.S. Private*, pg. 3767
S.S.W. MECHANICAL CONSTRUCTION, INC.; *U.S. Private*, pg. 3519
STANDARD PLUMBING & HEATING CO.; *U.S. Private*, pg. 3781
STANDARD REFRIGERATION CO. INC.; *U.S. Private*, pg. 3781
STAN'S HEATING & AIR CONDITIONING, INC.—See Catterton Management Company, LLC; *U.S. Private*, pg. 793
STARCON INC.; *U.S. Private*, pg. 3786
STASCO MECHANICAL CONTRACTORS; *U.S. Private*, pg. 3790
STEAM & CONTROL SYSTEMS, INC.; *U.S. Private*, pg. 3795
STEPHEN GOULD OF COLORADO, INC.—See Stephen Gould Corporation; *U.S. Private*, pg. 3802
STERLING BOILER & MECHANICAL INC.; *U.S. Private*, pg. 3804
STOKES MECHANICAL CONTRACTORS INC; *U.S. Private*, pg. 3816
STORO BLIKKENSLAGERVERKSTED AS—See AF Gruppen ASA; *Int'l*, pg. 184
STRICKLAND FIRE PROTECTION, INC.—See Pye-Barker Fire & Safety, LLC; *U.S. Private*, pg. 3309
STR MECHANICAL, LLC—See SkyKnight Capital LLC; *U.S. Private*, pg. 3685

238220 — PLUMBING, HEATING, ...

STROMBERG SHEET METAL WORKS INC.—See Metals Inc.; *U.S. Private*, pg. 2682
STROMEK EMIRATES FOUNDATIONS LLC—See Dubai Investments PJSC; *Int'l*, pg. 2219
SUBZERO CONSTRUCTORS, INC.; *U.S. Private*, pg. 3848
SUGIYAMAKANKOUSETUBI CO., LTD.—See Chudenko Corporation; *Int'l*, pg. 1594
SUMMIT FIRE PROTECTION CO.—See BlackRock, Inc.; *U.S. Public*, pg. 346
SUN LIGHT & POWER; *U.S. Private*, pg. 3863
SUNSET AIR INCORPORATED; *U.S. Private*, pg. 3871
SUNSHINE PLUMBING HEATING AIR LLC; *U.S. Private*, pg. 3872
SUPERIOR MECHANICAL SYSTEMS, INC.; *U.S. Private*, pg. 3879
SYCAMORE ENGINEERING; *U.S. Private*, pg. 3895
SYCLEF HOLDING SAS—See Ardian SAS; *Int'l*, pg. 556
SYMBIONT SERVICE CORP; *U.S. Private*, pg. 3899
SYSTENO GMBH—See Helaba Landesbank Hessen-Thuringen; *Int'l*, pg. 3328
T.A. SHEETS GENERAL CONTRACTORS, INC.; *U.S. Private*, pg. 3911
TAYLOR HEATING, INC.—See Brookfield Corporation; *Int'l*, pg. 1188
TD INDUSTRIES, INC.; *U.S. Private*, pg. 3943
TEBARCO MECHANICAL CORP.—See Modigent LLC; *U.S. Private*, pg. 2763
TECH MECHANICAL INC.—See Ares Management Corporation; *U.S. Public*, pg. 189
TECNO ARASAT SERVICIOS DE MANTENIMIENTO S.L.—See Brookfield Corporation; *Int'l*, pg. 1189
TECNOTEL CLIMA, S.L.—See ACS, Actividades de Construccion y Servicios, S.A.; *Int'l*, pg. 116
TELEDYNE OLDHAM SIMTRONICS SAS—See Teledyne Technologies Incorporated; *U.S. Public*, pg. 1994
TEMP-CONTROL MECHANICAL CORP.; *U.S. Private*, pg. 3963
TEMPERATURE SERVICE COMPANY, INC.; *U.S. Private*, pg. 3963
TESSIER'S, INC.—See APi Group Corporation; *Int'l*, pg. 514
TEWE ENERGIEVERSORGUNGSGESELLSCHAFT MBH—See EWE Aktiengesellschaft; *Int'l*, pg. 2575
TGA DEUTSCHLAND GMBH—See Fortive Corporation; *U.S. Public*, pg. 872
THERMA CORPORATION—See Blackstone Inc.; *U.S. Public*, pg. 361
THERMAL CONCEPTS, LLC—See Halmos Capital Partners; *U.S. Private*, pg. 1845
THERMAL CONCEPTS, LLC—See Trivest Partners, LP; *U.S. Private*, pg. 4241
THERMAL DYNAMICS INTERNATIONAL, INC.—See Page Management Co., Inc.; *U.S. Private*, pg. 3074
THIRD SUN SOLAR & WIND POWER, LTD.; *U.S. Private*, pg. 4145
THOMAS G. GALLAGHER, INC.; *U.S. Private*, pg. 4155
THRIFTY AIR CONDITIONING & REFRIGERATION, INC.—See Freeman Spogli & Co. Incorporated; *U.S. Private*, pg. 1606
TIMBIL MECHANICAL CORP; *U.S. Private*, pg. 4172
TIMOTHY OFF HEATING & AIR CONDITIONING; *U.S. Private*, pg. 4173
TODD-FORD INC.—See Todd-Ford Management Inc.; *U.S. Private*, pg. 4181
TODD-FORD MANAGEMENT INC.; *U.S. Private*, pg. 4181
TODD-FORD SHEETMETAL INC.—See Todd-Ford Management Inc.; *U.S. Private*, pg. 4181
TOLIN MECHANICAL SYSTEMS CO.—See The Jordan Company, L.P.; *U.S. Private*, pg. 4062
TOTAL BUILDING ENVIRONMENTS SOUTH, INC.—See Energy Control Consultants, Inc.; *U.S. Private*, pg. 1394
TOUGHER INDUSTRIES ENTERPRISES, LLC—See JWD Group Inc.; *U.S. Private*, pg. 2247
TOZOUR ENERGY SYSTEMS, INC.; *U.S. Private*, pg. 4199
TRADEWINDS MECHANICAL SERVICES, LLC.; *U.S. Private*, pg. 4202
TRAUTMAN & SHREVE, INC.—See EMCOR Group, Inc.; *U.S. Public*, pg. 739
TRIAD MECHANICAL INC.; *U.S. Private*, pg. 4225
TRIANGLE CONTRACTORS INC.; *U.S. Private*, pg. 4226
TRIANGLE REFRIGERATION CO.—See Ares Management Corporation; *U.S. Public*, pg. 189
TRI COUNTY AIR CONDITIONING & HEATING, INC.; *U.S. Private*, pg. 4220
TRINITY SOLAR, INC.; *U.S. Private*, pg. 4235
TRIPLE S AIR SYSTEMS, INC.; *U.S. Private*, pg. 4237
TRI TECH CONSTRUCTION CORP.; *U.S. Private*, pg. 4221
TRUFORM METALSERVICE INC—See McCarty Corporation; *U.S. Private*, pg. 2628
TUCKER MECHANICAL—See EMCOR Group, Inc.; *U.S. Public*, pg. 739
TUNNEL SAFETY TESTING, S.A.—See I Squared Capital Advisors (US) LLC; *U.S. Private*, pg. 2023
TUSTIN MECHANICAL SERVICES (LEHIGH VALLEY), LLC.; *U.S. Private*, pg. 4262
TWEET-GAROT MECHANICAL INC.; *U.S. Private*, pg. 4264
TWIN RIVERS PLUMBING INC.; *U.S. Private*, pg. 4266

TX SOLAR I LLC—See Duke Energy Corporation; *U.S. Public*, pg. 691
UCI CONSTRUCTION INC.; *U.S. Private*, pg. 4273
UKFM GROUP LTD—See Cordant Group PLC; *Int'l*, pg. 1796
THE UNDERFLOOR HEATING COMPANY LIMITED—See Georg Fischer AG; *Int'l*, pg. 2937
UNDERGROUND SPECIALTIES INC.—See Crestone Services Group LLC; *U.S. Private*, pg. 1097
UNIQUE AIR SERVICES INC.; *U.S. Private*, pg. 4286
UNIQUE ELEVATOR INTERIORS, INC.—See P4G Capital Management, LLC; *U.S. Private*, pg. 3062
UNITED AIR CONDITIONING & HEATING COMPANY, INC.; *U.S. Private*, pg. 4287
UNITED AIR-TEMP AC & HEATING; *U.S. Private*, pg. 4287
UNITED MECHANICAL, INC.; *U.S. Private*, pg. 4294
UNITED MECHANICAL INC.; *U.S. Private*, pg. 4294
UNITED MECHANICAL; *U.S. Private*, pg. 4294
UNIVERSAL RESTORATION, INC.—See Air Pros USA; *U.S. Private*, pg. 139
UNIVERSITY MECHANICAL & ENGINEERING CONTRACTORS, INC.—See EMCOR Group, Inc.; *U.S. Public*, pg. 737
UNIVERSITY MECHANICAL & ENGINEERING CONTRACTORS, INC.—See EMCOR Group, Inc.; *U.S. Public*, pg. 737
UPONOR INFRA OY—See Georg Fischer AG; *Int'l*, pg. 2937
UPONOR KFT—See Georg Fischer AG; *Int'l*, pg. 2938
US ENGINEERING COMPANY; *U.S. Private*, pg. 4318
USER FRIENDLY HOME SERVICES, LLC; *U.S. Private*, pg. 4322
VAN NATTA MECHANICAL INC.; *U.S. Private*, pg. 4340
VASEY COMMERCIAL HEATING & AC; *U.S. Private*, pg. 4347
VICTORIA AIR CONDITIONING, LTD.; *U.S. Private*, pg. 4378
VIKING AUTOMATIC SPRINKLER COMPANY—See APi Group Corporation; *Int'l*, pg. 514
VSC BUILDING PRODUCTS COMPANY LIMITED—See Hong Kong Shanghai Alliance Holdings Limited; *Int'l*, pg. 3467
WACO, INC.; *U.S. Private*, pg. 4424
THE WALDINGER CORPORATION; *U.S. Private*, pg. 4133
WALKER-J-WALKER, INC.—See EMCOR Group, Inc.; *U.S. Public*, pg. 739
WALTON & CO. INC.; *U.S. Private*, pg. 4434
WARKO ROOFING COMPANY INC.; *U.S. Private*, pg. 4442
WARREN'S AIR CONDITIONING & HEATING SERVICE, INC.; *U.S. Private*, pg. 4444
WARWICK PLUMBING AND HEATING CORPORATION; *U.S. Private*, pg. 4445
WAYNE AUTOMATIC FIRE SPRINKLERS, INC.; *U.S. Private*, pg. 4459
WAYNE CROUSE INC.; *U.S. Private*, pg. 4459
WAYNE MAPLES PLUMBING & HEATING; *U.S. Private*, pg. 4460
WB GUIMARIN & COMPANY INC.; *U.S. Private*, pg. 4461
WDF INC.—See WDF/Five Star Holding Corporation; *U.S. Private*, pg. 4462
WELDON MECHANICAL CORPORATION; *U.S. Private*, pg. 4474
WELSCH HEATING & COOLING CO.; *U.S. Private*, pg. 4479
WESTERN DRAIN SUPPLY, INC.—See Chemed Corporation; *U.S. Public*, pg. 484
WESTERN HEATING AND AIR CONDITIONING INC.—See The SEER Group LLC; *U.S. Private*, pg. 4115
WESTERN STATES FIRE PROTECTION—See APi Group Corporation; *Int'l*, pg. 514
W.G. TOMKO, INC.; *U.S. Private*, pg. 4420
WIEGMANN ASSOCIATES INC.; *U.S. Private*, pg. 4516
WIGINTON CORP.; *U.S. Private*, pg. 4517
WILLIAM E. WALTER INC.; *U.S. Private*, pg. 4523
WILLIAM R. NASH INC.; *U.S. Private*, pg. 4524
WILLIAMS MECHANICAL CORPORATION; *U.S. Private*, pg. 4526
WINGER CONTRACTING CO.; *U.S. Private*, pg. 4541
WINNER ENGINEERING PTE. LTD.—See EXEO Group Inc.; *Int'l*, pg. 2584
WINONA HEATING & VENT CO.; *U.S. Private*, pg. 4543
W. J. O'NEIL COMPANY; *U.S. Private*, pg. 4418
WM. F. MCDONOUGH PLUMBING, INC.; *U.S. Private*, pg. 4552
W.O. BLACKSTONE & COMPANY, INC.; *U.S. Private*, pg. 4422
WOLFFERTS HAUS- UND WARMETECHNIK GMBH—See Bilfinger SE; *Int'l*, pg. 1028
WOLVERINE FIRE PROTECTION CO.; *U.S. Private*, pg. 4555
WORRY FREE COMFORT SYSTEMS, INC—See Brookfield Corporation; *Int'l*, pg. 1188
WORTH & CO., INC.; *U.S. Private*, pg. 4570
WRENCH GROUP LLC—See Leonard Green & Partners, L.P.; *U.S. Private*, pg. 2430
WRIGHT TOTAL INDOOR COMFORT, INC.; *U.S. Private*, pg. 4573
W. SOULE & COMPANY; *U.S. Private*, pg. 4418

W.W. GAY MECHANICAL CONTRACTOR, INC.; *U.S. Private*, pg. 4423
XCEL MECHANICAL SYSTEMS, INC.; *U.S. Private*, pg. 4580
XL FIRE PROTECTION CO.; *U.S. Private*, pg. 4581
YANKEE ENERGY SERVICES COMPANY—See Eversource Energy; *U.S. Public*, pg. 802
YOUNG'S ENGINEERING COMPANY LIMITED—See FSE Services Group Limited; *Int'l*, pg. 2798
ZAMPELL REFRACTORIES; *U.S. Private*, pg. 4597
ZIPPER AIR CONDITIONING & HEATING COMPANY—See Defender Security Company; *U.S. Private*, pg. 1190

238290 — OTHER BUILDING EQUIPMENT CONTRACTORS

11400, INC.—See Clark Associates, Inc.; *U.S. Private*, pg. 912
1ST INSULATION PARTNERS LIMITED—See Carillion plc; *Int'l*, pg. 1380
9G ELEVATOR PTE. LTD.—See Otis Worldwide Corporation; *U.S. Public*, pg. 1622
A1 GARAGE DOOR SERVICES LLC; *U.S. Private*, pg. 29
ABC SUPPLY CO. INC.; *U.S. Private*, pg. 36
ADVANCED INDUSTRIAL SERVICES, INC.—See Cemtrex; *U.S. Public*, pg. 466
A+ INSULATION OF KANSAS CITY, LLC—See Installed Building Products, Inc.; *U.S. Public*, pg. 1131
ALGOL TECHNIQUES—See Algol Oy; *Int'l*, pg. 318
ALL CONSTRUCTION SERVICES, LLC—See Installed Building Products, Inc.; *U.S. Public*, pg. 1132
ALL IN ONE & MOORE BUILDING SYSTEMS, LLC—See Installed Building Products, Inc.; *U.S. Public*, pg. 1132
ALLTECH ENGINEERING CORP.; *U.S. Private*, pg. 194
ALPHA INSULATION & WATER PROOFING INC.—See Installed Building Products, Inc.; *U.S. Public*, pg. 1132
AMANO CLEANTECH MALAYSIA SDN. BHD.—See Amano Corporation; *Int'l*, pg. 410
ASK OKINAWA CORPORATION—See A&A Material Corporation; *Int'l*, pg. 18
ATM-TURAUTOMATIK GMBH—See dormakaba Holding AG; *Int'l*, pg. 2177
AZBIL EUROPE NV—See Azbil Corporation; *Int'l*, pg. 777
BANQUE SOLFEA SA—See ENGIE SA; *Int'l*, pg. 2428
BARTON MALOW YARD—See Barton Malow Enterprises, Inc.; *U.S. Private*, pg. 483
BELCORP, INC.; *U.S. Private*, pg. 517
BELGER CARTAGE SERVICE, INC.—See Belcorp Inc.; *U.S. Private*, pg. 517
BIGGE CRANE & RIGGING COMPANY; *U.S. Private*, pg. 555
BLATT GROUP; *U.S. Private*, pg. 580
BOA CONCEPT SA; *Int'l*, pg. 1094
B-ORGANIZED INSULATION, LLC—See Installed Building Products, Inc.; *U.S. Public*, pg. 1132
BRAUN THYSSENKRUPP ELEVATOR, LLC—See Advent International Corporation; *U.S. Private*, pg. 106
BRAUN THYSSENKRUPP ELEVATOR, LLC—See Cinven Limited; *Int'l*, pg. 1614
BUILDERS INSTALLED PRODUCTS OF VERMONT, LLC—See Installed Building Products, Inc.; *U.S. Public*, pg. 1132
CARDTRONICS CANADA, LTD.—See NCR Voyix Corporation.; *U.S. Public*, pg. 1501
C&C MILLWRIGHT MAINTENANCE CO.; *U.S. Private*, pg. 702
CDN MSOLAR CORP.; *Int'l*, pg. 1371
CENTURION INDUSTRIES INC.; *U.S. Private*, pg. 831
CENTURY CONVEYOR, INC.; *U.S. Private*, pg. 832
CHANCEY METALS, LLC—See Indigo South Capital, Inc.; *U.S. Private*, pg. 2063
CHEVALIER (E & M CONTRACTING) LIMITED—See Chevalier International Holdings Limited; *Int'l*, pg. 1473
CHIU TING MACHINERY CO., LTD.; *Int'l*, pg. 1574
CLEAN GREEN ENERGY, LLC—See CGE Energy Inc.; *U.S. Public*, pg. 477
CNIM SINGAPORE PTE LTD—See CNIM Constructions Industrielles de la Mediterranee SA; *Int'l*, pg. 1677
COGENIC, LLC; *U.S. Private*, pg. 962
COLUMBIA SWEEPING SERVICES INC.; *U.S. Private*, pg. 978
COMPACT POWER EQUIPMENT, INC.—See The Home Depot, Inc.; *U.S. Public*, pg. 2089
CON-PRO INDUSTRIES CANADA LTD.; *Int'l*, pg. 1763
CTR SYSTEMS INC.; *U.S. Private*, pg. 1119
C T R SYSTEMS INC.; *U.S. Private*, pg. 702
DELTA ELEVATOR SERVICE CORP.—See Otis Worldwide Corporation; *U.S. Public*, pg. 1623
DEPCOM POWER, INC.; *U.S. Private*, pg. 1208
DEVITT & FORAND CONTRACTORS INC.; *Int'l*, pg. 2089
DEYA ELEVATOR SERVICES, INC.; *U.S. Private*, pg. 1220
DFW MOVERS & ERECTORS INC.; *U.S. Private*, pg. 1221
DISTECH CONTROLS POLEN SP. Z O.O.—See Acuity Brands, Inc.; *U.S. Public*, pg. 37
DMW&H; *U.S. Private*, pg. 1249
DORMA DOOR CONTROLS LIMITED—See dormakaba Holding AG; *Int'l*, pg. 2178

N.A.I.C.S. INDEX

238310 — DRYWALL AND INSULAT...

DORMAKABA BRASIL SOLUCOES DE ACESSO LTDA.—See dormakaba Holding AG; *Int'l*, pg. 2178
DORMAKABA DEUTSCHL & GMBH—See dormakaba Holding AG; *Int'l*, pg. 2178
DORMAKABA KOREA INC.—See dormakaba Holding AG; *Int'l*, pg. 2179
DORMAKABA PORTUGAL, UNIPESSOAL LDA.—See dormakaba Holding AG; *Int'l*, pg. 2179
DORMAKABA ROMANIA S.R.L.—See dormakaba Holding AG; *Int'l*, pg. 2179
D.W. NICHOLSON CORPORATION; *U.S. Private*, pg. 1143
ECOLOGIC ENERGY SOLUTIONS, LLC—See Installed Building Products, Inc.; *U.S. Public*, pg. 1132
EDWARDS/MOONEY & MOSES, LLC—See Installed Building Products, Inc.; *U.S. Public*, pg. 1132
ELEVADORES OTIS LTDA.—See Otis Worldwide Corporation; *U.S. Public*, pg. 1623
EMMERT INDUSTRIAL CORPORATION; *U.S. Private*, pg. 1383
EPS B.V.—See The Sherwin-Williams Company; *U.S. Public*, pg. 2127
EUROPEAN PUMP SERVICES B.V.—See ITT Inc.; *U.S. Public*, pg. 1177
EV CHARGE PARTNER SWEDEN AB—See Garo AB; *Int'l*, pg. 2885
FIEDLER GROUP; *U.S. Private*, pg. 1503
FUJITEC INC.—See Fujitec Co., Ltd.; *Int'l*, pg. 2831
FUJITEC SAUDI ARABIA CO., LTD.—See Fujitec Co., Ltd.; *Int'l*, pg. 2831
FUJITEC UK LTD.—See Fujitec Co., Ltd.; *Int'l*, pg. 2831
GREEN ENERGY 4 SEASONS; *Int'l*, pg. 3071
GUY M. TURNER INC.; *U.S. Private*, pg. 1820
H2O SMILE CO., LTD.—See H2O Retailing Corp.; *Int'l*, pg. 3200
HANKS MACHINERY MOVERS, INC.—See Olympus Partners; *U.S. Private*, pg. 3013
HESCO SERVICES INC.—See Hoj Engineering & Sales Co., LLC; *U.S. Private*, pg. 1961
HIGGINS ERECTORS & HAULERS INC; *U.S. Private*, pg. 1935
HITACHI BUILDING SYSTEMS ENGINEERING CO., LTD.—See Hitachi, Ltd.; *Int'l*, pg. 3415
HITACHI ELEVATOR PHILIPPINES CORPORATION—See Hitachi, Ltd.; *Int'l*, pg. 3417
HITACHI ELEVATOR VIETNAM CO., LTD.—See Hitachi, Ltd.; *Int'l*, pg. 3417
JERSEY ELEVATOR CO. INC.—See Arcline Investment Management LP; *U.S. Private*, pg. 314
JUDLIN FERMETURES S.A.R.L.—See dormakaba Holding AG; *Int'l*, pg. 2177
KRV AS—See Addtech AB; *Int'l*, pg. 134
LANDMARK ELEVATOR, INC.—See L Squared Capital Management LP; *U.S. Private*, pg. 2362
LANGSON ENERGY, INC.; *U.S. Private*, pg. 2389
LAYMAN BROTHERS INSULATION, LLC—See Installed Building Products, Inc.; *U.S. Public*, pg. 1133
LIGHTWAVE SOLAR, LLC; *U.S. Private*, pg. 2454
THE LYDON COMPANY, LLC; *U.S. Private*, pg. 4073
MADDEN ELEVATOR COMPANY—See American Elevator Group; *U.S. Private*, pg. 231
MASTER TEK INTERNATIONAL, INC.—See Minol USA; *U.S. Private*, pg. 2744
MATTHEWS ENVIRONMENTAL SOLUTIONS LIMITED—See Matthews International Corporation; *U.S. Public*, pg. 1399
M & D INSULATION, LLC—See Installed Building Products, Inc.; *U.S. Public*, pg. 1133
MEI RIGGING & CRATING, LLC—See Olympus Partners; *U.S. Private*, pg. 3013
MERCURY ASCENSORE CO.,LTD.—See Otis Worldwide Corporation; *U.S. Public*, pg. 1623
METRIC GROUP LTD.—See Dutech Holdings Limited; *Int'l*, pg. 2235
MID-AMERICAN ELEVATOR EQUIPMENT CO., INC.; *U.S. Private*, pg. 2707
MIINC, LP—See SubSplit Services Group, L.P.; *U.S. Private*, pg. 3847
MORGAN INDUSTRIAL INC.; *U.S. Private*, pg. 2783
MULTIWAVE SENSORS INC.—See Hubbell Incorporated; *U.S. Public*, pg. 1067
NEWELL MACHINERY COMPANY INC.; *U.S. Private*, pg. 2914
NEW WAVE ATM INSTALLATIONS LIMITED—See NCR Voyix Corporation.; *U.S. Public*, pg. 1501
NORTHSTAR SCAFFOLD INC.—See Andover Capital Corporation; *Int'l*, pg. 451
NOTEMACHINE LIMITED—See The Brink's Company; *U.S. Public*, pg. 2043
OKINAWA HITACHI CO., LTD.—See Hitachi, Ltd.; *Int'l*, pg. 3423
OPTCONNECT, LLC; *U.S. Private*, pg. 3034
ORBIT MOVERS & ERECTORS—See Unitize Company Inc.; *U.S. Private*, pg. 4302
ORDERMATIC ELECTRONICS, INC.—See GLORY Ltd.; *Int'l*, pg. 3010
OTIS ELEVATOR COMPANY - PITTSBURGH—See Otis Worldwide Corporation; *U.S. Public*, pg. 1623

PACA ASCENSEURS SERVICES SAS—See ASSA ABLOY AB; *Int'l*, pg. 638
POMA-OTIS TRANSPORTATION SYSTEMS—See Otis Worldwide Corporation; *U.S. Public*, pg. 1623
PRECISION LIFT SERVICES LIMITED—See Analogue Holdings Limited; *Int'l*, pg. 446
PRO SERV SANDERS INC.; *U.S. Private*, pg. 3270
RESOURCE MECHANICAL INSULATION LLC—See The Rudolph/Libbe Companies; *U.S. Private*, pg. 4113
ROCKWELL AUTOMATION OF OHIO, INC.—See Rockwell Automation, Inc.; *U.S. Public*, pg. 1806
SEI GROUP, LLC—See Quad-C Management, Inc.; *U.S. Private*, pg. 3315
SHERRIN HIRE PTY LTD—See Boom Logistics Limited; *Int'l*, pg. 1110
SOUTHERN INSULATORS, LLC—See Installed Building Products, Inc.; *U.S. Public*, pg. 1133
SPECIALTY WELDING & TURNAROUNDS LLC—See Hastings Equity Partners, LLC; *U.S. Public*, pg. 1879
SUN RHINE ENTERPRISES LTD.—See Advent International Corporation; *U.S. Private*, pg. 106
SUN RHINE ENTERPRISES LTD.—See Cinven Limited; *Int'l*, pg. 1614
SUNRISE ELEVATOR CO., INC.—See Aldine Capital Partners, Inc.; *U.S. Private*, pg. 159
SUNRISE ELEVATOR CO., INC.—See Stoic Holdings LLC; *U.S. Private*, pg. 3816
SUPERIOR INSULATION SERVICES, LLC—See Installed Building Products, Inc.; *U.S. Public*, pg. 1133
SVABO KAROSS & HYDRAULSERVICE AB—See Heidelberg Materials AG; *Int'l*, pg. 3320
TCI CONTRACTING OF HILTON HEAD, LLC—See Installed Building Products, Inc.; *U.S. Public*, pg. 1133
THYSSENKRUPP ELEVADORES, S.A.—See Advent International Corporation; *U.S. Private*, pg. 106
THYSSENKRUPP ELEVADORES, S.A.—See Cinven Limited; *Int'l*, pg. 1614
THYSSENKRUPP ELEVATOR B.V.—See Advent International Corporation; *U.S. Private*, pg. 107
THYSSENKRUPP ELEVATOR B.V.—See Cinven Limited; *Int'l*, pg. 1615
THYSSENKRUPP ELEVATOR IRELAND, LTD.—See Advent International Corporation; *U.S. Private*, pg. 107
THYSSENKRUPP ELEVATOR IRELAND, LTD.—See Cinven Limited; *Int'l*, pg. 1615
THYSSENKRUPP ELEVATOR ITALIA S.P.A.—See Advent International Corporation; *U.S. Private*, pg. 107
THYSSENKRUPP ELEVATOR ITALIA S.P.A.—See Cinven Limited; *Int'l*, pg. 1615
THYSSENKRUPP ELEVATOR QUEENSLAND PTY. LTD.—See Advent International Corporation; *U.S. Private*, pg. 107
THYSSENKRUPP ELEVATOR QUEENSLAND PTY. LTD.—See Cinven Limited; *Int'l*, pg. 1615
THYSSENKRUPP ELEVATORS HELLAS S.A.—See Advent International Corporation; *U.S. Private*, pg. 107
THYSSENKRUPP ELEVATORS HELLAS S.A.—See Cinven Limited; *Int'l*, pg. 1615
THYSSENKRUPP ELEVATOR (SINGAPORE) PTE.LTD.—See Advent International Corporation; *U.S. Private*, pg. 106
THYSSENKRUPP ELEVATOR (SINGAPORE) PTE.LTD.—See Cinven Limited; *Int'l*, pg. 1614
THYSSENKRUPP ELEVATOR—See Advent International Corporation; *U.S. Private*, pg. 106
THYSSENKRUPP ELEVATOR—See Cinven Limited; *Int'l*, pg. 1615
THYSSENKRUPP ELEVATOR SRL—See Advent International Corporation; *U.S. Private*, pg. 107
THYSSENKRUPP ELEVATOR SRL—See Cinven Limited; *Int'l*, pg. 1615
THYSSENKRUPP ELEVATOR SVERIGE AB—See Advent International Corporation; *U.S. Private*, pg. 107
THYSSENKRUPP ELEVATOR SVERIGE AB—See Cinven Limited; *Int'l*, pg. 1615
THYSSENKRUPP ELEVATOR UK LTD.—See Advent International Corporation; *U.S. Private*, pg. 107
THYSSENKRUPP ELEVATOR UK LTD.—See Cinven Limited; *Int'l*, pg. 1615
THYSSENKRUPP ELEVATOR VIETNAM CO., LTD.—See Advent International Corporation; *U.S. Private*, pg. 107
THYSSENKRUPP ELEVATOR VIETNAM CO., LTD.—See Cinven Limited; *Int'l*, pg. 1615
TIDEWATER INSULATORS, LLC—See Installed Building Products, Inc.; *U.S. Public*, pg. 1134
TMR URUSHARTA (M) SDN. BHD.—See Damansara Realty Berhad; *Int'l*, pg. 1955
TOWN BUILDING SYSTEMS, LLC—See Installed Building Products, Inc.; *U.S. Public*, pg. 1134
TRANSIT ENGINEERING SERVICES, INC.—See Mattei Compressors Inc.; *U.S. Private*, pg. 2613
TUM-A-LUM LUMBER, INC.—See TAL Holdings LLC; *U.S. Private*, pg. 3925
UNITED DRILLING INC.; *U.S. Private*, pg. 4291
UNITED RIGGERS & ERECTORS INC.; *U.S. Private*, pg. 4296
UNITIZE COMPANY INC.; *U.S. Private*, pg. 4302
URBAN ELEVATOR SERVICE CA LLC—See Urban Elevator Service, LLC; *U.S. Private*, pg. 4314
URBAN ELEVATOR SERVICE, LLC; *U.S. Private*, pg. 4314
VERTICAL TRANSPORTATION EXCELLENCE—See OceanSound Partners, LP; *U.S. Private*, pg. 2991
WOOD-LAM STRUCTURES INC.—See Tumac Lumber Co. Inc.; *U.S. Private*, pg. 4258
WPS PARKING SYSTEMS BV—See Electricite de France S.A.; *Int'l*, pg. 2352
WYATT FIELD SERVICE CO.—See CIC Group, Inc.; *U.S. Private*, pg. 896

238310 — DRYWALL AND INSULATION CONTRACTORS

31-W INSULATION CO. INC.; *U.S. Private*, pg. 7
ABS COASTAL INSULATING COMPANY, LLC—See Installed Building Products, Inc.; *U.S. Public*, pg. 1132
ABS INSULATING COMPANY, INC.—See Installed Building Products, Inc.; *U.S. Public*, pg. 1132
ACCURATE INSULATION LLC—See Installed Building Products, Inc.; *U.S. Public*, pg. 1132
ACOUSTI ENGINEERING CO. OF FLORIDA—See Ardian SAS; *Int'l*, pg. 554
ACOUSTI INCORPORATED; *U.S. Private*, pg. 64
ADVANCED SPECIALTY CONTRACTORS—See Irex Corporation; *U.S. Private*, pg. 2137
AIRTITE CONTRACTORS INC.—See CDM Investment Group, Inc.; *U.S. Private*, pg. 802
ALLIED CONSTRUCTION SERVICES INC.; *U.S. Private*, pg. 185
ALL TEMP, INC.—See AT Industries, Inc.; *U.S. Private*, pg. 363
ALL WALL CONTRACTING, INC.; *U.S. Private*, pg. 173
ALPINE INSULATION CO, INC.—See Installed Building Products, Inc.; *U.S. Public*, pg. 1132
ALTAIR CONTRACTING—See Irex Corporation; *U.S. Private*, pg. 2137
ALTRAD PROFIX BVBA—See Altrad Investment Authority SAS; *Int'l*, pg. 397
AMERICAN SYNERGY CORPORATION; *U.S. Private*, pg. 256
ANCHOR INSULATION CO., INC.—See Installed Building Products, Inc.; *U.S. Public*, pg. 1132
ANN ARBOR CEILING & PARTITION CO.—See National Construction Enterprises Inc.; *U.S. Private*, pg. 2851
ANNING JOHNSON COMPANY—See Anson Industries, Inc.; *U.S. Private*, pg. 286
ANNING JOHNSON CO.—See Anson Industries, Inc.; *U.S. Private*, pg. 286
ANNING JOHNSON SAN FRANCISCO—See Anson Industries, Inc.; *U.S. Private*, pg. 286
ANSON INDUSTRIES, INC.; *U.S. Private*, pg. 286
API CONSTRUCTION COMPANY—See APi Group Corporation; *Int'l*, pg. 513
APPLE VALLEY INSULATION, A BDI COMPANY, INC.—See Installed Building Products, Inc.; *U.S. Public*, pg. 1132
ARCTIC EXPRESS INSULATION LLC—See Installed Building Products, Inc.; *U.S. Public*, pg. 1132
ARGUS CONTRACTING, INC—See Irex Corporation; *U.S. Private*, pg. 2137
ATLANTIC CONTRACTING & SPECIALTIES LLC—See Irex Corporation; *U.S. Private*, pg. 2137
AUSTIN COMPANY; *U.S. Private*, pg. 395
BAKER DRYWALL CO. INC.; *U.S. Private*, pg. 456
BARRIER CORP.—See Paul J. Krez Company; *U.S. Private*, pg. 3113
BAYTHERM INSULATION, LLC—See Installed Building Products, Inc.; *U.S. Public*, pg. 1132
BDI INSULATION OF IDAHO FALLS, INC.—See Installed Building Products, Inc.; *U.S. Public*, pg. 1132
BDI INSULATION OF SALT LAKE, LLC—See Installed Building Products, Inc.; *U.S. Public*, pg. 1132
BEAN DRYWALL, INC.; *U.S. Private*, pg. 506
BERGER BROS INC.; *U.S. Private*, pg. 530
BEST INTERIORS INC.; *U.S. Private*, pg. 543
BIG CITY INSULATION, INC.—See Installed Building Products, Inc.; *U.S. Public*, pg. 1132
BIG CITY INSULATION OF IDAHO, INC.—See Installed Building Products, Inc.; *U.S. Public*, pg. 1132
BILFINGER BERGER INDUSTRIAL SERVICES SPAIN S.A.—See Bilfinger SE; *Int'l*, pg. 1026
BILFINGER SALAMIS UK LIMITED—See Bilfinger SE; *Int'l*, pg. 1026
BIS INDUSTRIAL SERVICES BELGIE N.V.—See Bilfinger SE; *Int'l*, pg. 1025
BIS INSULATION B.V.—See Bilfinger SE; *Int'l*, pg. 1025
BIS ISENTA AB—See Bilfinger SE; *Int'l*, pg. 1025
BIS ISENTA NORR AB—See Bilfinger SE; *Int'l*, pg. 1025
BIS MULTISERWIS SP. Z O.O.—See Bilfinger SE; *Int'l*, pg. 1025
BIS PREFAL - ISOLAMENTOS TERMICOS LDA.—See Bilfinger SE; *Int'l*, pg. 1025
B.J. MCGLONE CO. INC.; *U.S. Private*, pg. 420
B J MCGLONE CO—See B.J. McGlone Co. Inc.; *U.S. Private*, pg. 420
BLOW IN BLANKET, LLC—See Masco Corporation; *U.S. Public*, pg. 1391

238310 — DRYWALL AND INSULAT...

BOCK CONSTRUCTION INC.; U.S. Private, pg. 607
BONITZ CONTRACTING COMPANY, INC.—See Bonitz Inc.; U.S. Private, pg. 614
BONITZ CONTRACTING COMPANY—See Bonitz Inc.; U.S. Private, pg. 614
BONITZ INC.; U.S. Private, pg. 614
BOUMA CORPORATION; U.S. Private, pg. 623
BOYETT CONSTRUCTION INC.; U.S. Private, pg. 628
BROKEN DRUM INSULATION VISALIA, INC.—See Installed Building Products, Inc.; U.S. Public, pg. 1132
BROKEN DRUM OF BAKERSFIELD, INC.—See Installed Building Products, Inc.; U.S. Public, pg. 1132
BRUSH MASTERS, INC.; U.S. Private, pg. 672
BURNHAM INDUSTRIAL CONTRACTORS INC.; U.S. Private, pg. 689
CADENA CONTRACTING, INC.; U.S. Private, pg. 712
CAJUN COMPANY; U.S. Private, pg. 714
CAPE EAST LIMITED—See Altrad Investment Authority SAS; Int'l, pg. 398
CAPE EAST LLC—See Altrad Investment Authority SAS; Int'l, pg. 398
CAPE EAST PRIVATE LIMITED—See Altrad Investment Authority SAS; Int'l, pg. 398
CAPE INDUSTRIAL SERVICES GROUP LIMITED—See Altrad Investment Authority SAS; Int'l, pg. 398
CAPE INDUSTRIAL SERVICES LIMITED—See Altrad Investment Authority SAS; Int'l, pg. 398
CATALYST ACOUSTICS GROUP—See KPS Capital Partners, LP; U.S. Private, pg. 2347
CAUDLE-HYATT, INC.; U.S. Private, pg. 794
C&D INSULATION, INC.; U.S. Private, pg. 702
CEILINGS & PARTITIONS, INC.; U.S. Private, pg. 805
CENTER BROTHERS INCORPORATED; U.S. Private, pg. 809
CENTRAL CEILING PARTITION INC.; U.S. Private, pg. 819
CERTAINTEED CEILINGS—See Compagnie de Saint-Gobain SA; Int'l, pg. 1729
CFI INSULATION, INC.—See Installed Building Products, Inc.; U.S. Public, pg. 1132
CGM ACOUSTICS; U.S. Private, pg. 844
CITY WIDE INSULATION OF MADISON INC.; U.S. Private, pg. 907
CITYWIDE INSULATION; U.S. Private, pg. 907
CLETON INSULATION BV—See Altrad Investment Authority SAS; Int'l, pg. 398
COLEMAN FLOOR CO.—See Littlejohn & Co., LLC; U.S. Private, pg. 2470
COLEMAN FLOOR CO.—See Platinum Equity, LLC; U.S. Private, pg. 3205
COMBEE INSULATION COMPANY, INC.—See Installed Building Products, Inc.; U.S. Public, pg. 1132
COMMERCIAL INTERIORS INC.; U.S. Private, pg. 983
COMMERCIAL PLASTERING INC.; U.S. Private, pg. 984
COMPONENT WEST, INC.—See Component Assembly Systems, Inc.; U.S. Private, pg. 1002
CONSTRUCTION SERVICES 2000, INC.; U.S. Private, pg. 1024
CORNHUSKER INSULATION, INC.—See Installed Building Products, Inc.; U.S. Public, pg. 1132
C.Q. INSULATION, INC.—See Installed Building Products, Inc.; U.S. Public, pg. 1132
CREATIVE CONSERVATION CO., INC.—See TopBuild Corp.; U.S. Public, pg. 2163
C & S DRYWALL INC.—See Paul Johnson Drywall, Inc.; U.S. Private, pg. 3113
CURTIS PARTITION CORP.; U.S. Private, pg. 1126
DAIKEN CORPORATION - OKAYAMA—See Daiken Corporation; Int'l, pg. 1931
DAVIDSON INSULATION & ACOUSTICS; U.S. Private, pg. 1171
DAVIS DRYWALL, INC.—See Swanson & Youngdale Inc.; U.S. Private, pg. 3890
DAW CONSTRUCTION GROUP, LLC; U.S. Private, pg. 1175
DECOUSTICS LIMITED—See Compagnie de Saint-Gobain SA; Int'l, pg. 1729
DELTA T CONSTRUCTION COMPANY; U.S. Private, pg. 1202
DENVER DRYWALL CO. INC.; U.S. Private, pg. 1207
DIVERSIFIED INTERIORS OF EL PASO INC.; U.S. Private, pg. 1242
DOWNSVIEW DRYWALL CONTRACTING; Int'l, pg. 2187
DRYVIT SYSTEMS CANADA LTD.—See RPM International Inc.; U.S. Public, pg. 1819
DRYVIT UK LIMITED—See RPM International Inc.; U.S. Public, pg. 1819
DUGGAN & MARCON INC.—See Marcon & Boyer Inc.; U.S. Private, pg. 2572
EASLEY & RIVERS INC.; U.S. Private, pg. 1315
EASTERN CONTRACTOR SERVICES, LIMITED LIABILITY COMPANY—See Installed Building Products, Inc.; U.S. Public, pg. 1132
E.B. BERGER INCORPORATED; U.S. Private, pg. 1304
EE-FIT PTY LIMITED—See Fletcher Building Limited; Int'l, pg. 2701
ELTEX ENTERPRISES 2002 LTD.; Int'l, pg. 2371
E.L. THOMPSON ASSOCIATES LLC; U.S. Private, pg. 1306

ENERGETIC PAINTING & DRYWALL; U.S. Private, pg. 1393
ENTRPRIZE CORPORATION; U.S. Private, pg. 1406
ENVIRONMENTAL SOLAR DESIGN, INC.—See Sigora Solar, LLC; U.S. Private, pg. 3651
EXTERIOR DESIGNS, LLC—See UFP Industries, Inc.; U.S. Public, pg. 2219
FH COMPANIES, INC.; U.S. Private, pg. 1501
F.L. CRANE & SONS, INC.; U.S. Private, pg. 1456
F.L. CRANE & SONS INC.; U.S. Private, pg. 1456
FORMAN INSULATION LIMITED—See Fletcher Building Limited; Int'l, pg. 2700
FREDERICK MEISWINKEL, INC.; U.S. Private, pg. 1602
FULLER AUSTIN INC.—See Bird Construction Inc.; Int'l, pg. 1047
GARLAND INSULATING, LTD.—See TopBuild Corp.; U.S. Public, pg. 2163
GENERAL CEILING & PARTITIONS, INC.—See Installed Building Products, Inc.; U.S. Public, pg. 1132
GIBSON-LEWIS, LLC—See National Construction Enterprises Inc.; U.S. Private, pg. 2851
GIBSON-LEWIS OF INDIANAPOLIS, LLC—See National Construction Enterprises Inc.; U.S. Private, pg. 2851
GOLD STAR INSULATION LP—See Installed Building Products, Inc.; U.S. Public, pg. 1132
GRAYHAWK LLC; U.S. Private, pg. 1761
GREGG INDUSTRIES INC.; U.S. Private, pg. 1782
GROUP BUILDERS INC.; U.S. Private, pg. 1793
GUARANTEE INTERIORS INC.; U.S. Private, pg. 1809
H. CARR & SONS INC.; U.S. Private, pg. 1824
HENDERSON-JOHNSON INC.; U.S. Private, pg. 1914
HERB RITSEMA CO.—See RDR Properties Inc.; U.S. Private, pg. 3364
HINKLE INSULATION & DRYWALL COMPANY, INCORPORATED—See Installed Building Products, Inc.; U.S. Public, pg. 1132
HOLT & HOLT, INC.; U.S. Private, pg. 1968
HUDAK INSULATION, INC.; U.S. Private, pg. 2001
INDUSTRIAL PROCESS INSULATORS, INC.—See Thermon Group Holdings, Inc.; U.S. Public, pg. 2155
INDY WALLS & CEILINGS INCORPORATED; U.S. Private, pg. 2069
INSTALLED BUILDING PRODUCTS, INC.; U.S. Public, pg. 1131
INSTALLED BUILDING PRODUCTS, LLC—See Installed Building Products, Inc.; U.S. Public, pg. 1133
INSTALLED BUILDING PRODUCTS OF MAINE, LLC—See Installed Building Products, Inc.; U.S. Public, pg. 1133
INSTALLED BUILDING PRODUCTS - PORTLAND, LLC—See Installed Building Products, Inc.; U.S. Public, pg. 1133
INSTALLED BUILDING SOLUTIONS II, LLC—See Installed Building Products, Inc.; U.S. Public, pg. 1133
INSULATION CONTRACTORS INC.—See Installed Building Products, Inc.; U.S. Public, pg. 1133
INSULMAX CONSTRUCTION SERVICES—See Irex Corporation; U.S. Private, pg. 2138
INSULVAIL, LLC—See Installed Building Products, Inc.; U.S. Public, pg. 1133
INTERIOR SYSTEMS INC.; U.S. Private, pg. 2111
IREX CORPORATION; U.S. Private, pg. 2137
JACOBSON & COMPANY, INC.; U.S. Private, pg. 2180
JAY HENGES ENTERPRISES INC.; U.S. Private, pg. 2191
JOE BANKS DRYWALL & ACOUSTICS INC.; U.S. Private, pg. 2218
JR INSULATION SALES & SERVICE; U.S. Private, pg. 2239
J&R PRODUCTS, INC.—See Pacific Avenue Capital Partners, LLC; U.S. Private, pg. 3065
JUDY'S INSULATION CO., INC.—See Quad-C Management, Inc.; U.S. Private, pg. 3315
JUST RITE ACOUSTICS INC.; U.S. Private, pg. 2245
KELLY SYSTEMS INC.—See Novinger Group, Inc.; U.S. Private, pg. 2968
KENYON COMPANIES; U.S. Private, pg. 2289
KENYON CONSTRUCTION, INC.; U.S. Private, pg. 2290
KEVOTHERMAL LIMITED—See Sealed Air Corporation; U.S. Public, pg. 1853
KING & COMPANY INC.; U.S. Private, pg. 2308
LAKESIDE INSULATION, LLC—See Installed Building Products, Inc.; U.S. Public, pg. 1133
LANECO CONSTRUCTION SYSTEMS INC.; U.S. Private, pg. 2388
LEE DRYWALL, INC.; U.S. Private, pg. 2411
LES FILE DRYWALL INCORPORATED; U.S. Private, pg. 2431
LIBERTY INDUSTRIAL GROUP, INC.—See Terra Millenium Corporation; U.S. Private, pg. 3970
LILIENTHAL INSULATION COMPANY, LLC—See Masco Corporation; U.S. Public, pg. 1391
LOTSPEICH CO. OF FLORIDA, INC.; U.S. Private, pg. 2497
LUSE THERMAL TECHNOLOGIES LLC—See Luse Holdings, Inc.; U.S. Private, pg. 2516
LYDALL THERMAL/ACOUSTICAL SALES, LLC—See Lydall, Inc.; U.S. Public, pg. 1350
MANGANARO NORTHEAST, LLC—See Manganaro MidAtlantic, LLC; U.S. Private, pg. 2563
MAP OF EASTON, INC.; U.S. Private, pg. 2568

CORPORATE AFFILIATIONS

MARCON & BOYER INC.; U.S. Private, pg. 2572
MAREK BROTHERS SYSTEMS, INC.; U.S. Private, pg. 2573
MARTIN BROS./MARCOWALL, INC.; U.S. Private, pg. 2594
MARV'S INSULATION, INC.—See Installed Building Products, Inc.; U.S. Public, pg. 1133
M. ECKER & CO. OF FLORIDA, INC.—See Ecker Enterprises Inc.; U.S. Private, pg. 1328
M. ECKER & CO. OF ILLINOIS, INC.—See Ecker Enterprises Inc.; U.S. Private, pg. 1328
MEGA CONSTRUCTION CORP. OF NJ; U.S. Private, pg. 2660
METALCLAD INSULATION CORPORATION—See Entrprize Corporation; U.S. Private, pg. 1406
METRO HOME INSULATION, LLC—See Installed Building Products, Inc.; U.S. Public, pg. 1133
MID SOUTH CONSTRUCTION AND BUILDING PRODUCTS, INC.—See Installed Building Products, Inc.; U.S. Public, pg. 1133
MIDWEST DRYWALL CO., INC.; U.S. Private, pg. 2720
MIKEN SPECIALTIES, LTD; U.S. Private, pg. 2726
MILLER INSULATION CO. INC.; U.S. Private, pg. 2734
MILLER PLASTERING & STUCCO, INC.; U.S. Private, pg. 2735
MILLS GROUP INC.; U.S. Private, pg. 2738
MINUTI-OGLE CO. INC.; U.S. Private, pg. 2745
M&O INSULATION COMPANY; U.S. Private, pg. 2525
M. & O. INSULATION COMPANY; U.S. Private, pg. 2526
NATIONAL CONSTRUCTION ENTERPRISES INC.; U.S. Private, pg. 2851
NATIONAL FIBER, INC.; U.S. Private, pg. 2853
NDI CONSTRUCTION; U.S. Private, pg. 2876
NEW SOUTH RESTORATIONS INC.; U.S. Private, pg. 2906
NORTHWEST INSULATION, LLC—See Installed Building Products, Inc.; U.S. Public, pg. 1133
NOVINGER GROUP, INC.; U.S. Private, pg. 2968
NOVINGER'S INC.—See Novinger Group, Inc.; U.S. Private, pg. 2968
NYCO, INC.—See API Group Corporation; Int'l, pg. 514
OCP CONTRACTORS, INC.; U.S. Private, pg. 2992
OJ INSULATION CO. INC.; U.S. Private, pg. 3006
OJ INSULATION, L.P.—See Installed Building Products, Inc.; U.S. Public, pg. 1133
OK INTERIORS CORP.; U.S. Private, pg. 3006
OLYMPIC COMPANIES INC.; U.S. Private, pg. 3012
OPTILINE ENTERPRISES, LLC; U.S. Private, pg. 3034
OTSEGO PAPER, INC.—See Gebr. Knauf KG; Int'l, pg. 2908
OZARK FOAM INSEALATORS, INC.—See TopBuild Corp.; U.S. Public, pg. 2163
PACIFIC CONSTRUCTION SYSTEMS INC.; U.S. Private, pg. 3067
PACIFIC PARTNERS INSULATION NORTH, A BDI COMPANY, LLC—See Installed Building Products, Inc.; U.S. Public, pg. 1133
PACIFIC PARTNERS INSULATION SOUTH, A BDI COMPANY, LLC—See Installed Building Products, Inc.; U.S. Public, pg. 1133
PAUL J. KREZ COMPANY; U.S. Private, pg. 3113
PAUL JOHNSON DRYWALL, INC.; U.S. Private, pg. 3113
PERFORMANCE CONTRACTING GROUP, INC.—See Performance Contracting Group; U.S. Private, pg. 3149
PERFORMANCE CONTRACTING, INC. - ISS DIVISION—See Performance Contracting Group; U.S. Private, pg. 3149
PERMAROCK PRODUCTS LIMITED—See Carillion plc; Int'l, pg. 1330
PETRIN CORP.—See Bernhard Capital Partners Management, LP; U.S. Private, pg. 537
PETRIN CORP.—See KBR, Inc.; U.S. Public, pg. 1216
PHASE 2 COMPANY; U.S. Private, pg. 3166
PILLAR CONSTRUCTION INC.; U.S. Private, pg. 3180
PONTIAC CEILING & PARTITION CO. LLC—See National Construction Enterprises Inc.; U.S. Private, pg. 2851
PRECISION WALLS, INC.; U.S. Private, pg. 3247
PROFESSIONAL FOAM INSULATORS LTD.—See Quad-C Management, Inc.; U.S. Private, pg. 3315
PROGROUP NETWORK INC.—See BrandPoint Services, Inc.; U.S. Private, pg. 638
QUALITY INSULATION & ROOFING; U.S. Private, pg. 3319
RDR PROPERTIES INC.; U.S. Private, pg. 3364
RED ROCK INSULATION LLC—See Installed Building Products, Inc.; U.S. Public, pg. 1133
SAINT GOBAIN ECOPHON AB—See Compagnie de Saint-Gobain SA; Int'l, pg. 1729
SCARECROW LATH & PLASTER INC.; U.S. Private, pg. 3561
SEARS CONTRACT, INC.; U.S. Private, pg. 3591
SELECTBUILD OF NEVADA—See Builders FirstSource, Inc.; U.S. Public, pg. 410
SIERRA INSULATION CONTRACTORS, INC.—See Installed Building Products, Inc.; U.S. Public, pg. 1133
SOUTH TEXAS LONE STAR DRYWALL; U.S. Private, pg. 3724
SPACECON, LLC—See Irex Corporation; U.S. Private, pg. 2138
SPACECON SOLUTIONS, LLC—See Irex Corporation; U.S. Private, pg. 2138

N.A.I.C.S. INDEX

238330 — FLOORING CONTRACTOR...

SPACECON SPECIALTY CONTRACTORS LLC—See Irex Corporation; *U.S. Private*, pg. 2138
SPEC 7 INSULATION CO., LLC—See Installed Building Products, Inc.; *U.S. Public*, pg. 1133
SPECIALTY INTERIORS INC.; *U.S. Private*, pg. 3750
SPECTRUM INTERIORS TENNESEE INC.—See Specialty Interiors Inc.; *U.S. Private*, pg. 3750
S&S DRYWALL INC.; *U.S. Private*, pg. 3514
S&S DRYWALL INSTALLERS INC—See S&S Drywall Inc.; *U.S. Private*, pg. 3514
STANDARD DRYWALL INC.; *U.S. Private*, pg. 3778
STATEWIDE INSULATION, INC.—See Installed Building Products, Inc.; *U.S. Public*, pg. 1133
SUBURBAN INSULATION, INC.—See Installed Building Products, Inc.; *U.S. Public*, pg. 1133
TAILORED FOAM OF FLORIDA, INC.—See SEI Group, Inc.; *U.S. Private*, pg. 3599
TASCON, INC.; *U.S. Private*, pg. 3934
TASMAN INSULATION NEW ZEALAND LIMITED—See Fletcher Building Limited; *Int'l*, pg. 2701
TCI CONTRACTING, LLC—See Installed Building Products, Inc.; *U.S. Public*, pg. 1133
THERMAL CONTROL INSULATION, LLC—See Installed Building Products, Inc.; *U.S. Public*, pg. 1133
THERMICO INC.; *U.S. Private*, pg. 4142
THOMAS RAWLINGS ASSOCIATES—See Thomas Rawlings Group Inc.; *U.S. Private*, pg. 4157
THOMAS RAWLINGS GROUP INC.; *U.S. Private*, pg. 4157
TOPBUILD CORP.; *U.S. Public*, pg. 2163
TRADEMARK ROOFING COMPANY, INC.—See Installed Building Products, Inc.; *U.S. Public*, pg. 1134
TRIANGLE ENTERPRISES INC.; *U.S. Private*, pg. 4226
TRUTEAM, LLC—See TopBuild Corp.; *U.S. Public*, pg. 2163
TRUTEAM OF CALIFORNIA, INC.—See TopBuild Corp.; *U.S. Public*, pg. 2163
UNITED SUBCONTRACTORS, INC.—See TopBuild Corp.; *U.S. Public*, pg. 2163
UNITEK TECHNICAL LLC—See Pacific Marine & Supply Co. Ltd. Inc.; *U.S. Private*, pg. 3068
UNIVERSAL LIMITED; *U.S. Private*, pg. 4305
USA INSULATION FRANCHISE, LLC—See Riverside Partners, LLC; *U.S. Private*, pg. 3446
U.S. INSULATION CORP.—See Installed Building Products, Inc.; *U.S. Public*, pg. 1134
VADEN'S ACOUSTICS & DRYWALL, INC.; *U.S. Private*, pg. 4329
VALCOM ENTERPRISES INCORPORATED; *U.S. Private*, pg. 4330
VALLEY INSULATION, INC.—See TopBuild Corp.; *U.S. Public*, pg. 2163
VALLEY INTERIOR SYSTEMS INC.; *U.S. Private*, pg. 4334
V & R DRYWALL, INC.; *U.S. Private*, pg. 4327
WALLDESIGN INC.; *U.S. Private*, pg. 4431
WALL SYSTEMS, INC.; *U.S. Private*, pg. 4430
WAL-MARK CONTRACTING GROUP INC.—See National Construction Enterprises Inc.; *U.S. Private*, pg. 2851
WCS CONTRACTORS, LTD.; *U.S. Private*, pg. 4461
WEATHERSEAL INSULATION CO., LLC—See Installed Building Products, Inc.; *U.S. Public*, pg. 1134
WESTERN PARTITIONS, INC.; *U.S. Private*, pg. 4495
WG VALENZUELA DRYWALL INC.; *U.S. Private*, pg. 4503
WILCO ENTERPRISES INC.; *U.S. Private*, pg. 4518
WILSON INSULATION COMPANY, LLC—See Installed Building Products, Inc.; *U.S. Public*, pg. 1134
WYATT INCORPORATED; *U.S. Private*, pg. 4575

238320 — PAINTING AND WALL COVERING CONTRACTORS

AALBERTS SURFACE TECHNOLOGIES GMBH—See Aalberts N.V.; *Int'l*, pg. 33
AALBERTS SURFACE TREATMENT TAMWORTH LIMITED—See Aalberts N.V.; *Int'l*, pg. 33
ALL-TECH DECORATING COMPANY; *U.S. Private*, pg. 174
AMERICAN PAINTING AND RENOVATIONS, INC.; *U.S. Private*, pg. 242
AVALOTIS CORPORATION; *U.S. Private*, pg. 403
BAYCOAT LTD.—See ArcelorMittal S.A.; *Int'l*, pg. 544
BEOPAN A.D.; *Int'l*, pg. 978
BLUE MOUNTAIN WALLCOVERINGS, INC.; *Int'l*, pg. 1069
BROCK SERVICES, LLC—See AIP, LLC; *U.S. Private*, pg. 134
CAMELEON B.V.—See E.ON SE; *Int'l*, pg. 2251
CHARLOTTE PAINT COMPANY INC.; *U.S. Private*, pg. 857
CHUGOKU PAINTS (MALAYSIA) SDN. BHD.—See Chugoku Marine Paints, Ltd.; *Int'l*, pg. 1595
COLLEGE WORKS PAINTING INC.—See National Services Group Inc.; *U.S. Private*, pg. 2863
COLLEGIATE ENTREPRENEURS; *U.S. Private*, pg. 968
COLOR WORLD HOUSEPAINTING, INC.—See Apax Partners LLP; *Int'l*, pg. 502
CONTINENTAL COATINGS—See Continental Plastics Co. Inc.; *U.S. Private*, pg. 1030
COSMOPOLITAN DECORATING CO.; *U.S. Private*, pg. 1062
CWPNC INC.—See National Services Group Inc.; *U.S. Private*, pg. 2863

D.C. VIENT INC.; *U.S. Private*, pg. 1141
DEBUSCHERE SA; *Int'l*, pg. 1999
DE MAESSCHALCK H N.V.—See LKQ Corporation; *U.S. Public*, pg. 1334
DUNKIN & BUSH INC.; *U.S. Private*, pg. 1289
D & W PAINTING INC.; *U.S. Private*, pg. 1136
ECKER ENTERPRISES INC.; *U.S. Private*, pg. 1328
ELIAS BROTHERS GROUP PAINTING & CONTRACTING, INC.; *U.S. Private*, pg. 1360
EMERAUDE S.A.S.—See Carlsberg A/S; *Int'l*, pg. 1340
EMPIE, INC.; *U.S. Private*, pg. 1384
ERA VALDIVIA CONTRACTORS, INC.; *U.S. Private*, pg. 1417
ETABLISSEMENTS ROCHE ET COMPAGNIE; *Int'l*, pg. 2519
EVERGREENE ARCHITECTURAL ARTS, INC.; *U.S. Private*, pg. 1440
F.D. THOMAS INC.—See Arctic Slope Regional Corporation; *U.S. Private*, pg. 316
FINISH LINE INDUSTRIES—See John S. Frey Enterprises; *U.S. Private*, pg. 2224
FIREMANS CONTRACTORS, INC.; *U.S. Public*, pg. 835
FIVE ARROWS INC.; *U.S. Private*, pg. 1537
FRANK NOVAK & SONS, INC.; *U.S. Private*, pg. 1595
FUJI SHOJI CO., LTD.—See Carlit Co., Ltd.; *Int'l*, pg. 1338
GALLITO LTD.—See Absolent Air Care Group AB; *Int'l*, pg. 70
GATEWAY COMPANY; *U.S. Private*, pg. 1650
GENERAL COATINGS CORPORATION; *U.S. Private*, pg. 1664
GEORGE E. MASKER, INC.; *U.S. Private*, pg. 1681
HARTMAN-WALSH CORPORATION; *U.S. Private*, pg. 1874
HEATHER PAINTING & DECORATING LTD—See Davian Construction Ltd.; *Int'l*, pg. 1983
INDUSTRIAL MAINTENANCE CONTRACTORS, INC.; *U.S. Private*, pg. 2067
JAPENAMELAC CORP.—See Leggett & Platt, Incorporated; *U.S. Public*, pg. 1302
JIMENEZ CUSTOM PAINTING, INC.; *U.S. Private*, pg. 2210
JVPK INC.; *U.S. Private*, pg. 2246
KLEIN-DICKERT CO. INC.; *U.S. Private*, pg. 2319
KOLONA PAINTING & GENERAL CONSTRUCTION, INC.—See Equal Earth Corp.; *U.S. Private*, pg. 1415
LAKESIDE PAINTING, INC.—See Painters USA, Inc.; *U.S. Private*, pg. 3076
LEADING EDGE MISSISSIPPI INC.; *U.S. Private*, pg. 2406
LEN-TEX CORP.; *U.S. Private*, pg. 2421
LONG PAINTING COMPANY; *U.S. Private*, pg. 2491
LOWE'S COMMERCIAL PAINTING; *U.S. Private*, pg. 2505
M & E PAINTING, LLC; *U.S. Private*, pg. 2522
METRO VALLEY PAINTING CORP.; *U.S. Private*, pg. 2686
M.L. MCDONALD SALES CO., INC.; *U.S. Private*, pg. 2529
NATIONAL SERVICES GROUP INC.; *U.S. Private*, pg. 2863
OMNI GLASS AND PAINT INC.; *U.S. Private*, pg. 3016
OTHER ART FAIRS AUSTRALIA PTY LTD—See Graham Holdings Company; *U.S. Public*, pg. 956
PAINTERS ON DEMAND, LLC; *U.S. Private*, pg. 3076
PAINTERS USA, INC.; *U.S. Private*, pg. 3076
PAINTZEN INC.—See PPG Industries, Inc.; *U.S. Public*, pg. 1710
PARAMOUNT PAINTING & INDUSTRIAL SERVICES, INC.—See Tailwind Capital Group, LLC; *U.S. Private*, pg. 3924
PETE KING CORPORATION—See JVPK Inc.; *U.S. Private*, pg. 2246
PHILLIPS PAINTING; *U.S. Private*, pg. 3171
PK CONTRACTING, INC.—See The Sterling Group, L.P.; *U.S. Private*, pg. 4123
RAINBOW INC.; *U.S. Private*, pg. 3347
REDWOOD PAINTING CO, INC.—See Arctic Slope Regional Corporation; *U.S. Private*, pg. 316
S C S CONTRACTING, INC.; *U.S. Private*, pg. 3512
SERVICE PAINTING CORPORATION—See Five Arrows Inc.; *U.S. Private*, pg. 1537
SHARPER IMPRESSIONS PAINTING COMPANY; *U.S. Private*, pg. 3627
SIPCO SERVICES INC.; *U.S. Private*, pg. 3671
THE SKY FACTORY, LC.; *U.S. Private*, pg. 4118
SPECTRUM CONTRACTING, INC.; *U.S. Private*, pg. 3752
SPF WATER ENGINEERING, LLC—See Lindsay Corporation; *U.S. Public*, pg. 1320
SPOTLESS GROUP LIMITED—See Downer EDI Limited; *Int'l*, pg. 2185
STRIPE-A-ZONE, INC.—See The Sterling Group, L.P.; *U.S. Private*, pg. 4123
STRIPING TECHNOLOGY L.P.; *U.S. Private*, pg. 3840
STUDENTPAINTERS.NET; *U.S. Private*, pg. 3843
SWANSON & YOUNGDALE INC.; *U.S. Private*, pg. 3890
VIABAL MANTENIMENT I CONSERVACIO, S.A.—See ACS, Actividades de Construccion y Servicios, S.A.; *Int'l*, pg. 114
VIVAX PRO PAINTING; *U.S. Private*, pg. 4406
WEST PARK PAINTING INC.—See Don C. Musick Construction Co., Inc.; *U.S. Private*, pg. 1257
WEST VIRGINIA PAINT LLC; *U.S. Private*, pg. 4487

238330 — FLOORING CONTRACTORS

2639-1862 QUEBEC, INC.; *Int'l*, pg. 4
AB GUSTAF KAHR—See Vestar Capital Partners, LLC; *U.S. Private*, pg. 4372
ACTION FLOORING; *Int'l*, pg. 119
AKO STONEWOOD INC.; *Int'l*, pg. 264
ALL TERIORS FLOOR COVERING, INC.; *U.S. Private*, pg. 173
ANTEX WESTERN LTD.; *Int'l*, pg. 482
ARBOR CONTRACT CARPET INC.; *U.S. Private*, pg. 308
ARCHITECTURAL FLOORING RESOURCE, INC.; *U.S. Private*, pg. 311
ARI PRODUCTS INC.; *U.S. Private*, pg. 322
ARLUN, INC.—See The Sterling Group, L.P.; *U.S. Private*, pg. 4121
BAUWERK GROUP AG—See Ernst Gohner Stiftung; *Int'l*, pg. 2495
BAYBRENT CONSTRUCTION CORP.; *U.S. Private*, pg. 495
BEAULIEU INTERNATIONAL GROUP NV HERMOSA PLANT—See Beaulieu International Group NV; *Int'l*, pg. 934
BEAULIEU INTERNATIONAL GROUP NV JUTEKS RU PLANT—See Beaulieu International Group NV; *Int'l*, pg. 934
BEAULIEU INTERNATIONAL GROUP NV LYNGDAL PLANT—See Beaulieu International Group NV; *Int'l*, pg. 934
BLACKTON, INC.; *U.S. Private*, pg. 577
BLACKTON INTERIORS OF ORLANDO—See Blackton, Inc.; *U.S. Private*, pg. 577
BONITZ FLOORING GROUP, INC.—See Bonitz Inc.; *U.S. Private*, pg. 614
B.T. MANCINI CO., INC.; *U.S. Private*, pg. 421
BUCHANAN HARDWOODS INC.; *U.S. Private*, pg. 676
BUDGE BUDGE FLOORCOVERINGS LIMITED—See Birla Corporation Ltd.; *Int'l*, pg. 1047
CAPITOL WOOD FLOORS & SUPPLIES INC.; *U.S. Private*, pg. 745
CARPET DECORATORS INC.; *U.S. Private*, pg. 770
CARPETLAND INC—See KW Leasing Inc.; *U.S. Private*, pg. 2359
CENTIMARK CORPORATION - QUESTMARK FLOORING DIVISION—See Centimark Corporation; *U.S. Private*, pg. 817
CENTURY CARPET, INC.; *U.S. Private*, pg. 832
CINCINNATI FLOOR COMPANY INC.; *U.S. Private*, pg. 897
COLEMAN FLOOR, LLC—See Littlejohn & Co., LLC; *U.S. Private*, pg. 2470
COLEMAN FLOOR, LLC—See Platinum Equity, LLC; *U.S. Private*, pg. 3205
CONNOR SPORT COURT INTERNATIONAL, INC.—See Cobepa S.A.; *Int'l*, pg. 1683
CONSOLIDATED CARPET-TRADE WORKROOM; *U.S. Private*, pg. 1020
CONTINENTAL INTERIORS INC.; *U.S. Private*, pg. 1030
CORPORATE FLOORS INC.; *U.S. Private*, pg. 1055
COVINGTON FLOORING COMPANY; *U.S. Private*, pg. 1073
CREATIVE DESIGN INTERIORS INC.; *U.S. Private*, pg. 1088
CREW2, INC.; *U.S. Private*, pg. 1099
CRITERION BROCK, INC.—See Wedbush Capital Partners; *U.S. Private*, pg. 4468
CROWN PRODUCTS, INC.—See ShoreView Industries, LLC; *U.S. Private*, pg. 3642
CTS FLOORING; *U.S. Private*, pg. 1119
DFS FLOORING, INC.; *U.S. Private*, pg. 1220
DIVERZIFY—See ACON Investments, LLC; *U.S. Private*, pg. 62
DURON ONTARIO LTD.; *Int'l*, pg. 2230
EVENTDECK—See Myers Industries, Inc.; *U.S. Public*, pg. 1488
EXPLORING.COM, INC.; *U.S. Private*, pg. 1450
FASHIONCRAFT FLOORS INC.; *U.S. Private*, pg. 1481
FEI GROUP—See CCA Global Partners, Inc.; *U.S. Private*, pg. 799
FORBO GIUBIASCO SA—See Forbo Holding Ltd.; *Int'l*, pg. 2729
GENERAL DE MINERALES, S.A. DE C.V.—See Grupo Lamosa S.A. de C.V.; *Int'l*, pg. 3131
GERFLOR USA, INC.—See Cobepa S.A.; *Int'l*, pg. 1683
GILFORD-JOHNSON FLOORING LLC; *U.S. Private*, pg. 1700
G-MES HOLDINGS INC.; *Int'l*, pg. 2862
GOMEZ FLOOR COVERING, INC.; *U.S. Private*, pg. 1737
GOOD BROTHERS FLOORING PLUS; *U.S. Private*, pg. 1737
GP LAND & CARPET CORPORATION; *U.S. Private*, pg. 1747
GREAT FLOORS, LLC—See The Sterling Group, L.P.; *U.S. Private*, pg. 4122
GUYS FLOOR SERVICE INCORPORATED; *U.S. Private*, pg. 1820
HID ULTRAVIOLET, LLC—See Amergraph Corporation; *U.S. Private*, pg. 219
HOOVER WELLS, INC.; *U.S. Private*, pg. 1978
HUMBL, INC.; *U.S. Public*, pg. 1071

238330 — FLOORING CONTRACTOR...

HUMMERVOLL INDUSTRIBELEGG AS—See RPM International Inc.; *U.S. Public*, pg. 1818
IDEAL FLOORCOVERINGS NV—See Beaulieu International Group NV; *Int'l*, pg. 934
IMPACT FLOORD OF TEXAS, LLC—See Blue Sage Capital, L.P.; *U.S. Private*, pg. 592
IMPACT SPECIALTIES, INC.—See Construction Specialties, Inc.; *U.S. Private*, pg. 1024
INTERIOR CONCEPTS, INC.—See Blue Sage Capital, L.P.; *U.S. Private*, pg. 592
INVISTA—See Koch Industries, Inc.; *U.S. Private*, pg. 2330
IRVINE ACCESS FLOORS INC.; *U.S. Private*, pg. 2141
ITALIAN TERRAZZO & TILE CO., OF BREVARD, INC.; *U.S. Private*, pg. 2149
JOHNSON FLOOR COMPANY, INC.; *U.S. Private*, pg. 2227
J.R. MCDADE COMPANY, INC.; *U.S. Private*, pg. 2170
KENNY'S TILE & FLOORING, INC.; *U.S. Private*, pg. 2287
KONINKLIJKE MOSA BV.—See Egeria Capital Management B.V.; *Int'l*, pg. 2323
LAMOSA REVESTIMIENTOS (GUADALAJARA), S.A. DE C.V.—See Grupo Lamosa S.A. de C.V.; *Int'l*, pg. 3132
LAMOSA REVESTIMIENTOS (MONTERREY), S.A. DE C.V.—See Grupo Lamosa S.A. de C.V.; *Int'l*, pg. 3132
LAMOSA REVESTIMIENTOS (TLAXCALA), S.A DE C.V.—See Grupo Lamosa S.A. de C.V.; *Int'l*, pg. 3132
LEONARD'S CARPET SERVICE INC.; *U.S. Private*, pg. 2430
LINOLEUMKOMPANIET AB—See BHG Group AB; *Int'l*, pg. 1014
LONGDEN COMPANY INC.; *U.S. Private*, pg. 2492
MALIBU ACCEPTANCE CORP.—See The Sterling Group, L.P.; *U.S. Private*, pg. 4122
METROPOLITAN CONTRACT CARPETS; *U.S. Private*, pg. 2688
MOHAWK FACTORING, INC.—See Mohawk Industries, Inc.; *U.S. Public*, pg. 1458
N&A ENTERPRISES INC.; *U.S. Private*, pg. 2826
NONN'S FLOORING INC.—See The Sterling Group, L.P.; *U.S. Private*, pg. 4122
PACIFIC CARPETS, INC.—See The Sterling Group, L.P.; *U.S. Private*, pg. 4122
PATRIOT FLOORING SUPPLY, INC.—See The Belknap White Group, LLC.; *U.S. Private*, pg. 3993
PENINSULA FLOORS, INC.; *U.S. Private*, pg. 3133
PHILLIPS' FLOORS, INC.; *U.S. Private*, pg. 3171
P&R METALS, INC.; *U.S. Private*, pg. 3059
PROFLOORS, LLC; *U.S. Private*, pg. 3277
PYRAMID FLOOR COVERING, INC.; *U.S. Private*, pg. 3310
RECLAMATION, LLC—See Peckham Industries, Inc.; *U.S. Private*, pg. 3127
RE:SOURCE COLORADO, INC.—See ACON Investments, LLC; *U.S. Private*, pg. 62
RITE RUG CO.—See Rite Rug Co.; *U.S. Private*, pg. 3441
ROMANOFF FLOOR COVERING; *U.S. Private*, pg. 3476
RUBENSTEIN'S CONTRACT CARPET, LLC; *U.S. Private*, pg. 3499
SANDERS HYLAND CORPORATION; *U.S. Private*, pg. 3543
SCI FLOOR COVERING, INC.—See Rainier Partners LP; *U.S. Private*, pg. 3348
SHERLAND & FARRINGTON INC.; *U.S. Private*, pg. 3633
SIGNATURE (FENCING AND FLOORING) SYSTEMS EUROPE, LTD.—See Myers Industries, Inc.; *U.S. Public*, pg. 1488
SIGNATURE SYSTEMS GROUP, LLC—See Myers Industries, Inc.; *U.S. Public*, pg. 1488
SNAPLOCK INDUSTRIES, INC.—See Cobepa S.A.; *Int'l*, pg. 1683
SOUTHERN CROSS BUILDING PRODUCTS, LLC—See Q.E.P. Co., Inc.; *U.S. Public*, pg. 1741
SPECTRA HOLDINGS, INC.—See ACON Investments, LLC; *U.S. Private*, pg. 62
STATICWORX, INC; *U.S. Private*, pg. 3793
STEPHENS FLOOR COVERING CO. INC.; *U.S. Private*, pg. 3803
STERLING QUAIL CREEK, LLC—See Sterling Real Estate Trust; *U.S. Private*, pg. 3807
STONCOR BENELUX B.V.—See RPM International Inc.; *U.S. Public*, pg. 1819
STONCOR CORROSION SPECIALISTS GROUP LTDA.—See RPM International Inc.; *U.S. Public*, pg. 1819
STONCOR (DEUTSCHLAND) GMBH—See RPM International Inc.; *U.S. Public*, pg. 1819
STONCOR ESPANA SL—See RPM International Inc.; *U.S. Public*, pg. 1819
STONHARD NEDERLAND B.V.—See RPM International Inc.; *U.S. Public*, pg. 1819
SUNRISE FLOOR SYSTEMS LLC; *U.S. Private*, pg. 3870
T.A.C. CERAMIC TILE CO.—See Littlejohn & Co., LLC; *U.S. Private*, pg. 2470
T.A.C. CERAMIC TILE CO.—See Platinum Equity, LLC; *U.S. Private*, pg. 3205
UNITED CARPET COMPANY, INC.—See Rainier Partners LP; *U.S. Private*, pg. 3348
VINTAGE DESIGN INC.—See The Sterling Group, L.P.; *U.S. Private*, pg. 4122
W.E. IMHOFF & CO. INC.; *U.S. Private*, pg. 4420

238340 — TILE AND TERRAZZO CONTRACTORS

ALAMO TILE CO. INC.; *U.S. Private*, pg. 149
CARRARA MARBLE CO. OF AMERICA INC.; *U.S. Private*, pg. 771
CLEVELAND MARBLE MOSAIC COMPANY; *U.S. Private*, pg. 941
DAVID ALLEN COMPANY INC.; *U.S. Private*, pg. 1169
D & J TILE COMPANY, INC.; *U.S. Private*, pg. 1136
DMI TILE & MARBLE CO.; *U.S. Private*, pg. 1248
ELLIS SKINNER COMPANY, INC.; *U.S. Private*, pg. 1374
EXCELLENCE IN STONE, INC.—See Walker & Zanger, Inc.; *U.S. Private*, pg. 4428
JOHN CARETTI & CO.—See Paul J. Krez Company; *U.S. Private*, pg. 3113
KDI ELEMENTS; *U.S. Private*, pg. 2270
PAUL G. WHITE TILE CO., INC.; *U.S. Private*, pg. 3112
PORT MORRIS TILE & MARBLE; *U.S. Private*, pg. 3230
QUALITY MARBLE, INC.; *U.S. Private*, pg. 3319
SOHO STUDIO, LLC—See AEA Investors LP; *U.S. Private*, pg. 115
TILE WEST INC.; *U.S. Private*, pg. 4170
UNITED PAINTS & CHEMICALS S.A.E—See Compagnie de Saint-Gobain SA; *Int'l*, pg. 1737
WESTERN TILE & MARBLE CONTRACTORS, INC.; *U.S. Private*, pg. 4497

238350 — FINISH CARPENTRY CONTRACTORS

5 STAR BUILDING PRODUCTS LLC—See Installed Building Products, Inc.; *U.S. Public*, pg. 1131
AL JABER CARPENTRY & DECOR L.L.C—See Al Jaber Group; *Int'l*, pg. 279
BEACH MOLD & TOOL VIRGINIA, INC.—See NYX Inc.; *U.S. Private*, pg. 2977
CAPITOL BUILDERS HARDWARE INC.; *U.S. Private*, pg. 743
CON-TECH COMPANIES; *U.S. Private*, pg. 1008
CYL CORPORATION BERHAD; *Int'l*, pg. 1896
EDON CONSTRUCTION COMPANY, INC.; *U.S. Private*, pg. 1338
EXPERT CONSTRUCTION INC.; *U.S. Private*, pg. 1450
FAR EAST ALUMINIUM WORKS CANADA CORPORATION—See China State Construction International Holdings Limited; *Int'l*, pg. 1554
FAR EAST ALUMINIUM WORKS (SINGAPORE) PTE. LTD.—See China State Construction International Holdings Limited; *Int'l*, pg. 1554
FERMATIC FRESNAIS S.A.S.—See dormakaba Holding AG; *Int'l*, pg. 2177
FORSTER GMBH—See BayWa AG; *Int'l*, pg. 918
FSN DOORS LIMITED—See Brickability Group plc; *Int'l*, pg. 1151
ISEC INCORPORATED; *U.S. Private*, pg. 2143
KOLE CONSTRUCTION COMPANY, INC.; *U.S. Private*, pg. 2341
MCCONNELL CABINETS, INC.; *U.S. Private*, pg. 2629
NETFORTUNE (SHANGHAI) ALUMINIUM WORKS CO. LTD.—See China State Construction International Holdings Limited; *Int'l*, pg. 1554
PARKER INSULATION AND BUILDING PRODUCTS, LLC—See Installed Building Products, Inc.; *U.S. Public*, pg. 1133
PROFESSIONAL CABINET SOLUTIONS—See American Woodmark Corporation; *U.S. Public*, pg. 113
RB INTERIOR TRIM; *U.S. Private*, pg. 3360
READ WINDOW PRODUCTS, LLC—See Culp, Inc.; *U.S. Public*, pg. 604
SHAWNLEE CONSTRUCTION, LLC—See UFP Industries, Inc.; *U.S. Public*, pg. 2219
SHEPARDVILLE CONSTRUCTION, LLC—See UFP Industries, Inc.; *U.S. Public*, pg. 2219
STOCKHAM CONSTRUCTION, INC.; *U.S. Private*, pg. 3815
WESTCOR CONSTRUCTION; *U.S. Private*, pg. 4489
WESTECH FRAMING LLC; *U.S. Private*, pg. 4489

238390 — OTHER BUILDING FINISHING CONTRACTORS

20 MCC PRIVATE LIMITED—See 20 Microns Limited; *Int'l*, pg. 4
A C HATHORN CO—See Altas Partners LP; *Int'l*, pg. 386
A.D. WILLIS COMPANY, INC.; *U.S. Private*, pg. 25
ALCAL SPECIALTY CONTRACTING, INC.—See Pacific Coast Building Products, Inc.; *U.S. Private*, pg. 3065
ALPHA INSULATION & WATER PROOFING COMPANY—See Installed Building Products, Inc.; *U.S. Public*, pg. 1132
ALUFORM MARKETING PTE LTD.—See Compact Metal Industries Ltd.; *Int'l*, pg. 1721
AMQ SOLUTIONS—See Steelcase Inc.; *U.S. Public*, pg. 1944

CORPORATE AFFILIATIONS

APB RESOURCES BERHAD; *Int'l*, pg. 507
A. PERIN ROOFING & SIDING, INC.; *U.S. Private*, pg. 23
ARIZONA BLINDS; *U.S. Private*, pg. 323
AT INDUSTRIAL SHEET METAL, INC.—See AT Industries, Inc.; *U.S. Private*, pg. 363
BB&W ASSOCIATES, INC—See Altas Partners LP; *Int'l*, pg. 387
BEST ENVIRONMENTAL SYSTEMS TECHNOLOGY, INC.—See EMP Management, LLC; *U.S. Private*, pg. 1384
BLEACHER RESTORATORS OF COLORADO, LLC; *U.S. Private*, pg. 580
BRISK WATERPROOFING COMPANY—See Western Construction Group; *U.S. Private*, pg. 4492
CANNON FABRICATION, INC.—See Vibration Mountings & Controls, Inc.; *U.S. Private*, pg. 4376
CEI ROOFING, INC.; *U.S. Private*, pg. 805
CENTRAL ALUMINUM SUPPLY CORP.—See Installed Building Products, Inc.; *U.S. Public*, pg. 1132
CENTURY REPROGRAPHICS—See American CyberSystems, Inc.; *U.S. Private*, pg. 229
CFM HOLDINGS LIMITED; *Int'l*, pg. 1430
CHILDERS ROOFING & SHEETMETAL, INC.—See Altas Partners LP; *Int'l*, pg. 386
CHRIS ANDERSEN ROOFING & ERECTING., CO.—See Altas Partners LP; *Int'l*, pg. 386
CINFAB INC.; *U.S. Private*, pg. 898
CITIROOF CORPORATION; *U.S. Private*, pg. 901
CLS INSULATION, LLC—See Installed Building Products, Inc.; *U.S. Public*, pg. 1132
COASTAL SHEET METAL, CORP.; *U.S. Private*, pg. 956
COBRA BEC, INC.; *U.S. Private*, pg. 958
COLLIS ROOFING, INC.; *U.S. Private*, pg. 969
COMMONWEALTH BLINDS & SHADES, INC.—See Contexture, Inc.; *U.S. Private*, pg. 1028
CONSTRUCTION LONGER INC.; *Int'l*, pg. 1778
COOL ROOFING SYSTEMS INC.; *U.S. Private*, pg. 1039
CORE ROOFING SYSTEMS LLC—See Shoreline Equity Partners, LLC; *U.S. Private*, pg. 3641
CRAM ROOFING COMPANY INC—See New State Capital Partners LLC; *U.S. Private*, pg. 2907
DESERTOAK LTD; *Int'l*, pg. 2045
DONALD B. SMITH INCORPORATED; *U.S. Private*, pg. 1259
DRH SOUTHWEST CONSTRUCTION, INC.—See D.R. Horton, Inc.; *U.S. Public*, pg. 620
DRY-PRO BASEMENT SYSTEMS, INC.; *U.S. Private*, pg. 1280
EAST MUSKEGON ROOFING & SHEET METAL COMPANY; *U.S. Private*, pg. 1317
EMECOLE METRO LLC—See Metropolitan Industries, Inc.; *U.S. Private*, pg. 2688
ENVIRONETX, LLC; *U.S. Private*, pg. 1407
EQUITIX INVESTMENT MANAGEMENT LIMITED; *Int'l*, pg. 2488
FIBERGLASS INSULATION, LLC—See Installed Building Products, Inc.; *U.S. Public*, pg. 1132
FIRMCO LTD.; *Int'l*, pg. 2679
FRONTIER ROOFING, INC—See EMP Management, LLC; *U.S. Private*, pg. 1384
FUGRO LOADTEST LTD.—See Fugro N.V.; *Int'l*, pg. 2806
F.W. WALTON ROOFING, INC.; *U.S. Private*, pg. 1457
GASTONIA SHEET METAL; *U.S. Private*, pg. 1649
GENERAL CUBICLE—See Construction Specialties, Inc.; *U.S. Private*, pg. 1024
GOLDEN EAGLE ROOFING COMPANY—See Cherubim Interests, Inc.; *U.S. Public*, pg. 485
HALL SHEET METAL WORKS, INC.; *U.S. Private*, pg. 1843
HASEKO COMMUNITY, INC.—See Haseko Corporation; *Int'l*, pg. 3283
HITACHI ELEVATOR ENGINEERING COMPANY (HONG KONG) LIMITED—See Hitachi, Ltd.; *Int'l*, pg. 3416
THE HOMAX GROUP, INC.—See PPG Industries, Inc.; *U.S. Public*, pg. 1710
I & E CONSTRUCTION, INC.; *U.S. Private*, pg. 2020
J.D. RIVET & CO., INC.; *U.S. Private*, pg. 2161
JOHNSON CONTRACTING COMPANY; *U.S. Private*, pg. 2227
JOLLY ROOFING & CONTRACTING CO., INC.; *U.S. Private*, pg. 2230
KATCHMARK CONSTRUCTION INC.—See Altas Partners LP; *Int'l*, pg. 386
KIRK & BLUM MANUFACTURING COMPANY INC.—See CECO Environmental Corp.; *U.S. Public*, pg. 463
KNOPE ROOFING & FURNACE CO.—See Eponk Group Ltd.; *U.S. Private*, pg. 1414
KPI 2 INCORPORATED; *U.S. Private*, pg. 2346
KRUEGER SHEET METAL; *U.S. Private*, pg. 2353
LABAIRE SYSTEMS CO—See Activar, Inc.; *U.S. Private*, pg. 68
LEO J. ROTH CORP.; *U.S. Private*, pg. 2422
MAD CITY WINDOWS & BATHS, LLC—See Florida Home Improvement Associates Inc.; *U.S. Private*, pg. 1549
MADDEN MANUFACTURING CO., INC.—See Caisse de Depot et Placement du Quebec; *Int'l*, pg. 1254
MANDAL'S, INC.; *U.S. Private*, pg. 2562
MERRICK CONSTRUCTION COMPANIES, INC.—See Merrick Industries Incorporated; *U.S. Private*, pg. 2675

N.A.I.C.S. INDEX　　　　　　　　　　　　　　　　　　　　　　　　238910 — SITE PREPARATION CO...

METCOE SKYLIGHT SPECIALTIES—See Weiss Sheet Metal Company; *U.S. Private,* pg. 4473
MIG BUILDING SYSTEMS, LLC—See Installed Building Products, Inc.; *U.S. Public,* pg. 1133
M&J MATERIALS INC.; *U.S. Private,* pg. 2524
NATIONWIDE GUTTER, LLC—See Installed Building Products, Inc.; *U.S. Public,* pg. 1133
NED STEVENS GUTTER CLEANING & GENERAL CONTRACTING, INC.—See AVALT, LLC; *U.S. Private,* pg. 403
NETH & SONS INC.; *U.S. Private,* pg. 2887
NIC GLOBAL MANUFACTURING SOLUTIONS, INC.; *U.S. Private,* pg. 2925
NORTH TEXAS WATERPROOFING & RESTORATION CO.—See Western Construction Group; *U.S. Private,* pg. 4492
OAK DRY LINING LIMITED—See Galliford Try Holdings plc; *Int'l,* pg. 2874
ORBIT SHEET METAL CO. INC.—See Unitize Company Inc.; *U.S. Private,* pg. 4302
PRATE ROOFING & INSTALLATIONS, LLC; *U.S. Private,* pg. 3243
R.L. JAMES INC.; *U.S. Private,* pg. 3338
ROCA TILES SPAIN, S.L.—See Grupo Lamosa S.A. de C.V.; *Int'l,* pg. 3132
SIMPSON PLASTERING LLC; *U.S. Private,* pg. 3668
STAINLESS SPECIALISTS INC.; *U.S. Private,* pg. 3776
STORM MASTER CO., INC.—See Installed Building Products, Inc.; *U.S. Public,* pg. 1133
STROMBERG METAL WORKS, INC.; *U.S. Private,* pg. 3840
SUPERIOR AIR HANDLING CORPORATION—See Harris Companies; *U.S. Private,* pg. 1869
SUPERIOR INSULATION, LLC—See Installed Building Products, Inc.; *U.S. Public,* pg. 1133
T4B LTD.—See Attard & Co. Ltd.; *Int'l,* pg. 696
TAR HEEL BASEMENT SYSTEMS LLC—See JES Construction, LLC; *U.S. Private,* pg. 2203
VALUE PLUS FLOORING, INC.—See The Sterling Group, L.P.; *U.S. Private,* pg. 4122
VOEGELE CO., INC.—See Burns & Scalo Roofing Co., Inc.; *U.S. Private,* pg. 690
WAITE SPECIALTY MACHINE, INC.; *U.S. Private,* pg. 4426
WALSH & ALBERT COMPANY, LTD.; *U.S. Private,* pg. 4432
WARENDORFER KUCHEN GMBH—See CoBe Capital LLC; *U.S. Private,* pg. 957
WEATHERPROOFING TECHNOLOGIES, INC.—See RPM International Inc.; *U.S. Public,* pg. 1818
WESTAR ROOFING CORPORATION; *U.S. Private,* pg. 4488
WESTERN RESTORATION & WATERPROOFING CO.—See Western Construction Group; *U.S. Private,* pg. 4492
WINDWARD ROOFING & CONSTRUCTION, INC.; *U.S. Private,* pg. 4539

238910 — SITE PREPARATION CONTRACTORS

3R LIMITED—See Anderson Group Limited; *Int'l,* pg. 450
ACCUTEMP HEATING-COOLING, INC.—See New Mountain Capital, LLC; *U.S. Private,* pg. 2902
AEGIS FIRE SYSTEMS, INC.—See Pye-Barker Fire & Safety, LLC; *U.S. Private,* pg. 3309
AF HARNOSAND BYGGRETURER AB—See AF Gruppen ASA; *Int'l,* pg. 184
AIR PROS; *U.S. Private,* pg. 139
AL-BAHA INVESTMENT AND DEVELOPMENT CO.; *Int'l,* pg. 284
ALOHA AIR CONDITIONING, INC.—See Marathon HVAC Services, LLC; *U.S. Private,* pg. 2570
AMBIENT TEMPERATURE CORP.—See Huron Capital Partners LLC; *U.S. Private,* pg. 2012
AMERICAN CONTRACTING INC.; *U.S. Private,* pg. 228
AMERICAN REFRIGERATION COMPANY, LLC—See Southfield Capital Advisors, LLC; *U.S. Private,* pg. 3736
AMERICAN WRECKING INC.; *U.S. Private,* pg. 258
AMI MECHANICAL, INC.—See Colorado Mechanical Services, LLC; *U.S. Private,* pg. 974
ANDERSON INDUSTRIAL CORPORATION; *Int'l,* pg. 450
ANGEL BROTHERS ENTERPRISES INC.; *U.S. Private,* pg. 281
ARVADA EXCAVATING CO.; *U.S. Private,* pg. 344
ASPLUNDH BRUSH CONTROL CO.—See Asplundh Tree Expert Co.; *U.S. Private,* pg. 353
ASTAR HEATING & AIR, LLC—See Morgan Stanley; *U.S. Public,* pg. 1474
AYERS BASEMENT SYSTEMS, LLC; *U.S. Private,* pg. 414
BADGER DAYLIGHTING—See Badger Infrastructure Solutions Ltd.; *Int'l,* pg. 796
BASETROPHY GROUP HOLDINGS LIMITED; *Int'l,* pg. 871
BAUER AKTIENGESELLSCHAFT; *Int'l,* pg. 891
BAUER FONDATIONS SPECIALES S.A.S.—See BAUER Aktiengesellschaft; *Int'l,* pg. 892
BAUER FUNDERINGSTECHNIEK B.V.—See BAUER Aktiengesellschaft; *Int'l,* pg. 892
BAUER ROMANIA S.R.L.—See BAUER Aktiengesellschaft; *Int'l,* pg. 892
BAUER SERVICES SINGAPORE PTE. LTD.—See BAUER Aktiengesellschaft; *Int'l,* pg. 892
BAUER SPEZIALTIEFBAU GESELLSCHAFT M.B.H.—See BAUER Aktiengesellschaft; *Int'l,* pg. 892
BAUER SPEZIALTIEFBAU GMBH.—See BAUER Aktiengesellschaft; *Int'l,* pg. 892
BAUER TECHNOLOGIES LIMITED—See BAUER Aktiengesellschaft; *Int'l,* pg. 892
BAUMGARDNER SERVICES INC.—See Applied Industrial Technologies, Inc.; *U.S. Public,* pg. 171
THE BEAVER EXCAVATING COMPANY, INC.; *U.S. Private,* pg. 3992
BEAVER GROUP (HOLDING) COMPANY LIMITED; *Int'l,* pg. 935
BENNETT CONTRACTING, INC.; *U.S. Private,* pg. 527
BENOURE PLUMBING & HEATING INC—See Empowered Ventures, Inc.; *U.S. Private,* pg. 1387
BIERLEIN COMPANIES INCORPORATED; *U.S. Private,* pg. 551
BIGRENTZ, INC.; *U.S. Private,* pg. 555
BILOTTA CONSTRUCTION CORP.; *U.S. Private,* pg. 559
BLACKHAWK SPECIALTY TOOLS, LLC—See Expro Group Holdings N.V.; *Int'l,* pg. 2591
BLASTING SOLUTIONS INC.—See Argosy Capital Group, LLC; *U.S. Private,* pg. 321
BRADFORD PRODUCTS, LLC; *U.S. Private,* pg. 632
BRADLEY EXCAVATING, INC.; *U.S. Private,* pg. 632
BRINLEY'S GRADING SERVICE, INC.; *U.S. Private,* pg. 655
BROKEN ARROW INCORPORATED; *U.S. Private,* pg. 661
BUCKNER'S HEATING & COOLING CO.—See Heartland Homecare Services, Inc.; *U.S. Private,* pg. 1900
BURKHARDT EXCAVATING; *U.S. Private,* pg. 688
BURTON SIGNWORKS, INC.; *U.S. Private,* pg. 693
C & A PAVING CO.—See Clyde Companies Inc.; *U.S. Private,* pg. 949
CAPE CRUSHING & EARTHMOVING CONTRACTORS PTY. LTD.—See CFC Group Pty Ltd.; *Int'l,* pg. 1429
CAPITOL ENGINEERING CO.—See Southfield Capital Advisors, LLC; *U.S. Private,* pg. 3736
CASTEEL HEATING AND COOLING, INC.—See New Mountain Capital, LLC; *U.S. Private,* pg. 2902
CATALYST OILFIELD SERVICES—See CES Energy Solutions Corp.; *Int'l,* pg. 1423
CENTRAL COOLING & HEATING INC.—See Morgan Stanley; *U.S. Public,* pg. 1474
CENTURY GROUP INTERNATIONAL HOLDINGS LIMITED; *Int'l,* pg. 1418
CH&D ENTERPRISES INC.; *U.S. Private,* pg. 844
CHINA DREDGING ENVIRONMENTAL PROTECTION HOLDING LIMITED; *Int'l,* pg. 1498
CHINA HONGBAO HOLDINGS LIMITED; *Int'l,* pg. 1508
CINELEASE, LLC—See Herc Holdings Inc.; *U.S. Public,* pg. 1028
CLARK FOUNDATION COMPANY; *U.S. Private,* pg. 913
CLEVE BATTE CONSTRUCTION INC.; *U.S. Private,* pg. 940
CLEVELAND WRECKING COMPANY—See AECOM; *U.S. Public,* pg. 51
CMA CONTRACTING PTY LIMITED—See Delta Group Pty Ltd; *Int'l,* pg. 2018
CMG GESELLSCHAFT FUR BAULOGISTIK GMBH—See Heijmans N.V.; *Int'l,* pg. 3322
COFFMAN EXCAVATION INC.; *U.S. Private,* pg. 961
CONCRETE CUTTING & BREAKING INC.; *U.S. Private,* pg. 1011
CONSOLIDATED MECHANICAL, INC.—See Limbach Holdings, Inc.; *U.S. Public,* pg. 1316
COOLING & HEATING SPECIALISTS, INC.—See Southfield Capital Advisors, LLC; *U.S. Private,* pg. 3736
COPART EXCAVATION, INC.—See Copart, Inc.; *U.S. Public,* pg. 575
COSTELLO DISMANTLING COMPANY, INC.; *U.S. Private,* pg. 1063
CRESTWOOD PLUMBING, INC.—See User Friendly Home Services, LLC; *U.S. Private,* pg. 4322
CRIMSON STEEL SUPPLY LLC—See Clayton, Dubilier & Rice, LLC; *U.S. Private,* pg. 930
CROPPMETCALFE, INC.—See Brookfield Corporation; *Int'l,* pg. 1188
CS BORED PILE SYSTEM PTE. LTD.—See CSC Holdings Limited; *Int'l,* pg. 1862
C S & W CONTRACTORS; *U.S. Private,* pg. 702
C. WATTS AND SONS CONSTRUCTION INC.; *U.S. Private,* pg. 705
DEMCO INC.; *U.S. Private,* pg. 1203
DEPATCO, INC.—See Clyde Companies Inc.; *U.S. Private,* pg. 949
D&E PLUMBING & HEATING INC.; *U.S. Private,* pg. 1137
DETROIT EXCAVATION, INC.—See Motor City Electric Co., Inc.; *U.S. Private,* pg. 2796
DEWITT EXCAVATION, LLC—See Sterling Infrastructure, Inc.; *U.S. Public,* pg. 1946
D.H. GRIFFIN OF TEXAS, INC—See D.H. Griffin Wrecking Co., Inc.; *U.S. Private,* pg. 1142
D.H. GRIFFIN WRECKING CO. INC.; *U.S. Private,* pg. 1142
DILLCO FLUID SERVICE, INC.—See Enservco Corporation; *U.S. Public,* pg. 775
DORE & ASSOCIATES CONTRACTING, INC.; *U.S. Private,* pg. 1262
DRAGON RISE GROUP HOLDINGS LIMITED; *Int'l,* pg. 2199
DRA TAGGART SITE SERVICES, LLC—See DRA Group Holdings Proprietary Limited; *Int'l,* pg. 2196
DRIGGS CORPORATION; *U.S. Private,* pg. 1277
DRILLCUT LIMITED—See GLORY FLAME HOLDINGS LIMITED; *Int'l,* pg. 3009
DUSTROL INC.; *U.S. Private,* pg. 1294
DYER CONSTRUCTION COMPANY, INC.; *U.S. Private,* pg. 1296
EARTH SERVICES & ABATEMENT, INC.; *U.S. Private,* pg. 1314
EGLENTOWICZ WRECKING LLC; *U.S. Private,* pg. 1344
ENERGY SAVERS OF GEORGIA, INC.—See NearU Services; *U.S. Private,* pg. 2877
ESI CONTRACTING, CORP.; *U.S. Private,* pg. 1425
FEECORP CORPORATION; *U.S. Private,* pg. 1492
FEENEY BROTHERS EXCAVATION LLC; *U.S. Private,* pg. 1493
FELDERS CONSTRUCTION, LLC; *U.S. Private,* pg. 1493
FERMA CORP.; *U.S. Private,* pg. 1497
FER-PAL CONSTRUCTION LTD.—See Blue Wolf Capital Partners LLC; *U.S. Private,* pg. 594
FORRISTALL ENTERPRISES, INC.; *U.S. Private,* pg. 1572
FRATTALONE COMPANIES, INC.; *U.S. Private,* pg. 1599
FRONTIER FIRE PROTECTION INC.—See Highview Capital, LLC; *U.S. Private,* pg. 1942
G.A. BLOCKER GRADING CONTRACTOR, INC.—See Curran Group, Inc.; *U.S. Private,* pg. 1125
GARELLI SA; *Int'l,* pg. 2884
G.D. HEIL INC.; *U.S. Private,* pg. 1630
GEIGER EXCAVATING, INC.; *U.S. Private,* pg. 1656
GENTRY AIR INC.—See Palladin Consumer Retail Partners, LLC; *U.S. Private,* pg. 3077
GEO GRADEL CO.; *U.S. Private,* pg. 1680
GEORGE J. IGEL & COMPANY, INC.; *U.S. Private,* pg. 1682
GFC CONSTRUCTION INC.; *U.S. Private,* pg. 1689
GLORY FLAME HOLDINGS LIMITED; *Int'l,* pg. 3009
GOLDEN STATE FIRE PROTECTION, INC.—See Fortis Fire & Safety, Inc.; *U.S. Private,* pg. 1576
GRADEX INC.; *U.S. Private,* pg. 1750
GRAYCOR BLASTING COMPANY INC.—See Graycor Inc.; *U.S. Private,* pg. 1761
GRIFFIN DEWATERING CORPORATION—See Crossplane Capital Management LP; *U.S. Private,* pg. 1107
GROGG'S HEATING & AIR CONDITIONING INC.—See NearU Services; *U.S. Private,* pg. 2878
GROUP FIVE PLANT & EQUIPMENT (PROPRIETARY) LIMITED—See Group Five Limited; *Int'l,* pg. 3089
GRUPO CARE SA—See Emeis SA; *Int'l,* pg. 2376
HAINES & KIBBLEHOUSE INC.; *U.S. Private,* pg. 1840
HARTLAND CONTROLS LLC—See Littelfuse, Inc.; *U.S. Public,* pg. 1327
HAZLETON SITE CONTRACTORS—See Haines & Kibblehouse Inc.; *U.S. Private,* pg. 1841
HEMLOCK EQUIPMENT LLC—See Evergreen Marine Corporation (Taiwan) Ltd.; *Int'l,* pg. 2566
HENEGHAN WRECKING & EXCAVATING CO., INC.—See J.F. Lehman & Company, Inc.; *U.S. Private,* pg. 2164
HILBIG SERVICES INC.—See Southland Industries; *U.S. Private,* pg. 3737
H.L. CHAPMAN PIPELINE CONSTRUCTION, INC.—See Quanta Services, Inc.; *U.S. Public,* pg. 1751
HONC INDUSTRIES, INC.; *U.S. Private,* pg. 1976
HORIZON SERVICES, LLC—See New Mountain Capital, LLC; *U.S. Private,* pg. 2902
HT SWEENEY & SON INC—See Southwest Gas Holdings, Inc.; *U.S. Public,* pg. 1913
HUCKESTEIN MECHANICAL SERVICES, INC.—See Leonard Green & Partners, L.P.; *U.S. Private,* pg. 2426
HYDRO TECHNOLOGIES, INC.—See Hughes Group, Inc.; *U.S. Private,* pg. 2003
ICON MECHANICAL CONSTRUCTION & ENGINEERING LLC.; *U.S. Private,* pg. 2032
INDEPENDENCE EXCAVATING, INC.; *U.S. Private,* pg. 2058
INDEPENDENCE RECYCLING DIVISION—See Independence Excavating, Inc.; *U.S. Private,* pg. 2058
INTERTEX, INC.—See Lasko Products, LLC; *U.S. Private,* pg. 2395
JAY DEE CONTRACTORS, INC.; *U.S. Private,* pg. 2191
JET SERVICES INC.—See Odyssey Investment Partners, LLC; *U.S. Private,* pg. 2995
JIMMIE CROWDER EXCAVATING INC.; *U.S. Private,* pg. 2210
JOHN DRIGGS COMPANY, INC.; *U.S. Private,* pg. 2221
JOHN L. JERSEY & SON INC.; *U.S. Private,* pg. 2222
JOHN W. GLEIM, JR. INC.; *U.S. Private,* pg. 2225
JONES SIGN CO., INC.; *U.S. Private,* pg. 2234
KAMMINGA & ROODVOETS INC.; *U.S. Private,* pg. 2258
KASS BROS INC.; *U.S. Private,* pg. 2264
K & E EXCAVATING INC.; *U.S. Private,* pg. 2249
KEITH ZARS POOLS; *U.S. Private,* pg. 2274

238910 — SITE PREPARATION CO...

KELPE CONTRACTING, INC.; *U.S. Private*, pg. 2277
KREAGER BROTHERS EXCAVATING; *U.S. Private*, pg. 2350
LAN-CO DEVELOPMENT INC.; *U.S. Private*, pg. 2381
LANDIS C. DECK & SONS SITE CONTRACTORS—See Haines & Kibblehouse Inc.; *U.S. Private*, pg. 1841
LARRY SNYDER & CO.; *U.S. Private*, pg. 2393
LARSON, INCORPORATED—See Paschal Home Services, LLC; *U.S. Private*, pg. 3104
LEEWARD CONSTRUCTION, INC.; *U.S. Private*, pg. 2415
LEGACY FIRE PROTECTION, INC.—See TruArc Partners, L.P.; *U.S. Private*, pg. 4244
LOCUST RIDGE CONTRACTORS—See Haines & Kibblehouse Inc.; *U.S. Private*, pg. 1841
LOVETT INC.; *U.S. Private*, pg. 2504
L P CIMINELLI CONSTRUCTION COMPANY INC.—See LPCiminelli Inc.; *U.S. Private*, pg. 2507
LPCIMINELLI INC.; *U.S. Private*, pg. 2507
MANAFORT BROTHERS INCORPORATED; *U.S. Private*, pg. 2559
MAROIS BROTHERS, INC.; *U.S. Private*, pg. 2586
MARUCCI AND GAFFNEY EXCAVATING CO.; *U.S. Private*, pg. 2597
MATECO GMBH—See Group Thermote & Vanhalst; *Int'l*, pg. 3090
MATRIX SERVICE CANADA ULC—See Matrix Service Company; *U.S. Public*, pg. 1397
MATRIX SERVICE COMPANY; *U.S. Public*, pg. 1397
MAX JANTZ EXCAVATING, LLC.; *U.S. Private*, pg. 2617
MECHANICAL ENGINEERING & CONSTRUCTION CORPORATION—See Ares Management Corporation; *U.S. Public*, pg. 189
MECHANICAL SOLUTIONS, INC.—See ABM Industries, Inc.; *U.S. Public*, pg. 26
MED-LOZ LEASE SERVICE INC.; *U.S. Private*, pg. 2650
MERRITT CONSTRUCTION SERVICES—See Merritt Management Corporation; *U.S. Private*, pg. 2676
MICHAEL THRASHER TRUCKING CO.; *U.S. Private*, pg. 2698
MINISCALCO CONSTRUCTION, L.L.C.—See Haines & Kibblehouse Inc.; *U.S. Private*, pg. 1841
M.L. ALBRIGHT & SONS, INC.; *U.S. Private*, pg. 2529
MORGAN CORP.; *U.S. Private*, pg. 2783
MORTON TRUCKING, INC.; *U.S. Private*, pg. 2792
MOUNTAIN AIR MECHANICAL CONTRACTORS, INC.—See DLVA, Inc.; *U.S. Private*, pg. 1248
NATIONAL EWP, INC.; *U.S. Private*, pg. 2853
NORTHEAST CONTRACTORS INC.; *U.S. Private*, pg. 2949
NORTHSTAR CONTRACTING GROUP, INC.—See J.F. Lehman & Company, Inc.; *U.S. Private*, pg. 2164
NORTHWEST DEMOLITION & DISMANTLING, INC.—See Arctic Slope Regional Corporation; *U.S. Private*, pg. 316
OFTEDAL CONSTRUCTION INC.; *U.S. Private*, pg. 3003
OLMOS EQUIPMENT INC.; *U.S. Private*, pg. 3011
OTI OPERATING, INC.—See L.B. Foster Company; *U.S. Public*, pg. 1279
PARHAM CONSTRUCTION CO.; *U.S. Private*, pg. 3094
PARK CONSTRUCTION CORP.; *U.S. Private*, pg. 3096
PAVEX INC.; *U.S. Private*, pg. 3115
PAVIMENTAL POLSKA SP Z.O.O.—See Edizione S.r.l.; *Int'l*, pg. 2312
PERRY ENGINEERING COMPANY, INC.; *U.S. Private*, pg. 3154
PETILLO, INC.—See Sterling Infrastructure, Inc.; *U.S. Public*, pg. 1946
PFISTER ENERGY INC.; *U.S. Private*, pg. 3165
PHOENIX FIRE SYSTEMS, INC.—See Pye-Barker Fire & Safety, LLC; *U.S. Private*, pg. 3309
PLANT RECLAMATION; *U.S. Private*, pg. 3197
PLATEAU EXCAVATION, INC.—See Sterling Infrastructure, Inc.; *U.S. Public*, pg. 1946
PLOTE CONSTRUCTION, INC.; *U.S. Private*, pg. 3214
POPPLE CONSTRUCTION, INC.; *U.S. Private*, pg. 3229
POTTS & CALLAHAN INC.; *U.S. Private*, pg. 3235
PRECISION FOUNDATIONS, INC.—See The Goldfield Corporation; *U.S. Public*, pg. 2076
PREMIER PACIFIC CONSTRUCTION, INC.; *U.S. Private*, pg. 3250
P.T. BAUER PRATAMA INDONESIA—See BAUER Aktiengesellschaft; *Int'l*, pg. 893
P.T. FERRO CONSTRUCTION INC.; *U.S. Private*, pg. 3061
PURGATOIRE VALLEY CONSTRUCTION; *U.S. Private*, pg. 3306
P&W EXCAVATING INC.; *U.S. Private*, pg. 3059
PYRAMID MATERIALS—See Haines & Kibblehouse Inc.; *U.S. Private*, pg. 1841
RAGSDALE HEATING & AIR CONDITIONING, INC.—See Leonard Green & Partners, L.P.; *U.S. Private*, pg. 2430
R.D. JOHNSON EXCAVATING COMPANY, LLC—See Summit Materials, Inc.; *U.S. Public*, pg. 1959
READING SITE CONTRACTORS—See Haines & Kibblehouse Inc.; *U.S. Private*, pg. 1841
REDING GRAVEL & EXCAVATING CO., INC.; *U.S. Private*, pg. 3378
RELIABLE PRODUCTION SERVICE, INC.; *U.S. Private*, pg. 3394
R.F. SCURLOCK COMPANY INC.; *U.S. Private*, pg. 3336
RICHARD E. PIERSON CONSTRUCTION COMPANY, INC.; *U.S. Private*, pg. 3428
R&L DEVELOPMENT COMPANY; *U.S. Private*, pg. 3332
ROBINSON EXCAVATING OF FLORIDA—See Ross Brothers Construction Co; *U.S. Private*, pg. 3485
RW RHINE INC.; *U.S. Private*, pg. 3508
THE RYAN COMPANIES, LLC; *U.S. Private*, pg. 4113
SACHS CIVIL INC.—See Sachs Electric Company; *U.S. Private*, pg. 3521
SAIIA CONSTRUCTION, LLC—See Insight Equity Holdings LLC; *U.S. Private*, pg. 2086
SAUDI BAUER FOUNDATION CONTRACTORS LTD.—See BAUER Aktiengesellschaft; *Int'l*, pg. 894
S.B. COX INC.; *U.S. Private*, pg. 3515
SCHACHTBAU NORDHAUSEN BAU GMBH—See BAUER Aktiengesellschaft; *Int'l*, pg. 894
SCHUETTE MOVERS; *U.S. Private*, pg. 3570
S.D. IRELAND BROTHERS CORP; *U.S. Private*, pg. 3517
SEALING AGENTS WATERPROOFING, INC.; *U.S. Private*, pg. 3585
SERVICE EXPERTS LLC; *U.S. Private*, pg. 3615
SERVICE SELECT, INC.; *U.S. Private*, pg. 3616
SHALLOW FORD CONSTRUCTION CO.; *U.S. Private*, pg. 3623
SHARP'S CONSTRUCTION SERVICES 2006 LTD.—See Quanta Services, Inc.; *U.S. Public*, pg. 1753
SHAUGHNESSY AND AHERN COMPANY—See Apollo Global Management, Inc.; *U.S. Public*, pg. 153
SHAW BROTHERS CONSTRUCTION; *U.S. Private*, pg. 3627
SHERWOOD CONSTRUCTION CO. INC.; *U.S. Private*, pg. 3634
SIMSCROFT-ECHO FARMS INC.; *U.S. Private*, pg. 3669
SITE ENGINEERING INC.; *U.S. Private*, pg. 3676
SITE WORK SPECIALISTS INC.; *U.S. Private*, pg. 3676
SMITH FILTER CORPORATION—See Audax Group, Limited Partnership; *U.S. Private*, pg. 389
SPIRTAS WRECKING CO. INC.; *U.S. Private*, pg. 3758
STRAND BROTHERS SERVICE EXPERTS HEATING & AIR CONDITIONING—See Service Experts LLC; *U.S. Private*, pg. 3615
STURGEON & SON INCORPORATED; *U.S. Private*, pg. 3844
SWIFT AIR INC.—See iAero Group; *U.S. Private*, pg. 2027
TETRIS SAS—See Jones Lang LaSalle Incorporated; *U.S. Public*, pg. 1206
THAI BAUER CO.LTD.—See BAUER Aktiengesellschaft; *Int'l*, pg. 894
THERMASERVE, INC.—See Huron Capital Partners LLC; *U.S. Private*, pg. 2012
TJADER & HIGHSTROM UTILITY SERVICES, LLC—See Dycom Industries, Inc.; *U.S. Public*, pg. 699
T.J. LAMBRECHT CONSTRUCTION; *U.S. Private*, pg. 3912
TOP NOTCH ENERGY SERVICES, INC.—See Intervale Capital, LLC; *U.S. Private*, pg. 2127
TUTT BRYANT GROUP LIMITED—See Affirma Capital Limited; *Int'l*, pg. 187
TYSAN FOUNDATION LIMITED—See Blackstone Inc.; *U.S. Public*, pg. 351
UAB PORTALPRO—See City Service SE; *Int'l*, pg. 1628
UNDERGROUND LOCATING & EXCAVATING—See Complete General Construction Co. Inc.; *U.S. Private*, pg. 1000
UNITED GHS INC.—See United Airlines Holdings, Inc.; *U.S. Public*, pg. 2229
US DISMANTLEMENT LLC; *U.S. Private*, pg. 4318
VOLLERS EXCAVATING & CONSTRUCTION INC.—See Vollers, Inc.; *U.S. Private*, pg. 4411
VOLLERS, INC.; *U.S. Private*, pg. 4410
WEIR BROS. INC.; *U.S. Private*, pg. 4472
WHOLESALE SHEET METAL INC.—See Ridgemont Partners Management LLC; *U.S. Private*, pg. 3433
WOODALL CONSTRUCTION CO. INC.; *U.S. Private*, pg. 4557
WORKBASE ENGINEERING LIMITED—See Basetrophy Group Holdings Limited; *Int'l*, pg. 871
WPM INC.; *U.S. Private*, pg. 4571
W.S. NEWELL, INC.; *U.S. Private*, pg. 4423
YENTER COMPANIES INC.; *U.S. Private*, pg. 4588
YOUNG & MCQUEEN GRADING COMPANY, INC.; *U.S. Private*, pg. 4592
ZEMBA BROS INC; *U.S. Private*, pg. 4601
ZOLADZ CONSTRUCTION CO., INC.; *U.S. Private*, pg. 4607
ZONE MECHANICAL, INC.—See Wind Point Advisors LLC; *U.S. Private*, pg. 4536

238990 — ALL OTHER SPECIALTY TRADE CONTRACTORS

A1 POOL PARTS; *U.S. Private*, pg. 29
A2Z ENVIRONMENTAL GROUP, LLC; *U.S. Private*, pg. 29
ABG CAULKING CONTRACTORS INC.; *U.S. Private*, pg. 38
A&B PROCESS SYSTEM CORP.; *U.S. Private*, pg. 19
ACI MECHANICAL, INC.—See Comfort Systems USA, Inc.; *U.S. Public*, pg. 543
ACT GLOBAL AMERICAS INC.—See Beaulieu International Group NV; *Int'l*, pg. 934
ACTION PRODUCTS MARKETING CORP.—See Edgewater Services, LLC; *U.S. Private*, pg. 1335
ADVANCED SYSTEMS GROUP—See EMCOR Group, Inc.; *U.S. Public*, pg. 739
A.H. BECK FOUNDATION CO. INC.; *U.S. Private*, pg. 26
AHERN FIRE PROTECTION—See J.F. Ahern Co.; *U.S. Private*, pg. 2162
ALAM CONSTRUCTIONS LTD.—See Alam Group of Companies; *Int'l*, pg. 289
ALCORN FENCE COMPANY; *U.S. Private*, pg. 154
ALLIANCE ENVIRONMENTAL GROUP, LLC; *U.S. Private*, pg. 182
ALL STATES AG PARTS, LLC—See Kinderhook Industries, LLC; *U.S. Private*, pg. 2306
ALTO CONSTRUCTION CO., INC.; *U.S. Private*, pg. 210
ALUMA SYSTEMS—See Brand Industrial Services, Inc.; *U.S. Private*, pg. 636
AMALGAMET CANADA—See Amalgamated Metal Corporation PLC; *Int'l*, pg. 409
AMENDOLAS FENCE CO.; *U.S. Private*, pg. 218
AMERICAN CLEANING SYSTEMS, INC.—See Valcourt Building Services LLC; *U.S. Private*, pg. 4330
AMERICAN FENCE COMPANY, INC.; *U.S. Private*, pg. 233
AMERICAN FENCE & SECURITY COMPANY—See American Fence Company, Inc.; *U.S. Private*, pg. 233
AMERICAN PARKS COMPANY—See Court Square Capital Partners, L.P.; *U.S. Private*, pg. 1069
AMERICAN SCAFFOLD—See J.F. Lehman & Company, Inc.; *U.S. Private*, pg. 2162
ANCHOR POST PRODUCTS OF TEXAS, INC.; *U.S. Private*, pg. 273
ANNING JOHNSON COMPANY—See Anson Industries, Inc.; *U.S. Private*, pg. 286
ANTHONY & SYLVAN POOLS CORPORATION; *U.S. Private*, pg. 287
ANTHONY & SYLVAN POOLS CORPORATION—See Anthony & Sylvan Pools Corporation; *U.S. Private*, pg. 287
ANVIL FENCE & SUPPLY CO. INC.—See The Fort Miller Group Inc.; *U.S. Private*, pg. 4029
APACHE CONSTRUCTION COMPANY, INC.; *U.S. Private*, pg. 290
API GROUP, INC.—See API Group Corporation; *Int'l*, pg. 513
AQUAHEAT NEW ZEALAND LIMITED—See Eastern Bay Energy Trust; *Int'l*, pg. 2271
AQUA POOL & SPA, INC.; *U.S. Private*, pg. 303
AQUATIC AMUSEMENT ASSOCIATES LTD.—See Aquatic Development Group, Inc.; *U.S. Private*, pg. 303
AQUATIC BUILDERS LTD.—See Aquatic Development Group, Inc.; *U.S. Private*, pg. 303
AQUATIC CONSTRUCTION LTD.—See Aquatic Development Group, Inc.; *U.S. Private*, pg. 303
AQUATIC DEVELOPMENT GROUP, INC.; *U.S. Private*, pg. 303
ARIZONA INDUSTRIAL & MUNICIPAL SERVICES LLC—See Mack Operations LLC; *U.S. Private*, pg. 2536
ASSOCIATED SPECIALTY CONTRACTING, INC.; *U.S. Private*, pg. 357
ASTRALPOOL S.A.—See Fluidra SA; *Int'l*, pg. 2713
ATALANTA FURNITURE SRL—See Gellert Global Group; *U.S. Private*, pg. 1656
ATF SERVICES PTY. LTD.—See CHAMP Private Equity Pty. Ltd.; *Int'l*, pg. 1439
ATLAS CLEAN AIR LTD.; *Int'l*, pg. 676
ATLAS COMPANIES, LLC; *U.S. Private*, pg. 375
AULSON CO. INC.; *U.S. Private*, pg. 393
AURORA BLACKTOP INC.; *U.S. Private*, pg. 393
AYCOCK, LLC—See Enerfab, Inc.; *U.S. Private*, pg. 1392
BACH PLUMBING & HEATING COMPANY OF CLAYTON, INC.—See Heidelberg Materials AG; *Int'l*, pg. 3313
BAE SYSTEMS-APPLIED TECHNOLOGIES—See BAE Systems plc; *Int'l*, pg. 797
BARNHART CRANE & RIGGING CO.; *U.S. Private*, pg. 478
BBV SYSTEMS GMBH—See Bilfinger SE; *Int'l*, pg. 1024
BELFOR (CANADA) INC.—See BELFOR USA Group, Inc.; *U.S. Private*, pg. 517
BELFOR USA GROUP, INC.; *U.S. Private*, pg. 517
BEN'S ASPHALT & SEAL COATING INC.; *U.S. Private*, pg. 523
BESTERRA CO., LTD.; *Int'l*, pg. 1000
BIG CITY ACCESS, INC.—See Brand Industrial Services, Inc.; *U.S. Private*, pg. 636
BILFINGER ARNHOLDT GMBH—See Bilfinger SE; *Int'l*, pg. 1026
BIS INDUSTRIER AS—See Bilfinger SE; *Int'l*, pg. 1025
BIS MIXAB AB—See Bilfinger SE; *Int'l*, pg. 1025
BIS PLETTAC SP. Z O.O.—See Bilfinger SE; *Int'l*, pg. 1026
BIS SALAMIS INTERNATIONAL LIMITED—See Bilfinger SE; *Int'l*, pg. 1026
BJC TRADING COMPANY LIMITED—See Berli Jucker Public Co. Ltd.; *Int'l*, pg. 985
BLAKLEY CORPORATION; *U.S. Private*, pg. 578
BLASTERS, INC.—See Federal Signal Corporation; *U.S. Public*, pg. 826
BLUE HAVEN POOLS NATIONAL INC.; *U.S. Private*, pg. 589

N.A.I.C.S. INDEX

238990 — ALL OTHER SPECIALTY...

BOYD PROPERTIES, LLC—See Pye-Barker Fire & Safety, LLC; *U.S. Private*, pg. 3309
BPG BUILDING PARTNERS GROUP GMBH—See Aurelius Equity Opportunities SE & Co. KGaA; *Int'l*, pg. 707
B+P GERUSTBAU GMBH—See Aurelius Equity Opportunities SE & Co. KGaA; *Int'l*, pg. 707
B+P GERUSTBAU HAMBURG GMBH—See Aurelius Equity Opportunities SE & Co. KGaA; *Int'l*, pg. 707
BRADY COMPANY/CENTRAL CALIFORNIA, INC.—See The Brady Companies; *U.S. Private*, pg. 3999
BRADY COMPANY/LOS ANGELES, INC.—See The Brady Companies; *U.S. Private*, pg. 3999
BRADY COMPANY/SAN DIEGO, INC.—See The Brady Companies; *U.S. Private*, pg. 3999
BRAND ENERGY & INFRASTRUCTURE SERVICES B.V.—See Brand Industrial Services, Inc.; *U.S. Private*, pg. 636
BRAND ENERGY & INFRASTRUCTURE SERVICES-HAZEL CREST—See Brand Industrial Services, Inc.; *U.S. Private*, pg. 636
BRAND ENERGY SOLUTIONS—See Brand Industrial Services, Inc.; *U.S. Private*, pg. 636
BRAND INDUSTRIAL SERVICES, INC.; *U.S. Private*, pg. 635
BRAND INSULATION SERVICES—See Brand Industrial Services, Inc.; *U.S. Private*, pg. 636
BRAND SCAFFOLDING SERVICES—See Brand Industrial Services, Inc.; *U.S. Private*, pg. 636
BSB BAU- UND SPEZIALGERUSTBAU GMBH—See Aurelius Equity Opportunities SE & Co. KGaA; *Int'l*, pg. 707
CAPE FOX CORPORATION; *U.S. Private*, pg. 737
CAPITAL TOWER & COMMUNICATIONS INC; *U.S. Private*, pg. 742
CARLTON POOLS INC.; *U.S. Private*, pg. 765
CASCADE SAWING & DRILLING, INC., *U.S. Private*, pg. 781
CASTELL SAFETY INTERNATIONAL LIMITED—See Halma plc; *Int'l*, pg. 3231
CATSCLAW AMERICAS, LLC—See PVPII - FNSS Acquisition, Inc.; *U.S. Private*, pg. 3308
CECO CONCRETE CONSTRUCTION LLC; *U.S. Private*, pg. 804
CEF SAFETY SYSTEMS B.V.—See Halma plc; *Int'l*, pg. 3230
CELL-CRETE CORPORATION; *U.S. Private*, pg. 807
CELTECH SP. Z O.O.—See Grupa Kety S.A.; *Int'l*, pg. 3117
C.E.MANAGEMENT INTEGRATED LABORATORY CO.LTD; *Int'l*, pg. 1240
CENTRAL CONCRETE CORPORATION; *U.S. Private*, pg. 819
CENTURY FENCE COMPANY; *U.S. Private*, pg. 833
CENTURY FENCE CO.—See Century Fence Company; *U.S. Private*, pg. 833
C.E. THURSTON & SONS INCORPORATED; *U.S. Private*, pg. 706
CHAPMAN WATERPROOFING CO.; *U.S. Private*, pg. 850
CHEMCO PRODUCTS COMPANY; *U.S. Private*, pg. 871
CH. KARNCHANG - TOKYU CONSTRUCTION CO LTD—See CH. Karnchang Public Company Limited; *Int'l*, pg. 1435
CIAO GROUP, INC.; *U.S. Private*, pg. 896
CINCINNATI UNITED CONTRACTORS, INC.; *U.S. Private*, pg. 898
CLARK MECHANICAL SERVICES, INC.—See Clark Associates, Inc.; *U.S. Private*, pg. 912
CLASSY CLOSETS ETC INC.; *U.S. Private*, pg. 917
CL COATINGS, LLC—See North American Coatings, Inc.; *U.S. Private*, pg. 2940
CLEAN EARTH OF NEW YORK, INC.—See Enviri Corporation; *U.S. Public*, pg. 780
CLEAN ENERGY DEVELOPMENTS CORP.—See Groundheat Energy Solar Wind Corp.; *Int'l*, pg. 3088
CLEANSERVE, INC.—See Mack Operations LLC; *U.S. Private*, pg. 2536
CLEANSTREET INC.—See Warburg Pincus LLC; *U.S. Private*, pg. 4440
CLESTRA HAUSERMAN, INC.—See Clestra Hauserman S.A.; *Int'l*, pg. 1658
CMC INC.; *U.S. Private*, pg. 950
COLORADO LINING INTERNATIONAL, INC.—See CNH Industrial N.V.; *Int'l*, pg. 1676
COLORADO SCAFFOLDING & EQUIPMENT CO INC.—See C&D Insulation, Inc.; *U.S. Private*, pg. 702
COLUMBIA SHELVING & MIRROR CO.—See Installed Building Products, Inc.; *U.S. Public*, pg. 1132
COMBINED GROUP CONTRACTING CO. W.L.L.—See Combined Group Contracting Company KSCC; *Int'l*, pg. 1709
COMBINED GROUP CONTRACTING GLOBAL CO. W.L.L.—See Combined Group Contracting Company KSCC; *Int'l*, pg. 1709
COM-ESCO, LLC; *U.S. Private*, pg. 980
COMMERCIAL POOL SPECIALIST, INC.; *U.S. Private*, pg. 984
COMMERCIAL RESINS COMPANY, CORROSION COATING AND TECHNOLOGY & SERVICES—See Commercial Resins Company; *U.S. Private*, pg. 984
COMMERCIAL RESINS COMPANY; *U.S. Private*, pg. 984

CORNERSTONE DETENTION PRODUCTS, INC.; *U.S. Private*, pg. 1052
CORNERSTONE SERVICES GROUP—See Irex Corporation; *U.S. Private*, pg. 2137
CORPORATE CONTRACTORS INC.—See Hendricks Holding Company, Inc.; *U.S. Private*, pg. 1915
CORPORATE INSTALLATION SERVICES; *U.S. Private*, pg. 1055
COSMO TRADE AND SERVICE CO., LTD.—See Cosmo Energy Holdings Co., Ltd.; *Int'l*, pg. 1812
COST OF WISCONSIN, INC.; *U.S. Private*, pg. 1062
THE COURT COMPANY; *U.S. Private*, pg. 4015
CREATIVE DESIGN INTERIORS OF NEVADA, LLC.; *U.S. Private*, pg. 1088
CREATIVE MAILBOX DESIGNS, LLC; *U.S. Private*, pg. 1089
CRETE MECHANICAL GROUP, INC.; *U.S. Private*, pg. 1099
CRITICAL POWER EXCHANGE LLC; *U.S. Private*, pg. 1101
CROWN FENCE COMPANY; *U.S. Private*, pg. 1111
CRTS, INC.—See New Mountain Capital, LLC; *U.S. Private*, pg. 2900
CURTAIN WALLS AND WINDOWS INC.—See The Berlin Steel Construction Company; *U.S. Private*, pg. 3994
CUSTOM BLAST SERVICES, INC.—See AIP, LLC; *U.S. Private*, pg. 134
CUSTOM BLAST SERVICES, INC.—See AIP, LLC; *U.S. Private*, pg. 134
CUSTOM PIPE COATING, INC.—See AIP, LLC; *U.S. Private*, pg. 134
CUSTOM POOL & SPA MECHANICS, INC.—See Astro Aerospace Ltd.; *U.S. Public*, pg. 217
DAIKEN ENGINEERING CORPORATION—See Daiken Corporation; *Int'l*, pg. 1931
DAI NIPPON CONSTRUCTION—See ENEOS Holdings, Inc.; *Int'l*, pg. 2415
DAMAGE CONTROL, INC.; *U.S. Private*, pg. 1150
DAMEN SHIPYARDS OOSTENDE NV—See Damen Shipyards Group; *Int'l*, pg. 1956
D-C ELEVATOR CO., INC. - LOUISVILLE—See D-C Elevator Co., Inc.; *U.S. Private*, pg. 1139
D-C ELEVATOR CO., INC.; *U.S. Private*, pg. 1139
DEBRINO CAULKING ASSOCIATES; *U.S. Private*, pg. 1186
DELTA CONTRACTING, INC.—See SurfaceCycle, Inc.; *U.S. Private*, pg. 3884
DESERT SPRINGS POOLS & SPAS; *U.S. Private*, pg. 1213
DESIREPATH MISSISSIPPI LLC—See The Thymes, LLC; *U.S. Private*, pg. 4127
D&H UNITED FUELING SOLUTIONS, INC.; *U.S. Private*, pg. 1137
DIVERSIFIED PROTECTION SYSTEMS INC.—See GTCR LLC; *U.S. Private*, pg. 1802
DOUBLE CHECK CO. INC.; *U.S. Private*, pg. 1265
DRILLING ENGINEERS INC.—See Terracon Consultants, Inc.; *U.S. Private*, pg. 3970
DUBAI CIVIL ENGINEERING EST—See Al Hamad Contracting Company LLC; *Int'l*, pg. 278
DYNATEC DRILLING, INC.; *U.S. Private*, pg. 1300
EASMUNT PAVING, INC.—See Advanced Pavement Group Corp.; *U.S. Private*, pg. 92
ELCAR FENCE & SUPPLY CO.; *U.S. Private*, pg. 1350
ELITE-WEILER POOLS, INC.; *U.S. Private*, pg. 1362
ELMENDORF STRATEGIES LLC—See Home Front Communications, LLC; *U.S. Private*, pg. 1971
ELMERS CRANE AND DOZER INC.; *U.S. Private*, pg. 1376
EMCOR SERVICES MESA INTEGRATED SOLUTIONS—See EMCOR Group, Inc.; *U.S. Public*, pg. 737
EMCOR SERVICES NEW YORK/NEW JERSEY—See EMCOR Group, Inc.; *U.S. Public*, pg. 737
EMCOR SERVICES TEAM MECHANICAL, INC.—See EMCOR Group, Inc.; *U.S. Public*, pg. 738
EMMTEC SERVICES B.V.—See GETEC Energie Holding GmbH; *Int'l*, pg. 2947
EMPACO EQUIPMENT CORP.; *U.S. Private*, pg. 1384
EMS WATER PTE LTD—See EMS Energy Limited; *Int'l*, pg. 2392
ENTR RATIONNELLE INSTALLATION ELECTRIQUE; *Int'l*, pg. 2452
ENVITEC BIOGAS AG; *Int'l*, pg. 2455
ESSEX SERVICES GROUP PLC; *Int'l*, pg. 2512
FENCEWORKS INC.—See Gemspring Capital Management, LLC; *U.S. Private*, pg. 1658
FENTON RIGGING & CONTRACTING, INC.; *U.S. Private*, pg. 1495
FERALCO—See Blackstone Inc.; *U.S. Public*, pg. 348
FEROELEKTRO D.D.; *Int'l*, pg. 2639
FIELD LINING SYSTEMS, INC.; *U.S. Private*, pg. 1504
FLUIDICS, INC.—See EMCOR Group, Inc.; *U.S. Public*, pg. 737
FLYNN CANADA LTD.; *Int'l*, pg. 2716
FOLEY CUSTOM POOLS INC.; *U.S. Private*, pg. 1558
FOODSERVICE TECHNOLOGIES, INC.—See HCI Equity Management, L.P.; *U.S. Private*, pg. 1889
FORTRESS INTERLOCKS LIMITED—See Halma plc; *Int'l*, pg. 3231

FRONT RANGE STONE, INC.—See Patrick Industries, Inc.; *U.S. Public*, pg. 1652
F+Z BAUGESELLSCHAFT MBH—See Bilfinger SE; *Int'l*, pg. 1024
GAPUMA CHINA—See Gapuma (UK) Limited; *Int'l*, pg. 2882
GAPUMA GHANA LIMITED—See Gapuma (UK) Limited; *Int'l*, pg. 2882
GAPUMA INDONESIA—See Gapuma (UK) Limited; *Int'l*, pg. 2883
GAPUMA NIGERIA LIMITED—See Gapuma (UK) Limited; *Int'l*, pg. 2883
GAPUMA ROMANIA—See Gapuma (UK) Limited; *Int'l*, pg. 2883
GAPUMA THAILAND—See Gapuma (UK) Limited; *Int'l*, pg. 2883
GAPUMA UGANDA LIMITED—See Gapuma (UK) Limited; *Int'l*, pg. 2883
GAPUMA (UK) LIMITED; *Int'l*, pg. 2882
GARCO, INC.—See EQT AB; *Int'l*, pg. 2474
GARNEY CONSTRUCTION COMPANY—See Garney Holding Company, Inc.; *U.S. Private*, pg. 1645
GEREMIA POOLS; *U.S. Private*, pg. 1686
GETEC HEAT & POWER AG—See GETEC Energie Holding GmbH; *Int'l*, pg. 2947
GLOBAL CRANES PTY LTD—See Berkshire Hathaway Inc.; *U.S. Public*, pg. 306
GLOBAL POWER GROUP, INC.; *U.S. Private*, pg. 1716
GLOBLEX HOLDING MANAGEMENT PUBLIC COMPANY LIMITED; *Int'l*, pg. 3007
GPL LIMPIEZAS, S.L.—See ACS, Actividades de Construccion y Servicios, S.A.; *Int'l*, pg. 112
GP ROADWAY SOLUTIONS, INC.—See Nan, Inc.; *U.S. Private*, pg. 2832
GREAT LAKES HOTEL SUPPLY CO.; *U.S. Private*, pg. 1764
GREGG DRILLING & TESTING INC.; *U.S. Private*, pg. 1782
GREGG INDUSTRIAL INSULATORS—See Gregg Industries Inc.; *U.S. Private*, pg. 1782
GROSOLAR INC.; *U.S. Private*, pg. 1792
GULF SHORE TEL-COM INC.; *U.S. Private*, pg. 1816
GUSTAV RAETZ GERUSTBAU GMBH—See Aurelius Equity Opportunities SE & Co. KGaA; *Int'l*, pg. 708
HARMON CONSTRUCTION INCORPORATED—See Harmon Group; *U.S. Private*, pg. 1866
HAVEL—See EMCOR Group, Inc.; *U.S. Public*, pg. 739
HEMPHILL CORPORATION; *U.S. Private*, pg. 1913
HENRY SCHEIN, INC. - NASHVILLE, TN—See Henry Schein, Inc.; *U.S. Public*, pg. 1026
HERCULES FENCE; *U.S. Private*, pg. 1921
HERCULES STEEL COMPANY INC.; *U.S. Private*, pg. 1921
HESSCOR, INC.; *U.S. Private*, pg. 1927
HOLLAND LP—See Curran Group, Inc.; *U.S. Private*, pg. 1125
HOME MOBILITY SOLUTIONS, INC.—See Rockwood Equity Partners, LLC; *U.S. Private*, pg. 3468
HOMESQUARE PRO, LLC—See Homesquare Holdings LLC; *U.S. Private*, pg. 1974
HOWARD BUILDING CORPORATION; *U.S. Private*, pg. 1994
HUGHES POOLS INC.; *U.S. Private*, pg. 2003
IBERVILLE INSULATIONS INC.; *U.S. Private*, pg. 2028
INCORP HOLDINGS, LLC; *U.S. Private*, pg. 2054
INDUSTRIAL COATINGS & FIREPROOFING—See North American Coatings, Inc.; *U.S. Private*, pg. 2940
INDUSTRIAL CONTRACTING OF FAIRMONT, INC.—See Victory of West Virginia, Inc.; *U.S. Private*, pg. 4379
INFOENGINE S.A.—See Gielda Papierow Wartosciowych w Warszawie S.A.; *Int'l*, pg. 2968
INFRASTRUCTURE ALTERNATIVES, INC.; *U.S. Private*, pg. 2075
INNOVATIVE, INC.; *U.S. Private*, pg. 2083
INSTAR SERVICES GROUP, LP—See BlackEagle Partners, LLC; *U.S. Private*, pg. 573
INSULATING SERVICES INC.; *U.S. Private*, pg. 2094
INSULATIONS INCORPORATED; *U.S. Private*, pg. 2094
INTEGRA MANTENIMENT, GESTIO I SERVEIS INTEGRATS, CENTRE ESPECIAL DE TREBALL, CATALUNYA, S.L—See ACS, Actividades de Construccion y Servicios, S.A.; *Int'l*, pg. 115
INTEGRA MANTENIMIENTO, GESTION Y SERVICIOS INTEGRADOS CENTRO ESPECIAL DE EMPLEO GALICIA S.L.—See ACS, Actividades de Construccion y Servicios, S.A.; *Int'l*, pg. 115
INTEGRA MANTENIMIENTO, GESTION Y SERVICIOS INTEGRADOS CENTRO ESPECIAL DE EMPLEO, S.L.—See ACS, Actividades de Construccion y Servicios, S.A.; *Int'l*, pg. 115
INTEGRO BUILDERS LLC; *U.S. Private*, pg. 2104
INTERIOR SPECIALTIES INC.; *U.S. Private*, pg. 2111
IRVINE - WHITLOCK LIMITED—See Heidelberg Materials AG; *Int'l*, pg. 3316
ISLAND FIRE SPRINKLER, INC.—See APi Group Corporation; *Int'l*, pg. 514
IVEY MECHANICAL COMPANY LLC; *U.S. Private*, pg. 2151
JACKSON DEAN CONSTRUCTION; *U.S. Private*, pg. 2176
JAMES GROUP, INC.; *U.S. Private*, pg. 2184

238990 — ALL OTHER SPECIALTY...

J.C. HIGGINS CORP.—See EMCOR Group, Inc.; *U.S. Public*, pg. 738
JEFF KERBER POOL PLASTERING, INC.; *U.S. Private*, pg. 2196
THE J. J. ELEMER CORP.—See Action Bag Company; *U.S. Private*, pg. 67
JOAN SMITH ENTERPRISES INC.; *U.S. Private*, pg. 2217
JOHNSON FINCH & MCCLURE CONSTRUCTION, INC.; *U.S. Private*, pg. 2227
JOHNSON WESTERN GUNITE COMPANY; *U.S. Private*, pg. 2229
JONES BROTHERS COMPANY INC.; *U.S. Private*, pg. 2231
J. PEREZ ASSOCIATES INC.; *U.S. Private*, pg. 2157
JR CLANCY, INC.—See Wenger Corporation; *U.S. Private*, pg. 4481
J.R. JOHNSON, INC.—See Basset Creek Capital, Inc.; *U.S. Private*, pg. 486
J.R. JOHNSON, INC.—See Gladstone Management Corporation; *U.S. Private*, pg. 1705
J&R UNDERGROUND LLC—See Quanta Services, Inc.; *U.S. Public*, pg. 1751
KALMAN FLOOR COMPANY; *U.S. Private*, pg. 2257
KAMRAN & COMPANY, INC.; *U.S. Private*, pg. 2259
K.C. PETROLEUM, INC.; *U.S. Private*, pg. 2251
KERBER BROS. POOL PLASTERING, INC.; *U.S. Private*, pg. 2290
K.H. SMITH COMMUNICATIONS, INC.—See Dycom Industries, Inc.; *U.S. Public*, pg. 698
KIMMINS CONTRACTING CORP.; *U.S. Private*, pg. 2305
KOEDYKER & KENYON CONSTRUCTION, INC.; *U.S. Private*, pg. 2336
LAKESIDE INDUSTRIES - MONROE PLANT—See Lakeside Industries; *U.S. Private*, pg. 2378
LANDCOAST INSULATION INC.; *U.S. Private*, pg. 2385
LASH EXCAVATING & PAVING; *U.S. Private*, pg. 2395
LCR CONTRACTORS, INC.—See TopBuild Corp.; *U.S. Public*, pg. 2163
L.G. HETAGER DRILLING, INC.—See OceanSound Partners, LP; *U.S. Private*, pg. 2991
LIME ENERGY CO.—See Willdan Group, Inc.; *U.S. Public*, pg. 2371
LIMPIEZAS DEYSE, S.L.—See ACS, Actividades de Construccion y Servicios, S.A.; *Int'l*, pg. 115
LIREBA SERVEIS INTEGRATS, S.L.—See ACS, Actividades de Construccion y Servicios, S.A.; *Int'l*, pg. 115
L. J. HUGHES & SONS, INC.; *U.S. Private*, pg. 2364
LOADTEST, INC.—See Fugro N.V.; *Int'l*, pg. 2805
LONG BROTHERS LANDSCAPING, LLC—See Aspen Grove Landscape Companies, LLC; *U.S. Private*, pg. 352
LONG FENCE COMPANY INC.; *U.S. Private*, pg. 2490
LONG FOUNDATION DRILLING CO.; *U.S. Private*, pg. 2490
LOUISVILLE PAVING COMPANY, INC.—See LPX, Inc.; *U.S. Private*, pg. 2507
LRE GROUND SERVICES, INC.; *U.S. Private*, pg. 2507
LUNDY SERVICES INC.; *U.S. Private*, pg. 2515
LUSE-STEVENSON CO. INC.—See Luse Holdings, Inc.; *U.S. Private*, pg. 2516
MACK OPERATIONS LLC; *U.S. Private*, pg. 2536
MAETEC POWER, INC.; *U.S. Private*, pg. 2545
MALCOLM DRILLING COMPANY INC.; *U.S. Private*, pg. 2557
MAPIDE, S.A.—See ACS, Actividades de Construccion y Servicios, S.A.; *Int'l*, pg. 115
MARIETTA SILOS LLC; *U.S. Private*, pg. 2574
MAXONS RESTORATIONS, INC.—See FirstService Corporation; *Int'l*, pg. 2691
MCHAL CORPORATION—See Victory of West Virginia, Inc.; *U.S. Private*, pg. 4379
MCINERNEY & ASSOCIATES, INC.; *U.S. Private*, pg. 2637
M-C MCLANE GROUP INTERNATIONAL—See McLane Group LP; *U.S. Private*, pg. 2640
MECHANICAL CONTRACTORS, INC.; *U.S. Private*, pg. 2648
MEDIGAS SERVICE & TESTING CO., INC.—See Atlas Copco AB; *Int'l*, pg. 681
MERRITT SAFETY ENVIRONMENTAL MANAGEMENT—See Gregg Industries Inc.; *U.S. Private*, pg. 1782
METALCOAT INC. OF FLORIDA; *U.S. Private*, pg. 2680
METROPOLITAN ASPHALT, INC.—See Peter A. Basile Sons, Inc.; *U.S. Private*, pg. 3157
MIDWEST PIPE COATING INC.—See C.S. McCrossan, Inc.; *U.S. Private*, pg. 709
MILLER & SON PAVING CO. INC.; *U.S. Private*, pg. 2732
MISSION POOLS OF ESCONDIDO; *U.S. Private*, pg. 2748
MITCHELL INDUSTRIAL CONTRACTORS, INC.; *U.S. Private*, pg. 2750
MOOSE BOATS, INC.—See Lind Marine, Inc.; *U.S. Private*, pg. 2459
NAPA VALLEY WEALTH MANAGEMENT—See TA Associates, Inc.; *U.S. Private*, pg. 3919
NASSAU POOLS CONSTRUCTION, INC.; *U.S. Private*, pg. 2837
NATIONAL POOL CONSTRUCTION; *U.S. Private*, pg. 2860
NATIONAL SPOT EXCHANGE LIMITED—See 63 moons technologies limited; *Int'l*, pg. 14

NCM ODOR CONTROL, INC.—See Palo Duro Capital, LLC; *U.S. Private*, pg. 3082
NET BRILL, S.L.—See ACS, Actividades de Construccion y Servicios, S.A.; *Int'l*, pg. 115
NEWBATH; *U.S. Private*, pg. 2913
NICHOLSON & HALL CORPORATION; *U.S. Private*, pg. 2925
NOBLE OIL SERVICES, INC.; *U.S. Private*, pg. 2933
NORTH AMERICAN COATINGS, INC.; *U.S. Private*, pg. 2940
NORTH AMERICAN SPECIALTY LAMINATIONS, LLC—See Building Industry Partners LLC; *U.S. Private*, pg. 683
NORTHERN COLORADO TRAFFIC CONTROL, INC.—See Kohlberg & Company, LLC; *U.S. Private*, pg. 2337
NORTHSTAR DEMOLITION AND REMEDIATION, LP—See J.F. Lehman & Company, Inc.; *U.S. Private*, pg. 2164
NORTHWEST FIRESTOP; *U.S. Private*, pg. 2960
NORTHWEST INSULATION CO. INC.; *U.S. Private*, pg. 2960
NORTHWEST TOWER CRANES—See The Sowles Company; *U.S. Private*, pg. 4119
OFFICE INSTALLERS INC.—See The Kane Company; *U.S. Private*, pg. 4064
OHIO STATE HOME SERVICES INC.; *U.S. Private*, pg. 3005
OHIO TAR ASPHALT—See Central Allied Enterprises; *U.S. Private*, pg. 818
THE OSCAR W. LARSON COMPANY INC.; *U.S. Private*, pg. 4089
PACIFIC NORTHERN ENVIRONMENTAL CORP; *U.S. Private*, pg. 3069
PADDOCK SWIMMING POOL COMPANY—See Colliers International Group Inc.; *Int'l*, pg. 1701
PATIO POOLS OF TUCSON INC.; *U.S. Private*, pg. 3109
PAVECON INC.; *U.S. Private*, pg. 3115
PAVECON UTILITIES INC.—See Pavecon Inc.; *U.S. Private*, pg. 3115
PEERLESS ENTERPRISES INC.; *U.S. Private*, pg. 3128
PENINSULATORS, INC.—See The Courtney Group, Incorporated; *U.S. Private*, pg. 4015
PERFORMANCE CONTRACTING GROUP; *U.S. Private*, pg. 3148
PERFORMANCE MECHANICAL, INC.—See EMCOR Group, Inc.; *U.S. Public*, pg. 737
PETROCHEM INSULATION, INC.—See Arctic Slope Regional Corporation; *U.S. Private*, pg. 316
PETROLEUM SOLUTIONS INC.—See MidOcean Partners, LLP; *U.S. Private*, pg. 2536
PHONEX-GEMA AG—See Armstrong World Industries, Inc.; *U.S. Public*, pg. 194
PIPELINE VIDEO INSPECTIONS & CLEANING LLC—See Mack Operations LLC; *U.S. Private*, pg. 2536
PLUMBING-HEATING-COOLING CONTRACTORS ASSOCIATION; *U.S. Private*, pg. 3215
PREMAC SPOL. S.R.O.—See CRH plc; *Int'l*, pg. 1848
PROMAS S.A—See ELLAKTOR S.A.; *Int'l*, pg. 2365
PROTHERM SERVICES GROUP, LLC—See Brand Industrial Services, Inc.; *U.S. Private*, pg. 636
PUGLIESE INTERIOR SYSTEMS INC.; *U.S. Private*, pg. 3303
PUMP & METER SERVICE INC.; *U.S. Private*, pg. 3303
QUALITY SOLUTIONS INC.—See TPG Capital, L.P.; *U.S. Public*, pg. 2173
RAM CONSTRUCTION SERVICES OF MICHIGAN, INC.; *U.S. Private*, pg. 3350
REDHORSE CORPORATION; *U.S. Private*, pg. 3378
REDPATH CANADA LIMITED—See ATON GmbH; *Int'l*, pg. 688
REDPATH MINING AUSTRALIA PTY. LTD.—See ATON GmbH; *Int'l*, pg. 688
REED CONTRACTING SERVICES, INC.; *U.S. Private*, pg. 3382
REELAN INDUSTRIES INC.; *U.S. Private*, pg. 3383
REFLECTIONS WINDOW AND PRESSURE WASHING—See ACON Investments, LLC; *U.S. Private*, pg. 62
RE KRAMIG & CO. INC.; *U.S. Private*, pg. 3364
RELIANCE FIRE PROTECTION, INC.—See APi Group Corporation; *U.S. Private*, pg. 514
REMATCH INC—See CME Group, Inc.; *U.S. Public*, pg. 517
RE-TRON TECHNOLOGIES—See WaveTech Global, Inc.; *U.S. Private*, pg. 4458
RICHARD GOETTLE INC.; *U.S. Private*, pg. 3428
RIVER CITY FABRICATION, INC.—See EverArc Holdings Limited; *U.S. Private*, pg. 2563
RMD HOLDINGS, LTD.; *U.S. Private*, pg. 3451
ROBERTSON INDUSTRIES, INC.—See Court Square Capital Partners, L.P.; *U.S. Private*, pg. 1070
ROBERT W. STANHOPE CO.; *U.S. Private*, pg. 3459
ROCKY MOUNTAIN MATERIALS & ASPHALT, INC.; *U.S. Private*, pg. 3469
ROYAL WINDOW FILMS, INC.—See Solar Art Window Film, Inc.; *U.S. Private*, pg. 3707
R.P. WEDDELL & SONS CO.; *U.S. Private*, pg. 3339
R.W. MERCER COMPANY, INC.; *U.S. Private*, pg. 3340
SCENARIOS, INC.—See GMA Holdings, Inc.; *Int'l*, pg. 3012
SCHNABEL FOUNDATION COMPANY; *U.S. Private*, pg. 3566

SCHROEDER MOVING SYSTEMS; *U.S. Private*, pg. 3569
SECOA, INC.—See Wenger Corporation; *U.S. Private*, pg. 4481
SECURITY VAULT WORKS INC.; *U.S. Private*, pg. 3596
SEI COATINGS, LLC—See North American Coatings, Inc.; *U.S. Private*, pg. 2940
SELLSTROM MANUFACTURING CO. - RTC FALL PROTECTION DIVISION—See Sellstrom Manufacturing Co.; *U.S. Private*, pg. 3603
SEMPRA ENERGY SERVICES—See Sempra; *U.S. Public*, pg. 1863
S.E.R.V. TRAYVOU INTERVERROUILLAGE SA—See Halma plc; *Int'l*, pg. 3232
SEVERN TRENT SERVICES, INC. - KATY OFFICE—See Severn Trent Services, Inc.; *U.S. Private*, pg. 3619
SEVERN TRENT SERVICES, INC.; *U.S. Private*, pg. 3619
SEV, INC.; *U.S. Private*, pg. 3618
SHASTA INDUSTRIES INC.; *U.S. Private*, pg. 3627
SIERRA LUMBER & FENCE—See Pacific States Industries Incorporated; *U.S. Private*, pg. 3071
SIERRA LUMBER & FENCE—See Pacific States Industries Incorporated; *U.S. Private*, pg. 3071
SJA INC.; *U.S. Private*, pg. 3678
SLEAD CONSTRUCTION, INC.—See Crossplane Capital Management LP; *U.S. Private*, pg. 1107
SMITHAHN CO., INC.; *U.S. Private*, pg. 3696
S&N COMMUNICATIONS—See Sun Capital Partners, Inc.; *U.S. Private*, pg. 3860
SOLAR ART WINDOW FILM, INC.; *U.S. Private*, pg. 3707
SOLARCITY CORP.—See Tesla, Inc.; *U.S. Public*, pg. 2021
SORDONI CONSTRUCTION SERVICES, INC.; *U.S. Private*, pg. 3715
SOS CORPORATION; *U.S. Private*, pg. 3716
SOUTHERN TIER INSULATIONS INC.; *U.S. Private*, pg. 3735
SOUTHWEST MERIDIAN CORP.; *U.S. Private*, pg. 3740
SPG SOLAR INC.; *U.S. Private*, pg. 3756
SPIE WHS LIMITED—See Clayton, Dubilier & Rice, LLC; *U.S. Private*, pg. 926
SPRAY INSULATIONS, INC.—See Paul J. Krez Company; *U.S. Private*, pg. 3113
STATEWIDE DISASTER RESTORATION, INC.; *U.S. Private*, pg. 3793
STEBBINS ENGINEERING & MANUFACTURING COMPANY; *U.S. Private*, pg. 3795
STEBBINS ENGINEERING & MANUFACTURING CO. - PORT ALLEN—See Stebbins Engineering & Manufacturing Company; *U.S. Private*, pg. 3795
STEBBINS ENGINEERING & MANUFACTURING CO. - SEATTLE—See Stebbins Engineering & Manufacturing Company; *U.S. Private*, pg. 3795
STENSTROM PETROLEUM SERVICES—See Stenstrom Companies Ltd.; *U.S. Private*, pg. 3801
STILL WATERS DESIGN/BUILD GROUP; *U.S. Private*, pg. 3812
STUART-DEAN CO. INC.; *U.S. Private*, pg. 3843
SUMIPAR, S.A.—See ACS, Actividades de Construccion y Servicios, S.A.; *Int'l*, pg. 116
SUN COUNTRY RESTORATION, LLC; *U.S. Private*, pg. 3863
SUNLAND BUILDERS; *U.S. Private*, pg. 3868
SUPERIOR GUNITE INCORPORATED; *U.S. Private*, pg. 3878
SUPERIOR POOLS OF SOUTHWEST FLORIDA INC.; *U.S. Private*, pg. 3879
SURECLEAN LIMITED—See Republic Services, Inc.; *U.S. Public*, pg. 1788
SURFACE PREPARATION TECHNOLOGIES, INC.—See Dominus Capital, L.P.; *U.S. Private*, pg. 1257
SVA VERKEHRSSICHERUNGS-ANLAGEN GESELLSCHAFT MIT BESCHRANKTER HAFTUNG—See Bilfinger SE; *Int'l*, pg. 1028
SWARTWOUT DIVISION—See Canada Pension Plan Investment Board; *Int'l*, pg. 1282
S&W CONTRACTING OF WNY, INC.; *U.S. Private*, pg. 3514
S.W. RODGERS COMPANY INC.; *U.S. Private*, pg. 3519
SYSTEMS CONNECTION OF MARYLAND; *U.S. Private*, pg. 3907
TCA HOLDINGS, LLC; *U.S. Private*, pg. 3942
T & D CONCRETE INC.; *U.S. Private*, pg. 3908
TEAM INDUSTRIAL SERVICES BELGIUM—See Team, Inc.; *U.S. Public*, pg. 1988
TEC ELEVATOR, INC.—See 3Phase Elevator Corp; *U.S. Private*, pg. 14
TECNICO CORPORATION—See American Maritime Holdings, Inc.; *U.S. Private*, pg. 240
TERMINAL CONSTRUCTION CORPORATION; *U.S. Private*, pg. 3969
TERRA STRUCTURES—See Haines & Kibblehouse Inc.; *U.S. Private*, pg. 1841
TEXAS CUSTOM POOLS INC.; *U.S. Private*, pg. 3975
THE TIBERTI FENCE COMPANY—See Tiberti Organization; *U.S. Private*, pg. 4167
TIBERTI ORGANIZATION; *U.S. Private*, pg. 4167
TITAN CONTRACTING & LEASING CO. INC.—See Charlesbank Capital Partners, LLC; *U.S. Private*, pg. 856
T.L. JONES LIMITED—See Halma plc; *Int'l*, pg. 3233

N.A.I.C.S. INDEX

TNS, INC.—See High Wire Networks Inc.; *U.S. Public*, pg. 1035
TNT POWER WASH, INC.; *U.S. Private*, pg. 4180
TOTAL OFFICE PLANNING SERVICES; *U.S. Private*, pg. 4191
TOWER PERFORMANCE, INC.—See Hastings Equity Partners, LLC; *U.S. Private*, pg. 1879
TRAIANA TECHNOLOGIES LIMITED—See CME Group, Inc.; *U.S. Public*, pg. 518
TRILBY TRADING LIMITED—See Endless LLP; *Int'l*, pg. 2403
TRIMARK RAYGAL INC—See Warburg Pincus LLC; *U.S. Private*, pg. 4440
TRIOPTIMA NORTH AMERICA LLC—See CME Group, Inc.; *U.S. Public*, pg. 517
TTS MARINE EQUIPMENT (DALIAN) CO., LTD.—See Cargotec Corporation; *Int'l*, pg. 1329
TYREE MAINTENANCE CO. INC.—See Tyree Organization, Ltd; *U.S. Private*, pg. 4269
UNDERGROUND PIERCING, INC.—See Comlink Contractors Inc.; *U.S. Private*, pg. 982
UNIVERSAL BUILDERS SUPPLY, INC.; *U.S. Private*, pg. 4304
U P SYSTEMS, INCORPORATED—See Vertiv Holdings Co; *U.S. Public*, pg. 2288
US FEDERAL CONTRACTOR REGISTRATION INC.; *U.S. Private*, pg. 4318
US STEEL MINNTAC—See United States Steel Corporation; *U.S. Public*, pg. 2237
VALLEY FENCE COMPANY—See Apache Construction Company, Inc.; *U.S. Private*, pg. 290
VECELLIO GROUP, INC.; *U.S. Private*, pg. 4349
VISTA WINDOW COMPANY, LLC; *U.S. Private*, pg. 4403
WAGNER POOLS; *U.S. Private*, pg. 4426
WALL-TECH, INC.; *U.S. Private*, pg. 4430
WALL WORKS USA INC.; *U.S. Private*, pg. 4430
WARCO CONSTRUCTION INC.; *U.S. Private*, pg. 4440
WASTE STREAM TECHNOLOGY, INC.—See Sevenson Environmental Services, Inc.; *U.S. Private*, pg. 3619
WAVEBAND CORPORATION—See Mercury Systems, Inc.; *U.S. Public*, pg. 1422
WAYNE PERRY, INC.; *U.S. Private*, pg. 4460
WEC CAROLINA ENERGY SOLUTIONS—See Brookfield Corporation; *Int'l*, pg. 1186
WEC WELDING & MACHINING LLC—See Brookfield Corporation; *Int'l*, pg. 1186
WELLNESS MARKETING CORPORATION—See Masco Corporation; *U.S. Public*, pg. 1392
WESTCO CLOSET CORPORATION; *U.S. Private*, pg. 4489
WESTERN CONSTRUCTION GROUP; *U.S. Private*, pg. 4492
WESTERN WATERPROOFING COMPANY INC.—See Western Construction Group; *U.S. Private*, pg. 4492
WETHERINGTON TRACTOR SERVICE, INC.; *U.S. Private*, pg. 4502
WILCOXON CONSTRUCTION, LLC—See Colliers International Group Inc.; *Int'l*, pg. 1701
WILLIAMS GROUP INTERNATIONAL, INC.; *U.S. Private*, pg. 4526
WILSON 5 SERVICE CO. INC.; *U.S. Private*, pg. 4530
WINDOW DOCTORS, INC.—See ACON Investments, LLC; *U.S. Private*, pg. 62
WINDOW SOLUTIONS, INC.—See Solar Art Window Film, Inc.; *U.S. Private*, pg. 3707
WORLDS OF WOW, LLC—See Court Square Capital Partners, L.P.; *U.S. Private*, pg. 1070
W. W. GAY FIRE & INTEGRATED SYSTEMS, INC.—See Huron Capital Partners LLC; *U.S. Private*, pg. 2012
WYNN O. JONES & ASSOCIATES; *U.S. Private*, pg. 4576
WYSEPOWER LIMITED—See Dubai World Corporation; *Int'l*, pg. 2220
XTRA GRASS—See ABN AMRO Group N.V.; *Int'l*, pg. 65
XTRA GRASS—See Gilde Buy Out Partners B.V.; *Int'l*, pg. 2975
ZIP MOVING & STORAGE INC.; *U.S. Private*, pg. 4606

311111 — DOG AND CAT FOOD MANUFACTURING

AGRI BRAND PURINA CANADA INC.—See Cargill, Inc.; *U.S. Private*, pg. 755
AGROBIOTHERS LABORATOIRE SAS—See Gimv NV; *Int'l*, pg. 2976
AINSWORTH PET NUTRITION, INC.—See The J.M. Smucker Company; *U.S. Public*, pg. 2106
AMERICAN NUTRITION, INC.—See J.H. Whitney & Co., LLC; *U.S. Private*, pg. 2166
ASIAN PETS CARE CORPORATION CO., LTD.—See Asian Sea Corporation Public Company Limited; *Int'l*, pg. 610
BANGKOK AGRO-INDUSTRIAL PRODUCTS PUBLIC COMPANY LIMITED—See Charoen Pokphand Foods Public Company Limited; *Int'l*, pg. 1451
BANGKOK FOOD PRODUCTS CO., LTD.—See Charoen Pokphand Foods Public Company Limited; *Int'l*, pg. 1451
BCCH, LLC; *U.S. Private*, pg. 499
BIG HEART PET BRANDS - BLOOMSBURG PLANT—See The J.M. Smucker Company; *U.S. Public*, pg. 2107
BIG HEART PET BRANDS—See The J.M. Smucker Company; *U.S. Public*, pg. 2106
BIL-JAC FOODS INC.; *U.S. Private*, pg. 556
BLUE BUFFALO CO., LTD.—See General Mills, Inc.; *U.S. Public*, pg. 921
BRIGTPET NUTRITION GROUP, LLC—See Alvarez & Marsal, Inc.; *U.S. Private*, pg. 212
BUTCHER'S PET CARE LTD.; *Int'l*, pg. 1229
CANNINES SUPPLIES DE MEXICO S. DE R.L. DE C.V.—See Spectrum Brands Holdings, Inc.; *U.S. Public*, pg. 1915
CARDINAL LABORATORIES, LLC—See Frontenac Company LLC; *U.S. Private*, pg. 1614
CARGILL ANIMAL NUTRITION—See Cargill, Inc.; *U.S. Private*, pg. 755
CARGILL ANIMAL NUTRITION—See Cargill, Inc.; *U.S. Private*, pg. 757
CARNIVORE MEAT COMPANY, LLC; *U.S. Private*, pg. 766
CEYLON GRAIN ELEVATORS PLC; *Int'l*, pg. 1426
CHAROEN POKPHAND NORTHEASTERN PUBLIC COMPANY LIMITED—See Charoen Pokphand Foods Public Company Limited; *Int'l*, pg. 1452
CHINA FOOD COMPANY PLC; *Int'l*, pg. 1503
CHUBU SHIRYO CO., LTD.; *Int'l*, pg. 1593
C.P. CAMBODIA CO., LTD.—See Charoen Pokphand Foods Public Company Limited; *Int'l*, pg. 1452
CROSSWIND PETFOODS, INC.—See Archer-Daniels-Midland Company; *U.S. Public*, pg. 184
DAEJOO CO.,LTD; *Int'l*, pg. 1907
DIMITRA SA—See ELLAKTOR S.A.; *Int'l*, pg. 2365
EARTH PET CO., LTD.—See Earth Corporation; *Int'l*, pg. 2268
EQUILLIUM AUS PTY. LTD.—See Equillium, Inc.; *U.S. Public*, pg. 787
EVIALIS GALICIA S.A.—See Archer-Daniels-Midland Company; *U.S. Public*, pg. 185
FIHUMIN-GESELLSCHAFT M.B.H.; *Int'l*, pg. 2661
FOUR PAWS PRODUCTS, LTD.—See Central Garden & Pet Company; *U.S. Public*, pg. 473
FRESHPET, INC.; *U.S. Public*, pg. 886
FROMM FAMILY PET FOODS, INC.; *U.S. Private*, pg. 1613
HALO, PURELY FOR PETS, INC.—See Better Choice Company, Inc.; *U.S. Public*, pg. 326
HEARTLAND PET FOOD MANUFACTURING IOWA, INC.—See General Mills, Inc.; *U.S. Public*, pg. 922
HEINZ NORTH AMERICA—See 3G Capital Inc.; *U.S. Private*, pg. 10
HEINZ NORTH AMERICA—See Berkshire Hathaway Inc.; *U.S. Public*, pg. 317
HILL'S PET NUTRITION ASIA-PACIFIC, PTE. LTD.—See Colgate-Palmolive Company; *U.S. Public*, pg. 532
HILL'S PET NUTRITION INDIANA, INC.—See Colgate-Palmolive Company; *U.S. Public*, pg. 533
HILL'S PET NUTRITION KOREA LTD.—See Colgate-Palmolive Company; *U.S. Public*, pg. 533
HILL'S PET NUTRITION LIMITED—See Colgate-Palmolive Company; *U.S. Public*, pg. 533
HILL'S PET NUTRITION MANUFACTURING, B.V.—See Colgate-Palmolive Company; *U.S. Public*, pg. 533
HILL'S PET NUTRITION NORWAY AS—See Colgate-Palmolive Company; *U.S. Public*, pg. 533
HILL'S PET NUTRITION S.N.C.—See Colgate-Palmolive Company; *U.S. Public*, pg. 533
HILL'S PET NUTRITION S.R.O.—See Colgate-Palmolive Company; *U.S. Public*, pg. 533
HILL'S PET NUTRITION SWEDEN AB—See Colgate-Palmolive Company; *U.S. Public*, pg. 533
THE HONEST KITCHEN, INC.; *U.S. Private*, pg. 4054
THE HYLAND COMPANY; *U.S. Private*, pg. 4055
IAMS EUROPE B.V.—See Spectrum Brands Holdings, Inc.; *U.S. Public*, pg. 1916
KENT PET GROUP, INC.—See Kent Corporation; *U.S. Private*, pg. 2287
MARS CANADA INC.—See Mars, Incorporated; *U.S. Private*, pg. 2589
MARS PETCARE—See Mars, Incorporated; *U.S. Private*, pg. 2590
MARS PETCARE—See Mars, Incorporated; *U.S. Private*, pg. 2590
MENU FOODS MIDWEST CORPORATION, INC—See Simmons Foods, Inc.; *U.S. Private*, pg. 3665
MID AMERICA PET FOOD LLC.; *U.S. Private*, pg. 2705
MIDWEST AG SUPPLEMENTS, LLC—See CHS INC.; *U.S. Public*, pg. 492
NL ENTERPRISES LLC—See Mid America Pet Food LLC.; *U.S. Private*, pg. 2705
NORMERICA INC—See Minerals Technologies, Inc.; *U.S. Public*, pg. 1449
NORTHWEST PET PRODUCTS INC.; *U.S. Private*, pg. 2961
NUTRADINE, LLC—See Archer-Daniels-Midland Company; *U.S. Public*, pg. 185
NUTRO PRODUCTS INC.—See Mars, Incorporated; *U.S. Private*, pg. 2590
OURPET'S COMPANY—See Hyper Pet, LLC; *U.S. Private*, pg. 2019
PATENT CO. DOO—See BayWa AG; *Int'l*, pg. 918
PERFORMANCE PET PRODUCTS, LLC—See Rosens Diversified, Inc.; *U.S. Private*, pg. 3484
PET CAROUSEL INC.—See Cargill, Inc.; *U.S. Private*, pg. 759
PET ECOLOGY BRANDS, INC.; *U.S. Public*, pg. 1678
PET FACTORY—See Alvarez & Marsal, Inc.; *U.S. Private*, pg. 213
PIED PIPER PET & WILDLIFE, INC.; *U.S. Private*, pg. 3176
POST BRANDS PET CARE, LLC—See Post Holdings, Inc.; *U.S. Public*, pg. 1704
PRIMAL PET FOODS INC.; *U.S. Private*, pg. 3260
PRO-PET, LLC - KANSAS CITY—See Cargill, Inc.; *U.S. Private*, pg. 755
PRO-PET, LLC—See Cargill, Inc.; *U.S. Private*, pg. 755
PROTEIN SOLUTIONS, LLC; *U.S. Private*, pg. 3289
ROBERTS MANUFACTURING COMPANY LTD—See Barbados Shipping & Trading Co. Ltd.; *Int'l*, pg. 858
ROYAL CANIN S.A.—See Mars, Incorporated; *U.S. Private*, pg. 2590
ROYAL CANIN USA INC.—See Mars, Incorporated; *U.S. Private*, pg. 2590
SCHELL & KAMPETER, INC.; *U.S. Private*, pg. 3564
SCHENCK CORPORATION—See Durr AG; *Int'l*, pg. 2233
SCHENCK MEXICO, S.A. DE C.V.—See Durr AG; *Int'l*, pg. 2233
SIMMONS PET FOOD, INC. - PENNSAUKEN—See Simmons Foods, Inc.; *U.S. Private*, pg. 3665
SIMMONS PET FOOD, INC. - STREETSVILLE—See Simmons Foods, Inc.; *U.S. Private*, pg. 3665
SK INTERNATIONAL, INC.; *U.S. Private*, pg. 3680
SOUTHWEST PET PRODUCTS INC.; *U.S. Private*, pg. 3740
SPECIALTY FEEDS, INC.; *U.S. Private*, pg. 3749
SPF NORTH AMERICA, INC.; *U.S. Private*, pg. 3756
STELLA & CHEWY'S; *U.S. Private*, pg. 3799
SUNSHINE MILLS INC. - HALIFAX DIVISION—See Sunshine Mills Inc.; *U.S. Private*, pg. 3872
SUNSHINE MILLS INC.; *U.S. Private*, pg. 3871
SUNSHINE MILLS INC. - TUPELO DIVISION—See Sunshine Mills Inc.; *U.S. Private*, pg. 3872
SUNSHINE MILLS OF VIRGINIA INC.—See Sunshine Mills Inc.; *U.S. Private*, pg. 3872
TDBBS LLC.—See Central Garden & Pet Company; *U.S. Public*, pg. 473
TEJAS INDUSTRIES; *U.S. Private*, pg. 3958
T. L. MONTGOMERY & ASSOCIATES; *U.S. Private*, pg. 3911
TREATCO, INC.; *U.S. Private*, pg. 4216
TRIPLE-T FOODS INC.—See Darling Ingredients Inc.; *U.S. Public*, pg. 634
TRIUMPH PET INDUSTRIES, INC.—See Sunshine Mills Inc.; *U.S. Private*, pg. 3872
TROPIKAL BAHCE VE EVCIL HAYVAN URUNLERI A.S.—See The Riverside Company; *U.S. Private*, pg. 4110
TRURX, LLC—See Bansk Group LLC; *U.S. Private*, pg. 469
TUFFYS PET FOODS INC—See KLN Enterprises Inc.; *U.S. Private*, pg. 2320
VET'S CHOICE JAPAN CORPORATION—See Arata Corporation; *Int'l*, pg. 536
WELLPET LLC—See Clearlake Capital Group, L.P.; *U.S. Private*, pg. 937
WHITEBRIDGE PET BRANDS, LLC—See Frontenac Company LLC; *U.S. Private*, pg. 1614
WORLD PET CARE—See Sunshine Mills Inc.; *U.S. Private*, pg. 3872

311119 — OTHER ANIMAL FOOD MANUFACTURING

8 IN 1 PET PRODUCTS GMBH—See Spectrum Brands Holdings, Inc.; *U.S. Public*, pg. 1916
ABO MIX S.A.; *Int'l*, pg. 65
ADISSEO FRANCE S.A.S.—See China National Chemical Corporation; *Int'l*, pg. 1526
ADM ALLIANCE NUTRITION OF PUERTO RICO, LLC—See Archer-Daniels-Midland Company; *U.S. Public*, pg. 181
ADM ALLIANCE NUTRITION—See Archer-Daniels-Midland Company; *U.S. Public*, pg. 181
ADM ALLIANCE NUTRITION—See Archer-Daniels-Midland Company; *U.S. Public*, pg. 181
ADM MILLING CO.—See Archer-Daniels-Midland Company; *U.S. Public*, pg. 182
ADM PORTUGAL, SA—See Archer-Daniels-Midland Company; *U.S. Public*, pg. 182
AFEED, A.S.—See Agrofert Holding, a.s.; *Int'l*, pg. 218
AFGRI ANIMAL FEEDS EASTERN CAPE (PTY) LTD.—See AFGRI Limited; *Int'l*, pg. 188
AFGRI ANIMAL FEEDS—See AFGRI Limited; *Int'l*, pg. 188
AFGRITECH LIMITED—See AFGRI Limited; *Int'l*, pg. 188
AFGRITECH LIMITED—See Carr's Group PLC; *Int'l*, pg. 1343
AGFEED ANIMAL NUTRITION HOLDINGS, INC.—See AgFeed Industries, Inc.; *Int'l*, pg. 209
AGFEED INDUSTRIES, INC.; *Int'l*, pg. 209
AGRAVIS EMS-JADE GMBH—See AGRAVIS Raiffeisen AG; *Int'l*, pg. 214
AGRAVIS MISCHFUTTER EMSLAND GMBH—See AGRA-

311119 — OTHER ANIMAL FOOD M...

VIS Raiffeisen AG; *Int'l*, pg. 214
AGRAVIS MISCHFUTTER OSTWESTFALEN-LIPPE GMBH—See AGRAVIS Raiffeisen AG; *Int'l*, pg. 214
AGRAVIS NIEDERSACHSEN-SUD GMBH—See AGRAVIS Raiffeisen AG; *Int'l*, pg. 215
AGRIBRANDS PURINA (LANGFANG) FEEDMILL CO., LTD.—See Cargill, Inc.; *U.S. Private*, pg. 754
AGRIBRANDS PURINA (XINJIANG) FEEDMILL CO., LTD.—See Cargill, Inc.; *U.S. Private*, pg. 755
AGRIBRANDS PURINA (ZHENGZHOU) FEEDMILL CO., LTD.—See Cargill, Inc.; *U.S. Private*, pg. 754
AGRICOLA GROUP LTD; *Int'l*, pg. 216
AGRI-FEEDS LIMITED—See Agria Corporation; *Int'l*, pg. 216
AGRIVEST INC.; *U.S. Private*, pg. 129
AGROMED AUSTRIA GMBH—See BayWa AG; *Int'l*, pg. 915
AGRONA, A. S.—See Agrofert Holding, a.s.; *Int'l*, pg. 218
AIK BAACKA TOPOLA A.D.; *Int'l*, pg. 232
AINSWORTH PET NUTRITION, INC. - AINSWORTH SPECIALTY BRANDS DIVISION—See The J.M. Smucker Company; *U.S. Public*, pg. 2106
AJOONI BIOTECH LIMITED; *Int'l*, pg. 258
AKEY—See Cargill, Inc.; *U.S. Private*, pg. 760
ALABAMA CATFISH FEEDMILL, LLC; *U.S. Private*, pg. 148
ALLIED FEEDS INC.; *U.S. Private*, pg. 186
ALLTECH, INC.; *U.S. Private*, pg. 194
AMAN FEED LTD.; *Int'l*, pg. 409
AMERICAN PROTEIN CORPORATION INC.—See Lauridsen Group Inc.; *U.S. Private*, pg. 2399
AMERICAN PROTEINS INC.; *U.S. Private*, pg. 244
AMERICAN SUPERIOR FEEDS INC.; *U.S. Private*, pg. 256
AMERI-PAC, INC.—See Wilbur-Ellis Company; *U.S. Private*, pg. 4517
AMPRO PRODUCTS INC.—See American Proteins Inc.; *U.S. Private*, pg. 244
ANANDA FOOD PTY. LTD.—See Elixinol Wellness Limited; *Int'l*, pg. 2363
ANCO ANIMAL NUTRITION COMPETENCE GMBH—See Archer-Daniels-Midland Company; *U.S. Public*, pg. 183
ANDRITZ FEED & BIOFUEL CANADA INC.—See ANDRITZ AG; *Int'l*, pg. 453
ANIMAL FEED SUPPLEMENT INC.—See Carr's Group PLC; *Int'l*, pg. 1343
ANIMAX, LLC—See Carr's Group PLC; *Int'l*, pg. 1343
ANIMIX, LLC—See Benford Capital Partners, LLC; *U.S. Private*, pg. 525
AN-PRO COMPANY—See The Procter & Gamble Company; *U.S. Public*, pg. 2120
ARABIAN AGRICULTURAL SERVICES CO.; *Int'l*, pg. 533
ARCHER DANIELS MIDLAND CO.-WEST PLANT—See Archer-Daniels-Midland Company; *U.S. Public*, pg. 184
ASCENDIS ANIMAL HEALTH (PTY) LTD—See Ascendis Health Limited; *Int'l*, pg. 601
ASPEN VETERINARY RESOURCES, LTD—See Patterson Companies, Inc.; *U.S. Public*, pg. 1653
ASTRAL FOODS LIMITED; *Int'l*, pg. 675
ATLANTIC POULTRY INC. - FEED MILL—See Atlantic Poultry Inc.; *Int'l*, pg. 675
AVANTI FEEDS LTD. - PRAWN FEED/FISH FEED FACTORIES—See Avanti Feeds Ltd.; *Int'l*, pg. 736
AVANTI FEEDS LTD.; *Int'l*, pg. 736
AVANTI THAI AQUA FEEDS PRIVATE LIMITED—See Avanti Feeds Ltd.; *Int'l*, pg. 736
BALANCEADOS NOVA SA BALNOVA—See Archer-Daniels-Midland Company; *U.S. Public*, pg. 184
BAR ALE, INC.; *U.S. Private*, pg. 471
BARTLETT MILLING COMPANY, L.P.—See Bartlett & Company; *U.S. Private*, pg. 483
BEAMING AGROTRADE SDN. BHD.—See Emivest Berhad; *Int'l*, pg. 2383
BEIT DICKSON KSCC—See Gulf Franchising Holding Company K.S.C.C.; *Int'l*, pg. 3180
BETAGRO PUBLIC COMPANY LIMITED; *Int'l*, pg. 1002
BIBBY AGRICULTURE LIMITED—See Carr's Group PLC; *Int'l*, pg. 1343
BIG GAIN INC.; *U.S. Private*, pg. 553
BIOMAR A/S—See Aktieselskabet Schouw & Co.; *Int'l*, pg. 265
BIOOREGON PROTEIN, INC.—See Dulcich, Inc.; *U.S. Private*, pg. 1286
BIOSCREEN TECHNOLOGIES SRL—See Balchem Corporation; *U.S. Public*, pg. 265
BIOTAY S.A.—See Phibro Animal Health Corporation; *U.S. Public*, pg. 1685
BIOZYME INCORPORATED; *U.S. Private*, pg. 563
BIRDBRAIN, INC.; *U.S. Private*, pg. 564
BIRMINGHAM HIDE & TALLOW COMPANY INC. - ABERDEEN DIVISION—See Birmingham Hide & Tallow Company Inc.; *U.S. Private*, pg. 565
BIRMINGHAM HIDE & TALLOW COMPANY INC. - ARLEY DIVISION—See Birmingham Hide & Tallow Company Inc.; *U.S. Private*, pg. 565
BIRMINGHAM HIDE & TALLOW COMPANY INC. - BESSEMER DIVISION—See Birmingham Hide & Tallow Company Inc.; *U.S. Private*, pg. 565
BIRMINGHAM HIDE & TALLOW COMPANY INC. - HUNTSVILLE DIVISION—See Birmingham Hide & Tallow Company Inc.; *U.S. Private*, pg. 565
BIRMINGHAM HIDE & TALLOW COMPANY INC. - LOXLEY DIVISION—See Birmingham Hide & Tallow Company Inc.; *U.S. Private*, pg. 565
BIRMINGHAM HIDE & TALLOW COMPANY INC. - MONTGOMERY DIVISION—See Birmingham Hide & Tallow Company Inc.; *U.S. Private*, pg. 565
BIRMINGHAM HIDE & TALLOW COMPANY INC. - PANAMA CITY DIVISION—See Birmingham Hide & Tallow Company Inc.; *U.S. Private*, pg. 565
BIRMINGHAM HIDE & TALLOW COMPANY INC. - RINGGOLD DIVISION—See Birmingham Hide & Tallow Company Inc.; *U.S. Private*, pg. 565
BLUE BUFFALO COMPANY, LTD.—See General Mills, Inc.; *U.S. Public*, pg. 921
BON SWEETS WLL—See Gulf Franchising Holding Company K.S.C.C.; *Int'l*, pg. 3180
B.P. FOOD PRODUCTS CO., LTD.—See Charoen Pokphand Foods Public Company Limited; *Int'l*, pg. 1451
BRANCH PROPERTIES, INC.; *U.S. Private*, pg. 635
BRAVO, LLC—See Alvarez & Marsal, Inc.; *U.S. Private*, pg. 212
BRENNER MILLS (PTY) LTD. - BRENNCO FEED MILLS—See Brenner Mills (Pty) Ltd.; *Int'l*, pg. 1146
BRENNER MILLS (PTY) LTD.; *Int'l*, pg. 1145
BRENNER MILLS (PTY) LTD. - TSWANA MILL—See Brenner Mills (Pty) Ltd.; *Int'l*, pg. 1146
BRENNER MILLS (PTY) LTD. - WARMBATHS MILL—See Brenner Mills (Pty) Ltd.; *Int'l*, pg. 1146
BRENNER MILLS (PTY) LTD. - ZOUTPANSBERG MILL—See Brenner Mills (Pty) Ltd.; *Int'l*, pg. 1146
BURKMANN INDUSTRIES INC.; *U.S. Private*, pg. 688
CALCIALIMENT; *Int'l*, pg. 1262
CALDWELL MILLING CO. INC.; *U.S. Private*, pg. 716
CANARIABIO INC.; *Int'l*, pg. 1288
CARGILL AGRICULTURA SRL - CARGILL NUTRITIE ANIMALA FACTROY—See Cargill, Inc.; *U.S. Private*, pg. 755
CARGILL AGRI PURINA, INC. - CHUNAN PLANT—See Cargill, Inc.; *U.S. Private*, pg. 755
CARGILL AGRI PURINA, INC. - KUNSAN PLANT—See Cargill, Inc.; *U.S. Private*, pg. 755
CARGILL AGRI PURINA, INC.—See Cargill, Inc.; *U.S. Private*, pg. 755
CARGILL ANIMAL NUTRITION (NANJING) CO., LTD—See Cargill, Inc.; *U.S. Private*, pg. 755
CARGILL ANIMAL NUTRITION—See Cargill, Inc.; *U.S. Private*, pg. 755
CARGILL ANIMAL NUTRITION—See Cargill, Inc.; *U.S. Private*, pg. 755
CARGILL ANIMAL NUTRITION—See Cargill, Inc.; *U.S. Private*, pg. 755
CARGILL ANIMAL NUTRITION—See Cargill, Inc.; *U.S. Private*, pg. 755
CARGILL ANIMAL NUTRITION—See Cargill, Inc.; *U.S. Private*, pg. 755
CARGILL ANIMAL NUTRITION—See Cargill, Inc.; *U.S. Private*, pg. 755
CARGILL ASIA PACIFIC FOOD SYSTEMS (BEIJING) LTD.—See Cargill, Inc.; *U.S. Private*, pg. 755
CARGILL AT & ENTERPRISE INC—See Cargill, Inc.; *U.S. Private*, pg. 755
CARGILL AUSTRALIA LTD—See Cargill, Inc.; *U.S. Private*, pg. 755
CARGILL CARIBE S.A.—See Cargill, Inc.; *U.S. Private*, pg. 755
CARGILL EUROPE LIMITED—See Cargill, Inc.; *U.S. Private*, pg. 756
CARGILL FEED SDN BHD—See Cargill, Inc.; *U.S. Private*, pg. 756
CARGILL, INC. - NUTRENA FEED—See Cargill, Inc.; *U.S. Private*, pg. 759
CARGILL INC.—See Cargill, Inc.; *U.S. Private*, pg. 757
CARGILL PAKISTAN HOLDINGS (PVT) LTD.—See Cargill, Inc.; *U.S. Private*, pg. 758
CARGILL SACI SUCURSAL URUGUAY—See Cargill, Inc.; *U.S. Private*, pg. 758
CARGILL SRL—See Cargill, Inc.; *U.S. Private*, pg. 758
CARGILL TAIWAN CORPORATION—See Cargill, Inc.; *U.S. Private*, pg. 758
CARGILL TURKEY PRODUCTS FEEDS, INC.—See Cargill, Inc.; *U.S. Private*, pg. 759
CARROLLTON FARMERS ELEVATOR CO., INC.—See CHS INC.; *U.S. Public*, pg. 492
CERES POWER HOLDINGS PLC; *Int'l*, pg. 1422
CHEVITA GMBH; *Int'l*, pg. 1474
CID LINES IBERICA SL—See Ecolab Inc.; *U.S. Public*, pg. 712
CID LINES NV—See Ecolab Inc.; *U.S. Public*, pg. 712
CID LINES SP. Z O. O.—See Ecolab Inc.; *U.S. Public*, pg. 712
CJ CHANGSHA FEED CO., LTD—See CJ Corporation; *Int'l*, pg. 1631
C.J. FOODS, INC.—See J.H. Whitney & Co., LLC; *U.S. Private*, pg. 2166
CJ (HAERBIN) FEED CO., LTD.—See CJ Corporation; *Int'l*, pg. 1631
CJ PHILIPPINES INC.—See CJ Corporation; *Int'l*, pg. 1633

CJ QINGDAO FEED CO., LTD.—See CJ Corporation; *Int'l*, pg. 1631
CJ TIANJIN FEED CO., LTD.—See CJ Corporation; *Int'l*, pg. 1631
CJ VINA AGRI CO., LTD.—See CJ Corporation; *Int'l*, pg. 1631
CJ ZHENGZHOU FEED CO., LTD.—See CJ Corporation; *Int'l*, pg. 1631
COMMODITY BLENDERS INC.; *U.S. Private*, pg. 985
CO-OPERATIVE ANIMAL HEALTH LIMITED—See Dairygold Co-Operative Society Ltd; *Int'l*, pg. 1940
CO-OPERATIVE ANIMAL HEALTH LIMITED—See Glanbia Co-Operative Society Limited; *Int'l*, pg. 2988
COOPER FARMS INC.; *U.S. Private*, pg. 1041
COVERIS FLEXIBLES US LLC - PET FOOD DIVISION—See Sun Capital Partners, Inc.; *U.S. Private*, pg. 3859
C.P. AQUACULTURE (BEIHAI) CO., LTD.—See Charoen Pokphand Foods Public Company Limited; *Int'l*, pg. 1451
CPF (INDIA) PRIVATE LTD.—See Charoen Pokphand Foods Public Company Limited; *Int'l*, pg. 1452
C.P. MERCHANDISING CO., LTD.—See Charoen Pokphand Foods Public Company Limited; *Int'l*, pg. 1452
C.P. STANDART GIDA SANAYI VE TICARET A.S.—See Charoen Pokphand Foods Public Company Limited; *Int'l*, pg. 1452
DABACO GROUP JOINT STOCK COMPANY; *Int'l*, pg. 1902
DABACO HIGH - TECH AGRICULTURE COMPANY LIMITED—See DABACO Group Joint Stock Company; *Int'l*, pg. 1902
DACHAN GREAT WALL GROUP; *Int'l*, pg. 1903
DAEHAN LIVESTOCK & FEED CO. LTD. - CHANGWON PLANT—See Daehan Flour Mills co., Ltd; *Int'l*, pg. 1906
DAEHAN LIVESTOCK & FEED CO. LTD. - INCHON PLANT—See Daehan Flour Mills co., Ltd; *Int'l*, pg. 1907
DAEHAN LIVESTOCK & FEED CO., LTD. - JEONJU PLANT—See Daehan Flour Mills co., Ltd; *Int'l*, pg. 1907
DAIRY FEEDS INC.; *U.S. Private*, pg. 1146
DAWE'S LABORATORIES; *U.S. Private*, pg. 1175
D&D COMMODITIES LTD.; *U.S. Private*, pg. 1137
DEKALB FEEDS INC.; *U.S. Private*, pg. 1192
DESA CARGILL SDN BHD—See Cargill, Inc.; *U.S. Private*, pg. 759
DHOFAR CATTLE FEED COMPANY SAOG; *Int'l*, pg. 2099
DIAMOND V MILLS, INC.; *U.S. Private*, pg. 1224
DODGEVILLE AGRI-SERVICE INC.—See Vita Plus Corporation; *U.S. Private*, pg. 4405
DOFU DONAUFUTTER GMBH—See AGRAVIS Raiffeisen AG; *Int'l*, pg. 215
DOMAIN INC.; *U.S. Private*, pg. 1255
DONGWON FARMS—See Dongwon Enterprise Co., Ltd.; *Int'l*, pg. 2170
DON'S FARM SUPPLY, INC.; *U.S. Private*, pg. 1259
EASY HOLDINGS CO., LTD.; *Int'l*, pg. 2275
ELANCO - AUGUSTA TECHNOLOGY CENTER—See Elanco Animal Health Incorporated; *U.S. Public*, pg. 722
ELENBAAS COMPANY; *U.S. Private*, pg. 1357
EMIVEST BERHAD; *Int'l*, pg. 2383
ENDRES PROCESSING LLC; *U.S. Private*, pg. 1392
ENVIROFLIGHT, LLC—See Darling Ingredients Inc.; *U.S. Public*, pg. 634
EPL FEED, LLC—See Elenbaas Company; *U.S. Private*, pg. 1357
EPL FEED, LLC—See Land O'Lakes, Inc.; *U.S. Private*, pg. 2383
E-P:N MINKINREHU OY; *Int'l*, pg. 2249
ERCROS SA - ANIMAL FEED DIVISION - CARTAGENA FACTORY—See Ercros SA; *Int'l*, pg. 2489
ERCROS SA - ANIMAL FEED DIVISION—See Ercros SA; *Int'l*, pg. 2489
ESCO INDUSTRIES, INC.; *U.S. Private*, pg. 1425
EVIALIS FRANCE—See Archer-Daniels-Midland Company; *U.S. Public*, pg. 185
EVOLVED INDUSTRIES, INC.; *U.S. Private*, pg. 1444
EWOS AS—See Cargill, Inc.; *U.S. Private*, pg. 759
EWOS CANADA LTD.—See Cargill, Inc.; *U.S. Private*, pg. 759
EWOS CHILE ALIMENTOS LTDA.—See Cargill, Inc.; *U.S. Private*, pg. 759
EWOS CHILE S.A.—See Cargill, Inc.; *U.S. Private*, pg. 759
EWOS LIMITED—See Cargill, Inc.; *U.S. Private*, pg. 759
FABRIKA STOCNE HRANE JABUKA A.D.; *Int'l*, pg. 2600
THE FAIR MANUFACTURING CO. LTD.—See Spectrum Brands Holdings, Inc.; *U.S. Public*, pg. 1917
FAIRVIEW MILLS INC.; *U.S. Private*, pg. 1464
FARMERS COOPERATIVE ELEVATOR COMPANY; *U.S. Private*, pg. 1477
FARMERS FEED MILL INC.; *U.S. Private*, pg. 1478
FARMERS RANCHERS COOP ASSOC.; *U.S. Private*, pg. 1478
FARMERS UNION MARKETING & PROCESSING ASSOCIATION; *U.S. Private*, pg. 1479
FARMSTORY CO., LTD.; *Int'l*, pg. 2620
FATENT CO. DOO LAKTASI—See BayWa AG; *Int'l*, pg. 917
FEDERACION DE ASC PECUARIAS PR; *U.S. Private*, pg. 1487
FEDERATED CO-OPERATIVES LIMITED - CALGARY

N.A.I.C.S. INDEX

311119 — OTHER ANIMAL FOOD M...

FEED PLANT—See Federated Co-operatives Limited; *Int'l*, pg. 2631
FEDERATED CO-OPERATIVES LIMITED - EDMONTON FEED PLANT—See Federated Co-operatives Limited; *Int'l*, pg. 2631
FEDERATED CO-OPERATIVES LIMITED - MOOSOMIN FEED PLANT—See Federated Co-operatives Limited; *Int'l*, pg. 2631
FEDERATED CO-OPERATIVES LIMITED - SASKATOON FEED PLANT—See Federated Co-operatives Limited; *Int'l*, pg. 2631
FEEDEX NUTRITION—See Agricola Group Ltd; *Int'l*, pg. 216
FEEDSTUFFS PROCESSING CO. INC.; *U.S. Private*, pg. 1493
FERMENTA USA LLC—See Fermenta Biotech Limited; *Int'l*, pg. 2639
FILOZOO SRL—See Archer-Daniels-Midland Company; *U.S. Public*, pg. 185
FISHBELT FEEDS INC.; *U.S. Private*, pg. 1533
FLINT RIVER MILLS; *U.S. Private*, pg. 1545
FORFARMERS GROUP B.V; *Int'l*, pg. 2732
FORM-A-FEED, INC.; *U.S. Private*, pg. 1569
FORMULA 1 FEEDS INC.; *U.S. Private*, pg. 1572
FUJIAN AONONG BIOLOGICAL TECHNOLOGY GROUP INCORPORATION LIMITED; *Int'l*, pg. 2817
FUJIAN TIANMA SCIENCE & TECHNOLOGY GROUP CO., LTD.; *Int'l*, pg. 2820
FUR BREEDERS AGRICULTURAL COOPERATIVE; *U.S. Private*, pg. 1623
FURST-MCNESS COMPANY; *U.S. Private*, pg. 1624
FWUSOW INDUSTRY CO., LTD. - SHA-LU FACTORY—See Fwusow Industry Co., Ltd.; *Int'l*, pg. 2859
FWUSOW INDUSTRY CO., LTD.; *Int'l*, pg. 2859
GARANT-TIERNAHRUNG GESELLSCHAFT M.B.H—See BayWa AG; *Int'l*, pg. 918
G.A. WINTZER AND SON COMPANY; *U.S. Private*, pg. 1630
GENE BIO TECH CO., LTD.; *Int'l*, pg. 2917
GENTRACO FEED JSC; *Int'l*, pg. 2929
GEORGE'S INC. - CASSVILLE FEED MILL—See George's Inc.; *U.S. Private*, pg. 1683
GEORGE'S INC. - HARRISONBURG FEED MILL—See George's Inc.; *U.S. Private*, pg. 1684
GEORGE'S INC. - MOUNT JACKSON FEED MILL—See George's Inc.; *U.S. Private*, pg. 1684
GEORGE'S INC. - SPRINGDALE FEED MILL—See George's Inc.; *U.S. Private*, pg. 1684
GERBER & SONS INC.; *U.S. Private*, pg. 1686
GODREJ AGROVET LTD.—See Godrej & Boyce Mfg. Co. Ltd.; *Int'l*, pg. 3020
GOLD COIN BIOTECHNOLOGIES SDN. BHD.—See Gold Coin Holdings Sdn Bhd; *Int'l*, pg. 3024
GOLD COIN FEEDMILL (DONGGUAN) CO. LTD.—See Gold Coin Holdings Sdn Bhd; *Int'l*, pg. 3024
GOLD COIN FEEDMILL (DONG NAI) CO LTD—See Gold Coin Holdings Sdn Bhd; *Int'l*, pg. 3024
GOLD COIN FEEDMILL (KUNMING) CO. LTD.—See Gold Coin Holdings Sdn Bhd; *Int'l*, pg. 3024
GOLD COIN FEEDMILL (SABAH) SDN. BHD.—See Gold Coin Holdings Sdn Bhd; *Int'l*, pg. 3024
GOLD COIN FEED MILLS (LANKA) LIMITED—See Gold Coin Holdings Sdn Bhd; *Int'l*, pg. 3024
GOLD COIN FEEDMILLS MALAYSIA SDN BHD—See Aboitiz Equity Ventures, Inc.; *Int'l*, pg. 67
GOLD COIN FEEDMILLS MALAYSIA—See Aboitiz Equity Ventures, Inc.; *Int'l*, pg. 67
GOLD COIN FEEDMILLS (M) SDN BHD—See Aboitiz Equity Ventures, Inc.; *Int'l*, pg. 67
GOLD COIN FEEDMILLS SDN BHD—See Aboitiz Equity Ventures, Inc.; *Int'l*, pg. 67
GOLD COIN SERVICES SINGAPORE PTE. LTD.—See Aboitiz Equity Ventures, Inc.; *Int'l*, pg. 66
GOLD COIN SPECIALITIES (THAILAND) CO. LTD.—See Gold Coin Holdings Sdn Bhd; *Int'l*, pg. 3024
GOLD COIN (ZHUHAI) CO., LTD.—See Aboitiz Equity Ventures, Inc.; *Int'l*, pg. 66
GOLDSBORO MILLING COMPANY; *U.S. Private*, pg. 1735
GORES INC.; *U.S. Private*, pg. 1743
GORMAN MILLING CO. INC.; *U.S. Private*, pg. 1744
GRAINCORP LIQUID FEEDS PTY LTD—See GrainCorp Limited; *Int'l*, pg. 3052
GRAND VALLEY FORTIFIERS LIMITED; *Int'l*, pg. 3057
GRISHAM FARM PRODUCTS, INC.; *U.S. Private*, pg. 1790
GROUPE PILARDIERE—See Archer-Daniels-Midland Company; *U.S. Public*, pg. 185
GUANGDONG HAID GROUP CO., LTD.; *Int'l*, pg. 3155
GUANGDONG VTR BIO-TECH CO., LTD.; *Int'l*, pg. 3161
GUANGDONG YUEHAI FEEDS GROUP CO., LTD.; *Int'l*, pg. 3162
GYMTECH FEEDMILL (M) SDN. BHD.—See Emivest Berhad; *Int'l*, pg. 2383
HAMPSHIRE PET PRODUCTS, LLC—See Red Collar Pet Foods, Inc.; *U.S. Private*, pg. 3374
HANGZHOU TIANYUAN PET PRODUCTS CO., LTD.; *Int'l*, pg. 3250
HANIL FEED CO., LTD.; *Int'l*, pg. 3252
HEALTHY PET, L.P.—See Kinderhook Industries, LLC; *U.S. Private*, pg. 2307

HERGERT MILLING INC.; *U.S. Private*, pg. 1921
HERITAGE NUTRIVET LIMITED—See Heritage Foods Ltd.; *Int'l*, pg. 3361
HERITAGE TECHNOLOGIES, LLC; *U.S. Private*, pg. 1924
HILL'S-COLGATE JAPAN LTD.—See Colgate-Palmolive Company; *U.S. Public*, pg. 533
HI-PRO FEEDS—See Friona Industries, LP; *U.S. Private*, pg. 1612
H.J. BAKER & BRO., INC.; *U.S. Private*, pg. 1834
HONEYWELL FLOUR MILLS PLC; *Int'l*, pg. 3465
HUNAN ZHENGHONG SCIENCE AND TECHNOLOGY DEVELOP CO., LTD.; *Int'l*, pg. 3534
I'ANSON BROTHERS LTD; *Int'l*, pg. 3562
IDEAL MULTIFEED (MALAYSIA) SDN BERHAD—See Emivest Berhad; *Int'l*, pg. 2383
IGENE BIOTECHNOLOGY, INC.; *U.S. Public*, pg. 1095
INTERNATIONAL INGREDIENT CORP.; *U.S. Private*, pg. 2118
INTERNATIONAL PET FOOD CO., LTD.—See Charoen Pokphand Foods Public Company Limited; *Int'l*, pg. 1452
JEIL FEED CO., LTD.—See Harim Holdings Co., Ltd.; *Int'l*, pg. 3275
JOHN A. VAN DEN BOSCH CO.; *U.S. Private*, pg. 2220
JUPE FEEDS, INC.; *U.S. Private*, pg. 2245
JUPE FEEDS, INC.; *U.S. Private*, pg. 2245
KALMBACH FEEDS, INC.; *U.S. Private*, pg. 2257
KANSAS FEEDS, INC.; *U.S. Private*, pg. 2261
KASSIK MILLING CO.; *U.S. Private*, pg. 2264
KAY FLO INDUSTRIES, INC.—See The Andersons Incorporated; *U.S. Public*, pg. 2034
KAYTEE PRODUCTS, INC.—See Central Garden & Pet Company; *U.S. Public*, pg. 473
KELLY FOODS CORPORATION; *U.S. Private*, pg. 2276
KENT NUTRITION GROUP, INC.—See Kent Corporation; *U.S. Private*, pg. 2287
KIRBY AGRI INC. - KIRBY AGRI INGREDIENTS FACILITY—See Kirby Agri Inc.; *U.S. Private*, pg. 2314
KOCH AGRICULTURE COMPANY—See Koch Industries, Inc.; *U.S. Private*, pg. 2331
KONZUL D.O.O.—See Ameropa AG; *Int'l*, pg. 424
LAKELAND ANIMAL NUTRITION, INC.—See Alltech, Inc.; *U.S. Private*, pg. 194
LAND O'LAKES, INC. - NASHVILLE—See Land O'Lakes, Inc.; *U.S. Private*, pg. 2383
LAND O'LAKES PURINA FEED LLC—See Land O'Lakes, Inc.; *U.S. Private*, pg. 2383
LAND O'LAKES PURINA FEED—See Land O'Lakes, Inc.; *U.S. Private*, pg. 2383
LFA CELTIC LIMITED—See Compagnie des Levures Lesaffre SA; *Int'l*, pg. 1738
LIANYUNGANG CHIA TAI FEED CO., LTD.—See Charoen Pokphand Foods Public Company Limited; *Int'l*, pg. 1453
LIND MARINE, INC.; *U.S. Private*, pg. 2459
MAHARD FEED MILL INC.; *U.S. Private*, pg. 2550
MANNA PRO PRODUCTS, LLC—See The Carlyle Group Inc.; *U.S. Public*, pg. 2049
MARK HERSHEY FARMS INC.; *U.S. Private*, pg. 2577
MARS HORSECARE US, INC.—See Mars, Incorporated; *U.S. Private*, pg. 2589
MASTERFEEDS INC.—See Alltech, Inc.; *U.S. Private*, pg. 194
MEADOW FEED MAURITIUS—See Astral Foods Limited; *Int'l*, pg. 658
MEADOW FEEDS CAPE—See Astral Foods Limited; *Int'l*, pg. 658
MEADOW FEEDS DELMAS—See Astral Foods Limited; *Int'l*, pg. 658
MEADOW FEEDS KWA-ZULU NATAL—See Astral Foods Limited; *Int'l*, pg. 658
MEADOW FEEDS PORT ELIZABETH—See Astral Foods Limited; *Int'l*, pg. 658
MEADOW FEEDS PTY. LTD.—See Astral Foods Limited; *Int'l*, pg. 658
MEADOW FEEDS RANDFONTEIN—See Astral Foods Limited; *Int'l*, pg. 658
MEADOW FEEDS ZAMBIA—See Astral Foods Limited; *Int'l*, pg. 658
MEADOW MOCAMBIQUE LIMITADA—See Astral Foods Limited; *Int'l*, pg. 658
MEADOW MOZAMBIQUE LDA—See Astral Foods Limited; *Int'l*, pg. 658
MICOBE, INC.; *U.S. Private*, pg. 2702
MID-SOUTH MILLING COMPANY, INC. - KANSAS PLANT—See Mid-South Milling Company, Inc.; *U.S. Private*, pg. 2709
MID-SOUTH MILLING COMPANY, INC.; *U.S. Private*, pg. 2709
MIDWEST PMS; *U.S. Private*, pg. 2722
MIRACLECORP PRODUCTS—See Alvarez & Marsal, Inc.; *U.S. Private*, pg. 212
MONAS FEED OY AB—See E-P:n Minkinrehu Oy; *Int'l*, pg. 2249
MONTI FOODS (PTY) LTD.—See Archer-Daniels-Midland Company; *U.S. Public*, pg. 185
MUENSTER MILLING COMPANY, LLC—See Kainos Capital, LLC; *U.S. Private*, pg. 2255
NATURAL BALANCE PET PRODUCTS, INC.—See The J.M. Smucker Company; *U.S. Public*, pg. 2107

NATURAL PRODUCTS, INC.—See Kent Corporation; *U.S. Private*, pg. 2287
NEOGEN CHILE SPA—See Neogen Corporation; *U.S. Public*, pg. 1505
NEOGEN URUGUAY—See Neogen Corporation; *U.S. Public*, pg. 1505
NEPRA FOODS INC.; *U.S. Public*, pg. 1506
NORLAC GMBH—See DMK Deutsches Milchkontor GmbH; *Int'l*, pg. 2146
NUTEC SOUTHERN AFRICA (PTY) LTD.—See Astral Foods Limited; *Int'l*, pg. 658
NUTEC SOUTHERN AFRICA (PTY) LTD.—See Cargill, Inc.; *U.S. Private*, pg. 759
NUTRENA FEEDS—See Cargill, Inc.; *U.S. Private*, pg. 759
NUTRI FEEDS (PTY) LIMITED - BLOEMFONTEIN FEED MILL—See Country Bird Holdings Limited; *Int'l*, pg. 1818
NUTRI FEEDS (PTY) LIMITED - MAFIKENG FEED MILL—See Country Bird Holdings Limited; *Int'l*, pg. 1818
NUTRI FEEDS (PTY) LIMITED—See Country Bird Holdings Limited; *Int'l*, pg. 1818
NUTRI FEEDS (PTY) LIMITED - VILJOENSKROON FEED MILL—See Country Bird Holdings Limited; *Int'l*, pg. 1818
NUTRIMIX FEED CO., INC.; *U.S. Private*, pg. 2974
NUTRIUS, LLC—See Cargill, Inc.; *U.S. Private*, pg. 760
OCALA BREEDERS' SALES COMPANY; *U.S. Private*, pg. 2988
PAN AMERICAN GRAIN COMPANY; *U.S. Private*, pg. 3083
PARTNER IN PET FOOD CZ S.R.O—See Cinven Limited; *Int'l*, pg. 1613
PARTNER IN PET FOOD HUNGARIA KFT.—See Cinven Limited; *Int'l*, pg. 1613
PATENT CO., DOO LAKTASI—See BayWa AG; *Int'l*, pg. 918
PETAG, INC.—See PBI/Gordon Corporation; *U.S. Private*, pg. 3118
PETDINE, LLC—See Archer-Daniels-Midland Company; *U.S. Public*, pg. 185
PHIBRO ANIMAL HEALTH CORPORATION; *U.S. Public*, pg. 1684
PHIBRO HAYVAN SAGLIGI URUNLERI SANAYI VE TICARET A.S.—See Phibro Animal Health Corporation; *U.S. Public*, pg. 1685
PHILLIPS PET FOOD & SUPPLIES; *U.S. Private*, pg. 3171
PINE MANOR INC.; *U.S. Private*, pg. 3182
POULIN GRAIN INC.; *U.S. Private*, pg. 3236
PRECISION PET PRODUCTS, INC.—See Texas Farm Products Company; *U.S. Private*, pg. 3975
PRINCE AGRI PRODUCTS, INC.—See Phibro Animal Health Corporation; *U.S. Public*, pg. 1685
PRODUCTOS QUIMICOS MAGIAR S.A.—See Neogen Corporation; *U.S. Public*, pg. 1505
PROFUMA SPEZIALFUTTERWERKE GMBH & CO. KG—See AGRAVIS Raiffeisen AG; *Int'l*, pg. 215
PROGRESSIVE NUTRITION, LLC—See Cargill, Inc.; *U.S. Private*, pg. 760
PROTEIN SOURCES, LLP; *U.S. Private*, pg. 3289
PROVIMI B.V.—See Cargill, Inc.; *U.S. Private*, pg. 760
PROVIMI FRANCE—See Cargill, Inc.; *U.S. Private*, pg. 760
PROVIMI NORTH AMERICA, INC.—See Cargill, Inc.; *U.S. Private*, pg. 760
PT CARGILL INDONESIA GUNUNG PUTRI—See Cargill, Inc.; *U.S. Private*, pg. 759
PT CARGILL INDONESIA—See Cargill, Inc.; *U.S. Private*, pg. 759
PT. CHEILJEDANG SUPERFEED—See CJ Corporation; *Int'l*, pg. 1631
PT CJ FEED & CARE INDONESIA—See CJ Corporation; *Int'l*, pg. 1634
PT. CJ FEED JOMBANG—See CJ Corporation; *Int'l*, pg. 1631
PT GOLD COIN SPECIALITIES—See Gold Coin Holdings Sdn Bhd; *Int'l*, pg. 3024
PT MALINDO FEEDMILL TBK—See Emerging Glory Sdn Bhd; *Int'l*, pg. 2379
PURINA GOLDEN SUN—See Land O'Lakes, Inc.; *U.S. Private*, pg. 2383
PURINA MILLS, LLC—See Land O'Lakes, Inc.; *U.S. Private*, pg. 2383
QUALI TECH LLC—See MidOcean Partners, LLP; *U.S. Private*, pg. 2717
RAGLAND MILLS, INC.; *U.S. Private*, pg. 3346
RAJBURI FOODS CO., LTD.—See Charoen Pokphand Foods Public Company Limited; *Int'l*, pg. 1453
RALCO NUTRITION, INC.; *U.S. Private*, pg. 3349
RANGEN, INC. - AQUACULTURE DIVISION—See Wilbur-Ellis Company; *U.S. Private*, pg. 4518
RANGEN, INC.—See Wilbur-Ellis Company; *U.S. Private*, pg. 4518
RECONSERVE, INC.—See ReConserve, Inc.; *U.S. Private*, pg. 3371
RECONSERVE OF CALIFORNIA-LOS ANGELES, INC.—See ReConserve, Inc.; *U.S. Private*, pg. 3371
RECONSERVE OF CALIFORNIA-STOCKTON, INC.—See ReConserve, Inc.; *U.S. Private*, pg. 3371
RECONSERVE OF MARYLAND—See ReConserve, Inc.; *U.S. Private*, pg. 3371
RECYCLE TO CONSERVE, TX, INC.—See ReConserve, Inc.; *U.S. Private*, pg. 3371
RED COLLAR PET FOODS, INC.; *U.S. Private*, pg. 3374

311119 — OTHER ANIMAL FOOD M...

R. & H. HALL LIMITED—See ARYZTA AG; *Int'l*, pg. 589
RIDLEY BLOCK OPERATIONS, INC.—See Alltech, Inc.; *U.S. Private*, pg. 194
ROBERT SMYTH & SONS LIMITED—See Fane Valley Co-operative Society Ltd.; *Int'l*, pg. 2613
SALT CREEK, INC.—See Benchmark Holdings Plc; *Int'l*, pg. 970
SAPHYTO SA—See Element Solutions Inc.; *U.S. Public*, pg. 728
SEABOARD OVERSEAS PERU S.A.—See Seaboard Corporation; *U.S. Public*, pg. 1851
SEMINOLE FEED CO.; *U.S. Private*, pg. 3604
SHAFER SEED COMPANY, INC.—See Wagner's LLC; *U.S. Private*, pg. 4426
SILO P. KRUSE BETRIEBS-GMBH & CO. KG—See Archer-Daniels-Midland Company; *U.S. Public*, pg. 185
SMARTPAK EQUINE, LLC—See Clayton, Dubilier & Rice, LLC; *U.S. Private*, pg. 921
SMARTPAK EQUINE, LLC—See TPG Capital, L.P.; *U.S. Public*, pg. 2170
SOJOURNER FARMS LLC—See Clearlake Capital Group, L.P.; *U.S. Private*, pg. 937
SONAC LUBIEN KUJAWSKI SPOLKA Z OGRANICZONA ODPOWIEDZIALNOSCIA—See Darling Ingredients Inc.; *U.S. Public*, pg. 634
SONAC USNICE SP.Z O.O.—See Darling Ingredients Inc.; *U.S. Public*, pg. 634
SOUTHERN STATES COOPERATIVE, INC.; *U.S. Private*, pg. 3735
SOVEREIGN FOOD INVESTMENTS LTD.—See Capitalworks Investment Partners (Pty) Ltd; *Int'l*, pg. 1314
STANDARD NUTRITION COMPANY; *U.S. Private*, pg. 3781
STAR FEEDMILLS (M) SDN. BHD.—See Charoen Pokphand Foods Public Company Limited; *Int'l*, pg. 1453
STAR MILLING COMPANY INC—See Mountaire Corporation; *U.S. Private*, pg. 2801
STILLWATER MILLING COMPANY INC.; *U.S. Private*, pg. 3812
STOLZ S.A.S.—See Alfa Laval AB; *Int'l*, pg. 312
STRAUSS FEEDS—See Strauss Veal Feeds Inc.; *U.S. Private*, pg. 3837
STRAUSS VEAL FEEDS INC.; *U.S. Private*, pg. 3837
TEO SENG FEEDMILL SDN BHD—See Emerging Glory Sdn Bhd; *Int'l*, pg. 2379
TETRA GMBH—See Spectrum Brands Holdings, Inc.; *U.S. Public*, pg. 1917
TETRA JAPAN K.K.—See Spectrum Brands Holdings, Inc.; *U.S. Public*, pg. 1917
TOBY/O, INC.; *U.S. Private*, pg. 4180
UNGA FARMCARE (EAST AFRICA) LIMITED—See Seaboard Corporation; *U.S. Public*, pg. 1851
UNITED ANIMAL HEALTH, INC.; *U.S. Private*, pg. 4287
UNITED PET GROUP, INC.—See Spectrum Brands Holdings, Inc.; *U.S. Public*, pg. 1917
UNITED PET POLSKA SP. Z.O.O.—See Spectrum Brands Holdings, Inc.; *U.S. Public*, pg. 1917
VALLEY PROTEINS, INC.—See Darling Ingredients Inc.; *U.S. Public*, pg. 634
VALLEY PROTEINS, INC.—See Darling Ingredients Inc.; *U.S. Public*, pg. 634
VIGORTONE AG PRODUCTS—See Cargill, Inc.; *U.S. Private*, pg. 760
VIRTUS NUTRITION, LLC—See Cargill, Inc.; *U.S. Private*, pg. 760
VITA PLUS CORPORATION; *U.S. Private*, pg. 4404
VITUSA CORP.; *U.S. Private*, pg. 4406
VP HOLDINGS CORPORATION; *U.S. Private*, pg. 4414
WENGER'S FEED MILL INC.; *U.S. Private*, pg. 4481
WESTWAY FEED PRODUCTS LLC—See ED&F Man Holdings Limited; *Int'l*, pg. 2303
WESTWAY FEED PRODUCTS LLC - WESTERN REGIONAL OFFICE—See ED&F Man Holdings Limited; *Int'l*, pg. 2303
WHERE FOOD COMES FROM, INC.; *U.S. Public*, pg. 2366
WHITE OAK MILLS INC.; *U.S. Private*, pg. 4509
WILBUR-ELLIS NUTRITION, LLC—See Wilbur-Ellis Company; *U.S. Private*, pg. 4517
ZEIGLER BROS INC.; *U.S. Private*, pg. 4599
ZINPRO CORPORATION; *U.S. Private*, pg. 4605
ZZN PELHRIMOV A. S.—See Agrofert Holding, a.s.; *Int'l*, pg. 219

311211 — FLOUR MILLING

ADM GRAIN—See Archer-Daniels-Midland Company; *U.S. Public*, pg. 181
ADM MILLING COMPANY—See Archer-Daniels-Midland Company; *U.S. Public*, pg. 184
ADM MILLING CO.—See Archer-Daniels-Midland Company; *U.S. Public*, pg. 182
ADM MILLING CO.—See Archer-Daniels-Midland Company; *U.S. Public*, pg. 182
ADM MILLING CO.—See Archer-Daniels-Midland Company; *U.S. Public*, pg. 182
ADM MILLING CO.—See Archer-Daniels-Midland Company; *U.S. Public*, pg. 182
ADM MILLING CO.—See Archer-Daniels-Midland Company; *U.S. Public*, pg. 182
ADM MILLING CO.—See Archer-Daniels-Midland Company; *U.S. Public*, pg. 184
AGRICOR INC.—See Grain Millers, Inc.; *U.S. Private*, pg. 1751
AMERICAN SUNNY FOODS, INC.—See Western Milling, LLC; *U.S. Private*, pg. 4494
ARCHER DANIELS MIDLAND CO.—See Archer-Daniels-Midland Company; *U.S. Public*, pg. 183
ARCHER DANIELS MIDLAND CO.—See Archer-Daniels-Midland Company; *U.S. Public*, pg. 183
ARCHER DANIELS MIDLAND CO.—See Archer-Daniels-Midland Company; *U.S. Public*, pg. 183
ARCHER DANIELS MIDLAND CO.—See Archer-Daniels-Midland Company; *U.S. Public*, pg. 183
ARCHER DANIELS MIDLAND CO.—See Archer-Daniels-Midland Company; *U.S. Public*, pg. 184
ARDENT MILLS, LLC—See Cargill, Inc.; *U.S. Private*, pg. 754
ARDENT MILLS, LLC—See CHS INC.; *U.S. Public*, pg. 491
ARDENT MILLS, LLC—See Conagra Brands, Inc.; *U.S. Public*, pg. 563
ARDENT MILLS—See Cargill, Inc.; *U.S. Private*, pg. 754
ARDENT MILLS—See CHS INC.; *U.S. Public*, pg. 491
ARDENT MILLS—See Conagra Brands, Inc.; *U.S. Public*, pg. 563
AXIANE MEUNERIE—See Axereal Union de Cooperatives Agricoles; *Int'l*, pg. 767
AZTECA MILLING LP—See Gruma, S.A.B. de C.V.; *Int'l*, pg. 3114
BAY STATE MILLING COMPANY; *U.S. Private*, pg. 494
BAY STATE MILLING COMPANY—See Bay State Milling Company; *U.S. Private*, pg. 494
BELARINA ALIMENTOS S.A.—See Seaboard Corporation; *U.S. Public*, pg. 1850
THE BIRKETT MILLS; *U.S. Private*, pg. 3995
BOB'S RED MILL NATURAL FOODS, INC.; *U.S. Private*, pg. 606
BONAVIA FOODS LLC.; *U.S. Private*, pg. 613
BUNGE MILLING (SOUTHWEST), INC.—See Bunge Limited; *U.S. Public*, pg. 411
CAKOVECKI MLINOVI D.D.; *Int'l*, pg. 1260
CARGILL DRY CORN INGREDIENTS INC—See Cargill, Inc.; *U.S. Private*, pg. 756
CARR'S FLOUR MILLS LTD.; *Int'l*, pg. 1343
CEREAL FOOD PROCESSORS INC. - BILLINGS FACILITY—See Cereal Food Processors Inc.; *U.S. Private*, pg. 840
CEREAL FOOD PROCESSORS INC. - CLEVELAND FACILITY—See Cereal Food Processors Inc.; *U.S. Private*, pg. 840
CEREAL FOOD PROCESSORS INC. - GREAT FALLS FACILITY—See Cereal Food Processors Inc.; *U.S. Private*, pg. 840
CEREAL FOOD PROCESSORS INC. - KANSAS CITY FACILITY—See Cereal Food Processors Inc.; *U.S. Private*, pg. 840
CEREAL FOOD PROCESSORS INC. - LOS ANGELES FACILITY—See Cereal Food Processors Inc.; *U.S. Private*, pg. 840
CEREAL FOOD PROCESSORS INC. - MCPHERSON FACILITY—See Cereal Food Processors Inc.; *U.S. Private*, pg. 840
CEREAL FOOD PROCESSORS INC. - OGDEN FACILITY—See Cereal Food Processors Inc.; *U.S. Private*, pg. 840
CEREAL FOOD PROCESSORS INC. - PORTLAND FACILITY—See Cereal Food Processors Inc.; *U.S. Private*, pg. 840
CEREAL FOOD PROCESSORS INC. - SALT LAKE CITY FACILITY—See Cereal Food Processors Inc.; *U.S. Private*, pg. 840
CEREAL FOOD PROCESSORS INC.; *U.S. Private*, pg. 840
CEREAL FOOD PROCESSORS INC. - WICHITA FACILITY—See Cereal Food Processors Inc.; *U.S. Private*, pg. 840
CERES S.A.—See Etablissements J. Soufflet; *Int'l*, pg. 2519
CHELSEA MILLING COMPANY; *U.S. Private*, pg. 870
C.H. GUENTHER & SON, INC. - PIONEER FLOUR MILL—See The Pritzker Group - Chicago, LLC; *U.S. Private*, pg. 4098
C.H. GUENTHER & SON, LLC—See The Pritzker Group - Chicago, LLC; *U.S. Private*, pg. 4098
CONAGRA FOOD INGREDIENTS CO.—See Conagra Brands, Inc.; *U.S. Public*, pg. 563
CONCERN TSESNA-ASTYK LLP—See Corporation Tsesna JSC; *Int'l*, pg. 1806
CORN PRODUCTS (THAILAND) CO. LTD.—See Ingredion Incorporated; *U.S. Public*, pg. 1123
CORRECTA INDUSTRIA E COMERCIO LTDO.—See Glencore plc; *Int'l*, pg. 2990
CP INGREDIENTS INDIA PVT. LTD.—See Ingredion Incorporated; *U.S. Public*, pg. 1123
CRUST CRAFT INC.; *Int'l*, pg. 1859
DAEHAN FLOUR MILLS CO., LTD; *Int'l*, pg. 1906
DERIVADOS DE MAIZ ALIMENTICIO, S.A.—See Gruma, S.A.B. de C.V.; *Int'l*, pg. 3114
DERIVADOS DE MAIZ DE EL SALVADOR, S.A.—See Gruma, S.A.B. de C.V.; *Int'l*, pg. 3114

DIDION MILLING INC.; *U.S. Private*, pg. 1227
DOVER FLOUR HALIFAX—See Excelsior Cooperative Avicole; *Int'l*, pg. 2578
DOVER FLOUR MILLS LTD.—See Excelsior Cooperative Avicole; *Int'l*, pg. 2578
EAST DELTA FLOUR MILLS; *Int'l*, pg. 2270
ELBISCO HOLDING S.A.; *Int'l*, pg. 2344
FLOUR MILLS KEPENOS S.A.; *Int'l*, pg. 2708
FLOUR MILLS OF FIJI LIMITED; *Int'l*, pg. 2708
FLOUR MILLS OF NIGERIA PLC.; *Int'l*, pg. 2708
FORESTAL Y AGRICOLA MONTEAGUILA S.A.—See Empresas CMPC S.A.; *Int'l*, pg. 2390
GENERAL MILLS, INC.; *U.S. Public*, pg. 921
GIUSTO SPECIALTY FOODS INC.; *U.S. Private*, pg. 1703
GOLDEN WHEAT MILLS COMPANY—See Arab Supply & Trading Co.; *Int'l*, pg. 532
GOODLUCK INDUSTRIES LTD.; *Int'l*, pg. 3040
GRAIN MILLERS, INC.; *U.S. Private*, pg. 1751
GRANEXPORT AD; *Int'l*, pg. 3058
GROUPE MINOTERIES SA; *Int'l*, pg. 3108
GRUMA, S.A.B. DE C.V.; *Int'l*, pg. 3114
GRUPO INDUSTRIAL MASECA, S.A.B. DE C.V.—See Gruma, S.A.B. de C.V.; *Int'l*, pg. 3114
GUJARAT AMBUJA EXPORTS LTD. - KARNATAKA DIVISION—See Gujarat Ambuja Exports Ltd.; *Int'l*, pg. 3175
GUJARAT AMBUJA EXPORTS LTD. - PITHAMPUR DIVISION—See Gujarat Ambuja Exports Ltd.; *Int'l*, pg. 3175
GUJARAT AMBUJA EXPORTS LTD. - UTTRANCHAL DIVISION—See Gujarat Ambuja Exports Ltd.; *Int'l*, pg. 3175
HANTOP INC.; *Int'l*, pg. 3261
HARINAS DE CHIHUAHUA, S.A. DE C.V.—See Grupo Xtra S.A. de C.V.; *Int'l*, pg. 3139
HARINERA DE MAIZ DE MEXICALI, S.A. DE C.V.—See Gruma, S.A.B. de C.V.; *Int'l*, pg. 3114
HARINERA LOS PIRINEOS, S.A DE C.V.—See Grupo La Moderna, S.A.B. de C.V.; *Int'l*, pg. 3131
HODGSON MILL, INC.—See Siemer Milling Company; *U.S. Private*, pg. 3646
HOPKINSVILLE MILLING CO.; *U.S. Private*, pg. 1979
HOUSE-AUTRY MILLS INC.; *U.S. Private*, pg. 1992
HOVIS LTD.—See The Gores Group, LLC; *U.S. Private*, pg. 4034
IDEAL RICE INDUSTRIES (PVT) LTD.—See Ideal Spinning Mills Ltd; *Int'l*, pg. 3589
INDUSTRIA MOLINERA MONTSERRAT, S.A. DE C.V.—See Bunge Limited; *U.S. Public*, pg. 412
INDUSTRIAS DEL MAIZ C.A.—See Ingredion Incorporated; *U.S. Public*, pg. 1123
INGREDION ANZ PTY LTD—See Ingredion Incorporated; *U.S. Public*, pg. 1123
INGREDION JAPAN K.K.—See Ingredion Incorporated; *U.S. Public*, pg. 1123
INGREDION MEXICO, S.A. DE C.V.—See Ingredion Incorporated; *U.S. Public*, pg. 1123
INGREDION PHILIPPINES, INC.—See Ingredion Incorporated; *U.S. Public*, pg. 1123
INGREDION SINGAPORE PTE. LTD.—See Ingredion Incorporated; *U.S. Public*, pg. 1123
INGREDION URUGUAY S.A.—See Ingredion Incorporated; *U.S. Public*, pg. 1123
J.R. SHORT MILLING COMPANY; *U.S. Private*, pg. 2170
KASHI COMPANY—See WK Kellogg Co; *U.S. Public*, pg. 2376
KHALEEJ NATIONAL FLOUR MILLS—See Al Ghurair Investment LLC; *Int'l*, pg. 278
THE KING ARTHUR FLOUR COMPANY, INC.; *U.S. Private*, pg. 4065
KING MILLING COMPANY; *U.S. Private*, pg. 2309
LES GRANDS MOULINS DE DAKAR—See Seaboard Corporation; *U.S. Public*, pg. 1850
LESOTHO FLOUR MILLS LIMITED—See Seaboard Corporation; *U.S. Public*, pg. 1850
MCSHARES, INC.; *U.S. Private*, pg. 2644
THE MENNEL MILLING COMPANY - BUCYRUS FLOUR MILL—See The Mennel Milling Company; *U.S. Private*, pg. 4077
THE MENNEL MILLING COMPANY OF ILLINOIS INC.—See The Mennel Milling Company; *U.S. Private*, pg. 4077
THE MENNEL MILLING COMPANY OF MICHIGAN INC.—See The Mennel Milling Company; *U.S. Private*, pg. 4077
THE MENNEL MILLING COMPANY OF VIRGINIA, INC.—See The Mennel Milling Company; *U.S. Private*, pg. 4077
THE MENNEL MILLING COMPANY; *U.S. Private*, pg. 4077
MENNEL MILLING LOGAN; *U.S. Private*, pg. 2666
MGP INGREDIENTS, INC.; *U.S. Public*, pg. 1435
MODERNA ALIMENTOS, S.A.—See Seaboard Corporation; *U.S. Public*, pg. 1850
MOINHO PACIFICO LTDA.—See Bunge Limited; *U.S. Public*, pg. 412
MOLINOS AZTECA, S.A. DE C.V.—See Gruma, S.A.B. de C.V.; *Int'l*, pg. 3114
MOLINOS DEL SUDESTE, S.A. DE C.V.—See Grupo La

N.A.I.C.S. INDEX

Moderna, S.A.B. de C.V.; *Int'l*, pg. 3131
MOLINOS MODERNOS, S.A.—See General Mills, Inc.; *U.S. Public*, pg. 922
MOLSA SAN SALVADOR—See General Mills, Inc.; *U.S. Public*, pg. 922
MOULINS SOUFFLET PANTIN S.A.—See Etablissements J. Soufflet; *Int'l*, pg. 2519
NATIONAL MILLS - LEBANON WLL—See Al Ghurair Investment LLC; *Int'l*, pg. 278
NATIONAL STARCH & CHEMICAL (THAILAND) LTD.—See Ingredion Incorporated; *U.S. Public*, pg. 1124
NIGERIA EAGLE FLOUR MILLS LIMITED—See Flour Mills of Nigeria Plc.; *Int'l*, pg. 2709
NORTH DAKOTA MILL & ELEVATOR ASSOCIATION; *U.S. Private*, pg. 2945
NORTHERN NIGERIA FLOUR MILLS PLC—See Flour Mills of Nigeria Plc.; *Int'l*, pg. 2709
PARRISH & HEIMBECKER, LIMITED - P&H FOODS HANOVER PROCESSING PLANT—See Exceldor Cooperative Avicole; *Int'l*, pg. 2578
PENNINE FOODS—See Boparan Holdings Limited; *Int'l*, pg. 1111
P&H MILLING GROUP—See Exceldor Cooperative Avicole; *Int'l*, pg. 2578
THE PILLSBURY COMPANY—See General Mills, Inc.; *U.S. Public*, pg. 922
PT. INGREDION INDONESIA—See Ingredion Incorporated; *U.S. Public*, pg. 1124
QUAKER OATS B.V.—See PepsiCo, Inc.; *U.S. Public*, pg. 1670
RAFHAN MAIZE PRODUCTS CO. LTD—See Ingredion Incorporated; *U.S. Public*, pg. 1124
RESEARCH PRODUCTS COMPANY—See McShares, Inc.; *U.S. Private*, pg. 2644
SERENDIB FLOUR MILLS (PVT) LTD.—See Al Ghurair Investment LLC; *Int'l*, pg. 278
SHAWNEE MILLING CO., INC.; *U.S. Private*, pg. 3628
SIEMER MILLING COMPANY - HOPKINSVILLE FACILITY—See Siemer Milling Company; *U.S. Private*, pg. 3646
SIEMER MILLING COMPANY; *U.S. Private*, pg. 3646
SPANGLERS FLOUR MILLS OF MT. JOY—See Wilkins-Rogers, Inc.; *U.S. Private*, pg. 4520
STAFFORD COUNTY FLOUR MILLS CO; *U.S. Private*, pg. 3775
STAR OF THE WEST MILLING CO.; *U.S. Private*, pg. 3785
THE SWEET LIFE ENTERPRISES; *U.S. Private*, pg. 4125
TABLEX MILLER, S.A. DE C.V.—See Grupo La Moderna, S.A.B. de C.V.; *Int'l*, pg. 3131
THAI FARM INTERNATIONAL LIMITED—See Flour Mills of Nigeria Plc.; *Int'l*, pg. 2709
TORTIMASA, S.A.—See Gruma, S.A.B. de C.V.; *Int'l*, pg. 3114
THE UHLMANN COMPANY; *U.S. Private*, pg. 4128
YEMEN COMPANY FOR FLOUR MILLS & SILOS-HODEIDAH—See Hayel Saeed Anam Group of Companies; *Int'l*, pg. 3291

311212 — RICE MILLING

AMERICAN RICE, INC.-FREEPORT—See Ebro Foods S.A.; *Int'l*, pg. 2287
AMERICAN RICE, INC.—See Ebro Foods S.A.; *Int'l*, pg. 2287
BOOST NUTRITION C.V.—See Ebro Foods S.A.; *Int'l*, pg. 2287
BUSCH AGRICULTURAL RESOURCES, INC.—See Anheuser-Busch InBev SA/NV; *Int'l*, pg. 465
CENTRAL MILLING COMPANY; *U.S. Private*, pg. 822
CHAMAN LAL SETIA EXPORT LTD.; *Int'l*, pg. 1439
CORMIER RICE MILLING COMPANY, INC.; *U.S. Private*, pg. 1050
EBROFROST DENMARK A/S—See Ebro Foods S.A.; *Int'l*, pg. 2286
EURYZA REIS GMBH—See Ebro Foods S.A.; *Int'l*, pg. 2286
FARMERS RICE COOPERATIVE; *U.S. Private*, pg. 1478
FAR WEST RICE; *U.S. Private*, pg. 1473
GOLDEN RESOURCES DEVELOPMENT LIMITED—See Golden Resources Development International Limited; *Int'l*, pg. 3031
GOLDEN RIDGE RICE MILLES, INC.—See RICEBRAN TECHNOLOGIES; *U.S. Public*, pg. 1797
GULF RICE ARKANSAS, LLC.; *U.S. Private*, pg. 1816
HERBA RICEMILLS ROM S.R.L.—See Ebro Foods S.A.; *Int'l*, pg. 2286
HERBA RICEMILLS, S.L.U.—See Ebro Foods S.A.; *Int'l*, pg. 2286
H. NAGEL & SON CO.; *U.S. Private*, pg. 1825
KAWTHER GRAIN (PRIVATE) LIMITED—See A.K. Al-Muhaidib & Sons Group of Companies; *Int'l*, pg. 25
KODA FARMS, INC.; *U.S. Private*, pg. 2336
LASSIE B.V.—See Ebro Foods S.A.; *Int'l*, pg. 2286
LOUISIANA RICE MILL, LLC.; *U.S. Private*, pg. 2500
MILLTEC MACHINERY PRIVATE LIMITED—See Ag Growth International Inc.; *Int'l*, pg. 198
MUNDI RISO S.R.L.—See Ebro Foods S.A.; *Int'l*, pg. 2287
MUNDIRIZ, S.A.—See Ebro Foods S.A.; *Int'l*, pg. 2287
PACIFIC INTERNATIONAL RICE MILLS—See Anheuser-Busch InBev SA/NV; *Int'l*, pg. 465
PENDLETON FLOUR MILLS, LLC.; *U.S. Private*, pg. 3132
PICRIC LIMITED—See A.K. Al-Muhaidib & Sons Group of Companies; *Int'l*, pg. 25
PLANTERS RICE MILL LLC.; *U.S. Private*, pg. 3197
PRODUCERS RICE MILL, INC.; *U.S. Private*, pg. 3273
PT BERSATU INTERNATIONAL FOOD INDUSTRIES—See EKA Noodles Berhad; *Int'l*, pg. 2338
REEM RICE MILLS (PRIVATE) LIMITED—See A.K. Al-Muhaidib & Sons Group of Companies; *Int'l*, pg. 24
RICEBRAN TECHNOLOGIES; *U.S. Public*, pg. 1797
RICELAND FOODS, INC.; *U.S. Private*, pg. 3425
RICELAND MAGYARORSZAG KFT—See Ebro Foods S.A.; *Int'l*, pg. 2287
RIVIANA FOODS INC.—See Ebro Foods S.A.; *Int'l*, pg. 2287
RIVIANA INTERNATIONAL INC.—See Ebro Foods S.A.; *Int'l*, pg. 2287
SAGE V FOODS, LLC; *U.S. Private*, pg. 3527
S&B HERBA FOODS, LTD.—See Ebro Foods S.A.; *Int'l*, pg. 2287
SUNWEST MILLING COMPANY, INC.; *U.S. Private*, pg. 3874
TWENTY-FIRST CENTURY GRAIN PROCESSING COOPERATIVE; *U.S. Private*, pg. 4264
VEETEE RICE LIMITED—See A.K. Al-Muhaidib & Sons Group of Companies; *Int'l*, pg. 24

311213 — MALT MANUFACTURING

BAIRDS MALT LTD.—See GrainCorp Limited; *Int'l*, pg. 3052
BARRETT BURSTON MALTING CO. PTY. LTD.—See GrainCorp Limited; *Int'l*, pg. 3052
BARRETT BURSTON MALTING CO. WA PTY. LIMITED—See GrainCorp Limited; *Int'l*, pg. 3052
BELGOMALT S.A.—See Axereal Union de Cooperatives Agricoles; *Int'l*, pg. 767
BOORTMALT N.V.—See Axereal Union de Cooperatives Agricoles; *Int'l*, pg. 767
BOUQUET COLLECTION, INC.; *U.S. Private*, pg. 624
BRIESS MALT & INGREDIENTS CO.; *U.S. Private*, pg. 650
CANADA MALTING CO LIMITED—See GrainCorp Limited; *Int'l*, pg. 3052
CARGILL MALT—See Axereal Union de Cooperatives Agricoles; *Int'l*, pg. 767
CARGILL MALT—See Axereal Union de Cooperatives Agricoles; *Int'l*, pg. 767
CARIB BREWERY LIMITED—See ANSA McAL Limited; pg. 477
COMPAGNIE DES LEVURES LESAFFRE SA; *Int'l*, pg. 1738
COUNTRY MALT GROUP; *U.S. Private*, pg. 1067
DANISH MALTING GROUP POLSKA SP. Z.O.O.—See Carlsberg A/S; *Int'l*, pg. 1340
ETABLISSEMENTS J. SOUFFLET; *Int'l*, pg. 2519
GREAT WESTERN MALTING CO.—See GrainCorp Limited; *Int'l*, pg. 3052
HEINRICH DURST MALZFABRIKEN GMBH & CO. KG—See Etablissements J. Soufflet; *Int'l*, pg. 2519
JOE WHITE MALTINGS PTY. LTD.—See Cargill, Inc.; *U.S. Private*, pg. 755
JSC FE EFES KAZAKHSTAN BREWERY—See Anadolu Efes Biracilik ve Malt Sanayii A.S.; *Int'l*, pg. 445
MAGIC VALLEY FRESH FROZEN, INC.; *U.S. Private*, pg. 2546
MALTERIES FRANC-BELGES S.A.—See Etablissements J. Soufflet; *Int'l*, pg. 2519
MALT PRODUCTS CORP. OF N.J.; *U.S. Private*, pg. 2558
NYP INC; *U.S. Private*, pg. 2976
PHILADELPHIA BEER WORKS INC.; *U.S. Private*, pg. 3168
PRAIRIE MALT LIMITED—See Cargill, Inc.; *U.S. Private*, pg. 759
PYRAMID GILMAN STREET PROPERTY, LLC—See Florida Ice and Farm Co. S.A.; *Int'l*, pg. 2708
RAHR MALTING CANADA LTD—See Rahr Malting Co. Inc.; *U.S. Private*, pg. 3346
RAHR MALTING CO. INC.; *U.S. Private*, pg. 3346
RAHR MALTING CO—See Rahr Corporation; *U.S. Private*, pg. 3346
SAFMEX SA DE CV—See Compagnie des Levures Lesaffre SA; *Int'l*, pg. 1739
SCOTGRAIN AGRICULTURE LTD.—See GrainCorp Limited; *Int'l*, pg. 3052
SEQUOIA ENTERPRISES, INC.; *U.S. Private*, pg. 3612
THE SOUTH AFRICAN BREWERIES MALTINGS (PTY) LTD—See Anheuser-Busch InBev SA/NV; *Int'l*, pg. 465
SUNNY CREEK FARM, LLC.; *U.S. Private*, pg. 3868
THE SWAEN B.V.—See Asahi Group Holdings Ltd.; *Int'l*, pg. 594
TAGAWA GREENHOUSES, INC.; *U.S. Private*, pg. 3922
VICGRAIN PTY LIMITED—See GrainCorp Limited; *Int'l*, pg. 3052
VITERRA LTD.—See Glencore plc; *Int'l*, pg. 2990

311221 — WET CORN MILLING AND STARCH MANUFACTURING

ADM AGRI-INDUSTRIES COMPANY—See Archer-Daniels-Midland Company; *U.S. Public*, pg. 184
ADM BAZANCOURT SASU—See Archer-Daniels-Midland Company; *U.S. Public*, pg. 181
ADM CLINTON BIOPROCESSING, INC.—See Archer-Daniels-Midland Company; *U.S. Public*, pg. 181
ADM NATURAL HEALTH & NUTRITION—See Archer-Daniels-Midland Company; *U.S. Public*, pg. 182
ADM NEW ZEALAND LTD.—See Archer-Daniels-Midland Company; *U.S. Public*, pg. 182
ADM NORTH AMERICAN OILSEED PROCESSING DIVISION—See Archer-Daniels-Midland Company; *U.S. Public*, pg. 182
ADM RAZGRAD EAD—See Archer-Daniels-Midland Company; *U.S. Public*, pg. 182
ADM SPECIALTY INGREDIENTS—See Archer-Daniels-Midland Company; *U.S. Public*, pg. 182
ADM TRADING AUSTRALIA PTY. LTD.—See Archer-Daniels-Midland Company; *U.S. Public*, pg. 182
ADM WILD VALENCIA—See Archer-Daniels-Midland Company; *U.S. Public*, pg. 183
AGRINATIONAL INSURANCE COMPANY—See Archer-Daniels-Midland Company; *U.S. Public*, pg. 183
AMAIZEINGLY GREEN PRODUCTS, L.P.; *Int'l*, pg. 408
AMYLON S.A.—See Boromir Prod SA Buzau; *Int'l*, pg. 1114
AMYLUM BULGARIA EAD—See Archer-Daniels-Midland Company; *U.S. Public*, pg. 183
AMYLUM NISASTA SANAYI TICARET ANONIM SIRKETI—See Archer-Daniels-Midland Company; *U.S. Public*, pg. 183
ANDERSON CUSTOM PROCESSING, INC. - BELLEVILLE PLANT—See Anderson Custom Processing, Inc.; *U.S. Private*, pg. 276
ANDERSON CUSTOM PROCESSING, INC.; *U.S. Private*, pg. 276
ANDRITZ FEED & BIOFUEL LTD.—See ANDRITZ AG; *Int'l*, pg. 453
ARCHER-DANIELS-MIDLAND COMPANY - CORN PROCESSING—See Archer-Daniels-Midland Company; *U.S. Public*, pg. 184
ARCHER DANIELS MIDLAND COMPNAY - CLINTON—See Archer-Daniels-Midland Company; *U.S. Public*, pg. 184
ARCHER DANIELS MIDLAND CO.—See Archer-Daniels-Midland Company; *U.S. Public*, pg. 183
ARCHER DANIELS MIDLAND CO.—See Archer-Daniels-Midland Company; *U.S. Public*, pg. 183
ARCHER DANIELS MIDLAND CO.—See Archer-Daniels-Midland Company; *U.S. Public*, pg. 183
CARGILL BENELUX B.V.—See Cargill, Inc.; *U.S. Private*, pg. 756
CARGILL CORN MILLING—See Cargill, Inc.; *U.S. Private*, pg. 756
CARGILL CORN MILLING—See Cargill, Inc.; *U.S. Private*, pg. 756
CARGILL GRAIN & OILSEEDS (NANTONG) CO., LTD.—See Cargill, Inc.; *U.S. Private*, pg. 756
CARGILL NORDIC OY—See Cargill, Inc.; *U.S. Private*, pg. 758
CHEMSTAR PRODUCTS COMPANY; *U.S. Private*, pg. 872
CHINA ESSENCE GROUP LTD.; *Int'l*, pg. 1500
CHINA SUN BIO-CHEM TECHNOLOGY GROUP COMPANY LTD.; *Int'l*, pg. 1556
CHIPPEWA VALLEY AGRAFUELS COOPERATIVE; *U.S. Private*, pg. 886
COLORADO SWEET GOLD LLC; *U.S. Private*, pg. 975
COPAM-COMPANHIA PORTUGUESA DE AMIDOS SA; *Int'l*, pg. 1792
CORN PRODUCTS BRASIL INGREDIENTES INDUSTRIAIS LTDA.—See Ingredion Incorporated; *U.S. Public*, pg. 1123
CORN PRODUCTS CHILE-INDUCORN S.A.—See Ingredion Incorporated; *U.S. Public*, pg. 1123
CORN PRODUCTS KENYA LTD.—See Ingredion Incorporated; *U.S. Public*, pg. 1123
CORN PRODUCTS SOUTHERN CONE S.A.—See Ingredion Incorporated; *U.S. Public*, pg. 1123
CORN PRODUCTS THAILAND CO., LTD.—See Ingredion Incorporated; *U.S. Public*, pg. 1123
CTI ASCEND CO., LTD.—See CTI Engineering Co., Ltd.; *Int'l*, pg. 1870
DAQING BORUN BIOTECHNOLOGY CO., LTD.—See CHINA NEW BORUN CORPORATION; *Int'l*, pg. 1534
EGYPTIAN STARCH & GLUCOSE COMPANY—See Cairo Three A Group; *Int'l*, pg. 1253
EMSLAND-STARKE ASIA PACIFIC PTE LTD.—See Emsland-Starke GmbH; *Int'l*, pg. 2394
EMSLAND-STARKE GMBH GOLSSEN FACTORY—See Emsland-Starke GmbH; *Int'l*, pg. 2394
EMSLAND-STARKE GMBH KYRITZ FACTORY—See Emsland-Starke GmbH; *Int'l*, pg. 2394
EMSLAND-STARKE GMBH WIETZENDORF FACTORY—See Emsland-Starke GmbH; *Int'l*, pg. 2394
EMSLAND-STARKE LOGISTICS GMBH & CO. KG—See Emsland-Starke GmbH; *Int'l*, pg. 2394

311221 — WET CORN MILLING AN...

GLUCOSAN COMPANY; *Int'l*, pg. 3011
GOLDEN TECHNOLOGIES COMPANY, INC.—See Ingredion Incorporated; *U.S. Public*, pg. 1123
GRAIN PROCESSING CORPORATION—See Kent Corporation; *U.S. Private*, pg. 2287
GTC OATS, INC.—See Ingredion Incorporated; *U.S. Public*, pg. 1123
HIGH SEA SUGAR INC.; *U.S. Private*, pg. 1936
INDUSTRIAS DEL MAIZ S.A.-CORN PRODUCTS ANDINA—See Ingredion Incorporated; *U.S. Public*, pg. 1123
INGREDION ANZ PTY LTD.—See Ingredion Incorporated; *U.S. Public*, pg. 1123
INGREDION ARGENTINA S.A.—See Ingredion Incorporated; *U.S. Public*, pg. 1123
INGREDION BRASIL INGREDIENTES INDUSTRIAIS LTDA.—See Ingredion Incorporated; *U.S. Public*, pg. 1123
INGREDION CANADA CORPORATION—See Ingredion Incorporated; *U.S. Public*, pg. 1123
INGREDION CHILE S.A.—See Ingredion Incorporated; *U.S. Public*, pg. 1123
INGREDION COLOMBIA S.A.—See Ingredion Incorporated; *U.S. Public*, pg. 1123
INGREDION INCORPORATED; *U.S. Public*, pg. 1122
INGREDION SOUTH AFRICA (PTY) LTD.—See Ingredion Incorporated; *U.S. Public*, pg. 1123
INGREDION UK LIMITED—See Ingredion Incorporated; *U.S. Public*, pg. 1123
INTER-NATIONAL STARCH INC.—See Ingredion Incorporated; *U.S. Public*, pg. 1124
MIWON VIETNAM CO., LTD. - TAY NINH TAPIOCA STARCH FACTORY—See Daesang Corporation; *Int'l*, pg. 1909
M & M MILLING, INC.; *U.S. Private*, pg. 2523
N-STARCH SDN. BHD.—See Ingredion Incorporated; *U.S. Public*, pg. 1124
OROWEAT FOODS—See Grupo Bimbo, S.A.B. de C.V.; *Int'l*, pg. 3122
PRODUCTOS DE MAIZ S.A.—See Ingredion Incorporated; *U.S. Public*, pg. 1124
PRODUCTOS DE MAIZ URUGUAY S.A.—See Ingredion Incorporated; *U.S. Public*, pg. 1124
PROGOLD LLC—See American Crystal Sugar Company; *U.S. Public*, pg. 98
PT SORINI AGRO ASIA CORPORINDO TBK.—See Cargill, Inc.; *U.S. Private*, pg. 759
RAFHAN MAIZE PRODUCTS CO. LTD.—See Ingredion Incorporated; *U.S. Public*, pg. 1124
SEMOLINA MISIR IRMIGI GIDA SANAYI VE TICARET A.S.—See Gruma, S.A.B. de C.V.; *Int'l*, pg. 3114
SERETRAM—See General Mills, Inc.; *U.S. Public*, pg. 922
SIOUXLAND ENERGY COOPERATIVE; *U.S. Private*, pg. 3671
STAMFORD FOOD INDUSTRIES SDN. BHD.—See Ingredion Incorporated; *U.S. Public*, pg. 1124
SUD-TREBER GMBH—See BayWa AG; *Int'l*, pg. 919
WESTFALISCHE LEBENSMITTEL WERKE LINDEMANN GMBH & CO. KG—See Bunge Limited; *U.S. Public*, pg. 412

311224 — SOYBEAN AND OTHER OILSEED PROCESSING

ADM AGRI-INDUSTRIES COMPANY—See Archer-Daniels-Midland Company; *U.S. Public*, pg. 184
ADM AGRI-INDUSTRIES COMPANY—See Archer-Daniels-Midland Company; *U.S. Public*, pg. 184
ADM AGRI-INDUSTRIES COMPANY—See Archer-Daniels-Midland Company; *U.S. Public*, pg. 184
ADM AGRI-INDUSTRIES COMPANY—See Archer-Daniels-Midland Company; *U.S. Public*, pg. 184
ADM ANTWERP NV—See Archer-Daniels-Midland Company; *U.S. Public*, pg. 181
ADM BIO-PRODUCTOS, S.A. DE C.V.—See Archer-Daniels-Midland Company; *U.S. Public*, pg. 181
AGRO HARAPAN LESTARI SDN. BHD.—See Carson Cumberbatch PLC; *Int'l*, pg. 1347
AJANTA SOYA LIMITED; *Int'l*, pg. 255
ALFA LAVAL COPENHAGEN A/S—See Alfa Laval AB; *Int'l*, pg. 309
ALFOREX SEEDS LLC—See Corteva, Inc.; *U.S. Public*, pg. 580
ARCHER DANIELS MIDLAND CO.—See Archer-Daniels-Midland Company; *U.S. Public*, pg. 183
ARCHER DANIELS MIDLAND CO.—See Archer-Daniels-Midland Company; *U.S. Public*, pg. 183
ARCHER DANIELS MIDLAND CO.—See Archer-Daniels-Midland Company; *U.S. Public*, pg. 183
ASHIANA AGRO INDUSTRIES LIMITED; *Int'l*, pg. 607
ASIA SEED CO., LTD.; *Int'l*, pg. 615
AUSTRALIAN AGRICULTURAL PROJECTS LTD; *Int'l*, pg. 720
BAYER CROPSCIENCE RAPS GMBH—See Bayer Aktiengesellschaft; *Int'l*, pg. 903
BERAKAN MAJU SDN BHD—See IJM Corporation Berhad; *Int'l*, pg. 3608
BIOSEED VIETNAM LIMITED—See DCM Shriram Limited; *Int'l*, pg. 1992
BUNGE ARGENTINA—See Bunge Limited; *U.S. Public*, pg. 411
BUNGE CANADA—See Bunge Limited; *U.S. Public*, pg. 411
BUNGE CORPORATION LTD.—See Bunge Limited; *U.S. Public*, pg. 411
BUNGE LODERS CROKLAAN OILS B.V.—See Bunge Limited; *U.S. Public*, pg. 411
BUNGE LODERS CROKLAAN OILS SDN BHD—See Bunge Limited; *U.S. Public*, pg. 411
BUNG LODERS CROKLAAN B.V.—See Bunge Limited; *U.S. Public*, pg. 411
CARGILL AGRI PURINA, INC. - SONGTAN PLANT—See Cargill, Inc.; *U.S. Private*, pg. 755
CARGILL GMBH—See Cargill, Inc.; *U.S. Private*, pg. 756
CARGILL INC.—See Cargill, Inc.; *U.S. Private*, pg. 756
CARGILL INC.—See Cargill, Inc.; *U.S. Private*, pg. 756
CARGILL INC.—See Cargill, Inc.; *U.S. Private*, pg. 757
CARGILL INTERNATIONAL S.A.—See Cargill, Inc.; *U.S. Private*, pg. 757
CARGILL JAPAN LIMITED—See Cargill, Inc.; *U.S. Private*, pg. 757
CARGILL LIMITED—See Cargill, Inc.; *U.S. Private*, pg. 757
CARGILL S.L.U.—See Cargill, Inc.; *U.S. Private*, pg. 758
CARGILL YUG, LLC—See Cargill, Inc.; *U.S. Private*, pg. 759
CHONGQING XINFU FOOD CO., LTD.—See COFCO Limited; *Int'l*, pg. 1692
CHS INC. - MANKATO OILSEED PROCESSING PLANT—See CHS INC.; *U.S. Public*, pg. 491
CHUMPORN PALM OIL INDUSTRY PUBLIC COMPANY LIMITED; *Int'l*, pg. 1596
COROMANDEL AGRO PRODUCTS & OILS LTD.; *Int'l*, pg. 1801
COVERCRESS INC.—See Bayer Aktiengesellschaft; *Int'l*, pg. 907
CPI AGROTECH CO., LTD.—See Chumporn Palm Oil Industry Public Company Limited; *Int'l*, pg. 1596
CRESTON BEAN PROCESSING, L.L.C.—See CHS INC.; *U.S. Public*, pg. 492
CVO PETROCHEMICAL REFINERY LIMITED; *Int'l*, pg. 1889
DAODAOQUAN GRAIN AND OIL CO LTD; *Int'l*, pg. 1970
DEKEL AGRI-VISION PLC; *Int'l*, pg. 2005
DELMAR COMMODITIES LTD. - NEWDALE ELEVATOR FACILITY—See Ceres Global Ag Corp.; *U.S. Public*, pg. 475
DELMAR COMMODITIES LTD. - SOMERSET ELEVATOR FACILITY—See Ceres Global Ag Corp.; *U.S. Public*, pg. 475
DELTA OIL MILL; *U.S. Private*, pg. 1201
DEOLEO, S.A.—See CVC Capital Partners SICAV-FIS S.A.; *Int'l*, pg. 1883
DESERT WHALE JOJOBA COMPANY, INC.—See H.I.G. Capital, LLC; *U.S. Private*, pg. 1832
DUNNS (LONG SUTTON) LTD; *Int'l*, pg. 2227
EARTH GEN-BIOFUEL INC.; *U.S. Public*, pg. 703
EDIBLE OIL COMPANY (D) LLC—See Al Ghurair Investment LLC; *Int'l*, pg. 278
EXTRACTED OIL & DERIVATIVES CO.; *U.S. Public*, pg. 813
FIRST RESOURCES LIMITED; *Int'l*, pg. 2687
FTN COCOA PROCESSORS PLC; *Int'l*, pg. 2800
FUJIAN DABOMB PROTEIN BIOTECH CORP.—See DaBomb Protein Corp.; *Int'l*, pg. 1903
FUJI FRESH FOODS CO., LTD.—See Fuji Oil Holdings Inc.; *Int'l*, pg. 2815
FWUSOW INDUSTRY CO., LTD. - TAICHUNG HARBOR FACTORY—See Fwusow Industry Co., Ltd.; *Int'l*, pg. 2859
G3 CANADA LIMITED—See Bunge Limited; *U.S. Public*, pg. 412
GLOBAL PALM RESOURCES HOLDINGS LIMITED; *Int'l*, pg. 3000
GOKUL AGRO RESOURCES LTD.—See Gokul Refoils and Solvent Limited; *Int'l*, pg. 3023
GOLDEN AGRI-RESOURCES IBERIA, S.L.—See Golden Agri-Resources Ltd.; *Int'l*, pg. 3028
GOLDEN PEANUT AND TREE NUT SA (PTY), LTD.—See Archer-Daniels-Midland Company; *U.S. Public*, pg. 185
GOLDEN WEB LTD.; *Int'l*, pg. 3032
GOODHOPE ASIA HOLDINGS LTD—See Carson Cumberbatch PLC; *Int'l*, pg. 1347
GUJARAT AMBUJA EXPORTS LTD. - KADI DIVISION—See Gujarat Ambuja Exports Ltd.; *Int'l*, pg. 3175
GULF VEGETABLE OIL COMPANY (NABATI)—See Ajwa Group for Food Industries Holding Ltd. Co.; *Int'l*, pg. 259
HARBIN GONG DA HIGH-TECH ENTERPRISE DEVELOPMENT CO., LTD.; *Int'l*, pg. 3270
HARN LEN CORPORATION BHD; *Int'l*, pg. 3278
HARTSVILLE OIL MILL; *U.S. Private*, pg. 1874
HOMEGROWN NATURAL FOODS INC.; *U.S. Private*, pg. 1973
IOWA RENEWABLE ENERGY, LLC; *U.S. Private*, pg. 2135
JORDAN VEGETABLE OIL INDUSTRIES COMPANY—See Arab Supply & Trading Co.; *Int'l*, pg. 532
KEHLIBAR EOOD—See Agria Group Holding JSC; *Int'l*, pg. 216
KILANG KOSFARM SDN BHD—See Far East Holdings Berhad; *Int'l*, pg. 2616
LODERS CROKLAAN FOR OILS S.A.E.—See Bunge Limited; *U.S. Public*, pg. 412
MARSA KRAFT JACOBS SUCHARD SABANCI GIDA SANAYI VE TICARET A.S.—See Haci Omer Sabanci Holding A.S.; *Int'l*, pg. 3204
MARSA KRAFT JACOBS SUCHARD SABANCI GIDA SANAYI VE TICARET A.S.—See Mondelez International, Inc.; *U.S. Public*, pg. 1462
MISR GULF OIL PROCESSING CO.—See Ajwa Group for Food Industries Holding Ltd. Co.; *Int'l*, pg. 259
NATURE SOY LLC—See Keystone Capital, Inc.; *U.S. Private*, pg. 2295
NEDIN PTY. LTD.—See AFGRI Limited; *Int'l*, pg. 188
OWENSBORO GRAIN COMPANY, LLC—See Cargill, Inc.; *U.S. Private*, pg. 759
PALMAJU EDIBLE OIL SDN. BHD.—See Fuji Oil Holdings Inc.; *Int'l*, pg. 2815
PLANTERS COTTON OIL MILL INC.; *U.S. Private*, pg. 3197
PRODUCERS COOP OIL MILL; *U.S. Private*, pg. 3272
PT AGRO HARAPAN LESTARI—See Carson Cumberbatch PLC; *Int'l*, pg. 1347
PT DAMI MAS SEJAHTERA—See Golden Agri-Resources Ltd.; *Int'l*, pg. 3028
PT DJUANDASAWIT LESTARI—See Golden Agri-Resources Ltd.; *Int'l*, pg. 3028
PT HARAPAN SAWIT LESTARI—See Cargill, Inc.; *U.S. Private*, pg. 759
PT SINAR MAS AGRO RESOURCES & TECHNOLOGY TBK—See Golden Agri-Resources Ltd.; *Int'l*, pg. 3028
PT SUMBER INDAHPERKASA—See Golden Agri-Resources Ltd.; *Int'l*, pg. 3028
PYCO INDUSTRIES, INC.; *U.S. Private*, pg. 3308
SAUDI TUNISIAN COMPANY—See Ajwa Group for Food Industries Holding Ltd. Co.; *Int'l*, pg. 259
SHANDONG LONGTENG FUJI FOODSTUFFS CO., LTD.—See Fuji Oil Holdings Inc.; *Int'l*, pg. 2815
SHANGHAI XUYANG FOOD CO., LTD.—See Fuji Oil Holdings Inc.; *Int'l*, pg. 2816
SHINING GOLD OILSEED CRUSHING (NINGBO) CO., LTD—See Golden Agri-Resources Ltd.; *Int'l*, pg. 3028
SOJAPROTEIN D.O.O.—See Archer-Daniels-Midland Company; *U.S. Public*, pg. 185
SONOCO BOARD MILLS LIMITED—See Sonoco Products Company; *U.S. Public*, pg. 1906
SOUTH DAKOTA SOYBEAN PROCESSORS, LLC; *U.S. Private*, pg. 3722
SOYAFARM CO., LTD.—See Fuji Oil Holdings Inc.; *Int'l*, pg. 2816
SOYA FARM USA INC.—See Fuji Oil Holdings Inc.; *Int'l*, pg. 2816
TIANJIN FUJI PROTEIN CO., LTD.—See Fuji Oil Holdings Inc.; *Int'l*, pg. 2816
VALLEY CO-OP OIL MILL INC.; *U.S. Private*, pg. 4333
VITASOY AUSTRALIA PRODUCTS PTY. LTD.—See Bega Cheese Ltd.; *Int'l*, pg. 940
WALTER RAU NEUSSER OL UND FETT AG—See Bunge Limited; *U.S. Public*, pg. 412
ZEELAND FARM SERVICES INC.; *U.S. Private*, pg. 4599

311225 — FATS AND OILS REFINING AND BLENDING

AAK AB; *Int'l*, pg. 31
AAK AUST. PTY. LTD.—See AAK AB; *Int'l*, pg. 31
AAK BELGIUM N.V.—See AAK AB; *Int'l*, pg. 31
AAK BF SARL—See AAK AB; *Int'l*, pg. 31
AAK BURKINA FASO SARL—See AAK AB; *Int'l*, pg. 31
AAK CANADA LTD.—See AAK AB; *Int'l*, pg. 31
AAK CHINA LTD.—See AAK AB; *Int'l*, pg. 31
AAK COTE D'IVOIRE SASU—See AAK AB; *Int'l*, pg. 31
AAK DALBY AB—See AAK AB; *Int'l*, pg. 32
AAK DENMARK AS—See AAK AB; *Int'l*, pg. 32
AAK DO BRASIL INDUSTRIA E COMERCIA DE OLEOS VEGETAIS LTDA—See AAK AB; *Int'l*, pg. 32
AAK DO BRASIL INDUSTRIA E COMERCIO DE OLEOS VEGETAIS LTDA—See AAK AB; *Int'l*, pg. 32
AAK GERMANY GMBH—See AAK AB; *Int'l*, pg. 32
AAK KAMANI PVT. LTD.—See AAK AB; *Int'l*, pg. 32
AAK MALAYSIA SDN. BHD.—See AAK AB; *Int'l*, pg. 32
AAK MALI SARL—See AAK AB; *Int'l*, pg. 32
AAK MIYOSHI JAPAN CO., LTD.—See AAK AB; *Int'l*, pg. 32
AAK NORWAY AS—See AAK AB; *Int'l*, pg. 32
AAK OOO—See AAK AB; *Int'l*, pg. 32
AAK POLAND SP. Z O. O.—See AAK AB; *Int'l*, pg. 32
AAK ROTTERDAM BV—See AAK AB; *Int'l*, pg. 32
AAK SINGAPORE PTE. LTD.—See AAK AB; *Int'l*, pg. 32
AAK TURKEY GIDA SANAYI VE TICARET LIMITED SIRKETI—See AAK AB; *Int'l*, pg. 32
AAK TURKEY GIDA SANAY VE TICARET LIMITED—See AAK AB; *Int'l*, pg. 32
AAK (UK) LIMITED—See AAK AB; *Int'l*, pg. 31
AAK (UK) LIMITED—See AAK AB; *Int'l*, pg. 31
AAK USA K1/K2 LLC—See AAK AB; *Int'l*, pg. 32
AAK USA RICHMOND CORP.—See AAK AB; *Int'l*, pg. 32
AARHUS 3 A/S—See AAK AB; *Int'l*, pg. 32

N.A.I.C.S. INDEX

311230 — BREAKFAST CEREAL MA...

AARHUSKARLSHAMN SWEDEN AB—See AAK AB; *Int'l*, pg. 32
AARHUS MALAYSIA SDN. BHD.—See AAK AB; *Int'l*, pg. 32
ADAMS VEGETABLE OILS, INC.—See The Adams Group Inc.; *U.S. Private*, pg. 3981
ADEKA FOODS (CHANGSHU) CO., LTD.—See Adeka Corporation; *Int'l*, pg. 141
ADEKA (SINGAPORE) PTE. LTD.—See Adeka Corporation; *Int'l*, pg. 141
ADM DO BRASIL LTDA—See Archer-Daniels-Midland Company; *U.S. Public*, pg. 184
AL-AHLIA VEGETABLE OIL COMPANY; *Int'l*, pg. 284
ALTINYAG KOMBINALARI AS; *Int'l*, pg. 393
AMBAR PROTEIN INDUSTRIES LIMITED; *Int'l*, pg. 413
ANGLO-EASTERN PLANTATIONS (M) SDN. BHD.—See Anglo Eastern Plantations PLC; *Int'l*, pg. 463
AOX PTY LTD—See Australian Agricultural Projects Ltd; *Int'l*, pg. 721
ARCHER DANIELS MIDLAND CO.—See Archer-Daniels-Midland Company; *U.S. Public*, pg. 183
ARCHER DANIELS MIDLAND CO.—See Archer-Daniels-Midland Company; *U.S. Public*, pg. 183
ARCHER DANIELS MIDLAND CO.—See Archer-Daniels-Midland Company; *U.S. Public*, pg. 184
ARGUS S.A.; *Int'l*, pg. 563
ASIA-POTASH INTERNATIONAL INVESTMENT (GUANGZHOU) CO., LTD.; *Int'l*, pg. 616
AUBADE HANDELS GMBH—See Calida Holding AG; *Int'l*, pg. 1264
AUSCOL PTY LTD—See GrainCorp Limited; *Int'l*, pg. 3052
BAKER COMMODITIES INC.-LOS ANGELES—See Baker Commodities, Inc.; *U.S. Private*, pg. 455
BIDCO OIL REFINERIES LIMITED; *Int'l*, pg. 1019
BIMAL D.D.; *Int'l*, pg. 1032
BIPORT BULKERS SDN. BHD.—See Bintulu Port Holdings Berhad; *Int'l*, pg. 1034
B.R. COHN WINERY—See Vintage Wine Estates, Inc.; *U.S. Public*, pg. 2298
BUNGE LODERS CROKLAAN (GHANA) LTD.—See Bunge Limited; *U.S. Public*, pg. 411
BUNGE LODERS CROKLAAN (SHANGHAI) TRADING CO. LTD.—See Bunge Limited; *U.S. Public*, pg. 411
BUNGE LODERS (XIAMEN) OILS TECHNOLOGY, CO. LTD.—See Bunge Limited; *U.S. Public*, pg. 411
BUNGE (NANJING) GRAIN AND OILS CO.,LTD.—See Bunge Limited; *U.S. Public*, pg. 411
BUNGE NORTH AMERICA EAST—See Bunge Limited; *U.S. Public*, pg. 411
CABIO BIOTECH WUHAN CO., LTD.; *Int'l*, pg. 1245
CALIFORNIA OLIVE RANCH INC.; *U.S. Private*, pg. 720
CARGILL INC.—See Cargill, Inc.; *U.S. Private*, pg. 757
CARGILL INC.—See Cargill, Inc.; *U.S. Private*, pg. 757
CARGILL NV—See Cargill, Inc.; *U.S. Private*, pg. 756
CARGILL OIL PACKERS BVBA—See Cargill, Inc.; *U.S. Private*, pg. 756
CARGILL OILS S.A.—See Cargill, Inc.; *U.S. Private*, pg. 755
CEPATWAWASAN GROUP BERHAD; *Int'l*, pg. 1420
CFC, INC.; *U.S. Private*, pg. 843
CIAN AGRO INDUSTRIES & INFRASTRUCTURE LIMITED; *Int'l*, pg. 1602
COAST PACKING COMPANY; *U.S. Private*, pg. 954
COBRAM ESTATE PTY LTD—See Boundary Bend Limited; *Int'l*, pg. 1119
CONTINENTAL PALMS PTE. LTD.—See C.I. Holdings Berhad; *Int'l*, pg. 1243
CONTINENTAL RESOURCES SDN. BHD.—See C.I. Holdings Berhad; *Int'l*, pg. 1243
CRODA EUROPE LTD.—See Croda International plc; *Int'l*, pg. 1852
DARLING INGREDIENTS INC.; *U.S. Public*, pg. 633
DELIMA OIL PRODUCTS SDN. BHD.—See FGV Holdings Bhd; *Int'l*, pg. 2649
DIJAMANT A.D; *Int'l*, pg. 2125
DILIGENT INDUSTRIES LIMITED; *Int'l*, pg. 2125
EA PALM NETWORK CO., LTD.—See Energy Absolute Public Company Limited; *Int'l*, pg. 2422
EASTERN LUBRICANTS BLENDERS LIMITED; *Int'l*, pg. 2273
EAST OCEAN OILS & GRAINS INDUSTRIES; *Int'l*, pg. 2270
EKIZ YAG VE SABUN SANAYI A.S.; *Int'l*, pg. 2338
FGV AGRI SERVICES SDN. BHD.—See FGV Holdings Bhd; *Int'l*, pg. 2649
FUJI OIL ASIA PTE. LTD.—See Fuji Oil Holdings Inc.; *Int'l*, pg. 2815
FUJI OIL EUROPE—See Fuji Oil Holdings Inc.; *Int'l*, pg. 2815
FUJI OIL GHANA LTD.—See Fuji Oil Holdings Inc.; *Int'l*, pg. 2815
FUJI OIL (THAILAND) CO., LTD.—See Fuji Oil Holdings Inc.; *Int'l*, pg. 2815
FUJI VEGETABLE OIL INC. - PLANT—See Fuji Oil Holdings Inc.; *Int'l*, pg. 2815
FUJI VEGETABLE OIL INC.—See Fuji Oil Holdings Inc.; *Int'l*, pg. 2815
GAR PAKISTAN (PVT.) LIMITED—See Golden Agri-Resources Ltd.; *Int'l*, pg. 3027
GEMINI EDIBLES & FATS INDIA PRIVATE LIMITED—See Golden Agri-Resources Ltd.; *Int'l*, pg. 3027
GODREJ INDUSTRIES LTD—See Godrej & Boyce Mfg. Co. Ltd.; *Int'l*, pg. 3020
GOKUL AGRI INTERNATIONAL LTD.—See Gokul Refoils and Solvent Limited; *Int'l*, pg. 3022
GOKUL REFOILS AND SOLVENT LIMITED - GANDHIDHAM UNIT—See Gokul Refoils and Solvent Limited; *Int'l*, pg. 3023
GOKUL REFOILS AND SOLVENT LIMITED; *Int'l*, pg. 3022
GOLDEN AGRI INTERNATIONAL (M) TRADING SDN. BHD.—See Golden Agri-Resources Ltd.; *Int'l*, pg. 3027
GOLDEN AGRI-RESOURCES COLOMBIA S.A.S.—See Golden Agri-Resources Ltd.; *Int'l*, pg. 3028
GOLDEN AGRI RESOURCES (INDIA) PRIVATE LIMITED—See Golden Agri-Resources Ltd.; *Int'l*, pg. 3027
GOLDEN FERTILIZER COMPANY LIMITED—See Flour Mills of Nigeria Plc.; *Int'l*, pg. 2709
GOOD HOPE PLC—See Carson Cumberbatch PLC; *Int'l*, pg. 1347
GUJARAT AMBUJA EXPORTS LTD. - AKOLA DIVISION—See Gujarat Ambuja Exports Ltd.; *Int'l*, pg. 3175
GUJARAT AMBUJA EXPORTS LTD. - MANDSAUR DIVISION—See Gujarat Ambuja Exports Ltd.; *Int'l*, pg. 3175
HANDAN CHENGUANG PRECIOUS OIL CO., LTD—See Chenguang Biotech Group Co., Ltd.; *Int'l*, pg. 1470
HENRY LAMOTTE OILS GMBH—See Henry Lamotte GmbH; *Int'l*, pg. 3355
HK FIBRE SDN. BHD.—See HHRG Berhad; *Int'l*, pg. 3379
HK GUA MUSANG SDN. BHD.—See HHRG Berhad; *Int'l*, pg. 3379
HK KITARAN SDN. BHD.—See HHRG Berhad; *Int'l*, pg. 3379
HOP HING GROUP HOLDINGS LIMITED; *Int'l*, pg. 3473
HWA HONG EDIBLE OIL INDUSTRIES PTE. LTD.—See Hwa Hong Corporation Limited; *Int'l*, pg. 3541
INDO-MALAY PLC—See Carson Cumberbatch PLC; *Int'l*, pg. 1347
ISOBIONICS B.V.—See BASF SE; *Int'l*, pg. 884
J.M. SMUCKER LLC—See The J.M. Smucker Company; *U.S. Public*, pg. 2107
KTC (EDIBLES) LIMITED—See Endless LLP; *Int'l*, pg. 2403
LODERS CROKLAAN USA, LLC—See Bunge Limited; *U.S. Public*, pg. 411
MAURIGO PTE.LTD.—See Gokul Refoils and Solvent Limited; *Int'l*, pg. 3023
MOBIL REFINING AUSTRALIA PTY LTD—See Exxon Mobil Corporation; *U.S. Public*, pg. 817
NEW LEYTE EDIBLE OIL MFG. CORP.—See Fuji Oil Holdings Inc.; *Int'l*, pg. 2815
NINGBO SHINING GOLD CEREAL OIL PORT CO., LTD—See Golden Agri-Resources Ltd.; *Int'l*, pg. 3028
OJSC EZHK—See Gruppa Kompaniy Rusagro OOO; *Int'l*, pg. 3140
OLEO-FATS INC—See D&L Industries, Inc.; *Int'l*, pg. 1899
OLEON N.V.—See Avril SCA; *Int'l*, pg. 750
PACIFIC OLEOCHEMICALS SDN BHD.—See Akzo Nobel N.V.; *Int'l*, pg. 274
PALMTOP SDN BHD—See C.I. Holdings Berhad; *Int'l*, pg. 1243
PAR-WAY TRYSON COMPANY; *U.S. Private*, pg. 3089
POMPEIAN, INC.; *U.S. Private*, pg. 3227
PONTIAN UNITED PLANTATIONS BERHAD—See FGV Holdings Bhd; *Int'l*, pg. 2650
PREDSTAVNISTVO AAK POLAND SP. Z O.O.—See AAK AB; *Int'l*, pg. 32
PREMIUM EDIBLE OIL PRODUCTS LIMITED—See Flour Mills of Nigeria Plc.; *Int'l*, pg. 2709
PREMIUM OILS & FATS SDN. BHD.—See Carson Cumberbatch PLC; *Int'l*, pg. 1347
PREMIUM VEGITABLE OILS SDN. BHD.—See Carson Cumberbatch PLC; *Int'l*, pg. 1347
PT ANGLO-EASTERN PLANTATIONS MANAGEMENT INDONESIA—See Anglo Eastern Plantations PLC; *Int'l*, pg. 463
PT KRESNA DUTA AGROINDO—See Golden Agri-Resources Ltd.; *Int'l*, pg. 3028
PT. MUSIM MAS-FUJI—See Fuji Oil Holdings Inc.; *Int'l*, pg. 2815
PT PURIMAS SASMITA—See Golden Agri-Resources Ltd.; *Int'l*, pg. 3028
PT. RIMBA PLAMA SEJAHTERA—See ELL Environmental Holdings Limited; *Int'l*, pg. 2364
PT SALIM IVOMAS PRATAMA TBK—See First Pacific Company Limited; *Int'l*, pg. 2686
SAMARAAGROPROMPERERABOTKA (SAPP)—See Gruppa Kompaniy Rusagro OOO; *Int'l*, pg. 3140
SELINSING PLC—See Carson Cumberbatch PLC; *Int'l*, pg. 1347
SHALIMAR (MALAY) PLC—See Carson Cumberbatch PLC; *Int'l*, pg. 1347
SHINING GOLD FOODSTUFFS (NINGBO) CO., LTD—See Golden Agri-Resources Ltd.; *Int'l*, pg. 3028
SOUTH CHICAGO PACKING CO.—See Ed Miniat, Inc.; *U.S. Private*, pg. 1331
SPECTRUM ORGANIC PRODUCTS, INC.—See The Hain Celestial Group, Inc.; *U.S. Public*, pg. 2087
UNIFUJI SDN. BHD.—See Fuji Oil Holdings Inc.; *Int'l*, pg. 2816
WENDY WEIHE STORLIE, INC.; *U.S. Private*, pg. 4481
YEMEN COMPANY FOR GHEE AND SOAP INDUSTRY LTD.—See Hayel Saeed Anam Group of Companies; *Int'l*, pg. 3291
YINGKOU CHENGUANG FOODS CO LTD—See Chenguang Biotech Group Co., Ltd.; *Int'l*, pg. 1470

311230 — BREAKFAST CEREAL MANUFACTURING

545 LLC—See Kellanova; *U.S. Public*, pg. 1218
8TH AVENUE FOOD & PROVISIONS, INC.—See Post Holdings, Inc.; *U.S. Public*, pg. 1703
AGROBACKA A.D.; *Int'l*, pg. 218
ALPEN FOOD COMPANY SOUTH AFRICA (PTY) LTD.—See Post Holdings, Inc.; *U.S. Public*, pg. 1703
ARROWHEAD MILLS, INC.—See Brynwood Partners Management LLC; *U.S. Private*, pg. 674
ASPEN NUTRITIONALS (PTY) LTD—See Groupe Lactalis SA; *Int'l*, pg. 3105
ATTUNE FOODS, INC.; *U.S. Private*, pg. 383
BAGLEY LATINOAMERICA S.A.—See Arcor Sociedad Anonima, Industrial y Comercial; *Int'l*, pg. 550
BAGLEY LATINOAMERICA S.A.—See Danone; *Int'l*, pg. 1965
BETTY CROCKER PRODUCTS—See General Mills, Inc.; *U.S. Public*, pg. 921
BIONEUTRA GLOBAL CORPORATION; *Int'l*, pg. 1040
BIONEUTRA NORTH AMERICA INC.—See BioNeutra Global Corporation; *Int'l*, pg. 1040
BLUE PLANET FOODS, INC.—See McKee Foods Corporation; *U.S. Private*, pg. 2637
BOKOMO FOODS (UK) LTD - PETERBOROUGH FACTORY—See PepsiCo, Inc.; *U.S. Public*, pg. 1672
CEREAL PARTNERS U.K.—See General Mills, Inc.; *U.S. Public*, pg. 921
CEREAL PARTNERS WORLDWIDE S.A.—See General Mills, Inc.; *U.S. Public*, pg. 921
C.P.D. CEREAL PARTNERS DEUTSCHLAND GMBH & CO. OHG—See General Mills, Inc.; *U.S. Public*, pg. 921
DAILYCER S.A.—See OEP Capital Advisors, L.P.; *U.S. Private*, pg. 2998
DAKOTA SPECIALTY MILLING COMPANY; *U.S. Private*, pg. 1147
DAWN FOOD PRODUCTS (CANADA), LTD.—See Dawn Food Products, Inc.; *U.S. Private*, pg. 1175
THE EGGO COMPANY—See Kellanova; *U.S. Public*, pg. 1218
EKA NOODLES BERHAD; *Int'l*, pg. 2337
FAUJI CEREALS—See Fauji Foundation; *Int'l*, pg. 2623
FROU FROU CEREALS LTD—See Alkis H. Hadjikyriacos (Frou Frou Biscuits) Public Ltd.; *Int'l*, pg. 331
GENERAL MILLS, CONSUMER FOODS SALES DIVISION—See General Mills, Inc.; *U.S. Public*, pg. 922
GRUPO LA MODERNA, S.A.B. DE C.V.; *Int'l*, pg. 3131
GRUPO MINSA, S.A.B. DE C.V.; *Int'l*, pg. 3133
GUILIN SEAMILD FOODS CO., LTD.; *Int'l*, pg. 3173
HINDUSTAN FOODS LIMITED; *Int'l*, pg. 3399
KAY'S PROCESSING, INC.—See American Securities LLC; *U.S. Private*, pg. 250
KELLOGG ASIA PRODUCTS SDN. BHD.—See Kellanova; *U.S. Public*, pg. 1217
KELLOGG (AUST.) PTY. LTD.—See Kellanova; *U.S. Public*, pg. 1217
KELLOGG (AUSTRALIA) PROPRIETARY LTD.—See Kellanova; *U.S. Public*, pg. 1217
KELLOGG CANADA, INC.—See Kellanova; *U.S. Public*, pg. 1217
KELLOGG CANADA INC.—See Kellanova; *U.S. Public*, pg. 1217
KELLOGG COMPANY MEXICO, S. DE R.L. DE C.V.—See Kellanova; *U.S. Public*, pg. 1218
KELLOGG COMPANY OF GREAT BRITAIN LIMITED—See Kellanova; *U.S. Public*, pg. 1218
KELLOGG COMPANY OF SOUTH AFRICA (PTY.) LTD.—See Kellanova; *U.S. Public*, pg. 1218
KELLOGG (DEUTSCHLAND) GMBH—See Kellanova; *U.S. Public*, pg. 1217
KELLOGG ESPANA, S.L.—See Kellanova; *U.S. Public*, pg. 1218
KELLOGG GROUP LIMITED—See Kellanova; *U.S. Public*, pg. 1218
KELLOGG INDIA PRIVATE LIMITED—See Kellanova; *U.S. Public*, pg. 1218
KELLOGG-LANCASTER PLANT—See WK Kellogg Co; *U.S. Public*, pg. 2376
KELLOGG MANUFACTURING ESPANA, S.L.—See Kellanova; *U.S. Public*, pg. 1218
KELLOGG-MEMPHIS PLANT—See WK Kellogg Co; *U.S. Public*, pg. 2376
KELLOGG (OSTERREICH) GMBH—See Kellanova; *U.S. Public*, pg. 1217
KELLOGG'S PRODUITS ALIMENTAIRES, S.A.—See Kellanova; *U.S. Public*, pg. 1218

311230 — BREAKFAST CEREAL MA...

KELLOGG (THAILAND) LIMITED—See Kellanova; *U.S. Public*, pg. 1217
KLUX A S.A.R.L.—See Kellanova; *U.S. Public*, pg. 1218
LEAN TEIK SOON SDN. BHD.—See ATA IMS Berhad; *Int'l*, pg. 665
LITTLE BEAR ORGANIC FOODS, INC.—See The Hain Celestial Group, Inc.; *U.S. Public*, pg. 2087
LOWAN WHOLE FOODS PTY. LIMITED—See Green's General Foods Pty. Limited; *Int'l*, pg. 3073
MAIZORO S.A. DE C.V.—See PepsiCo, Inc.; *U.S. Public*, pg. 1670
MARY LEE PACKAGING CORPORATION—See Gilster-Mary Lee Corporation; *U.S. Private*, pg. 1701
MASS FOOD SAE—See Kellanova; *U.S. Public*, pg. 1218
M & N FOODS LLC.; *U.S. Private*, pg. 2523
MOM BRANDS COMPANY, LLC—See Post Holdings, Inc.; *U.S. Public*, pg. 1703
NORDISK KELLOGGS APS—See Kellanova; *U.S. Public*, pg. 1218
PEACE CEREAL—See Attune Foods, Inc.; *U.S. Private*, pg. 383
PIONEER FOODS (UK) LIMITED—See PepsiCo, Inc.; *U.S. Public*, pg. 1672
POST FOODS CANADA CORP.—See Post Holdings, Inc.; *U.S. Public*, pg. 1704
POST FOODS, LLC - BATTLE CREEK PLANT—See Post Holdings, Inc.; *U.S. Public*, pg. 1704
POST FOODS, LLC - JONESBORO PLANT—See Post Holdings, Inc.; *U.S. Public*, pg. 1704
POST FOODS, LLC - MODESTO PLANT—See Post Holdings, Inc.; *U.S. Public*, pg. 1704
POST FOODS, LLC—See Post Holdings, Inc.; *U.S. Public*, pg. 1704
PRINGLES MANUFACTURING COMPANY—See Kellanova; *U.S. Public*, pg. 1218
QUAKER MANUFACTURING, LLC—See PepsiCo, Inc.; *U.S. Public*, pg. 1671
QUAKER OATS AUSTRALIA PTY LTD—See PepsiCo, Inc.; *U.S. Public*, pg. 1671
THE QUAKER OATS COMPANY—See PepsiCo, Inc.; *U.S. Public*, pg. 1670
QUAKER PERU S.R.L.—See PepsiCo, Inc.; *U.S. Public*, pg. 1671
QUAKER PRODUCTS (MALAYSIA) SDN BHD—See PepsiCo, Inc.; *U.S. Public*, pg. 1670
RALSTON FOODS, INC.—See Conagra Brands, Inc.; *U.S. Public*, pg. 564
RALSTON FOODS, INC.—See Conagra Brands, Inc.; *U.S. Public*, pg. 564
RALSTON FOODS, INC.—See Conagra Brands, Inc.; *U.S. Public*, pg. 564
RALSTON FOODS, INC.—See Conagra Brands, Inc.; *U.S. Public*, pg. 564
RALSTON FOODS—See Conagra Brands, Inc.; *U.S. Public*, pg. 564
SENSORYEFFECTS CEREAL SYSTEMS, INC.—See Balchem Corporation; *U.S. Public*, pg. 266
TELFORD FOODS LTD.—See Brand Partnership Ltd.; *Int'l*, pg. 1139
UNIVERSAL FOODS LIMITED—See Associated Brands Industries Limited; *Int'l*, pg. 648
U.S. MILLS, LLC—See Susquehanna International Group, LLP; *U.S. Private*, pg. 3886
WEETABIX EAST AFRICA LIMITED—See Post Holdings, Inc.; *U.S. Public*, pg. 1704
WEETABIX FOODS LIMITED—See Post Holdings, Inc.; *U.S. Public*, pg. 1704
WEETABIX LIMITED—See Post Holdings, Inc.; *U.S. Public*, pg. 1704
WEETABIX OF CANADA LIMITED—See Post Holdings, Inc.; *U.S. Public*, pg. 1704

311313 — BEET SUGAR MANUFACTURING

AMALGAMATED SUGAR CO.—See Snake River Sugar Co.; *U.S. Private*, pg. 3699
AMALGAMATED SUGAR CO.—See Snake River Sugar Co.; *U.S. Private*, pg. 3699
AMALGAMATED SUGAR CO.—See Snake River Sugar Co.; *U.S. Private*, pg. 3699
AMERICAN CRYSTAL SUGAR COMPANY; *U.S. Public*, pg. 98
BALRAMPUR OVERSEAS PVT. LTD.—See Balrampur Chini Mills Limited; *Int'l*, pg. 811
BOGO-MEDELLIN MILLING COMPANY, INC.; *Int'l*, pg. 1100
CHASHMA SUGAR MILLS LIMITED; *Int'l*, pg. 1457
CHERNYANSKY SUGAR—See Gruppa Kompaniy Rusagro OOO; *Int'l*, pg. 3140
CORBION GROUP NETHERLANDS B.V.—See Corbion N.V.; *Int'l*, pg. 1795
COSUMAR SA; *Int'l*, pg. 1815
CRESCENT COTTON MILLS LIMITED; *Int'l*, pg. 1839
DHAMPURE SPECIALTY SUGARS LTD; *Int'l*, pg. 2098
DUPONT NUTRITION BIOSCIENCES APS—See DuPont de Nemours, Inc.; *U.S. Public*, pg. 692
EMPRESA AGRARIA AZUCARERA ANDAHUASI S.A.A.; *Int'l*, pg. 2388
FELIX KOCH OFFENBACH COULEUR UND KARAMEL GMBH; *Int'l*, pg. 2633
GALACTIC S.A.—See Finasucre S.A.; *Int'l*, pg. 2670
GAYATRI SUGARS LIMITED; *Int'l*, pg. 2891
ISCAL SUGAR S.A./N.V.—See Finasucre S.A.; *Int'l*, pg. 2670
MALACO K/S—See Cloetta AB; *Int'l*, pg. 1661
MICHIGAN SUGAR COMPANY; *U.S. Private*, pg. 2701
MICHIGAN SUGAR COMPANY—See Michigan Sugar Company; *U.S. Private*, pg. 2701
MINN-DAK FARMERS COOPERATIVE; *U.S. Private*, pg. 2742
MPDL LTD.—See Apollo Global Management, Inc.; *U.S. Public*, pg. 152
NIKIFOROVSKY SUGAR—See Gruppa Kompaniy Rusagro OOO; *Int'l*, pg. 3140
OOO ZARYA—See Gruppa Kompaniy Rusagro OOO; *Int'l*, pg. 3140
POLETAEVSKOE LLC—See Gruppa Kompaniy Rusagro OOO; *Int'l*, pg. 3140
PURAC BIOCHEM BV—See Corbion N.V.; *Int'l*, pg. 1795
SC AGRANA ROMANIA SA—See AGRANA Beteiligungs-AG; *Int'l*, pg. 214
SIDNEY SUGARS INCORPORATED—See American Crystal Sugar Company; *U.S. Public*, pg. 98
SOUTHERN MINNESOTA BEET SUGAR COOPERATIVE; *U.S. Private*, pg. 3733
SPRECKELS SUGAR COMPANY, INC.—See Southern Minnesota Beet Sugar Cooperative; *U.S. Private*, pg. 3733
VALUIKISAKHAR SUGAR—See Gruppa Kompaniy Rusagro OOO; *Int'l*, pg. 3140
WHOLE EARTH BRANDS, INC.; *U.S. Public*, pg. 2369
ZHERDEVSKY SUGAR—See Gruppa Kompaniy Rusagro OOO; *Int'l*, pg. 3140
ZNAMENSKY SUGAR—See Gruppa Kompaniy Rusagro OOO; *Int'l*, pg. 3140

311314 — CANE SUGAR MANUFACTURING

ABDULLAH SHAH GHAZI SUGAR MILLS LIMITED; *Int'l*, pg. 59
ABDULLAH SUGAR MILLS LIMITED—See Haseeb Waqas Group of Companies; *Int'l*, pg. 3282
ADAM SUGAR MILLS LIMITED; *Int'l*, pg. 123
AGRANA BETEILIGUNGS-AG; *Int'l*, pg. 213
AGRANA ZUCKER GMBH—See AGRANA Beteiligungs-AG; *Int'l*, pg. 214
AGROGUACHAL SA; *Int'l*, pg. 219
AGROINDUSTRIAL LAREDO SAA; *Int'l*, pg. 219
AL-ABBAS SUGAR MILLS LIMITED - DHABEJI PLANT—See AL-ABBAS SUGAR Mills Limited; *Int'l*, pg. 284
AL-ABBAS SUGAR MILLS LIMITED - MIRWAH PLANT—See AL-ABBAS SUGAR Mills Limited; *Int'l*, pg. 284
AL-NOOR SUGAR MILLS LIMITED; *Int'l*, pg. 287
AMERICAN SUGAR REFINING, INC.—See Florida Crystals Corporation; *U.S. Private*, pg. 1548
ANSARI SUGAR MILLS LIMITED; *Int'l*, pg. 478
ATUL SUGAR SCREENS PRIVATE LIMITED—See IDEX Corp; *U.S. Public*, pg. 1089
BABA FARID SUGAR MILLS LIMITED—See Fecto Group of Companies; *Int'l*, pg. 2629
BAJAJ HINDUSTHAN SUGAR LTD. - KHAMBHAR KHERA - SUGAR UNIT—See Bajaj Hindustan Sugar Limited; *Int'l*, pg. 804
BALRAMPUR CHINI MILLS LIMITED; *Int'l*, pg. 811
BANAH INTERNATIONAL GROUP, INC.; *U.S. Private*, pg. 464
BAOTOU HUAZI INDUSTRY CO., LTD.; *Int'l*, pg. 856
BELAPUR INDUSTRIES LTD.; *Int'l*, pg. 963
BIEN HOA SUGAR JSC; *Int'l*, pg. 1020
BRYANT SUGAR HOUSE—See United States Sugar Corporation; *U.S. Private*, pg. 4300
BULGARSKA ZAHAR AD; *Int'l*, pg. 1213
BUNDABERG SUGAR LTD.—See Finasucre S.A.; *Int'l*, pg. 2670
BURIRAM SUGAR PUBLIC COMPANY LIMITED; *Int'l*, pg. 1224
CENTRAL AZUCARERA DE TARLAC, INC.—See CAT Resource & Asset Holdings, Inc.; *Int'l*, pg. 1358
C&H SUGAR COMPANY, INC.—See Florida Crystals Corporation; *U.S. Private*, pg. 1548
CONSTANCE LA GAIETE CO. LTD.; *Int'l*, pg. 1772
COPERSUCAR S.A.; *Int'l*, pg. 1793
CORA TEXAS MANUFACTURING CO., LLC; *U.S. Private*, pg. 1046
COSAN S.A.; *Int'l*, pg. 1809
CRVENKA FABRIKA SECERA A.D.; *Int'l*, pg. 1859
DANGOTE SUGAR REFINERY PLC—See Dangote Group Limited; *Int'l*, pg. 1962
DAVANGERE SUGAR COMPANY LIMITED; *Int'l*, pg. 1983
DCM SHRIRAM INDUSTRIES LIMITED; *Int'l*, pg. 1992
DCM SHRIRAM INDUSTRIES LIMITED - SUGAR DIVISION—See DCM Shriram Industries Limited; *Int'l*, pg. 1992
DELTA SUGAR COMPANY; *Int'l*, pg. 2020
DEWAN SUGAR MILLS LIMITED—See Dewan Farooque Motors Limited; *Int'l*, pg. 2091
DHAMPUR BIO ORGANICS LIMITED; *Int'l*, pg. 2098
DHAMPUR SUGAR MILLS LIMITED; *Int'l*, pg. 2098
DHARANI SUGARS & CHEMICALS LIMITED; *Int'l*, pg. 2099
DHARANI SUGARS & CHEMICALS LIMITED - UNIT III—See DHARANI SUGARS & CHEMICALS LIMITED; *Int'l*, pg. 2099
DHARANI SUGARS & CHEMICALS LIMITED - UNIT II—See DHARANI SUGARS & CHEMICALS LIMITED; *Int'l*, pg. 2099
DHARANI SUGARS & CHEMICALS LIMITED - UNIT I—See DHARANI SUGARS & CHEMICALS LIMITED; *Int'l*, pg. 2099
DOMINO FOODS - ARABI SUGAR REFINERY—See Florida Crystals Corporation; *U.S. Private*, pg. 1548
DOMINO FOODS - BALTIMORE SUGAR REFINERY—See Florida Crystals Corporation; *U.S. Private*, pg. 1548
DWARIKESH SUGAR INDUSTRIES LTD; *Int'l*, pg. 2236
ED&F MAN INGREDIENTS S.R.O.—See ED&F Man Holdings Limited; *Int'l*, pg. 2303
EMPEE SUGARS & CHEMICALS LTD.; *Int'l*, pg. 2385
ENSUIKO SUGAR REFINING CO., LTD.; *Int'l*, pg. 2449
ENVASADORA DE AZUCAR, INC.—See Able Sales Company, Inc.; *U.S. Private*, pg. 39
FARAN SUGAR MILLS LTD - SINDH MILL—See Faran Sugar Mills Ltd; *Int'l*, pg. 2618
FARAN SUGAR MILLS LTD; *Int'l*, pg. 2618
FECTO SUGAR MILLS LTD.—See Fecto Group of Companies; *Int'l*, pg. 2629
FINASUCRE S.A.; *Int'l*, pg. 2669
FIVES FLETCHER LIMITED—See FIVES, Societe Anonyme; *Int'l*, pg. 2696
FLORIDA SUGAR DISTRIBUTORS INC.—See Florida Crystals Corporation; *U.S. Private*, pg. 1548
GHAZVIN SUGAR COMPANY; *Int'l*, pg. 2959
GOLDEN SUGAR COMPANY LIMITED—See Flour Mills of Nigeria Plc.; *Int'l*, pg. 2709
GRUPPA KOMPANIY RUSAGRO OOO; *Int'l*, pg. 3140
GUANGXI RURAL INVESTMENT SUGAR INDUSTRY GROUP CO., LTD; *Int'l*, pg. 3163
GUANGXI YUEGUI GUANGYE HOLDINGS CO., LTD.; *Int'l*, pg. 3164
HABIB SUGAR MILLS LIMITED—See Habib Group of Companies; *Int'l*, pg. 3203
HASEEB WAQAS SUGAR MILLS LTD.—See Haseeb Waqas Group of Companies; *Int'l*, pg. 3282
HUNDLEY FARM INC.; *U.S. Private*, pg. 2007
INGENIO Y REFINERIA SAN MARTIN DEL TABACAL S.A.—See Seaboard Corporation; *U.S. Public*, pg. 1850
ISCAL SUGAR B.V.—See Finasucre S.A.; *Int'l*, pg. 2670
LULA-WESTFIELD LLC; *U.S. Private*, pg. 2513
MALAYAN SUGAR MANUFACTURING COMPANY BERHAD—See FGV Holdings Bhd; *Int'l*, pg. 2649
M.A. PATOUT & SON LIMITED; *U.S. Private*, pg. 2527
MERISANT AUSTRALIA PTY LTD—See MacAndrews & Forbes Incorporated; *U.S. Private*, pg. 2532
MERISANT INDIA PRIVATE LIMITED—See MacAndrews & Forbes Incorporated; *U.S. Private*, pg. 2532
MERISANT US, INC.—See MacAndrews & Forbes Incorporated; *U.S. Private*, pg. 2532
MICHIGAN SUGAR COMPANY—See Michigan Sugar Company; *U.S. Private*, pg. 2701
MON DESERT-ALMA SUGAR MILLING COMPANY LIMITED—See ENL Limited; *Int'l*, pg. 2441
MSM PERLIS SDN. BHD.—See FGV Holdings Bhd; *Int'l*, pg. 2650
MSM PRAI BERHAD—See FGV Holdings Bhd; *Int'l*, pg. 2650
MSM TRADING INTERNATIONAL DMCC—See FGV Holdings Bhd; *Int'l*, pg. 2650
NIKA SUGAR—See Gruppa Kompaniy Rusagro OOO; *Int'l*, pg. 3140
NORTHERN LAND HOLDINGS LTD—See Finasucre S.A.; *Int'l*, pg. 2670
OKEELANTA CORPORATION—See Florida Crystals Corporation; *U.S. Private*, pg. 1548
PREMIER MOLASSES COMPANY LIMITED—See Greencore Group plc; *Int'l*, pg. 3074
QUANG NGAI MINERAL INVESTMENT JOINT STOCK COMPANY—See 577 Investment Corporation; *Int'l*, pg. 13
RACELAND RAW SUGAR CORP.—See M.A. Patout & Son Limited; *U.S. Private*, pg. 2528
REDPATH SUGAR LTD.—See Florida Crystals Corporation; *U.S. Private*, pg. 1548
RZHEVSKY SUGAR—See Gruppa Kompaniy Rusagro OOO; *Int'l*, pg. 3140
THE SAVANNAH SUGAR MILLING COMPANY LTD.—See ENL Limited; *Int'l*, pg. 2441
SLOVENSKE CUKROVARY S.R.O.—See AGRANA Beteiligungs-AG; *Int'l*, pg. 214
STERLING SUGARS INC.—See M.A. Patout & Son Limited; *U.S. Private*, pg. 2528

N.A.I.C.S. INDEX

SUGAR & ALLIED INDUSTRIES LIMITED—See Alam Group of Companies; *Int'l*, pg. 289
SUGAR CANE GROWERS COOPERATIVE OF FLORIDA; *U.S. Private*, pg. 3849
SWEETENERS PLUS LLC—See Graycliff Partners LP; *U.S. Private*, pg. 1761
WHOLE EARTH SWEETENER COMPANY, LLC—See MacAndrews & Forbes Incorporated; *U.S. Private*, pg. 2532

311340 — NONCHOCOLATE CONFECTIONERY MANUFACTURING

ACTIVE NUTRITION INTERNATIONAL GMBH—See Post Holdings, Inc.; *U.S. Public*, pg. 1704
THE ALLAN CANDY COMPANY LIMITED—See The Hershey Co.; *U.S. Public*, pg. 2089
AMERICAN LICORICE CO. INC.; *U.S. Private*, pg. 239
AMERICAN SMOOTH WAVE VENTURES, INC.; *U.S. Private*, pg. 253
ARCOR DE PERU S.A.—See Arcor Sociedad Anonima, Industrial y Comercial; *Int'l*, pg. 550
ATKINSON CANDY COMPANY; *U.S. Private*, pg. 369
BAYAN SULU JSC; *Int'l*, pg. 901
BODEANS BAKING COMPANY LLC; *U.S. Private*, pg. 607
BROWN & HALEY; *U.S. Private*, pg. 666
CADBURY EIGHT LLP—See Mondelez International, Inc.; *U.S. Public*, pg. 1460
CADBURY FRANCE SAS—See Mondelez International, Inc.; *U.S. Public*, pg. 1460
CADBURY (SWAZILAND) (PTY) LIMITED—See Mondelez International, Inc.; *U.S. Public*, pg. 1460
CANDYWAREHOUSE.COM; *U.S. Private*, pg. 734
CE DE CANDY, INC.; *U.S. Private*, pg. 803
CHASE GENERAL CORPORATION; *U.S. Private*, pg. 860
COCOALAND HOLDINGS BERHAD; *Int'l*, pg. 1687
CONCORD CONFECTIONS LTD.—See Tootsie Roll Industries, Inc.; *U.S. Public*, pg. 2163
DADDY RAY—See J&J Snack Foods Corporation; *U.S. Public*, pg. 1179
DECOPAC, INC.—See Kohlberg & Company, LLC; *U.S. Private*, pg. 2337
DINDON FOODS CORP.; *U.S. Private*, pg. 1233
DOUMAK INC.; *U.S. Private*, pg. 1268
DRYDEN & PALMER COMPANY—See Founders Equity, Inc.; *U.S. Private*, pg. 1581
DURKEE-MOWER, INC.; *U.S. Private*, pg. 1293
EZAKI GLICO CO., LTD.; *Int'l*, pg. 2593
FARMERS CHOICE FOOD BRANDS—See Promotion In Motion, Inc.; *U.S. Private*, pg. 3283
F.B. WASHBURN CANDY CORP.; *U.S. Private*, pg. 1455
FORD GUM & MACHINE COMPANY, INC.; *U.S. Private*, pg. 1564
FOUR SEAS CONFECTIONERY (SHENZHEN) CO., LTD.—See Four Seas Mercantile Holdings Limited; *Int'l*, pg. 2755
FOX'S CONFECTIONERY LIMITED—See CapVest Limited; *Int'l*, pg. 1318
FUJI OIL CO., LTD. - CHIBA PLANT—See Fuji Oil Holdings Inc.; *Int'l*, pg. 2815
FUJI OIL CO., LTD. - ISHIKAWA PLANT—See Fuji Oil Holdings Inc.; *Int'l*, pg. 2815
FUJI OIL CO., LTD. - KANTO PLANT—See Fuji Oil Holdings Inc.; *Int'l*, pg. 2815
FUJI OIL CO., LTD. - KOBE PLANT—See Fuji Oil Holdings Inc.; *Int'l*, pg. 2815
FUJI OIL CO., LTD. - PROTEIN FOODS TSUKUBA PLANT—See Fuji Oil Holdings Inc.; *Int'l*, pg. 2815
FUJI OIL CO., LTD. - SAKAI PLANT—See Fuji Oil Holdings Inc.; *Int'l*, pg. 2815
FUJIYA KOBE CO., LTD.—See Fujiya Co., Ltd.; *Int'l*, pg. 2838
GLOBAL BIO-CHEM TECHNOLOGY GROUP COMPANY LIMITED; *Int'l*, pg. 2993
HAITAI CONFECTIONERY AND FOODS CO.,LTD.; *Int'l*, pg. 3217
HAPPY APPLE COMPANY; *U.S. Private*, pg. 1857
HARIBO AUSTRALIA PTY LIMITED—See HARIBO GmbH & Co. KG; *Int'l*, pg. 3275
HARIBO BELGIE B.V.B.A.—See HARIBO GmbH & Co. KG; *Int'l*, pg. 3275
HARIBO GMBH & CO. KG; *Int'l*, pg. 3275
HARIBO OF AMERICA INC.—See HARIBO GmbH & Co. KG; *Int'l*, pg. 3275
H.B. REESE CANDY CO.—See The Hershey Co.; *U.S. Public*, pg. 2088
HILLSIDE CANDY, LLC—See Highlander Partners, LP; *U.S. Private*, pg. 1939
HOSPITALITY MINTS LLC—See Mount Franklin Foods, LLC; *U.S. Private*, pg. 2798
IMPACT CONFECTIONS, INC.; *U.S. Private*, pg. 2048
JELLY BELLY CANDY COMPANY; *U.S. Private*, pg. 2198
JOYVA CORPORATION; *U.S. Private*, pg. 2239
JUST BORN, INC.; *U.S. Private*, pg. 2245
KENNY'S CANDY COMPANY INC.—See KLN Enterprises Inc.; *U.S. Private*, pg. 2320
KF (AUSTRALIA) PTY. LTD.—See Mondelez International, Inc.; *U.S. Public*, pg. 1461

KRAFT FOODS PANAMA, S.A.—See Mondelez International, Inc.; *U.S. Public*, pg. 1462
KRAFT FOODS (PUERTO RICO), LLC—See Mondelez International, Inc.; *U.S. Public*, pg. 1461
KRAFT FOODS SVERIGE HOLDING AB—See Mondelez International, Inc.; *U.S. Public*, pg. 1462
LEES OF SCOTLAND LIMITED—See DBAY Advisors Limited; *Int'l*, pg. 1986
LIBERTY ORCHARDS CO., INC.; *U.S. Private*, pg. 2446
MAFCO WORLDWIDE CORPORATION—See MacAndrews & Forbes Incorporated; *U.S. Private*, pg. 2532
MONDELEZ D.O.O. BEOGRAD—See Mondelez International, Inc.; *U.S. Public*, pg. 1464
MONDELEZ INTERNATIONAL RUS—See Mondelez International, Inc.; *U.S. Public*, pg. 1464
MONDELEZ SOUTH AFRICA (PTY) LTD.—See Mondelez International, Inc.; *U.S. Public*, pg. 1464
MONDELEZ (THAILAND) CO., LTD.—See Mondelez International, Inc.; *U.S. Public*, pg. 1461
MORLEY CANDY MAKERS, LLC—See Palladium Equity Partners, LLC; *U.S. Private*, pg. 3077
MOUNTAIN MAN NUT & FRUIT CO.; *U.S. Private*, pg. 2799
NEW ENGLAND CONFECTIONERY COMPANY INC.—See Ares Management Corporation; *U.S. Public*, pg. 190
OSCEOLA FARMS CO. INC.—See Florida Crystals Corporation; *U.S. Private*, pg. 1548
POWERBAR INC.—See Post Holdings, Inc.; *U.S. Public*, pg. 1704
PROMOTION IN MOTION, INC.; *U.S. Private*, pg. 3283
P.T. FREYABADI INDOTAMA—See Fuji Oil Holdings Inc.; *Int'l*, pg. 2815
RICHARDSON BRANDS COMPANY—See Founders Equity, Inc.; *U.S. Private*, pg. 1581
SERVICIOS INTEGRALES KRAFT, S. DE R.L. DE C.V.—See Mondelez International, Inc.; *U.S. Public*, pg. 1464
SPANGLER CANDY COMPANY; *U.S. Private*, pg. 3745
SPERLARI, S.R.L.—See Cloetta AB; *Int'l*, pg. 1661
SWEET ACQUISITIONS CA3, LLC—See Hilton Grand Vacations Inc.; *U.S. Public*, pg. 1039
SWEET CANDY COMPANY; *U.S. Private*, pg. 3892
SWEET PRODUCTIONS LTD.; *U.S. Private*, pg. 3892
SWEETWORKS, INC.; *U.S. Private*, pg. 3892
TAMANDA HOLDINGS USA INC.; *U.S. Private*, pg. 3928
TANGERINE CONFECTIONERY LTD.—See CapVest Limited; *Int'l*, pg. 1318
THOMPSON BRANDS LLC; *U.S. Private*, pg. 4158
THE TOOTSIE ROLL COMPANY—See Tootsie Roll Industries, Inc.; *U.S. Public*, pg. 2163
TOOTSIE ROLL MANAGEMENT INC—See Tootsie Roll Industries, Inc.; *U.S. Public*, pg. 2163
TOOTSIE ROLLS-LATIN AMERICA, INC.—See Tootsie Roll Industries, Inc.; *U.S. Public*, pg. 2163
VAN NETTEN GMBH—See Gigaset AG; *Int'l*, pg. 2972
WRIGLEY AUSTRIA GES.M.B.H.—See Mars, Incorporated; *U.S. Private*, pg. 2591
WRIGLEY CHEWING GUM COMPANY LTD.—See Mars, Incorporated; *U.S. Private*, pg. 2591
THE WRIGLEY COMPANY (E.A.) LTD.—See Mars, Incorporated; *U.S. Private*, pg. 2590
WRIGLEY & COMPANY LTD., JAPAN—See Mars, Incorporated; *U.S. Private*, pg. 2591
THE WRIGLEY COMPANY LTD.—See Mars, Incorporated; *U.S. Private*, pg. 2590
THE WRIGLEY COMPANY (MALAYSIA) SDN. BHD.—See Mars, Incorporated; *U.S. Private*, pg. 2590
THE WRIGLEY COMPANY (N.Z.) LIMITED—See Mars, Incorporated; *U.S. Private*, pg. 2590
THE WRIGLEY COMPANY PTY. LTD.—See Mars, Incorporated; *U.S. Private*, pg. 2591
WRIGLEY CO., S.A.U.—See Mars, Incorporated; *U.S. Private*, pg. 2591
WRIGLEY D.O.O.—See Mars, Incorporated; *U.S. Private*, pg. 2591
WRIGLEY FRANCE SNC—See Mars, Incorporated; *U.S. Private*, pg. 2591
WRIGLEY GMBH—See Mars, Incorporated; *U.S. Private*, pg. 2591
WRIGLEY PHILIPPINES, INC.—See Mars, Incorporated; *U.S. Private*, pg. 2591
WRIGLEY ROMANIA SRL—See Mars, Incorporated; *U.S. Private*, pg. 2591
WRIGLEY SCANDINAVIA AB—See Mars, Incorporated; *U.S. Private*, pg. 2591
WRIGLEY SCANDINAVIA AS—See Mars, Incorporated; *U.S. Private*, pg. 2591
WRIGLEY S.R.O.—See Mars, Incorporated; *U.S. Private*, pg. 2591
WRIGLEY TAIWAN LTD.—See Mars, Incorporated; *U.S. Private*, pg. 2591
YEMEN COMPANY FOR INDUSTRY AND COMMERCIAL LTD.—See Hayel Saeed Anam Group of Companies; *Int'l*, pg. 3291
Y & S CANDIES—See The Hershey Co.; *U.S. Public*, pg. 2089

311351 — CHOCOLATE AND CONFECTIONERY MANUFACTURING FROM CACAO BEANS

9101-9091 QUEBEC INC.; *Int'l*, pg. 16
ABTEY PRODUCTIONS; *Int'l*, pg. 70
ANDES CANDIES LP—See Tootsie Roll Industries, Inc.; *U.S. Public*, pg. 2163
APOLLO FOOD HOLDINGS BERHAD; *Int'l*, pg. 517
ARTISAN CONFECTIONS COMPANY—See The Hershey Co.; *U.S. Public*, pg. 2088
ARTISTA CHOCOLATES SA—See Compagnie du Bois Sauvage SA; *Int'l*, pg. 1740
ASTOR CHOCOLATE CORP.; *U.S. Private*, pg. 360
BLOMMER CHOCOLATE COMPANY - CALIFORNIA PLANT—See Fuji Oil Holdings Inc.; *Int'l*, pg. 2815
BLOMMER CHOCOLATE COMPANY - CHICAGO PLANT—See Fuji Oil Holdings Inc.; *Int'l*, pg. 2815
BLOMMER CHOCOLATE COMPANY - PENNSYLVANIA PLANT—See Fuji Oil Holdings Inc.; *Int'l*, pg. 2815
BLOMMER CHOCOLATE COMPANY—See Fuji Oil Holdings Inc.; *Int'l*, pg. 2815
BLOMMER CHOCOLATE MANUFACTURING (SHANGHAI) COMPANY LTD.—See Fuji Oil Company, Ltd.; *Int'l*, pg. 2815
BUDDY SQUIRREL, LLC; *U.S. Private*, pg. 679
BUHLER BARTH GMBH—See Buhler AG; *Int'l*, pg. 1212
BUHLER GMBH—See Buhler AG; *Int'l*, pg. 1212
CACHE CREEK FOODS, LLC.; *U.S. Private*, pg. 711
CADBURY CONFECTIONERY MALAYSIA SDN BHD—See Mondelez International, Inc.; *U.S. Public*, pg. 1460
CADBURY FOOD CO. LTD.—See Mondelez International, Inc.; *U.S. Public*, pg. 1460
CADBURY GHANA LTD.—See Mondelez International, Inc.; *U.S. Public*, pg. 1460
CADBURY INDIA LIMITED—See Mondelez International, Inc.; *U.S. Public*, pg. 1460
CADBURY IRELAND LTD.—See Mondelez International, Inc.; *U.S. Public*, pg. 1460
CADBURY JAPAN LTD.—See Mondelez International, Inc.; *U.S. Public*, pg. 1460
CADBURY KENYA LIMITED—See Mondelez International, Inc.; *U.S. Public*, pg. 1461
CADBURY LTD.—See Mondelez International, Inc.; *U.S. Public*, pg. 1460
CADBURY PAKISTAN LIMITED—See Mondelez International, Inc.; *U.S. Public*, pg. 1461
CADBURY SINGAPORE PTE. LTD.—See Mondelez International, Inc.; *U.S. Public*, pg. 1461
CADBURY SOUTH AFRICA (PTY) LTD.—See Mondelez International, Inc.; *U.S. Public*, pg. 1461
CADBURY STANI ADAMS ARGENTINA S.A.—See Mondelez International, Inc.; *U.S. Public*, pg. 1461
CARGILL CHOCOLATE BELGIUM SA—See Cargill, Inc.; *U.S. Private*, pg. 756
CARGILL COCOA & CHOCLATE CO., INC. - GEORGETOWN PLANT—See Cargill, Inc.; *U.S. Private*, pg. 755
CARGILL COCOA & CHOCOLATE CO. INC.—See Cargill, Inc.; *U.S. Private*, pg. 755
CARGILL COCOA & CHOCOLATE CO., INC.—See Cargill, Inc.; *U.S. Private*, pg. 755
CARGILL GHANA LIMITED—See Cargill, Inc.; *U.S. Private*, pg. 756
CARGILL WEST AFRICA S.A—See Cargill, Inc.; *U.S. Private*, pg. 759
CARLYLE COCOA CO., LLC—See Guan Chong Berhad; *Int'l*, pg. 3152
CARMIT CANDY INDUSTRIES LTD.; *Int'l*, pg. 1342
CHOCOLATE CANDY CREATIONS INC.; *U.S. Private*, pg. 887
CHRIS CANDIES, INC.—See Cemoi Chocolatier SAS; *Int'l*, pg. 1400
CLOETTA AB; *Int'l*, pg. 1660
CLOETTA SVERIGE AB—See Cloetta AB; *Int'l*, pg. 1661
COCOA PROCESSING COMPANY LIMITED; *Int'l*, pg. 1687
COFCO LE CONTE FOOD (SHENZHEN) CO., LTD.—See COFCO Limited; *Int'l*, pg. 1692
COKOLEND A.D.; *Int'l*, pg. 1696
COMPANIA NACIONAL DE CHOCOLATES DE PERU S.A.—See Grupo Nutresa S.A.; *Int'l*, pg. 3133
CONFECTIONERY & SNACKS (BARBADOS) LTD—See Associated Brands Industries Limited; *Int'l*, pg. 648
CONFECTIONERY & SNACKS (JAMAICA) LTD—See Associated Brands Industries Limited; *Int'l*, pg. 648
CORDIALSA BORICUA EMPAQUE, INC.—See Grupo Nutresa S.A.; *Int'l*, pg. 3133
CORNE PORT-ROYAL CHOCOLATIER S.A.—See Compagnie du Bois Sauvage SA; *Int'l*, pg. 1740
DELFI LIMITED; *Int'l*, pg. 2012
DROGA CHOCOLATES, LLC—See Hilton Grand Vacations Inc.; *U.S. Public*, pg. 1039
ETHEL M. CHOCOLATES, INC.—See Mars, Incorporated; *U.S. Private*, pg. 2589
EVROPA AD; *Int'l*, pg. 2574
THE FERRARA CANDY COMPANY—See Ferrero International S.A.; *Int'l*, pg. 2640
FERRERO ARDENNES S.A.—See Ferrero International S.A.; *Int'l*, pg. 2640
FERRERO ARGENTINA S.A.—See Ferrero International S.A.; *Int'l*, pg. 2640

311351 — CHOCOLATE AND CONFE...

FERRERO S.P.A.—See Ferrero International S.A.; *Int'l*, pg. 2640
F&F CO., LTD.—See Fuji Oil Holdings Inc.; *Int'l*, pg. 2815
FIRST BAKING CO., LTD.; *Int'l*, pg. 2682
FRANKFORD CANDY & CHOCOLATE CO.; *U.S. Private*, pg. 1596
FREYABADI (THAILAND) CO., LTD.—See Fuji Oil Holdings Inc.; *Int'l*, pg. 2815
FR. KAISER GMBH; *Int'l*, pg. 2758
FUJI GLOBAL CHOCOLATE (M) SDN. BHD.—See Fuji Oil Holdings Inc.; *Int'l*, pg. 2815
FUTURE ENTERPRISES PTE LTD—See Food Empire Holdings Limited; *Int'l*, pg. 2727
GCB COCOA SINGAPORE PTE. LTD.—See Guan Chong Berhad; *Int'l*, pg. 3152
GCB COCOA UK LIMITED—See Guan Chong Berhad; *Int'l*, pg. 3152
GCB FOODS SDN. BHD.—See Guan Chong Berhad; *Int'l*, pg. 3152
GERTRUDE HAWK CHOCOLATES, INC.; *U.S. Private*, pg. 1688
GHIRARDELLI CHOCOLATE COMPANY—See Chocoladefabriken Lindt & Sprungli AG; *Int'l*, pg. 1576
GREEN & BLACK'S LIMITED—See Mondelez International, Inc.; *U.S. Public*, pg. 1461
GUAN CHONG COCOA MANUFACTURER SDN. BHD.—See Guan Chong Berhad; *Int'l*, pg. 3152
GUITTARD CHOCOLATE COMPANY; *U.S. Private*, pg. 1814
HAIHA CONFECTIONERY JOINT STOCK COMPANY; *Int'l*, pg. 3210
HAITAI CONFECTIONERY AND FOODS CO.,LTD. - CHEONAN FACTORY—See Haitai Confectionery And Foods Co.,ltd.; *Int'l*, pg. 3217
HAITAI CONFECTIONERY AND FOODS CO.,LTD. - KWANGJU FACTORY—See Haitai Confectionery And Foods Co.,ltd.; *Int'l*, pg. 3217
HALLOREN SCHOKOLADENFABRIK AG; *Int'l*, pg. 3230
HAWAIIAN HOST INC.; *U.S. Private*, pg. 1882
HAWAII VINTAGE CHOCOLATE CO.; *U.S. Public*, pg. 988
THE HERSHEY CO.; *U.S. Public*, pg. 2088
HERSHEY INTERNATIONAL LTD.—See The Hershey Co.; *U.S. Public*, pg. 2089
HERSHEY MEXICO, S.A. DE C.V.—See The Hershey Co.; *U.S. Public*, pg. 2089
HOTEL CHOCOLAT GROUP LIMITED—See Mars, Incorporated; *U.S. Private*, pg. 2589
JACQUES TORRES CHOCOLATE; *U.S. Private*, pg. 2180
KENT GIDA MADDELERI SANAYII VE TICARET ANONIM SIRKETI—See Mondelez International, Inc.; *U.S. Public*, pg. 1461
KIND LLC; *U.S. Private*, pg. 2306
LES ATELIERS DU GOUT—See Sysco Corporation; *U.S. Public*, pg. 1974
LINDT & SPRUNGLI (CEE) S.R.O.—See Chocoladefabriken Lindt & Sprungli AG; *Int'l*, pg. 1576
LINDT & SPRUNGLI (NORDIC) AB—See Chocoladefabriken Lindt & Sprungli AG; *Int'l*, pg. 1576
LINDT & SPRUNGLI (SOUTH AFRICA) (PTY) LTD.—See Chocoladefabriken Lindt & Sprungli AG; *Int'l*, pg. 1576
LINDT & SPRUNGLI (USA) INC.—See Chocoladefabriken Lindt & Sprungli AG; *Int'l*, pg. 1576
LINETTE QUALITY CHOCOLATES, INC.—See Conagra Brands, Inc.; *U.S. Public*, pg. 564
MADELAINE CHOCOLATE NOVELTIES, INC.; *U.S. Private*, pg. 2539
MANTROSE UK LIMITED—See RPM International Inc.; *U.S. Public*, pg. 1817
MARS NORTH AMERICA—See Mars, Incorporated; *U.S. Private*, pg. 2589
MARS SWITZERLAND—See Mars, Incorporated; *U.S. Private*, pg. 2590
MERCATOR-EMBA D.D.—See Fortenova Group d.d.; *Int'l*, pg. 2738
MIYATA CO., LTD.—See Hong Kong Food Investment Holdings Limited; *Int'l*, pg. 3466
MONDELEZ HELLAS S.A.—See Mondelez International, Inc.; *U.S. Public*, pg. 1463
MONDELEZ OESTERREICH PRODUCTION GMBH—See Mondelez International, Inc.; *U.S. Public*, pg. 1464
MONDELEZ UK LIMITED—See Mondelez International, Inc.; *U.S. Public*, pg. 1463
MUNDO DULCE S.A. DE C.V.—See Arcor Sociedad Anonima, Industrial y Comercial; *Int'l*, pg. 550
MUNDO DULCE S.A. DE C.V.—See Grupo Bimbo, S.A.B. de C.V.; *Int'l*, pg. 3123
NEUHAUS NV—See Compagnie du Bois Sauvage SA; *Int'l*, pg. 1740
PEARSON CANDY COMPANY—See Brynwood Partners Management LLC; *U.S. Private*, pg. 674
PRIMROSE CANDY CO.; *U.S. Private*, pg. 3263
PT ASIA COCOA INDONESIA—See Guan Chong Berhad; *Int'l*, pg. 3152
R.M. PALMER COMPANY; *U.S. Private*, pg. 3339
ROCKY MOUNTAIN CHOCOLATE FACTORY, INC.—See Rocky Mountain Chocolate Factory, Inc.; *U.S. Public*, pg. 1807
SACO FOODS INC.—See Benford Capital Partners, LLC; *U.S. Private*, pg. 526
SEASON CONFECTIONARY & BAKERY SDN. BHD.—See ABR Holdings, Ltd.; *Int'l*, pg. 67
SEATTLE GOURMET FOODS, INC.; *U.S. Private*, pg. 3592
SUNSHINE INDUSTRIES LTD—See Associated Brands Industries Limited; *Int'l*, pg. 648
VOSGES HAUT-CHOCOLAT, LTD.; *U.S. Private*, pg. 4413
WHETSTONE CHOCOLATES, INC.; *U.S. Private*, pg. 4506
WILBUR CHOCOLATE CO., INC.—See Cargill, Inc.; *U.S. Private*, pg. 756
WILD THINGS SNACKS, LLC; *U.S. Private*, pg. 4519
WORLD'S FINEST CHOCOLATE, INC.; *U.S. Private*, pg. 4568
WRIGLEY INDIA PRIVATE LIMITED—See Mars, Incorporated; *U.S. Private*, pg. 2591
ZACHARY CONFECTIONS INC.; *U.S. Private*, pg. 4596

311352 — CONFECTIONERY MANUFACTURING FROM PURCHASED CHOCOLATE

ADM AGRO INDUSTRIES KOTA & AKOLA PRIVATE LIMITED—See Archer-Daniels-Midland Company; *U.S. Public*, pg. 181
ADM OLOMOUC S.R.O.—See Archer-Daniels-Midland Company; *U.S. Public*, pg. 182
ADM PROTEXIN LIMITED—See Archer-Daniels-Midland Company; *U.S. Public*, pg. 182
ADM (THAILAND) LTD.—See Archer-Daniels-Midland Company; *U.S. Public*, pg. 181
AMYLUM NISASTA SANAYI VE TICARET ANONIM SIRKETI—See Archer-Daniels-Midland Company; *U.S. Public*, pg. 183
ANASTASIA CONFECTIONS, INC.—See Hilton Grand Vacations Inc.; *U.S. Public*, pg. 1039
ANDES MANUFACTURING LLC—See Tootsie Roll Industries, Inc.; *U.S. Public*, pg. 2163
ANNABELLE CANDY COMPANY, INC.; *U.S. Private*, pg. 284
ANTHONY-THOMAS CANDY COMPANY; *U.S. Private*, pg. 288
ASHER'S CHOCOLATES, INC.; *U.S. Private*, pg. 349
AUJAN INDUSTRIES CO., L.L.C.; *Int'l*, pg. 704
BARCEL S.A. DE C.V.—See Grupo Bimbo, S.A.B. de C.V.; *Int'l*, pg. 3122
BETSY ANN CANDIES, INC.; *U.S. Private*, pg. 546
BISCOMISR—See Kellanova; *U.S. Public*, pg. 1217
BOYER CANDY COMPANY INC.; *U.S. Private*, pg. 628
BRITANNIA SUPERFINE LTD.; *Int'l*, pg. 1165
CADBURY NIGERIA PLC—See Mondelez International, Inc.; *U.S. Public*, pg. 1461
CADBURY UK LIMITED—See Mondelez International, Inc.; *U.S. Public*, pg. 1461
CAFFAREL S.P.A.—See Chocoladefabriken Lindt & Sprungli AG; *Int'l*, pg. 1577
CAMBRIDGE BRANDS, INC.—See Tootsie Roll Industries, Inc.; *U.S. Public*, pg. 2163
CAMPBELLS/BEWLEY GROUP; *Int'l*, pg. 1274
CHOCOLADEFABRIKEN LINDT & SPRUNGLI GMBH—See Chocoladefabriken Lindt & Sprungli AG; *Int'l*, pg. 1576
CHOCOLADEFABRIKEN LINDT & SPRUNGLI (SCHWEIZ) AG—See Chocoladefabriken Lindt & Sprungli AG; *Int'l*, pg. 1576
CHOCOLATE ACQUISITION SUB, LLC—See Hilton Grand Vacations Inc.; *U.S. Public*, pg. 1039
CHOCOLATES A LA CARTE, INC.; *U.S. Private*, pg. 888
CHOCOLATS CAMILLE BLOCH S.A.; *Int'l*, pg. 1577
CHOCOLATS HALBA—See Coop-Gruppe Genossenschaft; *Int'l*, pg. 1790
CLOETTA DANMARK APS—See Cloetta AB; *Int'l*, pg. 1661
CLOETTA DEUTSCHLAND GMBH—See Cloetta AB; *Int'l*, pg. 1661
CLOETTA HOLLAND B.V.—See Cloetta AB; *Int'l*, pg. 1661
CLOETTA ITALIA S.R.L.—See Cloetta AB; *Int'l*, pg. 1661
CLOETTA NORGE AS—See Cloetta AB; *Int'l*, pg. 1661
CLOETTA NUTISAL AB; *Int'l*, pg. 1661
CLOETTA SUOMI OY—See Cloetta AB; *Int'l*, pg. 1661
CLOETTA UK LTD.—See Cloetta AB; *Int'l*, pg. 1661
CORDON VERT CO., LTD—See AEON Co., Ltd.; *Int'l*, pg. 177
CROWN CONFECTIONERY CO., LTD.—See Crown Confectionery Co., Ltd.; *Int'l*, pg. 1857
CRYSTAL CANDY (PRIVATE) LTD.—See Mondelez International, Inc.; *U.S. Public*, pg. 1461
CUPID CANDIES, INC.—See Brown Sugar Bakery & Cafe, Inc.; *U.S. Private*, pg. 669
CYBELE CO., LTD.; *Int'l*, pg. 1891
DAGOBA ORGANIC CHOCOLATE—See The Hershey Co.; *U.S. Public*, pg. 2088
DEBRAND INC.; *U.S. Private*, pg. 1186
DOLLAR SWEETS COMPANY PTY LTD; *Int'l*, pg. 2158
ELMER CANDY CORPORATION; *U.S. Private*, pg. 1376
ENSTROM CANDIES, INC.; *U.S. Private*, pg. 1402
FUJI OIL (ZHANG JIA GANG) CO., LTD.—See Fuji Oil Holdings Inc.; *Int'l*, pg. 2815
GUAN CHONG BERHAD; *Int'l*, pg. 3152
HARRY LONDON CANDIES, INC.—See Ferrero International S.A.; *Int'l*, pg. 2640
HELEN GRACE CHOCOLATES, INC.—See Hilton Grand Vacations Inc.; *U.S. Public*, pg. 1040
HERSHEY CANADA, INC.—See The Hershey Co.; *U.S. Public*, pg. 2088
HERSHEY CHOCOLATE & CONFECTIONERY COMPANY—See The Hershey Co.; *U.S. Public*, pg. 2088
HERSHEY CHOCOLATE OF VIRGINIA, INC.—See The Hershey Co.; *U.S. Public*, pg. 2088
HERSHEY FOODS CORP.-HAZLETON PLANT—See The Hershey Co.; *U.S. Public*, pg. 2088
HERSHEY INDIA PRIVATE LIMITED—See The Hershey Co.; *U.S. Public*, pg. 2089
HOFFMANS CHOCOLATE, LLC—See Hilton Grand Vacations Inc.; *U.S. Public*, pg. 1039
KONINKLIJKE DE RUIJTER BV—See 3G Capital, Inc.; *U.S. Private*, pg. 9
KONINKLIJKE DE RUIJTER BV—See Berkshire Hathaway Inc.; *U.S. Public*, pg. 317
L.A. BURDICK CHOCOLATE; *U.S. Private*, pg. 2364
LA PIE QUI CHANTE SA—See Mondelez International, Inc.; *U.S. Public*, pg. 1461
LAZORD—See HAK Algahtani Group of Companies; *Int'l*, pg. 3219
LEES FOODS LIMITED—See DBAY Advisors Limited; *Int'l*, pg. 1986
LINDT & SPRUNGLI (AUSTRIA) GMBH—See Chocoladefabriken Lindt & Sprungli AG; *Int'l*, pg. 1576
LINDT & SPRUNGLI (BRAZIL) HOLDING LTDA.—See Chocoladefabriken Lindt & Sprungli AG; *Int'l*, pg. 1576
LINDT & SPRUNGLI (CHINA) LTD.—See Chocoladefabriken Lindt & Sprungli AG; *Int'l*, pg. 1576
LINDT & SPRUNGLI DE MEXICO SA DE CV—See Chocoladefabriken Lindt & Sprungli AG; *Int'l*, pg. 1577
LINDT & SPRUNGLI JAPAN CO., LTD.—See Chocoladefabriken Lindt & Sprungli AG; *Int'l*, pg. 1577
LINDT & SPRUNGLI (NORTH AMERICA) INC.—See Chocoladefabriken Lindt & Sprungli AG; *Int'l*, pg. 1576
LINDT & SPRUNGLI SA—See Chocoladefabriken Lindt & Sprungli AG; *Int'l*, pg. 1577
LINDT & SPRUNGLI S.P.A.—See Chocoladefabriken Lindt & Sprungli AG; *Int'l*, pg. 1577
MARS BELGIUM—See Mars, Incorporated; *U.S. Private*, pg. 2589
MARS CHOCOLAT FRANCE—See Mars, Incorporated; *U.S. Private*, pg. 2589
MARS FINLAND OY—See Mars, Incorporated; *U.S. Private*, pg. 2589
MARS, INCORPORATED; *U.S. Private*, pg. 2588
MARS SNACKFOODS U.S.—See Mars, Incorporated; *U.S. Private*, pg. 2590
MARS UK LTD.—See Mars, Incorporated; *U.S. Private*, pg. 2590
MASTER MIX OF TRINIDAD LIMITED—See Archer-Daniels-Midland Company; *U.S. Public*, pg. 185
MONDELEZ UK CONFECTIONERY PRODUCTION LIMITED—See Mondelez International, Inc.; *U.S. Public*, pg. 1461
NORMAN LOVE CONFECTIONS; *U.S. Private*, pg. 2938
PACKAGING PROGRESSIONS, INC.—See The Middleby Corporation; *U.S. Public*, pg. 2115
PALMER CANDY COMPANY; *U.S. Private*, pg. 3080
RUSSELL STOVER CANDIES, LLC—See Chocoladefabriken Lindt & Sprungli AG; *Int'l*, pg. 1576
SEE'S CANDY SHOPS, INC.—See Berkshire Hathaway Inc.; *U.S. Public*, pg. 316
SWEET ACQUISITONS UT1—See Hilton Grand Vacations Inc.; *U.S. Public*, pg. 1039
SWEET GARDEN CO., LTD.—See Fujiya Co., Ltd.; *Int'l*, pg. 2838
THE SWEET SHOP USA; *U.S. Private*, pg. 4125
TANGERINE CONFECTIONERY LTD. - LION CONFECTIONARY DIVISION—See CapVest Limited; *Int'l*, pg. 1318
THORNTONS LTD.—See Ferrero International S.A.; *Int'l*, pg. 2641
TOOTSIE ROLL INDUSTRIES, INC.; *U.S. Public*, pg. 2163
TOPPS CANADA, INC.—See Madison Dearborn Partners, LLC; *U.S. Private*, pg. 2542
TOPPS EUROPE LIMITED—See Madison Dearborn Partners, LLC; *U.S. Private*, pg. 2542
TOPPS IRELAND LTD.—See Madison Dearborn Partners, LLC; *U.S. Private*, pg. 2542
TOPPS ITALIA SRL—See Madison Dearborn Partners, LLC; *U.S. Private*, pg. 2542
TREBOR BASSETT SHARPS GMBH—See Mondelez International, Inc.; *U.S. Public*, pg. 1461
TRI INTERNATIONAL COMPANY—See Tootsie Roll Industries, Inc.; *U.S. Public*, pg. 2163
TUTSI S.A. DE C.V.—See Tootsie Roll Industries, Inc.; *U.S. Public*, pg. 2163
WORLD'S FINEST CHOCOLATE CANADA COMPANY—See World's Finest Chocolate, Inc.; *U.S. Private*, pg. 4568

N.A.I.C.S. INDEX

311411 — FROZEN FRUIT, JUICE, AND VEGETABLE MANUFACTURING

AGIS-AGROINDUSTRIJA; *Int'l*, pg. 210
AGRANA FRUCHT GMBH & CO KG—See AGRANA Beteiligungs-AG; *Int'l*, pg. 213
AGRANA FRUIT ARGENTINA S.A—See AGRANA Beteiligungs-AG; *Int'l*, pg. 213
AGRANA FRUIT AUSTRALIA PTY. LTD.—See AGRANA Beteiligungs-AG; *Int'l*, pg. 213
AGRANA FRUIT AUSTRIA GMBH—See AGRANA Beteiligungs-AG; *Int'l*, pg. 213
AGRANA FRUIT DACHANG CO. LTD—See AGRANA Beteiligungs-AG; *Int'l*, pg. 213
AGRANA FRUIT FIJI PTY. LTD.—See AGRANA Beteiligungs-AG; *Int'l*, pg. 213
AGRANA FRUIT FRANCE S.A.—See AGRANA Beteiligungs-AG; *Int'l*, pg. 213
AGRANA FRUIT ISTANBUL GIDA SAN VE TIC A.S.—See AGRANA Beteiligungs-AG; *Int'l*, pg. 213
AGRANA FRUIT KOREA CO. LTD.—See AGRANA Beteiligungs-AG; *Int'l*, pg. 213
AGRANA FRUIT MEXICO SA DE CV—See AGRANA Beteiligungs-AG; *Int'l*, pg. 213
AGRANA FRUIT POLSKA SP Z.O.O.—See AGRANA Beteiligungs-AG; *Int'l*, pg. 213
AGRANA FRUIT SOUTH AFRICA PTY. LTD..—See AGRANA Beteiligungs-AG; *Int'l*, pg. 213
AGRANA FRUIT US, INC.—See AGRANA Beteiligungs-AG; *Int'l*, pg. 213
AGROGORICA D.D.; *Int'l*, pg. 219
AGRO INDUSTRIAL EXPORTADORA, S.A. DE C.V.; *Int'l*, pg. 218
AGROINDUSTRIAS AIB S.A.; *Int'l*, pg. 219
AJINOMOTO WINDSOR, INC.—See Ajinomoto Company, Inc.; *Int'l*, pg. 257
AMERICAN BEVERAGE CORPORATION—See Brynwood Partners Management LLC; *U.S. Private*, pg. 674
ANADOLU ETAP PENKON GIDA VE TARIM URUNLERI SAN VE TIC. A.S.—See Anadolu Efes Biracilik ve Malt Sanayii A.S.; *Int'l*, pg. 445
APPLETISER SA (PTY) LTD.—See The Coca-Cola Company; *U.S. Public*, pg. 2063
AQUATUS A.D.; *Int'l*, pg. 528
ARDO A/B—See Ardo N.V.; *Int'l*, pg. 556
ARDO AUSTRIA FROST GMBH—See Ardo N.V.; *Int'l*, pg. 557
ARDO B.V.—See Ardo N.V.; *Int'l*, pg. 557
ARDO ITALIA SRL—See Ardo N.V.; *Int'l*, pg. 557
ARDO SA—See Ardo N.V.; *Int'l*, pg. 557
ARDO SHANGAI MARKETING CO. LTD—See Ardo N.V.; *Int'l*, pg. 557
ARDOVRIES ESPANA S.A.—See Ardo N.V.; *Int'l*, pg. 557
BEVOLUTION GROUP—See Highlander Partners, LP.; *U.S. Private*, pg. 1939
BOARDMAN FOODS INC.; *U.S. Private*, pg. 602
BRAMHULTS JUICE AB—See Eckes AG; *Int'l*, pg. 2290
B ROBERT'S FOODS LLC—See Bakkavor Group plc; *Int'l*, pg. 805
CAL PACIFIC SPECIALTY FOODS; *U.S. Private*, pg. 715
CAPFRUIT S.A.—See Hero AG; *Int'l*, pg. 3363
CCA BAYSWATER PTY LTD—See COCA-COLA EUROPACIFIC PARTNERS PLC; *Int'l*, pg. 1684
CELL-NIQUE CORPORATION; *U.S. Private*, pg. 807
CELSIUS HOLDINGS, INC.; *U.S. Public*, pg. 465
CHERRY GROWERS INC.; *U.S. Private*, pg. 874
CHIANGMAI FROZEN FOODS PUBLIC COMPANY LIMITED - CHIANGMAI FACTORY 1—See Chiangmai Frozen Foods Public Company Limited; *Int'l*, pg. 1476
CHIANGMAI FROZEN FOODS PUBLIC COMPANY LIMITED - CHIANGMAI FACTORY 2—See Chiangmai Frozen Foods Public Company Limited; *Int'l*, pg. 1476
CHIANGMAI FROZEN FOODS PUBLIC COMPANY LIMITED; *Int'l*, pg. 1476
CHINA HAISHENG JUICE HOLDINGS CO., LTD.; *Int'l*, pg. 1506
CHINA WANTIAN HOLDINGS LIMITED; *Int'l*, pg. 1562
CHIQUITA BRANDS INTERNATIONAL, INC.—See Banco Safra S.A.; *Int'l*, pg. 824
CHORDIA FOOD PRODUCTS LTD.; *Int'l*, pg. 1582
CLIFFSTAR LLC—See Primo Water Corporation; *U.S. Public*, pg. 1718
COCA-COLA EUROPACIFIC PARTNERS DEUTSCHLAND GMBH—See COCA-COLA EUROPACIFIC PARTNERS PLC; *Int'l*, pg. 1684
COCA-COLA NORTH AMERICA—See The Coca-Cola Company; *U.S. Public*, pg. 2064
COCA-COLA NORTH AMERICA—See The Coca-Cola Company; *U.S. Public*, pg. 2064
COLOMA FROZEN FOODS INC.; *U.S. Private*, pg. 970
COOPERATIVA A.D.; *Int'l*, pg. 1792
CRUSTA FRUIT JUICES PROPRIETARY LIMITED—See COCA-COLA EUROPACIFIC PARTNERS PLC; *Int'l*, pg. 1684
DELICA FOODS CO., LTD.—See Delica Foods Holdings Co., Ltd.; *Int'l*, pg. 2013
DELICA FOODS HOKKAIDO CO., LTD.—See Delica Foods Holdings Co., Ltd.; *Int'l*, pg. 2013
DELICA FOODS NAGASAKI CO., LTD.—See Delica Foods Holdings Co., Ltd.; *Int'l*, pg. 2013
DEL MAR FOOD PRODUCTS CORP.; *U.S. Private*, pg. 1192
DEL REY JUICE CO.; *U.S. Private*, pg. 1193
DESIGNER FOODS CO., LTD.—See Delica Foods Holdings Co., Ltd.; *Int'l*, pg. 2013
DIRAFROST FROZEN FRUIT INDUSTRY N.V.—See AGRANA Beteiligungs-AG; *Int'l*, pg. 214
DMC BEVERAGE CORP.; *U.S. Private*, pg. 1248
DOHLER-MILNE ASEPTICS LLC—See Dohler GmbH; *Int'l*, pg. 2156
DOHLER-MILNE ASEPTICS LLC—See Wyckoff Farms, Incorporated; *U.S. Private*, pg. 4575
ECKERT COLD STORAGE COMPANY; *U.S. Private*, pg. 1328
ECKES-GRANINI AUSTRIA GMBH—See Eckes AG; *Int'l*, pg. 2290
ECKES-GRANINI DEUTSCHLAND GMBH—See Eckes AG; *Int'l*, pg. 2290
ECKES-GRANINI FINLAND OY AB—See Eckes AG; *Int'l*, pg. 2291
ECKES-GRANINI (SUISSE) S.A.—See Eckes AG; *Int'l*, pg. 2290
ECOFROZ S.A.—See Air Water Inc.; *Int'l*, pg. 240
ENZAFOODS NEW ZEALAND LIMITED—See BayWa AG; *Int'l*, pg. 919
EQUATOR BEVERAGE COMPANY; *U.S. Public*, pg. 785
ERBORISTERIE D'ITALIA SRL—See Bioera S.p.A.; *Int'l*, pg. 1037
ERSU MEYVE VE GIDA SANAYI A.S.; *Int'l*, pg. 2499
EURO FRIGO A.D.; *Int'l*, pg. 2531
EXPORTADORA Y SERVICIOS EL PARQUE S.P.A.—See Dole plc; *Int'l*, pg. 2158
FOODS & INNS LTD.; *Int'l*, pg. 2727
FRUTTAGEL S.C.P.A.; *Int'l*, pg. 2797
FUTURE FINTECH GROUP INC.; *Int'l*, pg. 2856
GOLDEN VALLEY GRAPE JUICE & WINE; *U.S. Private*, pg. 1734
GOLD-PAK CO., LTD.—See Air Water Inc.; *Int'l*, pg. 240
GREENYARD N.V.; *Int'l*, pg. 3077
HAIXIN FOODS CO., LTD.; *Int'l*, pg. 3218
HALUCO B.V.—See Dole plc; *Int'l*, pg. 2158
HANOVER FOODS—See Hanover Foods Corporation; *U.S. Public*, pg. 984
HAPPY PLANET FOODS, INC.—See Agrifoods International Cooperative LTD; *Int'l*, pg. 217
HARVEY FRESH (1994) LTD.—See Groupe Lactalis SA; *Int'l*, pg. 3106
HENRY LAMOTTE FOOD GMBH—See Henry Lamotte GmbH; *Int'l*, pg. 3355
HERMISTON FOODS, LLC—See Norpac Foods, Inc.; *U.S. Private*, pg. 2939
IMPERIAL VALLEY FOODS INC.; *U.S. Private*, pg. 2049
INTERSTATE FOOD PROCESSING CORPORATION—See Oppenheimer Companies, Inc.; *U.S. Private*, pg. 3033
JOHN COPE'S FOOD PRODUCTS, INC.—See Farm Stand Foods; *U.S. Private*, pg. 1475
J.R. SIMPLOT COMPANY FOOD GROUP—See J.R. Simplot Company; *U.S. Private*, pg. 2170
J.R. SIMPLOT COMPANY; *U.S. Private*, pg. 2170
JUGOS DEL VALLE, S.A.B. DE C.V.—See Fomento Economico Mexicano, S.A.B. de C.V.; *Int'l*, pg. 2724
KD ACQUISITION I, LLC.; *U.S. Private*, pg. 2270
KINGSTON COMPANIES; *U.S. Private*, pg. 2312
KNUDSEN & SONS, INC.—See The J.M. Smucker Company; *U.S. Public*, pg. 2107
KRAFT HEINZ COMPANY - GRANITE CITY—See 3G Capital Inc.; *U.S. Private*, pg. 10
KRAFT HEINZ COMPANY - GRANITE CITY—See Berkshire Hathaway Inc.; *U.S. Public*, pg. 318
LUKTA POLSKA SP. Z O.O—See AGRANA Beteiligungs-AG; *Int'l*, pg. 214
LUKTA POLSKA SP. Z O.O—See BayWa AG; *Int'l*, pg. 919
MARIO CAMACHO FOODS, LLC; *U.S. Private*, pg. 2576
MARSTON IMPORT AGENCIES, INC.; *U.S. Private*, pg. 2593
M&B PRODUCTS INC.; *U.S. Private*, pg. 2524
MILNE FRUITS PRODUCTS, INC.—See Wyckoff Farms, Incorporated; *U.S. Private*, pg. 4575
MINUTE MAID COMPANY CANADA INC.—See The Coca-Cola Company; *U.S. Public*, pg. 2064
NATIONAL FROZEN FOODS CORPORATION - ALBANY—See National Frozen Foods Corporation; *U.S. Private*, pg. 2855
NATIONAL FROZEN FOODS CORPORATION - CHEHALIS—See National Frozen Foods Corporation; *U.S. Private*, pg. 2855
NATIONAL FROZEN FOODS CORPORATION - MOSES LAKE—See National Frozen Foods Corporation; *U.S. Private*, pg. 2855
NATIONAL FROZEN FOODS CORPORATION; *U.S. Private*, pg. 2854
NORPAC FOODS, INC. - PLANT 7—See Norpac Foods, Inc.; *U.S. Private*, pg. 2939
NORPAC FOODS, INC.; *U.S. Private*, pg. 2939

311412 — FROZEN SPECIALTY FO...

NORTHWEST NATURALS LLC—See Tree Top, Inc.; *U.S. Private*, pg. 4216
NUNHEMS INDIA PRIVATE LIMITED—See Bayer Aktiengesellschaft; *Int'l*, pg. 903
NUVIM, INC.; *U.S. Public*, pg. 1556
OREGON CHERRY GROWERS INC. - THE DALLES PLANT—See Oregon Cherry Growers Inc.; *U.S. Private*, pg. 3040
OSHAMANBE AGRI CO., LTD.—See ASTMAX Trading, Inc.; *Int'l*, pg. 655
OXFORD FROZEN FOODS LIMITED—See Bragg Group of Companies; *Int'l*, pg. 1136
PAGO INTERNATIONAL GMBH—See Eckes AG; *Int'l*, pg. 2290
THE PICTSWEET COMPANY; *U.S. Private*, pg. 4095
POM WONDERFUL LLC—See The Wonderful Company LLC; *U.S. Private*, pg. 4138
THE RADICAL FRUIT COMPANY OF NEW YORK—See PepsiCo, Inc.; *U.S. Public*, pg. 1672
RAPSONA AB—See AAK AB; *Int'l*, pg. 32
RYNKEBY FOODS A/S—See Arla Foods amba; *Int'l*, pg. 573
SEABROOK BROTHERS & SONS, INC.; *U.S. Private*, pg. 3583
SENSIENT NATURAL INGREDIENTS LLC—See Sensient Technologies Corporation; *U.S. Public*, pg. 1867
SIO-ECKES KFT.—See Eckes AG; *Int'l*, pg. 2291
SMITH FROZEN FOODS, INC.; *U.S. Private*, pg. 3694
SUNNY DELIGHT BEVERAGES CO.—See Brynwood Partners Management LLC; *U.S. Private*, pg. 674
SUN ORCHARD INCORPORATED—See Centre Partners Management LLC; *U.S. Private*, pg. 828
SUN ORCHARD OF FLORIDA INC.—See Centre Partners Management LLC; *U.S. Private*, pg. 828
TANGO SUPPLIES, INC.; *U.S. Private*, pg. 3931
TIM FOOD CO., LTD.—See House Foods Group Inc.; *Int'l*, pg. 3491
TREE TOP, INC. - PROSSER PLANT—See Tree Top, Inc.; *U.S. Private*, pg. 4216
TREE TOP, INC.; *U.S. Private*, pg. 4216
TROPICANA MANUFACTURING COMPANY, INC.—See PepsiCo, Inc.; *U.S. Public*, pg. 1672
TROY FOODS LTD—See Fylde Fresh & Fabulous Ltd.; *Int'l*, pg. 2860
TWIN CITY FOODS, INC.; *U.S. Private*, pg. 4265
UAB ECKES-GRANINI LIETUVA—See Eckes AG; *Int'l*, pg. 2291
VENTURA COASTAL LLC; *U.S. Private*, pg. 4357
WAWONA FROZEN FOODS INC.; *U.S. Private*, pg. 4459

311412 — FROZEN SPECIALTY FOOD MANUFACTURING

AJINOMOTO BETAGRO FROZEN FOODS (THAILAND) CO., LTD.—See Ajinomoto Company, Inc.; *Int'l*, pg. 256
AJINOMOTO BETAGRO FROZEN FOODS (THAILAND) CO., LTD.—See Betagro Public Company Limited; *Int'l*, pg. 1002
AJINOMOTO BETAGRO SPECIALTY FOODS (THAILAND) CO., LTD.—See Ajinomoto Company, Inc.; *Int'l*, pg. 256
AJINOMOTO BETAGRO SPECIALTY FOODS (THAILAND) CO., LTD.—See Betagro Public Company Limited; *Int'l*, pg. 1002
AJINOMOTO FOODS NORTH AMERICA, INC.—See Ajinomoto Company, Inc.; *Int'l*, pg. 256
AJINOMOTO FROZEN FOODS CO., INC.—See Ajinomoto Company, Inc.; *Int'l*, pg. 256
AL-JAZIRA MARINE RESOURCES COMPANY LTD.—See Hayel Saeed Anam Group of Companies; *Int'l*, pg. 3290
AL NABIL FOOD INDUSTRIES LLC—See Agthia Group PJSC; *Int'l*, pg. 222
ALNA TRADING & EXPORTS LTD.; *Int'l*, pg. 364
APETIT KASVIOLJY OY—See Apetit Plc; *Int'l*, pg. 509
APETIT PLC; *Int'l*, pg. 509
APETIT SUOMI OY—See Apetit Plc; *Int'l*, pg. 509
ARETTO WELLNESS INC.; *Int'l*, pg. 559
ARMANINO FOODS OF DISTINCTION, INC.; *U.S. Public*, pg. 193
ASAHI WELLNESS FOODS CO., LTD.—See Gourmet Kineya Co., Ltd.; *Int'l*, pg. 3044
ASTROCHEF, INC.; *U.S. Private*, pg. 362
ATEECO, INC.; *U.S. Private*, pg. 365
AUSSIE FOODS, LLC—See Downs Food Group; *U.S. Private*, pg. 1269
BAKKAVOR FRESH COOK LIMITED—See Bakkavor Group plc; *Int'l*, pg. 805
BAKKAVOR IBERICA S.A.—See Bakkavor Group plc; *Int'l*, pg. 805
BAKKAVOR LIMITED - BAKKAVOR DESSERTS HIGHBRIDGE FACILITY—See Bakkavor Group plc; *Int'l*, pg. 805
BAKKAVOR LIMITED - BAKKAVOR DESSERTS NEWARK FACILITY—See Bakkavor Group plc; *Int'l*, pg. 805
BAKKAVOR LIMITED - BAKKAVOR MEALS LONDON FACILITY—See Bakkavor Group plc; *Int'l*, pg. 805
BAKKAVOR LIMITED - BAKKAVOR MEALS SUTTON BRIDGE FACILITY—See Bakkavor Group plc; *Int'l*, pg. 805

311412 — FROZEN SPECIALTY FO...

BAKKAVOR LIMITED - MELROW SALADS FACILITY—See Bakkavor Group plc; *Int'l*, pg. 805
BAKKAVOR LIMITED - TILMANSTONE SALADS FACILITY—See Bakkavor Group plc; *Int'l*, pg. 805
BAKKAVOR LONDON LIMITED—See Bakkavor Group plc; *Int'l*, pg. 805
BAKKAVOR SPALDING LTD—See Bakkavor Group plc; *Int'l*, pg. 805
BARBER FOODS, LLC—See Tyson Foods, Inc.; *U.S. Public*, pg. 2209
BELLISIO FOODS, INC.—See Charoen Pokphand Foods Public Company Limited; *Int'l*, pg. 1451
BEN FORTUNE PASTRY MANUFACTURING (M) SDN BHD; *Int'l*, pg. 969
BERNARDI ITALIAN FOODS—See Ajinomoto Company, Inc.; *Int'l*, pg. 257
BERNATELLOS PIZZA INC.; *U.S. Private*, pg. 536
BETTER BAKED FOODS, INC.; *U.S. Private*, pg. 546
BLUE RIDGE FOODS LLC; *U.S. Private*, pg. 591
BOBOLI INTERNATIONAL, LLC; *U.S. Private*, pg. 607
BOCA FOODS COMPANY—See 3G Capital Inc.; *U.S. Private*, pg. 10
BOCA FOODS COMPANY—See Berkshire Hathaway Inc.; *U.S. Public*, pg. 317
BONDUELLE DEUTSCHLAND GMBH—See Bonduelle SAS; *Int'l*, pg. 1106
BONDUELLE IBERICA SAU—See Bonduelle SAS; *Int'l*, pg. 1106
BOTTOM LINE FOOD PROCESSORS, INC.—See Advent International Corporation; *U.S. Private*, pg. 98
BRIDGFORD FOOD PROCESSING OF TEXAS, L.P.—See Bridgford Foods Corporation; *U.S. Public*, pg. 382
BRIDGFORD FOODS CORPORATION; *U.S. Public*, pg. 382
CEDAR LAKE FOODS - MGM FOODS; *U.S. Private*, pg. 804
CESARE FIORUCCI S.P.A.—See ALFA, S.A.B. de C.V.; *Int'l*, pg. 313
CONAGRA FOODS - COMPTON—See Conagra Brands, Inc.; *U.S. Public*, pg. 563
CONAGRA FOODS - COUNCIL BLUFFS—See Conagra Brands, Inc.; *U.S. Public*, pg. 563
COPACK FRANCE S.A.R.L.—See FRoSTA AG; *Int'l*, pg. 2797
COPACK TIEFKUHLKOST-PRODUKTIONS GMBH—See FRoSTA AG; *Int'l*, pg. 2797
CUCINA SANO LTD—See Bakkavor Group plc; *Int'l*, pg. 806
CUISINE SOLUTIONS, INC.; *U.S. Public*, pg. 604
CUIZINA FOOD COMPANY—See Joshua Green Corporation; *U.S. Private*, pg. 2237
DAESANG AMERICA, INC.—See Daesang Holdings Co., Ltd.; *Int'l*, pg. 1909
DAIREI CO., LTD.; *Int'l*, pg. 1940
DAVIGEL SAS—See Sysco Corporation; *U.S. Public*, pg. 1973
DFG CONFECTIONARY LLC.; *U.S. Private*, pg. 1220
DOMINO'S PIZZA DEUTSCHLAND GMBH—See Domino's Pizza Enterprises Ltd.; *Int'l*, pg. 2162
DOMINO'S PIZZA NETHERLANDS B.V.—See Domino's Pizza Enterprises Ltd.; *Int'l*, pg. 2162
ELENA'S FOOD SPECIALTIES, INC.—See ADF Foods Ltd.; *Int'l*, pg. 145
EMPRESAS Y-NUINA, INC.; *U.S. Private*, pg. 1388
ENGLISH VILLAGE SALADS LIMITED—See Bakkavor Group plc; *Int'l*, pg. 806
ENTERPRISE FOODS (PTY) LIMITED—See Country Bird Holdings Limited; *Int'l*, pg. 1818
EUROFINS QKEN KK—See Eurofins Scientific S.E.; *Int'l*, pg. 2547
EVOL FOODS; *U.S. Private*, pg. 1442
EXCELLINE FOOD PRODUCTS, LLC; *U.S. Private*, pg. 1446
FAIRMONT FOODS OF MINNESOTA INC.; *U.S. Private*, pg. 1464
FARMFOODS LTD; *Int'l*, pg. 2619
FARMHOUSE FARE LIMITED—See The Hain Celestial Group, Inc.; *U.S. Public*, pg. 2086
FESCOPACK SP.ZO.O—See FLEXOPACK S.A.; *Int'l*, pg. 2705
FESTIVE FOODS, LLC.; *U.S. Private*, pg. 1499
FIOR FAMILIE GMBH; *Int'l*, pg. 2677
FIRST PLACE FOODS, LLC.—See Swander Pace Capital, LLC; *U.S. Private*, pg. 3890
FLEURY MICHON LOGISTIQUE—See Fleury Michon SA; *Int'l*, pg. 2701
FOOD AND DRINKS PUBLIC COMPANY LIMITED; *Int'l*, pg. 2727
FRA-MA-PIZZ S.A.S.—See Domino's Pizza Enterprises Ltd.; *Int'l*, pg. 2162
FRESH FACTORY B.C. LIMITED; *U.S. Private*, pg. 886
FROSTA AG; *Int'l*, pg. 2796
FROSTA FOODSERVICE GMBH—See FRoSTA AG; *Int'l*, pg. 2797
FROSTA ROMANIA S.R.L.—See FRoSTA AG; *Int'l*, pg. 2797
FROSTKRONE TIEFKUHLKOST GMBH—See EMERAM Capital Partners GmbH; *Int'l*, pg. 2452
FROZEN SPECIALTIES INC.—See Swander Pace Capital, LLC; *U.S. Private*, pg. 3890
FSI/MFP INCORPORATED—See Swander Pace Capital, LLC; *U.S. Private*, pg. 3890
G7 JAPAN FOOD SERVICE CO., LTD.—See G-7 HOLDINGS Inc.; *Int'l*, pg. 2862
G.A. FOOD SERVICES OF PINELLAS COUNTY INC.; *U.S. Private*, pg. 1630
GARDEN PROTEIN INTERNATIONAL INC.—See Conagra Brands, Inc.; *U.S. Public*, pg. 564
GARRETT PACKING CO.—See Smith Frozen Foods, Inc.; *U.S. Private*, pg. 3694
GBB TK GMBH; *Int'l*, pg. 2893
GELIT SRL—See Consilium SGR p.A.; *Int'l*, pg. 1770
GINGER BEEF CHOICE LTD.—See Ginger Beef Corporation; *Int'l*, pg. 2976
GINGER BEEF CORPORATION; *Int'l*, pg. 2976
THE GLOBAL GREEN COMPANY LIMITED—See Avantha Group; *Int'l*, pg. 736
GLOBAL GREEN INTERNATIONAL—See Avantha Group; *Int'l*, pg. 736
GOEL FOOD PRODUCTS LIMITED; *Int'l*, pg. 3021
GOLDEN TIGER—See Ajinomoto Company, Inc.; *Int'l*, pg. 257
GOODMAN FOOD PRODUCTS INC.; *U.S. Private*, pg. 1739
GOURMET EXPRESS LLC; *U.S. Private*, pg. 1746
GREAT RECIPES COMPANY, INC.; *U.S. Private*, pg. 1767
GREENCORE PREPARED MEALS—See Greencore Group plc; *Int'l*, pg. 3074
GREEN ISLE BRANDS LIMITED—See Boparan Holdings Limited; *Int'l*, pg. 1111
HAIN BPC, INC.—See The Hain Celestial Group, Inc.; *U.S. Public*, pg. 2086
HALLIBURTON INTERNATIONAL, INC.—See Halliburton Company; *U.S. Public*, pg. 980
HALONG CANNED FOOD JOINT STOCK CORPORATION; *Int'l*, pg. 3233
HAYLEYS AGRICULTURE HOLDINGS LIMITED—See Hayleys PLC; *Int'l*, pg. 3292
HEIRLER CENOVIS GMBH—See Coop-Gruppe Genossenschaft; *Int'l*, pg. 1790
HERITAGE FAMILY SPECIALTY FOODS, INC.; *U.S. Private*, pg. 1922
HERON FOODS LTD.—See B&M European Value Retail S.A.; *Int'l*, pg. 784
HIESTAND BETEILIGUNGSHOLDING GMBH & CO. KG—See ARYZTA AG; *Int'l*, pg. 589
HIMALAYA FOOD INTERNATIONAL LIMITED; *Int'l*, pg. 3396
HISTON SWEET SPREADS LIMITED—See The Hain Celestial Group, Inc.; *U.S. Public*, pg. 2087
HITCHEN FOODS LTD—See Bakkavor Group plc; *Int'l*, pg. 806
H.J. HEINZ FROZEN & CHILLED FOODS LIMITED—See 3G Capital Inc.; *U.S. Private*, pg. 10
H.J. HEINZ FROZEN & CHILLED FOODS LIMITED—See Berkshire Hathaway Inc.; *U.S. Public*, pg. 317
HOME RUN INN, INC.; *U.S. Private*, pg. 1972
HORMEL FOODS CORP. - REFRIGERATED FOODS DIVISION—See Hormel Foods Corporation; *U.S. Public*, pg. 1054
HUEGLI UK LTD.—See Coop-Gruppe Genossenschaft; *Int'l*, pg. 1790
HUGLI NAHRUNGSMITTEL GMBH—See Coop-Gruppe Genossenschaft; *Int'l*, pg. 1790
HUHTAMAKI FOODSERVICE GERMANY SALES GMBH & CO. KG—See Huhtamaki Oyj; *Int'l*, pg. 3525
THE ICEE COMPANY—See J&J Snack Foods Corporation; *U.S. Public*, pg. 1180
ICEE DE MEXICO, S.A. DE C.V.—See J&J Snack Foods Corporation; *U.S. Public*, pg. 1179
INNOVATIVE FOODS, INC.; *U.S. Private*, pg. 2082
INO FITA GMBH—See General Mills, Inc.; *U.S. Public*, pg. 922
IRVIN & JOHNSON HOLDING COMPANY (PTY) LIMITED—See AVI Limited; *Int'l*, pg. 740
ITALPIZZA S.R.L.—See Bakkavor Group plc; *Int'l*, pg. 806
JC COMSA CORPORATION - FOODS MANUFACTURING DIVISION—See Delsole Corporation; *Int'l*, pg. 2015
JUS BY JULIE LLC; *U.S. Private*, pg. 2245
KAHIKI FOODS, INC.—See CJ Corporation; *Int'l*, pg. 1631
KAJUN KETTLE FOODS, INC.; *U.S. Private*, pg. 2256
KODIAK CAKES, LLC—See Catterton Management Company, LLC; *U.S. Private*, pg. 793
KOHYO CO., LTD.—See AEON Co., Ltd.; *Int'l*, pg. 178
KORV-GORANS KEBAB OY—See Atria Plc; *Int'l*, pg. 694
KRAVE PURE FOODS, INC.—See Sonoma Brands LLC; *U.S. Private*, pg. 3714
KT'S KITCHENS, INC.; *U.S. Private*, pg. 2355
LAMB WESTON BSW, LLC—See Lamb Weston Holdings, Inc.; *U.S. Public*, pg. 1291
LAMB WESTON CANADA ULC—See Lamb Weston Holdings, Inc.; *U.S. Public*, pg. 1291
LAMB WESTON, INC.—See Lamb Weston Holdings, Inc.; *U.S. Public*, pg. 1291
LARU GMBH—See Darling Ingredients Inc.; *U.S. Public*, pg. 634
LA TERRA FINA, INC.; *U.S. Private*, pg. 2369
LITTLE LADY FOODS, INC.; *U.S. Private*, pg. 2469
LSG-SKY FOOD GMBH—See Deutsche Lufthansa AG; *Int'l*, pg. 2067
LUCKY INTERNATIONAL TRADING, INC.; *U.S. Private*, pg. 2511
MARCEL & HENRI SELECT MEATS, INC.; *U.S. Private*, pg. 2571
MARVEL PACKERS PTY. LTD.—See Lamb Weston Holdings, Inc.; *U.S. Public*, pg. 1291
MARZETTI FROZEN PASTA—See Lancaster Colony Corporation; *U.S. Public*, pg. 1291
MCCLANCY SEASONING CO.; *U.S. Private*, pg. 2628
METSOVO BAKING COMPANY; *U.S. Private*, pg. 2691
MICHAEL'S FINER MEATS, LLC—See The Chefs' Warehouse, Inc.; *U.S. Public*, pg. 2059
MISSION FOODS (SHANGHAI) CO., LTD.—See Gruma, S.A.B. de C.V.; *U.S. Public*, pg. 3114
MONDELEZ BRASIL LTDA.—See Mondelez International, Inc.; *U.S. Public*, pg. 1462
MONOGRAM APPETIZERS, LLC—See Monogram Food Solutions, LLC; *U.S. Private*, pg. 2771
MONTANA ALIMENTARI GMBH—See Cremonini S.p.A.; *Int'l*, pg. 1838
MOUNTAIN HOUSE—See OFD Foods, LLC; *U.S. Private*, pg. 3000
NALEWAY FOODS LTD.—See Beaumont Select Corporations Inc.; *Int'l*, pg. 934
NATIONAL FROZEN FOODS CORPORATION - QUINCY DIVISION—See National Frozen Foods Corporation; *U.S. Private*, pg. 2855
NATUREX S.P.A—See Givaudan S.A.; *Int'l*, pg. 2981
NEW PRIMEBAKE LTD—See Bakkavor Group plc; *Int'l*, pg. 806
NIPPON INDUSTRIES, INC.; *U.S. Private*, pg. 2928
ON-COR FROZEN FOODS LLC; *U.S. Private*, pg. 3018
THE ORIGINAL CHILI BOWL—See Ajinomoto Company, Inc.; *Int'l*, pg. 257
ORION FOOD SYSTEMS, LLC—See One Rock Capital Partners, LLC; *U.S. Private*, pg. 3022
O'TASTY FOODS, INC.; *U.S. Private*, pg. 2981
OVERHILL FARMS, INC.—See Charoen Pokphand Foods Public Company Limited; *Int'l*, pg. 1451
PENOBSCOT MCCRUM LLC; *U.S. Private*, pg. 3138
PHILLIPS GOURMET, INC.—See Phillips Mushroom Farms; *U.S. Private*, pg. 3171
PIE FIVE PIZZA COMPANY, INC.—See Rave Restaurant Group, Inc.; *U.S. Public*, pg. 1763
PINERIDGE FOODS INC.—See Swander Pace Capital, LLC; *U.S. Private*, pg. 3890
PINNACLE FOODS CANADA CORPORATION—See Conagra Brands, Inc.; *U.S. Public*, pg. 564
PIZZA INN, INC.—See Rave Restaurant Group, Inc.; *U.S. Public*, pg. 1763
PLENUS GROUP INC.; *U.S. Private*, pg. 3213
PLUSFOOD WREXHAM LTD.—See BRF S.A.; *Int'l*, pg. 1151
PREFERRED BRANDS INTERNATIONAL, INC.—See Mars, Incorporated; *U.S. Private*, pg. 2590
PRIMABAGUZ SDN. BHD.—See Johnsonville, LLC; *U.S. Private*, pg. 2229
PROPER FOODS, INC.; *U.S. Private*, pg. 3285
PROVENA FOODS INC.—See Hormel Foods Corporation; *U.S. Public*, pg. 1054
QUALITY CHEF FOODS—See 3G Capital Inc.; *U.S. Private*, pg. 10
QUALITY CHEF FOODS—See Berkshire Hathaway Inc.; *U.S. Public*, pg. 318
QZINA SPECIALTY FOODS, INC.—See The Chefs' Warehouse, Inc.; *U.S. Public*, pg. 2059
RAGOZZINO FOODS INC.; *U.S. Private*, pg. 3346
REBBL INC.; *U.S. Private*, pg. 3370
REQUEST FOODS INC.; *U.S. Private*, pg. 3403
RESER'S FINE FOODS—See Reser's Fine Foods Inc.; *U.S. Private*, pg. 3404
RHODES INTERNATIONAL—See Rhodes International, Inc.; *U.S. Private*, pg. 3422
RICH DO BRASIL LTDA. - MARINIQUE MANUFACTURING FACILITY—See Rich Holdings, Inc.; *U.S. Private*, pg. 3427
RICH PRODUCTS CORPORATION - MISSOURI CITY MANUFACTURING FACILITY—See Rich Holdings, Inc.; *U.S. Private*, pg. 3427
RICH PRODUCTS CORPORATION - SANTA FE SPRINGS - ANN STREET MANUFACTURING FACILITY—See Rich Holdings, Inc.; *U.S. Private*, pg. 3427
RICH PRODUCTS CORPORATION - VINELAND MANUFACTURING FACILITY—See Rich Holdings, Inc.; *U.S. Private*, pg. 3427
RISING SUN FARMS; *U.S. Private*, pg. 3440
RIVERSIDE FOODS, INC.; *U.S. Private*, pg. 3445
R.L.E. CORP.; *U.S. Private*, pg. 3338
RUIZ FOOD PRODUCTS, INC.; *U.S. Private*, pg. 3503
SANDERSON FARMS, INC. - FOODS DIVISION—See Cargill, Inc.; *U.S. Private*, pg. 760
SANDERSON FARMS, INC. - FOODS DIVISION—See Continental Grain Company; *U.S. Private*, pg. 1029
SAVANNAH FOOD COMPANY, INC.; *U.S. Private*, pg. 3555
THE SCHWAN FOOD COMPANY; *U.S. Private*, pg. 4115
SEAPAK SHRIMP & SEAFOOD COMPANY—See Rich Holdings, Inc.; *U.S. Private*, pg. 3427

311421 — FRUIT AND VEGETABLE...

SEVIROLI FOODS, INC.; *U.S. Private*, pg. 3619
SHANGHAI EUGLENA BIOTECHNOLOGY CO., LTD.—See euglena Co., Ltd.; *Int'l*, pg. 2526
SHAO TONG CHUANG (PHILIPHINE) FOODSTUFFS CO., LTD—See Hong Kong Kam Kee Foodstuffs Trading Co., Ltd.; *Int'l*, pg. 3466
SHAO TONG CHUAN VEGETARIAN FOODS MFG (SG) PTE. LTD.—See Hong Kong Kam Kee Foodstuffs Trading Co., Ltd.; *Int'l*, pg. 3466
SICILIAN CHEFS, INC.—See Consolidated Investment Group, LLC; *U.S. Private*, pg. 1021
SNOW BRAND PILLSBURY, INC.—See General Mills, Inc.; *U.S. Public*, pg. 922
SOCIETE POUR L'EXPANSION DES VENTES DES PRODUITS AGRICOLES ET ALIMENTAIRES—See Hopscotch Groupe S.A.; *Int'l*, pg. 3474
SOUTHEAST FOODS DISTRIBUTION; *U.S. Private*, pg. 3725
SUN HOUSE FOODS CORPORATION—See House Foods Group Inc.; *Int'l*, pg. 3490
SYLVIA WOODS, INC.; *U.S. Private*, pg. 3898
TABATCHNICK FINE FOODS, INC.; *U.S. Private*, pg. 3919
TIKO VERTRIEBSGESELLSCHAFT MBH—See FRoSTA AG; *Int'l*, pg. 2797
TILDA INDIA PRIVATE LIMITED—See Ebro Foods S.A.; *Int'l*, pg. 2287
TILDA LIMITED—See Ebro Foods S.A.; *Int'l*, pg. 2287
TILDA MARKETING INC.—See The Hain Celestial Group, Inc.; *U.S. Public*, pg. 2087
TOFUTTI BRANDS INC.; *U.S. Public*, pg. 2161
TURRI'S ITALIAN FOODS, INC.; *U.S. Private*, pg. 4262
TYSON FOODS, INC. - CHICAGO—See Tyson Foods, Inc.; *U.S. Public*, pg. 2210
VERTICAL SALES & MARKETING, INC.; *U.S. Private*, pg. 4370
WELCOME FOOD INGREDIENTS LTD—See Bakkavor Group plc; *Int'l*, pg. 806
WESTERN WAFFLES CORP.—See Conagra Brands, Inc.; *U.S. Public*, pg. 564
WHOLESOME & HEARTY FOODS COMPANY—See Annex Capital Management LLC; *U.S. Private*, pg. 285
WIBERG CANADA INC.—See International Flavors & Fragrances Inc.; *U.S. Public*, pg. 1154
WINDSOR FROZEN FOODS CO.; *U.S. Private*, pg. 4539
WIN SCHULER FOODS; *U.S. Private*, pg. 4532
WOODLAND FOODS INC.; *U.S. Private*, pg. 4559
YOPLAIT CANADA CO.—See General Mills, Inc.; *U.S. Public*, pg. 923
YOUNGWOO FROZEN FOODS CO., LTD.—See CJ Corporation; *Int'l*, pg. 1632

311421 — FRUIT AND VEGETABLE CANNING

AJINOMOTO BIOITALIA S.P.A.—See Ajinomoto Company, Inc.; *Int'l*, pg. 256
AJINOMOTO BIOLATINA INDUSTRIA E COMERCIO LTDA.—See Ajinomoto Company, Inc.; *Int'l*, pg. 256
AJINOMOTO (CHINA) CO., LTD.—See Ajinomoto Company, Inc.; *Int'l*, pg. 256
AJINOMOTO CO., (HONG KONG) LTD.—See Ajinomoto Company, Inc.; *Int'l*, pg. 256
AJINOMOTO CO. (THAILAND) LTD.—See Ajinomoto Company, Inc.; *Int'l*, pg. 256
AJINOMOTO DEL PERU S.A.—See Ajinomoto Company, Inc.; *Int'l*, pg. 257
AJINOMOTO EURO-ASPARTAME S.A.—See Ajinomoto Company, Inc.; *Int'l*, pg. 256
AJINOMOTO EUROPE S.A.S—See Ajinomoto Company, Inc.; *Int'l*, pg. 256
AJINOMOTO FOODS EUROPE SAS—See Ajinomoto Company, Inc.; *Int'l*, pg. 256
AJINOMOTO INTERAMERICANA INDUSTRIA E COMERCIO LTDA.—See Ajinomoto Company, Inc.; *Int'l*, pg. 256
AJINOMOTO (MALAYSIA) BERHAD—See Ajinomoto Company, Inc.; *Int'l*, pg. 256
AJINOMOTO PHARMACEUTICALS EUROPE LTD.—See Ajinomoto Company, Inc.; *Int'l*, pg. 257
AJINOMOTO PHILIPPINES CORPORATION—See Ajinomoto Company, Inc.; *Int'l*, pg. 257
AJINOMOTO POLAND SP. Z O.O.—See Ajinomoto Company, Inc.; *Int'l*, pg. 257
AJINOMOTO (SINGAPORE) PTE. LTD.—See Ajinomoto Company, Inc.; *Int'l*, pg. 256
AJINOMOTO VIETNAM CO., LTD.—See Ajinomoto Company, Inc.; *Int'l*, pg. 257
ALDRICH FARMS, LLC; *U.S. Private*, pg. 160
ALIMENTOS KERN DE GUATEMALA, S.A.—See Florida Ice and Farm Co. S.A.; *Int'l*, pg. 2707
AMERICAN FRUITS & FLAVORS LLC JUICE DIVISION—See Monster Beverage Corporation; *U.S. Public*, pg. 1465
AMERICAN ONION INC.; *U.S. Private*, pg. 242
AMYCEL, INC.—See Monterey Mushrooms, Inc.; *U.S. Private*, pg. 2776
AOHATA CORPORATION; *Int'l*, pg. 487
ASIA GREEN AGRICULTURE CORPORATION; *Int'l*, pg. 612
AUSTRIA JUICE GMBH—See AGRANA Beteiligungs-AG; *Int'l*, pg. 214
AUSTRIA JUICE GMBH—See BayWa AG; *Int'l*, pg. 919
AVOFUN EUROPE S.L.—See Dole plc; *Int'l*, pg. 2157
AYCO FARMS INC.; *U.S. Private*, pg. 414
BA-TAMPTE PICKLE PRODUCTS INCORPORATED; *U.S. Private*, pg. 421
BAUMER FOODS INC.; *U.S. Private*, pg. 490
BAY VALLEY FOODS—See TreeHouse Foods, Inc.; *U.S. Public*, pg. 2187
BAY VIEW FOOD PRODUCTS COMPANY; *U.S. Private*, pg. 495
BEAR STEWART CORPORATION; *U.S. Private*, pg. 506
BELL-CARTER FOODS, INC.; *U.S. Private*, pg. 519
BELL-CARTER PACKAGING—See Bell-Carter Foods, Inc.; *U.S. Private*, pg. 519
BIRDS EYE FOODS LLC—See Conagra Brands, Inc.; *U.S. Public*, pg. 564
BL PHARMTECH CORP; *Int'l*, pg. 1056
BOLTHOUSE JUICE PRODUCTS, LLC—See Campbell Soup Company; *U.S. Public*, pg. 426
BONDUELLE SAS; *Int'l*, pg. 1106
BOWMAN ANDROS PRODUCTS, LLC; *U.S. Private*, pg. 626
BURNETTE FOODS INC.; *U.S. Private*, pg. 689
BUSH BROTHERS & COMPANY PLANT—See Bush Brothers & Company; *U.S. Private*, pg. 694
CALIFORNIA MANUFACTURING CO., INC.—See Ajinomoto Company, Inc.; *Int'l*, pg. 257
CERES FRUIT JUICES (PTY) LTD—See PepsiCo, Inc.; *U.S. Public*, pg. 1672
CHEF MAESTRO GALICIA S.L.—See Dole plc; *Int'l*, pg. 2157
CHEF MAESTRO HORECA S.L.—See Dole plc; *Int'l*, pg. 2157
C.H.I. LIMITED—See The Coca-Cola Company; *U.S. Public*, pg. 2063
CHINA GREENFRESH GROUP CO., LTD.; *Int'l*, pg. 1505
CHIPICO PICKLES—See Vienna Sausage Mfg. Co.; *U.S. Private*, pg. 4381
CHIPPEWA VALLEY BEAN COMPANY INC.; *U.S. Private*, pg. 886
CHIQUITA DEUTSCHLAND GMBH—See Banco Safra S.A.; *Int'l*, pg. 824
CHIQUITA FRUIT BAR (GERMANY) GMBH—See Banco Safra S.A.; *Int'l*, pg. 824
CHIQUITA GUATEMALA, S.A.—See Banco Safra S.A.; *Int'l*, pg. 824
CHIQUITA LOGISTIC SERVICES EL SALVADOR LTDA.—See Banco Safra S.A.; *Int'l*, pg. 824
CHUANHUA AJINOMOTO CO., LTD.—See Ajinomoto Company, Inc.; *Int'l*, pg. 257
CINCINNATI PRESERVING COMPANY INC.—See Glencoe Capital LLC; *U.S. Private*, pg. 1709
CITRUS WORLD, INC.; *U.S. Public*, pg. 905
CLAUSSEN PICKLE CO.—See 3G Capital Inc.; *U.S. Private*, pg. 10
CLAUSSEN PICKLE CO.—See Berkshire Hathaway Inc.; *U.S. Public*, pg. 317
CLEMENTS FOODS COMPANY; *U.S. Private*, pg. 940
CONAGRA GROCERY PRODUCTS COMPANY, LLC—See Conagra Brands, Inc.; *U.S. Public*, pg. 564
COUNTRY PURE FOODS, INC.—See Blue Point Capital Partners, LLC; *U.S. Private*, pg. 590
CREMONINI S.P.A.; *Int'l*, pg. 1838
CSM BAKERY PRODUCTS - LANCASTER—See Rhone Group, LLC; *U.S. Private*, pg. 3423
DALTON'S BEST MAID PRODUCTS INC.; *U.S. Private*, pg. 1150
DEL MONTE (UK) LTD.—See Fresh Del Monte Produce Inc.; *U.S. Public*, pg. 885
DESERT FRESH, INC.; *U.S. Private*, pg. 1212
DILLMAN FARM; *U.S. Private*, pg. 1231
DOLE FOOD CO., INC. - HAWAII—See Dole plc; *Int'l*, pg. 2157
DOLE NORDIC AB—See Dole plc; *Int'l*, pg. 2157
EBARA FOODS INDUSTRY, INC.; *Int'l*, pg. 2284
ECKERT'S ORCHARDS; *U.S. Private*, pg. 1328
EL BURRITO MEXICAN FOOD PRODUCTS CORP.—See House Foods Group Inc.; *Int'l*, pg. 3490
ELMATAS A.S.—See Goltas Cimento A.S.; *Int'l*, pg. 3037
ESCALON PREMIER BRANDS—See 3G Capital Inc.; *U.S. Private*, pg. 10
ESCALON PREMIER BRANDS—See Berkshire Hathaway Inc.; *U.S. Public*, pg. 317
ETABLISSEMENTS GOUTOULY ET FILS; *Int'l*, pg. 2519
EXPRESS MICROBIOLOGY LIMITED—See Eurofins Scientific S.E.; *Int'l*, pg. 2550
FARIBAULT FOODS, INC.; *U.S. Private*, pg. 1474
FARIBAULT FOODS, INC.—See Faribault Foods, Inc.; *U.S. Private*, pg. 1474
FISCHER & WIESER SPECIALTY FOODS, INC.; *U.S. Private*, pg. 1532
THE FLEA MARKET, INC.; *U.S. Private*, pg. 4029
FLORIDA'S NATURAL GROWERS—See Citrus World, Inc.; *U.S. Public*, pg. 905
FOODSWING, INC.; *U.S. Private*, pg. 1562
THE FREMONT COMPANY; *U.S. Private*, pg. 4030
THE FREMONT CO.—See The Fremont Company; *U.S. Private*, pg. 4030
FRESH DEL MONTE PRODUCE INC.; *U.S. Public*, pg. 885
FRIEL LUMBER CO.; *U.S. Private*, pg. 1611
FROZSUN INC.; *U.S. Private*, pg. 1617
FRUITCROWN PRODUCTS CORP.; *U.S. Private*, pg. 1617
FRUIT DYNAMICS LLC.; *U.S. Private*, pg. 1617
FUJIYA SANYO LTD.—See Fujiya Co., Ltd.; *Int'l*, pg. 2838
FURMANO FOODS, INC.; *U.S. Private*, pg. 1624
GANYUAN FOODS CO., LTD.; *Int'l*, pg. 2882
GEDNEY FOODS COMPANY—See PMC Capital Partners, LLC; *U.S. Private*, pg. 3217
GIOVANNI FOOD COMPANY, INC.; *U.S. Private*, pg. 1702
GLK FOODS, LLC; *U.S. Private*, pg. 1711
G.L. MEZZETTA INC.; *U.S. Private*, pg. 1631
GOYA FOODS OF GREAT LAKES NEW YORK—See Goya Foods, Inc.; *U.S. Private*, pg. 1747
GRACE FOOD PROCESSORS (CANNING) LTD.—See GraceKennedy Limited; *Int'l*, pg. 3048
GRANOLIO D.D; *Int'l*, pg. 3059
G ROE WM & SONS INC.; *U.S. Private*, pg. 1628
THE HAIN DANIELS GROUP LIMITED—See The Hain Celestial Group, Inc.; *U.S. Public*, pg. 2087
HANOVER FOODS CORPORATION; *U.S. Public*, pg. 984
HANOVER FOODS CORP.—See Hanover Foods Corporation; *U.S. Public*, pg. 984
HAWAIIAN FRUIT SPECIALTIES LLC; *U.S. Private*, pg. 1882
HAWAIIAN SUN PRODUCTS INC.; *U.S. Private*, pg. 1882
HE BEI CHENG DE LOLO COMPANY LIMITED; *Int'l*, pg. 3300
HEINZ IBERICA, S.A.—See 3G Capital Inc.; *U.S. Private*, pg. 10
HEINZ IBERICA, S.A.—See Berkshire Hathaway Inc.; *U.S. Public*, pg. 317
HEINZ-UFE LTD.—See 3G Capital Inc.; *U.S. Private*, pg. 10
HEINZ-UFE LTD.—See Berkshire Hathaway Inc.; *U.S. Public*, pg. 318
HEINZ WATTIE'S LIMITED—See 3G Capital Inc.; *U.S. Private*, pg. 9
HEINZ WATTIE'S LIMITED—See Berkshire Hathaway Inc.; *U.S. Public*, pg. 317
HEVEAGRO SDN. BHD.—See HeveaBoard Berhad; *Int'l*, pg. 3367
HEY-SONG CORPORATION; *Int'l*, pg. 3373
HIRZEL CANNING CO & FARMS; *U.S. Private*, pg. 1951
H.J. HEINZ COMPANY LIMITED—See 3G Capital Inc.; *U.S. Private*, pg. 10
H.J. HEINZ COMPANY LIMITED—See Berkshire Hathaway Inc.; *U.S. Public*, pg. 317
H.J. HEINZ COMPANY OF CANADA LTD.—See 3G Capital Inc.; *U.S. Private*, pg. 9
H.J. HEINZ COMPANY OF CANADA LTD.—See Berkshire Hathaway Inc.; *U.S. Public*, pg. 317
HJ HEINZ POLSKA SP. Z O.O.—See 3G Capital Inc.; *U.S. Private*, pg. 10
HJ HEINZ POLSKA SP. Z O.O.—See Berkshire Hathaway Inc.; *U.S. Public*, pg. 317
HORTIFRUT SA; *Int'l*, pg. 3482
INDIAN SUMMER CO-OP, INC.; *U.S. Private*, pg. 2062
INGOMAR PACKING; *U.S. Private*, pg. 2076
INTERNATIONAL COMPANY FOR AGRICULTURAL INDUSTRIES PROJECTS (BEYTI) (SAE)—See Almarai Company Ltd.; *Int'l*, pg. 363
JASPER WYMAN & SON; *U.S. Private*, pg. 2190
J.L. DEGRAFFENREID & SONS, INC.—See DG Foods, LLC; *U.S. Private*, pg. 1221
J.LIEB FOODS, INC.; *U.S. Private*, pg. 2168
THE J.M. SMUCKER COMPANY; *U.S. Public*, pg. 2106
JOHANNA FOODS INC.; *U.S. Private*, pg. 2219
JOHNSON FOODS, INC.; *U.S. Private*, pg. 2228
KNOUSE FOODS COOPERATIVE INC. - BIGLERVILLE, PA. PLANT—See Knouse Foods Cooperative Inc.; *U.S. Private*, pg. 2323
KNOUSE FOODS COOPERATIVE INC. - CHAMBERSBURG, PA. PLANT—See Knouse Foods Cooperative Inc.; *U.S. Private*, pg. 2323
KNOUSE FOODS COOPERATIVE INC. - GARDNERS, PA. PLANT—See Knouse Foods Cooperative Inc.; *U.S. Private*, pg. 2323
KNOUSE FOODS COOPERATIVE INC. - ORRTANNA, PA. PLANT—See Knouse Foods Cooperative Inc.; *U.S. Private*, pg. 2323
KRAFT HEINZ COMPANY - GARLAND—See 3G Capital Inc.; *U.S. Private*, pg. 10
KRAFT HEINZ COMPANY - GARLAND—See Berkshire Hathaway Inc.; *U.S. Public*, pg. 318
KRIER FOODS, INC.; *U.S. Private*, pg. 2351
KROGAB SVERIGE AB—See Arla Foods amba; *Int'l*, pg. 573
KRUGER FOODS INC.; *U.S. Private*, pg. 2353
LAKESIDE FOODS, INC. - BROOTEN PLANT—See Lakeside Foods, Inc.; *U.S. Private*, pg. 2377
LAKESIDE FOODS, INC. - MANITOWOC PLANT—See Lakeside Foods, Inc.; *U.S. Private*, pg. 2377
LAKESIDE FOODS, INC. - RANDOM LAKE PLANT—See Lakeside Foods, Inc.; *U.S. Private*, pg. 2377
LAKESIDE FOODS, INC. - REEDSBURG PLANT—See

311421 — FRUIT AND VEGETABLE...

Lakeside Foods, Inc.; *U.S. Private*, pg. 2377
LAKESIDE FOODS, INC.; *U.S. Private*, pg. 2377
LAKESIDE FOODS—See Lakeside Foods, Inc.; *U.S. Private*, pg. 2377
LANCASTER FINE FOODS, INC.—See Wind Point Advisors LLC; *U.S. Private*, pg. 4536
LANGER JUICE COMPANY, INC.; *U.S. Private*, pg. 2389
LANKA CANNERIES LIMITED—See Hunter & Company PLC; *Int'l*, pg. 3536
LIANHUA AJINOMOTO CO., LTD.—See Ajinomoto Company, Inc.; *Int'l*, pg. 257
LOS OLIVOS PACKAGING INC.; *U.S. Private*, pg. 2497
LOUIS MAULL COMPANY; *U.S. Private*, pg. 2498
L&S PACKING CO., INC.; *U.S. Private*, pg. 2363
MANN PACKING CO., INC.—See Fresh Del Monte Produce Inc.; *U.S. Public*, pg. 886
MANU FRUTA SUR S.L.—See Dole plc; *Int'l*, pg. 2158
MARION FOODS, INC.—See Seneca Foods Corporation; *U.S. Public*, pg. 1864
MAUI LAND & PINEAPPLE COMPANY, INC.; *U.S. Public*, pg. 1401
MAUI PINEAPPLE COMPANY, LTD.—See Maui Land & Pineapple Company, Inc.; *U.S. Public*, pg. 1402
MAYER BROS. APPLE PRODUCTS, INC.; *U.S. Private*, pg. 2621
THE MINUTE MAID COMPANY—See The Coca-Cola Company; *U.S. Public*, pg. 2065
MONTEREY BAY BEVERAGE, INC.; *U.S. Private*, pg. 2776
MOODY DUNBAR FOODS CORPORATION—See Moody Dunbar Inc.; *U.S. Private*, pg. 2778
MOODY DUNBAR INC.; *U.S. Private*, pg. 2778
MORNING STAR PACKING CO. LP; *U.S. Private*, pg. 2785
MUSCO FAMILY OLIVE COMPANY; *U.S. Private*, pg. 2817
NATIONAL FRUIT PRODUCT COMPANY, INC.; *U.S. Private*, pg. 2855
NATIONAL GRAPE CO-OP ASSOCIATION, INC.; *U.S. Private*, pg. 2855
NORPAC FOODS, INC. - BROOKS PLANT—See Norpac Foods, Inc.; *U.S. Private*, pg. 2939
NORPAC FOODS, INC. - PLANT 6—See Norpac Foods, Inc.; *U.S. Private*, pg. 2939
NORTHWEST PACKING COMPANY INC.; *U.S. Private*, pg. 2961
OCEANA FOODS—See Cherry Central Cooperative, Inc.; *U.S. Private*, pg. 874
OCEAN SPRAY CRANBERRIES-BORDENTOWN PLANT—See Ocean Spray Cranberries, Inc.; *U.S. Private*, pg. 2990
OCEAN SPRAY CRANBERRIES, INC.; *U.S. Private*, pg. 2990
OCEAN SPRAY INTERNATIONAL SERVICES (UK) LIMITED—See Ocean Spray Cranberries, Inc.; *U.S. Private*, pg. 2990
OREGON CHERRY GROWERS—See Oregon Cherry Growers Inc.; *U.S. Private*, pg. 3040
OSTROM MUSHROOM FARMS LLC—See AGF Management Limited; *Int'l*, pg. 207
PACIFIC COAST PRODUCERS - LODI PLANT—See Pacific Coast Producers; *U.S. Private*, pg. 3066
PACIFIC COAST PRODUCERS - OROVILLE PLANT—See Pacific Coast Producers; *U.S. Private*, pg. 3066
PACIFIC COAST PRODUCERS; *U.S. Private*, pg. 3066
PACIFIC COAST PRODUCERS - WOODLAND PLANT—See Pacific Coast Producers; *U.S. Private*, pg. 3066
PAGE'S PRODUCE COMPANY; *U.S. Private*, pg. 3075
PAISLEY FARM, INC.—See The Fremont Company; *U.S. Private*, pg. 4030
PATRIOT PICKLE CO.—See Swander Pace Capital, LLC; *U.S. Private*, pg. 3890
PIE PIPER PRODUCTS, LTD.—See Vienna Sausage Mfg. Co.; *U.S. Private*, pg. 4381
PIONEER FOOD GROUP LIMITED—See PepsiCo, Inc.; *U.S. Public*, pg. 1671
PREMIER FOOD INDUSTRIES LTD—See Aga Khan Development Network; *Int'l*, pg. 199
PROCESSED FRUIT INGREDIENTS, BVBA—See Banco Safra S.A.; *Int'l*, pg. 824
P.T. AJINOMOTO INDONESIA—See Ajinomoto Company, Inc.; *Int'l*, pg. 257
PT. ANEKA BOGA NUSANTARA—See Daesang Corporation; *Int'l*, pg. 1909
P.T. KML ICHIMASA FOODS—See Ichimasa Kamaboko Co., Ltd.; *Int'l*, pg. 3580
RED GOLD INC. - ELWOOD FACILITY—See Red Gold Inc.; *U.S. Private*, pg. 3374
RED GOLD INC. - GENEVA FACILITY—See Red Gold Inc.; *U.S. Private*, pg. 3374
RED GOLD INC. - ORESTES FACILITY—See Red Gold Inc.; *U.S. Private*, pg. 3374
RED GOLD INC.; *U.S. Private*, pg. 3374
RED GOLD—See Red Gold Inc.; *U.S. Private*, pg. 3374
ROBINSON FRESH BV—See C.H. Robinson Worldwide, Inc.; *U.S. Public*, pg. 415
RWA SLOVENIJA D.O.O.—See BayWa AG; *Int'l*, pg. 918
SAN JOAQUIN TOMATO GROWERS, INC.; *U.S. Private*, pg. 3541

SATICOY FOODS CORPORATION—See Moody Dunbar Inc.; *U.S. Private*, pg. 2778
SEMINOLE FOODS, INC; *U.S. Private*, pg. 3604
SENECA FOODS-CENTRAL DIV.—See Seneca Foods Corporation; *U.S. Public*, pg. 1865
SENECA FOODS CORPORATION; *U.S. Public*, pg. 1864
SENECA FOODS L.L.C.—See Seneca Foods Corporation; *U.S. Public*, pg. 1865
SENECA FOODS-RIPON—See Seneca Foods Corporation; *U.S. Public*, pg. 1865
SENECA FOODS—See Seneca Foods Corporation; *U.S. Public*, pg. 1865
SENECA FOODS—See Seneca Foods Corporation; *U.S. Public*, pg. 1865
SENECA FOODS—See Seneca Foods Corporation; *U.S. Public*, pg. 1865
SENECA FOODS—See Seneca Foods Corporation; *U.S. Public*, pg. 1865
SENECA FOODS—See Seneca Foods Corporation; *U.S. Public*, pg. 1865
SENECA FOODS—See Seneca Foods Corporation; *U.S. Public*, pg. 1865
SFFI COMPANY, INC.; *U.S. Private*, pg. 3621
SMUCKER SPECIALTY FOODS COMPANY—See The J.M. Smucker Company; *U.S. Public*, pg. 2107
SNOKIST GROWERS CO-OP; *U.S. Private*, pg. 3700
SOMERSET CUISINE LIMITED—See Batu Kawan Berhad; *Int'l*, pg. 891
STONEWALL KITCHEN LLC—See TA Associates, Inc.; *U.S. Private*, pg. 3918
SUNKIST GROWERS, INC. - PROCESSED PRODUCTS—See Sunkist Growers, Inc.; *U.S. Private*, pg. 3867
SUN RICH FRESH FOODS, INC.—See Kainos Capital, LLC; *U.S. Private*, pg. 2255
SUNRISE FRESH PRODUCE, LLC—See Performance Food Group Company; *U.S. Public*, pg. 1676
TAISO COMMERCE, INC.—See Ajinomoto Company, Inc.; *Int'l*, pg. 257
TEASDALE FOODS, INC.—See TruArc Partners, L.P.; *U.S. Private*, pg. 4245
TEEBA INVESTMENT FOR DEVELOPED FOOD PROCESSING COMPANY—See Almarai Company Ltd.; *Int'l*, pg. 363
TFC HOLLAND B.V.—See BayWa AG; *Int'l*, pg. 919
THENERGY B.V.—See BayWa AG; *Int'l*, pg. 919
TIANJIN CHALTON TOMATO PRODUCT CO., LTD.—See Chalkis Health Industry Co., Ltd.; *Int'l*, pg. 1438
TIP TOP CANNING COMPANY; *U.S. Private*, pg. 4175
TRANSFRESH CORPORATION—See Banco Safra S.A.; *Int'l*, pg. 824
TREEHOUSE FOODS, INC.; *U.S. Public*, pg. 2187
TREE TOP, INC. - ROSS PLANT—See Tree Top, Inc.; *U.S. Private*, pg. 4217
TREE TOP, INC. - SELAH PLANT—See Tree Top, Inc.; *U.S. Private*, pg. 4217
TREE TOP, INC. - WENATCHEE PLANT—See Tree Top, Inc.; *U.S. Private*, pg. 4217
TRIPLE H FOOD PROCESSORS INCORPORATED; *U.S. Private*, pg. 4237
TRUITT BROS., INC.—See Seneca Foods Corporation; *U.S. Public*, pg. 1865
UNCLE MATT'S ORGANIC INC.—See Dean Foods Company; *U.S. Private*, pg. 1184
UNITED JUICE COMPANIES OF AMERICA, INC.; *U.S. Private*, pg. 4293
VALEO FOODS LTD.—See CapVest Limited; *Int'l*, pg. 1318
VALLEY PROCESSING, INC.—See Wyckoff Farms, Incorporated; *U.S. Private*, pg. 4575
V. B. HOOK VACUUM COOLING COMPANY—See V.B. Hook & Co., Inc.; *U.S. Private*, pg. 4328
VEGETABLE JUICES INC.—See Givaudan S.A.; *U.S. Private*, pg. 2981
VIE-DEL COMPANY; *U.S. Private*, pg. 4381
VITA-PAKT CITRUS PRODUCTS CO.; *U.S. Private*, pg. 4405
WAN THAI FOODS INDUSTRY CO., LTD.—See Ajinomoto Company, Inc.; *Int'l*, pg. 256
W. CANNING INTERNATIONAL B.V.—See Element Solutions Inc.; *U.S. Public*, pg. 728
WELCH FOODS INC.—See National Grape Co-Op Association, Inc.; *U.S. Private*, pg. 2855
WELCH'S INTERNATIONAL—See National Grape Co-Op Association, Inc.; *U.S. Private*, pg. 2855
WEST AFRICAN SEASONING CO., LTD.—See Ajinomoto Company, Inc.; *Int'l*, pg. 257
WHITLOCK HOLDING COMPANY; *U.S. Private*, pg. 4513

311422 — SPECIALTY CANNING

ALIMENTOS HEINZ C.A.—See 3G Capital Inc.; *U.S. Private*, pg. 9
ALIMENTOS HEINZ C.A.—See Berkshire Hathaway Inc.; *U.S. Public*, pg. 317
ARAB INTERNATIONAL FOOD FACTORIES & INVESTMENT COMPANY; *Int'l*, pg. 530
BALL METAL FOOD CONTAINER CORP.—See Ball Corporation; *U.S. Public*, pg. 267
BATCHELORS LTD.—See CapVest Limited; *Int'l*, pg. 1318

BECKMAN & GAST CO. INC.; *U.S. Private*, pg. 511
BEECH-NUT NUTRITION CORPORATION—See Hero AG; *Int'l*, pg. 3363
BERNARDIN LTD.—See Newell Brands Inc.; *U.S. Public*, pg. 1513
BISTRO SOUPS, LTD.—See Vienna Sausage Mfg. Co.; *U.S. Private*, pg. 4381
BUSH BROTHERS & COMPANY; *U.S. Private*, pg. 693
CAMPBELL COMPANY OF CANADA LTD—See Campbell Soup Company; *U.S. Public*, pg. 426
CAMPBELL SOUP COMPANY; *U.S. Public*, pg. 426
CAMPBELL SOUP CO. - PARIS PLANT—See Campbell Soup Company; *U.S. Public*, pg. 427
CAMPBELL SOUP SUPPLY COMPANY L.L.C.—See Campbell Soup Company; *U.S. Public*, pg. 427
CONAGRA FOODS CANADA, INC.—See Conagra Brands, Inc.; *U.S. Public*, pg. 563
DON MIGUEL MEXICAN FOODS, INC.—See Grupo Herdez, S.A.B. de C.V.; *Int'l*, pg. 3130
DON MIGUEL MEXICAN FOODS, INC.—See Hormel Foods Corporation; *U.S. Public*, pg. 1054
FIESTA CANNING CO., INC.; *U.S. Private*, pg. 1505
GOYA FOODS OF PUERTO RICO—See Goya Foods, Inc.; *U.S. Private*, pg. 1747
HUMANA ITALIA S.P.A.—See DMK Deutsches Milchkontor GmbH; *Int'l*, pg. 2146
HUMANA SPAIN S.L.—See DMK Deutsches Milchkontor GmbH; *Int'l*, pg. 2146
KETTLE CUISINE, LLC—See Kainos Capital, LLC; *U.S. Private*, pg. 2255
MORGAN FOODS, INC.; *U.S. Private*, pg. 2783
NEW MEXICO FOOD DISTRIBUTORS, INC.—See Tattooed Chef, Inc.; *U.S. Public*, pg. 1983
OSKAR BLUES BREWING COMPANY; *U.S. Private*, pg. 3047
PASTA LENSI, S.R.L.—See Conagra Brands, Inc.; *U.S. Public*, pg. 563
PASTORELLI FOOD PRODUCTS, INC.; *U.S. Private*, pg. 3104
SHINE FOOD, INC.; *U.S. Private*, pg. 3637
STAGG FOODS, INC.—See Hormel Foods Corporation; *U.S. Public*, pg. 1054
STIR FOODS, LLC—See Wind Point Advisors LLC; *U.S. Private*, pg. 4536
TODDS FOODS—See 3G Capital Inc.; *U.S. Private*, pg. 10
TODDS FOODS—See Berkshire Hathaway Inc.; *U.S. Public*, pg. 318
TODDS—See 3G Capital Inc.; *U.S. Private*, pg. 10
TODDS—See Berkshire Hathaway Inc.; *U.S. Public*, pg. 318
VANEE FOODS COMPANY INC.; *U.S. Private*, pg. 4343
YUCATAN FOODS, LLC—See Flagship Food Group, LLC; *U.S. Private*, pg. 1539

311423 — DRIED AND DEHYDRATED FOOD MANUFACTURING

A&B INGREDIENTS, INC.; *U.S. Private*, pg. 19
ACEITES BORGES PONT, S.A.; *Int'l*, pg. 95
AGROPLOD AD; *Int'l*, pg. 220
AL FOAH COMPANY LLC—See Agthia Group PJSC; *Int'l*, pg. 221
ALUSH (THAILAND) CO., LTD.—See Asia Cassava Resources Holdings Limited; *Int'l*, pg. 611
AMCOR FLEXIBLES A/S—See Amcor plc; *Int'l*, pg. 416
AMERICAS FOOD TECHNOLOGIES, INC.—See The Jordan Company, L.P.; *U.S. Private*, pg. 4062
ANDRE PROST, INC.; *U.S. Private*, pg. 279
ANS INDUSTRIES LIMITED; *Int'l*, pg. 476
ARIZONA PEPPER PRODUCTS CO., INC.; *U.S. Private*, pg. 324
ASSOCIATED BRANDS INC.—See TreeHouse Foods, Inc.; *U.S. Public*, pg. 2187
A.V.O.D. KURUTULMUS GIDA VE TARIM URUNLERI SAN. TIC. A.S.; *Int'l*, pg. 28
BARILLA HOLDING S.P.A.; *Int'l*, pg. 865
BASIC AMERICAN FOODS, INC.; *U.S. Private*, pg. 484
BELL-CARTER FOODS, INC. - CORNING PLANT—See Bell-Carter Foods, Inc.; *U.S. Private*, pg. 519
BERNARD FOOD INDUSTRIES INC.; *U.S. Private*, pg. 536
BESANA UK LIMITED; *Int'l*, pg. 998
BKI—See Standex International; *U.S. Public*, pg. 1930
BLAINE LARSEN FARMS INC.; *U.S. Private*, pg. 578
BLEDINA SA—See Danone; *Int'l*, pg. 1965
BOJUN AGRICULTURE HOLDINGS LIMITED; *Int'l*, pg. 1102
BORGES AGRICULTURAL & INDUSTRIAL NUTS S.A.; *Int'l*, pg. 1114
BRAND PARTNERSHIP LTD.; *Int'l*, pg. 1139
BRAN-ZAN CO. INC.; *U.S. Private*, pg. 635
BUCHER-GUYER AG FOOD TECH—See Bucher Industries AG; *Int'l*, pg. 1208
BWI, INC.; *U.S. Private*, pg. 700
CALIFORNIA NATURAL PRODUCTS, INC.—See Wind Point Advisors LLC; *U.S. Private*, pg. 4534
CALIFORNIA SUN DRY FOODS, INC.—See Benford Capital Partners, LLC; *U.S. Private*, pg. 526
CAMIL ALIMENTOS S.A.; *Int'l*, pg. 1272

N.A.I.C.S. INDEX

311511 — FLUID MILK MANUFACT...

CARGILL FOOD INGREDIENTS CANADA, INC.—See Cargill, Inc.; *U.S. Private*, pg. 756
C. CARDASSILARIS & SONS - CARDICO S.A.; *Int'l*, pg. 1240
CEVITAL FOOD PROCESSING INDUSTRY—See Cevital S.p.A.; *Int'l*, pg. 1425
CJ TUR YEM SANAYI VE TICARET ANONIM SIRKETI—See CJ Corporation; *Int'l*, pg. 1633
CLASSIC FOODS, L.P.; *U.S. Private*, pg. 916
CONAGRA BRANDS, INC.; *U.S. Public*, pg. 563
CONAGRA FOODS - GILROY—See Conagra Brands, Inc.; *U.S. Public*, pg. 563
CONAGRA FOODS - MODESTO—See Conagra Brands, Inc.; *U.S. Public*, pg. 563
CONAGRA STORE BRANDS—See Conagra Brands, Inc.; *U.S. Public*, pg. 564
CONSUMER GUILD FOODS, INC.; *U.S. Private*, pg. 1025
CREATIVE CONTRACT PACKAGING CORP.—See Hormel Foods Corporation; *U.S. Public*, pg. 1054
CULINARTE MARKETING GROUP, LLC—See Kainos Capital, LLC; *U.S. Private*, pg. 2255
DANISCO AUSTRALIA PTY. LTD.—See DuPont de Nemours, Inc.; *U.S. Public*, pg. 692
DANISCO USA, INC.—See DuPont de Nemours, Inc.; *U.S. Public*, pg. 692
DEL REAL FOODS; *U.S. Private*, pg. 1193
DOD BIOTECH PUBLIC COMPANY LIMITED; *Int'l*, pg. 2153
D.P. SUPPLY B.V—See DMK Deutsches Milchkontor GmbH; *Int'l*, pg. 2146
DROGA KOLINSKA D.D.—See ATLANTIC GRUPA d.d.; *Int'l*, pg. 675
DUPONT NUTRITION BIOSCIENCES - BRABRAND—See DuPont de Nemours, Inc.; *U.S. Public*, pg. 692
EBRO FOODS S.A.; *Int'l*, pg. 2286
ECOLAB (GUAM) LLC—See Ecolab Inc.; *U.S. Public*, pg. 712
EL POPOCATAPETL INDUSTRIES, INC.; *U.S. Private*, pg. 1349
ENWAVE CORPORATION; *Int'l*, pg. 2456
EXETER DEHYDRATOR INC.—See Sunshine Raisin Corporation; *U.S. Private*, pg. 3872
FADE GIDA YATIRIM SANAYI TICARET A.S.; *Int'l*, pg. 2601
FISHERS BAKERY & SANDWICH CO., INC.; *U.S. Private*, pg. 1535
FOODWELL CORPORATION - DAEGU FACTORY 1—See Foodwell Corporation; *Int'l*, pg. 2728
FOODWELL CORPORATION - DAEGU FACTORY 2—See Foodwell Corporation; *Int'l*, pg. 2728
FOODWELL CORPORATION; *Int'l*, pg. 2728
FREEWORLD TRADING LTD.; *Int'l*, pg. 2771
GABAN CO., LTD.—See House Foods Group Inc.; *Int'l*, pg. 3490
GALLA FOODS LTD.—See Amara Raja Energy & Mobility Limited; *Int'l*, pg. 411
GARDEN VALLEY CORPORATION; *U.S. Private*, pg. 1643
GENERAL MILLS KOREA CO. LTD.—See General Mills, Inc.; *U.S. Public*, pg. 922
GLANBIA CONSUMER FOODS LTD. - IRELAND—See Glanbia Co-Operative Society Limited; *Int'l*, pg. 2988
GLOBO FOODS LTD.; *Int'l*, pg. 3007
GRACE DAREX GMBH—See Standard Industries Holdings Inc.; *U.S. Private*, pg. 3779
GRACELAND FRUIT INC.; *U.S. Private*, pg. 1749
GRAINS NOIR—See The Hain Celestial Group, Inc.; *U.S. Public*, pg. 2086
GREENCORE GROUP PLC; *Int'l*, pg. 3073
GREGORIO, NUMO Y NOEL WERTHEIN S.A.; *Int'l*, pg. 3078
GRIFFITH COLOMBIA S.A.—See Griffith Laboratories, Inc.; *U.S. Private*, pg. 1789
GRIFFITH LABORATORIES, K.K.—See Griffith Laboratories, Inc.; *U.S. Private*, pg. 1789
GRIFFITH LABORATORIES LIMITED—See Griffith Laboratories, Inc.; *U.S. Private*, pg. 1789
GRIFFITH LABORATORIES LTD.—See Griffith Laboratories, Inc.; *U.S. Private*, pg. 1789
GRIFFITH LABORATORIES (PHILS.) INC.—See Griffith Laboratories, Inc.; *U.S. Private*, pg. 1789
HANKYU FOODS INC—See H2O Retailing Corp.; *Int'l*, pg. 3200
HAOXIANGNI HEALTH FOOD CO., LTD.; *Int'l*, pg. 3268
HEALTH AND PLANT PROTEIN GROUP LIMITED; *Int'l*, pg. 3303
HENA, INC.; *U.S. Private*, pg. 1913
H.J. HEINZ COMPANY AUSTRALIA LTD.—See 3G Capital Inc.; *U.S. Private*, pg. 9
H.J. HEINZ COMPANY AUSTRALIA LTD.—See Berkshire Hathaway Inc.; *U.S. Public*, pg. 317
HONG KONG KAM KEE FOODSTUFFS TRADING CO., LTD.; *Int'l*, pg. 3466
HUBEI WUCHANGYU CO., LTD.; *Int'l*, pg. 3518
IDAHO FRESH-PAK INC.; *U.S. Private*, pg. 2035
IDAHO PACIFIC CORPORATION—See Continental Grain Company; *U.S. Private*, pg. 1029
IDAHO SUPREME POTATOES, INC.; *U.S. Private*, pg. 2035
INVENTURE FOODS, INC.—See Utz Brands, Inc.; *U.S. Public*, pg. 2268

JOYCE FOOD PRODUCTS INC.; *U.S. Private*, pg. 2239
KENT PRECISION FOODS GROUP, INC.—See Kent Corporation; *U.S. Private*, pg. 2287
KRAFT HEINZ COMPANY - PLANTERS—See 3G Capital Inc.; *U.S. Private*, pg. 11
KRAFT HEINZ COMPANY - PLANTERS—See Berkshire Hathaway Inc.; *U.S. Public*, pg. 318
LABORATORIOS GRIFFITH DE CENTRO AMERICA S.A.—See Griffith Laboratories, Inc.; *U.S. Private*, pg. 1789
LIMA S.A./N.V.—See The Hain Celestial Group, Inc.; *U.S. Public*, pg. 2087
MARIANI PACKING COMPANY; *U.S. Private*, pg. 2574
MAVESA, S.A.—See Empresas Polar; *Int'l*, pg. 2391
MAXIMUM QUALITY FOODS; *U.S. Private*, pg. 2619
MCCORMICK FLAVOR DIVISION—See McCormick & Company, Incorporated; *U.S. Public*, pg. 1404
MCCORMICK-SALINAS PLANT—See McCormick & Company, Incorporated; *U.S. Public*, pg. 1404
MERCER FOODS LLC—See The Graham Group, Inc.; *U.S. Private*, pg. 4037
MINNESOTA DEHYDRATED VEGETABLES, INC.; *U.S. Private*, pg. 2743
MOJAVE FOODS CORPORATION—See McCormick & Company, Incorporated; *U.S. Public*, pg. 1404
NANTUCKET HARVEST CO., INC.; *U.S. Private*, pg. 2833
NIPPON FREEZE DRYING CO., LTD.—See Asahi Group Holdings Ltd.; *Int'l*, pg. 594
NISSIN-AJINOMOTO ALIMENTOS LTDA.—See Ajinomoto Company, Inc.; *Int'l*, pg. 257
NONPAREIL CORPORATION; *U.S. Private*, pg. 2934
NORSON ALIMENTOS S DE RL DE CV—See Agroindustrial del Noroeste S. de R.L. de C.V.; *Int'l*, pg. 219
NUTREX AG—See Coop-Gruppe Genossenschaft; *Int'l*, pg. 1790
N.V. GRIFFITH LABORATORIES S.A.—See Griffith Laboratories, Inc.; *U.S. Private*, pg. 1789
OREGON POTATO COMPANY; *U.S. Private*, pg. 3040
PLANTAIN PRODUCTS COMPANY; *U.S. Private*, pg. 3197
POWER PACKAGING, INC.—See HCI Equity Management, L.P.; *U.S. Private*, pg. 1889
PT INDOFOOD SUKSES MAKMUR TBK.—See First Pacific Company Limited; *Int'l*, pg. 2686
QINGDAO FOODWELL CORPORATION—See Foodwell Corporation; *Int'l*, pg. 2728
RIZHAO YUSHUN CASSAVA. CO., LTD.—See Asia Cassava Resources Holdings Limited; *Int'l*, pg. 611
R.J. VAN DRUNEN & SONS INC.; *U.S. Private*, pg. 3337
SARI FOODS, LLC—See Aterian, Inc.; *U.S. Public*, pg. 221
SCHIFF FOOD PRODUCTS CO., INC.; *U.S. Private*, pg. 3564
SENSIENT NATURAL INGREDIENTS—See Sensient Technologies Corporation; *U.S. Public*, pg. 1867
SENSIENT NATURAL TECHNOLOGIES LLC—See Sensient Technologies Corporation; *U.S. Public*, pg. 1867
SIMPLOT AUSTRALIA PTY. LTD.—See J.R. Simplot Company; *U.S. Private*, pg. 2171
SMALL PLANET FOODS INC.—See General Mills, Inc.; *U.S. Public*, pg. 922
SUNDOWN FOODS U.S.A., INC.—See A.V.O.D. Kurutulmus Gida ve Tarim Urunleri San. Tic. A.S.; *Int'l*, pg. 28
SUNSWEET DRYERS—See Sunsweet Growers, Inc.; *U.S. Private*, pg. 3873
SUNSWEET GROWERS, INC.; *U.S. Private*, pg. 3873
TREE TOP, INC. - MEDFORD OREGON PLANT—See Tree Top, Inc.; *U.S. Private*, pg. 4216
VALLEY VIEW PACKING; *U.S. Private*, pg. 4336
WINNEMUCCA FARMS INC.; *U.S. Private*, pg. 4542
THE WORNICK COMPANY—See Veritas Capital Fund Management, LLC; *U.S. Private*, pg. 4365
WRIGLEY HUNGARIA, KFT.—See Mars, Incorporated; *U.S. Private*, pg. 2591
WRIGLEY POLAND SP. ZO.O.—See Mars, Incorporated; *U.S. Private*, pg. 2591
ZORIA FARMS INC.; *U.S. Private*, pg. 4608

311511 — FLUID MILK MANUFACTURING

AGRIFOODS INTERNATIONAL COOPERATIVE LTD; *Int'l*, pg. 217
AGRI-MARK, INC.; *U.S. Private*, pg. 129
AGROPUR COOPERATIVE - DIVISION NATREL & FRESH PRODUCTS—See Agropur Cooperative; *Int'l*, pg. 220
AL RAWABI DAIRY COMPANY L.L.C.; *Int'l*, pg. 282
ALTA-DENA CERTIFIED DAIRY, LLC—See Dean Foods Company; *U.S. Private*, pg. 1183
AMRIT CORP LTD; *U.S. Private*, pg. 438
ANDERSEN DAIRY INC.; *U.S. Private*, pg. 275
ANDERSON DAIRY, INC.; *U.S. Private*, pg. 276
ANDERSON ERICKSON DAIRY COMPANY; *U.S. Private*, pg. 276
ARLA FOODS GMBH—See Arla Foods amba; *Int'l*, pg. 572
AT-TAHUR LTD.; *Int'l*, pg. 665
ATTITUDE DRINK COMPANY, INC.—See Attitude Drinks Incorporated; *U.S. Private*, pg. 383
AUBURN DAIRY PRODUCTS, INC.—See Instantwhip Foods, Incorporated; *U.S. Private*, pg. 2092

AURORA ORGANIC DAIRY CORPORATION—See Charlesbank Capital Partners, LLC; *U.S. Private*, pg. 854
BARBER DAIRIES, INC.—See Dean Foods Company; *U.S. Private*, pg. 1183
BAREMAN DAIRY INC.; *U.S. Private*, pg. 474
BAY VALLEY FOODS—See TreeHouse Foods, Inc.; *U.S. Public*, pg. 2187
BEIJING SANYUAN FOODS CO., LTD.—See Beijing Capital Agribusiness Group Co., Ltd.; *Int'l*, pg. 946
BERKELEY FARMS, LLC—See Dean Foods Company; *U.S. Private*, pg. 1183
BOBBIE BABY, INC.; *U.S. Private*, pg. 606
BORDEN DAIRY COMPANY OF FLORIDA—See Capitol Peak Partners, LLC; *U.S. Private*, pg. 744
BORDEN DAIRY COMPANY OF FLORIDA—See KKR & Co. Inc.; *U.S. Public*, pg. 1241
BORDEN MILK PRODUCTS—See Capitol Peak Partners, LLC; *U.S. Private*, pg. 744
BORDEN MILK PRODUCTS—See KKR & Co. Inc.; *U.S. Public*, pg. 1242
BRIGHT DAIRY & FOOD CO., LTD.—See Bright Food (Group) Co., Ltd.; *Int'l*, pg. 1161
BROUGHTON FOODS LLC—See Dean Foods Company; *U.S. Private*, pg. 1183
BYRNE DAIRY INC.; *U.S. Private*, pg. 701
CALIFORNIA DAIRIES, INC.; *U.S. Private*, pg. 718
CALPIS CO., LTD.—See Asahi Group Holdings Ltd.; *Int'l*, pg. 593
CALPIS FOODS SERVICE CO., LTD.—See Asahi Group Holdings Ltd.; *Int'l*, pg. 593
CASS-CLAY CREAMERY—See Associated Milk Producers, Inc.; *U.S. Private*, pg. 356
CATAMOUNT DAIRY HOLDINGS L.P.; *U.S. Private*, pg. 787
CENTRAL AREA COUNCIL—See Dairy Farmers of America, Inc.; *U.S. Private*, pg. 1145
CENTRAL DAIRY COMPANY; *U.S. Private*, pg. 820
CENTRALE LATTE RAPALLO S.P.A.—See Centrale del Latte di Torino & C. S.p.A.; *Int'l*, pg. 1410
CHESTER DAIRY COMPANY; *U.S. Private*, pg. 875
CLOVER DAIRY NAMIBIA (PTY) LTD.—See Clover Industries Limited; *Int'l*, pg. 1663
CLOVER FARMS DAIRY COMPANY; *U.S. Private*, pg. 947
CLOVER STORNETTA FARMS INC.; *U.S. Private*, pg. 947
CLOVER SWAZILAND (PTY) LTD.—See Clover Industries Limited; *Int'l*, pg. 1663
CLOVER WATERS (PTY) LTD.—See Clover Industries Limited; *Int'l*, pg. 1663
COBURG DAIRY—See Capitol Peak Partners, LLC; *U.S. Private*, pg. 744
COBURG DAIRY—See KKR & Co. Inc.; *U.S. Public*, pg. 1241
COCIO CHOKOLADEMAELK A/S—See Arla Foods amba; *Int'l*, pg. 573
COUNTRY DELITE—See Dean Foods Company; *U.S. Private*, pg. 1183
CREAMLAND DAIRIES, INC.—See Dean Foods Company; *U.S. Private*, pg. 1183
CROWLEY FOODS, INC.—See Catamount Dairy Holdings L.P.; *U.S. Private*, pg. 787
CRYSTAL CREAM & BUTTER COMPANY—See Atlas Holdings, LLC; *U.S. Private*, pg. 376
CUMBERLAND DAIRY INCORPORATED; *U.S. Private*, pg. 1122
DAIRIBORD MALAWI LIMITED—See Dairibord Holdings Limited; *Int'l*, pg. 1940
DAIRIBORD ZIMBABWE (PRIVATE) LIMITED—See Dairibord Holdings Limited; *Int'l*, pg. 1940
DAISY BRAND INC.; *U.S. Private*, pg. 1146
DAN-ED CORPORATION; *U.S. Private*, pg. 1152
THE DANNON COMPANY, INC.—See Danone; *Int'l*, pg. 1967
THE DANNON CO.—See Danone; *Int'l*, pg. 1967
THE DANNON CO.—See Danone; *Int'l*, pg. 1967
DANONE FOODS INC.—See Danone; *Int'l*, pg. 1967
DANONE INC. - MISSISSAUGA—See Danone; *Int'l*, pg. 1967
DANONE INC.—See Danone; *Int'l*, pg. 1967
DANONE JAPAN—See Danone; *Int'l*, pg. 1968
DANONE SA ESPANA—See Danone; *Int'l*, pg. 1968
DANYA FOODS LTD.—See Arla Foods amba; *Int'l*, pg. 573
DEAN DAIRY PRODUCTS COMPANY, LLC—See Dean Foods Company; *U.S. Private*, pg. 1183
DEAN FOODS COMPANY OF INDIANA, LLC—See Dean Foods Company; *U.S. Private*, pg. 1183
DEAN FOODS COMPANY—See Dean Foods Company; *U.S. Private*, pg. 1184
DEAN FOODS COMPANY—See Dean Foods Company; *U.S. Private*, pg. 1184
DEAN MILK COMPANY, LLC—See Dean Foods Company; *U.S. Private*, pg. 1183
DELAVAL S.A.—See Alfa Laval AB; *Int'l*, pg. 311
DMK DEUTSCHES MILCHKONTOR GMBH; *Int'l*, pg. 2146
DUTCH VALLEY FOOD COMPANY, INC.—See Weis Markets, Inc.; *U.S. Private*, pg. 2342
ELMHURST DAIRY, INC.; *U.S. Private*, pg. 1376
ETIKA DAIRIES NZ LIMITED—See Envictus International Holdings Limited; *Int'l*, pg. 2453

311511 — FLUID MILK MANUFACT...

ETIKA DAIRIES SDN. BHD.—See Asahi Group Holdings Ltd.; *Int'l*, pg. 593
FAN MILK LIMITED; *Int'l*, pg. 2612
FARMLAND DAIRIES LLC—See Grupo LALA S.A. de C.V.; *Int'l*, pg. 3131
FLAGSHIP ATLANTA DAIRY LLC—See Southeast Milk, Inc.; *U.S. Private*, pg. 3726
FONTERRA BRANDS INDONESIA, PT—See Fonterra Co-Operative Group Ltd.; *Int'l*, pg. 2726
FONTERRA BRANDS (MALAYSIA) SDN BHD—See Fonterra Co-Operative Group Ltd.; *Int'l*, pg. 2726
FONTERRA CO-OPERATIVE GROUP LTD.; *Int'l*, pg. 2726
FRANKLIN FOODS, INC.—See Hochland SE; *Int'l*, pg. 3437
FUJIYA MILK PRODUCT CO., LTD.—See Fujiya Co., Ltd.; *Int'l*, pg. 2838
GALLIKER DAIRY COMPANY INC.; *U.S. Private*, pg. 1639
GANDY'S DAIRIES, LLC—See Dean Foods Company; *U.S. Private*, pg. 1183
GARELICK FARMS, LLC—See Dean Foods Company; *U.S. Private*, pg. 1184
GLANBIA PLC—See Glanbia Co-Operative Society Limited; *Int'l*, pg. 2987
GROUPE LACTALIS SA; *Int'l*, pg. 3105
GRUPO LALA S.A. DE C.V.; *Int'l*, pg. 3131
GUANGDONG YANTANG DAIRY CO., LTD.; *Int'l*, pg. 3162
THE GUIDA-SEIBERT DAIRY COMPANY INC.; *U.S. Private*, pg. 4040
HALO FOOD CO. LIMITED; *Int'l*, pg. 3233
HASTINGS CO-OP CREAMERY COMPANY; *U.S. Private*, pg. 1879
HEBEI YANGYUAN ZHIHUI BEVERAGE CO., LTD.; *Int'l*, pg. 3306
HERITAGE FOODS INDIA LTD. - DAIRY DIVISION—See Heritage Foods Ltd.; *Int'l*, pg. 3361
HERITAGE FOODS LTD.; *Int'l*, pg. 3361
HILAND DAIRY FOODS COMPANY, LLC—See Dairy Farmers of America, Inc.; *U.S. Private*, pg. 1146
HILAND DAIRY FOODS COMPANY, LLC—See Prairie Farms Dairy, Inc.; *U.S. Private*, pg. 3242
H. MEYER DAIRY—See Capitol Peak Partners, LLC; *U.S. Private*, pg. 744
H. MEYER DAIRY—See KKR & Co. Inc.; *U.S. Public*, pg. 1242
HORIZON ORGANIC DAIRY, LLC—See Danone; *Int'l*, pg. 1967
HOUSE WELLNESS FOODS CORPORATION—See House Foods Group Inc.; *Int'l*, pg. 3490
HP HOOD LLC—See Catamount Dairy Holdings L.P.; *U.S. Private*, pg. 787
HUMANA GMBH—See DMK Deutsches Milchkontor GmbH; *Int'l*, pg. 2146
INDOC MILK GMBH—See DMK Deutsches Milchkontor GmbH; *Int'l*, pg. 2146
INSTANTWHIP-MINNEAPOLIS, INC.—See Instantwhip Foods, Inc.; *U.S. Private*, pg. 2092
JACKSON-MITCHELL, INC.—See Emmi AG; *Int'l*, pg. 2384
KASDORF S.A.—See Danone; *Int'l*, pg. 1966
KLEINPETER DAIRY FARM INC.; *U.S. Private*, pg. 2319
LACTALIS CANADA INC.—See Groupe Lactalis SA; *Int'l*, pg. 3106
LAKEVIEW FARMS, INC.; *U.S. Private*, pg. 2378
LAND O'LAKES, INC. - CARLISLE—See Land O'Lakes, Inc.; *U.S. Private*, pg. 2383
LAND-O-SUN DAIRIES LLC—See Dean Foods Company; *U.S. Private*, pg. 1183
MAOLA MILK & ICE CREAM COMPANY; *U.S. Private*, pg. 2567
MARCUS DAIRY, INC.; *U.S. Private*, pg. 2572
MAYFIELD DAIRY FARMS, LLC—See Dean Foods Company; *U.S. Private*, pg. 1183
MAYFIELD DAIRY FARMS—See Dean Foods Company; *U.S. Private*, pg. 1183
MEADOW BROOK DAIRY COMPANY—See Dean Foods Company; *U.S. Private*, pg. 1183
MEADOWFRESH DIARY CORPORATION—See Agrifoods International Cooperative LTD; *Int'l*, pg. 217
MIDWEST ICE CREAM COMPANY, LLC—See Dean Foods Company; *U.S. Private*, pg. 1184
MILKCO, INC.—See Ingles Markets, Incorporated; *U.S. Public*, pg. 1122
MILK SPECIALTIES COMPANY—See American Securities LLC; *U.S. Private*, pg. 250
MULLER-PINEHURST DAIRY INC.—See Prairie Farms Dairy, Inc.; *U.S. Private*, pg. 3242
NUMIL NUTRICION S.R.L.—See Danone; *Int'l*, pg. 1966
NUTRICIA LTD. - BABY NUTRITION—See Danone; *Int'l*, pg. 1966
OAK FARMS/SCHEPPS DAIRY—See Dean Foods Company; *U.S. Private*, pg. 1183
OAKHURST DAIRY; *U.S. Private*, pg. 2984
OBERWEIS DAIRY, INC.; *U.S. Private*, pg. 2987
OHIO PROCESSORS, INC.—See Instantwhip Foods, Inc.; *U.S. Private*, pg. 2093
OLD HOME FOODS, INC.; *U.S. Private*, pg. 3009
OLYMPIC DAIRY PRODUCTS INC.—See Agrifoods International Cooperative LTD; *Int'l*, pg. 217
OOO PETERBURGSKAYA NIVA—See Ekosem-Agrar GmbH; *Int'l*, pg. 2339
PARMALAT AUSTRALIA LTD.—See Groupe Lactalis SA; *Int'l*, pg. 3106
PARMALAT S.P.A.—See Groupe Lactalis SA; *Int'l*, pg. 3106
PEAK FOODS, LLC—See Lakeside Foods, Inc.; *U.S. Private*, pg. 2377
PLAINS DAIRY—See Affiliated Foods, Inc.; *U.S. Private*, pg. 122
PRAIRIE FARMS DAIRY, INC.; *U.S. Private*, pg. 3242
PROTEIN HOLDINGS INC.; *U.S. Private*, pg. 3289
PT NUTRICIA INDONESIA SEJAHTERA—See Danone; *Int'l*, pg. 1967
PT SARI HUSADA TBK—See Danone; *Int'l*, pg. 1967
REITER DAIRY, LLC—See Dean Foods Company; *U.S. Private*, pg. 1184
REITER DAIRY, LLC—See Dean Foods Company; *U.S. Private*, pg. 1184
ROSENBERGERS DAIRIES, LLC—See Catamount Dairy Holdings L.P.; *U.S. Private*, pg. 787
SANTEE DAIRIES, INC.—See Dean Foods Company; *U.S. Private*, pg. 1184
SCHNEIDER'S DAIRY HOLDINGS; *U.S. Private*, pg. 3567
SCHNEIDER'S DAIRY, INC.—See Schneider's Dairy Holdings; *U.S. Private*, pg. 3567
SCHREIBER FOODS, INC. - FULLERTON—See Schreiber Foods, Inc.; *U.S. Private*, pg. 3569
SHAMROCK FARMS DAIRY DIVISION—See Shamrock Foods Company; *U.S. Private*, pg. 3624
SINTON DAIRY FOODS COMPANY L.L.C.; *U.S. Private*, pg. 3670
SMITH BROTHERS FARMS, INC.; *U.S. Private*, pg. 3694
SMITH DAIRY PRODUCTS COMPANY INC.; *U.S. Private*, pg. 3694
STEWART'S PROCESSING CORP; *U.S. Private*, pg. 3812
STREMICKS HERITAGE FOODS LLC; *U.S. Private*, pg. 3839
SUPERIOR DAIRY, INC.; *U.S. Private*, pg. 3876
SUPER STORE INDUSTRIES; *U.S. Private*, pg. 3875
SWAN HILL MILK DISTRIBUTORS PTY. LTD.—See Groupe Lactalis SA; *Int'l*, pg. 3106
SWISS PREMIUM DAIRY, LLC—See Dean Foods Company; *U.S. Private*, pg. 1184
TURKEY HILL DAIRY, INC.—See Peak Rock Capital LLC; *U.S. Private*, pg. 3124
TURM-SAHNE GMBH—See DMK Deutsches Milchkontor GmbH; *Int'l*, pg. 2146
TURNER DAIRY FARMS, INC.; *U.S. Private*, pg. 4260
ULTIMA FOODS INC.—See Groupe Lactalis SA; *Int'l*, pg. 3106
UMPQUA DAIRY PRODUCTS CO. INC.; *U.S. Private*, pg. 4279
UNITED DAIRY, INC.; *U.S. Private*, pg. 4290
UNITED DAIRYMEN OF ARIZONA; *U.S. Private*, pg. 4291
UNITED DAIRY—See United Dairy, Inc.; *U.S. Private*, pg. 4291
UPSTATE NIAGARA COOPERATIVE, INC.; *U.S. Private*, pg. 4313
VAQUERIA TRES MONJITAS INC.; *U.S. Private*, pg. 4345
WAYNE DAIRY PRODUCTS, INC.—See Smith Dairy Products Company Inc.; *U.S. Private*, pg. 3694
WILCOX FARMS INC.; *U.S. Private*, pg. 4518
YASHILI NEW ZEALAND DAIRY CO. LTD.—See China Mengniu Dairy Company Limited; *Int'l*, pg. 1520
YOPLAIT USA, INC.—See General Mills, Inc.; *U.S. Public*, pg. 923

311512 — CREAMERY BUTTER MANUFACTURING

ARLA FOODS LIMITED—See Arla Foods amba; *Int'l*, pg. 573
BUTTER BUDS FOOD INGREDIENTS—See Cumberland Packing Corp.; *U.S. Private*, pg. 1122
CENTRALE DEL LATTE DI VICENZA S.P.A.—See Centrale del Latte di Torino & C. S.p.A.; *Int'l*, pg. 1410
DAIRYTOWN PRODUCTS LIMITED—See Agropur Cooperative; *Int'l*, pg. 220
GOLDCOIN HEALTH FOODS LIMITED; *Int'l*, pg. 3027
GRAF CREAMERY INC.; *U.S. Private*, pg. 1750
LAND O'LAKES, INC. - FOOD INGREDIENTS DIVISION—See Land O'Lakes, Inc.; *U.S. Private*, pg. 2383
LAND O'LAKES, INC. - INTERNATIONAL DIVISION—See Land O'Lakes, Inc.; *U.S. Private*, pg. 2383
LAND O'LAKES, INC. - KENT—See Land O'Lakes, Inc.; *U.S. Private*, pg. 2383
LAND O'LAKES, INC.; *U.S. Private*, pg. 2383
LARSENS CREAMERY INC.; *U.S. Private*, pg. 2393
MADISON DAIRY PRODUCE COMPANY—See Land O'Lakes, Inc.; *U.S. Private*, pg. 2383
SCHREIBER FOODS, INC. - WEST BEND—See Schreiber Foods, Inc.; *U.S. Private*, pg. 3569
TATURA MILK INDUSTRIES PTY LTD—See Bega Cheese Ltd.; *Int'l*, pg. 940
WEST POINT DAIRY PRODUCTS, LLC—See Grassland Dairy Products, Inc.; *U.S. Private*, pg. 1758

311513 — CHEESE MANUFACTURING

AGROPUR COOPERATIVE - ALLEGRO—See Agropur Cooperative; *Int'l*, pg. 220
AGROPUR COOPERATIVE - CHEESE & INGREDIENTS DIVISION—See Agropur Cooperative; *Int'l*, pg. 220
AGROPUR INC. - LITTLE CHUTE (APPLETON) PLANT—See Agropur Cooperative; *Int'l*, pg. 220
AGROPUR INC.—See Agropur Cooperative; *Int'l*, pg. 220
ARABIAN FOOD INDUSTRIES COMPANY; *Int'l*, pg. 533
ARLA FOODS INC.—See Arla Foods amba; *Int'l*, pg. 572
ARLA FOODS SP. Z O.O.—See Arla Foods amba; *Int'l*, pg. 573
ARTHUR SCHUMAN INC. (ASI); *U.S. Private*, pg. 342
ARTISANAL BRANDS, INC.; *U.S. Private*, pg. 343
BAKER CHEESE, INC.; *U.S. Private*, pg. 455
BEGA CHEESE LTD.; *Int'l*, pg. 940
BEGA CHEESE LTD. - STRATHMERTON PROCESS AND PACKAGING PLANT—See Bega Cheese Ltd.; *Int'l*, pg. 940
BELGIOIOSO CHEESE INC.; *U.S. Private*, pg. 517
BERGLAND GMBH—See Bayernland eG; *Int'l*, pg. 913
BLASER'S USA, INC.; *U.S. Private*, pg. 579
BONGARDS SOUTH LLC—See Bongards Creameries; *U.S. Private*, pg. 614
BOXHOLM MEJERI AB—See Arla Foods amba; *Int'l*, pg. 572
BREWSTER DAIRY INC.; *U.S. Private*, pg. 647
BUCOVINA SA; *Int'l*, pg. 1210
CACIQUE, INC.; *U.S. Private*, pg. 712
CADY CHEESE FACTORY, INC.; *U.S. Private*, pg. 713
CARBERY GROUP; *Int'l*, pg. 1320
CARR VALLEY CHEESE COMPANY, INC.; *U.S. Private*, pg. 771
CASTELLI UK LTD—See Groupe Lactalis SA; *Int'l*, pg. 3106
CASTRO CHEESE COMPANY INC.—See Dairy Farmers of America, Inc.; *U.S. Private*, pg. 1145
CERAMI SALES COMPANY, INC.; *U.S. Private*, pg. 835
CHEESE MERCHANTS OF AMERICA; *U.S. Private*, pg. 869
CHIANTI CHEESE COMPANY; *U.S. Private*, pg. 876
CLOVER FONTERRA INGREDIENTS (PTY) LTD.—See Clover Industries Limited; *Int'l*, pg. 1663
COLONNA BROS., INC.; *U.S. Private*, pg. 972
CORNISH COUNTRY LARDER LTD.—See Arla Foods amba; *Int'l*, pg. 573
DAILYCER BV—See OEP Capital Advisors, L.P.; *U.S. Private*, pg. 2998
DAILYCER NEDERLAND B.V., TILBURG—See OEP Capital Advisors, L.P.; *U.S. Private*, pg. 2998
DAIRICONCEPTS, L.P.—See Dairy Farmers of America, Inc.; *U.S. Private*, pg. 1145
DAIRICONCEPTS, L.P.—See Fonterra Co-Operative Group Ltd.; *Int'l*, pg. 2726
DAIRYFOOD USA INCORPORATED; *U.S. Private*, pg. 1146
DAIRYGOLD FINANCE LIMITED—See Dairygold Co-Operative Society Ltd; *Int'l*, pg. 1940
DAIRYGOLD FOOD INGREDIENTS LIMITED—See Dairygold Co-Operative Society Ltd; *Int'l*, pg. 1940
DAIRYGOLD FOOD INGREDIENTS (UK) LIMITED—See Dairygold Co-Operative Society Ltd; *Int'l*, pg. 1940
DANONE DE MEXICO SA DE CV—See Danone; *Int'l*, pg. 1967
DANONE SA—See Danone; *Int'l*, pg. 1968
DANONE S.P.A.—See Danone; *Int'l*, pg. 1968
DAVISCO INTERNATIONAL INC.; *U.S. Private*, pg. 1175
DIVI'S LABORATORIES EUROPE AG—See Divis Laboratories Limited; *Int'l*, pg. 2138
DIVIS LABORATORIES (USA) INC.—See Divis Laboratories Limited; *Int'l*, pg. 2138
EGIDIO GALBANI SPA—See Groupe Lactalis SA; *Int'l*, pg. 3106
ELLSWORTH COOPERATIVE CREAMERY; *U.S. Private*, pg. 1375
EMMI ROTH USA INC.—See Emmi AG; *Int'l*, pg. 2384
EMMI ROTH USA INC.—See Emmi AG; *Int'l*, pg. 2384
EMPIRE CHEESE, INC.—See The Great Lakes Cheese Co., Inc.; *U.S. Private*, pg. 4038
ENTREMONT S.A.—See BNP Paribas SA; *Int'l*, pg. 1090
ENTREMONT S.A.—See Frere-Bourgeois; *Int'l*, pg. 2773
EURO CHEESE VERTRIEBS-GMBH—See DMK Deutsches Milchkontor GmbH; *Int'l*, pg. 2146
FALBYGDENS OST AB—See Arla Foods amba; *Int'l*, pg. 573
FIRMENICH—See Firmenich International SA; *Int'l*, pg. 2680
FIRST DISTRICT ASSOCIATION; *U.S. Private*, pg. 1517
FORMAGGIO CHEESE; *U.S. Private*, pg. 1569
FROMAGERIE HENRI HUTIN S.A.R.L.—See Hochland SE; *Int'l*, pg. 3437
GALBANI FRANCE—See Danone; *Int'l*, pg. 1968
GALBANI—See Danone; *Int'l*, pg. 1968
GENNARO AURICCHIO S.P.A.; *Int'l*, pg. 2924
GILMAN CHEESE CORPORATION; *U.S. Private*, pg. 1701
GLANBIA FOODS INC.—See Glanbia Co-Operative Society Limited; *Int'l*, pg. 2988
GRANDE CHEESE COMPANY INC.; *U.S. Private*, pg. 1753
GRANDE CHEESE COMPANY LIMITED; *Int'l*, pg. 3057
GRANDE CHEESE COMPANY; *U.S. Private*, pg. 1753

N.A.I.C.S. INDEX

311514 — DRY, CONDENSED, AND...

THE GREAT LAKES CHEESE CO., INC.; *U.S. Private,* pg. 4038
GREAT LAKES CHEESE OF LA CROSSE WISCONSIN, INC.—See The Great Lakes Cheese Co., Inc.; *U.S. Private,* pg. 4038
GREAT LAKES CHEESE OF NEW YORK, INC.—See The Great Lakes Cheese Co., Inc.; *U.S. Private,* pg. 4038
HILMAR CHEESE COMPANY; *U.S. Private,* pg. 1947
HOCHLAND SE; *Int'l,* pg. 3437
HOOK'S CHEESE COMPANY, INC.; *U.S. Private,* pg. 1978
INGRETEC, LTD.; *U.S. Private,* pg. 2077
KEMPS LLC—See Dairy Farmers of America, Inc.; *U.S. Private,* pg. 1146
KRAFT CANADA, INC.-INGLESIDE—See 3G Capital Inc.; *U.S. Private,* pg. 10
KRAFT CANADA, INC.-INGLESIDE—See Berkshire Hathaway Inc.; *U.S. Public,* pg. 318
KRAFT CANADA, INC.-MOUNT-ROYAL—See 3G Capital Inc.; *U.S. Private,* pg. 10
KRAFT CANADA, INC.-MOUNT-ROYAL—See Berkshire Hathaway Inc.; *U.S. Public,* pg. 318
KRAFT HEINZ COMPANY - LEHIGH VALLEY—See 3G Capital Inc.; *U.S. Private,* pg. 10
KRAFT HEINZ COMPANY - LEHIGH VALLEY—See Berkshire Hathaway Inc.; *U.S. Public,* pg. 318
LACTALIS AMERICAN GROUP, INC.—See Groupe Lactalis SA; *Int'l,* pg. 3106
LACTALIS DELI, INC.—See Groupe Lactalis SA; *Int'l,* pg. 3106
LACTALIS MCLELLAND—See Groupe Lactalis SA; *Int'l,* pg. 3106
LAKE VIEW CHEESE CO.; *U.S. Private,* pg. 2376
LAND O'LAKES, INC. - KIEL—See Land O'Lakes, Inc.; *U.S. Private,* pg. 2383
LEPRINO FOODS COMPANY; *U.S. Private,* pg. 2431
MELROSE DAIRY PROTEINS, LLC.; *U.S. Private,* pg. 2663
MEXICAN CHEESE PRODUCERS, INC.—See ALFA, S.A.B. de C.V.; *Int'l,* pg. 314
MICELI DAIRY PRODUCTS CO.; *U.S. Private,* pg. 2697
MOLKEREI NIESKY GMBH—See DMK Deutsches Milchkontor GmbH; *Int'l,* pg. 2146
MURITZ MILCH GMBH—See DMK Deutsches Milchkontor GmbH; *Int'l,* pg. 2146
NELSON CHEESE FACTORY INC.; *U.S. Private,* pg. 2883
NUOVA CASTELLI SPA—See Groupe Lactalis SA; *Int'l,* pg. 3106
OLD EUROPE CHEESE, INC.; *U.S. Private,* pg. 3009
OLD FASHIONED FOODS INC.; *U.S. Private,* pg. 3009
PACE DAIRY FOODS—See The Kroger Co.; *U.S. Public,* pg. 2109
PARK CHEESE COMPANY INC.; *U.S. Private,* pg. 3095
PARMALAT SOUTH AFRICA (PTY) LTD.—See Groupe Lactalis SA; *Int'l,* pg. 3106
THE QUAY CORPORATION,INC.; *U.S. Private,* pg. 4101
ROTH KASE USA, LTD.; *U.S. Private,* pg. 3487
RUMIANO CHEESE COMPANY; *U.S. Private,* pg. 3503
SALERNO DAIRY PRODUCTS LIMITED—See Gay Lea Foods Co-operative Ltd.; *U.S. Private,* pg. 2891
SARGENTO FOODS INC. - CONSUMER PRODUCTS DIVISION—See Sargento Foods Inc.; *U.S. Private,* pg. 3550
SARGENTO FOODS INC. - FOOD SERVICE DIVISION—See Sargento Foods Inc.; *U.S. Private,* pg. 3550
SARGENTO FOODS INC.; *U.S. Private,* pg. 3550
SARTORI COMPANY; *U.S. Private,* pg. 3551
SARTORI INSPIRATIONS, LLC—See Sartori Company; *U.S. Private,* pg. 3551
SAUDI NEW ZEALAND MILK PRODUCTS COMPANY LIMITED—See Fonterra Co-Operative Group Ltd.; *Int'l,* pg. 2726
SCHREIBER FOODS, INC. - SHIPPENSBURG—See Schreiber Foods, Inc.; *U.S. Private,* pg. 3569
SCHREIBER FOODS, INC.; *U.S. Private,* pg. 3569
SCHREIBER MEXICO, S.A. DE C.V.—See Schreiber Foods, Inc.; *U.S. Private,* pg. 3569
SOCIETE COMTOISE DE SPECIALITES FROMAGERES—See Gimv NV; *Int'l,* pg. 2976
TILLAMOOK COUNTY CREAMERY ASSOCIATION; *U.S. Private,* pg. 4170
TROPICAL CHEESE INDUSTRIES, INC.; *U.S. Private,* pg. 4242
TROYER CHEESE, INC.—See Littlejohn & Co., LLC; *U.S. Private,* pg. 2472
V&V SUPREMO FOODS, INC.; *U.S. Private,* pg. 4327
WAPSIE VALLEY CREAMERY, INC.; *U.S. Private,* pg. 4436
WELCOME DAIRY INC.; *U.S. Private,* pg. 4473
WEYAUWEGA STAR DAIRY INC.; *U.S. Private,* pg. 4503
WOHLT CHEESE CORPORATION; *U.S. Private,* pg. 4553
ZENTHALKASEREI MV GMBH—See DMK Deutsches Milchkontor GmbH; *Int'l,* pg. 2146

311514 — DRY, CONDENSED, AND EVAPORATED DAIRY PRODUCT MANUFACTURING

ABBOTT NUTRITION—See Abbott Laboratories; *U.S. Public,* pg. 17
ABS ARGENTINA S.A.—See Genus Plc; *Int'l,* pg. 2930
ABS CHILE LIMITADA—See Genus Plc; *Int'l,* pg. 2930
ABS GLOBAL (CANADA) INC.—See Genus Plc; *Int'l,* pg. 2930
ABS ITALIA S.R.L.—See Genus Plc; *Int'l,* pg. 2930
ALIMENTS ULTIMA INC—See General Mills, Inc.; *U.S. Public,* pg. 921
ALPINA FOODS, INC.—See Alpina Productos Alimenticios S.A.; *Int'l,* pg. 371
ALPINA PRODUCTOS ALIMENTICIOS S.A.; *Int'l,* pg. 371
AMERICAN CASEIN COMPANY; *U.S. Private,* pg. 226
ANIK INDUSTRIES LTD.; *Int'l,* pg. 471
ARLA FOODS BANGLADESH LTD.—See Arla Foods amba; *Int'l,* pg. 572
ARLA FOODS KASEREINEN GMBH—See Arla Foods amba; *Int'l,* pg. 572
ARLA FOODS LTDA—See Arla Foods amba; *Int'l,* pg. 573
ARLA FOODS PRODUCTION LLC—See Arla Foods amba; *Int'l,* pg. 572
ARLA FOODS TRADING A/S—See Arla Foods amba; *Int'l,* pg. 573
ARLA FOODS (WESTBURY) LTD—See Arla Foods amba; *Int'l,* pg. 573
ARLA INGMAN OY AB—See Arla Foods amba; *Int'l,* pg. 572
ASH SHIPPING, INC.; *U.S. Private,* pg. 349
ASSOCIATED MILK PRODUCERS, INC.; *U.S. Private,* pg. 356
ATLANTIC S.R.L.—See ATLANTIC GRUPA d.d.; *Int'l,* pg. 675
AVI LIMITED; *Int'l,* pg. 740
BARBADOS DAIRY INDUSTRIES LTD.—See Anheuser-Busch InBev SA/NV; *Int'l,* pg. 464
BEGA DAIRY AND DRINKS PTY. LTD.—See Bega Cheese Ltd.; *Int'l,* pg. 940
BELUGA VENTURES, LLC.; *U.S. Private,* pg. 521
BESTON TECHNOLOGIES PTY LTD—See Beston Global Food Company Limited; *Int'l,* pg. 1000
BINGGRAE CO., LTD.; *Int'l,* pg. 1033
BLUEGRASS DAIRY AND FOOD, INC.—See Dubilier & Company, Inc.; *U.S. Private,* pg. 1283
BLUE GRASS DAIRY & FOOD LLC; *U.S. Private,* pg. 589
BONGARDS CREAMERIES; *U.S. Private,* pg. 614
BUBS AUSTRALIA LIMITED; *Int'l,* pg. 1206
CALIFORNIA DAIRIES, INC. - FRESNO PLANT—See California Dairies, Inc.; *U.S. Private,* pg. 718
CALIFORNIA DAIRIES, INC. - LOS BANOS PLANT—See California Dairies, Inc.; *U.S. Private,* pg. 718
CALIFORNIA DAIRIES, INC. - TIPTON PLANT—See California Dairies, Inc.; *U.S. Private,* pg. 718
CALIFORNIA DAIRIES, INC. - TURLOCK PLANT—See California Dairies, Inc.; *U.S. Private,* pg. 718
CANADA ROYAL MILK ULC—See China Feihe Limited; *Int'l,* pg. 1502
CARGILLS (CEYLON) PLC; *Int'l,* pg. 1325
CEDEVITA D.O.O.—See ATLANTIC GRUPA d.d.; *Int'l,* pg. 675
CENTRALE DEL LATTE DI TORINO & C. S.P.A.; *Int'l,* pg. 1410
CHINA FEIHE LIMITED; *Int'l,* pg. 1502
CHINA MENGNIU DAIRY COMPANY LIMITED; *Int'l,* pg. 1519
CLOVER S.A. (PTY) LTD—See Danone; *Int'l,* pg. 1965
COCO PURE BEVERAGE CORP.—See Herbal Dispatch Inc.; *Int'l,* pg. 3359
COMMERCIAL CREAMERY CO.; *U.S. Private,* pg. 983
CROWLEY FOODS, INC.—See Catamount Dairy Holdings L.P.; *U.S. Private,* pg. 787
DAIRY FARMERS OF AMERICA - READING PLANT—See Dairy Farmers of America, Inc.; *U.S. Private,* pg. 1146
DAIRYGOLD CO-OPERATIVE SOCIETY LTD; *Int'l,* pg. 1940
DAIRY QUEEN CANADA, INC.—See Berkshire Hathaway Inc.; *U.S. Public,* pg. 308
DANMARK PROTEIN A/S—See Arla Foods amba; *Int'l,* pg. 573
DANONE ARGENTINA SA—See Danone; *Int'l,* pg. 1967
DANONE GMBH—See Danone; *Int'l,* pg. 1968
DANONE INDIA—See Danone; *Int'l,* pg. 1968
DANONE KFT.—See Danone; *Int'l,* pg. 1968
DANONE LTD.—See Danone; *Int'l,* pg. 1968
DANONE OESTERREICH GMBH—See Danone; *Int'l,* pg. 1968
DANONE PORTUGAL, S.A.—See Danone; *Int'l,* pg. 1968
DANONE ROMANIA—See Danone; *Int'l,* pg. 1968
DANONE S.A.—See Danone; *Int'l,* pg. 1967
DANONE SP. Z O.O.—See Danone; *Int'l,* pg. 1968
DANONE (UK) LIMITED—See Danone; *Int'l,* pg. 1965
DASI CORPORATION; *U.S. Private,* pg. 1162
DEAN FOODS NORTH CENTRAL, LLC—See Dean Foods Company; *U.S. Private,* pg 1184
DIARYGOLD DEUTSCHLAND HANDLESGESELLSCHAFT MBH—See Dairygold Co-Operative Society Ltd; *Int'l,* pg. 1940
THE DIFFERENT DAIRY COMPANY LIMITED—See Donegal Investment Group Plc; *Int'l,* pg. 2163
DP SUPPLY GMBH—See DMK Deutsches Milchkontor GmbH; *Int'l,* pg. 2146
DXN HOLDINGS BHD.; *Int'l,* pg. 2237
EAGLE FAMILY FOODS GROUP LLC—See Kelso & Company, L.P.; *U.S. Private,* pg. 2278
ELGIN DAIRY FOODS, INC.; *U.S. Private,* pg. 1359
EMMI BENELUX B.V.—See Emmi AG; *Int'l,* pg. 2384
EMMI CANADA INC.—See Emmi AG; *Int'l,* pg. 2384
EMMI DEUTSCHLAND GMBH—See Emmi AG; *Int'l,* pg. 2384
EMMI OSTERREICH GMBH—See Emmi AG; *Int'l,* pg. 2384
EMMI UK LIMITED—See Emmi AG; *Int'l,* pg. 2384
ENVICTUS INTERNATIONAL HOLDINGS LIMITED; *Int'l,* pg. 2453
ERIE FOODS INTERNATIONAL, INC.; *U.S. Private,* pg. 1420
EVROFARMA SA; *Int'l,* pg. 2574
FAGE DAIRY INDUSTRY S.A.; *Int'l,* pg. 2601
FAGE USA DAIRY INDUSTRY, INC.—See Fage Dairy Industry S.A.; *Int'l,* pg. 2601
FAGE USA HOLDINGS, INC.—See Fage Dairy Industry S.A.; *Int'l,* pg. 2601
FARBEST-TALLMAN FOODS CORP.; *U.S. Private,* pg. 1473
FARMACIA PLUS D.O.O.—See ATLANTIC GRUPA d.d.; *Int'l,* pg. 675
FARM FRESH BERHAD; *Int'l,* pg. 2619
FEIHE INTERNATIONAL, INC.; *Int'l,* pg. 2632
FIDIFARM D.O.O.—See ATLANTIC GRUPA d.d.; *Int'l,* pg. 675
FRASCHERI S.P.A.—See Centrale del Latte di Torino & C. S.p.A.; *Int'l,* pg. 1410
FUDE + SERRAHN GMBH & CO. KG—See DMK Deutsches Milchkontor GmbH; *Int'l,* pg. 2146
GALAXY NUTRITIONAL FOODS, INC.—See GreenSpace Brands Inc.; *Int'l,* pg. 3076
GENUS ABS COLOMBIA SAS—See Genus Plc; *Int'l,* pg. 2930
GLANBIA - BALLYRAGGET FACTORY—See Glanbia Co-Operative Society Limited; *Int'l,* pg. 2987
GLANBIA NUTRITIONALS (EUROPE) LIMITED—See Glanbia Co-Operative Society Limited; *Int'l,* pg. 2988
GLANBIA NUTRITIONALS (IRELAND) LIMITED—See Glanbia Co-Operative Society Limited; *Int'l,* pg. 2988
GRUPO LECHE PASCUAL S.A.; *Int'l,* pg. 3132
HATSUN AGRO PRODUCTS LTD; *Int'l,* pg. 3284
HEALTHY TIMES, INC.—See Health and Happiness (H&H) International Holdings Limited; *Int'l,* pg. 3303
HIGH QUALITY FOOD S.P.A.; *Int'l,* pg. 3386
HOCHDORF HOLDING AG—See HOCHDORF Holding AG; *Int'l,* pg. 3437
HOCHDORF SWISS MILK LTD.—See HOCHDORF Holding AG; *Int'l,* pg. 3437
HORLICKS LIMITED—See GSK plc; *Int'l,* pg. 3149
ICECO INC.; *Int'l,* pg. 3579
ICREO CO., LTD.—See Ezaki Glico Co., Ltd.; *Int'l,* pg. 2593
I.D.Q. CANADA, INC.—See Berkshire Hathaway Inc.; *U.S. Public,* pg. 308
KINGDOM FOOD PRODUCTS APS—See Arla Foods amba; *Int'l,* pg. 573
LAKE COUNTRY FOODS; *U.S. Private,* pg. 2374
LESA LATARIA ENGIADINAISA SA—See Emmi AG; *Int'l,* pg. 2385
THE LIMU COMPANY LLC—See NewAge, Inc.; *U.S. Public,* pg. 1513
LION DAIRY & DRINKS PTY. LTD. - THEBARTON PLANT—See Bega Cheese Ltd.; *Int'l,* pg. 940
LLC GENUS ABS RUS—See Genus Plc; *Int'l,* pg. 2930
MAINLAND PRODUCTS LIMITED—See Fonterra Co-Operative Group Ltd.; *Int'l,* pg. 2726
MAIN STREET INGREDIENTS LLC; *U.S. Private,* pg. 2551
MALANDA DAIRYFOODS PTY. LIMITED—See Bega Cheese Ltd.; *Int'l,* pg. 940
MAPLE ISLAND INC.; *U.S. Private,* pg. 2568
MARQUEZ BROTHERS ENTERPRISES, INC.—See Marquez Brothers International, Inc.; *U.S. Private,* pg. 2587
MARQUEZ BROTHERS FOODS, INC.—See Marquez Brothers International, Inc.; *U.S. Private,* pg. 2587
MARQUEZ BROTHERS INTERNATIONAL S.A. DE C.V.—See Marquez Brothers International, Inc.; *U.S. Private,* pg. 2587
MARQUEZ BROTHERS RENO, INC.—See Marquez Brothers International, Inc.; *U.S. Private,* pg. 2587
MARQUEZ BROTHERS SOUTHERN CALIFORNIA, INC.—See Marquez Brothers International, Inc.; *U.S. Private,* pg. 2587
MARQUEZ BROTHERS TEXAS, LP—See Marquez Brothers International, Inc.; *U.S. Private,* pg. 2587
MEITEK TECHNOLOGY (QINGDAO) CO., LTD.—See Synutra International, Inc.; *U.S. Private,* pg. 3905
MILBURN DAIRY LIMITED—See Donegal Investment Group Plc; *Int'l,* pg. 2163
MILKO SVERIGE AB—See Arla Foods amba; *Int'l,* pg. 572
MILUPA GMBH—See Danone; *Int'l,* pg. 1966
MLEKARNA HLINSKO, A.S.—See Agrofert Holding, a.s.; *Int'l,* pg. 219
MOLKEREI BIEDERMANN AG—See Emmi AG; *Int'l,* pg. 2385
NATIONAL FOOD INDUSTRIES COMPANY LIMITED—See Adeptio LLC; *Int'l,* pg. 143
NESTLE MANUFACTURING (MALAYSIA) SDN. BHD. -

311514 — DRY, CONDENSED, AND...

SHAH ALAM COMPLEX FACTORY—See Groupe Lactalis SA; *Int'l*, pg. 3106
NOW HEALTH GROUP, INC.; *U.S. Private*, pg. 2968
NOX TECHNOLOGIES, INC.—See Nu Skin Enterprises, Inc.; *U.S. Public*, pg. 1552
NUTRICIA CUIJK B.V.—See Danone; *Int'l*, pg. 1966
OAO ISTRA-NUTRICIA—See Danone; *Int'l*, pg. 1966
OLMA, A.S.—See Agrofert Holding, a.s.; *Int'l*, pg. 219
OMU MILK PRODUCTS CO., LTD.—See Fuji Oil Holdings Inc.; *Int'l*, pg. 2815
PACE DAIRY FOODS COMPANY—See The Kroger Co.; *U.S. Public*, pg. 2109
PLAINVIEW MILK PRODUCTS ASSOCIATION; *U.S. Private*, pg. 3195
PLATINUM PERFORMANCE, INC.—See Zoetis, Inc.; *U.S. Public*, pg. 2409
RANUAN MEIJERI OY—See Arla Foods amba; *Int'l*, pg. 572
REDWOOD HILL FARM & CREAMERY, INC.—See Emmi AG; *Int'l*, pg. 2385
RICH PRODUCTS CORPORATION - GALLATIN MANUFACTURING FACILITY—See Rich Holdings, Inc.; *U.S. Private*, pg. 3426
SHENGYUAN NUTRITIONAL FOOD CO., LTD.—See Synutra International, Inc.; *U.S. Private*, pg. 3905
SILVADDEN AB—See Arla Foods amba; *Int'l*, pg. 572
STOLLE MILK BIOLOGICS INC.—See Spencer Trask & Co.; *U.S. Private*, pg. 3755
SUBCO FOODS OF WISCONSIN—See Subco Foods, Inc.; *U.S. Private*, pg. 3847
SUPER STORE INDUSTRIES - FAIRFIELD DAIRY DIVISION—See Super Store Industries; *U.S. Private*, pg. 3875
SUPER STORE INDUSTRIES - TURLOCK DAIRY DIVISION—See Super Store Industries; *U.S. Private*, pg. 3875
SYNUTRA, INC.—See Synutra International, Inc.; *U.S. Private*, pg. 3905
SYNUTRA INTERNATIONAL, INC.; *U.S. Private*, pg. 3905
TECNO-LECHE S.A.—See GEA Group Aktiengesellschaft; *Int'l*, pg. 2903
TRITENT INT'L AGRICULTURE, INC.; *U.S. Public*, pg. 2196
UMANG DAIRIES LTD.—See Bengal & Assam Company Ltd.; *Int'l*, pg. 973
VERNDALE PRODUCTS INC.; *U.S. Private*, pg. 4368
YOPLAIT S.A.S.—See General Mills, Inc.; *U.S. Public*, pg. 923
ZITERY S.A.—See Genus Plc; *Int'l*, pg. 2931

311520 — ICE CREAM AND FROZEN DESSERT MANUFACTURING

600 LB GORILLAS INC; *U.S. Private*, pg. 16
ABR HOLDINGS, LTD.; *Int'l*, pg. 67
AE FARMS, INC.—See Anderson Erickson Dairy Company; *U.S. Private*, pg. 276
AMERICAN DAIRY QUEEN CORPORATION—See Berkshire Hathaway Inc.; *U.S. Public*, pg. 308
ARENA HOLDING S.P.A. - CREMERIA DEL LATTAITO PLANT—See Arena Holding S.p.A.; *Int'l*, pg. 558
ASAEL FARR & SONS COMPANY; *U.S. Private*, pg. 345
ASPEN LEAF YOGURT, LLC—See Rocky Mountain Chocolate Factory, Inc.; *U.S. Public*, pg. 1807
BELFONTE ICE CREAM, INC.—See Belfonte Dairy Distribution Inc.; *U.S. Private*, pg. 517
BLISS UNLIMITED LLC—See HumanCo LLC; *U.S. Private*, pg. 2006
BLUE BELL CREAMERIES, L.P.; *U.S. Private*, pg. 585
BLUE BELL CREAMERIES—See Blue Bell Creameries, L.P.; *U.S. Private*, pg. 585
B-R 31 ICE CREAM CO., LTD.; *Int'l*, pg. 785
BROTHERS INTERNATIONAL DESSERTS, INC.; *U.S. Private*, pg. 665
BRUSTER'S REAL ICE CREAM, INC.; *U.S. Private*, pg. 673
BUBBIES HOMEMADE ICE CREAM & DESSERTS, INC.—See Kenex Holdings LLC; *U.S. Private*, pg. 2284
CAPRICORN HOLDINGS, INC.; *U.S. Private*, pg. 745
CARIBBEAN CREAM LTD.; *Int'l*, pg. 1330
CARVEL CORPORATION—See Roark Capital Group Inc.; *U.S. Private*, pg. 3454
CASPER'S ICE CREAM, INC.—See MidOcean Partners, LLP; *U.S. Private*, pg. 2716
CEDAR CREST SPECIALTIES INC.; *U.S. Private*, pg. 804
CF FOODS LLC.; *U.S. Private*, pg. 843
CREAMLAND DAIRIES, INC.—See Dean Foods Company; *U.S. Private*, pg. 1183
CREATIVE OCCASIONS INC.—See George Weston Limited; *Int'l*, pg. 2939
DAIRY-MIX, INC.; *U.S. Private*, pg. 1146
DEAN FOODS COMPANY; *U.S. Private*, pg. 1183
DELIZZA, INC.; *U.S. Private*, pg. 1197
DIPPIN' DOTS AUSTRALIA PTY. LTD.—See J&J Snack Foods Corporation; *U.S. Public*, pg. 1179
DIPPIN' DOTS, LLC—See J&J Snack Foods Corporation; *U.S. Public*, pg. 1179
DMK EIS GMBH—See DMK Deutsches Milchkontor GmbH; *Int'l*, pg. 2146
FIELDBROOK FOODS CORPORATION—See Wells Enterprises, Inc.; *U.S. Private*, pg. 4476
FLAVORITE FOODS LIMITED; *Int'l*, pg. 2698
FRIENDLYS MANUFACTURING AND RETAIL, LLC—See Dean Foods Company; *U.S. Private*, pg. 1184
GENERAL MILLS HELLAS S.A.—See General Mills, Inc.; *U.S. Public*, pg. 922
GENERAL MILLS UK LTD.—See General Mills, Inc.; *U.S. Public*, pg. 922
GOLD COAST MILK PTY. LTD.—See Groupe Lactalis SA; *Int'l*, pg. 3106
GOODBERRY CREAMERY INC.; *U.S. Private*, pg. 1738
GOOD OLD DAYS FOODS, INC.; *U.S. Private*, pg. 1738
GRAETER'S, INC.; *U.S. Private*, pg. 1750
HAAGEN-DAZS EUROPE—See General Mills, Inc.; *U.S. Public*, pg. 922
HAAGEN-DAZS JAPAN, INC.—See General Mills, Inc.; *U.S. Public*, pg. 922
HD CAFE LTD—See Hadco Limited; *Int'l*, pg. 3205
HERSHEY CREAMERY COMPANY; *U.S. Public*, pg. 1029
HIGH ROAD CRAFT ICE CREAM, INC.—See PMC Capital Partners, LLC; *U.S. Private*, pg. 3217
HORCHATA FROZEN DESSERT SANDWICH FARCHITECTURE BB, LLC; *U.S. Private*, pg. 1980
HOUSE OF FLAVORS, INC.; *U.S. Private*, pg. 1991
ICE CREAM SPECIALTIES, INC.—See Prairie Farms Dairy, Inc.; *U.S. Private*, pg. 3242
ICE CREAM SPECIALTIES, INC.—See Prairie Farms Dairy, Inc.; *U.S. Private*, pg. 3242
ITALIAN FRESH FOODS S.P.A.—See Emmi AG; *Int'l*, pg. 2384
J&J SNACK FOODS CORPORATION; *U.S. Public*, pg. 1179
J&J SNACK FOODS CORP.—See J&J Snack Foods Corporation; *U.S. Public*, pg. 1180
JOSH & JOHN'S HOME MADE ICE CREAM, INC.; *U.S. Private*, pg. 2237
KANSAI FROZEN DISTRIBUTION CO., LTD.—See Ezaki Glico Co., Ltd.; *Int'l*, pg. 2593
KLINKE BROTHERS ICE CREAM CO.; *U.S. Private*, pg. 2320
LAFAYETTE COMPANY; *U.S. Private*, pg. 2372
MEC3 OPTIMA SRL—See The Riverside Company; *U.S. Private*, pg. 4109
MEDICS ENTERPIRSES; *U.S. Private*, pg. 2656
MEDITTS MEDITERRANEAN HEALTHY SNACKS S.L.—See Dole plc; *Int'l*, pg. 2158
MILK PRODUCTS, L.P.—See Capitol Peak Partners, LLC; *U.S. Private*, pg. 744
MILK PRODUCTS, L.P.—See KKR & Co, Inc.; *U.S. Public*, pg. 1242
MINI MELTS INC.; *U.S. Private*, pg. 2742
NOOSA YOGHURT LLC—See Advent International Corporation; *U.S. Private*, pg. 105
PACIUGO FRANCHISING, LP; *U.S. Private*, pg. 3072
PARKER PRODUCTS, LLC—See The Riverside Company; *U.S. Private*, pg. 4109
PERRY'S ICE CREAM CO., INC.; *U.S. Private*, pg. 3154
PHILLY'S FAMOUS WATER ICE, INC.—See J&J Snack Foods Corporation; *U.S. Public*, pg. 1180
PIERRE'S FRENCH ICE CREAM COMPANY; *U.S. Private*, pg. 3179
PLM OPERATIONS, LLC—See Wind Point Advisors LLC; *U.S. Private*, pg. 4536
PRAIRIE FARMS DAIRY SUPPLY CORP.—See Prairie Farms Dairy, Inc.; *U.S. Private*, pg. 3242
PURITY DAIRIES - HOHENWALD PLANT—See Dean Foods Company; *U.S. Private*, pg. 1184
RAMAR FOODS INTERNATIONAL CORPORATION; *U.S. Private*, pg. 3351
REIS & IRVY'S, INC.—See Generation NEXT Franchise Brands, Inc.; *U.S. Private*, pg. 1668
REPICCI'S FRANCHISE GROUP, LLC—See Cardiff Lexington Corporation; *U.S. Public*, pg. 433
RICH ICE CREAM CO.; *U.S. Private*, pg. 3427
RICHIE'S SUPER PREMIUM ITALIAN ICE; *U.S. Private*, pg. 3430
RITA'S FRANCHISE COMPANY; *U.S. Private*, pg. 3441
ROCKY MOUNTAIN PIES, LLC.; *U.S. Private*, pg. 3469
ROSEN EISKREM SUD GMBH - PRENZLAU—See DMK Deutsches Milchkontor GmbH; *Int'l*, pg. 2146
R&S DAIRY QUEENS, INC.; *U.S. Private*, pg. 3333
SCHOEP'S ICE CREAM CO., INC.—See Brothers International Desserts, Inc.; *U.S. Private*, pg. 665
STONYFIELD FARM, INC.—See Groupe Lactalis SA; *Int'l*, pg. 3106
SUNSHINE STATE DAIRY FARMS—See Southeast Milk, Inc.; *U.S. Private*, pg. 3726
TLC BEATRICE INTERNATIONAL HOLDINGS INC.; *U.S. Private*, pg. 4178
TROPICALE FOODS, LLC—See Wind Point Advisors LLC; *U.S. Private*, pg. 4536
VELVET ICE CREAM COMPANY INC.; *U.S. Private*, pg. 4355
WELLS ENTERPRISES, INC.; *U.S. Private*, pg. 4476
WONDER ICE CREAM CO.; *U.S. Private*, pg. 4556
YOCREAM INTERNATIONAL INC.—See Danone; *Int'l*, pg. 1968
YUENGLING'S ICE CREAM CORPORATION; *U.S. Public*, pg. 2399

311611 — ANIMAL (EXCEPT POULTRY) SLAUGHTERING

ABBYLAND FOODS, INC.; *U.S. Private*, pg. 35
ABBYLAND PORK PACK—See Abbyland Foods, Inc.; *U.S. Private*, pg. 35
ADM ALLIANCE NUTRITION, INC.—See Archer-Daniels-Midland Company; *U.S. Public*, pg. 181
ADM ALLIANCE NUTRITION—See Archer-Daniels-Midland Company; *U.S. Public*, pg. 181
ADM ALLIANCE NUTRITION—See Archer-Daniels-Midland Company; *U.S. Public*, pg. 181
AGROPECUARIA DE GUISSONA, S. COOP. LTDA.; *Int'l*, pg. 220
ALL AMERICAN MEATS INC.; *U.S. Private*, pg. 169
ALPES PROVENCE AGNEAUX; *Int'l*, pg. 366
ALPINE MEATS INC.; *U.S. Private*, pg. 201
A&R PACKING CO.; *U.S. Private*, pg. 20
ASTRA FOODS, INC.; *U.S. Private*, pg. 361
AURORA PACKING CO., INC.; *U.S. Private*, pg. 394
BELL SCHWEIZ AG—See Coop-Gruppe Genossenschaft; *Int'l*, pg. 1789
BILL BAILEY MEAT PACKING CO INC.—See Square-H Brands Inc.; *U.S. Private*, pg. 3766
BINDAREE BEEF PTY. LIMITED; *Int'l*, pg. 1033
BOCM PAULS LTD.—See Agricola Group Ltd; *Int'l*, pg. 216
BROWN PACKING COMPANY INC.; *U.S. Private*, pg. 668
CAMBRIDGE PACKING CO., INC.—See The Chefs' Warehouse, Inc.; *U.S. Public*, pg. 2058
CARGILL FOODS LIMITED—See Cargill, Inc.; *U.S. Private*, pg. 757
CARGILL MEAT SOLUTIONS—See Cargill, Inc.; *U.S. Private*, pg. 758
CARGILL MEAT SOLUTIONS—See Cargill, Inc.; *U.S. Private*, pg. 758
CARGILL MEAT SOLUTIONS—See Cargill, Inc.; *U.S. Private*, pg. 758
CARGILL MEAT SOLUTIONS—See Cargill, Inc.; *U.S. Private*, pg. 758
CARGILL MEAT SOLUTIONS—See Cargill, Inc.; *U.S. Private*, pg. 758
CARGILL MEAT SOLUTIONS—See Cargill, Inc.; *U.S. Private*, pg. 758
CARGILL TURKEY PRODUCTS FARMS—See Cargill, Inc.; *U.S. Private*, pg. 759
CARL BUDDIG & COMPANY; *U.S. Private*, pg. 762
CENTRAL BEEF IND., L.L.C.; *U.S. Private*, pg. 819
CHIAPPETTI WHOLESALE MEAT CORPORATION; *U.S. Private*, pg. 876
CHINA XIANGTAI FOOD CO., LTD.; *Int'l*, pg. 1563
CHISESI BROTHERS MEAT PACKING CO.; *U.S. Private*, pg. 887
COFCO JOYCOME FOODS LIMITED; *Int'l*, pg. 1691
COLEMAN NATURAL FOODS, INC.—See Perdue Farms Incorporated; *U.S. Private*, pg. 3147
CONAGRA FOODS - ROSSVILLE—See Conagra Brands, Inc.; *U.S. Public*, pg. 563
CURTIS PACKING CO., INC.; *U.S. Private*, pg. 1126
DANISH CROWN AMBA; *Int'l*, pg. 1964
DIETZ & WATSON INC.; *U.S. Private*, pg. 1229
D.L. LEE & SONS INC.; *U.S. Private*, pg. 1142
ETABLISSEMENTS CHAZAUD; *Int'l*, pg. 2519
FAMILY BRANDS INTERNATIONAL LLC—See Cherokee Distributing Company, Inc.; *U.S. Private*, pg. 873
FORTUNE NG FUNG FOOD (HEBEI) CO., LTD.; *Int'l*, pg. 2744
FRESH MARK, INC—See Fresh Mark, Inc.; *U.S. Private*, pg. 1610
FURST-MCNESS OF CANADA—See Furst-McNess Company; *U.S. Private*, pg. 1624
GREATER OMAHA PACKING CO. INC.; *U.S. Private*, pg. 1770
GUSTO PACKING CO., INC.—See Maxwell Foods, LLC; *U.S. Private*, pg. 2619
GUSTO PACKING CO., INC.—See Seaboard Corporation; *U.S. Public*, pg. 1850
HARRIS RANCH BEEF COMPANY—See Central Valley Meat Holding Company; *U.S. Private*, pg. 826
HATFIELD QUALITY MEATS, INC.—See Clemens Family Corporation; *U.S. Private*, pg. 940
HFG SVERIGE AB—See Hilton Food Group plc; *Int'l*, pg. 3395
HILTON MEATS (RETAIL) LIMITED—See Hilton Food Group plc; *Int'l*, pg. 8395
HOFMANN SAUSAGE CO., INC.—See Trivest Partners, LP; *U.S. Private*, pg. 4241
HORMEL FOODS CORPORATION; *U.S. Public*, pg. 1053
H. R. JASPER & SON LTD.—See Dunbia Group; *Int'l*, pg. 2225
IOWA PACIFIC PROCESSORS INC.; *U.S. Private*, pg. 2135
J&B SAUSAGE COMPANY, INC.; *U.S. Private*, pg. 2153
J.H. ROUTH PACKING CO.; *U.S. Private*, pg. 2166
JOHN GRAVES FOOD SERVICE INC.—See Menu Maker Foods Inc.; *U.S. Private*, pg. 2667

N.A.I.C.S. INDEX

311612 — MEAT PROCESSED FROM...

KAYEM FOODS, INC.; *U.S. Private*, pg. 2266
LONE STAR BEEF PROCESSORS, L.P.; *U.S. Private*, pg. 2484
LONG IRON MEATS (PTY) LIMITED—See Country Bird Holdings Limited; *Int'l*, pg. 1818
LOWELL PACKING COMPANY; *U.S. Private*, pg. 2505
MANNING'S BEEF LLC.; *U.S. Private*, pg. 2565
METZGERMEISTER & RESEARCH CORP.; *U.S. Private*, pg. 2691
MPI HOLDINGS, INC.; *U.S. Private*, pg. 2804
MPS FRANCE, S.A.R.L.—See Equistone Partners Europe Limited; *Int'l*, pg. 2486
MPS GERMANY GMBH—See Equistone Partners Europe Limited; *Int'l*, pg. 2486
MPS MEAT PROCESSING SYSTEMS B.V.—See Equistone Partners Europe Limited; *Int'l*, pg. 2486
MPS NORTH AMERICA, INC.—See Equistone Partners Europe Limited; *Int'l*, pg. 2486
MPS RED MEAT SLAUGHTERING CO., LTD.—See Equistone Partners Europe Limited; *Int'l*, pg. 2486
MPS SPAIN, S.A.U.—See Equistone Partners Europe Limited; *Int'l*, pg. 2486
NEBRASKALAND; *U.S. Private*, pg. 2879
NICOLLET CATTLE COMPANY, INC.; *U.S. Private*, pg. 2926
NORTH AMERICAN BISON COOPERATIVE; *U.S. Private*, pg. 2940
NORTHWOOD FOODS INC.; *U.S. Private*, pg. 2963
OHIO PACKING COMPANY; *U.S. Private*, pg. 3005
OOO MPS RUS—See Equistone Partners Europe Limited; *Int'l*, pg. 2486
OSCEOLA FOODS, INC.—See Hormel Foods Corporation; *U.S. Public*, pg. 1054
PEORIA PACKING LTD.; *U.S. Private*, pg. 3143
PHILADELPHIA FOODS INC.; *U.S. Private*, pg. 3169
POLK'S MEAT PRODUCTS; *U.S. Private*, pg. 3224
PORK KING PACKING, INC.; *U.S. Private*, pg. 3229
PRECISION MICROBLENDERS INC.—See Archer-Daniels-Midland Company; *U.S. Public*, pg. 185
PREFERRED BEEF GROUP; *U.S. Private*, pg. 3247
PRG PACKING CORP.; *U.S. Private*, pg. 3257
PROVIMI FOODS INC; *U.S. Private*, pg. 3295
QUALITY PORK PROCESSORS, INC.; *U.S. Private*, pg. 3320
RABER PACKING CO.; *U.S. Private*, pg. 3341
RANDOLPH PACKING COMPANY; *U.S. Private*, pg. 3354
RECONSERVE, INC.—See ReConserve, Inc.; *U.S. Private*, pg. 3371
ROCHELLE FOODS, INC.—See Hormel Foods Corporation; *U.S. Public*, pg. 1054
RUSSELL & JILL HEFFNER, INC.; *U.S. Private*, pg. 3506
SADIA S.A.—See BRF S.A.; *Int'l*, pg. 1151
SAM KANE BEEF PROCESSORS, INC.; *U.S. Private*, pg. 3535
SCHENK PACKING CO. INC.; *U.S. Private*, pg. 3564
SERVICE PACKING COMPANY-UNITED FOOD GROUP; *U.S. Private*, pg. 3616
SIOUX-PREME PACKING CO.—See Perdue Farms Incorporated; *U.S. Private*, pg. 3147
SPARTANBURG MEAT PROCESSING CO., INC.; *U.S. Private*, pg. 3746
SPRINGTREE FARM GROUP; *U.S. Private*, pg. 3764
TRANSHUMANCE HOLDING COMPANY INC.; *U.S. Private*, pg. 4208
TYSON FRESH MEATS, INC.—See Tyson Foods, Inc.; *U.S. Public*, pg. 2210
TYSON FRESH MEATS, INC.—See Tyson Foods, Inc.; *U.S. Public*, pg. 2210
TYSON FRESH MEATS, INC.—See Tyson Foods, Inc.; *U.S. Public*, pg. 2210
TYSON FRESH MEATS, INC.—See Tyson Foods, Inc.; *U.S. Public*, pg. 2210
TYSON FRESH MEATS, INC.—See Tyson Foods, Inc.; *U.S. Public*, pg. 2210
TYSON FRESH MEATS, INC.—See Tyson Foods, Inc.; *U.S. Public*, pg. 2210
TYSON FRESH MEATS, INC.—See Tyson Foods, Inc.; *U.S. Public*, pg. 2210
TYSON FRESH MEATS, INC.—See Tyson Foods, Inc.; *U.S. Public*, pg. 2210
TYSON FRESH MEATS, INC.—See Tyson Foods, Inc.; *U.S. Public*, pg. 2210
TYSON FRESH MEATS, INC.—See Tyson Foods, Inc.; *U.S. Public*, pg. 2210
TYSON FRESH MEATS, INC.—See Tyson Foods, Inc.; *U.S. Public*, pg. 2210
VALLEY PRIDE PACK INC.; *U.S. Private*, pg. 4335
VALLEY PROTEINS, INC.—See Darling Ingredients Inc.; *U.S. Public*, pg. 634
VPP GROUP, LLC.; *U.S. Private*, pg. 4414
WAMPLERS FARM SAUSAGE CO. INC.; *U.S. Private*, pg. 4435
WEST LAKE FOOD CORPORATION; *U.S. Private*, pg. 4486
WOLVERINE PACKING CO.; *U.S. Private*, pg. 4555

311612 — MEAT PROCESSED FROM CARCASSES

AFFCO HOLDINGS LIMITED HOROTIU PLANT—See AFFCO Holdings Limited; *Int'l*, pg. 185
AFFCO HOLDINGS LIMITED IMLAY PLANT—See AFFCO Holdings Limited; *Int'l*, pg. 185
AFFCO HOLDINGS LIMITED INVERCARGILL PLANT—See AFFCO Holdings Limited; *Int'l*, pg. 186
AFFCO HOLDINGS LIMITED MALVERN PLANT—See AFFCO Holdings Limited; *Int'l*, pg. 186
AFFCO HOLDINGS LIMITED MANAWATU PLANT—See AFFCO Holdings Limited; *Int'l*, pg. 186
AFFCO HOLDINGS LIMITED - MOEREWA PLANT—See AFFCO Holdings Limited; *Int'l*, pg. 185
AFFCO HOLDINGS LIMITED RANGIURU PLANT—See AFFCO Holdings Limited; *Int'l*, pg. 186
AFFCO HOLDINGS LIMITED WAIROA PLANT—See AFFCO Holdings Limited; *Int'l*, pg. 186
AFFCO HOLDINGS LIMITED WANGANUI PLANT—See AFFCO Holdings Limited; *Int'l*, pg. 186
AGROINDUSTRIAL DEL NOROESTE S. DE R.L. DE C.V.; *Int'l*, pg. 219
AGROKOMBINAT A.D.; *Int'l*, pg. 219
AIDELLS SAUSAGE COMPANY, INC.—See Tyson Foods, Inc.; *U.S. Public*, pg. 2209
ALLANASONS PRIVATE LIMITED; *Int'l*, pg. 333
ALLIANCE GROUP LIMITED - DANNEVIRKE PLANT—See Alliance Group Limited; *Int'l*, pg. 339
ALLIANCE GROUP LIMITED - LEVIN PLANT—See Alliance Group Limited; *Int'l*, pg. 339
ALLIANCE GROUP LIMITED - LORNEVILLE PLANT—See Alliance Group Limited; *Int'l*, pg. 339
ALLIANCE GROUP LIMITED - MAKAREWA PLANT—See Alliance Group Limited; *Int'l*, pg. 339
ALLIANCE GROUP LIMITED - MATAURA PLANT—See Alliance Group Limited; *Int'l*, pg. 339
ALLIANCE GROUP LIMITED - NELSON PLANT—See Alliance Group Limited; *Int'l*, pg. 339
ALLIANCE GROUP LIMITED - PUKEURI PLANT—See Alliance Group Limited; *Int'l*, pg. 339
ALLIANCE GROUP LIMITED - SMITHFIELD PLANT—See Alliance Group Limited; *Int'l*, pg. 339
AMERICAN FOODSERVICE CORP.; *U.S. Private*, pg. 234
ANPULO FOOD, INC.; *Int'l*, pg. 475
A-PIHVI KAUHAJOKI OY—See Atria Plc; *Int'l*, pg. 693
ARENA HOLDING S.P.A. - MARSILI PLANT—See Arena Holding S.P.A.; *Int'l*, pg. 558
ARIES PREPARED BEEF CO.; *U.S. Private*, pg. 323
ATRIA CONCEPT AB—See Atria Plc; *Int'l*, pg. 693
ATRIA CONCEPT SP Z.O.O—See Atria Plc; *Int'l*, pg. 693
ATRIA EESTI AS—See Atria Plc; *Int'l*, pg. 693
ATRIA FINLAND LTD.—See Atria Plc; *Int'l*, pg. 693
ATRIA PLC; *Int'l*, pg. 693
ATRIA SCANDINAVIA AB—See Atria Plc; *Int'l*, pg. 693
AXYZ CO., LTD.; *Int'l*, pg. 773
BAR-S FOODS CO.—See ALFA, S.A.B. de C.V.; *Int'l*, pg. 314
BAVARIAN MEAT PRODUCTS, INC.; *U.S. Private*, pg. 491
BELL POLSKA SP. Z O.O—See Coop-Gruppe Genossenschaft; *Int'l*, pg. 1789
BERT HAZEKAMP & SON, INC.; *U.S. Private*, pg. 539
BEST PROVISION CO., INC.; *U.S. Private*, pg. 543
BLUE GRASS PROVISION COMPANY; *U.S. Private*, pg. 589
BLUE RIBBON, LP—See Altamont Capital Partners; *U.S. Private*, pg. 205
BOBAK SAUSAGE COMPANY; *U.S. Private*, pg. 606
BOB'S PROCESSING, INC.; *U.S. Private*, pg. 605
BRAEDT, S. A.—See ALFA, S.A.B. de C.V.; *Int'l*, pg. 313
BRIDGFORD FOOD PROCESSING CORPORATION—See Bridgford Foods Corporation; *U.S. Public*, pg. 382
BROWN PACKING CO., INC.; *U.S. Private*, pg. 668
BSA INDIA FOOD INGR. PVT. LTD.—See International Flavors & Fragrances Inc.; *U.S. Public*, pg. 1151
BURKE MARKETING CORPORATION; *U.S. Private*, pg. 688
BUSSETO FOODS, INC.—See Cremonini S.p.A.; *Int'l*, pg. 1838
CALUMET DIVERSIFIED MEATS INC.; *U.S. Private*, pg. 724
CAMPOFRIO FOOD GROUPE FRANCE HOLDING SAS—See ALFA, S.A.B. de C.V.; *Int'l*, pg. 314
CAMPOFRIO FOOD GROUP, S.A. - MANUFACTURING PITESTI—See ALFA, S.A.B. de C.V.; *Int'l*, pg. 314
CAMPOFRIO FOOD GROUP, S.A. - MANUFACTURING TULCEA—See ALFA, S.A.B. de C.V.; *Int'l*, pg. 314
CAPITAL WHOLESALE MEATS INC.; *U.S. Private*, pg. 742
CARGILL FOOD DISTRIBUTION—See Cargill, Inc.; *U.S. Private*, pg. 758
CARGILL FOOD DISTRIBUTION—See Cargill, Inc.; *U.S. Private*, pg. 758
CARLTON FOODS CORP—See Altamont Capital Partners; *U.S. Private*, pg. 205
CARMECO SA; *Int'l*, pg. 1341
CAROLI FOODS GROUP S. R. L.—See ALFA, S.A.B. de C.V.; *Int'l*, pg. 314

CASA DI BERTACCHI—See Rich Holdings, Inc.; *U.S. Private*, pg. 3426
CATALINA FINER FOOD CORPORATION—See Promise Holdings, LLC; *U.S. Private*, pg. 3283
CATTLEMAN'S, INC.; *U.S. Private*, pg. 794
CFG DEUTSCHLAND GMBH—See ALFA, S.A.B. de C.V.; *Int'l*, pg. 314
CHAIR CITY MEATS INC.; *U.S. Private*, pg. 845
CHICAGO MEAT AUTHORITY, INC.; *U.S. Private*, pg. 878
CHINA YURUN FOOD GROUP LIMITED; *Int'l*, pg. 1566
CIMPL'S, LLC—See Rosens Diversified, Inc.; *U.S. Private*, pg. 3484
CJ NUTRACON PTY.—See CJ Corporation; *Int'l*, pg. 1633
CLOVERDALE FOODS COMPANY INC.; *U.S. Private*, pg. 948
COLUMBUS MANUFACTURING, INC.—See Hormel Foods Corporation; *U.S. Public*, pg. 1054
COMINCA SA; *Int'l*, pg. 1713
CONAGRA FOODS - HEBREW NATIONAL KOSHER FOODS—See Conagra Brands, Inc.; *U.S. Public*, pg. 563
CPF FOOD PRODUCTS CO., LTD.—See Charoen Pokphand Foods Public Company Limited; *Int'l*, pg. 1452
CRANSWICK COUNTRY FOODS PLC—See Cranswick Plc; *Int'l*, pg. 1828
CREMINELLI FINE MEATS, LLC—See Entrepreneurial Equity Partners, LLC; *U.S. Private*, pg. 1406
CRETA FARM S.A.; *Int'l*, pg. 1842
DABECCA NATURAL FOODS INC.; *U.S. Private*, pg. 1143
DAKOTA PREMIUM FOODS, LLC—See Rosens Diversified, Inc.; *U.S. Private*, pg. 3484
DALEPAK FOODS—See Boparan Holdings Limited; *Int'l*, pg. 1111
DANISH CROWN FOODS FRANCE S.A.S.—See Danish Crown AmbA; *Int'l*, pg. 1964
DANISH CROWN FOODS GERMANY GMBH—See Danish Crown AmbA; *Int'l*, pg. 1964
DANISH CROWN FOODS HAARLEM B.V.—See Danish Crown AmbA; *Int'l*, pg. 1964
DANISH CROWN FOODS ITALY S.R.L.—See Danish Crown AmbA; *Int'l*, pg. 1964
DANISH CROWN FOODS JONKOPING AB—See Danish Crown AmbA; *Int'l*, pg. 1964
DANISH CROWN FOODS NORWAY AS—See Danish Crown AmbA; *Int'l*, pg. 1964
DANISH CROWN FOODS SWEDEN AB—See Danish Crown AmbA; *Int'l*, pg. 1964
DANISH CROWN TETEROWER FLEISCH GMBH—See Danish Crown AmbA; *Int'l*, pg. 1964
DEAN SAUSAGE COMPANY INC.; *U.S. Private*, pg. 1184
DELICO LIMITED—See Cranswick Plc; *Int'l*, pg. 1828
DEMAKES ENTERPRISES INC.; *U.S. Private*, pg. 1203
DEVAULT PACKING COMPANY, INC.—See Trivest Partners, LP; *U.S. Private*, pg. 4240
DONGRUI FOOD GROUP CO., LTD.; *Int'l*, pg. 2169
DOUBLE D FOODS—See Downs Food Group; *U.S. Private*, pg. 1269
DOUBLE R BRAND FOODS LLC.; *U.S. Private*, pg. 1266
ELABORADORA DE SUBPRODUTOS DE ORIGEM ANIMAL DO BRASIL LTDA.—See Danish Crown AmbA; *Int'l*, pg. 1965
ELORE ENTERPRISES LLC—See The Carlyle Group Inc.; *U.S. Public*, pg. 2047
EL SUPERIOR MEXICAN FOODS LLC.; *U.S. Private*, pg. 1349
EMGE FOODS, LLC—See Peer Foods Group, Inc.; *U.S. Private*, pg. 3128
ESS-FOOD HOLDING A/S—See Danish Crown AmbA; *Int'l*, pg. 1964
FAIR OAKS FARMS INC.; *U.S. Private*, pg. 1462
FARMER'S CHOICE LTD—See Aga Khan Development Network; *Int'l*, pg. 199
FELLS POINT WHOLESALE MEATS, INC.—See The Chefs' Warehouse, Inc.; *U.S. Public*, pg. 2059
FRED USINGER, INC.; *U.S. Private*, pg. 1601
FRESH MARK, INC.; *U.S. Private*, pg. 1609
FRILAND DEUTSCHLAND GMBH—See Danish Crown AmbA; *Int'l*, pg. 1965
G-7 MEAT TERABAYASHI CO., LTD.—See G-7 HOLDINGS Inc.; *Int'l*, pg. 2862
GAYTAN FOODS—See Wind Point Advisors LLC; *U.S. Private*, pg. 4534
GIBBON PACKING, LLC—See Rosens Diversified, Inc.; *U.S. Private*, pg. 3484
GOBARTO SA; *Int'l*, pg. 3018
GOLDEN STATE FOODS-GEORGIA DIVISION—See Golden State Foods Corp.; *U.S. Private*, pg. 1733
GREEN BAY DRESSED BEEF, LLC—See Rosens Diversified, Inc.; *U.S. Private*, pg. 3484
GROTE & WEIGEL INC.—See Rachael's Food Corporation; *U.S. Private*, pg. 3341
GRUPO BAFAR, S.A.B DE C.V.; *Int'l*, pg. 3121
HANSEL 'N GRETEL BRAND INC.; *U.S. Private*, pg. 1856
HARRINGTONS OF VERMONT, INC.; *U.S. Private*, pg. 1869
HICKORY FOODS, INC.; *U.S. Private*, pg. 1933
HILTON FOOD GROUP PLC; *Int'l*, pg. 3395
HOLISTA COLLTECH LIMITED; *Int'l*, pg. 3450

3259

311612 — MEAT PROCESSED FROM...

HOUSE FOODS AMERICA CORPORATION—See House Foods Group Inc.; *Int'l*, pg. 3490
IMPERIAL MEAT PRODUCTS N.V.—See ALFA, S.A.B. de C.V.; *Int'l*, pg. 314
INDUSTRIAS DE CARNES NOBRE S.A.—See ALFA, S.A.B. de C.V.; *Int'l*, pg. 314
INTERNATIONAL CASINGS GROUP, INC.; *U.S. Private*, pg. 2115
JBS ARGENTINA S.A.—See Compagnie Financiere Richemont S.A.; *Int'l*, pg. 1741
JOHNSONVILLE, LLC; *U.S. Private*, pg. 2229
KB JODDLAREN—See Atria Plc; *Int'l*, pg. 694
KLEMENT SAUSAGE CO., INC.—See Altamont Capital Partners; *U.S. Private*, pg. 205
KOEGEL MEATS INC.; *U.S. Private*, pg. 2336
KOWALSKI CO.; *U.S. Private*, pg. 2345
KOWALSKI COMPANIES INC.; *U.S. Private*, pg. 2345
KRAFT HEINZ COMPANY - OSCAR MAYER—See 3G Capital Inc.; *U.S. Private*, pg. 11
KRAFT HEINZ COMPANY - OSCAR MAYER—See Berkshire Hathaway Inc.; *U.S. Public*, pg. 318
LABELLA SAUSAGE, LLC—See The Anderson Group, LLC; *U.S. Private*, pg. 3986
LAND O'FROST, INC.; *U.S. Private*, pg. 2383
LAURA'S LEAN BEEF COMPANY—See Meyer Natural Angus, LLC; *U.S. Private*, pg. 2692
LEON'S FINE FOODS, INC.; *U.S. Private*, pg. 2423
LIGURIA FOODS, INC.—See Black Diamond Capital Holdings, LLC; *U.S. Private*, pg. 570
LIGURIA FOODS, INC.—See Massachusetts Mutual Life Insurance Company; *U.S. Private*, pg. 2605
LINK SNACKS, INC. - ANSBACH PLANT—See Link Snacks, Inc.; *U.S. Private*, pg. 2461
LINK SNACKS, INC.; *U.S. Private*, pg. 2461
LLOYDS BARBEQUE COMPANY, LLC—See Hormel Foods Corporation; *U.S. Public*, pg. 1054
LONG PRAIRIE PACKING LLC—See Rosens Diversified, Inc.; *U.S. Private*, pg. 3484
LOPEZ FOODS INC.; *U.S. Private*, pg. 2494
LOUIE'S FINER MEATS, INC.; *U.S. Private*, pg. 2498
LSI INC.; *U.S. Private*, pg. 2509
MAGLIO BROS INC.; *U.S. Private*, pg. 2546
MAID-RITE STEAK COMPANY INC.; *U.S. Private*, pg. 2551
MANDA PACKING CO. INC.; *U.S. Private*, pg. 2562
MANN'S INTERNATIONAL MEAT SPECIALTIES INC.; *U.S. Private*, pg. 2565
MARATHON ENTERPRISES, INC.; *U.S. Private*, pg. 2570
MEYER NATURAL ANGUS, LLC; *U.S. Private*, pg. 2692
M&M RESTAURANT SUPPLY—See Tyson Foods, Inc.; *U.S. Public*, pg. 2210
MONOGRAM MEAT SNACKS, LLC—See Monogram Food Solutions, LLC; *U.S. Private*, pg. 2771
NATIONWIDE FOODS INC.; *U.S. Private*, pg. 2865
OFD FOODS, LLC; *U.S. Private*, pg. 3000
OLD WISCONSIN SAUSAGE—See Carl Buddig & Company; *U.S. Private*, pg. 762
OMAHA STEAKS INTERNATIONAL, INC.; *U.S. Private*, pg. 3014
OOO CAMPOMOS—See Atria Plc; *Int'l*, pg. 694
PALMYRA BOLOGNA CO.; *U.S. Private*, pg. 3082
PARKER HOUSE SAUSAGE COMPANY; *U.S. Private*, pg. 3097
PEER FOODS GROUP, INC.; *U.S. Private*, pg. 3128
PERFECTION FOODS COMPANY, INC.; *U.S. Private*, pg. 3148
POLARIZED MEAT CO., INC.; *U.S. Private*, pg. 3223
PREMIO FOODS, INC.; *U.S. Private*, pg. 3251
PREMIUM PROTEIN PRODUCTS, LLC; *U.S. Private*, pg. 3252
PRIME FOOD PROCESSING CORP.; *U.S. Private*, pg. 3261
QUAKER MAID MEATS INC.; *U.S. Private*, pg. 3317
QUALITY BONELESS BEEF INC.; *U.S. Private*, pg. 3318
QUALITY SAUSAGE COMPANY; *U.S. Private*, pg. 3321
RALPH & PAUL ADAMS, INC.—See Jones Dairy Farm; *U.S. Private*, pg. 2232
REDI-SERVE FOODS—See On-Cor Frozen Foods LLC; *U.S. Private*, pg. 3018
RICE FIELD CORPORATION; *U.S. Private*, pg. 3425
RIDDERHEIMS AS—See Atria Plc; *Int'l*, pg. 694
R.L. ZEIGLER CO. INC.; *U.S. Private*, pg. 3338
ROSE PACKING COMPANY, INC.—See OSI Group, LLC; *U.S. Private*, pg. 3047
ROSINA FOOD PRODUCTS, INC.—See Rosina Holding, Inc.; *U.S. Private*, pg. 3484
ROSINA HOLDING, INC.; *U.S. Private*, pg. 3484
SALM PARTNERS, LLC.—See Johnsonville, LLC; *U.S. Private*, pg. 2229
SALOIR DE VIRIEU SAS—See Coop-Gruppe Genossenschaft; *Int'l*, pg. 1790
SAVOIE'S SAUSAGE & FOOD PRODUCTS, INC.; *U.S. Private*, pg. 3557
SCHALLER MANUFACTURING CORP.; *U.S. Private*, pg. 3563
SEABOARD ENERGY OKLAHOMA, LLC—See Seaboard Corporation; *U.S. Public*, pg. 1851
SHANGHAI MALING AQUARIUS CO., LTD.—See Bright Food (Group) Co., Ltd.; *Int'l*, pg. 1161
S I L INC.; *U.S. Private*, pg. 3512
SIMEUS FOODS INTERNATIONAL, INC.; *U.S. Private*, pg. 3665
SKYLARK MEATS, LLC—See Rosens Diversified, Inc.; *U.S. Private*, pg. 3484
SONAC OSETNICA SP.Z O.O.—See Darling Ingredients Inc.; *U.S. Public*, pg. 634
SPARRER SAUSAGE COMPANY, INC.; *U.S. Private*, pg. 3746
SQUARE-H BRANDS INC.; *U.S. Private*, pg. 3766
STAHL-MEYER FOODS, INC.; *U.S. Private*, pg. 3776
STAMPEDE MEAT, INC.—See Wynnchurch Capital, L.P.; *U.S. Private*, pg. 4578
STANDARD MEAT COMPANY; *U.S. Private*, pg. 3781
STEGEMAN B.V.—See ALFA, S.A.B. de C.V.; *Int'l*, pg. 314
SUGAR CREEK PACKING CO.; *U.S. Private*, pg. 3849
SUGARDALE FOODS INC.—See Fresh Mark, Inc.; *U.S. Private*, pg. 1610
SUNCREST FARMS COUNTRY HAMS, INC.; *U.S. Private*, pg. 3866
SUNHILL FOOD OF VERMONT, INC.—See Danish Crown AmbA; *Int'l*, pg. 1965
SUN SUPPLY CORPORATION—See House Foods Group Inc.; *Int'l*, pg. 3490
SUPERIOR'S BRAND MEATS—See Fresh Mark, Inc.; *U.S. Private*, pg. 1610
SURLEAN MEAT CO.—See L&H Packing Company; *U.S. Private*, pg. 2362
SYRACUSE'S SAUSAGE COMPANY—See Standard Meat Company; *U.S. Private*, pg. 3781
TENDERCUT MEATS LTD—See Argent Group Europe Limited; *Int'l*, pg. 560
THUMANN, INC.; *U.S. Private*, pg. 4165
TONY DOWNS FOODS—See Downs Food Group; *U.S. Private*, pg. 1269
TYSON DELI, INC.—See Tyson Foods, Inc.; *U.S. Public*, pg. 2210
TYSON REFRIGERATED PROCESSED MEATS, INC.—See Tyson Foods, Inc.; *U.S. Public*, pg. 2210
UNCLE CHARLEY'S SAUSAGE CO.; *U.S. Private*, pg. 4279
U.S. PREMIUM BEEF, LLC; *U.S. Private*, pg. 4271
VAL DE LYON SAS—See Coop-Gruppe Genossenschaft; *Int'l*, pg. 1790
VALLEY MEATS LLC—See North American Company; *U.S. Private*, pg. 2940
VINCENT GIORDANO CORPORATION; *U.S. Private*, pg. 4385
WEST LIBERTY FOODS - BOLINGBROOK—See Iowa Turkey Growers Cooperative; *U.S. Private*, pg. 2136
WILLIAMS SAUSAGE COMPANY, INC.—See Tyson Foods, Inc.; *U.S. Public*, pg. 2210
WIMMERS MEAT PRODUCTS INC.—See Land O'Frost, Inc.; *U.S. Private*, pg. 2383
WISCONSIN PACKING CO. INC. DELAWARE; *U.S. Private*, pg. 4548
WW JOHNSON MEAT COMPANY; *U.S. Private*, pg. 4575
ZIMBO HUSIPARI TERMELO KFT.—See Coop-Gruppe Genossenschaft; *Int'l*, pg. 1790

311613 — RENDERING AND MEAT BYPRODUCT PROCESSING

BAKER COMMODITIES, INC.; *U.S. Private*, pg. 455
BHJ A/S—See Lauridsen Group Inc.; *U.S. Private*, pg. 2399
BHJ UK FOOD LTD.—See Lauridsen Group Inc.; *U.S. Private*, pg. 2399
BHJ UK PROTEIN FOODS LTD—See Lauridsen Group Inc.; *U.S. Private*, pg. 2399
DARLING INGREDIENTS INTERNATIONAL HOLDING B.V.—See Darling Ingredients Inc.; *U.S. Public*, pg. 634
FERIA DE OSORNO S.A.; *Int'l*, pg. 2638
GES.CAR. S.R.L.—See Cremonini S.p.A.; *Int'l*, pg. 1838
GRIFFIN INDUSTRIES, INC.—See Darling Ingredients Inc.; *U.S. Public*, pg. 634
INALCA S.P.A.—See Cremonini S.p.A.; *Int'l*, pg. 1838
JDB INC.; *U.S. Private*, pg. 2195
JIF-PAK MANUFACTURING INC.—See Clayton, Dubilier & Rice, LLC; *U.S. Private*, pg. 926
KANE-MILLER CORP.; *U.S. Private*, pg. 2260
MONTANA ALIMENTARI S.P.A.—See Cremonini S.p.A.; *Int'l*, pg. 1838
MOUNTAIN VIEW RENDERING COMPANY; *U.S. Private*, pg. 2800
NEW ZEALAND LAMB COMPANY—See New Zealand Lamb Cooperative, Inc.; *U.S. Private*, pg. 2913
PRZEDSIEBIORSTWO PRODUKCYJNO HANDLOWE CONTO SP. Z O.O.—See Darling Ingredients Inc.; *U.S. Public*, pg. 634
RENDAC B.V.—See Darling Ingredients Inc.; *U.S. Public*, pg. 634
SONAC BURGUM B.V.—See Darling Ingredients Inc.; *U.S. Public*, pg. 634
SONAC B.V.—See Darling Ingredients Inc.; *U.S. Public*, pg. 634
VALLEY PROTEINS, INC.—See Darling Ingredients Inc.; *U.S. Public*, pg. 634
VALLEY PROTEINS, INC.—See Darling Ingredients Inc.; *U.S. Public*, pg. 634

311615 — POULTRY PROCESSING

2 SISTERS FOOD GROUP LIMITED—See Boparan Holdings Limited; *Int'l*, pg. 1111
AGRO-RYDZYNA SP. Z O.O.—See Dino Polska SA; *Int'l*, pg. 2127
ALLEN FAMILY FOODS, INC.; *U.S. Private*, pg. 178
ARENA HOLDING S.P.A. - LA FARAONA PLANT—See Arena Holding S.p.A.; *Int'l*, pg. 558
ASPEN FOODS—See Koch Foods, Inc.; *U.S. Private*, pg. 2326
AVICOLA CREVEDIA—See Agroli Group; *Int'l*, pg. 220
BACKA PALANKA A.D.; *George's Inc.; U.S. Private*, pg. 795
BAIADA POULTRY PTY LIMITED; *Int'l*, pg. 801
BEIJING SHUNXIN AGRICULTURE CO., LTD.; *Int'l*, pg. 956
BELL CARNI S.R.L.—See Cremonini S.p.A.; *Int'l*, pg. 1838
BELL & EVANS; *U.S. Private*, pg. 518
BELL NEDERLAND B.V.—See Coop-Gruppe Genossenschaft; *Int'l*, pg. 1789
BERNARD MATTHEWS FOODS LTD.—See Boparan Holdings Limited; *Int'l*, pg. 1111
BEYOND MEAT, INC.; *U.S. Public*, pg. 327
BRAKEBUSH BROTHERS INC.; *U.S. Private*, pg. 635
BROME LAKE DUCKS LTD; *Int'l*, pg. 1173
CAIRO POULTRY COMPANY—See Adeptio LLC; *Int'l*, pg. 143
CARGILL TURKEY PRODUCTS INC.—See Cargill, Inc.; *U.S. Private*, pg. 759
CASE FARMS, LLC - GOLDSBORO PROCESSING—See Case Foods, Inc.; *U.S. Private*, pg. 781
CASE FARMS, LLC - MORGANTON PRODUCTION & PROCESSING—See Case Foods, Inc.; *U.S. Private*, pg. 782
CASE FARMS, LLC - OHIO PROCESSING—See Case Foods, Inc.; *U.S. Private*, pg. 782
CASE FARMS, LLC—See Case Foods, Inc.; *U.S. Private*, pg. 781
CENTURY LEGEND HOLDINGS LTD; *Int'l*, pg. 1418
CHAROEN POKPHAND ENTERPRISE (TAIWAN) CO., LTD.—See Charoen Pokphand Foods Public Company Limited; *Int'l*, pg. 1452
CHAROEN POKPHAND FOODS (MALAYSIA) SDN. BHD.—See Charoen Pokphand Foods Public Company Limited; *Int'l*, pg. 1452
COLUMBIA FARMS INC.—See Nash Johnson & Sons Farms Inc.; *U.S. Private*, pg. 2836
CONTILATIN—See Continental Grain Company; *U.S. Private*, pg. 1029
COPAZ PACKING CORPORATION; *U.S. Private*, pg. 1044
COUNTRY BIRD HOLDINGS LIMITED; *Int'l*, pg. 1818
CRIDER INC.; *U.S. Private*, pg. 1100
C.W. BROWN FOODS, INC.; *U.S. Private*, pg. 709
DACHAN FOOD (ASIA) LIMITED; *Int'l*, pg. 1903
DCW CASING LLC—See Danish Crown AmbA; *Int'l*, pg. 1964
DELMON POULTRY CO. B.S.C.; *Int'l*, pg. 2014
DHOFAR POULTRY COMPANY SAOG; *Int'l*, pg. 2099
DOUX SA—See Avril SCA; *Int'l*, pg. 750
DOWNS FOOD GROUP; *U.S. Private*, pg. 1269
DRAPER VALLEY FARMS INC.—See Perdue Farms Incorporated; *U.S. Private*, pg. 3147
EGYPT FOR POULTRY; *Int'l*, pg. 2327
ELITE KSB HOLDINGS LIMITED; *Int'l*, pg. 2362
EMPIRE KOSHER POULTRY, INC.—See Palisades Associates, Inc.; *U.S. Private*, pg. 3077
EPIC PROVISIONS, LLC—See General Mills, Inc.; *U.S. Public*, pg. 921
EQUITY GROUP KENTUCKY DIVISION LLC—See Tyson Foods, Inc.; *U.S. Public*, pg. 2209
EXCELDOR COOPERATIVE AVICOLE - SAINT-ANSELME PLANT—See Exceldor Cooperative Avicole; *Int'l*, pg. 2577
EXCELDOR COOPERATIVE AVICOLE - SAINT-DAMASE PLANT—See Exceldor Cooperative Avicole; *Int'l*, pg. 2577
EXCELDOR COOPERATIVE AVICOLE; *Int'l*, pg. 2577
FARBEST FOODS, INC.; *U.S. Private*, pg. 1473
FARM'S BEST FOOD INDUSTRIES SDN. BHD.—See Cab Cakaran Corporation Berhad; *Int'l*, pg. 1245
FIELDALE FARMS CORPORATION; *U.S. Private*, pg. 1504
FIORANI & C. S.P.A—See Cremonini S.p.A.; *Int'l*, pg. 1838
FRUTAROM SAVORY SOLUTIONS AUSTRIA GMBH—See International Flavors & Fragrances Inc.; *U.S. Public*, pg. 1152
FUJIAN SUNNER DEVELOPMENT CO., LTD.; *Int'l*, pg. 2819
GEORGE'S INC. - CASSVILLE PROCESSING PLANT—See George's Inc.; *U.S. Private*, pg. 1683
GEORGE'S INC. - EDINBURG PROCESSING PLANT—See George's Inc.; *U.S. Private*, pg. 1683
GEORGE'S INC. - HARRISONBURG PROCESSING PLANT—See George's Inc.; *U.S. Private*, pg. 1684
GEORGE'S INC.; *U.S. Private*, pg. 1683

N.A.I.C.S. INDEX

311710 — SEAFOOD PRODUCT PRE...

GEORGE'S INC. - SPRINGDALE PLANT—See George's Inc.; *U.S. Private*, pg. 1684
GEORGE'S PROCESSING INC.—See George's Inc.; *U.S. Private*, pg. 1684
GODREJ TYSON FOODS LTD.—See Godrej & Boyce Mfg. Co. Ltd.; *Int'l*, pg. 3020
GOURMET FOODS, LTD.—See The Marygold Companies, Inc.; *U.S. Public*, pg. 2112
HAIN PURE PROTEIN CORPORATION—See Aterian Investment Management, L.P.; *U.S. Private*, pg. 366
HARIM CO., LTD.—See Harim Holdings Co., Ltd.; *Int'l*, pg. 3275
HENAN HUAYING AGRICULTURE DEVELOPMENT CO., LTD.; *Int'l*, pg. 3342
HERITAGE POULTRY LTD.; *Int'l*, pg. 3362
HOLMES FOODS INC.; *U.S. Private*, pg. 1967
HOUSE OF RAEFORD FARMS, INC.; *U.S. Private*, pg. 1991
HUBBARD LLC—See Groupe Grimaud La Corbiere SA; *Int'l*, pg. 3103
HUBBARD SAS—See Groupe Grimaud La Corbiere SA; *Int'l*, pg. 3103
HUNAN XIANGJIA ANIMAL HUSBANDRY CO., LTD.; *Int'l*, pg. 3534
INGHAMS ENTERPRISES PTY LTD.—See TPG Capital, L.P.; *U.S. Public*, pg. 2174
JENNIE-O TURKEY STORE, INC.—See Hormel Foods Corporation; *U.S. Public*, pg. 1054
KINGS DELIGHT LTD., INC.; *U.S. Private*, pg. 2311
KMOTR-MASNA KROMERIZ A.S.—See Agrofert Holding, a.s.; *Int'l*, pg. 219
KOCH FOODS LLC—See Koch Foods, Inc.; *U.S. Private*, pg. 2326
KOSTELECKE UZENINY A.S.—See Agrofert Holding, a.s.; *Int'l*, pg. 219
KRAFT HEINZ COMPANY - LOUIS RICH—See 3G Capital Inc.; *U.S. Private*, pg. 10
KRAFT HEINZ COMPANY - LOUIS RICH—See Berkshire Hathaway Inc.; *U.S. Public*, pg. 318
KRAHULIK - MASOZAVOD KRAHULCI, A.S.—See Agrofert Holding, a.s.; *Int'l*, pg. 219
MARR RUSSIA L.L.C.—See Cremonini S.p.A.; *Int'l*, pg. 1838
MAXI CANADA INC.—See Altamont Capital Partners; *U.S. Private*, pg. 205
MB CONSULTANTS LTD.; *U.S. Private*, pg. 2623
MINERVA S.A.—See Compagnie Financiere Richemont S.A.; *Int'l*, pg. 1741
MOUNTAIRE CORPORATION; *U.S. Private*, pg. 2801
NASH JOHNSON & SONS FARMS INC.; *U.S. Private*, pg. 2836
NEW MARKET POULTRY, LLC—See Tip Top Poultry, Inc.; *U.S. Private*, pg. 4175
NORMAN W. FRIES INC.; *U.S. Private*, pg. 2938
OZARK MOUNTAIN POULTRY, INC.—See George's Inc.; *U.S. Private*, pg. 1684
PECO FARMS OF MISSISSIPPI, LLC.—See Peco Foods Inc.; *U.S. Private*, pg. 3127
PECO FOODS INC. - BATESVILLE PROCESSING PLANT—See Peco Foods Inc.; *U.S. Private*, pg. 3127
PECO FOODS INC. - BROOKSVILLE PROCESSING PLANT—See Peco Foods Inc.; *U.S. Private*, pg. 3127
PECO FOODS INC. - CANTON FEATHER LANE PROCESSING PLANT—See Peco Foods Inc.; *U.S. Private*, pg. 3127
PECO FOODS INC. - CANTON WEST FULTON STREET PROCESSING PLANT—See Peco Foods Inc.; *U.S. Private*, pg. 3127
PECO FOODS INC. - TUSCALOOSA PROCESSING PLANT—See Peco Foods Inc.; *U.S. Private*, pg. 3127
PERDUE FARMS INCORPORATED; *U.S. Private*, pg. 3147
PETALUMA POULTRY—See Perdue Farms Incorporated; *U.S. Private*, pg. 3147
PLUSFOOD HOLLAND B.V.—See BRF S.A.; *Int'l*, pg. 1150
PLUSFOOD ITALY SRL—See BRF S.A.; *Int'l*, pg. 1150
PLUSFOOD UK LTD.—See BRF S.A.; *Int'l*, pg. 1151
QC SUPPLY LLC—See Charlesbank Capital Partners, LLC; *U.S. Private*, pg. 856
ROSE & SHORE; *U.S. Private*, pg. 3481
SAGA FOODS ZRT—See Boparan Holdings Limited; *Int'l*, pg. 1112
SANDERSON FARMS, INC. - PROCESSING DIVISION—See Cargill, Inc.; *U.S. Private*, pg. 760
SANDERSON FARMS, INC. - PROCESSING DIVISION—See Continental Grain Company; *U.S. Private*, pg. 1029
SANDERSON FARMS, INC.—See Cargill, Inc.; *U.S. Private*, pg. 760
SANDERSON FARMS, INC.—See Continental Grain Company; *U.S. Private*, pg. 1029
SIMMONS CUSTOM PROCESSING, INC.—See Simmons Foods, Inc.; *U.S. Private*, pg. 3665
SIMMONS FOODS, INC.; *U.S. Private*, pg. 3665
SIMMONS PET FOOD, INC.—See Simmons Foods, Inc.; *U.S. Private*, pg. 3665
SIMMONS PREPARED FOODS, INC.—See Simmons Foods, Inc.; *U.S. Private*, pg. 3665
SOONLY FOOD PROCESSING INDUSTRIES PTE LTD—See Emerging Glory Sdn Bhd; *Int'l*, pg. 2379
SOUTHERN QUALITY MEATS, INC.—See H.I.G. Capital, LLC; *U.S. Private*, pg. 1831
STOCKTON FURTHER PROCESSING—See Zacky Farms, Inc.; *U.S. Private*, pg. 4597
SUFFIELD POULTRY INC.; *U.S. Private*, pg. 3849
SUNRISE FARMS, INC.—See Eli Lilly & Company; *U.S. Public*, pg. 734
TECUMSEH POULTRY LLC—See Tyson Foods, Inc.; *U.S. Public*, pg. 2210
TIP TOP POULTRY, INC. - ROCKMART FACILITY—See Tip Top Poultry, Inc.; *U.S. Private*, pg. 4175
TIP TOP POULTRY, INC.; *U.S. Private*, pg. 4175
TWIN RIVERS FOODS INC.—See Twin Rivers Group Inc.; *U.S. Private*, pg. 4266
TWIN RIVERS PACKAGING INC.—See Twin Rivers Group Inc.; *U.S. Private*, pg. 4266
TYSON FOODS, INC. - CARTHAGE—See Tyson Foods, Inc.; *U.S. Public*, pg. 2210
TYSON FOODS ITALIA S.P.A.—See Tyson Foods, Inc.; *U.S. Public*, pg. 2210
VINELAND KOSHER POULTRY INC.; *U.S. Private*, pg. 4385
VODNANSKA DRUBEZ, A.S.—See Agrofert Holding, a.s.; *Int'l*, pg. 219
WAYNE FARMS LLC—See Continental Grain Company; *U.S. Private*, pg. 1029
WESTERN SUPREME INC.; *U.S. Private*, pg. 4497

311710 — SEAFOOD PRODUCT PREPARATION AND PACKAGING

602390 ONTARIO LIMITED; *Int'l*, pg. 14
ACI AGROLINKS LTD.—See Advanced Chemical Industries Limited; *Int'l*, pg. 158
ALFESCA HF.; *Int'l*, pg. 315
ALLIANCE SELECT FOODS INTERNATIONAL, INC.; *Int'l*, pg. 341
AMCO SP. Z O.O.—See International Flavors & Fragrances Inc.; *U.S. Public*, pg. 1151
AMERICAN SEAFOODS GROUP LLC—See American Seafoods, LP; *U.S. Private*, pg. 246
AMERICAN SEAFOODS, LP; *U.S. Private*, pg. 246
AMERICA'S CATCH, INC.; *U.S. Private*, pg. 220
ANGIANG FISHERIES IMPORT & EXPORT JOINT STOCK COMPANY; *Int'l*, pg. 460
APEX FOODS LIMITED—See Apex Holding Limited; *Int'l*, pg. 511
APP HUNG YEN COMPANY LIMITED—See Agriculture Printing & Packaging Joint Stock Company; *Int'l*, pg. 217
AQUAMAR, INC.—See Huron Capital Partners LLC; *U.S. Private*, pg. 2012
ARENA AGROINDUSTRIE ALIMENTARI SPA—See Arena Holding S.p.A.; *Int'l*, pg. 558
ARENA HOLDING S.P.A. - MARE PRONTO PLANT—See Arena Holding S.p.A.; *Int'l*, pg. 558
ARROWAC FISHERIES INC.; *U.S. Private*, pg. 336
ASIAN SEA CORPORATION PUBLIC COMPANY LIMITED; *Int'l*, pg. 619
ATLANTIC SAPPHIRE ASA; *U.S. Public*, pg. 222
ATRIA FOODSERVICE AB—See Atria Plc; *Int'l*, pg. 693
AUSTEVOLL FISKEINDUSTRI AS—See Austevoll Seafood ASA; *Int'l*, pg. 717
BANDON PACIFIC, INC.—See Dulcich, Inc.; *U.S. Private*, pg. 1286
BAR HARBOR FOODS; *U.S. Private*, pg. 471
BAYERN GOURMET FOOD COMPANY LIMITED—See Hopewell Holdings Limited; *Int'l*, pg. 3473
BEACH HATCHERY LIMITED; *Int'l*, pg. 932
BEHPAK INDUSTRIAL COMPANY LIMITED—See Behshahr Industrial Development Corp.; *Int'l*, pg. 942
BINH THANH IMPORT - EXPORT PRODUCTION & TRADE JSC; *Int'l*, pg. 1034
BIOMAR AS—See Aktieselskabet Schouw & Co.; *Int'l*, pg. 265
BIOMAR S.A.S.—See Aktieselskabet Schouw & Co.; *Int'l*, pg. 265
BLINI S.A.—See Alfesca hf.; *Int'l*, pg. 315
BLOUNT FINE FOODS CORPORATION; *U.S. Private*, pg. 584
BLUMAR S. A.; *Int'l*, pg. 1075
BON SECOUR FISHERIES INC.; *U.S. Private*, pg. 612
BORNSTEIN SEAFOODS INC.; *U.S. Private*, pg. 619
BRIVAIS VILNIS AS; *Int'l*, pg. 1171
BUMBLE BEE FOODS LLC—See FCF Co., Ltd.; *Int'l*, pg. 2627
BUMBLE BEE PUERTO RICO—See FCF Co., Ltd.; *Int'l*, pg. 2627
BUMBLE BEE SEAFOODS LLC—See FCF Co., Ltd.; *Int'l*, pg. 2627
CAITO FISHERIES INC.—See Prospect Enterprises Inc.; *U.S. Private*, pg. 3287
CALIFORNIA SHELLFISH COMPANY; *U.S. Private*, pg. 720
CAMIMEX GROUP JOINT STOCK COMPANY; *Int'l*, pg. 1272
CANADIAN GOLD SEAFOOD COMPANY; *Int'l*, pg. 1283
CERVANTES CORPORATION LIMITED; *Int'l*, pg. 1423

CHAROEN POKPHAND FOODS (OVERSEAS) LLC—See Charoen Pokphand Foods Public Company Limited; *Int'l*, pg. 1452
CHINA MARINE FOOD GROUP, LTD.; *Int'l*, pg. 1517
CHINA SHENGHAI GROUP LIMITED; *Int'l*, pg. 1551
CHOTIWAT MANUFACTURING PUBLIC COMPANY LIMITED; *Int'l*, pg. 1584
CLIPPER SEAFOODS LTD.—See Bristol Bay Native Corporation; *U.S. Private*, pg. 656
COASTAL CORPORATION LIMITED; *Int'l*, pg. 1681
COAST SEAFOODS COMPANY INC.—See Dulcich, Inc.; *U.S. Private*, pg. 1286
COLDWATER SEAFOOD (UK) LIMITED—See Enterprise Investment Fund slhf.; *Int'l*, pg. 2451
COMEAUS SEA FOODS LIMITED; *Int'l*, pg. 1710
CORPESCA S.A.—See AntarChile S.A.; *Int'l*, pg. 482
COUNTRY SELECT CATFISH COMPANY II, LLC—See Consolidated Catfish Companies, LLC; *U.S. Private*, pg. 1020
CPF PREMIUM FOODS CO., LTD—See Charoen Pokphand Foods Public Company Limited; *Int'l*, pg. 1452
CUSTOM PACK, INC.—See Global Seafood Technologies; *U.S. Private*, pg. 1717
DALIAN TIANBAO GREEN FOODS CO., LTD.; *Int'l*, pg. 1952
DAYBROOK HOLDINGS INC.; *U.S. Private*, pg. 1176
DOGGER AB—See BHG Group AB; *Int'l*, pg. 1014
EAST JAPAN FOODS CO.,LTD.—See Hanwa Co., Ltd.; *Int'l*, pg. 3262
EBARA FOODS INDUSTRY, INC. - GUNMA FACTORY—See Ebara Foods Industry, Inc.; *Int'l*, pg. 2284
FERD SEAFOODS—See Ferd AS; *Int'l*, pg. 2636
FISHERMAN'S MARKET INTERNATIONAL INC.; *Int'l*, pg. 2693
FRATELLO TRADE JSC BANJA LUKA; *Int'l*, pg. 2767
FRIOSUR PESQUERA SA; *Int'l*, pg. 2793
FUJICCO CO., LTD.; *Int'l*, pg. 2820
GALAXIDI MARINE FARM S.A.; *Int'l*, pg. 2871
GLOBAL SEAFOOD TECHNOLOGIES; *U.S. Private*, pg. 1717
GODACO SEAFOOD JOINT STOCK COMPANY; *Int'l*, pg. 3018
GOURMET OCEAN PRODUCTS INC.; *Int'l*, pg. 3044
THE GREAT GOURMET, INC.; *U.S. Private*, pg. 4038
GREEN FUTURE FOOD HYDROCOLLOID MARINE SCIENCE COMPANY LIMITED; *Int'l*, pg. 3071
GRIEG SEAFOOD ASA; *Int'l*, pg. 3083
HAIKUI SEAFOOD AG; *Int'l*, pg. 3211
HAN SUNG ENTERPRISE CO., LTD. - DANGGIIN FACTORY—See Han Sung Enterprise Co., Ltd.; *Int'l*, pg. 3240
HAN SUNG ENTERPRISE CO., LTD. - GURYONGPO FACTORY—See Han Sung Enterprise Co., Ltd.; *Int'l*, pg. 3240
HAN SUNG ENTERPRISE CO., LTD.; *Int'l*, pg. 3240
HAYASHIKANE SANGYO CO., LTD.; *Int'l*, pg. 3290
HB GRANDI HF; *Int'l*, pg. 3295
HEARTLAND CATFISH COMPANY, INC.; *U.S. Private*, pg. 1899
HEARTLAND CATFISH - GREENSBORO—See Heartland Catfish Company, Inc.; *U.S. Private*, pg. 1899
HIGH LINER FOODS (USA) INCORPORATED—See High Liner Foods Incorporated; *Int'l*, pg. 3385
HILLMAN OYSTER COMPANY; *U.S. Private*, pg. 1946
HIPAC LIMITED—See Goddard Enterprises Limited; *Int'l*, pg. 3019
HOY BROS. FISH & CRAB CO. INC.—See Dulcich, Inc.; *U.S. Private*, pg. 1286
HUNGHAU HOLDINGS; *Int'l*, pg. 3535
HUNG VUONG CORPORATION; *Int'l*, pg. 3535
ICICLE SEAFOODS, INC.—See Cooke, Inc.; *Int'l*, pg. 1788
IFP TRADING LTD.—See Enterprise Investment Fund slhf.; *Int'l*, pg. 2451
INLAND SEAFOOD-CHARLOTTE—See Inland Seafood; *U.S. Private*, pg. 2079
INLAND SEAFOOD; *U.S. Private*, pg. 2079
INLAND SEAFOOD—See Inland Seafood; *U.S. Private*, pg. 2079
JOHN KEELER & CO., INC.—See Blue Star Foods Corp.; *U.S. Public*, pg. 365
KODIAK FISHMEAL COMPANY; *U.S. Private*, pg. 2336
LA CAMPAGNOLA S.A.C.I.—See Arcor Sociedad Anonima, Industrial y Comercial; *Int'l*, pg. 550
LAMONICA FINE FOODS; *U.S. Private*, pg. 2380
LEROY SEAFOOD GROUP ASA—See Austevoll Seafood ASA; *Int'l*, pg. 717
LOUISIANA FISH FRY PRODUCTS LTD.—See Peak Rock Capital LLC; *U.S. Private*, pg. 3124
LOUIS KEMP SEAFOOD COMPANY—See Trident Seafoods Corporation; *U.S. Private*, pg. 4230
LYONS SEAFOODS LIMITED—See Alfesca hf.; *Int'l*, pg. 315
MONTEREY FISH COMPANY INC.; *U.S. Private*, pg. 2776
NEPTUNE FOODS—See Red Chamber Co.; *U.S. Private*, pg. 3373
NORTHWEST SEAFOOD PROCESSORS, INC.—See Odyssey Enterprises, Inc.; *U.S. Private*, pg. 2993
NORTON SOUND ECONOMIC DEVELOPMENT CORPO-

311710 — SEAFOOD PRODUCT PRE...

RATION; *U.S. Private*, pg. 2964
NORTON SOUND SEAFOOD PRODUCTS—See Norton Sound Economic Development Corporation; *U.S. Private*, pg. 2964
OCEAN BEAUTY SEAFOODS, INC.; *U.S. Private*, pg. 2989
OCEAN GOLD SEAFOODS, INC.; *U.S. Private*, pg. 2989
OMEGA PACKING COMPANY—See Dulcich, Inc.; *U.S. Private*, pg. 1286
OMEGA PROTEIN CORPORATION—See Cooke, Inc.; *Int'l*, pg. 1788
ORIZON S.A.—See AntarChile S.A.; *Int'l*, pg. 482
PACIFIC SEAFOOD CO., INC.—See Dulcich, Inc.; *U.S. Private*, pg. 1286
PACIFIC SHRIMP COMPANY—See Dulcich, Inc.; *U.S. Private*, pg. 1286
PAMLICO PACKING COMPANY INCORPORATED; *U.S. Private*, pg. 3083
PSH GROUP HOLDINGS, INC.; *U.S. Public*, pg. 1734
SALMOLUX, INC.—See Dulcich, Inc.; *U.S. Private*, pg. 1286
SAM HAE COMMERCIAL CO., LTD.—See CJ Corporation; *Int'l*, pg. 1634
SEAFOOD PRODUCERS COOPERATIVE; *U.S. Private*, pg. 3584
SEATRADE INTERNATIONAL COMPANY, INC.—See American Holdco Inc.; *U.S. Private*, pg. 236
SEA WATCH INTERNATIONAL, LTD. - MAPPSVILLE PLANT—See Sea Watch International, Ltd.; *U.S. Private*, pg. 3583
SEA WATCH INTERNATIONAL, LTD.; *U.S. Private*, pg. 3582
SHAW'S SOUTHERN BELLE FROZEN FOODS; *U.S. Private*, pg. 3628
SOCIETE DE CONSERVERIE EN AFRIQUE S.A.—See Dongwon Enterprise Co., Ltd.; *Int'l*, pg. 2171
SOUTHERN SHELL FISH CO. INC.; *U.S. Private*, pg. 3735
SOUTHFRESH AQUACULTURE; *U.S. Private*, pg. 3736
STARKIST CO.—See Dongwon Enterprise Co., Ltd.; *Int'l*, pg. 2171
STATE FISH COMPANY INC.; *U.S. Private*, pg. 3792
TRIDENT SEAFOODS CORPORATION; *U.S. Private*, pg. 4230
TRUE WORLD FOODS INTERNATIONAL, INC.—See Family Federation for World Peace & Unification; *U.S. Private*, pg. 1469
TRUE WORLD GROUP, INC.—See Family Federation for World Peace & Unification; *U.S. Private*, pg. 1469
THE TRU SHRIMP COMPANIES, INC.; *U.S. Public*, pg. 2136
VITA FOOD PRODUCTS, INC.—See SVB Food & Beverage Co.; *U.S. Private*, pg. 3888
VITAL CHOICE SEAFOOD LLC—See 1-800-FLOWERS.COM, Inc.; *U.S. Public*, pg. 1
WASHINGTON CRAB PRODUCERS INC.—See Dulcich, Inc.; *U.S. Private*, pg. 1286
YOU WANG CO., LTD.—See Dong Won Fisheries Co., Ltd.; *Int'l*, pg. 2164

311811 — RETAIL BAKERIES

ALESSI BAKERIES, INC.; *U.S. Private*, pg. 162
ALL ROUND FOODS BAKERY PRODUCTS INC.; *U.S. Private*, pg. 172
ALWAYS BAGELS, INC.; *U.S. Private*, pg. 214
ANJOST CORP.; *U.S. Private*, pg. 284
BAB, INC.; *U.S. Public*, pg. 262
BATTER UP, LLC; *U.S. Private*, pg. 488
BAY BREAD LLC—See Starbucks Corporation; *U.S. Public*, pg. 1938
BEWLEY'S LTD.—See Campbells/Bewley Group; *Int'l*, pg. 1274
BIAGGIS RISTORANTE ITALIANO; *U.S. Private*, pg. 550
BIMBO BAKERIES USA INC.—See Grupo Bimbo, S.A.B. de C.V.; *Int'l*, pg. 3122
BREADTALK PTE LTD.—See BreadTalk Group Pte Ltd.; *Int'l*, pg. 1143
BUBBLES BAKING CO.—See Surge Private Equity LLC; *U.S. Private*, pg. 3884
CINNABON, INC.—See Roark Capital Group Inc.; *U.S. Private*, pg. 3454
CONSOLIDATED BAKERIES (JAMAICA) LTD.; *Int'l*, pg. 1770
CRESTONE GROUP BAKING COMPANIES; *U.S. Private*, pg. 1097
DES INC.; *U.S. Private*, pg. 1210
EATZI'S TEXAS BEVERAGE CORP.; *U.S. Private*, pg. 1323
EGGFREE CAKE BOX LTD.—See Cake Box Holdings plc; *Int'l*, pg. 1260
ENTEMANN'S/OROWEAT—See Grupo Bimbo, S.A.B. de C.V.; *Int'l*, pg. 3122
EVERTASTE OY—See Deutsche Lufthansa AG; *Int'l*, pg. 2066
FLOWERS BAKING CO. OF BARDSTOWN, LLC.; *U.S. Private*, pg. 1552
GIGI'S CUPCAKES—See FundCorp, Inc.; *U.S. Private*, pg. 1623
GIULIANO'S DELICATESSEN & BAKERY; *U.S. Private*, pg. 1703
GREGGS PLC; *Int'l*, pg. 3078
HEIDELBERG PASTRY SHOPPE, INC.; *U.S. Private*, pg. 1904
HILL COUNTRY BAKERY; *U.S. Private*, pg. 1945
HOMEBOY INDUSTRIES; *U.S. Private*, pg. 1972
I BATT INC.; *U.S. Private*, pg. 2020
KRISPY KREME DOUGHNUT CORPORATION—See Krispy Kreme, Inc.; *U.S. Public*, pg. 1277
KRISPY KREME UK LTD.—See Alcuin Capital Partners LLP; *Int'l*, pg. 303
LE BOULANGER INC.; *U.S. Private*, pg. 2405
LISCIO'S ITALIAN BAKERY; *U.S. Private*, pg. 2466
MAMOLO'S CONTINENTAL & BAILEY BAKERIES INC.; *U.S. Private*, pg. 2559
MONTANA MILLS BREAD CO.—See Great Harvest Franchising, Inc.; *U.S. Private*, pg. 1763
MULTIPLE REWARD SDN BHD—See Focus Point Holdings Berhad; *Int'l*, pg. 2720
THE PITTSBURGH BAGEL FACTORY INC.; *U.S. Private*, pg. 4096
PORTUGESE BAKING COMPANY LP; *U.S. Private*, pg. 3233
PRIVECO INC.; *U.S. Private*, pg. 3268
SAINT HONORE HOLDINGS CO. LTD—See Convenience Retail Asia Limited; *Int'l*, pg. 1787
SHIPLEY DO-NUT FLOUR & SUPPLY CO.—See Peak Rock Capital LLC; *U.S. Private*, pg. 3124
SHIPLEY DO-NUTS FLOUR AND SUPPLY CO.; *U.S. Private*, pg. 3637
SHOW ME BREAD, INC.; *U.S. Private*, pg. 3643
SUNBEAM COUNTRY HEARTH THRIFT STORE; *U.S. Private*, pg. 3864
TATE'S BAKE SHOP—See Mondelez International, Inc.; *U.S. Public*, pg. 1464
TRADITIONAL BAKERY INC.; *U.S. Private*, pg. 4202
TRADITIONAL BAKERY INC.—See Traditional Bakery Inc.; *U.S. Private*, pg. 4202
TRUDEAU DISTRIBUTING COMPANY; *U.S. Private*, pg. 4247
UNITED STATES BAKERY - SPRINGFIELD PLANT—See United States Bakery; *U.S. Private*, pg. 4298
UNO ALLA VOLTA, LLC.; *U.S. Private*, pg. 4310
US MARKERBOARD; *U.S. Private*, pg. 4319
VIKTOR BENES BAKERY, INC.; *U.S. Private*, pg. 4383

311812 — COMMERCIAL BAKERIES

ADEKA FOODS (ASIA) SDN. BHD.—See Adeka Corporation; *Int'l*, pg. 141
AJINOMOTO BAKERY CO., LTD.—See Ajinomoto Company, Inc.; *Int'l*, pg. 256
ALFRED NICKLES BAKERY, INC. - LIMA—See Alfred Nickles Bakery, Inc.; *U.S. Private*, pg. 165
ALFRED NICKLES BAKERY, INC.; *U.S. Private*, pg. 165
ALPINE VALLEY BREAD COMPANY—See Flowers Foods, Inc.; *U.S. Public*, pg. 854
ALVARADO STREET BAKERY; *U.S. Private*, pg. 212
AMERICAN HARVEST BAKING; *U.S. Private*, pg. 235
ANA WING FELLOWS VIE OJI CO., LTD.—See ANA Holdings Inc.; *Int'l*, pg. 444
ANDRE-BOUDIN BAKERIES INC.; *U.S. Private*, pg. 279
ARTISAN BREAD CO., LLC—See Tyson Foods, Inc.; *U.S. Public*, pg. 2209
ARYZTA AG; *Int'l*, pg. 588
ARYZTA LTD.—See ARYZTA AG; *Int'l*, pg. 588
ATKINS INC.; *U.S. Private*, pg. 369
AVANA BAKERIES LTD.—See Boparan Holdings Limited; *Int'l*, pg. 1111
AVB, INC.—See Flowers Foods, Inc.; *U.S. Public*, pg. 854
A. ZORBAS & SONS PUBLIC LTD.; *Int'l*, pg. 22
BAILEY STREET BAKERY, LLC—See Flowers Foods, Inc.; *U.S. Public*, pg. 854
BAKE CRAFTERS FOOD COMPANY; *U.S. Private*, pg. 454
BAKERY EXPRESS - MID ATLANTIC, INC.; *U.S. Private*, pg. 457
BAKERY VAN DIERMEN BV—See Boboli International, LLC; *U.S. Public*, pg. 607
BALDINGER BAKING, LP—See The Pritzker Group - Chicago, LLC; *U.S. Private*, pg. 4098
BAMA COMPANIES INC.; *U.S. Private*, pg. 463
BAVARIAN SPECIALTY FOODS LLC; *U.S. Private*, pg. 491
B.C. BUNDT, INC.; *U.S. Private*, pg. 420
BECEJSKA PEKARA A.D.; *Int'l*, pg. 936
BENSON'S, INC.; *U.S. Private*, pg. 528
BEYOND BREAD; *U.S. Private*, pg. 548
BIMBO BAKERIES USA INC. - EARTH CITY—See Grupo Bimbo, S.A.B. de C.V.; *Int'l*, pg. 3122
BIMBO BAKERIES USA INC. - FREDERICK—See Grupo Bimbo, S.A.B. de C.V.; *Int'l*, pg. 3122
BIMBO BAKERIES USA INC. - GASTONIA—See Grupo Bimbo, S.A.B. de C.V.; *Int'l*, pg. 3122
BIMBO BAKERIES USA INC. - GRAND RAPIDS—See Grupo Bimbo, S.A.B. de C.V.; *Int'l*, pg. 3122
BIMBO BAKERIES USA INC. - LA CROSSE—See Grupo Bimbo, S.A.B. de C.V.; *Int'l*, pg. 3122
BIMBO BAKERIES USA INC. - MADISON—See Grupo Bimbo, S.A.B. de C.V.; *Int'l*, pg. 3122
BIMBO BAKERIES USA INC. - MILWAUKEE—See Grupo Bimbo, S.A.B. de C.V.; *Int'l*, pg. 3122
BIMBO BAKERIES USA INC. - MONTEBELLO—See Grupo Bimbo, S.A.B. de C.V.; *Int'l*, pg. 3122
BIMBO BAKERIES USA INC. - OCONOMOWOC—See Grupo Bimbo, S.A.B. de C.V.; *Int'l*, pg. 3122
BIMBO BAKERIES USA INC. - SAINT PAUL—See Grupo Bimbo, S.A.B. de C.V.; *Int'l*, pg. 3122
BIMBO S.A.—See Grupo Bimbo, S.A.B. de C.V.; *Int'l*, pg. 3123
BLE OR—See Groupe Limagrain Holding SA; *Int'l*, pg. 3107
BUTTER KRUST BAKING COMPANY; *U.S. Private*, pg. 698
CAJOLEBEN INC.; *U.S. Private*, pg. 714
CALIFORNIA CHURROS CORP.—See J&J Snack Foods Corporation; *U.S. Public*, pg. 1179
CALISE & SONS BAKERY INC.; *U.S. Private*, pg. 721
CANADA BREAD COMPANY LTD.—See Grupo Bimbo, S.A.B. de C.V.; *Int'l*, pg. 3123
CARLISLE FOOD INC.; *U.S. Private*, pg. 764
CARLO'S BAKERY LAS VEGAS LLC—See Las Vegas Sands Corp.; *U.S. Public*, pg. 1293
CHATTANOOGA BAKERY INC.; *U.S. Private*, pg. 868
THE CHEESECAKE FACTORY BAKERY INCORPORATED—See Cheesecake Factory Incorporated; *U.S. Public*, pg. 483
CHIPITA AMERICA, INC.—See Chipita S.A.; *Int'l*, pg. 1573
CHIPITA AMERICA, INC. - TULSA—See Chipita S.A.; *Int'l*, pg. 1573
CJ BAKERY, INC.—See CJ Corporation; *Int'l*, pg. 1631
CK SALES CO., LLC—See Flowers Foods, Inc.; *U.S. Public*, pg. 854
COLE'S QUALITY FOODS, INC.; *U.S. Private*, pg. 966
COLLIN STREET BAKERY; *U.S. Private*, pg. 969
COOKIE TREE BAKERIES; *U.S. Private*, pg. 1039
CORBIN-HILL, INC.; *U.S. Private*, pg. 1047
CORPUS CHRISTI BAKING CO., LLC—See Flowers Foods, Inc.; *U.S. Public*, pg. 854
COUNTRY STYLE FOODS LIMITED; *Int'l*, pg. 1819
CRNI MARKO A.D.; *Int'l*, pg. 1851
CROWN CONFECTIONERY CO., LTD.; *Int'l*, pg. 1857
CROWN SNACK CO., LTD.—See Crown Confectionery Co., Ltd.; *Int'l*, pg. 1857
CSM DEUTSCHLAND GMBH—See Rhone Group, LLC; *U.S. Private*, pg. 3423
CSM DEUTSCHLAND GMBH—See Rhone Group, LLC; *U.S. Private*, pg. 3423
CSM FRANCE SAS—See Rhone Group, LLC; *U.S. Private*, pg. 3423
CSM HELLAS SA—See Rhone Group, LLC; *U.S. Private*, pg. 3423
CSM ITALIA S.R.L.—See Rhone Group, LLC; *U.S. Private*, pg. 3423
CSM MAGYARORSZAG KFT.—See Rhone Group, LLC; *U.S. Private*, pg. 3423
CSM (UNITED KINGDOM) LTD.—See Rhone Group, LLC; *U.S. Private*, pg. 3423
CUISINE DE FRANCE INC.—See ARYZTA AG; *Int'l*, pg. 588
CUISINE DE FRANCE LIMITED—See ARYZTA AG; *Int'l*, pg. 588
CUISINE DE FRANCE (UK) LIMITED—See ARYZTA AG; *Int'l*, pg. 588
CYRUS OLEARYS PIES INC.; *U.S. Private*, pg. 1135
DANGEE DUMS LTD.; *Int'l*, pg. 1962
DANONE ASIA PTE. LTD.—See Danone; *Int'l*, pg. 1965
DAUNAT BRETAGNE; *Int'l*, pg. 1982
DAVID WOOD BAKING LIMITED; *Int'l*, pg. 1983
DERST BAKING COMPANY, LLC—See Flowers Foods, Inc.; *U.S. Public*, pg. 854
DIANNE'S FINE DESSERTS, INC.—See Wanxiang America Capital; *U.S. Private*, pg. 4436
DISTINCTIVE FOODS LLC.; *U.S. Private*, pg. 1239
D. LAZZARONI & C. S.P.A.; *Int'l*, pg. 1900
EAST BALT COMMISSARY LLC—See Grupo Bimbo, S.A.B. de C.V.; *Int'l*, pg. 3122
EAST BALT FRANCE S.A.R.L.—See Grupo Bimbo, S.A.B. de C.V.; *Int'l*, pg. 3122
EAST BALT ITALIA S.R.L.—See Grupo Bimbo, S.A.B. de C.V.; *Int'l*, pg. 3122
EB BAKERY OF BEIJING CO., LTD.—See Grupo Bimbo, S.A.B. de C.V.; *Int'l*, pg. 3122
EB BAKERY OF SHENYANG CO., LTD.—See Grupo Bimbo, S.A.B. de C.V.; *Int'l*, pg. 3122
EB GIDA SANAYI VE TICARET LTD. SIRKETI—See Grupo Bimbo, S.A.B. de C.V.; *Int'l*, pg. 3122
ELLISON BAKERY INC.—See MidOcean Partners, LLP; *U.S. Private*, pg. 2717
ENGELMANS BAKING CO.—See Shoreline Equity Partners, LLC; *U.S. Private*, pg. 3641
ENTENMANN'S BAKERY—See Grupo Bimbo, S.A.B. de C.V.; *Int'l*, pg. 3122
ENTEMANN'S/OROWEAT—See Grupo Bimbo, S.A.B. de C.V.; *Int'l*, pg. 3122
ENTEMANN'S/OROWEAT—See Grupo Bimbo, S.A.B. de C.V.; *Int'l*, pg. 3122
EUROGERM BRASIL PRODUTOS ALIMENTICIOS LIMITADA—See Eurogerm SA; *Int'l*, pg. 2552
EUROGERM IBERIA, S.L.U.—See Eurogerm SA; *Int'l*, pg. 2552

311812 — COMMERCIAL BAKERIES

EUROGERM SOUTH AFRICA (PTY) LTD.—See Eurogerm SA; *Int'l*, pg. 2552
FABRIKA HLEBA I MLEKA A.D.; *Int'l*, pg. 2599
FAMILY BAKERY SDN. BHD.; *Int'l*, pg. 2612
FFI HOLDINGS LIMITED; *Int'l*, pg. 2649
FIERA FOODS COMPANY; *Int'l*, pg. 2660
FLETCHERS BAKERIES LIMITED—See DBAY Advisors Limited; *Int'l*, pg. 1986
FLLC LEIPURIN—See Aspo Oyj; *Int'l*, pg. 631
FLOWERS BAKERIES BRANDS, LLC—See Flowers Foods, Inc.; *U.S. Public*, pg. 854
FLOWERS BAKERIES, LLC—See Flowers Foods, Inc.; *U.S. Public*, pg. 854
FLOWERS BAKERY OF CLEVELAND, LLC—See Flowers Foods, Inc.; *U.S. Public*, pg. 854
FLOWERS BAKERY OF CROSSVILLE, LLC—See Flowers Foods, Inc.; *U.S. Public*, pg. 854
FLOWERS BAKERY OF LONDON, LLC—See Flowers Foods, Inc.; *U.S. Public*, pg. 854
FLOWERS BAKERY OF MONTGOMERY, LLC—See Flowers Foods, Inc.; *U.S. Public*, pg. 854
FLOWERS BAKERY OF TEXARKANA, LLC—See Flowers Foods, Inc.; *U.S. Public*, pg. 854
FLOWERS BAKERY OF WINSTON-SALEM, LLC—See Flowers Foods, Inc.; *U.S. Public*, pg. 854
FLOWERS BAKING CO. OF BATESVILLE, LLC—See Flowers Foods, Inc.; *U.S. Public*, pg. 854
FLOWERS BAKING CO. OF BATON ROUGE, LLC—See Flowers Foods, Inc.; *U.S. Public*, pg. 854
FLOWERS BAKING CO. OF BIRMINGHAM, LLC—See Flowers Foods, Inc.; *U.S. Public*, pg. 854
FLOWERS BAKING CO. OF BRADENTON, LLC—See Flowers Foods, Inc.; *U.S. Public*, pg. 854
FLOWERS BAKING CO. OF DENTON, LLC—See Flowers Foods, Inc.; *U.S. Public*, pg. 854
FLOWERS BAKING CO. OF EL PASO, LLC—See Flowers Foods, Inc.; *U.S. Public*, pg. 854
FLOWERS BAKING CO. OF FLORIDA, LLC—See Flowers Foods, Inc.; *U.S. Public*, pg. 854
FLOWERS BAKING CO. OF JACKSONVILLE, LLC—See Flowers Foods, Inc.; *U.S. Public*, pg. 854
FLOWERS BAKING CO. OF JAMESTOWN, LLC—See Flowers Foods, Inc.; *U.S. Public*, pg. 854
FLOWERS BAKING CO. OF KNOXVILLE, LLC—See Flowers Foods, Inc.; *U.S. Public*, pg. 854
FLOWERS BAKING CO. OF LAFAYETTE, LLC—See Flowers Foods, Inc.; *U.S. Public*, pg. 854
FLOWERS BAKING CO. OF MCDONOUGH, LLC—See Flowers Foods, Inc.; *U.S. Public*, pg. 854
FLOWERS BAKING CO. OF MEMPHIS, LLC—See Flowers Foods, Inc.; *U.S. Public*, pg. 854
FLOWERS BAKING CO. OF NEW ORLEANS, LLC—See Flowers Foods, Inc.; *U.S. Public*, pg. 854
FLOWERS BAKING CO. OF NEWTON, LLC—See Flowers Foods, Inc.; *U.S. Public*, pg. 854
FLOWERS BAKING CO. OF NORFOLK, LLC—See Flowers Foods, Inc.; *U.S. Public*, pg. 854
FLOWERS BAKING CO. OF OHIO, LLC—See Flowers Foods, Inc.; *U.S. Public*, pg. 854
FLOWERS BAKING CO. OF OPELIKA, LLC—See Flowers Foods, Inc.; *U.S. Public*, pg. 854
FLOWERS BAKING CO. OF SAN ANTONIO, LLC—See Flowers Foods, Inc.; *U.S. Public*, pg. 854
FLOWERS BAKING CO. OF TUCKER, LLC—See Flowers Foods, Inc.; *U.S. Public*, pg. 855
FLOWERS BAKING CO. OF TUSCALOOSA, LLC—See Flowers Foods, Inc.; *U.S. Public*, pg. 855
FLOWERS BAKING CO. OF TYLER, LLC—See Flowers Foods, Inc.; *U.S. Public*, pg. 855
FLOWERS BAKING CO. OF VILLA RICA, LLC—See Flowers Foods, Inc.; *U.S. Public*, pg. 855
FLOWERS FOODS SPECIALTY GROUP, LLC—See Flowers Foods, Inc.; *U.S. Public*, pg. 855
FLOWERS SPECIALTY SNACK SALES, INC.—See Flowers Foods, Inc.; *U.S. Public*, pg. 855
FRANKLIN BAKING COMPANY, LLC—See Flowers Foods, Inc.; *U.S. Public*, pg. 855
FREED'S BAKERY LLC—See Swander Pace Capital, LLC; *U.S. Private*, pg. 3890
FULLBLOOM BAKING COMPANY; *U.S. Private*, pg. 1621
GEORGE WESTON CONSUMER SERVICES—See George Weston Limited; *Int'l*, pg. 2939
GEORGE WESTON LIMITED; *Int'l*, pg. 2938
GIULIANO-PAGANO CORPORATION; *U.S. Private*, pg. 1703
GOLD CRUST BAKING COMPANY, INC.; *U.S. Private*, pg. 1727
GOLD STANDARD BAKING, INC.—See 37 Baking Holdings, LLC; *U.S. Private*, pg. 8
GOMAN BAKERIET AS—See Coop Norge SA; *Int'l*, pg. 1789
GONNELLA BAKING COMPANY; *U.S. Private*, pg. 1737
GONNELLA FROZEN PRODUCTS—See Gonnella Baking Company; *U.S. Private*, pg. 1737
GREAT CIRCLE FAMILY FOODS LLC; *U.S. Private*, pg. 1762
GREAT HARVEST FRANCHISING, INC.; *U.S. Private*, pg. 1763

GRIUL SA; *Int'l*, pg. 3087
GUNSTONES BAKERY—See Boparan Holdings Limited; *Int'l*, pg. 1111
HANKYU BAKERY CO LTD—See H2O Retailing Corp.; *Int'l*, pg. 3200
HARTFORD BAKERY, INC.—See Lewis Brothers Bakeries, Inc.; *U.S. Private*, pg. 2438
HARTFORD CPL CO-OP, INC.; *U.S. Private*, pg. 1873
HERMAN SEEKAMP INC.; *U.S. Private*, pg. 1925
HIGH-5 CONGLOMERATE BERHAD; *Int'l*, pg. 3386
HOKKAIDO-SAINT-GERMAIN CO., LTD.—See create restaurants holdings inc.; *Int'l*, pg. 1832
HOLSUM BAKERY, INC.—See Flowers Foods, Inc.; *U.S. Public*, pg. 855
HORIZON SNACK FOODS OF CAL—See Horizon Food Group, Inc.; *U.S. Private*, pg. 1980
HOSTESS BRANDS, INC.—See The J.M. Smucker Company; *U.S. Public*, pg. 2107
HOSTESS BRANDS, LLC—See The J.M. Smucker Company; *U.S. Public*, pg. 2107
H&S BAKERY INC.; *U.S. Private*, pg. 1823
HURXLEY CORPORATION; *Int'l*, pg. 3538
ICEE OF HAWAII, INC.—See J&J Snack Foods Corporation; *U.S. Public*, pg. 1179
INTERNATIONAL DELIGHTS, LLC.; *U.S. Private*, pg. 2116
JACQUELINES WHOLESALE BAKERY, INC.—See Rich Holdings, Inc.; *U.S. Private*, pg. 3426
JACQUET MILCAMPS BENELUX—See Groupe Limagrain Holding SA; *Int'l*, pg. 3107
JSB INDUSTRIES INC.; *U.S. Private*, pg. 2241
KANGAROO BRANDS, INC.; *U.S. Private*, pg. 2260
KIM & SCOTT'S, INC.; *U.S. Private*, pg. 2305
KING'S HAWAIIAN HOLDING COMPANY, INC.; *U.S. Private*, pg. 2310
KLOSTERMAN BAKING COMPANY, INC.—See New Water Capital, L.P.; *U.S. Private*, pg. 2908
KRAFT HEINZ COMPANY - RICHMOND—See 3G Capital Inc.; *U.S. Private*, pg. 11
KRAFT HEINZ COMPANY - RICHMOND—See Berkshire Hathaway Inc.; *U.S. Public*, pg. 318
KRONOS FOODS CORP.—See Entrepreneurial Equity Partners, LLC; *U.S. Private*, pg. 1406
LA BAGUETTE FRENCH BREAD & PASTRY SHOP; *U.S. Private*, pg. 2368
LA BREA BAKERY, INC.—See ARYZTA AG; *Int'l*, pg. 588
LABRIOLA BAKING COMPANY; *Int'l*, pg. 2371
LAGKAGEHUSET A/S—See FSN Capital Partners AS; *Int'l*, pg. 2799
LA MODERNA DE TOLUCA, S.A. DE C.V.—See Grupo La Moderna, S.A.B. de C.V.; *Int'l*, pg. 3131
LAWLER FOODS LTD.—See Gryphon Investors, LLC; *U.S. Private*, pg. 1798
LEELAND BAKING CO., LLC—See Flowers Foods, Inc.; *U.S. Public*, pg. 855
LEIPURIN PLC—See Aspo Oyj; *Int'l*, pg. 631
LE PAFE, INC.; *U.S. Private*, pg. 2405
LEPAGE BAKERIES, INC.—See Flowers Foods, Inc.; *U.S. Public*, pg. 854
LEWIS BAKERIES—See Lewis Brothers Bakeries, Inc.; *U.S. Private*, pg. 2438
LEWIS BROTHERS BAKERIES, INC.; *U.S. Private*, pg. 2438
LLC LEIPURIN—See Aspo Oyj; *Int'l*, pg. 631
LOU MITCHELL'S INC.; *U.S. Private*, pg. 2498
LU POLSKA S.A.—See Mondelez International, Inc.; *U.S. Public*, pg. 1463
LY BROTHERS CORPORATION; *U.S. Private*, pg. 2519
MAGNOLIA BAKERY INC.; *U.S. Private*, pg. 2548
MAPLEHURST BAKERIES, INC.—See George Weston Limited; *Int'l*, pg. 2939
MARBO PRODUCT D.O.O. BEOGRAD—See PepsiCo, Inc.; *U.S. Public*, pg. 1669
MARGO - CSM SCHWEIZ AG—See Rhone Group, LLC; *U.S. Private*, pg. 3423
MARTIN'S FAMOUS PASTRY SHOPPES - SNACK DIVISION—See Martin's Famous Pastry Shoppes; *U.S. Private*, pg. 2596
MARTIN'S FAMOUS PASTRY SHOPPES; *U.S. Private*, pg. 2596
MASADA BAKERY, LLC—See Tennessee Bun Company, LLC; *U.S. Private*, pg. 3967
MCKEE FOODS CORPORATION; *U.S. Private*, pg. 2637
MEMORY LANE CAKES LIMITED—See DBAY Advisors Limited; *Int'l*, pg. 1987
METROPOLITAN BAKING COMPANY; *U.S. Private*, pg. 2688
METTE MUNK A/S—See ARYZTA AG; *Int'l*, pg. 589
MIKAWAYA LLC—See Lakeview Capital, Inc.; *U.S. Private*, pg. 2378
MIMI'S CAFE KANSAS, INC.—See Holding Le Duff SA; *Int'l*, pg. 3450
MIMI'S CAFE OF ROGERS, INC—See Holding Le Duff SA; *Int'l*, pg. 3450
ML BREADWORKS SDN BHD—See BreadTalk Group Pte Ltd.; *Int'l*, pg. 1143
MOLINOS SANTA MARTA S.A.S.—See Grupo Nutresa S.A.; *Int'l*, pg. 3133
MONDELEZ CANADA, INC.-SCARBOROUGH—See Mondelez International, Inc.; *U.S. Public*, pg. 1462
MONDELEZ JIANGMEN FOOD CO., LTD.—See Mondelez International, Inc.; *U.S. Public*, pg. 1462
MONDELEZ MALAYSIA SDN BHD.—See Mondelez International, Inc.; *U.S. Public*, pg. 1462
MONDELEZ TURKEY GIDA URETIM A.S.—See Mondelez International, Inc.; *U.S. Public*, pg. 1464
MRS BAIRD'S BAKERIES BUSINESS TRUST; *U.S. Private*, pg. 2806
MRS. BAIRD'S BAKERIES, INC.—See Grupo Bimbo, S.A.B. de C.V.; *Int'l*, pg. 3122
MRS. CUBBISON'S KITCHEN, LLC—See The Pritzker Group - Chicago, LLC; *U.S. Private*, pg. 4099
MULTIGRAINS, INC.; *U.S. Private*, pg. 2813
NATURAL OVENS BAKERY INC.—See Alpha Baking Company, Inc.; *U.S. Private*, pg. 196
NEWBERRY SPECIALTY BAKERS, INC.; *U.S. Public*, pg. 1513
NEW ENGLAND COUNTRY PIES, INC.; *U.S. Private*, pg. 2894
THE NEW FRENCH BAKERY, INC.—See Starbucks Corporation; *U.S. Public*, pg. 1939
NEW HORIZONS BAKING COMPANY; *U.S. Private*, pg. 2897
NEWLY WEDS FOODS, INC.—See Newly Weds Foods, Inc.; *U.S. Private*, pg. 2915
NEW SOUTHWEST BAKING COMPANY; *U.S. Private*, pg. 2906
NEW YORK FROZEN FOODS INC.—See Lancaster Colony Corporation; *U.S. Public*, pg. 1291
NICKLES BAKERY, INC.—See Alfred Nickles Bakery, Inc.; *U.S. Private*, pg. 165
NIHON SHOKUZAI CO., LTD.—See Fujiya Co., Ltd.; *Int'l*, pg. 2838
NORTHEAST FOODS, INC.; *U.S. Private*, pg. 2950
NORTHERN TIER BAKERY LLC—See Marathon Petroleum Corporation; *U.S. Public*, pg. 1363
NOVELTY CO.NE CO.—See Joy Cone Company; *U.S. Private*, pg. 2238
OAKHURST INDUSTRIES; *U.S. Private*, pg. 2984
O&H DANISH BAKERY; *U.S. Private*, pg. 2977
OPTIMA S.P.A.—See BPER BANCA S.p.A; *Int'l*, pg. 1132
THE ORLANDO BAKING COMPANY INC.; *U.S. Private*, pg. 4089
OTTENBERGS BAKERS INC.; *U.S. Private*, pg. 3049
PAIN JACQUET—See Groupe Limagrain Holding SA; *Int'l*, pg. 3107
PALAGONIA BAKERY, INC.; *U.S. Private*, pg. 3076
PANOFINA AG—See Coop-Gruppe Genossenschaft; *Int'l*, pg. 1790
PAN-O-GOLD BAKING CO.; *U.S. Private*, pg. 3084
PAN PEPIN INC.; *U.S. Private*, pg. 3084
PAULAUR CORPORATION; *U.S. Private*, pg. 3114
PECHTERS BAKING GROUP LLC; *U.S. Private*, pg. 3126
PEKARNA GROSUPLJE, D.D.—See Fortenova Group d.d.; *Int'l*, pg. 2738
PENAM, A.S.—See Agrofert Holding, a.s.; *Int'l*, pg. 219
PENAM SLOVAKIA, A.S.—See Agrofert Holding, a.s.; *Int'l*, pg. 219
PEPPERIDGE FARM, INC.—See Campbell Soup Company; *U.S. Public*, pg. 427
PIANTEDOSI BAKING CO. INC.; *U.S. Private*, pg. 3175
PIECE OF CAKE, INC—See Brentwood Associates; *U.S. Private*, pg. 646
PINKS ORIGINAL BAKERY, INC.; *U.S. Private*, pg. 3184
PIONEER FROZEN FOODS LLC—See The Pritzker Group - Chicago, LLC; *U.S. Private*, pg. 4098
PLAZA SWEETS, INC.; *U.S. Private*, pg. 3213
PLECIA CO., LTD.—See Air Water Inc.; *Int'l*, pg. 240
PRAIRIE CITY BAKERY, CO.—See McKee Foods Corporation; *U.S. Private*, pg. 2637
PRETZELS, INC.—See J&J Snack Foods Corporation; *U.S. Public*, pg. 1180
P.T. MONDELEZ INDONESIA—See Mondelez International, Inc.; *U.S. Public*, pg. 1462
PURITAN BAKERY, INC.; *U.S. Private*, pg. 3306
PURITY BAKERIES—See Goddard Enterprises Limited; *Int'l*, pg. 3019
QUALITY BAKERS GROUP, INC.; *U.S. Private*, pg. 3317
THE QUALITY BAKERY CO., INC.—See Lancaster Colony Corporation; *U.S. Public*, pg. 1292
QUALITY BAKERY PRODUCTS, INC.; *U.S. Private*, pg. 3317
REBORN COFFEE, INC.; *U.S. Public*, pg. 1769
RHODES INTERNATIONAL, INC.; *U.S. Private*, pg. 3422
ROCKLAND BAKERY; *U.S. Private*, pg. 3467
ROSKAM BAKING COMPANY INC.; *U.S. Private*, pg. 3484
ROTELLAS ITALIAN BAKERY INCORPORATED; *U.S. Private*, pg. 3486
RUBICON BAKERY LLC—See Trive Capital Inc.; *U.S. Private*, pg. 4240
RUBSCHLAGER BAKING CORPORATION—See George Weston Limited; *Int'l*, pg. 2939
RUDI'S ORGANIC BAKERY, INC.—See The Hain Celestial Group, Inc.; *U.S. Public*, pg. 2087
SAINT HONORE CAKE SHOP LIMITED—See Convenience Retail Asia Limited; *Int'l*, pg. 1787

311812 — COMMERCIAL BAKERIES

SARA LEE FROZEN BAKERY, LLC—See KKR & Co. Inc.; *U.S. Public*, pg. 1263
SCHMIDT BAKING CO., INC.; *U.S. Private*, pg. 3566
SCHULZE & BURCH BISCUIT COMPANY; *U.S. Private*, pg. 3570
SCHWEBEL BAKING CO. INC.; *U.S. Private*, pg. 3572
SHANGHAI BREADTALK CO., LTD.—See BreadTalk Group Pte Ltd.; *Int'l*, pg. 1144
SIGNATURE BREADS, INC.; *U.S. Private*, pg. 3649
SISTER SCHUBERT'S HOMEMADE ROLLS, INC.—See Lancaster Colony Corporation; *U.S. Public*, pg. 1292
SOUTHERN BAKERIES, INC.—See Flowers Foods, Inc.; *U.S. Public*, pg. 854
SOUTH FLORIDA BAKERY, INC.; *U.S. Private*, pg. 3722
SOUTHWEST BAKING COMPANY, LLC.; *U.S. Private*, pg. 3738
SOUTHWEST BAKING CO.; *U.S. Private*, pg. 3738
SPECIALTY BAKERS, INC.; *U.S. Private*, pg. 3749
STECK WHOLESALE FOODS, INC.—See Tennessee Bun Company, LLC; *U.S. Private*, pg. 3967
STERLING FOODS, LLC—See Cotton Creek Capital Management LLC; *U.S. Private*, pg. 1063
STROEHMANN BAKERIES, L.C.—See Grupo Bimbo, S.A.B. de C.V.; *Int'l*, pg. 3122
STROEHMANN BAKERIES—See Grupo Bimbo, S.A.B. de C.V.; *Int'l*, pg. 3122
SUNABON LIMITED PARTNERSHIP; *U.S. Private*, pg. 3864
SUNCOAST BAKERIES, INC.—See Shoreline Equity Partners, LLC; *U.S. Private*, pg. 3641
SUNRISE BAKING CO. LLC.; *U.S. Private*, pg. 3869
SUPERIOR CAKE PRODUCTS, INC.—See KKR & Co. Inc.; *U.S. Public*, pg. 1263
SVENHARD'S SWEDISH BAKERY INC.; *U.S. Private*, pg. 3888
SWEET SISTERS, INC.; *U.S. Private*, pg. 3892
TASTY BAKING COMPANY—See Flowers Foods, Inc.; *U.S. Public*, pg. 854
TASTY BAKING OXFORD, INC.—See Flowers Foods, Inc.; *U.S. Public*, pg. 854
TASTY BLEND FOODS, INC.; *U.S. Private*, pg. 3935
TENNESSEE BUN COMPANY, LLC - DICKSON PLANT—See Tennessee Bun Company, LLC; *U.S. Private*, pg. 3967
TENNESSEE BUN COMPANY, LLC; *U.S. Private*, pg. 3967
TEXAS FRENCH BREAD INC.; *U.S. Private*, pg. 3975
TOASTMASTER DE MEXICO S.A.—See Spectrum Brands Holdings, Inc.; *U.S. Public*, pg. 1917
TOO LEIPURIN—See Aspo Oyj; *Int'l*, pg. 631
TRIBECA OVEN, INC.—See The Pritzker Group - Chicago, LLC; *U.S. Private*, pg. 4098
TWIN CITY BAGEL, INC—See Grupo Bimbo, S.A.B. de C.V.; *Int'l*, pg. 3123
ULTRAEUROPA SP. Z O.O.—See DBAY Advisors Limited; *Int'l*, pg. 1987
UNITED STATES BAKERY - PORTLAND PLANT—See United States Bakery; *U.S. Private*, pg. 4298
UNITED STATES BAKERY - SEATTLE, 6TH AVE PLANT—See United States Bakery; *U.S. Private*, pg. 4298
UNITED STATES BAKERY - SEATTLE, WELLER STREET PLANT—See United States Bakery; *U.S. Private*, pg. 4298
UNITED STATES BAKERY; *U.S. Private*, pg. 4298
WAL-BON OF OHIO, INC.; *U.S. Private*, pg. 4427
WENNER BREAD PRODUCTS, INC.—See Europastry, S.A.; *Int'l*, pg. 2555
WESTERN BAGEL BAKING CORP.; *U.S. Private*, pg. 4490
WESTON BAKERIES LIMITED—See George Weston Limited; *Int'l*, pg. 2939
WESTON FOODS (CANADA) INC.—See George Weston Limited; *Int'l*, pg. 2939
WHITE CASTLE SYSTEM, INC.-EVENDEL—See White Castle System, Inc.; *U.S. Private*, pg. 4508
YOHAY BAKING COMPANY, INC.; *U.S. Private*, pg. 4589
ZITO LUKS A.D.—See Elbisco Holding S.A.; *Int'l*, pg. 2344

311813 — FROZEN CAKES, PIES, AND OTHER PASTRIES MANUFACTURING

A-27 S.P.A.—See Emmi AG; *Int'l*, pg. 2384
ALKIS H. HADJIKYRIACOS (FROU FROU BISCUITS) PUBLIC LTD.; *Int'l*, pg. 331
ARTUSO PASTRY FOODS, CORP.; *U.S. Private*, pg. 344
ARYZTA BAKERIES DEUTSCHLAND GMBH—See ARYZTA AG; *Int'l*, pg. 588
ARYZTA FOOD SOLUTIONS GMBH—See ARYZTA AG; *Int'l*, pg. 588
ARYZTA FOOD SOLUTIONS JAPAN CO., LTD.—See ARYZTA AG; *Int'l*, pg. 589
ARYZTA FOOD SOLUTIONS SCHWEIZ AG—See ARYZTA AG; *Int'l*, pg. 588
ARYZTA POLSKA SP.Z O.O.—See ARYZTA AG; *Int'l*, pg. 588
ATHENS FOODS, INC.; *U.S. Private*, pg. 367
BACKERHAUS VEIT LTD.—See Swander Pace Capital, LLC; *U.S. Private*, pg. 3889

BETTERMOO(D) FOOD CORPORATION; *Int'l*, pg. 1004
BOOSH PLANT-BASED BRANDS INC.; *Int'l*, pg. 1111
BOROMIR PROD SA BUZAU; *Int'l*, pg. 1114
BREADTALK CONCEPT HONG KONG LIMITED—See BreadTalk Group Pte Ltd.; *Int'l*, pg. 1143
BREADTALK INTERNATIONAL PTE. LTD.—See BreadTalk Group Pte Ltd.; *Int'l*, pg. 1143
BRIDOR FRANCE—See Holding Le Duff SA; *Int'l*, pg. 3450
BRIDOR INC.—See Holding Le Duff SA; *Int'l*, pg. 3450
BROWN SUGAR BAKERY & CAFE, INC.; *U.S. Private*, pg. 669
BURRY FOODS; *U.S. Private*, pg. 692
CAFE VALLEY INC.—See Swander Pace Capital, LLC; *U.S. Private*, pg. 3889
CAMPBELLS CAKE COMPANY LTD.—See DBAY Advisors Limited; *Int'l*, pg. 1986
C&G HOLDINGS, INC.—See Flowers Foods, Inc.; *U.S. Public*, pg. 854
CHARTER BAKING COMPANY, INC.—See The Hain Celestial Group, Inc.; *U.S. Public*, pg. 2086
CHRISTINE INTERNATIONAL HOLDINGS LIMITED; *Int'l*, pg. 1587
CPRAM CO., LTD.—See C.P. All Public Company Limited; *Int'l*, pg. 1243
CRUMBS BROADWAY LLC—See Fisher Enterprises, LLC; *U.S. Private*, pg. 1534
CRUMBS COLUMBUS LLC—See Fisher Enterprises, LLC; *U.S. Private*, pg. 1534
CRUMBS FEDERAL STREET, LLC—See Fisher Enterprises, LLC; *U.S. Private*, pg. 1534
CRUMBS GARMENT CENTER LLC—See Fisher Enterprises, LLC; *U.S. Private*, pg. 1534
CRUMBS GRAND CENTRAL LLC—See Fisher Enterprises, LLC; *U.S. Private*, pg. 1534
CRUMBS LEXINGTON LLC—See Fisher Enterprises, LLC; *U.S. Private*, pg. 1534
CRUMBS TIMES SQUARE LLC—See Fisher Enterprises, LLC; *U.S. Private*, pg. 1534
CRUMBS UNION SQUARE LLC—See Fisher Enterprises, LLC; *U.S. Private*, pg. 1534
CRUMBS UNION STATION LLC—See Fisher Enterprises, LLC; *U.S. Private*, pg. 1534
CSM BAKERY PRODUCTS - COLTON—See Rhone Group, LLC; *U.S. Private*, pg. 3423
CSM BAKERY SUPPLIES GIDA SAN. VE TIC. A.S—See Rhone Group, LLC; *U.S. Private*, pg. 3423
CSM BENELUX NV—See Rhone Group, LLC; *U.S. Private*, pg. 3423
DEIORIO FOODS, INC.—See LSCG Management, Inc.; *U.S. Private*, pg. 2508
DELICE DE FRANCE LIMITED; *Int'l*, pg. 2013
DE-LUXE FOOD SERVICES SDN. BHD.—See Envictus International Holdings Limited; *Int'l*, pg. 2453
DOBOJKA A.D.; *Int'l*, pg. 2153
ELI'S CHEESECAKE COMPANY; *U.S. Private*, pg. 1360
EMMI DESSERT ITALIA S.P.A—See Emmi AG; *Int'l*, pg. 2384
THE FATHER'S TABLE, LLC.; *U.S. Private*, pg. 4028
FB SOLUTION SAS—See Holding Le Duff SA; *Int'l*, pg. 3450
FINSBURY FOOD GROUP PLC—See DBAY Advisors Limited; *Int'l*, pg. 1986
FLOWERS BAKING CO. OF DENVER, LLC—See Flowers Foods, Inc.; *U.S. Public*, pg. 854
FLOWERS BAKING CO. OF HENDERSON, LLC—See Flowers Foods, Inc.; *U.S. Public*, pg. 854
FLOWERS BAKING CO. OF MODESTO, LLC—See Flowers Foods, Inc.; *U.S. Public*, pg. 854
FLOWERS BAKING CO. OF ORLANDO, LLC—See Flowers Foods, Inc.; *U.S. Public*, pg. 854
FLOWERS BAKING CO. OF THOMASVILLE, LLC—See Flowers Foods, Inc.; *U.S. Public*, pg. 855
FOOD REPUBLIC TAIWAN CO., LTD.—See BreadTalk Group Pte Ltd.; *Int'l*, pg. 1143
FORNETTI KFT—See ARYZTA AG; *Int'l*, pg. 588
FRESH START BAKERIES INDUSTRIAL LTDA—See ARYZTA AG; *Int'l*, pg. 588
FRICOPAN GMBH—See ARYZTA AG; *Int'l*, pg. 589
GALAXY DESSERTS; *U.S. Private*, pg. 1636
GENERAL MILLS ISRAEL LTD.—See General Mills, Inc.; *U.S. Public*, pg. 922
GOURMET BAKER, INC.—See Swander Pace Capital, LLC; *U.S. Private*, pg. 3890
GOYO FOODS INDUSTRY CO., LTD.; *Int'l*, pg. 3045
HEINEMANN'S BAKERIES L.L.C.; *U.S. Private*, pg. 1904
HIESTAND DEUTSCHLAND GMBH—See ARYZTA AG; *Int'l*, pg. 589
HIESTAND MALAYSIA SDN BHD—See ARYZTA AG; *Int'l*, pg. 589
HIESTAND & SUHR HANDELS UND LOGISTIK GMBH—See ARYZTA AG; *Int'l*, pg. 588
HILL & VALLEY, INC.—See J&J Snack Foods Corporation; *U.S. Public*, pg. 1179
HOM/ADE FOODS, INC.—See J&J Snack Foods Corporation; *U.S. Public*, pg. 1179
HYDRACT A/S; *Int'l*, pg. 3546
JAMES SKINNER BAKING COMPANY; *U.S. Private*, pg. 2185
J&J SNACK FOODS CORP. OF NEW JERSEY—See J&J Snack Foods Corporation; *U.S. Public*, pg. 1180
J&J SNACK FOODS TRANSPORT CORP.—See J&J Snack Foods Corporation; *U.S. Public*, pg. 1180
J.R BIRKETT AND SONS LIMITED—See Greggs plc; *Int'l*, pg. 3078
JTM FOODS, LLC—See Tenex Capital Management, L.P.; *U.S. Private*, pg. 3966
JUST DESSERTS, INC.—See Trive Capital Inc.; *U.S. Private*, pg. 4240
KAMPS GMBH—See Holding Le Duff SA; *Int'l*, pg. 3450
KAMPS INTERNATIONAL—See Holding Le Duff SA; *Int'l*, pg. 3450
KATE'S CAKES LTD—See Rhone Group, LLC; *U.S. Private*, pg. 3423
KELLANOVA CANADA INC.—See Kellanova; *U.S. Public*, pg. 1217
KELLOGG CONVENIENCE FOOD PLANT—See WK Kellogg Co; *U.S. Public*, pg. 2376
LEAGEL S.R.L.—See International Flavors & Fragrances Inc.; *U.S. Public*, pg. 1153
LIGHTBODY GROUP LTD.—See DBAY Advisors Limited; *Int'l*, pg. 1987
MEL-O-CREAM DONUTS INTERNATIONAL, INC.; *U.S. Private*, pg. 2661
MONDELEZ KINH DO VIETNAM JSC—See Mondelez International, Inc.; *U.S. Public*, pg. 1464
NEW YORK BAKERY COMPANY LIMITED—See Grupo Bimbo, S.A.B. de C.V.; *Int'l*, pg. 3123
NICHOLAS & HARRIS LTD.—See DBAY Advisors Limited; *Int'l*, pg. 1987
NORTH AMERICA CEREAL CO.—See Kellanova; *U.S. Public*, pg. 1218
PRE PAIN B.V.—See ARYZTA AG; *Int'l*, pg. 589
PRODUCTOS RICH S.A. DE C.V. - OCOYOACAC MANUFACTURING FACILITY—See Rich Holdings, Inc.; *U.S. Private*, pg. 3426
PRODUCTOS RICH S.A. DE C.V.—See Rich Holdings, Inc.; *U.S. Private*, pg. 3426
PURAC THAILAND LTD—See Corbion N.V.; *Int'l*, pg. 1795
RICH BAKERY PRODUCTS (TIANJIN) CO., LTD.—See Rich Holdings, Inc.; *U.S. Private*, pg. 3426
RICH DE ARGENTINA S.A.—See Rich Holdings, Inc.; *U.S. Private*, pg. 3427
RICH DE COLOMBIA S.A.S.—See Rich Holdings, Inc.; *U.S. Private*, pg. 3427
RICH DO BRASIL LTDA.—See Rich Holdings, Inc.; *U.S. Private*, pg. 3427
RICH GRAVISS PRODUCTS PVT. LTD. - KALA AMB MANUFACTURING FACILITY—See Rich Holdings, Inc.; *U.S. Private*, pg. 3426
RICH PRODUCTS AUSTRALIA PTY LTD.—See Rich Holdings, Inc.; *U.S. Private*, pg. 3426
RICH PRODUCTS CORPORATION - ARLINGTON MANUFACTURING FACILITY—See Rich Holdings, Inc.; *U.S. Private*, pg. 3426
RICH PRODUCTS CORPORATION - BROWNSVILLE MANUFACTURING FACILITY—See Rich Holdings, Inc.; *U.S. Private*, pg. 3426
RICH PRODUCTS CORPORATION - BRUNSWICK MANUFACTURING FACILITY—See Rich Holdings, Inc.; *U.S. Private*, pg. 3426
RICH PRODUCTS CORPORATION - BURLINGTON MANUFACTURING FACILITY—See Rich Holdings, Inc.; *U.S. Private*, pg. 3426
RICH PRODUCTS CORPORATION - EAGAN MANUFACTURING FACILITY—See Rich Holdings, Inc.; *U.S. Private*, pg. 3426
RICH PRODUCTS CORPORATION - FOUNTAIN INN MANUFACTURING FACILITY—See Rich Holdings, Inc.; *U.S. Private*, pg. 3426
RICH PRODUCTS CORPORATION - FRESNO MANUFACTURING FACILITY—See Rich Holdings, Inc.; *U.S. Private*, pg. 3426
RICH PRODUCTS CORPORATION - HILLIARD MANUFACTURING FACILITY—See Rich Holdings, Inc.; *U.S. Private*, pg. 3427
RICH PRODUCTS CORPORATION - MORRISTOWN MANUFACTURING FACILITY—See Rich Holdings, Inc.; *U.S. Private*, pg. 3427
RICH PRODUCTS CORPORATION - MURFREESBORO MANUFACTURING FACILITY—See Rich Holdings, Inc.; *U.S. Private*, pg. 3427
RICH PRODUCTS CORPORATION - NEW BRITAIN MANUFACTURING FACILITY—See Rich Holdings, Inc.; *U.S. Private*, pg. 3427
RICH PRODUCTS CORPORATION - NILES MANUFACTURING FACILITY—See Rich Holdings, Inc.; *U.S. Private*, pg. 3427
RICH PRODUCTS CORPORATION - ROCHESTER MANUFACTURING FACILITY—See Rich Holdings, Inc.; *U.S. Private*, pg. 3427
RICH PRODUCTS CORPORATION - SANTA ANA MANUFACTURING FACILITY—See Rich Holdings, Inc.; *U.S. Private*, pg. 3427
RICH PRODUCTS CORPORATION - SANTA FE SPRINGS - BUSCH PLACE MANUFACTURING FACILITY—See Rich Holdings, Inc.; *U.S. Private*, pg. 3427
RICH PRODUCTS CORPORATION - UNION CITY MANU-

N.A.I.C.S. INDEX

311824 — DRY PASTA, DOUGH, A...

FACTURING FACILITY—See Rich Holdings, Inc.; *U.S. Private*, pg. 3427
RICH PRODUCTS CORPORATION - WAYCROSS MANUFACTURING FACILITY—See Rich Holdings, Inc.; *U.S. Private*, pg. 3427
RICH PRODUCTS CORP. - SOUTH AFRICA—See Rich Holdings, Inc.; *U.S. Private*, pg. 3426
RICH PRODUCTS GIDA SANAYI VE TICARET LIMITED SIRKETI—See Rich Holdings, Inc.; *U.S. Private*, pg. 3427
RICH PRODUCTS LIMITED - KIDDERMINSTER MANUFACTURING FACILITY—See Rich Holdings, Inc.; *U.S. Private*, pg. 3427
RICH PRODUCTS LIMITED—See Rich Holdings, Inc.; *U.S. Private*, pg. 3427
RICH PRODUCTS LIMITED—See Rich Holdings, Inc.; *U.S. Private*, pg. 3427
RICH PRODUCTS MANUFACTURING (THAILAND) CO., LTD.—See Rich Holdings, Inc.; *U.S. Private*, pg. 3426
RICH PRODUCTS (M) SDN. BHD.—See Rich Holdings, Inc.; *U.S. Private*, pg. 3426
RICH PRODUCTS OF CANADA, LTD. - FORT ERIE MANUFACTURING FACILITY—See Rich Holdings, Inc.; *U.S. Private*, pg. 3427
RICH PRODUCTS OF CANADA, LTD.—See Rich Holdings, Inc.; *U.S. Private*, pg. 3427
RICH PRODUCTS (SUZHOU) CO., LTD.—See Rich Holdings, Inc.; *U.S. Private*, pg. 3426
RICH PRODUCTS (SUZHOU) CO., LTD. - SUZHOU PLANT MANUFACTURING FACILITY—See Rich Holdings, Inc.; *U.S. Private*, pg. 3426
SCHWAN'S BAKERY INC—See The Schwan Food Company; *U.S. Private*, pg. 4115
SHANGHAI INSTANTWHIP FOODS CO., LTD.—See Rich Holdings, Inc.; *U.S. Private*, pg. 3427
STEVEN ROBERTS ORIGINAL DESSERTS LLC.; *U.S. Private*, pg. 3808
SWEET STREET DESSERTS INC.; *U.S. Private*, pg. 3892
THIOLAT PACKAGING SA—See Groupe Guillin SA; *Int'l*, pg. 3104
TOOTIE PIE COMPANY, INC.; *U.S. Private*, pg. 4186
WHOLESOME HARVEST BAKING LLC—See Grupo Bimbo, S.A.B. de C.V.; *Int'l*, pg. 3123
WICKED GOOD CUPCAKES LLC—See Sun Capital Partners, Inc.; *U.S. Private*, pg. 3859

311821 — COOKIE AND CRACKER MANUFACTURING

ADM MILLING LIMITED—See Archer-Daniels-Midland Company; *U.S. Public*, pg. 182
ADM WILD NAUEN GMBH—See Archer-Daniels-Midland Company; *U.S. Public*, pg. 183
ALIMENTOS CARNICOS S.A.S.—See Grupo Nutresa S.A.; *Int'l*, pg. 3133
AMOS & CONNORS, INC.; *U.S. Private*, pg. 264
BAHLSEN GMBH & CO. KG; *Int'l*, pg. 800
BALOCCO S.P.A.; *Int'l*, pg. 810
BANGAS LIMITED; *Int'l*, pg. 832
BAPTISTA'S BAKERY, INC.—See Campbell Soup Company; *U.S. Public*, pg. 427
BASIC GRAIN PRODUCTS INC.; *U.S. Private*, pg. 485
BISCOMERICA CORP.; *U.S. Private*, pg. 565
BISCUITS LECLERC LTD.; *Int'l*, pg. 1049
BODEANS WAFER COMPANY, LLC; *U.S. Private*, pg. 607
BOURBON CORPORATION; *Int'l*, pg. 1120
BRAHMAPUTRA CRACKER AND POLYMER LTD.—See GAIL (India) Limited; *Int'l*, pg. 2869
BREMNER FOOD GROUP, INC.—See Conagra Brands, Inc.; *U.S. Public*, pg. 563
BROWNIE BRITTLE, LLC—See CapVest Limited; *Int'l*, pg. 1318
BUD'S BEST COOKIES, INC.; *U.S. Private*, pg. 679
BYRD COOKIE CO.; *U.S. Private*, pg. 700
CALIHAN PORK PROCESSORS, INC.—See Rosens Diversified, Inc.; *U.S. Private*, pg. 3484
CAMPBELL ARNOTTS LIMITED—See Campbell Soup Company; *U.S. Public*, pg. 426
CANUELAS MILL S.A.C.I.F.I.A; *Int'l*, pg. 1300
CHAMPADOR; *Int'l*, pg. 1439
CHARLIE'S SPECIALTIES INC.—See Byrnes & Kiefer Company; *U.S. Private*, pg. 701
CHERYL & CO.—See 1-800-FLOWERS.COM, Inc.; *U.S. Public*, pg. 1
CHICAGO BAR COMPANY LLC—See WK Kellogg Co; *U.S. Public*, pg. 2376
THE CHRISTIE COOKIE COMPANY—See Rich Holdings, Inc.; *U.S. Private*, pg. 3427
CJ BEIJING BAKERY CO., LTD.—See CJ Corporation; *Int'l*, pg. 1631
COMMERCIAL BAKERIES CORP.—See The Graham Group, Inc.; *U.S. Private*, pg. 4036
CONDOR CORP.; *U.S. Private*, pg. 1012
CONTINENTAL BAKERIES B.V.—See Silverfern Capital Management, LLC; *U.S. Private*, pg. 3663
CONTINENTAL BAKERIES B.V.—See The Goldman Sachs Group, Inc.; *U.S. Public*, pg. 2076

COOKIE KINGDOM INC.; *U.S. Private*, pg. 1039
CORNU SAS FONTAIN—See Cornu S.A.; *Int'l*, pg. 1801
CORNU S.A.; *Int'l*, pg. 1801
COUNTRY FRESH BATTER INC.; *U.S. Private*, pg. 1067
COUNTRYSIDE BAKING COMPANY, INC.—See Dawn Food Products, Inc.; *U.S. Private*, pg. 1175
DADDY RAY'S, INC.—See J&J Snack Foods Corporation; *U.S. Public*, pg. 1179
DANONE INDUSTRIA—See Danone; *Int'l*, pg. 1968
DARE FOODS LIMITED; *Int'l*, pg. 1972
DELYSE, INC.; *U.S. Private*, pg. 1202
FABRICA DE GALLETAS LA MODERNA, S.A. DE C.V.—See Grupo La Moderna, S.A.B. de C.V.; *Int'l*, pg. 3131
FAIRFIELD GOURMET FOOD CORP.; *U.S. Private*, pg. 1463
FAMOUS AMOS CHOCOLATE CHIP COOKIE CO., LLC—See Ferrero International S.A.; *Int'l*, pg. 2641
FOX'S BISCUITS LTD.—See Boparan Holdings Limited; *Int'l*, pg. 1111
FOX'S BISCUITS - PRESTON—See Boparan Holdings Limited; *Int'l*, pg. 1111
FOX'S BISCUITS - STAFFORDSHIRE—See Boparan Holdings Limited; *Int'l*, pg. 1111
GANSO CO., LTD.; *Int'l*, pg. 2881
THE GOLD CORPORATION; *U.S. Private*, pg. 4033
GOOD FORTUNES EAST, LLC—See Hilton Grand Vacations Inc.; *U.S. Public*, pg. 1039
GORJI BISCUIT COMPANY; *Int'l*, pg. 3043
GRIESSON DE BEUKELAER GMBH & CO. KG—See Danone; *Int'l*, pg. 1968
GRIESSON DE BEUKELAER OSTERREICH GMBH—See Danone; *Int'l*, pg. 1968
GRUPO GAMESA S. DE R.L. DE C.V—See PepsiCo, Inc.; *U.S. Public*, pg. 1670
GRUPO NUTRESA S.A.; *Int'l*, pg. 3133
GRUPO SIRO S.L.; *Int'l*, pg. 3135
GUENTHER BAKERIES UK LIMITED—See The Pritzker Group - Chicago, LLC; *U.S. Private*, pg. 4098
HAITAI CONFECTIONERY AND FOODS CO.,LTD. - DAGUE FACTORY—See Haitai Confectionery And Foods Co.,ltd.; *Int'l*, pg. 3217
HEARTHSIDE FOOD SOLUTIONS, LLC - MCCOMB—See Charlesbank Capital Partners, LLC; *U.S. Private*, pg. 855
HUP SENG INDUSTRIES BERHAD; *Int'l*, pg. 3537
HUP SENG PERUSAHAAN MAKANAN (M) SDN. BHD.—See Hup Seng Industries Berhad; *Int'l*, pg. 3538
HWA TAI FOOD INDUSTRIES (SABAH) SDN.BHD.—See Hwa Tai Industries Berhad; *Int'l*, pg. 3541
HWA TAI INDUSTRIES BERHAD - BATU PAHAT FACTORY—See Hwa Tai Industries Berhad; *Int'l*, pg. 3541
HWA TAI INDUSTRIES BERHAD; *Int'l*, pg. 3541
INTERBAKE FOODS LLC—See George Weston Limited; *Int'l*, pg. 2939
JOY CONE COMPANY; *U.S. Private*, pg. 2238
JOY CONE COMPANY - WESTERN FACILITY—See Joy Cone Company; *U.S. Private*, pg. 2238
KELLOGG CO. - COOKIES & SNACKS BUSINESS—See Ferrero International S.A.; *Int'l*, pg. 2640
KELSEN GROUP A/S—See Ferrero International S.A.; *Int'l*, pg. 2641
KRAFT MART—See AGCO Inc.; *U.S. Public*, pg. 126
LATE JULY SNACKS LLC; *U.S. Private*, pg. 2396
LU BISCUITS-BARCELONA—See Mondelez International, Inc.; *U.S. Public*, pg. 1463
LU GENERAL BISCUITS BELGIE N.V.—See Mondelez International, Inc.; *U.S. Public*, pg. 1463
LU GENERAL BISCUITS NEDERLAND B.V.—See Mondelez International, Inc.; *U.S. Public*, pg. 1463
MANISCHEWITZ COMPANY—See R.A.B. Holdings, Inc.; *U.S. Private*, pg. 3334
MARY'S GONE CRACKERS; *U.S. Private*, pg. 2599
MISSION FOODS (MALAYSIA) SDN. BHD.—See Gruma, S.A.B. de C.V.; *Int'l*, pg. 3114
MONDELEZ CHILE S.A.—See Mondelez International, Inc.; *U.S. Public*, pg. 1462
MONDELEZ ESPANA BISCUITS HOLDINGS Y CAMPANIA S.C.—See Mondelez International, Inc.; *U.S. Public*, pg. 1463
MONDELEZ ESPANA GALLETAS PRODUCTION, S.L.U.—See Mondelez International, Inc.; *U.S. Public*, pg. 1463
MONDELEZ EUROPEAN BUSINESS SERVICES CENTRE S.R.O.—See Mondelez International, Inc.; *U.S. Public*, pg. 1463
MONDELEZ FRANCE BISCUITS PRODUCTION SAS—See Mondelez International, Inc.; *U.S. Public*, pg. 1463
MONDELEZ NAMUR PRODUCTION SPRL—See Mondelez International, Inc.; *U.S. Public*, pg. 1463
MONDELEZ SCHWEIZ PRODUCTION GMBH—See Mondelez International, Inc.; *U.S. Public*, pg. 1463
MONDELEZ SHANGHAI FOOD CO., LTD.—See Mondelez International, Inc.; *U.S. Public*, pg. 1463
MONDELEZ SLOVAKIA S.R.O.—See Mondelez International, Inc.; *U.S. Public*, pg. 1463
MONDELEZ SUZHOU FOOD CO., LTD.—See Mondelez International, Inc.; *U.S. Public*, pg. 1462

MONDELEZ TAIWAN LIMITED—See Mondelez International, Inc.; *U.S. Public*, pg. 1462
MONDELEZ URUGUAY S.A.—See Mondelez International, Inc.; *U.S. Public*, pg. 1462
MRS. FIELDS GIFTS, INC.—See Capricorn Holdings, Inc.; *U.S. Private*, pg. 745
MRS. FIELDS' ORIGINAL COOKIES, INC.—See Capricorn Holdings, Inc.; *U.S. Private*, pg. 745
MURRAY BISCUIT COMPANY, L.L.C.—See Ferrero International S.A.; *Int'l*, pg. 2641
NEW DESSERTS; *U.S. Private*, pg. 2893
NONNI'S FOODS LLC—See Vestar Capital Partners, LLC; *U.S. Private*, pg. 4372
NONNI'S FOODS LLC—See Wind Point Advisors LLC; *U.S. Private*, pg. 4534
OPAVIA LU S.R.O.—See Mondelez International, Inc.; *U.S. Public*, pg. 1464
PARATI INDUSTRIA E COMERCIO DE ALIMENTOS LTDA—See Kellanova; *U.S. Public*, pg. 1218
PETRI BAKING PRODUCTS, INC.—See Conagra Brands, Inc.; *U.S. Public*, pg. 564
PHENIX GOURMET, LLC.; *U.S. Private*, pg. 3167
PINE VALLEY FOODS, INC.; *U.S. Private*, pg. 3183
POLAR BEVERAGE INC.; *U.S. Private*, pg. 3223
POZUELO, S.A.—See Ebro Foods S.A.; *Int'l*, pg. 2287
P.T. MONDELEZ INDONESIA MANUFACTURING—See Mondelez International, Inc.; *U.S. Public*, pg. 1462
ROLAND MURTEN AG—See Cornu S.A.; *Int'l*, pg. 1801
ROOTFRUIT SCANDINAVIA AB—See FMCG Business Partner AB; *Int'l*, pg. 2717
ROVIRA BISCUIT CORPORATION; *U.S. Private*, pg. 3490
SAIWA S.R.L.—See Mondelez International, Inc.; *U.S. Public*, pg. 1463
SELMA'S COOKIES, INC.—See Byrd Cookie Co.; *U.S. Private*, pg. 700
SHARPAK AYLESHAM LTD.—See Groupe Guillin SA; *Int'l*, pg. 3104
S-L SNACKS LOGISTICS, LLC—See Campbell Soup Company; *U.S. Public*, pg. 427
SMITH COOKIE COMPANY—See United States Bakery; *U.S. Private*, pg. 4298
SNYDER'S-LANCE, INC.—See Campbell Soup Company; *U.S. Public*, pg. 427
TROUSDALE LIMITED—See The Pritzker Group - Chicago, LLC; *U.S. Private*, pg. 4098
UNITED BAKING CO., INC.; *U.S. Private*, pg. 4288
VOORTMAN COOKIES LIMITED—See The J.M. Smucker Company; *U.S. Public*, pg. 2107
WALKERS SNACK FOODS LIMITED—See PepsiCo, Inc.; *U.S. Public*, pg. 1672
WESTMINSTER CRACKER COMPANY, INC.—See LSCG Management, Inc.; *U.S. Private*, pg. 2509

311824 — DRY PASTA, DOUGH, AND FLOUR MIXES MANUFACTURING FROM PURCHASED FLOUR

ACI PURE FLOUR LIMITED—See Advanced Chemical Industries Limited; *Int'l*, pg. 158
ADM MILLING CO.—See Archer-Daniels-Midland Company; *U.S. Public*, pg. 182
AGAINST THE GRAIN GOURMET LLC—See HumanCo LLC; *U.S. Private*, pg. 2006
ALB-GOLD TEIGWAREN GMBH; *Int'l*, pg. 292
AL DENTE PASTA COMPANY—See ALB-GOLD Teigwaren GmbH; *Int'l*, pg. 292
AMERICAN ITALIAN PASTA COMPANY—See Conagra Brands, Inc.; *U.S. Public*, pg. 563
AMERICAN QUALITY FOODS; *U.S. Private*, pg. 245
ARCHER DANIELS MIDLAND CO.—See Archer-Daniels-Midland Company; *U.S. Public*, pg. 183
A. ZEREGA'S SONS, INC.; *U.S. Private*, pg. 24
BAKEMARK INGREDIENTS-CANADA LTD.—See Rhone Group, LLC; *U.S. Private*, pg. 3423
BAKE 'N JOY FOODS INC.; *U.S. Private*, pg. 454
BARILLA AMERICA, INC.—See Barilla Holding S.p.A.; *Int'l*, pg. 865
BRAZI BITES LLC—See San Francisco Equity Partners; *U.S. Private*, pg. 3540
CARLAS PASTA INC.—See Tribe 9 Foods LLC; *U.S. Private*, pg. 4227
CONTINENTAL MILLS, INC.; *U.S. Private*, pg. 1030
CSM BAKERY PRODUCTS - MINNETONKA—See Rhone Group, LLC; *U.S. Private*, pg. 3423
DAKOTA GROWERS PASTA COMPANY, INC.—See Post Holdings, Inc.; *U.S. Public*, pg. 1703
DANUBIUS D.O.O. NOVI SAD—See Delta Holding; *Int'l*, pg. 2018
DARI COUSPATE S.A; *Int'l*, pg. 1972
DAWN FOOD PRODUCTS, INC.; *U.S. Private*, pg. 1175
DAWN FOODS B.V.—See Dawn Food Products, Inc.; *U.S. Private*, pg. 1175
DAYLIGHT DONUT FLOUR COMPANY LLC.; *U.S. Private*, pg. 1177
ELIS BREAD (ELI ZABAR) INC.; *U.S. Private*, pg. 1360
EUROPASTRY, S.A.; *Int'l*, pg. 2555
FLOUR MILLS C. SARANTOPOULOS S.A.; *Int'l*, pg. 2708

311824 — DRY PASTA, DOUGH, A...

FRATELLI DE CECCO DI FILIPPO FARA SAN MARTINO S.P.A.; *Int'l*, pg. 2766
FRY KRISP COMPANY; *U.S. Private*, pg. 1618
FUJIAN ANJOY FOODS CO LTD; *Int'l*, pg. 2817
GAC SUPPLY, LLC—See Fog Cutter Capital Group Inc.; *U.S. Private*, pg. 1557
GILSTER-MARY LEE CORPORATION; *U.S. Private*, pg. 1701
LITTLE CROW FOODS; *U.S. Private*, pg. 2468
NATIONAL BISCUITS & CONFECTIONERY COMPANY LTD.—See Hayel Saeed Anam Group of Companies; *Int'l*, pg. 3291
NATIONAL NOODLE INC.; *U.S. Private*, pg. 2860
NEW CARBON CO, LLC—See Arbor Private Investment Company, LLC; *U.S. Private*, pg. 309
NEWLY WEDS FOODS, INC.; *U.S. Private*, pg. 2915
NEWLY WEDS FOODS, INC.—See Newly Weds Foods, Inc.; *U.S. Private*, pg. 2915
NEW WORLD PASTA COMPANY—See Ebro Foods S.A.; *Int'l*, pg. 2287
NEW WORLD PASTA COMPANY—See Ebro Foods S.A.; *Int'l*, pg. 2287
NOODLES BY LEONARDO INC.; *U.S. Private*, pg. 2934
PASTA GALA SA—See Coop-Gruppe Genossenschaft; *Int'l*, pg. 1790
PASTAS COMARRICO S.A.S.—See Ihlas Holding A.S.; *Int'l*, pg. 3606
PHILADELPHIA MACARONI CO. INC.; *U.S. Private*, pg. 3169
PIZZA BLENDS INC.—See The Pritzker Group - Chicago, LLC; *U.S. Private*, pg. 4098
PORT CITY BAKERY INC.; *U.S. Private*, pg. 3230
PRODUCTOS ALIMENTICIOS LA MODERNA, S.A. DE C.V.—See Grupo La Moderna, S.A.B. de C.V.; *Int'l*, pg. 3131
READY BAKE FOODS INC.—See George Weston Limited; *Int'l*, pg. 2939
RHINO FOODS INC.; *U.S. Private*, pg. 3421
RUSTIC CRUST; *U.S. Private*, pg. 3507
SASKO PASTA (PTY) LTD—See PepsiCo, Inc.; *U.S. Public*, pg. 1672
SHENANDOAH MILLS, INC.; *U.S. Private*, pg. 3632
T. R. RIZZUTO PIZZA CRUST, INC.—See Rich Holdings, Inc.; *U.S. Private*, pg. 3427

311830 — TORTILLA MANUFACTURING

AREVALO'S TORTILLIARIA INC.; *U.S. Private*, pg. 318
AZTECA FOODS, INCORPORATED; *U.S. Private*, pg. 416
BERBER FOOD MANUFACTURING INC.; *U.S. Private*, pg. 529
BIMBO BAKERIES USA INC. - FORT WORTH—See Grupo Bimbo, S.A.B. de C.V.; *Int'l*, pg. 3122
EL MILAGRO INCORPORATED; *U.S. Private*, pg. 1349
EXQUISITA TORTILLAS INC.; *U.S. Private*, pg. 1452
GRUMA CORPORATION—See Gruma, S.A.B. de C.V.; *Int'l*, pg. 3114
GRUMA NETHERLANDS B.V.—See Gruma, S.A.B. de C.V.; *Int'l*, pg. 3114
GRUMA OCEANIA PTY. LTD.—See Gruma, S.A.B. de C.V.; *Int'l*, pg. 3114
LA BONITA OLE, INC.; *U.S. Private*, pg. 2368
LA ESPIGA DE ORO TORTILLA FACTORY; *U.S. Private*, pg. 2368
LA RANCHERA INC.; *U.S. Private*, pg. 2369
LA REINA COMPANY; *U.S. Private*, pg. 2369
LAROSA TORTILLA FACTORY; *U.S. Private*, pg. 2392
LA TAPATIA - NORCAL, INC.; *U.S. Private*, pg. 2369
LEO'S FOODS, INC.—See Flowers Foods, Inc.; *U.S. Public*, pg. 855
MANUEL VILLA ENTERPRISES INC.; *U.S. Private*, pg. 2567
MESA FOODS, LLC—See TruArc Partners, L.P.; *U.S. Private*, pg. 4246
NDF AZTECA MILLING EUROPE SRL—See Gruma, S.A.B. de C.V.; *Int'l*, pg. 3114
PUENTES BROTHERS INC.; *U.S. Private*, pg. 3302
ROBERT BERBER & SON INCORPORATED; *U.S. Private*, pg. 3457
ROMERO'S FOOD PRODUCTS, INCORPORATED; *U.S. Private*, pg. 3476
RUDY'S FOOD PRODUCTS, INC.—See TruArc Partners, L.P.; *U.S. Private*, pg. 4246
RUIZ MEXICAN FOODS INC.; *U.S. Private*, pg. 3503
SMOKEWOOD FOODS; *U.S. Private*, pg. 3698
TORTILLA KING INC.; *U.S. Private*, pg. 4190
ZAO SOLNTSE MEXICO—See Gruma, S.A.B. de C.V.; *Int'l*, pg. 3114

311911 — ROASTED NUTS AND PEANUT BUTTER MANUFACTURING

ALGOOD FOOD COMPANY; *U.S. Private*, pg. 166
A.L. SCHUTZMAN COMPANY INC.; *U.S. Private*, pg. 27
AMERICAN BLANCHING COMPANY—See Post Holdings, Inc.; *U.S. Public*, pg. 1703
BEER NUTS, INC.; *U.S. Private*, pg. 514
CAMILLA PECAN COMPANY; *U.S. Private*, pg. 729
CAMSON SEEDS LTD.; *Int'l*, pg. 1275
CLEMENTS NUT CO.—See Clements Foods Company; *U.S. Private*, pg. 940
COOP NORGE KAFFE AS—See Coop Norge SA; *Int'l*, pg. 1789
DIAMOND FOODS, LLC—See Campbell Soup Company; *U.S. Public*, pg. 427
EASTERN PRODUCE SOUTH AFRICA (PTY) LIMITED—See Camellia Plc; *Int'l*, pg. 1271
FES INDUSTRIES PTE LTD—See Food Empire Holdings Limited; *Int'l*, pg. 2727
FUTURE CORPORATION PTE LTD—See Food Empire Holdings Limited; *Int'l*, pg. 2727
GARUDAFOOD PUTRA PUTRI JAYA; *Int'l*, pg. 2886
GOLDEN BOY FOODS LTD.—See Post Holdings, Inc.; *U.S. Public*, pg. 1703
GOLDEN PEANUT ARGENTINA S.A.—See Archer-Daniels-Midland Company; *U.S. Public*, pg. 185
HAMMONS PRODUCTS COMPANY; *U.S. Private*, pg. 1850
HARVEST MANOR FARMS LLC—See Conagra Brands, Inc.; *U.S. Public*, pg. 564
HAZELNUT GROWERS OF OREGON; *U.S. Private*, pg. 1886
HH BIOTECHNOLOGY HOLDINGS COMPANY; *Int'l*, pg. 3378
ILLINOIS FOUNDATION SEEDS INC.; *U.S. Private*, pg. 2042
JIMBO'S JUMBOS—See Conagra Brands, Inc.; *U.S. Public*, pg. 564
JOHN B. SANFILIPPO & SON, INC.; *U.S. Public*, pg. 1190
JUSTIN'S LLC—See Hormel Foods Corporation; *U.S. Public*, pg. 1054
KANAN ENTERPRISES, INC.; *U.S. Private*, pg. 2259
KENLAKE FOODS—See The Kroger Co.; *U.S. Public*, pg. 2108
KING HENRY'S INC.; *U.S. Private*, pg. 2309
THE LEAVITT CORPORATION; *U.S. Private*, pg. 4068
LEAVITT INTERNATIONAL (FSC CORP.)—See The Leavitt Corporation; *U.S. Private*, pg. 4068
MELLACE FAMILY BRANDS, INC.; *U.S. Private*, pg. 2662
NUNHEMS FRANCE S.A.R.L.—See Bayer Aktiengesellschaft; *Int'l*, pg. 903
ONCE AGAIN NUT BUTTER COLLECTIVE INC.; *U.S. Private*, pg. 3019
ORIGINAL NUT HOUSE—See Conagra Brands, Inc.; *U.S. Public*, pg. 564
PEANUT BUTTER & CO.; *U.S. Private*, pg. 3125
PERFECT BAR, LLC—See Mondelez International, Inc.; *U.S. Public*, pg. 1464
PRIESTER PECAN CO., INC.; *U.S. Private*, pg. 3260
SAN SABA PECAN, INC.; *U.S. Private*, pg. 3542
SETTONS INTERNATIONAL FOODS, INC; *U.S. Private*, pg. 3618
SNAK CLUB, INC.—See Insignia Capital Group, L.P.; *U.S. Private*, pg. 2091
SUNGOLD FOOD INC.—See ACOMO N.V.; *Int'l*, pg. 108
TARA FOODS—See The Kroger Co.; *U.S. Public*, pg. 2109
TROPHY NUT CO.; *U.S. Private*, pg. 4242
YOUNG PECAN - LAS CRUCES PROCESSING PLANT—See King Ranch, Inc.; *U.S. Private*, pg. 2310

311919 — OTHER SNACK FOOD MANUFACTURING

ALIMENTS KRISPY KERNELS INC; *Int'l*, pg. 328
AMBO AGRITEC LIMITED; *Int'l*, pg. 415
AMERICAN IMPORTING COMPANY, INC.—See TreeHouse Foods, Inc.; *U.S. Public*, pg. 2187
AMERICOLD BARCELONA PALAU S.A.—See Americold Realty Trust, Inc.; *U.S. Public*, pg. 113
AMERICOLD FORWARDING AGENCY B.V.—See Americold Realty Trust, Inc.; *U.S. Public*, pg. 113
AMERICOLD LEIXOES UNIPESSOAL LDA—See Americold Realty Trust, Inc.; *U.S. Public*, pg. 113
AMERICOLD MAASVLAKTE B.V.—See Americold Realty Trust, Inc.; *U.S. Public*, pg. 113
AMERICOLD SINES UNIPESSOAL LDA.—See Americold Realty Trust, Inc.; *U.S. Public*, pg. 113
AMERICOLD URK B.V.—See Americold Realty Trust, Inc.; *U.S. Public*, pg. 113
AMERICOLD VALENCIA S.L.U.—See Americold Realty Trust, Inc.; *U.S. Public*, pg. 113
AMPLIFY SNACK BRANDS, INC.—See The Hershey Co.; *U.S. Public*, pg. 2088
ANITA'S MEXICAN FOODS CORP.—See La Reina Company; *U.S. Private*, pg. 2369
ARNOTT'S BISCUITS LTD.—See Campbell Soup Company; *U.S. Public*, pg. 426
ARNOTT'S NEW ZEALAND LIMITED—See Campbell Soup Company; *U.S. Public*, pg. 426
ASSOCIATED BRANDS INDUSTRIES LIMITED - BISCUIT DIVISION—See Associated Brands Industries Limited; *Int'l*, pg. 648
ASSOCIATED BRANDS INDUSTRIES LIMITED; *Int'l*, pg. 648
AUSTIN QUALITY FOODS, INC.—See Kellanova; *U.S. Public*, pg. 1217
BACK TO NATURE FOODS COMPANY, LLC—See B&G Foods, Inc.; *U.S. Public*, pg. 260
BAKER BOY; *U.S. Private*, pg. 455
BAKERS BEST SNACK FOOD CORP.—See J&J Snack Foods Corporation; *U.S. Public*, pg. 1179
BAKERS BEST TROTTER—See J&J Snack Foods Corporation; *U.S. Public*, pg. 1179
BAKLAWA MADE BETTER INVESTMENTS LLC—See Agthia Group PJSC; *Int'l*, pg. 222
BALLREICH SNACK FOOD COMPANY—See Grippo Potato Chip Company, Inc.; *U.S. Private*, pg. 1790
BAMBI-BANAT AD; *Int'l*, pg. 813
BARE FRUIT LLC; *U.S. Private*, pg. 474
BARREL O'FUN SNACK FOODS CO.—See KLN Enterprises, Inc.; *U.S. Private*, pg. 2320
BESTORE CO., LTD.; *Int'l*, pg. 1000
BETTER MADE SNACK FOODS INC.; *U.S. Private*, pg. 546
BETTY LOU'S, INC.; *U.S. Private*, pg. 547
BIKAJI FOODS INTERNATIONAL LIMITED; *Int'l*, pg. 1022
BJC FOODS (MALAYSIA) SDN. BHD.—See Berli Jucker Public Co. Ltd.; *Int'l*, pg. 985
BLUEBIRD FOODS LIMITED—See PepsiCo, Inc.; *U.S. Public*, pg. 1668
BLUE DINOSAUR PTY. LTD.—See Forbidden Foods Limited; *Int'l*, pg. 2729
BRANCHOUT FOOD INC.; *U.S. Public*, pg. 380
BREZELBACKEREI DITSCH GMBH—See Fomento Economico Mexicano, S.A.B. de C.V.; *Int'l*, pg. 2724
BT BRANDS, INC.; *U.S. Public*, pg. 409
BUHLER FARMILA VIETNAM LTD.—See Buhler AG; *Int'l*, pg. 1212
BUHLER LIMITED—See Buhler AG; *Int'l*, pg. 1212
BUHLER LTD.—See Buhler AG; *Int'l*, pg. 1212
BUHLER PAKISTAN (PVT.) LTD.—See Buhler AG; *Int'l*, pg. 1212
BUHLER VIETNAM COMPANY LIMITED—See Buhler AG; *Int'l*, pg. 1212
CALBEE AMERICA, INC.—See Calbee, Inc.; *Int'l*, pg. 1261
CALBEE GROUP (UK) LIMITED—See Calbee, Inc.; *Int'l*, pg. 1261
CALBEE, INC.; *Int'l*, pg. 1261
CALBEE MOH SENG PTE., LTD.—See Calbee, Inc.; *Int'l*, pg. 1261
CALBEE NORTH AMERICA, LLC—See Calbee, Inc.; *Int'l*, pg. 1261
CALIFORNIA PRETZEL COMPANY—See Conagra Brands, Inc.; *U.S. Public*, pg. 564
CAMBRIDGE SHARPE, INC.; *U.S. Private*, pg. 727
CAPE COD POTATO CHIP COMPANY INC.—See Campbell Soup Company; *U.S. Public*, pg. 427
CENTURY SNACKS, LLC—See Insignia Capital Group, L.P.; *U.S. Private*, pg. 2091
CHARKDELIKATESSER PRODUKTION AB—See Atria Plc; *Int'l*, pg. 694
CHIPITA LEFCO LLC—See Chipita S.A.; *Int'l*, pg. 1573
CHIPSY FOR FOOD INDUSTRIES SAE (CHIPSY)—See PepsiCo, Inc.; *U.S. Public*, pg. 1668
CHIRAG AFRICA LIMITED—See Flame Tree Group Holdings Ltd.; *Int'l*, pg. 2698
C.J. VITNER CO.—See Snak King Corp.; *U.S. Private*, pg. 3699
CLEM SNACKS INC.—See Utz Brands, Inc.; *U.S. Public*, pg. 2267
COCINA AUTENTICA, LLC—See PepsiCo, Inc.; *U.S. Public*, pg. 1668
COMERCIALIZADORA NACIONAL SAS LTDA.—See PepsiCo, Inc.; *U.S. Public*, pg. 1668
CONAGRA FOODS LTD.—See Conagra Brands, Inc.; *U.S. Public*, pg. 563
CONDOR SNACK COMPANY; *U.S. Private*, pg. 1012
CONSOLIDATED SNACKS INC.; *U.S. Private*, pg. 1022
CORINA SNACKS LIMITED—See PepsiCo, Inc.; *U.S. Public*, pg. 1670
CORNFIELDS, INC.—See Kelso & Company, L.P.; *U.S. Private*, pg. 2278
DAESUNG MACHINERY—See Mondelez International, Inc.; *U.S. Public*, pg. 1461
DALI FOODS GROUP CO. LTD.; *Int'l*, pg. 1951
DARK GREEN AUSTRALIA PTY LIMITED—See PepsiCo, Inc.; *U.S. Public*, pg. 1668
DENALI FLAVORS, INC.; *U.S. Private*, pg. 1204
DFM FOODS LIMITED; *Int'l*, pg. 2095
DITSCH USA LLC—See Fomento Economico Mexicano, S.A.B. de C.V.; *Int'l*, pg. 2724
DOC POPCORN FRANCHISING, INC.; *U.S. Private*, pg. 1251
ENJOY LIFE NATURAL BRANDS, LLC—See Mondelez International, Inc.; *U.S. Public*, pg. 1461
EUROPEAN FOOD—See European Drinks S.A.; *Int'l*, pg. 2556
EVANS FOOD GROUP LTD.—See Wind Point Advisors LLC; *U.S. Private*, pg. 4534
FATTORIE OSELLA S.P.A.—See Mondelez International, Inc.; *U.S. Public*, pg. 1461
FEDERAL PRETZEL BAKING COMPANY, LLC—See J&J Snack Foods Corporation; *U.S. Public*, pg. 1179

N.A.I.C.S. INDEX

311920 — COFFEE AND TEA MANU...

FLAGSTONE FOODS INC.—See Atlas Holdings, LLC; *U.S. Private*, pg. 376
FLODOR S.A.S.; *Int'l*, pg. 2707
FOOD SHOULD TASTE GOOD, INC.; *U.S. Private*, pg. 1561
FOUR SEAS MERCANTILE HOLDINGS LIMITED; *Int'l*, pg. 2755
FRITO-LAY-CHARLOTTE—See PepsiCo, Inc.; *U.S. Public*, pg. 1670
FRITO-LAY DE CHILE—See PepsiCo, Inc.; *U.S. Public*, pg. 1670
FRITO-LAY, INC.—See PepsiCo, Inc.; *U.S. Public*, pg. 1670
FRITO-LAY NORTH AMERICA, INC.—See PepsiCo, Inc.; *U.S. Public*, pg. 1670
FRITO-LAY TRADING COMPANY (EUROPE) GMBH—See PepsiCo, Inc.; *U.S. Public*, pg. 1670
GAMESA S. DE R.L. DE C.V.—See PepsiCo, Inc.; *U.S. Public*, pg. 1670
GARDETTO'S BAKERY, INC.—See General Mills, Inc.; *U.S. Public*, pg. 921
GEORGIA NUT COMPANY; *U.S. Private*, pg. 1684
GINBIS FOUR SEAS FOODS (SHANTOU) COMPANY LIMITED—See Four Seas Mercantile Holdings Limited; *Int'l*, pg. 2755
GLICO ASIA PACIFIC PTE. LTD—See Ezaki Glico Co., Ltd.; *Int'l*, pg. 2593
GOLDEN ENTERPRISES INC.—See Utz Brands, Inc.; *U.S. Public*, pg. 2268
GOLDEN FLAKE SNACK FOODS, INC.—See Utz Brands, Inc.; *U.S. Public*, pg. 2268
GOURMET FOOD NEW ZEALAND LTD.—See Mondelez International, Inc.; *U.S. Public*, pg. 1461
GRANDE FOODS CALIFORNIA CORPORATION; *U.S. Private*, pg. 1753
GREAT AMERICAN FOODS, INC—See Alliance Global Group, Inc.; *Int'l*, pg. 339
GRENADE (UK) LTD.—See Mondelez International, Inc.; *U.S. Public*, pg. 1461
GRIPPO POTATO CHIP COMPANY, INC.; *U.S. Private*, pg. 1790
GU, RENSOW LTD.; *Int'l*, pg. 3152
HAITAI CONFECTIONERY AND FOODS CO.,LTD. - CHONGJU FACTORY—See Haitai Confectionery And Foods Co.,ltd.; *Int'l*, pg. 3217
HERR FOODS INC.; *U.S. Private*, pg. 1926
HOUSTON HARVEST GIFT PRODUCTS LLC—See Marvin Traub Associates, Inc.; *U.S. Private*, pg. 2598
HUMPTY DUMPTY SNACK FOODS, INC.—See Old Dutch Foods, Inc.; *U.S. Private*, pg. 3008
HUP SRL—See Mondelez International, Inc.; *U.S. Public*, pg. 1461
INTERNATIONAL FOODSOURCE LLC.; *U.S. Private*, pg. 2117
JAG SPECIALTY FOODS, LLC.; *U.S. Private*, pg. 2181
JAPAN FRITO-LAY LTD.—See Calbee, Inc.; *Int'l*, pg. 1261
J&D SNACKS INC.—See Utz Brands, Inc.; *U.S. Public*, pg. 2267
J&J SNACK FOODS CORP. OF CALIFORNIA—See J&J Snack Foods Corporation; *U.S. Public*, pg. 1180
J & J SNACK FOODS INVESTMENT CORP.—See J&J Snack Foods Corporation; *U.S. Public*, pg. 1179
KANRO FOUR SEAS FOODS (SHANTOU) COMPANY LIMITED—See Four Seas Mercantile Holdings Limited; *Int'l*, pg. 2755
KAR NUT PRODUCTS COMPANY—See Palladium Equity Partners, LLC; *U.S. Private*, pg. 3077
KETTLE FOODS, INC.—See Campbell Soup Company; *U.S. Public*, pg. 427
KITCHEN COOKED, INC.—See Utz Brands, Inc.; *U.S. Public*, pg. 2268
KJELDSENS LIMITED—See Campbell Soup Company; *U.S. Public*, pg. 427
KJS INDIA PRIVATE LIMITED—See Mondelez International, Inc.; *U.S. Public*, pg. 1461
KLN ENTERPRISES INC.; *U.S. Private*, pg. 2320
LEGACY BAKEHOUSE, LLC—See Benford Capital Partners, LLC; *U.S. Private*, pg. 526
LENNY & LARRY'S; *U.S. Private*, pg. 2422
LI FOOK (QINGDAO) FOODS COMPANY LIMITED—See Four Seas Mercantile Holdings Limited; *Int'l*, pg. 2755
MARS MAGYARORSZAG ERTEKESITO BT.—See Mars, Incorporated; *U.S. Private*, pg. 2589
MARS PF FRANCE—See Mars, Incorporated; *U.S. Private*, pg. 2590
MARTINS POTATO CHIPS INC.; *U.S. Private*, pg. 2597
MASDAR AL HAYAT FOR FOOD INDUSTRIES, LTD.—See Ali Abdullah Al Tamimi Company; *Int'l*, pg. 319
MATUTANO-SOCIEDADE DE PRODUTOS ALIMENTARES, UNIPESOAL LDA.—See PepsiCo, Inc.; *U.S. Public*, pg. 1660
MCCLEARY INC.; *U.S. Private*, pg. 2628
MEDALLION FOODS, INC.—See Conagra Brands, Inc.; *U.S. Public*, pg. 564
MIKESELL'S POTATO CHIP CO.; *U.S. Private*, pg. 2726
MONDELEZ NEDERLAND B.V.—See Mondelez International, Inc.; *U.S. Public*, pg. 1464
MONDELEZ PAKISTAN LIMITED—See Mondelez International, Inc.; *U.S. Public*, pg. 1464
MONDELEZ POLSKA PRODUCTION SP. Z.O.O.—See Mondelez International, Inc.; *U.S. Public*, pg. 1464
NATIONAL BRANDS LIMITED—See AVI Limited; *Int'l*, pg. 740
NATIONAL BRANDS LIMITED—See AVI Limited; *Int'l*, pg. 740
NATIONAL BRANDS LIMITED—See AVI Limited; *Int'l*, pg. 740
NATIONAL BRANDS LIMITED—See AVI Limited; *Int'l*, pg. 740
NATIONAL PRETZEL COMPANY—See Conagra Brands, Inc.; *U.S. Public*, pg. 564
NATURAL FOOD WORKS, LLC—See Campbell Soup Company; *U.S. Public*, pg. 427
NELLSON NUTRACEUTICAL, LLC—See Kohlberg & Company, LLC; *U.S. Private*, pg. 2338
NETBRANDS CORP.; *U.S. Public*, pg. 1507
NEW YORK PRETZEL, LLC—See J&J Snack Foods Corporation; *U.S. Public*, pg. 1180
NICO FOUR SEAS (SHANTOU) COMPANY LIMITED—See Four Seas Mercantile Holdings Limited; *Int'l*, pg. 2755
NIGHTFOOD HOLDINGS, INC.; *U.S. Public*, pg. 1528
OLD DUTCH FOODS, INC.; *U.S. Private*, pg. 3008
OLD LYME GOURMET COMPANY; *U.S. Private*, pg. 3009
PALMEX ALIMENTOS SA DE CV—See Wind Point Advisors LLC; *U.S. Private*, pg. 4534
P.B.I. FRUIT JUICE COMPANY BVBA—See PepsiCo, Inc.; *U.S. Public*, pg. 1669
PEELED INC; *U.S. Private*, pg. 3128
PEPSICO AMERICAS FOODS—See PepsiCo, Inc.; *U.S. Public*, pg. 1670
PEPSICO DO BRASIL LTDA.—See PepsiCo, Inc.; *U.S. Public*, pg. 1671
PEPSICO EESTI—See PepsiCo, Inc.; *U.S. Public*, pg. 1671
PEPSICO FOODS CANADA - PETERBOROUGH PLANT—See PepsiCo, Inc.; *U.S. Public*, pg. 1671
PEPSICO FOODS CANADA—See PepsiCo, Inc.; *U.S. Public*, pg. 1671
PEPSICO IRELAND FOOD & BEVERAGES—See PepsiCo, Inc.; *U.S. Public*, pg. 1671
PEPSI-COLA MEXICANA, S. DE R.L. DE C.V.—See PepsiCo, Inc.; *U.S. Public*, pg. 1669
PEPSI FOODS PRIVATE LIMITED—See PepsiCo, Inc.; *U.S. Public*, pg. 1669
PIM BRANDS, LLC—See Promotion In Motion, Inc.; *U.S. Private*, pg. 3283
PIPERS CRISPS LIMITED—See PepsiCo, Inc.; *U.S. Public*, pg. 1671
POPCHIPS, INC.—See VMG Partners, LLC; *U.S. Private*, pg. 4408
THE POPCORN FACTORY, INC.—See 1-800-FLOWERS.COM, Inc.; *U.S. Public*, pg. 1
PORKIE COMPANY OF WISCONSIN—See Pork King Good; *U.S. Private*, pg. 3229
PORK KING GOOD; *U.S. Private*, pg. 3229
PREFERRED POPCORN LLC; *U.S. Private*, pg. 3248
PRETZELS, INC.—See Peak Rock Capital LLC; *U.S. Private*, pg. 3124
PRIME CHOICE FOODS, INC.; *U.S. Private*, pg. 3261
PRODUCTOS INDUSTRIALIZADOS SALTILLO, S. DE R.L. DE C.V.—See PepsiCo, Inc.; *U.S. Public*, pg. 1671
QUAKER OATS LIMITED—See PepsiCo, Inc.; *U.S. Public*, pg. 1670
QUEST NUTRITION, LLC—See The Simply Good Foods Company; *U.S. Public*, pg. 2130
READING BAKERY SYSTEMS, INC.—See Markel Group Inc.; *U.S. Public*, pg. 1369
RICO'S PRODUCTS COMPANY INC—See Liberto Specialty Company Inc.; *U.S. Private*, pg. 2443
RUDOLPH FOODS COMPANY - DALLAS FACILITY—See Rudolph Foods Company; *U.S. Private*, pg. 3502
RUDOLPH FOODS COMPANY - LAWRENCEVILLE FACILITY—See Rudolph Foods Company; *U.S. Private*, pg. 3502
RUDOLPH FOODS COMPANY - NEW HEBRON FACILITY—See Rudolph Foods Company; *U.S. Private*, pg. 3502
RUDOLPH FOODS COMPANY - SAN BERNARDINO FACILITY—See Rudolph Foods Company; *U.S. Private*, pg. 3502
RUDOLPH FOODS COMPANY; *U.S. Private*, pg. 3502
SABRA DIPPING COMPANY LLC—See PepsiCo, Inc.; *U.S. Public*, pg. 1670
SABRITAS, S.A. DE R.L. DE C.V.—See PepsiCo, Inc.; *U.S. Public*, pg. 1670
SAHALE SNACKS, INC.—See The J.M. Smucker Company; *U.S. Public*, pg. 2107
SAKATA RICE SNACKS AUSTRALIA PTY LTD—See PepsiCo, Inc.; *U.S. Public*, pg. 1671
SAVOR STREET FOODS INC.; *U.S. Private*, pg. 3557
SECOND NATURE SNACKS, INC—See CapVest Limited; *Int'l*, pg. 1318
SHANGHAI PEPSICO SNACKS COMPANY LIMITED—See PepsiCo, Inc.; *U.S. Public*, pg. 1671
SHEARER'S FOODS, LLC—See Clayton, Dubilier & Rice, LLC; *U.S. Private*, pg. 927
SHENZHEN MATCHLESS FOOD CO., LTD—See Four Seas Mercantile Holdings Limited; *Int'l*, pg. 2755
SMAKEN AV GRIMSTAD AS—See IKM Gruppen AS; *Int'l*, pg. 3612
SMITHS FOOD GROUP, B.V.—See PepsiCo, Inc.; *U.S. Public*, pg. 1672
THE SMITH'S SNACKFOOD COMPANY—See PepsiCo, Inc.; *U.S. Public*, pg. 1670
SNACK FACTORY, LLC—See Campbell Soup Company; *U.S. Public*, pg. 427
SNACK VENTURES S.A.—See PepsiCo, Inc.; *U.S. Public*, pg. 1672
SNAK KING CORP.; *U.S. Private*, pg. 3699
SNIKIDDY LLC; *U.S. Private*, pg. 3700
SNYDER OF BERLIN - CANAL FULTON DIVISION—See Utz Brands, Inc.; *U.S. Public*, pg. 2268
SNYDER OF BERLIN—See Utz Brands, Inc.; *U.S. Public*, pg. 2268
SOUTH GEORGIA PECAN COMPANY INC.; *U.S. Private*, pg. 3722
STACY'S PITA CHIP COMPANY, INC.—See PepsiCo, Inc.; *U.S. Public*, pg. 1670
STRETCH ISLAND FRUIT SALES L.L.C.—See Ferrero International S.A.; *Int'l*, pg. 2641
STRYVE FOODS, INC.; *U.S. Public*, pg. 1958
SUGAR CREEK FOODS INTERNATIONAL, INC.; *U.S. Private*, pg. 3849
TASTY FOODS S.A.—See PepsiCo, Inc.; *U.S. Public*, pg. 1672
THRIVE 365 LLC—See Mondelez International, Inc.; *U.S. Public*, pg. 1464
TROYER POTATO PRODUCTS, INC.—See Hanover Foods Corporation; *U.S. Public*, pg. 984
TSAKIRIS S.A.—See Coca-Cola HBC AG; *Int'l*, pg. 1686
TSUN FAT (HUI ZHOU) BISCUIT FACTORY LIMITED—See Four Seas Mercantile Holdings Limited; *Int'l*, pg. 2755
TURKEY CREEK PORK SKINS, LLC—See Wind Point Advisors LLC; *U.S. Private*, pg. 4534
TYRRELLS POTATO CRISPS LTD.—See The Hershey Co.; *U.S. Public*, pg. 2088
TYSON MEXICAN ORIGINAL, INC.—See Tyson Foods, Inc.; *U.S. Public*, pg. 2210
UAB LITHUANIAN SNACKS—See PepsiCo, Inc.; *U.S. Public*, pg. 1672
UNCLE RAY'S, LLC—See The H.T. Hackney Company; *U.S. Private*, pg. 4041
UTZ QUALITY FOODS, LLC—See Utz Brands, Inc.; *U.S. Public*, pg. 2268
VELOCITY SNACK BRANDS—See VMG Partners, LLC; *U.S. Private*, pg. 4408
VEURNE SNACK FOODS BVBA—See PepsiCo, Inc.; *U.S. Public*, pg. 1672
WARNOCK FOOD PRODUCTS, INC.—See Calbee, Inc.; *Int'l*, pg. 1261
WHITEFEATHER FOODS INC.—See Rudolph Foods Company; *U.S. Private*, pg. 3502
WIMBLE MANUFACTURING BELGIUM BVBA—See Kellanova; *U.S. Public*, pg. 1218
WISE FOODS, INC.—See Arca Continental, S.A.B. de C.V.; *Int'l*, pg. 540
WRIGLEY CONFECTIONS CR, KOM. SPOL.—See Mars, Incorporated; *U.S. Private*, pg. 2591
WYANDOT INC.; *U.S. Private*, pg. 4575
XTRAPACK LIMITED—See Mondelez International, Inc.; *U.S. Public*, pg. 1464
ZAKLADY TLUSZOZOWE W BODACZOWIE SP.Z.O.O.—See Glencore plc; *Int'l*, pg. 2991
ZAPP'S POTATO CHIPS, INC.; *U.S. Private*, pg. 4598

311920 — COFFEE AND TEA MANUFACTURING

AGROINDUSTRIAS ARRIBA DEL ECUADOR, AGROARRIBA S.A.—See Ecom Agroindustrial Corporation Ltd.; *Int'l*, pg. 2295
AGROINDUSTRIAS UNIDAS DE MEXICO S.A. DE C.V. (AMSA)—See Ecom Agroindustrial Corporation Ltd.; *Int'l*, pg. 2295
ALGODONERA GUARANI S.A.—See Ecom Agroindustrial Corporation Ltd.; *Int'l*, pg. 2296
ALLANN BROS. COFFEE, INC.; *U.S. Private*, pg. 174
ALOIS DALLMAYR KAFFEE OHG—See Alois Dallmayr KG; *Int'l*, pg. 365
ALOIS DALLMAYR KG; *Int'l*, pg. 365
AMERICAN COFFEE COMPANY, INC.; *U.S. Private*, pg. 227
AMERICAN PREMIUM WATER CORPORATION; *U.S. Public*, pg. 108
AMGOORIE INDIA LIMITED—See Camellia Plc; *Int'l*, pg. 1271
ANCORA COFFEE & TEA; *U.S. Private*, pg. 275
APEEJAY SURRENDRA GROUP LTD.; *Int'l*, pg. 508
ASIAN TEA & EXPORTS LIMITED; *Int'l*, pg. 619
ASPINWALL & CO. LTD., - COFFEE DIVISION—See Aspinwall & Co. Ltd.,; *Int'l*, pg. 630
ASSAM COMPANY INDIA LIMITED—See BRS Ventures Investment Ltd; *Int'l*, pg. 1199
ATLANTIC COMMODITIES VIETNAM LTD—See Ecom Agroindustrial Corporation Ltd.; *Int'l*, pg. 2296

311920 — COFFEE AND TEA MANU... CORPORATE AFFILIATIONS

N.A.I.C.S. Index

ATLANTIC (USA), INC., USA—See Ecom Agroindustrial Corporation Ltd.; *Int'l*, pg. 2296
AVT TEA SERVICES NORTH AMERICA LLC—See AVT Natural Products Ltd.; *Int'l*, pg. 751
B & A LIMITED; *Int'l*, pg. 783
BARISTAS COFFEE COMPANY, INC.; *U.S. Public*, pg. 276
BARRIE HOUSE COFFEE CO. INC.; *U.S. Private*, pg. 480
BEIJING G.E.O. COFFEE CO., LTD.—See Dynam Japan Holdings, Co., Ltd.; *Int'l*, pg. 2239
BEIJING OUTSELL HEALTH PRODUCT DEVELOPMENT CO., LTD.; *Int'l*, pg. 955
BEIJING STARBUCKS COFFEE COMPANY LTD.—See Starbucks Corporation; *U.S. Public*, pg. 1938
BENGAL TEA & FABRICS LTD; *Int'l*, pg. 974
BESUNYEN HOLDINGS COMPANY LIMITED; *Int'l*, pg. 1001
BLACK RIFLE COFFEE COMPANY LLC—See BRC Inc.; *U.S. Public*, pg. 380
BOGAWANTALAWA TEA CEYLON (PVT) LTD.—See Bogawantalawa Tea Estates PLC; *Int'l*, pg. 1100
BOGAWANTALAWA TEA ESTATES PLC; *Int'l*, pg. 1100
BONGO JAVA ROASTING CO.; *U.S. Private*, pg. 614
BOSTONBEAN COFFEE CO., INC.; *U.S. Private*, pg. 622
BOYD COFFEE COMPANY—See Farmer Brothers Co.; *U.S. Public*, pg. 821
BREWSTER'S FRANCHISE CORPORATION—See BAB, Inc.; *U.S. Public*, pg. 262
CADILLAC COFFEE COMPANY; *U.S. Private*, pg. 713
CAFE BRITT—See Grupo Britt N.V.; *Int'l*, pg. 3123
CAFES DE ESPECIALIDAD DE CHIAPAS, S.A.P.I. DE C.V—See Ecom Agroindustrial Corporation Ltd.; *Int'l*, pg. 2296
CAFE SOLUVEL BRASILIA SA; *Int'l*, pg. 1250
CAFETALERA AMAZONICA SAC—See Ecom Agroindustrial Corporation Ltd.; *Int'l*, pg. 2296
CAFETALERA DEL PACIFICO S.A DE C.V—See Ecom Agroindustrial Corporation Ltd.; *Int'l*, pg. 2296
CAFFE NERO GROUP LTD.; *Int'l*, pg. 1250
CAFFINO INC.; *U.S. Private*, pg. 714
CAFINTER S.A.—See Ecom Agroindustrial Corporation Ltd.; *Int'l*, pg. 2296
CARIBBEAN COFFEE COMPANY, INC.; *U.S. Private*, pg. 760
CASCADE COFFEE, INC.; *U.S. Private*, pg. 778
CCL PRODUCTS (INDIA) LIMITED; *Int'l*, pg. 1369
CELESTIAL SEASONINGS, INC.—See The Hain Celestial Group, Inc.; *U.S. Public*, pg. 2086
CEYLON TEA BROKERS PLC; *Int'l*, pg. 1426
CHEVIOT AGRO INDUSTRIES PVT. LTD.—See Cheviot Company Limited; *Int'l*, pg. 1474
CHEVIOT INTERNATIONAL LTD.—See Cheviot Company Limited; *Int'l*, pg. 1474
CHINA TEA CO., LTD.—See COFCO Limited; *Int'l*, pg. 1692
CHOP AIK SENG SDN. BHD.—See Hai-O Enterprise Berhad; *Int'l*, pg. 3209
CIA IGUACU DE CAFE SOLUVEL; *Int'l*, pg. 1602
COFFEE CONTACT (PROPRIETARY) LIMITED—See Famous Brands Limited; *Int'l*, pg. 2612
COFFEE DAY GLOBAL LTD. - FRESH & GROUND DIVISION—See Affirma Capital Limited; *Int'l*, pg. 187
COFFEE HOLDING COMPANY, INC.; *U.S. Public*, pg. 522
COFFEE KINETICS, L.L.C.—See Coffee Holding Company, Inc.; *U.S. Public*, pg. 522
THE COFFEE WORKS INC.; *U.S. Private*, pg. 4011
COMMUNITY COFFEE COMPANY LLC; *U.S. Private*, pg. 991
COMPAGNIE COLONIALE; *Int'l*, pg. 1722
COMPANHIA CACIQUE DE CAFE SOLUVEL; *Int'l*, pg. 1746
COMPANIA COLOMBIANA AGROINDUSTRIAL S.A.—See Ecom Agroindustrial Corporation Ltd.; *Int'l*, pg. 2296
CONDESA PTY LTD—See Ecom Agroindustrial Corporation Ltd.; *Int'l*, pg. 2296
COSTA LTD.—See The Coca-Cola Company; *U.S. Public*, pg. 2065
DAIDO PHARMACEUTICAL CORPORATION—See DyDo Group Holdings, Inc.; *Int'l*, pg. 2238
DAIOHS COFFEE COMMERCIAL TRADE (SHANGHAI) CO., LTD.—See Daiohs Corporation; *Int'l*, pg. 1940
DAVIDSTEA INC.; *Int'l*, pg. 1984
DECOTY COFFEE COMPANY; *U.S. Private*, pg. 1188
DHANYA AGROINDUSTRIAL PVT. LTD.—See Ecom Agroindustrial Corporation Ltd.; *Int'l*, pg. 2296
DHUNSERI TEA & INDUSTRIES LTD.; *Int'l*, pg. 2100
DIANA TEA COMPANY LIMITED; *Int'l*, pg. 2106
DILMAH CEYLON TEA SERVICES PLC; *Int'l*, pg. 2125
DONG-SUH FOODS CORPORATION—See Mondelez International, Inc.; *U.S. Public*, pg. 1461
DOUTOR COFFEE CO., LTD.—See Doutor-Nichires Holdings Co., Ltd.; *Int'l*, pg. 2182
DUNCAN BROTHERS LIMITED—See Camellia Plc; *Int'l*, pg. 1271
DUNN BROS COFFEE, INC.—See Gala Capital Partners, LLC; *U.S. Private*, pg. 1635
DYDO BEVERAGE SHIZUOKA, INC.—See DyDo Group Holdings, Inc.; *Int'l*, pg. 2238
EAAGADS LTD.; *Int'l*, pg. 2261
EASTERN PRODUCE KENYA LIMITED—See Camellia Plc; *Int'l*, pg. 1271
ECOM AGROINDUSTRIAL ASIA PTE LTD.—See Ecom Agroindustrial Corporation Ltd.; *Int'l*, pg. 2296
ECOM AGROINDUSTRIAL ASIA PTE. LTD.—See Ecom Agroindustrial Corporation Ltd.; *Int'l*, pg. 2296
ECOM AGROINDUSTRIAL CORP. LTD—See Ecom Agroindustrial Corporation Ltd.; *Int'l*, pg. 2296
ECOM AGROINDUSTRIAL CORPORATION LTD.; *Int'l*, pg. 2295
ECOM JAPAN LTD—See Ecom Agroindustrial Corporation Ltd.; *Int'l*, pg. 2296
ECOM TRADING (SHANGHAI) CO. LTD.—See Ecom Agroindustrial Corporation Ltd.; *Int'l*, pg. 2296
ECOM USA, INC., USA—See Ecom Agroindustrial Corporation Ltd.; *Int'l*, pg. 2296
EISA - EMPRESA INTERAGRICOLA S.A.—See Ecom Agroindustrial Corporation Ltd.; *Int'l*, pg. 2296
ELEV8 BRANDS, INC.; *U.S. Public*, pg. 728
ELPITIYA PLANTATIONS PLC; *Int'l*, pg. 2369
ESQUIRES COFFEE HOUSES IRELAND LIMITED—See Cooks Coffee Company Limited; *Int'l*, pg. 1788
ESQUIRES COFFEE UK LIMITED—See Cooks Coffee Company Limited; *Int'l*, pg. 1788
EXCELLENT COFFEE CO. INC.; *U.S. Private*, pg. 1446
EXECUTIVE COFFEE SERVICE INC; *U.S. Private*, pg. 1447
EXPORTADORA ATLANTIC S.A—See Ecom Agroindustrial Corporation Ltd.; *Int'l*, pg. 2296
FARMER BROS. CO.—See Farmer Brothers Co.; *U.S. Public*, pg. 821
FARMER BROTHERS CO.; *U.S. Public*, pg. 821
FES (VIETNAM) CO. LTD—See Food Empire Holdings Limited; *Int'l*, pg. 2727
F. GAVINA & SONS, INC.; *U.S. Private*, pg. 1455
FIRST COLONY COFFEE & TEA COMPANY; *U.S. Private*, pg. 1516
THE FOLGERS COFFEE COMPANY—See The J.M. Smucker Company; *U.S. Public*, pg. 2107
FOODAWORLD MARKETING PTE LTD—See Food Empire Holdings Limited; *Int'l*, pg. 2727
FREED, TELLER & FREED'S; *U.S. Private*, pg. 1603
FRESHBREW GROUP USA, L.P.; *U.S. Private*, pg. 1610
FUJIAN TEA IMPORT & EXPORT CO., LTD.—See COFCO Limited; *Int'l*, pg. 1692
GOODRICKE GROUP LIMITED—See Camellia Plc; *Int'l*, pg. 1271
GOODWEST INDUSTRIES, INC.—See The Jordan Company, L.P.; *U.S. Private*, pg. 4062
GRANDEUR PRODUCTS LIMITED; *Int'l*, pg. 3057
HALSSEN & LYON GMBH; *Int'l*, pg. 3233
HATTON PLANTATIONS PLC; *Int'l*, pg. 3285
HEALTHY COFFEE INTERNATIONAL, INC.; *U.S. Private*, pg. 1898
HEIMBS KAFFEE GMBH & CO. KG—See Alois Dallmayr KG; *Int'l*, pg. 365
HENDERSON COFFEE CORP—See Huron Capital Partners LLC; *U.S. Private*, pg. 2012
HVA FOODS PLC—See Citrus Leisure PLC; *Int'l*, pg. 1626
ICHITAN GROUP PUBLIC COMPANY LIMITED; *Int'l*, pg. 3581
ILLYCAFFE S.P.A. NIEDERLASSUNG DEUTSCHLAND—See illycaffe S.p.A.; *Int'l*, pg. 3615
ILLYCAFFE S.P.A.; *Int'l*, pg. 3615
IN-COMIX FOOD INDUSTRIES SDN. BHD.—See Hup Seng Industries Berhad; *Int'l*, pg. 3538
INSTANTINA NAHRUNGSMITTEL ENTWICKLUNGS- UND PRODUKTIONSGESELLSCHAFT M.B.H.—See AGRANA Beteiligungs-AG; *Int'l*, pg. 214
INTER-AMERICAN FOODS, INC.—See The Kroger Co.; *U.S. Public*, pg. 2108
JAMMIN JAVA CORP.; *U.S. Public*, pg. 1187
JAVA CITY; *U.S. Private*, pg. 2191
JAVO BEVERAGE COMPANY, INC.; *U.S. Private*, pg. 2191
JBR INC.; *U.S. Private*, pg. 2194
JING TEA LIMITED—See Camellia Plc; *Int'l*, pg. 1271
JOHN A. VASSILAROS & SON INC; *U.S. Private*, pg. 2220
KAKUZI PLC—See Camellia Plc; *Int'l*, pg. 1271
KAUAI COFFEE COMPANY, INC.—See Alexander & Baldwin, Inc.; *U.S. Public*, pg. 75
KAWACOM UGANDA LIMITED—See Ecom Agroindustrial Corporation Ltd.; *Int'l*, pg. 2296
KOHANA COFFEE LLC—See Westrock Coffee Company; *U.S. Public*, pg. 2361
KOOMBER TEA COMPANY LIMITED—See Camellia Plc; *Int'l*, pg. 1271
KRAFT HEINZ COMPANY - MAXWELL HOUSE COFFEE—See 3G Capital Inc.; *U.S. Private*, pg. 11
KRAFT HEINZ COMPANY - MAXWELL HOUSE COFFEE—See Berkshire Hathaway Inc.; *U.S. Public*, pg. 318
LA CREME COFFEE & TEA—See DeCoty Coffee Company; *U.S. Private*, pg. 1188
LEROY HILL COFFEE COMPANY INC.; *U.S. Private*, pg. 2431
LINGLE BROS COFFEE INC.; *U.S. Private*, pg. 2461
MABROC TEAS (PVT) LTD.—See Hayleys PLC; *Int'l*, pg. 3292
MAUIGROWN COFFEE DISTRIBUTORS, LLC—See Kaanapali Land, LLC; *U.S. Public*, pg. 1212
MAWENZI COFFEE EXPORTERS LTD.—See Ecom Agroindustrial Corporation Ltd.; *Int'l*, pg. 2296
MAXIMUS COFFEE GROUP, LLC.; *U.S. Private*, pg. 2619
MAYORGA COFFEE INC.; *U.S. Private*, pg. 2622
MELITTA BELGIE N.V.—See Eckes AG; *Int'l*, pg. 2291
M&M INTERNATIONAL TRADING; *U.S. Private*, pg. 2524
MONDELEZ ESPANA CONFECTIONERY PRODUCTION, SLU—See Mondelez International, Inc.; *U.S. Public*, pg. 1462
MONTANA COFFEE TRADERS INC.; *U.S. Private*, pg. 2775
NAMING'OMBA TEA ESTATES LIMITED—See Gillanders Arbuthnot & Co., Ltd.; *Int'l*, pg. 2976
NESTLE MANUFACTURING (MALAYSIA) SDN. BHD.—See Groupe Lactalis SA; *Int'l*, pg. 3106
NESTLE WATERS NORTH AMERICA INC. - COPPELL—See Metropoulos & Co.; *U.S. Private*, pg. 2690
NESTLE WATERS NORTH AMERICA INC. - COPPELL—See One Rock Capital Partners, LLC; *U.S. Private*, pg. 3021
NEW ENGLAND TEA & COFFEE COMPANY, LLC—See Reily Foods Company; *U.S. Private*, pg. 3391
NORTH AMERICAN TEA & COFFEE INC.—See TreeHouse Foods, Inc.; *U.S. Public*, pg. 2187
OLD TOWN COFFEE & TEA CO INC; *U.S. Private*, pg. 3009
OREGON COFFEE ROASTER, INC.; *U.S. Private*, pg. 3040
ORIGIN MERGER SUB II, LLC—See Westrock Coffee Company; *U.S. Public*, pg. 2361
PAN AMERICAN COFFEE COMPANY INC.; *U.S. Private*, pg. 3083
PAUL DE LIMA CO. INC.; *U.S. Private*, pg. 3112
PETRONCINI IMPIANTI S.P.A.—See I.M.A. Industria Macchine Automatiche S.p.A.; *Int'l*, pg. 3566
POD PACK INTERNATIONAL, LTD.; *U.S. Private*, pg. 3220
PONTIAC FOODS, INC.—See The Kroger Co.; *U.S. Public*, pg. 2109
PUERTO RICO COFFEE ROASTERS, LLC—See CC 1 Limited Partnership; *U.S. Private*, pg. 797
R.C. BIGELOW, INC.; *U.S. Private*, pg. 3334
ROGERS FAMILY COMPANY; *U.S. Private*, pg. 3471
RONNOCO COFFEE, LLC—See Huron Capital Partners LLC; *U.S. Private*, pg. 2012
ROYAL CUP INC.; *U.S. Private*, pg. 3492
SAN FRANCISCO HERB & NATURAL FOOD CO.; *U.S. Private*, pg. 3540
SANGANA COMMODITIES (K) LTD.—See Ecom Agroindustrial Corporation Ltd.; *Int'l*, pg. 2296
SHANDONG TENGJUNXIANG BIOTECHNOLOGY LTD.—See Tengjun Biotechnology Corp.; *U.S. Public*, pg. 2015
SHANGHAI WEISEN TRADING CO.LTD.—See Ecom Agroindustrial Corporation Ltd.; *Int'l*, pg. 2296
SHOFFEE INC.; *U.S. Private*, pg. 3639
SILOCAF OF NEW ORLEANS INC.—See B. Pacorini S.p.A.; *Int'l*, pg. 789
STAGECOACH COFFEE, INC.; *U.S. Private*, pg. 3775
STARBUCKS COFFEE COMPANY UK LTD.—See Starbucks Corporation; *U.S. Public*, pg. 1939
STARBUCKS CORPORATION; *U.S. Public*, pg. 1938
STARBUCKS MANUFACTURING EMEA B.V.—See Starbucks Corporation; *U.S. Public*, pg. 1939
STEEP & BREW, INC.—See Coffee Holding Company, Inc.; *U.S. Public*, pg. 522
STEWART'S PRIVATE BLEND FOODS INC.; *U.S. Private*, pg. 3811
SUSTAINABLE HARVEST COFFEE IMPORTERS; *U.S. Private*, pg. 3886
TEA HOUSE LLP—See Food Empire Holdings Limited; *Int'l*, pg. 2727
THANKSGIVING COFFEE COMPANY, INC.; *U.S. Private*, pg. 3980
TIRU TEA COMPANY LIMITED—See Camellia Plc; *Int'l*, pg. 1271
TORKE COFFEE ROASTING COMPANY; *U.S. Private*, pg. 4189
TRIPLE LEAF TEA, INC.; *U.S. Private*, pg. 4237
TROPICAL SMOOTHIE CAFE, LLC—See Levine Leichtman Capital Partners, LLC; *U.S. Private*, pg. 2436
UNCLE LEE'S TEA INC.; *U.S. Private*, pg. 4279
U.S. ROASTERIE, INC.—See Huron Capital Partners LLC; *U.S. Private*, pg. 2012
VAN REES B.V—See ACOMO N.V.; *Int'l*, pg. 108
VAN REES CEYLON LTD.—See ACOMO N.V.; *Int'l*, pg. 108
VAN REES GROUP—See Blackstone Inc.; *U.S. Public*, pg. 356
VOLCAFE FRANCE—See ED&F Man Holdings Limited; *Int'l*, pg. 2303
VOLCAFE SPECIALITY COFFEE LLC—See ED&F Man Holdings Limited; *Int'l*, pg. 2303
WALLINGFORD COFFEE MILLS INC.; *U.S. Private*, pg. 4431
WEST COAST COFFEE COMPANY INC.—See Farmer Brothers Co.; *U.S. Public*, pg. 821
WESTROCK COFFEE COMPANY; *U.S. Public*, pg. 2361
YARA COMMODITIES LTD.—See Ecom Agroindustrial Corporation Ltd.; *Int'l*, pg. 2296

N.A.I.C.S. INDEX

ZAMACOM S.A.—See Ecom Agroindustrial Corporation Ltd.; *Int'l*, pg. 2296

311930 — FLAVORING SYRUP AND CONCENTRATE MANUFACTURING

ADM WILD EUROPE GMBH & CO. KG—See Archer-Daniels-Midland Company; *U.S. Public*, pg. 183
AMERICAN FRUITS & FLAVORS LLC—See Monster Beverage Corporation; *U.S. Public*, pg. 1465
BALDWIN RICHARDSON FOODS CORPORATION—See Baldwin Richardson Foods Company; *U.S. Private*, pg. 459
BELL FLAVORS AND FRAGRANCES DO BRASIL INDUSTRIA—See Bell Flavors & Fragrances, Inc.; *U.S. Private*, pg. 518
BELL FLAVORS & FRAGRANCES DUFT UND AROMA GMBH—See Bell Flavors & Fragrances, Inc.; *U.S. Private*, pg. 518
CARIBBEAN REFRESCOS INC.—See The Coca-Cola Company; *U.S. Public*, pg. 2063
CHEFMASTER—See Byrnes & Kiefer Company; *U.S. Private*, pg. 701
CHENGUANG BIOTECH GROUP CO., LTD.; *Int'l*, pg. 1470
THE COCA-COLA COMPANY—See The Coca-Cola Company; *U.S. Public*, pg. 2065
THE COCA-COLA COMPANY—See The Coca-Cola Company; *U.S. Public*, pg. 2065
COCA-COLA HOLDINGS OVERSEAS LTD.—See The Coca-Cola Company; *U.S. Public*, pg. 2064
COCA-COLA NORTH AMERICA—See The Coca-Cola Company; *U.S. Public*, pg. 2064
COCA-COLA USA ONTARIO SYRUP—See The Coca-Cola Company; *U.S. Public*, pg. 2064
DAVID MICHAEL EUROPE S.A.S.—See International Flavors & Fragrances Inc.; *U.S. Public*, pg. 1154
DOUBLE-COLA CO.-USA; *U.S. Private*, pg. 1266
EMPIRE DISTRIBUTION (EUROPE) SPOLKA Z OGRANICZONA ODPOWIEDZIALNOSCIA—See Food Empire Holdings Limited; *Int'l*, pg. 2727
ENRICO GIOTTI SPA—See McCormick & Company, Incorporated; *U.S. Public*, pg. 1404
ETOL D.D.—See International Flavors & Fragrances Inc.; *U.S. Public*, pg. 1152
ETOL JVE D.O.O.—See International Flavors & Fragrances Inc.; *U.S. Public*, pg. 1152
ETOL RUS, LTD.—See International Flavors & Fragrances Inc.; *U.S. Public*, pg. 1152
ETOL SK S.R.O.—See International Flavors & Fragrances Inc.; *U.S. Public*, pg. 1152
ETOL UKRAJINA TZOV—See International Flavors & Fragrances Inc.; *U.S. Public*, pg. 1152
EVERGREEN SWEETENERS, INC.; *U.S. Private*, pg. 1440
FIRMENICH BELGIUM S.A.—See Firmenich International SA; *Int'l*, pg. 2680
FISA ANDINA S.A.S.—See Archer-Daniels-Midland Company; *U.S. Public*, pg. 185
FLAVOR & FRAGRANCE SPECIALTIES; *U.S. Private*, pg. 1541
FLAVOR INFUSION INTERNATIONAL, S.A.—See Archer-Daniels-Midland Company; *U.S. Public*, pg. 185
FLAYCO PRODUCTS, INC.; *U.S. Private*, pg. 1541
FLORIDA FOOD PRODUCTS, LLC—See Ardian SAS; *Int'l*, pg. 555
FRUTAROM ETOL D.O.O.—See International Flavors & Fragrances Inc.; *U.S. Public*, pg. 1152
FRUTAROM INDUSTRIES LTD.—See International Flavors & Fragrances Inc.; *U.S. Public*, pg. 1151
FRUTAROM USA INC.—See International Flavors & Fragrances Inc.; *U.S. Public*, pg. 1152
GIVAUDAN CANADA, INC.—See Givaudan S.A.; *Int'l*, pg. 2980
GIVAUDAN DEUTSCHLAND GMBH—See Givaudan S.A.; *Int'l*, pg. 2980
GIVAUDAN FLAVORS CORPORATION - ITASCA—See Givaudan S.A.; *Int'l*, pg. 2981
GIVAUDAN HUNGARY KFT—See Givaudan S.A.; *Int'l*, pg. 2980
GIVAUDAN UK LTD—See Givaudan S.A.; *Int'l*, pg. 2980
GROUPE MONIN SAS; *Int'l*, pg. 3109
GROW COMPANY INC—See International Flavors & Fragrances Inc.; *U.S. Public*, pg. 1152
HEG HOPFENEXTRAKTION GMBH—See S.S. Steiner Inc.; *U.S. Public*, pg. 3518
HOKKAIDO COCA-COLA BOTTLING CO., LTD.—See Dai Nippon Printing Co., Ltd.; *Int'l*, pg. 1915
IFF AROMA ESANS SANAYI VE TICARET A.S.—See International Flavors & Fragrances Inc.; *U.S. Public*, pg. 1152
INTERNATIONAL FLAVORS & FRAGRANCES (CHINA) LTD. - BEIJING OFFICE—See International Flavors & Fragrances Inc.; *U.S. Public*, pg. 1152
INTERNATIONAL FLAVORS & FRAGRANCES (CHINA) LTD. - SHANGHAI OFFICE—See International Flavors & Fragrances Inc.; *U.S. Public*, pg. 1152
INTERNATIONAL FLAVORS & FRAGRANCES I.F.F. (DEUTSCHLAND) GMBH—See International Flavors & Fragrances Inc.; *U.S. Public*, pg. 1153
INTERNATIONAL FLAVORS & FRAGRANCES I.F.F. (ESPANA) S.A. - BARCELONA—See International Flavors & Fragrances Inc.; *U.S. Public*, pg. 1153
INTERNATIONAL FLAVORS & FRAGRANCES I.F.F. (ESPANA) S.A.—See International Flavors & Fragrances Inc.; *U.S. Public*, pg. 1153
INTERNATIONAL FLAVORS & FRAGRANCES I.F.F. (FRANCE) S.A.S.—See International Flavors & Fragrances Inc.; *U.S. Public*, pg. 1153
INTERNATIONAL FLAVORS & FRAGRANCES I.F.F. (NEDERLAND) B.V. - TILBURG PLANT—See International Flavors & Fragrances Inc.; *U.S. Public*, pg. 1153
INTERNATIONAL FLAVORS & FRAGRANCES I.F.F. (NORDEN) AB—See International Flavors & Fragrances Inc.; *U.S. Public*, pg. 1153
INTERNATIONAL FLAVORS & FRAGRANCES I.F.F. (S.A.) (PTY) LTD.—See International Flavors & Fragrances Inc.; *U.S. Public*, pg. 1153
INTERNATIONAL FLAVORS & FRAGRANCES (JAPAN) LTD. - GOTEMBA PLANT—See International Flavors & Fragrances Inc.; *U.S. Public*, pg. 1152
INTERNATIONAL FLAVORS & FRAGRANCES (MEXICO) S.A. DE C.V.—See International Flavors & Fragrances Inc.; *U.S. Public*, pg. 1152
INTERNATIONAL FLAVORS & FRAGRANCES (PHILIPPINES), INC.—See International Flavors & Fragrances Inc.; *U.S. Public*, pg. 1153
INTERNATIONAL FLAVORS & FRAGRANCES S.R.L.—See International Flavors & Fragrances Inc.; *U.S. Public*, pg. 1153
INTERNATIONAL FLAVORS & FRAGRANCES (ZHEJIANG) CO., LTD.—See International Flavors & Fragrances Inc.; *U.S. Public*, pg. 1152
INTERNATIONAL FLAVOURS & FRAGRANCES (CIL) LIMITED—See International Flavors & Fragrances Inc.; *U.S. Public*, pg. 1153
THE JEL SERT COMPANY; *U.S. Private*, pg. 4058
KERR CONCENTRATES, INC.—See Ingredion Incorporated; *U.S. Public*, pg. 1124
MAFCO CONSOLIDATED GROUP INC—See MacAndrews & Forbes Incorporated; *U.S. Private*, pg. 2532
MCCORMICK DE CENTRO AMERICA, S.A. DE C.V.—See McCormick & Company, Incorporated; *U.S. Public*, pg. 1404
MCCORMICK DE MEXICO, S.A. DE C.V.—See Grupo Herdez, S.A.B. de C.V.; *Int'l*, pg. 3130
MCCORMICK DE MEXICO, S.A. DE C.V.—See McCormick & Company, Incorporated; *U.S. Public*, pg. 1404
MCCORMICK FOODS AUSTRALIA PTY. LTD.—See McCormick & Company, Incorporated; *U.S. Public*, pg. 1404
MCCORMICK GLENTHAM (PROPRIETARY) LIMITED—See McCormick & Company, Incorporated; *U.S. Public*, pg. 1404
MCCORMICK (GUANGZHOU) FOOD COMPANY LIMITED—See McCormick & Company, Incorporated; *U.S. Public*, pg. 1404
MCCORMICK PESA, S.A. DE C.V.—See McCormick & Company, Incorporated; *U.S. Public*, pg. 1404
MCCORMICK PHILIPPINES, INC.—See McCormick & Company, Incorporated; *U.S. Public*, pg. 1404
MONIN, INC.—See Groupe Monin SAS; *Int'l*, pg. 3109
MONT BLANC GOURMET; *U.S. Private*, pg. 2774
NATUREX S.A.—See Givaudan S.A.; *Int'l*, pg. 2981
THE PECAN DELUXE CANDY COMPANY INC.; *U.S. Private*, pg. 4091
PURECIRCLE LIMITED—See Ingredion Incorporated; *U.S. Public*, pg. 1124
QUALITY BEVERAGE LLC; *U.S. Private*, pg. 3317
SABORES Y FRAGANCIAS S.A.—See International Flavors & Fragrances Inc.; *U.S. Public*, pg. 1154
SENSIENT COLORS CANADA LTD.—See Sensient Technologies Corporation; *U.S. Public*, pg. 1867
SENSIENT COLORS LLC—See Sensient Technologies Corporation; *U.S. Public*, pg. 1867
SENSIENT COLORS SA DE CV—See Sensient Technologies Corporation; *U.S. Public*, pg. 1867
SENSIENT FLAVORS, LLC—See Sensient Technologies Corporation; *U.S. Public*, pg. 1867
SENSIENT FLAVORS LTD.—See Sensient Technologies Corporation; *U.S. Public*, pg. 1867
SENSIENT HOLDINGS UK—See Sensient Technologies Corporation; *U.S. Public*, pg. 1867
SENSIENT TECHNOLOGIES ASIA PACIFIC PTE. LTD.—See Sensient Technologies Corporation; *U.S. Public*, pg. 1867
SENSIENT TECHNOLOGIES AUSTRALIA PTY LTD—See Sensient Technologies Corporation; *U.S. Public*, pg. 1867
SENSIENT TECHNOLOGIES CORPORATION; *U.S. Public*, pg. 1867
SENSIENT TURKEY DOGAL MADDELER A.S.—See Sensient Technologies Corporation; *U.S. Public*, pg. 1868
SETHNESS-GREENLEAF, INC.—See Carbery Group; *Int'l*, pg. 1320
SETHNESS PRODUCTS COMPANY; *U.S. Private*, pg. 3617
SHANGHAI MCCORMICK FOODS COMPANY LIMITED—See McCormick & Company, Incorporated; *U.S. Public*, pg. 1404
SOFT DRINK SERVICES COMPANY—See The Coca-Cola Company; *U.S. Public*, pg. 2065
SYNERGY FLAVORS, INC.—See Carbery Group; *Int'l*, pg. 1320
TASTEPOINT, INC.—See International Flavors & Fragrances Inc.; *U.S. Public*, pg. 1154
TONE PRODUCTS INC.; *U.S. Private*, pg. 4184
TOTAL HEALTH CONCEPT SDN BHD—See Holista ColITech Limited; *Int'l*, pg. 3450
TREE TOP, INC. - OXNARD CALIFORNIA PLANT—See Tree Top, Inc.; *U.S. Private*, pg. 4216
TREE TOP, INC. - WOODBURN OREGON PLANT—See Tree Top, Inc.; *U.S. Private*, pg. 4217
UNGERER & COMPANY—See Givaudan S.A.; *Int'l*, pg. 2982
VERTEX BODY SCIENCES INC.; *U.S. Private*, pg. 4369
VIRGINIA DARE EXTRACT CO., INC.; *U.S. Private*, pg. 4387
WILD FLAVORS GMBH—See Archer-Daniels-Midland Company; *U.S. Public*, pg. 184
WILD VALENCIA S.A.—See Archer-Daniels-Midland Company; *U.S. Public*, pg. 184
WYNN STARR FLAVORS INC.; *U.S. Private*, pg. 4576

311941 — MAYONNAISE, DRESSING, AND OTHER PREPARED SAUCE MANUFACTURING

AARHUSKARLSHAMN UK LTD. - AAK FOODS—See AAK AB; *Int'l*, pg. 31
AATCO LLC—See Badr Investment Group LLC; *Int'l*, pg. 796
ADEKA FINE FOODS CORPORATION—See Adeka Corporation; *Int'l*, pg. 141
ADVANCED FOOD SYSTEMS, INC.; *U.S. Private*, pg. 89
AH-VEST LIMITED; *Int'l*, pg. 222
ALIMENTS FONTAINE SANTE, INC.; *Int'l*, pg. 328
AMERICAN SPICE COMPANY INC.; *U.S. Private*, pg. 255
AMOY FOOD LTD.—See CITIC Group Corporation; *Int'l*, pg. 1619
ARCOBASSO FOODS, INC.—See Golding Farms Foods, Inc.; *U.S. Private*, pg. 1735
AUTHENTIC SPECIALTY FOODS, INC.—See Grupo Kuo, S.A.B. de C.V.; *Int'l*, pg. 3131
BAY VALLEY FOODS—See TreeHouse Foods, Inc.; *U.S. Public*, pg. 2187
BAY VALLEY FOODS—See TreeHouse Foods, Inc.; *U.S. Public*, pg. 2187
BULL-DOG SAUCE CO., LTD.; *Int'l*, pg. 1214
CAINS FOODS, L.P.—See TreeHouse Foods, Inc.; *U.S. Public*, pg. 2187
CAIRO FOODS INDUSTRIES SAE—See 3G Capital Inc.; *U.S. Private*, pg. 9
CAIRO FOODS INDUSTRIES SAE—See Berkshire Hathaway Inc.; *U.S. Public*, pg. 317
CASA VISCO; *U.S. Private*, pg. 778
CHOICE FOOD OF AMERICA, LLC—See Choice Food Group, Inc.; *U.S. Private*, pg. 888
CHONGQING FULING ZHACAI GROUP CO., LTD.; *Int'l*, pg. 1579
CONWAY IMPORT CO. INC.; *U.S. Private*, pg. 1036
CONWAY IMPORT CO. INC.—See Conway Import Co. Inc.; *U.S. Private*, pg. 1036
CULINARY CONCEPTS INC.; *U.S. Private*, pg. 1120
DAESANG (BEIJING) FOODS CO LTD. - BEIJING FACTORY—See Daesang Corporation; *Int'l*, pg. 1909
DAESANG (BEIJING) FOODS CO LTD.—See Daesang Corporation; *Int'l*, pg. 1909
DAESANG FNF CORPORATION—See Daesang Corporation; *Int'l*, pg. 1909
DAESANG RICOR CORPORATION - CAGAYAN DE ORO FACTORY—See Daesang Corporation; *Int'l*, pg. 1909
DAESANG RICOR CORPORATION—See Daesang Corporation; *Int'l*, pg. 1909
DAISHO CO., LTD. - FUKUOKA FACTORY—See DAISHO Co., Ltd.; *Int'l*, pg. 1942
DAISHO CO., LTD. - FUKUOKA SECOND FACTORY—See DAISHO Co., Ltd.; *Int'l*, pg. 1942
DAISHO CO., LTD. - KANTO FACTORY—See DAISHO Co., Ltd.; *Int'l*, pg. 1942
DAISHO CO., LTD. - KYUSHU FACTORY—See DAISHO Co., Ltd.; *Int'l*, pg. 1942
DAISHO CO., LTD.; *Int'l*, pg. 1942
DAT-SCHAUB (PORTO) SA—See Danish Crown AmbA; *Int'l*, pg. 1964
DEL SOL FOOD COMPANY, INC.; *U.S. Private*, pg. 1193
DG FOODS, LLC; *U.S. Private*, pg. 1221
EBARA FOODS INDUSTRY, INC. - TOCHIGI FACTORY—See Ebara Foods Industry, Inc.; *Int'l*, pg. 2284
EBARA FOODS INDUSTRY, INC. - TSUYAMA FACTORY—See Ebara Foods Industry, Inc.; *Int'l*, pg. 2284
EBARA FOODS (SHANGHAI) CO., LTD.—See Ebara Foods Industry, Inc.; *Int'l*, pg. 2284
E.D. SMITH FOODS, LTD.—See TreeHouse Foods, Inc.; *U.S. Public*, pg. 2187
EXOTIC FOOD PUBLIC COMPANY LIMITED; *Int'l*, pg. 2586
THE FRENCH'S FOOD COMPANY LLC—See McCormick &

311941 — MAYONNAISE, DRESSIN...

Company, Incorporated; *U.S. Public*, pg. 1404
GARDEN FRESH GOURMET, LLC—See Aliments Fontaine Sante, Inc.; *Int'l*, pg. 328
GFF INC.; *U.S. Private*, pg. 1690
GOLDING FARMS FOODS, INC.; *U.S. Private*, pg. 1735
GOLD'S PURE FOODS, LLC—See LSCG Management, Inc.; *U.S. Private*, pg. 2509
GRAFFITI FOODS, LTD.—See New Horizons Baking Company; *U.S. Private*, pg. 2897
GRAVYMASTER INC.—See Founders Equity, Inc.; *U.S. Private*, pg. 1581
GREENCORE GROCERY LIMITED—See Greencore Group plc; *Int'l*, pg. 3074
GREENCORE GROUP PLC - GREENCORE FOOD TO GO MANTON WOOD FACILITY—See Greencore Group plc; *Int'l*, pg. 3074
HAZLEWOOD CONVENIENCE FOOD GROUP LIMITED—See Greencore Group plc; *Int'l*, pg. 3074
HEAD COUNTRY INC.—See Gladstone Management Corporation; *U.S. Private*, pg. 1705
H.J. HEINZ BELGIUM N.V.—See 3G Capital Inc.; *U.S. Private*, pg. 9
H.J. HEINZ BELGIUM N.V.—See Berkshire Hathaway Inc.; *U.S. Public*, pg. 317
H.J. HEINZ FRANCE S.A.S.—See 3G Capital Inc.; *U.S. Private*, pg. 10
H.J. HEINZ FRANCE S.A.S.—See Berkshire Hathaway Inc.; *U.S. Public*, pg. 317
HUNTSINGER FARMS INC.; *U.S. Private*, pg. 2010
ICHIMASA KAMABOKO CO., LTD.; *Int'l*, pg. 3580
ITALIAN ROSE GARLIC PRODUCTS, INC.—See Blue Point Capital Partners, LLC; *U.S. Private*, pg. 590
JMH INTERNATIONAL, LLC—See EagleTree Capital, LP; *U.S. Private*, pg. 1312
KEN'S FOODS, INC.; *U.S. Private*, pg. 2283
KRAFT HEINZ FOODS COMPANY—See 3G Capital Inc.; *U.S. Private*, pg. 9
KRAFT HEINZ FOODS COMPANY—See Berkshire Hathaway Inc.; *U.S. Public*, pg. 317
LIDESTRI FOODS, INC.; *U.S. Private*, pg. 2448
LITEHOUSE FOODS, INC.; *U.S. Private*, pg. 2467
LOS TIOS INC.; *U.S. Private*, pg. 2497
LOUISBURG CIDER MILL, INC.; *U.S. Private*, pg. 2499
LUCINI ITALIA COMPANY—See California Olive Ranch Inc.; *U.S. Private*, pg. 720
MARIE'S SALAD DRESSING—See Dean Foods Company; *U.S. Private*, pg. 1184
MARJON SPECIALTY FOODS, INC.; *U.S. Private*, pg. 2577
MCILHENNY COMPANY; *U.S. Private*, pg. 2636
MEGAMEX FOODS, LLC—See Grupo Herdez, S.A.B. de C.V.; *Int'l*, pg. 3130
MEGAMEX FOODS, LLC—See Hormel Foods Corporation; *U.S. Public*, pg. 1054
MILLCREST PRODUCTS CORPORATION—See Pacific Choice Brands, Inc.; *U.S. Private*, pg. 3065
MIWON VIETNAM CO., LTD.—See Daesang Corporation; *Int'l*, pg. 1909
MIWON VIETNAM CO., LTD. - VIET TRI FACTORY—See Daesang Corporation; *Int'l*, pg. 1909
MRS. CLARK'S FOODS L.C.; *U.S. Private*, pg. 2806
MULLINS FOOD PRODUCTS INC.; *U.S. Private*, pg. 2812
THE MUSHROOM COMPANY—See South Mill Mushrooms Sales, Inc.; *U.S. Private*, pg. 3723
NEWMAN'S OWN, INC.; *U.S. Private*, pg. 2916
OTT FOOD PRODUCTS—See Westin Foods, Inc.; *U.S. Private*, pg. 4498
PACIFICA FOODS LLC—See Wind Point Advisors LLC; *U.S. Private*, pg. 4534
PACIFIC CHOICE BRANDS, INC.; *U.S. Private*, pg. 3065
PARADISE TOMATO KITCHENS, INC.; *U.S. Private*, pg. 3090
PEPPER SOURCE, LTD.; *U.S. Private*, pg. 3144
PEPPERS UNLIMITED OF LOUISIANA, INC.; *U.S. Private*, pg. 3145
PLOCHMAN, INC.; *U.S. Private*, pg. 3214
PORTION PAC—See 3G Capital Inc.; *U.S. Private*, pg. 10
PORTION PAC—See Berkshire Hathaway Inc.; *U.S. Public*, pg. 318
PROVEEDORES DE INGENIERIA ALIMENTARIA, S.A. DE C.V.—See International Flavors & Fragrances Inc.; *U.S. Public*, pg. 1154
REILY FOODS COMPANY; *U.S. Private*, pg. 3391
RENEE'S GOURMET FOODS, INC.—See 3G Capital Inc.; *U.S. Private*, pg. 9
RENEE'S GOURMET FOODS, INC.—See Berkshire Hathaway Inc.; *U.S. Public*, pg. 317
SHANGHAI AMOY FOODS CO. LTD.—See Ajinomoto Company, Inc.; *Int'l*, pg. 257
SILVER SPRING FOODS, INC.—See Huntsinger Farms Inc.; *U.S. Private*, pg. 2010
STAR STABILIANTO ALIMENTARE S.P.A.—See Danone; *Int'l*, pg. 1968
SUPREME OIL COMPANY INC.; *U.S. Private*, pg. 3882
TASTY-TOPPINGS, INC.; *U.S. Private*, pg. 3935
TERRAPIN RIDGE FARMS, LLC; *U.S. Private*, pg. 3972
TIC GUMS, INC.—See Ingredion Incorporated; *U.S. Public*, pg. 1124

T. MARZETTI COMPANY—See Lancaster Colony Corporation; *U.S. Public*, pg. 1291
T. MARZETTI COMPANY - WEST—See Lancaster Colony Corporation; *U.S. Public*, pg. 1292
TULKOFF FOOD PRODUCTS, INC.—See The Graham Group, Inc.; *U.S. Private*, pg. 4037
VANLAW FOOD PRODUCTS, INC.—See Wind Point Advisors LLC; *U.S. Private*, pg. 4536
WALDEN FARMS, LLC—See Hammond, Kennedy, Whitney & Company, Inc.; *U.S. Private*, pg. 1850
WOEBER MUSTARD MANUFACTURING COMPANY; *U.S. Private*, pg. 4553

311942 — SPICE AND EXTRACT MANUFACTURING

ACI SALT LIMITED—See Advanced Chemical Industries Limited; *Int'l*, pg. 158
A.C. LEGG PACKING COMPANY, INC.; *U.S. Private*, pg. 24
A.M. TODD COMPANY; *U.S. Private*, pg. 27
A.M. TODD - INGREDIENTS & FLAVORS—See A.M. Todd Company; *U.S. Private*, pg. 27
ANJI FOODSTUFF CO., LTD.; *Int'l*, pg. 472
AVT MCCORMICK INGREDIENTS PVT LTD.—See McCormick & Company, Incorporated; *U.S. Public*, pg. 1403
AVT NATURAL PRODUCTS LTD.; *Int'l*, pg. 751
BLENDEX COMPANY; *U.S. Private*, pg. 580
BOHEN-KASEI CO., LTD.—See Astena Holdings Co., Ltd.; *Int'l*, pg. 653
BOTANICAL FOOD COMPANY, INC.—See McCormick & Company, Incorporated; *U.S. Public*, pg. 1404
BOTANICAL FOOD COMPANY PTY. LTD.—See McCormick & Company, Incorporated; *U.S. Public*, pg. 1404
BRADY ENTERPRISES, INC.; *U.S. Private*, pg. 633
CARGILL INC.—See Cargill, Inc.; *U.S. Private*, pg. 757
CARGILL SALT INC.—See Cargill, Inc.; *U.S. Private*, pg. 758
CARGILL SALT—See Cargill, Inc.; *U.S. Private*, pg. 758
CARGILL SALT—See Cargill, Inc.; *U.S. Private*, pg. 758
CARGILL SALT—See Cargill, Inc.; *U.S. Private*, pg. 758
CARGILL SALT—See Cargill, Inc.; *U.S. Private*, pg. 758
CARGILL SOUTH—See Cargill, Inc.; *U.S. Private*, pg. 758
CHOTHANI FOODS LIMITED; *Int'l*, pg. 1584
CHRISTIAN POTIER S.A.; *Int'l*, pg. 1586
COALESCENCE, LLC.—See New Horizons Baking Company; *U.S. Private*, pg. 2897
COMPASS MINERALS WINNIPEG UNLIMITED LIABILITY COMPANY—See Compass Minerals International, Inc.; *U.S. Public*, pg. 560
CP KELCO APS—See J.M. Huber Corporation; *U.S. Private*, pg. 2168
CP KELCO GERMANY GMBH—See J.M. Huber Corporation; *U.S. Private*, pg. 2168
DDW, INC.; *U.S. Private*, pg. 1181
DESSERT PRODUCTS INTERNATIONAL—See McCormick & Company, Incorporated; *U.S. Public*, pg. 1404
DROGHERIA E ALIMENTARI SPA—See McCormick & Company, Incorporated; *U.S. Public*, pg. 1404
EDLONG CORPORATION; *U.S. Private*, pg. 1337
ELAN CHEMICAL COMPANY INC.; *U.S. Private*, pg. 1349
EL ENCANTO INCORPORATED; *U.S. Private*, pg. 1349
ELITE SPICE, INC.; *U.S. Private*, pg. 1361
EL-NASR SALINE COMPANY—See Chemical Industries Holding Company; *Int'l*, pg. 1462
ESSEX LABORATORIES INC.—See Firmenich International SA; *Int'l*, pg. 2680
FERDINAND KREUTZER SABAMUHLE GMBH; *Int'l*, pg. 2637
FLAVOURS, INC.—See Excellere Capital Management LLC; *U.S. Private*, pg. 1446
FONA INTERNATIONAL, LLC—See McCormick & Company, Incorporated; *U.S. Public*, pg. 1404
FORAN SPICE COMPANY; *U.S. Private*, pg. 1562
FOSHAN HAITIAN FLAVOURING & FOOD COMPANY LTD.; *Int'l*, pg. 2748
FRONTIER NATURAL PRODUCTS CO-OP; *U.S. Private*, pg. 1615
FUCHS-GEWURZE GMBH; *Int'l*, pg. 2804
FUCHS NORTH AMERICA.—See FUCHS-Gewurze GmbH; *Int'l*, pg. 2804
GABAN SPICE MANUFACTURING (M) SDN. BHD.—See House Foods Group Inc.; *Int'l*, pg. 3490
GILES CHEMICAL CORP.; *U.S. Private*, pg. 1699
GLEN RESEARCH CORP.—See Maravai LifeSciences, Inc.; *U.S. Private*, pg. 2570
GOLD COAST INGREDIENTS, INC.; *U.S. Private*, pg. 1727
GOYAL SALT LIMITED; *Int'l*, pg. 3045
GRANDMA'S COUNTRY FOODS; *U.S. Private*, pg. 1754
GRIFFITH LABORATORIES, INC.; *U.S. Private*, pg. 1789
GSB & ASSOCIATES, INC.—See The Riverside Company; *U.S. Private*, pg. 4109
GS HALL & COMPANY LIMITED—See Health and Plant Protein Group Limited; *Int'l*, pg. 3303
GUILIN LAYN NATURAL INGREDIENTS CORP.; *Int'l*, pg. 3173
HOUSE AI-FACTORY CORPORATION—See House Foods Group Inc.; *Int'l*, pg. 3490

HUABAO INTERNATIONAL HOLDINGS LIMITED; *Int'l*, pg. 3510
KALAMAZOO HOLDINGS, INC.; *U.S. Private*, pg. 2256
KALSEC, INC.—See Kalamazoo Holdings, Inc.; *U.S. Private*, pg. 2257
KUSUM SPICES PRIVATE LIMITED—See Foods & Inns Ltd.; *Int'l*, pg. 2727
LA CIE MCCORMICK CANADA CO.—See McCormick & Company, Incorporated; *U.S. Public*, pg. 1404
LIFESPICE INGREDIENTS, LLC; *U.S. Private*, pg. 2451
MAFCO NATURAL PRODUCTS—See MacAndrews & Forbes Incorporated; *U.S. Private*, pg. 2532
MANCINI FOODS; *U.S. Private*, pg. 2562
MCCORMICK FOOD SERVICE DIVISION—See McCormick & Company, Incorporated; *U.S. Public*, pg. 1404
MCCORMICK INGREDIENTS SOUTHEAST ASIA PRIVATE LIMITED—See McCormick & Company, Incorporated; *U.S. Public*, pg. 1404
MCCORMICK SPICE MILL—See McCormick & Company, Incorporated; *U.S. Public*, pg. 1404
MODERN PRODUCTS, INC.; *U.S. Private*, pg. 2762
MORE THAN GOURMET, INC.—See Ajinomoto Company, Inc.; *Int'l*, pg. 256
NATIONAL FLAVORS, LLC—See The Riverside Company; *U.S. Private*, pg. 4109
NATURAL FLAVORS, INC.—See Firmenich International SA; *Int'l*, pg. 2680
NATURAL SEASONING COMPANY; *U.S. Private*, pg. 2867
NEWLY WEDS FOODS, INC.—See Newly Weds Foods, Inc.; *U.S. Private*, pg. 2915
NORTHWESTERN FLAVORS, LLC—See Mars, Incorporated; *U.S. Private*, pg. 2590
OCCIDENTAL INTERNATIONAL FOODS LLC; *U.S. Private*, pg. 2988
O S HOLDINGS, INC.; *U.S. Private*, pg. 2977
THE PERFECT PUREE OF NAPA VALLEY, LLC.; *U.S. Private*, pg. 4093
PHYTONE LIMITED—See FMC Corporation; *U.S. Public*, pg. 862
PT MIWON INDONESIA - GRESIK FACTORY—See Daesang Corporation; *Int'l*, pg. 1909
PT MIWON INDONESIA—See Daesang Corporation; *Int'l*, pg. 1909
QINGDAO ARIAKE FOODSTUFF CO., LTD.—See ARIAKE JAPAN Co., Ltd.; *Int'l*, pg. 564
QINGDAO RED BUTTERFLY PRECISION MATERIALS CO., LTD.—See Chori Co., Ltd.; *Int'l*, pg. 1583
RANI FOODS, INC.; *U.S. Private*, pg. 3355
RED MONKEY FOODS, INC.—See Wells Fargo & Company; *U.S. Public*, pg. 2344
RODELLE, INC.—See Archer-Daniels-Midland Company; *U.S. Public*, pg. 185
RUDOLF WILD GMBH & CO. KG—See Archer-Daniels-Midland Company; *U.S. Public*, pg. 184
SAMJO CELLTECH LTD.—See Dongwon Enterprise Co., Ltd.; *Int'l*, pg. 2171
SAUER BRANDS, INC.—See Falfurrias Capital Partners, LP; *U.S. Private*, pg. 1467
SAVOURY SYSTEMS INTERNATIONAL, INC.; *U.S. Private*, pg. 3557
SCHLOTTERBECK & FOSS, LLC—See Frontenac Company LLC; *U.S. Private*, pg. 1614
SENSIENT COLORS EUROPE GMBH—See Sensient Technologies Corporation; *U.S. Public*, pg. 1867
SENSIENT DEHYDRATED FLAVORS SAS—See Sensient Technologies Corporation; *U.S. Public*, pg. 1867
SENSIENT FLAVORS AND FRAGRANCES SOUTH AFRICA (PROPRIETARY) LTD—See Sensient Technologies Corporation; *U.S. Public*, pg. 1867
SENSIENT FLAVORS AUSTRIA GMBH—See Sensient Technologies Corporation; *U.S. Public*, pg. 1867
SENSIENT FLAVORS & FRAGRANCES INDUSTRY & TRADE LIMITED COMPANY—See Sensient Technologies Corporation; *U.S. Public*, pg. 1867
SENSIENT FLAVORS INTERNATIONAL, INC.—See Sensient Technologies Corporation; *U.S. Public*, pg. 1867
SENSIENT FLAVORS ITALY S.R.L.—See Sensient Technologies Corporation; *U.S. Public*, pg. 1867
SENSIENT FOOD COLORS ITALY S.R.L.—See Sensient Technologies Corporation; *U.S. Public*, pg. 1867
SENSIENT FOOD COLORS POLAND SP.ZO.O.—See Sensient Technologies Corporation; *U.S. Public*, pg. 1867
SENSIENT FOOD COLORS ROMANIA S.R.L.—See Sensient Technologies Corporation; *U.S. Public*, pg. 1867
SENSIENT FOOD COLORS THE NETHERLANDS BV—See Sensient Technologies Corporation; *U.S. Public*, pg. 1867
SENSIENT TECHNOLOGIES CORP. (CHINA) LTD—See Sensient Technologies Corporation; *U.S. Public*, pg. 1867
SENSIENT TECHNOLOGIES CORPORATION (JAPAN)—See Sensient Technologies Corporation; *U.S. Public*, pg. 1867
SOY VAY ENTERPRISES, INC.—See The Clorox Company; *U.S. Public*, pg. 2062
SPICE CHAIN CORPORATION—See iSpice LLC; *U.S. Private*, pg. 2146

N.A.I.C.S. INDEX

311991 — PERISHABLE PREPARED...

THE SPICE HUNTER—See Falfurrias Capital Partners, LP; *U.S. Private*, pg. 1467
STANGE (JAPAN) K.K.—See McCormick & Company, Incorporated; *U.S. Public*, pg. 1404
U.S. COATINGS LLC—See Henkel AG & Co. KGaA; *Int'l*, pg. 3354
US SALT, LLC—See Crestwood Equity Partners LP; *U.S. Public*, pg. 594
VITAMINSPICE; *U.S. Private*, pg. 4405
WATKINS INCORPORATED; *U.S. Private*, pg. 4455
WHITTLE & MUTCH, INC.—See Riverside Partners, LLC; *U.S. Private*, pg. 3446
WILD FLAVORS (CANADA) INC.—See Archer-Daniels-Midland Company; *U.S. Public*, pg. 184
WILD FLAVORS, INC.—See Archer-Daniels-Midland Company; *U.S. Public*, pg. 184
WILLIAMS FOODS LLC—See The Pritzker Group - Chicago, LLC; *U.S. Private*, pg. 4098
WIXON INDUSTRIES INC.; *U.S. Private*, pg. 4551

311991 — PERISHABLE PREPARED FOOD MANUFACTURING

ACI BIOTECH LIMITED—See Advanced Chemical Industries Limited; *Int'l*, pg. 158
ACI FOODS LIMITED—See Advanced Chemical Industries Limited; *Int'l*, pg. 158
AEON SAVEUR CO., LTD.—See AEON Co., Ltd.; *Int'l*, pg. 177
AEON TOPVALU VIETNAM COMPANY LIMITED—See AEON Co., Ltd.; *Int'l*, pg. 177
AGRICOLA NOVA INDEMIL LTDA—See General Mills, Inc.; *U.S. Public*, pg. 921
AHJIKAN CO., LTD.; *Int'l*, pg. 223
AL MUHAIDIB FOODS CO.—See A.K. Al-Muhaidib & Sons Group of Companies; *Int'l*, pg. 24
ALSEA, S.A.B. DE C.V.; *Int'l*, pg. 379
ALTYFOODS CO. LTD.—See AEON Co., Ltd.; *Int'l*, pg. 177
THE AMARNA CO.—See H.I.G. Capital, LLC; *U.S. Private*, pg. 1832
AMERICAN KITCHEN DELIGHTS; *U.S. Private*, pg. 239
ANTHONY'S COAL FIRED PIZZA OF AVENTURA, LLC—See BurgerFi International, Inc.; *U.S. Public*, pg. 412
ANTHONY'S COAL FIRED PIZZA OF BOCA RATON, LLC—See BurgerFi International, Inc.; *U.S. Public*, pg. 412
ANTHONY'S COAL FIRED PIZZA OF EDISON, LLC—See BurgerFi International, Inc.; *U.S. Public*, pg. 412
ANTHONY'S COAL FIRED PIZZA OF LITTLETON, LLC—See BurgerFi International, Inc.; *U.S. Public*, pg. 412
ANTHONY'S COAL FIRED PIZZA OF MONROEVILLE, LLC—See BurgerFi International, Inc.; *U.S. Public*, pg. 412
ANTHONY'S COAL FIRED PIZZA OF PLANTATION, LLC—See BurgerFi International, Inc.; *U.S. Public*, pg. 412
ANTHONY'S COAL FIRED PIZZA OF READING, LLC—See BurgerFi International, Inc.; *U.S. Public*, pg. 412
ANTHONY'S COAL FIRED PIZZA OF SOUTH TAMPA, LLC—See BurgerFi International, Inc.; *U.S. Public*, pg. 412
ANTHONY'S COAL FIRED PIZZA OF STONY BROOK, LLC—See BurgerFi International, Inc.; *U.S. Public*, pg. 412
ANTHONY'S COAL FIRED PIZZA OF TREXLERTOWN LLC—See BurgerFi International, Inc.; *U.S. Public*, pg. 412
ANTHONY'S COAL FIRED PIZZA OF WYNNEWOOD, LLC—See BurgerFi International, Inc.; *U.S. Public*, pg. 412
ARENA HOLDING S.P.A. - TU IN CUCINA PLANT—See Arena Holding S.p.A.; *Int'l*, pg. 558
ASAHIMATSU FOODS CO., LTD.; *Int'l*, pg. 599
ASIANA CUISINE ENTERPRISES, INC.; *U.S. Private*, pg. 351
ASK FOODS INC.; *U.S. Private*, pg. 351
BAKKAVOR LIMITED—See Bakkavor Group plc; *Int'l*, pg. 805
BAKKER BARENDRECHT B.V.—See Greenyard N.V.; *Int'l*, pg. 3077
BALDWIN RICHARDSON FOODS COMPANY - MACEDON MANUFACTURING FACILITY—See Baldwin Richardson Foods Company; *U.S. Private*, pg. 459
BEAR NAKED, INC.—See WK Kellogg Co; *U.S. Public*, pg. 2376
BEEOLOGICS INC.—See Bayer Aktiengesellschaft; *Int'l*, pg. 008
BIG-A COMPANY, INC.—See AEON Co., Ltd.; *Int'l*, pg. 177
BIMBOSAN AG—See HOCHDORF Holding AG; *Int'l*, pg. 3437
BHEATEC B.V.—See BRAIN Biotech AG; *Int'l*, pg. 1137
BRF GERMANY GMBH—See BRF S.A.; *Int'l*, pg. 1150
BRIDGFORD MARKETING COMPANY—See Bridgford Foods Corporation; *U.S. Public*, pg. 382
CHIN HUAY PUBLIC COMPANY LIMITED; *Int'l*, pg. 1480

CHUNG'S FOODS INC.; *U.S. Private*, pg. 894
CIPA INDUSTRIAL DE PRODUTOS ALIMENTARES LTDA.—See PepsiCo, Inc.; *U.S. Public*, pg. 1668
CJ FOODS USA INC.—See CJ Corporation; *Int'l*, pg. 1632
CJ FOODS VIETNAM CO., LTD.—See CJ Corporation; *Int'l*, pg. 1632
CJ RAVIOLLO RUS LLC—See CJ Corporation; *Int'l*, pg. 1633
CJ VIETNAM COMPANY LIMITED—See CJ Corporation; *Int'l*, pg. 1633
COFCO CEREAL WAY FOODS CO., LTD.—See COFCO Limited; *Int'l*, pg. 1691
COFCO LECONTE FOODS (SHENZHEN) CO., LTD.—See COFCO Limited; *Int'l*, pg. 1691
CONVENI B.V.; *Int'l*, pg. 1786
COOKIES-N-MILK, INC.—See Tenex Capital Management, L.P.; *U.S. Private*, pg. 3966
CTI FOODS, LLC - CARSON PLANT—See Black Diamond Capital Holdings, LLC; *U.S. Private*, pg. 570
CTI FOODS, LLC - CARSON PLANT—See Massachusetts Mutual Life Insurance Company; *U.S. Public*, pg. 2605
CUISINE SOLUTIONS FRANCE—See Cuisine Solutions, Inc.; *U.S. Public*, pg. 604
DDW COLOURS SDN. BHD.—See Givaudan S.A.; *Int'l*, pg. 2979
DELICA ACE CO., LTD.—See Ajinomoto Company, Inc.; *Int'l*, pg. 257
DELICA CHEF CORPORATION—See House Foods Group Inc.; *Int'l*, pg. 3490
DEL MONACO FOODS, INC.—See Kainos Capital, LLC; *U.S. Private*, pg. 2255
DELSOLE CORPORATION; *Int'l*, pg. 2015
DELTA AGRAR D.O.O.—See Delta Holding; *Int'l*, pg. 2018
DINEWISE, INC.; *U.S. Public*, pg. 667
DOMINOS PIZZA BELGIUM S.P.R.L.—See Domino's Pizza Enterprises Ltd.; *Int'l*, pg. 2162
DOMINO'S PIZZA NEW ZEALAND LIMITED—See Domino's Pizza Enterprises Ltd.; *Int'l*, pg. 2162
DYNAMIC FOODS—See Food Management Partners, Inc.; *U.S. Private*, pg. 1561
EARTH'S OWN FOOD COMPANY INC.—See Agrifoods International Cooperative LTD; *Int'l*, pg. 217
E.A. SWEEN COMPANY; *U.S. Private*, pg. 1304
EKA FOODSTUFF SDN. BHD.—See EKA Noodles Berhad; *Int'l*, pg. 2337
EURO-AMERICAN FOODS GROUP CO., INC.; *U.S. Private*, pg. 1433
EURO INDIA FRESH FOODS LTD.; *Int'l*, pg. 2531
FINAGAZ—See UGI Corporation; *U.S. Public*, pg. 2222
FLAGA NG GMBH—See UGI Corporation; *U.S. Public*, pg. 2222
FRESH & READY FOODS LLC—See Compass Group PLC; *Int'l*, pg. 1752
FSS, INC.; *U.S. Private*, pg. 1618
FUJI FOOD PRODUCTS, INC.—See Meruelo Group LLC; *U.S. Private*, pg. 2677
FUJIMOTO FOODS INC.; *Int'l*, pg. 2829
GOURMET BOUTIQUE; *U.S. Private*, pg. 1746
GRAPHIC PACKAGING INTERNATIONAL CANADA CORPORATION—See Graphic Packaging Holding Company; *U.S. Public*, pg. 958
GREENCORE NORTHAMPTON—See Greencore Group plc; *Int'l*, pg. 3074
GREENYARD FLOWERS NETHERLANDS B.V.—See Greenyard N.V.; *Int'l*, pg. 3077
GREENYARD FRESH AUSTRIA GMBH—See Greenyard N.V.; *Int'l*, pg. 3077
GREENYARD FRESH BELGIUM N.V.—See Greenyard N.V.; *Int'l*, pg. 3077
GREENYARD FRESH BRAZIL LTDA.—See Greenyard N.V.; *Int'l*, pg. 3077
GREENYARD FRESH CHILE LTDA.—See Greenyard N.V.; *Int'l*, pg. 3077
GREENYARD FRESH COLOMBIA SAS—See Greenyard N.V.; *Int'l*, pg. 3077
GREENYARD FRESH DIRECT BELGIUM N.V.—See Greenyard N.V.; *Int'l*, pg. 3077
GREENYARD FRESH FRANCE S.A.S.—See Greenyard N.V.; *Int'l*, pg. 3077
GREENYARD FRESH GERMANY GMBH—See Greenyard N.V.; *Int'l*, pg. 3077
GREENYARD FRESH HOLDING NL B.V.—See Greenyard N.V.; *Int'l*, pg. 3077
GREENYARD FRESH ITALY S.R.L.—See Greenyard N.V.; *Int'l*, pg. 3077
GREENYARD FRESH PERU SAC—See Greenyard N.V.; *Int'l*, pg. 3077
GREENYARD FRESH UK LTD.—See Greenyard N.V.; pg 3077
GREENYARD FROZEN BELGIUM N.V.—See Greenyard N.V.; *Int'l*, pg. 3077
GREENYARD FROZEN BRAZIL LTDA.—See Greenyard N.V.; *Int'l*, pg. 3077
GREENYARD FROZEN COMINES S.A.S.—See Greenyard N.V.; *Int'l*, pg. 3077
GREENYARD FROZEN FRANCE S.A.S.—See Greenyard N.V.; *Int'l*, pg. 3077

GREENYARD FROZEN POLAND SP. Z O.O.—See Greenyard N.V.; *Int'l*, pg. 3077
GREENYARD FROZEN UK LTD.—See Greenyard N.V.; *Int'l*, pg. 3077
GREENYARD LOGISTICS BELGIUM N.V.—See Greenyard N.V.; *Int'l*, pg. 3077
GREENYARD LOGISTICS POLAND SP. Z O.O.—See Greenyard N.V.; *Int'l*, pg. 3078
GREENYARD LOGISTICS USA INC.—See Greenyard N.V.; *Int'l*, pg. 3078
GREENYARD PREPARED BELGIUM N.V.—See Greenyard N.V.; *Int'l*, pg. 3078
GREENYARD PREPARED NETHERLANDS B.V.—See Greenyard N.V.; *Int'l*, pg. 3078
GREENYARD TRANSPORT BELGIUM N.V.—See Greenyard N.V.; *Int'l*, pg. 3078
HACHIBAN TRADING (THAILAND) CO., LTD.—See HACHI-BAN CO., LTD.; *Int'l*, pg. 3203
HALWANI BROS; *Int'l*, pg. 3234
HANKYU DELICA INC.—See H2O Retailing Corp.; *Int'l*, pg. 3200
THE HARRIS SOUP COMPANY—See Kainos Capital, LLC; *U.S. Private*, pg. 2255
HENG TAI CONSUMABLES GROUP LIMITED; *Int'l*, pg. 3345
HILD SAMEN GMBH—See Bayer Aktiengesellschaft; *Int'l*, pg. 908
HOME GROWN INDUSTRIES OF GEORGIA, INC.; *U.S. Private*, pg. 1971
HOT MAMA'S FOODS, INC.; *U.S. Private*, pg. 1988
HPK A.D.; *Int'l*, pg. 3501
J. G. TOWNSEND, JR. & COMPANY; *U.S. Private*, pg. 2156
J&J SNACK FOODS HANDHELDS CORP.—See J&J Snack Foods Corporation; *U.S. Public*, pg. 1180
JMS FOODSERVICE, LLC—See The J.M. Smucker Company; *U.S. Public*, pg. 2107
JOE CORBI'S WHOLESALE PIZZA INC.; *U.S. Private*, pg. 2218
KITCHEN FRESH FOODS INC.; *U.S. Private*, pg. 2316
LAND MARK PRODUCTS, INC.—See One Rock Capital Partners, LLC; *U.S. Private*, pg. 3022
LANDSHIRE, INC.; *U.S. Private*, pg. 2387
LET'S DO LUNCH, INC.; *U.S. Private*, pg. 2433
MAHINDRA GREENYARD PRIVATE LTD.—See Greenyard N.V.; *Int'l*, pg. 3078
MAMEDA INC.—See H2O Retailing Corp.; *Int'l*, pg. 3200
THE MARAMONT CORPORATION; *U.S. Private*, pg. 4074
MINMOR INDUSTRIES LLC; *U.S. Private*, pg. 2742
MRS. GERRY'S KITCHEN, INC.; *U.S. Private*, pg. 2806
NATURESEAL, INC.—See RPM International Inc.; *U.S. Public*, pg. 1817
NEW YORK RAVIOLI & PASTA CO.; *U.S. Private*, pg. 2912
NINA MIA, INC.; *U.S. Private*, pg. 2928
NURTURE INC.—See Danone; *Int'l*, pg. 1967
OHG REWE-FOODSERVICE GMBH & CO.—See Coop-Gruppe Genossenschaft; *Int'l*, pg. 1790
OKAMI, INC. - DENVER PLANT—See Meruelo Group LLC; *U.S. Private*, pg. 2677
OKAMI, INC.—See Meruelo Group LLC; *U.S. Private*, pg. 2677
ORCHARD HOUSE FOODS LIMITED—See Elaghmore GP LLP; *Int'l*, pg. 2342
PERONNE MANUFACTURING COMPANY LTD—See Barbados Shipping & Trading Co. Ltd.; *Int'l*, pg. 858
PIONEER FOODS UK LTD.—See PepsiCo, Inc.; *U.S. Public*, pg. 1671
THE PIZZA FACTORY—See Boparan Holdings Limited; *Int'l*, pg. 1111
READY PAC FOODS, INC.—See Bonduelle SAS; *Int'l*, pg. 1106
REED FOOD TECHNOLOGY; *U.S. Private*, pg. 3382
R.E. HANA II ENTERPRISES INC.; *U.S. Private*, pg. 3335
RIDGECREST HERBALS, INC.; *U.S. Private*, pg. 3432
SABA FRESH CUTS AB—See BAMA Gruppen AS; *Int'l*, pg. 813
SABROSURA FOODS, LLC—See Centre Partners Management LLC; *U.S. Private*, pg. 828
SANDRIDGE FOOD CORPORATION; *U.S. Private*, pg. 3544
THE SANDWICH FACTORY HOLDINGS LIMITED—See Greencore Group plc; *Int'l*, pg. 3074
SARA LEE FOODS, LLC—See Tyson Foods, Inc.; *U.S. Public*, pg. 2210
SARDUS LATTA MALTIDER AB—See Atria Plc; *Int'l*, pg. 694
SCHIFF'S FOOD SERVICE, INC.; *U.S. Private*, pg. 3564
SIGMA ALIMENTOS, S.A. DE C.V.—See ALFA, S.A.B. de C.V.; *Int'l*, pg. 313
SLIM-FAST NUTRITIONAL FOOD LLC; *U.S. Private*, pg. 3688
SO DELICIOUS DAIRY FREE—See Danone; *Int'l*, pg. 1967
SOVOS BRANDS INTERMEDIATE, INC.—See Advent International Corporation; *U.S. Private*, pg. 105
ST. CLAIR FOODS; *U.S. Private*, pg. 3771
SUNBURST FOODS INC.; *U.S. Private*, pg. 3865
SUN RICH FRESH FOODS, INC. - NORTHEAST FRESH FACILITY—See Kainos Capital, LLC; *U.S. Private*, pg. 2255
SUN RICH FRESH FOODS (USA) INC. - EASTERN FRESH

311991 — PERISHABLE PREPARED...

FACILITY—See Kainos Capital, LLC; *U.S. Private*, pg. 2255
SUN RICH FRESH FOODS (USA) INC.—See Kainos Capital, LLC; *U.S. Private*, pg. 2255
TANMIAH FOOD GROUP—See Dabbagh Group Holding Company Ltd.; *Int'l*, pg. 1903
TARAMI CORPORATION—See DyDo Group Holdings, Inc.; *Int'l*, pg. 2238
TASTY FRIES, INC.; *U.S. Public*, pg. 1983
TOPS FOODS NV—See Charoen Pokphand Foods Public Company Limited; *Int'l*, pg. 1453
TRANSGOURMET IMMOBILIEN GMBH & CO. KG—See Coop-Gruppe Genossenschaft; *Int'l*, pg. 1790
TRANSGOURMET SCHWEIZ AG—See Coop-Gruppe Genossenschaft; *Int'l*, pg. 1790
TYSON FOODS CANADA, INC.—See Tyson Foods, Inc.; *U.S. Public*, pg. 2210
UNAKA COMPANY INC.; *U.S. Private*, pg. 4279
US PERISHABLES; *U.S. Private*, pg. 4319
VANS INTERNATIONAL FOODS—See Tyson Foods, Inc.; *U.S. Public*, pg. 2210
THE WILLIAMSON GROUP, INC.—See Givaudan S.A.; *Int'l*, pg. 2982
YELLOW CHIPS BV—See Campbell Soup Company; *U.S. Public*, pg. 427

311999 — ALL OTHER MISCELLANEOUS FOOD MANUFACTURING

4C FOODS CORPORATION; *U.S. Private*, pg. 15
714607 ONTARIO LTD.; *Int'l*, pg. 14
AAK AUST. PTY LTD.—See AAK AB; *Int'l*, pg. 31
AAK AUSTRALIA PTY LTD.—See AAK AB; *Int'l*, pg. 31
AAK BD FOODS LTD.—See AAK AB; *Int'l*, pg. 31
AAK COLOMBIA S.A.S.—See AAK AB; *Int'l*, pg. 31
AAK CZECH REPUBLIC SPOL.S.R.O.—See AAK AB; *Int'l*, pg. 31
AAK CZECH REPUBLIC S.R.O.—See AAK AB; *Int'l*, pg. 31
AAK HAVNEN A/S—See AAK AB; *Int'l*, pg. 32
AAK MEXICO, S.A. DE C.V.—See AAK AB; *Int'l*, pg. 32
AAK NETHERLANDS BV—See AAK AB; *Int'l*, pg. 32
AAK SG PTE. LTD.—See AAK AB; *Int'l*, pg. 32
AAK SWEDEN AB—See AAK AB; *Int'l*, pg. 32
AARHUSKARLSHAMN BALTIC LTD.—See AAK AB; *Int'l*, pg. 32
AARHUSKARLSHAMN NORWAY AS—See AAK AB; *Int'l*, pg. 32
AARHUSKARLSHAMN POLAND SP.Z O.O.—See AAK AB; *Int'l*, pg. 32
AARHUSKARLSHAMN RU OOO—See AAK AB; *Int'l*, pg. 32
ABBOTT MANUFACTURING SINGAPORE PRIVATE LIMITED—See Abbott Laboratories; *U.S. Public*, pg. 16
ABBOTT NUTRITION—See Abbott Laboratories; *U.S. Public*, pg. 17
AB CARL A CARLSON CHARKUTERIER—See Atria Plc; *Int'l*, pg. 694
ABOVE FOOD CORP.—See Above Food Ingredients Inc.; *Int'l*, pg. 67
ABOVE FOOD INGREDIENTS INC.; *Int'l*, pg. 67
ADF FOODS LTD.; *Int'l*, pg. 145
ADM INTERNATIONAL SARL—See Archer-Daniels-Midland Company; *U.S. Public*, pg. 184
ADNAMS PLC; *Int'l*, pg. 152
ADRIAFRUIT ITALIA S.R.L.—See Coeclerici S.p.A.; *Int'l*, pg. 1688
ADVANCEPIERRE FOODS, INC.—See Tyson Foods, Inc.; *U.S. Public*, pg. 2209
AFRICAN AGRICULTURE, INC.—See African Agriculture Holdings Inc.; *U.S. Public*, pg. 57
AFRICAN CONSUMER CARE LTD.—See Dabur India Ltd; *Int'l*, pg. 1903
AGRANA FRUIT BRASIL INDUSTRIA, COMERCIO, IMPORTACAO E EXPORTACAO LTDA.—See AGRANA Beteiligungs-AG; *Int'l*, pg. 214
AGRANA FRUIT GERMANY GMBH—See AGRANA Beteiligungs-AG; *Int'l*, pg. 214
AGRANA FRUIT JAPAN CO., LTD.—See AGRANA Beteiligungs-AG; *Int'l*, pg. 214
AGRANA FRUIT (JIANGSU) COMPANY LIMITED—See AGRANA Beteiligungs-AG; *Int'l*, pg. 214
AGRANA FRUIT LUKA TOV—See AGRANA Beteiligungs-AG; *Int'l*, pg. 214
AGRANA FRUIT S.A.S.—See AGRANA Beteiligungs-AG; *Int'l*, pg. 214
AGRANA FRUIT SERVICES GMBH—See AGRANA Beteiligungs-AG; *Int'l*, pg. 214
AGRANA FRUIT UKRAINE TOV—See AGRANA Beteiligungs-AG; *Int'l*, pg. 214
AGRANA JUICE (XIANYANG) CO., LTD.—See AGRANA Beteiligungs-AG; *Int'l*, pg. 214
AGRANA RESEARCH & INNOVATION CENTER GMBH—See AGRANA Beteiligungs-AG; *Int'l*, pg. 214
AGRANA ROMANIA S.R.L.—See AGRANA Beteiligungs-AG; *Int'l*, pg. 214
AGRANA STARKE GMBH—See AGRANA Beteiligungs-AG; *Int'l*, pg. 214

AGRO TECH FOODS LTD.—See Conagra Brands, Inc.; *U.S. Public*, pg. 563
AGTHIA GROUP EGYPT LLC—See Agthia Group PJSC; *Int'l*, pg. 221
AGTHIA GROUP PJSC; *Int'l*, pg. 221
AGV PRODUCTS CORP.; *Int'l*, pg. 222
AIMIA FOODS LIMITED; *Int'l*, pg. 233
AJINOMOTO DO BRASIL IND. E COM. DE ALIMENTOS LTDA.—See Ajinomoto Company, Inc.; *Int'l*, pg. 257
AJINOMOTO FOODS EUROPE S.A.S—See Ajinomoto Company, Inc.; *Int'l*, pg. 256
AJINOMOTO FROZEN FOODS (THAILAND) CO., LTD.—See Ajinomoto Company, Inc.; *Int'l*, pg. 256
AJINOMOTO-GENETIKA RESEARCH INSTITUTE—See Ajinomoto Company, Inc.; *Int'l*, pg. 257
AJINOMOTO HEALTH & NUTRITION NORTH AMERICA, INC.—See Ajinomoto Company, Inc.; *Int'l*, pg. 256
AJINOMOTO INDIA PRIVATE LIMITED—See Ajinomoto Company, Inc.; *Int'l*, pg. 256
AJINOMOTO KOREA, INC.—See Ajinomoto Company, Inc.; *Int'l*, pg. 256
AJINOMOTO NORTH AMERICA, INC.—See Ajinomoto Company, Inc.; *Int'l*, pg. 257
AJINOMOTO TAIWAN INC.—See Ajinomoto Company, Inc.; *Int'l*, pg. 256
AL AIN FOOD & BEVERAGES PJSC—See Agthia Group PJSC; *Int'l*, pg. 221
ALDARIS JSC—See Carlsberg A/S; *Int'l*, pg. 1339
ALGIST BRUGGEMAN S.A.—See Compagnie des Levures Lesaffre SA; *Int'l*, pg. 1738
ALI-BIG INDUSTRIA ALIMENTARE S.R.L.—See Coop-Gruppe Genossenschaft; *Int'l*, pg. 1789
ALICORP S.A.—See Grupo Romero; *Int'l*, pg. 3134
ALIMENTOS FINOS DE OCCIDENTE, S.A. DE C.V.—See ALFA, S.A.B. de C.V.; *Int'l*, pg. 313
ALIMENTOS HEINZ DE COSTA RICA S.A—See 3G Capital Inc.; *U.S. Private*, pg. 9
ALIMENTOS HEINZ DE COSTA RICA S.A.—See Berkshire Hathaway Inc.; *U.S. Public*, pg. 317
ALLIANCE GRAIN TRADERS (TIANJIN) CO. LTD.—See AGT Food and Ingredients Inc.; *Int'l*, pg. 221
ALLIED BLENDING & INGREDIENTS, INC.—See Arsenal Capital Management LP; *U.S. Private*, pg. 337
ALLIED OLD ENGLISH, INC.; *U.S. Private*, pg. 187
ALLT SMORGAS—See Atria Plc; *Int'l*, pg. 694
ALMA FOODS, LLC—See Hormel Foods Corporation; *U.S. Public*, pg. 1053
AL MANAL PURIFICATION & BOTTLING OF MINERAL WATER LLC—See Agthia Group PJSC; *Int'l*, pg. 222
ALMER LTD.—See BERICAP GmbH & Co. KG; *Int'l*, pg. 980
ALPRO COMM.VA—See Danone; *Int'l*, pg. 1967
ALPRO GMBH—See Danone; *Int'l*, pg. 1967
ALPRO SOJA NEDERLAND B.V.—See Danone; *Int'l*, pg. 1967
ALPRO (UK) LIMITED—See Danone; *Int'l*, pg. 1967
AL SHAHEER CORP.; *Int'l*, pg. 282
AMERICAN POP CORN COMPANY; *U.S. Private*, pg. 244
AMI OPERATING, INC.—See Brynwood Partners Management LLC; *U.S. Private*, pg. 674
AMY'S KITCHEN, INC.; *U.S. Private*, pg. 270
ANGELIC BAKEHOUSE, INC.—See Benford Capital Partners, LLC; *U.S. Private*, pg. 526
ANGEL YEAST COMPANY LIMITED; *Int'l*, pg. 459
ANJANI FOODS LIMITED; *Int'l*, pg. 472
ANNIE'S, INC.—See General Mills, Inc.; *U.S. Public*, pg. 921
AOSTE FILIALE (SUISSE) SARL—See ALFA, S.A.B. de C.V.; *Int'l*, pg. 313
APETIT PAKASTE OY—See Apetit Plc; *Int'l*, pg. 509
APIS INDIA LIMITED; *Int'l*, pg. 515
A. POORTMAN (LONDON) LTD.—See AGT Food and Ingredients Inc.; *Int'l*, pg. 221
APPLE RUSH CO, INC.; *U.S. Public*, pg. 169
ARAMARK/CAMPBELL CATERING—See Aramark; *U.S. Public*, pg. 177
ARBEL GROUP—See AGT Food and Ingredients Inc.; *Int'l*, pg. 221
ARCHER DANIELS MIDLAND EUROPE BV—See Archer-Daniels-Midland Company; *U.S. Public*, pg. 184
ARCOPAR S.A.—See Arcor Sociedad Anonima, Industrial y Comercial; *Int'l*, pg. 550
ARCOR CANADA INC.—See Arcor Sociedad Anonima, Industrial y Comercial; *Int'l*, pg. 550
ARCOR DO BRASIL LIMITADA—See Arcor Sociedad Anonima, Industrial y Comercial; *Int'l*, pg. 550
ARCOR ECUADOR—See Arcor Sociedad Anonima, Industrial y Comercial; *Int'l*, pg. 550
ARCOR SOCIEDAD ANONIMA, INDUSTRIAL Y COMERCIAL; *Int'l*, pg. 550
ARCOR U.S.A. INC.—See Arcor Sociedad Anonima, Industrial y Comercial; *Int'l*, pg. 550
ARIAKE JAPAN CO., LTD.; *Int'l*, pg. 563
AROMOR FLAVORS & FRAGRANCES INC.—See International Flavors & Fragrances Inc.; *U.S. Public*, pg. 1151
AROTZ FOODS, S.A.—See Ebro Foods S.A.; *Int'l*, pg. 2286
AROUND NOON FOODS LIMITED; *Int'l*, pg. 577
ARROZEIRAS MUNDIARROZ, S.A.—See Ebro Foods S.A.; *Int'l*, pg. 2286
ASAHI L&C CORP.—See Hurxley Corporation; *Int'l*, pg. 3538

AS HKSCAN ESTONIA—See HKFoods Plc; *Int'l*, pg. 3429
ASTRA FOOD PROCESSING CO.—See Arab Supply & Trading Co.; *Int'l*, pg. 532
ATKINS NUTRITIONALS, INC.—See The Simply Good Foods Company; *U.S. Public*, pg. 2130
ATLANTA POLAND S.A.; *Int'l*, pg. 674
ATLANTIC ARGETA D.O.O.—See ATLANTIC GRUPA d.d.; *Int'l*, pg. 674
ATLANTIC DROGA KOLINSKA D.O.O.—See ATLANTIC GRUPA d.d.; *Int'l*, pg. 674
ATLANTIC STARK D.O.O.—See ATLANTIC GRUPA d.d.; *Int'l*, pg. 674
ATRIA RETAIL AB—See Atria Plc; *Int'l*, pg. 694
AUNT KITTY'S FOODS, INC—See Hanover Foods Corporation; *U.S. Public*, pg. 984
AUSTRALIAN OILSEEDS INVESTMENTS PTY LTD.—See Australian Oilseeds Holdings Limited; *Int'l*, pg. 722
AUSTRIA JUICE GERMANY GMBH—See AGRANA Beteiligungs-AG; *Int'l*, pg. 214
AUSTRIA JUICE ROMANIA S.R.L.—See AGRANA Beteiligungs-AG; *Int'l*, pg. 214
AUSTRIA JUICE UKRAINE TOV—See AGRANA Beteiligungs-AG; *Int'l*, pg. 214
AUTOCRAT, LLC; *U.S. Private*, pg. 398
AWETA FRANCE S.A.S.—See FPS Food Processing Systems B.V.; *Int'l*, pg. 2757
AZURE STANDARD; *U.S. Private*, pg. 416
BAKERY FOODS LIMITED—See CapVest Limited; *Int'l*, pg. 1318
BAKKAVOR PIZZA—See Bakkavor Group plc; *Int'l*, pg. 805
BALDWIN RICHARDSON FOODS COMPANY; *U.S. Private*, pg. 459
BAMA GRUPPEN AS; *Int'l*, pg. 813
BAMBINO AGRO INDUSTRIES LIMITED; *Int'l*, pg. 813
BARILLA AMERICA N.Y. INC.—See Barilla Holding S.p.A.; *Int'l*, pg. 865
BARILLA DEUTSCHLAND GMBH—See Barilla Holding S.p.A.; *Int'l*, pg. 865
BARILLA FRANCE SAS—See Barilla Holding S.p.A.; *Int'l*, pg. 865
BARILLA GIDA A.S.—See Barilla Holding S.p.A.; *Int'l*, pg. 865
BARILLA HELLAS S.A.—See Barilla Holding S.p.A.; *Int'l*, pg. 865
BARILLA SVERIGE AB—See Barilla Holding S.p.A.; *Int'l*, pg. 865
BARKMAN HONEY, LLC; *U.S. Private*, pg. 475
BAYN EUROPE AB; *Int'l*, pg. 914
BAY VALLEY FOODS, LLC—See TreeHouse Foods, Inc.; *U.S. Public*, pg. 2187
BAY VALLEY FOODS—See TreeHouse Foods, Inc.; *U.S. Public*, pg. 2187
BAY VALLEY FOODS—See TreeHouse Foods, Inc.; *U.S. Public*, pg. 2187
BAY VALLEY FOODS—See TreeHouse Foods, Inc.; *U.S. Public*, pg. 2187
BAYWA VENTURE GMBH—See BayWa AG; *Int'l*, pg. 916
BEIJING HORMEL FOODS CO. LTD.—See Hormel Foods Corporation; *U.S. Public*, pg. 1053
BEINGMATE CO., LTD.; *Int'l*, pg. 962
BELLAMY'S AUSTRALIA LIMITED—See China Mengniu Dairy Company Limited; *Int'l*, pg. 1520
BELL FLAVORS & FRAGRANCES, INC. - FRAGRANCE MANUFACTURING FACILITY—See Bell Flavors & Fragrances, Inc.; *U.S. Private*, pg. 518
BELL FOODS, LLC; *U.S. Private*, pg. 518
BERTAGNI 1882 SPA—See Ebro Foods S.A.; *Int'l*, pg. 2286
BETTER BEVERAGES, INC.; *U.S. Private*, pg. 546
B&G FOODS NORTH AMERICA, INC.—See B&G Foods, Inc.; *U.S. Public*, pg. 260
BICKEL'S SNACK FOODS, INC.—See Hanover Foods Corporation; *U.S. Public*, pg. 984
BIMBO-MARTINEZ COMERCIAL, S.L.—See Grupo Bimbo, S.A.B. de C.V.; *Int'l*, pg. 3123
BIOGEN KOREA—See Biogen Inc.; *U.S. Public*, pg. 336
BIO SPRINGER ASIA—See Compagnie des Levures Lesaffre SA; *Int'l*, pg. 1738
BIOSPRINGER GUANGXI YIPINXIAN CO. LTD—See Compagnie des Levures Lesaffre SA; *Int'l*, pg. 1738
BIO SPRINGER PACIFIC—See Compagnie des Levures Lesaffre SA; *Int'l*, pg. 1738
BIO SPRINGER S.A.—See Compagnie des Levures Lesaffre SA; *Int'l*, pg. 1738
BIO SPRINGER S.A. - YEAST EXTRACTS FACTORY—See Compagnie des Levures Lesaffre SA; *Int'l*, pg. 1738
BIO SPRINGER SOUTH AMERICA—See Compagnie des Levures Lesaffre SA; *Int'l*, pg. 1738
BOB EVANS FARMS, LLC—See Post Holdings, Inc.; *U.S. Public*, pg. 1703
BOREALIS FOODS INC.; *Int'l*, pg. 1114
BOURNE PREPARED PRODUCE—See Bakkavor Group plc; *Int'l*, pg. 805
BOURNE STIR FRY—See Bakkavor Group plc; *Int'l*, pg. 806
BREADWINNER FOODS LIMITED—See Greencore Group plc; *Int'l*, pg. 3074
BRUCE FOODS CORPORATION; *U.S. Private*, pg. 671
BUHLER AG; *Int'l*, pg. 1211
BUREAU DE LIAISON DOHLER FRANCE S.A.R.L.—See

N.A.I.C.S. INDEX

311999 — ALL OTHER MISCELLAN...

Dohler GmbH; *Int'l*, pg. 2155
BURLESON'S INC.; *U.S. Private*, pg. 688
CADBURY SOUTH AFRICA—See Mondelez International, Inc.; *U.S. Public*, pg. 1461
CALDIC B.V.; *Int'l*, pg. 1262
CALDIC USA INC.—See Caldic B.V.; *Int'l*, pg. 1262
CAMPBELL CHEONG CHAN MALAYSIA SDN BHD—See Campbell Soup Company; *U.S. Public*, pg. 426
CAMPBELL FOODS BELGIUM N.V./S.A.—See Campbell Soup Company; *U.S. Public*, pg. 426
CAMPBELL SOUP ASIA LIMITED—See Campbell Soup Company; *U.S. Public*, pg. 427
CAMPBELL SOUP SWEDEN AB—See Campbell Soup Company; *U.S. Public*, pg. 427
CAMPBELL SOUP TRADING (SHANGHAI) COMPANY LIMITED—See Campbell Soup Company; *U.S. Public*, pg. 427
CAMPBELL SOUTHEAST ASIA SDN BHD—See Campbell Soup Company; *U.S. Public*, pg. 427
CAMPBELL SWIRE (HK) LTD—See Campbell Soup Company; *U.S. Public*, pg. 427
CAMPOFRIO FOOD GROUP, S.A.—See ALFA, S.A.B. de C.V.; *Int'l*, pg. 313
CANYON CREEK FOOD COMPANY LTD.; *Int'l*, pg. 1300
CARABAO GROUP PUBLIC COMPANY LIMITED; *Int'l*, pg. 1319
CARAVAN INGREDIENTS—See Corbion N.V.; *Int'l*, pg. 1795
CAREMOLI SPA; *Int'l*, pg. 1324
CAREMOLI USA, INC.—See Caremoli SpA; *Int'l*, pg. 1324
CARGILL B.V.—See Cargill, Inc.; *U.S. Private*, pg. 756
CARGILL EUROPE BVBA—See Cargill, Inc.; *U.S. Private*, pg. 756
CARGILL KITCHEN SOLUTIONS—See Cargill, Inc.; *U.S. Private*, pg. 757
CARGILL KITCHEN SOLUTIONS—See Cargill, Inc.; *U.S. Private*, pg. 757
CARIBBEAN PRODUCERS JAMAICA LTD.; *Int'l*, pg. 1330
CARLSBERG MARSTON'S BREWING COMPANY LTD.—See Carlsberg A/S; *Int'l*, pg. 1340
CARNES SELECTAS 2000 S.A.—See ALFA, S.A.B. de C.V.; *Int'l*, pg. 314
CASTELLA IMPORTS, INC.; *U.S. Private*, pg. 784
CAVAGHAN & GRAY CARLISLE—See Boparan Holdings Limited; *Int'l*, pg. 1111
CAVA GROUP, INC.; *U.S. Public*, pg. 454
CCCL PEARL CITY FOOD PORT SEZ LIMITED—See Consolidated Construction Consortium Ltd; *Int'l*, pg. 1770
CEMOI CHOCOLATIER SAS; *Int'l*, pg. 1400
CENTURY FOODS INTERNATIONAL, LLC—See Hormel Foods Corporation; *U.S. Public*, pg. 1054
CENTURY PACIFIC FOOD, INC.; *Int'l*, pg. 1418
CEVITAL S.P.A.; *Int'l*, pg. 1425
CHADHA ORIENTAL FOODS LIMITED—See GraceKennedy Limited; *Int'l*, pg. 3048
CHAM FOODS (ISRAEL) LTD.; *Int'l*, pg. 1439
CHAMPION FOODS, L.L.C.—See Ilitch Holdings, Inc.; *U.S. Private*, pg. 2041
CHAMP, LLC—See Hormel Foods Corporation; *U.S. Public*, pg. 1054
CHANGCHUN DIHAO FOODSTUFF DEVELOPMENT CO., LTD.—See Global Sweeteners Holdings Limited; *Int'l*, pg. 3001
CHARKDELIKATESSER I HALMSTAD AB—See Atria Plc; *Int'l*, pg. 694
CHENGDU DALI FOODS CO., LTD.—See Dali Foods Group Co. Ltd.; *Int'l*, pg. 1951
CHEN KE MING FOOD MANUFACTURING CO., LTD; *Int'l*, pg. 1464
CHINA KANGDA FOOD COMPANY LIMITED; *Int'l*, pg. 1514
CHIN CHIN AGRO-INDUSTRIAL COMPANY; *Int'l*, pg. 1480
CHIPITA S.A.; *Int'l*, pg. 1573
CHOPPIES ENTERPRISES LTD.; *Int'l*, pg. 1582
CHUNG HWA FOOD INDUSTRIAL CO., LTD.; *Int'l*, pg. 1597
CJ BEIJING FOODS CO., LTD.—See CJ Corporation; *Int'l*, pg. 1631
CJ CHEILJEDANG CORP.—See CJ Corporation; *Int'l*, pg. 1631
CJ CORP. (BEIJING)—See CJ Corporation; *Int'l*, pg. 1632
CJ DCH GUANGDONG FROZEN FOOD CO., LTD.—See CJ Corporation; *Int'l*, pg. 1632
CJ ENM JAPAN INC.—See CJ Corporation; *Int'l*, pg. 1632
CJ FOODS MANUFACTURING, CORPORATION—See CJ Corporation; *Int'l*, pg. 1632
CJ FOODS MYANMAR CO., LTD.—See CJ Corporation; *Int'l*, pg. 1632
CJ FRESHWAY AMERICA CORPORATION—See CJ Corporation; *Int'l*, pg. 1632
CJ FRESHWAY QINGDAO CORPORATION—See CJ Corporation; *Int'l*, pg. 184
CJ GRAND, S.A. DE C.V.—See CJ Corporation; *Int'l*, pg. 1632
CJ LOGISTICS EUROPE GMBH—See CJ Corporation; *Int'l*, pg. 1633
CJ MAINFROST FOODS GMBH—See CJ Corporation; *Int'l*, pg. 1633
CJ N CITY CO., LTD.—See CJ Corporation; *Int'l*, pg. 1633

CJ OLIVE YOUNG (SHANGHAI) CORPORATION—See CJ Corporation; *Int'l*, pg. 1633
CJ OMNI, INC.—See CJ Corporation; *Int'l*, pg. 1631
CJ PACIFIC CORPORATION—See CJ Corporation; *Int'l*, pg. 1631
CLABBER GIRL CORPORATION—See B&G Foods, Inc.; *U.S. Public*, pg. 260
CLARMIL MANUFACTURING CORPORATION; *U.S. Private*, pg. 915
CLASSIC EGG PRODUCTS INC.—See Moark Productions Inc.; *U.S. Private*, pg. 2756
CLIF BAR & COMPANY—See Mondelez International, Inc.; *U.S. Public*, pg. 1461
CLOVER INDUSTRIES LIMITED; *Int'l*, pg. 1663
CLOVER PAKISTAN LTD.; *Int'l*, pg. 1663
COBB EUROPE LIMITED—See Tyson Foods, Inc.; *U.S. Public*, pg. 2209
COBB-VANTRESS BRASIL LTDA.—See Tyson Foods, Inc.; *U.S. Public*, pg. 2209
THE COCA-COLA COMPANY - AVIATION DEPARTMENT—See The Coca-Cola Company; *U.S. Public*, pg. 2065
COFCO TUNHE SUGAR CO., LTD.—See COFCO Limited; *Int'l*, pg. 1692
COFEED FEEDMILL (CHANGCHUN) CO., LTD.—See CJ Corporation; *Int'l*, pg. 1633
COLUMBIA NUTRITIONAL, LLC; *U.S. Private*, pg. 977
COMERCIAL NUTRESA S.A.S.—See Grupo Nutresa S.A.; *Int'l*, pg. 3133
COMO CO., LTD.; *Int'l*, pg. 1721
COMPANIA NACIONAL DE CHOCOLATES S.A.S.—See Grupo Nutresa S.A.; *Int'l*, pg. 3133
CONAGRA FOODS FOOD INGREDIENTS COMPANY, INC.—See Conagra Brands, Inc.; *U.S. Public*, pg. 563
CONAGRA FOODS - HAMBURG—See Conagra Brands, Inc.; *U.S. Public*, pg. 563
CONAGRA FOODS PACKAGED FOODS, LLC—See Conagra Brands, Inc.; *U.S. Public*, pg. 563
CONVENIENCE FOODS LANKA PLC; *Int'l*, pg. 1786
COOKS COFFEE COMPANY LIMITED; *Int'l*, pg. 1788
COOKTEK LLC—See The Middleby Corporation; *U.S. Public*, pg. 2113
COOPERATIVE REGIONS OF ORGANIC PRODUCER POOLS; *U.S. Private*, pg. 1043
COOP SCHWEIZ - SWISSMILL DIVISION—See Coop-Gruppe Genossenschaft; *Int'l*, pg. 1790
CORBION N.V.; *Int'l*, pg. 1795
COSMAX NBT, INC.; *Int'l*, pg. 1811
COSUCRA - GROUPE WARCOING; *Int'l*, pg. 1815
COUNTRY MAID, INC.; *U.S. Private*, pg. 1067
COWBOY FOOD COMPANY LIMITED—See Four Seas Mercantile Holdings Limited; *Int'l*, pg. 2755
CP KELCO—See J.M. Huber Corporation; *U.S. Private*, pg. 2168
C.P. PRODUCTS, INC.—See Charoen Pokphand Group Co., Ltd.; *Int'l*, pg. 1453
CRANSWICK GOURMET BACON COMPANY LIMITED—See Cranswick Plc; *Int'l*, pg. 1828
CRANSWICK GOURMET PASTRY COMPANY LIMITED—See Cranswick Plc; *Int'l*, pg. 1828
CRANSWICK GOURMET SAUSAGE COMPANY LIMITED—See Cranswick Plc; *Int'l*, pg. 1828
CRANSWICK PLC; *Int'l*, pg. 1828
CRESTCHEM LIMITED; *Int'l*, pg. 1841
CRIO INC.; *U.S. Private*, pg. 1101
CROWN CHICKEN LIMITED—See Cranswick Plc; *Int'l*, pg. 1828
CROWN I ENTERPRISES INC.—See Sysco Corporation; *U.S. Public*, pg. 1973
CRYOVAC LONDRINA LTDA.—See Sealed Air Corporation; *U.S. Public*, pg. 1852
CSM BAKERY PRODUCTS NORTH AMERICA—See Rhone Group, LLC; *U.S. Private*, pg. 3423
CSM BENELUX - GOES—See Rhone Group, LLC; *U.S. Private*, pg. 3423
CTH US INC.—See Darling Ingredients Inc.; *U.S. Public*, pg. 633
CTI FOODS, LLC—See Black Diamond Capital Holdings, LLC; *U.S. Private*, pg. 570
CTI FOODS, LLC—See Massachusetts Mutual Life Insurance Company; *U.S. Private*, pg. 2605
CUBA BEVERAGE COMPANY; *U.S. Public*, pg. 603
CULLY & SULLY LIMITED—See The Hain Celestial Group, Inc.; *U.S. Public*, pg. 2086
CURT GEORGI GMBH & CO. KG; *Int'l*, pg. 1880
CUSTOM CULINARY, INC.—See Griffith Laboratories, Inc.; *U.S. Private*, pg. 1789
CYTOSPORT, INC.—See PepsiCo, Inc.; *U.S. Public*, pg. 1668
DAAVISION BV—See Archer-Daniels-Midland Company; *U.S. Public*, pg. 184
DABOMB PROTEIN CORP.; *Int'l*, pg. 1903
DABUR INTERNATIONAL LTD.—See Dabur India Ltd; *Int'l*, pg. 1903
DAESANG CORPORATION; *Int'l*, pg. 1909
DAESANG CORPORATION - TAY NINH TAPIOCA STARCH FACTORY—See Daesang Corporation; *Int'l*, pg. 1909
DAICEL NANNING FOOD INGREDIENTS CO., LTD.—See Daicel Corporation; *Int'l*, pg. 1919

DAIRY FRUIT A/S—See Dohler GmbH; *Int'l*, pg. 2156
DAKOTA DRY BEAN INC.—See Benson Hills, Inc.; *U.S. Public*, pg. 296
DANONE DUMEX LTD.—See Danone; *Int'l*, pg. 1965
DANONE DUMEX—See Danone; *Int'l*, pg. 1965
DCL YEAST LIMITED—See Compagnie des Levures Lesaffre SA; *Int'l*, pg. 1738
D.D. WILLIAMSON & CO., INC.; *U.S. Private*, pg. 1141
DELIKATESS SKINKOR AB—See Atria Plc; *Int'l*, pg. 694
DELIMEX DE MEXICO S.A. DE C.V.—See 3G Capital Inc.; *U.S. Private*, pg. 9
DELIMEX DE MEXICO S.A. DE C.V.—See Berkshire Hathaway Inc.; *U.S. Public*, pg. 317
DEREK AND CONSTANCE LEE CORP.; *U.S. Private*, pg. 1209
DE WAFELBAKKERS, LLC—See Brynwood Partners Management LLC; *U.S. Private*, pg. 674
DIAMOND CRYSTAL BRANDS, INC.—See Peak Rock Capital LLC; *U.S. Private*, pg. 3123
DIANAS MEXICAN FOOD PRODUCTS; *U.S. Private*, pg. 1224
DIC LIFETEC CO., LTD.—See DIC Corporation; *Int'l*, pg. 2108
DIRAFROST MAROC SARL—See AGRANA Beteiligungs-AG; *Int'l*, pg. 214
DISCOVERY FOODS LTD.; *Int'l*, pg. 2134
DIVERSIFIED FOOD & SEASONING INC.; *U.S. Private*, pg. 1242
DNA BRANDS, INC.; *U.S. Public*, pg. 671
DNP INTERNATIONAL CO. INC.; *U.S. Private*, pg. 1249
DOHLER GMBH; *Int'l*, pg. 2155
DOLE FOOD COMPANY, INC.—See Dole plc; *Int'l*, pg. 2157
DOMRETOR OY—See Atria Plc; *Int'l*, pg. 694
DOUBLE B FOODS, INC.—See Atlantic Street Capital Management LLC; *U.S. Private*, pg. 374
DOUBLE FLOWERING CAMMELIA CO., LTD—See HACHIBAN CO., LTD.; *Int'l*, pg. 3203
DR SMOOTHIE BRANDS—See Highlander Partners, LP.; *U.S. Private*, pg. 1939
DUPONT & LEOSK ENTERPRISES SDN BHD; *Int'l*, pg. 2227
DXN INDUSTRIES (M) SDN. BHD.—See DXN Holdings Bhd.; *Int'l*, pg. 2237
DXN PHARMACEUTICAL SDN. BHD.—See DXN Holdings Bhd.; *Int'l*, pg. 2237
DXN (SINGAPORE) PTE LTD—See DXN Holdings Bhd.; *Int'l*, pg. 2237
EATEM CORP.—See Linsalata Capital Partners, Inc.; *U.S. Private*, pg. 2463
EBROFROST DENMARK A/S—See Ebro Foods S.A.; *Int'l*, pg. 2286
EBROFROST GERMANY GMBH—See Ebro Foods S.A.; *Int'l*, pg. 2286
EBROFROST UK LTD.—See Ebro Foods S.A.; *Int'l*, pg. 2286
EBRO INDIA PRIVATE LIMITED—See Ebro Foods S.A.; *Int'l*, pg. 2286
EBRO TILDA PRIVATE LIMITED—See Ebro Foods S.A.; *Int'l*, pg. 2286
ECHO LAKE FARM PRODUCE COMPANY INC.—See Elkin Co.; *U.S. Private*, pg. 1363
ECOAGRI ASIA LTD.—See AiFarm Ltd.; *Int'l*, pg. 231
ECOLAB B.V.B.A./S.P.R.L.—See Ecolab Inc.; *U.S. Public*, pg. 713
ECOLAB CO.—See Ecolab Inc.; *U.S. Public*, pg. 713
ECOLAB HYGIENE S.R.O.—See Ecolab Inc.; *U.S. Public*, pg. 713
EIPII EXPORTS PVT LTD.—See Bliss Gvs Pharma Ltd.; *Int'l*, pg. 1063
EKIZ KIMYA SANAYI VE TICARET A.S.; *Int'l*, pg. 2338
EMMSONS INTERNATIONAL LIMITED; *Int'l*, pg. 2385
ENERVIT S.P.A.; *Int'l*, pg. 2425
ERICH ZIEGLER GMBH—See Archer-Daniels-Midland Company; *U.S. Public*, pg. 185
EUROGERM SA; *Int'l*, pg. 2552
EV ACQUISITION INC.—See Darling Ingredients Inc.; *U.S. Public*, pg. 634
EVERYD.COM, INC.—See H2O Retailing Corp.; *Int'l*, pg. 3200
EXCLUSIVE MARK (M) SDN. BHD.—See Citra Nusa Holdings Berhad; *Int'l*, pg. 1626
EXPORT TRADING GROUP PTE LTD.; *Int'l*, pg. 2590
FAGERDALA (HUIYANG) PACKAGING CO., LTD.—See Sealed Air Corporation; *U.S. Public*, pg. 1853
FAGERDALA MALAYSIA SDN. BHD.—See Sealed Air Corporation; *U.S. Public*, pg. 1853
FAGERDALA PACKAGING INC.—See Sealed Air Corporation; *U.S. Public*, pg. 1853
FAGERDALA (SHANGHAI) FOAMS CO. LTD.—See Sealed Air Corporation; *U.S. Public*, pg. 1853
FAGERDALA (XIAMEN) PACKAGING CO. LTD.—See Sealed Air Corporation; *U.S. Public*, pg. 1853
FARMAX INDIA LIMITED; *Int'l*, pg. 2619
FARM FRESH FOODS, INC.—See Post Holdings, Inc.; *U.S. Public*, pg. 1703
FAZER FOOD SERVICES AB—See Compass Group PLC; *Int'l*, pg. 1752

311999 — ALL OTHER MISCELLAN...   CORPORATE AFFILIATIONS

FAZER FOOD SERVICES A/S—See Compass Group PLC; *Int'l*, pg. 1752
FAZER FOOD SERVICES AS—See Compass Group PLC; *Int'l*, pg. 1752
FAZER FOOD SERVICES OY—See Compass Group PLC; *Int'l*, pg. 1752
FBEC WORLDWIDE, INC., *U.S. Public*, pg. 824
F & B NUTRITION SDN. BHD.—See Can-One Berhad; *Int'l*, pg. 1276
FEINKOST DITTMANN REICHOLD FEINKOST GMBH; *Int'l*, pg. 2632
FERRERO ARGENTINA S.A. - PASTORA PLANT—See Ferrero International S.A.; *Int'l*, pg. 2640
FERRERO ASIA LIMITED—See Ferrero International S.A.; *Int'l*, pg. 2640
FERRERO ASIA LTD (SINGAPORE)—See Ferrero International S.A.; *Int'l*, pg. 2640
FERRERO ASIA LTD—See Ferrero International S.A.; *Int'l*, pg. 2640
FERRERO B.V.—See Ferrero International S.A.; *Int'l*, pg. 2640
FERRERO CANADA LTD.—See Ferrero International S.A.; *Int'l*, pg. 2640
FERRERO CESKA S.R.O.—See Ferrero International S.A.; *Int'l*, pg. 2640
FERRERO DEL ECUADOR S.A—See Ferrero International S.A.; *Int'l*, pg. 2640
FERRERO DE MEXICO S.A. DE C.V. E—See Ferrero International S.A.; *Int'l*, pg. 2640
FERRERO DEUTSCHLAND G.M.B.H—See Ferrero International S.A.; *Int'l*, pg. 2640
FERRERO DO BRASIL INDUSTRIA DOCEIRA E ALIMENTAR LTDA—See Ferrero International S.A.; *Int'l*, pg. 2641
FERRERO D.O.O.—See Ferrero International S.A.; *Int'l*, pg. 2640
FERRERO FRANCE S.A.—See Ferrero International S.A.; *Int'l*, pg. 2640
FERRERO FSC LUXEMBOURG S.A.—See Ferrero International S.A.; *Int'l*, pg. 2640
FERRERO IBERICA S.A.—See Ferrero International S.A.; *Int'l*, pg. 2640
FERRERO INDIA PRIVATE LIMITED—See Ferrero International S.A.; *Int'l*, pg. 2640
FERRERO IRELAND LIMITED—See Ferrero International S.A.; *Int'l*, pg. 2640
FERRERO ITHEMBA RSA (PTY) LTD—See Ferrero International S.A.; *Int'l*, pg. 2640
FERRERO JAPAN LTD—See Ferrero International S.A.; *Int'l*, pg. 2640
FERRERO LADM—See Ferrero International S.A.; *Int'l*, pg. 2640
FERRERO LANKA (PVT) LTD—See Ferrero International S.A.; *Int'l*, pg. 2640
FERRERO MAGYARORSZAG KFT.—See Ferrero International S.A.; *Int'l*, pg. 2640
FERRERO OSTERREICH HANDELS G. M.B.H.—See Ferrero International S.A.; *Int'l*, pg. 2640
FERRERO POLSKA SP. Z O.O.—See Ferrero International S.A.; *Int'l*, pg. 2640
FERRERO PUBBLIREGIA S.R.L.—See Ferrero International S.A.; *Int'l*, pg. 2640
FERRERO ROMANIA S.R.L.—See Ferrero International S.A.; *Int'l*, pg. 2640
FERRERO RUSSIA CJSC—See Ferrero International S.A.; *Int'l*, pg. 2640
FERRERO SCANDINAVIA A/B—See Ferrero International S.A.; *Int'l*, pg. 2640
FERRERO SCHWEIZ A.G.—See Ferrero International S.A.; *Int'l*, pg. 2640
FERRERO S.P.A. - ANGELO DEI LOMBARDI FACTORY—See Ferrero International S.A.; *Int'l*, pg. 2640
FERRERO S.P.A. - BALVANO FACTORY—See Ferrero International S.A.; *Int'l*, pg. 2640
FERRERO S.P.A GREECE SINGLE-PARTNER LIMITED LIABILITY COMPANY—See Ferrero International S.A.; *Int'l*, pg. 2640
FERRERO S.P.A. - POZZUOLO MARTESANA FACTORY—See Ferrero International S.A.; *Int'l*, pg. 2640
FERRERO TRADING DUBAI—See Ferrero International S.A.; *Int'l*, pg. 2640
FERRERO TRADING (SHANGHAI) COMPANY, LTD—See Ferrero International S.A.; *Int'l*, pg. 2640
FERRERO TURKIYE CIKOLATA VE TARIM URUNLERI SANAYI VE DIS TICARET A.S.—See Ferrero International S.A.; *Int'l*, pg. 2640
FERRERO UK LTD.—See Ferrero International S.A.; *Int'l*, pg. 2641
FERRERO UKRAINE LLC—See Ferrero International S.A.; *Int'l*, pg. 2641
F&G (BOTSWANA) (PTY) LIMITED—See Huabao International Holdings Limited; *Int'l*, pg. 3510
FLAGSHIP FOOD GROUP, LLC; *U.S. Private*, pg. 1539
FLAVOR INN CORPORATION SDN BHD—See Croda International plc; *Int'l*, pg. 1853
FLYING SPARK LTD.; *Int'l*, pg. 2716

FOREMOST GROUPS, INC.—See Foremost Groups, Inc.; *U.S. Private*, pg. 1565
FOREVERGREEN KOREA—See ForeverGreen Worldwide Corporation; *Int'l*, pg. 867
FOREVERGREEN WORLDWIDE CORPORATION; *U.S. Public*, pg. 867
FORMOSA OILSEED PROCESSING CO., LTD.; *Int'l*, pg. 2735
FORT DODGE FOODS, INC.—See Hormel Foods Corporation; *U.S. Public*, pg. 1054
FOUR SEAS (HEBEI) FOOD COMPANY LIMITED—See Four Seas Mercantile Holdings Limited; *Int'l*, pg. 2755
FOUR SEAS (SUZHOU) FOOD CO., LTD.—See Four Seas Mercantile Holdings Limited; *Int'l*, pg. 2755
FOUR WAY DISTRIBUTORS LTD.; *Int'l*, pg. 2755
FRUIT FORMULATIONS PRIVATE LIMITED; *Int'l*, pg. 2797
FRUTAROM PERU S.A—See International Flavors & Fragrances Inc.; *U.S. Public*, pg. 1152
FUJI EUROPE AFRICA B.V.—See Fuji Oil Holdings Inc.; *Int'l*, pg. 2815
FUJI OIL (CHINA) INVESTMENT CO., LTD.—See Fuji Oil Holdings Inc.; *Int'l*, pg. 2815
FUJI OIL CO., LTD. - RINKU PLANT—See Fuji Oil Holdings Inc.; *Int'l*, pg. 2815
FUNC FOOD FINLAND OY—See Celsius Holdings, Inc.; *U.S. Public*, pg. 466
FUNC FOOD GROUP OYJ—See Celsius Holdings, Inc.; *U.S. Public*, pg. 466
FUTURE BRIGHT HOLDINGS LIMITED; *Int'l*, pg. 2852
FU-WANG FOODS LTD.; *Int'l*, pg. 2801
G A CARLSSON AB - GEA'S—See Atria Plc; *Int'l*, pg. 694
GAIA HERBS INC.—See Givaudan S.A.; *Int'l*, pg. 2981
GAN SHMUEL FOODS LTD.; *Int'l*, pg. 2880
GANSU DALI FOODS CO., LTD.—See Dali Foods Group Co. Ltd.; *Int'l*, pg. 1951
GANSU YASHENG INDUSTRIAL (GROUP) CO., LTD.; *Int'l*, pg. 2882
GASLAMP POPCORN COMPANY, LLC—See Rudolph Foods Company; *U.S. Private*, pg. 3502
GEA NEDERLAND B.V.—See GEA Group Aktiengesellschaft; *Int'l*, pg. 2901
GEHL FOODS, LLC—See Wind Point Advisors LLC; *U.S. Private*, pg. 4534
GEINAN SHOKUHIN CO., LTD.—See Aohata Corporation; *Int'l*, pg. 487
GENERAL INDUSTRIES & PACKAGES COMPANY—See Hayel Saeed Anam Group of Companies; *Int'l*, pg. 3290
GENERAL MILLS ARGENTINA S.A.—See General Mills, Inc.; *U.S. Public*, pg. 921
GENERAL MILLS AUSTRALIA PTY. LTD.—See General Mills, Inc.; *U.S. Public*, pg. 922
GENERAL MILLS BRAZIL LTDA.—See General Mills, Inc.; *U.S. Public*, pg. 922
GENERAL MILLS CEREALS HOLDING (SOUTH AFRICA) PTY LIMITED—See General Mills, Inc.; *U.S. Public*, pg. 921
GENERAL MILLS DE VENEZUELA, C.A.; *Int'l*, pg. 2919
GENERAL MILLS FOODS, INC.—See General Mills, Inc.; *U.S. Public*, pg. 921
GENERAL MILLS FRANCE (SAS)—See General Mills, Inc.; *U.S. Public*, pg. 922
GENERAL MILLS GMBH—See General Mills, Inc.; *U.S. Public*, pg. 922
GENERAL MILLS HOLDING (AUSTRALIA) PTY LIMITED—See General Mills, Inc.; *U.S. Public*, pg. 921
GENERAL MILLS HOLDING ONE (GERMANY) GMBH—See General Mills, Inc.; *U.S. Public*, pg. 921
GENERAL MILLS HONG KONG LIMITED—See General Mills, Inc.; *U.S. Public*, pg. 922
GENERAL MILLS IBERICA, S.A.U.—See General Mills, Inc.; *U.S. Public*, pg. 922
GENERAL MILLS INDIA PRIVATE LIMITED—See General Mills, Inc.; *U.S. Public*, pg. 922
GENERAL MILLS MALAYSIA SDN. BHD.—See General Mills, Inc.; *U.S. Public*, pg. 921
GENERAL MILLS MANUFACTURING AUSTRALIA PTY LIMITED—See General Mills, Inc.; *U.S. Public*, pg. 921
GENERAL MILLS MIDDLE EAST & NORTH AFRICA FZE—See General Mills, Inc.; *U.S. Public*, pg. 921
GENERAL MILLS NEW ZEALAND LIMITED—See General Mills, Inc.; *U.S. Public*, pg. 922
GENERAL MILLS SALES SINGAPORE PTE. LTD.—See General Mills, Inc.; *U.S. Public*, pg. 921
GENERAL MILLS SAN ADRIAN, S.L. UNIPERSONAL—See General Mills, Inc.; *U.S. Public*, pg. 921
GENERAL MILLS SCANDINAVIA AB—See General Mills, Inc.; *U.S. Public*, pg. 921
GENERAL MILLS SOUTH AFRICA (PTY) LTD.—See General Mills, Inc.; *U.S. Public*, pg. 922
GENERAL MILLS TAIWAN LIMITED—See General Mills, Inc.; *U.S. Public*, pg. 922
GEOVITA S.R.L.—See Ebro Foods S.A.; *Int'l*, pg. 2286
GG UNIQUEFIBER AS—See The Hain Celestial Group, Inc.; *U.S. Public*, pg. 2086
GILSTER-MARY LEE CORPORATION—See Gilster-Mary Lee Corporation; *U.S. Private*, pg. 1701
GIVAUDAN AROMA VE ESANS SANAYI VE TICARET LTD. STI.—See Givaudan S.A.; *Int'l*, pg. 2980

GIVAUDAN AUSTRALIA PTY. LTD.—See Givaudan S.A.; *Int'l*, pg. 2980
GIVAUDAN AUSTRALIA PTY LTD.—See Givaudan S.A.; *Int'l*, pg. 2980
GIVAUDAN ERFTSTADT GMBH & CO. KG—See Givaudan S.A.; *Int'l*, pg. 2980
GIVAUDAN FLAVORS CORPORATION - ELGIN—See Givaudan S.A.; *Int'l*, pg. 2981
GIVAUDAN FLAVORS (SHANGHAI) LTD.—See Givaudan S.A.; *Int'l*, pg. 2981
GIVAUDAN JAPAN K.K. - YOKOHAMA—See Givaudan S.A.; *Int'l*, pg. 2980
GIVAUDAN NEDERLAND BV—See Givaudan S.A.; *Int'l*, pg. 2981
GIVAUDAN NORTH EUROPE AB—See Givaudan S.A.; *Int'l*, pg. 2981
GIVAUDAN NZ LTD.—See Givaudan S.A.; *Int'l*, pg. 2981
GIVAUDON RUS LLC—See Givaudan S.A.; *Int'l*, pg. 2981
GIVAUDAN UK LIMITED - WIRRAL—See Givaudan S.A.; *Int'l*, pg. 2980
GLOBAL EMPLOYMENT SERVICES, INC.—See Tyson Foods, Inc.; *U.S. Public*, pg. 2209
GLOBAL FOOD CREATORS CO., LTD.; *Int'l*, pg. 2996
GOLDA GIDA IHTIYAC MADDLER SAN. AND TRADE INC.—See Bera Holding A.S.; *Int'l*, pg. 978
GOLDEN PHEASANT FOODS LLC—See Swander Pace Capital, LLC; *U.S. Private*, pg. 3890
GOLD STAR CHILI INC.; *U.S. Public*, pg. 1728
GOURMET PRIMO CO., LTD.—See Bangkok Airways Public Company Limited; *Int'l*, pg. 832
GOURMET SERVICE AB—See Atria Plc; *Int'l*, pg. 693
GOYA EN ESPANA S.A.—See Goya Foods, Inc.; *U.S. Private*, pg. 1747
GOYA FOODS OF THE DOMINICAN REPUBLIC, S.A.—See Goya Foods, Inc.; *U.S. Private*, pg. 1747
GRACE FOOD PROCESSORS LTD.—See GraceKennedy Limited; *Int'l*, pg. 3048
GRACE FOODS & SERVICES COMPANY—See GraceKennedy Limited; *Int'l*, pg. 3048
GRACE FOODS (USA) INC.—See GraceKennedy Limited; *Int'l*, pg. 3049
GRACEKENNEDY (ONTARIO) INC.—See GraceKennedy Limited; *Int'l*, pg. 3049
GRACE, KENNEDY (U.S.A.) INC.—See GraceKennedy Limited; *Int'l*, pg. 3048
GRACEKENNEDY (USA) INC.—See GraceKennedy Limited; *Int'l*, pg. 3049
GRAINLI GMBH & CO. KG—See BayWa AG; *Int'l*, pg. 918
GRAND FOODS (PTY) LTD.—See Grand Parade Investments Limited; *Int'l*, pg. 3056
GREAT LAKES CHEESE OF WISCONSIN—See The Great Lakes Cheese Co., Inc.; *U.S. Private*, pg. 4038
GRECIAN DELIGHT FOODS INC.—See Entrepreneurial Equity Partners, LLC; *U.S. Private*, pg. 1406
GREENCORE DEVELOPMENTS LIMITED—See Greencore Group plc; *Int'l*, pg. 3074
GREENCORE FOOD TO GO LIMITED—See Greencore Group plc; *Int'l*, pg. 3074
GREENCORE PREPARED MEALS-KIVETON—See Greencore Group plc; *Int'l*, pg. 3074
GREENCORE SANDWICHES LTD.—See Greencore Group plc; *Int'l*, pg. 3074
GREENCORE SAUCES AND SOUPS LTD.—See Greencore Group plc; *Int'l*, pg. 3074
GREEN'S GENERAL FOODS PTY. LIMITED; *Int'l*, pg. 3073
GRIFFIN FOOD COMPANY—See Griffin Holdings Inc.; *U.S. Private*, pg. 1788
GRIFFITH LABORATORIES, INC. INNOVA DIVISION—See Griffith Laboratories, Inc.; *U.S. Private*, pg. 1789
GRUMA CORPORATION—See Gruma, S.A.B. de C.V.; *Int'l*, pg. 3114
GRUPA MASPEX SP. Z O.O.; *Int'l*, pg. 3117
GRUPO BIMBO, S.A.B. DE C.V.; *Int'l*, pg. 3122
GRUPO CHEN, S. DE R.L. DE C.V.—See ALFA, S.A.B. de C.V.; *Int'l*, pg. 314
GUANGDONG DALI FOODS CO., LTD.—See Dali Foods Group Co. Ltd.; *Int'l*, pg. 1951
GUANGDONG JIAHAO FOODSTUFF CO., LTD.—See Huabao International Holdings Limited; *Int'l*, pg. 3510
GULF COAST BLENDERS, INC.—See L.H. Hayward & Co., LLC; *U.S. Private*, pg. 2366
GYOZA KEIKAKU CO., LTD.—See CJ Corporation; *Int'l*, pg. 1634
HAAGEN-DAZS ARRAS SNC—See General Mills, Inc.; *U.S. Public*, pg. 922
HAAGEN-DAZS BELGIUM (SPRL)—See General Mills, Inc.; *U.S. Public*, pg. 922
HABIB RICE PRODUCT LIMITED; *Int'l*, pg. 3203
HAGOROMO FOODS CORPORATION; *Int'l*, pg. 3207
HAIN CELESTIAL BELGIUM BVBA—See The Hain Celestial Group, Inc.; *U.S. Public*, pg. 2086
HAIN CELESTIAL EUROPE B.V.—See The Hain Celestial Group, Inc.; *U.S. Public*, pg. 2086
THE HAIN CELESTIAL GROUP, INC.; *U.S. Public*, pg. 2086
HAIN CELESTIAL UK LIMITED—See The Hain Celestial Group, Inc.; *U.S. Public*, pg. 2087
HANGZHOU WAHAHA GROUP CO., LTD.; *Int'l*, pg. 3251

311999 — ALL OTHER MISCELLAN...

HANKYU DELICA I, INC.—See H2O Retailing Corp.; *Int'l*, pg. 3200
HANKYU FOOD PROCESS CO., LTD.—See H2O Retailing Corp.; *Int'l*, pg. 3200
HANKYU KITCHEN YELL KANSAI, INC.—See H2O Retailing Corp.; *Int'l*, pg. 3200
HANSELLS MASTERTON LTD.; *Int'l*, pg. 3259
HANS-GUNTER BERNER GMBH & CO. KG; *Int'l*, pg. 3259
HANSON FOODS LIMITED—See Heidelberg Materials AG; *Int'l*, pg. 3312
HARRY'S RESTAURATION SAS—See Barilla Holding S.p.A.; *Int'l*, pg. 865
HAUT BUYS (PVT) LTD—See Hi-Tech Lubricants Ltd.; *Int'l*, pg. 3381
HAZLEWOOD CONVENIENCE GROUP 1 LIMITED—See Greencore Group plc; *Int'l*, pg. 3074
HAZLEWOOD GROCERY LIMITED—See Greencore Group plc; *Int'l*, pg. 3074
HBL PRODUCTS S.A.—See Herbalife Nutrition Ltd.; *Int'l*, pg. 3359
HEARTHSIDE FOOD SOLUTIONS, LLC—See Charlesbank Capital Partners, LLC; *U.S. Private*, pg. 855
HEBEI DALI FOODS CO., LTD.—See Dali Foods Group Co. Ltd.; *Int'l*, pg. 1951
HEINZ ITALIA S.P.A.—See 3G Capital Inc.; *U.S. Private*, pg. 10
HEINZ ITALIA S.P.A.—See Berkshire Hathaway Inc.; *U.S. Public*, pg. 317
HENAN DALI FOODS CO., LTD.—See Dali Foods Group Co. Ltd.; *Int'l*, pg. 1951
HENNINGSEN FOODS, INC.—See Post Holdings, Inc.; *U.S. Public*, pg. 1704
HENNINGSEN NEDERLAND B.V.—See ARIAKE JAPAN Co., Ltd.; *Int'l*, pg. 564
HERBA BANGKOK, S.L.—See Ebro Foods S.A.; *Int'l*, pg. 2286
HERBA EGYPT RICEMILLS, LTD.—See Ebro Foods S.A.; *Int'l*, pg. 2286
HERBA INGREDIENTS, B.V.—See Ebro Foods S.A.; *Int'l*, pg. 2286
HERBALIFE BELA, LLC—See Herbalife Nutrition Ltd.; *Int'l*, pg. 3359
HERBALIFE BOLIVIA, LTDA.—See Herbalife Nutrition Ltd.; *Int'l*, pg. 3359
HERBALIFE CHINA, LLC—See Herbalife Nutrition Ltd.; *Int'l*, pg. 3359
HERBALIFE CZECH REPUBLIC, S.R.O—See Herbalife Nutrition Ltd.; *Int'l*, pg. 3359
HERBALIFE INTERNACIONAL DE MEXICO, S.A. DE C.V—See Herbalife Nutrition Ltd.; *Int'l*, pg. 3359
HERBALIFE INTERNATIONAL DEL COLOMBIA—See Herbalife Nutrition Ltd.; *Int'l*, pg. 3359
HERBALIFE INTERNATIONAL DEL ECUADOR, S.A.—See Herbalife Nutrition Ltd.; *Int'l*, pg. 3359
HERBALIFE INTERNATIONAL (THAILAND), LTD.—See Herbalife Nutrition Ltd.; *Int'l*, pg. 3359
HERBALIFE SLOVAKIA, S.R.O.—See Herbalife Nutrition Ltd.; *Int'l*, pg. 3360
HERBA NUTRICION, S.L.U.—See Ebro Foods S.A.; *Int'l*, pg. 2286
HERBSTREITH & FOX KG PEKTIN-FABRIKEN; *Int'l*, pg. 3360
HERO BENELUX B.V.—See Hero AG; *Int'l*, pg. 3363
HERO CZECH S.R.O.—See Hero AG; *Int'l*, pg. 3363
HERO ESPANA, S.A.—See Hero AG; *Int'l*, pg. 3363
HERO ITALIA SPA—See Hero AG; *Int'l*, pg. 3363
HERO POLSKA SP. Z O.O.—See Hero AG; *Int'l*, pg. 3363
HERO PORTUGAL LDA.—See Hero AG; *Int'l*, pg. 3363
HERO SLOVAKIA S.R.O.—See Hero AG; *Int'l*, pg. 3363
HIGHLAND SUGARWORKS, INCORPORATED; *U.S. Private*, pg. 1939
HILTON MEATS ZAANDAM B.V.—See Hilton Food Group plc; *Int'l*, pg. 3395
H.J. HEINZ B.V.—See 3G Capital Inc.; *U.S. Private*, pg. 9
H.J. HEINZ B.V.—See Berkshire Hathaway Inc.; *U.S. Public*, pg. 317
H.J. HEINZ COMPANY, L.P.—See 3G Capital Inc.; *U.S. Private*, pg. 9
H.J. HEINZ COMPANY, L.P.—See Berkshire Hathaway Inc.; *U.S. Public*, pg. 317
H.J. HEINZ CR/SR A.S.—See 3G Capital Inc.; *U.S. Private*, pg. 9
H.J. HEINZ CR/SR A.S.—See Berkshire Hathaway Inc.; *U.S. Public*, pg. 317
HKSCAN DENMARK A/S—See HKFoods Plc; *Int'l*, pg. 3429
HKSCAN FINLAND OY—See HKFoods Plc; *Int'l*, pg. 3429
HKSCAN LATVIA AS—See HKFoods Plc; *Int'l*, pg. 3429
HKSCAN SWEDEN AB—See HKFoods Plc; *Int'l*, pg. 3429
HOCHDORF NUTRICARE LTD.—See HOCHDORF Holding AG; *Int'l*, pg. 3437
HOCHDORF NUTRIFOOD LTD.—See HOCHDORF Holding AG; *Int'l*, pg. 3437
HOLIDAY SUPPORT FACILITY 2099; *U.S. Private*, pg. 1963
HOLTON FOOD PRODUCTS COMPANY—See RPM International Inc.; *U.S. Public*, pg. 1817
HOMETOWN FOOD COMPANY—See Brynwood Partners Management LLC; *U.S. Private*, pg. 674

HONEY GARDENS, INC.—See HGGC, LLC; *U.S. Private*, pg. 1930
HONIG MERKARTIKELEN—See 3G Capital Inc.; *U.S. Private*, pg. 9
HONIG MERKARTIKELEN—See Berkshire Hathaway Inc.; *U.S. Public*, pg. 317
HORMEL FOODS CORP. - SPECIALTY PRODUCTS DIVISION—See Hormel Foods Corporation; *U.S. Public*, pg. 1054
HORMEL FOODS JAPAN K.K.—See Hormel Foods Corporation; *U.S. Public*, pg. 1054
HOUSE FOODS CHINA INC.—See House Foods Group Inc.; *Int'l*, pg. 3490
HOUSE FOODS CORPORATION—See House Foods Group Inc.; *Int'l*, pg. 3490
HOUSE FOODS VIETNAM CO., LTD.—See House Foods Group Inc.; *Int'l*, pg. 3490
HOUSE OSOTSPA FOODS CO., LTD.—See House Foods Group Inc.; *Int'l*, pg. 3490
HPC FOODS, LTD.; *U.S. Private*, pg. 1996
HUGLI FOOD ELELMISZERIPARI KFT.—See Coop-Gruppe Genossenschaft; *Int'l*, pg. 1790
HUGLI FOOD POLSKA SP.Z O.O.—See Coop-Gruppe Genossenschaft; *Int'l*, pg. 1790
HUGLI FOOD SLOVAKIA S.R.O.—See Coop-Gruppe Genossenschaft; *Int'l*, pg. 1790
HUHTAMAKI FOODSERVICE (TIANJIN) LTD.—See Huhtamaki Oyj; *Int'l*, pg. 3525
HUMANA PHARMA INTERNATIONAL SPA—See DMK Deutsches Milchkontor GmbH; *Int'l*, pg. 2146
HUNG FOOK TONG GROUP HOLDINGS LTD; *Int'l*, pg. 3535
HUNYA FOODS CO., LTD.; *Int'l*, pg. 3537
H.WESTON & SONS LTD; *Int'l*, pg. 3199
HYUNDAI H&S CO., LTD.—See Hyundai Department Store Co., Ltd.; *Int'l*, pg. 3556
I.C.S. HERBALIFE MA, S.R.L.—See Herbalife Nutrition Ltd.; *Int'l*, pg. 3360
IINA DINING CO., LTD.—See Hankyu Hanshin Holdings Inc.; *Int'l*, pg. 3255
IMCD BENELUX BV—See IMCD N.V.; *Int'l*, pg. 3621
INDUSTRIA COLOMBIANA DE CAFE S.A.S.—See Grupo Nutresa S.A.; *Int'l*, pg. 3133
INDUSTRIA DE ALIMENTOS ZENU S.A.S.—See Grupo Nutresa S.A.; *Int'l*, pg. 3133
INDUSTRIA DOS EN UNO DE COLOMBIA LTDA—See Arcor Sociedad Anonima, Industrial y Comercial; *Int'l*, pg. 550
INDUSTRIAS ALIADAS S.A.S.—See Grupo Nutresa S.A.; *Int'l*, pg. 3133
INF - SOCIETA' AGRICOLA S.P.A.—See Assicurazioni Generali S.p.A.; *Int'l*, pg. 647
INGREDIENTS, INC.—See Cinven Limited; *Int'l*, pg. 1611
INGREDIENTS UNLIMITED, INC.—See Arsenal Capital Management LP; *U.S. Private*, pg. 337
INGREDION APAC EMEA SHARED SERVICES SDN. BHD.—See Ingredion Incorporated; *U.S. Public*, pg. 1123
INGREDION SOUTH AFRICA (PTY) LIMITED—See Ingredion Incorporated; *U.S. Public*, pg. 1123
INGREDION SWEETENER & STARCH (THAILAND) CO., LTD.—See Ingredion Incorporated; *U.S. Public*, pg. 1123
INNOVATION VENTURES LLC; *U.S. Private*, pg. 2081
INNOVATIVE FOOD PROCESSORS, INC.—See Balchem Corporation; *U.S. Public*, pg. 265
INTERNATIONAL FLAVORS & FRAGRANCES (HANGZHOU) CO. LTD—See International Flavors & Fragrances Inc.; *U.S. Public*, pg. 1152
INTERNATIONAL FLAVOURS & FRAGRANCES (NZ) LTD—See International Flavors & Fragrances Inc.; *U.S. Public*, pg. 1153
INTERNATURAL FOODS LLC.—See World Finer Foods, Inc.; *U.S. Private*, pg. 4565
INVITAE AUSTRALIA PTY. LTD.—See Invitae Corporation; *U.S. Public*, pg. 1165
IRAN MAYEH COMPANY—See Compagnie des Levures Lesaffre SA; *Int'l*, pg. 1739
IRAN MAYEH COMPANY - SOUTHEAST UNIT—See Compagnie des Levures Lesaffre SA; *Int'l*, pg. 1739
ISPICE LLC; *U.S. Private*, pg. 2146
IZICO KATWIJK B.V.—See Egeria Capital Management B.V.; *Int'l*, pg. 2323
IZICO NEDERLAND B.V.—See Egeria Capital Management B.V.; *Int'l*, pg. 2323
JACK GUTTMAN, INC.—See Kohlberg & Company, LLC; *U.S. Private*, pg. 2338
JIANGSU DALI FOODS CO., LTD.—See Dali Foods Group Co. Ltd.; *Int'l*, pg. 1951
JILIN DALI FOODS CO., LTD.—See Dali Foods Group Co. Ltd.; *Int'l*, pg. 1951
JINAN DALI FOODS CO., LTD.—See Dali Foods Group Co. Ltd.; *Int'l*, pg. 1951
JINZHOU YUANCHENG BIO-CHEM TECHNOLOGY CO., LTD.—See Global Sweeteners Holdings Limited; *Int'l*, pg. 3001
J&M FOOD PRODUCTS COMPANY—See My Own Meals, Inc.; *U.S. Public*, pg. 2823
J.P. INGLIS COMPANY LIMITED—See Four Seas Mercantile Holdings Limited; *Int'l*, pg. 2755
JSL FOODS INC.; *U.S. Private*, pg. 2241
JUICEBLENDZ INTERNATIONAL INC.; *U.S. Private*, pg. 2243
JUVER ALIMENTACION SA—See Hero AG; *Int'l*, pg. 3363
KALLE GMBH—See Clayton, Dubilier & Rice, LLC; *U.S. Private*, pg. 925
KARRAS S.A.—See Floridienne SA; *Int'l*, pg. 2708
KELLOGG DE MEXICO, S. DE R.L. DE C.V.—See Kellanova; *U.S. Public*, pg. 1218
KER CADELAC SA—See Compagnie Financiere et de Participations Roullier SA; *Int'l*, pg. 1740
KEY IMPACT & SALES SYSTEMS, INC.; *U.S. Private*, pg. 2293
KEYIMPACT SALES & SYSTEMS, INC.—See Prospect Hill Growth Partners, L.P.; *U.S. Private*, pg. 3288
KEYSTONE FOODS LLC—See Tyson Foods, Inc.; *U.S. Public*, pg. 2209
KIFISSIA PASTRIES S.A.—See General Mills, Inc.; *U.S. Public*, pg. 922
KILANG BIHUN BERSATU SDN BHD—See EKA Noodles Berhad; *Int'l*, pg. 2337
KLIPFEL HEFE AG—See Compagnie des Levures Lesaffre SA; *Int'l*, pg. 1738
KOSTO FOOD PRODUCTS CO.; *U.S. Private*, pg. 2345
KOZY SHACK ENTERPRISES INC.—See Land O'Lakes, Inc.; *U.S. Private*, pg. 2383
KRACIE FOODS, LTD.—See Hoyu Co., Ltd.; *Int'l*, pg. 3499
KRACIE FOODS SALES, LTD.—See Hoyu Co., Ltd.; *Int'l*, pg. 3499
KRAFT CANADA INC.—See 3G Capital Inc.; *U.S. Private*, pg. 10
KRAFT CANADA INC.—See Berkshire Hathaway Inc.; *U.S. Public*, pg. 318
KRAFT HEINZ COMPANY - CHARLOTTE—See 3G Capital Inc.; *U.S. Private*, pg. 10
KRAFT HEINZ COMPANY - CHARLOTTE—See Berkshire Hathaway Inc.; *U.S. Public*, pg. 318
KRAFT HEINZ COMPANY - COLUMBIA—See 3G Capital Inc.; *U.S. Private*, pg. 10
KRAFT HEINZ COMPANY - COLUMBIA—See Berkshire Hathaway Inc.; *U.S. Public*, pg. 318
KRAFT HEINZ COMPANY - COSHOCTON—See 3G Capital Inc.; *U.S. Private*, pg. 10
KRAFT HEINZ COMPANY - COSHOCTON—See Berkshire Hathaway Inc.; *U.S. Public*, pg. 318
KRAFT HEINZ COMPANY - DOVER—See 3G Capital Inc.; *U.S. Private*, pg. 10
KRAFT HEINZ COMPANY - DOVER—See Berkshire Hathaway Inc.; *U.S. Public*, pg. 318
KRAFT HEINZ COMPANY - FULLERTON—See 3G Capital Inc.; *U.S. Private*, pg. 10
KRAFT HEINZ COMPANY - FULLERTON—See Berkshire Hathaway Inc.; *U.S. Public*, pg. 318
KRAFT HEINZ COMPANY - IRVINE—See 3G Capital Inc.; *U.S. Private*, pg. 10
KRAFT HEINZ COMPANY - IRVINE—See Berkshire Hathaway Inc.; *U.S. Public*, pg. 318
KRAFT HEINZ COMPANY - LIVERMORE—See 3G Capital Inc.; *U.S. Private*, pg. 10
KRAFT HEINZ COMPANY - LIVERMORE—See Berkshire Hathaway Inc.; *U.S. Public*, pg. 318
KRAFT HEINZ COMPANY - LOWVILLE—See 3G Capital Inc.; *U.S. Private*, pg. 11
KRAFT HEINZ COMPANY - LOWVILLE—See Berkshire Hathaway Inc.; *U.S. Public*, pg. 318
KRAFT HEINZ COMPANY - MASON CITY—See 3G Capital Inc.; *U.S. Private*, pg. 11
KRAFT HEINZ COMPANY - MASON CITY—See Berkshire Hathaway Inc.; *U.S. Public*, pg. 318
KRAFT HEINZ COMPANY - NEW ULM—See 3G Capital Inc.; *U.S. Private*, pg. 11
KRAFT HEINZ COMPANY - NEW ULM—See Berkshire Hathaway Inc.; *U.S. Public*, pg. 318
KRAFT HEINZ COMPANY - SAN LEANDRO—See 3G Capital Inc.; *U.S. Private*, pg. 11
KRAFT HEINZ COMPANY - SAN LEANDRO—See Berkshire Hathaway Inc.; *U.S. Public*, pg. 318
KRAFT HEINZ COMPANY - SPRINGFIELD—See 3G Capital Inc.; *U.S. Private*, pg. 11
KRAFT HEINZ COMPANY - SPRINGFIELD—See Berkshire Hathaway Inc.; *U.S. Public*, pg. 318
KRAFT HEINZ COMPANY - TULARE—See 3G Capital Inc.; *U.S. Private*, pg. 11
KRAFT HEINZ COMPANY - TULARE—See Berkshire Hathaway Inc.; *U.S. Public*, pg. 318
KRAFT HEINZ COMPANY - WAUSAU—See 3G Capital Inc.; *U.S. Private*, pg. 11
KRAFT HEINZ COMPANY - WAUSAU—See Berkshire Hathaway Inc.; *U.S. Public*, pg. 318
KRAFT HEINZ COMPANY - WILKES BARRE—See 3G Capital Inc.; *U.S. Private*, pg. 11
KRAFT HEINZ COMPANY - WILKES BARRE—See Berkshire Hathaway Inc.; *U.S. Public*, pg. 318
K.U.K. HOFZUCKERBACKER CH. DEMEL—See DO & CO Aktiengesellschaft; *Int'l*, pg. 2152
KVASAC D.O.O.—See Compagnie des Levures Lesaffre SA; *Int'l*, pg. 1738

311999 — ALL OTHER MISCELLAN...   CORPORATE AFFILIATIONS

LABORATORIOS GRIFFITH DE MEXICO S.A. DE C.V.—See Griffith Laboratories, Inc.; *U.S. Private*, pg. 1789
LA FONTE DELLA VITA SRL—See Bioera S.p.A.; *Int'l*, pg. 1037
LAIRD SUPERFOOD, INC.; *U.S. Public*, pg. 1288
LAKE INTERNATIONAL TECHNOLOGIES (PTY) LIMITED—See AECI Limited; *Int'l*, pg. 171
LAKESIDE FOODS, INC. - OWATONNA PLANT—See Lakeside Foods, Inc.; *U.S. Private*, pg. 2377
LAKEVIEW FARMS, INC.—See Lakeview Farms, Inc.; *U.S. Private*, pg. 2378
LA REGINA DI SAN MARZANO USA; *U.S. Private*, pg. 2369
LARZUL SA—See Floridienne SA; *Int'l*, pg. 2708
LA SERRANA S.A.—See Arcor Sociedad Anonima, Industrial y Comercial; *Int'l*, pg. 550
LAURIDSEN GROUP INC.; *U.S. Private*, pg. 2399
LB CO., LTD.—See Asahi Group Holdings Ltd.; *Int'l*, pg. 594
LEMON-X CORPORATION—See Highlander Partners, LP.; *U.S. Private*, pg. 1939
LESAFFRE ARGENTINA S.A.—See Compagnie des Levures Lesaffre SA; *Int'l*, pg. 1738
LESAFFRE AUSTRALIA PACIFIC PTY LTD—See Compagnie des Levures Lesaffre SA; *Int'l*, pg. 1738
LESAFFRE AUSTRIA AG—See Compagnie des Levures Lesaffre SA; *Int'l*, pg. 1739
LESAFFRE COLOMBIA LTDA—See Compagnie des Levures Lesaffre SA; *Int'l*, pg. 1739
LESAFFRE IBERICA S.A.—See Compagnie des Levures Lesaffre SA; *Int'l*, pg. 1739
LESAFFRE ITALIA S.P.A.—See Compagnie des Levures Lesaffre SA; *Int'l*, pg. 1739
LESAFFRE MAGYARORSZAG ELESZTOGYARTO ES KERESKEDELMI KFT.—See Compagnie des Levures Lesaffre SA; *Int'l*, pg. 1739
LESAFFRE MANAGEMENT (SHANGHAI) CO., LTD—See Compagnie des Levures Lesaffre SA; *Int'l*, pg. 1739
LESAFFRE (MINGGUANG) CO., LTD.—See Compagnie des Levures Lesaffre SA; *Int'l*, pg. 1738
LESAFFRE PERU S.A.C.—See Compagnie des Levures Lesaffre SA; *Int'l*, pg. 1739
LESAFFRE POLSKA S.A.—See Compagnie des Levures Lesaffre SA; *Int'l*, pg. 1739
LESAFFRE ROMANIA S.R.L.—See Compagnie des Levures Lesaffre SA; *Int'l*, pg. 1739
LIANYUNGANG AJINOMOTO FROZEN FOODS CO., LTD.—See Ajinomoto Company, Inc.; *Int'l*, pg. 257
LIBERTY U.S.A., INC.—See Performance Food Group Company; *U.S. Public*, pg. 1674
LIHATUKKU HARRI TAMMINEN OY—See HKFoods Plc; *Int'l*, pg. 3429
THE LIVEKINDLY COMPANY, INC.; *U.S. Private*, pg. 4071
LOTUS SUPPLIES SDN. BHD.—See Citra Nusa Holdings Berhad; *Int'l*, pg. 1626
LOUISIANA FOOD COMPANY; *U.S. Public*, pg. 1342
LUCKY FOODS LLC—See Daesang Corporation; *Int'l*, pg. 1909
MA'ANSHAN DALI FOODS CO., LTD.—See Dali Foods Group Co. Ltd.; *Int'l*, pg. 1951
MAJD FOOD COMPANY-K.S.C.—See Al Imtiaz Investment Group Company- K.S.C.; *Int'l*, pg. 279
MALLET & COMPANY, INC.—See H.I.G. Capital, LLC; *U.S. Private*, pg. 1832
MALONY CO., LTD.—See House Foods Group Inc.; *Int'l*, pg. 3490
MARS AS—See Mars, Incorporated; *U.S. Public*, pg. 2589
MARS AUSTRALIA—See Mars, Incorporated; *U.S. Private*, pg. 2589
MARS AUSTRIA—See Mars, Incorporated; *U.S. Private*, pg. 2589
MARS BRAZIL—See Mars, Incorporated; *U.S. Private*, pg. 2589
MARS BULGARIA—See Mars, Incorporated; *U.S. Private*, pg. 2589
MARS CARIBBEAN & CENTRAL AMERICA—See Mars, Incorporated; *U.S. Public*, pg. 2589
MARS CROATIA—See Mars, Incorporated; *U.S. Private*, pg. 2589
MARS CZECH REPUBLIC—See Mars, Incorporated; *U.S. Private*, pg. 2589
MARS DENMARK A/S—See Mars, Incorporated; *U.S. Private*, pg. 2589
MARS ESPANA—See Mars, Incorporated; *U.S. Private*, pg. 2589
MARS FOOD (CHINA) CO., LTD.—See Mars, Incorporated; *U.S. Private*, pg. 2589
MARS FOOD EUROPE C.V.—See Mars, Incorporated; *U.S. Private*, pg. 2589
MARS GREECE—See Mars, Incorporated; *U.S. Private*, pg. 2589
MARS HONG KONG—See Mars, Incorporated; *U.S. Private*, pg. 2589
MARS INDONESIA—See Mars, Incorporated; *U.S. Private*, pg. 2589
MARS ITALIA S.P.A.—See Mars, Incorporated; *U.S. Private*, pg. 2589

MARS JAPAN—See Mars, Incorporated; *U.S. Private*, pg. 2589
MARS KOREA—See Mars, Incorporated; *U.S. Private*, pg. 2589
MARS LATVIA—See Mars, Incorporated; *U.S. Private*, pg. 2589
MARS LIETUVA—See Mars, Incorporated; *U.S. Private*, pg. 2589
MARS MALAYSIA—See Mars, Incorporated; *U.S. Private*, pg. 2589
MARS NEDERLAND B.V.—See Mars, Incorporated; *U.S. Private*, pg. 2589
MARS NEW ZEALAND LIMITED—See Mars, Incorporated; *U.S. Private*, pg. 2589
MARS NORWAY—See Mars, Incorporated; *U.S. Private*, pg. 2590
MARS PHILIPPINES—See Mars, Incorporated; *U.S. Private*, pg. 2590
MARS POLSKA SP. Z.O.O.—See Mars, Incorporated; *U.S. Private*, pg. 2590
MARS SINGAPORE—See Mars, Incorporated; *U.S. Private*, pg. 2590
MARS SOUTHERN CORE—See Mars, Incorporated; *U.S. Private*, pg. 2590
MARS TAIWAN—See Mars, Incorporated; *U.S. Private*, pg. 2590
MARS THAILAND, INC.—See Mars, Incorporated; *U.S. Private*, pg. 2590
MARTIN BRAUN-GRUPPE—See Dr. August Oetker KG; *Int'l*, pg. 2190
MARUCHAN AJINOMOTO INDIA PRIVATE LIMITED—See Ajinomoto Company, Inc.; *Int'l*, pg. 257
THE MASTERSON COMPANY, INC.; *U.S. Private*, pg. 4075
MCCORMICK & COMPANY, INCORPORATED; *U.S. Public*, pg. 1403
MCCORMICK COMPANY-SOUTH BEND—See McCormick & Company, Incorporated; *U.S. Public*, pg. 1404
MCCORMICK CONDIMENT PLANT—See McCormick & Company, Incorporated; *U.S. Public*, pg. 1404
MCNEIL NUTRITIONALS, LLC—See Kenvue Inc.; *U.S. Public*, pg. 1224
MEALS MERCADEO DE ALIMENTOS DE COLOMBIA S.A.S.—See Grupo Nutresa S.A.; *Int'l*, pg. 3133
MEXICAN ACCENT, LLC—See Hormel Foods Corporation; *U.S. Public*, pg. 1054
MICHAEL FOODS GROUP, INC.—See Post Holdings, Inc.; *U.S. Public*, pg. 1703
MICHAEL FOODS, INC.—See Post Holdings, Inc.; *U.S. Public*, pg. 1703
MILTE ITALIA SPA—See DMK Deutsches Milchkontor GmbH; *Int'l*, pg. 2146
MILUPA GMBH—See Danone; *Int'l*, pg. 1966
MINN-DAK YEAST COMPANY INC.—See Minn-Dak Farmers Cooperative; *U.S. Private*, pg. 2742
MISSION FOODS UK, LTD.—See Gruma, S.A.B. de C.V.; *Int'l*, pg. 3114
MISSISSIPPI BLENDING COMPANY, INC.—See Arsenal Capital Management LP; *U.S. Private*, pg. 337
MLO PRODUCTS INCORPORATED; *U.S. Private*, pg. 2754
MOCKLER BEVERAGE CO. LP; *U.S. Private*, pg. 2759
MOHEDA CHARK AB—See Atria Plc; *Int'l*, pg. 694
MOLINOS NACIONALES, C.A.—See Gruma, S.A.B. de C.V.; *Int'l*, pg. 3114
MQMARKET—See Momar, Inc.; *U.S. Private*, pg. 2768
MONA NATURPRODUKTE GMBH—See The Hain Celestial Group, Inc.; *U.S. Public*, pg. 2087
MONDELEZ ARGENTINA S.A.—See Mondelez International, Inc.; *U.S. Public*, pg. 1461
MONDELEZ AUSTRALIA (FOODS) LTD.—See Mondelez International, Inc.; *U.S. Public*, pg. 1461
MONDELEZ AUSTRALIA PTY. LTD. - FISHERMANS BEND—See Mondelez International, Inc.; *U.S. Public*, pg. 1462
MONDELEZ BELGIUM BISCUITS PRODUCTION NV—See Mondelez International, Inc.; *U.S. Public*, pg. 1462
MONDELEZ BELGIUM MANUFACTURING SERVICES BVBA—See Mondelez International, Inc.; *U.S. Public*, pg. 1462
MONDELEZ CANADA, INC.-MONTREAL—See Mondelez International, Inc.; *U.S. Public*, pg. 1462
MONDELEZ DEUTSCHLAND PROFESSIONAL GMBH—See Mondelez International, Inc.; *U.S. Public*, pg. 1463
MONDELEZ FRANCE SAS—See Mondelez International, Inc.; *U.S. Public*, pg. 1463
MONDELEZ INDIA FOODS PRIVATE LIMITED—See Mondelez International, Inc.; *U.S. Public*, pg. 1462
MONDELEZ INTERNATIONAL (THAILAND) CO., LTD—See Mondelez International, Inc.; *U.S. Public*, pg. 1464
MONDELEZ IRELAND PRODUCTION LIMITED—See Mondelez International, Inc.; *U.S. Public*, pg. 1464
MONDELEZ OSTERREICH GMBH—See Mondelez International, Inc.; *U.S. Public*, pg. 1463
MONDELEZ PHILIPPINES, INC.—See Mondelez International, Inc.; *U.S. Public*, pg. 1462
MONDELEZ POLSKA S.A.—See Mondelez International, Inc.; *U.S. Public*, pg. 1463
MONDELEZ PUERTO RICO LLC—See Mondelez International, Inc.; *U.S. Public*, pg. 1464

MONDELEZ SCHWEIZ GMBH—See Mondelez International, Inc.; *U.S. Public*, pg. 1463
MONOGRAM COMFORT FOODS, LLC—See Monogram Food Solutions, LLC; *U.S. Private*, pg. 2771
MOTO S.P.A.—See Cremonini S.p.A.; *Int'l*, pg. 1838
MOUNT FRANKLIN FOODS, LLC; *U.S. Public*, pg. 2798
MPEARLROCK LP—See MidOcean Partners, LLP; *U.S. Private*, pg. 2717
MPEARLROCK LP—See The Kroger Co.; *U.S. Public*, pg. 2108
MUHLEHOF GEWURZE AG—See International Flavors & Fragrances Inc.; *U.S. Public*, pg. 1154
MY OWN MEALS, INC.; *U.S. Private*, pg. 2823
NANCHANG DALI FOODS CO., LTD.—See Dali Foods Group Co. Ltd.; *Int'l*, pg. 1951
NATE'S FOOD CO.; *U.S. Public*, pg. 1492
NATFOOD PORTUGAL LDA—See Bioera S.p.A.; *Int'l*, pg. 1037
NATUMI AG—See The Hain Celestial Group, Inc.; *U.S. Public*, pg. 2087
NATURALAC NUTRITION LIMITED—See Hansells Masterton Ltd.; *Int'l*, pg. 3260
NATURAL AMERICAN FOODS, INC.—See Peak Rock Capital LLC; *U.S. Private*, pg. 3124
NATURE'S SELECTION FOODS—See AAB Holdings Pty Limited; *Int'l*, pg. 30
NATUREX UK LTD.—See Givaudan S.A.; *Int'l*, pg. 2981
NELLSON-SALT LAKE CITY POWDER DIVISION—See Kohlberg & Company, LLC; *U.S. Private*, pg. 2338
THE NEW COVENT GARDEN SOUP COMPANY LIMITED—See The Hain Celestial Group, Inc.; *U.S. Public*, pg. 2086
NEWLY WEDS FOODS, INC.—See Newly Weds Foods, Inc.; *U.S. Private*, pg. 2915
NIPPON SUPPLEMENT INC.—See Coca-Cola Bottlers Japan Holdings Inc.; *Int'l*, pg. 1684
NORFOLK FOODS (PRIVATE) LIMITED—See Charoen Pokphand Foods Public Company Limited; *Int'l*, pg. 1453
NORFRE FOOD INC.—See Cross Marketing Group Inc.; *Int'l*, pg. 1856
NORRBODA CHARKUTERIFABRIK AB—See Atria Plc; *Int'l*, pg. 694
NORTH AMERICA FOOD & BEVERAGE INC.; *U.S. Private*, pg. 2939
NOVAVENTA S.A.S.—See Grupo Nutresa S.A.; *Int'l*, pg. 3133
NUTRICIA BABY OY—See Danone; *Int'l*, pg. 1966
NUTRICIA DEVA A.S.—See ARX Equity Partners s.r.o.; *Int'l*, pg. 588
NUTRICIA GMBH—See Danone; *Int'l*, pg. 1966
NUTRICIA LTD. - ADVANCED MEDICAL NUTRITION—See Danone; *Int'l*, pg. 1966
NUTRICIA N.V.—See Danone; *Int'l*, pg. 1966
NUTRICIA PHARMACEUTICAL (WUXI) CO., LTD.—See Danone; *Int'l*, pg. 1967
NUTRI PHARMACEUTICALS RESEARCH, INC.; *U.S. Public*, pg. 1556
NUTROGANICS, INC.; *U.S. Public*, pg. 1556
OLIVIERI FOODS LIMITED—See Ebro Foods S.A.; *Int'l*, pg. 2287
OMEGA3 INNOVATIONS COMPANY; *U.S. Private*, pg. 3015
ORGANIC OILS S.P.A.—See Bioera S.p.A.; *Int'l*, pg. 1037
OSI GROUP, LLC; *U.S. Private*, pg. 3047
OSTERREICHISCHE RUBENSAMENZUCHT GESELLSCHAFT M.B.H.—See AGRANA Beteiligungs-AG; *Int'l*, pg. 214
OZMAYA SANAYI A.S.—See Compagnie des Levures Lesaffre SA; *Int'l*, pg. 1739
OZMAYA SANAYI A.S. - YEAST & INGREDIENT FACTORY—See Compagnie des Levures Lesaffre SA; *Int'l*, pg. 1739
PAIMION TEURASTAMO OY—See HKFoods Plc; *Int'l*, pg. 3429
PANCHOS MEXICAN FOODS, INC.—See Centre Partners Management LLC; *U.S. Private*, pg. 828
PANZANI, S.A.S.—See Ebro Foods S.A.; *Int'l*, pg. 2287
PAPETTI'S HYGRADE EGG PRODUCTS, INC.—See Post Holdings, Inc.; *U.S. Public*, pg. 1703
PARADISE, INC.; *U.S. Private*, pg. 3090
PARK 100 FOODS INC.—See OSI Group, LLC; *U.S. Private*, pg. 3047
PASSPORT FOOD GROUP, LLC—See Swander Pace Capital, LLC; *U.S. Private*, pg. 3890
PASTEJKOKET AB—See Atria Plc; *Int'l*, pg. 694
PASTIFICIO LUCIO GAROFALO S.P.A.—See Ebro Foods S.A.; *Int'l*, pg. 2287
PEOPLES CHOICE AB—See Celsius Holdings, Inc.; *U.S. Public*, pg. 466
PERFECT COMPANION GROUP COMPANY LIMITED—See Charoen Pokphand Group Co., Ltd.; *Int'l*, pg. 1453
PETE & GERRY'S ORGANICS, LLC—See Butterfly Equity LP; *U.S. Private*, pg. 698
PHILADELPHIA CHEESESTEAK COMPANY—See Tyson Foods, Inc.; *U.S. Public*, pg. 2210
PHILADELPHIA PRE-COOKED STEAK, INC.—See Tyson

N.A.I.C.S. INDEX
311999 — ALL OTHER MISCELLAN...

Foods, Inc.; *U.S. Public*, pg. 2210
- PILMICO FOODS CORPORATION—See Aboitiz Equity Ventures, Inc.; *Int'l*, pg. 67
- PINEDALE TRADING PTE LIMITED—See General Mills, Inc.; *U.S. Public*, pg. 922
- PINNACLE FOODS FORT MADISON LLC—See Conagra Brands, Inc.; *U.S. Public*, pg. 564
- PINNACLE FOODS INTERNATIONAL CORP.—See Conagra Brands, Inc.; *U.S. Public*, pg. 564
- THE PIZZERIA—See Bakkavor Group plc; *Int'l*, pg. 806
- PLUM, PBC—See Campbell Soup Company; *U.S. Public*, pg. 427
- **POPCORN, INDIANA LLC;** *U.S. Private*, pg. 3228
- PORTABLE FOODS MANUFACTURING COMPANY LIMITED—See Kellanova; *U.S. Public*, pg. 1218
- POWER HOUSE FOODS PTY LTD—See General Mills, Inc.; *U.S. Public*, pg. 922
- PREFERRED SNACKS, LLC—See Performance Food Group Company; *U.S. Public*, pg. 1675
- PREMIER FISHING & BRANDS LTD.—See African Equity Empowerment Investmts Limited; *Int'l*, pg. 191
- PROBLEND-EUROGERM LLC—See Eurogerm SA; *Int'l*, pg. 2552
- PRODUCTOS ALIMENTICIES LA MODERNA S.A. DE C.V.—See Grupo La Moderna, S.A.B. de C.V.; *Int'l*, pg. 3131
- PRODUCTOS ALIMENTICIOS DORIA S.A.S.—See Grupo Nutresa S.A.; *Int'l*, pg. 3133
- PRODUCTOS KRAFT S. DE R.L. DE C.V.—See Mondelez International, Inc.; *U.S. Public*, pg. 1462
- PRODUCTOS NATURELA S.A.S.—See Grupo Nutresa S.A.; *Int'l*, pg. 3133
- PROFILE FOOD INGREDIENTS, LLC—See RPM International Inc.; *U.S. Public*, pg. 1817
- **PRO FOOD SYSTEMS, INC.;** *U.S. Private*, pg. 3269
- PROGRESSIVE PROCESSING, LLC—See Hormel Foods Corporation; *U.S. Public*, pg. 1054
- PROLIANT INC.—See Lauridsen Group Inc.; *U.S. Private*, pg. 2400
- PROMASIDOR HOLDINGS LIMITED—See Ajinomoto Company, Inc.; *Int'l*, pg. 257
- **PROTEIN REACTOR COMBINED FUELS, INC.;** *U.S. Public*, pg. 1729
- PROTENERGY NATURAL FOODS CORPORATION—See TreeHouse Foods, Inc.; *U.S. Public*, pg. 2187
- PROTENERGY NATURAL FOODS, INC.—See TreeHouse Foods, Inc.; *U.S. Public*, pg. 2187
- PT. GIVAUDAN INDONESIA - DEPOK—See Givaudan S.A.; *Int'l*, pg. 2981
- PT HONGXIN ALGAE INTERNATIONA—See Green Future Food Hydrocolloid Marine Science Company Limited; *Int'l*, pg. 3071
- PT HOUSE & VOX INDONESIA—See House Foods Group Inc.; *Int'l*, pg. 3490
- PT IKAFOOD PUTRAMAS—See Brataco, PT; *Int'l*, pg. 1141
- PT JICO AGUNG—See Daesang Corporation; *Int'l*, pg. 1909
- PT SAF INDONESIA - SIDOARJO FACTORY—See Compagnie des Levures Lesaffre SA; *Int'l*, pg. 1739
- PT SAF INDONESIA—See Compagnie des Levures Lesaffre SA; *Int'l*, pg. 1739
- PUCHENG YONGFANG FRAGRANCE TECHNOLOGY CO., LTD.—See International Flavors & Fragrances Inc.; *U.S. Public*, pg. 1154
- PURAC POLSKA SP. Z O.O.—See Corbion N.V.; *Int'l*, pg. 1795
- PURECIRCLE AFRICA LIMITED—See Ingredion Incorporated; *U.S. Public*, pg. 1124
- PURECIRCLE (JIANGXI) CO. LTD—See Ingredion Incorporated; *U.S. Public*, pg. 1124
- PURECIRCLE NATURAL INGREDIENT INDIA PRIVATE LIMITED—See Ingredion Incorporated; *U.S. Public*, pg. 1124
- PURECIRCLE SOUTH AMERICA SOCIEDAD ANONIMA—See Ingredion Incorporated; *U.S. Public*, pg. 1124
- PURECIRCLE USA HOLDINGS INC—See Ingredion Incorporated; *U.S. Public*, pg. 1124
- PURFOODS, LLC—See Cressey & Company, LP; *U.S. Private*, pg. 1095
- **PYURE BRANDS, LLC;** *U.S. Private*, pg. 3311
- Q'SAI CO., LTD.—See Advantage Partners LLP; *Int'l*, pg. 164
- Q'SAI CO., LTD.—See euglena Co., Ltd.; *Int'l*, pg. 2526
- **QUALITY INGREDIENTS CORPORATION;** *U.S. Private*, pg. 3319
- QUALITY NATURALLY FOODS, INC.—See Yum Yum Donut Shops, Inc.; *U.S. Private*, pg. 4595
- QUANZHOU DALI FOODS CO., LTD.—See Dali Foods Group Co. Ltd.; *Int'l*, pg. 1951
- QUIK TRIP DISTRIBUTION—See QuikTrip Corporation; *U.S. Private*, pg. 3327
- **RACHAEL'S FOOD CORPORATION;** *U.S. Private*, pg. 3341
- **RAMONA'S MEXICAN FOOD PRODUCTS;** *U.S. Private*, pg. 3351
- **REAL BRANDS, INC.;** *U.S. Public*, pg. 1768
- **RECONSERVE, INC.;** *U.S. Public*, pg. 3371
- REDBROOK INGREDIENT SERVICES LIMITED—See International Flavors & Fragrances Inc.; *U.S. Public*, pg. 1154
- RED RIVER COMMODITIES INC—See ACOMO N.V.; *Int'l*, pg. 108
- **THE REDWOOD GROUP, LLC;** *U.S. Private*, pg. 4103
- **RELIANT FOODSERVICE;** *U.S. Private*, pg. 3395
- **RESER'S FINE FOODS INC.;** *U.S. Private*, pg. 3404
- RICHARD'S CAJUN FOODS CORP.—See Altamont Capital Partners; *U.S. Private*, pg. 205
- **RIENZI & SONS, INC.;** *U.S. Private*, pg. 3434
- **RIGHT ON BRANDS, INC.;** *U.S. Public*, pg. 1798
- RIVIANA FOODS CANADA CORPORATION—See Ebro Foods S.A.; *Int'l*, pg. 2287
- ROLAND FOODS, LLC—See Vestar Capital Partners, LLC; *U.S. Private*, pg. 4372
- SAF NEVA OOO - BREAD MAKING IMPROVERS FACTORY—See Compagnie des Levures Lesaffre SA; *Int'l*, pg. 1739
- SAF NEVA OOO - KURGAN YEAST FACTORY—See Compagnie des Levures Lesaffre SA; *Int'l*, pg. 1739
- SAF NEVA OOO - OUZLOVAYA YEAST FACTORY—See Compagnie des Levures Lesaffre SA; *Int'l*, pg. 1739
- SAF NEVA OOO—See Compagnie des Levures Lesaffre SA; *Int'l*, pg. 1739
- SAGE V FOODS, LLC - LITTLE ROCK PLANT—See Sage V Foods, LLC; *U.S. Private*, pg. 3527
- SAGE V FOODS, LLC - STUTTGART PLANT—See Producers Rice Mill, Inc.; *U.S. Private*, pg. 3273
- **SALTWORKS, INC.;** *U.S. Private*, pg. 3534
- SANTA RITA HARINAS, S.L.—See Ebro Foods S.A.; *Int'l*, pg. 2287
- **SAVANNAH BEE COMPANY INC;** *U.S. Private*, pg. 3555
- SAVOURY FLAVOURS LTD.—See International Flavors & Fragrances Inc.; *U.S. Public*, pg. 1154
- SAZONADORES DEL PACIFICO C. LTDA.—See Ajinomoto Company, Inc.; *Int'l*, pg. 257
- SCHWAN'S MAMA ROSA'S, LLC—See Schwan's Shared Services, LLC; *U.S. Private*, pg. 3572
- **SCHWAN'S SHARED SERVICES, LLC;** *U.S. Private*, pg. 3572
- SENSIENT FOOD COLORS CZECH REPUBLIC CZ S.R.O.—See Sensient Technologies Corporation; *U.S. Public*, pg. 1867
- SENSIENT NATURAL EXTRACTION INC.—See Sensient Technologies Corporation; *U.S. Public*, pg. 1867
- SENSIENT TECHNOLOGIES EUROPE GMBH—See Sensient Technologies Corporation; *U.S. Public*, pg. 1867
- SENSORYEFFECTS FLAVOR COMPANY—See Balchem Corporation; *U.S. Public*, pg. 266
- SENSORYEFFECTS POWDER SYSTEMS, INC.—See Balchem Corporation; *U.S. Public*, pg. 266
- SEPP'S GOURMET FOODS LTD.—See Conagra Brands, Inc.; *U.S. Public*, pg. 564
- SERVCATER INTERNACIONAL LTDA—See Deutsche Lufthansa AG; *Int'l*, pg. 2068
- SETAS COLOMBIANAS S.A.—See Grupo Nutresa S.A.; *Int'l*, pg. 3133
- SFK FOOD A/S—See Ardian SAS; *Int'l*, pg. 555
- SHANDONG KAIJIA FOOD COMPANY LIMITED—See China Kangda Food Company Limited; *Int'l*, pg. 1514
- SHANGHAI AJINOMOTO SEASONING CO., LTD.—See Ajinomoto Company, Inc.; *Int'l*, pg. 257
- SHANGHAI GIVAUDAN LTD—See Givaudan S.A.; *Int'l*, pg. 2981
- SHANGHAI HAO CHENG FOOD DEVELOPMENT CO., LTD.—See Global Sweeteners Holdings Limited; *Int'l*, pg. 3001
- SHANGHAI HORMEL FOODS CO. LTD.—See Hormel Foods Corporation; *U.S. Public*, pg. 1054
- SHANXI DALI FOODS CO., LTD.—See Dali Foods Group Co. Ltd.; *Int'l*, pg. 1951
- SHENG LONG BIO-TECH (INDIA) PVT. LTD.—See Guangdong Haid Group Co., Ltd.; *Int'l*, pg. 3155
- SHS INTERNATIONAL LTD.—See Danone; *Int'l*, pg. 1966
- SIA BALTIC FEED—See Apetit Plc; *Int'l*, pg. 509
- SIL FALA SARL—See Compagnie des Levures Lesaffre SA; *Int'l*, pg. 1739
- SILVA INTERNATIONAL, INC.—See Universal Corporation; *U.S. Public*, pg. 2254
- **SILVER SKY CAPITAL, LTD.;** *U.S. Private*, pg. 3662
- SIMPLOT KOREA INC—See J.R. Simplot Company; *U.S. Private*, pg. 2171
- **THE SIMPLY GOOD FOODS COMPANY;** *U.S. Public*, pg. 2130
- SK CHEMTRADE SERVICES PTY LTD—See Cinven Limited; *Int'l*, pg. 1611
- SLIM-FAST FOODS COMPANY—See Glanbia Co-Operative Society Limited; *Int'l*, pg. 2988
- SMUCKER FOODSERVICE, INC.—See The J.M. Smucker Company; *U.S. Public*, pg. 2107
- SMUCKER FOODS OF CANADA CORP.—See The J.M. Smucker Company; *U.S. Public*, pg. 2107
- SNICK EUROINGREDIENTS N.V.—See ACOMO N.V.; *Int'l*, pg. 108
- **SOKOL & COMPANY;** *U.S. Private*, pg. 3706
- SOKOLOW—See Danish Crown AmbA; *Int'l*, pg. 1965
- SOLBAR NINGBO FOOD CO., LTD.—See CHS INC.; *U.S. Public*, pg. 493
- SOLINA FRANCE SASU—See Ardian SAS; *Int'l*, pg. 556
- SONAC USA—See Darling Ingredients Inc.; *U.S. Public*, pg. 634
- SONGLIM FOOD CO., LTD.—See CJ Corporation; *Int'l*, pg. 1634
- SONSTEGARD FOODS OF GEORGIA—See Sonstegard Foods Company; *U.S. Private*, pg. 3715
- SPECIALTY CEREALS PTY LIMITED—See Kellanova; *U.S. Public*, pg. 1217
- SPECIALTY COMMODITIES, INC.—See Archer-Daniels-Midland Company; *U.S. Public*, pg. 182
- **SPORT STIX INC;** *U.S. Private*, pg. 3760
- STARFOOD FINLAND OY—See Deutsche Lufthansa AG; *Int'l*, pg. 2067
- STEENSMA B.V.—See Alberco Holding B.V.; *Int'l*, pg. 294
- **STEUBEN FOODS INC.;** *U.S. Public*, pg. 3807
- ST. HUBERT SAS—See Beijing Capital Agribusiness Group Co., Ltd.; *Int'l*, pg. 946
- ST. HUBERT SAS—See Fosun International Limited; *Int'l*, pg. 2752
- STOCKPOT INC.—See Campbell Soup Company; *U.S. Public*, pg. 427
- S.T. SPECIALTY FOODS, INC.—See TreeHouse Foods, Inc.; *U.S. Public*, pg. 2187
- STURM FOODS, INC.—See TreeHouse Foods, Inc.; *U.S. Public*, pg. 2188
- **SUBCO FOODS, INC.;** *U.S. Private*, pg. 3847
- SUMMIT HILL FOODS, INC.—See EagleTree Capital, LP; *U.S. Public*, pg. 1312
- SUPPORT PRODUTOS NUTRICIONAIS LTDA.—See Danone; *Int'l*, pg. 1967
- SUPREME FOODS PROCESSING COMPANY LTD.—See Dabbagh Group Holding Company Ltd.; *Int'l*, pg. 1903
- **SVB FOOD & BEVERAGE CO.;** *U.S. Private*, pg. 3888
- SWEET HARVEST FOODS CO.—See Peak Rock Capital LLC; *U.S. Private*, pg. 3124
- SYNERGY FLAVORS (OH). LLC—See Carbery Group; *Int'l*, pg. 1320
- SYNERGY WORLDWIDE ITALY S.R.L.—See Nature's Sunshine Products, Inc.; *U.S. Public*, pg. 1499
- SYNERGY WORLDWIDE NEW ZEALAND, ULC—See Nature's Sunshine Products, Inc.; *U.S. Public*, pg. 1500
- SYSCO EAST TEXAS, LLC—See Sysco Corporation; *U.S. Public*, pg. 1976
- TASTY BITE EATABLES LTD.—See Mars, Incorporated; *U.S. Private*, pg. 2590
- **TATTOOED CHEF, INC.;** *U.S. Public*, pg. 1983
- TAURA NATURAL INGREDIENTS LTD.—See International Flavors & Fragrances Inc.; *U.S. Public*, pg. 1154
- TELKO-POLAND SP. Z O.O.—See Aspo Oyj; *Int'l*, pg. 631
- TIC GUMS CHINA.—See Ingredion Incorporated; *U.S. Public*, pg. 1124
- TILDA RICE LIMITED—See The Hain Celestial Group, Inc.; *U.S. Public*, pg. 2087
- T.J. HARKINS BASIC COMMODITY BROKERS, INC—See Bay State Milling Company; *U.S. Private*, pg. 494
- TOHOKU AOHATA CO., LTD.—See Aohata Corporation; *Int'l*, pg. 487
- TOPNOTCH FOODS, INC.—See ReConserve, Inc.; *U.S. Private*, pg. 3371
- TOUS LES JOURS INTERNATIONAL CORP.—See CJ Corporation; *Int'l*, pg. 1632
- TRANSGOURMET SEAFOOD—See Coop-Gruppe Genossenschaft; *Int'l*, pg. 1790
- **TROPICAL BLOSSOM HONEY CO., INC.;** *U.S. Private*, pg. 4242
- TROPICAL COFFEE COMPANY S.A.S.—See Grupo Nutresa S.A.; *Int'l*, pg. 3133
- TRUDEAU FOODS, LLC—See United Natural Foods, Inc.; *U.S. Public*, pg. 2233
- TULIP FLEISCHWAREN OLDENBURG GMBH—See Danish Crown AmbA; *Int'l*, pg. 1965
- TYSON FOODS UK HOLDING LTD.—See Tyson Foods, Inc.; *U.S. Public*, pg. 2210
- TYSON PREPARED FOODS, INC.—See Tyson Foods, Inc.; *U.S. Public*, pg. 2210
- UAB HKSCAN LIETUVA—See HKFoods Plc; *Int'l*, pg. 3429
- UEHARA FOODS INDUSTRY CO., LTD—See Adeka Corporation; *Int'l*, pg. 142
- **UKROP'S HOMESTYLE FOODS, LLC.;** *U.S. Private*, pg. 4275
- UNIDAL VENEZUELA S.A.—See Arcor Sociedad Anonima, Industrial y Comercial; *Int'l*, pg. 550
- UNIQUE INGREDIENTS LIMITED—See International Flavors & Fragrances Inc.; *U.S. Public*, pg. 1154
- VAN DAM S.A.—See Arcor Sociedad Anonima, Industrial y Comercial; *Int'l*, pg. 550
- **VANTAGE INVESTMENT CORP.;** *U.S. Private*, pg. 4345
- VANTAGE SPECIALTY CHEMICALS, INC.—See H.I.G. Capital, LLC; *U.S. Private*, pg. 1832
- VERDESIAN LIFE SCIENCES, LLC—See AEA Investors LP; *U.S. Private*, pg. 116
- VIDEOJET TECHNOLOGIES GMBH—See Danaher Corporation; *U.S. Public*, pg. 632
- **VIGO IMPORTING COMPANY INC.;** *U.S. Private*, pg. 4382
- VITAL FARMS OF MISSOURI, LLC—See Vital Farms, Inc.; *U.S. Public*, pg. 2306
- VORONEZHSKIE DROJJI LLC—See Compagnie des Le-

311999 — ALL OTHER MISCELLAN...

vures Lesaffre SA; *Int'l*, pg. 1739
VOX TRADING CO., LTD.—See House Foods Group Inc.; *Int'l*, pg. 3491
VOX TRADING (THAILAND) CO., LTD.—See House Foods Group Inc.; *Int'l*, pg. 3491
WAKODO CO., LTD.—See Asahi Group Holdings Ltd.; *Int'l*, pg. 594
WALTER HOLLANDS—See Boparan Holdings Limited; *Int'l*, pg. 1111
WATSON LLC—See Glanbia Co-Operative Society Limited; *Int'l*, pg. 2988
WEETABIX COMPANY, LLC—See Post Holdings, Inc.; *U.S. Public*, pg. 1704
WELLNESS FOODS INC.—See The Simply Good Foods Company; *U.S. Public*, pg. 2130
WHEYCO GMBH—See DMK Deutsches Milchkontor GmbH; *Int'l*, pg. 2146
WHICH WICH, INC.; *U.S. Private*, pg. 4506
WHITFIELD FOODS, INC.; *U.S. Private*, pg. 4512
WILD JUICE SERVICES B.V.—See Archer-Daniels-Midland Company; *U.S. Public*, pg. 184
WINGLAND FOODS—See Bakkavor Group plc; *Int'l*, pg. 806
WINTER GARDENS QUALITY FOODS, INC.—See Sandridge Food Corporation; *U.S. Private*, pg. 3544
WONTON FOOD INC.; *U.S. Private*, pg. 4556
WOODLANDS SUNNY FOODS PTE. LTD.—See Fuji Oil Holdings Inc.; *Int'l*, pg. 2816
XIAMEN AJINOMOTO LIFE IDEAL FOODS CO., LTD.—See Ajinomoto Company, Inc.; *Int'l*, pg. 257
YOCABITO CO., LTD.—See Future Corporation; *Int'l*, pg. 2853
THE YOFARM COMPANY, INC.—See Danone; *Int'l*, pg. 1968
YONGZHOU SHANXIANG FLAVOUR CO., LTD.—See Huabao International Holdings Limited; *Int'l*, pg. 3511
YUHOR A.D.—See Delta Holding; *Int'l*, pg. 2018
YUNNAN DALI FOODS CO., LTD.—See Dali Foods Group Co. Ltd.; *Int'l*, pg. 1951
ZAO KONDI—See Barilla Holding S.p.A.; *Int'l*, pg. 865
ZATARAIN'S BRANDS, INC.—See McCormick & Company, Incorporated; *U.S. Public*, pg. 1404
ZEMCO INDUSTRIES, INC.—See Tyson Foods, Inc.; *U.S. Public*, pg. 2210

312111 — SOFT DRINK MANUFACTURING

24 LIGNE LLC—See Constellation Brands, Inc.; *U.S. Public*, pg. 570
ABARTA INC.; *U.S. Private*, pg. 34
ABTEX BEVERAGE LTD; *U.S. Private*, pg. 45
ACADIANA BOTTLING CO. INC.; *U.S. Private*, pg. 47
ACQUE DI CALTANISSETTA, S.P.A.—See Fomento de Construcciones y Contratas, S.A.; *Int'l*, pg. 2722
ADMIRAL BEVERAGE CORPORATION; *U.S. Private*, pg. 81
THE AKRON COCA-COLA BOTTLING COMPANY—See The Coca-Cola Company; *U.S. Public*, pg. 2065
ALACER CORP.—See Pfizer Inc.; *U.S. Public*, pg. 1679
ALIMENTOS DEL ISTMO, S.A.—See PepsiCo, Inc.; *U.S. Public*, pg. 1668
AMCAN BEVERAGES, INC.; *U.S. Private*, pg. 218
AMERICA'S BEVERAGE CO.—See The Kroger Co.; *U.S. Public*, pg. 2107
ANSARI & AUJAN COMPANY L.L.C.—See Aujan Industries Co., L.L.C.; *Int'l*, pg. 704
ARCA CONTINENTAL, S.A.B. DE C.V.; *Int'l*, pg. 540
ARWA MINERAL WATER COMPANY LTD.—See Hayel Saeed Anam Group of Companies; *Int'l*, pg. 3290
ASAHI SOFT DRINKS CO., LTD.—See Asahi Group Holdings Ltd.; *Int'l*, pg. 593
AS COCA-COLA HBC EESTI—See Coca-Cola HBC AG; *Int'l*, pg. 1685
ASIA CAN MANUFACTURING CO., LTD.—See Carabao Group Public Company Limited; *Int'l*, pg. 1319
ASIA PACIFIC GLASS CO., LTD.—See Carabao Group Public Company Limited; *Int'l*, pg. 1319
ASIA PACKAGING MANUFACTURING CO., LTD.—See Carabao Group Public Company Limited; *Int'l*, pg. 1319
ATLANTIC BOTTLING COMPANY; *U.S. Private*, pg. 371
ATLANTIC CEDEVITA D.O.O.—See ATLANTIC GRUPA d.d.; *Int'l*, pg. 674
AUGUSTA COCA-COLA BOTTLING COMPANY—See Coca-Cola Bottling Co. United, Inc.; *U.S. Private*, pg. 958
AUSTIN COCA-COLA BOTTLING COMPANY—See The Coca-Cola Company; *U.S. Public*, pg. 2064
BAGHDAD SOFT DRINKS CO.; *Int'l*, pg. 799
BARBADOS BOTTLING CO. LIMITED—See Anheuser-Busch InBev SA/NV; *Int'l*, pg. 464
BARFRESH FOOD GROUP INC.; *U.S. Public*, pg. 275
BATON ROUGE COCA-COLA BOTTLING COMPANY—See Coca-Cola Bottling Co. United, Inc.; *U.S. Private*, pg. 958
B&B DISTRIBUTION LTD.—See Anheuser-Busch InBev SA/NV; *Int'l*, pg. 464
BD THAI FOOD & BEVERAGE LTD.; *Int'l*, pg. 929
BEAUMONT COCA-COLA REFRESHMENTS; *U.S. Private*, pg. 508
BEFUN INC.; *U.S. Private*, pg. 514

BERNICK COMPANIES - BEMIDJI PLANT—See Bernick Companies; *U.S. Private*, pg. 537
BERNICK COMPANIES - BRAINERD PLANT—See Bernick Companies; *U.S. Private*, pg. 537
BERNICK COMPANIES - DRESSER PLANT—See Bernick Companies; *U.S. Private*, pg. 537
BERNICK COMPANIES - DULUTH PLANT—See Bernick Companies; *U.S. Private*, pg. 537
BERNICK COMPANIES - TWIN CITIES PLANT—See Bernick Companies; *U.S. Private*, pg. 537
BERNICK COMPANIES - WILLMAR PLANT—See Bernick Companies; *U.S. Private*, pg. 537
BEVCO SALES, INC.—See National Beverage Corp.; *U.S. Public*, pg. 1493
BEVERAGE CAPITAL CORPORATION—See Pepsi-Cola & National Brand Beverages, Ltd.; *U.S. Private*, pg. 3145
BEVERAGE DISTRIBUTION CENTER, INC.—See Pepsi-Cola & National Brand Beverages, Ltd.; *U.S. Private*, pg. 3145
BIG RED LTD.—See Court Square Capital Partners, L.P.; *U.S. Private*, pg. 1068
BIG SHOT BEVERAGES, INC.—See National Beverage Corp.; *U.S. Public*, pg. 1494
BIG SPRINGS INC.; *U.S. Private*, pg. 554
BIRMINGHAM COCA-COLA BOTTLING COMPANY—See Coca-Cola Bottling Co. United, Inc.; *U.S. Private*, pg. 958
BLUEBIRD FOODS LIMITED—See PepsiCo, Inc.; *U.S. Public*, pg. 1668
BLUEJAY HOLDINGS LLC—See PepsiCo, Inc.; *U.S. Public*, pg. 1668
BLUE SKY NATURAL BEVERAGE CO.—See Monster Beverage Corporation; *U.S. Public*, pg. 1465
BONNEVILLE CANNING COCA COLA; *U.S. Private*, pg. 615
BOTTLERS NEPAL LIMITED; *Int'l*, pg. 1119
BOTTLERS NEPAL (TERAI) LIMITED—See Bottlers Nepal Limited; *Int'l*, pg. 1119
BRICFRUIT SAS—See Britvic plc; *Int'l*, pg. 1171
BRITVIC SOFT DRINKS LTD.—See Britvic plc; *Int'l*, pg. 1171
BROOKLYN BOTTLING CO. OF MILTON, NY; *U.S. Private*, pg. 663
BROWN ENTERPRISES; *U.S. Private*, pg. 667
BRUNSWICK COCA-COLA BOTTLING COMPANY—See Coca-Cola Bottling Co. United, Inc.; *U.S. Private*, pg. 958
BUCHER UNIPEKTIN CO. LTD.—See Bucher Industries AG; *Int'l*, pg. 1208
BUFFALO ROCK COMPANY; *U.S. Private*, pg. 681
BULMERS LTD—See C&C Group Plc; *Int'l*, pg. 1238
CALPIS BEVERAGES CO., LTD.—See Asahi Group Holdings Ltd.; *Int'l*, pg. 593
CALYPSO SOFT DRINKS LIMITED—See KKR & Co. Inc.; *U.S. Public*, pg. 1263
CANADA DRY BOTTLING COMPANY OF NEW YORK, L.P.—See Pepsi-Cola & National Brand Beverages, Ltd.; *U.S. Private*, pg. 3145
CANADA DRY DELAWARE VALLEY BOTTLING COMPANY—See Pepsi-Cola & National Brand Beverages, Ltd.; *U.S. Private*, pg. 3145
CANADEAN LIMITED—See GlobalData Plc; *Int'l*, pg. 3003
CANEO SA; *Int'l*, pg. 1289
CARABAO TAWANDANG CO., LTD.—See Carabao Group Public Company Limited; *Int'l*, pg. 1319
CAROLINA CANNERS INC.; *U.S. Private*, pg. 767
CC 1 LIMITED PARTNERSHIP; *U.S. Private*, pg. 797
CC1 LIMITED PARTNERSHIP; *U.S. Private*, pg. 799
(CC) COMPANY FOR BEVERAGE INDUSTRY/LTD.—See Coca-Cola Icecek A.S.; *Int'l*, pg. 1686
CCEP HOLDINGS SVERIGE AB—See COCA-COLA EUROPACIFIC PARTNERS PLC; *Int'l*, pg. 1684
CCHBC ARMENIA CJSC—See Coca-Cola HBC AG; *Int'l*, pg. 1685
CCHBC BULGARIA AD—See Coca-Cola HBC AG; *Int'l*, pg. 1685
CENTRAL INVESTMENT LLC; *U.S. Private*, pg. 821
CENTRO-MEDITERRANEA DE BEBIDAS CARBONICAS PEPSICO, SL—See PepsiCo, Inc.; *U.S. Public*, pg. 1668
CHATTANOOGA COCA-COLA BOTTLING COMPANY—See Coca-Cola Bottling Co. United, Inc.; *U.S. Private*, pg. 958
CHESTERMAN CO.; *U.S. Private*, pg. 875
CHINA WU YI MOUNTAIN LTD.; *U.S. Private*, pg. 886
CHOICE USA BEVERAGE INC.; *U.S. Private*, pg. 888
CHUONG DUONG BEVERAGES JOINT STOCK COMPANY; *Int'l*, pg. 1600
CIPA NORDESTE INDUSTRIA DE PRODUTOS ALIMENTARES LTDA.—See PepsiCo, Inc.; *U.S. Public*, pg. 1668
CLASSIC DISTRIBUTING & BEVERAGE GROUP, INC.; *U.S. Private*, pg. 916
CLR ROASTERS, LLC—See Youngevity International Corp.; *U.S. Public*, pg. 2399
COCA-COLA AFRICA (PROPRIETARY) LIMITED—See The Coca-Cola Company; *U.S. Public*, pg. 2063
COCA-COLA AMATIL (FIJI) LTD—See COCA-COLA EUROPACIFIC PARTNERS PLC; *Int'l*, pg. 1684
COCA-COLA AMATIL PTY LTD—See COCA-COLA EUROPACIFIC PARTNERS PLC; *Int'l*, pg. 1684
COCA-COLA-ATLANTA—See The Coca-Cola Company; *U.S. Public*, pg. 2064

COCA-COLA BEVERAGES AUSTRIA GMBH—See Coca-Cola HBC AG; *Int'l*, pg. 1685
COCA-COLA BEVERAGES CESKA REPUBLIKA, S.R.O.—See Coca-Cola HBC AG; *Int'l*, pg. 1685
COCA-COLA BEVERAGES (SHANGHAI) COMPANY LIMITED—See The Coca-Cola Company; *U.S. Public*, pg. 2063
COCA-COLA BEVERAGES UKRAINE LTD.—See Coca-Cola HBC AG; *Int'l*, pg. 1685
COCA-COLA BISHKEK BOTTLERS CLOSED JOINT STOCK COMPANY—See Coca-Cola Icecek A.S.; *Int'l*, pg. 1686
COCA-COLA BOTTLERS CHISINAU S.R.L.—See Coca-Cola HBC AG; *Int'l*, pg. 1685
COCA-COLA BOTTLERS JAPAN HOLDINGS INC.; *Int'l*, pg. 1683
COCA-COLA BOTTLERS JAPAN INC.—See Coca-Cola Bottlers Japan Holdings Inc.; *Int'l*, pg. 1684
COCA-COLA BOTTLING CO. CONSOLIDATED - CHARLESTON, WV—See Coca-Cola Consolidated, Inc.; *U.S. Public*, pg. 521
COCA-COLA BOTTLING CO. CONSOLIDATED - COLUMBIA, TN—See Coca-Cola Consolidated, Inc.; *U.S. Public*, pg. 521
COCA-COLA BOTTLING CO. CONSOLIDATED - COLUMBUS, GA—See Coca-Cola Consolidated, Inc.; *U.S. Public*, pg. 521
COCA-COLA BOTTLING CO. CONSOLIDATED - MOBILE, AL—See Coca-Cola Consolidated, Inc.; *U.S. Public*, pg. 521
COCA-COLA BOTTLING CO. CONSOLIDATED - PANAMA CITY, FL—See Coca-Cola Consolidated, Inc.; *U.S. Public*, pg. 521
COCA-COLA BOTTLING CO. CONSOLIDATED - ROANOKE, VA—See Coca-Cola Consolidated, Inc.; *U.S. Public*, pg. 521
COCA-COLA BOTTLING COMPANY HIGH COUNTRY; *U.S. Private*, pg. 959
COCA-COLA BOTTLING COMPANY OF ELIZABETHTOWN—See Coca-Cola Bottling Works of Tullahoma, Inc.; *U.S. Private*, pg. 959
COCA-COLA BOTTLING COMPANY OF INDIANAPOLIS, INC.—See The Coca-Cola Company; *U.S. Public*, pg. 2064
THE COCA-COLA BOTTLING COMPANY OF JORDAN LIMITED—See Coca-Cola Icecek A.S.; *Int'l*, pg. 1686
COCA-COLA BOTTLING COMPANY OF KOKOMO INDIANA; *U.S. Private*, pg. 959
COCA-COLA BOTTLING COMPANY—See The Coca-Cola Company; *U.S. Public*, pg. 2064
COCA-COLA BOTTLING COMPANY—See The Coca-Cola Company; *U.S. Public*, pg. 2064
COCA-COLA BOTTLING COMPANY—See The Coca-Cola Company; *U.S. Public*, pg. 2064
COCA-COLA BOTTLING CO. OF NEW ENGLAND—See The Coca-Cola Company; *U.S. Public*, pg. 2064
THE COCA-COLA BOTTLING CO. OF NEW YORK, INC.—See The Coca-Cola Company; *U.S. Public*, pg. 2065
COCA-COLA BOTTLING CO. OF SHREVEPORT—See The Coca-Cola Company; *U.S. Public*, pg. 2064
COCA-COLA BOTTLING CO. OF TEXARKANA—See The Coca-Cola Company; *U.S. Public*, pg. 2064
COCA-COLA BOTTLING CO.—See The Coca-Cola Company; *U.S. Public*, pg. 2064
COCA-COLA BOTTLING CO.—See The Coca-Cola Company; *U.S. Public*, pg. 2064
COCA-COLA BOTTLING CO.—See The Coca-Cola Company; *U.S. Public*, pg. 2064
COCA-COLA BOTTLING CO. UNITED, INC.; *U.S. Private*, pg. 958
COCA-COLA BOTTLING CO. UNITED INC—See The Coca-Cola Company; *U.S. Public*, pg. 2063
COCA-COLA BOTTLING OF LOS ANGELES—See The Coca-Cola Company; *U.S. Public*, pg. 2064
COCA-COLA BOTTLING OF NORTH TEXAS—See The Coca-Cola Company; *U.S. Public*, pg. 2064
COCA-COLA BOTTLING WORKS OF TULLAHOMA, INC.; *U.S. Private*, pg. 959
COCA-COLA (CHINA) BEVERAGES LTD.—See The Coca-Cola Company; *U.S. Public*, pg. 2063
THE COCA-COLA COMPANY; *U.S. Public*, pg. 2063
THE COCA-COLA COMPANY—See The Coca-Cola Company; *U.S. Public*, pg. 2065
THE COCA-COLA COMPANY—See The Coca-Cola Company; *U.S. Public*, pg. 2065
THE COCA-COLA COMPANY—See The Coca-Cola Company; *U.S. Public*, pg. 2065
COCA-COLA CONSOLIDATED, INC.; *U.S. Public*, pg. 521
COCA-COLA DE ESPANA—See The Coca-Cola Company; *U.S. Public*, pg. 2065
COCA-COLA EMBONOR S.A.; *Int'l*, pg. 1684
COCA-COLA ENTERPRISE SAS—See COCA-COLA EUROPACIFIC PARTNERS PLC; *Int'l*, pg. 1685
COCA-COLA ENTERPRISES BELGIUM SPRL—See COCA-COLA EUROPACIFIC PARTNERS PLC; *Int'l*, pg. 1685
COCA-COLA ENTERPRISES LIMITED—See COCA-COLA

N.A.I.C.S. INDEX

312111 — SOFT DRINK MANUFACT...

EUROPACIFIC PARTNERS PLC; *Int'l*, pg. 1685
COCA-COLA ENTERPRISES NEDERLAND B.V.—See COCA-COLA EUROPACIFIC PARTNERS PLC; *Int'l*, pg. 1685
COCA-COLA ENTERPRISES NORGE AS—See COCA-COLA EUROPACIFIC PARTNERS PLC; *Int'l*, pg. 1685
COCA-COLA ENTERPRISES SVERIGE AB—See COCA-COLA EUROPACIFIC PARTNERS PLC; *Int'l*, pg. 1685
COCA-COLA ERFRISCHUNGSGETRANKE GMBH—See COCA-COLA EUROPACIFIC PARTNERS PLC; *Int'l*, pg. 1684
COCA-COLA EUROPACIFIC PARTNERS (FIJI) PTE. LIMITED—See COCA-COLA EUROPACIFIC PARTNERS PLC; *Int'l*, pg. 1684
COCA-COLA EUROPACIFIC PARTNERS GREAT BRITAIN LIMITED—See COCA-COLA EUROPACIFIC PARTNERS PLC; *Int'l*, pg. 1684
COCA-COLA EUROPACIFIC PARTNERS IBERIA, S.L.U.—See COCA-COLA EUROPACIFIC PARTNERS PLC; *Int'l*, pg. 1684
COCA-COLA EUROPACIFIC PARTNERS LUXEMBOURG SARL—See COCA-COLA EUROPACIFIC PARTNERS PLC; *Int'l*, pg. 1685
COCA-COLA EUROPACIFIC PARTNERS NEDERLAND B.V.—See COCA-COLA EUROPACIFIC PARTNERS PLC; *Int'l*, pg. 1685
COCA-COLA EUROPACIFIC PARTNERS PORTUGAL UNIPESSOAL LDA—See COCA-COLA EUROPACIFIC PARTNERS PLC; *Int'l*, pg. 1685
COCA-COLA EUROPACIFIC PARTNERS SERVICES BULGARIA EOOD—See COCA-COLA EUROPACIFIC PARTNERS PLC; *Int'l*, pg. 1685
COCA-COLA EUROPACIFIC PARTNERS SVERIGE AB—See COCA-COLA EUROPACIFIC PARTNERS PLC; *Int'l*, pg. 1685
COCA-COLA EUROPEAN PARTNERS FRANCE SAS—See COCA-COLA EUROPACIFIC PARTNERS PLC; *Int'l*, pg. 1685
COCA-COLA EUROPEAN PARTNERS IBERIA, S.L.U.—See COCA-COLA EUROPACIFIC PARTNERS PLC; *Int'l*, pg. 1685
COCA-COLA EUROPEAN PARTNERS ISLAND EHF.—See COCA-COLA EUROPACIFIC PARTNERS PLC; *Int'l*, pg. 1685
COCA-COLA EUROPEAN PARTNERS NEDERLAND B.V.—See COCA-COLA EUROPACIFIC PARTNERS PLC; *Int'l*, pg. 1685
COCA-COLA EUROPEAN PARTNERS NORGE AS—See COCA-COLA EUROPACIFIC PARTNERS PLC; *Int'l*, pg. 1685
COCA-COLA EUROPEAN PARTNERS PORTUGAL UNIPESSOAL, LDA—See COCA-COLA EUROPACIFIC PARTNERS PLC; *Int'l*, pg. 1685
THE COCA-COLA EXPORT CORPORATION—See The Coca-Cola Company; *U.S. Public*, pg. 2065
COCA-COLA HBC AUSTRIA GMBH—See Coca-Cola HBC AG; *Int'l*, pg. 1685
COCA-COLA HBC B-H D.O.O.—See Coca-Cola HBC AG; *Int'l*, pg. 1685
COCA-COLA HBC CESKA A SLOVENSKO, S.R.O.—See Coca-Cola HBC AG; *Int'l*, pg. 1686
COCA-COLA HBC CESKO A SLOVENSKO, S.R.O.—See Coca-Cola HBC AG; *Int'l*, pg. 1685
COCA-COLA HBC CYPRUS LTD.—See Coca-Cola HBC AG; *Int'l*, pg. 1685
COCA-COLA HBC HRVATSKA D.O.O.—See Coca-Cola HBC AG; *Int'l*, pg. 1685
COCA-COLA HBC HUNGARY LTD.—See Coca-Cola HBC AG; *Int'l*, pg. 1685
COCA-COLA HBC IRELAND LIMITED—See Coca-Cola HBC AG; *Int'l*, pg. 1685
COCA-COLA HBC ITALIA S.R.L.—See Coca-Cola HBC AG; *Int'l*, pg. 1686
COCA-COLA HBC NORTHERN IRELAND LIMITED—See Coca-Cola HBC AG; *Int'l*, pg. 1686
COCA-COLA HBC POLSKA SP. Z O.O.—See Coca-Cola HBC AG; *Int'l*, pg. 1686
COCA-COLA HBC ROMANIA LTD.—See Coca-Cola HBC AG; *Int'l*, pg. 1686
COCA-COLA HBC SLOVENIJA D.O.O.—See Coca-Cola HBC AG; *Int'l*, pg. 1686
COCA-COLA HBC-SRBIJA D.O.O.—See Coca-Cola HBC AG; *Int'l*, pg. 1686
COCA-COLA HBC SWITZERLAND LTD—See Coca-Cola HBC AG; *Int'l*, pg. 1686
COCA-COLA HOLDINGS (UNITED KINGDOM) LIMITED—See The Coca-Cola Company; *U.S. Public*, pg. 2063
COCA-COLA IBERIAN PARTNERS, S.A.U.—See COCA-COLA EUROPACIFIC PARTNERS PLC; *Int'l*, pg. 1685
COCA-COLA ICECEK A.S.; *Int'l*, pg. 1686
COCA-COLA INDIA LIMITED—See The Coca-Cola Company; *U.S. Public*, pg. 2064
COCA-COLA INTERAMERICAN CORP.—See The Coca-Cola Company; *U.S. Public*, pg. 2064
COCA-COLA ITALIA SRL—See The Coca-Cola Company; *U.S. Public*, pg. 2064
COCA-COLA (JAPAN) CO., LTD.—See The Coca-Cola Company; *U.S. Public*, pg. 2063
COCA-COLA LTD.—See The Coca-Cola Company; *U.S. Public*, pg. 2064
COCA-COLA LTD.—See The Coca-Cola Company; *U.S. Public*, pg. 2065
COCA-COLA LTD.—See The Coca-Cola Company; *U.S. Public*, pg. 2065
COCA-COLA OF TUCSON INC.—See The Coca-Cola Company; *U.S. Public*, pg. 2064
COCA-COLA REFRESHMENTS CANADA COMPANY—See The Coca-Cola Company; *U.S. Public*, pg. 2064
COCA-COLA REFRESHMENTS USA, INC. - BELLEVUE—See The Coca-Cola Company; *U.S. Public*, pg. 2064
COCA-COLA REFRESHMENTS USA, INC. - NILES—See The Coca-Cola Company; *U.S. Public*, pg. 2064
COCA-COLA SOUTH PACIFIC PTY LIMITED—See The Coca-Cola Company; *U.S. Public*, pg. 2065
COCA-COLA WEST DAISEN PRODUCTS CO., LTD.—See Coca-Cola Bottlers Japan Holdings Inc.; *Int'l*, pg. 1684
COLORADO SPRINGS COCA COLA BOTTLING; *U.S. Private*, pg. 974
THE CONCENTRATE MFR COMPANY OF IRELAND—See PepsiCo, Inc.; *U.S. Public*, pg. 1672
COOLACK SHARGH COMPANY (P.J.S)—See Azarbaijan Investment Development Company; *Int'l*, pg. 776
CORINTH COCA-COLA BOTTLING WORKS, INC.; *U.S. Private*, pg. 1050
CORPORACION LINDLEY S.A.—See Arca Continental, S.A.B. de C.V.; *Int'l*, pg. 540
COTT MAQUINARIA Y EQUIPO, S.A. DE C.V.—See Primo Water Corporation; *U.S. Public*, pg. 1718
CRAIG STEIN BEVERAGE; *U.S. Private*, pg. 1083
CRYSTAL SODA WATER CO.; *U.S. Private*, pg. 1115
CULLMAN COCA-COLA BOTTLING COMPANY—See Coca-Cola Bottling Co. United, Inc.; *U.S. Private*, pg. 958
CURATIVE BIOSCIENCES, INC.; *U.S. Public*, pg. 610
DANSA FOODS LIMITED—See Dangote Group Limited; *Int'l*, pg. 1962
DC BRANDS INTERNATIONAL, INC.; *U.S. Private*, pg. 1179
DELTA CORPORATION LIMITED; *Int'l*, pg. 2016
DHOFAR BEVERAGE AND FOOD STUFF COMPANY S.A.O.G; *Int'l*, pg. 2099
DRINKFINITY USA, INC.—See PepsiCo, Inc.; *U.S. Public*, pg. 1668
DUBAI REFRESHMENTS (P.S.C.) - DUBAI MAIN PRODUCTION FACILITY—See Dubai Refreshments (P.S.C.); *Int'l*, pg. 2220
DUBAI REFRESHMENTS (P.S.C.); *Int'l*, pg. 2220
DURHAM COCA COLA BOTTLING CO.; *U.S. Private*, pg. 1293
DUYVIS B.V.—See PepsiCo, Inc.; *U.S. Public*, pg. 1668
DYDO DRINCO INC.—See DyDo Group Holdings, Inc.; *Int'l*, pg. 2238
DYDO DRINCO TURKEY ICECEK SATIS VE PAZARLAMA A.S.—See DyDo Group Holdings, Inc.; *Int'l*, pg. 2238
EASTROC BEVERAGE GROUP CO., LTD.; *Int'l*, pg. 2275
ECKES-GRANINI FRANCE SNC—See Eckes AG; *Int'l*, pg. 2290
EMBOTELLADORA ANDINA S.A.; *Int'l*, pg. 2375
EMBOTELLADORA DE OCCIDENTE S.A. DE C.V.—See PepsiCo, Inc.; *U.S. Public*, pg. 1669
EMBOTELLADORA LAGUNERA, S.A. DE C.V.—See Arca Continental, S.A.B. de C.V.; *Int'l*, pg. 540
EMBOTELLADORA SAN LUIS, S.A. DE C.V.—See Arca Continental, S.A.B. de C.V.; *Int'l*, pg. 540
EPIC ENTERPRISES INC—See PepsiCo, Inc.; *U.S. Public*, pg. 1668
ESSENTUKSKY PLANT OF MINERAL WATERS ON KMV LTD.—See PepsiCo, Inc.; *U.S. Public*, pg. 1668
ETIKA BEVERAGES SDN. BHD.—See Envictus International Holdings Limited; *Int'l*, pg. 2453
EURO-JUICE G.M.B.H. IMPORT AND VERTRIEB—See PepsiCo, Inc.; *U.S. Public*, pg. 1668
EUROPEAN DRINKS S.A.; *Int'l*, pg. 2556
EVERCRISP SNACK PRODUCTOS DE CHILE S.A.—See PepsiCo, Inc.; *U.S. Public*, pg. 1668
EXCELLENCE SA; *Int'l*, pg. 2578
FAYGO BEVERAGES, INC.—See National Beverage Corp.; *U.S. Public*, pg. 1494
FERNHILL BEVERAGE, INC.—See V Group Inc.; *U.S. Private*, pg. 4327
FEROLITO, VULTAGGIO & SONS; *U.S. Private*, pg. 1498
FEVERTREE LIMITED—See Fevertree Drinks plc; *Int'l*, pg. 2648
FEVERTREE USA INC.—See Fevertree Drinks plc; *Int'l*, pg. 2648
FOMENTO ECONOMICO MEXICANO, S.A.B. DE C.V.; *Int'l*, pg. 2723
FREMONT BEVERAGES INC.; *U.S. Private*, pg. 1608
FRIGO-PAK GIDA MADDELERI SANAYI VE TICARET A.S.; *Int'l*, pg. 2792
FRITO-LAY POLAND SP.Z.O.O.—See PepsiCo, Inc.; *U.S. Public*, pg. 1668
FRITO-LAY TRADING COMPANY (POLAND) GMBH—See PepsiCo, Inc.; *U.S. Public*, pg. 1668
FRUITE SAS—See Britvic plc; *Int'l*, pg. 1171
FULL THROTTLE ENERGY COMPANY—See Monster Beverage Corporation; *U.S. Public*, pg. 1465
GAD-TEK PROPRIETARY LTD—See Bowler Metcalf Limited; *Int'l*, pg. 1124
GB INTERNATIONAL, INC.—See PepsiCo, Inc.; *U.S. Public*, pg. 1668
GDP GLOBAL DRINKS PARTNERSHIP GMBH—See Fevertree Drinks plc; *Int'l*, pg. 2649
G&J PEPSI-COLA BOTTLERS INC.; *U.S. Private*, pg. 1629
GLENBROOK COCA-COLA—See The Coca-Cola Company; *U.S. Public*, pg. 2065
GLENDIVE COCA COLA BOTTLING CO INC.—See Coca-Cola Bottling Company High Country; *U.S. Private*, pg. 959
GO FAST SPORTS & BEVERAGE CO.—See CBD Global Sciences, Inc.; *U.S. Public*, pg. 455
GREAT PLAINS COCA-COLA BOTTLING COMPANY—See Arca Continental, S.A.B. de C.V.; *Int'l*, pg. 540
GREATVIEW ASEPTIC PACKAGING COMPANY LIMITED; *Int'l*, pg. 3068
GRUPO CONTINENTAL, S.A.—See Arca Continental, S.A.B. de C.V.; *Int'l*, pg. 540
GULF STATES CANNERS INC.; *U.S. Private*, pg. 1816
HAAD THIP PUBLIC COMPANY LIMITED; *Int'l*, pg. 3201
HALL OF FAME BEVERAGES, INC.; *U.S. Public*, pg. 979
HANSEN BEVERAGE COMPANY—See Monster Beverage Corporation; *U.S. Public*, pg. 1465
HARRINGTON BOTTLING COMPANY; *U.S. Private*, pg. 1868
HEYSONG FOOD (SUZHOU) CO., LTD.—See Hey-Song Corporation; *Int'l*, pg. 3374
HILLEBRAND GORI HONG KONG LIMITED—See Deutsche Post AG; *Int'l*, pg. 2080
HILLEBRAND GORI JAPAN K.K.—See Deutsche Post AG; *Int'l*, pg. 2080
HILLEBRAND GORI KOREA LTD.—See Deutsche Post AG; *Int'l*, pg. 2080
HOKURIKU COCA-COLA BOTTLING CO., LTD.; *Int'l*, pg. 3444
HOME JUICE CORP.—See National Beverage Corp.; *U.S. Public*, pg. 1494
HONEST TEA—See The Coca-Cola Company; *U.S. Public*, pg. 2065
HOSHAKU INRYO CO., LTD.—See Aseed Holdings Co., Ltd.; *Int'l*, pg. 605
HUANLEJIA FOOD GROUP CO., LTD.; *Int'l*, pg. 3513
IBS PARTNERS LTD.; *U.S. Private*, pg. 2028
IGNITE ACQUISITION, INC.—See PepsiCo, Inc.; *U.S. Public*, pg. 1669
INDEPENDENT BEVERAGE COMPANY, LLC; *U.S. Private*, pg. 2058
INDUSTRIA DE REFRESCOS DEL NORESTE, S.R.L. DE C.V.—See PepsiCo, Inc.; *U.S. Public*, pg. 1669
INNOCENT LTD.—See The Coca-Cola Company; *U.S. Public*, pg. 2065
INTERCARABAO LIMITED—See Carabao Group Public Company Limited; *Int'l*, pg. 1319
INVERSIONES BORNEO S.R.L.—See PepsiCo, Inc.; *U.S. Public*, pg. 1669
INVITING FOODS LLC—See PepsiCo, Inc.; *U.S. Public*, pg. 1669
IZZE BEVERAGE COMPANY—See PepsiCo, Inc.; *U.S. Public*, pg. 1669
JC BOTTLING CO., LTD.—See Carlit Co., Ltd.; *Int'l*, pg. 1338
JEFFERSON CITY COCA-COLA BOTTLING CO.; *U.S. Private*, pg. 2197
JONES SODA (CANADA) INC.—See Jones Soda Company; *U.S. Public*, pg. 1206
JONES SODA COMPANY; *U.S. Public*, pg. 1206
JORDAN ICE AND AERATED WATER LTD.—See PepsiCo, Inc.; *U.S. Public*, pg. 1669
JSC LOMISI—See Anadolu Efes Biracilik ve Malt Sanayii A.S.; *Int'l*, pg. 445
J.V. COCA-COLA ALMATY BOTTLERS LIMITED LIABILITY PARTNERSHIP—See Coca-Cola Icecek A.S.; *Int'l*, pg. 1686
KALIL BOTTLING CO., INC.; *U.S. Private*, pg. 2257
KEVITA, INC.—See PepsiCo, Inc.; *U.S. Public*, pg. 1669
KONARED CORPORATION; *U.S. Public*, pg. 1271
LAFAYETTE COCA-COLA BOTTLING COMPANY—See Coca-Cola Bottling Co. United, Inc.; *U.S. Private*, pg. 958
LAKE CHARLES COCA COLA BOTTLING COMPANY—See Coca-Cola Bottling Co. United, Inc.; *U.S. Private*, pg. 958
LANCER EUROPE, S.A.—See Hoshizaki Corporation; *Int'l*, pg. 3484
LANITIS BROS PUBLIC LTD.—See Coca-Cola HBC AG; *Int'l*, pg. 1686
THE LAREDO COCA-COLA BOTTLING COMPANY, INC.—See The Coca-Cola Company; *U.S. Public*, pg. 2065
LEHRKINDS INC.; *U.S. Private*, pg. 2419
LLC COCA-COLA HBC EURASIA—See Coca-Cola HBC AG; *Int'l*, pg. 1686
LOVE BOTTLING CO.; *U.S. Private*, pg. 2501

312111 — SOFT DRINK MANUFACT...

MAHASKA BOTTLING COMPANY INC.; *U.S. Private*, pg. 2550
MANHATTAN SPECIAL BOTTLING CORP.; *U.S. Private*, pg. 2564
MARS DRINKS FRANCE—See Mars, Incorporated; *U.S. Private*, pg. 2589
MARS DRINKS—See Mars, Incorporated; *U.S. Private*, pg. 2590
MATILA NOMINEES PTY LIMITED—See COCA-COLA EUROPACIFIC PARTNERS PLC; *Int'l*, pg. 1684
MBA TULSA BEVERAGE COMPANY; *U.S. Private*, pg. 2624
MCCOMB COCA-COLA BOTTLING COMPANY—See Coca-Cola Bottling Co. United, Inc.; *U.S. Private*, pg. 958
MCRAE COCA-COLA BOTTLING COMPANY—See Coca-Cola Bottling Co. United, Inc.; *U.S. Private*, pg. 958
MD DRINKS, INC.—See Sunsweet Growers, Inc.; *U.S. Private*, pg. 3873
MERIDIAN COCA-COLA BOTTLING CO.; *U.S. Private*, pg. 2672
MEXICO BOTTLING SERVICES, S.A. DE C.V.—See Primo Water Corporation; *U.S. Public*, pg. 1718
MICHINOKU, LTD.—See DyDo Group Holdings, Inc.; *Int'l*, pg. 2238
MID-ATLANTIC COCA-COLA CO.—See The Coca-Cola Company; *U.S. Public*, pg. 2065
MIKE D. DIMICH & SONS, INC.; *U.S. Private*, pg. 2725
THE MONARCH BEVERAGE COMPANY, INC.; *U.S. Private*, pg. 4080
MONSTER ENERGY AUSTRIA GMBH—See Monster Beverage Corporation; *U.S. Public*, pg. 1465
MONTGOMERY COCA COLA BOTTLING CO.—See The Coca-Cola Company; *U.S. Public*, pg. 2065
NACKARD BOTTLING COMPANY; *U.S. Private*, pg. 2830
NATFOOD S.R.L.—See Bioera S.p.A.; *Int'l*, pg. 1037
NATIONAL BEVERAGE CORP.; *U.S. Public*, pg. 1493
NESTLE WATERS CANADA INC.—See Metropoulos & Co.; *U.S. Private*, pg. 2690
NESTLE WATERS CANADA INC.—See One Rock Capital Partners, LLC; *U.S. Private*, pg. 3021
NEWBEVCO, INC.—See National Beverage Corp.; *U.S. Public*, pg. 1494
NIGERIAN BOTTLING COMPANY LTD.—See Coca-Cola HBC AG; *Int'l*, pg. 1686
NOEL CANNING CORPORATION; *U.S. Private*, pg. 2933
NOR-CAL BEVERAGE CO., INC.; *U.S. Private*, pg. 2935
NORTH AMERICAN CANNABIS HOLDINGS, INC.; *U.S. Public*, pg. 1536
NORTHEAST HOT-FILL CO-OP, INC.; *U.S. Private*, pg. 2950
NORTHEAST MISSISSIPPI COCA-COLA BOTTLING CO., INC.—See C.C. Clark, Inc.; *U.S. Private*, pg. 706
NOS ENERGY COMPANY—See Monster Beverage Corporation; *U.S. Public*, pg. 1465
NOVAMEX, INC.; *U.S. Private*, pg. 2966
NUTRAFIZZ PRODUCTS CORP.—See National Beverage Corp.; *U.S. Public*, pg. 1494
NUUN & CO., INC.—See TSG Consumer Partners LLC; *U.S. Private*, pg. 4253
OC BEVERAGES, INC.; *U.S. Public*, pg. 1560
O-I SALES AND DISTRIBUTION ITALY S.R.L.—See O-I Glass, Inc.; *U.S. Public*, pg. 1559
OLD LINE SPIRITS, LLC—See Constellation Brands, Inc.; *U.S. Public*, pg. 571
OMEGA BRANDS INC.; *U.S. Private*, pg. 3015
ONE WORLD ENTERPRISES, LLC—See PepsiCo, Inc.; *U.S. Public*, pg. 1669
OZARKS COCA COLA/DR PEPPER BOTTLING COMPANY; *U.S. Private*, pg. 3058
PEPSI BEVERAGES COMPANY MEXICO—See PepsiCo, Inc.; *U.S. Public*, pg. 1669
PEPSI BEVERAGES COMPANY—See PepsiCo, Inc.; *U.S. Public*, pg. 1669
THE PEPSI BOTTLING GROUP (CANADA) ULC—See PepsiCo, Inc.; *U.S. Public*, pg. 1672
PEPSI BOTTLING - RALEIGH—See PepsiCo, Inc.; *U.S. Public*, pg. 1669
PEPSI BOTTLING VENTURES LLC—See PepsiCo, Inc.; *U.S. Public*, pg. 1669
PEPSICO AUSTRALIA HOLDINGS PTY LIMITED—See PepsiCo, Inc.; *U.S. Public*, pg. 1670
PEPSICO AZERBAIJAN LIMITED LIABILITY COMPANY—See PepsiCo, Inc.; *U.S. Public*, pg. 1670
PEPSICO BELUX BVBA—See PepsiCo, Inc.; *U.S. Public*, pg. 1670
PEPSICO BEVERAGES CANADA—See PepsiCo, Inc.; *U.S. Public*, pg. 1671
PEPSICO BEVERAGES ITALIA S.R.L.—See PepsiCo, Inc.; *U.S. Public*, pg. 1670
PEPSICO BEVERAGES SWITZERLAND GMBH—See PepsiCo, Inc.; *U.S. Public*, pg. 1670
PEPSICO (CHINA) CO., LTD.—See PepsiCo, Inc.; *U.S. Public*, pg. 1669
PEPSICO CZ S.R.O.—See PepsiCo, Inc.; *U.S. Public*, pg. 1671
PEPSICO DE ARGENTINA S.R.L.—See PepsiCo, Inc.; *U.S. Public*, pg. 1671

PEPSICO DEUTSCHLAND GMBH—See PepsiCo, Inc.; *U.S. Public*, pg. 1671
PEPSICO DEUTSCHLAND GMBH—See PepsiCo, Inc.; *U.S. Public*, pg. 1671
PEPSICO FOODS, A.I.E.—See PepsiCo, Inc.; *U.S. Public*, pg. 1671
PEPSICO, INC.; *U.S. Public*, pg. 1668
PEPSICO INDIA HOLDINGS PRIVATE LIMITED—See PepsiCo, Inc.; *U.S. Public*, pg. 1671
PEPSICO INTERNATIONAL LTD.—See PepsiCo, Inc.; *U.S. Public*, pg. 1671
PEPSICO (IRELAND)—See PepsiCo, Inc.; *U.S. Public*, pg. 1669
PEPSI-COLA BOTTLING COMPANY OF FARGO INC.—See Pohlad Companies; *U.S. Private*, pg. 3220
PEPSI-COLA BOTTLING CO. OF ABERDEEN, LLC—See Pohlad Companies; *U.S. Private*, pg. 3220
PEPSI COLA BOTTLING CO. OF CENTRAL VIRGINIA INC.; *U.S. Private*, pg. 3145
PEPSI COLA BOTTLING CO. OF GREENVILLE, SOUTH CAROLINA—See Carolina Canners Inc.; *U.S. Private*, pg. 767
PEPSI-COLA BOTTLING CO. OF LA CROSSE; *U.S. Private*, pg. 3145
PEPSI-COLA BOTTLING CO. OF NEW YORK, INC.—See Pepsi-Cola & National Brand Beverages, Ltd.; *U.S. Private*, pg. 3145
PEPSI-COLA BOTTLING CO. OF NORTON, VIRGINIA; *U.S. Private*, pg. 3145
PEPSI-COLA BOTTLING CO. OF SALINA INC.—See Mahaska Bottling Company Inc.; *U.S. Private*, pg. 2550
PEPSI-COLA BOTTLING OF CORBIN, KENTUCKY INC.; *U.S. Private*, pg. 3145
PEPSI-COLA BOTTLING OF HICKORY, NORTH CAROLINA INC.; *U.S. Private*, pg. 3145
PEPSI-COLA BOTTLING OF WORCESTER; *U.S. Private*, pg. 3145
PEPSI-COLA GENERAL BOTTLERS POLAND SP. Z.O.O.—See PepsiCo, Inc.; *U.S. Public*, pg. 1669
PEPSI-COLA INTERAMERICANA DE GUATEMALA S.A.—See PepsiCo, Inc.; *U.S. Public*, pg. 1669
PEPSI-COLA MANUFACTURING INTERNATIONAL LTD.—See PepsiCo, Inc.; *U.S. Public*, pg. 1670
PEPSI-COLA MEMPHIS BOTTLING CO., INC.; *U.S. Private*, pg. 3145
PEPSI-COLA OF FLORENCE, LLC; *U.S. Private*, pg. 3146
PEPSI-COLA OPERATING COMPANY OF CHESAPEAKE & INDIANAPOLIS—See PepsiCo, Inc.; *U.S. Public*, pg. 1669
PEPSI-COLA PRODUCTS PHILIPPINES, INC.—See PepsiCo, Inc.; *U.S. Public*, pg. 1669
PEPSI-COLA SR, S.R.O.—See PepsiCo, Inc.; *U.S. Public*, pg. 1669
PEPSI-COLA (THAI) TRADING COMPANY LIMITED—See PepsiCo, Inc.; *U.S. Public*, pg. 1669
PEPSICO NEDERLAND B.V.—See PepsiCo, Inc.; *U.S. Public*, pg. 1671
PEPSICO NEDERLAND B.V.—See PepsiCo, Inc.; *U.S. Public*, pg. 1671
PEPSICO NORDIC FINLAND OY—See PepsiCo, Inc.; *U.S. Public*, pg. 1671
PEPSICO PUERTO RICO, INC.—See PepsiCo, Inc.; *U.S. Public*, pg. 1671
PEPSICO SERVICES ASIA LTD.—See PepsiCo, Inc.; *U.S. Public*, pg. 1671
PEPSI LOGISTICS COMPANY, INC.—See PepsiCo, Inc.; *U.S. Public*, pg. 1669
PEPSI MIDAMERICA CO.; *U.S. Private*, pg. 3145
PEPSI NORTHWEST BEVERAGES LLC—See PepsiCo, Inc.; *U.S. Public*, pg. 1669
PHILADELPHIA COCA-COLA BOTTLING CO.—See The Coca-Cola Company; *U.S. Public*, pg. 2065
PLASTICOS NOVEL DO NORDESTE S.A.—See Myers Industries, Inc.; *U.S. Public*, pg. 1488
POLAR BEVERAGES; *U.S. Private*, pg. 3223
PORTLAND BOTTLING COMPANY—See Limnes Bottling Acquisition Co.; *U.S. Private*, pg. 2456
POSTAL PRESENTS PROPRIETARY LTD—See Bowler Metcalf Limited; *Int'l*, pg. 1124
POUCHTEC INDUSTRIES, LLC—See Kent Corporation; *U.S. Private*, pg. 2287
PREV PEPSICO SOCIEDADE PREVIDENCIARIA—See PepsiCo, Inc.; *U.S. Public*, pg. 1671
PRIDE ENGINEERING, LLC—See Arcline Investment Management LP; *U.S. Private*, pg. 315
PRIMROSE, LLC—See PepsiCo, Inc.; *U.S. Public*, pg. 1671
PROCESOS PLASTICOS S.R.L. DE C.V.—See PepsiCo, Inc.; *U.S. Public*, pg. 1671
PRS, INC.—See PepsiCo, Inc.; *U.S. Public*, pg. 1669
PT CALPIS INDONESIA—See Asahi Group Holdings Ltd.; *Int'l*, pg. 593
PT KREASI MAS INDAH—See Golden Agri-Resources Ltd.; *Int'l*, pg. 3028
PUNICA GETRANKE GMBH—See PepsiCo, Inc.; *U.S. Public*, pg. 1671
QUADRANT-AMROQ BEVERAGES S.R.L.—See PepsiCo, Inc.; *U.S. Public*, pg. 1671
QUALITY BEVERAGES 2000 PROPRIETARY LTD—See Bowler Metcalf Limited; *Int'l*, pg. 1124
QUEENCH, INC.; *U.S. Public*, pg. 1755
RANI SOFT DRINKS PRIVATE LTD.—See Aujan Industries Co., L.L.C.; *Int'l*, pg. 704
REED'S, INC.; *U.S. Public*, pg. 1771
REFRESCO BEVERAGES US INC. - SAN ANTONIO—See KKR & Co. Inc.; *U.S. Public*, pg. 1263
REFRESCO BEVERAGES US INC. - SIKESTON—See KKR & Co. Inc.; *U.S. Public*, pg. 1263
REFRESCO BEVERAGES US INC.—See KKR & Co. Inc.; *U.S. Public*, pg. 1263
REFRESCO B.V.—See KKR & Co. Inc.; *U.S. Public*, pg. 1263
REFRESCO DRINKS UK LTD.—See KKR & Co. Inc.; *U.S. Public*, pg. 1263
REFRESCO (NELSON) LIMITED—See KKR & Co. Inc.; *U.S. Public*, pg. 1263
RINGNES A/S—See Carlsberg A/S; *Int'l*, pg. 1341
ROCKSTAR INC.—See PepsiCo, Inc.; *U.S. Public*, pg. 1671
ROCKY MOUNTAIN HIGH BRANDS, INC.; *U.S. Public*, pg. 1807
ROGERS INVESTMENTS INC.; *U.S. Private*, pg. 3472
ROYAL CROWN BOTTLING CO. OF WINCHESTER INC.; *U.S. Private*, pg. 3492
RUSHNET, INC.; *U.S. Public*, pg. 1827
SAUDI SNACK FOODS COMPANY LIMITED—See PepsiCo, Inc.; *U.S. Public*, pg. 1671
SAVANNAH COCA-COLA BOTTLING COMPANY—See Coca-Cola Bottling Co. United, Inc.; *U.S. Private*, pg. 958
SCHWEPPES AUSTRALIA PTY LTD—See Asahi Group Holdings Ltd.; *Int'l*, pg. 594
S.C. UNITED ROMANIAN BREWERIES BEREPROD—See Eckes AG; *Int'l*, pg. 2291
SEVEN-UP BOTTLING COMPANY RENO; *U.S. Private*, pg. 3619
SHASTA BEVERAGES, INC.—See National Beverage Corp.; *U.S. Public*, pg. 1494
SHASTA, INC.—See National Beverage Corp.; *U.S. Public*, pg. 1494
SHASTA SALES, INC.—See National Beverage Corp.; *U.S. Public*, pg. 1494
SHIKOKU COCA-COLA BOTTLING CO., LTD.—See Coca-Cola Bottlers Japan Holdings Inc.; *Int'l*, pg. 1684
SIMBA (PROPRIETARY) LIMITED—See PepsiCo, Inc.; *U.S. Public*, pg. 1671
SMARTFOODS, INC.—See PepsiCo, Inc.; *U.S. Public*, pg. 1672
SMUCKER NATURAL FOODS, INC.—See The J.M. Smucker Company; *U.S. Public*, pg. 2107
SODASTREAM CANADA LTD.—See PepsiCo, Inc.; *U.S. Public*, pg. 1672
SODASTREAM ENTERPRISES N.V.—See PepsiCo, Inc.; *U.S. Public*, pg. 1672
SODASTREAM INTERNATIONAL LTD.—See PepsiCo, Inc.; *U.S. Public*, pg. 1672
SOUTH BEACH BEVERAGE COMPANY—See PepsiCo, Inc.; *U.S. Public*, pg. 1670
SOUTHWEST BOTTLING & CO-PACKING, LLC—See Regus Advisors, Inc.; *U.S. Public*, pg. 3389
SOUTHWEST CANNING & PACKAGING INC—See Kalil Bottling Co., Inc.; *U.S. Private*, pg. 2257
SPARTANBURG COCA-COLA BOTTLING CO.—See Coca-Cola Bottling Co. United, Inc.; *U.S. Private*, pg. 958
SPRINGFIELD PEPSI COLA BOTTLING CO. INC.; *U.S. Private*, pg. 3764
STAR FOODS BULGARIA EOOD—See PepsiCo, Inc.; *U.S. Public*, pg. 1672
STATESBORO COCA-COLA BOTTLING COMPANY—See Coca-Cola Bottling Co. United, Inc.; *U.S. Private*, pg. 959
STIRRINGS—See Nantucket Harvest Co., Inc.; *U.S. Private*, pg. 2833
STRATOSPHERE COMMUNICATIONS PTY LTD—See PepsiCo, Inc.; *U.S. Public*, pg. 1672
SUNCOKE ENERGY PARTNERS, L.P.—See SunCoke Energy, Inc.; *U.S. Public*, pg. 1964
SUN FOODS INC.—See PepsiCo, Inc.; *U.S. Public*, pg. 1672
SUNNY SKY PRODUCTS, LLC—See The Jordan Company, L.P.; *U.S. Private*, pg. 4062
TAL CONSOLIDATED INC.; *U.S. Private*, pg. 3925
TAMPICO BEVERAGES, INC.—See Houchens Industries, Inc.; *U.S. Private*, pg. 1990
TEISSEIRE FRANCE SAS—See Britvic plc; *Int'l*, pg. 1171
TEISSEIRE SAS—See Britvic plc; *Int'l*, pg. 1171
TEMPLE BOTTLING COMPANY LTD; *U.S. Private*, pg. 3963
TMLUC ARGENTINA S.A.—See Grupo Nutresa S.A.; *Int'l*, pg. 3133
TRIP DRINK LTD.—See 029 Group SE; *Int'l*, pg. 1
TROPICANA ALVALLE S.L.—See PepsiCo, Inc.; *U.S. Public*, pg. 1672
TROPICANA EUROPE N.V.—See PepsiCo, Inc.; *U.S. Public*, pg. 1672
TROPICANA LOOZA BENELUX BVBA—See PepsiCo, Inc.; *U.S. Public*, pg. 1672
TURKMENISTAN COCA-COLA BOTTLERS—See Coca-Cola Icecek A.S.; *Int'l*, pg. 1686

N.A.I.C.S. INDEX

UAB COCA-COLA HBC LIETUVA—See Coca-Cola HBC AG; *Int'l*, pg. 1686
UNISOURCE SAS—See Britvic plc; *Int'l*, pg. 1171
UPLIFT NUTRITION, INC.; *U.S. Private*, pg. 4312
VALSER SERVICES AG—See Coca-Cola HBC AG; *Int'l*, pg. 1686
VARNI BROTHERS CORPORATION—See KKR & Co. Inc.; *U.S. Public*, pg. 1263
VARUN BEVERAGES LIMITED—See Affirma Capital Limited; *Int'l*, pg. 188
VIENU CORPORATION; *U.S. Private*, pg. 4381
VIKING COCA COLA BOTTLING CO; *U.S. Private*, pg. 4382
VISION BEVERAGE CORP.; *U.S. Private*, pg. 4390
VIVARIS GETRANKE GMBH & CO. KG—See Berentzen-Gruppe AG; *Int'l*, pg. 978
VIVARIS GETRANKE VERWALTUNG GMBH—See Berentzen-Gruppe AG; *Int'l*, pg. 978
WALKERS GROUP LIMITED—See PepsiCo, Inc.; *U.S. Public*, pg. 1672
WALTON BEVERAGE CO.; *U.S. Private*, pg. 4434
WAYCROSS COCA-COLA BOTTLING COMPANY—See Coca-Cola Bottling Co. United, Inc.; *U.S. Private*, pg. 959
WEST ALABAMA COCA-COLA BOTTLING COMPANY—See Coca-Cola Bottling Co. United, Inc.; *U.S. Private*, pg. 959
WESTERN KENTUCKY COCA-COLA BOTTLING CO., INC.—See C.C. Clark, Inc.; *U.S. Private*, pg. 706
WILD AMAZON FLAVORS LTDA.—See Archer-Daniels-Midland Company; *U.S. Public*, pg. 185
WILD FLAVORS (BEIJING) LTD.—See Archer-Daniels-Midland Company; *U.S. Public*, pg. 185
WIS-PAK, INC.; *U.S. Private*, pg. 4547
YBBSTALER FRUIT AUSTRIA GMBH—See AGRANA Beteiligungs-AG; *Int'l*, pg. 214
YBBSTALER FRUIT AUSTRIA GMBH—See BayWa AG; *Int'l*, pg. 919
ZEVIA PBC; *U.S. Public*, pg. 2403
ZOLA—See KarpReilly, LLC; *U.S. Private*, pg. 2263

312112 — BOTTLED WATER MANUFACTURING

ABSOPURE WATER COMPANY INC.; *U.S. Private*, pg. 44
ADA COCA-COLA BOTTLING COMPANY; *U.S. Private*, pg. 72
AIGUES MINERALS DE VILAJUIGA, S.A.—See Grifols, S.A.; *Int'l*, pg. 3083
ALAMANCE FOODS INC.; *U.S. Private*, pg. 149
THE ALKALINE WATER COMPANY INC.; *U.S. Public*, pg. 2032
ALKAME HOLDINGS, INC.; *U.S. Public*, pg. 78
ALKAME WATER INC.—See Alkame Holdings, Inc.; *U.S. Public*, pg. 78
AMALGAMATED BEVERAGE INDUSTRIES—See Anheuser-Busch InBev SA/NV; *Int'l*, pg. 464
AQUA DIRECT LTD.—See Arjun Infrastructure Partners Limited; *Int'l*, pg. 568
AQUAESSENCE PTY LTD—See Beston Global Food Company Limited; *Int'l*, pg. 1000
AQUAGOLD INTERNATIONAL, INC.; *Int'l*, pg. 527
AQUAINTEC CORPORATION—See Air Water Inc.; *Int'l*, pg. 240
AQUASANA, INC.—See A. O. Smith Corporation; *U.S. Public*, pg. 11
BB MINAQUA AD; *Int'l*, pg. 920
BERKSHIRE MOUNTAIN SPRING WATER; *U.S. Private*, pg. 533
BRITVIC IRELAND—See Britvic plc; *Int'l*, pg. 1171
CASTLE CO-PACKERS LLC.; *U.S. Private*, pg. 784
CENTRAL STATES COCA-COLA BOTTLING COMPANY—See The Coca-Cola Company; *U.S. Public*, pg. 2064
CHAPEL DOWN GROUP PLC; *Int'l*, pg. 1447
CLEAR MOUNTAIN REFRESHMENT SERVICE, LLC—See Primo Water Corporation; *U.S. Public*, pg. 1717
CLEARSOURCE, INC.; *U.S. Private*, pg. 938
THE COCA-COLA BOTTLING CO. OF MEMPHIS, TENNESSEE—See The Coca-Cola Company; *U.S. Public*, pg. 2065
COCA COLA BOTTLING OF MEMPHIS—See The Coca-Cola Company; *U.S. Public*, pg. 2064
COCA-COLA LTD.—See The Coca-Cola Company; *U.S. Public*, pg. 2065
COTT BEVERAGES CANADA—See KKR & Co. Inc.; *U.S. Public*, pg. 1263
DANONE EAUX FRANCE—See Danone; *Int'l*, pg. 1967
DELAWARE COCA-COLA BOTTLING COMPANY, INC. Soo Tho Coca-Cola Company; *U.S. Public*, pg. 2064
DS SERVICES OF AMERICA, INC. - CRYSTAL SPRINGS—See Primo Water Corporation; *U.S. Public*, pg. 1718
DS SERVICES OF AMERICA, INC. - DEEP ROCK WATER CO.—See Primo Water Corporation; *U.S. Public*, pg. 1718
DS SERVICES OF AMERICA, INC. - HINCKLEY SPRINGS—See Primo Water Corporation; *U.S. Public*, pg. 1718
DS SERVICES OF AMERICA, INC. - MOUNT OLYMPUS—See Primo Water Corporation; *U.S. Public*, pg. 1718
DS SERVICES OF AMERICA, INC.—See Primo Water Corporation; *U.S. Public*, pg. 1718
EASYFILL AB; *Int'l*, pg. 2276
EAUX VIVES WATER INC.—See Morgan Stanley; *U.S. Public*, pg. 1472
ECOPACK LTD; *Int'l*, pg. 2298
EMIRATES REEM INVESTMENTS COMPANY P.J.S.C; *Int'l*, pg. 2382
ENERGY BRANDS, INC.—See The Coca-Cola Company; *U.S. Public*, pg. 2064
ERIE COCA-COLA BOTTLING COMPANY—See The Coca-Cola Company; *U.S. Public*, pg. 2064
ESVAL SA; *Int'l*, pg. 2519
FAMOUS RAMONA WATER, INC.; *U.S. Private*, pg. 1472
FERRARELLE S.P.A.; *Int'l*, pg. 2639
FIJI WATER COMPANY LLC—See The Wonderful Company LLC; *U.S. Private*, pg. 4138
FLORIDA COCA-COLA BOTTLING COMPANY—See The Coca-Cola Company; *U.S. Public*, pg. 2064
FONT VELLA SA—See Danone; *Int'l*, pg. 1968
THE GATORADE COMPANY—See PepsiCo, Inc.; *U.S. Public*, pg. 1670
GULFA GENERAL INVESTMENT COMPANY; *Int'l*, pg. 3182
GW SERVICES, LLC—See Primo Water Corporation; *U.S. Public*, pg. 1718
H2O TO GO/OPAL SPRINGS WATER COMPANY INC.; *U.S. Private*, pg. 1837
HALOSOURCE TECHNOLOGIES PVT. LTD.—See Halosource Corp.; *U.S. Private*, pg. 1846
HALOSOURCE WATER PURIFICATION TECHNOLOGY (SHANGHAI) CO. LTD.—See Halosource Corp.; *U.S. Private*, pg. 1846
HAWAIIAN SPRINGS, LLC; *U.S. Private*, pg. 1882
HICKORY SPRINGS WATER, INC.—See Silver Springs Bottled Water Co.; *U.S. Private*, pg. 3662
HIGHLAND MOUNTAIN WATER—See Primo Water Corporation; *U.S. Public*, pg. 1718
ICE RIVER SPRINGS WATER COMPANY INC.; *Int'l*, pg. 3579
INMEX CORPORATION—See The Coca-Cola Company; *U.S. Public*, pg. 2065
JA KIRSCH CORPORATION—See Gellert Global Group; *U.S. Public*, pg. 1657
JOHNSTON COCA-COLA BOTTLING GROUP, INC.—See The Coca-Cola Company; *U.S. Public*, pg. 2065
KNJAZ MILOS A.D.—See PepsiCo, Inc.; *U.S. Public*, pg. 1669
LEADER DISTRIBUTION SYSTEMS, INC.; *U.S. Private*, pg. 2406
LE BLEU CORPORATION; *U.S. Private*, pg. 2404
LINPEPCO PARTNERSHIP; *U.S. Private*, pg. 2462
MAPLEWOOD BEVERAGE PACKERS, LLC.; *U.S. Private*, pg. 2568
MEGA HOME CO., LTD.—See Home Product Center Public Company Limited; *Int'l*, pg. 3455
MIDDLESBORO COCA-COLA BOTTLING; *U.S. Public*, pg. 2713
MISTY MOUNTAIN SPRING WATER CO. LLC—See K-VA-T Food Stores, Inc.; *U.S. Private*, pg. 2251
MOUNTAIN GLACIER LLC—See Primo Water Corporation; *U.S. Public*, pg. 1718
MOUNTAIN PURE BEVERAGE COMPANY; *U.S. Private*, pg. 2799
MOUNTAIN VALLEY SPRING COMPANY, LLC—See Primo Water Corporation; *U.S. Public*, pg. 1718
NATFRESH BEVERAGES CORP.; *U.S. Private*, pg. 2838
NATURAL SPRINGS WATER GROUP, LLC—See The H.T. Hackney Company; *U.S. Private*, pg. 4041
NAYA WATERS INC.—See Champlain Financial Corporation; *Int'l*, pg. 1440
NEPTUNE-BENSON, INC.—See Xylem Inc.; *U.S. Public*, pg. 2394
NESTLE WATERS CANADA INC.—See Metropoulos & Co.; *U.S. Private*, pg. 2690
NESTLE WATERS CANADA INC.—See One Rock Capital Partners, LLC; *U.S. Private*, pg. 3021
NESTLE WATERS NORTH AMERICA INC. - FORT LAUDERDALE—See Metropoulos & Co.; *U.S. Private*, pg. 2690
NESTLE WATERS NORTH AMERICA INC. - FORT LAUDERDALE—See One Rock Capital Partners, LLC; *U.S. Private*, pg. 3021
NESTLE WATERS NORTH AMERICA INC. - LANHAM—See Metropoulos & Co.; *U.S. Private*, pg. 2690
NESTLE WATERS NORTH AMERICA INC. - LANHAM—See One Rock Capital Partners, LLC; *U.S. Private*, pg. 3021
NESTLE WATERS NORTH AMERICA INC. - NORTHBROOK—See Metropoulos & Co.; *U.S. Private*, pg. 2690
NESTLE WATERS NORTH AMERICA INC. - NORTHBROOK—See One Rock Capital Partners, LLC; *U.S. Private*, pg. 3021
NEVERFAIL BOTTLED WATER CO PTY LIMITED—See COCA-COLA EUROPACIFIC PARTNERS PLC; *Int'l*, pg. 1684
NICHIRO SUNPACK CO., LTD.—See Air Water Inc.; *Int'l*, pg. 240
NIRVANA, INC.; *U.S. Private*, pg. 2928
OASIS INTERNATIONAL—See Patriarch Partners, LLC; *U.S. Private*, pg. 3109
OZARKA WATER—See Metropoulos & Co.; *U.S. Private*, pg. 2690
OZARKA WATER—See One Rock Capital Partners, LLC; *U.S. Private*, pg. 3021
PEPSI-COLA GMBH—See PepsiCo, Inc.; *U.S. Public*, pg. 1669
PEPSI-COLA INTERNATIONAL (PVT) LIMITED—See PepsiCo, Inc.; *U.S. Public*, pg. 1669
POLAND SPRING CORPORATION—See Metropoulos & Co.; *U.S. Private*, pg. 2691
POLAND SPRING CORPORATION—See One Rock Capital Partners, LLC; *U.S. Private*, pg. 3021
POLYMEM S.A.—See Repligen Corporation; *U.S. Public*, pg. 1784
PT.HOKKAN INDONESIA—See Hokkan Holdings Limited; *Int'l*, pg. 3443
THE PULSE BEVERAGE CORPORATION; *U.S. Public*, pg. 2125
PURELY ALASKAN WATER INC.; *U.S. Private*, pg. 3306
RICHARDSON BOTTLING COMPANY; *U.S. Private*, pg. 3429
RIO DE JANEIRO REFRESCOS LTDA.—See Embotelladora Andina S.A.; *Int'l*, pg. 2375
THE ROBERTS GROUP, INC.; *U.S. Private*, pg. 4111
ROOSHINE, INC.; *U.S. Public*, pg. 1810
SA DES EAUX MINERALES D'EVIAN—See Danone; *Int'l*, pg. 1968
SARATOGA SPRING WATER COMPANY—See Metropoulos & Co.; *U.S. Private*, pg. 2691
SARATOGA SPRING WATER COMPANY—See One Rock Capital Partners, LLC; *U.S. Private*, pg. 3021
SARPES BEVERAGES, LLC—See Hygrovest Limited; *Int'l*, pg. 3549
SILVER SPRINGS BOTTLED WATER CO.; *U.S. Private*, pg. 3662
SOS HYDRATION INC.; *U.S. Private*, pg. 3716
SOUTHERN BEVERAGE PACKERS, INC.; *U.S. Private*, pg. 3729
TOP SHELF SPIRITS & WINE; *U.S. Private*, pg. 4186
VALLEY COCA-COLA BOTTLING COMPANY, INC.—See The Coca-Cola Company; *U.S. Public*, pg. 2065
VITAL AGUAS S.A.—See Embotelladora Andina S.A.; *Int'l*, pg. 2375
VOLTIC (GH) LIMITED—See The Coca-Cola Company; *U.S. Public*, pg. 2065
ZEPHYRHILLS SPRING WATER COMPANY—See Metropoulos & Co.; *U.S. Private*, pg. 2691
ZEPHYRHILLS SPRING WATER COMPANY—See One Rock Capital Partners, LLC; *U.S. Private*, pg. 3021

312113 — ICE MANUFACTURING

ARCTIC GLACIER INC.—See H.I.G. Capital, LLC; *U.S. Private*, pg. 1829
ARCTIC GLACIER PENNSYLVANIA, INC.—See H.I.G. Capital, LLC; *U.S. Private*, pg. 1829
ARCTIC GLACIER U.S.A., INC.—See H.I.G. Capital, LLC; *U.S. Private*, pg. 1829
ASIA MEWAH RESOURCES SDN. BHD.—See Haisan Resources Berhad; *Int'l*, pg. 3217
CITY ICE CO.—See Centerbridge Partners, L.P.; *U.S. Private*, pg. 815
FREEVILLE (M) SDN. BHD.—See Haisan Resources Berhad; *Int'l*, pg. 3217
HAI SAN & SONS SDN. BHD.—See Haisan Resources Berhad; *Int'l*, pg. 3217
HOME CITY ICE COMPANY INC.; *U.S. Private*, pg. 1970
JACK FROST ICE SERVICE, INC.—See H.I.G. Capital, LLC; *U.S. Private*, pg. 1829
PARADISE ICE PLANT; *U.S. Private*, pg. 3090
PONTIAN ICE FACTORY SDN. BHD.—See Haisan Resources Berhad; *Int'l*, pg. 3217
POSITIVE FOOD VENTURES PRIVATE LIMITED—See Food Empire Holdings Limited; *Int'l*, pg. 2727
REDDY ICE CORPORATION—See Centerbridge Partners, L.P.; *U.S. Private*, pg. 815
REDDY ICE—See Centerbridge Partners, L.P.; *U.S. Private*, pg. 815
SAINT JOHN ICE COMPANY; *U.S. Private*, pg. 3529
THERMAFREEZE PRODUCTS CORP.; *U.S. Public*, pg. 2145
VALLEY ICE, LLC—See Holtzman Oil Corp.; *U.S. Private*, pg. 1969

312120 — BREWERIES

6 SWEET BRIAR ROAD LIMITED—See ANSA McAL Limited; *Int'l*, pg. 476

312120 — BREWERIES

AB INBEV UK LIMITED—See Anheuser-Busch InBev SA/NV; *Int'l*, pg. 464
ABITA BREWING CO.; *U.S. Private,* pg. 39
AB SVYTURYS—See Carlsberg A/S; *Int'l*, pg. 1339
ACCRA BREWERY LIMITED—See Anheuser-Busch InBev SA/NV; *Int'l*, pg. 464
ADVADIS S.A.; *Int'l*, pg. 155
AFFINITY BEVERAGE GROUP, INC.; *U.S. Public,* pg. 57
ALASKAN BREWING COMPANY; *U.S. Private,* pg. 151
ALEFARM BREWING A/S; *Int'l*, pg. 306
ALSTONS LIMITED—See ANSA McAl Limited; *Int'l*, pg. 477
AMBEV S.A.—See Anheuser-Busch InBev SA/NV; *Int'l*, pg. 465
ANADOLU EFES BIRACILIK VE MALT SANAYII A.S.; *Int'l*, pg. 445
ANCHOR BREWERS & DISTILLERS, LLC—See The Griffin Group, LLC; *U.S. Private,* pg. 4039
ANHEUSER-BUSCH, INC.—See Anheuser-Busch InBev SA/NV; *Int'l*, pg. 465
ANHUI YINGJIA DISTILLERY CO., LTD.; *Int'l*, pg. 470
ANSA FINANCIAL HOLDINGS (BARBADOS) LIMITED—See ANSA McAl Limited; *Int'l*, pg. 476
ANSA MCAL ENTERPRISES LIMITED—See ANSA McAl Limited; *Int'l*, pg. 476
ANSA RE LIMITED—See ANSA McAl Limited; *Int'l*, pg. 476
APPALACHIAN MOUNTAIN BREWERY, INC.—See Anheuser-Busch InBev SA/NV; *Int'l*, pg. 465
ARCUS SWEDEN AB—See Arcus ASA; *Int'l*, pg. 552
ASAHI BEVERAGES PTY LTD—See Asahi Group Holdings Ltd.; *Int'l*, pg. 593
ASAHI BREWERIES, LTD.—See Asahi Group Holdings Ltd.; *Int'l*, pg. 593
ASAHI INTERNATIONAL, LTD.—See Asahi Group Holdings Ltd.; *Int'l*, pg. 593
A/S ALDARIS—See Carlsberg A/S; *Int'l*, pg. 1339
ASEPTIC SOLUTIONS USA VENTURES, LLC—See Glanbia Co-Operative Society Limited; *Int'l*, pg. 2987
ASSOCIATED MICROBREWERIES LTD.; *U.S. Private,* pg. 356
AS VIRU OLU—See Harboes Bryggeri A/S; *Int'l*, pg. 3271
BACKDRAFT BREWING COMPANY; *U.S. Private,* pg. 423
BALLAST POINT BREWING & SPIRITS, INC.—See Kings & Convicts Brewing Co.; *U.S. Private,* pg. 2311
BANJALUCKA PIVARA A.D., BANJA LUKA—See Altima Partners LLP; *Int'l*, pg. 393
BAVARIA SA - BARRANQUILLA BREWERY PLANT—See Anheuser-Busch InBev SA/NV; *Int'l*, pg. 464
BAVARIA SA—See Anheuser-Busch InBev SA/NV; *Int'l*, pg. 464
BAVARIA SA - TIBITO MALT PLANT—See Anheuser-Busch InBev SA/NV; *Int'l*, pg. 464
BAVARIA SA - TOCANCIPA BREWERY PLANT—See Anheuser-Busch InBev SA/NV; *Int'l*, pg. 464
BAVARIA SA - TROPICAL MALT PLANT—See Anheuser-Busch InBev SA/NV; *Int'l*, pg. 464
BAVARIA SA - VALLE BREWERY PLANT—See Anheuser-Busch InBev SA/NV; *Int'l*, pg. 464
BBD ACQUISITION CO—See Breckenridge Holding Company; *U.S. Private,* pg. 644
BEAR REPUBLIC BREWING CO., INC.; *U.S. Private,* pg. 506
BELHAVEN BREWERY COMPANY LIMITED—See CK Asset Holdings Limited; *Int'l*, pg. 1635
BELL'S BREWERY, INC.; *U.S. Private,* pg. 519
THE BENRIACH DISTILLERY CO. LTD.—See Brown-Forman Corporation; *U.S. Public,* pg. 403
BEOGRADSKA INDUSTRIJA PIVA A.D.; *Int'l*, pg. 978
BERGENBIER S.A.—See Molson Coors Beverage Company; *U.S. Public,* pg. 1459
BERMAS SA; *Int'l*, pg. 986
BIG ROCK BREWERY INC.; *Int'l*, pg. 1021
BIHACKA PIVOVARA D.D.; *Int'l*, pg. 1022
BIRRA PERONI S.R.L.—See Asahi Group Holdings Ltd.; *Int'l*, pg. 593
BITBURGER BRAUEREI TH. SIMON GMBH—See Bitburger Braugruppe GmbH; *Int'l*, pg. 1049
BITBURGER BRAUGRUPPE GMBH; *Int'l*, pg. 1049
BLUE POINT BREWING COMPANY, INC.—See Anheuser-Busch InBev SA/NV; *Int'l*, pg. 465
BONEYARD BEER LLC—See Deschutes Brewery Inc.; *U.S. Private,* pg. 1211
BORSODI SORGYAR KORLATOLT FELELOSSEGU TARSASAG—See Molson Coors Beverage Company; *U.S. Public,* pg. 1459
BORSODI SORGYAR ZRT.—See Molson Coors Beverage Company; *U.S. Public,* pg. 1459
THE BOSTON BEER COMPANY, INC.; *U.S. Public,* pg. 2041
BOSTON BREWING COMPANY, INC.—See The Boston Beer Company, Inc.; *U.S. Public,* pg. 2041
BOULEVARD BREWING CO.—See Fibemi NV; *Int'l*, pg. 2651
BRASSERIE D'ACHOUFFE NV—See Fibemi NV; *Int'l*, pg. 2651
BRASSERIE DE LUXEMBOURG MOUSEL - DIEKIRCH SA—See Anheuser-Busch InBev SA/NV; *Int'l*, pg. 465
BRASSERIES KRONENBOURG—See Carlsberg A/S; *Int'l*, pg. 1339

BRAUEREI BECK GMBH & CO. KG—See Anheuser-Busch InBev SA/NV; *Int'l*, pg. 465
BRAUEREI DIEBELS GMBH & CO. KG—See Anheuser-Busch InBev SA/NV; *Int'l*, pg. 465
BRAUEREI FOHRENBURG GMBH & CO KG; *Int'l*, pg. 1141
BRAUEREI MAX LEIBINGER GMBH; *Int'l*, pg. 1141
BRAUEREI ZOLLER-HOF GRAF-FLEISCHHUT GMBH & CO.KG; *Int'l*, pg. 1141
BRAUERGILDE HANNOVER AG—See Anheuser-Busch InBev SA/NV; *Int'l*, pg. 465
BRECKENRIDGE BREWERY—See Anheuser-Busch InBev SA/NV; *Int'l*, pg. 466
BREWBILT BREWING COMPANY; *U.S. Public,* pg. 381
BREWMASTER, INC.—See Full Circle Brewing Co., Ltd.; *U.S. Private,* pg. 1620
BROO LIMITED; *Int'l*, pg. 1174
BROUWERIJ BELAME LTD—See Fibemi NV; *Int'l*, pg. 2651
BROUWERIJ DE KONINCK NV—See Fibemi NV; *Int'l*, pg. 2651
BROUWERIJ VAN HOEGAARDEN N.V.—See Anheuser-Busch InBev SA/NV; *Int'l*, pg. 466
BROWN-FORMAN FINLAND OY—See Brown-Forman Corporation; *U.S. Public,* pg. 403
BROWN-FORMAN RO S.R.L.—See Brown-Forman Corporation; *U.S. Public,* pg. 403
BROWN-FORMAN RUS L.L.C.—See Brown-Forman Corporation; *U.S. Public,* pg. 403
BROWN-FORMAN SPAIN, S.L.—See Brown-Forman Corporation; *U.S. Public,* pg. 403
BSG CRAFTBREWING—See Rahr Corporation; *U.S. Private,* pg. 3346
BUDWEISER BREWING COMPANY APAC LIMITED; *Int'l*, pg. 1211
BUDWEISER WUHAN INTERNATIONAL BREWING COMPANY LIMITED—See Anheuser-Busch InBev SA/NV; *Int'l*, pg. 465
BUSCH PROPERTIES, INC.—See Anheuser-Busch InBev SA/NV; *Int'l*, pg. 465
BUTCOMBE BREWERY LTD.—See Caledonia Investments plc; *Int'l*, pg. 1262
CAMERONS BREWERY LTD.; *Int'l*, pg. 1272
CAPITAL BREWERY CO., INC.; *U.S. Private,* pg. 739
CARIBBEAN DEVELOPMENT COMPANY LIMITED—See ANSA McAl Limited; *Int'l*, pg. 477
CARIBBEAN DEVELOPMENT COMPANY (ST.KITTS) LIMITED—See ANSA McAl Limited; *Int'l*, pg. 477
CARLSBERG A/S; *Int'l*, pg. 1339
CARLSBERG BREWERIES A/S—See Carlsberg A/S; *Int'l*, pg. 1339
CARLSBERG BREWERY HONG KONG LIMITED—See Carlsberg A/S; *Int'l*, pg. 1339
CARLSBERG BREWERY MALAYSIA BERHAD—See Carlsberg A/S; *Int'l*, pg. 1339
CARLSBERG CHONGQING BREWERIES COMPANY LIMITED—See Carlsberg A/S; *Int'l*, pg. 1339
CARLSBERG CROATIA—See Carlsberg A/S; *Int'l*, pg. 1340
CARLSBERG DANMARK A/S—See Carlsberg A/S; *Int'l*, pg. 1340
CARLSBERG DENMARK A/S FREDERICIA—See Carlsberg A/S; *Int'l*, pg. 1340
CARLSBERG DEUTSCHLAND GMBH—See Carlsberg A/S; *Int'l*, pg. 1340
CARLSBERG GB LIMITED—See Carlsberg A/S; *Int'l*, pg. 1340
CARLSBERG IMPORTERS SA—See Carlsberg A/S; *Int'l*, pg. 1340
CARLSBERG INTERNATIONAL A/S—See Carlsberg A/S; *Int'l*, pg. 1340
CARLSBERG ITALIA S.P.A.—See Carlsberg A/S; *Int'l*, pg. 1340
CARLSBERG OKOCIM SA—See Carlsberg A/S; *Int'l*, pg. 1340
CARLSBERG POLSKA S. A.—See Carlsberg A/S; *Int'l*, pg. 1340
CARLSBERG (SINGAPORE) PTE. LTD.—See Carlsberg A/S; *Int'l*, pg. 1339
CARLSBERG SVERIGE AB—See Carlsberg A/S; *Int'l*, pg. 1340
CARLSBERG SWEDEN AB—See Carlsberg A/S; *Int'l*, pg. 1340
CARLTON & UNITED BEVERAGES LIMITED—See Anheuser-Busch InBev SA/NV; *Int'l*, pg. 464
CARLTON & UNITED BREWERIES PTY LTD—See Asahi Group Holdings Ltd.; *Int'l*, pg. 593
CAROLINA BEER & BEVERAGE, LLC.; *U.S. Private,* pg. 767
CASCADE BREWERY COMPANY; *Int'l*, pg. 1349
CASPIAN BEVERAGE HOLDING JSC; *Int'l*, pg. 1354
CASTEL MALAWI LIMITED—See Castel Freres SA; *Int'l*, pg. 1356
CATALINA PRODUCTS, LLC—See Coopers Brewery Limited; *Int'l*, pg. 1792
CERVECERIA ANDINA S.A.—See Anheuser-Busch InBev SA/NV; *Int'l*, pg. 464
CERVECERIA ARGENTINA S.A. ISENBECK—See Anheuser-Busch InBev SA/NV; *Int'l*, pg. 464
CERVECERIA BOLIVIANA NACIONAL S.A.—See Anheuser-Busch InBev SA/NV; *Int'l*, pg. 466

CERVECERIA CUAUHTEMOC MOCTEZUMA S.A. DE C.V.—See Anheuser-Busch InBev SA/NV; *Int'l*, pg. 466
CERVECERIA HONDURENA, S.A DE C.V—See Anheuser-Busch InBev SA/NV; *Int'l*, pg. 466
CERVECERIA NACIONAL (CN) SA—See Anheuser-Busch InBev SA/NV; *Int'l*, pg. 464
CERVECERIA NACIONAL, S.A.—See Anheuser-Busch InBev SA/NV; *Int'l*, pg. 464
CERVECERIA PARAGUAYA S.A.—See Anheuser-Busch InBev SA/NV; *Int'l*, pg. 464
CERVECERIA SAN JUAN S.A.—See Anheuser-Busch InBev SA/NV; *Int'l*, pg. 464
CERVECERIA Y MALTERIA QUILMES SAICA Y G—See Anheuser-Busch InBev SA/NV; *Int'l*, pg. 466
CEYLON BREWERY LTD.—See Carlsberg A/S; *Int'l*, pg. 1340
CHAMELEON BREWING—See Sprecher Brewing Company, LLC; *U.S. Private,* pg. 3762
CHONGQING BREWERY CO., LTD; *Int'l*, pg. 1579
CIGAR CITY BREWING LLC—See Fireman Capital Partners LLC; *U.S. Private,* pg. 1512
CITY BREWING COMPANY, LLC—See Brookfield Corporation; *Int'l*, pg. 1182
CITY BREWING COMPANY, LLC—See Charlesbank Capital Partners, LLC; *U.S. Private,* pg. 855
COCA-COLA BEVERAGES SLOVENIJA D.O.O.—See Coca-Cola HBC AG; *Int'l*, pg. 1685
COCA-COLA HELLENIC BOTTLING COMPANY-CRNA GORA D.O.O.—See Coca-Cola HBC AG; *Int'l*, pg. 1686
COCA-COLA HELLENIC PROCUREMENT GMBH—See Coca-Cola HBC AG; *Int'l*, pg. 1686
COLD SPRING BREWING CO.; *U.S. Private,* pg. 965
COLUMBIA BREWING COMPANY—See Anheuser-Busch InBev SA/NV; *Int'l*, pg. 466
COMPANIA CERVECERA AMBEV DOMINICANA—See Anheuser-Busch InBev SA/NV; *Int'l*, pg. 466
COMPANIA CERVECERA DE CANARIAS SA—See Anheuser-Busch InBev SA/NV; *Int'l*, pg. 464
COMPANIA CERVECERA DE PUERTO RICO; *U.S. Private,* pg. 998
CONSTELLATION BRANDS NEW ZEALAND LIMITED—See Constellation Brands, Inc.; *U.S. Public,* pg. 570
COOPERS BREWERY LIMITED; *Int'l*, pg. 1792
COORS BREWING COMPANY—See Molson Coors Beverage Company; *U.S. Public,* pg. 1459
CRAFT BREW ALLIANCE, INC.—See Anheuser-Busch InBev SA/NV; *Int'l*, pg. 465
CROWN BEERS INDIA LIMITED—See Anheuser-Busch InBev SA/NV; *Int'l*, pg. 466
DANIEL THWAITES BREWERY—See Daniel Thwaites PLC; *Int'l*, pg. 1962
DARGUNER BRAUEREI GMBH—See Harboes Bryggeri A/S; *Int'l*, pg. 3271
DBI BEVERAGE NAPA; *U.S. Private,* pg. 1179
DECRESCENTE DISTRIBUTING CO., INC.; *U.S. Private,* pg. 1188
DE KLOK DRANKEN B.V.—See Asahi Group Holdings Ltd.; *Int'l*, pg. 593
DELTA BEVERAGES (PVT) LIMITED—See Delta Corporation Limited; *Int'l*, pg. 2016
DESCHUTES BREWERY INC.; *U.S. Private,* pg. 1211
D.G. YUENGLING & SON INCORPORATED; *U.S. Private,* pg. 1142
DIAGEO IRELAND—See Diageo plc; *Int'l*, pg. 2102
DIAGEO NORTHERN IRELAND—See Diageo plc; *Int'l*, pg. 2102
DOGFISH HEAD CRAFT BREWERY, INC.—See The Boston Beer Company, Inc.; *U.S. Public,* pg. 2041
DRAFT BEER SERVICES OF ATLANTA, INC.—See Falconhead Capital, LLC; *U.S. Private,* pg. 1467
DUVEL MOORTGAT NV—See Fibemi NV; *Int'l*, pg. 2651
DYLAND BV—See Carlsberg A/S; *Int'l*, pg. 1340
EFES BREWERIES INTERNATIONAL N.V.—See Anadolu Efes Biracilik ve Malt Sanayii A.S.; *Int'l*, pg. 445
EFES VITANTA MOLDOVA BREWERY S.A—See Anadolu Efes Biracilik ve Malt Sanayii A.S.; *Int'l*, pg. 445
EINBECKER BRAUHAUS AG; *Int'l*, pg. 2332
ELYSIAN BREWING COMPANY—See Anheuser-Busch InBev SA/NV; *Int'l*, pg. 465
FALLS CITY BREWING COMPANY—See Neace Ventures; *U.S. Private,* pg. 2877
FAULTLINE BREWING CO. INC.; *U.S. Private,* pg. 1484
FELDSCHLOSSCHEN BEVERAGES LTD.—See Carlsberg A/S; *Int'l*, pg. 1340
FIELDWORK BREWING COMPANY; *U.S. Private,* pg. 1504
FIREHOUSE BREWING COMPANY, INC.; *U.S. Private,* pg. 1511
FIRESTEED CORPORATION—See Vintage Wine Estates, Inc.; *U.S. Public,* pg. 2298
FIRESTONE WALKER, LLC—See Fibemi NV; *Int'l*, pg. 2652
FNC S.A.—See Anheuser-Busch InBev SA/NV; *Int'l*, pg. 465
FORDHAM & DOMINION BREWING CO.; *U.S. Private,* pg. 1565
FOUNDERS BREWING CO.; *U.S. Private,* pg. 1580
FOUNTAIN ROCK MANAGEMENT CORPORATION; *U.S. Private,* pg. 1581
FOUR PEAKS BREWING COMPANY, INC.—See Anheuser-

N.A.I.C.S. INDEX

312130 — WINERIES

Busch InBev SA/NV; *Int'l*, pg. 466
FUJIAN YANJING HUIQUAN BREWERY CO., LTD.; *Int'l*, pg. 2820
FULL CIRCLE BREWING CO., LTD.; *U.S. Private*, pg. 1620
FULLER, SMITH & TURNER PLC; *Int'l*, pg. 2842
FULL SAIL BREWING CO.; *U.S. Private*, pg. 1621
THE F.X. MATT BREWING CO.; *U.S. Private*, pg. 4027
THE GAMBRINUS COMPANY; *U.S. Private*, pg. 4031
GANSU MOGAO INDUSTRIAL DEVELOPMENT CO., LTD.; *Int'l*, pg. 2881
GENERAL INVESTMENT CO., LTD.; *Int'l*, pg. 2919
GENESEE BREWING COMPANY—See Florida Ice and Farm Co. S.A.; *Int'l*, pg. 2707
GILDE BRAUEREI AG; *Int'l*, pg. 2973
GOOD DRINKS AUSTRALIA LTD.; *Int'l*, pg. 3038
GORKHA BREWERY LIMITED—See Carlsberg A/S; *Int'l*, pg. 1340
GOURMET BRYGGERIET APS—See Harboes Bryggeri A/S; *Int'l*, pg. 3271
GPBC INC.; *U.S. Private*, pg. 1748
GREAT NORTHERN BREWING COMPANY—See The McKenzie River Corporation; *U.S. Private*, pg. 4077
GREENE KING BREWING & RETAILING LIMITED—See CK Asset Holdings Limited; *Int'l*, pg. 1635
GRENADA BREWERIES LIMITED—See ANSA McAL Limited; *Int'l*, pg. 477
GRUPA ZYWIEC S.A.; *Int'l*, pg. 3117
GRUPO MODELO, S.A. DE C.V.—See Anheuser-Busch InBev SA/NV; *Int'l*, pg. 466
GUANGZHOU ZHUJIANG BREWERY GROUP CO., LTD.; *Int'l*, pg. 3168
GUINNESS GHANA BREWERIES PLC—See Diageo plc; *Int'l*, pg. 2102
HAINAN YEDAO (GROUP) CO., LTD.; *Int'l*, pg. 3216
HANOI BEER TRADING JSC; *Int'l*, pg. 3258
HANOI - HAI DUONG BEER JSC; *Int'l*, pg. 3258
HARBOES BRYGGERI A/S; *Int'l*, pg. 3271
HASSERODER BRAUEREI GMBH—See Anheuser-Busch InBev SA/NV; *Int'l*, pg. 466
HEINRICH'S SYNDICATE LIMITED—See Anheuser-Busch InBev SA/NV; *Int'l*, pg. 464
HILLIARD'S BEER—See Odin Brewing Co.; *U.S. Private*, pg. 2993
HOLSTEN-BRAUEREI AG—See Carlsberg A/S; *Int'l*, pg. 1340
HUE BREWERY LTD.—See Carlsberg A/S; *Int'l*, pg. 1340
HUSS BREWING CO. LLC; *U.S. Private*, pg. 2014
INBEV N.V.—See Anheuser-Busch InBev SA/NV; *Int'l*, pg. 466
INBEV SEDRIN BREWERY CO, LTD—See Anheuser-Busch InBev SA/NV; *Int'l*, pg. 466
INBEV UK LTD.—See Anheuser-Busch InBev SA/NV; *Int'l*, pg. 466
INDIAN RIVER BEVERAGE CORPORATION—See ANSA McAL Limited; *Int'l*, pg. 477
INDUSTRIAS LA CONSTANCIA S.A.—See Anheuser-Busch InBev SA/NV; *Int'l*, pg. 464
INTERBREW INTERNATIONAL B.V.—See Anheuser-Busch InBev SA/NV; *Int'l*, pg. 466
JACOB LEINENKUGEL BREWING COMPANY—See Molson Coors Beverage Company; *U.S. Public*, pg. 1459
KAMENITZA AD—See Anheuser-Busch InBev SA/NV; *Int'l*, pg. 466
KAZBEGI JSC—See Bank of Georgia Group PLC; *Int'l*, pg. 843
KINGS & CONVICTS BREWING CO.; *U.S. Private*, pg. 2311
KOMPANIA PIWOWARSKA S.A.—See Asahi Group Holdings Ltd.; *Int'l*, pg. 593
KONINKLIJKE GROLSCH N.V.—See Asahi Group Holdings Ltd.; *Int'l*, pg. 593
KORNBRENNEREI BERENTZEN GMBH—See Berentzen-Gruppe AG; *Int'l*, pg. 978
KOSTRITZER SCHWARZBIERBRAUEREI GMBH & CO.—See Bitburger Braugruppe GmbH; *Int'l*, pg. 1049
LABATT BREWERIES OF LONDON—See Anheuser-Busch InBev SA/NV; *Int'l*, pg. 466
LABATT BREWERIES OF NEWFOUNDLAND—See Anheuser-Busch InBev SA/NV; *Int'l*, pg. 466
LABATT BREWERIES ONTARIO LTD.—See Anheuser-Busch InBev SA/NV; *Int'l*, pg. 466
LABATT BREWERIES PRAIRIE REGION—See Anheuser-Busch InBev SA/NV; *Int'l*, pg. 466
LABATT BREWING COMPANY LIMITED—See Anheuser-Busch InBev SA/NV; *Int'l*, pg. 466
LA BRASSERIE LABATT—See Anheuser-Busch InBev SA/NV; *Int'l*, pg. 466
LACROIX SPARKLING WATER, INC.—See National Beverage Corp.; *U.S. Public*, pg. 1494
LAKE SUPERIOR BREWING COMPANY; *U.S. Private*, pg. 2376
LANDWIRTH'S GMBH—See Berentzen-Gruppe AG; *Int'l*, pg. 978
THE LION BREWERY, INC.—See Encore Associates Inc.; *U.S. Private*, pg. 1390
LITTLE HARPETH BREWING LLC—See H.S. Lipman Brewing Company, LLC; *U.S. Private*, pg. 3339
LONG TRAIL BREWING COMPANY—See Massachusetts Bay Brewing Co.; *U.S. Private*, pg. 2603

LOS GATOS BREWING CO.; *U.S. Private*, pg. 2497
MAC & JACK'S BREWERY, INC.—See Ackley Beverage Group, LLC; *U.S. Private*, pg. 60
MAGIC HAT BREWING CO. & PERFORMING ARTS CENTER INC.—See Florida Ice and Farm Co. S.A.; *Int'l*, pg. 2707
MASSACHUSETTS BAY BREWING CO.; *U.S. Private*, pg. 2603
MEANTIME BREWING COMPANY LTD.—See Asahi Group Holdings Ltd.; *Int'l*, pg. 594
MILLER BREWING COMPANY—See Molson Coors Beverage Company; *U.S. Public*, pg. 1459
MILLERCOORS LLC—See Molson Coors Beverage Company; *U.S. Public*, pg. 1459
MOLSON BREWERY - BRITISH COLUMBIA—See Molson Coors Beverage Company; *U.S. Public*, pg. 1459
MOLSON BREWERY - ONTARIO—See Molson Coors Beverage Company; *U.S. Public*, pg. 1459
MOLSON COORS BREWING COMPANY (UK) LTD.—See Molson Coors Beverage Company; *U.S. Public*, pg. 1459
MOLSON COORS CANADA INC.—See Molson Coors Beverage Company; *U.S. Public*, pg. 1459
MOLSON COORS CANADA—See Molson Coors Beverage Company; *U.S. Public*, pg. 1459
MOLSON INC.—See Molson Coors Beverage Company; *U.S. Public*, pg. 1459
MORGAN STREET BREWERY & TAVERN INC.; *U.S. Private*, pg. 2784
MYTHOS BREWERY S.A.—See Carlsberg A/S; *Int'l*, pg. 1340
NARRAGANSETT BREWING CO; *U.S. Private*, pg. 2835
NASHOBA VALLEY SPIRITS, LTD.; *U.S. Private*, pg. 2836
NEWAGE, INC.; *U.S. Public*, pg. 1513
NEW GLARUS BREWING COMPANY; *U.S. Private*, pg. 2896
NILE BREWERIES LTD.—See Anheuser-Busch InBev SA/NV; *Int'l*, pg. 466
NUUK IMEQ A/S—See Carlsberg A/S; *Int'l*, pg. 1340
OAO BALTIKA BREWERIES—See Carlsberg A/S; *Int'l*, pg. 1340
OAO VENA—See Carlsberg A/S; *Int'l*, pg. 1340
ODIN BREWING CO.; *U.S. Private*, pg. 2993
OOO VOSTOK SOLOD—See Anadolu Efes Biracilik ve Malt Sanayii A.S.; *Int'l*, pg. 445
ORIENTAL BREWERY CO., LTD.—See Anheuser-Busch InBev SA/NV; *Int'l*, pg. 466
OY SINEBRYCHOFF AB—See Carlsberg A/S; *Int'l*, pg. 1340
PABST BREWING COMPANY—See TSG Consumer Partners LLC; *U.S. Private*, pg. 4253
PABST & RICHARZ VERTRIEBS GMBH—See Berentzen-Gruppe AG; *Int'l*, pg. 978
PARADISE BEVERAGES (FIJI) LIMITED—See COCA-COLA EUROPACIFIC PARTNERS PLC; *Int'l*, pg. 1684
PARAG BREWERIES LTD—See Carlsberg A/S; *Int'l*, pg. 1340
PINE CREEK BREWING COMPANY LTD—See Big Rock Brewery Inc.; *Int'l*, pg. 1021
PITTSBURGH BREWING COMPANY—See Uni-World Capital, L.P.; *U.S. Private*, pg. 4281
PIVOVAR SAMSON A.S.—See Anheuser-Busch InBev SA/NV; *Int'l*, pg. 466
PIVOVARY STAROPRAMEN A.S.—See Molson Coors Beverage Company; *Int'l*, pg. 1460
PLZENSKY PRAZDROJ A.S.—See Asahi Group Holdings Ltd.; *Int'l*, pg. 594
PYRAMID BREWERIES INC.—See Florida Ice and Farm Co. S.A.; *Int'l*, pg. 2707
QUEENSLAND BREWERIES PTY LTD—See Anheuser-Busch InBev SA/NV; *Int'l*, pg. 464
RADEBERGER GRUPPE AG—See Dr. August Oetker KG; *Int'l*, pg. 2190
REED BEVERAGE, INC.; *U.S. Private*, pg. 3382
SABMILLER INDIA LIMITED—See Anheuser-Busch InBev SA/NV; *Int'l*, pg. 464
SABMILLER LATIN AMERICA—See Anheuser-Busch InBev SA/NV; *Int'l*, pg. 464
SABMILLER VIETNAM COMPANY LTD—See Anheuser-Busch InBev SA/NV; *Int'l*, pg. 464
THE SAINT LOUIS BREWERY, LLC.; *U.S. Private*, pg. 4113
SAKU OLLETEHASE AS—See Carlsberg A/S; *Int'l*, pg. 1341
SANTA BARBARA BREWING CO.; *U.S. Private*, pg. 3546
SEA DOG BREWING COMPANY; *U.S. Private*, pg. 3582
SEBAGO BREWING CO.; *U.S. Private*, pg. 3592
THE SHIPYARD BREWING COMPANY; *U.S. Private*, pg. 4117
SHMALTZ BREWING COMPANY; *U.S. Private*, pg. 3639
SHORT'S BREWING COMPANY; *U.S. Private*, pg. 3643
SIA COCA-COLA HBC LATVIA—See Coca-Cola HBC AG; *Int'l*, pg. 1686
SIERRA NEVADA BREWING CO.; *U.S. Private*, pg. 3647
SKAGIT RIVER BREWERY; *U.S. Private*, pg. 3681
SNYDER INTERNATIONAL BREWING GROUP LLC; *U.S. Private*, pg. 3701
THE SOUTH AFRICAN BREWERIES (PTY) LTD.—See Anheuser-Busch InBev SA/NV; *Int'l*, pg. 464
SOUTH-EAST ASIA BREWERY LTD.—See Carlsberg A/S; *Int'l*, pg. 1341
SOUTHERN SUDAN BEVERAGES LTD—See Anheuser-Busch InBev SA/NV; *Int'l*, pg. 465
SPATEN - FRANZISKANER - BRAU GMBH—See Anheuser-Busch InBev SA/NV; *Int'l*, pg. 466
S&P COMPANY INC.; *U.S. Private*, pg. 3513
SPRECHER BREWING COMPANY, LLC; *U.S. Private*, pg. 3762
STONE BREWING CO.; *U.S. Private*, pg. 3817
SUMMIT BREWING CO.; *U.S. Private*, pg. 3853
SUNSHINE BOTTLING, CO.; *U.S. Private*, pg. 3871
SUPERTIME DEVELOPMENT COMPANY LIMITED—See GDH Limited; *Int'l*, pg. 2896
SWEETWATER BREWING COMPANY, LLC; *U.S. Private*, pg. 3892
TANZANIA BREWERIES LIMITED—See Anheuser-Busch InBev SA/NV; *Int'l*, pg. 465
TENTH & BLAKE BEER COMPANY—See Molson Coors Beverage Company; *U.S. Public*, pg. 1459
THIRSTY BEAR BREWING CO. LLC.; *U.S. Private*, pg. 4145
TIN MAN BREWING CO.—See Neace Ventures; *U.S. Private*, pg. 2877
TRINKKONTOR BITBURGER BIER GMBH—See Bitburger Braugruppe GmbH; *Int'l*, pg. 1049
UGANDA BREWERIES LTD—See Diageo plc; *Int'l*, pg. 2102
UINTA BREWING CO.—See Riverside Partners, LLC; *U.S. Private*, pg. 3446
UNION DE CERVECERIAS PERUANAS BACKUS Y JOHNSTON S.A.A.—See Anheuser-Busch InBev SA/NV; *Int'l*, pg. 464
UNITED NATIONAL BREWERIES (SA) PTY LTD.—See Delta Corporation Limited; *Int'l*, pg. 2016
UNITED ROMANIAN BREWERIES BEREPROD SRL—See Carlsberg A/S; *Int'l*, pg. 1341
URSUS BREWERIES SA—See Anheuser-Busch InBev SA/NV; *Int'l*, pg. 465
VERMONT HARD CIDER COMPANY, LLC—See Northeast Drinks Group LLC; *U.S. Private*, pg. 2950
THE VITA COCO COMPANY, INC.; *U.S. Public*, pg. 2137
WATERLOO BREWING LTD.—See Carlsberg A/S; *Int'l*, pg. 1341
WATER STREET BREWERY; *U.S. Private*, pg. 4451
WATERTOWN HOPS COMPANY—See Molson Coors Beverage Company; *U.S. Public*, pg. 1459
WICKED WEED BREWING LLC—See Anheuser-Busch InBev SA/NV; *Int'l*, pg. 465
WISCONSIN BREWING COMPANY LLC; *U.S. Private*, pg. 4548
WYNWOOD BREWING COMPANY, LLC—See Anheuser-Busch InBev SA/NV; *Int'l*, pg. 465
YANTAI BEER ASAHI CO., LTD.—See Asahi Group Holdings Ltd.; *Int'l*, pg. 594
YARDS BREWING COMPANY; *U.S. Private*, pg. 4586
YUENGLING BEER COMPANY OF TAMPA, INC.—See D.G. Yuengling & Son Incorporated; *U.S. Private*, pg. 1142
ZAGREBACKA PIVOVARA D.D.—See Molson Coors Beverage Company; *U.S. Public*, pg. 1459
ZAO MOSCOW-EFES BREWERY—See Anadolu Efes Biracilik ve Malt Sanayii A.S.; *Int'l*, pg. 445

312130 — WINERIES

ABRAU-DURSO AO; *Int'l*, pg. 67
ACCOLADE WINES AUSTRALIA LIMITED—See The Carlyle Group Inc.; *U.S. Public*, pg. 2044
ACCOLADE WINES AUSTRALIA LTD. - BOTANY—See The Carlyle Group Inc.; *U.S. Public*, pg. 2044
ACCOLADE WINES AUSTRALIA LTD. - MOUNT WAVERLEY—See The Carlyle Group Inc.; *U.S. Public*, pg. 2044
ACCOLADE WINES LIMITED—See The Carlyle Group Inc.; *U.S. Public*, pg. 2044
ACCOLADE WINES NEW ZEALAND LIMITED—See The Carlyle Group Inc.; *U.S. Public*, pg. 2044
ADAMS WINE GROUP, LLC; *U.S. Private*, pg. 75
ADVINI POLSKA, SP. Z.O.O.—See AdVini S.A.; *Int'l*, pg. 168
ADVINI S.A.; *Int'l*, pg. 168
AFRICAN DISTILLERS LIMITED—See Delta Corporation Limited; *Int'l*, pg. 2016
ALDERBROOK WINERY—See The Terlato Wine Group; *U.S. Private*, pg. 4126
ALPHA BEVERAGES OY—See Altia Oyj; *Int'l*, pg. 392
ALTIA OYJ; *Int'l*, pg. 392
AMBRA S.A.; *Int'l*, pg. 415
ANDRETTI WINERY; *U.S. Private*, pg. 279
ANDREW PELLER LIMITED; *Int'l*, pg. 451
ANGOSTURA HOLDINGS LIMITED; *Int'l*, pg. 463
ANHUI GOLDEN SEED WINERY CO., LTD.; *Int'l*, pg. 467
ANHUI KOUZI DISTILLERY CO., LTD.; *Int'l*, pg. 469
ANTOINE MOUEIX SAS—See AdVini S.A.; *Int'l*, pg. 168
A. RACKE GMBH; *Int'l*, pg. 21
ARROWOOD VINEYARDS & WINERY—See Jackson Family Wines, Inc.; *U.S. Private*, pg. 2176
AUSCANN GROUP HOLDINGS PTY LTD; *Int'l*, pg. 715
AUSTRALIAN VINTAGE LTD.; *Int'l*, pg. 723
AUSTRALIAN VINTAGE (UK) LTD.—See Australian Vintage Ltd.; *Int'l*, pg. 723

312130 — WINERIES

BACARDI CAPITAL LIMITED—See Bacardi Limited; *Int'l*, pg. 793
BACARDI CENTROAMERICA, S.A.—See Bacardi Limited; *Int'l*, pg. 794
BACARDI INTERNATIONAL LIMITED—See Bacardi Limited; *Int'l*, pg. 794
BACARDI-MARTINI BELGIUM NV—See Bacardi Limited; *Int'l*, pg. 794
BACARDI-MARTINI URUGUAY S.A.—See Bacardi Limited; *Int'l*, pg. 794
BADEL 1862 D.D.; *Int'l*, pg. 795
BADEL D.O.O—See Badel 1862 d.d.; *Int'l*, pg. 795
BADEL D.O.O.E.L.—See Badel 1862 d.d.; *Int'l*, pg. 795
BADEL SARAJEVO D.O.O.—See Badel 1862 d.d.; *Int'l*, pg. 795
BALAI NI FRUITAS INC.; *Int'l*, pg. 806
BALLATORE CHAMPAGNE CELLARS—See E. & J. Gallo Winery; *U.S. Private*, pg. 1303
BARON DE LEY, S.A.; *Int'l*, pg. 866
BECLE, S.A.B. DE C.V.; *Int'l*, pg. 938
BELSAZAR GMBH—See Diageo plc; *Int'l*, pg. 2101
BENZIGER FAMILY WINERY LLC—See The Wine Group, Inc.; *U.S. Private*, pg. 4137
BIANCHI VINEYARDS—See Modern Development Company; *U.S. Private*, pg. 2760
BIGI S.P.A.—See Cantine Riunite & CIV S.C.Agr.; *Int'l*, pg. 1299
BILTMORE ESTATE WINE COMPANY; *U.S. Private*, pg. 560
BIN TO BOTTLE, LLC; *U.S. Private*, pg. 560
BLACK HILLS ESTATE WINERY INC.—See Andrew Peller Limited; *Int'l*, pg. 451
BODEGAS BILBAINAS, S.A.—See The Carlyle Group Inc.; *U.S. Public*, pg. 2045
BODEGAS BVBA—See Colruyt Group N.V.; *Int'l*, pg. 1705
BODEGAS RIOJANAS, S.A.; *Int'l*, pg. 1097
BOHAE BREWERY CO., LTD.; *Int'l*, pg. 1100
BOUVET LADUBAY SA; *Int'l*, pg. 1121
BRAND NEW VINTAGE LIMITED; *Int'l*, pg. 1139
BRONCO WINE COMPANY; *U.S. Private*, pg. 662
BUENA VISTA CARNEROS WINERY INC.—See Boisset, La Famille des Grands Vins; *Int'l*, pg. 1101
CAMERON HUGHES WINE—See Vintage Wine Estates, Inc.; *U.S. Public*, pg. 2298
CAMPARI S.P.A.—See Alicros S.p.A.; *Int'l*, pg. 327
CARLO ROSSI VINEYARDS—See E. & J. Gallo Winery; *U.S. Private*, pg. 1303
CARPENE MALVOLTI S.P.A.; *Int'l*, pg. 1343
CASELLA WINES PTY. LTD.; *Int'l*, pg. 1351
CASTEL FRERES SA; *Int'l*, pg. 1355
CASTELLO BANFI SRL—See Banfi Product Corp.; *U.S. Private*, pg. 465
CATOCTIN CREEK DISTILLING COMPANY LLC—See Constellation Brands, Inc.; *U.S. Public*, pg. 570
CECCHETTI WINE COMPANY; *U.S. Private*, pg. 804
CELLARMASTER WINES PTY LIMITED; *Int'l*, pg. 1392
CENTRAL COAST WINES; *U.S. Private*, pg. 819
CHADDSFORD WINERY LTD.; *U.S. Private*, pg. 845
CHALONE VINEYARD—See Diageo plc; *Int'l*, pg. 2102
CHAMPAGNE ALAIN THIENOT S.A.S.; *Int'l*, pg. 1439
CHAMPAGNE CANARD-DUCHENE S.A.—See Champagne Alain Thienot S.A.S.; *Int'l*, pg. 1439
CHAMPAGNE HENRIOT; *Int'l*, pg. 1439
CHAMPAGNE LAURENT-PERRIER; *Int'l*, pg. 1439
CHAMPAGNE POL ROGER; *Int'l*, pg. 1440
CHAPEL HILL WINERY PTY. LTD.—See Endeavour Group Limited; *Int'l*, pg. 2402
CHAROSA WINERIES LIMITED—See Grover Zampa Vineyards Limited; *Int'l*, pg. 3112
CHATEAU DASSAULT SA—See Groupe Industriel Marcel Dassault S.A.; *Int'l*, pg. 3104
CHATEAU LAROSE TRINTAUDON S.A.—See Allianz SE; *Int'l*, pg. 351
CHEVIOT BRIDGE LIMITED; *Int'l*, pg. 1474
CHIMNEY ROCK WINERY—See The Terlato Wine Group; *U.S. Private*, pg. 4126
CHINA DU KANG CO., LTD.; *Int'l*, pg. 1498
CHINA OUHUA WINERY HOLDINGS LIMITED; *Int'l*, pg. 1538
CHINA SHENSHAN ORCHARD HOLDINGS CO., LTD.; *Int'l*, pg. 1551
CHINA TONTINE WINES GROUP LIMITED; *Int'l*, pg. 1559
CITIC GUOAN WINE CO., LTD.; *Int'l*, pg. 1621
CLOS LACHANCE WINERY; *U.S. Private*, pg. 946
COCA-COLA EUROPACIFIC PARTNERS NEW ZEALAND LIMITED—See COCA-COLA EUROPACIFIC PARTNERS PLC; *Int'l*, pg. 1685
CODORNIU, S.A.; *Int'l*, pg. 1688
COMPANIA VINICOLA DEL NORTE DE ESPANA, S.A.; *Int'l*, pg. 1749
CONSTELLATION BEERS LTD.—See Constellation Brands, Inc.; *U.S. Public*, pg. 570
CONSTELLATION BRANDS, INC.; *U.S. Public*, pg. 570
CONSTELLATION WINES U.S.—See Constellation Brands, Inc.; *U.S. Public*, pg. 570
COPA DI VINO; *U.S. Private*, pg. 1044
COPPER & KINGS AMERICAN BRANDY COMPANY—See Constellation Brands, Inc.; *U.S. Public*, pg. 571

CORBETT CANYON VINEYARDS—See The Wine Group, Inc.; *U.S. Private*, pg. 4137
COURTSIDE CELLARS—See E. & J. Gallo Winery; *U.S. Private*, pg. 1303
CREW WINE COMPANY LLC—See Constellation Brands, Inc.; *U.S. Public*, pg. 571
CROFT JEREZ SA—See Diageo plc; *Int'l*, pg. 2102
DAVIDE CAMPARI-MILANO N.V.—See Alicros S.p.A.; *Int'l*, pg. 327
DEHESA BARON DE LEY S.A.—See Baron de Ley, S.A.; *Int'l*, pg. 867
DELEGAT'S GROUP LIMITED; *Int'l*, pg. 2010
DELEGAT—See Delegat's Group Limited; *Int'l*, pg. 2010
DELOACH VINEYARDS—See Boisset, La Famille des Grands Vins; *Int'l*, pg. 1101
DIAGEO CANADA, INC.—See Diageo plc; *Int'l*, pg. 2102
DIAGEO INDIA PRIVATE LIMITED—See Diageo plc; *Int'l*, pg. 2102
DIAGEO KOREA COMPANY LIMITED—See Diageo plc; *Int'l*, pg. 2102
DIAGEO UK—See Diageo plc; *Int'l*, pg. 2102
DIAGEO USVI INC.—See Diageo plc; *Int'l*, pg. 2102
DISTILLERIE MERLET ET FILS SARL; *Int'l*, pg. 2135
DONGWON WINEPLUS CO. LTD.—See Dongwon Enterprise Co., Ltd.; *Int'l*, pg. 2171
THE DONUM ESTATE, INC—See A. Racke GmbH; *Int'l*, pg. 21
THE DUCKHORN PORTFOLIO, INC.; *U.S. Public*, pg. 2067
DUCKHORN WINE COMPANY—See TSG Consumer Partners LLC; *U.S. Private*, pg. 4253
DYNASTY FINE WINES GROUP LIMITED; *Int'l*, pg. 2242
ECCO DOMANI USA INC.; *U.S. Private*, pg. 1326
EDNA VALLEY VINEYARD—See E. & J. Gallo Winery; *U.S. Private*, pg. 1303
E. & J. GALLO WINERY; *U.S. Private*, pg. 1303
EL COTO DE RIOJA S.A.—See Baron de Ley, S.A.; *Int'l*, pg. 867
EMPERADOR DISTILLERS, INC—See Alliance Global Group, Inc.; *Int'l*, pg. 339
ENARTIS PORTUGAL UNIPESSOAL, LDA—See Esseco Group SRL; *Int'l*, pg. 2509
ENARTIS SOUTH AFRICA LTD—See Esseco Group SRL; *Int'l*, pg. 2509
ENARTIS VINQUIRY INC.—See Esseco Group SRL; *Int'l*, pg. 2509
EPIC WINE & SPIRITS; *U.S. Private*, pg. 1413
EVERARDS BREWERY LTD.; *Int'l*, pg. 2563
EVER BRASIL INDUSTRIA E COMERCIO LTDA—See Esseco Group SRL; *Int'l*, pg. 2509
EVER TRADE S.R.O.—See Esseco Group SRL; *Int'l*, pg. 2509
FELDSCHLOSSCHEN BEVERAGES HOLDING LTD.—See Carlsberg A/S; *Int'l*, pg. 1340
FERRAR-CARANO VINEYARDS WINERY; *U.S. Private*, pg. 1498
FIELDBROOK VALLEY WINERY INC.; *U.S. Private*, pg. 1504
FIELD STONE WINERY & VINEYARD, INC.—See Jackson Family Wines, Inc.; *U.S. Public*, pg. 2176
FIRESTONE VINEYARD—See Foley Family Wines Holdings Inc; *U.S. Private*, pg. 1558
FOLEY FAMILY WINES, INC.—See Foley Family Wines Holdings Inc; *U.S. Private*, pg. 1558
FOLEY WINES LIMITED—See Foley Family Wines Holdings Inc; *U.S. Private*, pg. 1558
FOUR SEASONS WINES LTD.—See Grover Zampa Vineyards Limited; *Int'l*, pg. 3112
FRANCISCAN ESTATE WINERY—See Constellation Brands, Inc.; *U.S. Public*, pg. 570
FRANCISCAN VINEYARDS, INC.—See Constellation Brands, Inc.; *U.S. Public*, pg. 570
FRANCIS FORD COPPOLA WINERY; *U.S. Private*, pg. 1587
FRANZIA/SANGER WINERY; *U.S. Private*, pg. 1599
FRATELLI GANCIA & C. S.P.A.—See CJSC Russian Standard Corporation; *Int'l*, pg. 1634
FREIXENET S.A.—See Dr. August Oetker KG; *Int'l*, pg. 2190
FREIXENET SONOMA CAVES, INC.—See Dr. August Oetker KG; *Int'l*, pg. 2190
FRESH VINE WINE, INC.; *U.S. Public*, pg. 886
FUTO WINES—See Wilson Daniels Wholesale LLC; *U.S. Private*, pg. 4530
GASSIER SAS—See AdVini S.A.; *Int'l*, pg. 168
GENAGRICOLA S.P.A.—See Assicurazioni Generali S.p.A.; *Int'l*, pg. 644
GEYSER PEAK WINERY—See Francis Ford Coppola Winery; *U.S. Private*, pg. 1587
GIBSON WINE COMPANY; *U.S. Private*, pg. 1696
GOOSECROSS CELLARS, INC.—See Golden Equity Investments LLC; *U.S. Private*, pg. 1730
GRACE WINE HOLDINGS LTD.; *Int'l*, pg. 3048
GRAINVEST B.V.—See BayWa AG; *Int'l*, pg. 918
GROVER ZAMPA VINEYARDS LIMITED; *Int'l*, pg. 3112
HALL WINES OF NAPA, L.P.—See Hall Financial Group, Ltd.; *Int'l*, pg. 1843
HARDY'S TINTARA WINERY—See The Carlyle Group Inc.; *U.S. Public*, pg. 2044

CORPORATE AFFILIATIONS

HEBEI HENGSHUI LAOBAIGAN LIQUOR CO., LTD.; *Int'l*, pg. 3305
HECK ESTATES—See F. Korbel Bros. Inc.; *U.S. Private*, pg. 1455
HENRY ESTATE WINERY; *U.S. Private*, pg. 1918
HERACLES SA; *Int'l*, pg. 3357
HEXZA-MATHER SDN. BHD.—See Hexza Corporation Berhad; *Int'l*, pg. 3373
HIGH WEST DISTILLERY, LLC—See Constellation Brands, Inc.; *U.S. Public*, pg. 571
HIJOS DE ANTONIO BARCELO, S.A.—See Acciona, S.A.; *Int'l*, pg. 90
HONWORLD GROUP LIMITED; *Int'l*, pg. 3472
HOUGHTON WINES—See The Carlyle Group Inc.; *U.S. Public*, pg. 2044
IAN MACLEOD DISTILLERS & CO. LTD.; *Int'l*, pg. 3569
IAN MACLEOD DISTILLERS LTD.—See Ian Macleod Distillers & Co. Ltd.; *Int'l*, pg. 3569
IL TIGLIO - SOCIETA' AGRICOLA S.R.L.—See Assicurazioni Generali S.p.A.; *Int'l*, pg. 647
INTERNATIONAL WINE & SPIRITS OF LOUISIANA, INC.; *U.S. Private*, pg. 2122
J. LOHR WINERY CORPORATION; *U.S. Private*, pg. 2156
JOSEPH VICTORI WINES, INC.; *U.S. Private*, pg. 2237
JSC TELIANI VALLEY—See Bank of Georgia Group PLC; *Int'l*, pg. 843
JUSTERINI & BROOKS LTD.—See Diageo plc; *Int'l*, pg. 2102
JUSTIN VINEYARDS & WINERY LLC—See The Wonderful Company LLC; *U.S. Private*, pg. 4138
J VINEYARDS & WINERY—See E. & J. Gallo Winery; *U.S. Private*, pg. 1303
KB WINES, LLC—See TSG Consumer Partners LLC; *U.S. Private*, pg. 4253
KENDALL-JACKSON WINE ESTATES, LTD.—See Jackson Family Wines, Inc.; *U.S. Public*, pg. 2176
KING ESTATE OREGON WINES; *U.S. Private*, pg. 2309
KING ESTATE WINERY; *U.S. Private*, pg. 2309
KIONA VINEYARDS & WINERY; *U.S. Private*, pg. 2313
KIRRIBILLY VINEYARDS PTY LIMITED—See Cheviot Bridge Limited; *Int'l*, pg. 1474
LA CREMA, INC.—See Jackson Family Wines, Inc.; *U.S. Private*, pg. 2176
LAETITIA VINEYARD & WINERY—See Vintage Wine Estates, Inc.; *U.S. Public*, pg. 2298
L'AVENIR—See AdVini S.A.; *Int'l*, pg. 168
LEWIS CELLARS—See The Wonderful Company LLC; *U.S. Private*, pg. 4138
LONG MEADOW RANCH WINERY & FARMSTEAD; *U.S. Private*, pg. 2490
L.O. SMITH AB—See Constellation Brands, Inc.; *U.S. Public*, pg. 571
MAHOROBA FARM CO., LTD.—See DMG MORI Co., Ltd.; *Int'l*, pg. 2145
MATANZAS CREEK WINERY—See Jackson Family Wines, Inc.; *U.S. Public*, pg. 2176
MCCALL WINERIES & DISTILLERS—See E. & J. Gallo Winery; *U.S. Private*, pg. 1303
MEIER'S WINE CELLARS, INC.—See MGP Ingredients, Inc.; *U.S. Public*, pg. 1436
MEY ALKOLLU ICKILER SANAYI VE TICARET A.S.—See Diageo plc; *Int'l*, pg. 2102
MICHEL-SCHLUMBERGER WINES—See Adams Wine Group, LLC; *U.S. Private*, pg. 75
MOGEN DAVID WINE CORP.—See The Wine Group, Inc.; *U.S. Private*, pg. 4137
MOYER VINEYARDS INC.; *U.S. Private*, pg. 2802
M.S. WALKER, INC. - MSW NEW HAMPSHIRE FACILITY—See M.S. Walker, Inc.; *U.S. Private*, pg. 2529
MUD HOUSE WINE—See The Carlyle Group Inc.; *U.S. Public*, pg. 2044
MURPHY-GOODE WINERY—See Jackson Family Wines, Inc.; *U.S. Public*, pg. 2176
NAPA WINE CO. LLC—See Golden Triangle Ventures, Inc.; *U.S. Public*, pg. 951
NIVEN FAMILY WINE ESTATES; *U.S. Private*, pg. 2930
OGIER SAS—See Grupo Alimentario Argal SA; *Int'l*, pg. 3119
ONEHOPE WINE; *U.S. Private*, pg. 3025
ORIN SWIFT CELLARS LLC—See E. & J. Gallo Winery; *U.S. Private*, pg. 1303
OUTPOST WINES LLC—See AXA S.A.; *Int'l*, pg. 759
OYSTER BAY WINES USA, INC—See Delegat's Group Limited; *Int'l*, pg. 2011
PAHLMEYER, LLC—See E. & J. Gallo Winery; *U.S. Private*, pg. 1303
PATZ & HALL WINE COMPANY—See Altria Group, Inc.; *U.S. Public*, pg. 89
PENN SHORE WINERY & VINEYARDS; *U.S. Private*, pg. 3134
PETER LEHMANN WINES LIMITED—See Casella Wines Pty. Ltd.; *Int'l*, pg. 1351
PINE RIDGE WINERY, LLC—See Crimson Wine Group, Ltd.; *U.S. Public*, pg. 594
PRAGER WINERY & PORT WORKS, INC.; *U.S. Private*, pg. 3242
PURPLE WINE COMPANY; *U.S. Private*, pg. 3306

N.A.I.C.S. INDEX

312140 — DISTILLERIES

THE RANCH WINERY—See E. & J. Gallo Winery; *U.S. Private*, pg. 1303
RAVENSWOOD WINERY, INC.—See Constellation Brands, Inc.; *U.S. Public*, pg. 570
RED ROOSTER WINERY LTD.—See Andrew Peller Limited; *Int'l*, pg. 451
RIGAL SAS—See AdVini S.A.; *Int'l*, pg. 168
ROBERT MONDAVI WINERY—See Constellation Brands, Inc.; *U.S. Public*, pg. 570
ROBERT STEMMLER WINERY—See A. Racke GmbH; *Int'l*, pg. 21
ROMBAUER VINEYARDS, LLC—See E. & J. Gallo Winery; *U.S. Private*, pg. 1303
ROSENBLUM CELLARS—See Bronco Wine Company; *U.S. Private*, pg. 662
ROYAL WINE CORP.; *U.S. Private*, pg. 3494
RUBICON ESTATE WINERY; *U.S. Private*, pg. 3499
RUFFINO S.R.L.—See Constellation Brands, Inc.; *U.S. Public*, pg. 571
RUTHERFORD HILL WINERY—See The Terlato Wine Group; *U.S. Private*, pg. 4126
SANFORD WINERY—See The Terlato Wine Group; *U.S. Private*, pg. 4126
SAS DES DOMAINES DE LA BASTIDE ET DE LA CROIX—See Financiere de L'Odet; *Int'l*, pg. 2667
SCHRADER CELLARS, LLC—See Constellation Brands, Inc.; *U.S. Public*, pg. 571
SEAVIN, INC.; *U.S. Private*, pg. 3592
SEBASTIANI VINEYARDS, INC.—See Foley Family Wines Holdings Inc; *U.S. Private*, pg. 1558
SERENGETI BREWERIES LIMITED—See Diageo plc; *Int'l*, pg. 2103
SHANNON RIDGE, INC.; *U.S. Private*, pg. 3625
SICHUAN SWELLFUN CO., LTD.—See Diageo plc; *Int'l*, pg. 2103
SIDURI WINES, LLC—See Jackson Family Wines, Inc.; *U.S. Private*, pg. 2176
SILVERADO VINEYARDS INC.—See Foley Family Wines Holdings Inc; *U.S. Private*, pg. 1558
SIMI WINERY—See Constellation Brands, Inc.; *U.S. Public*, pg. 571
SOCIETA AGRICOLA SAN FELICE S.P.A.—See Allianz SE; *Int'l*, pg. 355
SOUFFLET VIGNE S.A.—See Etablissements J. Soufflet; *Int'l*, pg. 2519
STE. MICHELLE WINE ESTATES, LLC—See Altria Group, Inc.; *U.S. Public*, pg. 89
STICKS YARRA VALLEY PTY. LTD.—See BRAND NEW VINTAGE LIMITED; *Int'l*, pg. 1139
STONE BRIDGE CELLARS, INC.; *U.S. Private*, pg. 3817
STONE HILL WINERY; *U.S. Private*, pg. 3818
STONESTREET WINERY—See Jackson Family Wines, Inc.; *U.S. Private*, pg. 2176
STONY HILL VINEYARD—See Long Meadow Ranch Winery & Farmstead; *U.S. Private*, pg. 2491
STRYKER SONOMA—See Foley Family Wines Holdings Inc; *U.S. Private*, pg. 1558
ST. SUPERY, INC.—See Chanel S.A.; *Int'l*, pg. 1441
SWANSON VINEYARDS & WINERY—See Vintage Wine Estates, Inc.; *U.S. Public*, pg. 2298
TALBOTT VINEYARDS—See E. & J. Gallo Winery; *U.S. Private*, pg. 1303
TAMARACK CELLARS—See Vintage Wine Estates, Inc.; *U.S. Public*, pg. 2298
TATTERSALL COMPANIES, LLC; *U.S. Private*, pg. 3936
TEDESCHI VINEYARDS, LTD.; *U.S. Private*, pg. 3957
TERLATO WINES INTERNATIONAL INC.—See The Terlato Wine Group; *U.S. Private*, pg. 4126
TOTT'S CHAMPAGNE CELLARS—See E. & J. Gallo Winery; *U.S. Private*, pg. 1303
TRINCHERO FAMILY ESTATES; *U.S. Private*, pg. 4232
TRUETT-HURST, INC.; *U.S. Public*, pg. 2199
VAL VERDE WINERY; *U.S. Private*, pg. 4329
VERGELEGEN WINES (PTY) LTD.—See Anglo American PLC; *Int'l*, pg. 462
VIANSA WINERY; *U.S. Private*, pg. 4375
VIAS IMPORTS LTD.; *U.S. Private*, pg. 4375
VIGNADORO S.R.L.—See Assicurazioni Generali S.p.A.; *Int'l*, pg. 648
VIGNOBLES CLEMENT FAYAT ST EMILION—See FAYAT SAS; *Int'l*, pg. 2626
VILLA LA PAGLIAIA S.R.L.—See Allianz SE; *Int'l*, pg. 356
VINA CARMEN S.A.—See Compania Electro Metalurgica S.A.; *Int'l*, pg. 1749
VINEX SLAVIANTSI POLAND SP. Z.O.O.—See AMBRA S.A.; *Int'l*, pg. 415
W & A GILBEY SA—See Diageo plc; *Int'l*, pg. 2102
WAIPARA HILLS WINE—See The Carlyle Group Inc.; *U.S. Public*, pg. 2044
WARNER VINEYARDS, *U.S. Private*, pg. 4442
WEIBEL, INC.; *U.S. Private*, pg. 4470
WENTE VINEYARDS, *U.S. Private*, pg. 4481
WILLAMETTE VALLEY VINEYARDS, INC.; *U.S. Public*, pg. 2370
WINE AG VALENTIN & VON SALIS—See Coop-Gruppe Genossenschaft; *Int'l*, pg. 1790
WINEBID.COM, INC.—See Third Leaf Partners; *U.S. Private*, pg. 4145

WINERY EXCHANGE INC.; *U.S. Private*, pg. 4540
THE WINETASTING NETWORK—See 1-800-FLOWERS.COM, Inc.; *U.S. Public*, pg. 1
THE WOODFORD RESERVE DISTILLERY—See Brown-Forman Corporation; *U.S. Public*, pg. 403

312140 — DISTILLERIES

AB INBEV AFRICA B.V.—See Anheuser-Busch InBev SA/NV; *Int'l*, pg. 464
ALLIED BLENDERS AND DISTILLERS PVT. LTD.; *Int'l*, pg. 356
ANHEUSER-BUSCH AMERICAS HOLDINGS LLC—See Anheuser-Busch InBev SA/NV; *Int'l*, pg. 465
ARCTIC BLUE BEVERAGES AB; *Int'l*, pg. 551
ARCUS-GRUPPEN AS—See Arcus ASA; *Int'l*, pg. 552
AS LATVIJAS BALZAMS; *Int'l*, pg. 590
A. SMITH BOWMAN DISTILLERY—See Sazerac Company; *U.S. Private*, pg. 3559
AURANGABAD DISTILLERY LIMITED; *Int'l*, pg. 706
BACARDI CANADA, INC.—See Bacardi Limited; *Int'l*, pg. 793
BACARDI & COMPANY LIMITED—See Bacardi Limited; *Int'l*, pg. 793
BACARDI CORPORATION—See Bacardi Limited; *Int'l*, pg. 793
BACARDI ESPANA S.A.—See Bacardi Limited; *Int'l*, pg. 794
BACARDI FRANCE S.A.S.—See Bacardi Limited; *Int'l*, pg. 794
BACARDI GLOBAL BRANDS LIMITED—See Bacardi Limited; *Int'l*, pg. 794
BACARDI GMBH—See Bacardi Limited; *Int'l*, pg. 794
BACARDI-MARTINI ASIA-PACIFIC LIMITED—See Bacardi Limited; *Int'l*, pg. 794
BACARDI-MARTINI BV—See Bacardi Limited; *Int'l*, pg. 794
BACARDI-MARTINI CHILE S.A.—See Bacardi Limited; *Int'l*, pg. 794
BACARDI-MARTINI DANMARK A/S—See Bacardi Limited; *Int'l*, pg. 794
BACARDI-MARTINI FRANCE—See Bacardi Limited; *Int'l*, pg. 794
BACARDI-MARTINI GMBH—See Bacardi Limited; *Int'l*, pg. 794
BACARDI-MARTINI HUNGARY KFT.—See Bacardi Limited; *Int'l*, pg. 794
BACARDI-MARTINI INDIA LIMITED—See Bacardi Limited; *Int'l*, pg. 794
BACARDI-MARTINI PACIFIC PTY. LTD.—See Bacardi Limited; *Int'l*, pg. 794
BACARDI-MARTINI RUSSIA—See Bacardi Limited; *Int'l*, pg. 794
BACARDI-MARTINI (SUISSE) S.A.R.L.—See Bacardi Limited; *Int'l*, pg. 794
BACARDI-MARTINI UK LIMITED—See Bacardi Limited; *Int'l*, pg. 794
BACARDI NEDERLAND N.V.—See Bacardi Limited; *Int'l*, pg. 794
BACARDI SHANGHAI LIMITED—See Bacardi Limited; *Int'l*, pg. 794
BACARDI VENEZUELA C.A.—See Bacardi Limited; *Int'l*, pg. 794
BACARDI Y COMPANIA, S.A. DE C.V.—See Bacardi Limited; *Int'l*, pg. 794
BALAJI DISTILLERIES LTD.—See Diageo plc; *Int'l*, pg. 2103
THE BAR BEVERAGE, INC—See Alliance Global Group, Inc.; *Int'l*, pg. 339
BARDSTOWN BOURBON COMPANY, LLC—See The Pritzker Group - Chicago, LLC; *U.S. Private*, pg. 4098
BEIJING YANJING BREWERY CO., LTD.—See Beijing Enterprises Holdings Limited; *Int'l*, pg. 950
BERENTZEN-GRUPPE AG; *Int'l*, pg. 978
BEVCANNA ENTERPRISES, INC.; *Int'l*, pg. 1004
BHB BRAUHOLDING BAYERN-MITTE AG; *Int'l*, pg. 1014
BOLS HUNGARY, KFT—See CJSC Russian Standard Corporation; *Int'l*, pg. 1634
BRAVE SPIRITS LLC; *U.S. Private*, pg. 641
BROWN-FORMAN BEVERAGES—See Brown-Forman Corporation; *U.S. Public*, pg. 403
BROWN-FORMAN KOREA LTD.—See Brown-Forman Corporation; *U.S. Public*, pg. 403
CANADIAN MIST DISTILLERS LIMITED—See Brown-Forman Corporation; *U.S. Public*, pg. 403
CANSOURCE, LLC—See Ares Management Corporation; *U.S. Public*, pg. 191
CB SPIRITS CANADA, INC.—See Constellation Brands, Inc.; *U.S. Public*, pg. 570
CEDC INTERNATIONAL SP. Z O.O.—See Grupa Maspex Sp. z o.o.; *Int'l*, pg. 3117
CERVILLE INVESTMENTS SP. Z O.O.—See Eurocash S.A.; *Int'l*, pg. 2533
CHARLES JACQUIN ET CIE INC.—See Chatam International Incorporated; *U.S. Private*, pg. 860
CHATAM INTERNATIONAL INCORPORATED; *U.S. Private*, pg. 860
COGNAC FERRAND SASU; *Int'l*, pg. 1695
CONSTELLATION BRANDS SCHENLEY, INC.—See Constellation Brands, Inc.; *U.S. Public*, pg. 570

CUTWATER SPIRITS, LLC—See Anheuser-Busch InBev SA/NV; *Int'l*, pg. 465
DEMERARA DISTILLERS LTD.; *Int'l*, pg. 2025
DIAGEO CANADA INC.—See Diageo plc; *Int'l*, pg. 2102
DIAGEO CANADA INC.—See Diageo plc; *Int'l*, pg. 2102
DIAGEO NORTH AMERICA—See Diageo plc; *Int'l*, pg. 2102
DIAMOND ESTATES WINES & SPIRITS, INC.; *Int'l*, pg. 2105
DISTILLERIES COMPANY OF SRI LANKA PLC; *Int'l*, pg. 2135
DISTIL PLC; *Int'l*, pg. 2135
DRIFTLESS GLEN DISTILLERY LLC; *U.S. Private*, pg. 1277
DURHAM DISTILLERY LLC—See Constellation Brands, Inc.; *U.S. Public*, pg. 571
EARLY TIMES DISTILLERS COMPANY—See Brown-Forman Corporation; *U.S. Public*, pg. 403
EASTSIDE DISTILLING, INC.; *U.S. Public*, pg. 708
EL SILENCIO HOLDINGS, INC.—See Constellation Brands, Inc.; *U.S. Public*, pg. 571
EMPEE DISTILLERIES LIMITED; *Int'l*, pg. 2385
EMPRESAS SERRALLES INC.; *U.S. Private*, pg. 1388
FULL MOTION BEVERAGE, INC.; *U.S. Public*, pg. 892
GANSU HUANGTAI WINE-MARKETING INDUSTRY CO., LTD.; *Int'l*, pg. 2881
GEORGE A. DICKEL & CO.—See Diageo plc; *Int'l*, pg. 2102
GLENGLASSAUGH DISTILLERY LTD.—See Brown-Forman Corporation; *U.S. Public*, pg. 403
GLENMORE DISTILLERIES CO; *U.S. Private*, pg. 1710
GLOBUS SPIRITS LTD; *Int'l*, pg. 3008
G.M.BREWERIES LIMITED; *Int'l*, pg. 2866
GUALA CLOSURES S.P.A.; *Int'l*, pg. 3152
GURKTALER AKTIENGESELLSCHAFT; *Int'l*, pg. 3188
HERITAGE DISTILLING COMPANY, INC.—See Heritage Distilling Holding Company, Inc.; *U.S. Private*, pg. 1922
HITE JINRO CO., LTD. - CHEONGJU DISTILLERY FACTORY—See Hite Jinro Co., Ltd.; *Int'l*, pg. 3425
HITE JINRO CO., LTD. - GANGWON BREWERY FACTORY—See Hite Jinro Co., Ltd.; *Int'l*, pg. 3425
HITE JINRO CO., LTD. - ICHEON DISTILLERY FACTORY—See Hite Jinro Co., Ltd.; *Int'l*, pg. 3425
HITE JINRO CO., LTD. - IKSAN DISTILLERY FACTORY—See Hite Jinro Co., Ltd.; *Int'l*, pg. 3425
HITE JINRO CO., LTD. - JEONJU BREWERY FACTORY—See Hite Jinro Co., Ltd.; *Int'l*, pg. 3425
HITE JINRO CO., LTD. - MASAN BREWERY FACTORY—See Hite Jinro Co., Ltd.; *Int'l*, pg. 3425
HITE JINRO CO., LTD.; *Int'l*, pg. 3425
HOOD RIVER DISTILLERS INC.; *U.S. Private*, pg. 1978
JACK DANIEL DISTILLERY, LEM MOTLOW, PROP., INC.—See Brown-Forman Corporation; *U.S. Public*, pg. 403
JACK DANIEL'S PROPERTIES, INC.—See Brown-Forman Corporation; *U.S. Public*, pg. 403
KELLANOVA; *U.S. Public*, pg. 1217
KONA BREWERY LLC—See Anheuser-Busch InBev SA/NV; *Int'l*, pg. 465
LEBLON HOLDINGS LLC.—See Bacardi Limited; *Int'l*, pg. 794
LONGNORTH LIMITED—See Brown-Forman Corporation; *U.S. Public*, pg. 403
LUXCO, INC.—See MGP Ingredients, Inc.; *U.S. Public*, pg. 1436
MARANI BRANDS, INC.; *U.S. Public*, pg. 1363
MCCORMICK DISTILLING CO., INC.; *U.S. Private*, pg. 2630
MEY ICKI SANAYI VE TICARET A.S.—See Diageo plc; *Int'l*, pg. 2102
MILLENNIUM PRIME, INC.; *U.S. Public*, pg. 1446
MONTALVO SPIRITS, INC.; *U.S. Private*, pg. 2774
MONTANA DISTILLERS, LLC—See Constellation Brands, Inc.; *U.S. Public*, pg. 571
MONTEBELLO BRANDS INC.; *U.S. Private*, pg. 2775
M.S. WALKER, INC.; *U.S. Private*, pg. 2529
THE NIKKA WHISKY DISTILLING CO., LTD.—See Asahi Group Holdings Ltd.; *Int'l*, pg. 594
OCTOPI BREWING, LLC; *U.S. Private*, pg. 2993
THE PATRON SPIRITS COMPANY; *U.S. Private*, pg. 4091
PIONEER DISTILLERIES LIMITED—See Diageo plc; *Int'l*, pg. 2103
RENE LAURENT, A SOCIETE PAR ACTIONS SIMPLIFIEE—See International Flavors & Fragrances Inc.; *U.S. Public*, pg. 1154
RUSSIAN STANDARD VODKA—See CJSC Russian Standard Corporation; *Int'l*, pg. 1634
SAZERAC COMPANY, INC.; *U.S. Private*, pg. 3559
SCANDIC DISTILLERIES—See European Drinks S.A.; *Int'l*, pg. 2556
SOCIETE DES PRODUITS MARNIER-LAPOSTOLLE S.A.—See Alicros S.p.A.; *Int'l*, pg. 327
STOCK SPIRITS GROUP PLC—See CVC Capital Partners SICAV-FIS S.A.; *Int'l*, pg. 1888
TEQUILA PARTIDA DE MEXICO, S.A. DE C.V.—See Partida Tequila, LLC; *U.S. Private*, pg. 3101
UNIBEV LIMITED—See Globus Spirits Ltd; *Int'l*, pg. 3008
UNITED SPIRITS LTD.—See Diageo plc; *Int'l*, pg. 2103
UNITED STATES DISTILLED PRODUCTS CO., INC.; *U.S. Private*, pg. 4298

312140 — DISTILLERIES

VODKA BRANDS CORP.; *U.S. Public*, pg. 2308
THE WEST INDIES RUM DISTILLERY LIMITED—See Cognac Ferrand SASU; *Int'l*, pg. 1695
WHYTE & MACKAY LIMITED—See Alliance Global Group, Inc.; *Int'l*, pg. 339
WILD TURKEY DISTILLERY—See Alicros S.p.A.; *Int'l*, pg. 327
ZAREA S.A.—See AMBRA S.A.; *Int'l*, pg. 415

312230 — TOBACCO MANUFACTURING

ADRIS GRUPA D.D.; *Int'l*, pg. 153
AL-EQBAL INVESTMENT CO. (PLC); *Int'l*, pg. 285
AL FAKHER FOR TOBACCO TRADING & AGENCIES LLC—See Al-Eqbal Investment Co. (PLC); *Int'l*, pg. 285
ALLIANCE ONE BRASIL EXPORTADORA DE TABACOS LTDA.—See Pyxus International, Inc.; *U.S. Public*, pg. 1740
ALLIANCE ONE BRASIL EXPORTADORA DE TABACOS LTDA.—See Pyxus International, Inc.; *U.S. Public*, pg. 1740
ALLIANCE ONE BRASIL EXPORTADORA DE TABACOS LTDA.—See Pyxus International, Inc.; *U.S. Public*, pg. 1740
ALLIANCE ONE BRASIL EXPORTADORA DE TABACOS LTDA.—See Pyxus International, Inc.; *U.S. Public*, pg. 1740
ALLIANCE ONE SPECIALTY PRODUCTS LLC—See Pyxus International, Inc.; *U.S. Public*, pg. 1740
ALLIANCE ONE TOBACCO (MALAWI) LIMITED—See Pyxus International, Inc.; *U.S. Public*, pg. 1740
ALLIANCE ONE TOBACCO (MALAWI) LIMITED—See Pyxus International, Inc.; *U.S. Public*, pg. 1740
ALLIANCE ONE TOBACCO (MALAWI) LIMITED—See Pyxus International, Inc.; *U.S. Public*, pg. 1740
ALLIANCE ONE TOBACCO (MALAWI) LIMITED—See Pyxus International, Inc.; *U.S. Public*, pg. 1740
AL QURAISHI SERVICES—See Ali Zaid Al-Quraishi & Brothers Co.; *Int'l*, pg. 323
AMERICAN SNUFF COMPANY, LLC—See British American Tobacco plc; *Int'l*, pg. 1168
AMER TOBACCO LTD.—See ANTA Sports Products Limited; *Int'l*, pg. 480
AROMASCAPE DEVELOPMENT CENTRE GMBH—See Huabao International Holdings Limited; *Int'l*, pg. 3510
AVANTI CIGAR CORPORATION; *U.S. Private*, pg. 404
BADECO ADRIA D.D.; *Int'l*, pg. 795
B.A.T. (CYPRUS) LTD.—See British American Tobacco plc; *Int'l*, pg. 1165
B.A.T. SUCURSAL COSTA RICA—See British American Tobacco plc; *Int'l*, pg. 1165
B.A.T (U.K. AND EXPORT) LTD.—See British American Tobacco plc; *Int'l*, pg. 1165
BLAGOEVGRAD-BT AD—See Bulgarian Investment Holding; *Int'l*, pg. 1213
BOSANAC D.D.; *Int'l*, pg. 1116
THE BOTANIST, INC.—See Acreage Holdings, Inc.; *U.S. Public*, pg. 36
BRC ACOUSTICS & AUDIOVISUAL DESIGN—See Coffman Engineers, Inc.; *U.S. Private*, pg. 961
BRITISH AMERICAN TOBACCO - ALBANIA SH.P.K.—See British American Tobacco plc; *Int'l*, pg. 1166
BRITISH AMERICAN TOBACCO (ALGERIE) S.P.A.—See British American Tobacco plc; *Int'l*, pg. 1166
BRITISH AMERICAN TOBACCO ARGENTINA S.A.I.C.Y F.—See British American Tobacco plc; *Int'l*, pg. 1166
BRITISH AMERICAN TOBACCO AUSTRALASIA LTD.—See British American Tobacco plc; *Int'l*, pg. 1166
BRITISH AMERICAN TOBACCO AUSTRALIA LTD.—See British American Tobacco plc; *Int'l*, pg. 1166
BRITISH AMERICAN TOBACCO (AUSTRIA) GMBH—See British American Tobacco plc; *Int'l*, pg. 1166
BRITISH AMERICAN TOBACCO BANGLADESH CO. LTD.—See British American Tobacco plc; *Int'l*, pg. 1166
BRITISH AMERICAN TOBACCO-B.A.T. ANGOLA, LIMITADA—See British American Tobacco plc; *Int'l*, pg. 1167
BRITISH AMERICAN TOBACCO BELGIUM SA/NV—See British American Tobacco plc; *Int'l*, pg. 1166
BRITISH AMERICAN TOBACCO BOTSWANA (PTY) LIMITED—See British American Tobacco plc; *Int'l*, pg. 1166
BRITISH AMERICAN TOBACCO (BRANDS) LTD.—See British American Tobacco plc; *Int'l*, pg. 1166
BRITISH AMERICAN TOBACCO CAMEROUN S.A.—See British American Tobacco plc; *Int'l*, pg. 1166
BRITISH AMERICAN TOBACCO CHILE OPERACIONES S.A.—See British American Tobacco plc; *Int'l*, pg. 1166
BRITISH AMERICAN TOBACCO DEL PERU HOLDINGS S.A.—See British American Tobacco plc; *Int'l*, pg. 1167
BRITISH AMERICAN TOBACCO DENMARK—See British American Tobacco plc; *Int'l*, pg. 1166
BRITISH AMERICAN TOBACCO EGYPT LLC—See British American Tobacco plc; *Int'l*, pg. 1166
BRITISH AMERICAN TOBACCO ESPANA, S.A.—See British American Tobacco plc; *Int'l*, pg. 1166
BRITISH AMERICAN TOBACCO ESTONIA AS—See British American Tobacco plc; *Int'l*, pg. 1166
BRITISH AMERICAN TOBACCO (FIJI) MARKETING PTE LIMITED—See British American Tobacco plc; *Int'l*, pg. 1166
BRITISH AMERICAN TOBACCO FINLAND OY—See British American Tobacco plc; *Int'l*, pg. 1166
BRITISH AMERICAN TOBACCO FRANCE SAS—See British American Tobacco plc; *Int'l*, pg. 1166
BRITISH-AMERICAN TOBACCO (GERMANY) GMBH—See British American Tobacco plc; *Int'l*, pg. 1167
BRITISH AMERICAN TOBACCO HELLAS S.A.—See British American Tobacco plc; *Int'l*, pg. 1166
BRITISH AMERICAN TOBACCO (INDUSTRIE) GMBH—See British American Tobacco plc; *Int'l*, pg. 1166
BRITISH AMERICAN TOBACCO ITALIA S.P.A.—See British American Tobacco plc; *Int'l*, pg. 1166
BRITISH AMERICAN TOBACCO JAPAN, LTD.—See British American Tobacco plc; *Int'l*, pg. 1166
BRITISH AMERICAN TOBACCO KAZAKHSTAN TRADING LLP—See British American Tobacco plc; *Int'l*, pg. 1166
BRITISH AMERICAN TOBACCO KENYA PLC—See British American Tobacco plc; *Int'l*, pg. 1166
BRITISH AMERICAN TOBACCO KOREA LTD.—See British American Tobacco plc; *Int'l*, pg. 1166
BRITISH AMERICAN TOBACCO KOREA MANUFACTURING LTD.—See British American Tobacco plc; *Int'l*, pg. 1167
BRITISH AMERICAN TOBACCO KOSOVO SH.P.K.—See British American Tobacco plc; *Int'l*, pg. 1167
BRITISH AMERICAN TOBACCO (MALAWI) LIMITED—See British American Tobacco plc; *Int'l*, pg. 1166
BRITISH AMERICAN TOBACCO (MALAYSIA) BERHAD—See British American Tobacco plc; *Int'l*, pg. 1166
BRITISH AMERICAN TOBACCO (MALTA) LIMITED—See British American Tobacco plc; *Int'l*, pg. 1166
BRITISH AMERICAN TOBACCO MARKETING NIGERIA LIMITED—See British American Tobacco plc; *Int'l*, pg. 1167
BRITISH AMERICAN TOBACCO ME DMCC—See British American Tobacco plc; *Int'l*, pg. 1167
BRITISH AMERICAN TOBACCO MEXICO—See British American Tobacco plc; *Int'l*, pg. 1167
BRITISH AMERICAN TOBACCO-MOLDOVA S.R.L.—See British American Tobacco plc; *Int'l*, pg. 1167
BRITISH AMERICAN TOBACCO MOZAMBIQUE LIMITADA—See British American Tobacco plc; *Int'l*, pg. 1167
BRITISH AMERICAN TOBACCO MYANMAR LIMITED—See British American Tobacco plc; *Int'l*, pg. 1167
BRITISH AMERICAN TOBACCO NAMIBIA (PTY) LIMITED—See British American Tobacco plc; *Int'l*, pg. 1167
BRITISH AMERICAN TOBACCO NEDERLAND B.V.—See British American Tobacco plc; *Int'l*, pg. 1167
BRITISH AMERICAN TOBACCO (NEW ZEALAND) LTD.—See British American Tobacco plc; *Int'l*, pg. 1166
BRITISH AMERICAN TOBACCO NORWAY AS—See British American Tobacco plc; *Int'l*, pg. 1167
BRITISH-AMERICAN TOBACCO POLSKA S.A.—See British American Tobacco plc; *Int'l*, pg. 1167
BRITISH AMERICAN TOBACCO RCI SARL—See British American Tobacco plc; *Int'l*, pg. 1167
BRITISH AMERICAN TOBACCO (ROMANIA) TRADING SRL—See British American Tobacco plc; *Int'l*, pg. 1167
BRITISH AMERICAN TOBACCO SERVICES CONGO SARL—See British American Tobacco plc; *Int'l*, pg. 1167
BRITISH-AMERICAN TOBACCO (SINGAPORE) PTE. LTD.—See British American Tobacco plc; *Int'l*, pg. 1167
BRITISH AMERICAN TOBACCO SOUTH AFRICA—See British American Tobacco plc; *Int'l*, pg. 1167
BRITISH-AMERICAN TOBACCO TRADING COMPANY FOREIGN PRIVATE TRADING UNITARY ENTERPRISE—See British American Tobacco plc; *Int'l*, pg. 1167
BRITISH AMERICAN TOBACCO TRADING EOOD—See British American Tobacco plc; *Int'l*, pg. 1167
BRITISH AMERICAN TOBACCO TUTUN MAMULLERI SANAYI VE TICARET A.S.—See British American Tobacco plc; *Int'l*, pg. 1167
BRITISH AMERICAN TOBACCO (UGANDA) LTD.—See British American Tobacco plc; *Int'l*, pg. 1166
BRITISH AMERICAN TOBACCO VIETNAM LTD.—See British American Tobacco plc; *Int'l*, pg. 1167
BRITISH AMERICAN TOBACCO VRANJE A.D.—See British American Tobacco plc; *Int'l*, pg. 1167
BRITISH AMERICAN TOBACCO (ZAMBIA) PLC—See British American Tobacco plc; *Int'l*, pg. 1166
BRITISH AMERICAN TOBACCO ZIMBABWE (HOLDINGS) LIMITED—See British American Tobacco plc; *Int'l*, pg. 1167
BULGARTABAC-TRADING AD—See Bulgarian Investment Holding; *Int'l*, pg. 1213
C.A. CIGARRERA BIGOTT SUCS—See British American Tobacco plc; *Int'l*, pg. 1167
CARRERAS LIMITED—See British American Tobacco plc; *Int'l*, pg. 1167

CEYLON TOBACCO COMPANY LTD.; *Int'l*, pg. 1426
CHASE INVESTMENTS LIMITED—See Godfrey Phillips India Ltd.; *Int'l*, pg. 3019
CHINA BRASIL TABACOS EXPORTADORA S.A.—See China Tobacco International (HK) Company Limited; *Int'l*, pg. 1559
COKA DUVANSKA INDUSTRIJA A.D.; *Int'l*, pg. 1696
COMPANIA INDUSTRIAL DE TABACOS MONTE PAZ S.A.; *Int'l*, pg. 1749
COUGAR EXPRESS INC.—See Transportation and Logistics Systems, Inc.; *U.S. Public*, pg. 2184
CQENS TECHNOLOGIES INC.; *U.S. Private*, pg. 1081
C.T.O. PUBLIC COMPANY LTD.; *Int'l*, pg. 1244
DEMERARA TOBACCO CO. LTD.—See British American Tobacco plc; *Int'l*, pg. 1167
DEWAS SOYA LTD.—See Hind Syntex Limited; *Int'l*, pg. 3397
DICKINSON LEGG INC.—See Garbuio S.p.A.; *Int'l*, pg. 2883
DICKINSON LEGG LTD.—See Garbuio S.p.A.; *Int'l*, pg. 2883
DUBEK LTD.; *Int'l*, pg. 2222
DUVAN A.D.; *Int'l*, pg. 2236
DUVANSKA INDUSTRIJA A.D.; *Int'l*, pg. 2236
EASTERN COMPANY—See Chemical Industries Holding Company; *Int'l*, pg. 1461
EASTMAN FIBERS KOREA, LTD.—See Eastman Chemical Company; *U.S. Public*, pg. 705
ELOPAK DENMARK AS—See Ferd AS; *Int'l*, pg. 2635
FABRIKA DUHANA SARAJEVO D.D.—See CID Adriatic Investments GmbH; *Int'l*, pg. 1603
FIEDLER & LUNDGREN AB—See British American Tobacco plc; *Int'l*, pg. 1167
FINCK CIGAR CO.; *U.S. Private*, pg. 1508
GALLATIN REDRYING & STORAGE CO.—See R.C. Owen Holding Company; *U.S. Private*, pg. 3335
GEMINI GROUP GLOBAL CORP.; *U.S. Public*, pg. 910
GODFREY PHILLIPS INDIA LTD.; *Int'l*, pg. 3019
GODFREY PHILLIPS MIDDLEEAST DMCC—See Godfrey Phillips India Ltd.; *Int'l*, pg. 3019
GOTLANDS SNUS AB—See Philip Morris International Inc.; *U.S. Public*, pg. 1687
GPI KRAKOW SP. Z O.O.—See Graphic Packaging Holding Company; *U.S. Public*, pg. 958
GREEN LEAF INNOVATIONS, INC.; *U.S. Public*, pg. 963
GUANGDONG GOLDEN LEAF TECHNOLOGY DEVELOPMENT CO., LTD.—See Huabao International Holdings Limited; *Int'l*, pg. 3510
HARRYS INTERNATIONAL MANUFACTURING INC.—See Harrys Manufacturing Inc.; *Int'l*, pg. 3279
HARRYS MANUFACTURING INC.; *Int'l*, pg. 3279
HARRY WALKER AGENCY, INC.—See Silver Lake Group, LLC; *U.S. Private*, pg. 3654
HIGH TIDE, INC.; *Int'l*, pg. 3386
HOANG LONG GROUP JOINT STOCK COMPANY; *Int'l*, pg. 3436
HOUSE OF OLIVER TWIST A/S—See Philip Morris International Inc.; *U.S. Public*, pg. 1687
HUABAO FLAVOURS & FRAGRANCES CO., LTD.—See Huabao International Holdings Limited; *Int'l*, pg. 3510
HUMBLE JUICE CO., LLC—See Pyxus International, Inc.; *U.S. Public*, pg. 1740
IMPERIAL TOBACCO CANADA LIMITED—See British American Tobacco plc; *Int'l*, pg. 1167
INDUSTRIAS DEL TABACO, ALIMENTOS Y BEBIDAS S.A.—See Philip Morris International Inc.; *U.S. Public*, pg. 1685
INTERNATIONAL TOBACCO COMPANY LIMITED—See Godfrey Phillips India Ltd.; *Int'l*, pg. 3019
INTERTABA S.P.A.—See Philip Morris International Inc.; *U.S. Public*, pg. 1685
IPM INDIA WHOLESALE TRADING PRIVATE LIMITED—See Philip Morris International Inc.; *U.S. Public*, pg. 1685
ISRAEL TOBACCO CO. (M.T.) LTD.—See Dubek Ltd.; *Int'l*, pg. 2222
J.C. NEWMAN CIGAR CO.; *U.S. Private*, pg. 2160
JERUSALEM CIGARETTE CO. LTD.—See Dubek Ltd.; *Int'l*, pg. 2222
JOHN MIDDLETON INC.—See Altria Group, Inc.; *U.S. Public*, pg. 89
JSC JV UZBAT A.O.—See British American Tobacco plc; *Int'l*, pg. 1167
MASSALIN PARTICULARES S.A.—See Philip Morris International Inc.; *U.S. Public*, pg. 1685
M. MISTI CIGAR CO.; *U.S. Private*, pg. 2527
NATIONAL TOBACCO COMPANY LP—See North Atlantic Trading Company, Inc.; *U.S. Private*, pg. 2942
NOBLEZA PICCARDO SAIC Y F—See British American Tobacco plc; *Int'l*, pg. 1167
NUWAY TOBACCO COMPANY INC.; *U.S. Private*, pg. 2975
PAPASTRATOS CIGARETTE MANUFACTURING COMPANY—See Philip Morris International Inc.; *U.S. Public*, pg. 1685
PHILIP MORRIS ARMENIA LIMITED LIABILITY COMPANY—See Philip Morris International Inc.; *U.S. Public*, pg. 1686
PHILIP MORRIS ASIA LIMITED—See Philip Morris International Inc.; *U.S. Public*, pg. 1686

N.A.I.C.S. INDEX
313110 — FIBER, YARN, AND TH...
N.A.I.C.S. Index

PHILIP MORRIS (AUSTRALIA) LTD—See Philip Morris International Inc.; *U.S. Public*, pg. 1685
PHILIP MORRIS AUSTRIA GMBH—See Philip Morris International Inc.; *U.S. Public*, pg. 1686
PHILIP MORRIS BENELUX B.V.B.A.—See Philip Morris International Inc.; *U.S. Public*, pg. 1686
PHILIP MORRIS BRANDS S.A.R.L.—See Philip Morris International Inc.; *U.S. Public*, pg. 1686
PHILIP MORRIS BRASIL INDUSTRIA E COMERCIO LTDA.—See Philip Morris International Inc.; *U.S. Public*, pg. 1686
PHILIP MORRIS BULGARIA EOOD—See Philip Morris International Inc.; *U.S. Public*, pg. 1686
PHILIP MORRIS CHILE COMERCIALIZADORA LIMITADA—See Philip Morris International Inc.; *U.S. Public*, pg. 1686
PHILIP MORRIS COSTA RICA, SOCIEDAD ANONIMA—See Philip Morris International Inc.; *U.S. Public*, pg. 1686
PHILIP MORRIS DOMINICANA, S.A.—See Philip Morris International Inc.; *U.S. Public*, pg. 1686
PHILIP MORRIS EESTI OSAUHING—See Philip Morris International Inc.; *U.S. Public*, pg. 1686
PHILIP MORRIS EGYPT LIMITED LIABILITY COMPANY—See Philip Morris International Inc.; *U.S. Public*, pg. 1686
PHILIP MORRIS FINLAND OY—See Philip Morris International Inc.; *U.S. Public*, pg. 1686
PHILIP MORRIS FRANCE S.A.S.—See Philip Morris International Inc.; *U.S. Public*, pg. 1686
PHILIP MORRIS GMBH—See Philip Morris International Inc.; *U.S. Public*, pg. 1686
PHILIP MORRIS INTERNATIONAL MANAGEMENT SA—See Philip Morris International Inc.; *U.S. Public*, pg. 1686
PHILIP MORRIS INVESTMENTS B.V.—See Philip Morris International Inc.; *U.S. Public*, pg. 1686
PHILIP MORRIS JAPAN GODO-KAISHA INC.—See Philip Morris International Inc.; *U.S. Public*, pg. 1686
PHILIP MORRIS JAPAN KABUSHIKI KAISHA—See Philip Morris International Inc.; *U.S. Public*, pg. 1686
PHILIP MORRIS KAZAKHSTAN LLP—See Philip Morris International Inc.; *U.S. Public*, pg. 1686
PHILIP MORRIS KOREA INC.—See Philip Morris International Inc.; *U.S. Public*, pg. 1686
PHILIP MORRIS KOREA INC.—See Philip Morris International Inc.; *U.S. Public*, pg. 1686
PHILIP MORRIS LATIN AMERICA SERVICES S.R.L.—See Philip Morris International Inc.; *U.S. Public*, pg. 1686
PHILIP MORRIS LIMITED—See Philip Morris International Inc.; *U.S. Public*, pg. 1686
PHILIP MORRIS LJUBLJANA, STORITVENO PODJETJE, D.O.O.—See Philip Morris International Inc.; *U.S. Public*, pg. 1686
PHILIP MORRIS LTD.—See Philip Morris International Inc.; *U.S. Public*, pg. 1686
PHILIP MORRIS MAGHREB SARL—See Philip Morris International Inc.; *U.S. Public*, pg. 1686
PHILIP MORRIS MALAYSIA SDN. BHD.—See Philip Morris International Inc.; *U.S. Public*, pg. 1686
PHILIP MORRIS MANAGEMENT SERVICES (MIDDLE EAST) LIMITED—See Philip Morris International Inc.; *U.S. Public*, pg. 1686
PHILIP MORRIS MANUFACTURING GMBH—See Philip Morris International Inc.; *U.S. Public*, pg. 1686
PHILIP MORRIS MANUFACTURING SENEGAL S.A.R.L.—See Philip Morris International Inc.; *U.S. Public*, pg. 1686
PHILIP MORRIS MEXICO PRODUCTOS Y SERVICIOS, S. DE R.L. DE C.V.—See Philip Morris International Inc.; *U.S. Public*, pg. 1686
PHILIP MORRIS (NEW ZEALAND) LIMITED—See Philip Morris International Inc.; *U.S. Public*, pg. 1685
PHILIP MORRIS NORTH AFRICA SARL—See Philip Morris International Inc.; *U.S. Public*, pg. 1686
PHILIP MORRIS NORWAY AS—See Philip Morris International Inc.; *U.S. Public*, pg. 1686
PHILIP MORRIS OPERATIONS A.D.—See Philip Morris International Inc.; *U.S. Public*, pg. 1686
PHILIP MORRIS (PAKISTAN) LIMITED—See Philip Morris International Inc.; *U.S. Public*, pg. 1685
PHILIP MORRIS PANAMA SOCIEDAD EN COMANDITA POR ACCIONES—See Philip Morris International Inc.; *U.S. Public*, pg. 1686
PHILIP MORRIS PAZARLAMA VE SATIS A.S.—See Philip Morris International Inc.; *U.S. Public*, pg. 1686
PHILIP MORRIS POLSKA S.A.—See Philip Morris International Inc.; *U.S. Public*, pg. 1686
PHILIP MORRIS POLSKA TOBACCO SPOLKA Z OGRANICZONA ODPOWIEDZIALNOSCIA—See Philip Morris International Inc.; *U.S. Public*, pg. 1686
PHILIP MORRIS PRODUCTS S.A.—See Philip Morris International Inc.; *U.S. Public*, pg. 1686
PHILIP MORRIS REUNION S.A.R.L.—See Philip Morris International Inc.; *U.S. Public*, pg. 1686
PHILIP MORRIS SALES AND MARKETING LTD.—See Philip Morris International Inc.; *U.S. Public*, pg. 1687
PHILIP MORRIS SERVICES D.O.O.—See Philip Morris International Inc.; *U.S. Public*, pg. 1687
PHILIP MORRIS SEYAHAT PERAKENDE SATIS ANONIM SIRKETI—See Philip Morris International Inc.; *U.S. Public*, pg. 1687
PHILIP MORRIS SINGAPORE PTE. LTD.—See Philip Morris International Inc.; *U.S. Public*, pg. 1687
PHILIP MORRIS SOUTH AFRICA (PROPRIETARY) LIMITED—See Philip Morris International Inc.; *U.S. Public*, pg. 1687
PHILIP MORRIS SPAIN, S.L.—See Philip Morris International Inc.; *U.S. Public*, pg. 1687
PHILIP MORRIS SWITZERLAND SARL—See Philip Morris International Inc.; *U.S. Public*, pg. 1687
PHILIP MORRIS TUTUN MAMULLERI SANAYI VE TICARET A.S.—See Philip Morris International Inc.; *U.S. Public*, pg. 1687
PHILIP MORRIS USA INC.—See Altria Group, Inc.; *U.S. Public*, pg. 89
PHILIP MORRIS USA—See Altria Group, Inc.; *U.S. Public*, pg. 89
PHILIP MORRIS VIETNAM LIMITED LIABILITY COMPANY—See Philip Morris International Inc.; *U.S. Public*, pg. 1687
PHILIP MORRIS ZAGREB D.O.O.—See Philip Morris International Inc.; *U.S. Public*, pg. 1687
PHILSA PHILIP MORRIS SABANCI SIGARA VE TUTUNCULUK SANAYI VE TICARET A.S.—See Philip Morris International Inc.; *U.S. Public*, pg. 1685
P.J. CARROLL & CO. LTD.—See British American Tobacco plc; *Int'l*, pg. 1167
PLEVEN-BT AD—See Bulgarian Investment Holding; *Int'l*, pg. 1213
PMI GLOBAL SERVICES, INC.—See Philip Morris International Inc.; *U.S. Public*, pg. 1685
PMI SERVICE CENTER EUROPE SPOLKA Z OGRANICZONA ODPOWIEDZIALNOSCIA—See Philip Morris International Inc.; *U.S. Public*, pg. 1685
PRJSC PHILIP MORRIS UKRAINE—See Philip Morris International Inc.; *U.S. Public*, pg. 1687
PRJSC PHILIP MORRIS UKRAINE—See Philip Morris International Inc.; *U.S. Public*, pg. 1687
PT BENTOEL INTERNASIONAL INVESTAMA TBK—See British American Tobacco plc; *Int'l*, pg. 1167
PT HANJAYA MANDALA SAMPOERNA TBK.—See Philip Morris International Inc.; *U.S. Public*, pg. 1685
PT PHILIP MORRIS INDONESIA—See Philip Morris International Inc.; *U.S. Public*, pg. 1685
R.C. OWEN COMPANY OF TENNESSEE—See R.C. Owen Holding Company; *U.S. Private*, pg. 3335
R.C. OWEN HOLDING COMPANY; *U.S. Private*, pg. 3335
R.J. REYNOLDS GLOBAL PRODUCTS, INC.—See British American Tobacco plc; *Int'l*, pg. 1168
SANTA FE NATURAL TOBACCO COMPANY, INC.—See British American Tobacco plc; *Int'l*, pg. 1168
SHENZHEN HUACHANG INDUSTRIAL CO., LTD.—See China Boton Group Company Limited; *Int'l*, pg. 1487
SIA PHILIP MORRIS LATVIA—See Philip Morris International Inc.; *U.S. Public*, pg. 1687
SIMCOE LEAF TOBACCO COMPANY, LTD.—See Universal Corporation; *U.S. Public*, pg. 2254
SM CIGARS INC.—See Philip Morris International Inc.; *U.S. Public*, pg. 1687
SMD LOGISTICS AB—See Philip Morris International Inc.; *U.S. Public*, pg. 1687
SMOKEFREE INNOTEC, INC.; *U.S. Private*, pg. 3698
SOFIA-BT A.D.—See Bulgarian Investment Holding; *Int'l*, pg. 1213
SOLOMON ISLANDS TOBACCO COMPANY LIMITED—See British American Tobacco plc; *Int'l*, pg. 1168
SWEDISH MATCH AB—See Philip Morris International Inc.; *U.S. Public*, pg. 1687
SWEDISH MATCH DO BRASIL S/A—See Philip Morris International Inc.; *U.S. Public*, pg. 1687
SWEDISH MATCH DOMINICANA S.A.—See Philip Morris International Inc.; *U.S. Public*, pg. 1687
SWEDISH MATCH NORGE AS—See Philip Morris International Inc.; *U.S. Public*, pg. 1687
SWISHER INTERNATIONAL, INC.—See Hay Island Holding Corporation; *U.S. Private*, pg. 1884
TABACALERA HONDURENA SA—See British American Tobacco plc; *Int'l*, pg. 1168
TABACALERA ISTMENA SA—See British American Tobacco plc; *Int'l*, pg. 1168
TABACALERA NICARAGUENSE S.A.—See British American Tobacco plc; *Int'l*, pg. 1168
TDR D.O.O., BEOGRAD—See British American Tobacco plc; *Int'l*, pg. 1168
TDR D.O.O., BLAZUJ—See British American Tobacco plc; *Int'l*, pg. 1168
TDR D.O.O., ROVINJ—See British American Tobacco plc; *Int'l*, pg. 1168
TDR ROVITA D.O.O.—See British American Tobacco plc; *Int'l*, pg. 1168
TDR SKOPJE DOOEL—See British American Tobacco plc; *Int'l*, pg. 1168
TOBACCO MARKETING CONSULTANT BURKINA FASO SARL—See British American Tobacco plc; *Int'l*, pg. 1168
TURNING POINT BRANDS, INC.; *U.S. Public*, pg. 2205
UAB BRITISH AMERICAN TOBACCO LIETUVA—See British American Tobacco plc; *Int'l*, pg. 1168
UAB PHILIP MORRIS BALTIC—See Philip Morris International Inc.; *U.S. Public*, pg. 1687
UNIFILL S.P.A.—See Ferd AS; *Int'l*, pg. 2636
UNITED INDUSTRIES CO—See Hayel Saeed Anam Group of Companies; *Int'l*, pg. 3291
UPEXI, INC.; *U.S. Public*, pg. 2264
U.S. SMOKELESS TOBACCO COMPANY, LLC—See Altria Group, Inc.; *U.S. Public*, pg. 89
V2 TOBACCO A/S—See Philip Morris International Inc.; *U.S. Public*, pg. 1687
VAPORBRANDS INTERNATIONAL, INC.; *U.S. Public*, pg. 2275
WEE-CIG INTERNATIONAL CORP; *U.S. Public*, pg. 2342
WEST INDIAN TOBACCO LIMITED—See British American Tobacco plc; *Int'l*, pg. 1166
YAMBOL-TABAC A.D.—See Bulgarian Investment Holding; *Int'l*, pg. 1213
ZAO PHILIP MORRIS IZHORA—See Philip Morris International Inc.; *U.S. Public*, pg. 1688

313110 — FIBER, YARN, AND THREAD MILLS

AANANDA LAKSHMI SPINNING MILLS LIMITED; *Int'l*, pg. 36
ACME-MCCRARY CORPORATION; *U.S. Private*, pg. 61
ACS TECHNOLOGIES LIMITED; *Int'l*, pg. 109
ADIL TEXTILE MILLS LIMITED; *Int'l*, pg. 148
ADITYA SPINNERS LTD.; *Int'l*, pg. 149
A&E IPLIK SANAYI VE TICARET ANONIM SIRKETI—See The Kroger Co.; *U.S. Public*, pg. 2108
AI CHAMPDANY INDUSTRIES LIMITED; *Int'l*, pg. 226
AKARY FOR INDUSTRIES & REAL ESTATE INVESTMENTS PLC; *Int'l*, pg. 259
AKIN TEKSTIL A.S.; *Int'l*, pg. 263
AL-AZHAR TEXTILE MILLS LIMITED; *Int'l*, pg. 284
ALEXANDRIA SPINNING & WEAVING CO.; *Int'l*, pg. 307
AL-HAJ TEXTILE MILLS LIMITED; *Int'l*, pg. 285
ALI ASGHAR TEXTILE MILS LTD.; *Int'l*, pg. 320
ALIF MANUFACTURING COMPANY LTD.; *Int'l*, pg. 327
AL-QADIR TEXTILE MILLS LIMITED; *Int'l*, pg. 288
AL-QAIM TEXTILE MILLS LIMITED; *Int'l*, pg. 288
AMARJOTHI SPINNING MILLS LTD - AMARJOTHI DYEING DIVISION—See Amarjothi Spinning Mills Ltd; *Int'l*, pg. 412
AMARJOTHI SPINNING MILLS LTD; *Int'l*, pg. 412
AMBIKA COTTON MILLS LIMITED; *Int'l*, pg. 414
AMERICAN & EFIRD (A&E EUROPE), SUKANCI D.O.O.—See The Kroger Co.; *U.S. Public*, pg. 2108
AMERICAN & EFIRD DE MEXICO, S.A. DE C.V—See The Kroger Co.; *U.S. Public*, pg. 2108
AMERICAN & EFIRD ENTERPRISES, INC.—See The Kroger Co.; *U.S. Public*, pg. 2108
AMERICAN & EFIRD (G.B.) LIMITED—See The Kroger Co.; *U.S. Public*, pg. 2108
AMERICAN & EFIRD, LLC—See Platinum Equity, LLC; *U.S. Private*, pg. 3201
AMERICAN & EFIRD (MALAYSIA) SDN. BHD.—See The Kroger Co.; *U.S. Public*, pg. 2108
AMERICAN & EFIRD MILLS (S) PTE. LTD.—See The Kroger Co.; *U.S. Public*, pg. 2108
AMITAL SPINNING CORP.; *U.S. Private*, pg. 263
AMIT SPINNING INDUSTRIES LIMITED—See CLC Industries Limited; *Int'l*, pg. 1653
ANLIMA YARN DYEING LIMITED; *Int'l*, pg. 473
ANNOOR TEXTILE MILLS LIMITED; *Int'l*, pg. 474
APEX YARN DYEING LIMITED—See Apex Holding Limited; *Int'l*, pg. 511
APM INDUSTRIES LIMITED; *Int'l*, pg. 516
AQUAFIL S.P.A.—See Aquafin Holding S.p.A.; *Int'l*, pg. 527
AQUAFIL U.S.A., INC.—See Aquafin Holding S.p.A.; *Int'l*, pg. 527
ARAB POLVARA COMPANY FOR SPINNING & WEAVING COMPANY; *Int'l*, pg. 531
ASPINWALL & CO. LTD., - NATURAL FIBRE DIVISION—See Aspinwall & Co. Ltd.,; *Int'l*, pg. 630
ASPINWALL & CO. LTD., - SANDY SPRINGS BRANCH—See Aspinwall & Co. Ltd.,; *Int'l*, pg. 630
ASSOCIATED SERVICES LIMITED; *Int'l*, pg. 649
AZGARD NINE LIMITED; *Int'l*, pg. 778
BABRI COTTON MILLS LIMITED—See Bibojee Services Private Limited; *Int'l*, pg. 1018
BALA TECHNO GLOBAL LTD.; *Int'l*, pg. 806
BANSWARA FABRICS LIMITED—See Banswara Syntex Limited; *Int'l*, pg. 855
BANSWARA SYNTEX LIMITED; *Int'l*, pg. 854
BECO STEEL LIMITED; *Int'l*, pg. 938
BEL AIR INDUSTRIES; *Int'l*, pg. 962
BEXIMCO SYNTHETICS LIMITED; *Int'l*, pg. 1005
BHANERO TEXTILE MILLS LIMITED; *Int'l*, pg. 1010
BHILWARA SPINNERS LIMITED; *Int'l*, pg. 1015
BHUDEVI INFRA PROJECTS LTD.; *Int'l*, pg. 1016
BILAL FIBRES LIMITED; *Int'l*, pg. 1023
BILLION INDUSTRIAL HOLDINGS LIMITED; *Int'l*, pg. 1031

313110 — FIBER, YARN, AND TH...

BIRLIK MENSUCAT TICARET VE SANAYI ISLETMESI A.S.; *Int'l*, pg. 1048
BLESSED TEXTILES LIMITED; *Int'l*, pg. 1063
BONYAD PP FIBER PROD CO.; *Int'l*, pg. 1110
BROS EASTERN CO., LTD.; *Int'l*, pg. 1195
BROS HOLDING LTD.—See Bros Eastern Co., Ltd.; *Int'l*, pg. 1195
BROS SPINNING (SHENZHEN) CO., LTD.—See Bros Eastern Co., Ltd.; *Int'l*, pg. 1195
BROTHERS TEXTILE MILLS LIMITED; *Int'l*, pg. 1198
BUNNY'S LIMITED; *Int'l*, pg. 1216
CANDOUR TECHTEX LTD.; *Int'l*, pg. 1289
CAROLINA MILLS INC.; *U.S. Private*, pg. 768
CARON INTERNATIONAL—See National Spinning Company, Inc.; *U.S. Private*, pg. 2863
CAVALIER SPINNERS LIMITED—See Bremworth Limited; *Int'l*, pg. 1145
CELANESE ACETATE, LLC—See Celanese Corporation; *U.S. Public*, pg. 465
CENTENARI E ZINELLI SPA; *Int'l*, pg. 1402
CENTURY TEXTILES AND INDUSTRIES LIMITED - CENTURY RAYON DIVISION—See Century Textiles and Industries Limited; *Int'l*, pg. 1419
CENTURY TEXTILES AND INDUSTRIES LIMITED - CENTURY RAYON PLANT—See Century Textiles and Industries Limited; *Int'l*, pg. 1419
CENTURY TEXTILES AND INDUSTRIES LIMITED - CENTURY YARN DIVISION—See Century Textiles and Industries Limited; *Int'l*, pg. 1419
CENTURY TEXTILES AND INDUSTRIES LIMITED - CENTURY YARN WORKS—See Century Textiles and Industries Limited; *Int'l*, pg. 1420
CHAKWAL SPINNING MILLS LTD.; *Int'l*, pg. 1437
CHANGZHOU YINGFU TEXTILE CO., LTD.—See FUJIX Ltd.; *Int'l*, pg. 2838
CHAROENRUT KARNTAW CO., LTD.; *Int'l*, pg. 1454
CHHABRA SPINNERS LIMITED; *Int'l*, pg. 1474
CHINA GAOXIAN FIBRE FABRIC HOLDINGS LTD.; *Int'l*, pg. 1503
CHINA LONGEVITY GROUP COMPANY LIMITED; *Int'l*, pg. 1515
CHINA MAN-MADE FIBER CORPORATION; *Int'l*, pg. 1516
CHINA PAPER HOLDINGS LIMITED; *Int'l*, pg. 1539
CHINA RESOURCES TEXTILES CO., LTD.—See China Resources (Holdings) Co., Ltd.; *Int'l*, pg. 1548
CHINA WEAVING MATERIALS HOLDINGS LIMITED; *Int'l*, pg. 1563
CHONBANG CO., LTD.; *Int'l*, pg. 1578
CITIZEN YARNS LIMITED; *Int'l*, pg. 1625
CLC INDUSTRIES LIMITED; *Int'l*, pg. 1653
CLOVER YARNS INC.; *U.S. Private*, pg. 948
CLOVER YARNS—See Clover Yarns Inc.; *U.S. Private*, pg. 948
COATS AUSTRALIAN PTY LTD.—See Coats Group plc; *Int'l*, pg. 1682
COATS CADENA SA ARGENTINA—See Coats Group plc; *Int'l*, pg. 1682
COATS CANADA—See Comvest Group Holdings LLC; *U.S. Private*, pg. 1007
COATS & CLARK INC.—See Comvest Group Holdings LLC; *U.S. Private*, pg. 1007
COATS CORRENTE LTDA-FABRICA IPIRANGA—See Coats Group plc; *Int'l*, pg. 1682
COATS CUCIRINI S.P.A.—See Coats Group plc; *Int'l*, pg. 1682
COATS FABRA SA—See Coats Group plc; *Int'l*, pg. 1682
COATS GMBH—See Coats Group plc; *Int'l*, pg. 1682
COATS HARLANDER GES.M.B.H.—See Coats Group plc; *Int'l*, pg. 1682
COATS MANILA BAY, INC.—See Coats Group plc; *Int'l*, pg. 1682
COATS SOUTH AFRICA (PTY) LTD.—See Coats Group plc; *Int'l*, pg. 1682
COLONY TEXTILE MILLS LIMITED; *Int'l*, pg. 1702
COMPANIA DE LINHA COATS & CLARK, LDA.—See Coats Group plc; *Int'l*, pg. 1682
DAIWABO RAYON CO., LTD. - MASUDA MILL—See Daiwabo Holdings Co., Ltd.; *Int'l*, pg. 1949
DAMODAR INDUSTRIES LIMITED; *Int'l*, pg. 1957
DATA TEXTILES LIMITED; *Int'l*, pg. 1976
DCM LIMITED; *Int'l*, pg. 1992
DECHELETTE MALLEVAL SA; *Int'l*, pg. 2000
DEEPAK SPINNERS LIMITED; *Int'l*, pg. 2003
DELTA SPINNERS LIMITED; *Int'l*, pg. 2020
DERIVADOS ACRILICOS S.A. DE C.V. - AGUASCALIENTES PLANT—See Cydsa S.A.B. de C.V.; *Int'l*, pg. 1895
DILLON YARN CORPORATION; *U.S. Private*, pg. 1231
DIN TEXTILE MILLS LTD.; *Int'l*, pg. 2126
DMC (USA) CORPORATION—See Antofagasta plc; *Int'l*, pg. 484
DONGGUAN DONGMEI THREAD MFG. CO. LTD.—See The Kroger Co.; *U.S. Public*, pg. 2108
D.S. INDUSTRIES LIMITED; *Int'l*, pg. 1901
DULAMIA COTTON SPINNING MILLS LTD.; *Int'l*, pg. 2224
DUNAV A.D. GROCKA; *Int'l*, pg. 2225
DURAFIBER TECHNOLOGIES (DFT), INC. - SHELBY FACILITY—See Sun Capital Partners, Inc.; *U.S. Private*, pg. 3859
EASTERN SILK INDUSTRIES LIMITED; *Int'l*, pg. 2274
E.C. BIRCH PROPRIETARY LIMITED; *Int'l*, pg. 2251
ECO SPINDLES (PVT) LTD—See BPPL Holdings PLC; *Int'l*, pg. 1133
ELAHI COTTON MILLS LIMITED; *Int'l*, pg. 2342
EL. D. MOUZAKIS S.A.; *Int'l*, pg. 2341
ELVIP S.R.O.—See EL. D. MOUZAKIS S.A.; *Int'l*, pg. 2341
EUROTEX INDUSTRIES & EXPORTS LIMITED; *Int'l*, pg. 2558
EVEREST TEXTILE USA, LLC—See Everest Textile Co., Ltd.; *Int'l*, pg. 2565
FAISAL SPINNING MILLS LIMITED; *Int'l*, pg. 2609
FIBER INNOVATION TECHNOLOGY INC.—See CHA Technologies Inc.; *U.S. Private*, pg. 845
FILATEX INDIA LTD.; *Int'l*, pg. 2662
FILSYN CORPORATION; *Int'l*, pg. 2663
FIRESTONE FIBERS & TEXTILES DIVISION—See Bridgestone Corporation; *Int'l*, pg. 1156
FRONTIER SPINNING MILLS, INC.—See American Securities LLC; *U.S. Private*, pg. 249
FUJIAN FUNENG CO., LTD.; *Int'l*, pg. 2818
FUJIAN FYNEX TEXTILE SCIENCE & TECHNOLOGY CO., LTD.; *Int'l*, pg. 2818
FUJIBO HOLDINGS, INC.; *Int'l*, pg. 2820
FUJIX LTD.; *Int'l*, pg. 2838
FUJIX (SHANGHAI) THREAD LTD.—See FUJIX Ltd.; *Int'l*, pg. 2838
GADOON TEXTILE MILLS LIMITED; *Int'l*, pg. 2868
GANGOTRI TEXTILES LTD; *Int'l*, pg. 2881
GANGOTRI TEXTILES LTD - UNIT - III—See Gangotri Textiles Ltd; *Int'l*, pg. 2881
GANGOTRI TEXTILES LTD - UNIT - I—See Gangotri Textiles Ltd; *Int'l*, pg. 2881
GARDEN SILK MILLS PRIVATE LIMITED—See The Chatterjee Group; *U.S. Private*, pg. 4007
GATRON INDUSTRIES LIMITED; *Int'l*, pg. 2889
GEM SPINNERS INDIA LIMITED; *Int'l*, pg. 2915
GHAZI FABRICS INTERNATIONAL LIMITED; *Int'l*, pg. 2959
GIMSAN GEDIZ IPLIK VE MENSUCAT SANAYII AS; *Int'l*, pg. 2976
GLAMOUR TEXTILE MILLS LIMITED; *Int'l*, pg. 2987
GLEN RAVEN, INC.; *U.S. Private*, pg. 1709
GODFREY HIRST NZ LTD.—See Mohawk Industries, Inc.; *U.S. Public*, pg. 1457
GODFREY HIRST (SINGAPORE) PTE. LTD.—See Mohawk Industries, Inc.; *U.S. Public*, pg. 1457
GOKAK TEXTILES LTD.; *Int'l*, pg. 3022
GOLDLINK THREAD LIMITED—See Fountain Set (Holdings) Limited; *Int'l*, pg. 2754
GROVER INDUSTRIES INC.; *U.S. Private*, pg. 1795
GRUSCHWITZ TEXTILWERKE AG; *Int'l*, pg. 3141
GTN INDUSTRIES LTD; *Int'l*, pg. 3151
GTN TEXTILES LIMITED; *Int'l*, pg. 3151
GUJARAT AMBUJA EXPORTS LTD. - COTTON YARN DIVISION—See Gujarat Ambuja Exports Ltd.; *Int'l*, pg. 3175
GUJARAT COTEX LIMITED; *Int'l*, pg. 3176
GUJARAT CRAFT INDUSTRIES LIMITED; *Int'l*, pg. 3176
GUJARAT HYSPIN LIMITED; *Int'l*, pg. 3176
GULISTAN SPINNING MILLS LIMITED—See Gulistan Group; *Int'l*, pg. 3182
GULISTAN TEXTILE MILLS LIMITED—See Gulistan Group; *Int'l*, pg. 3182
GUNZE (SHANGHAI) INTERNATIONAL TRADING CO., LTD.—See Gunze Limited; *Int'l*, pg. 3185
HAJI MOHAMMAD ISMAIL MILLS LIMITED; *Int'l*, pg. 3219
HANDAN XURI COMMERCIAL & INDUSTRIAL CO., LTD.; *Int'l*, pg. 3243
HANORA SPINNING—See The First Republic Corporation of America; *U.S. Public*, pg. 2074
HHRG BERHAD; *Int'l*, pg. 3379
HIGHSCENE LIMITED—See Fountain Set (Holdings) Limited; *Int'l*, pg. 2754
HILOS A&E DE COSTA RICA, S.A.—See The Kroger Co.; *U.S. Public*, pg. 2108
HILOS A&E DE EL SALVADOR, S.A. DE C.V.—See The Kroger Co.; *U.S. Public*, pg. 2108
HILOS AMERICAN & EFIRD DE HONDURAS, S.A. DE C.V.—See The Kroger Co.; *U.S. Public*, pg. 2108
HIMACHAL FIBRES LIMITED; *Int'l*, pg. 3396
HINDOOSTAN MILLS LIMITED; *Int'l*, pg. 3397
HIND SYNTEX LIMITED; *Int'l*, pg. 3397
HISAR SPINNING MILLS LIMITED; *Int'l*, pg. 3406
HI-TECH FIBER GROUP CORPORATION—See China Hi-Tech Group Co., Ltd.; *Int'l*, pg. 1507
HONEYWELL NYLON LLC—See Honeywell International Inc.; *U.S. Public*, pg. 1051
HONG BI FIBER INDUSTRY CO., LTD.; *Int'l*, pg. 3469
HONG YI FIBER INDUSTRY CO., LTD. - YINGGE FACTORY—See Hong Yi Fiber Industry Co., Ltd.; *Int'l*, pg. 3469
HONG YI INTERNATION CO., LTD.—See Hong Yi Fiber Industry Co., Ltd.; *Int'l*, pg. 3469
HSIN SIN TEXTILE CO., LTD.; *Int'l*, pg. 3507
HUAFU FASHION CO., LTD.; *Int'l*, pg. 3512
HYOSUNG CORPORATION; *Int'l*, pg. 3550
HYOSUNG TNS INC.—See Hyosung Advanced Materials Co., Ltd.; *Int'l*, pg. 3550
IDEAL FIBRES & FABRICS COMINES SAS—See Beaulieu International Group NV; *Int'l*, pg. 934
I-HWA INDUSTRIAL CO., LTD. - TEXTILE DIVISION—See I-Hwa Industrial Co., Ltd.; *Int'l*, pg. 3563
ILSHIN SPINNING CO., LTD.; *Int'l*, pg. 3616
IMAGE PAKISTAN LIMITED; *Int'l*, pg. 3617
IZUMO APPAREL LTD.—See Gunze Limited; *Int'l*, pg. 3186
JEFFERSON YARNS; *U.S. Private*, pg. 2198
JONES COMPANIES LTD.; *U.S. Private*, pg. 2232
KAIPING HUI HUA TEXTILES LIMITED—See Fountain Set (Holdings) Limited; *Int'l*, pg. 2754
KENTWOOL COMPANY; *U.S. Private*, pg. 2289
KILKIS SPINNING MILLS S.A.—See Hellenic Fabrics S.A.; *Int'l*, pg. 3333
LANDMARK SPINNING INDUSTRIES LIMITED—See Hashwani Group; *Int'l*, pg. 3283
LUDLOW TEXTILES COMPANY, INC.; *U.S. Private*, pg. 2512
LUYANG ENERGY-SAVING MATERIALS CO., LTD.—See Clearlake Capital Group, L.P.; *U.S. Private*, pg. 937
MERIDIAN SPECIALTY YARN GROUP, INC.—See Meridian Industries, Inc.; *U.S. Private*, pg. 2673
MODERN COTTON YARN SPINNERS LTD.—See Bengal & Assam Company Ltd.; *Int'l*, pg. 973
MODERN POLY INDUSTRIES LTD.—See BSM Group Limited; *Int'l*, pg. 1202
NATIONAL SPINNING COMPANY, INC - ALAMANCE DYE PLANT—See National Spinning Company, Inc.; *U.S. Private*, pg. 2863
NATIONAL SPINNING COMPANY, INC - BEULAVILLE SPINNING PLANT—See National Spinning Company, Inc.; *U.S. Private*, pg. 2863
NATIONAL SPINNING COMPANY, INC.; *U.S. Private*, pg. 2863
NATIONAL SPINNING COMPANY LTD. CO.—See Al Abdullatif Industrial Investment Company; *Int'l*, pg. 275
NATIONAL SPINNING CO.—See National Spinning Company, Inc.; *U.S. Private*, pg. 2863
NATIONAL TEXTILES, LLC—See Hanesbrands Inc.; *U.S. Public*, pg. 983
O'MARA, INC.—See Aquafin Holding S.p.A.; *Int'l*, pg. 527
OOO SONOCO ALCORE—See Sonoco Products Company; *U.S. Public*, pg. 1904
PARAMOUNT SPINNING MILLS LIMITED—See Gulistan Group; *Int'l*, pg. 3182
PARKDALE AMERICA, LLC—See Parkdale, Inc.; *U.S. Private*, pg. 3097
PARKDALE MILLS INC.; *U.S. Private*, pg. 3097
PATRICK YARN MILL, INC.—See Coats Group plc; *Int'l*, pg. 1682
PROSPERLINK (MACAU COMMERCIAL OFFSHORE) LIMITED—See Fountain Set (Holdings) Limited; *Int'l*, pg. 2754
PT COATS REJO INDONESIA—See Coats Group plc; *Int'l*, pg. 1682
PT. HAGIHARA WESTJAVA INDUSTRIES—See Hagihara Industries Inc.; *Int'l*, pg. 3207
ROSELON INDUSTRIES INC.; *U.S. Private*, pg. 3483
SANS TECHNICAL FIBERS LLC—See AECI Limited; *Int'l*, pg. 171
SAPONA MANUFACTURING COMPANY, INC.—See Acme-McCrary Corporation; *U.S. Private*, pg. 61
SCHOELLER LITVINOV K.S.—See CLC Industries Limited; *Int'l*, pg. 1653
SCHOELLER TEXTILE (NETHERLANDS), B.V.—See CLC Industries Limited; *Int'l*, pg. 1653
SERRES GINNING S.A.—See EL. D. MOUZAKIS S.A.; *Int'l*, pg. 2341
SHANGHAI NEW FUJIX THREAD LTD.—See FUJIX Ltd.; *Int'l*, pg. 2838
SHENZHEN BROS EASTERN TEXTILE CO., LTD.—See Bros Eastern Co., Ltd.; *Int'l*, pg. 1195
SHRI DAMODAR YARN MANUFACTURING PVT. LTD.—See Damodar Industries Limited; *Int'l*, pg. 1957
SHUFORD MILLS LLC; *U.S. Private*, pg. 3644
SINOMA SCIENCE & TECHNOLOGY CO., LTD.—See China National Materials; *Int'l*, pg. 1532
SPENTEX INDUSTRIES LIMITED - BARAMATI UNIT—See CLC Industries Limited; *Int'l*, pg. 1653
SPENTEX INDUSTRIES LIMITED - SOLAPUR UNIT—See CLC Industries Limited; *Int'l*, pg. 1653
SPENTEX TASHKENT TOYTEPA LLC—See CLC Industries Limited; *Int'l*, pg. 1653
SPINRITE LP—See Comvest Group Holdings LLC; *U.S. Private*, pg. 1007
STI INDIA LIMITED—See Bombay Rayon Fashions Limited; *Int'l*, pg. 1104
STOWE-PHARR MILLS, INC.; *U.S. Private*, pg. 3832
THAI ASAHI KASEI SPANDEX CO., LTD. - AMPHUR SRIRACHA FACTORY—See Asahi Kasei Corporation; *Int'l*, pg. 597
TSEYU INTERNATIONAL TRADING COMPANY LIMITED—See Harbour Equine Holdings Limited; *Int'l*, pg. 3272
TSUYAMA GUNZE CO., LTD.—See Gunze Limited; *Int'l*, pg. 3186

N.A.I.C.S. INDEX

313210 — BROADWOVEN FABRIC M...

TUSCARORA YARNS INC.; *U.S. Private*, pg. 4262
ULTRAFAB INC.; *U.S. Private*, pg. 4278
UNIFI DO BRASIL, LTDA—See Unifi, Inc.; *U.S. Public*, pg. 2226
UNIFI LATIN AMERICA, S.A.S.—See Unifi, Inc.; *U.S. Public*, pg. 2226
UNIFI MANUFACTURING, INC,—See Unifi, Inc.; *U.S. Public*, pg. 2226
UNIFI TEXTILES—See Unifi, Inc.; *U.S. Public*, pg. 2226
UNIFI TEXTURED POLYESTER, LLC—See Unifi, Inc.; *U.S. Public*, pg. 2226
UNIFI TEXTURED YARNS EUROPE, LTD.—See Unifi, Inc.; *U.S. Public*, pg. 2226
U.S. FIBER, LLC—See Casella Waste Systems, Inc.; *U.S. Public*, pg. 446
VERSAX, S.A. DE C.V.—See ALFA, S.A.B. de C.V.; *Int'l*, pg. 314
VILLAGE PLASTICS CO.—See Keene Building Products Company, Inc.; *U.S. Private*, pg. 2272

313210 — BROADWOVEN FABRIC MILLS

ALBANY ENGINEERED COMPOSITES, INC.—See Albany International Corp.; *U.S. Public*, pg. 72
ALBANY INTERNATIONAL CORP.; *U.S. Public*, pg. 72
ALBANY INTERNATIONAL ENGINEERED FABRICS—See Albany International Corp.; *U.S. Public*, pg. 72
ALBANY INTERNATIONAL TECHNIWEAVE, INC.—See Albany International Corp.; *U.S. Public*, pg. 72
ALICE MANUFACTURING CO. INC.; *U.S. Private*, pg. 167
ALL ACCESS APPAREL INC.; *U.S. Private*, pg. 169
ALLISON CORPORATION; *U.S. Private*, pg. 192
AMERICAN FIBER & FINISHING INC.; *U.S. Private*, pg. 233
ANAHUAC SOUTH CAROLINA ELASTIC S.A. DE C.V.—See Rhode Island Textile Company, Inc.; *U.S. Private*, pg. 3422
APEX MILLS CORPORATION; *U.S. Private*, pg. 293
AREX INDUSTRIES LIMITED; *Int'l*, pg. 559
ARGON DENIMS LIMITED; *Int'l*, pg. 562
ARTISTIC DENIM MILLS LIMITED; *Int'l*, pg. 584
ARUJ INDUSTRIES LTD.; *Int'l*, pg. 586
ASHFAQ TEXTILE MILLS LIMITED; *Int'l*, pg. 606
ASHIMA LTD.; *Int'l*, pg. 607
ATD-AMERICAN CO. INC.; *U.S. Private*, pg. 365
AVERY DENNISON RETAIL BRANDING & INFORMATION SOLUTIONS - LENOIR—See Avery Dennison Corporation; *U.S. Public*, pg. 243
AVINTIV SPECIALTY MATERIALS INC.—See Berry Global Group, Inc; *U.S. Public*, pg. 320
A. WIMPFHEIMER & BROS., INC.; *U.S. Private*, pg. 24
BAJER DESIGN & MARKETING INC.; *U.S. Private*, pg. 454
BALLARD MATERIAL PRODUCTS INC.—See Ballard Power Systems, Inc.; *Int'l*, pg. 809
BAMBERGER KALIKO GMBH; *Int'l*, pg. 813
BANGALORE FORT FARMS LIMITED; *Int'l*, pg. 832
BEDFORD WEAVING MILLS INC.; *U.S. Private*, pg. 512
BEDGEAR LLC; *U.S. Private*, pg. 512
BEKAERT TEXTILES N.V.—See Franz Haniel & Cie. GmbH; *Int'l*, pg. 2762
BERKSHIRE BLANKET INCORPORATED—See China National Machinery Industry Corporation; *Int'l*, pg. 1531
BEXTEX LIMITED—See Bangladesh Export Import Co. Ltd.; *Int'l*, pg. 835
BGF INDUSTRIES INC.—See Groupe Porcher Industries; *Int'l*, pg. 3109
BILICI YATIRIM SANAYI VE TICARET A.S.; *Int'l*, pg. 1029
BLOOMSBURG MILLS INC.; *U.S. Private*, pg. 584
BLUE BLENDS (INDIA) LIMITED - DENIM DIVISION—See Blue Blends (India) Limited; *Int'l*, pg. 1067
BLUE BLENDS (INDIA) LIMITED; *Int'l*, pg. 1067
BLUE RIDGE TEXTILE MANUFACTURING, INC.—See Coyne International Enterprises Corp.; *U.S. Private*, pg. 1079
BRITISH MOHAIR SPINNERS LIMITED—See Dewavrin Groupe; *Int'l*, pg. 2091
BRITISH TRIMMINGS LTD.—See Conso International Corporation; *U.S. Private*, pg. 1020
BUDGE BUDGE COMPANY LTD.; *Int'l*, pg. 1211
CAMIRA FABRICS LTD. - LITHUANIA MANUFACTURING FACILITY—See Camira Fabrics Ltd.; *Int'l*, pg. 1273
CAMIRA FABRICS LTD. - MELTHAM MANUFACTURING FACILITY—See Camira Fabrics Ltd.; *Int'l*, pg. 1273
CAMIRA FABRICS LTD.; *Int'l*, pg. 1273
CAMIRA FABRICS SHANGHAI LTD—See Camira Fabrics Ltd.; *Int'l*, pg. 1273
CARAVAN EAST FABRICS LIMITED; *Int'l*, pg. 1320
CAROLE FABRICS CORP.—See 3G Capital Partners L.P.; *U.S. Private*, pg. 13
CAROLINA GLOVE COMPANY - CAROLINA SPECIALTY FABRICS DIVISION—See Carolina Glove Company; *U.S. Private*, pg. 768
CDS ENSEMBLES, INC.; *U.S. Private*, pg. 803
CENTURY TEXTILES AND INDUSTRIES LIMITED - CENTURY DENIM DIVISION—See Century Textiles and Industries Limited; *Int'l*, pg. 1419
CENTURY TEXTILES AND INDUSTRIES LIMITED - CENTURY DENIM WORKS—See Century Textiles and Industries Limited; *Int'l*, pg. 1419
CHANG-HO FIBRE CORPORATION - NANKAN FACTORY—See Chang-Ho Fibre Corporation; *Int'l*, pg. 1442
CHARGEURS WOOL (USA) INC.—See Chargeurs SA; *Int'l*, pg. 1449
CHARLES D. OWEN MFG. CO.—See Springs Global, Inc.; *U.S. Private*, pg. 3764
CHEVIOT COMPANY LIMITED; *Int'l*, pg. 1474
CHONBANG CO., LTD. - YOUNGAM FACTORY—See Chonbang Co., Ltd.; *Int'l*, pg. 1578
CHONGQING ZAISHENG TECHNOLOGY CORP., LTD.; *Int'l*, pg. 1581
CK STORES BELGIUM BVBA—See PVH Corp.; *U.S. Public*, pg. 1739
CK STORES DENMARK APS—See PVH Corp.; *U.S. Public*, pg. 1739
COMPANHIA DE FIACAO E TECIDOS CEDRO E CACHOEIRA; *Int'l*, pg. 1747
COPEN ASSOCIATES, INC.; *U.S. Private*, pg. 1044
COPLAND FABRICS, INC.; *U.S. Private*, pg. 1045
CRAFTEX MILLS INC. OF PENNSYLVANIA; *U.S. Private*, pg. 1082
CRESCENT JUTE PRODUCTS LIMITED; *Int'l*, pg. 1839
CROWN CRAFTS, INC.; *U.S. Public*, pg. 596
CROWN CRAFTS INFANT PRODUCTS, INC.—See Crown Crafts, Inc.; *U.S. Public*, pg. 596
CULP, INC.; *U.S. Public*, pg. 604
CURT BAUER GMBH; *Int'l*, pg. 1879
DARLINGTON FABRICS CORPORATION—See Moore Company; *U.S. Private*, pg. 2779
DAWSON FABRICS LTD.—See Dawson International PLC; *Int'l*, pg. 1984
DEWAN TEXTILE MILL LIMITED; *Int'l*, pg. 2091
THE DEWITT COMPANY, INC.; *U.S. Private*, pg. 4021
DYNAMIC ARCHISTRUCTURES LIMITED; *Int'l*, pg. 2240
EASTBANK TEXTILES, LLC—See Inman Holding Co. Inc.; *U.S. Private*, pg. 2079
ELEVATE TEXTILES INC.—See Platinum Equity, LLC; *U.S. Private*, pg. 3203
ELUXURY, LLC—See Culp, Inc.; *U.S. Public*, pg. 605
ETRO S.P.A.; *Int'l*, pg. 2524
EVEREST TEXTILE CO., LTD.; *Int'l*, pg. 2564
FABRIC DEVELOPMENT INC.—See Haci Omer Sabanci Holding A.S.; *Int'l*, pg. 3204
FABRIC RESOURCES INTERNATIONAL LTD.; *U.S. Private*, pg. 1458
FAIRWAY PRODUCTS—See Acme Mills Co. Inc.; *U.S. Private*, pg. 61
FARIBAULT MILLS, INC.; *U.S. Private*, pg. 1474
FEROZE1888 MILLS LIMITED—See 1888 Mills, LLC; *U.S. Private*, pg. 3
F.H. BONN COMPANY; *U.S. Private*, pg. 1456
FIBER GLASS INDUSTRIES INC.; *U.S. Private*, pg. 1501
THE FIRST REPUBLIC CORPORATION OF AMERICA; *U.S. Public*, pg. 2074
FLAMURA SA; *Int'l*, pg. 2698
FLORA TEXTILES LIMITED; *Int'l*, pg. 2707
FORELAND FABRICTECH HOLDINGS LIMITED; *Int'l*, pg. 2731
FORMOSA TAFFETA CORP.—See Formosa Petrochemical Corporation; *Int'l*, pg. 2735
FOV FABRICS AB; *Int'l*, pg. 2755
FRANCEBED CO., LTD.—See FRANCE BED HOLDINGS CO. LTD.; *Int'l*, pg. 2759
GAENSLEN VOELTER GMBH & CO. KG—See Gaenslen Voelter; *Int'l*, pg. 2868
GAENSLEN VOELTER; *Int'l*, pg. 2868
GALE PACIFIC INC.—See Gale Pacific Limited; *Int'l*, pg. 2872
GLEN RAVEN FILAMENT FABRICS LLC—See Glen Raven, Inc.; *U.S. Private*, pg. 1709
GLEN RAVEN TECHNICAL FABRICS, LLC—See Glen Raven, Inc.; *U.S. Private*, pg. 1709
GOLDEN SHIELD HOLDINGS (INDUSTRIAL) LTD.; *Int'l*, pg. 3031
GREEN MOUNTAIN KNITTING INC.; *U.S. Private*, pg. 1773
GREENWOOD MILLS, INC.—See GMI Holding, Inc.; *U.S. Private*, pg. 1722
GROUPE PORCHER INDUSTRIES; *Int'l*, pg. 3109
GUL AHMED TEXTILE MILLS LTD.; *Int'l*, pg. 3177
HAIHAO HIGH FASHION CO., LTD.—See Haixin Group Company Ltd.; *Int'l*, pg. 3219
HAINZ-KIMBERLY DEUTSCHLAND GMBH—See Kimberly-Clark Corporation; *U.S. Public*, pg. 1230
HAIXIN OHTSU CO., LTD.—See Haixin Group Company Ltd.; *Int'l*, pg. 3219
HAIXIN PLUSH CO., LTD.—See Haixin Group Company Ltd.; *Int'l*, pg. 3219
HALA ENTERPRISES LIMITED; *Int'l*, pg. 3227
HANGZHOU ASAHIKASEI TEXTILES CO., LTD.—See Asahi Kasei Corporation; *Int'l*, pg. 596
HARODITE INDUSTRIES, INC.; *U.S. Private*, pg. 1866
HARODITE S.A. DE C.V.—See Harodite Industries, Inc.; *U.S. Private*, pg. 1866
HARODITE S.A. DE C.V.—See Harodite Industries, Inc.; *U.S. Private*, pg. 1866
HENNIGES AUTOMOTIVE, INC. - FREDERICK—See Aviation Industry Corporation of China; *Int'l*, pg. 742
HIMATSINGKA AMERICA INC.—See Himatsingka Seide Limited; *Int'l*, pg. 3396
HIMATSINGKA LINENS—See Himatsingka Seide Limited; *Int'l*, pg. 3396
HIMATSINGKA SEIDE LIMITED; *Int'l*, pg. 3396
HIMATSINGKA SINGAPORE PTE. LTD.—See Himatsingka Seide Limited; *Int'l*, pg. 3396
HINGTEX HOLDINGS LTD.; *Int'l*, pg. 3401
HOFFMAN MILLS INC.; *U.S. Private*, pg. 1960
HONGDA HIGH-TECH HOLDING CO., LTD.; *Int'l*, pg. 3470
HUAFENG TRADING MACAO COMMERCIAL OFFSHORE LIMITED—See Blockchain Group Company Limited; *Int'l*, pg. 1064
HUIYIN HOLDINGS GROUP LIMITED; *Int'l*, pg. 3527
HUNAN HUASHENG CO., LTD.; *Int'l*, pg. 3532
HUYCK ARGENTINA SA—See ANDRITZ AG; *Int'l*, pg. 457
HUYCK.WANGNER AUSTRALIA PTY. LIMITED—See ANDRITZ AG; *Int'l*, pg. 457
HUYCK.WANGNER AUSTRIA GMBH—See ANDRITZ AG; *Int'l*, pg. 457
HUYCK.WANGNER JAPAN LIMITED—See ANDRITZ AG; *Int'l*, pg. 457
ICHIKAWA EUROPA GMBH—See ICHIKAWA CO. LTD.; *Int'l*, pg. 3580
I-HWA INDUSTRIAL CO., LTD.; *Int'l*, pg. 3563
IL JEONG INDUSTRIAL CO., LTD; *Int'l*, pg. 3612
INMAN MILLS INC.—See Inman Holding Co. Inc.; *U.S. Private*, pg. 2079
JAY FRANCO & SONS INC.; *U.S. Private*, pg. 2191
J.B. MARTIN COMPANY; *U.S. Private*, pg. 2158
JOE'S JEANS SUBSIDIARY, INC.—See Centric Brands Inc.; *U.S. Private*, pg. 829
JOHNSTON TEXTILES, INC.—See Meriturn Partners, LLC; *U.S. Private*, pg. 2675
JPS COMPOSITE MATERIALS CORPORATION—See Steel Partners Holdings L.P.; *U.S. Public*, pg. 1943
KIMBERLY-CLARK LIMITED—See Kimberly-Clark Corporation; *U.S. Public*, pg. 1230
LINTEX CO. INC.; *U.S. Private*, pg. 2463
L.W. PACKARD & CO., INC.; *U.S. Private*, pg. 2367
MANDHANA WEAVING HOUSE (SHIRTING DIVISION)—See GB Global Limited; *Int'l*, pg. 2892
MAQUILAS PAMI, S.A. DE C.V.—See Premier Brands Group Holdings LLC; *U.S. Private*, pg. 3249
MATERIAL TECHNOLOGY & LOGISTICS, INC.; *U.S. Private*, pg. 2609
MEHLER TEXNOLOGIES S.P.A—See Freudenberg SE; *Int'l*, pg. 2789
MICROFIBRES INC.; *U.S. Private*, pg. 2703
MILLIKEN & COMPANY; *U.S. Private*, pg. 2736
MILLIKEN FINE GOODS DIV.—See Milliken & Company; *U.S. Private*, pg. 2737
MILLIKEN FINISHED APPAREL DIV.—See Milliken & Company; *U.S. Private*, pg. 2737
MILLIKEN INDUSTRIAL DIV.—See Milliken & Company; *U.S. Private*, pg. 2737
MILLIKEN INTERIOR FURNISHINGS DIV.—See Milliken & Company; *U.S. Private*, pg. 2737
MONTEREY INC.; *U.S. Private*, pg. 2776
MORARJEE TEXTILES LTD—See Ashok Piramal Group; *Int'l*, pg. 608
MOUNT VERNON MILLS, INC.—See R.B. Pamplin Corporation; *U.S. Private*, pg. 3334
MUTUAL INDUSTRIES NORTH INC.; *U.S. Private*, pg. 2820
NATIONAL NONWOVENS; *U.S. Private*, pg. 2860
NEW RIVER INDUSTRIES INC.; *U.S. Private*, pg. 2906
NEWTEX INDUSTRIES INC.; *U.S. Private*, pg. 2918
NORTH CAROLINA FOAM INDUSTRIES, INC.—See Barnhardt Manufacturing Company; *U.S. Private*, pg. 478
OWENS CORNING OCV TECHNICAL FABRICS—See Owens Corning; *U.S. Public*, pg. 1627
PACIFIC COMPOSITES PTY. LTD—See Exel Composites Oyj; *Int'l*, pg. 2582
P&B FABRICS INC.; *U.S. Private*, pg. 3058
PERFORMANCE TEXTILES, INC.—See Praesidian Capital Corp.; *U.S. Private*, pg. 3241
POLARTEC LLC—See Milliken & Company; *U.S. Private*, pg. 2737
PORCHER INDUSTRIES ASIA-PACIFIC—See Groupe Porcher Industries; *Int'l*, pg. 3109
PORCHER INDUSTRIES, RUSSIA—See Groupe Porcher Industries; *Int'l*, pg. 3109
PORCHER INDUSTRIES, UK—See Groupe Porcher Industries; *Int'l*, pg. 3110
PORCHER ITALIANA—See Groupe Porcher Industries; *Int'l*, pg. 3110
PRECISION FABRICS GROUP INC.; *U.S. Private*, pg. 3244
PRINGLE OF SCOTLAND LTD.—See Fang Brothers Knitting Ltd.; *Int'l*, pg. 2613
PT ANEKA GARMENTAMA INDAH—See Carry Wealth Holdings Limited; *Int'l*, pg. 1346
PVH OSTERREICH GESMBH—See PVH Corp.; *U.S. Public*, pg. 1739
RAYONESE TEXTILES, INC.—See Culp, Inc.; *U.S. Public*, pg. 604
THE RUG BARN INC.—See The InterTech Group, Inc.; *U.S. Private*, pg. 4057

313210 — BROADWOVEN FABRIC M...

SAINT GOBAIN BTI—See Compagnie de Saint-Gobain SA; *Int'l*, pg. 1730
SAINT-GOBAIN CERAMIC MATERIALS WEILERSWIST GMBH—See Compagnie de Saint-Gobain SA; *Int'l*, pg. 1731
SAINT-GOBAIN VETROTEX DEUTSCHLAND GMBH—See Compagnie de Saint-Gobain SA; *Int'l*, pg. 1736
SANTISTA JEANSWEAR S.A.—See Camargo Correa S.A.; *Int'l*, pg. 1268
SCALAMANDRE, INC.; *U.S. Private*, pg. 3560
SCHNEIDER MILLS, INC.; *U.S. Private*, pg. 3566
SEAMAN CORPORATION; *U.S. Private*, pg. 3585
SHANGHAI PORCHER INDUSTRIES CO., LTD.—See Groupe Porcher Industries; *Int'l*, pg. 3110
SHERIDAN AUSTRALIA PTY. LIMITED—See Hanesbrands Inc.; *U.S. Public*, pg. 983
SINGLESOURCE APPAREL, INC.—See GMI Holding, Inc.; *U.S. Private*, pg. 1722
SOUTHERN MILLS, INC.—See ABN AMRO Group N.V.; *Int'l*, pg. 64
SOUTHERN MILLS, INC.—See Gilde Buy Out Partners B.V.; *Int'l*, pg. 2974
SPRINGS GLOBAL, INC.- BATH FASHIONS DIVISION—See Springs Global, Inc.; *U.S. Private*, pg. 3764
SPRINGS GLOBAL, INC.; *U.S. Private*, pg. 3764
SPRINGS GLOBAL PARTICIPACOES S.A.—See Coteminas Companhia de Tecidos Norte de Minas; *Int'l*, pg. 1817
SPRINGS GLOBAL PARTICIPACOES S.A.—See Springs Global, Inc.; *U.S. Private*, pg. 3764
SPRINGS GLOBAL US, INC.—See Coteminas Companhia de Tecidos Norte de Minas; *Int'l*, pg. 1817
SPRINGS GLOBAL US, INC.—See Springs Global, Inc.; *U.S. Private*, pg. 3764
STERN & STERN INDUSTRIES INC.; *U.S. Private*, pg. 3807
STOWE WOODWARD FINLAND OY—See ANDRITZ AG; *Int'l*, pg. 457
STOWE WOODWARD LLC—See ANDRITZ AG; *Int'l*, pg. 457
STRIBBONS INC.; *U.S. Private*, pg. 3839
SUNBURY TEXTILES MILLS, INC.—See Glen Raven, Inc.; *U.S. Private*, pg. 1709
SUPERIOR FABRICS, INC.; *U.S. Private*, pg. 3878
SWAVELLE/MILL CREEK FABRICS, INC.; *U.S. Private*, pg. 3891
SWIFT GALEY—See Patriarch Partners, LLC; *U.S. Private*, pg. 3109
TAISHAN FIBERGLASS INC.—See China National Materials; *Int'l*, pg. 1532
THERMAL ENGINEERING INTERNATIONAL LIMITED—See Babcock Power, Inc.; *U.S. Private*, pg. 422
TOYO CUSHION LANKA (PVT) LTD.—See Hayleys PLC; *Int'l*, pg. 3292
TRANSHIELD, INC.—See Patrick Industries, Inc.; *U.S. Public*, pg. 1653
TWITCHELL CORPORATION—See Highlander Partners, LP.; *U.S. Private*, pg. 1940
ULTRAFLEX SYSTEMS INC.; *U.S. Private*, pg. 4278
VALDESE WEAVERS, LLC—See CV Industries Inc.; *U.S. Private*, pg. 1132
VERATEX, INC.; *U.S. Private*, pg. 4359
VLISCO HELMOND B.V.—See General Atlantic Service Company, L.P.; *U.S. Private*, pg. 1661
WADE MANUFACTURING COMPANY; *U.S. Private*, pg. 4424
THE WARNACO GROUP, INC.—See PVH Corp.; *U.S. Public*, pg. 1739
WEARBEST SIL-TEX MILLS LTD.; *U.S. Private*, pg. 4462
WEAVE CORPORATION; *U.S. Private*, pg. 4463
WEAVEXX CORPORATION—See ANDRITZ AG; *Int'l*, pg. 457
WILMINGTON PRODUCTS-USA INC.; *U.S. Private*, pg. 4529
WOLF MANUFACTURING COMPANY; *U.S. Private*, pg. 4553
WOOLCAN, INC.—See Woolrich, Inc.; *U.S. Private*, pg. 4562
WOOLRICH, INC.; *U.S. Private*, pg. 4562
XERIUM CANADA INC.—See ANDRITZ AG; *Int'l*, pg. 457
XERIUM TECHNOLOGIES BRASIL INDUSTRIA E COMERCIO S.A.—See ANDRITZ AG; *Int'l*, pg. 457
XERIUM TECHNOLOGIES, INC.—See ANDRITZ AG; *Int'l*, pg. 457
XERIUM TECHNOLOGIES LIMITED—See ANDRITZ AG; *Int'l*, pg. 457
YUHAN-KIMBERLY, LIMITED—See Kimberly-Clark Corporation; *U.S. Public*, pg. 1230

313220 — NARROW FABRIC MILLS AND SCHIFFLI MACHINE EMBROIDERY

AHMAD HASSAN TEXTILE MILLS LIMITED; *Int'l*, pg. 225
ANGSTROM USA, LLC; *U.S. Private*, pg. 283
APOLO TUBULARS S.A.—See United States Steel Corporation; *U.S. Public*, pg. 2236
ASHEBORO ELASTICS CORPORATION; *U.S. Private*, pg. 349
ASHIMORI TEXTILE MANUFACTURING CO., LTD.—See Ashimori Industry Co., Ltd.; *Int'l*, pg. 607
AUSTRALIAN WOOL INDUSTRIES LTD.—See Alrov Properties & Lodgings Ltd.; *Int'l*, pg. 377
BALLY RIBBON MILLS; *U.S. Private*, pg. 461
BLUE STAR WEBBING CORP.; *U.S. Private*, pg. 593
BOSIDENG INTERNATIONAL HOLDINGS LIMITED; *Int'l*, pg. 1116
CALMON ABACUS TEXTILES PTE. LTD.—See Duroc AB; *Int'l*, pg. 2229
CAPITOL USA LLC; *U.S. Private*, pg. 744
CAROLACE EMBROIDERY CO., INC.; *U.S. Private*, pg. 767
CONSO INTERNATIONAL CORPORATION; *U.S. Private*, pg. 1020
CONTINENTAL TICKING CORPORATION AMERICA; *U.S. Private*, pg. 1031
DUNN MANUFACTURING CORPORATION; *U.S. Private*, pg. 1290
EVEREST TEXTILE (HK) CO. LTD.—See Everest Textile Co., Ltd.; *Int'l*, pg. 2565
FRANGI S.P.A; *Int'l*, pg. 2761
FURNIWEB HOLDINGS LIMITED; *Int'l*, pg. 2846
FURNIWEB (VIETNAM) SHAREHOLDING COMPANY—See Furniweb Holdings Limited; *Int'l*, pg. 2846
GINI SILK MILLS LIMITED; *Int'l*, pg. 2977
GSI MARULONTEX CO., LTD.—See GSI Creos Corporation; *Int'l*, pg. 3144
HAKATA TAKUMI KOUGEI INC.; *Int'l*, pg. 3219
HELLENIC FABRICS S.A.; *Int'l*, pg. 3333
HOLLYWOOD RIBBON INDUSTRIES INC.—See IG Design Group Plc; *Int'l*, pg. 3600
LABELTEX MILLS INCORPORATED; *U.S. Private*, pg. 2370
LAWRENCE SCHIFF SILK MILLS, INC.—See Revolution Capital Group, LLC; *U.S. Private*, pg. 3416
LION BROTHERS FAR EAST, LTD.—See Avery Dennison Corporation; *U.S. Public*, pg. 244
LION RIBBON COMPANY, LLC—See IG Design Group Plc; *Int'l*, pg. 3600
MURDOCK WEBBING COMPANY INCORPORATED; *U.S. Private*, pg. 2815
NARROW FABRIC AMERICA CORPORATION; *U.S. Private*, pg. 2835
NARROW FABRIC INDUSTRIES CORP.—See Cheynet S.A.S; *Int'l*, pg. 1474
PATRIOT PREMIUM THREADING SERVICES, LLC—See United States Steel Corporation; *U.S. Public*, pg. 2237
RHODE ISLAND TEXTILE COMPANY, INC.; *U.S. Private*, pg. 3422
SHELBY ELASTICS OF NORTH CAROLINA, LLC—See Beocare Group, Inc.; *U.S. Private*, pg. 529
SOLMAX—See ABN AMRO Group N.V.; *Int'l*, pg. 64
SOLMAX—See ABN AMRO Group N.V.; *Int'l*, pg. 64
SOLMAX—See Gilde Buy Out Partners B.V.; *Int'l*, pg. 2974
SOLMAX—See Gilde Buy Out Partners B.V.; *Int'l*, pg. 2974
SOUTH CAROLINA ELASTIC—See Industrial Value Partners, LLC; *U.S. Private*, pg. 2069
SOUTHERN WEAVING COMPANY; *U.S. Private*, pg. 3735
STATE NARROW FABRICS INC.; *U.S. Private*, pg. 3792
SUPREME ELASTIC CORP; *U.S. Private*, pg. 3882
TEN CATE DANMARK A/S—See ABN AMRO Group N.V.; *Int'l*, pg. 64
TEN CATE DANMARK A/S—See Gilde Buy Out Partners B.V.; *Int'l*, pg. 2974
TENCATE GEOSYNTHETICS MALAYSIA SDN BHD—See ABN AMRO Group N.V.; *Int'l*, pg. 64
TENCATE GEOSYNTHETICS MALAYSIA SDN BHD—See Gilde Buy Out Partners B.V.; *Int'l*, pg. 2975
TENCATE GEOSYNTHETICS NETHERLANDS B.V.—See ABN AMRO Group N.V.; *Int'l*, pg. 64
TENCATE GEOSYNTHETICS NETHERLANDS B.V.—See Gilde Buy Out Partners B.V.; *Int'l*, pg. 2975
TENCATE GEOSYNTHETICS (THAILAND) LTD—See ABN AMRO Group N.V.; *Int'l*, pg. 64
TENCATE GEOSYNTHETICS (THAILAND) LTD—See Gilde Buy Out Partners B.V.; *Int'l*, pg. 2975
TEN CATE GEOSYNTHETICS (UK) LIMITED—See ABN AMRO Group N.V.; *Int'l*, pg. 64
TEN CATE GEOSYNTHETICS (UK) LIMITED—See Gilde Buy Out Partners B.V.; *Int'l*, pg. 2974
TENCATE INDUSTRIAL ZHUHAI CO. LTD.—See ABN AMRO Group N.V.; *Int'l*, pg. 65
TENCATE INDUSTRIAL ZHUHAI CO. LTD.—See Gilde Buy Out Partners B.V.; *Int'l*, pg. 2975
TRIMTEX CO. INC.; *U.S. Private*, pg. 4232
TYGAFLOR LTD.—See Compagnie de Saint-Gobain SA; *Int'l*, pg. 1732
VALLEY METALS, LLC—See Leggett & Platt, Incorporated; *U.S. Public*, pg. 1304
WAYNE INDUSTRIES INC.; *U.S. Private*, pg. 4459

313230 — NONWOVEN FABRIC MILLS

ADS INC.; *Int'l*, pg. 153
AETNA FELT CORP.—See Industrial Opportunity Partners, LLC; *U.S. Private*, pg. 2067
ANDRITZ INC. - KUSTERS DIVISION—See ANDRITZ AG; *Int'l*, pg. 453
ANDRITZ KUSTERS GMBH—See ANDRITZ AG; *Int'l*, pg. 454
ASAHIOZU CORPORATION; *Int'l*, pg. 599
ATLAS RESOURCES INTERNATIONAL, INC.; *U.S. Public*, pg. 224
BALTA OUDENAARDE NV—See Balta Group NV; *Int'l*, pg. 812
BEN-TAM, INC.; *U.S. Public*, pg. 295
BERK WIPER CONVERTING & PACKAGING, LLC; *U.S. Private*, pg. 532
BONAR GMBH & CO. KG—See Freudenberg SE; *Int'l*, pg. 2789
BONTEX (ASIA) HOLDING COMPANY LIMITED—See Bontex, Inc.; *U.S. Public*, pg. 368
BOUCKAERT INDUSTRIAL TEXTILES, INC.—See Hyman Brickle & Son, Inc.; *U.S. Private*, pg. 2019
BRAND MARVEL WORLDWIDE CONSUMER PRODUCTS CORPORATION; *Int'l*, pg. 1139
BUSINESS PARTNERS CO., LTD.—See Dynam Japan Holdings, Co., Ltd.; *Int'l*, pg. 2239
CASCADES IFC—See Cascades Inc.; *Int'l*, pg. 1351
CHICOPEE EUROPE—See Berry Global Group, Inc; *U.S. Public*, pg. 321
CHICOPEE INC.—See Berry Global Group, Inc; *U.S. Public*, pg. 321
CHINA SLP FILTRATION TECHNOLOGY, INC.; *Int'l*, pg. 1552
CLARK-CUTLER-MCDERMOTT CO.; *U.S. Private*, pg. 914
COLBOND GEOSYNTHETICS SARL—See Freudenberg SE; *Int'l*, pg. 2789
DALCO NONWOVENS, LLC—See Snow Peak Capital, LLC; *U.S. Private*, pg. 3701
DK VINA CO., LTD.—See DK&D Co., Ltd.; *Int'l*, pg. 2139
DURAFIBER TECHNOLOGIES (DFT), INC.—See Sun Capital Partners, Inc.; *U.S. Private*, pg. 3859
DYNIC CORPORATION - FUJI FACTORY—See Dynic Corporation; *Int'l*, pg. 2242
DYNIC CORPORATION - MOKA FACTORY—See Dynic Corporation; *Int'l*, pg. 2242
DYNIC CORPORATION - OJI FACTORY—See Dynic Corporation; *Int'l*, pg. 2242
DYNIC CORPORATION - SHIGA FACTORY—See Dynic Corporation; *Int'l*, pg. 2242
DYNIC JUNO CO., LTD.—See Dynic Corporation; *Int'l*, pg. 2243
ELEPHANT NONWOVENS - NAO TECIDOS U.P., LDA.—See Aktieselskabet Schouw & Co.; *Int'l*, pg. 265
ESWEGEE VLIESSTOFF GMBH—See Hoftex Group AG; *Int'l*, pg. 3440
EVOLUTION SORBENT PRODUCTS, LLC—See National Packaging Services Corporation; *U.S. Private*, pg. 2860
EVORA S.A.; *Int'l*, pg. 2573
THE FELTERS GROUP; *U.S. Private*, pg. 4028
FIBERTEX, A.S.—See Aktieselskabet Schouw & Co.; *Int'l*, pg. 266
FIBERTEX FRANCE S.A.R.L.—See Aktieselskabet Schouw & Co.; *Int'l*, pg. 265
FIBERTEX NAOTECIDOS LTDA.—See Aktieselskabet Schouw & Co.; *Int'l*, pg. 265
FIBERTEX NONWOVENS A/S—See Aktieselskabet Schouw & Co.; *Int'l*, pg. 265
FIBERTEX NONWOVENS S.A.—See Aktieselskabet Schouw & Co.; *Int'l*, pg. 265
FIBERTEX NONWOVENS TEKSTIL SANAYI VE IHRACAT A.S.—See Aktieselskabet Schouw & Co.; *Int'l*, pg. 265
FIBERTEX PERSONAL CARE AG—See Aktieselskabet Schouw & Co.; *Int'l*, pg. 265
FIBERTEX PERSONAL CARE A/S—See Aktieselskabet Schouw & Co.; *Int'l*, pg. 265
FIBERTEX PERSONAL CARE CORPORATION—See Aktieselskabet Schouw & Co.; *Int'l*, pg. 265
FIBERTEX PERSONAL CARE SDN BHD—See Aktieselskabet Schouw & Co.; *Int'l*, pg. 266
FIBERTEX SOUTH AFRICA LTD.—See Aktieselskabet Schouw & Co.; *Int'l*, pg. 266
FIBERWEB (INDIA) LTD.; *Int'l*, pg. 2652
FIBRIX LLC—See Branford Castle, Inc.; *U.S. Private*, pg. 639
FITESA GERMANY GMBH—See Evora S.A.; *Int'l*, pg. 2573
FITESA ITALIA SRL—See Evora S.A.; *Int'l*, pg. 2573
FITESA MEXICO—See Evora S.A.; *Int'l*, pg. 2573
FITESA PERU S.A.C.—See Evora S.A.; *Int'l*, pg. 2573
FITESA SA—See Evora S.A.; *Int'l*, pg. 2573
FITESA SIMPSONVILLE, INC.—See Evora S.A.; *Int'l*, pg. 2573
FITESA SWEDEN AB—See Evora S.A.; *Int'l*, pg. 2573
FITESA WASHOUGAL, INC.—See Evora S.A.; *Int'l*, pg. 2573
FOSS MANUFACTURING COMPANY LLC; *U.S. Private*, pg. 1578
FOSS MANUFACTURING COMPANY LLC - THE KUNIN GROUP DIVISION—See Foss Manufacturing Company LLC; *U.S. Private*, pg. 1578

N.A.I.C.S. INDEX

313310 — TEXTILE AND FABRIC ...

FREUDENBERG ESPANA S.A., TELAS SIN TEJER S.EN—See Freudenberg SE; *Int'l*, pg. 2786
FREUDENBERG EVOLON S.A.R.L.—See Freudenberg SE; *Int'l*, pg. 2786
FREUDENBERG FAR EASTERN SPUNWEB COMP. LTD.—See Freudenberg SE; *Int'l*, pg. 2786
FREUDENBERG NAO-TECIDOS LTDA. & CIA.—See Freudenberg SE; *Int'l*, pg. 2787
FREUDENBERG NONWOVENS INDIA PVT. LTD.—See Freudenberg SE; *Int'l*, pg. 2787
FREUDENBERG NONWOVENS LIMITED PARTNERSHIP—See Freudenberg SE; *Int'l*, pg. 2787
FREUDENBERG NONWOVENS LP VILENE INTERLININGS—See Freudenberg SE; *Int'l*, pg. 2787
FREUDENBERG NONWOVENS (PTY.) LTD.—See Freudenberg SE; *Int'l*, pg. 2787
FREUDENBERG NONWOVENS TUFT DIVISION—See Freudenberg SE; *Int'l*, pg. 2787
FREUDENBERG S.P.A.—See Freudenberg SE; *Int'l*, pg. 2788
FREUDENBERG TELAS SIN TEJER S.A. DE C.V.—See Freudenberg SE; *Int'l*, pg. 2788
FREUDENBERG VERTRIEB EINLAGESTOFFE KG—See Freudenberg SE; *Int'l*, pg. 2788
FREUDENBERG VILENE NONWOVENS TAIWAN COMPANY LTD.—See Freudenberg SE; *Int'l*, pg. 2788
FREUDENBERG VILENE SP. Z.O.O.—See Freudenberg SE; *Int'l*, pg. 2788
FUJIKURA GRAPHICS, INC.—See Fujikura Composites Inc.; *Int'l*, pg. 2826
GALE PACIFIC FZE—See Gale Pacific Limited; *Int'l*, pg. 2872
GALE PACIFIC LIMITED; *Int'l*, pg. 2872
GALE PACIFIC (NZ) LIMITED—See Gale Pacific Limited; *Int'l*, pg. 2872
GAMMA GRUNDSTUCKSVERWALTUNGSGESELL-SCHAFT MBH—See Gilde Buy Out Partners B.V.; *Int'l*, pg. 2974
GHANA TEXTILE PRINTING COMPANY LTD.—See General Atlantic Service Company, L.P.; *U.S. Private*, pg. 1661
HANGZHOU BONYEE DAILY NECESSITY TECHNOLOGY CO., LTD.—See Hangzhou Nbond Nonwoven Co.,Ltd; *Int'l*, pg. 3249
HANGZHOU NBOND NONWOVEN CO.,LTD; *Int'l*, pg. 3249
HAVIX CORPORATION; *Int'l*, pg. 3287
HDK INDUSTRIES, INC.—See Branford Castle, Inc.; *U.S. Private*, pg. 639
HOFTEX GROUP AG; *Int'l*, pg. 3440
HYMAN BRICKLE & SON, INC. - BRANCH RIVER FACILITY—See Hyman Brickle & Son, Inc.; *U.S. Private*, pg. 2019
HYMAN BRICKLE & SON, INC. - BRICKLE FIBER TRADING DIVISION—See Hyman Brickle & Son, Inc.; *U.S. Private*, pg. 2019
INTISSEL SAS—See Chargeurs SA; *Int'l*, pg. 1450
JAPAN VILENE COMPANY, LTD.—See Freudenberg SE; *Int'l*, pg. 2789
JASON INCORPORATED—See Jason Industries, Inc.; *U.S. Private*, pg. 2189
JOHN WALKDEN ET COMPAGNIE S.A.—See General Atlantic Service Company, L.P.; *U.S. Private*, pg. 1661
JONES FIBER PRODUCTS INC.—See Jones Companies Ltd.; *U.S. Private*, pg. 2232
LYDALL FILTRATION/SEPARATION, INC. ROCHESTER OPERATION—See Lydall, Inc.; *U.S. Public*, pg. 1349
LYDALL FILTRATION SEPARATION S.A.S.—See Lydall, Inc.; *U.S. Public*, pg. 1349
LYDALL SOLUTECH B.V.—See Lydall, Inc.; *U.S. Public*, pg. 1350
LYDALL THERMIQUE/ACOUSTIQUE S.A.S.—See Lydall, Inc.; *U.S. Public*, pg. 1350
METCALF BROTHERS LLC—See Hyman Brickle & Son, Inc.; *U.S. Private*, pg. 2019
NEENAH TECHNICAL MATERIALS, INC.—See Mativ Holdings, Inc.; *U.S. Public*, pg. 1396
NIGER-AFRIQUE S.A.—See General Atlantic Service Company, L.P.; *U.S. Private*, pg. 1661
NORTHEASTERN NONWOVENS, INC.—See Metapoint Partners LP; *U.S. Private*, pg. 2682
PROPEX GEOSOLUTIONS CORPORATION—See Wayzata Investment Partners LLC; *U.S. Private*, pg. 4461
P.T. DAIWABO NONWOVEN INDONESIA—See Daiwabo Holdings Co., Ltd.; *Int'l*, pg. 1950
RESINTEX INDUSTRIALE S.R.L.—See Hoftex Group AG; *Int'l*, pg. 3440
SAINT-GOBAIN ADFORS AMERICA, INC.—See Compagnie de Saint-Gobain SA; *Int'l*, pg. 1730
SCAPA TAPES NORTH AMERICA—See Mativ Holdings, Inc.; *U.S. Public*, pg. 1397
SPERIAN PROTECTION ARMOR SAS—See Honeywell International Inc.; *U.S. Public*, pg. 1049
SUNFELT CO., LTD.—See Chiyoda Integre Co., Ltd.; *Int'l*, pg. 1575
TECHTEX GMBH VLIESTOFFE MITTWEIDA—See Hoftex Group AG; *Int'l*, pg. 3440

TPCNIC CO., LTD. - CHONBURI FACTORY—See Dynic Corporation; *Int'l*, pg. 2243
TPCNIC CO., LTD.—See Dynic Corporation; *Int'l*, pg. 2243
VAC GHANA—See General Atlantic Service Company, L.P.; *U.S. Private*, pg. 1661
VAC-TOGO S.A.—See General Atlantic Service Company, L.P.; *U.S. Private*, pg. 1661
VITA NONWOVENS, LLC; *U.S. Private*, pg. 4404
VITA NONWOVENS—See Vita Nonwovens, LLC; *U.S. Private*, pg. 4404
VLISCO FRANCE S.A.—See General Atlantic Service Company, L.P.; *U.S. Private*, pg. 1661
WM T. BURNETT & CO. - NONWOVENS DIVISION—See Wm T. Burnett & Co.; *U.S. Private*, pg. 4552

313240 — KNIT FABRIC MILLS

AMES TEXTILE CORPORATION; *U.S. Private*, pg. 262
ANJANI SYNTHETICS LTD. - AHMEDABAD PLANT—See Anjani Synthetics Ltd.; *Int'l*, pg. 472
ANLIMA TEXTILE LIMITED—See Anlima Yarn Dyeing Limited; *Int'l*, pg. 473
AVERY DENNISON S.R.L.—See Avery Dennison Corporation; *U.S. Public*, pg. 243
CLASSIC FILAMENTS LIMITED; *Int'l*, pg. 1652
DALMIA INDUSTRIAL DEVELOPMENT LIMITED; *Int'l*, pg. 1954
DAWOOD LAWRENCEPUR LIMITED—See Dawood Corporation (Pvt.) Ltd.; *Int'l*, pg. 1984
DENTELLE SOPHIE HALLETTE; *Int'l*, pg. 2033
DRAPER KNITTING CO., INC.; *U.S. Private*, pg. 1272
EMA S.A.R.L.; *Int'l*, pg. 2372
EVERTEX FABRINOLOGY LIMITED; *Int'l*, pg. 2569
FAB INDUSTRIES CORP.; *U.S. Private*, pg. 1458
FAR EAST KNITTING & DYEING INDUSTRIES LTD.; *Int'l*, pg. 2616
FIERATEX S.A.; *Int'l*, pg. 2660
FRIEDMAN'S LTD.—See CEPS PLC; *Int'l*, pg. 1420
FULIAN KNITTING CO., LTD—See Foreland Fabrictech Holdings Limited; *Int'l*, pg. 2731
GENERATION NEXT FASHIONS LIMITED; *Int'l*, pg. 2920
GILDAN ACTIVEWEAR INC.; *Int'l*, pg. 2973
GINZA INDUSTRIES LTD.; *Int'l*, pg. 2977
GRAVITY (INDIA) LIMITED; *Int'l*, pg. 3062
HAIXIN GROUP COMPANY LTD.; *Int'l*, pg. 3218
HALEX WOOLTON (M) SDN. BHD.—See Hextar Global Berhad; *Int'l*, pg. 3373
HARIA APPARELS LIMITED—See Haria Exports Limited; *Int'l*, pg. 3275
HONTEX INTERNATIONAL HOLDINGS CO., LTD.; *Int'l*, pg. 3472
HORNWOOD INC.; *U.S. Private*, pg. 1984
ICONIX CHINA LIMITED—See Iconix Acquisition LLC; *U.S. Private*, pg. 2033
JIANGYIN FUHUI TEXTILES LIMITED—See Fountain Set (Holdings) Limited; *Int'l*, pg. 2754
KLAUBER BROTHERS INC.; *U.S. Private*, pg. 2318
LACE LASTIC COMPANY; *U.S. Private*, pg. 2371
LAKE SIDE PRINTING FACTORY LIMITED—See Fountain Set (Holdings) Limited; *Int'l*, pg. 2754
LORRAINE LINENS INC.; *U.S. Private*, pg. 2496
MCMURRAY FABRICS INC.; *U.S. Private*, pg. 2643
OCEAN LANKA (PRIVATE) LIMITED—See Fountain Set (Holdings) Limited; *Int'l*, pg. 2754
PLANTATION PATTERNS, LLC—See Sycamore Partners Management, LP; *U.S. Private*, pg. 3896
PROSPERLINK (MACAO COMMERCIAL OFFSHORE) LIMITED—See Fountain Set (Holdings) Limited; *Int'l*, pg. 2754
QUAKER LACE—See Lorraine Linens Inc.; *U.S. Private*, pg. 2496
RAVAL LACE DIVISION—See Fab Industries Corp.; *U.S. Private*, pg. 1458
SOMERSET INDUSTRIES INC.; *U.S. Private*, pg. 3712
YANCHENG FUHUI TEXTILES LIMITED—See Fountain Set (Holdings) Limited; *Int'l*, pg. 2754
YUNSA YUNLU SANAYI VE TICARET A.S.—See Haci Omer Sabanci Holding A.S.; *Int'l*, pg. 3204

313310 — TEXTILE AND FABRIC FINISHING MILLS

5 B'S INC.; *U.S. Private*, pg. 15
AA WORLD CLASS CORP.; *U.S. Private*, pg. 30
ACENATURE BIOTECHNOLOGY CO., LTD.—See Acelon Chemicals & Fiber Corporation; *Int'l*, pg. 98
ADFA BLANKET COMPANY—See Al Abdullatif Industrial Investment Company; *Int'l*, pg. 275
AKM LACE AND EMBROTEX PRIVATE LIMITED; *Int'l*, pg. 264
AKRON TENT & AWNING CO.—See Ohio Awning & Manufacturing Co.; *U.S. Private*, pg. 3003
ALKA INDIA LIMITED; *Int'l*, pg. 330
ALLAWASAYA TEXTILE & FINISHING MILLS LTD.; *Int'l*, pg. 333
ALL STYLE APPAREL & ACTIVEWEAR; *U.S. Private*, pg. 173

ALLTEX INDUSTRIES LTD.; *Int'l*, pg. 360
THE ALMORE DYE HOUSE, INC.; *U.S. Private*, pg. 3984
AMBASSADOR INTRA HOLDINGS LTD.; *Int'l*, pg. 414
AMERBELLE TEXTILES, LLC; *U.S. Private*, pg. 219
AMERICAN APPAREL DYEING & FINISHING, INC.—See American Apparel, Inc.; *U.S. Private*, pg. 222
AMERICAN TEXTILE INDUSTRIES, LLC—See Monomoy Capital Partners LLC; *U.S. Private*, pg. 2772
ANGEL FIBERS LIMITED; *Int'l*, pg. 459
ANHUI HUAMAO TEXTILE COMPANY LIMITED; *Int'l*, pg. 468
ANHUI JINCHUN NONWOVEN CO., LTD.; *Int'l*, pg. 468
APEX (NANTONG) TEXTILE CO., LTD.—See De Licacy Industrial Co., Ltd.; *Int'l*, pg. 1996
ARCTIC CIRCLE ENTERPRISES INC.; *U.S. Private*, pg. 315
ARROW TEXTILES LTD.—See Delta Manufacturing Ltd; *Int'l*, pg. 2019
ASIA BRANDS BERHAD; *Int'l*, pg. 610
ASSOCIATED FABRICS CORPORATION; *U.S. Private*, pg. 355
AUBURN MANUFACTURING INC.; *U.S. Private*, pg. 385
AUTOLIV TEXTILES—See Autoliv, Inc.; *Int'l*, pg. 730
AVANTI LINENS, INC.; *U.S. Private*, pg. 404
A W HAINSWORTH & SONS LTD.; *Int'l*, pg. 18
AXITA COTTON LTD.; *Int'l*, pg. 770
AZTECHWB CO., LTD.; *Int'l*, pg. 781
BEN THANH TRADING & SERVICE JOINT STOCK COMPANY; *Int'l*, pg. 969
BEST TEXTILES ACQUISITION, LLC—See GHCL Limited; *Int'l*, pg. 2959
BIMATEX GMBH—See Dierig Holding AG; *Int'l*, pg. 2115
BINAYAK TEX PROCESSORS LIMITED; *Int'l*, pg. 1033
BIRLA CENTURY EXPORTS PRIVATE LIMITED—See Century Textiles and Industries Limited; *Int'l*, pg. 1419
BLUE CHIP TEX INDUSTRIES LTD.; *Int'l*, pg. 1067
BOMBAY RAYON FASHIONS LIMITED; *Int'l*, pg. 1104
BOSSA TICARET VE SANAYI ISLETMELERI TAS; *Int'l*, pg. 1117
BRAND & OPPENHEIMER CO., INC.—See Praesidian Capital Corp.; *U.S. Private*, pg. 3241
BRITTANY DYEING & PRINTING CORPORATION; *U.S. Private*, pg. 657
CARLISLE FINISHING, LLC—See Platinum Equity, LLC; *U.S. Private*, pg. 3203
CATEKS D.D.; *Int'l*, pg. 1359
CHAPMAN INNOVATIONS; *U.S. Private*, pg. 850
CHARGEURS FASHION TECHNOLOGIES—See Chargeurs SA; *Int'l*, pg. 1449
CHARGEURS NV; *Int'l*, pg. 1448
CHARGEURS WOOL (ARGENTINA) SA—See Chargeurs SA; *Int'l*, pg. 1449
CHARGEURS WOOL—See Chargeurs SA; *Int'l*, pg. 1449
CHIA HER INDUSTRIAL CO., LTD.; *Int'l*, pg. 1475
CHINA FIBRETECH LTD.; *Int'l*, pg. 1502
CHINA JISHAN HOLDINGS LIMITED; *Int'l*, pg. 1513
CHIRIPAL INDUSTRIES LTD.; *Int'l*, pg. 1573
CHRISTIAN DIERIG GMBH—See Dierig Holding AG; *Int'l*, pg. 2115
CIA DE TECIDOS DO NORTE DE MINAS - COTEMINAS; *Int'l*, pg. 1601
CIRCULAR KNIT DIVISION—See Fab Industries Corp.; *U.S. Private*, pg. 1458
CITIC GSI TOMIDA GROUP CO., LTD.—See CITIC Group Corporation; *Int'l*, pg. 1620
CITIC GSI TOMIDA GROUP CO., LTD.—See GSI Creos Corporation; *Int'l*, pg. 3144
CLOTHING PLUS ZHEJIANG LTD.—See Jabil Inc.; *U.S. Public*, pg. 1180
COMPANHIA INDUSTRIAL CATAGUASES; *Int'l*, pg. 1747
COMPANIA UNIVERSAL TEXTIL S.A.—See Grupo Romero; *Int'l*, pg. 3134
COMPOSITE FABRICS OF AMERICA LLC—See Schneider Mills, Inc.; *U.S. Private*, pg. 3567
CO-PROSPERITY HOLDINGS LIMITED; *Int'l*, pg. 1679
COTEMINAS COMPANHIA DE TECIDOS NORTE DE MINAS; *Int'l*, pg. 1817
CRANSTON PRINT WORKS COMPANY; *U.S. Private*, pg. 1086
CRYPTON LLC—See W.R. Berkley Corporation; *U.S. Public*, pg. 2317
CUTTING EDGE TEXSTYLES, LLC—See Praesidian Capital Corp.; *U.S. Private*, pg. 3241
DAIWABO SPINTEC CO., LTD.—See Daiwabo Holdings Co., Ltd.; *Int'l*, pg. 1949
DAMARTEX SA; *Int'l*, pg. 1955
DAMART—See Damartex SA; *Int'l*, pg. 1955
DCM TEXTILES LIMITED—See DCM Limited; *Int'l*, pg. 1992
DE LICACY INDUSTRIAL CO., LTD.; *Int'l*, pg. 1996
DEWAN MUSHTAQ TEXTILE MILLS LIMITED—See Dewan Farooque Motors Limited; *Int'l*, pg. 2091
DHANLAXMI FABRICS LTD.; *Int'l*, pg. 2098
DIERIG HOLDING AG; *Int'l*, pg. 2115
DONGGUAN HONMYUE TEXTILE LIMITED—See Honmyue Enterprise Co., Ltd.; *Int'l*, pg. 3472
DONGGUAN SHATIN LAKE SIDE TEXTILES PRINTING & DYEING CO., LTD.—See Fountain Set (Holdings) Limited; *Int'l*, pg. 2754

313310 — TEXTILE AND FABRIC ...

DUPONT SINGAPORE PTE. LTD.—See Corteva, Inc.; *U.S. Public*, pg. 584
DURO INDUSTRIES INC.; *U.S. Private*, pg. 1293
EASTERN TEXTILE COMPANY—See Al Abdullatif Industrial Investment Company; *Int'l*, pg. 275
ECLAT TEXTILE CO., LTD.; *Int'l*, pg. 2291
ENSURE GLOBAL CORP. LTD.; *Int'l*, pg. 2449
ERVINS GROUP, LLC—See Acme Mills Co. Inc.; *U.S. Private*, pg. 61
EUROFINS MODERN TESTING SERVICES BANGLADESH LIMITED—See Eurofins Scientific S.E.; *Int'l*, pg. 2546
EUROFINS MTS CONSUMER PRODUCT TESTING (HONG KONG) CO., LTD.—See Eurofins Scientific S.E.; *Int'l*, pg. 2545
EVEREST TEXTILE (SHANGHAI), LTD.—See Everest Textile Co., Ltd.; *Int'l*, pg. 2565
EVERLON FINANCIALS LTD.; *Int'l*, pg. 2568
EVINCE TEXTILES LTD.; *Int'l*, pg. 2570
FABRICUT INC.; *U.S. Private*, pg. 1459
FABRI-QUILT, INC.; *U.S. Private*, pg. 1458
FATEH TEXTILE MILLS LIMITED; *Int'l*, pg. 2622
FELLFAB LIMITED; *Int'l*, pg. 2633
FENDRICH INDUSTRIES INC.; *U.S. Private*, pg. 1494
FINETEX ENE, INC. - ROSARIO PLANT—See Finetex EnE, Inc.; *Int'l*, pg. 2674
F.N.C. TEXTILES INC.—See Carolace Embroidery Co., Inc.; *U.S. Private*, pg. 767
FRANCO MANUFACTURING CO. INC.; *U.S. Private*, pg. 1593
GABRIEL NORTH AMERICA INC.—See Gabriel Holding A/S; *Int'l*, pg. 2867
GALLS, LLC—See Charlesbank Capital Partners, LLC; *U.S. Private*, pg. 855
GANSU ENGINEERING CONSULTING GROUP CO., LTD.; *Int'l*, pg. 2881
GENTILI MOSCONI S.P.A.; *Int'l*, pg. 2928
GERLI & CO., INC.; *U.S. Private*, pg. 1686
GETALONG ENTERPRISE LIMITED; *Int'l*, pg. 2947
G-III APPAREL GROUP, LTD.; *U.S. Public*, pg. 893
GIOVANNI BOZZETTO S.P.A.—See Aimia Inc.; *Int'l*, pg. 233
GIRMES INTERNATIONAL GMBH; *Int'l*, pg. 2979
GLEN RAVEN CUSTOM FABRICS, LLC - ANDERSON PLANT—See Glen Raven, Inc.; *U.S. Private*, pg. 1709
GLEN RAVEN CUSTOM FABRICS, LLC - NORLINA PLANT—See Glen Raven, Inc.; *U.S. Private*, pg. 1709
GLEN RAVEN CUSTOM FABRICS, LLC - PLANT ONE—See Glen Raven, Inc.; *U.S. Private*, pg. 1709
GLEN RAVEN, INC.—See Glen Raven, Inc.; *U.S. Private*, pg. 1709
GLEN RAVEN, INC.—See Glen Raven, Inc.; *U.S. Private*, pg. 1709
GLEN RAVEN TECHNICAL FABRICS, LLC - PARK AVENUE FACILITY—See Glen Raven, Inc.; *U.S. Private*, pg. 1709
GSG GROUP INC.; *Int'l*, pg. 3144
GSI CREOS CORPORATION; *Int'l*, pg. 3144
GSI EUROPE-IMPORT & EXPORT GMBH—See GSI Creos Corporation; *Int'l*, pg. 3144
GSI HOLDING CORPORATION—See GSI Creos Corporation; *Int'l*, pg. 3144
GTM USA CORP.—See Gul Ahmed Textile Mills Ltd.; *Int'l*, pg. 3178
GUILFORD FRANCE—See Lear Corporation; *U.S. Public*, pg. 1297
GUILFORD MILLS - AUTOMOTIVE & UPHOLSTERY FABRICS—See Lear Corporation; *U.S. Public*, pg. 1297
GUILFORD MILLS EUROPE LIMITED—See Lear Corporation; *U.S. Public*, pg. 1297
GUILFORD MILLS, INC.—See Lear Corporation; *U.S. Public*, pg. 1297
GUL AHMED INTERNATIONAL LIMITED FZC—See Gul Ahmed Textile Mills Ltd.; *Int'l*, pg. 3178
HAMID FABRICS LTD.; *Int'l*, pg. 3237
HAMPSHIRE GROUP LIMITED; *U.S. Private*, pg. 1851
HANES BODYWEAR GERMANY GMBH—See Hanesbrands Inc.; *U.S. Public*, pg. 983
HANES COMPANIES, INC.—See Leggett & Platt, Incorporated; *U.S. Public*, pg. 1302
HANES COMPANIES - NEW JERSEY, LLC—See Leggett & Platt, Incorporated; *U.S. Public*, pg. 1302
HANES GEO COMPONENTS—See Leggett & Platt, Incorporated; *U.S. Public*, pg. 1302
HARYANA TEXPRINTS (OVERSEAS) LTD.; *Int'l*, pg. 3282
HAYLEYS FABRIC PLC; *Int'l*, pg. 3291
HCH. KETTELHACK GMBH & CO. KG; *Int'l*, pg. 3297
HEALTHCARE LINEN SERVICES GROUP—See York Capital Management Global Advisors, LLC; *U.S. Private*, pg. 4590
HEIQ AEONIQ GMBH—See HeiQ Plc; *Int'l*, pg. 3326
HEIQ CHEMTEX INC.—See HeiQ Plc; *Int'l*, pg. 3326
HEIQ (CHINA) MATERIAL TECH LTD.—See HeiQ Plc; *Int'l*, pg. 3326
HEIQ COMPANY LIMITED—See HeiQ Plc; *Int'l*, pg. 3326
HONMYUE ENTERPRISE (ZHEJIANG) CO., LTD.—See Honmyue Enterprise Co., Ltd.; *Int'l*, pg. 3472
HOWA CORPORATION; *Int'l*, pg. 3492
HUAFANG CO., LTD.; *Int'l*, pg. 3511
HUAJIN (HONG KONG) LIMITED—See Huayou Cobalt Co., Ltd.; *Int'l*, pg. 3516

HUNTER DOUGLAS BELGIUM N.V. - HELIOSCREEN FABRICS DIVISION—See 3G Capital Partners L.P.; *U.S. Private*, pg. 11
HUYCK.WANGNER UK LTD.—See ANDRITZ AG; *Int'l*, pg. 457
HYOSUNG BRASIL INDUSTRIA E COMERCIO DE FIBRAS LTDA.—See Hyosung TNC Co. Ltd.; *Int'l*, pg. 3552
HYOSUNG INDIA PVT. LTD.—See Hyosung TNC Co. Ltd.; *Int'l*, pg. 3552
HYOSUNG INTERNATIONAL TRADE (JIAXING) CO., LTD.—See Hyosung Corporation; *Int'l*, pg. 3551
HYOSUNG JAPAN—See Hyosung Corporation; *Int'l*, pg. 3551
HYOSUNG MEXICO CITY S.A. DE C.V.—See Hyosung TNC Co. Ltd.; *Int'l*, pg. 3552
HYOSUNG NEW MATERIAL & HIGHTECH (QUZHOU) CO., LTD.—See Hyosung TNC Co. Ltd.; *Int'l*, pg. 3552
HYOSUNG SPANDEX (QUZHOU) CO., LTD.—See Hyosung TNC Co. Ltd.; *Int'l*, pg. 3552
HYOSUNG SPANDEX (ZHUHAI) CO., LTD.—See Hyosung TNC Co. Ltd.; *Int'l*, pg. 3552
HYOSUNG TNC (TAIWAN) CORPORATION—See Hyosung TNC Co. Ltd.; *Int'l*, pg. 3552
IBRAHIM FIBRES LIMITED; *Int'l*, pg. 3576
IFG ASOTA GMBH—See Duc Long Gia Lai Group JSC; *Int'l*, pg. 2222
IFG EXELTO NV—See Duc Long Gia Lai Group JSC; *Int'l*, pg. 2222
IFL ENTERPRISES LTD.; *Int'l*, pg. 3599
ISOLIERERZEUGNISSE GROSSROHRSDORF GMBH—See Dortmunder Gussasphalt GmbH & Co. KG; *Int'l*, pg. 2180
JANLYNN CORPORATION; *U.S. Private*, pg. 2187
JASON PARTNERS HOLDINGS INC.—See Jason Industries, Inc.; *U.S. Private*, pg. 2190
JEONSANTEX CO., LTD.—See Chonbang Co., Ltd.; *Int'l*, pg. 1578
KENYON INDUSTRIES, INC.—See Hallwood Group, LLC; *U.S. Private*, pg. 1845
KITAN INDUSTRIES LTD.—See Access Industries, Inc.; *U.S. Private*, pg. 51
KUNSHAN STAFLEX TEXTILE CO., LTD. - JIANGSU FACTORY—See Dynic Corporation; *Int'l*, pg. 2243
KUNSHAN STAFLEX TEXTILE CO., LTD.—See Dynic Corporation; *Int'l*, pg. 2243
LANAS TRINIDAD SA—See Chargeurs SA; *Int'l*, pg. 1450
LIFE MATERIAL TECHNOLOGIES LIMITED—See HeiQ Plc; *Int'l*, pg. 3326
LION BROTHERS COMPANY, INC.—See Avery Dennison Corporation; *U.S. Public*, pg. 244
MAFATLAL INDUSTRIES LIMITED—See Arvind Mafatlal Group; *Int'l*, pg. 587
MANDHANA INDUSTRIES LIMITED - MANDHANA DYEING DIVISION—See GB Global Limited; *Int'l*, pg. 2892
MANDHANA INDUSTRIES LIMITED - MANDHANA DYEING UNIT-II—See GB Global Limited; *Int'l*, pg. 2892
MARY ANN INDUSTRIES INC.—See Leggett & Platt, Incorporated; *U.S. Public*, pg. 1303
MEDIKE, INC.; *U.S. Private*, pg. 2656
MODERN TESTING SERVICES (INDIA) PRIVATE LIMITED—See Eurofins Scientific S.E.; *Int'l*, pg. 2551
MODERN TESTING SERVICES (VIETNAM) CO., LTD.—See Eurofins Scientific S.E.; *Int'l*, pg. 2551
MONSANTO DEUTSCHLAND GMBH—See Bayer Aktiengesellschaft; *Int'l*, pg. 909
MONTEBELLO SRL—See Azgard Nine Limited; *Int'l*, pg. 778
MOORE COMPANY; *U.S. Private*, pg. 2779
OHIO AWNING COMPANY—See Ohio Awning & Manufacturing Co.; *U.S. Private*, pg. 3003
OJI FIBER CO., LTD.—See Daiwabo Holdings Co., Ltd.; *Int'l*, pg. 1949
OSBORN LIPPERT PVT. LTD.—See Jason Industries, Inc.; *U.S. Private*, pg. 2190
OWENS CORNING JAPAN LLC—See Owens Corning; *U.S. Public*, pg. 1628
PACIFIC CONTINENTAL TEXTILE, INC.—See Edmund Kim International Inc.; *U.S. Public*, pg. 1338
PALLAS TEXTILES—See Krueger International, Inc.; *U.S. Private*, pg. 2353
PEACE TEXTILE AMERICA INC.; *U.S. Private*, pg. 3122
THE PENN COMPANIES; *U.S. Private*, pg. 4092
PINNACLE TEXTILE INDUSTRIES, LLC; *U.S. Private*, pg. 3186
P.T. PRIMATEXCO INDONESIA—See Daiwabo Holdings Co., Ltd.; *Int'l*, pg. 1950
ROCKLAND INDUSTRIES, INC.; *U.S. Private*, pg. 3467
ROGERS B.V.B.A.—See Rogers Corporation; *U.S. Public*, pg. 1808
RONILE, INC.; *U.S. Private*, pg. 3478
RUSSELL CORPORATION—See Berkshire Hathaway Inc.; *U.S. Public*, pg. 305
SAINT-GOBAIN ADFORS FRANCE—See Compagnie de Saint-Gobain SA; *Int'l*, pg. 1735
SANTEE PRINT WORKS, INC.; *U.S. Private*, pg. 3548
SHASING SHAPHENG PRINTING & DYEING CO., LTD.—See Co-Prosperity Holdings Limited; *Int'l*, pg. 1680

SINA PEARSON TEXTILES, INC.—See Momentum Textiles Inc.; *U.S. Private*, pg. 2768
SLATER DYE WORKS INC.; *U.S. Private*, pg. 3687
STARENSIER INC.; *U.S. Private*, pg. 3786
SUNSPORTS, INC.; *U.S. Private*, pg. 3873
TDF, INC.—See Fluor Corporation; *U.S. Public*, pg. 859
TRIMIL S.A—See Giorgio Armani S.p.A.; *Int'l*, pg. 2978
T-SHIRT INTERNATIONAL INC.; *U.S. Private*, pg. 3911
T SHIRT PRINTERS PTY LIMITED—See Live Nation Entertainment, Inc.; *U.S. Public*, pg. 1331
UAB FURNMASTER—See Gabriel Holding A/S; *Int'l*, pg. 2867
UNIFI, INC.; *U.S. Public*, pg. 2226
UNIVERSAL DYEING & PRINTING, INC.; *U.S. Private*, pg. 4304
VISION LINENS LIMITED—See Icahn Enterprises L.P.; *U.S. Public*, pg. 1085
VITRULAN COMPOSITES OY—See ADCURAM Group AG; *Int'l*, pg. 128
VOYAGER EMBLEMS, INC.—See Grant Emblems Limited; *Int'l*, pg. 3059
WOLFE DYE & BLEACH WORKS INC.; *U.S. Private*, pg. 4554
XTRA TEXTIL, S.A. DE C.V.—See Grupo Xtra S.A. de C.V.; *Int'l*, pg. 3139
ZHEJIANG JISHAN PRINTING & DYEING CO., LTD.—See China Jishan Holdings Limited; *Int'l*, pg. 1513

313320 — FABRIC COATING MILLS

3M CZECH REPUBLIC—See 3M Company; *U.S. Public*, pg. 5
3M PAKISTAN (PVT) LTD.—See 3M Company; *U.S. Public*, pg. 6
3M POLAND SP. Z.O.O.—See 3M Company; *U.S. Public*, pg. 6
ABERDEEN ROAD COMPANY; *U.S. Private*, pg. 38
ADELL PLASTICS INC.; *U.S. Private*, pg. 77
ALPHA ASSOCIATES, INC.; *U.S. Private*, pg. 196
ANDRITZ KUFFERATH S.R.O.—See ANDRITZ AG; *Int'l*, pg. 454
ANGLO-DANISH FIBRE INDUSTRIES LTD—See Freudenberg SE; *Int'l*, pg. 2789
ANSELL LIMITED; *Int'l*, pg. 478
AOC, LLC—See The Alpha Corporation of Tennessee; *U.S. Private*, pg. 3984
BASF CONSTRUCTION CHEMICALS UK—See BASF SE; *Int'l*, pg. 874
BFS DIVERSIFIED PRODUCTS, LLC—See Bridgestone Corporation; *Int'l*, pg. 1156
BONAR YARNS & FABRICS LIMITED—See Freudenberg SE; *Int'l*, pg. 2789
BONDCOTE PERFORMANCE TEXTILES, LLC.—See XFS Global LLC; *U.S. Private*, pg. 4581
BRADFORD INDUSTRIES, INC.—See Wembly Enterprises LLC; *U.S. Private*, pg. 4480
BRUIN PLASTICS COMPANY, INC.; *U.S. Private*, pg. 671
CHANG-HO FIBRE CORPORATION; *Int'l*, pg. 1441
CHARGEURS FABRICS—See Chargeurs SA; *Int'l*, pg. 1449
CHARGEURS INTERLINING—See Chargeurs SA; *Int'l*, pg. 1449
CHERNG TAY TECHNOLOGY (INDIA) PRIVATE LIMITED—See Cherng Tay Technology Co., Ltd.; *Int'l*, pg. 1471
CLOISTER HOTEL—See Sea Island Company; *U.S. Private*, pg. 3582
COLBOND BV—See Freudenberg SE; *Int'l*, pg. 2789
DEITSCH PLASTICS COMPANY; *U.S. Private*, pg. 1192
DUKSUNG CO., LTD. - INCHEON FACTORY—See Duksung Co., Ltd.; *Int'l*, pg. 2224
DUKSUNG CO., LTD. - OSAN FACTORY—See Duksung Co., Ltd.; *Int'l*, pg. 2224
DUKSUNG CO., LTD. - PYEONGTAEK FACTORY—See Duksung Co., Ltd.; *Int'l*, pg. 2224
DUKSUNG CO., LTD.; *Int'l*, pg. 2224
DURO-LAST ROOFING, INC.; *U.S. Private*, pg. 1293
FERLAND INDUSTRIES INC.; *U.S. Private*, pg. 1497
FUJICHEMI KINKI CO., LTD.—See Fujikura Kasei Co., Ltd.; *Int'l*, pg. 2826
FUJICHEMI TOKYO CO., LTD.—See Fujikura Kasei Co., Ltd.; *Int'l*, pg. 2826
GREAT LAKES FOAM TECHNOLOGIES, INC.—See Taglich Private Equity LLC; *U.S. Private*, pg. 3922
THE HAARTZ CORPORATION - BLOOMFIELD HILLS—See The Haartz Corporation; *U.S. Private*, pg. 4041
THE HAARTZ CORPORATION; *U.S. Private*, pg. 4041
HENKEL CHEMBOND SURFACE TECHNOLOGIES LTD.—See Henkel AG & Co. KGaA; *Int'l*, pg. 3350
HERCON ENVIRONMENTAL CORPORATION—See Aberdeen Road Company; *U.S. Private*, pg. 38
HERCULITE PRODUCTS, INC.—See Aberdeen Road Company; *U.S. Private*, pg. 38
HYOSUNG TAEGU BUSINESS CENTER—See Hyosung Corporation; *Int'l*, pg. 3551
LAMINATING SERVICES INC.; *U.S. Private*, pg. 2380
MARLEN TEXTILES INC.—See Arsenal Capital Manage-

N.A.I.C.S. INDEX

314120 — CURTAIN AND LINEN M...

ment LP; *U.S. Private*, pg. 338
MEHLER TEXNOLOGIES GMBH—See Freudenberg SE; *Int'l*, pg. 2789
MEHLER TEXNOLOGIES INC—See Freudenberg SE; *Int'l*, pg. 2789
MEHLER TEXNOLOGIES LTD.—See Freudenberg SE; *Int'l*, pg. 2789
MEHLER TEXNOLOGIES S.A.R.L.—See Freudenberg SE; *Int'l*, pg. 2789
MEHLER TEXNOLOGIES S.I.A—See Freudenberg SE; *Int'l*, pg. 2789
MEHLER TEXNOLOGIES S.R.L—See Freudenberg SE; *Int'l*, pg. 2789
MEHLER TEXNOLOGIES S.R.O—See Freudenberg SE; *Int'l*, pg. 2789
OUTDRY TECHNOLOGIES S.R.L.—See Columbia Sportswear Company; *U.S. Public*, pg. 535
OXFORD INDUSTRIES, INC.; *U.S. Public*, pg. 1629
PARAMOUNT METALIZING DIV.—See Koller Enterprises, Inc.; *U.S. Private*, pg. 2341
PITCHMASTIC PMB LIMITED—See RPM International Inc.; *U.S. Public*, pg. 1817
PLASTATECH ENGINEERING LTD.; *U.S. Private*, pg. 3198
PRECISION TEXTILES LLC—See Chargeurs SA; *Int'l*, pg. 1449
PT CHERNG TAY INDONESIA—See Cherng Tay Technology Co., Ltd.; *Int'l*, pg. 1471
R.H. WYNER ASSOCIATES INC.; *U.S. Private*, pg. 3336
SAINT-GOBAIN PERFORMANCE PLASTICS CORPORATION—See Compagnie de Saint-Gobain SA; *Int'l*, pg. 1731
SAINT-GOBAIN PERFORMANCE PLASTICS IRELAND LTD—See Compagnie de Saint-Gobain SA; *Int'l*, pg. 1732
SENFA SAS—See Chargeurs SA; *Int'l*, pg. 1450
SWIFT TEXTILE METALIZING LLC—See Arcline Investment Management LP; *U.S. Private*, pg. 314
THANH THAI VIET NAM INDUSTRY TECHNOLOGY COMPANY LIMITED—See Cherng Tay Technology Co., Ltd.; *Int'l*, pg. 1471
TOMMY BAHAMA GLOBAL SOURCING LIMITED—See Oxford Industries, Inc.; *U.S. Public*, pg. 1629
TONOGA INC.; *U.S. Private*, pg. 4185
UNIROYAL ENGINEERED PRODUCTS, LLC—See Uniroyal Global Engineered Products, Inc.; *U.S. Public*, pg. 2228
UNIROYAL GLOBAL LIMITED—See Uniroyal Global Engineered Products, Inc.; *U.S. Public*, pg. 2228
VERSEIDAG-INDUTEX GMBH—See Gilde Buy Out Partners B.V.; *Int'l*, pg. 2974
VIETNAM CHERNG TAY TECHNOLOGY CO., LTD.—See Cherng Tay Technology Co., Ltd.; *Int'l*, pg. 1471
WATER-TITE COMPANY, LLC—See Installed Building Products, Inc.; *U.S. Public*, pg. 1134

314110 — CARPET AND RUG MILLS

AL ABDULLATIF INDUSTRIAL INVESTMENT COMPANY; *Int'l*, pg. 275
AL SORAYAI GROUP; *Int'l*, pg. 283
ANKER-TEPPICHBODEN GEBRUDER SCHOELLER GMBH & CO. KG - AVIATION DIVISION—See ANKER-Teppichboden Gebruder Schoeller GmbH & Co. KG; *Int'l*, pg. 472
ANKER-TEPPICHBODEN GEBRUDER SCHOELLER GMBH & CO. KG; *Int'l*, pg. 472
ARAB WEAVERS UNION COMPANY P.L.C.; *Int'l*, pg. 532
ARGOS CARPETS & FLOORING; *Int'l*, pg. 563
ASTRO CARPET MILLS LLC—See Live Ventures Incorporated; *U.S. Public*, pg. 1332
AUTO CUSTOM CARPETS INC.; *U.S. Private*, pg. 397
AUTOV CORPORATION SDN. BHD.—See Globaltec Formation Berhad; *Int'l*, pg. 3004
AXPRO FRANCE S.A—See Axel Johnson Gruppen AB; *Int'l*, pg. 762
BACOVA GUILD, LTD.—See Ronile, Inc.; *U.S. Private*, pg. 3478
BALTA FLOORCOVERING YER DAS, EMELERI SAN.VE TIC A.S.—See Balta Group NV; *Int'l*, pg. 811
BARRINGTON CARPETS INC.—See Argand Partners, LP; *U.S. Private*, pg. 319
BEAULIEU CANADA—See Beaulieu Group, LLC; *U.S. Private*, pg. 508
BEAULIEU GROUP, LLC; *U.S. Private*, pg. 508
BEAULIEU OF AUSTRALIA PTY LTD—See Beaulieu International Group NV; *Int'l*, pg. 934
BENTLEY PRINCE STREET, INC.—See Dominus Capital, L.P.; *U.S. Private*, pg. 1256
BETTER BACKERS INC.; *U.S. Private*, pg. 546
BIOKARPET ROMANIA S.R.L.—See Biokarpet S.A.; *Int'l*, pg. 1038
BIURO FORBO FLOORING POLAND—See Forbo Holding Ltd.; *Int'l*, pg. 2729
BLOOMSBURG CARPET INDUSTRIES INC.; *U.S. Private*, pg. 584
BLUE RIDGE ACQUISITION CO. LLC; *U.S. Private*, pg. 591
B&M NV—See Mohawk Industries, Inc.; *U.S. Public*, pg. 1457
BREMWORTH CARPETS AND RUGS LIMITED—See Bremworth Limited; *Int'l*, pg. 1145
BREMWORTH LIMITED; *Int'l*, pg. 1145
BRINTONS CARPETS ASIA PVT LTD.—See Argand Partners, LP; *U.S. Private*, pg. 319
BRINTONS CARPETS LIMITED—See Argand Partners, LP; *U.S. Private*, pg. 319
BRINTONS FRANCE S.A.R.L.—See Argand Partners, LP; *U.S. Private*, pg. 319
BRINTONS INDUSTRIA DE ALCATIFAS LDA.—See Argand Partners, LP; *U.S. Private*, pg. 319
BRINTONS PTY LTD—See Argand Partners, LP; *U.S. Private*, pg. 319
BRINTONS U.S. AXMINSTER, INC.—See Argand Partners, LP; *U.S. Private*, pg. 319
CAPEL INC.; *U.S. Private*, pg. 738
CAVALIER BREMWORTH LIMITED—See Bremworth Limited; *Int'l*, pg. 1145
CAVALIER BREMWORTH PTY. LIMITED—See Bremworth Limited; *Int'l*, pg. 1145
COCREATION GRASS CO., LTD.; *Int'l*, pg. 1687
CONTROLLED PRODUCTS, LLC—See Sentinel Capital Partners, L.L.C.; *U.S. Private*, pg. 3609
COURISTAN INC.; *U.S. Private*, pg. 1068
CROWN MATTING TECHNOLOGIES—See Ludlow Composites Corporation; *U.S. Private*, pg. 2512
DECOTEX JSC; *Int'l*, pg. 2001
THE DIXIE GROUP, INC.; *U.S. Public*, pg. 2067
DURA UNDERCUSHIONS LTD.; *Int'l*, pg. 2228
E&E CO., LTD.; *U.S. Private*, pg. 1301
EGETAEPPER A/S; *Int'l*, pg. 2324
ENGINEERED FLOORS, LLC; *U.S. Private*, pg. 1398
FABRICA INTERNATIONAL, INC.—See The Dixie Group, Inc.; *U.S. Public*, pg. 2067
FATES A.D.; *Int'l*, pg. 2622
FELTEX CARPETS LTD.—See Mohawk Industries, Inc.; *U.S. Public*, pg. 1457
FELTEX CARPETS PTY. LTD.—See Mohawk Industries, Inc.; *U.S. Public*, pg. 1457
FORBO FLOORING B.V.—See Forbo Holding Ltd.; *Int'l*, pg. 2729
FORBO FLOORING—See Forbo Holding Ltd.; *Int'l*, pg. 2730
FORBO FLOORING UK LTD.—See Forbo Holding Ltd.; *Int'l*, pg. 2729
FORBO SIEGLING (SHENYANG) BELTING CO. LTD—See Forbo Holding Ltd.; *Int'l*, pg. 2730
FORBO SIEGLING (SHENYANG)—See Forbo Holding Ltd.; *Int'l*, pg. 2730
GLOBAL TEXTILE SERVICES LLC; *U.S. Private*, pg. 1718
GODFREY HIRST AUSTRALIA PTY. LTD.—See Mohawk Industries, Inc.; *U.S. Public*, pg. 1457
GOLDEN CARPETS LIMITED; *Int'l*, pg. 3028
GULISTAN CARPET INC.; *U.S. Private*, pg. 1817
HOKANSON, INC.—See Scott Group Custom Carpets, Inc.; *U.S. Private*, pg. 3577
HYOSUNG ADVANCED MATERIALS CO., LTD.; *Int'l*, pg. 3550
INDIAN SUMMER CARPET MILLS, INC.; *U.S. Private*, pg. 2061
INTERFACE AMERICAS, INC.—See Interface, Inc.; *U.S. Public*, pg. 1144
INTERFACE EUROPE, LTD.—See Interface, Inc.; *U.S. Public*, pg. 1144
INTERFACE INTERNATIONAL B.V.—See Interface, Inc.; *U.S. Public*, pg. 1144
J&J FLOORING GROUP, LLC—See Engineered Floors, LLC; *U.S. Private*, pg. 1398
KIMBERLEY CARPETS PTY LIMITED—See Bremworth Limited; *Int'l*, pg. 1145
KLEEN-TEX DO BRAZIL—See Kleen-Tex Industries, Inc.; *U.S. Private*, pg. 2318
KLEEN-TEX INDUSTRIES GMBH—See Kleen-Tex Industries, Inc.; *U.S. Private*, pg. 2318
KLEEN-TEX INDUSTRIES, INC.; *U.S. Private*, pg. 2318
KLEEN-TEX INDUSTRIES LTD.—See Kleen-Tex Industries, Inc.; *U.S. Private*, pg. 2318
KLEEN-TEX JAPAN, INC.—See Kleen-Tex Industries, Inc.; *U.S. Private*, pg. 2318
KLEEN-TEX POLSKA, SP. Z.O.O.—See Kleen-Tex Industries, Inc.; *U.S. Private*, pg. 2318
KRAUS CARPET MILLS LIMITED—See Hilco Trading, LLC; *U.S. Private*, pg. 1944
LIMITED EDITION INC.—See Bon Fame Co., Ltd.; *Int'l*, pg. 1105
L&P SPRINGS DENMARK A/S—See Leggett & Platt, Incorporated; *U.S. Public*, pg. 1302
MANNINGTON CARPETS—See Mannington Mills, Inc.; *U.S. Private*, pg. 2566
MANUFACTURERS CHEMICALS, LLC—See Ascent Industries Co.; *U.S. Public*, pg. 210
MAPLES INDUSTRIES INC.; *U.S. Private*, pg. 2568
MASLAND CARPETS—See The Dixie Group, Inc.; *U.S. Public*, pg. 2067
THE MILLENNIUM MAT COMPANY, LLC—See Cintas Corporation; *U.S. Public*, pg. 496
MILLIKEN (AUSTRALIA) P/L—See Milliken & Company; *Int'l*, pg. 2737
MODULYSS NV—See Balta Group NV; *Int'l*, pg. 812
MOHAWK HOME—See Mohawk Industries, Inc.; *U.S. Public*, pg. 1458
MOHAWK INDUSTRIES, INC. - DALTON—See Mohawk Industries, Inc.; *U.S. Public*, pg. 1458
MOHAWK INDUSTRIES, INC.; *U.S. Public*, pg. 1457
MOHAWK UNILIN INTERNATIONAL BV—See Mohawk Industries, Inc.; *U.S. Public*, pg. 1458
MOUNTAIN RUG MILLS, INC.—See CAP Carpet, Inc.; *U.S. Private*, pg. 737
MOUNTVILLE MILLS CANADA—See Mountville Mills Inc.; *U.S. Private*, pg. 2801
MOUNTVILLE MILLS INC.; *U.S. Private*, pg. 2801
MURRAY FABRICS, INC.; *U.S. Private*, pg. 2816
NORMAN ELLISON CARPETS LIMITED—See Bremworth Limited; *Int'l*, pg. 1145
NORMAN ELLISON CARPETS PTY LIMITED—See Bremworth Limited; *Int'l*, pg. 1145
NPC SOUTH INC.—See Natco Products Corporation; *U.S. Private*, pg. 2838
ONTERA MODULAR CARPETS PTY LIMITED—See Bremworth Limited; *Int'l*, pg. 1145
PERSIKA SA—See Biokarpet S.A.; *Int'l*, pg. 1038
PLAYFIELD INTERNATIONAL, INC.; *U.S. Private*, pg. 3212
POSTON OF DALTON INC.; *U.S. Private*, pg. 3235
QUALITY FINISHERS, INC.; *U.S. Private*, pg. 3319
RACEMARK INTERNATIONAL, LLC—See Racemark International, LP; *U.S. Private*, pg. 3341
RACEMARK INTERNATIONAL, LP; *U.S. Private*, pg. 3341
ROYALTY CARPET MILLS INC.; *U.S. Private*, pg. 3494
RUGS AMERICA CORPORATION; *U.S. Private*, pg. 3502
RYALUX CARPETS LIMITED—See AIREA PLC; *Int'l*, pg. 247
SCOTT GROUP CUSTOM CARPETS, INC.; *U.S. Private*, pg. 3577
SHAW INDUSTRIES GROUP, INC.—See Berkshire Hathaway Inc.; *U.S. Public*, pg. 316
SHAW INDUSTRIES GROUP—See Berkshire Hathaway Inc.; *U.S. Public*, pg. 316
SIEGLING NEDERLAND B.V.—See Forbo Holding Ltd.; *Int'l*, pg. 2730
SYNTEC INDUSTRIES INC.; *U.S. Private*, pg. 3904
TDG OPERATIONS, LLC—See The Dixie Group, Inc.; *U.S. Public*, pg. 2067
TERZA, S.A. DE C.V.—See ALFA, S.A.B. de C.V.; *Int'l*, pg. 314
TERZA, S.A. DE C.V.—See Berkshire Hathaway Inc.; *U.S. Public*, pg. 316

314120 — CURTAIN AND LINEN MILLS

1888 MILLS, LLC; *U.S. Private*, pg. 3
AHMEDAHLS AB—See Almedahls Oy; *Int'l*, pg. 363
AL-ABID SILK MILLS LIMITED; *Int'l*, pg. 284
ALMEDAHL-KINNA AB—See Almedahls Oy; *Int'l*, pg. 363
AMERICAN DECORATIVE FABRICS, LLC; *U.S. Private*, pg. 230
AMERICAN DRAPERY BLIND & CARPET, INC.; *U.S. Private*, pg. 230
AMERICAN MILLS INCORPORATED; *U.S. Private*, pg. 241
AMTEX; *Int'l*, pg. 442
ARDEN COMPANIES; *U.S. Private*, pg. 317
ARLEE HOME FASHIONS INC.; *U.S. Private*, pg. 326
ASCOT ENTERPRISES, INC.; *U.S. Private*, pg. 348
BARDWIL INDUSTRIES INC.; *U.S. Private*, pg. 474
BARTH & DREYFUSS OF CALIFORNIA INC.—See BDK Holdings, Inc.; *U.S. Private*, pg. 500
BLACK & DECKER DO BRASIL LTDA.—See Stanley Black & Decker, Inc.; *U.S. Public*, pg. 1936
BUETTNER S.A. INDUSTRIA E COMERCIO; *Int'l*, pg. 1211
CALEFFI - S.P.A.; *Int'l*, pg. 1263
CARPENTER CO. - MORNING GLORY PRODUCTS DIV.—See Carpenter Co.; *U.S. Private*, pg. 770
CASUAL ELEGANCE ENTERPRISES, INC.; *U.S. Private*, pg. 786
CC INDUSTRIES, INC.—See Henry Crown & Company; *U.S. Private*, pg. 1917
CROSCILL HOME—See Patriarch Partners, LLC; *U.S. Private*, pg. 3109
CROSCILL, INC.—See Patriarch Partners, LLC; *U.S. Private*, pg. 3109
DELTA TEXTILES NEW YORK LTD.—See GMM Capital LLC; *U.S. Private*, pg. 1722
DOWN-LITE PRODUCTS INC.; *U.S. Private*, pg. 1269
ENCOMPASS GROUP LLC - TECHSTYLES DIVISION—See Encompass Group LLC; *U.S. Private*, pg. 1390
ENCOMPASS GROUP LLC - THE PILLOW FACTORY DIVISION—See Encompass Group LLC; *U.S. Private*, pg. 1390
EX-CELL HOME FASHIONS INC.; *U.S. Private*, pg. 1444
FAZE THREE LIMITED - WORKS II—See Faze Three Limited; *Int'l*, pg. 2627
FOAM CRAFT, INC.—See Future Foam, Inc.; *U.S. Private*, pg. 1626
GHCL LIMITED; *Int'l*, pg. 2959
GIBUS SPA; *Int'l*, pg. 2963
HILDEN AMERICA, INC.; *U.S. Private*, pg. 1944

314120 — CURTAIN AND LINEN M...

HIRA TEXTILE MILLS LIMITED; *Int'l*, pg. 3402
HOLLANDER SLEEP PRODUCTS LLC—See Centre Lane Partners, LLC; *U.S. Private*, pg. 827
HUNTER DOUGLAS HOSPITALITY, INC—See 3G Capital Partners L.P.; *U.S. Private*, pg. 13
THE IRONEES COMPANY; *U.S. Private*, pg. 4057
JLA HOME, INC.—See E&E Co., Ltd.; *U.S. Private*, pg. 1301
JOSIE ACCESSORIES INC.; *U.S. Private*, pg. 2237
KLEAR-VU CORPORATION; *U.S. Private*, pg. 2318
LEE'S CURTAIN CO., INC.; *U.S. Private*, pg. 2414
LINCOLN TEXTILE PRODUCTS CO.; *U.S. Private*, pg. 2459
LOUIS HORNICK & CO. INC.; *U.S. Private*, pg. 2498
LOUIS M. GERSON CO. INC.; *U.S. Private*, pg. 2498
LOUISVILLE BEDDING COMPANY; *U.S. Private*, pg. 2500
MADISON INDUSTRIES INC.; *U.S. Private*, pg. 2543
MANUAL WOODWORKERS & WEAVERS, INC.; *U.S. Private*, pg. 2567
MANUFACTURERS DISCOUNT FURNITURE & BEDDING, INC.; *U.S. Private*, pg. 2567
MILLER CURTAIN CO., INC.; *U.S. Private*, pg. 2733
MOHICAN MILLS, INC.—See Fab Industries Corp.; *U.S. Private*, pg. 1458
MOUNT VERNON MILLS, INC., RIEGEL CONSUMER PRODUCTS DIV.—See R.B. Pamplin Corporation; *U.S. Private*, pg. 3334
ORA HOME LLC—See Idrees Textile Mills Limited; *Int'l*, pg. 3596
PACIFIC COAST FEATHER COMPANY—See Centre Lane Partners, LLC; *U.S. Private*, pg. 827
PACIFIC COAST FEATHER CUSHION CO.—See Centre Lane Partners, LLC; *U.S. Private*, pg. 827
PDK REGENCY HOME FASHIONS INC.; *U.S. Private*, pg. 3122
PINNACLE FRAMES & ACCENTS, INC.—See Newcastle Partners LP; *U.S. Private*, pg. 2914
PINNACLE FRAMES AND ACCENTS, INC.—See Newcastle Partners LP; *U.S. Private*, pg. 2914
PRIVA INC.—See Fiberlinks Textiles Inc.; *Int'l*, pg. 2652
RADER GMBH—See Bastei Lubbe AG; *Int'l*, pg. 888
RIMBO WARE AG—See Rena-Ware Distributors Inc.; *U.S. Private*, pg. 3397
R&M INDUSTRIES INC.; *U.S. Private*, pg. 3332
SATURDAY KNIGHT LTD.; *U.S. Private*, pg. 3553
SHIMIZU SHOJI CO., LTD.—See AEON Co., Ltd.; *Int'l*, pg. 178
S. LICHTENBERG & CO. INC.; *U.S. Private*, pg. 3515
STANDARD TEXTILE BVBA—See Standard Textile Co., Inc.; *U.S. Private*, pg. 3782
SULTAN & SONS INC.; *U.S. Private*, pg. 3852
TALON INTERNATIONAL, INC.; *U.S. Public*, pg. 1979
THOMAS WEST INC.; *U.S. Private*, pg. 4158
TOWN & COUNTRY LINEN CORP.—See H.I.G. Capital, LLC; *U.S. Private*, pg. 1832
TRIBORO QUILT MANUFACTURING CORP.—See Gerber Childrenswear LLC; *U.S. Private*, pg. 1686
VIRGINIA QUILTING INC.; *U.S. Private*, pg. 4388
WESTPOINT HOME LLC—See Icahn Enterprises L.P.; *U.S. Public*, pg. 1085
WHITING MANUFACTURING CO., INC.; *U.S. Private*, pg. 4512

314910 — TEXTILE BAG AND CANVAS MILLS

AADI INDUSTRIES LTD.; *Int'l*, pg. 31
AMERICAN BILTRITE—See American Biltrite Inc.; *U.S. Public*, pg. 97
ANCHOR INDUSTRIES, INC.; *U.S. Private*, pg. 273
BAGMASTERS—See CTA Manufacturing, Inc.; *U.S. Private*, pg. 1118
BIANCHI INTERNATIONAL INC.—See BAE Systems plc; *Int'l*, pg. 796
BLUEWATER DEFENSE, INC.; *U.S. Private*, pg. 598
BRIDGESTONE INDUSTRIAL LTD.—See Bridgestone Corporation; *Int'l*, pg. 1159
BYON CO., LTD.; *Int'l*, pg. 1235
CAPSTONE POLYWEAVE PRIVATE LIMITED—See Clearlake Capital Group, L.P.; *U.S. Private*, pg. 935
CAREFREE OF COLORADO—See Berkshire Hathaway Inc.; *U.S. Public*, pg. 300
CARVER INDUSTRIES, INC.—See Covercraft Direct, LLC; *U.S. Private*, pg. 1072
CHASE & SONS DIVISION—See KKR & Co. Inc.; *U.S. Public*, pg. 1242
C & H MEKONG COMPANY LIMITED—See Dream International Ltd; *Int'l*, pg. 2202
C & H TARPS CO., LTD.—See Dream International Ltd; *Int'l*, pg. 2202
C & H VINA JOINT STOCK COMPANY—See Dream International Ltd; *Int'l*, pg. 2202
COMMERCIAL SYN BAGS LIMITED; *Int'l*, pg. 1715
CONTINENTAL BAG CO. INC.—See Langston Companies, Inc.; *U.S. Private*, pg. 2390
COVERCRAFT INDUSTRIES INC.—See Audax Group, Limited Partnership; *U.S. Private*, pg. 387
C.R. DANIELS, INC.; *U.S. Private*, pg. 708
CTA MANUFACTURING, INC.; *U.S. Private*, pg. 1118
DECCAN POLYPACKS LIMITED; *Int'l*, pg. 1999
DIAMOND BRAND CANVAS PRODUCTS CO., INC.; *U.S. Private*, pg. 1222
DONOVAN ENTERPRISES; *U.S. Private*, pg. 1261
DOWCO, INC.—See Patrick Industries, Inc.; *U.S. Public*, pg. 1652
DURASOL AWNINGS, INC.—See BAT S.p.A.; *Int'l*, pg. 888
EMINENT LUGGAGE CORP.; *Int'l*, pg. 2381
EMMBI INDUSTRIES LIMITED; *Int'l*, pg. 2384
THE ERGO BABY CARRIER, INC.—See Compass Diversified Holdings; *U.S. Public*, pg. 560
ESTEX MANUFACTURING COMPANY; *U.S. Private*, pg. 1429
FILATEX FASHIONS LIMITED; *Int'l*, pg. 2662
FREUDENBERG IBERICA S.A.—See Freudenberg SE; *Int'l*, pg. 2787
GIOIA SAILS INC.; *U.S. Private*, pg. 1702
GRANITE GEAR, INC.—See BRZZ Gear LLC; *U.S. Private*, pg. 674
GREAT LAKES BOAT TOP, LLC—See Patrick Industries, Inc.; *U.S. Public*, pg. 1652
GUJARAT RAFFIA INDUSTRIES LIMITED; *Int'l*, pg. 3177
HCP PLASTENE BULKPACK LTD.; *Int'l*, pg. 3299
HI-PLAINS BAG & BAGGING CO. INC.—See Langston Companies, Inc.; *U.S. Private*, pg. 2390
HMT (XIAMEN) NEW TECHNICAL MATERIALS CO., LTD.; *Int'l*, pg. 3433
HTS (USA) INC.—See OMNIQ Corp.; *U.S. Public*, pg. 1600
ICON POLYMER GROUP, LTD.; *Int'l*, pg. 3586
JANDD MOUNTAINEERING, INC.; *U.S. Private*, pg. 2186
J&M INDUSTRIES INC.; *U.S. Private*, pg. 2154
JOANNE PLASTICS—See Burlington Basket Co.; *U.S. Private*, pg. 688
THE JOHN JOHNSON CO.; *U.S. Private*, pg. 4059
KENNETH FOX SUPPLY CO.; *U.S. Private*, pg. 2286
LAFUMA GROUP GMBH—See Calida Holding AG; *Int'l*, pg. 1264
LBU, INC.; *U.S. Private*, pg. 2403
MENARDI-CRISWELL—See Hosokawa Micron Corporation; *Int'l*, pg. 3486
MEYCO PRODUCTS INC.; *U.S. Private*, pg. 2692
MILLET—See Calida Holding AG; *Int'l*, pg. 1264
NYP, LLC—See Granite Creek Capital Partners, LLC; *U.S. Private*, pg. 1755
OHIO AWNING & MANUFACTURING CO.; *U.S. Private*, pg. 3003
OUTDOOR RESEARCH INCORPORATED; *U.S. Private*, pg. 3051
OUTDOOR VENTURE CORP.; *U.S. Private*, pg. 3051
POLYTEX FIBERS CORPORATION—See ZL Star Inc.; *U.S. Private*, pg. 4606
ROLL-RITE, LLC—See Genstar Capital, LLC; *U.S. Private*, pg. 1676
SHUR-CO, LLC; *U.S. Private*, pg. 3644
SPRINGS DE MEXICO, S.A. DE C.V.—See Coteminas Companhia de Tecidos Norte de Minas; *Int'l*, pg. 1817
SPRINGS DE MEXICO, S.A. DE C.V.—See Springs Global, Inc.; *U.S. Private*, pg. 3764
STONE GLACIER, INC.; *U.S. Private*, pg. 3818
TAYLOR MADE GROUP, LLC—See LCI Industries; *U.S. Public*, pg. 1295
TENPAL CO., LTD.—See Bunka Shutter Co., Ltd.; *Int'l*, pg. 1216
THOMPSON MACHINES—See Burlington Basket Co.; *U.S. Private*, pg. 689
TRIMACO LLC—See Trimaco LLC; *U.S. Private*, pg. 4232
VLISCO NETHERLANDS B.V.—See General Atlantic Service Company, L.P.; *U.S. Private*, pg. 1661
WEST PHARMACEUTICAL SERVICES CORNWALL LIMITED—See West Pharmaceutical Services, Inc.; *U.S. Public*, pg. 2353
WEST PHARMACEUTICAL SERVICES DE COLOMBIA, S.A.—See West Pharmaceutical Services, Inc.; *U.S. Public*, pg. 2353
WEST PHARMACEUTICAL SERVICES ESPANA, S.A.—See West Pharmaceutical Services, Inc.; *U.S. Public*, pg. 2353
WEST PHARMACEUTICAL SERVICES LIMITED DANMARK A/S—See West Pharmaceutical Services, Inc.; *U.S. Public*, pg. 2353
XYMID LLC; *U.S. Private*, pg. 4584

314994 — ROPE, CORDAGE, TWINE, TIRE CORD, AND TIRE FABRIC MILLS

ALGOMA NET COMPANY—See Gleason Corporation; *U.S. Private*, pg. 1708
ANCRA INTERNATIONAL LLC—See The Heico Companies, L.L.C.; *U.S. Private*, pg. 4050
ANGKASA AMSTEEL PTE LTD—See Daehan Steel Co., Ltd.; *Int'l*, pg. 1907
APPLIED FIBER MANUFACTURING, LLC; *U.S. Private*, pg. 298
ASHAWAY LINE & TWINE MFG. CO.; *U.S. Private*, pg. 349
BENECKE-KALIKO AG—See Continental Aktiengesellschaft; *Int'l*, pg. 1780
BERWIN GROUP LIMITED—See HEXPOL AB; *Int'l*, pg. 3371
BEXCO N.V.—See Exmar N.V.; *Int'l*, pg. 2585
BRIDON CORDAGE LLC—See Universal Cooperatives, Inc.; *U.S. Private*, pg. 4304
BROWNELL & COMPANY, INC.; *U.S. Private*, pg. 669
BURLAN CORPORATION; *U.S. Private*, pg. 688
CABLECO—See The Carpenter Group; *U.S. Private*, pg. 4005
CANADA CORDAGE, INC.; *Int'l*, pg. 1277
CARISTRAP INTERNATIONAL INC.; *Int'l*, pg. 1331
CLIMBTECH; *U.S. Private*, pg. 943
CONTINENTAL INDUSTRIAS DEL CAUCHO S.A.—See Continental Aktiengesellschaft; *Int'l*, pg. 1781
CONTINENTAL ITALIA S.P.A.—See Continental Aktiengesellschaft; *Int'l*, pg. 1782
CONTINENTAL SUISSE S A—See Continental Aktiengesellschaft; *Int'l*, pg. 1783
CONTITECH AGES S.P.A.—See Continental Aktiengesellschaft; *Int'l*, pg. 1781
CONTITECH HYCOP AB—See Continental Aktiengesellschaft; *Int'l*, pg. 1781
CORTLAND LINE COMPANY, INC.; *U.S. Private*, pg. 1061
DETROIT CHAIN PRODUCTS INC.—See The Commercial Group Lifting Products; *U.S. Private*, pg. 4011
DN TYRE & RUBBER PLC; *Int'l*, pg. 2147
DONAGHYS LIMITED; *Int'l*, pg. 2163
DSR CORP.; *Int'l*, pg. 2210
FIRESTONE FIBERS & TEXTILES-KINGS MOUNTAIN—See Bridgestone Corporation; *Int'l*, pg. 1156
FIRESTONE TEXTILES-WOODSTOCK—See Bridgestone Corporation; *Int'l*, pg. 1156
FRANKLIN BRAID MANUFACTURING CO.—See Wayne Industries Inc.; *U.S. Private*, pg. 4459
GARWARE TECHNICAL FIBRES LTD.; *Int'l*, pg. 2887
HEXCEL REINFORCEMENTS UK LIMITED—See Hexcel Corporation; *U.S. Public*, pg. 1033
HICKORY BRANDS, INC.; *U.S. Private*, pg. 1933
HYOSUNG DONG NAI CO., LTD.—See Hyosung TNC Co. Ltd.; *Int'l*, pg. 3552
HYOSUNG USA, INC. - DECATUR PLANT—See Hyosung Corporation; *Int'l*, pg. 3551
HYOSUNG USA, INC.—See Hyosung Corporation; *Int'l*, pg. 3551
I&I SLING INC.; *U.S. Private*, pg. 2026
KOCH INDUSTRIES, INC.—See Hillman Solutions Corp.; *U.S. Public*, pg. 1038
KORDSA, INC.—See Haci Omer Sabanci Holding A.S.; *Int'l*, pg. 3204
ORION ROPEWORKS, INC.—See Canada Cordage, Inc.; *Int'l*, pg. 1278
PT GAJAH TUNGGAL TBK - PLANT 1—See Giti Tire Pte. Ltd.; *Int'l*, pg. 2979
PT GAJAH TUNGGAL TBK - PLANT 2—See Giti Tire Pte. Ltd.; *Int'l*, pg. 2979
SAMSON ROPE TECHNOLOGIES—See Wind River Holdings, L.P.; *U.S. Private*, pg. 4536
SICREM S.P.A.—See CAG Holding GmbH; *Int'l*, pg. 1250
SILVER STATE WIRE ROPE AND RIGGING, INC.—See Altamont Capital Partners; *U.S. Private*, pg. 205
SOUTHWEST SYNTHETIC SYSTEMS, INC.—See Dot Family Holdings LLC; *U.S. Private*, pg. 1264
TEXTILCORD STEINFORT S.A.—See CAG Holding GmbH; *Int'l*, pg. 1251
THAL LIMITED—See House of Habib; *Int'l*, pg. 3491
TUBBS CORDAGE INC.—See Frank W. Winne & Son, Inc.; *U.S. Private*, pg. 1596
UNICORD CORPORATION; *U.S. Private*, pg. 4282
UNICORD INTERNATIONAL LLC—See Unicord Corporation; *U.S. Private*, pg. 4282
VOLANKA EXPORTS LIMITED—See Hayleys PLC; *Int'l*, pg. 3292
WIRE ROPE CORPORATION OF THE PHILIPPINES—See DMCI Holdings, Inc.; *Int'l*, pg. 2143

314999 — ALL OTHER MISCELLANEOUS TEXTILE PRODUCT MILLS

1888 MILLS, LLC - GRIFFIN MILL—See 1888 Mills, LLC; *U.S. Private*, pg. 3
AADHAAR VENTURES INDIA LIMITED; *Int'l*, pg. 31
A B COTSPIN INDIA LIMITED; *Int'l*, pg. 17
A-B EMBLEMS AND CAPS—See Conrad Industries, Inc.; *U.S. Private*, pg. 1019
ACME MILLS CO. INC.; *U.S. Private*, pg. 61
ACTIVE QUILTING DIV.—See Rockville Fabrics Corporation; *U.S. Private*, pg. 3467
ADORE ME, INC.—See Victoria's Secret & Co.; *U.S. Public*, pg. 2296
AFX INDUSTRIES LLC—See Exco Technologies Limited; *Int'l*, pg. 218
AGRO ALLIANZ LIMITED; *Int'l*, pg. 218
AKSA AKRILIK KIMYA SANAYII A.S.; *Int'l*, pg. 264
AKSHAR SPINTEX LIMITED; *Int'l*, pg. 264
A.K. SPINTEX LTD.; *Int'l*, pg. 25
ALMEDAHLS OY; *Int'l*, pg. 363

N.A.I.C.S. INDEX

314999 — ALL OTHER MISCELLAN...

ALSTONE TEXTILES (INDIA) LTD.; *Int'l*, pg. 383
AMADEO FARELL S.A.U.—See Kadant Inc.; *U.S. Public*, pg. 1212
AMIT INTERNATIONAL LIMITED; *Int'l*, pg. 428
AMSAFE BRIDPORT LIMITED—See TransDigm Group Incorporated; *U.S. Public*, pg. 2182
ANAND RAYONS LTD.; *Int'l*, pg. 446
ANDREW INDUSTRIAL TEXTILE MANUFACTURING COMPANY (WUXI) LIMITED—See Lydall, Inc.; *U.S. Public*, pg. 1349
ANHUI HUAMAO IMPORT & EXPORT CO., LTD.—See Anhui Huamao Textile Company Limited; *Int'l*, pg. 468
ANHUI KORRUN CO., LTD.; *Int'l*, pg. 469
ANJANI SYNTHETICS LTD.; *Int'l*, pg. 472
ANNIN & COMPANY; *U.S. Private*, pg. 285
APEX SPINNING & KNITTING MILLS LIMITED—See Apex Holding Limited; *Int'l*, pg. 511
ARC-COM FABRICS INCORPORATED; *U.S. Private*, pg. 309
ARGAMAN INDUSTRIES LTD.; *Int'l*, pg. 560
ARGO PANTES TBK; *Int'l*, pg. 562
ARTISANS INC.; *U.S. Private*, pg. 343
ARVIND FASHIONS LTD.; *Int'l*, pg. 587
ASAHI INDUSTRIES LIMITED; *Int'l*, pg. 594
ASAHI KASEI ADVANCE CORP.—See Asahi Kasei Corporation; *Int'l*, pg. 595
ASAHI KASEI ADVANCE (SHANGHAI) CO., LTD.—See Asahi Kasei Corporation; *Int'l*, pg. 594
ASAHI KASEI ADVANCE THAILAND CO., LTD.—See Asahi Kasei Corporation; *Int'l*, pg. 595
ASAHI KASEI EUROPE GMBH—See Asahi Kasei Corporation; *Int'l*, pg. 595
ASAHI KASEI FIBERS (H.K.) LTD.—See Asahi Kasei Corporation; *Int'l*, pg. 595
ASAHI KASEI FIBERS ITALY SRL—See Asahi Kasei Corporation; *Int'l*, pg. 595
ASAHI KASEI INDIA PVT. LTD.—See Asahi Kasei Corporation; *Int'l*, pg. 595
ASAHI PROCESSING CO., LTD.—See Daiwabo Holdings Co., Ltd.; *Int'l*, pg. 1949
ASAHI-SCHWEBEL (TAIWAN) CO., LTD.—See Asahi Kasei Corporation; *Int'l*, pg. 596
ASCEND PERFORMANCE MATERIALS LLC—See SK Capital Partners, LP; *U.S. Private*, pg. 3679
AS FISKENETT—See Egersund Group AS; *Int'l*, pg. 2323
ASHNOOR TEXTILE MILLS LIMITED; *Int'l*, pg. 608
ASTENJOHNSON, INC. - KANATA R&D FACILITY—See AstenJohnson, Inc.; *U.S. Private*, pg. 360
ASTENJOHNSON, INC.; *U.S. Private*, pg. 360
ATA - A.T APPARELS, INC.; *U.S. Private*, pg. 363
ATALY, INC.; *U.S. Private*, pg. 364
AURORA S.A.; *Int'l*, pg. 714
AURORA SPECIALTY TEXTILES GROUP, INC.—See Meridian Industries, Inc.; *U.S. Private*, pg. 2673
BAINBRIDGE INTERNATIONAL INC.; *U.S. Private*, pg. 453
BAINBRIDGE INTERNATIONAL LTD.—See Bainbridge International Inc.; *U.S. Private*, pg. 453
BANGLADESH EXPORT IMPORT CO. LTD.; *Int'l*, pg. 835
BANNU WOOLLEN MILLS LIMITED; *Int'l*, pg. 851
BARCOS CO., LTD.; *Int'l*, pg. 864
BARNHARDT CUSHION-HICKORY PLANT—See Barnhardt Manufacturing Company; *U.S. Private*, pg. 478
BEAULIEU INTERNATIONAL GROUP NV KOMEN PLANT—See Beaulieu International Group NV; *Int'l*, pg. 934
BEKAERT TEXTILES USA, INC.—See Franz Haniel & Cie. GmbH; *Int'l*, pg. 2762
BELLA CASA FASHION & RETAIL LTD.; *Int'l*, pg. 966
BELTON INDUSTRIES, INC.; *U.S. Private*, pg. 521
BENTZON CARPETS APS—See Egetaepper A/S; *Int'l*, pg. 2324
BEST TEXTILES ACQUISITION, LLC—See Patriarch Partners, LLC; *U.S. Private*, pg. 3109
BETEX INDIA LIMITED; *Int'l*, pg. 1002
BETI PREJA D.O.O.—See Beti d.d.; *Int'l*, pg. 1002
BHILWARA TECHNICAL TEXTILES LIMITED; *Int'l*, pg. 1015
BIG SUNSHINE CO., LTD.; *Int'l*, pg. 1021
BIJLEE TEXTILES LIMITED; *Int'l*, pg. 1022
BILGUN TEKSTIL A.S—See Bilici Yatirim Sanayi ve Ticaret A.S.; *Int'l*, pg. 1029
BIRKO BIRLESIK KOYUNLULULAR MENSUCATTI-CARET VE SANAYI AS; *Int'l*, pg. 1047
BIXOLON MIDDLE EAST & AFRICA CO., LTD.—See Bixolon Co Ltd; *Int'l*, pg. 1052
BLOCKSOM & CO.; *U.S. Private*, pg. 583
BORUJERD TEXTILE CO (PUBLIC JOINT STOCK); *Int'l*, pg. 1115
BROOKWOOD COMPANIES INC.—See Hallwood Group, LLC; *U.S. Private*, pg. 1845
BURLINGTON WORLDWIDE INC.—See Platinum Equity, LLC; *U.S. Private*, pg. 3203
CAMEX LIMITED; *Int'l*, pg. 1272
CAPITAL INDIA FINANCE LIMITED; *Int'l*, pg. 1311
CAREFEEL COTTON INDUSTRIES (M) SDN. BHD.—See Hengan International Group Co. Ltd.; *Int'l*, pg. 3345
CASABLANCA GROUP LIMITED; *Int'l*, pg. 1349
CELULOSA Y DERIVADOS DE MONTERREY, S.A.—See Cydsa S.A.B. de C.V.; *Int'l*, pg. 1895
CENTRAL DE ABASTECIMIENTO LIMITADA—See Aramark; *U.S. Public*, pg. 177
CENTROTEXTIL A.D.; *Int'l*, pg. 1415
CENTURY ENKA LTD.—See CVC Capital Partners SICAV-FIS S.A.; *Int'l*, pg. 1886
CENTURY TEXTILES AND INDUSTRIES LIMITED - BIRLA CENTURY DIVISION—See Century Textiles and Industries Limited; *Int'l*, pg. 1419
CENTURY TEXTILES AND INDUSTRIES LIMITED - COTTONS BY CENTURY DIVISION—See Century Textiles and Industries Limited; *Int'l*, pg. 1420
CENTURY TEXTILES AND INDUSTRIES LIMITED; *Int'l*, pg. 1419
CHARGEURS ENTRETELAS (PORTUGAL) LTD—See Chargeurs SA; *Int'l*, pg. 1448
CHARGEURS INTERFODERE ITALIA S.P.A.—See Chargeurs SA; *Int'l*, pg. 1449
CHARGEURS INTERLINING (HK) LIMITED—See Chargeurs SA; *Int'l*, pg. 1449
CHARGEURS SA; *Int'l*, pg. 1448
CHARGEURS WOOL SALES (EUROPE) SRL—See Chargeurs SA; *Int'l*, pg. 1449
CHA TECHNOLOGIES INC.; *U.S. Private*, pg. 844
CHA TECHNOLOGIES INC.—See CHA Technologies Inc.; *U.S. Private*, pg. 845
CHEMANEX PLC; *Int'l*, pg. 1460
CHEMICA S.A.S—See Evolem S.A.; *Int'l*, pg. 2572
CHICAGO FLAG & DECORATING CO.; *U.S. Private*, pg. 877
CHINA DONGXIANG (GROUP) COMPANY LIMITED; *Int'l*, pg. 1498
CHINA GARMENTS CO., LTD.—See China Hi-Tech Group Corporation; *Int'l*, pg. 1508
CHINA LINEN TEXTILE INDUSTRY, LTD.; *Int'l*, pg. 1515
CHINA NATIONAL CHEMICAL FIBER CORPORATION—See China Hi-Tech Group Corporation; *Int'l*, pg. 1508
CHINA SILK INDUSTRIAL CORPORATION—See China Hi-Tech Group Corporation; *Int'l*, pg. 1508
CHINA TEXMATECH CO., LTD.—See China Hi-Tech Group Corporation; *Int'l*, pg. 1508
CHINA TEXTILE INDUSTRIAL CORPORATION FOR FOREIGN ECONOMIC & TECHNICAL COOPERATION—See China Hi-Tech Group Corporation; *Int'l*, pg. 1508
CHORI CO., LTD.; *Int'l*, pg. 1583
CHORI EUROPE GMBH—See Chori Co., Ltd.; *Int'l*, pg. 1583
CHORI SINGAPORE PTE. LTD.—See Chori Co., Ltd.; *Int'l*, pg. 1583
CHORI (TIANJIN) CO., LTD.—See Chori Co., Ltd.; *Int'l*, pg. 1583
CHORI TRADING MALAYSIA SDN BHD—See Chori Co., Ltd.; *Int'l*, pg. 1583
CIE INTL ANDRE TRIGANO; *Int'l*, pg. 1605
CLAREMONT FLOCK CORPORATION; *U.S. Private*, pg. 910
CLASSIC ACCESSORIES, LLC—See Z Capital Group, LLC; *U.S. Private*, pg. 4595
CLEAR EDGE FILTRATION (AUSTRALIA) PTY. LTD.—See Gilde Buy Out Partners B.V.; *Int'l*, pg. 2974
CLEAR EDGE FILTRATION CFE GMBH—See Gilde Buy Out Partners B.V.; *Int'l*, pg. 2974
CLEAR EDGE FILTRATION GMBH—See Gilde Buy Out Partners B.V.; *Int'l*, pg. 2974
CLEAR EDGE FILTRATION, INC.-SKANEATELES FALLS—See Gilde Buy Out Partners B.V.; *Int'l*, pg. 2974
CLEAR EDGE FILTRATION, INC.—See Gilde Buy Out Partners B.V.; *Int'l*, pg. 2974
CLEAR EDGE FILTRATION (NZ) LTD.—See Gilde Buy Out Partners B.V.; *Int'l*, pg. 2974
CLEAR EDGE FILTRATION POLSKA SP. Z O.O.—See Gilde Buy Out Partners B.V.; *Int'l*, pg. 2974
CLEAR EDGE FILTRATION SOUTH AFRICA PTY. LTD.—See Gilde Buy Out Partners B.V.; *Int'l*, pg. 2974
CLEAR EDGE FILTRATION UK LTD.—See Gilde Buy Out Partners B.V.; *Int'l*, pg. 2974
COATS BULGARIA EOOD—See Coats Group plc; *Int'l*, pg. 1682
COATS CADENA ANDINA SA—See Coats Group plc; *Int'l*, pg. 1682
COATS CADENA LTDA.—See Coats Group plc; *Int'l*, pg. 1682
COATS CADENA SA—See Coats Group plc; *Int'l*, pg. 1682
COATS CADENA SA—See Coats Group plc; *Int'l*, pg. 1682
COATS CADENA SA—See Coats Group plc; *Int'l*, pg. 1682
COATS CADENA SA—See Coats Group plc; *Int'l*, pg. 1682
COATS DE NICARAGUA SA—See Coats Group plc; *Int'l*, pg. 1682
COATS EESTI AS—See Coats Group plc; *Int'l*, pg. 1682
COATS EL SALVADOR, S.A. DE C.V.—See Coats Group plc; *Int'l*, pg. 1682
COATS HONDURAS, S.A.—See Coats Group plc; *Int'l*, pg. 1682
COATS INDUSTRIAL SCANDINAVIA AB—See Coats Group plc; *Int'l*, pg. 1682
COATS LLC—See Coats Group plc; *Int'l*, pg. 1682
COATS MAROC SA—See Coats Group plc; *Int'l*, pg. 1682
COATS MEXICO S.A. DE C.V.—See Coats Group plc; *Int'l*, pg. 1682
COATS OPTI GERMANY GMBH—See Coats Group plc; *Int'l*, pg. 1682
COATS PATONS (NEW ZEALAND) LTD.—See Coats Group plc; *Int'l*, pg. 1682
COATS POLSKA SP. Z O.O.—See Coats Group plc; *Int'l*, pg. 1682
COATS ROMANIA SRL—See Coats Group plc; *Int'l*, pg. 1682
COATS SHENZHEN LIMITED—See Coats Group plc; *Int'l*, pg. 1682
COATS STROPPEL AG—See Coats Group plc; *Int'l*, pg. 1682
COATS THREAD EXPORTS (PRIVATE) LIMITED—See Coats Group plc; *Int'l*, pg. 1682
COATS THREAD GERMANY GMBH—See Coats Group plc; *Int'l*, pg. 1682
COATS THREADS (THAILAND) LTD.—See Coats Group plc; *Int'l*, pg. 1682
COATS (TURKIYE) IPLIK SANAYII AS—See Coats Group plc; *Int'l*, pg. 1681
COATS UKRAINE LTD.—See Coats Group plc; *Int'l*, pg. 1682
COLBOND (NEDERLAND) BVARNHEM—See Freudenberg SE; *Int'l*, pg. 2789
COLONIAL LLC.; *U.S. Private*, pg. 971
CONE DENIM LLC—See Platinum Equity, LLC; *U.S. Private*, pg. 3203
CONRAD INDUSTRIES, INC.; *U.S. Private*, pg. 1019
CORPORACION CERVESUR S.A.A.; *Int'l*, pg. 1803
COSTA VERDE AERONAUTICA SA; *Int'l*, pg. 1814
THE CUSTOM COMPANY, INC.; *U.S. Private*, pg. 4017
DAIWABO HOLDINGS CO., LTD.; *Int'l*, pg. 1949
DAIWABO NEU CO., LTD.—See Daiwabo Holdings Co., Ltd.; *Int'l*, pg. 1949
DAIWABO RAYON CO., LTD.—See Daiwabo Holdings Co., Ltd.; *Int'l*, pg. 1949
DAIWABO TEX INC—See Daiwabo Holdings Co., Ltd.; *Int'l*, pg. 1949
DAIWABOUASOSHIE INC.—See Daiwabo Holdings Co., Ltd.; *Int'l*, pg. 1949
DAIWABOUPORITEKKU INC. - HARIMA PLANT—See Daiwabo Holdings Co., Ltd.; *Int'l*, pg. 1949
DAIWABOUPORITEKKU INC.—See Daiwabo Holdings Co., Ltd.; *Int'l*, pg. 1949
DAIWABOURAIFUSAPOTO INC.—See Daiwabo Holdings Co., Ltd.; *Int'l*, pg. 1949
DAIWA DO BRASIL TEXTIL LTDA.—See Daiwabo Holdings Co., Ltd.; *Int'l*, pg. 1949
DAIWA MARUESU INC.—See Daiwabo Holdings Co., Ltd.; *Int'l*, pg. 1949
DBW ADVANCED FIBER TECHNOLOGIES GMBH—See DMB Dr. Dieter Murmann Beteiligungsgesellschaft mbH; *Int'l*, pg. 2142
DBW HUNGARY KFT—See DMB Dr. Dieter Murmann Beteiligungsgesellschaft mbH; *Int'l*, pg. 2142
DBW IBERICA INDUSTRIA AUTOMOCION, S.A.—See DMB Dr. Dieter Murmann Beteiligungsgesellschaft mbH; *Int'l*, pg. 2142
DBW METALLVERARBEITUNG GMBH—See DMB Dr. Dieter Murmann Beteiligungsgesellschaft mbH; *Int'l*, pg. 2142
DESH GARMENTS LIMITED; *Int'l*, pg. 2045
DEWAN KHALID TEXTILE MILLS LIMITED; *Int'l*, pg. 2091
DE WITTE LIETAER INTERNATIONAL TEXTILES NV—See AUNDE Achter & Ebels GmbH; *Int'l*, pg. 705
DHJ INTERLINING LIMITED—See Chargeurs SA; *Int'l*, pg. 1450
DHJ (MALAYSIA) SDN BHD—See Chargeurs SA; *Int'l*, pg. 1450
DI DONG IL CORPORATION; *Int'l*, pg. 2101
DIENUPURODAKUTSU INC.—See Daiwabo Holdings Co., Ltd.; *Int'l*, pg. 1949
DISTRIBUIDORA COATS DE GUATEMALA S.A.—See Coats Group plc; *Int'l*, pg. 1682
D.M. TEXTILE MILLS LIMITED; *Int'l*, pg. 1901
DOLLFUS MIEG & CIE, S.A.—See Bernard Krief Consultants SA; *Int'l*, pg. 986
DOMINION TEXTILE (USA), LLC—See Berry Global Group, Inc; *U.S. Public*, pg. 321
DONEAR INDUSTRIES LTD; *Int'l*, pg. 2163
DOUNOR SAS—See Berry Global Group, Inc; *U.S. Public*, pg. 321
DUPONT-ASAHI FLASH SPUN PRODUCTS CO., LTD.—See Asahi Kasei Corporation; *Int'l*, pg. 596
DUPONT ASIA PACIFIC LIMITED—See Dow Inc.; *U.S. Public*, pg. 685
DUPONT (AUSTRALIA) LTD.—See Corteva, Inc.; *U.S. Public*, pg. 582
DUROS S.A.; *Int'l*, pg. 2230
DUVALTEX INC.; *Int'l*, pg. 2236
EDER FLAG MANUFACTURING CO.; *U.S. Private*, pg. 1333
EFFINGO TEXTILE & TRADING LIMITED; *Int'l*, pg. 2319
EMAS KIARA SDN. BHD.; *Int'l*, pg. 2374
ENGINEERED SPECIALTY TEXTILES LLC; *U.S. Private*, pg. 1398

314999 — ALL OTHER MISCELLAN...

ERB INDUSTRIES INC.; *U.S. Private,* pg. 1417
EREGLI TEKSTIL TURIZM SANAYI VE TICARET A.S.; *Int'l,* pg. 2490
EUREKA INDUSTRIES LIMITED; *Int'l,* pg. 2530
EVOLUTION BLOCKCHAIN GROUP INC.; *Int'l,* pg. 2572
EXSA EXPORT SANAYI MAMULLERI SATIS VE ARASTIRMA A.S.—See Haci Omer Sabanci Holding A.S.; *Int'l,* pg. 3204
EXXEL OUTDOORS, INC.; *U.S. Private,* pg. 1453
FALMAC TEXTILE (TIANJIN) LTD.—See Falmac Limited; *Int'l,* pg. 2611
FATEH INDUSTRIES LIMITED; *Int'l,* pg. 2622
FAZAL CLOTH MILLS LIMITED; *Int'l,* pg. 2626
FELTERS OF SC, LLC—See The Felters Group; *U.S. Private,* pg. 4028
FENNER, A.C.—See Compagnie Generale des Etablissements Michelin SCA; *Int'l,* pg. 1745
FERRARI S.A.; *Int'l,* pg. 2639
FERROBOTICS COMPLIANT ROBOT TECHNOLOGY GMBH—See Berndorf AG; *Int'l,* pg. 987
FIBERLINKS TEXTILES INC.; *Int'l,* pg. 2652
FIBERWEB ITALIA SPA—See Berry Global Group, Inc; *U.S. Public,* pg. 322
FIRESTONE FIBERS & TEXTILES COMPANY, LLC - GASTONIA MANUFACTURING FACILITY—See Bridgestone Corporation; *Int'l,* pg. 1156
FIRST WINNER INDUSTRIES LIMITED; *Int'l,* pg. 2688
FIRST WINNER LIFESTYLE LTD.—See First Winner Industries Limited; *Int'l,* pg. 2688
FN FACTORY OUTLET PCL; *Int'l,* pg. 2717
FORMOSA TAFFETA (CHANGSHU) CO., LTD.—See FORMOSA TAFFETA CO., LTD.; *Int'l,* pg. 2736
FORMOSA TAFFETA CO., LTD.; *Int'l,* pg. 2736
FORMOSA TAFFETA DONG NAI CO., LTD.—See FORMOSA TAFFETA CO., LTD.; *Int'l,* pg. 2736
FOUNTAIN SET (EUROPE) LIMITED—See Fountain Set (Holdings) Limited; *Int'l,* pg. 2754
FREUDENBERG EVOLON S.A.S.U.—See Freudenberg SE; *Int'l,* pg. 2786
FREUDENBERG GOSPODINJSKI PROIZVODI D.O.O.—See Freudenberg SE; *Int'l,* pg. 2786
GABRIEL HOLDING A/S; *Int'l,* pg. 2867
GARG FURNACE LTD.; *Int'l,* pg. 2884
GARLON POLYFAB INDUSTRIES LTD.; *Int'l,* pg. 2884
GARMEX SAIGON CORPORATION; *Int'l,* pg. 2884
GB GLOBAL LIMITED; *Int'l,* pg. 2892
GILLANDERS ARBUTHNOT & CO., LTD.; *Int'l,* pg. 2975
GLOBE TEXTILE MILLS (OE) LIMITED; *Int'l,* pg. 3006
GLOBUS KONFEKCIJA D.D.; *Int'l,* pg. 3008
GOBI JOINT STOCK COMPANY; *Int'l,* pg. 3018
GOLDEN TEXTILES & CLOTHES WOOL; *Int'l,* pg. 3032
GOTEX S.A.—See Coats Group plc; *Int'l,* pg. 1682
GP DESIGN, INC.; *U.S. Private,* pg. 1747
GRANFORD MANUFACTURING, INC.—See The Goodyear Tire & Rubber Company; *U.S. Public,* pg. 2084
GRANT EMBLEMS LIMITED; *Int'l,* pg. 3059
THE GRAPHIC EDGE, INC.; *U.S. Private,* pg. 4037
GREENFIELD RESEARCH, INC.; *U.S. Private,* pg. 1777
GSI CREOS (BEIJING) CO., LTD—See GSI Creos Corporation; *Int'l,* pg. 3144
G&T INDUSTRIES INC.; *U.S. Private,* pg. 1629
GUILFORD EUROPE LTD.—See Lear Corporation; *U.S. Public,* pg. 1297
GUILFORD MILLS AUTOMOTIVE (PORTUGAL) LIMITED—See Lear Corporation; *U.S. Public,* pg. 1296
GUILFORD PERFORMANCE TEXTILES, INC.—See Lear Corporation; *U.S. Public,* pg. 1297
GUILFORD SHANGHAI TRADING CO., LTD.—See Lear Corporation; *U.S. Public,* pg. 1297
GULISTAN GROUP; *Int'l,* pg. 3182
HAKKIM TEXTILE MILLS LIMITED; *Int'l,* pg. 3219
HAMID TEXTILE MILLS LIMITED; *Int'l,* pg. 3237
HAMMER TAEPPER A/S—See Egetaepper A/S; *Int'l,* pg. 2324
HANGZHOU ASAHIKASEI SPANDEX CO., LTD.—See Asahi Kasei Corporation; *Int'l,* pg. 596
HANGZHOU WENSLI SILK CULTURE CO., LTD.; *Int'l,* pg. 3251
HANKUK ADVANCED MATERIALS CO., LTD.—See HANKUK CARBON Co., LTD.; *Int'l,* pg. 3254
HANZA ALFARAM ELECTRIC (SUZHOU) CO., LTD.—See Hanza AB; *Int'l,* pg. 3267
HANZA CZECH REPUBLIC S.R.O—See Hanza AB; *Int'l,* pg. 3267
HANZA ELEKTROMEKAN AB—See Hanza AB; *Int'l,* pg. 3267
HANZA GMBH—See Hanza AB; *Int'l,* pg. 3267
HANZA MECHANICS NARVA AS—See Hanza AB; *Int'l,* pg. 3267
HANZA MECHANICS SWEDEN AB—See Hanza AB; *Int'l,* pg. 3267
HANZA MECHANICS TARTU AS—See Hanza AB; *Int'l,* pg. 3267
HANZA METALLISET OY—See Hanza AB; *Int'l,* pg. 3267
HANZA POLAND SP. Z.O.O—See Hanza AB; *Int'l,* pg. 3267
HANZA TOOLFAC OY—See Hanza AB; *Int'l,* pg. 3267
HARIA EXPORTS LIMITED; *Int'l,* pg. 3275
HARI GOVIND INTERNATIONAL LIMITED; *Int'l,* pg. 3275

HARODITE INDUSTRIES, INC. - SOUTH CAROLINA—See Harodite Industries, Inc.; *U.S. Private,* pg. 1866
HATEKS HATAY TEKSTIL ISLETMELERI A.S.; *Int'l,* pg. 3284
HEMISPHERE FASHION GROUP; *Int'l,* pg. 3341
HENAN XINYE TEXTILE CO., LTD.; *Int'l,* pg. 3343
HERITAGE HOUSE FABRICS INC.—See Jeffrey Fabrics Inc.; *U.S. Private,* pg. 2198
HIGHLAND INDUSTRIES INC.—See Takata Global Group; *U.S. Private,* pg. 3925
HOLLISTON, LLC; *U.S. Private,* pg. 1966
HOLOGENIX, LLC; *U.S. Private,* pg. 1968
HONMYUE ENTERPRISE CO., LTD.; *Int'l,* pg. 3472
H. SALB INTERNATIONAL; *Int'l,* pg. 3195
HUALE ACOUSTICS CORPORATION; *Int'l,* pg. 3512
HUESKER SYNTHETIC GMBH; *Int'l,* pg. 3522
HUNAN MENDALE HOMETEXTILE CO., LTD.; *Int'l,* pg. 3533
HUNG CHOU FIBER IND. CO., LTD.; *Int'l,* pg. 3535
HWA WELL TEXTILES (BD) LTD.; *Int'l,* pg. 3541
HYOSUNG CORPORATION - ANYANG PLANT—See Hyosung Corporation; *Int'l,* pg. 3550
HYOSUNG CORPORATION - DAEGU PLANT—See Hyosung Corporation; *Int'l,* pg. 3550
HYOSUNG CORPORATION - DAEJEON PLANT—See Hyosung Corporation; *Int'l,* pg. 3550
HYOSUNG CORPORATION - ICHEON PLANT—See Hyosung Corporation; *Int'l,* pg. 3550
HYOSUNG CORPORATION - JINCHEON PLANT—See Hyosung Corporation; *Int'l,* pg. 3550
HYOSUNG CORPORATION - KWANGHAEWON PLANT—See Hyosung Corporation; *Int'l,* pg. 3550
HYOSUNG CORPORATION - ULSAN PLANT—See Hyosung Corporation; *Int'l,* pg. 3550
HYOSUNG CORPORATION - YANGSAN PLANT—See Hyosung Corporation; *Int'l,* pg. 3550
HYOSUNG CORPORATION - YONGYEON PLANT 1—See Hyosung Corporation; *Int'l,* pg. 3550
HYOSUNG CORPORATION - YONGYEON PLANT 3—See Hyosung Corporation; *Int'l,* pg. 3550
HYOSUNG LUXEMBOURG S.A.—See Hyosung Corporation; *Int'l,* pg. 3551
HYOSUNG SPANDEX (GUANGDONG) CO., LTD.—See Hyosung Corporation; *Int'l,* pg. 3551
HYOSUNG TNC CO. LTD.; *Int'l,* pg. 3552
ICG HOLLISTON HOLDINGS CORPORATION; *U.S. Private,* pg. 2031
ICG/HOLLISTON—See ICG Holliston Holdings Corporation; *U.S. Private,* pg. 2031
IDEAL SPINNING MILLS LTD; *Int'l,* pg. 3589
INDES FUGGERHAUS TEXTIL GMBH—See A.S. Creation Tapeten AG; *Int'l,* pg. 28
INDIANA MILLS & MANUFACTURING, INC.; *U.S. Private,* pg. 2062
INDUSTRIAL COATINGS GROUP, INC.—See ICG Holliston Holdings Corporation; *U.S. Private,* pg. 2031
INDUSTRIAL FABRICS CORP.—See Gilde Buy Out Partners B.V.; *Int'l,* pg. 2974
JAMES THOMPSON & CO. INC.; *U.S. Private,* pg. 2185
JIUJIANG DEYU CO., LTD.—See Honmyue Enterprise Co., Ltd.; *Int'l,* pg. 3472
JOHNSON-FLUITEN S.R.L.—See Kadant Inc.; *U.S. Public,* pg. 1212
J & P COATS PAKISTAN (PVT) LIMITED—See Coats Group plc; *Int'l,* pg. 1682
KADANT BC- LAMORT UK LIMITED—See Kadant Inc.; *U.S. Public,* pg. 1212
KASBAR NATIONAL INDUSTRIES, INC.; *U.S. Private,* pg. 2263
KEBI INDUSTRY CO., LTD.—See Daiwabo Holdings Co., Ltd.; *Int'l,* pg. 1949
KORDSA TEKNIK TEKSTIL A.S.—See Haci Omer Sabanci Holding A.S.; *Int'l,* pg. 3204
LAINIERE DE PICARDIE KOREA CO. LTD—See Chargeurs SA; *Int'l,* pg. 1449
LEAR CORPORATION ASIENTOS S.L.—See Lear Corporation; *U.S. Public,* pg. 1297
LEAR MEXICAN TRIM OPERATIONS, S. DE R.L. DE C.V.—See Lear Corporation; *U.S. Public,* pg. 1297
LEIGH FIBERS, INC.; *U.S. Private,* pg. 2419
LONE STAR SPECIAL TEES INC.—See Periodical Management Group International Ltd.; *U.S. Private,* pg. 3150
LYDALL INDUSTRIAL FILTRATION TEXTILE MANUFACTURING (EMEA) LIMITED—See Lydall, Inc.; *U.S. Public,* pg. 1349
LYDALL INDUSTRIAL TEXTILE MANUFACTURING COMPANY (SHANGHAI) LIMITED—See Lydall, Inc.; *U.S. Public,* pg. 1349
MARCA PROTECCION LABORAL, S.L.U.—See Bunzl plc; *Int'l,* pg. 1219
MARCUS BROTHERS TEXTILES, INC.; *U.S. Private,* pg. 2572
MASTER SPORTS; *U.S. Private,* pg. 2607
MEHLER TEXNOLOGIES LOGISTICS GMBH—See Freudenberg SE; *Int'l,* pg. 2789
M&L ROSE ENTERPRISES INC.; *U.S. Private,* pg. 2524
MORARJEE INTERNATIONAL SRL—See Ashok Piramal Group; *Int'l,* pg. 608

NANDAN DENIM LIMITED—See Chiripal Industries Ltd.; *Int'l,* pg. 1573
NEFF MOTIVATION INC.; *U.S. Private,* pg. 2880
NEUTEX AG—See Bystronic AG; *Int'l,* pg. 1236
NEUTEX HOME DECO GMBH—See Hoftex Group AG; *Int'l,* pg. 3440
NICHOLSON MANUFACTURING LTD.—See Kadant Inc.; *U.S. Public,* pg. 1212
NINGBO CHARGEURS YAK TEXTILE TRADING CO. LTD—See Chargeurs SA; *Int'l,* pg. 1450
NISSHIN KOHGYO CORPORATION—See GSI Creos Corporation; *Int'l,* pg. 3145
NISSHO LINEN—See Aramark; *U.S. Public,* pg. 178
NITRO RIGGING, LLC.; *U.S. Private,* pg. 2929
NU IMAGE FABRICS INC.; *U.S. Private,* pg. 2971
NUOVA STIRERIA TAVOLETO SRL—See Aeffe SpA; *Int'l,* pg. 173
PACELINE, INC.; *U.S. Private,* pg. 3064
PARAMOUNT GLOBAL SURFACES—See Platinum Equity, LLC; *U.S. Private,* pg. 3206
PENN EMBLEM CO.—See The Penn Companies; *U.S. Private,* pg. 4092
PERFECT FIT INDUSTRIES, LLC—See The Anderson Group, LLC; *U.S. Private,* pg. 3986
PLASTIBERT & CIE NV—See Duroc AB; *Int'l,* pg. 2230
PRODUCTORA DE TEREFT DE ALTAMIRA, S.A. DE C.V.—See ALFA, S.A.B. de C.V.; *Int'l,* pg. 313
PT DAIWABO INDUSTRIAL FABRICS INDONESIA—See Daiwabo Holdings Co., Ltd.; *Int'l,* pg. 1950
PT DAYANI GARMENT INDONESIA (DGI)—See Daiwabo Holdings Co., Ltd.; *Int'l,* pg. 1950
P.T. SANDANG MUTIARA CEMERLANG—See Fountain Set (Holdings) Limited; *Int'l,* pg. 2754
PT TOKAI TEXPRINT INDONESIA (TTI)—See Daiwabo Holdings Co., Ltd.; *Int'l,* pg. 1950
PUBLIVENOR BVBA—See Encres Dubuit SA; *Int'l,* pg. 2402
QINGDAO COATS LIMITED—See Coats Group plc; *Int'l,* pg. 1682
QST INDUSTRIES, INC.; *U.S. Private,* pg. 3314
RAFFAELE CARUSO S.P.A.—See Fosun International Limited; *Int'l,* pg. 2751
RAMSHYAM TEXTILE INDUSTRIES LTD.—See First Winner Industries Limited; *Int'l,* pg. 2688
READY GARMENT TECHNOLOGY ITALIA SRL.—See Dr. Bock Industries AG; *Int'l,* pg. 2190
READY GARMENT TECHNOLOGY ROMANIA SRL—See Dr. Bock Industries AG; *Int'l,* pg. 2190
RICH LEGEND INTERNATIONAL LIMITED—See China Gas Holdings Limited; *Int'l,* pg. 1504
R.K. STRATMAN INCORPORATED; *U.S. Private,* pg. 3338
ROCKVILLE FABRICS CORPORATION; *U.S. Private,* pg. 3467
ROSS SPORTSWEAR INC.; *U.S. Private,* pg. 3485
SACKNER PRODUCTS INC.—See Leggett & Platt, Incorporated; *U.S. Public,* pg. 1303
SAINT-GOBAIN ADFORS CZ FABRICS S.R.O.—See Compagnie de Saint-Gobain SA; *Int'l,* pg. 1727
SANIN ASICS INDUSTRY CORP.—See ASICS Corporation; *Int'l,* pg. 621
SANSEGAL SPORTSWEAR, INC.; *U.S. Private,* pg. 3546
SCANDIA DOWN—See Chelsey Direct, LLC; *U.S. Private,* pg. 870
S EDWARD INC.; *U.S. Private,* pg. 3512
SERGE FERRARI AG—See Ferrari S.A.; *Int'l,* pg. 2639
SHANDONG HELON CO., LTD.—See China Hi-Tech Group Corporation; *Int'l,* pg. 1508
SHANGHAI COATS LIMITED—See Coats Group plc; *Int'l,* pg. 1682
SHANGHAI FUHUI TEXTILES TRADING CO., LTD.—See Fountain Set (Holdings) Limited; *Int'l,* pg. 2754
SILK SCREEN INK LTD.—See Delta Apparel, Inc.; *U.S. Public,* pg. 652
SNOW-LOTUS CASHMERE CO., LTD—See COFCO Limited; *Int'l,* pg. 1692
SOPHIA CORPORATION—See GSI Creos Corporation; *Int'l,* pg. 3145
STAHL'S INC.; *U.S. Private,* pg. 3776
STOWE-PHARR MILLS, INC. - PHARR PALOMAR PLANT—See Stowe-Pharr Mills, Inc.; *U.S. Private,* pg. 3832
SUPERIOR HEALTH LINENS, LLC—See York Capital Management Global Advisors, LLC; *U.S. Private,* pg. 4590
SUQIAN YOUNG TOP GARMENTS CO., LTD.—See Fountain Set (Holdings) Limited; *Int'l,* pg. 2754
SWAN FIBER CO., LTD.—See China Hi-Tech Group Corporation; *Int'l,* pg. 1508
TENCATE GEOSYNTHETICS ASIA SDN. BHD.—See ABN AMRO Group N.V.; *Int'l,* pg. 64
TENCATE GEOSYNTHETICS ASIA SDN. BHD.—See Gilde Buy Out Partners B.V.; *Int'l,* pg. 2975
TENCATE GEOSYNTHETICS AUSTRIA GES.M.B.H—See ABN AMRO Group N.V.; *Int'l,* pg. 64
TENCATE GEOSYNTHETICS AUSTRIA GES.M.B.H—See Gilde Buy Out Partners B.V.; *Int'l,* pg. 2975
TENOWO DE MEXIKO S. DE R.L. DE C.V.—See Hoftex Group AG; *Int'l,* pg. 3441
TENOWO HUZHOU NEW MATERIALS CO., LTD.—See Hoftex Group AG; *Int'l,* pg. 3440

N.A.I.C.S. INDEX

315210 — CUT AND SEW APPAREL...

TENOWO REICHENBACH GMBH—See Hoftex Group AG; *Int'l*, pg. 3441
TERRAM LIMITED—See Berry Global Group, Inc; *U.S. Public*, pg. 321
TEXNOLOGY NANO TEXTILE (CHINA) LIMITED—See Fullsun International Holdings Group Co., Limited; *Int'l*, pg. 2843
THAI CHORI CO., LTD.—See Chori Co., Ltd.; *Int'l*, pg. 1583
TIEDEMANN-BEVS INDUSTRIES, INC.—See Strength Capital Partners, LLC; *U.S. Private*, pg. 3839
TKO APPAREL, INC.; *U.S. Private*, pg. 4178
TONOWO INC.—See Hoftex Group AG; *Int'l*, pg. 3441
TOYO HEISEI POLYMER CO., LTD.—See Hagihara Industries Inc.; *Int'l*, pg. 3207
TRUE TEXTILES, INC.—See Duvaltex Inc.; *Int'l*, pg. 2236
UAB LITSPIN—See Egetaepper A/S; *Int'l*, pg. 2324
VALLEY FORGE FLAG COMPANY; *U.S. Private*, pg. 4334
VALON KONE OY—See Kadant Inc.; *U.S. Public*, pg. 1212
VALON KONE OY—See Kadant Inc.; *U.S. Public*, pg. 1212
VALON KONE OY—See Kadant Inc.; *U.S. Public*, pg. 1213
VALON KONE OY—See Kadant Inc.; *U.S. Public*, pg. 1213
VISION SUPPORT SERVICES LIMITED—See Icahn Enterprises L.P.; *U.S. Public*, pg. 1085
VISION SUPPORT SERVICES PAKISTAN LTD.—See Icahn Enterprises L.P.; *U.S. Public*, pg. 1085
VISION SUPPORT SERVICES PVT. LTD.—See Icahn Enterprises L.P.; *U.S. Public*, pg. 1085
WEILWOOD INDUSTRIES, INC.—See Santee Print Works, Inc.; *U.S. Private*, pg. 3548
WESTERN SLING COMPANY—See Altamont Capital Partners; *U.S. Private*, pg. 205
WNC CLOUD MERGER SUB, INC.—See WABASH NATIONAL CORPORATION; *U.S. Public*, pg. 2320
WORLD EMBLEM INTERNATIONAL, INC.; *U.S. Private*, pg. 4565

315120 — APPAREL KNITTING MILLS

ADDI INDUSTRIES LIMITED; *Int'l*, pg. 128
ALPHA INDUSTRIES INC.; *U.S. Private*, pg. 197
ALPHA MILLS CORP.; *U.S. Private*, pg. 198
ALPS SPORTSWEAR MANUFACTURING CO., INC.; *U.S. Private*, pg. 202
APEX TEXTILE PRINTING MILLS LIMITED—See Apex Holding Limited; *Int'l*, pg. 511
ARGO AG—See Coop-Gruppe Genossenschaft; *Int'l*, pg. 1789
B-52 CAPITAL PUBLIC COMPANY LIMITED; *Int'l*, pg. 784
BEIJING GSI HOSIERY CO., LTD.—See GSI Creos Corporation; *Int'l*, pg. 3144
BENETTON GROUP S.P.A.—See Edizione S.r.l.; *Int'l*, pg. 2311
BGI INVESTMENTS (1961) LTD.; *Int'l*, pg. 1008
BIFLEX INTIMATE GROUP, LLC; *U.S. Private*, pg. 552
BLAACANKA A.D.; *Int'l*, pg. 1056
BOSSONG HOSIERY MILLS, INC.; *U.S. Private*, pg. 620
BRANDS & FASHION NV—See Frasers Group plc; *Int'l*, pg. 2765
BRAND X CO., LTD.; *Int'l*, pg. 1139
BRIDGEDALE OUTDOOR LTD—See Bollin Group Ltd.; *Int'l*, pg. 1102
CANNON COUNTY KNIT MILLS, INC.; *U.S. Private*, pg. 734
CAROLINA HOSIERY MILLS INC.; *U.S. Private*, pg. 768
CARRY WEALTH LIMITED—See Carry Wealth Holdings Limited; *Int'l*, pg. 1346
CASTELBAJAC CO., LTD.; *Int'l*, pg. 1356
CATAWBA SOX LLC; *U.S. Private*, pg. 788
CAYSET FASHIONS LTD.; *U.S. Private*, pg. 795
CDU PLC; *Int'l*, pg. 1371
CHINATEX CORPORATION LIMITED—See COFCO Limited; *Int'l*, pg. 1692
CHUNG YICK TEXTILE FACTORY LIMITED—See GTI Holdings Limited; *Int'l*, pg. 3151
COLLETTE DINNIGAN PTY. LTD.; *Int'l*, pg. 1699
COLLINS FASHION (PVT) LTD.—See Collins Co., Ltd.; *Int'l*, pg. 1702
COLLTEX GARMENT MFY CO. LTD.—See Collins Co., Ltd.; *Int'l*, pg. 1702
COLOR IMAGE APPAREL INC.; *U.S. Private*, pg. 972
COMMONWEALTH HOSIERY MILLS; *U.S. Private*, pg. 987
CONFECTII VASLUI S.A.; *Int'l*, pg. 1767
C.P.G. GARMENT CO., LTD.—See Castle Peak Holdings Public Company Limited; *Int'l*, pg. 1357
CRESCENT HOSIERY MILLS INC.; *U.S. Private*, pg. 1093
CSP INTERNATIONAL FASHION GROUP S.P.A.; *Int'l*, pg. 1867
DAGI GIYIM SANAYI VE TICARET A.S.; *Int'l*, pg. 1912
DALIAN GUNZE FASHION GARMENTS CO., LTD.—See Gunze Limited; *Int'l*, pg. 3185
DAOHE GLOBAL GROUP LIMITED; *Int'l*, pg. 1970
DESOTO MILLS, INC.—See Berkshire Hathaway Inc.; *U.S. Public*, pg. 305
DOLLAR INDUSTRIES LIMITED; *Int'l*, pg. 2158
ECLAT TEXTILE (CAMBODIA) CO., LTD.—See Eclat Textile Co., Ltd.; *Int'l*, pg. 2291
ELLIS HOSIERY MILLS INC.; *U.S. Private*, pg. 1374

EL NASR CLOTHING & TEXTILES CO.; *Int'l*, pg. 2341
EMINENCE BENELUX S.A.—See GMM Capital LLC; *U.S. Private*, pg. 1723
EVEREST TEXTILE CO., LTD. - THAILAND FACTORY—See Everest Textile Co., Ltd.; *Int'l*, pg. 2565
FANG BROTHERS KNITTING LTD.; *Int'l*, pg. 2613
FASHION AVENUE KNITS, INC.; *U.S. Private*, pg. 1481
FATEH SPORTS WEAR LIMITED; *Int'l*, pg. 2622
FINE SHEER INDUSTRIES INC.; *U.S. Private*, pg. 1509
FRUIT OF THE LOOM, INC.—See Berkshire Hathaway Inc.; *U.S. Public*, pg. 305
GBG SOCKS, LLC—See Global Brands Group Holding Ltd; *Int'l*, pg. 2993
GILDAN ACTIVEWEAR (UK) LIMITED—See Gildan Activewear Inc.; *Int'l*, pg. 2973
GILDAN USA INC.—See Gildan Activewear Inc.; *Int'l*, pg. 2973
GOLDEN LADY S.P.A.; *Int'l*, pg. 3029
GRETEX INDUSTRIES LTD.; *Int'l*, pg. 3082
GUNZE LIMITED; *Int'l*, pg. 3185
HARRISS & COVINGTON HOSIERY MILLS; *U.S. Private*, pg. 1871
HERITAGE SPORTSWEAR, INC.; *U.S. Private*, pg. 1924
HIGHLAND MILLS INC.; *U.S. Private*, pg. 1938
HIGH STREET FILATEX LTD.; *Int'l*, pg. 3386
HOLT HOSIERY MILLS, INC.; *U.S. Private*, pg. 1968
HONG HO PRECISION TEXTILES CO., LTD.; *Int'l*, pg. 3465
HOT SOX COMPANY, INC.; *U.S. Private*, pg. 1988
THE HUBBARD COMPANY—See Individualized Apparel Group; *U.S. Private*, pg. 2064
IASON SA; *Int'l*, pg. 3569
INFINITY CLASSICS INTERNATIONAL; *U.S. Private*, pg. 2071
JERZEES—See Berkshire Hathaway Inc.; *U.S. Public*, pg. 305
JOCKEY INTERNATIONAL, INC.; *U.S. Private*, pg. 2217
KAMYN INDUSTRIES LTD—See Aga Khan Development Network; *Int'l*, pg. 199
KAYSER-ROTH CORPORATION—See Golden Lady S.p.A.; *Int'l*, pg. 3030
K.B. SOCKS, INC.; *U.S. Private*, pg. 2251
KNITCRAFT CORPORATION; *U.S. Private*, pg. 2322
KYUSHU GUNZE CO., LTD.—See Gunze Limited; *Int'l*, pg. 3186
LE BOURGET S.A.—See CSP International Fashion Group S.p.A.; *Int'l*, pg. 1867
LEG RESOURCE INC.; *U.S. Private*, pg. 2415
MAXLIN GARMENTS SDN. BHD.—See Baneng Holdings Bhd.; *Int'l*, pg. 831
MAYO KNITTING MILL INC.; *U.S. Private*, pg. 2622
MICHAEL SIMON INC.; *U.S. Private*, pg. 2698
MOUNTAIN HIGH KNITWEAR LTD.—See CCP Fund III Management LLC; *U.S. Private*, pg. 801
M. RUBIN & SONS INC.; *U.S. Private*, pg. 2527
MTM RECOGNITION CORPORATION; *U.S. Private*, pg. 2809
PARIS ACCESSORIES, INC.; *U.S. Private*, pg. 3094
PERFECTFORM—See Lady Ester Lingerie Corp.; *U.S. Private*, pg. 2372
PLEAS A.S.—See GMM Capital LLC; *U.S. Private*, pg. 1722
PRO FEET INC.; *U.S. Private*, pg. 3269
P.T. ECLAT TEXTILE INTERNATIONAL—See Eclat Textile Co., Ltd.; *Int'l*, pg. 2291
P.T. GUNZE SOCKS INDONESIA—See Gunze Limited; *Int'l*, pg. 3186
RECOVER GEAR, LLC; *U.S. Private*, pg. 3371
RELIABLE KNITTING WORKS, INC.; *U.S. Private*, pg. 3394
RENFRO CORPORATION—See The Renco Group Inc.; *U.S. Private*, pg. 4104
RENFRO INDIA PVT LTD.—See The Renco Group Inc.; *U.S. Private*, pg. 4104
RICHER POORER, INC.—See TerraMar Capital LLC; *U.S. Private*, pg. 3971
RIVER FALLS MANUFACTURING CO. INC.—See S. Rothschild & Co., Inc.; *U.S. Private*, pg. 3515
RUSSELL ATHLETIC—See Berkshire Hathaway Inc.; *U.S. Public*, pg. 305
RUSSELL CORP. ALEXANDER CITY—See Berkshire Hathaway Inc.; *U.S. Public*, pg. 305
SAN FRANCISCO KNITWORKS—See Hampshire Group Limited; *U.S. Private*, pg. 1851
SANPELLEGRINO POLSKA SP. Z O.O.—See CSP International Fashion Group S.p.A.; *Int'l*, pg. 1867
SCHIESSER INTERNATIONAL LTD.—See GMM Capital LLC; *U.S. Private*, pg. 1722
SCHIESSER SCHWEIZ AG—See GMM Capital LLC; *U.S. Private*, pg. 1722
SCULPTZ, INC.; *U.S. Private*, pg. 3581
SHANGHAI XINDIE TANAKA GARMENTS CO., LTD.—See Chori Co., Ltd.; *Int'l*, pg. 1583
SHOGREN HOSIERY MANUFACTURING CO., INC.—See Shogren Industries Inc.; *U.S. Private*, pg. 3639
SHOGREN INDUSTRIES INC.; *U.S. Private*, pg. 3639
SLANE HOSIERY MILLS, INC.; *U.S. Private*, pg. 3687
SOCK & ACCESSORY BRANDS GLOBAL, INC.—See Huron Capital Partners LLC; *U.S. Private*, pg. 2012
SPERIAN PROTECTION WORKWEAR SRL—See Honeywell International Inc.; *U.S. Public*, pg. 1049

ST. JOHN KNITS INTERNATIONAL, INC.—See Vestar/Gray Investors LLC; *U.S. Private*, pg. 4373
TEKBRANDS LLC—See WILsquare Capital LLC; *U.S. Private*, pg. 4532
THOR-LO, INC.; *U.S. Private*, pg. 4162
TOKYO KUTSUSHITA CO., LTD.—See Chori Co., Ltd.; *Int'l*, pg. 1583
TOPWELL GROUP DEVELOPMENT LTD—See Carry Wealth Holdings Limited; *Int'l*, pg. 1346
TRIMFIT COMPANY LIMITED—See Trimfit, Inc.; *U.S. Private*, pg. 4232
TRIMFIT, INC.; *U.S. Private*, pg. 4232
TRIUMPH LUCK LIMITED—See Fountain Set (Holdings) Limited; *Int'l*, pg. 2754
TWIN CITY KNITTING CO, INC.—See Huron Capital Partners LLC; *U.S. Private*, pg. 2012
UNI HOSIERY CO. INC.; *U.S. Private*, pg. 4281
UNION UNDERWEAR COMPANY, INC.—See Berkshire Hathaway Inc.; *U.S. Public*, pg. 305
US TEXTILE CORP.—See Sculptz, Inc.; *U.S. Private*, pg. 3581
WIGWAM MILLS, INC.; *U.S. Private*, pg. 4517
XERIANT, INC.; *U.S. Public*, pg. 2386

315210 — CUT AND SEW APPAREL CONTRACTORS

AEGIS ENGINEERING LIMITED—See Kanders & Company, Inc.; *U.S. Private*, pg. 2259
AMTEK HOLDINGS BERHAD; *Int'l*, pg. 441
ANTAEUS FASHIONS INC.—See Eclat Textile Co., Ltd.; *Int'l*, pg. 2291
AOYAMA TRADING CO. LTD.; *Int'l*, pg. 498
ARAMARK UNIFORM SERVICES (BALTIMORE) LLC—See Vestis Corp; *U.S. Public*, pg. 2290
ARAMARK UNIFORM SERVICES (TEXAS) LLC—See Vestis Corp; *U.S. Public*, pg. 2290
ASTRO APPAREL, INC.; *U.S. Private*, pg. 362
BEIJING COMPUTER TECHNOLOGY CO., LTD.—See Hyosung Corporation; *Int'l*, pg. 3550
BEIJING HYOSUNG CONTAINER CO., LTD.—See Hyosung Corporation; *Int'l*, pg. 3550
BEOCARE GROUP, INC.; *U.S. Private*, pg. 529
BETTY BARCLAY KLEIDERFABRIK GMBH; *Int'l*, pg. 1004
BGT CORPORATION PUBLIC COMPANY LIMITED; *Int'l*, pg. 1009
BINDAL EXPORTS LIMITED; *Int'l*, pg. 1033
BJORN BORG SWEDEN AB—See Bjorn Borg AB; *Int'l*, pg. 1054
BOSTON TEKNOWSYS (INDIA) LIMITED; *Int'l*, pg. 1118
CANADELLE L.P.—See Hanesbrands Inc.; *U.S. Public*, pg. 982
CANALI S.P.A.; *Int'l*, pg. 1287
CANALI USA INC.—See Canali S.p.A.; *Int'l*, pg. 1287
CARIBBEAN OUTERWEAR CORP.—See Standard Manufacturing Co., Inc.; *U.S. Private*, pg. 3781
CHANEL S.A.; *Int'l*, pg. 1441
CHEETAH HOLDINGS BERHAD; *Int'l*, pg. 1459
CJSC GLORIA JEANS CORPORATION; *Int'l*, pg. 1634
DELIA'S, INC.; *U.S. Private*, pg. 1197
DESTINATION MATERNITY CORPORATION; *U.S. Public*, pg. 656
DIANE VON FURSTENBERG COUTURE—See D.V.F. Studio; *U.S. Private*, pg. 1143
EAGLE NICE DEVELOPMENT LIMITED—See Eagle Nice (International) Holdings Ltd.; *Int'l*, pg. 2266
E-INSURE SERVICES, INC.—See Hellman & Friedman LLC; *U.S. Private*, pg. 1908
EMINENCE S.A.S.—See GMM Capital LLC; *U.S. Private*, pg. 1723
ESCADA FRANCE S.A.—See Regent, L.P.; *U.S. Private*, pg. 3387
ESCADA ITALIA S.R.L.—See Regent, L.P.; *U.S. Private*, pg. 3387
ESCADA JAPAN CO. LTD.—See Regent, L.P.; *U.S. Private*, pg. 3387
ESCADA KOREA LTD.—See Regent, L.P.; *U.S. Private*, pg. 3387
ESPRIT CANADA RETAIL LIMITED—See Esprit Holdings Limited; *Int'l*, pg. 2507
FAR EAST (EAG) LIMITED—See Eagle Nice (International) Holdings Ltd.; *Int'l*, pg. 2266
FORD GLORY INTERNATIONAL LIMITED; *Int'l*, pg. 2731
FRED PERRY LTD.—See Hit Union Company Ltd.; *Int'l*, pg. 3408
FRUIT OF THE LOOM SPORTS & LICENSING—See Berkshire Hathaway Inc.; *U.S. Public*, pg. 305
FUKURYO CO., LTD.—See AOYAMA TRADING Co. Ltd.; *Int'l*, pg. 498
FULIN PLASTIC INDUSTRY (CAYMAN) HOLDING CO., LTD.; *Int'l*, pg. 2842
G3 GLOBAL BERHAD; *Int'l*, pg. 2866
GARAN MANUFACTURING CORP.—See Berkshire Hathaway Inc.; *U.S. Public*, pg. 305
GERRY WEBER LIFE-STYLE FASHION GMBH—See GERRY WEBER International AG; *Int'l*, pg. 2944
GERRY WEBER SUPPORT S.R.L.—See GERRY WEBER

315210 — CUT AND SEW APPAREL...

International AG; *Int'l*, pg. 2945
GILDAN ACTIVEWEAR SRL—See Gildan Activewear Inc.; *Int'l*, pg. 2973
G&K SERVICES CANADA, INC.—See Cintas Corporation; *U.S. Public*, pg. 496
GOLDLION HOLDINGS LIMITED; *Int'l*, pg. 3033
GRAFTON FRASER, INC.; *Int'l*, pg. 3050
GUANGZHOU TAOBO SPORTS DEVELOPMENT COMPANY LIMITED—See Hillhouse Investment Management Limited; *Int'l*, pg. 3392
HIGH FASHION (CHINA) CO., LTD.—See High Fashion International Limited; *Int'l*, pg. 3385
HIGH FASHION GARMENTS COMPANY LIMITED—See High Fashion International Limited; *Int'l*, pg. 3385
HIGH FASHION (UK) LIMITED—See High Fashion International Limited; *Int'l*, pg. 3385
HIGHLAND RISK SERVICES LLC—See AmWINS Group, Inc.; *U.S. Private*, pg. 269
HIWAY TEXTILES LIMITED—See Fountain Set (Holdings) Limited; *Int'l*, pg. 2754
HORACE SMALL APPAREL COMPANY—See V. F. Corporation; *U.S. Public*, pg. 2269
HOUSE OF MONATIC (PTY) LTD.—See Brimstone Investment Corporation Ltd.; *Int'l*, pg. 1164
HYOGO GUNZE CO., LTD.—See Gunze Limited; *Int'l*, pg. 3186
HYOSUNG COMPUTER PERFORMANCE UNIT—See Hyosung Corporation; *Int'l*, pg. 3550
HYOSUNG CORPORATION BANGKOK—See Hyosung Corporation; *Int'l*, pg. 3550
HYOSUNG CORPORATION BEIJING—See Hyosung Corporation; *Int'l*, pg. 3550
HYOSUNG CORPORATION DUBAI—See Hyosung Corporation; *Int'l*, pg. 3551
HYOSUNG CORPORATION GUANGZHOU—See Hyosung Corporation; *Int'l*, pg. 3551
HYOSUNG CORPORATION HO CHI MINH—See Hyosung Corporation; *Int'l*, pg. 3551
HYOSUNG CORPORATION ISTANBUL—See Hyosung Corporation; *Int'l*, pg. 3551
HYOSUNG CORPORATION KAOHSIUNG—See Hyosung Corporation; *Int'l*, pg. 3551
HYOSUNG CORPORATION KUALA LUMPUR—See Hyosung Corporation; *Int'l*, pg. 3551
HYOSUNG CORPORATION MANILA—See Hyosung Corporation; *Int'l*, pg. 3551
HYOSUNG CORPORATION MOSCOW—See Hyosung Corporation; *Int'l*, pg. 3551
HYOSUNG CORPORATION SHANGHAI—See Hyosung Corporation; *Int'l*, pg. 3551
HYOSUNG CORPORATION TAIPEI—See Hyosung Corporation; *Int'l*, pg. 3551
HYOSUNG CORPORATION TEHRAN LIAISON OFFICE—See Hyosung Corporation; *Int'l*, pg. 3551
HYOSUNG EBARA ENVIRONMENTAL ENGINEERING CO. LTD.—See Hyosung Corporation; *Int'l*, pg. 3551
HYOSUNG (H.K.) LTD.—See Hyosung Corporation; *Int'l*, pg. 3550
HYOSUNG INFORMATION SYSTEMS CO., LTD.—See Hyosung Corporation; *Int'l*, pg. 3551
HYOSUNG MEDIA CO., LTD.—See Hyosung Corporation; *Int'l*, pg. 3551
HYOSUNG SINGAPORE PTE. LTD.—See Hyosung Corporation; *Int'l*, pg. 3551
JACLYN, INC.—See Golden Touch Imports, Inc.; *U.S. Private*, pg. 1734
JAMES C. GREENE COMPANY—See Tenco Services, Inc.; *U.S. Private*, pg. 3965
JEANSKOMPANIET AS—See Coala-Life Group AB; *Int'l*, pg. 1680
KENTUCKY APPAREL LLP; *U.S. Private*, pg. 2288
KURAYOSHI GUNZE CO., LTD.—See Gunze Limited; *Int'l*, pg. 3186
THE LAMARJEAN GROUP, INC.; *U.S. Private*, pg. 4067
LAURA ASHLEY LTD.—See Gordon Brothers Group, LLC; *U.S. Private*, pg. 1742
LEE JEANS—See Kontoor Brands, Inc.; *U.S. Public*, pg. 1271
LEVI STRAUSS & CO.—See Levi Strauss & Co.; *U.S. Public*, pg. 1308
LEVI STRAUSS POLAND SP Z.O.O.—See Levi Strauss & Co; *U.S. Public*, pg. 1309
MAHORSKY GROUP, INC—See Kelso & Company, L.P.; *U.S. Private*, pg. 2280
MANHATTAN BEACHWEAR, LLC—See Linsalata Capital Partners, Inc.; *U.S. Private*, pg. 2463
MARK J. BECKER & ASSOCIATES, LLC—See Arthur J. Gallagher & Co.; *U.S. Public*, pg. 206
MARSHALLS OF CA, LLC—See The TJX Companies, Inc.; *U.S. Public*, pg. 2134
MILLER INTERNATIONAL, INC. - CINCH JEANS AND SHIRTS DIVISION—See Miller International, Inc.; *U.S. Private*, pg. 2734
MOORES CLOTHING FOR MEN—See Tailored Brands, Inc.; *U.S. Public*, pg. 1979
MYANMAR HYOSUNG CO., LTD.—See Hyosung Corporation; *Int'l*, pg. 3552
NINGBO YOUNG TOP GARMENTS CO., LTD—See Fountain Set (Holdings) Limited; *Int'l*, pg. 2754

PAINTORY INC.—See Giftee, Inc.; *Int'l*, pg. 2970
PARKER UNIFORMS INC.; *U.S. Private*, pg. 3097
PHILLIPS-VAN HEUSEN CANADA, INC.—See PVH Corp.; *U.S. Public*, pg. 1739
QST DOMINICANA LLC—See QST Industries, Inc.; *U.S. Private*, pg. 3314
QST INDUSTRIAS DE MEXICO, S.A. DE R.L. DE C.V.—See QST Industries, Inc.; *U.S. Private*, pg. 3314
ROCKY OUTDOOR GEAR STORE, LLC—See Rocky Brands, Inc.; *U.S. Public*, pg. 1807
SALLY FOURMY & ASSOCIATES—See Cintas Corporation; *U.S. Public*, pg. 496
SCHIESSER AG—See GMM Capital LLC; *U.S. Private*, pg. 1722
SHOFF DARBY COMPANIES INC.—See Lawley Service Inc.; *U.S. Private*, pg. 2401
SPORTO CORP.; *U.S. Private*, pg. 3760
STANLEIGH INTERNATIONAL, INC.—See Kennington Ltd., Inc.; *U.S. Private*, pg. 2286
TAVE & ASSOCIATES, LLC—See Arthur J. Gallagher & Co.; *U.S. Public*, pg. 207
T.J. MAXX OF CA, LLC—See The TJX Companies, Inc.; *U.S. Public*, pg. 2134
TOHOKU GUNZE CO., LTD.—See Gunze Limited; *Int'l*, pg. 3186
TRACY EVANS LTD. INC.; *U.S. Private*, pg. 4201
UNDER ARMOUR, INC.; *U.S. Public*, pg. 2225
VEDANTA CREATIONS LIMITED—See Bang Overseas Ltd.; *Int'l*, pg. 832
VF IMAGEWEAR, INC.—See V. F. Corporation; *U.S. Public*, pg. 2269
WILLIAMSON-DICKIE APPAREL TRADING (SHANGHAI) CO. LTD—See V. F. Corporation; *U.S. Public*, pg. 2269
YABU APPAREL LTD.—See Gunze Limited; *Int'l*, pg. 3186
Z. CAVARICCI INC.—See Z. Cavaricci Inc.; *U.S. Private*, pg. 4596

315250 — CUT AND SEW APPAREL MANUFACTURING (EXCEPT CONTRACTORS)

7 FOR ALL MANKIND—See GMM Capital LLC; *U.S. Private*, pg. 1722
AARVEE DENIMS & EXPORTS LTD.; *Int'l*, pg. 38
ACNE STUDIO AB; *Int'l*, pg. 107
ACTIVE CLOTHING CO., LTD.; *Int'l*, pg. 120
ADDENTAX GROUP CORP.; *Int'l*, pg. 128
ADITRI INDUSTRIES LIMITED; *Int'l*, pg. 149
ADJMI APPAREL GROUP, INC.; *U.S. Private*, pg. 79
ADS, INC.; *U.S. Private*, pg. 82
ADVANCE LATEX PRODUCTS, INC.; *U.S. Private*, pg. 83
AFFINITY SPECIAL APPAREL, INC.—See Resilience Capital Partners, LLC; *U.S. Private*, pg. 3405
AFTER SIX, LLC—See The Anderson Group, LLC; *U.S. Private*, pg. 3986
AIMER CO., LTD.; *Int'l*, pg. 233
ALFRED ANGELO, INC.; *U.S. Private*, pg. 165
ALISON HAYES; *Int'l*, pg. 329
ALLESON OF ROCHESTER, INC.—See Platinum Equity, LLC; *U.S. Private*, pg. 3207
ALSCO BERUFSKLEIDUNGS-SERVICE GMBH—See Alsco Inc.; *U.S. Private*, pg. 202
ALYCE DESIGNS INC.; *U.S. Private*, pg. 214
AMAL SAMHA CO.; *Int'l*, pg. 408
AMCO INDIA INC.; *Int'l*, pg. 416
AMEREX KID'S GROUP—See Amerex Group, Inc.; *U.S. Private*, pg. 219
AMERICAN APPAREL, INC.; *U.S. Private*, pg. 222
AMERICAN APPAREL JAPAN YUGER KAISHA—See American Apparel, Inc.; *U.S. Private*, pg. 222
AMERICAN UNIFORM CO.—See Alsco Inc.; *U.S. Private*, pg. 202
A.M.E.'S UNIFORMS, INC.; *U.S. Private*, pg. 27
ANZHENG FASHION GROUP CO., LTD.; *Int'l*, pg. 487
APEX LINGERIE LIMITED—See Apex Holding Limited; *Int'l*, pg. 511
THE APPAREL GROUP, LTD.; *U.S. Private*, pg. 3987
APPAREL RESOURCES INC.; *U.S. Private*, pg. 295
APPARELWAY, INC.; *U.S. Private*, pg. 295
ARC OUTDOORS; *U.S. Private*, pg. 309
ARNAV INDUSTRIES, INC.; *U.S. Private*, pg. 332
ARROW SHIRT CO.—See PVH Corp.; *U.S. Public*, pg. 1739
ART LEWIN & CO.; *U.S. Private*, pg. 340
ATELIER GARDEUR GMBH; *Int'l*, pg. 668
ATHLETA—See The Gap, Inc.; *U.S. Public*, pg. 2074
ATSUGI CO., LTD.; *Int'l*, pg. 696
ATTITUDES IN DRESSING INC.; *U.S. Private*, pg. 383
AUBADE ITALIA S.R.L.—See Calida Holding AG; *Int'l*, pg. 1264
AUBADE PARIS SAS—See Calida Holding AG; *Int'l*, pg. 1264
AUBADE PARIS (UK) LTD.—See Calida Holding AG; *Int'l*, pg. 1264
AUGUSTA SPORTSWEAR, INC.—See Platinum Equity, LLC; *U.S. Private*, pg. 3207
AXARA; *Int'l*, pg. 761
BABY TOGS, INC.; *U.S. Private*, pg. 422

BADGER SPORTSWEAR, LLC—See Platinum Equity, LLC; *U.S. Private*, pg. 3207
BAGATELLE INTERNATIONAL INC.; *Int'l*, pg. 799
BALLIN, INC.; *Int'l*, pg. 809
BANENG HOLDINGS BHD.; *Int'l*, pg. 831
BANG OVERSEAS LTD.; *Int'l*, pg. 831
BAOXINIAO HOLDING CO., LTD.; *Int'l*, pg. 857
BARAKA FASHIONS LIMITED—See Baraka Power Limited; *Int'l*, pg. 858
BARBARA BUI SA; *Int'l*, pg. 858
BARCO UNIFORMS, INC.; *U.S. Private*, pg. 473
BARI-JAY FASHIONS INC.; *U.S. Private*, pg. 474
BARREL CO., LTD.; *Int'l*, pg. 869
BASICITALIA S.R.L.—See BasicNet S.p.A.; *Int'l*, pg. 886
BAUHAUS INTERNATIONAL (HOLDINGS) LIMITED; *Int'l*, pg. 894
BEBE STUDIO, INC.—See B. Riley Financial, Inc.; *U.S. Public*, pg. 262
BECCA & BEN LLC; *U.S. Private*, pg. 509
BEE DARLIN', INC.; *U.S. Private*, pg. 512
BELUGA INC.—See Adjmi Apparel Group, Inc.; *U.S. Private*, pg. 79
BENETTON U.S.A. CORPORATION—See Edizione S.r.l.; *Int'l*, pg. 2311
BERNARD CHAUS, INC.; *U.S. Private*, pg. 535
BEST MANUFACTURING GROUP LLC—See GHCL Limited; *Int'l*, pg. 2959
BETSY & ADAM LTD.; *U.S. Private*, pg. 546
BEYOND CLOTHING, LLC—See Compass Diversified Holdings; *U.S. Public*, pg. 559
BHANDARI HOSIERY EXPORTS LTD.; *Int'l*, pg. 1010
BHARTIYA INTERNATIONAL LTD.; *Int'l*, pg. 1013
BIBETTE (PTY) LTD.—See E Media Holdings Limited; *Int'l*, pg. 2246
BILL'S KHAKIS—See NEJ, Inc.; *U.S. Private*, pg. 2882
BILLWIN INDUSTRIES LIMITED; *Int'l*, pg. 1031
BJORN BORG AB; *Int'l*, pg. 1053
BLAUER MANUFACTURING COMPANY, INC.; *U.S. Private*, pg. 580
BLEACH GROUP, INC.; *U.S. Private*, pg. 580
BLEU OCEANE; *Int'l*, pg. 1063
BLUE CAST DENIM CO. INC.; *U.S. Private*, pg. 586
BLUE MAX BANNER LIMITED; *Int'l*, pg. 1069
BOARDRIDERS JAPAN CO., LTD.—See Leonard Green & Partners, L.P.; *U.S. Public*, pg. 2424
BONAVENTURE CO, LLC; *U.S. Private*, pg. 613
BONSOIR OF LONDON LTD.; *Int'l*, pg. 1109
BORCH TEXTILE GROUP A/S; *Int'l*, pg. 1113
BORGO 21 S.P.A.—See Giorgio Armani S.p.A.; *Int'l*, pg. 2978
BOUTIQUE NEWCITY PUBLIC COMPANY LIMITED; *Int'l*, pg. 1121
BOWE INDUSTRIES INC.; *U.S. Private*, pg. 625
BREMEN-BOWDON INVESTMENT CO; *U.S. Private*, pg. 645
BRISCO APPAREL CO. INC.; *U.S. Private*, pg. 655
BROOKHURST, INC.; *U.S. Private*, pg. 663
BROOKLYN INDUSTRIES; *U.S. Private*, pg. 663
THE BROWN & CHURCH COMPANY—See Individualized Apparel Group; *U.S. Public*, pg. 2064
BRUNELLO CUCINELLI AUSTRIA GMBH—See Brunello Cucinelli S.p.A.; *Int'l*, pg. 1200
BRUNELLO CUCINELLI BRASIL LTDA—See Brunello Cucinelli S.p.A.; *Int'l*, pg. 1200
BRUNELLO CUCINELLI DENMARK APS—See Brunello Cucinelli S.p.A.; *Int'l*, pg. 1200
BRUNELLO CUCINELLI HELLAS SA—See Brunello Cucinelli S.p.A.; *Int'l*, pg. 1200
BRUNELLO CUCINELLI NETHERLANDS B.V.—See Brunello Cucinelli S.p.A.; *Int'l*, pg. 1200
BRUNELLO CUCINELLI RETAIL SPAIN SL—See Brunello Cucinelli S.p.A.; *Int'l*, pg. 1200
BRUNELLO CUCINELLI (SICHUAN) FASHION CO. LTD.—See Brunello Cucinelli S.p.A.; *Int'l*, pg. 1200
BRUNELLO CUCINELLI S.P.A.; *Int'l*, pg. 1200
BRUNELLO CUCINELLI SUISSE SA—See Brunello Cucinelli S.p.A.; *Int'l*, pg. 1200
BSL LIMITED; *Int'l*, pg. 1202
BURLEN CORP.—See GMM Capital LLC; *U.S. Private*, pg. 1722
BUZZWIT CO., LTD.—See Adastria Co., Ltd.; *Int'l*, pg. 126
BYC CO., LTD.; *Int'l*, pg. 1234
BYER CALIFORNIA - LOS ANGELES FACTORY—See Byer California; *U.S. Private*, pg. 700
BYER CALIFORNIA; *U.S. Private*, pg. 700
CABBEEN FASHION LIMITED; *Int'l*, pg. 1245
CACHET INDUSTRIES INC.; *U.S. Private*, pg. 712
CALERES CANADA, INC.—See Caleres, Inc.; *U.S. Public*, pg. 422
CALHOUN APPAREL INC.; *U.S. Private*, pg. 717
CALIDA AG—See Calida Holding AG; *Int'l*, pg. 1264
CALIFORNIA MANUFACTURING CO. INC.; *U.S. Private*, pg. 719
CAMPBELLSVILLE APPAREL COMPANY, LLC; *U.S. Private*, pg. 731
CANADA GOOSE INC.—See Bain Capital, LP; *U.S. Private*, pg. 437
CANTOR GROUP, INC.; *U.S. Private*, pg. 736

N.A.I.C.S. INDEX

315250 — CUT AND SEW APPAREL...

CAPITAL MERCURY SHIRTMAKERS LLC; *U.S. Private*, pg. 741
CARHARTT, INC.; *U.S. Private*, pg. 760
CAROLE WREN, INC.; *U.S. Private*, pg. 767
CATHY DANIELS LTD.—See Jump Design Group; *U.S. Private*, pg. 2243
CC FILSON CO.; *U.S. Private*, pg. 799
CEDAR DEVELOPMENT CO., LTD.; *Int'l*, pg. 1388
CEENIK EXPORTS (INDIA) LIMITED; *Int'l*, pg. 1388
CELEBRITY FASHIONS LIMITED; *Int'l*, pg. 1392
CENTRAL MILLS INC.; *U.S. Private*, pg. 822
CENTRIC BRANDS INC.; *U.S. Private*, pg. 829
CEPOVETT; *Int'l*, pg. 1420
CHAMPION ATHLETICWEAR INC.—See Hanesbrands Inc.; *U.S. Public*, pg. 982
CHANO INTERNATIONAL INC.; *U.S. Private*, pg. 849
CHARLES KOMAR & SONS, INC.; *U.S. Private*, pg. 852
CHARLES TYRWHITT LLP.; *Int'l*, pg. 1450
CHENILLE INTERNATIONAL PTE. LTD.—See Baneng Holdings Bhd.; *Int'l*, pg. 831
CHETTA B INC.; *U.S. Private*, pg. 875
CHEYNET ASIA (CO.) LTD.—See Cheynet S.A.S.; *Int'l*, pg. 1474
CHEYNET TUNISIE—See Cheynet S.A.S.; *Int'l*, pg. 1474
CHICAGO PROTECTIVE APPAREL, INC.—See Gryphon Investors, LLC; *U.S. Private*, pg. 1798
CHINA ANCHU ENERGY STORAGE GROUP LIMITED; *Int'l*, pg. 1482
CHINA PARTYTIME CULTURE HOLDINGS LIMITED; *Int'l*, pg. 1539
CHINA TAISAN TECHNOLOGY GROUP HOLDINGS LIMITED; *Int'l*, pg. 1557
CHIRIPAL INDUSTRIES LTD. - FABRIC DIVISION—See Chiripal Industries Ltd.; *Int'l*, pg. 1573
CHIRIPAL INDUSTRIES LTD. - PETROCHEMICAL DIVISION—See Chiripal Industries Ltd.; *Int'l*, pg. 1573
CHOCOLATE SOUP INC.; *U.S. Private*, pg. 887
CIA TECIDOS SANTANENSE; *Int'l*, pg. 1602
CINTAS CORPORATION; *U.S. Public*, pg. 495
CIRCLE T WESTERN WEAR INC.; *U.S. Private*, pg. 900
CITYMAN LIMITED; *Int'l*, pg. 1629
CITY SITES SPORTSWEAR INC.; *U.S. Private*, pg. 907
CLASSITA (M) SDN. BHD.—See Classita Holdings Berhad; *Int'l*, pg. 1653
C.M. ALMY & SON, INC.; *U.S. Private*, pg. 708
COALA-LIFE GROUP AB; *Int'l*, pg. 1680
COATS BANGLADESH LIMITED—See Coats Group plc; *Int'l*, pg. 1681
COATS EGYPT FOR MANUFACTURING & DYEING SEWING THREAD SAE—See Coats Group plc; *Int'l*, pg. 1682
CODES COMBINE CO., LTD.; *Int'l*, pg. 1688
COLUMBIA BRANDS INTERNATIONAL SARL—See Columbia Sportswear Company; *U.S. Public*, pg. 534
COLUMBIA BRANDS USA, LLC—See Columbia Sportswear Company; *U.S. Public*, pg. 534
COMBI NEXT CORPORATION—See Combi Corporation; *Int'l*, pg. 1708
COMEFLY OUTDOOR CO LTD; *Int'l*, pg. 1710
CONCORDE APPAREL CO. LLC; *U.S. Private*, pg. 1010
CONFECCOES PORTO GRANDE, LDA; *Int'l*, pg. 1767
CONNECTED APPAREL COMPANY LLC; *U.S. Private*, pg. 1015
COOLIBAR, INC.; *U.S. Private*, pg. 1040
COOLWEAR INC.; *U.S. Private*, pg. 1040
COPPLEY, INC.—See Individualized Apparel Group; *U.S. Private*, pg. 2064
CP SHADES INC.; *U.S. Private*, pg. 1079
CREOS APPAREL CORPORATION—See GSI Creos Corporation; *Int'l*, pg. 3144
CROCODILE GARMENTS LIMITED; *Int'l*, pg. 1851
CRYSTAL INTERNATIONAL GROUP LIMITED; *Int'l*, pg. 1860
CRYSTAL MARTIN (VIETNAM) COMPANY LIMITED—See Crystal International Group Limited; *Int'l*, pg. 1860
CRYSTAL SPRINGS APPAREL LLC; *U.S. Private*, pg. 1115
CUPID FOUNDATIONS, INC.; *U.S. Private*, pg. 1123
CUT LOOSE; *U.S. Private*, pg. 1130
DAIDOH LIMITED; *Int'l*, pg. 1923
DAITOBO CO., LTD.; *Int'l*, pg. 1944
DAMART SERVIPOSTE S.A.—See Damartex SA; *Int'l*, pg. 1956
DANSKIN, INC.—See Iconix Acquisition LLC; *U.S. Private*, pg. 2032
DA-RUE OF CALIFORNIA, INC.; *U.S. Private*, pg. 1143
DASHAMERICA INC.; *U.S. Private*, pg. 1162
DAVID PEYSER SPORTSWEAR INC.; *U.S. Private*, pg. 1171
DBA DEUTSCHLAND GMBH—See Hanesbrands Inc.; *U.S. Public*, pg. 982
DBAPPAREL UK TRADING LTD—See Hanesbrands Inc.; *U.S. Public*, pg. 982
DECO&E CO., LTD.; *Int'l*, pg. 2001
DELONG SPORTSWEAR, INC.; *U.S. Private*, pg. 1198
DEL SOL LLC—See Pedersen Worldwide; *U.S. Private*, pg. 3128
DELTA GALIL GERMANY GMBH—See GMM Capital LLC; *U.S. Private*, pg. 1722

DELTA GALIL INDUSTRIES LTD.—See GMM Capital LLC; *U.S. Private*, pg. 1722
DELTA GALIL USA INC.—See GMM Capital LLC; *U.S. Private*, pg. 1722
DE MOULIN BROTHERS & COMPANY; *U.S. Private*, pg. 1181
DENIMATRIX S.A.—See Monomoy Capital Partners LLC; *U.S. Private*, pg. 2772
DEPECHE MODE COMPANY; *U.S. Private*, pg. 1208
DEVERNOIS SA; *Int'l*, pg. 2088
DEVIL DOG MANUFACTURING CO., INC.—See General Sportswear Co. Inc.; *U.S. Private*, pg. 1667
DIANA DOLLS FASHIONS INC.; *Int'l*, pg. 2106
DIMKO MITREV JSC; *Int'l*, pg. 2126
DIN LEATHER(PVT) LTD.—See Din Textile Mills Ltd.; *Int'l*, pg. 2126
D.J. BRONSON INC.; *U.S. Private*, pg. 1142
DMBM LLC; *U.S. Private*, pg. 1248
DODGER INDUSTRIES INC.—See The Greene Company of Virginia Inc.; *U.S. Private*, pg. 4039
DONCASTER—See Tanner Companies, LP; *U.S. Private*, pg. 3931
DOOSAN TOWER CORPORATION—See Doosan Corporation; *Int'l*, pg. 2173
DOUGLAS GILL INTERNATIONAL LIMITED—See POP Capital LLC; *U.S. Private*, pg. 3228
DPNK CO., LTD; *Int'l*, pg. 2189
DRAGON SWEATER & SPINNING LIMITED; *Int'l*, pg. 2199
DR. BOCK INDUSTRIES AG; *Int'l*, pg. 2190
DUNXIN FINANCIAL HOLDINGS LTD; *Int'l*, pg. 2227
DYNAMIC TEAM SPORTS INC.; *U.S. Private*, pg. 1299
EASYKNIT INTERNATIONAL HOLDINGS LTD.; *Int'l*, pg. 2276
ECLAT FABRICS (VIETNAM) CO., LTD.—See Eclat Textile Co., Ltd.; *Int'l*, pg. 2291
ECLAT TEXTILE (COMBODIA) CO., LTD.—See Eclat Textile Co., Ltd.; *Int'l*, pg. 2291
ECLAT TEXTILE (VIETNAM) CO., LTD.—See Eclat Textile Co., Ltd.; *Int'l*, pg. 2291
EDINTSVO AD; *Int'l*, pg. 2310
EDMUND KIM INTERNATIONAL INC.; *U.S. Private*, pg. 1337
EDMUND KIM PRODUCTIONS GROUP—See Edmund Kim International Inc.; *U.S. Private*, pg. 1338
EDUN APPAREL LTD.; *Int'l*, pg. 2316
EILEEN FISHER, INC.; *U.S. Private*, pg. 1347
E-LAND APPAREL LTD; *Int'l*, pg. 2248
E-LAND INTERNATIONAL FASHION (SHANGHAI) CO., LTD.—See E-Land World Ltd.; *Int'l*, pg. 2248
ELAN INDUSTRIES—See Etam Developpement SCA; *Int'l*, pg. 2520
ELBECO INCORPORATED—See Lakeland Industries, Inc.; *U.S. Public*, pg. 1288
ELDER MANUFACTURING COMPANY, INC.; *U.S. Private*, pg. 1351
ELEMENT RULE CO., LTD.—See Adastria Co., Ltd.; *Int'l*, pg. 126
ELIE TAHARI, LTD.; *U.S. Private*, pg. 1360
ELITE SPORTSWEAR, L.P.; *U.S. Private*, pg. 1361
ELK BRAND MANUFACTURING CO.; *U.S. Private*, pg. 1362
ELLA MOSS—See GMM Capital LLC; *U.S. Private*, pg. 1722
ELVE S.A.; *Int'l*, pg. 2371
ELZAY READY WEAR MANUFACTURING COMPANY; *Int'l*, pg. 2372
ENCOMPASS GROUP LLC; *U.S. Private*, pg. 1390
EPS CREATIVE HEALTH TECHNOLOGY GROUP LTD.—See EPS Holdings, Inc.; *Int'l*, pg. 2465
ERMENEGILDO ZEGNA HOLDITALIA S.P.A.; *Int'l*, pg. 2494
ESCADA CANADA INC.—See Regent, L.P.; *U.S. Private*, pg. 3387
ESSEX MANUFACTURING INC.; *U.S. Private*, pg. 1428
E.S. SUTTON INC.—See E.S. Sutton Inc.; *U.S. Private*, pg. 1307
ETAM DEVELOPPEMENT SCA; *Int'l*, pg. 2520
ETAM POLAND SP—See Etam Developpement SCA; *Int'l*, pg. 2520
ETON AB—See EQT AB; *Int'l*, pg. 2475
E-TOP (VIETNAM) CO., LTD.—See Eclat Textile Co., Ltd.; *Int'l*, pg. 2291
EURO ASIA EXPORTS LIMITED; *Int'l*, pg. 2530
EUROLEDER FASHION LIMITED; *Int'l*, pg. 2553
EVEREST TEXTILE CO., LTD. SHANGHAI FACTORY—See Everest Textile Co., Ltd.; *Int'l*, pg. 2565
EVER-GLORY INTERNATIONAL GROUP INC.; *Int'l*, pg. 2563
EVY OF CALIFORNIA, INC.; *U.S. Private*, pg. 1444
EXCEED COMPANY LTD.; *Int'l*, pg. 2577
EXCELHIGH INC.; *U.S. Private*, pg. 1445
EXCELLED SHEEPSKIN & LEATHER COAT CORPORATION; *U.S. Private*, pg. 1445
EXCELLED SHEEPSKIN & LEATHER COAT CORPORATION—See Excelled Sheepskin & Leather Coat Corporation; *U.S. Private*, pg. 1445
FAMILYTEX (BD) LIMITED; *Int'l*, pg. 2612
FANG CLOTHING INC.; *U.S. Private*, pg. 1472
FARRIS FASHIONS INC.; *U.S. Private*, pg. 1481

FASHION BOX GREECE S.A.—See Fashion Box S.p.A.; *Int'l*, pg. 2621
FASHION BOX S.P.A.; *Int'l*, pg. 2620
FAST LANE CLOTHING COMPANY, INC.; *U.S. Private*, pg. 1482
THE FECHHEIMER BROTHERS COMPANY—See Berkshire Hathaway Inc.; *U.S. Public*, pg. 316
FIELDSTON CLOTHES INC.—See S. Rothschild & Co., Inc.; *U.S. Private*, pg. 3515
FILIPPA K AB; *Int'l*, pg. 2663
FILWEL CO., LTD.—See Air Water Inc.; *Int'l*, pg. 240
FINANCIERE MARJOS SA; *Int'l*, pg. 2668
FINEBRAND DIVISION—See National Corset Supply House; *U.S. Private*, pg. 2852
FISHMAN & TOBIN, INC.; *U.S. Private*, pg. 1535
FLAX DESIGNS; *U.S. Private*, pg. 1541
FLYNN ENTERPRISES, LLC; *U.S. Private*, pg. 1553
FORD GLORY (CAMBODIA) MANUFACTURING LTD.—See Ford Glory International Limited; *Int'l*, pg. 2731
FORECASTER OF BOSTON INC.; *U.S. Private*, pg. 1565
FOR THE BRIDE BY DEMETRIOS; *U.S. Private*, pg. 1562
FORTUNE CASUALS, LLC; *U.S. Private*, pg. 1577
FOX HEAD, INC.—See Vista Outdoor Inc.; *U.S. Public*, pg. 2305
FREUDENBERG GYGLI AG—See Freudenberg SE; *Int'l*, pg. 2786
FRIGHT-RAGS, INC.; *U.S. Private*, pg. 1612
FUJIAN NUOQI CO., LTD.—See Aceso Life Science Group Limited; *Int'l*, pg. 102
FUJIAN SEPTWOLVES INDUSTRY CO., LTD.; *Int'l*, pg. 2819
FUNTEES—See Delta Apparel, Inc.; *U.S. Public*, pg. 652
GALLERY INDUSTRIES INC.; *U.S. Private*, pg. 1639
GARAN, INCORPORATED—See Berkshire Hathaway Inc.; *U.S. Public*, pg. 305
GARMENT MANTRA LIFESTYLE LTD.; *Int'l*, pg. 2884
GEARCO—See Hanesbrands Inc.; *U.S. Public*, pg. 983
GENERAL SPORTSWEAR CO. INC.; *U.S. Private*, pg. 1667
GERRY WEBER FASHION IBERICA S.L.—See GERRY WEBER International AG; *Int'l*, pg. 2944
GERSON & GERSON, INC.; *U.S. Private*, pg. 1688
GFSI, INC.—See Hanesbrands Inc.; *U.S. Public*, pg. 983
GILDAN ACTIVEWEAR DOMINICAN REPUBLIC TEXTILE COMPANY INC.—See Gildan Activewear Inc.; *Int'l*, pg. 2973
GILDAN HONDURAS—See Gildan Activewear Inc.; *Int'l*, pg. 2973
GIORDANO MIDDLE EAST FZE—See Giordano International Limited; *Int'l*, pg. 2978
GIORDANO (M) SDN. BHD.—See Giordano International Limited; *Int'l*, pg. 2977
GIORDANO (THAI) CO., LTD.—See Giordano International Limited; *Int'l*, pg. 2977
GLAMORISE FOUNDATIONS, INC.; *U.S. Private*, pg. 1706
GLOBAL GOLD, INC.—See Golden Touch Imports, Inc.; *U.S. Private*, pg. 1733
GLOBAL PRODUCTS INC.; *U.S. Private*, pg. 1717
GLOBE MANUFACTURING COMPANY, INC.—See MSA Safety Incorporated; *U.S. Public*, pg. 1481
GLORIA LANCE INC.; *U.S. Private*, pg. 1720
GLORIOUS SUN ENTERPRISES LIMITED; *Int'l*, pg. 3009
GNCO CO., LTD.; *Int'l*, pg. 3016
GOKALDAS EXPORTS LTD; *Int'l*, pg. 3022
GOLDEN WILL FASHIONS LIMITED; *Int'l*, pg. 3032
GOLF APPAREL BRANDS, INC.; *U.S. Private*, pg. 1735
GOOD PEOPLE CO., LTD; *Int'l*, pg. 3038
GREAT GROUP HOLDINGS LIMITED; *Int'l*, pg. 3064
GREATIME INTERNATIONAL HOLDINGS LIMITED; *Int'l*, pg. 3067
THE GREENE COMPANY OF VIRGINIA INC.; *U.S. Private*, pg. 4039
THE GREG NORMAN COLLECTION—See Hellman & Friedman LLC; *U.S. Private*, pg. 1907
GRIFFIN MEDICAL PRODUCTS INC.; *U.S. Private*, pg. 1788
GSG SCOVILL FASTENERS ASIA LIMITED—See The Gores Group, LLC; *U.S. Private*, pg. 4035
GSI CREOS KOREA CO., LTD.—See GSI Creos Corporation; *Int'l*, pg. 3144
GUARARAPES CONFECCOES S.A.; *Int'l*, pg. 3169
GUIRENNIAO CO., LTD.; *Int'l*, pg. 3174
HAGGAR CLOTHING CO.—See Randa Corp.; *U.S. Private*, pg. 3353
HAGGAR CORPORATION—See Perseus LLC; *U.S. Private*, pg. 3155
HANDSOME CORP.; *Int'l*, pg. 3243
HANES AUSTRALASIA PTY LTD—See Hanesbrands Inc.; *U.S. Public*, pg. 983
HANES AUSTRIA GMBH—See Hanesbrands Inc.; *U.S. Public*, pg. 983
HANESBRANDS INC.; *U.S. Public*, pg. 982
HANES FRANCE S.A.S.—See Hanesbrands Inc.; *U.S. Public*, pg. 982
HANSAE CO., LTD.—See Hansae Yes24 Holdings Co., Ltd.; *Int'l*, pg. 3259
HARARI INC.; *U.S. Private*, pg. 1857

315250 — CUT AND SEW APPAREL...

HARDWICK CLOTHES INC.; *U.S. Private*, pg. 1864
HBI RECEIVABLES LLC—See Hanesbrands Inc.; *U.S. Public*, pg. 983
HEADS UP VENTURES LIMITED—See GB Global Limited; *Int'l*, pg. 2892
HELIOS S.A.—See EL. D. MOUZAKIS S.A.; *Int'l*, pg. 2341
HELLY HANSEN AS—See Canadian Tire Corporation Limited; *Int'l*, pg. 1286
HELLY-HANSEN (US), INC.—See Canadian Tire Corporation Limited; *Int'l*, pg. 1286
HERFF JONES, INC. - CAP & GOWN DIVISION—See Bain Capital, LP; *U.S. Private*, pg. 451
HERFF JONES, INC. - COLLEGIATE CAP & GOWN, ARCOLA—See Bain Capital, LP; *U.S. Private*, pg. 452
HERMAN KAY BROMLEY INC.; *U.S. Private*, pg. 1925
HF MANUFACTURING CORP.; *U.S. Private*, pg. 1928
H. FREEMAN & SON, INC.; *U.S. Private*, pg. 1824
HICKEY FREEMAN TAILERED CLOTHING, INC.—See Grano Retail Investments Inc.; *Int'l*, pg. 3059
H M S PRODUCTIONS, INC.—See Bruderman & Co., LLC; *U.S. Private*, pg. 671
HOJEON LIMITED; *Int'l*, pg. 3442
HOLLOWAY SPORTSWEAR, INC.—See Platinum Equity, LLC; *U.S. Private*, pg. 3207
HONEYS HOLDINGS CO., LTD.; *Int'l*, pg. 3465
HOP LUN (HONG KONG) LIMITED—See Platinum Equity, LLC; *U.S. Private*, pg. 3203
HOSA INTERNATIONAL LIMITED; *Int'l*, pg. 3482
HOUSE OF PERFECTION, INC.; *U.S. Private*, pg. 1991
HUBEI MAILYARD SHARE CO., LTD.; *Int'l*, pg. 3518
HURLEY INTERNATIONAL LLC—See Bluestar Alliance LLC; *U.S. Private*, pg. 598
HYOSUNG CORPORATION EDUCATION CENTER—See Hyosung Corporation; *Int'l*, pg. 3551
HYOSUNG CORPORATION MEXICO—See Hyosung Corporation; *Int'l*, pg. 3551
HYOSUNG JAPAN OSAKA—See Hyosung Corporation; *Int'l*, pg. 3551
HYUNGJI INNOVATION AND CREATIVE COMPANY LIMITED; *Int'l*, pg. 3561
THE ICEBOX, LLC; *U.S. Private*, pg. 4055
IC GROUP A/S—See Friheden Invest A/S; *Int'l*, pg. 2792
ICON FASHION HOLDING AG; *Int'l*, pg. 3583
IFABRIC CORP.; *Int'l*, pg. 3598
IKEDDI ENTERPRISES INC.; *U.S. Private*, pg. 2041
IMAGE SOLUTIONS APPAREL, INC.; *U.S. Private*, pg. 2045
INDERA MILLS COMPANY—See Intradeco, Inc.; *U.S. Private*, pg. 2129
INDO BRITISH GARMENTS (P) LTD.—See Allied Universal Manager LLC; *U.S. Private*, pg. 190
ISFEL COMPANY, INC.; *U.S. Private*, pg. 2143
I. SPIEWAK & SONS, INC.; *U.S. Private*, pg. 2026
IT'S GREEK TO ME, INC.—See Hanesbrands Inc.; *U.S. Public*, pg. 983
IZOD—See PVH Corp.; *U.S. Public*, pg. 1739
JACQUES VERT GROUP LTD.—See Sun Capital Partners, Inc.; *U.S. Private*, pg. 3861
JAG APPAREL—See Apparel Group Pty. Ltd.; *Int'l*, pg. 519
JAKROO INC.; *U.S. Private*, pg. 2182
J. AMERICA, INC.—See Blue Point Capital Partners, LLC; *U.S. Private*, pg. 590
JANIE & JACK LLC—See The Gap, Inc.; *U.S. Public*, pg. 2074
JANTZEN APPAREL, LLC—See Perry Ellis International, Inc.; *U.S. Private*, pg. 3153
JAPANESE WEEKEND INC.; *U.S. Private*, pg. 2188
JAYA APPAREL; *U.S. Private*, pg. 2192
JBS LIMITED; *U.S. Private*, pg. 2194
JEANSWEAR SERVICES FAR EAST LTD.—See Fingen S.p.A.; *Int'l*, pg. 2674
JERASH GARMENTS AND FASHIONS MANUFACTURING CO. LTD.—See Ford Glory International Limited; *Int'l*, pg. 2731
JESSICA HOWARD, LTD.—See G-III Apparel Group, Ltd.; *U.S. Public*, pg. 894
JIANGMEN VA MANUFACTURING LTD.—See Ford Glory International Limited; *Int'l*, pg. 2731
J.JILL, INC.; *U.S. Public*, pg. 1180
JLM COUTURE, INC.; *U.S. Public*, pg. 1190
J. MENDEL, INC.—See Stallion, Inc.; *U.S. Private*, pg. 3776
JODI KRISTOPHER INC.; *U.S. Private*, pg. 2218
JOE BENBASSET INCORPORATED; *U.S. Private*, pg. 2218
JOE BOXER COMPANY, LLC—See Iconix Acquisition LLC; *U.S. Private*, pg. 2033
JOHN H. DANIEL COMPANY INC.; *U.S. Private*, pg. 2222
JOHNNY WAS, LLC—See Oxford Industries, Inc.; *U.S. Public*, pg. 1629
JOHN PAUL RICHARD INC.; *U.S. Private*, pg. 2223
JORO FASHIONS INCORPORATED; *U.S. Private*, pg. 2236
JUNONIA LTD.; *U.S. Private*, pg. 2245
JUST FOR WRAPS; *U.S. Private*, pg. 2245
KAHN-LUCAS-LANCASTER INC.; *U.S. Private*, pg. 2254
KAREN MILLER LTD.; *U.S. Private*, pg. 2262
KAYO OF CALIFORNIA, INC.; *U.S. Private*, pg. 2267
KAZOO, INC. - EDWARDS GARMENT DIVISION—See Kazoo, Inc.; *U.S. Private*, pg. 2268

KAZOO, INC.; *U.S. Private*, pg. 2267
KELLY'S KIDS; *U.S. Private*, pg. 2277
KENNINGTON LTD., INC.; *U.S. Private*, pg. 2286
KENTUCKY TEXTILES INC.; *U.S. Private*, pg. 2289
KEY INDUSTRIES, INC.; *U.S. Private*, pg. 2293
KIYONNA CLOTHING, INC.; *U.S. Private*, pg. 2317
KOBRA INTERNATIONAL LTD.; *U.S. Private*, pg. 2326
KREATIONS INC.; *U.S. Private*, pg. 2350
LA BELLE FASHIONS INC.; *U.S. Private*, pg. 2368
LADY ESTER LINGERIE CORP.; *U.S. Private*, pg. 2372
LAFUMA HUNGARIA—See Calida Holding AG; *Int'l*, pg. 1264
L.A. GLO INTERNATIONAL, INC.; *U.S. Private*, pg. 2364
L.A. MOVERS; *U.S. Private*, pg. 2364
LANDAU UNIFORMS INCORPORATED; *U.S. Private*, pg. 2384
LAND 'N SEA, INC.; *U.S. Private*, pg. 2382
LASTING IMPRESSIONS INC.; *U.S. Private*, pg. 2395
LCEL COLLECTIBLES INC.; *U.S. Private*, pg. 2403
LENG UNIVERSAL, INC.; *U.S. Private*, pg. 2422
LEON MAX INC.; *U.S. Private*, pg. 2423
LES DESSOUS BOUTIQUE DIFFUSION S.A.—See V. F. Corporation; *U.S. Public*, pg. 2268
LEVI STRAUSS (AUSTRALIA) PTY. LTD.—See Levi Strauss & Co.; *U.S. Public*, pg. 1308
LEVI STRAUSS & CO. APD—See Levi Strauss & Co.; *U.S. Public*, pg. 1308
LEVI STRAUSS & CO.; *U.S. Public*, pg. 1308
LEVI STRAUSS & CO.—See Levi Strauss & Co.; *U.S. Public*, pg. 1308
LEVI STRAUSS & CO.—See Levi Strauss & Co.; *U.S. Public*, pg. 1308
LEVI STRAUSS DE ESPANA S.A.—See Levi Strauss & Co.; *U.S. Public*, pg. 1309
LEVI STRAUSS DE MEXICO SA DE CV—See Levi Strauss & Co.; *U.S. Public*, pg. 1309
LEVI STRAUSS DO BRASIL INDUSTRIA E COMERCIO LTDA.—See Levi Strauss & Co.; *U.S. Public*, pg. 1309
LEVI STRAUSS EUROPE—See Levi Strauss & Co.; *U.S. Public*, pg. 1309
LEVI STRAUSS GERMANY GMBH—See Levi Strauss & Co.; *U.S. Public*, pg. 1309
LEVI STRAUSS HELLAS SA—See Levi Strauss & Co.; *U.S. Public*, pg. 1309
LEVI STRAUSS (HONG KONG) LIMITED—See Levi Strauss & Co.; *U.S. Public*, pg. 1308
LEVI STRAUSS INTERNATIONAL, INC.—See Levi Strauss & Co.; *U.S. Public*, pg. 1309
LEVI STRAUSS ISTANBUL KONFEKSIYON SANAYI VE TICARET A.S.—See Levi Strauss & Co.; *U.S. Public*, pg. 1309
LEVI STRAUSS ITALIA SRL—See Levi Strauss & Co.; *U.S. Public*, pg. 1309
LEVI STRAUSS JAPAN K.K.—See Levi Strauss & Co.; *U.S. Public*, pg. 1309
LEVI STRAUSS LISBON—See Levi Strauss & Co.; *U.S. Public*, pg. 1309
LEVI STRAUSS (MALAYSIA) SDN BHD—See Levi Strauss & Co.; *U.S. Public*, pg. 1308
LEVI STRAUSS NEW ZEALAND LIMITED—See Levi Strauss & Co.; *U.S. Public*, pg. 1309
LEVI STRAUSS NORWAY A/S—See Levi Strauss & Co.; *U.S. Public*, pg. 1309
LEVI STRAUSS (PHILIPPINES) INC.—See Levi Strauss & Co.; *U.S. Public*, pg. 1308
LEVI STRAUSS PRAHA, SPOL S.R.O.—See Levi Strauss & Co.; *U.S. Public*, pg. 1309
LEVI STRAUSS (SUISSE), SA—See Levi Strauss & Co.; *U.S. Public*, pg. 1309
LEVI STRAUSS TRADING KFT—See Levi Strauss & Co.; *U.S. Public*, pg. 1309
LEVI STRAUSS (UK) LIMITED—See Levi Strauss & Co.; *U.S. Public*, pg. 1309
LEVY GROUP, INC.; *U.S. Private*, pg. 2437
L.F. SPORTSWEAR INC.; *U.S. Private*, pg. 2365
LION APPAREL, INC.—See Lakeland Industries, Inc.; *U.S. Public*, pg. 1288
LION GROUP, INC—See Lakeland Industries, Inc.; *U.S. Public*, pg. 1288
LOOMWORKS APPAREL INC.—See GMM Capital LLC; *U.S. Private*, pg. 1722
LORD WEST FORMAL WEAR; *U.S. Private*, pg. 2495
LT APPAREL GROUP; *U.S. Private*, pg. 2509
THE LUNADA BAY CORPORATION; *U.S. Private*, pg. 4073
MABESA DO BRASIL LTDA—See Hypera Pharma S.A.; *Int'l*, pg. 3553
MACOPLEX S.A.—See EL. D. MOUZAKIS S.A.; *Int'l*, pg. 2341
MAGGY LONDON INTERNATIONAL LTD. INC.; *U.S. Private*, pg. 2545
MAIDENFORM BRANDS, LLC—See Hanesbrands Inc.; *U.S. Public*, pg. 983
MAIDENFORM LLC—See Hanesbrands Inc.; *U.S. Public*, pg. 983
MAJESTIC ATHLETIC LTD.—See V. F. Corporation; *U.S. Public*, pg. 2269
MARGARET O'LEARY INC.; *U.S. Private*, pg. 2573

MAR-MAC MANUFACTURING COMPANY, INC.; *U.S. Private*, pg. 2569
MAXINE OF HOLLYWOOD, INC.; *U.S. Private*, pg. 2619
MEDELITA, LLC; *U.S. Private*, pg. 2651
MEEMEE MEDIA INC.; *U.S. Public*, pg. 1414
M.G.T. INDUSTRIES INC.; *U.S. Private*, pg. 2529
MICHAEL KORS SPAIN, S.L.—See Capri Holdings Limited; *Int'l*, pg. 1316
MILCO INDUSTRIES INC.; *U.S. Private*, pg. 2727
MILLER INTERNATIONAL, INC.; *U.S. Private*, pg. 2734
MINERVA S.A.—See FIERATEX S.A.; *Int'l*, pg. 2660
MISYD CORP.; *U.S. Private*, pg. 2750
M. J. SOFFE, LLC—See Delta Apparel, Inc.; *U.S. Public*, pg. 652
M.L. KISHIGO MANUFACTURING COMPANY, LLC—See Bunzl plc; *Int'l*, pg. 1219
MOBILE EIGHT HOLDING LTD.; *U.S. Private*, pg. 2757
MODBE, INC.; *U.S. Private*, pg. 2759
MORTEX CORPORATION; *U.S. Private*, pg. 2791
NAKED BRAND GROUP INC.—See Cenntro Electric Group Limited; *Int'l*, pg. 1401
NAMYUE HOLDINGS LIMITED—See GDH Limited; *Int'l*, pg. 2896
NANETTE LEPORE; *U.S. Private*, pg. 2833
NATIONAL CORSET SUPPLY HOUSE; *U.S. Private*, pg. 2852
NATIONAL MILL INDUSTRY, INC.; *U.S. Private*, pg. 2859
THE NATURAL BABY COMPANY, LLC; *U.S. Private*, pg. 4082
NAUTICA APPAREL, INC.—See Leonard Green & Partners, L.P.; *U.S. Private*, pg. 2426
NAUTICA ENTERPRISES, INC.—See Leonard Green & Partners, L.P.; *U.S. Private*, pg. 2426
NINA PLASTICS, INC.; *U.S. Private*, pg. 2928
NORDSTROM FSB—See Nordstrom, Inc.; *U.S. Public*, pg. 1535
NYDJ APPAREL, LLC—See Falconhead Capital, LLC; *U.S. Private*, pg. 1467
OKAYAMA BEAUTY CORPORATION—See HOWA Corporation; *Int'l*, pg. 3492
OOBE, INC.; *U.S. Private*, pg. 3028
OSCAR DE LA RENTA LTD.; *U.S. Private*, pg. 3046
OUTERSTUFF, LTD.; *U.S. Private*, pg. 3051
PACIFIC CONTINENTAL TEXTILES, INC. APPAREL DIVISION (PCT-A)—See Edmund Kim International Inc.; *U.S. Private*, pg. 1338
PARIS BLUES, INC.; *U.S. Private*, pg. 3094
PATAGONIA, INC.—See Patagonia Works, Inc.; *U.S. Private*, pg. 3105
PAUL FRANK INDUSTRIES, INC.—See Saban Capital Group, Inc.; *U.S. Private*, pg. 3520
PENDLETON WOOLEN MILLS, INC.; *U.S. Private*, pg. 3132
PERCEPTIONS, INC.; *U.S. Private*, pg. 3146
PERFORM GROUP, LLC; *U.S. Private*, pg. 3148
PERRY ELLIS INTERNATIONAL EUROPE LIMITED—See Perry Ellis International, Inc.; *U.S. Private*, pg. 3154
PERRY ELLIS INTERNATIONAL HK LIMITED—See Perry Ellis International, Inc.; *U.S. Private*, pg. 3154
PERRY ELLIS INTERNATIONAL, INC.; *U.S. Private*, pg. 3153
PERRY ELLIS MENSWEAR, LLC—See Perry Ellis International, Inc.; *U.S. Private*, pg. 3154
PETIT VEHICULE S.A.—See Fast Retailing Co., Ltd.; *Int'l*, pg. 2621
PIEGE CO. INC.; *U.S. Private*, pg. 3178
PLAYTEX APPAREL, INC.—See Hanesbrands Inc.; *U.S. Public*, pg. 983
PL INDUSTRIES, LLC; *U.S. Private*, pg. 3194
POLKTON MANUFACTURING COMPANY; *U.S. Private*, pg. 3224
PRECEPT MEDICAL PRODUCTS INC.—See Audax Group, Limited Partnership; *U.S. Private*, pg. 386
PRIDE AND JOYS INC.; *U.S. Private*, pg. 3259
PRO EQUINE PRODUCTS INC.; *U.S. Private*, pg. 3269
PRONOVIAS SL—See BC Partners LLP; *Int'l*, pg. 925
PROPPER INTERNATIONAL, INC.; *U.S. Private*, pg. 3286
PROTREND LIMITED; *U.S. Private*, pg. 3291
PT CATERINDO GARMENT INDUSTRI—See Carry Wealth Holdings Limited; *Int'l*, pg. 1346
PT QUIKSILVER INDONESIA—See Leonard Green & Partners, L.P.; *U.S. Private*, pg. 2424
PT, V-APPAREL SEMARANG—See Ford Glory International Limited; *Int'l*, pg. 2731
PUTNAM SOURCING GROUP; *U.S. Private*, pg. 3307
PVH CORP.; *U.S. Public*, pg. 1739
QST VIETNAM CO., LTD—See QST Industries, Inc.; *U.S. Private*, pg. 3314
QUIKSILVER AUSTRALIA PTY LTD.—See Leonard Green & Partners, L.P.; *U.S. Private*, pg. 2424
QUIKSILVER EUROPE—See Leonard Green & Partners, L.P.; *U.S. Private*, pg. 2424
QUIKSILVER EYEWEAR, USA—See Leonard Green & Partners, L.P.; *U.S. Private*, pg. 2424
RADIANS CAROLINA—See Radians, Inc.; *U.S. Private*, pg. 3343
RAINFOREST INC.; *U.S. Private*, pg. 3348
RALPH LAUREN CORPORATION; *U.S. Public*, pg. 1761

315990 — APPAREL ACCESSORIES...

RAMPAGE CLOTHING COMPANY; *U.S. Private*, pg. 3351
RCM DESIGN—See S. Rothschild & Co., Inc.; *U.S. Private*, pg. 3515
RCM MANUFACTURING CORP.—See S. Rothschild & Co., Inc.; *U.S. Private*, pg. 3515
READY GARMENT TECHNOLOGY UKRAINE LTD.—See Dr. Bock Industries AG; *Int'l*, pg. 2190
REED MANUFACTURING COMPANY INC.; *U.S. Private*, pg. 3382
REFRIGIWEAR, INC.; *U.S. Private*, pg. 3385
RENAISSANCE KNITWEAR INC.; *U.S. Private*, pg. 3397
RG PARENT LLC—See Centric Brands Inc.; *U.S. Private*, pg. 829
RHODA LEE, INC.; *U.S. Private*, pg. 3421
RICHARD LEEDS INTERNATIONAL; *U.S. Private*, pg. 3428
RIPON ATHLETIC, INC.; *U.S. Private*, pg. 3439
R&M RICHARDS INC.; *U.S. Private*, pg. 3332
ROBERT GRAHAM DESIGNS LLC—See Tengram Capital Partners, Limited Partnership; *U.S. Private*, pg. 3967
ROBINSON MANUFACTURING COMPANY INC.; *U.S. Private*, pg. 3462
ROCKY MOUNTAIN CLOTHING CO.—See Miller International, Inc.; *U.S. Private*, pg. 2734
RONNI NICOLE II INC.; *U.S. Private*, pg. 3478
ROSENAU BECK INC.; *U.S. Private*, pg. 3483
ROSS DRESS FOR LESS, INC.—See Ross Stores, Inc.; *U.S. Public*, pg. 1815
ROUSSO APPAREL GROUP INC.; *U.S. Private*, pg. 3489
RUBIE'S COSTUME COMPANY INC.; *U.S. Private*, pg. 3500
RVCA CORPORATION—See Leonard Green & Partners, L.P.; *U.S. Private*, pg. 2424
SAIGON GARMENT MANUFACTURING TRADING JOINT STOCK COMPANY - AN NHON GARMENT FACTORY—See Garmex Saigon Corporation; *Int'l*, pg. 2884
SALLY LOU FASHIONS CORPORATION; *U.S. Private*, pg. 3533
SAMUELSOHN LIMITED—See Grano Retail Investments Inc.; *Int'l*, pg. 3059
SANGAR VALGA VABRIK AS—See AS Sangar; *Int'l*, pg. 591
S.A. SCHIESSER INTERNATIONAL N.V.—See GMM Capital LLC; *U.S. Private*, pg. 1722
SCHOOL APPAREL, INC.; *U.S. Private*, pg. 3568
SCHOTT BROTHERS, INC.; *U.S. Private*, pg. 3568
SCOTTYS FASHIONS, INC.; *U.S. Private*, pg. 3578
SEAMLESS PUERTO RICO, INC.—See Hanesbrands Inc.; *U.S. Public*, pg. 983
SEAN JOHN CLOTHING, INC.—See Global Brands Group Holding Ltd; *Int'l*, pg. 2993
SESSIONS INC.; *U.S. Private*, pg. 3617
SEWELL CLOTHING COMPANY INC.; *U.S. Private*, pg. 3620
SHADOWLINE INCORPORATED; *U.S. Private*, pg. 3622
SHANGHAI GMA FACTORY CO., LTD.—See GMA Accessories/Capelli of New York; *U.S. Private*, pg. 1721
SHANGHAI INTERMODA CLOTHING CO., LTD.—See Etam Developpement SCA; *Int'l*, pg. 2520
SHARON YOUNG INC.; *U.S. Private*, pg. 3626
SHAZDEH FASHIONS INC.; *U.S. Private*, pg. 3629
SHEAR ENTERPRISES, LLC; *U.S. Private*, pg. 3629
SHENZEN KORADIOR FASHION CO., LTD.—See EEKA Fashion Holdings Limited; *Int'l*, pg. 2317
SHENZHEN 1WOR UNITED DESIGN CO. LTD.—See Guangdong Bobaolon Co., Ltd.; *Int'l*, pg. 3153
SHINDONG CORPORATION—See Ilshin Spinning Co., Ltd.; *Int'l*, pg. 3616
SHINWA MFG. CO.—See EXEO Group Inc.; *Int'l*, pg. 2584
SIDRAN INC.; *U.S. Private*, pg. 3646
SIOUNI & ZAR CORP.; *U.S. Private*, pg. 3670
SISTER SISTER, INC.—See Adjmi Apparel Group, Inc.; *U.S. Private*, pg. 79
SKIP HOP, INC.—See Carter's, Inc.; *U.S. Public*, pg. 445
SOUTHERN TIDE, LLC—See Oxford Industries, Inc.; *U.S. Public*, pg. 1629
SOUTHWICK CLOTHING LLC; *U.S. Private*, pg. 3742
SP APPAREL, INC.—See NIKE, Inc.; *U.S. Public*, pg. 1529
SPIRITE INDUSTRIES, INC.; *U.S. Private*, pg. 3758
SPLENDID—See GMM Capital LLC; *U.S. Private*, pg. 1722
SPORT OBERMEYER LTD.; *U.S. Private*, pg. 3760
SPRL BRUNELLO CUCINELLI BELGIUM—See Brunello Cucinelli S.p.A.; *Int'l*, pg. 1200
S. ROTHSCHILD & CO., INC.; *U.S. Private*, pg. 3515
STALLION, INC.; *U.S. Private*, pg. 3776
STANBURY UNIFORMS, INC.—See Bain Capital, LP; *U.S. Private*, pg. 452
STANDARD MANUFACTURING CO., INC.; *U.S. Private*, pg. 3781
STANDARD SAFETY EQUIPMENT CO.; *U.S. Private*, pg. 3781
STANDARD TEXTILE CO., INC.; *U.S. Private*, pg. 3782
STEPHEN GOULD OF ARIZONA, INC.—See Stephen Gould Corporation; *U.S. Private*, pg. 3802
STRATEGIC PARTNERS, INC.—See New Mountain Capital, LLC; *U.S. Private*, pg. 2903
SUE & SAM CO. INC.; *U.S. Private*, pg. 3849
SUGARTOWN WORLDWIDE LLC—See Oxford Industries, Inc.; *U.S. Public*, pg. 1629

SUKARTIK CLOTHING PRIVATE LIMITED—See Garnet International Limited; *Int'l*, pg. 2885
SUPERIOR GROUP OF COMPANIES, INC.; *U.S. Public*, pg. 1966
SUPERIOR UNIFORM GROUP, INC. - SHANE UNIFORMS DIVISION—See Superior Group Of Companies, Inc.; *U.S. Public*, pg. 1966
SUPERIOR UNIFORM GROUP, INC. - WORKLON DIVISION—See Superior Group Of Companies, Inc.; *U.S. Public*, pg. 1966
SWAT FAME INC.; *U.S. Private*, pg. 3891
SWISSTEX COMPANY; *U.S. Private*, pg. 3894
TAIFUN-COLLECTION GERRY WEBER FASHION GMBH—See GERRY WEBER International AG; *Int'l*, pg. 2945
TAIL INC.; *U.S. Private*, pg. 3923
TAI-YUAN GARMENTS CO., LTD.—See Eclat Textile Co., Ltd.; *Int'l*, pg. 2291
TANNER COMPANIES, LP; *U.S. Private*, pg. 3931
TARRANT COMPANY LIMITED—See Sunrise Acquisition Corp.; *U.S. Private*, pg. 3869
TENNESSEE APPAREL CORP.; *U.S. Private*, pg. 3967
TENNIER INDUSTRIES INC.; *U.S. Private*, pg. 3968
THOMAS SCOTT (INDIA) LIMITED—See Bang Overseas Ltd.; *Int'l*, pg. 832
TIMBERLAND ITALY SRL—See V. F. Corporation; *U.S. Public*, pg. 2269
TOMMY HILFIGER CORPORATION—See PVH Corp.; *U.S. Public*, pg. 1739
TONY MARTERIE & ASSOCIATES; *U.S. Private*, pg. 4185
TRIMARK SPORTSWEAR GROUP INC.—See Charlesbank Capital Partners, LLC; *U.S. Private*, pg. 856
TRUE & CO.—See PVH Corp.; *U.S. Public*, pg. 1739
TRUE RELIGION APPAREL, INC.—See TowerBrook Capital Partners, L.P.; *U.S. Private*, pg. 4196
TURN-ON PRODUCTS INC.—See Steven Madden, Ltd.; *U.S. Public*, pg. 1947
UNGER FABRIK LLC; *U.S. Private*, pg. 4281
UNIQLO VIETNAM CO., LTD.—See Fast Retailing Co., Ltd.; *Int'l*, pg. 2621
UNIVERSAL GAMING CORPORATION; *U.S. Public*, pg. 2255
UNIVERSAL MANUFACTURING CORP.; *U.S. Private*, pg. 4305
UNIVERSAL OVERALL COMPANY; *U.S. Private*, pg. 4306
URBAN APPAREL GROUP INC.; *U.S. Private*, pg. 4313
VANTAGE CUSTOM CLASSICS, INC.; *U.S. Private*, pg. 4345
VARSITY BRANDS, INC.—See Bain Capital, LP; *U.S. Private*, pg. 452
VELMAR S.P.A—See Aeffe SpA; *Int'l*, pg. 173
VELVET, LLC—See Adastria Co., Ltd.; *Int'l*, pg. 126
VERA WANG BRIDAL HOUSE LTD.; *U.S. Private*, pg. 4359
VESTURE GROUP INC.; *U.S. Private*, pg. 4373
VF BRANDS INDIA PRIVATE LIMITED—See V. F. Corporation; *U.S. Public*, pg. 2269
VF COMMERCIALIZADORA LIMITADA—See V. F. Corporation; *U.S. Public*, pg. 2269
VF DO BRASIL LTDA.—See V. F. Corporation; *U.S. Public*, pg. 2269
VF EGE SOKE GIYIM SANAYI VE TICARET A.S.—See V. F. Corporation; *U.S. Public*, pg. 2269
VF GERMANY TEXTIL-HANDELS GMBH—See V. F. Corporation; *U.S. Public*, pg. 2269
VF IMAGEWEAR—See V. F. Corporation; *U.S. Public*, pg. 2269
VF INTERNATIONAL S.A.G.L—See V. F. Corporation; *U.S. Public*, pg. 2269
VF ITALIA, S.R.L.—See V. F. Corporation; *U.S. Public*, pg. 2269
VF ITALY SERVICES S.R.L.—See V. F. Corporation; *U.S. Public*, pg. 2269
VF JEANSWEAR DE MEXICO SA DE CV—See Kontoor Brands, Inc.; *U.S. Public*, pg. 1271
VF JEANSWEAR - EL PASO—See Kontoor Brands, Inc.; *U.S. Public*, pg. 1271
VF JEANSWEAR LIMITED PARTNERSHIP—See Kontoor Brands, Inc.; *U.S. Public*, pg. 1271
VF JEANSWEAR - SEMINOLE—See Kontoor Brands, Inc.; *U.S. Public*, pg. 1271
VF (J) FRANCE, S.A.—See Kontoor Brands, Inc.; *U.S. Public*, pg. 1271
VF LUXEMBOURG S.A.R.L.—See V. F. Corporation; *U.S. Public*, pg. 2269
VF NORTHERN EUROPE LTD.—See V. F. Corporation; *U.S. Public*, pg. 2269
VF NORTHERN EUROPE SERVICES LTD.—See V. F. Corporation; *U.S. Public*, pg. 2269
VF OUTDOOR (CANADA), INC.—See V. F. Corporation; *U.S. Public*, pg. 2269
VF SOURCING INDIA PRIVATE LIMITED—See V. F. Corporation; *U.S. Public*, pg. 2269
VICSA SAFETY COMERCIAL LIMITADA—See Bunzl plc; *Int'l*, pg. 1219
VINEYARD VINES LLC; *U.S. Private*, pg. 4385
VIRTUAL MIND HOLDING COMPANY LIMITED—See Guotai Junan Securities Co., Ltd.; *Int'l*, pg. 3187
VOMAX—See Triton Systems Inc.; *U.S. Private*, pg. 4239

WALLS INDUSTRIES LLC—See V. F. Corporation; *U.S. Public*, pg. 2269
WATCH LA JEANS; *U.S. Private*, pg. 4451
WHITESWAN/META—See Encompass Group LLC; *U.S. Private*, pg. 1390
WICKERS SPORTSWEAR INC.; *U.S. Private*, pg. 4515
WILLIAMSON-DICKIE CANADA COMPANY—See V. F. Corporation; *U.S. Public*, pg. 2269
WILLIAMSON-DICKIE EUROPE LIMITED—See V. F. Corporation; *U.S. Public*, pg. 2269
WILLIAMSON-DICKIE MANUFACTURING COMPANY—See V. F. Corporation; *U.S. Public*, pg. 2269
WOLFORD AG—See Fosun International Limited; *Int'l*, pg. 2752
WOLFORD CANADA INC.—See Fosun International Limited; *Int'l*, pg. 2752
WOLFORD DEUTSCHLAND GMBH—See Fosun International Limited; *Int'l*, pg. 2752
WOLFORD ESPANA, S.L.—See Fosun International Limited; *Int'l*, pg. 2752
WOLFORD ITALIA S.R.L.—See Fosun International Limited; *Int'l*, pg. 2752
WOLFORD LONDON LTD.—See Fosun International Limited; *Int'l*, pg. 2752
WOLFORD NEDERLAND B.V.—See Fosun International Limited; *Int'l*, pg. 2752
WOLFORD PARIS S.A.R.L.—See Fosun International Limited; *Int'l*, pg. 2752
WOLFORD SCANDINAVIA APS—See Fosun International Limited; *Int'l*, pg. 2752
WORTH COLLECTION LTD.—See New Water Capital, L.P.; *U.S. Private*, pg. 2908
W.S. EMERSON CO., INC.; *U.S. Private*, pg. 4422
YOKOTA APPAREL CO., LTD.—See Gunze Limited; *Int'l*, pg. 3186
Z. CAVARICCI INC.—See Z. Cavaricci Inc.; *U.S. Private*, pg. 4596
ZHUCHENG ETERNAL KNITTING CO., LIMITED—See Greatime International Holdings Limited; *Int'l*, pg. 3067

315990 — APPAREL ACCESSORIES AND OTHER APPAREL MANUFACTURING

ACI BRANDS INC.; *Int'l*, pg. 104
ACKNIT INDUSTRIES LTD.; *Int'l*, pg. 106
ACTIONWEAR SASKATOON INC.; *Int'l*, pg. 119
ADERANS CO., LTD.; *Int'l*, pg. 143
ADOLFO DOMINGUEZ, S.A.; *Int'l*, pg. 152
AGRI-COVER, INC.; *U.S. Private*, pg. 129
ALL AMERICAN SWIM; *U.S. Private*, pg. 170
ALLEGRA BRANDS; *U.S. Private*, pg. 177
ALPARGATAS SAIC—See Cambuhy Investimentos Ltda.; *Int'l*, pg. 1270
ALPS INDUSTRIES LIMITED; *Int'l*, pg. 377
AMERICAN ACCESSORIES INC.—See Kinderhook Industries, LLC; *U.S. Private*, pg. 2306
AMERICAN APPAREL AUSTRALIA PTY LTD.—See American Apparel, Inc.; *U.S. Private*, pg. 222
AMERICAN APPAREL (CARNABY) LIMITED—See American Apparel, Inc.; *U.S. Private*, pg. 222
AMERICAN APPAREL, INC.; *U.S. Private*, pg. 222
AMERICAN REBEL HOLDINGS, INC.; *U.S. Public*, pg. 109
ANDREW CHRISTIAN, INC.; *U.S. Private*, pg. 279
ANSELL INTERNATIONAL—See Ansell Limited; *Int'l*, pg. 478
ANTA SPORTS PRODUCTS LIMITED; *Int'l*, pg. 479
ARABIAN PLASTIC INDUSTRIAL CO. LTD.; *Int'l*, pg. 533
ARAPRINT B.V.—See Cimpress plc; *Int'l*, pg. 1609
ARC'TERYX EQUIPMENT, INC.—See ANTA Sports Products Limited; *Int'l*, pg. 480
ARENA BRANDS INC.—See Kainos Capital, LLC; *U.S. Private*, pg. 2254
AS SANGAR; *Int'l*, pg. 591
ATELIER DE PRODUCTION ET DE CREATION; *Int'l*, pg. 668
AVELANA—See Chargeurs SA; *Int'l*, pg. 1449
AVERY DENNISON RETAIL INFORMATION SERVICES LLC—See Avery Dennison Corporation; *U.S. Public*, pg. 243
BAILEY HATS COMPANY—See Bollman Hat Co.; *U.S. Private*, pg. 611
BARRIE KNITWEAR LTD.—See Chanel S.A.; *Int'l*, pg. 1441
BECKER GLOVE INTERNATIONAL INC.; *U.S. Private*, pg. 511
BEIJING JIAMAN DRESS CO., LTD.; *Int'l*, pg. 952
BENAY-HAT CO.; *U.S. Private*, pg. 523
BEN SHERMAN LIMITED—See Oxford Industries, Inc.; *U.S. Public*, pg. 1629
BERNE APPAREL CORP; *U.S. Private*, pg. 536
BETI D.D.; *Int'l*, pg. 1002
BHALCHANDRAM CLOTHING LIMITED; *Int'l*, pg. 1010
BISHRELT INDUSTRIAL JOINT STOCK COMPANY; *Int'l*, pg. 1049
BJORN BORG BRANDS AB—See Bjorn Borg AB; *Int'l*, pg. 1053
BJORN BORG CLOTHING AB—See Bjorn Borg AB; *Int'l*, pg. 1054

315990 — APPAREL ACCESSORIES...

BJORN BORG RETAIL AB—See Bjorn Borg AB; *Int'l*, pg. 1054
BOLLMAN HAT CO.; *U.S. Private*, pg. 611
BONIA CORPORATION BERHAD; *Int'l*, pg. 1107
BORBONESE SPA; *Int'l*, pg. 1112
BRIGHTON COLLECTIBLES, INC.; *U.S. Private*, pg. 652
BRIGHT ORIENT (HOLDING) LTD.; *Int'l*, pg. 1161
BROOKVILLE GLOVE MANUFACTURING COMPANY, INC.—See BSI Diversified LLC; *U.S. Private*, pg. 675
BRUNO SAINT HILAIRE SAS; *Int'l*, pg. 1200
BURMA BIBAS INC.; *U.S. Private*, pg. 689
BUYCOSTUMES.COM—See Rubie's Costume Company Inc.; *U.S. Private*, pg. 3500
BY MALENE BIRGER A/S—See Friheden Invest A/S; *Int'l*, pg. 2792
CALIDA GROUP DIGITAL GMBH—See Calida Holding AG; *Int'l*, pg. 1264
CAREGLOVE GLOBAL SDN. BHD.—See Careplus Group Berhad; *Int'l*, pg. 1325
CAREPLUS GROUP BERHAD; *Int'l*, pg. 1325
CARNIVAL INDUSTRIAL CORPORATION; *Int'l*, pg. 1342
CAROLINA GLOVE COMPANY; *U.S. Private*, pg. 768
CARRY WEALTH HOLDINGS LIMITED; *Int'l*, pg. 1346
CARTEL BLUE, INC.; *U.S. Private*, pg. 775
CASTLE PEAK HOLDINGS PUBLIC COMPANY LIMITED; *Int'l*, pg. 1357
CDRL S.A.; *Int'l*, pg. 1371
CHEYNET ELASTICS—See Cheynet S.A.S.; *Int'l*, pg. 1474
CHINA INTERNATIONAL DEVELOPMENT CORPORATION LIMITED; *Int'l*, pg. 1510
CHINA LILANG LIMITED; *Int'l*, pg. 1515
CIA. HERING - AVENIDA BRASIL - ANAPOLIS PLANT—See Grupo de Moda SOMA S.A.; *Int'l*, pg. 3126
CIA. HERING - DAIA - ANAPOLIS PLANT—See Grupo de Moda SOMA S.A.; *Int'l*, pg. 3126
CIA. HERING - GOIANESIA PLANT—See Grupo de Moda SOMA S.A.; *Int'l*, pg. 3126
CIA. HERING - PARAUNA PLANT—See Grupo de Moda SOMA S.A.; *Int'l*, pg. 3126
CIA. HERING - SANTA HELENA PLANT—See Grupo de Moda SOMA S.A.; *Int'l*, pg. 3126
CIA. HERING—See Grupo de Moda SOMA S.A.; *Int'l*, pg. 3126
CIEL LTD.; *Int'l*, pg. 1605
CIMPRESS AUSTRALIA PTY LTD—See Cimpress plc; *Int'l*, pg. 1609
CIMPRESS INDIA PRIVATE LIMITED—See Cimpress plc; *Int'l*, pg. 1609
COMASEC SAS—See Ansell Limited; *Int'l*, pg. 478
COMO DIFFUSION INC.; *Int'l*, pg. 1721
CONCEPT ONE ACCESSORIES; *U.S. Private*, pg. 1008
COTTON COUNTY RETAIL LIMITED; *Int'l*, pg. 1817
COUNTESS MARA, INC.—See Randa Corp.; *U.S. Private*, pg. 3353
COVER 50 S.P.A.; *Int'l*, pg. 1821
COX CO., LTD.; *Int'l*, pg. 1823
CUSTOMINK, LLC; *U.S. Private*, pg. 1130
DAE HYUN CO., LTD.; *Int'l*, pg. 1905
DAIWABOADVANCE CO., LTD.—See Daiwabo Holdings Co., Ltd.; *Int'l*, pg. 1949
DANIEL M. FRIEDMAN & ASSOCIATES, INC.—See Steven Madden, Ltd.; *U.S. Public*, pg. 1947
DC SHOES, INC.—See Leonard Green & Partners, L.P.; *U.S. Private*, pg. 2424
DECKERS ASIA PACIFIC LIMITED—See Deckers Outdoor Corporation; *U.S. Public*, pg. 645
DECKERS JAPAN GK—See Deckers Outdoor Corporation; *U.S. Public*, pg. 645
DESIGNERS REMIX A/S—See Friheden Invest A/S; *Int'l*, pg. 2792
DEVOLD OF NORWAY AS—See Flakk Holding AS; *Int'l*, pg. 2697
DHJ INTERNATIONAL—See Chargeurs SA; *Int'l*, pg. 1449
DINGXING LIDA HAT MAKING CO., LTD.—See Hebei Lihua Hat Manufacturing Group Co., Ltd.; *Int'l*, pg. 3306
DIPPED PRODUCTS PLC—See Hayleys PLC; *Int'l*, pg. 3291
DIRITEKS DIRILIS TEKSTIL SANAYI VE TICARET A.S.; *Int'l*, pg. 2130
DOHLER S.A.; *Int'l*, pg. 2156
DOLCE & GABBANA S.R.L.; *Int'l*, pg. 2157
DOME HEADWEAR CO.; *U.S. Private*, pg. 1255
DONALD J PLINER OF FLORIDA, INC.—See Castanea Partners, Inc.; *U.S. Private*, pg. 784
DRUCK.AT DRUCK- UND HANDELSGESELLSCHAFT GMBH—See Cimpress plc; *Int'l*, pg. 1609
EAGLE NICE (INTERNATIONAL) HOLDINGS LTD.; *Int'l*, pg. 2266
EASTERN TECHNOLOGIES, INC.; *U.S. Private*, pg. 1321
EDOARDOS MARTIN, S.A.B. DE C.V.; *Int'l*, pg. 2313
EIDER S.A.S.—See Calida Holding AG; *Int'l*, pg. 1264
EMANUEL UNGARO; *Int'l*, pg. 2374
EMERALD COAST SAS—See Leonard Green & Partners, L.P.; *U.S. Private*, pg. 2424
EMPRESAS TRICOT SA; *Int'l*, pg. 2392
ESOTIQ & HENDERSON SA; *Int'l*, pg. 2504
ESPRIT CANADA DISTRIBUTION LIMITED—See Esprit Holdings Limited; *Int'l*, pg. 2507

ESQUIRE KNIT COMPOSITE LTD.; *Int'l*, pg. 2507
EST GLOBAL APPAREL CO., LTD.; *Int'l*, pg. 2517
EUROPA EYEWEAR—See Blue Point Capital Partners, LLC; *U.S. Private*, pg. 590
EXAGROUP SAS—See Cimpress plc; *Int'l*, pg. 1609
FABRICA DE TECIDOS CARLOS RENAUX S.A.; *Int'l*, pg. 2599
FAIRFIELD LINE INC.; *U.S. Private*, pg. 1463
FENIX OUTDOOR INTERNATIONAL AG; *Int'l*, pg. 2634
F&F HOLDINGS CO., LTD.; *Int'l*, pg. 2595
FIACAO TEC SAO JOSE S.A.; *Int'l*, pg. 2650
FIN.PART S.P.A.; *Int'l*, pg. 2664
FIRESTONE INDUSTRIAL PRODUCTS-WILLIAMSBURG—See Bridgestone Corporation; *Int'l*, pg. 1156
FJ BENJAMIN HOLDINGS LTD.; *Int'l*, pg. 2697
F J BENJAMIN TRADING HK LTD—See FJ Benjamin Holdings Ltd.; *Int'l*, pg. 2697
FORSYTH HOLDINGS, INC.; *Int'l*, pg. 2737
FOTOKNUDSEN AS—See Cimpress plc; *Int'l*, pg. 1609
FOX GROUP CANADA LTD.—See Fox-Wizel Ltd.; *Int'l*, pg. 2756
FOX-WIZEL LTD.; *Int'l*, pg. 2756
FRUIT OF THE LOOM LIMITED—See Berkshire Hathaway Inc.; *U.S. Public*, pg. 305
FUXING GARMENTS CO., LTD.; *Int'l*, pg. 2858
GADZOOKS INC.; *U.S. Private*, pg. 1633
GALLANT QUALITY SDN. BHD.—See Comfort Gloves Berhad; *Int'l*, pg. 1711
GANT AB—See Gant Sweden; *Int'l*, pg. 2882
GANT SWEDEN; *Int'l*, pg. 2882
GANT SWEDEN—See Gant Sweden; *Int'l*, pg. 2882
GANT UK LTD—See Gant Sweden; *Int'l*, pg. 2882
GANT USA CORPORATION—See Gant Sweden; *Int'l*, pg. 2882
GAZAL APPAREL PTY LIMITED—See PVH Corp.; *U.S. Public*, pg. 1739
GEM-DANDY, INC.; *U.S. Private*, pg. 1657
GEORGE GLOVE CO, INC.; *U.S. Private*, pg. 1682
GERRY WEBER CANADA LTD.—See GERRY WEBER International AG; *Int'l*, pg. 2944
GERRY WEBER DENMARK APS—See GERRY WEBER International AG; *Int'l*, pg. 2944
GERRY WEBER FRANCE S.A.R.L.—See GERRY WEBER International AG; *Int'l*, pg. 2944
GERRY WEBER GMBH—See GERRY WEBER International AG; *Int'l*, pg. 2944
GERRY WEBER IBERICA S.L.U—See GERRY WEBER International AG; *Int'l*, pg. 2944
GERRY WEBER OUTLET BVBA—See GERRY WEBER International AG; *Int'l*, pg. 2945
GERRY WEBER UK LTD.—See GERRY WEBER International AG; *Int'l*, pg. 2945
GERRY WEBER WHOLESALE FASHION GMBH—See GERRY WEBER International AG; *Int'l*, pg. 2945
GETZNER TEXTIL AG; *Int'l*, pg. 2954
GIANNI VERSACE S.P.A—See Capri Holdings Limited; *Int'l*, pg. 1316
GIORGIO ARMANI S.P.A.; *Int'l*, pg. 2978
GLG CORP LTD.; *Int'l*, pg. 2992
GLOBAL BRANDS GROUP HOLDING LTD; *Int'l*, pg. 2993
GOLDROOSTER AG; *Int'l*, pg. 3034
GOLDWIN, INC.; *Int'l*, pg. 3035
GOTTEX MODELS LTD.—See Africa Israel Investments Ltd.; *Int'l*, pg. 190
THE GRANDOE CORPORATION; *U.S. Private*, pg. 4037
GRITEE, INC.; *Int'l*, pg. 3087
GROUPE ETAM SUISSE—See Etam Developpement SCA; *Int'l*, pg. 2520
GRUPO DE MODA SOMA S.A.; *Int'l*, pg. 3126
GRUPPO COIN S.P.A.; *Int'l*, pg. 3140
GUANGDONG HONGXING INDUSTRIAL CO., LTD.; *Int'l*, pg. 3156
GUD (NZ) LIMITED—See Amotiv Limited; *Int'l*, pg. 431
HANES GERMANY GMBH—See Hanesbrands Inc.; *U.S. Public*, pg. 983
HANES SOUTH AFRICA (PTY) LIMITED—See Hanesbrands Inc.; *U.S. Public*, pg. 983
HASKO TRADING INC.; *U.S. Private*, pg. 1878
HENNES MAURITZ (SHANGHAI) COMMERCIAL LTD CO—See H&M Hennes & Mauritz AB; *Int'l*, pg. 3192
HIGH FASHION INTERNATIONAL LIMITED; *Int'l*, pg. 3385
H&M HENNES & MAURITZ AB; *Int'l*, pg. 3192
H&M HENNES & MAURITZ UK LTD.—See H&M Hennes & Mauritz AB; *Int'l*, pg. 3192
HODGES BADGE COMPANY INC.; *U.S. Private*, pg. 1959
HONEYWELL FIRST RESPONDER PRODUCTS—See Honeywell International Inc.; *U.S. Public*, pg. 1049
HONEYWELL NORTH SAFETY PRODUCTS CANADA—See Honeywell International Inc.; *U.S. Public*, pg. 1049
HONEYWELL SAFETY PRODUCTS GLOVES USA, LLC—See Honeywell International Inc.; *U.S. Public*, pg. 1049
HONEYWELL SAFETY PRODUCTS—See Honeywell International Inc.; *U.S. Public*, pg. 1049
HW HOLDINGS, INC.; *U.S. Private*, pg. 2015
HYUNGJI ELITE INC.; *Int'l*, pg. 3561

IC COMPANYS POLAND SP. Z.O.O.—See Friheden Invest A/S; *Int'l*, pg. 2792
I.CENTURY HOLDING LIMITED; *Int'l*, pg. 3565
ICOGUANTI S.P.A.—See Hayleys PLC; *Int'l*, pg. 3291
IDREES TEXTILE MILLS LIMITED; *Int'l*, pg. 3596
IGUANAMED LLC; *U.S. Private*, pg. 2040
INTERLANA S.R.O—See Chargeurs SA; *Int'l*, pg. 1449
INTER-MODA GMBH—See CVC Capital Partners SICAV-FIS S.A.; *Int'l*, pg. 1883
INTERNATIONAL SOURCING COMPANY INC.—See Bunzl plc; *Int'l*, pg. 1217
IP HOLDINGS UNLTD LLC—See Iconix Acquisition LLC; *U.S. Private*, pg. 2032
JACOBSON HAT CO. INC.; *U.S. Private*, pg. 2180
J BRAND, INC.—See Fast Retailing Co., Ltd.; *Int'l*, pg. 2621
JIMMY SALES NECKWEAR CORP.; *U.S. Private*, pg. 2210
JOMAC CANADA—See Berkshire Hathaway Inc.; *U.S. Public*, pg. 311
JUMP DESIGN GROUP; *U.S. Private*, pg. 2243
JUNKFOOD CLOTHING COMPANY—See Delta Apparel, Inc.; *U.S. Public*, pg. 652
KATE SPADE & COMPANY LLC—See Tapestry, Inc.; *U.S. Public*, pg. 1981
KDH DEFENSE SYSTEMS, INC.—See Spanos Barber Jesse & Co.; *U.S. Private*, pg. 3745
KINCO, LLC; *U.S. Private*, pg. 2306
KLINGLER TEXTIL AG—See Getzner Textil AG; *Int'l*, pg. 2954
LAINIERE DE PICARDIE ARGENTINA S.A.—See Chargeurs SA; *Int'l*, pg. 1449
LAINIERE DE PICARDIE BC—See Chargeurs SA; *Int'l*, pg. 1449
LAINIERE DE PICARDIE DEUTSCHLAND GMBH—See Chargeurs SA; *Int'l*, pg. 1449
LAINIERE DE PICARDIE GOLAPLAST BRAZIL TEXTIL LTDA—See Chargeurs SA; *Int'l*, pg. 1449
LAINIERE DE PICARDIE UK LTD—See Chargeurs SA; *Int'l*, pg. 1449
LAINIERE DE PICARDIE URUGUAY S.A.—See Chargeurs SA; *Int'l*, pg. 1449
LAKELAND INDIA PRIVATE LIMITED—See Lakeland Industries, Inc.; *U.S. Public*, pg. 1289
LAKELAND PROTECTIVE WEAR, INC.—See Lakeland Industries, Inc.; *U.S. Public*, pg. 1289
L.C. INDUSTRIES INC.; *U.S. Private*, pg. 2365
LEPOUTRE TERNYNCK—See Chargeurs SA; *Int'l*, pg. 1449
LHD GROUP DEUTSCHLAND GMBH—See Lakeland Industries, Inc.; *U.S. Public*, pg. 1288
LIFE-STYLE FASHION GMBH—See GERRY WEBER International AG; *Int'l*, pg. 2945
LILLEBA & HERREMAN AS—See AcadeMedia AB; *Int'l*, pg. 77
L.L. BEAN, INC.; *U.S. Private*, pg. 2366
LSEB CREATIVE CORP.; *U.S. Public*, pg. 1344
LUCKY BRAND DUNGAREES, INC.—See Leonard Green & Partners, L.P.; *U.S. Private*, pg. 2426
LUCKY BRAND DUNGAREES, INC.—See Leonard Green & Partners, L.P.; *U.S. Private*, pg. 2426
MAGID GLOVE SAFETY MANUFACTURING CO. LLC; *U.S. Private*, pg. 2546
MARIGOLD INDUSTRIAL SDN. BHD.—See Ansell Limited; *Int'l*, pg. 478
MEYER MAYOR AG—See Getzner Textil AG; *Int'l*, pg. 2954
MIDWEST IMPRESSIONS INC.; *U.S. Private*, pg. 2721
MIDWEST QUALITY GLOVES, INC.; *U.S. Private*, pg. 2722
MIGLIARA S.A.—See Lakeland Industries, Inc.; *U.S. Public*, pg. 1289
MISS ELAINE INC.; *U.S. Private*, pg. 2746
MMG CORPORATION; *U.S. Private*, pg. 2754
MMS TRADING INC.; *U.S. Private*, pg. 2755
MOUNTCASTLE PTY LTD—See Hancock & Gore Ltd.; *Int'l*, pg. 3242
MUSGROVE MILLS, INC.; *U.S. Private*, pg. 2817
NAKAHATSU CO., LTD.—See CROSS PLUS INC.; *Int'l*, pg. 1856
NAMIFY LLC; *U.S. Private*, pg. 2832
NATHAN SPORTS—See Wells Fargo & Company; *U.S. Public*, pg. 2344
NATIONAL SAFETY APPAREL, INC.—See Blue Point Capital Partners, LLC; *U.S. Private*, pg. 590
NEFF, LLC—See Platinum Equity, LLC; *U.S. Private*, pg. 3205
NEW ERA CAP LLC—See ACON Investments, LLC; *U.S. Private*, pg. 62
NEW GUARDS GROUP HOLDING S.P.A—See Coupang, Inc.; *Int'l*, pg. 1819
NEW GUARDS GROUP HOLDING S.P.A—See Greenoaks Capital Partners LLC; *U.S. Private*, pg. 1779
NIKE ARGENTINA S.R.L.—See NIKE, Inc.; *U.S. Public*, pg. 1529
NOLAN ORIGINALS, LLC—See BioWorld Merchandising, Inc.; *U.S. Private*, pg. 563
NORTH EAST RIG-OUT LIMITED—See V. F. Corporation; *U.S. Public*, pg. 2268
THE NORTH FACE, INC.—See V. F. Corporation; *U.S. Public*, pg. 2269
NORTH SAFETY PRODUCTS EUROPE B.V.—See Honey-

N.A.I.C.S. INDEX

316210 — FOOTWEAR MANUFACTUR...

well International Inc.; *U.S. Public,* pg. 1049
ODCO SAS—See Delta Plus Group; *Int'l,* pg. 2020
OOO GERRY WEBER RUS—See GERRY WEBER International AG; *Int'l,* pg. 2945
OUTDOOR CAP COMPANY INC.; *U.S. Private,* pg. 3051
OWYHEE GROUP COMPANIES; *U.S. Private,* pg. 3055
PARAMOUNT APPAREL INTERNATIONAL INC.; *U.S. Private,* pg. 3092
PATRICIA FIELD BOUTIQUE; *U.S. Private,* pg. 3110
PEAK PERFORMANCE PRODUCTION AB—See ANTA Sports Products Limited; *Int'l,* pg. 481
PEDS LEGWEAR INC.—See Gildan Activewear Inc.; *Int'l,* pg. 2973
PEPPO FASHIONS GROUP COMPANY LMD—See FJ Benjamin Holdings Ltd.; *Int'l,* pg. 2697
PIXARTPRINTING S.P.A.—See Cimpress plc; *Int'l,* pg. 1609
POLO/RALPH LAUREN—See Ralph Lauren Corporation; *U.S. Public,* pg. 1761
PT QUIKSILVER INDONESIA—See Leonard Green & Partners, L.P.; *U.S. Private,* pg. 2424
QST ASIA LTD. HONG KONG—See QST Industries, Inc.; *U.S. Private,* pg. 3314
QST INDUSTRIES ASIA (S) PTE. LTD.—See QST Industries, Inc.; *U.S. Private,* pg. 3314
QUICK SERVICE TEXTILE GUATEMALA S.R.L—See QST Industries, Inc.; *U.S. Private,* pg. 3314
QUICK SERVICE TEXTILE MAROC—See QST Industries, Inc.; *U.S. Private,* pg. 3314
RAJ MANUFACTURING LLC—See Swander Pace Capital, LLC; *U.S. Private,* pg. 3890
RALPH LAUREN SCANDINAVIA AB—See Ralph Lauren Corporation; *U.S. Public,* pg. 1762
RHE HATCO, INC.—See Pro Equine Products Inc.; *U.S. Private,* pg. 3269
RL RETAIL FRANCE S.A.S.—See Ralph Lauren Corporation; *U.S. Public,* pg. 1761
ROBERTO CAVALLI S.P.A.—See DAMAC Group; *Int'l,* pg. 1955
ROBERT TALBOTT, INC.; *U.S. Private,* pg. 3459
ROUDIERE SA—See Chargeurs SA; *Int'l,* pg. 1449
THE SAFETY ZONE, LLC—See H.I.G. Capital, LLC; *U.S. Private,* pg. 1834
SAINT TROPEZ AF 1993 A/S—See DK Company A/S; *Int'l,* pg. 2138
SAL COMMERCIAL VENTURE ONE, S.A. DE C.V.—See Lakeland Industries, Inc.; *U.S. Public,* pg. 1289
SAS SAFETY CORP.—See Bunzl plc; *Int'l,* pg. 1218
SCOOP NYC; *U.S. Private,* pg. 3575
SCOVILL FASTENERS INDIA PRIVATE LIMITED—See The Gores Group, LLC; *U.S. Private,* pg. 4035
SHELBY GROUP INTERNATIONAL, INC.—See Bunzl plc; *Int'l,* pg. 1219
SIMPSON PERFORMANCE PRODUCTS—See Carousel Capital Partners; *U.S. Private,* pg. 770
SKINNYCORP L.L.C.; *U.S. Private,* pg. 3682
SMARTWOOL—See V. F. Corporation; *U.S. Public,* pg. 2268
SOUL BIOTECHNOLOGY CORPORATION; *U.S. Private,* pg. 3716
SPERIAN PROTECTION APPAREL LTD.—See Honeywell International Inc.; *U.S. Public,* pg. 1049
ST. CLAIR APPAREL, INC.; *U.S. Private,* pg. 3771
STEADFAST BRAND, INC.; *U.S. Private,* pg. 3794
STETSON HAT CO.—See Pro Equine Products Inc.; *U.S. Private,* pg. 3269
STROUD RILEY (PTY) LTD—See Chargeurs SA; *Int'l,* pg. 1449
TAPOUT LLC—See Leonard Green & Partners, L.P.; *U.S. Private,* pg. 2429
TEAMWORLD INC.; *U.S. Private,* pg. 3951
TED BAKER INTERNATIONAL LTD—See Leonard Green & Partners, L.P.; *U.S. Private,* pg. 2425
TED BAKER PLC—See Leonard Green & Partners, L.P.; *U.S. Private,* pg. 2425
TFE TEXTIL GMBH—See Getzner Textil AG; *Int'l,* pg. 2954
TIE RACK FRANCE SAS—See Fingen S.p.A.; *Int'l,* pg. 2675
TIE RACK LIMITED—See Fingen S.p.A.; *Int'l,* pg. 2675
TIE RACK RETAIL GROUP LIMITED—See Fingen S.p.A.; *Int'l,* pg. 2675
TIGER OF SWEDEN AB—See Friheden Invest A/S; *Int'l,* pg. 2792
TOPPS SAFETY APPAREL, INC.—See Pinnacle Textile Industries, LLC; *U.S. Private,* pg. 3186
TOPSON DOWNS OF CALIFORNIA, INC.; *U.S. Private,* pg. 4188
TOTES ISOTONER CORPORATION—See Freeman Spogli & Co. Incorporated; *U.S. Private,* pg. 1606
VINGAKER FACTORY OUTLET AB—See Friheden Invest A/S; *Int'l,* pg. 2793
VITAMIN BLUE, INC.; *U.S. Public,* pg. 2306
WELLS LAMONT INDUSTRY GROUP LLC—See Berkshire Hathaway Inc.; *U.S. Public,* pg. 312
WELLS LAMONT LLC—See Berkshire Hathaway Inc.; *U.S. Public,* pg. 311
WELLS LAMONT RETAIL GROUP—See Berkshire Hathaway Inc.; *U.S. Public,* pg. 312
WESFIL AUSTRALIA PTY. LTD.—See Amotiv Limited; *Int'l,* pg. 431
WEST MILL CLOTHES, TUXEDO ACCESSORIES DIVISION (DBA LORD WEST)—See Lord West Formal Wear; *U.S. Private,* pg. 2495
WILILAMSON-DICKIE MANUFACTURING COMPANY—See V. F. Corporation; *U.S. Public,* pg. 2269
WILLIAMSON-DICKIE NEDERLAND B.V.—See V. F. Corporation; *U.S. Public,* pg. 2270
WOLFORD BELGIUM N.V—See Fosun International Limited; *Int'l,* pg. 2752
WR WEBEREI RUSSIKON AG—See Getzner Textil AG; *Int'l,* pg. 2954
ZEPHYR GRAF-X INC.; *U.S. Private,* pg. 4602

316110 — LEATHER AND HIDE TANNING AND FINISHING

ACME SPONGE COMPANY—See Armaly Sponge Company, Inc.; *U.S. Private,* pg. 330
ACTION COMPANY; *U.S. Private,* pg. 67
ANDHRA PRADESH TANNERIES LTD.; *Int'l,* pg. 451
BIG TIME PRODUCTS, LLC—See Hillman Solutions Corp.; *U.S. Public,* pg. 1038
CHOKWANG LEATHER CO., LTD.; *Int'l,* pg. 1577
EAGLE OTTAWA LLC—See Lear Corporation; *U.S. Public,* pg. 1296
EDELMAN LEATHER, LLC—See MillerKnoll, Inc.; *U.S. Public,* pg. 1447
EDSIM LEATHER CO. INC.; *U.S. Private,* pg. 1338
FREUDENBERG HOUSEHOLD PRODUCTS B.V.—See Freudenberg SE; *Int'l,* pg. 2786
FURNISHED QUARTERS LLC; *U.S. Private,* pg. 1624
GILMORE & QUINN INDUSTRIES INC.; *U.S. Private,* pg. 1701
GM LEATHER S.P.A.; *Int'l,* pg. 3011
HOI TIN UNIVERSAL LIMITED; *Int'l,* pg. 3442
KAMALI LEATHER LLC; *U.S. Private,* pg. 2258
LINEA PELLE, INC.; *U.S. Private,* pg. 2460
MAJILITE CORPORATION—See Meridian Industries, Inc.; *U.S. Private,* pg. 2673
MOSSOP WESTERN LEATHERS (PTY) LTD—See Bolton Footwear (Pty) Ltd.; *Int'l,* pg. 1103
S.B. FOOT TANNING COMPANY CACTUS DIV.—See Red Wing Shoe Company, Inc.; *U.S. Private,* pg. 3376
S.B. FOOT TANNING COMPANY—See Red Wing Shoe Company, Inc.; *U.S. Private,* pg. 3376
SKINNY TAN PTY LTD.—See Brand Architekts Group plc; *Int'l,* pg. 1139
SOUTHWEST HIDE COMPANY; *U.S. Private,* pg. 3739
SPINNEYBECK ENTERPRISES, INC.—See MillerKnoll, Inc.; *U.S. Public,* pg. 1447
SPINNEYBECK IRELAND—See MillerKnoll, Inc.; *U.S. Public,* pg. 1447
TREBBIANNO LLC; *U.S. Private,* pg. 4216

316210 — FOOTWEAR MANUFACTURING

32 NORTH CORP.—See Berkshire Partners LLC; *U.S. Private,* pg. 535
ACHILLES CORPORATION; *Int'l,* pg. 103
ADIDAS KOREA TECHNICAL SERVICES LTD.—See adidas AG; *Int'l,* pg. 147
ALAN SCOTT INDUSTRIES LIMITED; *Int'l,* pg. 290
THE ALDEN SHOE COMPANY; *U.S. Private,* pg. 3983
ALLEN EDMONDS LLC—See Caleres, Inc.; *U.S. Public,* pg. 422
ALPARGATAS S.A. - CAMPINA GRANDE PLANT—See Cambuhy Investimentos Ltda.; *Int'l,* pg. 1270
ALPARGATAS S.A. - DUPE PLANT—See Cambuhy Investimentos Ltda.; *Int'l,* pg. 1270
ALPARGATAS S.A. - JOAO PESSOA PLANT—See Cambuhy Investimentos Ltda.; *Int'l,* pg. 1270
ALPARGATAS S.A. - MOGI MIRIM PLANT—See Cambuhy Investimentos Ltda.; *Int'l,* pg. 1270
ALPARGATAS S.A. - SANTA RITA PLANT—See Cambuhy Investimentos Ltda.; *Int'l,* pg. 1270
ALPARGATAS S.A.—See Cambuhy Investimentos Ltda.; *Int'l,* pg. 1270
ALPINA, D.D.; *Int'l,* pg. 371
ALTAMA FOOTWEAR—See Brand Velocity Partners; *U.S. Private,* pg. 637
AMERICAN SHOE S.A.—See Air Products & Chemicals, Inc.; *U.S. Public,* pg. 66
APEX FOOTWEAR LIMITED; *Int'l,* pg. 509
ARES ASIA LIMITED; *Int'l,* pg. 559
ARIAT INTERNATIONAL, INC.; *U.S. Private,* pg. 322
BAFFIN INC.—See Bain Capital, LP; *U.S. Private,* pg. 437
BANGKOK RUBBER PUBLIC CO., LTD.; *Int'l,* pg. 835
BATA INDIA LIMITED; *Int'l,* pg. 889
BATA PROPERTIES LIMITED—See Bata India Limited; *Int'l,* pg. 889
BEACONSFIELD FOOTWEAR LIMITED—See Epiris Managers LLP; *Int'l,* pg. 2461
BELLE WORLDWIDE LIMITED—See Hillhouse Investment Management Limited; *Int'l,* pg. 3392
THE BILTRITE CORPORATION; *U.S. Private,* pg. 3995
BINH TIEN DONG NAI IMEX CORP., PTE., LTD—See Binh Tien Imex Corp. Pte. Ltd.; *Int'l,* pg. 1034
BINH TIEN IMEX CORP. PTE. LTD.; *Int'l,* pg. 1034
BJORN BORG FOOTWEAR AB—See Bjorn Borg AB; *Int'l,* pg. 1054
BOLTON FOOTWEAR (PTY) LTD.; *Int'l,* pg. 1103
BRILL SHOE INDUSTRIES LTD.; *Int'l,* pg. 1163
BROOKS SPORTS INC.—See Berkshire Hathaway Inc.; *U.S. Public,* pg. 305
CALERES, INC.; *U.S. Public,* pg. 422
CAMPUS ACTIVEWEAR LIMITED; *Int'l,* pg. 1275
C.BANNER INTERNATIONAL HOLDINGS LIMITED; *Int'l,* pg. 1240
CESARE PACIOTTI S.P.A.; *Int'l,* pg. 1424
CHARGEURS ENTRETELAS (IBERICA) LTD.—See Chargeurs NV; *Int'l,* pg. 1448
CHEM-MAT TECHNOLOGIES CO., LTD.—See Evermore Chemical Industry Co., Ltd.; *Int'l,* pg. 2568
CHINA HONGXING SPORTS LIMITED; *Int'l,* pg. 1508
CHINA SPORTS INTERNATIONAL LIMITED; *Int'l,* pg. 1553
CHIYODA CO., LTD.; *Int'l,* pg. 1574
CHRISTIAN LOUBOUTIN SAS; *Int'l,* pg. 1586
C&J CLARK LIMITED; *Int'l,* pg. 1238
CLUJANA S.A.; *Int'l,* pg. 1664
COFLUSA S.A.; *Int'l,* pg. 1693
COLE HAAN COMPANY STORE—See Apax Partners LLP; *Int'l,* pg. 503
COUNTY FOOTWEAR LIMITED—See Patterson Companies, Inc.; *U.S. Public,* pg. 1653
COVE SHOE COMPANY—See Berkshire Hathaway Inc.; *U.S. Public,* pg. 299
COWTOWN BOOT COMPANY; *U.S. Private,* pg. 1074
CROCS ASIA PTE. LTD.—See Crocs, Inc.; *U.S. Public,* pg. 595
CROCS AUSTRALIA PTY. LTD.—See Crocs, Inc.; *U.S. Public,* pg. 595
CROCS AUSTRALIA PTY. LTD.—See Crocs, Inc.; *U.S. Public,* pg. 595
CROCS CANADA, INC.—See Crocs, Inc.; *U.S. Public,* pg. 595
CROCS HONG KONG LTD.—See Crocs, Inc.; *U.S. Public,* pg. 595
CROCS, INC.; *U.S. Public,* pg. 594
CROCS INDIA PRIVATE LIMITED—See Crocs, Inc.; *U.S. Public,* pg. 595
CROCS NORDIC OY—See Crocs, Inc.; *U.S. Public,* pg. 595
CROCS NZ LIMITED—See Crocs, Inc.; *U.S. Public,* pg. 595
CROCS PUERTO RICO, INC.—See Crocs, Inc.; *U.S. Public,* pg. 595
CROCS SINGAPORE PTE. LTD.—See Crocs, Inc.; *U.S. Public,* pg. 595
CROCS SOUTH AFRICA—See Crocs, Inc.; *U.S. Public,* pg. 595
DANNER, INC.—See ABC-Mart, Inc.; *Int'l,* pg. 57
DAN POST BOOT CO.—See McRae Industries, Inc.; *U.S. Public,* pg. 1409
DAPHNE INTERNATIONAL HOLDINGS LIMITED; *Int'l,* pg. 1970
DECKERS ASIA PACIFIC RETAIL LIMITED—See Deckers Outdoor Corporation; *U.S. Public,* pg. 645
DECKERS BENELUX BV—See Deckers Outdoor Corporation; *U.S. Public,* pg. 645
DECKERS CONSUMER DIRECT CORPORATION—See Deckers Outdoor Corporation; *U.S. Public,* pg. 645
DECKERS FOOTWEAR (SHANGHAI) CO., LTD.—See Deckers Outdoor Corporation; *U.S. Public,* pg. 645
DECKERS FRANCE 2 SAS—See Deckers Outdoor Corporation; *U.S. Public,* pg. 645
DECKERS FRANCE SAS—See Deckers Outdoor Corporation; *U.S. Public,* pg. 645
DECKERS OUTDOOR CORPORATION; *U.S. Public,* pg. 645
DECKERS UK, LTD—See Deckers Outdoor Corporation; *U.S. Public,* pg. 645
DEICHMANN SE; *Int'l,* pg. 2005
DEXTER SHOE COMPANY—See Berkshire Hathaway Inc.; *U.S. Public,* pg. 299
DIADORA INVICTA; *Int'l,* pg. 2101
DIANA E. KELLY, INC.; *U.S. Private,* pg. 1224
DIORK A.D.; *Int'l,* pg. 2128
DOUBLE H BOOT COMPANY—See Berkshire Hathaway Inc.; *U.S. Public,* pg. 299
DREW SHOE CORPORATION—See Wexford Capital Limited Partnership; *U.S. Private,* pg. 4502
DURANGO BOOT COMPANY, LLC—See Rocky Brands, Inc.; *U.S. Public,* pg. 1807
DVS FOOTWEAR INTERNATIONAL, LLC—See Elan-Polo Inc.; *U.S. Private,* pg. 1350
ECCO EMEA SALES SE—See Ecco Sko A/S; *Int'l,* pg. 2288
ECCOLET (PORTUGAL) FABRICA DE SAPATOS, LDA.—See Ecco Sko A/S; *Int'l,* pg. 2288
ECCO SKO A/S; *Int'l,* pg. 2288
ECCO (THAILAND) CO., LTD.—See Ecco Sko A/S; *Int'l,* pg. 2288
ECCO (XIAMEN) CO. LTD.—See Ecco Sko A/S; *Int'l,* pg. 2288
EGYPTIAN CO. FOR SHOES (BATA)—See Chemical Industries Holding Company; *Int'l,* pg. 1461
ELEFANTEN PORTUGUESA LDA. INDUSTRIA DE CALCADO—See Freudenberg SE; *Int'l,* pg. 2785

316210 — FOOTWEAR MANUFACTUR...

THE ENJOIYA GROUP, LLC; *U.S. Private*, pg. 4026
ERATAT LIFESTYLE LIMITED; *Int'l*, pg. 2489
EVERSUN FOOTWEAR CO., LTD.—See Fulgent Sun International (Holding) Co., Ltd.; *Int'l*, pg. 2842
EXO ITALIA, S.R.L.—See Crocs, Inc.; *U.S. Public*, pg. 595
FAST CASUALWEAR AG; *Int'l*, pg. 2621
FEELGOODZ, LLC; *U.S. Private*, pg. 1493
FELTEX HOLDINGS (PTY) LTD. - UNITED FRAM FOOTWEAR—See Bolton Footwear (Pty) Ltd.; *Int'l*, pg. 1103
FELTEX HOLDINGS (PTY) LTD. - WAYNE PLASTICS—See Bolton Footwear (Pty) Ltd.; *Int'l*, pg. 1103
FENG TAY ENTERPRISES CO., LTD.; *Int'l*, pg. 2634
FLAROS S.A.; *Int'l*, pg. 2698
FOOT PETALS, INC.—See Remington Products Company; *U.S. Private*, pg. 3396
FORTUNE SHOES LTD.; *Int'l*, pg. 2744
FOSHAN YOWANT TECHNOLOGY CO., LTD.; *Int'l*, pg. 2748
FREED OF LONDON LTD.; *Int'l*, pg. 2769
FREELAND S.R.L; *Int'l*, pg. 2770
FUGUINIAO CO., LTD.; *Int'l*, pg. 2808
FUJIAN LAYA OUTDOOR PRODUCTS CO., LTD.—See Fulgent Sun International (Holding) Co., Ltd.; *Int'l*, pg. 2842
FUJIAN SUNSHINE FOOTWEAR CO., LTD.—See Fulgent Sun International (Holding) Co., Ltd.; *Int'l*, pg. 2842
FULGENT SUN FOOTWEAR CO., LTD.—See Fulgent Sun International (Holding) Co., Ltd.; *Int'l*, pg. 2842
FULGENT SUN INTERNATIONAL (HOLDING) CO., LTD.; *Int'l*, pg. 2841
GENFOOT INC.; *Int'l*, pg. 2923
GENFOOT, INC.—See Genfoot Inc.; *Int'l*, pg. 2923
GEORGIA BOOT, LLC—See Rocky Brands, Inc.; *U.S. Public*, pg. 1807
GIANT STAR TRADING CO., LTD.—See Evermore Chemical Industry Co., Ltd.; *Int'l*, pg. 2568
GLOBE INTERNATIONAL LIMITED; *Int'l*, pg. 3006
GOLDEN SOLAR NEW ENERGY TECHNOLOGY HOLDINGS LIMITED; *Int'l*, pg. 3031
GOOD VIBRATIONS SHOES INC.; *U.S. Public*, pg. 951
GRENDENE S.A.; *Int'l*, pg. 3080
GRENSON SHOES LIMITED—See Grenson Limited; *Int'l*, pg. 3081
G. R. (HOLDINGS) PLC; *Int'l*, pg. 2864
GROUNDED PEOPLE APPAREL INC.; *Int'l*, pg. 3088
HEVEA B.V.; *Int'l*, pg. 3366
H.H. BROWN SHOE COMPANY, INC.—See Berkshire Hathaway Inc.; *U.S. Public*, pg. 299
HOLBROOK LTD.—See Deckers Outdoor Corporation; *U.S. Public*, pg. 645
HONGRONG LIGHT INDUSTRY CO., LTD.—See China Hongxing Sports Limited; *Int'l*, pg. 1508
HONGXING ERKE SPORTS GOODS CO., LTD—See China Hongxing Sports Limited; *Int'l*, pg. 1508
HUBEI SUNSMILE FOOTWEAR CO., LTD.—See Fulgent Sun International (Holding) Co., Ltd.; *Int'l*, pg. 2842
HWASEUNG AMERICA CORP.—See Hwaseung Industries Co., Ltd.; *Int'l*, pg. 3542
HWASEUNG CLIMATE CONTROL INDUSTRIES CO., LTD.—See Hwaseung Industries Co., Ltd.; *Int'l*, pg. 3542
HWASEUNG ENTERPRISE CO., LTD—See Hwaseung Industries Co., Ltd.; *Int'l*, pg. 3542
HWASEUNG EXWILL—See Hwaseung Industries Co., Ltd.; *Int'l*, pg. 3542
HWASEUNG MATERIAL CO., LTD.—See Hwaseung Industries Co., Ltd.; *Int'l*, pg. 3542
HWASEUNG NETWORKS CO., LTD.—See Hwaseung Industries Co., Ltd.; *Int'l*, pg. 3542
IDELIK FOOTWEAR, INC.; *U.S. Private*, pg. 2037
IMPLUS FOOTCARE, LLC—See Berkshire Partners LLC; *U.S. Private*, pg. 534
INNOVATION FOOTWEAR CO., LTD.—See Bangkok Rubber Public Co., Ltd.; *Int'l*, pg. 835
IPATH LLC—See Madison Parker Capital; *U.S. Private*, pg. 2544
JIMMY CHOO PLC—See Capri Holdings Limited; *Int'l*, pg. 1316
J.L. & COMPANY LIMITED—See Hermes International SCA; *Int'l*, pg. 3363
JOHN LOBB SAS—See Hermes International SCA; *Int'l*, pg. 3363
JONES & VINING INC. - CHINA FACTORY—See Jones & Vining Inc.; *U.S. Private*, pg. 2231
JONES & VINING INC. - LASTS FACTORY—See Jones & Vining Inc.; *U.S. Private*, pg. 2231
JONES & VINING INC. - MAINE FACTORY—See Jones & Vining Inc.; *U.S. Private*, pg. 2231
JONES & VINING INC. - TAIWAN TBC FACTORY—See Jones & Vining Inc.; *U.S. Private*, pg. 2231
JONES & VINING INC. - VIETNAM FACTORY—See Jones & Vining Inc.; *U.S. Private*, pg. 2231
JUMPING-JACKS SHOES DIV—See Munro & Company, Inc.; *U.S. Private*, pg. 2814
JUSTIN BOOT COMPANY—See Berkshire Hathaway Inc.; *U.S. Public*, pg. 308
JUSTIN BRANDS, INC.—See Berkshire Hathaway Inc.; *U.S. Public*, pg. 308

KEUKA FOOTWEAR, INC.—See Genesco Inc.; *U.S. Public*, pg. 930
KING'S SHOE MANUFACTURING PTE. LTD.—See Honeywell International Inc.; *U.S. Public*, pg. 1049
K S UK LIMITED—See E-Land World Ltd.; *Int'l*, pg. 2248
K-SWISS AUSTRALIA—See E-Land World Ltd.; *Int'l*, pg. 2248
K-SWISS CANADA—See E-Land World Ltd.; *Int'l*, pg. 2248
K-SWISS EUROPE B.V.—See E-Land World Ltd.; *Int'l*, pg. 2248
K-SWISS (HONG KONG) LTD.—See E-Land World Ltd.; *Int'l*, pg. 2248
K-SWISS INC.—See E-Land World Ltd.; *Int'l*, pg. 2248
K-SWISS PACIFIC INC.—See E-Land World Ltd.; *Int'l*, pg. 2248
K-SWISS RETAIL LTD.—See E-Land World Ltd.; *Int'l*, pg. 2248
K-SWISS SALES CORP.—See E-Land World Ltd.; *Int'l*, pg. 2248
LACROSSE FOOTWEAR, INC.—See ABC-Mart, Inc.; *Int'l*, pg. 57
L.A. GEAR CALIFORNIA, INC.—See ACI International; *U.S. Private*, pg. 59
L.A. GEAR, INC.—See ACI International; *U.S. Private*, pg. 59
LAKE CATHERINE—See Munro & Company, Inc.; *U.S. Private*, pg. 2814
THE LANGER GROUP—See PC GROUP, INC.; *U.S. Private*, pg. 3119
LAYA MAX TRADING CO., LTD.—See Fulgent Sun International (Holding) Co., Ltd.; *Int'l*, pg. 2842
LAYA OUTDOOR PRODUCTS LIMITED—See Fulgent Sun International (Holding) Co., Ltd.; *Int'l*, pg. 2842
LEHIGH OUTFITTERS, LLC—See Rocky Brands, Inc.; *U.S. Public*, pg. 1807
LIN WEN CHIH SUNBOW ENTERPRISES CO., LTD.—See Fulgent Sun International (Holding) Co., Ltd.; *Int'l*, pg. 2842
LUCCHESE, INC.—See Kainos Capital, LLC; *U.S. Private*, pg. 2254
MADISON FOOTWEAR CO. LTD.—See Mercury International Trading Corp.; *U.S. Private*, pg. 2670
MASON COMPANIES, INC.; *U.S. Private*, pg. 2602
MAURICE J. MARKELL SHOE CO., INC.; *U.S. Private*, pg. 2615
MCRAE FOOTWEAR DIVISION—See McRae Industries, Inc.; *U.S. Public*, pg. 1409
MCRAE INDUSTRIES, INC.; *U.S. Public*, pg. 1409
MGO GLOBAL INC.; *U.S. Public*, pg. 1435
MICHAEL KORS (BUCHAREST STORE) S.R.L.—See Capri Holdings Limited; *Int'l*, pg. 1316
MIRABELL INTERNATIONAL HOLDINGS LIMITED—See Hillhouse Investment Management Limited; *Int'l*, pg. 3393
MUNRO & COMPANY, INC.; *U.S. Private*, pg. 2814
NERI S.P.A.—See Bunzl plc; *Int'l*, pg. 1219
NEW BALANCE ATHLETIC SHOE, INC.; *U.S. Private*, pg. 2892
NGOC HUNG FOOTWEAR CO., LTD.—See Fulgent Sun International (Holding) Co., Ltd.; *Int'l*, pg. 2842
NIKE HONG KONG LIMITED—See NIKE, Inc.; *U.S. Public*, pg. 1529
NIKE (SWITZERLAND) GMBH—See NIKE, Inc.; *U.S. Public*, pg. 1528
OCEAN MINDED, INC.—See Crocs, Inc.; *U.S. Public*, pg. 595
ONGUARD INDUSTRIES LLC—See Ansell Limited; *Int'l*, pg. 478
THE ORIGINAL FOOTWEAR CO.—See Brand Velocity Partners; *U.S. Private*, pg. 637
THE OUTDOOR FOOTWEAR COMPANY—See V. F. Corporation; *U.S. Public*, pg. 2268
PAGODA INTERNATIONAL FOOTWEAR LIMITED—See Caleres, Inc.; *U.S. Public*, pg. 422
PHOENIX FOOTWEAR GROUP, INC.; *U.S. Public*, pg. 1689
POU CHIEN CHEMICAL CO., LTD.—See Evermore Chemical Industry Co., Ltd.; *Int'l*, pg. 2568
P.T. ECCO INDONESIA—See Ecco Sko A/S; *Int'l*, pg. 2288
P.T. FENG TAY INDONESIA ENTERPRISES—See Feng Tay Enterprises Co., Ltd.; *Int'l*, pg. 2634
P.W. MINOR & SON, INC.; *U.S. Private*, pg. 3061
REBECCA MINKOFF LLC; *U.S. Private*, pg. 3370
RED WING SHOE COMPANY, INC.; *U.S. Private*, pg. 3376
RED WING SHOE VASQUE DIV.—See Red Wing Shoe Company, Inc.; *U.S. Private*, pg. 3376
REEBOK INTERNATIONAL LTD.—See Leonard Green & Partners, L.P.; *U.S. Private*, pg. 2424
R.G. BARRY CORPORATION—See Mill Road Capital Management LLC; *U.S. Private*, pg. 2730
RHINO FOOTWEAR LTD.—See Alam Group of Companies; *Int'l*, pg. 289
RIKCO INTERNATIONAL LLC—See Enovis Corporation; *U.S. Public*, pg. 772
ROCKET DOG BRANDS, LLC—See Circle Peak Capital LLC; *U.S. Private*, pg. 900
ROCKET DOG BRANDS, LLC—See Golden Gate Capital Management II, LLC; *U.S. Public*, pg. 1731
THE ROCKPORT COMPANY, LLC—See Charlesbank Capital Partners, LLC; *U.S. Private*, pg. 856

ROCKY BRANDS, INC.; *U.S. Public*, pg. 1807
ROCKY BRANDS US, LLC—See Rocky Brands, Inc.; *U.S. Public*, pg. 1807
ROCKY OUTDOOR GEAR—See Rocky Brands, Inc.; *U.S. Public*, pg. 1807
SAUCONY, INC.—See Wolverine World Wide, Inc.; *U.S. Public*, pg. 2377
SCHWARTZ & BENJAMIN, INC.—See Steven Madden, Ltd.; *U.S. Public*, pg. 1947
SGFOOTWEAR, INC.; *U.S. Private*, pg. 3622
SHOES FOR CREWS, LLC—See CCMP Capital Advisors, LP; *U.S. Private*, pg. 801
SKECHERS POLAND SP. Z O.O.—See Skechers U.S.A., Inc.; *U.S. Public*, pg. 1891
SKECHERS SLOVAKIA S.R.O.—See Skechers U.S.A., Inc.; *U.S. Public*, pg. 1892
SKECHERS USA PORTUGAL UNIPESSOAL LIMITADA—See Skechers U.S.A., Inc.; *U.S. Public*, pg. 1891
SOFFT SHOE COMPANY, INC.—See Berkshire Hathaway Inc.; *U.S. Public*, pg. 299
SOUTH CONE, INC.—See Charlesbank Capital Partners, LLC; *U.S. Private*, pg. 856
SPENCO MEDICAL CORPORATION; *U.S. Private*, pg. 3755
STANBEE ASIA, LTD.—See Stanbee Company, Inc.; *U.S. Private*, pg. 3777
STANBEE COMPANY, INC.; *U.S. Private*, pg. 3777
STEVEN MADDEN, LTD.; *U.S. Public*, pg. 1947
SUNNY FOOTWEAR CO., LTD.—See Fulgent Sun International (Holding) Co., Ltd.; *Int'l*, pg. 2842
SUREFOOT INC; *U.S. Private*, pg. 3883
TECNO BOGA COMERCIAL LIMITADA—See Bunzl plc; *Int'l*, pg. 1219
TEXON INTERNATIONAL GROUP LTD.—See Coats Group plc; *Int'l*, pg. 1682
TIMBERLAND ASIA LLC—See V. F. Corporation; *U.S. Public*, pg. 2268
TIMBERLAND CANADA CO.—See V. F. Corporation; *U.S. Public*, pg. 2268
THE TIMBERLAND COMPANY—See V. F. Corporation; *U.S. Public*, pg. 2268
TIMBERLAND EUROPE SERVICES LTD.—See V. F. Corporation; *U.S. Public*, pg. 2268
TIMBERLAND HONG KONG LTD.—See V. F. Corporation; *U.S. Public*, pg. 2268
TIMBERLAND INTERNATIONAL, LLC—See V. F. Corporation; *U.S. Public*, pg. 2269
TIMBERLAND LLC—See V. F. Corporation; *U.S. Public*, pg. 2269
TINGLEY RUBBER CORPORATION—See Bunzl plc; *Int'l*, pg. 1219
TOPCO (SHANGHAI) CO., LTD.—See Evermore Chemical Industry Co., Ltd.; *Int'l*, pg. 2568
UNISA EUROPA SA—See Unisa Holdings Incorporated; *U.S. Private*, pg. 4286
VIKING FOOTWEAR AB—See Bertel O. Steen AS; *Int'l*, pg. 989
VIKING FOOTWEAR A/S—See Bertel O. Steen AS; *Int'l*, pg. 989
VIKING FOTTOY A/S—See Bertel O. Steen AS; *Int'l*, pg. 989
VIKING JALKINEET OY—See Bertel O. Steen AS; *Int'l*, pg. 989
WEINBRENNER SHOE COMPANY, INC.; *U.S. Private*, pg. 4471
WEST END FINANCIAL CORP.; *U.S. Private*, pg. 4485
WOLVERINE EUROPE RETAIL LIMITED—See Wolverine World Wide, Inc.; *U.S. Public*, pg. 2377
WOLVERINE INTERNATIONAL, S.L.—See Wolverine World Wide, Inc.; *U.S. Public*, pg. 2377
WOLVERINE WORLD WIDE - BATES FOOTWEAR—See Wolverine World Wide, Inc.; *U.S. Public*, pg. 2377
WOLVERINE WORLD WIDE, INC.; *U.S. Public*, pg. 2377
WOOD'S BOOTS—See Boot Barn Holdings, Inc.; *U.S. Public*, pg. 368
XSOVT BRANDS, INC.; *U.S. Public*, pg. 2393

316990 — OTHER LEATHER AND ALLIED PRODUCT MANUFACTURING

ACTON LEATHER CO. INC.; *Int'l*, pg. 121
AKI INDIA LIMITED; *Int'l*, pg. 263
ALLEGRO MANUFACTURING, INC.—See American Securities LLC; *U.S. Private*, pg. 247
AMERICAN ACCESSORIES INTERNATIONAL LLC; *U.S. Private*, pg. 221
AMIN TANNERY LIMITED; *Int'l*, pg. 427
AMVIG HOLDINGS LIMITED; *Int'l*, pg. 442
ANHUI ANLI MATERIAL TECHNOLOGY CO., LTD.; *Int'l*, pg. 466
ANKA INDIA LIMITED; *Int'l*, pg. 472
ANTLER LTD—See Centurion Group Ltd; *Int'l*, pg. 1417
ANVIL CASES, INC.—See Caltron Case Company; *U.S. Private*, pg. 724
ANYA HINDMARCH JAPAN CORPORATION—See ASHS Ltd.; *Int'l*, pg. 609
APEX TANNERY LIMITED; *Int'l*, pg. 512

N.A.I.C.S. INDEX

321113 — SAWMILLS

ASHS LTD.; *Int'l*, pg. 609
AUTOLIV BV & CO. KG—See Autoliv, Inc.; *Int'l*, pg. 728
AUTOMOTIVE TRIM DEVELOPMENTS; *Int'l*, pg. 731
BAGGALLINI INC.—See Mill Road Capital Management LLC; *U.S. Private*, pg. 2730
BARBOUR CORPORATION; *U.S. Private*, pg. 472
BARBOUR WELTING CO.—See Barbour Corporation; *U.S. Private*, pg. 472
BASLER JAPAN KK—See Basler AG; *Int'l*, pg. 887
BASLER KOREA INC.—See Basler AG; *Int'l*, pg. 887
BASLER NEUMUNSTER AG—See Basler AG; *Int'l*, pg. 887
BASLER VISION TECHNOLOGY (BEIJING) CO., LTD.—See Basler AG; *Int'l*, pg. 887
BATA PAKISTAN LIMITED; *Int'l*, pg. 889
BATA SHOE COMPANY (BANGLADESH) LIMITED; *Int'l*, pg. 889
B/E AEROSPACE FISCHER GMBH—See RTX Corporation; *U.S. Public*, pg. 1822
B/E AEROSPACE FISCHER GMBH—See The Boeing Company; *U.S. Public*, pg. 2040
BOISSY; *Int'l*, pg. 1101
BRAHMIN LEATHER WORKS, LLC—See Markel Group Inc.; *U.S. Public*, pg. 1367
BRZZ GEAR LLC; *U.S. Private*, pg. 674
CALZONE CASE CO., LTD.—See Caltron Case Company; *U.S. Private*, pg. 724
CHAI WATANA TANNERY GROUP PUBLIC COMPANY LIMITED; *Int'l*, pg. 1436
CHINA SKY CHEMICAL FIBRE CO., LTD.; *Int'l*, pg. 1552
CHRISTIAN DIOR S.A.; *Int'l*, pg. 1586
CIRCA CORPORATION; *U.S. Private*, pg. 899
COACH HONG KONG LIMITED—See Tapestry, Inc.; *U.S. Public*, pg. 1981
COACH INTERNATIONAL LIMITED—See Tapestry, Inc.; *U.S. Public*, pg. 1981
COACH SERVICES, INC.—See Tapestry, Inc.; *U.S. Public*, pg. 1981
COACH STORES BELGIUM—See Tapestry, Inc.; *U.S. Public*, pg. 1981
CPL GROUP PUBLIC COMPANY LIMITED; *Int'l*, pg. 1825
DAEWON CHEMICAL CO., LTD. - OSAN FACTORY—See DAEWON Chemical Co., Ltd.; *Int'l*, pg. 1910
DAEWON CHEMICAL CO., LTD.; *Int'l*, pg. 1910
DAPAI INTERNATIONAL HOLDINGS CO. LTD.; *Int'l*, pg. 1970
DERIMOD KONFEKSIYON AYAKKABI DERI SANAYI VE TICARET A.S.; *Int'l*, pg. 2042
DERLUKS YATIRIM HOLDING A.S.; *Int'l*, pg. 2042
DK&D CO., LTD.; *Int'l*, pg. 2138
DOGNESS (INTERNATIONAL) CORPORATION; *Int'l*, pg. 2154
DOONEY & BOURKE, INC.; *U.S. Private*, pg. 1261
DYNOMIGHTY DESIGN; *U.S. Private*, pg. 1300
EAGLE OTTAWA BRASIL INDUSTRIA E BENEFICIAMENTO DE COUROS LTDA.—See Lear Corporation; *U.S. Public*, pg. 1296
EAGLE OTTAWA CHINA LTD.—See Lear Corporation; *U.S. Public*, pg. 1296
EAGLE OTTAWA HUNGARY KFT.—See Lear Corporation; *U.S. Public*, pg. 1296
EAGLE OTTAWA NORTH AMERICA, LLC—See Lear Corporation; *U.S. Public*, pg. 1296
EAGLE OTTAWA (THAILAND) CO., LTD.—See Lear Corporation; *U.S. Public*, pg. 1296
ECCO LEATHER B.V.—See Ecco Sko A/S; *Int'l*, pg. 2288
ECO-BAGS PRODUCTS, INC.; *U.S. Private*, pg. 1328
E-LEATHER LTD.; *Int'l*, pg. 2248
ERIC SCOTT LEATHERS LTD.; *Int'l*, pg. 1419
ETRO USA INC.—See Etro S.p.A.; *Int'l*, pg. 2524
FENOPLAST LIMITED; *Int'l*, pg. 2634
FERRINI USA INC.; *U.S. Private*, pg. 1498
FJ BENJAMIN FASHIONS (SINGAPORE) PTE. LTD.—See FJ Benjamin Holdings Ltd.; *Int'l*, pg. 2697
FJ BENJAMIN (M) SDN. BHD.—See FJ Benjamin Holdings Ltd.; *Int'l*, pg. 2697
FLYING EAGLE PU TECHNICAL CORP.; *Int'l*, pg. 2716
FOGS D.D. SARAJEVO; *Int'l*, pg. 2721
FORANKRA POL SP. Z O.O.—See Axel Johnson Gruppen AB; *Int'l*, pg. 764
FORWARD INDUSTRIES, INC.; *U.S. Public*, pg. 874
FRANCES MARY ACCESSORIES, INC.; *U.S. Private*, pg. 1586
FULLER BOX COMPANY INC.; *U.S. Private*, pg. 1621
G-III LEATHER FASHIONS—See G-III Apparel Group, Ltd.; *U.S. Public*, pg. 894
GINO ROSSI S.A.—See CCC S.A.; *Int'l*, pg. 1366
GOULD & GOODRICH LEATHER, INC.—See JLL Partners, LLC; *U.S. Private*, pg. 2213
GPI FORANKRA SAS—See Axel Johnson Gruppen AB; *Int'l*, pg. 764
GROW-TECH LLC—See Dummen Orange Holding B.V.; *Int'l*, pg. 2225
GUANGDONG WANLIMA INDUSTRY CO LTD; *Int'l*, pg. 3161
HARSON TRADING (CHINA) CO., LTD.; *Int'l*, pg. 3279
HOBIE BAG COMPANY—See Hobie Cat Company; *U.S. Private*, pg. 1958
HUAFON MICROFIBRE (SHANGHAI) CO., LTD.; *Int'l*, pg. 3511
HUGO BOSCA COMPANY, INC.; *U.S. Private*, pg. 2004
IDENTITY STRONGHOLD, LLC; *U.S. Private*, pg. 2037
INDIA TRIMMINGS PRIVATE LIMITED—See IG Design Group Plc; *Int'l*, pg. 3600
INDONESIAN IMPORTS, INC.; *U.S. Private*, pg. 2064
INDUSTRIAS LAKELAND S.A. DE C.V.—See Lakeland Industries, Inc.; *U.S. Public*, pg. 1288
INITIALS, INC.; *U.S. Private*, pg. 2077
INTERCOM S.R.L.—See Heidelberg Materials AG; *Int'l*, pg. 3316
JONES & VINING INC.; *U.S. Private*, pg. 2231
JON HART DESIGN CO.; *U.S. Private*, pg. 2231
JUBA PERSONAL PROTECTIVE EQUIPMENT, S.L.U.—See Bunzl plc; *Int'l*, pg. 1218
JW HULME CO. LLC—See Olympus Holdings, LLC; *U.S. Private*, pg. 3013
KAMAN AUTOMATION, INC.—See Littlejohn & Co., LLC; *U.S. Private*, pg. 2471
K.J. QUINN S.A.S.—See Clariant AG; *Int'l*, pg. 1646
KOLTOV INC.; *U.S. Private*, pg. 2341
KUNSHAN ACHILLES ARTIFICIAL LEATHER CO., LTD.—See Achilles Corporation; *Int'l*, pg. 103
LAKELAND ARGENTINA, SRL—See Lakeland Industries, Inc.; *U.S. Public*, pg. 1289
LAKELAND (BEIJING) SAFETY PRODUCTS, CO., LTD.—See Lakeland Industries, Inc.; *U.S. Public*, pg. 1288
LAKELAND GLOVES AND SAFETY APPAREL PRIVATE LTD.—See Lakeland Industries, Inc.; *U.S. Public*, pg. 1289
LAKELAND INDUSTRIES EUROPE LTD.—See Lakeland Industries, Inc.; *U.S. Public*, pg. 1289
LAKELAND INDUSTRIES, INC. AGENCIA EN CHILE—See Lakeland Industries, Inc.; *U.S. Public*, pg. 1289
LANDES CANADA INC.—See Medike, Inc.; *U.S. Private*, pg. 2656
LANDES HONG KONG LIMITED—See Medike, Inc.; *U.S. Private*, pg. 2657
LANDES LEDERWARENFABRIK GMBH—See Medike, Inc.; *U.S. Private*, pg. 2656
LEAR SEWING (PTY.) LTD.—See Lear Corporation; *U.S. Public*, pg. 1297
LEATHER INDUSTRIES OF KENYA LTD—See Aga Khan Development Network; *Int'l*, pg. 199
LEE & MAN COMPANY LIMITED—See Best Food Holding Company Limited; *Int'l*, pg. 999
LEE & MAN HANDBAG MANUFACTURING CO. LTD.—See Best Food Holding Company Limited; *Int'l*, pg. 999
LYSSE—See E&A Industries, Inc.; *U.S. Private*, pg. 1301
MAD BY DESIGN LLC; *U.S. Private*, pg. 2538
MARY FRANCES ACCESSORIES, INC.; *U.S. Private*, pg. 2598
MERCURY LUGGAGE/SEWARD TRUNK; *U.S. Private*, pg. 2670
MERCURY LUGGAGE/SEWARD TRUNK—See Mercury; *U.S. Private*, pg. 2671
MORLANDS (GLASTONBURY) LIMITED—See G. R. (Holdings) plc; *Int'l*, pg. 2864
NEW ZEALAND LIGHT LEATHERS LTD—See Argent Group Europe Limited; *Int'l*, pg. 560
THE PEDRO COMPANIES, INC.; *U.S. Private*, pg. 4092
PIONEER INVESTMENT, INC.—See NCS Multistage Holdings, Inc.; *U.S. Public*, pg. 1503
POLYCHEM CORPORATION—See The Sterling Group, L.P.; *U.S. Private*, pg. 4123
RANDA ACCESSORIES LEATHER GOODS LLC—See Randa Corp.; *U.S. Private*, pg. 3353
RANDA LUGGAGE—See Randa Corp.; *U.S. Private*, pg. 3353
RHODIANA CORP.; *U.S. Private*, pg. 3422
RICARDO BEVERLY HILLS, INC.; *U.S. Private*, pg. 3425
RICKSHAW BAGWORKS; *U.S. Private*, pg. 3431
RICO INDUSTRIES INC.; *U.S. Private*, pg. 3431
ROSE-AMERICA CORPORATION; *U.S. Private*, pg. 3482
RYNN'S LUGGAGE CORPORATION; *U.S. Private*, pg. 3511
SAMSILL, INC.; *U.S. Private*, pg. 3538
SHOEAHOLICS LIMITED—See Cinven Limited; *Int'l*, pg. 1612
SIMPLICITY PTY LIMITED—See IG Design Group Plc; *Int'l*, pg. 3600
SKYWAY LUGGAGE COMPANY—See Ricardo Beverly Hills, Inc.; *U.S. Private*, pg. 3425
SUMMIT INDUSTRIES, INC. - LEXOL DIVISION—See Summit Industries, Inc.; *U.S. Private*, pg. 3854
SUN RAY MANUFACTORY, LIMITED—See China International Development Corporation Limited; *Int'l*, pg. 1510
SWANK, INC.—See Randa Corp.; *U.S. Private*, pg. 3353
TAMRAC, INC.; *U.S. Private*, pg. 3930
TANDY LEATHER FACTORY, INC.; *U.S. Public*, pg. 1980
TAPESTRY, INC.; *U.S. Public*, pg. 1981
TARA TOY CORP.—See Just Play Products, LLC; *U.S. Private*, pg. 2245
TARGUS ASIA PACIFIC LIMITED—See Targus Group International, Inc.; *U.S. Private*, pg. 3934
TARGUS ASIA PACIFIC PTE. LTD.—See Targus Group International, Inc.; *U.S. Private*, pg. 3934
TARGUS AUSTRALIA PTY. LTD.—See Targus Group International, Inc.; *U.S. Private*, pg. 3934
TARGUS CANADA LTD.—See Targus Group International, Inc.; *U.S. Private*, pg. 3934
TARGUS JAPAN LTD.—See Targus Group International, Inc.; *U.S. Private*, pg. 3934
TARGUS KOREA CO., LTD.—See Targus Group International, Inc.; *U.S. Private*, pg. 3934
TEX TAN WESTERN LEATHER COMPANY—See Action Company; *U.S. Private*, pg. 67
TIMBUK2 DESIGNS, INC.—See Exemplis LLC; *U.S. Private*, pg. 1448
THE TRAFALGAR COMPANY—See Randa Corp.; *U.S. Private*, pg. 3353
UNITED STATES LUGGAGE COMPANY, LLC; *U.S. Private*, pg. 4299
VALKYRIE COMPANY INC.; *U.S. Private*, pg. 4332
VERA BRADLEY DESIGNS, INC.—See Vera Bradley, Inc.; *U.S. Public*, pg. 2279
VERA BRADLEY, INC.; *U.S. Public*, pg. 2279
VERA BRADLEY SALES, LLC—See Vera Bradley, Inc.; *U.S. Public*, pg. 2279
VITASPRING BIOMEDICAL CO. LTD.; *U.S. Public*, pg. 2306
VOA CANADA, INC.—See Autoliv, Inc.; *Int'l*, pg. 730
WEAVER LEATHER, LLC—See Blue Point Capital Partners, LLC; *U.S. Public*, pg. 591
WEIFANG LAKELAND SAFETY PRODUCTS CO., LTD.—See Lakeland Industries, Inc.; *U.S. Public*, pg. 1289
WEIFANG MEIYANG PROTECTIVE PRODUCTS CO., LTD.—See Lakeland Industries, Inc.; *U.S. Public*, pg. 1289
WISE LUCK INTERNATIONAL (HK) LIMITED—See Come Sure Group (Holdings) Limited; *Int'l*, pg. 1710

321113 — SAWMILLS

84 LUMBER COMPANY - CHAROLETTE TRUSS PLANT—See 84 Lumber Company; *U.S. Private*, pg. 17
84 LUMBER COMPANY - COAL CENTER TRUSS PLANT—See 84 Lumber Company; *U.S. Private*, pg. 17
84 LUMBER COMPANY - MT AIRY TRUSS PLANT—See 84 Lumber Company; *U.S. Private*, pg. 17
ALLEGHENY WOOD PRODUCTS INC.; *U.S. Private*, pg. 176
ALLEGHENY WOOD PRODUCTS PRINCETON—See Allegheny Wood Products Inc.; *U.S. Private*, pg. 176
AMERICAN HARDWOOD INDUSTRIES, LLC—See Baillie Lumber Co., Inc.; *U.S. Private*, pg. 426
ANTHONY FOREST PRODUCTS CO., INC. - ARKANSAS SAWMILL—See Canfor Corporation; *Int'l*, pg. 1290
ANTHONY FOREST PRODUCTS CO., INC. - TEXAS CHIP MILL—See Canfor Corporation; *Int'l*, pg. 1290
ANTHONY FOREST PRODUCTS COMPANY, LLC—See Canfor Corporation; *Int'l*, pg. 1290
BABCOCK LUMBER COMPANY - FINEWOOD DIVISION—See Babcock Lumber Company; *U.S. Private*, pg. 422
BAILLIE LUMBER CO. INC. - BOONVILLE FACILITY—See Baillie Lumber Co., Inc.; *U.S. Private*, pg. 426
BAILLIE LUMBER CO. INC. - GALION FACILITY—See Baillie Lumber Co., Inc.; *U.S. Private*, pg. 426
BAILLIE LUMBER CO. INC. - LEITCHFIELD FACILITY—See Baillie Lumber Co., Inc.; *U.S. Private*, pg. 426
BAILLIE LUMBER CO. INC. - SMYRNA FACILITY—See Baillie Lumber Co., Inc.; *U.S. Private*, pg. 426
BAILLIE LUMBER CO. INC. - TITUSVILLE FACILITY—See Baillie Lumber Co., Inc.; *U.S. Private*, pg. 426
BAILLIE LUMBER SALES CO. INC.—See Baillie Lumber Co., Inc.; *U.S. Private*, pg. 426
BALFOUR LUMBER COMPANY, INC.—See Canfor Corporation; *Int'l*, pg. 1290
BEADLES LUMBER COMPANY—See Canfor Corporation; *Int'l*, pg. 1290
BECHTEL DESIGNS, INC.; *U.S. Private*, pg. 509
BEGLEY LUMBER COMPANY INC.; *U.S. Private*, pg. 514
BESSE FOREST PRODUCTS GROUP - THE BARAGA LUMBER DIVISION—See The Hoffmann Family of Companies; *U.S. Private*, pg. 4053
BESSE LUMBER COMPANY—See The Hoffmann Family of Companies; *U.S. Private*, pg. 4053
BESTWAY OF PENNSYLVANIA, INC.—See Bestway Enterprises Inc.; *U.S. Private*, pg. 544
BESTWAY SOUTH, INC.—See Bestway Enterprises Inc.; *U.S. Private*, pg. 544
BILL DE NOON LUMBER CO.; *U.S. Private*, pg. 556
BINDERHOLZ GMBH; *Int'l*, pg. 1033
BINDERHOLZ NORDIC OY—See Binderholz GmbH; *Int'l*, pg. 1033
BIRCHWOOD MANUFACTURING COMPANY—See The Hoffmann Family of Companies; *U.S. Private*, pg. 4053
BLUEBELL SAWMILLS LIMITED—See Grafton Group plc; *Int'l*, pg. 3050
BRADFORD FOREST, INC.—See Danzer AG; *Int'l*, pg. 1970

321113 — SAWMILLS

BSW TIMBER LTD.—See Endless LLP; *Int'l*, pg. 2403
BTM RESOURCES BERHAD; *Int'l*, pg. 1204
BUFFALO LUMBER & TIE CO.—See Midwest Hardwood Corporation; *U.S. Private*, pg. 2721
CANAL CHIP, LLC—See Canal Wood LLC; *U.S. Private*, pg. 733
CANFOR CORPORATION-POLAR DIVISION—See Canfor Corporation; *Int'l*, pg. 1291
CAPITAL BATTENS PTY LTD—See Brickworks Limited; *Int'l*, pg. 1152
CASCADE HARDWOOD LLC; *U.S. Private*, pg. 779
CEDA-PINE VENEER INC—See Idaho Veneer Company; *U.S. Private*, pg. 2035
CERSOSIMO LUMBER CO. INC.; *U.S. Private*, pg. 841
COASTAL FOREST RESOURCES COMPANY; *U.S. Private*, pg. 956
COMBIMILL OU; *Int'l*, pg. 1708
COMMONWEALTH PLYWOOD CO. LTD.; *Int'l*, pg. 1720
CREST NATURAL RESOURCES LLC—See Crest Industries, LLC; *U.S. Private*, pg. 1096
CUSTOM LUMBER MFG. CO.—See Lumber Group Inc.; *U.S. Private*, pg. 2513
DANZER UK LIMITED—See Danzer AG; *Int'l*, pg. 1970
DELTA CEDAR PRODUCTS LTD; *Int'l*, pg. 2015
DTE STAMPEN A/S—See Dansk Traeemballage A/S; *Int'l*, pg. 1969
ELLIOTT SAWMILLING COMPANY, INC.—See Canfor Corporation; *Int'l*, pg. 1291
EMPORIUM HARDWOODS, LLC—See H.I.G. Capital, LLC; *U.S. Private*, pg. 1832
F.H. STOLTZE LAND & LUMBER COMPANY; *U.S. Private*, pg. 1456
FOREST AUSTELL PRODUCTS INC.; *U.S. Private*, pg. 1566
FULGHUM FIBRES COLLINS, INC.—See Rentech, Inc.; *U.S. Private*, pg. 3400
GEARING MOSS SUPPLIES (PTY) LTD—See enX Group Limited; *Int'l*, pg. 2456
GEORGIA-PACIFIC CORPORATION—See Koch Industries, Inc.; *U.S. Private*, pg. 2327
GEORGIA-PACIFIC CORPORATION—See Koch Industries, Inc.; *U.S. Private*, pg. 2327
GEORGIA-PACIFIC FAYETTE LUMBER PLANT—See Koch Industries, Inc.; *U.S. Private*, pg. 2328
GEORGIA PACIFIC GURDON WOOD PRODUCTS COMPLEX—See Koch Industries, Inc.; *U.S. Private*, pg. 2328
GEORGIA-PACIFIC PINE CHIP & SAW MILL—See Koch Industries, Inc.; *U.S. Private*, pg. 2328
GEORGIA-PACIFIC SOFTWOOD SAWMILL—See Koch Industries, Inc.; *U.S. Private*, pg. 2328
GRAHAM LUMBER COMPANY, LLC—See Baillie Lumber Co., Inc.; *U.S. Private*, pg. 426
GUY BENNETT LUMBER COMPANY; *U.S. Private*, pg. 1820
HARTZELL HARDWOODS, INC.—See Hartzell Industries, Inc.; *U.S. Private*, pg. 1874
HASSELL & HUGHES LUMBER COMPANY, INC.; *U.S. Private*, pg. 1878
HILLS PRODUCTS GROUP, INC.—See Northwestern Engineering Company; *U.S. Private*, pg. 2962
HOLMEN TIMBER AB/IGGESUND SAWMILL—See Holmen AB; *Int'l*, pg. 3453
IDAHO FOREST GROUP, LLC; *U.S. Private*, pg. 2035
IDAHO TIMBER CORPORATION—See Jefferies Financial Group Inc.; *U.S. Public*, pg. 1188
JORDAN LUMBER & SUPPLY INC.; *U.S. Private*, pg. 2235
KAIBAB INDUSTRIES, INC.; *U.S. Private*, pg. 2254
KEENER LUMBER COMPANY INC.; *U.S. Private*, pg. 2272
KOPPERS INC.—See Koppers Holdings Inc.; *U.S. Public*, pg. 1271
KRETZ LUMBER CO., INC.; *U.S. Private*, pg. 2351
LACLEDE MILL—See Idaho Forest Group, LLC; *U.S. Private*, pg. 2035
THE LANGDALE COMPANY; *U.S. Private*, pg. 4067
LINDEN LUMBER, LLC—See H.I.G. Capital, LLC; *U.S. Private*, pg. 1832
LOUISIANA-PACIFIC CORPORATION; *U.S. Public*, pg. 1342
MANKE LUMBER COMPANY, INC.; *U.S. Private*, pg. 2564
MEISTER LOG & LUMBER CO.—See Midwest Hardwood Corporation; *U.S. Private*, pg. 2721
METTOWEE LUMBER & PLASTIC CO., INC.—See Telescope Casual Furniture Inc.; *U.S. Private*, pg. 3961
MILLAR WESTERN FOREST PRODUCTS LTD.—See Atlas Holdings, LLC; *U.S. Private*, pg. 377
MILLER & COMPANY, INC.; *U.S. Private*, pg. 2732
NORTHERN HARDWOODS—See H.I.G. Capital, LLC; *U.S. Private*, pg. 1832
NORTHERN INDUSTRIAL INC.; *U.S. Private*, pg. 2953
OCHOCO LUMBER COMPANY; *U.S. Private*, pg. 2992
PACIFIC LUMBER & SHIPPING CO.; *U.S. Private*, pg. 3068
PINELLI UNIVERSAL, S DE R.L. DE C.V.—See UFP Industries, Inc.; *U.S. Public*, pg. 2219
POST HARDWOODS, INC—See Littlejohn & Co., LLC; *U.S. Private*, pg. 2471
THE PRICE COMPANIES, INC.; *U.S. Private*, pg. 4098

PROTEQ PTY LTD.—See Altus Renewables Limited; *Int'l*, pg. 399
PYRAMID MOUNTAIN LUMBER; *U.S. Private*, pg. 3310
QUALITY HARDWOODS LTD.—See Goodfellow Inc.; *Int'l*, pg. 3040
RIVES & REYNOLDS LUMBER COMPANY, INC.; *U.S. Private*, pg. 3448
RSG FOREST PRODUCTS INC.; *U.S. Private*, pg. 3496
RY TIMBER INC.; *U.S. Private*, pg. 3509
SAGEBRUSH SALES COMPANY—See Jefferies Financial Group Inc.; *U.S. Public*, pg. 1188
SCOTCH & GULF LUMBER, LLC; *U.S. Private*, pg. 3576
SIERRA PACIFIC INDUSTRIES; *U.S. Private*, pg. 3647
SOMERSET HARDWOOD LUMBER, INC.—See Ernst Gohner Stiftung; *Int'l*, pg. 2495
STIMSON LUMBER COMPANY; *U.S. Private*, pg. 3812
STIMSON LUMBER TILLAMOOK—See Stimson Lumber Company; *U.S. Private*, pg. 3812
SWANSON GROUP INC.; *U.S. Private*, pg. 3891
TIMBER PRODUCTS COMPANY, LP; *U.S. Private*, pg. 4171
TREESOURCE INDUSTRIES, INC.; *U.S. Private*, pg. 4217
TRI-COUNTY LOGGING, INC.—See Hardwoods Distribution Inc.; *Int'l*, pg. 3273
TRICOYA TECHNOLOGIES LIMITED—See AccSys Technologies PLC; *Int'l*, pg. 93
UFP ASHBURN, LLC—See UFP Industries, Inc.; *U.S. Public*, pg. 2219
UFP AUBURNDALE, LLC—See UFP Industries, Inc.; *U.S. Public*, pg. 2219
UFP BLANCHESTER, LLC—See UFP Industries, Inc.; *U.S. Public*, pg. 2219
UFP CHANDLER, LLC—See UFP Industries, Inc.; *U.S. Public*, pg. 2219
UFP EATONTON, LLC—See UFP Industries, Inc.; *U.S. Public*, pg. 2219
UFP ELIZABETH CITY, LLC—See UFP Industries, Inc.; *U.S. Public*, pg. 2219
UFP GORDON, LLC—See UFP Industries, Inc.; *U.S. Public*, pg. 2220
UFP GRANGER, LLC—See UFP Industries, Inc.; *U.S. Public*, pg. 2220
UFP HALEYVILLE, LLC—See UFP Industries, Inc.; *U.S. Public*, pg. 2220
UFP HARRISONVILLE, LLC—See UFP Industries, Inc.; *U.S. Public*, pg. 2220
UFP JANESVILLE, LLC—See UFP Industries, Inc.; *U.S. Public*, pg. 2220
UFP LAFAYETTE, LLC—See UFP Industries, Inc.; *U.S. Public*, pg. 2220
UFP MID-ATLANTIC, LLC - JEFFERSON—See UFP Industries, Inc.; *U.S. Public*, pg. 2220
UFP MID-ATLANTIC, LLC—See UFP Industries, Inc.; *U.S. Public*, pg. 2220
UFP MILLRY, LLC—See UFP Industries, Inc.; *U.S. Public*, pg. 2220
UFP MINNEOTA, LLC—See UFP Industries, Inc.; *U.S. Public*, pg. 2220
UFP MOULTRIE, LLC—See UFP Industries, Inc.; *U.S. Public*, pg. 2220
UFP NEW LONDON, LLC—See UFP Industries, Inc.; *U.S. Public*, pg. 2220
UFP NEW WAVERLY, LLC—See UFP Industries, Inc.; *U.S. Public*, pg. 2220
UFP NEW WINDSOR, LLC—See UFP Industries, Inc.; *U.S. Public*, pg. 2220
UFP NEW YORK, LLC - CHAFFEE—See UFP Industries, Inc.; *U.S. Public*, pg. 2220
UFP NEW YORK, LLC - HUDSON—See UFP Industries, Inc.; *U.S. Public*, pg. 2220
UFP NEW YORK, LLC - SIDNEY—See UFP Industries, Inc.; *U.S. Public*, pg. 2220
UFP PARKER, LLC—See UFP Industries, Inc.; *U.S. Public*, pg. 2220
UFP RANSON, LLC—See UFP Industries, Inc.; *U.S. Public*, pg. 2220
UFP RIVERSIDE, LLC—See UFP Industries, Inc.; *U.S. Public*, pg. 2220
UFP SAGINAW, LLC—See UFP Industries, Inc.; *U.S. Public*, pg. 2220
UFP SCHERTZ, LLC—See UFP Industries, Inc.; *U.S. Public*, pg. 2220
UFP STOCKERTOWN, LLC—See UFP Industries, Inc.; *U.S. Public*, pg. 2220
UFP UNION CITY, LLC—See UFP Industries, Inc.; *U.S. Public*, pg. 2220
UFP WINDSOR, LLC—See UFP Industries, Inc.; *U.S. Public*, pg. 2221
UFP WOODBURN, LLC—See UFP Industries, Inc.; *U.S. Public*, pg. 2221
UPM-KYMMENE (AUSTRIA) GMBH - STEYRERMUHL SAWMILL—See Heinzel Holding GmbH; *Int'l*, pg. 3325
UPSHUR FOREST PRODUCTS, LLC—See UFP Industries, Inc.; *U.S. Public*, pg. 2221
USNR—See USNR; *U.S. Private*, pg. 4323
VAAGEN BROTHERS LUMBER, INC.; *U.S. Private*, pg. 4328
VANPORT MANUFACTURING, INC.; *U.S. Private*, pg. 4344

WASHINGTON ALDER, LLC; *U.S. Private*, pg. 4446
WELCO-SKOOKUM LUMBER USA—See Merrill & Ring; *U.S. Private*, pg. 2676
THE WESTERVELT COMPANY; *U.S. Private*, pg. 4134

321114 — WOOD PRESERVATION

ANTHONY FOREST PRODUCTS CO., INC. - ARKANSAS LAMINATING PLANT—See Canfor Corporation; *Int'l*, pg. 1290
ANTHONY FOREST PRODUCTS CO., INC. - GEORGIA LAMINATING PLANT—See Canfor Corporation; *Int'l*, pg. 1290
BALDWIN POLE & PILING COMPANY; *U.S. Private*, pg. 459
BAUER BULGARIA EOOD.—See BAUER Aktiengesellschaft; *Int'l*, pg. 892
BESTWAY OF NEW ENGLAND, INC.—See Bestway Enterprises Inc.; *U.S. Private*, pg. 544
BROWN WOOD PRESERVING COMPANY INC.—See Koppers Holdings Inc.; *U.S. Public*, pg. 1272
CHEMICAL COATINGS, INC.—See RPM International Inc.; *U.S. Public*, pg. 1819
COLLUM'S LUMBER MILL, INC.; *U.S. Private*, pg. 970
COLORSPEC COATINGS INTERNATIONAL; *U.S. Private*, pg. 975
COX INDUSTRIES, INC.; *U.S. Private*, pg. 1078
DR. WOLMAN GMBH—See BASF SE; *Int'l*, pg. 883
ESCUE WOOD PRESERVING, INC.—See Great Southern Wood Preserving, Incorporated; *U.S. Private*, pg. 1768
EXTERIOR WOOD INC.—See Avarga Limited; *Int'l*, pg. 737
FLAGSHIP TRADING CORP.; *U.S. Private*, pg. 1539
FLOORS-N-MORE, LLC—See ALJ Regional Holdings, Inc.; *U.S. Public*, pg. 78
FORTRESS WOOD PRODUCTS INC.—See The Lester Group Inc.; *U.S. Private*, pg. 4069
GREAT SOUTHERN WOOD PRESERVING, INCORPORATED; *U.S. Private*, pg. 1768
GREEN 2 BLUE ENERGY CORP.; *Int'l*, pg. 3069
HOOVER TREATED WOOD PRODUCTS, INC.—See Graham Holdings Company; *U.S. Public*, pg. 955
JEFFERSON HOMEBUILDERS INC.; *U.S. Private*, pg. 2198
JOHN A. BIEWER CO. INC.; *U.S. Private*, pg. 2219
JULIAN LUMBER CO. INC.; *U.S. Private*, pg. 2243
KOPPERS DEUTSCHLAND GMBH—See Koppers Holdings Inc.; *U.S. Public*, pg. 1271
KOPPERS LATVIA SIA—See Koppers Holdings Inc.; *U.S. Public*, pg. 1272
KOPPERS NORWAY AS—See Koppers Holdings Inc.; *U.S. Public*, pg. 1272
KOPPERS PERFORMANCE CHEMICALS INC.—See Koppers Holdings Inc.; *U.S. Public*, pg. 1272
KOPPERS PERFORMANCE CHEMICALS NEW ZEALAND—See Koppers Holdings Inc.; *U.S. Public*, pg. 1272
KOPPERS SPECIALTY CHEMICALS LIMITED—See Koppers Holdings Inc.; *U.S. Public*, pg. 1272
KOPPERS SWEDEN AB—See Koppers Holdings Inc.; *U.S. Public*, pg. 1272
KOPPERS (TIANJIN) TRADING CO., LTD.—See Koppers Holdings Inc.; *U.S. Public*, pg. 1271
KOPPERS UTILITY & INDUSTRIAL PRODUCTS INC.—See Koppers Holdings Inc.; *U.S. Public*, pg. 1272
NEUMANN ENTERPRISES, INC.; *U.S. Private*, pg. 2890
NORTHEAST TREATERS INC.; *U.S. Private*, pg. 2951
OSMOSE CHILE LIMITADA—See Koppers Holdings Inc.; *U.S. Public*, pg. 1272
OY KOPPERS FINLAND AB—See Koppers Holdings Inc.; *U.S. Public*, pg. 1272
PACIFIC WOOD PRESERVING OF BAKERSFIELD, INC.; *U.S. Private*, pg. 3071
PROTIM LTD.—See Koppers Holdings Inc.; *U.S. Public*, pg. 1272
ROBBINS MANUFACTURING COMPANY; *U.S. Private*, pg. 3457
SOUTHEAST WOOD TREATING INC.; *U.S. Private*, pg. 3727
TEXAS ELECTRIC COOPERATIVES, INC.; *U.S. Private*, pg. 3975
THOMAS WOOD PRESERVING INC.; *U.S. Private*, pg. 4158
TIMBER SPECIALTIES CO.—See Koppers Holdings Inc.; *U.S. Public*, pg. 1272
UNILIN ITALIA S.R.L.—See Mohawk Industries, Inc.; *U.S. Public*, pg. 1458
UNILIN SWISS GMBH—See Mohawk Industries, Inc.; *U.S. Public*, pg. 1458
WOOD PROTECTION LP—See Koppers Holdings Inc.; *U.S. Public*, pg. 1272

321211 — HARDWOOD VENEER AND PLYWOOD MANUFACTURING

ALLEGHENY DIMENSION LLP—See Allegheny Wood Products Inc.; *U.S. Private*, pg. 176

N.A.I.C.S. INDEX

321215 — ENGINEERED WOOD MEM...

AMERICAN CONSTRUCTION SUPPLY, INC.—See Avalon Holdings Corporation; *U.S. Public*, pg. 239
AMOS-HILL ASSOCIATES, INC.; *U.S. Private*, pg. 264
ANDERSON HARDWOOD FLOORS; *U.S. Private*, pg. 277
ANNUM BERHAD; *Int'l*, pg. 474
ANTHONY HARDWOOD COMPOSITES INC—See Anthony Timberlands, Inc.; *U.S. Private*, pg. 288
ARB BERHAD; *Int'l*, pg. 536
ARCHIDPLY INDUSTRIES LTD; *Int'l*, pg. 548
ATLANTA HARDWOOD CORPORATION - AHC CRYSTAL SPRING DIVISION—See Atlanta Hardwood Corporation; *U.S. Private*, pg. 370
ATLANTA HARDWOOD CORPORATION - AHC NORTH GEORGIA DIVISION—See Atlanta Hardwood Corporation; *U.S. Private*, pg. 370
ATLANTIC VENEER CORPORATION; *U.S. Private*, pg. 375
AURO SUNDRAM PLY & DOOR PVT. LTD.—See Century Plyboards (I) Ltd.; *Int'l*, pg. 1419
BAHIA PRODUTOS DE MADEIRA S.A.; *Int'l*, pg. 800
BANKS HARDWOODS, INC.—See Banks Hardwoods, Inc.; *U.S. Private*, pg. 468
BANKS HARDWOODS, INC.—See Banks Hardwoods, Inc.; *U.S. Private*, pg. 468
BERRYALLOC NV—See Beaulieu International Group NV; *Int'l*, pg. 934
BEST MOUNTAIN DEUTSCHLAND HOLZWIRTSCHAFT GMBH; *Int'l*, pg. 999
BIG RIVER CYPRESS & HARDWOOD, INC., *U.S. Private*, pg. 554
BIG RIVER INDUSTRIES LIMITED; *Int'l*, pg. 1021
BLOMBERGER HOLZINDUSTRIE B. HAUSMANN GMBH & CO. KG—See Delignit AG; *Int'l*, pg. 2013
BRINK GROUP OF COMPANIES; *Int'l*, pg. 1164
CALI BAMBOO LLC—See High Road Capital Partners, LLC; *U.S. Private*, pg. 1936
CEILINGS PLUS, INC.—See Gebr. Knauf KG; *Int'l*, pg. 2908
CENTURY PLYBOARDS (I) LTD.; *Int'l*, pg. 1419
CHINA WOOD, INC.; *Int'l*, pg. 1563
COLUMBIA FOREST PRODUCTS CORPORATION—See Columbia Forest Products Inc.; *U.S. Private*, pg. 976
COLUMBIA FOREST PRODUCTS INC.; *U.S. Private*, pg. 976
COLUMBIA FOREST PRODUCTS—See Columbia Forest Products Inc.; *U.S. Private*, pg. 976
COLUMBIA PLYWOOD CORPORATION—See Columbia Forest Products Inc.; *U.S. Private*, pg. 976
CORRUVEN, INC.; *Int'l*, pg. 1807
CYMAO PLYWOOD SDN. BHD.—See ANNUM BERHAD; *Int'l*, pg. 474
DAESUNG WOOD IND. CO., LTD.—See DONGWHA HOLDINGS CO., LTD.; *Int'l*, pg. 2170
DAIKEN SOUTHLAND LIMITED—See Daiken Corporation; *Int'l*, pg. 1931
DAI-WOOD CORPORATION—See Daiken Corporation; *Int'l*, pg. 1931
DANZER BOHEMIA-DYHARNA S.R.O.—See Danzer AG; *Int'l*, pg. 1970
DANZER VENEER AMERICAS, INC.—See Danzer AG; *Int'l*, pg. 1970
DAVID R. WEBB COMPANY, INC.—See Danzer AG; *Int'l*, pg. 1970
DAVIS WOOD PRODUCTS, INC.-MISSISSIPPI DIVISION—See Davis Wood Products, Inc.; *U.S. Private*, pg. 1174
DAVIS WOOD PRODUCTS, INC.; *U.S. Private*, pg. 1174
DONGWHA DUBAI—See DONGWHA HOLDINGS CO., LTD.; *Int'l*, pg. 2170
DONGWHA HONG KONG INTERNATIONAL CO LTD—See DONGWHA HOLDINGS CO., LTD.; *Int'l*, pg. 2170
DONGWHA INDIA PRIVATE LIMITED—See DONGWHA HOLDINGS CO., LTD.; *Int'l*, pg. 2170
DONGWHA MALAYSIA HOLDINGS SDN. BHD. - KULIM PLANT—See DONGWHA HOLDINGS CO., LTD.; *Int'l*, pg. 2170
DONGWHA MALAYSIA HOLDINGS SDN. BHD. - MERBOK PLANT—See DONGWHA HOLDINGS CO., LTD.; *Int'l*, pg. 2170
DONGWHA MALAYSIA HOLDINGS SDN. BHD. - NILAI PLANT—See DONGWHA HOLDINGS CO., LTD.; *Int'l*, pg. 2170
DONGWHA MALAYSIA HOLDINGS SDN. BHD.—See DONGWHA HOLDINGS CO., LTD.; *Int'l*, pg. 2170
DONGWHA SHENZHEN—See DONGWHA HOLDINGS CO., LTD.; *Int'l*, pg. 2170
D&R HENDERSON PTY. LTD.; *Int'l*, pg. 1899
DUROPLY INDUSTRIES LTD.; *Int'l*, pg. 2230
EAGON INDUSTRIAL CO., LTD.; *Int'l*, pg. 2267
EAGON USA CORP.—See Eagon Industrial Co., Ltd.; *Int'l*, pg. 2267
EDGEMATE, INC.; *U.S. Private*, pg. 1334
EIDAI CO., LTD.; *Int'l*, pg. 2328
ENCE, ENERGIA Y CELULOSA, S.A. - PONTEVEDRA MILL—See ENCE Energia y Celulosa, S.A.; *Int'l*, pg. 2401
FERCHE MILLWORK, INC.; *U.S. Private*, pg. 1496
FIBER PRO INC.—See Celstar Group Inc.; *U.S. Private*, pg. 808
FREEMAN CORPORATION; *U.S. Private*, pg. 1605

FUXIN SUMIRIN WOOD PRODUCTS CO., LTD.; *Int'l*, pg. 2858
G.D.S. VALORIBOIS INC.—See Groupe De Scieries G.D.S. Inc.; *Int'l*, pg. 3101
GEORGIA-PACIFIC CORPORATION—See Koch Industries, Inc.; *U.S. Private*, pg. 2327
GEORGIA-PACIFIC CORPORATION—See Koch Industries, Inc.; *U.S. Private*, pg. 2327
GEORGIA-PACIFIC CORPORATION—See Koch Industries, Inc.; *U.S. Private*, pg. 2327
GEORGIA-PACIFIC MONTICELLO PRE-FINISHED MDF PLANT—See Koch Industries, Inc.; *U.S. Private*, pg. 2328
GEORGIA-PACIFIC ORIENTED STRAND BOARD PLANT—See Koch Industries, Inc.; *U.S. Private*, pg. 2328
GEORGIA-PACIFIC ORIENTED STRAND BOARD PLANT—See Koch Industries, Inc.; *U.S. Private*, pg. 2328
GEORGIA-PACIFIC PLYWOOD PLANT—See Koch Industries, Inc.; *U.S. Private*, pg. 2328
GEORGIA-PACIFIC PLYWOOD PLANT—See Koch Industries, Inc.; *U.S. Private*, pg. 2328
GEORGIA-PACIFIC WOOD PRODUCTS LLC—See Koch Industries, Inc.; *U.S. Private*, pg. 2329
G-L VENEER CO. INC.; *U.S. Private*, pg. 1630
GOODMAN VENEER & LUMBER COMPANY—See The Hoffmann Family of Companies; *U.S. Private*, pg. 4053
GREENPLY INDUSTRIES LIMITED; *Int'l*, pg. 3076
G S HARRIS CO., INC.; *U.S. Private*, pg. 1628
GUANGZHOU PANYU DACHENG WOOD CO., LTD.—See Emerald Plantation Holdings Limited; *Int'l*, pg. 2377
HANSOL DEVELOPMENT CO. LTD.—See Hansol Group; *Int'l*, pg. 3260
HANSOL HOMEDECO CO. LTD.—See Hansol Group; *Int'l*, pg. 3260
HARTZELL VENEER PRODUCTS, LLC—See Hartzell Industries, Inc.; *U.S. Private*, pg. 1874
HOLLAND PANEL PRODUCTS, INC.—See Panel Processing, Inc.; *U.S. Private*, pg. 3086
INDIANA VENEERS CORP.; *U.S. Private*, pg. 2063
INDUSTRIAL PINE PRODUCTS, INC.—See Oregon Canadian Forest Products Inc.; *U.S. Private*, pg. 3039
INTERNATIONAL VENEER COMPANY—See IVC-USA Inc.; *U.S. Private*, pg. 2151
KARL DANZER GES.M.B.H.—See Danzer AG; *Int'l*, pg. 1970
KIRKHAM HARDWOODS, INC.—See Maley & Wertz, Inc.; *U.S. Private*, pg. 2557
LEGGETT & PLATT, INCORPORATED; *U.S. Public*, pg. 1301
MALEY & WERTZ, INC.; *U.S. Private*, pg. 2557
MANTHEI INC.; *U.S. Private*, pg. 2567
MARION PLYWOOD CORPORATION; *U.S. Private*, pg. 2576
MASISA COMPONENTES SPA—See GrupoNueva S.A.; *Int'l*, pg. 3139
MASISA DO BRASIL LTDA.—See AntarChile S.A.; *Int'l*, pg. 481
MILSO INDUSTRIES CORPORATION—See Matthews International Corporation; *U.S. Public*, pg. 1401
MODULAR WOOD SYSTEMS INC.—See Panel Processing, Inc.; *U.S. Private*, pg. 3086
MOHAWK/COLUMBIA FLOORING—See Mohawk Industries, Inc.; *U.S. Public*, pg. 1458
MT. BAKER PRODUCTS, INC.—See Swaner Hardwood Company, Inc.; *U.S. Private*, pg. 3890
MURPHY PLYWOOD—See Murphy Company; *U.S. Private*, pg. 2815
NORTHERN MICHIGAN VENEERS, INC.—See The Hoffmann Family of Companies; *U.S. Private*, pg. 4053
OXINOVA C.A.—See GrupoNueva S.A.; *Int'l*, pg. 3140
PACIFIC WOODTECH CORPORATION—See Daiken Corporation; *Int'l*, pg. 1931
PANEL PROCESSING OF COLDWATER, INC.—See Panel Processing, Inc.; *U.S. Private*, pg. 3086
PANEL PROCESSING OF INDIANA, INC.—See Panel Processing, Inc.; *U.S. Private*, pg. 3086
PERMINT PLYWOOD SDN BHD—See Golden Pharos Berhad; *Int'l*, pg. 3031
PERMINT TIMBER CORPORATION SDN BHD—See Golden Pharos Berhad; *Int'l*, pg. 3030
PHOENIX DOOR PANELS LIMITED—See Masco Corporation; *U.S. Public*, pg. 1391
PLYTECH INTERNATIONAL LIMITED—See Big River Industries Limited; *Int'l*, pg. 1021
PT. TECHNO WOOD INDONESIA—See AICA Kogyo Company, Limited; *Int'l*, pg. 229
RAJANG PLYWOOD (SABAH) SDN. BHD.—See Eksons Corporation Berhad; *Int'l*, pg. 2339
RAJANG PLYWOOD SAWMILL SDN. BHD.—See Eksons Corporation Berhad; *Int'l*, pg. 2339
ROSSI LUMBER COMPANY—See H.I.G. Capital, LLC; *U.S. Private*, pg. 1832
RUTLAND PLYWOOD CORP.; *U.S. Private*, pg. 3508
SARDA PLYWOOD INDUSTRIES LTD. - RAJKOT FACTORY—See Duroply Industries Ltd.; *Int'l*, pg. 2230
SOMERSET HARDWOOD FLOORING, INC.—See Ernst

Gohner Stiftung; *Int'l*, pg. 2495
STATES INDUSTRIES, LLC—See Renovo Capital, LLC; *U.S. Private*, pg. 3399
STATES INDUSTRIES, LLC—See The Rosewood Corporation; *U.S. Private*, pg. 4112
TAIGA BUILDING PRODUCTS USA LTD.—See Avarga Limited; *Int'l*, pg. 737
TIMBER PRODUCTS COMPANY—See Timber Products Company, LP; *U.S. Private*, pg. 4171
TOWER STRUCTURAL LAMINATING—See WABASH NATIONAL CORPORATION; *U.S. Public*, pg. 2320
TOYAMA DAIKEN CORPORATION—See Daiken Corporation; *Int'l*, pg. 1931
TRM INC.; *U.S. Private*, pg. 4241
VENEER TECHNOLOGIES INC.; *U.S. Private*, pg. 4356
WEST FRASER TIMBER CO., LTD. - SLAVE LAKE PULP DIVISION—See Atlas Holdings, LLC; *U.S. Private*, pg. 377
WISCONSIN VENEER & PLYWOOD, INC.—See The Hoffmann Family of Companies; *U.S. Private*, pg. 4053

321212 — SOFTWOOD VENEER AND PLYWOOD MANUFACTURING

CHEMICAL SPECIALTIES, LLC—See Huntsman Corporation; *U.S. Public*, pg. 1073
EAGLE VENEER INC.; *U.S. Private*, pg. 1311
EKSONS CORPORATION BERHAD; *Int'l*, pg. 2339
FOCUS LUMBER BERHAD; *Int'l*, pg. 2719
HARDEL MUTUAL PLYWOOD CORPORATION; *U.S. Private*, pg. 1862
HERB SHAW & SONS LIMITED; *Int'l*, pg. 3359
HOOD INDUSTRIES INC.; *U.S. Private*, pg. 1977
HOPPINGS SOFTWOOD PRODUCTS PLC; *Int'l*, pg. 3474
HUNT FOREST PRODUCTS INC.; *U.S. Private*, pg. 2009
IDAHO VENEER COMPANY; *U.S. Private*, pg. 2035
IDAHO VENEER CO.—See Idaho Veneer Company; *U.S. Private*, pg. 2035
IKE INTERNATIONAL CORPORATION—See Ike Trading Co. Ltd. Inc.; *U.S. Private*, pg. 2041
MURPHY COMPANY; *U.S. Private*, pg. 2815
PACIFIC WOOD LAMINATES INC.; *U.S. Private*, pg. 3071
ROSEBURG FOREST PRODUCTS CO.—See Roseburg Forest Products; *U.S. Private*, pg. 3482
ROSEBURG FOREST PRODUCTS; *U.S. Private*, pg. 3482
SCOTCH PLYWOOD COMPANY OF ALABAMA; *U.S. Private*, pg. 3576
SONAE INDUSTRIA, SGPS, S.A.—See Efanor Investimentos, SGPS, SA; *Int'l*, pg. 2318
SWANER HARDWOOD COMPANY, INC.; *U.S. Private*, pg. 3890
WILLAMINA LUMBER CO., INC.—See Hampton Affiliates; *U.S. Private*, pg. 1851

321215 — ENGINEERED WOOD MEMBER MANUFACTURING

84 COMPONENTS COMPANY—See 84 Lumber Company; *U.S. Private*, pg. 17
A-1 ROOF TRUSSES, LLC—See Builders FirstSource, Inc.; *U.S. Public*, pg. 409
ACI ELEVATION S.A.; *Int'l*, pg. 104
AIKBEE RESOURCES BERHAD; *Int'l*, pg. 232
ATLAS ENGINEERED PRODUCTS LTD.; *Int'l*, pg. 685
AURO HOLDINGS BERHAD; *Int'l*, pg. 711
AUSWEST TIMBERS HOLDINGS PTY LTD—See Brickworks Limited; *Int'l*, pg. 1152
AUTOMATED BUILDING COMPONENTS, INC.; *U.S. Private*, pg. 399
BMC SELECT - ABILENE TRUSS PLANT—See Builders FirstSource, Inc.; *U.S. Public*, pg. 409
BMC SELECT - EVERETT TRUSS PLANT—See Builders FirstSource, Inc.; *U.S. Public*, pg. 409
BMC SELECT - HELENA TRUSS PLANT—See Builders FirstSource, Inc.; *U.S. Public*, pg. 409
BMC SELECT - IDAHO FALLS TRUSS PLANT—See Builders FirstSource, Inc.; *U.S. Public*, pg. 409
BMC SELECT - INDIO TRUSS AND PANEL PLANT—See Builders FirstSource, Inc.; *U.S. Public*, pg. 409
BMC SELECT - KALISPELL TRUSS PLANT—See Builders FirstSource, Inc.; *U.S. Public*, pg. 409
BMC SELECT - MISSOULA TRUSS PLANT—See Builders FirstSource, Inc.; *U.S. Public*, pg. 409
BMC SELECT - NEW BRAUNFELS TRUSS AND PANEL PLANT—See Builders FirstSource, Inc.; *U.S. Public*, pg. 409
BMC SELECT - WEST JORDAN TRUSS PLANT—See Builders FirstSource, Inc.; *U.S. Public*, pg. 410
BTM MARKETING & TRADING SDN. BHD.—See BTM Resources Berhad; *Int'l*, pg. 1205
BUILDERS FIRSTSOURCE OF SUMTER—See Builders FirstSource, Inc.; *U.S. Public*, pg. 410
CALIFORNIA TRUSFRAME, LLC—See Builders FirstSource, Inc.; *U.S. Public*, pg. 410
CENTROTEC J I ASIA PTE. LTD.—See CENTROTEC SE; *Int'l*, pg. 1414

321215 — ENGINEERED WOOD MEM...

C.S. LUMBER CO., INC.; *Int'l*, pg. 1244
CUSTOM TRUSS LLC; *U.S. Private*, pg. 1129
DIS-TRAN WOOD PRODUCTS, LLC—See Crest Industries, LLC; *U.S. Private*, pg. 1096
D & M TRUSS CO. INC.—See Tibbetts Lumber Co., LLC; *U.S. Private*, pg. 4166
DOMINANT ENTERPRISE BERHAD; *Int'l*, pg. 2161
DOUBLE G COATINGS, INC.—See United States Steel Corporation; *U.S. Public*, pg. 2236
ELECO TIMBER FRAME LTD.—See Eleco Plc; *Int'l*, pg. 2348
EMERALD COAST TRUSS, LLC—See Bain Capital, LP; *U.S. Private*, pg. 450
EMOS LTD—See AKRITAS S.A.; *Int'l*, pg. 264
EVERMASTER GROUP BERHAD; *Int'l*, pg. 2568
FARGO TRUSS SYSTEMS INC.; *U.S. Private*, pg. 1473
FLORIDA FOREST PRODUCTS, LLC—See Tibbetts Lumber Co., LLC; *U.S. Private*, pg. 4166
FOXWORTH GALBRAITH TRUSS CO.—See Foxworth-Galbraith Lumber Company; *U.S. Private*, pg. 1585
GATES & SONS INCORPORATED; *U.S. Private*, pg. 1649
G. F. TRUSS, INC.; *U.S. Private*, pg. 1630
HANSON TRUSS INCORPORATED; *U.S. Private*, pg. 1857
HEART TRUSS & ENGINEERING; *U.S. Private*, pg. 1899
JAMES TRUSS COMPANY; *U.S. Private*, pg. 2185
KEN LUNEACK CONSTRUCTION CO.; *U.S. Private*, pg. 2282
LAMINATE TECHNOLOGIES INC.; *U.S. Private*, pg. 2380
LITTFIN LUMBER COMPANY; *U.S. Private*, pg. 2468
LUMBER SPECIALTIES LTD.; *U.S. Private*, pg. 2513
MAVERICK BUILDING SYSTEMS, LLC—See Zeeland Lumber & Supply Co.; *U.S. Private*, pg. 4599
MONTGOMERY TRUSS AND PANEL; *U.S. Private*, pg. 2777
NWP INDUSTRIES SDN. BHD.—See Auro Holdings Berhad; *Int'l*, pg. 711
OBAL-SERVIS, A.S. KOSICE—See United States Steel Corporation; *U.S. Public*, pg. 2236
OREGON TIMBER FRAME LIMITED—See Barratt Developments PLC; *Int'l*, pg. 868
OZARK STRUCTURES INC.; *U.S. Private*, pg. 3058
POUDRE VALLEY TRUSS, INC.; *U.S. Private*, pg. 3236
PREMIER BUILDING SYSTEMS—See Carlisle Companies Incorporated; *U.S. Public*, pg. 436
PRYDA AUSTRALIA—See Illinois Tool Works Inc.; *U.S. Public*, pg. 1110
QUALITY TRUSS INC.; *U.S. Private*, pg. 3321
REDBUILT LLC—See Atlas Holdings, LLC; *U.S. Private*, pg. 378
RICHCO STRUCTURES—See Richardson Industries, Inc.; *U.S. Private*, pg. 3429
RICHCO STRUCTURES—See Richardson Industries, Inc.; *U.S. Private*, pg. 3429
ROGERS MANUFACTURING CORP; *U.S. Private*, pg. 3472
SAM YODER & SON, LLC.; *U.S. Private*, pg. 3536
SANFORD RESOURCES CORPORATION; *U.S. Private*, pg. 3546
SIERRA TRUSS, LLC—See Clyde Companies Inc.; *U.S. Private*, pg. 949
SPACE COAST HOLDING CORP.—See Mercedes Homes Inc.; *U.S. Private*, pg. 2668
STANDARD STRUCTURES INC.; *U.S. Private*, pg. 3781
STONE TRUSS COMPANY, INC.—See Building Industry Partners LLC; *U.S. Private*, pg. 683
STRUCTURAL COMPONENT SYSTEMS INC; *U.S. Private*, pg. 3841
SUN STATE COMPONENTS OF NEVADA; *U.S. Private*, pg. 3864
SUPERIOR TRUSS SYSTEMS, LLC.; *U.S. Private*, pg. 3880
TEXAS & NORTHERN RAILWAY COMPANY—See United States Steel Corporation; *U.S. Public*, pg. 2236
THAL LIMITED-LAMINATES DIVISION—See House of Habib; *Int'l*, pg. 3491
TRIANGLE TRUSS INC.; *U.S. Private*, pg. 4226
TRI COUNTY TRUSS—See The Truss Company, Inc.; *U.S. Private*, pg. 4128
TRIM JOIST CORPORATION—See Sanford Resources Corporation; *U.S. Private*, pg. 3546
THE TRUSS COMPANY, INC.; *U.S. Private*, pg. 4128
TRUSS FAB, LLC—See Bain Capital, LP; *U.S. Private*, pg. 451
TRUSS-PRO'S, INC.; *U.S. Private*, pg. 4250
TRUSS SYSTEMS, INC.; *U.S. Private*, pg. 4250
TRUSS TECH INDUSTRIES INC.; *U.S. Private*, pg. 4250
TRUSSWAY LTD.; *U.S. Private*, pg. 4250
TRUS-WAY, INC.; *U.S. Private*, pg. 4250
TRUSWOOD INC.; *U.S. Private*, pg. 4251
UFP CALDWELL, LLC—See UFP Industries, Inc.; *U.S. Public*, pg. 2219
UFP MAGNA, LLC—See UFP Industries, Inc.; *U.S. Public*, pg. 2220
UNADILLA LAMINATED PRODUCTS—See Unadilla Silo Company Inc.; *U.S. Private*, pg. 4279
UNADILLA SILO COMPANY INC.; *U.S. Private*, pg. 4279
USS OILWELL TUBULAR, INC.—See United States Steel Corporation; *U.S. Public*, pg. 2237
U. S. STEEL EUROPE - GERMANY GMBH—See United States Steel Corporation; *U.S. Public*, pg. 2236
U. S. STEEL EUROPE (UK) LIMITED—See United States Steel Corporation; *U.S. Public*, pg. 2236
VALLEY TRUSS COMPANY—See Builders FirstSource, Inc.; *U.S. Public*, pg. 410
VILLAUME INDUSTRIES, INC.—See Bain Capital, LP; *U.S. Private*, pg. 451
WOOD STRUCTURES, INC.—See Roark Capital Group Inc.; *U.S. Private*, pg. 3456
YOUNGER BROTHERS COMPONENTS INC.—See Younger Brothers Group Inc.; *U.S. Private*, pg. 4594
YOUNGER BROTHERS CONSTRUCTION COMPANY—See Younger Brothers Group Inc.; *U.S. Private*, pg. 4594

321219 — RECONSTITUTED WOOD PRODUCT MANUFACTURING

AKRITAS S.A.; *Int'l*, pg. 264
ASIA CUANON TECHNOLOGY (SHANGHAI) CO., LTD.; *Int'l*, pg. 611
BLUE RIDGE FIBERBOARD, INC. - LISBON FALLS—See W. R. Meadows, Inc.; *U.S. Private*, pg. 4418
BLUE RIDGE FIBERBOARD, INC.—See W. R. Meadows, Inc.; *U.S. Private*, pg. 4418
CAROLINA NONWOVENS CORPORATION—See National Spinning Company, Inc.; *U.S. Private*, pg. 2863
CORENSO WISCONSIN BOARD, LLC—See Sonoco Products Company; *U.S. Public*, pg. 1904
DAIKEN MIRI SDN. BHD.—See Daiken Corporation; *Int'l*, pg. 1931
DAIKEN SARAWAK SDN. BHD.—See Daiken Corporation; *Int'l*, pg. 1931
DUFAYLITE DEVELOPMENTS LIMITED; *Int'l*, pg. 2223
ECOBOARD INDUSTRIES LTD; *Int'l*, pg. 2294
EGGER TURKIYE LTD.—See Fritz Egger GmbH & Co.; *Int'l*, pg. 2794
EVERGREEN FIBREBOARD (NILAI) SDN. BHD.—See Evergreen Fibreboard Berhad; *Int'l*, pg. 2565
FANCY WOOD INDUSTRIES PUBLIC COMPANY LIMITED - SURATTHANI FACTORY—See Fancy Wood Industries Public Company Limited; *Int'l*, pg. 2613
FIBERESIN INDUSTRIES, INC.; *U.S. Private*, pg. 1502
FORESTIA AS—See Byggma ASA; *Int'l*, pg. 1235
GUANGDONG WEIHUA CORPORATION (MEIZHOU MEDIUM-DENSITY FIBERBOARD FACTORY)—See Chengxin Lithium Group Co., Ltd.; *Int'l*, pg. 1470
HEVEABOARD BERHAD; *Int'l*, pg. 3367
HOKUSHIN CO., LTD.; *Int'l*, pg. 3445
HOMASOTE COMPANY; *U.S. Public*, pg. 1045
INDIAN COUNTRY INC.; *U.S. Private*, pg. 2061
JASPER CORP.; *U.S. Private*, pg. 2190
LAMINATE WORKS INC.; *U.S. Private*, pg. 2380
LOUISIANA-PACIFIC CHILE S.A.—See Louisiana-Pacific Corporation; *U.S. Public*, pg. 1342
MASISA ARGENTINA S.A.—See Fritz Egger GmbH & Co.; *Int'l*, pg. 2793
MDF LA BAIE INC.—See Compagnie de Saint-Gobain SA; *Int'l*, pg. 1723
NORPAL S. DE R.L. DE C.V.—See UFP Industries, Inc.; *U.S. Public*, pg. 2219
PANEL PROCESSING OF OREGON, INC.—See Panel Processing, Inc.; *U.S. Private*, pg. 3086
PANOLAM INDUSTRIES INTERNATIONAL, INC.—See Insight Equity Holdings LLC; *U.S. Private*, pg. 2086
PLACACENTRO MASISA MEXICO S.A. DE C.V.—See AntarChile S.A.; *Int'l*, pg. 481
QINGYUAN WEILIBANG WOOD CO., LTD.—See Chengxin Lithium Group Co., Ltd.; *Int'l*, pg. 1470
SIERRAPINE LIMITED; *U.S. Private*, pg. 3648
SIERRAPINE - MEDITE DIVISION—See SierraPine Limited; *U.S. Private*, pg. 3648
TECTUM, INC.—See Armstrong World Industries, Inc.; *U.S. Public*, pg. 194
TREX COMPANY, INC.; *U.S. Public*, pg. 2188
UNIBOARD CANADA, INC.-LDI DIVISION—See Compagnie de Saint-Gobain SA; *Int'l*, pg. 1724
UNIBOARD CANADA INC.—See Compagnie de Saint-Gobain SA; *Int'l*, pg. 1723
UNIBOARD FOSTORIA INC.—See Compagnie de Saint-Gobain SA; *Int'l*, pg. 1724
UNIBOARD MONT LAURIER INC.—See Compagnie de Saint-Gobain SA; *Int'l*, pg. 1724
UNIBOARD NEW LISKEARD, INC.—See Compagnie de Saint-Gobain SA; *Int'l*, pg. 1724
UNIBOARD SAYABEC, INC.—See Compagnie de Saint-Gobain SA; *Int'l*, pg. 1724
UNIBOARD SURFACE INC.—See Compagnie de Saint-Gobain SA; *Int'l*, pg. 1724
UNIBOARD VAL D'OR, INC.—See Compagnie de Saint-Gobain SA; *Int'l*, pg. 1724

321911 — WOOD WINDOW AND DOOR MANUFACTURING

A-1 DOOR AND BUILDING SOLUTIONS INC.; *U.S. Private*, pg. 21
AARON CARLSON CORPORATION; *U.S. Private*, pg. 32
ACTUAL FENSTER GMBH; *Int'l*, pg. 121
ADVANCE DOOR SYSTEMS LTD; *Int'l*, pg. 156
AG INDUSTRIES VIETNAM COMPANY LIMITED—See AG Industries Limited; *Int'l*, pg. 198
AISIN EUROPE MANUFACTURING (UK) LTD.—See AISIN Corporation; *Int'l*, pg. 252
ALCO DOORS, INC.—See Bain Capital, LP; *U.S. Private*, pg. 450
ALGOMA HARDWOODS, INC.—See Owens Corning; *U.S. Public*, pg. 1627
ALL WEATHER WINDOWS LTD.; *Int'l*, pg. 332
ALRO GMBH—See Gesco AG; *Int'l*, pg. 2945
ALSTA NASSAU BV—See ASSA ABLOY AB; *Int'l*, pg. 634
ALTWOOD GARAGE DOORS LTD.; *Int'l*, pg. 399
ALUMA-GLASS INDUSTRIES, INC.; *U.S. Private*, pg. 211
AMARR COMPANY—See ASSA ABLOY AB; *Int'l*, pg. 634
AMCC FENETRES ET PORTES SAS—See Atrya SAS; *Int'l*, pg. 694
AMERICA'S WINDOW, LLC—See West Shore Window & Door, Inc.; *U.S. Private*, pg. 4487
ANDERSEN WINDOWS, INC.—See Andersen Corporation; *U.S. Private*, pg. 275
ARCHITECTURAL WINDOWS & DOORS—See Peter Pan Bus Lines, Inc.; *U.S. Private*, pg. 3159
ASSA ABLOY ENTRANCE SYSTEMS DENMARK A/S—See ASSA ABLOY AB; *Int'l*, pg. 633
ASSA ABLOY ENTRANCE SYSTEMS ITALY SRL—See ASSA ABLOY AB; *Int'l*, pg. 633
ASSA ABLOY ENTRANCE SYSTEMS NV—See ASSA ABLOY AB; *Int'l*, pg. 633
ASSA ABLOY ENTRANCE SYSTEMS UK & IRELAND—See ASSA ABLOY AB; *Int'l*, pg. 634
ATLASS HARDWARE CORPORATION—See Frontenac Company LLC; *U.S. Private*, pg. 1613
ATRIUM WINDOWS & DOORS, INC.—See Kenner & Company, Inc.; *U.S. Private*, pg. 2285
ATRIUM WINDOWS & DOORS, INC.—See North Cove Partners; *U.S. Private*, pg. 2944
BALANCE UK LIMITED—See Quanex Building Products Corp.; *U.S. Public*, pg. 1749
BARBER & ROSS COMPANY INC.; *U.S. Private*, pg. 472
BIRTLEY GROUP LIMITED—See Hill & Smith PLC; *Int'l*, pg. 3391
BODE NORTH AMERICA INC.—See The Carlyle Group Inc.; *U.S. Public*, pg. 2053
BRIGHT WOOD CORP.; *U.S. Private*, pg. 651
BROWN WINDOW CORPORATION; *Int'l*, pg. 1198
BUFFELEN WOODWORKING COMPANY; *U.S. Private*, pg. 681
CALIFORNIA DELUXE WINDOWS; *U.S. Private*, pg. 718
CANA INC.—See Patrick Industries, Inc.; *U.S. Public*, pg. 1652
CARDO DOOR PRODUCTION AB—See ASSA ABLOY AB; *Int'l*, pg. 634
CARDO DOOR PRODUCTION B.V.—See ASSA ABLOY AB; *Int'l*, pg. 634
CASCADE OHIO INC.; *U.S. Private*, pg. 781
CHAPPELL DOOR CO. INC. MAIN OFFICE; *U.S. Private*, pg. 850
CHELSEA BUILDING PRODUCTS INC.—See aluplast GmbH; *Int'l*, pg. 401
CLEVER-CRAWFORD SA—See ASSA ABLOY AB; *Int'l*, pg. 634
CLOPAY BUILDING PRODUCTS COMPANY, INC.—See Griffon Corporation; *U.S. Public*, pg. 969
CONESTOGA WOOD SPECIALTIES CORP.; *U.S. Private*, pg. 1012
CONSUMERS CHOICE HOME IMPROVEMENTS CORP; *Int'l*, pg. 1778
CRAWFORD DEUR B.V.—See ASSA ABLOY AB; *Int'l*, pg. 634
CRAWFORD DOOR FORSALJNINGS AB—See ASSA ABLOY AB; *Int'l*, pg. 634
CRAWFORD DOOR M.E. AB—See ASSA ABLOY AB; *Int'l*, pg. 634
CRAWFORD HAFA AG—See ASSA ABLOY AB; *Int'l*, pg. 635
CRAWFORD HAFA GMBH-WENNINGSEN—See ASSA ABLOY AB; *Int'l*, pg. 635
CRAWFORD INTERNATIONAL AB—See ASSA ABLOY AB; *Int'l*, pg. 634
CRAWFORD NORMSTAHL N.V.—See ASSA ABLOY AB; *Int'l*, pg. 634
CRAWFORD POLAND SP. ZO.O.—See ASSA ABLOY AB; *Int'l*, pg. 634
CRAWFORD TOR GMBH—See ASSA ABLOY AB; *Int'l*, pg. 635
CRAWFORD UK LTD.—See ASSA ABLOY AB; *Int'l*, pg. 635
DAIFIT CO., LTD—See Daiken Corporation; *Int'l*, pg. 1931
DAI-TAC CORPORATION—See Daiken Corporation; *Int'l*, pg. 1931
DANMER, INC.; *U.S. Private*, pg. 1157
DECALU SOLUTIONS SP. Z O.O.—See Deceuninck NV; *Int'l*, pg. 1999
DESIGNER DOORS, INC.; *U.S. Private*, pg. 1214
DITEC SWISS S.A.—See ASSA ABLOY AB; *Int'l*, pg. 639
THE DOOR MILL, INC.—See Bain Capital, LP; *U.S. Private*, pg. 450

N.A.I.C.S. INDEX

DORMAKABA DANMARK A/S—See dormakaba Holding AG; *Int'l*, pg. 2178
DORMAKABA HRVATSKA D.O.O.—See dormakaba Holding AG; *Int'l*, pg. 2178
DORMAKABA MALAYSIA SDN. BHD.—See dormakaba Holding AG; *Int'l*, pg. 2178
DORMAKABA SINGAPORE PTE LTD—See dormakaba Holding AG; *Int'l*, pg. 2179
DORMAKABA SOUTH AFRICA PTY LTD.—See dormakaba Holding AG; *Int'l*, pg. 2179
DURABUILT WINDOWS & DOORS; *Int'l*, pg. 2228
EAGLE WINDOW & DOOR, INC.—See Andersen Corporation; *U.S. Private*, pg. 275
EAGON ENERGY CO., LTD.—See Eagon Holdings Co., Ltd.; *Int'l*, pg. 2266
EAGON GREEN TECH CO., LTD.—See Eagon Holdings Co., Ltd.; *Int'l*, pg. 2266
EAGON HOLDINGS CO., LTD.; *Int'l*, pg. 2266
EAGON LAUTARO S.A.—See Eagon Holdings Co., Ltd.; *Int'l*, pg. 2266
EAGON PACIFIC PLANTATION LTD.—See Eagon Holdings Co., Ltd.; *Int'l*, pg. 2266
EAGON WINDOWS & DOORS SYSTEM CO., LTD.—See Eagon Holdings Co., Ltd.; *Int'l*, pg. 2266
EAST HAVEN BUILDERS SUPPLY, INC.—See Bain Capital, LP; *U.S. Private*, pg. 450
ECKER WINDOW CORPORATION; *U.S. Private*, pg. 1328
EGGERS INDUSTRIES INC.—See VT Industries, Inc.; *U.S. Private*, pg. 4415
EGOKIEFER AG—See Arbonia AG; *Int'l*, pg. 538
EGOKIEFER SA—See Arbonia AG; *Int'l*, pg. 538
FLORIDA HOME IMPROVEMENT ASSOCIATES INC.; *U.S. Private*, pg. 1549
FLORIDA MADE DOOR CO.—See Owens Corning; *U.S. Public*, pg. 1626
FRESNO SHOWER DOOR, INC.—See Patrick Industries, Inc.; *U.S. Public*, pg. 1652
GARANT TUREN-UND ZARGEN GMBH—See Arbonia AG; *Int'l*, pg. 538
GENERAL DOORS CORP.; *U.S. Private*, pg. 1664
GOLDEN PHAROS DOORS SDN BHD—See Golden Pharos Berhad; *Int'l*, pg. 3030
GOLDEN WINDOWS LIMITED; *Int'l*, pg. 3032
GRABILL, INC.—See Pella Corporation; *U.S. Private*, pg. 3131
GRAHAM WOOD DOORS—See ASSA ABLOY AB; *Int'l*, pg. 636
GRAND BASKET, INC—See Z Capital Group, LLC; *U.S. Private*, pg. 4595
GRAND ENTRANCE; *U.S. Private*, pg. 1752
GUTTOMAT SEKTIONALTORE GMBH—See Atrya SAS; *Int'l*, pg. 694
HARBIN SAYYAS WINDOWS CO., LTD.; *Int'l*, pg. 3271
HARVEY INDUSTRIES, INC. - DARTMOUTH MANUFACTURING FACILITY—See Clayton, Dubilier & Rice, LLC; *U.S. Private*, pg. 920
HASLER FENSTER AG—See Atrya SAS; *Int'l*, pg. 694
HEHR INTERNATIONAL INC. - INDIANA WINDOW PLANT—See LCI Industries; *U.S. Public*, pg. 1295
HEHR INTERNATIONAL INC. - KANSAS WINDOW PLANT—See LCI Industries; *U.S. Public*, pg. 1295
HEHR INTERNATIONAL INC. - MICHIGAN WINDOW PLANT—See LCI Industries; *U.S. Public*, pg. 1295
HILZINGER FENSTER + TUEREN GMBH—See hilzinger Holding GmbH; *Int'l*, pg. 3395
HORMANN CHANGSHU DOOR PRODUCTION CO. LTD.—See Hormann KG Verkaufsgesellschaf; *Int'l*, pg. 3480
HORMANN OENSINGEN AG—See Hormann KG Verkaufsgesellschaf; *Int'l*, pg. 3481
HORMANN TIANJIN DOOR PRODUCTION CO. LTD.—See Hormann KG Verkaufsgesellschaf; *Int'l*, pg. 3481
H-PRODUKTER AS—See Flakk Holding AS; *Int'l*, pg. 2698
HUGA KG—See Hormann KG Verkaufsgesellschaf; *Int'l*, pg. 3481
INAMI DAIKEN CORPORATION—See Daiken Corporation; *Int'l*, pg. 1931
INVADO SP. Z.O.O.—See Arbonia AG; *Int'l*, pg. 538
JELD-WEN AUSTRALIA PTY LTD—See Platinum Equity, LLC; *U.S. Private*, pg. 3205
KERN DOOR COMPANY—See Installed Building Products, Inc.; *U.S. Public*, pg. 1133
KLW JOINERY PTE. LTD.—See HS Optimus Holdings Limited; *Int'l*, pg. 3503
KLW WOOD PRODUCTS SDN. BHD.—See HS Optimus Holdings Limited; *Int'l*, pg. 3503
KOETTER WOODWORKING INC.; *U.S. Private*, pg. 2336
KOLBE & KOLBE MILLWORK CO., INC.; *U.S. Private*, pg. 2341
KOUKOU SANGYO CORPORATION—See Daiken Corporation; *Int'l*, pg. 1931
LANG EXTERIOR, INC.; *U.S. Private*, pg. 2388
LINCOLN WOOD PRODUCTS, INC.; *U.S. Private*, pg. 2459
LINIAR LIMITED—See Quanex Building Products Corp.; *U.S. Public*, pg. 1749
MAPLE CITY WOODWORKING CORP.—See Patrick Industries, Inc.; *U.S. Public*, pg. 1652
MARLITE, INC.; *U.S. Private*, pg. 2585

MARSHFIELD DOORSYSTEMS, INC.—See Owens Corning; *U.S. Public*, pg. 1627
MARVIN WINDOWS & DOORS INC.; *U.S. Private*, pg. 2598
THE MARWIN COMPANY, INC.—See Validor Capital LLC; *U.S. Private*, pg. 4332
MASONITE CANADA CORPORATION—See Owens Corning; *U.S. Public*, pg. 1627
MASONITE CANADA CORP. - YARROW—See Owens Corning; *U.S. Public*, pg. 1627
MASONITE CORP. - CORNING—See Owens Corning; *U.S. Public*, pg. 1627
MASONITE CORP. - DICKSON—See Owens Corning; *U.S. Public*, pg. 1627
MASONITE CORP. - GREENVILLE—See Owens Corning; *U.S. Public*, pg. 1627
MASONITE CORP. - NORTH PLATTE—See Owens Corning; *U.S. Public*, pg. 1627
MASONITE CORPORATION—See Owens Corning; *U.S. Public*, pg. 1627
MASONITE CORP. - STANLEY—See Owens Corning; *U.S. Public*, pg. 1627
MAVIFLEX SAS—See Hormann KG Verkaufsgesellschaf; *Int'l*, pg. 3481
MEDALLION INDUSTRIES INC.; *U.S. Private*, pg. 2650
MEGADOOR AB—See ASSA ABLOY AB; *Int'l*, pg. 635
MIDWEST PREFINISHING INCORPORATED—See Building Industry Partners LLC; *U.S. Private*, pg. 683
MIKRON INDUSTRIES, INC.—See Quanex Building Products Corp.; *U.S. Public*, pg. 1749
MIWD HOLDING COMPANY LLC—See Koch Industries, Inc.; *U.S. Private*, pg. 2332
MI WINDOWS AND DOORS, LLC—See Koch Industries, Inc.; *U.S. Private*, pg. 2332
MODERN DOOR & EQUIPMENT SALES INC.; *U.S. Private*, pg. 2760
MOHAWK FLUSH DOORS, INC.—See Owens Corning; *U.S. Public*, pg. 1627
MOULURE ALEXANDRIA MOULDING INC.—See Specialty Building Products, LLC; *U.S. Private*, pg. 3749
MULTISOL RAAMBEKLEDING B.V.—See 3G Capital Partners L.P.; *U.S. Private*, pg. 13
MURPHY DOOR, INC.; *U.S. Private*, pg. 2815
MW MANUFACTURERS INC.—See Clayton, Dubilier & Rice, LLC; *U.S. Private*, pg. 921
NEWSOUTH WINDOW SOLUTIONS, LLC—See Koch Industries, Inc.; *U.S. Private*, pg. 2332
NEWSOUTH WINDOW SOLUTIONS OF PENSACOLA, LLC—See Koch Industries, Inc.; *U.S. Private*, pg. 2332
NORBA SA—See Atrya SAS; *Int'l*, pg. 694
NORMSTAHL CRAWFORD TOR GMBH—See ASSA ABLOY AB; *Int'l*, pg. 635
NORMSTAHL SCHWEIZ AG—See ASSA ABLOY AB; *Int'l*, pg. 635
PALM CITY MILLWORK, INC.—See Glenn Rieder, Inc.; *U.S. Private*, pg. 1711
PARRETT WINDOWS & DOORS, INC.; *U.S. Private*, pg. 3099
PASTURAL—See Compagnie de Saint-Gobain SA; *Int'l*, pg. 1724
PAUL ARGOE SCREENS, INC.; *U.S. Private*, pg. 3112
PELLA CORPORATION; *U.S. Private*, pg. 3131
PELLA WINDOWS & DOORS, INC. - DETROIT—See Pella Corporation; *U.S. Private*, pg. 3131
PERFORMANCE DOORSET SOLUTIONS, INC.—See Owens Corning; *U.S. Public*, pg. 1627
PHOENIX TIMBER FACTORY LLC—See Alpha Dhabi Holding PJSC; *Int'l*, pg. 367
POINT FIVE WINDOWS, INC.—See Kolbe & Kolbe Millwork Co., Inc.; *U.S. Private*, pg. 2341
PROVIA DOOR, INC.; *U.S. Private*, pg. 3291
QUANTUM WINDOWS & DOORS, INC.—See Swiftsure Capital LLC; *U.S. Private*, pg. 3893
RECORD NORTH AMERICA INC.—See ASSA ABLOY AB; *Int'l*, pg. 638
REILLY WINDOWS & DOORS—See Westny Building Products Co.; *U.S. Private*, pg. 4500
RESDOOR COMPANY, INC.—See R.E. Sweeney Company Inc.; *U.S. Private*, pg. 3335
RIVERBEND TIMBER FRAMING, LLC—See The Riverside Company; *U.S. Private*, pg. 4109
ROCHESTER COLONIAL MANUFACTURING; *U.S. Private*, pg. 3463
RSL WOODWORKING PRODUCTS CO.; *U.S. Private*, pg. 3497
SAFE-WAY GARAGE DOORS LLC—See CapitalWorks, LLC; *U.S. Private*, pg. 742
SAUDI CRAWFORD DOORS FACTORY LTD.—See ASSA ABLOY AB; *Int'l*, pg. 635
SCHORGHUBER SPEZIALTUREN KG—See Hormann KG Vorkaufsgesellschaf; *Int'l*, pg 3481
SECURIDOR LIMITED—See Quanex Building Products Corp.; *U.S. Public*, pg. 1750
SELLMORE INDUSTRIES INC.; *U.S. Private*, pg. 3603
SEUSTER KG—See Hormann KG Verkaufsgesellschaf; *Int'l*, pg. 3481
SIERRA PACIFIC WINDOWS—See Sierra Pacific Industries; *U.S. Private*, pg. 3647
SIMPSON DOOR COMPANY—See Simpson Investment Company; *U.S. Private*, pg. 3668
SLOVAKTUAL S.R.O.—See Arbonia AG; *Int'l*, pg. 538
SNE ENTERPRISES, INC.—See Weathershield Mfg. Inc.; *U.S. Private*, pg. 4463
SOLIDOR LIMITED—See Owens Corning; *U.S. Public*, pg. 1627
SOPROFEN—See Atrya SAS; *Int'l*, pg. 694
S R DOOR, INC.; *U.S. Private*, pg. 3512
STARGAZE WINDOWS LIMITED—See Emerson Developments (Holdings) Limited; *Int'l*, pg. 2380
STEVES & SONS, INC.; *U.S. Private*, pg. 3810
SUPERIOR TRIM & DOOR, INC.; *U.S. Private*, pg. 3880
SYNSEAL EXTRUSIONS LIMITED—See H.I.G. Capital, LLC; *U.S. Private*, pg. 1828
SYN TEC SEATING SOLUTIONS, LLC—See Indiana Mills & Manufacturing, Inc.; *U.S. Private*, pg. 2062
T. M. COBB COMPANY; *U.S. Private*, pg. 3911
TNR INDUSTRIAL DOORS INC.—See Hormann KG Verkaufsgesellschaf; *Int'l*, pg. 3481
TPO HOLZ-SYSTEME GMBH—See Arbonia AG; *Int'l*, pg. 538
TRUSSBILT, LLC.; *U.S. Private*, pg. 4250
TRUSTILE DOORS LLC—See Marvin Windows & Doors Inc.; *U.S. Private*, pg. 2598
ULDAL AS—See Byggma ASA; *Int'l*, pg. 1235
USA WOOD DOOR, INC.—See Owens Corning; *U.S. Public*, pg. 1627
VABA GMBH—See Axactor SE; *Int'l*, pg. 761
VTI OF GEORGIA, INC.—See VT Industries, Inc.; *U.S. Private*, pg. 4415
VTI OF IOWA, INC.—See VT Industries, Inc.; *U.S. Private*, pg. 4415
WEATHER SHIELD MANUFACTURING, INC.—See Weathershield Mfg. Inc.; *U.S. Private*, pg. 4463
WEATHERSHIELD MFG. INC.; *U.S. Private*, pg. 4462
WELLBORN CABINET, INC.—See HCI Equity Management, L.P.; *U.S. Private*, pg. 1889
WESTCOAST GATE & ENTRY SYSTEMS, INC.—See Aurora Capital Group, LLC; *U.S. Private*, pg. 394
WEST COAST SHUTTERS & SUNBURST, INC.; *U.S. Private*, pg. 4484
WEST TENNESSEE ORNAMENTAL DOOR CO., INC.; *U.S. Private*, pg. 4487
WINDOW & DOOR MANUFACTURERS ASSOCIATION—See Northeast Window & Door Association; *U.S. Private*, pg. 2951
WINDOWS AND WALLS UNLIMITED, INC.; *U.S. Private*, pg. 4539
WINDOW WORLD OF BATON ROUGE, LLC; *U.S. Private*, pg. 4538
WINDSOR WINDOWS & DOORS CO—See Woodgrain, Inc.; *U.S. Private*, pg. 4558
WOODGRAIN DOORS—See Woodgrain, Inc.; *U.S. Private*, pg. 4558
ZELUCK INC.; *U.S. Private*, pg. 4601
ZERO SEAL SYSTEMS LIMITED—See Allegion Public Limited Company; *Int'l*, pg. 336

321912 — CUT STOCK, RESAWING LUMBER, AND PLANING

AMA PLY LTD.—See Alam Group of Companies; *Int'l*, pg. 289
BATSON MILL L.L.C.—See Newpark Resources, Inc.; *U.S. Public*, pg. 1517
BEKY A.S.; *Int'l*, pg. 962
BROWN-FORMAN COOPERAGE—See Brown-Forman Corporation; *U.S. Public*, pg. 403
BUCHANAN FOREST PRODUCTS, LTD.; *Int'l*, pg. 1206
CHURCH & CHURCH LUMBER CO.; *U.S. Private*, pg. 894
CLENDENIN LUMBER COMPANY—See Baillie Lumber Co., Inc.; *U.S. Private*, pg. 426
THE COLLINS COMPANIES, INC.; *U.S. Private*, pg. 4011
CONNER INDUSTRIES, INC.; *U.S. Private*, pg. 1017
COULSON MANUFACTURING LTD.—See Coulson Group of Companies; *Int'l*, pg. 1817
COUSINEAUS HENNIKER—See Cousineau Inc.; *U.S. Private*, pg. 1071
DOCHTER LUMBER & SAWMILL, INC.; *U.S. Private*, pg. 1251
EOVATIONS, LLC—See UFP Industries, Inc.; *U.S. Public*, pg. 2219
FONTANA WOOD PRODUCTS INC.; *U.S. Private*, pg. 1560
FORESTAL CHOLGUAN S.A.; *Int'l*, pg. 2732
FRANCE BED HOLDINGS CO. LTD.; *Int'l*, pg. 2759
GLEN OAK LUMBER & MILLING INC.; *U.S. Private*, pg. 1709
GREWALS (MAURITIUS) LIMITED—See ENL Limited; *Int'l*, pg. 2441
GREWALS RODRIGUES LTD.—See ENL Limited; *Int'l*, pg. 2441
HAMPTON AFFILIATES - MORTON - COWLITZ DIVISION—See Hampton Affiliates; *U.S. Private*, pg. 1851
HAMPTON AFFILIATES - RANDLE - COWLITZ DIVISION—See Hampton Affiliates; *U.S. Private*, pg. 1851

321912 — CUT STOCK, RESAWING...

HAMPTON AFFILIATES - WASHINGTON MILLS—See Hampton Affiliates; *U.S. Private*, pg. 1851
JIM THORP LUMBER PRODUCTS, INC.; *U.S. Private*, pg. 2210
MARY'S RIVER LUMBER CO., INC.; *U.S. Private*, pg. 2599
MIDWEST HARDWOOD CORPORATION - LITTLE RIVER HARDWOODS FACILITY—See Midwest Hardwood Corporation; *U.S. Private*, pg. 2721
MIDWEST HARDWOOD CORPORATION - PARK FALLS HARDWOODS FACILITY—See Midwest Hardwood Corporation; *U.S. Private*, pg. 2721
MIDWEST HARDWOOD CORPORATION - REEDSBURG HARDWOODS FACILITY—See Midwest Hardwood Corporation; *U.S. Private*, pg. 2721
MIDWEST HARDWOOD CORPORATION - WESTBY HARDWOOD PRODUCTS FACILITY—See Midwest Hardwood Corporation; *U.S. Private*, pg. 2721
MISSOURI-PACIFIC LUMBER COMPANY; *U.S. Private*, pg. 2749
NEW ENGLAND WOOD PELLET, LLC—See Rentech, Inc.; *U.S. Private*, pg. 3400
NORTH CAROLINA LUMBER COMPANY; *U.S. Private*, pg. 2943
OREGON CANADIAN FOREST PRODUCTS INC.; *U.S. Private*, pg. 3039
PACIFIC FIBRE PRODUCTS INC.; *U.S. Private*, pg. 3067
PACIFIC TOPSOILS INC.—See GRO-WELL Brands Inc.; *U.S. Private*, pg. 1791
PRESTIGE ENTERPRISE INTERNATIONAL, INC.; *U.S. Private*, pg. 3256
PROFESSIONAL PRODUCTION PRODUCTS, INC.; *U.S. Private*, pg. 3276
REX LUMBER COMPANY; *U.S. Private*, pg. 3417
SUNBELT FOREST PRODUCTS CORPORATION—See UFP Industries, Inc.; *U.S. Public*, pg. 2219
SUNSET MOULDING CO., INC.; *U.S. Private*, pg. 3871
SUPERIOR HARDWOODS INC.—See J.T. Shannon Lumber Inc.; *U.S. Private*, pg. 2171
TILLAMOOK LUMBER COMPANY—See Hampton Affiliates; *U.S. Private*, pg. 1851
UFP SAN ANTONIO, LLC—See UFP Industries, Inc.; *U.S. Public*, pg. 2220
UFP THORNTON, LLC—See UFP Industries, Inc.; *U.S. Public*, pg. 2220
UNIVERSAL FOREST PRODUCTS OF CANADA, INC.—See UFP Industries, Inc.; *U.S. Public*, pg. 2221
WARREN WOOD INC.; *U.S. Private*, pg. 4444

321918 — OTHER MILLWORK (INCLUDING FLOORING)

3V COMPANY; *U.S. Private*, pg. 14
AACER FLOORING LLC; *U.S. Private*, pg. 31
ADAMS BROS. CABINETRY, INC.; *U.S. Private*, pg. 73
ALLEGHENY MILLWORK; *U.S. Private*, pg. 176
ALLOC AS—See Beaulieu International Group NV; *Int'l*, pg. 934
ARMSTRONG FLOORING, INC.; *U.S. Public*, pg. 193
ARMSTRONG WOOD PRODUCTS, INC.—See AIP, LLC; *U.S. Private*, pg. 134
BABCOCK LUMBER COMPANY; *U.S. Private*, pg. 422
BANKS HARDWOODS, INC. - NEWBERRY FACILITY—See Banks Hardwoods, Inc.; *U.S. Private*, pg. 468
BARBER & ROSS MILLWORK COMPANY INC.—See Barber & Ross Company Inc.; *U.S. Private*, pg. 472
BARLINEK S.A.; *Int'l*, pg. 866
BARNETT MILLWORKS, INC.; *U.S. Private*, pg. 477
BEAULIEU FIBRES INTERNATIONAL TERNI SRL—See Beaulieu International Group NV; *Int'l*, pg. 934
BEST MOULDING CORP; *U.S. Private*, pg. 543
BIG FLOORCOVERINGS NV—See Beaulieu International Group NV; *Int'l*, pg. 934
CARAUSTAR MILL GROUP, INC.—See Greif Inc.; *U.S. Public*, pg. 966
CASCADE WOOD PRODUCTS, INC.; *U.S. Private*, pg. 781
CEVOTEC GMBH; *Int'l*, pg. 1425
COLONIAL MILLWORKS LTD. INC.—See McDonough Corporation; *U.S. Private*, pg. 2632
THE COMBINATION DOOR CO.—See Paul Argoe Screens, Inc.; *U.S. Private*, pg. 3112
CONFORCE INTERNATIONAL, INC.; *Int'l*, pg. 1768
CONTACT INDUSTRIES; *U.S. Private*, pg. 1026
CORTLAND HARDWOOD PRODUCTS, LLC.; *U.S. Private*, pg. 1061
COX INTERIOR INC.; *U.S. Private*, pg. 1078
CUMBERLAND ARCHITECTURAL MILLWORK, INC.—See Orion Building Corporation; *U.S. Private*, pg. 3042
DAIKEN CORPORATION - MIE PLANT—See Daiken Corporation; *Int'l*, pg. 1931
DARLINGTON VENEER COMPANY; *U.S. Private*, pg. 1159
DESIGNED STAIRS INC.; *U.S. Private*, pg. 1214
DIVERSIFIED MILLWORK INC.—See Palo Duro Hardwoods Inc.; *U.S. Private*, pg. 3082
DIXIE PACIFIC MANUFACTURING CO.—See Ingersoll Rand Inc.; *U.S. Public*, pg. 1120
THE DORRIS LUMBER & MOULDING CO.; *U.S. Private*, pg. 4023

DUCHATEAU FLOORS; *U.S. Private*, pg. 1284
DURAWOOD PRODUCTS, INC.; *U.S. Private*, pg. 1293
ECORE INTERNATIONAL INC.; *U.S. Private*, pg. 1330
EMBELTON LIMITED; *Int'l*, pg. 2374
FIBREWORKS CORPORATION; *U.S. Private*, pg. 1502
FITZPATRICK & WELLER, INC.; *U.S. Private*, pg. 1536
GAF DECKING SYSTEMS LLC—See GAF Materials Corporation; *U.S. Private*, pg. 1633
GALLEHER LLC—See Transom Capital Group, LLC; *U.S. Private*, pg. 4209
GILES & KENDALL INC.; *U.S. Private*, pg. 1699
GLANBIA AGRIBUSINESS—See Glanbia Co-Operative Society Limited; *Int'l*, pg. 2987
GLENN RIEDER, INC.; *U.S. Private*, pg. 1711
G.P. EMBELTON & COMPANY PTY LTD.—See Embelton Limited; *Int'l*, pg. 2375
GRABILL CABINET COMPANY; *U.S. Private*, pg. 1748
HAVCO WOOD PRODUCTS LLC; *U.S. Private*, pg. 1880
HB&G BUILDING PRODUCTS, INC.; *U.S. Private*, pg. 1886
HERITAGE OAK FLOORING—See Mid America Hardwoods Inc.; *U.S. Private*, pg. 2705
HOFF COMPANIES INC.; *U.S. Private*, pg. 1959
HOLLYWOOD WOODWORK, INC.; *U.S. Private*, pg. 1966
IDEAL WOOD PRODUCTS, INC.—See Prophet Equity L.P.; *U.S. Private*, pg. 3286
INTER-STATE HARDWOODS COMPANY, INC.; *U.S. Private*, pg. 2107
JIAFENG WOOD (SUZHOU) CO., LTD.—See Emerald Plantation Holdings Limited; *Int'l*, pg. 2378
JOHNCARLO WOODWORKING, INC.; *U.S. Private*, pg. 2225
LAROCCO ENTERPRISES INC.; *U.S. Private*, pg. 2392
LEVOLOR INC.—See 3G Capital Partners L.P.; *U.S. Private*, pg. 13
L.J. SMITH INC.—See Hardwoods Distribution Inc.; *Int'l*, pg. 3273
LOUISIANA-PACIFIC SOUTHERN DIV.—See Louisiana-Pacific Corporation; *U.S. Public*, pg. 1343
MAGBEE CONTRACTORS SUPPLY; *U.S. Private*, pg. 2545
MANNINGTON WOOD FLOORS—See Mannington Mills, Inc.; *U.S. Private*, pg. 2566
MARK RICHEY WOODWORKING & DESIGN, INC.; *U.S. Private*, pg. 2578
MCDONOUGH CORPORATION; *U.S. Private*, pg. 2632
MENZNER LUMBER AND SUPPLY CO.; *U.S. Private*, pg. 2667
MGDM HOLDINGS CO.; *U.S. Private*, pg. 2694
MHJ GROUP INC.; *U.S. Private*, pg. 2695
MID AMERICA HARDWOODS INC.; *U.S. Private*, pg. 2705
MORTENSEN WOODWORK INC.; *U.S. Private*, pg. 2791
NAPLES SHUTTER, INC.; *U.S. Private*, pg. 2834
NICKELL MOULDING COMPANY INC.—See Patrick Industries, Inc.; *U.S. Public*, pg. 1653
NORTHANN CORP.; *U.S. Public*, pg. 1537
NYBRON FLOORING INTERNATIONAL CORPORATION—See Vestar Capital Partners, LLC; *U.S. Private*, pg. 4372
NYDREE FLOORING; *U.S. Private*, pg. 2976
ODL INCORPORATED; *U.S. Private*, pg. 2993
ORNAMENTAL PRODUCTS LLC; *U.S. Private*, pg. 3044
OSHKOSH FLOOR DESIGNS, INC.—See FCF Partners, LP; *U.S. Private*, pg. 1485
OVERSEAS HARDWOODS COMPANY; *U.S. Private*, pg. 3053
PIONEER CUT STOCK INC.—See Bright Wood Corp.; *U.S. Private*, pg. 651
POLY-PLY INDUSTRIES SDN. BHD.—See ANNUM BERHAD; *Int'l*, pg. 474
Q.E.P. AUSTRALIA PTY LIMITED—See Q.E.P. Co., Inc.; *U.S. Public*, pg. 1741
RENAISSANCE DOORS & WINDOWS INC.; *U.S. Private*, pg. 3397
ROBBINS, INC.—See L2 Capital Partners; *U.S. Private*, pg. 2367
SCHIELD FAMILY BRANDS—See Weathershield Mfg. Inc.; *U.S. Private*, pg. 4463
SETZER FOREST PRODUCTS INC.; *U.S. Private*, pg. 3618
SHAMROCK WOOD INDUSTRIES INC.—See J.T. Shannon Lumber Inc.; *U.S. Private*, pg. 2171
SHAW INDUSTRIES INC.—See Berkshire Hathaway Inc.; *U.S. Public*, pg. 316
SIGNATURE PARTNERS, LTD.; *U.S. Private*, pg. 3650
SINO-MAPLE (SHANGHAI) CO., LTD.—See Emerald Plantation Holdings Limited; *Int'l*, pg. 2378
SINO-PANEL (ASIA) INC.—See Emerald Plantation Holdings Limited; *Int'l*, pg. 2378
SISKIYOU FOREST PRODUCTS; *U.S. Private*, pg. 3675
SMITH FLOORING INC; *U.S. Private*, pg. 3694
SOMERSET WOOD PRODUCTS, CO.; *U.S. Private*, pg. 3712
SOUTHERN STAIRCASE INCORPORATED; *U.S. Private*, pg. 3735
STEPHENSON MILLWORK CO. INC.; *U.S. Private*, pg. 3803
STEVE WARD & ASSOCIATES INC.; *U.S. Private*, pg. 3808
THE TANEY CORPORATION; *U.S. Private*, pg. 4126
TRANS SP. Z O.O.—See Decora S.A.; *Int'l*, pg. 2001

UNILIN INDUSTRIES BVBA—See Mohawk Industries, Inc.; *U.S. Public*, pg. 1458
US DESIGN & MILL, CORP.; *U.S. Private*, pg. 4318
WARREN'S WOOD WORKS, INC.; *U.S. Private*, pg. 4444
WEABER, INC.—See Resilience Capital Partners, LLC; *U.S. Private*, pg. 3405
WESTEK ARCHITECTURAL WOODWORKING INC.; *U.S. Private*, pg. 4490
WINCHESTER WOODWORKING CORP.; *U.S. Private*, pg. 4533
WINDSOR MILL COMPANY; *U.S. Private*, pg. 4539
WOODGRAIN, INC.; *U.S. Private*, pg. 4558
YUBA RIVER MOULDING MILL WORK; *U.S. Private*, pg. 4595

321920 — WOOD CONTAINER AND PALLET MANUFACTURING

4077491 CANADA INC; *Int'l*, pg. 11
48FORTY SOLUTIONS, LLC—See Audax Group, Limited Partnership; *U.S. Public*, pg. 386
ALLEGHENY RECYCLED PRODUCTS, INC.—See Audax Group, Limited Partnership; *U.S. Public*, pg. 386
AMPCO PRODUCTS INC.; *U.S. Private*, pg. 265
ANDERSON FOREST PRODUCTS INC.; *U.S. Private*, pg. 277
ARRINGTON LUMBER & PALLET COMPANY, INC.; *U.S. Private*, pg. 335
ATLAS BOX & CRATING CO. INC.; *U.S. Private*, pg. 375
AVID PALLET SERVICES, LLC—See Hendricks Holding Company, Inc.; *U.S. Private*, pg. 1915
BARCO MATERIALS HANDLING LTD.; *Int'l*, pg. 863
BATTLE LUMBER COMPANY INC.; *U.S. Private*, pg. 490
BO'S PALLETS, INC.—See Audax Group, Limited Partnership; *U.S. Public*, pg. 386
CENTRAL GLASS PLANT SERVICES CO., LTD.—See Central Glass Co., Ltd.; *Int'l*, pg. 1406
CHEP SOUTH AFRICA (PTY) LTD.—See Brambles Limited; *Int'l*, pg. 1139
C & L WATER SOLUTIONS, INC.—See New Mountain Capital, LLC; *U.S. Private*, pg. 2899
COMMERCIAL LUMBER & PALLET CO.; *U.S. Private*, pg. 984
CONNER INDUSTRIES, INC. - ALAMO FACILITY—See Conner Industries, Inc.; *U.S. Private*, pg. 1017
CONNER INDUSTRIES, INC. - CONROE FACILITY—See Conner Industries, Inc.; *U.S. Private*, pg. 1017
CONNER INDUSTRIES, INC. - FAYETTEVILLE FACILITY—See Conner Industries, Inc.; *U.S. Private*, pg. 1017
CONNER INDUSTRIES, INC. - HASLET FACILITY—See Conner Industries, Inc.; *U.S. Private*, pg. 1017
CONNER INDUSTRIES, INC. - HOGANSVILLE FACILITY—See Conner Industries, Inc.; *U.S. Private*, pg. 1017
CONNER INDUSTRIES, INC. - HOUSTON FACILITY—See Conner Industries, Inc.; *U.S. Private*, pg. 1017
CONNER INDUSTRIES, INC. - STILWELL FACILITY—See Conner Industries, Inc.; *U.S. Private*, pg. 1017
COTELSA S.A.; *Int'l*, pg. 1817
CRATE TECH, INC.—See Delos Capital, LLC; *U.S. Private*, pg. 1198
DAMABOIS, INC.; *Int'l*, pg. 1955
DAYKEN PALLET COMPANY, INC.—See Gerrity Company Incorporated; *U.S. Private*, pg. 1687
DESTAMPES EMBALLAGES; *Int'l*, pg. 2046
DHANALAXMI ROTO SPINNERS LTD.; *Int'l*, pg. 2098
DMG MORI SEIKI CO., LTD. - NARA CAMPUS NO. 2 PLANT—See DMG MORI Co., Ltd.; *Int'l*, pg. 2145
DMI DISTRIBUTION INC.; *U.S. Private*, pg. 1248
DONALD B REMMEY INC.; *U.S. Private*, pg. 1259
DYNIC FACTORY SERVICE CO., LTD.—See Dynic Corporation; *Int'l*, pg. 2242
ELBERTA CRATE & BOX CO.; *U.S. Private*, pg. 1350
ENTERPRISE TRENCHLESS TECHNOLOGIES, INC—See Southwest Gas Holdings, Inc.; *U.S. Public*, pg. 1913
ENVIVA PELLETS AMORY, LLC—See Enviva Inc.; *U.S. Public*, pg. 782
E.R. PROBYN LTD.; *Int'l*, pg. 2260
FALCON CONTAINERS; *U.S. Private*, pg. 1466
FULUHASHI CORPORATION (THAILAND) LTD—See Fuluhashi EPO Corporation; *Int'l*, pg. 2844
GEORGIA BIOMASS, LLC—See Enviva Inc.; *U.S. Public*, pg. 782
GEORGIA CRATE & BASKET COMPANY; *U.S. Private*, pg. 1684
GIRARD WOOD PRODUCTS INC.; *U.S. Private*, pg. 1702
GLOBAL MECHANICAL, INC.; *U.S. Private*, pg. 1716
GRIDSOURCE, INC.—See Hastings Equity Partners, LLC; *U.S. Private*, pg. 1879
HARVEY PALLETS, INC.; *U.S. Private*, pg. 1878
HINCHCLIFF PRODUCTS COMPANY; *U.S. Private*, pg. 1948
IAD INDUSTRIEANLAGEN-DIENST GMBH—See Deufol SE; *Int'l*, pg. 2048
INDEPENDENT STAVE CO. INC.—See Isco Holding Company Inc.; *U.S. Private*, pg. 2143

N.A.I.C.S. INDEX

321992 — PREFABRICATED WOOD ...

INDUSTRIAL PACKAGING CORP.; *U.S. Private*, pg. 2067
INDUSTRIAL PALLET CORPORATION; *U.S. Private*, pg. 2067
INDUSTRIAL PALLET CORPORATION—See Industrial Pallet Corporation; *U.S. Private*, pg. 2067
INDUSTRIAL PALLET, LLC—See Audax Group, Limited Partnership; *U.S. Private*, pg. 386
INTERNATIONAL WOOD INDUSTRIES, INC.—See UFP Industries, Inc.; *U.S. Public*, pg. 2219
ISCO HOLDING COMPANY INC.; *U.S. Private*, pg. 2143
J.C. PALLET COMPANY, INC.; *U.S. Private*, pg. 2160
JIAXING CIMC WOOD CO., LTD.—See China International Marine Containers (Group) Co., Ltd.; *Int'l*, pg. 1511
JOHN ROCK, INC.—See Freeman Spogli & Co. Incorporated; *U.S. Private*, pg. 1606
J.P. TAYLOR COMPANY, L.L.C.—See Universal Corporation; *U.S. Public*, pg. 2254
KAMPS, INC.—See Freeman Spogli & Co. Incorporated; *U.S. Private*, pg. 1606
LARSON PACKAGING COMPANY, LLC; *U.S. Private*, pg. 2394
LATROBE PALLET, INC.; *U.S. Private*, pg. 2397
LIBERTY TECHNOLOGIES—See Millwood Inc.; *U.S. Private*, pg. 2738
LIM KET LENG TIMBER SDN. BHD.—See Classic Scenic Berhad; *Int'l*, pg. 1653
LOSCAM (HONG KONG) LIMITED—See China Merchants Group Limited; *Int'l*, pg. 1521
MADISON COUNTY WOOD PRODUCTS, INC.; *U.S. Private*, pg. 2540
MARTIN PALLET, INC.—See Burlington Capital Partners, LLC; *U.S. Private*, pg. 689
MCINTOSH BOX & PALLET CO. INC.; *U.S. Private*, pg. 2637
MERCURY LUGGAGE/SEWARD TRUNK—See Mercury; *U.S. Private*, pg. 2671
MICHIGAN BOX COMPANY; *U.S. Private*, pg. 2700
MILLARD LUMBER INC.; *U.S. Private*, pg. 2730
MILLWOOD INC.; *U.S. Private*, pg. 2738
MISSOURI COOPERAGE CO. INC.—See Isco Holding Company Inc.; *U.S. Private*, pg. 2143
MOMENCE PALLET CORPORATION; *U.S. Private*, pg. 2768
MURPHY PIPELINE CONTRACTORS, LLC—See J.F. Lehman & Company; *U.S. Private*, pg. 2163
NATIONAL COATING & LINING CO.—See Brand Industrial Services, Inc.; *U.S. Private*, pg. 636
NAZARETH PALLET CO., INC.—See Audax Group, Limited Partnership; *U.S. Private*, pg. 386
NEOPAL LLC; *U.S. Private*, pg. 2885
NORDIC PRODUCTS, INC.—See Monomoy Capital Partners LLC; *U.S. Private*, pg. 2772
OCL CORPORATION—See Hitachi Zosen Corporation; *Int'l*, pg. 3412
OREGON PALLET REPAIR, INC.; *U.S. Private*, pg. 3040
PACKING MATERIAL COMPANY INC.; *U.S. Private*, pg. 3073
PALLET CONSULTANTS CORP.; *U.S. Private*, pg. 3079
PALLETMAXX, INC.; *U.S. Private*, pg. 3079
PALLETONE, INC.—See UFP Industries, Inc.; *U.S. Public*, pg. 2219
PALLETONE OF ALABAMA, LLC—See UFP Industries, Inc.; *U.S. Public*, pg. 2219
PALLETS, INC.—See Damabois, Inc.; *Int'l*, pg. 1955
PIPE FREEZING SERVICES, INC.—See N2 Solutions LLC; *U.S. Private*, pg. 2829
POTOMAC SUPPLY, LLC—See AIP, LLC; *U.S. Private*, pg. 134
PRONET CO., LTD—See Core Corporation; *Int'l*, pg. 1797
PRZEDSIEBIORSTWO PRODUKCYJNO-HANDLOWE "TOR-PAL" SPOLKA Z OGRANICZONA ODPOWIEDZIALNOSCIA—See International Paper Company; *U.S. Public*, pg. 1158
PT. PANDU SATA UTAMA—See Universal Corporation; *U.S. Public*, pg. 2254
SCENIC WOOD PRODUCTS; *U.S. Private*, pg. 3562
SCHUTZ CONTAINER SYSTEMS, INC.—See BayernLB Holding AG; *Int'l*, pg. 914
SHANGHAI CIMC BAOWELL INDUSTRIES CO. LTD—See China International Marine Containers (Group) Co., Ltd.; *Int'l*, pg. 1512
STADIUM PACKING SERVICES LTD—See British Engines Ltd.; *Int'l*, pg. 1171
STAVE ASSOCIATES INTERNATIONAL, INC.—See Isco Holding Company Inc.; *U.S. Private*, pg. 2143
TAYLOR PALLETS & RECYCLING , INC—See Audax Group, Limited Partnership; *U.S. Private*, pg. 386
TIMBER CREEK RESOURCE, LLC.—See Delos Capital, LLC; *U.S. Private*, pg. 1198
TIMBERLINE, LLC; *U.S. Private*, pg. 4172
THE TIMBERMEN, INC.; *U.S. Private*, pg. 4127
TOSCA LIMITED—See Apax Partners LLP; *Int'l*, pg. 507
TOWER 16, INC.—See Sun Capital Partners, Inc.; *U.S. Private*, pg. 3860
TREE BRAND PACKAGING, INC.; *U.S. Private*, pg. 4216
TREEN BOX & PALLET, INC.—See Treen Box & Pallet Corp.; *U.S. Private*, pg. 4217
UFP FRANKLINTON, LLC—See UFP Industries, Inc.; *U.S. Public*, pg. 2219
UFP PACKAGING, LLC—See UFP Industries, Inc.; *U.S. Public*, pg. 2220
ULTOCO SERVICES, S.A.—See Universal Corporation; *U.S. Public*, pg. 2254
UNITED WHOLESALE LUMBER CO.—See Fruit Growers Supply Co.; *U.S. Private*, pg. 1617
WISCONSIN BOX COMPANY; *U.S. Private*, pg. 4548
WNC PALLET & FOREST PRODUCTS CO.; *U.S. Private*, pg. 4552
WOOD'N PALLETS, INC.; *U.S. Private*, pg. 4557

321991 — MANUFACTURED HOME (MOBILE HOME) MANUFACTURING

AMERICAN HOMESTAR CORPORATION; *U.S. Private*, pg. 236
ATHENS PARK HOMES, LLC—See Champion Homes, Inc.; *U.S. Public*, pg. 477
BIO HABITAT SAS—See Beneteau S.A.; *Int'l*, pg. 972
CAVALIER HOME BUILDERS, LLC—See Berkshire Hathaway Inc.; *U.S. Public*, pg. 304
CAVALIER HOMES, INC.—See Berkshire Hathaway Inc.; *U.S. Public*, pg. 304
CAVCO INDUSTRIES, INC.; *U.S. Public*, pg. 454
CHAMPION HOME BUILDERS INC.—See Champion Homes, Inc.; *U.S. Public*, pg. 477
CLAYTON HOMES, INC.—See Berkshire Hathaway Inc.; *U.S. Public*, pg. 304
CLAYTON PROPERTIES GROUP, INC.—See Berkshire Hathaway Inc.; *U.S. Public*, pg. 304
COLONY FACTORY CRAFTED HOMES—See Cavco Industries, Inc.; *U.S. Public*, pg. 455
THE COMMODORE CORPORATION—See Cavco Industries, Inc.; *U.S. Public*, pg. 455
DEER VALLEY CORPORATION—See LCV Capital Management, LLC; *U.S. Private*, pg. 2404
DEER VALLEY HOMEBUILDERS, INC.—See LCV Capital Management, LLC; *U.S. Private*, pg. 2404
ELLIOTT HOMES INC.—See Solitaire Homes, Inc.; *U.S. Private*, pg. 3709
FAIRMONT HOMES, INC.—See Cavco Industries, Inc.; *U.S. Public*, pg. 455
FLEETWOOD HOMES - DOUGLAS—See Cavco Industries, Inc.; *U.S. Public*, pg. 455
FLEETWOOD HOMES, INC.—See Cavco Industries, Inc.; *U.S. Public*, pg. 455
FLEETWOOD HOMES, INC.—See Cavco Industries, Inc.; *U.S. Public*, pg. 455
FLEETWOOD HOMES OF OREGON, INC.-WOODBURN/NORTH—See Cavco Industries, Inc.; *U.S. Public*, pg. 455
FLEETWOOD HOMES OF TEXAS, INC.-WACO/GHOLSON RD.—See Cavco Industries, Inc.; *U.S. Public*, pg. 455
FLEETWOOD HOMES OF VIRGINIA, INC.—See Cavco Industries, Inc.; *U.S. Public*, pg. 455
FLEETWOOD HOMES - WACO, TX—See Cavco Industries, Inc.; *U.S. Public*, pg. 455
FLEETWOOD PTY LTD—See Fleetwood Limited; *Int'l*, pg. 2699
FUTURO HOUSES, LLC—See US Lighting Group, Inc.; *U.S. Public*, pg. 2266
GAMMA ARREDAMENTI INT.I INC.—See Dexelance S.p.A.; *Int'l*, pg. 2092
GAMMA ARREDAMENTI INT.I S.P.A.—See Dexelance S.p.A.; *Int'l*, pg. 2092
GENERAL HOUSING INC.—See Strategic Investments & Holding Inc.; *U.S. Private*, pg. 3835
GERVASONI S.P.A.—See Dexelance S.p.A.; *Int'l*, pg. 2092
GLOBAL DIVERSIFIED INDUSTRIES, INC.; *U.S. Private*, pg. 1713
HANSE HAUS GMBH & CO. KG—See Equistone Partners Europe Limited; *Int'l*, pg. 2486
HOMESMART CONSTRUCTION—See Berkshire Hathaway Inc.; *U.S. Public*, pg. 304
HOMETTE CORPORATION—See Champion Homes, Inc.; *U.S. Public*, pg. 477
HORTON HOMES, INC.—See Horton Industries; *U.S. Private*, pg. 1984
HORTON INDUSTRIES, INC.; *U.S. Private*, pg. 1984
INDIANA BUILDING SYSTEMS LLC—See Pleasant Street Homes LLC; *U.S. Private*, pg. 3213
JACOBSEN MANUFACTURING, INC.; *U.S. Private*, pg. 2180
LEXINGTON HOMES, INC.—See Cavco Industries, Inc.; *U.S. Public*, pg. 455
LOSBERGER MODULAR SYSTEMS GMBH—See Gilde Buy Out Partners B.V.; *Int'l*, pg. 2975
MANUFACTURED STRUCTURES CORP.; *U.S. Private*, pg. 2567
MARK LINE INDUSTRIES; *U.S. Private*, pg. 2577
MARLETTE HOMES, INC.—See Berkshire Hathaway Inc.; *U.S. Public*, pg. 304
MERIDIANI S.R.L.—See Dexelance S.p.A.; *Int'l*, pg. 2092
MICRON SEMICONDUCTOR ASIA OPERATIONS PTE. LTD.—See Micron Technology, Inc.; *U.S. Public*, pg. 1438
MICRON SEMICONDUCTOR ITALIA S.R.L.—See Micron Technology, Inc.; *U.S. Public*, pg. 1438
MICRON SEMICONDUCTOR MALAYSIA SDN. BHD.—See Micron Technology, Inc.; *U.S. Public*, pg. 1438
MICRON TECHNOLOGY TAIWAN, INC.—See Micron Technology, Inc.; *U.S. Public*, pg. 1438
MODULINE INDUSTRIES (CANADA) LTD.—See Champion Homes, Inc.; *U.S. Public*, pg. 477
NADLER MODULAR STRUCTURES; *U.S. Private*, pg. 2830
NASHUA HOMES OF IDAHO INC.; *U.S. Private*, pg. 2836
O'HARA VACANCES SAS—See Beneteau S.A.; *Int'l*, pg. 972
PLEASANT STREET HOMES LLC; *U.S. Private*, pg. 3213
RED SEA HOUSING SERVICES COMPANY (PAPUA NEW GUINEA) LIMITED—See Dabbagh Group Holding Company Ltd.; *Int'l*, pg. 1902
RED SEA HOUSING SERVICES COMPANY—See Dabbagh Group Holding Company Ltd.; *Int'l*, pg. 1902
RED SEA HOUSING SERVICES (GHANA) LIMITED—See Dabbagh Group Holding Company Ltd.; *Int'l*, pg. 1903
RED SEA HOUSING SERVICES LLC—See Dabbagh Group Holding Company Ltd.; *Int'l*, pg. 1903
RED SEA HOUSING SERVICES (MOZAMBIQUE), LDA—See Dabbagh Group Holding Company Ltd.; *Int'l*, pg. 1903
RED SEA HOUSING SERVICES PTY LTD—See Dabbagh Group Holding Company Ltd.; *Int'l*, pg. 1903
RED SEA INTERNATIONAL COMPANY—See Dabbagh Group Holding Company Ltd.; *Int'l*, pg. 1902
SAMLING HOUSING PRODUCTS SDN. BHD.—See DIC Corporation; *Int'l*, pg. 2109
SARL RED SEA HOUSING SERVICES ALGERIA LIMITED—See Dabbagh Group Holding Company Ltd.; *Int'l*, pg. 1903
SAS LA LOUISIANE—See Clariane SE; *Int'l*, pg. 1644
SOUTHERN ENERGY HOMES, INC.—See Berkshire Hathaway Inc.; *U.S. Public*, pg. 304
SOUTHERN ENERGY HOMES—See Berkshire Hathaway Inc.; *U.S. Public*, pg. 304
SUNSHINE HOMES INC.—See Sunshine Mills Inc.; *U.S. Private*, pg. 3871
SURF S.R.L.—See Gruppo MutuiOnline S.p.A; *Int'l*, pg. 3141
TITAN MOBILE HOMES, INC.—See Champion Homes, Inc.; *U.S. Public*, pg. 477
TRUTANKLESS INC.; *U.S. Public*, pg. 2202
TURRI UK LTD.—See Dexelance S.p.A.; *Int'l*, pg. 2092
TURRI USA CORP.—See Dexelance S.p.A.; *Int'l*, pg. 2092
UMH PA CAMELOT WOODS, LLC—See UMH Properties, Inc.; *U.S. Public*, pg. 2225
WICK BUILDINGS, LLC; *U.S. Private*, pg. 4515

321992 — PREFABRICATED WOOD BUILDING MANUFACTURING

AICA LAMINATES INDIA PVT. LTD.—See AICA Kogyo Company, Limited; *Int'l*, pg. 228
ALL AMERICAN HOMES, LLC—See Innovative Building Systems LLC; *U.S. Private*, pg. 2082
ALL AMERICAN HOMES OF IOWA, LLC—See Innovative Building Systems LLC; *U.S. Private*, pg. 2082
APEX HOMES INC.; *U.S. Private*, pg. 292
APPALACHIAN LOG STRUCTURES; *U.S. Private*, pg. 295
ART'S WAY SCIENTIFIC, INC.—See Art's-Way Manufacturing Co., Inc.; *U.S. Public*, pg. 201
THE BARDEN & ROBESON CORPORATION; *U.S. Private*, pg. 3992
BARNA & COMPANY; *U.S. Private*, pg. 476
BENCHMARK INDUSTRIES; *U.S. Private*, pg. 524
THE BESPOKE BRICK COMPANY LIMITED—See Brickability Group plc; *Int'l*, pg. 1151
BIOLOGICAL MEDIATION SYSTEMS, LLC—See Worth Investment Group, LLC; *U.S. Private*, pg. 4570
BLAZER INDUSTRIES, INC.; *U.S. Private*, pg. 580
BLUE RIDGE LOG CABINS, LLC; *U.S. Private*, pg. 592
BLU HOMES, INC—See Dvele, Inc.; *U.S. Private*, pg. 1295
CAPSYS CORP.; *U.S. Private*, pg. 746
CITAIR INC.; *Int'l*, pg. 1619
CIVEO PREMIUM CAMP SERVICES LTD—See Civeo Corporation; *U.S. Public*, pg. 506
CIVEO USA LLC—See Civeo Corporation; *U.S. Public*, pg. 506
CLASSIC EQUINE EQUIPMENT, LLC—See Morton Buildings Inc.; *U.S. Private*, pg. 2792
DESIGN HOMES INC.; *U.S. Private*, pg. 1213
DYNAMIC HOMES, INC.; *U.S. Private*, pg. 1298
EASTERN EXTERIOR WALL SYSTEMS INC.—See Marcon & Boyer Inc.; *U.S. Private*, pg. 2572
EHI MODULAR COMPANY, INC.—See Innovative Building Systems LLC; *U.S. Private*, pg. 2082
EPOCH CORPORATION; *U.S. Public*, pg. 1414
FOREMOST INDUSTRIES INC.; *U.S. Private*, pg. 1566
GAMETIME LLC—See Court Square Capital Partners, L.P.; *U.S. Private*, pg. 1069
GENERAL HOUSING CORPORATION; *U.S. Private*, pg. 1665

321992 — PREFABRICATED WOOD ...

GOLDEN EAGLE LOG HOMES, INC.; *U.S. Private*, pg. 1730
GULF PREFAB HOUSES FACTORY LTD.—See Gulf General Investment Company PSC; *Int'l*, pg. 3180
HANDCRAFTED HOMES, LLC—See Innovative Building Systems LLC; *U.S. Private*, pg. 2082
HEARTHSTONE INC.; *U.S. Private*, pg. 1899
HOGE LUMBER COMPANY; *U.S. Private*, pg. 1961
HOME BRANDS, LLC—See Tuff Shed, Inc.; *U.S. Private*, pg. 4257
HUNTINGTON HOMES INC.; *U.S. Private*, pg. 2010
ISOLAFT AS—See Flakk Holding AS; *Int'l*, pg. 2698
KLAFS TECHNICAL LIMITED—See Kohler Company; *U.S. Private*, pg. 2339
KPS FUELING SOLUTIONS SDN. BHD.—See Dover, Corporation; *U.S. Public*, pg. 681
LANCASTER REDEVELOPMENT CORP; *U.S. Private*, pg. 2381
LINDAL BUILDING PRODUCTS—See Lindal Cedar Homes, Inc.; *U.S. Private*, pg. 2459
LINDAL CEDAR HOMES, INC.; *U.S. Private*, pg. 2459
LINDAL CEDAR HOMES, INC.—See Lindal Cedar Homes, Inc.; *U.S. Private*, pg. 2459
LOG CABIN HOMES LTD.; *U.S. Private*, pg. 2480
LOUISIANA-PACIFIC PARAGUAY S.A.—See Louisiana-Pacific Corporation; *U.S. Public*, pg. 1343
MAST UTILITY BARNS; *U.S. Private*, pg. 2607
MORGAN BUILDING & SPA MANUFACTURING CORPORATION—See GHM Corp.; *U.S. Private*, pg. 1690
NATIONAL GREENHOUSE COMPANY—See Gibraltar Industries, Inc.; *U.S. Public*, pg. 936
NATIONWIDE HOMES, INC.—See Cavco Industries, Inc.; *U.S. Public*, pg. 455
PALM HARBOR HOMES, INC.—See Cavco Industries, Inc.; *U.S. Public*, pg. 455
PENN LYON HOMES INC.; *U.S. Private*, pg. 3134
PLH PRODUCTS, INC.; *U.S. Private*, pg. 3214
PRUM-TURENWERK GMBH—See ACS, Actividades de Construccion y Servicios, S.A.; *Int'l*, pg. 114
RITZ-CRAFT CORP. OF PA; *U.S. Private*, pg. 3442
ROCKY MOUNTAIN LOG HOMES-CANADA, LLC; *U.S. Private*, pg. 3469
SAND CREEK POST & BEAM INC.; *U.S. Private*, pg. 3542
SATTERWHITE COMPANIES INC.; *U.S. Private*, pg. 3553
SIMPLEX CONSTRUCTION CO. INC.—See Simplex Industries Inc; *U.S. Private*, pg. 3667
SIMPLEX INDUSTRIES INC; *U.S. Private*, pg. 3667
SKYLINE HOMES, INC.—See Champion Homes, Inc;. *U.S. Public*, pg. 477
SPENARD BUILDERS SUPPLY LLC—See Builders First-Source, Inc.; *U.S. Public*, pg. 410
STERLING BUILDING SYSTEMS, INC.—See Wausau Homes, Inc.; *U.S. Private*, pg. 4457
STRATFORD HOMES LP; *U.S. Private*, pg. 3837
SUNBURST CONTEMPORARY HOMES INC.; *U.S. Private*, pg. 3865
TOMAHAWK LOG & COUNTRY HOMES, INC.; *U.S. Private*, pg. 4183
TOWN & COUNTRY CEDAR HOMES; *U.S. Private*, pg. 4196
TUFF SHED, INC.; *U.S. Private*, pg. 4257
VFP INC.; *U.S. Private*, pg. 4374
WAUSAU HOMES, INC.; *U.S. Private*, pg. 4457
WENTWORTH HOLDINGS; *U.S. Private*, pg. 4481
WEST COAST LAMINATING LLC—See The E.B. Bradley Co., Inc.; *U.S. Private*, pg. 4024
WESTVIEW PRODUCTS, INC.—See Sierra Pacific Industries; *U.S. Private*, pg. 3647
WILDERNESS LOG HOMES INC.; *U.S. Private*, pg. 4519
WISCONSIN HOMES INC.; *U.S. Private*, pg. 4548

321999 — ALL OTHER MISCELLANEOUS WOOD PRODUCT MANUFACTURING

4BIOFUELS S.A.—See 2Valorise N.V.; *Int'l*, pg. 5
A&A IBARAKI CORPORATION—See A&A Material Corporation; *Int'l*, pg. 18
A&A OSAKA CORPORATION—See A&A Material Corporation; *Int'l*, pg. 18
ACCSYS TECHNOLOGIES PLC; *Int'l*, pg. 93
AFFILIATED RESOURCES, INC.—See Forest City Trading Group, LLC; *U.S. Private*, pg. 1566
AGGLOTAP, S.A.—See CORTICEIRA AMORIM, S.G.P.S., S.A.; *Int'l*, pg. 1807
AHF, LLC—See Paceline Equity Partners LLC; *U.S. Private*, pg. 3064
AICA KOGYO COMPANY, LIMITED; *Int'l*, pg. 228
AJS & ASSOCIATES INC.—See Hankscraft Inc.; *U.S. Private*, pg. 1854
AKATI WOOD (VIETNAM) CO., LTD.—See Dominant Enterprise Berhad; *Int'l*, pg. 2161
ALABAMA INTER-FOREST CORP.; *U.S. Private*, pg. 148
ALFA WOOD BULGARIA S.A.; *Int'l*, pg. 312
ALL CLOSURES IN, S.A.—See CORTICEIRA AMORIM, S.G.P.S., S.A.; *Int'l*, pg. 1807
AMERICAN PAINT PADDLE CO.—See Hyde Manufacturing Company; *U.S. Private*, pg. 2016
AMERICAN WOOD FIBERS, INC.; *U.S. Private*, pg. 258
AMES TRUE TEMPER - BERNIE—See Griffon Corporation; *U.S. Public*, pg. 969
AMORIM BENELUX B.V.—See CORTICEIRA AMORIM, S.G.P.S., S.A.; *Int'l*, pg. 1807
AMORIM CORK BEIJING LTD.—See CORTICEIRA AMORIM, S.G.P.S., S.A.; *Int'l*, pg. 1807
AMORIM CORK BULGARIA EOOD—See CORTICEIRA AMORIM, S.G.P.S., S.A.; *Int'l*, pg. 1807
AMORIM CORK COMPOSITES INC.—See CORTICEIRA AMORIM, S.G.P.S., S.A.; *Int'l*, pg. 1807
AMORIM CORK COMPOSITES, S. A.—See CORTICEIRA AMORIM, S.G.P.S., S.A.; *Int'l*, pg. 1807
AMORIM CORK DEUTSCHLAND GMBH & CO KG—See CORTICEIRA AMORIM, S.G.P.S., S.A.; *Int'l*, pg. 1807
AMORIM CORK FLOORING, S.A.—See CORTICEIRA AMORIM, S.G.P.S., S.A.; *Int'l*, pg. 1807
AMORIM CORK INSULATION, S.A.—See CORTICEIRA AMORIM, S.G.P.S., S.A.; *Int'l*, pg. 1807
AMORIM CORK SOUTH AFRICA (PTY) LTD.—See CORTICEIRA AMORIM, S.G.P.S., S.A.; *Int'l*, pg. 1807
AMORIM CORK VENTURES, LDA.—See CORTICEIRA AMORIM, S.G.P.S., S.A.; *Int'l*, pg. 1807
AMORIM DEUTSCHLAND, GMBH—See CORTICEIRA AMORIM, S.G.P.S., S.A.; *Int'l*, pg. 1807
AMORIM FLOORING AUSTRIA GMBH—See CORTICEIRA AMORIM, S.G.P.S., S.A.; *Int'l*, pg. 1807
AMORIM FLOORING NORTH AMERICA INC.—See CORTICEIRA AMORIM, S.G.P.S., S.A.; *Int'l*, pg. 1807
AMORIM FLOORING SWEDEN AB—See CORTICEIRA AMORIM, S.G.P.S., S.A.; *Int'l*, pg. 1807
AMORIM FLOORING (SWITZERLAND) AG—See CORTICEIRA AMORIM, S.G.P.S., S.A.; *Int'l*, pg. 1807
AMORIM FLORESTAL ESPANA, SL—See CORTICEIRA AMORIM, S.G.P.S., S.A.; *Int'l*, pg. 1807
AMORIM FLORESTAL MEDITERRANEO, SL—See CORTICEIRA AMORIM, S.G.P.S., S.A.; *Int'l*, pg. 1807
AMORIM FLORESTAL, S.A.—See CORTICEIRA AMORIM, S.G.P.S., S.A.; *Int'l*, pg. 1807
AMORIM & IRMAOS, SGPS, S.A.—See CORTICEIRA AMORIM, S.G.P.S., S.A.; *Int'l*, pg. 1807
AMORIM ISOLAMENTOS, S.A.—See CORTICEIRA AMORIM, S.G.P.S., S.A.; *Int'l*, pg. 1807
AMORIM JAPAN CORPORATION—See CORTICEIRA AMORIM, S.G.P.S., S.A.; *Int'l*, pg. 1807
AMORIM REVESTIMENTOS, S.A.—See CORTICEIRA AMORIM, S.G.P.S., S.A.; *Int'l*, pg. 1807
AMORIM TOP SERIES, S.A.—See CORTICEIRA AMORIM, S.G.P.S., S.A.; *Int'l*, pg. 1807
AMORIM TUNISIE, S.A.R.L.—See CORTICEIRA AMORIM, S.G.P.S., S.A.; *Int'l*, pg. 1807
AMORIM (UK) LTD.—See CORTICEIRA AMORIM, S.G.P.S., S.A.; *Int'l*, pg. 1807
AMOSEALTEX CORK CO., LTD.—See CORTICEIRA AMORIM, S.G.P.S., S.A.; *Int'l*, pg. 1807
ANTENNA MAST INCORPORATED—See The Will-Burt Co., Inc.; *U.S. Private*, pg. 4136
APM, INC.; *U.S. Private*, pg. 294
ARAUCO DO BRASIL SA—See AntarChile S.A.; *Int'l*, pg. 481
ARCHITECTURAL COMPONENTS GROUP, INC.—See Armstrong World Industries, Inc.; *U.S. Public*, pg. 194
ASIAN PACIFIC TIMBER MARKETING PTY LTD—See Asian Pacific Timber Marketing Pty Ltd; *Int'l*, pg. 618
AUGUST HILDEBRANDT GMBH; *Int'l*, pg. 703
AVERBUCH FORMICA CENTER LTD.; *Int'l*, pg. 739
THE BACON VENEER COMPANY; *U.S. Private*, pg. 3990
BAKER MCMILLEN CO.; *U.S. Private*, pg. 456
BANKS HARDWOODS, INC. — MENOMONIE FACILITY—See Banks Hardwoods, Inc.; *U.S. Private*, pg. 468
BANKS HARDWOODS, INC.; *U.S. Private*, pg. 468
BARRETTE OUTDOOR LIVING, INC.—See CRH plc; *Int'l*, pg. 1845
BAWAN COMPANY; *Int'l*, pg. 900
BAWAN WOOD INDUSTRIES CO.—See Bawan Company; *Int'l*, pg. 900
BEAR MOUNTAIN FOREST PRODUCTS, INC.; *U.S. Private*, pg. 506
BERNINA OF AMERICA INC.—See Bernina Schweiz AG; *Int'l*, pg. 989
BIRMAN WOOD & HARDWARE LTD.; *Int'l*, pg. 1048
BLUE STAR OPPORTUNITIES CORP; *U.S. Public*, pg. 365
BORDER TIMBERS LIMITED; *Int'l*, pg. 1113
BOUCHONS PRIOUX SARL—See CORTICEIRA AMORIM, S.G.P.S., S.A.; *Int'l*, pg. 1807
BRAIME PRESSINGS LIMITED—See Braime Group Plc; *Int'l*, pg. 1136
BRIPANEL INDUSTRIES SDN. BHD.—See Dominant Enterprise Berhad; *Int'l*, pg. 2161
BURLINGTON TIMBER—See Burlington Basket Co.; *U.S. Private*, pg. 688
BURMATEX LIMITED—See AIREA PLC; *Int'l*, pg. 247
BURMATEX SP. Z.O.O.—See AIREA PLC; *Int'l*, pg. 247
CALI'CO HARDWOODS INC.—See Wynnchurch Capital, L.P.; *U.S. Private*, pg. 4578
CALIFORNIA CEDAR PRODUCTS COMPANY - PALOMINO BRANDS DIVISION—See California Cedar Products Company; *U.S. Private*, pg. 718
CALIFORNIA CEDAR PRODUCTS COMPANY; *U.S. Private*, pg. 718
CANFOR CORPORATION - CAMDEN PLANT—See Canfor Corporation; *Int'l*, pg. 1290
CANFOR CORPORATION - CANAL FLATS SAWMILL FACILITY—See Canfor Corporation; *Int'l*, pg. 1290
CANFOR CORPORATION - CHETWYND SAWMILL FACILITY—See Canfor Corporation; *Int'l*, pg. 1290
CANFOR CORPORATION - GRAHAM PLANT—See Canfor Corporation; *Int'l*, pg. 1290
CANFOR CORPORATION - ISLE PIERRE SAWMILL FACILITY—See Canfor Corporation; *Int'l*, pg. 1290
CANFOR CORPORATION - MARION PLANT—See Canfor Corporation; *Int'l*, pg. 1291
CANFOR CORPORATION - POLAR SAWMILL FACILITY—See Canfor Corporation; *Int'l*, pg. 1291
CANFOR CORPORATION - QUESNEL SAWMILL FACILITY—See Canfor Corporation; *Int'l*, pg. 1291
CARPENTER TAN HOLDINGS LIMITED; *Int'l*, pg. 1343
CARRIS OF CALIFORNIA, INC.—See Carris Financial Corp.; *U.S. Private*, pg. 772
CARRIS PLASTICS—See Carris Financial Corp.; *U.S. Private*, pg. 772
CARRIS REELS, INC.—See Carris Financial Corp.; *U.S. Private*, pg. 772
CASES BY SOURCE, INC.; *U.S. Private*, pg. 782
CATAWISSA WOOD & COMPONENTS INC.; *U.S. Private*, pg. 788
CEDAR SHAKE & SHINGLE BUREAU; *Int'l*, pg. 1388
CF ITALIA SRL; *Int'l*, pg. 1429
CHAHUA MODERN HOUSEWARES CO.LTD; *Int'l*, pg. 1436
CHINA ENVIRONMENTAL TECHNOLOGY & BIOENERGY HOLDINGS LIMITED; *Int'l*, pg. 1500
CHINA KING SPIRIT GROUP LTD.; *U.S. Private*, pg. 886
CHINAMATE (SHAANXI) NATURAL PRODUCTS CO. LTD.—See CORTICEIRA AMORIM, S.G.P.S., S.A.; *Int'l*, pg. 1807
CHINA WOOD OPTIMIZATION (HOLDINGS) LIMITED; *Int'l*, pg. 1563
CHROMASCAPE, LLC; *U.S. Private*, pg. 892
CLASSIC SCENIC BERHAD; *Int'l*, pg. 1653
CLEARWATER THRESHERS—See The Phillies, L.P.; *U.S. Private*, pg. 4095
CLW INC.; *U.S. Private*, pg. 949
CMPC MADERAS SPA—See Empresas CMPC S.A.; *Int'l*, pg. 2389
COGRA S.A.; *Int'l*, pg. 1695
COLONY DISPLAY LLC—See Kinzie Capital Partners LP; *U.S. Private*, pg. 2313
COMATRAL - C. DE MAROC. DE TRANSF. DU LIEGE, S.A.—See CORTICEIRA AMORIM, S.G.P.S., S.A.; *Int'l*, pg. 1807
CONIFEX TIMBER INC.; *Int'l*, pg. 1768
COOPER ENTERPRISES LLC—See Eaton Corporation plc; *Int'l*, pg. 2277
CORTEX KORKVERTRIEBS GMBH—See CORTICEIRA AMORIM, S.G.P.S., S.A.; *Int'l*, pg. 1807
CORTICEIRA AMORIM - FRANCE SAS—See CORTICEIRA AMORIM, S.G.P.S., S.A.; *Int'l*, pg. 1807
CORTICEIRA AMORIM, S.G.P.S., S.A.; *Int'l*, pg. 1807
CUTLER FOREST PRODUCTS INC.; *Int'l*, pg. 1881
CYPRUS FOREST INDUSTRIES PUBLIC LTD; *Int'l*, pg. 1897
DAAQUAM LUMBER INC.—See Canfor Corporation; *Int'l*, pg. 1291
DAIKEN CORPORATION - TAKAHAGI PLANT—See Daiken Corporation; *Int'l*, pg. 1931
DAIKEN NEW ZEALAND LIMITED—See Daiken Corporation; *Int'l*, pg. 1931
DAIWA CORE FACTORY CO., LTD.—See Daiwa House REIT Investment Corporation; *Int'l*, pg. 1947
DANIELSON DESIGNS, LTD.; *U.S. Private*, pg. 1156
DANSK TRAEEMBALLAGE A/S; *Int'l*, pg. 1969
DARE POWER DEKOR HOME CO., LTD.; *Int'l*, pg. 1972
DA SEN HOLDINGS GROUP LIMITED; *Int'l*, pg. 1902
DECOR CABINETS LTD.; *Int'l*, pg. 2001
DEHUA TB NEW DECORATION MATERIAL CO., LTD.; *Int'l*, pg. 2004
DELIGNIT AG; *Int'l*, pg. 2013
DENVER REEL & PALLET CO.—See Conner Industries, Inc.; *U.S. Private*, pg. 1017
DIAMOND BRANDS INCORPORATED; *U.S. Private*, pg. 1222
DISPLAY INDUSTRIES, LLC; *U.S. Private*, pg. 1238
DSG MANUFACTURING MALAYSIA SDN. BHD.—See Depa PLC; *Int'l*, pg. 2040
DSG PROJECTS MALAYSIA SDN. BHD.—See Depa PLC; *Int'l*, pg. 2040
DSG (THAILAND) CO., LTD.—See Depa PLC; *Int'l*, pg. 2040
DUC THANH WOOD PROCESSING JSC; *Int'l*, pg. 2223
DUKA & BOSNA D.D.; *Int'l*, pg. 2224
EAGLE INDUSTRIES LLC; *U.S. Private*, pg. 1309
ECOLOGIX RESOURCES GROUP, INC.; *U.S. Public*, pg. 717

N.A.I.C.S. INDEX

321999 — ALL OTHER MISCELLAN...

EDGEBUILDER, INC.—See Star Equity Holdings, Inc.; *U.S. Public*, pg. 1937
EGGER-ROL SA—See Fritz Egger GmbH & Co.; *Int'l*, pg. 2794
ELECO BAUPRODUKTE—See Eleco Plc; *Int'l*, pg. 2347
ELFVERSON & CO. AB—See CORTICEIRA AMORIM, S.G.P.S., S.A.; *Int'l*, pg. 1807
ELVILA S.A.; *Int'l*, pg. 2371
EMPIRE LUMBER COMPANY; *U.S. Private*, pg. 1385
ENVIRO-LOG, INC.—See Summit Equity Group, LLC; *U.S. Private*, pg. 3854
ENVIVA INC.; *U.S. Public*, pg. 781
ENVIVA LP—See Enviva Inc.; *U.S. Public*, pg. 782
ENVIVA PELLETS AHOSKIE, LLC—See Enviva Inc.; *U.S. Public*, pg. 782
ENVIVA PELLETS WIGGINS, LLC—See Enviva Inc.; *U.S. Public*, pg. 782
EO2 S.A.; *Int'l*, pg. 2457
ETABLISSEMENTS ALLIN; *Int'l*, pg. 2519
EUCATEX S.A. INDUSTRIA E COMERCIO - EUCATEX PAINTS AND VARNISHES PLANT—See Eucatex S.A. Industria e Comercio; *Int'l*, pg. 2525
EUCATEX S.A. INDUSTRIA E COMERCIO - FIBERBOARD FACILTY—See Eucatex S.A. Industria e Comercio; *Int'l*, pg. 2525
EUCATEX S.A. INDUSTRIA E COMERCIO - MDP AND LAMINATE FLOORING FACITLITY—See Eucatex S.A. Industria e Comercio; *Int'l*, pg. 2525
EUCATEX S.A. INDUSTRIA E COMERCIO - SEEDLINGS NURSERY UNIT—See Eucatex S.A. Industria e Comercio; *Int'l*, pg. 2525
EUCATEX S.A. INDUSTRIA E COMERCIO; *Int'l*, pg. 2525
EURO MULTIVISION LTD.; *Int'l*, pg. 2531
EVERGREEN FIBREBOARD BERHAD; *Int'l*, pg. 2565
FAMOS SA; *Int'l*, pg. 2612
FANCY WOOD INDUSTRIES PUBLIC COMPANY LIMITED; *Int'l*, pg. 2613
FAZERLES AD-SILISTRA; *Int'l*, pg. 2627
FB KETTEN HANDELS GMBH—See Addtech AB; *Int'l*, pg. 133
FEUTRES DEPLAND S.A.S.—See Gascogne SA; *Int'l*, pg. 2887
FIBER ENERGY PRODUCTS AR LLC—See EagleTree Capital, LP; *U.S. Private*, pg. 1311
FIPLASTO SA; *Int'l*, pg. 2678
FLAKEBOARD COMPANY LIMITED—See AntarChile S.A.; *Int'l*, pg. 481
FLETCHER WOOD PANELS (AUSTRALIA) PTY LIMITED—See Fletcher Building Limited; *Int'l*, pg. 2700
FOREST2MARKET, INC.—See Battery Ventures, L.P.; *U.S. Private*, pg. 489
FOREST INDUSTRIES, INC.—See Saunders Brothers; *U.S. Private*, pg. 3554
FORESTRY RESOURCES, INC.; *U.S. Private*, pg. 1567
FRAME USA, INC.—See Craig Frames, Inc.; *U.S. Private*, pg. 1082
FUJIAN YONGAN FORESTRY (GROUP) CO., LTD.; *Int'l*, pg. 2820
GARCY PIEDMONT—See Leggett & Platt, Incorporated; *U.S. Public*, pg. 1302
GASCOGNE BOIS ESCOURCE SAS—See Gascogne SA; *Int'l*, pg. 2887
GASCOGNE PACKAGING USA, INC.—See Gascogne SA; *Int'l*, pg. 2887
GASCOGNE SACK DEUTSCHLAND GMBH—See Gascogne SA; *Int'l*, pg. 2887
GASCOGNE SACS MIMIZAN SAS—See Gascogne SA; *Int'l*, pg. 2887
GASCOGNE SACS SAINT-HERBLAIN SAS—See Gascogne SA; *Int'l*, pg. 2888
GASCOGNE UK LTD—See Gascogne SA; *Int'l*, pg. 2888
GILCO LUMBER, INC.—See International Industries, Inc.; *U.S. Private*, pg. 2117
GINSEY INDUSTRIES, INC.; *U.S. Private*, pg. 1702
GLOBE ADHESIVE TECHNOLOGY (ZHUHAI) CO., LTD.—See Globe Industries Corporation; *Int'l*, pg. 3006
GLOBE INDUSTRIES CORPORATION; *Int'l*, pg. 3006
GOODFELLOW INC.; *Int'l*, pg. 3040
G-P WOOD & FIBER SUPPLY, LLC—See Koch Industries, Inc.; *U.S. Private*, pg. 2327
GREAT LAKES MDF, LLC.; *U.S. Private*, pg. 1764
GREAT NORTHERN BUILDING PRODUCTS, LLC; *U.S. Private*, pg. 1766
GREEN RIVER HOLDING CO., LTD.; *Int'l*, pg. 3072
GROUPE DE SCIERIES G.D.S. INC.; *Int'l*, pg. 3101
GUANGXI FENGLIN WOOD INDUSTRY GROUP CO., LTD.; *Int'l*, pg. 3163
HADLEY HOUSE COMPANY; *U.S. Private*, pg. 1839
HAMEL FOREST PRODUCTS, INC.; *U.S. Private*, pg. 1847
HAMPTON AFFILIATES - WARRENTON DIVISION—See Hampton Affiliates; *U.S. Private*, pg. 1851
HAN EXPRESS ENERGY SDN. BHD.—See HANEXPRESS CO, LTD.; *Int'l*, pg. 3244
HARDWOODS OF MICHIGAN, INC.—See Hardwoods Distribution Inc.; *Int'l*, pg. 3273
HANICH TEXTILE ENGINEERS LTD; *Int'l* pg. 3276
HARVEST GARDEN PRO, LLC—See Harvest Power Inc.; *U.S. Private*, pg. 1877

HASEKO FURNISHING CO.,LTD.—See Haseko Corporation; *Int'l*, pg. 3283
HEVEAMART SDN. BHD.—See HeveaBoard Berhad; *Int'l*, pg. 3367
HINOKI WOOD WORK COMPANY LIMITED—See Demeter Corporation Public Company Limited; *Int'l*, pg. 2025
HK WUSEJIE GROUP CO. LTD.; *Int'l*, pg. 3428
HOKUETSU FOREST CO., LTD.—See Hokuetsu Corporation; *Int'l*, pg. 3443
HOLMEN SKOG AB—See Holmen AB; *Int'l*, pg. 3453
HOLMQUIST FEEDMILL INC.; *U.S. Private*, pg. 1968
HOMAG KOREA CO., LTD—See Durr AG; *Int'l*, pg. 2232
HPI RESOURCES BERHAD; *Int'l*, pg. 3500
HUNGAROCORK, AMORIM, RT—See CORTICEIRA AMORIM, S.G.P.S., S.A.; *Int'l*, pg. 1808
H. WILSON COMPANY—See EBSCO Industries, Inc.; *U.S. Private*, pg. 1325
IDX CORPORATION—See UFP Industries, Inc.; *U.S. Public*, pg. 2221
INDUSTRIA CORCHERA, S.A.—See CORTICEIRA AMORIM, S.G.P.S., S.A.; *Int'l*, pg. 1808
JIANGXI JIACHANG FORESTRY DEVELOPMENT CO., LTD.—See Emerald Plantation Holdings Limited; *Int'l*, pg. 2378
JIM CARPENTER COMPANY—See The Lester Group Inc.; *U.S. Private*, pg. 4069
JOHN BOOS & CO.—See JBC Holding Co.; *U.S. Private*, pg. 2193
JOLLY GARDENER PRODUCTS INC.—See CRH plc; *Int'l*, pg. 1846
JURIHAN SDN. BHD.—See Dominant Enterprise Berhad; *Int'l*, pg. 2161
KALLESOE MACHINERY A/S—See Durr AG; *Int'l*, pg. 2233
KELLER KITCHEN CABINETS, INC.; *U.S. Private*, pg. 2275
KINCAID PRODUCTS, INC.; *U.S. Private*, pg. 2306
KING KOLD FROZEN FOODS, INC.—See Saveur Food Group, LLC; *U.S. Private*, pg. 3556
KORKKITRIO OY—See CORTICEIRA AMORIM, S.G.P.S., S.A.; *Int'l*, pg. 1808
LA CAFETIERE (UK) LIMITED—See Lifetime Brands, Inc.; *U.S. Public*, pg. 1313
LEWIS CONTROLS, INC—See Corley Manufacturing Co.; *U.S. Private*, pg. 1050
LEXINGTON MANUFACTURING INC.—See Watkins Associated Industries Inc.; *U.S. Private*, pg. 4455
LIFETIME BRANDS GLOBAL TRADING (SHANGHAI) COMPANY LIMITED—See Lifetime Brands, Inc.; *U.S. Public*, pg. 1313
LIGNETICS, INC.—See EagleTree Capital, LP; *U.S. Private*, pg. 1311
LYN-LAD GROUP LTD.; *U.S. Private*, pg. 2520
MAINE ORNAMENTAL, LLC—See UFP Industries, Inc.; *U.S. Public*, pg. 2219
MALHEUR LUMBER COMPANY—See Ochoco Lumber Company; *U.S. Private*, pg. 2992
MARQUIS INDUSTRIES, INC.—See Live Ventures Incorporated; *U.S. Public*, pg. 1332
MARTH WOOD SHAVING SUPPLY, INC.—See EagleTree Capital, LP; *U.S. Private*, pg. 1311
MASTIMBER INDUSTRIES SDN. BHD.—See EG Industries Berhad; *Int'l*, pg. 2322
MEADOW RIVER HARDWOOD, LLC.; *U.S. Private*, pg. 2647
MIDAH INDUSTRIES SDN BHD—See Chin Hin Group Berhad; *Int'l*, pg. 1480
MID ATLANTIC FRAMING, LLC—See UFP Industries, Inc.; *U.S. Public*, pg. 2219
MID-MICHIGAN RECYCLING, L.C.—See CMS Energy Corporation; *U.S. Public*, pg. 518
MIDWEST TOWERS INC.; *U.S. Private*, pg. 2723
THE MILLWORK, CO.; *U.S. Private*, pg. 4079
MOSSBERG INDUSTRIES - HUBBARD DIVISION—See Mossberg Industries, Inc.; *U.S. Private*, pg. 2794
MOSSBERG INDUSTRIES, INC.; *U.S. Private*, pg. 2794
NIELSEN DESIGN GMBH—See Sycamore Partners Management, LP; *U.S. Private*, pg. 3896
NORDAUTOMATION OY—See Addtech AB; *Int'l*, pg. 134
NORIDIAN HEALTHCARE SOLUTIONS, LLC—See Noridian Mutual Insurance Company; *U.S. Private*, pg. 2938
NORTH AMERICAN FOREST PRODUCTS, INC.—See Patrick Industries, Inc.; *U.S. Public*, pg. 1653
NORTHWEST HARDWOODS, INC.—See Littlejohn & Co., LLC; *U.S. Private*, pg. 2471
NOVO BUILDING PRODUCTS, LLC—See Hardwoods Distribution Inc.; *Int'l*, pg. 3273
OMEGA INDUSTRIES INC.; *U.S. Private*, pg. 3015
PACKNET, LTD.—See UFP Industries, Inc.; *U.S. Public*, pg. 2219
PANEL PROCESSING OF TEXAS, INC.—See Panel Processing, Inc.; *U.S. Private*, pg. 3086
PAPELES CORRUGADOS, S.A. DE C.V.—See Grupo La Moderna, S.A.B. de C.V.; *Int'l*, pg. 3131
PATTON PICTURE COMPANY—See Kohlberg & Company; *U.S. Private*, pg. 2338
PDM LTD.—See Compagnie de Saint-Gobain SA; *Int'l*, pg. 1733
PINNACLE RENEWABLE ENERGY, INC.—See Drax Group plc; *Int'l*, pg. 2200

PORTOCORK AMERICA, INC.—See CORTICEIRA AMORIM, S.G.P.S., S.A.; *Int'l*, pg. 1808
PORTOCORK ITALIA, S.R.L.—See CORTICEIRA AMORIM, S.G.P.S., S.A.; *Int'l*, pg. 1808
PREMIER WOODPROFILE SDN. BHD.—See Dominant Enterprise Berhad; *Int'l*, pg. 2161
PRIDE MANUFACTURING COMPANY, LLC—See Centre Partners Management LLC; *U.S. Private*, pg. 828
PROGRESSIVE FOAM TECHNOLOGIES, INC.; *U.S. Private*, pg. 3279
RENOGEN S.A.—See 2Valorise N.V.; *Int'l*, pg. 5
RICHWOOD INDUSTRIES, INC.—See Argosy Capital Group, LLC; *U.S. Private*, pg. 321
RICK'S CUSTOM FENCING & DECKING; *U.S. Private*, pg. 3431
ROCHESTER SHOE TREE COMPANY, INC.; *U.S. Private*, pg. 3464
ROMEX WORLD TRADE CO., L.L.C.—See Roy O. Martin Lumber Company, LLC; *U.S. Public*, pg. 3491
ROYAL WOODWORKING CO. LIMITED—See Specialty Building Products, LLC; *U.S. Private*, pg. 3749
SAINT-GOBAIN ISOVER G+H AG—See Compagnie de Saint-Gobain SA; *Int'l*, pg. 1726
SAINT-GOBAIN ISOVER S.A.—See Compagnie de Saint-Gobain SA; *Int'l*, pg. 1726
SAUDER FUNERAL PRODUCTS—See Sauder Woodworking Co.; *U.S. Private*, pg. 3554
SAUNDERS BROTHERS; *U.S. Private*, pg. 3554
SCANPOLE OY—See Iivari Mononen Oy; *Int'l*, pg. 3608
SCOTT PENN, INC.; *U.S. Private*, pg. 3577
SCOTTSDALE ART FACTORY LLC; *U.S. Private*, pg. 3578
SETZER FOREST PRODUCTS INC. - OROVILLE PLANT—See Setzer Forest Products Inc.; *U.S. Private*, pg. 3618
SEYMOUR MANUFACTURING LINK HANDLE DIVISION—See Seymour Midwest LLC; *U.S. Private*, pg. 3621
SHANTAWOOD SDN BHD—See DPS Resources Berhad; *Int'l*, pg. 2189
SIBL - SOCIETE INDUSTRIELLE BOIS LIEGE—See CORTICEIRA AMORIM, S.G.P.S., S.A.; *Int'l*, pg. 1808
SINO-PANEL (CHINA) INVESTMENTS LIMITED—See Emerald Plantation Holdings Limited; *Int'l*, pg. 2378
SINO-WOOD TRADING LIMITED—See Emerald Plantation Holdings Limited; *Int'l*, pg. 2378
SOCIETE GASCOGNE SACK TUNISIA—See Gascogne SA; *Int'l*, pg. 2888
SOFT-LITE LLC—See Clayton, Dubilier & Rice, LLC; *U.S. Private*, pg. 920
SOHO MYRIAD, LLC—See Longwater Opportunities LLC; *U.S. Private*, pg. 2493
STANDARD FURNITURE FACTORY D.D.—See Delta Holding; *Int'l*, pg. 2019
SUMMIT TREESTANDS, LLC—See EBSCO Industries, Inc.; *U.S. Private*, pg. 1325
SUPERIOR KILNS, INC.—See Midwest Hardwood Corporation; *U.S. Private*, pg. 2721
SUPERIOR WOOD TREATING—See Manke Lumber Company, Inc.; *U.S. Private*, pg. 2564
SWANSON BARK & WOOD PRODUCTS, INC.—See Denali Water Solutions LLC; *U.S. Private*, pg. 1204
TAIGA BUILDING PRODUCTS LTD.—See Avarga Limited; *Int'l*, pg. 737
TANNER SERVICES - TIMBER DIVISION—See Tanner Services, LLC; *U.S. Private*, pg. 3932
TAYLOR BROTHERS LUMBER COMPANY—See The Lester Group Inc.; *U.S. Private*, pg. 4069
TELEVISA CONSUMER PRODUCTS USA, LLC—See Grupo Televisa, S.A.B.; *Int'l*, pg. 3136
THOMASSON COMPANY; *U.S. Private*, pg. 4158
TIANJIN CUSTOM WOOD PROCESSING, CO. LTD—See California Cedar Products Company; *U.S. Private*, pg. 718
TITAN WOOD TECHNOLOGY B.V.—See AccSys Technologies PLC; *Int'l*, pg. 93
TREFINOS, S.L—See CORTICEIRA AMORIM, S.G.P.S., S.A.; *Int'l*, pg. 1808
TRENARY WOOD PRODUCTS—See Holmquist Feedmill Inc.; *U.S. Private*, pg. 1968
UFP SAUK RAPIDS, LLC—See UFP Industries, Inc.; *U.S. Public*, pg. 2220
UNIBOARD UNIRES, INC.—See Compagnie de Saint-Gobain SA; *Int'l*, pg. 1724
UNILIN FLOORING NC, LLC—See Mohawk Industries, Inc.; *U.S. Public*, pg. 1458
UNITED LUMBER & REMAN, LLC—See UFP Industries, Inc.; *U.S. Public*, pg. 2221
WALPOLE WOODWORKERS, INC.; *U.S. Private*, pg. 4432
WESTECH BUILDING PRODUCTS ULC—See Westlake Corporation; *U.S. Public*, pg. 2360
WEYERHAEUSER KOREA LTD.—See Weyerhaeuser Company; *U.S. Public*, pg. 2365
WHITE RIVER HARDWOODS-WOODWORKS, INC.; *U.S. Private*, pg. 4509
THE WILLAMETTE VALLEY COMPANY - IDAHO MILLING AND GRAIN DIVISION—See The Willamette Valley Company; *U.S. Private*, pg. 1136
WILL-BURT ADVANCED COMPOSITES, INC.—See The

321999 — ALL OTHER MISCELLAN...

Will-Burt Co., Inc.; *U.S. Private*, pg. 4136
WM COFFMAN RESOURCES LLC—See Prophet Equity L.P.; *U.S. Private*, pg. 3286
WOODCRAFT INDUSTRIES INC. - MOUNDS VIEW PLANT—See Quanex Building Products Corp.; *U.S. Public*, pg. 1750
WOODLORE—See Caleres, Inc.; *U.S. Public*, pg. 422
WR VERMILLION CO., INC.; *U.S. Private*, pg. 4571
YARD & HOME, LLC—See UFP Industries, Inc.; *U.S. Public*, pg. 2221

322110 — PULP MILLS

AGROMIN INC.; *U.S. Private*, pg. 130
ALBERTA-PACIFIC FOREST INDUSTRIES INC.—See Hokuetsu Corporation; *Int'l*, pg. 3443
ALTRI, SGPS, S.A.; *Int'l*, pg. 398
ANDRITZ INC. - PELL CITY—See ANDRITZ AG; *Int'l*, pg. 453
AS ESTONIAN CELL—See Heinzel Holding GmbH; *Int'l*, pg. 3325
ASIA PACIFIC RESOURCES INTERNATIONAL HOLDINGS LTD.; *Int'l*, pg. 613
BRACELL; *Int'l*, pg. 1134
BRUNSWICK CELLULOSE—See Koch Industries, Inc.; *U.S. Private*, pg. 2328
CELULOSAS DE ASTURIAS, S.A.—See ENCE Energia y Celulosa, S.A.; *Int'l*, pg. 2401
CENTURY TEXTILES AND INDUSTRIES LIMITED - CENTURY PULP AND PAPER DIVISION—See Century Textiles and Industries Limited; *Int'l*, pg. 1419
CHILENA DE MOLDEADOS S.A.—See Empresas CMPC S.A.; *Int'l*, pg. 2390
CMPC CELULOSA S.A.—See Empresas CMPC S.A.; *Int'l*, pg. 2389
COPAP INC.; *Int'l*, pg. 1792
COSMO SPECIALTY FIBERS, INC.—See The Gores Group, LLC; *U.S. Private*, pg. 4034
DOUBLE A (1991) PUBLIC COMPANY LIMITED; *Int'l*, pg. 2180
DOUBLE A INTERNATIONAL NETWORK B.V.—See Double A (1991) Public Company Limited; *Int'l*, pg. 2181
G.A. PAPER INTERNATIONAL INC.; *Int'l*, pg. 2865
GASCOGNE PAPIER SAS—See Gascogne SA; *Int'l*, pg. 2887
GP CELLULOSE, LLC—See Koch Industries, Inc.; *U.S. Private*, pg. 2328
HANSOL EME CO. LTD.—See Hansol Group; *Int'l*, pg. 3260
HEINZEL HOLDING GMBH; *Int'l*, pg. 3325
HEINZEL SALES ASIA PACIFIC SDN. BHD.—See Heinzel Holding GmbH; *Int'l*, pg. 3325
HEINZEL SALES CANADA INC.—See Heinzel Holding GmbH; *Int'l*, pg. 3325
IGGESUND PAPER BOARD—See Holmen AB; *Int'l*, pg. 3453
NORTH RIM PULP & PAPER INC.—See Heinzel Holding GmbH; *Int'l*, pg. 3325
PARSONS & WHITTEMORE, INC.; *U.S. Private*, pg. 3100
P. H. GLATFELTER COMPANY—See Glatfelter Corporation; *U.S. Public*, pg. 939
PT. ANDRITZ—See ANDRITZ AG; *Int'l*, pg. 456
RAUBLING PAPIER GMBH—See Heinzel Holding GmbH; *Int'l*, pg. 3325
ROTTNEROS AB—See Arctic Paper S.A.; *Int'l*, pg. 552
ROTTNEROS BRUK AB—See Arctic Paper S.A.; *Int'l*, pg. 552
ROTTNEROS MIRANDA SA—See Arctic Paper S.A.; *Int'l*, pg. 552
SIA ROTTNEROS BALTIC AB—See Arctic Paper S.A.; *Int'l*, pg. 552
SINGAPORE PULP (PTE) LTD.—See CellMark AB; *Int'l*, pg. 1394
SOUTHERN CELLULOSE PRODUCTS, INC.—See Archer-Daniels-Midland Company; *U.S. Public*, pg. 185
TECHNO-HOKUETSU, LTD.—See Hokuetsu Corporation; *Int'l*, pg. 3444
TRIOSIM CORPORATION; *U.S. Private*, pg. 4236
VALLVIKS BRUK AB—See Arctic Paper S.A.; *Int'l*, pg. 552
WESTROCK MINNESOTA CORPORATION—See WestRock Company; *U.S. Public*, pg. 2363
WOODLAND PULP, LLC—See Charmwell Holdings Ltd.; *Int'l*, pg. 1451
ZELLSTOFF POLS AG—See Heinzel Holding GmbH; *Int'l*, pg. 3326

322120 — PAPER MILLS

317298 SASKATCHEWAN LTD.—See Weyerhaeuser Company; *U.S. Public*, pg. 2365
3P LAND HOLDINGS LIMITED; *Int'l*, pg. 9
A.A. PULP MILL 2 COMPANY LIMITED—See Double A (1991) Public Company Limited; *Int'l*, pg. 2180
AGIO PAPER & INDUSTRIES LIMITED - BILASPUR MILL—See AGIO PAPER & INDUSTRIES LIMITED; *Int'l*, pg. 210
AGIO PAPER & INDUSTRIES LIMITED; *Int'l*, pg. 210
AGORA POLIGRAFIA SP. Z O.O.—See Agora S.A.; *Int'l*, pg. 212
AHLSTROM BRASIL LTDA.—See Ahlstrom Capital Oy; *Int'l*, pg. 224
AHLSTROM BRASIL LTDA.—See Bain Capital, LP; *U.S. Private*, pg. 429
AHLSTROM-MUNKSJO AB—See Ahlstrom Capital Oy; *Int'l*, pg. 224
AHLSTROM-MUNKSJO AB—See Bain Capital, LP; *U.S. Private*, pg. 429
AHLSTROM-MUNKSJO APPRIEU S.A.S—See Ahlstrom Capital Oy; *Int'l*, pg. 224
AHLSTROM-MUNKSJO APPRIEU S.A.S.—See Bain Capital, LP; *U.S. Private*, pg. 429
AHLSTROM-MUNKSJO ASPA BRUK AB—See Ahlstrom Capital Oy; *Int'l*, pg. 224
AHLSTROM-MUNKSJO ASPA BRUK AB—See Bain Capital, LP; *U.S. Private*, pg. 429
AHLSTROM-MUNKSJO BRASIL LTDA.—See Ahlstrom Capital Oy; *Int'l*, pg. 224
AHLSTROM-MUNKSJO BRASIL LTDA.—See Bain Capital, LP; *U.S. Private*, pg. 429
AHLSTROM-MUNKSJO CHIRNSIDE LIMITED - MANCHESTER PLANT—See Ahlstrom Capital Oy; *Int'l*, pg. 224
AHLSTROM-MUNKSJO CHIRNSIDE LIMITED - MANCHESTER PLANT—See Bain Capital, LP; *U.S. Private*, pg. 429
AHLSTROM-MUNKSJO FALUN AB—See Ahlstrom Capital Oy; *Int'l*, pg. 224
AHLSTROM-MUNKSJO FALUN AB—See Bain Capital, LP; *U.S. Private*, pg. 429
AHLSTROM-MUNKSJO FIBER COMPOSITES INDIA PRIVATE LTD.—See Ahlstrom Capital Oy; *Int'l*, pg. 224
AHLSTROM-MUNKSJO FIBER COMPOSITES INDIA PRIVATE LTD.—See Bain Capital, LP; *U.S. Private*, pg. 429
AHLSTROM-MUNKSJO FILTRATION LLC - MOUNT HOLLY SPRINGS PLANT—See Ahlstrom Capital Oy; *Int'l*, pg. 224
AHLSTROM-MUNKSJO FILTRATION LLC - MOUNT HOLLY SPRINGS PLANT—See Bain Capital, LP; *U.S. Private*, pg. 429
AHLSTROM-MUNKSJO FILTRATION LLC - TAYLORVILLE PLANT—See Ahlstrom Capital Oy; *Int'l*, pg. 224
AHLSTROM-MUNKSJO FILTRATION LLC - TAYLORVILLE PLANT—See Bain Capital, LP; *U.S. Private*, pg. 430
AHLSTROM-MUNKSJO NA SPECIALTY SOLUTIONS LLC - NICOLET PLANT—See Ahlstrom Capital Oy; *Int'l*, pg. 224
AHLSTROM-MUNKSJO NA SPECIALTY SOLUTIONS LLC - NICOLET PLANT—See Bain Capital, LP; *U.S. Private*, pg. 430
AHLSTROM-MUNKSJO NA SPECIALTY SOLUTIONS LLC—See Ahlstrom Capital Oy; *Int'l*, pg. 224
AHLSTROM-MUNKSJO NA SPECIALTY SOLUTIONS LLC—See Bain Capital, LP; *U.S. Private*, pg. 430
AHLSTROM-MUNKSJO OYJ - CAIEIRAS PLANT—See Ahlstrom Capital Oy; *Int'l*, pg. 224
AHLSTROM-MUNKSJO OYJ - CAIEIRAS PLANT—See Bain Capital, LP; *U.S. Private*, pg. 429
AHLSTROM-MUNKSJO OYJ - JACAREI PLANT—See Ahlstrom Capital Oy; *Int'l*, pg. 224
AHLSTROM-MUNKSJO OYJ - JACAREI PLANT—See Bain Capital, LP; *U.S. Private*, pg. 429
AHLSTROM-MUNKSJO OYJ - LOUVEIRA PLANT—See Ahlstrom Capital Oy; *Int'l*, pg. 224
AHLSTROM-MUNKSJO OYJ - LOUVEIRA PLANT—See Bain Capital, LP; *U.S. Private*, pg. 429
AHLSTROM-MUNKSJO OYJ—See Ahlstrom Capital Oy; *Int'l*, pg. 223
AHLSTROM-MUNKSJO OYJ—See Bain Capital, LP; *U.S. Private*, pg. 429
AHLSTROM-MUNKSJO PAPER GMBH—See Ahlstrom Capital Oy; *Int'l*, pg. 224
AHLSTROM-MUNKSJO PAPER GMBH—See Bain Capital, LP; *U.S. Private*, pg. 429
AHLSTROM-MUNKSJO PAPER S.A.—See Ahlstrom Capital Oy; *Int'l*, pg. 224
AHLSTROM-MUNKSJO PAPER S.A.—See Bain Capital, LP; *U.S. Private*, pg. 430
AHLSTROM-MUNKSJO PAPER (TAICANG) CO., LTD.—See Ahlstrom Capital Oy; *Int'l*, pg. 223
AHLSTROM-MUNKSJO PAPER (TAICANG) CO., LTD.—See Bain Capital, LP; *U.S. Private*, pg. 429
AHLSTROM-MUNKSJO PAPER TRADING (SHANGHAI) CO., LTD.—See Ahlstrom Capital Oy; *Int'l*, pg. 223
AHLSTROM-MUNKSJO PAPER TRADING (SHANGHAI) CO., LTD.—See Bain Capital, LP; *U.S. Private*, pg. 429
AHLSTROM-MUNKSJO ROTTERSAC S.A.S.—See Ahlstrom Capital Oy; *Int'l*, pg. 224
AHLSTROM-MUNKSJO ROTTERSAC S.A.S.—See Bain Capital, LP; *U.S. Private*, pg. 430
AHLSTROM-MUNKSJO RUS LLC—See Ahlstrom Capital Oy; *Int'l*, pg. 224
AHLSTROM-MUNKSJO RUS LLC—See Bain Capital, LP; *U.S. Private*, pg. 430
AHLSTROM-MUNKSJO SPECIALTIES S.A.S. - SAINT SEVERIN PLANT—See Ahlstrom Capital Oy; *Int'l*, pg. 224
AHLSTROM-MUNKSJO SPECIALTIES S.A.S. - SAINT SEVERIN PLANT—See Bain Capital, LP; *U.S. Private*, pg. 430
AHLSTROM SEOUL CO. LTD—See Ahlstrom Capital Oy; *Int'l*, pg. 223
AHLSTROM SEOUL CO. LTD—See Bain Capital, LP; *U.S. Private*, pg. 429
ALBANY INTERNATIONAL/ENGINEERED FABRICS—See Albany International Corp.; *U.S. Public*, pg. 72
ALKIM KAGIT SANAYI VE TICARET A.S.; *Int'l*, pg. 331
ALLEN PACKAGING CO.—See GenNx360 Capital Partners, L.P.; *U.S. Private*, pg. 1672
ALTRI FLORESTAL, S.A.—See Altri, SGPS, S.A.; *Int'l*, pg. 398
APC PAPER CO. INC.—See The Pritzker Group - Chicago, LLC; *U.S. Private*, pg. 4099
ARCTIC PAPER S.A.; *Int'l*, pg. 551
ARJOWIGGINS SECURITY SAS; *Int'l*, pg. 567
AWA PAPER (SHANGHAI) CO., LTD.—See Awa Paper & Technological Company Inc.; *Int'l*, pg. 751
AWA PAPER & TECHNOLOGICAL COMPANY INC.; *Int'l*, pg. 751
BALARAM PAPERS PVT LTD—See Astron Paper & Board Mill Limited; *Int'l*, pg. 662
BALLARPUR INDUSTRIES LIMITED—See Avantha Group; *Int'l*, pg. 735
BEAR ISLAND PAPER WB L.P.—See Black Diamond Capital Holdings, LLC; *U.S. Private*, pg. 570
BERLI JUCKER CELLOX LIMITED—See Berli Jucker Public Co. Ltd.; *Int'l*, pg. 985
BERNARD DUMAS S.A.S.—See Hokuetsu Corporation; *Int'l*, pg. 3443
BILLERUD FRANCE S.A—See Billerud AB; *Int'l*, pg. 1030
BILLERUD S.R.L.—See Billerud AB; *Int'l*, pg. 1030
BIO GREEN PAPERS LIMITED; *Int'l*, pg. 1035
BIO PAPPEL, S.A.B. DE C.V.; *Int'l*, pg. 1035
BIO PAPPEL SCRIBE, S.A. DE C.V.—See Bio Pappel, S.A.B. de C.V.; *Int'l*, pg. 1035
BPM INC.; *U.S. Private*, pg. 629
BURGO GROUP S.P.A.; *Int'l*, pg. 1223
BURROWS NETHERLANDS B.V.—See Burrows Paper Corporation; *U.S. Private*, pg. 692
BURROWS PAPER CORPORATION; *U.S. Private*, pg. 692
CALIFORNIA COMMUNITY NEWS CORPORATION—See Tribune Publishing Company; *U.S. Private*, pg. 4227
CANADIAN FOREST PRODUCTS - PRINCE GEORGE PULP & PAPER MILLS—See Canfor Corporation; *Int'l*, pg. 1290
CANFOR EUROPE—See Canfor Corporation; *Int'l*, pg. 1291
CARTIERA LUCCHESE S.P.A.; *Int'l*, pg. 1348
CARTONAJES INTERNATIONAL S.L.—See International Paper Company; *U.S. Public*, pg. 1155
CARVAJAL PULPA Y PAPEL S.A.—See Carvajal S.A.; *Int'l*, pg. 1349
CASCADE EVAPORATOR COMPANY; *U.S. Private*, pg. 779
CASCADES ENVIROPAC ST-CESAIRE—See Cascades Inc.; *Int'l*, pg. 1350
CASCADES GROUPE TISSU - AGINCOURT & SCARBOROUGH—See Cascades Inc.; *Int'l*, pg. 1351
CASCADES LA ROCHETTE—See Cascades Inc.; *Int'l*, pg. 1350
CASCADES TENDERCO INC.—See Cascades Inc.; *Int'l*, pg. 1351
CASCADES TISSUE GROUP - LACHUTE—See Cascades Inc.; *Int'l*, pg. 1351
CASCADES TISSUE GROUP - NEW YORK INC.—See Cascades Inc.; *Int'l*, pg. 1351
CASCADES TISSUE GROUP - OREGON INC.—See Cascades Inc.; *Int'l*, pg. 1351
CASCADES TISSUE GROUP - PENNSYLVANIA INC. (PITTSTON)—See Cascades Inc.; *Int'l*, pg. 1351
CASCADES TISSUE GROUP - PENNSYLVANIA INC. (RANSOM)—See Cascades Inc.; *Int'l*, pg. 1351
CASCADES TISSUE GROUP - TENNESSEE INC.—See Cascades Inc.; *Int'l*, pg. 1351
CAS PAPER MILL CO.—See Charoen Aksorn Holding Group Co. Ltd.; *Int'l*, pg. 1451
CELEST PAPER KLIPPAN AB; *Int'l*, pg. 1392
CELHART DONARIS SA; *Int'l*, pg. 1392
CELLA SPACE LTD.; *Int'l*, pg. 1392
CELULOSE BEIRA INDUSTRIAL (CELBI), S.A.—See Altri, SGPS, S.A.; *Int'l*, pg. 398
CENTURY PAPER & BOARD MILLS LIMITED; *Int'l*, pg. 1419
CHAM PAPER GROUP SCHWEIZ AG—See Cham Group AG; *Int'l*, pg. 1439
CHAROEN AKSORN TRADING CO., LTD.—See Charoen Aksorn Holding Group Co. Ltd.; *Int'l*, pg. 1451
CHINA TOBACCO MAUDUIT (JIANGMEN) PAPER INDUSTRY COMPANY LTD.—See Mativ Holdings, Inc.; *U.S. Public*, pg. 1396
CMPC PAPELES S.A.—See Empresas CMPC S.A.; *Int'l*, pg. 2389
CONDAT SAS—See CVC Capital Partners SICAV-FIS S.A.; *Int'l*, pg. 1806
COPAMEX EMPAQUE, S.A. DE C.V.—See Corporativo Copamex, S.A. de C.V.; *Int'l*, pg. 1806

N.A.I.C.S. INDEX

322120 — PAPER MILLS

CORAL NEWSPRINTS LTD.; *Int'l*, pg. 1794
CRANE & CO., INC.—See Fedrigoni SpA; *Int'l*, pg. 2631
CUMBERLAND EUROPE LTD.—See Harbour Group Industries, Inc.; *U.S. Private*, pg. 1860
DAIO MILL SUPPORT CO., LTD.—See Daio Paper Corporation; *Int'l*, pg. 1939
DAIO PAPER CORPORATION; *Int'l*, pg. 1939
DAIO PULP & PAPER CO., LTD.—See Daio Paper Corporation; *Int'l*, pg. 1939
DANUBE INDUSTRIES LIMITED; *Int'l*, pg. 1969
DIAMOND PAPER CORPORATION—See Gould Paper Corporation; *U.S. Private*, pg. 1745
DONG HAI JOINT STOCK COMPANY; *Int'l*, pg. 2163
DOUBLE A ALIZAY—See Double A (1991) Public Company Limited; *Int'l*, pg. 2180
DOUBLE A INTERNATIONAL BUSINESS (BEIJING) CO., LTD.—See Double A (1991) Public Company Limited; *Int'l*, pg. 2180
DOUBLE A INTERNATIONAL BUSINESS (GUANGZHOU) CO., LTD.—See Double A (1991) Public Company Limited; *Int'l*, pg. 2180
DOUBLE A INTERNATIONAL BUSINESS KOREA LTD—See Double A (1991) Public Company Limited; *Int'l*, pg. 2181
DOUBLE A INTERNATIONAL BUSINESS (SHANGHAI) CO., LTD—See Double A (1991) Public Company Limited; *Int'l*, pg. 2181
DOUBLE A INTERNATIONAL HONG KONG LIMITED—See Double A (1991) Public Company Limited; *Int'l*, pg. 2181
DOUBLE A INTERNATIONAL NETWORK (AUSTRALIA) PTY LTD—See Double A (1991) Public Company Limited; *Int'l*, pg. 2181
DOUBLE A INTERNATIONAL NETWORK CO., LTD—See Double A (1991) Public Company Limited; *Int'l*, pg. 2181
DOUBLE A INTERNATIONAL NETWORK CO. (PRIVATE) LIMITED—See Double A (1991) Public Company Limited; *Int'l*, pg. 2181
DOUBLE A INTERNATIONAL NETWORK (M) SDN BHD—See Double A (1991) Public Company Limited; *Int'l*, pg. 2181
DOUBLE A INTERNATIONAL NETWORK (PHILIPPINES) INC.—See Double A (1991) Public Company Limited; *Int'l*, pg. 2181
DOUBLE A PULP AND PAPER COMPANY LIMITED—See Double A (1991) Public Company Limited; *Int'l*, pg. 2181
DOUBLE A SERBIA. DOUBLE A INTERNATIONAL NETWORK COMPANY LIMITED—See Double A (1991) Public Company Limited; *Int'l*, pg. 2181
DR. FRANZ FEURSTEIN GMBH—See delfortgroup AG; *Int'l*, pg. 2013
DUCART INTERNATIONAL PAPER, LTD.; *Int'l*, pg. 2223
DUNAFIN KFT.—See delfortgroup AG; *Int'l*, pg. 2013
DUNMORE CORPORATION/BREWSTER—See Steel Partners Holdings L.P.; *U.S. Public*, pg. 1942
DUNN PAPER, INC.—See Arbor Private Investment Company, LLC; *U.S. Private*, pg. 309
ELLEAIR PAPER CO., LTD.—See Daio Paper Corporation; *Int'l*, pg. 1940
ELLEAIR TEXEL CORPORATION—See Daio Paper Corporation; *Int'l*, pg. 1940
EMAMI PAPER MILLS LTD.—See Emami Ltd; *Int'l*, pg. 2374
EMPRESAS CMPC S.A.; *Int'l*, pg. 2389
ERVING INDUSTRIES, INC.; *U.S. Private*, pg. 1424
FELIX SCHOELLER JR SHANGHAI—See Felix Schoeller Holding GmbH & Co. KG; *Int'l*, pg. 2633
FELIX SCHOELLER NORTH AMERICA—See Felix Schoeller Holding GmbH & Co. KG; *Int'l*, pg. 2633
FELIX SCHOELLER SUPPLY CHAIN TECHNOLOGIES GMBH & CO. KG—See Felix Schoeller Holding GmbH & Co. KG; *Int'l*, pg. 2633
FF SOUCY WB L.P.—See Black Diamond Capital Holdings, LLC; *U.S. Private*, pg. 570
FINCH PAPER LLC—See Atlas Holdings, LLC; *U.S. Private*, pg. 376
FLAMBEAU RIVER PAPERS LLC; *U.S. Private*, pg. 1540
FLAMINGO PRODUCTS, INC.—See Erving Industries, Inc.; *U.S. Private*, pg. 1424
FLEX-PAK PACKAGING PRODUCTS, INC.—See Jacsten Holdings, LLC; *U.S. Private*, pg. 2181
FLYING PAPER INDUSTRIES LTD.—See FLYING CEMENT COMPANY LIMITED; *Int'l*, pg. 2716
FORTRESS GLOBAL ENTERPRISES INC.; *Int'l*, pg. 2740
FOSHAN HUAXIN PACKAGING CO., LTD.; *Int'l*, pg. 2748
FRENCH PAPER CO.—See Atlas Holdings, LLC; *U.S. Private*, pg. 376
GENERAL COMPANY FOR PAPER INDUSTRY (RAKTA)—See Chemical Industries Holding Company; *Int'l*, pg. 1462
GEORGIA-PACIFIC CORPORATION—See Koch Industries, Inc.; *U.S. Private*, pg. 2329
GEORGIA-PACIFIC CORPORATION—See Koch Industries, Inc.; *U.S. Private*, pg. 2329
GEORGIA-PACIFIC MUSKOGEE—See Koch Industries, Inc.; *U.S. Private*, pg. 2329
GEORGIA-PACIFIC PALATKA PULP & PAPER OPERATIONS—See Koch Industries, Inc.; *U.S. Private*, pg. 2328
GEORGIA-PACIFIC PAPER DIVISION—See Koch Industries, Inc.; *U.S. Private*, pg. 2328
GEORGIA PACIFIC PULP & PAPER MILL—See Koch Industries, Inc.; *U.S. Private*, pg. 2327
GEORGIA-PACIFIC PULP & PAPER MILL—See Koch Industries, Inc.; *U.S. Private*, pg. 2328
GEORGIA-PACIFIC PULP & PAPER MILL—See Koch Industries, Inc.; *U.S. Private*, pg. 2328
GEORGIA-PACIFIC PULP & PAPER MILL—See Koch Industries, Inc.; *U.S. Private*, pg. 2328
GEORGIA-PACIFIC PULP & PAPER MILL—See Koch Industries, Inc.; *U.S. Private*, pg. 2328
GEORGIA-PACIFIC SAW MILL—See Koch Industries, Inc.; *U.S. Private*, pg. 2328
GLATFELTER CAERPHILLY LTD.—See Glatfelter Corporation; *U.S. Public*, pg. 939
GLATFELTER CORPORATION; *U.S. Public*, pg. 939
GLATFELTER GERNSBACH GMBH—See Glatfelter Corporation; *U.S. Public*, pg. 939
GLATFELTER LYDNEY, LTD.—See Glatfelter Corporation; *U.S. Public*, pg. 939
GLATFELTER SCAER SAS—See Glatfelter Corporation; *U.S. Public*, pg. 939
GOULD PAPER CORP. - CHICAGO—See Gould Paper Corporation; *U.S. Private*, pg. 1745
GOULD PAPER CORP. - METRO—See Gould Paper Corporation; *U.S. Private*, pg. 1745
GRAPHIC PACKAGING INTERNATIONAL, INC. - WEST MONROE—See Graphic Packaging Holding Company; *U.S. Public*, pg. 959
HAMMERMILL PAPER—See International Paper Company; *U.S. Public*, pg. 1155
HANKUK PAPER MFG CO LTD - ONSAN PLANT—See Haesung Industrial Co., Ltd.; *Int'l*, pg. 3205
HANKUK PAPER MFG CO LTD—See Haesung Industrial Co., Ltd.; *Int'l*, pg. 3205
HANSOL PAPER CO., LTD.—See Hansol Group; *Int'l*, pg. 3260
HARTFORD CITY PAPER LLC; *U.S. Private*, pg. 1873
HI-DE LINERS, LLC—See Sole Source Capital LLC; *U.S. Private*, pg. 3708
HOKUETSU CORPORATION; *Int'l*, pg. 3443
HOKUETSU KISHU PAPER CO., LTD. - OSAKA MILL—See Hokuetsu Corporation; *Int'l*, pg. 3443
HOKUETSU KISHU SALES CO., LTD.—See Hokuetsu Corporation; *Int'l*, pg. 3443
HOKUETSU TOYO FIBRE CO., LTD.—See Hokuetsu Corporation; *Int'l*, pg. 3444
HOLMEN DATA AB—See Holmen AB; *Int'l*, pg. 3452
HOLMEN PAPER AB—See Holmen AB; *Int'l*, pg. 3452
HOLMEN PAPER MADRID S.L.—See Holmen AB; *Int'l*, pg. 3453
HOLMEN SKOG AB-IGGESUND—See Holmen AB; *Int'l*, pg. 3453
HOLMEN SKOG AB-LYCKSELE—See Holmen AB; *Int'l*, pg. 3453
HOLMEN SKOG AB-ORNSKOLDSVIK—See Holmen AB; *Int'l*, pg. 3453
HOLMEN SKOG AB-ROBERTSFORS—See Holmen AB; *Int'l*, pg. 3453
HUHTAMAKI CONSUMER PACKAGING—See Huhtamaki Oyj; *Int'l*, pg. 3526
HUNG HING PRINTING (HESHAN) COMPANY LIMITED—See Hung Hing Printing Group Limited; *Int'l*, pg. 3535
IBERPAPEL GESTION SA; *Int'l*, pg. 3574
ID INFO BUSINESS SERVICES LTD.; *Int'l*, pg. 3587
IGGESUND PAPER LTD—See Holmen AB; *Int'l*, pg. 3453
IGGESUNDS BRUK—See Holmen AB; *Int'l*, pg. 3453
INDUSTRIAS FORESTALES S.A.—See Empresas CMPC S.A.; *Int'l*, pg. 2390
INLAND EMPIRE PAPER COMPANY INC.—See Cowles Company; *U.S. Private*, pg. 1073
INNOVIOPAPERS BV—See American Industrial Acquisition Corporation; *U.S. Private*, pg. 237
INTERNATIONAL CELLULOSE CORP.—See Compagnie de Saint-Gobain SA; *Int'l*, pg. 1730
INTERNATIONAL PAPER APPM LIMITED—See International Paper Company; *U.S. Public*, pg. 1155
INTERNATIONAL PAPER CARTOVAR, S.A.—See International Paper Company; *U.S. Public*, pg. 1156
INTERNATIONAL PAPER CO. - MANSFIELD MILL—See International Paper Company; *U.S. Public*, pg. 1156
INTERNATIONAL PAPER COMPANY - AUGUSTA LUMBER MILL—See International Paper Company; *U.S. Public*, pg. 1157
INTERNATIONAL PAPER COMPANY (EUROPE) LIMITED—See International Paper Company; *U.S. Public*, pg. 1157
INTERNATIONAL PAPER COMPANY; *U.S. Public*, pg. 1155
INTERNATIONAL PAPER COMPANY—See International Paper Company; *U.S. Public*, pg. 1156
INTERNATIONAL PAPER COMPANY—See International Paper Company; *U.S. Public*, pg. 1156
INTERNATIONAL PAPER COMPANY—See International Paper Company; *U.S. Public*, pg. 1156
INTERNATIONAL PAPER COMPANY—See International Paper Company; *U.S. Public*, pg. 1156
INTERNATIONAL PAPER COMPANY—See International Paper Company; *U.S. Public*, pg. 1156
INTERNATIONAL PAPER COMPANY - STAMFORD—See International Paper Company; *U.S. Public*, pg. 1157
INTERNATIONAL PAPER CO. - SNOW HILL CHIP MILL—See International Paper Company; *U.S. Public*, pg. 1156
INTERNATIONAL PAPER CO. - TICONDEROGA MILL—See International Paper Company; *U.S. Public*, pg. 1156
INTERNATIONAL PAPER DO BRASIL LTDA.—See International Paper Company; *U.S. Public*, pg. 1157
INTERNATIONAL PAPER (EUROPE) S.A.—See International Paper Company; *U.S. Public*, pg. 1155
INTERNATIONAL PAPER ITALIA S.P.A.—See International Paper Company; *U.S. Public*, pg. 1157
INTERNATIONAL PAPER - KWIDZYN SP. Z O.O.—See International Paper Company; *U.S. Public*, pg. 1155
INTERNATIONAL PAPER MANUFACTURING AND DISTRIBUTION LTD.—See International Paper Company; *U.S. Public*, pg. 1157
INTERNATIONAL PAPER MONTBLANC, S.L.—See International Paper Company; *U.S. Public*, pg. 1157
INTERNATIONAL PAPER MONTERREY, S. DE R.L. DE C.V.—See International Paper Company; *U.S. Public*, pg. 1157
INTERNATIONAL PAPER SAINT-AMAND—See International Paper Company; *U.S. Public*, pg. 1157
INTERNATIONAL PAPER—See International Paper Company; *U.S. Public*, pg. 1155
INTERNATIONAL PAPER (UK) LIMITED—See International Paper Company; *U.S. Public*, pg. 1155
INTERNATIONAL PULP SALES COMPANY—See International Paper Company; *U.S. Public*, pg. 1157
INTERSTATE CONTAINER READING LLC—See Interstate Resources, Inc.; *U.S. Private*, pg. 2125
IPEK KAGIT SAN. VE TIC. A.S.—See Eczacibasi Holding A.S.; *Int'l*, pg. 2301
IP SINGAPORE HOLDING PTE. LTD.—See International Paper Company; *U.S. Public*, pg. 1155
KIMBERLY-CLARK AUSTRALIA PTY. LTD.—See Kimberly-Clark Corporation; *U.S. Public*, pg. 1229
KIMBERLY-CLARK CANADA INC.—See Kimberly-Clark Corporation; *U.S. Public*, pg. 1229
KIMBERLY-CLARK CENTRAL AMERICAN HOLDINGS, S.A.—See Kimberly-Clark Corporation; *U.S. Public*, pg. 1229
KIMBERLY-CLARK CORPORATION - NEENAH PAPER—See Kimberly-Clark Corporation; *U.S. Public*, pg. 1229
KIMBERLY-CLARK CORPORATION; *U.S. Public*, pg. 1228
KIMBERLY-CLARK CORPORATION—See Kimberly-Clark Corporation; *U.S. Public*, pg. 1229
KIMBERLY-CLARK CORPORATION—See Kimberly-Clark Corporation; *U.S. Public*, pg. 1229
KIMBERLY-CLARK CORPORATION—See Kimberly-Clark Corporation; *U.S. Public*, pg. 1229
KIMBERLY-CLARK CORPORATION—See Kimberly-Clark Corporation; *U.S. Public*, pg. 1229
KIMBERLY-CLARK CORPORATION—See Kimberly-Clark Corporation; *U.S. Public*, pg. 1229
KIMBERLY-CLARK CORPORATION—See Kimberly-Clark Corporation; *U.S. Public*, pg. 1229
KIMBERLY-CLARK CORPORATION—See Kimberly-Clark Corporation; *U.S. Public*, pg. 1229
KIMBERLY-CLARK CORPORATION—See Kimberly-Clark Corporation; *U.S. Public*, pg. 1230
KIMBERLY-CLARK CORPORATION—See Kimberly-Clark Corporation; *U.S. Public*, pg. 1230
KIMBERLY-CLARK CORPORATION—See Kimberly-Clark Corporation; *U.S. Public*, pg. 1230
KIMBERLY-CLARK GLOBAL SALES, LLC—See Kimberly-Clark Corporation; *U.S. Public*, pg. 1230
KIMBERLY-CLARK, INC.-HUNTSVILLE—See Kimberly-Clark Corporation; *U.S. Public*, pg. 1230
KIMBERLY-CLARK INTERNATIONAL SERVICES CORP.—See Kimberly-Clark Corporation; *U.S. Public*, pg. 1229
KIMBERLY-CLARK MANUFACTURING (THAILAND) LIMITED—See Kimberly-Clark Corporation; *U.S. Public*, pg. 1230
KIMBERLY-CLARK PUERTO RICO, INC.—See Kimberly-Clark Corporation; *U.S. Public*, pg. 1231
KIMBERLY-CLARK THAILAND LTD.—See Kimberly-Clark Corporation; *U.S. Public*, pg. 1230
KLIPPAN AB—See Celest Paper Klippan AB; *Int'l*, pg. 1392
KNOWLTON TECHNOLOGIES LLC—See Eastman Chemical Company; *U.S. Public*, pg. 705
KURTZ BROS., INC.; *U.S. Public*, pg. 2358
LEGION PAPER CORPORATION—See Gould Paper Corporation; *U.S. Private*, pg. 1745
LEOCZECH SPOL S.R.O—See Huhtamaki Oyj; *Int'l*, pg. 3525
LIBERTY PAPER, INC.—See Liberty Diversified International Inc.; *U.S. Private*, pg. 2443
LITTLE RAPIDS CORPORATION; *U.S. Private*, pg. 2469
LONGVIEW FIBRE PAPER AND PACKAGING, INC.—See WestRock Company; *U.S. Public*, pg. 2361
LPS INDUSTRIES INC.; *U.S. Private*, pg. 2507

3315

322120 — PAPER MILLS

LTR INDUSTRIES S.A.—See Mativ Holdings, Inc.; *U.S. Public*, pg. 1396
LUCART SAS—See Cartiera Lucchese S.p.A.; *Int'l*, pg. 1348
MARUBISHI PAPER TEC. CORPORATION—See Daio Paper Corporation; *Int'l*, pg. 1940
THE MASA CORPORATION; *U.S. Private*, pg. 4075
MATIV HOLDINGS, INC.; *U.S. Public*, pg. 1396
MATUSSIERE & FOREST S.A.—See MatlinPatterson Global Advisers LLC; *U.S. Private*, pg. 2611
MIDWEST PAPER GROUP—See Industrial Assets Corp.; *U.S. Private*, pg. 2064
MONADNOCK PAPER MILLS, INC.; *U.S. Private*, pg. 2768
NANNING QIAOHONG NEW MATERIALS CO., LTD.—See Guangxi Rural Investment Sugar Industry Group Co. Ltd; *Int'l*, pg. 3163
NEENAH COLDENHOVE BV—See Mativ Holdings, Inc.; *U.S. Public*, pg. 1396
NEENAH, INC.—See Mativ Holdings, Inc.; *U.S. Public*, pg. 1396
NEENAH PAPER MICHIGAN, INC.—See Mativ Holdings, Inc.; *U.S. Public*, pg. 1396
NEWTECH PULP INC.—See Glatfelter Corporation; *U.S. Public*, pg. 939
NEW TOP WIN CORPORATION SDN. BHD.—See Hengan International Group Co. Ltd.; *Int'l*, pg. 3346
NEXTIER SOLUTIONS CORPORATION—See Billerud AB; *Int'l*, pg. 1030
NICE-PAK PRODUCTS, INC.; *U.S. Private*, pg. 2925
NORKOL CONVERTING CORPORATION; *U.S. Private*, pg. 2938
NORSKE SKOG JAMTLAND AB—See FriaSkog AB; *Int'l*, pg. 2791
NORTH PACIFIC PAPER COMPANY, LLC—See One Rock Capital Partners, LLC; *U.S. Private*, pg. 3022
ONYX SPECIALTY PAPERS, INC.; *U.S. Private*, pg. 3028
OP PAPIRNA, S.R.O.—See delfortgroup AG; *Int'l*, pg. 2013
ORCHIDS PAPER PRODUCTS COMPANY—See Cascades Inc.; *Int'l*, pg. 1351
PABCO BUILDING PRODUCTS, LLC - PABCO PAPER DIVISION—See Pacific Coast Building Products, Inc.; *U.S. Private*, pg. 3066
PACIFIC PULP MOLDING, INC—See Altamont Capital Partners; *U.S. Private*, pg. 205
PAPELERA DE CHIHUAHUA, S.A. DE C.V.—See Corporativo Copamex, S.A. de C.V.; *Int'l*, pg. 1806
PAPELERA GUIPUZCOANA DE ZICUNAGA, S.A.—See Iberpapel Gestion SA; *Int'l*, pg. 3574
PAPELERA MEXICANA SA DE CV, INDUSTRIAL—See Corporativo Copamex, S.A. de C.V.; *Int'l*, pg. 1806
PAPELES CORDILLERA SPA—See Empresas CMPC S.A.; *Int'l*, pg. 2389
PAPEL PRENSA S.A.I.C.F. Y DE M.—See Grupo Clarin S.A.; *Int'l*, pg. 3124
PAPETERIES DE MALAUCENE S.A.S.—See Mativ Holdings, Inc.; *U.S. Public*, pg. 1396
PAPETERIES DE SAINT-GIRONS S.A.S.—See Mativ Holdings, Inc.; *U.S. Public*, pg. 1396
PAPIERFABRIK WATTENS GMBH & CO. KG—See delfortgroup AG; *Int'l*, pg. 2013
PAPIER MASSON WB L.P.—See Black Diamond Capital Holdings, LLC; *U.S. Private*, pg. 570
PARENCO B.V.—See H2 Equity Partners B.V.; *Int'l*, pg. 3199
PERLEN PAPIER AG—See CPH Chemie + Papier Holding AG; *Int'l*, pg. 1824
PIXELLE ANDROSCOGGIN LLC—See Goldberg Lindsay & Co., LLC; *U.S. Private*, pg. 1729
PIXELLE SPECIALTY SOLUTIONS LLC—See Goldberg Lindsay & Co., LLC; *U.S. Private*, pg. 1729
PLYMKRAFT, INC.—See Unicord Corporation; *U.S. Private*, pg. 4282
PT AHLSTROM INDONESIA—See Ahlstrom Capital Oy; *Int'l*, pg. 223
PT AHLSTROM INDONESIA—See Bain Capital, LP; *U.S. Private*, pg. 429
R.D.M. OVARO—See Apollo Global Management, Inc.; *U.S. Public*, pg. 159
RENO DE MEDICI BLENDECQUES—See Apollo Global Management, Inc.; *U.S. Public*, pg. 159
RENO DE MEDICI SANTA GIUSTINA—See Apollo Global Management, Inc.; *U.S. Public*, pg. 159
ROLLAND ENTERPRISES INC.—See H.I.G. Capital, LLC; *U.S. Private*, pg. 1831
SAINT-GIRONS INDUSTRIES S.N.C.—See Mativ Holdings, Inc.; *U.S. Public*, pg. 1396
SCHNEIDER DOWNS & CO.—See Schneider Downs & Co., Inc.; *U.S. Private*, pg. 3566
SCHOELLER INDIA INDUSTRIES PVT. LTD.—See Felix Schoeller Holding GmbH & Co. KG; *Int'l*, pg. 2633
SCHOELLER INDUSTRIES—See Empteezy Ltd; *Int'l*, pg. 2392
SCHOELLER TECHNOCELL GMBH & CO. KG—See Felix Schoeller Holding GmbH & Co. KG; *Int'l*, pg. 2633
SCHWEITZER-MAUDUIT CANADA, INC.—See Mativ Holdings, Inc.; *U.S. Public*, pg. 1397
SEAMAN PAPER COMPANY OF MASSACHUSETTS INC.; *U.S. Private*, pg. 3585
SEHA CORPORATION—See Haesung Industrial Co., Ltd.; *Int'l*, pg. 3205

SERVICES PLUS, INC.—See Kimberly-Clark Corporation; *U.S. Public*, pg. 1230
SHUAIBA INDUSTRIAL COMPANY K.S.C.C.—See Al-Safwa Group Holding Co. K.P.S.C.; *Int'l*, pg. 288
SINGLE SOURCE PACKAGING CO. LLC.; *U.S. Private*, pg. 3670
SOCIETE MARTINIQUAISE DE CARTON ONDULE—See International Paper Company; *U.S. Public*, pg. 1158
SOUTHWORTH COMPANY INC.; *U.S. Private*, pg. 3742
SPECIALTY PACKAGING, INC.—See The Pritzker Group - Chicago, LLC; *U.S. Private*, pg. 4099
STADACONA WB L.P.—See Black Diamond Capital Holdings, LLC; *U.S. Private*, pg. 570
STAR PAPER INTERNATIONAL CO., LTD.—See Charoen Aksorn Holding Group Co. Ltd.; *Int'l*, pg. 1451
STRATHMORE ARTIST PAPERS—See F.I.L.A. - Fabbrica Italiana Lapis ed Affini S.p.A.; *Int'l*, pg. 2596
SYLVAMO CORPORATION; *U.S. Public*, pg. 1969
TECHNOCELL DEKOR SHANGHAI—See Felix Schoeller Holding GmbH & Co. KG; *Int'l*, pg. 2633
TECHNOCELL DEKOR USA—See Felix Schoeller Holding GmbH & Co. KG; *Int'l*, pg. 2633
TECHNOCELL INC.—See Felix Schoeller Holding GmbH & Co. KG; *Int'l*, pg. 2633
TERVAKOSKI OY—See delfortgroup AG; *Int'l*, pg. 2013
THAI UNITED AWA PAPER CO., LTD.—See Awa Paper & Technological Company Inc.; *Int'l*, pg. 751
TROY LAMINATING & COATING, INC.—See Chargeurs SA; *Int'l*, pg. 1449
TSG INC.; *U.S. Private*, pg. 4253
TST/IMPRESO, INC.—See Impreso, Inc.; *U.S. Public*, pg. 1114
TWIN RIVERS PAPER COMPANY; *U.S. Private*, pg. 4266
TWINSAVER GROUP—See TRG Management LP; *U.S. Private*, pg. 4220
UNICELL HOLDINGS INC.; *U.S. Private*, pg. 4281
UPM-KYMMENE (AUSTRIA) GMBH—See Heinzel Holding GmbH; *Int'l*, pg. 3325
UPM-KYMMENE (AUSTRIA) GMBH - STEYRERMUHL PAPER MILL—See Heinzel Holding GmbH; *Int'l*, pg. 3325
VERITIV DISTRIBUTION GROUP—See Clayton, Dubilier & Rice, LLC; *U.S. Private*, pg. 929
VERSO BUCKSPORT LLC—See Billerud AB; *Int'l*, pg. 1030
VERSO CORPORATION - ESCANABA MILL—See Billerud AB; *Int'l*, pg. 1030
VERSO CORPORATION - LUKE MILL—See Billerud AB; *Int'l*, pg. 1030
VERSO CORPORATION - STEVENS POINT MILL—See Goldberg Lindsay & Co., LLC; *U.S. Private*, pg. 1729
VERSO CORPORATION - WISCONSIN RAPIDS MILL—See Billerud AB; *Int'l*, pg. 1030
VERSO MAINE ENERGY LLC—See Billerud AB; *Int'l*, pg. 1030
VERSO PAPER LLC—See Billerud AB; *Int'l*, pg. 1030
VERSO QUINNESEC LLC—See Billerud AB; *Int'l*, pg. 1030
VERSO QUINNESEC REP LLC—See Billerud AB; *Int'l*, pg. 1030
VOITH IHI PAPER TECHNOLOGY CO., LTD.—See IHI Corporation; *Int'l*, pg. 3606
WATTENS VIETNAM CO. LTD.—See delfortgroup AG; *Int'l*, pg. 2013
WESTROCK RKT CO. - TACOMA MILL—See WestRock Company; *U.S. Public*, pg. 2363
WINBON SCHOELLER NEW MATERIALS CO., LTD.—See Felix Schoeller Holding GmbH & Co. KG; *Int'l*, pg. 2633
ZHANGJIAGANG CO., LTD.—See Haesung Industrial Co., Ltd.; *Int'l*, pg. 3205
ZIMMERLUND & CO.—See Amcor plc; *Int'l*, pg. 418

322130 — PAPERBOARD MILLS

ACCURATE BOX COMPANY, INC.; *U.S. Private*, pg. 55
AMERICRAFT CARTON GROUP, INC.—See Americraft Carton, Inc.; *U.S. Private*, pg. 259
ARTISTIC CARTON COMPANY—See Graphic Packaging Holding Company; *U.S. Public*, pg. 958
ASTRON PAPER & BOARD MILL LIMITED; *Int'l*, pg. 662
BARCELONA CARTONBOARD, S.A.U.—See Apollo Global Management, Inc.; *U.S. Public*, pg. 159
BAYCORR PACKAGING INCORPORATED—See Pioneer Packing Inc.; *U.S. Private*, pg. 3187
BILLERUD BEETHAM LTD—See Billerud AB; *Int'l*, pg. 1030
BILLERUD KARLSBORG AB—See Billerud AB; *Int'l*, pg. 1030
BILLERUD SKARBLACKA AB—See Billerud AB; *Int'l*, pg. 1030
BIO GREEN PAPERS LIMITED - SRIKAKULAM FACILITY—See Bio Green Papers Limited; *Int'l*, pg. 1035
BONG SVERIGE AB—See Bong AB; *Int'l*, pg. 1107
CARAUSTAR INDUSTRIES, INC. - BUCYRUS CONTRACT PACKAGING PLANT—See Greif Inc.; *U.S. Public*, pg. 966
CARAUSTAR INDUSTRIES, INC. - BURLINGTON RIGID BOX PLANT—See Greif Inc.; *U.S. Public*, pg. 966
CARAUSTAR INDUSTRIES, INC. - HARDEEVILLE RECYCLING PLANT—See Greif Inc.; *U.S. Public*, pg. 966
CARAUSTAR INDUSTRIES, INC. - ROCK HILL PLANT—See Greif Inc.; *U.S. Public*, pg. 966
CARAUSTAR INDUSTRIES, INC.—See Greif Inc.; *U.S. Public*, pg. 965
CARAUSTAR INDUSTRIES, INC. - TEXARKANA RECYCLING PLANT—See Greif Inc.; *U.S. Public*, pg. 966
CARAUSTAR INDUSTRIES—See Greif Inc.; *U.S. Public*, pg. 965
CARAUSTAR RECOVERED FIBER GROUP, INC.—See Greif Inc.; *U.S. Public*, pg. 966
CARAUSTAR RECYCLING PLANT—See Greif Inc.; *U.S. Public*, pg. 966
CARTIERE DEL GARDA SPA—See CVC Capital Partners SICAV-FIS S.A.; *Int'l*, pg. 1888
CASCADES BOXBOARD GROUP INC. - EAST ANGUS—See Cascades Inc.; *Int'l*, pg. 1350
CASCADES BOXBOARD GROUP INC. - LACHUTE—See Cascades Inc.; *Int'l*, pg. 1350
CASCADES BOXBOARD GROUP INC.—See Cascades Inc.; *Int'l*, pg. 1350
CASCADES CONVERSION, INC.—See Cascades Inc.; *Int'l*, pg. 1350
CASCADES EAST ANGUS, INC.—See Cascades Inc.; *Int'l*, pg. 1350
CASCADES FORMA-PAK, INC.—See Cascades Inc.; *Int'l*, pg. 1350
CASCADES GROUPE CARTON PLAT JONQUIERE—See Cascades Inc.; *Int'l*, pg. 1350
CASCADES INOPAK—See Cascades Inc.; *Int'l*, pg. 1350
CASCADES LUPEL, INC.—See Cascades Inc.; *Int'l*, pg. 1350
CASCADES MULTI-PRO, INC.—See Cascades Inc.; *Int'l*, pg. 1350
CASCADES PAPIER KINGSEY FALLS—See Cascades Inc.; *Int'l*, pg. 1350
CASCADES S.A.S.—See Cascades Inc.; *Int'l*, pg. 1350
CASCADES TISSUE GROUP - KINGSEY FALLS—See Cascades Inc.; *Int'l*, pg. 1351
CASCADES TISSUE GROUP—See Cascades Inc.; *Int'l*, pg. 1351
CHINA HUAJUN GROUP LIMITED; *Int'l*, pg. 1508
CINCINNATI PAPERBOARD—See Greif Inc.; *U.S. Public*, pg. 966
COLUMBUS RECYCLING PLANT—See Greif Inc.; *U.S. Public*, pg. 966
COME SURE GROUP (HOLDINGS) LIMITED; *Int'l*, pg. 1710
CONITEX-SONOCO—See Sonoco Products Company; *U.S. Public*, pg. 1906
COPAMEX CORRUGADOS, S.A. DE C.V.—See Corporativo Copamex, S.A. de C.V.; *Int'l*, pg. 1806
CORENSO NORTH AMERICA LLC—See Sonoco Products Company; *U.S. Public*, pg. 1904
COSBOARD INDUSTRIES LIMITED.; *Int'l*, pg. 1809
CRESCENT FIBRES LIMITED; *Int'l*, pg. 1839
DAEYANG PAPER MFG. CO., LTD.; *Int'l*, pg. 1911
EGGER BARONY LTD.—See Fritz Egger GmbH & Co.; *Int'l*, pg. 2793
EK SUCCESS LTD.—See GTCR LLC; *U.S. Private*, pg. 1806
ENVASES IMPRESOS S.A.—See Empresas CMPC S.A.; *Int'l*, pg. 2390
EXACTA PACKAGING DESIGNS, INC.; *U.S. Private*, pg. 1445
FIBERMARK INC.—See American Securities LLC; *U.S. Private*, pg. 248
FIBERMARK—See American Securities LLC; *U.S. Private*, pg. 248
FIELD CONTAINER QUERETARO (USA), L.L.C.—See Graphic Packaging Holding Company; *U.S. Public*, pg. 958
FIRST CLASS PACKAGING, INC.—See Larson Packaging Company, LLC; *U.S. Private*, pg. 2394
FISKEBY BOARD AB—See Fiskeby International Holding AB; *Int'l*, pg. 2695
FUJIAN QINGSHAN PAPER INDUSTRY CO., LTD.; *Int'l*, pg. 2819
FUSION PAPERBOARD - PAPER MILL—See OpenGate Capital Management, LLC; *U.S. Private*, pg. 3030
GANGA PAPERS INDIA LIMITED; *Int'l*, pg. 2880
GENTING SANYEN PAPERBOARD SDN BHD—See Genting Berhad; *Int'l*, pg. 2929
GLEASON INDUSTRIES, INC.; *U.S. Private*, pg. 1708
GL&V RUSSIA—See GL&V Pulp & Paper; *Int'l*, pg. 2986
GRAFOPROMET A.D.; *Int'l*, pg. 3050
GREEN BAY PACKAGING INC.; *U.S. Private*, pg. 1771
HAI PHONG HOANG HA PAPER JOINT STOCK COMPANY; *Int'l*, pg. 3209
HAKKANI PAPER & BOARD MILLS (PVT.) LTD.—See Hakkani Group; *Int'l*, pg. 3219
HANKUK PACKAGE CO., LTD.; *Int'l*, pg. 3254
HARTA PACKAGING INDUSTRIES (MALACCA) SDN. BHD.—See HPI Resources Berhad; *Int'l*, pg. 3500
HATILLO PAPER BOARD CORP.—See Borinquen Container Corp.; *U.S. Private*, pg. 618
HEIDELBERG POSTPRESS DEUTSCHLAND GMBH—See Heidelberger Druckmaschinen AG; *Int'l*, pg. 3321
HONGBO CO., LTD.; *Int'l*, pg. 3469

N.A.I.C.S. INDEX
322211 — CORRUGATED AND SOLI...

HONG WEI (ASIA) HOLDINGS COMPANY LIMITED; *Int'l*, pg. 3469
HOP FUNG GROUP HOLDINGS LTD; *Int'l*, pg. 3472
IGGESUND PAPERBOARD AB—See Holmen AB; *Int'l*, pg. 3453
IGGESUND PAPERBOARD ASIA PTE LTD—See Holmen AB; *Int'l*, pg. 3453
IGGESUND PAPERBOARD (WORKINGTON) LTD.—See Holmen AB; *Int'l*, pg. 3453
INTERNATIONAL PAPER ASIA LIMITED—See International Paper Company; *U.S. Public*, pg. 1155
INTERNATIONAL PAPER COMPANY - RIEGELWOOD MILL—See International Paper Company; *U.S. Public*, pg. 1157
INTERNATIONAL PAPER COMPANY—See International Paper Company; *U.S. Public*, pg. 1156
INTERNATIONAL PAPER COMPANY—See International Paper Company; *U.S. Public*, pg. 1156
INTERNATIONAL PAPER COMPANY—See International Paper Company; *U.S. Public*, pg. 1156
INTERNATIONAL PAPER COMPANY—See International Paper Company; *U.S. Public*, pg. 1156
INTERNATIONAL PAPER COMPANY - SPRINGHILL CONTAINER—See International Paper Company; *U.S. Public*, pg. 1157
INTERNATIONAL PAPER & SUN CARTONBOARD CO., LTD.—See International Paper Company; *U.S. Public*, pg. 1155
INTERSTATE PAPER LLC—See Interstate Resources, Inc.; *U.S. Private*, pg. 2125
INTERSTATE RESOURCES, INC.; *U.S. Private*, pg. 2125
ITW V.A.C. B.V.—See Illinois Tool Works Inc.; *U.S. Public*, pg. 1108
KAPSTONE CHARLESTON KRAFT, LLC—See WestRock Company; *U.S. Public*, pg. 2361
KAPSTONE KRAFT PAPER CORPORATION—See WestRock Company; *U.S. Public*, pg. 2361
KEYSTONE PAPER & BOX COMPANY, INC.—See Great Mill Rock LLC; *U.S. Private*, pg. 1766
KINGSEY COGENERATION—See Boralex Inc.; *Int'l*, pg. 1112
KORSNAS AB—See Billerud AB; *Int'l*, pg. 1030
LUDOWICI PACKAGING AUSTRALIA PTY LIMITED—See FLSmidth & Co. A/S; *Int'l*, pg. 2711
MAFCOTE INDUSTRIES INC.; *U.S. Private*, pg. 2545
MALNOVE INCORPORATED OF FLORIDA—See Malnove Incorporated; *U.S. Private*, pg. 2558
MALNOVE INCORPORATED OF UTAH—See Malnove Incorporated; *U.S. Private*, pg. 2558
MANCHESTER INDUSTRIES, INC. OF VIRGINIA—See Clearwater Paper Corporation; *U.S. Public*, pg. 513
MASISA S.A.—See GrupoNueva S.A.; *Int'l*, pg. 3139
MAT NUWOOD, LLC.—See Ancor Holdings, L.P.; *U.S. Private*, pg. 275
MELE COMPANIES, INC.; *U.S. Private*, pg. 2662
MENASHA CORPORATION; *U.S. Private*, pg. 2665
MENASHA PACKAGING COMPANY, LLC - CINCINNATI FACILITY—See Menasha Corporation; *U.S. Private*, pg. 2665
MENASHA PACKAGING COMPANY, LLC - FANFOLD PLANT—See Menasha Corporation; *U.S. Private*, pg. 2665
MENASHA PACKAGING COMPANY, LLC - YUKON PLANT—See Menasha Corporation; *U.S. Private*, pg. 2665
MODERN ALPINE SDN. BHD.—See Hengan International Group Co. Ltd.; *Int'l*, pg. 3346
MULTI-WALL PACKAGING CORP.—See Illinois Tool Works Inc.; *U.S. Public*, pg. 1109
NEW-INDY CONTAINERBOARD LLC—See Schwarz Partners, LP; *U.S. Private*, pg. 3572
NEW-INDY CONTAINERBOARD LLC—See The Kraft Group LLC; *U.S. Private*, pg. 4066
NORAMPAC INC. - DRUMMONDVILLE—See Cascades Inc.; *Int'l*, pg. 1350
NORAMPAC INC. - VAUDREUIL—See Cascades Inc.; *Int'l*, pg. 1350
NORAMPAC INDUSTRIES INC.—See Cascades Inc.; *Int'l*, pg. 1350
OX PAPERBOARD LLC—See Ox Paper Tube & Core, Inc.; *U.S. Private*, pg. 3056
PAPERWORKS INDUSTRIES, INC. - PHILADELPHIA MILL—See Sun Capital Partners, Inc.; *U.S. Private*, pg. 3860
PAPERWORKS INDUSTRIES, INC. - RICHMOND PLANT—See Sun Capital Partners, Inc.; *U.S. Private*, pg. 3860
PAPERWORKS INDUSTRIES, INC.—See Sun Capital Partners, Inc.; *U.S. Private*, pg. 3860
PAPERWORKS INDUSTRIES, INC. - WABASH MILL—See Sun Capital Partners, Inc.; *U.S. Private*, pg. 3860
PLASTIQUES CASCADES, INC.—See Cascades Inc.; *Int'l*, pg. 1350
PRESSED PAPERBOARD TECHNOLOGIES, LLC—See May River Capital, LLC; *U.S. Private*, pg. 2620
RAPID DISPLAYS, INC.—See Gemspring Capital Management, LLC; *U.S. Private*, pg. 1659

R.D.M ARNSBERG GMBH—See Cascades Inc.; *Int'l*, pg. 1351
R.D.M BARCELONA CARTONBOARD S.A.—See Cascades Inc.; *Int'l*, pg. 1351
REPUBLIC PAPERBOARD COMPANY LLC—See Eagle Materials Inc.; *U.S. Public*, pg. 702
RTS EMBALAJES DE ARGENTINA SA—See Sonoco Products Company; *U.S. Public*, pg. 1905
RTS EMPAQUES, S. DE R.L. DE CV—See Sonoco Products Company; *U.S. Public*, pg. 1905
RTS PACKAGING - ORANGE—See Sonoco Products Company; *U.S. Public*, pg. 1905
SONOCO-ALCORE OY—See Sonoco Products Company; *U.S. Public*, pg. 1909
SONOCO-ALCORE SP. Z.O.O.—See Sonoco Products Company; *U.S. Public*, pg. 1909
SONOCO BAKER—See Sonoco Products Company; *U.S. Public*, pg. 1908
SONOCO CANADA CORPORATION—See Sonoco Products Company; *U.S. Public*, pg. 1905
SONOCO CANADA CORPORATION—See Sonoco Products Company; *U.S. Public*, pg. 1905
SONOCO CANADA CORPORATION—See Sonoco Products Company; *U.S. Public*, pg. 1905
SONOCO CANADA CORPORATION—See Sonoco Products Company; *U.S. Public*, pg. 1905
SONOCO CANADA CORPORATION—See Sonoco Products Company; *U.S. Public*, pg. 1905
SONOCO CANADA CORPORATION—See Sonoco Products Company; *U.S. Public*, pg. 1905
SONOCO CANADA CORPORATION—See Sonoco Products Company; *U.S. Public*, pg. 1905
SONOCO CONSUMER PRODUCTS DORDRECHT B.V.—See Sonoco Products Company; *U.S. Public*, pg. 1906
SONOCO CONSUMER PRODUCTS EUROPE GMBH—See Sonoco Products Company; *U.S. Public*, pg. 1906
SONOCO CONSUMER PRODUCTS LTD.—See Sonoco Products Company; *U.S. Public*, pg. 1906
SONOCO CONSUMER PRODUCTS MECHELEN BVBA—See Sonoco Products Company; *U.S. Public*, pg. 1906
SONOCO CONSUMER PRODUCTS MONTANAY SAS—See Sonoco Products Company; *U.S. Public*, pg. 1906
SONOCO DE MEXICO, S.A. DE C.V.—See Sonoco Products Company; *U.S. Public*, pg. 1908
SONOCO DE MEXICO, S.A. DE C.V.—See Sonoco Products Company; *U.S. Public*, pg. 1908
SONOCO DO BRAZIL LTDA.—See Sonoco Products Company; *U.S. Public*, pg. 1908
SONOCO DO BRAZIL LTDA.—See Sonoco Products Company; *U.S. Public*, pg. 1908
SONOCO FLEXIBLE PACKAGING LIMITED—See Sonoco Products Company; *U.S. Public*, pg. 1906
SONOCO FLEXIBLE PACKAGING—See Sonoco Products Company; *U.S. Public*, pg. 1906
SONOCO HUTCHINSON, LLC—See Sonoco Products Company; *U.S. Public*, pg. 1906
SONOCO INTERNATIONAL, INC.—See Sonoco Products Company; *U.S. Public*, pg. 1905
SONOCO IPD FRANCE S.A.—See Sonoco Products Company; *U.S. Public*, pg. 1906
SONOCO MACHINERY INC.—See Sonoco Products Company; *U.S. Public*, pg. 1905
SONOCO PAPERBOARD SPECIALTIES—See Sonoco Products Company; *U.S. Public*, pg. 1907
SONOCO PAPER—See Sonoco Products Company; *U.S. Public*, pg. 1907
SONOCO PINA S.A.—See Sonoco Products Company; *U.S. Public*, pg. 1906
SONOCO PRODUCTS COMPANY - I.P.D. DIVISION—See Sonoco Products Company; *U.S. Public*, pg. 1908
SONOCO PRODUCTS COMPANY; *U.S. Public*, pg. 1904
SONOCO PRODUCTS COMPANY—See Sonoco Products Company; *U.S. Public*, pg. 1907
SONOCO PRODUCTS COMPANY—See Sonoco Products Company; *U.S. Public*, pg. 1907
SONOCO PRODUCTS COMPANY—See Sonoco Products Company; *U.S. Public*, pg. 1907
SONOCO PRODUCTS COMPANY—See Sonoco Products Company; *U.S. Public*, pg. 1907
SONOCO PRODUCTS COMPANY—See Sonoco Products Company; *U.S. Public*, pg. 1907
SONOCO PRODUCTS COMPANY—See Sonoco Products Company; *U.S. Public*, pg. 1907
SONOCO PRODUCTS COMPANY—See Sonoco Products Company; *U.S. Public*, pg. 1907
SONOCO PRODUCTS COMPANY—See Sonoco Products Company; *U.S. Public*, pg. 1907
SONOCO PRODUCTS COMPANY—See Sonoco Products Company; *U.S. Public*, pg. 1907

Company; *U.S. Public*, pg. 1907
SONOCO PRODUCTS COMPANY—See Sonoco Products Company; *U.S. Public*, pg. 1907
SONOCO PRODUCTS COMPANY—See Sonoco Products Company; *U.S. Public*, pg. 1907
SONOCO PRODUCTS COMPANY—See Sonoco Products Company; *U.S. Public*, pg. 1908
SONOCO PRODUCTS COMPANY—See Sonoco Products Company; *U.S. Public*, pg. 1908
SONOCO PRODUCTS COMPANY—See Sonoco Products Company; *U.S. Public*, pg. 1908
SONOCO PRODUCTS COMPANY—See Sonoco Products Company; *U.S. Public*, pg. 1908
SONOCO PRODUCTS COMPANY—See Sonoco Products Company; *U.S. Public*, pg. 1908
SONOCO PRODUCTS COMPANY—See Sonoco Products Company; *U.S. Public*, pg. 1908
SONOCO PRODUCTS COMPANY—See Sonoco Products Company; *U.S. Public*, pg. 1908
SONOCO RECYCLING—See Sonoco Products Company; *U.S. Public*, pg. 1907
SONOCO, S.A. DE C.V.—See Sonoco Products Company; *U.S. Public*, pg. 1908
SOUTHEASTERN PAPERBOARD INC.; *U.S. Private*, pg. 3728
SOUTHEASTERN PAPERBOARD INC.—See Southeastern Paperboard Inc.; *U.S. Private*, pg. 3728
SOUTH GAIN ENTERPRISES LIMITED—See Hung Hing Printing Group Limited; *Int'l*, pg. 3535
SPC CAPITAL MANAGEMENT, INC.—See Sonoco Products Company; *U.S. Public*, pg. 1905
SPC MANAGEMENT, INC.—See Sonoco Products Company; *U.S. Public*, pg. 1905
SULPACO WEST—See Sullivan Paper Company; *U.S. Private*, pg. 3851
SUNSHINE PAPER LLC; *U.S. Private*, pg. 3872
SUPERIOR PACKAGING SOLUTIONS; *U.S. Private*, pg. 3879
TEMPLE-INLAND INC.—See International Paper Company; *U.S. Public*, pg. 1158
UNIQUE-PRESCOTECH, INC.—See Taglich Private Equity LLC; *U.S. Private*, pg. 3922
UNITED CORRSTACK LLC—See Interstate Resources, Inc.; *U.S. Private*, pg. 2125
UNITED STATES BOX CORP.; *U.S. Private*, pg. 4298
U.S. PAPER MILLS CORP.—See Sonoco Products Company; *U.S. Public*, pg. 1909
WESTROCK CO. - COVINGTON—See WestRock Company; *U.S. Public*, pg. 2362
WESTROCK CO. - EVADALE MILL—See WestRock Company; *U.S. Public*, pg. 2362
WESTROCK CO. - MAHRT MILL - COTTONTON—See WestRock Company; *U.S. Public*, pg. 2362
WESTROCK CONVERTING COMPANY—See WestRock Company; *U.S. Public*, pg. 2363
WESTROCK MILL COMPANY, LLC—See WestRock Company; *U.S. Public*, pg. 2363
WESTROCK MWV, LLC—See WestRock Company; *U.S. Public*, pg. 2362
WHITE PIGEON PAPER COMPANY—See Graphic Packaging Holding Company; *U.S. Public*, pg. 958

322211 — CORRUGATED AND SOLID FIBER BOX MANUFACTURING

ABEX DISPLAY SYSTEMS; *U.S. Private*, pg. 38
ACORN PAPER PRODUCTS COMPANY—See Oak Paper Products Co. Inc.; *U.S. Private*, pg. 2984
ACTION BOX COMPANY INC.; *U.S. Private*, pg. 67
ADVANCE PACKAGING CORPORATION; *U.S. Private*, pg. 84
ADVANCE PAPER BOX COMPANY; *U.S. Private*, pg. 84
AG-BOX CO; *U.S. Private*, pg. 125
AHLSTROM-MUNKSJO CHIRNSIDE LTD.—See Ahlstrom Capital Oy; *Int'l*, pg. 224
AHLSTROM-MUNKSJO CHIRNSIDE LTD.—See Bain Capital, LP; *U.S. Private*, pg. 429
AHLSTROM-MUNKSJO ITALIA S.P.A.—See Ahlstrom Capital Oy; *Int'l*, pg. 224
AHLSTROM-MUNKSJO ITALIA S.P.A.—See Bain Capital, LP; *U.S. Private*, pg. 429
AHLSTROM-MUNKSJO KOREA CO., LTD.—See Ahlstrom Capital Oy; *Int'l*, pg. 223
AHLSTROM-MUNKSJO KOREA CO., LTD.—See Bain Capital, LP; *U.S. Private*, pg. 429
AHLSTROM-MUNKSJO STALLDALEN AB—See Ahlstrom Capital Oy; *Int'l*, pg. 224
AHLSTROM-MUNKSJO STALLDALEN AB—See Bain Capital, LP; *U.S. Private*, pg. 430
AKERS PACKAGING SERVICE INC.; *U.S. Private*, pg. 145
ALBAAD DEUTSCHLAND GMBH—See Albaad Massuot Yitzhak Ltd.; *Int'l*, pg. 293
ALLIANCE PACKAGING-BEAVERTON DIVISION—See Alliance Packaging LLC; *U.S. Private*, pg. 184
ALLIANCE PACKAGING LLC; *U.S. Private*, pg. 184
ALLIANCE PACKAGING-SEATTLE CORRUGATED

322211 — CORRUGATED AND SOLI...

DIVISION—See Alliance Packaging LLC; *U.S. Private,* pg. 184
ALL SIZE CORRUGATED—See Buckeye Corrugated Inc.; *U.S. Private,* pg. 677
ALPHA PACKAGING INC.; *U.S. Private,* pg. 199
ALTEX PACKAGING, INC.; *U.S. Private,* pg. 208
AMERICAN CORRUGATED PRODUCTS, INC.—See Welch Packaging Group, Inc.; *U.S. Private,* pg. 4473
AMERICAN PACKAGING CORPORATION—See American Packaging Corporation; *U.S. Private,* pg. 242
AMERICAN RIVER-PACKAGEONE INC.; *U.S. Private,* pg. 246
ANUROOP PACKAGING LIMITED; *Int'l,* pg. 486
A&R CARTON AB—See CVC Capital Partners SICAV-FIS S.A.; *Int'l,* pg. 1881
A&R CARTON A/S—See CVC Capital Partners SICAV-FIS S.A.; *Int'l,* pg. 1881
A&R CARTON CDF SA—See CVC Capital Partners SICAV-FIS S.A.; *Int'l,* pg. 1881
A&R CARTON LUND AB—See CVC Capital Partners SICAV-FIS S.A.; *Int'l,* pg. 1881
A&R CARTON NORTH AMERICA INC.—See CVC Capital Partners SICAV-FIS S.A.; *Int'l,* pg. 1881
A&R CARTON—See CVC Capital Partners SICAV-FIS S.A.; *Int'l,* pg. 1881
A&R CARTON ST PETERSBURG ZAO—See CVC Capital Partners SICAV-FIS S.A.; *Int'l,* pg. 1881
ARROWHEAD CONTAINERS INC.—See Southern Missouri Container Packaging Group; *U.S. Private,* pg. 3733
ARVCO CONTAINER CORPORATION; *U.S. Private,* pg. 344
ASIA PAPER MANUFACTURING CO., LTD.; *Int'l,* pg. 614
ATLAS CONTAINER CORPORATION; *U.S. Private,* pg. 375
ATLAS CONTAINER LLC—See Atlas Container Corporation; *U.S. Private,* pg. 375
AYEPEE LAMITUBES LIMITED; *Int'l,* pg. 775
BANA INC.; *U.S. Private,* pg. 464
BAODING INTERNATIONAL PAPER PACKAGING CO., LTD.—See International Paper Company; *U.S. Public,* pg. 1155
BARGER PACKAGING-IN—See Welch Packaging Group, Inc.; *U.S. Private,* pg. 4473
BAY CORRUGATED CONTAINER INC.; *U.S. Private,* pg. 492
BEACON CONTAINER CORPORATION; *U.S. Private,* pg. 504
BENNETT PACKAGING OF KANSAS CITY; *U.S. Private,* pg. 527
BERTAKO S.L.U.—See DS Smith Plc; *Int'l,* pg. 2207
BILLERUD AB; *Int'l,* pg. 1030
BILLERUDKORSNAS FINLAND OY—See Billerud AB; *Int'l,* pg. 1030
BILLERUDKORSNAS SKARBLACKA AB—See Billerud AB; *Int'l,* pg. 1030
BILOKALNIK-IPA D.D.—See DS Smith Plc; *Int'l,* pg. 2207
BINTANG SERIBU SDN. BHD.—See Can-One Berhad; *Int'l,* pg. 1276
BIRD PACKAGING LIMITED; *Int'l,* pg. 1047
BOBST LATINOAMERICA DO SUL LTDA—See Bobst Group S.A.; *Int'l,* pg. 1096
BOBST STUTTGART GMBH—See Bobst Group S.A.; *Int'l,* pg. 1096
BORINQUEN CONTAINER CORP.; *U.S. Private,* pg. 618
THE BOXMAKER INC.; *U.S. Private,* pg. 3998
BOX MANUFACTURING CO—See ENL Limited; *Int'l,* pg. 2441
BOX-PAK (MALAYSIA) BERHAD—See Can-One Berhad; *Int'l,* pg. 1276
BOX-PAK (VIETNAM) CO., LTD.—See Can-One Berhad; *Int'l,* pg. 1276
BRADFORD COMPANY; *U.S. Private,* pg. 631
BRETSCHNEIDER VERPACKUNGEN GMBH—See DS Smith Plc; *Int'l,* pg. 2207
BUCKEYE BOXES INC.; *U.S. Private,* pg. 677
BUCKEYE CONTAINER—See Buckeye Corrugated Inc.; *U.S. Private,* pg. 677
BUCKEYE CORRUGATED INC.; *U.S. Private,* pg. 677
BULK-PACK INC.; *U.S. Private,* pg. 684
CAESARS TRAVEL GROUP—See Caesars Group; *Int'l,* pg. 1249
CAL SHEETS, LLC—See Goldberg Lindsay & Co., LLC; *U.S. Private,* pg. 1729
CALUMET CARTON COMPANY; *U.S. Private,* pg. 724
CANO CONTAINER CORP.; *U.S. Private,* pg. 735
CARACAS PAPER COMPANY, S.A.; *Int'l,* pg. 1319
CARLISLE CONTAINER CO.; *U.S. Private,* pg. 764
CAROLINA CONTAINER COMPANY—See Schwarz Partners, LP; *U.S. Private,* pg. 3572
CAROLINA CONTAINER COMPANY—See The Kraft Group LLC; *U.S. Private,* pg. 4066
CARTOCOR S.A.—See Arcor Sociedad Anonima, Industrial y Comercial; *Int'l,* pg. 550
CARTONAJES UNION S.L.—See International Paper Company; *U.S. Public,* pg. 1155
CARTONAJES UNION S.L.—See International Paper Company; *U.S. Public,* pg. 1155
CARTON CRAFT CORPORATION—See Graphic Packaging Holding Company; *U.S. Public,* pg. 958

CARTON SERVICE INC.; *U.S. Private,* pg. 776
CARTON Y PAPEL RECICLADO, S.A.—See International Paper Company; *U.S. Public,* pg. 1155
CASCADES INC.; *Int'l,* pg. 1349
CENTRAL FLORIDA BOX CORPORATION—See WestRock Company; *U.S. Public,* pg. 2361
CENTURY CORRUGATED CONTAINER INC.—See Ozark Warehouses, Inc.; *U.S. Private,* pg. 3058
CEPAC LTD—See Hayel Saeed Anam Group of Companies; *Int'l,* pg. 3290
CHENGDU CHENG LOONG PACKING PRODUCTS CO., LTD.—See Cheng Loong Corp.; *Int'l,* pg. 1466
CHENG LOONG BINH DUONG CONTAINER CO., LTD.—See Cheng Loong Corp.; *Int'l,* pg. 1465
CHENG LOONG BINH DUONG PAPER CO., LTD.—See Cheng Loong Corp.; *Int'l,* pg. 1465
CHENG LOONG CORP. - CHUPEI MILL—See Cheng Loong Corp.; *Int'l,* pg. 1465
CHENG LOONG CORP. - HOULI MILL—See Cheng Loong Corp.; *Int'l,* pg. 1465
CHENG LOONG CORP. - HSINCHU MILL—See Cheng Loong Corp.; *Int'l,* pg. 1465
CHENG LOONG CORP. - LOS ANGELES BRANCH—See Cheng Loong Corp.; *Int'l,* pg. 1465
CHENG LOONG CORP. - MIAOLI PLANT—See Cheng Loong Corp.; *Int'l,* pg. 1465
CHENG LOONG CORP. - NEW JERSEY BRANCH—See Cheng Loong Corp.; *Int'l,* pg. 1465
CHENG LOONG CORP.; *Int'l,* pg. 1465
CHENG LOONG CORP. - TAICHUNG PLANT—See Cheng Loong Corp.; *Int'l,* pg. 1465
CHENG LOONG CORP. - TALIN PLANT—See Cheng Loong Corp.; *Int'l,* pg. 1466
CHENG LOONG CORP. - TAOYUAN MILL—See Cheng Loong Corp.; *Int'l,* pg. 1466
CHENG LOONG CORP. - TAOYUAN PLANT, FORM & PACKAGING MATERIALS—See Cheng Loong Corp.; *Int'l,* pg. 1466
CHENG LOONG CORP. - TAOYUAN PLANT II—See Cheng Loong Corp.; *Int'l,* pg. 1466
CHENG LOONG CORP. - TAOYUAN PLANT—See Cheng Loong Corp.; *Int'l,* pg. 1466
CHENG LOONG CORP. - YENCHAO PLANT—See Cheng Loong Corp.; *Int'l,* pg. 1466
CHENG LOONG (GWANGTUNG) PAPER CO., LTD.—See Cheng Loong Corp.; *Int'l,* pg. 1465
CHENG LOONG LONG AN CONTAINER CO., LTD.—See Cheng Loong Corp.; *Int'l,* pg. 1466
CHICAGO CONVERTING—See Menasha Corporation; *U.S. Private,* pg. 2665
CHINA SHENGDA PACKAGING GROUP INC.; *Int'l,* pg. 1550
CHONG QING CHENG LOONG PAPER CO., LTD.—See Cheng Loong Corp.; *Int'l,* pg. 1466
CHUNG LOONG PAPER HOLDINGS LIMITED—See Cheng Loong Corp.; *Int'l,* pg. 1466
CJ (CHANGCHUN) FEED CO., LTD.—See CJ Corporation; *Int'l,* pg. 1631
CJ (CHENGDU) FEED CO., LTD.—See CJ Corporation; *Int'l,* pg. 1631
CJ CORP.—See CJ Corporation; *Int'l,* pg. 1632
CJ (NANJING) FEED CO., LTD.—See CJ Corporation; *Int'l,* pg. 1631
CJ (SHENYANG) FEED CO., LTD.—See CJ Corporation; *Int'l,* pg. 1631
CMCP - INTERNATIONAL PAPER S.A.S.—See International Paper Company; *U.S. Public,* pg. 1155
CMPC PRODUCTOS DE PAPEL S.A.—See Empresas CMPC S.A.; *Int'l,* pg. 2389
COASTAL CORRUGATED, INC.—See Atlantic Corporation; *U.S. Private,* pg. 372
COASTAL GROUP; *U.S. Private,* pg. 956
COLD CHAIN TECHNOLOGIES, INC.—See Aurora Capital Group, LLC; *U.S. Private,* pg. 393
COLEPAK, INC.—See Greif Inc.; *U.S. Public,* pg. 967
COLUMBIA CORRUGATED BOX CO.; *U.S. Private,* pg. 976
CONCORD SPECIALTY CORRUGATED—See Buckeye Corrugated Inc.; *U.S. Private,* pg. 677
CONNECTICUT CONTAINER CORPORATION; *U.S. Private,* pg. 1015
CONNECT PACKAGING LTD.—See Corrugated Box Supplies Limited; *Int'l,* pg. 1807
CONSOLIDATED CONVERTING CO.—See Elliott Management Corporation; *U.S. Private,* pg. 1367
CONSOLIDATED CONVERTING CO.—See Veritas Capital Fund Management, LLC; *U.S. Private,* pg. 4361
CONTEMPO CARD CO., INC.; *U.S. Private,* pg. 1027
CORASIA CORP.—See Cheng Loong Corp.; *Int'l,* pg. 1466
CORBOX CORPORATION; *Int'l,* pg. 1795
CORRUGATED BOX SUPPLIES LIMITED; *Int'l,* pg. 1807
CORRUGATED CONTAINER CORP; *U.S. Private,* pg. 1059
CORRUGATED SUPPLIES CORP.; *U.S. Private,* pg. 1059
CRA-WAL—See Buckeye Corrugated Inc.; *U.S. Private,* pg. 677
CROWN KAMIKOGYO CO., LTD.—See Dynapac Co., Ltd.; *Int'l,* pg. 2241
CUSTOM PACKAGING INC.; *U.S. Private,* pg. 1129
DAELIM PAPER CO., LTD.; *Int'l,* pg. 1908

DAE YOUNG PACKAGING CO., LTD.; *Int'l,* pg. 1905
DALLAS CONTAINER CORPORATION; *U.S. Private,* pg. 1149
DEE PAPER COMPANY; *U.S. Private,* pg. 1189
DELTA CONTAINERS INC.—See Landaal Packaging Systems; *U.S. Private,* pg. 2384
DELTA PACKAGING SERVICES GMBH—See DS Smith Plc; *Int'l,* pg. 2209
DISC GRAPHICS INC.—See Dunsirn Partners LLC; *U.S. Private,* pg. 1291
DISC GRAPHICS INC.—See Pfingsten Partners, LLC; *U.S. Private,* pg. 3164
DIXIE REEL & BOX CO.—See Lone Star Corrugated Container Corporation; *U.S. Private,* pg. 2484
DONGGUAN CHUN YIK PAPER WARE FACTORY LIMITED—See Hop Fung Group Holdings Ltd; *Int'l,* pg. 3473
DONGGUANG CITY MING LOONG PAPER CO., LTD.—See Cheng Loong Corp.; *Int'l,* pg. 1466
DONGGUAN MING LOONG PAPER CO., LTD.—See Cheng Loong Corp.; *Int'l,* pg. 1466
DS SMITH BELISCE CROATIA D.O.O.—See DS Smith Plc; *Int'l,* pg. 2207
DS SMITH BULGARIA S.A.—See DS Smith Plc; *Int'l,* pg. 2207
DS SMITH HAMBURG DISPLAY GMBH—See DS Smith Plc; *Int'l,* pg. 2207
DS SMITH KAYSERSBERG S.A.S.—See DS Smith Plc; *Int'l,* pg. 2207
DS SMITH PACKAGING ALES SAS—See DS Smith Plc; *Int'l,* pg. 2207
DS SMITH PACKAGING ARENSHAUSEN MIVEPA GMBH—See DS Smith Plc; *Int'l,* pg. 2207
DS SMITH PACKAGING ARNSTADT GMBH—See DS Smith Plc; *Int'l,* pg. 2207
DS SMITH PACKAGING AUSTRIA GMBH—See DS Smith Plc; *Int'l,* pg. 2207
DS SMITH PACKAGING BALTIC HOLDING OY—See DS Smith Plc; *Int'l,* pg. 2207
DS SMITH PACKAGING BELGIUM N.V.—See DS Smith Plc; *Int'l,* pg. 2207
DS SMITH PACKAGING BH D.O.O.—See DS Smith Plc; *Int'l,* pg. 2207
DS SMITH PACKAGING CZECH REPUBLIC S.R.O.—See DS Smith Plc; *Int'l,* pg. 2207
DS SMITH PACKAGING DENMARK A/S—See DS Smith Plc; *Int'l,* pg. 2208
DS SMITH PACKAGING DPF SAS—See DS Smith Plc; *Int'l,* pg. 2207
DS SMITH PACKAGING DURTAL SAS—See DS Smith Plc; *Int'l,* pg. 2207
DS SMITH PACKAGING ESTONIA AS—See DS Smith Plc; *Int'l,* pg. 2207
DS SMITH PACKAGING FEGERSHEIM SAS—See DS Smith Plc; *Int'l,* pg. 2207
DS SMITH PACKAGING FUZESABONY KFT.—See DS Smith Plc; *Int'l,* pg. 2207
DS SMITH PACKAGING GALICIA S.A.—See DS Smith Plc; *Int'l,* pg. 2207
DS SMITH PACKAGING-HOLLY SPRINGS, LLC—See DS Smith Plc; *Int'l,* pg. 2208
DS SMITH PACKAGING ITALIA SPA—See DS Smith Plc; *Int'l,* pg. 2208
DS SMITH PACKAGING KAYPAC SAS—See DS Smith Plc; *Int'l,* pg. 2208
DS SMITH PACKAGING LAROUSSE SAS—See DS Smith Plc; *Int'l,* pg. 2208
DS SMITH PACKAGING LUCENA, S.L.—See DS Smith Plc; *Int'l,* pg. 2208
DS SMITH PACKAGING MEHUN-CIM SASU—See DS Smith Plc; *Int'l,* pg. 2208
DS SMITH PACKAGING PAKKAUSJALOSTE OY—See DS Smith Plc; *Int'l,* pg. 2208
DS SMITH PACKAGING PORTUGAL, S.A.—See DS Smith Plc; *Int'l,* pg. 2208
DS SMITH PACKAGING ROMANIA S.R.L.—See DS Smith Plc; *Int'l,* pg. 2208
DS SMITH PACKAGING SLOVAKIA S.R.O.—See DS Smith Plc; *Int'l,* pg. 2208
DS SMITH PACKAGING SUD EST SASU—See DS Smith Plc; *Int'l,* pg. 2208
DS SMITH PACKAGING SYSTEMS SAS—See DS Smith Plc; *Int'l,* pg. 2208
DS SMITH PACKAGING VELIN SASU—See DS Smith Plc; *Int'l,* pg. 2208
DS SMITH PAPER COULLONS SAS—See DS Smith Plc; *Int'l,* pg. 2208
DS SMITH PAPER ITALIA SRL—See DS Smith Plc; *Int'l,* pg. 2208
DS SMITH PAPER KAYSERSBERG SAS—See DS Smith Plc; *Int'l,* pg. 2208
DS SMITH PAPER ROUEN SAS—See DS Smith Plc; *Int'l,* pg. 2209
DS SMITH PAPER VIANA, S.A.—See DS Smith Plc; *Int'l,* pg. 2209
DS SMITH PAPER ZARNESTI, S.R.L.—See DS Smith Plc; *Int'l,* pg. 2209

N.A.I.C.S. INDEX

322211 — CORRUGATED AND SOLI...

DS SMITH PLC - KARTOTEX PLANT—See DS Smith Plc; *Int'l*, pg. 2209
DS SMITH POLSKA S.A.—See DS Smith Plc; *Int'l*, pg. 2207
DS SMITH SLOVENIJA D.O.O.—See DS Smith Plc; *Int'l*, pg. 2209
DS SMITH TRISS S.R.O.—See DS Smith Plc; *Int'l*, pg. 2209
DUROPACK GMBH—See DS Smith Plc; *Int'l*, pg. 2209
DUROPACK KRUSEVAC A. D.—See DS Smith Plc; *Int'l*, pg. 2209
DUROPACK STEMI LTD.—See DS Smith Plc; *Int'l*, pg. 2209
DUROPACK TRAKIA PAPIR S.A.—See DS Smith Plc; *Int'l*, pg. 2209
DUROPACK TURPAK OBALY A.S.—See DS Smith Plc; *Int'l*, pg. 2209
DYNAPAC CO., LTD. - FUKUSHIMA PLANT—See Dynapac Co., Ltd.; *Int'l*, pg. 2241
DYNAPAC CO., LTD. - KANIE PLANT—See Dynapac Co., Ltd.; *Int'l*, pg. 2241
DYNAPAC CO., LTD. - KAWAGOE PLANT—See Dynapac Co., Ltd.; *Int'l*, pg. 2241
DYNAPAC CO., LTD. - MATSUMOTO PLANT—See Dynapac Co., Ltd.; *Int'l*, pg. 2241
DYNAPAC CO., LTD. - MIYOSHI PLANT—See Dynapac Co., Ltd.; *Int'l*, pg. 2241
DYNAPAC CO., LTD. - SHIZUOKA PLANT—See Dynapac Co., Ltd.; *Int'l*, pg. 2241
DYNAPAC CO., LTD. - TSUKUBA PLANT—See Dynapac Co., Ltd.; *Int'l*, pg. 2241
DYNAPAC GF (MALAYSIA) SDN.BHD—See Dynapac Co., Ltd.; *Int'l*, pg. 2241
DYNAPAC (HAI PHONG) CO., LTD.—See Dynapac Co., Ltd.; *Int'l*, pg. 2241
DYNAPAC (HANOI) CO., LTD.—See Dynapac Co., Ltd.; *Int'l*, pg. 2241
DYNAPAC (HK) LTD.—See Dynapac Co., Ltd.; *Int'l*, pg. 2241
DYNAPAC (M) SDN. BHD.—See Dynapac Co., Ltd.; *Int'l*, pg. 2241
DYNAPAC (SUZHOU) CO., LTD.—See Dynapac Co., Ltd.; *Int'l*, pg. 2241
DYNAPAC (SZ) LTD.—See Dynapac Co., Ltd.; *Int'l*, pg. 2241
EMBALLAGES LAURENT SAS—See International Paper Company; *U.S. Public*, pg. 1155
ENVASES GRAU, S.L.—See International Paper Company; *U.S. Public*, pg. 1155
FABI BOLSAS INDUSTRIALES S.A.—See Empresas CMPC S.A.; *Int'l*, pg. 2390
FEDERAL METAL PRINTING FACTORY SDN. BHD.—See Can-One Berhad; *Int'l*, pg. 1276
FERGUSON SUPPLY & BOX MANUFACTURING CO; *U.S. Private*, pg. 1497
FLEETWOOD-FIBRE PACKAGING & GRAPHICS, INC.; *U.S. Private*, pg. 1542
FLINT PACKAGING, INC.—See Landaal Packaging Systems; *U.S. Private*, pg. 2384
FRUIT GROWERS SUPPLY CO.; *U.S. Private*, pg. 1617
GENERAL PACKAGING CORPORATION; *U.S. Private*, pg. 1666
GEORGIA-PACIFIC CORPORATION—See Koch Industries, Inc.; *U.S. Private*, pg. 2328
GEORGIA-PACIFIC CORPORATION—See Koch Industries, Inc.; *U.S. Private*, pg. 2328
GEORGIA-PACIFIC CORPORATION—See Koch Industries, Inc.; *U.S. Private*, pg. 2328
GEORGIA-PACIFIC CORPORATION—See Koch Industries, Inc.; *U.S. Private*, pg. 2328
GEORGIA-PACIFIC CORPORATION—See Koch Industries, Inc.; *U.S. Private*, pg. 2328
GEORGIA-PACIFIC CORPORATION—See Koch Industries, Inc.; *U.S. Private*, pg. 2328
GEORGIA-PACIFIC CORPORATION—See Koch Industries, Inc.; *U.S. Private*, pg. 2328
GEORGIA-PACIFIC CORPORATION—See Koch Industries, Inc.; *U.S. Private*, pg. 2328
GEORGIA-PACIFIC CORPORATION—See Koch Industries, Inc.; *U.S. Private*, pg. 2328
GEORGIA-PACIFIC CORPORATION—See Koch Industries, Inc.; *U.S. Private*, pg. 2328
GEORGIA-PACIFIC CORRUGATED-MARTINSVILLE FACILITY—See Koch Industries, Inc.; *U.S. Private*, pg. 2328
GEORGIA-PACIFIC PACKAGING - AUGUSTA—See Koch Industries, Inc.; *U.S. Private*, pg. 2328
GEORGIA-PACIFIC PACKAGING DIVISION—See Koch Industries, Inc.; *U.S. Private*, pg. 2328
GET MATCHES LLC; *U.S. Private*, pg. 1688
G.K.P PRINTING & PACKAGING LTD.; *Int'l*, pg. 2800
GLOBAL PACKAGING SOLUTIONS, INC.; *U.S. Private*, pg. 1716
GOLDEN BALES CORPORATION; *Int'l*, pg. 3028
GRAPH-CORR—See Dunsirn Partners LLC; *U.S. Private*, pg. 1291
GRAPH-CORR—See Pfingsten Partners, LLC; *U.S. Private*, pg. 3164
GRAPHIC PACKAGING INTERNATIONAL EUROPE NETHERLANDS B.V.—See CVC Capital Partners SICAV-FIS S.A.; *Int'l*, pg. 1881
GRAPHIC PACKAGING INTERNATIONAL, INC. - CAROL STREAM—See Graphic Packaging Holding Company; *U.S. Public*, pg. 959
GREAT LAKES PACKAGING CORP.; *U.S. Private*, pg. 1765
GREAT LITTLE BOX COMPANY LTD.; *Int'l*, pg. 3065
GREAT NORTHERN CORPORATION; *U.S. Private*, pg. 1766
GREAT SOUTHERN INDUSTRIES INC.; *U.S. Private*, pg. 1768
GREEN FOREST (QINGXIN) PAPER INDUSTRIAL LIMITED—See Hop Fung Group Holdings Ltd; *Int'l*, pg. 3473
GREIF CORRUGATED PRODUCTS—See Greif Inc.; *U.S. Public*, pg. 967
HAMBURGER HAFEN UND LOGISTIK AG; *Int'l*, pg. 3236
HARIMA PAPER TECH. CORPORATION—See Daio Paper Corporation; *Int'l*, pg. 1940
HARRIS PACKAGING CORPORATION; *U.S. Private*, pg. 1870
HARTA PACKAGING INDUSTRIES (PERAK) SDN. BHD.—See HPI Resources Berhad; *Int'l*, pg. 3500
HARTA PACKAGING INDUSTRIES SDN. BHD.—See HPI Resources Berhad; *Int'l*, pg. 3500
HAZMATPAC, INC.—See Cleveland Steel Container Corporation; *U.S. Private*, pg. 941
HENAN CHENG LOONG PACKING PRODUCTS CO., LTD.—See Cheng Loong Corp.; *Int'l*, pg. 1466
HERITAGE PACKAGING, LLC—See Welch Packaging Group, Inc.; *U.S. Private*, pg. 4473
HORN PACKAGING CORPORATION; *U.S. Private*, pg. 1983
HPI RESOURCES (OVERSEAS) SDN. BHD.—See HPI Resources Berhad; *Int'l*, pg. 3500
HUHTAMAKI LA ROCHELLE S.A.S.—See Huhtamaki Oyj; *Int'l*, pg. 3525
HUHTAMAKI NEW ZEALAND LIMITED—See Huhtamaki Oyj; *Int'l*, pg. 3525
IDEAL BOX CO.; *U.S. Private*, pg. 2035
INDEPENDENT II, LLC; *U.S. Private*, pg. 2059
INDIANA BOX CORP.—See Royal Continental Box Company Inc.; *U.S. Private*, pg. 3491
INDUSTRIA CARTONERA ASTURIANA, S.A.—See DS Smith Plc; *Int'l*, pg. 2209
INMARK, LLC—See Kelso & Company, L.P.; *U.S. Private*, pg. 2278
INTERNATIONAL PAPER AGROFLORESTAL LTDA.—See International Paper Company; *U.S. Public*, pg. 1155
INTERNATIONAL PAPER CARTONES LTDA.—See International Paper Company; *U.S. Public*, pg. 1156
INTERNATIONAL PAPER CHALON SAS—See International Paper Company; *U.S. Public*, pg. 1156
INTERNATIONAL PAPER (CHONGQING) PACKAGING CO., LTD—See International Paper Company; *U.S. Public*, pg. 1155
INTERNATIONAL PAPER COMPANY - FORT WAYNE—See International Paper Company; *U.S. Public*, pg. 1157
INTERNATIONAL PAPER COMPANY - FORT WORTH CONTAINER—See International Paper Company; *U.S. Public*, pg. 1157
INTERNATIONAL PAPER COMPANY - MOUNT CARMEL CONTAINER—See International Paper Company; *U.S. Public*, pg. 1157
INTERNATIONAL PAPER COMPANY - MURFREESBORO—See International Paper Company; *U.S. Public*, pg. 1157
INTERNATIONAL PAPER COMPANY - SAN ANTONIO—See International Paper Company; *U.S. Public*, pg. 1157
INTERNATIONAL PAPER COMPANY—See International Paper Company; *U.S. Public*, pg. 1156
INTERNATIONAL PAPER COMPANY—See International Paper Company; *U.S. Public*, pg. 1156
INTERNATIONAL PAPER COMPANY—See International Paper Company; *U.S. Public*, pg. 1156
INTERNATIONAL PAPER COMPANY—See International Paper Company; *U.S. Public*, pg. 1156
INTERNATIONAL PAPER COMPANY—See International Paper Company; *U.S. Public*, pg. 1156
INTERNATIONAL PAPER COMPANY—See International Paper Company; *U.S. Public*, pg. 1156
INTERNATIONAL PAPER COMPANY—See International Paper Company; *U.S. Public*, pg. 1156
INTERNATIONAL PAPER COMPANY—See International Paper Company; *U.S. Public*, pg. 1156
INTERNATIONAL PAPER COMPANY—See International Paper Company; *U.S. Public*, pg. 1156
INTERNATIONAL PAPER COMPANY—See International Paper Company; *U.S. Public*, pg. 1156
INTERNATIONAL PAPER COMPANY—See International Paper Company; *U.S. Public*, pg. 1156
INTERNATIONAL PAPER COMPANY—See International Paper Company; *U.S. Public*, pg. 1156
INTERNATIONAL PAPER COMPANY—See International Paper Company; *U.S. Public*, pg. 1156
INTERNATIONAL PAPER COMPANY—See International Paper Company; *U.S. Public*, pg. 1156
INTERNATIONAL PAPER COMPANY - WOOSTER CONTAINER PLANT—See International Paper Company; *U.S. Public*, pg. 1157
INTERNATIONAL PAPER CO. - STATESVILLE CONTAINER MILL—See International Paper Company; *U.S. Public*, pg. 1156
INTERNATIONAL PAPER CTA (MEXICO), S. DE R.L. DE C.V.—See International Paper Company; *U.S. Public*, pg. 1155
INTERNATIONAL PAPER CZECH REPUBLIC, S.R.O.—See International Paper Company; *U.S. Public*, pg. 1157
INTERNATIONAL PAPER (DEUTSCHLAND)GMBH—See International Paper Company; *U.S. Public*, pg. 1155
INTERNATIONAL PAPER DISTRIBUTION GROUP (TAIWAN) LIMITED—See International Paper Company; *U.S. Public*, pg. 1157
INTERNATIONAL PAPER DISTRIBUTION (SHANGHAI) LIMITED—See International Paper Company; *U.S. Public*, pg. 1157
INTERNATIONAL PAPER EMPAQUES INDUSTRIALES DE MEXICO S. DE R.L. DE C.V.—See International Paper Company; *U.S. Public*, pg. 1157
INTERNATIONAL PAPER ESPALY SAS—See International Paper Company; *U.S. Public*, pg. 1157
INTERNATIONAL PAPER (ESPANA), S. L.—See International Paper Company; *U.S. Public*, pg. 1155
INTERNATIONAL PAPER (INDIA) PRIVATE LIMITED—See International Paper Company; *U.S. Public*, pg. 1155
INTERNATIONAL PAPER (MALAYSIA) SDN BHD—See International Paper Company; *U.S. Public*, pg. 1155
INTERNATIONAL PAPER SINGAPORE—See International Paper Company; *U.S. Public*, pg. 1155
INTERSTATE CONTAINER - CAMBRIDGE—See Interstate Resources, Inc.; *U.S. Private*, pg. 2125
INTERSTATE CONTAINER LOWELL, LLC—See Interstate Resources, Inc.; *U.S. Private*, pg. 2125
INTERSTATE CONTAINER—See Interstate Resources, Inc.; *U.S. Private*, pg. 2125
IVEX PACKAGING CORPORATION—See Groupe IndusPac Emballage Inc.; *Int'l*, pg. 3104
IVEX PACKAGING LLC—See Groupe IndusPac Emballage Inc.; *Int'l*, pg. 3104
IWAKI DAIO PAPER CORPORATION—See Daio Paper Corporation; *Int'l*, pg. 1940
JAMESTOWN CONTAINER CORPORATION; *U.S. Private*, pg. 2185
JAMESTOWN CONTAINER CORP.—See Jamestown Container Corporation; *U.S. Private*, pg. 2185
JET BOX CO., INC.; *U.S. Private*, pg. 2203
JRD PACKAGING AND INDUSTRIAL SUPPLY; *U.S. Private*, pg. 2240
KANBARA DANBORU CO., LTD.—See Dynapac Co., Ltd.; *Int'l*, pg. 2241
KAPSTONE CONTAINER CORPORATION - AMSTERDAM—See WestRock Company; *U.S. Public*, pg. 2361
KAPSTONE CONTAINER CORPORATION—See WestRock Company; *U.S. Public*, pg. 2361
KAPSTONE OAKLAND—See WestRock Company; *U.S. Public*, pg. 2361
KAPSTONE PACKAGING - LAWRENCEBURG SHEET PLANT—See WestRock Company; *U.S. Public*, pg. 2361
KAPSTONE PACKAGING - MINNEAPOLIS CORRUGATOR PLANT—See WestRock Company; *U.S. Public*, pg. 2361
KAPSTONE PACKAGING PLANT—See WestRock Company; *U.S. Public*, pg. 2361
KAPSTONE PACKAGING PLANT - SOUTH CAROLINA—See WestRock Company; *U.S. Public*, pg. 2361
KAPSTONE PACKAGING - WEST SPRINGFIELD SHEET PLANT—See WestRock Company; *U.S. Public*, pg. 2361
KAPSTONE YAKIMA—See WestRock Company; *U.S. Public*, pg. 2361
KELLY BOX & PACKAGING CORP.; *U.S. Private*, pg. 2276
KEY CONTAINER CORPORATION; *U.S. Private*, pg. 2293
K&H CORRUGATED CASE CORP.—See Connecticut Container Corporation; *U.S. Private*, pg. 1015
KIAN JOO CANPACK SDN. BHD.—See Can-One Berhad; *Int'l*, pg. 1277
KIAN JOO CANPACK (SHAH ALAM) SDN. BHD.—See Can-One Berhad; *Int'l*, pg. 1276
KIAN JOO-VISYPAK SDN.BHD.—See Can-One Berhad; *Int'l*, pg. 1277
KIMBERLY-CLARK CORPORATION—See Kimberly-Clark Corporation; *U.S. Public*, pg. 1230
KINDLON ENTERPRISES, INC.; *U.S. Private*, pg. 2307
KJ CAN (SELANGOR) SDN. BHD.—See Can-One Berhad; *Int'l*, pg. 1276
KJM ALUMINIUM CAN SDN. BHD.—See Can-One Berhad; *Int'l*, pg. 1276

322211 — CORRUGATED AND SOLI...

KOCH CONTAINER—See Buckeye Corrugated Inc.; *U.S. Private*, pg. 677
KRAFCOR UNLIMITED—See Specialty Industries, Inc.; *U.S. Private*, pg. 3750
KUNFU PAPER (KUNSAN) CO., LTD.—See Cheng Loong Corp.; *Int'l*, pg. 1466
LANDAAL PACKAGING SYSTEMS; *U.S. Private*, pg. 2384
LAWRENCE PAPER COMPANY; *U.S. Private*, pg. 2401
LEAMAN CONTAINER INC.; *U.S. Private*, pg. 2407
LIBERTY DIVERSIFIED INTERNATIONAL INC.; *U.S. Private*, pg. 2443
LIQUI-BOX GERMANY GMBH—See Sealed Air Corporation; *U.S. Public*, pg. 1853
LONE STAR CORRUGATED CONTAINER CORPORATION; *U.S. Private*, pg. 2484
LONG FU PAPER (KUNSHAN) CO., LTD.—See Cheng Loong Corp.; *Int'l*, pg. 1466
LOONG FU PAPER (KUNSAN) CO., LTD.—See Cheng Loong Corp.; *Int'l*, pg. 1466
LOS ANGELES PAPER BOX, LLC—See Greif Inc.; *U.S. Public*, pg. 966
LOY-LANGE BOX COMPANY; *U.S. Private*, pg. 2506
MANNKRAFT CORPORATION—See Four M Holdings LLC; *U.S. Private*, pg. 1582
MASSACHUSETTS CONTAINER CORPORATION—See Connecticut Container Corporation; *U.S. Private*, pg. 1016
MASSILLON CONTAINER CO., INC.—See Vail Industries, Inc.; *U.S. Private*, pg. 4329
MCLEAN PACKAGING CORPORATION; *U.S. Private*, pg. 2641
MENASHA PACKAGING COMPANY, LLC - BROOKLYN PARK PLANT—See Menasha Corporation; *U.S. Private*, pg. 2665
MENASHA PACKAGING COMPANY, LLC - COLOMA—See Menasha Corporation; *U.S. Private*, pg. 2665
MENASHA PACKAGING COMPANY, LLC - ERIE—See Menasha Corporation; *U.S. Private*, pg. 2665
MENASHA PACKAGING COMPANY, LLC - PHILADELPHIA PLANT—See Menasha Corporation; *U.S. Private*, pg. 2665
MENASHA PACKAGING COMPANY, LLC - SANTA FE SPRINGS PLANT—See Menasha Corporation; *U.S. Private*, pg. 2665
METAL-PAK (MALAYSIA) SDN. BHD.—See Can-One Berhad; *Int'l*, pg. 1277
MICHIGAN PACKAGING CO.—See Greif Inc.; *U.S. Public*, pg. 967
MIDLAND CONTAINER CORPORATION—See Arbor Private Investment Company, LLC; *U.S. Private*, pg. 309
MIDWEST BOX COMPANY, INC.—See Jamestown Container Corporation; *U.S. Private*, pg. 2185
MILLER CONTAINER CORPORATION - CLINTON DIVISION—See Miller Container Corporation; *U.S. Private*, pg. 2733
MILLER CONTAINER CORPORATION; *U.S. Private*, pg. 2733
MING FONG PLASTIC (DONG GUAN) CO., LTD.—See Cheng Loong Corp.; *Int'l*, pg. 1466
MIYAGI DYNAPAC CO., LTD. - FURUKAWA PLANT—See Dynapac Co., Ltd.; *Int'l*, pg. 2241
MIYAGI DYNAPAC CO., LTD.—See Dynapac Co., Ltd.; *Int'l*, pg. 2241
MOHARRAM PRESS COMPANY—See Chemical Industries Holding Company; *Int'l*, pg. 1462
MONTEBELLO CONTAINER CORPORATION—See Goldberg Lindsay & Co., LLC; *U.S. Private*, pg. 1729
NEW ENGLAND WOODEN WARE CORP.; *U.S. Private*, pg. 2895
NORAMPAC INC. - NEWFOUNDLAND—See Cascades Inc.; *Int'l*, pg. 1350
NORAMPAC INDUSTRIES INC. - LANCASTER—See Cascades Inc.; *Int'l*, pg. 1350
NORAMPAC NEW ENGLAND INC.—See Cascades Inc.; *Int'l*, pg. 1350
NORAMPAC NEW YORK CITY INC.—See Cascades Inc.; *Int'l*, pg. 1350
NORAMPAC SCHENECTADY INC.—See Cascades Inc.; *Int'l*, pg. 1350
NORTH AMERICAN CONTAINER CORPORATION - CALHOUN FACILITY—See UFP Industries, Inc.; *U.S. Public*, pg. 2219
NORTH AMERICAN CONTAINER CORPORATION - LAWRENCEBURG FACILITY—See UFP Industries, Inc.; *U.S. Public*, pg. 2219
NORTH AMERICAN CONTAINER CORPORATION - MARTIN FACILITY—See UFP Industries, Inc.; *U.S. Public*, pg. 2219
NORTH AMERICAN CONTAINER CORPORATION - MCINTYRE FACILITY—See UFP Industries, Inc.; *U.S. Public*, pg. 2219
NORTH AMERICAN CONTAINER CORPORATION - NEWNAN FACILITY—See UFP Industries, Inc.; *U.S. Public*, pg. 2219
NORTH AMERICAN CONTAINER CORPORATION - ORANGEBURG FACILITY—See UFP Industries, Inc.; *U.S. Public*, pg. 2219
NORTH AMERICAN CONTAINER CORPORATION - SHARON FACILITY—See UFP Industries, Inc.; *U.S. Public*, pg. 2219
NORTH AMERICAN CONTAINER CORPORATION—See UFP Industries, Inc.; *U.S. Public*, pg. 2219
NORTHWEST PACKAGING INC.; *U.S. Private*, pg. 2961
NOVA DS SMITH EMBALAGEM, S.A.—See DS Smith Plc; *Int'l*, pg. 2209
NOVELART MANUFACTURING COMPANY; *U.S. Private*, pg. 2968
NUMAZU DYNAPAC CO., LTD.—See Dynapac Co., Ltd.; *Int'l*, pg. 2241
NUTMEG CONTAINER CORP.—See Connecticut Container Corporation; *U.S. Private*, pg. 1016
OAK PAPER PRODUCTS CO. INC.; *U.S. Private*, pg. 2983
OCKERLUND INDUSTRIES, INC.; *U.S. Private*, pg. 2992
OGURA SHIKI CO., LTD.—See Dynapac Co., Ltd.; *Int'l*, pg. 2241
OMAHA BOX COMPANY—See Liberty Diversified International Inc.; *U.S. Private*, pg. 2443
OTSU PAPER BOARD CO., LTD.—See Daio Paper Corporation; *Int'l*, pg. 1940
OZARK WAREHOUSES, INC.; *U.S. Private*, pg. 3058
PACKAGEONE, INC.—See Goldberg Lindsay & Co., LLC; *U.S. Private*, pg. 1729
PACKAGING CORPORATION OF AMERICA - CHICAGO FULL-LINE PLANT—See Packaging Corporation of America; *U.S. Public*, pg. 1633
PACKAGING CORPORATION OF AMERICA - HUNTSVILLE SHEET PLANT—See Packaging Corporation of America; *U.S. Public*, pg. 1633
THE PACKAGING HOUSE, INC.; *U.S. Private*, pg. 4090
PACKAGING UNLIMITED, LLC; *U.S. Private*, pg. 3073
PACKAGING UNLIMITED LLC—See Hood Industries Inc.; *U.S. Private*, pg. 1977
PAX CORRUGATED PRODUCTS, INC.—See Welch Packaging Group, Inc.; *U.S. Private*, pg. 4473
PCA SOUTHERN INDIANA CORRUGATED, LLC—See Packaging Corporation of America; *U.S. Public*, pg. 1633
PHILCORR LLC—See McLean Packaging Corporation; *U.S. Private*, pg. 2641
PHOENIX PACKAGING INC.; *U.S. Private*, pg. 3173
PLYMOUTH PACKAGING, INC.—See WestRock Company; *U.S. Public*, pg. 2362
POLYMER SOLUTIONS INTERNATIONAL, INC.; *U.S. Private*, pg. 3226
PRECISE PACKAGING, INC.—See The Pritzker Group - Chicago, LLC; *U.S. Private*, pg. 4099
PREFERRED PACKAGING & CRATING, INC.; *U.S. Private*, pg. 3248
PRESIDENT CONTAINER GROUP, INC.; *U.S. Private*, pg. 3254
PRESIDENT CONTAINER INC.—See President Container Group, Inc.; *U.S. Private*, pg. 3254
PRESIDENT INDUSTRIAL PRODUCTS—See President Container Group, Inc.; *U.S. Private*, pg. 3254
PROACTIVE PACKAGING AND DISPLAY, INC.—See Schwarz Partners, LP; *U.S. Private*, pg. 3572
PROACTIVE PACKAGING AND DISPLAY, INC.—See The Kraft Group LLC; *U.S. Private*, pg. 4066
PRO-PAK INDUSTRIES; *U.S. Private*, pg. 3271
PT INTERNATIONAL PAPER PACKAGING INDONESIA BATAM—See International Paper Company; *U.S. Public*, pg. 1157
PT. SUPER UNGGAS JAYA—See CJ Corporation; *Int'l*, pg. 1634
QINGDAO CHUNG LOONG PAPER CO., LTD.—See Cheng Loong Corp.; *Int'l*, pg. 1466
RAND-WHITNEY GROUP, LLC—See The Kraft Group LLC; *U.S. Private*, pg. 4066
RAPAK AD—See Sealed Air Corporation; *U.S. Public*, pg. 1853
RAPAK ASIA PACIFIC LIMITED—See Sealed Air Corporation; *U.S. Public*, pg. 1853
RAPAK, LLC—See Sealed Air Corporation; *U.S. Public*, pg. 1853
RAPAK, LLC - UNION CITY PLANT—See Sealed Air Corporation; *U.S. Public*, pg. 1853
RICHMOND CORRUGATED BOX INC.; *U.S. Private*, pg. 3430
RIGESA, CELULOSE, PAPEL E EMBALAGENS LTDA.—See WestRock Company; *U.S. Public*, pg. 2362
RIGESA, LTDA.—See WestRock Company; *U.S. Public*, pg. 2362
ROBERT MANN PACKAGING, INC.; *U.S. Private*, pg. 3458
ROMANOW INC.; *U.S. Private*, pg. 3476
ROYAL CONTINENTAL BOX COMPANY INC.; *U.S. Private*, pg. 3491
SECURITY PACKAGING INC.; *U.S. Private*, pg. 3596
SERVANTS INC.; *U.S. Private*, pg. 3614
SHAN FU PAPER (KUNSON) CO., LTD.—See Cheng Loong Corp.; *Int'l*, pg. 1466
SHANGHAI CHUNG HAO PAPER CO., LTD.—See Cheng Loong Corp.; *Int'l*, pg. 1466
SHANGHAI CHUNG LOONG PAPER CO., LTD.—See Cheng Loong Corp.; *Int'l*, pg. 1466
SHEETS & GRAPHIC SHEETS UNLIMITED; *U.S. Private*, pg. 3630

CORPORATE AFFILIATIONS

SHILLINGTON BOX COMPANY LLC; *U.S. Private*, pg. 3636
SIA DS SMITH PACKAGING LATVIA—See DS Smith Plc; *Int'l*, pg. 2209
SIAM FIBREBOARD COMPANY LIMITED—See Evergreen Fibreboard Berhad; *Int'l*, pg. 2565
SOCIETE GUADELOUPEENNE DE CARTON ONDULE SAS—See International Paper Company; *U.S. Public*, pg. 1158
SOCIETE MEDITERRANEENNE D EMBALLAGES SAS—See International Paper Company; *U.S. Public*, pg. 1158
SOCIETE NORMANDE DE CARTON ONDULE SAS—See International Paper Company; *U.S. Public*, pg. 1158
SONOCO CANADA CORPORATION—See Sonoco Products Company; *U.S. Public*, pg. 1905
SONOCO DE COLOMBIA LTDA.—See Sonoco Products Company; *U.S. Public*, pg. 1908
SONOCO DE MEXICO, S.A. DE C.V.—See Sonoco Products Company; *U.S. Public*, pg. 1908
SONOCO LTD.—See Sonoco Products Company; *U.S. Public*, pg. 1907
SONOCO MILNROW—See Sonoco Products Company; *U.S. Public*, pg. 1906
SONOCO PAPERBOARD SPECIALTIES—See Sonoco Products Company; *U.S. Public*, pg. 1907
SONOCO PRODUCTS CO. UK UNLIMITED—See Sonoco Products Company; *U.S. Public*, pg. 1907
SONOCO VENEZOLANA C.A.—See Sonoco Products Company; *U.S. Public*, pg. 1908
SOUTHEASTERN PACKAGING CO.—See Greif Inc.; *U.S. Public*, pg. 967
SOUTHERN CONTAINER LLC—See Kelso & Company, L.P.; *U.S. Private*, pg. 2278
SOUTHERN MISSOURI CONTAINER PACKAGING GROUP; *U.S. Private*, pg. 3733
SOUTH HAVEN PACKAGING, INC.—See Kindlon Enterprises, Inc.; *U.S. Private*, pg. 2307
SPECIALTY INDUSTRIES, INC.; *U.S. Private*, pg. 3750
SQUIRE CORRUGATED CONTAINER CORP.; *U.S. Private*, pg. 3766
STAND FAST PACKAGING PRODUCTS INC.; *U.S. Private*, pg. 3777
STEPHEN GOULD OF ALABAMA, INC.—See Stephen Gould Corporation; *U.S. Private*, pg. 3802
SUMMIT CONTAINER CORPORATION; *U.S. Private*, pg. 3854
SUMTER PACKAGING CORPORATION—See Hood Container Corporation; *U.S. Private*, pg. 1977
SUPPLYONE CLEVELAND, INC.—See Wellspring Capital Management LLC; *U.S. Private*, pg. 4478
SUPPLYONE, INC. - DALLAS PLANT—See Wellspring Capital Management LLC; *U.S. Private*, pg. 4478
SUPPLYONE, INC.—See Wellspring Capital Management LLC; *U.S. Private*, pg. 4477
SUPPLYONE TUCSON, INC. - ALBUQUERQUE PLANT—See Wellspring Capital Management LLC; *U.S. Private*, pg. 4478
SUPPLYONE TUCSON, INC.—See Wellspring Capital Management LLC; *U.S. Private*, pg. 4478
SUPPLYONE WEYERS CAVE, INC. - CHESAPEAKE PLANT—See Wellspring Capital Management LLC; *U.S. Private*, pg. 4478
SUPPLYONE WEYERS CAVE, INC.—See Wellspring Capital Management LLC; *U.S. Private*, pg. 4478
SUPPLYONE WISCONSIN, LLC—See Wellspring Capital Management LLC; *U.S. Private*, pg. 4478
SUZHOU CHENG LOONG PAPER CO., LTD.—See Cheng Loong Corp.; *Int'l*, pg. 1466
TAI HING PAPER PRODUCTS COMPANY, LIMITED—See Hung Hing Printing Group Limited; *Int'l*, pg. 3535
TAISEI PAPER CORPORATION—See Daio Paper Corporation; *Int'l*, pg. 1940
TAJIMI DYNAPAC CO., LTD.—See Dynapac Co., Ltd.; *Int'l*, pg. 2241
TAUNTON TRUSS, INC.; *U.S. Private*, pg. 3936
TAVENS CONTAINER INCORPORATED; *U.S. Private*, pg. 3936
TECHNOLOGY CONTAINER CORP.—See Connecticut Container Corporation; *U.S. Private*, pg. 1016
TECNICARTON FRANCE S.A.S.—See DS Smith Plc; *Int'l*, pg. 2209
TECNICARTON PORTUGAL UNIPESSOAL LDA—See DS Smith Plc; *Int'l*, pg. 2209
TECUMSEH PACKAGING SOLUTIONS—See Akers Packaging Service Inc.; *U.S. Private*, pg. 145
TENNESSEE PACKAGING—See Buckeye Corrugated Inc.; *U.S. Private*, pg. 677
THARCO CONTAINERS, INC.—See Packaging Corporation of America; *U.S. Public*, pg. 1633
THARCO CONTAINERS TEXAS, INC.—See Packaging Corporation of America; *U.S. Public*, pg. 1633
TIANJIN BOHAI INTERNATIONAL PAPER PACKAGING CO., LTD.—See International Paper Company; *U.S. Public*, pg. 1158
TIANJIN CHUNG LOONG PAPER CO., LTD.—See Cheng Loong Corp.; *Int'l*, pg. 1466

N.A.I.C.S. INDEX

TIN INC.—See International Paper Company; *U.S. Public*, pg. 1158
TITAN CORRUGATED, INC.—See UFP Industries, Inc.; *U.S. Public*, pg. 2220
TOKI DYNAPAC CO., LTD. - NAKATSUGAWA PLANT—See Dynapac Co., Ltd.; *Int'l*, pg. 2241
TOKI DYNAPAC CO., LTD.—See Dynapac Co., Ltd.; *Int'l*, pg. 2241
TOPAC GMBH—See Bertelsmann SE & Co. KGaA; *Int'l*, pg. 997
TOSCANA ONDULATI SPA—See DS Smith Plc; *Int'l*, pg. 2209
TRAMEC CONTINENTAL-AERO, LLC—See MacLean-Fogg Company; *U.S. Private*, pg. 2537
TRENT BOX MFG. CO., INC.; *U.S. Private*, pg. 4218
TRIAD PACKAGING DESIGN & DISPLAY INC.; *U.S. Private*, pg. 4225
TRIAD PACKAGING, INC. ATHENS, ALABAMA—See Triad Packaging Design & Display Inc.; *U.S. Private*, pg. 4225
TRISTATE CONTAINER CORP.—See Connecticut Container Corporation; *U.S. Private*, pg. 1016
TWP SENDIRIAN BERHAD—See Dai Nippon Printing Co., Ltd.; *Int'l*, pg. 1916
UAB DS SMITH PACKAGING LITHUANIA—See DS Smith Plc; *Int'l*, pg. 2209
UNICORR PACKAGING GROUP—See Connecticut Container Corporation; *U.S. Private*, pg. 1016
UNITED CARTON INDUSTRIES COMPANY LTD.—See Hayel Saeed Anam Group of Companies; *Int'l*, pg. 3291
U.S. CORRUGATED, INC. - CLEVELAND SHEET PLANT—See Bio Pappel, S.A.B. de C.V.; *Int'l*, pg. 1035
U.S. CORRUGATED, INC. - COAL CENTER CORRUGATOR PLANT—See Bio Pappel, S.A.B. de C.V.; *Int'l*, pg. 1035
U.S. CORRUGATED, INC. - MILWAUKEE SHEET PLANT—See Bio Pappel, S.A.B. de C.V.; *Int'l*, pg. 1035
U.S. CORRUGATED, INC.—See Bio Pappel, S.A.B. de C.V.; *Int'l*, pg. 1035
UTSUNOMIYA DYNAPAC CO., LTD.—See Dynapac Co., Ltd.; *Int'l*, pg. 2242
VANGUARD PACKAGING; *U.S. Private*, pg. 4344
VERICORR PACKAGING LLC; *U.S. Private*, pg. 4360
VIKING PAPER CORP.; *U.S. Private*, pg. 4382
VINA TAWANA CONTAINER CO., LTD.—See Cheng Loong Corp.; *Int'l*, pg. 1466
VIVABOX SOLUTIONS, LLC—See Clayton, Dubilier & Rice, LLC; *U.S. Private*, pg. 930
WEBCOR PACKAGING CORPORATION; *U.S. Private*, pg. 4464
WEBSTER PACKAGING CORP.; *U.S. Private*, pg. 4467
WELCH PACKAGING GROUP, INC.; *U.S. Private*, pg. 4473
WELCH PACKAGING—See Welch Packaging Group, Inc.; *U.S. Private*, pg. 4473
WESTERN INDUSTRIES CORP.—See Western Industries Corporation; *U.S. Private*, pg. 4494
WESTROCK CP, LLC—See WestRock Company; *U.S. Public*, pg. 2362
WESTROCK-PUERTO RICO, INC.—See WestRock Company; *U.S. Public*, pg. 2363
WESTROCK RKT CO. - DAYTON CONTAINER PLANT—See WestRock Company; *U.S. Public*, pg. 2362
WESTROCK RKT CO. - LIBERTY CONTAINER PLANT—See WestRock Company; *U.S. Public*, pg. 2363
WESTROCK RKT CO. - NORTH TONAWANDA CONTAINER PLANT—See WestRock Company; *U.S. Public*, pg. 2363
WESTROCK RKT CO. - PLYMOUTH FOOD SERVICE PACKAGING PLANT—See WestRock Company; *U.S. Public*, pg. 2363
WESTROCK RKT CO. - SAINT LOUIS FOOD SERVICE PACKAGING PLANT—See WestRock Company; *U.S. Public*, pg. 2363
WESTROCK RKT CO. - SAN JUAN CONTAINER PLANT—See WestRock Company; *U.S. Public*, pg. 2363
WESTROCK RKT CO. - SPRINGFIELD (MA) SHEET PLANT—See WestRock Company; *U.S. Public*, pg. 2363
WESTROCK RKT CO. - TUPELO CONTAINER PLANT—See WestRock Company; *U.S. Public*, pg. 2363
WESTROCK - SOUTHERN CONTAINER, LLC—See WestRock Company; *U.S. Public*, pg. 2362
WONDER STATE BOX CO.—See Southern Missouri Container Packaging Group; *U.S. Private*, pg. 3733
WORCESTER ENVELOPE COMPANY—See Moore DM Group, LLC; *U.S. Private*, pg. 2780
YAMAHATSU NIHON CO., LTD.—See Cheng Loong Corp.; *Int'l*, pg. 1466
ZAO SONOCO ALCORE—See Sonoco Products Company; *U.S. Public*, pg. 1906
ZHANGZHOU CHENG LOONG PAPER CO., LTD.—See Cheng Loong Corp.; *Int'l*, pg. 1466
ZHEJIANG GREAT SHENGDA PACKAGING CO., LTD.—See China Shengda Packaging Group Inc; *Int'l*, pg. 1551
ZHENGZHOU CHENG LOONG PACKING PRODUCTS CO., LTD.—See Cheng Loong Corp.; *Int'l*, pg. 1466

322212 — FOLDING PAPERBOARD BOX MANUFACTURING

ALFA LAVAL A/O—See Alfa Laval AB; *Int'l*, pg. 308
ALFA-LAVAL BENELUX N.V.—See Alfa Laval AB; *Int'l*, pg. 311
ALFA LAVAL DIS TICARET LTD STI—See Alfa Laval AB; *Int'l*, pg. 309
ALFA LAVAL K.K.—See Alfa Laval AB; *Int'l*, pg. 310
ALFA LAVAL KOREA LTD.—See Alfa Laval AB; *Int'l*, pg. 310
ALFA LAVAL LTD.—See Alfa Laval AB; *Int'l*, pg. 310
ALFA-LAVAL (MALAYSIA) SDN BHD—See Alfa Laval AB; *Int'l*, pg. 311
ALFA LAVAL OY—See Alfa Laval AB; *Int'l*, pg. 310
ALFA LAVAL PHILIPPINES, INC.—See Alfa Laval AB; *Int'l*, pg. 311
ALFA LAVAL POLSKA SP. ZOO—See Alfa Laval AB; *Int'l*, pg. 311
ALFA LAVAL SIA—See Alfa Laval AB; *Int'l*, pg. 311
ALFA LAVAL SOUTH EAST EUROPE LTD.—See Alfa Laval AB; *Int'l*, pg. 311
ALFA LAVAL, TAIWAN—See Alfa Laval AB; *Int'l*, pg. 311
ALFA LAVAL (THAILAND) LTD.—See Alfa Laval AB; *Int'l*, pg. 308
ALFA LAVAL TUMBA AB—See Alfa Laval AB; *Int'l*, pg. 311
ALL PACKAGING COMPANY—See Great Mill Rock LLC; *U.S. Private*, pg. 1766
AMERICRAFT CARTON, INC. - LOWELL PLANT—See Americraft Carton, Inc.; *U.S. Private*, pg. 259
AMERICRAFT CARTON, INC. - MEMPHIS PLANT—See Americraft Carton, Inc.; *U.S. Private*, pg. 259
AMERICRAFT CARTON, INC. - NORWALK PLANT—See Americraft Carton, Inc.; *U.S. Private*, pg. 259
AMERICRAFT CARTON, INC.; *U.S. Private*, pg. 259
AMERICRAFT CARTON INC.—See Americraft Carton, Inc.; *U.S. Private*, pg. 259
AMERICRAFT CARTON, INC.—See Americraft Carton, Inc.; *U.S. Private*, pg. 259
AMERICRAFT CARTON, INC.—See Americraft Carton, Inc.; *U.S. Private*, pg. 259
AMERICRAFT CARTON, INC. - ST. PAUL PLANT—See Americraft Carton, Inc.; *U.S. Private*, pg. 259
AMERICRAFT CARTON, INC. - STURGIS PLANT—See Americraft Carton, Inc.; *U.S. Private*, pg. 259
AMERICRAFT CARTON, INC. - WINSTON-SALEM PLANT—See Americraft Carton, Inc.; *U.S. Private*, pg. 259
AMG PACKAGING & PAPER COMPANY LTD.; *Int'l*, pg. 426
A&R CARTON OY—See CVC Capital Partners SICAV-FIS S.A.; *Int'l*, pg. 1881
ARKAY PACKAGING CORPORATION; *U.S. Private*, pg. 326
AR PACKAGING GROUP AB—See CVC Capital Partners SICAV-FIS S.A.; *Int'l*, pg. 1881
ARTISTIC CARTON COMPANY - AUBURN DIVISION—See Graphic Packaging Holding Company; *U.S. Public*, pg. 958
AUGUST FALLER GMBH & CO. KG; *Int'l*, pg. 703
BELLWYCK PACKAGING SOLUTIONS LTD.; *Int'l*, pg. 968
BEMIS FLEXIBLE PACKAGING CANADA LIMITED—See Amcor plc; *Int'l*, pg. 418
BERESFORD BOX COMPANY INC.; *Int'l*, pg. 979
BOX MANUFACTURING COMPANY LIMITED—See ENL Limited; *Int'l*, pg. 2441
BRITISH CONVERTING SOLUTIONS, LTD.; *Int'l*, pg. 1171
BURD & FLETCHER COMPANY; *U.S. Private*, pg. 686
CARAUSTAR CONVERTED PRODUCTS GROUP—See Greif Inc.; *U.S. Public*, pg. 966
CARAUSTAR INDUSTRIES, INC. - AUSTELL BOXBOARD MILL—See Greif Inc.; *U.S. Public*, pg. 965
CARAUSTAR INDUSTRIES, INC. - CHICAGO PACKAGING PLANT—See Greif Inc.; *U.S. Public*, pg. 966
CARAUSTAR INDUSTRIES, INC. - DENVER CARTON PLANT—See Greif Inc.; *U.S. Public*, pg. 966
CARAUSTAR INDUSTRIES, INC. - GRAND RAPIDS CARTON PLANT—See Greif Inc.; *U.S. Public*, pg. 966
CAREO S.R.L.—See Apollo Global Management, Inc.; *U.S. Public*, pg. 159
CASCADES BOXBOARD GROUP INC. - COBOURG—See Cascades Inc.; *Int'l*, pg. 1350
CASCADES BOXBOARD GROUP INC. - WINNIPEG—See Cascades Inc.; *Int'l*, pg. 1350
CASCADES DJUPAFORS A.B.—See Cascades Inc.; *Int'l*, pg. 1350
CASCADES MOULDED PULP, INC.—See Cascades Inc.; *Int'l*, pg. 1350
CASCADES SPECIALTY PRODUCTS GROUP—See Cascades Inc.; *Int'l*, pg. 1350
CHICAGO PACKAGING CORPORATION; *U.S. Private*, pg. 878
CLIMAX MANUFACTURING COMPANY—See DeltaPoint Capital Management, LLC; *U.S. Private*, pg. 1202
CLIMAX PACKAGING, INC—See DeltaPoint Capital Management, LLC; *U.S. Private*, pg. 1202
CLONDALKIN PHARMA & HEALTHCARE (PORT), INC.—See Egeria Capital Management B.V.; *Int'l*, pg. 2323

CM SUPPLY APS—See Bunzl plc; *Int'l*, pg. 1218
COLBERT PACKAGING CORPORATION; *U.S. Private*, pg. 965
CRESTEC PHILIPPINES, INC.—See Crestec Inc.; *Int'l*, pg. 1841
CURTIS CORPORATION; *U.S. Private*, pg. 1126
CURTIS PACKAGING CORPORATION—See Curtis Corporation; *U.S. Private*, pg. 1126
DAKOTA CORRUGATED BOX COMPANY—See Buckeye Corrugated Inc.; *U.S. Private*, pg. 677
DIAMOND PAPER BOX COMPANY; *U.S. Private*, pg. 1223
DIXIE PRINTING & PACKAGING, LLC—See Kollman Label Group, LLC; *U.S. Private*, pg. 2341
DOPACO, INC.—See Pactiv Evergreen Inc.; *U.S. Public*, pg. 1633
DURA-FIBRE, LLC.—See Dunsirn Partners LLC; *U.S. Private*, pg. 1290
EDELMANN (BEIJING) PHARMACEUTICAL PACKAGING & PRINTING, LTD.—See Edelmann GmbH; *Int'l*, pg. 2305
EDELMANN FRANCE—See Edelmann GmbH; *Int'l*, pg. 2305
EDELMANN HUNGARY PACKAGING ZRT.—See Edelmann GmbH; *Int'l*, pg. 2305
EDELMANN PACKAGING INDIA PRIVATE LIMITED—See Edelmann GmbH; *Int'l*, pg. 2305
EDELMANN PACKAGING MEXICO S.A. DE C.V.—See Edelmann GmbH; *Int'l*, pg. 2305
EDELMANN PHARMADRUCK GMBH—See Edelmann GmbH; *Int'l*, pg. 2305
EDELMANN POLAND SP.Z O.O.—See Edelmann GmbH; *Int'l*, pg. 2305
EDELMANN USA, INC. - PULASKI—See Edelmann GmbH; *Int'l*, pg. 2305
EDELMANN USA, INC.—See Edelmann GmbH; *Int'l*, pg. 2305
EMPIRE STATE CONTAINER INC—See Buckeye Corrugated Inc.; *U.S. Private*, pg. 677
FLOWER CITY PRINTING INC.; *U.S. Private*, pg. 1551
F.M. HOWELL & CO. INC.; *U.S. Private*, pg. 1456
FUSTELARKO BOREC BITOLA AD; *Int'l*, pg. 2850
GENERAL CONVERTING, INC.—See CORE Industrial Partners, LLC; *U.S. Private*, pg. 1048
GREEN BAY PACKAGING INC. - EL PASO DIVISION—See Green Bay Packaging Inc.; *U.S. Private*, pg. 1771
GREEN BAY PACKAGING INC. - FOLDING CARTON DIVISION—See Green Bay Packaging Inc.; *U.S. Private*, pg. 1771
GREEN BAY PACKAGING INC. - GREEN BAY DIVISION—See Green Bay Packaging Inc.; *U.S. Private*, pg. 1771
GREEN BAY PACKAGING INC. - KANSAS CITY DIVISION—See Green Bay Packaging Inc.; *U.S. Private*, pg. 1771
GREEN BAY PACKAGING INC. - TWIN CITIES DIVISION—See Green Bay Packaging Inc.; *U.S. Private*, pg. 1771
GREEN BAY PACKAGING INC. - WAUSAU DIVISION—See Green Bay Packaging Inc.; *U.S. Private*, pg. 1771
GRIFAL SPA; *Int'l*, pg. 3083
GUNTHER MELE LIMITED; *Int'l*, pg. 3185
GUNTHER MELE PACKAGING, INC.—See Gunther Mele Limited; *Int'l*, pg. 3185
HAWKEYE CORRUGATED BOX CO—See Buckeye Corrugated Inc.; *U.S. Private*, pg. 677
HUHTAMAKI, INC. - OHIO—See Huhtamaki Oyj; *Int'l*, pg. 3526
IMPRESSIONS INCORPORATED—See Great Mill Rock LLC; *U.S. Private*, pg. 1766
KAPSTONE CONTAINER CORP. - TWIN FALLS—See WestRock Company; *U.S. Public*, pg. 2361
KAPSTONE SEATTLE—See WestRock Company; *U.S. Public*, pg. 2361
KAPSTONE SPANISH FORK—See WestRock Company; *U.S. Public*, pg. 2361
MACK PAPER CO.—See Shorr Packaging Corp.; *U.S. Private*, pg. 3642
MALNOVE INCORPORATED OF NEBRASKA—See Malnove Incorporated.; *U.S. Private*, pg. 2558
MALNOVE INCORPORATED; *U.S. Private*, pg. 2558
MPS HOLLAND, INC.—See WestRock Company; *U.S. Public*, pg. 2362
MPS SOUTH PLAINFIELD, LLC—See WestRock Company; *U.S. Public*, pg. 2362
MULTI PACKAGING SOLUTIONS LIMITED—See WestRock Company; *U.S. Public*, pg. 2362
MULTI PACKAGING SOLUTIONS SERVICES GMBH—See WestRock Company; *U.S. Public*, pg. 2362
MURNANE PACKAGING CORPORATION; *U.S. Private*, pg. 2815
NAPCO, LLC; *U.S. Private*, pg. 2834
THE NATIONAL CARTON INDUSTRY COMPANY—See Arab Supply & Trading Co.; *Int'l*, pg. 532
NCALA, LLC; *U.S. Private*, pg. 2875
NEFF PACKAGING SOLUTIONS INC.; *U.S. Private*, pg. 2880
NEW DOMINION PACKAGING COMPANY INC.; *U.S. Private*, pg. 2893

322212 — FOLDING PAPERBOARD ...

NORAMPAC INC.—See Cascades Inc.; *Int'l*, pg. 1350
PAPERWORKS INDUSTRIES, INC. - HASTINGS—See Sun Capital Partners, Inc.; *U.S. Private*, pg. 3860
PAPERWORKS INDUSTRIES, INC. - MOUNT GILEAD—See Sun Capital Partners, Inc.; *U.S. Private*, pg. 3860
PARKSONS PACKAGING LTD.—See Warburg Pincus LLC; *U.S. Private*, pg. 4439
PRESTIGE BOX CORPORATION; *U.S. Private*, pg. 3255
PRYSTUP PACKAGING PRODUCTS; *U.S. Private*, pg. 3296
QUALITY CARTON INC.; *U.S. Private*, pg. 3318
RESOLUTION PACKAGING—See The Westervelt Company; *U.S. Private*, pg. 4134
RICE PACKAGING, INC.; *U.S. Private*, pg. 3425
ROYAL PAPER BOX OF CALIFORNIA; *U.S. Private*, pg. 3493
RTS EMBALAJES DE CHILE LIMITADA—See Sonoco Products Company; *U.S. Public*, pg. 1905
SEABOARD FOLDING BOX CORP.—See Vidya Brands Group LLC; *U.S. Private*, pg. 4381
SHOREWOOD PACKAGING LLC - LOS ANGELES PLANT—See Atlas Holdings, LLC; *U.S. Private*, pg. 378
SIMKINS/HARVARD FOLDING BOX COMPANY INC.; *U.S. Private*, pg. 3665
SONOCO ALLOYD-BATAVIA—See Sonoco Products Company; *U.S. Public*, pg. 1905
SOONER PACKAGING, INC.—See Southern Missouri Container Packaging Group; *U.S. Private*, pg. 3733
SOUTHERN CHAMPION TRAY CO. INC.; *U.S. Private*, pg. 3730
SOUTHERN CONVERTERS—See J.R. Cole Industries Inc.; *U.S. Private*, pg. 2170
SOUTHERN STANDARD CARTONS, INC.; *U.S. Private*, pg. 3735
STANDARD GROUP LLC—See Sun Capital Partners, Inc.; *U.S. Private*, pg. 3860
STERLING PAPER CO.; *U.S. Private*, pg. 3806
THIOLAT SAS—See Groupe Guillin SA; *Int'l*, pg. 3104
UTAH PAPER BOX COMPANY INC.; *U.S. Private*, pg. 4324
VAIL INDUSTRIES, INC.; *U.S. Private*, pg. 4329
WALTER G. ANDERSON INC.—See Graphic Packaging Holding Company; *U.S. Public*, pg. 959
WESTROCK CO. - CHICAGO—See WestRock Company; *U.S. Public*, pg. 2362
WESTROCK CO. - LANETT—See WestRock Company; *U.S. Public*, pg. 2362
WESTROCK CO. - MEBANE—See WestRock Company; *U.S. Public*, pg. 2362
WESTROCK KK—See WestRock Company; *U.S. Public*, pg. 2362
WESTROCK MANUFACTURING-BILBAO S.L.—See WestRock Company; *U.S. Public*, pg. 2362
WESTROCK PACKAGING SYSTEMS FRANCE SARL—See WestRock Company; *U.S. Public*, pg. 2362
WESTROCK PACKAGING SYSTEMS, LLC—See WestRock Company; *U.S. Public*, pg. 2362
WESTROCK PACKAGING SYSTEMS NETHERLANDS B.V.—See WestRock Company; *U.S. Public*, pg. 2362
WESTROCK PACKAGING SYSTEMS UK LTD.—See WestRock Company; *U.S. Public*, pg. 2362
WESTROCK RKT CO. - KNOX FOOD SERVICE PACKAGING PLANT—See WestRock Company; *U.S. Public*, pg. 2363
WESTROCK RKT COMPANY—See WestRock Company; *U.S. Public*, pg. 2362
WESTROCK RKT CO. - WINSTON-SALEM MERCHANDISING DISPLAYS—See WestRock Company; *U.S. Public*, pg. 2363
WESTROCK SERVICES, INC.—See WestRock Company; *U.S. Public*, pg. 2363
ZHONGSHAN HUNG HING PRINTING & PACKAGING COMPANY LIMITED—See Hung Hing Printing Group Limited; *Int'l*, pg. 3535
ZUMBIEL PACKAGING CO.-BEVERAGE DIVISION—See Zumbiel Packaging Co.; *U.S. Private*, pg. 4610
ZUMBIEL PACKAGING CO.; *U.S. Private*, pg. 4610

322219 — OTHER PAPERBOARD CONTAINER MANUFACTURING

3CI PACKAGING COMPANY—See Essentra plc; *Int'l*, pg. 2510
AHLSTROM MUNKSJO FIBER COMPOSITES INDIA PRIVATE LTD—See Ahlstrom Capital Oy; *Int'l*, pg. 224
AHLSTROM MUNKSJO FIBER COMPOSITES INDIA PRIVATE LTD—See Bain Capital, LP; *U.S. Private*, pg. 429
AJM PACKAGING CORPORATION; *U.S. Private*, pg. 144
AMCOR RIGID PLASTICS USA, INC.—See Amcor plc; *Int'l*, pg. 417
AMERICRAFT CARTON INC.—See Americraft Carton, Inc.; *U.S. Private*, pg. 259
AMSCAN INC.—See Thomas H. Lee Partners, L.P.; *U.S. Private*, pg. 4156
ARABIAN PAPER PRODUCTS COMPANY—See Huhtamaki Oyj; *Int'l*, pg. 3524
ASAHI KASEI SPANDEX EUROPE GMBH—See Asahi Kasei Corporation; *Int'l*, pg. 596
BAGHDAD FOR PACKING MATERIALS; *Int'l*, pg. 799
B&B TRIPLEWALL CONTAINERS LIMITED; *Int'l*, pg. 783
BEACHCOMBER HOT TUBS; *Int'l*, pg. 932
BORAX PAPER PRODUCTS—See Bain Capital, LP; *U.S. Private*, pg. 440
BORINQUEN FIBER DRUMS—See Borinquen Container Corp.; *U.S. Private*, pg. 618
BOX-PAK (HANOI) CO., LTD.—See Can-One Berhad; *Int'l*, pg. 1276
BP MPAK SDN. BHD.—See Can-One Berhad; *Int'l*, pg. 1276
CARAUSTAR INDUSTRIAL CANADA, INC.—See Greif Inc.; *U.S. Public*, pg. 965
CAROLINA PAPER TUBES INC.—See Ox Paper Tube & Core, Inc.; *U.S. Private*, pg. 3056
CASCADES CANADA ULC—See Cascades Inc.; *Int'l*, pg. 1350
CHANGYUAN ELECTRONICS (SHENZHEN) CO., LTD.—See ChangYuan Group Ltd.; *Int'l*, pg. 1444
COMPO TECH PLUS, SPOL. S R.O.—See Fukuda Corporation; *Int'l*, pg. 2839
CONSOLIDATED CONTAINER COMPANY LLC—See Stone Canyon Industries, LLC; *U.S. Private*, pg. 3817
CONTEGO PACKAGING—See Platinum Equity, LLC; *U.S. Private*, pg. 3202
CREATIVE CONVERTING—See Wellspring Capital Management LLC; *U.S. Private*, pg. 4477
CRESCENT BOX CORP.; *U.S. Private*, pg. 1093
CRYOVAC AUSTRALIA PTY. LTD.—See Sealed Air Corporation; *U.S. Public*, pg. 1852
DART CUP LTD—See Dart Container Corporation; *U.S. Private*, pg. 1160
DART PRODUCTS LTD—See Dart Container Corporation; *U.S. Private*, pg. 1160
DEL-TIN FIBER L.L.C.—See Roseburg Forest Products; *U.S. Private*, pg. 3482
DESIGN PACKAGING, INC.—See Clayton, Dubilier & Rice, LLC; *U.S. Private*, pg. 930
DS SMITH PACKAGING FINLAND OY—See DS Smith Plc; *Int'l*, pg. 2208
DS SMITH PACKAGING FRANCE—See DS Smith Plc; *Int'l*, pg. 2208
DS SMITH PACKAGING GHIMBAV SRL—See DS Smith Plc; *Int'l*, pg. 2208
DS SMITH PACKAGING ITALIA—See DS Smith Plc; *Int'l*, pg. 2208
DS SMITH PACKAGING MANNHEIM—See DS Smith Plc; *Int'l*, pg. 2208
DS SMITH PACKAGING SWEDEN AB—See DS Smith Plc; *Int'l*, pg. 2208
DS SMITH PACKAGING SWITZERLAND AG—See DS Smith Plc; *Int'l*, pg. 2208
DS SMITH PAPER DEUTSCHLAND GMBH—See DS Smith Plc; *Int'l*, pg. 2208
DUCKS CO.—See FP Corporation; *Int'l*, pg. 2756
DURAN DOGAN BASIM VE AMBALAJ SANAYI A.S.; *Int'l*, pg. 2228
ELOPAK A/S—See Ferd AS; *Int'l*, pg. 2635
EMS OFFSHORE PTE. LTD.—See EMS Energy Limited; *Int'l*, pg. 2392
EQUIPMENT STORAGE & SERVICE INC.—See Ed Bell Investments Company Inc.; *U.S. Private*, pg. 1331
EXEL COMPOSITES OYJ; *Int'l*, pg. 2581
F. BENDER LIMITED—See DOpla S.p.A.; *Int'l*, pg. 2174
F. BENDER LIMITED—See FLO S.p.A.; *Int'l*, pg. 2707
FLAMBEAU EUROPLAST, LTD.—See Nordic Group of Companies, Ltd.; *U.S. Private*, pg. 2936
FLO DEUTSCHLAND GMBH—See FLO S.p.A.; *Int'l*, pg. 2707
FLO VENDING—See FLO S.p.A.; *Int'l*, pg. 2707
FP CHUPA CORP.—See FP Corporation; *Int'l*, pg. 2756
FPCO AI PACK CO.—See FP Corporation; *Int'l*, pg. 2756
FPCO CHUBU CO.—See FP Corporation; *Int'l*, pg. 2756
FPCO DIA FOODS CO., LTD.—See FP Corporation; *Int'l*, pg. 2756
FPCO KASAOKA CO.—See FP Corporation; *Int'l*, pg. 2756
FPCO MINOSHIMA CO.—See FP Corporation; *Int'l*, pg. 2756
FP CORPORATION - FUKUYAMA PLANT—See FP Corporation; *Int'l*, pg. 2756
FP CORPORATION - HOKKAIDO PLANT—See FP Corporation; *Int'l*, pg. 2756
FPCO SHIMODATE, LTD.—See FP Corporation; *Int'l*, pg. 2756
FURUBAYASHI SHIKO CO., LTD.; *Int'l*, pg. 2846
FUSION PAPERBOARD US, INC.—See OpenGate Capital Management, LLC; *U.S. Private*, pg. 3030
GENPAK LLC—See First Atlantic Capital Ltd.; *U.S. Private*, pg. 1513
GENPAK—See First Atlantic Capital Ltd.; *U.S. Private*, pg. 1513
GEORGIA-PACIFIC CONTAINERBOARD LLC—See Koch Industries, Inc.; *U.S. Private*, pg. 2328
GREEN BAY PACKAGING INC. - ARKANSAS KRAFT DIVISION—See Green Bay Packaging Inc.; *U.S. Private*, pg. 1771
GREEN BAY PACKAGING INC. - BALTIMORE DIVISION—See Green Bay Packaging Inc.; *U.S. Private*, pg. 1771
GREEN BAY PACKAGING INC. - CHICKASHA DIVISION—See Green Bay Packaging Inc.; *U.S. Private*, pg. 1771
GREEN BAY PACKAGING INC. - CINCINNATI DIVISION—See Green Bay Packaging Inc.; *U.S. Private*, pg. 1771
GREEN BAY PACKAGING INC. - DE PERE DIVISION—See Green Bay Packaging Inc.; *U.S. Private*, pg. 1771
GREEN BAY PACKAGING INC. - FIBER RESOURCE DIVISION—See Green Bay Packaging Inc.; *U.S. Private*, pg. 1771
GREEN BAY PACKAGING INC. - FORT WORTH DIVISION—See Green Bay Packaging Inc.; *U.S. Private*, pg. 1771
GREEN BAY PACKAGING INC. - FREMONT DIVISION—See Green Bay Packaging Inc.; *U.S. Private*, pg. 1771
GREEN BAY PACKAGING INC. - GREEN BAY COATED PRODUCTS DIVISION—See Green Bay Packaging Inc.; *U.S. Private*, pg. 1771
GREEN BAY PACKAGING INC. - GREEN BAY MILL DIVISION—See Green Bay Packaging Inc.; *U.S. Private*, pg. 1771
GREEN BAY PACKAGING INC. - KALAMAZOO DIVISION—See Green Bay Packaging Inc.; *U.S. Private*, pg. 1771
GREEN BAY PACKAGING INC. - MINNEAPOLIS DIVISION—See Green Bay Packaging Inc.; *U.S. Private*, pg. 1771
GREEN BAY PACKAGING INC. - PINECREST LUMBER DIVISION—See Green Bay Packaging Inc.; *U.S. Private*, pg. 1771
GREEN BAY PACKAGING INC. - TULSA DIVISION—See Green Bay Packaging Inc.; *U.S. Private*, pg. 1771
GREEN BAY PACKAGING INC. - WINCHESTER DIVISION—See Green Bay Packaging Inc.; *U.S. Private*, pg. 1771
GREIF BROTHERS CANADA, INC.—See Greif Inc.; *U.S. Public*, pg. 967
GREIF DENMARK A/S—See Greif Inc.; *U.S. Public*, pg. 967
GREIF INC.; *U.S. Public*, pg. 965
GREIF - MASSILLON—See Greif Inc.; *U.S. Public*, pg. 967
GREIF RIVERVILLE MILL—See Greif Inc.; *U.S. Public*, pg. 968
HI-TECH WINDING SYSTEMS LTD.; *Int'l*, pg. 3382
HOFFMASTER GROUP, INC.—See Wellspring Capital Management LLC; *U.S. Private*, pg. 4477
HOOD CONTAINER CORPORATION; *U.S. Private*, pg. 1977
HOUSE OF PACKAGING INC.; *U.S. Private*, pg. 1991
HUHTAMAKI AUSTRALIA PTY. LTD.—See Huhtamaki Oyj; *Int'l*, pg. 3524
HUHTAMAKI CONSUMER PACKAGING INC.—See Huhtamaki Oyj; *Int'l*, pg. 3526
HUHTAMAKI FOODSERVICE GERMANY GMBH & CO. KG—See Huhtamaki Oyj; *Int'l*, pg. 3525
HUHTAMAKI FOODSERVICE GLIWICE SP. Z O.O.—See Huhtamaki Oyj; *Int'l*, pg. 3525
HUHTAMAKI FOODSERVICE (SHANGHAI) LIMITED—See Huhtamaki Oyj; *Int'l*, pg. 3525
HUHTAMAKI FOODSERVICE UKRAINE LLC—See Huhtamaki Oyj; *Int'l*, pg. 3525
HUHTAMAKI HENDERSON LTD.—See Huhtamaki Oyj; *Int'l*, pg. 3525
HUHTAMAKI MEXICANA S.A. DE C.V.—See Huhtamaki Oyj; *Int'l*, pg. 3525
HUHTAMAKI OYJ; *Int'l*, pg. 3524
IGNITE USA, LLC—See Newell Brands Inc.; *U.S. Public*, pg. 1514
INDIA FIBC CUSTOMER SERVICE CENTER—See Greif Inc.; *U.S. Public*, pg. 967
INDUSTRIAL CONTAINER SERVICES, LLC - CINCINNATI 26—See Stone Canyon Industries, LLC; *U.S. Private*, pg. 3817
INDUSTRIAL CONTAINER SERVICES, LLC - COLUMBUS—See Stone Canyon Industries, LLC; *U.S. Private*, pg. 3817
INDUSTRIAL CONTAINER SERVICES, LLC - DENVER—See Stone Canyon Industries, LLC; *U.S. Private*, pg. 3817
INDUSTRIAL CONTAINER SERVICES, LLC - LOUISVILLE—See Stone Canyon Industries, LLC; *U.S. Private*, pg. 3817
INDUSTRIAL CONTAINER SERVICES, LLC - ORLANDO—See Stone Canyon Industries, LLC; *U.S. Private*, pg. 3817
INDUSTRIAL CONTAINER SERVICES, LLC—See Stone Canyon Industries, LLC; *U.S. Private*, pg. 3817
INEX CORPORATION INC.; *U.S. Private*, pg. 2070
INTERNATIONAL PAPER COMPANY—See International Paper Company; *U.S. Public*, pg. 1156
INTERNATIONAL PAPER RETAIL DISPLAY & PACKAGING—See International Paper Company; *U.S. Public*, pg. 1157
INTERNATIONAL TUBE TECHNOLOGY (PTY) LTD—See Berry Global Group, Inc; *U.S. Public*, pg. 324

N.A.I.C.S. INDEX

322220 — PAPER BAG AND COATE...

KILMER WAGNER AND WISE PAPER CO. INC.—See Central National Gottesman Inc.; *U.S. Private*, pg. 823
KNIGHT PAPER BOX COMPANY; *U.S. Private*, pg. 2322
LBP MANUFACTURING LLC—See Sabert Corporation; *U.S. Private*, pg. 3520
LEADER ENERGY SERVICES LTD.—See Key Energy Services, Inc.; *U.S. Public*, pg. 1225
LIBERTY CARTON COMPANY—See Liberty Diversified International Inc.; *U.S. Private*, pg. 2443
MILLEN INDUSTRIES INCORPORATED; *U.S. Private*, pg. 2731
NEUVIBOX SAS—See Sonoco Products Company; *U.S. Public*, pg. 1904
NEW CREATURE; *U.S. Private*, pg. 2893
OWENS-CORNING (INDIA) LIMITED—See Owens Corning; *U.S. Public*, pg. 1628
PACIFIC PAPER TUBE, INC.—See Sky Island Capital LLC; *U.S. Private*, pg. 3684
PAPERTECH SL—See Sonoco Products Company; *U.S. Public*, pg. 1904
PARAMOUNT TUBE—See Auxo Investment Partners, LLC; *U.S. Private*, pg. 402
PLASTIC PRINTING PROFESSIONALS, INC.—See Bristol ID Technologies, Inc.; *U.S. Private*, pg. 656
PRECISION PAPER TUBE COMPANY; *U.S. Private*, pg. 3246
PRODUCEMBAL-PRODUCAO DE EMBALAGENS, LTDA—See Sealed Air Corporation; *U.S. Public*, pg. 1854
PT SONOCO INDONESIA—See Sonoco Products Company; *U.S. Public*, pg. 1905
R.D.M LA ROCHETTE S.A.S.—See Cascades Inc.; *Int'l*, pg. 1351
RENO DE MEDICI ARNSBERG—See Apollo Global Management, Inc.; *U.S. Public*, pg. 159
RENO DE MEDICI VILLA SANTA LUCIA—See Apollo Global Management, Inc.; *U.S. Public*, pg. 159
REYNOLDS FOOD PACKAGING LLC—See Pactiv Evergreen Inc.; *U.S. Public*, pg. 1634
ROBERT KARP CONTAINER CORP; *U.S. Private*, pg. 3458
RTS PACKAGING, LLC—See Sonoco Products Company; *U.S. Public*, pg. 1904
RUSKEN PACKAGING INC.; *U.S. Private*, pg. 3505
SACOPOR - SOCIEDADE DE EMBALAGENS E SACOS DE PAPEL S.A.—See Camargo Correa S.A.; *Int'l*, pg. 1268
SAS MECATEL—See Hiolle Industries SA; *Int'l*, pg. 3401
SEALED AIR (NEW ZEALAND)—See Sealed Air Corporation; *U.S. Public*, pg. 1854
SEALED AIR (NEW ZEALAND)—See Sealed Air Corporation; *U.S. Public*, pg. 1854
SHEBOYGAN PAPER BOX CO. INC.; *U.S. Private*, pg. 3629
SHIN-NIPPON INDUSTRIES SDN. BHD.—See Asahi Printing Co., Ltd.; *Int'l*, pg. 598
SHOREWOOD PACKAGING LLC - LOUISVILLE PLANT—See Atlas Holdings, LLC; *U.S. Private*, pg. 378
SHOREWOOD PACKAGING LLC—See Atlas Holdings, LLC; *U.S. Private*, pg. 378
SIMKINS CORPORATION; *U.S. Private*, pg. 3665
SONOCO ALCORE NV—See Sonoco Products Company; *U.S. Public*, pg. 1906
SONOCO AMBALAJ SANAYI VE TICARET A.S.—See Sonoco Products Company; *U.S. Public*, pg. 1906
SONOCO ASIA L.L.C.—See Sonoco Products Company; *U.S. Public*, pg. 1905
SONOCO AUSTRALIA PTY. LTD.—See Sonoco Products Company; *U.S. Public*, pg. 1905
SONOCO AUSTRALIA PTY. LTD.—See Sonoco Products Company; *U.S. Public*, pg. 1905
SONOCO CAPREX AG—See Sonoco Products Company; *U.S. Public*, pg. 1906
SONOCO COMERCIAL S. DE R.L. DE C.V.—See Sonoco Products Company; *U.S. Public*, pg. 1906
SONOCO CONSUMER PRODUCTS N.V.—See Sonoco Products Company; *U.S. Public*, pg. 1906
SONOCO CONSUMER PRODUCTS—See Sonoco Products Company; *U.S. Public*, pg. 1906
SONOCO DO BRASIL PARTICIPACOES LTDA—See Sonoco Products Company; *U.S. Public*, pg. 1906
SONOCO DO CHILE S.A.—See Sonoco Products Company; *U.S. Public*, pg. 1908
SONOCO HAYES, INC.—See Sonoco Products Company; *U.S. Public*, pg. 1906
SONOCO NEW ZEALAND LTD.—See Sonoco Products Company; *U.S. Public*, pg. 1905
SONOCO NORGE A/S—See Sonoco Products Company; *U.S. Public*, pg. 1907
SONOCO OF PUERTO RICO, INC.—See Sonoco Products Company; *U.S. Public*, pg. 1908
SONOCO PRODUCTS COMPANY - JACKSON—See Sonoco Products Company; *U.S. Public*, pg. 1908
SONOCO PRODUCTS COMPANY - ORLANDO—See Sonoco Products Company; *U.S. Public*, pg. 1908
SONOCO PRODUCTS COMPANY—See Sonoco Products Company; *U.S. Public*, pg. 1907
SONOCO PRODUCTS COMPANY—See Sonoco Products Company; *U.S. Public*, pg. 1907
SONOCO PRODUCTS COMPANY—See Sonoco Products Company; *U.S. Public*, pg. 1907
SONOCO PRODUCTS COMPANY—See Sonoco Products Company; *U.S. Public*, pg. 1907
SONOCO PRODUCTS COMPANY—See Sonoco Products Company; *U.S. Public*, pg. 1907
SONOCO PRODUCTS COMPANY—See Sonoco Products Company; *U.S. Public*, pg. 1907
SONOCO PRODUCTS COMPANY—See Sonoco Products Company; *U.S. Public*, pg. 1907
SONOCO PRODUCTS COMPANY—See Sonoco Products Company; *U.S. Public*, pg. 1907
SONOCO PRODUCTS COMPANY—See Sonoco Products Company; *U.S. Public*, pg. 1907
SONOCO PRODUCTS COMPANY—See Sonoco Products Company; *U.S. Public*, pg. 1907
SONOCO PRODUCTS COMPANY—See Sonoco Products Company; *U.S. Public*, pg. 1907
SONOCO PRODUCTS COMPANY—See Sonoco Products Company; *U.S. Public*, pg. 1907
SONOCO PRODUCTS COMPANY—See Sonoco Products Company; *U.S. Public*, pg. 1908
SONOCO PRODUCTS COMPANY—See Sonoco Products Company; *U.S. Public*, pg. 1908
SONOCO PRODUCTS COMPANY—See Sonoco Products Company; *U.S. Public*, pg. 1908
SONOCO PRODUCTS COMPANY—See Sonoco Products Company; *U.S. Public*, pg. 1908
SONOCO PRODUCTS COMPANY—See Sonoco Products Company; *U.S. Public*, pg. 1908
SONOCO PRODUCTS COMPANY—See Sonoco Products Company; *U.S. Public*, pg. 1908
SONOCO PRODUCTS COMPANY—See Sonoco Products Company; *U.S. Public*, pg. 1908
SONOCO PRODUCTS COMPANY—See Sonoco Products Company; *U.S. Public*, pg. 1908
SONOCO PRODUCTS COMPANY—See Sonoco Products Company; *U.S. Public*, pg. 1908
SONOCO RIGID PLASTICS—See Sonoco Products Company; *U.S. Public*, pg. 1908
SONOCO SINGAPORE PTE. LTD.—See Sonoco Products Company; *U.S. Public*, pg. 1905
SONOCO TAIWAN LIMITED—See Sonoco Products Company; *U.S. Public*, pg. 1905
SONOCO THAILAND LIMITED—See Sonoco Products Company; *U.S. Public*, pg. 1905
THE SPECIALIZED PACKAGING GROUP, INC—See Altamont Capital Partners; *U.S. Private*, pg. 205
SPECIALTY COATING & LAMINATING LLC; *U.S. Private*, pg. 3749
STONE INDUSTRIAL—See Auxo Investment Partners, LLC; *U.S. Private*, pg. 402
THE STRIVE GROUP LLC—See Menasha Corporation; *U.S. Private*, pg. 2665
TRANSPARENT CONTAINER CO., INC. - MEXICO FACILITY—See Wellspring Capital Management LLC; *U.S. Private*, pg. 4477
TRANSPARENT CONTAINER CO., INC. - PAPERBOARD FACILITY—See Wellspring Capital Management LLC; *U.S. Private*, pg. 4477
T&S PRODUCTS INC.; *U.S. Private*, pg. 3910
TUBO-TEC NORDESTE INDUSTRIA—See Sonoco Products Company; *U.S. Public*, pg. 1909
U.S. DISPLAY GROUP, INC.—See Four M Holdings LLC; *U.S. Private*, pg. 1582
U.S. DISPLAY GROUP—See Four M Holdings LLC; *U.S. Private*, pg. 1582
WEBCO INDUSTRIES INC.; *U.S. Public*, pg. 2341
WEIDENHAMMER HELLAS S.A.—See Sonoco Products Company; *U.S. Public*, pg. 1909
WESTROCK CONSUMER PAPERBOARD EMEA B.V.—See WestRock Company; *U.S. Public*, pg. 2362
WORLDCENTRIC.ORG; *U.S. Private*, pg. 4568

322220 — PAPER BAG AND COATED AND TREATED PAPER MANUFACTURING

3M AUSTRALIA PTY. LTD.—See 3M Company; *U.S. Public*, pg. 5
ACUCOTE INC.—See Fedrigoni SpA; *Int'l*, pg. 2631
ADCHEM CORPORATION—See Berry Global Group, Inc; *U.S. Public*, pg. 320
ADHESIVE PACKAGING SPECIALTIES, INC.; *U.S. Private*, pg. 79
ADMIRAL PACKAGING, INC.; *U.S. Private*, pg. 81
AGI SOLUTIONS INC.—See Ag Growth International Inc.; *Int'l*, pg. 198
AHLSTROM-MUNKSJO LA GERE S.A.S.—See Ahlstrom Capital Oy; *Int'l*, pg. 224
AHLSTROM-MUNKSJO LA GERE S.A.S.—See Bain Capital, LP; *U.S. Private*, pg. 429
AHLSTROM-MUNKSJO PAPER INC.—See Ahlstrom Capital Oy; *Int'l*, pg. 224
AHLSTROM-MUNKSJO PAPER INC.—See Bain Capital, LP; *U.S. Private*, pg. 430
AKZONOBEL—See Akzo Nobel N.V.; *Int'l*, pg. 272
AL ALAM INDUSTRIAL COMPANY LLC—See Hayel Saeed Anam Group of Companies; *Int'l*, pg. 3290
ALCAN PACKAGING BAIE D'URFE—See Amcor plc; *Int'l*, pg. 417
ALCAN PACKAGING IZMIR GRAVUR BASKILI KARTON SANAYI VE TICARET AS—See Amcor plc; *Int'l*, pg. 417
ALCAN PACKAGING LAINATE—See Amcor plc; *Int'l*, pg. 417
ALLIED SECURITY INNOVATIONS, INC.; *U.S. Public*, pg. 80
ALPHA BETA GLOBAL TAPES & ADHESIVES CO., LTD.—See 3M Company; *U.S. Public*, pg. 7
ALPHAFORM—See Groupe Guillin SA; *Int'l*, pg. 3103
ALPRINT S.A.; *Int'l*, pg. 375
AL TAWFIQ CO FOR PLASTIC & WOVEN SACKS INDUSTRIES LTD.—See Hayel Saeed Anam Group of Companies; *Int'l*, pg. 3290
ALUPOL FILMS SP. Z O.O.—See Grupa Kety S.A.; *Int'l*, pg. 3116
AMCOR FLEXIBLES BURGDORF GMBH—See Amcor plc; *Int'l*, pg. 417
AMCOR FLEXIBLES CRAMLINGTON LTD—See Amcor plc; *Int'l*, pg. 417
AMCOR FLEXIBLES EUROPE—See Amcor plc; *Int'l*, pg. 417
AMCOR FLEXIBLES GROUP PTY. LTD.—See Amcor plc; *Int'l*, pg. 416
AMCOR FLEXIBLES LUGO—See Amcor plc; *Int'l*, pg. 417
AMCOR FLEXIBLES PUERTO RICO INC.—See Amcor plc; *Int'l*, pg. 417
AMCOR FLEXIBLES SAINT MAUR—See Amcor plc; *Int'l*, pg. 417
AMCOR FLEXIBLES SARREBOURG S.A.S.—See Amcor plc; *Int'l*, pg. 417
AMCOR FLEXIBLES SINGAPORE PTE LTD—See Amcor plc; *Int'l*, pg. 417
AMCOR FLEXIBLES UK LTD.—See Amcor plc; *Int'l*, pg. 417
AMCOR FLEXIBLES ZUTPHEN B.V.—See Amcor plc; *Int'l*, pg. 417
AMCOR PTY LTD—See Amcor plc; *Int'l*, pg. 416
AMCOR TOBACCO PACKAGING BRABANT B.V.—See Amcor plc; *Int'l*, pg. 417
AMCOR TOBACCO PACKAGING SWITZERLAND GMBH—See Amcor plc; *Int'l*, pg. 417
AMERCAREROYAL, LLC—See HCI Equity Management, L.P.; *U.S. Public*, pg. 1889
AMERICAN BILTRITE FAR EAST, INC.—See American Biltrite Inc.; *U.S. Public*, pg. 97
AMERICAN PACKAGING CORPORATION - FLEXOGRAPHIC DIVISION—See American Packaging Corporation; *U.S. Private*, pg. 242
AMERICAN PACKAGING CORPORATION - ROTO GRAUVRE DIVISION—See American Packaging Corporation; *U.S. Private*, pg. 242
AMERICAN PACKAGING CORPORATION; *U.S. Private*, pg. 242
AMERITAPE, INC.—See Sur-Seal LLC; *U.S. Private*, pg. 3883
AMGRAPH PACKAGING INC.; *U.S. Private*, pg. 262
AMIFA CO., LTD.; *Int'l*, pg. 427
AMPAC FLEXIBLES AG—See The Pritzker Group - Chicago, LLC; *U.S. Public*, pg. 4099
ANDEX INDUSTRIES INC.; *U.S. Private*, pg. 278
ANTON DEBATIN GMBH; *Int'l*, pg. 484
API LAMINATES LIMITED—See Steel Partners Holdings L.P.; *U.S. Public*, pg. 1942
API (USA) HOLDINGS LIMITED—See Steel Partners Holdings L.P.; *U.S. Public*, pg. 1942
APPVION OPERATIONS, INC.—See Franklin Resources, Inc.; *U.S. Public*, pg. 880
ARCELORMITTAL - ARCELORMITTAL CANOSSA MILL—See ArcelorMittal S.A.; *Int'l*, pg. 543
ARGENT INTERNATIONAL; *U.S. Private*, pg. 320
ARKWRIGHT ADVANCED COATING, INC.—See ANDRITZ AG; *Int'l*, pg. 455
ARTINOVA AB; *Int'l*, pg. 584
ARTIN PAPIERVERTRIEBS GMBH—See Artinova AB; *Int'l*, pg. 584
A.S. CREATION (FRANCE) SAS—See A.S. Creation Tapeten AG; *Int'l*, pg. 28
A.S. CREATION TAPETEN AG; *Int'l*, pg. 28
ASTRAPAK LIMITED - CINQPLAST PLASTOP DENVER DIVISION—See Berry Global Group, Inc; *U.S. Public*, pg. 323
ASTRAPAK LIMITED - CITY PACKAGING DIVISION—See Berry Global Group, Inc; *U.S. Public*, pg. 323
ASTRAPAK LIMITED - PACKAGING CONSULTANTS DIVISION—See Berry Global Group, Inc; *U.S. Public*, pg. 323
ASTRAPAK LIMITED - PENINSULA PACKAGING DIVISION—See Berry Global Group, Inc; *U.S. Public*, pg. 323
ASTRAPAK LIMITED - PLASTFORM DIVISION—See Berry Global Group, Inc; *U.S. Public*, pg. 323
ASTRAPAK LIMITED - PLASTOP BRONKHORSTSPRUIT

322220 — PAPER BAG AND COATE...

DIVISION—See Berry Global Group, Inc; *U.S. Public*, pg. 323
ASTRAPAK LIMITED - TRISTAR PLASTICS DIVISION—See Berry Global Group, Inc; *U.S. Public*, pg. 323
ASTRAPAK LIMITED - ULTRAPAK DIVISION—See Berry Global Group, Inc; *U.S. Public*, pg. 323
ASTRAPAK MANUFACTURING HOLDINGS (PTY) LTD—See Berry Global Group, Inc; *U.S. Public*, pg. 323
ATLAPAC CORP.—See H.I.G. Capital, LLC; *U.S. Private*, pg. 1834
ATTRACTIVE VENTURE (JB) SDN. BHD.—See D'nonce Technology Bhd.; *Int'l*, pg. 1899
ATTRACTIVE VENTURE (KL) SDN. BHD.—See D'nonce Technology Bhd.; *Int'l*, pg. 1899
ATTRACTIVE VENTURE SDN. BHD.—See D'nonce Technology Bhd.; *Int'l*, pg. 1899
AVERY DENNISON CHILE S.A.—See Avery Dennison Corporation; *U.S. Public*, pg. 243
AVERY DENNISON COLOMBIA S. A.—See Avery Dennison Corporation; *U.S. Public*, pg. 243
AVERY DENNISON DO BRASIL LTDA.—See Avery Dennison Corporation; *U.S. Public*, pg. 244
AVERY DENNISON FASSON CANADA, INC.—See Avery Dennison Corporation; *U.S. Public*, pg. 244
AVERY DENNISON GROUP SINGAPORE (PTE) LIMITED—See Avery Dennison Corporation; *U.S. Public*, pg. 244
AVERY DENNISON - INDUSTRIAL & AUTOMOTIVE PRODUCTS DIVISION—See Avery Dennison Corporation; *U.S. Public*, pg. 243
AVERY DENNISON IRELAND LTD.—See Avery Dennison Corporation; *U.S. Public*, pg. 244
AVERY DENNISON ITALIA S.P.A.—See Avery Dennison Corporation; *U.S. Public*, pg. 244
AVERY DENNISON MATERIALS GMBH—See Avery Dennison Corporation; *U.S. Public*, pg. 244
AVERY DENNISON MATERIALS PTY LTD—See Avery Dennison Corporation; *U.S. Public*, pg. 244
AVERY DENNISON NTP A.S.—See Avery Dennison Corporation; *U.S. Public*, pg. 244
AVERY DENNISON - PERFORMANCE FILMS DIVISION, SCHERERVILLE—See Avery Dennison Corporation; *U.S. Public*, pg. 243
AVERY DENNISON - REFLECTIVE FILMS DIVISION, NILES—See Avery Dennison Corporation; *U.S. Public*, pg. 243
AVERY DENNISON RETAIL BRANDING & INFORMATION SOLUTIONS - GREENSBORO—See Avery Dennison Corporation; *U.S. Public*, pg. 243
AVERY DENNISON RETAIL INFORMATION SERVICES DE MEXICO, S.A. DE C.V.—See Avery Dennison Corporation; *U.S. Public*, pg. 244
AVERY DENNISON R.I.S. ITALIA S.R.L.—See Avery Dennison Corporation; *U.S. Public*, pg. 243
AVERY DENNISON RIS KOREA LTD.—See Avery Dennison Corporation; *U.S. Public*, pg. 243
AVERY DENNISON R.I.S. POLSKA SP.ZO.O—See Avery Dennison Corporation; *U.S. Public*, pg. 243
AVERY DENNISON RIS TAIWAN LTD.—See Avery Dennison Corporation; *U.S. Public*, pg. 243
AVERY DENNISON RIS VIETNAM CO. LTD.—See Avery Dennison Corporation; *U.S. Public*, pg. 244
AVERY DENNISON SINGAPORE (PTE) LTD.—See Avery Dennison Corporation; *U.S. Public*, pg. 244
AVERY DENNISON - SPECIALTY TAPE U.S.—See Avery Dennison Corporation; *U.S. Public*, pg. 243
AVERY DENNISON (SUZHOU) CO. LIMITED—See Avery Dennison Corporation; *U.S. Public*, pg. 243
AVERY DENNISON (THAILAND) LTD.—See Avery Dennison Corporation; *U.S. Public*, pg. 243
AVERY DENNISON U.K. LTD.—See Avery Dennison Corporation; *U.S. Public*, pg. 244
AVERY ETICHETTE ITALIA S.P.A.—See Avery Dennison Corporation; *U.S. Public*, pg. 244
AVERY GRAPHICS AND REFLECTIVE PRODUCTS DIVISION—See Avery Dennison Corporation; *U.S. Public*, pg. 244
AVERY OFFICE PRODUCTS PTY. LTD.—See CCL Industries Inc.; *Int'l*, pg. 1367
BAGCRAFT PAPERCORN I, LLC—See Apollo Global Management, Inc.; *U.S. Public*, pg. 153
BAKANLAR MEDYA A.S.; *Int'l*, pg. 804
BANCROFT BAG INC.; *U.S. Private*, pg. 464
B & A PACKAGING INDIA LIMITED; *Int'l*, pg. 783
BATES CARGO-PAK APS—See Illinois Tool Works Inc.; *U.S. Public*, pg. 1101
BEMIS ASIA PACIFIC SDN BHD—See Amcor plc; *Int'l*, pg. 418
BEMIS COMPANY, INC.—See Amcor plc; *Int'l*, pg. 418
BEMIS CUSTOM PRODUCTS—See Amcor plc; *Int'l*, pg. 418
BEMIS EUROPE FLEXIBLE PACKAGING—See Amcor plc; *Int'l*, pg. 418
BEMIS MONCEAU S.A.—See Amcor plc; *Int'l*, pg. 418
BEMIS PACKAGING SVERIGE A.B.—See Amcor plc; *Int'l*, pg. 418
BEMIS PACKAGING U.K. LTD.—See Kohlberg & Company, LLC; *U.S. Private*, pg. 2337

BEMIS PERFORMANCE PACKAGING, INC.—See Amcor plc; *Int'l*, pg. 418
BEMISS-JASON—See F.I.L.A. - Fabbrica Italiana Lapis ed Affini S.p.A.; *Int'l*, pg. 2596
BEMIS SWANSEA LTD.—See Kohlberg & Company, LLC; *U.S. Private*, pg. 2337
BEMIS VALKEAKOSKI OY—See Amcor plc; *Int'l*, pg. 418
BERYL CORPORATION; *U.S. Private*, pg. 541
BESIN AMBOISE SA—See Packaging Corporation of America; *U.S. Public*, pg. 1633
B&H BAG COMPANY—See Apollo Global Management, Inc.; *U.S. Public*, pg. 153
BILLERUD IBERICA S.L—See Billerud AB; *Int'l*, pg. 1030
BIOGROUPUSA, INC.; *U.S. Private*, pg. 562
BISCHOF + KLEIN GMBH & CO. KG; *Int'l*, pg. 1048
BOMARKO, INC.; *U.S. Private*, pg. 612
BONG RETAIL SOLUTIONS N.V.—See Bong AB; *Int'l*, pg. 1107
BONG S.A.S.—See Bong AB; *Int'l*, pg. 1107
BONTEX DE MEXICO, S.A. DE C.V.—See Bontex, Inc.; *U.S. Public*, pg. 368
BONTEX KOREA—See Bontex, Inc.; *U.S. Public*, pg. 368
BOSCH PACKAGING SYSTEMS AG—See CVC Capital Partners SICAV-FIS S.A.; *Int'l*, pg. 1884
BROWN PAPER GOODS COMPANY; *U.S. Private*, pg. 668
BRUSHFOIL—See Nicolet Capital Partners, LLC; *U.S. Private*, pg. 2926
BSC DRUKARNIA OPAKOWAN SA—See CVC Capital Partners SICAV-FIS S.A.; *Int'l*, pg. 1881
BURGO ARDENNES SA—See Burgo Group S.p.A.; *Int'l*, pg. 1223
BURGO DEUTSCHLAND GMBH—See Burgo Group S.p.A.; *Int'l*, pg. 1223
CANADIAN GENERAL TOWER LIMITED; *Int'l*, pg. 1283
CARIBBEAN LABEL CRAFTS LTD.—See Goddard Enterprises Limited; *Int'l*, pg. 3018
CASCADES ENVIROPAC HPM LLC—See Cascades Inc.; *Int'l*, pg. 1350
CASCADES ENVIROPAC INC—See Cascades Inc.; *Int'l*, pg. 1350
CASCADES USA INC.—See Cascades Inc.; *Int'l*, pg. 1351
CATTY CORPORATION; *U.S. Private*, pg. 794
CCL DESIGN GMBH—See CCL Industries Inc.; *Int'l*, pg. 1367
CCL LABEL (ASHFORD) LIMITED—See CCL Industries Inc.; *Int'l*, pg. 1368
CCL LABEL IRELAND—See CCL Industries Inc.; *Int'l*, pg. 1368
CCL LABEL LIMITED—See CCL Industries Inc.; *Int'l*, pg. 1368
CCL LABEL—See CCL Industries Inc.; *Int'l*, pg. 1367
CDG PACKAGING HOLDING AG; *Int'l*, pg. 1370
CELIA CORPORATION; *U.S. Private*, pg. 807
CELLO-FOIL PRODUCTS, INC.—See Sun Capital Partners, Inc.; *U.S. Private*, pg. 3858
CELLOGLAS LTD.—See Berggruen Holdings, Inc.; *U.S. Private*, pg. 531
CENTRAL NATIONAL GOTTESMAN INC. - CENTRAL NATIONAL DIVISION—See Central National Gottesman Inc.; *U.S. Private*, pg. 823
CHARGEURS PROTECTIVE FILMS—See Chargeurs SA; *Int'l*, pg. 1449
CHARTPAK INC—See GPC International, Inc.; *U.S. Private*, pg. 1748
CHIGA LIGHT INDUSTRIES SDN. BHD.—See HPI Resources Berhad; *Int'l*, pg. 3500
CHINA FILMS TECHNOLOGY INC.; *Int'l*, pg. 1502
CHURCH HILL CLASSICS; *U.S. Private*, pg. 894
CIC MARKETING SDN. BHD.—See Central Global Berhad; *Int'l*, pg. 1407
CLARK CONTAINER INCORPORATED; *U.S. Private*, pg. 912
CLONDALKIN PHARMA & HEALTHCARE (EVV), INC.—See Egeria Capital Management B.V.; *Int'l*, pg. 2323
CLOPAY PLASTIC PRODUCTS COMPANY—See Berry Global Group, Inc; *U.S. Public*, pg. 321
THE CLOROX COMPANY OF CANADA LTD.—See The Clorox Company; *U.S. Public*, pg. 2063
CLOSURE SYSTEMS INTERNATIONAL, INC.—See Cerberus Capital Management, L.P.; *U.S. Private*, pg. 837
COLONIAL BAG COMPANY; *U.S. Private*, pg. 970
COLORCON LTD.—See Berwind Corporation; *U.S. Private*, pg. 541
COLUMBINE SPECIALTY PRODUCTS, INC.; *U.S. Private*, pg. 978
COMITAL ALLUMINIO VOLPIANO—See Comital S.p.A.; *Int'l*, pg. 1714
COMITAL COFRESCO S.P.A.—See Comital S.p.A.; *Int'l*, pg. 1714
CONSTANTIA AFRIPACK—See One Rock Capital Partners, LLC; *U.S. Private*, pg. 3022
CONTEGO PACKAGING B.V.—See Platinum Equity, LLC; *U.S. Private*, pg. 3202
CONTEGO PACKAGING HOLDINGS LIMITED—See Platinum Equity, LLC; *U.S. Private*, pg. 3202
CONTEGO PACKAGING IRELAND LTD.—See Platinum Equity, LLC; *U.S. Private*, pg. 3202

CONTINENTAL DATALABEL; *U.S. Private*, pg. 1028
CONTIPAK NORON SDN. BHD.—See Computer Forms (Malaysia) Berhad; *Int'l*, pg. 1759
CORALLINE INVESTMENTS (PTY) LTD—See Berry Global Group, Inc; *U.S. Public*, pg. 323
CORAL PRODUCTS PLC; *Int'l*, pg. 1794
CORESA ARGENTINA S.A.—See Coresa S.A.; *Int'l*, pg. 1799
CORPORATIVO COPAMEX, S.A. DE C.V.; *Int'l*, pg. 1806
COSMO FIRST LIMITED; *Int'l*, pg. 1812
COVERIS ADVANCED COATINGS (NORTH WALES) LTD.—See Sun Capital Partners, Inc.; *U.S. Private*, pg. 3858
COVERIS ADVANCED COATINGS US LLC—See Sun Capital Partners, Inc.; *U.S. Private*, pg. 3859
C-P CONVERTERS, INC.—See First Atlantic Capital Ltd.; *U.S. Private*, pg. 1513
CROWN CORK & SEAL USA, INC.—See Crown Holdings, Inc.; *U.S. Public*, pg. 597
CROWN VAN GELDER B.V.—See Andlinger & Company, Inc.; *U.S. Private*, pg. 278
CURWOOD, INC.—See Amcor plc; *Int'l*, pg. 418
DAICEL PACK SYSTEMS LTD.—See Daicel Corporation; *Int'l*, pg. 1919
DAISAN SHIKA KOGYO CO., LTD.—See GSI Creos Corporation; *Int'l*, pg. 3144
DARET INC.; *U.S. Private*, pg. 1159
DATA2 INC.—See Data2 Corporation; *U.S. Private*, pg. 1164
DAVENPORT PAPER CO LIMITED—See Franz Haniel & Cie. GmbH; *Int'l*, pg. 2763
DEBATIN UK LTD—See Anton Debatin GmbH; *Int'l*, pg. 484
DETERLING COMPANY, INC.; *U.S. Private*, pg. 1216
DEUFOL ITALIA S.P.A.—See Deufol SE; *Int'l*, pg. 2048
DID CO., LTD.—See DAEWON Chemical Co., Ltd.; *Int'l*, pg. 1910
D.K. ENTERPRISES GLOBAL LIMITED; *Int'l*, pg. 1901
DNP NISHI NIPPON CO., LTD.—See Dai Nippon Printing Co., Ltd.; *Int'l*, pg. 1915
DNP TECHNOPACK CO., LTD.—See Dai Nippon Printing Co., Ltd.; *Int'l*, pg. 1915
DNP TOHOKU CO., LTD.—See Dai Nippon Printing Co., Ltd.; *Int'l*, pg. 1915
DONGGUAN NEW ISLAND PRINTING CO., LTD.—See China Huajun Group Limited; *Int'l*, pg. 1509
DONGGUAN WONDERFUL PACKAGING COMPANY LIMITED—See Amcor plc; *Int'l*, pg. 418
DS SMITH CORRUGATED PACKAGING LTD—See DS Smith Plc; *Int'l*, pg. 2208
DS SMITH PACKAGING LTD.—See DS Smith Plc; *Int'l*, pg. 2208
DS SMITH PACKAGING NEDERLAND BV—See DS Smith Plc; *Int'l*, pg. 2208
DS SMITH PACKAGING POLAND SP. Z O.O.—See DS Smith Plc; *Int'l*, pg. 2208
DS SMITH VERPACKUNG + DISPLAY VERTRIEBSGESELLSCHAFT MBH—See DS Smith Plc; *Int'l*, pg. 2208
DURO BAG MANUFACTURING CO. BROWNSVILLE—See Apollo Global Management, Inc.; *U.S. Public*, pg. 153
DURO BAG MANUFACTURING CO. - ELIZABETH—See Apollo Global Management, Inc.; *U.S. Public*, pg. 153
DURO BAG MANUFACTURING COMPANY—See Apollo Global Management, Inc.; *U.S. Public*, pg. 153
DURO BAG MANUFACTURING CO. - RICHWOOD—See Apollo Global Management, Inc.; *U.S. Public*, pg. 153
D&W FINE PACK LLC - FOUNTAIN INN—See Mid Oaks Investments LLC; *U.S. Private*, pg. 2706
D&W FINE PACK LLC - LAKE ZURICH—See Mid Oaks Investments LLC; *U.S. Private*, pg. 2706
D&W FINE PACK LLC—See Mid Oaks Investments LLC; *U.S. Private*, pg. 2706
DYNAPAC CO., LTD.; *Int'l*, pg. 2241
DYNAPLAST SA—See Groupe Guillin SA; *Int'l*, pg. 3103
ECO-PRODUCTS, INC.—See Apollo Global Management, Inc.; *U.S. Public*, pg. 154
EL AHRAM FOR PACKING S.A.E.; *Int'l*, pg. 2340
EMPRESA REGIONAL DE SERVICIO PU DE EL SA; *Int'l*, pg. 2388
EPL LTD.—See Blackstone Inc.; *U.S. Public*, pg. 353
ETERNABOND, LLC—See H.B. Fuller Company; *U.S. Public*, pg. 977
FAERCH PLAST BUNOL S.L.U.—See Advent International Corporation; *U.S. Private*, pg. 101
FASSON ROLL NORTH AMERICA - FORT WAYNE—See Avery Dennison Corporation; *U.S. Public*, pg. 244
FASSON ROLL NORTH AMERICA - PEACHTREE—See Avery Dennison Corporation; *U.S. Public*, pg. 244
FAUBEL & CO. NACHFOLGER GMBH—See CCL Industries Inc.; *Int'l*, pg. 1369
FIBERMARK NORTH AMERICA, INC.—See American Securities LLC; *U.S. Private*, pg. 248
FILMCO INDUSTRIES INC.—See Thermwell Products Co., Inc.; *U.S. Private*, pg. 4143
FLEXTRUS AB—See CVC Capital Partners SICAV-FIS S.A.; *Int'l*, pg. 1881
FOREST PACKAGING GROUP CO., LTD.; *Int'l*, pg. 2732
FORMICA CANADA, INC.—See HAL Trust N.V.; *Int'l*, pg. 3223

322220 — PAPER BAG AND COATE...

FORMICA NETHERLAND B.V.—See HAL Trust N.V.; *Int'l*, pg. 3223
FORMICA (SINGAPORE) PTE. LTD—See HAL Trust N.V.; *Int'l*, pg. 3223
FORTIFIBER CORPORATION; *U.S. Private*, pg. 1576
FP CORPORATION; *Int'l*, pg. 2756
FRITZ EGGER GMBH & CO.; *Int'l*, pg. 2793
GASCOGNE SACK AIGIS SA—See Gascogne SA; *Int'l*, pg. 2887
GASCOGNE SA; *Int'l*, pg. 2887
GASCOGNE USA, INC. - ORANGEVALE—See Gascogne SA; *Int'l*, pg. 2888
GASTON SYSTEMS, INC.—See Tubular Textile Machinery, Inc.; *U.S. Private*, pg. 4256
G-BOX SA DE CV.—See Graphic Packaging Holding Company; *U.S. Public*, pg. 958
GC PACKAGING, LLC—See Graphic Converting Inc.; *U.S. Private*, pg. 1757
GEBR. GRUNEWALD GMBH & CO. KG; *Int'l*, pg. 2905
GEBRUDER DURRBECK KUNSTSTOFFE GMBH; *Int'l*, pg. 2909
GEORGIA-PACIFIC CONSUMER PRODUCTS LP—See Koch Industries, Inc.; *U.S. Private*, pg. 2328
GEORGIA-PACIFIC CORPORATION—See Koch Industries, Inc.; *U.S. Private*, pg. 2329
GLATFELTER DRESDEN GMBH—See Glatfelter Corporation; *U.S. Public*, pg. 939
GLATFELTER OBERSCHMITTEN GMBH—See Glatfelter Corporation; *U.S. Public*, pg. 939
GPI UK—See Groupe Guillin SA; *Int'l*, pg. 3103
GRACE JAPAN K.K.—See Standard Industries Holdings Inc.; *U.S. Private*, pg. 3780
GRAPHIC PACKAGING INTERNATIONAL, INC. - ELK GROVE VILLAGE—See Graphic Packaging Holding Company; *U.S. Public*, pg. 959
GRAPHIC PACKAGING INTERNATIONAL, INC. - SALT LAKE CITY—See Graphic Packaging Holding Company; *U.S. Public*, pg. 959
GRAPHIC PACKAGING INTERNATIONAL, LLC—See Graphic Packaging Holding Company; *U.S. Public*, pg. 958
GREATPAC SDN. BHD.—See Doka Wawasan TKH Holdings Berhad; *Int'l*, pg. 2156
GREATPAC (S) PTE. LTD.—See Doka Wawasan TKH Holdings Berhad; *Int'l*, pg. 2156
GREATVIEW ASEPTIC PACKAGING EUROPE GMBH—See Greatview Aseptic Packaging Company Limited; *Int'l*, pg. 3068
GREATVIEW ASEPTIC PACKAGING MANUFACTURING GMBH—See Greatview Aseptic Packaging Company Limited; *Int'l*, pg. 3068
GREIF FLEXIBLE PRODUCTS & SERVICES—See Greif Inc.; *U.S. Public*, pg. 967
GREIF FLEXIBLES USA INC.—See Greif Inc.; *U.S. Public*, pg. 968
GREINER ASSISTEC LERESTI ROMANIA SA—See Greiner Holding AG; *Int'l*, pg. 3079
GRIGEO BALTWOOD UAB—See Grigeo AB; *Int'l*, pg. 3085
GROUPE GUILLIN SA; *Int'l*, pg. 3103
GROUPE INDUSPAC EMBALLAGE INC.; *Int'l*, pg. 3104
GTA-NHT, INC.—See 3M Company; *U.S. Public*, pg. 8
GUANGDONG GUANHAO HIGH-TECH CO., LTD.; *Int'l*, pg. 3155
GUANGDONG HONGMING INTELLIGENT JOINT STOCK CO., LTD.; *Int'l*, pg. 3155
GUANGZHOU HUAYAN PRECISION MACHINERY CO., LTD.; *Int'l*, pg. 3166
GUILLIN EMBALLAGES—See Groupe Guillin SA; *Int'l*, pg. 3103
GUILLIN ESPANA SL—See Groupe Guillin SA; *Int'l*, pg. 3104
HANDY WACKS CORPORATION; *U.S. Private*, pg. 1853
HARTA FLEKSIPAK SDN. BHD.—See HPI Resources Berhad; *Int'l*, pg. 3500
HAZEN PAPER COMPANY; *U.S. Private*, pg. 1886
HENKEL CONSUMER ADHESIVES, INC.—See Henkel AG & Co. KGaA; *Int'l*, pg. 3353
HINDUSTAN ADHESIVES LTD.; *Int'l*, pg. 3399
HOOD PACKAGING CORPORATION; *U.S. Private*, pg. 1977
HOOMARK ARTEX SP. Z O.O—See IG Design Group Plc; *Int'l*, pg. 3600
HOOMARK B.V.—See IG Design Group Plc; *Int'l*, pg. 3600
HOOMARK GIFT-WRAP PARTNERS BV—See IG Design Group Plc; *Int'l*, pg. 3600
H.S. CROCKER CO., INC.; *U.S. Private*, pg. 1835
HUANGSHAN NOVEL CO., LTD.; *Int'l*, pg. 3513
HUHTAMAKI ALF ZWEIGNIEDERLASSUNG DER HUHTAMAKI DEUTSCHLAND GMBH & CO KG—See Huhtamaki Oyj; *Int'l*, pg. 3525
HUHTAMAKI AUSTRALIA PTY LTD - FLEXIBLE PACKAGING SALES UNIT—See Huhtamaki Oyj; *Int'l*, pg. 3524
HUHTAMAKI AUSTRALIA PTY LTD - FOOD SERVICE BUSINESS UNIT—See Huhtamaki Oyj; *Int'l*, pg. 3524
HUHTAMAKI ESTONIA LTD.—See Huhtamaki Oyj; *Int'l*, pg. 3524
HUHTAMAKI FOODSERVICE FINLAND OY—See Huhtamaki Oyj; *Int'l*, pg. 3525

HUHTAMAKI FOODSERVICE POLAND SP. Z.O.O. - XPS PLANT—See Huhtamaki Oyj; *Int'l*, pg. 3525
HUHTAMAKI FORCHHEIM ZWEIGNIEDERLASSUNG DER HUHTAMAKI DEUTSCHLAND GMBH & CO KG—See Huhtamaki Oyj; *Int'l*, pg. 3525
HUHTAMAKI (GUANGZHOU) LIMITED—See Huhtamaki Oyj; *Int'l*, pg. 3524
HUHTAMAKI HENDERSON LIMITED - FOOD SERVICE BUSINESS UNIT—See Huhtamaki Oyj; *Int'l*, pg. 3525
HUHTAMAKI HONG KONG LIMITED—See Huhtamaki Oyj; *Int'l*, pg. 3525
HUHTAMAKI NEW ZEALAND LIMITED - FLEXIBLE FOOD PACKAGING BUSINESS UNIT—See Huhtamaki Oyj; *Int'l*, pg. 3524
HUHTAMAKI RONSBERG - ZWEIGNIEDERLASSUNG DER HUHTAMAKI DEUTSCHLAND GMBH & CO KG—See Huhtamaki Oyj; *Int'l*, pg. 3525
HUHTAMAKI (THAILAND) LIMITED - PLANT 1—See Huhtamaki Oyj; *Int'l*, pg. 3524
HUHTAMAKI (THAILAND) LIMITED - PLANT 2—See Huhtamaki Oyj; *Int'l*, pg. 3524
HUHTAMAKI (THAILAND) LIMITED—See Huhtamaki Oyj; *Int'l*, pg. 3524
HUHTAMAKI (VIETNAM) LTD—See Huhtamaki Oyj; *Int'l*, pg. 3524
HYOSUNG CHEMICALS GUMI PLANT I—See Hyosung Corporation; *Int'l*, pg. 3550
HYOSUNG CORPORATION - GWANGHYEWON PLANT—See Hyosung Corporation; *Int'l*, pg. 3550
ICI PACKAGING COATINGS LTDA.—See Akzo Nobel N.V.; *Int'l*, pg. 274
IDEAL TAPE-BELGIUM—See American Biltrite Inc.; *U.S. Public*, pg. 97
IDEAL TAPE COMPANY—See American Biltrite Inc.; *U.S. Public*, pg. 97
IG DESIGN GROUP BV—See IG Design Group Plc; *Int'l*, pg. 3600
IMAFLEX USA INC.—See Imaflex Inc.; *Int'l*, pg. 3617
INNO-PAK, LLC; *U.S. Private*, pg. 2080
INTERNATIONAL PAPER CANADA, INC.—See International Paper Company; *U.S. Public*, pg. 1155
INTERNATIONAL PAPER PACKAGING MALAYSIA (KUALA LUMPUR) SDN. BHD.—See International Paper Company; *U.S. Public*, pg. 1157
INTERNATIONAL PAPER SWITZERLAND GMBH—See International Paper Company; *U.S. Public*, pg. 1157
INTERTAPE POLYMER GROUP INC.—See Clearlake Capital Group, L.P.; *U.S. Private*, pg. 935
INTERWRAP CORP.—See Owens Corning; *U.S. Public*, pg. 1628
INTERWRAP, INC.—See Owens Corning; *U.S. Public*, pg. 1628
ISOLA GROUP LTD.—See TPG Capital, L.P.; *U.S. Public*, pg. 2174
ITW FOILS B.V.—See Illinois Tool Works Inc.; *U.S. Public*, pg. 1106
ITW FOILS—See Illinois Tool Works Inc.; *U.S. Public*, pg. 1105
ITW NEW ZEALAND LIMITED—See Illinois Tool Works Inc.; *U.S. Public*, pg. 1106
JIANGMEN XINGHUI PAPER MILL CO., LTD.—See Hokuetsu Corporation; *Int'l*, pg. 3444
J. JOSEPHSON, INC.; *U.S. Private*, pg. 2156
JOHNSON BRYCE INC—See Bryce Corporation; *U.S. Private*, pg. 674
KDV LABEL CO., INC.; *U.S. Private*, pg. 2270
KENDALL PACKAGING CORPORATION - JEFFERSON—See Kendall Packaging Corporation; *U.S. Private*, pg. 2283
KENDALL PACKAGING CORPORATION; *U.S. Private*, pg. 2283
KENNEDY GROUP INC.; *U.S. Private*, pg. 2285
KIERAN LABEL CORP.—See I.D. Images LLC; *U.S. Private*, pg. 2027
KNOX ENTERPRISES INC.; *U.S. Private*, pg. 2324
KORSNAS GMBH—See Billerud AB; *Int'l*, pg. 1030
KORSNAS SHANGHAI TRADING LTD.—See Billerud AB; *Int'l*, pg. 1030
KWIK LOK AUSTRALIA PTY LTD—See KLC Holdings, Ltd.; *U.S. Private*, pg. 2318
KWIK LOK JAPAN LTD.—See KLC Holdings, Ltd.; *U.S. Private*, pg. 2318
KWIK LOK LTD.—See KLC Holdings, Ltd.; *U.S. Private*, pg. 2318
LABELS WEST, INC.—See Ares Management Corporation; *U.S. Public*, pg. 190
LANGSTON COMPANIES, INC.; *U.S. Private*, pg. 2389
LECTA S.A.—See CVC Capital Partners SICAV-FIS S.A.; *Int'l*, pg. 1887
LOFTON LABEL, INC.—See Leonard Green & Partners, L.P.; *U.S. Private*, pg. 2428
LUX GLOBAL LABEL COMPANY, LLC—See Resilience Capital Partners, LLC; *U.S. Private*, pg. 3405
MAIN TAPE COMPANY, INC.—See Chargeurs SA; *Int'l*, pg. 1449
MAJOR BUSINESS SYSTEMS, INC.—See Ennis, Inc.; *U.S. Public*, pg. 769
MANJUSHREE TECHNOPACK LIMITED—See Advent International Corporation; *U.S. Private*, pg. 103
MANUFACTURAS SONOCO, S.A. DE C.V.—See Sonoco Products Company; *U.S. Public*, pg. 1904
MASTER DESIGN LLC; *U.S. Private*, pg. 2607
MCLEAN PACKAGING CORPORATION - CORRUGATED DIVISION—See McLean Packaging Corporation; *U.S. Private*, pg. 2641
MCLEAN PACKAGING CORPORATION - RIGID PAPER BOX DIVISION—See McLean Packaging Corporation; *U.S. Private*, pg. 2641
M&C SPECIALTIES COMPANY—See Illinois Tool Works Inc.; *U.S. Public*, pg. 1109
METRO LABEL CORP.; *U.S. Private*, pg. 2685
MICHELSEN PACKAGING OF CALIFORNIA INC.—See Michelsen Packaging Co. Inc.; *U.S. Private*, pg. 2700
MINIGRIP/ZIP-PAK—See Illinois Tool Works Inc.; *U.S. Public*, pg. 1109
MOHAWK FINE PAPERS, INC.—See Fedrigoni SpA; *Int'l*, pg. 2631
MULTI-FIX BVBA—See Avery Dennison Corporation; *U.S. Public*, pg. 244
NASHUA MERRIMACK COATED PAPER PRODUCTS PLANT—See Cenveo, Inc.; *U.S. Private*, pg. 835
NEENAH GESSNER GMBH—See Mativ Holdings, Inc.; *U.S. Public*, pg. 1396
NEW ISLAND PRINTING (LIAONING) COMPANY LIMITED—See China Huajun Group Limited; *Int'l*, pg. 1509
NIHON PACKAGING MATERIAL CO., LTD.—See DIC Corporation; *Int'l*, pg. 2109
NOSCO, INC.—See Holden Industries, Inc.; *U.S. Private*, pg. 1962
NOVACEL, INC.—See Chargeurs SA; *Int'l*, pg. 1449
N.S. PACKAGING LLC; *U.S. Private*, pg. 2828
NYCO FLEXIBLE PACKAGING GMBH—See FairCap GmbH; *Int'l*, pg. 2605
OLIVER PRODUCTS COMPANY INC.—See Berwind Corporation; *U.S. Private*, pg. 541
OOO A.S. CREATION (RUS)—See A.S. Creation Tapeten AG; *Int'l*, pg. 28
OOO HUHTAMAKI S.N.G.—See Huhtamaki Oyj; *Int'l*, pg. 3526
OPTIMUM PLASTICS, INC.—See Bloomer Plastics, Inc.; *U.S. Private*, pg. 584
PACKAGING CONCEPTS INC.; *U.S. Private*, pg. 3072
PACKAGING CORPORATION OF AMERICA; *U.S. Public*, pg. 1632
PACKAGING PERSONIFIED, INC.; *U.S. Private*, pg. 3072
PACKAGING RESOURCES, INC.; *U.S. Private*, pg. 3072
PAC NATIONAL INC.—See PAC Worldwide Corporation; *U.S. Private*, pg. 3063
PACTIV LLC—See Pactiv Evergreen Inc.; *U.S. Public*, pg. 1633
PARADISE PLASTICS, INC.—See Paradise, Inc.; *U.S. Private*, pg. 3090
PATRIOT CONVERTING, INC.—See Brixey & Meyer, Inc.; *U.S. Private*, pg. 658
PBM GRAPHICS, INC - PACKAGING DIVISION—See Chatham Asset Management, LLC; *U.S. Private*, pg. 863
PERFECSEAL, INC.—See Amcor plc; *Int'l*, pg. 418
PIONEER INDUSTRIES, INC. - BATLINER CONVERTING DIVISION—See Pioneer Industries, Inc.; *U.S. Private*, pg. 3187
PIONEER PACKAGING INC.—See Pioneer Packing Inc.; *U.S. Private*, pg. 3188
PLASCON GROUP; *U.S. Private*, pg. 3198
PLASTIC PACKAGING TECHNOLOGIES, LLC—See GTCR LLC; *U.S. Private*, pg. 1806
POLIPAK SP. Z O.O.—See Gr. Sarantis S.A.; *Int'l*, pg. 3047
POLYAIR INTER PACK INC. - SACRAMENTO DIVISION—See Clearlake Capital Group, L.P.; *U.S. Private*, pg. 935
POLYPRIDE, INC.—See Sealed Air Corporation; *U.S. Public*, pg. 1854
PORTCO CORPORATION; *U.S. Private*, pg. 3231
PPA INTERNATIONAL LIMITED—See HH Global Group Limited; *Int'l*, pg. 3379
PRECISION DYNAMICS—See Brady Corporation; *U.S. Public*, pg. 379
PRECISION PACKAGING INC.—See Goddard Enterprises Limited; *Int'l*, pg. 3019
PRINT-O-TAPE, INC.; *U.S. Private*, pg. 3265
PRINTPACK INC.; *U.S. Private*, pg. 3266
PROFESSIONAL PACKAGING SERVICES LIMITED—See HH Global Group Limited; *Int'l*, pg. 3379
PROLAMINA CORPORATION—See The Pritzker Group - Chicago, LLC; *U.S. Private*, pg. 4099
PROVENTUS BINA SDN. BHD.—See Central Global Berhad; *Int'l*, pg. 1407
PT AVERY DENNISON INDONESIA—See Avery Dennison Corporation; *U.S. Public*, pg. 244
PURE-STAT TECHNOLOGIES, INC.—See Huhtamaki Oyj; *Int'l*, pg. 3526
REDI-TAG CORP.—See Tops Products; *U.S. Private*, pg. 4188
REPACORP INC.; *U.S. Private*, pg. 3400
REUTHER VERPACKUNG GMBH & CO. KG—See Sun Capital Partners, Inc.; *U.S. Private*, pg. 3862

322220 — PAPER BAG AND COATE...

REVERE PACKAGING; *U.S. Private*, pg. 3414
REYNOLDS CONSUMER PRODUCTS INC.—See Pactiv Evergreen Inc.; *U.S. Public*, pg. 1633
REYNOLDS FOOD PACKAGING—See Pactiv Evergreen Inc.; *U.S. Public*, pg. 1634
REYNOLDS FOOD PACKAGING—See Pactiv Evergreen Inc.; *U.S. Public*, pg. 1634
RIO TINTO ALCAN PACKAGING GROUP—See Amcor plc; *Int'l*, pg. 417
ROLLED EDGE, INC.—See WestRock Company; *U.S. Public*, pg. 2362
ROLLPRINT PACKAGING PRODUCTS INC.; *U.S. Private*, pg. 3475
ROTTNEROS PACKAGING AB—See Arctic Paper S.A.; *Int'l*, pg. 552
SARANTIS POLSKA S.A.—See Gr. Sarantis S.A.; *Int'l*, pg. 3047
SCAPA NORTH AMERICA INC.—See Mativ Holdings, Inc.; *U.S. Public*, pg. 1397
SCHOLLE PACKAGING, INC.—See Scholle Corporation; *U.S. Private*, pg. 3567
SCOTT OFFICE SYSTEMS—See Longwood Industries Holdings, LLC; *U.S. Private*, pg. 2493
SCRIBE MANUFACTURING, INC.—See H.I.G. Capital, LLC; *U.S. Private*, pg. 1831
SEALED AIR AFRICA (PTY) LTD.—See Sealed Air Corporation; *U.S. Public*, pg. 1854
SEALED AIR AUSTRALIA PTY. LIMITED—See Sealed Air Corporation; *U.S. Public*, pg. 1854
SEALED AIR (CANADA) CO.—See Sealed Air Corporation; *U.S. Public*, pg. 1854
SEALED AIR JAPAN G.K.—See Sealed Air Corporation; *U.S. Public*, pg. 1854
SEALED AIR KOREA LIMITED—See Sealed Air Corporation; *U.S. Public*, pg. 1854
SEALED AIR LIMITED—See Sealed Air Corporation; *U.S. Public*, pg. 1854
SEALED AIR (NEW ZEALAND)—See Sealed Air Corporation; *U.S. Public*, pg. 1854
SEALED AIR NORGE AS—See Sealed Air Corporation; *U.S. Public*, pg. 1854
SEALED AIR OY—See Sealed Air Corporation; *U.S. Public*, pg. 1854
SEALED AIR PACKAGING (SHANGHAI) CO. LTD.—See Sealed Air Corporation; *U.S. Public*, pg. 1854
SEALED AIR PACKAGING S.R.L.—See Sealed Air Corporation; *U.S. Public*, pg. 1854
SEALED AIR (PHILIPPINES) INC.—See Sealed Air Corporation; *U.S. Public*, pg. 1854
SEALED AIR POLSKA SP. Z.O.O.—See Sealed Air Corporation; *U.S. Public*, pg. 1855
SEALED AIR VERPACKUNGEN GMBH—See Sealed Air Corporation; *U.S. Public*, pg. 1855
SELLERS & JOSEPHSON—See Whippoorwill Associates, Inc.; *U.S. Private*, pg. 4507
SHANGHAI NEW ISLAND PACKAGING PRINTING CO., LTD.—See China Huajun Group Limited; *Int'l*, pg. 1509
SHANGHAI REX PACKAGING CO., LTD.—See Hong Leong Investment Holdings Pte. Ltd.; *Int'l*, pg. 3469
SHAWSHEEN RUBBER CO., INC.—See Wembly Enterprises LLC; *U.S. Private*, pg. 4480
SHIPPERS EUROPE SRL—See Crown Holdings, Inc.; *U.S. Public*, pg. 599
SHORELINE CONTAINER INC.—See Schwarz Partners, LP; *U.S. Private*, pg. 3572
SHORELINE CONTAINER INC.—See The Kraft Group LLC; *U.S. Private*, pg. 4066
SHUFORD DEVELOPMENT CO. INC.—See CV Industries Inc.; *U.S. Private*, pg. 1132
SIERRA COATING TECHNOLOGIES LLC; *U.S. Private*, pg. 3647
SIGNATURE FLEXIBLE PACKAGING—See H.I.G. Capital, LLC; *U.S. Private*, pg. 1831
SIGNODE INDUSTRIAL GROUP - ANGLEBOARD—See Crown Holdings, Inc.; *U.S. Public*, pg. 599
SILGAN TUBES LLC—See Silgan Holdings, Inc.; *U.S. Public*, pg. 1879
SIMPLICITY CREATIVE CORP.—See IG Design Group Plc; *Int'l*, pg. 3600
SINTER IBERICA PACKAGING—See Fluor Corporation; *U.S. Public*, pg. 860
SOLIANT, LLC—See Akzo Nobel N.V.; *Int'l*, pg. 275
SONOCO-ALCORE OU—See Sonoco Products Company; *U.S. Public*, pg. 1908
SONOCO PACKAGING SERVICES—See Sonoco Products Company; *U.S. Public*, pg. 1907
SONOCO PAPER MILL & IPD HELLAS SA—See Sonoco Products Company; *U.S. Public*, pg. 1907
SONOCO PRODUCTS COMPANY—See Sonoco Products Company; *U.S. Public*, pg. 1907
SONOCO PRODUCTS COMPANY—See Sonoco Products Company; *U.S. Public*, pg. 1907
SONOCO PRODUCTS COMPANY—See Sonoco Products Company; *U.S. Public*, pg. 1907
SONOCO PRODUCTS COMPANY—See Sonoco Products Company; *U.S. Public*, pg. 1907
SONOCO PRODUCTS COMPANY—See Sonoco Products Company; *U.S. Public*, pg. 1908
SPEAR USA LLC—See Spear USA LLC; *U.S. Private*, pg. 3747
STRETCHTAPE, INC.—See Akoya Capital LLC; *U.S. Private*, pg. 146
SUGARCANE ECOWARE CO., LTD.—See Buriram Sugar Public Company Limited; *Int'l*, pg. 1224
SUPERIOR SPECIALTIES, INC.—See The Van Hoof Companies; *U.S. Private*, pg. 4130
SYLVAMO SWEDEN AB—See Sylvamo Corporation; *U.S. Public*, pg. 1969
TAPECOAT COMPANY—See KKR & Co. Inc.; *U.S. Public*, pg. 1243
TART S.R.O—See Sealed Air Corporation; *U.S. Public*, pg. 1855
TAYLOR MADE LABELS—See Ares Management Corporation; *U.S. Public*, pg. 191
TECHNICOTE INC.; *U.S. Private*, pg. 3954
TEKNI-PLEX, INC.—See Genstar Capital, LLC; *U.S. Private*, pg. 1678
TEMKIN INTERNATIONAL INC.—See GTCR LLC; *U.S. Private*, pg. 1806
TOPFLIGHT CORPORATION; *U.S. Private*, pg. 4187
TRIDENT GRAPHICS CANADA CORPORATION—See Sonoco Products Company; *U.S. Public*, pg. 1909
TRIOPLANEX FRANCE SAS—See Altor Equity Partners AB; *Int'l*, pg. 396
TRIOPLAST LANDSKRONA AB—See Altor Equity Partners AB; *Int'l*, pg. 396
TRIOPLAST SIFAB AB—See Altor Equity Partners AB; *Int'l*, pg. 396
TRIOWORLD BOTTNARYD AB—See Altor Equity Partners AB; *Int'l*, pg. 396
TRIOWORLD INDUSTRIER AB—See Altor Equity Partners AB; *Int'l*, pg. 396
TRIOWORLD VARBERG AB—See Altor Equity Partners AB; *Int'l*, pg. 397
TROJAN LITHOGRAPH CORPORATION—See Great Mill Rock LLC; *U.S. Private*, pg. 1766
TST/IMPRESO, INC.—See Impreso, Inc.; *U.S. Public*, pg. 1114
TUBETEX NV—See Sonoco Products Company; *U.S. Public*, pg. 1909
TULSACK, INC.—See The Pritzker Group - Chicago, LLC; *U.S. Private*, pg. 4099
TYDENBROOKS STOFFEL SEALS CORPORATION—See Bertram Capital Management, LLC; *U.S. Private*, pg. 540
TYDENBROOKS STOFFEL SEALS CORPORATION—See Crimson Investment; *U.S. Private*, pg. 1100
UNIFOIL CORPORATION; *U.S. Private*, pg. 4283
UNISTAR PLASTICS LLC; *U.S. Private*, pg. 4287
US VINYL MANUFACTURING CORP.; *U.S. Private*, pg. 4320
VEECOR CO., INC—See Coastal Group; *U.S. Private*, pg. 956
VENTURE TAPE CORP.—See 3M Company; *U.S. Public*, pg. 6
VINISA FUEGUINA S.R.L—See Amcor plc; *Int'l*, pg. 418
VONCO PRODUCTS, LLC—See Jacsten Holdings, LLC; *U.S. Private*, pg. 2181
WAUSAU COATED PRODUCTS INC.; *U.S. Private*, pg. 4457
WEB INDUSTRIES INC.; *U.S. Private*, pg. 4463
WEB INDUSTRIES INC.—See Web Industries Inc.; *U.S. Private*, pg. 4464
WEST CARROLLTON PARCHMENT & CONVERTING, INC.; *U.S. Private*, pg. 4483
WESTERN STATES ENVELOPE & LABEL - KENTUCKY DIVISION—See Western States Envelope & Label; *U.S. Private*, pg. 4497
WESTERN STATES ENVELOPE & LABEL - LABEL DIVISION—See Western States Envelope & Label; *U.S. Private*, pg. 4497
WESTERN STATES ENVELOPE & LABEL - MINNESOTA DIVISION—See Western States Envelope & Label; *U.S. Private*, pg. 4497
WESTERN STATES ENVELOPE & LABEL - OHIO DIVISION—See Western States Envelope & Label; *U.S. Private*, pg. 4497
WESTMARK INDUSTRIES INC.; *U.S. Private*, pg. 4499
WESTROCK CONSUMER PACKAGING GROUP, LLC—See WestRock Company; *U.S. Public*, pg. 2362
WESTROCK RKT CO. - PLYMOUTH LAMINATING FOOD SERVICE PLANT—See WestRock Company; *U.S. Public*, pg. 2363
W. R. GRACE ITALIANA S.P.A.—See Standard Industries Holdings Inc.; *U.S. Public*, pg. 3780
YORK WALLCOVERINGS, INC.—See High Road Capital Partners, LLC; *U.S. Private*, pg. 1936
ZENITH SPECIALTY BAG CO. INC.—See Apollo Global Management, Inc.; *U.S. Public*, pg. 154
ZHUHAI SINGYES CURTAIN WALL ENGINEERING CO., LTD—See China Shuifa Singyes Energy Holdings Limited; *Int'l*, pg. 1551
ZHUHAI SINGYES RENEWABLE ENERGY TECHNOLOGY CO., LTD.—See China Shuifa Singyes Energy Holdings Limited; *Int'l*, pg. 1551
ZIP-PAK—See Illinois Tool Works Inc.; *U.S. Public*, pg. 1109

322230 — STATIONERY PRODUCT MANUFACTURING

3M COMPANY - CONOVER PLANT—See 3M Company; *U.S. Public*, pg. 5
ACCO UK LIMITED—See ACCO Brands Corporation; *U.S. Public*, pg. 32
ADEL KALEMCILIK TICARET VE SANAYI A.S.; *Int'l*, pg. 142
ADVEO GROUP INTERNATIONAL, S.A.; *Int'l*, pg. 167
AMERICANCHURCH, INC.—See Our Sunday Visitor, Inc.; *U.S. Private*, pg. 3050
AMERICAN STATIONERY CO., INC.; *U.S. Private*, pg. 255
AMSTERDAM PRINTING & LITHO—See Taylor Corporation; *U.S. Private*, pg. 3938
ARTPRESTO CO., LTD.—See BANDAI NAMCO Holdings Inc.; *Int'l*, pg. 828
ATLAS AXILLIA CO. (PVT) LTD.—See Hemas Holdings PLC; *Int'l*, pg. 3340
AVERY DENNISON PRAHA SPOL. S.R.O.—See Avery Dennison Corporation; *U.S. Public*, pg. 244
BARTON NELSON INC.; *U.S. Private*, pg. 483
BENESSE CORPORATION CHINA—See EQT AB; *Int'l*, pg. 2467
BONG AB; *Int'l*, pg. 1106
BONG BELGIUM S.A.—See Bong AB; *Int'l*, pg. 1106
BONG CALY SWIAT KOPERT SP Z O.O.—See Bong AB; *Int'l*, pg. 1106
BONG EESTI OU—See Bong AB; *Int'l*, pg. 1106
BONG GMBH—See Bong AB; *Int'l*, pg. 1106
BONG LJUNGDAHL SVERIGE AB—See Bong AB; *Int'l*, pg. 1107
BONG NORGE AS—See Bong AB; *Int'l*, pg. 1107
BONG NORGE AS—See Bong AB; *Int'l*, pg. 1107
BONG POLSKA S.P. Z.O.O.—See Bong AB; *Int'l*, pg. 1107
BONG SECURITY SOLUTIONS S.A.—See Bong AB; *Int'l*, pg. 1107
BONG SUOMI OY—See Bong AB; *Int'l*, pg. 1107
B&W PRESS, INC.; *U.S. Private*, pg. 419
CAMPAP MAREKETING SDN. BHD.—See CWG Holdings Berhad; *Int'l*, pg. 1890
CAMPAP MARKETING SDN. BHD.—See CWG Holdings Berhad; *Int'l*, pg. 1890
CANSON SAS—See F.I.L.A. - Fabbrica Italiana Lapis ed Affini S.p.A.; *Int'l*, pg. 2596
CHINA STATIONERY LIMITED; *Int'l*, pg. 1554
CLAIREFONTAINE SA—See Carrefour SA; *Int'l*, pg. 1344
COMPENDIUM, INC.; *U.S. Private*, pg. 1000
CRE8 DIRECT (NINGBO) CO., LTD.; *Int'l*, pg. 1830
CTCI AMERICAS, INC.—See CTCI Corporation; *Int'l*, pg. 1870
DIXON STATIONERY COMPANY LTD.—See F.I.L.A. - Fabbrica Italiana Lapis ed Affini S.p.A.; *Int'l*, pg. 2596
D'NONCE (KELANTAN) SDN. BHD.—See D'nonce Technology Bhd.; *Int'l*, pg. 1900
D'NONCE (K.L) SDN. BHD.—See D'nonce Technology Bhd.; *Int'l*, pg. 1900
D'NONCE (M) SDN. BHD.—See D'nonce Technology Bhd.; *Int'l*, pg. 1900
DOMS INDUSTRIES PVT. LTD.—See F.I.L.A. - Fabbrica Italiana Lapis ed Affini S.p.A.; *Int'l*, pg. 2596
DUROPACK LTD; *Int'l*, pg. 2230
EDDING EXPRESSIVE SKIN GMBH—See Edding AG; *Int'l*, pg. 2304
EFI (CANADA), INC.—See Siris Capital Group, LLC; *U.S. Private*, pg. 3672
ENVEL EUROPA S.A.—See Bong AB; *Int'l*, pg. 1107
ESSELTE LEITZ BURO MALZEMELERI SANAYI VE TICARET A.S.—See ACCO Brands Corporation; *U.S. Public*, pg. 33
ESSELTE OFFICE PRODUCTS GMBH—See ACCO Brands Corporation; *U.S. Public*, pg. 33
ESSELTE SALES S.R.L—See ACCO Brands Corporation; *U.S. Public*, pg. 33
FILA ART PRODUCTS AG—See F.I.L.A. - Fabbrica Italiana Lapis ed Affini S.p.A.; *Int'l*, pg. 2597
F.I.L.A. CHILE LTDA—See F.I.L.A. - Fabbrica Italiana Lapis ed Affini S.p.A.; *Int'l*, pg. 2596
FILA HELLAS S.A.—See F.I.L.A. - Fabbrica Italiana Lapis ed Affini S.p.A.; *Int'l*, pg. 2597
F.I.L.A. HISPANIA S.L.—See F.I.L.A. - Fabbrica Italiana Lapis ed Affini S.p.A.; *Int'l*, pg. 2597
FILA IBERIA S. L.—See F.I.L.A. - Fabbrica Italiana Lapis ed Affini S.p.A.; *Int'l*, pg. 2597
FILALYRA GB LTD.—See F.I.L.A. - Fabbrica Italiana Lapis ed Affini S.p.A.; *Int'l*, pg. 2596
FILA SA PTY. LTD.—See F.I.L.A. - Fabbrica Italiana Lapis ed Affini S.p.A.; *Int'l*, pg. 2597
FILA STATIONARY AND OFFICE EQUIPMENT INDUSTRY LTD. CO.—See F.I.L.A. - Fabbrica Italiana Lapis ed Affini S.p.A.; *Int'l*, pg. 2597
FINE IMPRESSIONS, INC.—See Taylor Corporation; *U.S. Private*, pg. 3938
FLIP FILE (PTY) LTD.—See Caxton and CTP Publishers and Printers Ltd.; *Int'l*, pg. 1363
FORMAT WERK GMBH & CO. KG; *Int'l*, pg. 2733
FOTO-WEAR INC.; *U.S. Private*, pg. 1579

N.A.I.C.S. INDEX

322291 — SANITARY PAPER PROD...

FRANK G. LOVE ENVELOPES INC.; *U.S. Private*, pg. 1594
GARTNER STUDIOS, INC.; *U.S. Private*, pg. 1646
GRACE CHINA LTD.—See Standard Industries Holdings Inc.; *U.S. Private*, pg. 3779
GREAT NORTHERN INDUSTRIES INC.; *U.S. Private*, pg. 1766
GROUPE HAMELIN S.A.; *Int'l*, pg. 3104
GRUPO F.I.L.A.-DIXON, S.A. DE C.V.—See F.I.L.A. - Fabbrica Italiana Lapis ed Affini S.p.A.; *Int'l*, pg. 2597
GUANGBO GROUP STOCK CO., LTD.; *Int'l*, pg. 3152
GUSSCO MANUFACTURING, INC.—See Selco Industries, Inc.; *U.S. Private*, pg. 3600
HALLMARK CARDS, INC. - LIBERTY DISTRIBUTION CENTER—See Hallmark Cards, Inc.; *U.S. Private*, pg. 1844
HAMELIN A/S—See Groupe Hamelin S.A.; *Int'l*, pg. 3104
HAMELIN BRANDS LTD—See Groupe Hamelin S.A.; *Int'l*, pg. 3104
HAMELIN GMBH—See Groupe Hamelin S.A.; *Int'l*, pg. 3104
HARPER + SCOTT, LLC; *U.S. Private*, pg. 1867
HEINRICH ENVELOPE CORPORATION—See Taylor Corporation; *U.S. Private*, pg. 3938
HOKUETSU PACKAGE CO., LTD.—See Hokuetsu Corporation; *Int'l*, pg. 3444
HUSKY ENVELOPE PRODUCTS INCORPORATED; *U.S. Private*, pg. 2013
IKAN PAPER CRAFTS LTD.—See Aurelius Equity Opportunities SE & Co. KGaA; *Int'l*, pg. 710
IMPRESSIONS DIRECT, INC.—See Ennis, Inc.; *U.S. Public*, pg. 769
ITW IMTRAN—See Illinois Tool Works Inc.; *U.S. Public*, pg. 1106
JOHANN FROESCHEIS LYRA BLEISTIFT-FABRIK GMBH & CO. KG—See F.I.L.A. - Fabbrica Italiana Lapis ed Affini S.p.A.; *Int'l*, pg. 2597
KONIGSFURT URANIA VERLAG GMBH—See Cartamundi N.V.; *Int'l*, pg. 1348
LA CARTERIE HALLMARK—See Hallmark Cards, Inc.; *U.S. Private*, pg. 1845
LEADER PAPER PRODUCTS INC.; *U.S. Private*, pg. 2406
LEARN-S CO., LTD.—See EQT AB; *Int'l*, pg. 2467
LICYN MERCANTIL INDUSTRIAL LTDA—See F.I.L.A. - Fabbrica Italiana Lapis ed Affini S.p.A.; *Int'l*, pg. 2597
LOUISIANA ASSOCIATION FOR THE BLIND; *U.S. Private*, pg. 2499
LYRA ASIA PTE LTD.—See F.I.L.A. - Fabbrica Italiana Lapis ed Affini S.p.A.; *Int'l*, pg. 2597
LYRA SCANDINAVIA AB—See F.I.L.A. - Fabbrica Italiana Lapis ed Affini S.p.A.; *Int'l*, pg. 2597
MACKAYMITCHELL ENVELOPE COMPANY - IOWA MANUFACTURING FACILITY—See MackayMitchell Envelope Company; *U.S. Private*, pg. 2536
MACKAYMITCHELL ENVELOPE COMPANY; *U.S. Private*, pg. 2536
NATIONAL IMPRINT CORPORATION—See Ennis, Inc.; *U.S. Public*, pg. 769
NORCOM INC.; *U.S. Private*, pg. 2936
NORTHEASTERN ENVELOPE COMPANY; *U.S. Private*, pg. 2951
OLES ENVELOPE CORPORATION; *U.S. Private*, pg. 3010
OMYACOLOR S.A.—See F.I.L.A. - Fabbrica Italiana Lapis ed Affini S.p.A.; *Int'l*, pg. 2597
PAPERLY—See JRjr33, Inc.; *U.S. Private*, pg. 2240
PCI, PAPER CONVERSION INC.—See Matt Industries Inc.; *U.S. Private*, pg. 2613
PK KOPERTY SP. Z O.O—See Bong AB; *Int'l*, pg. 1107
PLASTOREG SMIDT GMBH (OFFICE SUPPLIES DIVISION)—See Asia File Corporation Bhd.; *Int'l*, pg. 612
PLASTOREG SMIDT GMBH (SPECIALS DIVISION)—See Asia File Corporation Bhd.; *Int'l*, pg. 612
POSTAC LLC—See Bong AB; *Int'l*, pg. 1107
PT. LYRA AKRELUX—See F.I.L.A. - Fabbrica Italiana Lapis ed Affini S.p.A.; *Int'l*, pg. 2597
RITE-MADE PAPER CONVERTERS; *U.S. Private*, pg. 3442
THE R.J. MARSHALL COMPANY EUROPE BVBA—See The R.J. Marshall Company; *U.S. Private*, pg. 4102
ROSELLE PAPER CO., INC.; *U.S. Private*, pg. 3482
ROSE MOON INC.—See Mattel, Inc.; *U.S. Public*, pg. 1398
THE RYTEX COMPANY—See American Stationery Co., Inc.; *U.S. Private*, pg. 255
SCAPA TAPES MALAYSIA SDN BHD—See Mativ Holdings, Inc.; *U.S. Public*, pg. 1397
STM PACKAGING GROUP LTD.—See DPG Media Group NV; *Int'l*, pg. 2189
SUN-STAR STATIONERY CO., LTD.—See BANDAI NAMCO Holdings Inc.; *Int'l*, pg. 829
S&W MANUFACTURING—See Smead Manufacturing Company; *U.S. Private*, pg. 3693
TAB DATA FILE—See H.S. Morgan Limited Partnership; *U.S. Private*, pg. 1835
TAMIMI TAPE MANUFACTURING CO. LTD—See Ali Abdullah Al Tamimi Company; *Int'l*, pg. 320
TENSION ENVELOPE CORPORATION; *U.S. Private*, pg. 3968
TOPEKA PRODUCTION CENTER—See Hallmark Cards, Inc.; *U.S. Private*, pg. 1845
TOP FLIGHT, INC.; *U.S. Private*, pg. 4186

TRIO PAPER MILLS SDN. BHD.—See HPI Resources Berhad; *Int'l*, pg. 3501
TRI-STATE ENVELOPE CORPORATION; *U.S. Private*, pg. 4224
UNITED ENVELOPE LLC—See Palm Beach Capital Partners LLC; *U.S. Private*, pg. 3079
WESTERN STATES ENVELOPE & LABEL; *U.S. Private*, pg. 4497
WISCO ENVELOPE—See Ennis, Inc.; *U.S. Public*, pg. 769

322291 — SANITARY PAPER PRODUCT MANUFACTURING

ABU-PLAST GMBH—See Aliaxis S.A./N.V.; *Int'l*, pg. 323
AFKAR HOLDING CO.—See Gulf Investment House K.S.C.P.; *Int'l*, pg. 3181
AGILE PURSUITS FRANCHISING, INC.—See The Procter & Gamble Company; *U.S. Public*, pg. 2120
AIRTISSUE S.R.L.—See Cartiera Lucchese S.p.A.; *Int'l*, pg. 1348
AKABIRA PAPER CORPORATION—See Daio Paper Corporation; *Int'l*, pg. 1939
AMERICAN INNOTEK, INC; *U.S. Private*, pg. 237
ANDRITZ DIATEC S.R.L.—See ANDRITZ AG; *Int'l*, pg. 452
ANDRITZ KUFFERATH GMBH—See ANDRITZ AG; *Int'l*, pg. 454
ARQUEST INC.; *U.S. Private*, pg. 334
ART CORPORATION LIMITED - KADOMA PAPER MILLS DIVISION—See Amalgamated Regional Trading (ART) Holdings Ltd.; *Int'l*, pg. 409
ASALEO CARE LIMITED—See Essity Aktiebolag; *Int'l*, pg. 2516
BENTLEY MANUFACTURING INC.—See Playgirl Industries, Inc.; *U.S. Private*, pg. 3212
BERK WIPER INTERNATIONAL LLC; *U.S. Private*, pg. 532
BRAUN-GILLETTE IMMOBILIEN GMBH & CO. KG—See The Procter & Gamble Company; *U.S. Public*, pg. 2124
BROWN & WHITE, INC.—See Bain Capital, LP; *U.S. Private*, pg. 441
CAN HYGIENE SPA—See Hygianis SpA; *Int'l*, pg. 3549
CASCADES TISSUE GROUP - LAVAL—See Cascades Inc.; *Int'l*, pg. 1351
CASCADES TISSUE GROUP - ROCKINGHAM—See Cascades Inc.; *Int'l*, pg. 1351
CELLUCAP MANUFACTURING CO.; *U.S. Private*, pg. 807
CHONGQING BAIYA SANITARY PRODUCTS CO., LTD.; *Int'l*, pg. 1579
CLEARWATER FIBER, LLC—See Clearwater Paper Corporation; *U.S. Public*, pg. 513
CMPC TISSUE S.A.—See Empresas CMPC S.A.; *Int'l*, pg. 2389
CODI INTERNATIONAL B.V.—See Active Capital Company Holding BV; *Int'l*, pg. 120
C&S PAPER CO., LTD.; *Int'l*, pg. 1239
DAINICHI PAPER CORPORATION—See Daio Paper Corporation; *Int'l*, pg. 1939
DAIO PAPER PRODUCTS CORPORATION—See Daio Paper Corporation; *Int'l*, pg. 1939
DALLMER GMBH & CO. KG; *Int'l*, pg. 1954
DISPOSABLE SOFT GOODS LIMITED—See DSG International Limited; *Int'l*, pg. 2210
DISPOSABLE SOFT GOODS (MALAYSIA) SDN. BHD.—See DSG International Limited; *Int'l*, pg. 2210
DISPOSABLE SOFT GOODS (S) PTE. LTD.—See DSG International Limited; *Int'l*, pg. 2210
DRYLOCK TECHNOLOGIES NV; *Int'l*, pg. 2207
DSG INTERNATIONAL LIMITED; *Int'l*, pg. 2209
DSG INTERNATIONAL (THAILAND) PUBLIC COMPANY LIMITED—See DSG International Limited; *Int'l*, pg. 2209
DSG (MALAYSIA) SDN. BHD.—See DSG International Limited; *Int'l*, pg. 2209
DUNI AB; *Int'l*, pg. 2226
DUNI AG—See Duni AB; *Int'l*, pg. 2226
DUNI & CO. KG—See Duni AB; *Int'l*, pg. 2226
DUNI GMBH—See Duni AB; *Int'l*, pg. 2226
DUNI IBERICA S.L.—See Duni AB; *Int'l*, pg. 2226
DUNI LTD.—See Duni AB; *Int'l*, pg. 2227
ELLEAIR INTERNATIONAL KOREA CO., LTD.—See Daio Paper Corporation; *Int'l*, pg. 1940
ELLEAIR INTERNATIONAL (THAILAND) CO., LTD.—See Daio Paper Corporation; *Int'l*, pg. 1940
ELOPAK, INC.—See Ferd AS; *Int'l*, pg. 2636
ESSITY CZECH REPUBLIC S.R.O.—See Essity Aktiebolag; *Int'l*, pg. 2517
ESSITY DENMARK A/S—See Essity Aktiebolag; *Int'l*, pg. 2517
ESSITY GERMANY GMBH—See Essity Aktiebolag; *Int'l*, pg. 2517
ESSITY HIJYEN URUNLERI SANAYI VE TICARET A.S.—See Essity Aktiebolag; *Int'l*, pg. 2517
ESSITY HUNGARY KFT—See Essity Aktiebolag; *Int'l*, pg. 2517
ESSITY NORWAY AS—See Essity Aktiebolag; *Int'l*, pg. 2517
FATER S.P.A.—See Angelini ACRAF S.p.A.; *Int'l*, pg. 460
FATER S.P.A.—See The Procter & Gamble Company; *U.S. Public*, pg. 2120

FEMPRO INC.—See First Quality Enterprises, Inc.; *U.S. Private*, pg. 1524
FIRST QUALITY FIBERS, LLC—See First Quality Enterprises, Inc.; *U.S. Private*, pg. 1524
FOX CONVERTING INC.; *U.S. Private*, pg. 1584
FU BURG INDUSTRIAL CO., LTD.; *Int'l*, pg. 2800
FUJIAN HENGAN HOLDING CO., LTD.—See Hengan International Group Co. Ltd.; *Int'l*, pg. 3345
GEBERIT A/S—See Geberit AG; *Int'l*, pg. 2904
GEBERIT INDIA MANUFACTURING PVT. LTD.—See Geberit AG; *Int'l*, pg. 2904
GEBERIT OZORKOW SP. Z O.O.—See Geberit AG; *Int'l*, pg. 2905
GEBERIT PRODUCTION OY—See Geberit AG; *Int'l*, pg. 2905
GEBERIT PRODUKCJA SP. Z O.O.—See Geberit AG; *Int'l*, pg. 2905
GEBERIT PROIZVODNJA D.O.O.—See Geberit AG; *Int'l*, pg. 2905
GEBERIT SERVICE OY—See Geberit AG; *Int'l*, pg. 2905
GEORGIA-PACIFIC GREEN BAY OPERATIONS—See Koch Industries, Inc.; *U.S. Private*, pg. 2328
GILLETTE INTERNATIONAL B.V.—See The Procter & Gamble Company; *U.S. Public*, pg. 2124
GILLETTE POLAND INTERNATIONAL SP. ZO.O.—See The Procter & Gamble Company; *U.S. Public*, pg. 2124
GREAT LAKES TISSUE COMPANY, INC.; *U.S. Private*, pg. 1765
GREEN INNOVATIONS LTD.; *U.S. Private*, pg. 1773
HANGZHOU COCO HEALTHCARE PRODUCTS CO., LTD.; *Int'l*, pg. 3247
HANGZHOU HAOYUE PERSONAL CARE CO., LTD.; *Int'l*, pg. 3247
HENAN YINGE INDUSTRIAL INVESTMENT CO., LTD.; *Int'l*, pg. 3343
HIGIENE INFANTIL DE MEXICO, S.A. DE C.V.—See Corporativo Copamex, S.A. de C.V.; *Int'l*, pg. 1806
HYGIANIS SPA; *Int'l*, pg. 3549
IBEREUCALIPTOS, S.A.U.—See Iberpapel Gestion SA; *Int'l*, pg. 3574
IBERPAPEL ON LINE, S.L.U.—See Iberpapel Gestion SA; *Int'l*, pg. 3574
IPEK KAGIT KAZAKHSTAN LLP—See Eczacibasi Holding A.S.; *Int'l*, pg. 2302
JINJIANG HAINA MACHINERY COMPANY LIMITED—See Haina Intelligent Equipment International Holdings Limited; *Int'l*, pg. 3211
JOHNSON & JOHNSON DE ARGENTINA, S.A.C.E I.—See Kenvue Inc.; *U.S. Public*, pg. 1224
JOHNSON & JOHNSON GMBH—See Kenvue Inc.; *U.S. Public*, pg. 1224
JOHNSON & JOHNSON (IRELAND) LTD.—See Johnson & Johnson; *U.S. Public*, pg. 1198
K-C AFC MANUFACTURING, S. DE R.L. DE C. V.—See Kimberly-Clark Corporation; *U.S. Public*, pg. 1229
KCSSA EAST AFRICA LIMITED—See Kimberly-Clark Corporation; *U.S. Public*, pg. 1229
KIMBERLY BOLIVIA S.A.—See Kimberly-Clark Corporation; *U.S. Public*, pg. 1229
KIMBERLY-CLARK AMSTERDAM HOLDINGS B.V.—See Kimberly-Clark Corporation; *U.S. Public*, pg. 1229
KIMBERLY-CLARK ARGENTINA S.A.—See Kimberly-Clark Corporation; *U.S. Public*, pg. 1229
KIMBERLY-CLARK ASIA HOLDINGS PTE. LTD.—See Kimberly-Clark Corporation; *U.S. Public*, pg. 1229
KIMBERLY-CLARK ASIA PACIFIC PTE. LTD.—See Kimberly-Clark Corporation; *U.S. Public*, pg. 1229
KIMBERLY-CLARK BOLIVIA S.A.—See Kimberly-Clark Corporation; *U.S. Public*, pg. 1229
KIMBERLY-CLARK BRASIL INDUSTRIA E COMERCIO DE PRODUTOS DE HIGIENE LTDA.—See Kimberly-Clark Corporation; *U.S. Public*, pg. 1229
KIMBERLY-CLARK CHILE S.A.—See Kimberly-Clark Corporation; *U.S. Public*, pg. 1229
KIMBERLY-CLARK CHILE S.A.—See Kimberly-Clark Corporation; *U.S. Public*, pg. 1229
KIMBERLY-CLARK CONWAY MILLS—See Kimberly-Clark Corporation; *U.S. Public*, pg. 1230
KIMBERLY-CLARK CORPORATION - MOBILE—See Kimberly-Clark Corporation; *U.S. Public*, pg. 1229
KIMBERLY-CLARK CORPORATION—See Kimberly-Clark Corporation; *U.S. Public*, pg. 1230
KIMBERLY-CLARK CORPORATION—See Kimberly-Clark Corporation; *U.S. Public*, pg. 1230
KIMBERLY-CLARK CORPORATION—See Kimberly-Clark Corporation; *U.S. Public*, pg. 1230
KIMBERLY-CLARK DE CENTRO AMERICA S.A.—See Kimberly-Clark Corporation; *U.S. Public*, pg. 1231
KIMBERLY-CLARK DE MEXICO, S.A.B. DE C.V.—See Kimberly-Clark Corporation; *U.S. Public*, pg. 1231
KIMBERLY-CLARK ECUADOR S.A.—See Kimberly-Clark Corporation; *U.S. Public*, pg. 1230
KIMBERLY-CLARK EUROPE LIMITED—See Kimberly-Clark Corporation; *U.S. Public*, pg. 1230
KIMBERLY-CLARK FINANCE LIMITED—See Kimberly-Clark Corporation; *U.S. Public*, pg. 1230
KIMBERLY-CLARK GMBH—See Kimberly-Clark Corporation; *U.S. Public*, pg. 1230

322291 — SANITARY PAPER PROD...

KIMBERLY-CLARK GMBH—See Kimberly-Clark Corporation; *U.S. Public*, pg. 1230
KIMBERLY-CLARK GMBH—See Kimberly-Clark Corporation; *U.S. Public*, pg. 1230
KIMBERLY-CLARK GUATEMALA, LIMITADA—See Kimberly-Clark Corporation; *U.S. Public*, pg. 1230
KIMBERLY-CLARK (HONG KONG) LIMITED—See Kimberly-Clark Corporation; *U.S. Public*, pg. 1229
KIMBERLY-CLARK HYGIENE PRODUCTS PRIVATE LIMITED—See Kimberly-Clark Corporation; *U.S. Public*, pg. 1230
KIMBERLY-CLARK INC.—See Kimberly-Clark Corporation; *U.S. Public*, pg. 1230
KIMBERLY-CLARK INDIA PRIVATE LIMITED—See Kimberly-Clark Corporation; *U.S. Public*, pg. 1230
KIMBERLY-CLARK LDA.—See Kimberly-Clark Corporation; *U.S. Public*, pg. 1230
KIMBERLY-CLARK PAPER (SHANGHAI) CO. LTD.—See Kimberly-Clark Corporation; *U.S. Public*, pg. 1230
KIMBERLY-CLARK PARAGUAY, S.A.—See Kimberly-Clark Corporation; *U.S. Public*, pg. 1231
KIMBERLY-CLARK PERU S.R.L.—See Kimberly-Clark Corporation; *U.S. Public*, pg. 1231
KIMBERLY-CLARK S.A.S.—See Kimberly-Clark Corporation; *U.S. Public*, pg. 1231
KIMBERLY-CLARK SAS—See Kimberly-Clark Corporation; *U.S. Public*, pg. 1231
KIMBERLY-CLARK (SINGAPORE) FINANCE PTE. LTD.—See Kimberly-Clark Corporation; *U.S. Public*, pg. 1229
KIMBERLY-CLARK SINGAPORE PTE. LTD.—See Kimberly-Clark Corporation; *U.S. Public*, pg. 1230
KIMBERLY-CLARK S.L.U.—See Kimberly-Clark Corporation; *U.S. Public*, pg. 1230
KIMBERLY-CLARK S.L.U.—See Kimberly-Clark Corporation; *U.S. Public*, pg. 1231
KIMBERLY-CLARK S.R.L.—See Kimberly-Clark Corporation; *U.S. Public*, pg. 1230
KIMBERLY-CLARK S.R.L.—See Kimberly-Clark Corporation; *U.S. Public*, pg. 1231
KIMBERLY-CLARK TAIWAN—See Kimberly-Clark Corporation; *U.S. Public*, pg. 1231
KIMBERLY CLARK TRADING (MALAYSIA) SDN. BHD.—See Kimberly-Clark Corporation; *U.S. Public*, pg. 1230
KIMBERLY-CLARK TRADING (M) SDN. BHD.—See Kimberly-Clark Corporation; *U.S. Public*, pg. 1231
KIMBERLY-CLARK TUKETIM MALLARI SANAYI VE TICARET A.S.—See Kimberly-Clark Corporation; *U.S. Public*, pg. 1231
KIMBERLY-CLARK UK OPERATIONS LIMITED—See Kimberly-Clark Corporation; *U.S. Public*, pg. 1231
KIMBERLY-CLARK UKRAINE LLC—See Kimberly-Clark Corporation; *U.S. Public*, pg. 1231
KIMBERLY CLARK URUGUAY S.A.—See Kimberly-Clark Corporation; *U.S. Public*, pg. 1229
KIMBERLY-CLARK VIETNAM LTD.—See Kimberly-Clark Corporation; *U.S. Public*, pg. 1231
KIMNICA SOCIEDAD ANONIMA—See Kimberly-Clark Corporation; *U.S. Public*, pg. 1231
LINDSTROM & SONDEN AB—See BHG Group AB; *Int'l*, pg. 1015
MORCON, INC.; *U.S. Private*, pg. 2782
NATIONAL PACKAGING SERVICES CORPORATION; *U.S. Private*, pg. 2860
NICE PAK INTERNATIONAL LTD.—See Nice-Pak Products, Inc.; *U.S. Private*, pg. 2925
OOO KIMBERLY-CLARK—See Kimberly-Clark Corporation; *U.S. Public*, pg. 1231
OY ESSITY FINLAND AB—See Essity Aktiebolag; *Int'l*, pg. 2517
PAPER CHEMICAL SUPPLY COMPANY; *U.S. Private*, pg. 3087
PRESTO ABSORBENT PRODUCTS, INC.—See Drylock Technologies NV; *Int'l*, pg. 2207
PRODUCTOS FAMILIA S.A.—See Essity Aktiebolag; *Int'l*, pg. 2517
PRODUCTOS TISSUE DEL ECUADOR S.A.—See Empresas CMPC S.A.; *Int'l*, pg. 2390
PROFESSIONAL DISPOSABLES INTERNATIONAL, INC.—See Nice-Pak Products, Inc.; *U.S. Private*, pg. 2925
PROPAPER INDUSTRIA E COMERCIO DE PAPEIS LTDA.—See Illinois Tool Works Inc.; *U.S. Public*, pg. 1110
PROTISA COLOMBIA S.A.—See Empresas CMPC S.A.; *Int'l*, pg. 2390
PT DSG SURYA MAS INDONESIA—See DSG International Limited; *Int'l*, pg. 2210
QS NEDERLAND B.V.—See Bunzl plc; *Int'l*, pg. 1219
QUALITY HERO CORPORATION SDN. BHD.—See Hengan International Group Co. Ltd.; *Int'l*, pg. 3346
REXCELL TISSUE & AIRLAID AB—See Duni AB; *Int'l*, pg. 2227
RLG INVESTMENTS, INC. -U.S.A; *U.S. Private*, pg. 3450
ROSE'S SOUTHWEST PAPERS, INC.; *U.S. Private*, pg. 3482
ROYAL PAPER CONVERTING INC.; *U.S. Private*, pg. 3493

SANCELA CHILE S.A.—See Essity Aktiebolag; *Int'l*, pg. 2517
SANITAIRE ACCESSOIRES SERVICES S.A.S.—See Aliaxis S.A./N.V.; *Int'l*, pg. 325
SANITARTECHNIK EISENBERG GMBH—See Aliaxis S.A./N.V.; *Int'l*, pg. 325
S.C. JOHNSON & SON OF SOUTH AFRICA—See S.C. Johnson & Son, Inc.; *U.S. Private*, pg. 3516
SELCO INDUSTRIES, INC.; *U.S. Private*, pg. 3600
SHIKMA—See Kimberly-Clark Corporation; *U.S. Public*, pg. 1229
SOUNDVIEW PAPER CO. LLC—See Atlas Holdings, LLC; *U.S. Private*, pg. 378
ST. PAPER, LLC; *U.S. Private*, pg. 3770
TECNOSUR S.A.—See Kimberly-Clark Corporation; *U.S. Public*, pg. 1231
THE TRANZONIC COMPANIES—See The PNC Financial Services Group, Inc.; *U.S. Public*, pg. 2120
VINDA PAPER (SICHUAN) LIMITED—See Essity Aktiebolag; *Int'l*, pg. 2517
VINDA PAPER (ZHEJIANG) COMPANY LIMITED—See Essity Aktiebolag; *Int'l*, pg. 2517
VON DREHLE CORPORATION—See Atlas Holdings, LLC; *U.S. Private*, pg. 378
ZHEJIANG NEW YUHONG INTELLIGENT EQUIPMENT CO., LTD.—See CSG Smart Science & Technology Co., Ltd.; *Int'l*, pg. 1865

322299 — ALL OTHER CONVERTED PAPER PRODUCT MANUFACTURING

3M PURIFICATION INC.—See 3M Company; *U.S. Public*, pg. 7
AERO COPY D.O.O.—See Aero d.d.; *Int'l*, pg. 180
AERO PAPIROTTI D.O.O.—See Aero d.d.; *Int'l*, pg. 180
AHLSTROM-MUNKSJO BRIGNOUD SAS—See Ahlstrom Capital Oy; *Int'l*, pg. 224
AHLSTROM-MUNKSJO BRIGNOUD SAS—See Bain Capital, LP; *U.S. Private*, pg. 429
AHLSTROM-MUNKSJO FIBERCOMPOSITES (BINZHOU) LIMITED—See Ahlstrom Capital Oy; *Int'l*, pg. 223
AHLSTROM-MUNKSJO FIBERCOMPOSITES (BINZHOU) LIMITED—See Bain Capital, LP; *U.S. Private*, pg. 429
AHLSTROM-MUNKSJO ITALIA S.P.A.—See Ahlstrom Capital Oy; *Int'l*, pg. 224
AHLSTROM-MUNKSJO ITALIA S.P.A.—See Bain Capital, LP; *U.S. Private*, pg. 429
AHLSTROM-MUNKSJO MALMEDY SA—See Ahlstrom Capital Oy; *Int'l*, pg. 224
AHLSTROM-MUNKSJO MALMEDY SA—See Bain Capital, LP; *U.S. Private*, pg. 429
AHLSTROM-MUNKSJO NA SPECIALTY SOLUTIONS LLC - RHINELANDER MILL—See Ahlstrom Capital Oy; *Int'l*, pg. 224
AHLSTROM-MUNKSJO NA SPECIALTY SOLUTIONS LLC - RHINELANDER MILL—See Bain Capital, LP; *U.S. Private*, pg. 430
AHLSTROM-MUNKSJO NONWOVENS LLC—See Ahlstrom Capital Oy; *Int'l*, pg. 224
AHLSTROM-MUNKSJO NONWOVENS LLC—See Bain Capital, LP; *U.S. Private*, pg. 429
AHLSTROM-MUNKSJO SPECIALTIES S.A.S.—See Ahlstrom Capital Oy; *Int'l*, pg. 224
AHLSTROM-MUNKSJO SPECIALTIES S.A.S.—See Bain Capital, LP; *U.S. Private*, pg. 430
AHLSTROM-MUNKSJO TAMPERE OY—See Ahlstrom Capital Oy; *Int'l*, pg. 225
AHLSTROM-MUNKSJO TAMPERE OY—See Bain Capital, LP; *U.S. Private*, pg. 430
AHLSTROM RESEARCH AND SERVICES SA—See Ahlstrom Capital Oy; *Int'l*, pg. 224
AHLSTROM RESEARCH AND SERVICES SA—See Bain Capital, LP; *U.S. Private*, pg. 429
ALLAN MOULD MANUFACTURING LIMITED—See Allan International Holdings Limited; *Int'l*, pg. 332
ALLEN-BAILEY TAG & LABEL INC.; *U.S. Private*, pg. 180
ALL STATE PACKAGING, INC.—See PMC Capital Partners, LLC; *U.S. Private*, pg. 3217
AMERICAN FUJI SEAL, INC.—See Fuji Seal International, Inc.; *Int'l*, pg. 2816
AMERICAN PAPER OPTICS, LLC—See Westshore Capital Partners LLC; *U.S. Private*, pg. 4500
AMERICAN SHOPPING CARTS INC—See Americana Companies, Inc.; *U.S. Private*, pg. 258
AMJ LAND HOLDINGS LIMITED; *Int'l*, pg. 428
AMORIM CORK HUNGARY ZRT—See CORTICEIRA AMORIM, S.G.P.S., S.A.; *Int'l*, pg. 1807
AMORIM CORK ITALIA, SPA—See CORTICEIRA AMORIM, S.G.P.S., S.A.; *Int'l*, pg. 1807
ANHUI GENUINE PAPER PACKING CO., LTD.; *Int'l*, pg. 467
AP-TELA OY—See Lone Star Funds; *U.S. Private*, pg. 2487
ARAKAWA CHEMICAL INDUSTRIES, LTD. - MIZUSHIMA PLANT—See Arakawa Chemical Industries, Ltd.; *Int'l*, pg. 534
ARCTIC PAPER GRYCKSBO AB—See Arctic Paper S.A.; *Int'l*, pg. 551

ARCTIC PAPER KOSTRZYN S.A.—See Arctic Paper S.A.; *Int'l*, pg. 551
ARCTIC PAPER MOCHENWANGEN GMBH—See Arctic Paper S.A.; *Int'l*, pg. 551
ARCTIC PAPER MUNKEDALS AB—See Arctic Paper S.A.; *Int'l*, pg. 551
ARTINOVA POLAND SP. Z O.O.—See Artinova AB; *Int'l*, pg. 584
ATLANTIC CORPORATION; *U.S. Private*, pg. 372
AVERY DENNISON (FUZHOU) CONVERTED PRODUCTS LIMITED—See Avery Dennison Corporation; *U.S. Public*, pg. 243
AVERY DENNISON, S.A. DE C.V.—See Avery Dennison Corporation; *U.S. Public*, pg. 244
AVERY DENNISON SYSTEMES D'ETIQUETAGE FRANCE S.A.S.—See Avery Dennison Corporation; *U.S. Public*, pg. 243
AVERY PRODUCTS CORPORATION—See CCL Industries Inc.; *Int'l*, pg. 1367
BADGER PAPER MILLS, INC.; *U.S. Private*, pg. 424
BAI SHA TECHNOLOGY CO., LTD.; *Int'l*, pg. 801
BALKRISHNA PAPER MILLS LIMITED; *Int'l*, pg. 809
BALTERM, L.L.P.—See Blue Wolf Capital Partners LLC; *U.S. Private*, pg. 595
BARIL CORPORATION—See Clearlake Capital Group, L.P.; *U.S. Private*, pg. 937
BARTON ENTERPRISES INC.; *U.S. Private*, pg. 483
BASHUNDHARA PAPER MILLS LTD.; *Int'l*, pg. 886
THE BEISTLE COMPANY, INC.; *U.S. Private*, pg. 3993
BEMIS BRISBANE PTY LTD—See Amcor plc; *Int'l*, pg. 418
BIELY & SHOAF CO.; *U.S. Private*, pg. 551
BIL ENERGY SYSTEMS LIMITED; *Int'l*, pg. 1023
BOISE PAPER - IDAHO—See Packaging Corporation of America; *U.S. Public*, pg. 1632
BOISE WHITE PAPER, LLC—See Packaging Corporation of America; *U.S. Public*, pg. 1633
BONG NETHERLANDS BV—See Bong AB; *Int'l*, pg. 1107
BRANDON INTERNATIONAL; *U.S. Private*, pg. 638
BULKLEY DUNTON, INC.—See Clayton, Dubilier & Rice, LLC; *U.S. Private*, pg. 928
BURGO CENTRAL EUROPE GMBH—See Burgo Group S.p.A.; *Int'l*, pg. 1223
BURGO EASTERN EUROPE SP. Z O.O.—See Burgo Group S.p.A.; *Int'l*, pg. 1223
BURGO FRANCE SARL—See Burgo Group S.p.A.; *Int'l*, pg. 1224
BURGO IBERICA PAPEL SA—See Burgo Group S.p.A.; *Int'l*, pg. 1224
BUTLER MERCHANDISING SOLUTIONS, INC.—See Presence From Innovation, LLC; *U.S. Private*, pg. 3254
CAESAR PAC CARTON & PAPER PRODUCTS CO.—See Caesars Group; *Int'l*, pg. 1249
CANFOR CORPORATION - INTERCONTINENTAL PULP (CPLP) FACILITY—See Canfor Corporation; *Int'l*, pg. 1290
CANFOR CORPORATION - PRINCE GEORGE PULP & PAPER (CPLP) FACILITY—See Canfor Corporation; *Int'l*, pg. 1291
CANFOR PULP PRODUCTS INC.; *Int'l*, pg. 1291
CANSON INC.—See Groupe Hamelin A.; *Int'l*, pg. 3104
CARAUSTAR INDUSTRIES, INC. - ARLINGTON TUBE PLANT—See Greif Inc.; *U.S. Public*, pg. 965
CARAUSTAR INDUSTRIES, INC. - AUSTELL TUBE PLANT—See Greif Inc.; *U.S. Public*, pg. 965
CARAUSTAR INDUSTRIES, INC. - BEARDSTOWN TUBE PLANT—See Greif Inc.; *U.S. Public*, pg. 965
CARAUSTAR INDUSTRIES, INC. - CANTONMENT TUBE PLANT—See Greif Inc.; *U.S. Public*, pg. 966
CARAUSTAR INDUSTRIES, INC. - CHICAGO CARTON PLANT—See Greif Inc.; *U.S. Public*, pg. 966
CARAUSTAR INDUSTRIES, INC. - CORINTH TUBE PLANT—See Greif Inc.; *U.S. Public*, pg. 966
CARAUSTAR INDUSTRIES, INC. - DALTON TUBE PLANT—See Greif Inc.; *U.S. Public*, pg. 966
CARAUSTAR INDUSTRIES, INC. - FRANKLIN, KY TUBE PLANT—See Greif Inc.; *U.S. Public*, pg. 966
CARAUSTAR INDUSTRIES, INC. - KERNERSVILLE TUBE PLANT—See Greif Inc.; *U.S. Public*, pg. 966
CARAUSTAR INDUSTRIES, INC. - KINGSTON SPRINGS CARTON PLANT—See Greif Inc.; *U.S. Public*, pg. 966
CARAUSTAR INDUSTRIES, INC. - KINGSTON TUBE PLANT—See Greif Inc.; *U.S. Public*, pg. 966
CARAUSTAR INDUSTRIES, INC. - LANCASTER TUBE PLANT—See Greif Inc.; *U.S. Public*, pg. 966
CARAUSTAR INDUSTRIES, INC. - MINERVA TUBE PLANT—See Greif Inc.; *U.S. Public*, pg. 966
CARAUSTAR INDUSTRIES, INC. - PHOENIX TUBE PLANT—See Greif Inc.; *U.S. Public*, pg. 966
CARAUSTAR INDUSTRIES, INC. - SAGINAW TUBE PLANT—See Greif Inc.; *U.S. Public*, pg. 966
CARAUSTAR INDUSTRIES, INC. - SALT LAKE CITY TUBE PLANT—See Greif Inc.; *U.S. Public*, pg. 966
CARAUSTAR INDUSTRIES, INC. - SILSBEE TUBE PLANT—See Greif Inc.; *U.S. Public*, pg. 966
CARAUSTAR INDUSTRIES, INC. - TACOMA TUBE PLANT—See Greif Inc.; *U.S. Public*, pg. 966
CARAUSTAR INDUSTRIES, INC. - TEXARKANA TUBE PLANT—See Greif Inc.; *U.S. Public*, pg. 966

N.A.I.C.S. INDEX

322299 — ALL OTHER CONVERTED...

CARAUSTAR INDUSTRIES, INC. - TOLEDO TUBE PLANT—See Greif Inc.; *U.S. Public*, pg. 966
CARAUSTAR INDUSTRIES, INC. - TORONTO TUBE PLANT—See Greif Inc.; *U.S. Public*, pg. 966
CARAUSTAR INDUSTRIES, INC. - WEST MONROE TUBE PLANT—See Greif Inc.; *U.S. Public*, pg. 966
CARAUSTAR INDUSTRIES, INC. - WEYERS CAVE TUBE PLANT—See Greif Inc.; *U.S. Public*, pg. 966
CARAUSTAR INDUSTRIES, INC. - WINNIPEG TUBE PLANT—See Greif Inc.; *U.S. Public*, pg. 966
CCL LABEL, INC.—See CCL Industries Inc.; *Int'l*, pg. 1367
CELULOSA ARGENTINA S.A.; *Int'l*, pg. 1396
CENPA S.A.S.—See Accursia Capital GmbH; *Int'l*, pg. 94
CENTRAL FIBER LLC; *U.S. Private*, pg. 820
CENTRAL NATIONAL GOTTESMAN EUROPE GMBH—See Central National Gottesman Inc.; *U.S. Private*, pg. 823
CENVEO MCLAREN MORRIS AND TODD COMPANY—See Cenveo, Inc.; *U.S. Public*, pg. 835
CF CARD FACTORY GMBH—See Die Schweizerische Post AG; *Int'l*, pg. 2112
CHADHA PAPERS LTD.; *Int'l*, pg. 1436
CHERAT PACKAGING LIMITED; *Int'l*, pg. 1471
CHICAGO COATING SYSTEMS; *U.S. Private*, pg. 877
CHILCOTE COMPANY; *U.S. Private*, pg. 881
CHINA SUNSHINE PAPER HOLDINGS COMPANY LIMITED; *Int'l*, pg. 1556
CHUETSU PULP & PAPER CO., LTD.; *Int'l*, pg. 1594
CHUNG HWA PULP CORP.; *Int'l*, pg. 1597
CLEAN & SCIENCE CO., LTD. - HANAM FACTORY—See CLEAN & SCIENCE Co., Ltd.; *Int'l*, pg. 1653
CLEAN & SCIENCE CO., LTD. - JEONGEUP FACTORY—See CLEAN & SCIENCE Co., Ltd.; *Int'l*, pg. 1654
CLEAN & SCIENCE CO., LTD.; *Int'l*, pg. 1653
CLEARWATER PAPER CORPORATION; *U.S. Public*, pg. 513
COASTAL WOOD PRODUCTS, INC.—See McConnell Cabinets, Inc.; *U.S. Private*, pg. 2629
CONBUZZ CO., LTD.; *Int'l*, pg. 1763
CONITEX SONOCO HELLAS S.A.—See Sonoco Products Company; *U.S. Public*, pg. 1904
CONITEX SONOCO INDIA PVT. LTD.—See Sonoco Products Company; *U.S. Public*, pg. 1904
CONITEX SONOCO TAIWAN LTD.—See Sonoco Products Company; *U.S. Public*, pg. 1904
CONITEX SONOCO UK LIMITED—See Sonoco Products Company; *U.S. Public*, pg. 1904
CONITEX SONOCO USA, INC.—See Sonoco Products Company; *U.S. Public*, pg. 1904
COOK LABO CO., LTD.—See FP Corporation; *Int'l*, pg. 2756
CORRCHOICE, INC.—See Greif Inc.; *U.S. Public*, pg. 967
COXON INDUSTRIAL LTD. - GUANGDONG PLASTIC & MOULD PLANT—See COXON Precise Industrial Co., Ltd.; *Int'l*, pg. 1823
CPA GMBH—See Artinova AB; *Int'l*, pg. 584
CRESCENT CARDBOARD COMPANY, L.L.C.—See Potomac Corporation; *U.S. Private*, pg. 3235
CUNO ENGINEERED PRODUCTS, INC.—See 3M Company; *U.S. Public*, pg. 7
CURTIS 1000 FRANCE SARL—See Bong AB; *Int'l*, pg. 1107
CUSTOM PRINTED PRODUCTS; *U.S. Private*, pg. 1129
DELTACRAFT PAPER & CONVERTING COMPANY—See The Millcraft Paper Company Inc.; *U.S. Private*, pg. 4079
DE LUXE GROUP INC.—See Apollo Global Management, Inc.; *U.S. Public*, pg. 153
DENNECREPE CORPORATION—See Seaman Paper Company of Massachusetts Inc.; *U.S. Private*, pg. 3585
DIETZGEN CORPORATION; *U.S. Private*, pg. 1229
DISCOUNT LABELS, INC.—See Cenveo, Inc.; *U.S. Private*, pg. 834
DIXIE CONSUMER PRODUCTS LLC—See Koch Industries, Inc.; *U.S. Private*, pg. 2327
DIXON TICONDEROGA ART ULC—See F.I.L.A. - Fabbrica Italiana Lapis ed Affini S.p.A.; *Int'l*, pg. 2596
DNP HOKKAIDO CO., LTD.—See Dai Nippon Printing Co., Ltd.; *Int'l*, pg. 1914
DNP TECHNOPACK TOKAI CO., LTD.—See Dai Nippon Printing Co., Ltd.; *Int'l*, pg. 1915
DPV DRUCK UND PAPIERVEREDELUNG GMBH; *Int'l*, pg. 2189
DS SMITH PAPER LIMITED—See DS Smith Plc; *Int'l*, pg. 2208
DS SMITH PAPER LTD - HIGHER KINGS PAPER MILL—See DS Smith Plc; *Int'l*, pg. 2208
DS SMITH PAPER LTD - HOLLINS PAPER MILL—See DS Smith Plc; *Int'l*, pg. 2208
DS SMITH PAPER LTD - WANSBROUGH PAPER MILL—See DS Smith Plc; *Int'l*, pg. 2208
DS SMITH PLC; *Int'l*, pg. 2207
DS SMITH RECYCLING GROUP—See DS Smith Plc; *Int'l*, pg. 2209
DS SMITH WITZENHAUSEN MILL—See DS Smith Plc; *Int'l*, pg. 2208
DUNI (CZ) S.R.O.—See Duni AB; *Int'l*, pg. 2226
ECOLOGICAL FIBERS INC.; *U.S. Private*, pg. 1329
EGAA OFFSET A/S—See Bong AB; *Int'l*, pg. 1107
E&H CO., LTD.; *Int'l*, pg. 2247

EKOTAB AD KOCHERINOVO; *Int'l*, pg. 2339
ELOF HANSSON INC. - FIBER DIVISION—See Elof Hansson AB; *Int'l*, pg. 2368
EMMAUS PACK S.R.L.—See Apollo Global Management, Inc.; *U.S. Public*, pg. 159
EMPEROR PAPER INDUSTRIES LTD.; *U.S. Private*, pg. 1384
ERVING PAPER PRODUCTS, INC.—See Erving Industries, Inc.; *U.S. Private*, pg. 1424
ESSENTRA FILTER PRODUCTS LIMITED—See Essentra plc; *Int'l*, pg. 2511
EUROPAPIER POLSKA SP.Z.O.O.—See Heinzel Holding GmbH; *Int'l*, pg. 3325
EXCELSIOR ENVELOPPEN BV—See Bong AB; *Int'l*, pg. 1107
FATO PROFESSIONAL S.P.A.—See Cartiera Lucchese S.p.A.; *Int'l*, pg. 1348
FDS MANUFACTURING COMPANY INCORPORATED; *U.S. Private*, pg. 1486
FLEENOR; *U.S. Private*, pg. 1541
FORTIFIBER BUILDING SYSTEMS GROUP—See Fortifiber Corporation; *U.S. Private*, pg. 1576
FRANK CROSSLEY & SON LTD—See Artinova AB; *Int'l*, pg. 584
FUJI PACKAGING SERVICES, INC—See Fuji Seal International, Inc.; *Int'l*, pg. 2816
GATEWAY PACKAGING COMPANY LLC—See The Pritzker Group - Chicago, LLC; *U.S. Public*, pg. 4099
GENTAS AS; *Int'l*, pg. 2928
GEORGIA-PACIFIC WEST, INC.—See Koch Industries, Inc.; *U.S. Private*, pg. 2329
G.G. McGUIGGAN CORP.; *U.S. Private*, pg. 1631
GLATFELTER COSTA RICA, S.R.L.—See Glatfelter Corporation; *U.S. Public*, pg. 939
GLATFELTER FALKENHAGEN GMBH—See Glatfelter Corporation; *U.S. Public*, pg. 939
GLATFELTER GATINEAU, LTEE.—See Glatfelter Corporation; *U.S. Public*, pg. 939
GOLDEN FRONTIER BERHAD; *Int'l*, pg. 3029
GORDON PAPER COMPANY INCORPORATED; *U.S. Private*, pg. 1743
GRIGEO AB; *Int'l*, pg. 3085
GUANGDONG GANHUA SCIENCE & INDUSTRY CO LTD.; *Int'l*, pg. 3154
GUANGDONG SONGYANG RECYCLE RESOURCES CO., LTD.; *Int'l*, pg. 3160
GULF PAPER MANUFACTURING COMPANY K.S.C.; *Int'l*, pg. 3181
HAKKANI PAPER MILLS (PVT.) LTD.—See Hakkani Group; *Int'l*, pg. 3219
HAKKANI PULP & PAPER MILLS LTD.—See Hakkani Group; *Int'l*, pg. 3219
HANCHANG PAPER CO., LTD; *Int'l*, pg. 3242
HANGZHOU HUAWANG NEW MATERIAL TECHNOLOGY CO., LTD.; *Int'l*, pg. 3248
HANGZHOU MCN PAPER TECH CO., LTD.—See Huazhang Technology Holding Limited; *Int'l*, pg. 3516
HAPACO GROUP JOINT STOCK COMPANY; *Int'l*, pg. 3268
HARVEST CONSUMER INSULATION, INC.; *U.S. Private*, pg. 1875
HEIWA PAPER CO., LTD.; *Int'l*, pg. 3327
HEXACOMB CORPORATION—See Packaging Corporation of America; *U.S. Public*, pg. 1633
HFS HOLDING CORPORATION—See Magnetic Ticket & Label Corp.; *U.S. Private*, pg. 2547
HOLMEN B.V.—See Holmen AB; *Int'l*, pg. 3452
HOLMES PACKAGING AUSTRALIA PTY. LTD.—See Sealed Air Corporation; *U.S. Public*, pg. 1853
HONEYMOON PAPER PRODUCTS, INC.—See Southern Champion Tray Co. Inc.; *U.S. Private*, pg. 3730
HUAT LAI PAPER PRODUCTS SDN. BHD.—See Huat Lai Resources Berhad; *Int'l*, pg. 3514
HUHTAMAKI NEW ZEALAND LIMITED - MOLDED FIBER BUSINESS UNIT—See Huhtamaki Oyj; *Int'l*, pg. 3524
HYGINETT KFT—See The Procter & Gamble Company; *U.S. Public*, pg. 2120
INSULAIR, INC.—See Koch Industries, Inc.; *U.S. Private*, pg. 2327
INTERNATIONAL PAPER CABOURG SAS—See International Paper Company; *U.S. Public*, pg. 1155
INTERNATIONAL PAPER CELLULOSE FIBERS (POLAND) SP. Z O.O.—See International Paper Company; *U.S. Public*, pg. 1156
INTERNATIONAL PAPER CELLULOSE FIBERS SALES SARL—See International Paper Company; *U.S. Public*, pg. 1156
INTERNATIONAL PAPER CO. - GEORGETOWN CONTAINER—See International Paper Company; *U.S. Public*, pg. 1156
INTERNATIONAL PAPER COMPANY (JAPAN) LTD—See International Paper Company; *U.S. Public*, pg. 1157
INTERNATIONAL PAPER FOODSERVICE EUROPE LIMITED—See International Paper Company; *U.S. Public*, pg. 1157
INTERNATIONAL PAPER FOODSERVICE (SHANGHAI) CO., LTD.—See Huhtamaki Oyj; *Int'l*, pg. 3526
INTERNATIONAL PAPER GRINON, S.L.—See International Paper Company; *U.S. Public*, pg. 1157

INTERNATIONAL PAPER GROUP, S. DE R.L. DE C.V.—See International Paper Company; *U.S. Public*, pg. 1157
INTERNATIONAL PAPER POLSKA SP. Z O.O.—See International Paper Company; *U.S. Public*, pg. 1157
INTERNATIONAL PAPER VALLS, S.A.—See International Paper Company; *U.S. Public*, pg. 1157
I.P. CONTAINER HOLDINGS (SPAIN) S.L.—See International Paper Company; *U.S. Public*, pg. 1155
ITALTUBETTI, SPA—See Sonoco Products Company; *U.S. Public*, pg. 1904
JAPROTEK OY AB—See Lone Star Funds; *U.S. Private*, pg. 2486
J.R. COLE INDUSTRIES INC.; *U.S. Private*, pg. 2170
KIMBERLY-CLARK CORPORATION - CONSUMER TISSUE SECTOR—See Kimberly-Clark Corporation; *U.S. Public*, pg. 1229
KIMBERLY-CLARK CORPORATION - PROFESSIONAL & OTHER AND HEALTH CARE SECTOR—See Kimberly-Clark Corporation; *U.S. Public*, pg. 1230
KIMBERLY-CLARK PHILIPPINES INC.—See Kimberly-Clark Corporation; *U.S. Public*, pg. 1231
KNIGHTS LIMITED—See Barbados Shipping & Trading Co. Ltd.; *Int'l*, pg. 858
KORSNAS AB - FROVI—See Billerud AB; *Int'l*, pg. 1030
LABELTEC—See J.R. Cole Industries Inc.; *U.S. Private*, pg. 2170
LAKELAND PAPER CORPORATION; *U.S. Private*, pg. 2376
LEGACY CONVERTING, INC.—See Essity Aktiebolag; *Int'l*, pg. 2517
MAGNETIC TICKET & LABEL CORP.; *U.S. Private*, pg. 2547
MARTES ENTERPRISES, LLC—See DRG Technologies, Inc.; *U.S. Private*, pg. 1277
MATERIALS CONVERTING, INC.—See ADDEV Material SAS; *Int'l*, pg. 128
McCOURT LABEL COMPANY; *U.S. Private*, pg. 2630
MC XPEDX, S. DE R.L. DE C.V.—See Clayton, Dubilier & Rice, LLC; *U.S. Private*, pg. 928
MILTON MANUFACTURING INC.—See Align Capital Partners, LLC; *U.S. Private*, pg. 167
M.K. PRINTPACK (P) LTD.—See Warburg Pincus LLC; *U.S. Private*, pg. 4439
MODERNISTIC INC.; *U.S. Private*, pg. 2763
NAKED PAPERS BRANDS, INC.—See Telco Cuba, Inc.; *U.S. Public*, pg. 1992
NEEKO-SUAVE, INC.; *U.S. Private*, pg. 2880
NELIPAK B.V.—See Kohlberg & Company, LLC; *U.S. Private*, pg. 2338
NEW MIND (HONG KONG) LIMITED—See China Healthwise Holdings Limited; *Int'l*, pg. 1507
NORTHERN TECHNOLOGIES INTERNATIONAL CORPORATION; *U.S. Public*, pg. 1537
OAK HILLS CARTON CO.; *U.S. Private*, pg. 2983
OHIO PACKAGING CO.—See Greif Inc.; *U.S. Public*, pg. 967
OX PAPER TUBE & CORE, INC.; *U.S. Private*, pg. 3055
PACIFIC PAPER—See Salt Creek Capital Management, LLC; *U.S. Public*, pg. 3533
PACK-TIGER GMBH—See Sealed Air Corporation; *U.S. Public*, pg. 1854
PACON CORPORATION—See F.I.L.A. - Fabbrica Italiana Lapis ed Affini S.p.A.; *Int'l*, pg. 2596
PAC PAPER, LLC—See Apollo Global Management, Inc.; *U.S. Public*, pg. 154
PANELTECH INTERNATIONAL HOLDINGS, INC.; *U.S. Public*, pg. 1635
PAPER ONE S.R.L—See Artinova AB; *Int'l*, pg. 584
PAPER SYSTEMS INC.; *U.S. Private*, pg. 3088
PAP-R PRODUCTS COMPANY; *U.S. Private*, pg. 3087
PATERSON PACIFIC PARCHMENT CO.—See Wellspring Capital Management LLC; *U.S. Private*, pg. 4477
PENN JERSEY PAPER CO.; *U.S. Private*, pg. 3134
PERFORMANCE PAPER LLC; *U.S. Private*, pg. 3149
PERISCOPE PRINTING & PACKAGING INDIA PRIVATE LIMITED—See Quad/Graphics, Inc.; *U.S. Public*, pg. 1744
PERLEN DEUTSCHLAND GMBH—See CPH Chemie + Papier Holding AG; *Int'l*, pg. 1824
PIERCE BOX & PAPER CORP.—See Welch Packaging Group, Inc.; *U.S. Private*, pg. 4473
PINNACLE COATING & CONVERTING, INC.; *U.S. Private*, pg. 3184
PLC UUTECHNIC GROUP OYJ—See Lone Star Funds; *U.S. Private*, pg. 2486
PM COMPANY LLC; *U.S. Private*, pg. 3216
POTOMAC CORPORATION; *U.S. Private*, pg. 3235
PRO-CON PROGRESSIVE CONVERTING, INC.; *U.S. Private*, pg. 3270
PUDUMJEE PAPER PRODUCTS LTD.—See 3P Land Holdings Limited; *Int'l*, pg. 9
RANPAK CORP. - RENO—See Ranpak Holdings Corp.; *U.S. Public*, pg. 1763
RANPAK CORP.—See Ranpak Holdings Corp.; *U.S. Public*, pg. 1763
RENO DE MEDICI S.P.A.—See Apollo Global Management, Inc.; *U.S. Public*, pg. 159

322299 — ALL OTHER CONVERTED...

ROOSEVELT PAPER COMPANY; *U.S. Private,* pg. 3480
SEALED AIR AUSTRALIA (HOLDINGS) PTY. LIMITED—See Sealed Air Corporation; *U.S. Public,* pg. 1854
SEALED AIR DE MEXICO S. DE R.L. DE C.V—See Sealed Air Corporation; *U.S. Public,* pg. 1855
SEALED AIR LUXEMBOURG S.A.R.L—See Sealed Air Corporation; *U.S. Public,* pg. 1854
SEALED AIR S.R.L—See Sealed Air Corporation; *U.S. Public,* pg. 1855
SEALED AIR VITEMBAL S.L.—See Sealed Air Corporation; *U.S. Public,* pg. 1855
SECOPA S.L.—See Artinova AB; *Int'l,* pg. 584
SE (ENVELOPE MANUFACTURING) LTD—See Bong AB; *Int'l,* pg. 1107
SELKASAN KAGIT VE PAKETLEME MALZEMELERI IMALATI SAN. VE TIC. A.S.—See Cukurova Holding A.S.; *Int'l,* pg. 1876
SELKASAN KAGIT VE PAKETLEME MALZEMELERI IMALATI SAN. VE TIC. A.S.—See DS Smith Plc; *Int'l,* pg. 2208
SETTER GMBH & CO. PAPIERVERARBEITUNG—See Gesco AG; *Int'l,* pg. 2946
SETTERSTIX CORP.—See Gesco AG; *Int'l,* pg. 2946
SHAMROCK CORPORATION; *U.S. Private,* pg. 3624
SHANDONG CENTURY SUNSHINE PAPER GROUP CO., LTD.—See China Sunshine Paper Holdings Company Limited; *Int'l,* pg. 1556
SMEAD MANUFACTURING COMPANY; *U.S. Private,* pg. 3693
SMYTH COMPANIES, INC.; *U.S. Private,* pg. 3699
SONOCO OPV HUELSEN GMBH—See Sonoco Products Company; *U.S. Public,* pg. 1906
STELZER RUHRTECHNIK INTERNATIONAL GMBH—See Lone Star Funds; *U.S. Private,* pg. 2486
STEVA OY—See Lone Star Funds; *U.S. Private,* pg. 2486
ST. REGIS PAPER COMPANY LIMITED—See DS Smith Plc; *Int'l,* pg. 2209
SUGARMADE, INC.; *U.S. Private,* pg. 1959
SULLIVAN PAPER COMPANY; *U.S. Private,* pg. 3851
SURREY ENVELOPES LTD—See Bong AB; *Int'l,* pg. 1107
TAGS & LABELS—See Heartwood Partners, LLC; *U.S. Private,* pg. 1901
TEO SENG PAPER PRODUCTS SDN BHD—See Emerging Glory Sdn Bhd; *Int'l,* pg. 2379
THERMAL PAPER DIRECT INC.; *U.S. Private,* pg. 4142
THOMPSON PRODUCTS, INC.; *U.S. Private,* pg. 4160
TORRASPAPEL, S.A.—See CVC Capital Partners SICAV-FIS S.A.; *Int'l,* pg. 1888
TUFCO TECHNOLOGIES, INC.—See Griffin Holdings, LLC; *U.S. Private,* pg. 1788
UNISOURCE BELGIUM BVBA—See Clayton, Dubilier & Rice, LLC; *U.S. Private,* pg. 928
UNIVERSITY PRODUCTS INC.; *U.S. Private,* pg. 4310
US GREENFIBER LLC; *U.S. Private,* pg. 4318
VAAHTO PAPER TECHNOLOGY LTD.—See Lone Star Funds; *U.S. Private,* pg. 2487
VALLEY CONVERTING CO., INC.; *U.S. Private,* pg. 4333
VANGUARD LABEL, INC.; *U.S. Private,* pg. 4343
VENLOP B.V.—See Bong AB; *Int'l,* pg. 1107
VERITIV EXPRESS—See Clayton, Dubilier & Rice, LLC; *U.S. Private,* pg. 929
VINDA NORTH PAPER (BEIJING) COMPANY LIMITED—See Essity Aktiebolag; *Int'l,* pg. 2517
VINDA PAPER (CHINA) COMPANY LIMITED—See Essity Aktiebolag; *Int'l,* pg. 2517
WESTERN PULP PRODUCTS CO.; *U.S. Private,* pg. 4496
WEST FRASER TIMBER CO., LTD. - QUESNEL RIVER PULP DIVISION—See Atlas Holdings, LLC; *U.S. Private,* pg. 377
WS PACKAGING GROUP INC.—See Platinum Equity, LLC; *U.S. Private,* pg. 3206
XPEDX, S.A. DE C.V—See Clayton, Dubilier & Rice, LLC; *U.S. Private,* pg. 930
ZAO SLALOM—See Lone Star Funds; *U.S. Private,* pg. 2487
ZHUHAI SHENGLONG BAR CODE TECHNOLOGY CO., LTD.—See Guangdong Guanhao High-Tech Co., Ltd.; *Int'l,* pg. 3155

323111 — COMMERCIAL PRINTING (EXCEPT SCREEN AND BOOKS)

333D LTD.; *Int'l,* pg. 6
3G GRAPHIC SOLUTIONS; *U.S. Private,* pg. 13
4OVER, INC.; *U.S. Private,* pg. 15
ABC IMAGING LLC; *U.S. Private,* pg. 36
ABC PRINTING CO.—See Greater Georgia Printers, Inc.; *U.S. Private,* pg. 1769
ABNOTE AUSTRALASIA PTY. LTD.—See American Banknote Corporation; *U.S. Private,* pg. 224
ABNOTE NORTH AMERICA—See American Banknote Corporation; *U.S. Private,* pg. 224
ABSORBENT, INK.; *U.S. Private,* pg. 44
ACCENT INTERMEDIA, LLC—See Cuentas Inc.; *U.S. Public,* pg. 604
ACCO BRANDS CANADA INC.—See ACCO Brands Corporation; *U.S. Public,* pg. 32
ACCO BRANDS CORPORATION; *U.S. Public,* pg. 32
ACCO INTERNATIONAL HOLDINGS, INC.—See ACCO Brands Corporation; *U.S. Public,* pg. 33
ACCU COPY OF GREENVILLE, INC.—See Taylor Corporation; *U.S. Private,* pg. 3939
ACE LITHOGRAPHERS OF MORRIS COUNTY, INC.; *U.S. Private,* pg. 57
ACTA PRINT TAMPERE—See Alma Media Corporation; *Int'l,* pg. 362
ACTIGROUP—See DPG Media Group NV; *Int'l,* pg. 2188
ADAIR PRINTING COMPANY; *U.S. Private,* pg. 73
THE ADAM GROUP; *U.S. Private,* pg. 3981
ADAMS MCCLURE, LP—See Ennis, Inc.; *U.S. Public,* pg. 768
ADM ENDEAVORS, INC.; *U.S. Public,* pg. 41
ADMORE, INC.—See Ennis, Inc.; *U.S. Public,* pg. 768
ADMORE WEST—See Ennis, Inc.; *U.S. Public,* pg. 768
ADVANCED LABELWORX, INC. - ANDERSON—See Advanced Labelworx, Inc.; *U.S. Private,* pg. 90
ADVANCED LABELWORX, INC.; *U.S. Private,* pg. 90
ADVANCED NETWORK MARKETING, INC.; *U.S. Private,* pg. 91
ADVANCED VISION TECHNOLOGY LTD.—See Danaher Corporation; *U.S. Public,* pg. 624
ADVANCED WEB TECHNOLOGIES, INC.; *U.S. Private,* pg. 93
ADVANTEST MEDIA SERVICE CORPORATION—See Advantest Corporation; *Int'l,* pg. 166
ADVERTISERS PRESS INCORPORATED; *U.S. Private,* pg. 109
ADVOCATE PRINTING & PUBLISHING CO. LTD. - DARTMOUTH PLANT—See Advocate Printing & Publishing Co. Ltd.; *Int'l,* pg. 168
ADVOCATE PRINTING & PUBLISHING CO. LTD.; *Int'l,* pg. 168
AEOON TECHNOLOGIES GMBH; *Int'l,* pg. 179
AFE INDUSTRIES, INC.; *U.S. Private,* pg. 121
AGRICULTURE PRINTING & PACKAGING JOINT STOCK COMPANY; *Int'l,* pg. 217
AGS CUSTOM GRAPHICS, INC.—See Chatham Asset Management, LLC; *U.S. Private,* pg. 862
AIDA DO BRASIL COMERCIO DE MAQUINAS LTDA.—See AIDA Engineering, Ltd.; *Int'l,* pg. 231
AIDA EUROPE GMBH—See AIDA Engineering, Ltd.; *Int'l,* pg. 230
AIDA GREATER ASIA PHILIPPINES, INC.—See AIDA Engineering, Ltd.; *Int'l,* pg. 230
AIDA INDIA PVT. LTD.—See AIDA Engineering, Ltd.; *Int'l,* pg. 230
AIDA MANUFACTURING (ASIA) SDN. BHD.—See AIDA Engineering, Ltd.; *Int'l,* pg. 230
AIDA MAROC SARL—See AIDA Engineering, Ltd.; *Int'l,* pg. 230
AIDA PRESS MACHINERY SYSTEMS CO., LTD.—See AIDA Engineering, Ltd.; *Int'l,* pg. 231
AIDA (THAILAND) CO., LTD.—See AIDA Engineering, Ltd.; *Int'l,* pg. 230
AIDA VIETNAM CO., LTD.—See AIDA Engineering, Ltd.; *Int'l,* pg. 230
AJ BART INC.; *U.S. Private,* pg. 143
AKEBONO 123 CO., LTD.—See Akebono Brake Industry Co., Ltd.; *Int'l,* pg. 261
AKI, INC.; *U.S. Private,* pg. 145
THE ALC GROUP—See Burd & Fletcher Company; *U.S. Private,* pg. 686
ALCOM PRINTING GROUP, INC.; *U.S. Private,* pg. 154
AL EMAN PRINTING PRESS CO—See HAK Algahtani Group of Companies; *Int'l,* pg. 3219
ALEXANDER'S HOLDINGS, LC; *U.S. Private,* pg. 164
ALEX WILSON COLDSTREAM LTD.; *Int'l,* pg. 306
ALL ABOUT PACKAGING; *U.S. Private,* pg. 169
ALLEN PRINTING, INC.; *U.S. Private,* pg. 179
ALLIANCE PRINTING & PUBLISHING, INC.—See Corporate Document Solutions, Inc.; *U.S. Private,* pg. 1054
THE ALLIED GROUP INC.—See Atlantic Street Capital Management LLC; *U.S. Private,* pg. 374
ALLIED PRINTING SERVICES, INC.; *U.S. Private,* pg. 187
ALL-STATE INTERNATIONAL, INC.; *U.S. Private,* pg. 173
ALPENPLAKAT AG—See APG/SGA SA; *Int'l,* pg. 513
ALRAI MEDIA GROUP COMPANY K.S.C.; *Int'l,* pg. 377
AMARIN PRINTING & PUBLISHING PUBLIC COMPANY LIMITED; *Int'l,* pg. 412
AMBA CO., PROIZVODNJA IN TRGOVINA D.O.O., LJUBLJANA—See CETIS, d.d.; *Int'l,* pg. 1424
AMEDIA AS; *Int'l,* pg. 420
AMERICAN DIRECT LLC—See Tidewater Direct LLC; *U.S. Private,* pg. 4168
AMERICAN LITHO INC.; *U.S. Private,* pg. 240
AMERICAN PRESS LLC; *U.S. Private,* pg. 244
AMERICAN PRINTING COMPANY INC.; *U.S. Private,* pg. 244
AMERICAN SLIDE-CHART CO.; *U.S. Private,* pg. 253
AMERICAN SPIRIT GRAPHICS CORPORATION; *U.S. Private,* pg. 255
AMERICAN THERMOPLASTIC COMPANY; *U.S. Private,* pg. 257
AMERICAN WEB INC.; *U.S. Private,* pg. 258
AMERICHIP, INC.; *U.S. Private,* pg. 259
AMERIPRINT CORPORATION—See Ennis, Inc.; *U.S. Public,* pg. 768
AMSIVE LLC—See H.I.G. Capital, LLC; *U.S. Private,* pg. 1829
ANCHOR PRINTING COMPANY—See Harvest Partners L.P.; *U.S. Private,* pg. 1876
ANDERSON LA, INC.—See Chatham Asset Management, LLC; *U.S. Private,* pg. 866
ANDERSON & VREELAND INC.—See Anderson & Vreeland, Inc.; *U.S. Private,* pg. 276
ANDREWS CONNECTICUT—See Chatham Asset Management, LLC; *U.S. Private,* pg. 866
ANGSTROM GRAPHICS INC. - ANGSTROM GRAPHICS CREATIVE DIVISION—See Mittera Group, Inc.; *U.S. Private,* pg. 2751
ANGSTROM GRAPHICS INC.-MIDWEST—See Mittera Group, Inc.; *U.S. Private,* pg. 2751
ANGSTROM GRAPHICS INC.—See Mittera Group, Inc.; *U.S. Private,* pg. 2751
ANNAN & BIRD LITHOGRAPHERS, INC.—See Chatham Asset Management, LLC; *U.S. Private,* pg. 862
ANRO INC.; *U.S. Private,* pg. 285
ANSELMO L. MORVILLO, S.A.—See Quad/Graphics, Inc.; *U.S. Private,* pg. 1744
ANTOK NYOMDAIPARI KFT—See CirclePrinters Holding BV; *Int'l,* pg. 1618
APOGEE CORPORATION (JERSEY) LIMITED—See HP Inc.; *U.S. Public,* pg. 1062
APPERSON PRINT RESOURCES, INC. - APPERSON EDUCATION PRODUCTS DIVISION—See Apperson Print Resources, Inc.; *U.S. Private,* pg. 296
APPERSON PRINT RESOURCES, INC.; *U.S. Private,* pg. 296
APPLE GRAPHICS, INC.—See Chatham Asset Management, LLC; *U.S. Private,* pg. 862
APTARA, INC.—See iEnergizer Limited; *Int'l,* pg. 3597
ARANDELL CORPORATION—See Saothair Capital Partners LLC; *U.S. Private,* pg. 3548
ARC DOCUMENT SOLUTIONS, INC. - ATLANTA—See ARC DOCUMENT SOLUTIONS, INC.; *U.S. Public,* pg. 179
ARC DOCUMENT SOLUTIONS, INC.—See ARC DOCUMENT SOLUTIONS, INC.; *U.S. Public,* pg. 179
ARC DOCUMENT SOLUTIONS, INC.—See ARC DOCUMENT SOLUTIONS, INC.; *U.S. Public,* pg. 179
ARC DOCUMENT SOLUTIONS, INC.—See ARC DOCUMENT SOLUTIONS, INC.; *U.S. Public,* pg. 179
ARC DOCUMENT SOLUTIONS, INC.—See ARC DOCUMENT SOLUTIONS, INC.; *U.S. Public,* pg. 179
ARC DOCUMENT SOLUTIONS, INC.—See ARC DOCUMENT SOLUTIONS, INC.; *U.S. Public,* pg. 179
ARC DOCUMENT SOLUTIONS, INC.—See ARC DOCUMENT SOLUTIONS, INC.; *U.S. Public,* pg. 179
ARKLE PRINT LTD; *Int'l,* pg. 571
ARROW GAMES CORPORATION—See Arrow International, Inc.; *U.S. Private,* pg. 335
ARROW INTERNATIONAL, INC.; *U.S. Private,* pg. 335
THE ARTCRAFT COMPANY; *U.S. Private,* pg. 3988
ARTES GRAFICAS RIOPLATENSE S.A.—See Grupo Clarin S.A.; *Int'l,* pg. 3124
ASAP PRINTING CORP—See 4OVER, Inc.; *U.S. Private,* pg. 15
AS PRINTALL—See AS Ekspress Grupp; *Int'l,* pg. 589
ASUKANET COMPANY LIMITED; *Int'l,* pg. 663
ATLAS TAG & LABEL—See Ennis, Inc.; *U.S. Public,* pg. 768
ATLAS TRADE DISTRIBUTION SRL—See ANY Security Printing Company PLC; *Int'l,* pg. 486
AUGUSTUS MARTIN LTD.; *Int'l,* pg. 704
AUS-TEX PRINTING & MAILING; *U.S. Private,* pg. 395
AUTOMATED GRAPHIC SYSTEMS, INC.—See Chatham Asset Management, LLC; *U.S. Private,* pg. 862
AVANT IMAGING & INFORMATION MANAGEMENT, INC.; *Int'l,* pg. 735
AVERY DENNISON HOLDING LIMITED—See Avery Dennison Corporation; *U.S. Public,* pg. 243
BA INTERNATIONAL—See Giesecke & Devrient GmbH; *Int'l,* pg. 2969
BANG PRINTING OF OHIO, INC.—See Bang Printing; *U.S. Private,* pg. 465
BANG PRINTING; *U.S. Private,* pg. 465
BANTA GLOBAL TURNKEY, S.R.O.—See Chatham Asset Management, LLC; *U.S. Private,* pg. 862
BAUER MEDIA FRANCE SNC—See Heinrich Bauer Verlag KG; *Int'l,* pg. 3323
BAUER PRINT CIECHANOW SP. Z O.O.—See Heinrich Bauer Verlag KG; *Int'l,* pg. 3323
BAUER PRINT WYKROTY SP. Z O.O.—See Heinrich Bauer Verlag KG; *Int'l,* pg. 3323
BAY STATE ENVELOPE INC.; *U.S. Private,* pg. 494
BAZAAR & NOVELTY LTD.—See Arrow International, Inc.; *U.S. Private,* pg. 335
B&D LITHO OF ARIZONA, INC.—See Ennis, Inc.; *U.S. Public,* pg. 769
BEIJING SHENGTONG PRINTING CO., LTD.; *Int'l,* pg. 955
BELMARK INC.; *U.S. Private,* pg. 520
BERLIN DIVISION—See American Litho Inc.; *U.S. Private,* pg. 240
BEST LABEL COMPANY INC.—See Ares Management Cor-

N.A.I.C.S. INDEX

323111 — COMMERCIAL PRINTING...

poration; *U.S. Public*, pg. 190
BFS BUSINESS PRINTING INC.; *U.S. Private*, pg. 548
BIBBERO SYSTEMS INC.; *U.S. Private*, pg. 550
BIEGELAAR BV; *Int'l*, pg. 1020
BILLBOARD JSC; *Int'l*, pg. 1030
BINGO KING COMPANY—See Arrow International, Inc.; *U.S. Private*, pg. 335
BIZXCHANGE INCORPORATED; *U.S. Private*, pg. 568
BLOCK GRAPHICS, INC.—See Ennis, Inc.; *U.S. Public*, pg. 769
BLOOMINGTON OFFSET PROCESS; *U.S. Private*, pg. 584
BLUE OCEAN PRESS, INC.; *U.S. Private*, pg. 589
THE BLUE PRINT INDEPENDENCE—See ARC DOCUMENT SOLUTIONS, INC.; *U.S. Public*, pg. 179
BLUE RIDGE PRINTING CO., INC.; *U.S. Private*, pg. 592
BLUE STAR PRINT GROUP LIMITED—See CHAMP Private Equity Pty. Ltd.; *Int'l*, pg. 1439
BNBS, INC.—See Deluxe Corporation; *U.S. Public*, pg. 652
BORAC H & H A.D.; *Int'l*, pg. 1112
BOUTWELL OWENS & CO. INC.; *U.S. Private*, pg. 624
BOWNE INTERNATIONAL LTD.—See Chatham Asset Management, LLC; *U.S. Private*, pg. 862
BPI REPRO, LLC—See ARC DOCUMENT SOLUTIONS, INC.; *U.S. Public*, pg. 179
THE BRANDT CO.; *U.S. Private*, pg. 4000
BRAVE, INC.—See Faith, Inc.; *Int'l*, pg. 2609
BREHM COMMUNICATIONS INC. - GOLD COUNTRY PRINTING DIVISION—See Brehm Communications Inc.; *U.S. Private*, pg. 644
BREHM COMMUNICATIONS INC.; *U.S. Private*, pg. 644
BRIDGECOM LLC; *U.S. Private*, pg. 649
BRIDGETOWN PRINTING CO.—See Chatham Asset Management, LLC; *U.S. Private*, pg. 862
BROWN INDUSTRIES, INC.; *U.S. Private*, pg. 667
BR PRINTERS, INC.; *U.S. Private*, pg. 630
THE BUREAU OF ENGRAVING, INC.; *U.S. Private*, pg. 4002
BUSINESS CARD SERVICE INC.; *U.S. Private*, pg. 694
C2 IMAGING, LLC-NEW YORK—See Vomela Specialty Company; *U.S. Private*, pg. 4412
CADMUS COMMUNICATIONS - HURLOCK—See Cenveo, Inc.; *U.S. Private*, pg. 834
CADMUS JOURNAL SERVICES, INC.—See Cenveo, Inc.; *U.S. Private*, pg. 834
CALIBRATED FORMS CO., INC.—See Ennis, Inc.; *U.S. Public*, pg. 769
CALICO TAG & LABEL INC—See AFE Industries, Inc.; *U.S. Private*, pg. 121
CALIFORNIA OFFSET PRINTERS, INC.—See COP Communications; *U.S. Private*, pg. 1044
CALLIGRAPHEN AB—See HAL Trust N.V.; *Int'l*, pg. 3224
CALLIGRAPHEN APS—See HAL Trust N.V.; *Int'l*, pg. 3224
CALLIGRAPHEN OY—See HAL Trust N.V.; *Int'l*, pg. 3224
CAMELOT GHANA LIMITED; *Int'l*, pg. 1271
CAMELOT SECURITY SOLUTIONS LIMITED—See Camelot Ghana Limited; *Int'l*, pg. 1271
CANFIELD & TACK INCORPORATED; *U.S. Private*, pg. 734
CAPTIVA GROUP INC.; *U.S. Private*, pg. 747
CARDINAL CO., LTD.; *Int'l*, pg. 1321
CARDINAL PRINTING CO., INC.—See Deluxe Corporation; *U.S. Public*, pg. 653
CARLSON CRAFT CATALOG—See Taylor Corporation; *U.S. Private*, pg. 3938
CARLSON CRAFT—See Taylor Corporation; *U.S. Private*, pg. 3938
CAROLINA CUT SHEETS, INC.—See Champion Industries, Inc.; *U.S. Public*, pg. 478
CARTAMUNDI ESPANA, S.L.—See Cartamundi N.V.; *Int'l*, pg. 1348
CARTAMUNDI ITALY SA—See Cartamundi N.V.; *Int'l*, pg. 1348
CARTAMUNDI NORDIC AB—See Cartamundi N.V.; *Int'l*, pg. 1348
CARTAMUNDI NORTH AMERICA EAST LONGMEADOW LLC—See Cartamundi N.V.; *Int'l*, pg. 1348
CARTAMUNDI POLSKA SP. Z O.O.—See Cartamundi N.V.; *Int'l*, pg. 1348
CARVEL PRINT SERIGRAPH, INC.—See Serigraph, Inc.; *U.S. Private*, pg. 3613
CATHEDRAL CORPORATION; *U.S. Private*, pg. 788
CAXTON AND CTP PUBLISHERS AND PRINTERS LTD.; *Int'l*, pg. 1363
CCL LABEL—See CCL Industries Inc.; *Int'l*, pg. 1367
CCL LABEL—See CCL Industries Inc.; *Int'l*, pg. 1367
CCL LABEL (VIC) PTY. LTD.—See CCL Industries Inc.; *Int'l*, pg. 1368
CCL SECURE PTY LTD—See CCL Industries Inc.; *Int'l*, pg. 1368
CDS PUBLICATIONS—See Chatham Asset Management, LLC; *U.S. Private*, pg. 862
CEFLA ASIA PTE LTD—See Cefla S.C.; *Int'l*, pg. 1389
CEFLA FINISHING EUROPE DEUTSCHLAND—See Cefla S.C.; *Int'l*, pg. 1389
CEFLA FINISHING EUROPE—See Cefla S.C.; *Int'l*, pg. 1389
CEFLA FINISHING INDIA PVT. LTD.—See Cefla S.C.; *Int'l*, pg. 1389

CEFLA FINISHING RUSSIA—See Cefla S.C.; *Int'l*, pg. 1389
CEFLA MIDDLE EAST FZE—See Cefla S.C.; *Int'l*, pg. 1389
CEFLA POLSKA SP. Z.O.O.—See Cefla S.C.; *Int'l*, pg. 1389
CEFLA S.C. - DUSPOHL PLANT—See Cefla S.C.; *Int'l*, pg. 1389
CEFLA S.C. - FALCIONI PLANT—See Cefla S.C.; *Int'l*, pg. 1389
CELLOTAPE, INC.—See Ares Management Corporation; *U.S. Public*, pg. 190
CELLO-WRAP PRINTING COMPANY, INC.—See Carroll Products, Inc.; *U.S. Private*, pg. 773
CENTRAL STATES BUSINESS FORMS—See Adams Investment Company; *U.S. Private*, pg. 74
CENTRAL STATES BUSINESS FORMS - SUWANEE PLANT—See Adams Investment Company; *U.S. Private*, pg. 74
CENTURY MARKETING SOLUTIONS, LLC—See Lumen Technologies, Inc.; *U.S. Public*, pg. 1345
CENVEO COMMERCIAL PRINTING & PACKAGING - ST. LOUIS—See Cenveo, Inc.; *U.S. Private*, pg. 834
CENVEO CORPORATION—See Cenveo, Inc.; *U.S. Private*, pg. 834
CENVEO PUBLISHER SERVICES—See Cenveo, Inc.; *U.S. Private*, pg. 834
CERQA COPYRIGHT—See Nationwide Argosy Solutions, LLC; *U.S. Private*, pg. 2865
CETIS, D.D.; *Int'l*, pg. 1424
CETIS-ZG D.O.O.—See CETIS, d.d.; *Int'l*, pg. 1424
CEWE MAGYARORSZAG KFT—See CEWE Stiftung & Co. KGaA; *Int'l*, pg. 1425
CEWE SP. Z O. O.—See CEWE Stiftung & Co. KGaA; *Int'l*, pg. 1425
CFM PRINTING & STATIONERY SDN. BHD—See Computer Forms (Malaysia) Berhad; *Int'l*, pg. 1759
CFM TOPPAN FORMS (MALAYSIA) SDN. BHD.—See Computer Forms (Malaysia) Berhad; *Int'l*, pg. 1759
CGX YAMAGATA JAPAN GK—See Chatham Asset Management, LLC; *U.S. Private*, pg. 862
CHAINTECH TECHNOLOGY CORP.; *Int'l*, pg. 1437
THE CHALLENGE PRINTING COMPANY; *U.S. Private*, pg. 4007
CHAMPION GRAPHIC COMMUNICATIONS—See Champion Industries, Inc.; *U.S. Public*, pg. 478
CHAMPION INDUSTRIES, INC.; *U.S. Public*, pg. 477
THE CHAPMAN PRINTING COMPANY, INC. - CHARLESTON—See Champion Industries, Inc.; *U.S. Public*, pg. 478
THE CHAPMAN PRINTING COMPANY, INC. - LEXINGTON—See Champion Industries, Inc.; *U.S. Public*, pg. 478
THE CHAPMAN PRINTING COMPANY, INC. - PARKERSBURG—See Champion Industries, Inc.; *U.S. Public*, pg. 478
THE CHAPMAN PRINTING COMPANY, INC.—See Champion Industries, Inc.; *U.S. Public*, pg. 478
CHARMING PRINTING LIMITED—See Cirtek Holdings Limited; *Int'l*, pg. 1618
CHECKS IN THE MAIL, INC.—See MacAndrews & Forbes Incorporated; *U.S. Private*, pg. 2532
CHENGDU B-RAY MEDIA CO., LTD.; *Int'l*, pg. 1467
CHOICE DEVELOPMENT, INC. - LINKOU FACTORY—See Choice Development, Inc.; *Int'l*, pg. 1577
CHOICE DEVELOPMENT, INC. - TAINAN FACTORY—See Choice Development, Inc.; *Int'l*, pg. 1577
CHRISTMAS CITY PRINTING CO., INC.—See Alcom Printing Group, Inc.; *U.S. Private*, pg. 154
CHROMALINE SCREEN PRINT PRODUCTS—See Terawulf Inc.; *U.S. Public*, pg. 2018
CHROMOS GROUP AG—See Basler AG; *Int'l*, pg. 887
CIMPRESS JAPAN CO., LTD.—See Cimpress plc; *Int'l*, pg. 1609
CIPI S.P.A—See Cifin S.r.l.; *Int'l*, pg. 1605
CIRCLE GRAPHICS, INC.—See H.I.G. Capital, LLC; *U.S. Private*, pg. 1827
CIRCLE PRESSROOM, INC.; *U.S. Private*, pg. 900
CLARION SAFETY SYSTEMS, LLC; *U.S. Private*, pg. 911
CL&D GRAPHICS, INC.; *U.S. Private*, pg. 909
CLEAR VISIONS, INC.—See Chatham Asset Management, LLC; *U.S. Private*, pg. 862
CMC CORPORATION; *Int'l*, pg. 1668
COASTAL PRINTING, INC.—See Intech Printing & Direct Mail; *U.S. Private*, pg. 2097
COASTAL TAG & LABEL INC.—See AFE Industries, Inc.; *U.S. Private*, pg. 121
COAST LABEL COMPANY—See Ares Management Corporation; *U.S. Public*, pg. 190
COFFEE GMBH—See Bechtle AG; *Int'l*, pg. 937
THE COLAD GROUP, INC.—See Bindagraphics Inc.; *U.S. Private*, pg. 560
COLLOTYPE LABELS INTERNATIONAL PTY. LTD.—See Platinum Equity, LLC; *U.S. Private*, pg. 3206
COLLOTYPE LABELS IRELAND LIMITED—See Platinum Equity, LLC; *U.S. Private*, pg. 3206
COLLOTYPE LABELS USA INC.—See Platinum Equity, LLC; *U.S. Private*, pg. 3206
COLONIAL PARTNERS, INC.; *U.S. Private*, pg. 971
COLOR-BRIDGE PRINTING & PACKAGING COMPANY LIMITED - DONGGUAN COLOR-BRIDGE PRINTING &

PAPER PRODUCTS FACTORY—See Evershine Group Holdings Limited; *Int'l*, pg. 2569
COLOR-BRIDGE PRINTING & PACKAGING COMPANY LIMITED—See Evershine Group Holdings Limited; *Int'l*, pg. 2569
COLOR COMMUNICATIONS, INC.; *U.S. Private*, pg. 972
COLORCRAFT OF VIRGINIA, INC.—See Corporate Press Inc.; *U.S. Private*, pg. 1055
COLOREP, INC.; *U.S. Private*, pg. 975
COLORFX LLC—See Mittera Group, Inc.; *U.S. Private*, pg. 2751
COLORGRAPHICS, INC. - SAN FRANCISCO—See Cenveo, Inc.; *U.S. Private*, pg. 835
COLORGRAPHICS, INC. - SEATTLE—See Cenveo, Inc.; *U.S. Private*, pg. 835
COLOR IMPRESSIONS, INC.—See Docuplex, Inc.; *U.S. Private*, pg. 1252
COLOR INK, INC.; *U.S. Private*, pg. 972
COLT PRINT SERVICES, INC.; *U.S. Private*, pg. 975
COLWELL INDUSTRIES, INC.; *U.S. Private*, pg. 979
COLWELL NORTH AMERICA—See Colwell Industries, Inc.; *U.S. Private*, pg. 980
COMMAND WEB OFFSET CO.—See Unimac Graphics; *U.S. Private*, pg. 4284
COMMUNISIS PLC—See Aquiline Capital Partners LLC; *U.S. Private*, pg. 304
COMMUNISIS UK LIMITED—See Aquiline Capital Partners LLC; *U.S. Private*, pg. 304
COMPASS DISPLAY GROUP, INC.—See Edison Lithographing & Printing Corp.; *U.S. Private*, pg. 1336
COMPUTER FORMS (MALAYSIA) BERHAD; *Int'l*, pg. 1759
COMPUTER STOCK FORMS, INC.—See Rotary Forms Press, Inc.; *U.S. Private*, pg. 3486
COMPUTYPE INC.; *U.S. Private*, pg. 1006
CONCORD LITHO GROUP; *U.S. Private*, pg. 1010
CONCORD PUBLISHING HOUSE INC.—See Rust Communications; *U.S. Private*, pg. 3507
CONLEY PUBLISHING GROUP LTD.; *U.S. Private*, pg. 1014
CONSOLIDATED CARQUEVILLE PRINTING COMPANY—See Chatham Asset Management, LLC; *U.S. Private*, pg. 862
CONSOLIDATED GRAPHIC COMMUNICATIONS—See Champion Industries, Inc.; *U.S. Public*, pg. 478
CONSOLIDATED GRAPHICS GROUP, INC.; *U.S. Private*, pg. 1020
CONSOLIDATED GRAPHICS, INC.—See Chatham Asset Management, LLC; *U.S. Private*, pg. 862
CONSOLIDATED PRESS, INC.; *U.S. Private*, pg. 1021
CONTENT MANAGEMENT CORPORATION—See BR Printers, Inc.; *U.S. Private*, pg. 630
CONTINENTAL WEB PRESS, INC.; *U.S. Private*, pg. 1031
CONTINENTAL WEB PRESS OF KENTUCKY—See Continental Web Press, Inc.; *U.S. Private*, pg. 1031
CONVENIENCE STORE DECISIONS—See Telapex Inc.; *U.S. Private*, pg. 3959
COPAC, INC.; *U.S. Private*, pg. 1044
COPAG DA AMAZONIA S.A.—See Cartamundi N.V.; *Int'l*, pg. 1348
COP COMMUNICATIONS; *U.S. Private*, pg. 1044
COPY-MOR, INC.—See Chatham Asset Management, LLC; *U.S. Private*, pg. 862
CORAL GRAPHIC SERVICES, INC.; *U.S. Private*, pg. 1046
CORPORATE COLOR, INC.—See Corporate Press Inc.; *U.S. Private*, pg. 1055
CORPORATE DIRECT INC.—See Corporate Press Inc.; *U.S. Private*, pg. 1055
CORPORATE GRAPHICS INTERNATIONAL—See Taylor Corporation; *U.S. Private*, pg. 3938
CORPORATE GRAPHICS INTERNATIONAL—See Taylor Corporation; *U.S. Private*, pg. 3938
CORPORATE PRESS INC.; *U.S. Private*, pg. 1055
COSMOPOLITAN—See The Hearst Corporation; *U.S. Private*, pg. 4046
COSMOS COMMUNICATIONS; *U.S. Private*, pg. 1062
COTT INDEX CO.; *U.S. Private*, pg. 1063
COUNTRY LIVING—See The Hearst Corporation; *U.S. Private*, pg. 4046
COURIER GRAPHICS CORP.; *U.S. Private*, pg. 1068
COVERDELL CANADA CORPORATION—See Arthur J. Gallagher & Co.; *U.S. Public*, pg. 204
CRANE CURRENCY MALTA LTD.—See Crane NXT, Co.; *U.S. Public*, pg. 590
CREATIVEPRO.COM—See PrintingForLess.com, Inc.; *U.S. Private*, pg. 3266
CREEL PRINTING, LLC—See Atlas Holdings, LLC; *U.S. Private*, pg. 377
CREPS UNITED PUBLICATIONS; *U.S. Private*, pg. 1093
CROSSMARK GRAPHICS INC.; *U.S. Private*, pg. 1107
CUBIC KOREA INC.; *Int'l*, pg. 1875
CURTIS 1000, INC.—See Taylor Corporation; *U.S. Private*, pg. 3938
CURTIS 1000, INC.—See Taylor Corporation; *U.S. Private*, pg. 3938
CURTIS 1000, INC.—See Taylor Corporation; *U.S. Private*, pg. 3938
CURTIS 1000, INC.—See Taylor Corporation; *U.S. Private*, pg. 3938

323111 — COMMERCIAL PRINTING...   CORPORATE AFFILIATIONS

CURTIS BUSINESS FORMS INC.—See Ennis, Inc.; *U.S. Public*, pg. 769
CUSHING AND COMPANY INC.; *U.S. Private*, pg. 1127
CUSTOMCD, INC.—See Siris Capital Group, LLC; *U.S. Private*, pg. 3672
CUSTOM PRINTING INC.; *U.S. Private*, pg. 1129
CUSTOM PRINT NOW; *U.S. Private*, pg. 1129
THE CYRIL-SCOTT COMPANY—See Chatham Asset Management, LLC; *U.S. Private*, pg. 863
DALB, INC.; *U.S. Private*, pg. 1148
DARMON IMPRESSIONS; *Int'l*, pg. 1973
DARTMOUTH PRINTING CO. INC.—See CJK Group, Inc.; *U.S. Private*, pg. 909
DARWILL PRESS, INC., *U.S. Private*, pg. 1160
DASCO SYSTEMS, INC.—See Sole Source Capital LLC; *U.S. Private*, pg. 3708
DATA LABEL INC.; *U.S. Private*, pg. 1163
DATA PAPERS INC.; *U.S. Private*, pg. 1163
DATA SERVICE SOLUTIONS, INC.—See The Segerdahl Corporation; *U.S. Private*, pg. 4116
DATATEL RESOURCES CORPORATION; *U.S. Private*, pg. 1166
DAY-TIMERS, INC.—See ACCO Brands Corporation; *U.S. Public*, pg. 33
DB PRINT GMBH—See Deutsche Bank Aktiengesellschaft; *Int'l*, pg. 2056
DECHAN II, INC.; *U.S. Private*, pg. 1187
DECK THE WALLS—See Franchise Concepts, Inc.; *U.S. Private*, pg. 1587
DEDALO HELIOCOLOR—See Dedalo Grupo Grafico, S.L.; *Int'l*, pg. 2002
DE LA RUE CURRENCY AND SECURITY PRINT LIMITED—See De La Rue plc; *Int'l*, pg. 1996
DE LA RUE CURRENCY AND SECURITY PRINT—See De La Rue plc; *Int'l*, pg. 1996
DE LA RUE CURRENCY AND SECURITY PRINT—See De La Rue plc; *Int'l*, pg. 1996
DE LA RUE INTERNATIONAL LIMITED—See De La Rue plc; *Int'l*, pg. 1996
DE LA RUE MALAYSIA SDN. BHD.—See De La Rue plc; *Int'l*, pg. 1996
DE LA RUE MEXICO, S.A. DE C.V—See De La Rue plc; *Int'l*, pg. 1996
DE LA RUE PLC; *Int'l*, pg. 1996
DE LA RUE SECURITY PRINT INC.—See De La Rue plc; *Int'l*, pg. 1996
DE LA RUE SECURITY PRODUCTS—See De La Rue plc; *Int'l*, pg. 1996
DE LA RUE SECURITY PRODUCTS—See De La Rue plc; *Int'l*, pg. 1996
DE LA RUE SECURITY PRODUCTS—See De La Rue plc; *Int'l*, pg. 1996
DE LA RUE SMURFIT LIMITED—See De La Rue plc; *Int'l*, pg. 1996
DELLE VEDOVE S.P.A.—See Cefla S.C.; *Int'l*, pg. 1390
DELUXE PACKAGES—See Amcor plc; *Int'l*, pg. 417
DELUXE SMALL BUSINESS SALES, INC.—See Deluxe Corporation; *U.S. Public*, pg. 652
DELZER LITHOGRAPH COMPANY; *U.S. Private*, pg. 1202
DEMOCRAT PRINTING & LITHOGRAPH COMPANY; *U.S. Private*, pg. 1204
DESIGNTEX - PORTLAND—See Steelcase Inc.; *U.S. Public*, pg. 1944
THE DETROIT NEWS - STERLING HEIGHTS PRINTING FACILITY—See Alden Global Capital LLC; *U.S. Private*, pg. 158
DG3 ASIA LIMITED—See Diversified Global Graphics Group, LLC; *U.S. Private*, pg. 1242
DG3 EUROPE LTD.—See Diversified Global Graphics Group, LLC; *U.S. Private*, pg. 1242
DG3 JAPAN LIMITED—See Diversified Global Graphics Group, LLC; *U.S. Private*, pg. 1242
DG3 MANILA LTD.—See Diversified Global Graphics Group, LLC; *U.S. Private*, pg. 1242
DG3 NORTH AMERICA, INC.—See Diversified Global Graphics Group, LLC; *U.S. Private*, pg. 1242
DGI COMMUNICATIONS, LLC—See Kirkwood Printing Company, Inc.; *U.S. Private*, pg. 2315
DIGIGRAPH XPRESS LLC—See Next Page, Inc.; *U.S. Private*, pg. 2920
DIGIMARC CORPORATION; *U.S. Public*, pg. 662
DIGITAL COLOR GRAPHICS; *U.S. Private*, pg. 1230
DIGITAL DOGMA CORP.—See Harvest Partners L.P.; *U.S. Private*, pg. 1876
DIGITAL LABEL SOLUTIONS, LLC—See Genstar Capital, LLC; *U.S. Private*, pg. 1676
DIGITAL PRINT IMPRESSIONS, INC.—See Merrick Industries Incorporated; *U.S. Private*, pg. 2675
DIMENSIONAL GRAPHICS CORPORATION; *U.S. Private*, pg. 1233
DIRECT CONNECT GROUP (DCG) LLC; *U.S. Private*, pg. 1235
DIRECTFX SOLUTIONS INC.; *U.S. Private*, pg. 1236
DIRECT TECHNOLOGIES, INC.—See GI Manager L.P.; *U.S. Private*, pg. 1692
DIS ARTWORKS CO., LTD.—See Daiwabo Holdings Co., Ltd.; *Int'l*, pg. 1949
DISPLAY ART PLC; *Int'l*, pg. 2135

DIVERSIFIED GLOBAL GRAPHICS GROUP, LLC; *U.S. Private*, pg. 1242
DNP DATA TECHNO KANSAI CO., LTD.—See Dai Nippon Printing Co., Ltd.; *Int'l*, pg. 1914
DNP FOTOLUSIO CO., LTD.—See Dai Nippon Printing Co., Ltd.; *Int'l*, pg. 1914
DNP GRAPHICA CO., LTD.—See Dai Nippon Printing Co., Ltd.; *Int'l*, pg. 1914
DNP INTERNATIONAL TRADING (SHANGHAI) CO., LTD.—See Dai Nippon Printing Co., Ltd.; *Int'l*, pg. 1914
DNP MEDIA ART CO., LTD.—See Dai Nippon Printing Co., Ltd.; *Int'l*, pg. 1915
DNP MULTI PRINT CO., LTD.—See Dai Nippon Printing Co., Ltd.; *Int'l*, pg. 1915
DNP SHIKOKU CO., LTD.—See Dai Nippon Printing Co., Ltd.; *Int'l*, pg. 1915
DNP TECHNOPACK YOKOHAMA CO., LTD.—See Dai Nippon Printing Co., Ltd.; *Int'l*, pg. 1915
DNP TOTAL PROCESS MAEBASHI CO., LTD.—See Dai Nippon Printing Co., Ltd.; *Int'l*, pg. 1915
DNP TOTAL PROCESS NAGAOKA CO., LTD.—See Dai Nippon Printing Co., Ltd.; *Int'l*, pg. 1915
DNP UNIPROCESS CO., LTD.—See Dai Nippon Printing Co., Ltd.; *Int'l*, pg. 1915
DOCUPLEX, INC.; *U.S. Private*, pg. 1252
DOCUSOURCE OF NC, LLC; *U.S. Private*, pg. 1252
DOCUTREND; *U.S. Private*, pg. 1252
DONGILI INVESTMENT GROUP, INC.; *U.S. Private*, pg. 1260
DONIHE GRAPHICS, INC.—See Champion Industries, Inc.; *U.S. Public*, pg. 478
DOODAD; *U.S. Private*, pg. 1261
DOT PRINTER, INC.; *U.S. Private*, pg. 1265
DOWLING GRAPHICS, INC.; *U.S. Private*, pg. 1268
DRAKE INDUSTRIES, INC.—See Cubbison Company; *U.S. Private*, pg. 1120
DRESCHER FULL-SERVICE VERSAND GMBH—See Exela Technologies, Inc.; *U.S. Public*, pg. 806
DRG TECHNOLOGIES, INC.; *U.S. Private*, pg. 1277
DRUKWERKDEAL.NL PRODUCTIE B.V.—See Cimpress plc; *Int'l*, pg. 1609
DS GRAPHICS INC.; *U.S. Private*, pg. 1281
DSI/DYNAMATIC CORPORATION; *U.S. Private*, pg. 1281
DUKE GRAPHICS, INC.—See Heeter Printing Co., Inc.; *U.S. Private*, pg. 1903
DUNCAN-PARNELL—See Duncan-Parnell, Inc.; *U.S. Private*, pg. 1288
DUNCAN-PARNELL—See Duncan-Parnell, Inc.; *U.S. Private*, pg. 1288
DUNCAN-PARNELL—See Duncan-Parnell, Inc.; *U.S. Private*, pg. 1288
DUNLAP MANUFACTURING CO.—See The Vernon Company; *U.S. Private*, pg. 4130
DUPLI ENVELOPES & GRAPHICS - MALVERN—See Matt Industries Inc.; *U.S. Private*, pg. 2613
DUPLI PRINT SAS; *Int'l*, pg. 2227
DURATECH INDUSTRIES INC.; *U.S. Private*, pg. 1293
DV-SYSTEM—See Cefla S.C.; *Int'l*, pg. 1389
DYNAMIC GRAPHICS INC.—See Bertelsmann SE & Co. KGaA; *Int'l*, pg. 990
DYNAMIC REPROGRAPHICS, INC.—See Thomas Reprographics, Inc.; *U.S. Private*, pg. 4157
EAGLE GRAPHICS; *U.S. Private*, pg. 1309
EAGLE PRESS, INC.; *U.S. Private*, pg. 1310
EAGLE:XM; *U.S. Private*, pg. 1311
EARTHCOLOR, INC.—See Mittera Group, Inc.; *U.S. Private*, pg. 2751
EARTHDIGITAL—See Mittera Group, Inc.; *U.S. Private*, pg. 2751
EARTH THEBAULT—See Mittera Group, Inc.; *U.S. Private*, pg. 2751
EASTERN POWER GROUP PUBLIC COMPANY LIMITED; *Int'l*, pg. 2273
EASTMAN KODAK PRINTING—See Eastman Kodak Company; *U.S. Public*, pg. 707
EBSCO INDUSTRIES, INC. - EBSCO MEDIA DIVISION—See EBSCO Industries, Inc.; *U.S. Private*, pg. 1325
ECM PRINTING—See Adams Publishing Group, LLC; *U.S. Private*, pg. 75
THE ECONOMY ADVERTISING COMPANY INC.; *U.S. Private*, pg. 4025
ECONO-PRINT INC.; *U.S. Private*, pg. 1329
ECO PRODUCCIONES, S.A. DE C.V.—See Grupo Televisa, S.A.B.; *Int'l*, pg. 3136
EDEL GERMANY GMBH—See Edel SE & Co KGaA; *Int'l*, pg. 2305
EDELMANN LEAFLET SOLUTIONS GMBH—See Edelmann GmbH; *Int'l*, pg. 2305
EDISON LITHOGRAPHING & PRINTING CORP.; *U.S. Private*, pg. 1336
EDIT'66 SAE—See HAL Trust N.V.; *Int'l*, pg. 3224
EDIT'66 SAS—See HAL Trust N.V.; *Int'l*, pg. 3224
EDITORIAL GYJ TELEVISA, S.A. DE C.V.—See Grupo Televisa, S.A.B.; *Int'l*, pg. 3136
EGT PRINTING SOLUTIONS, LLC—See Chatham Asset Management, LLC; *U.S. Private*, pg. 862
ELANDERS AB—See Carl Bennet AB; *Int'l*, pg. 1331

ELANDERS (BEIJING) PRINTING COMPANY LTD—See Carl Bennet AB; *Int'l*, pg. 1331
ELANDERS HUNGARY KFT—See Carl Bennet AB; *Int'l*, pg. 1331
ELANDERS REPRODUCAO DE IMAGENS LTDA—See Carl Bennet AB; *Int'l*, pg. 1331
ELANDERSUSA, LLC—See Carl Bennet AB; *Int'l*, pg. 1331
ELBE-CESCO INC.—See The Union Group; *U.S. Private*, pg. 4129
ELECTRIC CITY PRINTING COMPANY—See Chatham Asset Management, LLC; *U.S. Private*, pg. 862
ELECTRONIC DATA MAGNETICS, INC.; *U.S. Private*, pg. 1355
ELECTRONICS FOR IMAGING, INC. - PITTSBURGH—See Siris Capital Group, LLC; *U.S. Private*, pg. 3672
EMERALD CITY GRAPHICS, INC.—See Chatham Asset Management, LLC; *U.S. Private*, pg. 862
ENFOCUS NV—See Danaher Corporation; *U.S. Public*, pg. 626
ENGAGE PRINT, INC.—See Neuger Communications Group, Inc.; *U.S. Private*, pg. 2890
ENGLE PRINTING & PUBLISHING CO., INC.; *U.S. Private*, pg. 1399
ENK DRUCK & MEDIA GMBH; *Int'l*, pg. 2439
ENNIS BUSINESS FORMS OF KANSAS, INC.—See Ennis, Inc.; *U.S. Public*, pg. 769
ENNIS, INC. - CHATHAM—See Ennis, Inc.; *U.S. Public*, pg. 769
ENNIS, INC. - COSHOCTON—See Ennis, Inc.; *U.S. Public*, pg. 769
ENNIS, INC. - DEWITT—See Ennis, Inc.; *U.S. Public*, pg. 769
ENNIS, INC. - ENNIS, TX—See Ennis, Inc.; *U.S. Public*, pg. 769
ENNIS, INC. - KNOXVILLE—See Ennis, Inc.; *U.S. Public*, pg. 769
ENNIS, INC. - MOULTRIE—See Ennis, Inc.; *U.S. Public*, pg. 769
ENNIS, INC. - PASO ROBLES—See Ennis, Inc.; *U.S. Public*, pg. 769
ENNIS, INC.; *U.S. Public*, pg. 768
ENNIS, INC. - WOLFE CITY—See Ennis, Inc.; *U.S. Public*, pg. 769
ENTERPRISE PRESS, INC.; *U.S. Public*, pg. 1404
E.P. GRAPHICS, INC.—See Dynamic Resource Group, Inc.; *U.S. Private*, pg. 1299
ESKO BVBA—See Danaher Corporation; *U.S. Public*, pg. 626
ESKO GRAPHICS IMAGING GMBH—See Danaher Corporation; *U.S. Public*, pg. 626
ESKO GRAPHICS KONGSBERG AS—See Danaher Corporation; *U.S. Public*, pg. 626
EST IMPRIMERIE; *Int'l*, pg. 2517
ETABLISSEMENTS MARTINENQ; *Int'l*, pg. 2519
EVERGREEN PRINTING COMPANY; *U.S. Private*, pg. 1440
EXCELSIOR PRINTING COMPANY; *U.S. Private*, pg. 1446
EXECUTIVE SERVICES, INC.; *U.S. Private*, pg. 1448
EXTOR GMBH—See Delticom AG; *Int'l*, pg. 2021
FACTOR FORMS LTD; *Int'l*, pg. 2601
FASTFORMS INC.; *Int'l*, pg. 2622
FAUBEL PHARMA SERVICES CORP.—See CCL Industries Inc.; *Int'l*, pg. 1369
F.B. JOHNSTON GRAPHICS—See Fred B. Johnston Company, Inc.; *U.S. Private*, pg. 1600
F.C.L. GRAPHICS; *U.S. Private*, pg. 1456
FEDERAL BUSINESS PRODUCTS, INC.; *U.S. Private*, pg. 1487
FEDEX KINKO'S CANADA LIMITED—See FedEx Corporation; *U.S. Public*, pg. 827
FEDEX OFFICE & PRINT SERVICES, INC.—See FedEx Corporation; *U.S. Public*, pg. 827
FETTER PRINTING COMPANY; *U.S. Private*, pg. 1500
FINANCIAL STATEMENT SERVICES; *U.S. Private*, pg. 1508
FINE LINE GRAPHICS CORP.; *U.S. Private*, pg. 1509
FISHER PRINTING INC.; *U.S. Private*, pg. 1534
THE FLESH COMPANY—See Ennis, Inc.; *U.S. Public*, pg. 769
FLEXOGRAPHIC PACKAGING CO.—See The Graham Group, Inc.; *U.S. Public*, pg. 4036
FLEXO-GRAPHICS, LLC—See AEA Investors LP; *U.S. Private*, pg. 114
FLEXO IMPRESSIONS—See Taylor Corporation; *U.S. Private*, pg. 3938
FLEXO TRANSPARENT, LLC—See First Atlantic Capital Ltd.; *U.S. Private*, pg. 1513
FLM GRAPHICS CORPORATION; *U.S. Private*, pg. 1546
F.L. MOTHERAL CO. INC.; *U.S. Private*, pg. 1456
FLORAMEDIA AUSTRIA GMBH—See HAL Trust N.V.; *Int'l*, pg. 3224
FLORAMEDIA BELGIUM N.V.—See HAL Trust N.V.; *Int'l*, pg. 3224
FLORAMEDIA DEUTSCHLAND KG—See HAL Trust N.V.; *Int'l*, pg. 3224
FLORAMEDIA ESPANA, S.A.U.—See HAL Trust N.V.; *Int'l*, pg. 3224
FLORAMEDIA FRANCE—See HAL Trust N.V.; *Int'l*, pg. 3224

N.A.I.C.S. INDEX

323111 — COMMERCIAL PRINTING...

FLORAMEDIA GROUP B.V.—See HAL Trust N.V.; *Int'l*, pg. 3224

FLORAMEDIA POLSKA SP.Z O.O.—See HAL Trust N.V.; *Int'l*, pg. 3224

FLORAMEDIA SCHWEIZ AG—See HAL Trust N.V.; *Int'l*, pg. 3224

FLORAMEDIA UK LTD—See HAL Trust N.V.; *Int'l*, pg. 3224

FMA COMMUNICATIONS, INC.; *U.S. Private*, pg. 1553

F&M EXPRESSIONS UNLIMITED; *U.S. Private*, pg. 1455

FOLDER FACTORY, INC.; *U.S. Private*, pg. 1558

FOLIUM GROUP LTD; *Int'l*, pg. 2721

FONG BROTHERS PRINTING INC.; *U.S. Private*, pg. 1559

FORMS MANUFACTURERS INC.—See Ennis, Inc.; *U.S. Public*, pg. 769

FORM SYSTEMS, INC.—See Deluxe Corporation; *U.S. Public*, pg. 653

FORSSA PRINT—See Alma Media Corporation; *Int'l*, pg. 362

FORT DEARBORN - BOWLING GREEN—See Advent International Corporation; *U.S. Private*, pg. 101

FORWARD GRAPHIC ENTERPRISE CO., LTD.; *Int'l*, pg. 2747

FOSTER PRINTING SERVICE, INC.; *U.S. Private*, pg. 1579

FOUR POINT PRODUCTS—See American Thermoplastic Company; *U.S. Private*, pg. 257

FOXFIRE PRINTING & PACKAGING; *U.S. Private*, pg. 1585

FOX PRINTING COMPANY, INC.—See Harman Press; *U.S. Private*, pg. 1866

F.P. HORAK COMPANY; *U.S. Private*, pg. 1457

FRANCIS EMORY FITCH, INCORPORATED—See The Hearst Corporation; *U.S. Private*, pg. 4044

FRANKLIN-DODD COMMUNICATIONS LLC—See Nationwide Argosy Solutions, LLC; *U.S. Private*, pg. 2865

FRED B. JOHNSTON COMPANY, INC., *U.S. Private*, pg. 1600

FREDERIC PRINTING COMPANY—See Chatham Asset Management, LLC; *U.S. Private*, pg. 862

FREEDOM GRAPHIC SYSTEMS INC.; *U.S. Private*, pg. 1603

FREEDOM IMAGING SYSTEMS INC.—See Freedom Graphic Systems Inc.; *U.S. Private*, pg. 1603

FREEPORT PRESS INC.; *U.S. Private*, pg. 1606

FRY COMMUNICATIONS INC.; *U.S. Private*, pg. 1617

FUJICOLOR BENELUX B.V.—See FUJIFILM Holdings Corporation; *Int'l*, pg. 2822

FUJI SEAL, INC.—See Fuji Seal International, Inc.; *Int'l*, pg. 2816

FULFILLMENT CORPORATION OF AMERICA—See Palladium Equity Partners, LLC; *U.S. Private*, pg. 3078

FUSION IMAGING, INC.—See Vomela Specialty Company; *U.S. Private*, pg. 4412

GARLOCK PRINTING AND CONVERTING INC—See Seaman Paper Company of Massachusetts Inc.; *U.S. Private*, pg. 3585

GARNER PRINTING COMPANY—See Chatham Asset Management, LLC; *U.S. Private*, pg. 862

GASCH PRINTING LLC; *U.S. Private*, pg. 1648

GATEWAY PRESS, INC.; *U.S. Private*, pg. 1650

GEMGROUP INC.—See Angel Holdings Godo Kaisha; *Int'l*, pg. 459

GENERAL FINANCIAL SUPPLY, INC.—See Ennis, Inc.; *U.S. Public*, pg. 769

GENERAL PACKAGING PRODUCTS INC.; *U.S. Private*, pg. 1666

GEO GRAPHICS, INC.; *U.S. Private*, pg. 1680

GEORGE SCHMITT & CO. INC.; *U.S. Private*, pg. 1683

GHP MEDIA, INC.; *U.S. Private*, pg. 1691

GIESECKE & DEVRIENT GMBH; *Int'l*, pg. 2969

GILBRETH PACKAGING SYSTEMS—See Genstar Capital, LLC; *U.S. Private*, pg. 1676

GILFORD GRAPHICS INTERNATIONAL; *U.S. Private*, pg. 1699

GINTZLER GRAPHICS, INC.—See Ares Management Corporation; *U.S. Public*, pg. 190

GL DIRECT—See Great Lakes Integrated; *U.S. Private*, pg. 1764

GLOBAL TRIM SALES INC.—See Crane NXT, Co.; *U.S. Public*, pg. 592

GOLD BOND INC.; *U.S. Private*, pg. 1727

GOODING CO., INC.—See Holden Industries, Inc.; *U.S. Private*, pg. 1962

GOODWAY GRAPHICS OF VA INC.; *U.S. Private*, pg. 1740

GORENJSKI TISK STORITVE D.O.O.; *Int'l*, pg. 3043

GP & J BAKER—See Kravet Fabrics Inc.; *U.S. Private*, pg. 2350

GPM ASSOCIATES LLC; *U.S. Private*, pg. 1748

GRAFICA EDITORA AQUARELA S.A.—See Cimpress plc; *Int'l*, pg. 1609

GRAFICAS INTEGRADAS S.A.—See Dedalo Grupo Grafico, S.L.; *Int'l*, pg. 2002

GRAND RAPIDS LABEL CO.; *U.S. Private*, pg. 1753

GRANDVILLE PRINTING COMPANY; *U.S. Private*, pg. 1754

GRAPHCOM, LLC—See Chatham Asset Management, LLC; *U.S. Private*, pg. 862

GRAPHIC INFORMATION SYSTEMS INC.; *U.S. Private*, pg. 1757

GRAPHIC PRESS GROUP SDN BHD—See Berjaya Corporation Berhad; *Int'l*, pg. 984

GRAPHICS PLUS, INC.—See Blooming Color, Inc.; *U.S. Private*, pg. 584

GRAPHICS WEST, INC.—See Nationwide Argosy Solutions, LLC; *U.S. Private*, pg. 2865

GRAPHIC TECHNOLOGY OF MARYLAND, INC.—See Chatham Asset Management, LLC; *U.S. Private*, pg. 862

GRAPHIC VISUAL SOLUTIONS, INC.; *U.S. Private*, pg. 1758

GRAPHIX PRODUCTS, INC.—See Kelmscott Communications, Inc.; *U.S. Private*, pg. 2277

GRAPHTEC—See Chatham Asset Management, LLC; *U.S. Private*, pg. 862

GREAT EASTERN COLOR LITHOGRAPHIC; *U.S. Private*, pg. 1762

GREATER GEORGIA PRINTERS, INC.; *U.S. Private*, pg. 1769

THE GREAT FRAME UP—See Franchise Concepts, Inc.; *U.S. Private*, pg. 1587

GREAT LAKES INTEGRATED; *U.S. Private*, pg. 1764

GRENVILLE PRINTING LTD.; *Int'l*, pg. 3081

GREYSTONE GRAPHICS, INC.; *U.S. Private*, pg. 1786

GRUPO NACION GN, S.A.; *Int'l*, pg. 3133

GRUPUL EDITORILOR SI DIFUZORILOR DE PRESA SA; *Int'l*, pg. 3141

GSB DIGITAL INC.; *U.S. Private*, pg. 1800

GSL FINE LITHOGRAPHERS—See Chatham Asset Management, LLC; *U.S. Private*, pg. 862

GSP PRINT PTY LTD—See ARN Media Limited; *Int'l*, pg. 576

GYOMAI KNER NYOMDA ZRT.—See ANY Security Printing Company PLC; *Int'l*, pg. 486

HALLMARK CANADA, INC.—See Hallmark Cards, Inc.; *U.S. Private*, pg. 1844

HALLMARK CARDS AUSTRALIA LTD.—See Hallmark Cards, Inc.; *U.S. Private*, pg. 1844

HALLMARK CARDS NEDERLAND, B.V.—See Hallmark Cards, Inc.; *U.S. Private*, pg. 1844

HAMMER PACKAGING CORP.—See Advent International Corporation; *U.S. Private*, pg. 101

HAMPTON TEXTILE PRINTING—See Safer Prints Inc.; *U.S. Private*, pg. 3524

HANSAPRINT ELANDERS KFT—See Hansaprint Oy; *Int'l*, pg. 3259

HANSAPRINT OY; *Int'l*, pg. 3259

HARMAN PRESS; *U.S. Private*, pg. 1866

HARPER ENGRAVING & PRINTING CO.; *U.S. Private*, pg. 1867

HARRIER LLC—See District Photo Inc.; *U.S. Private*, pg. 1239

HART INTERCIVIC INC.; *U.S. Private*, pg. 1873

THE HARTY PRESS INC.; *U.S. Private*, pg. 4043

HATTERAS PRESS INC.; *U.S. Private*, pg. 1880

HAWK RIDGE SYSTEMS, LLC; *U.S. Private*, pg. 1882

HEDERMAN BROTHERS, LLC; *U.S. Private*, pg. 1903

HEETER PRINTING CO., INC.; *U.S. Private*, pg. 1903

HEIDELBERG ASIA PTE LTD.—See Heidelberger Druckmaschinen AG; *Int'l*, pg. 3321

HEIDELBERG JAPAN K.K.—See Heidelberger Druckmaschinen AG; *Int'l*, pg. 3321

HEIDELBERG KOREA LTD.—See Heidelberger Druckmaschinen AG; *Int'l*, pg. 3321

HEIDELBERG MALAYSIA SDN BHD—See Heidelberger Druckmaschinen AG; *Int'l*, pg. 3321

HEIDELBERG MEXICO S. DE R.L. DE C.V.—See Heidelberger Druckmaschinen AG; *Int'l*, pg. 3321

HEIDELBERG PHILIPPINES, INC.—See Heidelberger Druckmaschinen AG; *Int'l*, pg. 3321

HEINN CHAPMAN CORPORATION; *U.S. Private*, pg. 1905

HEINRICH BAUER PRODUKTIONS KG—See Heinrich Bauer Verlag KG; *Int'l*, pg. 3324

HENDERSONS PRINTING INC.; *U.S. Private*, pg. 1914

THE HENNEGAN COMPANY—See Chatham Asset Management, LLC; *U.S. Private*, pg. 863

HENRY WURST INC.; *U.S. Private*, pg. 1919

THE HERALD, INC.; *U.S. Private*, pg. 4051

HERFF JONES FINE PAPERS - IOLA—See Bain Capital, LP; *U.S. Private*, pg. 452

HERFF JONES FINE PAPERS—See Bain Capital, LP; *U.S. Private*, pg. 452

HERFF JONES, INC. - YEARBOOKS—See Bain Capital, LP; *U.S. Private*, pg. 452

HERFF JONES, INC. - YEARBOOKS—See Bain Capital, LP; *U.S. Private*, pg. 452

HICKORY PRINTING SOLUTIONS—See Chatham Asset Management, LLC; *U.S. Private*, pg. 862

HICKORY PRINTING—See Chatham Asset Management, LLC; *U.S. Private*, pg. 862

HIGHLAND COMPUTER FORMS INC.; *U.S. Private*, pg. 1938

HIKARI BUSINESS FORM CO., LTD.; *Int'l*, pg. 3389

HILLSBORO ARGUS—See Advance Publications, Inc.; *U.S. Private*, pg. 86

HIMMER AG; *Int'l*, pg. 3397

HITACHI DOCUMENT PRINTING CO., LTD.—See Hitachi, Ltd.; *Int'l*, pg. 3416

HITECH PRINT SYSTEMS LTD.—See Anjani Portland Cement Ltd.; *Int'l*, pg. 472

HITI DIGITAL AMERICA, INC.—See HiTi Digital Inc.; *Int'l*, pg. 3426

HM GRAPHICS INC.—See Color Ink, Inc.; *U.S. Private*, pg. 972

H&N PRINTING & GRAPHICS, INC.—See Chatham Asset Management, LLC; *U.S. Private*, pg. 862

HOECHSTETTER PRINTING—See Chatham Asset Management, LLC; *U.S. Private*, pg. 862

HOKUTO PRINTING CO, LTD.; *Int'l*, pg. 3445

HOLDEN GRAPHIC SERVICES; *U.S. Private*, pg. 1962

HOLLIMANN S.A.—See Hubert Burda Media Holding Kommanditgesellschaft; *Int'l*, pg. 3519

HOLLY'S CUSTOM PRINT, INC.; *U.S. Private*, pg. 1966

HOT FROG PRINT MEDIA LLC; *U.S. Private*, pg. 1988

H.S. CROCKER CO., INC.—See H.S. Crocker Co., Inc.; *U.S. Private*, pg. 1835

HUAFA PROPERTY SERVICES GROUP COMPANY LIMITED; *Int'l*, pg. 3511

HUBCAST, INC.—See mimeo.com, Inc.; *U.S. Private*, pg. 2740

HUNG HING OFF-SET PRINTING COMPANY, LIMITED—See Hung Hing Printing Group Limited; *Int'l*, pg. 3535

HUNG HING PRINTING (CHINA) COMPANY LIMITED—See Hung Hing Printing Group Limited; *Int'l*, pg. 3535

HYBRID SOFTWARE GROUP PLC; *Int'l*, pg. 3544

HYGRADE BUSINESS GROUP INC.; *U.S. Private*, pg. 2018

IC GROUP; *U.S. Private*, pg. 2029

I/D/E/A/ INC.; *U.S. Private*, pg. 2027

IMAGEMARK BUSINESS SERVICES; *U.S. Private*, pg. 2045

IMAGIC—See H.I.G. Capital, LLC; *U.S. Private*, pg. 1827

IMAGINE! PRINT SOLUTIONS, INC.—See Keystone Group, L.P.; *U.S. Private*, pg. 2298

IMMEDIA, INC.—See Liberty Diversified International Inc.; *U.S. Private*, pg. 2443

IMPACT INNOVATIONS, INC.—See IG Design Group Plc; *Int'l*, pg. 3600

IMPERIAL PRINTING PRODUCTS CO., INC.—See Imagemark Business Services; *U.S. Private*, pg. 2045

IMPRESSIONS INCORPORATED—See Vivid Impact Corporation; *U.S. Private*, pg. 4406

IMPRESSIONS PRINTING & COPYING SERVICES; *U.S. Private*, pg. 2051

IMPRIPOST TECNOLOGIAS S.A—See Grupo Clarin S.A.; *Int'l*, pg. 3124

INDEPENDENT PRINTING CO., INC.—See Independent Printing; *U.S. Private*, pg. 2061

INDEPENDENT PRINTING COMPANY, INC.; *U.S. Private*, pg. 2060

INDEPENDENT PRINTING COMPANY, INC.—See Ennis, Inc.; *U.S. Public*, pg. 769

INDEPENDENT RESOURCES, INC.; *U.S. Private*, pg. 2061

INDIANA PRINTING & PUBLISHING CO., INC.; *U.S. Private*, pg. 2062

INDOX SERVICES—See SBI Incorporated; *U.S. Private*, pg. 3560

INDUSTRIAL COLOR PRODUCTIONS, INC.—See Frontenac Company LLC; *U.S. Private*, pg. 1613

INFINEER, LTD.—See Chazak Value Corp.; *U.S. Private*, pg. 868

INFOSEAL, LLC—See Ennis, Inc.; *U.S. Public*, pg. 769

INKED PRODUCTIONS, INC.—See The Walt Disney Company; *U.S. Public*, pg. 2140

INKJET INTERNATIONAL, LTD.; *U.S. Private*, pg. 2077

INNERWORKINGS, INC. - NEW YORK CITY OFFICE—See HH Global Group Limited; *Int'l*, pg. 3379

INNOVATIVE PRINT & MEDIA GROUP—See Deluxe Corporation; *U.S. Public*, pg. 653

INNOVATIVE TECHNOLOGIES IN PRINT—See Continental Press Inc.; *U.S. Private*, pg. 1030

INSPEC TECH, INC.; *U.S. Private*, pg. 2092

THE INSTANT WEB COMPANIES; *U.S. Private*, pg. 4056

INTECH PRINTING & DIRECT MAIL; *U.S. Private*, pg. 2097

INTELLIGENCER PRINTING COMPANY INC.; *U.S. Private*, pg. 2123

INTERFLEX ACQUISITION COMPANY, LLC—See Nicolet Capital Partners, LLC; *U.S. Private*, pg. 2926

INTERFORM CORPORATION—See Champion Industries, Inc.; *U.S. Public*, pg. 478

INTERMEC MEDIA PRODUCTS—See Honeywell International Inc.; *U.S. Public*, pg. 1050

INTERNATIONAL GAMCO INC.; *U.S. Private*, pg. 2117

INTERPRINT INCORPORATED—See Morten Enterprises Inc.; *U.S. Private*, pg. 2791

INTERPRINT INC.; *U.S. Private*, pg. 2123

INVESTMENT ENTERPRISES INC.; *U.S. Private*, pg. 2132

IONE FINANCIAL PRESS LIMITED—See Huafa Property Services Group Company Limited; *Int'l*, pg. 3511

IPAGSA TECHNOLOGIES S.L.U.—See Agfa-Gevaert N.V.; *Int'l*, pg. 208

IPC PRINT SERVICES, INC.—See Walsworth Publishing Company, Inc.; *U.S. Private*, pg. 4433

IPD PRINTING—See Chatham Asset Management, LLC; *U.S. Private*, pg. 863

323111 — COMMERCIAL PRINTING...   CORPORATE AFFILIATIONS

IPG MARKETING SOLUTIONS PTY LTD—See Domino's Pizza Enterprises Ltd.; *Int'l*, pg. 2162
IP HOLDINGS AND MANAGEMENT CORPORATION—See Iconix Acquisition LLC; *U.S. Private*, pg. 2032
I PRINT OY—See Ilkka Yhtymae Oyj; *Int'l*, pg. 3615
IRONWOOD LITHOGRAPHERS, INC.—See Chatham Asset Management, LLC; *U.S. Private*, pg. 862
IRWIN-HODSON COMPANY; *U.S. Private*, pg. 2142
ISSGR, INC.; *U.S. Private*, pg. 2147
ITOWNSTORE LLC; *U.S. Private*, pg. 2150
JACKSON COUNTY NEWSPAPERS INC.—See New West Newspapers Inc.; *U.S. Private*, pg. 2908
THE JACKSON GROUP CORPORATION—See Chatham Asset Management, LLC; *U.S. Private*, pg. 863
JACOB NORTH LLC—See Midstates Group Company; *U.S. Private*, pg. 2718
JACO BRYANT PRINTING LLC—See Westshore Capital Partners LLC; *U.S. Private*, pg. 4500
JAPAN LUTRAVIL COMPANY LTD.—See Freudenberg SE; *Int'l*, pg. 2789
JAPS-OLSON COMPANY—See Monomoy Capital Partners LLC; *U.S. Private*, pg. 2772
THE JARVIS PRESS, INC.—See Chatham Asset Management, LLC; *U.S. Private*, pg. 863
JAY PACKAGING GROUP, INC.—See Wellspring Capital Management LLC; *U.S. Private*, pg. 4477
J.B. KENEHAN, LLC; *U.S. Private*, pg. 2158
JET INC.; *U.S. Private*, pg. 2204
J.J. COLLINS SONS INC.; *U.S. Private*, pg. 2167
JML UNLIMITED; *U.S. Private*, pg. 2216
JOHN H. HARLAND CO. OF PUERTO RICO—See MacAndrews & Forbes Incorporated; *U.S. Private*, pg. 2532
JOHN ROBERTS COMPANY; *U.S. Private*, pg. 2224
THE JOHNSON GROUP—See Deluxe Corporation; *U.S. Public*, pg. 653
JONES COMPANY—See Nationwide Argosy Solutions, LLC; *U.S. Private*, pg. 2865
J & P INVESTMENTS, INC.—See Revitalize Capital; *U.S. Private*, pg. 3416
J.S. MCCARTHY INC.; *U.S. Private*, pg. 2171
J. THOMSON COLOUR PRINTERS LTD.—See Bell & Bain Ltd.; *Int'l*, pg. 965
K-1 PACKAGING GROUP—See Dunes Point Capital, LLC; *U.S. Private*, pg. 1288
KAPPA GRAPHICS, LP; *U.S. Private*, pg. 2262
KATSUYA (THAILAND) CO., LTD.—See AAPICO Hitech plc; *Int'l*, pg. 37
KAYE-SMITH; *U.S. Private*, pg. 2266
KAY GRAFICAS AUTOMOTRICES S.A. DE C.V.—See Kay Screen Printing, Inc.; *U.S. Private*, pg. 2266
KAY SCREEN PRINTING, INC.; *U.S. Private*, pg. 2266
KAY TOLEDO TAG, INC.—See Ennis, Inc.; *U.S. Public*, pg. 769
K&COMPANY, LLC—See GTCR LLC; *U.S. Private*, pg. 1806
THE KELLY COMPANIES; *U.S. Private*, pg. 4064
KELVYN PRESS INC.; *U.S. Private*, pg. 2281
KEYS PRINTING COMPANY—See Chatham Asset Management, LLC; *U.S. Private*, pg. 862
KING BUSINESS FORMS CORP.; *U.S. Private*, pg. 2309
KINGERY PRINTING COMPANY; *U.S. Private*, pg. 2310
KIRKWOOD PRINTING COMPANY, INC.; *U.S. Private*, pg. 2315
KNOX ATTORNEY SERVICE INC.; *U.S. Private*, pg. 2324
KODAK GMBH—See Eastman Kodak Company; *U.S. Public*, pg. 707
KOLORFUSION INTERNATIONAL, INC.; *U.S. Public*, pg. 1270
KOPCO INC.; *U.S. Private*, pg. 2343
KOPY KWEEN INCORPORATED; *U.S. Private*, pg. 2343
K/P CORPORATION; *U.S. Private*, pg. 2252
KREPE-KRAFT, INC.—See MOD-PAC CORP.; *U.S. Private*, pg. 2759
KUBIN-NICHOLSON CORP., CHICAGO—See Kubin-Nicholson Corporation; *U.S. Private*, pg. 2356
KUBIN-NICHOLSON CORPORATION; *U.S. Private*, pg. 2355
KUBIN-NICHOLSON CORP.—See Kubin-Nicholson Corporation; *U.S. Private*, pg. 2356
KUTTNER PRINTS INC.—See Safer Prints Inc.; *U.S. Private*, pg. 3524
LABEL IMPRESSION, INC.—See Genstar Capital, LLC; *U.S. Private*, pg. 1676
LABEL TECH, INC.—See Harvest Partners L.P.; *U.S. Private*, pg. 1876
LABEL WORKS—See Taylor Corporation; *U.S. Private*, pg. 3938
LAKE COUNTY PRESS; *U.S. Private*, pg. 2375
LAMINEX, INC.; *U.S. Private*, pg. 2380
LANDMARK COMMUNITY NEWSPAPERS, LLC—See Irish Times; *U.S. Private*, pg. 2138
LANE PRESS, INC.; *U.S. Private*, pg. 2388
LASER LIGHT TECHNOLOGIES, LLC—See DuPont de Nemours, Inc.; *U.S. Public*, pg. 694
LASERMASTER INTERNATIONAL; *U.S. Public*, pg. 1294
LASER PRINT PLUS, INC.—See GI Manager L.P.; *U.S. Private*, pg. 1692
LASER REPRODUCTIONS INC.—See Trilantic Capital Management L.P.; *U.S. Private*, pg. 4231

LASERTEC, INC.; *U.S. Private*, pg. 2395
LA SUPPLY CO.; *U.S. Private*, pg. 2369
L.A WEB OFFSET PRINTING INC.; *U.S. Private*, pg. 2364
LEED SELLING TOOLS CORPORATION; *U.S. Private*, pg. 2414
LEHMAN PRINTING CENTER—See Alden Global Capital LLC; *U.S. Private*, pg. 157
LEIGH-MARDON PACIFIC PACKAGING PTE LTD.—See AMVIG Holdings Limited; *Int'l*, pg. 442
LEW A. CUMMINGS CO., INC.; *U.S. Private*, pg. 2437
LEWISBURG PRINTING, INC.—See Radial Equity Partners LP; *U.S. Private*, pg. 3343
LIBERTY PAPER & PRINTING; *U.S. Private*, pg. 2446
LIFEPICS INC.; *U.S. Private*, pg. 2450
LIFESTYLE MAGAZINES PUBLISHING PTE LTD—See Bacui Technologies International Ltd.; *Int'l*, pg. 795
THE LIGATURE—See Taylor Corporation; *U.S. Private*, pg. 3939
LIGHTHOUSE EDISCOVERY—See Lightyear Capital LLC; *U.S. Private*, pg. 2454
LITHOCRAFT, INC.—See Graphic Packaging Holding Company; *U.S. Public*, pg. 959
LITHOGRAPHICS INC.; *U.S. Private*, pg. 2467
LITHOGRAPHIX, INC.; *U.S. Private*, pg. 2467
LITHO-KROME COMPANY—See Hallmark Cards, Inc.; *U.S. Private*, pg. 1845
LITHOTONE INC.; *U.S. Private*, pg. 2468
LITHOTYPE COMPANY, INC. - MIDWEST FACILITY—See Lithotype Company, Inc.; *U.S. Private*, pg. 2468
LITHOTYPE COMPANY, INC.; *U.S. Private*, pg. 2468
LITOTIPOGRAFIA ALCIONE S.R.L.—See Cimpress plc; *Int'l*, pg. 1609
LMI PACKAGING SOLUTIONS, INC.; *U.S. Private*, pg. 2476
LOBER DRUCK UND KUVERT GMBH—See Bong AB; *Int'l*, pg. 1107
LOGONATION, INC.; *U.S. Private*, pg. 2482
LOWEN VISUAL IMAGING—See Lowen Corporation; *U.S. Private*, pg. 2505
L.P. THEBAULT COMPANY; *U.S. Private*, pg. 2367
LSC COMMUNICATIONS INC.—See Atlas Holdings, LLC; *U.S. Private*, pg. 376
LYKE CORPORATION—See Walsworth Publishing Company, Inc.; *U.S. Private*, pg. 4433
MADDEN COMMUNICATIONS INC.—See HH Global Group Limited; *Int'l*, pg. 3379
MADISON/GRAHAM COLORGRAPHICS, INC.—See Cenveo, Inc.; *U.S. Private*, pg. 835
MAGICARD LTD.—See Brady Corporation; *U.S. Public*, pg. 379
MAGNA IV; *U.S. Private*, pg. 2546
MAILING AND PRINT SERVICES—See AAB Holdings Pty Limited; *Int'l*, pg. 30
MAINLINE PRINTING INC.; *U.S. Private*, pg. 2553
MANROLAND GOSS WEB SYSTEMS GMBH—See AIP, LLC; *U.S. Private*, pg. 134
MANROLAND WEB SYSTEMS (UK) LTD.—See AIP, LLC; *U.S. Private*, pg. 134
MARKET SHARE DEVELOPMENT; *U.S. Private*, pg. 2579
MARTIN LITHOGRAPH, INC.; *U.S. Private*, pg. 2595
MARYLAND COMPOSITION—See Chatham Asset Management, LLC; *U.S. Private*, pg. 862
MATT INDUSTRIES INC.; *U.S. Private*, pg. 2613
MAXIMUM GRAPHICS—See Chatham Asset Management, LLC; *U.S. Private*, pg. 862
MAXISAVER GROUP, INC.; *U.S. Private*, pg. 2619
MCARDLE PRINTING CO., INC.—See Bloomberg L.P.; *U.S. Private*, pg. 584
MCCORMICK ARMSTRONG CO. INC.; *U.S. Private*, pg. 2630
MCC POLSKA SA—See Platinum Equity, LLC; *U.S. Private*, pg. 3206
THE MCKAY PRESS, INC.—See Chatham Asset Management, LLC; *U.S. Private*, pg. 863
MEDIA PRINTING CORPORATION; *U.S. Private*, pg. 2652
MEDLIT SOLUTIONS, LLC—See Ares Management Corporation; *U.S. Public*, pg. 190
MENASHA PACKAGING COMPANY, LLC—See Menasha Corporation; *U.S. Private*, pg. 2665
MERCURY PRINTING COMPANY, LLC—See Chatham Asset Management, LLC; *U.S. Private*, pg. 863
MERCURY PRINTING, INC.—See Chatham Asset Management, LLC; *U.S. Private*, pg. 863
MEREDITH-WEBB PRINTING CO. INC.; *U.S. Private*, pg. 2672
MERRICK INDUSTRIES INCORPORATED; *U.S. Private*, pg. 2675
THE MERRICK PRINTING COMPANY INC.—See Merrick Industries Incorporated; *U.S. Private*, pg. 2675
MERRILL CORPORATION CANADA—See aPriori Capital Partners L.P.; *U.S. Private*, pg. 302
MERRILL CORPORATION CANADA—See aPriori Capital Partners L.P.; *U.S. Private*, pg. 302
MERRILL CORPORATION - CHICAGO OFFICE—See aPriori Capital Partners L.P.; *U.S. Private*, pg. 301
MERRILL CORPORATION - DENVER OFFICE—See aPriori Capital Partners L.P.; *U.S. Private*, pg. 301
MERRILL CORPORATION - HOUSTON OFFICE—See aPriori Capital Partners L.P.; *U.S. Private*, pg. 301

MERRILL CORPORATION - IRVINE OFFICE—See aPriori Capital Partners L.P.; *U.S. Private*, pg. 301
MERRILL CORPORATION - LA MIRADA OFFICE—See aPriori Capital Partners L.P.; *U.S. Private*, pg. 301
MERRILL CORPORATION LIMITED—See aPriori Capital Partners L.P.; *U.S. Private*, pg. 302
MERRILL CORPORATION - LOS ANGELES (SOUTH GRAND) OFFICE—See aPriori Capital Partners L.P.; *U.S. Private*, pg. 301
MERRILL CORPORATION - MONROE OFFICE—See aPriori Capital Partners L.P.; *U.S. Private*, pg. 301
MERRILL CORPORATION - ST. CLOUD OFFICE—See aPriori Capital Partners L.P.; *U.S. Private*, pg. 301
MERRILL CORPORATION - WASHINGTON, DC OFFICE—See aPriori Capital Partners L.P.; *U.S. Private*, pg. 302
MERRILL/DANIELS, INC.—See aPriori Capital Partners L.P.; *U.S. Private*, pg. 302
THE MERTEN COMPANY—See Champion Industries, Inc.; *U.S. Public*, pg. 478
METROPOLITAN LOOSE LEAF—See The Union Group; *U.S. Private*, pg. 4129
METROPOLITAN PRINTING SERVICES, LLC—See Chatham Asset Management, LLC; *U.S. Private*, pg. 863
METRO PRINTED PRODUCTS, INC.; *U.S. Private*, pg. 2686
MEYERS PRINTING COMPANY INC.; *U.S. Private*, pg. 2693
MICKELBERRY COMMUNICATIONS INC.; *U.S. Private*, pg. 2701
MID-ATLANTIC PRINTERS LTD.; *U.S. Private*, pg. 2707
MIDLAND INFORMATION RESOURCES INC.—See Carl Bennet AB; *Int'l*, pg. 1332
MIDSTATES PRINTING INC.; *U.S. Private*, pg. 2718
THE MILL POND PRESS COMPANIES, INC.—See Mill Pond Holdings LLC; *U.S. Private*, pg. 2730
MOBILITY, INC.—See Chatham Asset Management, LLC; *U.S. Private*, pg. 863
MODERN LITHO-KANSAS CITY—See Modern Litho-Print Co.; *U.S. Private*, pg. 2761
MODERN LITHO-PRINT CO.; *U.S. Private*, pg. 2761
MODERN LITHO - ST LOUIS—See Modern Litho-Print Co.; *U.S. Private*, pg. 2761
MOLENAAR, LLC—See Fey Industries, Inc.; *U.S. Private*, pg. 1500
MONARCH ART PLASTICS LLC; *U.S. Private*, pg. 2768
MONARCH LITHO INC.; *U.S. Private*, pg. 2769
MOORE CANADA CORPORATION—See DATA Communications Management Corp.; *Int'l*, pg. 1976
MOORE IMS BV—See Chatham Asset Management, LLC; *U.S. Private*, pg. 863
MOORE PARAGON (CARIBBEAN) LTD.—See Chatham Asset Management, LLC; *U.S. Private*, pg. 864
MOORE RESPONSE MARKETING B.V.—See Chatham Asset Management, LLC; *U.S. Private*, pg. 864
MORAN PRINTING INC.; *U.S. Private*, pg. 2781
MORRISON COMMUNICATIONS, INC.; *U.S. Private*, pg. 2789
MORRIS PRINTING GROUP, INC.; *U.S. Private*, pg. 2788
MORTEN ENTERPRISES INC.; *U.S. Private*, pg. 2791
MOSAIC; *U.S. Private*, pg. 2792
MOTORBOATING—See Bonnier AB; *Int'l*, pg. 1108
MOUNT VERNON PRINTING COMPANY—See Chatham Asset Management, LLC; *U.S. Private*, pg. 863
MRI FLEXIBLE PACKAGING COMPANY—See First Atlantic Capital Ltd.; *U.S. Private*, pg. 1513
MULTI-COLOR CLYDEBANK SCOTLAND LIMITED—See Platinum Equity, LLC; *U.S. Private*, pg. 3206
MULTI-COLOR CORPORATION—See Platinum Equity, LLC; *U.S. Private*, pg. 3206
MULTI-COLOR CORPORATION - WATERTOWN PLANT—See Platinum Equity, LLC; *U.S. Private*, pg. 3206
MULTI-COLOR DAVENTRY ENGLAND LTD.—See Platinum Equity, LLC; *U.S. Private*, pg. 3206
MULTI-COLOR (GRIFFITH) PTY. LTD.—See Platinum Equity, LLC; *U.S. Private*, pg. 3206
MULTI-COLOR HARO SPAIN, S.L.—See Platinum Equity, LLC; *U.S. Private*, pg. 3206
MULTI-COLOR ITALIA S.P.A.—See Platinum Equity, LLC; *U.S. Private*, pg. 3206
MULTI-COLOR SUISSE S.A.—See Platinum Equity, LLC; *U.S. Private*, pg. 3206
MWM DEXTER INC.; *U.S. Private*, pg. 2822
MYFONTS, INC.—See HGGC, LLC; *U.S. Private*, pg. 1930
MYPRINT CORP.—See Triton Pacific Capital Partners LLC; *U.S. Private*, pg. 4239
NASHUA CORPORATION—See Cenveo, Inc.; *U.S. Private*, pg. 835
NATIONAL COMMUNICATIONS GROUP, INC.—See Duggal Visual Solutions, Inc.; *U.S. Private*, pg. 1285
NATIONAL HANOVER PRESS LTD.; *U.S. Private*, pg. 2855
NATIONAL PRINT GROUP-DIGITAL & SCREEN—See Wingate Partners, LLP; *U.S. Private*, pg. 4541
NATIONAL PRINT GROUP, INC.—See Wingate Partners, LLP; *U.S. Private*, pg. 4541
NATIONAL RECOGNITION PRODUCTS, INC.—See Taylor

N.A.I.C.S. INDEX

323111 — COMMERCIAL PRINTING...

Corporation; *U.S. Private*, pg. 3938
NATIONAL REPROGRAPHICS INC.; *U.S. Private*, pg. 2862
NATIONAL TICKET COMPANY; *U.S. Private*, pg. 2864
NAVITOR EAST—See Taylor Corporation; *U.S. Private*, pg. 3938
NAYLOR PUBLICATIONS INCORPORATED—See Clarity Partners, L.P.; *U.S. Private*, pg. 912
NAYLOR PUBLICATIONS INCORPORATED—See Zelnick-Media Corp.; *U.S. Private*, pg. 4600
NCL COMMUNICATIONS—See Consolidated Press, Inc.; *U.S. Private*, pg. 1021
NCL GRAPHIC SPECIALTIES, INC.; *U.S. Private*, pg. 2876
NCP SOLUTIONS, LLC—See Aquiline Capital Partners LLC; *U.S. Private*, pg. 305
NEW ERA PORTFOLIO; *U.S. Private*, pg. 2896
NEW ISLAND PRINTING COMPANY LIMITED—See China Huajun Group Limited; *Int'l*, pg. 1509
NEW ISLAND PRINTING (US) INC.—See China Huajun Group Limited; *Int'l*, pg. 1509
NEW JERSEY BUSINESS FORMS MANUFACTURING CORPORATION; *U.S. Private*, pg. 2897
NEWS MEDIA CORPORATION—See News Media Corporation; *U.S. Private*, pg. 2917
NEXT PAGE, INC.; *U.S. Private*, pg. 2920
NICHOLAS EARTH PRINTING—See Mittera Group, Inc.; *U.S. Private*, pg. 2752
NIES/ARTCRAFT COMPANIES, INC.—See Chatham Asset Management, LLC; *U.S. Private*, pg. 863
NIES/ARTCRAFT, INC.—See Chatham Asset Management, LLC; *U.S. Private*, pg. 864
NORTHSTAR COMPUTER FORMS, INC.—See Ennis, Inc.; *U.S. Public*, pg. 769
NORTHWEST WEB CO.; *U.S. Private*, pg. 2962
NOSCO, INC.—See Holden Industries, Inc.; *U.S. Private*, pg. 1962
NOVA MARKETING SERVICES LLC; *U.S. Private*, pg. 2966
NOVATECH, INC.—See Perpetual Capital, LLC; *U.S. Private*, pg. 3153
NOVAVISION, INC.—See Incline MGMT Corp.; *U.S. Private*, pg. 2054
NPC, INC.; *U.S. Private*, pg. 2969
NPG PRINTING CO.—See News-Press & Gazette Company; *U.S. Private*, pg. 2917
NTA GRAPHICS INC.; *U.S. Private*, pg. 2970
NTA GRAPHICS SOUTH, INC.—See NTA Graphics Inc.; *U.S. Private*, pg. 2970
NTVB MEDIA, INC.; *U.S. Private*, pg. 2971
NUTIS PRESS INC.; *U.S. Private*, pg. 2974
OATMEAL STUDIOS, INC.—See Biely & Shoaf Co.; *U.S. Private*, pg. 551
OBERTHUR FIDUCIAIRE SAS—See Francois-Charles Oberthur Fiduciaire S.A.; *Int'l*, pg. 2760
OCE PRINTING SYSTEMS GMBH—See Canon Inc.; *Int'l*, pg. 1294
ODELL PUBLISHING INC; *U.S. Private*, pg. 2993
OHNO PRINTING CO., LTD.—See Crestec Inc.; *Int'l*, pg. 1841
THE OLD TRAIL PRINTING CO., INC.; *U.S. Private*, pg. 4088
OLIVER PRINTING & PACKAGING CO., LLC—See Dunsirn Partners LLC; *U.S. Private*, pg. 1290
OLIVER PRINTING & PACKAGING CO., LLC—See Pfingsten Partners, LLC; *U.S. Private*, pg. 3164
OMNIPRINT INTERNATIONAL INC.; *U.S. Private*, pg. 3017
O'NEIL DATA SYSTEMS, INC.—See William O'Neil & Co., Inc.; *U.S. Private*, pg. 4524
ONETOUCHPOINT EAST CORP.—See ICV Partners, LLC; *U.S. Private*, pg. 2034
ONETOUCHPOINT MIDWEST CORP.—See ICV Partners, LLC; *U.S. Private*, pg. 2034
ONETOUCHPOINT WEST CORP. - TEMPE OFFICE—See ICV Partners, LLC; *U.S. Private*, pg. 2034
OOO AIDA—See AIDA Engineering, Ltd.; *Int'l*, pg. 231
OPSEC SECURITY LIMITED—See Crane NXT, Co.; *U.S. Public*, pg. 592
ORANGE COUNTY PRINTING—See Chatham Asset Management, LLC; *U.S. Private*, pg. 863
ORIGINAL IMPRESSIONS, LLC—See Postal Center International; *U.S. Private*, pg. 3234
O.T. DRESCHER AG—See Exela Technologies, Inc.; *U.S. Public*, pg. 806
P2 ENERGY SOLUTIONS, INC. - SAN ANTONIO—See Advent International Corporation; *U.S. Private*, pg. 105
PACE EDITIONS INC.; *U.S. Private*, pg. 3063
PACE PRESS, INC.; *U.S. Private*, pg. 3063
PACKAGING SPECIALTIES INC.; *U.S. Private*, pg. 3072
THE PADUCAH SUN NEWSPAPER—See Paxton Media Group LLC; *U.S. Private*, pg. 3116
PAGOSA SPRINGS SUN PUBLISHING, INC.—See O'Rourke Media Group, LLC; *U.S. Private*, pg. 2980
PALADIN COMMERCIAL PRINTERS, LLC—See Marketing Solutions Unlimited, Inc.; *U.S. Private*, pg. 2580
PAMCO LABEL COMPANY; *U.S. Private*, pg. 3083
PAPERWORKS INDUSTRIES, INC. - BALDWINSVILLE—See Sun Capital Partners, Inc.; *U.S. Private*, pg. 3860
PARADIGM LABEL, INC—See Genstar Capital, LLC; *U.S. Private*, pg. 1676

PARIS ART LABEL CO., INC.—See WestRock Company; *U.S. Public*, pg. 2362
PARIS BUSINESS PRODUCTS, INC.; *U.S. Private*, pg. 3094
PARKSONS CARTAMUNDI PVT. LTD.—See Cartamundi N.V.; *Int'l*, pg. 1348
PARS INTERNATIONAL CORP.; *U.S. Private*, pg. 3100
PATSON'S MEDIA GROUP; *U.S. Private*, pg. 3111
PBM GRAPHICS INC.—See Chatham Asset Management, LLC; *U.S. Private*, pg. 863
PBM GRAPHICS, INC - TRIAD DIVISION—See Chatham Asset Management, LLC; *U.S. Private*, pg. 863
PCA, LLC—See Chatham Asset Management, LLC; *U.S. Private*, pg. 863
PDQ PRINT CENTER, INC.; *U.S. Private*, pg. 3122
PEAKE PRINTERS, INC.; *U.S. Private*, pg. 3125
PEARL-PRESSMAN-LIBERTY COMMUNICATIONS GROUP; *U.S. Private*, pg. 3125
PEGASUS PRINTING—See AAB Holdings Pty Limited; *Int'l*, pg. 30
PEND OREILLE PRINTERS INC.—See The Hagadone Corporation; *U.S. Private*, pg. 4041
PFG VENTURES L.P.; *U.S. Private*, pg. 3164
PHILIPP LITHOGRAPHING COMPANY; *U.S. Private*, pg. 3170
PHOENIX COLOR CORP.—See Atlas Holdings, LLC; *U.S. Private*, pg. 376
PHONECARD EXPRESS, LLC—See Magnet LLC; *U.S. Private*, pg. 2547
PHOTOCRAFT, INC.—See Taylor Corporation; *U.S. Private*, pg. 3938
PICTORIAL OFFSET CORPORATION; *U.S. Private*, pg. 3176
PIONEER PHOTO ALBUMS INC.; *U.S. Private*, pg. 3188
PIP PRINTING, INC.—See KOA Holdings Inc.; *U.S. Private*, pg. 2325
PITNEY BOWES ASTERION SAS—See Pitney Bowes Inc.; *U.S. Public*, pg. 1694
PLANTA SAN JUAN DEL RIO UNIDAD DE NEGOCIOS IMPRESION COMERCIAL—See Atlas Holdings, LLC; *U.S. Public*, pg. 377
PLURAL GRAFICA E EDITORA LTDA—See Quad/Graphics, Inc.; *U.S. Public*, pg. 1744
PLYMOUTH PRINTING CO. INC.; *U.S. Private*, pg. 3216
POHJANMAAN LAHISANOMAT OY—See Ilkka Yhtymae Oyj; *Int'l*, pg. 3615
POLESTAR APPLIED SOLUTIONS LIMITED—See Sun Capital Partners, Inc.; *U.S. Private*, pg. 3862
POLESTAR APPLIED SOLUTIONS LTD. - LEEDS—See Sun Capital Partners, Inc.; *U.S. Private*, pg. 3862
POLESTAR CHANTRY LIMITED—See Sun Capital Partners, Inc.; *U.S. Private*, pg. 3862
POLESTAR COLCHESTER LIMITED—See Sun Capital Partners, Inc.; *U.S. Private*, pg. 3862
POLESTAR PETTY LIMITED—See Sun Capital Partners, Inc.; *U.S. Private*, pg. 3862
POLESTAR SHEFFIELD LIMITED—See Sun Capital Partners, Inc.; *U.S. Private*, pg. 3862
POLESTAR STONES—See Sun Capital Partners, Inc.; *U.S. Private*, pg. 3862
POLESTAR UK PRINT LIMITED—See Sun Capital Partners, Inc.; *U.S. Private*, pg. 3862
POLY-FLEX CORP; *U.S. Private*, pg. 3225
POPULAR MECHANICS—See The Hearst Corporation; *U.S. Private*, pg. 4046
PORTOLA REPORTER—See Feather Publishing Co., Inc.; *U.S. Private*, pg. 1486
POST OAK GRAPHICS—See Gulf International Corporation; *U.S. Private*, pg. 1816
POST PRINTING CO. INC.; *U.S. Private*, pg. 3234
PPS, INC.; *U.S. Private*, pg. 3240
PRECISION LITHO, INC.—See Chatham Asset Management, LLC; *U.S. Private*, pg. 863
PRECISION PRINTING, INC.—See Icahn Enterprises L.P.; *U.S. Public*, pg. 1085
PREMIER GRAPHICS, LLC; *U.S. Private*, pg. 3250
PRESENTATION SERVICES, INC.—See Phase 3 Media, LLC; *U.S. Private*, pg. 3166
PRICE CHOPPER, LLC; *U.S. Private*, pg. 3258
PRIME LABEL & PACKAGING, LLC—See Kollman Label Group, LLC; *U.S. Private*, pg. 2341
PRINOVIS GMBH & CO. KG—See Bertelsmann SE & Co. KGaA; *Int'l*, pg. 995
PRINOVIS GMBH & CO. KG—See Bertelsmann SE & Co. KGaA; *Int'l*, pg. 995
PRINOVIS UK LIMITED—See Bertelsmann SE & Co. KGaA; *Int'l*, pg. 993
PRINT APPEAL, INC.—See Thomas H. Lee Partners, L.P.; *U.S. Private*, pg. 4156
THE PRINTED GROUP LIMITED—See Silver Lake Group, LLC; *U.S. Private*, pg. 3661
PRINTEGRA CORPORATION—See Ennis, Inc.; *U.S. Public*, pg. 769
PRINTERON CORPORATION—See HP Inc.; *U.S. Public*, pg. 1065
PRINTERS SQUARE, INC.; *U.S. Private*, pg. 3265
PRINTFLEX GRAPHICS, INC.; *U.S. Private*, pg. 3266
PRINTFLY CORP.; *U.S. Private*, pg. 3266

PRINTFUL, INC.; *U.S. Private*, pg. 3266
PRINTGRAPHICS, LLC—See Ennis, Inc.; *U.S. Public*, pg. 769
PRINTING CONTROL GRAPHICS—See Chatham Asset Management, LLC; *U.S. Private*, pg. 863
PRINTINGFORLESS.COM, INC.; *U.S. Private*, pg. 3266
PRINT NW LLC; *U.S. Private*, pg. 3265
PRINTPLACE.COM, LLC; *U.S. Private*, pg. 3266
PRINTRUNNER, INC.; *U.S. Private*, pg. 3266
PRINT SOUTH CORPORATION; *U.S. Private*, pg. 3265
PRINTSOUTH CORPORATION; *U.S. Private*, pg. 3266
PRINT TIME INC.; *U.S. Private*, pg. 3265
PRINTXCEL—See Ennis, Inc.; *U.S. Public*, pg. 769
PRINTXCEL - VISALIA PLANT—See Ennis, Inc.; *U.S. Public*, pg. 769
PRISMA GRAPHIC CORPORATION; *U.S. Private*, pg. 3267
PROCESS DISPLAYS CO; *U.S. Private*, pg. 3271
PROFESSIONAL OFFICE SERVICES INC.; *U.S. Private*, pg. 3275
PROFESSIONAL OFFICE SERVICES—See Professional Office Services Inc.; *U.S. Private*, pg. 3275
PROFORMA GPS GLOBAL PROMOTIONAL SOURCING; *U.S. Private*, pg. 3277
PROFORMA GRAPHIC SERVICES; *U.S. Private*, pg. 3277
PROFORMA POWERHOUSE SOLUTIONS; *U.S. Private*, pg. 3277
PROFORMA PRINT & PROMOTIONS; *U.S. Private*, pg. 3277
PROFORMA PROGRESSIVE MARKETING; *U.S. Private*, pg. 3277
PROFORMA PROMOTION CONSULTANTS; *U.S. Private*, pg. 3277
PROFORMA SIGNATURE SOLUTIONS; *U.S. Private*, pg. 3277
PROGRESS PRINTING COMPANY; *U.S. Private*, pg. 3278
PRO PRINT, INC.; *U.S. Private*, pg. 3270
PSPRINT LLC; *U.S. Private*, pg. 3297
PT. AIDA INDONESIA—See AIDA Engineering, Ltd.; *Int'l*, pg. 231
QUAD/GRAPHICS, INC. - ATGLEN—See Quad/Graphics, Inc.; *U.S. Public*, pg. 1744
QUAD/GRAPHICS, INC. - CHICAGO PREMEDIA—See Quad/Graphics, Inc.; *U.S. Public*, pg. 1744
QUAD/GRAPHICS, INC. - DICKSON—See Quad/Graphics, Inc.; *U.S. Public*, pg. 1744
QUAD/GRAPHICS, INC. - EFFINGHAM—See Quad/Graphics, Inc.; *U.S. Public*, pg. 1744
QUAD/GRAPHICS, INC. - ENFIELD—See Quad/Graphics, Inc.; *U.S. Public*, pg. 1744
QUAD/GRAPHICS, INC. - FAIRFIELD—See Quad/Graphics, Inc.; *U.S. Public*, pg. 1744
QUAD/GRAPHICS, INC. - FERNLEY—See Quad/Graphics, Inc.; *U.S. Public*, pg. 1745
QUAD/GRAPHICS, INC. - FRANKLIN—See Quad/Graphics, Inc.; *U.S. Public*, pg. 1745
QUAD/GRAPHICS, INC. - HAZLETON—See Quad/Graphics, Inc.; *U.S. Public*, pg. 1745
QUAD/GRAPHICS, INC. - LEOMINSTER—See Quad/Graphics, Inc.; *U.S. Public*, pg. 1745
QUAD/GRAPHICS, INC. - MIDLAND—See Quad/Graphics, Inc.; *U.S. Public*, pg. 1745
QUAD/GRAPHICS, INC. - PEWAUKEE—See Quad/Graphics, Inc.; *U.S. Public*, pg. 1745
QUAD/GRAPHICS, INC.; *U.S. Public*, pg. 1744
QUAD/GRAPHICS, INC. - ST. CLOUD—See Quad/Graphics, Inc.; *U.S. Public*, pg. 1745
QUAD/GRAPHICS, INC. - TAUNTON—See Quad/Graphics, Inc.; *U.S. Public*, pg. 1745
QUAD/GRAPHICS, INC. - VERSAILLES—See CJK Group, Inc.; *U.S. Private*, pg. 909
QUAD/GRAPHICS, INC. - WAUKEE—See Quad/Graphics, Inc.; *U.S. Public*, pg. 1745
QUAD/GRAPHICS, INC. - WOBURN—See Quad/Graphics, Inc.; *U.S. Public*, pg. 1745
QUAD/GRAPHICS QUERATARO S.A. DE C.V.—See Quad/Graphics, Inc.; *U.S. Public*, pg. 1744
QUAD/TECH EUROPE, INC.—See Quad/Graphics, Inc.; *U.S. Public*, pg. 1745
QUADTECH EUROPE—See Quad/Graphics, Inc.; *U.S. Public*, pg. 1745
QUADTECH IRELAND—See Quad/Graphics, Inc.; *U.S. Public*, pg. 1745
QUADTECH (SHANGHAI) TRADING COMPANY LIMITED—See Quad/Graphics, Inc.; *U.S. Public*, pg. 1745
QUADWINKOWSKI—See Quad/Graphics, Inc.; *U.S. Public*, pg. 1745
QUAD/WINKOWSKI SP. ZOO—See Quad/Graphics, Inc.; *U.S. Public*, pg. 1745
QUALITY ASSURED ENTERPRISES, INC.; *U.S. Private*, pg. 3317
QUALITY ASSURED LABEL, INC.—See Quality Assured Enterprises, Inc.; *U.S. Private*, pg. 3317
QUIK PRINT; *U.S. Private*, pg. 3327
RAINBOW GRAPHICS INC.; *U.S. Private*, pg. 3347
RAND GRAPHICS INC.; *U.S. Private*, pg. 3353
RAYPRESS CORP.—See Ares Management Corporation; *U.S. Public*, pg. 191

REDBOOK—See The Hearst Corporation; *U.S. Private*, pg. 4046
REDFIELD & COMPANY INC.; *U.S. Private*, pg. 3378
REGAL PRESS INC.; *U.S. Private*, pg. 3385
REGENCY THERMOGRAPHERS—See Taylor Corporation; *U.S. Private*, pg. 3939
REINDL PRINTING INC.; *U.S. Private*, pg. 3392
REISCHLING PRESS, INC.; *U.S. Private*, pg. 3392
REPLICO CORPORATION—See Bain Capital, LP; *U.S. Private*, pg. 438
REPRODUCCIONES FOTOMECANICAS S.A. DE C.V.—See Quad/Graphics, Inc.; *U.S. Public*, pg. 1745
REPROFLEX GMBH LEIPZIG—See Matthews International Corporation; *U.S. Public*, pg. 1399
RESOURCE LABEL GROUP, LLC—See Ares Management Corporation; *U.S. Public*, pg. 190
RESOURCE ONE—See Moore DM Group, LLC; *U.S. Private*, pg. 2780
RESPONSE ENVELOPE INC.; *U.S. Private*, pg. 3408
REYNOLDS FLEXIBLE PACKAGING-BELLWOOD PRINTING PLANT—See Pactiv Evergreen Inc.; *U.S. Public*, pg. 1634
REYNOLDS & REYNOLDS (CANADA) LTD.—See The Reynolds & Reynolds Company; *U.S. Private*, pg. 4106
RICHARD SCHERPE GMBH & CO.—See Aurelius Equity Opportunities SE & Co. KGaA; *Int'l*, pg. 709
RICHARDSON & EDWARDS PRINTING, INC.—See Wellspring Capital Management LLC; *U.S. Private*, pg. 4477
RICH LTD.—See San Francisco Equity Partners; *U.S. Private*, pg. 3540
RIDER DICKERSON, INC.; *U.S. Private*, pg. 3432
RIPON PRINTERS - MILWAUKEE—See Walsworth Publishing Company, Inc.; *U.S. Private*, pg. 4433
RIVER CITIES PRINTING—See Champion Industries, Inc.; *U.S. Public*, pg. 478
THE R.L BRYAN COMPANY; *U.S. Private*, pg. 4102
ROBINETTE COMPANY; *U.S. Private*, pg. 3460
ROBYN, INC.; *U.S. Private*, pg. 3463
ROCK COMMUNICATIONS LTD.; *U.S. Private*, pg. 3464
ROHRER CORP. - PRINTING SERVICES—See Wellspring Capital Management LLC; *U.S. Private*, pg. 4477
RONPAK INC.; *U.S. Private*, pg. 3478
ROSS NETWORK INC.; *U.S. Private*, pg. 3485
ROTARY FORMS PRESS, INC.; *U.S. Private*, pg. 3486
ROTARY MULTIFORMS, INC.; *U.S. Private*, pg. 3486
ROTARY OFFSET PRESS—See Blethen Corporation; *U.S. Private*, pg. 581
ROTARY OFFSET PRESS—See Chatham Asset Management, LLC; *U.S. Private*, pg. 867
ROYAL BUSINESS FORMS, INC.—See Ennis, Inc.; *U.S. Public*, pg. 769
ROYLE CORPORATE PRINT LTD.—See Chevrillon Philippe Industrie; *Int'l*, pg. 1474
ROYLE FINANCIAL PRINT LTD—See Chevrillon Philippe Industrie; *Int'l*, pg. 1474
ROYLE PRINTING; *U.S. Private*, pg. 3494
RPC BEBO PRINT PATENT GMBH—See Berry Global Group, Inc; *U.S. Public*, pg. 324
RRD DUTCH HOLDCO, INC.—See Chatham Asset Management, LLC; *U.S. Private*, pg. 865
RR DONNELLEY ASIA PRINTING SOLUTIONS LIMITED—See Chatham Asset Management, LLC; *U.S. Private*, pg. 865
R. R. DONNELLEY-ATLANTA WEST PLANT—See Chatham Asset Management, LLC; *U.S. Private*, pg. 864
RR DONNELLEY (AUSTRALIA) PTY LIMITED—See Chatham Asset Management, LLC; *U.S. Private*, pg. 865
RR DONNELLEY (CHENGDU) PRINTING CO., LTD.—See Chatham Asset Management, LLC; *U.S. Private*, pg. 865
R.R. DONNELLEY COMMERCIAL PRESS—See Chatham Asset Management, LLC; *U.S. Private*, pg. 865
R.R. DONNELLEY DE COSTA RICA S.A.—See Chatham Asset Management, LLC; *U.S. Private*, pg. 865
R. R. DONNELLEY DE EL SALVADOR, S.A. DE C.V.—See Chatham Asset Management, LLC; *U.S. Private*, pg. 864
R. R. DONNELLEY DE GUATEMALA, S.A.—See Chatham Asset Management, LLC; *U.S. Private*, pg. 864
R. R. DONNELLEY DEUTSCHLAND GMBH—See Chatham Asset Management, LLC; *U.S. Private*, pg. 864
R. R. DONNELLEY DOCUMENT SOLUTIONS (SWITZERLAND) GMBH—See Chatham Asset Management, LLC; *U.S. Private*, pg. 864
RR DONNELLEY EDITORA E GRAFICA LTDA.—See Chatham Asset Management, LLC; *U.S. Private*, pg. 865
RR DONNELLEY ELECTRONICS (SUZHOU) CO., LTD.—See Chatham Asset Management, LLC; *U.S. Private*, pg. 865
R. R. DONNELLEY EUROPE SP. Z O.O—See Chatham Asset Management, LLC; *U.S. Private*, pg. 864
RR DONNELLEY FINANCIAL COMUNICACAO CORPORATIVA LTDA.—See Chatham Asset Management, LLC; *U.S. Private*, pg. 865
RR DONNELLEY FINLAND OY—See Chatham Asset Management, LLC; *U.S. Private*, pg. 865
RR DONNELLEY GLOBAL TURNKEY SOLUTIONS MEXICO, S. DE R.L. DE C.V.—See Chatham Asset Management, LLC; *U.S. Private*, pg. 865
RR DONNELLEY INDIA OUTSOURCE PRIVATE LIMITED—See Chatham Asset Management, LLC; *U.S. Private*, pg. 865
RR DONNELLEY INTERNATIONAL DE MEXICO, S.A. DE C.V.—See Chatham Asset Management, LLC; *U.S. Private*, pg. 865
RR DONNELLEY KOREA ELECTRONIC SOLUTION LLC—See Chatham Asset Management, LLC; *U.S. Private*, pg. 865
R. R. DONNELLEY LIMITED—See Chatham Asset Management, LLC; *U.S. Private*, pg. 864
R.R. DONNELLEY - LITHO PLANT—See Chatham Asset Management, LLC; *U.S. Private*, pg. 865
RR DONNELLEY LOGISTICS SERVICES WORLDWIDE, INC.—See Chatham Asset Management, LLC; *U.S. Private*, pg. 865
R.R. DONNELLEY NORWEST INC.—See Chatham Asset Management, LLC; *U.S. Private*, pg. 865
R.R. DONNELLEY OF PUERTO RICO—See Chatham Asset Management, LLC; *U.S. Private*, pg. 865
R. R. DONNELLEY PRINTING COMPANY—See Chatham Asset Management, LLC; *U.S. Private*, pg. 865
R.R. DONNELLEY RECEIVABLES, INC.—See Chatham Asset Management, LLC; *U.S. Private*, pg. 865
R.R. DONNELLEY RESPONSE MARKETING SERVICES—See Chatham Asset Management, LLC; *U.S. Private*, pg. 865
R.R. DONNELLEY SEYMOUR INC.—See Chatham Asset Management, LLC; *U.S. Private*, pg. 865
R. R. DONNELLEY & SONS COMPANY—See Chatham Asset Management, LLC; *U.S. Private*, pg. 862
R. R. DONNELLEY & SONS CO. - NASHVILLE—See Chatham Asset Management, LLC; *U.S. Private*, pg. 865
R. R. DONNELLEY & SONS CO. - PINEVILLE—See Chatham Asset Management, LLC; *U.S. Private*, pg. 865
R.R. DONNELLEY & SONS CO.—See Chatham Asset Management, LLC; *U.S. Private*, pg. 864
R.R. DONNELLEY & SONS CO.—See Chatham Asset Management, LLC; *U.S. Private*, pg. 864
R.R. DONNELLEY & SONS CO.—See Chatham Asset Management, LLC; *U.S. Private*, pg. 864
R.R. DONNELLEY & SONS CO.—See Chatham Asset Management, LLC; *U.S. Private*, pg. 864
R.R. DONNELLEY & SONS CO.—See Chatham Asset Management, LLC; *U.S. Private*, pg. 864
R.R. DONNELLEY & SONS CO.—See Chatham Asset Management, LLC; *U.S. Private*, pg. 865
R.R. DONNELLEY—See Chatham Asset Management, LLC; *U.S. Private*, pg. 864
R.R. DONNELLEY—See Chatham Asset Management, LLC; *U.S. Private*, pg. 864
R.R. DONNELLEY—See Chatham Asset Management, LLC; *U.S. Private*, pg. 864
R.R. DONNELLEY—See Chatham Asset Management, LLC; *U.S. Private*, pg. 864
R.R. DONNELLEY—See Chatham Asset Management, LLC; *U.S. Private*, pg. 864
R.R. DONNELLEY—See Chatham Asset Management, LLC; *U.S. Private*, pg. 864
R.R. DONNELLEY—See Chatham Asset Management, LLC; *U.S. Private*, pg. 864
R. R. DONNELLEY STARACHOWICE SP. Z O.O—See Chatham Asset Management, LLC; *U.S. Private*, pg. 864
R. R. DONNELLEY (U.K.) LIMITED—See Chatham Asset Management, LLC; *U.S. Private*, pg. 864
RRD PENDAFLEX DE MEXICO, S. DE R.L. DE C.V.—See Chatham Asset Management, LLC; *U.S. Private*, pg. 865
RRD SECAUCUS FINANCIAL, INC.—See Chatham Asset Management, LLC; *U.S. Private*, pg. 865
RRD STARACHOWICE SP. Z O.O.—See Chatham Asset Management, LLC; *U.S. Private*, pg. 865
RUSSELLVILLE NEWSPAPERS INC.—See Paxton Media Group LLC; *U.S. Private*, pg. 3116
RYAN PRINTING, INC; *U.S. Public*, pg. 3510
SAFEGUARD BUSINESS SYSTEMS, INC.—See Deluxe Corporation; *U.S. Public*, pg. 652
SAFEGUARD FRANCHISE SALES, INC.—See Deluxe Corporation; *U.S. Public*, pg. 653
SAFEPRINTS LLC—See AEA Investors LP; *U.S. Private*, pg. 114
SALEM PRINTING; *U.S. Private*, pg. 3531
SANDY ALEXANDER, INC.—See Snow Peak Capital, LLC; *U.S. Private*, pg. 3701
SANOMALEHTI ILKKA OY—See Ilkka Yhtymae Oyj; *Int'l*, pg. 3615
SAXOPRINT AG—See CEWE Stiftung & Co. KGaA; *Int'l*, pg. 1425
SAXOPRINT EURL—See CEWE Stiftung & Co. KGaA; *Int'l*, pg. 1425
SAXOPRINT GMBH—See CEWE Stiftung & Co. KGaA; *Int'l*, pg. 1425
SAXOPRINT LTD.—See CEWE Stiftung & Co. KGaA; *Int'l*, pg. 1425
SCANSTAT TECHNOLOGIES, LLC—See NewSpring Capital LLC; *U.S. Private*, pg. 2918
SCHAWK INDIA PVT. LTD.—See Matthews International Corporation; *U.S. Public*, pg. 1400
SCHMIDT PRINTING—See Taylor Corporation; *U.S. Private*, pg. 3939
SCHUMANN PRINTERS, INC.; *U.S. Private*, pg. 3571
SCIENTIFIC GAMES INTERNATIONAL—See Light & Wonder, Inc.; *U.S. Public*, pg. 1315
SCIENTIFIC GAMES PUERTO RICO, LLC—See Light & Wonder, Inc.; *U.S. Public*, pg. 1315
SEARCY NEWSPAPERS INC.—See Paxton Media Group LLC; *U.S. Private*, pg. 3116
SEAWAY PRINTING COMPANY, INC.; *U.S. Private*, pg. 3592
SECUPRINT INC.—See DSS, Inc.; *U.S. Public*, pg. 689
SECURITY PRINTING CORPORATION (BANGLADESH) LTD.—See Bangladesh Bank; *Int'l*, pg. 835
THE SEGERDAHL CORPORATION; *U.S. Private*, pg. 4116
SEP COMMUNICATIONS, LLC—See Southeastern Printing Company Inc.; *U.S. Private*, pg. 3728
SERVICE LITHO-PRINT, INC.; *U.S. Private*, pg. 3615
SERVICE PRINTERS, INC.—See Hederman Brothers, LLC; *U.S. Private*, pg. 1903
SERVICE WEB OFFSET CORPORATION; *U.S. Private*, pg. 3616
SG360—See The Segerdahl Corporation; *U.S. Private*, pg. 4116
SHAPEWAYS HOLDINGS, INC.; *U.S. Public*, pg. 1873
SHAPEWAYS, INC.—See Shapeways Holdings, Inc.; *U.S. Public*, pg. 1873
SHENZHEN HEIDELBERG NETWORX TECHNOLOGY CO., LTD.—See Heidelberger Druckmaschinen AG; *Int'l*, pg. 3322
SHERIDAN BOOKS, INC.—See CJK Group, Inc.; *U.S. Private*, pg. 909
THE SHERIDAN GROUP, INC.—See CJK Group, Inc.; *U.S. Private*, pg. 909
SHERIDAN MAGAZINE SERVICES—See CJK Group, Inc.; *U.S. Private*, pg. 909
THE SHERIDAN PRESS—See CJK Group, Inc.; *U.S. Private*, pg. 909
SHOREWOOD PACKAGING LLC - HENDERSONVILLE PLANT—See Atlas Holdings, LLC; *U.S. Private*, pg. 378
SHOREWOOD PACKAGING LLC - MELROSE PARK—See Atlas Holdings, LLC; *U.S. Private*, pg. 378
SIGNATURE OFFSET, INC.; *U.S. Private*, pg. 3650
SINCLAIR PRINTING COMPANY; *U.S. Private*, pg. 3669
SLATE GROUP; *U.S. Private*, pg. 3687
SMART SOURCE OF GEORGIA, LLC; *U.S. Private*, pg. 3691
SMITH-EDWARDS-DUNLAP COMPANY; *U.S. Private*, pg. 3696
SOUTHEASTERN PRINTING COMPANY INC.; *U.S. Private*, pg. 3728
SOUTHEAST MEDIA, INC.; *U.S. Private*, pg. 3726
SOUTHERN ATLANTIC LABEL CO., INC.—See Platinum Equity, LLC; *U.S. Public*, pg. 3206
SOUTHERN GRAPHIC SYSTEMS, INC. - GRAVURE DIVISON—See HPS Investment Partners, LLC; *U.S. Private*, pg. 1997
SOUTHLAND PRINTING CO., INC.; *U.S. Private*, pg. 3737
SOUTHWESTERN STATIONERY & BANK SUPPLY, INC.; *U.S. Private*, pg. 3742
SOUTHWEST PRECISION PRINTERS, L.P.; *U.S. Private*, pg. 3740
SOVEREIGN BUSINESS FORMS INC.—See Ennis, Inc.; *U.S. Public*, pg. 769
SPANDEX BELGIUM NV—See Chequers SA; *Int'l*, pg. 1471
SPANDEX LTD—See Chequers SA; *Int'l*, pg. 1471
SPANGLER GRAPHICS, LLC—See Chatham Asset Management, LLC; *U.S. Private*, pg. 863
SPEAR USA LLC; *U.S. Private*, pg. 3747
SPEAR USA LLC—See Spear USA LLC; *U.S. Private*, pg. 3747
SPECIALIZED PRINTED FORMS, INC.—See Ennis, Inc.; *U.S. Public*, pg. 769
SPECIAL SERVICE PARTNERS CORPORATION—See Ennis, Inc.; *U.S. Public*, pg. 769
SPECIALTY MANUFACTURING, INC.—See Arrow International, Inc.; *U.S. Private*, pg. 335
SPECIMEN PAPIR ES NYOMDAIPARI ZRT.—See ANY Security Printing Company PLC; *Int'l*, pg. 486
SPECTRATEK TECHNOLOGIES INC.; *U.S. Private*, pg. 3751
SPECTRUM LABEL CORPORATION—See Ares Management Corporation; *U.S. Public*, pg. 191
SPECTRUM PRINTING INC.—See Mount Royal Printing & Communications, Inc.; *U.S. Private*, pg. 2798
STAMPA NAPOLI 2015 SRL—See Caltagirone Editore S.p.A.; *Int'l*, pg. 1266
STANDARD OFFSET PRINTING CO.; *U.S. Private*, pg. 3781
STANDARD REGISTER, INC.—See Taylor Corporation; *U.S. Private*, pg. 3939
ST. CROIX PRESS, INC.; *U.S. Private*, pg. 3771
STEFANO'S PRINTING, INC.—See Ford Business Machines, Inc.; *U.S. Private*, pg. 1564
STEFANO'S PRINTING, INC.—See Unity Printing Co., Inc.; *U.S. Private*, pg. 4303
STELLAR PRINTING INC.—See Family Federation for World Peace & Unification; *U.S. Private*, pg. 1470

N.A.I.C.S. INDEX

323111 — COMMERCIAL PRINTING...

STEPHENSON PRINTING, INC.; *U.S. Private*, pg. 3803
STERLING BUSINESS FORMS INC.; *U.S. Private*, pg. 3804
STEVEN LABEL CORPORATION; *U.S. Private*, pg. 3808
STORK AVENUE, INC.; *U.S. Private*, pg. 3831
STORTERCHILDS PRINTING CO., INC.—See Chatham Asset Management, LLC; *U.S. Private*, pg. 865
STORTER CHILDS PRINTING COMPANY, INC.—See Chatham Asset Management, LLC; *U.S. Private*, pg. 863
STRATA GRAPHICS, INC.; *U.S. Private*, pg. 3833
STRINE PRINTING COMPANY INC.—See Menasha Corporation; *U.S. Private*, pg. 2665
STUART & ASSOCIATES, INC.; *U.S. Private*, pg. 3843
STYLECRAFT PRINTING, CO.—See Ennis, Inc.; *U.S. Public*, pg. 769
SUCCESSORIES.COM LLC—See TWS Partnership LLC; *U.S. Private*, pg. 4267
SUMMIT PRINTING (AUSTRALIA) PTY LIMITED—See Centurion Corporation Limited; *Int'l*, pg. 1417
SUNCOAST FORMS & SYSTEMS, INC.; *U.S. Private*, pg. 3865
SUNCRAFT TECHNOLOGIES INC.; *U.S. Private*, pg. 3866
SUN GRAPHICS INC.; *U.S. Private*, pg. 3863
SUN GRAPHICS PRINTING, INC.; *U.S. Private*, pg. 3863
SUN PRINTING INC.; *U.S. Private*, pg. 3863
SUNRISE DIGITAL; *U.S. Private*, pg. 3870
SUPERIOR PRINT & EXHIBIT, INC.; *U.S. Private*, pg. 3879
SUTHERLAND PRINTING, INC.—See Nationwide Argosy Solutions, LLC; *U.S. Private*, pg. 2865
SUTTLE-STRAUS INC.—See Telephone & Data Systems, Inc.; *U.S. Public*, pg. 1997
SYMETA N.V.—See Colruyt Group N.V.; *Int'l*, pg. 1705
TAMARACK PACKAGING LIMITED—See Channellock, Inc.; *U.S. Private*, pg. 849
TANASEYBERT; *U.S. Private*, pg. 3930
TANDEM PUBLISHING GROUP, INC.; *U.S. Private*, pg. 3930
TAPEMARK, INC.—See dievini Hopp BioTech holding GmbH & Co. KG; *Int'l*, pg. 2117
TARADEL, LLC; *U.S. Private*, pg. 3933
TARGET PRINT & MAIL; *U.S. Private*, pg. 3933
TAYLOR CORPORATION; *U.S. Private*, pg. 3937
TAYMARK, INC.—See Taylor Corporation; *U.S. Private*, pg. 3939
TECHNICAL IMAGE PRODUCTS, INC.; *U.S. Private*, pg. 3954
TECHTARGET GERMANY GMBH—See TechTarget, Inc.; *U.S. Public*, pg. 1989
TECHTARGET (SINGAPORE) PTE. LTD.—See TechTarget, Inc.; *U.S. Public*, pg. 1989
TELDON MEDIA GROUP, INC—See CARDON Group Inc.; *Int'l*, pg. 1323
TEMPOGRAPHICS INC.; *U.S. Private*, pg. 3964
TEUTEBERG INCORPORATED; *U.S. Private*, pg. 3974
TEWELL WARREN PRINTING COMPANY—See Chatham Asset Management, LLC; *U.S. Private*, pg. 863
TFP DATA SYSTEMS—See Taylor Corporation; *U.S. Private*, pg. 3939
THAYER PUBLISHING—See Taylor Corporation; *U.S. Private*, pg. 3938
THEO DAVIS SONS, INCORPORATED—See Chatham Asset Management, LLC; *U.S. Private*, pg. 863
THOMAS REPROGRAPHICS, INC.; *U.S. Private*, pg. 4157
THOROUGHBRED TIMES COMPANY INC.—See Fancy Publications Inc.; *U.S. Private*, pg. 1472
THOUSAND OAKS PRINTING & SPECIALTIES, INC.—See Chatham Asset Management, LLC; *U.S. Private*, pg. 863
TIDEWATER DIRECT LLC; *U.S. Private*, pg. 4168
TIMBERTECH, INC.; *U.S. Private*, pg. 4172
TIMES PRINTING COMPANY, INC.—See PDQ Print Center, Inc.; *U.S. Private*, pg. 3122
TIPO DIRECT SERV SRL—See ANY Security Printing Company PLC; *Int'l*, pg. 486
TOOF COMMERCIAL PRINTING; *U.S. Private*, pg. 4185
THE TOPPS COMPANY, INC.—See Madison Dearborn Partners, LLC; *U.S. Private*, pg. 2542
TRABON PRINTING COMPANY INC.; *U.S. Private*, pg. 4200
TRADEPRINT DISTRIBUTION LIMITED—See Cimpress plc; *Int'l*, pg. 1609
TRANSACT TECHNOLOGIES LTD.—See TransAct Technologies Incorporated; *U.S. Public*, pg. 2179
TRANSPRINT USA, INC.—See Colorep, Inc.; *U.S. Private*, pg. 975
TRAVEL TAGS, INC.—See Taylor Corporation; *U.S. Private*, pg. 3939
TRAY, INC.; *U.S. Private*, pg. 4215
TREND OFFSET PRINTING SERVICES, INC.—See Mittera Group, Inc.; *U.S. Private*, pg. 2752
TREND OFFSET PRINTING SERVICES - SOUTHEAST DIVISION—See Mittera Group, Inc.; *U.S. Private*, pg. 2752
TRI-C BUSINESS FORMS, INC.—See Ennis, Inc.; *U.S. Public*, pg. 769
TRI-CITY HERALD—See Chatham Asset Management, LLC; *U.S. Private*, pg. 867
TRIENT, LLC—See Audax Group, Limited Partnership; *U.S. Private*, pg. 387

TRILITERAL LLC—See Atlas Holdings, LLC; *U.S. Private*, pg. 377
TRINITY GRAPHIC USA, INC.; *U.S. Private*, pg. 4233
TRISTAR WEB GRAPHICS INC—See Tristar Holdings Inc.; *U.S. Private*, pg. 4238
TUCKER PRINTERS, INC.—See Chatham Asset Management, LLC; *U.S. Private*, pg. 863
TULLY-WIHR COMPANY; *U.S. Private*, pg. 4258
TURSACK INCORPORATED—See Chatham Asset Management, LLC; *U.S. Private*, pg. 863
TURSSO COMPANIES INCORPORATED; *U.S. Private*, pg. 4262
TWEDDLE LITHO COMPANY; *U.S. Private*, pg. 4264
TWILL, INC.—See Ace Lithographers of Morris County, Inc.; *U.S. Private*, pg. 57
UNIFIED PACKAGING, INC.; *U.S. Private*, pg. 4283
THE UNION GROUP; *U.S. Private*, pg. 4129
UNION PRINTING—See The Union Group; *U.S. Private*, pg. 4129
UNITED LITHO, INC.—See CJK Group, Inc.; *U.S. Private*, pg. 909
UNITED PRINTING AND PUBLISHING—See Abu Dhabi Media; *Int'l*, pg. 72
UNITS SETS, INC.—See Rotary Forms Press, Inc.; *U.S. Private*, pg. 3486
UNIVERSAL BUSINESS SOLUTIONS, NA; *U.S. Private*, pg. 4304
UNIVERSAL MANUFACTURING COMPANY—See WNC Corporation; *U.S. Private*, pg. 4552
UNIVERSAL NUTRITION; *U.S. Private*, pg. 4306
UNIVERSAL PRINTING COMPANY; *U.S. Private*, pg. 4306
UNIVERSAL PRODUCTS INC.; *U.S. Private*, pg. 4306
UNIVERSAL WILDE; *U.S. Private*, pg. 4307
THE UPPER DECK COMPANY, LLC; *U.S. Private*, pg. 4129
UPRINTING.COM; *U.S. Private*, pg. 4312
US1COM INC.—See AFE Industries, Inc.; *U.S. Private*, pg. 121
U.S. LEGAL FORMS, INC.—See USLegal, Inc.; *U.S. Private*, pg. 4323
U.S. PRESS, LLC; *U.S. Private*, pg. 4272
US TAG & TICKET—See Champion Industries, Inc.; *U.S. Public*, pg. 478
US WEB INCORPORATED; *U.S. Private*, pg. 4320
V3 PRINTING CORPORATION; *U.S. Private*, pg. 4328
VAASA OY—See Ilkka Yhtymae Oyj; *Int'l*, pg. 3615
VAASSEN, INC.—See Egeria Capital Management B.V.; *Int'l*, pg. 2323
VALASSIS COMMUNICATIONS, INC.—See MacAndrews & Forbes Incorporated; *U.S. Private*, pg. 2532
VALCOUR PRINTING, INC.—See Chatham Asset Management, LLC; *U.S. Private*, pg. 863
VALMARK INDUSTRIES, INC.—See Jordan Industries, Inc.; *U.S. Private*, pg. 2235
VANGUARD PRINTING LLC; *U.S. Private*, pg. 4344
VELOCITY PRINT SOLUTIONS; *U.S. Private*, pg. 4354
VERICAST—See MacAndrews & Forbes Incorporated; *U.S. Private*, pg. 2532
VERIDOS GMBH—See Bundesdruckerei GmbH; *Int'l*, pg. 1216
VERIDOS GMBH—See Giesecke & Devrient GmbH; *Int'l*, pg. 2970
VERIDOS MATSOUKIS S.A.—See Giesecke & Devrient GmbH; *Int'l*, pg. 2970
VERITAS DOCUMENT SOLUTIONS, LLC—See Chatham Asset Management, LLC; *U.S. Private*, pg. 863
VERITIV OPERATING COMPANY—See Clayton, Dubilier & Rice, LLC; *U.S. Private*, pg. 928
VIATECH PUBLISHING SOLUTIONS LIMITED—See ViaTech Publishing Solutions; *U.S. Private*, pg. 4376
VIATECH PUBLISHING SOLUTIONS; *U.S. Private*, pg. 4376
VIDEOJET TECHNOLOGIES INC.—See Danaher Corporation; *U.S. Public*, pg. 632
VISION ENVELOPE, INC.—See Western States Envelope & Label; *U.S. Private*, pg. 4497
VISION GRAPHICS INC.; *U.S. Private*, pg. 4390
VISION INTEGRATED GRAPHICS GROUP; *U.S. Private*, pg. 4391
VISTA COLOR CORPORATION; *U.S. Private*, pg. 4394
VISTAPRINT B.V.—See Cimpress plc; *Int'l*, pg. 1609
VISTAPRINT CANADA LIMITED—See Cimpress plc; *Int'l*, pg. 1609
VISTAPRINT CORPORATE SOLUTIONS INCORPORATED—See Cimpress plc; *Int'l*, pg. 1609
VISTAPRINT ESPANA S.L.—See Cimpress plc; *Int'l*, pg. 1609
VISTAPRINT JAMAICA LIMITED—See Cimpress plc; *Int'l*, pg. 1609
VISTAPRINT NETHERLANDS B.V.—See Cimpress plc; *Int'l*, pg. 1609
VISTAPRINT NORTH AMERICAN SERVICES CORP.—See Cimpress plc; *Int'l*, pg. 1609
VISTAPRINT USA, INCORPORATED—See Cimpress plc; *Int'l*, pg. 1609
VISUAL CONTROLS/CHAMP INC.; *U.S. Private*, pg. 4404
VITEX PACKAGING GROUP—See The Pritzker Group - Chicago, LLC; *U.S. Private*, pg. 4099
VIVID IMPACT CORPORATION; *U.S. Private*, pg. 4406

VOMELA SPECIALTY COMPANY; *U.S. Private*, pg. 4412
VULCAN INFORMATION PACKAGING—See NAPCO, Inc.; *U.S. Private*, pg. 2834
WALLE CORPORATION; *U.S. Private*, pg. 4431
WALLMONKEYS, LLC—See HC Brands; *U.S. Private*, pg. 1888
WALNUT CIRCLE PRESS, INC.—See Chatham Asset Management, LLC; *U.S. Private*, pg. 866
WARD/KRAFT, INC. - KANSAS PLANT—See Ward/Kraft, Inc.; *U.S. Private*, pg. 4441
WARD/KRAFT, INC.; *U.S. Private*, pg. 4441
WATERMARK PRESS, LTD.—See Chatham Asset Management, LLC; *U.S. Private*, pg. 866
W.E. ANDREWS—See Chatham Asset Management, LLC; *U.S. Private*, pg. 866
W.E. BAXTER LIMITED—See B.L.L. Holdings Ltd; *Int'l*, pg. 790
WEBB-MASON INC.; *U.S. Private*, pg. 4464
WEB GRAPHICS, INC.—See Taylor Corporation; *U.S. Private*, pg. 3939
WEGENER GRAFISCHE GROEP BV—See DPG Media Group NV; *Int'l*, pg. 2189
WELDON, WILLIAMS & LICK, INC.; *U.S. Private*, pg. 4474
WENTWORTH CORPORATION—See Chatham Asset Management, LLC; *U.S. Private*, pg. 863
WENTWORTH PRINTING CORPORATION—See Chatham Asset Management, LLC; *U.S. Private*, pg. 863
WESTERN BLUE PRINT COMPANY LLC; *U.S. Private*, pg. 4491
WESTERN ROTO ENGRAVERS INC.; *U.S. Private*, pg. 4496
WESTERN SHIELD ACQUISITIONS LLC—See Heartwood Partners, LLC; *U.S. Private*, pg. 1901
WESTERN YANKEE, INC.—See AFE Industries, Inc.; *U.S. Private*, pg. 121
WESTLAND PRINTERS, INC.—See Chatham Asset Management, LLC; *U.S. Private*, pg. 866
WESTLAND PRINTERS—See Chatham Asset Management, LLC; *U.S. Private*, pg. 866
WETZEL BROTHERS, LLC—See Chatham Asset Management, LLC; *U.S. Private*, pg. 863
WHITE HOUSE CUSTOM COLOUR, INC.; *U.S. Private*, pg. 4509
THE WHITE QUILL PRESS—See Chevrillon Philippe Industrie; *Int'l*, pg. 1474
WHITLAM GROUP, INC.; *U.S. Private*, pg. 4512
WILLIAM E. COUTTS CO., LTD.—See Hallmark Cards, Inc.; *U.S. Private*, pg. 1845
WINKOWSKI DEUTSCHLAND GMBH—See Quad/Graphics, Inc.; *U.S. Public*, pg. 1745
WINSTON PRINTING COMPANY; *U.S. Private*, pg. 4544
WIRMACHENDRUCK GMBH—See Cimpress plc; *Int'l*, pg. 1609
WISE BUSINESS FORMS INCORPORATED - COMMERCIAL PRINTING PLANT—See Wise Business Forms Incorporated; *U.S. Private*, pg. 4549
WISE BUSINESS FORMS INCORPORATED - INDIANA PLANT—See Wise Business Forms Incorporated; *U.S. Private*, pg. 4549
WISE BUSINESS FORMS INCORPORATED - PENNSYLVANIA PLANT—See Wise Business Forms Incorporated; *U.S. Private*, pg. 4549
WISE BUSINESS FORMS INCORPORATED; *U.S. Private*, pg. 4549
WISE BUSINESS FORMS INCORPORATED - SOUTH CAROLINA PLANT—See Wise Business Forms Incorporated; *U.S. Private*, pg. 4549
WISE BUSINESS—See Wise Business Forms Incorporated; *U.S. Private*, pg. 4549
WITT PRINTING COMPANY—See Ennis, Inc.; *U.S. Public*, pg. 769
WORTH HIGGINS & ASSOCIATES INC.; *U.S. Private*, pg. 4570
WRIGHT BUSINESS FORMS, INC. - CHINO FACILITY—See Wright Business Forms, Inc.; *U.S. Private*, pg. 4572
WRIGHT BUSINESS FORMS, INC. - KENT FACILITY—See Wright Business Forms, Inc.; *U.S. Private*, pg. 4572
WRIGHT BUSINESS FORMS, INC.; *U.S. Private*, pg. 4572
WRIGHT GRAPHICS INC.; *U.S. Private*, pg. 4573
WRIGHT IMAGING SOLUTIONS—See Wright Business Forms, Inc.; *U.S. Private*, pg. 4572
WS PACKAGING GROUP INC. - FRANKLIN—See Platinum Equity, LLC; *U.S. Private*, pg. 3206
WS PACKAGING GROUP INC. - MASON—See Platinum Equity, LLC; *U.S. Private*, pg. 3206
XEIKON JAPAN CO., LTD.—See Koch Industries, Inc.; *U.S. Private*, pg. 2327
XEIKON JAPAN CO., LTD.—See The Goldman Sachs Group, Inc.; *U.S. Public*, pg. 2077
XEIKON MANUFACTURING AND R&D CENTER—See Koch Industries, Inc.; *U.S. Private*, pg. 2327
XEIKON MANUFACTURING AND R&D CENTER—See The Goldman Sachs Group, Inc.; *U.S. Public*, pg. 2077
XEROX REPROGRAPHISCHE SERVICES GMBH—See Xerox Holdings Corporation; *U.S. Public*, pg. 2390
XPRESS MEDIA PTE LTD—See A-Smart Holdings Ltd.; *Int'l*, pg. 20

323111 — COMMERCIAL PRINTING...

XPRESS PRINT (AUSTRALIA) PTY LTD—See A-Smart Holdings Ltd.; *Int'l*, pg. 20
XPRESS PRINT (PTE) LTD.—See A-Smart Holdings Ltd.; *Int'l*, pg. 20
YORK GRAPHIC SERVICES CO.; *U.S. Private*, pg. 4590
ZAZZLE, INC.; *U.S. Private*, pg. 4598
ZEBRA IMAGING, INC.; *U.S. Private*, pg. 4599
ZIPPER SERVICES SRL—See ANY Security Printing Company PLC; *Int'l*, pg. 486
ZOOOM PRINTING; *U.S. Private*, pg. 4608

323113 — COMMERCIAL SCREEN PRINTING

ALLIED ADVERTISING AGENCY, INC.; *U.S. Private*, pg. 185
ARC DOCUMENT SOLUTIONS, LLC—See ARC DOCUMENT SOLUTIONS, INC.; *U.S. Public*, pg. 179
ARES SPORTSWEAR, LTD.; *U.S. Private*, pg. 318
ARES SPORTSWEAR—See Dyenomite, LLC; *U.S. Private*, pg. 1296
ARTCO (US), INC.—See Taylor Corporation; *U.S. Private*, pg. 3938
ARTISSIMO DESIGNS INC.—See Artissimo Holdings, Inc.; *U.S. Private*, pg. 343
ARTISSIMO U.S., LLC—See Artissimo Holdings, Inc.; *U.S. Private*, pg. 343
BACOVA GUILD, LTD.—See Ronile, Inc.; *U.S. Private*, pg. 3478
BLUECOTTON, INC.; *U.S. Private*, pg. 596
BRADY CORPORATION HONG KONG LIMITED—See Brady Corporation; *U.S. Public*, pg. 378
THE BRANDING AGENCY, LLC; *U.S. Private*, pg. 3999
BRAVE PRECISION MFG. SUZHOU CO., LTD.—See Brave C&H Supply Co., Ltd.; *Int'l*, pg. 1141
BRAVE TECHNOLOGY (CHENGDU) CO., LTD.—See Brave C&H Supply Co., Ltd.; *Int'l*, pg. 1141
CARD FULFILLMENT SERVICES INC—See Taylor Corporation; *U.S. Private*, pg. 3938
CARDINAL INDUSTRIES, INC.; *U.S. Private*, pg. 750
CCA OCCASIONS LTD—See Taylor Corporation; *U.S. Private*, pg. 3938
COLUMBUS PRODUCTIONS, INC.—See Global Payments Inc.; *U.S. Public*, pg. 944
CORPORATE GRAPHICS COMMERCIAL—See Taylor Corporation; *U.S. Private*, pg. 3938
DAMY CORP.; *U.S. Private*, pg. 1151
DIGITAL ROOM, LLC—See Sycamore Partners Management, LP; *U.S. Private*, pg. 3895
DTG2GO, LLC—See Delta Apparel, Inc.; *U.S. Public*, pg. 652
EBSCO INDUSTRIES, INC. - EBSCO RECEPTION ROOM SUBSCRIPTION SERVICES DIVISION—See EBSCO Industries, Inc.; *U.S. Private*, pg. 1325
EMPIRE SCREEN PRINTING, INC.; *U.S. Private*, pg. 1385
ENCRES DUBUIT SA; *Int'l*, pg. 2402
FBL FINANCIAL GROUP, INC.—See Iowa Farm Bureau Federation; *U.S. Private*, pg. 2134
FELLAZO CORP.; *Int'l*, pg. 2633
FINE DESIGNS STORE; *U.S. Private*, pg. 1509
FOREST CORP.; *U.S. Private*, pg. 1567
FURMANITE CORPORATION—See Team, Inc.; *U.S. Public*, pg. 1987
GEM GROUP INC.; *U.S. Private*, pg. 1657
GFX INTERNATIONAL INC.—See Keystone Group, L.P.; *U.S. Private*, pg. 2298
GOULD PAPER CORPORATION; *U.S. Private*, pg. 1745
GRAPHICS GROUP LTD.; *U.S. Private*, pg. 1758
GREAT BIG PICTURES, INC.—See GSP Marketing Technologies, Inc.; *U.S. Private*, pg. 1801
GSP MARKETING TECHNOLOGIES, INC.; *U.S. Private*, pg. 1801
HAIDEMENOS S.A.; *Int'l*, pg. 3209
HBP, INC.; *U.S. Private*, pg. 1887
HOOGHLY PRINTING COMPANY LTD.—See Andrew Yule & Company Ltd.; *Int'l*, pg. 452
INNERWORKINGS DANMARK A/S—See HH Global Group Limited; *Int'l*, pg. 3378
INNOVIZE, INC.—See Vance Street Capital LLC; *U.S. Private*, pg. 4342
INTERNATIONAL GRAPHICS ULC—See Taylor Corporation; *U.S. Private*, pg. 3938
ITW GRAPHICS—See Illinois Tool Works Inc.; *U.S. Public*, pg. 1106
J.N. WHITE ASSOCIATES, INC.; *U.S. Private*, pg. 2169
KERUSSO ACTIVEWEAR, INC.; *U.S. Private*, pg. 2291
KG SPECIALTIES LLC—See PEP Printing, Inc.; *U.S. Private*, pg. 3143
KOALA TEE, INC.; *U.S. Private*, pg. 2325
KOKOLO SAS—See Leonard Green & Partners, L.P.; *U.S. Private*, pg. 2424
LITHO TECH, INC.—See Taylor Corporation; *U.S. Private*, pg. 3938
LOGOSPORTSWEAR.COM; *U.S. Private*, pg. 2482
LSI GRAPHIC SOLUTIONS PLUS—See LSI Industries Inc.; *U.S. Public*, pg. 1344
LSI GRAPHIC SOLUTIONS PLUS—See LSI Industries Inc.; *U.S. Public*, pg. 1344

LSI INTEGRATED GRAPHICS L.P.—See LSI Industries Inc.; *U.S. Public*, pg. 1344
MARQUIS BOOK PRINTING INC.—See Atlas Holdings, LLC; *U.S. Private*, pg. 377
MODAGRAFICS INC.; *U.S. Private*, pg. 2759
OBERTHUR FIDUCIAIRE (UK) LIMITED—See Francois-Charles Oberthur Fiduciaire S.A.; *Int'l*, pg. 2760
THE OCCASIONS GROUP, INC.—See Taylor Corporation; *U.S. Private*, pg. 3939
ORIGINAL SMITH PRINTING—See Taylor Corporation; *U.S. Private*, pg. 3938
PHARMACEUTIC LITHO & LABEL COMPANY, INC.—See Ares Management Corporation; *U.S. Public*, pg. 191
PINE DECALS—See PPS, Inc.; *U.S. Private*, pg. 3240
PLOCKMATIC INTERNATIONAL AB—See Grimaldi Industri AB; *Int'l*, pg. 3086
POLESTAR BICESTER LTD—See Sun Capital Partners, Inc.; *U.S. Private*, pg. 3862
PRATT CORPORATION—See Vomela Specialty Company; *U.S. Private*, pg. 4412
PRECISION PRESS, INC.—See Taylor Corporation; *U.S. Private*, pg. 3939
PRINT SYSTEMS, INC.—See HH Global Group Limited; *Int'l*, pg. 3379
PROGRESSIVE COMMUNICATIONS INTERNATIONAL—See Taylor Corporation; *U.S. Private*, pg. 3939
RD&G HOLDINGS CORPORATION; *U.S. Private*, pg. 3362
REPROFLEX VIETNAM LIMITED COMPANY—See Matthews International Corporation; *U.S. Public*, pg. 1400
RX TECHNOLOGY CORP.—See Cenveo, Inc.; *U.S. Private*, pg. 835
RYONET CORP.; *U.S. Private*, pg. 3511
SAFECOM UK LIMITED—See Microsoft Corporation; *U.S. Public*, pg. 1443
SCREENED IMAGES, INC.—See HH Global Group Limited; *Int'l*, pg. 3379
SCREEN TRYCK AB—See Bergman & Beving AB; *Int'l*, pg. 980
SERIGRAPH, INC.; *U.S. Private*, pg. 3613
SHARPRINT; *U.S. Private*, pg. 3627
SHERRY MANUFACTURING CO. INC.; *U.S. Private*, pg. 3634
SHUMANI MILLS COMMUNICATIONS (PTY) LTD.—See Caxton and CTP Publishers and Printers Ltd.; *Int'l*, pg. 1363
SIA PLOCKMATIC—See Grimaldi Industri AB; *Int'l*, pg. 3086
SPARTAN PRODUCTS, LLC—See Vulcan Materials Company; *U.S. Public*, pg. 2314
SPECIALTY GRAPHIC IMAGING ASSOCIATION; *U.S. Private*, pg. 3749
SUPERIOR IMAGING GROUP, INC.—See Vomela Specialty Company; *U.S. Private*, pg. 4412
TAINOL, S.A.—See American CyberSystems, Inc.; *U.S. Private*, pg. 230
TATEX INC.—See Taylor Corporation; *U.S. Private*, pg. 3939
TEAM IP.COM; *U.S. Private*, pg. 3949
TENNESSEE VALLEY SIGN & PRINTING, INC.; *U.S. Private*, pg. 3968
T ENTERPRISES, INC.; *U.S. Private*, pg. 3909
THAI CUBIC TECHNOLOGY CO., LTD.—See Cubic Korea INC.; *Int'l*, pg. 1875
TRAU & LOEVNER INCORPORATED; *U.S. Private*, pg. 4212
TREND OFFSET PRINTING SERVICES - SOUTHWEST DIVISION—See Mittera Group, Inc.; *U.S. Private*, pg. 2752
UNDERGROUND PRINTING; *U.S. Private*, pg. 4279
UNITY PRINTING CO., INC.; *U.S. Private*, pg. 4303
VAUGHN PRINTERS INCORPORATED—See Cenveo, Inc.; *U.S. Private*, pg. 835
VINCENT PRINTING COMPANY INCORPORATED; *U.S. Private*, pg. 4385
VISTAPRINT AUSTRALIA PTY LTD—See Cimpress plc; *Int'l*, pg. 1609
VOLT ROAD BORING CORP.—See American CyberSystems, Inc.; *U.S. Private*, pg. 230
WESTERN GRAPHICS & DATA—See Taylor Corporation; *U.S. Private*, pg. 3939
WETZEL GMBH—See Matthews International Corporation; *U.S. Public*, pg. 1401
WORLD WIDE LINE, INC.—See Gold Bond Inc.; *U.S. Private*, pg. 1727

323117 — BOOKS PRINTING

ACADEMY PRESS PLC.; *Int'l*, pg. 77
BANG PRINTING - VALENCIA—See Bang Printing; *U.S. Private*, pg. 465
BERRYVILLE GRAPHICS INC.—See Bertelsmann SE & Co. KGaA; *Int'l*, pg. 990
BINDAGRAPHICS SOUTH, INC.—See Bindagraphics Inc.; *U.S. Private*, pg. 560
BINDTECH LLC; *U.S. Private*, pg. 560
BOOKMARQUE—See Chevrillon Philippe Industrie; *Int'l*, pg. 1474

CENVEO PUBLISHER SERVICES—See Cenveo, Inc.; *U.S. Private*, pg. 835
CHEVRILLON PHILIPPE INDUSTRIE; *Int'l*, pg. 1474
CPI BLACKPRINT IBERICA, S.L.—See Chevrillon Philippe Industrie; *Int'l*, pg. 1474
CPI GROUP (UK) LTD—See Chevrillon Philippe Industrie; *Int'l*, pg. 1474
CPI MORAVIA BOOKS S.R.O.—See Chevrillon Philippe Industrie; *Int'l*, pg. 1474
DICKINSON PRESS, INC.; *U.S. Private*, pg. 1227
EBSCO INDUSTRIES, INC.; *U.S. Private*, pg. 1324
EDWARDS BROTHERS - CAROLINA—See Edwards Brothers, Inc.; *U.S. Private*, pg. 1341
EDWARDS BROTHERS, INC.; *U.S. Private*, pg. 1341
GEYER PRINTING COMPANY, INC.—See Chatham Asset Management, LLC; *U.S. Private*, pg. 862
GRAPHICS EAST, INC.—See Detroit Legal News Company; *U.S. Public*, pg. 657
THE HF GROUP LLC - BOOK PARTNER DIVISION—See The HF Group LLC; *U.S. Private*, pg. 4052
HOSTER BINDERY, INC.—See The HF Group LLC; *U.S. Private*, pg. 4052
KONINKLIJKE WOHRMANN B.V.—See Chevrillon Philippe Industrie; *Int'l*, pg. 1474
LAKESIDE BOOK COMPANY—See Atlas Holdings, LLC; *U.S. Private*, pg. 376
LIGHTNING SOURCE, INC.—See Ingram Industries, Inc.; *U.S. Private*, pg. 2076
MALLOY INC.; *U.S. Private*, pg. 2558
THE MAPLE PRESS COMPANY—See The Maple-Vail Book Manufacturing Group; *U.S. Private*, pg. 4074
THE MAPLE-VAIL BOOK MANUFACTURING GROUP; *U.S. Private*, pg. 4074
MCNAUGHTON & GUNN, INC.; *U.S. Private*, pg. 2643
ODCOMBE PRESS LP—See Apax Partners LLP; *Int'l*, pg. 502
ODCOMBE PRESS LP—See TowerBrook Capital Partners, L.P.; *U.S. Private*, pg. 4195
OGUCHI BOOK BINDING & PRINTING CO., LTD.—See Dai Nippon Printing Co., Ltd.; *Int'l*, pg. 1916
OVERSEAS PRINTING CORPORATION—See HH Global Group Limited; *Int'l*, pg. 3379
THE P.A. HUTCHISON COMPANY; *U.S. Private*, pg. 4089
POLESTAR CHROMOWORKS LIMITED—See Sun Capital Partners, Inc.; *U.S. Private*, pg. 3862
POLESTAR PURNELL LIMITED—See Sun Capital Partners, Inc.; *U.S. Private*, pg. 3862
PORT CITY PRESS, INC.—See Cenveo, Inc.; *U.S. Private*, pg. 835
PUBLISHERS' GRAPHICS, LLC; *U.S. Private*, pg. 3301
PUBLISHERS PRESS, LLC—See Atlas Holdings, LLC; *U.S. Private*, pg. 377
R.D. MANUFACTURING CORPORATION—See RDA Holding Co.; *U.S. Private*, pg. 3363
REVAI NYOMEDA—See Sun Capital Partners, Inc.; *U.S. Private*, pg. 3862
ROSE PRINTING COMPANY, INC.; *U.S. Private*, pg. 3481
R.R. DONNELLEY MANUFACTURING—See Chatham Asset Management, LLC; *U.S. Private*, pg. 865
R.R. DONNELLEY & SONS CO.—See Chatham Asset Management, LLC; *U.S. Private*, pg. 864
R.R. DONNELLEY & SONS CO.—See Chatham Asset Management, LLC; *U.S. Private*, pg. 864
R.R. DONNELLEY & SONS CO.—See Chatham Asset Management, LLC; *U.S. Private*, pg. 865
R.R. DONNELLEY—See Chatham Asset Management, LLC; *U.S. Private*, pg. 864
R.R. DONNELLEY—See Chatham Asset Management, LLC; *U.S. Private*, pg. 864
R.R. DONNELLEY—See Chatham Asset Management, LLC; *U.S. Private*, pg. 864
SENTINEL PRINTING CO., INC.—See Bang Printing; *U.S. Private*, pg. 465
SHIPWRECK HERITAGE PRESS LLC—See Odyssey Marine Exploration, Inc.; *U.S. Public*, pg. 1564
SOURCEBOOKS, INC.; *U.S. Private*, pg. 3718
SPV-DRUCK GESELLSCHAFT M.B.H—See Erste Group Bank AG; *Int'l*, pg. 2499
VERSA PRESS, INC.; *U.S. Private*, pg. 4369
VICKS LITHOGRAPH & PRINTING; *U.S. Private*, pg. 4377
WALSWORTH PUBLISHING COMPANY, INC. - MARCELINE PRINTING AND BINDERY FACILITY—See Walsworth Publishing Company, Inc.; *U.S. Private*, pg. 4433
WALSWORTH PUBLISHING COMPANY, INC. - SAINT JOSEPH PRINTING AND BINDERY FACILITY—See Walsworth Publishing Company, Inc.; *U.S. Private*, pg. 4433
WEBCRAFTERS INC.; *U.S. Private*, pg. 4464
WORZALLA, INC.—See CJK Group, Inc.; *U.S. Private*, pg. 909

323120 — SUPPORT ACTIVITIES FOR PRINTING

360 IMAGING INC.—See Seaman Paper Company of Massachusetts Inc.; *U.S. Private*, pg. 3585
AGFA GRAPHICS NV—See Agfa-Gevaert N.V.; *Int'l*, pg. 208
AMSKY TECHNOLOGY CO., LTD.; *Int'l*, pg. 441

N.A.I.C.S. INDEX

324110 — PETROLEUM REFINERIE...

ANOCOIL CORPORATION; *U.S. Private*, pg. 285
ARC PHILADELPHIA—See ARC DOCUMENT SOLUTIONS, INC.; *U.S. Public*, pg. 179
ASML KOREA CO., LTD.—See ASML Holding N.V.; *Int'l*, pg. 627
ASML (TIANJIN) CO. LTD.—See ASML Holding N.V.; *Int'l*, pg. 627
ASML US, INC.—See ASML Holding N.V.; *Int'l*, pg. 627
BANC STATEMENTS, INC. (BSI); *U.S. Private*, pg. 464
BELL & BAIN LTD.; *Int'l*, pg. 965
BINDAGRAPHICS INC.; *U.S. Private*, pg. 560
BLOOMING COLOR, INC.; *U.S. Private*, pg. 584
BOUND TO STAY BOUND BOOKS INC.; *U.S. Private*, pg. 623
BRADY COMPANY INDIA PRIVATE LIMITED—See Brady Corporation; *U.S. Public*, pg. 378
BRANDMARK CREATIVE INC.—See Winbrook Inc.; *U.S. Private*, pg. 4533
CANADIAN BANK NOTE COMPANY LIMITED; *Int'l*, pg. 1282
CANADIAN BANK NOTE DESIGN INC.—See Canadian Bank Note Company Limited; *Int'l*, pg. 1282
CBN LOTTERY GROUP—See Canadian Bank Note Company Limited; *Int'l*, pg. 1282
CFC PRINT SOLUTIONS; *U.S. Private*, pg. 843
CHOICE DEVELOPMENT, INC.; *Int'l*, pg. 1577
CIRCLEPRINTERS HOLDING BV; *Int'l*, pg. 1617
COLERIDGE DESIGN & IMAGING, INC.—See Greystone Graphics, Inc.; *U.S. Private*, pg. 1786
COLOR OPTICS INC.—See Atlas Holdings, LLC; *U.S. Private*, pg. 376
COMPUTER COMPOSITION OF CANADA LP—See Stagwell, Inc.; *U.S. Public*, pg. 1926
CONTRACT CONVERTING LLC; *U.S. Private*, pg. 1032
CREATIVE LABEL INC.; *U.S. Private*, pg. 1089
DAVID DOBBS ENTERPRISES INC.; *U.S. Private*, pg. 1169
DESK TOP GRAPHICS INC.; *U.S. Private*, pg. 1215
DOBBS APPAREL—See David Dobbs Enterprises Inc.; *U.S. Private*, pg. 1169
DOBBS BUSINESS PRODUCTS—See David Dobbs Enterprises Inc.; *U.S. Private*, pg. 1169
DOME PUBLISHING COMPANY, INC.; *U.S. Private*, pg. 1255
DPV DEUTSCHER PRESSEVERTRIEB GMBH—See Bertelsmann SE & Co. KGaA; *Int'l*, pg. 992
DYNIC (HK) LTD.—See Dynic Corporation; *Int'l*, pg. 2242
ECKHART & COMPANY, INC.—See BindTech LLC; *U.S. Private*, pg. 560
EPRINT GROUP LIMITED; *Int'l*, pg. 2465
EVADIX SA; *Int'l*, pg. 2560
FILMOLUX CO., LTD.—See Blue Cap AG; *Int'l*, pg. 1067
FILMOLUX SARL—See Blue Cap AG; *Int'l*, pg. 1067
FRAMOS ELECTRONICS LTD.—See FRAMOS GmbH; *Int'l*, pg. 2759
FRAMOS FRANCE SA—See FRAMOS GmbH; *Int'l*, pg. 2759
FRAMOS ITALIA SRL—See FRAMOS GmbH; *Int'l*, pg. 2759
FRAMOS TECHNOLOGIES INC.—See FRAMOS GmbH; *Int'l*, pg. 2759
G6 MATERIALS CORP.; *U.S. Public*, pg. 894
GANNETT PUBLISHING SERVICES, LLC—See Gannett Co., Inc.; *U.S. Public*, pg. 897
GENERAL BOOKBINDING COMPANY—See The HF Group LLC; *U.S. Private*, pg. 4052
GIESECKE & DEVRIENT AMERICA, INC.—See Giesecke & Devrient GmbH; *Int'l*, pg. 2969
GOODTECH GERMANY GMBH—See Goodtech ASA; *Int'l*, pg. 3041
GRAPHIC COMMUNICATIONS UK—See Clayton, Dubilier & Rice, LLC; *U.S. Private*, pg. 928
HAGADONE PRINTING COMPANY INC.—See The Hagadone Corporation; *U.S. Private*, pg. 4041
HAWAII LIBRARY BINDERY INC.—See The HF Group LLC; *U.S. Private*, pg. 4052
THE HF GROUP LLC; *U.S. Private*, pg. 4052
HOAG & SONS BOOK BINDERY INC.—See The HF Group LLC; *U.S. Private*, pg. 4052
HUNG HING PRINTING GROUP LIMITED; *Int'l*, pg. 3535
HUSTON-PATTERSON CORPORATION—See Radial Equity Partners LP; *U.S. Private*, pg. 3343
I.D. IMAGES LLC; *U.S. Private*, pg. 2027
INNERWORKINGS, INC. - CINCINNATI OFFICE—See HH Global Group Limited; *Int'l*, pg. 3378
INNERWORKINGS, INC. - EAST BRUNSWICK OFFICE—See HH Global Group Limited; *Int'l*, pg. 3379
INNERWORKINGS, INC.—See HH Global Group Limited; *Int'l*, pg. 3378
INTERNATIONAL PAPER COMPANY—See International Paper Company; *U.S. Public*, pg. 1156
IR ENGRAVING LLC—See Standex International; *U.S. Public*, pg. 1930
IRIDIO COLOR SERVICE INC.—See Chatham Asset Management, LLC; *U.S. Private*, pg. 863
JOHN C. OTTO COMPANY, INC.—See Chatham Asset Management, LLC; *U.S. Private*, pg. 862
KGP GROUP, INC.; *U.S. Private*, pg. 2301
KINGSPORT BOOK, INC.—See Signet LLC; *U.S. Private*, pg. 3650

KREBER L.L.C.—See Kreber Graphics Inc.; *U.S. Private*, pg. 2350
LASER IMAGE CORPORATION—See Didit.com, Inc.; *U.S. Private*, pg. 1228
LIBRARY BINDING SERVICE INC.; *U.S. Private*, pg. 2447
LTI PRINTING, INC.—See Max Solutions Inc.; *U.S. Private*, pg. 2617
MACDERMID AUTOTYPE (ASIA) PTE LTD—See Element Solutions Inc.; *U.S. Public*, pg. 726
MACDERMID AUTOTYPE INC—See Element Solutions Inc.; *U.S. Public*, pg. 727
MACDERMID AUTOTYPE LTD—See Element Solutions Inc.; *U.S. Public*, pg. 727
MAESTRO PRINT MANAGEMENT LLC; *U.S. Private*, pg. 2544
MARION DAILY REPUBLICAN; *U.S. Private*, pg. 2576
MATTHEWS INTERNATIONAL CORP. - GRAPHICS IMAGING—See Matthews International Corporation; *U.S. Public*, pg. 1400
MATTHEWS PACKAGING GRAPHICS & DESIGN—See Matthews International Corporation; *U.S. Public*, pg. 1400
MATTHEWS PACKAGING GRAPHICS—See Matthews International Corporation; *U.S. Public*, pg. 1400
MCARA PRINTING—See Canadian Bank Note Company Limited; *Int'l*, pg. 1282
MI5 PRINT & DIGITAL COMMUNICATIONS; *U.S. Private*, pg. 2696
MICRODYNAMICS GROUP; *U.S. Private*, pg. 2703
MID ATLANTIC BOOK BINDERY INC.—See The HF Group LLC; *U.S. Private*, pg. 4052
MOUNT ROYAL PRINTING & COMMUNICATIONS, INC.; *U.S. Private*, pg. 2798
MOVAD, LLC—See Strata Graphics, Inc.; *U.S. Private*, pg. 3833
MULTI PACKAGING SOLUTIONS, INC. - ALLEGAN; *U.S. Private*, pg. 2812
NORTH CENTRAL DIGITAL SYSTEMS, INC.—See Wells Fargo & Company; *U.S. Public*, pg. 2344
OCE-HUNGARIA KFT.—See Canon Inc.; *Int'l*, pg. 1294
OLYMPUS GROUP; *U.S. Private*, pg. 3012
PAPERPLUS—See Clayton, Dubilier & Rice, LLC; *U.S. Private*, pg. 929
PERFORMANCE PRESS, INC.; *U.S. Private*, pg. 3149
PERRY PRINTING CO.—See Hot Frog Print Media LLC; *U.S. Private*, pg. 1988
PIGUET GRAPHIC & PRINTS COMPANY LIMITED—See Hung Hing Printing Group Limited; *Int'l*, pg. 3535
PRINTALL AS—See AS Ekspress Grupp; *Int'l*, pg. 590
PRINT PLANNER (BEIJING) CO., LTD.—See A-Smart Holdings Ltd.; *Int'l*, pg. 20
PROFESSIONAL PUBLICATIONS, INC.—See Graham Holdings Company; *U.S. Public*, pg. 956
PROMISE NETWORK PRINTING LIMITED—See eprint Group Limited; *Int'l*, pg. 2465
QUANTUM COLOR GRAPHICS LLC; *U.S. Private*, pg. 3322
RAINMAKER DOCUMENT TECHNOLOGIES, INC.—See Sentinel Capital Partners, L.L.C.; *U.S. Private*, pg. 3609
REPRO-BUSEK GMBH & CO. KG—See Matthews International Corporation; *U.S. Public*, pg. 1399
REPROSERVICE EURODIGITAL GMBH—See Matthews International Corporation; *U.S. Public*, pg. 1399
ROSWELL BOOKBINDING CORP.—See Signet LLC; *U.S. Private*, pg. 3650
RUDOLF REPROFLEX GMBH & CO. KG—See Matthews International Corporation; *U.S. Public*, pg. 1399
SAN VAL INC.—See GL Group, Inc.; *U.S. Private*, pg. 1704
SCHAWK ASIA PACIFIC PTE. LTD.—See Matthews International Corporation; *U.S. Public*, pg. 1400
SCHAWK INDIA LTD.—See Matthews International Corporation; *U.S. Public*, pg. 1400
SCHOLLER GMBH & CO. KG—See Matthews International Corporation; *U.S. Public*, pg. 1400
SEED PRINT—See Excelsior Printing Company; *U.S. Private*, pg. 1446
SGS INTERNATIONAL, INC.—See HPS Investment Partners, LLC; *U.S. Private*, pg. 1997
SHERIDAN DEXTER INC.—See CJK Group, Inc.; *U.S. Private*, pg. 909
SHUMAN-HERITAGE PRINTING CO. LLC—See Mount Royal Printing & Communications, Inc.; *U.S. Private*, pg. 2798
SOUTHEAST LIBRARY BINDERY INC.—See The HF Group LLC; *U.S. Private*, pg. 4052
SOUTHERN GRAPHIC SYSTEMS, INC. - FLEXO DIVISON—See HPS Investment Partners, LLC; *U.S. Private*, pg. 1997
SOUTHERN GRAPHIC SYSTEMS, INC.—See HPS Investment Partners, LLC; *U.S. Private*, pg. 1997
SOUTHERN LITHOPLATE, INC.; *U.S. Private*, pg. 3732
SOUTHWEST PLASTIC BINDING COMPANY; *U.S. Private*, pg. 3740
SPECTRAGRAPHIC NEW ENGLAND—See Spectra Group Ltd.; *U.S. Private*, pg. 3751
STANDEX INTERNATIONAL GMBH—See Standex International; *U.S. Public*, pg. 1931
STANDEX INTERNATIONAL S.R.L. - INTERNATIONAL ENGRAVING DIVISION—See Standex International; *U.S. Public*, pg. 1930
THE STEVENSON COLOR COMPANY, INC.—See HPS Investment Partners, LLC; *U.S. Private*, pg. 1997
STEVENSON THE COLOR COMPANY; *U.S. Private*, pg. 3810
STRAFFORD PUBLICATIONS, INC.—See Francisco Partners Management, LP; *U.S. Public*, pg. 1588
SUPERIOR PRESS, INC.; *U.S. Private*, pg. 3879
SYMPRES CO., LTD.—See EQT AB; *Int'l*, pg. 2467
TEK LABEL AND PRINTING, INC.—See Ares Management Corporation; *U.S. Public*, pg. 191
THOMAS TECHNOLOGY SOLUTIONS INC.—See Thomas Publishing Company LLC; *U.S. Public*, pg. 4157
TICKETS PLUS, INC.—See Intelli-Mark Technologies, Inc.; *U.S. Private*, pg. 2105
TRUMBULL PRINTING INC.—See Hersam Acorn Newspapers LLC; *U.S. Private*, pg. 1926
TSI GRAPHICS INC.; *U.S. Private*, pg. 4253
UNISOURCE CANADA INC.—See Clayton, Dubilier & Rice, LLC; *U.S. Private*, pg. 929
UNIVERSAL ENGRAVING INC.; *U.S. Private*, pg. 4305
WISCONSIN TECHNICOLOR LLC; *U.S. Private*, pg. 4549
XPRESS PRINT (SHENYANG) CO., LTD.—See A-Smart Holdings Ltd.; *Int'l*, pg. 20
ZENFOLIO, INC.—See Centre Lane Partners, LLC; *U.S. Private*, pg. 828
ZHUHAI BROTHER INDUSTRIES CO., LTD.—See Brother Industries, Ltd.; *Int'l*, pg. 1198

324110 — PETROLEUM REFINERIES

ABU DHABI OIL REFINING COMPANY—See Abu Dhabi National Oil Company; *Int'l*, pg. 73
AEKYUNG HONGKONG CO., LTD.—See AK Holdings, Inc.; *Int'l*, pg. 259
AGERATEC AB—See Alfa Laval AB; *Int'l*, pg. 308
AGIP S.P.A.—See Eni S.p.A.; *Int'l*, pg. 2436
AKTOBE REFINERY LLP; *Int'l*, pg. 267
ALFA, S.A.B. DE C.V.; *Int'l*, pg. 312
ALON BRANDS, INC.—See Delek Group Ltd.; *Int'l*, pg. 2011
ALON USA ENERGY, INC.—See Delek Group Ltd.; *Int'l*, pg. 2011
ALON USA PARTNERS, LP—See Delek Group Ltd.; *Int'l*, pg. 2011
ALPEK, S.A. DE C.V.—See ALFA, S.A.B. de C.V.; *Int'l*, pg. 313
AMERICAN REFINING GROUP INC.; *U.S. Private*, pg. 245
AMERIGAS FINANCE CORP.—See UGI Corporation; *U.S. Public*, pg. 2221
AMPOL LIMITED; *Int'l*, pg. 436
ANADARKO GATHERING COMPANY LLC—See Western Midstream Partners, LP; *U.S. Public*, pg. 2356
APOLLO (THAILAND) CO., LTD.—See Idemitsu Kosan Co., Ltd.; *Int'l*, pg. 3590
ASBURY GRAPHITE INC. OF CALIFORNIA—See Great Mill Rock LLC; *U.S. Private*, pg. 1765
ASHLAND CHEMICAL HISPANIA, S.L.—See Ashland Inc.; *U.S. Public*, pg. 211
ASHLAND SPECIALTIES SOUTH AFRICA PROPRIETARY LIMITED—See Ashland Inc.; *U.S. Public*, pg. 212
ASTRON ENERGY—See Glencore plc; *Int'l*, pg. 2990
ATTOCK PETROLEUM LIMITED—See Attock Refinery Ltd; *Int'l*, pg. 697
ATTOCK REFINERY LTD; *Int'l*, pg. 697
AXION ENERGY—See BP plc; *Int'l*, pg. 1131
AXION ENERGY—See Bridas Corporation; *Int'l*, pg. 1152
THE BANGCHAK BIOFUEL CO., LTD.—See Bangchak Corporation Public Company Limited; *Int'l*, pg. 832
BARD HOLDING, INC.; *U.S. Private*, pg. 473
BATON ROUGE FRACTIONATORS LLC—See The Williams Companies, Inc.; *U.S. Public*, pg. 2142
BHARAT OMAN REFINERIES LIMITED—See Bharat Petroleum Corporation Limited; *Int'l*, pg. 1011
BHARAT PETROLEUM CORPORATION LIMITED - KOCHI REFINERY—See Bharat Petroleum Corporation Limited; *Int'l*, pg. 1011
BHARAT PETROLEUM CORPORATION LIMITED; *Int'l*, pg. 1011
BHARAT SHELL LIMITED—See Bharat Petroleum Corporation Limited; *Int'l*, pg. 1011
BIG RIVER PROPANE SERVICE LLC—See Big River Oil Company Inc.; *U.S. Private*, pg. 554
BIG WEST OIL, LLC—See FJ Management, Inc.; *U.S. Private*, pg. 1538
BIODIESEL OF LAS VEGAS INC.—See New-Com Inc.; *U.S. Private*, pg. 2913
BIOGAS HERZBERG GMBH & CO. KG—See EnviTec Biogas AG; *Int'l*, pg. 2455
BIOGAS NIEHEIM GMBH & CO. KG—See EnviTec Biogas AG; *Int'l*, pg. 2455
BLACK EAGLE LLC—See HF Sinclair Corporation; *U.S. Public*, pg. 1033
BP AMERICA - WEST—See BP plc; *Int'l*, pg. 1126
BP CHEMICALS INC.—See BP plc; *Int'l*, pg. 1126
BP COMPANY NORTH AMERICA INC.—See BP plc; *Int'l*, pg. 1128

324110 — PETROLEUM REFINERIE...

BP CORPORATION NORTH AMERICA INC.—See BP plc; *Int'l*, pg. 1126
BP CORPORATION NORTH AMERICA INC.—See BP plc; *Int'l*, pg. 1126
BP FRANCE SA—See BP plc; *Int'l*, pg. 1129
BP HUSKY REFINERY—See BP plc; *Int'l*, pg. 1127
BP HUSKY REFINERY—See Cenovus Energy Inc.; *Int'l*, pg. 1401
BP MEXICO S.A. DE C.V.—See BP plc; *Int'l*, pg. 1129
BP MIDDLE EAST LTD.—See BP plc; *Int'l*, pg. 1129
BP OIL CO.—See BP plc; *Int'l*, pg. 1127
BP OIL REFINERIA DE CASTELLON, S.A.U.—See BP plc; *Int'l*, pg. 1128
BP OIL U.K.—See BP plc; *Int'l*, pg. 1129
BP PIPELINES NORTH AMERICA INC.—See BP plc; *Int'l*, pg. 1126
BP PRODUCTS NORTH AMERICA INC.—See BP plc; *Int'l*, pg. 1127
BP REFINING & PETROCHEMICALS GMBH—See BP plc; *Int'l*, pg. 1131
BPRL VENTURES BV—See Bharat Petroleum Corporation Limited; *Int'l*, pg. 1011
BP SOUTHERN AFRICA PTY LTD.—See BP plc; *Int'l*, pg. 1129
BP WHITING REFINERY—See BP plc; *Int'l*, pg. 1127
BULGARIAN PETROLEUM REFINERY LTD—See Chimimport AD; *Int'l*, pg. 1479
BYCO PETROLEUM PAKISTAN LIMITED; *Int'l*, pg. 1234
CALIFORNIA RESOURCES ELK HILLS, LLC—See California Resources Corporation; *U.S. Public*, pg. 423
CALS REFINERIES LIMITED; *Int'l*, pg. 1265
CALTEX AUSTRALIA CUSTODIANS PTY LTD—See Ampol Limited; *Int'l*, pg. 436
CALUMET DICKINSON REFINING, LLC—See Calumet, Inc.; *U.S. Public*, pg. 425
CALUMET KARNS CITY REFINING, LLC—See Calumet, Inc.; *U.S. Public*, pg. 425
CAMECO FUEL MANUFACTURING INC—See Cameco Corporation; *Int'l*, pg. 1270
CASTLE FUELS INC.; *Int'l*, pg. 1357
CASTROL (SHENZHEN) CO. LTD.—See BP plc; *Int'l*, pg. 1130
CENTURION PIPELINE LP, INC.—See Occidental Petroleum Corporation; *U.S. Public*, pg. 1561
CHALMETTE REFINING, L.L.C.—See PBF Energy Inc.; *U.S. Public*, pg. 1657
CHANNEL INFRASTRUCTURE NZ LIMITED; *Int'l*, pg. 1446
CHEMCHINA PETROCHEMICAL CO., LTD—See China National Chemical Corporation; *Int'l*, pg. 1526
CHEMOIL ENERGY PTE LIMITED—See Glencore plc; *Int'l*, pg. 2990
CHEVRON, INC.—See Miller Industries, Inc.; *U.S. Public*, pg. 1446
CHEVRON INTERNATIONAL PTE. LTD.—See Chevron Corporation; *U.S. Public*, pg. 486
CHIMCOMPLEX S.A. BORZESTI; *Int'l*, pg. 1479
CHINA PETROCHEMICAL DEVELOPMENT CORP. - DASHE PLANT—See China Petrochemical Development Corp.; *Int'l*, pg. 1540
CHINA PETROCHEMICAL DEVELOPMENT CORP. - HSIAOKANG PLANT—See China Petrochemical Development Corp.; *Int'l*, pg. 1540
CHINA PETROCHEMICAL DEVELOPMENT CORP. - TOUFEN PLANT—See China Petrochemical Development Corp.; *Int'l*, pg. 1540
CHRYSAOR PRODUCTION (U.K.) LIMITED—See Harbour Energy plc; *Int'l*, pg. 3271
CHS MCPHERSON REFINERY INC.—See CHS INC.; *U.S. Public*, pg. 491
CINCO INVESTMENTS PLC; *Int'l*, pg. 1609
CONCERN BELNEFTEKHIM; *Int'l*, pg. 1764
CONOCOPHILLIPS AUSTRIA GES, M.B.H.—See Conoco-Phillips; *U.S. Public*, pg. 568
CONOCOPHILLIPS; *U.S. Public*, pg. 568
CONTINENTAL REFINING COMPANY; *U.S. Private*, pg. 1031
COSMO OIL COMPANY, LIMITED—See Cosmo Energy Holdings Co., Ltd.; *Int'l*, pg. 1811
COSMO PETRO SERVICE CO., LTD.—See Cosmo Energy Holdings Co., Ltd.; *Int'l*, pg. 1811
COSMO TECHNO YOKKAICHI CO., LTD.—See Cosmo Energy Holdings Co., Ltd.; *Int'l*, pg. 1812
COUNTRYMARK ENERGY RESOURCES, LLC—See Countrymark Cooperative, Inc.; *U.S. Private*, pg. 1067
CPC CORPORATION; *Int'l*, pg. 1823
CROWN CENTRAL LLC—See Rosemore Inc.; *U.S. Private*, pg. 3483
CTAS CORPORATION—See CTCI Corporation; *Int'l*, pg. 1870
CTCI SINGAPORE PTE. LTD.—See CTCI Corporation; *Int'l*, pg. 1870
CVR REFINING, LP—See Icahn Enterprises L.P.; *U.S. Public*, pg. 1084
DAISEKI CO. LTD.; *Int'l*, pg. 1941
DALIAN IDEMITSU CHINAOIL CO., LTD.—See Idemitsu Kosan Co., Ltd.; *Int'l*, pg. 3590
DAQING ZHONGLAN PETROCHEMICAL CO LTD—See China National Chemical Corporation; *Int'l*, pg. 1526

DELAWARE CITY REFINING COMPANY LLC—See PBF Energy Inc.; *U.S. Public*, pg. 1657
DELEK REFINING, INC.—See Delek Group Ltd.; *Int'l*, pg. 2011
DELEK REFINING, LTD.—See Delek Group Ltd.; *Int'l*, pg. 2012
DELEK RENEWABLES, LLC—See Delek Group Ltd.; *Int'l*, pg. 2012
DEUTSCHE BP AG—See BP plc; *Int'l*, pg. 1131
DEZHOU SHIHUA CHEMICAL CO., LTD.—See China National Chemical Corporation; *Int'l*, pg. 1527
DIALOG GROUP BERHAD; *Int'l*, pg. 2104
DIAXON ABEE—See HELLENiQ ENERGY Holdings S.A.; *Int'l*, pg. 3334
ECO HUILE SA—See Aurea, S.A.; *Int'l*, pg. 707
ECOPETROL S.A.; *Int'l*, pg. 2298
ELPET VALKANIKI SA—See HELLENiQ ENERGY Holdings S.A.; *Int'l*, pg. 3334
ENI AUSTRIA MARKETING GMBH—See Eni S.p.A.; *Int'l*, pg. 2437
ENI DEUTSCHLAND GMBH—See Eni S.p.A.; *Int'l*, pg. 2437
ENI USA R&M CO INC—See Eni S.p.A.; *Int'l*, pg. 2438
ENTERPRISE PRODUCTS OPERATING LLC—See Enterprise Products Partners L.P.; *U.S. Public*, pg. 778
ENVITEC BIOGAS BALTICS SIA—See EnviTec Biogas AG; *Int'l*, pg. 2455
ENVITEC BIOGAS CENTRAL EUROPE S.R.O.—See EnviTec Biogas AG; *Int'l*, pg. 2455
ENVITEC BIOGAS FRANCE S.A.R.L.—See EnviTec Biogas AG; *Int'l*, pg. 2455
ENVITEC BIOGAS NEDERLAND B.V.—See EnviTec Biogas AG; *Int'l*, pg. 2455
ENVITEC BIOGAS ROMANIA S.R.L—See EnviTec Biogas AG; *Int'l*, pg. 2455
ENVITEC BIOGAS SOUTH EAST EUROPE LTD.—See EnviTec Biogas AG; *Int'l*, pg. 2455
ENVITEC GREEN POWER GMBH & CO. KG—See EnviTec Biogas AG; *Int'l*, pg. 2455
ENVITEC GREEN POWER VERWALTUNGS GMBH—See EnviTec Biogas AG; *Int'l*, pg. 2455
EQUINOR REFINING DENMARK A/S—See Equinor ASA; *Int'l*, pg. 2484
EQUINOR TANZANIA AS—See Equinor ASA; *Int'l*, pg. 2484
EQUINOR USA ONSHORE PROPERTIES INC.—See Equinor ASA; *Int'l*, pg. 2485
ERGON, INC.; *U.S. Private*, pg. 1417
ERGON REFINING, INC.—See Ergon, Inc.; *U.S. Private*, pg. 1418
ERGON WEST VIRGINIA, INC.—See Ergon, Inc.; *U.S. Private*, pg. 1418
ESSO SOCIETE ANONYME FRANCAISE—See Exxon Mobil Corporation; *U.S. Public*, pg. 814
ETERNAL ELECTRONIC MATERIAL (THAILAND) CO., LTD.—See Eternal Materials Co., Ltd.; *Int'l*, pg. 2520
ETFT ENVITEC FILTRATION TECHNIK GMBH—See EnviTec Biogas AG; *Int'l*, pg. 2455
EXXONMOBIL ASIA PACIFIC PTE LTD.—See Exxon Mobil Corporation; *U.S. Public*, pg. 814
EXXONMOBIL CHEMICAL OPERATIONS PRIVATE LIMITED—See Exxon Mobil Corporation; *U.S. Public*, pg. 814
EXXONMOBIL OIL CORPORATION—See Exxon Mobil Corporation; *U.S. Public*, pg. 815
EXXON MOBIL PETROLEUM CHEMICAL—See Exxon Mobil Corporation; *U.S. Public*, pg. 814
EXXONMOBIL REFINING & SUPPLY COMPANY—See Exxon Mobil Corporation; *U.S. Public*, pg. 816
EXXONMOBIL REFINING & SUPPLY—See Exxon Mobil Corporation; *U.S. Public*, pg. 816
EXXONMOBIL UK LIMITED—See Exxon Mobil Corporation; *U.S. Public*, pg. 816
FABRICATION & CONSTRUCTION SERVICES, LP; *U.S. Private*, pg. 1459
FORMOSAN UNION CHEMICAL CORP.; *Int'l*, pg. 2736
FREEHOLD RESOURCES LTD.—See Freehold Royalties Ltd.; *Int'l*, pg. 2770
FREUDENBERG NOK-SEALANT PRODUCTS—See Freudenberg SE; *Int'l*, pg. 2788
FRONTIER EL DORADO REFINERY COMPANY—See HF Sinclair Corporation; *U.S. Public*, pg. 1033
FRONTIER REFINING, INC.—See HF Sinclair Corporation; *U.S. Public*, pg. 1033
GARDNER OIL COMPANY INC.; *U.S. Private*, pg. 1644
GE TRANSPORTATION—See Westinghouse Air Brake Technologies Corporation; *U.S. Public*, pg. 2358
GOENERGY COMPANY LIMITED—See GOIL PLC; *Int'l*, pg. 3022
GOLDEN WEST REFINING COMPANY—See Thrifty Oil Co.; *U.S. Private*, pg. 4165
GS CALTEX CORPORATION—See GS Holdings Corp.; *Int'l*, pg. 3141
GS ECOMETAL CO., LTD.—See GS Holdings Corp.; *Int'l*, pg. 3142
GUNVOR RAFFINERIE INGOLSTADT GMBH—See Gunvor Group Ltd.; *Int'l*, pg. 3185
HAOHUA JUNHUA GROUP CO., LTD.—See China National Chemical Corporation; *Int'l*, pg. 1527
HBOIL JSC; *Int'l*, pg. 3297

HEILONGJIANG CHEMICAL GROUP CO., LTD.—See China National Chemical Corporation; *Int'l*, pg. 1528
HEP EL DORADO LLC—See HF Sinclair Corporation; *U.S. Public*, pg. 1033
HOKURIKU DAISEKI CO., LTD.—See Daiseki Co. Ltd.; *Int'l*, pg. 1941
HOLLYCORP AVIATION, LLC—See HF Sinclair Corporation; *U.S. Public*, pg. 1034
HOLLYFRONTIER ASPHALT COMPANY LLC—See HF Sinclair Corporation; *U.S. Public*, pg. 1033
HOLLYFRONTIER EL DORADO REFINING LLC—See HF Sinclair Corporation; *U.S. Public*, pg. 1033
HOLLYFRONTIER NAVAJO REFINING LLC—See HF Sinclair Corporation; *U.S. Public*, pg. 1033
HOLLY LOGISTIC SERVICES, L.L.C.—See HF Sinclair Corporation; *U.S. Public*, pg. 1033
HOLLY PETROLEUM, INC.—See HF Sinclair Corporation; *U.S. Public*, pg. 1033
HOLLY REFINING COMMUNICATIONS, INC.—See HF Sinclair Corporation; *U.S. Public*, pg. 1033
HOLLY REFINING & MARKETING COMPANY—See HF Sinclair Corporation; *U.S. Public*, pg. 1033
HOLLY REFINING & MARKETING COMPANY - WOODS CROSS LLC—See HF Sinclair Corporation; *U.S. Public*, pg. 1033
H&R ANZ PTY. LTD.—See H&R KGaA; *Int'l*, pg. 3193
H&R CHEMPHARM (THAILAND) LTD.—See H&R KGaA; *Int'l*, pg. 3193
H&R CHINA (DAXIE) CO., LTD.—See H&R KGaA; *Int'l*, pg. 3193
H&R CHINA (FUSHUN) CO., LTD.—See H&R KGaA; *Int'l*, pg. 3193
H&R CHINA (HONG KONG) CO., LTD.—See H&R KGaA; *Int'l*, pg. 3193
H&R GROUP US, INC.—See H&R KGaA; *Int'l*, pg. 3193
H&R SINGAPORE PTE. LTD.—See H&R KGaA; *Int'l*, pg. 3193
HUNT REFINING COMPANY INC.—See Hunt Consolidated, Inc.; *U.S. Private*, pg. 2008
HYDRODEC NORTH AMERICAN HOLDINGS INC—See Hydrodec Group plc; *Int'l*, pg. 3547
HYTHANE COMPANY LLC—See Eden Innovations Ltd.; *Int'l*, pg. 2306
HYUNDAI OILBANK CO., LTD. - DAESAN REFINERY PLANT—See Hyundai Oilbank Co., Ltd.; *Int'l*, pg. 3560
HYUNDAI OILBANK CO., LTD.; *Int'l*, pg. 3560
HYUNDAI OILBANK SINGAPORE PTE LTD—See Hyundai Oilbank Co., Ltd.; *Int'l*, pg. 3560
IDEMITSU APOLLO CORPORATION—See Idemitsu Kosan Co., Ltd.; *Int'l*, pg. 3590
IDEMITSU KOSAN CO., LTD.; *Int'l*, pg. 3590
IDEMITSU LUBE (SINGAPORE) PTE.LTD.—See Idemitsu Kosan Co., Ltd.; *Int'l*, pg. 3591
IL SEUNG CO., LTD.; *Int'l*, pg. 3613
IMPERIAL OIL, LIMITED PRODUCTS & CHEMICALS DIVISION—See Exxon Mobil Corporation; *U.S. Public*, pg. 816
IMPERIAL OIL LIMITED—See Exxon Mobil Corporation; *U.S. Public*, pg. 816
IMPERIAL OIL LIMITED—See Exxon Mobil Corporation; *U.S. Public*, pg. 816
INDEPENDENCE OILFIELD CHEMICALS LLC—See Innospec Inc.; *U.S. Public*, pg. 1125
INDEPENDENT BELGIAN REFINERY N.V.—See Gunvor Group Ltd.; *Int'l*, pg. 3185
INEOS PARAFORM GMBH & CO. KG—See One Rock Capital Partners, LLC; *U.S. Private*, pg. 3022
INGLESIDE COGENERATION LIMITED PARTNERSHIP—See Occidental Petroleum Corporation; *U.S. Public*, pg. 1561
INNOSPEC FRANCE S.A.—See Innospec Inc.; *U.S. Public*, pg. 1125
INNOSPEC FUEL SPECIALTIES LLC—See Innospec Inc.; *U.S. Public*, pg. 1125
INNOSPEC HELLAS LTD.—See Innospec Inc.; *U.S. Public*, pg. 1125
INTERGULF CORPORATION—See EQT AB; *Int'l*, pg. 2473
ISLAND PETROLEUM, INC.—See Par Pacific Holdings, Inc.; *U.S. Public*, pg. 1636
JASPER OIL, INC.—See AIP, LLC; *U.S. Private*, pg. 136
JAYHAWK PIPELINE, LLC—See CHS INC.; *U.S. Public*, pg. 491
JIA SHI LUBRICANTS TRADING (SHANGHAI) CO., LTD.—See HF Sinclair Corporation; *U.S. Public*, pg. 1034
KANSAI COSMO LOGISTICS CO., LTD.—See Cosmo Energy Holdings Co., Ltd.; *Int'l*, pg. 1812
KAOHSIUNG REFINERY—See CPC Corporation; *Int'l*, pg. 1824
KAUAI PETROLEUM CO., LTD.—See Par Pacific Holdings, Inc.; *U.S. Public*, pg. 1636
KCBX—See Koch Industries, Inc.; *U.S. Private*, pg. 2331
KENTS OIL SERVICE—See MDU Resources Group, Inc.; *U.S. Public*, pg. 1410
KERN OIL & REFINING COMPANY—See Casey Co.; *U.S. Private*, pg. 782
KOCH ASPHALT SOLUTIONS—See Koch Industries, Inc.; *U.S. Private*, pg. 2331

N.A.I.C.S. INDEX

324121 — ASPHALT PAVING MIXT...

KOCH EXPLORATION COMPANY LLC; *U.S. Private*, pg. 2326
KOCH OIL COMPANY—See Koch Industries, Inc.; *U.S. Private*, pg. 2333
KONYA PETROL A.S.—See Bera Holding A.S.; *Int'l*, pg. 978
KUO HORNG CO., LTD.—See Idemitsu Kosan Co., Ltd.; *Int'l*, pg. 3591
LEADING EDGE JET CENTER LLC—See Leading Edge Aviation, Inc.; *U.S. Private*, pg. 2406
LION OIL COMPANY—See Delek Group Ltd.; *Int'l*, pg. 2012
LIQUID MINERALS GROUP LTD.—See Pilot Chemical Company; *U.S. Private*, pg. 3181
LODERS CROKLAAN CANADA INC.—See Bunge Limited; *U.S. Public*, pg. 411
LOREFCO, INC.—See HF Sinclair Corporation; *U.S. Public*, pg. 1034
LOTOS OIL S.A.—See Grupa LOTOS S.A.; *Int'l*, pg. 3117
MARATHON PETROLEUM COMPANY LLC—See Marathon Petroleum Corporation; *U.S. Public*, pg. 1364
MARATHON PETROLEUM COMPANY LLC—See Marathon Petroleum Corporation; *U.S. Public*, pg. 1364
MARATHON PETROLEUM COMPANY LLC—See Marathon Petroleum Corporation; *U.S. Public*, pg. 1364
MARATHON PETROLEUM CORPORATION; *U.S. Public*, pg. 1363
MARKWEST ENERGY PARTNERS, L.P. - CARTHAGE PROCESSING FACILITY—See Marathon Petroleum Corporation; *U.S. Public*, pg. 1364
MOBIL OIL A.G.—See Exxon Mobil Corporation; *U.S. Public*, pg. 814
MONROE ENERGY, LLC—See Delta Air Lines, Inc.; *U.S. Public*, pg. 652
MONTANA REFINING COMPANY INC.—See Calumet, Inc.; *U.S. Public*, pg. 425
MOOSE JAW REFINERY PARTNERSHIP—See Gibson Energy Inc.; *Int'l*, pg. 2963
MURCO PETROLEUM LTD.—See Murphy Oil Corporation; *U.S. Public*, pg. 1487
MURPHY OIL CORPORATION; *U.S. Public*, pg. 1487
MURPHY'S WASTE OIL SERVICE, INC.—See Clean Harbors, Inc.; *U.S. Public*, pg. 510
NAVAJO HOLDINGS, INC.—See HF Sinclair Corporation; *U.S. Public*, pg. 1034
NAVAJO REFINING LP, L.L.C.—See HF Sinclair Corporation; *U.S. Public*, pg. 1034
NETHERLANDS REFINING COMPANY B.V.—See BP plc; *Int'l*, pg. 1129
NEUMIN PRODUCTION COMPANY—See Formosa Plastics Corporation; *Int'l*, pg. 2736
NIIGATA JOINT OIL STOCKPILING CO., LTD—See Idemitsu Kosan Co., Ltd.; *Int'l*, pg. 3592
NIPPON OIL-DHABI—See ENEOS Holdings, Inc.; *Int'l*, pg. 2417
NIPPON OIL FINANCE (NETHERLANDS) B.V.—See ENEOS Holdings, Inc.; *Int'l*, pg. 2417
NIPPON OIL (U.K.) PLC—See ENEOS Holdings, Inc.; *Int'l*, pg. 2417
NIPPON PETROLEUM REFINING CO., LTD.—See ENEOS Holdings, Inc.; *Int'l*, pg. 2417
NK ASPHALT PARTNERS—See HF Sinclair Corporation; *U.S. Public*, pg. 1034
NORTH ATLANTIC REFINING LTD.—See Silverpeak Strategic Partners LP; *U.S. Private*, pg. 3663
NORTHERN PROJECT & CONSTRUCTION DIVISION—See CPC Corporation; *Int'l*, pg. 1824
NORTHERN TIER ENERGY LLC—See Marathon Petroleum Corporation; *U.S. Public*, pg. 1363
OCCIDENTAL CHEMICAL CHILE LIMITADA—See Occidental Petroleum Corporation; *U.S. Public*, pg. 1561
OHGISHIMA OIL TERMINAL CO., LTD.—See Idemitsu Kosan Co., Ltd.; *Int'l*, pg. 3592
OKTA A.D.—See HELLENiQ ENERGY Holdings S.A.; *Int'l*, pg. 3334
OXBOW MIDWEST CALCINING LLC—See Oxbow Corporation; *U.S. Private*, pg. 3056
OXY VINYLS, LP—See Occidental Petroleum Corporation; *U.S. Public*, pg. 1562
PAR HAWAII REFINING, LLC—See Par Pacific Holdings, Inc.; *U.S. Public*, pg. 1636
PATRIOT FUELS BIODIESEL, LLC—See CHS INC.; *U.S. Public*, pg. 492
PAULSBORO REFINING COMPANY LLC—See PBF Energy Inc.; *U.S. Public*, pg. 1657
PBF ENERGY COMPANY LLC—See PBF Energy Inc.; *U.S. Public*, pg. 1657
PBF ENERGY INC.; *U.S. Public*, pg. 1657
PBF ENERGY WESTERN REGION LLC—See PBF Energy Inc.; *U.S. Public*, pg. 1657
PBF FINANCE CORPORATION—See PBF Energy Inc.; *U.S. Public*, pg. 1657
PETRO-CANADA LUBRICANTS INC.—See HF Sinclair Corporation; *U.S. Public*, pg. 1034
PETRO STAR INC.—See Arctic Slope Regional Corporation; *U.S. Private*, pg. 316
PETROTEC AG—See Chevron Corporation; *U.S. Public*, pg. 487
PHILADELPHIA ENERGY SOLUTIONS, LLC—See Energy Transfer LP; *U.S. Public*, pg. 764

POWER SERVICE PRODUCTS, INC.; *U.S. Private*, pg. 3238
PREMIER OIL DO BRASIL PETROLEO E GAS LTDA.—See Harbour Energy plc; *Int'l*, pg. 3271
PREOL, A.S.—See Agrofert Holding, a.s.; *Int'l*, pg. 219
PT HUR SALES INDONESIA—See H&R KGaA; *Int'l*, pg. 3193
PT PACIFIC PALMINDO INDUSTRY—See Hayel Saeed Anam Group of Companies; *Int'l*, pg. 3291
PTT ASAHI CHEMICAL CO., LTD.—See Asahi Kasei Corporation; *Int'l*, pg. 596
QINGDAO ANBANG PETROCHEMICAL CO LTD—See China National Chemical Corporation; *Int'l*, pg. 1526
RAG HUNGARY KFT.—See EVN AG; *Int'l*, pg. 2571
REED & GRAHAM, INC. - GEOSYNTHETICS DIVISION—See Reed & Graham Inc.; *U.S. Private*, pg. 3381
REED & GRAHAM INC.; *U.S. Private*, pg. 3381
REFINERIA DE CARTAGENA S.A.S.—See Ecopetrol S.A.; *Int'l*, pg. 2299
REG HOUSTON, LLC—See Chevron Corporation; *U.S. Public*, pg. 488
REPRO BEBER GMBH & CO. KG—See EnviTec Biogas AG; *Int'l*, pg. 2456
SAFETY-KLEEN SYSTEMS, INC.—See Clean Harbors, Inc.; *U.S. Public*, pg. 510
SAN JOAQUIN REFINING CO., INC.; *U.S. Private*, pg. 3541
SAUDI ARAMCO LUBRICATING OIL REFINING COMPANY—See Exxon Mobil Corporation; *U.S. Public*, pg. 817
SAUDI ARAMCO MOBIL REFINERY COMPANY LTD.—See Exxon Mobil Corporation; *U.S. Public*, pg. 817
SENECA PETROLEUM CO. INC.; *U.S. Private*, pg. 3606
SINCLAIR OIL LLC—See HF Sinclair Corporation; *U.S. Public*, pg. 1034
SINGAPORE REFINING CO. PTE. LTD.—See Chevron Corporation; *U.S. Public*, pg. 486
SINGAPORE REFINING CO. PTE. LTD.—See China National Petroleum Corporation; *Int'l*, pg. 1533
SOCIETE DE LA RAFFINERIE DE DUNKERQUE—See OpenGate Capital Management, LLC; *U.S. Private*, pg. 3031
SOUTHEAST PROPANE, LLC—See CHS INC.; *U.S. Public*, pg. 493
ST. PAUL PARK REFINING CO. LLC—See Marathon Petroleum Corporation; *U.S. Public*, pg. 1363
SUNOCO INC. - MARCUS HOOK REFINERY—See Energy Transfer LP; *U.S. Public*, pg. 764
SUNOCO INC. - PHILADELPHIA REFINERY—See Energy Transfer LP; *U.S. Public*, pg. 764
SUNOCO, INC.—See Energy Transfer LP; *U.S. Public*, pg. 763
SUPERIOR GRAPHITE EUROPE, LTD.—See Superior Graphite Co.; *U.S. Private*, pg. 3878
TEXAS ALLIED HOLDINGS INC.; *U.S. Private*, pg. 3974
TOA OIL CO., LTD.—See Idemitsu Kosan Co., Ltd.; *Int'l*, pg. 3592
TOLEDO REFINING COMPANY LLC—See PBF Energy Inc.; *U.S. Public*, pg. 1657
TORRANCE REFINING COMPANY—See PBF Energy Inc.; *U.S. Public*, pg. 1657
UNITED REFINING COMPANY—See Red Apple Group, Inc.; *U.S. Private*, pg. 3373
U.S. OIL - CHEBOYGAN TERMINAL—See U.S. Venture, Inc.; *U.S. Private*, pg. 4272
U.S. OIL TRADING LLC—See Par Pacific Holdings, Inc.; *U.S. Public*, pg. 1636
VALERO ENERGY CORPORATION; *U.S. Public*, pg. 2272
VALERO PARTNERS SOUTH TEXAS, LLC—See Valero Energy Corporation; *U.S. Public*, pg. 2272
VALERO REFINING COMPANY-ARUBA N.V.—See Valero Energy Corporation; *U.S. Public*, pg. 2272
VALERO REFINING COMPANY-CALIFORNIA—See Valero Energy Corporation; *U.S. Public*, pg. 2272
VALERO REFINING-TEXAS, L.P.—See Valero Energy Corporation; *U.S. Public*, pg. 2272
VARO REFINING CRESSIER S.A.—See AtlasInvest; *Int'l*, pg. 686
VERTEC BIOSOLVENTS, INC.; *U.S. Private*, pg. 4369
VP RACING FUELS INC.—See Texas Allied Holdings Inc.; *U.S. Private*, pg. 3974
WAGNER & BROWN, LTD.; *U.S. Private*, pg. 4426
WD-40 MANUFACTURING CO.—See WD-40 Company; *U.S. Public*, pg. 2339
WESTERN REFINING CO. - GALLUP REFINERY—See Marathon Petroleum Corporation; *U.S. Public*, pg. 1364
WESTERN REFINING, INC.—See Marathon Petroleum Corporation; *U.S. Public*, pg. 1363
WESTERN REFINING SOUTHWEST, INC.—See Marathon Petroleum Corporation; *U.S. Public*, pg. 1363
WILHELMSHAVENER RAFFINERIEGESELLSCHAFT MBH—See Riverstone Holdings LLC; *U.S. Private*, pg. 3447
WILLIAMS ENERGY SERVICES—See The Williams Companies, Inc.; *U.S. Public*, pg. 2142
WOODS CROSS REFINING COMPANY, LLC—See HF Sinclair Corporation; *U.S. Public*, pg. 1034
XINJIANG JICHUANG ASSET MANAGEMENT CO.,

LTD.—See GI Technology Group Co., Ltd.; *Int'l*, pg. 2960
ZIEGLER CHEMICAL & MINERAL CORPORATION; *U.S. Private*, pg. 4604
ZUREX CORPORATION SDN. BHD.—See Graphene Nanochem plc; *Int'l*, pg. 3060

324121 — ASPHALT PAVING MIXTURE AND BLOCK MANUFACTURING

AGGREGATE INDUSTRIES UK LIMITED—See Holcim Ltd.; *Int'l*, pg. 3446
AJAX PAVING INDUSTRIES, INC. - BALD MOUNTAIN PLANT—See Ajax Paving Industries, Inc.; *U.S. Private*, pg. 143
AJAX PAVING INDUSTRIES, INC. - INKSTER ROAD PLANT—See Ajax Paving Industries, Inc.; *U.S. Private*, pg. 143
AJAX PAVING INDUSTRIES, INC. - LARGO PLANT—See Ajax Paving Industries, Inc.; *U.S. Private*, pg. 143
AJAX PAVING INDUSTRIES, INC. - NEW HAVEN PLANT—See Ajax Paving Industries, Inc.; *U.S. Private*, pg. 143
AJAX PAVING INDUSTRIES, INC. - NOKOMIS PLANT—See Ajax Paving Industries, Inc.; *U.S. Private*, pg. 143
AJAX PAVING INDUSTRIES, INC. - ODESSA PLANT—See Ajax Paving Industries, Inc.; *U.S. Private*, pg. 143
AJAX PAVING INDUSTRIES, INC. - PLANT 5—See Ajax Paving Industries, Inc.; *U.S. Private*, pg. 143
AJAX PAVING INDUSTRIES, INC. - PORT MANATEE PLANT—See Ajax Paving Industries, Inc.; *U.S. Private*, pg. 143
AJAX PAVING INDUSTRIES, INC. - PUNTA GORDA PLANT—See Ajax Paving Industries, Inc.; *U.S. Private*, pg. 143
AJAX PAVING INDUSTRIES, INC. - TAMPA PLANT—See Ajax Paving Industries, Inc.; *U.S. Private*, pg. 143
ALCO CORPORATION; *U.S. Private*, pg. 153
ALEX FRASER PTY LIMITED - ASPHALT - LAVERTON PLANT—See Heidelberg Materials AG; *Int'l*, pg. 3311
ALON ASPHALT COMPANY—See Marathon Petroleum Corporation; *U.S. Public*, pg. 1363
ANDRE VOSS ERDBAU UND TRANSPORT GMBH; *Int'l*, pg. 451
THE ANGELO IAFRATE COMPANIES; *U.S. Private*, pg. 3986
APAC-ARKANSAS - MCCLINTON ANCHOR DIVISION—See CRH plc; *Int'l*, pg. 1846
APAC-ATLANTIC - ASHEVILLE DIVISION—See CRH plc; *Int'l*, pg. 1846
APAC-ATLANTIC - HARRISON DIVISION—See CRH plc; *Int'l*, pg. 1846
APAC-MISSISSIPPI, INC.—See CRH plc; *Int'l*, pg. 1846
APAC-TEXAS - TROTTI & THOMSON DIVISION—See CRH plc; *Int'l*, pg. 1846
ARTISTIC PAVERS MANUFACTURING, INC.; *U.S. Private*, pg. 343
ASPHALT MATERIALS INC.—See Heritage Group; *U.S. Private*, pg. 1923
ATLANTIC SOUTHERN PAVING & SEALCOATING, CO.—See Harbor Beach Capital, LLC; *U.S. Private*, pg. 1858
ATLAS ASPHALT INC.; *U.S. Private*, pg. 375
AUSTIN MATERIALS, LLC—See Summit Materials, Inc.; *U.S. Public*, pg. 1960
BAKER INFRASTRUCTURE GROUP, INC.—See Reeves Construction Company; *U.S. Private*, pg. 3384
BALDWIN PAVING COMPANY INC. - PLANT 1—See Baldwin Paving Company Inc.; *U.S. Private*, pg. 459
BALDWIN PAVING COMPANY INC. - PLANT 2—See Baldwin Paving Company Inc.; *U.S. Private*, pg. 459
BALDWIN PAVING COMPANY INC. - PLANT 3—See Baldwin Paving Company Inc.; *U.S. Private*, pg. 459
BALDWIN PAVING COMPANY INC. - PLANT 4—See Baldwin Paving Company Inc.; *U.S. Private*, pg. 459
BALDWIN PAVING COMPANY INC. - PLANT 5—See Baldwin Paving Company Inc.; *U.S. Private*, pg. 459
BALDWIN PAVING COMPANY INC. - PLANT 6—See Baldwin Paving Company Inc.; *U.S. Private*, pg. 459
BARBER BROTHERS CONTRACTING COMPANY - ASPHALT PLANT 1—See Barber Brothers Contracting Company; *U.S. Private*, pg. 472
BARBER BROTHERS CONTRACTING COMPANY - ASPHALT PLANT 6—See Barber Brothers Contracting Company; *U.S. Private*, pg. 472
BASIN CONTRACTING LIMITED; *Int'l*, pg. 887
BECHTELSVILLE ASPHALT—See Haines & Kibblehouse Inc.; *U.S. Private*, pg. 1840
BERKELEY ASPHALT COMPANY; *U.S. Private*, pg. 532
BETONGRUPPEN RBR A/S—See CRH plc; *Int'l*, pg. 1843
BITUMINOUS ROADWAYS, INC.; *U.S. Private*, pg. 567
BKEP MATERIALS LLC—See Ergon, Inc.; *U.S. Private*, pg. 1418
BLACKLIDGE EMULSIONS, INC.; *U.S. Private*, pg. 576
BROX INDUSTRIES INC.; *U.S. Private*, pg. 670
CALAVERAS MATERIALS INC. - HUGHSON PLANT—See Heidelberg Materials AG; *Int'l*, pg. 3313

324121 — ASPHALT PAVING MIXT...

CALIFORNIA COMMERCIAL ASPHALT CORP.; *U.S. Private*, pg. 718
CARLSON PAVING PRODUCTS, INC.—See Astec Industries, Inc.; *U.S. Public*, pg. 216
CIMPOR BETAO - INDUSTRIA DE BETAO PRONTO S.A.—See Camargo Correa S.A.; *Int'l*, pg. 1267
COLORADO RIVER CONCRETE, LP—See Holcim Ltd.; *Int'l*, pg. 3446
CRAFCO, INC.—See Ergon, Inc.; *U.S. Private*, pg. 1418
CURRAN CONTRACTING COMPANY, INC. - LAKE BLUFF PLANT—See Curran Group, Inc.; *U.S. Private*, pg. 1125
CURRAN CONTRACTING COMPANY, INC. - MCHENRY PLANT—See Curran Group, Inc.; *U.S. Private*, pg. 1125
DANSK NATURSTEN A/S—See Holcim Ltd.; *Int'l*, pg. 3446
DELTA SAND & GRAVEL, INC.; *U.S. Private*, pg. 1201
DES MOINES ASPHALT & PAVING CO.—See CRH plc; *Int'l*, pg. 1847
D&G TECHNOLOGY HOLDING CO., LTD.; *Int'l*, pg. 1899
DICKERSON & BOWEN, INC.—See Granite Construction Incorporated; *U.S. Public*, pg. 957
DITECPESA, S.A.—See Ferrovial S.A.; *Int'l*, pg. 2644
DOLOMITE PRODUCTS COMPANY INC.—See CRH plc; *Int'l*, pg. 1847
DORTMUNDER GUSSASPHALT GMBH & CO. KG; *Int'l*, pg. 2180
DUNMORE MATERIALS—See Haines & Kibblehouse Inc.; *U.S. Private*, pg. 1841
ERGON ASFALTOS MEXICO S. DE R.L. DE C.V.—See Ergon, Inc.; *U.S. Private*, pg. 1418
ERGON ASPHALT & EMULSIONS, INC.—See Ergon, Inc.; *U.S. Private*, pg. 1417
EUREKA STONE QUARRY INC.; *U.S. Private*, pg. 1433
EVERETT HOLDING COMPANY; *U.S. Private*, pg. 1438
FRANCIS O. DAY CO., INC.; *U.S. Private*, pg. 1587
FREETECH ROAD RECYCLING TECHNOLOGY (HOLDINGS) LIMITED; *Int'l*, pg. 2771
GEIGER EXCAVATING, INC.—See Zemba Bros Inc; *U.S. Private*, pg. 4601
GENERAL COMBUSTION CORPORATION—See Gencor Industries, Inc.; *U.S. Public*, pg. 911
GERNATT ASPHALT PRODUCTS INC.; *U.S. Private*, pg. 1687
GLASGOW INC.; *U.S. Private*, pg. 1706
GRANGER-LYNCH CORP.—See J.H. Lynch & Sons Inc.; *U.S. Private*, pg. 2166
HENRY G. MEIGS, LLC—See Heritage Group; *U.S. Private*, pg. 1923
HINKLE CONTRACTING CO., LLC - JACKSON—See Summit Materials, Inc.; *U.S. Public*, pg. 1960
HINKLE CONTRACTING CO., LLC - SOMERSET—See Summit Materials, Inc.; *U.S. Public*, pg. 1960
HUBEI GUOCHUANG HI-TECH MATERIAL CO., LTD.; *Int'l*, pg. 3517
IDAHO ASPHALT SUPPLY INC.; *U.S. Private*, pg. 2034
INDUSTRIAL ASPHALT, LLC—See Summit Materials, Inc.; *U.S. Public*, pg. 1960
J.H. BERRA PAVING CO., INC.—See J.H. Berra Holding Co., Inc.; *U.S. Private*, pg. 2165
KARSON ASPHALT PAVING INC.—See Aecon Group Inc.; *Int'l*, pg. 172
KB INDUSTRIES, INC.—See Atlantic Wind & Solar, Inc.; *U.S. Private*, pg. 676
KILGORE COMPANIES, LLC—See Summit Materials, Inc.; *U.S. Public*, pg. 1960
KING ASPHALT, INC.—See Construction Partners, Inc.; *U.S. Public*, pg. 572
KOKOSING MATERIALS, INC. - CLEVELAND PLANT—See Kokosing Construction Company, Inc.; *U.S. Private*, pg. 2340
KOKOSING MATERIALS, INC. - COLUMBIA STATION PLANT—See Kokosing Construction Company, Inc.; *U.S. Private*, pg. 2340
KOKOSING MATERIALS, INC. - COLUMBUS PLANT—See Kokosing Construction Company, Inc.; *U.S. Private*, pg. 2340
KOKOSING MATERIALS, INC. - EAST CLARIDON PLANT—See Kokosing Construction Company, Inc.; *U.S. Private*, pg. 2340
KOKOSING MATERIALS, INC. - GARFIELD PLANT—See Kokosing Construction Company, Inc.; *U.S. Private*, pg. 2341
KOKOSING MATERIALS, INC.—See Kokosing Construction Company, Inc.; *U.S. Private*, pg. 2340
LANGFANG D&G MACHINERY TECHNOLOGY COMPANY LIMITED—See D&G TECHNOLOGY HOLDING CO., LTD.; *Int'l*, pg. 1899
LONGVIEW ASPHALT INC.—See Madden Contracting Company Inc.; *U.S. Private*, pg. 2539
LORUSSO CORPORATION; *U.S. Private*, pg. 2496
MANCIL'S TRACTOR SERVICE, INC.—See Construction Partners, Inc.; *U.S. Public*, pg. 572
MARINI INDIA PRIVATE LTD—See FAYAT SAS; *Int'l*, pg. 2625
MARINI SPA—See FAYAT SAS; *Int'l*, pg. 2625
MARINI UK LIMITED—See FAYAT SAS; *Int'l*, pg. 2625
MARTIN ASPHALT COMPANY—See Martin Resource Management Corporation; *U.S. Private*, pg. 2595
MARTIN ASPHALT COMPANY—See Martin Resource Management Corporation; *U.S. Private*, pg. 2595
MCASPHALT INDUSTRIES LIMITED—See Bouygues S.A.; *Int'l*, pg. 1122
MIBAU BAUSTOFFHANDEL GMBH—See Heidelberg Materials AG; *Int'l*, pg. 3318
MIBAU HOLDING GMBH—See Heidelberg Materials AG; *Int'l*, pg. 3318
MIDDLEPORT TERMINAL, INC.—See CRH plc; *Int'l*, pg. 1847
MOBILE ASPHALT CO., LLC - ATMORE PLANT—See Mobile Asphalt Co., LLC; *U.S. Private*, pg. 2757
MOBILE ASPHALT CO., LLC - BAY MINETTE PLANT—See Mobile Asphalt Co., LLC; *U.S. Private*, pg. 2757
MOBILE ASPHALT CO., LLC - FOLEY PLANT—See Mobile Asphalt Co., LLC; *U.S. Private*, pg. 2757
MOBILE ASPHALT CO., LLC - SARALAND PLANT—See Mobile Asphalt Co., LLC; *U.S. Private*, pg. 2757
MOBILE ASPHALT CO., LLC; *U.S. Private*, pg. 2757
MOBILE ASPHALT CO., LLC - SUMMERDALE PLANT—See Mobile Asphalt Co., LLC; *U.S. Private*, pg. 2757
MOBILE ASPHALT CO., LLC - WHATLEY PLANT—See Mobile Asphalt Co., LLC; *U.S. Private*, pg. 2757
MOORE BROTHERS ASPHALT INC.; *U.S. Private*, pg. 2779
MUCH ASPHALT (PROPRIETARY) LIMITED—See AECI Limited; *Int'l*, pg. 171
NIBLOCK EXCAVATING INC.; *U.S. Private*, pg. 2924
OHIO VALLEY ASPHALT, LLC—See Summit Materials, Inc.; *U.S. Public*, pg. 1960
OLDCASTLE MATERIAL TEXAS INC.—See CRH plc; *Int'l*, pg. 1846
OLDCASTLE SOUTHERN GROUP, INC.—See CRH plc; *Int'l*, pg. 1848
PALMETTO PAVING CORPORATION; *U.S. Private*, pg. 3081
PARAMOUNT-NEVADA ASPHALT COMPANY, LLC—See Marathon Petroleum Corporation; *U.S. Public*, pg. 1363
PECKHAM INDUSTRIES, INC.; *U.S. Private*, pg. 3126
PECKHAM MATERIALS CORPORATION—See Peckham Industries, Inc.; *U.S. Private*, pg. 3127
PENNSY SUPPLY, INC.—See CRH plc; *Int'l*, pg. 1847
PIONEER ASPHALTS (U.K.) LIMITED—See Heidelberg Materials AG; *Int'l*, pg. 3318
PIONEER NORTH QUEENSLAND PTY LTD—See Heidelberg Materials AG; *Int'l*, pg. 3311
P.J. KEATING COMPANY—See CRH plc; *Int'l*, pg. 1847
POSILLICO MATERIALS, LLC—See Posillico, Inc.; *U.S. Private*, pg. 3233
PREFERRED MATERIALS, INC.—See CRH plc; *Int'l*, pg. 1848
PUTNAM MATERIALS CORP.—See Peckham Industries, Inc.; *U.S. Private*, pg. 3127
RC BETON A/S—See CRH plc; *Int'l*, pg. 1848
REEVES CONSTRUCTION COMPANY; *U.S. Private*, pg. 3384
REKISEI KAGAKU K.K.—See Idemitsu Kosan Co., Ltd.; *Int'l*, pg. 3592
REYNOLDS ASPHALT & CONSTRUCTION COMPANY; *U.S. Private*, pg. 3418
ROSTOCKER ZEMENTUMSCHLAGSGESELLSCHAFT MBH—See Heidelberg Materials AG; *Int'l*, pg. 3319
SEACO, INC.—See Ergon, Inc.; *U.S. Private*, pg. 1418
THE SHELLY CO. - COLUMBUS DIVISION—See CRH plc; *Int'l*, pg. 1847
THE SHELLY COMPANY—See CRH plc; *Int'l*, pg. 1847
THE SHELLY CO. - NORTHEAST DIVISION—See CRH plc; *Int'l*, pg. 1847
THE SHELLY CO. - NORTHWEST DIVISION—See CRH plc; *Int'l*, pg. 1847
THE SHELLY CO. - SOUTHERN DIVISION—See CRH plc; *Int'l*, pg. 1847
SIMOSA OIL CORPORATION—See Formosa Petrochemical Corporation; *Int'l*, pg. 2735
SIMPSON CONSTRUCTION MATERIALS; *U.S. Private*, pg. 3668
SMAC SA—See OpenGate Capital Management, LLC; *U.S. Private*, pg. 3031
SOUTHERN WEST VIRGINIA ASPHALT, INC.—See CRH plc; *Int'l*, pg. 1848
SOUTH READING BLACKTOP—See Haines & Kibblehouse Inc.; *U.S. Private*, pg. 1841
STEMA SHIPPING A/S—See Heidelberg Materials AG; *Int'l*, pg. 3319
STEMA SHIPPING FRANCE S.A.S.—See Heidelberg Materials AG; *Int'l*, pg. 3319
SUIT-KOTE CORP.; *U.S. Private*, pg. 3850
SUPERIOR ASPHALT INC.—See W.G. Yates & Sons Construction Company; *U.S. Private*, pg. 4420
SYAR INDUSTRIES, INC. - HEALDSBURG PLANT—See Syar Industries, Inc.; *U.S. Private*, pg. 3895
SYAR INDUSTRIES, INC. - TODD ROAD PLANT—See Syar Industries, Inc.; *U.S. Private*, pg. 3895
THOMPSON-ARTHUR PAVING & CONSTRUCTION—See CRH plc; *Int'l*, pg. 1847
TILCON CONNECTICUT INC.—See CRH plc; *Int'l*, pg. 1848
TILCON NEW YORK INC. - NEW JERSEY—See CRH plc; *Int'l*, pg. 1848
TILCON NEW YORK INC.—See CRH plc; *Int'l*, pg. 1848
UNITED CONTRACTORS MIDWEST, INC.; *U.S. Private*, pg. 4290
U.S. PAVEMENT SERVICES INC.; *U.S. Private*, pg. 4271
VANCE BROTHERS INCORPORATED; *U.S. Private*, pg. 4342
WABASH VALLEY ASPHALT CO., LLC—See Milestone Contractors, LP; *U.S. Private*, pg. 2728
WALSH & KELLY, INC.—See Milestone Contractors, LP; *U.S. Private*, pg. 2728
WARREN MATERIALS—See Haines & Kibblehouse Inc.; *U.S. Private*, pg. 1841
WELDON ASPHALT CORP.; *U.S. Private*, pg. 4474
WESTERN EMULSIONS, INC.—See Idaho Asphalt Supply Inc.; *U.S. Private*, pg. 2034
WINGDALE MATERIALS LLC—See Peckham Industries, Inc.; *U.S. Private*, pg. 3127
WOLF PAVING & EXCAVATING OF MADISON—See Lowell Wolf Industries Inc.; *U.S. Private*, pg. 2505

324122 — ASPHALT SHINGLE AND COATING MATERIALS MANUFACTURING

AMERICAN ROCKWOOL, INC.—See Owens Corning; *U.S. Public*, pg. 1626
ARAMIT LIMITED—See Aramit Group; *Int'l*, pg. 535
ATLAS ROOFING CORP.—See Atlas Roofing Corp.; *U.S. Private*, pg. 380
ATLAS ROOFING CORP.—See Atlas Roofing Corp.; *U.S. Private*, pg. 380
ATLAS ROOFING CORP.—See Atlas Roofing Corp.; *U.S. Private*, pg. 380
BETUMAT QUIMICA LTDA.—See RPM International Inc.; *U.S. Public*, pg. 1816
BIM AD; *Int'l*, pg. 1031
BITEC INC.; *U.S. Private*, pg. 567
BRASILIT SA—See Compagnie de Saint-Gobain SA; *Int'l*, pg. 1722
THE BREWER COMPANY; *U.S. Private*, pg. 4000
BUILDING MATERIALS CORPORATION OF AMERICA—See GAF Materials Corporation; *U.S. Private*, pg. 1633
BUILDING PRODUCTS OF CANADA CORP.—See Compagnie de Saint-Gobain SA; *Int'l*, pg. 1722
CANROOF CORPORATION INC.—See IKO Enterprises Ltd.; *Int'l*, pg. 3612
CARLISLE, LLC—See Carlisle Companies Incorporated; *U.S. Public*, pg. 437
CARLISLE SYNTEC INC.—See Carlisle Companies Incorporated; *U.S. Public*, pg. 436
CERTAINTEED—See Compagnie de Saint-Gobain SA; *Int'l*, pg. 1729
C.I.M. INDUSTRIES, INC.—See KKR & Co. Inc.; *U.S. Public*, pg. 1242
CITADEL RESTORATION AND REPAIR, INC.—See RPM International Inc.; *U.S. Public*, pg. 1816
CONKLIN COMPANY INC.; *U.S. Private*, pg. 1014
DERBIGUM AMERICAS, INC.; *U.S. Private*, pg. 1209
DIAMOND MATERIALS CO., LTD.—See Diamond Building Products Public Company Limited; *Int'l*, pg. 2105
DIC COLOR COATINGS, INC.—See DIC Corporation; *Int'l*, pg. 2107
DPI PLASTICS SDN. BHD.—See DPI Holdings Berhad; *Int'l*, pg. 2189
ELKCORP.—See GAF Materials Corporation; *U.S. Private*, pg. 1633
ELK PREMIUM BUILDING PRODUCTS, INC.—See GAF Materials Corporation; *U.S. Private*, pg. 1633
EMENITE LTD.—See Etex SA/NV; *Int'l*, pg. 2521
FEUMAS GMBH—See GAF Materials Corporation; *U.S. Private*, pg. 1633
FLYNN BROTHERS CONTRACTING INC. - ASPHALT MATERIAL PLANT—See Flynn Brothers Contracting Inc.; *U.S. Private*, pg. 1553
F T MORRELL & COMPANY LIMITED—See RPM International Inc.; *U.S. Public*, pg. 1817
GAP ROOFING INC.; *U.S. Private*, pg. 1642
GARDNER-GIBSON, INC.—See Audax Group, Limited Partnership; *U.S. Private*, pg. 388
THE GARLAND COMPANY INC.—See Garland Industries Inc.; *U.S. Private*, pg. 1644
GARLAND INDUSTRIES INC.; *U.S. Private*, pg. 1644
GASCOGNE FLEXIBLE GERMANY GMBH—See Gascogne SA; *Int'l*, pg. 2887
GMX—See Garland Industries Inc.; *U.S. Private*, pg. 1644
HENRY COMPANY LLC - KIMBERTON—See Carlisle Companies Incorporated; *U.S. Public*, pg. 437
HENRY COMPANY LLC—See Carlisle Companies Incorporated; *U.S. Public*, pg. 437
HOLLYFRONTIER REFINING & MARKETING LLC—See HF Sinclair Corporation; *U.S. Public*, pg. 1033
ICHIKAWA CHINA CO., LTD.—See ICHIKAWA CO. LTD.; *Int'l*, pg. 3580
ICOPAL AB—See GAF Materials Corporation; *U.S. Private*, pg. 1633
ICOPAL APS—See GAF Materials Corporation; *U.S. Private*, pg. 1633

N.A.I.C.S. INDEX

324191 — PETROLEUM LUBRICATI...

ICOPAL AS—See GAF Materials Corporation; *U.S. Private*, pg. 1633
ICOPAL GMBH—See GAF Materials Corporation; *U.S. Private*, pg. 1633
ICOPAL HISPANIA S.L.—See Siris Capital Group, LLC; *U.S. Private*, pg. 3674
ICOPAL LTD—See GAF Materials Corporation; *U.S. Private*, pg. 1633
ICOPAL OY—See GAF Materials Corporation; *U.S. Private*, pg. 1634
ICOPAL SIPLAST SAS—See GAF Materials Corporation; *U.S. Private*, pg. 1634
ICOPAL SP. Z O.O.—See GAF Materials Corporation; *U.S. Private*, pg. 1634
ICOPAL S.R.L.—See GAF Materials Corporation; *U.S. Private*, pg. 1634
IKO INDUSTRIES LTD.—See IKO Enterprises Ltd.; *Int'l*, pg. 3612
IKO MIDWEST INC.—See IKO Enterprises Ltd.; *Int'l*, pg. 3612
IKO PLC—See IKO Enterprises Ltd.; *Int'l*, pg. 3612
IKO PRODUCTION INC.—See IKO Enterprises Ltd.; *Int'l*, pg. 3612
INLAND COATINGS CORPORATION—See Midwest Growth Partners, LLLP; *U.S. Private*, pg. 2721
KENT'S OIL SERVICE—See MDU Resources Group, Inc.; *U.S. Public*, pg. 1410
KOKOSING MATERIALS, INC. - SHEFFIELD PLANT—See Kokosing Construction Company, Inc.; *U.S. Private*, pg. 2341
MALARKEY ROOFING PRODUCTS; *U.S. Private*, pg. 2556
MATICH CORPORATION - CABAZON ASPHALT PLANT—See Matich Corporation; *U.S. Private*, pg. 2611
MATICH CORPORATION - REDLANDS ASPHALT PLANT—See Matich Corporation; *U.S. Private*, pg. 2611
MATICH CORPORATION - RIALTO ASPHALT PLANT—See Matich Corporation; *U.S. Private*, pg. 2611
MEXALIT—See Grupo Empresarial Kaluz S.A. de C.V.; *Int'l*, pg. 3127
MONARFLEX S.R.O.—See GAF Materials Corporation; *U.S. Private*, pg. 1634
NORTHERN ELASTOMERIC, INC.—See Owens Corning; *U.S. Public*, pg. 1627
NV SOUTHWESTERN PETROLEUM EUROPE, SA—See Southwestern Petroleum Corporation; *U.S. Private*, pg. 3742
OCV MEXICO S. DE R.L. DE C.V.—See Owens Corning; *U.S. Public*, pg. 1627
OWENS CORNING COMPOSITES (BEIJING) CO., LTD.—See Owens Corning; *U.S. Public*, pg. 1628
OWENS CORNING COMPOSITES (CHINA) CO., LTD.—See Owens Corning; *U.S. Public*, pg. 1628
OWENS CORNING; *U.S. Public*, pg. 1626
PABCO BUILDING PRODUCTS, LLC - PABCO ROOFING PRODUCTS DIVISION—See Pacific Coast Building Products, Inc.; *U.S. Private*, pg. 3066
PLYCEM—See Grupo Empresarial Kaluz S.A. de C.V.; *Int'l*, pg. 3127
RICHARD E. PIERSON CONSTRUCTION COMPANY, INC. - ASPHALT PLANT—See Richard E. Pierson Construction Company, Inc.; *U.S. Private*, pg. 3428
RPM/BELGIUM N.V.—See RPM International Inc.; *U.S. Public*, pg. 1819
SALES STRETCHER ENTERPRISES (SSE)—See W.H. Maze Company; *U.S. Private*, pg. 4420
SAS GASCOGNE FLEXIBLE—See Gascogne SA; *Int'l*, pg. 2888
SHERWIN-WILLIAMS IRELAND LTD.—See The Sherwin-Williams Company; *U.S. Public*, pg. 2128
SIPLAST ICOPAL INC.—See GAF Materials Corporation; *U.S. Private*, pg. 1634
SOUTHWESTERN PETROLEUM CORPORATION; *U.S. Private*, pg. 3742
S&P CLEVER REINFORCEMENT COMPANY BENELUX B.V.—See Simpson Manufacturing Company, Inc.; *U.S. Public*, pg. 1882
S&P CLEVER REINFORCEMENT GMBH—See Simpson Manufacturing Company, Inc.; *U.S. Public*, pg. 1882
S&P REINFORCEMENT SP. Z O.O.—See Simpson Manufacturing Company, Inc.; *U.S. Public*, pg. 1883
TAMKO ROOFING PRODUCTS INC.; *U.S. Private*, pg. 3928
TARCO INC.; *U.S. Private*, pg. 3933
TARCO OF TEXAS, INC.—See Tarco Inc.; *U.S. Private*, pg. 3933
TRANSANDINA DE COMERCIO S.A.—See Owens Corning; *U.S. Public*, pg. 1628
TREMCO ILLBRUCK GMBH—See RPM International Inc.; *U.S. Public*, pg. 1820
TRUCO INC.; *U.S. Private*, pg. 4247

324191 — PETROLEUM LUBRICATING OIL AND GREASE MANUFACTURING

ACHESON COLLOIDS COMPANY—See Henkel AG & Co. KGaA; *Int'l*, pg. 3353
ACHESON DO BRASIL IND. E COM LTDA.—See Henkel AG & Co. KGaA; *Int'l*, pg. 3353
ACHESON INDUSTRIES (EUROPE) LTD.—See Henkel AG & Co. KGaA; *Int'l*, pg. 3353
AEROSPACE LUBRICANTS, INC.—See Amsoil Inc.; *U.S. Private*, pg. 267
AGS AUTOMOTIVE SOLUTIONS LLC—See 3 Rivers Capital, LLC; *U.S. Private*, pg. 7
ALEXANDRIA MINERAL OILS CO.; *Int'l*, pg. 307
ALHAMRANI-FUCHS PETROLEUM SAUDI ARABIA LTD.—See Alhamrani Group; *Int'l*, pg. 319
ALHAMRANI-FUCHS PETROLEUM SAUDI ARABIA LTD.—See FUCHS SE; *Int'l*, pg. 2802
ALPHA PACIFIC PETROLEUM (S) PTE LTD—See AP Oil International Ltd.; *Int'l*, pg. 499
AMALIE OIL COMPANY; *U.S. Private*, pg. 215
AMSOIL INC.; *U.S. Private*, pg. 267
AP OIL INTERNATIONAL LTD.; *Int'l*, pg. 499
AP OIL PTE LTD—See AP Oil International Ltd.; *Int'l*, pg. 499
AP OIL SINGAPORE (CHONGQING) LTD.—See AP Oil International Ltd.; *Int'l*, pg. 499
AP OIL SINGAPORE (SHANGHAI) LIMITED—See AP Oil International Ltd.; *Int'l*, pg. 499
ARABIAN PETROLEUM LIMITED; *Int'l*, pg. 533
ARCHER DANIELS MIDLAND CO.—See Archer-Daniels-Midland Company; *U.S. Public*, pg. 183
ARMORED AUTOGROUP INC.—See Energizer Holdings, Inc.; *U.S. Public*, pg. 760
AXEL AMERICAS LLC; *U.S. Private*, pg. 412
AXEL PLASTICS RESEARCH LABORATORIES, INC.; *U.S. Private*, pg. 412
BARDAHL MANUFACTURING CORPORATION - BARDAHL EUROPE DIVISION—See Bardahl Manufacturing Corporation; *U.S. Private*, pg. 474
BARDAHL MANUFACTURING CORPORATION; *U.S. Private*, pg. 473
BATTENFELD-AMERICAN, INC.—See Battenfeld Management Inc.; *U.S. Private*, pg. 488
BATTENFELD GREASE & OIL CORP—See Battenfeld Management Inc.; *U.S. Private*, pg. 488
BATTENFELD MANAGEMENT INC.; *U.S. Private*, pg. 488
BEL-RAY COMPANY, LLC—See Calumet, Inc.; *U.S. Public*, pg. 425
BENZ OIL INC.—See Amsoil Inc.; *U.S. Private*, pg. 267
BERNER OY; *Int'l*, pg. 988
BG PRODUCTS, INC.; *U.S. Private*, pg. 548
BINOL AB—See Quaker Chemical Corporation; *U.S. Public*, pg. 1745
BJ SERVICES COMPANY ITALIA S.R.L.—See Baker Hughes Company; *U.S. Public*, pg. 264
B & N BASE OILS LTD.—See FUCHS SE; *Int'l*, pg. 2803
BP CASTROL CONSUMER NORTH AMERICA INC.—See BP plc; *Int'l*, pg. 1127
BP CASTROL K.K.—See BP plc; *Int'l*, pg. 1130
BP - CASTROL (THAILAND) LIMITED—See BP plc; *Int'l*, pg. 1126
BP CASTROL (THAILAND) LIMITED—See BP plc; *Int'l*, pg. 1129
BP FRANCE LUBRIFIANTS INDUSTRIELS & SERVICES—See BP plc; *Int'l*, pg. 1130
BP ITALIA SPA—See BP plc; *Int'l*, pg. 1129
BP LUBRICANTS USA INC.—See BP plc; *Int'l*, pg. 1127
BP LUBRICANTS USA INC.—See BP plc; *Int'l*, pg. 1127
BP OIL AUSTRALIA PTY. LTD.—See BP plc; *Int'l*, pg. 1129
BP TAIWAN MARKETING LIMITED—See BP plc; *Int'l*, pg. 1130
BREAK-FREE—See BAE Systems plc; *Int'l*, pg. 796
BREMER & LEGUIL GMBH—See FUCHS SE; *Int'l*, pg. 2802
BURMAH CASTROL AUSTRALIA PTY LTD.—See BP plc; *Int'l*, pg. 1130
CALUMET MISSOURI, LLC—See Calumet, Inc.; *U.S. Public*, pg. 425
CALUMET OPERATING, LLC—See Calumet, Inc.; *U.S. Public*, pg. 425
CALUMET PRINCETON REFINING, LLC—See Calumet, Inc.; *U.S. Public*, pg. 425
CALUMET SHREVEPORT REFINING, LLC—See Calumet, Inc.; *U.S. Public*, pg. 425
CASTROL CROATIA D.O.O.—See BP plc; *Int'l*, pg. 1130
CASTROL INDIA LIMITED—See BP plc; *Int'l*, pg. 1130
CASTROL INDUSTRIAL NORTH AMERICA INC.—See BP plc; *Int'l*, pg. 1127
CASTROL INDUSTRIAL NORTH AMERICA—See BP plc; *Int'l*, pg. 1127
CASTROL LIMITED—See BP plc; *Int'l*, pg. 1130
CASTROL LUBRICANTS (CR), S.R.O.—See BP plc; *Int'l*, pg. 1130
CASTROL NORTH AMERICA AUTO—See BP plc; *Int'l*, pg. 1127
CASTROL NORTH AMERICA INC.—See BP plc; *Int'l*, pg. 1127
CASTROL SLOVENIJA D.O.O.—See BP plc; *Int'l*, pg. 1130
CASTROL (U.K.) LIMITED—See BP plc; *Int'l*, pg. 1130
CASTROL VIETNAM LTD.—See BP plc; *Int'l*, pg. 1131
CHAMPION BRANDS LLC; *U.S. Private*, pg. 846
CHEMIE TECHNIK GMBH; *Int'l*, pg. 1462
CHEMTOOL, INC.—See Berkshire Hathaway Inc.; *U.S. Public*, pg. 318
CHEM-TREND (DEUTSCHLAND) GMBH—See Freudenberg SE; *Int'l*, pg. 2785
CHEM-TREND LIMITED PARTNERSHIP—See Freudenberg SE; *Int'l*, pg. 2785
CHEMTURA CHEMICALS INDIA PRIVATE LIMITED—See Element Solutions Inc.; *U.S. Public*, pg. 725
CHEVRON LATIN AMERICA—See Chevron Corporation; *U.S. Public*, pg. 486
CHEVRON LUBRICANTS LANKA PLC; *Int'l*, pg. 1474
CHEVRON ORONITE S.A.—See Chevron Corporation; *U.S. Public*, pg. 486
CHEVRON (THAILAND) LIMITED—See Chevron Corporation; *U.S. Public*, pg. 486
CHEVRON UNITED KINGDOM LIMITED—See Chevron Corporation; *U.S. Public*, pg. 487
COMPLEX CHEMICAL COMPANY, INC.; *U.S. Private*, pg. 1001
CONFIDENCE PETROLEUM INDIA LTD; *Int'l*, pg. 1768
CONTINENTAL PETROLEUMS LIMITED; *Int'l*, pg. 1784
COSMO OIL LUBRICANTS CO., LTD.—See Cosmo Energy Holdings Co., Ltd.; *Int'l*, pg. 1812
CRC INDUSTRIES, INC.—See Berwind Corporation; *U.S. Private*, pg. 541
CROSS OIL REFINING & MARKETING COMPANY; *U.S. Private*, pg. 1105
D-A LUBRICANT COMPANY; *U.S. Private*, pg. 1139
DA STUART SHANGHAI CO.—See Quaker Chemical Corporation; *U.S. Public*, pg. 1745
DELTA PETROLEUM COMPANY INC.—See Aurora Capital Group, LLC; *U.S. Private*, pg. 394
DELTA PETROLEUM COMPANY INC.—See The Jordan Company, L.P.; *U.S. Private*, pg. 4061
ECLI PRODUCTS, LLC—See Quaker Chemical Corporation; *U.S. Public*, pg. 1745
ECO-TEK GROUP INC.; *Int'l*, pg. 2293
ENGINEERED CUSTOM LUBRICANTS GMBH—See Quaker Chemical Corporation; *U.S. Public*, pg. 1745
EVERGREEN HOLDINGS INC.; *U.S. Private*, pg. 1439
EVEXIA LIFECARE LIMITED; *Int'l*, pg. 2570
EXCELDA MANUFACTURING COMPANY; *U.S. Private*, pg. 1445
EXXONMOBIL MEXICO S.A. DE C.V.—See Exxon Mobil Corporation; *U.S. Public*, pg. 815
FABRIKA MAZIVA FAM A.D. KRUSEVAC; *Int'l*, pg. 2599
FISKE BROTHERS REFINING COMPANY; *U.S. Private*, pg. 1535
FISKE BROTHERS REFINING COMPANY - TOLEDO DIVISION—See Fiske Brothers Refining Company; *U.S. Private*, pg. 1535
FLOW MANAGEMENT DEVICES, LLC—See IDEX Corp; *U.S. Public*, pg. 1090
FORSYTHE LUBRICATION ASSOCIATES LIMITED; *Int'l*, pg. 2737
FRAGOL BETEILIGUNGS GMBH + CO.KG; *Int'l*, pg. 2758
FUCHS ARGENTINA S.A.—See FUCHS SE; *Int'l*, pg. 2802
FUCHS AUSTRIA SCHMIERMITTEL GES. MBH—See FUCHS SE; *Int'l*, pg. 2802
FUCHS BELGIUM N.V.—See FUCHS SE; *Int'l*, pg. 2802
FUCHS BRASIL S.A.—See FUCHS SE; *Int'l*, pg. 2802
FUCHS CORPORATION—See FUCHS SE; *Int'l*, pg. 2802
FUCHS DO BRASIL S.A.—See FUCHS SE; *Int'l*, pg. 2802
FUCHS EUROPE SCHMIERSTOFFE GMBH & CO. KG—See FUCHS SE; *Int'l*, pg. 2802
FUCHS EUROPE SCHMIERSTOFFE GMBH - EXPORT DIVISION—See FUCHS SE; *Int'l*, pg. 2802
FUCHS EUROPE SCHMIERSTOFFE GMBH - KIEL PLANT—See FUCHS SE; *Int'l*, pg. 2802
FUCHS FINANZSERVICE GMBH—See FUCHS SE; *Int'l*, pg. 2802
FUCHS HELLAS S.A.—See FUCHS SE; *Int'l*, pg. 2802
FUCHS JAPAN LTD. - CHIBA FACTORY—See FUCHS SE; *Int'l*, pg. 2803
FUCHS JAPAN LTD. - IGA UENO FACTORY—See FUCHS SE; *Int'l*, pg. 2803
FUCHS JAPAN LTD.—See FUCHS SE; *Int'l*, pg. 2803
FUCHS LUBRICANTES S.A.—See FUCHS SE; *Int'l*, pg. 2802
FUCHS LUBRICANTS (AUSTRALASIA) PTY. LTD.—See FUCHS SE; *Int'l*, pg. 2803
FUCHS LUBRICANTS BENELUX N.V. / S.A—See FUCHS SE; *Int'l*, pg. 2802
FUCHS LUBRICANTS CANADA LTD.—See FUCHS SE; *Int'l*, pg. 2803
FUCHS LUBRICANTS (CHINA) LTD.—See FUCHS SE; *Int'l*, pg. 2803
FUCHS LUBRICANTS CO. - FUCHS LUBRITECH USA DIVISION—See FUCHS SE; *Int'l*, pg. 2803
FUCHS LUBRICANTS CO.—See FUCHS SE; *Int'l*, pg. 2803
FUCHS LUBRICANTS (INDIA) PVT. LTD.—See FUCHS SE; *Int'l*, pg. 2803
FUCHS LUBRICANTS-KANSAS CITY DIVISION—See FUCHS SE; *Int'l*, pg. 2803
FUCHS LUBRICANTS (KOREA) LTD.—See FUCHS SE; *Int'l*, pg. 2803
FUCHS LUBRICANTS (KOREA) LTD. - ULSAN PLANT—See FUCHS SE; *Int'l*, pg. 2803
FUCHS LUBRICANTS PTE. LTD.—See FUCHS SE; *Int'l*, pg. 2803

324191 — PETROLEUM LUBRICATI...

FUCHS LUBRICANTS (S.A.) (PTY.) LTD.—See FUCHS SE; *Int'l,* pg. 2802
FUCHS LUBRICANTS TAIWAN CORP.—See FUCHS SE; *Int'l,* pg. 2803
FUCHS LUBRICANTS (YINGKOU) LTD.—See FUCHS SE; *Int'l,* pg. 2803
FUCHS LUBRIFIANT FRANCE S.A.—See FUCHS SE; *Int'l,* pg. 2803
FUCHS LUBRIFICANTES, UNIP. LDA.—See FUCHS SE; *Int'l,* pg. 2803
FUCHS LUBRIFICANTI S.P.A.—See FUCHS SE; *Int'l,* pg. 2802
FUCHS LUBRITECH GMBH - DOHNA PLANT—See FUCHS SE; *Int'l,* pg. 2803
FUCHS LUBRITECH GMBH - FLT OBERFLACHENTECH-NIK PLANT—See FUCHS SE; *Int'l,* pg. 2803
FUCHS LUBRITECH GMBH - MOLY-PAUL DIVISION—See FUCHS SE; *Int'l,* pg. 2803
FUCHS LUBRITECH GMBH—See FUCHS SE; *Int'l,* pg. 2803
FUCHS LUBRITECH S.A.S—See FUCHS SE; *Int'l,* pg. 2802
FUCHS LUBRITECH (UK) LTD.—See FUCHS SE; *Int'l,* pg. 2803
FUCHS MAZIVA D.O.O.—See FUCHS SE; *Int'l,* pg. 2803
FUCHS MAZIVA LSL D.O.O—See FUCHS SE; *Int'l,* pg. 2802
FUCHS OIL CORPORATION (CZ) SPOL. S R.O.—See FUCHS SE; *Int'l,* pg. 2803
FUCHS OIL CORPORATION (PL) SP. Z O.O.—See FUCHS SE; *Int'l,* pg. 2803
FUCHS OIL CORP. (SK), SPOL. S RO—See FUCHS SE; *Int'l,* pg. 2802
FUCHS OIL FINLAND OY—See FUCHS SE; *Int'l,* pg. 2803
FUCHS OIL HUNGARIA KFT—See FUCHS SE; *Int'l,* pg. 2802
FUCHS OIL MIDDLE EAST LTD.—See FUCHS SE; *Int'l,* pg. 2803
FUCHS PETROLEUM S.A.R.L.—See FUCHS SE; *Int'l,* pg. 2802
FUCHS PETROLUB AG - CASSIDA DIVISION—See FUCHS SE; *Int'l,* pg. 2803
FUCHS PETROLUB AG - HEIN DE WINDT DIVISION—See FUCHS SE; *Int'l,* pg. 2803
FUCHS PETROLUB AG - PACIFIC DIVISION—See FUCHS SE; *Int'l,* pg. 2804
FUCHS PETROLUB AG—See FUCHS SE; *Int'l,* pg. 2803
FUCHS SE; *Int'l,* pg. 2802
FUCHS WISURA GMBH—See FUCHS SE; *Int'l,* pg. 2804
GHI ASIA PACIFIC PTE. LTD.—See Quaker Chemical Corporation; *U.S. Public,* pg. 1745
GOCL CORPORATION LIMITED—See Hinduja Group Ltd.; *Int'l,* pg. 3398
GOLD EAGLE COMPANY - INTERNATIONAL DIVISION—See Gold Eagle Company; *U.S. Private,* pg. 1728
GOLD EAGLE COMPANY - PRIVATE LABEL DIVISION—See Gold Eagle Company; *U.S. Private,* pg. 1728
GOLD EAGLE COMPANY - THE GOLDEN TOUCH DIVISION—See Gold Eagle Company; *U.S. Private,* pg. 1728
GOLD EAGLE COMPANY - WHOLESALE/RETAIL DIVISION—See Gold Eagle Company; *U.S. Private,* pg. 1728
GP PETROLEUMS LTD.; *Int'l,* pg. 3046
GREEN PLANET GROUP, INC.; *U.S. Public,* pg. 964
GREEN STAR PRODUCTS, INC.; *U.S. Public,* pg. 964
GROENEVELD GROEP HOLDING B.V.—See The Timken Company; *U.S. Public,* pg. 2132
GROENEVELD ITALIA S.R.L.—See The Timken Company; *U.S. Public,* pg. 2132
GULF OIL ARGENTINA SA—See Hinduja Group Ltd.; *Int'l,* pg. 3398
GULF OIL CORPN. LTD. - LUBES DIVISION—See Hinduja Group Ltd.; *Int'l,* pg. 3398
GULF OIL MIDDLE EAST LTD - JEBEL ALI FACILITY—See Hinduja Group Ltd.; *Int'l,* pg. 3399
GULF OIL MIDDLE EAST LTD—See Hinduja Group Ltd.; *Int'l,* pg. 3398
GULF OIL PHILIPPINES, INC.—See Hinduja Group Ltd.; *Int'l,* pg. 3398
HAROON OILS LIMITED; *Int'l,* pg. 3278
HARVESTONE GROUP LLC; *U.S. Private,* pg. 1877
HENKEL NEDERLAND B.V., SCHEEMDA—See Henkel AG & Co. KGaA; *Int'l,* pg. 3353
HI-TECH LUBRICANTS LTD.; *Int'l,* pg. 3381
HORRISON RESOURCES INC.; *Int'l,* pg. 3482
H&R LUBE BLENDING GMBH—See H&R KGaA; *Int'l,* pg. 3193
H&R OLWERKE SCHINDLER GMBH—See H&R KGaA; *Int'l,* pg. 3193
HYDRASPECMA OY—See Aktieselskabet Schouw & Co.; *Int'l,* pg. 266
HYDROTEX PARTNERS LTD.; *U.S. Private,* pg. 2018
HYFCO TRADING AND INVESTMENTS COMPANY LIMITED—See Henderson Land Development Co, Ltd.; *Int'l,* pg. 3345
INDUSTRIAL OILS UNLIMITED, LLC—See KFM Enterprises, LLC; *U.S. Private,* pg. 2301

INFINEUM INTERNATIONAL LTD.—See Exxon Mobil Corporation; *U.S. Public,* pg. 814
INNOSPEC DEUTSCHLAND GMBH—See Innospec Inc.; *U.S. Public,* pg. 1125
INTERLUBES GMBH—See BayWa AG; *Int'l,* pg. 918
ITW ROCOL—See Illinois Tool Works Inc.; *U.S. Public,* pg. 1107
JAPAN SUN OIL COMPANY, LTD.—See Energy Transfer LP; *U.S. Public,* pg. 764
KLUBER LUBRICATION AUSTRIA GMBH—See Freudenberg SE; *Int'l,* pg. 2785
KLUBER LUBRICATION BENELUX S.A.—See Freudenberg SE; *Int'l,* pg. 2785
KLUBER LUBRICATION GMBH IBERICA S.EN C.—See Freudenberg SE; *Int'l,* pg. 2785
KLUBER LUBRICATION ITALIA S.A.S.—See Freudenberg SE; *Int'l,* pg. 2785
KLUBER LUBRICATION (KOREA) LTD.—See Freudenberg SE; *Int'l,* pg. 2785
KLUBER LUBRICATION LUBRIFICANTES ESPECIAIS LTDA. & CIA.—See Freudenberg SE; *Int'l,* pg. 2786
KLUBER LUBRICATION MEXICANA S.A. DE C.V.—See Freudenberg SE; *Int'l,* pg. 2786
KLUBER LUBRICATION MUNCHEN SE & CO. KG—See Freudenberg SE; *Int'l,* pg. 2786
KLUBER LUBRICATION NORTH AMERICA LP—See Freudenberg SE; *Int'l,* pg. 2786
KLUBER LUBRICATION SOUTH EAST ASIA PTE. LTD.—See Freudenberg SE; *Int'l,* pg. 2786
KLUBER LUBRICATION YAGLAMA URUNLERI SANAYI VE TICARET A.S.—See Freudenberg SE; *Int'l,* pg. 2786
KOREA HOUGHTON CORPORATION—See Quaker Chemical Corporation; *U.S. Public,* pg. 1746
LATIN ENERGY ARGENTINA—See BP plc; *Int'l,* pg. 1131
LUBRICANTS UK LTD—See BP plc; *Int'l,* pg. 1131
LUBRICATING SPECIALTIES COMPANY INC.—See Amalie Oil Company; *U.S. Private,* pg. 216
LUBRICATION ENGINEERS, INC.; *U.S. Private,* pg. 2510
LUBRIPLATE LUBRICANTS—See Fiske Brothers Refining Company; *U.S. Private,* pg. 1535
LUCAS OIL PRODUCTS INC.; *U.S. Private,* pg. 2510
MACDERMID CANNING—See Element Solutions Inc.; *U.S. Public,* pg. 727
MAKOTO-FUCHS K.K.—See FUCHS SE; *Int'l,* pg. 2804
MASTER CHEMICAL CORPORATION; *U.S. Private,* pg. 2607
MESA OIL INC.; *U.S. Private,* pg. 2677
METHES ENERGIES INTERNATIONAL LTD.; *U.S. Public,* pg. 1428
MICROGLEIT SPEZIALSCHMIERSTOFFE, GMBH—See Element Solutions Inc.; *U.S. Public,* pg. 728
MILLER INDUSTRIAL FLUIDS, LLC—See PetroChoice LLC; *U.S. Private,* pg. 3162
MOTOREX AG LANGENTHAL—See FUCHS SE; *Int'l,* pg. 2804
NANOSAVE TECHNOLOGIES, INC.; *U.S. Private,* pg. 2833
NEW FLUID SOLUTIONS INC.—See OMNOVA Solutions Inc.; *U.S. Public,* pg. 3017
NIPPON GREASE CO., LTD.—See Idemitsu Kosan Co., Ltd.; *Int'l,* pg. 3592
NOK-KLUBER CO., LTD.—See Freudenberg SE; *Int'l,* pg. 2786
NYE LUBRICANTS, INC.—See FUCHS SE; *Int'l,* pg. 2804
OIL CENTER RESEARCH INTERNATIONAL, LLC; *U.S. Private,* pg. 3006
OLYMPIC OIL, LTD.—See Aurora Capital Group, LLC; *U.S. Private,* pg. 394
OLYMPIC OIL, LTD.—See The Jordan Company, L.P.; *U.S. Private,* pg. 4061
OOO FUCHS OIL—See FUCHS SE; *Int'l,* pg. 2804
OPTIMOL OELWERKE INDUSTRIE GMBH & CO. KG—See BP plc; *Int'l,* pg. 1131
PARAFLUID MINERALOELGESELLSCHAFT MBH—See FUCHS SE; *Int'l,* pg. 2804
PERMAWICK COMPANY, INC.; *U.S. Private,* pg. 3152
PETROMIN CORPORATION—See Dabbagh Group Holding Company Ltd.; *Int'l,* pg. 1902
PETROMIN EGYPT—See Dabbagh Group Holding Company Ltd.; *Int'l,* pg. 1902
PETRON CORPORATION—See Wechco, Inc.; *U.S. Public,* pg. 4468
PROMOTORA FUCHS S.A. DE C.V.—See FUCHS SE; *Int'l,* pg. 2804
PT FEDERAL KARYATAMA—See Exxon Mobil Corporation; *U.S. Public,* pg. 817
PT FUCHS INDONESIA—See FUCHS SE; *Int'l,* pg. 2803
QUAKER CHEMICAL CORP. - MANUFACTURING & LOGISTICS - STEEL PRODUCTS—See Quaker Chemical Corporation; *U.S. Public,* pg. 1746
RAJ PETRO SPECIALITIES PRIVATE LIMITED—See BRENNTAG SE; *Int'l,* pg. 1149
RAJ PETRO SPECIALTIES DMCC—See BRENNTAG SE; *Int'l,* pg. 1149
RAVENSBERGER SCHMIERSTOFFVERTRIEB GMBH—See FUCHS SE; *Int'l,* pg. 2804
RESTORE INCORPORATED; *U.S. Private,* pg. 3410
RICHARDSAPEX INC.; *U.S. Private,* pg. 3429

ROCK VALLEY OIL & CHEMICAL COMPANY; *U.S. Private,* pg. 3465
ROYAL MANUFACTURING CO. INC.; *U.S. Private,* pg. 3492
SAFETY-KLEEN OIL RECOVERY CO.—See Clean Harbors, Inc.; *U.S. Public,* pg. 510
SCHAEFFER MANUFACTURING CO; *U.S. Private,* pg. 3563
SHANXI JAPAN ENERGY LUBRICANTS CO., LTD.—See ENEOS Holdings, Inc.; *Int'l,* pg. 2417
SILOGRAM LUBRICANTS CORP.; *U.S. Private,* pg. 3653
SOUTH COAST TERMINALS LP; *U.S. Private,* pg. 3721
SOUTHERN PLAINS OIL CORP.; *U.S. Public,* pg. 1912
SOUTHWESTERN PETROLEUM CANADA LTD.—See Southwestern Petroleum Corporation; *U.S. Private,* pg. 3742
SPUR ENERGY PARTNERS LLC—See KKR & Co. Inc.; *U.S. Public,* pg. 1264
STONER INC.; *U.S. Private,* pg. 3830
SUMMIT LUBRICANTS, INC.—See Quaker Chemical Corporation; *U.S. Public,* pg. 1747
TEXAS REFINERY CORP. - LUBRICANTS DIVISION—See Texas Refinery Corp.; *U.S. Private,* pg. 3977
TEXAS REFINERY CORP OF CANADA LIMITED—See Texas Refinery Corp.; *U.S. Private,* pg. 3977
TEXAS REFINERY CORP. - PROTECTIVE COATINGS DIVISION—See Texas Refinery Corp.; *U.S. Private,* pg. 3977
TEXAS REFINERY CORP.; *U.S. Private,* pg. 3977
THOMPSON INDUSTRIAL SUPPLY—See Thompson Industrial Services, LLC; *U.S. Private,* pg. 4159
U.S. LUBRICANTS—See U.S. Venture, Inc.; *U.S. Private,* pg. 4272
VALERO ENERGY INC.—See Valero Energy Corporation; *U.S. Public,* pg. 2272
VALERO REFINING-MERAUX LLC—See Valero Energy Corporation; *U.S. Public,* pg. 2272
WAKAYAMA PETROLEUM REFINING CO., LTD.—See ENEOS Holdings, Inc.; *Int'l,* pg. 2417
WARREN DISTRIBUTION, INC.; *U.S. Private,* pg. 4443
WHITMORE EUROPE LIMITED—See CSW Industrials, Inc.; *U.S. Public,* pg. 602
WYNN OIL COMPANY—See Illinois Tool Works Inc.; *U.S. Public,* pg. 1111

324199 — ALL OTHER PETROLEUM AND COAL PRODUCTS MANUFACTURING

ABDULLA FOUAD-SUPPLY & SERVICES DIVISION—See Abdulla Fouad Holding Co.; *Int'l,* pg. 59
ACE ETHANOL LLC; *U.S. Private,* pg. 56
ADKINS ENERGY LLC; *U.S. Private,* pg. 79
ADMIN NUCOAL; *Int'l,* pg. 151
ADVANCE METALS LIMITED; *Int'l,* pg. 156
AI ENERGY PUBLIC COMPANY LIMITED; *Int'l,* pg. 226
ALGENOL BIOFUELS GERMANY GMBH—See Algenol Biofuels Inc.; *U.S. Private,* pg. 166
ALGENOL BIOFUELS INC.; *U.S. Private,* pg. 166
ALUMINIUM SERVICES UK LIMITED—See Reliance Steel & Aluminum Co.; *U.S. Public,* pg. 1779
ANTHRACITE INDUSTRIES, INC.—See Great Mill Rock LLC; *U.S. Private,* pg. 1765
ARCELORMITTAL GEEL—See ArcelorMittal S.A.; *Int'l,* pg. 544
ARDOVA PLC.; *Int'l,* pg. 557
ASIA BIOMASS PUBLIC COMPANY LIMITED; *Int'l,* pg. 610
AUROMA COKE LIMITED; *Int'l,* pg. 713
BAOTAILONG NEW MATERIALS CO., LTD.; *Int'l,* pg. 856
BBHC, INC.; *U.S. Public,* pg. 284
BIODIESEL OKAYAMA CO., LTD.—See Dowa Holdings Co., Ltd.; *Int'l,* pg. 2183
BLUE BIOFUELS, INC.; *U.S. Public,* pg. 364
BP PRODUCTS NORTH AMERICA INC.—See BP plc; *Int'l,* pg. 1127
BUCYRUS (LANGFANG) MINING MACHINERY CO. LTD.—See Caterpillar, Inc.; *U.S. Public,* pg. 450
BYCO ISOMERISATION PAKISTAN (PRIVATE) LIMITED—See Byco Petroleum Pakistan Limited; *Int'l,* pg. 1234
CABOT ARGENTINA S.A.I.C.—See Cabot Corporation; *U.S. Public,* pg. 416
CALIFORNIA HEAVY OIL, INC.—See Occidental Petroleum Corporation; *U.S. Public,* pg. 1561
CALUMET BRANDED PRODUCTS, LLC—See Calumet, Inc.; *U.S. Public,* pg. 425
CALUMET REFINING, LLC—See Calumet, Inc.; *U.S. Public,* pg. 425
C & D PROPANE—See UGI Corporation; *U.S. Public,* pg. 2221
CHANGCHUN GAS CO., LTD.; *Int'l,* pg. 1442
CHARAH, INC.; *U.S. Private,* pg. 850
CHELSEA SANDWICH LLC—See Global Partners LP; *U.S. Public,* pg. 942
CHINA CLEAN ENERGY INC.; *Int'l,* pg. 1489
CHINA OILFIELD TECHNOLOGY SERVICES GROUP LIMITED; *Int'l,* pg. 1538
CHINA RISUN GROUP LTD.; *Int'l,* pg. 1549

N.A.I.C.S. INDEX

325110 — PETROCHEMICAL MANUF...

CHINA STEEL CHEMICAL CO., LTD.—See China Steel Corporation; *Int'l*, pg. 1555
CHINA STEEL CHEMICAL CORP.—See China Steel Corporation; *Int'l*, pg. 1555
CHK OIL LIMITED; *Int'l*, pg. 1575
CLEAN COAL TECHNOLOGIES, INC.; *U.S. Public*, pg. 508
CNX GAS CORPORATION—See CNX Resources Corporation; *U.S. Public*, pg. 520
COAL INDIA LIMITED; *Int'l*, pg. 1680
CONDEPOLS, S.A.; *Int'l*, pg. 1766
COPETRO, S.A.—See Oxbow Corporation; *U.S. Private*, pg. 3056
COSKATA, INC.; *U.S. Private*, pg. 1062
COSMO ENERGY EXPLORATION AND DEVELOPMENT LTD.—See Cosmo Energy Holdings Co., Ltd.; *Int'l*, pg. 1812
DAIDO STEEL (AMERICA) INC—See Daido Steel Co., Ltd.; *Int'l*, pg. 1923
DAVENPORT ENERGY INC.; *U.S. Private*, pg. 1169
DELEK PI GLILOT - LIMITED PARTNERSHIP—See Delek Group Ltd.; *Int'l*, pg. 2012
DGP CO.,LTD.; *Int'l*, pg. 2097
DHC SOLVENT CHEMIE GMBH—See BP plc; *Int'l*, pg. 1131
DORNOD AUTO ZAM JOINT STOCK COMPANY; *Int'l*, pg. 2179
DRUMMOND COMPANY, INC. - ABC COKE DIVISION—See Drummond Company, Inc.; *U.S. Private*, pg. 1280
E-COMMODITIES HOLDINGS LIMITED; *Int'l*, pg. 2247
ECOSLOPS SA; *Int'l*, pg. 2299
ENERGY ABSOLUTE PUBLIC COMPANY LIMITED; *Int'l*, pg. 2422
ENOC PROCESSING COMPANY LLC—See Emirates National Oil Company Limited; *Int'l*, pg. 2381
ENVIRO ENERGY INTERNATIONAL HOLDINGS LIMITED; *Int'l*, pg. 2454
ETERNA PLC.; *Int'l*, pg. 2520
EUGLENA CO., LTD.; *Int'l*, pg. 2526
FORESIGHT ENERGY LP; *U.S. Public*, pg. 867
FORMOSA HYDROCARBONS COMPANY, INC.—See Formosa Plastics Corporation; *Int'l*, pg. 2735
FORUM PACIFIC INC.; *Int'l*, pg. 2744
FREEDOM HOLDINGS, INC.; *U.S. Public*, pg. 884
FUCHS LUBRICANTS CO. - MINING DIVISION—See FUCHS SE; *Int'l*, pg. 2803
FUCHS SMORJMEDEL SVERIGE AB—See FUCHS SE; *Int'l*, pg. 2802
FUTUREFUEL CORP.; *U.S. Public*, pg. 893
GALILEE ENERGY LIMITED; *Int'l*, pg. 2873
GENOL GESELLSCHAFT MBH—See BayWa AG; *Int'l*, pg. 918
GENUINE BIO-FUEL, INC.; *U.S. Private*, pg. 1680
GIB OIL LIMITED—See World Kinect Corporation; *U.S. Public*, pg. 2380
GILBARCO CHINA CO. LTD—See Vontier Corporation; *U.S. Public*, pg. 2308
GILBARCO QUEENSLAND PTY. LTD.—See Vontier Corporation; *U.S. Public*, pg. 2308
GLOBAL NUCLEAR FUEL - JAPAN CO., LTD.—See General Electric Company; *U.S. Public*, pg. 920
GOA CARBON LTD.; *Int'l*, pg. 3017
GOOD ENERGY GROUP PLC; *Int'l*, pg. 3038
GRAND OCEAN RESOURCES COMPANY LIMITED; *Int'l*, pg. 3055
GREAT WALL INTERNATIONAL ACG CO., LTD.; *Int'l*, pg. 3065
GRIGEO KLAIPEDA AB—See Grigeo AB; *Int'l*, pg. 3085
GUANGZHOU DEVOTION THERMAL TECHNOLOGY CO., LTD.; *Int'l*, pg. 3165
GUJARAT NRE COKE LTD.; *Int'l*, pg. 3177
HAVERHILL NORTH COKE COMPANY—See SunCoke Energy, Inc.; *U.S. Public*, pg. 1963
HENAN JINMA ENERGY COMPANY LIMITED; *Int'l*, pg. 3342
HENAN SHEN HUO COAL INDUSTRY & ELECTRICITY POWER CO., LTD.; *Int'l*, pg. 3343
HUTA POKOJ S.A.; *Int'l*, pg. 3540
IDEMITSU LUBE (CHINA) CO., LTD.—See Idemitsu Kosan Co., Ltd.; *Int'l*, pg. 3591
IDEMITSU LUBE SOUTH AMERICA LTDA.—See Idemitsu Kosan Co., Ltd.; *Int'l*, pg. 3591
IDEMITSU LUBRICANTS AMERICA CORPORATION—See Idemitsu Kosan Co., Ltd.; *Int'l*, pg. 3591
IDEMITSU LUBRICANTS RUS LLC—See Idemitsu Kosan Co., Ltd.; *Int'l*, pg. 3591
INDIANA HARBOR COKE CORPORATION—See Energy Transfer LP; *U.S. Public*, pg. 764
JEWELL COAL & COKE COMPANY, INC.—See SunCoke Energy, Inc.; *U.S. Public*, pg. 1964
JEWELL RESOURCES CORPORATION—See SunCoke Energy, Inc.; *U.S. Public*, pg. 1963
KELLER ENTERPRISES, INC.; *U.S. Private*, pg. 2274
KILDAIR SERVICE ULC—See Axel Johnson Gruppen AB; *Int'l*, pg. 765
KIOR, INC.; *U.S. Private*, pg. 2313
KOCH CARBON, LLC—See Koch Industries, Inc.; *U.S. Private*, pg. 2331
KOCH MINERALS, LLC—See Koch Industries, Inc.; *U.S. Private*, pg. 2333
LAIDLAW ENERGY GROUP, INC.; *U.S. Private*, pg. 2373
LUBRICANTES FUCHS DE MEXICO S.A. DE C.V.—See FUCHS SE; *Int'l*, pg. 2804
MID-CONTINENT COAL & COKE COMPANY—See Mid-Continent Minerals Corporation; *U.S. Private*, pg. 2708
MIDDLE EAST RESOURCES CO.—See Al-Osais International Holding Company; *Int'l*, pg. 288
MOUNTAIN STATE CARBON, LLC—See Cleveland-Cliffs, Inc.; *U.S. Public*, pg. 514
NEW AMERICA ENERGY CORP.; *U.S. Public*, pg. 1511
NEWMARKET CORPORATION; *U.S. Public*, pg. 1516
NEXLUBE TAMPA LLC; *U.S. Private*, pg. 2919
NIPPON OIL LUBRICANTS (AMERICA) LLC—See ENEOS Holdings, Inc.; *Int'l*, pg. 2417
NOV MISSION PRODUCTS UK LIMITED—See NOV, Inc.; *U.S. Public*, pg. 1545
NUCOR STEEL JACKSON, INC.—See Nucor Corporation; *U.S. Public*, pg. 1554
NUCOR STEEL-SOUTH CAROLINA—See Nucor Corporation; *U.S. Public*, pg. 1554
NYNAS AB—See Bitumina Industries Ltd.; *Int'l*, pg. 1050
NYNAS UK AB—See Bitumina Industries Ltd.; *Int'l*, pg. 1051
OCCIDENTAL ENERGY VENTURES CORP.—See Occidental Petroleum Corporation; *U.S. Public*, pg. 1561
OXBOW CALCINING LLC—See Oxbow Corporation; *U.S. Private*, pg. 3056
OXBOW COAL S.A.R.L.—See Oxbow Corporation; *U.S. Private*, pg. 3056
OXBOW CORPORATION; *U.S. Private*, pg. 3056
OXBOW GMBH—See Oxbow Corporation; *U.S. Private*, pg. 3056
PACIFIC ETHANOL COLUMBIA, LLC—See Alto Ingredients, Inc.; *U.S. Public*, pg. 88
PACIFIC ETHANOL MADERA LLC—See Alto Ingredients, Inc.; *U.S. Public*, pg. 88
PACIFIC ETHANOL MAGIC VALLEY, LLC—See Alto Ingredients, Inc.; *U.S. Public*, pg. 88
PEABODY ENERGY AUSTRALIA COAL PTY LTD—See Peabody Energy Corporation; *U.S. Public*, pg. 1659
PE OP CO.—See Alto Ingredients, Inc.; *U.S. Public*, pg. 88
PETROTEC BIODIESEL GMBH—See Chevron Corporation; *U.S. Public*, pg. 487
PHILLIPS 66 PARTNERS LP—See Phillips 66 Company; *U.S. Public*, pg. 1688
QUANTUM SCREENING AND CRUSHING (PROPRIETARY) LIMITED—See Canaf Investments Inc.; *Int'l*, pg. 1287
RAAB KARCHER FRANCE S.A.—See Compagnie de Saint-Gobain SA; *Int'l*, pg. 1733
RAIL BEARING SERVICE CORP.—See The Timken Company; *U.S. Public*, pg. 2133
REG SYNTHETIC FUELS, LLC—See Chevron Corporation; *U.S. Public*, pg. 488
RENEWABLE FUEL CORP.; *U.S. Private*, pg. 3398
ROYAL OAK ENTERPRISES, INC.; *U.S. Private*, pg. 3493
SAFE&CEC S.R.L.—See Clean Energy Fuels Corp.; *U.S. Public*, pg. 508
SANTOKU CORPORATION—See Hitachi, Ltd.; *Int'l*, pg. 3424
SAUDI ARABIAN CHEVRON INC.—See Chevron Corporation; *U.S. Public*, pg. 488
SCHRADENBIOGAS GMBH & CO. KG—See BayWa AG; *Int'l*, pg. 919
SEABOARD ENERGY KANSAS, LLC—See Seaboard Corporation; *U.S. Public*, pg. 1851
SEADRIFT COKE L.P.—See Brookfield Corporation; *U.S. Public*, pg. 1187
SHOWA YOKKAICHI SEKIYU CO., LTD.—See Idemitsu Kosan Co., Ltd.; *Int'l*, pg. 3592
SOUTHERN POST COMPANY—See Commercial Metals Company; *U.S. Public*, pg. 546
SUNCOKE ENERGY, INC.; *U.S. Public*, pg. 1963
SUNFIELD RESOURCES PTY. LIMITED—See China Coal Energy Company Limited; *Int'l*, pg. 1490
SYNTHESIS ENERGY SYSTEMS, INC.; *U.S. Public*, pg. 1972
TEXAS INDUSTRIES, INC.—See Martin Marietta Materials, Inc.; *U.S. Public*, pg. 1389
TIDELANDS ROYALTY TRUST B; *U.S. Public*, pg. 2158
TOMATO COAL CENTER—See Hokkaido Electric Power Co., Inc.; *Int'l*, pg. 3443
TONAWANDA COKE CORP; *U.S. Private*, pg. 4184
TRAMP OIL DISTRIBUIDORA LTDA.—See World Kinect Corporation; *U.S. Public*, pg. 2381
UNIVERSAL BIOENERGY, INC.; *U.S. Private*, pg. 4303
VERTEX ENERGY, INC.; *U.S. Public*, pg. 2287
VIASPACE GREEN ENERGY INC.—See VIASPACE INC.; *U.S. Public*, pg. 2292
VIASPACE INC.; *U.S. Public*, pg. 2292
WINTERSHALL AG—See BASF SE; *Int'l*, pg. 885
XCELPLUS INTERNATIONAL, INC.; *U.S. Public*, pg. 2385

325110 — PETROCHEMICAL MANUFACTURING

AARVI ENGINEERING & CONSULTANTS PRIVATE LIMITED—See Aarvi Encon Ltd.; *Int'l*, pg. 38
ADVANCED PETROCHEMICAL COMPANY; *Int'l*, pg. 161
ADVANCE PETROCHEMICALS LIMITED - AHMEDABAD WORKS—See Advance Petrochemicals Limited; *Int'l*, pg. 156
ADVANCE PETROCHEMICALS LIMITED; *Int'l*, pg. 156
AEKYUNG CHEMICAL CO., LTD.—See AK Holdings, Inc.; *Int'l*, pg. 259
AGC VINYTHAI PUBLIC COMPANY LIMITED—See AGC Inc.; *Int'l*, pg. 203
AGPRO (N.Z.) LTD.—See RPM International Inc.; *U.S. Public*, pg. 1819
AKRA POLYESTER, S.A. DE C.V.—See ALFA, S.A.B. de C.V.; *Int'l*, pg. 313
ALBEMARLE SORBENT TECHNOLOGIES—See Albemarle Corporation; *U.S. Public*, pg. 73
ALFA CORPORATIVO, S.A. DE C.V.—See ALFA, S.A.B. de C.V.; *Int'l*, pg. 313
ALPEK POLYESTER S.A. DE C.V.—See ALFA, S.A.B. de C.V.; *Int'l*, pg. 313
ALPHAGARY LIMITED—See Grupo Empresarial Kaluz S.A. de C.V.; *Int'l*, pg. 3127
ANDES CHEMICAL CORPORATION—See IMCD N.V.; *Int'l*, pg. 3621
ANGUS CHEMIE GMBH—See Golden Gate Capital Management II, LLC; *U.S. Private*, pg. 1730
ASSAM PETRO-CHEMICALS LTD.; *Int'l*, pg. 641
BASF FINA PETROCHEMICALS LP—See BASF SE; *Int'l*, pg. 876
BASF-YPC COMPANY LIMITED—See BASF SE; *Int'l*, pg. 877
BASF-YPC COMPANY LIMITED—See China Petrochemical Corporation; *Int'l*, pg. 1539
BIOAMBER INC.; *Int'l*, pg. 1036
BOUBYAN PETROCHEMICAL CO. KSC; *Int'l*, pg. 1119
BP AMOCO CHEMICAL COMPANY—See BP plc; *Int'l*, pg. 1126
BRUNEL INDIA PRIVATE LTD.—See Brunel International N.V.; *Int'l*, pg. 1200
CALUMET PACKAGING, LLC—See Calumet, Inc.; *U.S. Public*, pg. 425
CALUMET SAN ANTONIO REFINING, LLC—See Calumet, Inc.; *U.S. Public*, pg. 425
CALUMET SPECIALTY PRODUCTS PARTNERS, L.P.—See Calumet, Inc.; *U.S. Public*, pg. 425
CHANDRA PRABHU INTERNATIONAL LTD.; *Int'l*, pg. 1441
CHEVRON ORONITE COMPANY LLC—See Chevron Corporation; *U.S. Public*, pg. 486
CHEVRON PHILLIPS CHEMICAL COMPANY LLC—See Chevron Corporation; *U.S. Public*, pg. 486
CHEVRON PHILLIPS CHEMICAL COMPANY LLC—See Phillips 66 Company; *U.S. Public*, pg. 1688
CHINA JINSHAN ASSOCIATED TRADING CORP.—See China Petrochemical Corporation; *Int'l*, pg. 1539
CHINESE PETROLEUM ENGINEERING CORPORATION; *Int'l*, pg. 1569
CIL NOVA PETROCHEMICALS LIMITED—See Chiripal Industries Ltd.; *Int'l*, pg. 1573
CLEANSORB LIMITED—See Newpark Resources, Inc.; *U.S. Public*, pg. 1517
CONSTRUCTION SPECIALTIES (SINGAPORE) PTE. LTD.—See Construction Specialties, Inc.; *U.S. Private*, pg. 1024
COSMO ENGINEERING CO., LTD.—See Cosmo Energy Holdings Co., Ltd.; *Int'l*, pg. 1812
CROSS TIMBERS ENERGY SERVICES, INC.—See Exxon Mobil Corporation; *U.S. Public*, pg. 813
DAELIM CORPORATION—See Daelim Industrial Co., Ltd.; *Int'l*, pg. 1908
DAQING HUAKE COMPANY LIMITED; *Int'l*, pg. 1971
DC ALABAMA, INC.—See Dow Inc.; *U.S. Public*, pg. 683
DCW LIMITED - SAHUPURAM UNIT—See DCW Limited; *Int'l*, pg. 1993
DIAMOND K RANCH LLC—See Valero Energy Corporation; *U.S. Public*, pg. 2272
DIOKI D.D.; *Int'l*, pg. 2127
DL CHEMICAL CO. LTD.—See Daelim Industrial Co., Ltd.; *Int'l*, pg. 1908
DMC-NORTHERN PETROLIUM CHEMICALS JOINT STOCK COMPANY; *Int'l*, pg. 2142
DOVER CHEMICAL—See ICC Industries, Inc.; *U.S. Private*, pg. 2029
DOW AUSTRIA GESELLSCHAFT M.B.H—See Dow Inc.; *U.S. Public*, pg. 683
DOW BRASIL SUDESTE INDUSTRIAL LTDA.—See Dow Inc.; *U.S. Public*, pg. 683
DOW CHEMICAL BANGLADESH PRIVATE LIMITED—See Dow Inc.; *U.S. Public*, pg. 683
DOW CHEMICAL ROMANIA S.R.L.—See Dow Inc.; *U.S. Public*, pg. 684
DOW CHEMICAL (SICHUAN) CO., LTD.—See Dow Inc.; *U.S. Public*, pg. 683
DOW CHEMICAL SILICONES KOREA, LTD.—See Dow Inc.; *U.S. Public*, pg. 684
DOW CHEMICAL THAILAND LTD.—See Dow Inc.; *U.S. Public*, pg. 684
DOW CHEMICAL VIETNAM LLC—See Dow Inc.; *U.S. Public*, pg. 684

325110 — PETROCHEMICAL MANUF...

DOW EGYPT SERVICES LIMITED—See Dow Inc.; *U.S. Public*, pg. 684
DOW ITALIA DIVISIONE COMMERCIALE S.R.L—See Dow Inc.; *U.S. Public*, pg. 685
DOW MATERIALS SCIENCE SAUDI ARABIA LIMITED—See Dow Inc.; *U.S. Public*, pg. 685
DOW PERU S.A.—See Dow Inc.; *U.S. Public*, pg. 685
DOW QUIMICA MEXICANA S.A. DE C.V.—See Dow Inc.; *U.S. Public*, pg. 685
DOW SILICONES DEUTSCHLAND GMBH—See Dow Inc.; *U.S. Public*, pg. 685
DOW SILICONES (SHANGHAI) CO., LTD.—See Dow Inc.; *U.S. Public*, pg. 685
DOW SILICONES (ZHANGJIAGANG) CO., LTD.—See Dow Inc.; *U.S. Public*, pg. 685
DOW SILOXANES (ZHANGJIAGANG) CO., LTD.—See Dow Inc.; *U.S. Public*, pg. 685
DYNAMIC CHEMICAL PTE. LTD.—See Ancom Nylex Berhad; *Int'l*, pg. 449
ENEOS CORPORATION—See ENEOS Holdings, Inc.; *Int'l*, pg. 2415
ENERCHEM INTERNATIONAL, INC.; *Int'l*, pg. 2418
EXXONMOBIL CHEMICAL COMPANY—See Exxon Mobil Corporation; *U.S. Public*, pg. 814
FERRO CORPORATION - SPECIALTY COLOR DIVISION—See American Securities LLC; *U.S. Private*, pg. 251
FHR PROPYLENE LLC—See Koch Industries, Inc.; *U.S. Private*, pg. 2327
FIRST CHEMICAL TEXAS, L.P.—See The Chemours Company; *U.S. Public*, pg. 2059
FORMOSA IDEMITSU PETROCHEMICAL CORPORATION—See Idemitsu Kosan Co., Ltd.; *Int'l*, pg. 3590
FORMOSA PETROCHEMICAL TRANSPORTATION CORPORATION—See Formosa Plastics Corporation; *Int'l*, pg. 2735
FUJIAN GREEN PINE CO., LTD.; *Int'l*, pg. 2818
GLOBAL INDUSTRIAL CORPORATION—See Dow Inc.; *U.S. Public*, pg. 685
GREENCHEM INDUSTRIES LLC; *U.S. Private*, pg. 1776
GREEN POWER GENERATION JSC; *Int'l*, pg. 3072
GRUPO ZULIANO, C.A.; *Int'l*, pg. 3139
GUANGDONG HONGCHUAN SMART LOGISTICS CO., LTD.; *Int'l*, pg. 3155
HAIKE CHEMICAL GROUP LTD; *Int'l*, pg. 3210
HALDIA PETROCHEMICALS LIMITED—See The Chatterjee Group; *U.S. Private*, pg. 4007
HANWHA SOLUTIONS CORPORATION; *Int'l*, pg. 3267
HAWTHORNE PAINT COMPANY, INC.—See SK Capital Partners, LP; *U.S. Private*, pg. 3679
HELPE ARTA PREVEZA SA—See HELLENiQ ENERGY Holdings S.A.; *Int'l*, pg. 3334
HENKEL MEXICANA S.A. DE C.V.—See Henkel AG & Co. KGaA; *Int'l*, pg. 3351
HERSHEY ENVIRONMENTAL TECHNOLOGY CO., LTD.—See Formosan Union Chemical Corp.; *Int'l*, pg. 2736
HINDUSTAN COLAS PVT. LTD.—See Bouygues S.A.; *Int'l*, pg. 1123
HORIZON SINGAPORE TERMINALS PRIVATE LIMITED—See Emirates National Oil Company Limited; *Int'l*, pg. 2381
HUIZHOU LCY ELASTOMERS CORP.—See KKR & Co. Inc.; *U.S. Public*, pg. 1258
HUNTSMAN DE MEXICO, S.A. DE C.V.—See Huntsman Corporation; *U.S. Public*, pg. 1074
HYUNDAI COSMO PETROCHEMICAL CO., LTD.—See Cosmo Energy Holdings Co., Ltd.; *Int'l*, pg. 1812
IDEMITSU CHEMICALS SOUTHEAST ASIA PTE. LTD.—See Idemitsu Kosan Co., Ltd.; *Int'l*, pg. 3590
IDEMITSU CHEMICALS U.S.A. CORPORATION—See Idemitsu Kosan Co., Ltd.; *Int'l*, pg. 3590
IDEMITSU PETROCHEMICAL CO., LTD.—See Idemitsu Kosan Co., Ltd.; *Int'l*, pg. 3591
IDEMITSU SM (MALAYSIA) SDN. BHD.—See Idemitsu Kosan Co., Ltd.; *Int'l*, pg. 3591
IG PETROCHEMICALS LTD.; *Int'l*, pg. 3601
INDUSTRIAS CYDSA BAYER, S.A. DE C.V.—See Cydsa S.A.B. de C.V.; *Int'l*, pg. 1895
INDUSTRIENETZGESELLSCHAFT SCHKOPAU MBH—See Dow Inc.; *U.S. Public*, pg. 683
KOZHAN JSC—See Geo-Jade Petroleum Corporation; *Int'l*, pg. 2932
LCY ELASTOMERS LP—See KKR & Co. Inc.; *U.S. Public*, pg. 1258
LEE CHANG YUNG TECHNOLOGY CORPORATION—See KKR & Co. Inc.; *U.S. Public*, pg. 1258
LOTOS PARAFINY SP. Z O.O.—See Grupa LOTOS S.A.; *Int'l*, pg. 3117
LUMASENSE, VENDAS BRASIL—See Advanced Energy Industries, Inc.; *U.S. Public*, pg. 47
MARUZEN PETROCHEMICAL CO., LTD.—See Cosmo Energy Holdings Co., Ltd.; *Int'l*, pg. 1812
MUNA NOOR MANUFACTURING AND TRADING CO. L.L.C—See Boubyan Petrochemical Co. KSC; *Int'l*, pg. 1119
NORTH AMERICAN SPECIALTY PRODUCTS LLC—See Westlake Corporation; *U.S. Public*, pg. 2360
ORBIA ADVANCE CORPORATION, S.A.B. DE C.V.—See Grupo Empresarial Kaluz S.A. de C.V.; *Int'l*, pg. 3127
PETROCHEMICALS (MALAYSIA) SDN. BHD.—See Idemitsu Kosan Co., Ltd.; *Int'l*, pg. 3592
POLIMERI EUROPA SPA—See Eni S.p.A.; *Int'l*, pg. 2438
POLIOLES S.A. DE C.V.—See ALFA, S.A.B. de C.V.; *Int'l*, pg. 313
POLIOLES S.A. DE C.V.—See BASF SE; *Int'l*, pg. 876
PORT NECHES FUELS, LLC—See First Reserve Management, L.P.; *U.S. Private*, pg. 1526
PORT NECHES FUELS, LLC—See SK Capital Partners, LP; *U.S. Private*, pg. 3680
PRIME POLYMER CO., LTD.—See Idemitsu Kosan Co., Ltd.; *Int'l*, pg. 3592
PROEN SCAFFOLD PTE. LTD.—See Hiap Seng Engineering Limited; *Int'l*, pg. 3382
P.T. ADVANCED AGRI INDONESIA—See Advanced Holdings Ltd.; *Int'l*, pg. 159
QUANZHOU GRAND PACIFIC CHEMICAL CO., LTD.—See Grand Pacific Petrochemical Corporation; *Int'l*, pg. 3055
R.C. MULTIBOND DURAL S.R.L.—See CFS Group, Inc.; *Int'l*, pg. 1430
ROHM AND HAAS KIMYA SANAYI LIMITED SIRKETI—See Dow Inc.; *U.S. Public*, pg. 686
SANYO PETROCHEMICAL CO., LTD.—See Asahi Kasei Corporation; *Int'l*, pg. 597
SAUDI TECHNOLOGY & LOGISTICS SERVICES LIMITED—See BAE Systems plc; *Int'l*, pg. 799
SHANGHAI SECCO PETROCHEMICAL CO., LTD.—See BP plc; *Int'l*, pg. 1131
SHANGHAI SECCO PETROCHEMICAL CO., LTD.—See China Petrochemical Corporation; *Int'l*, pg. 1539
SI GROUP, INC.—See SK Capital Partners, LP; *U.S. Private*, pg. 3679
SI GROUP INDIA LTD—See SK Capital Partners, LP; *U.S. Private*, pg. 3679
SINOPEC BEIJING YANHUA PETROCHEMICAL COMPANY LIMITED—See China Petrochemical Corporation; *Int'l*, pg. 1539
SINOPEC FUJIAN REFINING & CHEMICAL CO., LTD.—See China Petrochemical Corporation; *Int'l*, pg. 1539
SINOPEC GUANGZHOU COMPANY—See China Petrochemical Corporation; *Int'l*, pg. 1539
SINOPEC QILU PETROCHEMICAL CO., LTD.—See China Petrochemical Corporation; *Int'l*, pg. 1539
SINOPEC SHENGLI OILFIELD CO., LTD.—See China Petrochemical Corporation; *Int'l*, pg. 1539
SINOPEC TAISHAN OIL PRODUCTS CO., LTD.—See China Petrochemical Corporation; *Int'l*, pg. 1539
SINOPEC WUHAN PHOENIX CO., LTD.—See China Petrochemical Corporation; *Int'l*, pg. 1540
SINOPEC ZHENHAI REFINING & CHEMICAL CO., LTD.—See China Petrochemical Corporation; *Int'l*, pg. 1540
SOUTH HAMPTON RESOURCES, INC.—See Balmoral Funds LLC; *U.S. Private*, pg. 462
TEXAS BUTYLENE CHEMICAL CORPORATION—See First Reserve Management, L.P.; *U.S. Private*, pg. 1526
TEXAS BUTYLENE CHEMICAL CORPORATION—See SK Capital Partners, LP; *U.S. Private*, pg. 3680
TONEN CHEMICAL CORPORATION—See ENEOS Holdings, Inc.; *Int'l*, pg. 2417
TPC GROUP INC.—See First Reserve Management, L.P.; *U.S. Private*, pg. 1526
TPC GROUP INC.—See SK Capital Partners, LP; *U.S. Private*, pg. 3680
TRECORA, LLC—See Balmoral Funds LLC; *U.S. Private*, pg. 461
VALERO MARKETING AND SUPPLY DE MEXICO S.A. DE C.V.—See Valero Energy Corporation; *U.S. Public*, pg. 2272
VALERO TERMINALING AND DISTRIBUTION DE MEXICO, S.A. DE C.V.—See Valero Energy Corporation; *U.S. Public*, pg. 2272
WESTLAKE OLEFINS CORPORATION—See Westlake Corporation; *U.S. Public*, pg. 2360
WESTLAKE VINNOLIT GMBH & CO. KG—See Westlake Corporation; *U.S. Public*, pg. 2361
WESTLAKE VINYLS COMPANY LP—See Westlake Corporation; *U.S. Public*, pg. 2361
WPT LLC—See Westlake Corporation; *U.S. Public*, pg. 2360
YEOCHUN NCC CO., LTD.—See Daelim Industrial Co., Ltd.; *Int'l*, pg. 1908
YEOCHUN NCC CO., LTD.—See Hanwha Group; *Int'l*, pg. 3266
ZHENJIANG LCY WAREHOUSING & STORAGE CO., LTD.—See KKR & Co. Inc.; *U.S. Public*, pg. 1258

325120 — INDUSTRIAL GAS MANUFACTURING

ABDULLA HASHIM GASES & EQUIPMENT CO. LIMITED—See Air Products & Chemicals, Inc.; *U.S. Public*, pg. 64
ABDULLAH HASHIM INDUSTRIAL GASES & EQUIPMENT CO. LTD.; *Int'l*, pg. 59
ABU DHABI GAS INDUSTRIES LIMITED—See Abu Dhabi National Oil Company; *Int'l*, pg. 72
AEROPRES CORPORATION-SIBLEY PLANT—See Aeropres Corporation; *U.S. Private*, pg. 119
AEROPRES CORPORATION; *U.S. Private*, pg. 119
AIR LIQUIDE AL-KHAFRAH INDUSTRIAL GASES LLC—See Abdullah Hashim Industrial Gases & Equipment Co. Ltd.; *Int'l*, pg. 59
AIR LIQUIDE BENIN S.A.—See Adenia Partners Ltd; *Int'l*, pg. 143
AIR LIQUIDE BURKINA FASO S.A.—See Adenia Partners Ltd; *Int'l*, pg. 143
AIR LIQUIDE CAMEROUN S.A.—See Adenia Partners Ltd; *Int'l*, pg. 143
AIR LIQUIDE CONGO S.A.—See Adenia Partners Ltd; *Int'l*, pg. 143
AIR LIQUIDE COTE D'IVOIRE S.A.—See Adenia Partners Ltd; *Int'l*, pg. 143
AIR LIQUIDE GHANA LTD.—See Adenia Partners Ltd; *Int'l*, pg. 143
AIR LIQUIDE MADAGASCAR S.A.—See Adenia Partners Ltd; *Int'l*, pg. 143
AIR LIQUIDE MALI S.A.—See Adenia Partners Ltd; *Int'l*, pg. 143
AIR LIQUIDE SENEGAL S.A.—See Adenia Partners Ltd; *Int'l*, pg. 143
AIR LIQUIDE TOGO S.A.—See Adenia Partners Ltd; *Int'l*, pg. 143
AIR PRODUCTS AND CHEMICALS (NANJING) CO., LTD.—See Air Products & Chemicals, Inc.; *U.S. Public*, pg. 66
AIR PRODUCTS ASIA, INC.—See Air Products & Chemicals, Inc.; *U.S. Public*, pg. 64
AIR PRODUCTS A/S—See Air Products & Chemicals, Inc.; *U.S. Public*, pg. 64
AIR PRODUCTS BRASIL LTDA.—See Air Products & Chemicals, Inc.; *U.S. Public*, pg. 64
AIR PRODUCTS CANADA LTD.—See Air Products & Chemicals, Inc.; *U.S. Public*, pg. 64
AIR PRODUCTS CHILE S. A.—See Air Products & Chemicals, Inc.; *U.S. Public*, pg. 64
AIR PRODUCTS GB LIMITED—See Air Products & Chemicals, Inc.; *U.S. Public*, pg. 65
AIR PRODUCTS GMBH—See Air Products & Chemicals, Inc.; *U.S. Public*, pg. 65
AIR PRODUCTS GMBH—See Air Products & Chemicals, Inc.; *U.S. Public*, pg. 65
AIR PRODUCTS ITALIA—See Air Products & Chemicals, Inc.; *U.S. Public*, pg. 65
AIR PRODUCTS KOREA, INC.—See Air Products & Chemicals, Inc.; *U.S. Public*, pg. 65
AIR PRODUCTS MANUFACTURING CORPORATION—See Air Products & Chemicals, Inc.; *U.S. Public*, pg. 65
AIR PRODUCTS (MIDDLE EAST) FZE—See Air Products & Chemicals, Inc.; *U.S. Public*, pg. 64
AIR PRODUCTS NEDERLAND B.V.—See Air Products & Chemicals, Inc.; *U.S. Public*, pg. 65
AIR PRODUCTS NEDERLAND B.V.—See Air Products & Chemicals, Inc.; *U.S. Public*, pg. 65
AIR PRODUCTS NEDERLAND B.V.—See Air Products & Chemicals, Inc.; *U.S. Public*, pg. 65
AIR PRODUCTS NEDERLAND B.V.—See Air Products & Chemicals, Inc.; *U.S. Public*, pg. 65
AIR PRODUCTS PERU S.A.—See Air Products & Chemicals, Inc.; *U.S. Public*, pg. 65
AIR PRODUCTS PLC—See Air Products & Chemicals, Inc.; *U.S. Public*, pg. 65
AIR PRODUCTS PLC—See Air Products & Chemicals, Inc.; *U.S. Public*, pg. 65
AIR PRODUCTS SAN FU GAS CO., LTD.—See Air Products & Chemicals, Inc.; *U.S. Public*, pg. 65
AIR PRODUCTS S.A.—See Air Products & Chemicals, Inc.; *U.S. Public*, pg. 65
AIR PRODUCTS SINGAPORE INDUSTRIAL GASES PTE. LTD.—See Air Products & Chemicals, Inc.; *U.S. Public*, pg. 65
AIR PRODUCTS SINGAPORE PTE LTD.—See Air Products & Chemicals, Inc.; *U.S. Public*, pg. 66
AIR PRODUCTS SOUTH AFRICA (PTY) LTD.—See Air Products & Chemicals, Inc.; *U.S. Public*, pg. 66
AIR PRODUCTS STB—See Air Products & Chemicals, Inc.; *U.S. Public*, pg. 65
AIR PRODUCTS STB—See Air Products & Chemicals, Inc.; *U.S. Public*, pg. 65
AIR PRODUCTS TAIWAN CO., LTD.—See Air Products & Chemicals, Inc.; *U.S. Public*, pg. 66
AIR WATER CARBONIC INC.—See Air Water Inc.; *Int'l*, pg. 239
AIR WATER INC. - HOKKAIDO—See Air Water Inc.; *Int'l*, pg. 239
AIR WATER INC.; *Int'l*, pg. 239
AIR WATER, INC. - TOKYO—See Air Water Inc.; *Int'l*, pg. 239
ALPHA BILLION SDN. BHD.—See B.I.G. Industries Berhad; *Int'l*, pg. 790
APPLIED NATURAL GAS FUELS, INC.; *U.S. Private*, pg. 299

N.A.I.C.S. INDEX

BANGKOK INDUSTRIAL GAS CO., LTD.—See Air Products & Chemicals, Inc.; *U.S. Public*, pg. 66
BANGKOK INDUSTRIAL GAS CO., LTD.—See Bangkok Bank Public Company Limited; *Int'l*, pg. 833
BEIJING AP BAIF GAS INDUSTRY CO., LTD.—See Air Products & Chemicals, Inc.; *U.S. Public*, pg. 64
BHAGAWATI OXYGEN LIMITED; *Int'l*, pg. 1009
B.I.G. INDUSTRIAL GAS SDN. BHD.—See B.I.G. Industries Berhad; *Int'l*, pg. 790
B.I.G. INDUSTRIES BERHAD; *Int'l*, pg. 789
BIOGAZ FEJLESZTO KFT.—See AGRANA Beteiligungs-AG; *Int'l*, pg. 214
BOMBAY OXYGEN INVESTMENTS LTD.; *Int'l*, pg. 1104
BRUMIT OIL CO. INC.; *U.S. Private*, pg. 672
CARBIDE INDUSTRIES, LLC.; *U.S. Private*, pg. 748
CARVEMAGERE MANUTENCAO E ENERGIAS RENOVAVEIS LDA—See Enel S.p.A.; *Int'l*, pg. 2411
CELLA ACQUISITION LTD.—See Persephone Capital Partners LLC; *U.S. Private*, pg. 3154
CHARBONE HYDROGEN CORPORATION; *Int'l*, pg. 1448
CHART FEROX A.S.—See Chart Industries, Inc.; *U.S. Public*, pg. 481
CHART LATIN AMERICA S.A.S.—See Chart Industries, Inc.; *U.S. Public*, pg. 481
CHEMOGAS N.V.—See Balchem Corporation; *U.S. Public*, pg. 265
CHENZHOU XIANGNENG SEMICONDUCTOR GAS CO., LTD.—See Guangdong Huate Gas Co., Ltd.; *Int'l*, pg. 3156
CHILL BRANDS GROUP PLC; *Int'l*, pg. 1478
CHUBU LIQUID OXYGEN CO., LTD.—See Chubu Electric Power Co., Inc.; *Int'l*, pg. 1593
CLEAN POWER HYDROGEN GROUP LIMITED—See Clean Power Hydrogen Plc; *Int'l*, pg. 1654
COALFIELD PIPELINE COMPANY—See CNX Resources Corporation; *U.S. Public*, pg. 520
CONTSE, S.A.U.—See Air Products & Chemicals, Inc.; *U.S. Public*, pg. 66
CRYOGENMASH PJSC—See Gazprombank JSC; *Int'l*, pg. 2892
CRYOINFRA S.A. DE C.V.—See Air Products & Chemicals, Inc.; *U.S. Public*, pg. 66
DECCAN ALLOY METAL INDUSTRIES PVT. LTD.—See Chowgule & Company Pvt. Ltd.; *Int'l*, pg. 1585
DELILLE OXYGEN CO.; *U.S. Private*, pg. 1197
DENKA SINGAPORE PRIVATE LIMITED—See Denki Company Limited; *Int'l*, pg. 2027
EAGLE LNG PARTNERS LLC—See Ferus Inc.; *Int'l*, pg. 2646
EKC INTERNATIONAL FZE—See Everest Kanto Cylinder Limited; *Int'l*, pg. 2564
ELLENBARRIE INDUSTRIAL GASES LTD.—See Air Water Inc.; *Int'l*, pg. 240
ENAPTER AG; *Int'l*, pg. 2396
ENVIRI CORPORATION; *U.S. Public*, pg. 780
ENVITEC BIOGAS BALTIC SIA—See EnviTec Biogas AG; *Int'l*, pg. 2455
ENVITEC BIOGAS CHINA LTD.—See EnviTec Biogas AG; *Int'l*, pg. 2455
ENVITEC BIOGAS SERVICE BALTIC SIA—See EnviTec Biogas AG; *Int'l*, pg. 2455
ENVITEC BIOGAS S.R.L.—See EnviTec Biogas AG; *Int'l*, pg. 2455
ENVITEC SERVICE APS—See EnviTec Biogas AG; *Int'l*, pg. 2456
ENVITEC SERVICE SARL—See EnviTec Biogas AG; *Int'l*, pg. 2456
ERRE DUE S.P.A.; *Int'l*, pg. 2497
EVERFUEL A/S; *Int'l*, pg. 2565
FERUS INC. - DAWSON CREEK N2 PLANT—See Ferus Inc.; *Int'l*, pg. 2646
FERUS INC. - JOFFRE N2 PLANT—See Ferus Inc.; *Int'l*, pg. 2646
FERUS INC. - UTAH CO2 PLANT—See Ferus Inc.; *Int'l*, pg. 2646
FOOSUNG CO., LTD.; *Int'l*, pg. 2728
GASES INDUSTRIALES DE COLUMBIA S.A.—See Air Products & Chemicals, Inc.; *U.S. Public*, pg. 66
GASIN II UNIPESSOAL LDA—See Air Products & Chemicals, Inc.; *U.S. Public*, pg. 66
GHANI GLOBAL HOLDINGS LIMITED; *Int'l*, pg. 2958
GLOBAL GAS CORPORATION; *U.S. Public*, pg. 942
GOVIND POY OXYGEN LTD.; *Int'l*, pg. 3044
GREEN AIR CO., LTD.—See Hyundai Steel Company; *Int'l*, pg. 3560
GREEN HYDROGEN SYSTEMS A/S; *Int'l*, pg. 3071
HANSON QUARRY PRODUCTS (PERAK) SDN BHD—See Heidelberg Materials AG; *Int'l*, pg. 3312
HEXAGON PURUS ASA; *Int'l*, pg. 3370
HINDUSTAN WIRES LIMITED; *Int'l*, pg. 3400
HOSHIZAKI CHUGOKU CO., LTD.—See Hoshizaki Corporation; *Int'l*, pg. 3483
HOSHIZAKI (THAILAND) LIMITED—See Hoshizaki Corporation; *Int'l*, pg. 3483
HUNAN KAIMEITE GASES CO., LTD.; *Int'l*, pg. 3533
H.V. BOWEN & SONS (QUARRY) LTD.—See Breedon Group plc; *Int'l*, pg. 1144

HYDROGENICS EUROPE N.V.—See Cummins Inc.; *U.S. Public*, pg. 607
HYDROGENICS USA, INC.—See Cummins Inc.; *U.S. Public*, pg. 607
HYDROGEN REFUELING SOLUTIONS SA; *Int'l*, pg. 3547
HYNION AS; *Int'l*, pg. 3550
HYON AS; *Int'l*, pg. 3550
HYPOWER FUEL, INC.; *U.S. Private*, pg. 2020
I3 ENERGY CANADA LIMITED—See i3 Energy Plc; *Int'l*, pg. 3566
I.C.S. DRY-ICE EXPRESS B.V.—See Cryoport, Inc.; *U.S. Public*, pg. 600
ILJIN HYSOLUS CO., LTD.; *Int'l*, pg. 3615
INDURA ARGENTINA S.A.—See Air Products & Chemicals, Inc.; *U.S. Public*, pg. 66
INDURA S.A.—See Air Products & Chemicals, Inc.; *U.S. Public*, pg. 66
INDUSTRIAL SCIENTIFIC CANADA ULC—See Fortive Corporation; *U.S. Public*, pg. 870
INFRA DEL SUR, S.A. DE C.V.—See Air Products & Chemicals, Inc.; *U.S. Public*, pg. 66
INFRA, S.A. DE C.V.—See Air Products & Chemicals, Inc.; *U.S. Public*, pg. 66
INOX AIR PRODUCTS PVT. LTD.—See Air Products & Chemicals, Inc.; *U.S. Public*, pg. 66
JAZAN GAS PROJECTS COMPANY—See Air Products & Chemicals, Inc.; *U.S. Public*, pg. 66
KOLHAPUR OXYGEN AND ACETYLENE PRIVATE LIMITED—See Chowgule & Company Pvt. Ltd.; *Int'l*, pg. 1585
KULIM INDUSTRIAL GASES SDN. BHD.—See Air Products & Chemicals, Inc.; *U.S. Public*, pg. 66
LIDERGAS S.A. E.S.P.—See Air Products & Chemicals, Inc.; *U.S. Public*, pg. 66
LINDSAY CORPORATION; *U.S. Public*, pg. 1319
MESSER GAS LLC—See CVC Capital Partners SICAV-FIS S.A.; *Int'l*, pg. 1885
M&M GASES LIMITED—See Air Products & Chemicals, Inc.; *U.S. Public*, pg. 66
MOLECULAR PRODUCTS GROUP LIMITED—See Madison Industries Holdings LLC; *U.S. Private*, pg. 2543
NGL ENERGY PARTNERS LP; *U.S. Public*, pg. 1527
NITRO LIFT TECHNOLOGIES, LLC—See H.I.G. Capital, LLC; *U.S. Private*, pg. 1834
NRG ENERGY SERVICES LLC—See NRG Energy, Inc.; *U.S. Public*, pg. 1550
ORION ENGINEERED CARBONS FRANCE SAS—See Rhone Group, LLC; *U.S. Private*, pg. 3424
OSAIR INC.; *U.S. Private*, pg. 3046
OXYGAS LTD.—See Alam Group of Companies; *Int'l*, pg. 289
OXYGEN & ARGON WORKS, LTD.—See Air Products & Chemicals, Inc.; *U.S. Public*, pg. 66
PERMEA CHINA, LTD.—See Air Products & Chemicals, Inc.; *U.S. Public*, pg. 67
PERMEA INC.—See Air Products & Chemicals, Inc.; *U.S. Public*, pg. 67
PORTAGAS, INC.—See Celanese Corporation; *U.S. Public*, pg. 465
PT AIR PRODUCTS INDONESIA—See Air Products & Chemicals, Inc.; *U.S. Public*, pg. 67
PT UNITED AIR PRODUCTS INDONESIA—See Air Products & Chemicals, Inc.; *U.S. Public*, pg. 67
RADIOMETER BASEL AG—See Danaher Corporation; *U.S. Public*, pg. 630
RECLAMATION TECHNOLOGIES, INC.—See A-Gas Limited; *Int'l*, pg. 19
RENAGEN INC.—See EnviTec Biogas AG; *Int'l*, pg. 2456
S.E. CARBUROS METALICOS S.A.—See Air Products & Chemicals, Inc.; *U.S. Public*, pg. 67
SOCIETE D'INSTALLATIONS ET DE DIFFUSION DE MATERIEL TECHNIQUE S.P.A.—See Adenia Partners Ltd; *Int'l*, pg. 143
TARGA MIDSTREAM SERVICES LLC - CAMERON—See Targa Resources Corp.; *U.S. Public*, pg. 1982
TEGA-TECHNISCHE GASE UND GASETECHNIK GMBH—See DCC plc; *Int'l*, pg. 1991
TEMPIL, INC.—See Illinois Tool Works Inc.; *U.S. Public*, pg. 1111
TRONOX HOLDINGS PLC; *U.S. Public*, pg. 2197
TURBOGAS - PRODUTORA ENERGIA S.A.—See ENGIE SA; *Int'l*, pg. 2433
TYCZKA INDUSTRIE-GASE GMBH—See Air Products & Chemicals, Inc.; *U.S. Public*, pg. 67
UNI-MIX CONCRETE PRODUCTS SDN. BHD.—See B.I.G. Industries Berhad; *Int'l*, pg. 790
VITALOX INDUSTRIAL S.L.U.—See Air Products & Chemicals, Inc.; *U.S. Public*, pg. 67
WASKOM GAS PROCESSING CO.—See CenterPoint Energy, Inc.; *U.S. Public*, pg. 472
WATERBURY COMPANIES, INC.; *U.S. Private*, pg. 4452
WELDSHIP INDUSTRIES, INC.—See Markel Group Inc.; *U.S. Public*, pg. 1369
WORTHINGTON INDUSTRIES POLAND SP. Z O.O.—See Worthington Industries, Inc.; *U.S. Public*, pg. 2383

325130 — SYNTHETIC DYE AND PIGMENT MANUFACTURING

AECI LIMITED; *Int'l*, pg. 171
ALCHEMIE EUROPE LTD.—See Aarti Industries Ltd.; *Int'l*, pg. 38
ALTAIRNANO, INC.—See Altair Nanotechnologies Inc.; *U.S. Private*, pg. 204
ALTAIR NANOTECHNOLOGIES INC.; *U.S. Private*, pg. 204
AMERICHEM INC.; *U.S. Private*, pg. 259
APOLLO COLORS INC.; *U.S. Private*, pg. 294
ARCHROMA PAKISTAN LTD.—See SK Capital Partners, LP; *U.S. Private*, pg. 3679
ASAHI SONGWON COLORS LTD.; *Int'l*, pg. 598
AZO LTD.—See AZO GmbH & Co. KG; *Int'l*, pg. 780
BASF AUXILIARY CHEMICALS CO. LTD.—See BASF SE; *Int'l*, pg. 877
BASF CATALYSTS LLC - QUINCY—See BASF SE; *Int'l*, pg. 875
BASF CATALYSTS LLC - SEPARATION SYSTEMS & VENTURES—See BASF SE; *Int'l*, pg. 875
BASF COLORS & EFFECTS JAPAN LTD.—See BASF SE; *Int'l*, pg. 874
BASF COLORS & EFFECTS KOREA LTD.—See BASF SE; *Int'l*, pg. 874
BASF PERFORMANCE PRODUCTS FRANCE SA—See BASF SE; *Int'l*, pg. 879
BASF PERFORMANCE PRODUCTS PLC - PAISLEY PLANT—See BASF SE; *Int'l*, pg. 882
BASF PERFORMANCE PRODUCTS PLC - PIGMENTS DIVISION—See BASF SE; *Int'l*, pg. 882
BHAGERIA INDUSTRIES LIMITED; *Int'l*, pg. 1009
BIOVILL CO., LTD.; *Int'l*, pg. 1045
BODAL CHEMICALS LTD.; *Int'l*, pg. 1097
BRENNTAG SPECIALTIES, INC.—See BRENNTAG SE; *Int'l*, pg. 1148
CELANESE EMULSIONS NORDEN AB—See Celanese Corporation; *U.S. Public*, pg. 464
CERAMIC COLOR & CHEMICAL MFG. CO.; *U.S. Private*, pg. 835
CHROMAFLO TECHNOLOGIES CORPORATION—See American Securities LLC; *U.S. Private*, pg. 250
CHYANG SHENG DYEING & FINISHING CO., LTD.; *Int'l*, pg. 1600
CLARIANT (ARGENTINA) S.A.—See Clariant AG; *Int'l*, pg. 1645
CLARIANT (AUSTRALIA) PTY. LTD.—See Clariant AG; *Int'l*, pg. 1645
CLARIANT BENELUX SA/NV—See Clariant AG; *Int'l*, pg. 1646
CLARIANT (CANADA), INC.—See Clariant AG; *Int'l*, pg. 1645
CLARIANT CHEMICALS (CHINA) LTD.—See Clariant AG; *Int'l*, pg. 1645
CLARIANT CHEMICALS (GUANGZHOU) LTD.—See Clariant AG; *Int'l*, pg. 1645
CLARIANT CHEMICALS (THAILAND) LTD.—See Clariant AG; *Int'l*, pg. 1646
CLARIANT (CHINA) LTD.—See Clariant AG; *Int'l*, pg. 1645
CLARIANT (COLOMBIA) S.A.—See Clariant AG; *Int'l*, pg. 1645
CLARIANT COLORQUIMICA (CHILE) LTDA.—See Clariant AG; *Int'l*, pg. 1646
CLARIANT (DENMARK) A/S—See Clariant AG; *Int'l*, pg. 1645
CLARIANT (DEUTSCHLAND) GMBH—See Clariant AG; *Int'l*, pg. 1647
CLARIANT (EGYPT) S.A.E.-EGCODAR—See Clariant AG; *Int'l*, pg. 1646
CLARIANT (EGYPT) S.A.E.—See Clariant AG; *Int'l*, pg. 1646
CLARIANT (FINLAND) OY—See Clariant AG; *Int'l*, pg. 1646
CLARIANT (FRANCE)—See Clariant AG; *Int'l*, pg. 1646
CLARIANT GMBH—See Clariant AG; *Int'l*, pg. 1647
CLARIANT (HELLAS) S.A.—See Clariant AG; *Int'l*, pg. 1646
CLARIANT HUNINGUE—See Clariant AG; *Int'l*, pg. 1646
CLARIANT IBERICA S.A.—See Clariant AG; *Int'l*, pg. 1647
CLARIANT (INDIA) LTD.—See Clariant AG; *Int'l*, pg. 1646
CLARIANT INDUSTRIES (KOREA) LTD.—See Clariant AG; *Int'l*, pg. 1647
CLARIANT (ITALIA) S.P.A.—See Clariant AG; *Int'l*, pg. 1646
CLARIANT (JAPAN) K.K.—See Clariant AG; *Int'l*, pg. 1646
CLARIANT (MALAYSIA) SDN. BHD.—See Clariant AG; *Int'l*, pg. 1646
CLARIANT (MAROC) S.A.—See Clariant AG; *Int'l*, pg. 1646
CLARIANT MASTERBATCHES THAILAND LTD—See Clariant AG; *Int'l*, pg. 1645
CLARIANT MASTERBATCH GMBH & CO. OHG—See Clariant AG; *Int'l*, pg. 1647
CLARIANT (MEXICO) S.A. DE C.V.—See Clariant AG; *Int'l*, pg. 1646
CLARIANT (NEW ZEALAND) LTD.—See Clariant AG; *Int'l*, pg. 1646
CLARIANT (NORGE) AS—See Clariant AG; *Int'l*, pg. 1646
CLARIANT (OSTERREICH) GMBH—See Clariant AG; *Int'l*, pg. 1646
CLARIANT (PERU) S.A.—See Clariant AG; *Int'l*, pg. 1646

325130 — SYNTHETIC DYE AND P...

CLARIANT POLSKA SP. Z.O.O.—See Clariant AG; *Int'l*, pg. 1647
CLARIANT PRODUCTOS QUIMICOS S.A. DE C. V.—See Clariant AG; *Int'l*, pg. 1646
CLARIANT QUIMICOS (PORTUGAL) LTD.—See Clariant AG; *Int'l*, pg. 1647
CLARIANT S.A.—See Clariant AG; *Int'l*, pg. 1647
CLARIANT (SINGAPORE) PTE. LTD.—See Clariant AG; *Int'l*, pg. 1646
CLARIANT (SVERIGE) AB—See Clariant AG; *Int'l*, pg. 1646
CLARIANT (TAIWAN) CO. LTD.—See Clariant AG; *Int'l*, pg. 1646
CLARIANT (TIANJIN) LTD.—See Clariant AG; *Int'l*, pg. 1645
CLARIANT (TIANJIN) PIGMENTS CO. LTD.—See Clariant AG; *Int'l*, pg. 1645
CLARIANT TUNISIE S.A.—See Clariant AG; *Int'l*, pg. 1648
CLARIANT (TURKIYE) A.S.—See Clariant AG; *Int'l*, pg. 1646
CLARIANT UK LTD.—See Clariant AG; *Int'l*, pg. 1648
CLARIANT (VENEZUELA) S.A.—See Clariant AG; *Int'l*, pg. 1646
CLARIANT VERWALTUNGSGESELLSCHAFT MBH—See Clariant AG; *Int'l*, pg. 1647
COLOR MASTER, INC.; *U.S. Private*, pg. 972
COLORMATRIX CORPORATION—See Avient Corporation; *U.S. Public*, pg. 247
COLORMATRIX GROUP, INC.—See Avient Corporation; *U.S. Public*, pg. 247
COLORS FOR PLASTICS INC.; *U.S. Private*, pg. 975
COTELLE S.A.—See Colgate-Palmolive Company; *U.S. Public*, pg. 532
CROMEX S/A; *Int'l*, pg. 1853
DANE COLOR UK LIMITED—See RPM International Inc.; *U.S. Public*, pg. 1816
DAY-GLO COLOR CORP.—See RPM International Inc.; *U.S. Public*, pg. 1819
DIC COLORANTS TAIWAN CO., LTD.—See DIC Corporation; *Int'l*, pg. 2107
DIC COMPOUNDS (MALAYSIA) SDN. BHD.—See DIC Corporation; *Int'l*, pg. 2107
DIVAR CHEMICALS, INC.; *U.S. Private*, pg. 1240
DYNAMIC COLOURS LIMITED; *Int'l*, pg. 2240
DYNAMIC INDUSTRIES LIMITED; *Int'l*, pg. 2240
DYNEMIC PRODUCTS LTD.; *Int'l*, pg. 2242
EGYPTIAN CHEMICAL INDUSTRIES CO. (KIMA)—See Chemical Industries Holding Company; *Int'l*, pg. 1461
EPOLIN, LLC—See Arsenal Capital Management LP; *U.S. Private*, pg. 337
ESTA FINE COLOR CORPORATION—See Dainichiseika Color & Chemicals Mfg. Co., Ltd.; *Int'l*, pg. 1939
EUROPEAN COLOUR (PIGMENTS) LIMITED—See European Colour Plc; *Int'l*, pg. 2556
FARBCHEMIE BRAUN KG; *Int'l*, pg. 2618
FERRO CORPORATION - PERFORMANCE COLORS & GLASS DIVISION—See American Securities LLC; *U.S. Private*, pg. 251
FERRO CORPORATION - PERFORMANCE COLORS & GLASS, ORRVILLE PLANT—See American Securities LLC; *U.S. Private*, pg. 251
FUJIAN KUNCAI MATERIAL TECHNOLOGY CO., LTD.; *Int'l*, pg. 2818
FUJIFILM IMAGING COLORANTS INC.—See FUJIFILM Holdings Corporation; *Int'l*, pg. 2823
FUNDVISER CAPITAL (INDIA) LTD.; *Int'l*, pg. 2845
FURUKAWA DENSHI CO., LTD.—See Furukawa Co., Ltd.; *Int'l*, pg. 2847
GENERAL COLOR & CHEMICAL CO., INC.; *U.S. Private*, pg. 1664
GREENVILLE COLORANTS, LLC—See ChromaScape, LLC; *U.S. Private*, pg. 892
GUANGDONG DOWSTONE TECHNOLOGY CO., LTD.; *Int'l*, pg. 3154
HANSOL CHEMICAL CO. LTD.—See Hansol Group; *Int'l*, pg. 3260
HEUCOTECH LTD.; *U.S. Private*, pg. 1928
HOLLAND COLOURS AMERICAS INC—See Holland Colours NV; *Int'l*, pg. 3451
HOLLAND COLOURS CHINA LTD—See Holland Colours NV; *Int'l*, pg. 3451
HOLLAND COLOURS HUNGARIA KFT—See Holland Colours NV; *Int'l*, pg. 3451
HOLLAND COLOURS NV; *Int'l*, pg. 3451
HOOVER COLOR CORPORATION—See Cathay Industries Europe N.V.; *Int'l*, pg. 1360
HUNTSMAN P&A FINLAND OY—See Huntsman Corporation; *U.S. Public*, pg. 1073
HUNTSMAN PIGMENTS (UK) LIMITED—See Huntsman Corporation; *U.S. Public*, pg. 1074
HUNTSMAN TEXTILE EFFECTS - CHARLOTTE PLANT—See Huntsman Corporation; *U.S. Public*, pg. 1074
HUNTSMAN TEXTILE EFFECTS DIVISION—See Huntsman Corporation; *U.S. Public*, pg. 1074
HUNTSMAN TEXTILE EFFECTS (GERMANY) GMBH—See Huntsman Corporation; *U.S. Public*, pg. 1074
HUNTSMAN TEXTILE EFFECTS - HIGH POINT PLANT—See Huntsman Corporation; *U.S. Public*, pg. 1074
ITALTINTO S.R.L.—See I.C.T.C. Holdings Corporation; *Int'l*, pg. 3565
J.M. HUBER FINLAND OY—See J.M. Huber Corporation; *U.S. Private*, pg. 2168
KEYSTONE ANILINE CORP. - LIQUID MANUFACTURING TECHNICAL FACILITY—See Milliken & Company; *U.S. Private*, pg. 2737
KEYSTONE ANILINE CORP. - PACIFIC DIVISION—See Milliken & Company; *U.S. Private*, pg. 2737
KRONOS LOUISIANA, INC.—See Contran Corporation; *U.S. Private*, pg. 1033
KRONOS NORGE A/S—See Contran Corporation; *U.S. Private*, pg. 1033
KUNCAI AMERICAS LLC—See Fujian Kuncai Material Technology Co., Ltd.; *Int'l*, pg. 2818
KUNCAI EUROPE B.V.—See Fujian Kuncai Material Technology Co., Ltd.; *Int'l*, pg. 2818
KUNCAI INTERNATIONAL INDIA PVT. LTD.—See Fujian Kuncai Material Technology Co., Ltd.; *Int'l*, pg. 2818
KVK USA INC.—See DIC Corporation; *Int'l*, pg. 2109
LOUISIANA PIGMENT COMPANY L.P.—See Contran Corporation; *U.S. Private*, pg. 1033
MATEX BANGLADESH LIMITED—See Apex Holding Limited; *Int'l*, pg. 511
MEDIASTREET, INC.; *U.S. Private*, pg. 2654
MESA INDUSTRIES, INC.—See Avient Corporation; *U.S. Public*, pg. 247
MESGO IRIDE COLORS SRL—See HEXPOL AB; *Int'l*, pg. 3372
MLPC INTERNATIONAL SA—See Arkema S.A.; *Int'l*, pg. 571
NANTONG DIC COLOR CO., LTD.—See DIC Corporation; *Int'l*, pg. 2109
NL ENVIRONMENTAL MANAGEMENT SERVICES, INC.—See Contran Corporation; *U.S. Private*, pg. 1033
NUBIOLA BULGARIA ODD—See American Securities LLC; *U.S. Private*, pg. 252
NUBIOLA INDIA PRIVATE, LIMITED—See American Securities LLC; *U.S. Private*, pg. 252
NUBIOLA PIGMENTS (SHANGHAI) CO., LTD.—See American Securities LLC; *U.S. Private*, pg. 252
NUBIOLA ROMANIA SRL—See American Securities LLC; *U.S. Private*, pg. 252
NUBIOLA USA, INC.—See American Securities LLC; *U.S. Private*, pg. 252
ORGANIC DYES AND PIGMENTS, LLC; *U.S. Private*, pg. 3041
PENN COLOR INC. - ELMWOOD PARK FACILITY—See Penn Color Inc.; *U.S. Private*, pg. 3133
PENN COLOR INC. - MILTON FACILITY—See Penn Color Inc.; *U.S. Private*, pg. 3133
PENN COLOR INC. - RINGGOLD FACILITY—See Penn Color Inc.; *U.S. Private*, pg. 3133
PENN COLOR INC.; *U.S. Private*, pg. 3133
PLASTIC COLOR CORPORATION, INC.—See PMC Capital Partners, LLC; *U.S. Private*, pg. 3218
PRISM CHEMICALS—See Banner Chemicals Limited; *Int'l*, pg. 851
P.T. CLARIANT INDONESIA—See Clariant AG; *Int'l*, pg. 1648
PT DIC ASTRA CHEMICALS—See DIC Corporation; *Int'l*, pg. 2109
SAMBO FINE CHEMICALS MFG. CO., LTD.—See Dainichiseika Color & Chemicals Mfg. Co., Ltd.; *Int'l*, pg. 1939
SENSIENT COLORS UK LTD.—See Sensient Technologies Corporation; *U.S. Public*, pg. 1867
SENSIENT COSMETIC TECHNOLOGIES USA—See Sensient Technologies Corporation; *U.S. Public*, pg. 1867
SILBERLINE MANUFACTURING CO., INC.; *U.S. Private*, pg. 3652
SINLOIHI CO., LTD.—See Dai Nippon Toryo Co., Ltd.; *Int'l*, pg. 1916
STANDRIDGE COLOR CORPORATION; *U.S. Private*, pg. 3782
SUN CHEMICAL CORPORATION OF MICHIGAN—See DIC Corporation; *Int'l*, pg. 2110
SUN CHEMICAL CORPORATION, PIGMENTS DIVISION—See DIC Corporation; *Int'l*, pg. 2110
SUN CHEMICAL, D.O.O.—See DIC Corporation; *Int'l*, pg. 2111
SUQIAN LINTONG NEW MATERIAL CO., LTD.—See DIC India Ltd; *Int'l*, pg. 2111
SUQIAN LINTONG NEW MATERIALS CO., LTD.—See DIC Corporation; *Int'l*, pg. 2111
SWISSNOVACHEM LTD.—See Clariant AG; *Int'l*, pg. 1648
SYNTHESIA, A.S.—See Agrofert Holding, a.s.; *Int'l*, pg. 219
TECXO FARBEN PRODUKTIONSGESELLSCHAFT MBH—See Farbchemie Braun KG; *Int'l*, pg. 2618
TETRA TECHNOLOGIES DE MEXICO, S.A. DE C.V.—See TETRA Technologies, Inc.; *U.S. Public*, pg. 2024
TETRA TECHNOLOGIES, INC.; *U.S. Public*, pg. 2024
TIGERTURF AUSTRALIA PTY LTD—See ABN AMRO Group N.V.; *Int'l*, pg. 65
TIGERTURF AUSTRALIA PTY LTD—See Gilde Buy Out Partners B.V.; *Int'l*, pg. 2975
TIOXIDE EUROPE SAS—See Huntsman Corporation; *U.S. Public*, pg. 1075
TIOXIDE EUROPE S.R.L.—See Huntsman Corporation; *U.S. Public*, pg. 1075
TIOXIDE (MALAYSIA) SDN. BHD.—See Huntsman Corporation; *U.S. Public*, pg. 1075
TIOXIDE SOUTHERN AFRICA (PTY) LTD.—See Huntsman Corporation; *U.S. Public*, pg. 1075
TOR MINERALS MALAYSIA, SDN. BHD.—See TOR Minerals International Inc.; *U.S. Public*, pg. 2164
TOR PROCESSING & TRADE BV—See TOR Minerals International Inc.; *U.S. Public*, pg. 2164
TP&T (TOR PROCESSING & TRADE) B.V.—See TOR Minerals International Inc.; *U.S. Public*, pg. 2164
TRONOX B.V.—See Tronox Holdings plc; *U.S. Public*, pg. 2197
TRONOX INCORPORATED—See Tronox Holdings plc; *U.S. Public*, pg. 2197
TRONOX KZN SANDS PROPRIETARY LIMITED—See Tronox Holdings plc; *U.S. Public*, pg. 2197
TRONOX LLC—See Tronox Holdings plc; *U.S. Public*, pg. 2197
TRONOX PIGMENTS (HOLLAND) B.V.—See Tronox Holdings plc; *U.S. Public*, pg. 2197
TRONOX PIGMENTS (NETHERLANDS) B.V.—See Tronox Holdings plc; *U.S. Public*, pg. 2197
TRONOX PIGMENTS (SINGAPORE) PTE. LTD.—See Tronox Holdings plc; *U.S. Public*, pg. 2197
TRONOX WESTERN AUSTRALIA PTY. LTD.—See Tronox Holdings plc; *U.S. Public*, pg. 2197
UNITED COLOR MANUFACTURING; *U.S. Private*, pg. 4289
VIBRANTZ TECHNOLOGIES INC—See American Securities LLC; *U.S. Private*, pg. 250
WAYNE PIGMENT CORP.; *U.S. Private*, pg. 4460

325180 — OTHER BASIC INORGANIC CHEMICAL MANUFACTURING

ABA CHEMICALS (SHANGHAI) LIMITED—See ABA Chemicals Corporation; *Int'l*, pg. 47
ADVANCED ENERGY MINERALS INC.; *Int'l*, pg. 158
ADVANCE SYNTEX LIMITED; *Int'l*, pg. 157
ADVANTAGE LITHIUM CORP.—See Allkem Limited; *Int'l*, pg. 359
AGC CHEMICALS VIETNAM CO., LTD.—See AGC Inc.; *Int'l*, pg. 203
AGC SI-TECH CO., LTD.—See AGC Inc.; *Int'l*, pg. 202
AGLOBIS GMBH—See Chemtrade Logistics Income Fund; *Int'l*, pg. 1464
AHMAD ALBINALI & TETRA ARABIA COMPANY LTD.—See TETRA Technologies, Inc.; *U.S. Public*, pg. 2024
AIR PRODUCTS AND CHEMICALS (CHINA) INVESTMENT CO. LTD.—See Air Products & Chemicals, Inc.; *U.S. Public*, pg. 66
AIR PRODUCTS AND CHEMICALS (SHANGHAI) CO. LTD.—See Air Products & Chemicals, Inc.; *U.S. Public*, pg. 66
AIR PRODUCTS AND CHEMICALS (SHANGHAI) GASES CO., LTD.—See Air Products & Chemicals, Inc.; *U.S. Public*, pg. 66
AIR PRODUCTS (BR) LIMITED—See Air Products & Chemicals, Inc.; *U.S. Public*, pg. 64
AIR PRODUCTS (CHEMICALS) PUBLIC LIMITED COMPANY—See Air Products & Chemicals, Inc.; *U.S. Public*, pg. 64
AIR PRODUCTS HELIUM, INC.—See Air Products & Chemicals, Inc.; *U.S. Public*, pg. 65
AIR PRODUCTS HOLDINGS B.V.—See Air Products & Chemicals, Inc.; *U.S. Public*, pg. 65
AIR PRODUCTS INVESTMENTS B.V.—See Air Products & Chemicals, Inc.; *U.S. Public*, pg. 65
AJINOMOTO EUROLYSINE S.A.S.—See Ajinomoto Company, Inc.; *Int'l*, pg. 256
AKZONOBEL SURFACE CHEMISTRY—See Akzo Nobel N.V.; *Int'l*, pg. 273
ALKIM ALKALI KIMYA A.S.; *Int'l*, pg. 331
AL-KOUT INDUSTRIAL PROJECTS COMPANY K.S.C.C.; *Int'l*, pg. 286
ALUFLUORIDE LIMITED; *Int'l*, pg. 400
AMERICAN CHEMET CORPORATION; *U.S. Private*, pg. 227
AMERICAN CHEMET EXPORT CORPORATION—See American Chemet Corporation; *U.S. Private*, pg. 227
AMERICAN GAS & CHEMICAL CO., LTD.; *U.S. Private*, pg. 235
AMERICAN GCI RESITOP, INC.—See Gun Ei Chemical Industry Co., Ltd.; *Int'l*, pg. 3183
AMERICAN NANO SILICON TECHNOLOGIES, INC.; *Int'l*, pg. 422
AMERICAN PACIFIC CORPORATION—See H.I.G. Capital, LLC; *U.S. Private*, pg. 1828
ANGLO DUTCH WATER CARBONS LTD.—See Cabot Corporation; *U.S. Public*, pg. 416
ANSA MCAL CHEMICALS LTD.—See ANSA McAL Limited; *Int'l*, pg. 476
APEX RESOURCES, INC.; *U.S. Private*, pg. 293
APOLLO CHEMICAL CORP.; *U.S. Private*, pg. 294

N.A.I.C.S. INDEX

325180 — OTHER BASIC INORGAN...

APOLLO SCIENTIFIC LIMITED—See Central Glass Co., Ltd.; *Int'l*, pg. 1406
ARAB FERTILIZERS AND CHEMICALS INDUSTRIES LTD.—See Arab Potash Company PLC; *Int'l*, pg. 531
ARAKAWA CHEMICAL (CHINA) INC.—See Arakawa Chemical Industries, Ltd.; *Int'l*, pg. 534
ARAKAWA CHEMICAL INDUSTRIES, LTD - FUJI PLANT—See Arakawa Chemical Industries, Ltd.; *Int'l*, pg. 534
ARAKAWA CHEMICAL INDUSTRIES, LTD - KUSHIRO PLANT—See Arakawa Chemical Industries, Ltd.; *Int'l*, pg. 534
ARAKAWA CHEMICAL INDUSTRIES, LTD. - ONAHAMA PLANT—See Arakawa Chemical Industries, Ltd.; *Int'l*, pg. 534
ARAKAWA CHEMICAL INDUSTRIES, LTD - OSAKA PLANT—See Arakawa Chemical Industries, Ltd.; *Int'l*, pg. 534
ARAKAWA CHEMICAL INDUSTRIES, LTD. - TOKUSHIMA PLANT—See Arakawa Chemical Industries, Ltd.; *Int'l*, pg. 534
ARAKAWA CHEMICAL INDUSTRIES, LTD - TSURUSAKI PLANT—See Arakawa Chemical Industries, Ltd.; *Int'l*, pg. 534
ARKEMA CANADA INC.—See Arkema S.A.; *Int'l*, pg. 569
ARKEMA CANADA INC.—See Arkema S.A.; *Int'l*, pg. 569
ARKEMA CHANGSHU CHEMICALS CO. LTD—See Arkema S.A.; *Int'l*, pg. 569
ARKEMA (CHANGSHU) FLUOROCHEMICAL CO. LTD—See Arkema S.A.; *Int'l*, pg. 568
ARKEMA HYDROGEN PEROXIDE CO., LTD.—See Arkema S.A.; *Int'l*, pg. 569
ARMAND PRODUCTS COMPANY—See Church & Dwight Co., Inc.; *U.S. Public*, pg. 493
ARMAND PRODUCTS COMPANY—See Occidental Petroleum Corporation; *U.S. Public*, pg. 1561
ASAHI CARBON CO., LTD—See Bridgestone Corporation; *Int'l*, pg. 1155
ASAHI KASEI CHEMICALS CORPORATION—See Asahi Kasei Corporation; *Int'l*, pg. 595
ASIAN PETROPRODUCTS & EXPORTS LIMITED; *Int'l*, pg. 619
ASTRON CORPORATION LIMITED; *Int'l*, pg. 662
AUTOMOTIVE CLEANING CHEMICALS LTD.—See Berner SE; *Int'l*, pg. 988
AVANTOR PERFORMANCE MATERIALS, LLC—See Avantor, Inc.; *U.S. Public*, pg. 241
AVECIA SPAIN S.L.—See Avecia Ltd.; *Int'l*, pg. 737
B2E CORPORATION—See Central Garden & Pet Company; *U.S. Public*, pg. 473
BALAJI AMINES LIMITED; *Int'l*, pg. 806
BASF CATALYSTS LLC - APPEARANCE & PERFORMANCE TECHNOLOGIES—See BASF SE; *Int'l*, pg. 875
BASF CORP. - EVANS CITY PLANT—See BASF SE; *Int'l*, pg. 876
BASF CORP. - LAGRANGE - NUTRITION & HEALTH—See BASF SE; *Int'l*, pg. 876
BASF CORP. - TARRYTOWN RESEARCH FACILITY—See BASF SE; *Int'l*, pg. 876
BASF GASTRONOMIE GMBH—See BASF SE; *Int'l*, pg. 879
BASF PETRONAS CHEMICALS SDN. BHD.—See BASF SE; *Int'l*, pg. 878
BASF PETRONAS CHEMICALS SDN. BHD.—See BASF SE; *Int'l*, pg. 878
BAZNA HEMIJA D.D.; *Int'l*, pg. 920
BHS SPECIALTY CHEMICALS; *U.S. Private*, pg. 549
BIO-CIDE INTERNATIONAL, INC.—See Kemin Industries, Inc.; *U.S. Private*, pg. 2281
BIOQUELL GMBH—See Ecolab Inc.; *U.S. Public*, pg. 712
BIOQUELL SAS—See Ecolab Inc.; *U.S. Public*, pg. 712
BIOQUELL TECHNOLOGY (SHENZHEN) LTD.—See Ecolab Inc.; *U.S. Public*, pg. 712
BIRKO CORPORATION—See Platinum Equity, LLC; *U.S. Private*, pg. 3204
BORD NA MONA FUELS LIMITED—See Bord na Mona Plc; *Int'l*, pg. 1113
BP PETRONAS ACETYLS SDN BHD—See BP plc; *Int'l*, pg. 1128
BRENNTAG INORGANIC CHEMICALS (THETFORD) LTD.—See BRENNTAG SE; *Int'l*, pg. 1147
BRENNTAG KENYA LIMITED—See BRENNTAG SE; *Int'l*, pg. 1147
BRENNTAG LUBRICANTS (THAILAND) CO., LTD.—See BRENNTAG SE; *Int'l*, pg. 1147
BREWER SCIENCE LIMITED—See Brewer Science, Inc.; *U.S. Private*, pg. 647
BUCK-CHEMIE GMBH; *Int'l*, pg. 1209
BUSH BOAKE ALLEN DO BRASIL INDUSTRIA E COMERCIO LTDA.—See International Flavors & Fragrances Inc.; *U.S. Public*, pg. 1151
CABOT ACTIVATED CARBON B.V.—See Cabot Corporation; *U.S. Public*, pg. 416
CABOT CANADA LTD.—See Cabot Corporation; *U.S. Public*, pg. 416
CABOT CARBON LIMITED—See Cabot Corporation; *U.S. Public*, pg. 416
CABOT (CHINA) LIMITED—See Cabot Corporation; *U.S. Public*, pg. 416

CABOT CORPORATION CARBON BLACK DIVISION—See Cabot Corporation; *U.S. Public*, pg. 416
CABOT CORPORATION; *U.S. Public*, pg. 416
CABOT NORIT ITALIA S.P.A.—See Cabot Corporation; *U.S. Public*, pg. 417
CABOT NORIT SINGAPORE PTE. LTD.—See Cabot Corporation; *U.S. Public*, pg. 417
CABOT PLASTICS BELGIUM S.A.—See Cabot Corporation; *U.S. Public*, pg. 417
CABOT PLASTICS CANADA LP—See Cabot Corporation; *U.S. Public*, pg. 417
CABOT RHEINFELDEN GMBH & CO. KG—See Cabot Corporation; *U.S. Public*, pg. 417
CAHYA MATA PHOSPHATE INDUSTRIES SDN. BHD.—See Cahya Mata Sarawak Berhad; *Int'l*, pg. 1251
CALACHEM LTD.—See Aurelius Equity Opportunities SE & Co. KGaA; *Int'l*, pg. 708
CAMPINE N.V.; *Int'l*, pg. 1275
CAPPELLE FRERES (UK) LTD.—See Cappelle Pignenes N.V.; *Int'l*, pg. 1315
CAPPELLE INC.—See Cappelle Pignenes N.V.; *Int'l*, pg. 1315
CARBODERIVADOS S.A.—See China National Chemical Corporation; *Int'l*, pg. 1527
CARBONXT GROUP LIMITED; *Int'l*, pg. 1320
CARUS CHEMICAL COMPANY—See Carus Corporation; *U.S. Private*, pg. 776
CARUS CORPORATION; *U.S. Private*, pg. 776
CARUS PHOSPHATES, INC.—See Carus Corporation; *U.S. Private*, pg. 776
CATALYST REFINERS—See Ames Goldsmith Corp.; *U.S. Private*, pg. 262
CATHAY CHEMICAL WORKS, INC.; *Int'l*, pg. 1360
CATHAY INDUSTRIES EUROPE N.V.; *Int'l*, pg. 1360
CECA ITALIANA S.P.A—See Arkema S.A.; *Int'l*, pg. 571
CELANESE CORPORATION; *U.S. Public*, pg. 464
C-GREEN CARBON MANAGEMENT SOLUTIONS INC.—See HTC Purenergy Inc.; *Int'l*, pg. 3508
CHANGCHUN PETROCHEMICAL CO., LTD.—See Chang-Chun Group; *Int'l*, pg. 1442
CHANGSHU COATEX ADDITIVES CO. LTD—See Arkema S.A.; *Int'l*, pg. 571
CHAYSECHEM INC.—See Charkit Chemical Company, LLC; *U.S. Private*, pg. 851
CHEMALLOY COMPANY INC.; *U.S. Private*, pg. 871
CHEMCONTROL LIMITED—See BASF SE; *Int'l*, pg. 882
CHEMFAB ALKALIS LIMITED; *Int'l*, pg. 1461
CHEMICAL MANUFACTURE AND REFINING LIMITED—See Heidelberg Materials AG; *Int'l*, pg. 3309
CHEMIPHOS SA (PTY) LIMITED—See AECI Limited; *Int'l*, pg. 171
CHEMOL COMPANY, INC.—See The Seydel Companies, Inc.; *U.S. Private*, pg. 4117
CHEMTRADE REFINERY SERVICES INC.—See Chemtrade Logistics Income Fund; *Int'l*, pg. 1464
CHEMTURA NETHERLANDS B.V.—See Element Solutions Inc.; *U.S. Public*, pg. 725
CHESSCO PROCESS RESEARCH PRODUCTS—See Chessco Industries, Inc.; *U.S. Private*, pg. 875
CHINA REFORM CULTURE HOLDINGS CO., LTD.; *Int'l*, pg. 1547
CHINA SYNTHETIC RUBBER CORPORATION; *Int'l*, pg. 1557
CHINA TUHSU FLAVOURS & FRAGRANCES IMPORT & EXPORT CORPORATION—See COFCO Limited; *Int'l*, pg. 1692
CHONGQING DAZU RED BUTTERFLY STRONTIUM INDUSTRY CO., LTD.—See Guizhou Redstar Development Co., Ltd.; *Int'l*, pg. 3175
CHONGQING DAZU RED BUTTERFLY STRONTIUM INDUSTRY CO., LTD. - YONGXI FACTORY—See Guizhou Redstar Development Co., Ltd.; *Int'l*, pg. 3175
CHURCH & DWIGHT SPECIALTY PRODUCTS DIVISION—See Church & Dwight Co., Inc.; *U.S. Public*, pg. 493
CLARIANT CORPORATION—See Clariant AG; *Int'l*, pg. 1647
CLEARON CORP.—See Platinum Equity, LLC; *U.S. Private*, pg. 3204
CLEER VISION WINDOWS, INC.—See Thor Industries, Inc.; *U.S. Public*, pg. 2156
CLORO DE TEHUANTEPEC, S.A. DE C.V.—See Grupo Empresarial Kaluz S.A. de C.V.; *Int'l*, pg. 3127
CNNC HUAYUAN TITANIUM DIOXIDE CO., LTD.; *Int'l*, pg. 1677
CNSIG INNER MONGOLIA CHEMICAL INDUSTRY CO., LTD.; *Int'l*, pg. 1678
COGNIS FRANCE S.A.S.—See BASF SE; *Int'l*, pg. 883
COLUMBIA RIVER CARBONATES; *U.S. Private*, pg. 977
CONTINENTAL CARBON COMPANY—See China Synthetic Rubber Corporation; *Int'l*, pg. 1557
CONTINENTAL CARBON INDIA LTD.—See China Synthetic Rubber Corporation; *Int'l*, pg. 1557
COSMO CHEMICAL CO., LTD. - ONSAN FACTORY—See Cosmo Chemical Co., Ltd.; *Int'l*, pg. 1811
COSMO CHEMICAL CO., LTD.; *Int'l*, pg. 1811
CP KELCO OY—See J.M. Huber Corporation; *U.S. Private*, pg. 2168

CP KELCO POLAND SP. Z.O.O.—See J.M. Huber Corporation; *U.S. Private*, pg. 2168
CRISTAL MINING AUSTRALIA LIMITED - AUSTRALIND PLANT—See One Rock Capital Partners, LLC; *U.S. Private*, pg. 3023
CRI-TECH INC.—See Daikin Industries, Ltd.; *Int'l*, pg. 1932
CRODA CHEMICALS INTERNATIONAL LTD—See Croda International plc; *Int'l*, pg. 1851
CRYSTAL CLEAR ELECTRONIC MATERIAL CO., LTD; *Int'l*, pg. 1860
CYANCO COMPANY, LLC—See Cerberus Capital Management, L.P.; *U.S. Private*, pg. 837
CYANCO CORPORATION—See Cerberus Capital Management, L.P.; *U.S. Private*, pg. 837
CYANCO INTERNATIONAL, LLC - HOUSTON PLANT—See Cerberus Capital Management, L.P.; *U.S. Private*, pg. 837
CYANCO INTERNATIONAL, LLC—See Cerberus Capital Management, L.P.; *U.S. Private*, pg. 837
DAHUA GROUP DALIAN CHEMICAL INDUSTRY CO., LTD.; *Int'l*, pg. 1913
DAICEL ABOSHI SANGYO CO. LTD.—See Daicel Corporation; *Int'l*, pg. 1918
DAICEL ARAI CHEMICAL LTD.—See Daicel Corporation; *Int'l*, pg. 1918
DAIKIN CHEMICAL FRANCE S.A.S.—See Daikin Industries, Ltd.; *Int'l*, pg. 1934
DAIKIN CHEMICAL NETHERLANDS B.V.—See Daikin Industries, Ltd.; *Int'l*, pg. 1934
DAIKIN INDUSTRIES, LTD. - KASHIMA PLANT—See Daikin Industries, Ltd.; *Int'l*, pg. 1934
THE DALLAS GROUP OF AMERICA, INC.; *U.S. Private*, pg. 4017
DAREX PUERTO RICO, INC.—See Standard Industries Holdings Inc.; *U.S. Private*, pg. 3779
DA STUART INDIA PRIVATE LIMITED—See Quaker Chemical Corporation; *U.S. Public*, pg. 1745
DCW LIMITED; *Int'l*, pg. 1993
DEZA, A.S.—See Agrofert Holding, a.s.; *Int'l*, pg. 219
DIGITAL SPECIALTY CHEMICALS LIMITED—See Entegris, Inc.; *U.S. Public*, pg. 776
DONGIL-BANDO CO., LTD.—See Bando Chemical Industries, Ltd.; *Int'l*, pg. 830
DONGSUNG FINETEC CO., LTD.; *Int'l*, pg. 2170
DOODEH SANATI PARS COMPANY; *Int'l*, pg. 2172
DOVER CHEMICAL CORPORATION—See ICC Industries, Inc.; *U.S. Private*, pg. 2029
THE DOW CHEMICAL COMPANY - TEXAS OPERATIONS—See Dow Inc.; *U.S. Public*, pg. 686
DOW EUROPE GMBH—See Dow Inc.; *U.S. Public*, pg. 684
DOW SILICONES CORPORATION—See Dow Inc.; *U.S. Public*, pg. 684
DR. O.K. WACK CHEMIE GMBH; *Int'l*, pg. 2194
DU PONT (AUSTRALIA) PTY LTD.—See DuPont de Nemours, Inc.; *U.S. Public*, pg. 692
DYMATIC CHEMICALS INC.; *Int'l*, pg. 2238
EASTMAN CHEMICAL URUAPAN, S.A. DE C.V.—See Eastman Chemical Company; *U.S. Public*, pg. 705
ECKERT & ZIEGLER ANALYTICS, LNC.—See Eckert & Ziegler Strahlen- und Medizintechnik AG; *Int'l*, pg. 2290
ECKERT & ZIEGLER EURO-PET BERLIN GMBH—See Eckert & Ziegler Strahlen- und Medizintechnik AG; *Int'l*, pg. 2290
ECKERT & ZIEGLER EUROTOPE GMBH—See Eckert & Ziegler Strahlen- und Medizintechnik AG; *Int'l*, pg. 2290
EG CORPORATION; *Int'l*, pg. 2322
EG METAL CORPORATION—See EG Corporation; *Int'l*, pg. 2322
EG POTECH CO. LTD—See EG Corporation; *Int'l*, pg. 2322
EG TECH CORP.—See EG Corporation; *Int'l*, pg. 2322
EGYPTIAN INTERNATIONAL INDUSTRIAL MINERALS S.A.E.—See Gruppo Minerali Maffei S.p.A.; *Int'l*, pg. 3140
ELECTRO QUIMICA MEXICANA S.A. DE C.V.—See FMC Corporation; *U.S. Public*, pg. 861
ELEMENTIS CHROMIUM, LP—See Elementis plc; *Int'l*, pg. 2359
ELEMENTIS LTP, LT—See Elementis plc; *Int'l*, pg. 2359
ELEMENTIS PHARMA GMBH—See Elementis plc; *Int'l*, pg. 2359
ELEMENTIS S.E.A. (MALAYSIA) SDN BHD—See Elementis plc; *Int'l*, pg. 2359
EMC INDUSTRIAL GROUP LIMITED—See Endress+Hauser (International) Holding AG; *Int'l*, pg. 2406
EMERSON & CUMING—See Henkel AG & Co. KGaA; *Int'l*, pg. 3353
EMMESSAR BIOTECH & NUTRITION LTD.; *Int'l*, pg. 2384
EMS-CHEMIE (FRANCE) S.A.—See EMS-Chemie Holding AG; *Int'l*, pg. 2393
ENDRESS+HAUSER (H.K.) LTD.—See Endress+Hauser (International) Holding AG; *Int'l*, pg. 2406
ENERGETIC SERVICES INC. - EDSON FACILITY—See Energetic Services Inc.; *Int'l*, pg. 2419
ENERGETIC SERVICES INC. - FORT NELSON FACILITY—See Energetic Services Inc.; *Int'l*, pg. 2419
ENERGETIC SERVICES INC. - GRANDE PRAIRIE FACILITY—See Energetic Services Inc.; *Int'l*, pg. 2419

325180 — OTHER BASIC INORGAN...

ENERSUL INC.—See Berkshire Hathaway Inc.; *U.S. Public*, pg. 311
ENERSUL OPERATIONS—See Berkshire Hathaway Inc.; *U.S. Public*, pg. 311
ENTERGY NUCLEAR FUELS COMPANY—See Entergy Corporation; *U.S. Public*, pg. 777
ENTERPRISE METALS LIMITED; *Int'l*, pg. 2452
ENTHONE GMBH—See Element Solutions Inc.; *U.S. Public*, pg. 726
ENTHONE-OMI DE MEXICO S.A. DE C.V.—See Element Solutions Inc.; *U.S. Public*, pg. 726
ENVIRO TECH JAPAN CO., LTD.; *Int'l*, pg. 2454
E.ON KERNKRAFT GMBH—See E.ON SE; *Int'l*, pg. 2253
ERCROS SA - ANIMAL FEED DIVISION - FLIX FACTORY—See Ercros SA; *Int'l*, pg. 2489
ERCROS SA - BASIC CHEMICALS DIVISION - FLIX FACTORY—See Ercros SA; *Int'l*, pg. 2489
ERCROS SA - BASIC CHEMICALS DIVISION - SABINANIGO FACTORY—See Ercros SA; *Int'l*, pg. 2489
ESSECO GROUP SRL; *Int'l*, pg. 2509
ESSECO UK LIMITED—See Esseco Group SRL; *Int'l*, pg. 2509
EURO BAT TRI—See Floridienne SA; *Int'l*, pg. 2708
EXCEL INDUSTRIES LIMITED; *Int'l*, pg. 2577
FENICE S.P.A.—See Electricite de France S.A.; *Int'l*, pg. 2351
FERRO ELECTRONIC MATERIALS INC. - PENN YAN—See American Securities LLC; *U.S. Private*, pg. 251
FERTIGAMA, S.L.; *Int'l*, pg. 2646
FIRESTONE POLYMERS, LLC—See Bridgestone Corporation; *Int'l*, pg. 1157
FLEXIBLE SOLUTIONS, INC.—See Flexible Solutions International, Inc.; *Int'l*, pg. 2704
FLUID ENERGY PROCESSING & EQUIPMENT CO.; *U.S. Private*, pg. 1552
FLUOR HANFORD, INC.—See Fluor Corporation; *U.S. Public*, pg. 859
FMC CORP. - INDUSTRIAL CHEMICALS GROUP—See FMC Corporation; *U.S. Public*, pg. 862
FMC OF CANADA LIMITED—See FMC Corporation; *U.S. Public*, pg. 862
FORMOSA PLASTICS CORPORATION - POLYOLEFIN DIVISION—See Formosa Plastics Corporation; *Int'l*, pg. 2735
FORMOSA PLASTICS CORPORATION - POLYPROPYLENE DIVISION—See Formosa Plastics Corporation; *Int'l*, pg. 2735
FUJIAN ZHONGDE TECHNOLOGY CO., LTD.—See CHINA CLEAN ENERGY INC.; *Int'l*, pg. 1489
FUKUVI CHEMICAL INDUSTRY CO., LTD.; *Int'l*, pg. 2841
FUSO CHEMICAL CO., LTD - KYOTO FIRST FACTORY—See Fuso Chemical Co., Ltd.; *Int'l*, pg. 2850
FUSO CHEMICAL CO., LTD - KYOTO SECOND FACTORY—See Fuso Chemical Co., Ltd.; *Int'l*, pg. 2850
GALAXY LITHIUM (CANADA) INC.—See Allkem Limited; *Int'l*, pg. 359
GALAXY LITHIUM (SAL DE VIDA) S.A.—See Allkem Limited; *Int'l*, pg. 359
GEBROEDERS CAPPELLE FRERES S.A.R.L.—See Cappelle Pignenes N.V.; *Int'l*, pg. 1315
GE HEALTHCARE BIO-SCIENCES EUROPE GMBH—See GE HealthCare Technologies Inc.; *U.S. Public*, pg. 909
GE HEALTHCARE BIO-SCIENCES—See GE HealthCare Technologies Inc.; *U.S. Public*, pg. 909
GENERAL CHEMICAL GROUP, INC.; *U.S. Public*, pg. 913
GENERAL CHEMICAL PERFORMANCE PRODUCTS LLC—See American Securities LLC; *U.S. Private*, pg. 249
GFS CHEMICALS, INC.; *U.S. Private*, pg. 1690
GPRO TITANIUM INDUSTRY CO., LTD.; *Int'l*, pg. 3046
GRACE DAVISON DISCOVERY SCIENCES—See Standard Industries Holdings Inc.; *U.S. Private*, pg. 3779
GRACE H-G, INC.—See Standard Industries Holdings Inc.; *U.S. Private*, pg. 3780
GRACE PAR CORPORATION—See Standard Industries Holdings Inc.; *U.S. Private*, pg. 3780
GSL CORPORATION—See Compass Minerals International, Inc.; *U.S. Public*, pg. 560
GUANGXI WUZHOU ARAKAWA CHEMICAL INDUSTRIES, LTD.—See Arakawa Chemical Industries, Ltd.; *Int'l*, pg. 534
GUANGZHOU SAIFU CHEMICAL CO., LTD.—See BRENNTAG SE; *Int'l*, pg. 1149
GUIZHOU HONGXING DEVELOPMENT CO., LTD.—See Guizhou Redstar Development Co., Ltd.; *Int'l*, pg. 3175
GUIZHOU REDSTAR DEVELOPMENT CO., LTD.; *Int'l*, pg. 3175
GUIZHOU RED STAR DEVELOPMENT DRAGON CHEMICAL INDUSTRY CO., LTD.—See Guizhou Redstar Development Co., Ltd.; *Int'l*, pg. 3175
GUIZHOU RED STAR DEVELOPMENT FANJINGSHAN COLD WATER FISHERIES CO., LTD.—See Guizhou Redstar Development Co., Ltd.; *Int'l*, pg. 3175
GUIZHOU RED STAR DEVELOPMENT IMPORT & EXPORT CO., LTD.—See Guizhou Redstar Development Co., Ltd.; *Int'l*, pg. 3175
GUJARAT ALKALIES & CHEMICALS LTD; *Int'l*, pg. 3175

GUJARAT NCODE SOLUTIONS LIMITED—See Gujarat Narmada Valley Fertilizers & Chemicals Limited; *Int'l*, pg. 3176
GULSHAN POLYOLS LTD.; *Int'l*, pg. 3183
HAMMOND GROUP, INC.; *U.S. Private*, pg. 1849
HAMMOND LEAD PRODUCTS—See Hammond Group, Inc.; *U.S. Private*, pg. 1849
HANIL CHEMICAL IND. CO., LTD.; *Int'l*, pg. 3252
HARDIDE COATINGS INCORPORATED—See Hardide Plc; *Int'l*, pg. 3273
H.C. STARCK GMBH & CO. KG—See Advent International Corporation; *U.S. Private*, pg. 102
H.C. STARCK GMBH & CO. KG—See The Carlyle Group Inc.; *U.S. Public*, pg. 2047
HEMLOCK SEMICONDUCTOR OPERATIONS LLC—See Corning Incorporated; *U.S. Public*, pg. 579
HEMLOCK SEMICONDUCTOR OPERATIONS LLC—See Dow Inc.; *U.S. Public*, pg. 684
HENRY H. OTTENS MANUFACTURING CO., INC.—See International Flavors & Fragrances Inc.; *U.S. Public*, pg. 1152
HERTZ LITHIUM INC.; *Int'l*, pg. 3365
HOKKAIDO SODA CO., LTD.—See AGC Inc.; *Int'l*, pg. 204
HOLITECH TECHNOLOGY CO., LTD.; *Int'l*, pg. 3451
HOSOKAWA MICRON POWDERS GMBH—See Hosokawa Micron Corporation; *Int'l*, pg. 3486
HOWW MANUFACTURING COMPANY INC.—See Arch Promo Group LLC; *U.S. Private*, pg. 310
HUBEI ZHENHUA CHEMICAL CO., LTD; *Int'l*, pg. 3518
HUBER ENGINEERED MATERIALS, LLC - HAVRE DE GRACE—See J.M. Huber Corporation; *U.S. Private*, pg. 2168
HUBER SPECIALTY HYDRATES, LLC—See J.M. Huber Corporation; *U.S. Private*, pg. 2168
HULAMIN LIMITED; *Int'l*, pg. 3527
HUNTSMAN ADVANCED MATERIALS (HONG KONG) LTD—See Huntsman Corporation; *U.S. Public*, pg. 1073
HUNTSMAN P&A GERMANY GMBH—See Huntsman Corporation; *U.S. Public*, pg. 1073
HYDRO CARBIDE, INC. - GULFPORT FACILITY—See HBD Industries, Inc.; *U.S. Private*, pg. 1887
HYDRO CARBIDE, INC. - LATROBE FACILITY—See HBD Industries, Inc.; *U.S. Private*, pg. 1887
IFF TURKEY AROMA VE ESANS URUNLERI SATIS TICARET ANONIM SIRKETI—See International Flavors & Fragrances Inc.; *U.S. Public*, pg. 1152
IKA GMBH & CO.KG—See Floridienne SA; *Int'l*, pg. 2708
IMERYS MINERALS AB—See Groupe Bruxelles Lambert SA; *Int'l*, pg. 3100
IMPERIAL OIL LIMITED—See Exxon Mobil Corporation; *U.S. Public*, pg. 816
INEOS CALABRIAN—See One Rock Capital Partners, LLC; *U.S. Private*, pg. 3023
INNOPHOS MEXICANA S.A. DE C.V.—See One Rock Capital Partners, LLC; *U.S. Private*, pg. 3022
INNOSPEC INC.; *U.S. Public*, pg. 1125
INTERNATIONAL CHEMICAL CORP.; *U.S. Private*, pg. 2115
INTERNATIONAL FLAVORS & FRAGRANCES I.F.F. (MIDDLE EAST) FZE—See International Flavors & Fragrances Inc.; *U.S. Public*, pg. 1153
INTERNATIONAL FLAVORS & FRAGRANCES (LUXEMBOURG) S.A.R.L.—See International Flavors & Fragrances Inc.; *U.S. Public*, pg. 1152
INTERNATIONAL FLAVORS & FRAGRANCES (MIDDLE EAST) FZ-LLC—See International Flavors & Fragrances Inc.; *U.S. Public*, pg. 1152
INTERNATIONAL FLAVOURS & FRAGRANCES (THAILAND) LIMITED—See International Flavors & Fragrances Inc.; *U.S. Public*, pg. 1153
INTERNATIONAL FLAVOURS & FRAGRANCES (VIETNAM) LIMITED LIABILITY COMPANY—See International Flavors & Fragrances Inc.; *U.S. Public*, pg. 1153
IQAP CZECH, S.R.O.—See Avient Corporation; *U.S. Public*, pg. 247
IQAP MASTERBATCH GROUP, S.L.—See Avient Corporation; *U.S. Public*, pg. 247
ISAGRO HELLAS LTD—See Gowan Company LLC; *U.S. Private*, pg. 1747
JACOBS ADVANCED MANUFACTURING BV—See Jacobs Engineering Group, Inc.; *U.S. Public*, pg. 1185
JACOBS CHINA LIMITED—See Jacobs Engineering Group, Inc.; *U.S. Public*, pg. 1184
JCI JONES CHEMICALS, INC.-CORPORATE FINANCIAL CENTER—See JCI Jones Chemicals, Inc.; *U.S. Private*, pg. 2195
JCI JONES CHEMICALS, INC.-CSC—See JCI Jones Chemicals, Inc.; *U.S. Private*, pg. 2195
JIANGXI DATANG CHEMICALS CO., LTD.—See Daikin Industries, Ltd.; *Int'l*, pg. 1935
J.M. HUBER CORPORATION; *U.S. Private*, pg. 2168
JONES-HAMILTON CO.; *U.S. Private*, pg. 2234
JORDAN MAGNESIA COMPANY—See Arab Potash Company PLC; *Int'l*, pg. 531
KANTO SODIUM SILICATE GLASS CO., LTD.—See Adeka Corporation; *Int'l*, pg. 142
KEIYO MONOMER CO., LTD.—See AGC Inc.; *Int'l*, pg. 204
KIMFLOR AS—See Floridienne SA; *Int'l*, pg. 2708

KMG DE MEXICO, SA DE CV—See Entegris, Inc.; *U.S. Public*, pg. 776
KOATSU CHEMICAL INDUSTRIES, LTD.—See Arakawa Chemical Industries, Ltd.; *Int'l*, pg. 534
KOPPERS HOLDINGS INC.; *U.S. Public*, pg. 1271
KRONOS CANADA, INC.—See Contran Corporation; *U.S. Private*, pg. 1033
KRONOS TITAN GMBH—See Contran Corporation; *U.S. Private*, pg. 1033
KUEHNE CHEMICAL COMPANY, INC.; *U.S. Private*, pg. 2356
LAWTER, INC.—See Harima Chemicals Group, Inc.; *Int'l*, pg. 3276
LEWIS CHEMICAL COMPANY; *U.S. Private*, pg. 2438
LIVENT CORPORATION; *U.S. Public*, pg. 1332
LUCAS MEYER COSMETICS AUSTRALIA PTY LTD—See International Flavors & Fragrances Inc.; *U.S. Public*, pg. 1153
LUMIGEN, INC—See Danaher Corporation; *U.S. Public*, pg. 625
MADISON INDUSTRIES, INC.; *U.S. Private*, pg. 2543
MAGNETICS INTERNATIONAL, INC.—See International Steel Services, Inc.; *U.S. Private*, pg. 2121
MAGNIFIN MAGNESIAPRODUKTE GMBH & CO KG—See J.M. Huber Corporation; *U.S. Private*, pg. 2168
MATERION ADVANCED CHEMICALS INC.—See Materion Corporation; *U.S. Public*, pg. 1395
MECS, INC.—See DuPont de Nemours, Inc.; *U.S. Public*, pg. 694
MERCK & CO. INC.—See Merck & Co., Inc.; *U.S. Public*, pg. 1419
MERICHEM CHEMICALS & REFINING SERVICES LLC—See Merichem Company; *U.S. Private*, pg. 2672
MESGO ASIA KAUCUK SAN. VE TIC. LTD.—See HEXPOL AB; *Int'l*, pg. 3372
METALS AND ADDITIVES CORPORATION, INC.; *U.S. Private*, pg. 2681
MEXICHEM FLUOR—See Grupo Empresarial Kaluz S.A. de C.V.; *Int'l*, pg. 3127
MINERALS TECHNOLOGIES EUROPE N.V.—See Minerals Technologies, Inc.; *U.S. Public*, pg. 1449
MINERALS TECHNOLOGIES INDIA PRIVATE LIMITED—See Minerals Technologies, Inc.; *U.S. Public*, pg. 1449
NATIONAL TITANIUM DIOXIDE COMPANY LTD.—See Tronox Holdings plc; *U.S. Public*, pg. 2197
NAVARRA DE COMPONENTES ELECTRONICOS SA (NACESA)—See Parker Hannifin Corporation; *U.S. Public*, pg. 1643
NEVCO, INC.—See Neville Chemical Company; *U.S. Private*, pg. 2891
NHUMO, S.A.P.I. DE C.V.—See Cabot Corporation; *U.S. Public*, pg. 417
NOAH TECHNOLOGIES CORPORATION; *U.S. Private*, pg. 2932
NOURYON CHEMICALS ARGENTINA SAU—See GIC Pte. Ltd.; *Int'l*, pg. 2968
NOURYON CHEMICALS ARGENTINA SAU—See GIC Pte. Ltd.; *Int'l*, pg. 2968
NOURYON CHEMICALS ARGENTINA SAU—See The Carlyle Group Inc.; *U.S. Public*, pg. 2051
NOURYON CHEMICALS ARGENTINA SAU—See The Carlyle Group Inc.; *U.S. Public*, pg. 2051
NUCLEAR FUEL SERVICES, INC.—See Electricite de France S.A.; *Int'l*, pg. 2351
NUFLUX LLC—See Speyside Equity LLC; *U.S. Private*, pg. 3756
OCCIDENTAL CHEMICAL CORPORATION—See Occidental Petroleum Corporation; *U.S. Public*, pg. 1561
OJSC EVRAZ VANADY TULA—See Evraz plc; *Int'l*, pg. 2574
OLIN CHLOR ALKALI PRODUCTS—See Olin Corporation; *U.S. Public*, pg. 1570
OLIN CORPORATION - CHLOR ALKALI PRODUCTS DIVISION—See Olin Corporation; *U.S. Public*, pg. 1570
OLIN CORPORATION; *U.S. Public*, pg. 1570
ORION ENGINEERED CARBONS GMBH—See Rhone Group, LLC; *U.S. Private*, pg. 3424
ORION ENGINEERED CARBONS LLC—See Rhone Group, LLC; *U.S. Private*, pg. 3424
OTSUKA-MGC CHEMICAL COMPANY, INC.—See Earth Corporation; *Int'l*, pg. 2268
PACIFIC GREEN ENERGY STORAGE TECHNOLOGIES INC.—See PACIFIC GREEN TECHNOLOGIES INC.; *U.S. Public*, pg. 1631
PENINSULA COPPER INDUSTRIES; *U.S. Private*, pg. 3133
PENN UNITED TECHNOLOGIES, INC. - CARBIDE DIVISION—See Penn United Technologies, Inc.; *U.S. Private*, pg. 3135
PLASMINE TECHNOLOGY, INC.—See Harima Chemicals Group, Inc.; *Int'l*, pg. 3276
PMC SPECIALTIES GROUP, INC.—See PMC Capital Partners, LLC; *U.S. Private*, pg. 3217
PQLYMER PRODUCTS COMPANY, INC.—See PMC Group, Inc.; *U.S. Private*, pg. 3218
POLYNT COMPOSITES USA INC.—See Reichhold, Inc.; *U.S. Public*, pg. 3390
POLYNT S.P.A. - SAN GIOVANNI VALDARNO PLANT—See Reichhold, Inc.; *U.S. Public*, pg. 3391

N.A.I.C.S. INDEX

325193 — ETHYL ALCOHOL MANUF...

POLYNT S.P.A.—See Reichhold, Inc.; *U.S. Private*, pg. 3390
POROCEL CORP.—See Porocel Industries, LLC; *U.S. Private*, pg. 3229
POWERLAB INC.; *U.S. Private*, pg. 3239
PQ AUSTRALIA PTY. LTD.—See The Carlyle Group Inc.; *U.S. Public*, pg. 2052
PQ CHEMICALS (THAILAND) LTD.—See The Carlyle Group Inc.; *U.S. Public*, pg. 2052
PQ CORPORATION—See The Carlyle Group Inc.; *U.S. Public*, pg. 2052
PQ EUROPE GMBH—See The Carlyle Group Inc.; *U.S. Public*, pg. 2052
PQ FINLAND OY—See The Carlyle Group Inc.; *U.S. Public*, pg. 2052
PQ FRANCE S.A.S.—See The Carlyle Group Inc.; *U.S. Public*, pg. 2052
PQ ITALY S.R.L.—See The Carlyle Group Inc.; *U.S. Public*, pg. 2052
PQ NEDERLAND B.V.—See The Carlyle Group Inc.; *U.S. Public*, pg. 2052
PQ SILICATES LTD.—See The Carlyle Group Inc.; *U.S. Public*, pg. 2052
PQ SWEDEN AB—See The Carlyle Group Inc.; *U.S. Public*, pg. 2052
PQ (TIANJIN) SILICATES TECHNOLOGY CO. LTD.—See The Carlyle Group Inc.; *U.S. Public*, pg. 2052
PROTAMEEN CHEMICALS INC.; *U.S. Private*, pg. 3289
PRYOR CHEMICAL COMPANY—See LSB Industries, Inc.; *U.S. Public*, pg. 1344
PUR-SYSTEMS VERWANTUNGSGESELLSCHAFT MBH—See Huntsman Corporation; *U.S. Public*, pg. 1073
PVS CHEMICALS SOLUTIONS INC. - BUFFALO—See PVS Chemicals, Inc.; *U.S. Private*, pg. 3308
Q2 TECHNOLOGIES, LLC—See Quaker Chemical Corporation; *U.S. Public*, pg. 1746
QINGDAO HONGXING CHEMICAL GROUP INORGANIC NEW MATERIAL TECHNOLOGY DEVELOPMENT CO., LTD.—See Guizhou Redstar Development Co., Ltd.; *Int'l*, pg. 3175
QINGDAO NATURAL PIGMENTS LIMITED—See Guizhou Redstar Development Co., Ltd.; *Int'l*, pg. 3175
RADCO INDUSTRIES, INC.; *U.S. Private*, pg. 3342
REAGENT CHEMICAL & RESEARCH INC.—See Wynnchurch Capital, L.P.; *U.S. Private*, pg. 4578
THE RENEWABLE CORPORATION; *U.S. Public*, pg. 2125
RETORTE GMBH—See Aurubis AG; *Int'l*, pg. 715
THE R.J. MARSHALL COMPANY; *U.S. Private*, pg. 4101
ROHM AND HAAS CHEMICALS LLC - BRISTOL PLANT—See Dow Inc.; *U.S. Public*, pg. 686
ROHM AND HAAS CHEMICALS LLC—See Dow Inc.; *U.S. Public*, pg. 685
SAINT-GOBAIN CERAMIC MATERIALS GMBH—See Compagnie de Saint-Gobain SA; *Int'l*, pg. 1728
SAINT-GOBAIN CERAMICS & PLASTICS—See Compagnie de Saint-Gobain SA; *Int'l*, pg. 1732
SASCO CHEMICAL GROUP, LLC—See Polymer Solutions (PSI); *U.S. Private*, pg. 3226
SCIENTIFIC DESIGN COMPANY, INC.—See Clariant AG; *Int'l*, pg. 1647
SHAMROCK TECHNOLOGIES INC.; *U.S. Private*, pg. 3624
SHANDONG DONGYUE CHEMICAL CO., LTD.—See Dongyue Group Limited; *Int'l*, pg. 2172
SHANDONG SINOBROM ALBEMARLE BROMINE CHEMICALS COMPANY LIMITED—See Albemarle Corporation; *U.S. Public*, pg. 73
SHANGHAI AJINOMOTO AMINO ACID CO., LTD.—See Ajinomoto Company, Inc.; *Int'l*, pg. 257
THE SHEPHERD CHEMICAL COMPANY, INC.; *U.S. Private*, pg. 4117
SIAPA S.R.L.—See Gowan Company LLC; *U.S. Private*, pg. 1747
SIA TIKKURILA—See PPG Industries, Inc.; *U.S. Public*, pg. 1710
SID RICHARDSON CARBON & ENERGY LTD.; *U.S. Private*, pg. 3645
SILBERLINE ASIA PACIFIC PTE. LTD.—See Silberline Manufacturing Co., Inc.; *U.S. Private*, pg. 3652
SILBERLINE MANUFACTURING CO., INC. - SILBERLINE MANUFACTURING FACILITY—See Silberline Manufacturing Co., Inc.; *U.S. Private*, pg. 3652
SILBERLINE PIGMENT (SUZHOU) COMPANY LIMITED—See Silberline Manufacturing Co., Inc.; *U.S. Private*, pg. 3652
SILICATOS Y DERIVADOS S.A. DE C.V.—See The Carlyle Group Inc.; *U.S. Public*, pg. 2052
SKYBITZ PETROLEUM LOGISTICS LLC—See AMETEK, Inc.; *U.S. Public*, pg. 122
SKYBITZ TANK MONITORING CORPORATION—See AMETEK, Inc.; *U.S. Public*, pg. 122
SOCIETE NOUVELLE D'AFFINAGE DES METAUX - SNAM S.A.S.—See Floridienne SA; *Int'l*, pg. 2708
SOLVAY PORTUGAL - PRODUTOS QUIMICOS S.A.—See A4F-Algae for Future SA; *Int'l*, pg. 30
SOLVAY PORTUGAL - PRODUTOS QUIMICOS S.A.—See GREEN AQUA Company SGPS, S.A.; *Int'l*, pg. 3069
SOUTHERN IONICS, INC.; *U.S. Private*, pg. 3732
SOUTHERN STATES CHEMICAL, INC.—See Dulany Industries Inc.; *U.S. Private*, pg. 1286
SOUTHERN STATES CHEMICAL, INC. - WILMINGTON PLANT—See Dulany Industries Inc.; *U.S. Private*, pg. 1286
SPECIALTY MINERALS FRANCE S.P.A.S.—See Minerals Technologies, Inc.; *U.S. Public*, pg. 1449
SPECIALTY MINERALS GMBH—See Minerals Technologies, Inc.; *U.S. Public*, pg. 1449
SPECIALTY MINERALS NORDIC OY AB—See Minerals Technologies, Inc.; *U.S. Public*, pg. 1449
STAR INTERNATIONAL SAINT-PETERSBURG LLC—See GHW International; *Int'l*, pg. 2960
SUD-CHEMIE INC.-AIR PURIFICATION—See Clariant AG; *Int'l*, pg. 1647
SYNQUEST LABORATORIES, INC.—See Central Glass Co., Ltd.; *Int'l*, pg. 1407
TAIAN HAVAY GROUP CO., LTD.—See GHW International; *Int'l*, pg. 2960
TAIWAN ARAKAWA CHEMICAL INDUSTRIES, LTD.—See Arakawa Chemical Industries, Ltd.; *Int'l*, pg. 535
TAIWAN CHLORINE INDUSTRIES LTD.—See China Petrochemical Development Corp.; *Int'l*, pg. 1540
TAIWAN CHLORINE INDUSTRIES LTD.—See Westlake Corporation; *U.S. Public*, pg. 2360
TEES VALLEY LITHIUM LIMITED—See Alkemy Capital Investments Plc; *Int'l*, pg. 331
TETRA CHEMICALS EUROPE AB—See TETRA Technologies, Inc.; *U.S. Public*, pg. 2024
TETRA CHEMICALS EUROPE OY—See TETRA Technologies, Inc.; *U.S. Public*, pg. 2024
TEXAS UNITED CHEMICAL COMPANY LLC—See United Salt Corporation; *U.S. Private*, pg. 4297
THAI ETHOXYLATE COMPANY LIMITED—See BASF SE; *Int'l*, pg. 885
THERMOX PERFORMANCE MATERIALS LTD.—See Amalgamated Metal Corporation PLC; *Int'l*, pg. 409
TOB BRENNTAG UKRAINE LLC—See BRENNTAG SE; *Int'l*, pg. 1150
TOKAI CARBON (TIANJIN) CO., LTD.—See Cabot Corporation; *U.S. Public*, pg. 417
TRECORA CHEMICAL, INC—See Balmoral Funds LLC; *U.S. Private*, pg. 462
TRONOX LLC - GREEN RIVER SODA ASH PLANT—See Tronox Holdings plc; *U.S. Public*, pg. 2197
TRONOX PIGMENTS PTY. LIMITED—See Tronox Holdings plc; *U.S. Public*, pg. 2197
UMICORE BUILDING PRODUCTS USA INC.—See Fedrus International NV; *Int'l*, pg. 2631
UOP LLC - HOUSTON—See Honeywell International Inc.; *U.S. Public*, pg. 1052
UOP LLC—See Honeywell International Inc.; *U.S. Public*, pg. 1052
VALSPAR REFINISH, INC.—See The Sherwin-Williams Company; *U.S. Public*, pg. 2129
VELSICOL CHEMICAL CORPORATION—See Arsenal Capital Management LP; *U.S. Private*, pg. 339
VERTELLUS HEALTH & SPECIALTY PRODUCTS LLC - ELMA—See Black Diamond Capital Holdings, LLC; *U.S. Private*, pg. 571
VERTELLUS HEALTH & SPECIALTY PRODUCTS LLC - ELMA—See Brightwood Capital Advisors, LLC; *U.S. Private*, pg. 653
VERTEX CHEMICAL CORPORATION—See Hawkins, Inc.; *U.S. Public*, pg. 989
VIANCE, LLC—See Dow Inc.; *U.S. Public*, pg. 686
VIANCE, LLC—See Huntsman Corporation; *U.S. Public*, pg. 1075
WATER ENGINEERING, INC.—See Nolan Capital, Inc.; *U.S. Private*, pg. 2934
WATERSAVR GLOBAL SOLUTIONS INC.—See Flexible Solutions International, Inc.; *Int'l*, pg. 2704
WILLIAMS GAS PIPELINE—See The Williams Companies, Inc.; *U.S. Public*, pg. 2143
W. R. GRACE KOREA INC.—See Standard Industries Holdings Inc.; *U.S. Public*, pg. 3780
W. R. GRACE LIMITED—See Standard Industries Holdings Inc.; *U.S. Public*, pg. 3780
YANGTZE RIVER ACETYLS CO. LTD.—See BP plc; *Int'l*, pg. 1128
ZEOLYST INTERNATIONAL—See The Carlyle Group Inc.; *U.S. Public*, pg. 2052
ZHEJIANG DEWEI CEMENTED CARBIDE MANUFACTURING CO., LTD.—See GEM Co., Ltd.; *Int'l*, pg. 2914
ZHUZHOU CEMENTED CARBIDE WORKS IMPORT & EXPORT COMPANY—See Hunan Nonferrous Metals Corporation Ltd.; *Int'l*, pg. 3533
Z-TECH LLC—See Compagnie de Saint-Gobain SA; *Int'l*, pg. 1732

325193 — ETHYL ALCOHOL MANUFACTURING

ABENGOA BIOENERGY CORP.—See Abengoa S.A.; *Int'l*, pg. 59
ADVANCED BIOENERGY, LLC; *U.S. Public*, pg. 46
AEMETIS ADVANCED FUELS KEYES, INC.—See Aemetis, Inc.; *U.S. Public*, pg. 52
ASSOCIATED ALCOHOLS & BREWERIES LTD.; *Int'l*, pg. 648
BADGER STATE ETHANOL LLC; *U.S. Private*, pg. 424
BAJAJ HINDUSTAN SUGAR LIMITED; *Int'l*, pg. 804
BLAZE PRODUCTS CORPORATION—See BCP Inc.; *U.S. Private*, pg. 499
BLUE FLINT ETHANOL LLC—See Great River Energy; *U.S. Private*, pg. 1767
CARDINAL ETHANOL, LLC; *U.S. Private*, pg. 750
CHANGHAE ETHANOL CO., LTD.; *Int'l*, pg. 1443
CHEMICAL INDUSTRIES (MALAYA) SDN. BHD.—See Hexza Corporation Berhad; *Int'l*, pg. 3373
CHIEF ETHANOL FUELS, INC.—See Chief Industries, Inc.; *U.S. Private*, pg. 881
CHINA BEIDAHUANG INDUSTRY GROUP HOLDINGS LTD.; *Int'l*, pg. 1486
COMMONWEALTH AGRI-ENERGY, LLC—See Hopkinsville Elevator Company, Inc.; *U.S. Private*, pg. 1979
DINS KANSAI CO., LTD.—See Daiei Kankyo Co., Ltd.; *Int'l*, pg. 1924
ETERNAL ENERGY PUBLIC COMPANY LIMITED; *Int'l*, pg. 2520
ETHANOL ENERGY A.S.—See Agrofert Holding, a.s.; *Int'l*, pg. 219
ETHANOL TECHNOLOGIES LIMITED; *Int'l*, pg. 2523
GRANITE FALLS ENERGY, LLC; *U.S. Private*, pg. 1755
GREEN PLAINS ATKINSON LLC—See Green Plains Inc.; *U.S. Public*, pg. 963
GREEN PLAINS BLUFFTON LLC—See Valero Energy Corporation; *U.S. Public*, pg. 2272
GREEN PLAINS CENTRAL CITY LLC—See Green Plains Inc.; *U.S. Public*, pg. 963
GREEN PLAINS COMMODITIES LLC—See Green Plains Inc.; *U.S. Public*, pg. 963
GREEN PLAINS FAIRMONT LLC—See Green Plains Inc.; *U.S. Public*, pg. 963
GREEN PLAINS HEREFORD LLC—See Green Plains Inc.; *U.S. Public*, pg. 963
GREEN PLAINS INC.; *U.S. Public*, pg. 963
GREEN PLAINS ORD LLC—See Green Plains Inc.; *U.S. Public*, pg. 963
GREEN PLAINS OTTER TAIL LLC—See Green Plains Inc.; *U.S. Public*, pg. 963
GREEN PLAINS SHENANDOAH LLC—See Green Plains Inc.; *U.S. Public*, pg. 963
GREEN PLAINS WOOD RIVER LLC—See Green Plains Inc.; *U.S. Public*, pg. 964
GTL RESOURCES PLC—See Harwood Capital LLP; *Int'l*, pg. 3282
HERON LAKE BIOENERGY, LLC—See Granite Falls Energy, LLC; *U.S. Private*, pg. 1755
HIGHWATER ETHANOL, LLC; *U.S. Private*, pg. 1942
HOMELAND ENERGY SOLUTIONS, LLC; *U.S. Private*, pg. 1973
HUSKER AG, LLC; *U.S. Private*, pg. 2013
ILLINOIS RIVER ENERGY, LLC—See CHS INC.; *U.S. Public*, pg. 492
LAKE AREA CORN PROCESSORS, LLC; *U.S. Private*, pg. 2374
LINCOLNWAY ENERGY, LLC; *U.S. Private*, pg. 2459
MARQUIS ENERGY LLC - NECEDAH WI PLANT—See Marquis Grain, Inc.; *U.S. Private*, pg. 2587
NORTHERN GROWERS LLC; *U.S. Public*, pg. 1537
NUGEN ENERGY, LLC—See REX American Resources Corporation; *U.S. Public*, pg. 1795
PACIFIC ETHANOL AURORA EAST, LLC—See Alto Ingredients, Inc.; *U.S. Public*, pg. 88
PACIFIC ETHANOL CENTRAL, LLC—See Alto Ingredients, Inc.; *U.S. Public*, pg. 88
PACIFIC ETHANOL PEKIN, INC.—See Alto Ingredients, Inc.; *U.S. Public*, pg. 88
PHARMCO-AAPER—See GreenField Specialty Alcohols Inc.; *Int'l*, pg. 3074
RED STAR DAQING LVYOU NATURAL PIGMENT CO., LTD.—See Guizhou Redstar Development Co., Ltd.; *Int'l*, pg. 3175
RED TRAIL ENERGY, LLC; *U.S. Public*, pg. 1770
RTW RETAILWINDS, INC.; *U.S. Public*, pg. 1820
SIOUXLAND ETHANOL, LLC.; *U.S. Private*, pg. 3671
UNICOL.—See Cherat Cement Company Limited; *Int'l*, pg. 1471
UNITED WISCONSIN GRAIN PRODUCERS, LLC; *U.S. Private*, pg. 4302
UTICA ENERGY, LLC.; *U.S. Private*, pg. 4325
VALERO RENEWABLE FUELS CO., LLC - ALBION—See Valero Energy Corporation; *U.S. Public*, pg. 2272
VALERO RENEWABLE FUELS CO., LLC - AURORA—See Valero Energy Corporation; *U.S. Public*, pg. 2272
VALERO RENEWABLE FUELS CO., LLC - BLOOMINGBURG—See Valero Energy Corporation; *U.S. Public*, pg. 2273
VALERO RENEWABLE FUELS CO., LLC - CHARLES CITY—See Valero Energy Corporation; *U.S. Public*, pg. 2273
VALERO RENEWABLE FUELS CO., LLC - FORT DODGE—See Valero Energy Corporation; *U.S. Public*, pg. 2273
VALERO RENEWABLE FUELS CO., LLC - HARTLEY—See Valero Energy Corporation; *U.S. Public*, pg. 2273
VALERO RENEWABLE FUELS CO., LLC - LINDEN—See

325193 — ETHYL ALCOHOL MANUF...

Valero Energy Corporation; *U.S. Public*, pg. 2273
VALERO RENEWABLE FUELS CO., LLC WELCOME—See Valero Energy Corporation; *U.S. Public*, pg. 2273
WESTERN PLAINS ENERGY, LLC.; *U.S. Private*, pg. 4495

325194 — CYCLIC CRUDE, INTERMEDIATE, AND GUM AND WOOD CHEMICAL MANUFACTURING

ALFREBRO, LLC—See Archer-Daniels-Midland Company; *U.S. Public*, pg. 183
AMERICAN XANTHAN CORPORATION; *U.S. Private*, pg. 258
APERAM BIOENERGIA LTDA—See Aperam SA; *Int'l*, pg. 508
ASHLAND INDUSTRIES AUSTRIA GMBH—See Ashland Inc.; *U.S. Public*, pg. 212
ASHLAND INDUSTRIES BELGIUM BVBA—See Ashland Inc.; *U.S. Public*, pg. 212
ASHLAND INDUSTRIES DEUTSCHLAND GMBH—See Ashland Inc.; *U.S. Public*, pg. 212
ASHLAND INDUSTRIES FINLAND OY—See Ashland Inc.; *U.S. Public*, pg. 212
ASHLAND INDUSTRIES SWEDEN AB—See Ashland Inc.; *U.S. Public*, pg. 212
AUSON AB; *Int'l*, pg. 716
BIO METHANOL CHEMIE NEDERLAND BV; *Int'l*, pg. 1035
CALUMET COTTON VALLEY REFINING, LLC—See Calumet, Inc.; *U.S. Public*, pg. 425
CARBOLINEUM WOOD PRESERVING CO.; *U.S. Private*, pg. 748
C.A. SPENCER INC.; *Int'l*, pg. 1240
CHEMCRUX ENTERPRISES LIMITED; *Int'l*, pg. 1461
CROWLEY TAR PRODUCTS CO., INC.—See Palo Duro Capital, LLC; *U.S. Private*, pg. 3082
EXXONMOBIL PETROLEUM & CHEMICAL BVBA—See Exxon Mobil Corporation; *U.S. Public*, pg. 816
FULCRUM BIOENERGY, INC.; *U.S. Private*, pg. 1620
HERCULES INCORPORATED—See Ashland Inc.; *U.S. Public*, pg. 212
HUNAN LEAD POWER TECHNOLOGY GROUP CO., LTD.; *Int'l*, pg. 3533
THE KINGSFORD PRODUCTS COMPANY—See The Clorox Company; *U.S. Public*, pg. 2063
KOPPERS ASHCROFT INC.—See Koppers Holdings Inc.; *U.S. Public*, pg. 1271
KOPPERS WORLDWIDE VENTURES CORPORATION—See Koppers Holdings Inc.; *U.S. Public*, pg. 1272
LAWTER INC. - R&D—See Harima Chemicals Group, Inc.; *Int'l*, pg. 3276
MOBIL OIL NEW ZEALAND LIMITED—See Exxon Mobil Corporation; *U.S. Public*, pg. 817
NORTH TEXAS ENERGY, INC.; *U.S. Private*, pg. 2948
PAKISTAN GUM INDUSTRIES LIMITED—See Ashland Inc.; *U.S. Public*, pg. 212

325199 — ALL OTHER BASIC ORGANIC CHEMICAL MANUFACTURING

AAK NETHERLANDS BV—See AAK AB; *Int'l*, pg. 32
ABS MATERIALS, INC.—See AQUANEX, Servicio Domiciliario del Agua de EXTREMADURA SA; *U.S. Public*, pg. 527
ACCESSORIES MARKETING, INC.—See Illinois Tool Works Inc.; *U.S. Public*, pg. 1101
ACP BELGIUM NV—See Air Products & Chemicals, Inc.; *U.S. Public*, pg. 64
ACTION PIN SA—See Firmenich International SA; *Int'l*, pg. 2681
ADA-ES, INC.—See Advanced Emissions Solutions, Inc.; *U.S. Public*, pg. 46
ADEKA CORPORATION; *Int'l*, pg. 141
ADEKA FINE CHEMICAL (SHANGHAI) CO., LTD.—See Adeka Corporation; *Int'l*, pg. 141
ADEKA FINE CHEMICAL TAIWAN CORP.—See Adeka Corporation; *Int'l*, pg. 141
ADVANCED APPLICATIONS INSTITUTE, INC.; *U.S. Private*, pg. 87
ADVANCED BIO-AGRO TECH LIMITED—See Advanced Enzyme Technologies Limited; *Int'l*, pg. 159
ADVANCED ENZYMES USA, INC.—See Advanced Enzyme Technologies Limited; *Int'l*, pg. 159
ADVANCED ENZYME TECHNOLOGIES LIMITED; *Int'l*, pg. 158
AJINOMOTO AMINOSCIENCE LLC—See Ajinomoto Company, Inc.; *Int'l*, pg. 257
AKZO NOBEL CHEMICALS LLC—See GIC Pte. Ltd.; *Int'l*, pg. 2967
AKZO NOBEL CHEMICALS LLC—See The Carlyle Group Inc.; *U.S. Public*, pg. 2050
AKZO NOBEL CHEMICALS PTY LTD—See GIC Pte. Ltd.; *Int'l*, pg. 2968
AKZO NOBEL CHEMICALS PTY LTD—See The Carlyle Group Inc.; *U.S. Public*, pg. 2050
AKZO NOBEL CHEMICALS SA DE CV—See GIC Pte. Ltd.; *Int'l*, pg. 2968
AKZO NOBEL CHEMICALS SA DE CV—See The Carlyle Group Inc.; *U.S. Public*, pg. 2051
AKZO NOBEL INC.—See Akzo Nobel N.V.; *Int'l*, pg. 271
ALBEMARLE CHEMICALS SOUTH AFRICA (PTY) LTD.—See Albemarle Corporation; *U.S. Public*, pg. 73
ALBEMARLE CHEMICALS U.K. LIMITED—See Albemarle Corporation; *U.S. Public*, pg. 73
ALBEMARLE CORP. - PENNSYLVANIA—See Albemarle Corporation; *U.S. Public*, pg. 73
ALBERT VIEILLE S.A.S.—See Givaudan S.A.; *Int'l*, pg. 2979
ALKANE, INC.; *U.S. Public*, pg. 78
ALLERGAN BOTOX LIMITED—See AbbVie Inc.; *U.S. Public*, pg. 22
ALTAIR CHIMICA SPA—See Esseco Group SRL; *Int'l*, pg. 2509
ALTEO HOLDING SAS—See H.I.G. Capital, LLC; *U.S. Private*, pg. 1828
ALTIVIA CORPORATION—See BRENNTAG SE; *Int'l*, pg. 1148
ALTIVIA OXIDE CHEMICALS, LLC—See BRENNTAG SE; *Int'l*, pg. 1148
ALTIVIA PETROCHEMICALS, LLC—See BRENNTAG SE; *Int'l*, pg. 1148
ALTO INGREDIENTS, INC.; *U.S. Public*, pg. 88
AMAL LIMITED; *Int'l*, pg. 408
AMAX INDUSTRIAL PRODUCTS; *U.S. Private*, pg. 216
THE AMBER CHEMICAL COMPANY LTD.—See Akoya Capital LLC; *U.S. Private*, pg. 146
THE AMBER CHEMICAL COMPANY LTD.—See Century Park Capital Partners, LLC; *U.S. Private*, pg. 833
AMERICAN ACRYL LP—See Arkema S.A.; *Int'l*, pg. 569
AMPACET SHANGHAI (TRADING) CO., LTD.—See Ampacet Corporation; *U.S. Private*, pg. 264
AMPACET SPECIALTY PRODUCTS PRIVATE LTD.—See Ampacet Corporation; *U.S. Private*, pg. 264
ANAEROBICOS SRL—See Illinois Tool Works Inc.; *U.S. Public*, pg. 1101
ANDA SEMICONDUCTOR TECHNOLOGY (SUZHOU) CO., LTD.—See Everlight Chemical Industrial Co.; *Int'l*, pg. 2567
ANGUS CHEMICAL COMPANY—See Golden Gate Capital Management II, LLC; *U.S. Private*, pg. 1730
ANHUI COFCO BIOCHEMICAL & GALACTIC LACTIC ACID CO., LTD.—See Cofco Biotechnology Co., Ltd.; *Int'l*, pg. 1691
ANHUI COFCO BIOCHEMICAL & GALACTIC LACTIC ACID CO., LTD.—See Finasucre S.A.; *Int'l*, pg. 2670
ANUPAM RASAYAN INDIA LIMITED; *Int'l*, pg. 486
ANYGEN CO LTD; *Int'l*, pg. 487
ARABIAN AMINES COMPANY—See Huntsman Corporation; *U.S. Public*, pg. 1073
ARASCO CHEMICAL CO.—See Arabian Agricultural Services Co.; *Int'l*, pg. 533
ARCHEAN CHEMICAL INDUSTRIES LIMITED; *Int'l*, pg. 547
ARCHEM QUIMICA LTDA—See Illinois Tool Works Inc.; *U.S. Public*, pg. 1101
ARCHER DANIELS MIDLAND CO.—See Archer-Daniels-Midland Company; *U.S. Public*, pg. 183
ARCHIT ORGANOSYS LTD.; *Int'l*, pg. 549
ARGO LIVING SOILS CORP.; *Int'l*, pg. 562
ARGUS (SHANGHAI) TEXTILE CHEMICALS CO., LTD.; *Int'l*, pg. 563
ARKEMA EUROPE SA—See Arkema S.A.; *Int'l*, pg. 569
ARKEMA PTE LTD—See Arkema S.A.; *Int'l*, pg. 569
ARKEMA QUIMICA LTDA—See Arkema S.A.; *Int'l*, pg. 569
ARKEMA SRL—See Arkema S.A.; *Int'l*, pg. 570
ARLA FOODS INGREDIENTS AMBA—See Arla Foods amba; *Int'l*, pg. 572
ARLA FOODS INGREDIENTS S.A.—See Arla Foods amba; *Int'l*, pg. 572
AROMCO LTD.—See International Flavors & Fragrances Inc.; *U.S. Public*, pg. 1151
ARRAN CHEMICAL COMPANY—See Almac Sciences Group Ltd.; *Int'l*, pg. 363
ARRMAZ PRODUCTS, LP—See Golden Gate Capital Management II, LLC; *U.S. Private*, pg. 1731
ARVEE LABORATORIES (INDIA) LIMITED; *Int'l*, pg. 587
ASAHI TENNANTS COLOR PRIVATE LIMITED—See Asahi Songwon Colors Ltd.; *Int'l*, pg. 598
ASHLAND SPECIALTY INGREDIENTS—See Ashland Inc.; *U.S. Public*, pg. 212
ASHOK ALCO CHEM LIMITED; *Int'l*, pg. 608
ASIA POLYMER CORPORATION - LIN YUAN PLANT—See Asia Polymer Corporation; *Int'l*, pg. 615
AVADH SUGAR & ENERGY LIMITED; *Int'l*, pg. 734
AVOCADO RESEARCH CHEMICALS LIMITED—See Thermo Fisher Scientific Inc.; *U.S. Public*, pg. 2145
AXYNTIS SAS—See Argos Wityu S.A.; *Int'l*, pg. 563
AZELIS GROUP NV—See EQT AB; *Int'l*, pg. 2469
BAJAJ HINDUSTAN LTD. - KINAUNI - SUGAR UNIT—See Bajaj Hindustan Sugar Limited; *Int'l*, pg. 804
BAJAJ HINDUSTHAN LTD. - RUDAULI - SUGAR UNIT—See Bajaj Hindustan Sugar Limited; *Int'l*, pg. 804
BALCHEM BV—See Balchem Corporation; *U.S. Public*, pg. 265
BANGCHAK RETAIL CO., LTD.—See Bangchak Corporation Public Company Limited; *Int'l*, pg. 832
BANNER CHEMICALS-OXYGENATED SOLVENTS & INTERMEDIATES—See Banner Chemicals Limited; *Int'l*, pg. 851
BAOJI FUFENG BIOTECHNOLOGIES CO., LTD.—See Fufeng Group Limited; *Int'l*, pg. 2804
BAOTOU TOMORROW TECHNOLOGY CO., LTD.; *Int'l*, pg. 857
BASF BEAUTY CARE SOLUTIONS FRANCE SAS - LYON—See BASF SE; *Int'l*, pg. 878
BASF BEAUTY CARE SOLUTIONS FRANCE SAS—See BASF SE; *Int'l*, pg. 878
BASF BEAUTY CARE SOLUTIONS LLC—See BASF SE; *Int'l*, pg. 879
BASF CATALYSTS INDIA PVT. LTD.—See BASF SE; *Int'l*, pg. 872
BASF COATINGS SERVICES SP. Z O.O.—See BASF SE; *Int'l*, pg. 872
BASF CORP. - LIVONIA PLANT—See BASF SE; *Int'l*, pg. 876
BASF HOCK MINING CHEMICAL (CHINA) COMPANY LTD.—See BASF SE; *Int'l*, pg. 879
BASF HONG KONG LTD.—See BASF SE; *Int'l*, pg. 879
BASF MEXICANA, S.A. DE C.V.—See BASF SE; *Int'l*, pg. 880
BASF TURK KIMYA SAN. VE TIC. LTD. STI.—See BASF SE; *Int'l*, pg. 881
BATU KAWAN BERHAD; *Int'l*, pg. 890
BAYER D.O.O.—See Bayer Aktiengesellschaft; *Int'l*, pg. 906
BAYER JINLING POLYURETHANE CO., LTD.—See Bayer Aktiengesellschaft; *Int'l*, pg. 905
BBGI PUBLIC COMPANY LIMITED—See Bangchak Corporation Public Company Limited; *Int'l*, pg. 832
BCP INGREDIENTS, INC.—See Balchem Corporation; *U.S. Public*, pg. 265
BEIJING JWGB SCI. & TECH. CO., LTD.; *Int'l*, pg. 953
BEIJING SCITOP BIO-TECH CO., LTD.; *Int'l*, pg. 955
BELL FLAVORS & FRAGRANCES, INC.; *U.S. Private*, pg. 518
BENECHIM S.P.R.L.—See PMC Capital Partners, LLC; *U.S. Private*, pg. 3217
BERLI JUCKER SPECIALTIES LTD.—See Berli Jucker Public Co. Ltd.; *Int'l*, pg. 985
BGB GIOVANNI BOZZETTO, S.A.—See Aimia Inc.; *U.S. Public*, pg. 233
BHATIA COLOUR CHEM LIMITED; *Int'l*, pg. 1014
BIOLAC GMBH & CO. KG—See Arla Foods amba; *Int'l*, pg. 572
BLH SAS; *Int'l*, pg. 1063
BLUE CUBE COLOMBIA LTDA.—See Olin Corporation; *U.S. Public*, pg. 1570
BNT CHEMICALS GMBH—See IBU-Tec Advanced Materials AG; *Int'l*, pg. 3577
BONA VIDA, INC.—See Better Choice Company, Inc.; *U.S. Public*, pg. 326
BONTERRA LTD.—See Hayleys PLC; *Int'l*, pg. 3291
BOULDER IONICS CORPORATION—See Molson Coors Beverage Company; *U.S. Public*, pg. 1459
BOULDER SCIENTIFIC COMPANY; *U.S. Private*, pg. 623
BOZZETTO GMBH—See Aimia Inc.; *U.S. Public*, pg. 233
BOZZETTO KIMYA SAN.VE TIC . A.S.—See Aimia Inc.; *Int'l*, pg. 234
BP CHEMICALS, INC.—See BP plc; *Int'l*, pg. 1126
B.R. CHEMICALS CO., LTD.—See Black Rose Industries Ltd.; *Int'l*, pg. 1060
BRENNTAG MID-SOUTH, INC.—See BRENNTAG SE; *Int'l*, pg. 1148
BRENNTAG UKRAINE LTD—See BRENNTAG SE; *Int'l*, pg. 1148
BUCKMAN LABORATORIES, INC.—See Bulab Holdings, Inc.; *U.S. Private*, pg. 683
BYOTROL CONSUMER PRODUCTS LIMITED—See Byotrol Limited; *Int'l*, pg. 1235
CARBACID INVESTMENTS PLC; *Int'l*, pg. 1320
CARBIDE CHEMICAL (THAILAND) LIMITED—See Dow Inc.; *U.S. Public*, pg. 686
CARDIOXYL PHARMACEUTICALS, INC.—See Bristol-Myers Squibb Company; *U.S. Public*, pg. 385
CARDOLITE CORPORATION; *U.S. Private*, pg. 751
CARGILL FOOD INGREDIENTS—See Cargill, Inc.; *U.S. Private*, pg. 756
CASDA BIOMATERIALS CO., LTD.—See Arkema S.A.; *Int'l*, pg. 570
CASELLA ORGANICS—See Casella Waste Systems, Inc.; *U.S. Public*, pg. 446
CELANESE CHEMICALS, INC.—See Celanese Corporation; *U.S. Public*, pg. 465
CELANESE PROPERTY GERMANY GMBH & CO. KG—See Celanese Corporation; *U.S. Public*, pg. 465
CELANESE SERVICES GERMANY GMBH—See Celanese Corporation; *U.S. Public*, pg. 465
CELESTE INDUSTRIES CORPORATION—See Illinois Tool Works Inc.; *U.S. Public*, pg. 1102
CENTAURI TECHNOLOGIES, LP—See The Pritzker Group - Chicago, LLC; *U.S. Private*, pg. 4098
THE CHAMPION COMPANY INC.; *U.S. Private*, pg. 4007
CHANG CHIANG CHEMICAL (SHANGHAI) CO., LTD.—See

N.A.I.C.S. INDEX

325199 — ALL OTHER BASIC ORG...

ChangChun Group; *Int'l*, pg. 1442
CHANG CHUN CHEMICAL (JIANGSU) CO., LTD.—See ChangChun Group; *Int'l*, pg. 1442
CHANG CHUN CHEMICAL (ZHANGZHOU) CO., LTD.—See ChangChun Group; *Int'l*, pg. 1442
CHANGCHUN GBT BIO-CHEMICAL CO., LTD.—See Global Bio-chem Technology Group Company Limited; *Int'l*, pg. 2993
CHANG LONG CHEMICAL (SHENZHEN) CO., LTD.—See ChangChun Group; *Int'l*, pg. 1442
CHEMETALL GMBH—See BASF SE; *Int'l*, pg. 873
CHEMICAL INITIATIVES (PTY) LIMITED—See AECI Limited; *Int'l*, pg. 171
CHEMIESYNTH (VAPI) LTD.; *Int'l*, pg. 1462
CHEMSIL SILICONES, INC.—See Innospec Inc.; *U.S. Public*, pg. 1125
CHINA ZENITH CHEMICAL GROUP LIMITED; *Int'l*, pg. 1566
CHIPLUN FINE CHEMICALS LTD.; *Int'l*, pg. 1573
CHRISAL N.V.—See HeiQ Plc; *Int'l*, pg. 3326
C.I.B.A. COMPANIA INTRODUCTORA DE BUENOS AIRES S.A.—See FV S.A.; *Int'l*, pg. 2859
CIRCHEM AB; *Int'l*, pg. 1617
CJ LIAO CHENG BIOTECH CO., LTD.—See CJ Corporation; *Int'l*, pg. 1632
CLARIANT CORPORATION—See Clariant AG; *Int'l*, pg. 1647
CLARIANT PAKISTAN (PRIVATE) LIMITED—See Clariant AG; *Int'l*, pg. 1647
CLEAN SCIENCE & TECHNOLOGY LIMITED; *Int'l*, pg. 1654
CLOPAY EUROPE GMBH—See Griffon Corporation; *U.S. Public*, pg. 969
COATEX CENTRAL EASTERN EUROPE S.R.O.—See Arkema S.A.; *Int'l*, pg. 571
COATEX INC.—See Arkema S.A.; *Int'l*, pg. 569
COFCO BIOTECHNOLOGY CO., LTD.; *Int'l*, pg. 1691
COMMONWEALTH OIL CORPORATION—See Quaker Chemical Corporation; *U.S. Public*, pg. 1745
CONCENTRADOS INDUSTRIALES, S.A. DE C.V.—See Arca Continental, S.A.B. de C.V.; *Int'l*, pg. 540
COOGEE CHEMICALS (MT ISA) PTY LTD—See Coogee Chemicals Pty Ltd.; *Int'l*, pg. 1788
COOGEE CHEMICALS PTY LTD. - METHANOL FACILITY—See Coogee Chemicals Pty Ltd.; *Int'l*, pg. 1788
COOKSON ENTHONE CHEMISTRY TRADING (SHANGHAI) CO LTD—See Element Solutions Inc.; *U.S. Public*, pg. 726
COOKSON INDIA PRIVATE LIMITED - ENTHONE INDIA DIVISION—See Element Solutions Inc.; *U.S. Public*, pg. 726
CORAL SEAS - CONSUMER PRODUCTS DIVISION—See Coral Chemical Company; *U.S. Private*, pg. 1046
CORNERSTONE CHEMICAL COMPANY B.V.—See Littlejohn & Co., LLC; *U.S. Private*, pg. 2470
CORNHUSKER ENERGY LEXINGTON, LLC—See ACI Capital Co. LLC; *U.S. Private*, pg. 59
CORTEVA AGRISCIENCE BOLIVIA S.A.—See Corteva, Inc.; *U.S. Public*, pg. 581
CORTEVA AGRISCIENCE CZECH S.R.O.—See Corteva, Inc.; *U.S. Public*, pg. 581
COVESTRO A/S—See Bayer Aktiengesellschaft; *Int'l*, pg. 907
CP INGREDIENTS INDIA PRIVATE LIMITED—See Ingredion Incorporated; *U.S. Public*, pg. 1123
CRISTAL PIGMENT UK LTD.—See One Rock Capital Partners, LLC; *U.S. Private*, pg. 3023
CRODA CHILE LTDA.—See Croda International plc; *Int'l*, pg. 1851
CRODA CHINA TRADING COMPANY LTD.—See Croda International plc; *Int'l*, pg. 1851
CRODA INDIA COMPANY PRIVATE LTD.—See Croda International plc; *Int'l*, pg. 1852
CRODA INTERNATIONAL PLC; *Int'l*, pg. 1851
CRODA JAPAN KK—See Croda International plc; *Int'l*, pg. 1852
CRODA KIMYA TICARET LIMITED SIRKET—See Croda International plc; *Int'l*, pg. 1852
CRODA KOREA CO, LTD.—See Croda International plc; *Int'l*, pg. 1852
CRODA MAGYARORSZAG KFT.—See Croda International plc; *Int'l*, pg. 1852
CRODA PARS TRADING CO—See Croda International plc; *Int'l*, pg. 1852
CRODA RUS LLC—See Croda International plc; *Int'l*, pg. 1852
CRODA (SA) (PTY) LTD.—See Croda International plc; *Int'l*, pg. 1851
CRODA SIPO (SICHUAN) CO., LTD.—See Croda International plc; *Int'l*, pg. 1852
CRODA SPOL. S.R.O—See Croda International plc; *Int'l*, pg. 1852
CROP LIFE SCIENCE LIMITED; *Int'l*, pg. 1855
CROWLEY CHEMICAL COMPANY, INC.—See Palo Duro Capital, LLC; *U.S. Private*, pg. 3082
CROWN PRODUCTS & SERVICES, INC.—See Merit Capital Partners; *U.S. Private*, pg. 2674

CTRACK (PTY) LTD—See Inseego Corp.; *U.S. Public*, pg. 1129
CTRACK UK LTD—See Inseego Corp.; *U.S. Public*, pg. 1129
CUMBERLAND PACKING CORP.; *U.S. Private*, pg. 1122
CURIA GERMANY GMBH—See GTCR LLC; *U.S. Private*, pg. 1805
CURIA GERMANY GMBH—See The Carlyle Group Inc.; *U.S. Public*, pg. 2046
CURIA MISSOURI, INC.—See GTCR LLC; *U.S. Private*, pg. 1805
CURIA MISSOURI, INC.—See The Carlyle Group Inc.; *U.S. Public*, pg. 2046
C.UYEMURA & CO., LTD. - HIRAKATA CHEMICAL PLANT—See C.Uyemura & Co., Ltd.; *Int'l*, pg. 1244
CZECH SILICAT S.R.O.—See Gruppo Minerali Maffei S.p.A.; *Int'l*, pg. 3140
DACRO B.V.—See Illinois Tool Works Inc.; *U.S. Public*, pg. 1102
DAICEL CORPORATION; *Int'l*, pg. 1918
DAICEL OHTAKE SANGYO CO., LTD.—See Daicel Corporation; *Int'l*, pg. 1919
DAI-ICHI KARKARIA LIMITED; *Int'l*, pg. 1917
DAIKIN ARKEMA REFRIGERANTS ASIA LTD.—See Daikin Industries, Ltd.; *Int'l*, pg. 1934
DAINICHI CHEMICAL CORP.—See Daicel Corporation; *Int'l*, pg. 1919
DAINICHI COLOR VIETNAM CO., LTD.—See Dainichiseika Color & Chemicals Mfg. Co., Ltd.; *Int'l*, pg. 1939
DANISCO DEUTSCHLAND GMBH—See DuPont de Nemours, Inc.; *U.S. Public*, pg. 692
DANISCO JAPAN LTD.—See DuPont de Nemours, Inc.; *U.S. Public*, pg. 692
DANISCO (UK) LTD. - BEAMINSTER—See DuPont de Nemours, Inc.; *U.S. Public*, pg. 692
DANISCO (UK) LTD. - REIGATE—See DuPont de Nemours, Inc.; *U.S. Public*, pg. 692
DANISCO (UK) LTD.—See DuPont de Nemours, Inc.; *U.S. Public*, pg. 692
DANISCO USA, INC. - NEW CENTURY—See DuPont de Nemours, Inc.; *U.S. Public*, pg. 692
DAVIDSON ORGANICS, LLC; *U.S. Private*, pg. 1172
DC ALABAMA, INC.—See Dow Inc.; *U.S. Public*, pg. 684
DEEP POLYMERS LTD.; *Int'l*, pg. 2002
DELAMINE B.V.—See GIC Pte. Ltd.; *Int'l*, pg. 2967
DELAMINE B.V.—See The Carlyle Group Inc.; *U.S. Public*, pg. 2050
DENKA ADVANCED MATERIALS (SUZHOU) CO. LTD.—See Denki Company Limited; *Int'l*, pg. 2027
DENKA ADVANTECH PRIVATE LIMITED—See Denki Company Limited; *Int'l*, pg. 2027
DENKI COMPANY LIMITED; *Int'l*, pg. 2027
DESTILACIJA A.D.; *Int'l*, pg. 2046
DEVELOPPEMENT ACTIVITES CHIMIQUES DISTRIBUTION SA; *Int'l*, pg. 2088
DGL GROUP LIMITED; *Int'l*, pg. 2096
DHARMAJ CROP GUARD LIMITED; *Int'l*, pg. 2099
DIAMINES AND CHEMICALS LIMITED; *Int'l*, pg. 2104
DIC ALKYLPHENOL SINGAPORE PTE., LTD.—See DIC Corporation; *Int'l*, pg. 2107
DINTEC AGROQUIMICA PRODUTOS QUIMICOS, LDA.—See Corteva, Inc.; *U.S. Public*, pg. 581
DIXIE CHEMICAL COMPANY, INC.—See DX Holding Company Inc.; *U.S. Private*, pg. 1296
DNF CO LTD - FINE CHEMICAL DIVISION—See DNF Co., Ltd.; *Int'l*, pg. 2148
DNP FINE CHEMICALS CO., LTD.—See Dai Nippon Printing Co., Ltd.; *Int'l*, pg. 1914
DODGE COMPANY INC.; *U.S. Private*, pg. 1252
DONGGUAN BOTON FLAVOR & FRAGRANCES COMPANY LIMITED—See China Boton Group Company Limited; *Int'l*, pg. 1487
DORF-KETAL CHEMICALS INDIA PVT. LTD.; *Int'l*, pg. 2176
DOSITEC SISTEMAS SL—See Dover Corporation; *U.S. Public*, pg. 678
DOW AGROSCIENCES PARAGUAY S.A.—See Corteva, Inc.; *U.S. Public*, pg. 582
DOW AGROSCIENCES TECHNOLOGY GMBH—See Corteva, Inc.; *U.S. Public*, pg. 582
DOW CHEMICAL CANADA ULC—See Dow Inc.; *U.S. Public*, pg. 683
DOW CHEMICAL CANADA ULC—See Dow Inc.; *U.S. Public*, pg. 683
THE DOW CHEMICAL COMPANY - LOUISIANA OPERATIONS—See Dow Inc.; *U.S. Public*, pg. 686
DOW CHEMICAL INTERNATIONAL PVT. LTD.—See Dow Inc.; *U.S. Public*, pg. 684
DOW CORNING SINGAPORE PTE. LTD.—See Dow Inc.; *U.S. Public*, pg. 684
DOW PERFORMANCE MATERIALS (AUSTRALIA) PTY. LTD.—See Dow Inc.; *U.S. Public*, pg. 685
DOW SILICONES BELGIUM SPRL—See Dow Inc.; *U.S. Public*, pg. 685
DOW SILICONES CORPORATION - KENDALLVILLE SITE—See Dow Inc.; *U.S. Public*, pg. 684
DOW SILICONES UK LIMITED—See Dow Inc.; *U.S. Public*, pg. 685
DOW VERWALTUNGSGESELLSCHAFT MBH—See Dow Inc.; *U.S. Public*, pg. 685

DUPONT TURKEY ENDUSTRI URUNLERI LIMITED SIRKETI—See Corteva, Inc.; *U.S. Public*, pg. 582
DX HOLDING COMPANY INC.; *U.S. Private*, pg. 1296
DYCENT BIOTECH (SHANGHAI) CO. LTD.; *Int'l*, pg. 2238
DYNEA PAKISTAN LIMITED - GADOON UNIT—See Dynea Pakistan Limited; *Int'l*, pg. 2242
DYNEA PAKISTAN LIMITED - HUB UNIT—See Dynea Pakistan Limited; *Int'l*, pg. 2242
EDIBLE GARDEN AG INCORPORATED; *U.S. Public*, pg. 719
EGYPTIAN FINANCIAL & INDUSTRIAL CO.; *Int'l*, pg. 2327
ELAN A.D.; *Int'l*, pg. 2342
EL DORADO AMMONIA L.L.C.—See LSB Industries, Inc.; *U.S. Public*, pg. 1344
ELIN VERD S.A.; *Int'l*, pg. 2361
ELITE FOREIGN TRADING INC.—See Everlight Chemical Industrial Co.; *Int'l*, pg. 2567
ELIXENS AMERICA INC.—See Elixens S.A.; *Int'l*, pg. 2363
ELIXENS S.A.; *Int'l*, pg. 2363
ELIXENS UK LTD—See Elixens S.A.; *Int'l*, pg. 2363
ELMER'S PRODUCTS CANADA, CORPORATION—See Newell Brands Inc.; *U.S. Public*, pg. 1514
EMA KIMYA SISTEMLERI SANAYI VE TICARET A.S.—See Huntsman Corporation; *U.S. Public*, pg. 1073
EMISSION PARTICLE SOLUTION SWEDEN AB—See De-Tai New Energy Group Limited; *Int'l*, pg. 2047
EMS-CHEMIE (JAPAN) LTD.—See EMS-Chemie Holding AG; *Int'l*, pg. 2393
ENTERNAL EDGE SDN. BHD.—See Batu Kawan Berhad; *Int'l*, pg. 891
ENTHONE GMBH—See Element Solutions Inc.; *U.S. Public*, pg. 726
ENVIRONMENTAL MANUFACTURING SOLUTIONS, LLC; *U.S. Private*, pg. 1408
ENVIRO TECH CHEMICAL SERVICES, INC.; *U.S. Private*, pg. 1406
ENZYME DEVELOPMENT CORPORATION; *U.S. Private*, pg. 1410
ENZYME INNOVATION, INC.—See Advanced Enzyme Technologies Limited; *Int'l*, pg. 159
ERCO WORLDWIDE—See Birch Hill Equity Partners Management Inc.; *Int'l*, pg. 1046
ERCO WORLDWIDE (USA) INC.—See Birch Hill Equity Partners Management Inc.; *Int'l*, pg. 1046
ERCROS SA - BASIC CHEMICALS DIVISION - TARRAGONA FACTORY—See Ercros SA; *Int'l*, pg. 2489
ERCROS SA - BASIC CHEMICALS DIVISION - VILA-SECA I FACTORY—See Ercros SA; *Int'l*, pg. 2490
ERCROS SA - INTERMEDIATE CHEMICALS DIVISION—See Ercros SA; *Int'l*, pg. 2490
ERCROS SA - INTERMEDIATE CHEMICALS DIVISION - TORTOSA FACTORY—See Ercros SA; *Int'l*, pg. 2490
ESSECO USA LLC—See Esseco Group SRL; *Int'l*, pg. 2509
ESTERCHEM LTD.; *Int'l*, pg. 2518
ETHICAL INTERNATIONAL TRADING & WAREHOUSING (SHANGHAI) CO., LTD.—See Everlight Chemical Industrial Co.; *Int'l*, pg. 2567
ETHICAL (QINGDAO) LTD.—See Everlight Chemical Industrial Co.; *Int'l*, pg. 2567
ETHICAL TRADING COMPANY—See Everlight Chemical Industrial Co.; *Int'l*, pg. 2567
EVERLIGHT CHEMICAL INDUSTRIAL CO.; *Int'l*, pg. 2567
EVERLIGHT CHEMICAL INDUSTRIAL CO. - TAOYUAN 1ST PLANT—See Everlight Chemical Industrial Co.; *Int'l*, pg. 2567
EVERLIGHT CHEMICAL INDUSTRIAL CO. - TAOYUAN 2ND PLANT—See Everlight Chemical Industrial Co.; *Int'l*, pg. 2567
EVERLIGHT CHEMICAL INDUSTRIAL CO. - TAOYUAN 3RD PLANT—See Everlight Chemical Industrial Co.; *Int'l*, pg. 2567
EVERLIGHT CHEMICAL INDUSTRIAL CO. - TAOYUAN 4TH PLANT—See Everlight Chemical Industrial Co.; *Int'l*, pg. 2567
EVERLIGHT EUROPE B.V.—See Everlight Chemical Industrial Co.; *Int'l*, pg. 2567
EVERLIGHT HONG KONG LIMITED—See Everlight Chemical Industrial Co.; *Int'l*, pg. 2567
EVERLIGHT (SUZHOU) ADVANCED CHEMICALS LTD.—See Everlight Chemical Industrial Co.; *Int'l*, pg. 2567
EVERLIGHT USA, INC.—See Everlight Chemical Industrial Co.; *Int'l*, pg. 2567
EVER S.R.L.—See Esseco Group SRL; *Int'l*, pg. 2509
EXTRACTION (PAKISTAN) LIMITED; *Int'l*, pg. 2592
EXXONMOBIL CHEMICAL HOLLAND B.V.—See Exxon Mobil Corporation; *U.S. Public*, pg. 814
FC PRO, LLC—See Flotek Industries, Inc.; *U.S. Public*, pg. 853
FERMENTA BIOTECH LIMITED; *Int'l*, pg. 2639
FERRO PFANSTIEHL LABORATORIES, INC.—See American Securities LLC; *U.S. Private*, pg. 252
FIBER INTERMEDIATE PRODUCTS COMPANY; *Int'l*, pg. 2652
FINNFEEDS FINLAND OY-NAANTALI—See DuPont de Nemours, Inc.; *U.S. Public*, pg. 693
FINNFEEDS FINLAND OY—See DuPont de Nemours, Inc.; *U.S. Public*, pg. 693

325199 — ALL OTHER BASIC ORG...   CORPORATE AFFILIATIONS

FINNFEEDS OY—See DuPont de Nemours, Inc.; *U.S. Public*, pg. 693
FIRESTONE SYNTHETIC RUBBER & LATEX-ORANGE—See Bridgestone Corporation; *Int'l*, pg. 1156
FIRMENICH PRODUCTIONS S.A.S.—See Firmenich International SA; *Int'l*, pg. 2680
FIRMENICH—See Firmenich International SA; *Int'l*, pg. 2680
FIRST CHEMICAL CORP.—See The Chemours Company; *U.S. Public*, pg. 2059
FLAVORS AND ESSENCES UK LIMITED—See International Flavors & Fragrances Inc.; *U.S. Public*, pg. 1151
FLINT HILLS RESOURCES CHEMICAL INTERMEDIATES, LLC—See Koch Industries, Inc.; *U.S. Private*, pg. 2327
FLORIDA CHEMICAL COMPANY, INC.—See Archer-Daniels-Midland Company; *U.S. Public*, pg. 185
FLOTEK CHEMISTRY, LLC—See Flotek Industries, Inc.; *U.S. Public*, pg. 853
FLOW POLYMERS LLC—See The Jordan Company, L.P.; *U.S. Private*, pg. 4061
FMC CHEMICALS LIMITED—See FMC Corporation; *U.S. Public*, pg. 862
FOR THE EARTH CORP.; *U.S. Public*, pg. 864
FPG OLEOCHEMICALS SDN. BHD.—See The Procter & Gamble Company; *U.S. Public*, pg. 2120
FRAGRANCE OILS (INTERNATIONAL) LIMITED—See Givaudan S.A.; *Int'l*, pg. 2980
FUFENG GROUP LIMITED; *Int'l*, pg. 2804
FUJIFILM HUNT CHEMICALS SPECIALTY PRODUCTS CO.—See FUJIFILM Holdings Corporation; *Int'l*, pg. 2823
FUJIKURA KASEI VIETNAM CO., LTD.—See Fujikura Kasei Co., Ltd.; *Int'l*, pg. 2827
FULGHUM FIBREFUELS, LTD.—See Rentech, Inc.; *U.S. Private*, pg. 3400
FURUKAWA CHEMICALS CO., LTD.—See Furukawa Co., Ltd.; *Int'l*, pg. 2847
FUSO CHEMICAL CO., LTD - JUSO FACTORY—See Fuso Chemical Co., Ltd.; *Int'l*, pg. 2850
FUSO CHEMICAL CO., LTD - OSAKA FACTORY—See Fuso Chemical Co., Ltd.; *Int'l*, pg. 2850
FUTURISTIC OFFSHORE SERVICES & CHEMICAL LIMITED; *Int'l*, pg. 2858
GAGE CORPORATION; *U.S. Private*, pg. 1634
GAGE PRODUCTS COMPANY—See Gage Corporation; *U.S. Private*, pg. 1634
GANESH BENZOPLAST LTD.; *Int'l*, pg. 2880
GARODIA CHEMICALS LIMITED; *Int'l*, pg. 2885
GAYATRI BIOORGANICS LTD.; *Int'l*, pg. 2891
GELITA AG; *Int'l*, pg. 2913
GENENCOR INTERNATIONAL OY - HANKO—See DuPont de Nemours, Inc.; *U.S. Public*, pg. 693
GENENCOR INTERNATIONAL OY—See DuPont de Nemours, Inc.; *U.S. Public*, pg. 692
GENERAL ATOMICS - CRYOTECH DEICING TECHNOLOGY DIVISION—See General Atomics; *U.S. Private*, pg. 1663
GEOCEL LIMITED—See The Sherwin-Williams Company; *U.S. Public*, pg. 2127
GFBIOCHEMICALS ITALY SPA; *Int'l*, pg. 2956
GHW INTERNATIONAL; *Int'l*, pg. 2960
GIOVANNI BOZZETTO (SHANGHAI) CHEMICAL TRADING CO., LTD.—See Aimia Inc.; *Int'l*, pg. 234
GIVAUDAN ARGENTINA S.A.—See Givaudan S.A.; *Int'l*, pg. 2980
GIVAUDAN FLAVORS CORPORATION—See Givaudan S.A.; *Int'l*, pg. 2980
GLOBAL SWEETENERS HOLDINGS LIMITED; *Int'l*, pg. 3001
GOLDEN GRAIN ENERGY, LLC; *U.S. Private*, pg. 1732
GRANULES INDIA LTD; *Int'l*, pg. 3059
GRAUER & WEIL INDIA LTD - DADRA PLANT—See Grauer & Weil India Limited; *Int'l*, pg. 3061
GRAUER & WEIL INDIA LTD - VAPI PLANT—See Grauer & Weil India Limited; *Int'l*, pg. 3061
GRUPA AZOTY ATT POLYMERS GMBH—See Grupa Azoty S.A.; *Int'l*, pg. 3115
GRUPA AZOTY JEDNOSTKA RATOWNICTWA CHEMICZNEGO SP. Z.O.O.—See Grupa Azoty S.A.; *Int'l*, pg. 3115
GRUPA AZOTY POLSKIE KONSORCJUM CHEMICZNE SP. Z O.O.—See Grupa Azoty S.A.; *Int'l*, pg. 3115
GRUPA AZOTY S.A.; *Int'l*, pg. 3115
GRUPA AZOTY ZAKIADY AZOTOWE CHORZOW S.A.—See Grupa Azoty S.A.; *Int'l*, pg. 3116
GRUPA AZOTY ZAKLADY AZOTOWE KEDZIERZYN S.A.—See Grupa Azoty S.A.; *Int'l*, pg. 3116
GRUPA AZOTY ZAKLADY CHEMICZNE "POLICE" S.A.—See Grupa Azoty S.A.; *Int'l*, pg. 3116
GRUPPO MINERALI DO BRASIL LTDA—See Gruppo Minerali Maffei S.p.A.; *Int'l*, pg. 3140
GUANGZHOU ETHICAL TRADING COMPANY—See Everlight Chemical Industrial Co.; *Int'l*, pg. 2567
GUANGZHOU LINGWE TECHNOLOGY CO., LTD.; *Int'l*, pg. 3166
GUIZHOU CRYSTAL CHEMICAL CO LTD—See China National Chemical Corporation; *Int'l*, pg. 1527
GUIZHOU CRYSTAL ORGANIC CHEMICAL (GROUP) CO., LTD.—See China National Chemical Corporation; *Int'l*, pg. 1527

GUJARAT ORGANICS LIMITED; *Int'l*, pg. 3177
GUJCHEM DISTILLERIES INDIA LTD.; *Int'l*, pg. 3177
GULF RESOURCES, INC.; *Int'l*, pg. 3182
HA INTERNATIONAL LLC—See Huettenes-Albertus Chemische Werke GmbH; *Int'l*, pg. 3522
HALEX INDUSTRIES (M) SDN. BHD.—See Hextar Global Berhad; *Int'l*, pg. 3373
THE HALLSTAR COMPANY; *U.S. Private*, pg. 4042
HALOCARBON LABORATORIES—See Halocarbon Products Corporation; *U.S. Public*, pg. 1846
HALTERMANN CARLESS DEUTSCHLAND GMBH—See H.I.G. Capital, LLC; *U.S. Private*, pg. 1828
HA MINERALS GMBH—See Huettenes-Albertus Chemische Werke GmbH; *Int'l*, pg. 3523
HANNONG CHEMICALS INC; *Int'l*, pg. 3257
HAOHUA EAST CHINA CHEMICAL CO., LTD.—See China National Chemical Corporation; *Int'l*, pg. 1527
HAOHUA HONGHE CHEMICAL CO., LTD.—See China National Chemical Corporation; *Int'l*, pg. 1527
HAOHUA YUHANG CHEMICAL CO., LTD.—See China National Chemical Corporation; *Int'l*, pg. 1528
HARCROS CHEMICALS INC. ORGANICS DIVISION—See Harcros Chemicals Inc.; *U.S. Private*, pg. 1862
HARDCASTLE & WAUD MANUFACTURING COMPANY LIMITED; *Int'l*, pg. 3272
HARIMA M.I.D., INC.—See Harima Chemicals Group, Inc.; *Int'l*, pg. 3276
HAYDALE LTD.—See Haydale Graphene Industries plc; *Int'l*, pg. 3290
HAYDALE TECHNOLOGIES KOREA CO., LTD.—See Haydale Graphene Industries plc; *Int'l*, pg. 3290
HAYDALE TECHNOLOGIES THAILAND LTD.—See Haydale Graphene Industries plc; *Int'l*, pg. 3290
H.B. S.R.L.—See Dana Incorporated; *U.S. Public*, pg. 623
HEALTH SCIENCES GROUP, INC.; *U.S. Public*, pg. 1015
HEBEI SHENGHUA CHEMICAL CO., LTD.—See China National Chemical Corporation; *Int'l*, pg. 1528
HEILONGJIANG HAOHUA CHEMICAL CO., LTD.—See China National Chemical Corporation; *Int'l*, pg. 1528
HEIQ IBERIA UNIPESSOAL LDA.—See HeiQ Plc; *Int'l*, pg. 3326
HEIQ MATERIALS AG—See HeiQ Plc; *Int'l*, pg. 3326
HEIQ RAS AG—See HeiQ Plc; *Int'l*, pg. 3326
HELM ITALIA S.R.L.—See HELM AG; *Int'l*, pg. 3337
HEMLOCK SEMICONDUCTOR, LLC—See Corning Incorporated; *U.S. Public*, pg. 579
HEMLOCK SEMICONDUCTOR, LLC—See Dow Inc.; *U.S. Public*, pg. 684
HENAN JINDAN LACTIC ACID TECHNOLOGY CO., LTD.; *Int'l*, pg. 3342
HENKEL OF AMERICA INC.—See Henkel AG & Co. KGaA; *Int'l*, pg. 3352
HENKEL SINGAPORE PTE., LTD.—See Henkel AG & Co. KGaA; *Int'l*, pg. 3349
HENKEL US OPERATIONS CORPORATION—See Henkel AG & Co. KGaA; *Int'l*, pg. 3352
HERAEUS PRECIOUS METALS NORTH AMERICA DAYCHEM LLC—See Heraeus Holding GmbH; *Int'l*, pg. 3357
HEXION INC.—See American Securities LLC; *U.S. Private*, pg. 249
HEXZA CORPORATION BERHAD; *Int'l*, pg. 3373
HIGH PLAINS BIOENERGY, LLC—See Seaboard Corporation; *U.S. Public*, pg. 1850
HILLSTREET FUND LP; *U.S. Private*, pg. 1947
HINDUSTAN FLUOROCARBONS LIMITED—See Hindustan Organic Chemicals Limited; *Int'l*, pg. 3400
HINDUSTAN ORGANIC CHEMICALS LIMITED; *Int'l*, pg. 3400
HISSAN TRADING CO., LTD.—See Denki Company Limited; *Int'l*, pg. 2027
HODOGAYA CHEMICAL CO., LTD.; *Int'l*, pg. 3438
HODOGAYA CONTRACT LABORATORY CO., LTD.—See Hodogaya Chemical Co., Ltd.; *Int'l*, pg. 3438
HOLLIDAY FRANCE S.A.S.—See Huntsman Corporation; *U.S. Public*, pg. 1073
HONEYWELL BURDICK & JACKSON—See Honeywell International Inc.; *U.S. Public*, pg. 1051
HONSHU CHEMICAL INDUSTRY CO., LTD.; *Int'l*, pg. 3472
HOSHINE SILICON INDUSTRY CO., LTD.; *Int'l*, pg. 3482
HSIN-LI CHEMICAL INDUSTRIAL CORP.; *Int'l*, pg. 3507
HUABAO FLAVOURS & FRAGRANCES (HK) LIMITED—See Huabao International Holdings Limited; *Int'l*, pg. 3510
HUBEI SHUANGHUAN SCIENCE & TECHNOLOGY STOCK CO., LTD.; *Int'l*, pg. 3518
HUDSON MARKETING PTY LTD—See Hudson Investment Group Limited; *Int'l*, pg. 3522
HUETTENES-ALBERTUS KOREA CO., LTD.—See Huettenes-Albertus Chemische Werke GmbH; *Int'l*, pg. 3523
HULUNBEIER NORTH EAST FUFENG BIOTECHNOLOGIES CO., LTD.—See Fufeng Group Limited; *Int'l*, pg. 2804
HUNAN DONGTING CITRIC ACID CHEMICAL CO. LIMITED—See Hunan Er-Kang Pharmaceutical Co., Ltd.; *Int'l*, pg. 3532
HUNTSMAN ADVANCED MATERIALS (AUSTRIA) GMBH—See Huntsman Corporation; *U.S. Public*, pg. 1073

HUNTSMAN ADVANCED MATERIALS (INDIA) PRIVATE LIMITED—See Huntsman Corporation; *U.S. Public*, pg. 1073
HUNTSMAN ADVANCED MATERIALS (ITALY) SRL—See Huntsman Corporation; *U.S. Public*, pg. 1073
HUNTSMAN ADVANCED MATERIALS LLC—See Huntsman Corporation; *U.S. Public*, pg. 1073
HUNTSMAN ADVANCED MATERIALS (NANJING) COMPANY LIMITED.—See Huntsman Corporation; *U.S. Public*, pg. 1073
HUNTSMAN ADVANCED MATERIALS (TAIWAN) CORPORATION—See Huntsman Corporation; *U.S. Public*, pg. 1073
HUNTSMAN ADVANCED MATERIALS (UAE) FZE—See Huntsman Corporation; *U.S. Public*, pg. 1073
HUNTSMAN ADVANCED MATERIALS (UK) LIMITED—See Huntsman Corporation; *U.S. Public*, pg. 1073
HUNTSMAN (BELGIUM) BVBA—See Huntsman Corporation; *U.S. Public*, pg. 1073
HUNTSMAN CHEMICAL TRADING (SHANGHAI) LTD.—See Huntsman Corporation; *U.S. Public*, pg. 1073
HUNTSMAN (EUROPE) BVBA—See Huntsman Corporation; *U.S. Public*, pg. 1073
HUNTSMAN INTERNATIONAL (INDIA) PRIVATE LIMITED—See Huntsman Corporation; *U.S. Public*, pg. 1074
HUNTSMAN NORDEN AB—See Huntsman Corporation; *U.S. Public*, pg. 1074
HUNTSMAN PIGMENTS AMERICAS LLC—See Huntsman Corporation; *U.S. Public*, pg. 1074
HUNTSMAN PIGMENTS S.P.A.—See Huntsman Corporation; *U.S. Public*, pg. 1074
HUNTSMAN POLYURETHANES SHANGHAI LTD.—See Huntsman Corporation; *U.S. Public*, pg. 1074
HUNTSMAN (RUSSIA INVESTMENTS) B.V.—See Huntsman Corporation; *U.S. Public*, pg. 1073
HUNTSMAN SURFACE SCIENCES FRANCE SAS—See Huntsman Corporation; *U.S. Public*, pg. 1074
HUNTSMAN SURFACE SCIENCES ITALIA S.R.L.—See Huntsman Corporation; *U.S. Public*, pg. 1074
HUNTSMAN TEXTILE EFFECTS (BELGIUM) BVBA—See Huntsman Corporation; *U.S. Public*, pg. 1073
HUNTSMAN TEXTILE EFFECTS (QINGDAO) CO., LTD—See Huntsman Corporation; *U.S. Public*, pg. 1074
HYOSUNG CHEMICALS (JIAXING) CO., LTD.—See Hyosung Corporation; *Int'l*, pg. 3550
IAF LTD.; *U.S. Private*, pg. 2027
IBERCHEM SOUTH AFRICA (PTY) LTD.—See Croda International plc; *Int'l*, pg. 1853
IBU-TEC ADVANCED MATERIALS AG; *Int'l*, pg. 3577
IFF INTERNATIONAL FLAVORS & FRAGRANCES INC.—See International Flavors & Fragrances Inc.; *U.S. Public*, pg. 1152
IFF (KOREA) INC.—See International Flavors & Fragrances Inc.; *U.S. Public*, pg. 1152
IMPERIAL CHEMICAL INDUSTRIES PLC—See Akzo Nobel N.V.; *Int'l*, pg. 274
INCON PROCESSING SYSTEMS, INC.—See Cooke, Inc.; *Int'l*, pg. 1788
INCOTEC (BEIJING) AGRICULTURAL TECHNOLOGY CO., LTD.—See Croda International plc; *Int'l*, pg. 1853
INCOTEC MALAYSIA SDN. BHD.—See Croda International plc; *Int'l*, pg. 1853
INCOTEC (TIANJIN) AGRICULTURAL TECHNOLOGY CO., LTD.—See Croda International plc; *Int'l*, pg. 1853
INDSPEC CHEMICAL EXPORT SALES, LLC—See Occidental Petroleum Corporation; *U.S. Public*, pg. 1561
INDUSTRIAL OLEOCHEMICAL PRODUCTS (PTY) LIMITED—See AECI Limited; *Int'l*, pg. 171
INEOS MELAMINES GMBH—See One Rock Capital Partners, LLC; *U.S. Private*, pg. 3022
INTEGRATED COATING & SEED TECHNOLOGY INDIA PVT. LTD.—See Croda International plc; *Int'l*, pg. 1853
INTEGRATED DNA TECHNOLOGIES PTE. LTD.—See Danaher Corporation; *U.S. Public*, pg. 627
INTERACTIVE LEISURE SYSTEMS, INC.; *U.S. Public*, pg. 1140
INTERNATIONALE METALL IMPRAGNIER GMBH—See Quaker Chemical Corporation; *U.S. Public*, pg. 1746
INTERNATIONAL FLAVORS E FRAGRANCES IFF (ITALIA) S.R.L.—See International Flavors & Fragrances Inc.; *U.S. Public*, pg. 1153
INTERNATIONAL FLAVORS & FRAGRANCES S.R.L.—See International Flavors & Fragrances Inc.; *U.S. Public*, pg. 1153
INTERNATIONAL FLAVOURS & FRAGRANCES (INDIA) LTD.—See International Flavors & Fragrances Inc.; *U.S. Public*, pg. 1153
INTERNATIONAL FLAVOURS & FRAGRANCES (NEW ZEALAND) LTD.—See International Flavors & Fragrances Inc.; *U.S. Public*, pg. 1153
INTERNATIONAL FLAVOURS & FRAGRANCES (NZ) LIMITED—See International Flavors & Fragrances Inc.; *U.S. Public*, pg. 1153
INTERNATIONAL FRAGRANCE & TECHNOLOGY; *U.S. Private*, pg. 2117

N.A.I.C.S. INDEX

325199 — ALL OTHER BASIC ORG...

INTERNATIONAL POLYURETHANE INVESTMENTS B.V.—See Huntsman Corporation; *U.S. Public*, pg. 1074
IOCHEM CORPORATION; *U.S. Private*, pg. 2133
IP BEAUTY, INC.—See Inter Parfums, Inc.; *U.S. Public*, pg. 1140
ISLECHEM, LLC—See Aceto Corporation; *U.S. Private*, pg. 58
ISP ARGENTINA S.R.L.—See Ashland Inc.; *U.S. Public*, pg. 212
ISP BIOCHEMA SCHWABEN GMBH—See Ashland Inc.; *U.S. Public*, pg. 212
ISP CHEMICAL PRODUCTS LLC—See Ashland Inc.; *U.S. Public*, pg. 213
ISP GLOBAL TECHNOLOGIES INC.—See Ashland Inc.; *U.S. Public*, pg. 213
ISP INDIA PVT. LTD—See Ashland Inc.; *U.S. Public*, pg. 213
ISP MARL GMBH—See Ashland Inc.; *U.S. Public*, pg. 213
ISP (THAILAND) CO., LTD—See Ashland Inc.; *U.S. Public*, pg. 212
ITW CHEMICAL PRODUCTS LTDA—See Illinois Tool Works Inc.; *U.S. Public*, pg. 1105
ITW CHEMICAL PRODUCTS SCANDINAVIA APS—See Illinois Tool Works Inc.; *U.S. Public*, pg. 1105
ITW LLC & CO. KG—See Illinois Tool Works Inc.; *U.S. Public*, pg. 1106
JAPAN FORMALIN COMPANY, INC.—See DIC Corporation; *Int'l*, pg. 2109
JARCHEM INDUSTRIES, INC.; *U.S. Private*, pg. 2188
JATRODIESEL, INC.; *U.S. Private*, pg. 2191
JC BIOTECH PRIVATE LIMITED—See Advanced Enzyme Technologies Limited; *Int'l*, pg. 159
JIANGSU WEIMING NEW MATERIAL CO., LTD.—See China Petrochemical Development Corp.; *Int'l*, pg. 1540
KAWAKEN FINE CHEMICALS CO., LTD.—See Ajinomoto Company, Inc.; *Int'l*, pg. 257
KAWASAKI KASEI CHEMICALS LTD. - KAWASAKI PLANT—See Air Water Inc.; *Int'l*, pg. 240
KAWASAKI KASEI CHEMICALS LTD.—See Air Water Inc.; *Int'l*, pg. 240
KAYAKU AKZO CORPORATION—See Akzo Nobel N.V.; *Int'l*, pg. 274
KELP INDUSTRIES PTY. LTD.—See International Flavors & Fragrances Inc.; *U.S. Public*, pg. 1153
KMG CHEMICALS DO BRASIL LTDA—See Entegris, Inc.; *U.S. Public*, pg. 776
KMG SINGAPORE PTE. LTD.—See Entegris, Inc.; *U.S. Public*, pg. 776
KPX FINE CHEMICAL CO., LTD.—See Hanwha Group; *Int'l*, pg. 3266
KUNMING FIRMENICH AROMATICS CO. LTD.—See Firmenich International SA; *Int'l*, pg. 2681
KYODO SAKUSAN CO. LTD.—See Daicel Corporation; *Int'l*, pg. 1919
KYUSHU DAINICHISEIKA KOGYO CO., LTD—See Dainichiseika Color & Chemicals Mfg. Co., Ltd.; *Int'l*, pg. 1939
LABORATOIRE MONIQUE REMY—See International Flavors & Fragrances Inc.; *U.S. Public*, pg. 1153
LIAOCHENG LANTIAN COGENERATION PLANT CO., LTD.—See CJ Corporation; *Int'l*, pg. 1634
LINDAU CHEMICALS INC.; *U.S. Private*, pg. 2459
LIPESA COLOMBIA SA—See Danaher Corporation; *U.S. Public*, pg. 628
LUBRICOR, INC.—See Quaker Chemical Corporation; *U.S. Public*, pg. 1746
LUBRIZOL ADVANCED MATERIALS INTERNATIONAL, INC.—See Berkshire Hathaway Inc.; *U.S. Public*, pg. 319
LUBRIZOL OVERSEAS TRADING CORPORATION—See Berkshire Hathaway Inc.; *U.S. Public*, pg. 319
LYVEN S.A.—See Etablissements J. Soufflet; *Int'l*, pg. 2519
MALAY-SINO CHEMICAL INDUSTRIES SDN. BHD. - KEMAMAN PLANT—See Batu Kawan Berhad; *Int'l*, pg. 891
MALAY-SINO CHEMICAL INDUSTRIES SDN. BHD.—See Batu Kawan Berhad; *Int'l*, pg. 891
MATERIA, INC.; *U.S. Private*, pg. 2609
MCGEAN-ROHCO SINGAPORE PTE LTD—See McGean-Rohco, Inc.; *U.S. Private*, pg. 2634
MCGEAN ROHCO (UK) LTD.—See McGean-Rohco, Inc.; *U.S. Private*, pg. 2634
MCPI PRIVATE LIMITED—See The Chatterjee Group; *U.S. Private*, pg. 4007
MELTEX ASIA (THAILAND) CO., LTD.—See Astena Holdings Co., Ltd.; *Int'l*, pg. 653
MELTEX INC. - KUMAGAYA FACTORY—See Astena Holdings Co., Ltd.; *Int'l*, pg. 653
MELTEX INC.—See Astena Holdings Co., Ltd.; *Int'l*, pg. 653
MERICHEM COMPANY; *U.S. Private*, pg. 2672
MERISANT CORP.—See MacAndrews & Forbes Incorporated; *U.S. Private*, pg. 2532
MERISANT UK, LTD.—See MacAndrews & Forbes Incorporated; *U.S. Private*, pg. 2532
MERISOL ANTIOXIDANTS LLC—See Merichem Company; *U.S. Private*, pg. 2672
MEXICHEM ARGENTINA, S.A.—See Grupo Empresarial Kaluz S.A. de C.V.; *Int'l*, pg. 3127
MICHELMAN INC.; *U.S. Private*, pg. 2699
THE MIGHTY COMPANY LIMITED—See International Flavors & Fragrances Inc.; *U.S. Public*, pg. 1154

MINERALI INDUSTIALI TUNISIA SA—See Gruppo Minerali Maffei S.p.A.; *Int'l*, pg. 3140
MISR CO. FOR AROMATIC PRODUCTS (MARP) S.A.E.—See International Flavors & Fragrances Inc.; *U.S. Public*, pg. 1154
MIZUSHIMA PLASTICIZER CO., LTD.—See Adeka Corporation; *Int'l*, pg. 142
MOLECULAR BIOLOGY RESOURCES; *U.S. Private*, pg. 2767
MONSANTO JAPAN LTD.—See Bayer Aktiengesellschaft; *Int'l*, pg. 909
MONTGOMERY MANUFACTURING CO.; *U.S. Private*, pg. 2777
MPD CHEMICALS LLC—See Entegris, Inc.; *U.S. Public*, pg. 777
NARDI ARMOAS LTDA.—See International Flavors & Fragrances Inc.; *U.S. Public*, pg. 1154
NATIONAL ENZYME COMPANY; *U.S. Private*, pg. 2853
NATIONAL PLASTICS COLOR INC.; *U.S. Private*, pg. 2860
NEIMENGGU FUFENG BIOTECHNOLOGIES CO., LTD.—See Fufeng Group Limited; *Int'l*, pg. 2805
NIPPON ALUMINUM ALKYLS, LTD.—See Albemarle Corporation; *U.S. Public*, pg. 73
NOBEL INDUSTRIES USA INC.—See Akzo Nobel N.V.; *Int'l*, pg. 274
NORAC COMPANY INC.; *U.S. Private*, pg. 2935
NORMAN HAY ENGINEERING LTD.—See Quaker Chemical Corporation; *U.S. Public*, pg. 1746
NORQUAY TECHNOLOGY, INC.—See Entegris, Inc.; *U.S. Public*, pg. 777
NOURYON CHEMICALS ARGENTINA SAU—See GIC Pte. Ltd.; *Int'l*, pg. 2968
NOURYON CHEMICALS ARGENTINA SAU—See The Carlyle Group Inc.; *U.S. Public*, pg. 2051
NU-MEGA INGREDIENTS PTY. LTD.—See Clover Corporation Limited; *Int'l*, pg. 1663
NUTRAFUR S.A.—See International Flavors & Fragrances Inc.; *U.S. Public*, pg. 1154
THE NUTRASWEET COMPANY—See Prospect Hill Growth Partners, L.P.; *U.S. Private*, pg. 3288
NUVOSUN, INC.—See Dow Inc.; *U.S. Public*, pg. 685
OAK-BARK CORPORATION; *U.S. Private*, pg. 2984
OCCIDENTAL CHEMICAL ASIA, LIMITED—See Occidental Petroleum Corporation; *U.S. Public*, pg. 1561
OCCIDENTAL CHEMICAL BELGIUM B.V.B.A.—See Occidental Petroleum Corporation; *U.S. Public*, pg. 1561
OCCIDENTAL RESEARCH CORPORATION—See Occidental Petroleum Corporation; *U.S. Public*, pg. 1561
OLIGO SA—See Huntsman Corporation; *U.S. Public*, pg. 1075
ONE EARTH ENERGY, LLC—See REX American Resources Corporation; *U.S. Public*, pg. 1795
ORGANIC PRODUCTS TRADING COMPANY, LLC—See Coffee Holding Company, Inc.; *U.S. Public*, pg. 522
OWENSBORO GRAIN BIODIESEL, LLC—See Cargill, Inc.; *U.S. Private*, pg. 759
OXIRANE CHEMICAL CORPORATION—See Adeka Corporation; *Int'l*, pg. 142
OXYCHEM - LUDINGTON—See Occidental Petroleum Corporation; *U.S. Public*, pg. 1561
OY SHERWIN-WILLIAMS FINLAND AB—See The Sherwin-Williams Company; *U.S. Public*, pg. 2128
PCAS CHINA—See Eurazeo SE; *Int'l*, pg. 2530
PEARL ENGINEERED SOLUTIONS PTE. LTD.—See Platinum Equity, LLC; *U.S. Private*, pg. 3207
PENTA-91 OOO—See Illinois Tool Works Inc.; *U.S. Public*, pg. 1109
PENTA INTERNATIONAL CORP.; *U.S. Private*, pg. 3139
PERFORMANCE ADDITIVES OF AMERICA, LLC—See Behn Meyer (D) Holding AG & Co.; *Int'l*, pg. 941
PERFUME HOLDING S.P.A.—See BI-Invest Advisors S.A.; *Int'l*, pg. 1017
PETROCHEM CARLESS BVBA—See H.I.G. Capital, LLC; *U.S. Private*, pg. 1828
PH BEAUTY LABS, INC.—See Yellow Wood Partners LLC; *U.S. Private*, pg. 4587
PHOSTECH LITHIUM INC.—See Clariant AG; *Int'l*, pg. 1645
PILOT INDUSTRIES OF TEXAS INC.—See Pilot Chemical Company; *U.S. Private*, pg. 3181
PIONEER AMERICAS LLC—See Olin Corporation; *U.S. Public*, pg. 1570
PLANET RESOURCE RECOVERY, INC.; *U.S. Public*, pg. 1697
PLASGOM S.A.U.—See OpenGate Capital Management, LLC; *U.S. Private*, pg. 3031
PLATFORM DELAWARE HOLDINGS, INC—See Element Solutions Inc.; *U.S. Public*, pg. 728
PMC BIOGENIX, INC.—See PMC Group, Inc.; *U.S. Private*, pg. 3218
PMP FERMENTATION PRODUCTS, INC.—See Fuso Chemical Co., Ltd.; *Int'l*, pg. 2850
POLY EXPLOSIVES CO., LTD.—See China Poly Group Corporation; *Int'l*, pg. 1541
POLYMER SOLUTIONS GROUP LLC—See The Jordan Company, L.P.; *U.S. Private*, pg. 4061
PORTIONPAC CHEMICAL CORP.; *U.S. Private*, pg. 3232
PRODUITS CHIMIQUES AUXILIAIRES ET DE SYNTHESE SA - USINE DE LIMAY PLANT—See Eurazeo SE; *Int'l*, pg. 2530
PT. CHEILJEDANG INDONESIA (PASURUAN)—See CJ Corporation; *Int'l*, pg. 1631
PT.CHEIL JEDANG INDONESIA—See CJ Corporation; *Int'l*, pg. 1634
PT ISP CHEMICALS INDONESIA—See Ashland Inc.; *U.S. Public*, pg. 213
PT SOCI MAS—See Golden Agri-Resources Ltd.; *Int'l*, pg. 3028
PURAC JAPAN K.K.—See Corbion N.V.; *Int'l*, pg. 1795
PURECIRCLE SDN. BHD—See Ingredion Incorporated; *U.S. Public*, pg. 1124
PUR-SYSTEMS GMBH—See Huntsman Corporation; *U.S. Public*, pg. 1073
QUAKER CHEMICAL CORPORATION; *U.S. Public*, pg. 1745
RASCHIG GMBH - ESPENHAIN—See PMC Capital Partners, LLC; *U.S. Private*, pg. 3217
REG SENECA, LLC—See Chevron Corporation; *U.S. Public*, pg. 488
RICHLAND RESEARCH CORPORATION; *U.S. Private*, pg. 3430
ROHM AND HAAS ELECTRONIC MATERIALS TAIWAN LTD.—See DuPont de Nemours, Inc.; *U.S. Public*, pg. 694
ROHM AND HAAS ESPANA PRODUCTION HOLDING, S.L.—See Dow Inc.; *U.S. Public*, pg. 686
ROYCE ASSOCIATES; *U.S. Private*, pg. 3494
R P ADAM LIMITED—See Ecolab Inc.; *U.S. Public*, pg. 716
SACHEM INC.; *U.S. Private*, pg. 3521
S.A. CITRIQUE BELGE N.V.—See ADCURAM Group AG; *Int'l*, pg. 128
SAFISIS—See Compagnie des Levures Lesaffre SA; *Int'l*, pg. 1739
SAMEDAN METHANOL—See Chevron Corporation; *U.S. Public*, pg. 487
SASIL S.P.A.—See Gruppo Minerali Maffei S.p.A.; *Int'l*, pg. 3140
SASOL-HUNTSMAN VERWALTUNGS-GMBH—See Huntsman Corporation; *U.S. Public*, pg. 1075
SCF NATURAL SP.Z.O.O.—See Grupa Azoty S.A.; *Int'l*, pg. 3116
SEACHEM LABORATORIES INC.; *U.S. Private*, pg. 3583
SEE SEN CHEMICAL BHD. - PASIR GUDANG FACILITY—See Batu Kawan Berhad; *Int'l*, pg. 891
SEE SEN CHEMICAL BHD.—See Batu Kawan Berhad; *Int'l*, pg. 891
SEGETIS—See GFBiochemicals Italy SpA; *Int'l*, pg. 2956
SEKI ARKEMA CO LTD—See Arkema S.A.; *Int'l*, pg. 571
SENSIENT FRAGRANCES MEXICO, S.A. DE C.V.—See Sensient Technologies Corporation; *U.S. Public*, pg. 1867
SENSIENT FRAGRANCES, S.A.—See Sensient Technologies Corporation; *U.S. Public*, pg. 1867
SHANDONG FUFENG FERMENTATION CO., LTD.—See Fufeng Group Limited; *Int'l*, pg. 2805
SHANDONG HUAXIA SHENZHOU NEW CO., LTD.—See Dongyue Group Limited; *Int'l*, pg. 2172
SHANGHAI ARKEMA GAOYUAN CHEMICALS CO. LTD—See Arkema S.A.; *Int'l*, pg. 571
SHARE CORPORATION; *U.S. Private*, pg. 3626
SHERWIN-WILLIAMS BALKAN S.R.L.—See The Sherwin-Williams Company; *U.S. Public*, pg. 2128
SHERWIN-WILLIAMS BEL—See The Sherwin-Williams Company; *U.S. Public*, pg. 2128
SHERWIN-WILLIAMS BENELUX NV—See The Sherwin-Williams Company; *U.S. Public*, pg. 2128
SIGRANO NEDERLAND B.V.—See EUROQUARZ GmbH; *Int'l*, pg. 2558
SILBERLINE LIMITED—See Silberline Manufacturing Co., Inc.; *U.S. Private*, pg. 3652
SIMON DUTRIAUX S.A.S.—See Floridienne SA; *Int'l*, pg. 2708
SIPING HAOHUA CHEMICAL CO.—See China National Chemical Corporation; *Int'l*, pg. 1529
SITELARK, LLC—See Flotek Industries, Inc.; *U.S. Public*, pg. 853
SKC HAAS POLSKA SP.Z O. O.—See Dow Inc.; *U.S. Public*, pg. 686
SOLAE LLC—See DuPont de Nemours, Inc.; *U.S. Public*, pg. 692
SONNEBORN, LLC; *U.S. Private*, pg. 3714
SOTECNA S.A.—See Floridienne SA; *Int'l*, pg. 2708
SOUTHERN COMPONENTS, INC.; *U.S. Private*, pg. 3730
SOVEMA GROUP S.P.A.—See ANDRITZ AG; *Int'l*, pg. 456
SPECIALTY MATERIALS, INC.; *U.S. Private*, pg. 3750
SPECIALTY SILICONE PRODUCTS, INC.—See HEICO Corporation; *U.S. Public*, pg. 1021
SPURRIER CHEMICAL COMPANIES, INC.; *U.S. Private*, pg. 3765
STEPAN CANADA, INC.—See Stepan Company; *U.S. Public*, pg. 1945
STEPAN COMPANY - ELWOOD POLYMER & SURFACTANT PLANT—See Stepan Company; *U.S. Public*, pg. 1945
STEPAN DEUTSCHLAND GMBH—See Stepan Company; *U.S. Public*, pg. 1945

325199 — ALL OTHER BASIC ORG...

STEPAN MEXICO, S.A. DE C.V.—See Stepan Company; *U.S. Public*, pg. 1945
STEPAN QUIMICA LTDA.—See Stepan Company; *U.S. Public*, pg. 1945
STEPAN UK LIMITED—See Stepan Company; *U.S. Public*, pg. 1945
ST. MARKS POWDER, INC.—See General Dynamics Corporation; *U.S. Public*, pg. 914
SUGAR FOODS CORPORATION—See The Pritzker Group - Chicago, LLC; *U.S. Private*, pg. 4099
SUMACHEM LLC—See Sealed Air Corporation; *U.S. Public*, pg. 1855
SUN-UP RECYCLING CO., LTD.—See Air Water Inc.; *Int'l*, pg. 240
SURFACTANTS INTERNATIONAL LLC—See Galaxy Surfactants Limited; *Int'l*, pg. 2872
SUZHOU FIRMENICH AROMATICS CO. LTD.—See Firmenich International SA; *Int'l*, pg. 2681
SUZHOU LINTONG CHEMICAL SCIENCE CORP.—See DIC Corporation; *Int'l*, pg. 2111
SYNGENTA AGRO, S.A. DE C.V.—See China National Chemical Corporation; *Int'l*, pg. 1529
SYNTHEXIM SAS—See Argos Wityu S.A.; *Int'l*, pg. 563
SYSTEA S.P.A.—See Focused Photonics (Hangzhou), Inc.; *Int'l*, pg. 2720
SYSTEMCARE PRODUCTS LIMITED—See Illinois Tool Works Inc.; *U.S. Public*, pg. 1111
TAIXING SUNKE CHEMICALS CO., LTD.—See Arkema S.A.; *Int'l*, pg. 571
TASTEPOINT INC.—See International Flavors & Fragrances Inc.; *U.S. Public*, pg. 1154
TC HEARTLAND LLC; *U.S. Private*, pg. 3942
TECHWAX LIMITED—See Ashland Inc.; *U.S. Public*, pg. 213
TEKNA PLASMA EUROPE SAS—See Arendals Fossekompani ASA; *Int'l*, pg. 559
TEKNA SYSTEMES PLASMA INC—See Arendals Fossekompani ASA; *Int'l*, pg. 559
TETRA TECHNOLOGIES DO BRASIL, LIMITADA—See TETRA Technologies, Inc.; *U.S. Public*, pg. 2024
TETRA TECHNOLOGIES UK LIMITED—See TETRA Technologies, Inc.; *U.S. Public*, pg. 2024
TIANJIN UNIVTECH CO., LTD.—See China National Chemical Corporation; *Int'l*, pg. 1530
TOA-DIC ZHANGJIAGANG CHEMICAL CO., LTD.—See DIC Corporation; *Int'l*, pg. 2111
TOKAI MELTEX INC.—See Astena Holdings Co., Ltd.; *Int'l*, pg. 653
TRADEWORKS GROUP INC.—See One Rock Capital Partners, LLC; *U.S. Private*, pg. 3022
TREND TONE IMAGING, INC.—See Everlight Chemical Industrial Co.; *Int'l*, pg. 2567
TROY CORPORATION; *U.S. Private*, pg. 4243
ULTRASEAL CHONGQING LIMITED—See Quaker Chemical Corporation; *U.S. Public*, pg. 1747
ULTRASEAL INTERNATIONAL GROUP LTD.—See Quaker Chemical Corporation; *U.S. Public*, pg. 1747
ULTRASEAL SHANGHAI LIMITED—See Quaker Chemical Corporation; *U.S. Public*, pg. 1747
UNGERER DE COLOMBIA LTDA—See Givaudan S.A.; *Int'l*, pg. 2982
UNION CARBIDE CORPORATION—See Dow Inc.; *U.S. Public*, pg. 686
UNION CARBIDE CORPORATION—See Dow Inc.; *U.S. Public*, pg. 686
UNISON TRANSFORMER SERVICES, INC.—See Dow Inc.; *U.S. Public*, pg. 686
UNITED INITIATORS GMBH & CO. KG—See Equistone Partners Europe Limited; *Int'l*, pg. 2487
UNITED INITIATORS, INC.—See Equistone Partners Europe Limited; *Int'l*, pg. 2487
UNITED INITIATORS PTY. LTD.—See Equistone Partners Europe Limited; *Int'l*, pg. 2487
UP HUNTSMAN-NMG—See Huntsman Corporation; *U.S. Public*, pg. 1075
VALUEPARK TERNEUZEN BEHEER B.V.—See Dow Inc.; *U.S. Public*, pg. 685
VANTAGE OLEOCHEMICALS, INC.—See H.I.G. Capital, LLC; *U.S. Private*, pg. 1832
VANTAGE SPECIALTY INGREDIENTS, INC.—See H.I.G. Capital, LLC; *U.S. Private*, pg. 1832
VERA CHIMIE DEVELOPPEMENTS S.A.S.—See Floridienne SA; *Int'l*, pg. 2708
VERTELLUS HEALTH & SPECIALTY PRODUCTS LLC - DELAWARE WATER GAP—See Black Diamond Capital Holdings, LLC; *U.S. Private*, pg. 571
VERTELLUS HEALTH & SPECIALTY PRODUCTS LLC - DELAWARE WATER GAP—See Brightwood Capital Advisors, LLC; *U.S. Private*, pg. 653
VERTELLUS PERFORMANCE MATERIALS, INC.—See Black Diamond Capital Holdings, LLC; *U.S. Private*, pg. 571
VERTELLUS PERFORMANCE MATERIALS, INC.—See Brightwood Capital Advisors, LLC; *U.S. Private*, pg. 654
VERTELLUS SPECIALTIES INC.—See Black Diamond Capital Holdings, LLC; *U.S. Private*, pg. 571
VERTELLUS SPECIALTIES INC.—See Brightwood Capital Advisors, LLC; *U.S. Private*, pg. 653
VERTELLUS SPECIALTIES UK LTD.—See Black Diamond Capital Holdings, LLC; *U.S. Private*, pg. 571
VERTELLUS SPECIALTIES UK LTD.—See Brightwood Capital Advisors, LLC; *U.S. Private*, pg. 654
VIGON INTERNATIONAL, INC.—See EQT AB; *Int'l*, pg. 2469
VIKING CHEMICAL COMPANY—See Arkema S.A.; *Int'l*, pg. 569
WALLOVER OIL COMPANY INCORPORATED—See Quaker Chemical Corporation; *U.S. Public*, pg. 1747
WESTERN POLYMER CORPORATION—See Ingredion Incorporated; *U.S. Public*, pg. 1124
WESTLAKE CORPORATION; *U.S. Public*, pg. 2360
WESTLAKE LONGVIEW CORPORATION—See Westlake Corporation; *U.S. Public*, pg. 2360
WIGO CHEMIE GMBH—See Berner SE; *Int'l*, pg. 988
WISCONSIN BIOPRODUCTS—See Molecular Biology Resources; *U.S. Private*, pg. 2767
WORLD ENERGY ALTERNATIVES, LLC; *U.S. Private*, pg. 4565
WUHAN GRAND HOYO COMPANY LIMITED—See Grand Pharmaceutical Group Limited; *Int'l*, pg. 3056
XINGTAI HENGYUAN CHEMICAL GROUP CO., LTD.—See China National Chemical Corporation; *Int'l*, pg. 1530
XINJIANG FUFENG BIOTECHNOLOGIES CO., LTD.—See Fufeng Group Limited; *Int'l*, pg. 2805
YAMATO SHIKO CO., LTD.—See Dynic Corporation; *Int'l*, pg. 2243
ZAO HUNTSMAN-NMG—See Huntsman Corporation; *U.S. Public*, pg. 1075
ZEOCHEM L.L.C—See CPH Chemie + Papier Holding AG; *Int'l*, pg. 1824
ZHONGHAO ALKALI INDUSTRY CO., LTD.—See China National Chemical Corporation; *Int'l*, pg. 1527
ZUARI MAROC PHOSPHATES LIMITED—See Adventz Group; *Int'l*, pg. 167

325211 — PLASTICS MATERIAL AND RESIN MANUFACTURING

9116-4509 QUEBEC INC; *Int'l*, pg. 16
ABU DHABI POLYMERS CO. LTD—See Abu Dhabi National Oil Company; *Int'l*, pg. 73
ACCELLA POLYURETHANE SYSTEMS, LLC—See Carlisle Companies Incorporated; *U.S. Public*, pg. 436
ACCESSIBLE PRODUCTS COMPANY - TECHLITE INSULATION DIVISION—See The Zippertubing Company; *U.S. Private*, pg. 4140
ACCURATE PLASTICS INC.; *U.S. Private*, pg. 55
ADM TRONICS UNLIMITED, INC.; *U.S. Public*, pg. 42
ADVANCED MEDICAL SOLUTIONS GROUP PLC; *Int'l*, pg. 161
ADVANCED PROTECTIVE COATINGS INC.; *U.S. Private*, pg. 92
ADVANSIX INC.; *U.S. Public*, pg. 49
AEI COMPOUNDS LIMITED—See Saco Polymers Inc.; *U.S. Private*, pg. 3522
AEOLIAN CORPORATION—See Dainichiseika Color & Chemicals Mfg. Co., Ltd.; *Int'l*, pg. 1938
AGVA CORPORATION LIMITED; *Int'l*, pg. 222
AHIMSA INDUSTRIES LIMITED; *Int'l*, pg. 223
AICA ASIA PACIFIC HOLDING PTE. LTD.—See AICA Kogyo Company, Limited; *Int'l*, pg. 228
AICA HARIMA KOGYO CO., LTD.—See AICA Kogyo Company, Limited; *Int'l*, pg. 228
AICA HATYAI CO., LTD.—See AICA Kogyo Company, Limited; *Int'l*, pg. 228
AICA NZ LTD.—See AICA Kogyo Company, Limited; *Int'l*, pg. 228
AIR WATER BELLPEARL INC.—See Air Water Inc.; *Int'l*, pg. 239
AKITA RECYCLE & FINEPACK CO., LTD.—See Dowa Holdings Co., Ltd.; *Int'l*, pg. 2182
AL COMPOSITES MATERIALS FZE—See China XD Plastics Company Ltd.; *Int'l*, pg. 1563
ALIANCYS AG—See CVC Capital Partners SICAV-FIS S.A.; *Int'l*, pg. 1886
ALLNEX RESINS AUSTRALIA PTY. LTD.—See Advent International Corporation; *U.S. Private*, pg. 98
ALLPACK INDUSTRIES LTD—See Aga Khan Development Network; *Int'l*, pg. 199
ALPEK POLYESTER ARGENTINA S.A.—See ALFA, S.A.B. de C.V.; *Int'l*, pg. 313
ALPEK POLYESTER BRASIL S.A.—See ALFA, S.A.B. de C.V.; *Int'l*, pg. 313
ALPEK POLYESTER PERNAMBUCO S. A.—See ALFA, S.A.B. de C.V.; *Int'l*, pg. 313
ALPEK POLYESTER UK LTD.—See ALFA, S.A.B. de C.V.; *Int'l*, pg. 313
ALPHA RESINS—See Covia Holdings Corporation; *U.S. Private*, pg. 1072
ALRO STEEL CORPORATION - ALRO PLASTICS DIVISION—See Alro Steel Corporation; *U.S. Private*, pg. 202
AMERIKAN LLC—See Myers Industries, Inc.; *U.S. Public*, pg. 1488
ANHUI SHENJIAN NEW MATERIALS CO., LTD.; *Int'l*, pg. 469
ANTI-HYDRO INTERNATIONAL, INC.; *U.S. Private*, pg. 288
A.O.C. CANADA, INC.—See The Alpha Corporation of Tennessee; *U.S. Private*, pg. 3984
AOC INDIA PVT. LTD.—See The Alpha Corporation of Tennessee; *U.S. Private*, pg. 3984
AOC, LLC - AOC CALIFORNIA PLANT—See The Alpha Corporation of Tennessee; *U.S. Private*, pg. 3984
AOC, LLC - AOC FLORIDA PLANT—See The Alpha Corporation of Tennessee; *U.S. Private*, pg. 3984
AOC, LLC - AOC INDIANA PLANT—See The Alpha Corporation of Tennessee; *U.S. Private*, pg. 3984
AOC, LLC - AOC MEXICO PLANT—See The Alpha Corporation of Tennessee; *U.S. Private*, pg. 3984
AOC, LLC - AOC ONTARIO PLANT—See The Alpha Corporation of Tennessee; *U.S. Private*, pg. 3984
AOC, LLC - AOC TENNESSEE PLANT—See The Alpha Corporation of Tennessee; *U.S. Private*, pg. 3984
AOC NEDERLAND B.V.—See CVC Capital Partners SICAV-FIS S.A.; *Int'l*, pg. 1886
APPLIED DB PUBLIC COMPANY LIMITED; *Int'l*, pg. 521
AQUALON FRANCE B.V.—See Ashland Inc.; *U.S. Public*, pg. 212
ARAKAWA EUROPE GMBH—See Arakawa Chemical Industries, Ltd.; *Int'l*, pg. 534
ARGHA KARYA PRIMA INDUSTRY TBK; *Int'l*, pg. 561
ARISAWA MANUFACTURING CO., LTD.; *Int'l*, pg. 565
ARISTECH ACRYLICS LLC - AVONITE SURFACES—See SK Capital Partners, LP; *U.S. Private*, pg. 3679
ARISTECH ACRYLICS LLC—See SK Capital Partners, LP; *U.S. Private*, pg. 3679
ARKEMA S.A.; *Int'l*, pg. 568
ARKEMA VLISSINGEN B.V.—See Arkema S.A.; *Int'l*, pg. 568
ARNETTE POLYMERS, LLC—See RPM International Inc.; *U.S. Public*, pg. 1818
ARTISON INVESTMENTS, LTD.; *U.S. Private*, pg. 343
ASAHI CHEMICAL (H.K.) LTD.—See Asahi Kasei Corporation; *Int'l*, pg. 594
ASAHI KASEI-BEIJING—See Asahi Kasei Corporation; *Int'l*, pg. 596
ASAHIKASEI PLASTICS (AMERICA) INC.—See Asahi Kasei Corporation; *Int'l*, pg. 596
ASAHI KASEI PLASTICS LTD.—See Asahi Kasei Corporation; *Int'l*, pg. 595
ASAHI KASEI PLASTICS NORTH AMERICA, INC.—See Asahi Kasei Corporation; *Int'l*, pg. 595
ASAHI KASEI-SHANGHAI—See Asahi Kasei Corporation; *Int'l*, pg. 596
ASAHI ORGANIC CHEMICALS INDUSTRY CO., LTD. - AICHI PLANT—See Asahi Yukizai Corporation; *Int'l*, pg. 598
ASAHI ORGANIC CHEMICALS INDUSTRY CO., LTD. - HIROSIMA PLANT—See Asahi Yukizai Corporation; *Int'l*, pg. 598
ASAHI ORGANIC CHEMICALS (NANTONG) CO., LTD.—See Asahi Yukizai Corporation; *Int'l*, pg. 598
ASAHI YUKIZAI CORPORATION; *Int'l*, pg. 598
ASHLAND SERVICES B.V.—See Ashland Inc.; *U.S. Public*, pg. 211
ASIA POLY INDUSTRIAL SDN. BHD.—See Asia Poly Holdings Berhad; *Int'l*, pg. 615
ASIA POLYMER CORPORATION; *Int'l*, pg. 615
ASK CHEMICALS GMBH - WERK WULFRATH—See Rhone Group, LLC; *U.S. Private*, pg. 3423
ASK CHEMICALS LP—See Rhone Group, LLC; *U.S. Private*, pg. 3423
ASTRAPAK KWAZULU-NATAL (PTY) LTD—See Berry Global Group, Inc; *U.S. Public*, pg. 323
ATCOAT GMBH; *Int'l*, pg. 667
ATCOAT HAMBURG GMBH—See ATCOAT GmbH; *Int'l*, pg. 667
AVIENT CANADA ULC—See Avient Corporation; *U.S. Public*, pg. 246
AVIENT COLORANTS ITALY S.R.L.—See Avient Corporation; *U.S. Public*, pg. 246
AVIENT CORPORATION; *U.S. Public*, pg. 246
AVIENT TH. BERGMANN GMBH—See Avient Corporation; *U.S. Public*, pg. 247
AVI POLYMERS LIMITED; *Int'l*, pg. 740
AXEL POLYMERS LIMITED; *Int'l*, pg. 765
BALOCHISTAN PARTICLE BOARD LIMITED; *Int'l*, pg. 810
BAOTOU NEW DAMAO RARE EARTH CO., LTD.—See Hongda Xingye Co., Ltd.; *Int'l*, pg. 3470
BASF CORP. - ENGINEERING PLASTICS NAFTA—See BASF SE; *Int'l*, pg. 876
BASF CROATIA D.O.O.—See BASF SE; *Int'l*, pg. 876
BASF DE MEXICO S.A. DE C.V.—See BASF SE; *Int'l*, pg. 876
BASF ESPANOLA S.L.—See BASF SE; *Int'l*, pg. 878
BASF ESPANOLA S.L.—See BASF SE; *Int'l*, pg. 883
BASF IRELAND DAC—See BASF SE; *Int'l*, pg. 879
BASF KANOO POLYURETHANES LLC—See BASF SE; *Int'l*, pg. 879
BASF PERFORMANCE POLYAMIDES KOREA CO., LTD.—See BASF SE; *Int'l*, pg. 880
BASF POLYURETHANE INDUSTRY AND TRADE CO., LTD. STI—See BASF SE; *Int'l*, pg. 883

N.A.I.C.S. INDEX

325211 — PLASTICS MATERIAL A...

BASF POLYURETHANES (CHINA) CO., LTD.—See BASF SE; *Int'l*, pg. 877
BASF POLYURETHANES NORTH AMERICA—See BASF SE; *Int'l*, pg. 876
BASF SCHWARZHEIDE GMBH—See BASF SE; *Int'l*, pg. 883
BAYER INTERNATIONAL TRADE SERVICES CORPORATION—See Bayer Aktiengesellschaft; *Int'l*, pg. 902
BAYER MALIBU POLYMERS PRIVATE LIMITED—See Bayer Aktiengesellschaft; *Int'l*, pg. 907
BAYER MATERIALSCIENCE B.V.—See Bayer Aktiengesellschaft; *Int'l*, pg. 907
BAYER MATERIALSCIENCE LTD.—See Bayer Aktiengesellschaft; *Int'l*, pg. 907
BAYER URETECH LTD.—See Bayer Aktiengesellschaft; *Int'l*, pg. 906
BBIGPLAS POLY PVT LTD.; *Int'l*, pg. 920
BCC PRODUCTS INC.—See Arsenal Capital Management LP; *U.S. Private*, pg. 339
BEAULIEU INTERNATIONAL GROUP NV DISTRIPLAST PLANT—See Beaulieu International Group NV; *Int'l*, pg. 934
BEAULIEU INTERNATIONAL GROUP NV PINNACLE PLANT—See Beaulieu International Group NV; *Int'l*, pg. 934
BEAULIEU INTERNATIONAL GROUP NV TERNI PLANT—See Beaulieu International Group NV; *Int'l*, pg. 934
BEAULIEU RIZHAO FLOORCOVERINGS CO. LTD.—See Beaulieu International Group NV; *Int'l*, pg. 934
BEMIS HONG KONG LTD.—See Bemis Associates Inc.; *U.S. Private*, pg. 522
BERRY SUPERFOS BESANCON SAS—See Berry Global Group, Inc; *U.S. Public*, pg. 321
BGFECOMATERIALS CO., LTD.; *Int'l*, pg. 1007
BHANSALI ENGINEERING POLYMERS LIMITED; *Int'l*, pg. 1010
BIOFINA, INC.; *U.S. Private*, pg. 561
BP AMERICA, INC. - COOPER RIVER PLANT—See BP plc; *Int'l*, pg. 1126
BP CHEMICAL TRELLEBORG AB—See BP plc; *Int'l*, pg. 1128
BP ZHUHAI CHEMICAL COMPANY LIMITED—See BP plc; *Int'l*, pg. 1130
BRADY MEXICO, S. DE R.L. DE C.V.—See Brady Corporation; *U.S. Public*, pg. 379
BRAI-COST S.P.A.; *Int'l*, pg. 1136
BRIGHT BROTHERS LIMITED; *Int'l*, pg. 1161
BUFA COMPOSITE SYSTEMS GMBH & CO. KG—See BUFA GmbH & Co. KG; *Int'l*, pg. 1211
CAROLINA COLOR CORPORATION OF OHIO—See Arsenal Capital Management LP; *U.S. Private*, pg. 337
CAROLINA COLOR CORPORATION—See Arsenal Capital Management LP; *U.S. Private*, pg. 337
CBC AMERICA CORP. - LOS ANGELES DIVISION—See CBC Co., Ltd.; *Int'l*, pg. 1365
CBC (BEIJING) TRADING CO., LTD.—See CBC Co., Ltd.; *Int'l*, pg. 1365
CBC CO., LTD. - MISHIMA FACTORY—See CBC Co., Ltd.; *Int'l*, pg. 1365
CBC CO., LTD.; *Int'l*, pg. 1365
CBC CORPORATION (INDIA) PVT. LTD.—See CBC Co., Ltd.; *Int'l*, pg. 1365
CBC EUROPE S.R.L.—See CBC Co., Ltd.; *Int'l*, pg. 1365
CBC FORMA C.O.—See CBC Co., Ltd.; *Int'l*, pg. 1365
CBC (GUANGZHOU) TRADING CO., LTD.—See CBC Co., Ltd.; *Int'l*, pg. 1365
CBC (H.K.) CO., LTD. - KWUN TONG BRANCH—See CBC Co., Ltd.; *Int'l*, pg. 1365
CBC (H.K.) CO., LTD.—See CBC Co., Ltd.; *Int'l*, pg. 1365
CBC IBERIA S.A.—See CBC Co., Ltd.; *Int'l*, pg. 1365
CBC INGS (CHANGSHU) CO., LTD.—See CBC Co., Ltd.; *Int'l*, pg. 1365
CBC INGS (DONG GUAN) CO., LTD.—See CBC Co., Ltd.; *Int'l*, pg. 1365
CBC OPTRONICS (BD) CO., LTD.—See CBC Co., Ltd.; *Int'l*, pg. 1365
CBC (SHANGHAI) TRADING CO., LTD.—See CBC Co., Ltd.; *Int'l*, pg. 1365
CBC.S PTE LTD. - DISTRIBUTION DIVISION—See CBC Co., Ltd.; *Int'l*, pg. 1365
CBC (THAILAND) CO., LTD.—See CBC Co., Ltd.; *Int'l*, pg. 1365
CENTROPLAST ENGINEERING PLASTICS GMBH—See CENTROTEC SE; *Int'l*, pg. 1415
CHANG CHIANG CHEMICAL CO., LTD.—See Adeka Corporation; *Int'l*, pg. 142
CHANG CHIANG CHEMICAL CO., LTD. Soo ChangChun Group; *Int'l*, pg. 1442
CHANGZHOU HUARI NEW MATERIAL CO., LTD.—See DIC Corporation; *Int'l*, pg. 2107
CHASE CORPORATION - PITTSBURGH—See KKR & Co. Inc.; *U.S. Public*, pg. 1242
CHEMTRUSION, INC.; *U.S. Private*, pg. 872
CHEMVIN PLASTICS LTD—See Aliaxis S.A./N.V.; *Int'l*, pg. 323

CHIA LUNG CHEMICAL INDUSTRIAL CORP.—See DIC Corporation; *Int'l*, pg. 2107
CHINA GENERAL PLASTICS CORPORATION; *Int'l*, pg. 1504
CHINA GENERAL PLASTICS CORPORATION - TOUFEN PLANT—See China General Plastics Corporation; *Int'l*, pg. 1504
CHINA PETROCHEMICAL DEVELOPMENT CORP.; *Int'l*, pg. 1540
CHINYANG CHEMICAL CORPORATION; *Int'l*, pg. 1571
CLARIANT ADVANCED MATERIALS GMBH—See Clariant AG; *Int'l*, pg. 1647
CLARIANT CORPORATION—See Clariant AG; *Int'l*, pg. 1647
CLARIANT CORPORATION—See Clariant AG; *Int'l*, pg. 1647
CLOPAY DOMBUHL GMBH—See Griffon Corporation; *U.S. Public*, pg. 969
CMC KOREA CO., LTD.—See Entegris, Inc.; *U.S. Public*, pg. 776
COASTLINE PLASTICS L.L.C.—See Spears Manufacturing Company; *U.S. Public*, pg. 3748
COGNIS CHEMICALS (CHINA) CO. LTD.—See BASF SE; *Int'l*, pg. 883
COGNIS GMBH - ILLERTISSEN—See BASF SE; *Int'l*, pg. 883
COLONIAL BAG CORPORATION—See Ardian SAS; *Int'l*, pg. 554
COMMAND POLYMERS LIMITED; *Int'l*, pg. 1714
COMMONWEALTH LAMINATING & COATING (HONG KONG) LIMITED—See Eastman Chemical Company; *U.S. Public*, pg. 704
COMMONWEALTH LAMINATING & COATING (SHANGHAI) CO., LTD.—See Eastman Chemical Company; *U.S. Public*, pg. 704
CONSTANTIA AFRIPACK LABELS PINETOWN—See One Rock Capital Partners, LLC; *U.S. Private*, pg. 3022
COORSTEK, INC. - COORSTEK VISTA FACILITY—See CoorsTek, Inc.; *U.S. Private*, pg. 1044
CRESCENT PLASTICS, INC.—See Cresline Plastic Pipe Co., Inc.; *U.S. Private*, pg. 1094
CROSSFIELD PRODUCTS CORPORATION; *U.S. Private*, pg. 1106
CUKUROVA KIMYA ENDUSTRISI A.S.—See Cukurova Holding A.S.; *Int'l*, pg. 1876
CULTURED STONE CORPORATION—See Owens Corning; *U.S. Public*, pg. 1626
CUSTOM RESINS INC.—See Polymeric Resources Corp.; *U.S. Public*, pg. 1701
DAICEL CHEMICALS CO LTD—See Daicel Corporation; *Int'l*, pg. 1918
DAICEL-CYTEC COMPANY, LTD.—See Daicel Corporation; *Int'l*, pg. 1919
DAICEL-EVONIK LTD.—See Daicel Corporation; *Int'l*, pg. 1919
DAICEL MIRAIZU (THAILAND) CO., LTD.—See Daicel Corporation; *Int'l*, pg. 1919
DAICEL-POLYMER (HONG KONG) LIMITED—See Daicel Corporation; *Int'l*, pg. 1919
DAICEL POLYMER LTD.—See Daicel Corporation; *Int'l*, pg. 1919
DAICOLOR DO BRASIL IND. E COM. LTDA.—See Dainichiseika Color & Chemicals Mfg. Co., Ltd.; *Int'l*, pg. 1939
DAIDO SIGNAL CO., LTD.; *Int'l*, pg. 1922
DAINICHI COLOR INDIA PRIVATE LTD.—See Dainichiseika Color & Chemicals Mfg. Co., Ltd.; *Int'l*, pg. 1939
DAINICHI COLOR (THAILAND) LTD.—See Dainichiseika Color & Chemicals Mfg. Co., Ltd.; *Int'l*, pg. 1939
DAINICHISEIKA COLOR & CHEMICALS MFG. CO., LTD.; *Int'l*, pg. 1938
DAINICHISEIKA (H.K.) COLOURING CO., LTD.—See Dainichiseika Color & Chemicals Mfg. Co., Ltd.; *Int'l*, pg. 1939
DAINICHISEIKA (H.K.) LTD.—See Dainichiseika Color & Chemicals Mfg. Co., Ltd.; *Int'l*, pg. 1939
DAINICHISEIKA (SHANGHAI) TRADING LTD.—See Dainichiseika Color & Chemicals Mfg. Co., Ltd.; *Int'l*, pg. 1939
DAK AMERICAS MISSISSIPPI INC.—See ALFA, S.A.B. de C.V.; *Int'l*, pg. 313
DAK RESINAS AMERICAS MEXICO, S.A. DE C.V.—See ALFA, S.A.B. de C.V.; *Int'l*, pg. 313
DDEV PLASTIKS INDUSTRIES LIMITED; *Int'l*, pg. 1993
DEKALB MOLDED PLASTICS INC.; *U.S. Private*, pg. 1192
DE LA RUE AUTHENTICATION SOLUTIONS INC.—See De La Rue plc; *Int'l*, pg. 1996
DELTECH RESIN CO.—See SK Capital Partners, LP; *U.S. Private*, pg. 3679
DENSO TEN TECHNOSEPTA LIMITED—See Denso Corporation; *Int'l*, pg. 2030
DEQING DIC SYNTHETIC RESINS, LTD.—See DIC Corporation; *Int'l*, pg. 2109
DIC BERLIN GMBH R & D LABORATORY—See DIC Corporation; *Int'l*, pg. 2107
DIC COVESTRO POLYMER LTD.—See DIC Corporation; *Int'l*, pg. 2107
DIC DECOR, INC.—See DIC Corporation; *Int'l*, pg. 2107
DIC EP CORP.—See DIC Corporation; *Int'l*, pg. 2107
DIC EPOXY (MALAYSIA) SDN. BHD.—See DIC Corporation; *Int'l*, pg. 2107

DIC IMAGING PRODUCTS USA INC.—See DIC Corporation; *Int'l*, pg. 2108
DIC KITANIHON POLYMER CO., LTD.—See DIC Corporation; *Int'l*, pg. 2108
DIC KYUSHU POLYMER CO., LTD.—See DIC Corporation; *Int'l*, pg. 2108
DIC MATERIAL INC.—See DIC Corporation; *Int'l*, pg. 2108
DIC PERFORMANCE RESINS GMBH—See DIC Corporation; *Int'l*, pg. 2108
DIC SYNTHETIC RESINS (ZHONGSHAN) CO., LTD.—See DIC Corporation; *Int'l*, pg. 2108
DIC ZHANGJIAGANG CHEMICALS CO., LTD.—See DIC Corporation; *Int'l*, pg. 2108
DISTRIPLAST SAS—See Beaulieu International Group NV; *Int'l*, pg. 934
DNO NORGE AS—See DNO ASA; *Int'l*, pg. 2148
DNO TECHNICAL SERVICES AS—See DNO ASA; *Int'l*, pg. 2148
DOCK RESINS CORPORATION—See Lifecore Biomedical, Inc.; *U.S. Public*, pg. 1312
DOMO CAPROLEUNA GMBH—See Domo NV; *Int'l*, pg. 2162
DONG GUAN DAINICHI CHEMICAL MANUFACTURING CO., LTD.—See Dainichiseika Color & Chemicals Mfg. Co., Ltd.; *Int'l*, pg. 1939
DONGSUNG CHEMICAL CO., LTD. - SIHWA FACTORY—See Dongsung Chemical Co., Ltd.; *Int'l*, pg. 2170
DONGSUNG CHEMICAL CO., LTD.; *Int'l*, pg. 2169
DORLYL SNC—See Arkema S.A.; *Int'l*, pg. 571
DOW AGROSCIENCES (THAILAND) LTD.—See Corteva, Inc.; *U.S. Public*, pg. 582
DOW CORNING TORAY SILICON CO., LTD.—See Dow Inc.; *U.S. Public*, pg. 684
DOW HELLAS SA—See Dow Inc.; *U.S. Public*, pg. 685
DRT PINOVA INC.—See Firmenich International SA; *Int'l*, pg. 2679
DSM IDEMITSU CORP. LTD.—See Idemitsu Kosan Co., Ltd.; *Int'l*, pg. 3590
DUJODWALA PAPER CHEMICALS LIMITED; *Int'l*, pg. 2224
DU PONT DE NEMOURS (BELGIUM) BVBA—See DuPont de Nemours, Inc.; *U.S. Public*, pg. 692
DUPONT DE NEMOURS (DEUTSCHLAND) GMBH—See DuPont de Nemours, Inc.; *U.S. Public*, pg. 693
DUPONT DE NEMOURS (NEDERLAND) B.V.—See DuPont de Nemours, Inc.; *U.S. Public*, pg. 693
DUPONT MITSUI FLUOROCHEMICALS CO., LTD.—See DuPont de Nemours, Inc.; *U.S. Public*, pg. 692
DUPONT MITSUI POLYCHEMICALS CO., LTD.—See DuPont de Nemours, Inc.; *U.S. Public*, pg. 692
DUPONT SPECIALTY PRODUCTS INDIA PRIVATE LIMITED—See DuPont de Nemours, Inc.; *U.S. Public*, pg. 693
DUPONT STYRO CORPORATION—See DuPont de Nemours, Inc.; *U.S. Public*, pg. 693
DYNEA N.V.—See Ackermans & van Haaren NV; *Int'l*, pg. 106
DYNEA PAKISTAN LIMITED; *Int'l*, pg. 2242
DYNEON GMBH—See 3M Company; *U.S. Public*, pg. 5
EASTMAN CHEMICAL (CHINA) CO., LTD.—See Eastman Chemical Company; *U.S. Public*, pg. 704
EASTMAN CHEMICAL COMPANY INVESTMENTS, INC.—See Eastman Chemical Company; *U.S. Public*, pg. 704
EASTMAN CHEMICAL COMPANY SOUTH CAROLINA OPERATIONS—See Eastman Chemical Company; *U.S. Public*, pg. 704
EASTMAN CHEMICAL GERMANY GMBH—See Eastman Chemical Company; *U.S. Public*, pg. 704
EASTMAN CHEMICAL INDIA PRIVATE LIMITED—See Eastman Chemical Company; *U.S. Public*, pg. 704
EASTMAN CHEMICAL INTERNATIONAL GMBH—See Eastman Chemical Company; *U.S. Public*, pg. 705
EASTMAN CHEMICAL RESINS, INC.—See Eastman Chemical Company; *U.S. Public*, pg. 705
EASTMAN CHEMICAL TEXAS CITY, INC.—See Eastman Chemical Company; *U.S. Public*, pg. 705
EASTMAN COGENERATION L.P.—See Eastman Chemical Company; *U.S. Public*, pg. 705
EASTMAN MAZZUCCHELLI PLASTICS (SHENZHEN) COMPANY LIMITED—See Eastman Chemical Company; *U.S. Public*, pg. 705
EASTMAN SPECIALTIES OU—See Eastman Chemical Company; *U.S. Public*, pg. 705
ECHO ENGINEERING & PRODUCTION SUPPLIES, INC.; *U.S. Private*, pg. 1327
ECOLOC NV—See RPM International Inc.; *U.S. Public*, pg. 1816
EIDP, INC.—See Corteva, Inc.; *U.S. Public*, pg. 582
E.I. DUPONT DE NEMOURS & CO.—See Corteva, Inc.; *U.S. Public*, pg. 584
ELASTOGRAN FRANCE S.A.S—See BASF SE; *Int'l*, pg. 883
ELASTOGRAN ITALIA S.P.A.—See BASF SE; *Int'l*, pg. 883
ELASTOGRAN LAGOMAT NORDIC AB—See BASF SE; *Int'l*, pg. 883
ELASTOGRAN UK LIMITED—See BASF SE; *Int'l*, pg. 883

325211 — PLASTICS MATERIAL A...   CORPORATE AFFILIATIONS

ELEMENTIA S.A.—See Grupo Empresarial Kaluz S.A. de C.V.; *Int'l*, pg. 3126
ELITE COLOR ENVIRONMENTAL RESOURCES SCIENCE & TECHNOLOGY CO., LTD.; *Int'l*, pg. 2362
EMATEC - CUERNAVACA PLANT—See Ematec II S. de R. L. de C.V.; *Int'l*, pg. 2374
EMATEC II S. DE R. L. DE C.V. - GUADALAJARA PLANT—See Ematec II S. de R. L. de C.V.; *Int'l*, pg. 2374
EMATEC II S. DE R. L. DE C.V. - GUADALUPE PLANT—See Ematec II S. de R. L. de C.V.; *Int'l*, pg. 2374
EMATEC II S. DE R. L. DE C.V. - HERMOSILLO PLANT—See Ematec II S. de R. L. de C.V.; *Int'l*, pg. 2374
EMATEC II S. DE R. L. DE C.V.; *Int'l*, pg. 2374
EMS-CHEMIE (NORTH AMERICA) INC.—See EMS-Chemie Holding AG; *Int'l*, pg. 2393
ENDURANCE TECHNOLOGIES, INC.—See Arsenal Capital Management LP; *U.S. Private*, pg. 339
ENDURIS EXTRUSIONS, INC.; *U.S. Private*, pg. 1392
ENGRO POLYMER & CHEMICALS LIMITED—See Engro Corporation Limited; *Int'l*, pg. 2435
ENSINGER COMPOSITES SCHWEIZ GMBH—See Ensinger GmbH; *Int'l*, pg. 2447
ENSINGER MACHINING SA—See Ensinger GmbH; *Int'l*, pg. 2447
ENSINGER PENN FIBRE INC.—See Ensinger GmbH; *Int'l*, pg. 2447
ENSINGER POLSKA SP. Z O.O.—See Ensinger GmbH; *Int'l*, pg. 2447
ENSINGER PRECISION COMPONENTS INC.—See Ensinger GmbH; *Int'l*, pg. 2447
ENVIRONMENTAL TECHNOLOGY, INC.—See Arsenal Capital Management LP; *U.S. Private*, pg. 339
EP BIOCOMPOSITES LIMITED; *Int'l*, pg. 2458
EPIC RESINS; *U.S. Private*, pg. 1412
EPOXY BASE ELECTRONIC MATERIAL CORPORATION LIMITED; *Int'l*, pg. 2463
EPSILYTE HOLDINGS LLC—See Balmoral Funds LLC; *U.S. Private*, pg. 461
ERCROS SA - INTERMEDIATE CHEMICALS DIVISION - CERDANYOLA FACTORY—See Ercros SA; *Int'l*, pg. 2490
ESENTTIA S.A.—See Ecopetrol S.A.; *Int'l*, pg. 2299
E & S HOME OF COLOR B.V.—See Dainichiseika Color & Chemicals Mfg. Co., Ltd.; *Int'l*, pg. 1939
ESSCHEM INC.; *U.S. Private*, pg. 1427
ETERNAL CHEMICAL (CHENGDU) CO., LTD.—See Eternal Materials Co., Ltd.; *Int'l*, pg. 2520
ETERNAL CHEMICAL CO., LTD. - LU-CHU PLANT—See China Petrochemical Development Corp.; *Int'l*, pg. 1540
ETERNAL CHEMICAL CO., LTD. - PING-NAN PLANT—See Eternal Materials Co., Ltd.; *Int'l*, pg. 2520
ETERNAL CHEMICAL (GUANGDONG) CO., LTD.—See Eternal Materials Co., Ltd.; *Int'l*, pg. 2520
ETERNAL CHEMICAL (JAPAN) CO., LTD.—See Eternal Materials Co., Ltd.; *Int'l*, pg. 2520
ETERNAL CHEMICAL (TIANJIN) CO., LTD.—See Eternal Materials Co., Ltd.; *Int'l*, pg. 2520
ETERNAL MATERIALS (GUANGDONG) CO., LTD.—See Eternal Materials Co., Ltd.; *Int'l*, pg. 2520
ETERNAL MATERIALS (MALAYSIA) SDN. BHD.—See Eternal Materials Co., Ltd.; *Int'l*, pg. 2521
ETERNAL SPECIALTY CHEMICAL (ZHUHAI) CO., LTD.—See Eternal Materials Co., Ltd.; *Int'l*, pg. 2521
ETERNAL SPECIALTY MATERIALS (ZHUHAI) CO., LTD.—See Eternal Materials Co., Ltd.; *Int'l*, pg. 2521
ETERNAL SYNTHETIC RESINS (CHANGSHU) CO., LTD.—See Eternal Materials Co., Ltd.; *Int'l*, pg. 2521
EVERMORE CHEMICAL INDUSTRY CO., LTD.; *Int'l*, pg. 2568
EXCALA GROUP; *Int'l*, pg. 2577
EXXONMOBIL CHEMICAL COMPANY INC.—See Exxon Mobil Corporation; *U.S. Public*, pg. 814
EXXONMOBIL CHEMICAL COMPANY - MONT BELVIEU PLASTICS PLANT—See Exxon Mobil Corporation; *U.S. Public*, pg. 814
FARS CHEMICAL INDUSTRIES COMPANY; *Int'l*, pg. 2620
FASOPLAST S.A.—See Aga Khan Development Network; *Int'l*, pg. 199
FEMTO ENGINEERING S.R.L.—See LCI Industries; *U.S. Public*, pg. 1295
FIBERWEB GEOSYNTHETICS LTD—See Berry Global Group, Inc.; *U.S. Public*, pg. 321
FILLING & PACKING MATERIALS MANUFACTURING COMPANY; *Int'l*, pg. 2663
FILMTEC CORPORATION—See DuPont de Nemours, Inc.; *U.S. Public*, pg. 693
FILPASSION SA—See Dainichiseika Color & Chemicals Mfg. Co., Ltd.; *Int'l*, pg. 1939
FLEXFAB SOUTH AMERICA LTDA.—See Flexfab Horizons International, LLC; *U.S. Private*, pg. 1544
FLEXSYS AMERICA CO.—See Eastman Chemical Company; *U.S. Public*, pg. 705
FLEXTRONICS INTERNATIONAL KFT—See Flex Ltd.; *Int'l*, pg. 2702
FLEXTRONICS INTERNATIONAL KFT—See Flex Ltd.; *Int'l*, pg. 2702
FLEXTRONICS (MALAYSIA) SDN. BHD.—See Flex Ltd.; *Int'l*, pg. 2702

FLEXTRONICS TECHNOLOGY SDN BHD—See Flex Ltd.; *Int'l*, pg. 2704
FLUID POLYMERS—See KKR & Co. Inc.; *U.S. Public*, pg. 1243
FORMOSA PLASTICS CORPORATION, U.S.A.—See Formosa Plastics Corporation; *Int'l*, pg. 2735
FO-SHAN CITY SHANSHUI LIANMEI CHEMICAL CO., LTD.—See Headway Advanced Materials Inc.; *Int'l*, pg. 3302
FRIGOCEL—See Grupo Empresarial Kaluz S.A. de C.V.; *Int'l*, pg. 3127
FUKOKU CO., LTD. - GUNMA PLANT 2—See Fukoku Co., Ltd.; *Int'l*, pg. 2838
FUTURA POLYESTERS LTD.; *Int'l*, pg. 2852
GAUDLITZ PRECISION TECHNOLOGY (WUXI) CO., LTD.—See H&R KGaA; *Int'l*, pg. 3193
GENERAL POLYMERIC CORP.; *U.S. Private*, pg. 1666
GENTAS KIMYA SANAYI VE TICARET PAZARLAMA A.S.—See Gentas AS; *Int'l*, pg. 2928
GEO-TECH POLYMERS, LLC—See Wastren Advantage, Inc.; *U.S. Private*, pg. 4451
GERRESHEIMER PLASTIC PACKAGING (CHANGZHOU) CO., LTD.—See Gerresheimer AG; *Int'l*, pg. 2944
GERRESHEIMER SINGAPORE PTE. LTD.—See Gerresheimer AG; *Int'l*, pg. 2944
GGB GMBH—See Hirsch Servo AG; *Int'l*, pg. 3405
GINAR TECHNOLOGY CO., LTD.; *Int'l*, pg. 2976
GLASFORMS, INC.—See Avient Corporation; *U.S. Public*, pg. 247
GNOSJOPLAST AB—See Duroc AB; *Int'l*, pg. 2229
GOO CHEMICAL CO., LTD. - FUKUI FACTORY—See GOO Chemical Co., Ltd.; *Int'l*, pg. 3037
GOO CHEMICAL CO., LTD. - SHIGA FACTORY—See GOO Chemical Co., Ltd.; *Int'l*, pg. 3037
GOOD NATURED PRODUCTS INC.; *Int'l*, pg. 3038
GOODYEAR S.A.—See The Goodyear Tire & Rubber Company; *U.S. Public*, pg. 2084
GRAFO WIREMARKERS PTY. LTD.—See Brady Corporation; *U.S. Public*, pg. 379
GRAHAM PACKAGING COMPANY INC.—See Pactiv Evergreen Inc.; *U.S. Public*, pg. 1633
GRAHAM PACKAGING FRANCE, S.A.S.—See Pactiv Evergreen Inc.; *U.S. Public*, pg. 1633
GREAT LAKES TEXTILES INCORPORATED; *U.S. Private*, pg. 1749
GREENCHEM HOLDING B.V.—See Agrofert Holding, a.s.; *Int'l*, pg. 219
GUANGDONG DIC TOD RESINS CO., LTD.—See DIC India Ltd; *Int'l*, pg. 2111
GUANGDONG PLASTICS EXCHANGE CO., LTD.—See Hongda Xingye Co., Ltd.; *Int'l*, pg. 3470
GUANGDONG QUANWEI TECHNOLOGY CO., LTD.; *Int'l*, pg. 3159
GUANGDONG RONGTAI INDUSTRY CO., LTD.; *Int'l*, pg. 3159
GUANGZHOU DONGSUNG CHEMICAL CO., LTD.—See Dongsung Chemical Co., Ltd.; *Int'l*, pg. 2170
GUANGZHOU LIDYE RESIN CO., LTD.—See DIC Corporation; *Int'l*, pg. 2109
GUILIN HENKEL DETERGENTS & CLEANING PRODUCTS CO. LTD.—See Henkel AG & Co. KGaA; *Int'l*, pg. 3348
GUJARAT PETROSYNTHESE LTD; *Int'l*, pg. 3177
GUN EI CHEMICAL INDUSTRY CO., LTD. - SHIGA PLANT—See Gun Ei Chemical Industry Co., Ltd.; *Int'l*, pg. 3183
GUN EI CHEMICAL INDUSTRY CO., LTD.; *Int'l*, pg. 3183
GURIT AMERICAS INC.—See Gurit Holding AG; *Int'l*, pg. 3188
GURIT HOLDING AG; *Int'l*, pg. 3187
GURIT (TIANJIN) COMPOSITE MATERIAL CO., LTD.—See Gurit Holding AG; *Int'l*, pg. 3188
HAGIHARA INDUSTRIES INC.; *Int'l*, pg. 3206
HAHL FILAMENTS GMBH—See Global Equity Partners Beteiligungs-Management AG; *Int'l*, pg. 2996
HAHL INC.—See Global Equity Partners Beteiligungs-Management AG; *Int'l*, pg. 2996
HANGZHOU FIRST APPLIED MATERIAL CO., LTD.; *Int'l*, pg. 3247
HANGZHOU JUHESHUN NEW MATERIAL CO., LTD.; *Int'l*, pg. 3249
HANWHA ADVANCED MATERIALS CZECH S.R.O.—See Hanwha Group; *Int'l*, pg. 3264
HARIMATEC INC.—See Harima Chemicals Group, Inc.; *Int'l*, pg. 3297
HCD INVESTMENT PRODUCING & TRADING JOINT STOCK CO; *Int'l*, pg. 3297
HEADWAY ADVANCED MATERIALS INC.; *Int'l*, pg. 3302
HEADWAY ADVANCED MATERIALS (SHANGHAI) CO., LTD.—See Headway Advanced Materials Inc.; *Int'l*, pg. 3302
HEADWAY ADVANCED MATERIALS (VIETNAM) CO., LTD.—See Headway Advanced Materials Inc.; *Int'l*, pg. 3302
HEADWAY POLYURETHANE CO., LTD.—See Headway Advanced Materials Inc.; *Int'l*, pg. 3302
HEBEI HUAXIA ENTERPRISE CO.LTD.—See Avery Dennison Corporation; *U.S. Public*, pg. 245

HENGYI PETROCHEMICAL CO., LTD.; *Int'l*, pg. 3347
HENKEL ADHESIVES CO., LTD.—See Henkel AG & Co. KGaA; *Int'l*, pg. 3348
HENKEL CENTROAMERICANA S.A.—See Henkel AG & Co. KGaA; *Int'l*, pg. 3350
HENKEL COSMETICS (ZHAOQING) CO., LTD.—See Henkel AG & Co. KGaA; *Int'l*, pg. 3348
HENKEL CROATIA D.O.O.—See Henkel AG & Co. KGaA; *Int'l*, pg. 3350
HENKEL CR SPOL.S.R.O.—See Henkel AG & Co. KGaA; *Int'l*, pg. 3350
HENKEL MAKROFLEX OY—See Henkel AG & Co. KGaA; *Int'l*, pg. 3352
HENKEL NORDEN AB—See Henkel AG & Co. KGaA; *Int'l*, pg. 3351
HENKEL POLSKA S.A.—See Henkel AG & Co. KGaA; *Int'l*, pg. 3350
HENKEL ROMANIA SRL—See Henkel AG & Co. KGaA; *Int'l*, pg. 3350
HENKEL TEROSON GMBH—See Henkel AG & Co. KGaA; *Int'l*, pg. 3352
HERCULES TIANPU CHEMICALS COMPANY LIMITED—See Ashland Inc.; *U.S. Public*, pg. 212
HEXAGON COMPOSITE SDN. BHD.—See Hexagon Holdings Berhad; *Int'l*, pg. 3370
HEXAGON DISTRIBUTORS SDN. BHD.—See Hexagon Holdings Berhad; *Int'l*, pg. 3370
HEXCEL CORPORATION; *U.S. Public*, pg. 1032
HEXION B.V.—See American Securities LLC; *U.S. Private*, pg. 249
HINDUSTHAN SPECIALITY CHEMICALS LTD.—See Hindusthan Urban Infrastructure Ltd.; *Int'l*, pg. 3400
HITECH CORPORATION LTD.; *Int'l*, pg. 3425
HL PLASTICS LTD.—See Quanex Building Products Corp.; *U.S. Public*, pg. 1749
HOFFMAN PLASTIC COMPOUNDS, INC.; *U.S. Private*, pg. 1960
HONGDA XINGYE CO., LTD.; *Int'l*, pg. 3470
HP POLYMERS, LTD.—See PPG Industries, Inc.; *U.S. Public*, pg. 1711
HUNTSMAN MEXICO S. DE R.L. DE C.V.—See Huntsman Corporation; *U.S. Public*, pg. 1075
HUNTSMAN P&A AMERICAS LLC—See Huntsman Corporation; *U.S. Public*, pg. 1075
HUNTSMAN POLYURETHANES (AUSTRALIA) PTY LTD.—See Huntsman Corporation; *U.S. Public*, pg. 1074
HUNTSMAN POLYURETHANES—See Huntsman Corporation; *U.S. Public*, pg. 1074
HUNTSMAN POLYURETHANES (UK) LTD.—See Huntsman Corporation; *U.S. Public*, pg. 1074
HUNTSMAN PRODUCTS GMBH—See Huntsman Corporation; *U.S. Public*, pg. 1075
HUNTSMAN PURSAN CHEMICALS KIMYA SANAYI VE TICARET LIMITED SIRKETI—See Huntsman Corporation; *U.S. Public*, pg. 1075
HUNTSMAN TEXTILE EFFECTS (SWITZERLAND) GMBH—See Huntsman Corporation; *U.S. Public*, pg. 1075
HYDRATEC INDUSTRIES NV; *Int'l*, pg. 3546
IBIDEN JUSHI CO., LTD.—See Ibiden Co., Ltd.; *Int'l*, pg. 3575
ID ADDITIVES, INC.; *U.S. Private*, pg. 2034
IDEAL CHEMI PLAST PRIVATE LIMITED—See DIC Corporation; *Int'l*, pg. 2109
IDEMITSU UNITECH CO., LTD. - CHIBA PLANT—See Idemitsu Kosan Co., Ltd.; *Int'l*, pg. 3591
IDEMITSU UNITECH CO., LTD. - HYOGO PLANT—See Idemitsu Kosan Co., Ltd.; *Int'l*, pg. 3591
IDEMITSU UNITECH CO., LTD. - SYIZUOKA PLANT—See Idemitsu Kosan Co., Ltd.; *Int'l*, pg. 3591
ILPEA INC.; *U.S. Private*, pg. 2043
INDELPRO, S.A. DE C.V.—See ALFA, S.A.B. de C.V.; *Int'l*, pg. 313
INEOS CHLORVINYLS BELGIUM NV—See One Rock Capital Partners, LLC; *U.S. Private*, pg. 3022
INEOS COMPOUNDS FRANCE SAS—See One Rock Capital Partners, LLC; *U.S. Private*, pg. 3022
INEOS COMPOUNDS ITALIA SRL—See One Rock Capital Partners, LLC; *U.S. Private*, pg. 3022
INEOS COMPOUNDS SWEDEN AB—See One Rock Capital Partners, LLC; *U.S. Private*, pg. 3022
INEOS COMPOUNDS SWITZERLAND AG—See One Rock Capital Partners, LLC; *U.S. Private*, pg. 3022
INEOS COMPOUNDS UK LTD.—See One Rock Capital Partners, LLC; *U.S. Private*, pg. 3023
INFRASTRUCTURE PRODUCTS AUSTRALIA PTY. LTD.—See CRH plc; *Int'l*, pg. 1844
INIT POLYMERS B.V.—See Sun Capital Partners, Inc.; *U.S. Private*, pg. 3861
INNER MONGOLIA WUHAI CHEMICAL INDUSTRY CO., LTD.—See Hongda Xingye Co., Ltd.; *Int'l*, pg. 3470
INNER MONGOLIA ZHONGGU MINING INDUSTRY CO., LTD.—See Hongda Xingye Co., Ltd.; *Int'l*, pg. 3470
INNO POLYTECH CORPORATION—See GS Holdings Corp.; *Int'l*, pg. 3142
INNOVATIVE HESS PRODUCTS, LLC.; *U.S. Private*, pg. 2082

N.A.I.C.S. INDEX

325211 — PLASTICS MATERIAL A...

INOLEX CHEMICAL COMPANY—See Inolex Group Inc.; *U.S. Private*, pg. 2084
INOLEX GROUP INC.; *U.S. Private*, pg. 2084
INTERGROUP INTERNATIONAL, LTD.; *U.S. Private*, pg. 2110
INTERPLASTIC CORPORATION; *U.S. Private*, pg. 2122
INTERPLASTIC CORPORATION—See Interplastic Corporation; *U.S. Private*, pg. 2123
INTERPLASTIC CORPORATION—See Interplastic Corporation; *U.S. Private*, pg. 2123
INVISTA GMBH—See Koch Industries, Inc.; *U.S. Private*, pg. 2330
INVISTA S.A.R.L.—See Koch Industries, Inc.; *U.S. Private*, pg. 2330
ITW PHILADELPHIA RESINS—See Illinois Tool Works Inc.; *U.S. Private*, pg. 1107
ITW SMPI S.A.S.—See Illinois Tool Works Inc.; *U.S. Public*, pg. 1107
ITW SPECIALTY FILMS ITALY S.R.L.—See Illinois Tool Works Inc.; *U.S. Public*, pg. 1107
JADCORE LLC—See Arsenal Capital Management LP; *U.S. Private*, pg. 339
JIANGSU GOLDEN MATERIAL TECHNOLOGY CO., LTD.—See Hongda Xingye Co., Ltd.; *Int'l*, pg. 3470
JIANGXI ANDELI HIGH TECH CO., LTD.—See Foshan Golden Milky Way Intelligent Equipment Co., Ltd.; *Int'l*, pg. 2748
JOHNS MANVILLE CANADA INC.—See Berkshire Hathaway Inc.; *U.S. Public*, pg. 308
JOINT STOCK COMPANY HUNTSMAN-NMG B.V.—See Huntsman Corporation; *U.S. Public*, pg. 1075
JSP INTERNATIONAL; *U.S. Private*, pg. 2241
KANBO PRAS CORPORATION—See Daiwabo Holdings Co., Ltd.; *Int'l*, pg. 1949
KANGNAM CHEMICAL CO., LTD.—See DIC Corporation; *Int'l*, pg. 2109
KARMAY INDUSTRIAL LIMITED—See Cosmos Machinery Enterprises Limited; *Int'l*, pg. 1813
KARMAY PLASTIC PRODUCTS (ZHUHAI) CO., LTD—See Cosmos Machinery Enterprises Limited; *Int'l*, pg. 1813
KCA PARTNERS, LTD.; *U.S. Private*, pg. 2269
KEM ONE S.A.S.—See OpenGate Capital Management, LLC; *U.S. Private*, pg. 3030
KIRKHILL-TA—See TransDigm Group Incorporated; *U.S. Public*, pg. 2181
KKALPANA PLASTICK LTD.—See Bbigplas Poly Pvt Ltd.; *Int'l*, pg. 920
KRATON POLYMERS DO BRASIL INDUSTRIA E COMERCIO DE PRODUTOS PETROQUIMICOS LTDA.—See Daelim Industrial Co., Ltd.; *Int'l*, pg. 1908
KRATON POLYMERS U.S. LLC—See Daelim Industrial Co., Ltd.; *Int'l*, pg. 1908
KYOUDOU POLYMER CO., LTD.—See Daicel Corporation; *Int'l*, pg. 1919
LAKESIDE PLASTICS, INC.; *U.S. Private*, pg. 2378
LES DERIVES RESINIQUES ET TERPENIQUES SA—See Firmenich International SA; *Int'l*, pg. 2681
LIBERTY CHEMICALS PRIVATE LIMITED—See Control Print Ltd.; *Int'l*, pg. 1785
LIDYE CHEMICAL CO., LTD.—See DIC Corporation; *Int'l*, pg. 2109
LIFECORE BIOMEDICAL, INC.; *U.S. Public*, pg. 1312
LIFELAST INC.—See Henkel AG & Co. KGaA; *Int'l*, pg. 3354
LINSHINE ENGINEERING PLASTICS (SUZHOU) CO., LTD.—See Chi Mei Group; *Int'l*, pg. 1475
LION COPOLYMER GEISMAR, LLC—See Lion Copolymer Holdings, LLC; *U.S. Private*, pg. 2463
LION ELASTOMERS LLC—See Lion Copolymer Holdings, LLC; *U.S. Private*, pg. 2463
LION IDEMITSU COMPOSITES CO., LTD—See Idemitsu Kosan Co., Ltd.; *Int'l*, pg. 3591
LLC TELKO CENTRAL ASIA—See Aspo Oyj; *Int'l*, pg. 631
MACROMERIC—See Saco Polymers Inc.; *U.S. Private*, pg. 3522
MACRO-M, S.A. DE C.V.—See Grupo Kuo, S.A.B. de C.V.; *Int'l*, pg. 3131
MAPA SPONTEX S.A.—See Newell Brands Inc.; *U.S. Public*, pg. 1514
MAQUILA PRODUCTS DEL NOROESTE S.DE R.L. DE C.V.—See Brady Corporation; *U.S. Public*, pg. 379
MARCOM PLASTICS (PTY) LTD—See Berry Global Group, Inc; *U.S. Public*, pg. 324
MEMSTAR PTE. LTD.—See CITIC Group Corporation; *Int'l*, pg. 1620
MENASHA CORP., POLY HI SOLIDUR—See Menasha Corporation; *U.S. Private*, pg. 2665
MEXICHEM PANAMA, S.A.—See Grupo Empresarial Kaluz S.A. de C.V.; *Int'l*, pg. 3128
MEXICHEM RESINAS COLOMBIA S.A.—See Grupo Empresarial Kaluz S.A. de C.V.; *Int'l*, pg. 3127
MEXICHEM RESINAS VINILICAS, S.A. DE C.V.—See Grupo Empresarial Kaluz S.A. de C.V.; *Int'l*, pg. 3128
MIDBEC AB—See Dainichiseika Color & Chemicals Mfg. Co., Ltd.; *Int'l*, pg. 1939
MINOVA INTERNATIONAL LIMITED—See Aurelius Equity Opportunities SE & Co. KGaA; *Int'l*, pg. 709
MODERN DISPERSIONS SOUTH, INC.—See Modern Dispersions, Inc.; *U.S. Private*, pg. 2760

MRC POLYMERS, INC.; *U.S. Private*, pg. 2805
MULTIBASE INDIA LIMITED—See Dow Inc.; *U.S. Public*, pg. 684
NATIONAL STARCH PERSONAL CARE—See Akzo Nobel N.V.; *Int'l*, pg. 274
NETZSCH INSTRUMENTS NORTH AMERICA, LLC—See Erich Netzsch GmbH & Co. Holding KG; *Int'l*, pg. 2493
NEU SPECIALTY ENGINEERED MATERIALS, LLC—See Avient Corporation; *U.S. Public*, pg. 247
NEVILLE CHEMICAL COMPANY; *U.S. Private*, pg. 2891
NEXT POLYMERS LIMITED—See Celanese Corporation; *U.S. Public*, pg. 465
NICOLL S.A.—See Aliaxis S.A./N.V.; *Int'l*, pg. 325
NIPPONEX INC.—See Bayer Aktiengesellschaft; *Int'l*, pg. 902
NOBLE POLYMERS LLC—See Cascade Engineering, Inc.; *U.S. Private*, pg. 779
NOR-AM AGRO LLC—See Bayer Aktiengesellschaft; *Int'l*, pg. 902
NORSECHEM RESINS SDN. BERHAD—See Hexza Corporation Berhad; *Int'l*, pg. 3373
NORTH AMERICAN COMPOSITES—See Interplastic Corporation; *U.S. Private*, pg. 2123
NORTON PAMPUS GMBH—See Compagnie de Saint-Gobain SA; *Int'l*, pg. 1731
NUC CORPORATION—See ENEOS Holdings, Inc.; *Int'l*, pg. 2417
NUSIL TECHNOLOGY LLC—See New Mountain Capital, LLC; *U.S. Private*, pg. 2903
NYLON CORPORATION OF AMERICA—See Wembly Enterprises LLC; *U.S. Private*, pg. 4480
OMNOVA PERFORMANCE CHEMICALS (UK) LTD.—See OMNOVA Solutions Inc.; *U.S. Private*, pg. 3017
OOO HENKEL SUD—See Henkel AG & Co. KGaA; *Int'l*, pg. 3350
OUVRIE PMC, SAS—See PMC Group, Inc.; *U.S. Private*, pg. 3218
OWENS-CORNING CANADA—See Owens Corning; *U.S. Public*, pg. 1628
OXY VINYLS CANADA CO.—See Occidental Petroleum Corporation; *U.S. Public*, pg. 1562
OY. AVANE TRADING LTD.—See Dainichiseika Color & Chemicals Mfg. Co., Ltd.; *Int'l*, pg. 1939
PARKWAY PRODUCTS, LLC - LOVELAND FACILITY—See Heartwood Partners, LLC; *U.S. Private*, pg. 1901
PARKWAY PRODUCTS, LLC - SALTILLO FACILITY—See Heartwood Partners, LLC; *U.S. Private*, pg. 1901
PARKWAY PRODUCTS, LLC - SENECA FACILITY—See Heartwood Partners, LLC; *U.S. Private*, pg. 1901
PELNOX, LTD.—See Arakawa Chemical Industries, Ltd.; *Int'l*, pg. 535
PET PROCESSORS, LLC—See Diefenthal Holdings, LLC; *U.S. Private*, pg. 1228
PLALLOY MTD B.V.—See Dainichiseika Color & Chemicals Mfg. Co., Ltd.; *Int'l*, pg. 1939
PLASCOAT SYSTEMS LIMITED—See Axalta Coating Systems Ltd.; *U.S. Public*, pg. 255
PLASMINE TECHNOLOGY, INC. - BAY MINETTE—See Harima Chemicals Group, Inc.; *Int'l*, pg. 3276
PLASTEX EXTRUDERS, INC.USA—See Enterprises International; *U.S. Private*, pg. 1404
PLASTICS ENGINEERING COMPANY INC.; *U.S. Private*, pg. 3199
PLASTI-FAB LTD. - DELTA PLANT—See The Riverside Company; *U.S. Private*, pg. 4109
PLASTIPAK ARGENTINA SA—See Plastipak Holdings, Inc.; *U.S. Private*, pg. 3199
PLASTIPAK, CZECH REPUBLIC S.R.O.—See Plastipak Holdings, Inc.; *U.S. Private*, pg. 3199
PLASTIPAK PACKAGING DA AMAZONIA—See Plastipak Holdings, Inc.; *U.S. Private*, pg. 3200
POLY-CARB, INC.—See Dow Inc.; *U.S. Public*, pg. 685
POLYCHIM INDUSTRIE SAS—See Beaulieu International Group NV; *Int'l*, pg. 934
POLYNT COMPOSITES AUSTRALIA PTY LTD.—See Reichhold, Inc.; *U.S. Private*, pg. 3390
POLYNT COMPOSITES BRAZIL LTDA.—See Reichhold, Inc.; *U.S. Private*, pg. 3390
POLYNT COMPOSITES KOREA CO. LTD—See Reichhold, Inc.; *U.S. Private*, pg. 3390
POLYNT HONG KONG CO., LIMITED—See Reichhold, Inc.; *U.S. Private*, pg. 3390
POLYNT IBERICA, S.L.—See Reichhold, Inc.; *U.S. Private*, pg. 3390
POLYONE JAPAN K.K.—See Avient Corporation; *U.S. Public*, pg. 248
POLYONE POLYMERS INDIA PVT. LTD—See Avient Corporation; *U.S. Public*, pg. 248
POLYONE SHANGHAI, CHINA—See Avient Corporation; *U.S. Public*, pg. 248
POLYONE SHENZHEN CO. LTD—See Avient Corporation; *U.S. Public*, pg. 248
POLYONE SINGAPORE, LTD.—See Avient Corporation; *U.S. Public*, pg. 248
POLYONE SUZHOU, CHINA—See Avient Corporation; *U.S. Public*, pg. 248
POLYPLASTIC B.V.—See LCI Industries; *U.S. Public*, pg. 1296

POLYPLASTICS ASIA PACIFIC SDN. BHD.—See Daicel Corporation; *Int'l*, pg. 1919
POLYPLASTICS ASIA PACIFIC SINGAPORE PTE. LTD.—See Daicel Corporation; *Int'l*, pg. 1919
POLYPLASTICS CHINA LTD.—See Daicel Corporation; *Int'l*, pg. 1919
POLYPLASTICS CO., LTD.—See Daicel Corporation; *Int'l*, pg. 1919
POLYPLASTICS EUROPE GMBH—See Daicel Corporation; *Int'l*, pg. 1920
POLYPLASTICS KOREA LTD.—See Daicel Corporation; *Int'l*, pg. 1920
POLYPLASTICS MARKETING MEXICO, S.A. DE C.V.—See Daicel Corporation; *Int'l*, pg. 1920
POLYPLASTICS (NANTONG) LTD.—See Daicel Corporation; *Int'l*, pg. 1920
POLYPLASTICS TAIWAN CO., LTD.—See Daicel Corporation; *Int'l*, pg. 1920
POLYPLASTICS USA, INC.—See Daicel Corporation; *Int'l*, pg. 1920
PRE CON INC.; *U.S. Private*, pg. 3243
PREFERE RESINS HOLDING GMBH—See One Rock Capital Partners, LLC; *U.S. Private*, pg. 3022
PRIME RESINS, INC.—See RPM International Inc.; *U.S. Public*, pg. 1820
PRIMEX PLASTICS LIMITED—See ICC Industries, Inc.; *U.S. Private*, pg. 2030
PRITT PRODUKTIONSGESELLSCHAFT GMBH—See Henkel AG & Co. KGaA; *Int'l*, pg. 3354
P.T. AICA INDONESIA—See AICA Kogyo Company, Limited; *Int'l*, pg. 229
P.T. AVIENT COLORANTS INDONESIA—See Avient Corporation; *U.S. Public*, pg. 248
PT. CBC PRIMA—See CBC Co., Ltd.; *Int'l*, pg. 1365
PT. CHANG CHUN DPN CHEMICAL INDUSTRY—See ChangChun Group; *Int'l*, pg. 1442
P.T. DONGSUNG JAKARTA—See Dongsung Chemical Co., Ltd.; *Int'l*, pg. 2170
PTFE POLAR PACKAGING MFG./SEALS APS—See Parker Hannifin Corporation; *U.S. Public*, pg. 1648
P.T. PARDIC JAYA CHEMICALS—See DIC Corporation; *Int'l*, pg. 2109
PUROLITE CORPORATION—See Ecolab Inc.; *U.S. Public*, pg. 716
PUYLAERT DESIGNS OF THE TIME N.V.—See Dainichiseika Color & Chemicals Mfg. Co., Ltd.; *Int'l*, pg. 1939
QUANTUM COMPOSITES INC.—See Premix, Inc.; *U.S. Private*, pg. 3252
RAPAC INC.—See MSD Capital, L.P.; *U.S. Private*, pg. 2807
RASCHIG GMBH—See PMC Capital Partners, LLC; *U.S. Private*, pg. 3217
RECYCLED POLYMERIC MATERIALS, INC.—See Diversified Chemical Technologies Inc.; *U.S. Private*, pg. 1241
REDI S.P.A.—See Aliaxis S.A./N.V.; *Int'l*, pg. 325
REICHHOLD AS—See Reichhold, Inc.; *U.S. Private*, pg. 3391
REICHHOLD, INC.; *U.S. Private*, pg. 3390
REICHHOLD LIMITED—See Reichhold, Inc.; *U.S. Private*, pg. 3391
REICHHOLD UK LIMITED—See Reichhold, Inc.; *U.S. Private*, pg. 3391
RESIMON, C.A.—See Corimon, C.A.; *Int'l*, pg. 1801
RESINALL CORP; *U.S. Private*, pg. 3406
RESIRENE, S.A. DE C.V.—See Grupo Kuo, S.A.B. de C.V.; *Int'l*, pg. 3131
REVOLUTION SUSTAINABLE SOLUTIONS, LLC—See Arsenal Capital Management LP; *U.S. Private*, pg. 339
RHETECH LLC—See HEXPOL AB; *Int'l*, pg. 3372
RHETECH THERMOCOLOR LLC—See HEXPOL AB; *Int'l*, pg. 3372
RIONIL COMPOSTOS VINILCOS LTDA—See Arkema S.A.; *Int'l*, pg. 571
ROGERS CORP. - HIGH PERFORMANCE FOAMS DIVISION - BISCO SILICONES—See Rogers Corporation; *U.S. Public*, pg. 1808
ROGERS CORP. - HIGH PERFORMANCE FOAMS DIVISION - COMPOSITE MATERIALS—See Rogers Corporation; *U.S. Public*, pg. 1808
ROGERS CORP. - HIGH PERFORMANCE FOAMS DIVISION - PORON URETHANES—See Rogers Corporation; *U.S. Public*, pg. 1808
ROGERS INOAC CORPORATION—See Rogers Corporation; *U.S. Public*, pg. 1808
ROGERS TECHNOLOGIES (SUZHOU) CO., LTD.—See Rogers Corporation; *U.S. Public*, pg. 1808
ROGERS TECHNOLOGY (SUZHOU) CO., LTD.—See Rogers Corporation; *U.S. Public*, pg. 1808
ROLF SCHMIDT INDUSTRI PLAST A/S—See CENTROTEC SE; *Int'l*, pg. 1414
RPC BEBO POLSKA SP. Z O.O.—See Berry Global Group, Inc; *U.S. Public*, pg. 324
RPC CONTAINERS LTD.—See Berry Global Group, Inc; *U.S. Public*, pg. 324
RPC PACKAGING KERKRADE BV—See Berry Global Group, Inc; *U.S. Public*, pg. 324
RPM PERFORMANCE COATINGS GROUP, INC.—See RPM International Inc.; *U.S. Public*, pg. 1818
RTP COMPANY; *U.S. Private*, pg. 3498

325211 — PLASTICS MATERIAL A...

RUNELANDHS FORSALJNINGS AB—See Brady Corporation; *U.S. Public*, pg. 379
SAINT-GOBAIN PERFORMANCE PLASTICS COLOGNE GMBH—See Compagnie de Saint-Gobain SA; *Int'l*, pg. 1732
SAINT-GOBAIN PERFORMANCE PLASTICS VERNERET—See Compagnie de Saint-Gobain SA; *Int'l*, pg. 1735
SAMDONG INDUSTRY CO., LTD.—See Chonbang Co., Ltd.; *Int'l*, pg. 1578
SANTROL (YIXING) PROPPANT CO. LTD—See Covia Holdings Corporation; *U.S. Private*, pg. 1072
SCANDIA PLASTICS—See Odyssey Investment Partners, LLC; *U.S. Private*, pg. 2995
SCHNELLER ASIA PTE. LTD.—See TransDigm Group Incorporated; *U.S. Public*, pg. 2183
SCHNELLER S.A.R.L.—See TransDigm Group Incorporated; *U.S. Public*, pg. 2183
THE SDI DIVESTITURE CORPORATION—See Bayer Aktiengesellschaft; *Int'l*, pg. 902
S.E.R. PLAST S.R.L.—See ACEA S.p.A.; *Int'l*, pg. 95
SETUP PERFORMANCE SAS—See BASF SE; *Int'l*, pg. 885
SHANDONG HUAXIA SHENZHOU NEW MATERIALS CO., LTD.—See Dongyue Group Limited; *Int'l*, pg. 2172
SHANGHAI BASF POLYURETHANE CO., LTD.—See BASF SE; *Int'l*, pg. 877
SHANGHAI DAICEL POLYMERS, LTD.—See Daicel Corporation; *Int'l*, pg. 1920
SHANGHAI HENKEL CHEMICALS CO., LTD.—See Henkel AG & Co. KGaA; *Int'l*, pg. 3349
SHANGHAI MITSUI PLASTIC COMPOUNDS LTD.—See Dainichiseika Color & Chemicals Mfg. Co., Ltd.; *Int'l*, pg. 1939
SHANGHAI XIN YU RESIN CO., LTD.—See Headway Advanced Materials, Inc.; *Int'l*, pg. 3302
SIAM CHEMICAL INDUSTRY CO., LTD.—See DIC Corporation; *Int'l*, pg. 2109
SI GROUP-SWITZERLAND—See SK Capital Partners, LP; *U.S. Private*, pg. 3680
SINOPEC SHANGHAI PETROCHEMICAL COMPANY LIMITED—See China Petrochemical Corporation; *Int'l*, pg. 1539
SO.F.TER BRASIL COMPOSTOS TERMOPLASTICOS LTDA.—See Celanese Corporation; *U.S. Public*, pg. 465
SOLUTIA INC.—See Eastman Chemical Company; *U.S. Public*, pg. 705
SOUTHERN POLYMER, INC.—See Audia International, Inc.; *U.S. Private*, pg. 390
SPARTECH - CAPE GIRARDEAU—See The Jordan Company, L.P.; *U.S. Private*, pg. 4062
SPARTECH - GOODYEAR—See The Jordan Company, L.P.; *U.S. Private*, pg. 4062
SPARTECH - SALISBURY—See The Jordan Company, L.P.; *U.S. Private*, pg. 4062
SPARTECH - TOWNSEND—See The Jordan Company, L.P.; *U.S. Private*, pg. 4062
SPECIALTY POLYMERS INC.; *U.S. Private*, pg. 3750
SPILLTECH ENVIRONMENTAL INC—See New Pendulum Corporation; *U.S. Private*, pg. 2905
STARRFOAM MANUFACTURING INC.; *U.S. Private*, pg. 3788
STELLANA DEUTSCHLAND GMBH—See HEXPOL AB; *Int'l*, pg. 3372
STYRON DEUTSCHLAND ANLAGENGESELLSCHAFT MBH—See Bain Capital, LP; *U.S. Private*, pg. 449
STYRON DEUTSCHLAND GMBH—See Bain Capital, LP; *U.S. Private*, pg. 449
STYRON DO BRASIL COMERCIO DE PRODUTOS QUIMICOS LTDA.—See Bain Capital, LP; *U.S. Private*, pg. 449
STYRON SVERIGE AB—See Bain Capital, LP; *U.S. Private*, pg. 449
SUMIKA BAYER URETHANE CO., LTD.—See Bayer Aktiengesellschaft; *Int'l*, pg. 910
SUMITOMO BAKELITE (TAIWAN) CORPORATION LIMITED—See ChangChun Group; *Int'l*, pg. 1442
SUN PLASTECH INC.—See Asahi Kasei Corporation; *Int'l*, pg. 597
SUZHOU HUIYE CHEMICAL & LIGHT INDUSTRY CO., LTD.—See Dynamic Colours Limited; *Int'l*, pg. 2240
TAI CHIN CHEMICAL INDUSTRY CO., LTD.—See Dainichiseika Color & Chemicals Mfg. Co., Ltd.; *Int'l*, pg. 1939
TAIWAN AICA KOGYO CO., LTD.—See AICA Kogyo Company, Limited; *Int'l*, pg. 229
T-CBC (TAIWAN) CO., LTD.—See CBC Co., Ltd.; *Int'l*, pg. 1365
TECHMER PM, LLC; *U.S. Private*, pg. 3952
TECHNETICS GROUP—See Enpro Inc.; *U.S. Public*, pg. 775
TECHNICAL POLYMERS, LLC—See Domo NV; *Int'l*, pg. 2162
TECNOELASTOMERI S.R.L.—See Huntsman Corporation; *U.S. Public*, pg. 1075
TEKNOR APEX ASIA PACIFIC PTE. LTD.—See Teknor Apex Company; *U.S. Private*, pg. 3958
TEKNOR APEX COMPANY - THERMOPLASTIC ELASTOMER DIVISION—See Teknor Apex Company; *U.S. Private*, pg. 3958
TEKNOR APEX ELASTOMERS, INC.—See Teknor Apex Company; *U.S. Private*, pg. 3958
TEKNOR APEX (SUZHOU) ADVANCED POLYMER COMPOUNDS CO. PTE LTD.—See Teknor Apex Company; *U.S. Private*, pg. 3958
TEKNOR APEX VERMONT COMPANY—See Teknor Apex Company; *U.S. Private*, pg. 3959
TEKNOR COLOR CO.—See Teknor Apex Company; *U.S. Private*, pg. 3959
TELKO ROMANIA SRL—See Aspo Oyj; *Int'l*, pg. 631
TELKO SOLUTION LLC—See Aspo Oyj; *Int'l*, pg. 631
TELKO SWEDEN AB—See Aspo Oyj; *Int'l*, pg. 631
TELKO UAB—See Aspo Oyj; *Int'l*, pg. 631
TENNESSEE EASTMAN DIVISION—See Eastman Chemical Company; *U.S. Public*, pg. 706
TENSAR INTERNATIONAL B.V.—See Commercial Metals Company; *U.S. Public*, pg. 547
TENSAR INTERNATIONAL SARL—See Commercial Metals Company; *U.S. Public*, pg. 547
TERRA FRUCTI S.A.S.—See CBC Co., Ltd.; *Int'l*, pg. 1365
TEXMARK CHEMICALS, INC.—See Chemical Exchange Industries, Inc.; *U.S. Private*, pg. 871
THAI GCI RESITOP CO., LTD.—See Gun Ei Chemical Industry Co., Ltd.; *Int'l*, pg. 3183
THERMO FISHER SCIENTIFIC—See Thermo Fisher Scientific Inc.; *U.S. Public*, pg. 2153
THERMOFORM ENGINEERED QUALITY LLC—See Sonoco Products Company; *U.S. Public*, pg. 1909
THERMOPLASTIC SERVICES INC.—See Netrix LLC; *U.S. Private*, pg. 2888
TJM PRODUCTS PTY. LTD.—See Eastern Polymer Group Public Company Limited; *Int'l*, pg. 2273
TOHOKU U-LOID INDUSTRY CO., LTD.—See Gun Ei Chemical Industry Co., Ltd.; *Int'l*, pg. 3183
TONE ZOOM INDUSTRY CO., LTD.—See Chung-Hsin Electric & Machinery Manufacturing Corp.; *Int'l*, pg. 1597
TOPAS ADVANCED POLYMERS GMBH—See Daicel Corporation; *Int'l*, pg. 1920
TOTAL SYSTEMS TECHNOLOGY INC.; *U.S. Private*, pg. 4191
TOYO STYRENE CO., LTD.—See Daicel Corporation; *Int'l*, pg. 1920
TRIMAX BUILDING PRODUCTS; *U.S. Private*, pg. 4232
TRINSEO EUROPE GMBH—See Bain Capital, LP; *U.S. Private*, pg. 450
TRINSEO NETHERLANDS B.V.—See Bain Capital, LP; *U.S. Private*, pg. 450
TRINSEO S.A.—See Bain Capital, LP; *U.S. Public*, pg. 449
TYGAVAC ADVANCED MATERIALS LTD.—See Airtech International Inc.; *U.S. Private*, pg. 142
UNIFI CENTRAL AMERICA, LTDA. DE CV—See Unifi, Inc.; *U.S. Public*, pg. 2226
UNION CARBIDE CORPORATION—See Dow Inc.; *U.S. Public*, pg. 686
UNIVERSAL ENVIRONMENTAL SERVICES, LLC—See Avista Oil AG; *Int'l*, pg. 745
USI CORPORATION - KAOHSIUNG PLANT—See Chun Yu Works & Co., Ltd.; *Int'l*, pg. 1596
VALLEY ROLLER COMPANY, INC.—See Berwind Corporation; *U.S. Private*, pg. 541
VERTEC POLYMERS, INC.—See Edgewater Capital Partners, L.P.; *U.S. Private*, pg. 1334
VESTOLIT GMBH—See Grupo Empresarial Kaluz S.A. de C.V.; *Int'l*, pg. 3128
VIANT MEDICAL, LLC; *U.S. Private*, pg. 4375
VICOM 2002 S.L.—See HEXPOL AB; *Int'l*, pg. 3373
VINNOLIT GMBH & CO. KG—See Westlake Corporation; *U.S. Public*, pg. 2360
VINNOLIT HILLHOUSE LTD.—See Westlake Corporation; *U.S. Public*, pg. 2360
WAVIN POLYFEMOS AS—See Bharti Enterprises Limited; *Int'l*, pg. 1013
WESTLAKE PETROCHEMICALS LLC—See Westlake Corporation; *U.S. Public*, pg. 2360
WESTLAKE POLYMERS LLC—See Westlake Corporation; *U.S. Public*, pg. 2360
WESTLAKE STYRENE LLC—See Westlake Corporation; *U.S. Public*, pg. 2360
WESTLAKE VINYLS, INC.—See Westlake Corporation; *U.S. Public*, pg. 2361
WEST PHARMACEUTICAL SERVICES ARGENTINA S.A.—See West Pharmaceutical Services, Inc.; *U.S. Public*, pg. 2353
WOODRUFF CORPORATION—See ICC Industries, Inc.; *U.S. Private*, pg. 2030
WUHAI GUANGYU CHEMICAL METALLURGY CO., LTD.—See Hongda Xingye Co., Ltd.; *Int'l*, pg. 3470
WUZHOU ARAKAWA CHEMICAL INDUSTRIES, LTD.—See Arakawa Chemical Industries, Ltd.; *Int'l*, pg. 535
YU CHENG MATERIALS CO., LTD.—See Headway Advanced Materials Inc.; *Int'l*, pg. 3302
ZHANGZHOU CHIMEI CHEMICAL CO., LTD.—See Chi Mei Group; *Int'l*, pg. 1475

325212 — SYNTHETIC RUBBER MANUFACTURING

ACRYLIC DESIGN ASSOCIATES—See Taylor Corporation; *U.S. Private*, pg. 3938
ALL SERV INDUSTRIAL LLC.—See HCI Equity Management, L.P.; *U.S. Private*, pg. 1889
ALPHAKAT GMBH; *Int'l*, pg. 370
AMERICAN SYNTHETIC RUBBER COMPANY—See Compagnie Generale des Etablissements Michelin SCA; *Int'l*, pg. 1743
APCOTEX INDUSTRIES LIMITED; *Int'l*, pg. 508
ARMSTRONG RUBBER & CHEMICAL PRODUCTS COMPANY LIMITED—See Armstrong Industrial Corporation Ltd.; *Int'l*, pg. 575
ASAHI KASEI SYNTHETIC RUBBER SINGAPORE PTE. LTD.—See Asahi Kasei Corporation; *Int'l*, pg. 596
BRIDGESTONE APM COMPANY—See Bridgestone Corporation; *Int'l*, pg. 1156
CHASE-WALTON ELASTOMERS INC.; *U.S. Private*, pg. 860
CPR GOMU INDUSTRIAL PUBLIC COMPANY LIMITED; *Int'l*, pg. 1826
CRY -TECHINC; *U.S. Private*, pg. 1114
C.W. MACKIE PLC; *Int'l*, pg. 1244
DENKA PERFORMANCE ELASTOMER LLC—See Denki Company Limited; *Int'l*, pg. 2027
DICAR, INC.; *U.S. Private*, pg. 1225
DMK MEXICO, S.A. DE C.V.—See Palmer International, Inc.; *U.S. Private*, pg. 3081
EAST WEST COPOLYMER LLC; *U.S. Private*, pg. 1318
FIRESTONE POLYMERS, LLC - LAKE CHARLES PLANT—See Bridgestone Corporation; *Int'l*, pg. 1157
FIRESTONE POLYMERS, LLC - ORANGE PLANT—See Bridgestone Corporation; *Int'l*, pg. 1157
FREUDENBERG-NOK INC.—See Freudenberg SE; *Int'l*, pg. 2788
GACO WESTERN INC.—See Bridgestone Corporation; *Int'l*, pg. 1157
GURIT (UK) LIMITED—See Gurit Holding AG; *Int'l*, pg. 3188
HEXTAR RUBBER SDN. BHD.—See Hextar Global Berhad; *Int'l*, pg. 3373
HITACHI ZOSEN YANGLING CO., LTD.—See Hitachi Zosen Corporation; *Int'l*, pg. 3411
HRS CO., LTD. - ASAN FACTORY—See HRS Co., Ltd.; *Int'l*, pg. 3502
HRS CO., LTD. - PYEONGTAEK FACTORY—See HRS Co., Ltd.; *Int'l*, pg. 3502
HRS CO., LTD.; *Int'l*, pg. 3502
HRS CO., LTD. - SUZHOU FACTORY—See HRS Co., Ltd.; *Int'l*, pg. 3502
HYLOAD, INC.—See IKO Enterprises Ltd.; *Int'l*, pg. 3612
INTERNATIONAL RUBBER CO. LLC—See Dubai Investments PJSC; *Int'l*, pg. 2219
ISP SYNTHETIC ELASTOMERS LLC—See Ashland Inc.; *U.S. Public*, pg. 213
JAPAN ELASTOMER CO., LTD.—See Asahi Kasei Corporation; *Int'l*, pg. 596
KAIMANN GMBH—See Compagnie de Saint-Gobain SA; *Int'l*, pg. 1723
KENT ELASTOMER PRODUCTS, INC.—See Meridian Industries, Inc.; *U.S. Private*, pg. 2673
KLEEN-TEX SOUTH AFRICA (PTY) LTD.—See Kleen-Tex Industries, Inc.; *U.S. Private*, pg. 2318
LMC TYRE & RUBBER LIMITED—See GlobalData Plc; *Int'l*, pg. 3003
MEREDIAN HOLDINGS GROUP INC.—See Danimer Scientific, Inc.; *U.S. Public*, pg. 632
MESGO SPA—See HEXPOL AB; *Int'l*, pg. 3372
NOCIL LIMITED—See Arvind Mafatlal Group; *Int'l*, pg. 587
OMNICON VERWALTUNGS GMBH—See Starwood Capital Group Global I, LLC; *U.S. Private*, pg. 3789
POLYTEK DEVELOPMENT CORP.—See Arsenal Capital Management LP; *U.S. Private*, pg. 339
PRECISION ASSOCIATES INC.; *U.S. Private*, pg. 3244
ROGERS CORPORATION - DELAWARE FACILITY—See Rogers Corporation; *U.S. Public*, pg. 1808
RUBBER COMPOUNDING HOLLAND B.V.—See Elgi Rubber Company Limited; *Int'l*, pg. 2360
SAINT-GOBAIN PERFORMANCE PLASTICS KONTICH NV—See Compagnie de Saint-Gobain SA; *Int'l*, pg. 1735
SHANXI SYNTHETIC RUBBER GROUP CO LTD—See Bluestar Adisseo Company Limited; *Int'l*, pg. 1074
STYRON FRANCE SAS—See Bain Capital, LP; *U.S. Private*, pg. 449
STYRON HOLDINGS ASIA PTE LTD.—See Bain Capital, LP; *U.S. Private*, pg. 449
STYRON (HONG KONG) LIMITED—See Bain Capital, LP; *U.S. Private*, pg. 449
STYRON ITALIA S.R.L.—See Bain Capital, LP; *U.S. Private*, pg. 449
STYRON KOREA LTD.—See Bain Capital, LP; *U.S. Private*, pg. 449
STYRON SPAIN, S.L.—See Bain Capital, LP; *U.S. Private*, pg. 449
TAIWAN STYRON LIMITED—See Bain Capital, LP; *U.S. Private*, pg. 450
TECHNO RUBBER COMPANY—See Dubai Investments PJSC; *Int'l*, pg. 2219
TRINSEO JAPAN Y.K.—See Bain Capital, LP; *U.S. Private*, pg. 450

N.A.I.C.S. INDEX

YUNHONG GREEN CTI LTD.; *U.S. Public*, pg. 2400

325220 — ARTIFICIAL AND SYNTHETIC FIBERS AND FILAMENTS MANUFACTURING

ACEGREEN ECO-MATERIAL TECHNOLOGY CO., LTD.—See Acelon Chemicals & Fiber Corporation; *Int'l*, pg. 98
ACELON CHEMICALS & FIBER CORPORATION; *Int'l*, pg. 98
ACETATE PRODUCTS LTD.—See CVC Capital Partners SICAV-FIS S.A.; *Int'l*, pg. 1886
ACORDIS BV—See CVC Capital Partners SICAV-FIS S.A.; *Int'l*, pg. 1886
ACRY FAB INC.—See The Vollrath Company LLC; *U.S. Private*, pg. 4132
ADVANCED FIBER, LLC—See Installed Building Products, Inc.; *U.S. Public*, pg. 1132
ALTIME SPORT & LEISURE GMBH—See Cocreation Grass Co., Ltd.; *Int'l*, pg. 1687
AMES CORPORATION—See Grafoid, Inc.; *Int'l*, pg. 3050
APEX ENTERPRISES LIMITED—See Apex Footwear Limited; *Int'l*, pg. 509
ARTIFICIAL TURF SUPPLY LLC—See Blackford Capital LLC; *U.S. Private*, pg. 574
ASOTA GMBH—See Duroc AB; *Int'l*, pg. 2230
BARODA RAYON CORP LTD.; *Int'l*, pg. 866
BAYER SA—See Bayer Aktiengesellschaft; *Int'l*, pg. 906
BEAUFLOR USA, LLC—See Beaulieu International Group NV; *Int'l*, pg. 934
BONTEX, INC.; *U.S. Public*, pg. 368
BUFFALO BATT & FELT, LLC—See Leggett & Platt, Incorporated; *U.S. Public*, pg. 1301
CFF BELGIUM N.V.—See CFF GmbH & Co. KG; *Int'l*, pg. 1429
CFF GMBH & CO. KG; *Int'l*, pg. 1429
CHENGXIN LITHIUM GROUP CO., LTD.; *Int'l*, pg. 1470
CHINA TAIFENG BEDDINGS HOLDINGS LIMITED; *Int'l*, pg. 1557
CHTC HELON CO., LTD.; *Int'l*, pg. 1589
CONSOLIDATED FIBERS, INC.; *U.S. Private*, pg. 1020
CRAILAR TECHNOLOGIES INC.; *Int'l*, pg. 1827
CYDSA S.A. DE C.V. - ENVIRONMENTAL SERVICES DIVISION—See Cydsa S.A.B. de C.V.; *Int'l*, pg. 1895
DAK AMERICAS LLC—See ALFA, S.A.B. de C.V.; *Int'l*, pg. 313
DCM SHRIRAM INDUSTRIES LIMITED - RAYONS DIVISION—See DCM Shriram Industries Limited; *Int'l*, pg. 1992
DCM SHRIRAM INDUSTRIES LIMITED - SHRIRAM RAYONS WORKS—See DCM Shriram Industries Limited; *Int'l*, pg. 1992
DEWAN SALMAN FIBRE LIMITED; *Int'l*, pg. 2091
DOLAN GMBH—See Dralon GmbH; *Int'l*, pg. 2200
DONGGUAN SALIPT CO., LTD.—See ChangYuan Group Ltd.; *Int'l*, pg. 1444
DRALON GMBH; *Int'l*, pg. 2200
DU PONT-TORAY CO., LTD.—See DuPont de Nemours, Inc.; *U.S. Public*, pg. 692
DURAFIBER TECHNOLOGIES (DFT), INC. - SALISBURY PLANT—See Sun Capital Partners, Inc.; *U.S. Private*, pg. 3859
DURAFIBER TECHNOLOGIES (DFT), INC. - WINNSBORO PLANT—See Sun Capital Partners, Inc.; *U.S. Private*, pg. 3859
EASTMAN SHUANGWEI FIBERS COMPANY LIMITED—See Eastman Chemical Company; *U.S. Public*, pg. 705
E.I. DUPONT DE NEMOURS & CO.—See Corteva, Inc.; *U.S. Public*, pg. 584
FAIRFIELD PROCESSING CORP.; *U.S. Private*, pg. 1463
FIBER-LINE INTERNATIONAL B.V.—See Avient Corporation; *U.S. Public*, pg. 247
FIBER-LINE, LLC—See Avient Corporation; *U.S. Public*, pg. 247
FIBON AUSTRALIA PTY LTD—See Fibon Berhad; *Int'l*, pg. 2652
FIBRECHEM TECHNOLOGIES LIMITED; *Int'l*, pg. 2653
GARWARE SYNTHETICS LIMITED; *Int'l*, pg. 2887
GCH POLYMER MATERIAL (HONGKONG) CO. LIMITED—See GCH Technology Co., Ltd.; *Int'l*, pg. 2895
GLOTECH ELECTRONICS (SUZHOU) CORP.—See Glotech Industrial Corp.; *Int'l*, pg. 3011
GLOTECH TECHNICAL MATERIALS CORP.—See Glotech Industrial Corp.; *Int'l*, pg. 3011
GUANGDONG HUATIE TONGDA HIGH-SPEED RAILWAY EQUIPMENT CO., LTD.; *Int'l*, pg. 3156
GUANGDONG MODERN HIGH-TECH FIBER CO., LTD.; *Int'l*, pg. 3158
GUANGDONG XINHUI MEIDA NYLON CO., LTD.; *Int'l*, pg. 3162
HEXCEL FIBERS INC.—See Hexcel Corporation; *U.S. Public*, pg. 1033
HONGWEI TECHNOLOGIES LIMITED; *Int'l*, pg. 3471
HUAFON CHEMICAL CO., LTD.; *Int'l*, pg. 3511
HUBEI XIANGYUAN NEW MATERIAL TECHNOLOGY, INC.; *Int'l*, pg. 3518

HUVIS CORPORATION; *Int'l*, pg. 3540
HYOSUNG CORPORATION PANAMA—See Hyosung Corporation; *Int'l*, pg. 3551
HYOSUNG DO BRAZIL—See Hyosung Corporation; *Int'l*, pg. 3551
HYOSUNG R&DB LABS—See Hyosung Corporation; *Int'l*, pg. 3551
HYOSUNG SPANDEX (JIAXING) CO., LTD.—See Hyosung Corporation; *Int'l*, pg. 3551
HYOSUNG TECHNICAL RESEARCH INSTITUTE—See Hyosung Corporation; *Int'l*, pg. 3551
IDEAL FIBRES & FABRICS WIELSBEKE NV—See Beaulieu International Group NV; *Int'l*, pg. 934
IFG DRAKE LTD.—See Duroc AB; *Int'l*, pg. 2230
INTERNATIONAL FIBER CORP.—See Arsenal Capital Management LP; *U.S. Private*, pg. 338
JANCO ENGINEERED PRODUCTS, LLC—See MacLean-Fogg Company; *U.S. Private*, pg. 2537
KINGSTON DISTRIBUTION CENTER—See Corteva, Inc.; *U.S. Public*, pg. 584
MAGENTA MASTER FIBERS S.R.L—See Avient Corporation; *U.S. Public*, pg. 247
MARTIN COLOR-FI, INC.—See Dimeling, Schreiber & Park; *U.S. Private*, pg. 1232
NINGBO DA-AN CHEMICAL INDUSTRIES CO., LTD.—See Daicel Corporation; *Int'l*, pg. 1919
NORTH THIN PLY TECHNOLOGY, SARL—See Windway Capital Corp.; *U.S. Private*, pg. 4539
POLYLOOM CORPORATION OF AMERICA—See ABN AMRO Group N.V.; *Int'l*, pg. 64
POLYLOOM CORPORATION OF AMERICA—See Gilde Buy Out Partners B.V.; *Int'l*, pg. 2974
PROPEX OPERATING COMPANY, LLC—See Wayzata Investment Partners LLC; *U.S. Private*, pg. 4461
SHANGHAI CHENGHE INTERNATIONAL CO. LTD.—See GCH Technology Co., Ltd.; *Int'l*, pg. 2895
SPEED LINE SOUTH AFRICA (PTY) LTD.—See Emak S.p.A.; *Int'l*, pg. 2373
SPEED SOUTH AMERICA S.P.A.—See Emak S.p.A.; *Int'l*, pg. 2373
TEN CATE THIOBAC BV—See ABN AMRO Group N.V.; *Int'l*, pg. 64
TEN CATE THIOBAC BV—See Gilde Buy Out Partners B.V.; *Int'l*, pg. 2974
TEN CATE THIOLON B.V.—See Crestview Partners, L.P.; *U.S. Private*, pg. 1099
TEN CATE THIOLON USA INC.—See Crestview Partners, L.P.; *U.S. Private*, pg. 1099
TESSUTICA NV—See Beaulieu International Group NV; *Int'l*, pg. 934
UNIVERSAL FIBERS SYSTEMS LLC; *U.S. Private*, pg. 4305
WALSRODER CASINGS GMBH—See Icahn Enterprises L.P.; *U.S. Public*, pg. 1085
WARP TECHNOLOGIES INC.; *U.S. Private*, pg. 4443
XI'AN HUIDA CHEMICAL INDUSTRIES CO., LTD.—See Daicel Corporation; *Int'l*, pg. 1920
ZIP-PAK INTERNATIONAL B.V.—See Illinois Tool Works Inc.; *U.S. Public*, pg. 1111

325311 — NITROGENOUS FERTILIZER MANUFACTURING

ABU QIR FERTILIZERS AND CHEMICAL INDUSTRIES CO.; *Int'l*, pg. 74
AGGRENE CORPORATION; *U.S. Private*, pg. 127
AGLUKON SPEZIALDUNGER GMBH & CO. KG; *Int'l*, pg. 211
AGROQUIMICOS Y SEMILLAS SA DE CV—See Element Solutions Inc.; *U.S. Public*, pg. 725
AG RX, INC.; *U.S. Private*, pg. 125
ALEX FERT CO. - S.A.E.—See Egyptian Kuwaiti Holding; *Int'l*, pg. 2327
AMAIZEINGLY GREEN VALUE PRODUCTS ULC—See Amaizeingly Green Products, L.P.; *Int'l*, pg. 408
ANCOM CROP CARE SDN. BHD.—See Ancom Nylex Berhad; *Int'l*, pg. 449
ANHUI HUAERTAI CHEMICAL CO., LTD.; *Int'l*, pg. 468
ANHUI SIERTE FERTILIZER INDUSTRY CO., LTD.; *Int'l*, pg. 469
APACHE NITROGEN PRODUCTS, INC.; *U.S. Private*, pg. 290
ASTRACHEM MOROCCO CO.—See ASTRA INDUSTRIAL GROUP COMPANY; *Int'l*, pg. 657
ASTRACHEM SAUDI ARABIA CO.—See ASTRA INDUSTRIAL GROUP COMPANY; *Int'l*, pg. 657
ASTRA INDUSTRIAL COMPLEX CO. FOR FERTILIZERS & AGROCHEMICALS—See ASTRA INDUSTRIAL GROUP COMPANY; *Int'l*, pg. 657
ASTRA INDUSTRIAL COMPLEX FOR FERTILIZERS & AGROCHEMICALS CO. LTD.—See Arab Supply & Trading Co.; *Int'l*, pg. 532
ASTRA INDUSTRIAL GROUP COMPANY; *Int'l*, pg. 657
AZOMURES S.A.—See Ameropa AG; *Int'l*, pg. 424
BASF PLANT SCIENCE GMBH—See BASF SE; *Int'l*, pg. 877
BEIJING TIANJUYUAN FERTILIZER CO., LTD.—See China Green Agriculture, Inc.; *Int'l*, pg. 1505

325311 — NITROGENOUS FERTILI...

BIONITROGEN HOLDINGS CORP.; *U.S. Public*, pg. 338
CF INDUSTRIES HOLDINGS, INC.; *U.S. Public*, pg. 477
CF INDUSTRIES, INC. - DONALDSONVILLE NITROGEN COMPLEX—See CF Industries Holdings, Inc.; *U.S. Public*, pg. 477
CF INDUSTRIES, INC.—See CF Industries Holdings, Inc.; *U.S. Public*, pg. 477
CF INDUSTRIES, INC. - WOODWARD PLANT—See CF Industries Holdings, Inc.; *U.S. Public*, pg. 477
CF INDUSTRIES, INC. - YAZOO CITY PLANT—See CF Industries Holdings, Inc.; *U.S. Public*, pg. 477
CF INDUSTRIES NITROGEN, LLC—See CF Industries Holdings, Inc.; *U.S. Public*, pg. 477
CHEROKEE NITROGEN HOLDINGS, INC.—See LSB Industries, Inc.; *U.S. Public*, pg. 1344
CHEROKEE NITROGEN LLC—See LSB Industries, Inc.; *U.S. Public*, pg. 1344
COMPAGNIE FINANCIERE ET DE PARTICIPATIONS ROULLIER SA; *Int'l*, pg. 1740
COMPO EXPERT ASIA PACIFIC SDN. BHD.—See Grupa Azoty S.A.; *Int'l*, pg. 3115
COMPO EXPERT BRASIL FERTILIZANTES LTDA.—See Grupa Azoty S.A.; *Int'l*, pg. 3115
COMPO EXPERT GMBH—See Grupa Azoty S.A.; *Int'l*, pg. 3115
COMPO EXPERT HELLAS S.A.—See Grupa Azoty S.A.; *Int'l*, pg. 3115
COMPO EXPERT ITALIA S.R.L.—See Grupa Azoty S.A.; *Int'l*, pg. 3115
COMPO EXPERT POLSKA SP. Z O.O.—See Grupa Azoty S.A.; *Int'l*, pg. 3115
COMPO EXPERT PORTUGAL, UNIPESSOAL LDA.—See Grupa Azoty S.A.; *Int'l*, pg. 3115
COMPO EXPERT SPAIN S.L.—See Grupa Azoty S.A.; *Int'l*, pg. 3115
COMPO EXPERT TECHN. (SHENZHEN) CO., LTD.—See Grupa Azoty S.A.; *Int'l*, pg. 3115
COMPO EXPERT UK LTD.—See Grupa Azoty S.A.; *Int'l*, pg. 3115
COMPO EXPERT USA & CANADA INC.—See Grupa Azoty S.A.; *Int'l*, pg. 3115
CONNOILS LLC; *U.S. Private*, pg. 1018
DAIKYO FERTILIZER CO., LTD.—See euglena Co., Ltd.; *Int'l*, pg. 2526
DONGBU ORGANIC FOODS—See Dongbu Group; *Int'l*, pg. 2166
EARTH2EARTH PROPRIETARY LIMITED—See Groupe Seche SAS; *Int'l*, pg. 3110
EL-DELTA COMPANY—See Chemical Industries Holding Company; *Int'l*, pg. 1461
EL DORADO NITRIC LLC—See LSB Industries, Inc.; *U.S. Public*, pg. 1344
ENZYME ENVIRONMENTAL SOLUTIONS, INC.; *U.S. Private*, pg. 1410
EUROCHEM AGRO GMBH—See EuroChem Mineral Chemical Company, OJSC; *Int'l*, pg. 2533
EUROCHEM AGRO HELLAS SA—See EuroChem Mineral Chemical Company, OJSC; *Int'l*, pg. 2533
EUROCHEM AGRO IBERIA, S.L.—See EuroChem Mineral Chemical Company, OJSC; *Int'l*, pg. 2533
FERTIGLOBE PLC—See Abu Dhabi National Oil Company; *Int'l*, pg. 73
FRIT INDUSTRIES INC.—See Frit Incorporated; *U.S. Private*, pg. 1612
GENERAL MATERIALS BIOCHEMISTRY FERTILIZER JOINT STOCK COMPANY; *Int'l*, pg. 2919
G.F.C. GREEN FIELDS CAPITAL LTD.; *Int'l*, pg. 2865
GIVNFLOW COMPANY LIMITED—See Greenyield Berhad; *Int'l*, pg. 3078
GK BIO INTERNATIONAL SDN. BHD.—See All Cosmos Bio-Tech Holding Corporation; *Int'l*, pg. 332
GOULDING CHEMICALS LIMITED—See ARYZTA AG; *Int'l*, pg. 589
GRASSLAND FERTILIZERS LIMITED—See Greencore Group plc; *Int'l*, pg. 3074
GREEN VALLEY CHEMICAL CORP.; *U.S. Private*, pg. 1774
GREEN VISION BIOTECHNOLOGY CORP.; *Int'l*, pg. 3073
GREENYIELD INDUSTRIES (M) SDN. BHD.—See Greenyield Berhad; *Int'l*, pg. 3078
GRUPA AZOTY ZAKIADY AZOTOWE KEDZIERZYN S. A.—See Grupa Azoty S.A.; *Int'l*, pg. 3115
GRUPA AZOTY ZAKIADY CHEMICZNE POLICE S. A.—See Grupa Azoty S.A.; *Int'l*, pg. 3116
GUJARAT NARMADA VALLEY FERTILIZERS & CHEMICALS LIMITED; *Int'l*, pg. 3176
HAIFA CHEMICALS LTD.—See Trans-Resources, Inc.; *U.S. Private*, pg. 4206
HANOI INVESTMENT GENERAL CORPORATION; *Int'l*, pg. 3258
HENAN XINLIANXIN BLUE ENVIRONMENTAL PROTECTION TECHNOLOGY CO., LTD.—See China XLX Fertiliser Ltd; *Int'l*, pg. 1563
HOA BINH URBAN ENVIRONMENTAL SERVICES JOINT STOCK COMPANY; *Int'l*, pg. 3435
JIUJIANG XINLIANXIN FERTILISER CO., LTD.—See China XLX Fertiliser Ltd; *Int'l*, pg. 1563
KAIHATSUHIRYOU CO., LTD.—See Electric Power Devel-

325311 — NITROGENOUS FERTILI...

opment Co., Ltd.; *Int'l*, pg. 2349
KELLOGG SUPPLY INC.; *U.S. Private*, pg. 2276
KEY BRAND FERTILIZER COMPANY LIMITED—See Buriram Sugar Public Company Limited; *Int'l*, pg. 1224
KOCH NITROGEN COMPANY, LLC—See Koch Industries, Inc.; *U.S. Private*, pg. 2333
KUGLER COMPANY - CULBERTSON PRODUCTION PLANT—See Kugler Company; *U.S. Private*, pg. 2356
KUGLER COMPANY - RAPID CITY PRODUCTION PLANT—See Kugler Company; *U.S. Private*, pg. 2356
KUGLER COMPANY - STERLING PRODUCTION PLANT—See Kugler Company; *U.S. Private*, pg. 2356
KUGLER COMPANY - ULYSSES PRODUCTION PLANT—See Kugler Company; *U.S. Private*, pg. 2356
KYNOCH FERTILIZERS (PTY) LTD.—See Farmsecure Holdings (Pty) Ltd.; *Int'l*, pg. 2620
LIFOSA AB—See EuroChem Mineral Chemical Company, OJSC; *Int'l*, pg. 2534
LOVOCHEMIE, A.S.—See Agrofert Holding, a.s.; *Int'l*, pg. 219
MARTIN RESOURCE MANAGEMENT CORP. - PAX DIVISION—See Martin Resource Management Corporation; *U.S. Private*, pg. 2596
MARTIN RESOURCES, INC.—See Martin Resource Management Corporation; *U.S. Private*, pg. 2596
THE MAURITIUS CHEMICAL & FERTILIZER INDUSTRY LIMITED—See Harel Mallac & Co. Ltd.; *Int'l*, pg. 3274
MIRACLE-GRO LAWN PRODUCTS, INC.—See The Scotts Miracle-Gro Company; *U.S. Public*, pg. 2127
NATIONAL FERTILIZER CORPORATION OF PAKISTAN (PRIVATE) LIMITED—See Agritech Limited; *Int'l*, pg. 218
NEW EEZY-GRO INC.—See The Andersons Incorporated; *U.S. Public*, pg. 2034
NOVOMOSKOVSKIY AZOT, OJSC—See EuroChem Mineral Chemical Company, OJSC; *Int'l*, pg. 2534
ORIENTAL CHEMICAL INDUSTRIAL CORP LTD.—See China National Chemical Corporation; *Int'l*, pg. 1527
ORIGIN ENTERPRISES PLC—See ARYZTA AG; *Int'l*, pg. 589
PAKARAB FERTILIZERS LIMITED—See Aisha Steel Mills Limited; *Int'l*, pg. 251
PIONEER AG-CHEM INC.; *U.S. Private*, pg. 3186
PK FERTILIZERS (SARAWAK) SDN. BHD.—See Hextar Industries Berhad; *Int'l*, pg. 3373
POINT LISAS NITROGEN LIMITED—See CF Industries Holdings, Inc.; *U.S. Public*, pg. 477
POINT LISAS NITROGEN LIMITED—See Koch Industries, Inc.; *U.S. Private*, pg. 2333
PRECHEZA, A.S.—See Agrofert Holding, a.s.; *Int'l*, pg. 219
PRO FARM OU—See Bioceres S.A.; *Int'l*, pg. 1036
PRO FARM TECHNOGIES COMERCIO DE INSUMOS AGRICOLAS DO BRAISIL LTDA—See Bioceres S.A.; *Int'l*, pg. 1036
PRO FARM TECHNOLOGIES OY—See Bioceres S.A.; *Int'l*, pg. 1036
REED & PERRINE SALES, INC.; *U.S. Private*, pg. 3382
RENTECH ENERGY MIDWEST CORPORATION—See Rentech, Inc.; *U.S. Private*, pg. 3400
ROD MCLELLAN COMPANY—See The Scotts Miracle-Gro Company; *U.S. Public*, pg. 2127
SABAH SOFTWOODS HYBRID FERTILISER SDN. BHD.—See All Cosmos Bio-Tech Holding Corporation; *Int'l*, pg. 332
THE SCOTTS COMPANY—See The Scotts Miracle-Gro Company; *U.S. Public*, pg. 2127
THE SCOTTS COMPANY—See The Scotts Miracle-Gro Company; *U.S. Public*, pg. 2127
THE SCOTTS COMPANY—See The Scotts Miracle-Gro Company; *U.S. Public*, pg. 2127
THE SCOTTS COMPANY—See The Scotts Miracle-Gro Company; *U.S. Public*, pg. 2127
THE SCOTTS COMPANY—See The Scotts Miracle-Gro Company; *U.S. Public*, pg. 2127
THE SCOTTS COMPANY—See The Scotts Miracle-Gro Company; *U.S. Public*, pg. 2127
SCOTTS-SIERRA HORTICULTURAL PRODUCTS CO.—See The Scotts Miracle-Gro Company; *U.S. Public*, pg. 2127
SCOTTS TEMECULA OPERATIONS, LLC—See The Scotts Miracle-Gro Company; *U.S. Public*, pg. 2127
SHAANXI TECHTEAM JINONG HUMIC ACID PRODUCT CO., LTD—See China Green Agriculture, Inc.; *Int'l*, pg. 1505
SLIR, S.L.—See Fertigama, S.L.; *Int'l*, pg. 2646
SMART CANNABIS CORP.; *U.S. Public*, pg. 1895
SMG GROWING MEDIA, INC.—See The Scotts Miracle-Gro Company; *U.S. Public*, pg. 2127
STOLLER COLOMBIA S.A.—See Corteva, Inc.; *U.S. Public*, pg. 584
STOLLER EUROPE, S.L.U.—See Corteva, Inc.; *U.S. Public*, pg. 584
SUPRA AGROCHEMIA SP. Z O.O.—See Grupa Azoty S.A.; *Int'l*, pg. 3116
SWISS FARMS PRODUCTS, INC—See The Scotts Miracle-Gro Company; *U.S. Public*, pg. 2127
SYNGENTA AG—See China National Chemical Corporation; *Int'l*, pg. 1529
TERRA NITROGEN COMPANY, L.P.—See CF Industries Holdings, Inc.; *U.S. Public*, pg. 477
TRAMMO AG—See Trammo, Inc.; *U.S. Private*, pg. 4204
TRANSAMMONIA AG—See Trammo, Inc.; *U.S. Private*, pg. 4205
TRANSAMMONIA B.V.—See Trammo, Inc.; *U.S. Private*, pg. 4205
TRANSAMMONIA LTD.—See Trammo, Inc.; *U.S. Private*, pg. 4205
TRANSAMMONIA S.A.R.L.—See Trammo, Inc.; *U.S. Private*, pg. 4205
TRANSAMMONIA (SHANGHAI) TRADING CO., LTD.—See Trammo, Inc.; *U.S. Private*, pg. 4205
VEGALAB, INC.; *U.S. Private*, pg. 4353
VEGALAB LLC—See Vegalab, Inc.; *U.S. Private*, pg. 4353
XINJIANG XINLIANXIN ENERGY CHEMICAL CO., LTD.—See China XLX Fertiliser Ltd; *Int'l*, pg. 1564
ZAKLADY AZOTOWE PULAWY S.A.—See Grupa Azoty S.A.; *Int'l*, pg. 3116
ZUARI AGRO CHEMICALS LIMITED—See Adventz Group; *Int'l*, pg. 167
ZUARI GLOBAL LTD.—See Adventz Group; *Int'l*, pg. 167

325312 — PHOSPHATIC FERTILIZER MANUFACTURING

AGROZZN, A.S.—See Agrofert Holding, a.s.; *Int'l*, pg. 218
ARAB POTASH COMPANY PLC; *Int'l*, pg. 531
ARIES AGRO LIMITED; *Int'l*, pg. 564
BOHRA INDUSTRIES LTD.; *Int'l*, pg. 1101
COG MARKETERS LTD.; *U.S. Private*, pg. 961
COPEBRAS LIMITADA—See Anglo American PLC; *Int'l*, pg. 461
CYTOZYME LABORATORIES, INC.—See AEA Investors LP; *U.S. Private*, pg. 116
DCM SHRIRAM LIMITED; *Int'l*, pg. 1992
DULANY INDUSTRIES INC.; *U.S. Private*, pg. 1286
DUSLO, A.S.—See Agrofert Holding, a.s.; *Int'l*, pg. 219
ELEMENTAL ALTUS ROYALTIES CORP.; *Int'l*, pg. 2358
EUROCHEM - BELORECHENSKIE MINUDOBRENIA, LLC—See EuroChem Mineral Chemical Company, OJSC; *Int'l*, pg. 2533
FAUJI FERTILIZER BIN QASIM LIMITED—See Fauji Foundation; *Int'l*, pg. 2623
FERTOZ LTD.; *Int'l*, pg. 2646
GROWERS FERTILIZER CORPORATION; *U.S. Private*, pg. 1795
GUANGXI HECHI CHEMICAL CO., LTD.—See China National Chemical Corporation; *Int'l*, pg. 1527
GUIZHOU CHANHEN CHEMICAL CORPORATION; *Int'l*, pg. 3174
HAYLEYS AGRO FERTILIZERS (PVT) LTD.—See Hayleys PLC; *Int'l*, pg. 3292
HAZARA PHOSPHATE FERTILIZERS (PRIVATE) LIMITED—See Azgard Nine Limited; *Int'l*, pg. 778
HOWARD FERTILIZER COMPANY INC.; *U.S. Private*, pg. 1994
HUBEI FORBON TECHNOLOGY CO., LTD.; *Int'l*, pg. 3517
HUBEI YIHUA CHEMICAL INDUSTRY CO., LTD.; *Int'l*, pg. 3518
IHO-AGRO INTERNATIONAL, INC.; *Int'l*, pg. 3607
IMPACT FERTILISERS PTY LTD—See Ameropa AG; *Int'l*, pg. 424
ITAFOS; *U.S. Public*, pg. 1175
ITRONICS METALLURGICAL, INC.—See Itronics Inc.; *U.S. Public*, pg. 1176
J.R. SIMPLOT COMPANY, AGRI BUSINESS—See J.R. Simplot Company; *U.S. Private*, pg. 2170
MALAYSIAN PHOSPHATE ADDITIVES (SARAWAK) SDN. BHD.—See Cahya Mata Sarawak Berhad; *Int'l*, pg. 1251
THE MOSAIC COMPANY—See The Mosaic Company; *U.S. Public*, pg. 2116
THE MOSAIC COMPANY—See The Mosaic Company; *U.S. Public*, pg. 2116
MOSAIC FERTILIZANTES P&K S.A.—See The Mosaic Company; *U.S. Public*, pg. 2116
MOSAIC FERTILIZER, LLC—See The Mosaic Company; *U.S. Public*, pg. 2116
MOSAIC GLOBAL HOLDINGS INC.—See The Mosaic Company; *U.S. Public*, pg. 2116
NICHII GREEN FARM COMPANY—See Bain Capital, LP; *U.S. Private*, pg. 442
ORGANIC PLANT HEALTH, INC.; *U.S. Private*, pg. 3041
OXBOW SULPHUR CANADA ULC—See H.J. Baker & Bro., Inc.; *U.S. Private*, pg. 1834
OXBOW SULPHUR & FERTILISER (BRAZIL) LTDA—See Oxbow Corporation; *U.S. Private*, pg. 3056
OXBOW SULPHUR & FERTILISER (SINGAPORE) PTE LTD—See Oxbow Corporation; *U.S. Private*, pg. 3056
PARADEEP PHOSPHATES LTD—See Adventz Group; *Int'l*, pg. 167
PHOSPHORIT INDUSTRIAL GROUP, LLC—See EuroChem Mineral Chemical Company, OJSC; *Int'l*, pg. 2534
PLANTABBS PRODUCTS COMPANY—See Tango Industries Ltd.; *U.S. Private*, pg. 3931
SEAGATE HANDLING INC—See Dulany Industries Inc.; *U.S. Private*, pg. 1286
SIMPLOT PARTNERS—See J.R. Simplot Company; *U.S. Private*, pg. 2171
SIMPLOT PHOSPHATES, LLC—See J.R. Simplot Company; *U.S. Private*, pg. 2171
SUN BIOMASS, INC.; *U.S. Private*, pg. 3858
TANGO INDUSTRIES LTD.; *U.S. Private*, pg. 3931
TIMAC AGRO INTERNATIONAL SAS—See Compagnie Financiere et de Participations Roullier SA; *Int'l*, pg. 1740
TSOU SEEN CHEMICAL INDUSTRIES CORPORATION—See China Petrochemical Development Corp.; *Int'l*, pg. 1540
TWIN STATE INC.; *U.S. Private*, pg. 4266
ZUARI FERTILISERS & CHEMICALS LIMITED—See Adventz Group; *Int'l*, pg. 167

325314 — FERTILIZER (MIXING ONLY) MANUFACTURING

AGRICO CANADA LIMITED; *Int'l*, pg. 216
AGRITECH LIMITED; *Int'l*, pg. 218
AGRO-100 LTEE; *Int'l*, pg. 218
ALL COSMOS BIO-TECH HOLDING CORPORATION; *Int'l*, pg. 331
AMERICAN PLANT FOOD CORP.; *U.S. Private*, pg. 243
AMEROPA GRAINS SA; *Int'l*, pg. 424
THE ANDERSONS, SOUTHERN REGION—See The Andersons Incorporated; *U.S. Public*, pg. 2034
ANHUI LIUGUO CHEMICAL CO., LTD.; *Int'l*, pg. 469
ASAHI INDUSTRIES CO., LTD. - CHIBA PLANT—See Godo Steel, Ltd.; *Int'l*, pg. 3020
ASAHI INDUSTRIES CO., LTD. - KANSAI PLANT—See Godo Steel, Ltd.; *Int'l*, pg. 3020
BANDIRMA GUBRE FABRIKALARI A.S.; *Int'l*, pg. 830
BAYER CROPSCIENCE (PORTUGAL) PRODUTOS PARA A AGRICULTURA, LDA.—See Bayer Aktiengesellschaft; *Int'l*, pg. 903
BHARAT AGRI FERT & REALTY LIMITED; *Int'l*, pg. 1010
BIOLCHIM S.P.A.—See Chequers SA; *Int'l*, pg. 1471
BIOLCHIM S.P.A.—See Neuberger Berman Group LLC; *U.S. Private*, pg. 2890
BONUS CROP FERTILIZER, INC.; *U.S. Private*, pg. 615
BRANDT CONSOLIDATED, INC.; *U.S. Private*, pg. 638
CAPRO CORP.; *Int'l*, pg. 1317
CENTRAL CHEMICAL CO., LTD.—See Central Glass Co., Ltd.; *Int'l*, pg. 1406
CENTRAL KASEI CHEMICAL CO., LTD.—See Central Glass Co., Ltd.; *Int'l*, pg. 1407
CENTURY SUNSHINE GROUP HOLDINGS LIMITED; *Int'l*, pg. 1419
CHEMINOVA AGROQUIMICA S.A. DE C.V.—See FMC Corporation; *U.S. Public*, pg. 861
CHINA ENVIRONMENTAL RESOURCES GROUP LIMITED; *Int'l*, pg. 1500
CHINA GREEN AGRICULTURE, INC.; *Int'l*, pg. 1505
CHINA XLX FERTILISER LTD; *Int'l*, pg. 1563
CHOBI COMPANY LIMITED; *Int'l*, pg. 1576
CLINTON NURSERY PRODUCTS INC.; *U.S. Private*, pg. 945
COASTAL AGROBUSINESS INC.; *U.S. Private*, pg. 955
COMPANIA AGROPECUARIA COPEVAL S.A.; *Int'l*, pg. 1748
COMPO EXPERT ARGENTINA SRL—See Grupa Azoty S.A.; *Int'l*, pg. 3115
COMPO EXPERT AUSTRIA GMBH—See Grupa Azoty S.A.; *Int'l*, pg. 3115
COMPO EXPERT BENELUX N. V.—See Grupa Azoty S.A.; *Int'l*, pg. 3115
COMPO EXPERT CHILE FERTILIZANTES LTDA.—See Grupa Azoty S.A.; *Int'l*, pg. 3115
COMPO EXPERT FRANCE SAS—See Grupa Azoty S.A.; *Int'l*, pg. 3115
COMPO EXPERT INDIA PRIVATE LIMITED—See Grupa Azoty S.A.; *Int'l*, pg. 3115
COMPO EXPERT MEXICO S. A. DE C. V.—See Grupa Azoty S.A.; *Int'l*, pg. 3115
COMPO EXPERT SOUTH AFRICA (PTY) LTD.—See Grupa Azoty S.A.; *Int'l*, pg. 3115
COMPO EXPERT TURKIYE TARIM SAN.VE TIC. LTD.—See Grupa Azoty S.A.; *Int'l*, pg. 3115
CONSUMERS COOP ASSOCIATION LITCHFIELD; *U.S. Private*, pg. 1026
CREATIVE SERVICES, INC.; *U.S. Private*, pg. 1090
DAWOOD HERCULES CORPORATION LIMITED—See Dawood Corporation (Pvt.) Ltd.; *Int'l*, pg. 1984
EGE GUBRE SANAYI A.S.; *Int'l*, pg. 2322
EL NASR COMPANY FOR FERTILIZERS & CHEMICAL INDUSTRIES—See Chemical Industries Holding Company; *Int'l*, pg. 1461
ENGRO CORPORATION LIMITED; *Int'l*, pg. 2435
ENGRO FERTILIZERS LIMITED—See Engro Corporation Limited; *Int'l*, pg. 2435
EUROCHEM ANTWERPEN NV—See EuroChem Mineral Chemical Company, OJSC; *Int'l*, pg. 2533
EVERGREEN GARDEN CARE (UK) LTD.—See Exponent Private Equity LLP; *Int'l*, pg. 2590
FARMERS COOPERATIVE, INC.; *U.S. Private*, pg. 1477
FARMWAY CO-OP INC. - BELOIT FERTILIZER

N.A.I.C.S. INDEX

325320 — PESTICIDE AND OTHER...

PLANT—See Farmway Co-Op Inc.; *U.S. Private*, pg. 1480
FARMWAY CO-OP INC. - NORKAN PLANT—See Farmway Co-Op Inc.; *U.S. Private*, pg. 1480
FAUJI FERTILIZER COMPANY LIMITED—See Fauji Foundation; *Int'l*, pg. 2623
FERTILIZER COMPANY OF ARIZONA; *U.S. Private*, pg. 1499
GOOD EARTH CANADA LIMITED—See Good Earth, Inc.; *U.S. Private*, pg. 1738
GREENLEAF LLC—See Ford Motor Company; *U.S. Public*, pg. 866
GUBRE FABRIKALARI T.A.S.; *Int'l*, pg. 3171
GUJARAT STATE FERTILIZERS & CHEMICALS LTD.; *Int'l*, pg. 3177
HARRELLS INC.; *U.S. Private*, pg. 1868
HEXTAR FERTILIZERS SDN. BHD.—See Hextar Holdings Sdn. Bhd.; *Int'l*, pg. 3373
H.J. BAKER & BRO., INC. - SULPHUR PLANT—See H.J. Baker & Bro., Inc.; *U.S. Private*, pg. 1834
HOWARD JOHNSON'S ENTERPRISES INC.; *U.S. Private*, pg. 1995
HYOSUNG ONB CO, LTD - ASAN FACTORY—See Hyosung ONB Co, Ltd; *Int'l*, pg. 3552
HYOSUNG ONB CO, LTD - CHEONGDO FACTORY—See Hyosung ONB Co, Ltd; *Int'l*, pg. 3552
HYOSUNG ONB CO, LTD - EUISUNG FACTORY—See Hyosung ONB Co, Ltd; *Int'l*, pg. 3552
HYOSUNG ONB CO, LTD - HAMPYEONG FACTORY—See Hyosung ONB Co, Ltd; *Int'l*, pg. 3552
HYOSUNG ONB CO, LTD; *Int'l*, pg. 3552
HYOSUNG ONB CO, LTD - SRI LANKA FACTORY—See Hyosung ONB Co, Ltd; *Int'l*, pg. 3552
INNER MONGOLIA LIANFENG RARE EARTH CHEMICAL INSTITUTE CO., LTD.—See Hongda Xingye Co., Ltd.; *Int'l*, pg. 3470
INNER MONGOLIA MENGHUA HAIBOWAN POWER GENERATION CO., LTD.—See Hongda Xingye Co., Ltd.; *Int'l*, pg. 3470
INNER MONGOLIA ZHONGKE EQUIPMENT CO., LTD.—See Hongda Xingye Co., Ltd.; *Int'l*, pg. 3470
INTREPID POTASH, INC.; *U.S. Public*, pg. 1159
JCAM AGRI CO., LTD.—See Asahi Kasei Corporation; *Int'l*, pg. 596
JH BIOTECH, INC.; *U.S. Private*, pg. 2207
KIRBY AGRI INC.; *U.S. Private*, pg. 2314
KIRBY AGRI SERVICES—See Kirby Agri Inc.; *U.S. Private*, pg. 2314
KIWA BIO-TECH PRODUCTS GROUP CORP.; *U.S. Public*, pg. 1237
KOCH FERTILISER AUSTRALIA PTY LTD—See Koch Industries, Inc.; *U.S. Private*, pg. 2333
KOCH FERTILISER, LTD—See Koch Industries, Inc.; *U.S. Private*, pg. 2333
KOCH FERTILIZER CANADA, ULC—See Koch Industries, Inc.; *U.S. Private*, pg. 2333
KUGLER OIL CO.; *U.S. Private*, pg. 2356
LEBANON SEABOARD CORPORATION; *U.S. Private*, pg. 2409
LONG ISLAND COMPOST CORP.; *U.S. Private*, pg. 2490
MOSAIC CROP NUTRITION, LLC—See The Mosaic Company; *U.S. Public*, pg. 2116
NACHURS ALPINE SOLUTIONS, LLC—See Wilbur-Ellis Company; *U.S. Private*, pg. 4517
NEW MILFORD FARMS—See Hendricks Holding Company, Inc.; *U.S. Private*, pg. 1915
ORIGIN FERTILISERS (UK) LIMITED—See ARYZTA AG; *Int'l*, pg. 589
OXBOW SULPHUR & FERTILISER (UK) LIMITED—See Oxbow Corporation; *U.S. Private*, pg. 3056
PACIFICO COMPANIA DE SEGUROS Y REASEGUROS S.A.—See Credicorp Ltd.; *Int'l*, pg. 1834
PAYGRO—See Hendricks Holding Company, Inc.; *U.S. Private*, pg. 1915
PHOENIX SOIL, LLC—See Enviri Corporation; *U.S. Public*, pg. 780
PRO SOL INC.—See Frit Incorporated; *U.S. Private*, pg. 1612
REGAL CHEMICAL COMPANY—See SiteOne Landscape Supply, Inc.; *U.S. Public*, pg. 1889
THE SCOTTS COMPANY LLC—See The Scotts Miracle-Gro Company; *U.S. Public*, pg. 2127
THE SCOTTS COMPANY—See The Scotts Miracle-Gro Company; *U.S. Public*, pg. 2127
THE SCOTTS COMPANY—See The Scotts Miracle-Gro Company; *U.S. Public*, pg. 2127
THE SCOTTS COMPANY—See The Scotts Miracle-Gro Company; *U.S. Public*, pg. 2127
THE SCOTTS COMPANY—See The Scotts Miracle-Gro Company; *U.S. Public*, pg. 2127
SCOTTS EARTHGRO—See The Scotts Miracle-Gro Company; *U.S. Public*, pg. 2127
SMARTCHEM TECHNOLOGIES LIMITED—See Deepak Fertilisers & Petrochemicals Corporation Limited; *Int'l*, pg. 2003
SOCIETE COMMERCIALE DES POTASSES ET DE L'AZOTE—See Entreprise Miniere et Chimique SA; *Int'l*, pg. 2453
TIGER-SUL PRODUCTS (CANADA) CO.—See Platte River Ventures, LLC; *U.S. Private*, pg. 3211
TIGER-SUL PRODUCTS LLC—See Platte River Ventures, LLC; *U.S. Private*, pg. 3211
TIGER-SUL PRODUCTS LLC - STOCKTON PLANT—See Platte River Ventures, LLC; *U.S. Private*, pg. 3211
TURFGRASS, LLC; *U.S. Private*, pg. 4259
UNITED PRAIRIE, LLC; *U.S. Private*, pg. 4295
VOGEL SEED & FERTILIZER, INC.; *U.S. Private*, pg. 4409
WARNER FERTILIZER COMPANY; *U.S. Private*, pg. 4442
WESTERN ENVIRONMENTAL PROTECTION CO., LTD.—See Hongda Xingye Co., Ltd.; *Int'l*, pg. 3470
WOLFKILL FEED & FERTILIZER CORPORATION; *U.S. Private*, pg. 4554
YARGUS MANUFACTURING—See Ag Growth International Inc.; *Int'l*, pg. 198

325320 — PESTICIDE AND OTHER AGRICULTURAL CHEMICAL MANUFACTURING

ACI FORMULATIONS LIMITED—See Advanced Chemical Industries Limited; *Int'l*, pg. 158
ADAMA AGRICULTURAL SOLUTIONS LTD.—See China National Chemical Corporation; *Int'l*, pg. 1526
ADAMA AGRICULTURAL SOLUTIONS S.R.L.—See China National Chemical Corporation; *Int'l*, pg. 1526
ADAMA AGRICULTURAL SOLUTIONS UK LTD.—See China National Chemical Corporation; *Int'l*, pg. 1526
ADAMA AGRICULTURE ESPANA, S.A.—See China National Chemical Corporation; *Int'l*, pg. 1526
ADAMA ANDINA B.V. SUCURSAL COLOMBIA—See China National Chemical Corporation; *Int'l*, pg. 1526
ADAMA ARGENTINA S.A.—See China National Chemical Corporation; *Int'l*, pg. 1526
ADAMA BRASIL S.A.—See China National Chemical Corporation; *Int'l*, pg. 1526
ADAMA FRANCE S.A.S—See China National Chemical Corporation; *Int'l*, pg. 1526
ADAMA ITALIA S.R.L.—See China National Chemical Corporation; *Int'l*, pg. 1526
ADAMA LTD.—See China National Chemical Corporation; *Int'l*, pg. 1526
ADAMA MAKHTESHIM LTD.—See China National Chemical Corporation; *Int'l*, pg. 1526
ADD-SHOP ERETAIL LTD.; *Int'l*, pg. 128
AGCO INTERNATIONAL LTD.—See AGCO Corporation; *U.S. Public*, pg. 58
AGRAUXINE S.A. - LOCHES FACTORY—See Compagnie des Levures Lesaffre SA; *Int'l*, pg. 1738
AGRAUXINE S.A. - PLOMELIN FACTORY—See Compagnie des Levures Lesaffre SA; *Int'l*, pg. 1738
AGRAUXINE S.A.—See Compagnie des Levures Lesaffre SA; *Int'l*, pg. 1738
AGRICULTURAL CHEMICALS (MALAYSIA) SDN. BHD.—See Adeka Corporation; *Int'l*, pg. 142
AGRIPHAR ITALIA SRL—See Element Solutions Inc.; *U.S. Public*, pg. 725
AGRO CHEMICALS INC—See Barbados Shipping & Trading Co. Ltd.; *Int'l*, pg. 858
AGROFRESH INC.—See Paine Schwartz Partners, LLC; *U.S. Public*, pg. 3075
AGRO-KANESHO CO., LTD.; *Int'l*, pg. 218
AGRO PHOS INDIA LTD.; *Int'l*, pg. 218
AGRO TECHNICA LTD.—See Hayleys PLC; *Int'l*, pg. 3292
AIMCO PESTICIDES LIMITED; *Int'l*, pg. 232
ALBAUGH INC.; *U.S. Private*, pg. 152
ALFA AGRICULTURAL SUPPLIES S.A.—See China National Chemical Corporation; *Int'l*, pg. 1526
ALL COSMOS INDUSTRIES SDN. BHD.—See All Cosmos Bio-Tech Holding Corporation; *Int'l*, pg. 331
ALLIED AGRONOMY, LLC—See CHS INC.; *U.S. Public*, pg. 491
AMVAC CHEMICAL CORPORATION—See American Vanguard Corporation; *U.S. Public*, pg. 111
AMVAC CHEMICAL CORPORATION—See American Vanguard Corporation; *U.S. Public*, pg. 111
AMVAC NETHERLANDS BV—See American Vanguard Corporation; *U.S. Public*, pg. 111
ANHUI GUANGXIN AGROCHEMICAL CO., LTD.; *Int'l*, pg. 467
ARABIA FELIX INDUSTRIAL LTD.—See Hayel Saeed Anam Group of Companies; *Int'l*, pg. 3290
ARCADIA BIOSCIENCES, INC.; *U.S. Public*, pg. 179
ASTRACHEM TURKEY—See ASTRA INDUSTRIAL GROUP COMPANY; *Int'l*, pg. 657
ASTRA INDUSTRIAL COMPLEX CO. FOR FERTILIZERS AND PESTICIDES LTD.—See ASTRA INDUSTRIAL GROUP COMPANY; *Int'l*, pg. 657
ASTRA NOVA CO.—See ASTRA INDUSTRIAL GROUP COMPANY; *Int'l*, pg. 657
AVIMA (PTY) LTD—See Ascendis Health Limited; *Int'l*, pg. 704
BAM AGRICULTURAL SOLUTIONS, INC.—See Zero Gravity Solutions, Inc.; *U.S. Public*, pg. 2403
BASANT AGRO TECH (INDIA) LTD.; *Int'l*, pg. 871
BASF AGRICULTURAL PRODUCTS DE PUERTO RICO—See BASF SE; *Int'l*, pg. 877
BASF AGRI-PRODUCTION S.A.S.—See BASF SE; *Int'l*, pg. 877
BASF AGRO SAS—See BASF SE; *Int'l*, pg. 877
BASF ASIA PACIFIC (INDIA) PVT. LTD.—See BASF SE; *Int'l*, pg. 877
BASF CONTROLS LTD.—See BASF SE; *Int'l*, pg. 875
BASF CORP. - BEAUMONT AGRICULTURAL PRODUCTS PLANT—See BASF SE; *Int'l*, pg. 877
BASF CORP. - PALMYRA (HANNIBAL) AGRICULTURAL PRODUCTS PLANT—See BASF SE; *Int'l*, pg. 877
BASF HELLAS S.A.—See BASF SE; *Int'l*, pg. 879
BASF PEST CONTROL SOLUTIONS—See BASF SE; *Int'l*, pg. 882
BASF PLANT SCIENCE LP—See BASF SE; *Int'l*, pg. 877
BAUTECHNIK GESELLSCHAFT M.B.H—See BayWa AG; *Int'l*, pg. 915
BAYER AGCO LIMITED—See Bayer Aktiengesellschaft; *Int'l*, pg. 902
BAYER AGRICULTURE LIMITED—See Bayer Aktiengesellschaft; *Int'l*, pg. 902
BAYER ALGERIE S.P.A.—See Bayer Aktiengesellschaft; *Int'l*, pg. 902
BAYER BIOSCIENCE PVT. LTD.—See Bayer Aktiengesellschaft; *Int'l*, pg. 904
BAYER CROPSCIENCE AG—See Bayer Aktiengesellschaft; *Int'l*, pg. 902
BAYER CROPSCIENCE AUSTRALIA PTY. LTD.—See Bayer Aktiengesellschaft; *Int'l*, pg. 902
BAYER CROPSCIENCE (CHINA) COMPANY LTD.—See Bayer Aktiengesellschaft; *Int'l*, pg. 902
BAYER CROPSCIENCE GUATEMALA, LIMITADA—See Bayer Aktiengesellschaft; *Int'l*, pg. 904
BAYER CROPSCIENCE K.K.—See Bayer Aktiengesellschaft; *Int'l*, pg. 903
BAYER CROPSCIENCE LIMITED—See Bayer Aktiengesellschaft; *Int'l*, pg. 903
BAYER CROPSCIENCE LP—See Bayer Aktiengesellschaft; *Int'l*, pg. 903
BAYER CROPSCIENCE LTD.—See Bayer Aktiengesellschaft; *Int'l*, pg. 903
BAYER CROPSCIENCE—See Bayer Aktiengesellschaft; *Int'l*, pg. 903
BAYER CROPSCIENCE VERMOGENSVERWALTUNGSGESELLSCHAFT MBH—See Bayer Aktiengesellschaft; *Int'l*, pg. 903
BAYER D.O.O. SARAJEVO—See Bayer Aktiengesellschaft; *Int'l*, pg. 906
BAYER MEDICAL CARE B.V.—See Bayer Aktiengesellschaft; *Int'l*, pg. 905
BAYER MOZAMBIQUE, LIMITADA—See Bayer Aktiengesellschaft; *Int'l*, pg. 905
BAYER SAUDI ARABIA LLC—See Bayer Aktiengesellschaft; *Int'l*, pg. 906
BAYER TURK KIMYA SANAYI LIMITED SIRKETI—See Bayer Aktiengesellschaft; *Int'l*, pg. 906
BAYER VAPI PRIVATE LIMITED—See Bayer Aktiengesellschaft; *Int'l*, pg. 906
BAYER WEST-CENTRAL AFRICA S.A.—See Bayer Aktiengesellschaft; *Int'l*, pg. 906
BAYER ZIMBABWE (PRIVATE) LIMITED—See Bayer Aktiengesellschaft; *Int'l*, pg. 906
BECKER UNDERWOOD, INC.—See BASF SE; *Int'l*, pg. 877
BEE VECTORING TECHNOLOGIES INTERNATIONAL INC.; *Int'l*, pg. 939
BEIHAI GOFAR CHUANSHAN BIOLOGICAL CO., LTD.; *Int'l*, pg. 942
BELL LABORATORIES, INC.; *U.S. Private*, pg. 518
BERNER EESTI OY—See Berner Oy; *Int'l*, pg. 988
BHAGIRADHA CHEMICALS & INDUSTRIES LTD.; *Int'l*, pg. 1009
BHARAT RASAYAN LIMITED; *Int'l*, pg. 1011
BIOMASS HEATING SOLUTIONS LTD.; *Int'l*, pg. 1039
BIOSAFE SYSTEMS, LLC; *U.S. Private*, pg. 562
BIOWORKS, INC.—See Floridienne SA; *Int'l*, pg. 2708
BOMBAY SUPER HYBRID SEEDS LTD.; *Int'l*, pg. 1104
BONIFICHE FERRARESI S.P.A; *Int'l*, pg. 1107
CAN THO PESTICIDES JOINT STOCK COMPANY; *Int'l*, pg. 1276
CARGILL INC.—See Cargill, Inc.; *U.S. Private*, pg. 757
CHEMCEL BIO-TECH LIMITED; *Int'l*, pg. 1461
CHEMINOVA A/S—See FMC Corporation; *U.S. Public*, pg. 861
CHEMINOVA DEUTSCHLAND GMBH & CO. KG—See FMC Corporation; *U.S. Public*, pg. 861
CHEM-TECH, LTD.—See Neogen Corporation; *U.S. Public*, pg. 1505
CHEMTURA PTY LIMITED—See Element Solutions Inc.; *U.S. Public*, pg. 725
CHINA AGRI-BUSINESS, INC.; *Int'l*, pg. 1481
CLEANING SOLUTIONS, INC.; *U.S. Private*, pg. 931
THE CLIMATE CORPORATION—See Bayer Aktiengesellschaft; *Int'l*, pg. 909
COFLE SPA; *Int'l*, pg. 1692
COMERCIALIZADORA TIMAC AGRO CHILE LIMITADA—See Compagnie Financiere et de Participations Roullier SA; *Int'l*, pg. 1740
CORTEVA AGRISCIENCE ARGENTINA S.R.L.—See Corteva, Inc.; *U.S. Public*, pg. 581
CORTEVA AGRISCIENCE GERMANY GMBH—See Corteva, Inc.; *U.S. Public*, pg. 581

325320 — PESTICIDE AND OTHER...

CORTEVA AGRISCIENCE LLC—See Corteva, Inc.; *U.S. Public*, pg. 580
CORTEVA AGRISCIENCE (SINGAPORE) PTE. LTD.—See Corteva, Inc.; *U.S. Public*, pg. 581
CORTEVA AGRISCIENCE UK LIMITED—See Corteva, Inc.; *U.S. Public*, pg. 581
C.Q. PHARMACEUTICAL HOLDING CO., LTD.; *Int'l*, pg. 1244
CU DEUTERO + AGRO AG—See CPH Chemie + Papier Holding AG; *Int'l*, pg. 1824
DALIAN BIO-CHEM COMPANY LIMITED - LVSHUN FACTORY—See Dalian Bio-Chem Company Limited; *Int'l*, pg. 1951
DALIAN BIO-CHEM COMPANY LIMITED - SONGMUDAO FACTORY—See Dalian Bio-Chem Company Limited; *Int'l*, pg. 1951
DBJ ENTERPRISES DE COLOMBIA S.A.—See Corteva, Inc.; *U.S. Public*, pg. 584
DHANUKA AGRITECH LIMITED; *Int'l*, pg. 2098
DONGBANG AGRO CORP.; *Int'l*, pg. 2165
DONGYING HI-TECH SPRING CHEMICAL CO., LTD.—See HaiKe Chemical Group Ltd; *Int'l*, pg. 3211
DOW AGROSCIENCES B.V—See Corteva, Inc.; *U.S. Public*, pg. 581
DOW AGROSCIENCES CANADA INC. - SASKATOON—See Corteva, Inc.; *U.S. Public*, pg. 582
DOW AGROSCIENCES CANADA INC.—See Corteva, Inc.; *U.S. Public*, pg. 582
DOW AGROSCIENCES CHILE S.A.—See Corteva, Inc.; *U.S. Public*, pg. 582
DOW AGROSCIENCES COSTA RICA S.A.—See Corteva, Inc.; *U.S. Public*, pg. 582
DOW AGROSCIENCES IBERICA S.A.—See Corteva, Inc.; *U.S. Public*, pg. 582
DOW AGROSCIENCES INDIA PVT. LTD.—See Corteva, Inc.; *U.S. Public*, pg. 582
DOW AGROSCIENCES (MALAYSIA) SDN BHD—See Corteva, Inc.; *U.S. Public*, pg. 581
DOW AGROSCIENCES (NZ) LIMITED—See Corteva, Inc.; *U.S. Public*, pg. 581
DOW AGROSCIENCES POLSKA SP Z.O.O.—See Corteva, Inc.; *U.S. Public*, pg. 582
THE DOW CHEMICAL CO. - BAYPORT PLANT—See Dow Inc.; *U.S. Public*, pg. 686
THE DOW CHEMICAL COMPANY - WASHINGTON, DC—See Dow Inc.; *U.S. Public*, pg. 686
DOW DEUTSCHLAND ANLAGENGESELLSCHAFT MBH—See Dow Inc.; *U.S. Public*, pg. 684
DREXEL CHEMICAL COMPANY INC.; *U.S. Private*, pg. 1276
DUPONT AGRICULTURAL CHEMICALS LTD. SHANGHAI—See FMC Corporation; *U.S. Public*, pg. 861
DUPONT AGRICULTURE & NUTRITION—See Corteva, Inc.; *U.S. Public*, pg. 582
DUPONT DE NEMOURS (FRANCE) S.A.S, CERNAY PLANT—See Corteva, Inc.; *U.S. Public*, pg. 584
DUPONT DE NEMOURS SOUTH AFRICA (PTY) LTD.—See Corteva, Inc.; *U.S. Public*, pg. 584
DUPONT, S.A. DE C.V.—See DuPont de Nemours, Inc.; *U.S. Public*, pg. 693
DUPONT (U.K.) INDUSTRIAL LIMITED—See DuPont de Nemours, Inc.; *U.S. Public*, pg. 692
DUPONT UKRAINE LLC—See Corteva, Inc.; *U.S. Public*, pg. 584
DYNAMIC SOLUTIONS WORLDWIDE, LLC—See Vestar Capital Partners, LLC; *U.S. Private*, pg. 4372
DYNAMITE PLANT FOOD—See Florikan ESA LLC; *U.S. Private*, pg. 1551
EARTH ALIVE CLEAN TECHNOLOGIES INC.; *Int'l*, pg. 2268
EARTH CORPORATION; *Int'l*, pg. 2268
EARTH CORPORATION—See Earth Corporation; *Int'l*, pg. 2268
EARTH HOME PRODUCTS (MALAYSIA) SDN. BHD.—See Earth Corporation; *Int'l*, pg. 2268
EARTH (THAILAND) CO., LTD.—See Earth Corporation; *Int'l*, pg. 2268
EDEN RESEARCH PLC; *Int'l*, pg. 2307
EFEKTO CARE (PTY) LTD—See Ascendis Health Limited; *Int'l*, pg. 601
EMERALD BIOAGRICULTURE CORP.; *U.S. Private*, pg. 1379
ENBIO CO., LTD.; *Int'l*, pg. 2396
EUROFINS AGROSCIENCE SERVICES LTD—See Eurofins Scientific S.E.; *Int'l*, pg. 2537
EUROFINS AGROSCIENCES SERVICES SRL—See Eurofins Scientific S.E.; *Int'l*, pg. 2537
EVERGREEN GARDEN CARE DEUTSCHLAND GMBH—See Exponent Private Equity LLP; *Int'l*, pg. 2590
FEDEA S.A.—See Corteva, Inc.; *U.S. Public*, pg. 582
FLORIKAN ESA LLC; *U.S. Private*, pg. 1551
FMC AGRO LTD.—See FMC Corporation; *U.S. Public*, pg. 861
FMC AGROQUIMICA DE MEXICO S.R.L. DE C.V.—See FMC Corporation; *U.S. Public*, pg. 861
FMC AUSTRALASIA PTY LTD.—See FMC Corporation; *U.S. Public*, pg. 861

FUMAKILLA AMERICA, S.A. DE C.V.—See Fumakilla Limited; *Int'l*, pg. 2844
FUMAKILLA LIMITED; *Int'l*, pg. 2844
FUMAKILLA MALAYSIA BERHAD—See Fumakilla Limited; *Int'l*, pg. 2844
GALENIKA-FITOFARMACIJA A.D.; *Int'l*, pg. 2872
GARD ROGARD INC.; *U.S. Private*, pg. 1642
GEECEE VENTURES LIMITED; *Int'l*, pg. 2910
GHARDA CHEMICALS LIMITED - DOMBIVILI PLANT—See Gharda Chemicals Limited; *Int'l*, pg. 2958
GHARDA CHEMICALS LIMITED - LOTE PLANT—See Gharda Chemicals Limited; *Int'l*, pg. 2958
GHARDA CHEMICALS LIMITED - PANOLI PLANT—See Gharda Chemicals Limited; *Int'l*, pg. 2958
GHARDA CHEMICALS LIMITED; *Int'l*, pg. 2958
GRAUER & WEIL INDIA LIMITED; *Int'l*, pg. 3061
GROW MORE, INC.; *U.S. Private*, pg. 1795
GSFC AGROTECH LIMITED—See Gujarat State Fertilizers & Chemicals Ltd.; *Int'l*, pg. 3177
GUJARAT INSECTICIDES LIMITED—See Gharda Chemicals Limited; *Int'l*, pg. 2958
HACCO, INC.—See Neogen Corporation; *U.S. Public*, pg. 1505
HAI AGROCHEM JOINT STOCK COMPANY; *Int'l*, pg. 3208
HAI AGROCHEM JOINT STOCK COMPANY—See HAI Agrochem Joint Stock Company; *Int'l*, pg. 3208
HAILIR PESTICIDES & CHEMICALS GROUP; *Int'l*, pg. 3211
HALDER VENTURES LIMITED; *Int'l*, pg. 3227
HANDSON PARTICIPACOES S.A.—See Cosan S.A.; *Int'l*, pg. 1809
HAYLEYS AGRO PRODUCTS LIMITED—See Hayleys PLC; *Int'l*, pg. 3292
HEDLEY TECHNOLOGIES (USA) INC.—See BioSyent Inc.; *Int'l*, pg. 1042
HEFEI FENGLE SEED CO., LTD.; *Int'l*, pg. 3307
HEKTAS TICARET T.A.S.; *Int'l*, pg. 3327
HERANBA INDUSTRIES LIMITED; *Int'l*, pg. 3358
HERBICIDES PRODUCTION COMPANY; *Int'l*, pg. 3360
HEXTAR CHEMICALS SDN. BHD.—See Hextar Holdings Sdn. Bhd.; *Int'l*, pg. 3373
HODOGAYA UPL CO., LTD.—See Hodogaya Chemical Co., Ltd.; *Int'l*, pg. 3438
HOKKO CHEMICAL INDUSTRY CO., LTD. - OKAYAMA FACTORY—See HOKKO CHEMICAL INDUSTRY CO., LTD.; *Int'l*, pg. 3443
HOKKO CHEMICAL INDUSTRY CO., LTD.; *Int'l*, pg. 3443
HUBEI GRAND FUCHI PHARMACEUTICAL & CHEMICAL COMPANY LIMITED—See Grand Pharmaceutical Group Limited; *Int'l*, pg. 3056
HUIKWANG CORP.; *Int'l*, pg. 3526
HUI KWANG (THAILAND) CO., LTD.—See Huikwang Corp.; *Int'l*, pg. 3526
HUNAN HAILI CHEMICAL INDUSTRY CO., LTD.; *Int'l*, pg. 3532
HUNAN HAILI CHEMICAL INDUSTRY STOCK CO., LTD.—See Hunan Haili Chemical Industry Co., Ltd.; *Int'l*, pg. 3532
HUNAN HAOHUA CHEMICAL CO LTD.—See China National Corporation; *Int'l*, pg. 1528
IMASPRO CORPORATION BERHAD; *Int'l*, pg. 3620
INAGRO SDN. BHD.—See Analabs Resources Berhad; *Int'l*, pg. 446
INNOVATIVE PEST MANAGEMENT (PTY) LTD—See Ascendis Health Limited; *Int'l*, pg. 601
INTERPROVINCIAL COOPERATIVE LIMITED—See Federated Co-operatives Limited; *Int'l*, pg. 2631
INTERPROVINCIAL COOPERATIVE LIMITED—See Growmark, Inc.; *U.S. Private*, pg. 1795
ISAGRO S.P.A.—See Gowan Company LLC; *U.S. Private*, pg. 1747
ISAGRO USA, INC.—See Gowan Company LLC; *U.S. Private*, pg. 1747
J.R. SIMPLOT COMPANY LATHROP PLANT—See J.R. Simplot Company; *U.S. Private*, pg. 2170
J.R. SIMPLOT COMPANY—See J.R. Simplot Company; *U.S. Private*, pg. 2170
KALO, INC.; *U.S. Private*, pg. 2258
KLUB M5 (PTY) LTD—See Ascendis Health Limited; *Int'l*, pg. 601
LANDEC AG—See Lifecore Biomedical, Inc.; *U.S. Public*, pg. 1312
LIMAGRAIN CEREALES INGREDIENTS—See Groupe Limagrain Holding SA; *Int'l*, pg. 3107
MAGAN KOREA CO. LTD.—See China National Chemical Corporation; *Int'l*, pg. 1526
MAHYCO MONSANTO BIOTECH (INDIA) LIMITED—See Bayer Aktiengesellschaft; *Int'l*, pg. 908
MATSON, LLC—See Central Garden & Pet Company; *U.S. Public*, pg. 473
MILLER CHEMICAL & FERTILIZER, LLC—See J.M. Huber Corporation; *U.S. Private*, pg. 2169
MINERAL FEED, S.L.—See Huntsman Corporation; *U.S. Public*, pg. 1075
MONSANTO AGRICOLTURA ITALIA S.P.A.—See Bayer Aktiengesellschaft; *Int'l*, pg. 908
MONSANTO AGRICULTURE FRANCE SAS—See Bayer Aktiengesellschaft; *Int'l*, pg. 908

CORPORATE AFFILIATIONS

MONSANTO ARGENTINA SRL—See Bayer Aktiengesellschaft; *Int'l*, pg. 908
MONSANTO AUSTRALIA LTD.—See Bayer Aktiengesellschaft; *Int'l*, pg. 908
MONSANTO CANADA, INC. - TILLSONBURG CORN & SOYBEAN MANUFACTURING/DISTRIBUTION—See Bayer Aktiengesellschaft; *Int'l*, pg. 908
MONSANTO CHILE S.A.—See Bayer Aktiengesellschaft; *Int'l*, pg. 908
MONSANTO CO. - DAVIS—See Bayer Aktiengesellschaft; *Int'l*, pg. 908
MONSANTO CO. - JANESVILLE—See Bayer Aktiengesellschaft; *Int'l*, pg. 908
MONSANTO CO. - KAHAHEO—See Bayer Aktiengesellschaft; *Int'l*, pg. 908
MONSANTO CO. - KEARNEY—See Bayer Aktiengesellschaft; *Int'l*, pg. 908
MONSANTO CO. - MARSHALL—See Bayer Aktiengesellschaft; *Int'l*, pg. 908
MONSANTO CO. - MATTHEWS—See Bayer Aktiengesellschaft; *Int'l*, pg. 908
MONSANTO COMERCIAL, S DE RL DE CV—See Bayer Aktiengesellschaft; *Int'l*, pg. 909
MONSANTO COMMERCIAL, S.A. DE C.V.—See Bayer Aktiengesellschaft; *Int'l*, pg. 909
MONSANTO COMPANY—See Bayer Aktiengesellschaft; *Int'l*, pg. 908
MONSANTO CO. - MUSCATINE PLANT—See Bayer Aktiengesellschaft; *Int'l*, pg. 908
MONSANTO CO. - MYSTIC—See Bayer Aktiengesellschaft; *Int'l*, pg. 909
MONSANTO CO. - SODA SPRINGS PLANT—See Bayer Aktiengesellschaft; *Int'l*, pg. 909
MONSANTO CO. - STONINGTON—See Bayer Aktiengesellschaft; *Int'l*, pg. 909
MONSANTO CO. - WILLIAMSBURG—See Bayer Aktiengesellschaft; *Int'l*, pg. 909
MONSANTO EUROPE S.A./N.V. (BELGIUM)—See Bayer Aktiengesellschaft; *Int'l*, pg. 909
MONSANTO FAR EAST LTD.—See Bayer Aktiengesellschaft; *Int'l*, pg. 909
MONSANTO HOLDINGS PRIVATE LTD.—See Bayer Aktiengesellschaft; *Int'l*, pg. 909
MONSANTO HOLLAND BV—See Bayer Aktiengesellschaft; *Int'l*, pg. 909
MONSANTO INTERNATIONAL S.A.R.L—See Bayer Aktiengesellschaft; *Int'l*, pg. 909
MONSANTO (MALAYSIA) SDN BHD—See Bayer Aktiengesellschaft; *Int'l*, pg. 908
MONSANTO ROMANIA SRL—See Bayer Aktiengesellschaft; *Int'l*, pg. 909
MONSANTO SINGAPORE COMPANY (PTE.) LTD.—See Bayer Aktiengesellschaft; *Int'l*, pg. 909
MONSANTO UK LTD.—See Bayer Aktiengesellschaft; *Int'l*, pg. 909
MONTEREY CHEMICAL COMPANY INC.—See Brandt Consolidated, Inc.; *U.S. Public*, pg. 638
THE MOSAIC COMPANY; *U.S. Public*, pg. 2116
MOSAIC FERTILIZANTES P&K LTDA—See The Mosaic Company; *U.S. Public*, pg. 2116
MOSFLY INTERNATIONAL SDN. BHD.—See IMASPRO Corporation Berhad; *Int'l*, pg. 3620
NANTONG DAS CHEMICAL CO., LTD.—See Corteva, Inc.; *U.S. Public*, pg. 580
NAP-STOLLER THAILAND—See Corteva, Inc.; *U.S. Public*, pg. 584
NICHINO AMERICA INC.—See Adeka Corporation; *Int'l*, pg. 142
NICHINO CHEMICAL INDIA PVT. LTD.—See Adeka Corporation; *Int'l*, pg. 142
NICHINO RYOKKA CO., LTD.—See Adeka Corporation; *Int'l*, pg. 142
NIHON ECOTECH CO., LTD.—See Adeka Corporation; *Int'l*, pg. 142
NIHON NOHYAKU CO., LTD.—See Adeka Corporation; *Int'l*, pg. 142
NISSO BASF AGRO CO., LTD.—See BASF SE; *Int'l*, pg. 878
NORTH AMERICAN GREEN INC.—See Commercial Metals Company; *U.S. Public*, pg. 547
NORTHWEST AGRICULTURAL PRODUCTS, INC.—See AEA Investors LP; *U.S. Private*, pg. 116
NOVON PROTECTA (PTY) LTD—See Element Solutions Inc.; *U.S. Public*, pg. 728
OHP, INC.—See American Vanguard Corporation; *U.S. Public*, pg. 111
OMG (ASIA) ELECTRONIC CHEMICALS CO. LTD.—See Element Solutions Inc.; *U.S. Public*, pg. 728
OVERUM INDUSTRIES AB—See FairCap GmbH; *Int'l*, pg. 2605
OXITEC DO BRASIL TECNOLOGIA DE INSETOS LTDA—See Precigen, Inc.; *U.S. Public*, pg. 1713
OXITEC LTD.—See Precigen, Inc.; *U.S. Public*, pg. 1713
PACE INTERNATIONAL, LLC—See Paine Schwartz Partners, LLC; *U.S. Private*, pg. 3075
PARADIGM CONVERGENCE TECHNOLOGIES CORPORATION—See PCT LTD; *U.S. Public*, pg. 1658
PBI/GORDON CORPORATION; *U.S. Private*, pg. 3118
PERFORMANCE CHEMISERVE LIMITED—See Deepak

N.A.I.C.S. INDEX

325411 — MEDICINAL AND BOTAN...

Fertilisers & Petrochemicals Corporation Limited; *Int'l*, pg. 2003
PLANT NUTRIENT GROUP—See The Andersons Incorporated; *U.S. Public*, pg. 2034
PLANT SCIENCE SWEDEN AB—See BASF SE; *Int'l*, pg. 877
PRIME SOURCE, LLC—See Bunzl plc; *Int'l*, pg. 1219
PRO FARM GROUP, INC.—See Bioceres S.A.; *Int'l*, pg. 1036
PRP-GP LLC—See The Mosaic Company; *U.S. Public*, pg. 2116
P.T. FUMAKILLA INDONESIA—See Fumakilla Limited; *Int'l*, pg. 2844
PT TECHNOPIA JAKARTA—See Fumakilla Limited; *Int'l*, pg. 2844
QUIMICAS STOLLER DE CENTROAMERICA, S.A.—See Corteva, Inc.; *U.S. Public*, pg. 584
ROGAMA INDUSTRIA COMERCIO LTDA.—See Neogen Corporation; *U.S. Public*, pg. 1505
ROHM AND HAAS ITALIA SRL—See Dow Inc.; *U.S. Public*, pg. 686
ROLLINS SUPPLY, INC.—See Rollins, Inc.; *U.S. Public*, pg. 1809
RWA MAGYARORSZAG KFT—See BayWa AG; *Int'l*, pg. 918
RWA RAIFFEISEN AGRO ROMANIA S.R.L.—See BayWa AG; *Int'l*, pg. 918
RWA SLOVAKIA SPOL. S.R.O.—See BayWa AG; *Int'l*, pg. 918
RWA SRBIJA D.O.O.—See BayWa AG; *Int'l*, pg. 918
SCHIRM GMBH-LUBECK—See AECI Limited; *Int'l*, pg. 172
SCHIRM GMBH-SCHONEBECK—See AECI Limited; *Int'l*, pg. 172
SCHIRM GMBH—See AECI Limited; *Int'l*, pg. 171
SCHIRM USA, INC.—See AECI Limited; *Int'l*, pg. 172
THE SCOTTS COMPANY (MANUFACTURING) LIMITED—See Exponent Private Equity LLP; *Int'l*, pg. 2590
THE SCOTTS COMPANY—See The Scotts Miracle-Gro Company; *U.S. Public*, pg. 2127
SCOTTS MANUFACTURING COMPANY—See The Scotts Miracle-Gro Company; *U.S. Public*, pg. 2127
SCOTTS PROFESSIONAL PRODUCTS CO.—See The Scotts Miracle-Gro Company; *U.S. Public*, pg. 2127
SDS BIOTECH KKS—See Idemitsu Kosan Co., Ltd.; *Int'l*, pg. 3592
SEPRO CORPORATION; *U.S. Private*, pg. 3611
SHANGHAI HKC LTD.—See Huikwang Corp.; *Int'l*, pg. 3526
SIA BAYER—See Bayer Aktiengesellschaft; *Int'l*, pg. 910
SIAMONS INTERNATIONAL INC.—See RPM International Inc.; *U.S. Public*, pg. 1820
SINOAGRO CHEMICALS CO., LTD.—See Hailir Pesticides & Chemicals Group; *Int'l*, pg. 3211
SIPCAM EUROPE S.P.A—See Adeka Corporation; *Int'l*, pg. 142
SIPCAM NICHINO BRASIL S.A.—See Adeka Corporation; *Int'l*, pg. 142
SKW STICKSTOFFWERKE PIESTERITZ GMBH—See E.ON SE; *Int'l*, pg. 2259
SOREX LTD.—See BASF SE; *Int'l*, pg. 882
SPECIALTY FERTILIZER PRODUCTS, LLC—See AEA Investors LP; *U.S. Private*, pg. 116
SQM - VITAS BRASIL LTDA.—See Compagnie Financiere et de Participations Roullier SA; *Int'l*, pg. 1740
SQM VITAS PERU S.A.C.—See Compagnie Financiere et de Participations Roullier SA; *Int'l*, pg. 1740
S.T.I.M.A. S.A.R.L.—See BASF SE; *Int'l*, pg. 884
STOLLER ARGENTINA—See Corteva, Inc.; *U.S. Public*, pg. 584
STOLLER AUSTRALIA PTY. LTD.—See Corteva, Inc.; *U.S. Public*, pg. 584
STOLLER CHEMICAL COMPANY OF CANADA LTD.—See Corteva, Inc.; *U.S. Public*, pg. 584
STOLLER DE CHILE, S.A.—See Corteva, Inc.; *U.S. Public*, pg. 584
STOLLER DO BRASIL, LTDA.—See Corteva, Inc.; *U.S. Public*, pg. 584
STOLLER ENTERPRISES DE MEXICO, SA DE CV—See Corteva, Inc.; *U.S. Public*, pg. 584
STOLLER ENTERPRISES, LTD.—See Corteva, Inc.; *U.S. Public*, pg. 584
STOLLER GROUP, INC.—See Corteva, Inc.; *U.S. Public*, pg. 584
STOLLER IBERICA, S.L.—See Corteva, Inc.; *U.S. Public*, pg. 584
STOLLER - PERU S.A.—See Corteva, Inc.; *U.S. Public*, pg. 584
STOLLER PHILLIPINNES, INC.—See Corteva, Inc.; *U.S. Public*, pg. 584
SUPPLIVA GMBH—See AlzChem Group AG; *Int'l*, pg. 402
SUSPA VERTRIEBSGESELLSCHAFT MBH—See Andlinger & Company, Inc.; *U.S. Private*, pg. 279
SYNGENTA AGRO AG—See China National Chemical Corporation; *Int'l*, pg. 1529
SYNGENTA AGRO S.A.—See China National Chemical Corporation; *Int'l*, pg. 1529
SYNGENTA BULGARIA EOOD—See China National Chemical Corporation; *Int'l*, pg. 1529
SYNGENTA CROP PROTECTION AG—See China National Chemical Corporation; *Int'l*, pg. 1530
SYNGENTA CROP PROTECTION, INC.—See China National Chemical Corporation; *Int'l*, pg. 1529
SYNGENTA CROP PROTECTION LIMITED—See China National Chemical Corporation; *Int'l*, pg. 1530
SYNGENTA CROP PROTECTION, LLC—See China National Chemical Corporation; *Int'l*, pg. 1529
SYNGENTA CROP PROTECTION MUNCHWILEN AG—See China National Chemical Corporation; *Int'l*, pg. 1530
SYNGENTA CROP PROTECTION S.A.—See China National Chemical Corporation; *Int'l*, pg. 1530
SYNGENTA PROTECAO DE CULTIVOS LTDA.—See China National Chemical Corporation; *Int'l*, pg. 1530
TAFT PRODUCTION COMPANY—See Oil-Dri Corporation of America; *U.S. Public*, pg. 1566
TAIWAN NIHON NOHYAKU CO., LTD.—See Adeka Corporation; *Int'l*, pg. 142
TECHNOPIA (THAILAND) LTD.—See Fumakilla Limited; *Int'l*, pg. 2844
TIGER-SUL PRODUCTS LLC—See Platte River Ventures, LLC; *U.S. Private*, pg. 3211
TIMAB MAGNESIUM SAS—See Compagnie Financiere et de Participations Roullier SA; *Int'l*, pg. 1740
TIMAC AGRO ALGERIE, SARL—See Compagnie Financiere et de Participations Roullier SA; *Int'l*, pg. 1740
TIMAC AGRO ARGENTINA S.A.—See Compagnie Financiere et de Participations Roullier SA; *Int'l*, pg. 1740
TIMAC AGRO MAROC SA—See Compagnie Financiere et de Participations Roullier SA; *Int'l*, pg. 1740
TIMAC AGRO PARAGUAY S.A—See Compagnie Financiere et de Participations Roullier SA; *Int'l*, pg. 1740
TIMAC AGRO POLSKA SP.Z.O.O.—See Compagnie Financiere et de Participations Roullier SA; *Int'l*, pg. 1740
TIMAC AGRO ROMANIA SRL—See Compagnie Financiere et de Participations Roullier SA; *Int'l*, pg. 1740
TIMAC AGRO SVERIGE AB—See Compagnie Financiere et de Participations Roullier SA; *Int'l*, pg. 1740
TIMAC AGRO UK LTD.—See Compagnie Financiere et de Participations Roullier SA; *Int'l*, pg. 1740
TIMAC AGRO UKRAINE LLC—See Compagnie Financiere et de Participations Roullier SA; *Int'l*, pg. 1740
TIMAC AGRO URUGUAY S.A.—See Compagnie Financiere et de Participations Roullier SA; *Int'l*, pg. 1740
TIMAC AGRO USA INC.—See Compagnie Financiere et de Participations Roullier SA; *Int'l*, pg. 1740
TITAN AG PTY LTD—See Elders Limited; *Int'l*, pg. 2346
TRICAL INC.; *U.S. Private*, pg. 4228
TROY BIOSCIENCES, INC.—See Troy Corporation; *U.S. Private*, pg. 4243
TROY CHEMICAL COMPANY LIMITED—See Troy Corporation; *U.S. Private*, pg. 4243
TROY CHEMICAL CORPORATION—See Troy Corporation; *U.S. Private*, pg. 4243
TYRATECH, INC.—See American Vanguard Corporation; *U.S. Public*, pg. 112
UNITED INDUSTRIES CORP. - BRIDGETON—See Spectrum Brands Holdings, Inc.; *U.S. Public*, pg. 1917
UNITED INDUSTRIES CORPORATION—See Spectrum Brands Holdings, Inc.; *U.S. Public*, pg. 1917
VCM PRODUCTS, LLC; *U.S. Private*, pg. 4349
WILLERT HOME PRODUCTS, INC.—See Spectrum Brands Holdings, Inc.; *U.S. Public*, pg. 4521
WINFIELD UNITED, LLC; *U.S. Private*, pg. 4541
WISCONSIN PHARMACAL COMPANY, LLC; *U.S. Private*, pg. 4548
WUHAN KERNEL BIO-TECHNOLOGY CO., LTD.—See Grand Pharmaceutical Group Limited; *Int'l*, pg. 3056
ZEP INC. - ENFORCER PRODUCTS—See New Mountain Capital, LLC; *U.S. Private*, pg. 2904

325411 — MEDICINAL AND BOTANICAL MANUFACTURING

4LIFE RESEARCH LC; *U.S. Private*, pg. 15
AARTI HEALTHCARE LTD.—See Aarti Industries Ltd.; *Int'l*, pg. 38
ABATTIS BIOCEUTICALS CORPORATION; *Int'l*, pg. 48
ABBVIE BIOTHERAPEUTICS INC.—See AbbVie Inc.; *U.S. Public*, pg. 21
AB CERNELLE—See Dermapharm Holding SE; *Int'l*, pg. 2043
ABL BIO, INC.; *Int'l*, pg. 62
ABNOVA GMBH—See Abnova (Taiwan) Corporation; *Int'l*, pg. 65
ACORIS RESEARCH LIMITED—See Hikal Limited; *Int'l*, pg. 3389
ADEKA AL GHURAIR ADDITIVES LLC—See Al Ghurair Group; *Int'l*, pg. 277
ADIA NUTRITION, INC.; *U.S. Public*, pg. 41
AEGERION PHARMACEUTICALS, INC.—See Chiesi Farmaceutici SpA; *Int'l*, pg. 1477
AFFINOR GROWERS INC.; *Int'l*, pg. 187
AIM INTERNATIONAL, INC.; *U.S. Private*, pg. 132
AION THERAPEUTIC INC.; *Int'l*, pg. 234
AIR WATER INC. - KASHIMA PLANT—See Air Water Inc.; *Int'l*, pg. 239
ALAND LIMITED—See Golden Resources Development International Limited; *Int'l*, pg. 3031
ALAPIS HOLDING INDUSTRIAL & COMMERCIAL SA; *Int'l*, pg. 291
ALFA WASSERMANN SRL—See Alfa-Wassermann S.p.A.; *Int'l*, pg. 314
ALKALOID BUCHUREST SRL—See Alkaloid A.D. Skopje; *Int'l*, pg. 330
ALLERGOPHARMA (BEIJING) PHARMACEUTICAL TECHNOLOGY CO., LTD.—See Dermapharm Holding SE; *Int'l*, pg. 2043
ALLIANCE GROWERS CORP.; *Int'l*, pg. 339
ALPHA-TEC SYSTEMS, INC.—See StoneCalibre, LLC; *U.S. Private*, pg. 3827
ALTERNATIVE LABORATORIES, LLC—See Alpine 4 Holdings, Inc.; *U.S. Public*, pg. 85
AMERICAN GREEN, INC.; *U.S. Public*, pg. 103
AMERINIC, INC.—See Universal Corporation; *U.S. Public*, pg. 2254
A.M. TODD BOTANICAL THERAPEUTICS—See A.M. Todd Company; *U.S. Private*, pg. 27
ANTEROGEN CO., LTD—See Bukwang Pharmaceutical Co., Ltd.; *Int'l*, pg. 1213
ANTIBIOTICE S.A.; *Int'l*, pg. 483
APOTEX NZ LTD—See SK Capital Partners, LP; *U.S. Private*, pg. 3678
ARAGON PHARMACEUTICALS, INC.—See Johnson & Johnson; *U.S. Public*, pg. 1194
AREV LIFE SCIENCES GLOBAL CORP.; *Int'l*, pg. 559
ASIAN PHYTOCEUTICALS PUBLIC COMPANY LIMITED; *Int'l*, pg. 619
ASSERTIO HOLDINGS, INC.; *U.S. Public*, pg. 214
AURORA CANNABIS INC.; *Int'l*, pg. 713
AVANTI POLAR LIPIDS, INC.—See Croda International plc; *Int'l*, pg. 1851
AXIM BIOTECHNOLOGIES, INC.; *U.S. Public*, pg. 255
AXON COMMUNICATIONS INC.—See Mountaingate Capital Management, L.P.; *U.S. Private*, pg. 2801
AXYGEN BIOSCIENCE, INC.—See Corning Incorporated; *U.S. Public*, pg. 578
AYR WELLNESS INC.; *Int'l*, pg. 775
BABYCARE LTD.—See Gull Holdings, Ltd.; *U.S. Private*, pg. 1817
BAXTER BIOSCIENCE DIVISION—See Baxter International Inc.; *U.S. Public*, pg. 280
BBI BASIC CANADA INC.—See BBI Life Sciences Corporation; *Int'l*, pg. 920
BC CRAFT SUPPLY CO., LTD.; *Int'l*, pg. 921
BERONI GROUP LIMITED; *Int'l*, pg. 989
BEST WORLD INTERNATIONAL LTD.; *Int'l*, pg. 999
BETTA PHARMACEUTICALS CO., LTD.; *Int'l*, pg. 1003
BIFIDO CO., LTD.; *Int'l*, pg. 1020
BIOADAPTIVES, INC.; *U.S. Public*, pg. 334
BIOALPHA HOLDINGS BERHAD; *Int'l*, pg. 1036
BIOATLA, INC; *U.S. Public*, pg. 335
BIOCATALYSTS LTD.—See BRAIN Biotech AG; *Int'l*, pg. 1137
BIOME GROW, INC.; *Int'l*, pg. 1039
BIOMETICS INTERNATIONAL, INC.; *U.S. Private*, pg. 562
BIO-RAD QSD DIVISION—See Bio-Rad Laboratories, Inc.; *U.S. Public*, pg. 333
BIOXYNE INTERNATIONAL MALAYSIA SDN BHD—See Bioxyne Limited; *Int'l*, pg. 1045
BLACKMORES LIMITED; *Int'l*, pg. 1061
BLUEBONNET NUTRITION, CORP.; *U.S. Private*, pg. 596
BOIRON GROUP; *Int'l*, pg. 1101
BOIRON USA INC.—See Boiron Group; *Int'l*, pg. 1101
THE BOUNTIFUL COMPANY—See KKR & Co. Inc.; *U.S. Public*, pg. 1264
CAMLIN FINE SCIENCES LTD.; *Int'l*, pg. 1273
CAMURUS PTY. LTD.—See Camurus AB; *Int'l*, pg. 1275
CANAQUEST MEDICAL CORP; *Int'l*, pg. 1287
THE CANNABIS DEPOT HOLDING CORP.; *U.S. Private*, pg. 4004
CANNAGROW HOLDINGS, INC.; *U.S. Public*, pg. 430
CANNDESCENT LLC; *U.S. Private*, pg. 734
CANN GROUP LIMITED; *Int'l*, pg. 1291
CANOPY GROWTH CORPORATION; *Int'l*, pg. 1298
CANSORTIUM, INC.; *U.S. Public*, pg. 430
CAPTEK SOFTGEL INTERNATIONAL, INC.—See Swander Pace Capital, LLC; *U.S. Private*, pg. 3890
CBI LABORATORIES, INC.—See SunTx Capital Partners, L.P.; *U.S. Private*, pg. 3874
CELESTIAL BIOLABS LIMITED; *Int'l*, pg. 1392
CELL TECH INTERNATIONAL INCORPORATED; *U.S. Public*, pg. 465
CHARLIE'S HOLDINGS, INC.; *U.S. Public*, pg. 480
CHINA GINSENG HOLDINGS, INC.; *Int'l*, pg. 1504
CHINA HOLDINGS, INC.; *Int'l*, pg. 1508
CHINA MEHECO TOPFOND PHARMA CO., LTD.—See China Meheco Group Co., Ltd.; *Int'l*, pg. 1519
CHINA NATIONAL GROUP CORPORATION OF TRADITIONAL & HERBAL MEDICINE—See China National Pharmaceutical Group Corporation; *Int'l*, pg. 1533
CHINA PENGFEI GROUP LIMITED; *Int'l*, pg. 1539
CHROMADEX ANALYTICS, INC.—See ChromaDex Corporation; *U.S. Public*, pg. 490
CHROMADEX, INC.—See ChromaDex Corporation; *U.S. Public*, pg. 490

N.A.I.C.S. Index

325411 — MEDICINAL AND BOTAN... CORPORATE AFFILIATIONS

CHUMA HOLDINGS INC.; *U.S. Private*, pg. 894
CJ BIO AMERICA INC.—See CJ Corporation; *Int'l*, pg. 1631
CJ CORP. (MOSCOW)—See CJ Corporation; *Int'l*, pg. 1632
COMMONWEALTH ALTERNATIVE CARE, INC.—See TILT Holdings Inc.; *U.S. Public*, pg. 2159
CORBION - PURAC DIVISION—See Corbion N.V.; *Int'l*, pg. 1795
CRONOS GROUP INC.; *Int'l*, pg. 1855
CYANOTECH CORPORATION; *U.S. Public*, pg. 616
CY BIOTECH; *Int'l*, pg. 1891
DAEDONG KOREA GINSENG CO., LTD.; *Int'l*, pg. 1906
DAKO SCHWEIZ GMBH—See Agilent Technologies, Inc.; *U.S. Public*, pg. 61
DELPHARM EVREUX SAS—See Delpharm S.A.S.; *Int'l*, pg. 2015
DELPHARM TOURS SAS—See Delpharm S.A.S.; *Int'l*, pg. 2015
DESERET LABORATORIES, INC.; *U.S. Private*, pg. 1212
DESIGNING HEALTH, INC.; *U.S. Private*, pg. 1215
DISC MEDICINE, INC.; *U.S. Public*, pg. 668
DOCTOR'S NATURAL; *U.S. Private*, pg. 1251
DR. WILLMAR SCHWABE GMBH & CO. KG; *Int'l*, pg. 2195
EARTHRISE NUTRITIONAL LLC—See DIC Corporation; *Int'l*, pg. 2109
EASTWOOD BIO-MEDICAL CANADA INC.; *Int'l*, pg. 2275
ELECTROCORE, INC.; *U.S. Public*, pg. 723
ELEMENTS OF HEALTH AND WELLNESS, INC.—See ASC Global Inc.; *U.S. Private*, pg. 345
ELITE ONE SOURCE NUTRISCIENCES—See Ampersand Management LLC; *U.S. Private*, pg. 265
ELIXINOL BV—See Elixinol Wellness Limited; *Int'l*, pg. 2363
ELIXINOL WELLNESS LIMITED; *Int'l*, pg. 2363
EMAMI INTERNATIONAL FZE—See Emami Ltd; *Int'l*, pg. 2374
EMAMI REALTY LIMITED—See Emami Ltd; *Int'l*, pg. 2374
EMERGENT BIOSOLUTIONS INC.; *U.S. Public*, pg. 739
EMERGING WORLD PHARMA, INC.; *U.S. Private*, pg. 1381
ENTEC GESELLSCHAFT FUR ENDOKRINOLOGISCHE TECHNOLOGIE GMBH—See Bayer Aktiengesellschaft; *Int'l*, pg. 904
ENTEC GESELLSCHAFT FUR ENDOKRINOLOGISCHE TECHNOLOGIE MBH—See Bayer Aktiengesellschaft; *Int'l*, pg. 904
ENTOURAGE HEALTH CORP.; *Int'l*, pg. 2452
ENZYMATIC THERAPY INC.—See Dr. Willmar Schwabe GmbH & Co. KG; *Int'l*, pg. 2195
EPICENTRE TECHNOLOGIES CORPORATION—See Illumina, Inc.; *U.S. Public*, pg. 1112
ERCROS SA - BASIC CHEMICALS DIVISION—See Ercros SA; *Int'l*, pg. 2489
ESENSE-LAB LTD; *Int'l*, pg. 2502
ESSENTIAL OILS OF TASMANIA PTY LTD—See Atlas Pearls Ltd.; *Int'l*, pg. 686
THE ESTER-C COMPANY—See KKR & Co. Inc.; *U.S. Public*, pg. 1264
EUROMED S.A.—See Dermapharm Holding SE; *Int'l*, pg. 2043
EU YAN SANG (SINGAPORE) PTE LTD—See Eu Yan Sang International Ltd.; *Int'l*, pg. 2525
EVERGREEN BAMBOO INTERNATIONAL LIMITED; *Int'l*, pg. 2565
EXCELSIOR BIOPHARMA, INC.; *Int'l*, pg. 2578
FARMHOUSE, INC.; *U.S. Public*, pg. 822
FITLIFE BRANDS, INC.; *U.S. Public*, pg. 851
FLORA INC.—See Flora Manufacturing & Distributing Ltd.; *Int'l*, pg. 2707
FLORA MANUFACTURING & DISTRIBUTING LTD.; *Int'l*, pg. 2707
FOOD SCIENCES CORPORATION; *U.S. Private*, pg. 1561
FORMOSA PHARMACEUTICALS, INC.—See Formosa Laboratories, Inc.; *Int'l*, pg. 2735
FRESH TRACKS THERAPEUTICS, INC.; *U.S. Public*, pg. 886
FRUTAROM USA INC.—See International Flavors & Fragrances Inc.; *U.S. Public*, pg. 1152
GANGA PHARMACEUTICALS LTD.; *Int'l*, pg. 2880
GASPARI NUTRITION, INC.—See Gaspari Nutra LLC; *U.S. Private*, pg. 1648
GB CHEMICALS PTE LTD—See AP Oil International Ltd.; *Int'l*, pg. 499
GELITA HEALTH GMBH—See Gelita AG; *Int'l*, pg. 2913
GENEXINE INC. - NEW YORK BRANCH—See Genexine Inc.; *Int'l*, pg. 2923
GENEXINE INC.; *Int'l*, pg. 2923
GENOTECH CORPORATION; *Int'l*, pg. 2925
GLOBAL ROUNDTABLE CORPORATION; *U.S. Public*, pg. 945
GNOMESTAR CRAFT INC.; *Int'l*, pg. 3017
GRAPE KING BIO LTD.; *Int'l*, pg. 3060
GREAT TREE PHARMACY CO., LTD.; *Int'l*, pg. 3065
H2OCEAN, INC.; *U.S. Private*, pg. 1837
HAINAN DIC MICROALGAE CO., LTD.—See DIC Corporation; *Int'l*, pg. 2109
HALO COLLECTIVE INC.; *Int'l*, pg. 3233
HARBIN MEDISAN PHARMACEUTICAL CO., LTD.; *Int'l*, pg. 3270
HARBIN YEW SCIENCE AND TECHNOLOGY DEVELOPMENT CO., LTD.—See Yew Bio-Pharm Group, Inc.; *U.S. Private*, pg. 4589
HARVEST ENTERPRISES, INC.—See Trulieve Cannabis Corp.; *U.S. Public*, pg. 2201
HAW PAR LAND (MALAYSIA) SDN. BHD.—See Haw Par Corporation Limited; *Int'l*, pg. 3287
HAW PAR LEISURE PTE LTD—See Haw Par Corporation Limited; *Int'l*, pg. 3287
HEALIXA INC.; *U.S. Public*, pg. 1014
HEALTH AND HAPPINESS (H&H) INTERNATIONAL HOLDINGS LIMITED; *Int'l*, pg. 3303
HEALTH PRODUCTS CORPORATION; *U.S. Private*, pg. 1894
THE HEALTHY BACK INSTITUTE; *U.S. Private*, pg. 4044
HEINRICH HAGNER GMBH & CO.; *Int'l*, pg. 3324
HEMPACCO CO., INC.; *U.S. Public*, pg. 1025
HEMP, INC.; *U.S. Public*, pg. 1025
HERSHEY ENGINEERING COMPANY, LTD.—See Formosan Union Chemical Corp.; *Int'l*, pg. 2736
HL SCIENCE CO., LTD.; *Int'l*, pg. 3430
HOVIONE LIMITED—See Hovione Farma Ciencia S.A.; *Int'l*, pg. 3492
HVL INC.; *U.S. Private*, pg. 2015
THE HYBRID CREATIVE LLC—See Greenlane Holdings, Inc.; *U.S. Public*, pg. 965
HYUPJIN CO., LTD.; *Int'l*, pg. 3561
IDBYDNA INC.—See Illumina, Inc.; *U.S. Public*, pg. 1112
IFP, INC.; *U.S. Private*, pg. 2039
IM CANNABIS CORP.; *Int'l*, pg. 3617
IMPACT FUSION INTERNATIONAL, INC.; *U.S. Public*, pg. 1113
INERGETICS, INC.; *U.S. Private*, pg. 2069
INNOVATIVE HOLDINGS ALLIANCE, INC.; *U.S. Public*, pg. 1127
ION LABS, INC.—See DCC plc; *Int'l*, pg. 1990
JANSSEN PRODUCTS, LP—See Johnson & Johnson; *U.S. Public*, pg. 1197
JEUNESSE GLOBAL LLC; *U.S. Private*, pg. 2204
JEUNIQUE INTERNATIONAL INC.; *U.S. Private*, pg. 2204
KALEXSYN, INC.—See Dipharma Francis S.r.l.; *Int'l*, pg. 2128
KELATRON CORPORATION—See One Rock Capital Partners, LLC; *U.S. Private*, pg. 3022
KORVER CORP.; *U.S. Public*, pg. 1275
LIMITLESS VENTURE GROUP, INC.; *U.S. Public*, pg. 1316
MANNATECH, INCORPORATED; *U.S. Public*, pg. 1356
MANNATECH JAPAN, INC.—See Mannatech, Incorporated; *U.S. Public*, pg. 1357
MANNATECH TAIWAN CORPORATION—See Mannatech, Incorporated; *U.S. Public*, pg. 1357
MATRIXX INITIATIVES, INC.—See Gryphon Investors, LLC; *U.S. Private*, pg. 1799
MEDA MANUFACTURING GMBH—See Viatris Inc.; *U.S. Public*, pg. 2293
MEDA PHARMA GMBH & CO. KG—See Viatris Inc.; *U.S. Public*, pg. 2293
MEDA PHARMA GMBH—See Viatris Inc.; *U.S. Public*, pg. 2293
MEDICAL MARIJUANA INC.; *U.S. Public*, pg. 1412
MEDIPHARMA LTD—See Hikal Limited; *Int'l*, pg. 3389
MEI PHARMA, INC.; *U.S. Public*, pg. 1414
MELALEUCA INC.; *U.S. Private*, pg. 2661
MERCK SHARP & DOHME, LIMITADA—See Merck & Co., Inc.; *U.S. Public*, pg. 1420
MERIDIAN LIFE SCIENCE, INC.—See Meridian Bioscience Inc.; *U.S. Public*, pg. 1424
MJARDIN GROUP, INC.; *U.S. Public*, pg. 1452
MTI PHARMA SOLUTIONS, INC.—See Catalent, Inc.; *U.S. Public*, pg. 448
MYM NUTRACEUTICALS INC.—See IM Cannabis Corp.; *Int'l*, pg. 3617
NAI EUROPE—See Natural Alternatives International, Inc.; *U.S. Public*, pg. 1499
NATROL, LLC—See Aurobindo Pharma Ltd.; *Int'l*, pg. 712
NATURAL ALTERNATIVES INTERNATIONAL, INC.; *U.S. Public*, pg. 1498
NATURE'S SUNSHINE PRODUCTS DE VENEZUELA, C.A.—See Nature's Sunshine Products, Inc.; *U.S. Public*, pg. 1499
NATUREX INC.—See Givaudan S.A.; *Int'l*, pg. 2981
NEWAYS INC.; *U.S. Private*, pg. 2913
NOTIS GLOBAL, INC.; *U.S. Public*, pg. 1543
NULAB, INC.; *U.S. Private*, pg. 2973
NULEAF NATURALS, LLC—See High Tide, Inc.; *Int'l*, pg. 3386
NUTRACEUTICAL INTERNATIONAL CORPORATION—See HGGC, LLC; *U.S. Private*, pg. 1930
NUTRA MANUFACTURING, INC.—See Ares Management Corporation; *U.S. Public*, pg. 189
NUTRAMED, INC.—See Ampersand Management LLC; *U.S. Private*, pg. 265
NUTRANOMICS INC.; *U.S. Public*, pg. 1556
NUTRASCIENCE LABS, INC.—See Twinlab Consolidated Holdings, Inc.; *U.S. Public*, pg. 2207
NUTRITIONAL LABORATORIES INTERNATIONAL, INC.—See Ampersand Management LLC; *U.S. Private*, pg. 265
OBAGI COSMECEUTICALS LLC—See Waldencast plc; *U.S. Public*, pg. 2321
OCI CO., LTD. - INCHEON PLANT—See HJ Shipbuilding & Construction Company, Ltd.; *Int'l*, pg. 3428
ONCOLOGY ANALYTICS, INC.; *U.S. Private*, pg. 3019
ONE WORLD VENTURES, INC.; *U.S. Public*, pg. 1602
OPTIGENEX, INC.; *U.S. Private*, pg. 3034
ORTHO-MCNEIL PHARMACEUTICAL, INC.—See Johnson & Johnson; *U.S. Public*, pg. 1197
PACIFICHEALTH LABORATORIES, INC.; *U.S. Public*, pg. 1632
PERMA-FIX MEDICAL S.A—See Perma-Fix Environmental Services, Inc.; *U.S. Public*, pg. 1676
PFIZER PRODUCTS INC.—See Pfizer Inc.; *U.S. Public*, pg. 1682
PHARMETICS - BURLINGTON OPERATIONS—See Monitor Clipper Partners, LLC; *U.S. Private*, pg. 2771
PLUS PRODUCTS INC; *U.S. Public*, pg. 1699
P.T. SYNERGY WORLDWIDE INDONESIA—See Nature's Sunshine Products, Inc.; *U.S. Public*, pg. 1499
PUCHENG CHIA TAI BIOCHEMISTRY CO., LTD.—See Charoen Pokphand Foods Public Company Limited; *Int'l*, pg. 1452
PUCHENG CHIA TAI BIOCHEMISTRY LTD.—See Charoen Pokphand Foods Public Company Limited; *Int'l*, pg. 1453
PURAC BIOQUIMICA S.A.—See Corbion N.V.; *Int'l*, pg. 1795
PURAC SINTESES—See Corbion N.V.; *Int'l*, pg. 1795
PURE FRUIT TECHNOLOGIES, LLC; *U.S. Private*, pg. 3305
PURITAN'S PRIDE, INC.—See KKR & Co. Inc.; *U.S. Public*, pg. 1264
QINGDAO HUAZHONG PHARMACEUTICALS CO., LTD.—See China National Pharmaceutical Group Corporation; *Int'l*, pg. 1534
QINGDAO HUAZHONG PHARMACEUTICALS CO., LTD.—See Hoyu Co., Ltd.; *Int'l*, pg. 3499
QUANTUM, INC.; *U.S. Private*, pg. 3323
RAINBOW LIGHT NUTRITIONAL SYSTEMS, INC.; *U.S. Private*, pg. 3347
REIGN BEVERAGE COMPANY LLC—See Monster Beverage Corporation; *U.S. Public*, pg. 1465
RELIV INTERNATIONAL, INC.; *U.S. Public*, pg. 1782
REPLIGEN GMBH—See Repligen Corporation; *U.S. Public*, pg. 1784
RIMROCK GOLD CORP.; *U.S. Public*, pg. 1799
SATIPHARM AG—See Hygrovest Limited; *Int'l*, pg. 3549
SCIGEN BIOPHARMA PVT LTD—See BIOTON S.A.; *Int'l*, pg. 1043
SIMAFEX—See Guerbet SA; *Int'l*, pg. 3172
SINO-SWED PHARMACEUTICAL CORP., LTD.—See China National Pharmaceutical Group Corporation; *Int'l*, pg. 1534
SINO-SWED PHARMACEUTICAL CORP., LTD.—See Fresenius SE & Co. KGaA; *Int'l*, pg. 2778
SIRTON PHARMACEUTICALS SPA—See 3SBio Inc.; *Int'l*, pg. 9
SOLAE LLC - PRYOR OFFICE—See DuPont de Nemours, Inc.; *U.S. Public*, pg. 692
SOLGAR, INC.—See KKR & Co. Inc.; *U.S. Public*, pg. 1264
SOLIANCE S.A.—See Givaudan S.A.; *Int'l*, pg. 2982
SPECTRUM LABS INDIA PVT. LTD.—See Repligen Corporation; *U.S. Public*, pg. 1785
SWING CORPORATION—See Ebara Corporation; *Int'l*, pg. 2284
SWISSE WELLNESS PTY LTD—See Health and Happiness (H&H) International Holdings Limited; *Int'l*, pg. 3303
SYNERGY WORLDWIDE AUSTRALIA PTY LTD.—See Nature's Sunshine Products, Inc.; *U.S. Public*, pg. 1499
SYNERGY WORLDWIDE INC.—See Nature's Sunshine Products, Inc.; *U.S. Public*, pg. 1499
SYNERGY WORLDWIDE MARKETING SDN BHD—See Nature's Sunshine Products, Inc.; *U.S. Public*, pg. 1499
SYNERGY WORLDWIDE PHILIPPINES DISTRIBUTION INC.—See Nature's Sunshine Products, Inc.; *U.S. Public*, pg. 1500
SYNERGY WORLDWIDE (S) PTE LTD.—See Nature's Sunshine Products, Inc.; *U.S. Public*, pg. 1499
TACTICAL RELIEF, LLC—See Allied Corp.; *Int'l*, pg. 357
TASMANIAN ALKALOIDS PTY. LTD.—See SK Capital Partners, LP; *U.S. Private*, pg. 3680
TECHLAB, INC.—See Adelis Equity Partners AB; *Int'l*, pg. 142
THERAPEUTICSMD, INC.; *U.S. Public*, pg. 2144
TOBAHMAOZ, INC.; *U.S. Private*, pg. 4180
TRIARCO INDUSTRIES, LLC—See One Rock Capital Partners, LLC; *U.S. Private*, pg. 3022
TWINLAB CONSOLIDATION CORPORATION—See Twinlab Consolidated Holdings, Inc.; *U.S. Public*, pg. 2207
TWINLAB CORPORATION—See Twinlab Consolidated Holdings, Inc.; *U.S. Public*, pg. 2207
TWINLAB CORP. - UTAH FACILITY—See Twinlab Consolidated Holdings, Inc.; *U.S. Public*, pg. 2207
UHS ESSENTIAL HEALTH PHILIPPINES, INC.—See Gull Holdings, Ltd.; *U.S. Private*, pg. 1817
UHS PRODUCTS (MALAYSIA) SDN BHD—See Gull Holdings, Ltd.; *U.S. Private*, pg. 1817
UNITED PERFORMANCE MATERIALS CORP.—See For-

N.A.I.C.S. INDEX

325412 — PHARMACEUTICAL PREP...

mosan Union Chemical Corp.; *Int'l*, pg. 2736
UNRIVALED BRANDS, INC.; *U.S. Public*, pg. 2263
USANA HEALTH SCIENCES, INC.—See Gull Holdings, Ltd.; *U.S. Private*, pg. 1817
UST CORPORATION—See Heartwood Partners, LLC; *U.S. Private*, pg. 1901
VITAMIN CLASSICS INC.; *U.S. Private*, pg. 4405
VITAMINHAUS PTY LTD—See The Procter & Gamble Company; *U.S. Public*, pg. 2124
WEISSBIOTECH GMBH—See BRAIN Biotech AG; *Int'l*, pg. 1137
WENG LI SDN. BHD.—See Eu Yan Sang International Ltd.; *Int'l*, pg. 2525
WESTAR NUTRITION CORP.; *U.S. Private*, pg. 4488
WESTERN SIERRA RESOURCE CORP.; *U.S. Private*, pg. 2356
XANGO, LLC; *U.S. Private*, pg. 4580
YEW BIO-PHARM GROUP, INC.; *U.S. Private*, pg. 4589
YIN YANG SPA PRODUCTS PTE LTD—See Eu Yan Sang International Ltd.; *Int'l*, pg. 2525
YOUR SUPERFOODS GMBH—See The Healing Company Inc.; *U.S. Public*, pg. 2088
ZACK DARLING CREATIVE ASSOCIATES, LLC—See Greenlane Holdings, Inc.; *U.S. Public*, pg. 965
ZENTIVA INHALATIONSPRODUKTE GMBH—See Advent International Corporation; *U.S. Private*, pg. 108
ZHEJIANG XIANJU XIANLE PHARMACEUTICAL COMPANY LIMITED—See Grand Pharmaceutical Group Limited; *Int'l*, pg. 3056

325412 — PHARMACEUTICAL PREPARATION MANUFACTURING

024 PHARMA, INC.; *U.S. Private*, pg. 1
1CM INC.; *Int'l*, pg. 3
1NKEMIA IUCT GROUP, S.A.; *Int'l*, pg. 3
21ST CENTURY BIOCHEMICALS; *U.S. Private*, pg. 5
2CUREX GMBH—See 2cureX AB; *Int'l*, pg. 4
3-D MATRIX EUROPE SAS—See 3-D Matrix, Ltd.; *Int'l*, pg. 6
3-D MATRIX, INC.—See 3-D Matrix, Ltd.; *Int'l*, pg. 6
3M HEALTH CARE LTD.—See Solventum Corporation; *U.S. Public*, pg. 1901
3M SVENSKA AB—See 3M Company; *U.S. Public*, pg. 7
4D PHARMA PLC; *Int'l*, pg. 11
4FRONT VENTURES CORP.; *U.S. Public*, pg. 9
60 DEGREES PHARMACEUTICALS, INC.; *U.S. Public*, pg. 9
AAREY DRUGS & PHARMACEUTICALS LTD.; *Int'l*, pg. 37
AARTI DRUGS LTD.; *Int'l*, pg. 38
AB-BIOTICS S.A.; *Int'l*, pg. 47
ABBOTT AG-DIAGNOSTICS—See Abbott Laboratories; *U.S. Public*, pg. 14
ABBOTT AG-NUTRITIONALS—See Abbott Laboratories; *U.S. Public*, pg. 17
ABBOTT AG—See Abbott Laboratories; *U.S. Public*, pg. 14
ABBOTT ARZNEIMITTEL GMBH—See Abbott Laboratories; *U.S. Public*, pg. 17
ABBOTT BIOLOGICALS BV—See Abbott Laboratories; *U.S. Public*, pg. 14
ABBOTT B.V.—See Abbott Laboratories; *U.S. Public*, pg. 14
ABBOTT CAPITAL INDIA LIMITED—See Abbott Laboratories; *U.S. Public*, pg. 14
ABBOTT DIABETES CARE B.V.—See Abbott Laboratories; *U.S. Public*, pg. 14
ABBOTT DIABETES CARE—See Abbott Laboratories; *U.S. Public*, pg. 14
ABBOTT-ESTABLISHED PRODUCTS DIVISION—See Abbott Laboratories; *U.S. Public*, pg. 17
ABBOTT GESELLSCHAFT M.B.H.—See Abbott Laboratories; *U.S. Public*, pg. 15
ABBOTT GMBH & CO. KG - PHARMACEUTICAL DIVISION—See Abbott Laboratories; *U.S. Public*, pg. 15
ABBOTT GMBH & CO. KG—See Abbott Laboratories; *U.S. Public*, pg. 15
ABBOTT HEALTHCARE PRODUCTS B.V.—See Abbott Laboratories; *U.S. Public*, pg. 17
ABBOTT HEALTHCARE VIETNAM COMPANY LIMITED—See Abbott Laboratories; *U.S. Public*, pg. 15
ABBOTT INDIA LIMITED—See Abbott Laboratories; *U.S. Public*, pg. 15
ABBOTT INFORMATICS EUROPE LIMITED—See Abbott Laboratories; *U.S. Public*, pg. 15
ABBOTT INFORMATICS FRANCE—See Abbott Laboratories; *U.S. Public*, pg. 15
ABBOTT INTERNATIONAL LLC—See Abbott Laboratories; *U.S. Public*, pg. 15
ABBOTT IRELAND—See Abbott Laboratories; *U.S. Public*, pg. 15
ABBOTT JAPAN CO., LTD.—See Abbott Laboratories; *U.S. Public*, pg. 15
ABBOTT KOREA LIMITED—See Abbott Laboratories; *U.S. Public*, pg. 15
ABBOTT LABORATORIES ARGENTINA, S.A.—See Abbott Laboratories; *U.S. Public*, pg. 15
ABBOTT LABORATORIES A/S—See Abbott Laboratories; *U.S. Public*, pg. 15
ABBOTT LABORATORIES BALTICS—See Abbott Laboratories; *U.S. Public*, pg. 15
ABBOTT LABORATORIES B.V.—See Abbott Laboratories; *U.S. Public*, pg. 15
ABBOTT LABORATORIES, C.A.—See Abbott Laboratories; *U.S. Public*, pg. 16
ABBOTT LABORATORIES DE CHILE LIMITADA—See Abbott Laboratories; *U.S. Public*, pg. 16
ABBOTT LABORATORIES DE COLOMBIA, S.A.—See Abbott Laboratories; *U.S. Public*, pg. 16
ABBOTT LABORATORIES D.O.O—See Abbott Laboratories; *U.S. Public*, pg. 16
ABBOTT LABORATORIES DRUZBA ZA FARMACIJO IN DIAGNOSTIKO D.O.O.—See Abbott Laboratories; *U.S. Public*, pg. 16
ABBOTT LABORATORIES GMBH—See Abbott Laboratories; *U.S. Public*, pg. 15
ABBOTT LABORATORIES (HELLAS) S.A.—See Abbott Laboratories; *U.S. Public*, pg. 15
ABBOTT LABORATORIES, LIMITED—See Abbott Laboratories; *U.S. Public*, pg. 16
ABBOTT LABORATORIES LIMITED—See Abbott Laboratories; *U.S. Public*, pg. 16
ABBOTT LABORATORIES (MALAYSIA) SDN. BHD.—See Abbott Laboratories; *U.S. Public*, pg. 15
ABBOTT LABORATORIES (N.Z.) LTD.—See Abbott Laboratories; *U.S. Public*, pg. 15
ABBOTT LABORATORIES PACIFIC LTD.—See Abbott Laboratories; *U.S. Public*, pg. 16
ABBOTT LABORATORIES (PAKISTAN) LIMITED—See Abbott Laboratories; *U.S. Public*, pg. 15
ABBOTT LABORATORIES PHARMACEUTICALS (PR) LTD.—See Abbott Laboratories; *U.S. Public*, pg. 17
ABBOTT LABORATORIES (PHILIPPINES)—See Abbott Laboratories; *U.S. Public*, pg. 15
ABBOTT LABORATORIES POLAND SP Z.O.O.—See Abbott Laboratories; *U.S. Public*, pg. 15
ABBOTT LABORATORIES (PUERTO RICO) INCORPORATED—See Abbott Laboratories; *U.S. Public*, pg. 15
ABBOTT LABORATORIES, S.A.—See Abbott Laboratories; *U.S. Public*, pg. 16
ABBOTT LABORATORIES (SINGAPORE) PRIVATE LIMITED—See Abbott Laboratories; *U.S. Public*, pg. 15
ABBOTT LABORATORIES SLOVAKIA S.R.O.—See Abbott Laboratories; *U.S. Public*, pg. 16
ABBOTT LABORATORIES; *U.S. Public*, pg. 14
ABBOTT LABORATORIES SOUTH AFRICA (PROPRIETARY) LIMITED—See Abbott Laboratories; *U.S. Public*, pg. 16
ABBOTT LABORATORIES S.R.O.—See Abbott Laboratories; *U.S. Public*, pg. 16
ABBOTT LABORATORIES TAIWAN—See Abbott Laboratories; *U.S. Public*, pg. 16
ABBOTT LABORATORIES URUGUAY S.A.—See Abbott Laboratories; *U.S. Public*, pg. 16
ABBOTT LABORATORIOS DEL ECUADOR CIA. LTDA.—See Abbott Laboratories; *U.S. Public*, pg. 16
ABBOTT LABORATORIOS DO BRASIL LTDA—See Abbott Laboratories; *U.S. Public*, pg. 16
ABBOTT LABORATORIOS, LIMITADA—See Abbott Laboratories; *U.S. Public*, pg. 16
ABBOTT LABORATORIOS S.A.—See Abbott Laboratories; *U.S. Public*, pg. 16
ABBOTT LABORATUARLARI ITHALAT IHRACAT VE TECARET LIMITED SIRKETI—See Abbott Laboratories; *U.S. Public*, pg. 16
ABBOTT LABORATUARLARI ITHALAT IHRACAT VE TICARET LIMITED SIRKETI—See Abbott Laboratories; *U.S. Public*, pg. 16
ABBOTT MEDICAL AUSTRALIA PTY. LTD.—See Abbott Laboratories; *U.S. Public*, pg. 16
ABBOTT MEDICAL LABORATORIES LTD—See Abbott Laboratories; *U.S. Public*, pg. 17
ABBOTT MEDICAL NEDERLAND B.V.—See Abbott Laboratories; *U.S. Public*, pg. 17
ABBOTT MOLECULAR INC.—See Abbott Laboratories; *U.S. Public*, pg. 14
ABBOTT NORGE AS—See Abbott Laboratories; *U.S. Public*, pg. 17
ABBOTT NUTRITION—See Abbott Laboratories; *U.S. Public*, pg. 17
ABBOTT OY—See Abbott Laboratories; *U.S. Public*, pg. 17
ABBOTT PHARMACEUTICAL CORPORATION—See Abbott Laboratories; *U.S. Public*, pg. 17
ABBOTT PRODUCTS AG—See Abbott Laboratories; *U.S. Public*, pg. 17
ABBOTT PRODUCTS OPERATIONS AG—See Abbott Laboratories; *U.S. Public*, pg. 17
ABBOTT PRODUCTS ROMANIA S.R.L.—See Abbott Laboratories; *U.S. Public*, pg. 17
ABBOTT RAPID DIAGNOSTICS SCHWEIZ GMBH—See Abbott Laboratories; *U.S. Public*, pg. 17
ABBOTT RAPID DX NORTH AMERICA, LLC—See Abbott Laboratories; *U.S. Public*, pg. 18
ABBOTT SA/NV - DIAGNOSTICS DIVISION—See Abbott Laboratories; *U.S. Public*, pg. 18
ABBOTT S.A.—See Abbott Laboratories; *U.S. Public*, pg. 18
ABBOTT SCANDINAVIA A.B.—See Abbott Laboratories; *U.S. Public*, pg. 18
ABBOTT S.R.L.—See Abbott Laboratories; *U.S. Public*, pg. 18
ABBOTT TRUECARE PHARMA PRIVATE LIMITED—See Abbott Laboratories; *U.S. Public*, pg. 18
ABBOTT VASCULAR DEUTSCHLAND GMBH—See Abbott Laboratories; *U.S. Public*, pg. 18
ABBVIE AB—See AbbVie Inc.; *U.S. Public*, pg. 21
ABBVIE AG—See AbbVie Inc.; *U.S. Public*, pg. 21
ABBVIE A/S; *Int'l*, pg. 57
ABBVIE AS—See AbbVie Inc.; *U.S. Public*, pg. 21
ABBVIE B.V.—See AbbVie Inc.; *U.S. Public*, pg. 21
ABBVIE CORPORATION—See AbbVie Inc.; *U.S. Public*, pg. 21
ABBVIE DEUTSCHLAND GMBH & CO. KG—See AbbVie Inc.; *U.S. Public*, pg. 21
ABBVIE D.O.O.—See AbbVie Inc.; *U.S. Public*, pg. 22
ABBVIE ENDOCRINOLOGY INC.—See AbbVie Inc.; *U.S. Public*, pg. 21
ABBVIE FARMACEUTICA, S.L.U.—See AbbVie Inc.; *U.S. Public*, pg. 21
ABBVIE FARMACEUTICOS, S.A. DE C.V.—See AbbVie Inc.; *U.S. Public*, pg. 21
ABBVIE GK—See AbbVie Inc.; *U.S. Public*, pg. 21
ABBVIE GMBH—See AbbVie Inc.; *U.S. Public*, pg. 21
ABBVIE HEALTHCARE INDIA PRIVATE LIMITED—See AbbVie Inc.; *U.S. Public*, pg. 21
ABBVIE INC.; *U.S. Public*, pg. 21
ABBVIE IRELAND LIMITED—See AbbVie Inc.; *U.S. Public*, pg. 21
ABBVIE IRELAND NL B.V.—See AbbVie Inc.; *U.S. Public*, pg. 21
ABBVIE KFT.—See AbbVie Inc.; *U.S. Public*, pg. 21
ABBVIE, L.DA—See AbbVie Inc.; *U.S. Public*, pg. 22
ABBVIE LIMITED—See AbbVie Inc.; *U.S. Public*, pg. 21
ABBVIE LIMITED—See AbbVie Inc.; *U.S. Public*, pg. 21
ABBVIE LIMITED—See AbbVie Inc.; *U.S. Public*, pg. 21
ABBVIE LTD.—See AbbVie Inc.; *U.S. Public*, pg. 21
ABBVIE LTD—See AbbVie Inc.; *U.S. Public*, pg. 21
ABBVIE LTD—See AbbVie Inc.; *U.S. Public*, pg. 21
ABBVIE OY—See AbbVie Inc.; *U.S. Public*, pg. 22
ABBVIE POLSKA SP. Z O.O.—See AbbVie Inc.; *U.S. Public*, pg. 22
ABBVIE PRODUCTOS FARMACEUTICOS LIMITADA—See AbbVie Inc.; *U.S. Public*, pg. 22
ABBVIE PTE. LTD.—See AbbVie Inc.; *U.S. Public*, pg. 22
ABBVIE PTY LTD—See AbbVie Inc.; *U.S. Public*, pg. 22
ABBVIE SARL—See AbbVie Inc.; *U.S. Public*, pg. 22
ABBVIE S.A.—See AbbVie Inc.; *U.S. Public*, pg. 22
ABBVIE SA—See AbbVie Inc.; *U.S. Public*, pg. 22
ABBVIE S.A.—See AbbVie Inc.; *U.S. Public*, pg. 22
ABBVIE S.A.S.—See AbbVie Inc.; *U.S. Public*, pg. 22
ABBVIE SDN. BHD.—See AbbVie Inc.; *U.S. Public*, pg. 22
ABBVIE SPAIN, S.L.—See AbbVie Inc.; *U.S. Public*, pg. 22
ABBVIE SP. Z O.O.—See AbbVie Inc.; *U.S. Public*, pg. 22
ABBVIE, S.R.L.—See AbbVie Inc.; *U.S. Public*, pg. 22
ABBVIE S.R.O.—See AbbVie Inc.; *U.S. Public*, pg. 22
ABBVIE S.R.O.—See AbbVie Inc.; *U.S. Public*, pg. 22
ABBVIE TIBBI ILACLAR SANAYI VE TICARET LIMITED SIRKETI—See AbbVie Inc.; *U.S. Public*, pg. 22
ABBVIE TIBBI LIACLAR SANAYI VE TICARET LIMITED SIRKETI—See AbbVie Inc.; *U.S. Public*, pg. 22
ABCAM KK—See Danaher Corporation; *U.S. Public*, pg. 624
ABCHECK S.R.O.; *Int'l*, pg. 57
ABC MEDICAL, LLC—See AdaptHealth Corp.; *U.S. Public*, pg. 38
ABCUR AB—See ADVANZ PHARMA Corp. Limited; *Int'l*, pg. 166
ABEONA THERAPEUTICS INC.; *U.S. Public*, pg. 24
ABIC BIOLOGICAL LABORATORIES LTD.—See Phibro Animal Health Corporation; *U.S. Public*, pg. 1685
ABILENE NUCLEAR, LLC—See Cardinal Health, Inc.; *U.S. Public*, pg. 433
ABINGDON HEALTH PLC; *Int'l*, pg. 61
ABION, INC.; *Int'l*, pg. 61
ABIONYX PHARMA SA; *Int'l*, pg. 61
ABIVAX SA; *Int'l*, pg. 62
ABLIVA AB; *Int'l*, pg. 63
ABON BIOPHARM (HANGZHOU) CO., LTD.—See Abbott Laboratories; *U.S. Public*, pg. 18
AB SCIENCE SA; *Int'l*, pg. 41
AB SCIEX GERMANY GMBH—See Danaher Corporation; *U.S. Public*, pg. 623
AB SCIEX KK—See Danaher Corporation; *U.S. Public*, pg. 623
ABTEK (BIOLOGICALS) LTD.—See Neogen Corporation; *U.S. Public*, pg. 1505
ABURAIHAN PHARMACEUTICAL COMPANY; *Int'l*, pg. 74
ABVC BIOPHARMA, INC.; *U.S. Public*, pg. 27
ABZENA PLC—See Welsh, Carson, Anderson & Stowe; *U.S. Private*, pg. 4479
ACACIA PHARMA GROUP PLC—See Eagle Pharmaceuticals, Inc.; *U.S. Public*, pg. 703
ACACIA PHARMA INC.—See Eagle Pharmaceuticals, Inc.; *U.S. Public*, pg. 703
ACADIA PHARMACEUTICALS INC.; *U.S. Public*, pg. 31
ACCELERATED ENROLLMENT SOLUTIONS, INC.—See

325412 — PHARMACEUTICAL PREP...

Thermo Fisher Scientific Inc.; *U.S. Public*, pg. 2150
ACCELERON PHARMA INC.—See Merck & Co., Inc.; *U.S. Public*, pg. 1415
ACCENT MICROCELL LTD.; *Int'l*, pg. 81
ACCREDO HEALTH, INCORPORATED—See The Cigna Group; *U.S. Public*, pg. 2062
ACCUCAPS INDUSTRIES LIMITED—See Catalent, Inc.; *U.S. Public*, pg. 448
ACENZIA, INC.—See Novo Integrated Sciences, Inc.; *U.S. Public*, pg. 1549
ACERTA PHARMA B.V.—See AstraZeneca PLC; *Int'l*, pg. 659
ACERUS PHARMACEUTICALS CORPORATION; *Int'l*, pg. 102
ACETO PHARMA INDIA PVT. LTD.—See Aceto Corporation; *U.S. Private*, pg. 58
ACHIEVE LIFE SCIENCES, INC.; *Int'l*, pg. 103
ACHILLION PHARMACEUTICALS, INC.—See AstraZeneca PLC; *Int'l*, pg. 659
ACI HEALTHCARE LTD.—See Advanced Chemical Industries Limited; *Int'l*, pg. 158
AC IMMUNE SA; *Int'l*, pg. 74
ACINO PHARMA AG—See Avista Capital Partners, L.P.; *U.S. Private*, pg. 408
ACIS ARZNEIMITTEL GMBH—See Dermapharm Holding SE; *Int'l*, pg. 2043
ACLARIS THERAPEUTICS, INC.; *U.S. Public*, pg. 35
ACROTECH BIOPHARMA LLC—See Aurobindo Pharma Ltd.; *Int'l*, pg. 712
ACRUX DDS PTY LTD—See Acrux Limited; *Int'l*, pg. 109
ACRUX PHARMA PTY LTD—See Acrux Limited; *Int'l*, pg. 109
ACS DOBFAR SPA; *Int'l*, pg. 109
ACTINIUM PHARMACEUTICALS, INC.; *U.S. Public*, pg. 36
ACTIVE FINE CHEMICALS LIMITED; *Int'l*, pg. 120
ACUMEDIA MANUFACTURERS, INC.—See Neogen Corporation; *U.S. Public*, pg. 1505
ACURA PHARMACEUTICALS, INC.—See Galen Partners, L.P.; *U.S. Private*, pg. 1637
ACURA PHARMACEUTICAL TECHNOLOGIES, INC.—See Galen Partners, L.P.; *U.S. Private*, pg. 1637
ADALTA LIMITED; *Int'l*, pg. 123
ADAMAS PHARMACEUTICALS, INC.—See Supernus Pharmaceuticals, Inc.; *U.S. Public*, pg. 1967
ADAMIS CORPORATION—See DMK Pharmaceuticals Corporation; *U.S. Public*, pg. 671
ADAPTIMMUNE THERAPEUTICS PLC; *Int'l*, pg. 125
ADAPT PHARMA OPERATIONS LIMITED—See Emergent BioSolutions Inc.; *U.S. Public*, pg. 739
ADHERA THERAPEUTICS, INC.; *U.S. Public*, pg. 41
ADHESYS MEDICAL GMBH—See Grunenthal GmbH; *Int'l*, pg. 3114
ADH HEALTH PRODUCTS, INC.; *U.S. Private*, pg. 79
ADIMMUNE CORPORATION; *Int'l*, pg. 148
ADINATH BIO-LABS LTD.; *Int'l*, pg. 148
ADL BIONATUR SOLUTIONS; *Int'l*, pg. 150
ADLEY FORMULATIONS PRIVATE LIMITED—See Beta Drugs Limited; *Int'l*, pg. 1001
ADLINE CHEM LAB LIMITED; *Int'l*, pg. 150
ADNEXUS, A BRISTOL-MYERS SQUIBB R&D COMPANY—See Bristol-Myers Squibb Company; *U.S. Public*, pg. 384
ADVANCED BIOLOGICS, LLC—See Thompson Street Capital Manager LLC; *U.S. Private*, pg. 4161
ADVANCED CHEMICAL INDUSTRIES LIMITED; *Int'l*, pg. 158
ADVANCED CHROMATOGRAPHY TECHNOLOGIES LTD.—See Avantor, Inc.; *U.S. Public*, pg. 241
ADVANCED ONCOTHERAPY PLC; *Int'l*, pg. 161
ADVANCED PROTEOME THERAPEUTICS CORPORATION; *U.S. Public*, pg. 49
ADVANCED VISION RESEARCH, INC.—See Akorn, Inc.; *U.S. Private*, pg. 145
ADVANCED VITAL ENZYMES PVT. LTD.; *Int'l*, pg. 163
ADVENT PHARMA LIMITED; *Int'l*, pg. 167
ADVERIO PHARMA GMBH—See Bayer Aktiengesellschaft; *Int'l*, pg. 901
ADVERUM BIOTECHNOLOGIES, INC.; *U.S. Public*, pg. 50
ADVICENNE S.A.; *Int'l*, pg. 168
AENOVA HOLDING GMBH—See BC Partners LLP; *Int'l*, pg. 922
AEOLUS PHARMACEUTICALS, INC.; *U.S. Public*, pg. 52
AEON BIOPHARMA SUB, INC.—See AEON Biopharma, Inc.; *U.S. Public*, pg. 52
AEON PROCARE PRIVATE LIMITED—See Ashapura Minechem Limited; *Int'l*, pg. 606
AEQUUS PHARMACEUTICALS INC.; *Int'l*, pg. 179
AERIE PHARMACEUTICALS, INC.—See Alcon Inc.; *Int'l*, pg. 302
AETERNA ZENTARIS GMBH—See COSCIENS Biopharma Inc.; *U.S. Public*, pg. 585
AETHER INDUSTRIES LIMITED; *Int'l*, pg. 183
AFC AGRO BIOTECH LIMITED; *Int'l*, pg. 185
AFC-HD AMS LIFE SCIENCE CO., LTD.; *Int'l*, pg. 185
AFFIMED N.V.; *Int'l*, pg. 186
AFFYMAX, INC.; *U.S. Public*, pg. 57
AFT PHARMACEUTICALS LIMITED; *Int'l*, pg. 196
AGC BIOLOGICS S.P.A—See AGC Inc.; *Int'l*, pg. 201

AGC PHARMA CHEMICALS EUROPE, S.L.U.—See AGC Inc.; *Int'l*, pg. 203
AGC WAKASA CHEMICALS CO., LTD.—See AGC Inc.; *Int'l*, pg. 203
AGENTUS THERAPEUTICS, INC.—See Agenus Inc.; *U.S. Public*, pg. 60
AGENUS INC.; *U.S. Public*, pg. 60
AGE REVERSAL, INC.; *U.S. Private*, pg. 126
AGILA SPECIALTIES POLSKA SP. ZO.O—See Viatris Inc.; *U.S. Public*, pg. 2293
AGILE THERAPEUTICS, INC.; *U.S. Public*, pg. 60
AGIOS PHARMACEUTICALS INC.; *U.S. Public*, pg. 62
AGNO PHARMA; *U.S. Private*, pg. 128
AGOURON PHARMACEUTICALS, INC.—See Pfizer Inc.; *U.S. Public*, pg. 1679
AGTECH PRODUCTS, INC.—See International Flavors & Fragrances Inc.; *U.S. Public*, pg. 1151
AHG OF NEW YORK, INC.—See The Cigna Group; *U.S. Public*, pg. 2062
AHLCON PARENTERALS (INDIA) LTD.—See B. Braun Melsungen AG; *Int'l*, pg. 785
AHN-GOOK PHARMACEUTICAL CO., LTD.; *Int'l*, pg. 225
AIDA PHARMACEUTICALS, INC.; *Int'l*, pg. 231
AINOS, INC.; *U.S. Public*, pg. 64
AIREHEALTH, LLC; *U.S. Private*, pg. 141
AJANTA PHARMA LIMITED; *Int'l*, pg. 255
AJANTA PHARMA (MAURITIUS) LIMITED—See Ajanta Pharma Limited; *Int'l*, pg. 255
AJANTA PHARMA PHILIPPINES INC.—See Ajanta Pharma Limited; *Int'l*, pg. 255
AJANTA PHARMA USA INC.—See Ajanta Pharma Limited; *Int'l*, pg. 255
AJINOMOTO ALTHEA, INC—See Ajinomoto Company, Inc.; *Int'l*, pg. 257
AJINOMOTO KOHJIN BIO CO., LTD.—See Ajinomoto Company, Inc.; *Int'l*, pg. 257
AKANDA CORP.; *Int'l*, pg. 259
AKARI THERAPEUTICS, PLC; *Int'l*, pg. 259
AKEBIA THERAPEUTICS, INC.; *U.S. Public*, pg. 69
AKESO, INC.; *Int'l*, pg. 263
AKORN AG—See Akorn, Inc.; *U.S. Private*, pg. 146
AKORN, INC.; *U.S. Private*, pg. 145
AKORN (NEW JERSEY), INC.—See Akorn, Inc.; *U.S. Private*, pg. 146
ALAUNOS THERAPEUTICS, INC.; *U.S. Public*, pg. 72
ALBEMARLE CHEMICALS (SHANGHAI) COMPANY LIMITED—See Albemarle Corporation; *U.S. Public*, pg. 73
ALBEMARLE DEUTSCHLAND GMBH—See Albemarle Corporation; *U.S. Public*, pg. 73
ALBEMARLE EUROPE SPRL—See Albemarle Corporation; *U.S. Public*, pg. 73
ALBEMARLE JAPAN CORPORATION—See Albemarle Corporation; *U.S. Public*, pg. 73
ALBEMARLE KOREA CORPORATION—See Albemarle Corporation; *U.S. Public*, pg. 73
ALBEMARLE SINGAPORE PTE LTD—See Albemarle Corporation; *U.S. Public*, pg. 73
ALBERT DAVID LTD. - KOLKATTA UNIT—See Albert David Ltd.; *Int'l*, pg. 297
ALBERT DAVID LTD; *Int'l*, pg. 297
ALBIREO PHARMA, INC.; *U.S. Public*, pg. 74
ALBORZ BULK RAW MATERIALS COMPANY—See Alborz Investment Company; *Int'l*, pg. 299
ALBORZ DAROU PHARMACEUTICAL COMPANY; *Int'l*, pg. 299
ALCALIBER S.A; *Int'l*, pg. 300
ALCAMI CAROLINAS CORPORATION—See Ares Management Corporation; *U.S. Public*, pg. 188
ALDAGEN, INC.—See Nuo Therapeutics, Inc.; *U.S. Public*, pg. 1555
ALDEYRA THERAPEUTICS, INC.; *U.S. Public*, pg. 74
ALEMBIC LIMITED; *Int'l*, pg. 306
ALEMBIC PHARMACEUTICALS LIMITED—See Alembic Limited; *Int'l*, pg. 306
ALERE GMBH—See Abbott Laboratories; *U.S. Public*, pg. 18
ALERE HEALTH BVBA—See Abbott Laboratories; *U.S. Public*, pg. 18
ALERE HEALTH B.V.—See Abbott Laboratories; *U.S. Public*, pg. 18
ALERE HEALTHCARE INC.—See Abbott Laboratories; *U.S. Public*, pg. 18
ALERE HEALTHCARE (PTY) LIMITED—See Abbott Laboratories; *U.S. Public*, pg. 18
ALERE HOME MONITORING INC—See Abbott Laboratories; *U.S. Public*, pg. 18
ALERE MEDICAL CO., LTD.—See Abbott Laboratories; *U.S. Public*, pg. 18
ALERE MEDICAL PRIVATE LIMITED—See Abbott Laboratories; *U.S. Public*, pg. 18
ALERE S.A.—See Abbott Laboratories; *U.S. Public*, pg. 18
ALERE SAS—See Abbott Laboratories; *U.S. Public*, pg. 18
ALERE SPAIN, S.L.—See Abbott Laboratories; *U.S. Public*, pg. 19
ALERE S.R.L.—See Abbott Laboratories; *U.S. Public*, pg. 18
ALERE TECHNOLOGIES GMBH—See Abbott Laboratories; *U.S. Public*, pg. 19

ALERE TOXICOLOGY, INC.—See Abbott Laboratories; *U.S. Public*, pg. 19
ALEXION PHARMACEUTICALS, INC.—See AstraZeneca PLC; *Int'l*, pg. 659
ALEXION PHARMACEUTICALS (SHANGHAI) COMPANY LIMITED—See AstraZeneca PLC; *Int'l*, pg. 659
ALEXION PHARMA GMBH—See AstraZeneca PLC; *Int'l*, pg. 659
ALEXION PHARMA INTERNATIONAL OPERATIONS UNLIMITED COMPANY—See AstraZeneca PLC; *Int'l*, pg. 659
ALEXION PHARMA INTERNATIONAL SARL—See AstraZeneca PLC; *Int'l*, pg. 659
ALEX PHARM LTD.; *Int'l*, pg. 306
ALEXZA PHARMACEUTICALS, INC.—See Grupo Ferrer Internacional, S.A.; *Int'l*, pg. 3129
ALFASIGMA S.P.A; *Int'l*, pg. 315
AL FATH TRADING CO. LTD.; *Int'l*, pg. 277
ALFA WASSERMANN CZECH S. R. O.—See Alfa-Wassermann S.p.A.; *Int'l*, pg. 314
ALFA WASSERMANN MAGHREB S.A.R.L.—See Alfa-Wassermann S.p.A.; *Int'l*, pg. 314
ALFA WASSERMANN PHARMA SAS—See Alfa-Wassermann S.p.A.; *Int'l*, pg. 314
ALFA WASSERMANN POLSKA SP.Z O.O—See Alfa-Wassermann S.p.A.; *Int'l*, pg. 314
ALFA WASSERMANN PRODUTOS FARMACEUTICOS, LDA.—See Alfa-Wassermann S.p.A.; *Int'l*, pg. 314
ALFA WASSERMANN S.A. DE C.V.—See Alfa-Wassermann S.p.A.; *Int'l*, pg. 314
ALFA WASSERMANN S.P.A. - ALANNO MANUFACTURING DIVISION—See Alfa-Wassermann S.p.A.; *Int'l*, pg. 314
ALFA WASSERMANN S.P.A. - MILANO INTERNATIONAL DIVISION—See Alfa-Wassermann S.p.A.; *Int'l*, pg. 314
ALFA-WASSERMANN S.P.A.; *Int'l*, pg. 314
ALFA WASSERMANN TUNISIE SARL—See Alfa-Wassermann S.p.A.; *Int'l*, pg. 314
ALFRESA FINE CHEMICAL CORPORATION—See Alfresa Holdings Corporation; *Int'l*, pg. 317
ALFRESA PHARMA CORPORATION—See Alfresa Holdings Corporation; *Int'l*, pg. 317
ALGERNON PHARMACEUTICALS, INC.; *Int'l*, pg. 318
ALGOL OY; *Int'l*, pg. 318
ALIGN PHARMACEUTICALS, LLC—See Cyclacel Pharmaceuticals, Inc.; *U.S. Public*, pg. 617
ALIMENTOS LIQUIDOS INDUSTRIALES—See Able Sales Company, Inc.; *U.S. Private*, pg. 39
ALIMERA SCIENCES EUROPE LIMITED—See ANI Pharmaceuticals, Inc.; *U.S. Public*, pg. 137
ALIMERA SCIENCES, INC.—See ANI Pharmaceuticals, Inc.; *U.S. Public*, pg. 137
ALIMERA SCIENCES LIMITED—See ANI Pharmaceuticals, Inc.; *U.S. Public*, pg. 137
ALINAMIN PHARMACEUTICAL CO., LTD.—See Blackstone Inc.; *U.S. Public*, pg. 347
ALIUD PHARMA GMBH—See Bain Capital, LP; *U.S. Private*, pg. 443
ALIUD PHARMA GMBH—See Cinven Limited; *Int'l*, pg. 1613
ALIUD PHARMA VERWALTUNGS-GMBH—See Bain Capital, LP; *U.S. Private*, pg. 443
ALIUD PHARMA VERWALTUNGS-GMBH—See Cinven Limited; *Int'l*, pg. 1613
AL JAZEERAH PHARMACEUTICAL INDUSTRIES LTD.—See Hikma Pharmaceuticals PLC; *Int'l*, pg. 3390
ALKA-LAB DOO—See Alkaloid A.D. Skopje; *Int'l*, pg. 330
ALKALOID A.D. SKOPJE; *Int'l*, pg. 330
ALKALOID ILAC TLS—See Alkaloid A.D. Skopje; *Int'l*, pg. 330
ALKALOID INT DOO—See Alkaloid A.D. Skopje; *Int'l*, pg. 330
ALKALOID KIEV CO, LTD.—See Alkaloid A.D. Skopje; *Int'l*, pg. 330
ALKALOID VELEDROGERIJA DOO—See Alkaloid A.D. Skopje; *Int'l*, pg. 330
ALKANO CHEMICAL, INC.; *U.S. Private*, pg. 169
ALKEM LABORATORIES LTD.; *Int'l*, pg. 330
ALKEM LABORATORIES (PTY) LIMITED—See Alkem Laboratories Ltd.; *Int'l*, pg. 330
ALKERMES CONTROLLED THERAPEUTICS, INC.—See Alkermes plc; *Int'l*, pg. 331
ALKERMES, INC.—See Alkermes plc; *Int'l*, pg. 331
ALKERMES, INC. - WILMINGTON FACILITY—See Alkermes plc; *Int'l*, pg. 331
ALKERMES PHARMA IRELAND LIMITED—See Alkermes plc; *Int'l*, pg. 331
ALKERMES PLC; *Int'l*, pg. 331
AL KINDI OF VETERINARY VACCINES CO.; *Int'l*, pg. 281
ALLENA PHARMACEUTICALS, INC.; *U.S. Public*, pg. 79
ALLERGAN AG—See AbbVie Inc.; *U.S. Public*, pg. 22
ALLERGAN AS—See AbbVie Inc.; *U.S. Public*, pg. 22
ALLERGAN BIOLOGICS LIMITED—See AbbVie Inc.; *U.S. Public*, pg. 23
ALLERGAN B.V.—See AbbVie Inc.; *U.S. Public*, pg. 22
ALLERGAN C.I.S. SARL—See AbbVie Inc.; *U.S. Public*, pg. 22
ALLERGAN COLOMBIA S.A.—See AbbVie Inc.; *U.S. Public*, pg. 22
ALLERGAN GMBH—See AbbVie Inc.; *U.S. Public*, pg. 22

325412 — PHARMACEUTICAL PREP...

ALLERGAN HOLDINGS LIMITED—See AbbVie Inc.; *U.S. Public*, pg. 23
ALLERGAN HONG KONG LIMITED—See AbbVie Inc.; *U.S. Public*, pg. 23
ALLERGAN INDUSTRIE S.A.S.—See AbbVie Inc.; *U.S. Public*, pg. 23
ALLERGAN KOREA LTD.—See AbbVie Inc.; *U.S. Public*, pg. 23
ALLERGAN LABORATORIOS LTDA.—See AbbVie Inc.; *U.S. Public*, pg. 23
ALLERGAN-LOA S.A.—See AbbVie Inc.; *U.S. Public*, pg. 23
ALLERGAN NEW ZEALAND LIMITED—See AbbVie Inc.; *U.S. Public*, pg. 23
ALLERGAN NORDEN AB—See AbbVie Inc.; *U.S. Public*, pg. 23
ALLERGAN N.V.—See AbbVie Inc.; *U.S. Public*, pg. 23
ALLERGAN PHARMACEUTICALS IRELAND (EUROCENTRE)—See AbbVie Inc.; *U.S. Public*, pg. 23
ALLERGAN PHARMA CO.—See AbbVie Inc.; *U.S. Public*, pg. 23
ALLERGAN SINGAPORE PTE. LTD.—See AbbVie Inc.; *U.S. Public*, pg. 23
ALLERGOPHARMA ESPANA S.L.—See Dermapharm Holding SE; *Int'l*, pg. 2043
ALLFLEX INDIA PRIVATE LIMITED—See Merck & Co., Inc.; *U.S. Public*, pg. 1415
ALLIANCE PHARMACEUTICALS LIMITED—See Alliance Pharma PLC; *Int'l*, pg. 340
ALLIANCE PHARMACEUTICALS (THAILAND) CO., LTD.—See Alliance Pharma PLC; *Int'l*, pg. 340
ALLIANCE PHARMA S.R.L.—See Alliance Pharma PLC; *Int'l*, pg. 340
ALL PHARMA (SHANGHAI) TRADING COMPANY LIMITED—See Aurobindo Pharma Ltd.; *Int'l*, pg. 712
ALLSTAR HEALTH BRANDS, INC.; *Int'l*, pg. 360
ALMAC CLINICAL SERVICES—See Almac Sciences Group Ltd.; *Int'l*, pg. 362
ALMAC CO., LTD.; *Int'l*, pg. 362
ALMAC PHARMACEUTICAL SERVICES K.K.—See Almac Sciences Group Ltd.; *Int'l*, pg. 362
ALMAC PHARMA SERVICES—See Almac Sciences Group Ltd.; *Int'l*, pg. 362
AL MANSOUR COMPANY FOR PHARMACEUTICAL INDUSTRIES; *Int'l*, pg. 281
ALMIRALL APS—See Almirall, S.A.; *Int'l*, pg. 364
ALMIRALL B.V.—See Almirall, S.A.; *Int'l*, pg. 364
ALMIRALL GMBH—See Almirall, S.A.; *Int'l*, pg. 364
ALMIRALL HERMAL GMBH—See Almirall, S.A.; *Int'l*, pg. 364
ALMIRALL LIMITED—See Almirall, S.A.; *Int'l*, pg. 364
ALMIRALL - PRODUTOS FARMACEUTICOS LDA.—See Almirall, S.A.; *Int'l*, pg. 364
ALMIRALL, S.A. DE C.V.—See Almirall, S.A.; *Int'l*, pg. 364
ALMIRALL, S.A.; *Int'l*, pg. 364
ALMIRALL, SAS—See Almirall, S.A.; *Int'l*, pg. 364
ALMIRALL, S.P.A.—See Almirall, S.A.; *Int'l*, pg. 364
ALMIRALL SP. Z O.O.—See Almirall, S.A.; *Int'l*, pg. 364
ALNYLAM PHARMACEUTICALS, INC.; *U.S. Public*, pg. 81
ALNYLAM PHARMACEUTICALS SPAIN SL—See Alnylam Pharmaceuticals, Inc.; *U.S. Public*, pg. 82
ALNYLAM UK LIMITED—See Alnylam Pharmaceuticals, Inc.; *U.S. Public*, pg. 82
ALPA LABORATORIES LTD; *Int'l*, pg. 365
ALPHA CO., LTD.; *Int'l*, pg. 367
ALPHAPHARM PTY LTD; *Int'l*, pg. 370
ALPHARMA DE ARGENTINA S.R.L.—See Zoetis, Inc.; *U.S. Public*, pg. 2409
ALPHARMA DO BRASIL LTDA.—See Zoetis, Inc.; *U.S. Public*, pg. 2409
ALPHARMA PHARMACEUTICALS LLC—See Pfizer Inc.; *U.S. Public*, pg. 1679
ALPHA THERAPEUTIC ITALIA, S.P.A.—See Grifols, S.A.; *Int'l*, pg. 3084
ALPINE IMMUNE SCIENCES, INC.—See Vertex Pharmaceuticals Incorporated; *U.S. Public*, pg. 2287
ALSERES PHARMACEUTICALS, INC.; *U.S. Public*, pg. 85
ALTAMIRA THERAPEUTICS LTD.; *Int'l*, pg. 385
ALTASCIENCES COMPANY INC.; *Int'l*, pg. 387
ALTEOGEN INC.; *Int'l*, pg. 391
ALTERITY THERAPEUTICS LIMITED; *Int'l*, pg. 391
ALTERNATE HEALTH CORP.; *Int'l*, pg. 391
ALTO NEUROSCIENCE, INC.; *U.S. Public*, pg. 88
ALTOS BIOLOGICS CO., LTD.—See Alteogen Inc.; *Int'l*, pg. 391
ALTRAZEAL LIFE SCIENCES INC.; *U.S. Private*, pg. 210
ALVA/AMCO PHARMACAL COMPANIES, INC.; *U.S. Private*, pg. 211
ALZECURE PHARMA AB; *Int'l*, pg. 402
AMAG PHARMACEUTICALS, INC.; *U.S. Private*, pg. 215
AMARANTUS BIOSCIENCE HOLDINGS, INC.; *U.S. Public*, pg. 90
AMARIN CORPORATION PLC; *Int'l*, pg. 412
AMAVITA APOTHEKEN GALENICARE AG—See CSL Limited; *Int'l*, pg. 1866
AMBALAL SARABHAI ENTERPRISES LTD.; *Int'l*, pg. 413
AMBEE PHARMACEUTICALS LIMITED; *Int'l*, pg. 414
AMBRILIA BIOPHARMA INC.; *Int'l*, pg. 415

AMBRX, INC.—See China Everbright Group Limited; *Int'l*, pg. 1501
AMBRX, INC.—See HOPU Investment Management Co., Ltd.; *Int'l*, pg. 3474
A MENARINI INDUSTRIE FARMACEUTICHE RIUNITE SRL; *Int'l*, pg. 18
AMERICAN BIOTECH LABS; *U.S. Private*, pg. 224
AMERICAN BOTANICALS, LLC; *U.S. Private*, pg. 225
AMERICAN GLOBAL HEALTH GROUP, LLC; *U.S. Private*, pg. 235
AMERICAN HEALTH NETWORK OF INDIANA, LLC—See UnitedHealth Group Incorporated; *U.S. Public*, pg. 2238
AMERICAN HEALTH NETWORK OF OHIO, LLC—See UnitedHealth Group Incorporated; *U.S. Public*, pg. 2238
AMERICAN HOME MEDICAL, INC.—See AdaptHealth Corp.; *U.S. Public*, pg. 38
AMERICAN LABORATORIES INC.; *U.S. Private*, pg. 239
AMERICAN ORIENTAL BIOENGINEERING, INC.; *Int'l*, pg. 422
AMERICAN REGENT, INC.—See Daiichi Sankyo Co., Ltd.; *Int'l*, pg. 1930
AMERILAB TECHNOLOGIES, INC.—See DCC plc; *Int'l*, pg. 1990
AMERISOURCE HEALTH SERVICES CORPORATION—See Cencora, Inc.; *U.S. Public*, pg. 466
AMGEN COLORADO, INC.—See Amgen Inc.; *U.S. Public*, pg. 122
AMGEN DEVELOPMENT CORPORATION—See Amgen Inc.; *U.S. Public*, pg. 122
AMGEN FREMONT INC.—See Amgen Inc.; *U.S. Public*, pg. 123
AMGEN GLOBAL FINANCE B.V.—See Amgen Inc.; *U.S. Public*, pg. 123
AMGEN HOLDING, INC.—See Amgen Inc.; *U.S. Public*, pg. 123
AMGEN USA INC.—See Amgen Inc.; *U.S. Public*, pg. 123
AMICUS THERAPEUTICS CANADA INC.—See Amicus Therapeutics, Inc.; *U.S. Public*, pg. 124
AMICUS THERAPEUTICS, INC.; *U.S. Public*, pg. 124
AMICUS THERAPEUTICS S.L.U.—See Amicus Therapeutics, Inc.; *U.S. Public*, pg. 124
AMIN PHARMACEUTICAL COMPANY; *Int'l*, pg. 427
AMI ORGANICS LIMITED; *Int'l*, pg. 426
AMNEAL PHARMACEUTICALS COMPANY GMBH—See Amneal Pharmaceuticals, Inc.; *U.S. Public*, pg. 125
AMNEAL PHARMACEUTICALS LLC—See Amneal Pharmaceuticals, Inc.; *U.S. Public*, pg. 125
AMNEAL PHARMACEUTICALS OF NEW YORK LLC—See Amneal Pharmaceuticals, Inc.; *U.S. Public*, pg. 125
AMOUN PHARMACEUTICAL COMPANY S.A.E.; *Int'l*, pg. 431
AMOY DIAGNOSTICS CO., LTD.; *Int'l*, pg. 431
AMPHASTAR PHARMACEUTICALS, INC.; *U.S. Public*, pg. 126
AMPIO PHARMACEUTICALS, INC.; *U.S. Public*, pg. 132
AMPLIA THERAPEUTICS LIMITED; *Int'l*, pg. 435
AMRUTANJAN HEALTH CARE LIMITED; *Int'l*, pg. 438
AMRYT PHARMA PLC—See Chiesi Farmaceutici SpA; *Int'l*, pg. 1477
ANAPTYSBIO, INC.; *U.S. Public*, pg. 136
ANATARA LIFESCIENCES LTD; *Int'l*, pg. 447
ANAZAOHEALTH INC.—See Fagron NV; *Int'l*, pg. 2602
ANBC, INC.; *Int'l*, pg. 447
A.N.B. LABORATORIES CO., LTD.—See Bangkok Dusit Medical Services Public Company Limited; *Int'l*, pg. 833
A.N.B. LABORATORY CO., LTD.—See Bangkok Dusit Medical Services Public Company Limited; *Int'l*, pg. 833
ANGELINI ACRAF S.P.A.; *Int'l*, pg. 460
ANGELINI PHARMA CESKA REPUBLIKA S.R.O.—See Angelini ACRAF S.p.A.; *Int'l*, pg. 460
ANGELINI PHARMA INC.—See Angelini ACRAF S.p.A.; *Int'l*, pg. 460
ANGELINI PHARMA POLSKA SP.ZO.O.—See Angelini ACRAF S.p.A.; *Int'l*, pg. 460
ANGIOGENEX, INC.; *U.S. Public*, pg. 137
ANG LIFESCIENCES INDIA LIMITED; *Int'l*, pg. 459
ANHUI FENGYUAN PHARMACEUTICAL CO., LTD.; *Int'l*, pg. 467
ANHUI SUNHERE PHARMACEUTICAL EXCIPIENTS CO., LTD.; *Int'l*, pg. 469
ANIMAL HEALTH INTERNATIONAL, INC.—See Patterson Companies, Inc.; *U.S. Public*, pg. 1654
ANIMEDICA GMBH—See AGRAVIS Raiffeisen AG; *Int'l*, pg. 216
ANI PHARMACEUTICALS, INC.; *U.S. Public*, pg. 137
ANITOX CORP—See The Riverside Company; *U.S. Private*, pg. 4107
ANTARES PHARMA AG—See Halozyme Therapeutics, Inc.; *U.S. Public*, pg. 981
ANTENGENE CORPORATION LIMITED; *Int'l*, pg. 482
ANTERIS TECHNOLOGIES LTD.; *Int'l*, pg. 482
ANTHERA PHARMACEUTICALS, INC.; *U.S. Public*, pg. 140
ANTIBE THERAPEUTICS INC.; *Int'l*, pg. 483
ANTON HUBNER GMBH & CO. KG—See Dermapharm Holding SE; *Int'l*, pg. 2043
ANUH PHARMA LTD.; *Int'l*, pg. 485

AOI PHARMACEUTICALS, INC.—See Akebia Therapeutics, Inc.; *U.S. Public*, pg. 69
AOXING PHARMACEUTICAL COMPANY, INC.; *U.S. Private*, pg. 289
APATECH LIMITED—See Baxter International Inc.; *U.S. Public*, pg. 280
APDC, INC.—See I Squared Capital Advisors (US) LLC; *U.S. Private*, pg. 2025
APELLIS PHARMACEUTICALS, INC.; *U.S. Public*, pg. 144
APELOA PHARMACEUTICAL CO., LTD.; *Int'l*, pg. 508
APEX HEALTHCARE BERHAD; *Int'l*, pg. 510
APEX PHARMA LIMITED—See Apex Footwear Limited; *Int'l*, pg. 509
APEX RETAIL SDN BHD—See Apex Healthcare Berhad; *Int'l*, pg. 511
APICORE US LLC—See Viatris Inc.; *U.S. Public*, pg. 2293
APL CHEMI NATURA LTD.—See Aurobindo Pharma Ltd.; *Int'l*, pg. 712
APLICARE INC.—See The Clorox Company; *U.S. Public*, pg. 2062
APL RESEARCH CENTRE LIMITED—See Aurobindo Pharma Ltd.; *Int'l*, pg. 712
APL SWIFT SERVICES (MALTA) LTD.—See Aurobindo Pharma Ltd.; *Int'l*, pg. 712
APL THAI LIMITED—See Aurobindo Pharma Ltd.; *Int'l*, pg. 712
APOLLO MEDICAL HOLDINGS INC.—See Alfresa Holdings Corporation; *Int'l*, pg. 317
APONTIS PHARMA AG—See Advent International Corporation; *U.S. Private*, pg. 108
APOTEX EUROPE B.V.—See Aurobindo Pharma Ltd.; *Int'l*, pg. 712
APOTEX INC.—See SK Capital Partners, LP; *U.S. Private*, pg. 3678
APOTHECARY PRODUCTS, LLC—See Wells Fargo & Company; *U.S. Public*, pg. 2344
APOTHECON B.V.—See Viatris Inc.; *U.S. Public*, pg. 2293
APOTHECON, INC.—See Bristol-Myers Squibb Company; *U.S. Public*, pg. 384
APPILI THERAPEUTICS, INC.; *Int'l*, pg. 520
APPLIKON BIOTECHNOLOGY B.V.—See Getinge AB; *Int'l*, pg. 2947
APP PHARMACEUTICALS, INC.—See Fresenius SE & Co. KGaA; *Int'l*, pg. 2777
APROGEN BIOLOGICS, INC.; *Int'l*, pg. 522
APROGEN HEALTHCARE & GAMES INC.; *Int'l*, pg. 522
APTABIO THERAPEUTICS INC.; *Int'l*, pg. 523
APTERYX IMAGING INC.—See Level Equity Management, LLC; *U.S. Private*, pg. 2434
APTEVO THERAPEUTICS INC.; *U.S. Public*, pg. 175
APTINYX, INC.; *U.S. Public*, pg. 175
APTIV INTERNATIONAL LTD.—See ICON plc; *Int'l*, pg. 3584
APTIV INTERNATIONAL LTD.—See ICON plc; *Int'l*, pg. 3584
APTORUM GROUP LIMITED; *Int'l*, pg. 526
APTOSE BIOSCIENCES INC.; *Int'l*, pg. 526
APTUIT (OXFORD) LIMITED—See Evotec SE; *Int'l*, pg. 2573
APTUIT (VERONA) SRL—See Evotec SE; *Int'l*, pg. 2573
AQUAGESTION CAPACITACION S.A.—See Abbott Laboratories; *U.S. Public*, pg. 19
AQUAGESTION S.A.—See Abbott Laboratories; *U.S. Public*, pg. 19
ARAB CENTER FOR PHARMACEUTICAL & CHEMICAL INDUSTRIES CO.; *Int'l*, pg. 529
ARAB PHARMACEUTICAL MANUFACTURING CO.—See Hikma Pharmaceuticals PLC; *Int'l*, pg. 3390
ARATANA THERAPEUTICS, INC.—See Elanco Animal Health Incorporated; *U.S. Public*, pg. 722
ARAVIVE, INC.; *U.S. Public*, pg. 178
ARBOR PHARMACEUTICALS LLC—See NovaQuest Capital Management, LLC; *U.S. Private*, pg. 2967
ARBUTUS BIOPHARMA CORPORATION; *U.S. Public*, pg. 178
ARCH BIOPARTNERS INC.; *Int'l*, pg. 546
ARCHER DANIELS MIDLAND CO.—See Archer-Daniels-Midland Company; *U.S. Public*, pg. 183
ARCH PHARMALABS LIMITED; *Int'l*, pg. 547
ARCTICZYMES TECHNOLOGIES ASA; *Int'l*, pg. 552
ARCTURUS THERAPEUTICS LTD.—See Arcturus Therapeutics Holdings Inc.; *U.S. Public*, pg. 187
ARDELYX, INC.; *U.S. Public*, pg. 187
ARENA PHARMACEUTICALS, INC.—See Pfizer Inc.; *U.S. Public*, pg. 1679
ARGENICA THERAPEUTICS LIMITED; *Int'l*, pg. 560
ARGENX JAPAN KK—See ARGENX SE; *Int'l*, pg. 561
ARISTA MOLECULAR, INC.—See Danaher Corporation; *U.S. Public*, pg. 625
ARMATA PHARMACEUTICALS, INC.; *U.S. Public*, pg. 193
ARMSTRONG LABORATORIOS DE MEXICO S.A. DE C.V.—See Bago Group; *Int'l*, pg. 799
ARMSTRONG PHARMACEUTICALS, INC.—See Amphastar Pharmaceuticals, Inc.; *U.S. Public*, pg. 126
AROVELLA THERAPEUTICS LIMITED; *Int'l*, pg. 578
ARQULE, INC.—See Merck & Co., Inc.; *U.S. Public*, pg. 1419

ARRAY BIOPHARMA INC.—See Pfizer Inc.; *U.S. Public*, pg. 1679
ARSEUS TEC NV—See Fagron NV; *Int'l*, pg. 2603
ARTELO BIOSCIENCES, INC.; *U.S. Public*, pg. 201
ARTESYN BIOSOLUTIONS ESTONIA OU—See Repligen Corporation; *U.S. Public*, pg. 1784
ARTESYN BIOSOLUTIONS IRELAND LIMITED—See Repligen Corporation; *U.S. Public*, pg. 1784
ARTESYN BIOSOLUTIONS USA, LLC—See Repligen Corporation; *U.S. Public*, pg. 1784
ARVINAS, INC.; *U.S. Public*, pg. 208
ARVIND REMEDIES LTD; *Int'l*, pg. 588
ARX, LLC—See Adhesive Research, Inc.; *U.S. Private*, pg. 79
ASAHI FOOD & HEALTHCARE CO., LTD.—See Asahi Group Holdings Ltd.; *Int'l*, pg. 593
ASAHI KASEI PHARMA (BEIJING) CO., LTD.—See Asahi Kasei Corporation; *Int'l*, pg. 596
ASAHI KASEI PHARMA—See Asahi Kasei Corporation; *Int'l*, pg. 596
ASANA BIOSCIENCES, LLC—See Erasca, Inc.; *U.S. Public*, pg. 792
ASARINA PHARMA AB; *Int'l*, pg. 599
ASCELIA PHARMA AB; *Int'l*, pg. 601
ASCENDIS HEALTH DIRECT (PTY) LTD—See Ascendis Health Limited; *Int'l*, pg. 601
ASCENDIS PHARMA A/S; *Int'l*, pg. 602
ASCENDIS PHARMA GMBH—See Ascendis Pharma A/S; *Int'l*, pg. 602
ASCENDIS PHARMA, INC.—See Ascendis Pharma A/S; *Int'l*, pg. 602
ASCEND LABORATORIES LLC—See Alkem Laboratories Ltd.; *Int'l*, pg. 330
ASCEND LABORATORIES SPA—See Alkem Laboratories Ltd.; *Int'l*, pg. 330
ASCENSUS SPECIALTIES LLC—See Wind Point Advisors LLC; *U.S. Private*, pg. 4533
ASCENTAGE PHARMA GROUP INC.—See Ascentage Pharma Group International; *Int'l*, pg. 602
ASCENTAGE PHARMA GROUP INTERNATIONAL; *Int'l*, pg. 602
ASCHE CHIESI GMBH—See Chiesi Farmaceutici SpA; *Int'l*, pg. 1477
ASCLETIS PHARMA, INC.; *Int'l*, pg. 602
ASC NETWORK, LLC—See UnitedHealth Group Incorporated; *U.S. Public*, pg. 2238
ASEGUA THERAPEUTICS, LLC—See Gilead Sciences, Inc.; *U.S. Public*, pg. 936
ASHLAND FINLAND OY—See Ashland Inc; *U.S. Public*, pg. 211
ASHLEY-MARTIN MANUFACTURING LLC—See Designs for Health, Inc.; *U.S. Private*, pg. 1215
ASIA RESOURCES HOLDINGS LIMITED; *Int'l*, pg. 615
ASKA ANIMAL HEALTH CO., LTD.—See ASKA Pharmaceutical Co., Ltd.; *Int'l*, pg. 621
ASKA PHARMACEUTICAL CO., LTD.; *Int'l*, pg. 621
ASLAN PHARMACEUTICALS LIMITED; *Int'l*, pg. 625
ASLAN PHARMACEUTICALS (SHANGHAI) CO. LTD.—See ASLAN Pharmaceuticals Limited; *Int'l*, pg. 625
ASLAN PHARMACEUTICALS TAIWAN LTD.—See ASLAN Pharmaceuticals Limited; *Int'l*, pg. 625
ASMECO (THAILAND) LTD.; *Int'l*, pg. 627
AS OLAINFARM; *Int'l*, pg. 590
ASPEN API INC.—See Aspen Pharmacare Holdings Limited; *Int'l*, pg. 629
ASPEN ASIA COMPANY LIMITED—See Aspen Pharmacare Holdings Limited; *Int'l*, pg. 629
ASPEN COLOMBIANA S.A.S.—See Aspen Pharmacare Holdings Limited; *Int'l*, pg. 629
ASPEN HEALTHCARE MALTA LTD.—See Aspen Pharmacare Holdings Limited; *Int'l*, pg. 629
ASPEN HEALTHCARE TAIWAN LIMITED—See Aspen Pharmacare Holdings Limited; *Int'l*, pg. 629
ASPEN NOTRE DAME DE BONDEVILLE SAS—See Aspen Pharmacare Holdings Limited; *Int'l*, pg. 629
ASPEN PHARMACARE AUSTRALIA PTY. LTD.—See Aspen Pharmacare Holdings Limited; *Int'l*, pg. 629
ASPEN PHARMACARE UK LIMITED—See Aspen Pharmacare Holdings Limited; *Int'l*, pg. 629
ASPEN PHARMA - INDUSTRIA FARMACEUTICA LTDA.—See Aspen Pharmacare Holdings Limited; *Int'l*, pg. 629
ASPEN PHARMA IRELAND LIMITED—See Aspen Pharmacare Holdings Limited; *Int'l*, pg. 629
ASPEN PHARMA (PTY) LIMITED—See Aspen Pharmacare Holdings Limited; *Int'l*, pg. 629
ASPEN PHARMA TRADING LIMITED—See Aspen Pharmacare Holdings Limited; *Int'l*, pg. 629
ASPIAIR GMBH—See ATON GmbH; *Int'l*, pg. 688
ASPREVA INTERNATIONAL LIMITED—See CSL Limited; *Int'l*, pg. 1866
ASSEMBLY BIOSCIENCES, INC.; *U.S. Public*, pg. 214
ASSEMBLY PHARMACEUTICALS, INC.—See Assembly Biosciences, Inc.; *U.S. Public*, pg. 214
ASTALLAS PHARMA SP—See Astellas Pharma Inc.; *Int'l*, pg. 652
ASTAREAL AB—See Fuji Chemical Industries Co., Ltd; *Int'l*, pg. 2809
ASTAREAL CO., LTD.—See Fuji Chemical Industries Co., Ltd; *Int'l*, pg. 2809
ASTAREAL, INC.—See Fuji Chemical Industries Co., Ltd; *Int'l*, pg. 2809
ASTAREAL, INC. - WASHINGTON—See Fuji Chemical Industries Co., Ltd; *Int'l*, pg. 2809
ASTAREAL (INDIA) PRIVATE LIMITED—See Fuji Chemical Industries Co., Ltd; *Int'l*, pg. 2809
ASTAVITA, INC.—See Fuji Chemical Industries Co., Ltd; *Int'l*, pg. 2809
ASTELLAS BUSINESS SERVICE CO., LTD.—See Astellas Pharma Inc.; *Int'l*, pg. 651
ASTELLAS B.V.—See Astellas Pharma Inc.; *Int'l*, pg. 652
ASTELLAS FARMA COLOMBIA SAS—See Astellas Pharma Inc.; *Int'l*, pg. 651
ASTELLAS FARMA LIMITADA—See Astellas Pharma Inc.; *Int'l*, pg. 651
ASTELLAS IRELAND—See Astellas Pharma Inc.; *Int'l*, pg. 652
ASTELLAS LEARNING INSTITUTE CO., LTD.—See Astellas Pharma Inc.; *Int'l*, pg. 651
ASTELLAS LTD.—See Astellas Pharma Inc.; *Int'l*, pg. 652
ASTELLAS PHARMA AB—See Astellas Pharma Inc.; *Int'l*, pg. 652
ASTELLAS PHARMA AE—See Astellas Pharma Inc.; *Int'l*, pg. 652
ASTELLAS PHARMA A.G.—See Astellas Pharma Inc.; *Int'l*, pg. 652
ASTELLAS PHARMA A/S—See Astellas Pharma Inc.; *Int'l*, pg. 652
ASTELLAS PHARMA B.V.—See Astellas Pharma Inc.; *Int'l*, pg. 652
ASTELLAS PHARMA CO., LIMITED—See Astellas Pharma Inc.; *Int'l*, pg. 652
ASTELLAS PHARMA DMCC—See Astellas Pharma Inc.; *Int'l*, pg. 652
ASTELLAS PHARMA EUROPE B.V.—See Astellas Pharma Inc.; *Int'l*, pg. 652
ASTELLAS PHARMA EUROPE LTD.—See Astellas Pharma Inc.; *Int'l*, pg. 652
ASTELLAS PHARMA EUROPE—See Astellas Pharma Inc.; *Int'l*, pg. 652
ASTELLAS PHARMA GES.MBH—See Astellas Pharma Inc.; *Int'l*, pg. 652
ASTELLAS PHARMA HONG KONG CO., LTD.—See Astellas Pharma Inc.; *Int'l*, pg. 652
ASTELLAS PHARMA ILAC TICARET VE SANAYI A.S.—See Astellas Pharma Inc.; *Int'l*, pg. 652
ASTELLAS PHARMA INC.; *Int'l*, pg. 651
ASTELLAS PHARMA KFT.—See Astellas Pharma Inc.; *Int'l*, pg. 652
ASTELLAS PHARMA LTDA—See Astellas Pharma Inc.; *Int'l*, pg. 652
ASTELLAS PHARMA LTD.—See Astellas Pharma Inc.; *Int'l*, pg. 652
ASTELLAS PHARMA PHILIPPINES INC.—See Astellas Pharma Inc.; *Int'l*, pg. 652
ASTELLAS PHARMA (PTY) LIMITED—See Astellas Pharma Inc.; *Int'l*, pg. 652
ASTELLAS PHARMA SARL—See Astellas Pharma Inc.; *Int'l*, pg. 652
ASTELLAS PHARMA, S.A.—See Astellas Pharma Inc.; *Int'l*, pg. 652
ASTELLAS PHARMA S.A.S—See Astellas Pharma Inc.; *Int'l*, pg. 652
ASTELLAS PHARMA S.P.A.—See Astellas Pharma Inc.; *Int'l*, pg. 652
ASTELLAS PHARMA S.R.O—See Astellas Pharma Inc.; *Int'l*, pg. 652
ASTELLAS PHARMA TAIWAN, INC.—See Astellas Pharma Inc.; *Int'l*, pg. 652
ASTELLAS PHARMA US, INC.—See Astellas Pharma Inc.; *Int'l*, pg. 653
ASTELLAS RESEARCH TECHNOLOGIES CO., LTD.—See Astellas Pharma Inc.; *Int'l*, pg. 653
ASTELLAS TOKAI CO., LTD.—See Astellas Pharma Inc.; *Int'l*, pg. 653
ASTELLAS US HOLDING, INC.—See Astellas Pharma Inc.; *Int'l*, pg. 653
ASTENA HOLDINGS CO., LTD.; *Int'l*, pg. 653
ASTERIAS BIOTHERAPEUTICS, INC.—See Lineage Cell Therapeutics, Inc.; *U.S. Public*, pg. 1320
ASTRAZENECA AB—See AstraZeneca PLC; *Int'l*, pg. 659
ASTRAZENECA AG—See AstraZeneca PLC; *Int'l*, pg. 659
ASTRAZENECA ARGENTINA S.A.—See AstraZeneca PLC; *Int'l*, pg. 660
ASTRAZENECA A/S—See AstraZeneca PLC; *Int'l*, pg. 659
ASTRAZENECA AS—See AstraZeneca PLC; *Int'l*, pg. 659
ASTRAZENECA BELGIUM—See AstraZeneca PLC; *Int'l*, pg. 659
ASTRAZENECA BULGARIA—See AstraZeneca PLC; *Int'l*, pg. 659
ASTRAZENECA CANADA INC.—See AstraZeneca PLC; *Int'l*, pg. 660
ASTRAZENECA CHILE S.A.—See AstraZeneca PLC; *Int'l*, pg. 660
ASTRAZENECA COLOMBIA S.A.—See AstraZeneca PLC; *Int'l*, pg. 660
ASTRAZENECA DO BRASIL LTDA.—See AstraZeneca PLC; *Int'l*, pg. 660
ASTRAZENECA EGYPT LLC—See AstraZeneca PLC; *Int'l*, pg. 661
ASTRAZENECA FARMACEUTICA SPAIN S.A.—See AstraZeneca PLC; *Int'l*, pg. 660
ASTRAZENECA FRANCE—See AstraZeneca PLC; *Int'l*, pg. 660
ASTRAZENECA FZ-LLC—See AstraZeneca PLC; *Int'l*, pg. 660
ASTRAZENECA GMBH—See AstraZeneca PLC; *Int'l*, pg. 660
ASTRAZENECA GULF FZ LLC—See AstraZeneca PLC; *Int'l*, pg. 660
ASTRAZENECA HONG KONG LTD.—See AstraZeneca PLC; *Int'l*, pg. 660
ASTRAZENECA INDIA PVT LIMITED—See AstraZeneca PLC; *Int'l*, pg. 660
ASTRAZENECA KK—See AstraZeneca PLC; *Int'l*, pg. 660
ASTRAZENECA KONTOR EESTIS—See AstraZeneca PLC; *Int'l*, pg. 661
ASTRAZENECA LATVIA—See AstraZeneca PLC; *Int'l*, pg. 660
ASTRAZENECA LIETUVA UAB—See AstraZeneca PLC; *Int'l*, pg. 660
ASTRAZENECA LLAC SANAYI VE TIC. LTD. STI.—See AstraZeneca PLC; *Int'l*, pg. 661
ASTRAZENECA LP—See AstraZeneca PLC; *Int'l*, pg. 660
ASTRAZENECA LP—See AstraZeneca PLC; *Int'l*, pg. 660
ASTRAZENECA OSTERREICH GMBH—See AstraZeneca PLC; *Int'l*, pg. 660
ASTRAZENECA PERU S.A.—See AstraZeneca PLC; *Int'l*, pg. 660
ASTRAZENECA PHARMACEUTICAL CO. LTD.—See AstraZeneca PLC; *Int'l*, pg. 660
ASTRAZENECA PHARMACEUTICALS LP—See AstraZeneca PLC; *Int'l*, pg. 660
ASTRAZENECA PHARMACEUTICALS PAKISTAN (PRIVATE) LIMITED—See AstraZeneca PLC; *Int'l*, pg. 661
ASTRAZENECA PHARMACEUTICALS (PHILS.) INC.—See AstraZeneca PLC; *Int'l*, pg. 660
ASTRAZENECA PHARMACEUTICALS (PTY) LTD—See AstraZeneca PLC; *Int'l*, pg. 660
ASTRAZENECA PHARMA INDIA LIMITED—See AstraZeneca PLC; *Int'l*, pg. 660
ASTRAZENECA (PHILIPPINES) INC.—See AstraZeneca PLC; *Int'l*, pg. 659
ASTRAZENECA PRODUTOS FARMACEUTICOS, LDA.—See AstraZeneca PLC; *Int'l*, pg. 661
ASTRAZENECA PTY. LTD.—See AstraZeneca PLC; *Int'l*, pg. 661
ASTRAZENECA RUSSIA—See AstraZeneca PLC; *Int'l*, pg. 661
ASTRAZENECA S.A. DE C.V.—See AstraZeneca PLC; *Int'l*, pg. 660
ASTRAZENECA S.A.—See AstraZeneca PLC; *Int'l*, pg. 661
ASTRAZENECA SDN BHD.—See AstraZeneca PLC; *Int'l*, pg. 661
ASTRAZENECA (SINGAPORE) PTE. LTD.—See AstraZeneca PLC; *Int'l*, pg. 659
ASTRAZENECA S.P.A.—See AstraZeneca PLC; *Int'l*, pg. 661
ASTRAZENECA TAIWAN LIMITED—See AstraZeneca PLC; *Int'l*, pg. 661
ASTRAZENECA (THAILAND) LTD.—See AstraZeneca PLC; *Int'l*, pg. 659
ASTRAZENECA UK LTD.—See AstraZeneca PLC; *Int'l*, pg. 661
ASTRAZENECA UK MANUFACTURING—See AstraZeneca PLC; *Int'l*, pg. 661
ASTRAZENECA UKRAINE LLC—See AstraZeneca PLC; *Int'l*, pg. 661
ASTRAZENECA URUGUAY SA—See AstraZeneca PLC; *Int'l*, pg. 661
ASTRIA THERAPEUTICS, INC.; *U.S. Public*, pg. 217
ASUBIO PHARMA CO., LTD.—See Daiichi Sankyo Co., Ltd.; *Int'l*, pg. 1929
ASYMCHEM LABORATORIES TIAN JIN CO LTD; *Int'l*, pg. 664
ATARA BIOTHERAPEUTICS, INC.; *U.S. Public*, pg. 220
ATHENEX PHARMACEUTICAL DIVISION, LLC—See Athenex, Inc.; *U.S. Public*, pg. 221
ATHENEX PHARMA SOLUTIONS, LLC—See Athenex, Inc.; *U.S. Public*, pg. 221
ATHERONOVA INC.; *U.S. Private*, pg. 368
ATHERSYS, INC.—See Healios K.K.; *Int'l*, pg. 3302
ATI PHARMED PHARMACEUTICAL COMPANY—See Alborz Investment Company; *Int'l*, pg. 299
ATLANTIC GRUPA D.D.; *Int'l*, pg. 674
ATLANTIC MEDICAL, INC.—See AdaptHealth Corp.; *U.S. Public*, pg. 38
ATLANTIC PRO-NUTRIENTS, INC.; *U.S. Private*, pg. 374
ATLAS FARMACEUTICA S.A.—See Abbott Laboratories; *U.S. Public*, pg. 19
ATLAS THERAPEUTICS AB—See Alligator Bioscience AB; *Int'l*, pg. 359
ATOMO DIAGNOSTICS LIMITED; *Int'l*, pg. 688

ATON PHARMA, INC.—See Bausch Health Companies Inc.; *Int'l*, pg. 898
ATOSSA THERAPEUTICS, INC.; *U.S. Public*, pg. 225
ATS LABORATORIES INC.—See Abbott Laboratories; *U.S. Public*, pg. 18
ATYR PHARMA, INC.; *U.S. Public*, pg. 225
AU NATUREL INC.—See HGGC, LLC; *U.S. Private*, pg. 1930
AUREX B.V.—See Aurobindo Pharma Ltd.; *Int'l*, pg. 712
AURIGENE DISCOVERY TECHNOLOGIES (MALAYSIA) SDN BHD—See Dr. Reddy's Laboratories Limited; *Int'l*, pg. 2195
AURINIA PHARMACEUTICALS INC.; *Int'l*, pg. 711
AURISCO PHARMACEUTICAL CO., LTD.; *Int'l*, pg. 711
AURIS MEDICAL LTD.—See Altamira Therapeutics Ltd.; *Int'l*, pg. 385
AUROBINDO (DATONG) BIO-PHARMA CO. LTD.—See Aurobindo Pharma Ltd.; *Int'l*, pg. 712
AUROBINDO (H.K.) LIMITED—See Aurobindo Pharma Ltd.; *Int'l*, pg. 712
AUROBINDO ILAC SANAYI VE TICARET LTD—See Aurobindo Pharma Ltd.; *Int'l*, pg. 712
AUROBINDO PHARMA B.V.—See Aurobindo Pharma Ltd.; *Int'l*, pg. 712
AUROBINDO PHARMA COLOMBIA SAS—See Aurobindo Pharma Ltd.; *Int'l*, pg. 712
AUROBINDO PHARMA FRANCE SARL—See Aurobindo Pharma Ltd.; *Int'l*, pg. 712
AUROBINDO PHARMA GMBH—See Aurobindo Pharma Ltd.; *Int'l*, pg. 712
AUROBINDO PHARMA INDUSTRIA PHARMACEUTICA LTDA—See Aurobindo Pharma Ltd.; *Int'l*, pg. 712
AUROBINDO PHARMA (ITALIA) S.R.L—See Aurobindo Pharma Ltd.; *Int'l*, pg. 712
AUROBINDO PHARMA JAPAN K.K—See Aurobindo Pharma Ltd.; *Int'l*, pg. 712
AUROBINDO PHARMA LTD.; *Int'l*, pg. 712
AUROBINDO PHARMA (PORTUGAL) UNIPESSOAL LDA—See Aurobindo Pharma Ltd.; *Int'l*, pg. 712
AUROBINDO PHARMA PRODUCTOS FARMACEUTICOS LTDA—See Aurobindo Pharma Ltd.; *Int'l*, pg. 712
AUROBINDO PHARMA PRODUTOS FARMACEUTICOS LTDA—See Aurobindo Pharma Ltd.; *Int'l*, pg. 712
AUROBINDO PHARMA (PTY) LIMITED—See Aurobindo Pharma Ltd.; *Int'l*, pg. 712
AUROBINDO PHARMA ROMANIA SRL—See Aurobindo Pharma Ltd.; *Int'l*, pg. 712
AUROBINDO PHARMA USA INC.—See Aurobindo Pharma Ltd.; *Int'l*, pg. 712
AUROBINDO SWITZERLAND AG—See Aurobindo Pharma Ltd.; *Int'l*, pg. 712
AUROBINDO TONGLING (DATONG) PHARMACEUTICAL CO. LTD.—See Aurobindo Pharma Ltd.; *Int'l*, pg. 712
AURO HEALTH LLC—See Aurobindo Pharma Ltd.; *Int'l*, pg. 712
AURO LABORATORIES LIMITED; *Int'l*, pg. 711
AUROLIFE PHARMA LLC—See Aurobindo Pharma Ltd.; *Int'l*, pg. 712
AURORA OPTOELECTRONICS CO., LTD.; *Int'l*, pg. 714
AUROVIDA FARMACEUTICA S.A. DE C.V—See Aurobindo Pharma Ltd.; *Int'l*, pg. 712
AUROVITAS PHARMA POLSKA SP. Z O.O.—See Aurobindo Pharma Ltd.; *Int'l*, pg. 712
AUROVITAS SPAIN SA.—See Aurobindo Pharma Ltd.; *Int'l*, pg. 713
AUROVITAS SPOL S.R.O—See Aurobindo Pharma Ltd.; *Int'l*, pg. 713
AUROVITAS UNIPESSOAL LDA.—See Aurobindo Pharma Ltd.; *Int'l*, pg. 712
AVACTA LIFE SCIENCES LIMITED—See Avacta Group plc; *Int'l*, pg. 733
AVADEL PHARMACEUTICALS PLC; *Int'l*, pg. 734
AVADIM HEALTH, INC.—See British Columbia Investment Management Corp.; *Int'l*, pg. 1169
AVALO THERAPEUTICS, INC.; *U.S. Public*, pg. 239
AVARA AIKEN PHARMACEUTICAL SERVICES, INC.—See American Industrial Acquisition Corporation; *U.S. Private*, pg. 237
AVARA PHARMACEUTICAL SERVICES, INC.—See American Industrial Acquisition Corporation; *U.S. Private*, pg. 237
AVARA PHARMACEUTICAL TECHNOLOGIES, INC.—See American Industrial Acquisition Corporation; *U.S. Private*, pg. 237
AVECHO BIOTECHNOLOGY LTD.; *Int'l*, pg. 737
AVECIA LTD. - CINCINNATI FACILITY—See Avecia Ltd.; *Int'l*, pg. 737
AVECIA LTD. - MILFORD FACILITY—See Avecia Ltd.; *Int'l*, pg. 737
AVECIA LTD., *Int'l*, pg. 737
AVELLA OF DEER VALLEY, INC.; *U.S. Private*, pg. 405
AVELLA OF PHOENIX III, INC.—See UnitedHealth Group Incorporated; *U.S. Public*, pg. 2239
AVELLA OF SACRAMENTO, INC.—See UnitedHealth Group Incorporated; *U.S. Public*, pg. 2239
AVELLA OF SCOTTSDALE, INC.—See Avella of Deer Valley, Inc.; *U.S. Private*, pg. 405
AVESTHAGEN LIMITED; *Int'l*, pg. 740

AVI BIOPHARMA INTERNATIONAL LIMITED—See Sarepta Therapeutics, Inc.; *U.S. Public*, pg. 1841
AVICANNA, INC.; *Int'l*, pg. 743
AVID BIOSERVICES, INC.; *U.S. Public*, pg. 246
AVID RADIOPHARMACEUTICALS, INC.—See Eli Lilly & Company; *U.S. Public*, pg. 731
AVOCA, INC.—See Ashland Inc.; *U.S. Public*, pg. 213
AVRICORE HEALTH INC.; *Int'l*, pg. 750
AV THERAPEUTICS, INC.; *U.S. Private*, pg. 402
AVVAA WORLD HEALTH CARE PRODUCTS INC.; *Int'l*, pg. 751
AXICORP GMBH—See Dermapharm Holding SE; *Int'l*, pg. 2043
AXIUM PHARMACEUTICALS, INC.; *U.S. Private*, pg. 414
AXM PHARMA, INC.; *U.S. Private*, pg. 414
AXSOME THERAPEUTICS, INC.; *U.S. Public*, pg. 256
AXXZIA, INC.; *Int'l*, pg. 773
AYALA PHARMACEUTICALS, INC.; *U.S. Public*, pg. 256
AYERST-WYETH PHARMACEUTICALS LLC—See Pfizer Inc.; *U.S. Public*, pg. 1679
AYRTON DRUGS MANUFACTURING COMPANY LIMITED; *Int'l*, pg. 775
AZURITY PHARMACEUTICALS, INC.—See NovaQuest Capital Management, LLC; *U.S. Private*, pg. 2967
BACHEM AMERICAS, INC.—See Bachem Holding AG; *Int'l*, pg. 795
BACHEM JAPAN K.K.—See Bachem Holding AG; *Int'l*, pg. 795
BACHEM SA—See Bachem Holding AG; *Int'l*, pg. 795
BAFNA PHARMACEUTICALS LIMITED; *Int'l*, pg. 799
BAINBRIDGE & KNIGHT LABORATORIES; *U.S. Private*, pg. 453
BAJAJ HEALTHCARE LIMITED; *Int'l*, pg. 804
BAL PHARMA LTD; *Int'l*, pg. 806
BAMA-GEVE, S.L.U.—See Alfa-Wassermann S.p.A.; *Int'l*, pg. 314
BANCO DE VIDA S.A.—See Abbott Laboratories; *U.S. Public*, pg. 19
BANNER CHEMICALS-PHARMACEUTICAL PRODUCTS—See Banner Chemicals Limited; *Int'l*, pg. 851
BARENTZ B.V.—See Cinven Limited; *Int'l*, pg. 1611
BARENTZ (ROMANIA) S.R.L.—See Cinven Limited; *Int'l*, pg. 1611
BASF HEALTH AND CARE PRODUCTS FRANCE S.A.S.—See BASF SE; *Int'l*, pg. 879
BASF PHARMA (CALLANISH) LIMITED—See BASF SE; *Int'l*, pg. 882
BASF-PJPC NEOPENTYLGLYCOL CO. LTD.—See BASF SE; *Int'l*, pg. 882
BASF VITAMINS COMPANY LTD.—See BASF SE; *Int'l*, pg. 882
BASILEA PHARMACEUTICA INTERNATIONAL LTD.—See Basilea Pharmaceutica Ltd.; *Int'l*, pg. 887
BASILEA PHARMACEUTICA LTD.; *Int'l*, pg. 887
BAUDAX BIO, INC.; *U.S. Public*, pg. 280
BAUSCH HEALTH, CANADA INC.—See Bausch Health Companies Inc.; *Int'l*, pg. 897
BAUSCH HEALTH HELLAS SINGLE-MEMBER PHARMACEUTICALS SA—See Bausch Health Companies Inc.; *Int'l*, pg. 897
BAUSCH HEALTH LIMITED LIABILITY COMPANY—See Bausch Health Companies Inc.; *Int'l*, pg. 897
BAUSCH HEALTH LIMITED LIABILITY COMPANY—See Bausch Health Companies Inc.; *Int'l*, pg. 897
BAUSCH HEALTH LLC—See Bausch Health Companies Inc.; *Int'l*, pg. 897
BAUSCH HEALTH LLP—See Bausch Health Companies Inc.; *Int'l*, pg. 897
BAUSCH HEALTH MAGYARORSZAG KFT—See Bausch Health Companies Inc.; *Int'l*, pg. 897
BAUSCH HEALTH PERU S.R.L.—See Bausch Health Companies Inc.; *Int'l*, pg. 897
BAUSCH HEALTH ROMANIA SRL—See Bausch Health Companies Inc.; *Int'l*, pg. 897
BAUSCH HEALTH SLOVAKIA S.R.O.—See Bausch Health Companies Inc.; *Int'l*, pg. 897
BAUSCH HEALTH TRADING DWC-LLC—See Bausch Health Companies Inc.; *Int'l*, pg. 897
BAUSCH HEALTH UKRAINE LLC—See Bausch Health Companies Inc.; *Int'l*, pg. 897
BAUSCH & LOMB PHARMACEUTICALS, INC.—See Bausch Health Companies Inc.; *Int'l*, pg. 896
BAUSCH PHARMA KAZAKHSTAN LLP—See Bausch Health Companies Inc.; *Int'l*, pg. 897
BAUSCH RUMO LLC—See Bausch Health Companies Inc.; *Int'l*, pg. 897
BAVARIAN NORDIC A/S; *Int'l*, pg. 900
BAXTAR AS—See Baxter International Inc.; *U.S. Public*, pg. 280
BAXTER BIOSCIENCE MANUFACTURING SARL—See Baxter International Inc.; *U.S. Public*, pg. 280
BAXTER CARIBE, INC.—See Baxter International Inc.; *U.S. Public*, pg. 280
BAXTER HEALTHCARE (GUANGZHOU) COMPANY LTD—See Baxter International Inc.; *U.S. Public*, pg. 280
BAXTER HEALTHCARE LIMITED—See Baxter International Inc.; *U.S. Public*, pg. 280

BAXTER HEALTHCARE LIMITED—See Baxter International Inc.; *U.S. Public*, pg. 280
BAXTER HEALTHCARE LIMITED—See Baxter International Inc.; *U.S. Public*, pg. 280
BAXTER HEALTHCARE LIMITED—See Baxter International Inc.; *U.S. Public*, pg. 280
BAXTER HEALTHCARE LIMITED—See Baxter International Inc.; *U.S. Public*, pg. 280
BAXTER HEALTHCARE PTY LTD—See Baxter International Inc.; *U.S. Public*, pg. 280
BAXTER (HELLAS) EPE—See Baxter International Inc.; *U.S. Public*, pg. 280
BAXTER HOLDING B.V.—See Baxter International Inc.; *U.S. Public*, pg. 281
BAXTER HOLDING MEXICO, S. DE R.L. DE C.V.—See Baxter International Inc.; *U.S. Public*, pg. 281
BAXTER HOSPITALAR LTDA.—See Baxter International Inc.; *U.S. Public*, pg. 280
BAXTER (INDIA) PRIVATE LIMITED—See Baxter International Inc.; *U.S. Public*, pg. 280
BAXTER INNOVATIONS GMBH—See Baxter International Inc.; *U.S. Public*, pg. 281
BAXTER PHARMACEUTICAL SOLUTIONS LLC—See Baxter International Inc.; *U.S. Public*, pg. 280
BAXTER S.A. DE C.V.—See Baxter International Inc.; *U.S. Public*, pg. 281
BAXTER S.L.—See Baxter International Inc.; *U.S. Public*, pg. 281
BAXTER S.P.A.—See Baxter International Inc.; *U.S. Public*, pg. 281
BAYBRIDGE PHARMACY CORP.; *U.S. Private*, pg. 495
BAYER AB—See Bayer Aktiengesellschaft; *Int'l*, pg. 902
BAYER AGRICULTURE BVBA—See Bayer Aktiengesellschaft; *Int'l*, pg. 902
BAYER ANIMAL HEALTH—See Elanco Animal Health Incorporated; *U.S. Public*, pg. 722
BAYER ANIMAL HEALTH - USA—See Elanco Animal Health Incorporated; *U.S. Public*, pg. 722
BAYER ARGENTINA S.A.—See Bayer Aktiengesellschaft; *Int'l*, pg. 902
BAYER AS—See Bayer Aktiengesellschaft; *Int'l*, pg. 902
BAYER A/S—See Bayer Aktiengesellschaft; *Int'l*, pg. 902
BAYER AUSTRALIA LIMITED—See Bayer Aktiengesellschaft; *Int'l*, pg. 902
BAYER BOLIVIANA LTDA.—See Bayer Aktiengesellschaft; *Int'l*, pg. 902
BAYER BULGARIA EOOD—See Bayer Aktiengesellschaft; *Int'l*, pg. 902
BAYER CROPSCIENCE SCHWEIZ AG—See Bayer Aktiengesellschaft; *Int'l*, pg. 904
BAYER DE MEXICO, S.A. DE C.V.—See Bayer Aktiengesellschaft; *Int'l*, pg. 906
BAYER D.O.O.—See Bayer Aktiengesellschaft; *Int'l*, pg. 906
BAYER HEALTHCARE AG - DERMATOLOGY UNIT—See Bayer Aktiengesellschaft; *Int'l*, pg. 904
BAYER HEALTHCARE AG—See Bayer Aktiengesellschaft; *Int'l*, pg. 904
BAYER HEALTHCARE AUSTRALIA—See Bayer Aktiengesellschaft; *Int'l*, pg. 902
BAYER HEALTHCARE BIOLOGICAL PRODUCTS—See Bayer Aktiengesellschaft; *Int'l*, pg. 904
BAYER HEALTHCARE CO. LTD.—See Bayer Aktiengesellschaft; *Int'l*, pg. 904
BAYER HEALTHCARE MANUFACTURING S.R.L.—See Bayer Aktiengesellschaft; *Int'l*, pg. 904
BAYER HEALTHCARE PHARMACEUTICALS CANADA—See Bayer Aktiengesellschaft; *Int'l*, pg. 904
BAYER HEALTHCARE PHARMA—See Bayer Aktiengesellschaft; *Int'l*, pg. 904
BAYERHEALTH CARE—See Bayer Aktiengesellschaft; *Int'l*, pg. 904
BAYER HISPANIA SL—See Bayer Aktiengesellschaft; *Int'l*, pg. 905
BAYER HOLDING (THAILAND) CO., LTD.—See Bayer Aktiengesellschaft; *Int'l*, pg. 905
BAYER INC.—See Bayer Aktiengesellschaft; *Int'l*, pg. 905
BAYER ISRAEL LTD.—See Bayer Aktiengesellschaft; *Int'l*, pg. 905
BAYER LIMITED EGYPT LLC—See Bayer Aktiengesellschaft; *Int'l*, pg. 905
BAYER NETHERLANDS B.V.—See Bayer Aktiengesellschaft; *Int'l*, pg. 905
BAYER NEW ZEALAND LIMITED—See Bayer Aktiengesellschaft; *Int'l*, pg. 905
BAYER NORDIC SE—See Bayer Aktiengesellschaft; *Int'l*, pg. 905
BAYER OY—See Bayer Aktiengesellschaft; *Int'l*, pg. 904
BAYER OY—See Bayer Aktiengesellschaft; *Int'l*, pg. 905
BAYER PAKISTAN (PRIVATE) LIMITED—See Bayer Aktiengesellschaft; *Int'l*, pg. 905
BAYER PARSIAN AG—See Bayer Aktiengesellschaft; *Int'l*, pg. 905
BAYER PARSIAN P.J.S. CO.—See Bayer Aktiengesellschaft; *Int'l*, pg. 905
BAYER PHARMA AG—See Bayer Aktiengesellschaft; *Int'l*, pg. 904
BAYER PHARMA AG - WUPPERTAL—See Bayer Aktiengesellschaft; *Int'l*, pg. 904

325412 — PHARMACEUTICAL PREP...

BAYER PHILIPPINES, INC.—See Bayer Aktiengesellschaft; *Int'l*, pg. 905
BAYER PORTUGAL, LDA.—See Bayer Aktiengesellschaft; *Int'l*, pg. 905
BAYER PORTUGAL S.A.—See Bayer Aktiengesellschaft; *Int'l*, pg. 905
BAYER (PROPRIETARY) LIMITED—See Bayer Aktiengesellschaft; *Int'l*, pg. 901
BAYER S.A. DE C.V.—See Bayer Aktiengesellschaft; *Int'l*, pg. 906
BAYER SANTE SAS—See Bayer Aktiengesellschaft; *Int'l*, pg. 906
BAYER S.A.—See Bayer Aktiengesellschaft; *Int'l*, pg. 905
BAYER S.A.—See Bayer Aktiengesellschaft; *Int'l*, pg. 905
BAYER S.A.—See Bayer Aktiengesellschaft; *Int'l*, pg. 905
BAYER S.A.—See Bayer Aktiengesellschaft; *Int'l*, pg. 905
BAYER S.A.—See Bayer Aktiengesellschaft; *Int'l*, pg. 959
BAYER S.A.—See Bayer Aktiengesellschaft; *Int'l*, pg. 906
BAYER S.A.—See Bayer Aktiengesellschaft; *Int'l*, pg. 906
BAYER S.A.—See Bayer Aktiengesellschaft; *Int'l*, pg. 906
BAYER SA—See Bayer Aktiengesellschaft; *Int'l*, pg. 906
BAYER S.A.S.—See Bayer Aktiengesellschaft; *Int'l*, pg. 906
BAYER SCHERING PHARMA AG—See Bayer Aktiengesellschaft; pg. 904
BAYER SOUTH AFRICA (PTY.) LTD.—See Bayer Aktiengesellschaft; *Int'l*, pg. 906
BAYER S.P.A.—See Bayer Aktiengesellschaft; *Int'l*, pg. 904
BAYER SP. Z O.O.—See Bayer Aktiengesellschaft; *Int'l*, pg. 906
BAYER S.R.O.—See Bayer Aktiengesellschaft; *Int'l*, pg. 904
BAYER TAIWAN CO., LTD.—See Bayer Aktiengesellschaft; *Int'l*, pg. 906
BAYER THAI COMPANY LIMITED—See Bayer Aktiengesellschaft; *Int'l*, pg. 904
BAYER VITAL GMBH—See Bayer Aktiengesellschaft; *Int'l*, pg. 905
BAYER WEIMAR GMBH & CO. KG—See Bayer Aktiengesellschaft; *Int'l*, pg. 906
BAYER WR LLC—See Bayer Aktiengesellschaft; *Int'l*, pg. 906
BAYER YAKUHIN, LTD.—See Bayer Aktiengesellschaft; *Int'l*, pg. 906
BAYER ZAMBIA LIMITED—See Bayer Aktiengesellschaft; *Int'l*, pg. 906
BAYHEALTH, S.L.—See Bayer Aktiengesellschaft; *Int'l*, pg. 906
BAYHILL THERAPEUTICS, INC.; *U.S. Private*, pg. 496
BAYTACARE PHARMACEUTICAL CO., LTD; *Int'l*, pg. 915
B&B PHARMACEUTICALS, INC.—See Fagron NV; *Int'l*, pg. 2603
BCWORLD PHARM CO., LTD.; *Int'l*, pg. 929
BCWORLD PHARM CO., LTD. - YEOJU FACTORY—See Bcworld Pharm Co., Ltd.; *Int'l*, pg. 929
BDH INDUSTRIES LTD.; *Int'l*, pg. 929
BD RX INC.—See Becton, Dickinson & Company; *U.S. Public*, pg. 288
BEACH PRODUCTS, INC.; *U.S. Private*, pg. 503
BEACON PHARMACEUTICALS LTD.; *Int'l*, pg. 932
BECKMAN COULTER AB—See Danaher Corporation; *U.S. Public*, pg. 624
BECKMAN COULTER BIOMEDICAL GMBH—See Danaher Corporation; *U.S. Public*, pg. 624
BECKMAN COULTER CESKA REPUBLIKA S.R.O.—See Danaher Corporation; *U.S. Public*, pg. 624
BECKMAN COULTER COMMERCIAL ENTERPRISE (CHINA) CO., LTD.—See Danaher Corporation; *U.S. Public*, pg. 624
BECKMAN COULTER DO BRASIL COMERCIO E IMPORTACAO DE PRODUTOS DE LABORATORIO LTDA.—See Danaher Corporation; *U.S. Public*, pg. 625
BECKMAN COULTER D.O.O.—See Danaher Corporation; *U.S. Public*, pg. 625
BECKMAN COULTER INDIA PRIVATE LIMITED—See Danaher Corporation; *U.S. Public*, pg. 624
BECKMAN COULTER IRELAND INC.—See Danaher Corporation; *U.S. Public*, pg. 624
BECKMAN COULTER KOREA LTD.—See Danaher Corporation; *U.S. Public*, pg. 624
BECKMAN COULTER NEDERLAND B.V.—See Danaher Corporation; *U.S. Public*, pg. 625
BECKMAN COULTER POLSKA SP. Z.O.O.—See Danaher Corporation; *U.S. Public*, pg. 625
BECKMAN COULTER SLOVENSKA REPUBLIKA S.R.O.—See Danaher Corporation; *U.S. Public*, pg. 625
BECTON DICKINSON BENELUX N.V.—See Becton, Dickinson & Company; *U.S. Public*, pg. 289
BECTON DICKINSON PTY. LTD.—See Becton, Dickinson & Company; *U.S. Public*, pg. 290
BEIGENE AUS PTY LTD.—See BeiGene, Ltd.; *Int'l*, pg. 942
BEIGENE (BEIJING) CO., LIMITED—See BeiGene, Ltd.; *Int'l*, pg. 942
BEIGENE (SHANGHAI) CO., LIMITED—See BeiGene, Ltd.; *Int'l*, pg. 942
BEIGENE (SUZHOU) CO., LIMITED—See BeiGene, Ltd.; *Int'l*, pg. 942
BEIGENE SWITZERLAND GMBH—See BeiGene, Ltd.; *Int'l*, pg. 942

BEIJING BEILU PHARMACEUTICAL CO., LTD.; *Int'l*, pg. 946
BEIJING BIOSINO-AGIACCU BIOTECHNOLOGY CO., LTD—See BioSino Bio-technology & Science Inc.; *Int'l*, pg. 1042
BEIJING CONTINENT PHARMACEUTICAL CO., LTD.—See GNI Group Ltd.; *Int'l*, pg. 3017
BEIJING FRESENIUS PHARMACEUTICAL CO., LTD.—See Fresenius SE & Co. KGaA; *Int'l*, pg. 2777
BEIJING KONRUNS PHARMACEUTICAL CO., LTD.; *Int'l*, pg. 954
BEIJING MEHECO BAITAI PHARMACEUTICAL TECHNOLOGY CO., LTD.—See China Meheco Group Co., Ltd.; *Int'l*, pg. 1518
BEIJING MEHECO YONSTRON PHARMACEUTICAL CO., LTD.—See China Meheco Group Co., Ltd.; *Int'l*, pg. 1518
BEIJING MICROVISION TECHNOLOGY CO., LTD.—See Beijing Tongtech Company Limited; *Int'l*, pg. 959
BEIJING SCIENCE SUN PHARMACEUTICAL CO., LTD.; *Int'l*, pg. 955
BEIJING SL PHARMACEUTICAL CO., LTD.; *Int'l*, pg. 957
BEIJING TONG REN TANG AUSTRALIA PTY, LTD.—See Beijing Tong Ren Tang Chinese Medicine Company Limited; *Int'l*, pg. 958
BEIJING TONGRENTANG CO., LTD.; *Int'l*, pg. 959
BEIJING WANTAI BIOLOGICAL PHARMACY ENTERPRISE CO., LTD.; *Int'l*, pg. 960
BELCHER PHARMACEUTICALS, LLC; *U.S. Private*, pg. 517
BELEAVE, INC.; *Int'l*, pg. 963
BELLEROPHON THERAPEUTICS, INC.; *U.S. Public*, pg. 295
BELLICUM PHARMACEUTICALS, INC.; *U.S. Public*, pg. 295
BELLUS HEALTH INC.—See GSK plc; *Int'l*, pg. 3145
BENCHMARK HOLDINGS PLC; *Int'l*, pg. 970
BEN TRE PHARMACEUTICAL JSC; *Int'l*, pg. 969
BERGENBIO ASA; *Int'l*, pg. 979
BERGENBIO LIMITED—See BerGenBio ASA; *Int'l*, pg. 979
BERLIMED-PRODUCTOS QUIMICOS FARMACEUTICOS E BIOLOGICOS LTDA.—See Bayer Aktiengesellschaft; *Int'l*, pg. 904
BERLIMED, S.A.—See Bayer Aktiengesellschaft; *Int'l*, pg. 904
BERLIN-CHEMIE AG—See A Menarini Industrie Farmaceutiche Riunite Srl; *Int'l*, pg. 18
BERLIS AG—See Bayer Aktiengesellschaft; *Int'l*, pg. 901
BERMELE PLC; *Int'l*, pg. 986
BERNA BIOTECH KOREA CORP.—See Johnson & Johnson; *U.S. Public*, pg. 1194
BERONI BIOTECH INC.—See Beroni Group Limited; *Int'l*, pg. 989
BERONI JAPAN INC.—See Beroni Group Limited; *Int'l*, pg. 989
BERONI USA CORPORATION—See Beroni Group Limited; *Int'l*, pg. 989
BERYL DRUGS LTD.; *Int'l*, pg. 998
BESTCO, INC.—See Tamanda Holdings USA Inc.; *U.S. Private*, pg. 3928
BETA DRUGS LIMITED; *Int'l*, pg. 1001
BETA HEALTHCARE INTERNATIONAL LTD—See Aspen Pharmacare Holdings Limited; *Int'l*, pg. 629
BETA HEALTHCARE (UGANDA) LIMITED—See Aspen Pharmacare Holdings Limited; *Int'l*, pg. 629
BETAPHARM ARZNEIMITTEL GMBH—See Dr. Reddy's Laboratories Limited; *Int'l*, pg. 2195
THE BETTER BEING CO.; *U.S. Public*, pg. 2038
BETTERLIFE PHARMA INC.; *Int'l*, pg. 1004
BEUTLICH PHARMACEUTICALS LP; *U.S. Private*, pg. 547
BEXIMCO PHARMACEUTICALS LIMITED; *Int'l*, pg. 1005
BEYOND AIR, INC.; *U.S. Public*, pg. 327
BF BIOSCIENCES LIMITED—See Ferozsons Laboratories Limited; *Int'l*, pg. 2639
BG MEDICINE, INC.; *U.S. Public*, pg. 327
BGP PRODUCTS GMBH—See Viatris Inc.; *U.S. Public*, pg. 2293
BHARAT IMMUNOLOGICALS AND BIOLOGICALS CORPORATION LIMITED; *Int'l*, pg. 1011
BHARAT PARENTERALS LIMITED; *Int'l*, pg. 1011
BIEFFE MEDITAL S.P.A.—See Baxter International Inc.; *U.S. Public*, pg. 280
BILCARE TECHNOLOGIES SINGAPORE PTE. LTD.—See Bilcare Limited; *Int'l*, pg. 1023
BI MEDICAL, INC.—See Bellsystem24 holdings, Inc.; *Int'l*, pg. 967
THE BINDING SITE CORPORATION LIMITED—See Thermo Fisher Scientific Inc.; *U.S. Public*, pg. 2152
THE BINDING SITE PORTUGAL, SPECIALIST PROTEIN COMPANY, UNIP LDA.—See Thermo Fisher Scientific Inc.; *U.S. Public*, pg. 2152
THE BINDING SITE PTE LTD.—See Thermo Fisher Scientific Inc.; *U.S. Public*, pg. 2152
THE BINDING SITE PTY LIMITED—See Thermo Fisher Scientific Inc.; *U.S. Public*, pg. 2152
THE BINDING SITE S.R.O.—See Thermo Fisher Scientific Inc.; *U.S. Public*, pg. 2152
BINEX CO., LTD.; *Int'l*, pg. 1033
BIO-AMERICA, INC.; *Int'l*, pg. 1035

CORPORATE AFFILIATIONS

BIOBLOCKS, INC.—See Genesis Biotechnology Group, LLC; *U.S. Private*, pg. 1669
BIO-BRIDGE SCIENCE, INC.; *U.S. Public*, pg. 332
BIOCARDIA LIFESCIENCES, INC.—See BioCardia, Inc.; *U.S. Public*, pg. 335
BIOCARE MEDICAL, LLC; *U.S. Private*, pg. 561
BIOCARE TECHNOLOGY COMPANY LIMITED—See Fresenius Medical Care AG; *Int'l*, pg. 2775
BIOCHROM LTD.—See Harvard Bioscience, Inc.; *U.S. Public*, pg. 987
BIOCODEX, INC.—See Biocodex SA; *Int'l*, pg. 1036
BIOCODEX SA; *Int'l*, pg. 1036
BIOCON BIOLOGICS LIMITED—See Eris Lifesciences Limited; *Int'l*, pg. 2493
BIOCON LTD.; *Int'l*, pg. 1036
BIOCON SDN. BHD.—See Biocon Ltd.; *Int'l*, pg. 1036
BIODELIVERY SCIENCES INTERNATIONAL, INC.—See Collegium Pharmaceutical, Inc.; *U.S. Public*, pg. 533
BIODEXA PHARMACEUTICALS PLC; *Int'l*, pg. 1037
BIODUE S.P.A.; *Int'l*, pg. 1037
BIODURO LLC—See Advent International Corporation; *U.S. Private*, pg. 98
BIO-ENGINEERED SUPPLEMENTS & NUTRITION, INC.—See Glanbia Co-Operative Society Limited; *Int'l*, pg. 2987
BIO ESSENCE HERBAL ESSENTIALS INC.; *U.S. Private*, pg. 561
BIOFARMA SRL—See Ardian SAS; *Int'l*, pg. 555
BIOFIL CHEMICALS & PHARMACEUTICALS LIMITED; *Int'l*, pg. 1037
BIOFOCUS DPI AG—See Charles River Laboratories International, Inc.; *U.S. Public*, pg. 480
BIOFOCUS, INC.—See Charles River Laboratories International, Inc.; *U.S. Public*, pg. 480
BIOFRONTERA AG; *Int'l*, pg. 1037
BIOGAIA PHARMA AB—See Biogaia Ab; *Int'l*, pg. 1038
BIOGEN BELGIUM N.V./S.A.—See Biogen Inc.; *U.S. Public*, pg. 336
BIOGEN BRASIL PRODUTOS FARMACEUTICOS LTDA—See Biogen Inc.; *U.S. Public*, pg. 336
BIOGEN (CZECH REPUBLIC) S.R.O.—See Biogen Inc.; *U.S. Public*, pg. 336
BIOGEN (DENMARK) A/S—See Biogen Inc.; *U.S. Public*, pg. 336
BIOGENESIS BAGO S.A.—See Bago Group; *Int'l*, pg. 799
BIOGEN FINLAND OY—See Biogen Inc.; *U.S. Public*, pg. 336
BIOGEN FRANCE S.A.S.—See Biogen Inc.; *U.S. Public*, pg. 336
BIOGEN GMBH—See Biogen Inc.; *U.S. Public*, pg. 336
BIOGEN HUNGARY KFT—See Biogen Inc.; *U.S. Public*, pg. 336
BIOGEN IDEC BELGIUM S.A./N.V.—See Biogen Inc.; *U.S. Public*, pg. 336
BIOGEN IDEC (DENMARK) MANUFACTURING APS—See Biogen Inc.; *U.S. Public*, pg. 336
BIOGEN IDEC FRANCE—See Biogen Inc.; *U.S. Public*, pg. 336
BIOGEN IDEC GMBH—See Biogen Inc.; *U.S. Public*, pg. 336
BIOGEN IDEC GMBH—See Biogen Inc.; *U.S. Public*, pg. 336
BIOGEN IDEC IBERIA—See Biogen Inc.; *U.S. Public*, pg. 336
BIOGEN IDEC INTERNATIONAL B.V.—See Biogen Inc.; *U.S. Public*, pg. 336
BIOGEN IDEC INTERNATIONAL GMBH—See Biogen Inc.; *U.S. Public*, pg. 336
BIOGEN IDEC JAPAN LTD.—See Biogen Inc.; *U.S. Public*, pg. 336
BIOGEN IDEC LIMITED—See Biogen Inc.; *U.S. Public*, pg. 336
BIOGEN IDEC PORTUGAL SOCIEDADE FARMACEUTICA, UNIPESSOAL, LDA.—See Biogen Inc.; *U.S. Public*, pg. 336
BIOGEN IDEC RESEARCH & CORPORATE CAMPUS—See Biogen Inc.; *U.S. Public*, pg. 336
BIOGEN IDEC SWEDEN AB—See Biogen Inc.; *U.S. Public*, pg. 336
BIOGEN INTERNATIONAL GMBH—See Biogen Inc.; *U.S. Public*, pg. 336
BIOGEN NETHERLANDS B.V.—See Biogen Inc.; *U.S. Public*, pg. 336
BIOGEN PORTUGAL SOCIEDADE FARMACEUTICA, UNIPESSOAL, LDA.—See Biogen Inc.; *U.S. Public*, pg. 337
BIOGEN SPAIN, S.L.—See Biogen Inc.; *U.S. Public*, pg. 337
BIOGEN SWITZERLAND AG—See Biogen Inc.; *U.S. Public*, pg. 337
BIOHAVEN PHARMACEUTICAL HOLDING COMPANY LTD.—See Pfizer Inc.; *U.S. Public*, pg. 1679
BIOINVENT INTERNATIONAL AB; *Int'l*, pg. 1038
BIOKIRCH GMBH—See Dermapharm Holding SE; *Int'l*, pg. 2043
BIOLAND CO., LTD - ANSAN PLANT—See Hyundai Bioland Co., Ltd.; *Int'l*, pg. 3555
BIOLAND CO., LTD - OCHANG PLANT—See Hyundai Bioland Co., Ltd.; *Int'l*, pg. 3555
BIOLAND CO., LTD - OSONG PLANT—See Hyundai Bio-

325412 — PHARMACEUTICAL PREP...

land Co., Ltd.; *Int'l*, pg. 3555
BIOLASCO TAIWAN CO., LTD.; *Int'l*, pg. 1038
BIOLIFE, LLC; *U.S. Private*, pg. 562
BIOLINE GMBH—See Meridian Bioscience Inc.; *U.S. Public*, pg. 1424
BIOLINE LTD.—See Meridian Bioscience Inc.; *U.S. Public*, pg. 1424
BIOLINE REAGENTS LTD.—See Meridian Bioscience Inc.; *U.S. Public*, pg. 1424
BIOLINERX LTD.; *Int'l*, pg. 1039
BIOLINE USA INC.—See Meridian Bioscience Inc.; *U.S. Public*, pg. 1424
BIOLOGISCHE HEILMITTEL HEEL GMBH—See Delton AG; *Int'l*, pg. 2021
BIOMARIN INTERNATIONAL LTD—See BioMarin Pharmaceutical Inc.; *U.S. Public*, pg. 337
BIOMARIN LEIDEN HOLDING BV—See BioMarin Pharmaceutical Inc.; *U.S. Public*, pg. 337
BIOMED LABORATORIES INC.—See Mativ Holdings, Inc.; *U.S. Public*, pg. 1396
BIOMED-LUBLIN WYTWORNIA SUROWIC I SZCZEPIONEK S.A.; *Int'l*, pg. 1039
BIOMM S. A.; *Int'l*, pg. 1040
BIONOMICS LIMITED; *Int'l*, pg. 1040
BIONOTE, INC.—See Abbott Laboratories; *U.S. Public*, pg. 19
BIO-PATH HOLDINGS, INC.; *U.S. Public*, pg. 332
BIOPHARMA CREDIT PLC; *Int'l*, pg. 1041
BIOPHARMA MANUFACTURING SOLUTIONS, INC.; *U.S. Private*, pg. 562
BIOPLUS CO., LTD.; *Int'l*, pg. 1041
BIOPORTO A/S; *Int'l*, pg. 1041
BIOQUANTA SA; *Int'l*, pg. 1041
BIO-RAD LABORATORIES—See Bio-Rad Laboratories, Inc.; *U.S. Public*, pg. 332
BIO-RAD—See Bio-Rad Laboratories, Inc.; *U.S. Public*, pg. 332
BIOSCIENCE BRANDS LIMITED; *Int'l*, pg. 1041
BIOSENSE WEBSTER (ISRAEL) LTD.—See Johnson & Johnson; *U.S. Public*, pg. 1194
BIOSINO BIO-TECHNOLOGY & SCIENCE INC.; *Int'l*, pg. 1042
BIOSKIN GMBH—See Eurofins Scientific S.E.; *Int'l*, pg. 2552
BIOSPECIFICS TECHNOLOGIES CORP.—See Endo International plc; *Int'l*, pg. 2403
BIOSPECTRA INC.; *U.S. Private*, pg. 563
BIOSPLICE THERAPEUTICS, INC.; *U.S. Private*, pg. 563
BIOSTAR PHARMACEUTICALS, INC.; *Int'l*, pg. 1042
BIOSTRIDE, INC.—See DevCo Partners Oy; *Int'l*, pg. 2086
BIOSYENT INC.; *Int'l*, pg. 1042
BIOSYN ARZNEIMITTEL GMBH; *Int'l*, pg. 1042
BIOSYN CORPORATION—See biosyn Arzneimittel GmbH; *Int'l*, pg. 1042
BIOTECHLOGIC, INC.—See Dark Horse Consulting; *U.S. Private*, pg. 1159
BIO-TECHNOLOGY GENERAL (ISRAEL) LTD.—See Ferring Holding SA; *Int'l*, pg. 2642
BIOTEST AG; *Int'l*, pg. 1043
BIOTEST AUSTRIA GMBH—See Biotest AG; *Int'l*, pg. 1043
BIOTEST FARMACEUTICA LTDA.—See Biotest AG; *Int'l*, pg. 1043
BIOTEST GRUNDSTUCKSVERWALTUNGS GMBH—See Biotest AG; *Int'l*, pg. 1043
BIOTEST HUNGARIA KFT.—See Biotest AG; *Int'l*, pg. 1043
BIOTEST ITALIA S.R.L.—See Biotest AG; *Int'l*, pg. 1043
BIO-THERA SOLUTIONS LTD.; *Int'l*, pg. 1035
BIOTIKA, A.S.—See Fiera Capital Corporation; *Int'l*, pg. 2660
BIOTIKA BOHEMIA SPOL. S R.O.; *Int'l*, pg. 1043
BIOTON S.A.; *Int'l*, pg. 1043
BIOVAIL PHARMACEUTICALS CANADA—See Bausch Health Companies Inc.; *Int'l*, pg. 898
BIOVET JSC—See Huvepharma EOOD; *Int'l*, pg. 3540
BIOVICA INTERNATIONAL AB; *Int'l*, pg. 1045
BIOVIE, INC.; *U.S. Public*, pg. 339
BIOWORKSHOPS LIMITED—See CSPC Pharmaceutical Group Limited; *Int'l*, pg. 1867
BIOXYNE LIMITED; *Int'l*, pg. 1045
BIOZYME HOLDINGS LIMITED—See Abbott Laboratories; *U.S. Public*, pg. 19
BIRZEIT PHARMACEUTICAL COMPANY; *Int'l*, pg. 1048
BLACKMORES INTERNATIONAL PTE. LIMITED—See Blackmores Limited; *Int'l*, pg. 1061
BLISS GVS PHARMA LTD.; *Int'l*, pg. 1063
BLIS TECHNOLOGIES LIMITED; *Int'l*, pg. 1063
BLISTEX LIMITED—See Blistex, Inc.; *U.S. Private*, pg. 582
BLUEBERRY THERAPEUTICS LIMITED—See China Medical System Holdings Ltd.; *Int'l*, pg. 1518
BLUEJAY DIAGNOSTICS, INC.; *U.S. Public*, pg. 365
BLUE JET HEALTHCARE LIMITED; *Int'l*, pg. 1068
BLUEPRINT MEDICINES CORPORATION; *U.S. Public*, pg. 366
BMN MSI CO., LTD.—See BioLASCO Taiwan Co., Ltd.; *Int'l*, pg. 1038
BMS HOLDINGS SPAIN, S.L.—See Bristol-Myers Squibb Company; *U.S. Public*, pg. 384
BMS PHARMACEUTICAL KOREA LIMITED—See Bristol-Myers Squibb Company; *U.S. Public*, pg. 384

BNC KOREA CO., LTD.; *Int'l*, pg. 1078
BOCAGREENMD, INC.—See TherapeuticsMD, Inc.; *U.S. Public*, pg. 2145
BOEHRINGER INGELHEIM AB—See C.H. Boehringer Sohn AG & Co. KG; *Int'l*, pg. 1241
BOEHRINGER INGELHEIM ANIMAL HEALTH AUSTRALIA PTY. LTD.—See C.H. Boehringer Sohn AG & Co. KG; *Int'l*, pg. 1241
BOEHRINGER INGELHEIM ANIMAL HEALTH BELGIUM S.A.—See C.H. Boehringer Sohn AG & Co. KG; *Int'l*, pg. 1241
BOEHRINGER INGELHEIM ANIMAL HEALTH DO BRASIL LTDA.—See C.H. Boehringer Sohn AG & Co. KG; *Int'l*, pg. 1241
BOEHRINGER INGELHEIM ANIMAL HEALTH JAPAN CO., LTD.—See C.H. Boehringer Sohn AG & Co. KG; *Int'l*, pg. 1241
BOEHRINGER INGELHEIM ANIMAL HEALTH NETHERLANDS B.V.—See C.H. Boehringer Sohn AG & Co. KG; *Int'l*, pg. 1241
BOEHRINGER INGELHEIM ANIMAL HEALTH NEW ZEALAND LIMITED—See C.H. Boehringer Sohn AG & Co. KG; *Int'l*, pg. 1241
BOEHRINGER INGELHEIM ANIMAL HEALTH SOUTH AFRICA PTY. LTD.—See C.H. Boehringer Sohn AG & Co. KG; *Int'l*, pg. 1241
BOEHRINGER INGELHEIM AUSTRIA GMBH—See C.H. Boehringer Sohn AG & Co. KG; *Int'l*, pg. 1241
BOEHRINGER INGELHEIM B.V.—See C.H. Boehringer Sohn AG & Co. KG; *Int'l*, pg. 1241
BOEHRINGER INGELHEIM DANMARK A/S—See C.H. Boehringer Sohn AG & Co. KG; *Int'l*, pg. 1241
BOEHRINGER INGELHEIM DO BRASIL QUIMICA E FARMACEUTICA LTDA.—See C.H. Boehringer Sohn AG & Co. KG; *Int'l*, pg. 1242
BOEHRINGER INGELHEIM ELLAS AE—See C.H. Boehringer Sohn AG & Co. KG; *Int'l*, pg. 1241
BOEHRINGER INGELHEIM ESPANA, S.A.—See C.H. Boehringer Sohn AG & Co. KG; *Int'l*, pg. 1241
BOEHRINGER INGELHEIM FRANCE S.A.S.—See C.H. Boehringer Sohn AG & Co. KG; *Int'l*, pg. 1241
BOEHRINGER INGELHEIM (HONG KONG) LTD.—See C.H. Boehringer Sohn AG & Co. KG; *Int'l*, pg. 1241
BOEHRINGER INGELHEIM ILAC TICARET A.S.—See C.H. Boehringer Sohn AG & Co. KG; *Int'l*, pg. 1242
BOEHRINGER INGELHEIM INDIA PRIVATE LTD.—See C.H. Boehringer Sohn AG & Co. KG; *Int'l*, pg. 1242
BOEHRINGER INGELHEIM ITALIA S.P.A.—See C.H. Boehringer Sohn AG & Co. KG; *Int'l*, pg. 1242
BOEHRINGER INGELHEIM KOREA LTD.—See C.H. Boehringer Sohn AG & Co. KG; *Int'l*, pg. 1242
BOEHRINGER INGELHEIM LTDA.—See C.H. Boehringer Sohn AG & Co. KG; *Int'l*, pg. 1242
BOEHRINGER INGELHEIM LTD.—See C.H. Boehringer Sohn AG & Co. KG; *Int'l*, pg. 1242
BOEHRINGER INGELHEIM MICROPARTS GMBH—See C.H. Boehringer Sohn AG & Co. KG; *Int'l*, pg. 1242
BOEHRINGER INGELHEIM PERU S.A.C.—See C.H. Boehringer Sohn AG & Co. KG; *Int'l*, pg. 1242
BOEHRINGER INGELHEIM PHARMACEUTICALS, INC.—See C.H. Boehringer Sohn AG & Co. KG; *Int'l*, pg. 1241
BOEHRINGER INGELHEIM PHARMA GES.M.B.H.—See C.H. Boehringer Sohn AG & Co. KG; *Int'l*, pg. 1241
BOEHRINGER INGELHEIM PHARMA GMBH & CO. KG—See C.H. Boehringer Sohn AG & Co. KG; *Int'l*, pg. 1242
BOEHRINGER INGELHEIM (PHILIPPINES) INC.—See C.H. Boehringer Sohn AG & Co. KG; *Int'l*, pg. 1241
BOEHRINGER INGELHEIM PROMECO, S.A. DE C.V.—See C.H. Boehringer Sohn AG & Co. KG; *Int'l*, pg. 1242
BOEHRINGER INGELHEIM PTY. LTD.—See C.H. Boehringer Sohn AG & Co. KG; *Int'l*, pg. 1242
BOEHRINGER INGELHEIM S.A./N.V.—See C.H. Boehringer Sohn AG & Co. KG; *Int'l*, pg. 1242
BOEHRINGER INGELHEIM S.A.—See C.H. Boehringer Sohn AG & Co. KG; *Int'l*, pg. 1242
BOEHRINGER INGELHEIM S.A.—See C.H. Boehringer Sohn AG & Co. KG; *Int'l*, pg. 1242
BOEHRINGER INGELHEIM (SCHWEIZ) GMBH—See C.H. Boehringer Sohn AG & Co. KG; *Int'l*, pg. 1241
BOEHRINGER INGELHEIM SEIYAKU CO., LTD.—See C.H. Boehringer Sohn AG & Co. KG; *Int'l*, pg. 1243
BOEHRINGER INGELHEIM SHANGHAI PHARMACEUTICALS CO., LTD.—See C.H. Boehringer Sohn AG & Co. KG; *Int'l*, pg. 1242
BOEHRINGER INGELHEIM SPOL. S R.O.—See C.H. Boehringer Sohn AG & Co. KG; *Int'l*, pg. 1242
BOEHRINGER INGELHEIM SP. Z O.O.—See C.H. Boehringer Sohn AG & Co. KG; *Int'l*, pg. 1241
BOEHRINGER INGELHEIM S.R.O.—See C.H. Boehringer Sohn AG & Co. KG; *Int'l*, pg. 1241
BOEHRINGER INGELHEIM TAIWAN LTD.—See C.H. Boehringer Sohn AG & Co. KG; *Int'l*, pg. 1242
BOEHRINGER INGELHEIM (THAI) LTD.—See C.H. Boehringer Sohn AG & Co. KG; *Int'l*, pg. 1241
BOEHRINGER INGELHEIM VETERINARY RESEARCH CENTER GMBH & CO. KG—See C.H. Boehringer Sohn

AG & Co. KG; *Int'l*, pg. 1242
BOEHRINGER INGELHEIM VETMEDICA GMBH—See C.H. Boehringer Sohn AG & Co. KG; *Int'l*, pg. 1242
BOEHRINGER INGELHEIM VETMEDICA JAPAN—See C.H. Boehringer Sohn AG & Co. KG; *Int'l*, pg. 1243
BOEHRINGER INGELHEIM VETMEDICA S.A. DE C.V.—See C.H. Boehringer Sohn AG & Co. KG; *Int'l*, pg. 1242
BOHAI PHARMACEUTICALS GROUP, INC.; *Int'l*, pg. 1100
BOIRON BG EOOD—See Boiron Group; *Int'l*, pg. 1101
BOIRON CANADA INC.—See Boiron Group; *Int'l*, pg. 1101
BOIRON CZ S.R.O.—See Boiron Group; *Int'l*, pg. 1101
BOIRON HUNGARIA KFT—See Boiron Group; *Int'l*, pg. 1101
BOIRON INC—See Boiron Group; *Int'l*, pg. 1101
BOIRON MEDICAMENTOS HOMEOPATICOS LTDA—See Boiron Group; *Int'l*, pg. 1101
BOIRON PORTUGAL LTDA—See Boiron Group; *Int'l*, pg. 1101
BOIRON RUSSIE O.O.O—See Boiron Group; *Int'l*, pg. 1101
BOIRON SA—See Boiron Group; *Int'l*, pg. 1101
BOIRON SK S.R.O—See Boiron Group; *Int'l*, pg. 1101
BOIRON SOCIEDAD IBERICA DE HOMEOPATIA—See Boiron Group; *Int'l*, pg. 1101
BOIRON SP Z.O.O—See Boiron Group; *Int'l*, pg. 1101
BOIRON SRL—See Boiron Group; *Int'l*, pg. 1101
BOIRON SUISSE SA—See Boiron Group; *Int'l*, pg. 1101
BOIRON TN SARL—See Boiron Group; *Int'l*, pg. 1101
BOLAK COMPANY LIMITED; *Int'l*, pg. 1102
BONESUPPORT HOLDING AB; *Int'l*, pg. 1106
BORA PHARMACEUTICALS CO., LTD.; *Int'l*, pg. 1112
BORYUNG PHARMACEUTICAL - ANSAN FACTORY—See Boryung Pharmaceutical; *Int'l*, pg. 1115
BORYUNG PHARMACEUTICAL; *Int'l*, pg. 1115
BOSNALIJEK D.D.; *Int'l*, pg. 1116
BOTANECO SPECIALTY INGREDIENTS INC.—See AVAC, Ltd.; *U.S. Public*, pg. 733
BOUCHER & MUIR PTY LIMITED—See ADVANZ PHARMA Corp. Limited; *Int'l*, pg. 166
BRACCO DIAGNOSTICS INC.—See Bracco S.p.A.; *Int'l*, pg. 1134
BRACCO-EISAI CO., LTD.—See Bracco S.p.A.; *Int'l*, pg. 1134
BRACCO-EISAI CO., LTD.—See Eisai Co., Ltd.; *Int'l*, pg. 2334
BRACCO IMAGING DEUTSCHLAND GMBH—See Bracco S.p.A.; *Int'l*, pg. 1134
BRACCO IMAGING S.P.A.—See Bracco S.p.A.; *Int'l*, pg. 1134
BRACCO INTERNATIONAL B.V.—See Bracco S.p.A.; *Int'l*, pg. 1134
BRACCO S.P.A.; *Int'l*, pg. 1134
BRAEBURN INC.; *U.S. Private*, pg. 633
BRAMTON COMPANY INC.—See NCH Corporation; *U.S. Private*, pg. 2875
BRATACO, PT; *Int'l*, pg. 1140
BRAUN (SHANGHAI) CO. LTD.—See The Procter & Gamble Company; *U.S. Public*, pg. 2124
BRAWN BIOTECH LTD.; *Int'l*, pg. 1142
BRIDGE BIOTHERAPEUTICS, INC.; *Int'l*, pg. 1152
BRIGHTGENE FERMENTATION TECHNOLOGY CO. LTD.—See BrightGene Bio-Medical Technology Co., Ltd.; *Int'l*, pg. 1162
BRIGHTGENE FINE CHEMICAL CO. LTD.—See BrightGene Bio-Medical Technology Co., Ltd.; *Int'l*, pg. 1162
BRIGHTGENE PHARMACEUTICAL CO. LTD.—See BrightGene Bio-Medical Technology Co., Ltd.; *Int'l*, pg. 1162
BRIGHTPATH BIOTHERAPEUTICS CO., LTD.; *Int'l*, pg. 1163
BRIOSCHI INTERNATIONAL CORP.—See Brioschi Pharmaceuticals International, LLC; *U.S. Private*, pg. 655
BRIOSCHI PHARMACEUTICALS INTERNATIONAL, LLC; *U.S. Private*, pg. 655
BRISTOL-MYERS PHARMACEUTICAL—See Bristol-Myers Squibb Company; *U.S. Public*, pg. 384
BRISTOL-MYERS SQUIBB AB—See Bristol-Myers Squibb Company; *U.S. Public*, pg. 384
BRISTOL-MYERS SQUIBB ARGENTINA S.R.L.—See Bristol-Myers Squibb Company; *U.S. Public*, pg. 385
BRISTOL-MYERS SQUIBB AUSTRALIA PTY. LTD.—See Bristol-Myers Squibb Company; *U.S. Public*, pg. 385
BRISTOL-MYERS SQUIBB BELGIUM S.A.—See Bristol-Myers Squibb Company; *U.S. Public*, pg. 385
BRISTOL-MYERS SQUIBB CANADA INTERNATIONAL LIMITED—See Bristol-Myers Squibb Company; *U.S. Public*, pg. 385
BRISTOL-MYERS SQUIBB COMPANY - LAWRENCEVILLE R&D FACILITY—See Bristol-Myers Squibb Company; *U.S. Public*, pg. 385
BRISTOL-MYERS SQUIBB COMPANY; *U.S. Public*, pg. 384
BRISTOL-MYERS SQUIBB DENMARK FILIAL OF BRISTOL-MYERS SQUIBB AB—See Bristol-Myers Squibb Company; *U.S. Public*, pg. 385
BRISTOL-MYERS SQUIBB DENMARK—See Bristol-Myers Squibb Company; *U.S. Public*, pg. 385
BRISTOL-MYERS SQUIBB FARMACEUTICA PORTU-

325412 — PHARMACEUTICAL PREP...

GUESA S.A.—See Bristol-Myers Squibb Company; *U.S. Public*, pg. 385
BRISTOL-MYERS SQUIBB GES. M.B.H.—See Bristol-Myers Squibb Company; *U.S. Public*, pg. 385
BRISTOL-MYERS SQUIBB GMBH—See Bristol-Myers Squibb Company; *U.S. Public*, pg. 385
BRISTOL-MYERS SQUIBB HOLDINGS GERMANY VERWALTUNGS GMBH—See Bristol-Myers Squibb Company; *U.S. Public*, pg. 385
BRISTOL-MYERS SQUIBB ILACLARI, INC.—See Bristol-Myers Squibb Company; *U.S. Public*, pg. 385
BRISTOL-MYERS SQUIBB INDIA PVT. LTD.—See Bristol-Myers Squibb Company; *U.S. Public*, pg. 385
BRISTOL-MYERS SQUIBB (ISRAEL) LTD—See Bristol-Myers Squibb Company; *U.S. Public*, pg. 384
BRISTOL-MYERS SQUIBB K.K.—See Bristol-Myers Squibb Company; *U.S. Public*, pg. 385
BRISTOL-MYERS SQUIBB LIMITED LIABILITY COMPANY—See Bristol-Myers Squibb Company; *U.S. Public*, pg. 385
BRISTOL-MYERS SQUIBB NORWAY LTD.—See Bristol-Myers Squibb Company; *U.S. Public*, pg. 385
BRISTOL-MYERS SQUIBB PERU S.A.—See Bristol-Myers Squibb Company; *U.S. Public*, pg. 385
BRISTOL-MYERS SQUIBB PHARMACEUTICALS LIMITED—See Bristol-Myers Squibb Company; *U.S. Public*, pg. 385
BRISTOL-MYERS SQUIBB PHARMACEUTICALS UNLIMITED COMPANY—See Bristol-Myers Squibb Company; *U.S. Public*, pg. 385
BRISTOL-MYERS SQUIBB PHARMA (THAILAND) CO. LTD.—See Bristol-Myers Squibb Company; *U.S. Public*, pg. 385
BRISTOL-MYERS SQUIBB POLSKA SP.Z.O.O.—See Bristol-Myers Squibb Company; *U.S. Public*, pg. 385
BRISTOL-MYERS SQUIBB PUERTO RICO, INC. - MANATI PLANT—See Bristol-Myers Squibb Company; *U.S. Public*, pg. 385
BRISTOL-MYERS SQUIBB S.A.—See Bristol-Myers Squibb Company; *U.S. Public*, pg. 385
BRISTOL-MYERS SQUIBB SERVICES SP. Z O.O.—See Bristol-Myers Squibb Company; *U.S. Public*, pg. 385
BRISTOL-MYERS SQUIBB (SINGAPORE) PTE. LIMITED—See Bristol-Myers Squibb Company; *U.S. Public*, pg. 384
BRISTOL-MYERS SQUIBB SPOL. S R.O.—See Bristol-Myers Squibb Company; *U.S. Public*, pg. 385
BRISTOL-MYERS SQUIBB S.R.L.—See Bristol-Myers Squibb Company; *U.S. Public*, pg. 385
BRISTOL-MYERS SQUIBB (TAIWAN) LTD.—See Bristol-Myers Squibb Company; *U.S. Public*, pg. 384
BRITANNIA PHARMACEUTICALS LTD.—See Bain Capital, LP; *U.S. Private*, pg. 443
BRITANNIA PHARMACEUTICALS LTD.—See Cinven Limited; *Int'l*, pg. 1613
BROOKS LABORATORIES LIMITED; *Int'l*, pg. 1194
BRUNEL HEALTHCARE MANUFACTURING LIMITED—See Elder Pharmaceuticals Ltd.; *Int'l*, pg. 2346
BTG AUSTRALASIA PTY LIMITED—See Boston Scientific Corporation; *U.S. Public*, pg. 373
BTG PLC—See Boston Scientific Corporation; *U.S. Public*, pg. 373
BUCHANG PHARMACEUTICAL,INC; *Int'l*, pg. 1206
BUCHER DENWEL, SPOL. S R.O.—See Bucher Industries AG; *Int'l*, pg. 1207
BUKWANG PHARMACEUTICAL CO., LTD.; *Int'l*, pg. 1213
BUNKER INDUSTRIA FARMACEUTICA LTDA.—See Bausch Health Companies Inc.; *Int'l*, pg. 897
BURGWEDEL BIOTECH GMBH—See Merck & Co., Inc.; *U.S. Public*, pg. 1415
BURROUGHS WELLCOME (INDIA) LTD.—See GSK plc; *Int'l*, pg. 3145
BUSHU PHARMACEUTICALS LTD. - MISATO PLANT—See EQT AB; *Int'l*, pg. 2469
BUSHU PHARMACEUTICALS LTD.—See EQT AB; *Int'l*, pg. 2469
BUSINESS SUPPORT SOLUTION S.A.—See CEPD N.V.; *Int'l*, pg. 1420
C3I SUPPORT SERVICES PRIVATE LIMITED—See Merck & Co., Inc.; *U.S. Public*, pg. 1415
CACHET PHARMACEUTICALS PRIVATE LIMITED—See Alkem Laboratories Ltd.; *Int'l*, pg. 330
CAI LAY VETERINARY PHARMACEUTICAL JOINT STOCK COMPANY; *Int'l*, pg. 1252
CALITHERA BIOSCIENCES, INC.; *U.S. Public*, pg. 424
CALLIDITAS THERAPEUTICS AB—See Asahi Kasei Corporation; *Int'l*, pg. 596
CALLITAS THERAPEUTICS, INC.—See Callitas Health Inc.; *U.S. Private*, pg. 722
CAMBIUM BIO LIMITED; *Int'l*, pg. 1268
CAMBRIDGE COGNITION HOLDINGS PLC; *Int'l*, pg. 1269
CAMBRIDGE LIFE SCIENCES LTD.; *Int'l*, pg. 1269
CAMURUS AB; *Int'l*, pg. 1275
CAMURUS GMBH—See Camurus AB; *Int'l*, pg. 1275
CAMURUS LTD.—See Camurus AB; *Int'l*, pg. 1275
CANADIAN CANNABIS CORP.; *Int'l*, pg. 1283
CANAFARMA HEMP PRODUCTS CORP.; *Int'l*, pg. 1287

CANBAS CO., LTD.; *Int'l*, pg. 1288
CANBRIDGE PHARMACEUTICALS INC.; *Int'l*, pg. 1288
CANCER PREVENTION PHARMACEUTICALS, INC.—See Panbela Therapeutics, Inc.; *U.S. Public*, pg. 1635
CAN-FITE BIOPHARMA LTD.; *Int'l*, pg. 1276
CANGENE BIOPHARMA, INC.—See Emergent BioSolutions Inc.; *U.S. Public*, pg. 739
CANNABINOID BIOSCIENCES, INC.; *U.S. Private*, pg. 734
CANNABIS POLAND S.A.; *Int'l*, pg. 1291
CANNABIS SUISSE CORP; *Int'l*, pg. 1292
CANNAMERICA BRANDS CORP.; *Int'l*, pg. 1292
CANNAPHARMARX, INC.; *Int'l*, pg. 1292
CANNAPOWDER, INC.; *U.S. Public*, pg. 430
CANNARA BIOTECH, INC.; *Int'l*, pg. 1292
CANNIMED LTD.—See Aurora Cannabis Inc.; *Int'l*, pg. 713
CANNOVUM CANNABIS AG; *Int'l*, pg. 1292
CANNTAB THERAPEUTICS LIMITED; *Int'l*, pg. 1292
CANTARGIA AB; *Int'l*, pg. 1299
CAPLIN POINT LABORATORIES LIMITED - CP-I FACTORY—See Caplin Point Laboratories Limited; *Int'l*, pg. 1315
CAPLIN POINT LABORATORIES LIMITED - CP-II FACTORY—See Caplin Point Laboratories Limited; *Int'l*, pg. 1315
CAPLIN POINT LABORATORIES LIMITED; *Int'l*, pg. 1315
CAPRICOR THERAPEUTICS, INC.; *U.S. Public*, pg. 432
CAPSTONE THERAPEUTICS CORP.; *U.S. Public*, pg. 432
CAPSUGEL DE MEXICO, S. DE R.L. DE C.V.—See Pfizer Inc.; *U.S. Public*, pg. 1679
CAPSUGEL HEALTHCARE LIMITED—See Pfizer Inc.; *U.S. Public*, pg. 1679
CAPSULINE, INC.; *U.S. Private*, pg. 746
CARA THERAPEUTICS, INC.; *U.S. Public*, pg. 432
CARBOGEN AMCIS LTD. (U.K.)—See Dishman Carbogen Amcis Limited; *Int'l*, pg. 2135
CARBOGEN AMCIS REAL ESTATE SAS—See Dishman Carbogen Amcis Limited; *Int'l*, pg. 2135
CARDAX PHARMA, INC.—See Cardax Pharmaceuticals, Inc.; *U.S. Private*, pg. 749
CARDINAL ASSOCIATES INC.—See Balchem Corporation; *U.S. Public*, pg. 265
CARDINAL HEALTH 104 LP—See Cardinal Health, Inc.; *U.S. Public*, pg. 433
CARDINAL HEALTH 222 (THAILAND) LTD.—See Cardinal Health, Inc.; *U.S. Public*, pg. 433
CARDINAL HEALTH 418, INC.—See Cardinal Health, Inc.; *U.S. Public*, pg. 433
CARDINAL HEALTH, INC. - DENVER—See Cardinal Health, Inc.; *U.S. Public*, pg. 434
CARDINAL HEALTH MALTA 212 LIMITED—See Cardinal Health, Inc.; *U.S. Public*, pg. 433
CARDINAL HEALTH SINGAPORE 225 PTE. LTD.—See Cardinal Health, Inc.; *U.S. Public*, pg. 433
CARDINAL HEALTH SYSTEMS, INC.—See Cardinal Health, Inc.; *U.S. Public*, pg. 434
CARDIOL THERAPEUTICS, INC.; *Int'l*, pg. 1321
CARDIOVASCULAR SYSTEMS, INC.—See Abbott Laboratories; *U.S. Public*, pg. 19
CARDOZ AB—See Forbion Capital Partners Management Holding BV; *Int'l*, pg. 2729
CARISMA THERAPEUTICS INC.; *U.S. Public*, pg. 435
CARNA BIOSCIENCES INC.; *Int'l*, pg. 1342
CAROL INFO SERVICES LTD.; *Int'l*, pg. 1342
CARTESIAN THERAPEUTICS, INC.; *U.S. Public*, pg. 445
CASCADIAN THERAPEUTICS, INC.—See Seagen Inc.; *U.S. Public*, pg. 1852
CASI PHARMACEUTICALS (CHINA) CO., LTD.—See CASI Pharmaceuticals, Inc.; *Int'l*, pg. 1352
CASSAVA SCIENCES, INC.; *U.S. Public*, pg. 447
CASSIOPEA SPA—See Cosmo Pharmaceuticals N.V.; *Int'l*, pg. 1813
CASTLE CREEK PHARMACEUTICALS HOLDINGS, INC.; *U.S. Public*, pg. 447
CATALENT ANAGNI S.R.L.—See Catalent, Inc.; *U.S. Public*, pg. 448
CATALENT BRASIL LTDA—See Catalent, Inc.; *U.S. Public*, pg. 448
CATALENT DUSSELDORF GMBH—See Catalent, Inc.; *U.S. Public*, pg. 448
CATALENT GERMANY EBERBACH GMBH—See Catalent, Inc.; *U.S. Public*, pg. 448
CATALENT GERMANY SCHORNDORF GMBH—See Catalent, Inc.; *U.S. Public*, pg. 448
CATALENT HARMANS ROAD, LLC—See Catalent, Inc.; *U.S. Public*, pg. 448
CATALENT HOUSTON, LLC—See Catalent, Inc.; *U.S. Public*, pg. 448
CATALENT, INC.; *U.S. Public*, pg. 448
CATALENT JAPAN K.K.—See Catalent, Inc.; *U.S. Public*, pg. 448
CATALENT MICRON TECHNOLOGIES, INC.—See Catalent, Inc.; *U.S. Public*, pg. 448
CATALENT NOTTINGHAM LIMITED—See Catalent, Inc.; *U.S. Public*, pg. 448
CATALENT OXFORD LIMITED—See Catalent, Inc.; *U.S. Public*, pg. 448
CATALENT PHARMA SOLUTIONS, LLC - RALEIGH—See Catalent, Inc.; *U.S. Public*, pg. 448

CATALENT PHARMA SOLUTIONS LTD. - BOLTON—See Catalent, Inc.; *U.S. Public*, pg. 448
CATALENT PRINCETON, LLC—See Catalent, Inc.; *U.S. Public*, pg. 448
CATALENT SAN DIEGO, INC.—See Catalent, Inc.; *U.S. Public*, pg. 448
CATALENT SAN DIEGO INC.—See Catalent, Inc.; *U.S. Public*, pg. 448
CATALYST BIO, INC.—See GNI Group Ltd.; *Int'l*, pg. 3017
CATALYST PHARMACEUTICALS, INC.; *U.S. Public*, pg. 449
CATHAY INTERNATIONAL HOLDINGS LIMITED; *Int'l*, pg. 1360
CATO SMS; *Int'l*, pg. 1361
CAYMAN CHEMICAL COMPANY, INC.; *U.S. Private*, pg. 795
CCM PHARMACEUTICALS SDN BHD—See Batu Kawan Berhad; *Int'l*, pg. 891
CCM PHARMACEUTICALS (S) PTE LTD.—See Batu Kawan Berhad; *Int'l*, pg. 891
CDK KOREA CORPORATION—See CKD Corporation; *Int'l*, pg. 1639
CEAPRO INC.—See COSCIENS Biopharma Inc.; *U.S. Public*, pg. 585
CEAUTAMED WORLDWIDE LLC—See Smart for Life, Inc.; *U.S. Public*, pg. 1895
CECEP SOLAR ENERGY CO., LTD.; *Int'l*, pg. 1373
CELGENE AB—See Bristol-Myers Squibb Company; *U.S. Public*, pg. 386
CELGENE AB—See Bristol-Myers Squibb Company; *U.S. Public*, pg. 386
CELGENE APS—See Bristol-Myers Squibb Company; *U.S. Public*, pg. 386
CELGENE AVILOMICS RESEARCH, INC.—See Bristol-Myers Squibb Company; *U.S. Public*, pg. 386
CELGENE BVBA—See Bristol-Myers Squibb Company; *U.S. Public*, pg. 386
CELGENE B.V.—See Bristol-Myers Squibb Company; *U.S. Public*, pg. 386
CELGENE CHEMICALS SARL—See Bristol-Myers Squibb Company; *U.S. Public*, pg. 386
CELGENE CORPORATION—See Bristol-Myers Squibb Company; *U.S. Public*, pg. 385
CELGENE CO.—See Bristol-Myers Squibb Company; *U.S. Public*, pg. 386
CELGENE EUROPE, LIMITED—See Bristol-Myers Squibb Company; *U.S. Public*, pg. 386
CELGENE GMBH—See Bristol-Myers Squibb Company; *U.S. Public*, pg. 386
CELGENE GMBH—See Bristol-Myers Squibb Company; *U.S. Public*, pg. 386
CELGENE GMBH—See Bristol-Myers Squibb Company; *U.S. Public*, pg. 386
CELGENE INC.—See Bristol-Myers Squibb Company; *U.S. Public*, pg. 386
CELGENE INTERNATIONAL SARL—See Bristol-Myers Squibb Company; *U.S. Public*, pg. 386
CELGENE LIMITED—See Bristol-Myers Squibb Company; *U.S. Public*, pg. 386
CELGENE LIMITED—See Bristol-Myers Squibb Company; *U.S. Public*, pg. 386
CELGENE LLAC PAZARLAMA VE TIC.LTD. STI.—See Bristol-Myers Squibb Company; *U.S. Public*, pg. 386
CELGENE LOGISTICS SARL—See Bristol-Myers Squibb Company; *U.S. Public*, pg. 386
CELGENE NETHERLANDS BV—See Bristol-Myers Squibb Company; *U.S. Public*, pg. 386
CELGENE PTE LTD—See Bristol-Myers Squibb Company; *U.S. Public*, pg. 386
CELGENE PTY LIMITED—See Bristol-Myers Squibb Company; *U.S. Public*, pg. 386
CELGENE QUANTICEL RESEARCH, INC.—See Bristol-Myers Squibb Company; *U.S. Public*, pg. 386
CELGENE SARL—See Bristol-Myers Squibb Company; *U.S. Public*, pg. 386
CELGENE, S. DE R.L. DE C.V.—See Bristol-Myers Squibb Company; *U.S. Public*, pg. 386
CELGENE, SL—See Bristol-Myers Squibb Company; *U.S. Public*, pg. 386
CELGENE SOCIEDADE UNIPESSOAL LDA—See Bristol-Myers Squibb Company; *U.S. Public*, pg. 386
CELGENE SP. ZOO—See Bristol-Myers Squibb Company; *U.S. Public*, pg. 386
CELGENE SRL—See Bristol-Myers Squibb Company; *U.S. Public*, pg. 386
CELLDEX THERAPEUTICS, INC.; *U.S. Public*, pg. 465
CELLECTAR BIOSCIENCES, INC.; *U.S. Public*, pg. 465
CELLID CO., LTD.; *Int'l*, pg. 1393
CELLIVERY THERAPEUTICS INC.; *Int'l*, pg. 1393
CELL PHARM GESELLSCHAFT FUR PHARMAZEUTISCHE UND DIAGNOSTISCHE PRAPARATE MBH—See Bain Capital, LP; *U.S. Private*, pg. 444
CELL PHARM GESELLSCHAFT FUR PHARMAZEUTISCHE UND DIAGNOSTISCHE PRAPARATE MBH—See Cinven Limited; *Int'l*, pg. 1614
CELLTRION HEALTHCARE CO., LTD.—See Celltrion Pharm, Inc.; *Int'l*, pg. 1394
CELLTRION, INC.; *Int'l*, pg. 1394

N.A.I.C.S. INDEX

325412 — PHARMACEUTICAL PREP...

CELLTRION PHARM. INC. - JINCHEON FACTORY—See Celltrion Pharm. Inc.; *Int'l*, pg. 1394
CELLTRION PHARM. INC.; *Int'l*, pg. 1394
CELLTRION USA, INC.—See Celltrion, Inc.; *Int'l*, pg. 1395
CELLULAR BIOMEDICINE GROUP, INC.; *U.S. Private*, pg. 807
CELLZOME GMBH—See GSK plc; *Int'l*, pg. 3145
CELON PHARMA SA; *Int'l*, pg. 1395
CELTIC PHARMA LIMITED; *Int'l*, pg. 1396
CELYAD ONCOLOGY SA; *Int'l*, pg. 1396
CENTRAFARM NEDERLAND B.V.—See Bain Capital, LP; *U.S. Private*, pg. 443
CENTRAFARM NEDERLAND B.V.—See Cinven Limited; *Int'l*, pg. 1613
CENTRAFARM PHARMACEUTICALS B.V.—See Bain Capital, LP; *U.S. Private*, pg. 443
CENTRAFARM PHARMACEUTICALS B.V.—See Cinven Limited; *Int'l*, pg. 1613
CENTRAL ADMIXTURE PHARMACY SERVICES, INC.—See B. Braun Melsungen AG; *Int'l*, pg. 787
CENTRAL GLASS CHEMSPEC COMPANY LTD.—See Central Glass Co., Ltd.; *Int'l*, pg. 1406
CENTRAL GLASS CZECH S.R.O.—See Central Glass Co., Ltd.; *Int'l*, pg. 1406
CENTRAL PHARMACEUTICALS LIMITED; *Int'l*, pg. 1409
CENTREXION THERAPEUTICS CORPORATION; *U.S. Private*, pg. 829
CEPHAZONE PHARMA LLC—See Aurobindo Pharma Ltd.; *Int'l*, pg. 712
CEREBAIN BIOTECH CORP.; *U.S. Private*, pg. 840
CERENIS THERAPEUTICS INC.—See Abionyx Pharma SA; *Int'l*, pg. 62
CEREP LTD.—See Eurofins Scientific S.E.; *Int'l*, pg. 2542
CERES F&D INC.—See Alteogen Inc.; *Int'l*, pg. 391
CEREVEL THERAPEUTICS, LLC—See AbbVie Inc.; *U.S. Public*, pg. 24
CERUS CORPORATION; *U.S. Public*, pg. 476
CERUS EUROPE B.V.—See Cerus Corporation; *U.S. Public*, pg. 476
CERVOMED INC.; *U.S. Public*, pg. 476
CESSATECH A/S; *Int'l*, pg. 1424
CG PHARMACEUTICALS, INC.—See CrystalGenomics, Inc.; *Int'l*, pg. 1860
CHA BIOTECH CO., LTD.; *Int'l*, pg. 1435
CHAMPION NUTRITION, INC.; *U.S. Private*, pg. 846
CHAMPIONS ONCOLOGY, INC.; *U.S. Public*, pg. 478
CHANDRA BHAGAT PHARMA LTD.; *Int'l*, pg. 1441
CHANGCHUN EXTRAWELL PHARMACEUTICAL CO., LTD.—See Extrawell Pharmaceutical Holdings Ltd.; *Int'l*, pg. 2592
CHANGCHUN HIGH & NEW TECHNOLOGY INDUSTRY (GROUP) INC.; *Int'l*, pg. 1442
CHANGSHAN BIOCHEMICAL PHARMACEUTICAL (JIANGSU) CO., LTD.—See Hebei Changshan Biochemical Pharmaceutical Co. Ltd.; *Int'l*, pg. 3305
CHANGSHAN CONJUCHEM BIOLOGICAL PHARMACEUTICAL R&D CO., LTD.—See Hebei Changshan Biochemical Pharmaceutical Co. Ltd.; *Int'l*, pg. 3305
CHANGZHOU QIANHONG BIO-PHARMA CO., LTD.; *Int'l*, pg. 1445
CHARLES RIVER LABORATORIES—See Charles River Laboratories International, Inc.; *U.S. Public*, pg. 480
CHARLOTTE'S WEB HOLDINGS, INC.; *U.S. Public*, pg. 480
CHECKPOINT THERAPEUTICS, INC.—See Fortress Biotech, Inc.; *U.S. Public*, pg. 872
CHECKPOINT TRENDS LIMITED; *Int'l*, pg. 1459
CHEIL BIO CO., LTD.; *Int'l*, pg. 1459
CHEMCOM SA—See Floridienne SA; *Int'l*, pg. 2708
CHEMICAL WORKS OF GEDEON RICHTER PLC; *Int'l*, pg. 1462
CHEMI DAROU INDUSTRIAL COMPANY; *Int'l*, pg. 1461
CHEMISCHE FABRIK BERG GMBH—See PMC Capital Partners, LLC; *U.S. Private*, pg. 3217
CHEMOMAB THERAPEUTICS LTD.; *Int'l*, pg. 1463
CHEMO PHARMA LABORATORIES LTD; *Int'l*, pg. 1462
CHEMTREAT INTERNATIONAL, INC.—See Danaher Corporation; *U.S. Public*, pg. 625
CHENGDA PHARMACEUTICALS CO., LTD.; *Int'l*, pg. 1467
CHENGDU EASTON BIOPHARMACEUTICALS CO., LTD.; *Int'l*, pg. 1467
CHENGDU HUASUN TECHNOLOGY GROUP INC.; *Int'l*, pg. 1468
CHENGDU KANGHONG PHARMACEUTICALS GROUP CO., LTD.; *Int'l*, pg. 1468
CHENGDU OLYMVAX BIOPHARMACEUTICALS, INC.; *Int'l*, pg. 1468
CHENGDU SHENGNUO BIOPHARMACEUTICAL CO., LTD.; *Int'l*, pg. 1469
CHENGDU TONGTECH CO., LTD.—See Beijing Tongtooh Company Limited; *Int'l*, pg. 959
CHENGZHI CO., LTD.; *Int'l*, pg. 1470
CHIASMA, INC.—See Chiesi Farmaceutici SpA; *Int'l*, pg. 1477
CHIASMA (ISRAEL) LTD.—See Chiesi Farmaceutici SpA; *Int'l*, pg. 1477
CHIESI AUSTRALIA PTY LTD—See Chiesi Farmaceutici SpA; *Int'l*, pg. 1477

CHIESI ESPANA S.A.—See Chiesi Farmaceutici SpA; *Int'l*, pg. 1477
CHIESI FARMACEUTICAL ITALIA—See Chiesi Farmaceutici SpA; *Int'l*, pg. 1477
CHIESI FARMACEUTICA LTDA.—See Chiesi Farmaceutici SpA; *Int'l*, pg. 1477
CHIESI FARMACEUTICI SPA; *Int'l*, pg. 1477
CHIESI HELLAS A.E.B.E.—See Chiesi Farmaceutici SpA; *Int'l*, pg. 1477
CHIESI ITALIA S.P.A.—See Chiesi Farmaceutici SpA; *Int'l*, pg. 1477
CHIESI LTD.—See Chiesi Farmaceutici SpA; *Int'l*, pg. 1477
CHIESI PHARMA AB—See Chiesi Farmaceutici SpA; *Int'l*, pg. 1477
CHIESI PHARMACEUTICALS INC.—See Chiesi Farmaceutici SpA; *Int'l*, pg. 1478
CHIESI PHARMACEUTICALS (PVT) LIMITED—See Chiesi Farmaceutici SpA; *Int'l*, pg. 1477
CHIESI ROMANIA S.R.L.—See Chiesi Farmaceutici SpA; *Int'l*, pg. 1478
CHIESI S.A.—See Chiesi Farmaceutici SpA; *Int'l*, pg. 1478
CHIESI USA INC.—See Chiesi Farmaceutici SpA; *Int'l*, pg. 1478
CHIMERIX, INC.; *U.S. Public*, pg. 489
CHIMPHARM JSC; *Int'l*, pg. 1480
CHINA ANIMAL HEALTHCARE LTD.; *Int'l*, pg. 1482
CHINA ANIMAL HUSBANDRY INDUSTRY CO., LTD.; *Int'l*, pg. 1482
CHINA BCT PHARMACY GROUP, INC.; *Int'l*, pg. 1486
CHINA CHEMICAL & PHARMACEUTICAL CO., LTD. - HSINFONG PLANT—See China Chemical & Pharmaceutical Co., Ltd.; *Int'l*, pg. 1488
CHINA CHEMICAL & PHARMACEUTICAL CO., LTD.; *Int'l*, pg. 1488
CHINA CHEMICAL & PHARMACEUTICAL CO., LTD. - TAICHUNG PLANT—See China Chemical & Pharmaceutical Co., Ltd.; *Int'l*, pg. 1488
CHINA DONGSHENG INTERNATIONAL, INC.; *Int'l*, pg. 1498
CHINA GENERAL TECHNOLOGY (GROUP) PHARMACEUTICAL HOLDING CO., LTD.—See China Meheco Group Co., Ltd.; *Int'l*, pg. 1518
CHINA GEWANG BIOTECHNOLOGY, INC.; *Int'l*, pg. 1504
CHINA HEALTH GROUP INC.; *Int'l*, pg. 1507
CHINA HEALTH INDUSTRIES HOLDINGS, INC.; *Int'l*, pg. 1507
CHINA HEALTH RESOURCE, INC.; *Int'l*, pg. 1507
CHINA ISOTOPE & RADIATION CORPORATION—See China National Nuclear Corporation; *Int'l*, pg. 1532
CHINA LSOTOPE & RADIATION CORPORATION; *Int'l*, pg. 1515
CHINA MEDICAL (INTERNATIONAL) GROUP LIMITED; *Int'l*, pg. 1518
CHINA MEDICAL SYSTEM HOLDINGS LTD.; *Int'l*, pg. 1518
CHINA MEDICINE CORPORATION; *Int'l*, pg. 1518
CHINA MEHECO CO., LTD. - TANGGU PROCESSING PLANT—See China Meheco Group Co., Ltd.; *Int'l*, pg. 1518
CHINA MEHECO GREAT WALL PHARMA CO., LTD.—See China Meheco Group Co., Ltd.; *Int'l*, pg. 1518
CHINA MEHECO GROUP CO., LTD.; *Int'l*, pg. 1518
CHINA MEHECO INTERNATIONAL CO., LTD.—See China Meheco Group Co., Ltd.; *Int'l*, pg. 1518
CHINA MEHECO KANGLI PHARMA CO., LTD.—See China Meheco Group Co., Ltd.; *Int'l*, pg. 1519
CHINA MEHECO KEYI PHARMA CO., LTD.—See China Meheco Group Co., Ltd.; *Int'l*, pg. 1519
CHINA MEHECO MED-TECH SERVICE CO., LTD.—See China Meheco Group Co., Ltd.; *Int'l*, pg. 1519
CHINA MEHECO SANYANG PHARMA CO., LTD.—See China Meheco Group Co., Ltd.; *Int'l*, pg. 1519
CHINA MEHECO TOPFOND TRADITIONAL CHINESE MEDICINE CO., LTD.—See China Meheco Group Co., Ltd.; *Int'l*, pg. 1519
CHINA MEHECO XINJIANG PHARMA CO., LTD.—See China Meheco Group Co., Ltd.; *Int'l*, pg. 1519
CHINA NATIONAL ACCORD MEDICINES CORP., LTD.; *Int'l*, pg. 1525
CHINA NATIONAL PHARMACEUTICAL GROUP CORPORATION; *Int'l*, pg. 1533
CHINA NT PHARMA GROUP COMPANY LIMITED; *Int'l*, pg. 1536
CHINA QINBA PHARMACEUTICALS, INC.; *Int'l*, pg. 1542
CHINA REFORM HEALTH MANAGEMENT AND SERVICES GROUP CO., LTD.; *Int'l*, pg. 1547
CHINA RESOURCES DOUBLE-CRANE PHARMACEUTICAL CO., LTD.; *Int'l*, pg. 1548
CHINA RESOURCES PHARMACEUTICAL GROUP LIMITED—See China Resources (Holdings) Co., Ltd.; *Int'l*, pg. 1548
CHINA RESOURCES SANJIU MEDICAL & PHARMACEUTICAL CO., LTD.; *Int'l*, pg. 1549
CHINA SHENGHUO PHARMACEUTICAL HOLDINGS, INC.; *Int'l*, pg. 1551
CHINA SKY ONE MEDICAL, INC.; *Int'l*, pg. 1552
CHINA SXT PHARMACEUTICALS, INC.; *Int'l*, pg. 1556
CHINA TRADITIONAL CHINESE MEDICINE HOLDINGS

CO. LTD.—See China National Pharmaceutical Group Corporation; *Int'l*, pg. 1534
CHIOME BIOSCIENCE INC.; *Int'l*, pg. 1572
CHIRAL QUEST, INC.—See Chiral Quest Corp.; *U.S. Private*, pg. 886
CHIRAL QUEST (JIASHAN) CO., LTD.—See Chiral Quest Corp.; *U.S. Private*, pg. 886
CHLORKING, LLC—See Hayward Holdings, Inc.; *U.S. Public*, pg. 990
CHOA PHARMACEUTICAL CO., LTD.; *Int'l*, pg. 1576
CHO-A PHARM. CO., LTD. - HAMAN FACTORY—See CHO-A Pharm. Co., Ltd.; *Int'l*, pg. 1576
CHO-A PHARM. CO., LTD.; *Int'l*, pg. 1576
CHOKSI LABORATORIES LIMITED; *Int'l*, pg. 1577
CHONG KUN DANG BIO CO., LTD. - ANSAN PLANT—See Chong Kun Dang Holdings Corp.; *Int'l*, pg. 1578
CHONG KUN DANG BIO CO., LTD.—See Chong Kun Dang Holdings Corp.; *Int'l*, pg. 1578
CHONG KUN DANG HEALTHCARE CORP. - DANGJINGUN FACTORY—See Chong Kun Dang Holdings Corp.; *Int'l*, pg. 1578
CHONG KUN DANG HEALTHCARE CORP.—See Chong Kun Dang Holdings Corp.; *Int'l*, pg. 1578
CHONG KUN DANG HOLDINGS CORP.; *Int'l*, pg. 1578
CHONG KUN DANG PHARMACEUTICAL CORP. - CHEONAN FACTORY—See Chong Kun Dang Holdings Corp.; *Int'l*, pg. 1578
CHONG KUN DANG PHARMACEUTICAL CORP.—See Chong Kun Dang Holdings Corp.; *Int'l*, pg. 1578
CHONGQING LUMMY PHARMACEUTICAL CO., LTD.; *Int'l*, pg. 1580
CHONGQING PHARSCIN PHARMACEUTICAL CO., LTD.; *Int'l*, pg. 1580
CHONGQING TAIJI INDUSTRY (GROUP) CO., LTD.; *Int'l*, pg. 1581
CHONGQING ZHIFEI BIOLOGICAL PRODUCTS CO.,LTD; *Int'l*, pg. 1582
CHOONGANG VACCINE LABORATORY CO., LTD.; *Int'l*, pg. 1582
CHO PHARMA, INC.; *Int'l*, pg. 1576
CHURCH & DWIGHT CANADA CORP.—See Church & Dwight Co., Inc.; *U.S. Public*, pg. 493
CIAN HEALTHCARE LIMITED; *Int'l*, pg. 1602
CIDARA THERAPEUTICS, INC.; *U.S. Public*, pg. 494
CILAG ADVANCED TECHNOLOGIES GMBH—See Johnson & Johnson; *U.S. Public*, pg. 1196
CILAG AG—See Johnson & Johnson; *U.S. Public*, pg. 1196
CINCOR PHARMA, INC.—See AstraZeneca PLC; *Int'l*, pg. 661
CIPHER PHARMACEUTICALS INC.; *Int'l*, pg. 1616
CIPLA AGRIMED (PTY) LTD.—See Cipla Ltd.; *Int'l*, pg. 1617
CIPLA (EU) LIMITED—See Cipla Ltd.; *Int'l*, pg. 1616
CIPLA EUROPE NV—See Cipla Ltd.; *Int'l*, pg. 1617
CIPLA LTD.; *Int'l*, pg. 1616
CIPLA MEDPRO MANUFACTURING (PTY) LIMITED—See Cipla Ltd.; *Int'l*, pg. 1617
CIPLA MEDPRO (PTY) LIMITED—See Cipla Ltd.; *Int'l*, pg. 1617
CIPLA MEDPRO SOUTH AFRICA LIMITED—See Cipla Ltd.; *Int'l*, pg. 1617
CIPLA QUALITY CHEMICAL INDUSTRIES LIMITED—See Africa Capitalworks Holdings; *Int'l*, pg. 189
CIPLA USA INC.—See Cipla Ltd.; *Int'l*, pg. 1617
CIPLA VET (PTY) LIMITED—See Cipla Ltd.; *Int'l*, pg. 1617
CIRPRO DE DELICIAS S.A. DE C.V.—See Cardinal Health, Inc.; *U.S. Public*, pg. 434
CISBIO BIOASSAYS SAS—See Revvity, Inc.; *U.S. Public*, pg. 1794
CISEN PHARMACEUTICAL CO., LTD.; *Int'l*, pg. 1618
CITA NEUROPHARMACEUTICALS INC—See Ligand Pharmaceuticals Incorporated; *U.S. Public*, pg. 1314
CJSC GEDEON RICHTER - RUS—See Gedeon Richter Plc.; *Int'l*, pg. 2909
CKD BIO CORP.; *Int'l*, pg. 1639
CKP PRODUCTS LIMITED; *Int'l*, pg. 1640
CKW PHARMA-EXTRAKT GMBH & CO. KG—See Danish Crown AmbA; *Int'l*, pg. 1964
CLARION CORP.—See FORVIA SE; *Int'l*, pg. 2745
CLARITY PHARMACEUTICALS LIMITED; *Int'l*, pg. 1649
CLARUS THERAPEUTICS, INC.—See Clarus Therapeutics Holdings, Inc.; *U.S. Public*, pg. 508
CLEARSIDE BIOMEDICAL, INC.; *U.S. Public*, pg. 513
CLEVER GLOBAL SA; *Int'l*, pg. 1658
CLINICAL SPECIALTIES, INC.; *U.S. Private*, pg. 944
CLINICAL TRIAL CONSULTANTS AB; *Int'l*, pg. 1660
CLINILABS, INC.; *U.S. Private*, pg. 944
CLINOMICS INC.; *Int'l*, pg. 1660
CLINUVEL AG—See Clinuvel Pharmaceuticals Limited; *Int'l*, pg. 1660
CLINUVEL PHARMACEUTICALS LIMITED; *Int'l*, pg. 1660
CLONMEL HEALTHCARE LIMITED—See Bain Capital, LP; *U.S. Private*, pg. 443
CLONMEL HEALTHCARE LIMITED—See Cinven Limited; *Int'l*, pg. 1613
CLOVIS ONCOLOGY, INC.; *U.S. Public*, pg. 515
CLOVIS ONCOLOGY UK LIMITED—See Clovis Oncology, Inc.; *U.S. Public*, pg. 515
CLP HUANYU (SHANDONG) BIOMASS HEAT AND

325412 — PHARMACEUTICAL PREP...   CORPORATE AFFILIATIONS

POWER COMPANY LIMITED—See CLP Holdings Limited; *Int'l*, pg. 1663
CMG PHARMACEUTICAL CO., LTD.; *Int'l*, pg. 1669
CMIC ASIA-PACIFIC PTE. LTD.—See CMIC Holdings Co., Ltd.; *Int'l*, pg. 1670
CMIC (BEIJING) CO.LTD.—See CMIC Holdings Co., Ltd.; *Int'l*, pg. 1670
CMIC CMO CO., LTD.—See CMIC Holdings Co., Ltd.; *Int'l*, pg. 1670
CMIC CMO KOREA CO., LTD.—See CMIC Holdings Co., Ltd.; *Int'l*, pg. 1670
CMIC CMO NISHINE CO., LTD.—See CMIC Holdings Co., Ltd.; *Int'l*, pg. 1670
CMIC KOREA CO.LTD.—See CMIC Holdings Co., Ltd.; *Int'l*, pg. 1670
CMIC SS CMO CO. LTD.—See CMIC Holdings Co., Ltd.; *Int'l*, pg. 1670
CN BIO INNOVATIONS LIMITED—See CN Innovations Holdings Limited; *Int'l*, pg. 1672
CNBX PHARMACEUTICALS INC.; *U.S. Public*, pg. 519
COBRA BIOLOGICS LIMITED—See Cobra Biologics Holding AB; *Int'l*, pg. 1683
COCRYSTAL DISCOVERY, INC.—See Cocrystal Pharma, Inc.; *U.S. Public*, pg. 521
CODY LABORATORIES, INC.—See Lannett Company, Inc.; *U.S. Public*, pg. 1292
COEPTIS THERAPEUTICS HOLDINGS, INC.; *U.S. Public*, pg. 521
COGENT HEALTHCARE, INC.—See UnitedHealth Group Incorporated; *U.S. Public*, pg. 2240
COGNATE BIOSERVICES, INC.—See Charles River Laboratories International, Inc.; *U.S. Public*, pg. 480
COHBAR, INC.; *U.S. Public*, pg. 525
COIMMUNE, INC.—See Genexine Inc.; *Int'l*, pg. 2923
COLAND HOLDINGS LIMITED; *Int'l*, pg. 1697
COLAND PHARMACEUTICAL CO., LTD.—See Coland Holdings Limited; *Int'l*, pg. 1697
COLEY PHARMACEUTICAL GROUP, LTD.—See Pfizer Inc.; *U.S. Public*, pg. 1679
COLGATE ORAL PHARMACEUTICAL—See Colgate-Palmolive Company; *U.S. Public*, pg. 531
COLINZ LABORATORIES LIMITED; *Int'l*, pg. 1698
COLLEGIUM PHARMACEUTICAL, INC.; *U.S. Public*, pg. 533
COLORCON, INC. - NORTH AMERICA HEADQUARTERS—See Berwind Corporation; *U.S. Private*, pg. 541
COLORCON, INC.—See Berwind Corporation; *U.S. Private*, pg. 541
COLUMBIA PETRO CHEM PVT. LTD.; *Int'l*, pg. 1706
COMBAT DRUGS LIMITED; *Int'l*, pg. 1708
COMBE INTERNATIONAL LIMITED—See Combe Incorporated; *U.S. Private*, pg. 980
COMECER S.P.A.—See ATS Corporation; *Int'l*, pg. 695
COMPANIA FARMACEUTICA UPJOHN, S.A.—See Pfizer Inc.; *U.S. Public*, pg. 1679
THE COMPOUNDING PHARMACY OF SOUTH AFRICA (PTY) LTD—See Ascendis Health Limited; *Int'l*, pg. 601
COMSORT, INC.—See Merck & Co., Inc.; *U.S. Public*, pg. 1415
CONCEPTUS, SAS—See Bayer Aktiengesellschaft; *Int'l*, pg. 905
CONCORD DRUGS LIMITED; *Int'l*, pg. 1765
CONCORDIA HEALTHCARE INC.—See Advanz Pharma Corp.; *Int'l*, pg. 166
CONFAB LABORATORIES, INC.—See RoundTable Healthcare Management, Inc.; *U.S. Private*, pg. 3489
CONFLUENCE DISCOVERY TECHNOLOGIES, INC.—See Aclaris Therapeutics, Inc.; *U.S. Public*, pg. 35
CONSUN PHARMACEUTICAL GROUP LIMITED; *Int'l*, pg. 1778
CONTENTCHECKED HOLDINGS INC.; *U.S. Private*, pg. 1027
CONTRACT PHARMACAL CORP; *U.S. Private*, pg. 1032
CONTRACT PHARMACEUTICALS LIMITED—See Aterian Investment Management, L.P.; *U.S. Private*, pg. 366
CONTRAFECT CORPORATION; *U.S. Public*, pg. 573
CONVERTORS DE MEXICO S.A. DE C.V.—See Cardinal Health, Inc.; *U.S. Public*, pg. 434
COOPERSURGICAL, INC.—See The Cooper Companies, Inc.; *U.S. Public*, pg. 2066
COPHAR LTD.—See CSL Limited; *Int'l*, pg. 1866
CORBUS PHARMACEUTICALS, INC.—See Corbus Pharmaceuticals Holdings, Inc.; *U.S. Public*, pg. 575
CORCEPT THERAPEUTICS INCORPORATED; *U.S. Public*, pg. 575
CORDEN PHARMA BERGAMO S.P.A.—See Astorg Partners S.A.S.; *Int'l*, pg. 656
CORDEN PHARMA BOULDER, INC.—See Astorg Partners S.A.S.; *Int'l*, pg. 656
CORDEN PHARMACHEM IRELAND LTD.—See Astorg Partners S.A.S.; *Int'l*, pg. 656
CORDEN PHARMA COLORADO INC.—See Astorg Partners S.A.S.; *Int'l*, pg. 656
CORDEN PHARMA INTERNATIONAL GMBH—See Astorg Partners S.A.S.; *Int'l*, pg. 656
CORDEN PHARMA LATINA S.P.A.—See Astorg Partners S.A.S.; *Int'l*, pg. 656

CORDEN PHARMA S.P.A.—See Astorg Partners S.A.S.; *Int'l*, pg. 656
CORDEN PHARMA SWITZERLAND LLC—See Astorg Partners S.A.S.; *Int'l*, pg. 656
CORDOVACANN CORP.; *Int'l*, pg. 1796
CORE ONE LABS INC.; *Int'l*, pg. 1798
COREPHARMA, LLC; *U.S. Private*, pg. 1049
CORERX, INC.—See NovaQuest Capital Management, LLC; *U.S. Private*, pg. 2967
CORESTEM INC.; *Int'l*, pg. 1800
CORIUM INTERNATIONAL, INC.—See Gurnet Point Capital LLC; *U.S. Private*, pg. 1819
CORMEDIX INC.; *U.S. Public*, pg. 577
CORNERSTONE BIOPHARMA, INC.—See Chiesi Farmaceutici SpA; *Int'l*, pg. 1478
CORNERSTONE THERAPEUTICS, INC.—See Chiesi Farmaceutici SpA; *Int'l*, pg. 1478
CORPORACION BONIMA S.A. DE C.V.—See Bayer Aktiengesellschaft; *Int'l*, pg. 907
CORRELATE ENERGY CORP.; *U.S. Public*, pg. 580
CORREVIO PHARMA CORP.; *Int'l*, pg. 1806
CORREVIO SAS—See Advanz Pharma Corp.; *Int'l*, pg. 166
CORVIGLIA-APOTHEKE AG—See CSL Limited; *Int'l*, pg. 1866
CORVUS PHARMACEUTICALS, INC.; *U.S. Public*, pg. 585
COSAR PHARMACEUTICAL COMPANY; *Int'l*, pg. 1809
COSCIENS BIOPHARMA INC.; *U.S. Public*, pg. 585
COTINGA PHARMACEUTICALS INC.; *Int'l*, pg. 1817
COVALON TECHNOLOGIES LTD.; *Int'l*, pg. 1820
COVESTRO—See Bayer Aktiengesellschaft; *Int'l*, pg. 907
COVX RESEARCH LLC—See Pfizer Inc.; *U.S. Public*, pg. 1679
COVX TECHNOLOGIES IRELAND LIMITED—See Pfizer Inc.; *U.S. Public*, pg. 1679
CPEC LLC—See Endo International plc; *Int'l*, pg. 2404
CPEX PHARMACEUTICALS, INC.—See Xstelos Holdings, Inc.; *U.S. Private*, pg. 4583
CPINGREDIENTES, S.A. DE C.V.—See Ingredion Incorporated; *U.S. Public*, pg. 1123
C.P.M. CONTRACTPHARMA GMBH & CO. KG—See BC Partners LLP; *U.S. Private*, pg. 923
CRAWFORD HEALTHCARE HOLDINGS LIMITED; *Int'l*, pg. 1828
CREAGRI, INC.; *U.S. Private*, pg. 1087
CREOSALUS, INC.; *U.S. Private*, pg. 1092
CRIMSON PHARMACEUTICAL (SHANGHAI) COMPANY LIMITED—See First Shanghai Investments Limited; *Int'l*, pg. 2687
CRINETICS PHARMACEUTICALS, INC.; *U.S. Public*, pg. 594
CRISI MEDICAL SYSTEMS, INC.—See Becton, Dickinson & Company; *U.S. Public*, pg. 291
CROMA MEDIC, INC.—See Bain Capital, LP; *U.S. Private*, pg. 443
CROMA MEDIC, INC.—See Cinven Limited; *Int'l*, pg. 1613
CROSSPHARMA LTD.—See Bain Capital, LP; *U.S. Private*, pg. 443
CROSSPHARMA LTD.—See Cinven Limited; *Int'l*, pg. 1613
CROSS VETPHARM GROUP LIMITED—See Zoetis, Inc.; *U.S. Public*, pg. 2409
CRUCELL HOLLAND B.V.—See Johnson & Johnson; *U.S. Public*, pg. 1194
CRUCELL SPAIN, S.A.—See Johnson & Johnson; *U.S. Public*, pg. 1194
CRYOSITE LIMITED; *Int'l*, pg. 1860
CRYSTALGENOMICS, INC.; *Int'l*, pg. 1860
CSL BEHRING CANADA INC.—See CSL Limited; *Int'l*, pg. 1865
CSL BIOTHERAPIES GMBH.—See CSL Limited; *Int'l*, pg. 1865
CSPC HEBEI ZHONGNUO PHARMACEUTICAL (SHIJIAZ-HUANG) CO., LTD.—See CSPC Pharmaceutical Group Limited; *Int'l*, pg. 1867
CSPC PHARMACEUTICAL GROUP LIMITED; *Int'l*, pg. 1867
CSPC WEISHENG PHARMACEUTICAL (SHIJIAZHUANG) CO., LTD—See CSPC Pharmaceutical Group Limited; *Int'l*, pg. 1867
CSTONE PHARMACEUTICALS; *Int'l*, pg. 1868
CS YAKUHIN CO., LTD.—See Alfresa Holdings Corporation; *Int'l*, pg. 317
CTC BIO, INC.; *Int'l*, pg. 1869
CTC INTERNATIONAL, INC—See CTC Bio, Inc.; *Int'l*, pg. 1869
CUMBERLAND PHARMACEUTICALS, INC.; *U.S. Public*, pg. 605
CURASAN AG; *Int'l*, pg. 1878
CURASCRIPT, INC.—See The Cigna Group; *U.S. Public*, pg. 2061
CURATEK PHARMACEUTICALS LTD.—See Tang Industries Inc.; *U.S. Private*, pg. 3930
CURATIS HOLDING AG; *Int'l*, pg. 1878
CUREVAC SE—See CureVac N.V.; *Int'l*, pg. 1878
CUREXA HEALTH (PRIVATE) LIMITED—See Highnoon Laboratories Limited; *Int'l*, pg. 3388
CURIA MASSACHUSETTS, INC.—See GTCR LLC; *U.S. Private*, pg. 1805

CURIA MASSACHUSETTS, INC.—See The Carlyle Group Inc.; *U.S. Public*, pg. 2046
CURIA NEW YORK, INC.—See GTCR LLC; *U.S. Private*, pg. 1805
CURIA NEW YORK, INC.—See The Carlyle Group Inc.; *U.S. Public*, pg. 2046
CURIA (SCOTLAND) LIMITED—See GTCR LLC; *U.S. Private*, pg. 1805
CURIA (SCOTLAND) LIMITED—See The Carlyle Group Inc.; *U.S. Public*, pg. 2046
CURIA SERVICES, INC.—See GTCR LLC; *U.S. Private*, pg. 1805
CURIA SERVICES, INC.—See The Carlyle Group Inc.; *U.S. Public*, pg. 2046
CURIUM US LLC—See Curium SAS; *Int'l*, pg. 1879
CURRAX PHARMACEUTICALS LLC—See JPMorgan Chase & Co.; *U.S. Public*, pg. 1207
CUTANEA LIFE SCIENCES, INC.—See Biofrontera AG; *Int'l*, pg. 1037
CUU LONG PHARMACEUTICAL JOINT STOCK CORPORATION; *Int'l*, pg. 1881
CV SCIENCES, INC.; *U.S. Public*, pg. 613
CYCLACEL LIMITED—See Cyclacel Pharmaceuticals, Inc.; *U.S. Public*, pg. 617
CYCLACEL PHARMACEUTICALS, INC.; *U.S. Public*, pg. 617
CYCLOMEDICA AUSTRALIA PTY LTD—See Cyclopharm Limited; *Int'l*, pg. 1894
CYCLOMEDICA CANADA LIMITED—See Cyclopharm Limited; *Int'l*, pg. 1894
CYCLOPET PTY LTD—See Cyclopharm Limited; *Int'l*, pg. 1894
CYDEX PHARMACEUTICALS, INC.—See Ligand Pharmaceuticals Incorporated; *U.S. Public*, pg. 1314
CYMABAY THERAPEUTICS, INC.—See Gilead Sciences, Inc.; *U.S. Public*, pg. 936
CYPROTEX US—See Evotec SE; *Int'l*, pg. 2573
CYTODYN INC.; *U.S. Public*, pg. 618
CYTOMED THERAPEUTICS LIMITED; *Int'l*, pg. 1897
CYTOMX THERAPEUTICS, INC.; *U.S. Public*, pg. 618
CYXONE AB; *Int'l*, pg. 1898
DABUR INDIA LTD - BADDI - ORAL CARE UNIT—See Dabur India Ltd; *Int'l*, pg. 1903
DABUR INDIA LTD - NASHIK UNIT—See Dabur India Ltd; *Int'l*, pg. 1903
DAEBONG LS CO., LTD.; *Int'l*, pg. 1905
DAEHAN NEW PHARM CO., LTD.; *Int'l*, pg. 1907
DAE HWA PHARMACEUTICAL CO., LTD.; *Int'l*, pg. 1905
DAE HWA PHARM CO., LTD.; *Int'l*, pg. 1905
DAEJUNG EM CO., LTD.—See Daejung Chemicals & Metals Co., Ltd.; *Int'l*, pg. 1907
DAE SUNG MICROBIOLOGICAL LABS. CO., LTD.; *Int'l*, pg. 1905
DAEWON PHARMACEUTICAL CO., LTD. - HYANGNAM FACTORY—See Daewon Pharmaceutical Co., Ltd.; *Int'l*, pg. 1910
DAEWON PHARMACEUTICAL CO., LTD.; *Int'l*, pg. 1910
DAEWOONG PHARMACEUTICAL CO., LTD.; *Int'l*, pg. 1911
DAI HAN PHARMACEUTICAL CO., LTD.; *Int'l*, pg. 1913
DAIICHI SANKYO ALTKIRCH SARL—See Daiichi Sankyo Co., Ltd.; *Int'l*, pg. 1929
DAIICHI SANKYO BRASIL FARMACEUTICA LTDA.—See Daiichi Sankyo Co., Ltd.; *Int'l*, pg. 1929
DAIICHI SANKYO CHEMICAL PHARMA CO., LTD.—See Daiichi Sankyo Co., Ltd.; *Int'l*, pg. 1929
DAIICHI SANKYO (CHINA) HOLDINGS CO., LTD.—See Daiichi Sankyo Co., Ltd.; *Int'l*, pg. 1929
DAIICHI SANKYO CO., LTD. - AKITA PLANT—See Daiichi Sankyo Co., Ltd.; *Int'l*, pg. 1929
DAIICHI SANKYO CO., LTD. - HIRATSUKA PLANT—See Daiichi Sankyo Co., Ltd.; *Int'l*, pg. 1929
DAIICHI SANKYO CO., LTD. - ODAWARA PLANT—See Daiichi Sankyo Co., Ltd.; *Int'l*, pg. 1929
DAIICHI SANKYO CO., LTD. - ONAHAMA PLANT—See Daiichi Sankyo Co., Ltd.; *Int'l*, pg. 1929
DAIICHI SANKYO CO., LTD. - TAKATSUKI PLANT—See Daiichi Sankyo Co., Ltd.; *Int'l*, pg. 1929
DAIICHI SANKYO DEUTSCHLAND GMBH—See Daiichi Sankyo Co., Ltd.; *Int'l*, pg. 1930
DAIICHI SANKYO DEVELOPMENT LTD.—See Daiichi Sankyo Co., Ltd.; *Int'l*, pg. 1930
DAIICHI SANKYO ESPHA CO., LTD.—See Daiichi Sankyo Co., Ltd.; *Int'l*, pg. 1929
DAIICHI SANKYO ILAC TICARET LTD. STI.—See Daiichi Sankyo Co., Ltd.; *Int'l*, pg. 1930
DAIICHI SANKYO, INC.—See Daiichi Sankyo Co., Ltd.; *Int'l*, pg. 1930
DAIICHI SANKYO INDIA PVT. LTD.—See Daiichi Sankyo Co., Ltd.; *Int'l*, pg. 1930
DAIICHI SANKYO IRELAND LTD.—See Daiichi Sankyo Co., Ltd.; *Int'l*, pg. 1930
DAIICHI SANKYO NORDICS APS—See Daiichi Sankyo Co., Ltd.; *Int'l*, pg. 1930
DAIICHI SANKYO NORTHERN EUROPE GMBH—See Daiichi Sankyo Co., Ltd.; *Int'l*, pg. 1930
DAIICHI SANKYO PORTUGAL, UNIPESSOAL LDA.—See Daiichi Sankyo Co., Ltd.; *Int'l*, pg. 1930

N.A.I.C.S. INDEX

325412 — PHARMACEUTICAL PREP...

DAIICHI SANKYO PROPHARMA CO., LTD.—See Daiichi Sankyo Co., Ltd.; *Int'l*, pg. 1930
DAIICHI SANKYO (THAILAND) LTD.—See Daiichi Sankyo Co., Ltd.; *Int'l*, pg. 1929
DAIICHI SANKYO VIETNAM CO., LTD.—See Daiichi Sankyo Co., Ltd.; *Int'l*, pg. 1930
DAIKYO SEIKO, LTD.—See West Pharmaceutical Services, Inc.; *U.S. Public*, pg. 2352
DAITO PHARMACEUTICAL (CHINA) CO., LTD.—See Daito Pharmaceutical Co., Ltd.; *Int'l*, pg. 1943
DAITO PHARMACEUTICAL CO., LTD.; *Int'l*, pg. 1943
DAITO PHARMACEUTICALS AMERICA, INC.—See Daito Pharmaceutical Co., Ltd.; *Int'l*, pg. 1943
DALIAN BIO-CHEM COMPANY LIMITED; *Int'l*, pg. 1951
DALI PHARMACEUTICAL CO., LTD.; *Int'l*, pg. 1951
DAMLORAN RAZAK PHARMACEUTICAL COMPANY; *Int'l*, pg. 1957
DANCANN PHARMA A/S; *Int'l*, pg. 1958
DANCE BIOPHARM INC.; *U.S. Private*, pg. 1153
DAR AL DAWA DEVELOPMENT & INVESTMENT CO.; *Int'l*, pg. 1971
DAR AL-SHIFA'A FOR THE MANUFACTURING OF PHARMACEUTICALS; *Int'l*, pg. 1971
DARE BIOSCIENCE, INC.; *U.S. Public*, pg. 633
DAROUPAKHSH HOLDING COMPANY; *Int'l*, pg. 1973
DAROU PAKHSH PHARMACEUTICAL MFG CO.; *Int'l*, pg. 1973
DASHENLIN PHARMACEUTICAL GROUP CO., LTD.; *Int'l*, pg. 1973
DAVI II FARMACEUTICA S.A.; *Int'l*, pg. 1983
DAWNRAYS PHARMACEUTICAL (HOLDINGS) LTD; *Int'l*, pg. 1984
DB (PHILIPPINES), INC.—See Batu Kawan Berhad; *Int'l*, pg. 891
DBV TECHNOLOGIES S.A.; *Int'l*, pg. 1989
DCC HEALTH AND BEAUTY SOLUTIONS LIMITED—See DCC plc; *Int'l*, pg. 1989
DDD LTD.; *Int'l*, pg. 1993
DECCAN HEALTH CARE LTD.; *Int'l*, pg. 1999
DECHRA LIMITED—See EQT AB; *Int'l*, pg. 2474
DECHRA PHARMACEUTICALS MANUFACTURING - UK—See EQT AB; *Int'l*, pg. 2474
DECHRA PRODUCTOS VETERINARIOS, S.A. DE C.V.—See EQT AB; *Int'l*, pg. 2474
DECHRA VETERINARY PRODUCTS (AUSTRALIA) PTY LIMITED—See EQT AB; *Int'l*, pg. 2474
DECHRA VETERINARY PRODUCTS, INC.—See EQT AB; *Int'l*, pg. 2474
DECHRA VETERINARY PRODUCTS SP. Z O.O.—See EQT AB; *Int'l*, pg. 2474
DECIBEL CANNABIS COMPANY, INC.; *Int'l*, pg. 2000
DECISION BIOMARKERS, INC.; *U.S. Private*, pg. 1187
DEEPVERGE PLC; *Int'l*, pg. 2003
DELPHARM S.A.S. - BRETIGNY PLANT—See Delpharm S.A.S.; *Int'l*, pg. 2015
DELPHARM S.A.S. - DIJON PLANT—See Delpharm S.A.S.; *Int'l*, pg. 2015
DELPHARM S.A.S. - DROGENBOS PLANT—See Delpharm S.A.S.; *Int'l*, pg. 2015
DELPHARM S.A.S. - GAILLARD PLANT—See Delpharm S.A.S.; *Int'l*, pg. 2015
DELPHARM S.A.S. - HUNINGUE PLANT—See Delpharm S.A.S.; *Int'l*, pg. 2015
DELPHARM S.A.S. - LILLE PLANT—See Delpharm S.A.S.; *Int'l*, pg. 2015
DELPHARM S.A.S. - LYON BIOTECH PLANT—See Delpharm S.A.S.; *Int'l*, pg. 2015
DELPHARM S.A.S. - REIMS PLANT—See Delpharm S.A.S.; *Int'l*, pg. 2015
DELPHARM S.A.S.; *Int'l*, pg. 2015
DELTASELECT GMBH—See aligna AG; *Int'l*, pg. 327
DELTON HEALTH AG—See Delton AG; *Int'l*, pg. 2021
DENDREON PHARMACEUTICALS LLC—See Bausch Health Companies Inc.; *Int'l*, pg. 897
DENDRON LTD.—See DDD LTD.; *Int'l*, pg. 1993
DENIS CHEM LAB LIMITED; *Int'l*, pg. 2026
DENTECO 2000 SA—See Fagron NV; *Int'l*, pg. 2603
DENTSPLY SIRONA KOREA—See DENTSPLY SIRONA Inc.; *U.S. Public*, pg. 655
DEREN ILAC SANAYI VE DIS TICARET ANONIM SIRKETI—See Ecolab Inc.; *U.S. Public*, pg. 712
DERMAPHARM AG—See Dermapharm Holding SE; *Int'l*, pg. 2043
DERMAPHARM AG—See Dermapharm Holding SE; *Int'l*, pg. 2043
DERMAPHARM HOLDING SE; *Int'l*, pg. 2042
DERMIRA, INC.—See Eli Lilly & Company; *U.S. Public*, pg. 731
DESH RAKSHAK AUSHDHALAYA LIMITED; *Int'l*, pg. 2045
DESIGNS FOR HEALTH, INC.; *U.S. Private*, pg. 1215
DESTINY PHARMA PLC; *Int'l*, pg. 2047
DEVA HOLDINGS (NZ) LTD.—See Eastpharma Ltd.; *Int'l*, pg. 2274
DEVICORE MEDICAL PRODUCTS INC.—See Danaher Corporation; *U.S. Public*, pg. 626
DEVONIAN HEALTH GROUP, INC.; *Int'l*, pg. 2089
DEXTECH MEDICAL AB; *Int'l*, pg. 2093

DEXTRAN PRODUCTS LIMITED—See Biospectra Inc.; *U.S. Private*, pg. 563
DEZHAN HEALTH CO., LTD.; *Int'l*, pg. 2094
DFB PHARMACEUTICALS, INC.; *U.S. Private*, pg. 1220
DIACEUTICS PLC; *Int'l*, pg. 2101
DIAGNOSTIC GRIFOLS, S.A.—See Grifols, S.A.; *Int'l*, pg. 3084
DIAMEDICA THERAPEUTICS INC.; *U.S. Public*, pg. 658
DIAMONDBACK DRUGS, LLC—See Tailwind Capital Group, LLC; *U.S. Private*, pg. 3924
DIASORIN AB—See DiaSorin S.p.A.; *Int'l*, pg. 2106
DIASORIN LTD.—See DiaSorin S.p.A.; *Int'l*, pg. 2106
DICERNA PHARMACEUTICALS, INC.; *U.S. Public*, pg. 659
DICE THERAPEUTICS, INC.—See Eli Lilly & Company; *U.S. Public*, pg. 731
DIECKMANN ARZNEIMITTEL GMBH—See Merck & Co., Inc.; *U.S. Public*, pg. 1416
DIFGEN PHARMACEUTICALS PVT. LTD.; *Int'l*, pg. 2118
DIGIMEDICAL SOLUTIONS, INC; *U.S. Private*, pg. 1229
DIPHARMA FRANCIS S.R.L.; *Int'l*, pg. 2128
DIPNA PHARMACHEM LIMITED; *Int'l*, pg. 2129
DISHMAN CARBOGEN AMCIS LIMITED; *Int'l*, pg. 2135
DISHMAN EUROPE LIMITED—See Dishman Carbogen Amcis Limited; *Int'l*, pg. 2135
DISHMAN INTERNATIONAL TRADE (SHANGHAI) CO., LTD.—See Dishman Carbogen Amcis Limited; *Int'l*, pg. 2135
DISHMAN JAPAN LTD.—See Dishman Carbogen Amcis Limited; *Int'l*, pg. 2135
DISHMAN SWITZERLAND LTD.—See Dishman Carbogen Amcis Limited; *Int'l*, pg. 2135
DISHMAN USA INC.—See Dishman Carbogen Amcis Limited; *Int'l*, pg. 2135
DIURNAL EUROPE B.V.—See Neurocrine Biosciences Inc.; *U.S. Public*, pg. 1510
DIURNAL GROUP PLC—See Neurocrine Biosciences Inc.; *U.S. Public*, pg. 1510
DMK PHARMACEUTICALS CORPORATION; *U.S. Public*, pg. 671
DMS IMAGING SA; *Int'l*, pg. 2146
DNA ELECTRONICS, INC.—See Genting Berhad; *Int'l*, pg. 2928
DNA ELECTRONICS, INC.—See Genting Berhad; *Int'l*, pg. 2928
DOMANTIS LTD.—See GSK plc; *Int'l*, pg. 3145
DOMESCO MEDICAL JOINT STOCK CORPORATION; *Int'l*, pg. 2159
DOMES PHARMA SA; *Int'l*, pg. 2159
DONG-A SOCIO HOLDINGS CO., LTD.; *Int'l*, pg. 2164
DONG-A ST CO., LTD.—See Dong-A Socio Holdings Co., Ltd.; *Int'l*, pg. 2165
DONG-EE-JIAO CO., LTD.; *Int'l*, pg. 2165
DONGKOO BIO & PHARMA CO., LTD.; *Int'l*, pg. 2168
DONG KOOK LIFESCIENCE CO., LTD.—See Dongkook Pharmaceutical Co., Ltd.; *Int'l*, pg. 2168
DONGKOOK PHARMACEUTICAL CO., LTD.; *Int'l*, pg. 2168
DONGSHENG PHARMACEUTICAL INTERNATIONAL CO., LTD.; *Int'l*, pg. 2169
DONGSUNG BIOPOL CO., LTD.—See Dongsung Chemical Co., Ltd.; *Int'l*, pg. 2170
DONG SUNG PHARMACEUTICAL COMPANY LTD. - ASAN FACTORY—See Dong Sung Pharmaceutical Company Ltd.; *Int'l*, pg. 2164
DONG SUNG PHARMACEUTICAL COMPANY LTD.; *Int'l*, pg. 2164
DONG WHA PHARM CO., LTD.; *Int'l*, pg. 2164
DOTTIKON ES AMERICA, INC.—See Dottikon ES Holding AG; *Int'l*, pg. 2180
DOUGLAS LABORATORIES; *U.S. Private*, pg. 1267
DOW PHARMACEUTICAL SCIENCES, INC.—See Bausch Health Companies Inc.; *Int'l*, pg. 898
D-PHARM LTD.; *Int'l*, pg. 1900
DPT LABORATORIES, LTD.—See RoundTable Healthcare Management, Inc.; *U.S. Private*, pg. 3489
DPT LAKEWOOD, INC.—See RoundTable Healthcare Management, Inc.; *U.S. Private*, pg. 3489
DR. ABIDI PHARMACEUTICALS PJSC; *Int'l*, pg. 2190
DRAGENOPHARM APOTHEKER PUSCHL GMBH & CO. KG—See BC Partners LLP; *Int'l*, pg. 922
DREAM PHARMA CORP.—See Hanwha Group; *Int'l*, pg. 3264
DR.E.GRAUB AG—See AGRAVIS Raiffeisen AG; *Int'l*, pg. 215
DR. GERHARD MANN CHEM.-PHARM. FABRIK GMBH—See Bausch Health Companies Inc.; *Int'l*, pg. 897
DR KULICH PHARMA S.R.O.—See Fagron NV; *Int'l*, pg. 2603
DR. LAL PATH LABS BANGLADESH PRIVATE LIMITED—See Dr. Lal PathLabs Ltd.; *Int'l*, pg. 2194
DR. LAL PATHLABS NEPAL PRIVATE LIMITED—See Dr. Lal PathLabs Ltd.; *Int'l*, pg. 2194
DR. REDDY'S LABORATORIES LIMITED; *Int'l*, pg. 2194
DR. SCHUMACHER GMBH; *Int'l*, pg. 2195
DR. WILLMAR SCHWABE INDIA PVT. LTD.—See Dr. Willmar Schwabe GmbH & Co. KG; *Int'l*, pg. 2195
DSM SINOCHEM PHARMACEUTICALS NETHERLANDS B.V.—See Bain Capital, LP; *U.S. Private*, pg. 439
DUNCAN FARMACEUTICA, S.A.—See GSK plc; *Int'l*, pg. 3148
DUNCAN PHARMACEUTICALS PHILIPPINES INC.—See GSK plc; *Int'l*, pg. 3145
DUOPHARMA BIOTECH BERHAD—See Batu Kawan Berhad; *Int'l*, pg. 891
DUPONT NUTRITION MANUFACTURING UK LIMITED—See DuPont de Nemours, Inc.; *U.S. Public*, pg. 693
DURECT CORPORATION; *U.S. Public*, pg. 694
DVIRIA NANO TECH SDN. BHD.—See Ho Wah Genting Berhad; *Int'l*, pg. 3435
D. WESTERN THERAPEUTICS INSTITUTE, INC.; *Int'l*, pg. 1900
DXN HERBAL MANUFACTURING (INDIA) PRIVATE LIMITED—See DXN Holdings Bhd.; *Int'l*, pg. 2237
DYMATIZE ENTERPRISES, INC.—See Post Holdings, Inc.; *U.S. Public*, pg. 1703
DYNAVAX EUROPE GMBH—See Dynavax Technologies Corporation; *U.S. Public*, pg. 700
DYNAVAX GMBH—See Dynavax Technologies Corporation; *U.S. Public*, pg. 700
DYNAVAX TECHNOLOGIES CORPORATION; *U.S. Public*, pg. 700
EAGLE HEALTH HOLDINGS LIMITED; *Int'l*, pg. 2264
EAGLE PHARMACEUTICALS, INC.; *U.S. Public*, pg. 702
EAGLE VETERINARY TECHNOLOGY CO., LTD.; *Int'l*, pg. 2266
EAGLE VET. TECH CO., LTD.; *Int'l*, pg. 2266
EA PHARMA CO., LTD.—See Eisai Co., Ltd.; *Int'l*, pg. 2334
EARTH SCIENCE TECH, INC.; *U.S. Public*, pg. 703
EASTGATE BIOTECH CORP.; *Int'l*, pg. 2274
EASTGATE PHARMACEUTICALS, INC.—See EastGate Biotech Corp.; *Int'l*, pg. 2274
EASTON PHARMACEUTICALS, INC.; *Int'l*, pg. 2274
EASTPHARMA LTD.; *Int'l*, pg. 2274
EASYWELL BIOMEDICALS, INC.; *Int'l*, pg. 2277
EB PHARMA, LLC—See Eiger BioPharmaceuticals, Inc.; *U.S. Public*, pg. 721
EB SUB, INC.—See EPIRUS Biopharmaceuticals, Inc.; *U.S. Private*, pg. 1413
ECKERT & ZIEGLER CESIO S.R.O.—See Eckert & Ziegler Strahlen- und Medizintechnik AG; *Int'l*, pg. 2290
ECKERT & ZIEGLER ISOTOPE PRODUCTS, GMBH—See Eckert & Ziegler Strahlen- und Medizintechnik AG; *Int'l*, pg. 2290
ECLAT PHARMACEUTICALS, LLC—See AVADEL PHARMACEUTICALS PLC; *Int'l*, pg. 734
ECTYCELL SASU—See Cellectis S.A.; *Int'l*, pg. 1393
ECUPHAR GMBH—See Animalcare Group plc; *Int'l*, pg. 471
ECUPHAR NV/SA—See Animalcare Group plc; *Int'l*, pg. 471
EDESA BIOTECH, INC.; *Int'l*, pg. 2308
EGETIS THERAPEUTICS AB; *Int'l*, pg. 2324
EGF THERAMED HEALTH CORP; *Int'l*, pg. 2324
EG LABO SAS - LABORATOIRES EUROGENERICS SAS—See Bain Capital, LP; *U.S. Private*, pg. 443
EG LABO SAS - LABORATOIRES EUROGENERICS SAS—See Cinven Limited; *Int'l*, pg. 1613
EG S.A.—See Bain Capital, LP; *U.S. Private*, pg. 443
EG S.A.—See Cinven Limited; *Int'l*, pg. 1613
EG S.P.A.—See Bain Capital, LP; *U.S. Private*, pg. 443
EG S.P.A.—See Cinven Limited; *Int'l*, pg. 1613
EGYPTIAN INTERNATIONAL PHARMACEUTICAL INDUSTRIES COMPANY; *Int'l*, pg. 2327
EIRGENIX, INC.; *Int'l*, pg. 2334
EIRGEN PHARMA LTD.—See OPKO Health, Inc.; *U.S. Public*, pg. 1608
EISAI AUSTRALIA PTY. LTD.—See Eisai Co., Ltd.; *Int'l*, pg. 2334
EISAI B.V.—See Eisai Co., Ltd.; *Int'l*, pg. 2335
EISAI CHINA HOLDINGS LTD.—See Eisai Co., Ltd.; *Int'l*, pg. 2334
EISAI CHINA INC.—See Eisai Co., Ltd.; *Int'l*, pg. 2334
EISAI CHINA INC. - SUZHOU FACTORY—See Eisai Co., Ltd.; *Int'l*, pg. 2334
EISAI CO., LTD. - KASHIMA PLANT—See Eisai Co., Ltd.; *Int'l*, pg. 2335
EISAI CO., LTD.; *Int'l*, pg. 2334
EISAI FOOD & CHEMICALS CO., LTD.—See Eisai Co., Ltd.; *Int'l*, pg. 2335
EISAI HONG KONG CO., LTD.—See Eisai Co., Ltd.; *Int'l*, pg. 2335
EISAI INC. - RESEARCH TRIANGLE PARK—See Eisai Co., Ltd.; *Int'l*, pg. 2335
EISAI INC.—See Eisai Co., Ltd.; *Int'l*, pg. 2335
EISAI LABORATORIOS LTDA.—See Eisai Co., Ltd.; *Int'l*, pg. 2335
EISAI LABORATORIOS, S. DE R.L. DE C.V.—See Eisai Co., Ltd.; *Int'l*, pg. 2335
EISAI (LIAONING) PHARMACEUTICAL CO.—See Eisai Co., Ltd.; *Int'l*, pg. 2334
EISAI LIMITED—See Eisai Co., Ltd.; *Int'l*, pg. 2335
EISAI MANUFACTURING LTD.—See Eisai Co., Ltd.; *Int'l*, pg. 2335
EISAI PHARMACEUTICALS INDIA PRIVATE LTD.—See Eisai Co., Ltd.; *Int'l*, pg. 2335
EISAI PHARMATECHNOLOGY & MANUFACTURING PVT.

325412 — PHARMACEUTICAL PREP...

LTD.—See Eisai Co., Ltd.; *Int'l*, pg. 2335
EISAI SA/NV—See Eisai Co., Ltd.; *Int'l*, pg. 2335
EISAI (SUZHOU) TRADING CO., LTD.—See Eisai Co., Ltd.; *Int'l*, pg. 2334
EISAI TAIWAN, INC.—See Eisai Co., Ltd.; *Int'l*, pg. 2335
EISAI (THAILAND) MARKETING CO., LTD.—See Eisai Co., Ltd.; *Int'l*, pg. 2334
EISAI VIETNAM CO., LTD.—See Eisai Co., Ltd.; *Int'l*, pg. 2335
EIS ECZACIBASI ILAC, SINAI VE FINANSAL YATIRIMLAR SANAYI VE TICARET A.S.—See Eczacibasi Holding A.S.; *Int'l*, pg. 2301
ELANCO AH PORTUGAL, UNIPESSOAL LDA—See Elanco Animal Health Incorporated; *U.S. Public*, pg. 722
ELANCO ANIMAL HEALTH INCORPORATED; *U.S. Public*, pg. 722
ELANCO ANIMAL HEALTH UK LIMITED—See Eli Lilly and Company; *U.S. Public*, pg. 731
ELANCO ARGENTINA S.R.L.—See Elanco Animal Health Incorporated; *U.S. Public*, pg. 722
ELANCO BELGIUM BVBA—See Elanco Animal Health Incorporated; *U.S. Public*, pg. 722
ELANCO CHILE SPA—See Elanco Animal Health Incorporated; *U.S. Public*, pg. 722
ELANCO COLOMBIA S.A.S.—See Elanco Animal Health Incorporated; *U.S. Public*, pg. 722
ELANCO DENMARK APS—See Elanco Animal Health Incorporated; *U.S. Public*, pg. 722
ELANCO FRANCE S.A.S.—See Eli Lilly & Company; *U.S. Public*, pg. 731
ELANCO HAYVAN SAGLIGI LIMITED SIRKETI—See Elanco Animal Health Incorporated; *U.S. Public*, pg. 722
ELANCO INDIA PRIVATE LIMITED—See Eli Lilly & Company; *U.S. Public*, pg. 731
ELANCO ITALIA S.P.A.—See Eli Lilly & Company; *U.S. Public*, pg. 731
ELANCO MALAYSIA SDN. BHD.—See Elanco Animal Health Incorporated; *U.S. Public*, pg. 722
ELANCO NEW ZEALAND—See Elanco Animal Health Incorporated; *U.S. Public*, pg. 722
ELANCO PHILIPPINES INC.—See Elanco Animal Health Incorporated; *U.S. Public*, pg. 723
ELANCO SALUD ANIMAL SA DE CV—See Eli Lilly & Company; *U.S. Public*, pg. 731
ELANCO SAUDE ANIMAL LTDA.—See Eli Lilly & Company; *U.S. Public*, pg. 731
ELANCO (SHANGHAI) ANIMAL HEALTH CO., LTD.—See Eli Lilly & Company; *U.S. Public*, pg. 731
ELANCO S.R.L.—See Elanco Animal Health Incorporated; *U.S. Public*, pg. 723
ELANCO (TAIWAN) ANIMAL HEALTH CO. LTD.—See Eli Lilly & Company; *U.S. Public*, pg. 731
ELANCO (THAILAND) LTD.—See Eli Lilly & Company; *U.S. Public*, pg. 731
ELANCO TIERGESUNDHEIT AG—See Eli Lilly & Company; *U.S. Public*, pg. 731
ELANCO VALQUIMICA S.A.—See Elanco Animal Health Incorporated; *U.S. Public*, pg. 723
ELANCO VIETNAM COMPANY LIMITED—See Elanco Animal Health Incorporated; *U.S. Public*, pg. 723
ELANIX BIOTECHNOLOGIES AG; *Int'l*, pg. 2343
ELDER PHARMACEUTICALS LTD.; *Int'l*, pg. 2346
ELDER PROJECTS LIMITED; *Int'l*, pg. 2346
ELECTROMEDICAL TECHNOLOGIES, INC.; *U.S. Public*, pg. 723
ELEDON PHARMACEUTICALS, INC.; *U.S. Public*, pg. 725
ELEISON PHARMACEUTICALS INC.; *U.S. Private*, pg. 1356
ELEKTA GMBH—See Elekta AB; *Int'l*, pg. 2355
ELEMENT NUTRITIONAL SCIENCES INC.; *Int'l*, pg. 2358
ELICIO THERAPEUTICS, INC; *U.S. Public*, pg. 734
ELI LILLY AND COMPANY (INDIA) PVT. LTD.—See Eli Lilly & Company; *U.S. Public*, pg. 733
ELI LILLY AND COMPANY (N.Z.) LIMITED—See Eli Lilly & Company; *U.S. Publia*, pg. 732
ELI LILLY AND COMPANY (TAIWAN), INC.—See Eli Lilly & Company; *U.S. Public*, pg. 732
ELI LILLY ASIAN OPERATIONS, LIMITED—See Eli Lilly & Company; *U.S. Public*, pg. 732
ELI LILLY ASIA PACIFIC SSC SDN BHD—See Eli Lilly & Company; *U.S. Public*, pg. 732
ELI LILLY AUSTRALIA PTY. LIMITED—See Eli Lilly & Company; *U.S. Public*, pg. 732
ELI LILLY B-H D.O.O.—See Eli Lilly & Company; *U.S. Public*, pg. 732
ELI LILLY CANADA, INC.—See Eli Lilly & Company; *U.S. Public*, pg. 732
ELI LILLY & COMPANY (INDIA) PVT. LTD.—See Eli Lilly & Company; *U.S. Public*, pg. 731
ELI LILLY & COMPANY LIMITED—See Eli Lilly & Company; *U.S. Public*, pg. 732
ELI LILLY & COMPANY; *U.S. Public*, pg. 731
ELI LILLY CORK LIMITED—See Eli Lilly & Company; *U.S. Public*, pg. 732
ELI LILLY CR S.R.O.—See Eli Lilly & Company; *U.S. Public*, pg. 732
ELI LILLY CR S.R.O.—See Eli Lilly & Company; *U.S. Public*, pg. 732

ELI LILLY DE MEXICO S.A. DE C.V.—See Eli Lilly & Company; *U.S. Public*, pg. 732
ELI LILLY DO BRASIL LTDA.—See Eli Lilly & Company; *U.S. Public*, pg. 733
ELI LILLY EGYPT—See Eli Lilly & Company; *U.S. Public*, pg. 732
ELI LILLY EXPORT S.A.—See Eli Lilly & Company; *U.S. Public*, pg. 732
ELI LILLY FARMACEVTSKA DRUZBA, D.O.O.—See Eli Lilly & Company; *U.S. Public*, pg. 733
ELI LILLY GES.M.B.H.—See Eli Lilly & Company; *U.S. Public*, pg. 732
ELI LILLY INTERAMERICA, INC.—See Eli Lilly & Company; *U.S. Public*, pg. 732
ELI LILLY ITALIA, S.P.A.—See Eli Lilly & Company; *U.S. Public*, pg. 732
ELI LILLY ITALIA SPA—See Eli Lilly & Company; *U.S. Public*, pg. 732
ELI LILLY LITHUANIA UAB—See Eli Lilly & Company; *U.S. Public*, pg. 732
ELI LILLY (MALAYSIA) SDN. BHD.—See Eli Lilly & Company; *U.S. Public*, pg. 731
ELI LILLY (MALAYSIA) SDN. BHD.—See Eli Lilly & Company; *U.S. Public*, pg. 731
ELI LILLY NEDERLAND B.V.—See Eli Lilly & Company; *U.S. Public*, pg. 732
ELI LILLY NORGE A.S.—See Eli Lilly & Company; *U.S. Public*, pg. 733
ELI LILLY NORGE A.S.—See Eli Lilly & Company; *U.S. Public*, pg. 733
ELI LILLY PAKISTAN (PVT.) LTD.—See Eli Lilly & Company; *U.S. Public*, pg. 732
ELI LILLY (PHILIPPINES), INCORPORATED—See Eli Lilly & Company; *U.S. Public*, pg. 731
ELI LILLY (PHILIPPINES), INCORPORATED—See Eli Lilly & Company; *U.S. Public*, pg. 731
ELI LILLY POLSKA SP. Z.O.O. (LTD.)—See Eli Lilly & Company; *U.S. Public*, pg. 732
ELI LILLY ROMANIA SRL—See Eli Lilly & Company; *U.S. Public*, pg. 733
ELI LILLY (S.A.) (PROPRIETARY) LIMITED—See Eli Lilly & Company; *U.S. Public*, pg. 732
ELI LILLY SAUDI ARABIA LIMITED—See Eli Lilly & Company; *U.S. Public*, pg. 733
ELI LILLY SLOVAKIA SRO—See Eli Lilly & Company; *U.S. Public*, pg. 733
ELI LILLY SPAIN HOLDING ETVE, S.L.—See Eli Lilly & Company; *U.S. Public*, pg. 732
ELI LILLY (SUISSE) S.A.—See Eli Lilly & Company; *U.S. Public*, pg. 732
ELI LILLY SUZHOU PHARMACEUTICAL CO. LTD.—See Eli Lilly & Company; *U.S. Public*, pg. 732
ELI LILLY SWEDEN AB—See Eli Lilly & Company; *U.S. Public*, pg. 732
ELI LILLY VOSTOK SA—See Eli Lilly & Company; *U.S. Public*, pg. 733
ELI LILLY Y COMPANIA DE MEXICO, S.A. DE C.V.—See Eli Lilly & Company; *U.S. Public*, pg. 733
ELITECHGROUP CLINICAL SYSTEMS SAS—See Bruker Corporation; *U.S. Public*, pg. 406
ELITE PHARMACEUTICALS, INC.; *U.S. Public*, pg. 734
EL-NILE CO. FOR PHARMACEUTICALS & CHEMICAL INDUSTRIES; *Int'l*, pg. 2341
EMBER THERAPEUTICS, INC.; *U.S. Public*, pg. 736
EMBREX DE MEXICO S. DE R.L. DE C.V.—See Zoetis, Inc.; *U.S. Public*, pg. 2410
EMERALD HEALTH BOTANICALS, INC.—See Skye Bioscience, Inc.; *U.S. Public*, pg. 1892
EMERALD HEALTH THERAPEUTICS, INC.—See Skye Bioscience, Inc.; *U.S. Public*, pg. 1892
EMERGENT BIOSOLUTIONS, INC.—See Emergent BioSolutions Inc.; *U.S. Public*, pg. 739
EMERGENT HEALTH CORP.; *U.S. Public*, pg. 740
EMERGENT PRODUCT DEVELOPMENT SEATTLE LLC—See Emergent BioSolutions Inc.; *U.S. Public*, pg. 740
EMI HOLDING, INC.—See Emmaus Life Sciences, Inc.; *U.S. Public*, pg. 752
EMO-FARM LTD.—See Bausch Health Companies Inc.; *Int'l*, pg. 897
ENANTA PHARMACEUTICALS, INC.; *U.S. Public*, pg. 754
ENANTIGEN THERAPEUTICS, INC.—See Arbutus Biopharma Corporation; *U.S. Public*, pg. 178
ENCYSIVE PHARMACEUTICALS INC.—See Pfizer Inc.; *U.S. Public*, pg. 1679
ENDEAVOUR CH PTY LTD—See EBOS Group Limited; *Int'l*, pg. 2285
ENDOCEUTICS INC.; *Int'l*, pg. 2405
ENDO HEALTH SOLUTIONS INC.—See Endo International plc; *Int'l*, pg. 2404
ENDO PHARMACEUTICALS SOLUTIONS INC. - NEW JERSEY—See Endo International plc; *Int'l*, pg. 2404
ENDO PHARMACEUTICALS SOLUTIONS INC.—See Endo International plc; *Int'l*, pg. 2404
ENIA LIPOTECH SL—See Ascendis Health Limited; *Int'l*, pg. 601
ENLIVEX THERAPEUTICS LTD.; *Int'l*, pg. 2442
ENOX BIOPHARMA, INC.; *Int'l*, pg. 2444

ENSOL BIOSCIENCES, INC.; *Int'l*, pg. 2448
ENTASIS THERAPEUTICS HOLDINGS INC.—See Innoviva, Inc.; *U.S. Public*, pg. 1127
ENTERIS BIOPHARMA, INC.—See Carlson Capital, L.P.; *U.S. Private*, pg. 764
ENTERO THERAPEUTICS, INC.; *U.S. Public*, pg. 777
ENTEST GROUP, INC.; *Int'l*, pg. 2452
ENTIA BIOSCIENCES, INC.; *U.S. Private*, pg. 1405
ENWEI PHARMACEUTICAL CO., LTD.; *Int'l*, pg. 2456
ENZAL CHEMICALS (INDIA) LTD.; *Int'l*, pg. 2456
ENZENE BIOSCIENCES LIMITED—See Alkem Laboratories Ltd.; *Int'l*, pg. 330
ENZO LIFE SCIENCES—See Enzo Biochem Inc.; *U.S. Public*, pg. 782
ENZYCHEM LIFESCIENCES CORPORATION - JECHEON FACTORY—See Enzychem Lifesciences Corporation; *Int'l*, pg. 2456
ENZYCHEM LIFESCIENCES CORPORATION; *Int'l*, pg. 2456
ENZYCHEM LIFESCIENCES INC.—See Enzychem Lifesciences Corporation; *Int'l*, pg. 2456
ENZYMATICA AB; *Int'l*, pg. 2456
ENZYMES OF AMERICA HOLDING CORP.; *U.S. Public*, pg. 782
EOM PHARMACEUTICALS, INC.—See EOM Pharmaceutical Holdings, Inc.; *U.S. Public*, pg. 782
EPAX NORWAY AS—See Austevoll Seafood ASA; *Int'l*, pg. 717
EPICEPT CORPORATION—See Immune Pharmaceuticals Inc.; *U.S. Public*, pg. 1113
EPICEPT GMBH—See Immune Pharmaceuticals Inc.; *U.S. Public*, pg. 1113
EPIC PHARMA, LLC—See Humanwell Healthcare (Group) Co., Ltd.; *Int'l*, pg. 3530
EPIRUS BIOPHARMACEUTICALS, INC.; *U.S. Private*, pg. 1413
EPIRUS SWITZERLAND GMBH—See EPIRUS Biopharmaceuticals, Inc.; *U.S. Private*, pg. 1413
EP-MINT CO., LTD.—See EPS Holdings, Inc.; *Int'l*, pg. 2465
EPRUF S.A.—See CEPD N.V.; *Int'l*, pg. 1420
EPSILON HEALTHCARE LTD.; *Int'l*, pg. 2466
ERCROS SA - PHARMACEUTICAL DIVISION-FYSE—See Ercros SA; *Int'l*, pg. 2490
ERIS LIFESCIENCES LIMITED; *Int'l*, pg. 2493
ERIS PHARMACEUTICALS AUSTRALIA PTY LTD.; *Int'l*, pg. 2493
ERNO LASZLO, INC.—See CITIC Group Corporation; *Int'l*, pg. 1619
E. R. SQUIBB & SONS LIMITED—See Bristol-Myers Squibb Company; *U.S. Public*, pg. 386
ESI MAIL ORDER PROCESSING, INC.—See The Cigna Group; *U.S. Public*, pg. 2061
ESPEE BIOPHARMA & FINECHEM, LLC; *U.S. Private*, pg. 1426
ESPERION THERAPEUTICS, INC.; *U.S. Public*, pg. 794
ESPERO BIOPHARMA, INC.; *U.S. Private*, pg. 1426
ESPERO PHARMACEUTICALS, INC.—See Espero BioPharma, Inc.; *U.S. Private*, pg. 1427
ESSA PHARMA INC.; *Int'l*, pg. 2508
ESSENTIAL PHARMACEUTICAL CORP.; *U.S. Private*, pg. 1427
ESSEX BIO-TECHNOLOGY LIMITED; *Int'l*, pg. 2512
ESSEX CHEMIE AG—See Merck & Co., Inc.; *U.S. Public*, pg. 1416
ESS GROUP, INC.—See TRC Companies, Inc.; *U.S. Private*, pg. 4215
ESSIX BIOSCIENCES LIMITED; *Int'l*, pg. 2517
ESTEVE PHARMACEUTICALS S.A.; *Int'l*, pg. 2518
ETELA ALBORZ INVESTMENT COMPANY—See Alborz Investment Company; *Int'l*, pg. 299
ETEX FARMACEUTICA LIMITADA—See GSK plc; *Int'l*, pg. 3145
ETUBICS CORPORATION—See NantWorks, LLC; *U.S. Private*, pg. 2833
EUBIOCO S.A.—See CEPD N.V.; *Int'l*, pg. 1420
EUROAPI SAS; *Int'l*, pg. 2532
EUROESPES S.A.; *Int'l*, pg. 2534
EUROFINS CEREP SA—See Eurofins Scientific S.E.; *Int'l*, pg. 2542
EUROFINS PANLABS, INC.—See Eurofins Scientific S.E.; *Int'l*, pg. 2542
EUROFINS PHARMA QUALITY CONTROL DENMARK A/S—See Eurofins Scientific S.E.; *Int'l*, pg. 2547
EUROFINS PROXY LABORATORIES BV—See Eurofins Scientific S.E.; *Int'l*, pg. 2546
EUROFINS SELCIA LIMITED—See Eurofins Scientific S.E.; *Int'l*, pg. 2548
EUROIMMUN US INC.—See Revvity, Inc.; *U.S. Public*, pg. 1794
EURO-MED LABORATORIES PHIL., INC.; *Int'l*, pg. 2531
EUROPEAN INSTITUTE OF SCIENCE AB; *Int'l*, pg. 2556
EUROPEAN MEDICAL CONTRACT MANUFACTURING B.V.—See aap Implantate AG; *Int'l*, pg. 36
EUROSCREEN S.A.; *Int'l*, pg. 2558
EUSA PHARMA (UK) LIMITED—See Essex Woodlands Management, Inc.; *U.S. Private*, pg. 1428
EVANS MEDICAL PLC; *Int'l*, pg. 2560
EVEREST ORGANICS LIMITED MEDAK FACTORY—See

N.A.I.C.S. INDEX

325412 — PHARMACEUTICAL PREP...

Everest Organics Limited; *Int'l*, pg. 2564
EVEREST ORGANICS LIMITED; *Int'l*, pg. 2564
EVERSANA LIFE SCIENCE SERVICES, LLC—See JLL Partners, LLC; *U.S. Private*, pg. 2212
EVERSANA LIFE SCIENCE SERVICES, LLC—See Water Street Healthcare Partners, LLC; *U.S. Private*, pg. 4452
EVGEN PHARMA PLC; *Int'l*, pg. 2570
EVOFEM BIOSCIENCES, INC.; *U.S. Public*, pg. 804
EVOKE PHARMA, INC.; *U.S. Public*, pg. 804
EVOLVA A/S—See Evolva Holding SA; *Int'l*, pg. 2572
EVOLVA HOLDING SA; *Int'l*, pg. 2572
EVOQ REMEDIES LIMITED; *Int'l*, pg. 2573
EVOTEC (INDIA) PRIVATE LTD.—See Evotec SE; *Int'l*, pg. 2573
EVOTEC SE; *Int'l*, pg. 2573
EXCELLA GMBH—See Fareva SA; *Int'l*, pg. 2618
EXCITEPCR, CORPORATION—See PositiveID Corporation; *U.S. Private*, pg. 3233
EXELIXIS, INC.; *U.S. Public*, pg. 806
EXERGY21 CO., LTD.; *Int'l*, pg. 2584
EXIR PHARMACEUTICAL COMPANY; *Int'l*, pg. 2585
EXOPHARM LTD.; *Int'l*, pg. 2586
EYEGENE INC.; *Int'l*, pg. 2593
EYEPOINT PHARMACEUTICALS, INC.; *U.S. Public*, pg. 817
EYEPOINT PHARMACEUTICALS US, INC.—See EyePoint Pharmaceuticals, Inc.; *U.S. Public*, pg. 817
FABINO LIFE SCIENCES LIMITED; *Int'l*, pg. 2599
FAES FARMA DEL ECUADOR SA—See FAES Farma, S.A.; *Int'l*, pg. 2601
FAES FARMA, S.A.; *Int'l*, pg. 2601
FAGRON A.S.—See Fagron NV; *Int'l*, pg. 2603
FAGRON BV—See Fagron NV; *Int'l*, pg. 2603
FAGRON CANADA INC.—See Fagron NV; *Int'l*, pg. 2603
FAGRON COLOMBIA SAS—See Fagron NV; *Int'l*, pg. 2603
FAGRON GMBH & CO KG—See Fagron NV; *Int'l*, pg. 2603
FAGRON GROUP BV—See Fagron NV; *Int'l*, pg. 2603
FAGRON IBERICA SAU—See Fagron NV; *Int'l*, pg. 2603
FAGRON, INC.—See Fagron NV; *Int'l*, pg. 2603
FAGRON NORDIC A/S—See Fagron NV; *Int'l*, pg. 2603
FAGRON SAS—See Fagron NV; *Int'l*, pg. 2603
FAGRON SERVICES BVBA—See Fagron NV; *Int'l*, pg. 2603
FAGRON SH LTD.—See Fagron NV; *Int'l*, pg. 2603
FAGRON SOUTH AFRICA LTD.—See Fagron NV; *Int'l*, pg. 2603
FAGRON SP. Z O.O—See Fagron NV; *Int'l*, pg. 2603
FAGRON UK LTD—See Fagron NV; *Int'l*, pg. 2603
FAIR DEAL CORPORATION PHARMACEUTICAL SA (PTY.) LIMITED—See FDC Ltd; *Int'l*, pg. 2629
FARABI PHARMACEUTICAL.CO; *Int'l*, pg. 2617
FAREVA SA; *Int'l*, pg. 2618
FARMABIOS SPA—See Groupe Bruxelles Lambert SA; *Int'l*, pg. 3099
FARMACEUTICI FORMENTI S.P.A.—See Grunenthal GmbH; *Int'l*, pg. 3114
FARMACOLOGIA EN AQUACULTURA VETERINARIA FAV ECUADOR S.A.—See Abbott Laboratories; *U.S. Public*, pg. 19
FARMACOLOGIA EN AQUACULTURA VETERINARIA FAV S.A.—See Abbott Laboratories; *U.S. Public*, pg. 19
FARMAK JSC; *Int'l*, pg. 2619
FARMALAB INDUSTRIAS QUIIMICAS E FARMACEUTICAS LTDA—See Chiesi Farmaceutici SpA; *Int'l*, pg. 1478
FARMASIX-PRODUTOS FARMACEUTICOS, LDA—See Merck & Co., Inc.; *U.S. Public*, pg. 1416
FARM-SERWIS SP. Z O.O.—See CEPD N.V.; *Int'l*, pg. 1420
FARON PHARMACEUTICALS; *Int'l*, pg. 2620
FARSIGHT BIOSCIENCE LIMITED; *Int'l*, pg. 2620
FAST INTERNATIONAL CO.; *Int'l*, pg. 2621
FATE THERAPEUTICS, INC.; *U.S. Public*, pg. 824
FDC LTD; *Int'l*, pg. 2628
THE F. DOHMEN COMPANY—See Cardinal Health, Inc.; *U.S. Public*, pg. 434
FEMPHARM PTY LTD—See Acrux Limited; *Int'l*, pg. 109
FENNEC PHARMACEUTICALS, INC.; *U.S. Public*, pg. 829
FERNDALE LABORATORIES INC.; *U.S. Private*, pg. 1497
FEROZSONS LABORATORIES LIMITED; *Int'l*, pg. 2639
FERRER ESPANA, S.A.—See Grupo Ferrer Internacional, S.A.; *Int'l*, pg. 3129
FERRING AG—See Ferring Holding SA; *Int'l*, pg. 2641
FERRING ARZNEIMITTEL GESMBH—See Ferring Holding SA; *Int'l*, pg. 2641
FERRING ARZNEIMITTEL GMBH—See Ferring Holding SA; *Int'l*, pg. 2641
FERRING BV—See Ferring Holding SA; *Int'l*, pg. 2642
FERRING CONTROLLED THERAPEUTICS LTD—See Ferring Holding SA; *Int'l*, pg. 2641
FERRING GALENISCHES LABOR AG—See Ferring Holding SA; *Int'l*, pg. 2641
FERRING GMBH—See Ferring Holding SA; *Int'l*, pg. 2641
FERRING HELLAS PHARMACEUTICALS E.P.E.—See Ferring Holding SA; *Int'l*, pg. 2641
FERRING HUNGARY PHARMACEUTICAL TRADING CO LTD—See Ferring Holding SA; *Int'l*, pg. 2641
FERRING ILAC SANAYI VE TICARET LTD STI—See Ferring Holding SA; *Int'l*, pg. 2641
FERRING INC.—See Ferring Holding SA; *Int'l*, pg. 2641

FERRING INTERNATIONAL CENTER SA—See Ferring Holding SA; *Int'l*, pg. 2642
FERRING INTERNATIONAL PHARMASCIENCE CENTER U.S. INC.—See Ferring Holding SA; *Int'l*, pg. 2642
FERRING INTERNATIONAL PHARMA-SCIENCE CENTRE (CHINA) CO. LTD.—See Ferring Holding SA; *Int'l*, pg. 2641
FERRING (IRELAND) LTD.—See Ferring Holding SA; *Int'l*, pg. 2641
FERRING LAAKKEET OY—See Ferring Holding SA; *Int'l*, pg. 2641
FERRING LAEGEMIDLER A/S—See Ferring Holding SA; *Int'l*, pg. 2641
FERRING LAKEMEDEL AB—See Ferring Holding SA; *Int'l*, pg. 2641
FERRING LECIVA AS—See Ferring Holding SA; *Int'l*, pg. 2641
FERRING LEGEMIDLER AS—See Ferring Holding SA; *Int'l*, pg. 2641
FERRING NV—See Ferring Holding SA; *Int'l*, pg. 2641
FERRING PHARMACEUTICAL (CHINA) COMPANY LIMITED—See Ferring Holding SA; *Int'l*, pg. 2642
FERRING PHARMACEUTICALS (ASIA) CO. LTD.—See Ferring Holding SA; *Int'l*, pg. 2641
FERRING PHARMACEUTICALS CO. LTD.—See Ferring Holding SA; *Int'l*, pg. 2641
FERRING PHARMACEUTICALS KOREA CO., LTD.—See Ferring Holding SA; *Int'l*, pg. 2641
FERRING PHARMACEUTICALS LLC—See Ferring Holding SA; *Int'l*, pg. 2641
FERRING PHARMACEUTICALS LTD.—See Ferring Holding SA; *Int'l*, pg. 2641
FERRING PHARMACEUTICALS POLAND SP. Z O.O.—See Ferring Holding SA; *Int'l*, pg. 2642
FERRING PHARMACEUTICALS PTE LTD.—See Ferring Holding SA; *Int'l*, pg. 2642
FERRING PHARMACEUTICALS PTY LTD—See Ferring Holding SA; *Int'l*, pg. 2642
FERRING PHARMACEUTICALS PVT LTD—See Ferring Holding SA; *Int'l*, pg. 2642
FERRING PHARMACEUTICALS ROMANIA S.R.L.—See Ferring Holding SA; *Int'l*, pg. 2642
FERRING PHARMACEUTICALS SA—See Ferring Holding SA; *Int'l*, pg. 2642
FERRING PORTUGUESA PRODUTOS FARMACEUTICOS SOCIEDADE UNIPESSOAL, LDA.—See Ferring Holding SA; *Int'l*, pg. 2642
FERRING PRODUCTOS FARMACEUTICOS SPA—See Ferring Holding SA; *Int'l*, pg. 2642
FERRING PTY LTD—See Ferring Holding SA; *Int'l*, pg. 2642
FERRING SA DE CV—See Ferring Holding SA; *Int'l*, pg. 2642
FERRING S.A.S.—See Ferring Holding SA; *Int'l*, pg. 2642
FERRING SAU—See Ferring Holding SA; *Int'l*, pg. 2642
FERRING SDN BHD—See Ferring Holding SA; *Int'l*, pg. 2642
FERRING SLOVAKIA S.R.O.—See Ferring Holding SA; *Int'l*, pg. 2642
FERRING SPA—See Ferring Holding SA; *Int'l*, pg. 2642
FERRING THERAPEUTICS PRIVATE LTD.—See Ferring Holding SA; *Int'l*, pg. 2642
FERROSAN A/S—See Altor Equity Partners AB; *Int'l*, pg. 394
FERROSAN DO BRASIL LTDA.—See Altor Equity Partners AB; *Int'l*, pg. 394
FERROSAN INTERNATIONAL A/S—See Altor Equity Partners AB; *Int'l*, pg. 394
FERROSAN NORGE AS—See Altor Equity Partners AB; *Int'l*, pg. 394
FERROSAN POLAND SP. Z.O.O.—See Altor Equity Partners AB; *Int'l*, pg. 394
FERROSAN S.R.L—See Altor Equity Partners AB; *Int'l*, pg. 394
FERTIN PHARMA A/S—See Philip Morris International Inc.; *U.S. Public*, pg. 1685
FERVENT SYNERGIES LIMITED; *Int'l*, pg. 2646
FIBROGEN, INC.; *U.S. Public*, pg. 830
FIDSON HEALTHCARE PLC; *Int'l*, pg. 2655
FILAMENT HEALTH CORP.; *Int'l*, pg. 2662
FINCANNA CAPITAL CORP.; *Int'l*, pg. 2670
FINE CHEMICALS CORPORATION (PTY) LTD—See Aspen Pharmacare Holdings Limited; *Int'l*, pg. 629
FINE FOODS & PHARMACEUTICALS N.T.M. S.P.A.; *Int'l*, pg. 2673
FIREBRICK PHARMA LIMITED; *Int'l*, pg. 2678
FISHER & PAYKEL HEALTHCARE PROPERTIES LIMITED—See Fisher & Paykel Healthcare Corporation Limited; *Int'l*, pg. 2693
FIT BIOTECH OY; *Int'l*, pg. 2695
FITVIA GMBH—See Dermapharm Holding SE; *Int'l*, pg. 2043
FIVE PRIME THERAPEUTICS, INC.—See Amgen Inc.; *U.S. Public*, pg. 123
FIXEDSPRING LIMITED—See GSK plc; *Int'l*, pg. 3145
FLEET LABORATORIES INC.—See DDD Ltd.; *Int'l*, pg. 1993
FLEMING PHARMACEUTICALS; *U.S. Private*, pg. 1542
FLEXION THERAPEUTICS, INC.—See Pacira BioSciences, Inc.; *U.S. Public*, pg. 1632
FLEX-POWER INC.; *U.S. Private*, pg. 1543
FLORA GROWTH CORP.; *Int'l*, pg. 2707

FLUOROPHARMA MEDICAL, INC.; *U.S. Public*, pg. 860
FMC CHEMICAL SPRL—See FMC Corporation; *U.S. Public*, pg. 862
FMC CHEMICALS (THAILAND) LTD—See FMC Corporation; *U.S. Public*, pg. 862
FMC ITALY SRL—See FMC Corporation; *U.S. Public*, pg. 862
FMC NORWAY HOLDING AS—See FMC Corporation; *U.S. Public*, pg. 862
FMC SPECIALTY ALKALI CORPORATION—See FMC Corporation; *U.S. Public*, pg. 862
FMC WYOMING CORPORATION—See FMC Corporation; *U.S. Public*, pg. 862
FORESEE PHARMACEUTICALS CO., LTD.; *Int'l*, pg. 2731
FOREST LABORATORIES IRELAND LIMITED—See AbbVie Inc.; *U.S. Public*, pg. 23
FOREST TOSARA LTD.—See AbbVie Inc.; *U.S. Public*, pg. 23
FOREVERGREEN INTERNATIONAL, LLC—See ForeverGreen Worldwide Corporation; *U.S. Public*, pg. 867
FORGIVEN BOTTLING GROUP, INC.; *U.S. Private*, pg. 1568
FORMULA PHARMACEUTICALS, INC.—See Genexine Inc.; *Int'l*, pg. 2923
FORMYCON AG; *Int'l*, pg. 2737
FORTRESS BIOTECH, INC.; *U.S. Public*, pg. 872
FORWARD PHARMA A/S; *Int'l*, pg. 2747
FORWARD PHARMA USA, LLC—See Forward Pharma A/S; *Int'l*, pg. 2747
FOSHAN DEZHONG PHARMACEUTICAL CO., LTD.—See China National Pharmaceutical Group Corporation; *Int'l*, pg. 1534
FOSUN PHARMA KITE BIOTECHNOLOGY CO., LTD.—See Gilead Sciences, Inc.; *U.S. Public*, pg. 937
FOURNIER PHARMA GMBH—See Abbott Laboratories; *U.S. Public*, pg. 19
FPZ DEUTSCHLAND DEN RUCKEN STARKEN GMBH—See Pfizer Inc.; *U.S. Public*, pg. 1679
FRALEX THERAPEUTICS INC.—See Boston Scientific Corporation; *U.S. Public*, pg. 374
FREDUN PHARMACEUTICALS LTD.; *Int'l*, pg. 2769
FRESENIUS HEMOCARE DEUTSCHLAND GMBH—See Fresenius SE & Co. KGaA; *Int'l*, pg. 2777
FRESENIUS HEMOCARE ITALIA S.R.L—See Fresenius SE & Co. KGaA; *Int'l*, pg. 2777
FRESENIUS KABI AB—See Fresenius SE & Co. KGaA; *Int'l*, pg. 2777
FRESENIUS KABI AG—See Fresenius SE & Co. KGaA; *Int'l*, pg. 2777
FRESENIUS KABI ARGENTINA SA—See Fresenius SE & Co. KGaA; *Int'l*, pg. 2777
FRESENIUS KABI ASIA-PACIFIC LIMITED—See Fresenius SE & Co. KGaA; *Int'l*, pg. 2777
FRESENIUS KABI AUSTRIA GMBH—See Fresenius SE & Co. KGaA; *Int'l*, pg. 2777
FRESENIUS KABI BRAZIL LTDA.—See Fresenius SE & Co. KGaA; *Int'l*, pg. 2777
FRESENIUS KABI COMPOUNDING LLC—See Fagron NV; *Int'l*, pg. 2603
FRESENIUS KABI DEUTSCHLAND GMBH—See Fresenius SE & Co. KGaA; *Int'l*, pg. 2777
FRESENIUS KABI ESPANA S.A.—See Fresenius SE & Co. KGaA; *Int'l*, pg. 2777
FRESENIUS KABI FRANCE S.A.S.—See Fresenius SE & Co. KGaA; *Int'l*, pg. 2777
FRESENIUS KABI ITALIA S.R.L.—See Fresenius SE & Co. KGaA; *Int'l*, pg. 2777
FRESENIUS KABI KOREA LTD.—See Fresenius SE & Co. KGaA; *Int'l*, pg. 2777
FRESENIUS KABI LTD.—See Fresenius SE & Co. KGaA; *Int'l*, pg. 2777
FRESENIUS KABI MEXICO S.A. DE C.V.—See Fresenius SE & Co. KGaA; *Int'l*, pg. 2777
FRESENIUS KABI NORGE A.S.—See Fresenius SE & Co. KGaA; *Int'l*, pg. 2777
FRESENIUS KABI ONCOLOGY LIMITED—See Fresenius SE & Co. KGaA; *Int'l*, pg. 2777
FRESENIUS KABI POLSKA SP Z.O.O.—See Fresenius SE & Co. KGaA; *Int'l*, pg. 2778
FRESENIUS KABI (SCHWEIZ) AG—See Fresenius SE & Co. KGaA; *Int'l*, pg. 2777
FRESENIUS KABI SOUTH AFRICA (PTY) LTD.—See Fresenius SE & Co. KGaA; *Int'l*, pg. 2778
FRESENIUS KABI USA, LLC—See Fresenius SE & Co. KGaA; *Int'l*, pg. 2778
FRESENIUS MEDICAL CARE POLSKA S.A.—See Fresenius Medical Care AG; *Int'l*, pg. 2775
FRESENIUS VIAL S.A.S.—See Fresenius SE & Co. KGaA; *Int'l*, pg. 2778
FRONTAGE LABORATORIES, INC.—See Hangzhou Tigermed Consulting Co., Ltd.; *Int'l*, pg. 3251
FRONTIER BIOTECHNOLOGIES, INC.; *Int'l*, pg. 2794
FUAN PHARMACEUTICAL (GROUP) CO., LTD.; *Int'l*, pg. 2801
FUJIAN COSUNTER PHARMACEUTICAL CO., LTD.; *Int'l*, pg. 2817
FUJI CHEMICAL INDUSTRIES CO., LTD.

325412 — PHARMACEUTICAL PREP...

GOHKAKIZAWA—See Fuji Chemical Industries Co., Ltd; *Int'l*, pg. 2809
FUJI CHEMICAL INDUSTRIES CO., LTD; *Int'l*, pg. 2808
FUJI CHEMICAL INDUSTRIES CO., LTD. - TOKYO—See Fuji Chemical Industries Co., Ltd; *Int'l*, pg. 2809
FUJI CHEMICAL INDUSTRIES USA, INC.—See Fuji Chemical Industries Co., Ltd; *Int'l*, pg. 2809
FUJIFILM DIOSYNTH BIOTECHNOLOGIES INC.—See FUJIFILM Holdings Corporation; *Int'l*, pg. 2822
FUJIFILM DIOSYNTH BIOTECHNOLOGIES TEXAS, LLC—See FUJIFILM Holdings Corporation; *Int'l*, pg. 2824
FUJIFILM DIOSYNTH BIOTECHNOLOGIES UK LIMITED—See FUJIFILM Holdings Corporation; *Int'l*, pg. 2821
FUJIFILM IRVINE SCIENTIFIC, INC.—See FUJIFILM Holdings Corporation; *Int'l*, pg. 2824
FUJIFILM PHARMA CO., LTD.—See FUJIFILM Holdings Corporation; *Int'l*, pg. 2824
FUJIFILM RI PHARMA CO., LTD.—See FUJIFILM Holdings Corporation; *Int'l*, pg. 2825
FUJIFILM WAKO PURE CHEMICAL CORPORATION—See FUJIFILM Holdings Corporation; *Int'l*, pg. 2823
FUJI PHARMA CO., LTD.; *Int'l*, pg. 2816
FUJIREBIO DIAGNOSTICS AB—See H.U. Group Holdings, Inc.; *Int'l*, pg. 3196
FUJIREBIO INC.—See H.U. Group Holdings, Inc.; *Int'l*, pg. 3196
FUJIREBIO TAIWAN, INC.—See H.U. Group Holdings, Inc.; *Int'l*, pg. 3196
FUJISAWA SA—See Astellas Pharma Inc.; *Int'l*, pg. 652
FUJISAWA SYNTHELABO PHARMACEUTICALS CO., LTD.—See Astellas Pharma Inc.; *Int'l*, pg. 653
FUJISAWA TAIWAN CO., LTD.—See Astellas Pharma Inc.; *Int'l*, pg. 653
FUNDACION ABBVIE—See AbbVie Inc.; *U.S. Public*, pg. 24
FUNDACION BIOGEN—See Biogen Inc.; *U.S. Public*, pg. 337
FUNPEP CO., LTD.; *Int'l*, pg. 2846
FUREN GROUP PHARMACEUTICAL CO., LTD.; *Int'l*, pg. 2846
FUSEN PHARMACEUTICAL CO., LTD.; *Int'l*, pg. 2849
FUSION ANTIBODIES PLC; *Int'l*, pg. 2849
FUSO PHARMACEUTICAL INDUSTRIES, LTD.; *Int'l*, pg. 2850
FUSS BRANDS CORP.; *U.S. Public*, pg. 893
FUTURA MEDICAL DEVELOPMENTS LIMITED—See Futura Medical plc; *Int'l*, pg. 2852
FUTURA MEDICAL PLC; *Int'l*, pg. 2852
FUTURECHEM CO LTD; *Int'l*, pg. 2857
FUTURE MEDICINE CO., LTD; *Int'l*, pg. 2856
G1 THERAPEUTICS, INC.; *U.S. Private*, pg. 1632
GABY INC.; *Int'l*, pg. 2868
GAKO DEUTSCHLAND GMBH—See Fagron NV; *Int'l*, pg. 2603
GALAPAGOS SASU—See Galapagos N.V.; *Int'l*, pg. 2870
GALAXY DIGITAL HOLDINGS LTD.; *U.S. Public*, pg. 894
GALDERMA CANADA, INC.—See Abu Dhabi Investment Authority; *Int'l*, pg. 71
GALDERMA CANADA, INC.—See EQT Corporation; *U.S. Public*, pg. 785
GALDERMA LABORATORIES, L.P.—See Abu Dhabi Investment Authority; *Int'l*, pg. 71
GALDERMA LABORATORIES, L.P.—See EQT Corporation; *U.S. Public*, pg. 785
GALDERMA LABORATORIUM GMBH—See Abu Dhabi Investment Authority; *Int'l*, pg. 71
GALDERMA LABORATORIUM GMBH—See EQT Corporation; *U.S. Public*, pg. 785
GALDERMA PRODUCTION CANADA INC.—See Abu Dhabi Investment Authority; *Int'l*, pg. 71
GALDERMA PRODUCTION CANADA INC.—See EQT Corporation; *U.S. Public*, pg. 785
GALECTIN THERAPEUTICS, INC.; *U.S. Public*, pg. 895
GALEN PHARMA IRELAND LIMITED—See Almac Sciences Group Ltd.; *Int'l*, pg. 363
GALMED PHARMACEUTICALS LTD.; *Int'l*, pg. 2875
GAN & LEE PHARMACEUTICALS CO., LTD.; *Int'l*, pg. 2879
GANSU LONGSHENRONGFA PHRMCTCL IND CO LTD; *Int'l*, pg. 2881
GARDEN OF LIFE, INC.; *U.S. Private*, pg. 1643
GC BIOPHARMA CORP.; *Int'l*, pg. 2893
GC BIOPHARMA USA, INC.—See GC Biopharma Corp.; *Int'l*, pg. 2893
G.C. HANFORD MANUFACTURING COMPANY; *U.S. Private*, pg. 1630
GC HEALTH CARE CORPORATION—See GC Biopharma Corp.; *Int'l*, pg. 2893
GC JBP CORPORATION—See GC Biopharma Corp.; *Int'l*, pg. 2893
GC MOGAM, INC.—See Green Cross WellBeing Corp.; *Int'l*, pg. 3070
GEA PHARMA SYSTEMS LIMITED—See GEA Group Aktiengesellschaft; *Int'l*, pg. 2901
GEDEON RICHTER BULGARIA LTD.—See Gedeon Richter Plc.; *Int'l*, pg. 2909

GEDEON RICHTER COLOMBIA S.A.S.—See Gedeon Richter Plc.; *Int'l*, pg. 2910
GEDEON RICHTER FRANCE S.A.R.L—See Gedeon Richter Plc.; *Int'l*, pg. 2910
GEDEON RICHTER IBERICA S.A—See Gedeon Richter Plc.; *Int'l*, pg. 2910
GEDEON RICHTER ITALIA S.R.L—See Gedeon Richter Plc.; *Int'l*, pg. 2910
GEDEON RICHTER KZ LLP—See Chemical Works of Gedeon Richter Plc; *Int'l*, pg. 1462
GEDEON RICHTER MARKETING CR S.R.O.—See Gedeon Richter Plc.; *Int'l*, pg. 2910
GEDEON RICHTER PHARMA GMBH—See Gedeon Richter Plc.; *Int'l*, pg. 2910
GEDEON RICHTER PHARMA O.O.O.—See Gedeon Richter Plc.; *Int'l*, pg. 2910
GEDEON RICHTER PLC.; *Int'l*, pg. 2909
GEDEON RICHTER POLSKA SP. Z O.O—See Gedeon Richter Plc.; *Int'l*, pg. 2910
GEDEON RICHTER - RETEA FARMACEUTICA S.R.L—See Gedeon Richter Plc.; *Int'l*, pg. 2909
GEDEON RICHTER ROMANIA S.A—See Gedeon Richter Plc.; *Int'l*, pg. 2910
GEDEON RICHTER SLOVENIJA, D.O.O.—See Gedeon Richter Plc.; *Int'l*, pg. 2910
GEDEON RICHTER UA TOV—See Chemical Works of Gedeon Richter Plc; *Int'l*, pg. 1462
GEDEON RICHTER UA V.A.T.—See Gedeon Richter Plc.; *Int'l*, pg. 2910
GEDEON RICHTER UK LTD—See Gedeon Richter Plc.; *Int'l*, pg. 2910
GEDEON RICHTER USA, INC—See Gedeon Richter Plc.; *Int'l*, pg. 2910
GE HEALTHCARE PHARMA LIMITED—See GE HealthCare Technologies Inc.; *U.S. Public*, pg. 909
GELESIS, INC.—See Gelesis Holdings, Inc.; *U.S. Public*, pg. 910
GELSTAT CORPORATION; *U.S. Public*, pg. 910
GELTEQ LIMITED; *Int'l*, pg. 2914
GENE BIOTHERAPEUTICS INC.; *U.S. Public*, pg. 911
GENENCOR INTERNATIONAL INC. - ROCHESTER—See DuPont de Nemours, Inc.; *U.S. Public*, pg. 692
GENENCOR INTERNATIONAL, INC.—See DuPont de Nemours, Inc.; *U.S. Public*, pg. 692
GENERA D.O.O. SARAJEVO—See EQT AB; *Int'l*, pg. 2475
GENERAL BIOLOGICALS CORPORATION; *Int'l*, pg. 2918
GENERAL HOSPITAL PRODUCTS PCL—See Bangkok Dusit Medical Services Public Company Limited; *Int'l*, pg. 834
GENERA PHARMA D.O.O.—See EQT AB; *Int'l*, pg. 2474
GENEREX BIOTECHNOLOGY CORPORATION; *U.S. Public*, pg. 930
GENERIS FARMACEUTICA, S.A.—See Aurobindo Pharma Ltd.; *Int'l*, pg. 713
GENERIS PHAR, UNIPESSOAL LD WOS—See Aurobindo Pharma Ltd.; *Int'l*, pg. 713
GENERTEC MEHECO TIBET ZHONGJIAN CO., LTD.—See China Meheco Group Co., Ltd.; *Int'l*, pg. 1519
GENESCIENCE PHARMACEUTICALS CO., LTD.—See Changchun High & New Technology Industry (Group) Inc.; *Int'l*, pg. 1442
GENESIS DRUG DISCOVERY & DEVELOPMENT LLC—See Genesis Biotechnology Group, LLC; *U.S. Private*, pg. 1669
GENEURO SA; *Int'l*, pg. 2922
GENEXTRA S.P.A.; *Int'l*, pg. 2923
GENFIT S.A.; *Int'l*, pg. 2923
GENFLOW BIOSCIENCES S.R.L—See Genflow Biosciences Plc; *Int'l*, pg. 2923
GENINUS INC.; *Int'l*, pg. 2924
GENIX PHARMACEUTICALS CORPORATION; *Int'l*, pg. 2924
GENKY DRUGSTORES CO., LTD.; *Int'l*, pg. 2924
GENKYOTEX S.A.—See Asahi Kasei Corporation; *Int'l*, pg. 596
GENMAB US, INC.—See Genmab A/S; *Int'l*, pg. 2924
GENOCEA BIOSCIENCES, INC.; *U.S. Public*, pg. 931
GENO LLC; *U.S. Private*, pg. 1672
GENOME & COMPANY; *Int'l*, pg. 2925
GENOR BIOPHARMA CO., LTD.; *Int'l*, pg. 2925
GENOTECH CORPORATION - GMP PLANT—See Geno-Tech Corporation; *Int'l*, pg. 2925
GENOVATE BIOTECHNOLOGY CO., LTD.; *Int'l*, pg. 2926
GENPREX, INC.; *U.S. Public*, pg. 931
GENSENTA ILAC SANAYI VE TICARET ANONIM SIRKETI—See Amgen Inc.; *U.S. Public*, pg. 123
GENTIAN USA INC.—See Gentian Diagnostics AS; *Int'l*, pg. 2928
GENUS PHARMACEUTICALS LTD.—See Bain Capital, LP; *U.S. Private*, pg. 443
GENUS PHARMACEUTICALS LTD.—See Cinven Limited; *Int'l*, pg. 1613
GENVEC, INC.—See Precigen, Inc.; *U.S. Public*, pg. 1713
GEOVAX LABS, INC.; *U.S. Public*, pg. 934
GERITREX CORP.—See BelHealth Investment Partners LLC; *U.S. Private*, pg. 518
GEROLYMATOS INC—See Gerolymatos Group of Companies; *Int'l*, pg. 2943

GERON CORPORATION; *U.S. Public*, pg. 934
GERRESHEIMER GLASS INC. - FOREST GROVE PLANT—See Gerresheimer AG; *Int'l*, pg. 2943
GERRESHEIMER QUERETARO S.A.—See Gerresheimer AG; *Int'l*, pg. 2944
GETINGE CETREA A/S—See Getinge AB; *Int'l*, pg. 2949
GETINGE COLOMBIA SAS—See Getinge AB; *Int'l*, pg. 2949
GETINGE DEUTSCHLAND GMBH—See Getinge AB; *Int'l*, pg. 2949
GETINGE DO BRASIL EQUIPAMENTOS MEDICOS LTDA.—See Getinge AB; *Int'l*, pg. 2951
GETINGE FINANCIAL SERVICES GMBH—See Getinge AB; *Int'l*, pg. 2949
GETINGE GROUP HONG KONG LTD.—See Getinge AB; *Int'l*, pg. 2949
GETINGE GROUP LOGISTICS AMERICAS, LLC—See Getinge AB; *Int'l*, pg. 2949
GETINGE GROUP MIDDLE EAST FZ-LLC—See Getinge AB; *Int'l*, pg. 2949
GETINGE GROUP PORTUGAL UNIPESSOAL LDA.—See Getinge AB; *Int'l*, pg. 2949
GETINGE GROUP SOUTH EAST EUROPE D.O.O—See Getinge AB; *Int'l*, pg. 2949
GETINGE GROUP SPAIN SL—See Getinge AB; *Int'l*, pg. 2949
GETINGE GROUP TAIWAN CO., LTD.—See Getinge AB; *Int'l*, pg. 2949
GETINGE IC PRODUCTION POLAND SP. Z O.O.—See Getinge AB; *Int'l*, pg. 2950
GETINGE IRELAND LTD.—See Getinge AB; *Int'l*, pg. 2950
GETINGE IT SOLUTIONS GMBH—See Getinge AB; *Int'l*, pg. 2950
GETINGE IT SOLUTIONS LTD.—See Getinge AB; *Int'l*, pg. 2950
GETINGE MEDICAL INDIA PVT LTD.—See Getinge AB; *Int'l*, pg. 2950
GETINGE MEDICAL KOREA CO., LTD.—See Getinge AB; *Int'l*, pg. 2950
GETINGE MEDIKAL SISTEMLER SAN VE TIC A.S—See Getinge AB; *Int'l*, pg. 2950
GETINGE OSTERREICH GMBH—See Getinge AB; *Int'l*, pg. 2950
GETINGE POLSKA SP. Z O.O.—See Getinge AB; *Int'l*, pg. 2950
GETINGE SHARED SERVICES SP. Z O.O.—See Getinge AB; *Int'l*, pg. 2950
GETINGE SLOVAKIA S.R.O.—See Getinge AB; *Int'l*, pg. 2950
GETINGE SOUTH EAST ASIA PTE. LTD.—See Getinge AB; *Int'l*, pg. 2950
GETINGE STERICOOL MEDIKAL ALETLER SAN. VE TIC. A.S.—See Getinge AB; *Int'l*, pg. 2950
GETINGE TREASURY IRELAND DAC—See Getinge AB; *Int'l*, pg. 2950
GETINGE USA SALES, LLC—See Getinge AB; *Int'l*, pg. 2951
GETINGE VIETNAM COMPANY LTD.—See Getinge AB; *Int'l*, pg. 2951
GEYSER BRANDS, INC.; *Int'l*, pg. 2955
GILEAD ALBERTA ULC—See Gilead Sciences, Inc.; *U.S. Public*, pg. 937
GILEAD CONNECTICUT, INC.—See Gilead Sciences, Inc.; *U.S. Public*, pg. 937
GILEAD SCIENCES CANADA, INC.—See Gilead Sciences, Inc.; *U.S. Public*, pg. 937
GILEAD SCIENCES FARMACEUTICA DO BRASIL LTDA—See Gilead Sciences, Inc.; *U.S. Public*, pg. 937
GILEAD SCIENCES INTERNATIONAL LTD.—See Gilead Sciences, Inc.; *U.S. Public*, pg. 937
GILEAD SCIENCES IRELAND UC—See Gilead Sciences, Inc.; *U.S. Public*, pg. 937
GILEAD SCIENCES LTD.—See Gilead Sciences, Inc.; *U.S. Public*, pg. 937
GILEAD SCIENCES POLAND—See Gilead Sciences, Inc.; *U.S. Public*, pg. 937
GILEAD SCIENCES SAS—See Gilead Sciences, Inc.; *U.S. Public*, pg. 937
GILEAD SCIENCES (SHANGHAI) CONSULTING CO., LTD.—See Gilead Sciences, Inc.; *U.S. Public*, pg. 937
GILEAD YM ULC—See Gilead Sciences, Inc.; *U.S. Public*, pg. 937
GINWA ENTERPRISE (GROUP) INC.; *Int'l*, pg. 2977
GIVAUDAN ARGENTINA SA—See Givaudan S.A.; *Int'l*, pg. 2980
GLAND PHARMA LIMITED—See Fosun International Limited; *Int'l*, pg. 2751
GLATT AIR TECHNIQUES, INC.; *U.S. Private*, pg. 1707
GLAXOCHEM PTE LTD—See GSK plc; *Int'l*, pg. 3148
GLAXOSMITHKLINE AB—See GSK plc; *Int'l*, pg. 3146
GLAXOSMITHKLINE AG—See GSK plc; *Int'l*, pg. 3146
GLAXOSMITHKLINE ALGERIA SPA—See GSK plc; *Int'l*, pg. 3146
GLAXOSMITHKLINE ARGENTINA SA—See GSK plc; *Int'l*, pg. 3146
GLAXOSMITHKLINE AS—See GSK plc; *Int'l*, pg. 3146
GLAXOSMITHKLINE AUSTRALIA PTY. LTD. - CONSUMER HEALTHCARE DIVISION—See GSK plc; *Int'l*, pg. 3146

N.A.I.C.S. INDEX — 325412 — PHARMACEUTICAL PREP...

GLAXOSMITHKLINE AUSTRALIA PTY LTD.—See GSK plc; *Int'l*, pg. 3146
GLAXOSMITHKLINE BIOLOGICALS KFT.—See GSK plc; *Int'l*, pg. 3146
GLAXOSMITHKLINE BIOLOGICALS S.A.S.—See GSK plc; *Int'l*, pg. 3146
GLAXOSMITHKLINE BRASIL LTDA.—See GSK plc; *Int'l*, pg. 3147
GLAXOSMITHKLINE B.V.—See GSK plc; *Int'l*, pg. 3146
GLAXOSMITHKLINE CHILE FARMACEUTICA LIMITADA—See GSK plc; *Int'l*, pg. 3147
GLAXOSMITHKLINE (CHINA) INVESTMENT CO. LTD—See GSK plc; *Int'l*, pg. 3146
GLAXOSMITHKLINE (CHINA) LIMITED—See GSK plc; *Int'l*, pg. 3146
GLAXOSMITHKLINE COLOMBIA S.A.—See GSK plc; *Int'l*, pg. 3147
GLAXOSMITHKLINE CONSUMER HEALTHCARE A/S—See GSK plc; *Int'l*, pg. 3147
GLAXOSMITHKLINE CONSUMER HEALTHCARE GMBH & CO KG—See GSK plc; *Int'l*, pg. 3147
GLAXOSMITHKLINE CONSUMER HEALTHCARE (IRELAND) LIMITED—See GSK plc; *Int'l*, pg. 3147
GLAXOSMITHKLINE CONSUMER HEALTHCARE (PVT) LTD—See GSK plc; *Int'l*, pg. 3147
GLAXOSMITHKLINE CONSUMER HEALTHCARE SDN. BHD.—See GSK plc; *Int'l*, pg. 3147
GLAXOSMITHKLINE CONSUMER HEALTHCARE—See GSK plc; *Int'l*, pg. 3147
GLAXOSMITHKLINE CONSUMER HEALTHCARE S.P.A.—See GSK plc; *Int'l*, pg. 3147
GLAXOSMITHKLINE CONSUMER HEALTHCARE S.P.A.—See GSK plc; *Int'l*, pg. 3147
GLAXOSMITHKLINE CONSUMER HEALTHCARE SP.Z O.O.—See GSK plc; *Int'l*, pg. 3147
GLAXOSMITHKLINE COSTA RICA S.A.—See GSK plc; *Int'l*, pg. 3147
GLAXOSMITHKLINE D.O.O—See GSK plc; *Int'l*, pg. 3149
GLAXOSMITHKLINE D.O.O.—See GSK plc; *Int'l*, pg. 3149
GLAXOSMITHKLINE DUNGARVAN LTD.—See GSK plc; *Int'l*, pg. 3147
GLAXOSMITHKLINE ECUADOR S.A.—See GSK plc; *Int'l*, pg. 3147
GLAXOSMITHKLINE EESTI OU—See GSK plc; *Int'l*, pg. 3147
GLAXOSMITHKLINE EGYPT—See GSK plc; *Int'l*, pg. 3147
GLAXOSMITHKLINE EHF—See GSK plc; *Int'l*, pg. 3147
GLAXOSMITHKLINE EL SALVADOR, S.A. DE C.V.—See GSK plc; *Int'l*, pg. 3147
GLAXOSMITHKLINE EOOD—See GSK plc; *Int'l*, pg. 3147
GLAXOSMITHKLINE - EVREUX PLANT—See GSK plc; *Int'l*, pg. 3149
GLAXOSMITHKLINE EXPORT LTD.—See GSK plc; *Int'l*, pg. 3147
GLAXOSMITHKLINE FARMACEUTICA LTDA.—See GSK plc; *Int'l*, pg. 3147
GLAXOSMITHKLINE FINANCE PLC—See GSK plc; *Int'l*, pg. 3147
GLAXOSMITHKLINE GMBH & CO. KG—See GSK plc; *Int'l*, pg. 3147
GLAXOSMITHKLINE (GSK) S.R.L.—See GSK plc; *Int'l*, pg. 3146
GLAXOSMITHKLINE ILACLARI SANAYI VE TICARET A.S.—See GSK plc; *Int'l*, pg. 3148
GLAXOSMITHKLINE ILAC SANAYI VE TICARET AS—See GSK plc; *Int'l*, pg. 3148
GLAXO SMITH KLINE INC.—See Bora Pharmaceuticals Co., Ltd.; *Int'l*, pg. 1112
GLAXOSMITHKLINE (IRELAND) LIMITED—See GSK plc; *Int'l*, pg. 3146
GLAXOSMITHKLINE ISRAEL—See GSK plc; *Int'l*, pg. 3148
GLAXOSMITHKLINE KFT.—See GSK plc; *Int'l*, pg. 3148
GLAXOSMITHKLINE K.K.—See GSK plc; *Int'l*, pg. 3148
GLAXOSMITHKLINE - KOREA—See GSK plc; *Int'l*, pg. 3146
GLAXOSMITHKLINE LIMITED—See GSK plc; *Int'l*, pg. 3148
GLAXOSMITHKLINE LTD.—See GSK plc; *Int'l*, pg. 3148
GLAXOSMITHKLINE (MALTA) LIMITED—See GSK plc; *Int'l*, pg. 3146
GLAXOSMITHKLINE (MANUFACTURING) LTD.—See Thermo Fisher Scientific Inc.; *U.S. Public*, pg. 2148
GLAXOSMITHKLINE MANUFACTURING S.P.A.—See GSK plc; *Int'l*, pg. 3148
GLAXOSMITHKLINE MAROC S.A.—See GSK plc; *Int'l*, pg. 3148
GLAXOSMITHKLINE MDR-BOSTON FACILITY—See GSK plc; *Int'l*, pg. 3148
GLAXOSMITHKLINE MEXICO S.A. DE C.V.—See GSK plc; *Int'l*, pg. 3148
GLAXOSMITHKLINE (NZ) LTD. CONSUMER HEALTH DIV.—See GSK plc; *Int'l*, pg. 3146
GLAXOSMITHKLINE (NZ) LTD.—See GSK plc; *Int'l*, pg. 3146
GLAXOSMITHKLINE OTC INC.—See GSK plc; *Int'l*, pg. 3148
GLAXOSMITHKLINE OY—See GSK plc; *Int'l*, pg. 3148
GLAXOSMITHKLINE PAKISTAN LTD.—See GSK plc; *Int'l*, pg. 3148

GLAXOSMITHKLINE PERU S.A.—See GSK plc; *Int'l*, pg. 3148
GLAXOSMITHKLINE PHARMA A/S—See GSK plc; *Int'l*, pg. 3148
GLAXOSMITHKLINE PHARMACEUTICAL SDN. BHD.—See GSK plc; *Int'l*, pg. 3148
GLAXOSMITHKLINE PHARMACEUTICALS LTD.—See GSK plc; *Int'l*, pg. 3148
GLAXOSMITHKLINE PHARMACEUTICALS LTD—See GSK plc; *Int'l*, pg. 3148
GLAXOSMITHKLINE PHARMACEUTICALS S.A.—See GSK plc; *Int'l*, pg. 3148
GLAXOSMITHKLINE PHARMACEUTICALS S.A.—See GSK plc; *Int'l*, pg. 3148
GLAXOSMITHKLINE PHARMACEUTICALS UKRAINE LLC—See GSK plc; *Int'l*, pg. 3148
GLAXOSMITHKLINE PHARMA GMBH—See GSK plc; *Int'l*, pg. 3147
GLAXOSMITHKLINE PHARMA GMBH—See GSK plc; *Int'l*, pg. 3148
GLAXOSMITHKLINE PHILIPPINES, INC.—See GSK plc; *Int'l*, pg. 3148
GLAXOSMITHKLINE PRODUTOS FARMACEUTICOS LTDA.—See GSK plc; *Int'l*, pg. 3148
GLAXOSMITHKLINE (PROPRIETARY) LIMITED—See GSK plc; *Int'l*, pg. 3146
GLAXOSMITHKLINE PTE. LTD. - NEURAL PATHWAYS DISCOVERY PERFORMANCE UNIT—See GSK plc; *Int'l*, pg. 3148
GLAXOSMITHKLINE PTE. LTD.—See GSK plc; *Int'l*, pg. 3148
GLAXOSMITHKLINE REPUBLICA DOMINICANA S.A.—See GSK plc; *Int'l*, pg. 3148
GLAXOSMITHKLINE S.A.E.—See GSK plc; *Int'l*, pg. 3148
GLAXOSMITHKLINE SANTE GRAND PUBLIC—See GSK plc; *Int'l*, pg. 3149
GLAXOSMITHKLINE S.A.—See GSK plc; *Int'l*, pg. 3148
GLAXOSMITHKLINE S.A.—See GSK plc; *Int'l*, pg. 3148
GLAXOSMITHKLINE SAUDI ARABIA—See GSK plc; *Int'l*, pg. 3148
GLAXOSMITHKLINE SERVICES UNLIMITED—See GSK plc; *Int'l*, pg. 3149
GLAXOSMITHKLINE SLOVAKIA S.R.O.—See GSK plc; *Int'l*, pg. 3149
GLAXOSMITHKLINE—See Bora Pharmaceuticals Co., Ltd.; *Int'l*, pg. 1112
GLAXOSMITHKLINE—See GSK plc; *Int'l*, pg. 3145
GLAXOSMITHKLINE—See GSK plc; *Int'l*, pg. 3145
GLAXOSMITHKLINE—See GSK plc; *Int'l*, pg. 3145
GLAXOSMITHKLINE—See GSK plc; *Int'l*, pg. 3146
GLAXOSMITHKLINE—See GSK plc; *Int'l*, pg. 3146
GLAXOSMITHKLINE—See GSK plc; *Int'l*, pg. 3146
GLAXOSMITHKLINE—See GSK plc; *Int'l*, pg. 3146
GLAXOSMITHKLINE—See GSK plc; *Int'l*, pg. 3146
GLAXOSMITHKLINE—See GSK plc; *Int'l*, pg. 3146
GLAXOSMITHKLINE—See GSK plc; *Int'l*, pg. 3146
GLAXOSMITHKLINE SOUTH AFRICA (PTY) LIMITED—See GSK plc; *Int'l*, pg. 3149
GLAXOSMITHKLINE S.P.A.—See GSK plc; *Int'l*, pg. 3148
GLAXOSMITHKLINE S.R.L.—See GSK plc; *Int'l*, pg. 3148
GLAXOSMITHKLINE SRO—See GSK plc; *Int'l*, pg. 3148
GLAXOSMITHKLINE (THAILAND) LIMITED—See GSK plc; *Int'l*, pg. 3146
GLAXOSMITHKLINE (TIANJIN) CO. LTD.—See GSK plc; *Int'l*, pg. 3146
GLAXOSMITHKLINE UK LIMITED—See GSK plc; *Int'l*, pg. 3149
GLAXOSMITHKLINE VENEZUELA C.A.—See GSK plc; *Int'l*, pg. 3149
GLAXO WELLCOME CEYLON LIMITED—See GSK plc; *Int'l*, pg. 3145
GLAXO WELLCOME (KENYA) LIMITED—See GSK plc; *Int'l*, pg. 3145
GLAXO WELLCOME MANUFACTURING PTE LTD—See GSK plc; *Int'l*, pg. 3148
GLAXO WELLCOME S.A.—See GSK plc; *Int'l*, pg. 3145
GLAXO WELLCOME TAIWAN LIMITED—See GSK plc; *Int'l*, pg. 3145
GLENMARK ARZNEIMITTEL GMBH—See Glenmark Pharmaceuticals Limited; *Int'l*, pg. 2991
GLENMARK FARMACEUTICA LTDA.—See Glenmark Pharmaceuticals Limited; *Int'l*, pg. 2991
GLENMARK GENERICS INC.—See Glenmark Pharmaceuticals Limited; *Int'l*, pg. 2991
GLENMARK GENERICS LIMITED—See Glenmark Pharmaceuticals Limited; *Int'l*, pg. 2991
GLENMARK GENERICS S.A.—See Glenmark Pharmaceuticals Limited; *Int'l*, pg. 2992
GLENMARK PHARMACEUTICALS B.V.—See Glenmark Pharmaceuticals Limited; *Int'l*, pg. 2992
GLENMARK PHARMACEUTICALS ECUADOR S.A.—See Glenmark Pharmaceuticals Limited; *Int'l*, pg. 2992
GLENMARK PHARMACEUTICALS EUROPE LTD.—See Glenmark Pharmaceuticals Limited; *Int'l*, pg. 2992
GLENMARK PHARMACEUTICALS INC.—See Glenmark Pharmaceuticals Limited; *Int'l*, pg. 2992

GLENMARK PHARMACEUTICALS LIMITED; *Int'l*, pg. 2991
GLENMARK PHARMACEUTICALS MALAYSIA SDN. BHD.—See Glenmark Pharmaceuticals Limited; *Int'l*, pg. 2992
GLENMARK PHARMACEUTICALS NORDIC AB—See Glenmark Pharmaceuticals Limited; *Int'l*, pg. 2992
GLENMARK PHARMACEUTICALS SOUTH AFRICA (PTY) LTD.—See Glenmark Pharmaceuticals Limited; *Int'l*, pg. 2992
GLENMARK PHILIPPINES INC.—See Glenmark Pharmaceuticals Limited; *Int'l*, pg. 2992
GLENMARK UKRAINE LLC—See Glenmark Pharmaceuticals Limited; *Int'l*, pg. 2992
GLENWOOD LLC; *U.S. Private*, pg. 1711
GLOBAL ANALYTICAL DEVELOPMENT LLC—See Abbott Laboratories; *U.S. Public*, pg. 19
GLOBAL ANIMAL MANAGEMENT, INC.—See Merck & Co., Inc.; *U.S. Public*, pg. 1416
GLOBAL BLOOD THERAPEUTICS, INC.—See Pfizer Inc.; *U.S. Public*, pg. 1679
GLOBAL CONSORTIUM, INC.; *U.S. Public*, pg. 941
GLOBAL DISPOMEDIKA, PT; *Int'l*, pg. 2994
GLOBAL MEDICAL SOLUTIONS, LTD.; *U.S. Private*, pg. 1716
GLOBALPHARMA COMPANY LLC—See Dubai Investments PJSC; *Int'l*, pg. 2219
GLOBAL PHARMATECH, INC.; *Int'l*, pg. 3000
GLOBEIMMUNE, INC.—See NantWorks, LLC; *U.S. Private*, pg. 2833
GLS PHARMA LIMITED—See Aurobindo Pharma Ltd.; *Int'l*, pg. 713
GLUCOSE HEALTH, INC.; *U.S. Public*, pg. 947
GLYCOMIMETICS, INC.; *U.S. Public*, pg. 947
GMED HEALTHCARE BVBA—See Johnson & Johnson; *U.S. Public*, pg. 1196
GNI GROUP LTD.; *Int'l*, pg. 3017
GODAVARI DRUGS LIMITED; *Int'l*, pg. 3018
GOLDENCROSS PHARMA PVT. LTD.—See Cipla Ltd.; *Int'l*, pg. 1617
GO LIFE INTERNATIONAL LTD.; *Int'l*, pg. 3017
GOSSAMER BIO, INC.; *U.S. Public*, pg. 952
GOUR MEDICAL AG; *Int'l*, pg. 3044
GP GRENZACH PRODUKTIONS GMBH—See Bayer Aktiengesellschaft; *Int'l*, pg. 905
GRAMON BAGO DE URUGUAY S.A.—See Bago Group; *Int'l*, pg. 799
GRANDPA BRANDS COMPANY; *U.S. Private*, pg. 1754
GRAND PHARMA (CHINA) CO, LTD.—See Grand Pharmaceutical Group Limited; *Int'l*, pg. 3056
GRANT INDUSTRIES INC.; *U.S. Private*, pg. 1756
GREEN CROSS CELL CORP.; *Int'l*, pg. 3070
GREEN CROSS CORPORATION - HWASUN PLANT—See GC Biopharma Corp.; *Int'l*, pg. 2894
GREEN CROSS CORPORATION - OCHANG PLANT—See GC Biopharma Corp.; *Int'l*, pg. 2894
GREEN CROSS HEALTH SCIENCE—See GC Biopharma Corp.; *Int'l*, pg. 2894
GREENFIELD-PRODUTOS FARMACEUTICOS, LDA.—See Eli Lilly & Company; *U.S. Public*, pg. 733
GREEN GOLD CO., LTD.—See Asian Phytoceuticals Public Company Limited; *Int'l*, pg. 619
GREEN GROWTH BRANDS, INC.; *Int'l*, pg. 3071
GREEN LIFE SCIENCE CO., LTD; *Int'l*, pg. 3071
GREENSTONE LLC—See Viatris Inc.; *U.S. Public*, pg. 2293
GREEN THUMB INDUSTRIES, INC.; *U.S. Public*, pg. 964
GRIFOLS ARGENTINA, S.A.—See Grifols, S.A.; *Int'l*, pg. 3084
GRIFOLS ASIA PACIFIC PTE LTD—See Grifols, S.A.; *Int'l*, pg. 3084
GRIFOLS CHILE, S.A.—See Grifols, S.A.; *Int'l*, pg. 3084
GRIFOLS COLOMBIA, LTDA—See Grifols, S.A.; *Int'l*, pg. 3084
GRIFOLS DEUTSCHLAND GMBH—See Grifols, S.A.; *Int'l*, pg. 3084
GRIFOLS DIAGNOSTICS EQUIPMENT TAIWAN LIMITED—See Grifols, S.A.; *Int'l*, pg. 3084
GRIFOLS FRANCE, S.A.R.L.—See Grifols, S.A.; *Int'l*, pg. 3084
GRIFOLS (H.K.), LIMITED—See Grifols, S.A.; *Int'l*, pg. 3084
GRIFOLS INDIA HEALTHCARE PRIVATE LTD.—See Grifols, S.A.; *Int'l*, pg. 3084
GRIFOLS ITALIA S.P.A.—See Grifols, S.A.; *Int'l*, pg. 3084
GRIFOLS JAPAN K.K.—See Grifols, S.A.; *Int'l*, pg. 3084
GRIFOLS MALAYSIA SDN BHD—See Grifols, S.A.; *Int'l*, pg. 3084
GRIFOLS MEXICO, S.A. DE C.V.—See Grifols, S.A.; *Int'l*, pg. 3084
GRIFOLS MOVACO, S.A.—See Grifols, S.A.; *Int'l*, pg. 3084
GRIFOLS PHARMACEUTICAL TECHNOLOGY (SHANGHAI) CO., LTD.—See Grifols, S.A.; *Int'l*, pg. 3084
GRIFOLS POLSKA SP.Z.O.O—See Grifols, S.A.; *Int'l*, pg. 3084
GRIFOLS PORTUGAL PRODUTOS FARMACEUTICOS E HOSPITALARES, LDA.—See Grifols, S.A.; *Int'l*, pg. 3084
GRIFOLS PORTUGAL PRODUTOS FARMACEUTICOS E HOSPITALARES, LDA.—See Grifols, S.A.; *Int'l*, pg. 3084
GRIFOLS, S.A.; *Int'l*, pg. 3083

325412 — PHARMACEUTICAL PREP... CORPORATE AFFILIATIONS

GRIFOLS S.R.O.—See Grifols, S.A.; *Int'l*, pg. 3084
GRIFOLS THAILAND LTD.—See Grifols, S.A.; *Int'l*, pg. 3084
GRIFOLS U.K. LTD.—See Grifols, S.A.; *Int'l*, pg. 3084
GRIFOLS USA, INC.—See Grifols, S.A.; *Int'l*, pg. 3084
GRIFOLS VIAJES, S.A.—See Grifols, S.A.; *Int'l*, pg. 3084
GRIFOLS WORLDWIDE OPERATIONS LIMITED—See Grifols, S.A.; *Int'l*, pg. 3084
GRINDEKS AS; *Int'l*, pg. 3086
GROUPE GLAXOSMITHKLINE SAS—See GSK plc; *Int'l*, pg. 3149
GRUNENTHAL B.V.—See Grunenthal GmbH; *Int'l*, pg. 3114
GRUNENTHAL CHILENA LTDA—See Grunenthal GmbH; *Int'l*, pg. 3114
GRUNENTHAL COLOMBIANA S.A.—See Grunenthal GmbH; *Int'l*, pg. 3114
GRUNENTHAL DE MEXICO S.A. DE C.V.—See Grunenthal GmbH; *Int'l*, pg. 3115
GRUNENTHAL DENMARK APS—See Grunenthal GmbH; *Int'l*, pg. 3114
GRUNENTHAL ECUATORIANA C. LTDA—See Grunenthal GmbH; *Int'l*, pg. 3114
GRUNENTHAL GMBH; *Int'l*, pg. 3114
GRUNENTHAL ITALIA S.R.L.—See Grunenthal GmbH; *Int'l*, pg. 3114
GRUNENTHAL LTD.—See Grunenthal GmbH; *Int'l*, pg. 3114
GRUNENTHAL NORWAY AS—See Grunenthal GmbH; *Int'l*, pg. 3114
GRUNENTHAL PERUANA S.A.—See Grunenthal GmbH; *Int'l*, pg. 3114
GRUNENTHAL PHARMA AG—See Grunenthal GmbH; *Int'l*, pg. 3114
GRUNENTHAL PHARMA LTD.—See Grunenthal GmbH; *Int'l*, pg. 3114
GRUNENTHAL PHARMA SA—See Grunenthal GmbH; *Int'l*, pg. 3114
GRUNENTHAL S.A.—See Grunenthal GmbH; *Int'l*, pg. 3114
GRUNENTHAL SWEDEN AB—See Grunenthal GmbH; *Int'l*, pg. 3114
GRUNENTHAL USA, INC.—See Grunenthal GmbH; *Int'l*, pg. 3114
GRUNENTHAL VENEZOLANA FARMACEUTICA C.A.—See Grunenthal GmbH; *Int'l*, pg. 3115
GRUPO FARMACEUTICO SOMAR—See Advent International Corporation; *U.S. Private*, pg. 102
GRUPO INTERNATIONAL, INC.; *U.S. Public*, pg. 972
G&S ENTERPRISES, INCORPORATED—See Pernix Therapeutics Holdings, Inc.; *U.S. Private*, pg. 3152
GSK CONSUMER HEALTHCARE CHILE SPA—See Haleon Plc; *Int'l*, pg. 3228
GSK MOLDOVA—See GSK plc; *Int'l*, pg. 3145
GSK PSC POLAND SP. Z O.O.—See GSK plc; *Int'l*, pg. 3145
GT BIOPHARMA, INC.; *U.S. Public*, pg. 973
GT DIAGNOSTICS (UK) LIMITED—See Genting Berhad; *Int'l*, pg. 2928
GUANGDONG JIANGMEN CENTER FOR BIOTECH DEVELOPMENT CO., LTD.; *Int'l*, pg. 3156
GUANGDONG JIAYING PHARMACEUTICAL CO., LTD.; *Int'l*, pg. 3156
GUANGDONG LIFESTRONG PHARMACY CO., LTD.; *Int'l*, pg. 3158
GUANGDONG NT PHARMA CO., LTD.—See China NT Pharma Group Company Limited; *Int'l*, pg. 1536
GUANGDONG POLY PHARMACEUTICAL CO., LTD—See China Poly Group Corporation; *Int'l*, pg. 1541
GUANGDONG TAIANTANG PHAMACEUTICAL CO., LTD.; *Int'l*, pg. 3161
GUANGDONG TAIENKANG PHARMACEUTICAL CO., LTD.; *Int'l*, pg. 3161
GUANGDONG WENS DAHUANONG BIOTECHNOLOGY CO., LTD.; *Int'l*, pg. 3161
GUANGDONG ZHONGSHENG PHARMACEUTICAL CO., LTD.; *Int'l*, pg. 3162
GUANGXI BOKE PHARMACEUTICAL CO., LTD.—See AMERICAN ORIENTAL BIOENGINEERING, INC.; *Int'l*, pg. 422
GUANGXI WUZHOU ZHONGHENG GROUP CO., LTD.; *Int'l*, pg. 3164
GUANGYUYUAN CHINESE HERBAL MEDICINE CO., LTD.; *Int'l*, pg. 3164
GUANGZHOU WONDFO BIOTECH CO., LTD.; *Int'l*, pg. 3168
GUARDION HEALTH SCIENCES, INC.; *U.S. Public*, pg. 973
GUERBET AG—See Guerbet SA; *Int'l*, pg. 3172
GUERBET ASIA PACIFIC LTD—See Guerbet SA; *Int'l*, pg. 3172
GUERBET GMBH—See Guerbet SA; *Int'l*, pg. 3172
GUERBET LLC—See Guerbet SA; *Int'l*, pg. 3172
GUERBET NEDERLAND B.V.—See Guerbet SA; *Int'l*, pg. 3172
GUERBET SA; *Int'l*, pg. 3172
GUERBET S.P.A.—See Guerbet SA; *Int'l*, pg. 3172
GUERBET TAIWAN CO., LTD.—See Guerbet SA; *Int'l*, pg. 3172
GUFIC BIOSCIENCES LIMITED; *Int'l*, pg. 3173
GUILIN SANJIN PHARMACEUTICAL CO., LTD.; *Int'l*, pg. 3173

GUIYANG XINTIAN PHARMACEUTICAL CO., LTD.; *Int'l*, pg. 3174
GUIZHOU BAILING GROUP PHARMACEUTICAL CO., LTD.; *Int'l*, pg. 3174
GUIZHOU SANLI PHARMACEUTICAL CO., LTD.; *Int'l*, pg. 3175
GUIZHOU XINBANG PHARMACEUTICAL CO., LTD.; *Int'l*, pg. 3175
GUIZHOU YIBAI PHARMACEUTICAL CO., LTD.; *Int'l*, pg. 3175
GUJARAT INJECT (KERALA) LTD.; *Int'l*, pg. 3176
GUJARAT TERCE LABORATORIES LIMITED; *Int'l*, pg. 3177
GUJARAT THEMIS BIOSYN LIMITED; *Int'l*, pg. 3177
GULF COAST NUTRITIONALS, INC.; *U.S. Private*, pg. 1815
GULF PHARMACEUTICAL INDUSTRIES P.S.C.; *Int'l*, pg. 3182
GUY & O'NEILL, INC.—See Centre Partners Management LLC; *U.S. Private*, pg. 828
G&W LABORATORIES INC.; *U.S. Private*, pg. 1630
GYROS U.S. INC.—See Mesa Laboratories, Inc.; *U.S. Public*, pg. 1426
HAEDONG SS PHARMACEUTICAL CO, LTD—See CMIC Holdings Co., Ltd.; *Int'l*, pg. 1670
HAINAN GENERAL SANYANG PHARMACEUTICAL CO., LTD.—See China Meheco Group Co., Ltd.; *Int'l*, pg. 1519
HAINAN HAIYAO CO., LTD.; *Int'l*, pg. 3212
HAINAN HULUWA PHARMACEUTICAL GROUP CO., LTD.; *Int'l*, pg. 3212
HAINAN POLY. CO., LTD.—See Hainan Poly Pharm.Co.,Ltd.; *Int'l*, pg. 3212
HAINAN POLY PHARM.CO.,LTD.; *Int'l*, pg. 3212
HAINAN SHUANGCHENG PHARMACEUTICALS CO., LTD.; *Int'l*, pg. 3212
HAI-O ENTERPRISE BERHAD; *Int'l*, pg. 3209
HAI-O MEDICINE SDN. BHD.—See Hai-O Enterprise Berhad; *Int'l*, pg. 3209
HAISCO PHARMACEUTICAL GROUP CO., LTD.; *Int'l*, pg. 3217
HALEON ITALY S.R.L.—See Haleon Plc; *Int'l*, pg. 3228
HALEON NETHERLANDS B.V.—See Haleon Plc; *Int'l*, pg. 3228
HALEON NEW ZEALAND ULC—See Haleon Plc; *Int'l*, pg. 3228
HALEON PAKISTAN LIMITED—See Haleon Plc; *Int'l*, pg. 3228
HALOZYME THERAPEUTICS, INC.; *U.S. Public*, pg. 981
HAMAD MEDICAL CORPORATION—See Dar Al Dawa Development & Investment Co.; *Int'l*, pg. 1971
HANALL BIOPHARMA CO., LTD.; *Int'l*, pg. 3241
HANA PHARM CO., LTD.; *Int'l*, pg. 3241
HANDA PHARMACEUTICALS, INC.; *U.S. Private*, pg. 1852
HANDOK INC. - HANDOK EUMSEONG FACTORY—See Handok Inc.; *Int'l*, pg. 3243
HANDOK INC.; *Int'l*, pg. 3243
HANGOVER JOE'S HOLDING CORPORATION; *U.S. Private*, pg. 1853
HANGZHOU BIO-SINCERITY PHARMA-TECH CO., LTD.; *Int'l*, pg. 3246
HANGZHOU TIANMUSHAN PHARMACEUTICAL ENTERPRISE CO.; *Int'l*, pg. 3250
HANMI FINE CHEMICAL CO., LTD—See Hanmi Pharmaceutical Co., Ltd.; *Int'l*, pg. 3256
HANMI JAPAN PHARMACEUTICAL CO., LTD—See Hanmi Pharmaceutical Co., Ltd.; *Int'l*, pg. 3256
HANMI PHARMACEUTICAL CO., LTD.; *Int'l*, pg. 3256
HANSA BIOPHARMA AB; *Int'l*, pg. 3259
HAO WEN HOLDINGS LIMITED; *Int'l*, pg. 3267
HAPPY JACK INC.; *U.S. Private*, pg. 1857
HARBIN GLORIA PHARMACEUTICAL CO., LTD.; *Int'l*, pg. 3270
HARBOR DIVERSIFIED, INC.; *U.S. Public*, pg. 984
HARBOR THERAPEUTICS, INC.—See Harbor Diversified, Inc.; *U.S. Public*, pg. 984
HARRISVACCINES, INC.—See Merck & Co., Inc.; *U.S. Public*, pg. 1416
HARVARD APPARATUS LIMITED—See Harvard Bioscience, Inc.; *U.S. Public*, pg. 987
HARVARD APPARATUS S.A.R.L.—See Harvard Bioscience, Inc.; *U.S. Public*, pg. 987
HA TAY PHARMACEUTICAL JOINT STOCK COMPANY; *Int'l*, pg. 3201
HAUPT PHARMA AG—See BC Partners LLP; *Int'l*, pg. 922
HAUPT PHARMA AMAREG GMBH—See BC Partners LLP; *Int'l*, pg. 922
HAUPT PHARMA BERLIN GMBH—See BC Partners LLP; *Int'l*, pg. 922
HAUPT PHARMA INC.—See BC Partners LLP; *Int'l*, pg. 922
HAUPT PHARMA LATINA S.R.L.—See BC Partners LLP; *Int'l*, pg. 922
HAUPT PHARMA LIVRON S.A.S.—See BC Partners LLP; *Int'l*, pg. 922
HAUPT PHARMA MUNSTER GMBH—See BC Partners LLP; *Int'l*, pg. 922
HAUPT PHARMA TORIDE CO., LTD.—See BC Partners LLP; *Int'l*, pg. 922

HAUPT PHARMA WOLFRATSHAUSEN GMBH—See BC Partners LLP; *Int'l*, pg. 922
HAUPT PHARMA WULFING GMBH—See BC Partners LLP; *Int'l*, pg. 923
HAW PAR CORPORATION LIMITED; *Int'l*, pg. 3287
HAW PAR LAND (M) SDN. BHD.—See Haw Par Corporation Limited; *Int'l*, pg. 3287
HBM PHARMA S.R.O.—See GRINDEKS AS; *Int'l*, pg. 3086
HC BERLIN PHARMA AG; *Int'l*, pg. 3297
HEALTH-CHEM CORP.; *U.S. Public*, pg. 1015
HEALTH-RIGHT DISCOVERIES, INC.; *U.S. Private*, pg. 1894
HEALTH WRIGHT PRODUCTS, INC.—See International Flavors & Fragrances Inc.; *U.S. Public*, pg. 1152
HEALTHYPHARM B.V.—See Bain Capital, LP; *U.S. Private*, pg. 443
HEALTHYPHARM B.V.—See Cinven Limited; *Int'l*, pg. 1613
HEBEI CHANGSHAN BIOCHEMICAL PHARMACEUTICAL CO. LTD.; *Int'l*, pg. 3305
HEBEI CHANGSHAN KAIKUDE BIOTECHNOLOGY CO., LTD.—See Hebei Changshan Biochemical Pharmaceutical Co. Ltd.; *Int'l*, pg. 3305
HEBEI CHANGSHAN KAILA BIOTECHNOLOGY CO., LTD.—See Hebei Changshan Biochemical Pharmaceutical Co. Ltd.; *Int'l*, pg. 3305
HEBEI CHANGSHAN KAILUONITE BIOTECHNOLOGY CO.—See Hebei Changshan Biochemical Pharmaceutical Co. Ltd.; *Int'l*, pg. 3305
HEBEI CHANGSHAN LONG KANG BIOTECHNOLOGY CO., LTD.—See Hebei Changshan Biochemical Pharmaceutical Co. Ltd.; *Int'l*, pg. 3305
HEC PHARM CO., LTD.; *Int'l*, pg. 3307
HEEL CANADA INC.; *Int'l*, pg. 3307
HEEL DO BRASIL BIOMEDICA LTDA.—See Delton AG; *Int'l*, pg. 2021
HEFEI LIFEON PHARMACEUTICAL CO., LTD.; *Int'l*, pg. 3307
HEILONGJIANG ZBD PHARMACEUTICAL CO., LTD.; *Int'l*, pg. 3323
HELIOS KLINIKEN BREISGAU HOCHSCHWARZWALD GMBH—See Fresenius SE & Co. KGaA; *Int'l*, pg. 2779
HELIOS KLINIKEN GMBH—See Fresenius SE & Co. KGaA; *Int'l*, pg. 2778
HELIX BIOMEDIX, INC.; *U.S. Public*, pg. 1024
HELIX BIOPHARMA CORP.; *Int'l*, pg. 3331
HELIX HEALTHCARE B.V.—See Aurobindo Pharma Ltd.; *Int'l*, pg. 712
HEMAS PHARMACEUTICALS (PVT.) LTD.—See Hemas Holdings PLC; *Int'l*, pg. 3340
HEMAS SURGICALS & DIAGNOSTICS (PVT.) LTD.—See Hemas Holdings PLC; *Int'l*, pg. 3340
HEMISPHERX BIOPHARMA EUROPE—See AIM ImmunoTech Inc.; *U.S. Public*, pg. 63
HEMOFARM A.D.—See Bain Capital, LP; *U.S. Private*, pg. 443
HEMOFARM A.D.—See Cinven Limited; *Int'l*, pg. 1613
HEMOFARM BANJA LUKA D.O.O.—See Bain Capital, LP; *U.S. Private*, pg. 443
HEMOFARM BANJA LUKA D.O.O.—See Cinven Limited; *Int'l*, pg. 1613
HEMOFARM KONCERN A.D.—See Bain Capital, LP; *U.S. Private*, pg. 443
HEMOFARM KONCERN A.D.—See Cinven Limited; *Int'l*, pg. 1613
HEMOGENYX PHARMACEUTICALS PLC; *Int'l*, pg. 3341
HEMOMONT D.O.O.—See Bain Capital, LP; *U.S. Private*, pg. 443
HEMOMONT D.O.O.—See Cinven Limited; *Int'l*, pg. 1613
HEMO ORGANIC LIMITED; *Int'l*, pg. 3341
HEMOPHARM GMBH—See Bain Capital, LP; *U.S. Private*, pg. 443
HEMOPHARM GMBH—See Cinven Limited; *Int'l*, pg. 1613
HENAN LINGRUI PHARMACEUTICAL CO., LTD.; *Int'l*, pg. 3342
HENAN NEWLAND PHARMACEUTICAL CO., LTD.; *Int'l*, pg. 3342
HENAN PROVINCE PHARMACEUTICAL CO., LTD.—See China Meheco Group Co., Ltd.; *Int'l*, pg. 1519
HENAN TALOPH PHARMACEUTICAL STOCK CO., LTD.; *Int'l*, pg. 3343
HENAN TOPFOND PHARMACEUTICAL CO.,LTD.; *Int'l*, pg. 3343
HENKEL GENTHIN GMBH—See Henkel AG & Co. KGaA; *Int'l*, pg. 3351
HEPION PHARMACEUTICALS, INC.; *U.S. Public*, pg. 1027
HERANTIS PHARMA PLC; *Int'l*, pg. 3359
HERBAL DISPATCH INC.; *Int'l*, pg. 3359
HERBAPOL LUBLIN S.A.; *Int'l*, pg. 3360
HERBORIUM GROUP, INC.; *U.S. Public*, pg. 1027
HERO INTERNATIONAL USA HOLDING CORP.; *U.S. Public*, pg. 1029
HERON THERAPEUTICS, INC.; *U.S. Public*, pg. 1029
HESKA AG—See Mars, Incorporated; *U.S. Private*, pg. 2588
HESTER BIOSCIENCES NEPAL PRIVATE LIMITED—See Hester Biosciences Limited; *Int'l*, pg. 3365
HEYL CHEMISCH-PHARMAZEUTISCHE FABRIK GMBH UND CO. KG; *Int'l*, pg. 3374

N.A.I.C.S. INDEX

325412 — PHARMACEUTICAL PREP...

HI-EISAI PHARMACEUTICALS, INC.—See Eisai Co., Ltd.; *Int'l*, pg. 2335
HIGHNOON LABORATORIES LIMITED; *Int'l*, pg. 3388
HIGH TECH PHARM CO., LTD.; *Int'l*, pg. 3386
HIKMA EMERGING MARKETS & ASIA PACIFIC FZ LLC—See Hikma Pharmaceuticals PLC; *Int'l*, pg. 3390
HIKMA FARMACEUTICA S.A.—See Hikma Pharmaceuticals PLC; *Int'l*, pg. 3390
HIKMA ITALIA S.P.A.—See Hikma Pharmaceuticals PLC; *Int'l*, pg. 3390
HIKMA LIBAN S.A.R.L—See Hikma Pharmaceuticals PLC; *Int'l*, pg. 3390
HIKMA PHARMA ALGERIA S.A.R.L—See Hikma Pharmaceuticals PLC; *Int'l*, pg. 3390
HIKMA PHARMACEUTICALS LLC—See Hikma Pharmaceuticals PLC; *Int'l*, pg. 3390
HIKMA PHARMACEUTICALS PLC; *Int'l*, pg. 3390
HIKMA PHARMACEUTICALS USA INC.—See Hikma Pharmaceuticals PLC; *Int'l*, pg. 3390
HIKMA PHARMA GMBH—See Hikma Pharmaceuticals PLC; *Int'l*, pg. 3390
HIKMA PHARMA SAE—See Hikma Pharmaceuticals PLC; *Int'l*, pg. 3390
HIKMA SLOVAKIA S.R.O.—See Hikma Pharmaceuticals PLC; *Int'l*, pg. 3390
HIKMA SPECIALITY USA INC.—See Hikma Pharmaceuticals PLC; *Int'l*, pg. 3390
HIKU BRANDS COMPANY LTD.—See Canopy Growth Corporation; *Int'l*, pg. 1298
HIMALAYA DRUG COMPANY; *Int'l*, pg. 3396
HINDUSTAN BIO SCIENCES LIMITED; *Int'l*, pg. 3399
HIRAN ORGOCHEM LTD.; *Int'l*, pg. 3403
HISAMITSU FARMACEUTICA DO BRASIL LTDA.—See Hisamitsu Pharmaceutical Co., Inc.; *Int'l*, pg. 3406
HISAMITSU PHARMACEUTICAL CO., INC.; *Int'l*, pg. 3406
HISAMITSU UK LTD.—See Hisamitsu Pharmaceutical Co., Inc.; *Int'l*, pg. 3406
HISAMITSU VIETNAM PHARMACEUTICAL CO., LTD.—See Hisamitsu Pharmaceutical Co., Inc.; *Int'l*, pg. 3406
HISTOGEN, INC.; *U.S. Public*, pg. 1042
HITIQ LIMITED; *Int'l*, pg. 3426
HK INNO.N CORP.; *Int'l*, pg. 3428
HLB PHARMACEUTICAL CO LTD; *Int'l*, pg. 3430
HOAN PHARMACEUTICALS—See Bora Corporation; *Int'l*, pg. 1112
HOECHST PAKISTAN LIMITED; *Int'l*, pg. 3439
HOLOGIC ITALIA S.R.L.—See Hologic, Inc.; *U.S. Public*, pg. 1045
HONZ PHARMACEUTICAL CO., LTD.; *Int'l*, pg. 3472
HORIZON PHARMACEUTICAL LLC—See Amgen Inc.; *U.S. Public*, pg. 123
HORIZON PHARMA SWITZERLAND GMBH—See Amgen Inc.; *U.S. Public*, pg. 123
HORIZON PHARMA USA, INC. - ROSWELL, GEORGIA OFFICE—See Amgen Inc.; *U.S. Public*, pg. 123
HORUS B.V.—See Merck & Co., Inc.; *U.S. Public*, pg. 1416
HOSPIRA ASEPTIC SERVICES LIMITED—See Pfizer Inc.; *U.S. Public*, pg. 1680
HOSPIRA AUSTRALIA PTY. LTD.—See Pfizer Inc.; *U.S. Public*, pg. 1680
HOSPIRA DEUTSCHLAND GMBH—See Pfizer Inc.; *U.S. Public*, pg. 1680
HOSPIRA INVICTA SA—See Pfizer Inc.; *U.S. Public*, pg. 1680
HOSPIRA ITALIA S.R.L.—See Pfizer Inc.; *U.S. Public*, pg. 1680
HOSPIRA PHILIPPINES, INC.—See Pfizer Inc.; *U.S. Public*, pg. 1680
HOSPIRA SLOVAKIA, S.R.O.—See Pfizer Inc.; *U.S. Public*, pg. 1680
HOSPIRA UK LIMITED—See Pfizer Inc.; *U.S. Public*, pg. 1680
HOSPIRA WORLDWIDE, LLC—See Pfizer Inc.; *U.S. Public*, pg. 1680
HOVERINK BIOTECHNOLOGIES, INC.; *U.S. Private*, pg. 1994
HOVIONE FARMA CIENCIA S.A.; *Int'l*, pg. 3492
HOVIONE LIMITED—See Hovione Farma Ciencia S.A.; *Int'l*, pg. 3492
HOVIONE LLC—See Hovione Farma Ciencia S.A.; *Int'l*, pg. 3492
HOVIONE PHARMASCIENCE LTD.—See Hovione Farma Ciencia S.A.; *Int'l*, pg. 3492
HOVIONE SA—See Hovione Farma Ciencia S.A.; *Int'l*, pg. 3492
HOYE'S PHARMACY; *U.S. Private*, pg. 1996
HP INGREDIENTS; *U.S. Private*, pg. 1996
HRA PHARMA, SA—See Astorg Partners S.A.S.; *Int'l*, pg. 656
HRA PHARMA, SA—See The Goldman Sachs Group, Inc.; *U.S. Public*, pg. 2077
HR PHARMACEUTICALS, INC.; *U.S. Private*, pg. 1998
HST GLOBAL, INC.; *U.S. Public*, pg. 1065
HTP HUISAPOTHEEK B.V.—See Bain Capital, LP; *U.S. Private*, pg. 443
HTP HUISAPOTHEEK B.V.—See Cinven Limited; *Int'l*, pg. 1613

HUABO BIOPHARM (SHANGHAI) CO., LTD.; *Int'l*, pg. 3511
HUADONG MEDICINE CO., LTD.; *Int'l*, pg. 3511
HUA HAN HEALTH INDUSTRY HOLDINGS LIMITED; *Int'l*, pg. 3509
HUA MEDICINE LTD.; *Int'l*, pg. 3509
HUAPONT LIFE SCIENCES CO., LTD.; *Int'l*, pg. 3514
HUAREN PHARMACEUTICAL CO., LTD.; *Int'l*, pg. 3514
HUBEI BIOCAUSE PHARMACEUTICAL CO., LTD.; *Int'l*, pg. 3517
HUBEI GOTO BIOPHARM CO., LTD.; *Int'l*, pg. 3517
HUBEI GUANGJI PHARMACEUTICAL CO., LTD.; *Int'l*, pg. 3517
HUBEI JUMPCAN PHARMACEUTICAL CO., LTD.; *Int'l*, pg. 3518
HUBEI KEYI PHARMACEUTICAL CO., LTD.—See China Meheco Group Co., Ltd.; *Int'l*, pg. 1519
HUBEI MINKANG PHARMACEUTICAL LTD.; *Int'l*, pg. 3518
HUBNER NATURARZNEIMITTEL GMBH—See Dermapharm Holding SE; *Int'l*, pg. 2043
HUGEL, INC.; *Int'l*, pg. 3524
HUMACYTE GLOBAL, INC.—See Humacyte, Inc.; *U.S. Public*, pg. 1069
HUMANIGEN, INC.; *U.S. Public*, pg. 1070
HUMANWELL HEALTHCARE (GROUP) CO., LTD.; *Int'l*, pg. 3530
HUMCO HOLDING GROUP, INC.—See Fagron NV; *Int'l*, pg. 2603
HUMEDIX CO., LTD.; *Int'l*, pg. 3530
HUNAN DAJIAWEIKANG PHARMACEUTICAL INDUSTRY CO., LTD.; *Int'l*, pg. 3532
HUNAN DEHAI PHARMACEUTICAL CO., LTD.—See Dahu Aquaculture Company Limited; *Int'l*, pg. 1913
HUNAN ER-KANG PHARMACEUTICAL CO., LTD.; *Int'l*, pg. 3532
HUNAN FANGSHENG PHARMACEUTICAL CO., LTD.; *Int'l*, pg. 3532
HUNAN HANSEN PHARMACEUTICAL CO., LTD.; *Int'l*, pg. 3532
HUNAN JINGFENG PHARMACEUTICAL CO., LTD.; *Int'l*, pg. 3533
HUNAN JIUDIAN PHARMACEUTICAL CO., LTD.; *Int'l*, pg. 3533
HUNAN NUCIEN PHARMACEUTICAL CO., LTD.; *Int'l*, pg. 3533
THE HUNTER RIVER COMPANY PTY LTD—See Elders Limited; *Int'l*, pg. 2346
HUONS GLOBAL CO., LTD.; *Int'l*, pg. 3537
HUVEPHARMA EOOD; *Int'l*, pg. 3540
HUVEPHARMA, INC.—See Huvepharma EOOD; *Int'l*, pg. 3540
HUVEPHARMA NV—See Huvepharma EOOD; *Int'l*, pg. 3540
HWAIL PHARMACEUTICAL CO.,LTD.; *Int'l*, pg. 3542
HWGB BIOTECH SDN. BHD.—See Ho Wah Genting Berhad; *Int'l*, pg. 3435
HYBIO PHARMACEUTICAL CO., LTD.; *Int'l*, pg. 3544
HYBRIGENICS S.A.—See Diagnostic Medical Systems S.A.; *Int'l*, pg. 2103
HYCLONE UK LIMITED—See Thermo Fisher Scientific Inc.; *U.S. Public*, pg. 2148
HYCOR BIOMEDICAL GMBH—See Linden LLC; *U.S. Private*, pg. 2460
HYCOR BIOMEDICAL, INC.—See Linden LLC; *U.S. Private*, pg. 2460
HYLORIS PHARMACEUTICALS SA; *Int'l*, pg. 3549
HYPERA PHARMA S.A.; *Int'l*, pg. 3553
HYPHENS PHARMA INTERNATIONAL LIMITED; *Int'l*, pg. 3553
HYUNDAI BIOLAND CO., LTD.; *Int'l*, pg. 3555
HYUNDAI PHARMACEUTICAL CO., LTD.; *Int'l*, pg. 3560
HYUNDAI PHARM CO., LTD.; *Int'l*, pg. 3560
IBC PHARMACEUTICALS, INC.—See Gilead Sciences, Inc.; *U.S. Public*, pg. 937
IBIO, INC.; *U.S. Public*, pg. 1083
ICAGEN, INC.; *U.S. Private*, pg. 2029
ICAGEN-T, INC.—See Icagen, Inc.; *U.S. Private*, pg. 2029
ICN POLFA RZESZOW S.A.—See Bausch Health Companies Inc.; *Int'l*, pg. 897
ICON CLINICAL RESEARCH—See ICON plc; *Int'l*, pg. 3584
IDENIX PHARMACEUTICALS, INC.—See Merck & Co., Inc.; *U.S. Public*, pg. 1416
IDEXX B.V.—See IDEXX Laboratories, Inc.; *U.S. Public*, pg. 1092
IDEXX EUROPE B.V.—See IDEXX Laboratories, Inc.; *U.S. Public*, pg. 1092
IDEXX GMBH—See IDEXX Laboratories, Inc.; *U.S. Public*, pg. 1092
IDEXX LABORATORIES INC.—See IDEXX Laboratories, Inc.; *U.S. Public*, pg. 1092
IDEXX LABORATORIES ITALIA S.R.L.—See IDEXX Laboratories, Inc.; *U.S. Public*, pg. 1092
IDEXX LABORATORIES, KK—See IDEXX Laboratories, Inc.; *U.S. Public*, pg. 1093
IDEXX LABORATORIES LIMITED—See IDEXX Laboratories, Inc.; *U.S. Public*, pg. 1092
IDEXX LABORATORIES LIMITED—See IDEXX Laboratories, Inc.; *U.S. Public*, pg. 1092
IDEXX LABORATORIES PTY. LTD.—See IDEXX Laboratories, Inc.; *U.S. Public*, pg. 1093

ries, Inc.; *U.S. Public*, pg. 1093
IDEXX LABORATORIES PTY. LTD.—See IDEXX Laboratories, Inc.; *U.S. Public*, pg. 1093
IDEXX LABORATORIOS, S.L.—See IDEXX Laboratories, Inc.; *U.S. Public*, pg. 1093
IDEXX S.A.R.L.—See IDEXX Laboratories, Inc.; *U.S. Public*, pg. 1093
IGC PHARMA LLC—See IGC Pharma, Inc.; *U.S. Public*, pg. 1095
IG INNOVATIONS LIMITED—See Abbott Laboratories; *U.S. Public*, pg. 19
ILDONG PHARMACEUTICAL CO., LTD. - CHEONGJU PLANT—See Ildong Pharmaceutical Co., Ltd.; *Int'l*, pg. 3613
ILDONG PHARMACEUTICAL CO., LTD.; *Int'l*, pg. 3613
ILSUNG PHARMACEUTICALS CO., LTD; *Int'l*, pg. 3616
ILYANG PHARMACEUTICAL CO., LTD.; *Int'l*, pg. 3617
IMA LIFE (BEIJING) PHARMACEUTICAL SYSTEMS CO. LTD.—See I.M.A. Industria Macchine Automatiche S.p.A.; *Int'l*, pg. 3565
IMA LIFE NORTH AMERICA INC.—See I.M.A. Industria Macchine Automatiche S.p.A.; *Int'l*, pg. 3565
IMA LIFE THE NETHERLANDS B.V.—See I.M.A. Industria Macchine Automatiche S.p.A.; *Int'l*, pg. 3565
IMMUNE DESIGN CORP.—See Merck & Co., Inc.; *U.S. Public*, pg. 1416
IMMUNE PHARMACEUTICALS INC.; *U.S. Public*, pg. 1113
IMMUNE THERAPEUTICS, INC.; *U.S. Public*, pg. 1113
IMMUNIC AG—See Immunic, Inc.; *U.S. Public*, pg. 1113
IMMUNIC, INC.; *U.S. Public*, pg. 1113
IMMUNITYBIO, INC.—See NantWorks, LLC; *U.S. Private*, pg. 2833
IMMUNOGEN, INC.—See AbbVie Inc.; *U.S. Public*, pg. 24
IMMUNOMEDICS, INC.—See Gilead Sciences, Inc.; *U.S. Public*, pg. 937
IMMUNOTECH SRO—See Danaher Corporation; *U.S. Public*, pg. 627
IMPAX LABORATORIES, LLC—See Amneal Pharmaceuticals, Inc.; *U.S. Public*, pg. 125
IMQUEST BIOSCIENCES INC.; *U.S. Private*, pg. 2051
INCYTE BIOSCIENCES BENELUX B.V.—See Incyte Corporation; *U.S. Public*, pg. 1115
INCYTE BIOSCIENCES NORDIC AB—See Incyte Corporation; *U.S. Public*, pg. 1115
INDCHEMIE HEALTH SPECIALITIES PRIVATE LIMITED—See Alkem Laboratories Ltd.; *Int'l*, pg. 330
INDCHEM INTERNATIONAL—See IMCD N.V.; *Int'l*, pg. 3622
INDUSTRIA ITALIANA INTEGRATORI TREI S.P.A.—See AGRAVIS Raiffeisen AG; *Int'l*, pg. 215
INDUSTRIAL VETERINARIA, S.A.—See Espiga Capital Gestion S.G.E.C.R, S.A.; *Int'l*, pg. 2506
INDUSTRIAS QUIMICAS FALCON DE MEXICO, S.A. DE CV—See Dr. Reddy's Laboratories Limited; *Int'l*, pg. 2195
INFINITY DISCOVERY, INC.—See Infinity Pharmaceuticals, Inc.; *U.S. Public*, pg. 1117
INFINITY PHARMA BV—See Fagron NV; *Int'l*, pg. 2603
INFINITY PHARMACEUTICALS, INC.; *U.S. Public*, pg. 1117
INGELHEIM PHARMACEUTICALS (PTY.) LTD.—See C.H. Boehringer Sohn AG & Co. KG; *Int'l*, pg. 1241
INNOCOLL HOLDINGS PLC—See Gurnet Point Capital LLC; *U.S. Private*, pg. 1819
INNOVATION PHARMACEUTICALS INC.; *U.S. Public*, pg. 1126
INNOVAX SDN BHD—See Batu Kawan Berhad; *Int'l*, pg. 891
INNOVIVA, INC.; *U.S. Public*, pg. 1127
INNOVUS PHARMACEUTICALS, INC.—See Aytu BioPharma, Inc.; *U.S. Public*, pg. 257
INOVA PHARMACEUTICALS (AUSTRALIA) PTY LIMITED—See The Carlyle Group Inc.; *U.S. Public*, pg. 2057
INOVA PHARMACEUTICALS (PTY) LIMITED—See The Carlyle Group Inc.; *U.S. Public*, pg. 2057
INPELLIS, INC.; *U.S. Private*, pg. 2084
INSMED INCORPORATED; *U.S. Public*, pg. 1130
INSPIRE PHARMACEUTICALS, INC.—See Merck & Co., Inc.; *U.S. Public*, pg. 1419
INSYS MANUFACTURING, LLC—See Insys Therapeutics, Inc.; *U.S. Private*, pg. 2096
INSYS PHARMA, INC.—See Insys Therapeutics, Inc.; *U.S. Private*, pg. 2096
INSYS THERAPEUTICS, INC.; *U.S. Private*, pg. 2096
INTARCIA THERAPEUTICS, INC.; *U.S. Private*, pg. 2097
INTEGRATED BIOPHARMA, INC.; *U.S. Public*, pg. 1136
INTEGRATED DNA TECHNOLOGIES BVBA—See Danaher Corporation; *U.S. Public*, pg. 627
INTELLECT NEUROSCIENCES, INC.; *U.S. Private*, pg. 2105
INTENDIS DERMA, S.L.—See Bayer Aktiengesellschaft; *Int'l*, pg. 908
INTERCEPT PHARMACEUTICALS, INC.—See Alfasigma S.p.A; *Int'l*, pg. 315
INTERNATIONAL MEDICATION SYSTEMS, LIMITED—See Amphastar Pharmaceuticals, Inc.; *U.S. Public*, pg. 126
INTERVET AB—See Merck & Co., Inc.; *U.S. Public*, pg. 1416

325412 — PHARMACEUTICAL PREP... CORPORATE AFFILIATIONS

INTERVET AGENCIES B.V.—See Merck & Co., Inc.; *U.S. Public*, pg. 1416
INTERVET ARGENTINA S.A.—See Merck & Co., Inc.; *U.S. Public*, pg. 1416
INTERVET AUSTRALIA PTY LTD—See Merck & Co., Inc.; *U.S. Public*, pg. 1416
INTERVET CANADA CORP.—See Merck & Co., Inc.; *U.S. Public*, pg. 1416
INTERVET COLOMBIA LTDA—See Merck & Co., Inc.; *U.S. Public*, pg. 1416
INTERVET DENMARK A/S—See Merck & Co., Inc.; *U.S. Public*, pg. 1416
INTERVET GES MBH—See Merck & Co., Inc.; *U.S. Public*, pg. 1416
INTERVET HUNGARIA KFT—See Merck & Co., Inc.; *U.S. Public*, pg. 1416
INTERVET INC. - ELKHORN—See Merck & Co., Inc.; *U.S. Public*, pg. 1416
INTERVET INC. - MILLSBORO—See Merck & Co., Inc.; *U.S. Public*, pg. 1416
INTERVET INC.—See Merck & Co., Inc.; *U.S. Public*, pg. 1416
INTERVET INDIA PVT. LTD—See Merck & Co., Inc.; *U.S. Public*, pg. 1417
INTERVET INDIA PVT. LTD—See Merck & Co., Inc.; *U.S. Public*, pg. 1417
INTERVET MEXICO S.A. DE C.V.—See Merck & Co., Inc.; *U.S. Public*, pg. 1417
INTERVET (M) SDN BHD—See Merck & Co., Inc.; *U.S. Public*, pg. 1416
INTERVET NEDERLAND B.V.—See Merck & Co., Inc.; *U.S. Public*, pg. 1417
INTERVET PHILIPPINES, INC.—See Merck & Co., Inc.; *U.S. Public*, pg. 1417
INTERVET ROMANIA SRL—See Merck & Co., Inc.; *U.S. Public*, pg. 1417
INTERVET SCHERING-PLOUGH ANIMAL HEALTH PTY LTD—See Merck & Co., Inc.; *U.S. Public*, pg. 1417
INTERVET SP. Z O.O.—See Merck & Co., Inc.; *U.S. Public*, pg. 1417
INTERVET SP. Z O.O.—See Merck & Co., Inc.; *U.S. Public*, pg. 1417
INTERVET (THAILAND) LTD.—See Merck & Co., Inc.; *U.S. Public*, pg. 1416
INTERVET U.K. LTD.—See Merck & Co., Inc.; *U.S. Public*, pg. 1417
INTERVET VENEZOLANA SA—See Merck & Co., Inc.; *U.S. Public*, pg. 1417
INTERVET VETERINARIA CHILE LTDA—See Merck & Co., Inc.; *U.S. Public*, pg. 1417
INTERVET VIETNAM CO., LTD.—See Merck & Co., Inc.; *U.S. Public*, pg. 1417
INTEZYNE TECHNOLOGIES, INC.; *U.S. Private*, pg. 2128
INTRA-CELLULAR THERAPIES, INC.; *U.S. Public*, pg. 1159
INVAGEN PHARMACEUTICALS INC.—See Cipla Ltd.; *Int'l*, pg. 1617
INVETEK, INC.; *U.S. Private*, pg. 2132
INVIBE LABS, LLC—See JLL Partners, LLC; *U.S. Private*, pg. 2212
INVIBE LABS, LLC—See Water Street Healthcare Partners, LLC; *U.S. Private*, pg. 4452
INYX, INC.; *U.S. Private*, pg. 2133
IONIS PHARMACEUTICALS, INC.; *U.S. Public*, pg. 1166
IOVANCE BIOTHERAPEUTICS, INC.; *U.S. Public*, pg. 1167
IPR PHARMACEUTICAL INC.—See AstraZeneca PLC; *Int'l*, pg. 660
IQUINOSA FARMA S.A.—See FAES Farma, S.A.; *Int'l*, pg. 2601
IRAN DAROU COMPANY—See Alborz Investment Company; *Int'l*, pg. 299
IROKO PHARMACEUTICALS INC.; *U.S. Private*, pg. 2139
IRONWOOD PHARMACEUTICALS, INC.; *U.S. Public*, pg. 1174
IRX THERAPEUTICS, INC.; *U.S. Private*, pg. 2142
ISAGENIX INTERNATIONAL, LLC; *U.S. Private*, pg. 2142
ISTITUTO DI RICHERCHE DI BIOLOGIA MOLECOLARE S.P.A.—See Merck & Co., Inc.; *U.S. Public*, pg. 1417
ITI, INC.—See Intra-Cellular Therapies, Inc.; *U.S. Public*, pg. 1159
ITONIS, INC.; *U.S. Public*, pg. 1175
IVERIC BIO, INC.—See Astellas Pharma Inc.; *Int'l*, pg. 653
IWAKI SEIYAKU CO., LTD.—See Astena Holdings Co., Ltd.; *Int'l*, pg. 653
JAGUAR HEALTH, INC.; *U.S. Public*, pg. 1186
JANSSEN ALZHEIMER IMMUNOTHERAPY RESEARCH & DEVELOPMENT, LLC—See Johnson & Johnson; *U.S. Public*, pg. 1196
JANSSEN BIOLOGICS B.V.—See Johnson & Johnson; *U.S. Public*, pg. 1196
JANSSEN BIOLOGICS (IRELAND)—See Johnson & Johnson; *U.S. Public*, pg. 1196
JANSSEN-CILAG A/S—See Johnson & Johnson; *U.S. Public*, pg. 1197
JANSSEN-CILAG FARMACEUTICA, LDA.—See Johnson & Johnson; *U.S. Public*, pg. 1197
JANSSEN-CILAG FARMACEUTICA LTDA.—See Johnson & Johnson; *U.S. Public*, pg. 1197

JANSSEN CILAG FARMACEUTICA S.A.—See Johnson & Johnson; *U.S. Public*, pg. 1196
JANSSEN-CILAG LTD.—See Johnson & Johnson; *U.S. Public*, pg. 1197
JANSSEN-CILAG LTD.—See Johnson & Johnson; *U.S. Public*, pg. 1197
JANSSEN-CILAG OY—See Johnson & Johnson; *U.S. Public*, pg. 1197
JANSSEN-CILAG PHARMACEUTICA LIMITED—See Johnson & Johnson; *U.S. Public*, pg. 1197
JANSSEN-CILAG POLSKA, SP. Z O.O.—See Johnson & Johnson; *U.S. Public*, pg. 1197
JANSSEN-CILAG, S.A. DE C.V.—See Johnson & Johnson; *U.S. Public*, pg. 1197
JANSSEN-CILAG S.A.—See Johnson & Johnson; *U.S. Public*, pg. 1197
JANSSEN-CILAG S.A.—See Johnson & Johnson; *U.S. Public*, pg. 1197
JANSSEN-CILAG S.P.A.—See Johnson & Johnson; *U.S. Public*, pg. 1197
JANSSEN-CILAG S.R.O.—See Johnson & Johnson; *U.S. Public*, pg. 1197
JANSSEN-ORTHO, INC.—See Johnson & Johnson; *U.S. Public*, pg. 1197
JANSSEN ORTHO, LLC—See Johnson & Johnson; *U.S. Public*, pg. 1196
JANSSEN ORTHO LLC—See Johnson & Johnson; *U.S. Public*, pg. 1196
JANSSEN PHARMACEUTICAL LTD.—See Johnson & Johnson; *U.S. Public*, pg. 1197
JANSSEN PHARMACEUTICALS, INC.—See Johnson & Johnson; *U.S. Public*, pg. 1196
JANSSEN PHARMACEUTICA N.V.—See Johnson & Johnson; *U.S. Public*, pg. 1196
JANSSEN PHARMACEUTICA (PTY) LIMITED—See Johnson & Johnson; *U.S. Public*, pg. 1196
JANSSEN PHARMACEUTICA—See Johnson & Johnson; *U.S. Public*, pg. 1196
JANSSEN VACCINE CORP.—See Johnson & Johnson; *U.S. Public*, pg. 1197
JANSSEN VACCINES AG—See Johnson & Johnson; *U.S. Public*, pg. 1195
JANSSEN VACCINES & PREVENTION B.V.—See Johnson & Johnson; *U.S. Public*, pg. 1197
JARROW INDUSTRIES INCORPORATED; *U.S. Private*, pg. 2188
JCEL CO., LTD.—See Central Glass Co., Ltd.; *Int'l*, pg. 1407
JENAPHARM GMBH & CO, KG—See Bayer Aktiengesellschaft; *Int'l*, pg. 904
JIANGSU BROTHER VITAMINS CO., LTD.—See Brother Enterprises Holding Co., Ltd.; *Int'l*, pg. 1196
JIANGSU SHENHUA PHARMACEUTICAL CO., LTD.—See Fufeng Group Limited; *Int'l*, pg. 2804
JIANGXI BROTHER PHARMACEUTICAL CO., LTD.—See Brother Enterprises Holding Co., Ltd.; *Int'l*, pg. 1196
JIANGXI PROVINCE PHARMACEUTICAL GROUP CORPORATION—See China Meheco Group Co., Ltd.; *Int'l*, pg. 1519
JIANGXI TINCI CENTRAL ADVANCED MATERIALS CO., LTD.—See Central Glass Co., Ltd.; *Int'l*, pg. 1407
JILIN EXTRAWELL CHANGBAISHAN PHARMACEUTICAL CO., LTD.—See Extrawell Pharmaceutical Holdings Ltd.; *Int'l*, pg. 2592
JOHNSON & JOHNSON CONSUMER B.V.—See Kenvue Inc.; *U.S. Public*, pg. 1223
JOHNSON & JOHNSON CONSUMER PRODUCTS—See Kenvue Inc.; *U.S. Public*, pg. 1223
JOHNSON & JOHNSON CONSUMER PRODUCTS—See Kenvue Inc.; *U.S. Public*, pg. 1223
JOHNSON & JOHNSON DEL ECUADOR S.A.—See Kenvue Inc.; *U.S. Public*, pg. 1224
JOHNSON & JOHNSON DE URUGUAY S.A.—See Johnson & Johnson; *U.S. Public*, pg. 1199
JOHNSON & JOHNSON GESELLSCHAFT M.B.H—See Kenvue Inc.; *U.S. Public*, pg. 1223
JOHNSON & JOHNSON HEMISFERICA S.A.—See Johnson & Johnson; *U.S. Public*, pg. 1198
JOHNSON & JOHNSON INNOVATION LLC—See Johnson & Johnson; *U.S. Public*, pg. 1198
JOHNSON & JOHNSON KOREA, LTD.—See Kenvue Inc.; *U.S. Public*, pg. 1224
JOHNSON & JOHNSON MEDICAL KOREA LIMITED—See Johnson & Johnson; *U.S. Public*, pg. 1198
JOHNSON & JOHNSON MEDICAL LTD.—See Johnson & Johnson; *U.S. Public*, pg. 1198
JOHNSON & JOHNSON MEDICAL LTD.—See Johnson & Johnson; *U.S. Public*, pg. 1198
JOHNSON & JOHNSON MEDICAL N.V.—See Johnson & Johnson; *U.S. Public*, pg. 1199
JOHNSON & JOHNSON MEDICAL PRODUCTS GMBH—See Johnson & Johnson; *U.S. Public*, pg. 1199
JOHNSON & JOHNSON MEDICAL (PTY) LIMITED—See Johnson & Johnson; *U.S. Public*, pg. 1199
JOHNSON & JOHNSON (MIDDLE EAST) INC.—See Johnson & Johnson; *U.S. Public*, pg. 1198
JOHNSON & JOHNSON NORDIC AB—See Johnson & Johnson; *U.S. Public*, pg. 1199
JOHNSON & JOHNSON PRIVATE LIMITED—See Johnson & Johnson; *U.S. Public*, pg. 1199

JOHNSON & JOHNSON, PRODAJA MEDICINSKIH IN FARMACEVTSKIH IZDELKOV, D.O.O—See Johnson & Johnson; *U.S. Public*, pg. 1199
JOHNSON & JOHNSON (PROPRIETARY) LIMITED—See Johnson & Johnson; *U.S. Public*, pg. 1198
JOHNSON & JOHNSON PTE. LTD.—See Kenvue Inc.; *U.S. Public*, pg. 1224
JOHNSON & JOHNSON PTY. LIMITED—See Kenvue Inc.; *U.S. Public*, pg. 1224
JOHNSON & JOHNSON ROMANIA S.R.L.—See Johnson & Johnson; *U.S. Public*, pg. 1199
JOHNSON & JOHNSON SANTE BEAUTE FRANCE—See Kenvue Inc.; *U.S. Public*, pg. 1224
JOHNSON & JOHNSON S.E. D.O.O.—See Johnson & Johnson; *U.S. Public*, pg. 1199
JOHNSON & JOHNSON SERVICES INC.—See Johnson & Johnson; *U.S. Public*, pg. 1199
JOHNSON & JOHNSON, SPOL. S.R.O.—See Johnson & Johnson; *U.S. Public*, pg. 1199
JOHNSON & JOHNSON, S.R.O.—See Johnson & Johnson; *U.S. Public*, pg. 1199
JOHNSON & JOHNSON, S.R.O.—See Johnson & Johnson; *U.S. Public*, pg. 1199
JOHN WYETH & BROTHER LIMITED—See Pfizer Inc.; *U.S. Public*, pg. 1680
JOINT-STOCK COMPANY OLAINFARM KAZAKHSTAN—See AS Olainfarm; *Int'l*, pg. 590
JOURNEY MEDICAL CORPORATION; *U.S. Public*, pg. 1206
JSJ PHARMACEUTICALS; *U.S. Private*, pg. 2241
JUNIPER PHARMACEUTICALS (FRANCE) SA—See Catalent, Inc.; *U.S. Public*, pg. 448
JUNIPER PHARMACEUTICALS, INC.—See Catalent, Inc.; *U.S. Public*, pg. 448
JUNIPER PHARMA SERVICES LIMITED—See Catalent, Inc.; *U.S. Public*, pg. 448
JUNO THERAPEUTICS, INC.—See Bristol-Myers Squibb Company; *U.S. Public*, pg. 386
JUVENTEDC INC.—See COSCIENS Biopharma Inc.; *U.S. Public*, pg. 585
J.W.S. DELAVAU CO. INC.; *U.S. Private*, pg. 2172
KALILA MEDICAL, INC.—See Abbott Laboratories; *U.S. Public*, pg. 20
KALVISTA PHARMACEUTICALS, INC.; *U.S. Public*, pg. 1214
KAMBAL INTERNATIONAL CO.—See Dar Al Dawa Development & Investment Co.; *Int'l*, pg. 1971
KAPPA BIOSCIENCE AS—See Balchem Corporation; *U.S. Public*, pg. 265
KARO PHARMA AB—See EQT AB; *Int'l*, pg. 2478
KARYOPHARM EUROPE GMBH—See Karyopharm Therapeutics Inc.; *U.S. Public*, pg. 1214
KARYOPHARM THERAPEUTICS INC.; *U.S. Public*, pg. 1214
KBI-E INC.—See Merck & Co., Inc.; *U.S. Public*, pg. 1417
KELLER MEDICAL, INC.—See AbbVie Inc.; *U.S. Public*, pg. 23
KEMIN INDUSTRIES, INC.; *U.S. Private*, pg. 2281
KENFARMA, S.A.—See Pfizer Inc.; *U.S. Public*, pg. 1680
KENTUCKY BIOPROCESSING, INC.—See British American Tobacco plc; *Int'l*, pg. 1168
KERYX BIOPHARMACEUTICALS, INC.—See Akebia Therapeutics, Inc.; *U.S. Public*, pg. 69
KINDRED BIOSCIENCES, INC.—See Elanco Animal Health Incorporated; *U.S. Public*, pg. 723
KINETA, INC.; *U.S. Public*, pg. 1234
KINGDOMWAY NUTRITION, INC.; *U.S. Private*, pg. 2310
KINTARA THERAPEUTICS, INC.; *U.S. Public*, pg. 1235
KIORA PHARMACEUTICALS, INC.; *U.S. Public*, pg. 1235
KIRKMAN GROUP, INC.—See Hemptown Organics Corp.; *Int'l*, pg. 3341
KITE PHARMA, INC.—See Gilead Sciences, Inc.; *U.S. Public*, pg. 938
KODIAK SCIENCES INC.; *U.S. Public*, pg. 1270
KOFFOLK ANIMAL HEALTH & NUTRITION—See Phibro Animal Health Corporation; *U.S. Public*, pg. 1685
KOLON TISSUEGENE, INC.; *U.S. Public*, pg. 1270
KOMPETENZZENTRUM FUR SICHERE ENTSORGUNG GMBH—See Eckert & Ziegler Strahlen- und Medizintechnik AG; *Int'l*, pg. 2290
KONEKSA HEALTH LLC—See Merck & Co., Inc.; *U.S. Public*, pg. 1417
KONSYL PHARMACEUTICALS INC.—See ICC Industries, Inc.; *U.S. Private*, pg. 2030
KRACIE PHARMACEUTICAL, LTD.—See Hoyu Co., Ltd.; *Int'l*, pg. 3499
KRACIE PHARMA, LTD.—See Hoyu Co., Ltd.; *Int'l*, pg. 3499
KRELE, LLC—See TONIX PHARMACEUTICALS HOLDING CORP.; *U.S. Public*, pg. 2162
KREMOINT PHARMA PRIVATE LIMITED—See Bliss Gvs Pharma Ltd.; *Int'l*, pg. 1063
KROK BROTHERS HOLDINGS (PTY) LTD—See Aspen Pharmacare Holdings Limited; *Int'l*, pg. 629
KRYSTAL BIOTECH, INC.; *U.S. Public*, pg. 1277
KUNMING SHENGHUO PHARMACEUTICAL (GROUP) CO., LTD.—See China Resources Sanjiu Medical & Pharmaceutical Co., Ltd.; *Int'l*, pg. 1549

325412 — PHARMACEUTICAL PREP...

KURA ONCOLOGY, INC.; *U.S. Public*, pg. 1277
KVP PHARMA+VETERINAR PRODUKTE GMBH—See Bayer Aktiengesellschaft; *Int'l*, pg. 905
KYRON LABORATORIES (PTY) LTD—See Ascendis Health Limited; *Int'l*, pg. 601
LABESFAL LABORATORIOS ALMIRO S.A—See Fresenius SE & Co. KGaA; *Int'l*, pg. 2778
LABORATOIRES BOIRON SRL—See Boiron Group; *Int'l*, pg. 1101
LABORATOIRES GALDERMA SAS—See Abu Dhabi Investment Authority; *Int'l*, pg. 71
LABORATOIRES GALDERMA SAS—See EQT Corporation; *U.S. Public*, pg. 785
LABORATOIRES GRUNENTHAL S.A.S.—See Grunenthal GmbH; *Int'l*, pg. 3115
LABORATORIO FRANCO COLOMBIANO LAFRANCOL S.A.S.—See Abbott Laboratories; *U.S. Public*, pg. 20
LABORATORIO LKM SA—See Advent International Corporation; *U.S. Private*, pg. 103
LABORATORIOS BAGO COLOMBIA—See Bago Group; *Int'l*, pg. 799
LABORATORIOS BAGO DE BOLIVIA S.A.—See Bago Group; *Int'l*, pg. 799
LABORATORIOS BAGO DE GUATEMALA S.A.—See Bago Group; *Int'l*, pg. 799
LABORATORIOS BAGO DEL ECUADOR S.A.—See Bago Group; *Int'l*, pg. 799
LABORATORIOS BAGO DEL PERU S.A.—See Bago Group; *Int'l*, pg. 799
LABORATORIOS BAGO DO BRASIL S.A.—See Bago Group; *Int'l*, pg. 799
LABORATORIOS BAGO S.A.—See Bago Group; *Int'l*, pg. 799
LABORATORIOS DELTA SA—See Viatris Inc.; *U.S. Public*, pg. 2293
LABORATORIOS FARMACEUTICOS GUERBET S.A.—See Guerbet SA; *Int'l*, pg. 3172
LABORATORIOS FERRING LTDA—See Ferring Holding SA; *Int'l*, pg. 2642
LABORATORIOS FERRING SA—See Ferring Holding SA; *Int'l*, pg. 2642
LABORATORIOS FROSST, S.A.—See Merck & Co., Inc.; *U.S. Public*, pg. 1417
LABORATORIOS GROSSMAN, S.A.—See Bausch Health Companies Inc.; *Int'l*, pg. 897
LABORATORIOS INTERVET S.A.—See Merck & Co., Inc.; *U.S. Public*, pg. 1417
LABORATORIOS PARKE DAVIS, S.L.—See Pfizer Inc.; *U.S. Public*, pg. 1680
LABORATORIOS PFIZER, LDA.—See Pfizer Inc.; *U.S. Public*, pg. 1680
LABORATORIOS PFIZER LTDA.—See Pfizer Inc.; *U.S. Public*, pg. 1680
LABORATORIOS PHOENIX SOCIEDAD ANONIMA INDUSTRIAL COMERCIAL Y FINANCIERA—See GSK plc; *Int'l*, pg. 3149
LABORATORIOS RECALCINE S.A.—See Abbott Laboratories; *U.S. Public*, pg. 20
LABORATORIOS SILESIA S.A.—See Grunenthal GmbH; *Int'l*, pg. 3115
LABORATORIO STADA, S.L—See Bain Capital, LP; *U.S. Private*, pg. 443
LABORATORIO STADA, S.L—See Cinven Limited; *Int'l*, pg. 1613
LABORATORIOS VITORIA S.A.—See FAES Farma, S.A.; *Int'l*, pg. 2601
LABORCHEMIE APOLDA GMBH—See HEYL Chemisch-pharmazeutische Fabrik GmbH und Co. KG; *Int'l*, pg. 3374
LABORMED PHARMA S.A.—See Advent International Corporation; *U.S. Private*, pg. 103
LAFRANCOL INTERNACIONAL S.A.S.—See Abbott Laboratories; *U.S. Public*, pg. 20
LAKE CONSUMER PRODUCTS, INC.—See Wisconsin Pharmacal Company, LLC; *U.S. Private*, pg. 4548
LAKEWOOD-AMEDEX INC.; *U.S. Private*, pg. 2379
LALEHAM HEALTHCARE LIMITED—See DCC plc; *Int'l*, pg. 1991
LANCER USA INC.—See Getinge AB; *Int'l*, pg. 2949
LANNETT COMPANY, INC.; *U.S. Public*, pg. 1292
LARIMAR THERAPEUTICS, INC.; *U.S. Public*, pg. 1293
LAUREATE BIOPHARMACEUTICAL SERVICES, INC.—See Saints Capital, LLC; *U.S. Private*, pg. 3530
LAURUS LABS LIMITED—See Evotec SE; *Int'l*, pg. 2573
LAZLO INTERNATIONAL SA—See FAES Farma, S.A.; *Int'l*, pg. 2601
LEAP THERAPEUTICS LTD.—See Leap Therapeutics, Inc.; *U.S. Public*, pg. 1296
LEE BIOSOLUTIONS, INC.—See DevCo Partners Oy; *Int'l*, pg. 2086
LEEHAR DISTRIBUTORS, LLC—See UnitedHealth Group Incorporated; *U.S. Public*, pg. 2247
LEE PHARMACEUTICALS; *U.S. Public*, pg. 1300
LESCARDEN, INC.; *U.S. Public*, pg. 1308
LEXICON PHARMACEUTICALS, INC.; *U.S. Public*, pg. 1309
LEXICON PHARMACEUTICALS, INC.—See Lexicon Pharmaceuticals, Inc.; *U.S. Public*, pg. 1309

LIAONING HAISCO PHARMACEUTICAL CO., LTD.—See Haisco Pharmaceutical Group Co., Ltd.; *Int'l*, pg. 3217
LIDCO GROUP PLC—See Masimo Corporation; *U.S. Public*, pg. 1392
LIEBEL-FLARSHEIM COMPANY LLC—See Guerbet SA; *Int'l*, pg. 3172
LIEBEL-FLARSHEIM IRELAND LIMITED—See Guerbet SA; *Int'l*, pg. 3172
LIFEMD, INC.; *U.S. Public*, pg. 1313
LIFESCAN, INC.—See Platinum Equity, LLC; *U.S. Private*, pg. 3205
LIFEVANTAGE CORPORATION; *U.S. Public*, pg. 1313
LIGAND PHARMACEUTICALS INCORPORATED; *U.S. Public*, pg. 1314
LIL' DRUG STORE PRODUCTS, INC.; *U.S. Private*, pg. 2455
LILLY DEL CARIBE INC.—See Eli Lilly & Company; *U.S. Public*, pg. 733
LILLY DEUTSCHLAND GMBH—See Eli Lilly & Company; *U.S. Public*, pg. 733
LILLY FRANCE S.A.—See Eli Lilly & Company; *U.S. Public*, pg. 733
LILLY HUNGARIA KFT—See Eli Lilly & Company; *U.S. Public*, pg. 733
LILLY ILAC TICARET LIMITED SIRKETI—See Eli Lilly & Company; *U.S. Public*, pg. 733
LILLY KOREA LIMITED—See Eli Lilly & Company; *U.S. Public*, pg. 732
LILLY PHARMACEUTICALS—See Eli Lilly & Company; *U.S. Public*, pg. 733
LILLY-PORTUGAL PRODUTOS FARMACEUTICOS, LDA.—See Eli Lilly & Company; *U.S. Public*, pg. 733
LILLY, S.A.—See Eli Lilly & Company; *U.S. Public*, pg. 733
LILLY TIPPECANOE LABORATORIES—See Eli Lilly & Company; *U.S. Public*, pg. 733
LILLY USA, LLC—See Eli Lilly & Company; *U.S. Public*, pg. 733
LIMINAL BIOSCIENCES INC.—See Thomvest Ventures LLC; *U.S. Private*, pg. 4162
LIMITED LIABILITY COMPANY EISAI—See Eisai Co., Ltd.; *Int'l*, pg. 2335
LIMITED LIABILITY COMPANY OLAINFARM ASIA—See AS Olainfarm; *Int'l*, pg. 591
LIMITED LIABILITY COMPANY OLAINFARM AZERBAIJAN—See AS Olainfarm; *Int'l*, pg. 591
LIMITED LIABILITY COMPANY OLAINFARM OZBAXT—See AS Olainfarm; *Int'l*, pg. 591
LIMITED LIABILITY COMPANY OLAINFARM PHARMACEUTICAL & MEDICAL PRODUCTS INDUSTRY & TRADE—See AS Olainfarm; *Int'l*, pg. 591
LINVATEC BIOMATERIALS, LTD.—See CONMED Corporation; *U.S. Public*, pg. 567
LINVATEC EUROPE SPRL—See CONMED Corporation; *U.S. Public*, pg. 567
LIPA PHARMACEUTICALS LIMITED—See CK Hutchison Holdings Limited; *Int'l*, pg. 1637
LIPOCINE INC.; *U.S. Public*, pg. 1320
LIPOCINE OPERATING INC.—See Lipocine Inc.; *U.S. Public*, pg. 1320
LIVEWIRE ERGOGENICS INC.; *U.S. Private*, pg. 2473
LIVISTO GROUP GMBH—See AGRAVIS Raiffeisen AG; *Int'l*, pg. 215
LIVISTO SP. Z O.O.—See AGRAVIS Raiffeisen AG; *Int'l*, pg. 215
LIXTE BIOTECHNOLOGY HOLDINGS, INC.; *U.S. Public*, pg. 1333
LKM PERU S.A.—See Advent International Corporation; *U.S. Private*, pg. 103
LOGICBIO THERAPEUTICS, INC.—See AstraZeneca PLC; *Int'l*, pg. 659
LOHMANN ANIMAL HEALTH GMBH—See Eli Lilly & Company; *U.S. Public*, pg. 733
LOMAPHARM GMBH—See Daicel Corporation; *Int'l*, pg. 1919
LOXO ONCOLOGY, INC.—See Eli Lilly & Company; *U.S. Public*, pg. 734
LTS LOHMANN THERAPIE-SYSTEME AG—See dievini Hopp BioTech holding GmbH & Co. KG; *Int'l*, pg. 2117
LTS LOHMANN THERAPY SYSTEMS CORP.—See dievini Hopp BioTech holding GmbH & Co. KG; *Int'l*, pg. 2117
LUITPOLD PHARMACEUTICALS, INC. - NORRISTOWN OFFICE—See Daiichi Sankyo Co., Ltd.; *Int'l*, pg. 1930
LUMARA HEALTH INC.—See AMAG Pharmaceuticals, Inc.; *U.S. Private*, pg. 215
LUMARA HEALTH SERVICES LTD.—See AMAG Pharmaceuticals, Inc.; *U.S. Private*, pg. 215
LUMICERA HEALTH SERVICES LLC—See SSM Health Care Corporation; *U.S. Private*, pg. 3769
LUMINEX MOLECULAR DIAGNOSTICS—See DiaSorin S.p.A.; *Int'l*, pg. 2106
LUMOS PHARMA, INC.; *U.S. Public*, pg. 1348
LUNG BIOENGINEERING INC.—See United Therapeutics Corporation; *U.S. Public*, pg. 2238
LUYE PHARMA AG—See AsiaPharma Holdings Ltd.; *Int'l*, pg. 620
LUYE PHARMA GROUP LTD.—See AsiaPharma Holdings Ltd.; *Int'l*, pg. 620
MACROGENICS, INC.; *U.S. Public*, pg. 1353

MADRIGAL PHARMACEUTICALS, INC.; *U.S. Public*, pg. 1354
MAH PHARMACY, LLC—See The Cigna Group; *U.S. Public*, pg. 2061
MAKERS NUTRITION, LLC; *U.S. Private*, pg. 2556
MALLINCKRODT MEDICAL B.V.—See Curium SAS; *Int'l*, pg. 1878
MANAGEMENT & NETWORK SERVICES LLC—See CVS Health Corporation; *U.S. Public*, pg. 616
MANHATTAN DRUG COMPANY, INC.—See Integrated Biopharma, Inc.; *U.S. Public*, pg. 1136
MANIFESTSEVEN HOLDINGS CORPORATION; *U.S. Public*, pg. 1356
MANNKIND CORPORATION; *U.S. Public*, pg. 1357
MANZO PHARMACEUTICALS, INC.; *U.S. Private*, pg. 2567
MAQUET CARDIOPULMONARY MEDIKAL TEKNIK SANTIC LTD. STI—See Getinge AB; *Int'l*, pg. 2951
MAQUET SOUTHERN AFRICA (PTY) LTD.—See Getinge AB; *Int'l*, pg. 2952
MARINUS PHARMACEUTICALS INC.; *U.S. Public*, pg. 1367
MARIZYME, INC.; *U.S. Public*, pg. 1367
MARKER GENE TECHNOLOGIES, INC.—See Danaher Corporation; *U.S. Public*, pg. 624
MARKER THERAPEUTICS, INC.; *U.S. Public*, pg. 1369
MARLEX PHARMACEUTICALS, INC.; *U.S. Private*, pg. 2583
MARTI FARM LTD.—See Hangzhou Tigermed Consulting Co., Ltd.; *Int'l*, pg. 3251
MASTIX MEDICA, LLC—See GelStat Corporation; *U.S. Public*, pg. 910
MATINAS BIOPHARMA HOLDINGS, INC.; *U.S. Public*, pg. 1396
MATRIX LABORATORIES (XIAMEN) LTD.—See Viatris Inc.; *U.S. Public*, pg. 2293
MATYS HEALTHY PRODUCTS LLC—See Bayer Aktiengesellschaft; *Int'l*, pg. 908
MAXCYTE, INC.; *U.S. Public*, pg. 1402
MCDERMOTT LABORATORIES LTD.—See Viatris Inc.; *U.S. Public*, pg. 2293
MCKESSON CANADA—See McKesson Corporation; *U.S. Public*, pg. 1408
MCKESSON EUROPE AG—See McKesson Corporation; *U.S. Public*, pg. 1408
MCM VACCINE B.V.1—See Merck & Co., Inc.; *U.S. Public*, pg. 1417
MCNEIL AB—See Kenvue Inc.; *U.S. Public*, pg. 1224
MCNEIL CONSUMER HEALTHCARE GMBH—See Kenvue Inc.; *U.S. Public*, pg. 1224
MCNEIL CONSUMER PHARMACEUTICALS CO.—See Kenvue Inc.; *U.S. Public*, pg. 1224
MCNEIL DENMARK APS—See Kenvue Inc.; *U.S. Public*, pg. 1224
MCNEIL GMBH & CO. OHG—See Kenvue Inc.; *U.S. Public*, pg. 1224
MCNEIL SWEDEN AB—See Kenvue Inc.; *U.S. Public*, pg. 1224
MDCP, LLC—See BioCryst Pharmaceuticals, Inc.; *U.S. Public*, pg. 335
MEDA AB—See Viatris Inc.; *U.S. Public*, pg. 2293
MEDA AS—See Viatris Inc.; *U.S. Public*, pg. 2293
MEDAFOR, INC.—See Becton, Dickinson & Company; *U.S. Public*, pg. 291
MEDA MANUFACTURING SAS—See Viatris Inc.; *U.S. Public*, pg. 2293
MEDA PHARMA B.V.—See Viatris Inc.; *U.S. Public*, pg. 2293
MEDA PHARMACEUTICALS A.E.—See Viatris Inc.; *U.S. Public*, pg. 2293
MEDA PHARMACEUTICALS INC.—See Viatris Inc.; *U.S. Public*, pg. 2293
MEDA PHARMACEUTICALS LIMITED—See Viatris Inc.; *U.S. Public*, pg. 2293
MEDA PHARMACEUTICALS MEA FZ-LLC—See Viatris Inc.; *U.S. Public*, pg. 2294
MEDA PHARMA GMBH—See Viatris Inc.; *U.S. Public*, pg. 2293
MEDA PHARMA ILAC SANAYI VE TICARET LIMITED SIRKETI—See Viatris Inc.; *U.S. Public*, pg. 2293
MEDA PHARMA ILAC SAN VE TIC LTD. STI—See Viatris Inc.; *U.S. Public*, pg. 2293
MEDA PHARMA PRODUTOS FARMACEUTICOS, S.A.—See Viatris Inc.; *U.S. Public*, pg. 2293
MEDA PHARMA S.A.—See Viatris Inc.; *U.S. Public*, pg. 2293
MEDA PHARMA S.P.A.—See Viatris Inc.; *U.S. Public*, pg. 2293
MEDAVANTE-PROPHASE, INC—See Leonard Green & Partners, L.P.; *U.S. Private*, pg. 2430
MEDCAL SALES LLC—See Medline Industries, LP; *U.S. Private*, pg. 2657
MED-FARE DRUG & PHARMACEUTICAL COMPOUNDING, LLC—See Parkview Capital Credit, Inc.; *U.S. Private*, pg. 3098
MEDICHEMIE BIOLINE AG—See CSL Limited; *Int'l*, pg. 1866
MEDICIA HOLDINGS LLC—See Joshua Partners, LLC; *U.S. Private*, pg. 2237
MEDICINE SHOPPE INTERNATIONAL, INC.—See Cardinal

325412 — PHARMACEUTICAL PREP... CORPORATE AFFILIATIONS

Health, Inc.; *U.S. Public*, pg. 434
MEDICINOVA, INC.; *U.S. Public*, pg. 1412
MEDICIS AESTHETICS INC.—See Bausch Health Companies Inc.; *Int'l*, pg. 898
MEDICIS GLOBAL SERVICES CORPORATION—See Bausch Health Companies Inc.; *Int'l*, pg. 898
MEDIMMUNE LIMITED—See AstraZeneca PLC; *Int'l*, pg. 661
MEDIMPEX FRANCE S.A.R.L.—See Gedeon Richter Plc.; *Int'l*, pg. 2910
MEDIMPEX UK LTD.—See Gedeon Richter Plc.; *Int'l*, pg. 2910
MEDIPOLIS GMP OY—See BIOTON S.A.; *Int'l*, pg. 1043
MEDIWOUND LTD.—See Access Industries, Inc.; *U.S. Private*, pg. 51
MEDLINE INTERNATIONAL GERMANY GMBH—See Medline Industries, LP; *U.S. Private*, pg. 2658
MEDLINE INTERNATIONAL ITALY S.R.L.—See Medline Industries, LP; *U.S. Private*, pg. 2658
MED-PHARMEX, INC.—See EQT AB; *Int'l*, pg. 2475
MEGALITH PHARMACEUTICALS INC.—See CSPC Pharmaceutical Group Limited; *Int'l*, pg. 1867
MELINTA SUBSIDIARY CORP.—See Deerfield Management Company L.P.; *U.S. Private*, pg. 1190
MERCK CANADA—See Merck & Co., Inc.; *U.S. Public*, pg. 1419
MERCK & CO., INC. - MANUFACTURING DIVISION—See Merck & Co., Inc.; *U.S. Public*, pg. 1419
MERCK & CO. INC.—See Merck & Co., Inc.; *U.S. Public*, pg. 1418
MERCK & CO. INC.—See Merck & Co., Inc.; *U.S. Public*, pg. 1419
MERCK & CO., INC. - SPRINGFIELD—See Merck & Co., Inc.; *U.S. Public*, pg. 1419
MERCK & CO., INC. - VACCINE DIVISION—See Merck & Co., Inc.; *U.S. Public*, pg. 1419
MERCK & CO. RESEARCH & DEVELOPMENT—See Merck & Co., Inc.; *U.S. Public*, pg. 1419
MERCK SHARP & DOHME (ARGENTINA) INC.—See Merck & Co., Inc.; *U.S. Public*, pg. 1419
MERCK SHARP & DOHME ASIA PACIFIC SERVICES PTE. LTD.—See Merck & Co., Inc.; *U.S. Public*, pg. 1419
MERCK SHARP & DOHME-CHIBRET AG—See Merck & Co., Inc.; *U.S. Public*, pg. 1420
MERCK SHARP & DOHME-CHIBRET - MIRABEL—See Merck & Co., Inc.; *U.S. Public*, pg. 1420
MERCK SHARP & DOHME (CHINA) LTD.—See Merck & Co., Inc.; *U.S. Public*, pg. 1419
MERCK SHARP & DOHME CYPRUS LIMITED—See Merck & Co., Inc.; *U.S. Public*, pg. 1420
MERCK SHARP & DOHME DE ESPANA, S.A.—See Merck & Co., Inc.; *U.S. Public*, pg. 1420
MERCK SHARP & DOHME DE MEXICO S.A. DE C.V.—See Merck & Co., Inc.; *U.S. Public*, pg. 1420
MERCK SHARP & DOHME D.O.O.—See Merck & Co., Inc.; *U.S. Public*, pg. 1420
MERCK SHARP & DOHME FARMACEUTICA LTDA—See Merck & Co., Inc.; *U.S. Public*, pg. 1420
MERCK SHARP & DOHME GESELLSCHAFT M.B.H.—See Merck & Co., Inc.; *U.S. Public*, pg. 1420
MERCK SHARP & DOHME (HOLDINGS) LIMITED—See Merck & Co., Inc.; *U.S. Public*, pg. 1419
MERCK SHARP & DOHME (I.A.) LLC—See Merck & Co., Inc.; *U.S. Public*, pg. 1419
MERCK SHARP & DOHME INOVATIVNA ZDRAVILA D.O.O.—See Merck & Co., Inc.; *U.S. Public*, pg. 1420
MERCK SHARP & DOHME (IRELAND) LTD.—See Merck & Co., Inc.; *U.S. Public*, pg. 1419
MERCK SHARP & DOHME (ITALIA) S.P.A.—See Merck & Co., Inc.; *U.S. Public*, pg. 1419
MERCK SHARP & DOHME LATVIJA—See Merck & Co., Inc.; *U.S. Public*, pg. 1420
MERCK SHARP & DOHME OU—See Merck & Co., Inc.; *U.S. Public*, pg. 1420
MERCK SHARP & DOHME QUIMICA DE PUERTO RICO, INC.—See Merck & Co., Inc.; *U.S. Public*, pg. 1419
MERCK SHARP & DOHME ROMANIA SRL—See Merck & Co., Inc.; *U.S. Public*, pg. 1420
MERCK SHARP & DOHME SAUDE ANIMAL LTDA.—See Merck & Co., Inc.; *U.S. Public*, pg. 1420
MERCK SHARP & DOHME S. DE R.L. DE C.V.—See Merck & Co., Inc.; *U.S. Public*, pg. 1420
MERCK SHARP & DOHME, S.R.O.—See Merck & Co., Inc.; *U.S. Public*, pg. 1420
MERCK SHARP & DOHME S.R.O.—See Merck & Co., Inc.; *U.S. Public*, pg. 1420
MERCURY PHARMACEUTICALS (IRELAND) LIMITED—See ADVANZ PHARMA Corp. Limited; *Int'l*, pg. 166
MERICAL LLC; *U.S. Private*, pg. 2672
MERIDIAN BIOSCIENCE INC.; *U.S. Public*, pg. 1424
MERIDIAN BIOSCIENCE UK LTD.—See Meridian Bioscience Inc.; *U.S. Public*, pg. 1424
MERIT MEDICAL KOREA CO., LTD.—See Merit Medical Systems, Inc.; *U.S. Public*, pg. 1425
MERIT MEDICAL MALAYSIA SDN. BHD—See Merit Medical Systems, Inc.; *U.S. Public*, pg. 1425
MERIT MEDICAL SYSTEMS INDIA PRIVATE LIMITED—See Merit Medical Systems, Inc.; *U.S. Public*, pg. 1425
MERTIVA AB—See Arbona AB; *Int'l*, pg. 537
METENOVA AB—See Repligen Corporation; *U.S. Public*, pg. 1784
METREX RESEARCH, LLC—See Danaher Corporation; *U.S. Public*, pg. 628
(MFG) TECH GROUP PUERTO RICO, LLC—See West Pharmaceutical Services, Inc.; *U.S. Public*, pg. 2352
MIBE GMBH ARZNEIMITTEL—See Dermapharm Holding SE; *Int'l*, pg. 2043
MIBE PHARMACEUTICALS D.O.O—See Dermapharm Holding SE; *Int'l*, pg. 2043
MIBE PHARMA ITALIA SRL—See Dermapharm Holding SE; *Int'l*, pg. 2043
MIBE PHARMA UK LTD.—See Dermapharm Holding SE; *Int'l*, pg. 2043
MIBE UKRAINE LLC—See Dermapharm Holding SE; *Int'l*, pg. 2043
MICRON TECHNOLOGIES LIMITED—See Catalent, Inc.; *U.S. Public*, pg. 449
MIDATECH PHARMA US INC.—See Massachusetts Mutual Life Insurance Company; *U.S. Public*, pg. 2605
MIKART INC.; *U.S. Private*, pg. 2724
MILLER TECHNOLOGIES INTERNATIONAL; *U.S. Private*, pg. 2735
MILPHARM LIMITED—See Aurobindo Pharma Ltd.; *Int'l*, pg. 713
MIMI'S ROCK CORP.—See FitLife Brands, Inc.; *U.S. Public*, pg. 851
MIND-NRG SA—See Minerva Neurosciences, Inc.; *U.S. Public*, pg. 1449
MINERVA NEUROSCIENCES, INC.; *U.S. Public*, pg. 1449
MIRA PHARMACEUTICALS, INC.; *U.S. Public*, pg. 1449
MIRIXA CORPORATION—See Cardinal Health, Inc.; *U.S. Public*, pg. 434
MIROMATRIX MEDICAL INC.—See United Therapeutics Corporation; *U.S. Public*, pg. 2238
MIRREN (PTY) LTD.—See Cipla Ltd.; *Int'l*, pg. 1617
MISSION PHARMACAL COMPANY INC.; *U.S. Private*, pg. 2748
MJ BIOPHARM PVT LTD—See BIOTON S.A.; *Int'l*, pg. 1043
MJ BIOTECH, INC.; *U.S. Private*, pg. 2752
MOBERG PHARMA NORTH AMERICA LLC—See RoundTable Healthcare Management, Inc.; *U.S. Private*, pg. 3489
MOBERG PHARMA NORTH AMERICA LLC—See Signet Healthcare Partners, LLC; *U.S. Private*, pg. 3650
MOLOGIC LIMITED—See Abbott Laboratories; *U.S. Public*, pg. 19
MONARCH NUTRACEUTICALS, INC.—See HGGC, LLC; *U.S. Private*, pg. 1930
MONSANTO PAKISTAN (PRIVATE) LIMITED—See Bayer Aktiengesellschaft; *Int'l*, pg. 909
THE MONTICELLO COMPANIES, INC.; *U.S. Private*, pg. 4080
MONTICELLO DRUG CO.—See The Monticello Companies, Inc.; *U.S. Private*, pg. 4080
MORISON LIMITED—See Hemas Holdings PLC; *Int'l*, pg. 3341
MOTIF BIO PLC; *U.S. Private*, pg. 2795
MOUNTAIN HIGH PRODUCTS, LLC; *U.S. Private*, pg. 2799
MPX BIOCEUTICAL CORPORATION—See iAnthus Capital Holdings, Inc.; *U.S. Public*, pg. 1083
MSD ANIMAL HEALTH BVBA—See Merck & Co., Inc.; *U.S. Public*, pg. 1417
MSD ANIMAL HEALTH DANUBE BIOTECH GMBH—See Merck & Co., Inc.; *U.S. Public*, pg. 1417
MSD ANIMAL HEALTH GMBH—See Merck & Co., Inc.; *U.S. Public*, pg. 1417
MSD ANIMAL HEALTH INNOVATION AS—See Merck & Co., Inc.; *U.S. Public*, pg. 1417
MSD ANIMAL HEALTH KOREA LTD.—See Merck & Co., Inc.; *U.S. Public*, pg. 1417
MSD ANIMAL HEALTH, LDA.—See Merck & Co., Inc.; *U.S. Public*, pg. 1418
MSD ANIMAL HEALTH LIMITED—See Merck & Co., Inc.; *U.S. Public*, pg. 1418
MSD ANIMAL HEALTH (PHILS.), INC.—See Merck & Co., Inc.; *U.S. Public*, pg. 1417
MSD ANIMAL HEALTH S.R.L.—See Merck & Co., Inc.; *U.S. Public*, pg. 1418
MSD ARGENTINA SRL—See Merck & Co., Inc.; *U.S. Public*, pg. 1418
MSD AUSTRALIA - MANUFACTURING DIVISION—See Merck & Co., Inc.; *U.S. Public*, pg. 1418
MSD AUSTRALIA—See Merck & Co., Inc.; *U.S. Public*, pg. 1418
MSD BELGIUM BVBA/SPRL—See Merck & Co., Inc.; *U.S. Public*, pg. 1418
MSD BRAZIL—See Merck & Co., Inc.; *U.S. Public*, pg. 1420
MSD BV HAARLEM—See Merck & Co., Inc.; *U.S. Public*, pg. 1418
MSD CHIBROPHARM GMBH—See Merck & Co., Inc.; *U.S. Public*, pg. 1418
MSD DANMARK APS—See Merck & Co., Inc.; *U.S. Public*, pg. 1418
MSD FRANCE S.A.S.—See Merck & Co., Inc.; *U.S. Public*, pg. 1418
MSD (ITALIA) S.R.L.—See Merck & Co., Inc.; *U.S. Public*, pg. 1417
MSD ITALIA S.R.L.—See Merck & Co., Inc.; *U.S. Public*, pg. 1418
MSD K.K.—See Merck & Co., Inc.; *U.S. Public*, pg. 1418
MSD MERCK SHARP & DOHME AG—See Merck & Co., Inc.; *U.S. Public*, pg. 1418
MSD MEXICO—See Merck & Co., Inc.; *U.S. Public*, pg. 1420
MSD PHARMACEUTICALS—See Merck & Co., Inc.; *U.S. Public*, pg. 1418
MSD PHARMA HUNGARY KORLATOLT FELELOSSEGU TARSASAG—See Merck & Co., Inc.; *U.S. Public*, pg. 1418
MSD (PTY) LTD—See Merck & Co., Inc.; *U.S. Public*, pg. 1417
MSD SHARP & DOHME GESELLSCHAFT MIT BESCHRANKTER HAFTUNG—See Merck & Co., Inc.; *U.S. Public*, pg. 1418
MSD SHARP & DOHME GMBH—See Merck & Co., Inc.; *U.S. Public*, pg. 1418
MSD-SP LTD.—See Merck & Co., Inc.; *U.S. Public*, pg. 1418
MSD SWORDS—See Merck & Co., Inc.; *U.S. Public*, pg. 1418
MSD UKRAINE LIMITED LIABILITY COMPANY—See Merck & Co., Inc.; *U.S. Public*, pg. 1418
MSD VERWALTUNGS GMBH—See Merck & Co., Inc.; *U.S. Public*, pg. 1418
MSM PROTEIN TECHNOLOGIES, INC.; *U.S. Private*, pg. 2807
MUELLER SPORTS MEDICINE, INC.; *U.S. Private*, pg. 2810
MULTICORP INTERNATIONAL, INC.; *U.S. Public*, pg. 1486
MULTIDENT GMBH—See Fagron NV; *Int'l*, pg. 2603
MUREX DIAGNOSTICOS S.A.—See Abbott Laboratories; *U.S. Public*, pg. 20
MUSCLEPHARM CORPORATION—See FitLife Brands, Inc.; *U.S. Public*, pg. 852
MUSTANG BIO, INC.; *U.S. Public*, pg. 1487
MYCOVIA PHARMACEUTICALS, INC.—See NovaQuest Capital Management, LLC; *U.S. Private*, pg. 2967
MYLAN AB—See Viatris Inc.; *U.S. Public*, pg. 2294
MYLAN APS—See Viatris Inc.; *U.S. Public*, pg. 2294
MYLAN BERTEK PHARMACEUTICALS, INC.—See Viatris Inc.; *U.S. Public*, pg. 2294
MYLAN BVBA—See Viatris Inc.; *U.S. Public*, pg. 2294
MYLAN EMEA S.A.S.—See Viatris Inc.; *U.S. Public*, pg. 2294
MYLAN EPD KFT.—See Viatris Inc.; *U.S. Public*, pg. 2294
MYLAN GENERICS FRANCE HOLDING S.A.S.—See Viatris Inc.; *U.S. Public*, pg. 2294
MYLAN GROUP B.V.—See Viatris Inc.; *U.S. Public*, pg. 2294
MYLAN HEALTHCARE NORGE AS—See Viatris Inc.; *U.S. Public*, pg. 2293
MYLAN HEALTHCARE S.P. Z O.O.—See Viatris Inc.; *U.S. Public*, pg. 2293
MYLAN HEALTH PTY. LTD.—See Viatris Inc.; *U.S. Public*, pg. 2293
MYLAN II B.V.—See Viatris Inc.; *U.S. Public*, pg. 2293
MYLAN, INC.—See Viatris Inc.; *U.S. Public*, pg. 2293
MYLAN INSTITUTIONAL INC.—See Viatris Inc.; *U.S. Public*, pg. 2294
MYLAN INSTITUTIONAL LLC—See Viatris Inc.; *U.S. Public*, pg. 2294
MYLAN LABORATORIES INC.—See Viatris Inc.; *U.S. Public*, pg. 2294
MYLAN LABORATORIES LIMITED—See Viatris Inc.; *U.S. Public*, pg. 2294
MYLAN NETHERLANDS B.V.—See Viatris Inc.; *U.S. Public*, pg. 2294
MYLAN NEW ZEALAND LTD—See Viatris Inc.; *U.S. Public*, pg. 2294
MYLAN PHARMACEUTICALS INC.—See Viatris Inc.; *U.S. Public*, pg. 2294
MYLAN PHARMACEUTICALS PRIVATE LIMITED—See Viatris Inc.; *U.S. Public*, pg. 2294
MYLAN PHARMACEUTICALS SP. Z O.O.—See Viatris Inc.; *U.S. Public*, pg. 2294
MYLAN PHARMACEUTICALS ULC—See Viatris Inc.; *U.S. Public*, pg. 2294
MYLAN PHARMA UK LIMITED—See Viatris Inc.; *U.S. Public*, pg. 2294
MYLAN SEIYAKU LTD.—See Viatris Inc.; *U.S. Public*, pg. 2294
MYLAN SPECIALTY L.P.—See Viatris Inc.; *U.S. Public*, pg. 2294
MYLAN SPECIALTY LP—See Viatris Inc.; *U.S. Public*, pg. 2294
MYLAN SWITZERLAND GMBH—See Viatris Inc.; *U.S. Public*, pg. 2294
MYLAN TECHNOLOGIES, INCORPORATED—See Viatris Inc.; *U.S. Public*, pg. 2294
MYLAN TEORANTA—See Viatris Inc.; *U.S. Public*, pg. 2294
MYONEX, LLC; *U.S. Private*, pg. 2825
MYREXIS, INC.; *U.S. Public*, pg. 1489
NALPROPION PHARMACEUTICALS, INC.—See JPMorgan Chase & Co.; *U.S. Public*, pg. 1207

N.A.I.C.S. INDEX
325412 — PHARMACEUTICAL PREP...

NALPROPION PHARMACEUTICALS, INC.—See Pernix Therapeutics Holdings, Inc.; *U.S. Private*, pg. 3152
NALPROPION PHARMACEUTICALS, INC.—See Whitebox Advisors, LLC; *U.S. Private*, pg. 4511
NANOMIX CORPORATION; *U.S. Public*, pg. 1490
NANO MOBILE HEALTHCARE, INC.; *U.S. Public*, pg. 1490
NANOPHARM LTD.—See AptarGroup, Inc.; *U.S. Public*, pg. 174
NANOVIRICIDES, INC.; *U.S. Public*, pg. 1490
NAPO PHARMACEUTICALS, INC.—See Jaguar Health, Inc.; *U.S. Public*, pg. 1186
NASCENT BIOTECH INC.; *U.S. Public*, pg. 1491
NATIONAL FOUNDATION LIFE INSURANCE COMPANY—See UnitedHealth Group Incorporated; *U.S. Public*, pg. 2242
NATIONAL VITAMIN CO. INC.; *U.S. Private*, pg. 2864
NATTOPHARMA ASA—See Compagnie des Levures Lesaffre SA; *Int'l*, pg. 1739
NATTOPHARMA USA, INC.—See Compagnie des Levures Lesaffre SA; *Int'l*, pg. 1739
NATURAL ORGANICS, INC.; *U.S. Private*, pg. 2867
NATUREPLEX LLC; *U.S. Private*, pg. 2867
NATURE'S PRODUCTS, INC.—See The Clorox Company; *U.S. Public*, pg. 2062
NATURE'S SUNSHINE PRODUCTS, INC.; *U.S. Public*, pg. 1499
NATURESTAR BIO-TEC INC.; *U.S. Private*, pg. 2868
NATURE'S VALUE, INC.; *U.S. Private*, pg. 2867
NBTY ACQUISITION, LLC—See KKR & Co. Inc.; *U.S. Public*, pg. 1264
NEKTAR THERAPEUTICS; *U.S. Public*, pg. 1504
NEOCARE B.V.—See Bain Capital, LP; *U.S. Private*, pg. 443
NEOCARE B.V.—See Cinven Limited; *Int'l*, pg. 1613
NEOGEN BIO-SCIENTIFIC TECHNOLOGY (SHANGHAI) CO., LTD.—See Neogen Corporation; *U.S. Public*, pg. 1505
NEOGEN CORPORATION; *U.S. Public*, pg. 1505
NEOGEN DO BRASIL PRODUTOS PARA LABRATORIOS LTDA.—See Neogen Corporation; *U.S. Public*, pg. 1505
NEOGEN EUROPE LIMITED—See Neogen Corporation; *U.S. Public*, pg. 1505
NEOGEN LATINOAMERICA S.A.P.I. DE C.V.—See Neogen Corporation; *U.S. Public*, pg. 1505
NEOLEUKIN THERAPEUTICS, INC.; *U.S. Public*, pg. 1506
NEOS THERAPEUTICS, INC.—See Aytu BioPharma, Inc.; *U.S. Public*, pg. 257
NEPHRON PHARMACEUTICALS CORPORATION; *U.S. Private*, pg. 2885
NEUBASE THERAPEUTICS, INC.; *U.S. Public*, pg. 1509
NEUMORA THERAPEUTICS, INC.; *U.S. Public*, pg. 1510
NEUROBO PHARMACEUTICALS, INC.; *U.S. Public*, pg. 1510
NEUROGENESIS, INC.; *U.S. Public*, pg. 1510
NEW BRUNSWICK SCIENTIFIC CO., INC.—See Eppendorf AG; *Int'l*, pg. 2464
NEW CHAPTER, INC.—See The Procter & Gamble Company; *U.S. Public*, pg. 2121
NEW CLICKS SOUTH AFRICA (PROPRIETARY) LIMITED—See Clicks Group Limited; *Int'l*, pg. 1658
NEW EARTH LIFE SCIENCES, INC.; *U.S. Private*, pg. 2893
NEW VISION USA, INC.; *U.S. Private*, pg. 2907
NEWYOU, INC.; *U.S. Public*, pg. 1521
NEXTPHARMA TECHNOLOGIES HOLDING LTD.—See Sun Capital Partners, Inc.; *U.S. Private*, pg. 3862
NEXUS PHARMACEUTICALS, INC.; *U.S. Private*, pg. 2922
NHA TRANG VACCINES & BIOLOGICAL PRODUCTS JOINT-STOCK COMPANY—See Ben Tre Pharmaceutical JSC; *Int'l*, pg. 969
NH.CO NUTRITION S.A.S.—See Chiesi Farmaceutici SpA; *Int'l*, pg. 1478
NICONOVUM AB—See British American Tobacco plc; *Int'l*, pg. 1168
NIHON APOCH CO., LTD.—See Alfresa Holdings Corporation; *Int'l*, pg. 317
NIKA PHARMACEUTICALS, INC.; *U.S. Public*, pg. 1528
NINA BIOTHERAPEUTICS, INC—See Atara Biotherapeutics, Inc.; *U.S. Public*, pg. 220
NIPPON BECTON DICKINSON COMPANY, LTD.—See Becton, Dickinson & Company; *U.S. Public*, pg. 292
NIPPON WELLCOME KK—See GSK plc; *Int'l*, pg. 3149
NITIN LIFESCIENCES LTD.—See TA Associates, Inc.; *U.S. Private*, pg. 3918
NOHO HEALTH INC.—See Bayer Aktiengesellschaft; *Int'l*, pg. 909
NOLTE GMBH—See Fagron NV; *Int'l*, pg. 2603
NORAMCO, INC.—See SK Capital Partners, LP; *U.S. Private*, pg. 3679
NORCHIM S.A.S.—See PMC Capital Partners, LLC; *U.S. Private*, pg. 3217
NORDIC NATURALS, INC.; *U.S. Private*, pg. 2937
NORDSVITEN AB—See ACADIA Pharmaceuticals Inc.; *U.S. Public*, pg. 31
NORTH STAR PROCESSING, LLC—See Welcome Dairy Inc.; *U.S. Private*, pg. 4473
NORTHWEST BIOTHERAPEUTICS, INC.; *U.S. Public*, pg. 1542
NOUVEAU LIFE PHARMACEUTICALS, INC.; *U.S. Public*, pg. 1543

NOVABAY PHARMACEUTICALS, INC.; *U.S. Public*, pg. 1547
NOVARTIS RINGASKIDDY LIMITED—See GHO Capital Partners LLP; *Int'l*, pg. 2959
NOVATEC IMMUNDIAGNOSTICA GMBH—See Eurofins Scientific S.E.; *Int'l*, pg. 2551
NOVAVAX AB—See Novavax, Inc.; *U.S. Public*, pg. 1548
NOVEN PHARMACEUTICALS, INC.—See Hisamitsu Pharmaceutical Co., Inc.; *Int'l*, pg. 3406
NOVIRA THERAPEUTICS, INC.—See Johnson & Johnson; *U.S. Public*, pg. 1200
NOVOHEART HOLDINGS, INC.; *U.S. Public*, pg. 1549
NT BIOPHARMACEUTICALS CHANGSHA CO., LTD.—See China NT Pharma Group Company Limited; *Int'l*, pg. 1536
NT BIOPHARMACEUTICALS JIANGSU CO., LTD.—See China NT Pharma Group Company Limited; *Int'l*, pg. 1536
NT PHARMA (JIANGSU) CO., LTD.—See China NT Pharma Group Company Limited; *Int'l*, pg. 1536
NT TONG ZHOU (BEIJING) PHARMACEUTICALS CO., LTD.—See China NT Pharma Group Company Limited; *Int'l*, pg. 1536
NUGENEREX IMMUNO-ONCOLOGY, INC.—See Generex Biotechnology Corporation; *U.S. Public*, pg. 930
NUOVA FARMEC S.R.L.—See Ecolab Inc.; *U.S. Public*, pg. 716
NUTRACEUTICAL CORPORATION—See HGGC, LLC; *U.S. Private*, pg. 1930
NUTRALIFE BIOSCIENCES, INC.; *U.S. Public*, pg. 1556
NUTRAMAX LABORATORIES, INC.; *U.S. Private*, pg. 2974
NUTRANEXT, LLC—See The Clorox Company; *U.S. Public*, pg. 2062
NUTRA PHARMA CORP.; *U.S. Public*, pg. 1555
NUTRAWISE CORPORATION; *U.S. Private*, pg. 2974
NUTRIBAND INC.; *U.S. Public*, pg. 1556
NUTRI-FORCE NUTRITION, INC.; *U.S. Private*, pg. 2974
NUTRI GRANULATIONS, INC.—See IMCD N.V.; *Int'l*, pg. 3622
NUTRITIONAL HOLDINGS, INC; *U.S. Private*, pg. 2974
NUVATION BIO INC.; *U.S. Public*, pg. 1556
NUVECTIS PHARMA, INC.; *U.S. Public*, pg. 1556
OCULAR THERAPEUTIX, INC.; *U.S. Public*, pg. 1563
OCULUS TECHNOLOGIES OF MEXICO, S.A. DE C.V.—See Sonoma Pharmaceuticals, Inc.; *U.S. Public*, pg. 1909
OCUPHIRE PHARMA, INC.; *U.S. Public*, pg. 1564
ODYSSEY HEALTH, INC.; *U.S. Public*, pg. 1564
OLIC (THAILAND) LIMITED—See Fuji Pharma Co., Ltd.; *Int'l*, pg. 2816
OLTA PHARMACEUTICALS CORP.—See Akorn, Inc.; *U.S. Private*, pg. 146
OLVE FARMACEUTICA LIMITADA—See FAES Farma, S.A.; *Int'l*, pg. 2601
OMEROS CORPORATION; *U.S. Public*, pg. 1572
OMNI BIO PHARMACEUTICAL, INC.; *U.S. Private*, pg. 3016
OMNILAB S.R.L—See Abbott Laboratories; *U.S. Public*, pg. 20
OMRIX BIOPHARMACEUTICALS LTD—See Johnson & Johnson; *U.S. Public*, pg. 1196
OMTHERA PHARMACEUTICALS, INC.—See AstraZeneca PLC; *Int'l*, pg. 661
ONCODESIGN SA—See Edmond de Rothschild Holding S.A.; *Int'l*, pg. 2313
ONCTERNAL THERAPEUTICS, INC.; *U.S. Public*, pg. 1602
ONKURE, INC.—See OnKure Therapeutics, Inc.; *U.S. Public*, pg. 1605
ONKURE THERAPEUTICS, INC.; *U.S. Public*, pg. 1605
OOO ALFA WASSERMANN—See Alfa-Wassermann S.p.A.; *Int'l*, pg. 315
OOO HEMOFARM—See Bain Capital, LP; *U.S. Private*, pg. 443
OOO HEMOFARM—See Cinven Limited; *Int'l*, pg. 1613
OPKO HEALTH EUROPE, S.L.—See OPKO Health, Inc.; *U.S. Public*, pg. 1608
OPKO HEALTH, INC.; *U.S. Public*, pg. 1608
OPTEC INTERNATIONAL, INC.; *U.S. Public*, pg. 1608
OPTIMUM CHOICE, INC.—See UnitedHealth Group Incorporated; *U.S. Public*, pg. 2243
OPTINOSE US, INC.—See OptiNose, Inc.; *U.S. Public*, pg. 1609
OPTUMCARE FLORIDA, LLC—See UnitedHealth Group Incorporated; *U.S. Public*, pg. 2247
OPTUMCARE MANAGEMENT, LLC—See UnitedHealth Group Incorporated; *U.S. Public*, pg. 2247
OPTUMCARE SOUTH FLORIDA, LLC—See UnitedHealth Group Incorporated; *U.S. Public*, pg. 2248
OPTUM GLOBAL SOLUTIONS (INDIA) PRIVATE LIMITED—See UnitedHealth Group Incorporated; *U.S. Public*, pg. 2243
OPTUM PHARMACY 701, LLC—See UnitedHealth Group Incorporated; *U.S. Public*, pg. 2243
OPTUMSERVE TECHNOLOGY SERVICES, INC.—See UnitedHealth Group Incorporated; *U.S. Public*, pg. 2248
OPTUM SERVICES (IRELAND) LIMITED—See UnitedHealth Group Incorporated; *U.S. Public*, pg. 2243

OPUS HEALTHCARE LIMITED—See Alliance Pharma PLC; *Int'l*, pg. 340
ORAGENICS, INC.; *U.S. Public*, pg. 1614
ORAMED LTD—See Oramed Pharmaceuticals Inc.; *U.S. Public*, pg. 1614
ORAMED PHARMACEUTICALS INC.; *U.S. Public*, pg. 1614
ORAPHARMA, INC.—See Bausch Health Companies Inc.; *Int'l*, pg. 898
ORE PHARMACEUTICALS INC.; *U.S. Private*, pg. 3039
ORFI-FARMA S.L.—See Pfizer Inc.; *U.S. Public*, pg. 1680
ORGANON ARGENTINA S.R.L.—See Organon & Co.; *U.S. Public*, pg. 1616
ORGANON ASIA PACIFIC SERVICES PTE. LTD.—See Organon & Co.; *U.S. Public*, pg. 1616
ORGANON AUSTRIA GMBH—See Organon & Co.; *U.S. Public*, pg. 1616
ORGANON BELGIUM BV—See Organon & Co.; *U.S. Public*, pg. 1616
ORGANON CANADA HOLDINGS LLC—See Organon & Co.; *U.S. Public*, pg. 1616
ORGANON CENTRAL EAST GMBH—See Organon & Co.; *U.S. Public*, pg. 1616
ORGANON COLOMBIA S.A.S.—See Organon & Co.; *U.S. Public*, pg. 1616
ORGANON COMERCIALIZADORA, S. DE R.L. DE C.V.—See Organon & Co.; *U.S. Public*, pg. 1616
ORGANON & CO.; *U.S. Public*, pg. 1616
ORGANON CZECH REPUBLIC S.R.O.—See Organon & Co.; *U.S. Public*, pg. 1616
ORGANON DENMARK APS—See Organon & Co.; *U.S. Public*, pg. 1616
ORGANON - ECUADOR S.A.—See Organon & Co.; *U.S. Public*, pg. 1616
ORGANON EGYPT LTD—See Organon & Co.; *U.S. Public*, pg. 1616
ORGANON FINLAND OY—See Organon & Co.; *U.S. Public*, pg. 1616
ORGANON FRANCE—See Organon & Co.; *U.S. Public*, pg. 1616
ORGANON GLOBAL INC.—See Organon & Co.; *U.S. Public*, pg. 1616
ORGANON HEALTHCARE GMBH—See Organon & Co.; *U.S. Public*, pg. 1616
ORGANON HONG KONG LIMITED—See Organon & Co.; *U.S. Public*, pg. 1616
ORGANON INTERNATIONAL SERVICES GMBH—See Organon & Co.; *U.S. Public*, pg. 1616
ORGANON (IRELAND) LTD—See Organon & Co.; *U.S. Public*, pg. 1616
ORGANON ITALIA SPA—See Organon & Co.; *U.S. Public*, pg. 1616
ORGANON ITALIA S.R.L.—See Organon & Co.; *U.S. Public*, pg. 1616
ORGANON KOREA CO. LTD.—See Organon & Co.; *U.S. Public*, pg. 1616
ORGANON KSA GMBH—See Organon & Co.; *U.S. Public*, pg. 1616
ORGANON LLC—See Organon & Co.; *U.S. Public*, pg. 1616
ORGANON MALAYSIA SDN. BHD.—See Organon & Co.; *U.S. Public*, pg. 1616
ORGANON MAROC S.A.R.L.—See Organon & Co.; *U.S. Public*, pg. 1616
ORGANON NEW ZEALAND LIMITED—See Organon & Co.; *U.S. Public*, pg. 1616
ORGANON PHARMA B.V.—See Organon & Co.; *U.S. Public*, pg. 1616
ORGANON PHARMA FZ-LLC—See Organon & Co.; *U.S. Public*, pg. 1616
ORGANON PHARMA HOLDINGS LLC—See Organon & Co.; *U.S. Public*, pg. 1616
ORGANON PHARMA PTY LTD—See Organon & Co.; *U.S. Public*, pg. 1616
ORGANON PHARMA S. DE R.L.—See Organon & Co.; *U.S. Public*, pg. 1616
ORGANON (PHILIPPINES) INC.—See Organon & Co.; *U.S. Public*, pg. 1616
ORGANON POLSKA SP. Z O.O.—See Organon & Co.; *U.S. Public*, pg. 1616
ORGANON PORTUGAL SOCIEDADE UNIPESSOAL LDA—See Organon & Co.; *U.S. Public*, pg. 1616
ORGANON SALUD, S.L.—See Organon & Co.; *U.S. Public*, pg. 1616
ORGANON (SHANGHAI) PHARMACEUTICAL TECHNOLOGY CO., LTD.—See Organon & Co.; *U.S. Public*, pg. 1616
ORGANON SINGAPORE PTE. LTD.—See Organon & Co.; *U.S. Public*, pg. 1616
ORGANON SLOVAKIA S.R.O.—See Organon & Co.; *U.S. Public*, pg. 1616
ORGANON SOUTH AFRICA (PTY) LTD.—See Organon & Co.; *U.S. Public*, pg. 1616
ORGANON (THAILAND) LTD.—See Organon & Co.; *U.S. Public*, pg. 1616
ORGANON TRADE LLC—See Organon & Co.; *U.S. Public*, pg. 1616
ORGANON TURKEY ILACLARI LIMITED SIRKETI—See Organon & Co.; *U.S. Public*, pg. 1616

325412 — PHARMACEUTICAL PREP...

ORGENICS LTD.—See Abbott Laboratories; *U.S. Public*, pg. 19
ORIC PHARMACEUTICALS, INC.; *U.S. Public*, pg. 1617
ORIGENE WUXI—See OriGene Technologies, Inc.; *U.S. Private*, pg. 3042
ORION GENOMICS, LLC; *U.S. Private*, pg. 3043
ORTHO BIOLOGICS, LLC—See Johnson & Johnson; *U.S. Public*, pg. 1197
ORTHOPEDICS NORTH AMERICA—See Orthofix Medical Inc.; *U.S. Public*, pg. 1619
ORTHOFIX ORTHOPEDICS—See Orthofix Medical Inc.; *U.S. Public*, pg. 1619
ORTHOFIX SPORTS MEDICINE BREG, INC.—See Orthofix Medical Inc.; *U.S. Public*, pg. 1619
OSA LOGISTIK GMBH—See Die Schweizerische Post AG; *Int'l*, pg. 2113
OSI ONCOLOGY DEVELOPMENT—See Astellas Pharma Inc.; *Int'l*, pg. 653
OSMOTICA ARGENTINA, S.A.—See RVL Pharmaceuticals plc; *U.S. Public*, pg. 1827
OSMOTICA KERESKEDELMI ES SZOLGALTATO KFT—See RVL Pharmaceuticals plc; *U.S. Public*, pg. 1827
OTONOMY, INC.; *U.S. Public*, pg. 1623
OXFORD IMMUNOTEC K.K.—See Revvity, Inc.; *U.S. Public*, pg. 1794
OXFORD IMMUNOTEC LTD—See Revvity, Inc.; *U.S. Public*, pg. 1794
OY BRISTOL-MYERS SQUIBB (FINLAND) AB—See Bristol-Myers Squibb Company; *U.S. Public*, pg. 387
OY ELI LILLY FINLAND AB—See Eli Lilly & Company; *U.S. Public*, pg. 733
OY FERROSAN AB—See Altor Equity Partners AB; *Int'l*, pg. 394
OY MEDIX BIOCHEMICA AB—See DevCo Partners Oy; *Int'l*, pg. 2086
PACE ANALYTICAL LIFE SCIENCES LLC—See Leonard Green & Partners, L.P.; *U.S. Private*, pg. 2426
PACGEN LIFE SCIENCE CORPORATION—See General Biologicals Corporation; *Int'l*, pg. 2918
PACIRA BIOSCIENCES, INC.; *U.S. Public*, pg. 1632
PACIRA CRYOTECH, INC.—See Pacira BioSciences, Inc.; *U.S. Public*, pg. 1632
PACIRA PHARMACEUTICALS, INC.—See Pacira BioSciences, Inc.; *U.S. Public*, pg. 1632
PAKHSH ALBORZ COMPANY—See Alborz Investment Company; *Int'l*, pg. 299
PALADIN LABS INC.—See Endo International plc; *Int'l*, pg. 2404
PALATIN TECHNOLOGIES INC.; *U.S. Public*, pg. 1634
PAN AMERICAN LABORATORIES INC.; *U.S. Private*, pg. 3084
PANBELA THERAPEUTICS, INC.; *U.S. Public*, pg. 1635
PAN PROBE BIOTECH, INC.—See EarlyDETECT Inc.; *U.S. Private*, pg. 1314
PANTHERX SPECIALTY, LLC—See General Atlantic Service Company, L.P.; *U.S. Public*, pg. 1663
PANTHERX SPECIALTY, LLC—See Nautic Partners, LLC; *U.S. Private*, pg. 2871
PANTHERX SPECIALTY, LLC—See The Vistria Group, LP; *U.S. Private*, pg. 4132
PAR ACTIVE TECHNOLOGIES PRIVATE LIMITED—See Endo International plc; *Int'l*, pg. 2404
PARAGON BIOSERVICES, INC.—See Catalent, Inc.; *U.S. Public*, pg. 449
PARATA SYSTEMS, LLC—See Becton, Dickinson & Company; *U.S. Public*, pg. 292
PARATEK PHARMACEUTICALS, LLC—See Gurnet Point Capital LLC; *U.S. Private*, pg. 1819
PAR BIOSCIENCES PRIVATE LIMITED—See Endo International plc; *Int'l*, pg. 2404
PAR FORMULATIONS PRIVATE LIMITED—See Endo International plc; *Int'l*, pg. 2404
PARKE-DAVIS & COMPANY LIMITED—See Pfizer Inc.; *U.S. Public*, pg. 1680
PARMED PHARMACEUTICALS, INC.—See Cardinal Health, Inc.; *U.S. Public*, pg. 434
PAR PHARMACEUTICAL HOLDINGS, INC.—See Endo International plc; *Int'l*, pg. 2404
PAR PHARMACEUTICAL, INC.—See Endo International plc; *Int'l*, pg. 2404
PAR STERILE PRODUCTS, LLC—See Endo International plc; *Int'l*, pg. 2404
PATHEON API SERVICES, INC.—See Thermo Fisher Scientific Inc.; *U.S. Public*, pg. 2151
PATHEON BURLINGTON CENTURY OPERATIONS—See Thermo Fisher Scientific Inc.; *U.S. Public*, pg. 2151
PATHEON FLORENCE - EAST—See Thermo Fisher Scientific Inc.; *U.S. Public*, pg. 2151
PATHEON INC TORONTO YORK MILLS OPERATIONS—See Thermo Fisher Scientific Inc.; *U.S. Public*, pg. 2151
PATHEON ITALIA S.P.A.—See Thermo Fisher Scientific Inc.; *U.S. Public*, pg. 2151
PATHEON MOVA—See Thermo Fisher Scientific Inc.; *U.S. Public*, pg. 2151
PATHEON UK LIMITED—See Thermo Fisher Scientific Inc.; *U.S. Public*, pg. 2151

PATHFINDER CELL THERAPY, INC.; *U.S. Public*, pg. 1651
PCAS AMERICA INC.—See Eurazeo SE; *Int'l*, pg. 2530
PD HOLDINGS, LLC—See Edgewater Capital Partners, L.P.; *U.S. Private*, pg. 1335
PDS BIOTECHNOLOGY CORPORATION.; *U.S. Public*, pg. 1658
PEGASUS LABORATORIES INC.—See PBI/Gordon Corporation; *U.S. Private*, pg. 3118
PEGASUS PHARMACEUTICALS, INC.; *U.S. Public*, pg. 1660
PEPROTECH EC LTD.—See Thermo Fisher Scientific Inc.; *U.S. Public*, pg. 2151
PEPROTECH FRANCE S.A.S—See Thermo Fisher Scientific Inc.; *U.S. Public*, pg. 2151
PEPROTECH GMBH—See Thermo Fisher Scientific Inc.; *U.S. Public*, pg. 2151
PEPTISYNTHA S.A.—See Astorg Partners S.A.S.; *Int'l*, pg. 656
PETIQ, INC.—See Bansk Group LLC; *U.S. Private*, pg. 469
PETLIFE PHARMACEUTICALS, INC.; *U.S. Public*, pg. 1678
PETROS PHARMACEUTICALS, INC.; *U.S. Public*, pg. 1678
PETVIVO HOLDINGS, INC.; *U.S. Public*, pg. 1679
PFIZER AB—See Pfizer Inc.; *U.S. Public*, pg. 1680
PFIZER AG—See Pfizer Inc.; *U.S. Public*, pg. 1680
PFIZER ANIMAL PHARMA PRIVATE LIMITED—See Zoetis, Inc.; *U.S. Public*, pg. 2409
PFIZER APS—See Pfizer Inc.; *U.S. Public*, pg. 1680
PFIZER ARGENTINA—See Pfizer Inc.; *U.S. Public*, pg. 1680
PFIZER ASIA PACIFIC PTE LTD.—See Pfizer Inc.; *U.S. Public*, pg. 1680
PFIZER A/S—See Pfizer Inc.; *U.S. Public*, pg. 1680
PFIZER AS—See Pfizer Inc.; *U.S. Public*, pg. 1680
PFIZER AUSTRALIA HOLDINGS PTY LIMITED—See Pfizer Inc.; *U.S. Public*, pg. 1680
PFIZER AUSTRALIA INVESTMENTS PTY. LTD.—See Pfizer Inc.; *U.S. Public*, pg. 1680
PFIZER AUSTRALIA PTY LIMITED—See Pfizer Inc.; *U.S. Public*, pg. 1680
PFIZER BIOTECH CORPORATION—See Pfizer Inc.; *U.S. Public*, pg. 1681
PFIZER BIOTECHNOLOGY IRELAND—See Pfizer Inc.; *U.S. Public*, pg. 1681
PFIZER B.V.—See Pfizer Inc.; *U.S. Public*, pg. 1681
PFIZER CANADA INC.—See Pfizer Inc.; *U.S. Public*, pg. 1681
PFIZER CHILE S.A.—See Pfizer Inc.; *U.S. Public*, pg. 1681
PFIZER (CHINA) RESEARCH AND DEVELOPMENT CO. LTD.—See Pfizer Inc.; *U.S. Public*, pg. 1680
PFIZER CIA. LTDA.—See Pfizer Inc.; *U.S. Public*, pg. 1681
PFIZER CONSUMER HEALTHCARE GMBH—See Pfizer Inc.; *U.S. Public*, pg. 1681
PFIZER CORPORATION AUSTRIA GESELLSCHAFT M.B.H.—See Pfizer Inc.; *U.S. Public*, pg. 1681
PFIZER CORPORATION HONG KONG LIMITED—See Pfizer Inc.; *U.S. Public*, pg. 1681
PFIZER CORPORATION—See Pfizer Inc.; *U.S. Public*, pg. 1681
PFIZER CROATIA D.O.O.—See Pfizer Inc.; *U.S. Public*, pg. 1681
PFIZER CROATIA D.O.O.—See Pfizer Inc.; *U.S. Public*, pg. 1681
PFIZER DEUTSCHLAND GMBH—See Pfizer Inc.; *U.S. Public*, pg. 1681
PFIZER ENTERPRISES SARL—See Pfizer Inc.; *U.S. Public*, pg. 1681
PFIZER ESBJERG A/S—See Pfizer Inc.; *U.S. Public*, pg. 1681
PFIZER EUROPEAN SERVICE CENTER BVBA—See Pfizer Inc.; *U.S. Public*, pg. 1681
PFIZER EXPORT COMPANY—See Pfizer Inc.; *U.S. Public*, pg. 1681
PFIZER FRANCE INTERNATIONAL INVESTMENTS SAS—See Pfizer Inc.; *U.S. Public*, pg. 1681
PFIZER GLOBAL SUPPLY JAPAN INC.—See Pfizer Inc.; *U.S. Public*, pg. 1681
PFIZER GROUP LIMITED—See Pfizer Inc.; *U.S. Public*, pg. 1681
PFIZER GYOGYSZERKERESKEDELMI KFT.—See Pfizer Inc.; *U.S. Public*, pg. 1681
PFIZER HEALTH AB—See Pfizer Inc.; *U.S. Public*, pg. 1681
PFIZER HEALTHCARE INDIA PRIVATE LIMITED—See Pfizer Inc.; *U.S. Public*, pg. 1681
PFIZER HEALTHCARE IRELAND—See Pfizer Inc.; *U.S. Public*, pg. 1681
PFIZER HELLAS, A.E.—See Pfizer Inc.; *U.S. Public*, pg. 1681
PFIZER HK SERVICE COMPANY LIMITED—See Pfizer Inc.; *U.S. Public*, pg. 1681
PFIZER HOLDING FRANCE (S.C.A.)—See Pfizer Inc.; *U.S. Public*, pg. 1681
PFIZER HOLDING ITALY S.P.A.—See Pfizer Inc.; *U.S. Public*, pg. 1681
PFIZER ILACLARI, A.S.—See Pfizer Inc.; *U.S. Public*, pg. 1681
PFIZER ILACLARI LIMITED SIRKETI—See Pfizer Inc.; *U.S. Public*, pg. 1681

PFIZER INC.; *U.S. Public*, pg. 1679
PFIZER, INC.—See Pfizer Inc.; *U.S. Public*, pg. 1683
PFIZER INTERNATIONAL CORPORATION—See Pfizer Inc.; *U.S. Public*, pg. 1681
PFIZER INTERNATIONAL LLC—See Pfizer Inc.; *U.S. Public*, pg. 1681
PFIZER INTERNATIONAL TRADING (SHANGHAI) LIMITED—See Pfizer Inc.; *U.S. Public*, pg. 1681
PFIZER IRELAND PHARMACEUTICALS—See Pfizer Inc.; *U.S. Public*, pg. 1681
PFIZER ITALIA S.R.L.—See Pfizer Inc.; *U.S. Public*, pg. 1681
PFIZER JAPAN INC.—See Pfizer Inc.; *U.S. Public*, pg. 1681
PFIZER LABORATORIES PFE (PTY) LTD—See Pfizer Inc.; *U.S. Public*, pg. 1681
PFIZER LABORATORIES (PTY) LIMITED—See Pfizer Inc.; *U.S. Public*, pg. 1681
PFIZER LIMITED—See Pfizer Inc.; *U.S. Public*, pg. 1682
PFIZER LIMITED—See Pfizer Inc.; *U.S. Public*, pg. 1682
PFIZER LIMITED—See Pfizer Inc.; *U.S. Public*, pg. 1682
PFIZER LIMITED (TAIWAN)—See Pfizer Inc.; *U.S. Public*, pg. 1682
PFIZER LUXEMBOURG SARL—See Pfizer Inc.; *U.S. Public*, pg. 1682
PFIZER MALAYSIA SDN BHD—See Pfizer Inc.; *U.S. Public*, pg. 1682
PFIZER MANUFACTURING BELGIUM N.V.—See Pfizer Inc.; *U.S. Public*, pg. 1682
PFIZER MANUFACTURING DEUTSCHLAND GMBH—See Pfizer Inc.; *U.S. Public*, pg. 1682
PFIZER MEDICAL SYSTEMS, INC.—See Pfizer Inc.; *U.S. Public*, pg. 1682
PFIZER MEDICAL TECHNOLOGY GROUP (NETHERLANDS) B.V.—See Pfizer Inc.; *U.S. Public*, pg. 1682
PFIZER NETHERLANDS B.V.—See Pfizer Inc.; *U.S. Public*, pg. 1682
PFIZER NEW ZEALAND LIMITED—See Pfizer Inc.; *U.S. Public*, pg. 1682
PFIZER NORGE AS—See Pfizer Inc.; *U.S. Public*, pg. 1682
PFIZER N.V./S.A.—See Pfizer Inc.; *U.S. Public*, pg. 1682
PFIZER OVERSEAS LLC—See Pfizer Inc.; *U.S. Public*, pg. 1681
PFIZER OY—See Pfizer Inc.; *U.S. Public*, pg. 1682
PFIZER PAKISTAN LIMITED—See Pfizer Inc.; *U.S. Public*, pg. 1682
PFIZER (PERTH) PTY LIMITED—See Pfizer Inc.; *U.S. Public*, pg. 1680
PFIZER PFE (MALAYSIA) SDN. BHD.—See Pfizer Inc.; *U.S. Public*, pg. 1682
PFIZER PFE, SPOL. S R.O.—See Pfizer Inc.; *U.S. Public*, pg. 1682
PFIZER PHARMACEUTICALS ISRAEL LTD.—See Pfizer Inc.; *U.S. Public*, pg. 1682
PFIZER PHARMACEUTICALS KOREA LTD.—See Pfizer Inc.; *U.S. Public*, pg. 1682
PFIZER PHARMACEUTICALS LTD.—See Pfizer Inc.; *U.S. Public*, pg. 1682
PFIZER PHARMACEUTICALS TUNISIE SARL—See Pfizer Inc.; *U.S. Public*, pg. 1682
PFIZER PHARMACEUTICAL (WUXI) CO., LTD.—See Pfizer Inc.; *U.S. Public*, pg. 1682
PFIZER PHARMA GMBH—See Pfizer Inc.; *U.S. Public*, pg. 1682
PFIZER POLSKA SP. Z.O.O.—See Pfizer Inc.; *U.S. Public*, pg. 1682
PFIZER PREV-SOCIEDADE DE PREVIDENCIA PRIVADA—See Pfizer Inc.; *U.S. Public*, pg. 1682
PFIZER PRODUCTS INDIA PRIVATE LIMITED—See Pfizer Inc.; *U.S. Public*, pg. 1682
PFIZER ROMANIA SRL—See Pfizer Inc.; *U.S. Public*, pg. 1682
PFIZER SA (BELGIUM)—See Pfizer Inc.; *U.S. Public*, pg. 1683
PFIZER, S.A. DE C.V.—See Pfizer Inc.; *U.S. Public*, pg. 1683
PFIZER S.A.—See Pfizer Inc.; *U.S. Public*, pg. 1683
PFIZER S.A.S.—See Pfizer Inc.; *U.S. Public*, pg. 1683
PFIZER SAUDI LIMITED—See Pfizer Inc.; *U.S. Public*, pg. 1683
PFIZER SERVICE COMPANY BVBA—See Pfizer Inc.; *U.S. Public*, pg. 1683
PFIZER SERVICE COMPANY IRELAND—See Pfizer Inc.; *U.S. Public*, pg. 1683
PFIZER S.G.P.S. LDA.—See Pfizer Inc.; *U.S. Public*, pg. 1683
PFIZER SHARED SERVICES—See Pfizer Inc.; *U.S. Public*, pg. 1683
PFIZER, S.L.—See Pfizer Inc.; *U.S. Public*, pg. 1683
PFIZER—See Pfizer Inc.; *U.S. Public*, pg. 1680
PFIZER SPAIN S.A.—See Pfizer Inc.; *U.S. Public*, pg. 1683
PFIZER SPECIALTIES LIMITED—See Pfizer Inc.; *U.S. Public*, pg. 1683
PFIZER SRB D.O.O.—See Pfizer Inc.; *U.S. Public*, pg. 1683
PFIZER S.R.L.—See Pfizer Inc.; *U.S. Public*, pg. 1683
PFIZER S.R.L.—See Pfizer Inc.; *U.S. Public*, pg. 1683
PFIZER S.R.O.—See Pfizer Inc.; *U.S. Public*, pg. 1683
PFIZER TAIWAN LTD.—See Pfizer Inc.; *U.S. Public*, pg. 1683

N.A.I.C.S. INDEX 325412 — PHARMACEUTICAL PREP...

PFIZER (THAILAND) LIMITED—See Pfizer Inc.; *U.S. Public*, pg. 1680

PFIZER VENEZUELA, S.A.—See Pfizer Inc.; *U.S. Public*, pg. 1683

PFIZER (VIETNAM) LIMITED COMPANY—See Pfizer Inc.; *U.S. Public*, pg. 1680

THE P.F. LABORATORIES INC.—See Purdue Pharma LP; *U.S. Private*, pg. 3305

PGM EUROPEAN LOGISTICS CENTER—See Pfizer Inc.; *U.S. Public*, pg. 1682

PHARMACARE LTD—See Aspen Pharmacare Holdings Limited; *Int'l*, pg. 629

PHARMACEUTICAL ASSOCIATES, INC.—See Beach Products, Inc.; *U.S. Private*, pg. 503

PHARMACHEM LABORATORIES, LLC—See Ashland Inc.; *U.S. Public*, pg. 213

PHARMACIA (SOUTH AFRICA) (PTY) LTD—See Pfizer Inc.; *U.S. Public*, pg. 1683

PHARMACIA & UPJOHN LLC—See Pfizer Inc.; *U.S. Public*, pg. 1683

PHARMACIN B.V.—See Aurobindo Pharma Ltd.; *Int'l*, pg. 712

PHARMACOR PTY LIMITED—See Alkem Laboratories Ltd.; *Int'l*, pg. 330

PHARMACOS EXAKTA S.A. DE C.V.—See OPKO Health, Inc.; *U.S. Public*, pg. 1608

PHARMACYCLICS LLC—See AbbVie Inc.; *U.S. Public*, pg. 24

PHARMACYTE BIOTECH, INC.; *U.S. Public*, pg. 1684

PHARMADERM LABORATORIES LTD.—See Helix BioPharma Corp.; *Int'l*, pg. 3331

PHARMAFLORE SA—See Fagron NV; *Int'l*, pg. 2603

PHARMA IXIR CO. LTD.—See Hikma Pharmaceuticals PLC; *Int'l*, pg. 3390

PHARMALINK SP. Z O.O.—See CEPD N.V.; *Int'l*, pg. 1420

PHARM-ALLERGAN GMBH—See AbbVie Inc.; *U.S. Public*, pg. 23

PHARMALOZ MANUFACTURING INC.—See ProPhase Labs, Inc.; *U.S. Public*, pg. 1727

PHARMAPOD LTD.—See Beedie Capital Partners; *Int'l*, pg. 939

PHARMASERVE-LILLY S.A.C.I.—See Eli Lilly & Company; *U.S. Public*, pg. 733

PHARMASWISS BH D.O.O.—See Bausch Health Companies Inc.; *Int'l*, pg. 897

PHARMASWISS CESKA REPUBLIKA S.R.O.—See Bausch Health Companies Inc.; *Int'l*, pg. 897

PHARMASWISS DOO—See Bausch Health Companies Inc.; *Int'l*, pg. 897

PHARMASWISS D.O.O.—See Bausch Health Companies Inc.; *Int'l*, pg. 897

PHARMASWISS DRUSTVO S OGRANICENOM ODGOVORNOSCU ZA TRGOVINU I USLUGE—See Bausch Health Companies Inc.; *Int'l*, pg. 897

PHARMASWISS HELLAS S.A.—See Bausch Health Companies Inc.; *Int'l*, pg. 897

PHARMASWISS S.A.—See Bausch Health Companies Inc.; *Int'l*, pg. 897

PHARMA TECH INDUSTRIES INC.; *U.S. Private*, pg. 3165

PHARMATEL FRESENIUS KABI PTY LTD.—See Fresenius SE & Co. KGaA; *Int'l*, pg. 2778

PHARMATHENE US CORPORATION—See Altimmune, Inc; *U.S. Public*, pg. 88

PHARMATON S.A.—See C.H. Boehringer Sohn AG & Co. KG; *Int'l*, pg. 1241

PHARMAZELL GMBH—See Groupe Bruxelles Lambert SA; *Int'l*, pg. 3099

PHARMEDIUM SERVICES, LLC—See Cencora, Inc.; *U.S. Public*, pg. 467

PHARMENA S.A.—See CEPD N.V.; *Int'l*, pg. 1420

PHARMETICS, INC.—See Monitor Clipper Partners, LLC; *U.S. Private*, pg. 2771

PHARMLOG PHARMA LOGISTIK GMBH—See GSK plc; *Int'l*, pg. 3149

PHASEBIO PHARMACEUTICALS, INC.; *U.S. Public*, pg. 1684

PHERIN PHARMACEUTICALS, INC.—See VistaGen Therapeutics, Inc.; *U.S. Public*, pg. 2305

PHERMPEP BIOTECHNOLOGY CO., LTD.—See China Chemical & Pharmaceutical Co., Ltd.; *Int'l*, pg. 1488

PHIO PHARMACEUTICALS CORP.; *U.S. Public*, pg. 1689

PHOENIX TISSUE REPAIR, INC.—See BridgeBio Pharma, Inc.; *U.S. Public*, pg. 382

PHYSICIANS' PHARMACEUTICAL CORPORATION; *U.S. Private*, pg. 3175

PIERIS PHARMACEUTICALS, INC.; *U.S. Public*, pg. 1690

PILLAR 5 PHARMA INC.—See ANJAC SAS; *Int'l*, pg. 472

PINNACLE BIOLOGICS, INC.—See Advanz Pharma Corp.; *Int'l*, pg. 166

PIXCELL MEDICAL TECHNOLOGIES LTD.—See KLA Corporation; *U.S. Public*, pg. 1269

PLAZMASZOLGALAT KFT.—See Biotest AG; *Int'l*, pg. 1043

PL DEVELOPMENT, INC. - LYNWOOD PLANT—See PL Development, Inc.; *U.S. Private*, pg. 3194

PL DEVELOPMENT, INC.; *U.S. Private*, pg. 3194

PLIXXENT GMBH & CO. KG—See Bayer Aktiengesellschaft; *Int'l*, pg. 907

PLUS THERAPEUTICS, INC.; *U.S. Public*, pg. 1699

PLX OPCO INC.—See PLx Pharma Inc.; *U.S. Public*, pg. 1699

PMSI, LLC—See UnitedHealth Group Incorporated; *U.S. Public*, pg. 2249

POA PHARMA SCANDINAVIA AB—See Almac Sciences Group Ltd.; *Int'l*, pg. 363

POCONO PHARMACEUTICALS INC.—See NutriBand Inc.; *U.S. Public*, pg. 1556

POLNET ID SPOLKA Z OGRANICZONA ODPOWIEDZIALNOSCIA—See Merck & Co., Inc.; *U.S. Public*, pg. 1421

POLYDEX PHARMACEUTICALS LIMITED—See Biospectra Inc.; *U.S. Private*, pg. 563

POLYMED THERAPEUTICS, INC.—See Athenex, Inc.; *U.S. Public*, pg. 221

PONIARD PHARMACEUTICALS, INC.; *U.S. Public*, pg. 1701

POTENTIA PHARMACEUTICALS, INC.—See Apellis Pharmaceuticals, Inc.; *U.S. Public*, pg. 144

POTTERS LIMITED—See CSL Limited; *Int'l*, pg. 1866

PPD PHARMACEUTICAL DEVELOPMENT PHILIPPINES CORP.—See Thermo Fisher Scientific Inc.; *U.S. Public*, pg. 2150

PRA HEALTH SCIENCES, INC.—See ICON plc; *Int'l*, pg. 3585

PRAXSYN CORPORATION; *U.S. Private*, pg. 3243

PREGLEM SA—See Gedeon Richter Plc.; *Int'l*, pg. 2910

PREMIER BIOMEDICAL, INC.; *U.S. Public*, pg. 1714

PRESCOTT HOLDINGS, INC.; *U.S. Public*, pg. 3254

PRESIDIO PHARMACEUTICALS, INC.—See Panorama Capital Corp.; *U.S. Public*, pg. 1636

PRESTIGE CONSUMER HEALTHCARE INC.; *U.S. Public*, pg. 1716

PRESTIGE SERVICES CORP.—See Prestige Consumer Healthcare Inc.; *U.S. Public*, pg. 1716

PRETECT AS—See Gentian Diagnostics AS; *Int'l*, pg. 2928

PREVACUS, INC.; *U.S. Private*, pg. 3257

PRIMORIGEN BIOSCIENCES INC.—See Nucleus Biologics LLC; *U.S. Private*, pg. 2972

PRIMUS THERAPEUTICS, INC.; *U.S. Private*, pg. 3263

PRISMIC PHARMACEUTICALS, INC.—See FSD Pharma Inc.; *U.S. Public*, pg. 2798

PRN PHARMACAL INC—See PBI/Gordon Corporation; *U.S. Private*, pg. 3118

PROBIOTICA LABORATORIOS LTDA.—See Bausch Health Companies Inc.; *Int'l*, pg. 897

PROCESSA PHARMACEUTICALS, INC.; *U.S. Public*, pg. 1723

PROCTER & GAMBLE HEALTH LTD.—See The Procter & Gamble Company; *U.S. Public*, pg. 2123

PROCTER & GAMBLE HEALTH PRODUCTS—See The Procter & Gamble Company; *U.S. Public*, pg. 2122

PROCTER & GAMBLE PORTUGAL - PRODUTOS DE CONSUMO, HIGIENE E SAUDE S.A.—See The Procter & Gamble Company; *U.S. Public*, pg. 2123

PROCYON CORP.; *U.S. Public*, pg. 1724

PRODUCT QUEST MANUFACTURING, LLC.; *U.S. Private*, pg. 3273

PRODUITS CHIMIQUES AUXILIAIRES ET DE SYNTHESE SA - USINE DE COUTERNE PLANT—See Eurazeo SE; *Int'l*, pg. 2530

PROGENICS PHARMACEUTICALS, INC.—See Avista Capital Partners, L.P.; *U.S. Public*, pg. 408

PROMETHEUS BIOSCIENCES, INC.—See Merck & Co., Inc.; *U.S. Public*, pg. 1421

PROMETHEUS LABORATORIES, INC.—See Merck & Co., Inc.; *U.S. Public*, pg. 1421

PROMETIC BIOSCIENCES INC.—See Thomvest Ventures LLC; *U.S. Private*, pg. 4162

PROMETIC BIOSCIENCES LTD—See Thomvest Ventures LLC; *U.S. Private*, pg. 4162

PROMETIC BIOTHERAPEUTICS, INC.—See Thomvest Ventures LLC; *U.S. Private*, pg. 4162

PRONDIL SOCIEDAD ANONIMA—See Merck & Co., Inc.; *U.S. Public*, pg. 1421

PRONOVA BIOPHARMA ASA—See BASF SE; *Int'l*, pg. 872

PRONOVA BIOPHARMA NORGE AS—See BASF SE; *Int'l*, pg. 872

PRO PAC LABS, INC.—See MeriCal LLC; *U.S. Private*, pg. 2672

PROPHASE LABS, INC.; *U.S. Public*, pg. 1727

PROQUIMIO PRODUTOS QUIMICOS OPOTERAPICOS LTDA.—See Akzo Nobel N.V.; *Int'l*, pg. 274

PROTALIX BIOTHERAPEUTICS, INC.; *U.S. Public*, pg. 1729

PROTARA THERAPEUTICS, INC.; *U.S. Public*, pg. 1729

PROTEA BIOSCIENCES GROUP, INC.; *U.S. Private*, pg. 3289

PROTEIN POLYMER TECHNOLOGIES, INC.; *U.S. Private*, pg. 3289

PROTEO, INC.; *U.S. Public*, pg. 1729

PROTHERICS UK LIMITED—See Boston Scientific Corporation; *U.S. Public*, pg. 374

PROTHERICS UTAH INC.—See Boston Scientific Corporation; *U.S. Public*, pg. 374

PROTIDE PHARMACEUTICALS, INC.; *U.S. Private*, pg. 1729

PROVECTUS BIOPHARMACEUTICALS, INC.; *U.S. Public*, pg. 1730

PRUGEN, INC.; *U.S. Private*, pg. 3296

PSC "VEROPHARM"—See Abbott Laboratories; *U.S. Public*, pg. 20

PT. ABBOTT INDONESIA—See Abbott Laboratories; *U.S. Public*, pg. 20

P.T. ASTELLAS PHARMA INDONESIA—See Astellas Pharma Inc.; *Int'l*, pg. 653

PT ASTRAZENECA INDONESIA—See AstraZeneca PLC; *Int'l*, pg. 661

P.T. BAYER INDONESIA—See Bayer Aktiengesellschaft; *Int'l*, pg. 909

PT BOEHRINGER INGELHEIM INDONESIA—See C.H. Boehringer Sohn AG & Co. KG; *Int'l*, pg. 1243

PT. BRATACO CHEMICA—See Brataco, PT; *Int'l*, pg. 1141

PT. CAPSUGEL INDONESIA—See Pfizer Inc.; *U.S. Public*, pg. 1680

PT CLARIS LIFESCIENCES INDONESIA—See Claris Lifesciences Ltd.; *Int'l*, pg. 1649

PTC THERAPEUTICS, INC.; *U.S. Public*, pg. 1735

PTC THERAPEUTICS INTERNATIONAL LIMITED—See PTC Therapeutics, Inc.; *U.S. Public*, pg. 1735

PT DAEWOONG PHARMACEUTICAL COMPANY—See Daewoong Pharmaceutical Co., Ltd.; *Int'l*, pg. 1911

PT DARYA-VARIA LABORATORIA TBK—See First Pacific Company Limited; *Int'l*, pg. 2686

PT DISTRIVERSA BUANAMAS—See Brataco, PT; *Int'l*, pg. 1141

PT. EISAI INDONESIA - BOGOR FACTORY—See Eisai Co., Ltd.; *Int'l*, pg. 2335

PT. EISAI INDONESIA—See Eisai Co., Ltd.; *Int'l*, pg. 2335

PT GLAXOSMITHKLINE INDONESIA—See GSK plc; *Int'l*, pg. 3149

PT IKAPHARMINDO PUTRAMAS—See Brataco, PT; *Int'l*, pg. 1141

P.T. MERCK SHARP & DOHME INDONESIA—See Merck & Co., Inc.; *U.S. Public*, pg. 1420

P.T. MERCK SHARP & DOHME INDONESIA—See Merck & Co., Inc.; *U.S. Public*, pg. 1420

PT MERCK SHARP DOHME PHARMA TBK—See Merck & Co., Inc.; *U.S. Public*, pg. 1420

P.T. MONAGRO KIMIA—See Bayer Aktiengesellschaft; *Int'l*, pg. 909

PT. PFIZER INDONESIA—See Pfizer Inc.; *U.S. Public*, pg. 1680

PT SCHERING INDONESIA—See Bayer Aktiengesellschaft; *Int'l*, pg. 904

P.T. SOLVAY PHARMA INDONESIA—See Abbott Laboratories; *U.S. Public*, pg. 20

PT ZOETIS ANIMALHEALTH INDONESIA—See Zoetis, Inc.; *U.S. Public*, pg. 2409

PULMATRIX, INC.; *U.S. Public*, pg. 1736

PULMOQUINE THERAPEUTICS, INC.—See Innoviva, Inc.; *U.S. Public*, pg. 1127

PUMA BIOTECHNOLOGY, INC.; *U.S. Public*, pg. 1738

PURACAP CARIBE LLC—See PuraCap Pharmaceutical LLC; *U.S. Private*, pg. 3304

PURACAP LABORATORIES LLC—See PuraCap Pharmaceutical LLC; *U.S. Private*, pg. 3304

PURACAP PHARMACEUTICAL LLC; *U.S. Private*, pg. 3304

PURAMED BIOSCIENCE INC.; *U.S. Private*, pg. 3304

PURDUE PHARMACEUTICALS L.P.—See Purdue Pharma LP; *U.S. Private*, pg. 3305

PURDUE PHARMA LP; *U.S. Private*, pg. 3305

PURE BIOSCIENCE, INC.; *U.S. Public*, pg. 1738

PUREN PHARMA GMBH & CO. KG.—See Aurobindo Pharma Ltd.; *Int'l*, pg. 713

PURETECH HEALTH PLC; *U.S. Public*, pg. 1738

PURETEK CORPORATION; *U.S. Private*, pg. 3306

PWH CO MFG, INC.; *U.S. Private*, pg. 3308

Q-MED (SWEDEN) AUSTRALIA PTY LTD.—See Abu Dhabi Investment Authority; *Int'l*, pg. 71

Q-MED (SWEDEN) AUSTRALIA PTY LTD.—See EQT Corporation; *U.S. Public*, pg. 785

Q THERAPEUTICS, INC.; *U.S. Private*, pg. 3312

QUADRALENE LTD.—See Getinge AB; *Int'l*, pg. 2952

QUALIGEN THERAPEUTICS, INC.; *U.S. Public*, pg. 1748

QUATRX PHARMACEUTICALS CO.; *U.S. Private*, pg. 3324

QUEST PRODUCTS, INC.—See Promus Holdings, LLC; *U.S. Private*, pg. 3284

QUICK-MED TECHNOLOGIES, INC.; *U.S. Public*, pg. 1756

QUIDEL CORPORATION - SANTA CLARA—See QuidelOrtho Corporation; *U.S. Public*, pg. 1757

QUIMICA FARMACEUTICA BAYER, S.A.—See Bayer Aktiengesellschaft; *Int'l*, pg. 905

QUIMICAS UNIDAS S.A.—See Bayer Aktiengesellschaft; *Int'l*, pg. 910

QYH BIOTECH CO., LTD.—See China Animal Husbandry Industry Co., Ltd.; *Int'l*, pg. 1482

RADIUS HEALTH, INC.—See Gurnet Point Capital LLC; *U.S. Private*, pg. 1819

RADIUS HEALTH, INC.—See Patient Square Capital, L.P.; *U.S. Private*, pg. 3107

RAKS PHARMA PVT. LTD.—See Amneal Pharmaceuticals, Inc.; *U.S. Public*, pg. 125

RAMUNELES VAISTINE UAB—See Walgreens Boots Alli-

325412 — PHARMACEUTICAL PREP...

ance, Inc.; *U.S. Public*, pg. 2322
REATA PHARMACEUTICALS, INC.—See Biogen Inc.; *U.S. Public*, pg. 337
REBUS HOLDINGS INC.; *U.S. Public*, pg. 1769
RECEPTOS SERVICES LLC—See Bristol-Myers Squibb Company; *U.S. Public*, pg. 386
RECIPHARM HOGANAS AB—See Blue Wolf Capital Partners LLC; *U.S. Private*, pg. 595
RECIPHARM KARLSKOGA AB—See Blue Wolf Capital Partners LLC; *U.S. Private*, pg. 595
RECIPHARM OT CHEMISTRY AB—See Blue Wolf Capital Partners LLC; *U.S. Private*, pg. 595
RECIPHARM PARETS SL—See Blue Wolf Capital Partners LLC; *U.S. Private*, pg. 595
RECIPHARM PESSAC S.A.S.—See Blue Wolf Capital Partners LLC; *U.S. Private*, pg. 595
RECIPHARM PHARMACEUTICAL DEVELOPMENT AB—See Blue Wolf Capital Partners LLC; *U.S. Private*, pg. 595
RECIPHARM STRANGNAS AB—See Blue Wolf Capital Partners LLC; *U.S. Private*, pg. 595
RECIPHARM UPPSALA AB—See Clinical Trial Consultants AB; *Int'l*, pg. 1660
RECRO GAINESVILLE LLC—See NovaQuest Capital Management, LLC; *U.S. Private*, pg. 2967
REDWOOD BIOSCIENCE INC.—See Catalent, Inc.; *U.S. Public*, pg. 449
REDWOOD SCIENTIFIC TECHNOLOGIES, INC.; *U.S. Private*, pg. 3381
REDWOOD TOXICOLOGY LABORATORY, INC.—See Abbott Laboratories; *U.S. Public*, pg. 19
REDX ANTI-INFECTIVES LTD—See Redmile Group LLC; *U.S. Private*, pg. 3379
REDX PHARMA PLC—See Redmile Group LLC; *U.S. Private*, pg. 3379
REGEN BIOPHARMA, INC.—See Bio-Matrix Scientific Group, Inc.; *U.S. Public*, pg. 332
REGENERON CANADA COMPANY—See Regeneron Pharmaceuticals, Inc.; *U.S. Public*, pg. 1775
REGENERON IRELAND DESIGNATED ACTIVITY COMPANY—See Regeneron Pharmaceuticals, Inc.; *U.S. Public*, pg. 1775
REGENERON NL B.V.—See Regeneron Pharmaceuticals, Inc.; *U.S. Public*, pg. 1775
REGENERON PHARMACEUTICALS, INC.; *U.S. Public*, pg. 1774
REGENERON—See Regeneron Pharmaceuticals, Inc.; *U.S. Public*, pg. 1775
REGENERX BIOPHARMACEUTICALS INC.; *U.S. Public*, pg. 1775
REGENESIS BIOMEDICAL, INC; *U.S. Private*, pg. 3387
RELIABLE BIOPHARMACEUTICAL LLC—See Avantor, Inc.; *U.S. Public*, pg. 241
RELIV, INC.—See Reliv International, Inc.; *U.S. Public*, pg. 1782
RELMADA THERAPEUTICS, INC.; *U.S. Public*, pg. 1782
REMEDICA LTD.—See Ascendis Health Limited; *Int'l*, pg. 601
REMEGENIX, INC.; *U.S. Private*, pg. 3396
REMEL EUROPE LIMITED—See Thermo Fisher Scientific Inc.; *U.S. Public*, pg. 2151
RENEW LIFE CANADA INC.—See The Clorox Company; *U.S. Public*, pg. 2062
RENOVARO BIOSCIENCES INC.; *U.S. Public*, pg. 1783
REPLIGEN IRELAND LIMITED—See Repligen Corporation; *U.S. Public*, pg. 1784
REPROS THERAPEUTICS INC.—See AbbVie Inc; *U.S. Public*, pg. 23
RESPIRERX PHARMACEUTICALS INC.; *U.S. Public*, pg. 1792
REST EZ, INC.; *U.S. Public*, pg. 1792
RETRIEVE MEDICAL HOLDINGS, INC.; *U.S. Public*, pg. 1792
RETROSENSE THERAPEUTICS, LLC—See AbbVie Inc.; *U.S. Public*, pg. 23
REVANCE THERAPEUTICS, INC.; *U.S. Public*, pg. 1792
REVIVA PHARMACEUTICALS HOLDINGS, INC.; *U.S. Public*, pg. 1793
REVIVICOR, INC.—See United Therapeutics Corporation; *U.S. Public*, pg. 2238
REVOLUTION MEDICINES, INC.; *U.S. Public*, pg. 1793
REZOLUTE, INC.; *U.S. Public*, pg. 1795
RHODES TECHNOLOGIES L.P.—See Purdue Pharma LP; *U.S. Private*, pg. 3305
RHYTHM HOLDING COMPANY, INC.; *U.S. Private*, pg. 3424
RICHIE PHARMACAL COMPANY INC.; *U.S. Private*, pg. 3430
RICH PHARMACEUTICALS, INC.; *U.S. Private*, pg. 3427
RICHTER-HELM BIOLOGIC MANAGEMENT GMBH—See Gedeon Richter Plc.; *Int'l*, pg. 2910
RICHTER-HELM BIOLOGICS GMBH & CO KG—See Gedeon Richter Plc.; *Int'l*, pg. 2910
RICHTER-THEMIS MEDICARE (INDIA) PRIVATE LTD.—See Gedeon Richter Plc.; *Int'l*, pg. 2910
RIEMSER PHARMA GMBH—See Ardian SAS; *Int'l*, pg. 556
RIGEL PHARMACEUTICALS, INC.; *U.S. Public*, pg. 1798

RITE AID DRUG PALACE, INC.—See New Rite Aid, LLC; *U.S. Private*, pg. 2905
RITE AID OF ALABAMA, INC.—See New Rite Aid, LLC; *U.S. Private*, pg. 2905
RITE AID OF SOUTH CAROLINA, INC.—See New Rite Aid, LLC; *U.S. Private*, pg. 2906
ROBINSON PHARMA INC.; *U.S. Private*, pg. 3462
ROCK CREEK PHARMACEUTICALS, INC.; *U.S. Public*, pg. 1804
ROCKET PHARMACEUTICALS, INC.; *U.S. Public*, pg. 1805
ROMARK LABORATORIES, L.C.; *U.S. Private*, pg. 3476
RVL PHARMACEUTICALS PLC; *U.S. Public*, pg. 1827
RX FOR FLEAS INC.; *U.S. Private*, pg. 3509
S1 BIOPHARMA, INC.; *U.S. Private*, pg. 3519
SAFETY SHOT, INC.; *U.S. Public*, pg. 1835
SAGENT AGILA LLC—See Viatris Inc.; *U.S. Public*, pg. 2294
SAGE THERAPEUTICS, INC.; *U.S. Public*, pg. 1835
SALARIUS PHARMACEUTICALS, INC.; *U.S. Public*, pg. 1836
SAMBAZON, INC.; *U.S. Private*, pg. 3536
SAMSUNG PHARM HEALTHCARE CO., LTD.—See GemVax & KAEL Co., Ltd.; *Int'l*, pg. 2916
SANGART, INC.—See Jefferies Financial Group Inc.; *U.S. Public*, pg. 1189
SANOFI PASTEUR MSD—See Merck & Co., Inc.; *U.S. Public*, pg. 1421
SANOVAS, INC.; *U.S. Private*, pg. 3546
SARABHAI CHEMICALS (INDIA) PVT. LTD.—See Ambalal Sarabhai Enterprises Ltd.; *Int'l*, pg. 413
SAREPTA THERAPEUTICS, INC.; *U.S. Public*, pg. 1841
SAVANNAH PHARMACEUTICAL INDUSTRIES CO. LTD.—See Hikma Pharmaceuticals PLC; *Int'l*, pg. 3390
SAVARA INC.; *U.S. Public*, pg. 1842
SA VETO-PHARMA—See Element Solutions Inc.; *U.S. Public*, pg. 728
SBH SCIENCE, INC.; *U.S. Private*, pg. 3559
SBL PVT. LTD—See Boiron Group; *Int'l*, pg. 1101
S & B PHARMA INC.—See Alkem Laboratories Ltd.; *Int'l*, pg. 330
SCANDINAVIAN PHARMACEUTICALS-GENERICS AB—See Viatris Inc.; *U.S. Public*, pg. 2294
SCANTIBODIES LABORATORY INC.; *U.S. Private*, pg. 3561
SC BAYER SRL—See Bayer Aktiengesellschaft; *Int'l*, pg. 910
SC. DAR AL DAWAPHARMA SRL—See Dar Al Dawa Development & Investment Co.; *Int'l*, pg. 1971
SCHERING AG REGIONAL SCIENTIFIC OFFICE, MALAYSIA—See Bayer Aktiengesellschaft; *Int'l*, pg. 904
SCHERING AG—See Bayer Aktiengesellschaft; *Int'l*, pg. 904
SCHERING DE CHILE S.A.—See Bayer Aktiengesellschaft; *Int'l*, pg. 905
SCHERING DO BRASIL LTDA—See Bayer Aktiengesellschaft; *Int'l*, pg. 905
SCHERING GMBH & CO. PRODUKTIONS KG—See Bayer Aktiengesellschaft; *Int'l*, pg. 904
SCHERING NORGE A/S—See Bayer Aktiengesellschaft; *Int'l*, pg. 904
SCHERING PHARMACEUTICAL LIMITED—See Bayer Aktiengesellschaft; *Int'l*, pg. 904
SCHERING-PLOUGH CANADA INC.—See Merck & Co., Inc.; *U.S. Public*, pg. 1421
SCHERING-PLOUGH LABO NV—See Organon & Co.; *U.S. Public*, pg. 1616
SCHERING-PLOUGH SANTE ANIMALE—See Merck & Co., Inc.; *U.S. Public*, pg. 1421
SCHERING PREDSTAVNISTVO U JUGOSLAVIJII—See Bayer Aktiengesellschaft; *Int'l*, pg. 904
SCHERING TAIWAN LTD.—See Bayer Aktiengesellschaft; *Int'l*, pg. 905
SCHICK-WILKINSON SWORD—See Edgewell Personal Care Company; *U.S. Public*, pg. 718
SCHOTT FRANCE PHARMA SYSTEMS SAS—See Carl-Zeiss-Stiftung; *Int'l*, pg. 1337
SCHULKE & MAYR AG—See EQT AB; *Int'l*, pg. 2479
SCHULKE & MAYR (ASIA) PTE. LTD.—See EQT AB; *Int'l*, pg. 2479
SCICLONE PHARMACEUTICALS CHINA LTD.—See SciClone Pharmaceuticals, Inc.; *U.S. Private*, pg. 3573
SCICLONE PHARMACEUTICALS HONG KONG LIMITED—See SciClone Pharmaceuticals, Inc.; *U.S. Private*, pg. 3573
SCICLONE PHARMACEUTICALS, INC.; *U.S. Private*, pg. 3573
SCICLONE PHARMACEUTICALS INTERNATIONAL LTD.—See SciClone Pharmaceuticals, Inc.; *U.S. Private*, pg. 3573
SCIENION GMBH—See BICO Group AB; *Int'l*, pg. 1019
SCIENTURE, INC.—See Scienture Holdings, Inc.; *U.S. Public*, pg. 1849
SCIENTURE, LLC—See Scienture Holdings, Inc.; *U.S. Public*, pg. 1849
SCIFORMIX CORPORATION—See Laboratory Corporation of America Holdings; *U.S. Public*, pg. 1287
SCIFORMIX PHILIPPINES, INC.—See Laboratory Corporation of America Holdings; *U.S. Public*, pg. 1287
SCIFORMIX TECHNOLOGIES PRIVATE LIMITED—See Laboratory Corporation of America Holdings; *U.S. Public*, pg. 1287
SCIGATE TECHNOLOGY CORP.—See BioLASCO Taiwan Co.; *Int'l*, pg. 1038
SCITECH SPECIALITIES PRIVATE LIMITED—See Advanced Enzyme Technologies Limited; *Int'l*, pg. 159
SCIVAC LTD.—See VBI Vaccines Inc.; *U.S. Public*, pg. 2276
S.C.I. VAL PROMERY—See AbbVie Inc.; *U.S. Public*, pg. 23
SCORPIUS HOLDINGS, INC.; *U.S. Public*, pg. 1849
SCYNEXIS, INC.; *U.S. Public*, pg. 1850
SEAGEN AUSTRIA GMBH—See Seagen Inc.; *U.S. Public*, pg. 1852
SEAGEN SPAIN, S.L.—See Seagen Inc.; *U.S. Public*, pg. 1852
SEA STARR ANIMAL HEALTH, LLC.; *U.S. Private*, pg. 3582
SEELOS THERAPEUTICS, INC.; *U.S. Public*, pg. 1856
SEKPHARMA (PTY) LTD—See African Equity Empowerment Investmts Limited; *Int'l*, pg. 191
SENSEONICS HOLDINGS, INC.; *U.S. Public*, pg. 1866
SENTOSA PHARMACY SDN BHD—See Batu Kawan Berhad; *Int'l*, pg. 891
SEQIRUS USA INC.—See CSL Limited; *Int'l*, pg. 1866
SERACARE LIFE SCIENCES, INC.—See KKR & Co. Inc.; *U.S. Public*, pg. 1258
SERADYN, INC.—See Thermo Fisher Scientific Inc.; *U.S. Public*, pg. 2152
SERES THERAPEUTICS, INC.; *U.S. Public*, pg. 1868
SG GLOBAL BIOTECH SDN. BHD.—See Hai-O Enterprise Berhad; *Int'l*, pg. 3209
SHANDONG SHENGLI BIO-ENGINEERING CO., LTD.—See China Animal Husbandry Industry Co., Ltd.; *Int'l*, pg. 1482
SHANGHAI ABBOTT PHARMACEUTICAL CO., LTD.—See Abbott Laboratories; *U.S. Public*, pg. 17
SHANGHAI GENOMICS TECHNOLOGY, LTD.—See GNI Group Ltd.; *Int'l*, pg. 3017
SHANGHAI GRAPE KING ENTERPRISE CO., LTD.—See Grape King Bio Ltd.; *Int'l*, pg. 3060
SHANGHAI JOHNSON & JOHNSON PHARMACEUTICALS, LTD.—See Johnson & Johnson; *U.S. Public*, pg. 1200
SHANGHAI PUKANG PHARMACEUTICAL CO., LTD.—See China Meheco Group Co., Ltd.; *Int'l*, pg. 1519
SHANGHAI TONGTECH SOFTWARE CO., LTD.—See Beijing Tongtech Company Limited; *Int'l*, pg. 959
SHAPE PHARMACEUTICALS PTY LTD—See TetraLogic Pharmaceuticals Corporation; *U.S. Public*, pg. 2025
SHENYANG SUNSHINE PHARMACEUTICAL CO., LIMITED—See 3SBio Inc.; *Int'l*, pg. 9
SHENZHEN SCIPROGEN BIO-PHARMACEUTICAL CO., LTD.—See 3SBio Inc.; *Int'l*, pg. 9
SHIJIAZHUANG CHANGSHAN PHARMACY CO., LTD.—See Hebei Changshan Biochemical Pharmaceutical Co. Ltd.; *Int'l*, pg. 3305
SHINE STAR (HUBEI) BIOLOGICAL ENGINEERING CO., LTD.—See Fosun International Limited; *Int'l*, pg. 2752
SHUTTLE PHARMACEUTICALS, INC.; *U.S. Private*, pg. 3644
SICHUAN HEZHENG PHARMACY CO., LTD.—See Chongqing Lummy Pharmaceutical Co., Ltd.; *Int'l*, pg. 1580
SICHUAN QINGMU PHARMACEUTICAL CO., LTD.—See Chengdu Easton Biopharmaceuticals Co., Ltd.; *Int'l*, pg. 1467
SIERRA RADIOPHARMACY, LLC—See Cardinal Health, Inc.; *U.S. Public*, pg. 434
SIGA TECHNOLOGIES, INC.—See MacAndrews & Forbes Incorporated; *U.S. Private*, pg. 2534
SIGNANT HEALTH MGT LLP; *U.S. Private*, pg. 3649
SIGNPATH PHARMA INC.; *U.S. Public*, pg. 1878
SIHUAN PHARMACEUTICAL HOLDINGS GROUP LTD.—See Morgan Stanley; *U.S. Public*, pg. 1473
SILARX PHARMACEUTICALS, INC.—See Lannett Company, Inc.; *U.S. Public*, pg. 1293
SILVER CREEK PHARMACEUTICALS, INC.—See Merrimack Pharmaceuticals, Inc.; *U.S. Public*, pg. 1425
SILVERGATE PHARMACEUTICALS INC.—See NovaQuest Capital Management, LLC; *U.S. Private*, pg. 2967
SIMESA SPA.—See AstraZeneca PLC; *Int'l*, pg. 661
SIMPLEX HEALTHCARE, INC.; *U.S. Private*, pg. 3667
SINCLAIR IS PHARMA MANUFACTURING & LOGISTICS—See Huadong Medicine Co., Ltd.; *Int'l*, pg. 3511
SINCLAIR PHARMACEUTICALS LTD.—See Huadong Medicine Co., Ltd.; *Int'l*, pg. 3511
SINCLAIR PHARMA PLC—See Huadong Medicine Co., Ltd.; *Int'l*, pg. 3511
SINGAPORE CAMBO BIOLOGICAL TECHNOLOGY PTE. LTD.—See China GreenFresh Group Co., Ltd.; *Int'l*, pg. 1505
SINO-AMERICAN SHANGHAI SQUIBB PHARMACEUTICALS LTD.—See Bristol-Myers Squibb Company; *U.S. Public*, pg. 387
SINO-AMERICAN TIANJIN SMITH KLINE & FRENCH LABORATORIES LTD—See GSK plc; *Int'l*, pg. 3149
SIRTEX SIR-SPHERES PTY. LTD.—See CDH China Management Company Limited; *Int'l*, pg. 1371

325412 — PHARMACEUTICAL PREP...

SIRTRIS PHARMACEUTICALS—See GSK plc; *Int'l*, pg. 3149
SITE REALTY, INC.—See Pfizer Inc.; *U.S. Public*, pg. 1683
SKINVISIBLE, INC.; *U.S. Public*, pg. 1892
SKYE BIOSCIENCE, INC.; *U.S. Public*, pg. 1892
SKY UNITED TRADING LIMITED—See China Medical System Holdings Ltd.; *Int'l*, pg. 1518
SMITHERS AVANZA—See The Smithers Group; *U.S. Private*, pg. 4118
SMITHKLINE BEECHAM CONSUMER BRANDS LIMITED—See GSK plc; *Int'l*, pg. 3149
SMITHKLINE BEECHAM (CORK) LIMITED—See GSK plc; *Int'l*, pg. 3149
SMITHKLINE BEECHAM DE PANAMA S.A.—See GSK plc; *Int'l*, pg. 3149
SMITHKLINE BEECHAM HONDURAS S.A.—See GSK plc; *Int'l*, pg. 3149
SMITHKLINE BEECHAM (IRELAND) LIMITED—See GSK plc; *Int'l*, pg. 3149
SMITHKLINE BEECHAM LIMITED—See GSK plc; *Int'l*, pg. 3149
SOBHAN DAROU COMPANY—See Alborz Investment Company; *Int'l*, pg. 299
SOBHAN ONCOLOGY PHARMACEUTICAL COMPANY—See Alborz Investment Company; *Int'l*, pg. 299
SOCHINAZ SA—See Bachem Holding AG; *Int'l*, pg. 795
SOCIETAL CDMO, INC.—See NovaQuest Capital Management, LLC; *U.S. Private*, pg. 2967
SOCIETE DE PROMOTION PHARMACEUTIQUE DU MAGHREB S.A.—See Hikma Pharmaceuticals PLC; *Int'l*, pg. 3390
SOHM, INC.; *U.S. Public*, pg. 1899
SOLANA AGRO PECUARIA LTDA.—See C.H. Boehringer Sohn AG & Co. KG; *Int'l*, pg. 1242
SOLESIS, INC.—See Altaris Capital Partners, LLC; *U.S. Private*, pg. 206
SOLIGENIX, INC.; *U.S. Public*, pg. 1901
SOLUBLE THERAPEUTICS, INC.—See Predictive Oncology Inc.; *U.S. Public*, pg. 1713
SOMACEUTICA, INC.—See Marizyme, Inc.; *U.S. Public*, pg. 1367
SOMAHLUTION, INC.—See Marizyme, Inc.; *U.S. Public*, pg. 1367
SOMERSET THERAPEUTICS LIMITED—See Veego Pharma LLC; *U.S. Private*, pg. 4353
S-OM SA—See CSL Limited; *Int'l*, pg. 1866
SONOMA PHARMACEUTICALS, INC.; *U.S. Public*, pg. 1909
SOS BRANDS, INC.—See HealthEdge Investment Partners, LLC; *U.S. Private*, pg. 1896
SOURCE NATURALS—See Threshold Enterprises, Ltd.; *U.S. Private*, pg. 4164
SPA AL DAR AL ARABIA POUR LA FABRICATION DE MEDICAMENTS—See Hikma Pharmaceuticals PLC; *Int'l*, pg. 3390
SPECTRUM ONCOLOGY PRIVATE LIMITED—See Assertio Holdings, Inc.; *U.S. Public*, pg. 214
SPECTRUM PHARMACEUTICALS, INC.—See Assertio Holdings, Inc.; *U.S. Public*, pg. 214
SPINE SOLUTIONS GMBH—See Johnson & Johnson; *U.S. Public*, pg. 1200
SPRUYT HILLEN BV—See Fagron NV; *Int'l*, pg. 2603
SPYRE THERAPEUTICS, INC.; *U.S. Public*, pg. 1922
SRPS, LLC—See UnitedHealth Group Incorporated; *U.S. Public*, pg. 2250
SSB HOLDINGS, INC.—See The Rosewood Corporation; *U.S. Private*, pg. 4112
STADA ARZNEIMITTEL AG—See Bain Capital, LP; *U.S. Private*, pg. 442
STADA ARZNEIMITTEL AG—See Cinven Limited; *Int'l*, pg. 1613
STADA ARZNEIMITTEL GESELLSCHAFT M.B.H.—See Bain Capital, LP; *U.S. Private*, pg. 443
STADA ARZNEIMITTEL GESELLSCHAFT M.B.H.—See Cinven Limited; *Int'l*, pg. 1613
STADA CONSUMER HEALTH & STADAPHARM GMBH—See Bain Capital, LP; *U.S. Private*, pg. 443
STADA CONSUMER HEALTH & STADAPHARM GMBH—See Cinven Limited; *Int'l*, pg. 1613
STADA GMBH—See Bain Capital, LP; *U.S. Private*, pg. 443
STADA GMBH—See Cinven Limited; *Int'l*, pg. 1613
STADA HEMOFARM S.R.L.—See Bain Capital, LP; *U.S. Private*, pg. 443
STADA HEMOFARM S.R.L.—See Cinven Limited; *Int'l*, pg. 1613
STADA NORDIC APS—See Bain Capital, LP; *U.S. Private*, pg. 444
STADA NORDIC APS—See Cinven Limited; *Int'l*, pg. 1614
STADA PHARMA BULGARIA EOOD—See Bain Capital, LP; *U.S. Private*, pg. 443
STADA PHARMA BULGARIA EOOD—See Cinven Limited; *Int'l*, pg. 1613
STADA PHARMACEUTICALS (ASIA) LTD.—See Bain Capital, LP; *U.S. Private*, pg. 443
STADA PHARMACEUTICALS (ASIA) LTD.—See Cinven Limited; *Int'l*, pg. 1613
STADA PHARMACEUTICALS (BEIJING) LTD.—See Bain Capital, LP; *U.S. Private*, pg. 443
STADA PHARMACEUTICALS (BEIJING) LTD.—See Cinven Limited; *Int'l*, pg. 1613
STADA PHARMA CZ, S.R.O.—See Bain Capital, LP; *U.S. Private*, pg. 443
STADA PHARMA CZ, S.R.O.—See Cinven Limited; *Int'l*, pg. 1613
STADAPHARM GMBH—See Bain Capital, LP; *U.S. Private*, pg. 444
STADAPHARM GMBH—See Cinven Limited; *Int'l*, pg. 1614
STADA R&D GMBH—See Bain Capital, LP; *U.S. Private*, pg. 443
STADA R&D GMBH—See Cinven Limited; *Int'l*, pg. 1613
STADA SERVICE HOLDING B.V.—See Bain Capital, LP; *U.S. Private*, pg. 443
STADA SERVICE HOLDING B.V.—See Cinven Limited; *Int'l*, pg. 1613
STAFFORD MILLER (IRELAND) LIMITED—See GSK plc; *Int'l*, pg. 3149
STALLERGENES SAS—See B-FLEXION Group Holdings SA; *Int'l*, pg. 785
STANBIO LABORATORY LP—See EKF Diagnostics Holdings PLC; *Int'l*, pg. 2338
STANDARD HOMEOPATHIC COMPANY; *U.S. Private*, pg. 3778
STANDING STONE LLC—See Abbott Laboratories; *U.S. Public*, pg. 19
STAUBER CALIFORNIA, INC.—See Hawkins, Inc.; *U.S. Public*, pg. 989
STEADYMED LTD.—See United Therapeutics Corporation; *U.S. Public*, pg. 2238
STE D'INDUSTRIEE PHARMACEUTIQUE IBN AL BAYTAR—See Hikma Pharmaceuticals PLC; *Int'l*, pg. 3390
STE MEDICEF—See Hikma Pharmaceuticals PLC; *Int'l*, pg. 3390
STEMLINE THERAPEUTICS, INC.—See A Menarini Industrie Farmaceutiche Riunite Srl; *Int'l*, pg. 18
STERITEC PRODUCTS MFG. CO., INC.—See Getinge AB; *Int'l*, pg. 2952
STERLING PHARMA SOLUTIONS LTD.—See GHO Capital Partners LLP; *Int'l*, pg. 2959
STERN APOTHEKE AG—See CSL Limited; *Int'l*, pg. 1866
STIEFEL LABORATORIES, INC.—See GSK plc; *Int'l*, pg. 3149
ST PHARM CO., LTD.—See Dong-A Socio Holdings Co., Ltd.; *Int'l*, pg. 2165
STRAIGHT ARROW PRODUCTS, INC.; *U.S. Private*, pg. 3833
STRECK LABORATORIES INC.; *U.S. Private*, pg. 3838
STRONGBRIDGE BIOPHARMA LIMITED—See Xeris Biopharma Holdings, Inc.; *U.S. Public*, pg. 2386
STWB INC.—See Bayer Aktiengesellschaft; *Int'l*, pg. 902
SUMMIT INDUSTRIES, INC.; *U.S. Private*, pg. 3854
SUMMIT (OXFORD) LIMITED—See Summit Therapeutics Inc.; *U.S. Public*, pg. 1961
SUMMIT THERAPEUTICS LIMITED—See Summit Therapeutics Inc.; *U.S. Public*, pg. 1961
SUN-FARM SP. Z O.O.—See Dermapharm Holding SE; *Int'l*, pg. 2043
THE SUNRIDER CORPORATION; *U.S. Private*, pg. 4125
SUNSET ISLAND GROUP, INC.; *U.S. Public*, pg. 1966
SUNSHINE GUOJIAN PHARMACEUTICALS (SHANGHAI) CO., LTD.—See 3SBio Inc.; *Int'l*, pg. 9
SUNSHINE GUOJIAN PHARMACEUTICALS (SHANGHAI) CO., LTD.—See 3SBio Inc.; *Int'l*, pg. 9
SUPERNUS PHARMACEUTICALS, INC.; *U.S. Public*, pg. 1967
THE SUPREME CANNABIS COMPANY, INC.—See Canopy Growth Corporation; *Int'l*, pg. 1298
SUVANZA; *U.S. Private*, pg. 3887
SUVEN PHARMACEUTICALS LIMITED—See Advent International Corporation; *U.S. Private*, pg. 105
SUYASH LABORATORIES LTD.—See Aarti Drugs Ltd.; *Int'l*, pg. 38
SUZHOU CAPSUGEL LTD.—See Pfizer Inc.; *U.S. Public*, pg. 1683
SUZHOU DAWNRAYS PHARMACEUTICAL CO., LTD.—See Dawnrays Pharmaceutical (Holdings) Ltd; *Int'l*, pg. 1984
SUZHOU FIRST PHARMACEUTICAL CO., LTD.—See China NT Pharma Group Company Limited; *Int'l*, pg. 1536
SWISS-AMERICAN PRODUCTS, INC.; *U.S. Private*, pg. 3894
SWISS CAPS AG—See BC Partners LLP; *Int'l*, pg. 923
SWISSCO SERVICES AG—See BC Partners LLP; *Int'l*, pg. 923
SYMMETRY GLOBAL, LLC; *U.S. Private*, pg. 3899
SYNAPTOGENIX, INC.; *U.S. Public*, pg. 1969
SYNCO (H.K.) LIMITED—See Eu Yan Sang International Ltd.; *Int'l*, pg. 2525
SYNDAX PHARMACEUTICALS, INC.; *U.S. Public*, pg. 1970
SYNERGY PHARMACEUTICALS, INC.—See Bausch Health Companies Inc.; *Int'l*, pg. 898
SYNLOGIC, INC; *U.S. Public*, pg. 1970
SYNOKEM PHARMACEUTICALS LTD.—See TA Associates, Inc.; *U.S. Private*, pg. 3918
SYNOVIA PHARMA PLC.—See Beximco Pharmaceuticals Limited; *Int'l*, pg. 1005
SYNPAC-KINGDOM PHARMACEUTICAL CO., LTD.—See China Synthetic Rubber Corporation; *Int'l*, pg. 1557
SYNTACOLL GMBH—See Gurnet Point Capital LLC; *U.S. Private*, pg. 1819
SYROS PHARMACEUTICALS, INC.; *U.S. Public*, pg. 1972
TAAV BIOMANUFACTURING SOLUTIONS, S.L.U.—See Bayer Aktiengesellschaft; *Int'l*, pg. 910
TABLABS INC.—See Philip Morris International Inc.; *U.S. Public*, pg. 1687
TABUK PHARMACEUTICAL MANUFACTURING COMPANY—See ASTRA INDUSTRIAL GROUP COMPANY; *Int'l*, pg. 657
TABUK PHARMACEUTICALS LTD.—See ASTRA INDUSTRIAL GROUP COMPANY; *Int'l*, pg. 657
TAILOR MADE COMPOUNDING, LLC; *U.S. Private*, pg. 3923
TAIRX, INC.—See Formosa Laboratories, Inc.; *Int'l*, pg. 2735
TAISHO TOYAMA PHARMACEUTICAL CO., LTD.—See FUJIFILM Holdings Corporation; *Int'l*, pg. 2826
TAIVEX THERAPEUTICS INC.—See China Petrochemical Development Corp.; *Int'l*, pg. 1540
TALIS CLINICAL LLC—See Getinge AB; *Int'l*, pg. 2952
TALPHERA, INC.; *U.S. Public*, pg. 1980
TANNING RESEARCH LABORATORIES, LLC—See Edgewell Personal Care Company; *U.S. Public*, pg. 718
TARGETED CELL THERAPIES, LLC; *U.S. Private*, pg. 3933
TARGETED MEDICAL PHARMA, INC.; *U.S. Public*, pg. 1982
TEARSCIENCE, INC.—See Johnson & Johnson; *U.S. Public*, pg. 1200
TEC LABORATORIES, INC.—See Promus Holdings, LLC; *U.S. Private*, pg. 3284
TECNANDINA S.A.—See Grunenthal GmbH; *Int'l*, pg. 3115
TECNOFARMA, S.A. DE C.V.—See Bausch Health Companies Inc.; *Int'l*, pg. 898
TECNONUCLEAR S.A.—See Eckert & Ziegler Strahlen- und Medizintechnik AG; *Int'l*, pg. 2290
TECTRION GMBH—See Bayer Aktiengesellschaft; *Int'l*, pg. 910
TELIGENT, INC.; *U.S. Public*, pg. 1998
TELOMIR PHARMACEUTICALS, INC.; *U.S. Public*, pg. 1999
TEMMLER IRELAND LTD.—See BC Partners LLP; *Int'l*, pg. 923
TEMMLER ITALIA S.R.L.—See BC Partners LLP; *Int'l*, pg. 923
TEMMLER PHARMA GMBH & CO. KG—See BC Partners LLP; *Int'l*, pg. 923
TEMMLER WERKE GMBH—See BC Partners LLP; *Int'l*, pg. 923
TENAX THERAPEUTICS, INC.; *U.S. Public*, pg. 2001
TENDER CORPORATION; *U.S. Private*, pg. 3966
TENDYNE MEDICAL, INC.—See Abbott Laboratories; *U.S. Public*, pg. 21
TEORA HEALTH LTD.—See Aequus Pharmaceuticals Inc.; *Int'l*, pg. 179
TEPHA, INC.; *U.S. Private*, pg. 3969
TERGENE BIOTECH PRIVATE LIMITED—See Aurobindo Pharma Ltd.; *Int'l*, pg. 713
TERRANUEVA CORPORATION—See Goldflare Exploration Inc.; *Int'l*, pg. 3033
TESARO, INC.—See GSK plc; *Int'l*, pg. 3149
TETHYS BIOSCIENCE, INC.; *U.S. Private*, pg. 3973
TETRALOGIC PHARMACEUTICALS CORPORATION; *U.S. Public*, pg. 2024
TETRAPHASE PHARMACEUTICALS, INC.; *U.S. Public*, pg. 2025
TETRIS PHARMA LTD.—See Arecor Therapeutics Plc; *Int'l*, pg. 557
TG THERAPEUTICS, INC.; *U.S. Public*, pg. 2030
THARIMMUNE, INC.; *U.S. Public*, pg. 2030
THAR PHARMACEUTICALS, INC.—See Grunenthal GmbH; *Int'l*, pg. 3115
THERACOM LLC—See Cencora, Inc.; *U.S. Public*, pg. 467
THERAVANCE BIOPHARMA, INC.; *U.S. Public*, pg. 2145
THERAVANCE BIOPHARMA IRELAND LIMITED—See Theravance Biopharma, Inc.; *U.S. Public*, pg. 2145
THERAVANCE BIOPHARMA US, INC.—See Theravance Biopharma, Inc.; *U.S. Public*, pg. 2145
THERIVA BIOLOGICS, INC.; *U.S. Public*, pg. 2145
THOMPSON & CAPPER LIMITED—See DCC plc; *Int'l*, pg. 1991
THORNE RESEARCH, INC.; *U.S. Private*, pg. 4162
THORNTON & ROSS LIMITED—See Bain Capital, LP; *U.S. Private*, pg. 444
THORNTON & ROSS LIMITED—See Cinven Limited; *Int'l*, pg. 1614
THRESHOLD ENTERPRISES, LTD.; *U.S. Private*, pg. 4164
THYMOORGAN PHARMAZIE GMBH—See Hikma Pharmaceuticals PLC; *Int'l*, pg. 3390
TIAN'AN PHARMACEUTICAL CO., LTD.; *U.S. Public*, pg. 2157
TIANJIN BERONI BIOTECHNOLOGY CO., LIMITED—See Beroni Group Limited; *Int'l*, pg. 989

325412 — PHARMACEUTICAL PREP...

TIANJIN JINGMING NEW TECHNOLOGICAL DEVELOPMENT CO., LTD—See Grand Pharmaceutical Group Limited; *Int'l*, pg. 3056
TIANJIN TANABE SEIYAKU CO., LTD.—See Grand Pharmaceutical Group Limited; *Int'l*, pg. 3056
TIBOTEC BVBA—See Johnson & Johnson; *U.S. Public*, pg. 1200
TIBOTEC PHARMACEUTICALS LTD.—See Johnson & Johnson; *U.S. Public*, pg. 1200
TIBOTEC-VIRCO VIROLOGY BVBA—See Johnson & Johnson; *U.S. Public*, pg. 1200
TIGER BALM (MALAYSIA) SDN BHD—See Haw Par Corporation Limited; *Int'l*, pg. 3287
TIMM HEALTH CARE BV—See Fagron NV; *Int'l*, pg. 2603
TISHCON CORP.; *U.S. Private*, pg. 4176
TOLID DAROU PHARMACEUTICAL COMPANY—See Alborz Investment Company; *Int'l*, pg. 299
TOLMAR, INC.; *U.S. Private*, pg. 4182
TOLMAR PHARMACEUTICALS, INC.—See TOLMAR, Inc.; *U.S. Private*, pg. 4182
TONGLI PHARMACEUTICALS (USA), INC.; *U.S. Private*, pg. 4184
TONIX PHARMACEUTICALS HOLDING CORP.; *U.S. Public*, pg. 2162
TOPFOND PHARMACEUTICAL CO., LTD.—See China Meheco Group Co., Ltd.; *Int'l*, pg. 1519
TORII PHARMACEUTICAL CO., LTD. - SAKURA PLANT—See Astena Holdings Co., Ltd.; *Int'l*, pg. 653
TORREX CHIESI PHARMA GMBH—See Chiesi Farmaceutici SpA; *Int'l*, pg. 1478
TOYAMA CHEMICAL CO., LTD.—See FUJIFILM Holdings Corporation; *Int'l*, pg. 2826
TRACON PHARMACEUTICALS, INC.; *U.S. Public*, pg. 2178
TRANSITION THERAPEUTICS INC.—See OPKO Health, Inc.; *U.S. Public*, pg. 1608
TRAVERE THERAPEUTICS, INC.; *U.S. Public*, pg. 2186
TRAWS PHARMA, INC; *U.S. Public*, pg. 2186
TREVENA, INC.; *U.S. Public*, pg. 2188
TRICIDA, INC.; *U.S. Public*, pg. 2189
TRIGEN LABORATORIES, LLC—See RVL Pharmaceuticals plc; *U.S. Public*, pg. 1827
TRILLIUM THERAPEUTICS INC.—See Pfizer Inc.; *U.S. Public*, pg. 1683
TRIM NUTRITION INC.; *U.S. Private*, pg. 4232
TRIS PHARMA, INC.; *U.S. Private*, pg. 4238
TRISTAR WELLNESS SOLUTIONS, INC.; *U.S. Public*, pg. 2196
TROMMSDORFF GMBH & CO. KG—See Dermapharm Holding SE; *Int'l*, pg. 2043
TROPICAL BOTANICS SDN BHD—See Holista ColITech Limited; *Int'l*, pg. 3451
TWI PHARMACEUTICALS USA, INC.—See Bora Pharmaceuticals Co., Ltd.; *Int'l*, pg. 1112
TWISTDX LIMITED—See Abbott Laboratories; *U.S. Public*, pg. 19
THE TYLENOL COMPANY—See Johnson & Johnson; *U.S. Public*, pg. 1200
UAB BAYER—See Bayer Aktiengesellschaft; *Int'l*, pg. 910
UAB MERCK SHARP & DOHME—See Merck & Co., Inc.; *U.S. Public*, pg. 1421
UAB PHARMASWISS—See Bausch Health Companies Inc.; *Int'l*, pg. 898
UCKELE HEALTH NUTRITION; *U.S. Private*, pg. 4274
ULTRAGENYX GERMANY GMBH—See Ultragenyx Pharmaceutical Inc.; *U.S. Public*, pg. 2224
ULTRAGENYX PHARMACEUTICAL INC.; *U.S. Public*, pg. 2223
UNDA S.A—See Boiron Group; *Int'l*, pg. 1101
UNION CHEMICAL & PHARMACEUTICAL CO., LTD.—See Bora Pharmaceuticals Co., Ltd.; *Int'l*, pg. 1112
UNIPACK, INC.—See BelHealth Investment Partners LLC; *U.S. Private*, pg. 518
UNIPHARM INC.; *U.S. Private*, pg. 4285
UNIQUE PHARMACY (IPOH) SDN BHD—See Batu Kawan Berhad; *Int'l*, pg. 891
UNITED BIOSOURCE HOLDING (UK) LIMITED—See Avista Capital Partners, L.P.; *U.S. Private*, pg. 409
THE UNITED DRUG (1996) CO. LTD.—See Diethelm Keller Holding Limited; *Int'l*, pg. 2117
UNITEDHEALTHCARE SERVICE LLC—See UnitedHealth Group Incorporated; *U.S. Public*, pg. 2251
UNITED MEDCO, LLC—See Medline Industries, LP; *U.S. Private*, pg. 2658
UNITED THERAPEUTICS CORPORATION; *U.S. Public*, pg. 2238
UNITHER PHARMACEUTICALS SAS—See Equistone Partners Europe Limited; *Int'l*, pg. 2487
UNLIMIT HEALTH LIMITED—See Eisai Co., Ltd.; *Int'l*, pg. 2336
UPM PHARMACEUTICALS, INC.; *U.S. Private*, pg. 4312
UPSHER-SMITH LABORATORIES, LLC—See Bora Pharmaceuticals Co., Ltd.; *Int'l*, pg. 1112
URIGEN PHARMACEUTICALS, INC.; *U.S. Private*, pg. 4315
UROGEN PHARMA LTD.; *U.S. Public*, pg. 2266
USANA AUSTRALIA PTY, LTD.—See Gull Holdings, Ltd.; *U.S. Private*, pg. 1817

USANA CANADA CO.—See Gull Holdings, Ltd.; *U.S. Private*, pg. 1817
USANA HEALTH SCIENCES KOREA LTD.—See Gull Holdings, Ltd.; *U.S. Private*, pg. 1818
USANA HEALTH SCIENCES (NZ) CORP.—See Gull Holdings, Ltd.; *U.S. Private*, pg. 1818
USANA HEALTH SCIENCES SINGAPORE PTE, LTD.—See Gull Holdings, Ltd.; *U.S. Private*, pg. 1818
USANA HONG KONG LTD.—See Gull Holdings, Ltd.; *U.S. Private*, pg. 1818
USANA JAPAN, INC.—See Gull Holdings, Ltd.; *U.S. Private*, pg. 1818
U.S. COMPOUNDING, INC.—See DMK Pharmaceuticals Corporation; *U.S. Public*, pg. 671
USF HEALTHCARE SA—See Ecolab Inc.; *U.S. Public*, pg. 717
US WORLDMEDS, LLC; *U.S. Private*, pg. 4320
VACCINOGEN, INC.; *U.S. Private*, pg. 4329
VALEANT CANADA LTD.—See Bausch Health Companies Inc.; *Int'l*, pg. 898
VALEANT CANADA S.E.C./VALEANT CANADA LP—See Bausch Health Companies Inc.; *Int'l*, pg. 898
VALEANT CZECH PHARMA S.R.O.—See Bausch Health Companies Inc.; *Int'l*, pg. 898
VALEANT FARMACEUTICA DO BRASIL LTDA.—See Bausch Health Companies Inc.; *Int'l*, pg. 898
VALEANT FARMACEUTICA, S.A. DE C.V.—See Bausch Health Companies Inc.; *Int'l*, pg. 898
VALEANT FARMACUETICA PANAMA S.A.—See Bausch Health Companies Inc.; *Int'l*, pg. 898
VALEANT MED SP. Z O.O.—See Bausch Health Companies Inc.; *Int'l*, pg. 897
VALEANT PHARMACEUTICALS INTERNATIONAL CORPORATION—See Bausch Health Companies Inc.; *Int'l*, pg. 898
VALEANT PHARMACEUTICALS INTERNATIONAL—See Bausch Health Companies Inc.; *Int'l*, pg. 898
VALEANT PHARMACEUTICALS NORTH AMERICA LLC—See Bausch Health Companies Inc.; *Int'l*, pg. 898
VALEANT PHARMA HUNGARY COMMERCIAL LLC—See Bausch Health Companies Inc.; *Int'l*, pg. 898
VALOIS S.A.S.—See AptarGroup, Inc.; *U.S. Public*, pg. 175
VANDA PHARMACEUTICALS GERMANY GMBH—See Vanda Pharmaceuticals Inc.; *U.S. Public*, pg. 2275
VANDA PHARMACEUTICALS INC.; *U.S. Public*, pg. 2274
VANRX PHARMASYSTEMS INC.—See Danaher Corporation; *U.S. Public*, pg. 631
VASOACTIVE PHARMACEUTICALS, INC.; *U.S. Private*, pg. 4347
VASONOVA, INC.—See Teleflex Incorporated; *U.S. Public*, pg. 1996
VCG&A, INC.—See IQVIA Holdings Inc.; *U.S. Public*, pg. 1170
VECTURA GMBH—See Philip Morris International Inc.; *U.S. Public*, pg. 1688
VECTURA GROUP PLC - NOTTINGHAM—See Philip Morris International Inc.; *U.S. Public*, pg. 1688
VECTURA GROUP PLC—See Philip Morris International Inc.; *U.S. Public*, pg. 1688
VECTURA INC—See Philip Morris International Inc.; *U.S. Public*, pg. 1688
VEEGO PHARMA LLC; *U.S. Private*, pg. 4353
VELOXIS PHARMACEUTICALS A/S—See Asahi Kasei Corporation; *Int'l*, pg. 597
VELOXIS PHARMACEUTICALS, INC.—See Asahi Kasei Corporation; *Int'l*, pg. 597
VENCO FARMACEUTICA S.A.—See Merck & Co., Inc.; *U.S. Public*, pg. 1421
VERASTEM, INC.; *U.S. Public*, pg. 2280
VERDE SCIENCE, INC.; *U.S. Public*, pg. 2280
VERNALIS DEVELOPMENT LIMITED—See Ligand Pharmaceuticals Incorporated; *U.S. Public*, pg. 1314
VERNALIS PLC—See Ligand Pharmaceuticals Incorporated; *U.S. Public*, pg. 1314
VERNALIS (R&D) LTD—See Ligand Pharmaceuticals Incorporated; *U.S. Public*, pg. 1314
VERRICA PHARMACEUTICALS, INC.; *U.S. Public*, pg. 2287
VERSEON CORPORATION; *U.S. Public*, pg. 2287
VERTEX PHARMACEUTICALS (EUROPE) LIMITED—See Vertex Pharmaceuticals Incorporated; *U.S. Public*, pg. 2287
VERTEX PHARMACEUTICALS INCORPORATED; *U.S. Public*, pg. 2287
VESTERALENS NATURPRODUKTER AB—See Pfizer Inc.; *U.S. Public*, pg. 1683
VESTERALENS NATURPRODUKTER AS—See Pfizer Inc.; *U.S. Public*, pg. 1683
VET PHARMA FRIESOYTHE GMBH—See Merck & Co., Inc.; *U.S. Public*, pg. 1421
VET PHARM, INC.; *U.S. Private*, pg. 4373
VIADERMA, INC.; *U.S. Public*, pg. 2291
VIATRIS INC.; *U.S. Public*, pg. 2293
VICTORIA SEGUROS S.A.—See Bago Group; *Int'l*, pg. 799
VICTUS, INC.; *U.S. Public*, pg. 4380
VICURON PHARMACEUTICALS, INC—See AbbVie Inc.; *U.S. Public*, pg. 23

CORPORATE AFFILIATIONS

VIDA CELL S.A.—See Abbott Laboratories; *U.S. Public*, pg. 21
VIFOR AG—See CSL Limited; *Int'l*, pg. 1866
VIFOR (INTERNATIONAL) INC.—See CSL Limited; *Int'l*, pg. 1866
VIFOR PHARMA AMERICA LATINA S.A.—See CSL Limited; *Int'l*, pg. 1866
VIFOR PHARMA ASIA PACIFIC PTE. LIMITED—See CSL Limited; *Int'l*, pg. 1866
VIFOR PHARMA ASPREVA INTERNATIONAL LTD.—See CSL Limited; *Int'l*, pg. 1866
VIFOR PHARMA ASPREVA PHARMACEUTICALS INC.—See CSL Limited; *Int'l*, pg. 1866
VIFOR PHARMA ASPREVA PHARMACEUTICALS LIMITED—See CSL Limited; *Int'l*, pg. 1866
VIFOR PHARMA ASPREVA PHARMACEUTICALS SA—See CSL Limited; *Int'l*, pg. 1866
VIFOR PHARMA BELGIE NV—See CSL Limited; *Int'l*, pg. 1866
VIFOR PHARMA DEUTSCHLAND GMBH—See CSL Limited; *Int'l*, pg. 1866
VIFOR PHARMA ESPANA, S.L.—See CSL Limited; *Int'l*, pg. 1866
VIFOR PHARMA ITALIA S.R.L.—See CSL Limited; *Int'l*, pg. 1867
VIFOR PHARMA LTD.—See CSL Limited; *Int'l*, pg. 1866
VIFOR PHARMA MANAGEMENT LTD.—See CSL Limited; *Int'l*, pg. 1867
VIFOR PHARMA NORDISKA AB—See CSL Limited; *Int'l*, pg. 1867
VIFOR PHARMA OSTERREICH GMBH—See CSL Limited; *Int'l*, pg. 1867
VIFOR PHARMA PTY LTD.—See CSL Limited; *Int'l*, pg. 1867
VIFOR PHARMA ROMANIA S.R.L.—See CSL Limited; *Int'l*, pg. 1867
VIFOR PHARMA—See CSL Limited; *Int'l*, pg. 1866
VIFOR PHARMA UK LIMITED—See CSL Limited; *Int'l*, pg. 1867
VIIV HEALTHCARE—See GSK plc; *Int'l*, pg. 3149
VIIV HEALTHCARE—See Pfizer Inc.; *U.S. Public*, pg. 1683
VIKING THERAPEUTICS, INC.; *U.S. Public*, pg. 2297
VIRACTA THERAPEUTICS, INC.; *U.S. Public*, pg. 2298
VIRALGEN COMMERCIAL THERAPEUTIC VECTOR CORE, S.L.—See Bayer Aktiengesellschaft; *Int'l*, pg. 910
VIRALGEN VECTOR CORE, S.L.—See Bayer Aktiengesellschaft; *Int'l*, pg. 910
VIRCO BVBA—See Johnson & Johnson; *U.S. Public*, pg. 1200
VIREO GROWTH INC.; *U.S. Public*, pg. 2299
VIRIDAX CORPORATION; *U.S. Private*, pg. 4388
VIRIDIAN THERAPEUTICS, INC.; *U.S. Public*, pg. 2299
VIRMEDICA INC.—See General Atlantic Service Company, L.P.; *U.S. Private*, pg. 1662
VIROBAY, INC.; *U.S. Public*, pg. 4388
VIRPAX PHARMACEUTICALS, INC.; *U.S. Public*, pg. 2299
VISO FARMACEUTICA S.L.U.—See Glenmark Pharmaceuticals Limited; *Int'l*, pg. 2992
VISTAGEN THERAPEUTICS, INC.—See VistaGen Therapeutics, Inc.; *U.S. Public*, pg. 2305
VISTAPHARM, INC.—See Warburg Pincus LLC; *U.S. Private*, pg. 4440
VITACARE PRESCRIPTION SERVICES, INC.—See GoodRx Holdings, Inc.; *U.S. Public*, pg. 952
VITAKEM NUTRACEUTICAL, INC.; *U.S. Private*, pg. 4405
VITALINK INDUSTRY (SHENZHEN) COMPANY LIMITED-PINGHU—See CN Innovations Holdings Limited; *Int'l*, pg. 1673
VITALINK INDUSTRY (SHENZHEN) COMPANY LIMITED—See CN Innovations Holdings Limited; *Int'l*, pg. 1673
VITAL PHARMACEUTICALS, INC.—See Monster Beverage Corporation; *U.S. Public*, pg. 1465
VITAMEDMD, LLC—See TherapeuticsMD, Inc.; *U.S. Public*, pg. 2145
VITAMIN WORLD USA CORPORATION—See China Feihe Limited; *Int'l*, pg. 1502
VITA QUEST INTERNATIONAL INC.; *U.S. Private*, pg. 4405
VIT-BEST NUTRITION, INC.—See Kingdomway Nutrition, Inc.; *U.S. Private*, pg. 2310
VIVITIDE, LLC—See Ampersand Management LLC; *U.S. Private*, pg. 266
VIVUS, INC.; *U.S. Public*, pg. 2307
VOGUE INTERNATIONAL LLC—See Kenvue Inc.; *U.S. Public*, pg. 1224
VON HEYDEN PHARMA GMBH—See Bristol-Myers Squibb Company; *U.S. Public*, pg. 387
VR LABORATORIES, LLC; *U.S. Private*, pg. 4415
VS HERCULES LLC—See B. Riley Financial, Inc.; *U.S. Public*, pg. 261
VS HERCULES LLC—See Irradiant Partners, LP; *U.S. Private*, pg. 2141
VTV THERAPEUTICS LLC—See MacAndrews & Forbes Incorporated; *U.S. Private*, pg. 2534
VYNE PHARMACEUTICALS LTD.—See VYNE Therapeutics Inc.; *U.S. Public*, pg. 2315
WARNER CHILCOTT COMPANY, LLC—See AbbVie Inc.; *U.S. Public*, pg. 24

N.A.I.C.S. INDEX

325413 — IN-VITRO DIAGNOSTIC...

WARNER CHILCOTT CORPORATION—See AbbVie Inc.; *U.S. Public*, pg. 24
WARNER CHILCOTT DEUTSCHLAND GMBH—See AbbVie Inc.; *U.S. Public*, pg. 24
WARNER CHILCOTT (IRELAND) LIMITED—See AbbVie Inc.; *U.S. Public*, pg. 24
WARNER CHILCOTT ITALY S.R.L.—See AbbVie Inc.; *U.S. Public*, pg. 24
WARNER CHILCOTT PHARMACEUTICALS B.V.B.A.—See AbbVie Inc.; *U.S. Public*, pg. 24
WARNER CHILCOTT PUERTO RICO LLC—See AbbVie Inc.; *U.S. Public*, pg. 24
WARNER CHILCOTT UK LTD.—See AbbVie Inc.; *U.S. Public*, pg. 24
WARNER CHILCOTT (US), LLC—See AbbVie Inc.; *U.S. Public*, pg. 24
WARNER LAMBERT DEL URUGUAY S.A.—See Pfizer Inc.; *U.S. Public*, pg. 1683
WATERFILTERS.NET LLC.; *U.S. Private*, pg. 4453
WAVELENGTH ENTERPRISES, INC.—See SK Capital Partners, LP; *U.S. Private*, pg. 3680
WAVELENGTH PHARMACEUTICALS LTD.—See SK Capital Partners, LP; *U.S. Private*, pg. 3680
WAYPOINT BIOMEDICAL HOLDINGS, INC.; *U.S. Public*, pg. 2338
WC PHARMACEUTICALS I LIMITED—See AbbVie Inc.; *U.S. Public*, pg. 24
WELLPARTNER, INC.; *U.S. Private*, pg. 4476
WELLSPRING PHARMACEUTICAL CORPORATION—See Avista Capital Partners, L.P.; *U.S. Private*, pg. 409
WEST PHARMACEUTICAL SERVICES BRASIL LTDA.—See West Pharmaceutical Services, Inc.; *U.S. Public*, pg. 2353
WEST PHARMACEUTICAL SERVICES LAKEWOOD, INC.—See West Pharmaceutical Services, Inc.; *U.S. Public*, pg. 2353
WESTPOINT VETERINARY GROUP—See August Equity LLP; *Int'l*, pg. 703
WEST-WARD PHARMACEUTICALS CORP.—See Hikma Pharmaceuticals PLC; *Int'l*, pg. 3390
WHITE RIVER ENERGY CORP.; *U.S. Public*, pg. 2369
WICK PHARMA—See The Procter & Gamble Company; *U.S. Public*, pg. 2122
WIKILEAF TECHNOLOGIES, INC.; *U.S. Public*, pg. 2370
WINSTON PHARMACEUTICALS, INC.; *U.S. Public*, pg. 2374
WORLDWIDE CLINICAL TRIALS, INC.—See The Jordan Company, L.P.; *U.S. Private*, pg. 4063
WUHAN BIOCAUSE PHARMACEUTICAL DEVELOPMENT CO., LTD.—See Hubei Biocause Pharmaceutical Co., Ltd.; *Int'l*, pg. 3517
WUHAN WUYAO PHARMACEUTICAL CO., LTD.—See Grand Pharmaceutical Group Limited; *Int'l*, pg. 3056
WUXI YUSHOU MEDICAL APPLIANCES CO., LTD.—See Canmax Technologies Co., Ltd.; *Int'l*, pg. 1291
WYETH LEDERLE S.R.L.—See Pfizer Inc.; *U.S. Public*, pg. 1683
WYETH (MALAYSIA) SDN. BHD.—See Pfizer Inc.; *U.S. Public*, pg. 1683
WYETH NUTRITIONAL (CHINA) CO., LTD.—See Pfizer Inc.; *U.S. Public*, pg. 1683
WYETH PAKISTAN LIMITED—See Pfizer Inc.; *U.S. Public*, pg. 1683
WYETH PHARMACEUTICAL CO., LTD.—See Pfizer Inc.; *U.S. Public*, pg. 1683
XBIOTECH INC.; *U.S. Public*, pg. 2385
XENCOR, INC.; *U.S. Public*, pg. 2385
XENETIC BIOSCIENCES, INC.; *U.S. Public*, pg. 2386
XENETIC BIOSCIENCES PLC—See Xenetic Biosciences, Inc.; *U.S. Public*, pg. 2386
XEPA-SOUL PATTINSON (MALAYSIA) SDN. BHD.—See Apex Healthcare Berhad; *Int'l*, pg. 511
XERIS PHARMACEUTICALS, INC.—See Xeris Biopharma Holdings, Inc.; *U.S. Public*, pg. 2386
XF ENTERPRISES INC.; *U.S. Private*, pg. 4581
XIAMEN EAGLE DON PHARMACEUTICALS CO., LTD.—See Eagle Health Holdings Limited; *Int'l*, pg. 2264
XIAMEN TIGER MEDICALS CO., LTD.—See Haw Par Corporation Limited; *Int'l*, pg. 3287
XIAN BEILIN PHARMACEUTICAL COMPANY LIMITED—See Grand Pharmaceutical Group Limited; *Int'l*, pg. 3056
XIAN-JANSSEN PHARMACEUTICAL LTD.—See Johnson & Johnson; *U.S. Public*, pg. 1197
XINJIANG TIANSHAN PHARMACEUTICALS INDUSTRY CO., LTD.—See China Meheco Group Co., Ltd.; *Int'l*, pg. 1519
XINJIANG TOPFOND HENGDE PHARMACEUTICAL CO., LTD.—See China Mohooo Group Co., Ltd.; *Int'l*, pg. 1519
XOMA CORPORATION; *U.S. Public*, pg. 2391
XTTRIUM LABORATORIES INC.; *U.S. Private*, pg. 4583
XYLEM MANUFACTURING AUSTRIA GMBH—See Xylem Inc.; *U.S. Public*, pg. 2397
YABROFARMA LDA—See Astellas Pharma Inc.; *Int'l*, pg. 652
YAEYAMA SHOKUSAN CO., LTD.—See euglena Co., Ltd.; *Int'l*, pg. 2526
YAMANOUCHI (THAILAND) CO., LTD.—See Astellas Pharma Inc.; *Int'l*, pg. 653
YANGLING DAILYHEALTH BIO-ENGINEERING TECHNOLOGY CO. LIMITED—See Cathay International Holdings Limited; *Int'l*, pg. 1360
YICHANG HEC CHANGJIANG PHARMACEUTICAL CO., LTD.—See Guangdong Hec Technology Holding Co., Ltd.; *Int'l*, pg. 3155
Y-MABS THERAPEUTICS A/S—See Y-mAbs Therapeutics, Inc.; *U.S. Public*, pg. 2398
Y-MABS THERAPEUTICS, INC.; *U.S. Public*, pg. 2398
YORK S.A—See Hypera Pharma S.A.; *Int'l*, pg. 3553
ZAO ASTELLAS PHARMA—See Astellas Pharma Inc.; *Int'l*, pg. 653
ZARBEE'S, INC.—See Kenvue Inc.; *U.S. Public*, pg. 1224
ZDRAVIJE AD—See Frontier Pharma Limited; *Int'l*, pg. 2795
ZENAD GROUP CO. FOR TRADING & CONTRACTING. & PHARMASOM LTD.—See Dar Al Dawa Development & Investment Co.; *Int'l*, pg. 1971
ZENTIVA GROUP, A.S.—See Advent International Corporation; *U.S. Private*, pg. 108
ZENTIVA INTERNATIONAL A.S.—See Advent International Corporation; *U.S. Private*, pg. 108
ZENTIVA SAGLIK URUNLERI SAN.VE TIC.A.S.—See Advent International Corporation; *U.S. Private*, pg. 108
ZENTIVA S.A.—See Advent International Corporation; *U.S. Private*, pg. 108
ZEVRA THERAPEUTICS, INC.; *U.S. Public*, pg. 2403
ZHEJIANG ECO BIOK ANIMAL HEALTH PRODUCTS LIMITED—See ECO Animal Health Group plc; *Int'l*, pg. 2292
ZHEJIANG POLY. CO., LTD.—See Hainan Poly Pharm.Co.,Ltd.; *Int'l*, pg. 3212
ZHEJIANG WANSHENG PHARMACEUTICAL CO., LTD.—See 3SBio Inc.; *Int'l*, pg. 9
ZHENGJIANG WANSHENG PHARMACEUTICAL CO., LTD. - QINGSHAN PLANT—See 3SBio Inc.; *Int'l*, pg. 10
ZHENGJIANG WANSHENG PHARMACEUTICAL CO., LTD.—See 3SBio Inc.; *Int'l*, pg. 10
ZICAM LLC—See Gryphon Investors, LLC; *U.S. Private*, pg. 1799
ZOETIS ARGENTINA S.R.L.—See Zoetis, Inc.; *U.S. Public*, pg. 2410
ZOETIS BELGIUM S.A.—See Zoetis, Inc.; *U.S. Public*, pg. 2410
ZOETIS B.V.—See Zoetis, Inc.; *U.S. Public*, pg. 2410
ZOETIS CANADA INC.—See Zoetis, Inc.; *U.S. Public*, pg. 2410
ZOETIS, C.A.—See Zoetis, Inc.; *U.S. Public*, pg. 2410
ZOETIS COSTA RICA, S.R.L.—See Zoetis, Inc.; *U.S. Public*, pg. 2410
ZOETIS DE CHILE S.A.—See Zoetis, Inc.; *U.S. Public*, pg. 2410
ZOETIS DEUTSCHLAND GMBH—See Zoetis, Inc.; *U.S. Public*, pg. 2410
ZOETIS EGYPT LLC—See Zoetis, Inc.; *U.S. Public*, pg. 2410
ZOETIS FINLAND OY—See Zoetis, Inc.; *U.S. Public*, pg. 2410
ZOETIS HELLAS S.A.—See Zoetis, Inc.; *U.S. Public*, pg. 2410
ZOETIS HUNGARY KFT.—See Zoetis, Inc.; *U.S. Public*, pg. 2410
ZOETIS, INC. - LINCOLN—See Zoetis, Inc.; *U.S. Public*, pg. 2410
ZOETIS, INC.; *U.S. Public*, pg. 2409
ZOETIS, INC. - WHITE HALL—See Zoetis, Inc.; *U.S. Public*, pg. 2410
ZOETIS INDIA LIMITED—See Zoetis, Inc.; *U.S. Public*, pg. 2410
ZOETIS INDUSTRIA DE PRODUTOS VETERINARIOS LTDA.—See Zoetis, Inc.; *U.S. Public*, pg. 2410
ZOETIS IRELAND LIMITED—See Zoetis, Inc.; *U.S. Public*, pg. 2410
ZOETIS JAPAN K.K.—See Zoetis, Inc.; *U.S. Public*, pg. 2410
ZOETIS KOREA LTD.—See Zoetis, Inc.; *U.S. Public*, pg. 2410
ZOETIS MALAYSIA SDN. BHD.—See Zoetis, Inc.; *U.S. Public*, pg. 2410
ZOETIS MEXICO, S. DE R.L. DE C.V.—See Zoetis, Inc.; *U.S. Public*, pg. 2410
ZOETIS OOO—See Zoetis, Inc.; *U.S. Public*, pg. 2410
ZOETIS POLSKA SP. Z O.O—See Zoetis, Inc.; *U.S. Public*, pg. 2410
ZOETIS PORTUGAL, LDA.—See Zoetis, Inc.; *U.S. Public*, pg. 2410
ZOETIS ROMANIA S.R.L.—See Zoetis, Inc.; *U.S. Public*, pg. 2410
ZOETIS SALUD ANIMAL, C.A.—See Zoetis, Inc.; *U.S. Public*, pg. 2410
ZOETIS SCHWEIZ GMBH—See Zoetis, Inc.; *U.S. Public*, pg. 2410
ZOETIS SOUTH AFRICA (PTY) LTD.—See Zoetis, Inc.; *U.S. Public*, pg. 2410
ZOETIS SPAIN, S.L.—See Zoetis, Inc.; *U.S. Public*, pg. 2410
ZOETIS S.R.L.—See Zoetis, Inc.; *U.S. Public*, pg. 2410
ZOETIS TAIWAN LIMITED—See Zoetis, Inc.; *U.S. Public*, pg. 2410
ZOETIS UK LIMITED—See Zoetis, Inc.; *U.S. Public*, pg. 2410
ZOETIS UKRAINE LLC—See Zoetis, Inc.; *U.S. Public*, pg. 2410
ZOETIS VIETNAM LIMITED LIABILITY COMPANY—See Zoetis, Inc.; *U.S. Public*, pg. 2410
ZOMEDICA CORP.; *U.S. Public*, pg. 2410
ZOSANO PHARMA CORPORATION; *U.S. Public*, pg. 2411
ZS PHARMA, INC.—See AstraZeneca PLC; *Int'l*, pg. 661
ZYMETECH EHF—See Enzymatica AB; *Int'l*, pg. 2457
ZYMEWORKS BC INC.—See Zymeworks Inc.; *U.S. Public*, pg. 2414
ZYMEWORKS INC.; *U.S. Public*, pg. 2414
ZYNERBA PHARMACEUTICALS, INC.—See Harmony Biosciences Holdings, Inc.; *U.S. Public*, pg. 986
ZYVERSA THERAPEUTICS, INC.; *U.S. Public*, pg. 2414

325413 — IN-VITRO DIAGNOSTIC SUBSTANCE MANUFACTURING

4BASEBIO S.L.U—See 2invest AG; *Int'l*, pg. 5
ABBOTT DIABETES CARE, INC.—See Abbott Laboratories; *U.S. Public*, pg. 14
ABBOTT FRANCE S.A.—See Abbott Laboratories; *U.S. Public*, pg. 15
ABBOTT LABORATORIES, LIMITADA—See Abbott Laboratories; *U.S. Public*, pg. 16
ABBOTT RAPID DIAGNOSTICS JENA GMBH—See Abbott Laboratories; *U.S. Public*, pg. 17
AGENDIA NV; *Int'l*, pg. 205
AJ INNUSCREEN GMBH—See Endress+Hauser (International) Holding AG; *Int'l*, pg. 2405
ALERE INC.—See Abbott Laboratories; *U.S. Public*, pg. 18
ALLERGOPHARMA VERTRIEBSGES, MBH—See Dermapharm Holding SE; *Int'l*, pg. 2043
AMERICAN CRYOSTEM CORPORATION; *U.S. Public*, pg. 98
AMERICAN VIETNAMESE BIOTECH INCORPORATION; *Int'l*, pg. 423
ANATECH, LTD.—See Cancer Diagnostics, Inc.; *U.S. Private*, pg. 733
ARCA BIOPHARMA, INC.; *U.S. Public*, pg. 179
ATHENA DIAGNOSTICS, INC.—See Quest Diagnostics, Inc.; *U.S. Public*, pg. 1755
BAIYE TRADING (SHANGHAI) CO., LTD.; *Int'l*, pg. 803
BANYAN BIOMARKERS INC.; *U.S. Private*, pg. 470
BEIJING IDEXX LABORATORIES CO. LIMITED—See IDEXX Laboratories, Inc.; *U.S. Public*, pg. 1092
BEIJING LEADMAN BIOCHEMISTRY CO., LTD.; *Int'l*, pg. 954
BEIJING PHADIA DIAGNOSTICS CO LTD—See Thermo Fisher Scientific Inc.; *U.S. Public*, pg. 2145
BEIJING STRONG BIOTECHNOLOGIES, INC.; *Int'l*, pg. 958
BIOCARTIS GROUP NV; *Int'l*, pg. 1036
BIONIME AUSTRALIA PTY LIMITED—See Bionime Corporation; *Int'l*, pg. 1040
BIONIME GMBH—See Bionime Corporation; *Int'l*, pg. 1040
BIONIME USA CORPORATION—See Bionime Corporation; *Int'l*, pg. 1040
BIO-RAD LABORATORII LLC—See Bio-Rad Laboratories, Inc.; *U.S. Public*, pg. 333
BIOSYNEX SA; *Int'l*, pg. 1042
BONE THERAPEUTICS SA; *Int'l*, pg. 1106
B.R.A.H.M.S GMBH—See Thermo Fisher Scientific Inc.; *U.S. Public*, pg. 2145
CANAG DIAGNOSTICS (BEIJING) CO., LTD.—See H.U. Group Holdings, Inc.; *Int'l*, pg. 3196
CARDIFF ONCOLOGY, INC.; *U.S. Public*, pg. 433
CELLSCREEN DIRECT LIMITED; *Int'l*, pg. 1394
CELLSEED INC.; *Int'l*, pg. 1394
CELL SOURCE, INC.; *U.S. Public*, pg. 465
CENTRUS INTERNATIONAL, INC.—See Neogen Corporation; *U.S. Public*, pg. 1505
CHROMOLOGIC LLC; *U.S. Private*, pg. 892
COMPUMED, INC.; *U.S. Public*, pg. 561
CORGENIX MEDICAL CORPORATION—See Caisse de Depot et Placement du Quebec; *Int'l*, pg. 1255
CORGENIX MEDICAL CORPORATION—See CVC Capital Partners SICAV-FIS S.A.; *Int'l*, pg. 1884
CURETIS USA—See OpGen, Inc.; *U.S. Public*, pg. 1607
CYNATA THERAPEUTICS LIMITED; *Int'l*, pg. 1896
DAKO BELGIUM N.V.—See Agilent Technologies, Inc.; *U.S. Public*, pg. 61
DAKO DENMARK A/S—See Agilent Technologies, Inc.; *U.S. Public*, pg. 61
DAKO ITALIA S.P.A.—See Agilent Technologies, Inc.; *U.S. Public*, pg. 61
DAKO SWEDEN AB—See Agilent Technologies, Inc.; *U.S. Public*, pg. 61
DENKA SEIKEN CO., LTD.—See Denki Company Limited; *Int'l*, pg. 2027
DIAGNOSTIC CONSULTING NETWORK, INC.; *U.S. Private*, pg. 1222
DIAGNOSTIC HYBRIDS, INC.—See QuidelOrtho Corporation; *U.S. Public*, pg. 1757

325413 — IN-VITRO DIAGNOSTIC...

DIASORIN DEUTSCHLAND GMBH—See DiaSorin S.p.A.; *Int'l*, pg. 2106
DIASORIN INC.—See DiaSorin S.p.A.; *Int'l*, pg. 2106
DIASORIN S.P.A.; *Int'l*, pg. 2106
EARLYDETECT INC.; *U.S. Private*, pg. 1314
EPIGENOMICS INC.—See Epigenomics AG; *Int'l*, pg. 2460
EUROFINS ABRAXIS, INC.—See Eurofins Scientific S.E.; *Int'l*, pg. 2536
FALCO BIOSYSTEMS LTD.—See FALCO Holdings Co. Ltd.; *Int'l*, pg. 2610
GENTIAN DIAGNOSTICS AS; *Int'l*, pg. 2928
GETEIN BIOTECH, INC.; *Int'l*, pg. 2947
GREEN CROSS MEDICAL SCIENCE CORPORATION—See GC Biopharma Corp.; *Int'l*, pg. 2894
GRIFOLS AUSTRALIA PTY LTD.—See Grifols, S.A.; *Int'l*, pg. 3084
GRIFOLS CHIRON DIAGNOSTICS CORP.—See Grifols, S.A.; *Int'l*, pg. 3084
GUANGDONG HYBRIBIO BIOTECH CO., LTD.; *Int'l*, pg. 3156
HEALTH DISCOVERY CORPORATION; *U.S. Public*, pg. 1014
IDEXX LABORATORIES, INC.; *U.S. Public*, pg. 1092
IMMUCELL CORPORATION; *U.S. Public*, pg. 1112
IMMUNOMEDICS, B.V.—See Gilead Sciences, Inc.; *U.S. Public*, pg. 938
IMMUNOMEDICS GMBH—See Gilead Sciences, Inc.; *U.S. Public*, pg. 938
INNOMINATA—See Eurobio Scientific SA; *Int'l*, pg. 2533
INTERPACE DIAGNOSTICS CORPORATION—See Interpace Biosciences, Inc.; *U.S. Public*, pg. 1158
INTERPACE DIAGNOSTICS, LLC—See Interpace Biosciences, Inc.; *U.S. Public*, pg. 1158
JS GENETICS, INC.—See Interpace Biosciences, Inc.; *U.S. Public*, pg. 1158
LABORATORY SPECIALITIES PROPRIETARY LTD.—See Thermo Fisher Scientific Inc.; *U.S. Public*, pg. 2147
LAUNCH DIAGNOSTICS LIMITED—See Avacta Group plc; *Int'l*, pg. 733
LINKAGE BIOSCIENCES, INC.—See Thermo Fisher Scientific Inc.; *U.S. Public*, pg. 2149
LIPOSCIENCE, INC.—See Laboratory Corporation of America Holdings; *U.S. Public*, pg. 1287
MASTHERCELL GLOBAL, INC.—See Catalent, Inc.; *U.S. Public*, pg. 448
MASTHERCELL, S.A.—See Catalent, Inc.; *U.S. Public*, pg. 448
MASTHERCELL U.S., LLC—See Catalent, Inc.; *U.S. Public*, pg. 448
MERIDIAN BIOSCIENCE EUROPE B.V.—See Meridian Bioscience Inc.; *U.S. Public*, pg. 1424
MERIDIAN BIOSCIENCE EUROPE FRANCE—See Meridian Bioscience Inc.; *U.S. Public*, pg. 1424
MERIDIAN BIOSCIENCE EUROPE S.A.—See Meridian Bioscience Inc.; *U.S. Public*, pg. 1424
MWG BIOTECH INC.—See Eurofins Scientific S.E.; *Int'l*, pg. 2549
MYRIAD GENETICS, INC.; *U.S. Public*, pg. 1489
NAVIDEA BIOPHARMACEUTICALS, INC.; *U.S. Public*, pg. 1500
ORCHID BIOMEDICAL SYSTEMS PVT LTD.—See Revvity, Inc.; *U.S. Public*, pg. 1795
ORGENESIS INC.; *U.S. Public*, pg. 1616
ORTHO-CLINICAL DIAGNOSTICS GMBH—See QuidelOrtho Corporation; *U.S. Public*, pg. 1756
ORTHO-CLINICAL DIAGNOSTICS, INC. ROCHESTER—See QuidelOrtho Corporation; *U.S. Public*, pg. 1757
ORTHO-CLINICAL DIAGNOSTICS, INC.—See QuidelOrtho Corporation; *U.S. Public*, pg. 1756
ORTHO-CLINICAL DIAGNOSTICS K.K.—See QuidelOrtho Corporation; *U.S. Public*, pg. 1756
ORTHO-CLINICAL DIAGNOSTICS N.V.—See QuidelOrtho Corporation; *U.S. Public*, pg. 1756
ORTHO-CLINICAL DIAGNOSTICS S.A.—See QuidelOrtho Corporation; *U.S. Public*, pg. 1756
ORTHO-CLINICAL DIAGNOSTICS—See QuidelOrtho Corporation; *U.S. Public*, pg. 1756
ORTHO-CLINICAL DIAGNOSTICS S.P.A.—See QuidelOrtho Corporation; *U.S. Public*, pg. 1756
OSI PHARMACEUTICALS, INC.—See Astellas Pharma Inc.; *Int'l*, pg. 653
OXFORD IMMUNOTEC GLOBAL LIMITED—See Revvity, Inc.; *U.S. Public*, pg. 1794
OXFORD IMMUNOTEC, INC.—See Revvity, Inc.; *U.S. Public*, pg. 1794
PHADIA AG—See Thermo Fisher Scientific Inc.; *U.S. Public*, pg. 2147
PHADIA APS—See Thermo Fisher Scientific Inc.; *U.S. Public*, pg. 2147
PHADIA AUSTRIA GMBH—See Thermo Fisher Scientific Inc.; *U.S. Public*, pg. 2147
PHADIA B.V.—See Thermo Fisher Scientific Inc.; *U.S. Public*, pg. 2147
PHADIA DIAGNOSTICOS LTDA.—See Thermo Fisher Scientific Inc.; *U.S. Public*, pg. 2147
PHADIA GMBH—See Thermo Fisher Scientific Inc.; *U.S. Public*, pg. 2147
PHADIA K.K.—See Thermo Fisher Scientific Inc.; *U.S. Public*, pg. 2147
PHADIA KOREA CO. LTD.—See Thermo Fisher Scientific Inc.; *U.S. Public*, pg. 2147
PHADIA LTD.—See Thermo Fisher Scientific Inc.; *U.S. Public*, pg. 2147
PHADIA MULTIPLEXING DIAGNOSTICS GMBH—See Thermo Fisher Scientific Inc.; *U.S. Public*, pg. 2147
PHADIA NV/SA—See Thermo Fisher Scientific Inc.; *U.S. Public*, pg. 2147
PHADIA OY—See Thermo Fisher Scientific Inc.; *U.S. Public*, pg. 2148
PHADIA SOCIEDADE UNIPESSOAL LDA—See Thermo Fisher Scientific Inc.; *U.S. Public*, pg. 2148
PHADIA SPAIN S.L.—See Thermo Fisher Scientific Inc.; *U.S. Public*, pg. 2148
PHADIA S.R.O.—See Thermo Fisher Scientific Inc.; *U.S. Public*, pg. 2148
PHADIA TAIWAN INC.—See Thermo Fisher Scientific Inc.; *U.S. Public*, pg. 2148
PRINCETON BIOMEDITECH CORP.; *U.S. Private*, pg. 3264
PROGNOST SYSTEMS INC.—See Burckhardt Compression Holding AG; *Int'l*, pg. 1221
PROTEINTECH GROUP, INC.; *U.S. Private*, pg. 3289
QUIDEL CORPORATION—See QuidelOrtho Corporation; *U.S. Public*, pg. 1757
REGENXBIO INC.; *U.S. Public*, pg. 1775
RIDGE DIAGNOSTICS, INC.; *U.S. Private*, pg. 3432
SOMAGEN DIAGNOSTICS INC.—See Diploma PLC; *Int'l*, pg. 2129
SSI DIAGNOSTICA A/S—See Adelis Equity Partners AB; *Int'l*, pg. 142
T2 BIOSYSTEMS, INC.; *U.S. Public*, pg. 1978
TEARLAB CORP.—See Accelmed Partners II Management, LLC; *U.S. Private*, pg. 50
TEMPEST THERAPEUTICS, INC.; *U.S. Public*, pg. 1999
THERMO FISHER DIAGNOSTICS SPA—See Thermo Fisher Scientific Inc.; *U.S. Public*, pg. 2148
THIRD WAVE AGBIO, INC.—See Hologic, Inc.; *U.S. Public*, pg. 1045
THIRD WAVE TECHNOLOGIES, INC.—See Hologic, Inc.; *U.S. Public*, pg. 1045
TULIP DIAGNOSTICS PVT LTD.—See Revvity, Inc.; *U.S. Public*, pg. 1795
TURNER IMAGING SYSTEMS, INC.—See RadNet, Inc.; *U.S. Public*, pg. 1761
VIGEO ITALIA S.R.L—See Moody's Corporation; *U.S. Public*, pg. 1469
VITATEX INC.—See Applied DNA Sciences, Inc.; *U.S. Public*, pg. 170

325414 — BIOLOGICAL PRODUCT (EXCEPT DIAGNOSTIC) MANUFACTURING

ABNOVA (TAIWAN) CORPORATION; *Int'l*, pg. 65
ACERAGEN, INC.; *U.S. Public*, pg. 34
ACORDA THERAPEUTICS, INC.; *U.S. Public*, pg. 36
ACTIVE MOTIF, INC.; *U.S. Private*, pg. 70
ACTIVE MOTIF-JAPAN—See Active Motif, Inc.; *U.S. Private*, pg. 70
ADBIOTECH CO., LTD.; *Int'l*, pg. 126
AGC BIOLOGICS A/S—See AGC Inc.; *Int'l*, pg. 201
AGC BIOLOGICS INC.—See AGC Inc.; *Int'l*, pg. 201
AGENNIX INCORPORATED—See Agennix AG; *Int'l*, pg. 205
AGRISOMA BIOSCIENCES INC.—See Calyx Ventures Inc.; *Int'l*, pg. 1266
AGRITECH WORLWIDE, INC.; *U.S. Private*, pg. 129
AIM IMMUNOTECH INC.; *U.S. Public*, pg. 63
AIM VACCINE CO., LTD.; *Int'l*, pg. 232
AIRBORNE, INC.—See GF Capital Management & Advisors, LLC; *U.S. Private*, pg. 1689
AIRTECH EQUIPMENT PTE. LTD.—See AIRTECH JAPAN, LTD.; *Int'l*, pg. 249
ALDEVRON, LLC—See Danaher Corporation; *U.S. Public*, pg. 624
ALLABINC DE MEXICO, S.A. DE C.V.—See Zoetis, Inc.; *U.S. Public*, pg. 2409
AMGEN INC.; *U.S. Public*, pg. 122
AMGEN MANUFACTURING, LIMITED—See Amgen Inc.; *U.S. Public*, pg. 123
AMGEN RESEARCH (MUNICH) GMBH—See Amgen Inc.; *U.S. Public*, pg. 123
AMGEN SINGAPORE MANUFACTURING PTE. LTD.—See Amgen Inc.; *U.S. Public*, pg. 123
AMOEBA BIOCIDE SAS; *Int'l*, pg. 429
ANIKA THERAPEUTICS, INC.; *U.S. Public*, pg. 137
ANTIBODIES INCORPORATED—See Janel Corporation; *U.S. Public*, pg. 1187
APPLIED BIOCODE CORP.; *U.S. Public*, pg. 169
APPLIED BIOSYSTEMS DE MEXICO S. DE R.L. DE C.V.—See Thermo Fisher Scientific Inc.; *U.S. Public*, pg. 2148
APRINNOVA, LLC—See Amyris, Inc.; *U.S. Public*, pg. 134
ARBOR BIOSCIENCES (BIODISCOVERY LLC)—See Daicel Corporation; *Int'l*, pg. 1918
ARROWHEAD PHARMACEUTICALS, INC.; *U.S. Public*, pg. 200
ASPEN GERMANY GMBH—See Aspen Pharmacare Holdings Limited; *Int'l*, pg. 629
ASPEN PHARMACARE ESPANA S.L.—See Aspen Pharmacare Holdings Limited; *Int'l*, pg. 629
ASPEN PHARMACARE NIGERIA LIMITED—See Aspen Pharmacare Holdings Limited; *Int'l*, pg. 629
ASPEN PHILIPPINES INCORPORATED—See Aspen Pharmacare Holdings Limited; *Int'l*, pg. 629
ASTRAZENECA NIJMEGEN B.V.—See AstraZeneca PLC; *Int'l*, pg. 661
ATVIO BIOTECH LTD.—See Orgenesis Inc.; *U.S. Public*, pg. 1617
AUDENTES THERAPEUTICS, INC.—See Astellas Pharma Inc.; *Int'l*, pg. 653
BAOLINGBAO BIOLOGY CO., LTD.; *Int'l*, pg. 856
BAVARIAN NORDIC GMBH—See Bavarian Nordic A/S; *Int'l*, pg. 900
BAVARIAN NORDIC, INC.—See Bavarian Nordic A/S; *Int'l*, pg. 900
BAXTER INTERNATIONAL INC.; *U.S. Public*, pg. 280
BAYER (SICHUAN) ANIMAL HEALTH CO., LTD.—See Bayer Aktiengesellschaft; *Int'l*, pg. 901
BEIJING TIANTAN BIOLOGICAL PRODUCTS CORPORATION LIMITED—See China National Pharmaceutical Group Corporation; *Int'l*, pg. 1533
BIO BASIC CANADA INC.—See BBI Life Sciences Corporation; *Int'l*, pg. 920
BIOCRYST PHARMACEUTICALS, INC.; *U.S. Public*, pg. 335
BIOD,LLC—See Integra LifeSciences Holdings Corporation; *U.S. Public*, pg. 1135
BIOENZYMES PTY LTD.; *Int'l*, pg. 1037
BIOGEN CANADA INC.—See Biogen Inc.; *U.S. Public*, pg. 336
BIOGEN (DENMARK) A/S—See Biogen Inc.; *U.S. Public*, pg. 336
BIOGEN HEMOPHILIA INC.—See Biogen Inc.; *U.S. Public*, pg. 336
BIOGEN IDEC (IRELAND) LTD.—See Biogen Inc.; *U.S. Public*, pg. 336
BIOGEN IDEC (SINGAPORE) PTE LTD—See Biogen Inc.; *U.S. Public*, pg. 336
BIOGEN INC.; *U.S. Public*, pg. 335
BIOGEN ITALIA SRL—See Biogen Inc.; *U.S. Public*, pg. 336
BIOGEN JAPAN LTD.—See Biogen Inc.; *U.S. Public*, pg. 336
BIOGEN NORWAY AS—See Biogen Inc.; *U.S. Public*, pg. 336
BIOGEN NZ BIOPHARMA LTD.—See Biogen Inc.; *U.S. Public*, pg. 336
BIOGEN PHARMA, FARMACEVTSKA IN BIOTEHNOLOSKA DRUZBA D.O.O—See Biogen Inc.; *U.S. Public*, pg. 336
BIOGEN POLAND SP. Z.O.O—See Biogen Inc.; *U.S. Public*, pg. 336
BIOGEN SLOVAKIA S.R.O.—See Biogen Inc.; *U.S. Public*, pg. 337
BIOIVT, LLC; *U.S. Private*, pg. 562
BIOLEADERS CORPORATION; *Int'l*, pg. 1038
BIOLIFE SOLUTIONS, INC.; *U.S. Public*, pg. 337
BIOLOGICAL E. LIMITED; *Int'l*, pg. 1039
BIONORDIKA (DENMARK) A/S—See AddLife AB; *Int'l*, pg. 129
BIONORDIKA (SWEDEN) AB—See AddLife AB; *Int'l*, pg. 129
BIONOR IMMUNO AS—See Bionor Holding AS; *Int'l*, pg. 1040
BIONTECH INNOVATIVE MANUFACTURING SERVICES GMBH—See BioNTech SE; *Int'l*, pg. 1041
BIOPREMIER - INOVACAO E SERVICOS EM BIOTECNOLOGIA S.A.; *Int'l*, pg. 1041
BIOQUELL PLC—See Ecolab Inc.; *U.S. Public*, pg. 712
BIOQUELL UK LIMITED—See Ecolab Inc.; *U.S. Public*, pg. 712
BIORESTORATIVE THERAPIES, INC.; *U.S. Public*, pg. 338
BIORIGINAL EUROPE/ASIA B.V.—See Cooke, Inc.; *Int'l*, pg. 1788
BIOSOLUTION CO., LTD.; *Int'l*, pg. 1042
BIOTA SCIENTIFIC MANAGEMENT PTY. LTD.—See Vaxart, Inc.; *U.S. Public*, pg. 2276
BIOTEST PHARMACEUTICALS CORPORATION—See Biotest AG; *Int'l*, pg. 1043
BOEHRINGER INGELHEIM FREMONT, INC.—See C.H. Boehringer Sohn AG & Co. KG; *Int'l*, pg. 1241
BOEHRINGER INGELHEIM VETMEDICA, INC.—See C.H. Boehringer Sohn AG & Co. KG; *Int'l*, pg. 1241
BONUS BIOGROUP LTD.; *Int'l*, pg. 1109
BOTANIX PHARMACEUTICALS LIMITED; *Int'l*, pg. 1118
BP BIOFUELS LOUISIANA LLC—See BP plc; *U.S. Public*, pg. 1126
BRAMMER BIO, LLC—See Thermo Fisher Scientific Inc.; *U.S. Public*, pg. 2145
CALIDI THERAPEUTICS (NEVADA), INC.—See Calidi Biotherapeutics, Inc.; *U.S. Public*, pg. 423
CANSINO BIOLOGICS, INC.; *Int'l*, pg. 1298
CARNABIO USA INC.—See Carna Biosciences Inc.; *Int'l*, pg. 1342
CASTELLUM, INC.; *U.S. Public*, pg. 447

N.A.I.C.S. INDEX

325414 — BIOLOGICAL PRODUCT ...

CELL BIOTECH CO., LTD.; *Int'l*, pg. 1392
CELL BIOTECH INTERNATIONAL CO., LTD.—See Cell Biotech Co., Ltd.; *Int'l*, pg. 1392
CELLECT BIOTECHNOLOGY LTD.; *Int'l*, pg. 1392
CELLERO, LLC—See Charles River Laboratories International, Inc.; *U.S. Public*, pg. 479
CEL-SCI CORPORATION; *U.S. Public*, pg. 464
CHARLES RIVER LABORATORIES, INC.—See Charles River Laboratories International, Inc.; *U.S. Public*, pg. 480
CHARLES RIVER LABORATORIES INTERNATIONAL, INC.; *U.S. Public*, pg. 479
CHA VACCINE INSTITUTE; *Int'l*, pg. 1436
CHINA BIOLOGIC PRODUCTS HOLDINGS, INC.; *Int'l*, pg. 1486
CHINA-BIOTICS, INC.; *Int'l*, pg. 1568
CHINA RESOURCES BOYA BIO-PHARMACEUTICAL GROUP CO., LTD.; *Int'l*, pg. 1548
CLINIQA CORPORATION—See Bio-Techne Corporation; *U.S. Public*, pg. 334
COBRA BIOLOGICS HOLDING AB; *Int'l*, pg. 1683
COBRA BIOLOGICS LTD - MICROBIAL PRODUCTION & FILL FINISH FACILITY—See Cobra Biologics Holding AB; *Int'l*, pg. 1683
COHERUS BIOSCIENCES, INC.; *U.S. Public*, pg. 529
COLORADO SERUM CO.; *U.S. Private*, pg. 974
COMPUGEN LTD.; *Int'l*, pg. 1755
COMPUGEN USA, INC.—See Compugen Ltd.; *Int'l*, pg. 1755
CONVERGENCE PHARMACEUTICALS LTD.—See Biogen Inc.; *U.S. Public*, pg. 337
CORLINE BIOMEDICAL AB; *Int'l*, pg. 1801
CPA LABORATORIES LTD.—See Eurofins Scientific S.E.; *Int'l*, pg. 2535
CREATIVE MEDICAL TECHNOLOGIES, INC.—See Creative Medical Technology Holdings, Inc.; *U.S. Public*, pg. 593
CRODAROM SAS—See Croda International plc; *Int'l*, pg. 1852
CRYSTAL BIOSCIENCE, INC.—See Ligand Pharmaceuticals Incorporated; *U.S. Public*, pg. 1314
CSL BEHRING AG—See CSL Limited; *Int'l*, pg. 1865
CSL BEHRING (AUSTRALIA) PTY LTD.—See CSL Limited; *Int'l*, pg. 1865
CSL BEHRING GMBH—See CSL Limited; *Int'l*, pg. 1865
CSL BEHRING LDA.—See CSL Limited; *Int'l*, pg. 1865
CSL BEHRING LLC—See CSL Limited; *Int'l*, pg. 1865
CSL BEHRING N.V.—See CSL Limited; *Int'l*, pg. 1865
CSL BEHRING S.A.—See CSL Limited; *Int'l*, pg. 1865
CSL BEHRING S.P.A.—See CSL Limited; *Int'l*, pg. 1865
CSL BEHRING UK LTD.—See CSL Limited; *Int'l*, pg. 1865
CSL BIOTHERAPIES LTD.—See CSL Limited; *Int'l*, pg. 1865
CSL LIMITED; *Int'l*, pg. 1865
CSL PLASMA GMBH—See CSL Limited; *Int'l*, pg. 1865
CUREVAC NETHERLANDS B.V.—See CureVac N.V.; *Int'l*, pg. 1878
CUREVAC SWISS AG—See CureVac N.V.; *Int'l*, pg. 1878
CURIS, INC.; *U.S. Public*, pg. 610
CYTENA GMBH—See BICO Group AB; *Int'l*, pg. 1019
DA AN GENE CO., LTD.; *Int'l*, pg. 1901
DAIICHI SANKYO BIOTECH CO., LTD.—See Daiichi Sankyo Co., Ltd.; *Int'l*, pg. 1929
DELTA-FLY PHARMA, INC.; *Int'l*, pg. 2020
DHANVANTARI BOTANICALS, PVT., LTD.—See Avesthagen Limited; *Int'l*, pg. 740
DIAMOND ANIMAL HEALTH, INC.—See Mars, Incorporated; *U.S. Private*, pg. 2588
DYADIC INTERNATIONAL, INC.; *U.S. Public*, pg. 698
EIRGENIX EUROPE GMBH—See EirGenix, Inc.; *Int'l*, pg. 2334
ELUSYS THERAPEUTICS, INC.; *U.S. Private*, pg. 1377
EMERGENT SALES AND MARKETING GERMANY GMBH—See Emergent BioSolutions Inc.; *U.S. Public*, pg. 740
EMERGENT SALES AND MARKETING SINGAPORE PTE. LTD.—See Emergent BioSolutions Inc.; *U.S. Public*, pg. 740
ENVIRONMENTAL LUBRICANTS MANUFACTURING, INC.; *U.S. Private*, pg. 1408
ENZON PHARMACEUTICALS, INC.; *U.S. Public*, pg. 782
EPICORE ECUADOR S.A.—See Archer-Daniels-Midland Company; *U.S. Public*, pg. 185
ETEX CORPORATION—See Zimmer Biomet Holdings, Inc.; *U.S. Public*, pg. 2406
ETINPRO (BEIJING) CO., LTD.—See Beijing Kawin Technology Share-Holding Co., Ltd.; *Int'l*, pg. 954
EUBIOLOGICS CO., LTD.; *Int'l*, pg. 2525
EXTREME BIODIESEL, INC.; *U.S. Public*, pg. 813
FIBERGEL TECHNOLOGIES, INC.—See Agritech Worlwide, Inc.; *U.S. Private*, pg. 129
FIBROCELL SCIENCE, INC.—See Castle Creek Pharmaceuticals Holdings, Inc.; *U.S. Public*, pg. 447
FILAVIE S.A.S—See Groupe Grimaud La Corbiere SA; *Int'l*, pg. 3103
FISHER SCIENTIFIC SPRL—See Thermo Fisher Scientific Inc.; *U.S. Public*, pg. 2154
FUJIFILM DIOSYNTH BIOTECHNOLOGIES DENMARK APS—See FUJIFILM Holdings Corporation; *Int'l*, pg. 2821
FUJIFILM DIOSYNTH BIOTECHNOLOGIES HOLDINGS DENMARK APS—See FUJIFILM Holdings Corporation; *Int'l*, pg. 2824
GALVANI BIOELECTRONICS LIMITED—See GSK plc; *Int'l*, pg. 3145
G&E HERBAL BIOTECHNOLOGY CO., LTD.; *Int'l*, pg. 2862
GEMINI BIO-PRODUCTS, LLC—See BelHealth Investment Partners LLC; *U.S. Private*, pg. 517
GENESIS INVEST AG; *Int'l*, pg. 2921
GENOMAS INC.—See Rennova Health, Inc.; *U.S. Public*, pg. 1783
GENOWAY S.A.; *Int'l*, pg. 2926
GENUFOOD ENERGY ENZYMES CORP.; *U.S. Public*, pg. 932
GET YOUR FEELZ ON; *U.S. Public*, pg. 935
GILEAD SCIENCES BELGIUM BVBA/SPRL—See Gilead Sciences, Inc.; *U.S. Public*, pg. 937
GILEAD SCIENCES GES M.B.H.—See Gilead Sciences, Inc.; *U.S. Public*, pg. 937
GILEAD SCIENCES GMBH—See Gilead Sciences, Inc.; *U.S. Public*, pg. 937
GILEAD SCIENCES HELLAS .EPE—See Gilead Sciences, Inc.; *U.S. Public*, pg. 937
GILEAD SCIENCES, INC.; *U.S. Public*, pg. 936
GILEAD SCIENCES, LDA.—See Gilead Sciences, Inc.; *U.S. Public*, pg. 937
GILEAD SCIENCES LLAC LTD—See Gilead Sciences, Inc.; *U.S. Public*, pg. 937
GILEAD SCIENCES NETHERLANDS BV—See Gilead Sciences, Inc.; *U.S. Public*, pg. 937
GILEAD SCIENCES PTY LTD—See Gilead Sciences, Inc.; *U.S. Public*, pg. 937
GILEAD SCIENCES, S.L.—See Gilead Sciences, Inc.; *U.S. Public*, pg. 937
GILEAD SCIENCES S.R.L—See Gilead Sciences, Inc.; *U.S. Public*, pg. 937
GILEAD SCIENCES SWEDEN AB—See Gilead Sciences, Inc.; *U.S. Public*, pg. 937
GREEN AQUA POVOA, S.A.—See GREEN AQUA Company SGPS, S.A.; *Int'l*, pg. 3069
GREER LABORATORIES, INC.—See B-FLEXION Group Holdings SA; *Int'l*, pg. 785
GSK BIOLOGICALS—See GSK plc; *Int'l*, pg. 3146
GYROS PROTEIN TECHNOLOGY AB—See Mesa Laboratories, Inc.; *U.S. Public*, pg. 1426
HANGZHOU AGS MED TECH CO. LTD.—See Da An Gene Co., Ltd.; *Int'l*, pg. 1901
HELIXMITH CO., LTD.; *Int'l*, pg. 3331
HEPAHOPE KOREA, INC.; *Int'l*, pg. 3356
HESTER BIOSCIENCES LIMITED; *Int'l*, pg. 3365
HOFSETH BIOCARE AS; *Int'l*, pg. 3440
HORIZON DISCOVERY GROUP, PLC—See Revvity, Inc.; *U.S. Public*, pg. 1794
HUMAN METABOLOME TECHNOLOGIES AMERICA, INC.—See Human Metabolome Technologies Inc.; *Int'l*, pg. 3529
HUMAN METABOLOME TECHNOLOGIES EUROPE B.V.—See Human Metabolome Technologies Inc.; *Int'l*, pg. 3529
HUMANOPTICS AG; *Int'l*, pg. 3530
HUMANZYME, INC.—See Proteintech Group, Inc.; *U.S. Private*, pg. 3290
HURUM CO., LTD.; *Int'l*, pg. 3538
ICURE PHARMACEUTICAL, INC.; *Int'l*, pg. 3587
IMMTECH PHARMACEUTICALS, INC.; *U.S. Private*, pg. 2047
IMMUNETRICS INC.—See Simulations Plus, Inc.; *U.S. Public*, pg. 1884
INGREDIENTES NATURALES SELECCIONADOS S.L.—See International Flavors & Fragrances Inc.; *U.S. Public*, pg. 1152
INHIBITEX, L.L.C.—See Bristol-Myers Squibb Company; *U.S. Public*, pg. 386
INNOPHARMA, INC.—See Pfizer Inc.; *U.S. Public*, pg. 1680
INTEGRA ORTHOBIOLOGICS, INC.—See Integra LifeSciences Holdings Corporation; *U.S. Public*, pg. 1136
INTEGRATED DNA TECHNOLOGIES, INC.—See Danaher Corporation; *U.S. Public*, pg. 627
IRVINE SCIENTIFIC SALES COMPANY, INC.—See FUJIFILM Holdings Corporation; *Int'l*, pg. 2823
ISOLAGEN EUROPE LTD.—See Castle Creek Pharmaceuticals Holdings, Inc.; *U.S. Public*, pg. 447
JPT PEPTIDE TECHNOLOGIES GMBH—See BioNTech SE; *Int'l*, pg. 1041
KAMA INDUSTRIES LIMITED—See Aspen Pharmacare Holdings Limited; *Int'l*, pg. 629
KEMP PROTEINS, LLC—See Six.02 Bioservices, LLC; *U.S. Private*, pg. 3677
LADRX CORPORATION; *U.S. Public*, pg. 1288
LA JOLLA PHARMACEUTICAL COMPANY—See Innoviva, Inc.; *U.S. Public*, pg. 1127
LATTICE BIOLOGICS LTD.; *U.S. Public*, pg. 1294
LIFECORE BIOMEDICAL, INC.—See Lifecore Biomedical, Inc.; *U.S. Public*, pg. 1312
LIFE TECHNOLOGIES CORPORATION—See Thermo Fisher Scientific Inc.; *U.S. Public*, pg. 2148
LIFE TECHNOLOGIES GMBH—See Thermo Fisher Scientific Inc.; *U.S. Public*, pg. 2149
LIFE TECHNOLOGIES HOLDINGS PTE LTD.—See Thermo Fisher Scientific Inc.; *U.S. Public*, pg. 2149
LIFE TECHNOLOGIES JAPAN LIMITED—See Thermo Fisher Scientific Inc.; *U.S. Public*, pg. 2149
LIFE TECHNOLOGIES LIMITED—See Thermo Fisher Scientific Inc.; *U.S. Public*, pg. 2149
LIFE TECHNOLOGIES LIMITED—See Thermo Fisher Scientific Inc.; *U.S. Public*, pg. 2149
LIFE TECHNOLOGIES MAGYARORSZAG KFT.—See Thermo Fisher Scientific Inc.; *U.S. Public*, pg. 2149
LIFE TECHNOLOGIES NEW ZEALAND LTD.—See Thermo Fisher Scientific Inc.; *U.S. Public*, pg. 2149
LIFE TECHNOLOGIES SAS—See Thermo Fisher Scientific Inc.; *U.S. Public*, pg. 2149
LINEAGE CELL THERAPEUTICS, INC.; *U.S. Public*, pg. 1320
LIST BIOLOGICAL LABORATORIES, INC.—See Genome & Company; *Int'l*, pg. 2925
LYOPHILIZATION SERVICES OF NEW ENGLAND, INC.—See Kohlberg & Company, LLC; *U.S. Private*, pg. 2339
MEDIATECH, INC.—See Corning Incorporated; *U.S. Public*, pg. 578
MEGAZYME, LTD.—See Neogen Corporation; *U.S. Public*, pg. 1505
MESA LABORATORIES, INC. - BIOLOGICAL INDICATOR FACILITY—See Mesa Laboratories, Inc.; *U.S. Public*, pg. 1426
MICROARRAYS, INC.—See Spectrum Solutions L.L.C.; *U.S. Private*, pg. 3753
MIRATI THERAPEUTICS, INC.—See Bristol-Myers Squibb Company; *U.S. Public*, pg. 386
MITOSCIENCES INC.—See Danaher Corporation; *U.S. Public*, pg. 624
MODERNA GERMANY GMBH—See Moderna, Inc.; *U.S. Public*, pg. 1454
MODERNA ITALY S.R.L.—See Moderna, Inc.; *U.S. Public*, pg. 1454
MOLECULAR PROBES, INC.—See Thermo Fisher Scientific Inc.; *U.S. Public*, pg. 2149
MONOGRAM BIOSCIENCES, INC.—See Laboratory Corporation of America Holdings; *U.S. Public*, pg. 1287
MUNDIPHARMA INTERNATIONAL LTD.—See Purdue Pharma LP; *U.S. Private*, pg. 3305
MUSTAFA NEVZAT ILAC SANAYII ANONIM SIRKETI—See Amgen Inc.; *U.S. Public*, pg. 123
MWG BIOTECH AG—See Eurofins Scientific S.E.; *Int'l*, pg. 2551
MWG BIOTECH PVT LTD.—See Eurofins Scientific S.E.; *Int'l*, pg. 2551
NANTCELL, INC.—See NantWorks, LLC; *U.S. Private*, pg. 2833
NATUREWORKS LLC—See Cargill, Inc.; *U.S. Private*, pg. 759
NEOGEN ARGENTINA S.A.—See Neogen Corporation; *U.S. Public*, pg. 1505
NEUROCRINE BIOSCIENCES INC.; *U.S. Public*, pg. 1510
NIKA BIOTECHNOLOGY, INC.—See Nika Pharmaceuticals, Inc.; *U.S. Public*, pg. 1528
NOVAVAX CZ—See Novavax, Inc.; *U.S. Public*, pg. 1548
NOVAVAX, INC.; *U.S. Public*, pg. 1548
NOVUS BIOLOGICALS, LLC—See Bio-Techne Corporation; *U.S. Public*, pg. 334
NUO THERAPEUTICS, INC.; *U.S. Public*, pg. 1555
OMJ PHARMACEUTICALS, INC.—See Johnson & Johnson; *U.S. Public*, pg. 1197
OMNICANNA HEALTH SOLUTIONS, INC.; *U.S. Public*, pg. 1572
ONCOTELIC THERAPEUTICS, INC.; *U.S. Public*, pg. 1602
ORGANOGENESIS INC.—See Organogenesis Holdings Inc.; *U.S. Public*, pg. 1615
OSPREY BIOTECHNICS, INC.—See Phibro Animal Health Corporation; *U.S. Public*, pg. 1685
OUTLOOK THERAPEUTICS, INC.; *U.S. Public*, pg. 1625
OXOID AUSTRALIA PTY. LIMITED—See Thermo Fisher Scientific Inc.; *U.S. Public*, pg. 2150
PAH LUXEMBOURG 2 SARL—See Zoetis, Inc.; *U.S. Public*, pg. 2409
PDL BIOPHARMA INC.; *U.S. Private*, pg. 3122
PELICAN EXPRESSION TECHNOLOGY—See Ligand Pharmaceuticals Incorporated; *U.S. Public*, pg. 1314
PEPROTECH ASIA LTD.—See Thermo Fisher Scientific Inc.; *U.S. Public*, pg. 2151
PEPTIDES INTERNATIONAL, INC.—See Ampersand Management LLC; *U.S. Private*, pg. 266
PERBIO SCIENCE DEUTSCHLAND—See Thermo Fisher Scientific Inc.; *U.S. Public*, pg. 2154
PERBIO SCIENCE FRANCE—See Thermo Fisher Scientific Inc.; *U.S. Public*, pg. 2154
PERBIO SCIENCE NEDERLAND BV—See Thermo Fisher Scientific Inc.; *U.S. Public*, pg. 2154
PERBIO SCIENCE UK LTD.—See Thermo Fisher Scientific Inc.; *U.S. Public*, pg. 2154
PFIZER MANUFACTURING AUSTRIA G.M.B.H.—See Pfizer Inc.; *U.S. Public*, pg. 1682
PFIZER MANUFACTURING DEUTSCHLAND PFE

325414 — BIOLOGICAL PRODUCT ...

GMBH—See Pfizer Inc.; *U.S. Public*, pg. 1682
PFIZER - MIDDLETON—See Pfizer Inc.; *U.S. Public*, pg. 1680
PFIZER PFE ILACLARI ANONIM SIRKETI—See Pfizer Inc.; *U.S. Public*, pg. 1682
PHARMAQ AS CHILE LIMITADA—See Zoetis, Inc.; *U.S. Public*, pg. 2409
PHARMAQ AS—See Zoetis, Inc.; *U.S. Public*, pg. 2409
PHARMAQ CA PANAMA INC.—See Zoetis, Inc.; *U.S. Public*, pg. 2409
PHARMAQ HONG KONG LIMITED—See Zoetis, Inc.; *U.S. Public*, pg. 2409
PHARMAQ LTD—See Zoetis, Inc.; *U.S. Public*, pg. 2409
PHARMAQ SPAIN AQUA SL—See Zoetis, Inc.; *U.S. Public*, pg. 2409
PHARMAQ VETERINAR ECZA DEPOSU VE SU URUN-LERI TICARET LTD SKI—See Zoetis, Inc.; *U.S. Public*, pg. 2409
PHARMAQ VIETNAM COMPANY LIMITED—See Zoetis, Inc.; *U.S. Public*, pg. 2409
PHOSPHOSOLUTIONS, LLC—See Janel Corporation; *U.S. Public*, pg. 1187
POINT OF CARE NANO-TECHNOLOGY, INC.; *U.S. Private*, pg. 3222
PROFESSIONAL BIOLOGICAL COMPANY—See Colorado Serum Co.; *U.S. Private*, pg. 974
PROMEGA CORPORATION; *U.S. Private*, pg. 3282
PROTOX CO., LTD.—See DSK Co., Ltd.; *Int'l*, pg. 2210
QTEROS, INC.; *U.S. Private*, pg. 3314
QUAT-CHEM LTD.—See Neogen Corporation; *U.S. Public*, pg. 1505
REGENICIN, INC.; *U.S. Public*, pg. 1775
REJUVENATION LABS—See Crocker Ventures LLC; *U.S. Private*, pg. 1102
RELIEF THERAPEUTICS SA—See Sonnet BioTherapeutics Holdings, Inc.; *U.S. Public*, pg. 1904
REPLIGEN CORPORATION; *U.S. Public*, pg. 1784
REPLIGEN SWEDEN AB—See Repligen Corporation; *U.S. Public*, pg. 1784
REPREVE RENEWABLES, LLC—See Unifi, Inc.; *U.S. Public*, pg. 2226
RICETEC, INC.; *U.S. Private*, pg. 3425
RICHTER-HELM BIOLOGICS MANAGE - MENT GMBH—See Chemical Works of Gedeon Richter Plc; *Int'l*, pg. 1462
RIGONTEC GMBH—See Merck & Co., Inc.; *U.S. Public*, pg. 1421
SANOFI PASTEUR MSD AG—See Merck & Co., Inc.; *U.S. Public*, pg. 1421
SANOFI PASTEUR MSD GMBH—See Merck & Co., Inc.; *U.S. Public*, pg. 1421
SANOFI PASTEUR MSD GMBH—See Merck & Co., Inc.; *U.S. Public*, pg. 1421
SANOFI PASTEUR MSD N.V.—See Merck & Co., Inc.; *U.S. Public*, pg. 1421
SANOFI PASTEUR MSD OY—See Merck & Co., Inc.; *U.S. Public*, pg. 1421
SANOFI PASTEUR MSD, SA—See Merck & Co., Inc.; *U.S. Public*, pg. 1421
SANOFI PASTEUR MSD, SNC—See Merck & Co., Inc.; *U.S. Public*, pg. 1421
SANOFI PASTEUR MSD SPA—See Merck & Co., Inc.; *U.S. Public*, pg. 1421
SCIVAC (ISRAEL) LTD.—See VBI Vaccines Inc.; *U.S. Public*, pg. 2276
SDIX, LLC—See OriGene Technologies, Inc.; *U.S. Private*, pg. 3042
SEAGEN INC.; *U.S. Public*, pg. 1852
SELLAS LIFE SCIENCES GROUP, INC.; *U.S. Public*, pg. 1863
SEMPRAE LABORATORIES, INC.—See Aytu BioPharma, Inc.; *U.S. Public*, pg. 257
SEQIRUS PTY LTD.—See CSL Limited; *Int'l*, pg. 1866
SEQIRUS UK LIMITED—See CSL Limited; *Int'l*, pg. 1866
SERINA THERAPEUTICS, INC.; *U.S. Public*, pg. 1868
SHANGHAI HUAXIN BIOTECHNOLOGY CO., LTD.—See EPS Holdings, Inc.; *Int'l*, pg. 2466
SHANGHAI LIFE TECHNOLOGIES BIOTECHNOLOGY CO. LIMITED—See Thermo Fisher Scientific Inc.; *U.S. Public*, pg. 2149
SHANGHAI PRIMEGENE BIO-TECH CO., LTD.—See Bio-Techne Corporation; *U.S. Public*, pg. 334
SMARTMETRIC, INC.; *U.S. Public*, pg. 1895
STABILITY INC.—See MiMedx Group, Inc.; *U.S. Public*, pg. 1448
STRATAGENE CORP.—See Agilent Technologies, Inc.; *U.S. Public*, pg. 62
SURMODICS, INC.; *U.S. Public*, pg. 1967
SYNBIOTICS CORPORATION—See Zoetis, Inc.; *U.S. Public*, pg. 2409
TETRAGENETICS, INC.—See AbCellera Biologics Inc.; *Int'l*, pg. 57
THERMO FISHER SCIENTIFIC INC.—See Thermo Fisher Scientific Inc.; *U.S. Public*, pg. 2154
THERMO FISHER SCIENTIFIC (MILWAUKEE) LLC—See Thermo Fisher Scientific Inc.; *U.S. Public*, pg. 2153
THERMO FISHER SCIENTIFIC—See Thermo Fisher Scientific Inc.; *U.S. Public*, pg. 2153

TISSUE REPAIR COMPANY—See Gene Biotherapeutics Inc.; *U.S. Public*, pg. 911
TITAN PHARMACEUTICALS, INC.; *U.S. Public*, pg. 2160
TOCRIS COOKSON LIMITED—See Bio-Techne Corporation; *U.S. Public*, pg. 334
US BIOTEC, INC.; *U.S. Public*, pg. 2266
VACCEX, INC.; *U.S. Private*, pg. 4329
VARIATION BIOTECHNOLOGIES (US), INC.—See VBI Vaccines Inc.; *U.S. Public*, pg. 2276
VAXART BIOSCIENCES, INC.—See Vaxart, Inc.; *U.S. Public*, pg. 2276
VELICO MEDICAL; *U.S. Private*, pg. 4354
VERICEL CORPORATION; *U.S. Public*, pg. 2280
VERIS FARMACEUTICA LIMITADA—See FAES Farma, S.A.; *Int'l*, pg. 2601
WESTBRIDGE RESEARCH GROUP; *U.S. Private*, pg. 4488
WINDTREE THERAPEUTICS, INC.; *U.S. Public*, pg. 2373
XIAMEN INNOVAX BIOTECH CO., LTD.—See Beijing Wantai Biological Pharmacy Enterprise Co., Ltd.; *Int'l*, pg. 960
XOMA (US) LLC—See XOMA Corporation; *U.S. Public*, pg. 2391
XTANT MEDICAL HOLDINGS, INC.; *U.S. Public*, pg. 2393
ZEPTOMETRIX CORPORATION—See GTCR LLC; *U.S. Private*, pg. 1804
ZHONGSHAN BIO-TECH CO., LTD.—See Da An Gene Co., Ltd.; *Int'l*, pg. 1901
ZLB BIOPLASMA INC.—See CSL Limited; *Int'l*, pg. 1865
ZOETIS GLOBAL POULTRY—See Zoetis, Inc.; *U.S. Public*, pg. 2410

325510 — PAINT AND COATING MANUFACTURING

2002 PERLINDUSTRIA, S.L.U.—See RPM International Inc.; *U.S. Public*, pg. 1816
3M NORTHALLERTON—See 3M Company; *U.S. Public*, pg. 7
ABSOLUTE COATINGS, INC.—See Huron Capital Partners LLC; *U.S. Private*, pg. 2011
ACE HARDWARE CORPORATION - PAINT DIVISION—See Ace Hardware Corporation; *U.S. Private*, pg. 56
ADVANCE MULTITECH LTD.; *Int'l*, pg. 156
AERVOE INDUSTRIES INCORPORATED; *U.S. Private*, pg. 120
AEXCEL CORP.; *U.S. Private*, pg. 121
AFRICAN PAINTS (NIGERIA) PLC.; *Int'l*, pg. 192
AGC COAT-TECH CO., LTD.—See AGC Inc.; *Int'l*, pg. 201
AGC POLYMER MATERIAL CO., LTD.—See AGC Inc.; *Int'l*, pg. 202
AHC B.V.—See Aalberts N.V.; *Int'l*, pg. 33
AHC SPECIAL COATINGS GMBH—See Aalberts N.V.; *Int'l*, pg. 33
AJISCO-DNT (NINGBO) PAINT CO.,LTD.—See Dai Nippon Toryo Co., Ltd.; *Int'l*, pg. 1916
AKZO COATINGS LTDA -TINTAS—See Akzo Nobel N.V.; *Int'l*, pg. 272
AKZO NOBEL AB—See Akzo Nobel N.V.; *Int'l*, pg. 268
AKZO NOBEL AEROSPACE COATINGS GMBH—See Akzo Nobel N.V.; *Int'l*, pg. 268
AKZO NOBEL AEROSPACE COATINGS LTD—See Akzo Nobel N.V.; *Int'l*, pg. 268
AKZO NOBEL ARGENTINA S.A.—See Akzo Nobel N.V.; *Int'l*, pg. 268
AKZONOBEL (ASIA PACIFIC) PTE. LTD.—See Akzo Nobel N.V.; *Int'l*, pg. 273
AKZO NOBEL ASSURANTIE N.V.—See Akzo Nobel N.V.; *Int'l*, pg. 268
AKZO NOBEL (AUSTRALIA) PTY LTD—See Akzo Nobel N.V.; *Int'l*, pg. 268
AKZO NOBEL AUTOMOTIVE AND AEROSPACE COATINGS MEXICO S.A. DE C.V.—See Akzo Nobel N.V.; *Int'l*, pg. 268
AKZO NOBEL BALTICS, UAB—See Akzo Nobel N.V.; *Int'l*, pg. 268
AKZO NOBEL BOYA SANAYI VE TICARET AS—See Akzo Nobel N.V.; *Int'l*, pg. 268
AKZO NOBEL BYGGLIM AB—See Akzo Nobel N.V.; *Int'l*, pg. 268
AKZO NOBEL CANADA INC.—See Akzo Nobel N.V.; *Int'l*, pg. 268
AKZO NOBEL CAR REFINISHES A/S—See Akzo Nobel N.V.; *Int'l*, pg. 269
AKZO NOBEL CAR REFINISHES AUSTRALIA PTY LTD—See Akzo Nobel N.V.; *Int'l*, pg. 269
AKZO NOBEL CAR REFINISHES BV—See Akzo Nobel N.V.; *Int'l*, pg. 272
AKZO NOBEL CAR REFINISHES INDIA PVT LTD—See Akzo Nobel N.V.; *Int'l*, pg. 269
AKZO NOBEL CAR REFINISHES (IRELAND) LTD—See Akzo Nobel N.V.; *Int'l*, pg. 269
AKZO NOBEL CAR REFINISHES KOREA CO. LTD—See Akzo Nobel N.V.; *Int'l*, pg. 269
AKZO NOBEL CAR REFINISHES SAS—See Akzo Nobel N.V.; *Int'l*, pg. 269
AKZO NOBEL CAR REFINISHES (SINGAPORE) PTE. LTD.—See Akzo Nobel N.V.; *Int'l*, pg. 269

AKZO NOBEL CAR REFINISHES SL—See Akzo Nobel N.V.; *Int'l*, pg. 269
AKZO NOBEL CAR REFINISHES (SUZHOU) CO. LTD—See Akzo Nobel N.V.; *Int'l*, pg. 269
AKZO NOBEL CENTER ENERGIE B.V.—See Akzo Nobel N.V.; *Int'l*, pg. 269
AKZO NOBEL CHANGCHENG COATING (LANGFANG) CO., LTD.—See Akzo Nobel N.V.; *Int'l*, pg. 269
AKZO NOBEL CHANG CHENG COATINGS (GUANGDONG) CO LTD—See Akzo Nobel N.V.; *Int'l*, pg. 269
AKZO NOBEL CHANG CHENG COATINGS (SUZHOU) CO LTD—See Akzo Nobel N.V.; *Int'l*, pg. 269
AKZO NOBEL CHANG CHENG LIMITED—See Akzo Nobel N.V.; *Int'l*, pg. 269
AKZO NOBEL COATINGS A.E.—See Akzo Nobel N.V.; *Int'l*, pg. 269
AKZO NOBEL COATINGS AG—See Akzo Nobel N.V.; *Int'l*, pg. 269
AKZO NOBEL COATINGS B.V.—See Akzo Nobel N.V.; *Int'l*, pg. 269
AKZO NOBEL COATINGS (DONGGUAN) CO. LTD.—See Akzo Nobel N.V.; *Int'l*, pg. 269
AKZO NOBEL COATINGS GMBH—See Akzo Nobel N.V.; *Int'l*, pg. 269
AKZO NOBEL COATINGS INC. (MI)—See Akzo Nobel N.V.; *Int'l*, pg. 272
AKZO NOBEL COATINGS INC.—See Akzo Nobel N.V.; *Int'l*, pg. 272
AKZO NOBEL COATINGS INC.—See Akzo Nobel N.V.; *Int'l*, pg. 272
AKZO NOBEL COATINGS INC.—See Akzo Nobel N.V.; *Int'l*, pg. 272
AKZO NOBEL COATINGS INC.—See Akzo Nobel N.V.; *Int'l*, pg. 272
AKZO NOBEL COATINGS INC.—See Akzo Nobel N.V.; *Int'l*, pg. 272
AKZO NOBEL COATINGS INC.—See Akzo Nobel N.V.; *Int'l*, pg. 272
AKZO NOBEL COATINGS INDIA PRIVATE LTD—See Akzo Nobel N.V.; *Int'l*, pg. 269
AKZO NOBEL COATINGS INTERNATIONAL B.V.—See Akzo Nobel N.V.; *Int'l*, pg. 269
AKZO NOBEL COATINGS (JIAXING) CO. LTD—See Akzo Nobel N.V.; *Int'l*, pg. 269
AKZO NOBEL COATINGS K.K.—See Akzo Nobel N.V.; *Int'l*, pg. 269
AKZO NOBEL COATINGS LTD.—See Akzo Nobel N.V.; *Int'l*, pg. 272
AKZO NOBEL COATINGS OY—See Akzo Nobel N.V.; *Int'l*, pg. 269
AKZO NOBEL COATINGS SA—See Akzo Nobel N.V.; *Int'l*, pg. 272
AKZO NOBEL COATINGS SA—See Akzo Nobel N.V.; *Int'l*, pg. 272
AKZO NOBEL COATINGS, S.L.—See Akzo Nobel N.V.; *Int'l*, pg. 269
AKZO NOBEL COATINGS S.P.A.—See Akzo Nobel N.V.; *Int'l*, pg. 272
AKZO NOBEL COATINGS (TIANJIN) CO., LTD.—See Akzo Nobel N.V.; *Int'l*, pg. 269
AKZO NOBEL COATINGS TRADING LTD—See Akzo Nobel N.V.; *Int'l*, pg. 269
AKZO NOBEL COATINGS VIETNAM LIMITED—See Akzo Nobel N.V.; *Int'l*, pg. 269
AKZONOBEL COATINGS VIETNAM LTD.—See Akzo Nobel N.V.; *Int'l*, pg. 272
AKZO NOBEL COATINGS ZRT—See Akzo Nobel N.V.; *Int'l*, pg. 269
AKZO NOBEL COIL COATINGS SA—See Akzo Nobel N.V.; *Int'l*, pg. 269
AKZO NOBEL DECO A/S—See Akzo Nobel N.V.; *Int'l*, pg. 269
AKZO NOBEL DECO GMBH—See Akzo Nobel N.V.; *Int'l*, pg. 269
AKZONOBEL DECO GMBH—See Akzo Nobel N.V.; *Int'l*, pg. 273
AKZO NOBEL DECORATIVE COATINGS A/S—See Akzo Nobel N.V.; *Int'l*, pg. 269
AKZO NOBEL DECORATIVE COATINGS BV—See Akzo Nobel N.V.; *Int'l*, pg. 269
AKZO NOBEL DECORATIVE COATINGS B.V.—See Akzo Nobel N.V.; *Int'l*, pg. 270
AKZO NOBEL DECORATIVE COATINGS B.V.—See Akzo Nobel N.V.; *Int'l*, pg. 270
AKZO NOBEL DECORATIVE COATINGS B.V.—See Akzo Nobel N.V.; *Int'l*, pg. 270
AKZO NOBEL DECORATIVE COATINGS SVERIGE AB—See Akzo Nobel N.V.; *Int'l*, pg. 269
AKZO NOBEL DECORATIVE COATINGS TURKEY B.V.—See Akzo Nobel N.V.; *Int'l*, pg. 269
AKZO NOBEL DECORATIVE PAINTS BELGIUM NV—See Akzo Nobel N.V.; *Int'l*, pg. 271
AKZO NOBEL DECORATIVE PAINTS—See Akzo Nobel N.V.; *Int'l*, pg. 269
AKZONOBEL DECORATIVE PAINTS—See Akzo Nobel N.V.; *Int'l*, pg. 271
AKZO NOBEL DECORATIVE PAINTS SP. Z O.O—See Akzo Nobel N.V.; *Int'l*, pg. 271

325510 — PAINT AND COATING M...

AKZO NOBEL DECORATIVE PAINTS, USA—See Akzo Nobel N.V.; *Int'l*, pg. 272
AKZO NOBEL DISTRIBUTION LLE DE FRANCE S.A.S.—See Akzo Nobel N.V.; *Int'l*, pg. 271
AKZO NOBEL DISTRIBUTION SAS—See Akzo Nobel N.V.; *Int'l*, pg. 271
AKZO NOBEL ENERGIE HENGELO B.V.—See Akzo Nobel N.V.; *Int'l*, pg. 271
AKZO NOBEL ENGINEERING & OPERATIONAL SOLUTIONS B.V.—See Akzo Nobel N.V.; *Int'l*, pg. 271
AKZO NOBEL FARBEN BETEILIGUNGS-GMBH—See Akzo Nobel N.V.; *Int'l*, pg. 271
AKZO NOBEL FASER PENSIONSVERWALTUNGS-GMBH—See Akzo Nobel N.V.; *Int'l*, pg. 271
AKZO NOBEL GMBH—See Akzo Nobel N.V.; *Int'l*, pg. 271
AKZO NOBEL INDA, S.A. DE C.V.—See Akzo Nobel N.V.; *Int'l*, pg. 271
AKZO NOBEL INDIA LIMITED—See Akzo Nobel N.V.; *Int'l*, pg. 271
AKZONOBEL INDIA LTD.—See Akzo Nobel N.V.; *Int'l*, pg. 273
AKZO NOBEL INDUSTRIAL COATINGS AB—See Akzo Nobel N.V.; *Int'l*, pg. 271
AKZO NOBEL INDUSTRIAL COATINGS KOREA LTD.—See Akzo Nobel N.V.; *Int'l*, pg. 273
AKZO NOBEL INDUSTRIAL COATINGS MEXICO SA DE CV—See Akzo Nobel N.V.; *Int'l*, pg. 271
AKZO NOBEL INDUSTRIAL COATINGS SA—See Akzo Nobel N.V.; *Int'l*, pg. 271
AKZO NOBEL INDUSTRIAL COATINGS SDN BHD—See Akzo Nobel N.V.; *Int'l*, pg. 271
AKZO NOBEL INDUSTRIAL COATINGS SP. Z O.O.—See Akzo Nobel N.V.; *Int'l*, pg. 271
AKZO NOBEL INDUSTRIAL FINISHES AB—See Akzo Nobel N.V.; *Int'l*, pg. 270
AKZO NOBEL INDUSTRIAL FINISHES GMBH—See Akzo Nobel N.V.; *Int'l*, pg. 271
AKZO NOBEL INDUSTRIAL PAINTS, S.L.—See Akzo Nobel N.V.; *Int'l*, pg. 271
AKZO NOBEL INDUSTRIES LIMITED—See Akzo Nobel N.V.; *Int'l*, pg. 271
AKZO NOBEL KEMIPOL A.S.—See Akzo Nobel N.V.; *Int'l*, pg. 271
AKZO NOBEL LAKOKRASKA LTD—See Akzo Nobel N.V.; *Int'l*, pg. 271
AKZO NOBEL LIMITED—See Akzo Nobel N.V.; *Int'l*, pg. 272
AKZONOBEL LTD.—See Akzo Nobel N.V.; *Int'l*, pg. 270
AKZO NOBEL NIPPON PAINT ESPANIA SA—See Akzo Nobel N.V.; *Int'l*, pg. 270
AKZO NOBEL NIPPON PAINT GMBH—See Akzo Nobel N.V.; *Int'l*, pg. 270
AKZO NOBEL NIPPON PAINT LIMITED—See Akzo Nobel N.V.; *Int'l*, pg. 270
AKZO NOBEL NIPPON PAINT SRL—See Akzo Nobel N.V.; *Int'l*, pg. 270
AKZO NOBEL PACKAGE COATINGS GMBH—See Akzo Nobel N.V.; *Int'l*, pg. 272
AKZO NOBEL PACKAGING COATINGS LTD.—See Akzo Nobel N.V.; *Int'l*, pg. 272
AKZO NOBEL PACKAGING COATINGS S.A.—See Akzo Nobel N.V.; *Int'l*, pg. 272
AKZO NOBEL PACKAGING COATINGS S.A.S.—See Akzo Nobel N.V.; *Int'l*, pg. 272
AKZONOBEL PAINTS (ASIA PACIFIC) PTE LTD—See Akzo Nobel N.V.; *Int'l*, pg. 270
AKZO NOBEL PAINTS BELGIUM NV/SA—See Akzo Nobel N.V.; *Int'l*, pg. 270
AKZONOBEL PAINTS ESPANA—See Akzo Nobel N.V.; *Int'l*, pg. 270
AKZO NOBEL PAINTS (PUERTO RICO) INC.—See Akzo Nobel N.V.; *Int'l*, pg. 272
AKZO NOBEL PAINTS (SINGAPORE) PTE LIMITED—See Akzo Nobel N.V.; *Int'l*, pg. 272
AKZONOBEL PAINTS (SINGAPORE) PTE LTD.—See Akzo Nobel N.V.; *Int'l*, pg. 270
AKZO NOBEL PAINTS TAIWAN LIMITED—See Akzo Nobel N.V.; *Int'l*, pg. 270
AKZO NOBEL PAINTS (THAILAND) LTD., EKA BANGKOK BRANCH—See Akzo Nobel N.V.; *Int'l*, pg. 270
AKZO NOBEL PAKISTAN LIMITED—See Akzo Nobel N.V.; *Int'l*, pg. 272
AKZO NOBEL PERU S.A.C.—See Akzo Nobel N.V.; *Int'l*, pg. 272
AKZONOBEL POLSKA SP. ZO.O.—See Akzo Nobel N.V.; *Int'l*, pg. 273
AKZO NOBEL POWDER COATINGS A.E.—See Akzo Nobel N.V.; *Int'l*, pg. 272
AKZO NOBEL POWDER COATINGS B.V.—See Akzo Nobel N.V.; *Int'l*, pg. 272
AKZO NOBEL POWDER COATINGS (CHENGDU) CO., LTD.—See Akzo Nobel N.V.; *Int'l*, pg. 272
AKZO NOBEL POWDER COATINGS FZE—See Akzo Nobel N.V.; *Int'l*, pg. 273
AKZO NOBEL POWDER COATINGS GMBH—See Akzo Nobel N.V.; *Int'l*, pg. 273
AKZO NOBEL POWDER COATINGS GMBH—See Akzo Nobel N.V.; *Int'l*, pg. 273
AKZO NOBEL POWDER COATINGS KOREA CO., LIMITED—See Akzo Nobel N.V.; *Int'l*, pg. 273
AKZO NOBEL POWDER COATINGS (LANGFANG) CO. LTD.—See Akzo Nobel N.V.; *Int'l*, pg. 272
AKZO NOBEL POWDER COATINGS LTD.—See Akzo Nobel N.V.; *Int'l*, pg. 272
AKZO NOBEL POWDER COATINGS (NINGBO) CO., LTD.—See Akzo Nobel N.V.; *Int'l*, pg. 272
AKZO NOBEL POWDER COATINGS SNC—See Akzo Nobel N.V.; *Int'l*, pg. 273
AKZO NOBEL POWDER COATINGS SOUTH AFRICA (PROPRIETARY) LIMITED—See Akzo Nobel N.V.; *Int'l*, pg. 273
AKZO NOBEL POWDER COATINGS (SUZHOU) CO., LTD.—See Akzo Nobel N.V.; *Int'l*, pg. 272
AKZO NOBEL POWDER COATINGS (VIETNAM) CO., LTD.—See Akzo Nobel N.V.; *Int'l*, pg. 272
AKZO NOBEL PROTECTIVE COATINGS (SUZHOU) CO. LTD.—See Akzo Nobel N.V.; *Int'l*, pg. 273
AKZO NOBEL REPRESENTATIVE OFFICES B.V.—See Akzo Nobel N.V.; *Int'l*, pg. 273
AKZONOBEL SDN BHD—See Akzo Nobel N.V.; *Int'l*, pg. 273
AKZO NOBEL (SHANGHAI) CO. LTD.—See Akzo Nobel N.V.; *Int'l*, pg. 268
AKZO NOBEL SINO COATINGS B.V.—See Akzo Nobel N.V.; *Int'l*, pg. 273
AKZO NOBEL—See Akzo Nobel N.V.; *Int'l*, pg. 268
AKZONOBEL—See Akzo Nobel N.V.; *Int'l*, pg. 270
AKZONOBEL—See Akzo Nobel N.V.; *Int'l*, pg. 270
AKZO NOBEL SWIRE PAINTS (GUANGZHOU) LIMITED—See Akzo Nobel N.V.; *Int'l*, pg. 273
AKZO NOBEL SWIRE PAINTS LIMITED—See Akzo Nobel N.V.; *Int'l*, pg. 273
AKZO NOBEL TINTAS PARA AUTOMOVEIS LDA—See Akzo Nobel N.V.; *Int'l*, pg. 273
AKZO NOBEL UK LTD—See Akzo Nobel N.V.; *Int'l*, pg. 273
ALABASTINE HOLLAND BV—See Akzo Nobel N.V.; *Int'l*, pg. 270
ALBI PROTECTIVE COATINGS—See SK Capital Partners, LP; *U.S. Private*, pg. 3679
ALCRO-BECKERS AB—See PPG Industries, Inc.; *U.S. Public*, pg. 1710
ALFA S.R.L.—See Currys plc; *Int'l*, pg. 1879
AL JABER PROTECTIVE COATING L.L.C.—See Al Jaber Group; *Int'l*, pg. 279
ALLNEX BELGIUM SA/NV - DROGENBOS—See Advent International Corporation; *U.S. Private*, pg. 98
ALLNEX BELGIUM SA/NV - SCHOONAARDE—See Advent International Corporation; *U.S. Private*, pg. 98
ALLNEX BELGIUM SA/NV—See Advent International Corporation; *U.S. Private*, pg. 98
ALLNEX GERMANY GMBH - HAMBURG PLANT—See Advent International Corporation; *U.S. Private*, pg. 98
ALLNEX GERMANY GMBH—See Advent International Corporation; *U.S. Private*, pg. 98
ALLNEX USA, INC. - KALAMAZOO PLANT—See Advent International Corporation; *U.S. Private*, pg. 98
ALLNEX USA, INC.—See Advent International Corporation; *U.S. Private*, pg. 98
ALLNEX USA, INC. - WALLINGFORD PLANT—See Advent International Corporation; *U.S. Private*, pg. 98
ALLNEX USA, INC. - WILLOW ISLAND PLANT—See Advent International Corporation; *U.S. Private*, pg. 98
ALPHA COATINGS INC—See PPG Industries, Inc.; *U.S. Public*, pg. 1711
ALPHA COATING TECHNOLOGIES, LLC—See PPG Industries, Inc.; *U.S. Public*, pg. 1707
AMBANI ORGOCHEM LIMITED; *Int'l*, pg. 413
AMERICAN COATINGS; *U.S. Private*, pg. 227
AMOL DICALITE LTD.—See RGP Holding, Inc.; *U.S. Private*, pg. 3420
AMOS CO., LTD.—See Amorepacific Corp.; *Int'l*, pg. 430
ANALABS RESOURCES BERHAD; *Int'l*, pg. 446
ANCHOR PAINT MANUFACTURING CO. INC.; *U.S. Private*, pg. 273
ANEST IWATA MOTHERSON COATING EQUIPMENT PRIVATE LTD.—See ANEST IWATA Corporation; *Int'l*, pg. 458
ANEST IWATA RUS LLC—See ANEST IWATA Corporation; *Int'l*, pg. 458
ANSA COATINGS LIMITED—See ANSA McAL Limited; *Int'l*, pg. 476
APCO COATINGS LTD.—See Asian Paints Limited; *Int'l*, pg. 618
APCO COATINGS—See Asian Paints Limited; *Int'l*, pg. 618
A.P.I. APPLICAZIONI PLASTICHE INDUSTRIALI S.P.A.—See RPM International Inc.; *U.S. Public*, pg. 1818
API USA, INC.—See RPM International Inc.; *U.S. Public*, pg. 1818
APOLLO CHEMICALS LIMITED—See H.B. Fuller Company; *U.S. Public*, pg. 977
A P RESINAS, S.A. DE C.V.—See PPG Industries, Inc.; *U.S. Public*, pg. 1707
ARAB COMPANY FOR PAINT PRODUCTS; *Int'l*, pg. 530
ARIZONA POLYMER FLOORING—See Audax Group, Limited Partnership; *U.S. Private*, pg. 388
ASAHIPEN CORPORATION; *Int'l*, pg. 599
ASIAN PAINTS (BANGLADESH) LIMITED—See Asian Paints Limited; *Int'l*, pg. 618
ASIAN PAINTS INDUSTRIAL COATINGS LTD.—See Asian Paints Limited; *Int'l*, pg. 618
ASIAN PAINTS INTERNATIONAL PRIVATE LIMITED—See Asian Paints Limited; *Int'l*, pg. 618
ASIAN PAINTS (LANKA) LIMITED—See Asian Paints Limited; *Int'l*, pg. 618
ASIAN PAINTS LIMITED; *Int'l*, pg. 618
ASIAN PAINTS (NEPAL) PVT. LIMITED—See Asian Paints Limited; *Int'l*, pg. 618
ASIAN PAINTS (S.I.) LIMITED—See Asian Paints Limited; *Int'l*, pg. 618
ASIAN PAINTS (VANUATU) LIMITED—See Asian Paints Limited; *Int'l*, pg. 618
AS TIKKURILA—See PPG Industries, Inc.; *U.S. Public*, pg. 1710
THE ATLAS COMPANIES, INC.—See Betco Corporation; *U.S. Private*, pg. 545
ATOMIX CO., LTD.; *Int'l*, pg. 688
AUGUSTA COATING & MANUFACTURING, LLC; *U.S. Private*, pg. 392
AXALTA COATING SYSTEMS AUSTRALIA PTY LTD—See Axalta Coating Systems Ltd.; *U.S. Public*, pg. 255
AXALTA COATING SYSTEMS CANADA COMPANY—See Axalta Coating Systems Ltd.; *U.S. Public*, pg. 254
AXALTA COATING SYSTEMS FRANCE SAS—See Axalta Coating Systems Ltd.; *U.S. Public*, pg. 255
AXALTA COATING SYSTEMS, LLC—See Axalta Coating Systems Ltd.; *U.S. Public*, pg. 255
AXALTA COATING SYSTEMS MEXICO, S. DE R.L. DE C.V.—See Axalta Coating Systems Ltd.; *U.S. Public*, pg. 255
AXALTA POWDER COATING SYSTEMS USA, INC.—See Axalta Coating Systems Ltd.; *U.S. Public*, pg. 255
BALAKOM SLOVAKIA S.R.O.—See Akzo Nobel N.V.; *Int'l*, pg. 273
BARLOWORLD EQUIPMENT MARTEX—See Barloworld Ltd.; *Int'l*, pg. 866
BARLOWORLD PLASCON (PTY) LTD.—See Barloworld Ltd.; *Int'l*, pg. 866
BASF ARGENTINA S.A.—See BASF SE; *Int'l*, pg. 872
BASF CATALYSTS LLC - EAST WINDSOR—See BASF SE; *Int'l*, pg. 875
BASF CATALYSTS LLC - PAPER PIGMENTS & ADDITIVES—See BASF SE; *Int'l*, pg. 875
BASF COATINGS A.S.—See BASF SE; *Int'l*, pg. 872
BASF COATINGS AUSTRALIA PTY. LTD.—See BASF SE; *Int'l*, pg. 872
BASF COATINGS DE MEXICO S.A. DE C.V.—See BASF SE; *Int'l*, pg. 873
BASF COATINGS GMBH—See BASF SE; *Int'l*, pg. 873
BASF COATINGS PRIVATE LTD.—See BASF SE; *Int'l*, pg. 873
BASF COATINGS S.A.—See BASF SE; *Int'l*, pg. 873
BASF COATINGS S.A.S.—See BASF SE; *Int'l*, pg. 873
BASF COATINGS SERVICES B.V.—See BASF SE; *Int'l*, pg. 873
BASF COATINGS SERVICES GMBH—See BASF SE; *Int'l*, pg. 873
BASF COATINGS SERVICES ITLAY SRL—See BASF SE; *Int'l*, pg. 873
BASF COATINGS SERVICES S.A./N.V.—See BASF SE; *Int'l*, pg. 873
BASF COATINGS SERVICES S.A.R.L.—See BASF SE; *Int'l*, pg. 873
BASF COATINGS SERVICES S.A.S.—See BASF SE; *Int'l*, pg. 873
BASF COATINGS SERVICES S.A.U.—See BASF SE; *Int'l*, pg. 874
BASF COATINGS SERVICES SP. Z O.O.—See BASF SE; *Int'l*, pg. 873
BASF COATINGS SERVICES SP. Z.O.O.—See BASF SE; *Int'l*, pg. 874
BASF COATINGS, STORITVE ZA AVTOMOBILSKE PREMAZE, D.O.O.—See BASF SE; *Int'l*, pg. 873
BASF CORP. - GREENVILLE PLANT—See BASF SE; *Int'l*, pg. 876
BASF CORP. - SOUTHFIELD SITE—See BASF SE; *Int'l*, pg. 876
BASF QTECH INC.—See BASF SE; *Int'l*, pg. 881
BASF S.A.—See BASF SE; *Int'l*, pg. 873
BASF SA—See BASF SE; *Int'l*, pg. 881
BASF SHANGHAI COATINGS CO. LTD.—See BASF SE; *Int'l*, pg. 877
BASF, SIA—See BASF SE; *Int'l*, pg. 882
BEHR PROCESS CORPORATION—See Masco Corporation; *U.S. Public*, pg. 1390
BEHR PROCESS PAINTS (INDIA) PRIVATE LIMITED—See Masco Corporation; *U.S. Public*, pg. 1390
BEIJING ORIENTAL YUHONG WATERPROOF TECHNOLOGY CO., LTD.; *Int'l*, pg. 955
BENDA-LUTZ-ALPOCO SP.Z O.O.—See DIC Corporation; *Int'l*, pg. 2109
BENDA-LUTZ CORPORATION—See DIC Corporation; *Int'l*, pg. 2109
BENDA-LUTZ WERKE GMBH—See DIC Corporation; *Int'l*, pg. 2109

325510 — PAINT AND COATING M...

BENJAMIN MOORE & CO.—See Berkshire Hathaway Inc.; *U.S. Public*, pg. 300
BENJAMIN MOORE & CO.—See Berkshire Hathaway Inc.; *U.S. Public*, pg. 300
BERCEN INC.—See Cranston Print Works Company; *U.S. Private*, pg. 1086
BERGER INTERNATIONAL LTD.—See Asian Paints Limited; *Int'l*, pg. 618
BERGER JENSON & NICHOLSON (NEPAL) PRIVATE LIMITED—See Berger Paints India Limited; *Int'l*, pg. 979
BERGER PAINTS BAHRAIN W.L.L.—See Asian Paints Limited; *Int'l*, pg. 618
BERGER PAINTS BANGLADESH LIMITED; *Int'l*, pg. 979
BERGER PAINTS BARBADOS LTD.—See ANSA McAL Limited; *Int'l*, pg. 476
BERGER PAINTS EMIRATES LIMITED—See Asian Paints Limited; *Int'l*, pg. 618
BERGER PAINTS INDIA LIMITED; *Int'l*, pg. 979
BERGER PAINTS JAMAICA LIMITED—See ANSA McAL Limited; *Int'l*, pg. 476
BERGER PAINTS NIGERIA PLC.; *Int'l*, pg. 980
BERGER PAINTS NINGBO CO. LTD.—See Asian Paints Limited; *Int'l*, pg. 619
BERGER PAINTS (THAILAND) LTD—See Asian Paints Limited; *Int'l*, pg. 618
BERMUDA PAINT COMPANY LIMITED—See Devonshire Industries Limited; *Int'l*, pg. 2089
BIONI CS GMBH FZE—See Bioni CS GmbH; *Int'l*, pg. 1040
BIONI CS GMBH; *Int'l*, pg. 1040
BIONI SYSTEM GMBH—See Bioni CS GmbH; *Int'l*, pg. 1040
BIONI USA AND AMERICAS LLC.—See Bioni CS GmbH; *Int'l*, pg. 1040
BOAT S.P.A.—See Boero Bartolomeo S.p.A.; *Int'l*, pg. 1100
BQ CHEMICAL CO., LTD.—See Dai Nippon Toryo Co., Ltd.; *Int'l*, pg. 1916
BODYCOTE K-TECH, INC.—See Bodycote plc; *Int'l*, pg. 1098
BOERO BARTOLOMEO S.P.A.; *Int'l*, pg. 1100
BOERO COLORI FRANCE S.A.R.L—See Boero Bartolomeo S.p.A.; *Int'l*, pg. 1100
BOLIX S.A.—See Berger Paints India Limited; *Int'l*, pg. 980
BOLIX UKRAINA SP. Z O.O.—See Berger Paints India Limited; *Int'l*, pg. 980
BOSTON TAPES S.P.A—See Chargeurs SA; *Int'l*, pg. 1449
BREWER SCIENCE, INC.; *U.S. Private*, pg. 647
BREWER SCIENCE, INC.—See Brewer Science, Inc.; *U.S. Private*, pg. 647
BREWER SCIENCE, INC.—See Brewer Science, Inc.; *U.S. Private*, pg. 647
BREWER SCIENCE, INC.—See Brewer Science, Inc.; *U.S. Private*, pg. 647
BREWER SCIENCE, INC.—See Brewer Science, Inc.; *U.S. Private*, pg. 647
BREWER SCIENCE JAPAN, G.K.—See Brewer Science, Inc.; *U.S. Private*, pg. 647
BROWN BROTHERS DISTRIBUTION LIMITED—See PPG Industries, Inc.; *U.S. Public*, pg. 1707
B-TEAM CONSULT AND SERVICES SRL—See 2G Energy AG; *Int'l*, pg. 5
BUXLY PAINTS LIMITED; *Int'l*, pg. 1229
CALIFORNIA PRODUCTS CORPORATION—See Audax Group, Limited Partnership; *U.S. Private*, pg. 388
CALIFORNIA PRODUCTS CORP. - PAINT DIVISION—See Audax Group, Limited Partnership; *U.S. Private*, pg. 388
CALIFORNIA PRODUCTS CORP. - RECREATIONAL PRODUCTS DIVISION—See Audax Group, Limited Partnership; *U.S. Private*, pg. 388
CAM SRL—See Group Thermote & Vanhalst; *Int'l*, pg. 3089
CANADIAN WILLAMETTE INDUSTRIES, INC.—See The Willamette Valley Company; *U.S. Private*, pg. 4136
CANLAK COATINGS, INC—See SK Capital Partners, LP; *U.S. Private*, pg. 3679
CANNON SLINE INDUSTRIAL, INC. - WILMINGTON DIVISION—See The Halifax Group LLC; *U.S. Private*, pg. 4042
CAPPELLE PIGMENTS NV—See American Securities LLC; *U.S. Private*, pg. 251
CARBOLINE COMPANY—See RPM International Inc.; *U.S. Public*, pg. 1818
CARBOLINE DUBAI CORPORATION—See RPM International Inc.; *U.S. Public*, pg. 1818
CARBOLINE FRANCE S.A.S.—See RPM International Inc.; *U.S. Public*, pg. 1818
CARBOLINE GLOBAL, INC.—See RPM International Inc.; *U.S. Public*, pg. 1816
CARBOLINE ITALIA S.P.A.—See RPM International Inc.; *U.S. Public*, pg. 1818
CARBOLINE NORGE AS—See RPM International Inc.; *U.S. Public*, pg. 1818
CARDINAL INDUSTRIAL FINISHES, INC. - POWDER COATING MANUFACTURING—See Cardinal Industrial Finishes, Inc.; *U.S. Private*, pg. 750
CARDINAL INDUSTRIAL FINISHES, INC.; *U.S. Private*, pg. 750
CARELAA B.V.—See Akzo Nobel N.V.; *Int'l*, pg. 273
CARLISLE COATINGS & WATERPROOFING INC.—See Carlisle Companies Incorporated; *U.S. Public*, pg. 436
CARLISLE FLUID TECHNOLOGIES, INC.—See Carlisle Companies Incorporated; *U.S. Public*, pg. 436
CARPENTER POWDER PRODUCTS AB—See Carpenter Technology Corporation; *U.S. Public*, pg. 439
CASS HOLDING LLC; *U.S. Private*, pg. 783
CAUSEWAY PAINTS LANKA (PRIVATE) LIMITED—See Asian Paints Limited; *Int'l*, pg. 619
CCM POLYMERS SDN. BHD.—See Batu Kawan Berhad; *Int'l*, pg. 890
CENTURY INDUSTRIAL COATINGS INCORPORATED—See Axalta Coating Systems Ltd.; *U.S. Public*, pg. 255
CERAM-TRAZ CORPORATION; *U.S. Private*, pg. 835
CETEK, LTD.—See J.F. Lehman & Company, Inc.; *U.S. Private*, pg. 2163
CFC EUROPE GMBH—See Illinois Tool Works Inc.; *U.S. Public*, pg. 1102
CFC INTERNATIONAL, INC.—See Illinois Tool Works Inc.; *U.S. Public*, pg. 1102
CHARTER CHEMICAL & COATING CORPORATION—See Chugoku Marine Paints, Ltd.; *Int'l*, pg. 1595
CHEMETALL DANMARK A/S—See BASF SE; *Int'l*, pg. 882
CHEMETALL KFT.—See BASF SE; *Int'l*, pg. 882
CHIBA KAKO CO., LTD.—See Dai Nippon Toryo Co., Ltd.; *Int'l*, pg. 1916
THE CHINA PAINT MANUFACTURING COMPANY (1932) LIMITED—See CNT Group Limited; *Int'l*, pg. 1678
THE CHINA PAINT MANUFACTURING (SHENZHEN) CO., LTD.—See CNT Group Limited; *Int'l*, pg. 1678
THE CHINA PAINT MFG. CO., (XINFENG) LTD.—See CNT Group Limited; *Int'l*, pg. 1678
CHOKWANG PAINT CO., LTD.; *Int'l*, pg. 1577
CHOKWANG VINA CO., LTD.—See Chokwang Paint Co., Ltd.; *Int'l*, pg. 1578
CHONGQING SANXIA PAINTS CO., LTD.; *Int'l*, pg. 1581
CHROMA COLOR CORPORATION—See Arsenal Capital Management LP; *U.S. Private*, pg. 337
CHROMAFLO TECHNOLOGIES CHINA MANUFACTURING LTD.—See American Securities LLC; *U.S. Private*, pg. 251
CHROMAFLO TECHNOLOGIES EUROPE B.V.—See American Securities LLC; *U.S. Private*, pg. 251
CHROMATICS, INC.—See Avient Corporation; *U.S. Public*, pg. 247
CHUGOKU MARINE PAINTS, LTD.; *Int'l*, pg. 1595
CHUGOKU MARINE PAINTS (NAGASAKI), LTD.—See Chugoku Marine Paints, Ltd.; *Int'l*, pg. 1595
CHUGOKU MARINE PAINTS (SHANGHAI), LTD. - FACTORY & TECHNICAL CENTER—See Chugoku Marine Paints, Ltd.; *Int'l*, pg. 1595
CHUGOKU MARINE PAINTS (SHANGHAI), LTD.—See Chugoku Marine Paints, Ltd.; *Int'l*, pg. 1595
CHUGOKU MARINE PAINTS (SINGAPORE) PTE. LTD.—See Chugoku Marine Paints, Ltd.; *Int'l*, pg. 1595
CHUGOKU PAINTS (INDIA) PRIVATE LIMITED—See Chugoku Marine Paints, Ltd.; *Int'l*, pg. 1595
CHUGOKU PAINTS (MALAYSIA) SDN. BHD. - JOHOR FACTORY—See Chugoku Marine Paints, Ltd.; *Int'l*, pg. 1595
CHUGOKU-SAMHWA PAINTS LTD. - GYEONGNAM FACTORY—See Chugoku Marine Paints, Ltd.; *Int'l*, pg. 1595
CHUGOKU SAMHWA PAINTS LTD.—See Chugoku Marine Paints, Ltd.; *Int'l*, pg. 1595
CHUGOKU SOFT DEVELOPMENT CO. LTD.—See Chugoku Marine Paints, Ltd.; *Int'l*, pg. 1595
CIANBRO FABRICATION & COATING CORPORATION—See Cianbro Corporation; *U.S. Private*, pg. 896
CLARIANT CHEMICALS (INDIA) LIMITED—See Clariant AG; *Int'l*, pg. 1646
CLOVERDALE PAINT INC.; *Int'l*, pg. 1663
CMA ROBOTER GMBH—See EFORT Intelligent Equipment Co., Ltd.; *Int'l*, pg. 2321
CMA ROBOTICS S.P.A.—See EFORT Intelligent Equipment Co., Ltd.; *Int'l*, pg. 2321
COATING & ADHESIVES CORPORATION; *U.S. Private*, pg. 957
COLORANT CHROMATICS AG—See Avient Corporation; *U.S. Public*, pg. 247
COLORMATRIX ASIA LIMITED—See Avient Corporation; *U.S. Public*, pg. 247
COLORMATRIX EUROPE BV—See Avient Corporation; *U.S. Public*, pg. 247
COLORMATRIX RUSSIA LLC—See Avient Corporation; *U.S. Public*, pg. 247
COLORMATRIX UK LIMITED—See Avient Corporation; *U.S. Public*, pg. 247
COLOR WHEEL PAINT MANUFACTURING CO. INC.; *U.S. Private*, pg. 973
COLUMBIA PAINT & COATINGS—See The Sherwin-Williams Company; *U.S. Public*, pg. 2127
COMERCIAL MEXICANA DE PINTURAS, S.A. DE C.V.—See PPG Industries, Inc.; *U.S. Public*, pg. 1709
COMEX INDUSTRIAL COATINGS, S.A. DE C.V.—See PPG Industries, Inc.; *U.S. Public*, pg. 1707
COMPANIA MEXICANA DE PINTURAS INTERNATIONAL SA DE CV—See Akzo Nobel N.V.; *Int'l*, pg. 273
COMPANIA SHERWIN-WILLIAMS, S.A. DE C.V.—See The Sherwin-Williams Company; *U.S. Public*, pg. 2127
CONSORSIO COMEX, S.A. DE C.V.—See PPG Industries, Inc.; *U.S. Public*, pg. 1707
CONSTRUCTIEWERKHUIZEN G. VERBRUGGEN NV—See Nordson Corporation; *U.S. Public*, pg. 1532
THE CONTINENTAL PRODUCTS COMPANY, INC.—See Keene Building Products Company, Inc.; *U.S. Private*, pg. 2272
CORIMON, C.A.; *Int'l*, pg. 1800
CORIMON PINTURAS, C.A.—See Corimon, C.A.; *Int'l*, pg. 1801
COVERIGHT SURFACES USA CO.—See Lone Star Funds; *U.S. Private*, pg. 2484
CPM S.P.A.—See Durr AG; *Int'l*, pg. 2230
CROWN PAINTS KENYA LTD.; *Int'l*, pg. 1858
CROWN PAINTS KENYA PLC; *Int'l*, pg. 1858
CROWN PAINTS LTD.—See Hempel A/S; *Int'l*, pg. 3341
CUPRINOL LIMITED—See Akzo Nobel N.V.; *Int'l*, pg. 273
DAGE DEUTSCHLAND GMBH—See Nordson Corporation; *U.S. Public*, pg. 1532
DAGE (SEASIA) PTE. LTD.—See Nordson Corporation; *U.S. Public*, pg. 1532
DAILY POLYMER CO., LTD.; *Int'l*, pg. 1938
DAINICHISEIKA COLOR & CHEMICALS S.A.—See Dainichiseika Color & Chemicals Mfg. Co., Ltd.; *Int'l*, pg. 1939
DAI NIPPON TORYO CO., LTD.; *Int'l*, pg. 1916
DAI NIPPON TORYO HOKKAIDO CO., LTD.—See Dai Nippon Toryo Co., Ltd.; *Int'l*, pg. 1916
DAI NIPPON TORYO MEXICANA S. A. DE C. V.—See Dai Nippon Toryo Co., Ltd.; *Int'l*, pg. 1916
DAISHIN CHEMICAL CO., LTD.; *Int'l*, pg. 1941
DAVIS-FROST INC.; *U.S. Private*, pg. 1174
DAVIS PAINT COMPANY; *U.S. Private*, pg. 1174
DECOART INC—See MPE Partners, LLC; *U.S. Private*, pg. 2803
DECORATIVE OUEST S.A.S.—See Akzo Nobel N.V.; *Int'l*, pg. 273
DEFT, INC. OF OHIO—See PPG Industries, Inc.; *U.S. Public*, pg. 1707
DEFT, INC.—See PPG Industries, Inc.; *U.S. Public*, pg. 1707
DEJMARK KFT.—See Dejmark Group s.r.o.; *Int'l*, pg. 2005
DEKRO PAINTS (PTY) LTD; *Int'l*, pg. 2010
DELTA LABORATORIES INC.; *U.S. Private*, pg. 1201
DE SIKKENS GROSSIER B.V.—See Akzo Nobel N.V.; *Int'l*, pg. 273
DEUTSCHE NANOSCHICHT GMBH—See BASF SE; *Int'l*, pg. 883
DIAMOND VOGEL PAINT, INC.; *U.S. Private*, pg. 1224
DICALITE EUROPE NORD, S.A.—See RGP Holding, Inc.; *U.S. Private*, pg. 3420
DIC INDIA LTD; *Int'l*, pg. 2111
DIMET (SIAM) PUBLIC COMPANY LIMITED; *Int'l*, pg. 2126
DNT KANSAI MEXICANA S.A. DE C.V.—See Dai Nippon Toryo Co., Ltd.; *Int'l*, pg. 1916
DNT PAINT (MALAYSIA) SDN. BHD.—See Dai Nippon Toryo Co., Ltd.; *Int'l*, pg. 1916
DNT SANYO CHEMICAL CO., LTD.—See Dai Nippon Toryo Co., Ltd.; *Int'l*, pg. 1916
DNT (SHANGHAI) CO.,LTD.—See Dai Nippon Toryo Co., Ltd.; *Int'l*, pg. 1916
DNT SINGAPORE PTE. LTD.—See Dai Nippon Toryo Co., Ltd.; *Int'l*, pg. 1916
DONG A PAINT JSC; *Int'l*, pg. 2163
DONGGUAN LILLY PAINT INDUSTRIES LIMITED—See The Sherwin-Williams Company; *U.S. Public*, pg. 2129
DONGLAI COATING TECHNOLOGY SHANGHAI CO., LTD.; *Int'l*, pg. 2169
DONG NAI PAINT CORPORATION; *Int'l*, pg. 2163
DPG BV; *Int'l*, pg. 2188
DPI ALLIANCE PTE. LTD.—See DPI Holdings Berhad; *Int'l*, pg. 2189
DPI CHEMICALS SDN. BHD.—See DPI Holdings Berhad; *Int'l*, pg. 2189
DUCKBACK PRODUCTS—See The Sherwin-Williams Company; *U.S. Public*, pg. 2127
DUDICK, INC.—See RPM International Inc.; *U.S. Public*, pg. 1818
DUGA HOLDING AD; *Int'l*, pg. 2224
DULUX BOTSWANA (PTY) LIMITED—See Akzo Nobel N.V.; *Int'l*, pg. 273
DULUX PAINTS ZA—See Akzo Nobel N.V.; *Int'l*, pg. 274
DULUX SWAZILAND (PTY) LIMITED—See Akzo Nobel N.V.; *Int'l*, pg. 274
DUNCAN ENTERPRISES—See Duncan Financial Corporation; *U.S. Private*, pg. 1287
DUPLI-COLOR PRODUCTS COMPANY—See The Sherwin-Williams Company; *U.S. Public*, pg. 2127
DURA COAT PRODUCTS, INC.—See Axalta Coating Systems Ltd.; *U.S. Public*, pg. 255
DURA COAT PRODUCTS OF ALABAMA, INC.—See Axalta Coating Systems Ltd.; *U.S. Public*, pg. 255
DURR PAINTSHOP SYSTEMS ENGINEERING (SHANGHAI) CO. LTD.—See Durr AG; *Int'l*, pg. 2231
DURR SOUTH AFRICA (PTY.) LTD—See Durr AG; *Int'l*, pg. 2231
DURR SYSTEMS SLOVAKIA SPOL. S R.O.—See Durr AG; *Int'l*, pg. 2231
DURR SYSTEMS WOLFSBURG GMBH—See Durr AG; *Int'l*, pg. 2231

N.A.I.C.S. INDEX

325510 — PAINT AND COATING M...

DYNAMIC PAINT PRODUCTS INC.—See Centre Lane Partners, LLC; *U.S. Private*, pg. 828
DYRUP A/S—See PPG Industries, Inc.; *U.S. Public*, pg. 1707
DYRUP GMBH—See PPG Industries, Inc.; *U.S. Public*, pg. 1707
DYRUP SAS—See PPG Industries, Inc.; *U.S. Public*, pg. 1707
DYRUP SP. Z.O.O.—See PPG Industries, Inc.; *U.S. Public*, pg. 1707
EASON & CO PUBLIC COMPANY LTD.; *Int'l*, pg. 2269
ECL ENVIROCLEAN VENTURES LTD.; *Int'l*, pg. 2291
ECP INCORPORATED—See Daubert Industries, Inc.; *U.S. Private*, pg. 1167
E.E. ZIMMERMAN COMPANY—See Zimmerman Holding Company; *U.S. Private*, pg. 4605
EFORT EUROPE S.R.L—See EFORT Intelligent Equipment Co., Ltd.; *Int'l*, pg. 2321
ELEMENTIS SPECIALTIES, INC.—See Elementis plc; *Int'l*, pg. 2359
ENCAPSYS LLC; *U.S. Private*, pg. 1390
ENCO MANUFACTURING CORP.; *U.S. Private*, pg. 1390
ENDEKA CERAMICS S.R.L.—See American Securities LLC; *U.S. Private*, pg. 251
ENGINEERED POLYMER SOLUTIONS, INC.—See The Sherwin-Williams Company; *U.S. Public*, pg. 2129
ENNIS-FLINT, INC.—See PPG Industries, Inc.; *U.S. Public*, pg. 1707
ENNIS PAINT INC.—See Brazos Private Equity Partners, LLC; *U.S. Private*, pg. 642
ENVIROCOAT TECHNOLOGIES INC.—See ECL Enviro-Clean Ventures Ltd.; *Int'l*, pg. 2291
EP MINERALS EUROPE GMBH & CO. KG—See Apollo Global Management, Inc.; *U.S. Public*, pg. 165
EPS/CCA—See The Sherwin-Williams Company; *U.S. Public*, pg. 2129
ES SADOLIN AS—See Akzo Nobel N.V.; *Int'l*, pg. 274
THE EUCLID CHEMICAL COMPANY—See RPM International Inc.; *U.S. Public*, pg. 1818
EUROPLASMA NV—See Gimv NV; *Int'l*, pg. 2976
FABRESINES—See Compagnie de Saint-Gobain SA; *Int'l*, pg. 1723
FABRICA DE PINTURAS UNIVERSALES, S.A. DE C.V.—See PPG Industries, Inc.; *U.S. Public*, pg. 1707
FABRYKA FARB I LAKIEROW SNIEZKA S.A.; *Int'l*, pg. 2600
FABRYO CORPORATION SRL—See Akzo Nobel N.V.; *Int'l*, pg. 274
FALTON INVESTMENT LIMITED—See China Automobile New Retail (Holdings) Limited; *Int'l*, pg. 1484
FARRELL-CALHOUN INC.; *U.S. Private*, pg. 1481
FAST & FLUID MANAGEMENT AUSTRALIA PTY. LTD.—See IDEX Corp; *U.S. Public*, pg. 1090
FAST & FLUID MANAGEMENT B.V.—See IDEX Corp; *U.S. Public*, pg. 1090
FAST & FLUID MANAGEMENT NETHERLANDS—See IDEX Corp; *U.S. Public*, pg. 1090
FAST & FLUID MANAGEMENT SRL—See IDEX Corp; *U.S. Public*, pg. 1090
FERRO ARGENTINA, S.A.—See American Securities LLC; *U.S. Private*, pg. 251
FERRO COLOMBIA PIGMENTOS S.A.S.—See American Securities LLC; *U.S. Private*, pg. 251
FERRO CORPORATION - COLOR DIVISION—See American Securities LLC; *U.S. Private*, pg. 251
FERRO CORPORATION - INDUSTRIAL COATINGS DIVISION—See American Securities LLC; *U.S. Private*, pg. 251
FERRO CORPORATION—See American Securities LLC; *U.S. Private*, pg. 251
FERRO ENAMEL DO BRASIL LTDA.—See American Securities LLC; *U.S. Private*, pg. 251
FERRO ENAMEL ESPANOLA, S.A.—See American Securities LLC; *U.S. Private*, pg. 252
FERRO FRANCE S.A.R.L.—See American Securities LLC; *U.S. Private*, pg. 251
FERRO GMBH—See American Securities LLC; *U.S. Private*, pg. 252
FERRO (GREAT BRITAIN) LTD—See American Securities LLC; *U.S. Private*, pg. 251
FERRO INDUSTRIAS QUIMICAS (PORTUGAL) LDA—See American Securities LLC; *U.S. Private*, pg. 251
FERRO MEXICANA, S.A. DE C.V.—See American Securities LLC; *U.S. Private*, pg. 252
FERRO PERFORMANCE PIGMENTS BELGIUM NV—See American Securities LLC; *U.S. Private*, pg. 252
FERRO PERFORMANCE PIGMENTS FRANCE SAS—See American Securities LLC; *U.S. Private*, pg. 251
FERRO PERFORMANCE PIGMENTS ROMANIA SRL—See American Securities LLC; *U.S. Private*, pg. 252
FERRO PERFORMANCE PIGMENTS (SHANGHAI) CO., LTD.—See American Securities LLC; *U.S. Private*, pg. 252
FERRO TURKEY KAPLAMA CAM VE RENK COZUMLERI SANAYI VE TICARET LIMITED SIRKETI—See American Securities LLC; *U.S. Private*, pg. 252

THE FLECTO COMPANY, INC.—See RPM International Inc.; *U.S. Public*, pg. 1817
FLINT TRADING, INC.—See Brazos Private Equity Partners, LLC; *U.S. Private*, pg. 642
FLORIDA PAINTS & COATINGS LLC; *U.S. Private*, pg. 1550
FLUGGER DENMARK A/S—See Flugger Group A/S; *Int'l*, pg. 2712
FLUGGER GROUP A/S; *Int'l*, pg. 2712
FLUGGER ICELAND EHF.—See Flugger Group A/S; *Int'l*, pg. 2712
FLUGGER NORWAY AS—See Flugger Group A/S; *Int'l*, pg. 2712
FLUGGER POLAND SP. Z O.O.—See Flugger Group A/S; *Int'l*, pg. 2712
FLUGGER SWEDEN AB—See Flugger Group A/S; *Int'l*, pg. 2712
FLUID MANAGEMENT EUROPE B.V.—See IDEX Corp; *U.S. Public*, pg. 1090
FORREST PAINT CO.; *U.S. Private*, pg. 1572
FORTECH PRODUCTS, INC.; *U.S. Private*, pg. 1575
FOX VALLEY SYSTEMS, INC.; *U.S. Private*, pg. 1585
FOY-JOHNSTON INC.; *U.S. Public*, pg. 877
FREUND CORPORATION; *Int'l*, pg. 2791
FRONTKEN (SINGAPORE) PTE. LTD. - JURONG PLANT 2—See Frontken Corporation Berhad; *Int'l*, pg. 2796
FRONTKEN (SINGAPORE) PTE. LTD.—See Frontken Corporation Berhad; *Int'l*, pg. 2796
FSW COATINGS LIMITED; *Int'l*, pg. 2800
FUJICHEM SONNEBORN LTD. - CHESTERFIELD PLANT—See Fujikura Kasei Co., Ltd.; *Int'l*, pg. 2826
FUJICHEM SONNEBORN LTD.—See Fujikura Kasei Co., Ltd.; *Int'l*, pg. 2826
FUJIKURA KASEI CO., LTD. - SANO PLANT 1—See Fujikura Kasei Co., Ltd.; *Int'l*, pg. 2826
FUJIKURA KASEI CO., LTD. - SANO PLANT 2—See Fujikura Kasei Co., Ltd.; *Int'l*, pg. 2826
FULLER WESTERN RUBBER LININGS LTD.—See Corrosion & Abrasion Solutions Ltd.; *Int'l*, pg. 1806
GEMINI INDUSTRIES INC.; *U.S. Private*, pg. 1658
GENERAL COATINGS TECHNOLOGIES; *U.S. Private*, pg. 1664
GLAS TROSCH AG HY-TECH-GLASS—See Glas Trosch Holding AG; *Int'l*, pg. 2988
GML COATINGS, LLC—See Primoris Services Corporation; *U.S. Public*, pg. 1718
GREAT LAKE WOODS INC.; *U.S. Private*, pg. 1764
GUANGDONG HUARUN PAINTS CO., LTD.—See The Sherwin-Williams Company; *U.S. Public*, pg. 2127
GUARDSMAN INDUSTRIES LIMITED—See The Sherwin-Williams Company; *U.S. Public*, pg. 2128
HADROKOR SP. Z O.O.—See Fabryka Farb i Lakierow Sniezka S.A.; *Int'l*, pg. 2600
HALLMAN LINDSAY PAINTS INC.; *U.S. Private*, pg. 1844
HAMMERITE PRODUCTS LIMITED—See Akzo Nobel N.V.; *Int'l*, pg. 274
HARDER & STEENBECK GMBH & CO. KG—See ANEST IWATA Corporation; *Int'l*, pg. 458
HARDIDE PLC; *Int'l*, pg. 3272
HARRISON PAINT COMPANY - EXCELSIOR COATINGS DIVISION—See Harrison Paint Company; *U.S. Private*, pg. 1870
HARRISON PAINT COMPANY; *U.S. Private*, pg. 1870
HCI CHEMTEC, INC.; *U.S. Private*, pg. 1888
HCI HOLLAND COATINGS INDUSTRIES—See 3G Capital Partners L.P.; *U.S. Private*, pg. 11
HEMMELRATH AUTOMOTIVE COATINGS (JILIN) CO., LTD.—See PPG Industries, Inc.; *U.S. Public*, pg. 1707
HEMOTEQ AG; *Int'l*, pg. 3341
HEMPEL A/S; *Int'l*, pg. 3341
HEMPEL (CHINA) LTD.—See Hempel A/S; *Int'l*, pg. 3341
HEMPEL (USA) INC.—See Hempel A/S; *Int'l*, pg. 3341
HENTZEN COATINGS INC.; *U.S. Private*, pg. 1920
HICHEM PAINT TECHNOLOGIES PTY. LIMITED—See RPM International Inc.; *U.S. Public*, pg. 1817
HIGHLAND ELECTROPLATERS LTD.—See DMI UK Ltd.; *Int'l*, pg. 2146
HIRSHFIELD'S PAINT MANUFACTURING INC.—See Hirshfield's Inc.; *U.S. Private*, pg. 1951
H-I-S PAINT MANUFACTURING COMPANY INC.; *U.S. Private*, pg. 1824
HOA BINH PAINT CO., LTD.—See Hoa Binh Construction Group JSC; *Int'l*, pg. 3435
HODIJ COATINGS B.V.—See PPG Industries, Inc.; *U.S. Public*, pg. 1707
HOMAX PRODUCTS, INC.—See PPG Industries, Inc.; *U.S. Public*, pg. 1708
HUMISEAL INDIA PRIVATE LIMITED—See KKR & Co. Inc.; *U.S. Public*, pg. 1243
HUNTSMAN BUILDING SOLUTIONS (FRANCE) SAS—See Huntsman Corporation; *U.S. Public*, pg. 1072
HYBRID COATING TECHNOLOGIES INC.; *U.S. Public*, pg. 1078
ICA DEUTSCHLAND LACKE GMBH—See The Sherwin-Williams Company; *U.S. Public*, pg. 2128
ICA POLSKA SP. Z O.O.—See The Sherwin-Williams Company; *U.S. Public*, pg. 2128

ICI INDIA LTD.-PAINTS DIVISION—See Akzo Nobel N.V.; *Int'l*, pg. 273
ICI OMICRON B.V.—See Akzo Nobel N.V.; *Int'l*, pg. 274
ICI PAINTS CZ SPOL.S.R.O.—See Akzo Nobel N.V.; *Int'l*, pg. 274
ICI PAINTS DECO FRANCE SA—See Akzo Nobel N.V.; *Int'l*, pg. 274
ICI PAINTS MERCOSUR B.V.—See Akzo Nobel N.V.; *Int'l*, pg. 274
ICI THETA B.V.—See Akzo Nobel N.V.; *Int'l*, pg. 274
IDEAPAINT, INC.—See Audax Group, Limited Partnership; *U.S. Private*, pg. 388
IFS COATINGS, INC.—See CFS Group, Inc.; *Int'l*, pg. 1430
IMPREGLON CELLRAMIC—See Aalberts N.V.; *Int'l*, pg. 34
INDUPLEX, INC.—See RGP Holding, Inc.; *U.S. Private*, pg. 3420
INDUSTRIA CHIMICA REGGIANA I.C.R. SPA—See PPG Industries, Inc.; *U.S. Public*, pg. 1707
INDUSTRIA MAIMERI S.P.A.—See F.I.L.A. - Fabbrica Italiana Lapis ed Affini S.p.A.; *Int'l*, pg. 2597
INSL-X PRODUCTS CORP.—See Berkshire Hathaway Inc.; *U.S. Public*, pg. 300
INTEGRATED GLOBAL SERVICES, INC.—See J.F. Lehman & Company, Inc.; *U.S. Private*, pg. 2163
INTERNATIONAL COATINGS LTD—See Akzo Nobel N.V.; *Int'l*, pg. 274
INTERNATIONAL COATINGS PTE LTD—See Akzo Nobel N.V.; *Int'l*, pg. 274
INTERNATIONAL FARBENWERKE GMBH—See Akzo Nobel N.V.; *Int'l*, pg. 274
INTERNATIONAL FARG AB—See Akzo Nobel N.V.; *Int'l*, pg. 274
INTERNATIONAL MALING A/S—See Akzo Nobel N.V.; *Int'l*, pg. 274
INTERNATIONAL PAINT (BELGIUM) NV—See Akzo Nobel N.V.; *Int'l*, pg. 270
INTERNATIONAL PAINT (EAST RUSSIA) LTD—See Akzo Nobel N.V.; *Int'l*, pg. 270
INTERNATIONAL PAINT FRANCE S.A.—See Akzo Nobel N.V.; *Int'l*, pg. 270
INTERNATIONAL PAINT (HELLAS) S.A.—See Akzo Nobel N.V.; *Int'l*, pg. 270
INTERNATIONAL PAINT (HONG KONG) LIMITED—See Akzo Nobel N.V.; *Int'l*, pg. 270
INTERNATIONAL PAINT INC.—See Akzo Nobel N.V.; *Int'l*, pg. 274
INTERNATIONAL PAINT ITALIA SPA—See Akzo Nobel N.V.; *Int'l*, pg. 270
INTERNATIONAL PAINT JAPAN K.K.—See Akzo Nobel N.V.; *Int'l*, pg. 270
INTERNATIONAL PAINT (KOREA) LTD - CHILSEO FACTORY—See Akzo Nobel N.V.; *Int'l*, pg. 270
INTERNATIONAL PAINT (KOREA) LTD—See Akzo Nobel N.V.; *Int'l*, pg. 270
INTERNATIONAL PAINT LBERIA, LDA—See Akzo Nobel N.V.; *Int'l*, pg. 271
INTERNATIONAL PAINT LTD—See Akzo Nobel N.V.; *Int'l*, pg. 270
INTERNATIONAL PAINT OF SHANGHAI CO LTD—See Akzo Nobel N.V.; *Int'l*, pg. 271
INTERNATIONAL PAINT PAZARLAMA LIMITED SIRKETI—See Akzo Nobel N.V.; *Int'l*, pg. 271
INTERNATIONAL PAINT (RESEARCH) LTD—See Akzo Nobel N.V.; *Int'l*, pg. 270
INTERNATIONAL PAINT SDN BHD—See Akzo Nobel N.V.; *Int'l*, pg. 271
INTERNATIONAL PAINT SINGAPORE PTE LTD—See Akzo Nobel N.V.; *Int'l*, pg. 271
INTERNATIONAL PAINT (TAIWAN) LTD—See Akzo Nobel N.V.; *Int'l*, pg. 270
INTERNATIONAL PEINTURE S.A.—See Akzo Nobel N.V.; *Int'l*, pg. 271
INVER EAST MED S.A.—See The Sherwin-Williams Company; *U.S. Public*, pg. 2129
INVER FRANE SAS—See The Sherwin-Williams Company; *U.S. Public*, pg. 2129
INVER GMBH—See The Sherwin-Williams Company; *U.S. Public*, pg. 2129
INVER POLSKA SPOLKA Z O.O.—See The Sherwin-Williams Company; *U.S. Public*, pg. 2128
INVER POLSKA SP.Z.O.O.—See The Sherwin-Williams Company; *U.S. Public*, pg. 2129
INVER S.P.A.—See The Sherwin-Williams Company; *U.S. Public*, pg. 2129
IONBOND AG—See IHI Corporation; *Int'l*, pg. 3605
IONBOND CZECHCOATING CZECHCOATING S.R.O.—See IHI Corporation; *Int'l*, pg. 3605
IONBOND CZECHIA, S.R.O.—See IHI Corporation; *Int'l*, pg. 3605
IONBOND ICC PARIS INNOVATIVE COATING CO.—See IHI Corporation; *Int'l*, pg. 3605
IONBOND LLC—See IHI Corporation; *Int'l*, pg. 3605
IONBOND (MALAYSIA) SDN. BHD.—See IHI Corporation; *Int'l*, pg. 3605
IONBOND MULHOUSE—See IHI Corporation; *Int'l*, pg. 3605
IONBOND TINKAP ISTANBUL TINKAP VAKUM PLAZMA TEK. LTD.—See IHI Corporation; *Int'l*, pg. 3605

325510 — PAINT AND COATING M...

IONIC TECHNOLOGIES, INC.—See Aalberts N.V.; *Int'l*, pg. 34
ITW DEVCON FUTURA COATINGS—See Illinois Tool Works Inc.; *U.S. Public*, pg. 1105
ITW - EVERCOAT—See Illinois Tool Works Inc.; *U.S. Public*, pg. 1104
ITW SPECIALTY FILM LLC—See Illinois Tool Works Inc.; *U.S. Public*, pg. 1107
ITW SPECIALTY MATERIALS (SUZHOU) CO., LTD.—See Illinois Tool Works Inc.; *U.S. Public*, pg. 1107
ITW THERMAL FILMS (SHANGHAI) CO., LTD.—See Illinois Tool Works Inc.; *U.S. Public*, pg. 1108
JAPAN POWDER COATINGS MANUFACTURING CO., LTD.—See Dai Nippon Toryo Co., Ltd.; *Int'l*, pg. 1916
JIANGSU PULANNA COATING CO., LTD.—See The Sherwin-Williams Company; *U.S. Public*, pg. 2128
JONES-BLAIR COMPANY, LLC—See Hempel A/S; *Int'l*, pg. 3341
KADISCO PAINT & ADHESIVE INDUSTRY S.C.—See Asian Paints Limited; *Int'l*, pg. 619
KARL WOERWAG LACK-UND FARBENFABRIK GMBH & CO. KG—See PPG Industries, Inc.; *U.S. Public*, pg. 1707
KELLY-MOORE PAINT COMPANY, INC.; *U.S. Private*, pg. 2277
KOBE PAINTS, LTD.—See Chugoku Marine Paints, Ltd.; *Int'l*, pg. 1595
KOP-COAT, INC.—See RPM International Inc.; *U.S. Public*, pg. 1819
KOP-COAT NEW ZEALAND LTD.—See RPM International Inc.; *U.S. Public*, pg. 1819
KRONOS INTERNATIONAL, INC.—See Contran Corporation; *U.S. Private*, pg. 1033
KRONOS WORLDWIDE, INC.—See Contran Corporation; *U.S. Private*, pg. 1033
KUWAIT PAINT CO.—See Al-Babtain Group; *Int'l*, pg. 284
LAFARGE ROAD MARKING—See Holcim Ltd.; *Int'l*, pg. 3449
LAPOLLA INDUSTRIES, INC.—See Huntsman Corporation; *U.S. Public*, pg. 1075
LILLY INDUSTRIES (SHANGHAI) LIMITED—See The Sherwin-Williams Company; *U.S. Public*, pg. 2129
LNTERQUIM S.A.—See Akzo Nobel N.V.; *Int'l*, pg. 275
LORD FAR EAST, INC.—See Parker Hannifin Corporation; *U.S. Public*, pg. 1641
LORD SUISSE SARL—See Parker Hannifin Corporation; *U.S. Public*, pg. 1641
LYMTAL INTERNATIONAL, INC.; *U.S. Private*, pg. 2520
MAGNUM ENERGY SERVICES LTD.—See Corrosion & Abrasion Solutions Ltd.; *Int'l*, pg. 1806
MANTROSE-HAEUSER CO.—See RPM International Inc.; *U.S. Public*, pg. 1817
MARICOGEN A/S—See Akzo Nobel N.V.; *Int'l*, pg. 274
MARTIN MATHYS NV—See RPM International Inc.; *U.S. Public*, pg. 1817
MASTERCHEM INDUSTRIES, LLC—See Masco Corporation; *U.S. Public*, pg. 1392
MASTER COATING TECHNOLOGIES, INC.—See Audax Group, Limited Partnership; *U.S. Private*, pg. 388
MCCORMICK PAINT WORKS COMPANY; *U.S. Private*, pg. 2630
MERCURY PAINT CORP.; *U.S. Private*, pg. 2671
METALFX TECHNOLOGY LTD.—See BASF SE; *Int'l*, pg. 884
METOKOTE CANADA LTD.—See PPG Industries, Inc.; *U.S. Public*, pg. 1707
METOKOTE CORPORATION, INC.—See PPG Industries, Inc.; *U.S. Public*, pg. 1707
METOKOTE DEUTSCHLAND GMBH—See PPG Industries, Inc.; *U.S. Public*, pg. 1707
METOKOTE U.K. LIMITED—See PPG Industries, Inc.; *U.S. Public*, pg. 1707
MILLER PAINT COMPANY, INC.—See Cloverdale Paint Inc.; *Int'l*, pg. 1663
ML CAMPBELL & FABULON—See The Sherwin-Williams Company; *U.S. Public*, pg. 2128
MOBILE PAINT MANUFACTURING COMPANY OF DELAWARE INC.; *U.S. Private*, pg. 2757
MOHAWK FINISHING PRODUCTS, INC.—See RPM International Inc.; *U.S. Public*, pg. 1817
MORRELLS WOODFINISHES LIMITED—See RPM International Inc.; *U.S. Public*, pg. 1817
NATIONAL PAINT INDUSTRIES, INC.—See Huron Capital Partners LLC; *U.S. Private*, pg. 2012
NCP COATINGS INC.; *U.S. Private*, pg. 2876
NEOGARD CONSTRUCTION COATINGS—See Hempel A/S; *Int'l*, pg. 3341
NEW NAUTICAL COATINGS, INC.—See Akzo Nobel N.V.; *Int'l*, pg. 274
NIPPO DENKO CO., LTD.—See Dai Nippon Toryo Co., Ltd.; *Int'l*, pg. 1916
NITTO CHEMICAL CO., LTD.—See Dai Nippon Toryo Co., Ltd.; *Int'l*, pg. 1916
NITTO SANWA TORYO CO., LTD.—See Dai Nippon Toryo Co., Ltd.; *Int'l*, pg. 1916
NITTO SERVICE CO., LTD.—See Dai Nippon Toryo Co., Ltd.; *Int'l*, pg. 1916
NORDSON AB—See Nordson Corporation; *U.S. Public*, pg. 1533

NORDSON OSTERREICH GMBH—See Nordson Corporation; *U.S. Public*, pg. 1534
NOVACEL GMBH—See Chargeurs SA; *Int'l*, pg. 1449
NOVACEL IBERICA S.P.A.—See Chargeurs SA; *Int'l*, pg. 1449
NOVACEL ITALIA S.R.L—See Chargeurs SA; *Int'l*, pg. 1449
NOVACEL SHANGHAI—See Chargeurs SA; *Int'l*, pg. 1449
NOVACEL—See Chargeurs SA; *Int'l*, pg. 1449
NOVACEL UK LTD—See Chargeurs SA; *Int'l*, pg. 1449
OASIS-AMERON COMPANY LTD.—See PPG Industries, Inc.; *U.S. Public*, pg. 1709
OKAYAMA KAKO CO., LTD.—See Dai Nippon Toryo Co., Ltd.; *Int'l*, pg. 1916
OLPIDURR S.P.A.—See Durr AG; *Int'l*, pg. 2233
OMNOVA SOLUTIONS SAS—See OMNOVA Solutions Inc.; *U.S. Private*, pg. 3017
ONA POLYMERS LLC—See CFS Group, Inc.; *Int'l*, pg. 1430
ONE SHOT LLC—See PPG Industries, Inc.; *U.S. Public*, pg. 1707
OOO AKZO NOBEL WOOD COATINGS—See Akzo Nobel N.V.; *Int'l*, pg. 274
OOO BASF WOSTOK—See BASF SE; *Int'l*, pg. 886
OOO GAMMA INDUSTRIAL COATINGS—See PPG Industries, Inc.; *U.S. Public*, pg. 1710
OOO PETROKOM-LIPETSK—See Akzo Nobel N.V.; *Int'l*, pg. 274
OOO TIKKURILA—See PPG Industries, Inc.; *U.S. Public*, pg. 1710
OSKAR NOLTE GMBH—See The Sherwin-Williams Company; *U.S. Public*, pg. 2128
PANTER B.V.—See Akzo Nobel N.V.; *Int'l*, pg. 274
PEINTURE DE PARIS SAS—See PPG Industries, Inc.; *U.S. Public*, pg. 1710
PEMCO BRUGGE BVBA—See American Securities LLC; *U.S. Private*, pg. 253
PEMCO CORPORATION—See American Securities LLC; *U.S. Private*, pg. 253
PEMCO EMELIER S.A.—See American Securities LLC; *U.S. Private*, pg. 253
PENTA PAINTS CARIBBEAN LIMITED—See ANSA McAL Limited; *Int'l*, pg. 476
PERFORMANCE COATINGS INTERNATIONAL LABORATORIES, LLC; *U.S. Private*, pg. 3148
PERLITA Y VERMICULITA, S.L.U.—See RPM International Inc.; *U.S. Public*, pg. 1818
PERRY & DERRICK CO.; *U.S. Private*, pg. 3153
THE PERVO PAINT COMPANY; *U.S. Private*, pg. 4093
PETTIT PAINT COMPANY—See RPM International Inc.; *U.S. Public*, pg. 1819
PICEU GROUP LIMITED, INC.; *U.S. Private*, pg. 3176
PIGROL FARBEN GMBH—See PPG Industries, Inc.; *U.S. Public*, pg. 1710
PINTURAS BENICARLO, S.L.—See American Securities LLC; *U.S. Private*, pg. 252
PINTURAS DYRUP, S.A.—See PPG Industries, Inc.; *U.S. Public*, pg. 1710
PINTURAS INCA S.A.—See Akzo Nobel N.V.; *Int'l*, pg. 271
PLASTICOS ENVOLVENTES, S.A. DE C.V.—See PPG Industries, Inc.; *U.S. Public*, pg. 1710
PLASTI-KOTE COMPANY INC.—See The Sherwin-Williams Company; *U.S. Public*, pg. 2129
POSTER STORE SVERIGE AB—See Desenio Group AB; *Int'l*, pg. 2044
POWDERMET, INC.—See ABAKAN INC.; *U.S. Private*, pg. 34
POWDER PAINTS AND VARNISHES PLANT LTD.—See Fabryka Farb i Lakierow Sniezka S.A.; *Int'l*, pg. 2600
POWDERTECH, LLC—See Great Plains Ventures, Inc.; *U.S. Private*, pg. 1767
PPG AEROSPACE MATERIALS (SUZHOU) CO. LTD.—See PPG Industries, Inc.; *U.S. Public*, pg. 1708
PPG AEROSPACE—See PPG Industries, Inc.; *U.S. Public*, pg. 1707
PPG AP RESINAS, S.A. DE C.V.—See PPG Industries, Inc.; *U.S. Public*, pg. 1707
PPG ARCHITECTURAL COATINGS EMEA—See PPG Industries, Inc.; *U.S. Public*, pg. 1708
PPG ARCHITECTURAL COATINGS—See PPG Industries, Inc.; *U.S. Public*, pg. 1708
PPG ARCHITECTURAL COATINGS—See PPG Industries, Inc.; *U.S. Public*, pg. 1708
PPG ARCHITECTURAL COATINGS UK LIMITED—See PPG Industries, Inc.; *U.S. Public*, pg. 1708
PPG ARCHITECTURAL FINISHES, INC.—See PPG Industries, Inc.; *U.S. Public*, pg. 1708
PPG (AUSTRIA) HANDELS GMBH—See PPG Industries, Inc.; *U.S. Public*, pg. 1707
PPG CAMEROUN SA—See PPG Industries, Inc.; *U.S. Public*, pg. 1708
PPG CEE PREMAZI (D.O.O.)—See PPG Industries, Inc.; *U.S. Public*, pg. 1708
PPG CEE PREMAZI—See PPG Industries, Inc.; *U.S. Public*, pg. 1708
PPG COATINGS BELGIUM BV—See PPG Industries, Inc.; *U.S. Public*, pg. 1708
PPG COATINGS BELUX N.V.—See PPG Industries, Inc.; *U.S. Public*, pg. 1708

PPG COATINGS BV—See PPG Industries, Inc.; *U.S. Public*, pg. 1708
PPG COATINGS EUROPE B.V.—See PPG Industries, Inc.; *U.S. Public*, pg. 1708
PPG COATINGS (HONG KONG) CO., LIMITED—See PPG Industries, Inc.; *U.S. Public*, pg. 1708
PPG COATINGS (KUNSHAN) CO., LTD.—See PPG Industries, Inc.; *U.S. Public*, pg. 1708
PPG COATINGS MANUFACTURING SARL—See PPG Industries, Inc.; *U.S. Public*, pg. 1708
PPG COATINGS S.A.—See PPG Industries, Inc.; *U.S. Public*, pg. 1708
PPG COATINGS (SINGAPORE) PTE LTD—See PPG Industries, Inc.; *U.S. Public*, pg. 1708
PPG COATINGS (TIANJIN) CO., LTD.—See PPG Industries, Inc.; *U.S. Public*, pg. 1708
PPG DAIHAN PACKAGING COATINGS, LTD.—See PPG Industries, Inc.; *U.S. Public*, pg. 1708
PPG DECO CZECH A.S.—See PPG Industries, Inc.; *U.S. Public*, pg. 1708
PPG DECO POLSKA SP. Z O.O.—See PPG Industries, Inc.; *U.S. Public*, pg. 1709
PPG DECORATIVE COATINGS-CAROLINA—See PPG Industries, Inc.; *U.S. Public*, pg. 1710
PPG DECORATIVE COATINGS-CARROLLTON—See PPG Industries, Inc.; *U.S. Public*, pg. 1710
PPG DECORATIVE COATINGS-HURON—See PPG Industries, Inc.; *U.S. Public*, pg. 1710
PPG DEUTSCHLAND BUSINESS SUPORT GMBH—See PPG Industries, Inc.; *U.S. Public*, pg. 1708
PPG GUADELOUPE SAS—See PPG Industries, Inc.; *U.S. Public*, pg. 1708
PPG HEMMELRATH LACKFABRIK GMBH—See PPG Industries, Inc.; *U.S. Public*, pg. 1708
PPG IBERICA, S.A.—See PPG Industries, Inc.; *U.S. Public*, pg. 1708
PPG INDUSTRIAL COATINGS B.V.—See PPG Industries, Inc.; *U.S. Public*, pg. 1708
PPG INDUSTRIES AUSTRALIA PTY. LIMITED—See PPG Industries, Inc.; *U.S. Public*, pg. 1708
PPG INDUSTRIES CHEMICALS B.V.—See PPG Industries, Inc.; *U.S. Public*, pg. 1709
PPG INDUSTRIES DE MEXICO, SA DE CV—See PPG Industries, Inc.; *U.S. Public*, pg. 1709
PPG INDUSTRIES EUROPE SARL—See PPG Industries, Inc.; *U.S. Public*, pg. 1709
PPG INDUSTRIES FRANCE SAS—See PPG Industries, Inc.; *U.S. Public*, pg. 1709
PPG INDUSTRIES, INC.; *U.S. Public*, pg. 1706
PPG INDUSTRIES ITALIA S.P.A.—See PPG Industries, Inc.; *U.S. Public*, pg. 1709
PPG INDUSTRIES ITALIA SRL—See PPG Industries, Inc.; *U.S. Public*, pg. 1709
PPG INDUSTRIES KIMYA SANAYI VE TICARET ANONIM SIRKETI—See PPG Industries, Inc.; *U.S. Public*, pg. 1709
PPG INDUSTRIES (KOREA) LTD.—See PPG Industries, Inc.; *U.S. Public*, pg. 1708
PPG INDUSTRIES LACKFABRIK GMBH—See PPG Industries, Inc.; *U.S. Public*, pg. 1709
PPG INDUSTRIES LLC—See PPG Industries, Inc.; *U.S. Public*, pg. 1709
PPG INDUSTRIES NETHERLANDS B.V.—See PPG Industries, Inc.; *U.S. Public*, pg. 1709
PPG INDUSTRIES NEW ZEALAND LIMITED—See PPG Industries, Inc.; *U.S. Public*, pg. 1709
PPG INDUSTRIES OHIO, INC.—See PPG Industries, Inc.; *U.S. Public*, pg. 1709
PPG INDUSTRIES POLAND SP. Z O.O.—See PPG Industries, Inc.; *U.S. Public*, pg. 1709
PPG INDUSTRIES (UK) LTD.—See PPG Industries, Inc.; *U.S. Public*, pg. 1708
PPG ITALIA SALES & SERVICES SRL—See PPG Industries, Inc.; *U.S. Public*, pg. 1709
PPG KOREA LTD.—See PPG Industries, Inc.; *U.S. Public*, pg. 1709
PPG LUXEMBOURG FINANCE S.AR.L.—See PPG Industries, Inc.; *U.S. Public*, pg. 1709
PPG MANAGEMENT (SHANGHAI) CO., LTD—See PPG Industries, Inc.; *U.S. Public*, pg. 1709
PPG PACKAGING COATINGS (SUZHOU) CO., LTD.—See PPG Industries, Inc.; *U.S. Public*, pg. 1709
PPG PERFORMANCE COATINGS (MALAYSIA) SDN. BHD.—See PPG Industries, Inc.; *U.S. Public*, pg. 1709
PPG PMC JAPAN CO LTD—See PPG Industries, Inc.; *U.S. Public*, pg. 1709
PPG PREMAZI CEE (D.O.O.)—See PPG Industries, Inc.; *U.S. Public*, pg. 1709
PPG PROTECTIVE & MARINE COATINGS—See PPG Industries, Inc.; *U.S. Public*, pg. 1709
PPG REUNION SAS—See PPG Industries, Inc.; *U.S. Public*, pg. 1709
PPG ROMANIA S.A.—See PPG Industries, Inc.; *U.S. Public*, pg. 1709
PPG SSC CO., LTD.—See PPG Industries, Inc.; *U.S. Public*, pg. 1709
PPG TRILAK KFT.—See PPG Industries, Inc.; *U.S. Public*, pg. 1709

N.A.I.C.S. INDEX

325510 — PAINT AND COATING M...

PPG UNIVER S.P.A.—See PPG Industries, Inc.; *U.S. Public*, pg. 1709
PPG WORWAG COATINGS GMBH & CO. KG—See PPG Industries, Inc.; *U.S. Public*, pg. 1710
PP PROFESSIONAL PAINT A/S—See Flugger Group A/S; *Int'l*, pg. 2712
PRC-DESOTO INTERNATIONAL, INC. - MOUNT LAUREL—See PPG Industries, Inc.; *U.S. Public*, pg. 1708
PRC-DESOTO INTERNATIONAL, INC.—See PPG Industries, Inc.; *U.S. Public*, pg. 1708
PRIMALEX A.S.—See PPG Industries, Inc.; *U.S. Public*, pg. 1710
PRINCE MINERALS ITALY S.R.L.—See American Securities LLC; *U.S. Private*, pg. 253
PROTEC PTY. LTD.—See PPG Industries, Inc.; *U.S. Public*, pg. 1709
PT AKZO NOBEL CAR REFINISHES INDONESIA—See Akzo Nobel N.V.; *Int'l*, pg. 274
PT ASIAN PAINTS INDONESIA—See Asian Paints Limited; *Int'l*, pg. 619
PT CASCO PERSADA—See Akzo Nobel N.V.; *Int'l*, pg. 273
P.T. CHUGOKU PAINTS INDONESIA—See Chugoku Marine Paints, Ltd.; *Int'l*, pg. 1595
PT. DNT INDONESIA—See Dai Nippon Toryo Co., Ltd.; *Int'l*, pg. 1916
PT FERRO MATERIALS UTAMA—See American Securities LLC; *U.S. Private*, pg. 252
PT. PPG COATINGS INDONESIA—See PPG Industries, Inc.; *U.S. Public*, pg. 1710
QUIMICER POLSKA SP. Z O.O.—See American Securities LLC; *U.S. Private*, pg. 252
QUIMICER PORTUGAL S.A.—See American Securities LLC; *U.S. Private*, pg. 252
QUIMICER, S.A.—See American Securities LLC; *U.S. Private*, pg. 252
RADIANT COLOR N.V.—See RPM International Inc.; *U.S. Public*, pg. 1820
RAVEN LINING SYSTEMS, INC.—See Cohesant, Inc.; *U.S. Private*, pg. 963
RED SPOT PAINT & VARNISH CO., INC.—See Fujikura Ltd.; *Int'l*, pg. 2829
RED SPOT WESTLAND INC.—See Fujikura Ltd.; *Int'l*, pg. 2829
REGAL PAINTS UGANDA LIMITED—See Crown Paints Kenya Plc; *Int'l*, pg. 1858
REMMERT HOLLAND B.V.—See Akzo Nobel N.V.; *Int'l*, pg. 274
REPUBLIC POWDERED METALS, INC.—See RPM International Inc.; *U.S. Public*, pg. 1817
REVOCOAT FRANCE SAS—See PPG Industries, Inc.; *U.S. Public*, pg. 1710
REVOCOAT IBERICA SL—See PPG Industries, Inc.; *U.S. Public*, pg. 1710
RHINO LININGS CORPORATION; *U.S. Private*, pg. 3421
RHONE SUD EST DECORATION S.A.—See Akzo Nobel N.V.; *Int'l*, pg. 274
RICHARD'S PAINT MANUFACTURING COMPANY, INC.; *U.S. Private*, pg. 3428
RODDA PAINT CO.—See Cloverdale Paint Inc.; *Int'l*, pg. 1663
ROOF CARE CO.—See Henkel AG & Co. KGaA; *Int'l*, pg. 3354
RPM CANADA—See RPM International Inc.; *U.S. Public*, pg. 1818
RPM, INC.—See RPM International Inc.; *U.S. Public*, pg. 1819
RUST-OLEUM AUSTRALIA & NEW ZEALAND PTY. LTD.—See RPM International Inc.; *U.S. Public*, pg. 1820
RUST-OLEUM AUSTRALIA PTY. LTD.—See RPM International Inc.; *U.S. Public*, pg. 1820
RUST-OLEUM CORPORATION—See RPM International Inc.; *U.S. Public*, pg. 1817
RUST-OLEUM JAPAN CORPORATION—See RPM International Inc.; *U.S. Public*, pg. 1817
RUST-OLEUM UK LIMITED—See RPM International Inc.; *U.S. Public*, pg. 1820
SA ALBA (DECO PAINTS LATIN AMERICA)—See Akzo Nobel N.V.; *Int'l*, pg. 271
SAMOA PAINTS LIMITED—See Asian Paints Limited; *Int'l*, pg. 619
SAMPSON COATINGS INC.—See Penn Color Inc.; *U.S. Private*, pg. 3133
S.A NOVACEL BELGIUM NV—See Chargeurs SA; *Int'l*, pg. 1449
SANYO KOSAN CO., LTD.—See Chugoku Marine Paints, Ltd.; *Int'l*, pg. 1595
THE SAVOGRAN COMPANY; *U.S. Private*, pg. 4114
SBL SPECIALTY COATINGS PRIVATE LIMITED—See Berger Paints India Limited; *Int'l*, pg. 980
SC AZUR SA—See ICC Industries, Inc.; *U.S. Private*, pg. 2030
SCHENECTADY AUSTRALIA PTY. LTD.—See SK Capital Partners, LP; *U.S. Private*, pg. 3680
SCHENECTADY BRASIL LIMITADA—See SK Capital Partners, LP; *U.S. Private*, pg. 3680
SCHENECTADY EUROPE, S.A.—See SK Capital Partners, LP; *U.S. Private*, pg. 3680

SCHENECTADY MEXICO, S.A. DE C.V.—See SK Capital Partners, LP; *U.S. Private*, pg. 3680
SCHRAMM HOLDING AG—See Akzo Nobel N.V.; *Int'l*, pg. 275
SCOTTISH AGRICULTURAL INDUSTRIES LIMITED—See Akzo Nobel N.V.; *Int'l*, pg. 275
SEALANTS EUROPE SAS—See PPG Industries, Inc.; *U.S. Public*, pg. 1710
SEALMASTER INDUSTRIES INC.; *U.S. Private*, pg. 3585
SERVER BOYA MATBAA MUREKKEPLERI VE VERNIK SANAYI VE TICARET A.S.—See Akzo Nobel N.V.; *Int'l*, pg. 275
SEYMOUR OF SYCAMORE, INC.; *U.S. Private*, pg. 3621
SHANGHAI EFTEC CHEMICAL PRODUCTS LTD.—See EMS-Chemie Holding AG; *Int'l*, pg. 2394
SHANGHAI HUNTSMAN POLYURETHANES SPECIALTIES CO., LTD.—See Huntsman Corporation; *U.S. Public*, pg. 1074
SHEBOYGAN PAINT COMPANY; *U.S. Private*, pg. 3629
SHERWIN-WILLIAMS CHILE S.A.—See The Sherwin-Williams Company; *U.S. Public*, pg. 2128
SHERWIN-WILLIAMS COATINGS INDIA PRIVATE LIMITED—See The Sherwin-Williams Company; *U.S. Public*, pg. 2128
SHERWIN-WILLIAMS CO. - DIVERSIFIED BRANDS DIVISION—See The Sherwin-Williams Company; *U.S. Public*, pg. 2128
SHERWIN WILLIAMS COLOMBIA S.A.S.—See The Sherwin-Williams Company; *U.S. Public*, pg. 2128
THE SHERWIN-WILLIAMS COMPANY; *U.S. Public*, pg. 2127
THE SHERWIN-WILLIAMS CO. - SAN DIEGO (FRAZEE PAINT) PLANT—See The Sherwin-Williams Company; *U.S. Public*, pg. 2129
SHERWIN-WILLIAMS CZECH REPUBLIC SPOL. S.R.O.—See The Sherwin-Williams Company; *U.S. Public*, pg. 2128
SHERWIN-WILLIAMS DEUTSCHLAND GMBH—See The Sherwin-Williams Company; *U.S. Public*, pg. 2128
SHERWIN-WILLIAMS DIVERSIFIED BRANDS LIMITED—See The Sherwin-Williams Company; *U.S. Public*, pg. 2128
SHERWIN-WILLIAMS DO BRASIL INDUSTRIA E COMERCIO LIMITADA—See The Sherwin-Williams Company; *U.S. Public*, pg. 2129
SHERWIN-WILLIAMS FRANCE FINISHES SAS—See The Sherwin-Williams Company; *U.S. Public*, pg. 2128
SHERWIN-WILLIAMS ITALY S.R.L.—See The Sherwin-Williams Company; *U.S. Public*, pg. 2128
SHERWIN-WILLIAMS NORWAY AS—See The Sherwin-Williams Company; *U.S. Public*, pg. 2128
SHERWIN-WILLIAMS PERU S.R.L.—See The Sherwin-Williams Company; *U.S. Public*, pg. 2129
SHERWIN-WILLIAMS POLAND SP. Z O.O—See The Sherwin-Williams Company; *U.S. Public*, pg. 2129
SHERWIN-WILLIAMS PROTECTIVE & MARINE COATINGS—See The Sherwin-Williams Company; *U.S. Public*, pg. 2129
SHERWIN-WILLIAMS SERVICES (MALAYSIA) SDN. BHD.—See The Sherwin-Williams Company; *U.S. Public*, pg. 2129
SHERWIN-WILLIAMS (SHANGHAI) LIMITED—See The Sherwin-Williams Company; *U.S. Public*, pg. 2128
SHERWIN-WILLIAMS SPAIN COATINGS S.L.—See The Sherwin-Williams Company; *U.S. Public*, pg. 2129
SHERWIN-WILLIAMS SWEDEN AB—See The Sherwin-Williams Company; *U.S. Public*, pg. 2129
SHERWIN-WILLIAMS (THAILAND) CO., LTD.—See The Sherwin-Williams Company; *U.S. Public*, pg. 2128
SHERWIN-WILLIAMS UK COATINGS LIMITED—See The Sherwin-Williams Company; *U.S. Public*, pg. 2129
SHERWIN-WILLIAMS URUGUAY S.A.—See The Sherwin-Williams Company; *U.S. Public*, pg. 2129
SHERWIN-WILLIAMS (WEST INDIES) LTD.—See The Sherwin-Williams Company; *U.S. Public*, pg. 2128
SIGMA COATINGS PROPRIETARY LIMITED—See PPG Industries, Inc.; *U.S. Public*, pg. 1710
SIGMA SAMSUNG COATINGS CO., LTD—See PPG Industries, Inc.; *U.S. Public*, pg. 1710
SILCOTEC, INC.—See Avient Corporation; *U.S. Public*, pg. 248
SISSONS PAINTS (GRENADA) LIMITED—See ANSA McAL Limited; *Int'l*, pg. 476
SISSONS PAINTS LIMITED—See ANSA McAL Limited; *Int'l*, pg. 476
SOCIETE TUNISIENNE DE PEINTURES ASTRAL S.A.—See Akzo Nobel N.V.; *Int'l*, pg. 275
SPECIALTY CONSTRUCTION BRANDS, INC.—See H.B. Fuller Company; *U.S. Public*, pg. 978
SPECIALTY POLYMER COATINGS INC.—See RPM International Inc.; *U.S. Public*, pg. 1818
SPRAYLAT COATINGS (SHANGHAI) LIMITED—See PPG Industries, Inc.; *U.S. Public*, pg. 1710
SPS B.V.—See RPM International Inc.; *U.S. Public*, pg. 1820
STAR BRONZE COMPANY, INC.; *U.S. Private*, pg. 3784
STARKEN PAINT SDN BHD—See Chin Hin Group Berhad; *Int'l*, pg. 1480
STEELBLAST COATINGS AND PAINTING INC.—See HTC

Purenergy Inc.; *Int'l*, pg. 3508
STIWEX - FLUGGER SWEDEN AB—See Flugger Group A/S; *Int'l*, pg. 2712
STIWEX SRL—See Flugger Group A/S; *Int'l*, pg. 2712
STO CORPORATION; *U.S. Private*, pg. 3814
STONCOR AFRICA PTY. LTD.—See RPM International Inc.; *U.S. Public*, pg. 1819
STONCOR GROUP, INC.—See RPM International Inc.; *U.S. Public*, pg. 1818
STRATHMORE PRODUCTS INC.—See CSW Industrials, Inc.; *U.S. Public*, pg. 602
STRONGSVILLE AUTOMOTIVE COATINGS—See PPG Industries, Inc.; *U.S. Public*, pg. 1710
SUN PAINTS & COATINGS, INC.; *U.S. Private*, pg. 3863
SURFACE TECHNOLOGIES CORP; *U.S. Private*, pg. 3884
SUZHOU EKA TRADE CO. LTD—See Akzo Nobel N.V.; *Int'l*, pg. 275
SYNTEMA I VAGGERYD AB—See The Sherwin-Williams Company; *U.S. Public*, pg. 2129
TAPEL WILLAMETTE INC. S.A.—See The Willamette Valley Company; *U.S. Private*, pg. 4136
TCI, INC.—See RPM International Inc.; *U.S. Public*, pg. 1819
TCI POWDER COATING CANADA INC.—See RPM International Inc.; *U.S. Public*, pg. 1820
TCI POWDER COATINGS DE MEXICO, S.A. DE C.V.—See RPM International Inc.; *U.S. Public*, pg. 1820
TECHCOTE INDUSTRIAL COATING, LTD.—See Tailwind Capital Group, LLC; *U.S. Private*, pg. 3924
TECHNI-COAT GERMANY GMBH—See Akzo Nobel N.V.; *Int'l*, pg. 275
TEKNOS DEUTSCHLAND GMBH—See Arbonia AG; *Int'l*, pg. 537
TEKNOS FEYCO AG—See Arbonia AG; *Int'l*, pg. 538
TEKNOS US, INC.—See Arbonia AG; *Int'l*, pg. 538
TEKYAR TEKNIK YARDIM A. S.—See Akzo Nobel N.V.; *Int'l*, pg. 275
THE TESTOR CORPORATION—See RPM International Inc.; *U.S. Public*, pg. 1817
THAI DNT PAINT MANUFACTURING CO., LTD.—See Dai Nippon Toryo Co., Ltd.; *Int'l*, pg. 1917
THERMAL SPRAY INDUSTRIES LTD.—See Corrosion & Abrasion Solutions Ltd.; *Int'l*, pg. 1806
TIANJIN COSCO KANSAI PAINT & CHEMICALS CO., LTD.—See China COSCO Shipping Corporation Limited; *Int'l*, pg. 1492
TIGER DRYLAC USA INC.; *U.S. Private*, pg. 4169
TIKKURILA DANMARK A/S—See PPG Industries, Inc.; *U.S. Public*, pg. 1710
TIKKURILA NORGE A/S—See PPG Industries, Inc.; *U.S. Public*, pg. 1710
TIKKURILA OYJ—See PPG Industries, Inc.; *U.S. Public*, pg. 1710
TIKKURILA POLSKA S.A.—See PPG Industries, Inc.; *U.S. Public*, pg. 1710
TIKKURILA SVERIGE AB—See PPG Industries, Inc.; *U.S. Public*, pg. 1711
TIKKURILA ZORKA D.O.O.—See PPG Industries, Inc.; *U.S. Public*, pg. 1710
TINTAS CORAL LTDA—See Akzo Nobel N.V.; *Int'l*, pg. 271
TINTAS DYRUP, S.A.—See PPG Industries, Inc.; *U.S. Public*, pg. 1707
TNEMEC COMPANY INC.; *U.S. Private*, pg. 4180
TOR COATINGS LIMITED—See RPM International Inc.; *U.S. Public*, pg. 1820
TOXEMENT, S.A.—See RPM International Inc.; *U.S. Public*, pg. 1820
TREMCO ILLBRUCK DIS TICARET A.S.—See RPM International Inc.; *U.S. Public*, pg. 1820
TREMCO ILLBRUCK KFT—See RPM International Inc.; *U.S. Public*, pg. 1820
TREMCO ILLBRUCK LIMITED—See RPM International Inc.; *U.S. Public*, pg. 1820
TREMCO ILLBRUCK OOO—See RPM International Inc.; *U.S. Public*, pg. 1820
TREMCO ILLBRUCK PRODUCTION SAS—See RPM International Inc.; *U.S. Public*, pg. 1820
TREMCO ILLBRUCK PRODUKTION GMBH—See RPM International Inc.; *U.S. Public*, pg. 1820
TREMCO ILLBRUCK SAS—See RPM International Inc.; *U.S. Public*, pg. 1820
TREMCO ILLBRUCK, S.L.U.—See RPM International Inc.; *U.S. Public*, pg. 1820
TREMCO ILLBRUCK S.R.O.—See RPM International Inc.; *U.S. Public*, pg. 1820
TREMCO ILLBRUCK SWISS AG—See RPM International Inc.; *U.S. Public*, pg. 1820
TRIMACO LLC; *U.S. Private*, pg. 4232
TRIMACO LLC—See Trimaco LLC; *U.S. Private*, pg. 4232
UAB SHERWIN-WILLIAMS BALTIC—See The Sherwin-Williams Company; *U.S. Public*, pg. 2130
UCAR EMULSION SYSTEMS INTERNATIONAL, INC.—See Dow Inc.; *U.S. Public*, pg. 686
ULTRA ADDITIVES INC.; *U.S. Private*, pg. 4277
UNICELL NORDIC A/S—See Flugger Group A/S; *Int'l*, pg. 2712
UNITECTA ITALIANA S.P.A.—See Akzo Nobel N.V.; *Int'l*, pg. 271
UNITED PAINT & CHEMICAL CORPORATION—See Piceu

325510 — PAINT AND COATING M...

Group Limited, Inc.; *U.S. Private,* pg. 3176
VALSPAR B.V.—See The Sherwin-Williams Company; *U.S. Public,* pg. 2130
THE VALSPAR CORPORATION—See The Sherwin-Williams Company; *U.S. Public,* pg. 2129
THE VALSPAR (FINLAND) CORPORATION OY—See The Sherwin-Williams Company; *U.S. Public,* pg. 2129
THE VALSPAR (FRANCE) CORPORATION, S.A.S.—See The Sherwin-Williams Company; *U.S. Public,* pg. 2129
THE VALSPAR (H.K.) CORPORATION LIMITED—See The Sherwin-Williams Company; *U.S. Public,* pg. 2129
VALSPAR INC.—See The Sherwin-Williams Company; *U.S. Public,* pg. 2129
VALSPAR INDUSTRIES GMBH—See The Sherwin-Williams Company; *U.S. Public,* pg. 2129
VALSPAR MEXICANA, S.A. DE C.V.—See The Sherwin-Williams Company; *U.S. Public,* pg. 2130
THE VALSPAR (NANTES) CORPORATION, S.A.S.—See The Sherwin-Williams Company; *U.S. Public,* pg. 2129
VALSPAR PAINT (AUSTRALIA) PTY LTD—See The Sherwin-Williams Company; *U.S. Public,* pg. 2129
VALSPAR ROCK CO., LTD.—See The Sherwin-Williams Company; *U.S. Public,* pg. 2129
THE VALSPAR (SOUTH AFRICA) CORPORATION (PTY) LTD.—See The Sherwin-Williams Company; *U.S. Public,* pg. 2129
THE VALSPAR (SWITZERLAND) CORPORATION AG—See The Sherwin-Williams Company; *U.S. Public,* pg. 2129
THE VALSPAR (UK) CORPORATION LIMITED—See The Sherwin-Williams Company; *U.S. Public,* pg. 2129
VANEX, INC.—See PPG Industries, Inc.; *U.S. Public,* pg. 1711
VAN NOORDENNE VERF B.V.—See Akzo Nobel N.V.; *Int'l,* pg. 275
VANTACO OY—See The Sherwin-Williams Company; *U.S. Public,* pg. 2130
VERSAFLEX, INC.—See PPG Industries, Inc.; *U.S. Public,* pg. 1711
VISTA PAINT CORPORATION; *U.S. Private,* pg. 4403
VIVECHROM DR. STEFANOS D. PATERAS S.A.—See Akzo Nobel N.V.; *Int'l,* pg. 275
VOGEL PAINT, INC.; *U.S. Private,* pg. 4409
WATCO GMBH—See RPM International Inc.; *U.S. Public,* pg. 1820
WATCO S.A.R.L.—See RPM International Inc.; *U.S. Public,* pg. 1820
WATCO UK LIMITED—See RPM International Inc.; *U.S. Public,* pg. 1820
WATSON-STANDARD COMPANY—See Watson Industries, Inc.; *U.S. Private,* pg. 4455
WATTYL AUSTRALIA PTY LTD—See The Sherwin-Williams Company; *U.S. Public,* pg. 2130
WATTYL AUSTRALIA PTY LTD—See The Sherwin-Williams Company; *U.S. Public,* pg. 2130
WATTYL AUSTRALIA PTY LTD—See The Sherwin-Williams Company; *U.S. Public,* pg. 2130
WATTYL LIMITED—See The Sherwin-Williams Company; *U.S. Public,* pg. 2129
WATTYL (NZ) LTD.—See The Sherwin-Williams Company; *U.S. Public,* pg. 2129
WEATHERFORD AEROSPACE, INC.—See KKR & Co. Inc.; *U.S. Public,* pg. 1262
WESTFIELD COATINGS CORP.—See RPM International Inc.; *U.S. Public,* pg. 1819
WHITFORD ESPANA S.L.—See PPG Industries, Inc.; *U.S. Public,* pg. 1711
WHITFORD GMBH—See PPG Industries, Inc.; *U.S. Public,* pg. 1711
WHITFORD INDIA PRIVATE LIMITED—See PPG Industries, Inc.; *U.S. Public,* pg. 1711
WHITFORD JIANGMEN LTD.—See PPG Industries, Inc.; *U.S. Public,* pg. 1711
WHITFORD LTD.—See PPG Industries, Inc.; *U.S. Public,* pg. 1711
WHITFORD LTD.—See PPG Industries, Inc.; *U.S. Public,* pg. 1711
WHITFORD PTE LTD—See PPG Industries, Inc.; *U.S. Public,* pg. 1711
WHITFORD SARL—See PPG Industries, Inc.; *U.S. Public,* pg. 1711
WHITFORD S.R.L.—See PPG Industries, Inc.; *U.S. Public,* pg. 1711
THE WHITMORE MANUFACTURING COMPANY—See CSW Industrials, Inc.; *U.S. Public,* pg. 602
THE WILLAMETTE VALLEY COMPANY - MIDWEST DIVISION—See The Willamette Valley Company; *U.S. Private,* pg. 4136
THE WILLAMETTE VALLEY COMPANY - WESTERN DIVISION—See The Willamette Valley Company; *U.S. Private,* pg. 4136
XIOM CORP.—See Environmental Infrastructure Holdings Corp.; *U.S. Private,* pg. 1408
X-RITE EUROPE GMBH—See Danaher Corporation; *U.S. Public,* pg. 632
XYLAZEL S.A.—See Akzo Nobel N.V.; *Int'l,* pg. 275
YACHT SYSTEMS S.R.L—See Boero Bartolomeo S.p.A.; *Int'l,* pg. 1100

YENKIN-MAJESTIC PAINT CORPORATION; *U.S. Private,* pg. 4588
ZAO AKZO NOBEL DEKOR—See Akzo Nobel N.V.; *Int'l,* pg. 275
ZC&R COATINGS FOR OPTICS, INC.—See The Graham Group, Inc.; *U.S. Private,* pg. 4036
ZERUST PREVENCAO DE CORROSAO S.A.—See Northern Technologies International Corporation; *U.S. Public,* pg. 1538
ZHONGSHAN DIC COLOUR CO., LTD.—See DIC Corporation; *Int'l,* pg. 2111
ZINSSER BRANDS COMPANY—See RPM International Inc.; *U.S. Public,* pg. 1817
ZINSSER CO., INC.—See RPM International Inc.; *U.S. Public,* pg. 1817

325520 — ADHESIVE MANUFACTURING

3M BRICOLAGE AND BATIMENT—See 3M Company; *U.S. Public,* pg. 5
3M CHINA LIMITED—See 3M Company; *U.S. Public,* pg. 5
3M COMPANY; *U.S. Public,* pg. 4
3M ESPANA S.A.—See 3M Company; *U.S. Public,* pg. 5
3M FRANCE S.A.S—See 3M Company; *U.S. Public,* pg. 6
3M INDUSTRIAL ADHESIVES & TAPES DIVISION—See 3M Company; *U.S. Public,* pg. 6
3M MEXICO S.A. DE C.V.—See 3M Company; *U.S. Public,* pg. 6
AABBITT ADHESIVES INC.; *U.S. Private,* pg. 30
AALBORG PORTLAND (ANQING) CO., LTD.—See Cementir Holding N.V.; *Int'l,* pg. 1397
AALBORG PORTLAND BELGIUM SA—See Cementir Holding N.V.; *Int'l,* pg. 1397
AALBORG PORTLAND MALAYSIA SDN BHD—See Cementir Holding N.V.; *Int'l,* pg. 1397
ABLESTIK (SHANGHAI) LTD.—See Henkel AG & Co. KGaA; *Int'l,* pg. 3348
AB TEBECO—See Beijer Alma AB; *Int'l,* pg. 942
ACI INDUSTRIES PTE LTD—See Asian Micro Holdings Ltd.; *Int'l,* pg. 618
AC PRODUCTS, INC.—See Quaker Chemical Corporation; *U.S. Public,* pg. 1745
ADCO INC.—See Atlan Plastics Inc.; *U.S. Private,* pg. 370
ADDEV MATERIAL SAS; *Int'l,* pg. 128
ADECOL INDUSTRIA QUIMICA LTDA.—See H.B. Fuller Company; *U.S. Public,* pg. 977
ADHESIVE RESEARCH, INC.; *U.S. Private,* pg. 79
ADHESIVES SPECIALISTS, INC.—See EUKALIN Spezial-Klebstoff Fabrik GmbH; *Int'l,* pg. 2526
ADHESIVES TECHNOLOGY CORP.—See Arsenal Capital Management LP; *U.S. Private,* pg. 339
ADHESIVE SYSTEMS INC.—See Diversified Chemical Technologies Inc.; *U.S. Private,* pg. 1241
ADHESIVE TECHNOLOGIES INC.; *U.S. Private,* pg. 79
ADHESIVOS DE JALISCO (LEON), S.A. DE C.V.—See Grupo Lamosa S.A. de C.V.; *Int'l,* pg. 3131
ADHESIVOS DE JALISCO, S.A. DE C.V.—See Grupo Lamosa S.A. de C.V.; *Int'l,* pg. 3131
ADHESIVOS PERDURA, S. A. DE C. V.—See Grupo Lamosa S.A. de C.V.; *Int'l,* pg. 3131
ADVANCED BIOMEDICAL TECHNOLOGIES, INC.; *U.S. Public,* pg. 46
ADVANCED POLYMERS INTERNATIONAL—See H.B. Fuller Company; *U.S. Public,* pg. 978
AERO EXCLUSIVE D.O.O.—See Aero d.d.; *Int'l,* pg. 180
AERO ZAGREB D.O.O.—See Aero d.d.; *Int'l,* pg. 180
AFINITICA TECHNOLOGIES S.L.—See Arkema S.A.; *Int'l,* pg. 568
AICA ADTEK SDN. BHD.—See AICA Kogyo Company, Limited; *Int'l,* pg. 228
AICA BANGKOK CO., LTD.—See AICA Kogyo Company, Limited; *Int'l,* pg. 228
AICA DONG NAI CO., LTD.—See AICA Kogyo Company, Limited; *Int'l,* pg. 228
AICA MALAYSIA SDN. BHD.—See AICA Kogyo Company, Limited; *Int'l,* pg. 228
AICA NANJING CO., LTD.—See AICA Kogyo Company, Limited; *Int'l,* pg. 228
AICA TRADING (SHANGHAI) CO., LTD.—See AICA Kogyo Company, Limited; *Int'l,* pg. 228
AISLANTES NACIONALES S.A.—See Henkel AG & Co. KGaA; *Int'l,* pg. 3348
AKEMI CHEMISCH TECHNISCHE SPEZIALFABRIK GMBH; *Int'l,* pg. 262
AKZO NOBEL AEROSPACE COATINGS—See Akzo Nobel N.V.; *Int'l,* pg. 272
AKZO NOBEL COATINGS INC, (KY)—See Akzo Nobel N.V.; *Int'l,* pg. 272
AKZO NOBEL PAINTS LLC—See Akzo Nobel N.V.; *Int'l,* pg. 272
AKZO NOBEL WOOD FINISHES AND ADHESIVES—See Akzo Nobel N.V.; *Int'l,* pg. 273
AMERICAN SEALANTS, INC.—See Arsenal Capital Management LP; *U.S. Private,* pg. 339
ANABOND LIMITED; *Int'l,* pg. 444
ANHUI HYEA AROMAS CO., LTD.; *Int'l,* pg. 468

APPLICHEM, INC.—See Illinois Tool Works Inc.; *U.S. Public,* pg. 1101
APPLIED PRODUCTS, INC.—See Goldner Hawn Johnson & Morrison Inc.; *U.S. Public,* pg. 1735
AQUABOND TECHNOLOGIES, INC.—See Universal Photonics, Inc.; *U.S. Private,* pg. 4306
ARCHEMICS LTD—See Harel Mallac & Co. Ltd.; *Int'l,* pg. 3274
ARCLIN INC.—See Lone Star Funds; *U.S. Private,* pg. 2484
ARCLIN USA, LLC—See Lone Star Funds; *U.S. Private,* pg. 2484
ASHLAND PERFORMANCE MATERIALS - OAK CREEK—See Ashland Inc.; *U.S. Public,* pg. 211
ASHWA TECHNOLOGIES CO. LTD.—See Henkel AG & Co. KGaA; *Int'l,* pg. 3348
ASSEMS INC.; *Int'l,* pg. 642
ATLANTIC PASTE & GLUE CO. INC.; *U.S. Private,* pg. 374
ATLAS MINERALS & CHEMICALS, INC.; *U.S. Private,* pg. 379
AVERY DENNISON PERFORMANCE POLYMERS—See Avery Dennison Corporation; *U.S. Public,* pg. 244
AVEVA DRUG DELIVERY SYSTEMS, INC—See DifGen Pharmaceuticals Pvt. Ltd.; *Int'l,* pg. 2118
AXIOM MATERIALS, INC.—See Haci Omer Sabanci Holding A.S.; *Int'l,* pg. 3204
BACON INDUSTRIES, INC.—See H.B. Fuller Company; *U.S. Public,* pg. 978
BARRDAY, INC.; *Int'l,* pg. 868
BARRIER TECHNOLOGY CORP.; *U.S. Private,* pg. 480
BAR'S PRODUCTS, INC.; *U.S. Private,* pg. 471
BASF COATINGS, INC.—See BASF SE; *Int'l,* pg. 873
BASF COATINGS JAPAN LTD.—See BASF SE; *Int'l,* pg. 872
BASF CONSTRUCTION CHEMICALS GMBH - FRANKFURT AM MAIN—See BASF SE; *Int'l,* pg. 874
BASF CONSTRUCTION CHEMICALS, LLC—See BASF SE; *Int'l,* pg. 875
BASF CORP. - BUILDING SYSTEMS—See BASF SE; *Int'l,* pg. 875
BASIC ADHESIVES INC.; *U.S. Private,* pg. 484
BEARDOW ADAMS A.B.—See H.B. Fuller Company; *U.S. Public,* pg. 977
BEARDOW ADAMS DO BRASIL ADHESIVES LTDA.—See H.B. Fuller Company; *U.S. Public,* pg. 977
BEARDOW ADAMS GMBH—See H.B. Fuller Company; *U.S. Public,* pg. 977
BEARDOW ADAMS HOT MELT WERK GMBH—See H.B. Fuller Company; *U.S. Public,* pg. 977
BEARDOWADAMS, INC.—See H.B. Fuller Company; *U.S. Public,* pg. 977
BEARDOW ADAMS OY—See H.B. Fuller Company; *U.S. Public,* pg. 977
BEARDOW ADAMS S.A.S.—See H.B. Fuller Company; *U.S. Public,* pg. 977
BEARDOW AND ADAMS (ADHESIVES) LIMITED—See H.B. Fuller Company; *U.S. Public,* pg. 977
BEIJING COMENS NEW MATERIALS CO., LTD.; *Int'l,* pg. 948
BEMIS ASSOCIATES INC.; *U.S. Private,* pg. 522
THE BERGQUIST COMPANY SHENZHEN LTD.—See Henkel AG & Co. KGaA; *Int'l,* pg. 3354
THE BERGQUIST COMPANY ZHUHAI LTD.—See Henkel AG & Co. KGaA; *Int'l,* pg. 3354
BESTOLIFE CORPORATION—See Quexco Incorporated; *U.S. Private,* pg. 3326
BESTWAY CEMENT LIMITED—See Bestway (Holdings) Limited; *Int'l,* pg. 1001
BIRLA CORPORATION LTD.; *Int'l,* pg. 1047
BOIARDI PRODUCTS CORPORATION—See Q.E.P. Co., Inc.; *U.S. Public,* pg. 1741
BOSIG BAUKUNSTSTOFFE GMBH—See BOSIG Holding GmbH & Co. KG; *Int'l,* pg. 1116
BOSIG GMBH—See BOSIG Holding GmbH & Co. KG; *Int'l,* pg. 1116
BOSIG HOLDING GMBH & CO. KG; *Int'l,* pg. 1116
BOSIG POLSKA SP. Z O.O.—See BOSIG Holding GmbH & Co. KG; *Int'l,* pg. 1116
BOSTIK AB—See Arkema S.A.; *Int'l,* pg. 570
BOSTIK AEROSOLS GMBH—See Arkema S.A.; *Int'l,* pg. 570
BOSTIK ARGENTINA S.A.—See Arkema S.A.; *Int'l,* pg. 570
BOSTIK A/S—See Arkema S.A.; *Int'l,* pg. 570
BOSTIK BELUX S.A. - N.V.—See Arkema S.A.; *Int'l,* pg. 570
BOSTIK B.V. CONSTRUCTION DIVISION—See Arkema S.A.; *Int'l,* pg. 570
BOSTIK B.V. INDUSTRIAL DIVISION—See Arkema S.A.; *Int'l,* pg. 570
BOSTIK EGYPT FOR PRODUCTION OF ADHESIVES S.A.E—See Arkema S.A.; *Int'l,* pg. 570
BOSTIK FINDLEY (MALAYSIA) SDN. BHD.—See Arkema S.A.; *Int'l,* pg. 570
BOSTIK GMBH—See Arkema S.A.; *Int'l,* pg. 570
BOSTIK HELLAS S.A.—See Arkema S.A.; *Int'l,* pg. 570
BOSTIK, INC. - BOSTON—See Arkema S.A.; *Int'l,* pg. 570
BOSTIK, INC. - CONYERS—See Arkema S.A.; *Int'l,* pg. 570
BOSTIK, INC. - GREENVILLE—See Arkema S.A.; *Int'l,* pg. 570
BOSTIK, INC. - LOUISVILLE—See Arkema S.A.; *Int'l,* pg. 570

N.A.I.C.S. INDEX

325520 — ADHESIVE MANUFACTUR...

BOSTIK, INC.—See Arkema S.A.; *Int'l*, pg. 570
BOSTIK, INC. - TEMECULA—See Arkema S.A.; *Int'l*, pg. 570
BOSTIK INDIA PRIVATE LTD.—See Arkema S.A.; *Int'l*, pg. 570
BOSTIK INDUSTRIES LIMITED—See Arkema S.A.; *Int'l*, pg. 570
BOSTIK KIMYA SANAYI VE TICARET A.S.—See Arkema S.A.; *Int'l*, pg. 570
BOSTIK LTD—See Arkema S.A.; *Int'l*, pg. 570
BOSTIK MEXICANA S.A. DE C.V.—See Arkema S.A.; *Int'l*, pg. 570
BOSTIK NETHERLAND B.V.—See Arkema S.A.; *Int'l*, pg. 570
BOSTIK NEW ZEALAND LTD.—See Arkema S.A.; *Int'l*, pg. 570
BOSTIK OY—See Arkema S.A.; *Int'l*, pg. 570
BOSTIK PHILIPPINES INC.—See Arkema S.A.; *Int'l*, pg. 570
BOSTIK ROMANIA S.R.L—See Arkema S.A.; *Int'l*, pg. 570
BOSTIK SA—See Arkema S.A.; *Int'l*, pg. 570
BOSTIK (SHANGHAI) MANAGEMENT CO., LTD.—See Arkema S.A.; *Int'l*, pg. 570
BOSTIK SP Z.O.O.—See Arkema S.A.; *Int'l*, pg. 570
BOSTIK TECHNOLOGY GMBH—See Arkema S.A.; *Int'l*, pg. 570
BOSTIK (THAILAND) CO., LTD.—See Arkema S.A.; *Int'l*, pg. 570
BOSTIK UAB—See Arkema S.A.; *Int'l*, pg. 570
BRADLEY COATING INC.; *U.S. Private*, pg. 632
BRITE-LINE TECHNOLOGIES, INC.—See Independence Capital Partners, LLC; *U.S. Private*, pg. 2057
BSM CHEMICAL CO., LTD.; *Int'l*, pg. 1202
CAN-CELL INDUSTRIES INC.; *Int'l*, pg. 1276
CARAUSTAR INDUSTRIES, INC. - KERNERSVILLE ADHESIVES PLANT—See Greif Inc.; *U.S. Public*, pg. 966
CARIBBEAN CONSTRUCTION AND DEVELOPMENT LTD.—See Grupo Argos S.A.; *Int'l*, pg. 3121
CASCO ADHESIVES AB—See Akzo Nobel N.V.; *Int'l*, pg. 273
CENTRAL GLOBAL BERHAD; *Int'l*, pg. 1407
CENTURY INDUSTRIES—See Century Container, LLC; *U.S. Private*, pg. 832
CG PPI ADHESIVE PRODUCTS LIMITED—See Avantha Group; *Int'l*, pg. 736
CHANGCHUN HENKEL SURFACE TECHNOLOGIES CO. LTD.—See Henkel AG & Co. KGaA; *Int'l*, pg. 3348
CHANGTIAN PLASTIC & CHEMICAL LIMITED; *Int'l*, pg. 1444
CHEMBOND CHEMICALS LTD - BADDI PLANT—See Chembond Chemicals Ltd; *Int'l*, pg. 1461
CHEMBOND CHEMICALS LTD - CHENNAI PLANT—See Chembond Chemicals Ltd; *Int'l*, pg. 1461
CHEMBOND CHEMICALS LTD - TARAPUR PLANT—See Chembond Chemicals Ltd; *Int'l*, pg. 1461
CHENGDU GUIBAO; *Int'l*, pg. 1467
CHENGDU HENKEL ADHESIVE TECHNOLOGIES CO., LTD.—See Henkel AG & Co. KGaA; *Int'l*, pg. 3348
CHENGDU HENKEL ADHESIVE TECHONOLOGIES CO. LTD.—See Henkel AG & Co. KGaA; *Int'l*, pg. 3348
CHERAT CEMENT COMPANY LIMITED; *Int'l*, pg. 1471
CHERNG TAY TECHNOLOGY CO., LTD.; *Int'l*, pg. 1471
CIMENTERIES CBR S.A.—See Heidelberg Materials AG; *Int'l*, pg. 3309
CLH INC.; *U.S. Private*, pg. 942
COAT-IT INC.—See Diversified Chemical Technologies Inc.; *U.S. Private*, pg. 1241
CONROS CORPORATION; *Int'l*, pg. 1769
COROPLAST FRITZ MULLER GMBH UND CO. KG; *Int'l*, pg. 1802
COVALENCE SPECIALTY ADHESIVES LLC—See Berry Global Group, Inc; *U.S. Public*, pg. 321
CREST (MEXICO CITY), S.A. DE C.V.—See Grupo Lamosa S.A. de C.V.; *Int'l*, pg. 3131
CREST NORTEAMERICA, S. A. DE C. V.—See Grupo Lamosa S.A. de C.V.; *Int'l*, pg. 3131
CREST, S.A. DE C.V.—See Grupo Lamosa S.A. de C.V.; *Int'l*, pg. 3131
CREST (TIZAYUCA), S.A. DE C.V.—See Grupo Lamosa S.A. de C.V.; *Int'l*, pg. 3131
CUSTOM TAPE CO INC.—See CGR Products Inc.; *U.S. Private*, pg. 844
THE CUTLER CORPORATION; *U.S. Private*, pg. 4017
CYBERBOND CS S.R.O.—See H.B. Fuller Company; *U.S. Public*, pg. 977
CYBERBOND EUROPE GMBH—See H.B. Fuller Company; *U.S. Public*, pg. 977
CYBERBOND FRANCE S.A.R.L.—See H.B. Fuller Company; *U.S. Public*, pg. 977
CYBERBOND IBERICA S.L.—See H.B. Fuller Company; *U.S. Public*, pg. 977
CYBERBOND, LLC—See H.B. Fuller Company; *U.S. Public*, pg. 977
CYBERBOND UK LTD—See H.B. Fuller Company; *U.S. Public*, pg. 977
DAP GLOBAL, INC.—See RPM International Inc.; *U.S. Public*, pg. 1816
DAP PRODUCTS, INC.—See RPM International Inc.; *U.S. Public*, pg. 1817

DELPHON INDUSTRIES, LLC; *U.S. Private*, pg. 1199
DEN BRAVEN FRANCE S.A.R.L.—See Arkema S.A.; *Int'l*, pg. 571
DEN BRAVEN SA (PROPRIETARY) LTD.—See Arkema S.A.; *Int'l*, pg. 571
DEN BRAVEN SEALANTS GMBH—See Arkema S.A.; *Int'l*, pg. 571
DENOVUS L.L.C.—See Orscheln Group; *U.S. Private*, pg. 3045
DIVERSIFIED CHEMICAL TECHNOLOGIES INC.; *U.S. Private*, pg. 1241
DIVERSIFIED CHEMICAL TECHNOLOGIES OPERATING COMPANY INC.—See Diversified Chemical Technologies Inc.; *U.S. Private*, pg. 1241
D&K GROUP, INC.; *U.S. Private*, pg. 1138
D&K INTERNATIONAL INC.—See D&K Group, Inc.; *U.S. Private*, pg. 1138
DOMINION SURE SEAL LTD.; *Int'l*, pg. 2161
DONGSUNG NSC COMPANY LTD.; *Int'l*, pg. 2170
DONGSUNG NSC VIETNAM COMPANY LTD.—See Dongsung NSC Company Ltd.; *Int'l*, pg. 2170
D PLAST-EFTEC UA—See EMS-Chemie Holding AG; *Int'l*, pg. 2393
DYMAX CORP.; *U.S. Private*, pg. 1296
EAGLEBURGMANN TAIWAN CORPORATION—See Freudenberg SE; *Int'l*, pg. 2784
EAGLE INDUSTRY TAIWAN CORPORATION—See Eagle Industry Co., Ltd.; *Int'l*, pg. 2265
EAST AFRICAN PORTLAND CEMENT COMPANY LIMITED; *Int'l*, pg. 2269
EDGE ADHESIVES, INC.—See Gladstone Management Corporation; *U.S. Private*, pg. 1705
EFTEC AG—See EMS-Chemie Holding AG; *Int'l*, pg. 2393
EFTEC BRASIL LTDA.—See EMS-Chemie Holding AG; *Int'l*, pg. 2393
EFTEC CHINA LTD.—See EMS-Chemie Holding AG; *Int'l*, pg. 2393
EFTEC ENGINEERING GMBH—See EMS-Chemie Holding AG; *Int'l*, pg. 2393
EFTEC (INDIA) PVT. LTD.—See EMS-Chemie Holding AG; *Int'l*, pg. 2393
EFTEC-PLACOSA—See EMS-Chemie Holding AG; *Int'l*, pg. 2393
EFTEC (ROMANIA) S.R.L.—See EMS-Chemie Holding AG; *Int'l*, pg. 2393
ELMER'S PRODUCTS, INC.—See Newell Brands Inc.; *U.S. Public*, pg. 1514
THE EUCLID CHEMICAL COMPANY—See RPM International Inc.; *U.S. Public*, pg. 1818
EUKALIN SPEZIAL-KLEBSTOFF FABRIK GMBH; *Int'l*, pg. 2526
EVANS ADHESIVE CORPORATION—See Arsenal Capital Management LP; *U.S. Private*, pg. 339
EVERGREEN ADHESIVE & CHEMICALS SDN. BHD.—See Evergreen Fibreboard Berhad; *Int'l*, pg. 2565
FEDERAL PROCESS CORPORATION; *U.S. Private*, pg. 1489
FIBER FIX, LLC; *U.S. Private*, pg. 1501
FINDTAPE.COM LLC; *U.S. Private*, pg. 1509
FLEXCON GLENROTHES LTD—See FLEXcon Corporation; *U.S. Private*, pg. 1543
FLURO GELENKLAGER GMBH—See Brd. Klee A/S; *Int'l*, pg. 1143
FLYING CEMENT COMPANY LIMITED; *Int'l*, pg. 2716
FOCUS HOTMELT COMPANY LTD.; *Int'l*, pg. 2719
FORBO ERFURT GMBH—See Forbo Holding Ltd.; *Int'l*, pg. 2729
FORBO EUROCOL BV—See Forbo Holding Ltd.; *Int'l*, pg. 2729
FORBO SIEGLING GMBH—See Forbo Holding Ltd.; *Int'l*, pg. 2730
FORBO SIEGLING JAPAN LIMITED—See Forbo Holding Ltd.; *Int'l*, pg. 2730
FOURNY NV—See H.B. Fuller Company; *U.S. Public*, pg. 977
FRANKLIN INTERNATIONAL INC.; *U.S. Private*, pg. 1597
GCH TECHNOLOGY CO., LTD.; *Int'l*, pg. 2895
GEOCEL CORPORATION; *U.S. Private*, pg. 1680
GHARIBWAL CEMENT LIMITED; *Int'l*, pg. 2959
GLUEFAST COMPANY, INC.; *U.S. Private*, pg. 1721
GRACE AUSTRALIA PTY. LTD.—See Standard Industries Holdings Inc.; *U.S. Private*, pg. 3779
GRACE CANADA, INC.—See Standard Industries Holdings Inc.; *U.S. Private*, pg. 3779
GRACE HELLAS E.P.E.—See Standard Industries Holdings Inc.; *U.S. Private*, pg. 3780
GRACE PRODUCTS (SINGAPORE) PRIVATE LIMITED—See Standard Industries Holdings Inc.; *U.S. Private*, pg. 3780
GRUPO CCRR; pg. 3124
GUANGZHOU HENKEL SURFACE TECHNOLOGIES CO. LTD.—See Henkel AG & Co. KGaA; *Int'l*, pg. 3348
GUANGZHOU JOINTAS CHEMICAL CO., LTD.; *Int'l*, pg. 3166
GUANGZHOU SANFU NEW MATERIALS TECHNOLOGY CO., LTD.; *Int'l*, pg. 3167
GURIT (USA) INC—See Gurit Holding AG; *Int'l*, pg. 3188
HARPER-LOVE ADHESIVES CORPORATION—See HBM Holdings Company; *U.S. Private*, pg. 1887
H.B. FULLER ADHESIVES DEUTSCHLAND GMBH—See H.B. Fuller Company; *U.S. Public*, pg. 977
H.B. FULLER ADHESIVES FRANCE SAS—See H.B. Fuller Company; *U.S. Public*, pg. 977
H.B. FULLER ADHESIVES HONG KONG LIMITED—See H.B. Fuller Company; *U.S. Public*, pg. 977
H.B. FULLER ADHESIVES ITALIA S.P.A.—See H.B. Fuller Company; *U.S. Public*, pg. 977
H.B. FULLER ARGENTINA, S.A.I.C—See H.B. Fuller Company; *U.S. Public*, pg. 977
H.B. FULLER BELGIE BVBA—See H.B. Fuller Company; *U.S. Public*, pg. 977
H.B. FULLER CANADA (PARTNERSHIP)—See H.B. Fuller Company; *U.S. Public*, pg. 977
H.B. FULLER CENTROAMERICA, S.A.—See H.B. Fuller Company; *U.S. Public*, pg. 977
H.B. FULLER CHILE, S.A.—See H.B. Fuller Company; *U.S. Public*, pg. 977
H.B. FULLER (CHINA) ADHESIVES, LTD.—See H.B. Fuller Company; *U.S. Public*, pg. 977
H.B. FULLER COLOMBIA S.A.S.—See H.B. Fuller Company; *U.S. Public*, pg. 977
H.B. FULLER COMPANY AUSTRALIA PTY. LTD.—See H.B. Fuller Company; *U.S. Public*, pg. 977
H.B. FULLER COMPANY; *U.S. Public*, pg. 976
H.B. FULLER DEUTSCHLAND GMBH—See H.B. Fuller Company; *U.S. Public*, pg. 977
H.B. FULLER GREECE S.A.I.C—See H.B. Fuller Company; *U.S. Public*, pg. 978
H.B. FULLER GROUP LIMITED—See H.B. Fuller Company; *U.S. Public*, pg. 978
H.B. FULLER (GUANGZHOU) ADHESIVES CO., LTD—See H.B. Fuller Company; *U.S. Public*, pg. 977
H.B. FULLER INTERNATIONAL, INC.—See H.B. Fuller Company; *U.S. Public*, pg. 978
H.B. FULLER (PHILIPPINES), INC.—See H.B. Fuller Company; *U.S. Public*, pg. 977
H.B. FULLER (PHILS.) INC.—See Filinvest Development Corporation; *Int'l*, pg. 2663
H.B. FULLER RUS LTD.—See H.B. Fuller Company; *U.S. Public*, pg. 978
H.B. FULLER (SHANGHAI) CO. LTD.—See H.B. Fuller Company; *U.S. Public*, pg. 977
H.B. FULLER TAIWAN CO., LTD.—See H.B. Fuller Company; *U.S. Public*, pg. 978
H.B. FULLER (THAILAND) CO., LTD.—See H.B. Fuller Company; *U.S. Public*, pg. 977
HENKEL ADHESIVES CORPORATION—See Henkel AG & Co. KGaA; *Int'l*, pg. 3353
HENKEL ADHESIVES TECHNOLOGIES (GUANGDONG) CO. LIMITED—See Henkel AG & Co. KGaA; *Int'l*, pg. 3348
HENKEL ADHESIVES TECHNOLOGIES INDIA PRIVATE LIMITED—See Henkel AG & Co. KGaA; *Int'l*, pg. 3348
HENKEL ADHESIVE TECHNOLOGIES CANADA—See Henkel AG & Co. KGaA; *Int'l*, pg. 3350
HENKEL ADHESIVE TECHNOLOGIES NORDEN AB—See Henkel AG & Co. KGaA; *Int'l*, pg. 3351
HENKEL ADHESIVE TECHNOLOGIES SDN. BHD.—See Henkel AG & Co. KGaA; *Int'l*, pg. 3348
HENKEL ARGENTINA S.A.—See Henkel AG & Co. KGaA; *Int'l*, pg. 3348
HENKEL BALTI OPERATIONS OU—See Henkel AG & Co. KGaA; *Int'l*, pg. 3349
HENKEL BALTI—See Henkel AG & Co. KGaA; *Int'l*, pg. 3349
HENKEL BAUTECHNIK KAZAKHSTAN LLP—See Henkel AG & Co. KGaA; *Int'l*, pg. 3350
HENKEL BAUTECHNIK TAA—See Henkel AG & Co. KGaA; *Int'l*, pg. 3350
HENKEL BELGIUM N.V.—See Henkel AG & Co. KGaA; *Int'l*, pg. 3350
HENKEL BELGIUM OPERATIONS N.V.—See Henkel AG & Co. KGaA; *Int'l*, pg. 3350
HENKEL BH D.O.O.—See Henkel AG & Co. KGaA; *Int'l*, pg. 3349
HENKEL CAPITAL S.A. DE C.V.—See Henkel AG & Co. KGaA; *Int'l*, pg. 3350
HENKEL CHEMICAL TECHNOLOGIES (SHANGHAI) LTD.—See Henkel AG & Co. KGaA; *Int'l*, pg. 3348
HENKEL CHILE LTDA.—See Henkel AG & Co. KGaA; *Int'l*, pg. 3350
HENKEL CHILE S.A.—See Henkel AG & Co. KGaA; *Int'l*, pg. 3350
HENKEL (CHINA) CO. LTD.—See Henkel AG & Co. KGaA; *Int'l*, pg. 3348
HENKEL (CHINA) INVESTMENT CO. LTD.—See Henkel AG & Co. KGaA; *Int'l*, pg. 3348
HENKEL DENMARK A/S—See Henkel AG & Co. KGaA; *Int'l*, pg. 3350
HENKEL DONGSUNG (THAILAND) LTD.—See Henkel AG & Co. KGaA; *Int'l*, pg. 3349
HENKEL DONGSUNG VIETNAM CO. LTD.—See Henkel AG & Co. KGaA; *Int'l*, pg. 3349
HENKEL EASTERN EUROPE GMBH—See Henkel AG & Co. KGaA; *Int'l*, pg. 3350
HENKEL EGYPT FOR INDUSTRY & TRADE SAE—See Henkel AG & Co. KGaA; *Int'l*, pg. 3351

325520 — ADHESIVE MANUFACTUR...

HENKEL ELECTRONIC MATERIALS (BELGIUM) N.V.—See Henkel AG & Co. KGaA; *Int'l*, pg. 3350
HENKEL ELECTRONICS MATERIALS N.V.—See Henkel AG & Co. KGaA; *Int'l*, pg. 3351
HENKEL FINLAND OY—See Henkel AG & Co. KGaA; *Int'l*, pg. 3351
HENKEL FRANCE OPERATIONS S.A.—See Henkel AG & Co. KGaA; *Int'l*, pg. 3351
HENKEL GLOBAL SUPPLY CHAIN B.V.—See Henkel AG & Co. KGaA; *Int'l*, pg. 3351
HENKEL HELLAS SA—See Henkel AG & Co. KGaA; *Int'l*, pg. 3350
HENKEL HOME CARE KOREA LTD. - ANSAN PLANT—See Henkel AG & Co. KGaA; *Int'l*, pg. 3349
HENKEL HONG KONG LTD.—See Henkel AG & Co. KGaA; *Int'l*, pg. 3349
HENKEL INDUSTRIAL ADHESIVES PAKISTAN PVT. LTD.—See Henkel AG & Co. KGaA; *Int'l*, pg. 3352
HENKEL IP MANAGEMENT AND IC SERVICES GMBH—See Henkel AG & Co. KGaA; *Int'l*, pg. 3351
HENKEL IRELAND LTD.—See Henkel AG & Co. KGaA; *Int'l*, pg. 3351
HENKEL ITALIA OPERATIONS S.R.L.—See Henkel AG & Co. KGaA; *Int'l*, pg. 3351
HENKEL ITALIA S.R.L.—See Henkel AG & Co. KGaA; *Int'l*, pg. 3351
HENKEL JAMAICA LIMITED—See Henkel AG & Co. KGaA; *Int'l*, pg. 3351
HENKEL JEBEL ALI FZCO—See Henkel AG & Co. KGaA; *Int'l*, pg. 3351
HENKEL (JIANGSU) AUTO PARTS CO., LTD.—See Henkel AG & Co. KGaA; *Int'l*, pg. 3348
HENKEL KENYA LTD.—See Henkel AG & Co. KGaA; *Int'l*, pg. 3351
HENKEL LABORATORIES—See Henkel AG & Co. KGaA; *Int'l*, pg. 3353
HENKEL LATVIA SIA—See Henkel AG & Co. KGaA; *Int'l*, pg. 3351
HENKEL LOCTITE BRASIL LTDA.—See Henkel AG & Co. KGaA; *Int'l*, pg. 3351
HENKEL LOCTITE (CHINA) CO. LTD.—See Henkel AG & Co. KGaA; *Int'l*, pg. 3351
HENKEL LOCTITE DEUTSCHLAND GMBH—See Henkel AG & Co. KGaA; *Int'l*, pg. 3351
HENKEL LOCTITE DE VENEZUELA, C.A.—See Henkel AG & Co. KGaA; *Int'l*, pg. 3352
HENKEL LOCTITE ESPANA, S.A.—See Henkel AG & Co. KGaA; *Int'l*, pg. 3351
HENKEL LOCTITE FRANCE SAS—See Henkel AG & Co. KGaA; *Int'l*, pg. 3351
HENKEL LOCTITE HONG KONG LIMITED—See Henkel AG & Co. KGaA; *Int'l*, pg. 3349
HENKEL LOCTITE ITALIA S.P.A.—See Henkel AG & Co. KGaA; *Int'l*, pg. 3352
HENKEL LOCTITE KOREA LTD.—See Henkel AG & Co. KGaA; *Int'l*, pg. 3349
HENKEL LTD., LINTON—See Henkel AG & Co. KGaA; *Int'l*, pg. 3353
HENKEL MARIBOR D.O.O.—See Henkel AG & Co. KGaA; *Int'l*, pg. 3351
HENKEL NEDERLAND OPERATIONS B.V.—See Henkel AG & Co. KGaA; *Int'l*, pg. 3351
HENKELORBSEAL—See Henkel AG & Co. KGaA; *Int'l*, pg. 3353
HENKEL POLSKA OPERATIONS SP. Z O.O.—See Henkel AG & Co. KGaA; *Int'l*, pg. 3352
HENKEL POLYBIT INDUSTRIES LTD.—See Henkel AG & Co. KGaA; *Int'l*, pg. 3352
HENKEL PUERTO RICO, INC.—See Henkel AG & Co. KGaA; *Int'l*, pg. 3352
HENKEL REPUBLICA DOMINICANA SRL—See Henkel AG & Co. KGaA; *Int'l*, pg. 3352
HENKEL (SIAM) ADHESIVE TECHNOLOGIES LTD.—See Henkel AG & Co. KGaA; *Int'l*, pg. 3348
HENKEL-STORITVE D.O.O.—See Henkel AG & Co. KGaA; *Int'l*, pg. 3354
HENKEL SURFACE TECHNOLOGIES NORDIC AB—See Henkel AG & Co. KGaA; *Int'l*, pg. 3351
HENKEL SWEDEN OPERATIONS AB—See Henkel AG & Co. KGaA; *Int'l*, pg. 3352
HENKEL SWITZERLAND OPERATIONS AG—See Henkel AG & Co. KGaA; *Int'l*, pg. 3352
HENKEL TAIWAN LTD. - P'INGCHEN—See Henkel AG & Co. KGaA; *Int'l*, pg. 3349
HENKEL TECHNOLOGIES FRANCE SAS—See Henkel AG & Co. KGaA; *Int'l*, pg. 3351
HENKEL TECHNOLOGIES (KOREA) LTD. - BUSAN PLANT—See Henkel AG & Co. KGaA; *Int'l*, pg. 3349
HENKEL TECHNOLOGIES (KOREA) LTD. - CHUNAN PLANT—See Henkel AG & Co. KGaA; *Int'l*, pg. 3349
HENKEL TECHNOLOGIES (KOREA) LTD.—See Henkel AG & Co. KGaA; *Int'l*, pg. 3349
HENKEL TECHNOLOGIES—See Henkel AG & Co. KGaA; *Int'l*, pg. 3353
HENKEL (THAILAND) LTD.—See Henkel AG & Co. KGaA; *Int'l*, pg. 3348
HENKEL VENEZOLANA S.A.—See Henkel AG & Co. KGaA; *Int'l*, pg. 3352

HENKEL XIANGHUA ADHESIVES CO. LTD.—See Henkel AG & Co. KGaA; *Int'l*, pg. 3349
HERNON MANUFACTURING, INC.; *U.S. Private*, pg. 1925
HEXZACHEM SARAWAK SDN. BHD.—See Hexza Corporation Berhad; *Int'l*, pg. 3373
HEXZACHEM SARAWAK SDN. BHD.—See Hexza Corporation Berhad; *Int'l*, pg. 3373
HEXZACHEM SARAWAK SDN. BHD.—See Hexza Corporation Berhad; *Int'l*, pg. 3373
HEXZACHEM SARAWAK SDN. BHD.—See Hexza Corporation Berhad; *Int'l*, pg. 3373
HUBEI HUITIAN NEW MATERIALS CO., LTD.; *Int'l*, pg. 3518
HUNAN SOKAN NEW MATERIALS CO., LTD.; *Int'l*, pg. 3533
ICP ADHESIVES & SEALANTS, INC.—See Audax Group, Limited Partnership; *U.S. Private*, pg. 388
IFS INDUSTRIES, INC.—See CFS Group, Inc.; *Int'l*, pg. 1430
INDUSTRIAS NIASA, S.A. DE C.V.—See Grupo Lamosa S.A. de C.V.; *Int'l*, pg. 3132
INOVEX INDUSTRIES INC.; *U.S. Private*, pg. 2084
INTER-NATIONAL STARCH & CHEMICAL CO., INC.—See Ingredion Incorporated; *U.S. Public*, pg. 1123
IPS ADHESIVES (JIASHAN) CO., LTD.—See IPS Corporation; *U.S. Private*, pg. 2137
IPS CORPORATION; *U.S. Private*, pg. 2137
ITW DEVCON—See Illinois Tool Works Inc.; *U.S. Public*, pg. 1105
ITW DYNATEC ADHESIVE EQUIPMENT (SUZHOU) CO. LTD.—See Illinois Tool Works Inc.; *U.S. Public*, pg. 1105
ITW DYNATEC—See Illinois Tool Works Inc.; *U.S. Public*, pg. 1105
ITW INDIA LIMITED—See Illinois Tool Works Inc.; *U.S. Public*, pg. 1106
ITW PERFORMANCE POLYMERS TRADING (SHANGHAI) CO. LTD.—See Illinois Tool Works Inc.; *U.S. Public*, pg. 1107
ITW PERMATEX, INC.—See Illinois Tool Works Inc.; *U.S. Public*, pg. 1107
ITW POLYMERS ADHESIVES NORTH AMERICA—See Illinois Tool Works Inc.; *U.S. Public*, pg. 1107
ITW POLYMERS SEALANTS NORTH AMERICA INC. - EASTERN DIVISION OFFICE—See Illinois Tool Works Inc.; *U.S. Public*, pg. 1107
ITW POLYMERS SEALANTS NORTH AMERICA INC.—See Illinois Tool Works Inc.; *U.S. Public*, pg. 1107
ITW POLY MEX, S. DE R.L. DE C.V.—See Illinois Tool Works Inc.; *U.S. Public*, pg. 1107
ITW PPF BRASIL ADESIVOS LTDA.—See Illinois Tool Works Inc.; *U.S. Public*, pg. 1106
KARNAK CORPORATION; *U.S. Private*, pg. 2263
KARS CIMENTO AS—See Cementir Holding N.V.; *Int'l*, pg. 1397
KK ENTERPRISE (KUNSHAN) CO., LTD.—See Grand Pacific Petrochemical Corporation; *Int'l*, pg. 3055
KK ENTERPRISE (MALAYSIA) SDN. BHD.—See Grand Pacific Petrochemical Corporation; *Int'l*, pg. 3055
KOMMERLING CHEMISCHE FABRIK GMBH—See H.B. Fuller Company; *U.S. Public*, pg. 978
KRATON FORMOSA POLYMERS CORPORATION—See Daelim Industrial Co., Ltd.; *Int'l*, pg. 1908
KUNSHAN AICA KOGYO CO., LTD.—See AICA Kogyo Company, Limited; *Int'l*, pg. 229
LANCO MANUFACTURING CORP.; *U.S. Private*, pg. 2382
L.D. DAVIS INDUSTRIES INC.; *U.S. Private*, pg. 2365
LEMTAPES OY—See H.B. Fuller Company; *U.S. Public*, pg. 978
LOCTITE INTERNATIONAL B.V.—See Henkel AG & Co. KGaA; *Int'l*, pg. 3351
LOCTITE (OVERSEAS) LTD.—See Henkel AG & Co. KGaA; *Int'l*, pg. 3351
LOCTITE PUERTO RICO, INC.—See Henkel AG & Co. KGaA; *Int'l*, pg. 3353
LORD CORPORATION—See Parker Hannifin Corporation; *U.S. Public*, pg. 1641
LORD ITALIA S.R.L.—See Parker Hannifin Corporation; *U.S. Public*, pg. 1641
LORD KOREA, LTD.—See Parker Hannifin Corporation; *U.S. Public*, pg. 1641
LORD SOLUTIONS FRANCE—See Parker Hannifin Corporation; *U.S. Public*, pg. 1641
LORD (THAILAND) LTD.—See Parker Hannifin Corporation; *U.S. Public*, pg. 1641
LUCIGEN CORP.—See KKR & Co. Inc.; *U.S. Public*, pg. 1258
MACTAC DEUTSCHLAND GMBH—See Avery Dennison Corporation; *U.S. Public*, pg. 244
MACTAC EUROPE SPRL—See Avery Dennison Corporation; *U.S. Public*, pg. 244
MACTAC FRANCE SARL—See Avery Dennison Corporation; *U.S. Public*, pg. 244
MASTER BOND INC.; *U.S. Private*, pg. 2607
MEM BAUCHEMIE GMBH—See Arkema S.A.; *Int'l*, pg. 571
MIMA FILMS SPRL—See Illinois Tool Works Inc.; *U.S. Public*, pg. 1109
MULTIBIND BIOTECH GMBH—See Illinois Tool Works Inc.; *U.S. Public*, pg. 1109

MULTISEAL INC.; *U.S. Private*, pg. 2813
MYDRIN FINDLEY SRL—See Arkema S.A.; *Int'l*, pg. 570
NATIONAL ADHESIVES CO. LTD.—See Henkel AG & Co. KGaA; *Int'l*, pg. 3349
NATIONAL CASEIN CO. INC.; *U.S. Private*, pg. 2850
NATIONAL STARCH & CHEMICAL LTD.-NAM DINH—See Ingredion Incorporated; *U.S. Public*, pg. 1124
NATIONAL STARCH & CHEMICAL PTY LTD.—See Ingredion Incorporated; *U.S. Public*, pg. 1124
NATIONAL STARCH & CHEMICAL—See Ingredion Incorporated; *U.S. Public*, pg. 1124
NATIONAL STARCH SPECIALTIES (SHANGHAI) LTD.—See Ingredion Incorporated; *U.S. Public*, pg. 1124
ND ADHESIVES & SEALANTS DIVISION—See H.B. Fuller Company; *U.S. Public*, pg. 978
NORDSON CANADA LTD.—See Nordson Corporation; *U.S. Public*, pg. 1533
NORDSON ENGINEERING GMBH—See Nordson Corporation; *U.S. Public*, pg. 1533
NORDSON TEST AND INSPECTION AMERICAS, INC.—See Nordson Corporation; *U.S. Public*, pg. 1534
NORDSON (U.K.) LIMITED—See Nordson Corporation; *U.S. Public*, pg. 1533
OKON, INC.—See RPM International Inc.; *U.S. Public*, pg. 1817
OOO HENKEL BAUTECHNIK—See Henkel AG & Co. KGaA; *Int'l*, pg. 3354
OOO HENKEL RUS—See Henkel AG & Co. KGaA; *Int'l*, pg. 3350
OY H.B. FULLER NORDIC AB—See H.B. Fuller Company; *U.S. Public*, pg. 978
PACER TECHNOLOGY—See AC MARCA, S.A.; *Int'l*, pg. 74
PALMER INTERNATIONAL, INC.; *U.S. Private*, pg. 3081
PANACOL-ELOSOL GMBH—See Dr. Honle AG; *Int'l*, pg. 2192
PARKER CHOMERICS—See Parker Hannifin Corporation; *U.S. Public*, pg. 1643
PARKER HANNIFIN ENGINEERED POLYMER SYSTEMS DIV.—See Parker Hannifin Corporation; *U.S. Public*, pg. 1643
PARKER HANNIFIN SEAL GROUP - ENGINEERED POLYMER SYSTEMS DIVISION—See Parker Hannifin Corporation; *U.S. Public*, pg. 1649
PARR TECHNOLOGIES, LLC—See Gladstone Management Corporation; *U.S. Private*, pg. 1705
PECORA CORPORATION—See Navigation Capital Partners, Inc.; *U.S. Private*, pg. 2873
PERFORMANCE POLYMER SOLUTIONS INC.—See Proof Research, Inc.; *U.S. Private*, pg. 3284
PIMACO AUTOADESIVOS LTDA.—See Grupo CCRR; *Int'l*, pg. 3124
PLANTA CREST MONTERREY—See Grupo Lamosa S.A. de C.V.; *Int'l*, pg. 3131
POLYMERIC SYSTEMS, INC.—See PPG Industries, Inc.; *U.S. Public*, pg. 1711
POLYNT COMPOSITES CANADA INC.—See Reichhold, Inc.; *U.S. Private*, pg. 3390
POWERBAND INDUSTRIES PRIVATE LIMITED—See Clearlake Capital Group, L.P.; *U.S. Private*, pg. 935
PRC-DESOTO AUSTRALIA PTY LTD.—See PPG Industries, Inc.; *U.S. Public*, pg. 1710
PROPAMSA, S.A.U.—See Cementos Molins S.A.; *Int'l*, pg. 1397
PT.AICA INDRIA—See AICA Kogyo Company, Limited; *Int'l*, pg. 229
PT BOSTIK INDONESIA—See Arkema S.A.; *Int'l*, pg. 571
P.T. HI-TECH INK INDONESIA—See Dainichiseika Color & Chemicals Mfg. Co., Ltd.; *Int'l*, pg. 1939
PT NATIONAL STARCH & CHEMICAL INDONESIA—See Ingredion Incorporated; *U.S. Public*, pg. 1124
PT. SLIONTEC EKADHARMA INDONESIA—See Hitachi, Ltd.; *Int'l*, pg. 3424
QUANEX IG SYSTEMS, INC.—See Quanex Building Products Corp.; *U.S. Public*, pg. 1749
QUISS QUALITATS-LNSPEKTIONSSYSTEMEUND SERVICE AG—See Atlas Copco AB; *Int'l*, pg. 684
RAAB KARCHER NEDERLAND B.V.—See Compagnie de Saint-Gobain SA; *Int'l*, pg. 1733
RAIN GUARD; *U.S. Private*, pg. 3347
RESIN DESIGNS, LLC—See KKR & Co. Inc.; *U.S. Public*, pg. 1243
RESINOVA CHEMIE LIMITED—See Astral Limited; *Int'l*, pg. 658
RESIN TECHNOLOGY GROUP LLC—See Henkel AG & Co. KGaA; *Int'l*, pg. 3353
ROMAN HOLDINGS CORPORATION; *U.S. Private*, pg. 3475
ROYAL ADHESIVES & SEALANTS, LLC—See H.B. Fuller Company; *U.S. Public*, pg. 978
ROYAL ADHESIVES & SEALANTS, LLC - WAYNE—See H.B. Fuller Company; *U.S. Public*, pg. 978
RUBEX, INC.—See Gladstone Management Corporation; *U.S. Private*, pg. 1705
THE RUSCOE COMPANY; *U.S. Private*, pg. 4113
SAINT-GOBAIN CONSTRUCTION PRODUCTS SLOVAKIA S.R.O.—See Compagnie de Saint-Gobain SA; *Int'l*, pg. 1726
SAINT-GOBAIN GRADBENI IZDELKI D.O.O.—See Com-

pagnie de Saint-Gobain SA; *Int'l*, pg. 1728
SAINT-GOBAIN PERFORMANCE PLASTICS CORBY LTD.—See Compagnie de Saint-Gobain SA; *Int'l*, pg. 1735
SAINT-GOBAIN WEBER (INDIA) LTD—See Compagnie de Saint-Gobain SA; *Int'l*, pg. 1728
SAINT-GOBAIN WEBER SOUTH AFRICA (PTY) LTD. - ALRODE FACTORY—See Compagnie de Saint-Gobain SA; *Int'l*, pg. 1727
SCAPA FRANCE S.A.—See Mativ Holdings, Inc.; *U.S. Public*, pg. 1397
SCAPA GROUP PLC—See Mativ Holdings, Inc.; *U.S. Public*, pg. 1396
SCAPA HOLDINGS GMBH—See Mativ Holdings, Inc.; *U.S. Public*, pg. 1397
SCAPA HONG KONG LTD—See Mativ Holdings, Inc.; *U.S. Public*, pg. 1397
SCAPA ITALIA S.P.A.—See Mativ Holdings, Inc.; *U.S. Public*, pg. 1397
SCAPA (SCHWEIZ) AG—See Mativ Holdings, Inc.; *U.S. Public*, pg. 1397
SCAPA TAPES (KOREA) CO. LTD—See Mativ Holdings, Inc.; *U.S. Public*, pg. 1397
SCAPA TAPES UK LTD.—See Mativ Holdings, Inc.; *U.S. Public*, pg. 1397
SCHUL INTERNATIONAL CO., LLC—See RPM International Inc.; *U.S. Public*, pg. 1818
SEAL-KRETE INC.—See RPM International Inc.; *U.S. Public*, pg. 1817
SEA S.A.—See Etex SA/NV; *Int'l*, pg. 2522
SEKISUI FULLER CO. LTD.—See H.B. Fuller Company; *U.S. Public*, pg. 978
SERVICIOS DE ADMINISTRACION DE ADHESIVOS, S.A. DE C.V.—See Grupo Lamosa S.A. de C.V.; *Int'l*, pg. 3132
SHANGHAI GAOQIAO BASF DISPERSIONS CO., LTD.—See BASF SE; *Int'l*, pg. 877
SHANGHAI GAOQIAO BASF DISPERSIONS CO., LTD.—See China Petrochemical Corporation; *Int'l*, pg. 1539
SHANGHAI JOHNSON & JOHNSON LTD.—See Johnson & Johnson; *U.S. Public*, pg. 1200
SHANGHAI S3 BUILDING MATERIALS CO LTD—See En-Gro Corporation Limited; *Int'l*, pg. 2436
SHENYANG AICA-HOPE KOGYO CO., LTD.—See AICA Kogyo Company, Limited; *Int'l*, pg. 229
SHERWIN-WILLIAMS CONSUMER GROUP—See The Sherwin-Williams Company; *U.S. Public*, pg. 2128
SHURTAPE SPECIALTY COATING, LLC—See STM Industries, Inc.; *U.S. Private*, pg. 3813
SHURTAPE TECHNOLOGIES, LLC—See STM Industries, Inc.; *U.S. Private*, pg. 3813
SIEGLING BRASIL LTDA.—See Forbo Holding Ltd.; *Int'l*, pg. 2730
SIEGLING MEXICO S.A. DE C.V.—See Forbo Holding Ltd.; *Int'l*, pg. 2730
SIEGLING (SCHWEIZ) AG—See Forbo Holding Ltd.; *Int'l*, pg. 2730
SIGNODE LIMITED—See Crown Holdings, Inc.; *U.S. Public*, pg. 600
SINAI WHITE PORTLAND CEMENT CO. SAE—See Cementir Holding N.V.; *Int'l*, pg. 1753
SLUYTER COMPANY LTD.—See Devjo Industries, Inc.; *Int'l*, pg. 2089
SOCIEDAD DE COMERCIO, ACHESON COLLOIDS—See Henkel AG & Co. KGaA; *Int'l*, pg. 3353
SOCIETE MAROCAINE DES COLLES—See Arkema S.A.; *Int'l*, pg. 571
SONDERHOFF CHEMICALS GMBH—See Henkel AG & Co. KGaA; *Int'l*, pg. 3354
SONDERHOFF ENGINEERING GMBH—See Henkel AG & Co. KGaA; *Int'l*, pg. 3354
SONDERHOFF HOLDING GMBH—See Henkel AG & Co. KGaA; *Int'l*, pg. 3354
SONDERHOFF ITALIA S.R.L.—See Henkel AG & Co. KGaA; *Int'l*, pg. 3354
SONDERHOFF POLYMER-SERVICES AUSTRIA GMBH—See Henkel AG & Co. KGaA; *Int'l*, pg. 3354
SONDERHOFF SERVICES GMBH—See Henkel AG & Co. KGaA; *Int'l*, pg. 3354
SONDERHOFF (SUZHOU) SEALING SYSTEM CO., LTD.—See Henkel AG & Co. KGaA; *Int'l*, pg. 3354
SONDERHOFF USA LLC—See Henkel AG & Co. KGaA; *Int'l*, pg. 3353
SOUTHERN GROUT & MORTARS INC.; *U.S. Private*, pg. 3732
SOVEREIGN SPECIALTY CHEMICALS, INC.—See Henkel AG & Co. KGaA; *Int'l*, pg. 3353
SOVEREIGN SPECIALTY CHEMICALS—See Henkel AG & Co. KGaA; *Int'l*, pg. 3353
SPECIALTY ADHESIVES, INC.; *U.S. Private*, pg. 3749
SPECIALTY CONSTRUCTION BRANDS - PALATINE—See H.B. Fuller Company; *U.S. Public*, pg. 978
STOKVIS DANMARK AS—See Illinois Tool Works Inc.; *U.S. Public*, pg. 1110
STOKVIS TAPE GROUP B.V.—See Illinois Tool Works Inc.; *U.S. Public*, pg. 1110
STOKVIS TAPES (BEIJING) CO. LTD.—See Illinois Tool Works Inc.; *U.S. Public*, pg. 1110

STOKVIS TAPES BVBA—See Illinois Tool Works Inc.; *U.S. Public*, pg. 1110
STOKVIS TAPES DEUTSCHLAND GMBH—See Illinois Tool Works Inc.; *U.S. Public*, pg. 1110
STOKVIS TAPES FRANCE SAS—See Illinois Tool Works Inc.; *U.S. Public*, pg. 1111
STOKVIS TAPES ITALIA S.R.L.—See Illinois Tool Works Inc.; *U.S. Public*, pg. 1111
STOKVIS TAPES LIMITED LIABILITY COMPANY—See Illinois Tool Works Inc.; *U.S. Public*, pg. 1111
STOKVIS TAPES MAGYARORSZAG KFT—See Illinois Tool Works Inc.; *U.S. Public*, pg. 1111
STOKVIS TAPES NORGE AS—See Illinois Tool Works Inc.; *U.S. Public*, pg. 1111
STOKVIS TAPES OY—See Illinois Tool Works Inc.; *U.S. Public*, pg. 1111
STOKVIS TAPES (SHANGHAI) CO. LTD.—See Illinois Tool Works Inc.; *U.S. Public*, pg. 1110
STOKVIS TAPES (SHENZHEN) CO. LTD.—See Illinois Tool Works Inc.; *U.S. Public*, pg. 1110
STOKVIS TAPES SVERIGE AB—See Illinois Tool Works Inc.; *U.S. Public*, pg. 1111
STOKVIS TAPES (TAIWAN) CO. LTD.—See Illinois Tool Works Inc.; *U.S. Public*, pg. 1110
STOKVIS TAPES (TIANJIN) CO. LTD.—See Illinois Tool Works Inc.; *U.S. Public*, pg. 1110
STRUCTIL SASU—See Hexcel Corporation; *U.S. Public*, pg. 1033
SUPER GLUE CORPORATION—See AC MARCA, S.A; *Int'l*, pg. 74
SUZHOU GIGA SOLAR MATERIALS CORP.—See Giga Solar Materials Corp.; *Int'l*, pg. 2971
SUZHOU TONSAN ADHESIVE CO., LTD.—See H.B. Fuller Company; *U.S. Public*, pg. 978
TASEK CORPORATION BERHAD—See Hong Leong Investment Holdings Pte. Ltd.; *Int'l*, pg. 3469
TECNOCRETO, S.A.—See Grupo Lamosa S.A. de C.V.; *Int'l*, pg. 3132
TEKNOL INC.; *U.S. Private*, pg. 3958
TEXTILE RUBBER & CHEMICAL CO., INC.; *U.S. Private*, pg. 3978
TONSAN ADHESIVE, INC.—See H.B. Fuller Company; *U.S. Public*, pg. 978
TREMCO ASIA PTE. LTD.—See RPM International Inc.; *U.S. Public*, pg. 1818
TREMCO AUSTRALIA—See RPM International Inc.; *U.S. Public*, pg. 1818
TREMCO BARRIER SOLUTIONS, INC.—See RPM International Inc.; *U.S. Public*, pg. 1818
TREMCO ILLBRUCK GROUP GMBH—See RPM International Inc.; *U.S. Public*, pg. 1820
TREMCO INCORPORATED—See RPM International Inc.; *U.S. Public*, pg. 1817
TREMCO PTY. LTD.—See RPM International Inc.; *U.S. Public*, pg. 1818
ULTRASEAL USA INC.—See Quaker Chemical Corporation; *U.S. Public*, pg. 1747
ULTRATAPE INDUSTRIES—See Delphon Industries, LLC; *U.S. Private*, pg. 1199
VAL-A CHICAGO, INC.—See LHB Industries, Inc.; *U.S. Private*, pg. 2442
VETEK SAU—See Arkema S.A.; *Int'l*, pg. 571
WEN TRADING CO., LTD.—See Chugoku Marine Paints, Ltd.; *Int'l*, pg. 1595
WF HOLDINGS INC.; *U.S. Private*, pg. 4503
WF TAYLOR CO., INC.—See Arsenal Capital Management LP; *U.S. Public*, pg. 339
WHITFORD CORPORATION—See PPG Industries, Inc.; *U.S. Public*, pg. 1711
WHITFORD WORLDWIDE COMPANY—See PPG Industries, Inc.; *U.S. Public*, pg. 1711
WILTIC CHEMICAL MANUFACTURING—See Genova Products, Inc.; *U.S. Public*, pg. 1673
W. R. GRACE HOLDINGS, S.A. DE C.V.—See Standard Industries Holdings Inc.; *U.S. Private*, pg. 3780
W. R. GRACE (PHILIPPINES), INC.—See Standard Industries Holdings Inc.; *U.S. Private*, pg. 3780
W. R. GRACE S.A.—See Standard Industries Holdings Inc.; *U.S. Private*, pg. 3780
WUHU EFTEC CHEMICAL PRODUCTS LTD.—See EMS-Chemie Holding AG; *Int'l*, pg. 2394
XCHEM INTERNATIONAL LLC—See H.B. Fuller Company; *U.S. Public*, pg. 978
YONGLE TAPE CO., LTD.—See Avery Dennison Corporation; *U.S. Public*, pg. 245

325611 — SOAP AND OTHER DETERGENT MANUFACTURING

AFRINAT PROPRIETARY LIMITED—See AYO Technology Solutions Ltd.; *Int'l*, pg. 775
ALBEMARLE AMENDMENTS, LLC—See Albemarle Corporation; *U.S. Public*, pg. 73
ALBUS A.D.; *Int'l*, pg. 299
ALCONOX, INC.; *U.S. Private*, pg. 154
ARBORA & AUSONIA, S.L.—See The Procter & Gamble Company; *U.S. Public*, pg. 2120

ARM & HAMMER CONSUMER PRODUCTS—See Church & Dwight Co., Inc.; *U.S. Public*, pg. 493
B&D LIFE HEALTH CO.,LTD.; *Int'l*, pg. 784
BOMBRIL S.A.; *Int'l*, pg. 1104
BRILLIANT N.E.V. CORP.; *Int'l*, pg. 1163
BULLEN MIDWEST INC.—See Hospeco Brands Group; *U.S. Private*, pg. 1985
CAIRO OIL & SOAP COMPANY; *Int'l*, pg. 1253
CALVATIS GMBH; *Int'l*, pg. 1266
CALVATIS OOO—See Calvatis GmbH; *Int'l*, pg. 1266
CALVATIS SRL—See Calvatis GmbH; *Int'l*, pg. 1266
CARTER PRODUCTS (N.Z.) INC.—See Church & Dwight Co., Inc.; *U.S. Public*, pg. 493
CAVINKARE PVT. LTD.; *Int'l*, pg. 1362
CERTOL INTERNATIONAL, LLC—See MicroCare, LLC; *U.S. Private*, pg. 2703
CHINA GOLDEN CLASSIC GROUP LIMITED; *Int'l*, pg. 1505
CHINA LUDAO TECHNOLOGY COMPANY LIMITED; *Int'l*, pg. 1515
CHUNGHWA BIOMEDICAL TECHNOLOGY CO., LTD.—See Chunghwa Chemical Synthesis & Biotech Co., Ltd.; *Int'l*, pg. 1598
CLARO PRODUCTS GMBH; *Int'l*, pg. 1651
COLGATE-PALMOLIVE AB—See Colgate-Palmolive Company; *U.S. Public*, pg. 531
COLGATE-PALMOLIVE AG—See Colgate-Palmolive Company; *U.S. Public*, pg. 531
COLGATE-PALMOLIVE (ARKANSAS)—See Colgate-Palmolive Company; *U.S. Public*, pg. 531
COLGATE-PALMOLIVE BELGIUM S.A.—See Colgate-Palmolive Company; *U.S. Public*, pg. 531
COLGATE-PALMOLIVE C.A.—See Colgate-Palmolive Company; *U.S. Public*, pg. 531
COLGATE-PALMOLIVE (CENTRAL AMERICA), INC.—See Colgate-Palmolive Company; *U.S. Public*, pg. 531
COLGATE-PALMOLIVE (CENTRAL AMERICA), INC.—See Colgate-Palmolive Company; *U.S. Public*, pg. 531
COLGATE-PALMOLIVE (CENTRAL AMERICA)—See Colgate-Palmolive Company; *U.S. Public*, pg. 531
COLGATE-PALMOLIVE CHILE S.A.—See Colgate-Palmolive Company; *U.S. Public*, pg. 531
COLGATE-PALMOLIVE CIA—See Colgate-Palmolive Company; *U.S. Public*, pg. 531
COLGATE-PALMOLIVE COMPANY; *U.S. Public*, pg. 530
COLGATE-PALMOLIVE DEL ECUADOR, S.A.—See Colgate-Palmolive Company; *U.S. Public*, pg. 532
COLGATE-PALMOLIVE DE PUERTO RICO, INC.—See Colgate-Palmolive Company; *U.S. Public*, pg. 532
COLGATE-PALMOLIVE, (DR), INC.—See Colgate-Palmolive Company; *U.S. Public*, pg. 532
COLGATE-PALMOLIVE (EASTERN) PTE. LTD.—See Colgate-Palmolive Company; *U.S. Public*, pg. 531
COLGATE-PALMOLIVE (FIJI) LTD.—See Colgate-Palmolive Company; *U.S. Public*, pg. 531
COLGATE-PALMOLIVE GHANA LIMITED—See Colgate-Palmolive Company; *U.S. Public*, pg. 532
COLGATE-PALMOLIVE GMBH—See Colgate-Palmolive Company; *U.S. Public*, pg. 532
COLGATE-PALMOLIVE GMBH—See Colgate-Palmolive Company; *U.S. Public*, pg. 532
COLGATE-PALMOLIVE (GUYANA) LTD.—See Colgate-Palmolive Company; *U.S. Public*, pg. 531
COLGATE-PALMOLIVE HOUSEHOLD PRODUCTS DIVISION—See Colgate-Palmolive Company; *U.S. Public*, pg. 532
COLGATE-PALMOLIVE INC. S.A.—See Colgate-Palmolive Company; *U.S. Public*, pg. 532
COLGATE-PALMOLIVE, INC.—See Colgate-Palmolive Company; *U.S. Public*, pg. 532
COLGATE-PALMOLIVE (INDIA) LTD.—See Colgate-Palmolive Company; *U.S. Public*, pg. 531
COLGATE-PALMOLIVE ITALIA SRL—See Colgate-Palmolive Company; *U.S. Public*, pg. 532
COLGATE-PALMOLIVE LTD.—See Colgate-Palmolive Company; *U.S. Public*, pg. 532
COLGATE-PALMOLIVE LTD.—See Colgate-Palmolive Company; *U.S. Public*, pg. 532
COLGATE-PALMOLIVE (MYANMAR) LIMITED—See Colgate-Palmolive Company; *U.S. Public*, pg. 531
COLGATE-PALMOLIVE NEDERLAND B.V.—See Colgate-Palmolive Company; *U.S. Public*, pg. 532
COLGATE-PALMOLIVE (PAKISTAN) LTD.; *Int'l*, pg. 1698
COLGATE-PALMOLIVE PERSONAL CARE PRODUCTS DIVISION—See Colgate-Palmolive Company; *U.S. Public*, pg. 532
COLGATE-PALMOLIVE PHILIPPINES INC.—See Colgate-Palmolive Company; *U.S. Public*, pg. 532
COLGATE-PALMOLIVE (ROMANIA) SRL—See Colgate-Palmolive Company; *U.S. Public*, pg. 531
COLGATE-PALMOLIVE, S.A. DE C.V.—See Colgate-Palmolive Company; *U.S. Public*, pg. 532
COLGATE-PALMOLIVE S.P.A.—See Colgate-Palmolive Company; *U.S. Public*, pg. 532
COLGATE-PALMOLIVE (THAILAND) LIMITED—See Colgate-Palmolive Company; *U.S. Public*, pg. 531
COLGATE U.S.A.—See Colgate-Palmolive Company; *U.S. Public*, pg. 531

325611 — SOAP AND OTHER DETE...

COMPANIA QUIMICA S.A.—See The Procter & Gamble Company; *U.S. Public*, pg. 2120
CO-OP CLEAN CO., LTD.—See Adeka Corporation; *Int'l*, pg. 142
CR BRANDS, INC.—See Resilience Capital Partners, LLC; *U.S. Private*, pg. 3405
DALLI-DE KLOK B.V.—See DALLI-WERKE GmbH & Co. KG; *Int'l*, pg. 1954
DALLI-WIN IBERICA SL—See DALLI-WERKE GmbH & Co. KG; *Int'l*, pg. 1954
DIAL INTERNATIONAL, INC.—See Henkel AG & Co. KGaA; *Int'l*, pg. 3353
DIAMOND CHEMICAL CO., INC.; *U.S. Private*, pg. 1222
DIVERSEY INDIA PRIVATE LIMITED—See Sealed Air Corporation; *U.S. Public*, pg. 1852
DIVERSEY ISRAEL LTD.—See Sealed Air Corporation; *U.S. Public*, pg. 1852
DIVERSEY ITALY PRODUCTION S.R.L.—See Sealed Air Corporation; *U.S. Public*, pg. 1852
DIVERSEY NETHERLANDS PRODUCTION B.V.—See Sealed Air Corporation; *U.S. Public*, pg. 1853
ECOLAB AB—See Ecolab Inc.; *U.S. Public*, pg. 713
ECOLAB AS—See Ecolab Inc.; *U.S. Public*, pg. 713
ECOLAB CANADA—See Ecolab Inc.; *U.S. Public*, pg. 713
ECOLAB D.O.O.—See Ecolab Inc.; *U.S. Public*, pg. 714
ECOLAB G.K.—See Ecolab Inc.; *U.S. Public*, pg. 713
ECOLAB GLOBAL INSTITUTIONAL GROUP—See Ecolab Inc.; *U.S. Public*, pg. 713
ECOLAB LIMITED—See Ecolab Inc.; *U.S. Public*, pg. 713
ECOLAB LLC—See Ecolab Inc.; *U.S. Public*, pg. 713
ECOLAB NEW ZEALAND LTD.—See Ecolab Inc.; *U.S. Public*, pg. 713
ECOLAB PTE. LTD.—See Ecolab Inc.; *U.S. Public*, pg. 714
ECOLAB (PTY) LTD.—See Ecolab Inc.; *U.S. Public*, pg. 712
ECOLAB PTY. LTD.—See Ecolab Inc.; *U.S. Public*, pg. 714
ECOLAB USA INC. - FOOD & BEVERAGE PROCESSING—See Ecolab Inc.; *U.S. Public*, pg. 714
ECOVER BELGIUM NV; *Int'l*, pg. 2300
ELCH GMBH—See Henkel AG & Co. KGaA; *Int'l*, pg. 3348
ENVIROCON TECHNOLOGIES, INC.; *U.S. Private*, pg. 1406
FARIA CORPORATION; *U.S. Private*, pg. 1474
FATER PORTUGAL UNIPESSOAL LDA—See The Procter & Gamble Company; *U.S. Public*, pg. 2120
GLISSEN CHEMICAL CO. INC.; *U.S. Private*, pg. 1711
GODREJ CONSUMER PRODUCTS LIMITED—See Godrej & Boyce Mfg. Co. Ltd.; *Int'l*, pg. 3020
GOJO INDUSTRIES, INC.; *U.S. Private*, pg. 1726
GRANDPA SOAP COMPANY—See Grandpa Brands Company; *U.S. Public*, pg. 1754
GURTLER INDUSTRIES INC; *U.S. Private*, pg. 1819
HENKEL ABLESTIK JAPAN LTD.—See Henkel AG & Co. KGaA; *Int'l*, pg. 3349
HENKEL ALGERIE S.P.A.—See Henkel AG & Co. KGaA; *Int'l*, pg. 3352
HENKEL ALKI DISTRIBUTION S.A.R.L.—See Henkel AG & Co. KGaA; *Int'l*, pg. 3352
HENKEL ARABIA FOR HOME AND PERSONAL CARE PRODUCTS CO. LTD.—See Henkel AG & Co. KGaA; *Int'l*, pg. 3352
HENKEL AUSTRIA GROUP—See Henkel AG & Co. KGaA; *Int'l*, pg. 3350
HENKEL & CIE AG—See Henkel AG & Co. KGaA; *Int'l*, pg. 3348
HENKEL CONSUMER GOODS CANADA, INC.—See Henkel AG & Co. KGaA; *Int'l*, pg. 3350
HENKEL CONSUMER GOODS INC.—See Henkel AG & Co. KGaA; *Int'l*, pg. 3353
HENKEL FRANCE S.A.—See Henkel AG & Co. KGaA; *Int'l*, pg. 3351
HENKEL HOME CARE KOREA LTD.—See Henkel AG & Co. KGaA; *Int'l*, pg. 3349
HENKEL IBERICA S.A.—See Henkel AG & Co. KGaA; *Int'l*, pg. 3351
HENKEL JORDAN PSC—See Henkel AG & Co. KGaA; *Int'l*, pg. 3352
HENKEL LA LUZ S.A.—See Henkel AG & Co. KGaA; *Int'l*, pg. 3351
HENKEL MAGYARORSZAG KFT.—See Henkel AG & Co. KGaA; *Int'l*, pg. 3350
HENKEL NEDERLAND B.V.—See Henkel AG & Co. KGaA; *Int'l*, pg. 3351
HENKEL PDC EGYPT SAE—See Henkel AG & Co. KGaA; *Int'l*, pg. 3352
HENKEL SAUDI ARABIA DETERGENTS CO. LTD.—See Henkel AG & Co. KGaA; *Int'l*, pg. 3352
HENKEL S.P.A.—See Henkel AG & Co. KGaA; *Int'l*, pg. 3352
HENKEL SRBIJA D.O.O. - INDJIJA PLANT—See Henkel AG & Co. KGaA; *Int'l*, pg. 3352
HENKEL SRBIJA D.O.O. - KRUSEVAC PLANT—See Henkel AG & Co. KGaA; *Int'l*, pg. 3352
HENKEL SRBIJA D.O.O.—See Henkel AG & Co. KGaA; *Int'l*, pg. 3352
HENKEL SURFACE TECHNOLOGIES—See Henkel AG & Co. KGaA; *Int'l*, pg. 3352
HENKEL UKRAINE TOW—See Henkel AG & Co. KGaA; *Int'l*, pg. 3352

HIGH RIDGE BRANDS CO.—See Clayton, Dubilier & Rice, LLC; *U.S. Private*, pg. 924
HIPOLIN LIMITED; *Int'l*, pg. 3402
HUNAN LICHEN INDUSTRIAL CO., LTD.; *Int'l*, pg. 3533
JAMES AUSTIN CO.; *U.S. Private*, pg. 2183
JOHNSON COMPANY, LTD.—See S.C. Johnson & Son, Inc.; *U.S. Private*, pg. 3516
JOHNSONS WAX DE PORTUGAL, LDA.—See S.C. Johnson & Son, Inc.; *U.S. Private*, pg. 3516
JOHNSONWAX DEL ECUADOR S.A.—See S.C. Johnson & Son, Inc.; *U.S. Private*, pg. 3516
JOHNSON WAX (EGYPT) CO—See S.C. Johnson & Son, Inc.; *U.S. Private*, pg. 3516
JOHNSON WAX NEW ZEALAND LIMITED—See S.C. Johnson & Son, Inc.; *U.S. Private*, pg. 3516
JOHNSON WAX NIGERIA LIMITED—See S.C. Johnson & Son, Inc.; *U.S. Private*, pg. 3516
JOHNSON WAX S.P.A.—See S.C. Johnson & Son, Inc.; *U.S. Private*, pg. 3516
KETJEN CATALYSTS (SHANGHAI) COMPANY LIMITED—See Albemarle Corporation; *U.S. Public*, pg. 73
KETJEN CORPORATION—See Albemarle Corporation; *U.S. Public*, pg. 73
KETJEN HUNGARY LIMITED LIABILITY COMPANY—See Albemarle Corporation; *U.S. Public*, pg. 73
KETJEN INDIA PRIVATE LIMITED—See Albemarle Corporation; *U.S. Public*, pg. 73
KETJEN JAPAN GK—See Albemarle Corporation; *U.S. Public*, pg. 73
KETJEN KOREA LIMITED—See Albemarle Corporation; *U.S. Public*, pg. 73
KETJEN MALAYSIA SDN BHD.—See Albemarle Corporation; *U.S. Public*, pg. 73
KETJEN NETHERLANDS B.V.—See Albemarle Corporation; *U.S. Public*, pg. 73
KETJEN SINGAPORE PRIVATE LIMITED—See Albemarle Corporation; *U.S. Public*, pg. 73
KETJEN VIETNAM LIMITED LIABILITY CO., LTD.—See Albemarle Corporation; *U.S. Public*, pg. 73
KIK (VIRGINIA) LLC—See Centerbridge Partners, L.P.; *U.S. Private*, pg. 815
KOREA JOHNSON CO., LTD.—See S.C. Johnson & Son, Inc.; *U.S. Private*, pg. 3516
KOREX CORPORATION—See Pensler Capital Corporation; *U.S. Private*, pg. 3139
LANMAN & KEMP-BARCLAY CO., INC.; *U.S. Private*, pg. 2390
LOCTITE ITALIA S.P.A.—See Henkel AG & Co. KGaA; *Int'l*, pg. 3352
MAESA INC—See F&B Group; *Int'l*, pg. 2595
MAESA UK LTD—See F&B Group; *Int'l*, pg. 2595
MANUFACTURERS SOAP AND CHEMICALS COMPANY—See Ascent Industries Co.; *U.S. Public*, pg. 210
MARIETTA CORP. - LOS ANGELES—See Ares Management Corporation; *U.S. Public*, pg. 189
MARIETTA CORP. - OLIVE BRANCH—See Ares Management Corporation; *U.S. Public*, pg. 189
MARIETTA CORPORATION—See Ares Management Corporation; *U.S. Public*, pg. 189
METHOD PRODUCTS, INC.—See Ecover Belgium NV; *Int'l*, pg. 2300
OCUSOFT, INC.; *U.S. Private*, pg. 2993
OLIVINE INDUSTRIES (PRIVATE) LIMITED—See Cottco Holdings Limited; *Int'l*, pg. 1817
OOO HENKEL RUS—See Henkel AG & Co. KGaA; *Int'l*, pg. 3354
ORIGINAL BRADFORD SOAP WORKS, INC.; *U.S. Private*, pg. 3042
PANAMEX NEW ZEALAND—See Panamex Pacific, Inc; *U.S. Private*, pg. 3085
P&G ISRAEL M.D.O. LTD.—See The Procter & Gamble Company; *U.S. Public*, pg. 2121
P&G K.K.—See The Procter & Gamble Company; *U.S. Public*, pg. 2122
PIEDMONT CHEMICAL INDUSTRIES, INC.; *U.S. Private*, pg. 3177
PILOT CHEMICAL CO. OF OHIO INC.—See Pilot Chemical Company; *U.S. Private*, pg. 3181
PILOT LABORATORIES INC.—See Pilot Chemical Company; *U.S. Private*, pg. 3181
PROCTER & GAMBLE AUSTRALIA PROPRIETARY LIMITED—See The Procter & Gamble Company; *U.S. Public*, pg. 2121
PROCTER & GAMBLE AUSTRIA GMBH—See The Procter & Gamble Company; *U.S. Public*, pg. 2121
PROCTER & GAMBLE COMMERCIAL COMPANY—See The Procter & Gamble Company; *U.S. Public*, pg. 2121
PROCTER & GAMBLE DO BRASIL S/A—See The Procter & Gamble Company; *U.S. Public*, pg. 2123
PROCTER & GAMBLE DO BRAZIL, LLC—See The Procter & Gamble Company; *U.S. Public*, pg. 2123
PROCTER & GAMBLE ESPANA, S.A.—See The Procter & Gamble Company; *U.S. Public*, pg. 2121
PROCTER & GAMBLE FRANCE S.A.S.—See The Procter & Gamble Company; *U.S. Public*, pg. 2121
PROCTER & GAMBLE GMBH—See The Procter & Gamble Company; *U.S. Public*, pg. 2121

PROCTER & GAMBLE INC.—See The Procter & Gamble Company; *U.S. Public*, pg. 2122
PROCTER & GAMBLE INTERNATIONAL FUNDING SCA—See The Procter & Gamble Company; *U.S. Public*, pg. 2122
PROCTER & GAMBLE MANUFACTURING BELGIUM N.V.—See The Procter & Gamble Company; *U.S. Public*, pg. 2122
PROCTER & GAMBLE MANUFACTURING COMPANY—See The Procter & Gamble Company; *U.S. Public*, pg. 2122
PROCTER & GAMBLE MANUFACTURING (THAILAND) LTD.—See The Procter & Gamble Company; *U.S. Public*, pg. 2122
PROCTER & GAMBLE NIGERIA LIMITED—See The Procter & Gamble Company; *U.S. Public*, pg. 2122
PROCTER & GAMBLE PRODUCT SUPPLY (U.K.) LIMITED—See The Procter & Gamble Company; *U.S. Public*, pg. 2123
PROCTER & GAMBLE-RAKONA, S.R.O.—See The Procter & Gamble Company; *U.S. Public*, pg. 2123
PROCTER & GAMBLE SERVICES GMBH—See The Procter & Gamble Company; *U.S. Public*, pg. 2123
PROCTER & GAMBLE SINGAPORE PTE. LTD.—See The Procter & Gamble Company; *U.S. Public*, pg. 2123
PROCTER & GAMBLE SWEDEN—See The Procter & Gamble Company; *U.S. Public*, pg. 2123
PROCTER & GAMBLE U.K.—See The Procter & Gamble Company; *U.S. Public*, pg. 2123
P.T. S.C. JOHNSON & SON (INDONESIA) LTD.—See S.C. Johnson & Son, Inc.; *U.S. Private*, pg. 3516
PURE-CHEM PRODUCTS CO., INC.—See Alex C. Ferguson, Inc.; *U.S. Private*, pg. 162
QINGDAO HONGXING CHEMICAL GROUP CO., LTD.—See Guizhou Redstar Development Co., Ltd.; *Int'l*, pg. 3175
RAINING ROSE, INC.; *U.S. Private*, pg. 3348
ROYAL CHEMICAL COMPANY—See Paro Services Corp.; *U.S. Private*, pg. 3099
RUBIA INDUSTRIES LIMITED—See Berli Jucker Public Co. Ltd.; *Int'l*, pg. 985
RUSTIC ESCENTUALS—See Incline MGMT Corp.; *U.S. Private*, pg. 2054
SCHWARZKOPF & HENKEL K.K.—See Henkel AG & Co. KGaA; *Int'l*, pg. 3354
S.C. JOHNSON CANADA—See S.C. Johnson & Son, Inc.; *U.S. Private*, pg. 3517
S.C. JOHNSON DE CENTROAMERICA S.A.—See S.C. Johnson & Son, Inc.; *U.S. Private*, pg. 3517
S.C. JOHNSON, LTD.—See S.C. Johnson & Son, Inc.; *U.S. Private*, pg. 3517
S.C. JOHNSON LTD—See S.C. Johnson & Son, Inc.; *U.S. Private*, pg. 3517
S.C. JOHNSON & SON COLOMBIANA S.A.—See S.C. Johnson & Son, Inc.; *U.S. Private*, pg. 3516
S.C. JOHNSON & SON DE ARGENTINA S.A.I.C.—See S.C. Johnson & Son, Inc.; *U.S. Private*, pg. 3516
S.C. JOHNSON & SON DE VENEZUELA, C.A.—See S.C. Johnson & Son, Inc.; *U.S. Private*, pg. 3516
S.C. JOHNSON & SON (HELLAS) E.P.E.—See S.C. Johnson & Son, Inc.; *U.S. Private*, pg. 3516
S.C. JOHNSON & SON, LTD.—See S.C. Johnson & Son, Inc.; *U.S. Private*, pg. 3517
S.C. JOHNSON & SON PTE. LIMITED—See S.C. Johnson & Son, Inc.; *U.S. Private*, pg. 3516
S C JOHNSON & SON S.A. DE C.V—See S.C. Johnson & Son, Inc.; *U.S. Private*, pg. 3516
S.C. JOHNSON & SON TAIWAN, LTD.—See S.C. Johnson & Son, Inc.; *U.S. Private*, pg. 3516
S.C. JOHNSON UKRAINE, INC.—See S.C. Johnson & Son, Inc.; *U.S. Private*, pg. 3517
S. C. JOHNSON WAX LTD.—See S.C. Johnson & Son, Inc.; *U.S. Private*, pg. 3516
SCOTT'S LIQUID GOLD-INC.; *U.S. Public*, pg. 1849
SERVICE FOUR EQUIPMENT COMPANY, INC.; *U.S. Private*, pg. 3615
SEVEN RIVERS, INC.—See Harima Chemicals Group, Inc.; *Int'l*, pg. 3276
SPD SWISS PRECISION DIAGNOSTICS GMBH—See The Procter & Gamble Company; *U.S. Public*, pg. 2123
THE SPIC & SPAN COMPANY—See Prestige Consumer Healthcare Inc.; *U.S. Public*, pg. 1716
STAR BRITE EUROPE, LLC—See OneWater Marine Inc.; *U.S. Public*, pg. 1604
STARCO CHEMICAL—See Diamond Chemical Co., Inc.; *U.S. Private*, pg. 1223
STATE INDUSTRIAL PRODUCTS CORPORATION; *U.S. Private*, pg. 3792
STERLING PRODUCTS LIMITED—See Edward B. Beharry & Co. Ltd.; *Int'l*, pg. 2316
SWSH DALEY MFG, INC.—See Ecolab Inc.; *U.S. Public*, pg. 716
THEOCHEM LABORATORIES, INC.—See Theochem Laboratories, Inc.; *U.S. Private*, pg. 4141
THERA COSMETIC GMBH—See Henkel AG & Co. KGaA; *Int'l*, pg. 3354
TIANJIN HENKEL DETERGENTS & CLEANING PROD-

N.A.I.C.S. INDEX

325612 — POLISH AND OTHER SA...

UCTS CO. LTD.—See Henkel AG & Co. KGaA; *Int'l*, pg. 3349
TOKYO REINE, LTD.—See Hoyu Co., Ltd.; *Int'l*, pg. 3499
TOM'S OF MAINE, INC.—See Colgate-Palmolive Company; *U.S. Public*, pg. 533
TURK HENKEL KIMYA SANAYI VE TICARET A.S.—See Henkel AG & Co. KGaA; *Int'l*, pg. 3354
TWINCRAFT, INC.—See PC GROUP, INC.; *U.S. Private*, pg. 3119
UNITED-GUARDIAN, INC.; *U.S. Public*, pg. 2238
VALEANT GROUPE COSMODERME INC.—See Bausch Health Companies Inc.; *Int'l*, pg. 898
VALLEY PRODUCTS CO.; *U.S. Private*, pg. 4335
THE VALUE BRANDS COMPANY DE ARGENTINA S.C.A.—See Grupo Romero; *Int'l*, pg. 3134
WIN WARTH GMBH—See DALLI-WERKE GmbH & Co. KG; *Int'l*, pg. 1954
YAMAHATSU (THAILAND) CO. LTD.—See Henkel AG & Co. KGaA; *Int'l*, pg. 3349
ZOHAR DALIA—See Ecolab Inc.; *U.S. Public*, pg. 717
ZUF ACQUISITIONS I LLC—See EVI Industries, Inc.; *U.S. Public*, pg. 803

325612 — POLISH AND OTHER SANITATION GOOD MANUFACTURING

151 PRODUCTS LTD.; *Int'l*, pg. 2
ABC COMPOUNDING COMPANY, INC.; *U.S. Private*, pg. 35
ACS INDUSTRIES, INC. - SCRUBBLE PRODUCTS DIVISION—See ACS Industries, Inc.; *U.S. Private*, pg. 66
ADCO, INC.—See Mentor Partners LLC; *U.S. Private*, pg. 2667
AERO BALKAN, D.O.O.—See Aero d.d.; *Int'l*, pg. 180
A.J. FUNK & CO. INC.; *U.S. Private*, pg. 26
ALBEMARLE HUNGARY LTD.—See Albemarle Corporation; *U.S. Public*, pg. 73
ALBEMARLE MIDDLE EAST CORPORATION FZE—See Albemarle Corporation; *U.S. Public*, pg. 73
ALEX C. FERGUSSON, INC.; *U.S. Private*, pg. 162
A.L. WILSON CHEMICAL CO.; *U.S. Private*, pg. 27
AMREP, INC.—See New Mountain Capital, LLC; *U.S. Private*, pg. 2904
APOLLO INDUSTRIES INC.; *U.S. Private*, pg. 294
AVMOR LTEE; *Int'l*, pg. 748
BHH MIKROMED SP. Z O.O.—See Acciaierie Valbruna S.p.A.; *Int'l*, pg. 89
BIO-CLEAN INTERNATIONAL, INC.; *U.S. Public*, pg. 332
BIOLAB, INC.—See Centerbridge Partners, L.P.; *U.S. Private*, pg. 815
BIZOTIC COMMERCIAL LIMITED; *Int'l*, pg. 1053
BLSA INDUSTRIES (PTY) LTD.—See Centerbridge Partners, L.P.; *U.S. Private*, pg. 815
BLUE CROSS LABORATORIES; *U.S. Private*, pg. 588
BRASSCRAFT CANADA LTD.—See Masco Corporation; *U.S. Public*, pg. 1390
BRONDOW, INC.; *U.S. Private*, pg. 662
BROPLAST S.A.R.L—See Aurea, S.A.; *Int'l*, pg. 707
THE BRULIN CORPORATION; *U.S. Private*, pg. 4001
BUCKEYE INTERNATIONAL INC.; *U.S. Private*, pg. 677
CADIE PRODUCTS CORP.; *U.S. Private*, pg. 713
CAL-TEX PROTECTIVE COATINGS INC.—See Cornell Capital LLC; *U.S. Private*, pg. 1051
CALVATIS ASIA PACIFIC CO., LTD—See Calvatis GmbH; *Int'l*, pg. 1266
CAMCO CHEMICAL COMPANY INC.; *U.S. Private*, pg. 727
CAR-FRESHENER CORPORATION; *U.S. Private*, pg. 748
CAR-FRESHNER CORPORATION; *U.S. Private*, pg. 748
CARROLL COMPANY - CLEANWORKS DIVISION—See Montgomery Manufacturing Co.; *U.S. Private*, pg. 2777
CARROLL COMPANY—See Montgomery Manufacturing Co.; *U.S. Private*, pg. 2777
CELLO PROFESSIONAL PRODUCTS—See Montgomery Manufacturing Co.; *U.S. Private*, pg. 2777
CHEM-DRY FRANCHISING LIMITED; *Int'l*, pg. 1460
CHEMICAL PACKAGING CORPORATION; *U.S. Private*, pg. 871
CHEMICAL SPECIALTIES MANUFACTURING CORP.—See RPM International Inc.; *U.S. Public*, pg. 1819
CHEMPACE CORPORATION; *U.S. Private*, pg. 872
CHEMSEARCH—See NCH Corporation; *U.S. Private*, pg. 2875
CHEMSTAR CORP.—See Ecolab Inc.; *U.S. Public*, pg. 712
CHURCH & DWIGHT CO., INC.; *U.S. Public*, pg. 493
CHURCH & DWIGHT DOMESTIC CONSUMER PRODUCTS—See Church & Dwight Co., Inc.; *U.S. Public*, pg. 493
CHURCH & DWIGHT INTERNATIONAL CONSUMER PRODUCTS—See Church & Dwight Co., Inc.; *U.S. Public*, pg. 493
THE CLAIRE MANUFACTURING COMPANY—See The Pritzker Group - Chicago, LLC; *U.S. Private*, pg. 4099
CLEAN CONTROL CORPORATION; *U.S. Private*, pg. 931
CLEANUP LOGISTICS CO., LTD.—See Cleanup Corporation; *Int'l*, pg. 1656

CLOROX AFRICA HOLDINGS (PROPRIETARY) LTD.—See The Clorox Company; *U.S. Public*, pg. 2063
CLOROX ARGENTINA S.A.—See The Clorox Company; *U.S. Public*, pg. 2062
CLOROX AUSTRALIA PTY. LTD.—See The Clorox Company; *U.S. Public*, pg. 2063
THE CLOROX COMPANY; *U.S. Public*, pg. 2062
CLOROX DE MEXICO S.A. DE C.V.—See The Clorox Company; *U.S. Public*, pg. 2063
CLOROX DOMINICANA S.R.L.—See The Clorox Company; *U.S. Public*, pg. 2062
CLOROX MANUFACTURING COMPANY OF PUERTO RICO, INC.—See The Clorox Company; *U.S. Public*, pg. 2063
CLOROX MANUFACTURING COMPANY OF PUERTO RICO, INC.—See The Clorox Company; *U.S. Public*, pg. 2063
CLOROX MANUFACTURING COMPANY OF PUERTO RICO, INC.—See The Clorox Company; *U.S. Public*, pg. 2063
CLOROX MEXICANA S. DE R.L. DE C.V.—See The Clorox Company; *U.S. Public*, pg. 2063
CLOROX NEW ZEALAND LIMITED—See The Clorox Company; *U.S. Public*, pg. 2063
CLOROX PRODUCTS MANUFACTURING COMPANY—See The Clorox Company; *U.S. Public*, pg. 2062
CLOROX PROFESSIONAL PRODUCTS COMPANY—See The Clorox Company; *U.S. Public*, pg. 2062
CLOROX SERVICES COMPANY—See The Clorox Company; *U.S. Public*, pg. 2062
COLGATE-PALMOLIVE (MARKETING) SDN BHD—See Colgate-Palmolive Company; *U.S. Public*, pg. 531
CONNOISSEURS PRODUCTS CORPORATION; *U.S. Private*, pg. 1018
CORAL CHEMICAL COMPANY; *U.S. Private*, pg. 1046
CREALIS S.A.S.—See A.S. Creation Tapeten AG; *Int'l*, pg. 28
CRITZAS INDUSTRIES, INC.; *U.S. Private*, pg. 1102
CUSTOM CHEMICAL FORMULATORS, INC.; *U.S. Private*, pg. 1128
DAIDO ECOMET CO., LTD.—See Daido Steel Co., Ltd.; *Int'l*, pg. 1922
DELTA FOREMOST CHEMICAL CORP.; *U.S. Private*, pg. 1200
DIVERSEY BELGIUM BVBA—See Platinum Equity, LLC; *U.S. Private*, pg. 3204
DIVERSEY B.V.—See Platinum Equity, LLC; *U.S. Private*, pg. 3204
DIVERSEY CANADA, INC.—See Platinum Equity, LLC; *U.S. Private*, pg. 3204
DIVERSEY CARE—See Platinum Equity, LLC; *U.S. Private*, pg. 3204
DIVERSEY CESKA REPUBLIKA S.R.O.—See Platinum Equity, LLC; *U.S. Private*, pg. 3204
DIVERSEY DEUTSCHLAND GMBH & CO. OHG—See Platinum Equity, LLC; *U.S. Private*, pg. 3204
DIVERSEY ESPANA, S.L.—See Platinum Equity, LLC; *U.S. Private*, pg. 3204
DIVERSEY (FRANCE) S.A.S.—See Platinum Equity, LLC; *U.S. Private*, pg. 3204
DIVERSEY HONG KONG LIMITED—See Platinum Equity, LLC; *U.S. Private*, pg. 3204
DIVERSEY, INC.—See Platinum Equity, LLC; *U.S. Private*, pg. 3204
DIVERSEY LIMITED—See Platinum Equity, LLC; *U.S. Private*, pg. 3204
DIVERSEY POLSKA SP. Z O.O.—See Platinum Equity, LLC; *U.S. Private*, pg. 3204
DIVERSEY S.R.L.—See Platinum Equity, LLC; *U.S. Private*, pg. 3204
EARTH FRIENDLY PRODUCTS—See Venus Laboratories Inc.; *U.S. Private*, pg. 4358
EBIOX LIMITED; *Int'l*, pg. 2285
ECOLAB USA INC. - TUCSON—See Ecolab Inc.; *U.S. Public*, pg. 714
ECOLAB VIETNAM COMPANY LIMITED—See Ecolab Inc.; *U.S. Public*, pg. 714
ELCO LABORATORIES INC.; *U.S. Private*, pg. 1350
ELECTROLUX HOME CARE PRODUCTS, INC.—See Bissell Homecare, Inc.; *U.S. Private*, pg. 566
ELSAN LTD.; *Int'l*, pg. 2370
ERGOPACK LLC—See Gr. Sarantis S.A.; *Int'l*, pg. 3047
FAULTLESS STARCH/BON AMI COMPANY; *U.S. Private*, pg. 1483
FERRENGI HOUSEHOLD PRODUCTS (PTY) LTD.—See Excellerate Holdings Ltd.; *Int'l*, pg. 2578
FLOW CONTROL HOLDINGS, LLC—See Audax Group, Limited Partnership; *U.S. Private*, pg. 388
FRANK B. ROSS CO. INC.; *U.S. Private*, pg. 1593
FRESH AS A DAISY, INC.; *U.S. Private*, pg. 1609
THE FULLER BRUSH COMPANY, INC.—See Victory Park Capital Advisors, LLC; *U.S. Private*, pg. 4379
FULLER COMPANY—See FLSmidth & Co. A/S; *Int'l*, pg. 2710
GALLOO HALLUIN—See Galloo n.v.; *Int'l*, pg. 2875
GENLABS; *U.S. Private*, pg. 1672

THE GLAD PRODUCTS COMPANY—See The Clorox Company; *U.S. Public*, pg. 2063
GO JO INDUSTRIES, INC.; *U.S. Private*, pg. 1723
GOODMAID CHEMICAL CORPORATION SDN BHD—See CIMB Group Holdings Berhad; *Int'l*, pg. 1608
GOODMAID MARKETING SDN BHD—See CIMB Group Holdings Berhad; *Int'l*, pg. 1608
GOODWIN AMMONIA COMPANY; *U.S. Private*, pg. 1741
GREENCAT SP. Z O.O.—See The Timken Company; *U.S. Public*, pg. 2132
GREEN EARTH TECHNOLOGIES, INC.; *U.S. Private*, pg. 1772
GUARDIAN TECHNOLOGIES LLC—See Lasko Products, LLC; *U.S. Private*, pg. 2395
GUARDSMAN AUSTRALIA PTY LIMITED—See The Sherwin-Williams Company; *U.S. Public*, pg. 2127
HORTON HYGIENE CO.—See Elsan Ltd.; *Int'l*, pg. 2370
HSIN FENG BUFF FACTORY CO., LTD.—See Jason Industries, Inc.; *U.S. Private*, pg. 2190
HV MANUFACTURING COMPANY—See The Clorox Company; *U.S. Public*, pg. 2062
IFC DISPOSABLES INC.—See Cascades Inc.; *Int'l*, pg. 1351
INOUE KOSAN CO., LTD.—See Cleanup Corporation; *Int'l*, pg. 1656
INTERCON CHEMICAL COMPANY—See C&I Holdings Inc.; *U.S. Private*, pg. 703
ITW AUTO WAX COMPANY, INC.—See Illinois Tool Works Inc.; *U.S. Public*, pg. 1104
ITW PERMATEX CANADA—See Illinois Tool Works Inc.; *U.S. Public*, pg. 1107
ITW TEXWIPE—See Illinois Tool Works Inc.; *U.S. Public*, pg. 1108
J.A. WRIGHT & CO.—See TA Associates, Inc.; *U.S. Private*, pg. 3919
J.A. WRIGHT & CO.—See The Carlyle Group Inc.; *U.S. Public*, pg. 2057
KAY CHEMICAL COMPANY—See Ecolab Inc.; *U.S. Public*, pg. 714
KIK CUSTOM PRODUCTS INC.—See Centerbridge Partners, L.P.; *U.S. Private*, pg. 815
KIK (GEORGIA) LLC—See Centerbridge Partners, L.P.; *U.S. Private*, pg. 815
KINGSFORD MANUFACTURING COMPANY—See The Clorox Company; *U.S. Public*, pg. 2063
KINPAK, INC.—See OneWater Marine Inc.; *U.S. Public*, pg. 1604
KRUD KUTTER, INC.—See RPM International Inc.; *U.S. Public*, pg. 1817
KYZEN CORPORATION; *U.S. Private*, pg. 2361
LABORATOIRES ANIOS S.A.—See Ecolab Inc.; *U.S. Public*, pg. 714
LAUTUS TRADING BVBA—See Elsan Ltd.; *Int'l*, pg. 2370
LEGEND BRANDS, INC.—See RPM International Inc.; *U.S. Public*, pg. 1817
LHB INDUSTRIES, INC.; *U.S. Private*, pg. 2442
L&R MANUFACTURING COMPANY; *U.S. Private*, pg. 2363
MACDERMID, INC. - CONNECTICUT—See Element Solutions Inc.; *U.S. Public*, pg. 727
MALCO PRODUCTS, INC.; *U.S. Private*, pg. 2556
MATCHLESS METAL POLISH COMPANY—See Jason Industries, Inc.; *U.S. Private*, pg. 2189
MICROCARE, LLC; *U.S. Private*, pg. 2703
MILLER-STEPHENSON CHEMICAL COMPANY, INC.; *U.S. Private*, pg. 2736
MIRACLE SEALANTS COMPANY, LLC—See RPM International Inc.; *U.S. Public*, pg. 1817
MOC PRODUCTS COMPANY, INC.; *U.S. Private*, pg. 2758
MOMAR, INC.; *U.S. Private*, pg. 2767
NATIONAL CLEANING PRODUCTS LTD.—See The Clorox Company; *U.S. Public*, pg. 2063
NATURAL CHEMISTRY, INC.; *U.S. Private*, pg. 2867
NCH CORPORATION PUERTO RICO—See NCH Corporation; *U.S. Private*, pg. 2875
NCH CORPORATION; *U.S. Private*, pg. 2875
NEW PIG CORPORATION—See New Pendulum Corporation; *U.S. Private*, pg. 2905
NEXT FILM SP. Z O.O.—See Agora S.A.; *Int'l*, pg. 212
NILODOR, INC.; *U.S. Private*, pg. 2927
OCEAN BIO-CHEM, LLC—See OneWater Marine Inc.; *U.S. Public*, pg. 1604
ODYSSEY MANUFACTURING CO.; *U.S. Private*, pg. 2996
OIL-DRI SARL—See Oil-Dri Corporation of America; *U.S. Public*, pg. 1566
PACIFIC SANDS, INC.; *U.S. Private*, pg. 3070
PARADISE ROAD LLC—See Surf City Garage, LLC; *U.S. Private*, pg. 3883
PAULSBORO PACKAGING CO.—See The Clorox Company; *U.S. Public*, pg. 2062
PCI, INC.—See Lewis & Clark Capital LLC; *U.S. Private*, pg. 2437
PENETONE CORPORATION—See Wechco, Inc.; *U.S. Private*, pg. 4468
PIONEER ECLIPSE CORPORATION—See Amano Corporation; *Int'l*, pg. 411
PREMIERE PACKAGING, INC.; *U.S. Private*, pg. 3251
PRESERVE, INC.—See Neogen Corporation; *U.S. Public*, pg. 1505

325612 — POLISH AND OTHER SA...

PROCTER & GAMBLE HELLAS SINGLE MEMBER LTD.—See The Procter & Gamble Company; *U.S. Public,* pg. 2122
PURA NATURALS, INC.; *U.S. Private,* pg. 3304
QUENETS PROPRIETARY LIMITED—See Dis-Chem Pharmacies Ltd.; *Int'l,* pg. 2131
ROCHESTER MIDLAND CORPORATION; *U.S. Private,* pg. 3463
THE ROOTO CORPORATION; *U.S. Private,* pg. 4112
ROYAL CHEMICAL COMPANY—See Paro Services Corp.; *U.S. Private,* pg. 3099
RPS PRODUCTS, INC.; *U.S. Private,* pg. 3496
SAUDI JOHNSON CO. LTD.—See S.C. Johnson & Son, Inc.; *U.S. Private,* pg. 3517
SC JOHNSON AND SON CHILE LTDA.—See S.C. Johnson & Son, Inc.; *U.S. Private,* pg. 3517
S. C. JOHNSON DE PUERTO RICO, INC.—See S.C. Johnson & Son, Inc.; *U.S. Private,* pg. 3516
S. C. JOHNSON EUROPE SARL—See S.C. Johnson & Son, Inc.; *U.S. Private,* pg. 3516
S.C. JOHNSON GMBH—See S.C. Johnson & Son, Inc.; *U.S. Private,* pg. 3517
S. C. JOHNSON ISRAEL LTD.—See S.C. Johnson & Son, Inc.; *U.S. Private,* pg. 3516
S.C. JOHNSON ITALY SRL PREDSTAVNISTVO—See S.C. Johnson & Son, Inc.; *U.S. Private,* pg. 3517
S.C. JOHNSON ITALY S.R.L.—See S.C. Johnson & Son, Inc.; *U.S. Private,* pg. 3517
S.C. JOHNSON KFT.—See S.C. Johnson & Son, Inc.; *U.S. Private,* pg. 3517
S.C. JOHNSON & SON, INC.; *U.S. Private,* pg. 3515
S.C. JOHNSON & SON, INC.—See S.C. Johnson & Son, Inc.; *U.S. Private,* pg. 3517
S.C. JOHNSON & SON, INC. - WASHINGTON, DC—See S.C. Johnson & Son, Inc.; *U.S. Private,* pg. 3517
SC JOHNSON WAX SRL—See S.C. Johnson & Son, Inc.; *U.S. Private,* pg. 3517
SCOT LABORATORIES—See Berkshire Hathaway Inc.; *U.S. Public,* pg. 300
SCRUB DADDY, INC.; *U.S. Private,* pg. 3580
SEATEX, LLC—See Cotton Creek Capital Management LLC; *U.S. Private,* pg. 1063
SHANGHAI JOHNSON LTD.—See S.C. Johnson & Son, Inc.; *U.S. Private,* pg. 3517
SIMONIZ USA, INC.; *U.S. Private,* pg. 3666
SISTEMAS Y VEHICULOS DE ALTA TECNOLOGIA, S.A.—See Fomento de Construcciones y Contratas, S.A.; *Int'l,* pg. 2723
SPARTAN CHEMICAL CO. INC.; *U.S. Private,* pg. 3746
SPLASH PRODUCTS INC.; *U.S. Private,* pg. 3759
SPRAY NINE CORPORATION—See Illinois Tool Works Inc.; *U.S. Public,* pg. 1107
SPRAYWAY, INC.—See The Pritzker Group - Chicago, LLC; *U.S. Private,* pg. 4099
STAR BRITE CORP.—See OneWater Marine Inc.; *U.S. Public,* pg. 1604
STAR BRITE DISTRIBUTING, INC.—See OneWater Marine Inc.; *U.S. Public,* pg. 1604
SURF CITY GARAGE, LLC; *U.S. Private,* pg. 3883
SYSCO GUEST SUPPLY CANADA INC.—See Sysco Corporation; *U.S. Public,* pg. 1976
SYSCO GUEST SUPPLY EUROPE LIMITED—See Sysco Corporation; *U.S. Public,* pg. 1976
TECH ENTERPRISES, INC.; *U.S. Private,* pg. 3951
THEOCHEM LABORATORIES, INC.; *U.S. Private,* pg. 4141
TRANSTAR AUTOBODY TECHNOLOGIES, INC.—See Blue Point Capital Partners, LLC; *U.S. Private,* pg. 591
TRU VUE, INC.—See Apogee Enterprises, Inc.; *U.S. Public,* pg. 145
TURTLE WAX, INC.; *U.S. Private,* pg. 4262
UNITED LABORATORIES, INC.; *U.S. Private,* pg. 4293
U.N.X. INCORPORATED; *U.S. Private,* pg. 4269
US NONWOVENS CORP.—See Wind Point Advisors LLC; *U.S. Private,* pg. 4536
VENUS LABORATORIES INC.; *U.S. Private,* pg. 4358
VERIDIEN CORP.; *U.S. Private,* pg. 4360
VILEDA GMBH—See Freudenberg SE; *Int'l,* pg. 2791
VIRACON, INC.—See Apogee Enterprises, Inc.; *U.S. Public,* pg. 145
VIRAL SHIELD LIFE SCIENCE SDN. BHD.—See Ideal Capital Berhad; *Int'l,* pg. 3589
WALTER G. LEGGE COMPANY, INC.; *U.S. Private,* pg. 4433
WEST PENETONE, INC.—See Wechco, Inc.; *U.S. Private,* pg. 4468
WHINK PRODUCTS COMPANY—See RPM International Inc.; *U.S. Public,* pg. 1817
WHIZ AUTOMOTIVE CHEMICALS DIV—See Malco Products, Inc.; *U.S. Private,* pg. 2556
WINBRO GROUP LTD.; *U.S. Private,* pg. 4533
W.J. HAGERTY & SONS, LTD., INC.; *U.S. Private,* pg. 4421
W.M. BARR & COMPANY, INC.; *U.S. Private,* pg. 4421
WU HOLDCO, INC.—See TA Associates, Inc.; *U.S. Private,* pg. 3919
WU HOLDCO, INC.—See The Carlyle Group Inc.; *U.S. Public,* pg. 2057
ZEP INDUSTRIES B.V.—See New Mountain Capital, LLC; *U.S. Private,* pg. 2904

ZEP UK LIMITED—See New Mountain Capital, LLC; *U.S. Private,* pg. 2904
ZHEJIANG KAWAMOTO HEALTH CARE PRODUCTS CO., LTD.—See Air Water Inc.; *Int'l,* pg. 241
ZHEJIANG LUDAO TECHNOLOGY CO., LTD.—See China Ludao Technology Company Limited; *Int'l,* pg. 1515

325613 — SURFACE ACTIVE AGENT MANUFACTURING

AARTI SURFACTANTS LIMITED; *Int'l,* pg. 38
AKZO NOBEL SURFACE CHEMISTRY LLC—See GIC Pte. Ltd.; *Int'l,* pg. 2968
AKZO NOBEL SURFACE CHEMISTRY LLC—See The Carlyle Group Inc.; *U.S. Public,* pg. 2050
ATLAS REFINERY, INC.; *U.S. Private,* pg. 379
BEIJING BERNDORF TECHNOLOGY DEVELOPMENT CO., LTD.—See Berndorf AG; *Int'l,* pg. 986
BERNDORF BAND ENGINEERING GMBH—See Berndorf AG; *Int'l,* pg. 987
BERNDORF BAND GMBH—See Berndorf AG; *Int'l,* pg. 986
CARGILL TEXTURIZING SOLUTIONS DEUTSCHLAND GMBH & CO. KG—See Cargill, Inc.; *U.S. Private,* pg. 759
CUSTOM SYNTHESIS, LLC—See Piedmont Chemical Industries, Inc.; *U.S. Private,* pg. 3177
DOOLEY CHEMICALS LLC—See Piedmont Chemical Industries, Inc.; *U.S. Private,* pg. 3177
ETHOX CHEMICALS LLC—See Piedmont Chemical Industries, Inc.; *U.S. Private,* pg. 3177
GREEN CHEMICAL CO., LTD.; *Int'l,* pg. 3069
HI-MAR SPECIALTY CHEMICALS, LLC—See Elementis plc; *Int'l,* pg. 2359
HOWARD INDUSTRIES INC.; *U.S. Private,* pg. 1994
HUECK RHEINISCHE GMBH—See Berndorf AG; *Int'l,* pg. 987
HUNTSMAN POLYURETHANES—See Huntsman Corporation; *U.S. Public,* pg. 1074
HUSEIN INDUSTRIES LIMITED; *Int'l,* pg. 3538
KLK KOLB SPECIALTIES BV—See Batu Kawan Berhad; *Int'l,* pg. 891
KLK TENSACHEM SA—See Batu Kawan Berhad; *Int'l,* pg. 891
LSG CO., LTD.—See EPS Holdings, Inc.; *Int'l,* pg. 2466
LUBRIZOL ADVANCED MATERIALS, INC. - PASO ROBLES—See Berkshire Hathaway Inc.; *U.S. Public,* pg. 319
LUCOAT POWDER COATINGS TLD—See Akzo Nobel N.V.; *Int'l,* pg. 272
MAGNAFLUX LIMITED—See Illinois Tool Works Inc.; *U.S. Public,* pg. 1109
PILOT CHEMICAL COMPANY; *U.S. Private,* pg. 3181
PILOT CHEMICAL CO. OF CALIFORNIA, INC.—See Pilot Chemical Company; *U.S. Private,* pg. 3181
RESOPAL GMBH—See Clayton, Dubilier & Rice, LLC; *U.S. Private,* pg. 930
SCHULKE & MAYR (ASIA) SDN.BHD.—See EQT AB; *Int'l,* pg. 2479

325620 — TOILET PREPARATION MANUFACTURING

220 LABORATORIES INC.—See The Pritzker Group - Chicago, LLC; *U.S. Private,* pg. 4099
AARHUSKARLSHAMN GHANA LTD.—See AAK AB; *Int'l,* pg. 32
ABLE C&C CO., LTD.; *Int'l,* pg. 62
ACCRAPLY CANADA, INC.—See Barry-Wehmiller Companies, Inc.; *U.S. Private,* pg. 481
ADERANS INC—See Aderans Co., Ltd.; *Int'l,* pg. 143
ADJUVANT HOLDINGS CO., LTD.; *Int'l,* pg. 150
ADOR MULTIPRODUCTS LTD.—See Ador Welding Ltd; *Int'l,* pg. 152
AEKYUNG INDUSTRIAL CO., LTD.—See AK Holdings, Inc.; *Int'l,* pg. 259
AFFINITY BEAUTY BRANDS; *U.S. Private,* pg. 122
AGEL ENTERPRISES ARGENTINA SRL—See JRjr33, Inc.; *U.S. Private,* pg. 2240
AGEL ENTERPRISES, INC.—See JRjr33, Inc.; *U.S. Private,* pg. 2240
AGEL ENTERPRISES (MALAYSIA) SDN. BHD.—See JRjr33, Inc.; *U.S. Private,* pg. 2240
AGEL ENTERPRISES PTE. LTD.—See JRjr33, Inc.; *U.S. Private,* pg. 2240
AGEL ENTERPRISES RS LLC—See JRjr33, Inc.; *U.S. Private,* pg. 2240
AGILEX FLAVORS & FRAGRANCES, INC.—See Firmenich International SA; *Int'l,* pg. 2680
AKD SA; *Int'l,* pg. 261
ALASTIN SKINCARE, INC—See Abu Dhabi Investment Authority; *Int'l,* pg. 71
ALASTIN SKINCARE, INC—See EQT Corporation; *U.S. Public,* pg. 785
ALBAAD MASSUOT YITZHAK LTD.; *Int'l,* pg. 293
AMERICAN CREW, INC.—See MacAndrews & Forbes Incorporated; *U.S. Private,* pg. 2534

CORPORATE AFFILIATIONS

AMERICAN DISTILLING & MANUFACTURING CO.; *U.S. Private,* pg. 230
AMOREPACIFIC CANADA INC.—See Amorepacific Corp.; *Int'l,* pg. 430
AMOREPACIFIC CORP.; *Int'l,* pg. 429
AMOREPACIFIC EUROPE S.A.S—See Amorepacific Corp.; *Int'l,* pg. 430
AMOREPACIFIC HONG KONG CO., LIMITED—See Amorepacific Corp.; *Int'l,* pg. 430
AMOREPACIFIC (SHANGHAI) R&I CENTER CO., LTD.—See Amorepacific Corp.; *Int'l,* pg. 430
AMOREPACIFIC TAIWAN CO., LTD.—See Amorepacific Corp.; *Int'l,* pg. 430
AMOREPACIFIC VIETNAM LTD.—See Amorepacific Corp.; *Int'l,* pg. 430
AMPRO INDUSTRIES INC.; *U.S. Private,* pg. 266
ANTI-AGING HOUSE HOLDING LIMITED; *Int'l,* pg. 483
APROS CO., LTD.—See Astena Holdings Co., Ltd.; *Int'l,* pg. 653
AQUA BIO TECHNOLOGY ASA; *Int'l,* pg. 527
ARABIAN OUD COMPANY; *Int'l,* pg. 533
ARBONNE INTERNATIONAL, LLC—See Groupe Rocher Operations SAS; *Int'l,* pg. 3110
AROMATECH HOLDING COMPANY—See Jordan Industries, Inc.; *U.S. Private,* pg. 2235
AROMATHERAPY ASSOCIATES LTD.—See B&B Investment Partners LLP; *Int'l,* pg. 783
ARRESTAGE INTERNATIONAL, INC.; *U.S. Private,* pg. 334
ARTSANA S.P.A.—See BI-Invest Advisors S.A.; *Int'l,* pg. 1016
ASA JOINT STOCK COMPANY; *Int'l,* pg. 592
ATLANTIC COAST MEDIA GROUP; *U.S. Private,* pg. 372
AT LAST NATURALS, INC.; *U.S. Private,* pg. 363
AUBREY ORGANICS INC.; *U.S. Private,* pg. 385
AUSUPREME INTERNATIONAL HOLDINGS LIMITED; *Int'l,* pg. 724
AVALON NATURAL PRODUCTS, INC.—See The Hain Celestial Group, Inc.; *U.S. Public,* pg. 2086
AVEDA CORPORATION—See The Estee Lauder Companies, Inc.; *U.S. Public,* pg. 2073
AVEDA SERVICES INC.—See The Estee Lauder Companies Inc.; *U.S. Public,* pg. 2073
BABOR COSMETICS AMERICA CORP.—See Dr. BABOR GmbH & Co. KG; *Int'l,* pg. 2190
BAJAJ CONSUMER CARE LIMITED—See Bajaj Hindustan Sugar Limited; *Int'l,* pg. 804
BARI COSMETICS LTD; *U.S. Private,* pg. 474
BASF PERSONAL CARE AND NUTRITION GMBH—See BASF SE; *Int'l,* pg. 880
BATHCLIN CORPORATION—See Earth Corporation; *Int'l,* pg. 2268
BAWANG INTERNATIONAL (GROUP) HOLDING LIMITED; *Int'l,* pg. 900
BAYER CROPSCIENCE S.A.S.—See Bayer Aktiengesellschaft; *Int'l,* pg. 903
B&B KOREA CORPORATION—See Hitejinro Holdings Co., Ltd.; *Int'l,* pg. 3426
BEAUTY BIOSCIENCES LLC—See Nu Skin Enterprises, Inc.; *U.S. Public,* pg. 1551
BEAUTYGE BEAUTY GROUP, S.L.—See MacAndrews & Forbes Incorporated; *U.S. Private,* pg. 2533
BEAUTYGE FRANCE SAS—See MacAndrews & Forbes Incorporated; *U.S. Private,* pg. 2533
BEAUTYGE GERMANY GMBH—See MacAndrews & Forbes Incorporated; *U.S. Private,* pg. 2533
BEAUTYGE LOGISTICS SERVICES, S.L.—See MacAndrews & Forbes Incorporated; *U.S. Private,* pg. 2533
BEAUTYGE PORTUGAL - PRODUTOS COSMETICOS E PROFISSIONAIS LDA.—See MacAndrews & Forbes Incorporated; *U.S. Private,* pg. 2533
BEAUTYGE PROFESSIONAL LIMITED—See MacAndrews & Forbes Incorporated; *U.S. Private,* pg. 2533
BEAUTY SKIN CO., LTD.; *Int'l,* pg. 935
BEIJING DABAO COSMETICS CO., LTD.—See Johnson & Johnson; *U.S. Public,* pg. 1194
BELCAM INC.; *U.S. Private,* pg. 516
BELHASA BIOTEK SOLUTIONS LLC—See Belhasa Group of Companies; *Int'l,* pg. 964
BELMAY, INC.; *U.S. Private,* pg. 520
BERNER OY - HEINAVESI PLANT—See Berner Oy; *Int'l,* pg. 988
BEST WORLD VIETNAM COMPANY LIMITED—See Best World International Ltd.; *Int'l,* pg. 1000
BETTER FOR YOU WELLNESS, INC.; *U.S. Public,* pg. 326
BIOELEMENTS, INC.; *U.S. Private,* pg. 561
BLISTEX, INC.; *U.S. Private,* pg. 582
BOCCHI LABORATORIES, INC.—See Aterian Investment Management, L.P.; *U.S. Private,* pg. 366
BOD SCIENCE LIMITED; *Int'l,* pg. 1097
THE BODY SHOP GERMANY GMBH—See Aurelius Equity Opportunities SE & Co. KGaA; *Int'l,* pg. 710
THE BODY SHOP INTERNATIONAL LIMITED—See Aurelius Equity Opportunities SE & Co. KGaA; *Int'l,* pg. 709
THE BODY SHOP INTERNATIONAL (PTE) LTD.—See Aurelius Equity Opportunities SE & Co. KGaA; *Int'l,* pg. 710
BOERLIND GESELLSCHAFT FUER ERZEUGNISSE MBH; *Int'l,* pg. 1099
BOGDANA CORPORATION; *U.S. Private,* pg. 609

N.A.I.C.S. INDEX

325620 — TOILET PREPARATION ...

BOIRON ASIA LIMITED—See Boiron Group; *Int'l*, pg. 1101
BOIRON (HANGZHOU) TRADING CO., LTD.—See Boiron Group; *Int'l*, pg. 1101
BOOMERANG LABORATORIES, INC.—See Centre Partners Management LLC; *U.S. Private*, pg. 828
BORUTA-ZACHEM SA; *Int'l*, pg. 1115
BRAND ARCHITEKTS GROUP PLC; *Int'l*, pg. 1139
BRANDS, LLC; *U.S. Private*, pg. 638
BRISTOL-MYERS SQUIBB (HONG KONG) LIMITED—See Bristol-Myers Squibb Company; *U.S. Public*, pg. 384
BRONNER BROTHERS INC.; *U.S. Private*, pg. 662
BWL HEALTH & SCIENCES, INC.—See Best World International Ltd.; *Int'l*, pg. 1000
BWL KOREA CO., LTD.—See Best World International Ltd.; *Int'l*, pg. 1000
CALIFORNIA PACIFIC RESEARCH, INC.; *U.S. Private*, pg. 720
CANNABIS SATIVA, INC.; *U.S. Public*, pg. 428
CARIBBEAN PACIFIC MARKETING, INC.; *U.S. Private*, pg. 761
C.B. FLEET COMPANY, INC.—See Prestige Consumer Healthcare Inc.; *U.S. Public*, pg. 1716
C'BON COSMETICS CO., LTD.; *Int'l*, pg. 1239
C'BON COSMETICS CO., LTD. - TOCHIGI FACTORY—See C'BON Cosmetics Co., Ltd.; *Int'l*, pg. 1239
CCA INDUSTRIES, INC.; *U.S. Public*, pg. 460
C&C INTERNATIONAL CO., LTD.; *Int'l*, pg. 1238
CCL LABEL DE MEXICO S.A. DE C.V.—See CCL Industries Inc.; *Int'l*, pg. 1368
CEDAROME CANADA INC.; *Int'l*, pg. 1388
CHANEL, INC.—See Chanel S.A.; *Int'l*, pg. 1441
CHEMSTER GMBH—See BASF SE; *Int'l*, pg. 882
CHLITINA HOLDING LIMITED; *Int'l*, pg. 1576
CHURCH & DWIGHT CANADA CORP.—See Church & Dwight Co., Inc.; *U.S. Public*, pg. 493
CHURCH & DWIGHT DO BRASIL LTDA—See Church & Dwight Co., Inc.; *U.S. Public*, pg. 493
CHURCH & DWIGHT SERVICIOS DE R.L. DE C.V.—See Church & Dwight Co., Inc.; *U.S. Public*, pg. 493
CI:Z HOLDINGS CO. LTD.—See Johnson & Johnson; *U.S. Public*, pg. 1194
CLARINS S.A.; *Int'l*, pg. 1648
CLASSIC COSMETICS, INC.; *U.S. Private*, pg. 916
CLINIQUE LABORATORIES, INC.—See The Estee Lauder Companies Inc.; *U.S. Public*, pg. 2073
CLIO COSMETICS CO LTD; *Int'l*, pg. 1660
CLYNOL GMBH—See Henkel AG & Co. KGaA; *Int'l*, pg. 3348
CNP COSMETICS SINGAPORE PTE. LIMITED—See Cornerstone Financial Holdings Limited; *Int'l*, pg. 1801
CODIBEL SA/NV; *Int'l*, pg. 1688
COFINLUXE S.A.; *Int'l*, pg. 1692
COLGATE PALMOLIVE ARGENTINA S.A.—See Colgate-Palmolive Company; *U.S. Public*, pg. 531
COLGATE-PALMOLIVE A/S—See Colgate-Palmolive Company; *U.S. Public*, pg. 531
COLGATE-PALMOLIVE CANADA INC.—See Colgate-Palmolive Company; *U.S. Public*, pg. 531
COLGATE-PALMOLIVE (CENTRAL AMERICA) S.A.—See Colgate-Palmolive Company; *U.S. Public*, pg. 531
COLGATE-PALMOLIVE CESKA REPUBLIKA, S.R.O.—See Colgate-Palmolive Company; *U.S. Public*, pg. 531
COLGATE-PALMOLIVE FRANCE—See Colgate-Palmolive Company; *U.S. Public*, pg. 532
COLGATE-PALMOLIVE (HELLAS) S.A.I.C.—See Colgate-Palmolive Company; *U.S. Public*, pg. 531
COLGATE-PALMOLIVE IRELAND—See Colgate-Palmolive Company; *U.S. Public*, pg. 532
COLGATE-PALMOLIVE LTDA.—See Colgate-Palmolive Company; *U.S. Public*, pg. 532
COLGATE-PALMOLIVE LTD.—See Colgate-Palmolive Company; *U.S. Public*, pg. 532
COLGATE-PALMOLIVE (MALAYSIA) SDN. BHD.—See Colgate-Palmolive Company; *U.S. Public*, pg. 531
COLGATE-PALMOLIVE PERU S.A.—See Colgate-Palmolive Company; *U.S. Public*, pg. 532
COLGATE-PALMOLIVE (POLAND) SP. Z O.O.—See Colgate-Palmolive Company; *U.S. Public*, pg. 531
COLGATE-PALMOLIVE PORTUGUESE LTDA—See Colgate-Palmolive Company; *U.S. Public*, pg. 532
COLGATE-PALMOLIVE PTY. LTD.—See Colgate-Palmolive Company; *U.S. Public*, pg. 532
COLGATE-PALMOLIVE SERVICES S.A.—See Colgate-Palmolive Company; *U.S. Public*, pg. 532
COLGATE-PALMOLIVE SLOVENSKO, S.R.O.—See Colgate-Palmolive Company; *U.S. Public*, pg. 532
COLGATE-PALMOLIVE TEMIZLIK URUNLERI SANAYI VE TICARET ANONIM SIRKETI—See Colgate-Palmolive Company; *U.S. Public*, pg. 532
THE COLOMER GROUP—See MacAndrews & Forbes Incorporated; *U.S. Private*, pg. 2533
COLOMER USA, INC.—See MacAndrews & Forbes Incorporated; *U.S. Private*, pg. 2534
COLORADO PRODUCT CONCEPTS, INC.—See Scott's Liquid Gold-Inc.; *U.S. Public*, pg. 1849
COLORAY INTERNATIONAL INVESTMENT CO., LTD.; *Int'l*, pg. 1704
COLORESCIENCE, INC.; *U.S. Private*, pg. 975

COMBE INCORPORATED; *U.S. Private*, pg. 980
CONAIR LIQUIDS DIVISION—See American Securities LLC; *U.S. Private*, pg. 248
COOP SCHWEIZ - CWK-SCS DIVISION—See Coop-Gruppe Genossenschaft; *Int'l*, pg. 1790
COREANA COSMETICS CO., LTD.; *Int'l*, pg. 1798
COSMAX BTI INC.; *Int'l*, pg. 1811
COSMAX INC.; *Int'l*, pg. 1811
COSMAX (THAILAND) CO., LTD.—See Cosmax Inc.; *Int'l*, pg. 1811
COSMECCA FOSHAN, LTD.—See Cosmecca Korea Co.,Ltd.; *Int'l*, pg. 1811
COSMECCA KOREA CO.,LTD.; *Int'l*, pg. 1811
COSMED, INC.—See Elah Holdings, Inc.; *U.S. Public*, pg. 722
COSME SCIENCE CO., LTD.—See Hokkan Holdings Limited; *Int'l*, pg. 3443
COSMETIC SUPPLIERS PTY. LTD.—See The Procter & Gamble Company; *U.S. Public*, pg. 2120
COSON CO., LTD. - OSAN FACTORY—See Coson Co., Ltd.; *Int'l*, pg. 1814
COSON CO., LTD.; *Int'l*, pg. 1814
COSVISION CO., LTD.—See Amorepacific Corp.; *Int'l*, pg. 430
COTA CO., LTD.; *Int'l*, pg. 1815
COVER GIRL COSMETICS—See The Procter & Gamble Company; *U.S. Public*, pg. 2120
CREATIVE NAIL DESIGN, INC.—See MacAndrews & Forbes Incorporated; *U.S. Private*, pg. 2534
CREIGHTONS PLC; *Int'l*, pg. 1837
CRODA CHOCQUES SAS—See Croda International plc; *Int'l*, pg. 1851
CROWN LABORATORIES, INC.; *U.S. Private*, pg. 1111
C&T DREAM CO., LTD.; *Int'l*, pg. 1239
CTK COSMETICS; *Int'l*, pg. 1871
CURE CO., LTD.—See 4Cs Holdings Co., Ltd.; *Int'l*, pg. 11
DABUR EGYPT LTD.—See Dabur India Ltd; *Int'l*, pg. 1903
DABUR INDIA LTD - JAMMU UNIT I , II & III—See Dabur India Ltd; *Int'l*, pg. 1903
DABUR INDIA LTD; *Int'l*, pg. 1903
DABUR INTERNATIONAL LIMITED—See Dabur India Ltd; *Int'l*, pg. 1903
DABUR NEPAL PVT. LTD.—See Dabur India Ltd; *Int'l*, pg. 1903
DAEBONG LS CO., LTD. - INCHEON FACTORY—See Daebong LS Co., Ltd.; *Int'l*, pg. 1905
DAEBONG LS CO., LTD. - JEJU FACTORY—See Daebong LS Co., Ltd.; *Int'l*, pg. 1905
DAIICHI SANKYO HEALTHCARE CO., LTD.—See Daiichi Sankyo Co., Ltd.; *Int'l*, pg. 1930
DANA CLASSIC FRAGRANCES, INC.—See Dimeling, Schreiber & Park; *U.S. Private*, pg. 1232
DELAGAR DIVISION—See Belcam Inc.; *U.S. Private*, pg. 516
DERMADOCTOR, LLC; *U.S. Private*, pg. 1209
DERMAZONE SOLUTIONS, INC.; *U.S. Private*, pg. 1210
DIAMOND WIPES INTERNATIONAL, INC.; *U.S. Private*, pg. 1224
DINAIR AIRBRUSH MAKE-UP SYSTEM, INC.; *U.S. Private*, pg. 1233
DIVERSEY MAROC S.A.—See Sealed Air Corporation; *U.S. Public*, pg. 1853
DIVERSIFIED MANUFACTURING CORPORATION—See San Francisco Equity Partners; *U.S. Private*, pg. 3540
D-NEE COSMETICS CO., LTD.—See Arata Corporation; *Int'l*, pg. 536
DO DAY DREAM PCL; *Int'l*, pg. 2152
DONGGUAN BOTON FLAVORS & FRAGRANCES COMPANY LIMITED—See China Boton Group Company Limited; *Int'l*, pg. 1487
DR. BABOR GMBH & CO. KG; *Int'l*, pg. 2190
DRT-ANTHEA AROMA CHEMICALS PRIVATE LIMITED—See Firmenich International SA; *Int'l*, pg. 2679
DR. THEISS NATURWAREN GMBH; *Int'l*, pg. 2195
DR.WU SKINCARE CO., LTD.; *Int'l*, pg. 2196
DS HEALTHCARE GROUP, INC.; *U.S. Private*, pg. 1281
DSM-FIRMENICH AG; *Int'l*, pg. 2210
ECOFIRST PRODUCTS SDN BHD—See EcoFirst Consolidated Bhd; *Int'l*, pg. 2295
EDGEWELL PERSONAL CARE - ORMOND BEACH—See Edgewell Personal Care Company; *U.S. Public*, pg. 718
ELIZABETH ARDEN (DENMARK) APS—See MacAndrews & Forbes Incorporated; *U.S. Private*, pg. 2533
ELIZABETH ARDEN, INC.—See MacAndrews & Forbes Incorporated; *U.S. Private*, pg. 2533
ELIZABETH ARDEN INTERNATIONAL HOLDING, INC.—See MacAndrews & Forbes Incorporated; *U.S. Private*, pg. 2533
ELIZABETH ARDEN INTERNATIONAL S.A.R.L.—See MacAndrews & Forbes Incorporated; *U.S. Private*, pg. 2533
ELIZABETH ARDEN KOREA YUHAN HOESA—See MacAndrews & Forbes Incorporated; *U.S. Private*, pg. 2533
ELIZABETH ARDEN (SOUTH AFRICA) (PTY) LTD.—See MacAndrews & Forbes Incorporated; *U.S. Private*, pg. 2533
ELIZABETH ARDEN (UK) LTD.—See MacAndrews & Forbes Incorporated; *U.S. Private*, pg. 2533
EMINENCE ORGANIC SKIN CARE INC.; *Int'l*, pg. 2380

ENERGIZER PERSONAL CARE, LLC—See Edgewell Personal Care Company; *U.S. Public*, pg. 718
ENG KAH CORPORATION BERHAD; *Int'l*, pg. 2425
ENG KAH ENTERPRISE (KL) SDN. BHD.—See Eng Kah Corporation Berhad; *Int'l*, pg. 2425
ENG KAH ENTERPRISE SDN. BHD.—See Eng Kah Corporation Berhad; *Int'l*, pg. 2425
ENGLEWOOD LAB, LLC; *U.S. Public*, pg. 1400
ENGLEWOOD LAB; *Int'l*, pg. 2435
ENHANCE SKIN PRODUCTS INC.; *U.S. Public*, pg. 768
EPAULER CO., LTD.—See euglena Co., Ltd.; *Int'l*, pg. 2526
EQOLOGY ASA; *Int'l*, pg. 2466
ESSENTIAL WHOLESALE; *U.S. Private*, pg. 1427
ESTEE LAUDER CLINIQUE & ARAMIS—See The Estee Lauder Companies Inc.; *U.S. Public*, pg. 2073
THE ESTEE LAUDER COMPANIES INC.; *U.S. Public*, pg. 2073
ESTEE LAUDER COSMETICS LTD.—See The Estee Lauder Companies Inc.; *U.S. Public*, pg. 2073
ESTEE LAUDER—See The Estee Lauder Companies Inc.; *U.S. Public*, pg. 2073
ESTEE LAUDER S.R.L.—See The Estee Lauder Companies Inc.; *U.S. Public*, pg. 2073
E.T. BROWNE DRUG COMPANY, INC.; *U.S. Private*, pg. 1307
EUROPEENNE DE PRODUITS DE BEAUTE S.A.S.—See MacAndrews & Forbes Incorporated; *U.S. Private*, pg. 2533
EXPRESSIONS PARFUMEES S.A.S.—See Givaudan S.A.; *Int'l*, pg. 2980
FARCENT ENTERPRICE CO., LTD.; *Int'l*, pg. 2618
FIN-MARK S.R.L.—See Providence Equity Partners L.L.C.; *U.S. Private*, pg. 3292
FIN-MARK S.R.L.—See Searchlight Capital Partners, L.P.; *U.S. Private*, pg. 3587
FIRMENICH AROMATICS (CHINA) CO. LTD.—See Firmenich International SA; *Int'l*, pg. 2680
FIRMENICH AROMATICS (INDIA) PVT LTD.—See Firmenich International SA; *Int'l*, pg. 2680
FIRMENICH AROMATICS PRODUCTION (INDIA) PVT. LTD.—See Firmenich International SA; *Int'l*, pg. 2680
FIRMENICH AROMATICS (SHANGHAI) CO.—See Firmenich International SA; *Int'l*, pg. 2680
FIRMENICH AROMATICS (ZHANGJIAGANG) CO.,LTD.—See Firmenich International SA; *Int'l*, pg. 2680
FIRMENICH ASIA PTE. LTD.—See Firmenich International SA; *Int'l*, pg. 2680
FIRMENICH & CIA. LTDA.—See Firmenich International SA; *Int'l*, pg. 2680
FIRMENICH & CIE. S.A.S.—See Firmenich International SA; *Int'l*, pg. 2680
FIRMENICH DE MEXICO S.A. DE C.V.—See Firmenich International SA; *Int'l*, pg. 2680
FIRMENICH GES.M.B.H.—See Firmenich International SA; *Int'l*, pg. 2680
FIRMENICH INCORPORATED—See Firmenich International SA; *Int'l*, pg. 2680
FIRMENICH LIMITED—See Firmenich International SA; *Int'l*, pg. 2680
FIRMENICH (PHILIPPINES), INC.—See Firmenich International SA; *Int'l*, pg. 2680
FIRMENICH (PTY.) LTD.—See Firmenich International SA; *Int'l*, pg. 2680
FIRMENICH S.A.I.C. Y F.—See Firmenich International SA; *Int'l*, pg. 2680
FIRMENICH S.A.—See Firmenich International SA; *Int'l*, pg. 2680
FIRMENICH S.A.—See Firmenich International SA; *Int'l*, pg. 2680
FIRMENICH SP.Z O.O—See Firmenich International SA; *Int'l*, pg. 2680
FIRMENICH (THAILAND) LTD.—See Firmenich International SA; *Int'l*, pg. 2680
FIRMENICH UK LTD.—See Firmenich International SA; *Int'l*, pg. 2680
FIRMENICH UK LTD.—See Firmenich International SA; *Int'l*, pg. 2680
FOREVERGREEN SINGAPORE—See ForeverGreen Worldwide Corporation; *U.S. Public*, pg. 867
FORMULATED SOLUTIONS, LLC.; *U.S. Private*, pg. 1572
FRAGRANCE OILS LIMITED—See Givaudan S.A.; *Int'l*, pg. 2980
FRAMESI S.P.A.; *Int'l*, pg. 2759
FREDRIC'S CORPORATION; *U.S. Private*, pg. 1602
FUJIFILM HEALTHCARE LABORATORY CO., LTD.—See FUJIFILM Holdings Corporation; *Int'l*, pg. 2824
GAIA CORPORATION CO., LTD.; *Int'l*, pg. 2868
GARCOA INC.—See Vitamin Classics Inc.; *U.S. Private*, pg. 4405
GDMI INC.; *U.S. Private*, pg. 1654
GEBERIT ISRAEL LTD.—See Geberit AG; *Int'l*, pg. 2904
GEMINI COSMETICS, INC.; *U.S. Private*, pg. 1657
GENIC CO., LTD. - NONSAN 1ST PLANT—See Genic Co., Ltd.; *Int'l*, pg. 2923
GENIC CO., LTD. - NONSAN 2ND PLANT—See Genic Co., Ltd.; *Int'l*, pg. 2923
GENIC CO., LTD.; *Int'l*, pg. 2923

325620 — TOILET PREPARATION ...

GENOMMA LAB INTERNATIONAL SAB DE CV; *Int'l*, pg. 2925
GILCHRIST & SOAMES HOLDINGS CORPORATION—See Sysco Corporation; *U.S. Public*, pg. 1974
GILCHRIST & SOAMES, INC.—See Sysco Corporation; *U.S. Public*, pg. 1976
GILCHRIST & SOAMES UK LIMITED—See Sysco Corporation; *U.S. Public*, pg. 1974
THE GILLETTE COMPANY—See The Procter & Gamble Company; *U.S. Public*, pg. 2124
GILLETTE DEL URUGUAY, S.A.—See The Procter & Gamble Company; *U.S. Public*, pg. 2120
GILLETTE DOMINICANA, S.A.—See The Procter & Gamble Company; *U.S. Public*, pg. 2120
GILLETTE—See The Procter & Gamble Company; *U.S. Public*, pg. 2124
GIVAUDAN ARGENTINA SERVICIOS SA—See Givaudan S.A.; *Int'l*, pg. 2980
GIVAUDAN BUSINESS SOLUTIONS KFT—See Givaudan S.A.; *Int'l*, pg. 2980
GIVAUDAN COLOMBIA SAS—See Givaudan S.A.; *Int'l*, pg. 2980
GIVAUDAN DE MEXICO S.A. DE C.V.—See Givaudan S.A.; *Int'l*, pg. 2981
GIVAUDAN DE MEXICO SA DE CV—See Givaudan S.A.; *Int'l*, pg. 2981
GIVAUDAN DO BRASIL LTDA—See Givaudan S.A.; *Int'l*, pg. 2980
GIVAUDAN EGYPT FRAGRANCE LLC—See Givaudan S.A.; *Int'l*, pg. 2980
GIVAUDAN EGYPT SAE—See Givaudan S.A.; *Int'l*, pg. 2980
GIVAUDAN FLAVORS AND FRAGRANCES, INC.—See Givaudan S.A.; *Int'l*, pg. 2981
GIVAUDAN FLAVORS (NANTONG) LTD.—See Givaudan S.A.; *Int'l*, pg. 2980
GIVAUDAN FLAVOURS & FRAGRANCES MALAYSIA SDN. BHD.—See Givaudan S.A.; *Int'l*, pg. 2980
GIVAUDAN FRAGRANCES CORPORATION—See Givaudan S.A.; *Int'l*, pg. 2981
GIVAUDAN FRAGRANCES (GUANGZHOU) CO. LTD.—See Givaudan S.A.; *Int'l*, pg. 2980
GIVAUDAN FRAGRANCES (SHANGHAI) LTD.—See Givaudan S.A.; *Int'l*, pg. 2980
GIVAUDAN FRANCE FRAGRANCES SAS—See Givaudan S.A.; *Int'l*, pg. 2980
GIVAUDAN FRANCE NATURALS S.A.S.—See Givaudan S.A.; *Int'l*, pg. 2980
GIVAUDAN GUATEMALA S.A.—See Givaudan S.A.; *Int'l*, pg. 2980
GIVAUDAN HONG KONG LTD.—See Givaudan S.A.; *Int'l*, pg. 2980
GIVAUDAN (INDIA) PVT. LTD.—See Givaudan S.A.; *Int'l*, pg. 2980
GIVAUDAN INTERNATIONAL SA—See Givaudan S.A.; *Int'l*, pg. 2980
GIVAUDAN ITALIA S.P.A—See Givaudan S.A.; *Int'l*, pg. 2980
GIVAUDAN JAPAN K.K.—See Givaudan S.A.; *Int'l*, pg. 2980
GIVAUDAN KOREA LTD.—See Givaudan S.A.; *Int'l*, pg. 2980
GIVAUDAN MALAYSIA SDN. BHD—See Givaudan S.A.; *Int'l*, pg. 2981
GIVAUDAN MIDDLE EAST & AFRICA FZE—See Givaudan S.A.; *Int'l*, pg. 2981
GIVAUDAN NEDERLAND FINANCE BV—See Givaudan S.A.; *Int'l*, pg. 2981
GIVAUDAN S.A.; *Int'l*, pg. 2979
GIVAUDAN SINGAPORE PTE LTD. PHILIPPINES—See Givaudan S.A.; *Int'l*, pg. 2981
GIVAUDAN SINGAPORE PTE LTD.—See Givaudan S.A.; *Int'l*, pg. 2981
GIVAUDAN SPECIALTY PRODUCTS (SHANGHAI) LTD—See Givaudan S.A.; *Int'l*, pg. 2981
GIVAUDAN SUISSE SA—See Givaudan S.A.; *Int'l*, pg. 2981
GIVAUDAN (THAILAND) LTD.—See Givaudan S.A.; *Int'l*, pg. 2980
GIVAUDAN TREASURY INTERNATIONAL B.V.—See Givaudan S.A.; *Int'l*, pg. 2981
GIVAUDAN UK LIMITED—See Givaudan S.A.; *Int'l*, pg. 2980
GIVAUDAN UNITED STATES, INC.—See Givaudan S.A.; *Int'l*, pg. 2981
GIVAUDAN VENEZUELA SA—See Givaudan S.A.; *Int'l*, pg. 2981
GLAXOSMITHKLINE—See GSK plc; *Int'l*, pg. 3146
GODREJ GLOBAL MID EAST FZE—See Godrej & Boyce Mfg. Co. Ltd.; *Int'l*, pg. 3020
GOLDEN MOOR INC.; *Int'l*, pg. 3030
GOLDEN SUN, INC.; *U.S. Private*, pg. 1733
GOLD MEDAL HAIR PRODUCTS, INC.; *U.S. Private*, pg. 1728
THE GOOD COLLECTIVE PTY LTD.—See BWX Limited; *Int'l*, pg. 1233
GOODIER COSMETICS, INC.—See RoundTable Healthcare Management, Inc.; *U.S. Private*, pg. 3489
GRESHAM COSMETICS PTY. LTD.—See The Procter & Gamble Company; *U.S. Public*, pg. 2120

GROUPE MARCELLE, INC.; *Int'l*, pg. 3108
GR. SARANTIS S.A.; *Int'l*, pg. 3047
GUANGDONG MARUBI BIOTECHNOLOGY CO., LTD.; *Int'l*, pg. 3158
GUARDIAN LABORATORIES DIVISION—See United-Guardian, Inc.; *U.S. Public*, pg. 2238
H2O PLUS, LLC—See The Goldman Sachs Group, Inc.; *U.S. Public*, pg. 2081
H2O PLUS, LLC—See The Williams Capital Group, L.P.; *U.S. Public*, pg. 4136
HABA LABORATORIES, INC.; *Int'l*, pg. 3201
HANGZHOU MARY KAY COSMETICS CO. LTD.—See Mary Kay Holding Corporation; *U.S. Private*, pg. 2599
HANKOOK COSMETICS MANUFACTURING CO., LTD.; *Int'l*, pg. 3253
HANS SCHWARZKOPF & HENKEL GMBH & CO, KG—See Henkel AG & Co. KGaA; *Int'l*, pg. 3348
THE HAPPY COMPANY—See Tender Loving Things Inc.; *U.S. Private*, pg. 3966
HARPER HYGIENICS S.A.—See iCotton SIA; *Int'l*, pg. 3586
HASK TOILETRIES—See Inspired Beauty Brands Inc.; *U.S. Private*, pg. 2092
HAWLEY & HAZEL CHEMICAL CO., (HK) LTD.—See Colgate-Palmolive Company; *U.S. Public*, pg. 532
HAYWARD LABORATORIES—See E.T. Browne Drug Company, Inc.; *U.S. Private*, pg. 1307
HENKEL CENTRAL ASIA & CAUCASUS TOO—See Henkel AG & Co. KGaA; *Int'l*, pg. 3350
HENKEL CENTRAL EASTERN EUROPE GMBH—See Henkel AG & Co. KGaA; *Int'l*, pg. 3350
HENKEL CONSUMER GOODS, INC.—See Henkel AG & Co. KGaA; *Int'l*, pg. 3353
HENKEL VIETNAM CO. LTD.—See Henkel AG & Co. KGaA; *Int'l*, pg. 3349
HILLHOUSE NATURALS FARM, LTD.; *U.S. Private*, pg. 1946
HOLIDAY VACATIONS, LLC—See The Anschutz Corporation; *U.S. Private*, pg. 3987
HOYU CO., LTD.; *Int'l*, pg. 3499
HUM&C CO., LTD.; *Int'l*, pg. 3528
ICERA LLC—See NVIDIA Corporation; *U.S. Public*, pg. 1558
ICOTTON SIA; *Int'l*, pg. 3586
IDEAL STANDARD INTERNATIONAL NV—See Anchorage Capital Group, L.L.C.; *U.S. Private*, pg. 274
IDEAL STANDARD INTERNATIONAL NV—See CVC Capital Partners SICAV-FIS S.A.; *Int'l*, pg. 1888
IFAMIYSC CO., LTD.; *Int'l*, pg. 3598
IFF BENICARLO, S.A.—See International Flavors & Fragrances Inc.; *U.S. Public*, pg. 1153
INCOMA SAL—See Holdal s.a.l.; *Int'l*, pg. 3449
INDIGO BRANDS—See AVI Limited; *Int'l*, pg. 740
INDOLA GMBH—See Henkel AG & Co. KGaA; *Int'l*, pg. 3354
I-NE CO., LTD.; *Int'l*, pg. 3563
INNOVADERMA PLC—See Brand Architekts Group plc; *Int'l*, pg. 1139
INNOVASCIENCE INC.—See Brand Architekts Group plc; *Int'l*, pg. 1139
INSPIRED BEAUTY BRANDS INC.; *U.S. Private*, pg. 2092
INSTANATURAL, LLC; *U.S. Private*, pg. 2092
INTERNATIONAL FLAVORS & FRAGRANCES (JAPAN) LTD.—See International Flavors & Fragrances Inc.; *U.S. Public*, pg. 1152
INTER PARFUMS GRAND PUBLIC, S.A.—See Inter Parfums, Inc.; *U.S. Public*, pg. 1140
INTERPARFUMS SA—See Inter Parfums, Inc.; *U.S. Public*, pg. 1140
INTPROPCO S.A.—See The Procter & Gamble Company; *U.S. Public*, pg. 2120
IREDALE MINERAL COSMETICS LTD.—See San Francisco Equity Partners; *U.S. Private*, pg. 3540
IT WORKS! GLOBAL, INC.; *U.S. Private*, pg. 2148
JACK BLACK, L.L.C.—See Edgewell Personal Care Company; *U.S. Public*, pg. 718
JALSOSA, S.L.—See Helvetia Holding AG; *Int'l*, pg. 3340
JASON NATURAL PRODUCTS INC.—See The Hain Celestial Group, Inc.; *U.S. Public*, pg. 2087
JEAN PHILIPPE FRAGRANCES, LLC—See Inter Parfums, Inc.; *U.S. Public*, pg. 1140
JOHNSON & JOHNSON COMERCIO E DISTRIBUICAO LTDA.—See Johnson & Johnson; *U.S. Public*, pg. 1198
JOHNSON & JOHNSON CONSUMER INC.—See Kenvue Inc.; *U.S. Public*, pg. 1223
JOHNSON & JOHNSON LDA.—See Johnson & Johnson; *U.S. Public*, pg. 1198
JOHNSON & JOHNSON TAIWAN LTD.—See Johnson & Johnson; *U.S. Public*, pg. 1199
JOICO LABORATORIES INC.—See Henkel AG & Co. KGaA; *Int'l*, pg. 3354
J. STEPHEN SCHERER INC.; *U.S. Private*, pg. 2157
J. STRICKLAND & COMPANY; *U.S. Private*, pg. 2157
JUNE JACOBS SPA COLLECTION—See Peter Thomas Roth Labs LLC; *U.S. Private*, pg. 3159
KARA VITA, INC.—See Dermazone Solutions, Inc.; *U.S. Private*, pg. 1210
KENRA PROFESSIONAL, LLC—See Henkel AG & Co. KGaA; *Int'l*, pg. 3353
KEYSTONE LABORATORIES, INC.; *U.S. Private*, pg. 2300
KIMBERLY-CLARK KAZAKHSTAN LIMITED LIABILITY PARTNERSHIP—See Kimberly-Clark Corporation; *U.S. Public*, pg. 1230

CORPORATE AFFILIATIONS

KIMBERLY PARRY ORGANICS, CORP.; *U.S. Public*, pg. 1228
KIRKER ENTERPRISES, INC.—See RPM International Inc.; *U.S. Public*, pg. 1817
KISSTIXX, LLC; *U.S. Private*, pg. 2315
KLEEN TEST PRODUCTS DIVISION, MEQUON PLANT—See Meridian Industries, Inc.; *U.S. Private*, pg. 2673
KONINKLIJKE SANDERS BV—See 3i Group plc; *Int'l*, pg. 9
KRACIE HOME PRODUCTS, LTD.—See Hoyu Co., Ltd.; *Int'l*, pg. 3499
LABORATOIRES CLARINS—See Clarins S.A.; *Int'l*, pg. 1649
LABORATORIE DR RENAUD INC.—See Bausch Health Companies Inc.; *Int'l*, pg. 898
LABORATORIOS VICKS, S.L.—See The Procter & Gamble Company; *U.S. Public*, pg. 2120
LADY PRIMROSE'S, INC.; *U.S. Private*, pg. 2372
LAVISH LABORATORY COMPANY LIMITED—See Gift Infinite Public Company Limited; *Int'l*, pg. 2970
LAYERTEX S.L.—See Helvetia Holding AG; *Int'l*, pg. 3340
LEE DENTAL & ORTHODONTICS DIVISION—See Lee Pharmaceuticals; *U.S. Public*, pg. 1300
LEONARD DRAKE (M) SDN. BHD.—See Esthetics International Group Berhad; *Int'l*, pg. 2518
LEVLAD, LLC—See Harvest Partners L.P.; *U.S. Private*, pg. 1876
LIFELINE SKINCARE, INC—See International Stem Cell Corporation; *U.S. Public*, pg. 1158
LIGUNA INC.—See euglena Co., Ltd.; *Int'l*, pg. 2526
LILLEBORG AS—See Platinum Equity, LLC; *U.S. Private*, pg. 3204
LION IDEMITSU COMPOSITES (HONG KONG) LIMITED—See Idemitsu Kosan Co., Ltd.; *Int'l*, pg. 3591
LION IDEMITSU COMPOSITES (INDIA) PRIVATE LIMITED—See Idemitsu Kosan Co., Ltd.; *Int'l*, pg. 3591
LION IDEMITSU COMPOSITES (SHANGHAI) CO., LTD.—See Idemitsu Kosan Co., Ltd.; *Int'l*, pg. 3591
LION IDEMITSU COMPOSITES (THAILAND) CO., LTD.—See Idemitsu Kosan Co., Ltd.; *Int'l*, pg. 3592
LIPOTEC, S.A.—See Berkshire Hathaway Inc.; *U.S. Public*, pg. 308
LIPOTEC USA, INC.—See Berkshire Hathaway Inc.; *U.S. Public*, pg. 319
LIQUID TECHNOLOGIES, INC.—See The Pritzker Group - Chicago, LLC; *U.S. Private*, pg. 4099
LISE WATIER COSMETIQUES INC.—See Groupe Marcelle, Inc.; *Int'l*, pg. 3108
LIZ EARLE BEAUTY CO. LIMITED—See Walgreens Boots Alliance, Inc.; *U.S. Public*, pg. 2322
LOFTA, INC.—See Owens & Minor, Inc.; *U.S. Public*, pg. 1625
LUBRIZOL LUXEMBOURG S.A.R.L.—See Berkshire Hathaway Inc.; *U.S. Public*, pg. 319
LUCAS MEYER COSMETICS—See Clariant AG; *Int'l*, pg. 1648
LUSTER PRODUCTS INC.; *U.S. Private*, pg. 2516
LUZIER PERSONALIZED COSMETICS, INC.; *U.S. Private*, pg. 2518
M.A.C. COSMETICS—See The Estee Lauder Companies Inc.; *U.S. Public*, pg. 2073
MAESA SA—See F&B Group; *Int'l*, pg. 2595
MAJOR INTERNATIONAL LTD.—See Givaudan S.A.; *Int'l*, pg. 2981
MANA PRODUCTS, INC.—See Marvin Traub Associates, Inc.; *U.S. Private*, pg. 2598
MANSFIELD-KING LLC—See The Pritzker Group - Chicago, LLC; *U.S. Private*, pg. 4099
MARKWINS INTERNATIONAL CORPORATION; *U.S. Private*, pg. 2582
MARY KAY (HONG KONG) LIMITED—See Mary Kay Holding Corporation; *U.S. Private*, pg. 2599
MARY KAY INC.—See Mary Kay Holding Corporation; *U.S. Private*, pg. 2599
MCBRIDE PLC - IEPER PERSONAL CARE FACTORY—See 3i Group plc; *Int'l*, pg. 9
MED-NAP LLC—See Acme United Corporation; *U.S. Public*, pg. 35
MEKON SCIENCE NETWORKS GMBH—See BRAIN Biotech AG; *Int'l*, pg. 1137
MERLE NORMAN COSMETICS, INC.; *U.S. Private*, pg. 2675
MISSION HILLS, S.A. DE C.V.—See Colgate-Palmolive Company; *U.S. Public*, pg. 533
MODERN PRODUCTS COMPANY - JEDDAH—See The Procter & Gamble Company; *U.S. Public*, pg. 2120
MYSPRAY THERAPEUTICS INC.—See SOUL BIOTECHNOLOGY CORPORATION; *U.S. Public*, pg. 3716
NANCY MYERS BEAUTY SHOP; *U.S. Private*, pg. 2833
NATERA INTERNATIONAL, INC.—See Natera, Inc.; *U.S. Public*, pg. 1493
NATERRA INTERNATIONAL INC.; *U.S. Private*, pg. 2838
NATUREX AUSTRALIA PTY LTD—See Givaudan S.A.; *Int'l*, pg. 2981
NATUREX GMBH—See Givaudan S.A.; *Int'l*, pg. 2981
NATUREX HOLDINGS SINGAPORE PTE. LTD.—See

N.A.I.C.S. INDEX 325620 — TOILET PREPARATION ...

N.A.I.C.S. Index

Givaudan S.A.; *Int'l*, pg. 2981
NATUREX INDIA PRIVATE LIMITED—See Givaudan S.A.; *Int'l*, pg. 2981
NATUREX K.K.—See Givaudan S.A.; *Int'l*, pg. 2981
NATUREX LTD.—See Givaudan S.A.; *Int'l*, pg. 2981
NEUTROGENA CORPORATION—See Johnson & Johnson; *U.S. Public*, pg. 1200
NIHON FIRMENICH K.K. - OSAKA BRANCH—See Firmenich International SA; *Int'l*, pg. 2681
NIHON FIRMENICH K.K.—See Firmenich International SA; *Int'l*, pg. 2681
NORTHTEC LLC—See The Estee Lauder Companies Inc.; *U.S. Public*, pg. 2073
NOX BELLCOW COSMETICS CO., LTD.—See Fujian Green Pine Co., Ltd.; *Int'l*, pg. 2818
NOXELL CORPORATION—See The Procter & Gamble Company; *U.S. Public*, pg. 2121
NUMEIRA MIXED SALTS & MUD CO.—See Arab Potash Company PLC; *Int'l*, pg. 531
NU SKIN ENTERPRISES PHILIPPINES, INC.—See Nu Skin Enterprises, Inc.; *U.S. Public*, pg. 1552
NU SKIN ENTERPRISES (THAILAND), LTD.—See Nu Skin Enterprises, Inc.; *U.S. Public*, pg. 1552
NU SKIN ENTERPRISES UNITED STATES, INC.—See Nu Skin Enterprises, Inc.; *U.S. Public*, pg. 1552
NU SKIN NORWAY AS—See Nu Skin Enterprises, Inc.; *U.S. Public*, pg. 1552
NUTRIMETICS AUSTRALIA PTY. LTD.—See Tupperware Brands Corporation; *U.S. Public*, pg. 2204
NUTRIMETICS FRANCE SNC—See Tupperware Brands Corporation; *U.S. Public*, pg. 2204
NUTRIMETICS INTERNATIONAL (NZ) LIMITED—See Tupperware Brands Corporation; *U.S. Public*, pg. 2204
OLAY COMPANY, INC.—See The Procter & Gamble Company; *U.S. Public*, pg. 2121
OLIVEDA INTERNATIONAL, INC.; *U.S. Public*, pg. 1570
ONDAL FRANCE SARL—See The Procter & Gamble Company; *U.S. Public*, pg. 2121
ORAL-B LABORATORIES, G.P.—See The Procter & Gamble Company; *U.S. Public*, pg. 2121
ORGANIX SOUTH, INC.—See HGGC, LLC; *U.S. Private*, pg. 1930
ORLY INTERNATIONAL, INC.; *U.S. Private*, pg. 3044
PARFUMS DE COEUR LTD.—See Yellow Wood Partners LLC; *U.S. Private*, pg. 4587
PARLUX FRAGRANCES, LLC—See Perfumania Holdings, Inc.; *U.S. Private*, pg. 3150
PAULA'S CHOICE LLC—See TA Associates, Inc.; *U.S. Private*, pg. 3917
PAXAN YERAVAN CO.—See Behshahr Industrial Development Corp.; *Int'l*, pg. 942
PEOPLESWAY.COM, INC.; *U.S. Public*, pg. 1668
PERSONNA INTERNATIONAL ISRAEL LTD.—See Edgewell Personal Care Company; *U.S. Public*, pg. 718
PETER THOMAS ROTH LABS LLC; *U.S. Private*, pg. 3159
PEVONIA INTERNATIONAL, LLC; *U.S. Private*, pg. 3163
PGIO S.A. AGENCIA EN CHILE—See The Procter & Gamble Company; *U.S. Public*, pg. 2121
P&G PRESTIGE PRODUCTS N.V.—See The Procter & Gamble Company; *U.S. Public*, pg. 2122
P&G PRESTIGE PRODUCTS—See The Procter & Gamble Company; *U.S. Public*, pg. 2121
P&G PRESTIGE SERVICE GMBH—See The Procter & Gamble Company; *U.S. Public*, pg. 2121
PHARMASOL CORPORATION; *U.S. Private*, pg. 3165
PHYSICIANS FORMULA COSMETICS, INC.—See Markwins International Corporation; *U.S. Private*, pg. 2582
P&K SKIN RESEARCH CENTER CO., LTD.—See Daebong LS Co., Ltd.; *Int'l*, pg. 1906
POTTER & MOORE INNOVATIONS LIMITED—See Creightons plc; *Int'l*, pg. 1837
PRESTIGE COSMETICS CORP.; *U.S. Private*, pg. 3256
PRIMAL LIFE ORGANICS, LLC—See Society Brands, Inc.; *U.S. Private*, pg. 3703
PROBEMEX SA DE CV—See Tupperware Brands Corporation; *U.S. Public*, pg. 2204
PROCTER & GAMBLE ASIA HOLDING B.V.—See The Procter & Gamble Company; *U.S. Public*, pg. 2121
PROCTER & GAMBLE BLOIS S.A.S.—See The Procter & Gamble Company; *U.S. Public*, pg. 2121
PROCTER & GAMBLE BRAZIL HOLDINGS B.V.—See The Procter & Gamble Company; *U.S. Public*, pg. 2121
PROCTER & GAMBLE BULGARIA EOOD—See The Procter & Gamble Company; *U.S. Public*, pg. 2121
PROCTER & GAMBLE CHILE LIMITADA—See The Procter & Gamble Company; *U.S. Public*, pg. 2121
PROCTER & GAMBLE COMMERCIAL COMPANY—See The Procter & Gamble Company; *U.S. Public*, pg. 2121
THE PROCTER & GAMBLE COMPANY; *U.S. Public*, pg. 2120
PROCTER & GAMBLE CZECH REPUBLIC S.R.O.—See The Procter & Gamble Company; *U.S. Public*, pg. 2121
PROCTER & GAMBLE DANMARK APS—See The Procter & Gamble Company; *U.S. Public*, pg. 2121
PROCTER & GAMBLE DETERGENT (BEIJING) LTD.—See The Procter & Gamble Company; *U.S. Public*, pg. 2121
PROCTER & GAMBLE DISTRIBUTING NEW ZEALAND—See The Procter & Gamble Company; *U.S. Public*, pg. 2121
PROCTER & GAMBLE DISTRIBUTION COMPANY (EUROPE) BVBA—See The Procter & Gamble Company; *U.S. Public*, pg. 2122
PROCTER & GAMBLE D.O.O.—See The Procter & Gamble Company; *U.S. Public*, pg. 2123
PROCTER & GAMBLE (EGYPT) MANUFACTURING COMPANY—See The Procter & Gamble Company; *U.S. Public*, pg. 2121
PROCTER & GAMBLE GERMANY GMBH & CO. OPERATIONS OHG—See The Procter & Gamble Company; *U.S. Public*, pg. 2121
PROCTER & GAMBLE GERMANY GMBH—See The Procter & Gamble Company; *U.S. Public*, pg. 2121
PROCTER & GAMBLE GRUNDSTUCKS-UND VERMOGENSVERWALTUNGS GMBH & CO. KG—See The Procter & Gamble Company; *U.S. Public*, pg. 2122
PROCTER & GAMBLE HEALTH & BEAUTY CARE BELGIUM—See The Procter & Gamble Company; *U.S. Public*, pg. 2122
PROCTER & GAMBLE HEALTH & BEAUTY CARE LIMITED—See The Procter & Gamble Company; *U.S. Public*, pg. 2122
PROCTER & GAMBLE HOLDING GMBH—See The Procter & Gamble Company; *U.S. Public*, pg. 2122
PROCTER & GAMBLE HOLDING (HK) LIMITED—See The Procter & Gamble Company; *U.S. Public*, pg. 2122
PROCTER & GAMBLE HOLDING S.R.L.—See The Procter & Gamble Company; *U.S. Public*, pg. 2122
PROCTER & GAMBLE HOLDING (THAILAND) LIMITED—See The Procter & Gamble Company; *U.S. Public*, pg. 2122
PROCTER & GAMBLE HOME PRODUCTS LIMITED—See The Procter & Gamble Company; *U.S. Public*, pg. 2122
PROCTER & GAMBLE HONG KONG LIMITED—See The Procter & Gamble Company; *U.S. Public*, pg. 2122
PROCTER & GAMBLE HYGIENE AND HEALTH CARE LIMITED—See The Procter & Gamble Company; *U.S. Public*, pg. 2122
PROCTER & GAMBLE INTERNATIONAL OPERATIONS PTE. LTD.—See The Procter & Gamble Company; *U.S. Public*, pg. 2122
PROCTER & GAMBLE (IRELAND) LIMITED—See The Procter & Gamble Company; *U.S. Public*, pg. 2121
PROCTER & GAMBLE ITALIA, S.P.A.—See The Procter & Gamble Company; *U.S. Public*, pg. 2122
PROCTER & GAMBLE LLC—See The Procter & Gamble Company; *U.S. Public*, pg. 2122
PROCTER & GAMBLE MANUFACTURING BERLIN GMBH—See The Procter & Gamble Company; *U.S. Public*, pg. 2121
PROCTER & GAMBLE MANUFACTURING COLOGNE GMBH—See The Procter & Gamble Company; *U.S. Public*, pg. 2121
PROCTER & GAMBLE MARKETING AND SERVICES DOO—See The Procter & Gamble Company; *U.S. Public*, pg. 2122
PROCTER & GAMBLE MARKETING ROMANIA SRL—See The Procter & Gamble Company; *U.S. Public*, pg. 2122
PROCTER & GAMBLE NEDERLAND B.V.—See The Procter & Gamble Company; *U.S. Public*, pg. 2122
PROCTER & GAMBLE NETHERLANDS SERVICES B.V.—See The Procter & Gamble Company; *U.S. Public*, pg. 2122
PROCTER & GAMBLE NORDIC LLC—See The Procter & Gamble Company; *U.S. Public*, pg. 2122
PROCTER & GAMBLE NORGE AS—See The Procter & Gamble Company; *U.S. Public*, pg. 2122
PROCTER & GAMBLE PAKISTAN (PRIVATE) LIMITED—See The Procter & Gamble Company; *U.S. Public*, pg. 2123
PROCTER & GAMBLE PAPER PRODUCTS COMPANY—See The Procter & Gamble Company; *U.S. Public*, pg. 2123
PROCTER & GAMBLE PERU S.R.L.—See The Procter & Gamble Company; *U.S. Public*, pg. 2123
PROCTER & GAMBLE POLSKA-SPOLKA Z O.O—See The Procter & Gamble Company; *U.S. Public*, pg. 2123
PROCTER & GAMBLE PORTO - FABRICACAO DE PRODUTOS DE CONSUMO, SOCIEDADE UNIPESSOAL LDA—See The Procter & Gamble Company; *U.S. Public*, pg. 2123
PROCTER & GAMBLE SA (PTY) LTD.—See The Procter & Gamble Company; *U.S. Public*, pg. 2123
PROCTER & GAMBLE SATIS VE DAGITIM LTD. STI.—See The Procter & Gamble Company; *U.S. Public*, pg. 2123
PROCTER & GAMBLE SERVICE GMBH—See The Procter & Gamble Company; *U.S. Public*, pg. 2121
PROCTER & GAMBLE SERVICES LT—See The Procter & Gamble Company; *U.S. Public*, pg. 2123
PROCTER & GAMBLE SERVICES (SWITZERLAND) SA—See The Procter & Gamble Company; *U.S. Public*, pg. 2123
PROCTER & GAMBLE S.R.L.—See The Procter & Gamble Company; *U.S. Public*, pg. 2123
PROCTER & GAMBLE SVERIGE AB—See The Procter & Gamble Company; *U.S. Public*, pg. 2123
PROCTER & GAMBLE SWITZERLAND SARL—See The Procter & Gamble Company; *U.S. Public*, pg. 2123
PROCTER & GAMBLE TAIWAN LIMITED—See The Procter & Gamble Company; *U.S. Public*, pg. 2123
PROCTER & GAMBLE TRADING (THAILAND) LIMITED—See The Procter & Gamble Company; *U.S. Public*, pg. 2123
PROCTER & GAMBLE UK LTD.—See The Procter & Gamble Company; *U.S. Public*, pg. 2123
PROCTER & GAMBLE UK PARENT COMPANY LTD.—See The Procter & Gamble Company; *U.S. Public*, pg. 2123
PROCTER & GAMBLE UKRAINE—See The Procter & Gamble Company; *U.S. Public*, pg. 2123
THE PROCTER & GAMBLE U.S. BUSINESS SERVICES COMPANY—See The Procter & Gamble Company; *U.S. Public*, pg. 2124
PROFESSIONAL HAIR LABS, INC.; *U.S. Private*, pg. 3275
PT BWL INDONESIA—See Best World International Ltd.; *Int'l*, pg. 1000
P.T. COGNIS INDONESIA—See BASF SE; *Int'l*, pg. 883
PT FIRMENICH INDONESIA—See Firmenich International SA; *Int'l*, pg. 2681
P.T. GAMATA UTAMA—See Bioxyne Limited; *Int'l*, pg. 1045
PT. GIVAUDAN INDONESIA—See Givaudan S.A.; *Int'l*, pg. 2981
PTI ROYSTON, LLC.; *U.S. Private*, pg. 3298
PT SOFTEX INDONESIA—See Kimberly-Clark Corporation; *U.S. Public*, pg. 1231
Q-MED ICT S.R.L.—See Abu Dhabi Investment Authority; *Int'l*, pg. 71
Q-MED ICT S.R.L.—See EQT Corporation; *U.S. Public*, pg. 785
Q-PACK (M) SDN BHD—See Citra Nusa Holdings Berhad; *Int'l*, pg. 1626
RADICAL COSMETICS, LLC; *U.S. Private*, pg. 3343
REJUVEL BIO-SCIENCES, INC.; *U.S. Public*, pg. 1778
REVIV3 PROCARE COMPANY; *U.S. Public*, pg. 1793
REVLON AUSTRALIA PTY LIMITED—See MacAndrews & Forbes Incorporated; *U.S. Private*, pg. 2533
REVLON CANADA INC.—See MacAndrews & Forbes Incorporated; *U.S. Private*, pg. 2533
REVLON CONSUMER PRODUCTS CORPORATION—See MacAndrews & Forbes Incorporated; *U.S. Private*, pg. 2533
REVLON GOVERNMENT SALES, INC.—See MacAndrews & Forbes Incorporated; *U.S. Private*, pg. 2533
REVLON GROUP LIMITED—See MacAndrews & Forbes Incorporated; *U.S. Private*, pg. 2533
REVLON MANUFACTURING LTD.—See MacAndrews & Forbes Incorporated; *U.S. Private*, pg. 2533
REVLON NEW ZEALAND LIMITED—See MacAndrews & Forbes Incorporated; *U.S. Private*, pg. 2533
REVLON REAL ESTATE CORPORATION—See MacAndrews & Forbes Incorporated; *U.S. Private*, pg. 2533
REVLON, S.A. DE C.V.—See MacAndrews & Forbes Incorporated; *U.S. Private*, pg. 2533
REVLON SOUTH AFRICA (PROPRIETARY) LIMITED—See MacAndrews & Forbes Incorporated; *U.S. Private*, pg. 2533
REVLON S.P.A.—See MacAndrews & Forbes Incorporated; *U.S. Private*, pg. 2533
REVLON (SUISSE) S.A.—See MacAndrews & Forbes Incorporated; *U.S. Private*, pg. 2533
RICH BRANDS, LLC; *U.S. Private*, pg. 3426
RILKEN COSMETICS INDUSTRY S.A.—See Henkel AG & Co. KGaA; *Int'l*, pg. 3350
ROBANDA INTERNATIONAL, INC.; *U.S. Private*, pg. 3456
RODAN & FIELDS, LLC; *U.S. Private*, pg. 3469
ROUX LABORATORIES, INC.—See MacAndrews & Forbes Incorporated; *U.S. Private*, pg. 2533
SARANTIS BELGRADE D.O.O.—See Gr. Sarantis S.A.; *Int'l*, pg. 3047
S.C. ELMI PRODFARM S.R.L.—See Gr. Sarantis S.A.; *Int'l*, pg. 3047
SCHICK JAPAN K.K.—See Edgewell Personal Care Company; *U.S. Public*, pg. 718
SCHWARZKOPF, INC.—See Henkel AG & Co. KGaA; *Int'l*, pg. 3354
SCIENTIFIC RESEARCH PRODUCTS, INC.—See The Stephan Company; *U.S. Public*, pg. 2132
SCOTT'S LIQUID GOLD- ADVERTISING PROMOTIONS, INC.—See Scott's Liquid Gold-Inc.; *U.S. Public*, pg. 1849
SEDERMA GMBH—See Croda International plc; *Int'l*, pg. 1853
SEDERMA INC.—See Croda International plc; *Int'l*, pg. 1853
SEGUIN NATURAL HAIR PRODUCTS, INC.; *U.S. Private*, pg. 3598
SENSIENT COSMETIC TECHNOLOGIES E CORANTES, IMPORTACAO E EXPORTACAO DO—See Sensient Technologies Corporation; *U.S. Public*, pg. 1867
SENSIENT COSMETIC TECHNOLOGIES POLAND, SP. Z.O.O.—See Sensient Technologies Corporation; *U.S. Public*, pg. 1867
SENSIENT COSMETIC TECHNOLOGIES—See Sensient Technologies Corporation; *U.S. Public*, pg. 1867
SHAANXI AIERFU ACTIVTISSUE ENGINEERING COMPANY LIMITED—See China Regenerative Medicine International Co., Ltd.; *Int'l*, pg. 1547

325620 — TOILET PREPARATION ...

SHEFFIELD LABORATORIES—See Faria Corporation; *U.S. Private*, pg. 1474
SIAM SNAIL COMPANY LIMITED—See E for L Aim Public Company Limited; *Int'l*, pg. 2246
SIMPLE SUGARS; *U.S. Private*, pg. 3667
SMALL WORLD TRADING CO, INC.; *U.S. Private*, pg. 3690
SNOWBERRY NEW ZEALAND LIMITED—See The Procter & Gamble Company; *U.S. Public*, pg. 2123
SOUTHERN CROSS BOTANICALS PTY. LTD.—See Clariant AG; *Int'l*, pg. 1648
SPEXIMO AB—See International Flavors & Fragrances Inc.; *U.S. Public*, pg. 1154
SPINCONTROL AMERIQUE DU NORD, INC.—See Eurofins Scientific S.E.; *Int'l*, pg. 2551
STARFLOWER ESSENTIALS ORGANIC SKIN CARE; *U.S. Private*, pg. 3786
STEARNS PRODUCTS INC.; *U.S. Private*, pg. 3795
THE STEPHAN COMPANY; *U.S. Public*, pg. 2132
STIEFEL INDIA PRIVATE LIMITED—See GSK plc; *Int'l*, pg. 3149
STIEFEL LABORATORIES (IRELAND) LIMITED—See GSK plc; *Int'l*, pg. 3149
STIEFEL LABORATORIES (U.K.) LTD.—See GSK plc; *Int'l*, pg. 3149
STILA CORP.—See Patriarch Partners, LLC; *U.S. Private*, pg. 3109
SUMMIT LABORATORIES INC.; *U.S. Private*, pg. 3855
SUNLESS INC.—See Castle Harlan, Inc.; *U.S. Private*, pg. 785
SUN & SKIN CARE RESEARCH, LLC; *U.S. Private*, pg. 3858
SUREFIL LLC; *U.S. Private*, pg. 3883
SV LABS CORPORATION—See San Francisco Equity Partners; *U.S. Private*, pg. 3540
SWISS AMERICAN CDMO, LLC; *U.S. Private*, pg. 3894
SYSCO GUEST SUPPLY, LLC—See Sysco Corporation; *U.S. Public*, pg. 1976
TATA'S NATURAL ALCHEMY, LLC—See Amorepacific Corp.; *Int'l*, pg. 430
TENDER LOVING THINGS INC.; *U.S. Private*, pg. 3966
TEVCO ENTERPRISES, INC.—See RPM International Inc.; *U.S. Public*, pg. 1820
TOO FACED COSMETICS, LLC—See The Estee Lauder Companies Inc.; *U.S. Public*, pg. 2073
TRANS-INDIA PRODUCTS, INC.; *U.S. Private*, pg. 4206
TRESSA, INC.; *U.S. Private*, pg. 4218
TRIGG LABORATORIES, INC.; *U.S. Private*, pg. 4230
TRILOGY INTERNATIONAL LIMITED—See CITIC Group Corporation; *Int'l*, pg. 1620
TRISH MCEVOY LTD.; *U.S. Private*, pg. 4238
TRI TECH LABORATORIES, INC.; *U.S. Private*, pg. 4221
UCL CO., LTD. - INCHEON FACTORY—See Daebong LS Co., Ltd.; *Int'l*, pg. 1906
UCL CO., LTD. - JEJU FACTORY—See Daebong LS Co., Ltd.; *Int'l*, pg. 1906
UCL CO., LTD.—See Daebong LS Co., Ltd.; *Int'l*, pg. 1906
UNGERER INDUSTRIES, INC—See Givaudan S.A.; *Int'l*, pg. 2982
URBAN DECAY COSMETICS LLC—See Castanea Partners, Inc.; *U.S. Private*, pg. 784
USA LABS INC.; *U.S. Private*, pg. 4321
USA LABS INC.—See USA Labs Inc.; *U.S. Private*, pg. 4321
U.S. COTTON, LLC; *U.S. Private*, pg. 4270
VALOIS ESPANA S.A.—See AptarGroup, Inc.; *U.S. Public*, pg. 175
VERU INC.; *U.S. Public*, pg. 2289
VI-JON, INC.—See Berkshire Partners LLC; *U.S. Private*, pg. 535
VI-JON, INC.—See Berkshire Partners LLC; *U.S. Private*, pg. 535
VIKA B.V.—See Givaudan S.A.; *Int'l*, pg. 2982
VITALIBIS, INC.; *U.S. Public*, pg. 2306
VITAL SCIENCE CORP.—See Bausch Health Companies Inc.; *Int'l*, pg. 898
VOYANT BEAUTY—See Wind Point Advisors LLC; *U.S. Private*, pg. 4536
WESSCO INTERNATIONAL LTD.; *U.S. Private*, pg. 4483
WILLERT HOME PRODUCTS (SHANGHAI) CO., LTD.—See Willert Home Products, Inc.; *U.S. Private*, pg. 4522
WIN AEROSOL GMBH & CO. KG—See DALLI-WERKE GmbH & Co. KG; *Int'l*, pg. 1954
WIN COSMETIC GMBH & CO. KG.—See DALLI-WERKE GmbH & Co. KG; *Int'l*, pg. 1954
YOUNGEVITY RUSSIA, LLC—See Youngevity International Corp.; *U.S. Public*, pg. 2399
ZIRH HOLDINGS LLC—See The Procter & Gamble Company; *U.S. Public*, pg. 2124
ZOTOS INTERNATIONAL, INC.—See Henkel AG & Co. KGaA; *Int'l*, pg. 3354

325910 — PRINTING INK MANUFACTURING

A.J. DAW PRINTING INK CO.; *U.S. Private*, pg. 26
AKZONOBEL—See GIC Pte. Ltd.; *Int'l*, pg. 2968
AKZONOBEL—See The Carlyle Group Inc.; *U.S. Public*, pg. 2051
AMERICAN INKS & COATINGS CORPORATION—See Mosley Holdings Limited Partnership; *U.S. Private*, pg. 2793
THE BRADEN SUTPHIN INK COMPANY; *U.S. Private*, pg. 3999
CENTRAL INK CORPORATION; *U.S. Private*, pg. 821
CHROMATIC TECHNOLOGIES, INC.; *U.S. Private*, pg. 892
CITRONIX INC.—See Brother Industries, Ltd.; *Int'l*, pg. 1197
COATES BROTHERS (CARIBBEAN) LTD.—See DIC Corporation; *Int'l*, pg. 2109
COATES BROTHERS (ZAMBIA) LTD.—See DIC Corporation; *Int'l*, pg. 2109
COATES ELECTROGRAPHICS INC.—See DIC Corporation; *Int'l*, pg. 2109
COATES SCREEN INKS GMBH—See DIC Corporation; *Int'l*, pg. 2109
COLORPAK INDONESIA TBK; *Int'l*, pg. 1704
CORDES & CO. GMBH—See Henkel AG & Co. KGaA; *Int'l*, pg. 3348
DAICOLOR ITALY S.R.L.—See Dainichiseika Color & Chemicals Mfg. Co., Ltd.; *Int'l*, pg. 1939
DAINICHISEIKA INK (GUANGZHOU) LTD.—See Dainichiseika Color & Chemicals Mfg. Co., Ltd.; *Int'l*, pg. 1939
DAINIPPON INK & CHEMICALS, INC.—See DIC Corporation; *Int'l*, pg. 2108
DAINIPPON INK & CHEMICALS (PHILIPPINES), INC.—See DIC Corporation; *Int'l*, pg. 2108
DAINIPPON INK & CHEMICALS (SINGAPORE) PTE., LTD.—See DIC Corporation; *Int'l*, pg. 2108
DATACOLOR ASIA PACIFIC (HK) LIMITED—See Datacolor AG; *Int'l*, pg. 1977
DIC ASIA PACIFIC PTE LTD.—See DIC Corporation; *Int'l*, pg. 2107
DIC AUSTRALIA PTY LTD.—See DIC Corporation; *Int'l*, pg. 2107
DIC (CHINA) CO., LTD.—See DIC Corporation; *Int'l*, pg. 2107
DIC CORPORATION; *Int'l*, pg. 2107
DIC EUROPE GMBH—See DIC Corporation; *Int'l*, pg. 2107
DIC FINE CHEMICALS PRIVATE LIMITED—See DIC Corporation; *Int'l*, pg. 2108
DIC GRAPHICS CHIA LUNG CORP.—See DIC Corporation; *Int'l*, pg. 2108
DIC GRAPHICS CORPORATION - CHIBA PLANT—See DIC Corporation; *Int'l*, pg. 2108
DIC GRAPHICS CORPORATION - GUNMA PLANT—See DIC Corporation; *Int'l*, pg. 2108
DIC GRAPHICS CORPORATION - HOKURIKU PLANT—See DIC Corporation; *Int'l*, pg. 2108
DIC GRAPHICS CORPORATION - KANSAI PLANT—See DIC Corporation; *Int'l*, pg. 2108
DIC GRAPHICS CORPORATION - KASHIMA PLANT—See DIC Corporation; *Int'l*, pg. 2108
DIC GRAPHICS CORPORATION - KOMAKI PLANT—See DIC Corporation; *Int'l*, pg. 2108
DIC GRAPHICS CORPORATION—See DIC Corporation; *Int'l*, pg. 2108
DIC GRAPHICS CORPORATION - TOKYO PLANT—See DIC Corporation; *Int'l*, pg. 2108
DIC GRAPHICS (DONGGUAN) LTD.—See DIC Corporation; *Int'l*, pg. 2108
DIC GRAPHICS (GUANGZHOU) LTD.—See DIC Corporation; *Int'l*, pg. 2108
DIC GRAPHICS (HONG KONG) LTD.—See DIC Corporation; *Int'l*, pg. 2108
DIC GRAPHICS (SHENYANG) CO., LTD.—See DIC Corporation; *Int'l*, pg. 2108
DIC GRAPHICS TAIYUAN CO., LTD.—See DIC Corporation; *Int'l*, pg. 2108
DIC GRAPHICS (THAILAND) CO., LTD.—See DIC Corporation; *Int'l*, pg. 2108
DIC KOREA CORP.—See DIC Corporation; *Int'l*, pg. 2108
DIC LANKA (PRIVATE) LTD.—See DIC Corporation; *Int'l*, pg. 2108
DIC NEW ZEALAND LTD.—See DIC Corporation; *Int'l*, pg. 2108
DIC PAKISTAN LTD.—See DIC Corporation; *Int'l*, pg. 2108
DIC PHILIPPINES, INC.—See DIC Corporation; *Int'l*, pg. 2108
DIC (VIETNAM) CO., LTD.—See DIC Corporation; *Int'l*, pg. 2108
DOMINO CODING LTD.—See EAC Invest AS; *Int'l*, pg. 2261
DRUCKFARBEN HELLAS S.A.; *Int'l*, pg. 2206
E.I. DUPONT DE NEMOURS & CO.—See Corteva, Inc.; *U.S. Public*, pg. 584
ELECTRONICS FOR IMAGING INDIA PRIVATE LIMITED—See Siris Capital Group, LLC; *U.S. Private*, pg. 3672
ELECTRONICS FOR IMAGING JAPAN YK—See Siris Capital Group, LLC; *U.S. Private*, pg. 3673
ELECTRONICS FOR IMAGING UNITED KINGDOM LIMITED—See Siris Capital Group, LLC; *U.S. Private*, pg. 3673
ENJET CO., LTD.; *Int'l*, pg. 2439
ENVIRONMENTAL INKS & COATINGS CORP.; *U.S. Private*, pg. 1408
FLINT GROUP, INC.—See Koch Industries, Inc.; *U.S. Private*, pg. 2327
FLINT GROUP, INC.—See The Goldman Sachs Group, Inc.; *U.S. Public*, pg. 2076
FUJIFILM IMAGING COLORANTS LIMITED—See FUJIFILM Holdings Corporation; *Int'l*, pg. 2822
FUJIFILM PRINTING PLATE (CHINA) CO., LTD.—See FUJIFILM Holdings Corporation; *Int'l*, pg. 2825
FUJI FILM SERICOL AG—See FUJIFILM Holdings Corporation; *Int'l*, pg. 2823
FUJIFILM SERICOL INDIA PRIVATE LIMITED—See FUJIFILM Holdings Corporation; *Int'l*, pg. 2823
FUJIFILM SERICOL NEDERLAND BV—See FUJIFILM Holdings Corporation; *Int'l*, pg. 2823
FUJIFILM SERICOL UK LIMITED—See FUJIFILM Holdings Corporation; *Int'l*, pg. 2823
FUJIFILM SERICOL USA, INC.—See FUJIFILM Holdings Corporation; *Int'l*, pg. 2823
FUJIFILM SPECIALITY INK SYSTEMS, LTD.—See FUJIFILM Holdings Corporation; *Int'l*, pg. 2823
FUKUSHIMA CANON INC.—See Canon Inc.; *Int'l*, pg. 1297
FUNAI LEXINGTON TECHNOLOGY CORPORATION—See Funai Electric Co., *Int'l*, pg. 2845
GANS INK & SUPPLY COMPANY, INC.; *U.S. Private*, pg. 1641
GRANDPRIX LEISURE SYSTEM CO., LTD.—See Brother Industries, Ltd.; *Int'l*, pg. 1198
GRAND RAPIDS PRINTING INK COMPANY; *U.S. Private*, pg. 1753
GRAPHIC SCIENCES INC.; *U.S. Private*, pg. 1758
GREAT WESTERN INK, INC.; *U.S. Private*, pg. 1768
GUANGDONG TLOONG TECHNOLOGY GROUP CO., LTD.; *Int'l*, pg. 3161
HARIMA CHEMICALS, INC.—See Harima Chemicals Group, Inc.; *Int'l*, pg. 3276
HARTMANN DRUCKFARBEN GMBH—See DIC Corporation; *Int'l*, pg. 2110
HARTMANN-SUN CHEMICAL EOOD—See DIC Corporation; *Int'l*, pg. 2110
HENKEL CORPORATION, ONTARIO—See Henkel AG & Co. KGaA; *Int'l*, pg. 3353
HEWLETT-PACKARD INDIGO B.V.—See HP Inc.; *U.S. Public*, pg. 1063
HI-TECH COLOR, INC.—See Dainichiseika Color & Chemicals Mfg. Co., Ltd.; *Int'l*, pg. 1939
HUBERGROUP USA, INC. - ARLINGTON HEIGHTS—See Hubergroup Deutschland GmbH; *Int'l*, pg. 3519
HUBERGROUP USA, INC.—See Hubergroup Deutschland GmbH; *Int'l*, pg. 3519
ICREATE LIMITED—See CN Innovations Holdings Limited; *Int'l*, pg. 1673
IMS CONCEPTS S.A./N.V.—See DIC Corporation; *Int'l*, pg. 2109
INC.JET, INC.—See Norwix Inc.; *U.S. Public*, pg. 1543
INKJETMADNESS.COM, INC.; *U.S. Private*, pg. 2077
INK MILL CORP.—See Avery Dennison Corporation; *U.S. Public*, pg. 244
INKSOLUTIONS, LLC; *U.S. Private*, pg. 2078
INK SYSTEMS INC.; *U.S. Private*, pg. 2077
INTERNATIONAL UNITED TECHNOLOGY CO., LTD.—See ASUSTeK Computer Inc.; *Int'l*, pg. 664
JK GROUP SPA—See Dover Corporation; *U.S. Public*, pg. 681
JK GROUP USA, INC.—See Dover Corporation; *U.S. Public*, pg. 681
KENNEDY INK CO, INC.; *U.S. Private*, pg. 2285
KEYSTONE PRINTING INK CO.; *U.S. Private*, pg. 2300
KIIAN DIGITAL (SHANGHAI) CO., LTD.—See Dover Corporation; *U.S. Public*, pg. 681
LIQUECOLOR INKJET GROUP; *U.S. Private*, pg. 2465
MAGNA COLOURS LIMITED—See Avient Corporation; *U.S. Public*, pg. 247
MONARCH COLOR CORPORATION; *U.S. Private*, pg. 2768
MOSLEY HOLDINGS LIMITED PARTNERSHIP; *U.S. Private*, pg. 2793
NAZDAR LTD.—See Thrall Enterprises, Inc.; *U.S. Private*, pg. 4163
NOCOPI TECHNOLOGIES, INC.; *U.S. Public*, pg. 1531
NOR-COTE INTERNATIONAL INC.; *U.S. Private*, pg. 2935
PAN TECHNOLOGY INC.; *U.S. Private*, pg. 3084
POST JET SYSTEMS LTD.—See Brother Industries, Ltd.; *Int'l*, pg. 1198
PREMIER INK SYSTEMS INC.; *U.S. Private*, pg. 3250
PT DIC GRAPHICS—See DIC Corporation; *Int'l*, pg. 2109
PT. DIC TRADING INDONESIA—See DIC Corporation; *Int'l*, pg. 2109
QINGDAO DIC FINECHEMICALS CO., LTD.—See DIC Corporation; *Int'l*, pg. 2109
QUANTUM INK COMPANY; *U.S. Private*, pg. 3323
RUTLAND GROUP, INC.—See Avient Corporation; *U.S. Public*, pg. 248
RUTLAND PLASTIC TECHNOLOGIES, INC.—See Avient Corporation; *U.S. Public*, pg. 248
SENSIENT IMAGING TECHNOLOGIES INC.—See Sensient Technologies Corporation; *U.S. Public*, pg. 1867
SERICOL SAS—See FUJIFILM Holdings Corporation; *Int'l*, pg. 2823
SHANGHAI DIC INK CO., INC.—See DIC Corporation; *Int'l*, pg. 2109

N.A.I.C.S. INDEX

SHENZHEN DIC CHEMICALS CO., LTD.—See DIC Corporation; *Int'l*, pg. 2109
SHENZHEN-DIC CO., LTD.—See DIC Corporation; *Int'l*, pg. 2109
SIHL LLC—See ANDRITZ AG; *Int'l*, pg. 455
SPECTRA ANALYSIS INSTRUMENTS, INC.—See DANI Instruments SpA; *Int'l*, pg. 1962
SUN CHEMICAL AB—See DIC Corporation; *Int'l*, pg. 2110
SUN CHEMICAL AG—See DIC Corporation; *Int'l*, pg. 2110
SUN CHEMICAL AG—See DIC Corporation; *Int'l*, pg. 2110
SUN CHEMICAL ALBANIA SHPK—See DIC Corporation; *Int'l*, pg. 2110
SUN CHEMICAL A/S—See DIC Corporation; *Int'l*, pg. 2109
SUN CHEMICAL A/S—See DIC Corporation; *Int'l*, pg. 2109
SUN CHEMICAL B.V.—See DIC Corporation; *Int'l*, pg. 2110
SUN CHEMICAL CHILE S.A.—See DIC Corporation; *Int'l*, pg. 2110
SUN CHEMICAL CORPORATION—See DIC Corporation; *Int'l*, pg. 2109
SUN CHEMICAL DE CENTRO AMERICA, S.A. DE C.V.—See DIC Corporation; *Int'l*, pg. 2110
SUN CHEMICAL DE PANAMA, S.A.—See DIC Corporation; *Int'l*, pg. 2110
SUN CHEMICAL DO BRASIL LTDA.—See DIC Corporation; *Int'l*, pg. 2110
SUN CHEMICAL DRUCKFARBEN GMBH—See DIC Corporation; *Int'l*, pg. 2110
SUN CHEMICAL ECP S.A./N.V.—See DIC Corporation; *Int'l*, pg. 2110
SUN CHEMICAL GROUP COOPERATIEF U.A.—See DIC Corporation; *Int'l*, pg. 2110
SUN CHEMICAL GROUP S.P.A.—See DIC Corporation; *Int'l*, pg. 2110
SUN CHEMICAL, INC. S.A.—See DIC Corporation; *Int'l*, pg. 2111
SUN CHEMICAL, INC. S.A.—See DIC Corporation; *Int'l*, pg. 2111
SUN CHEMICAL INKS A/S—See DIC Corporation; *Int'l*, pg. 2110
SUN CHEMICAL INKS LTD.—See DIC Corporation; *Int'l*, pg. 2110
SUN CHEMICAL INK—See DIC Corporation; *Int'l*, pg. 2110
SUN CHEMICAL INKS S.A.—See DIC Corporation; *Int'l*, pg. 2110
SUN CHEMICAL LASFELDE GMBH—See DIC Corporation; *Int'l*, pg. 2110
SUN CHEMICAL LIMITED—See DIC Corporation; *Int'l*, pg. 2110
SUN CHEMICAL LTD.—See DIC Corporation; *Int'l*, pg. 2109
SUN CHEMICAL LTD.—See DIC Corporation; *Int'l*, pg. 2110
SUN CHEMICAL MATBAA MUREKKEPLERI VE GERECLERI SANAYII VE TICARET A.S.—See DIC Corporation; *Int'l*, pg. 2110
SUN CHEMICAL MOSCOW—See DIC Corporation; *Int'l*, pg. 2110
SUN CHEMICAL N.V./S.A.—See DIC Corporation; *Int'l*, pg. 2110
SUN CHEMICAL NYOMDAFESTEK KERESKEDELMI ES GYARTO KFT—See DIC Corporation; *Int'l*, pg. 2110
SUN CHEMICAL OSTERODE DRUCKFARBEN GMBH—See DIC Corporation; *Int'l*, pg. 2110
SUN CHEMICAL OY—See DIC Corporation; *Int'l*, pg. 2110
SUN CHEMICAL PIGMENTS S.L.—See DIC Corporation; *Int'l*, pg. 2110
SUN CHEMICAL PORTUGAL TINTAS GRAFICAS UNIPESSOAL, LTDA.—See DIC Corporation; *Int'l*, pg. 2110
SUN CHEMICAL PRINTING INK D.O.O.—See DIC Corporation; *Int'l*, pg. 2110
SUN CHEMICAL S.A. DE C.V.—See DIC Corporation; *Int'l*, pg. 2110
SUN CHEMICAL S.A.—See DIC Corporation; *Int'l*, pg. 2110
SUN CHEMICAL S.A.S.—See DIC Corporation; *Int'l*, pg. 2110
SUN CHEMICAL S.P.A.—See DIC Corporation; *Int'l*, pg. 2110
SUN CHEMICAL SP. ZO.O.—See DIC Corporation; *Int'l*, pg. 2110
SUN CHEMICAL S.R.L.—See DIC Corporation; *Int'l*, pg. 2110
SUN CHEMICAL S.R.O.—See DIC Corporation; *Int'l*, pg. 2111
SUN CHEMICAL S.R.O.—See DIC Corporation; *Int'l*, pg. 2111
SUN CHEMICALS—See DIC Corporation; *Int'l*, pg. 2111
SUN CHEMICAL TRADING (SHANGHAI) CO., LTD.—See DIC Corporation; *Int'l*, pg. 2111
SUN CHEMICAL ZAO—See DIC Corporation; *Int'l*, pg. 2110
SUPERIOR PRINTING INK COMPANY INCORPORATED; *U.S. Private*, pg. 3880
THINK INK, INC.; *U.S. Private*, pg. 4144
UNICAT CATALYST TECHNOLOGIES, INC.—See White Deer Management LLC; *U.S. Private*, pg. 4509
US INK CORPORATION, EASTERN REGION—See DIC Corporation; *Int'l*, pg. 2111
US INK CORPORATION, MIDWEST REGION—See DIC Corporation; *Int'l*, pg. 2111
US INK CORPORATION—See DIC Corporation; *Int'l*, pg. 2111
US INK CORPORATION, SOUTHERN REGION—See DIC Corporation; *Int'l*, pg. 2111
US INK CORPORATION, SOUTHWEST REGION—See DIC Corporation; *Int'l*, pg. 2111
US INK CORPORATION, WESTERN REGION—See DIC Corporation; *Int'l*, pg. 2111
WIKOFF COLOR CORPORATION; *U.S. Private*, pg. 4517
WOLKE INKS & PRINTERS GMBH—See Danaher Corporation; *U.S. Public*, pg. 632

325920 — EXPLOSIVES MANUFACTURING

AFRICAN EXPLOSIVES (BOTSWANA) LIMITED—See AECI Limited; *Int'l*, pg. 171
AFRICAN EXPLOSIVES LIMITED—See AECI Limited; *Int'l*, pg. 171
AFRICAN EXPLOSIVES (TANZANIA) LIMITED—See AECI Limited; *Int'l*, pg. 171
AL FAJAR AL ALAMIA COMPANY SAOG; *Int'l*, pg. 277
ANHUI JIANGNAN CHEMICAL INDUSTRY CO., LTD.; *Int'l*, pg. 468
AUSTIN POWDER COMPANY—See Davis Mining & Manufacturing Inc.; *U.S. Private*, pg. 1174
BIAFO INDUSTRIES LIMITED; *Int'l*, pg. 1017
BUCKLEY POWDER CO.; *U.S. Private*, pg. 678
CHEMRING DEFENCE SPAIN S.L.—See Chemring Group PLC; *Int'l*, pg. 1463
CHEMRING NOBEL AS—See Chemring Group PLC; *Int'l*, pg. 1463
DAVIS MINING & MANUFACTURING INC.; *U.S. Private*, pg. 1173
DETNET SOUTH AFRICA (PTY) LTD.—See AECI Limited; *Int'l*, pg. 171
DREW MARINE SIGNAL AND SAFETY UK LTD—See Court Square Capital Partners, L.P.; *U.S. Private*, pg. 1069
DST DEFENCE SERVICE TRACKS GMBH—See Diehl Stiftung & Co. KG; *Int'l*, pg. 2114
DYNAENERGETICS GMBH & CO. KG—See DMC Global Inc.; *U.S. Public*, pg. 671
DYNITEC GMBH—See Diehl Stiftung & Co. KG; *Int'l*, pg. 2115
EXPLOSIVE CO., LTD.; *Int'l*, pg. 2588
GUANGDONG HONGDA HOLDINGS GROUP CO., LTD.; *Int'l*, pg. 3155
HANWHA CORPORATION—See Hanwha Group; *Int'l*, pg. 3265
HODGDON POWDER COMPANY; *U.S. Private*, pg. 1959
HUBEI KAILONG CHEMICAL GROUP CO., LTD.; *Int'l*, pg. 3518
HYPEX BIO EXPLOSIVES TECHNOLOGY AB; *Int'l*, pg. 3553
JUNGHANS MICROTEC GMBH—See Diehl Stiftung & Co. KG; *Int'l*, pg. 2115
JUNGHANS T2M SAS—See Diehl Stiftung & Co. KG; *Int'l*, pg. 2115
KELTECH ENERGIES LTD.—See Chowgule & Company Pvt. Ltd.; *Int'l*, pg. 1585
NELSON BROTHERS INC.; *U.S. Private*, pg. 2883
PACIFIC SCIENTIFIC ENERGETIC MATERIALS COMPANY (ARIZONA) LLC—See Fortive Corporation; *U.S. Public*, pg. 871
PERFOLINE—See DMC Global Inc.; *U.S. Public*, pg. 671
SNPE SA—See GIAT Industries S.A.; *Int'l*, pg. 2962
SPECTRA TECHNOLOGIES, LLC—See National Presto Industries, Inc; *U.S. Public*, pg. 1497
TECHNICAL DRILLING AND BLASTING CO. LLC—See Al Fajar Al Alamia Company SAOG; *Int'l*, pg. 277
TELEDYNE RISI, INC.—See Teledyne Technologies Incorporated; *U.S. Public*, pg. 1995

325991 — CUSTOM COMPOUNDING OF PURCHASED RESINS

AKROTEX EXTUSION & RECYCLING INC.—See Akrotex, Inc.; *U.S. Private*, pg. 146
ALLOY POLYMERS, INC.—See RTP Company; *U.S. Private*, pg. 3498
ALLOY POLYMERS TEXAS, LP—See RTP Company; *U.S. Private*, pg. 3498
ALPHAGARY CORPORATION—See Grupo Empresarial Kaluz S.A. de C.V.; *Int'l*, pg. 3127
ARKEMA COATING RESINS - ALSIP—See Arkema S.A.; *Int'l*, pg. 569
ARKEMA COATING RESINS—See Arkema S.A.; *Int'l*, pg. 569
ARKEMA COATING RESINS - TORRANCE PLANT—See Arkema S.A.; *Int'l*, pg. 569
AZON USA INC.; *U.S. Private*, pg. 415
BEAULIEU INTERNATIONAL GROUP NV KRUISHOUTEM PLANT—See Beaulieu International Group NV; *Int'l*, pg. 934
CAHYA MATA ALAM SDN. BHD.—See Cahya Mata Sarawak Berhad; *Int'l*, pg. 1251
CAMPINE RECYCLED POLYMERS S.A.S.—See Campine N.V.; *Int'l*, pg. 1275
CLARIANT-MASTERBATCHES DIVISION—See Clariant AG; *Int'l*, pg. 1647
COLONIAL DIVERSIFIED POLYMER PRODUCTS LLC; *U.S. Private*, pg. 970
COLORITE SPECIALTY RESINS—See Genstar Capital, LLC; *U.S. Private*, pg. 1678
DELTECH LLC—See SK Capital Partners, LP; *U.S. Private*, pg. 3679
EARTHMINDED BENELUX NV—See Greif Inc.; *U.S. Public*, pg. 967
EARTHMINDED FRANCE S.A.S.—See Greif Inc.; *U.S. Public*, pg. 967
EARTHMINDED GERMANY GMBH—See Greif Inc.; *U.S. Public*, pg. 967
EARTH MINDED LLC—See Greif Inc.; *U.S. Public*, pg. 967
EARTHMINDED NETHERLANDS B.V.—See Greif Inc.; *U.S. Public*, pg. 967
FINPROJECT S.P.A.; *Int'l*, pg. 2676
FREEMAN MANUFACTURING & SUPPLY COMPANY; *U.S. Private*, pg. 1605
GAUDLITZ GMBH—See H&R KGaA; *Int'l*, pg. 3193
IDI THERMOSET MOLDING COMPOUNDS SHENZHEN COMPANY, LTD.—See Hidden Harbor Capital Partners; *U.S. Private*, pg. 1934
INDUSTRIAL DIELECTRICS (UK) LTD.—See Industrial Dielectrics Holdings, Inc.; *U.S. Private*, pg. 2065
INNOVATIVE SOLUTIONS & SUPPORT, INC.; *U.S. Public*, pg. 1127
INTERCONTINENTAL EXPORT IMPORT INC.; *U.S. Private*, pg. 2109
IPS - INNOVA PACKAGING SYSTEMS NV—See CABKA Group GmbH; *Int'l*, pg. 1245
JX NIPPON ANCI CORP. - NARITA PLANT—See ENEOS Holdings, Inc.; *Int'l*, pg. 2417
JX NIPPON ANCI CORPORATION—See ENEOS Holdings, Inc.; *Int'l*, pg. 2417
JX NIPPON ANCI, INC.—See ENEOS Holdings, Inc.; *Int'l*, pg. 2417
MILLER WASTE MILLS, INC.; *U.S. Private*, pg. 2735
MODERN DISPERSIONS, INC.; *U.S. Private*, pg. 2760
PLASGRAN LIMITED—See Berry Global Group, Inc; *U.S. Public*, pg. 322
POLYMERIC RESOURCES CORP.; *U.S. Public*, pg. 1701
POLYSOURCE, LLC; *U.S. Private*, pg. 3226
PROTECH PERFORMANCE PLASTICS LTD—See Madison Dearborn Partners, LLC; *U.S. Private*, pg. 2541
RECAN ORGANIZACJA ODZYSKU S.A.—See Ball Corporation; *U.S. Public*, pg. 268
RESILIA S.R.L.—See OpenGate Capital Management, LLC; *U.S. Private*, pg. 3031
RESINOPLAST S.A.—See OpenGate Capital Management, LLC; *U.S. Private*, pg. 3031
RESIN & PIGMENT TECHNOLOGIES PTE LTD—See En-Gro Corporation Limited; *Int'l*, pg. 2435
RETURN POLYMERS, INC.—See The AZEK Company Inc.; *U.S. Public*, pg. 2035
RHETECH, INC.—See HEXPOL AB; *Int'l*, pg. 3372
RLA POLYMERS PTY. LTD.—See TPG Capital, L.P.; *U.S. Public*, pg. 2175
SABLE POLYMER SOLUTIONS, LLC—See RiskOn International, Inc.; *U.S. Public*, pg. 1799
SACO POLYMERS INC.; *U.S. Private*, pg. 3522
SUZHOU HUIYE PLASTIC INDUSTRY CO., LTD.—See Dynamic Colours Limited; *Int'l*, pg. 2240
TECHMER ENGINEERED SOLUTIONS, LLC—See SK Capital Partners, LP; *U.S. Private*, pg. 3680
TEKNOR APEX COMPANY; *U.S. Private*, pg. 3958
UNIFORM COLOR COMPANY—See Audia International, Inc.; *U.S. Private*, pg. 390
URETHANE ENGINEERING INC.—See Bunker Corporation; *U.S. Private*, pg. 685
VIKING POLYMERS, LLC—See Teknor Apex Company; *U.S. Private*, pg. 3959
WASHINGTON PENN PLASTIC CO., INC. - FRANKFORT DIVISION—See Audia International, Inc.; *U.S. Private*, pg. 391
WASHINGTON PENN PLASTIC CO., INC.—See Audia International, Inc.; *U.S. Private*, pg. 390

325992 — PHOTOGRAPHIC FILM, PAPER, PLATE, CHEMICAL, AND COPY TONER MANUFACTURING

AGFA-GEVAERT A.E.B.E.—See Agfa-Gevaert N.V.; *Int'l*, pg. 208
AGFA HEALTHCARE MEXICO S.A. DE C.V.—See Agfa-Gevaert N.V.; *Int'l*, pg. 208
AGFA LIMITED—See Agfa-Gevaert N.V.; *Int'l*, pg. 207
AVI PRODUCTS INDIA LIMITED; *Int'l*, pg. 741
BIXOLON CO LTD; *Int'l*, pg. 1052
CANON DALIAN BUSINESS MACHINES, INC.—See Canon Inc.; *Int'l*, pg. 1292
CANON INC.; *Int'l*, pg. 1292
CANON SOLUTIONS AMERICA, INC. - CHICAGO—See Canon Inc.; *Int'l*, pg. 1297
CHANGHE INTERNATIONAL TRADING (GZFTZ) CO., LTD.—See Eternal Materials Co., Ltd.; *Int'l*, pg. 2520

325992 — PHOTOGRAPHIC FILM, ...

CHARTER NEX FILMS, INC.—See Keystone Group, L.P.; *U.S. Private*, pg. 2297
CHARTER NEX FILMS, INC.—See Leonard Green & Partners, L.P.; *U.S. Private*, pg. 2425
CHEMIPRO KASEI KAISHA LTD. - AIOI PLANT—See Chemipro Kasei Kaisha Ltd.; *Int'l*, pg. 1462
CHEMIPRO KASEI KAISHA LTD. - AKASHI PLANT—See Chemipro Kasei Kaisha Ltd.; *Int'l*, pg. 1462
CHEMIPRO KASEI KAISHA LTD. - FUKUSHIMA PLANT—See Chemipro Kasei Kaisha Ltd.; *Int'l*, pg. 1462
CHEMIPRO KASEI KAISHA LTD. - HIMEJI PLANT—See Chemipro Kasei Kaisha Ltd.; *Int'l*, pg. 1462
CHEMIPRO KASEI KAISHA LTD. - OSAKA PLANT—See Chemipro Kasei Kaisha Ltd.; *Int'l*, pg. 1462
CHEMIPRO KASEI KAISHA LTD.; *Int'l*, pg. 1462
CIAAT CO., LTD.; *Int'l*, pg. 1602
COSMO AM & T CO., LTD.; *Int'l*, pg. 1811
CREDENT TECHNOLOGY ASIA PTE. LTD.—See Hexagon AB; *Int'l*, pg. 3368
DAITO CHEMIX CORPORATION; *Int'l*, pg. 1943
DIRECT PRINTER SERVICE GMBH—See ECO Supplies Europe AB; *Int'l*, pg. 2292
DNP PHOTOMASK EUROPE S.P.A.—See Dai Nippon Printing Co., Ltd.; *Int'l*, pg. 1915
DS CHEMPORT (AUSTRALIA) PTY LTD—See FUJIFILM Holdings Corporation; *Int'l*, pg. 2821
DYNIC CORPORATION; *Int'l*, pg. 2242
ETERNAL CHEMICAL CO., LTD. - TA-FA PLANT—See Eternal Materials Co., Ltd.; *Int'l*, pg. 2520
ETERNAL CHEMICAL (GUANGZHOU) CO., LTD.—See Eternal Materials Co., Ltd.; *Int'l*, pg. 2520
ETERNAL ELECTRONIC MATERIAL (GUANGZHOU) CO., LTD.—See Eternal Materials Co., Ltd.; *Int'l*, pg. 2520
ETERNAL ELECTRONIC (SUZHOU) CO., LTD.—See Eternal Materials Co., Ltd.; *Int'l*, pg. 2520
ETERNAL PHOTOELECTRIC MATERIAL INDUSTRY (YINGKOU) CO., LTD.—See Eternal Materials Co., Ltd.; *Int'l*, pg. 2521
FUJIFILM HUNT CHEMICALS EUROPE N.V.—See FUJIFILM Holdings Corporation; *Int'l*, pg. 2821
FUJIFILM HUNT CHEMICALS SINGAPORE PTE. LTD.—See FUJIFILM Holdings Corporation; *Int'l*, pg. 2822
FUJIFILM HUNT CHEMICALS USA, INC.—See FUJIFILM Holdings Corporation; *Int'l*, pg. 2823
FUJIFILM HUNT DO BRASIL - PRODUCAO DE QUIMICOS LTDA—See FUJIFILM Holdings Corporation; *Int'l*, pg. 2823
FUJIFILM IMAGING PRODUCTS & SOLUTIONS GMBH & CO. KG.—See FUJIFILM Holdings Corporation; *Int'l*, pg. 2824
FUJIFILM IMAGING PROTEC CO., LTD.—See FUJIFILM Holdings Corporation; *Int'l*, pg. 2824
FUJIFILM MANUFACTURING EUROPE B.V.—See FUJIFILM Holdings Corporation; *Int'l*, pg. 2821
FUJIFILM MEDICAL SYSTEMS BENELUX N.V.—See FUJIFILM Holdings Corporation; *Int'l*, pg. 2822
FUJIFILM MEDICAL SYSTEMS TAIWAN CO., LTD.—See FUJIFILM Holdings Corporation; *Int'l*, pg. 2824
FUJIFILM PHILIPPINES INC.—See FUJIFILM Holdings Corporation; *Int'l*, pg. 2824
FUJIFILM PHOTO MANUFACTURING CO., LTD.—See FUJIFILM Holdings Corporation; *Int'l*, pg. 2824
FUJIFILM SHIZUOKA CO., LTD.—See FUJIFILM Holdings Corporation; *Int'l*, pg. 2825
FUJI XEROX TAIWAN CORPORATION—See FUJIFILM Holdings Corporation; *Int'l*, pg. 2825
GENERAL PLASTIC INDUSTRIAL CO., LTD.; *Int'l*, pg. 2919
GENTHERM AUTOMOTIVE SYSTEMS (CHINA) LTD.—See Gentherm Incorporated; *U.S. Public*, pg. 931
GENTHERM ENTERPRISES GMBH—See Gentherm Incorporated; *U.S. Public*, pg. 931
GENTHERM HUNGARY KFT—See Gentherm Incorporated; *U.S. Public*, pg. 932
GENTHERM JAPAN INC.—See Gentherm Incorporated; *U.S. Public*, pg. 932
GENTHERM KOREA INC.—See Gentherm Incorporated; *U.S. Public*, pg. 932
GENTHERM U.K. LTD.—See Gentherm Incorporated; *U.S. Public*, pg. 932
GREAT RICH TECHNOLOGIES LTD; *Int'l*, pg. 3065
GUANGDONG LEARY NEW MATERIAL TECHNOLOGY CO., LTD.; *Int'l*, pg. 3158
GUNZE PACKAGING SYSTEMS CO., LTD.—See Gunze Limited; *Int'l*, pg. 3185
HANGZHOU HESHUN TECHNOLOGY CO., LTD.; *Int'l*, pg. 3247
HITI DIGITAL INC.; *Int'l*, pg. 3426
HORIZONS INCORPORATED; *U.S. Private*, pg. 1983
HUBEI W OLF PHOTOELECTRIC TECHNOLOGY CO., LTD.; *Int'l*, pg. 3518
IKONICS CORPORATION—See Terawulf Inc.; *U.S. Public*, pg. 2018
INTELICOAT TECHNOLOGIES, LLC—See Sun Capital Partners, Inc.; *U.S. Private*, pg. 3859
INTERGRAPH CORPORATION TAIWAN—See Hexagon AB; *Int'l*, pg. 3368

INTERGRAPH (ESPANA) S.A.—See Hexagon AB; *Int'l*, pg. 3368
INTERGRAPH (ESPANA) S.A.—See Hexagon AB; *Int'l*, pg. 3368
INTERGRAPH POLSKA SP. Z O.O.—See Hexagon AB; *Int'l*, pg. 3369
INTERGRAPH (SWITZERLAND) AG—See Hexagon AB; *Int'l*, pg. 3368
JESSUP MANUFACTURING COMPANY, INC.; *U.S. Private*, pg. 2203
KODAK DA AMAZONIA INDUSTRIA E COMERCIO LTDA.—See Eastman Kodak Company; *U.S. Public*, pg. 708
KODAK (HONG KONG) LIMITED—See Eastman Kodak Company; *U.S. Public*, pg. 707
LUMIERE IMAGING FRANCE SAS—See Ilford Imaging Switzerland GmbH; *Int'l*, pg. 3614
MACDERMID DO BRAZIL LTDA—See Element Solutions Inc.; *U.S. Public*, pg. 728
MACDERMID PRINTING SOLUTIONS, LLC - SAN MARCOS—See Element Solutions Inc.; *U.S. Public*, pg. 727
MICRON CONSUMER PRODUCTS GROUP, INC.—See Micron Technology, Inc.; *U.S. Public*, pg. 1437
PROFILE SYSTEMS, INC.; *U.S. Private*, pg. 3277
REPROGRAPHICS ONE INC.; *U.S. Private*, pg. 3401
TAYANGAN UNGGUL SDN. BHD.—See Astro All Asia Networks plc; *Int'l*, pg. 662
TEUWEN ONE IMAGE, INC.—See Evins Communications, Ltd.; *U.S. Private*, pg. 1442
TOPIC CO., LTD.—See DIC Corporation; *Int'l*, pg. 2111
UNIVERSAL BLUEPRINT PAPER COMPANY, LLC; *U.S. Private*, pg. 4304
UYEMURA (MALAYSIA) SDN. BHD.—See C.Uyemura & Co., Ltd.; *Int'l*, pg. 1244
UYEMURA (SHENZHEN) CO., LTD.—See C.Uyemura & Co., Ltd.; *Int'l*, pg. 1244
VEECO SIC CVD SYSTEMS AB—See Veeco Instruments Inc.; *U.S. Public*, pg. 2277
WEST POINT PRODUCTS LLC; *U.S. Private*, pg. 4487

325998 — ALL OTHER MISCELLANEOUS CHEMICAL PRODUCT AND PREPARATION MANUFACTURING

3M BELGIUM N.V./S.A.—See 3M Company; *U.S. Public*, pg. 5
3M EGYPT LTD.—See 3M Company; *U.S. Public*, pg. 5
A-1 ACID LIMITED; *Int'l*, pg. 19
AARTECH SOLONICS LIMITED; *Int'l*, pg. 37
ABA CHEMICALS CORPORATION; *Int'l*, pg. 47
A BRITE COMPANY; *U.S. Private*, pg. 18
ABTECH INDUSTRIES, INC.—See ABTECH HOLDINGS, INC.; *U.S. Private*, pg. 45
ABUNDANCE INTERNATIONAL LTD.; *Int'l*, pg. 74
ACC SILICONES LTD.—See Akoya Capital LLC; *U.S. Private*, pg. 146
ACC SILICONES LTD.—See Century Park Capital Partners, LLC; *U.S. Private*, pg. 833
ACHESON VENTURES, LLC—See Henkel AG & Co. KGaA; *Int'l*, pg. 3352
ACOBAL S.A.S.—See Northern Technologies International Corporation; *U.S. Public*, pg. 1537
ADA CARBON SOLUTIONS, LLC—See Advanced Emissions Solutions, Inc.; *U.S. Public*, pg. 46
ADDENDA CHEMICAL CORPORATION LIMITED—See Metals and Additives; *U.S. Private*, pg. 2682
ADDENDA CORPORATION—See Metals and Additives; *U.S. Private*, pg. 2682
ADDIVANT USA, LLC—See SK Capital Partners, LP; *U.S. Private*, pg. 3678
ADEKA AL OTAIBA MIDDLE EAST LLC—See Adeka Corporation; *Int'l*, pg. 141
ADEKA EUROPE GMBH—See Adeka Corporation; *Int'l*, pg. 141
ADEKA FINE CHEMICAL (CHANGSHU) CO., LTD.—See Adeka Corporation; *Int'l*, pg. 141
ADEKA FINE CHEMICAL (THAILAND) CO., LTD.—See Adeka Corporation; *Int'l*, pg. 141
ADEKA INDIA PVT. LTD.—See Adeka Corporation; *Int'l*, pg. 141
ADEKA POLYMER ADDITIVES EUROPE SAS—See Adeka Corporation; *Int'l*, pg. 142
AD FIRE PROTECTION SYSTEMS INC.—See RPM International Inc.; *U.S. Public*, pg. 1816
ADRIACHEM D.D.; *Int'l*, pg. 153
ADVANCED AROMATICS, LLC—See Heritage Group; *U.S. Private*, pg. 1923
ADVANCED CHEMICAL COMPANY; *U.S. Private*, pg. 88
ADVANCED CHEMICAL CONCEPTS, INC.; *U.S. Private*, pg. 88
ADVANCED CHEMTECH—See CreoSalus Inc.; *U.S. Private*, pg. 1092
ADVANCED FOOD TECHNOLOGIES, INC.—See Zoetis Inc.; *U.S. Public*, pg. 2409
ADVANCED NANO PRODUCTS CO., LTD.; *Int'l*, pg. 161
ADVANCED REFINING TECHNOLOGIES, LLC - CATALYSTS—See Chevron Corporation; *U.S. Public*, pg. 486
ADVANCED REFINING TECHNOLOGIES, LLC—See Chevron Corporation; *U.S. Public*, pg. 486
ADVANCE ZINTECK LIMITED; *Int'l*, pg. 157
ADVANSIX'S HOPEWELL FACILITY—See Honeywell International Inc.; *U.S. Public*, pg. 1047
AEGIS CHEMICAL SOLUTIONS, LLC—See Intervale Capital, LLC; *U.S. Private*, pg. 2127
AEKYUNG (NINGBO) CHEMICAL CO., LTD.—See AK Holdings, Inc.; *Int'l*, pg. 259
AETHER CATALYST SOLUTIONS, INC.; *Int'l*, pg. 183
AFRICAN FINE CARBON (PTY) LIMITED—See Glencore plc; *Int'l*, pg. 2990
AFTON CHEMICAL ASIA PTE. LTD.—See Newmarket Corporation; *U.S. Public*, pg. 1516
AFTON CHEMICAL CANADA CORPORATION—See Newmarket Corporation; *U.S. Public*, pg. 1516
AFTON CHEMICAL CORPORATION—See Newmarket Corporation; *U.S. Public*, pg. 1516
AFTON CHEMICAL GMBH—See Newmarket Corporation; *U.S. Public*, pg. 1516
AFTON CHEMICAL INDIA PRIVATE LIMITED—See Newmarket Corporation; *U.S. Public*, pg. 1516
AFTON CHEMICAL INTANGIBLES LLC—See Newmarket Corporation; *U.S. Public*, pg. 1516
AFTON CHEMICAL LIMITED—See Newmarket Corporation; *U.S. Public*, pg. 1516
AFTON CHEMICAL S.P.R.L.—See Newmarket Corporation; *U.S. Public*, pg. 1516
A-GAS LIMITED; *Int'l*, pg. 19
AGC CHEMICALS AMERICAS, INC. - THORNDALE MANUFACTURING PLANT—See AGC Inc.; *Int'l*, pg. 200
AGC CHEMICALS (THAILAND) CO., LTD. - PHRAPRADAENG PLANT—See AGC Inc.; *Int'l*, pg. 201
AGC CHEMICALS (THAILAND) CO., LTD. - RAYONG PLANT—See AGC Inc.; *Int'l*, pg. 201
AGC INC.; *Int'l*, pg. 200
AGRI-EMPRESA INC.; *U.S. Private*, pg. 129
AGROSTULLN GMBH—See ASTRA INDUSTRIAL GROUP COMPANY; *Int'l*, pg. 657
AGSTAR PLC; *Int'l*, pg. 221
AICA THAI CHEMICAL LTD.—See AICA Kogyo Company, Limited; *Int'l*, pg. 228
A.I.M. CHEMICAL INDUSTRIES PTE LTD—See AP Oil International Ltd.; *Int'l*, pg. 499
AIR PRODUCTS CANADA LTD.—See Air Products & Chemicals, Inc.; *U.S. Public*, pg. 64
AIR PRODUCTS CANADA LTD.—See Air Products & Chemicals, Inc.; *U.S. Public*, pg. 64
AIR PRODUCTS CANADA LTD.—See Air Products & Chemicals, Inc.; *U.S. Public*, pg. 64
AIR PRODUCTS CANADA LTD.—See Air Products & Chemicals, Inc.; *U.S. Public*, pg. 64
AIR PRODUCTS CANADA LTD.—See Air Products & Chemicals, Inc.; *U.S. Public*, pg. 64
AIR PRODUCTS CHINA INC.—See Air Products & Chemicals, Inc.; *U.S. Public*, pg. 64
AIR PRODUCTS NEDERLAND B.V.-CHEMICALS DIV—See Air Products & Chemicals, Inc.; *U.S. Public*, pg. 65
AIR PRODUCTS N.V.—See Air Products & Chemicals, Inc.; *U.S. Public*, pg. 65
AIR PRODUCTS N.V.—See Air Products & Chemicals, Inc.; *U.S. Public*, pg. 65
AIR PRODUCTS PLC—See Air Products & Chemicals, Inc.; *U.S. Public*, pg. 65
AIR PRODUCTS SAN FU CO., LTD.—See Air Products & Chemicals, Inc.; *U.S. Public*, pg. 65
AIR PRODUCTS-SPECIALTY GASES FACILITY—See Air Products & Chemicals, Inc.; *U.S. Public*, pg. 66
AIRSEC S.A.S.—See Clariant AG; *Int'l*, pg. 1646
AISLAPOL S.A.—See BASF SE; *Int'l*, pg. 872
AKITA ZINC RECYCLING CO., LTD.—See Dowa Holdings Co., Ltd.; *Int'l*, pg. 2183
AKSHARCHEM (INDIA) LIMITED; *Int'l*, pg. 264
AK VINA CO., LTD.—See AK Holdings, Inc.; *Int'l*, pg. 259
AKZO NOBEL CHEMICAL LTD.—See GIC Pte. Ltd.; *Int'l*, pg. 2967
AKZO NOBEL CHEMICAL LTD.—See The Carlyle Group Inc.; *U.S. Public*, pg. 2050
AKZO NOBEL CHEMICALS S.A.—See GIC Pte. Ltd.; *Int'l*, pg. 2968
AKZO NOBEL CHEMICALS S.A.—See The Carlyle Group Inc.; *U.S. Public*, pg. 2051
AKZO NOBEL CROSS LINKING PEROXIDES (NINGBO) CO. LTD—See Akzo Nobel N.V.; *Int'l*, pg. 269
AKZO NOBEL FUNCTIONAL CHEMICALS AB—See GIC Pte. Ltd.; *Int'l*, pg. 2968
AKZO NOBEL FUNCTIONAL CHEMICALS AB—See The Carlyle Group Inc.; *U.S. Public*, pg. 2051
AKZO NOBEL FUNCTIONAL CHEMICALS VERWALTUNGS-GMBH—See GIC Pte. Ltd.; *Int'l*, pg. 2968
AKZO NOBEL FUNCTIONAL CHEMICALS VERWALTUNGS-GMBH—See The Carlyle Group Inc.; *U.S. Public*, pg. 2051
AKZONOBEL INDIA LTD.—See Akzo Nobel N.V.; *Int'l*, pg. 273

N.A.I.C.S. INDEX

325998 — ALL OTHER MISCELLAN...

AKZO NOBEL INDUSTRIAL CHEMICALS AB—See GIC Pte. Ltd.; *Int'l*, pg. 2968
AKZO NOBEL INDUSTRIAL CHEMICALS AB—See The Carlyle Group Inc.; *U.S. Public*, pg. 2051
AKZO NOBEL LTDA.—See Akzo Nobel N.V.; *Int'l*, pg. 272
AKZO NOBEL NEDERLAND BV—See Akzo Nobel N.V.; *Int'l*, pg. 272
AKZO NOBEL PERFORMANCE COATINGS—See Akzo Nobel N.V.; *Int'l*, pg. 272
AKZO NOBEL POLYMER CHEMICALS (NINGBO) CO., LTD.—See Akzo Nobel N.V.; *Int'l*, pg. 272
AKZO NOBEL PULP AND PERFORMANCE CHEMICALS AB—See GIC Pte. Ltd.; *Int'l*, pg. 2968
AKZO NOBEL PULP AND PERFORMANCE CHEMICALS AB—See The Carlyle Group Inc.; *U.S. Public*, pg. 2051
AKZO NOBEL PULP AND PERFORMANCE CHEMICALS NORWAY AS—See GIC Pte. Ltd.; *Int'l*, pg. 2968
AKZO NOBEL PULP AND PERFORMANCE CHEMICALS NORWAY AS—See The Carlyle Group Inc.; *U.S. Public*, pg. 2051
AKZO NOBEL SALT B.V.—See Akzo Nobel N.V.; *Int'l*, pg. 273
AKZO NOBEL S.A.S.—See Akzo Nobel N.V.; *Int'l*, pg. 273
AKZO NOBEL SOURCING B.V.—See Akzo Nobel N.V.; *Int'l*, pg. 273
AKZO NOBEL UK LIMITED—See GIC Pte. Ltd.; *Int'l*, pg. 2968
AKZO NOBEL UK LIMITED—See The Carlyle Group Inc.; *U.S. Public*, pg. 2051
ALAC INTERNATIONAL, INC.; *U.S. Private*, pg. 148
ALBEMARLE CORPORATION; *U.S. Public*, pg. 72
ALBEMARLE GERMANY GMBH—See Albemarle Corporation; *U.S. Public*, pg. 73
ALBEMARLE LIMITADA—See Albemarle Corporation; *U.S. Public*, pg. 73
ALBEMARLE LITHIUM PTY. LTD.—See Albemarle Corporation; *U.S. Public*, pg. 73
ALBEMARLE U.S., INC.—See Albemarle Corporation; *U.S. Public*, pg. 73
ALBI MANUFACTURING—See SK Capital Partners, LP; *U.S. Private*, pg. 3679
ALDEN LEEDS, INC.; *U.S. Private*, pg. 159
ALKALI METALS LIMITED; *Int'l*, pg. 330
ALLIED UNIVERSAL CORP.—See Allied Universal Holding Corporation; *U.S. Private*, pg. 188
ALLNEX AUSTRIA GMBH—See Advent International Corporation; *U.S. Private*, pg. 98
ALLNEX NORGE KS—See Advent International Corporation; *U.S. Private*, pg. 98
ALLTECH APPLIED SCIENCE B.V.—See Standard Industries Holdings Inc.; *U.S. Private*, pg. 3779
ALS LIMITED; *Int'l*, pg. 377
ALTECH BATTERIES LIMITED; *Int'l*, pg. 388
ALZCHEM HOLDING GMBH—See BLUO SICAV-SIF; *Int'l*, pg. 1075
ALZCHEM LLC—See AlzChem Group AG; *Int'l*, pg. 402
ALZCHEM TROSTBERG GMBH—See BLUO SICAV-SIF; *Int'l*, pg. 1075
ALZCHEM UK LTD.—See AlzChem Group AG; *Int'l*, pg. 402
AMARAK CHEMICALS FZC—See Aries Agro Limited; *Int'l*, pg. 564
AMBER SILICONES (TIANJIN) CO. LTD.—See Akoya Capital LLC; *U.S. Private*, pg. 146
AMBER SILICONES (TIANJIN) CO. LTD.—See Century Park Capital Partners, LLC; *U.S. Private*, pg. 834
AMBICA AGARBATHIES & AROMA INDUSTRIES LTD.; *Int'l*, pg. 414
AMERICAN AZIDE CORPORATION—See H.I.G. Capital, LLC; *U.S. Private*, pg. 1829
AMERICAN COLLOID COMPANY—See Minerals Technologies, Inc.; *U.S. Public*, pg. 1448
AMETEK CHEMICAL PRODUCTS—See AMETEK, Inc.; *U.S. Public*, pg. 117
AMG VANADIUM, INC.—See AMG Critical Materials N.V.; *Int'l*, pg. 425
AMICOGEN, INC. - 2ND MANUFACTURING FACILITY—See Amicogen, Inc.; *Int'l*, pg. 427
AMICOGEN, INC.; *Int'l*, pg. 427
AMINCO CHOLINE CHLORIDE (SHANGHAI) CO., LTD.—See Eastman Chemical Company; *U.S. Public*, pg. 706
AMINES & PLASTICIZERS LIMITED; *Int'l*, pg. 427
AMINES & PLASTICIZERS LIMITED - UNIT-II—See AMINES & PLASTICIZERS LIMITED; *Int'l*, pg. 428
AMINES & PLASTICIZERS LIMITED - UNIT-I—See AMINES & PLASTICIZERS LIMITED; *Int'l*, pg. 428
AMIR SEMEL PACKAGING & CHEMICALS LTD.—See BERICAP GmbH & Co. KG; *Int'l*, pg. 980
AM STABILIZERS CORP.—See Adeka Corporation; *Int'l*, pg. 142
ANATRACE PRODUCTS, LLC—See StoneCalibre, LLC; *U.S. Private*, pg. 3827
ANCHOR CHEMICALS (PTY) LTD—See Hobart Enterprises Ltd; *Int'l*, pg. 3436
ANDERSON CHEMICAL COMPANY INC.—See NCH Corporation; *U.S. Public*, pg. 2876
THE ANDERSONS DENISON ETHANOL LLC—See The Andersons Incorporated; *U.S. Public*, pg. 2035

ANGSTROM TECHNOLOGIES INC.; *U.S. Public*, pg. 137
ANHUI ANNADA TITANIUM INDUSTRY CO., LTD.; *Int'l*, pg. 466
ANHUI HUANGSHAN CAPSULE CO., LTD.; *Int'l*, pg. 468
ANHUI HUAYE AROMAS HEFEI CO., LTD.—See Anhui Hyea Aromas Co., Ltd.; *Int'l*, pg. 468
ANHUI JINHE INDUSTRIAL CO., LTD.; *Int'l*, pg. 468
ANHUI WANWEI UPDATED HI-TECH MATERIAL INDUSTRY COMPANY LIMITED; *Int'l*, pg. 470
ANPARIO PLC; *Int'l*, pg. 474
ANSHAN HIFICHEM CO., LTD.; *Int'l*, pg. 479
ANTONG HOLDINGS CO., LTD.; *Int'l*, pg. 485
APEXICAL, INC.; *U.S. Private*, pg. 293
APISCENT LABS, LLC; *U.S. Private*, pg. 294
APPLE FLAVOR & FRAGRANCE GROUP CO., LTD.; *Int'l*, pg. 520
APPLICHEM GMBH—See Illinois Tool Works Inc.; *U.S. Public*, pg. 1101
APPLIED BIOCHEMIST INC.—See SePRO Corporation; *U.S. Private*, pg. 3611
APYRON TECHNOLOGIES, INC.—See Streamline Capital, Inc.; *U.S. Private*, pg. 3838
ARAB POTASH COMPANY PLC - POTASH PLANT—See Arab Potash Company PLC; *Int'l*, pg. 531
ARAKAWA CHEMICAL INDUSTRIES, LTD.; *Int'l*, pg. 534
ARAKAWA CHEMICAL (USA) INC.—See Arakawa Chemical Industries, Ltd.; *Int'l*, pg. 534
ARCHROMA MANAGEMENT GMBH—See SK Capital Partners, LP; *U.S. Private*, pg. 3679
ARGUS (SHANGHAI) TEXTILE AUXILIARY CO., LTD.—See Argus (Shanghai) Textile Chemicals Co., Ltd.; *Int'l*, pg. 563
ARKEMA (CHANGSHU) POLYAMIDES CO., LTD.—See Arkema S.A.; *Int'l*, pg. 568
ARKEMA CHEMICALS INDIA PRIVATE LTD.—See Arkema S.A.; *Int'l*, pg. 568
ARKEMA CHEMICALS SAUDI ARABIA—See Arkema S.A.; *Int'l*, pg. 568
ARKEMA COATING RESINS LTD.—See Arkema S.A.; *Int'l*, pg. 569
ARKEMA COATING RESINS MALAYSIA SDN. BHD.—See Arkema S.A.; *Int'l*, pg. 569
ARKEMA COMPANY LTD.—See Arkema S.A.; *Int'l*, pg. 569
ARKEMA GMBH—See Arkema S.A.; *Int'l*, pg. 569
ARKEMA INC.—See Arkema S.A.; *Int'l*, pg. 569
ARKEMA INICIADORES SA DE CV—See Arkema S.A.; *Int'l*, pg. 569
ARKEMA KIMYA SANAYI VE TICARET AS—See Arkema S.A.; *Int'l*, pg. 569
ARKEMA ROTTERDAM BV—See Arkema S.A.; *Int'l*, pg. 568
ARKEMA (SUZHOU) POLYAMIDES CO., LTD.—See Arkema S.A.; *Int'l*, pg. 568
ARKION LIFE SCIENCES L.L.C.; *U.S. Private*, pg. 326
AROMA CELTE SA; *Int'l*, pg. 577
ARRMAZ CHEMICALS (YUNNAN) CO., LTD.—See Arkema S.A.; *Int'l*, pg. 570
ARR-MAZ DO BRASIL LTDA.—See Arkema S.A.; *Int'l*, pg. 570
ARRMAZ GULF CHEMICAL COMPANY LTD.—See Arkema S.A.; *Int'l*, pg. 570
ARRMAZ MOROCCO SARLAU—See Arkema S.A.; *Int'l*, pg. 570
ASAHI GLASS CO., LTD. - CHIBA PLANT—See AGC Inc.; *Int'l*, pg. 203
ASAHI KASEI (CHINA) CO., LTD.—See Asahi Kasei Corporation; *Int'l*, pg. 594
ASAHI KASEI EPOXY CO., LTD.—See Asahi Kasei Corporation; *Int'l*, pg. 595
ASAHI KASEI FINECHEM CO., LTD.—See Asahi Kasei Corporation; *Int'l*, pg. 595
ASAHIKASEI PLASTICS (THAILAND) CO., LTD.—See Asahi Kasei Corporation; *Int'l*, pg. 596
ASAHI PHOTOPRODUCTS EUROPE N.V./S.A.—See Asahi Kasei Corporation; *Int'l*, pg. 595
ASHLAND CANADA CORP.—See Ashland Inc.; *U.S. Public*, pg. 211
ASHLAND (CHINA) HOLDINGS CO., LTD.—See Ashland Inc.; *U.S. Public*, pg. 211
ASHLAND FRANCE SAS—See Ashland Inc.; *U.S. Public*, pg. 211
ASHLAND INDUSTRIES FRANCE SAS—See Ashland Inc.; *U.S. Public*, pg. 212
ASHLAND INDUSTRIES ITALIA S.R.L.—See Ashland Inc.; *U.S. Public*, pg. 212
ASHLAND INDUSTRIES NEDERLAND B.V.—See Ashland Inc.; *U.S. Public*, pg. 212
ASHLAND INDUSTRIES UK LIMITED—See Ashland Inc.; *U.S. Public*, pg. 212
ASHLAND PERFORMANCE MATERIALS—See Ashland Inc.; *U.S. Public*, pg. 211
ASHLAND SPECIALTY INGREDIENTS—See Ashland Inc.; *U.S. Public*, pg. 212
ASK CHEMICALS GMBH—See Rhone Group, LLC; *U.S. Private*, pg. 3423
ASPEN AEROGELS, INC.; *U.S. Public*, pg. 213
ASTEC LIFESCIENCES LTD; *Int'l*, pg. 651
ATCO INTERNATIONAL CORPORATION; *U.S. Private*, pg. 365

ATLAS CONSOLIDATED INDUSTRIES (PTY) LIMITED—See AECI Limited; *Int'l*, pg. 171
AURORIUM HOLDINGS LLC—See The Pritzker Group - Chicago, LLC; *U.S. Public*, pg. 4098
AVANTIUM HOLDING BV; *Int'l*, pg. 736
AVANTOR PERFORMANCE MATERIALS S.A. DE C.V.—See Avantor, Inc.; *U.S. Public*, pg. 241
AVANTOR PERFORMANCE MATERIALS SDN BHD—See Avantor, Inc.; *U.S. Public*, pg. 241
AVCHEM, INC.—See Platinum Equity, LLC; *U.S. Private*, pg. 3210
AVECIA NV/SA—See Avecia Ltd.; *Int'l*, pg. 737
AVIAN ENTERPRISES, LLC; *U.S. Private*, pg. 406
AVIENT COLORANTS MALAYSIA SDN. BHD.—See Avient Corporation; *U.S. Public*, pg. 246
AVIENT COLORANTS SINGAPORE PTE. LTD.—See Avient Corporation; *U.S. Public*, pg. 247
AVIENT COLORANTS (THAILAND) LTD.—See Avient Corporation; *U.S. Public*, pg. 246
AVIENT SINGAPORE PTE. LTD.—See Avient Corporation; *U.S. Public*, pg. 247
AXICHEM AB; *Int'l*, pg. 768
AXYS INDUSTRIAL SOLUTIONS, INC.; *U.S. Private*, pg. 414
AZELIS A/S—See EQT AB; *Int'l*, pg. 2469
AZELIS FOOD & HEALTH—See EQT AB; *Int'l*, pg. 2469
AZUMA BUSSAN LTD.—See BASF SE; *Int'l*, pg. 871
BACHEM DISTRIBUTION SERVICES GMBH—See Bachem Holding AG; *Int'l*, pg. 795
BACHEM (UK) LTD.—See Bachem Holding AG; *Int'l*, pg. 794
BACHMAN SERVICES INC.—See Innospec Inc.; *U.S. Public*, pg. 1125
BACTIGUARD HOLDING AB; *Int'l*, pg. 795
BAKER PETROLITE LLC—See Baker Hughes Company; *U.S. Public*, pg. 265
BALCHEM ITALIA, S.R.L.—See Balchem Corporation; *U.S. Public*, pg. 265
BANNER CHEMICALS-BIOCIDES—See Banner Chemicals Limited; *Int'l*, pg. 851
BANNER CHEMICALS-COSMETICS & PERSONAL CARE—See Banner Chemicals Limited; *Int'l*, pg. 851
BANNER CHEMICALS-HYDROCARBON SOLVENTS—See Banner Chemicals Limited; *Int'l*, pg. 851
BANNER CHEMICALS LIMITED; *Int'l*, pg. 851
BANNER CHEMICALS-PRECISION & ELECTRONICS CLEANING—See Banner Chemicals Limited; *Int'l*, pg. 851
BAOTOU DONGBAO BIO-TECH CO., LTD.; *Int'l*, pg. 856
BARENTZ INTERNATIONAL B.V.—See Cinven Limited; *Int'l*, pg. 1611
BASECLICK GMBH—See BASF SE; *Int'l*, pg. 886
BASF AGRICULTURAL PRODUCTS GROUP CORPORATION—See BASF SE; *Int'l*, pg. 872
BASF AGRO B.V. - ARNHEM (NL)—See BASF SE; *Int'l*, pg. 877
BASF AGRO HELLAS INDUSTRIAL AND COMMERCIAL S.A.—See BASF SE; *Int'l*, pg. 877
BASF AGRO, —See BASF SE; *Int'l*, pg. 877
BASF ANTWERPEN N.V.—See BASF SE; *Int'l*, pg. 872
BASF A/S—See BASF SE; *Int'l*, pg. 871
BASF A/S—See BASF SE; *Int'l*, pg. 874
BASF BANGLADESH LIMITED—See BASF SE; *Int'l*, pg. 878
BASF BAUTECHNIK GMBH—See BASF SE; *Int'l*, pg. 872
BASF BELGIUM COORDINATION CENTER COMMV—See BASF SE; *Int'l*, pg. 872
BASF BETEILIGUNGSGESELLSCHAFT MBH—See BASF SE; *Int'l*, pg. 872
BASF BIORENEWABLE BETEILIGUNGS GMBH & CO. KG—See BASF SE; *Int'l*, pg. 872
BASF CANADA INC.—See BASF SE; *Int'l*, pg. 875
BASF CARE CHEMICALS (SHANGHAI) CO. LTD.—See BASF SE; *Int'l*, pg. 877
BASF CATALYST CANADA ULC—See BASF SE; *Int'l*, pg. 875
BASF CATALYSTS CANADA B.V.—See BASF SE; *Int'l*, pg. 875
BASF CATALYSTS DELAWARE LLC—See BASF SE; *Int'l*, pg. 875
BASF CATALYSTS GRUNDBESITZ GMBH—See BASF SE; *Int'l*, pg. 872
BASF CATALYSTS LLC - PROCESS TECHNOLOGIES—See BASF SE; *Int'l*, pg. 875
BASF CATALYSTS (SHANGHAI) CO. LTD.—See BASF SE; *Int'l*, pg. 875
BASF CHEMICALS (SHANGHAI) CO., LTD.—See BASF SE; *Int'l*, pg. 877
BASF CHEMIKALIEN GMBH—See BASF SE; *Int'l*, pg. 872
BASF (CHINA) CO., LTD. - BEIJING—See BASF SE; *Int'l*, pg. 877
BASF (CHINA) CO., LTD. - GUANGZHOU—See BASF SE; *Int'l*, pg. 877
BASF (CHINA) CO., LTD.—See BASF SE; *Int'l*, pg. 877
BASF CHINA LTD.—See BASF SE; *Int'l*, pg. 877
BASF COATING SERVICES (PTY) LTD.—See BASF SE; *Int'l*, pg. 872

325998 — ALL OTHER MISCELLAN...

BASF COATING SERVICES S.A.S.—See BASF SE; *Int'l*, pg. 872
BASF COATINGS GMBH—See BASF SE; *Int'l*, pg. 872
BASF COATINGS INDIA PRIVATE LTD.—See BASF SE; *Int'l*, pg. 872
BASF COATINGS NEDERLAND B.V.—See BASF SE; *Int'l*, pg. 872
BASF COATINGS SERVICES AG—See BASF SE; *Int'l*, pg. 873
BASF COATINGS SERVICES S.R.O.—See BASF SE; *Int'l*, pg. 873
BASF COATINGS S.P.A.—See BASF SE; *Int'l*, pg. 873
BASF COLORS & EFFECTS SWITZERLAND AG—See BASF SE; *Int'l*, pg. 874
BASF COLOR SOLUTIONS GERMANY GMBH—See BASF SE; *Int'l*, pg. 874
BASF CONSTRUCTION ADDITIVES GMBH—See BASF SE; *Int'l*, pg. 874
BASF CONSTRUCTION CHEMICALS ALGERIA S.A.R.L.—See BASF SE; *Int'l*, pg. 874
BASF CONSTRUCTION CHEMICALS EUROPE AG—See BASF SE; *Int'l*, pg. 874
BASF CONSTRUCTION CHEMICALS GRUNDBESITZ GMBH & CO. KG—See BASF SE; *Int'l*, pg. 875
BASF CONSTRUCTION CHEMICALS ITALIA SPA—See BASF SE; *Int'l*, pg. 874
BASF CONSTRUCTION CHEMICALS LTDA.—See BASF SE; *Int'l*, pg. 874
BASF CONSTRUCTION CHEMICALS PERU S.A.—See BASF SE; *Int'l*, pg. 874
BASF CONSTRUCTION CHEMICALS (PTY) LTD—See BASF SE; *Int'l*, pg. 874
BASF CONSTRUCTION SOLUTIONS GMBH—See BASF SE; *Int'l*, pg. 875
BASF CONSTRUCTION SYSTEMS (CHINA) CO. LTD.—See BASF SE; *Int'l*, pg. 875
BASF COORDINATION CENTER COMM.V.—See BASF SE; *Int'l*, pg. 875
BASF CORP. - AMBLER - CARE CHEMICALS—See BASF SE; *Int'l*, pg. 876
BASF CORP. - APPLETON PLANT—See BASF SE; *Int'l*, pg. 876
BASF CORP. - FREEPORT PLANT—See BASF SE; *Int'l*, pg. 876
BASF CORP. - GEISMAR PLANT—See BASF SE; *Int'l*, pg. 876
BASF CORP. - INDEPENDENCE—See BASF SE; *Int'l*, pg. 876
BASF CORP. - MONACA POLYMERS PLANT—See BASF SE; *Int'l*, pg. 876
BASF CORP. - WASHINGTON PLANT—See BASF SE; *Int'l*, pg. 876
BASF CORP. - WEST MEMPHIS PLANT—See BASF SE; *Int'l*, pg. 876
BASF CORP. - WHITE STONE PLANT—See BASF SE; *Int'l*, pg. 876
BASF (CZECH) SPOL. S R.O.—See BASF SE; *Int'l*, pg. 871
BASF DE GUATEMALA, S.A.—See BASF SE; *Int'l*, pg. 882
BASF DE NICARAGUA S.A.—See BASF SE; *Int'l*, pg. 882
BASF ELECTRONIC MATERIALS TAIWAN—See BASF SE; *Int'l*, pg. 878
BASF EOOD—See BASF SE; *Int'l*, pg. 877
BASF FINANCE EUROPE N.V.—See BASF SE; *Int'l*, pg. 880
BASF FINE CHEMICALS SWITZERLAND SA—See BASF SE; *Int'l*, pg. 871
BASF FOOD—See BASF SE; *Int'l*, pg. 878
BASF FZE—See BASF SE; *Int'l*, pg. 878
BASF GRENZACH GMBH—See BASF SE; *Int'l*, pg. 879
BASF HELLAS INDUSTRIAL AND COMMERCIAL S.A.—See BASF SE; *Int'l*, pg. 879
BASF IDEMITSU CO., LTD.—See BASF SE; *Int'l*, pg. 878
BASF IDEMITSU CO., LTD.—See Idemitsu Kosan Co., Ltd.; *Int'l*, pg. 3591
BASF IMMOBILIEN PIGMENT GMBH—See BASF SE; *Int'l*, pg. 879
BASF INDIA LTD.—See BASF SE; *Int'l*, pg. 878
BASF INDUSTRIAL METALS LLC—See BASF SE; *Int'l*, pg. 879
BASF INTERSERVICE SPA—See BASF SE; *Int'l*, pg. 879
BASF INTERTRADE AG—See BASF SE; *Int'l*, pg. 871
BASF IRAN (PJS) CO.—See BASF SE; *Int'l*, pg. 879
BASF IRELAND LIMITED—See BASF SE; *Int'l*, pg. 879
BASF ITALIA - CENTRO CUOIO—See BASF SE; *Int'l*, pg. 879
BASF ITALIA - CENTRO RICERCA E SVILUPPO—See BASF SE; *Int'l*, pg. 879
BASF ITALIA - ESPANSI—See BASF SE; *Int'l*, pg. 879
BASF JAPAN LTD. - OSAKA—See BASF SE; *Int'l*, pg. 878
BASF JAPAN LTD.—See BASF SE; *Int'l*, pg. 878
BASF KAISTEN AG—See BASF SE; *Int'l*, pg. 871
BASF LAMPERTHEIM GMBH—See BASF SE; *Int'l*, pg. 880
BASF-LANKA (PVT.) LTD.—See BASF SE; *Int'l*, pg. 878
BASF LEUNA GMBH—See BASF SE; *Int'l*, pg. 880
BASF (MALAYSIA) SDN. BHD.—See BASF SE; *Int'l*, pg. 878
BASF METALS GMBH—See BASF SE; *Int'l*, pg. 880
BASF METALS JAPAN LTD.—See BASF SE; *Int'l*, pg. 880
BASF METALS LTD.—See BASF SE; *Int'l*, pg. 880

BASF MOBILIENLEASING GMBH—See BASF SE; *Int'l*, pg. 880
BASF NEDERLAND B.V.—See BASF SE; *Int'l*, pg. 880
BASF NEDERLAND B.V.—See BASF SE; *Int'l*, pg. 880
BASF OPERATIONS B.V.—See BASF SE; *Int'l*, pg. 880
BASF OSTERREICH GMBH—See BASF SE; *Int'l*, pg. 880
BASF OY - WOLMAN DIVISION—See BASF SE; *Int'l*, pg. 880
BASF PAPER CHEMICALS (JIANGSU) CO. LTD.—See BASF SE; *Int'l*, pg. 880
BASF PERFORMANCE PRODUCTS FRANCE - GRON PLANT—See BASF SE; *Int'l*, pg. 879
BASF PERFORMANCE PRODUCTS GMBH—See BASF SE; *Int'l*, pg. 880
BASF PERFORMANCE PRODUCTS LTD.—See BASF SE; *Int'l*, pg. 880
BASF PERFORMANCE PRODUCTS PLC - BRADFORD PLANT—See BASF SE; *Int'l*, pg. 882
BASF PERUANA S.A.—See BASF SE; *Int'l*, pg. 880
BASF PIGMENT GMBH—See BASF SE; *Int'l*, pg. 880
BASF POLIURETANI ITALIA SPA—See BASF SE; *Int'l*, pg. 881
BASF POLIURETANOS LTDA.—See BASF SE; *Int'l*, pg. 881
BASF POLIURETANOS S.A.—See BASF SE; *Int'l*, pg. 872
BASF POLSKA SP. Z O. O—See BASF SE; *Int'l*, pg. 880
BASF POLYURETHANE LICENSING GMBH—See BASF SE; *Int'l*, pg. 881
BASF POLYURETHANES BENELUX B.V.—See BASF SE; *Int'l*, pg. 881
BASF POLYURETHANES (CHONGQING) CO. LTD.—See BASF SE; *Int'l*, pg. 881
BASF POLYURETHANES NORDIC AB—See BASF SE; *Int'l*, pg. 881
BASF POLYURETHANE SPECIALTIES (CHINA) CO. LTD.—See BASF SE; *Int'l*, pg. 881
BASF PROCESS CATALYSTS GMBH—See BASF SE; *Int'l*, pg. 881
BASF REPRESENTATION BELARUS—See BASF SE; *Int'l*, pg. 881
BASF S.A.—See BASF SE; *Int'l*, pg. 881
BASF (SCHWEIZ) AG—See BASF SE; *Int'l*, pg. 871
BASF SEE SEN SDN. BHD.—See BASF SE; *Int'l*, pg. 878
BASF SE - EUROPEAN GOVERNMENTAL AFFAIRS—See BASF SE; *Int'l*, pg. 872
BASF SERVICES (MALAYSIA) SDN. BHD.—See BASF SE; *Int'l*, pg. 881
BASF STAVEBNI HMOTY CESKA REPUBLIKA S.R.O.—See BASF SE; *Int'l*, pg. 881
BASF TAIWAN B.V.—See BASF SE; *Int'l*, pg. 881
BASF TAIWAN LTD.—See BASF SE; *Int'l*, pg. 878
BASF (THAI) LTD.—See BASF SE; *Int'l*, pg. 878
BASF TRADING EGYPT S.A.E.—See BASF SE; *Int'l*, pg. 881
BASF TURK KIMYA SANAYI VE TICARET LTD. STI.—See BASF SE; *Int'l*, pg. 882
BASF UAB—See BASF SE; *Int'l*, pg. 882
BASF URUGUAYA S.A.—See BASF SE; *Int'l*, pg. 882
BASF VENEZOLANA, S.A.—See BASF SE; *Int'l*, pg. 882
BASF VENEZUELA S.A.—See BASF SE; *Int'l*, pg. 882
BASF VIETNAM CO. LTD.—See BASF SE; *Int'l*, pg. 882
BASF WOHNEN + BAUEN GMBH—See BASF SE; *Int'l*, pg. 882
BASLINI S.P.A.; *Int'l*, pg. 887
BAYER CHEMICALS AG—See Bayer Aktiengesellschaft; *Int'l*, pg. 902
BAYER CROPSCIENCE N.V.—See Bayer Aktiengesellschaft; *Int'l*, pg. 903
BAYER MATERIALSCIENCE AUSTRALIA—See Bayer Aktiengesellschaft; *Int'l*, pg. 902
BAYER MATERIALSCIENCE (CHINA) COMPANY LIMITED—See Bayer Aktiengesellschaft; *Int'l*, pg. 907
BAYER SA-NV—See Bayer Aktiengesellschaft; *Int'l*, pg. 906
BAYER S.P.A.—See Bayer Aktiengesellschaft; *Int'l*, pg. 906
BAYPO I LLC—See Bayer Aktiengesellschaft; *Int'l*, pg. 902
BBC BIOCHEMICAL CORP—See Audax Group, Limited Partnership; *U.S. Private*, pg. 389
BBCC-BUSINESS BELUX-BTC—See BASF SE; *Int'l*, pg. 882
BBCC - EU GOVERNMENT RELATIONS BASF GROUP B.V.—See BASF SE; *Int'l*, pg. 882
BEFAR GROUP CO., LTD.; *Int'l*, pg. 939
BEIJING APPLE KAIXIN FOODS TECH CO., LTD.—See Apple Flavor & Fragrance Group Co., Ltd.; *Int'l*, pg. 520
BEIJING CHOSTAR EQUIPMENT ENGINEERING TECHNOLOGY CO., LTD.—See Chori Co., Ltd.; *Int'l*, pg. 1583
BEIJING HAIXIN ENERGY TECHNOLOGY CO., LTD.; *Int'l*, pg. 951
BEST CHEM, LTD.—See Momar, Inc.; *U.S. Private*, pg. 2767
BETCO CORPORATION; *U.S. Private*, pg. 545
BHASKAR AGROCHEMICALS LTD.; *Int'l*, pg. 1013
BIDACHEM S.P.A.—See C.H. Boehringer Sohn AG & Co. KG; *Int'l*, pg. 1242
BIO-GATE AG; *Int'l*, pg. 1035
BIOLARGO ENGINEERING, SCIENCE & TECHNOLOGIES, LLC—See BioLargo, Inc.; *U.S. Public*, pg. 337
BIOLARGO, INC.; *U.S. Public*, pg. 337
BIONEUTRAL GROUP, INC.; *U.S. Private*, pg. 562

CORPORATE AFFILIATIONS

BIOSCIENCE NEUTRACEUTICALS, INC.; *U.S. Public*, pg. 338
BIOU (ZHEJIANG) FOOD INDUSTRY CO., LTD.—See Apple Flavor & Fragrance Group Co., Ltd.; *Int'l*, pg. 520
BITUMINEX COCHIN PVT LTD—See Agarwal Industrial Corporation Ltd.; *Int'l*, pg. 200
BLACK ROSE INDUSTRIES LTD.; *Int'l*, pg. 1060
BLI LEGACY, INC.—See New Water Capital, L.P.; *U.S. Private*, pg. 2907
BLUEPRINT PRODUCTS N.V.—See Heidelberger Druckmaschinen AG; *Int'l*, pg. 3321
BLUESTAR ADISSEO COMPANY LIMITED; *Int'l*, pg. 1074
BLUESTAR (BEIJING) CHEMICAL MACHINERY CO., LTD.—See Bluestar Adisseo Company Limited; *Int'l*, pg. 1074
BLUESTAR HARBIN PETROCHEMICAL CORPORATION—See Bluestar Adisseo Company Limited; *Int'l*, pg. 1074
BLUESTAR SILICON MATERIAL CO. LTD.—See Bluestar Adisseo Company Limited; *Int'l*, pg. 1074
BLUESTAR WUXI PETROCHEMICAL CO LTD—See Bluestar Adisseo Company Limited; *Int'l*, pg. 1074
BOAI NKY MEDICAL HOLDINGS LTD.; *Int'l*, pg. 1094
BOEHRINGER INGELHEIM CHEMICALS, INC.—See C.H. Boehringer Sohn AG & Co. KG; *Int'l*, pg. 1241
BONIDE PRODUCTS, INC.—See China National Chemical Corporation; *Int'l*, pg. 1526
BORCHERS SAS—See The Jordan Company, L.P.; *U.S. Private*, pg. 4060
BORDER CHEMICAL CO., LTD.; *Int'l*, pg. 1113
BORREGAARD ASA; *Int'l*, pg. 1115
BORYSZEW S.A.; *Int'l*, pg. 1115
BOSTIK FINDLEY CHINA CO., LTD.—See Arkema S.A.; *Int'l*, pg. 570
BOSTIK L.L.C.—See Arkema S.A.; *Int'l*, pg. 570
BOSTIK-NITTA CO., LTD.—See Arkema S.A.; *Int'l*, pg. 570
BP BELGIUM NV/SA—See BP plc; *Int'l*, pg. 1128
BP CHEMBEL N.V.—See BP plc; *Int'l*, pg. 1128
BPI BY-PRODUCT INDUSTRIES; *U.S. Private*, pg. 629
BRAND-NU LABORATORIES INC.; *U.S. Private*, pg. 637
BREATHABLEBABY, LLC—See Transom Capital Group, LLC; *U.S. Private*, pg. 4209
BRENNTAG ARGENTINA S.A.—See BRENNTAG SE; *Int'l*, pg. 1147
BRENNTAG BOLIVIA SRL—See BRENNTAG SE; *Int'l*, pg. 1147
BRENNTAG BRASIL LTDA.—See BRENNTAG SE; *Int'l*, pg. 1147
BRENNTAG BULGARIA LTD—See BRENNTAG SE; *Int'l*, pg. 1146
BRENNTAG CANADA INC.—See BRENNTAG SE; *Int'l*, pg. 1146
BRENNTAG CARIBE S.A.—See BRENNTAG SE; *Int'l*, pg. 1147
BRENNTAG CHILE LTDA.—See BRENNTAG SE; *Int'l*, pg. 1147
BRENNTAG COLOMBIA S. A.—See BRENNTAG SE; *Int'l*, pg. 1147
BRENNTAG ECUADOR S. A.—See BRENNTAG SE; *Int'l*, pg. 1147
BRENNTAG GMBH—See BRENNTAG SE; *Int'l*, pg. 1147
BRENNTAG GREAT LAKES, LLC—See BRENNTAG SE; *Int'l*, pg. 1148
BRENNTAG GUATEMALA S. A.—See BRENNTAG SE; *Int'l*, pg. 1147
BRENNTAG INGREDIENTS (INDIA) PRIVATE LIMITED—See BRENNTAG SE; *Int'l*, pg. 1147
BRENNTAG LATIN AMERICA, INC.—See BRENNTAG SE; *Int'l*, pg. 1147
BRENNTAG MEXICO, S. A. DE C. V.—See BRENNTAG SE; *Int'l*, pg. 1147
BRENNTAG NICARAGUA, S.A.—See BRENNTAG SE; *Int'l*, pg. 1147
BRENNTAG NORTHEAST, INC.—See BRENNTAG SE; *Int'l*, pg. 1148
BRENNTAG PERU A. C.—See BRENNTAG SE; *Int'l*, pg. 1147
BRENNTAG SOUTHEAST, INC.—See BRENNTAG SE; *Int'l*, pg. 1148
BRENNTAG SOUTHWEST, INC.—See BRENNTAG SE; *Int'l*, pg. 1148
BRI-CHEM CORP.; *Int'l*, pg. 1151
BRIDGESTONE DIVERSIFIED CHEMICAL PRODUCTS CO., LTD.—See Bridgestone Corporation; *Int'l*, pg. 1158
BRILLIANT LAVENDER SDN BHD—See Momar, Inc.; *U.S. Private*, pg. 2767
BROTHER ENTERPRISES HOLDING CO., LTD.; *Int'l*, pg. 1196
BUCKMAN LABORATORIES, K.K.—See Bulab Holdings, Inc.; *U.S. Private*, pg. 683
BUCKMAN LABORATORIES, N.V.—See Bulab Holdings, Inc.; *U.S. Private*, pg. 684
BUCKMAN LABORATORIES PTY LTD.—See Bulab Holdings, Inc.; *U.S. Private*, pg. 683
BUDENHEIM USA, INC.—See Dr. August Oetker KG; *Int'l*, pg. 2190
BULGARIAN ROSE PLC; *Int'l*, pg. 1213
BULK CHEMICAL SERVICES, LLC - SANDERSVILLE

N.A.I.C.S. INDEX

325998 — ALL OTHER MISCELLAN...

PLANT—See Bulk Chemical Services, LLC; *U.S. Private*, pg. 684
BULK CHEMICAL SERVICES, LLC; *U.S. Private*, pg. 684
BURGESS PIGMENT COMPANY—See Burgess Pigment Company; *U.S. Private*, pg. 687
BURNISHINE PRODUCTS—See TA Associates, Inc.; *U.S. Private*, pg. 3919
BURNISHINE PRODUCTS—See The Carlyle Group Inc.; *U.S. Public*, pg. 2057
BURZYNSKI RESEARCH INSTITUTE, INC.; *U.S. Public*, pg. 412
BYUCKSAN CORPORATION - HUNA PLANT 1—See Byucksan Corporation; *Int'l*, pg. 1237
BYUCKSAN CORPORATION - HUNA PLANT 2—See Byucksan Corporation; *Int'l*, pg. 1237
BYUCKSAN PAINT & COATINGS CO., LTD.—See Byucksan Corporation; *Int'l*, pg. 1237
CABOT GMBH—See Cabot Corporation; *U.S. Public*, pg. 416
CABOT MALAYSIA SDN. BHD.—See Cabot Corporation; *U.S. Public*, pg. 417
CABOT MICROELECTRONICS JAPAN K.K.—See Entegris, Inc.; *U.S. Public*, pg. 776
CABOT PERFORMANCE MATERIALS (ZHUHAI) CO., LTD.—See Cabot Corporation; *U.S. Public*, pg. 417
CABOT SANMAR LTD.—See Cabot Corporation; *U.S. Public*, pg. 417
CABOT SPECIALTY CHEMICALS, INC.—See Cabot Corporation; *U.S. Public*, pg. 417
CABOT SPECIALTY CHEMICALS MEXICO S.A.P.I. DE C.V.—See Cabot Corporation; *U.S. Public*, pg. 417
CAF LLC; *U.S. Private*, pg. 714
CALCITECH LTD.; *Int'l*, pg. 1262
CALUMET PARALOGICS, INC.—See Calumet, Inc.; *U.S. Public*, pg. 425
CAMCO MANUFACTURING INC.; *U.S. Private*, pg. 727
CANGZHOU DAHUA GROUP CO., LTD.—See China National Chemical Corporation; *Int'l*, pg. 1526
CANON CHEMICALS, INC.—See Canon Inc.; *Int'l*, pg. 1293
CANSA PTY LTD.—See Momar, Inc.; *U.S. Private*, pg. 2767
CAPITOL W.B.C. PLC; *Int'l*, pg. 1314
CAPROLACTAM CHEMICALS LIMITED; *Int'l*, pg. 1317
CARAMBA CHEMIE GMBH & CO. KG—See Berner SE; *Int'l*, pg. 988
CARAMBA HOLDING GMBH—See Berner SE; *Int'l*, pg. 988
CARBIDE SWEDEN AB—See Akzo Nobel N.V.; *Int'l*, pg. 273
CARBOGEN AMCIS AG—See Dishman Carbogen Amcis Limited; *Int'l*, pg. 2135
CARBOSULF CHEMISCHE WERKE GMBH—See GIC Pte. Ltd.; *Int'l*, pg. 2968
CARBOSULF CHEMISCHE WERKE GMBH—See The Carlyle Group Inc.; *U.S. Public*, pg. 2051
CARPENTER POWDER PRODUCTS GMBH—See Carpenter Technology Corporation; *U.S. Public*, pg. 439
CARST & WALKER (PTY) LTD.—See Hobart Enterprises Ltd; *Int'l*, pg. 3436
CATHAY INDUSTRIAL BIOTECH LTD.; *Int'l*, pg. 1360
CAUSTIC JSC—See Central-Asian Power Energy Company JSC; *Int'l*, pg. 1410
CCM INNOVATIVE SOLUTIONS SDN BHD—See Batu Kawan Berhad; *Int'l*, pg. 890
CCM SINGAPORE PTE LTD—See Batu Kawan Berhad; *Int'l*, pg. 890
CCM USAHA KIMIA (M) SDN BHD—See Batu Kawan Berhad; *Int'l*, pg. 891
CCM WATERCARE SDN BHD—See Batu Kawan Berhad; *Int'l*, pg. 891
CCR TECHNOLOGIES LIMITED; *Int'l*, pg. 1369
CDEX INC.; *U.S. Private*, pg. 802
CECA S.A.—See Arkema S.A.; *Int'l*, pg. 571
CELANESE (CHINA) HOLDING CO., LTD.—See Celanese Corporation; *U.S. Public*, pg. 464
CELANESE EMULSIONS B.V.—See Celanese Corporation; *U.S. Public*, pg. 464
CELANESE EMULSIONS LTD.—See Celanese Corporation; *U.S. Public*, pg. 464
CELANESE EVA PERFORMANCE POLYMERS INC.—See Celanese Corporation; *U.S. Public*, pg. 464
CELANESE FAR EAST LTD.—See Celanese Corporation; *U.S. Public*, pg. 464
CELANESE KOREA LTD.—See Celanese Corporation; *U.S. Public*, pg. 465
CELANESE PRODUCTION SWITZERLAND AG—See Celanese Corporation; *U.S. Public*, pg. 465
CELANESE PTE. LTD.—See Celanese Corporation; *U.S. Public*, pg. 465
CELANESE S.A./N.V.—See Celanese Corporation; *U.S. Public*, pg. 465
CFI ANFSF (SHANGHAI) POLYMERS CO., LTD.—See Celanese Corporation; *U.S. Public*, pg. 464
CELANESE SINGAPORE PTE. LTD.—See Celanese Corporation; *U.S. Public*, pg. 465
CELANESE SWITZERLAND AG—See Celanese Corporation; *U.S. Public*, pg. 465
CELANESE (THAILAND) LIMITED—See Celanese Corporation; *U.S. Public*, pg. 465
CELEMICS, INC.; *Int'l*, pg. 1392

CENTAK CHEMICALS LTD.—See Akzo Nobel N.V.; *Int'l*, pg. 271
CENTRAL DE DROGAS S.A. DE C.V.—See Fagron NV; *Int'l*, pg. 2603
CENTRAL PETROVIETNAM FERTILIZER & CHEMICALS JOINT STOCK COMPANY; *Int'l*, pg. 1409
CENTRAL VAPORS, LLC; *U.S. Private*, pg. 826
CENXI DONGLIN ROSIN CO., LTD.—See Harima Chemicals Group, Inc.; *Int'l*, pg. 3276
CERTIFIED LABORATORIES—See NCH Corporation; *U.S. Private*, pg. 2875
C&E SERVICES INC. WASHINGTON—See C&E Services Inc.; *U.S. Private*, pg. 703
CHANGCHUN CHEMETALL CHEMICALS CO., LTD.—See BASF SE; *Int'l*, pg. 873
CHANG CHUN PETROCHEMICAL CO., LTD.—See ChangChun Group; *Int'l*, pg. 1442
CHANGMAO BIOCHEMICAL ENGINEERING COMPANY LIMITED; *Int'l*, pg. 1443
CHANGZHOU TRONLY NEW ELECTRONIC MATERIALS CO., LTD.; *Int'l*, pg. 1446
CHARKIT CHEMICAL COMPANY, LLC; *U.S. Private*, pg. 851
CHARM SCIENCES, INC.; *U.S. Private*, pg. 858
CHAR TECHNOLOGY (PTY) LIMITED—See Glencore plc; *Int'l*, pg. 2990
CHEMBOND CHEMICALS LTD - BALASORE PLANT—See Chembond Chemicals Ltd; *Int'l*, pg. 1461
CHEMBOND CHEMICALS LTD - DUDHWADA PLANT—See Chembond Chemicals Ltd; *Int'l*, pg. 1461
CHEMBOND CHEMICALS LTD; *Int'l*, pg. 1460
CHEMBRIDGE CORPORATION; *U.S. Private*, pg. 871
CHEMCON SPECIALITY CHEMICALS LIMITED; *Int'l*, pg. 1461
CHEMDESIGN PRODUCTS, INC.—See Lubar & Co., Inc.; *U.S. Private*, pg. 2510
CHEMETALL AB—See BASF SE; *Int'l*, pg. 873
CHEMETALL ASIA PTE. LTD.—See BASF SE; *Int'l*, pg. 873
CHEMETALL (AUSTRALASIA) PTY. LTD.—See BASF SE; *Int'l*, pg. 873
CHEMETALL B.V.—See BASF SE; *Int'l*, pg. 873
CHEMETALL HONG KONG LTD.—See BASF SE; *Int'l*, pg. 873
CHEMETALL ITALIA S.R.L.—See BASF SE; *Int'l*, pg. 873
CHEMETALL LIMITED—See BASF SE; *Int'l*, pg. 873
CHEMETALL MEXICANA, S.A. DE C.V.—See BASF SE; *Int'l*, pg. 873
CHEMETALL (NEW ZEALAND) LTD.—See BASF SE; *Int'l*, pg. 873
CHEMETALL POLSKA SP.Z O.O.—See BASF SE; *Int'l*, pg. 873
CHEMETALL (PTY) LTD.—See BASF SE; *Int'l*, pg. 873
CHEMETALL SANAYI KIMYASALLARI TICARET VE SANAYI A.S.—See BASF SE; *Int'l*, pg. 873
CHEMETALL S.A.—See BASF SE; *Int'l*, pg. 873
CHEMETALL S.A.S.—See BASF SE; *Int'l*, pg. 873
CHEMETALL S.R.L.—See BASF SE; *Int'l*, pg. 873
CHEMETALL (THAILAND) CO. LTD.—See BASF SE; *Int'l*, pg. 873
CHEMETALL US, INC.—See BASF SE; *Int'l*, pg. 873
CHEMETICS, INC.—See Jacobs Engineering Group, Inc.; *U.S. Public*, pg. 1185
CHEMICAL INDUSTRIES HOLDING COMPANY; *Int'l*, pg. 1461
CHEMICAL PACKAGING CORP.; *U.S. Private*, pg. 871
CHEMIEPARK BITTERFELD-WOLFEN GMBH—See IBU-Tec Advanced Materials AG; *Int'l*, pg. 3577
CHEMIPLASTICA S.P.A.; *Int'l*, pg. 1462
CHEMISCHE FABRIK BUDENHEIM KG—See Dr. August Oetker KG; *Int'l*, pg. 2190
CHEMOFAST ANCHORING GMBH—See Henkel AG & Co. KGaA; *Int'l*, pg. 3348
CHEMOFORM AG; *Int'l*, pg. 1462
CHEMOLAK; *Int'l*, pg. 1463
CHEMOLUTIONS CHEMICALS LTD.—See Camlin Fine Sciences Ltd.; *Int'l*, pg. 1273
THE CHEMOURS COMPANY; *U.S. Public*, pg. 2059
CHEMOVATOR GMBH—See BASF SE; *Int'l*, pg. 882
CHEMOXY INTERNATIONAL LIMITED; *Int'l*, pg. 1463
CHEMQUEST CHEMICALS LLC—See Cotton Creek Capital Management LLC; *U.S. Private*, pg. 1063
CHEMRING DEFENCE UK LTD; *Int'l*, pg. 1463
CHEMRING GROUP PLC; *Int'l*, pg. 1463
CHEMSPEC INTERNATIONAL LIMITED; *Int'l*, pg. 1463
CHEM-TEX LABORATORIES, INC.—See HeiQ Plc; *Int'l*, pg. 3326
CHEMTRADE ELECTROCHEM INC.—See Chemtrade Logistics Income Fund; *Int'l*, pg. 1464
CHEMTRADE LOGISTICS, INC.—See Chemtrade Logistics Income Fund; *Int'l*, pg. 1464
CHEMTRADE LOGISTICS (US), INC.—See Chemtrade Logistics Income Fund; *Int'l*, pg. 1464
CHEMTRADE PERFORMANCE CHEMICALS US, LLC—See Chemtrade Logistics Income Fund; *Int'l*, pg. 1464
CHEMTRADE PULP CHEMICALS LIMITED—See Canfor Corporation; *Int'l*, pg. 1291

CHEMTREAT, INC.—See Danaher Corporation; *U.S. Public*, pg. 625
CHEM-TREND JAPAN K.K.—See Freudenberg SE; *Int'l*, pg. 2782
CHEM-TREND ROMANIA S.R.L.—See Freudenberg SE; *Int'l*, pg. 2782
CHEMTROVINA CO. LTD.—See Chemtronics Co., Ltd.; *Int'l*, pg. 1464
CHENGDU WINTRUE HOLDING CO., LTD.; *Int'l*, pg. 1469
CHEVRON CORPORATION; *U.S. Public*, pg. 486
CHEVRON PHILLIPS CHEMICALS INTERNATIONAL N.V.—See Chevron Corporation; *U.S. Public*, pg. 486
CHEVRON PHILLIPS CHEMICALS INTERNATIONAL N.V.—See Phillips 66 Company; *U.S. Public*, pg. 1688
CHIA TAI ENTERPRISES INTERNATIONAL LTD.—See Charoen Pokphand Foods Public Company Limited; *Int'l*, pg. 1452
CHICAGO AEROSOL, LLC; *U.S. Private*, pg. 877
CHINA AMERICAN PETROCHEMICAL CO., LTD.—See BP plc; *Int'l*, pg. 1131
CHINA BLUESTAR INTERNATIONAL CHEMICAL CORPORATION—See Bluestar Adisseo Company Limited; *Int'l*, pg. 1074
CHINA CHEMICAL CORP.; *Int'l*, pg. 1488
CHINA GREEN MATERIAL TECHNOLOGIES, INC.; *Int'l*, pg. 1505
CHINA NATIONAL BLUESTAR (GROUP) CO., LTD.—See China National Chemical Corporation; *Int'l*, pg. 1526
CHINA NEW BORUN CORPORATION; *Int'l*, pg. 1534
CHINA RUITAI INTERNATIONAL HOLDINGS CO., LTD.; *Int'l*, pg. 1549
CHINA SANJIANG FINE CHEMICALS COMPANY LIMITED; *Int'l*, pg. 1549
CHINA SUN GROUP HIGH-TECH CO.; *Int'l*, pg. 1556
CHIRAL TECHNOLOGIES-EUROPE S.A.R.L.—See Daicel Corporation; *Int'l*, pg. 1918
CHITEC TECHNOLOGY CO., LTD.; *Int'l*, pg. 1574
CHONG-WAH NTIA SDN. BHD.—See Chong Wah Plastics Sdn Bhd; *Int'l*, pg. 1578
CHONG-WAH NTIA SDN. BHD.—See Northern Technologies International Corporation; *U.S. Public*, pg. 1537
CHORI MIDDLE EAST FZE—See Chori Co., Ltd.; *Int'l*, pg. 1583
CHOWGULE KOSTER (INDIA) CONSTRUCTION CHEMICALS PVT. LTD.—See Chowgule & Company Pvt. Ltd.; *Int'l*, pg. 1585
CHROMATIC INDIA LIMITED; *Int'l*, pg. 1588
CHRYSO, INC.—See Compagnie de Saint-Gobain SA; *Int'l*, pg. 1723
CHRYSO SAS—See Compagnie de Saint-Gobain SA; *Int'l*, pg. 1722
CHRYSO UK LTD.—See Compagnie de Saint-Gobain SA; *Int'l*, pg. 1722
CHS SPIRITWOOD FERTILIZER LLC—See CHS INC.; *U.S. Public*, pg. 491
CHUNG HWA CHEMICAL INDUSTRIAL WORKS LTD.; *Int'l*, pg. 1597
CHUNGHWA CHEMICAL SYNTHESIS & BIOTECH CO., LTD.; *Int'l*, pg. 1597
CIMCOOL INDUSTRIAL PRODUCTS B.V.—See Altas Partners LP; *Int'l*, pg. 386
CIMCOOL INDUSTRIAL PRODUCTS LLC—See Altas Partners LP; *Int'l*, pg. 386
CINKARNA CELJE D.D.; *Int'l*, pg. 1611
CITRASOURCE HOLDINGS, LLC—See International Flavors & Fragrances Inc.; *U.S. Public*, pg. 1151
CITRUS AND ALLIED ESSENCES LTD.; *U.S. Private*, pg. 904
C.J.GELATINE PRODUCTS LIMITED; *Int'l*, pg. 1243
CLARIANT BENTONITE (JIANGSU) CO., LTD.—See Clariant AG; *Int'l*, pg. 1646
CLARIANT CATALYSTS (JAPAN) K.K.—See Clariant AG; *Int'l*, pg. 1646
CLARIANT CHEMICALS (HUIZHOU) LTD.—See Clariant AG; *Int'l*, pg. 1646
CLARIANT CHEMICALS (TAIWAN) CO., LTD—See Clariant AG; *Int'l*, pg. 1646
CLARIANT CHEMICALS TECHNOLOGY (SHANGHAI) LTD.—See Clariant AG; *Int'l*, pg. 1646
CLARIANT (CHILE) LTDA.—See Clariant AG; *Int'l*, pg. 1645
CLARIANT (GULF) FZE—See Clariant AG; *Int'l*, pg. 1646
CLARIANT HUAJIN CATALYSTS (PANJIN) LTD.—See Clariant AG; *Int'l*, pg. 1647
CLARIANT IBERICA PRODUCCION S.A.—See Clariant AG; *Int'l*, pg. 1647
CLARIANT IBERICA SERVICIOS S.L.—See Clariant AG; *Int'l*, pg. 1647
CLARIANT (KOREA) LTD.—See Clariant AG; *Int'l*, pg. 1646
CLARIANT MASTERBATCHES (BEIJING) LTD—See Clariant AG; *Int'l*, pg. 1645
CLARIANT MASTERBATCHES BENELUX SA—See Clariant AG; *Int'l*, pg. 1647
CLARIANT MASTERBATCHES (FINLAND) OY—See Clariant AG; *Int'l*, pg. 1647
CLARIANT MASTERBATCHES IRELAND LIMITED—See Clariant AG; *Int'l*, pg. 1647
CLARIANT MASTERBATCHES (ITALIA) S.P.A.—See Clariant AG; *Int'l*, pg. 1647

325998 — ALL OTHER MISCELLAN...

CLARIANT MASTERBATCHES NORDEN AB—See Clariant AG; *Int'l*, pg. 1647
CLARIANT MASTERBATCHES (SAUDI ARABIA) LTD—See Clariant AG; *Int'l*, pg. 1645
CLARIANT MASTERBATCH IBERICA—See Clariant AG; *Int'l*, pg. 1647
CLARIANT MATERIAL SCIENCE (GUANGZHOU) LTD.—See Avient Corporation; *U.S. Public*, pg. 247
CLARIANT OIL SERVICES UK LTD.—See Clariant AG; *Int'l*, pg. 1648
CLARIANT PIGMENTS (TIANJIN) LTD—See Clariant AG; *Int'l*, pg. 1645
CLARIANT PLASTICS AND COATINGS (RUS) LLC—See Avient Corporation; *U.S. Public*, pg. 247
CLARIANT PLASTICS & COATINGS (FRANCE)—See Avient Corporation; *U.S. Public*, pg. 247
CLARIANT PLASTICS & COATINGS (ITALIA) S.P.A.—See Avient Corporation; *U.S. Public*, pg. 247
CLARIANT PLASTICS & COATINGS (JAPAN) K.K.—See Clariant AG; *Int'l*, pg. 1647
CLARIANT PLASTICS & COATINGS MEXICO, S.A. DE C.V.—See Clariant AG; *Int'l*, pg. 1647
CLARIANT PLASTICS & COATINGS (POLSKA) SP. Z O.O.—See Avient Corporation; *U.S. Public*, pg. 247
CLARIANT PLASTICS & COATINGS SOUTHERN AFRICA (PTY) LTD.—See Clariant AG; *Int'l*, pg. 1647
CLARIANT PLASTICS & COATINGS (TAIWAN) CO., LTD.—See Avient Corporation; *U.S. Public*, pg. 247
CLARIANT PLASTICS & COATINGS (THAILAND) LTD.—See Avient Corporation; *U.S. Public*, pg. 247
CLARIANT POLAND SPOLKA Z.O.O.—See Clariant AG; *Int'l*, pg. 1647
CLARIANT PRODOTTI (ITALIA) S.P.A.—See Clariant AG; *Int'l*, pg. 1647
CLARIANT PRODUCTS (SCHWEIZ) AG—See Clariant AG; *Int'l*, pg. 1647
CLARIANT PRODUKTE (DEUTSCHLAND) GMBH—See Clariant AG; *Int'l*, pg. 1647
CLARIANT QATAR W.L.L.—See Clariant AG; *Int'l*, pg. 1647
CLARIANT (RUS) LLC—See Clariant AG; *Int'l*, pg. 1646
CLARIANT SANGHO LTD.—See Clariant AG; *Int'l*, pg. 1648
CLARIANT SASOL CATALYSTS LTD.—See Clariant AG; *Int'l*, pg. 1648
CLARIANT SE - BRANCH MUTTENZ—See Clariant AG; *Int'l*, pg. 1648
CLARIANT SERVICES (FRANCE) SAS—See Clariant AG; *Int'l*, pg. 1648
CLARIANT SERVICES (POLAND) SP. Z O.O.—See Clariant AG; *Int'l*, pg. 1648
CLARIANT SOUTHERN AFRICA (PTY) LTD.—See Clariant AG; *Int'l*, pg. 1648
CLARIANT SPECIALTY CHEMICALS (ZHENJIANG) CO., LTD.—See Clariant AG; *Int'l*, pg. 1648
CLARIANT (THAILAND) LTD.—See Clariant AG; *Int'l*, pg. 1646
CLARIANT UKRAINE LLC—See Clariant AG; *Int'l*, pg. 1648
CLARIANT (URUGUAY) SA—See Clariant AG; *Int'l*, pg. 1646
CLAVIAG AG—See GIC Pte. Ltd.; *Int'l*, pg. 2968
CLAVIAG AG—See The Carlyle Group Inc.; *U.S. Public*, pg. 2051
CLEAN SOLUTIONS GROUP, INC.—See Branford Castle, Inc.; *U.S. Private*, pg. 639
CLEAR LAKE CHEMICALS LLC—See Platte River Ventures, LLC; *U.S. Private*, pg. 3211
CLIMAX MOLYBDENUM COMPANY—See Freeport-McMoRan Inc.; *U.S. Public*, pg. 884
CLINICAL DIAGNOSTICS SOLUTIONS INC.—See Boule Diagnostics AB; *Int'l*, pg. 1119
CNMC (GUANGXI) PINGGUI PGMA CO., LTD. - TITANIUM DIOXIDE PLANT—See China Nonferrous Metal Mining (Group) Co., Ltd.; *Int'l*, pg. 1535
COATES BROTHERS (SOUTH AFRICA) (PTY). LTD.—See DIC Corporation; *Int'l*, pg. 2107
COATEX ASIA PACIFIC INC.—See Arkema S.A.; *Int'l*, pg. 571
COATEX SAS—See Arkema S.A.; *Int'l*, pg. 570
CODEXIS, INC.; *U.S. Public*, pg. 521
COGNIS AUSTRALIA PTY. LTD.—See BASF SE; *Int'l*, pg. 883
COGNIS S.A.—See BASF SE; *Int'l*, pg. 883
COGNIS THAI LTD.—See BASF SE; *Int'l*, pg. 883
COLBOND GMBH AND CO. KG—See Freudenberg SE; *Int'l*, pg. 2789
COLEX SPOLKA Z O.O.—See Clariant AG; *Int'l*, pg. 1647
COLONY GUMS LLC—See BRENNTAG SE; *Int'l*, pg. 1149
COLORANT CHROMATICS EUROPE B.V.—See Avient Corporation; *U.S. Public*, pg. 247
COLORANTS SOLUTIONS (ARGENTINA) S.A.—See Clariant AG; *Int'l*, pg. 1648
COLORANTS SOLUTIONS (BRAZIL) LTDA.—See Clariant AG; *Int'l*, pg. 1648
COLORANTS SOLUTIONS (THAILAND) LTD.—See Clariant AG; *Int'l*, pg. 1648
COLORMATRIX SOUTH AFRICA (PTY) LTD.—See Avient Corporation; *U.S. Public*, pg. 247
COMAIS S.R.L.—See Etex SA/NV; *Int'l*, pg. 2521

COMPANHIA BRASILEIRA DE BENTONITA LTDA.—See Clariant AG; *Int'l*, pg. 1648
CONTINENTAL ALUMINUM COMPANY—See Metal Exchange Corporation; *U.S. Private*, pg. 2680
CONTINENTAL CHEMICALS LIMITED; *Int'l*, pg. 1783
CONTRACT CHEMICALS LTD.; *Int'l*, pg. 1785
CONTRAF-NICOTEX-TOBACCO GMBH; *Int'l*, pg. 1785
CONVENIENCE PRODUCTS, INC.—See Clayton Corporation; *U.S. Private*, pg. 918
COOGEE CHEMICALS PTY LTD.; *Int'l*, pg. 1788
COREMAX NINGBO CHEMICAL CO., LTD.—See Coremax Corp.; *Int'l*, pg. 1798
COREMAX (THAILAND) CO., LTD.—See Coremax Corp.; *Int'l*, pg. 1798
COREMAX (ZHANGZHOU) CHEMICAL CO., LTD.—See Coremax Corp.; *Int'l*, pg. 1798
COREMAX ZHUHAI CHEMICAL CO., LTD.—See Coremax Corp.; *Int'l*, pg. 1798
CORNERSTONE CHEMICAL COMPANY—See Littlejohn & Co., LLC; *U.S. Private*, pg. 2470
CORTEC CORPORATION; *U.S. Private*, pg. 1060
CORTEVA AGRISCIENCE DENMARK A/S—See Corteva, Inc.; *U.S. Public*, pg. 581
CORTEVA AGRISCIENCE FRANCE SAS—See Corteva, Inc.; *U.S. Public*, pg. 581
COSMO BIO USA, INC.—See COSMO BIO Co., Ltd.; *Int'l*, pg. 1811
COVENTYA AB—See Element Solutions Inc.; *U.S. Public*, pg. 725
COVENTYA ENVIRONMENTAL PLATING TECHNOLOGY (JIANGSU) CO., LTD.—See Element Solutions Inc.; *U.S. Public*, pg. 725
COVENTYA GMBH—See Element Solutions Inc.; *U.S. Public*, pg. 725
COVENTYA KIMYA SANAYI VE TICARET ANONIM SIRKETI—See Element Solutions Inc.; *U.S. Public*, pg. 725
COVENTYA KOREA CO., LIMITED—See Element Solutions Inc.; *U.S. Public*, pg. 725
COVENTYA LIMITED—See Element Solutions Inc.; *U.S. Public*, pg. 725
COVENTYA MALAYSIA SDN. BHD.—See Element Solutions Inc.; *U.S. Public*, pg. 725
COVENTYA QUIMICA LTDA—See Element Solutions Inc.; *U.S. Public*, pg. 725
COVENTYA TECHNOLOGIES S.L.—See Element Solutions Inc.; *U.S. Public*, pg. 725
CPAC AFRICA (PTY.) LTD.—See Buckingham Capital, LLC; *U.S. Private*, pg. 678
CPAC ASIA IMAGING PRODUCTS LIMITED—See Buckingham Capital, LLC; *U.S. Private*, pg. 678
CP KELCO APS—See J.M. Huber Corporation; *U.S. Private*, pg. 2168
CP KELCO ARGENTINA S.A.—See J.M. Huber Corporation; *U.S. Private*, pg. 2168
CP KELCO B.V.—See J.M. Huber Corporation; *U.S. Private*, pg. 2168
CP KELCO JAPAN APS—See J.M. Huber Corporation; *U.S. Private*, pg. 2168
CP KELCO SINGAPORE PTE., LTD.—See J.M. Huber Corporation; *U.S. Private*, pg. 2168
CP KELCO—See J.M. Huber Corporation; *U.S. Private*, pg. 2168
CP KELCO UK LIMITED—See J.M. Huber Corporation; *U.S. Private*, pg. 2168
CPS PERFORMANCE MATERIALS CORP.—See Arsenal Capital Management LP; *U.S. Private*, pg. 337
CPS TECHNOLOGIES CORPORATION; *U.S. Public*, pg. 588
CQV CO., LTD.; *Int'l*, pg. 1826
CRI TOLLING, LLC—See Ascent Industries Co.; *U.S. Public*, pg. 210
CRODA AUSTRALIA—See Croda International plc; *Int'l*, pg. 1852
CRODA CHEMICALS EUROPE LTD—See Croda International plc; *Int'l*, pg. 1851
CRODA CHEMICALS (INDIA) PVT LTD—See Croda International plc; *Int'l*, pg. 1852
CRODA CHEMICALS SA PTY LTD—See Croda International plc; *Int'l*, pg. 1851
CRODA DO BRASIL LTDA—See Croda International plc; *Int'l*, pg. 1852
CRODA FRANCE SAS—See Croda International plc; *Int'l*, pg. 1852
CRODA GMBH—See Croda International plc; *Int'l*, pg. 1852
CRODA HONG KONG—See Croda International plc; *Int'l*, pg. 1852
CRODA HUNGARY LTD.—See Croda International plc; *Int'l*, pg. 1852
CRODA IBERICA SA—See Croda International plc; *Int'l*, pg. 1852
CRODA INC.—See Croda International plc; *Int'l*, pg. 1852
CRODA ITALIANA S.P.A.—See Croda International plc; *Int'l*, pg. 1852
CRODA KOREA CHEMICAL INTERNATIONAL LTD.—See Croda International plc; *Int'l*, pg. 1852
CRODA NEDERLAND B.V.—See Croda International plc; *Int'l*, pg. 1852

CORPORATE AFFILIATIONS

CRODA NORDICA AB—See Croda International plc; *Int'l*, pg. 1852
CRODA OLEOCHEMICALS IBERICA, S.A.—See Croda International plc; *Int'l*, pg. 1852
CRODAROM—See Croda International plc; *Int'l*, pg. 1852
CRODA SHANGHAI—See Croda International plc; *Int'l*, pg. 1852
CRODA SINGAPORE PTE. LTD.—See Croda International plc; *Int'l*, pg. 1852
CROWN ASIA CHEMICALS CORPORATION; *Int'l*, pg. 1857
CRYSTAL, INC. - PMC—See PMC Group, Inc.; *U.S. Private*, pg. 3218
CTCI CHEMICALS CORP.—See CTCI Corporation; *Int'l*, pg. 1870
CU CHEMIE UETIKON GMBH—See Eurazeo SE; *Int'l*, pg. 2530
CURIA FRANCE SAS—See GTCR LLC; *U.S. Private*, pg. 1805
CURIA FRANCE SAS—See The Carlyle Group Inc.; *U.S. Public*, pg. 2046
CUSTOM BLENDERS, INC.—See Darling Ingredients Inc.; *U.S. Public*, pg. 633
C.UYEMURA & CO., LTD.; *Int'l*, pg. 1244
CVC THERMOSET SPECIALTIES—See Huntsman Corporation; *U.S. Public*, pg. 1072
CYANTEK CORPORATION—See Entegris, Inc.; *U.S. Public*, pg. 776
CYDSA S.A.B. DE C.V.; *Int'l*, pg. 1895
CYDSA S.A. DE C.V. - LA PRESA PLANT—See Cydsa S.A.B. de C.V.; *Int'l*, pg. 1895
DAEJUNG CHEMICALS & METALS CO., LTD.; *Int'l*, pg. 1907
DAICEL-ALLNEX LTD.—See Daicel Corporation; *Int'l*, pg. 1919
DAICEL AMERICA HOLDINGS,INC.—See Daicel Corporation; *Int'l*, pg. 1918
DAICEL (ASIA) PTE. LTD.—See Daicel Corporation; *Int'l*, pg. 1918
DAICEL BEYOND LTD.—See Daicel Corporation; *Int'l*, pg. 1918
DAICEL (CHINA) INVESTMENT CO.,LTD.—See Daicel Corporation; *Int'l*, pg. 1918
DAICEL MIRAIZU LTD.—See Daicel Corporation; *Int'l*, pg. 1919
DAICEL SAFETY SYSTEMS AMERICAS, INC.—See Daicel Corporation; *Int'l*, pg. 1919
DAICEN MEMBRANE-SYSTEMS LTD.—See Daicel Corporation; *Int'l*, pg. 1919
DAICOLOR SHANGHAI MFG. CO., LTD.—See Dainichiseika Color & Chemicals Mfg. Co., Ltd.; *Int'l*, pg. 1939
DAI-ICHI CERAMO CO., LTD.—See DKS Co. Ltd.; *Int'l*, pg. 2139
DAI-ICHI KENKOU CO., LTD.—See DKS Co. Ltd.; *Int'l*, pg. 2139
DAIICHI KIGENSO KAGAKU KOGYO CO., LTD.; *Int'l*, pg. 1927
DAIICHI SANKYO RD NOVARE CO., LTD.—See Daiichi Sankyo Co., Ltd.; *Int'l*, pg. 1930
DAIKAFFIL CHEMICALS INDIA LIMITED.; *Int'l*, pg. 1930
DAIKIN HVAC SOLUTION KINKI CO., LTD.—See Daikin Industries, Ltd.; *Int'l*, pg. 1934
DAIKIN HVAC SOLUTION KYUSHU CO., LTD.—See Daikin Industries, Ltd.; *Int'l*, pg. 1934
DAIKIN HVAC SOLUTION TOKAI CO., LTD.—See Daikin Industries, Ltd.; *Int'l*, pg. 1934
DAIKIN INDUSTRIES, LTD. - YODOGAWA PLANT—See Daikin Industries, Ltd.; *Int'l*, pg. 1934
DAIKIN SUNRISE SETTSU CO., LTD.—See Daikin Industries, Ltd.; *Int'l*, pg. 1935
DAIREN CHEMICAL CORPORATION—See ChangChun Group; *Int'l*, pg. 1442
DAIREN CHEMICAL (JIANGSU) CO. LTD.—See ChangChun Group; *Int'l*, pg. 1442
DAIREN CHEMICAL (M) SDN. BHD.—See ChangChun Group; *Int'l*, pg. 1442
DAITO CHEMICAL CO., LTD.—See Air Water Inc.; *Int'l*, pg. 240
DALIAN APPLE FOODS INGREDIENTS CO., LTD.—See Apple Flavor & Fragrance Group Co., Ltd.; *Int'l*, pg. 520
DALIAN SHIDE PLASTICS INDUSTRY CO., LTD.—See Dalian Shide Group Co., Ltd.; *Int'l*, pg. 1952
DANCHEM TECHNOLOGIES, INC—See Ascent Industries Co.; *U.S. Public*, pg. 210
DANHUA CHEMICAL TECHNOLOGY CO., LTD.; *Int'l*, pg. 1962
DAOMING OPTICS AND CHEMICAL CO., LTD.; *Int'l*, pg. 1970
DAQO NEW ENERGY CORP.; *Int'l*, pg. 1971
DATONG COAL MINE GROUP CO., LTD.; *Int'l*, pg. 1982
DAWOOD HERCULES CHEMICALS SHEIKHUPURA—See Dawood Corporation (Pvt.) Ltd.; *Int'l*, pg. 1984
DAXIN MATERIALS CORPORATION; *Int'l*, pg. 1985
DBC CO., LTD.—See Doosan Corporation; *Int'l*, pg. 2172
DCM SHRIRAM INDUSTRIES LIMITED - CHEMICAL & ALCOHOL DIVISION—See DCM Shriram Industries Limited; *Int'l*, pg. 1992
D.D. BEAN & SONS CO.; *U.S. Private*, pg. 1141

N.A.I.C.S. INDEX

325998 — ALL OTHER MISCELLAN...

DEEPAK FERTILISERS & PETROCHEMICALS CORPORATION LIMITED; *Int'l*, pg. 2003
DEEPAK NITRITE LIMITED; *Int'l*, pg. 2003
DEINOVE SA; *Int'l*, pg. 2005
DELAWARE CHEMICALS CORPORATION—See Arkema S.A.; *Int'l*, pg. 569
DE MATTOS & SULLIVAN LIMITED—See BASF SE; *Int'l*, pg. 883
DENKA ADVANCED MATERIALS VIETNAM CO., LTD.—See Denki Company Limited; *Int'l*, pg. 2027
DENKA CHEMICALS DEVELOPMENT SUZHOU CO., LTD.—See Denki Company Limited; *Int'l*, pg. 2027
DENKA CHEMICALS HOLDINGS ASIA PACIFIC PTE. LTD.—See Denki Company Limited; *Int'l*, pg. 2027
DENKA CONSULTANT & ENGINEERING CO., LTD.—See Denki Company Limited; *Int'l*, pg. 2027
DENKA ELECTRONICS MATERIALS DALIAN CO., LTD.—See Denki Company Limited; *Int'l*, pg. 2027
DENKA INFRASTRUCTURE TECHNOLOGIES SHANGHAI CO,. LTD.—See Denki Company Limited; *Int'l*, pg. 2027
DENKA INORGANIC MATERIALS (TIANJIN) CO., LTD.—See Denki Company Limited; *Int'l*, pg. 2027
DENKA KOREA CO., LTD.—See Denki Company Limited; *Int'l*, pg. 2027
DENKA LIFE INNOVATION RESEARCH PTE. LTD.—See Denki Company Limited; *Int'l*, pg. 2027
DENKA SEIKEN (SHANGHAI) CO., LTD.—See Denki Company Limited; *Int'l*, pg. 2027
DENKA SEIKEN USA INCORPORATED—See Denki Company Limited; *Int'l*, pg. 2027
DENKA TAIWAN CORPORATION—See Denki Company Limited; *Int'l*, pg. 2027
DEPOSITION SCIENCES, INC.—See Lockheed Martin Corporation; *U.S. Public*, pg. 1337
DERYPOL SA—See Ecolab Inc.; *U.S. Public*, pg. 712
DEVJO INDUSTRIES, INC.; *Int'l*, pg. 2089
DEXERIALS AMERICA CORPORATION—See Development Bank of Japan, Inc.; *Int'l*, pg. 2087
DEXERIALS CORPORATION—See Development Bank of Japan, Inc.; *Int'l*, pg. 2087
DEXERIALS EUROPE B.V.—See Development Bank of Japan, Inc.; *Int'l*, pg. 2087
D & H INDIA LIMITED - UNIT LL—See D & H India Limited; *Int'l*, pg. 1898
DIAMOND INDUSTRIES LIMITED; *Int'l*, pg. 2105
DIAZYME LABORATORIES, INC.—See General Atomics; *U.S. Private*, pg. 1663
DISTA, S.A.—See Eli Lilly & Company; *U.S. Public*, pg. 731
THE DISTILLATA COMPANY; *U.S. Private*, pg. 4021
DIVERSITAK, INC.—See Diversified Chemical Technologies Inc.; *U.S. Private*, pg. 1241
DIVIS LABORATORIES LIMITED; *Int'l*, pg. 2137
DKS CO. LTD.; *Int'l*, pg. 2139
DNF CO., LTD.; *Int'l*, pg. 2148
DOBER CHEMICAL CORP. - GLENWOOD PLANT—See Dober Chemical Corp.; *U.S. Private*, pg. 1250
DOBER CHEMICAL CORP. - MIDLOTHIAN PLANT—See Dober Chemical Corp.; *U.S. Private*, pg. 1250
DOBER CHEMICAL CORP.; *U.S. Private*, pg. 1250
DO-FLUORIDE NEW MATERIALS CO LTD; *Int'l*, pg. 2152
DOMO CHEMICAL GMBH; *Int'l*, pg. 2162
DONETSKKOKS PJSC; *Int'l*, pg. 2163
DONGBU FINE CHEMICAL CO., LTD.—See Dongbu Group; *Int'l*, pg. 2166
DONGFENG SCI-TECH GROUP CO., LTD.; *Int'l*, pg. 2166
DONGGUAN HANGHUA-HARIMA PAPER CHEMICALS CO., LTD.—See Harima Chemicals Group, Inc.; *Int'l*, pg. 3276
DONGGUAN HUAJIA SURFACE TECHNOLOGY CO., LTD.—See PPG Industries, Inc.; *U.S. Public*, pg. 1707
DONGNAM CHEMICAL CO., LTD.; *Int'l*, pg. 2169
DONGSUNG CHEMICAL CO., LTD. - SINPYEONG FACTORY—See Dongsung Chemical Co., Ltd.; *Int'l*, pg. 2170
DONGSUNG CHEMICAL CO., LTD. - YEOCHEON FACTORY—See Dongsung Chemical Co., Ltd.; *Int'l*, pg. 2170
DONGSUNG ECORE CO., LTD.—See Dongsung Chemical Co., Ltd.; *Int'l*, pg. 2170
DONGYUE GROUP LIMITED; *Int'l*, pg. 2172
DOTTIKON ES HOLDING AG; *Int'l*, pg. 2180
DOUBLE BOND CHEMICAL IND. CO., LTD.; *Int'l*, pg. 2181
DOUGLAS PRODUCTS & PACKAGING COMPANY LLC—See Brightstar Capital Partners, L.P.; *U.S. Private*, pg. 653
DOWA F-TEC CO., LTD.—See Dowa Holdings Co., Ltd.; *Int'l*, pg. 2183
DOW AGROSCIENCES B.V.-PHILIPPINES—See Corteva, Inc.; *U.S. Public*, pg. 582
DOW AGROSCIENCES TAIWAN LTD.—See Corteva, Inc.; *U.S. Public*, pg. 582
DOWA HIGHTECH CO., LTD.—See Dowa Holdings Co., Ltd.; *Int'l*, pg. 2183
DOW BELGIUM B.V.B.A—See Dow Inc.; *U.S. Public*, pg. 684
DOW BENELUX B.V.—See Dow Inc.; *U.S. Public*, pg. 685
DOW CHEMICAL (AUSTRALIA) PTY LTD.—See Dow Inc.; *U.S. Public*, pg. 683

THE DOW CHEMICAL CO. - HAYWARD PLANT—See Dow Inc.; *U.S. Public*, pg. 686
THE DOW CHEMICAL COMPANY - KNOXVILLE PLANT—See Dow Inc.; *U.S. Public*, pg. 686
DOW CHEMICAL COMPANY LIMITED—See Dow Inc.; *U.S. Public*, pg. 684
DOW CHEMICAL (GUANGZHOU) COMPANY LIMITED—See Dow Inc.; *U.S. Public*, pg. 684
DOW CHEMICAL IBERICA S.A.—See Dow Inc.; *U.S. Public*, pg. 684
DOW CHEMICAL KOREA LIMITED—See Dow Inc.; *U.S. Public*, pg. 684
DOW CHEMICAL (MALAYSIA) SDN. BHD.—See Dow Inc.; *U.S. Public*, pg. 684
DOW CHEMICAL (NZ) LIMITED—See Dow Inc.; *U.S. Public*, pg. 683
DOW CHEMICAL PACIFIC (SINGAPORE) PTE LTD.—See Dow Inc.; *U.S. Public*, pg. 684
DOW CHEMICAL PHILIPPINES, INC.—See Dow Inc.; *U.S. Public*, pg. 684
DOW CHEMICAL TAIWAN LIMITED—See Dow Inc.; *U.S. Public*, pg. 684
DOW DEUTSCHLAND BETEILIGUNGSGESELLSCHAFT MBH—See Dow Inc.; *U.S. Public*, pg. 684
DOW FRANCE S.A.S.—See Dow Inc.; *U.S. Public*, pg. 685
DOW FRANCE S.A.S.—See Dow Inc.; *U.S. Public*, pg. 685
DOW HUNGARY LTD.—See Dow Inc.; *U.S. Public*, pg. 685
DOW INVESTMENT ARGENTINA S.R.L.—See Dow Inc.; *U.S. Public*, pg. 685
DOW ITALIA S.R.L.—See Dow Inc.; *U.S. Public*, pg. 685
DOW MATERIAL SCIENCES LTD.—See Dow Inc.; *U.S. Public*, pg. 683
DOW POLSKA SP.Z.O.O.—See Dow Inc.; *U.S. Public*, pg. 685
DOW PORTUGAL - PRODUTOS QUIMICOS UNIPESSOAL, LDA.—See Dow Inc.; *U.S. Public*, pg. 685
DOW (SHANGHAI) HOLDING CO., LTD.—See Dow Inc.; *U.S. Public*, pg. 683
DOW SOUTHERN AFRICA (PTY) LTD.—See Dow Inc.; *U.S. Public*, pg. 685
DOW SVERIGE AB—See Dow Inc.; *U.S. Public*, pg. 685
DOW TORAY CO., LTD.—See Dow Inc.; *U.S. Public*, pg. 683
DOW TURKIYE KIMYA SANAYI VE TICARET LTD STI—See Dow Inc.; *U.S. Public*, pg. 685
DRAGER HISPANIA S.A.U.—See Draegerwerk AG & Co. KGaA; *Int'l*, pg. 2197
DR. REDDY'S LABORATORIES—See Dr. Reddy's Laboratories Limited; *Int'l*, pg. 2195
DRUCKFARBEN ROMANIA S.R.L.—See Druckfarben Hellas S.A.; *Int'l*, pg. 2206
DRYVIT SYSTEMS, INC.—See RPM International Inc.; *U.S. Public*, pg. 1819
DRYVIT SYSTEMS USA (EUROPE) SP. Z O.O.—See RPM International Inc.; *U.S. Public*, pg. 1819
DS CHEMPORT (MALAYSIA) SDN. BHD.—See FUJIFILM Holdings Corporation; *Int'l*, pg. 2821
DUBOIS CHEMICALS, INC.—See Altas Partners LP; *Int'l*, pg. 386
DUC GIANG CHEMICALS GROUP JOINT STOCK COMPANY; *Int'l*, pg. 2222
DU PONT CHINA HOLDING COMPANY LTD.—See DuPont de Nemours, Inc.; *U.S. Public*, pg. 692
DUPONT DO BRASIL S.A.—See Corteva, Inc.; *U.S. Public*, pg. 584
DUPONT HELLAS S.A.—See Corteva, Inc.; *U.S. Public*, pg. 582
DUPONT KABUSHIKI KAISHA—See DuPont de Nemours, Inc.; *U.S. Public*, pg. 692
DUPONT (KOREA) INC.—See DuPont de Nemours, Inc.; *U.S. Public*, pg. 692
DUPONT MEXICO, S.A. DE C.V.—See DuPont de Nemours, Inc.; *U.S. Public*, pg. 693
DUPONT PAKISTAN OPERATIONS (PVT.) LIMITED—See DuPont de Nemours, Inc.; *U.S. Public*, pg. 693
DUPONT POLAND SP Z O.O.—See Corteva, Inc.; *U.S. Public*, pg. 582
DUPONT TAIWAN LTD.—See DuPont de Nemours, Inc.; *U.S. Public*, pg. 693
DUPONT (U.K.) LTD.—See Corteva, Inc.; *U.S. Public*, pg. 582
EASTERN POLYMER GROUP PUBLIC COMPANY LIMITED; *Int'l*, pg. 2273
EASTMAN CHEMICAL BARCELONA, S.L.—See Eastman Chemical Company; *U.S. Public*, pg. 704
EASTMAN CHEMICAL B.V.—See Eastman Chemical Company; *U.S. Public*, pg. 704
EASTMAN CHEMICAL B.V., THE HAGUE, ZUG BRANCH—See Eastman Chemical Company; *U.S. Public*, pg. 704
EASTMAN CHEMICAL COMPANY; *U.S. Public*, pg. 704
EASTMAN CHEMICAL COMPANY—See Eastman Chemical Company; *U.S. Public*, pg. 704
EASTMAN CHEMICAL GMBH—See Eastman Chemical Company; *U.S. Public*, pg. 704
EASTMAN CHEMICAL IBERICA, S.L.—See Eastman Chemical Company; *U.S. Public*, pg. 704
EASTMAN CHEMICAL INTERNATIONAL AG—See Eastman Chemical Company; *U.S. Public*, pg. 704

EASTMAN CHEMICAL (MALAYSIA) SDN. BHD.—See Eastman Chemical Company; *U.S. Public*, pg. 704
EASTMAN CHEMICAL MIDDELBURG, B.V.—See Eastman Chemical Company; *U.S. Public*, pg. 704
EASTMAN CHEMICAL PRODUCTS SINGAPORE PTE. LTD.—See Eastman Chemical Company; *U.S. Public*, pg. 705
EASTMAN CHEMICAL SINGAPORE PTE. LTD.—See Eastman Chemical Company; *U.S. Public*, pg. 705
EASTMAN ESPANA S.L.—See Eastman Chemical Company; *U.S. Public*, pg. 705
EASTMAN MFG JAPAN LTD.—See Eastman Chemical Company; *U.S. Public*, pg. 705
EBITO CHEMIEBETEILIGUNGEN AG—See Clariant AG; *Int'l*, pg. 1648
ECOGREEN FINE CHEMICALS B.V.—See EcoGreen International Group Limited; *Int'l*, pg. 2295
ECOGREEN FINE CHEMICALS LIMITED—See EcoGreen International Group Limited; *Int'l*, pg. 2295
ECOGREEN INTERNATIONAL GROUP LIMITED; *Int'l*, pg. 2295
ECOLAB APS—See Ecolab Inc.; *U.S. Public*, pg. 713
ECOLAB S.R.L.—See Ecolab Inc.; *U.S. Public*, pg. 714
ECOLOGIC BRANDS, INC.—See Jabil Inc.; *U.S. Public*, pg. 1180
ECOSYNTHETIX, INC.; *Int'l*, pg. 2300
ECOVYST CATALYST TECHNOLOGIES UK LTD.—See Ecovyst Inc.; *U.S. Public*, pg. 717
ECRONOVA POLYMER GMBH—See Michelman Inc.; *U.S. Private*, pg. 2699
ECZACIBASI-BAXTER HASTANE URUNLERI SANAYI VE TICARET A.S.—See Baxter International Inc.; *U.S. Public*, pg. 281
EFTEC (SHANGHAI) SERVICES CO., LTD.—See EMS-Chemie Holding AG; *Int'l*, pg. 2393
E.I. DUPONT CANADA COMPANY—See Corteva, Inc.; *U.S. Public*, pg. 584
E.I. DUPONT INDIA PRIVATE LIMITED—See Corteva, Inc.; *U.S. Public*, pg. 584
EKA CHEMICALS (AUSTRALIA) PTY LTD—See GIC Pte. Ltd.; *Int'l*, pg. 2968
EKA CHEMICALS (AUSTRALIA) PTY LTD—See The Carlyle Group Inc.; *U.S. Public*, pg. 2051
EKA CHEMICALS CANADA, INC.—See GIC Pte. Ltd.; *Int'l*, pg. 2968
EKA CHEMICALS CANADA, INC.—See The Carlyle Group Inc.; *U.S. Public*, pg. 2051
EKA CHEMICALS DO BRASIL S.A.—See GIC Pte. Ltd.; *Int'l*, pg. 2968
EKA CHEMICALS DO BRASIL S.A.—See The Carlyle Group Inc.; *U.S. Public*, pg. 2051
EKA CHEMICALS (GUANGZHOU) CO., LTD.—See GIC Pte. Ltd.; *Int'l*, pg. 2968
EKA CHEMICALS (GUANGZHOU) CO., LTD.—See The Carlyle Group Inc.; *U.S. Public*, pg. 2051
EKC TECHNOLOGY, INC.—See DuPont de Nemours, Inc.; *U.S. Public*, pg. 693
ELASTOGRAN INNOVATIONSPROJEKTE BETEILIGUNGSGESELLSCHAFT MBH—See BASF SE; *Int'l*, pg. 883
EL DORADO CHEMICAL COMPANY—See LSB Industries, Inc.; *U.S. Public*, pg. 1344
ELECTROLUBE LIMITED—See Element Solutions Inc.; *U.S. Public*, pg. 726
ELECTRO-SCIENCE LABORATORIES, LLC—See American Securities LLC; *U.S. Private*, pg. 251
ELEKEIROZ S.A.—See H.I.G. Capital, LLC; *U.S. Private*, pg. 1828
ELEMENTIS CHROMIUM—See Elementis plc; *Int'l*, pg. 2359
ELEMENTIS PLC; *Int'l*, pg. 2358
ELEVANCE RENEWABLE SCIENCES, INC.; *U.S. Private*, pg. 1358
ELLBA EASTERN (PTE) LTD.—See BASF SE; *Int'l*, pg. 878
EL MEX SALINES CO.—See Chemical Industries Holding Company; *Int'l*, pg. 1461
EMS-CHEMIE (PRODUKTION) AG—See EMS-Chemie Holding AG; *Int'l*, pg. 2393
EMS-CHEMIE (SWITZERLAND) AG—See EMS-Chemie Holding AG; *Int'l*, pg. 2393
EMS-GRILTECH AG—See EMS-Chemie Holding AG; *Int'l*, pg. 2393
ENCHEM CO., LTD.; *Int'l*, pg. 2401
ENECO REFRESH LIMITED; *Int'l*, pg. 2411
ENERG2 TECHNOLOGIES, INC.—See BASF SE; *Int'l*, pg. 883
ENERKEM INC.; *Int'l*, pg. 2423
ENERTECK CORPORATION; *U.S. Public*, pg. 768
ENF TECHNOLOGY CO., LTD. - ASAN PLANT—See ENF Technology Co., Ltd.; *Int'l*, pg. 2425
ENF TECHNOLOGY CO., LTD.; *Int'l*, pg. 2425
ENF TECHNOLOGY CO., LTD. - ULSAN PLANT—See ENF Technology Co., Ltd.; *Int'l*, pg. 2425
ENTHONE INC.—See Element Solutions Inc.; *U.S. Public*, pg. 726
ENZOLYTICS, INC.; *U.S. Public*, pg. 782
ENZYMEBIOSYSTEMS; *U.S. Private*, pg. 1410
ENZYMEDICA, INC.; *U.S. Private*, pg. 1410

325998 — ALL OTHER MISCELLAN...

EPI ENVIRONMENTAL PRODUCTS INC.—See EPI Environmental Technologies Inc.; *Int'l*, pg. 2460
EPI ENVIRONMENTAL PRODUCTS INC.—See EPI Environmental Technologies Inc.; *Int'l*, pg. 2460
EPI ENVIRONMENTAL TECHNOLOGIES INC.; *Int'l*, pg. 2459
EPOCH MATERIAL CO., LTD.—See Entegris, Inc.; *U.S. Public*, pg. 776
EQUATE PETROCHEMICAL COMPANY K.S.C.C.—See Dow Inc.; *U.S. Public*, pg. 685
ERAMET MANGANESE—See Eramet SA; *Int'l*, pg. 2489
ERCO WORLDWIDE, INC.—See Birch Hill Equity Partners Management Inc.; *Int'l*, pg. 1046
ERCROS SA; *Int'l*, pg. 2489
ERCROS SA - WATER TREATMENT DIVISION - SABINANIGO FACTORY—See Ercros SA; *Int'l*, pg. 2490
ERCROS SA - WATER TREATMENT DIVISION—See Ercros SA; *Int'l*, pg. 2490
ERSHIGS, INC.—See NOV, Inc.; *U.S. Public*, pg. 1544
ESNAAD—See Abu Dhabi National Oil Company; *Int'l*, pg. 73
ESTI CHEM A/S; *Int'l*, pg. 2518
ETERNAL PHOTO ELECTRONIC MATERIALS (GUANGZHOU) CO., LTD.—See Eternal Materials Co., Ltd.; *Int'l*, pg. 2521
ETERNAL SPECIALTY MATERIALS (SUZHOU) CO., LTD.—See Eternal Materials Co., Ltd.; *Int'l*, pg. 2521
ETERNIT B.V.—See Etex SA/NV; *Int'l*, pg. 2521
ETOL AROMA VE BAHARAT GIDA URUNLERI SAN.VE TIC.A.S.—See International Flavors & Fragrances Inc.; *U.S. Public*, pg. 1151
EUCLID ADMIXTURE CANADA INC.—See RPM International Inc.; *U.S. Public*, pg. 1816
EUREKA CHEMICAL COMPANY; *U.S. Private*, pg. 1433
EURENCO BOFORS AB—See GIAT Industries S.A.; *Int'l*, pg. 2962
EURENCO—See GIAT Industries S.A.; *Int'l*, pg. 2962
EUROCAPS LIMITED—See DCC plc; *Int'l*, pg. 1990
EUROCARB PRODUCTS LTD.—See Hayleys PLC; *Int'l*, pg. 3291
EUROFINS MWG SYNTHESIS GMBH—See Eurofins Scientific S.E.; *Int'l*, pg. 2551
EUROKERN GIESSEREITECHNIK GMBH—See Huettenes-Albertus Chemische Werke GmbH; *Int'l*, pg. 3522
EUROPEAN COLOUR PLC; *Int'l*, pg. 2556
EVERLIGHT CHEMICALS (VIETNAM) COMPANY LIMITED—See Everlight Chemical Industrial Co.; *Int'l*, pg. 2567
EVOQUA WATER TECHNOLOGIES—See Xylem Inc.; *U.S. Public*, pg. 2394
EVOQUA WATER TECHNOLOGIES—See Xylem Inc.; *U.S. Public*, pg. 2394
EWG SLUPSK SP. Z.O.O; *Int'l*, pg. 2576
EXCELITAS NOBLELIGHT LIMITED—See AEA Investors LP; *U.S. Private*, pg. 113
EXCOR GMBH—See Northern Technologies International Corporation; *U.S. Public*, pg. 1537
EXCOR IBERICA—See Northern Technologies International Corporation; *U.S. Public*, pg. 1537
EXCOR SP. Z.O.O.—See Northern Technologies, International Corporation; *U.S. Public*, pg. 1537
EXPANSIA S.A.S.—See Eurazeo SE; *Int'l*, pg. 2530
EXPRESSION SYSTEMS, LLC—See Golden Gate Capital Management II, LLC; *U.S. Private*, pg. 1730
EXTER B.V.; *Int'l*, pg. 2591
EXXONMOBIL CHEMICAL COMPANY INC.—See Exxon Mobil Corporation; *U.S. Public*, pg. 814
EXXONMOBIL CHEMICAL COMPANY INC.—See Exxon Mobil Corporation; *U.S. Public*, pg. 814
FAIR CHEM INDUSTRIES PTE LTD.—See GKE Corporation Limited; *Int'l*, pg. 2983
FAIRCHEM ORGANICS LIMITED; *Int'l*, pg. 2605
FAVORITE PRODUCTS COMPANY LTD.—See Oil-Dri Corporation of America; *U.S. Public*, pg. 1566
FEBEX S.A.—See Arkema S.A.; *Int'l*, pg. 571
FELDER GMBH; *Int'l*, pg. 2632
FERMENTALG SA; *Int'l*, pg. 2639
FERNOX LIMITED—See Element Solutions Inc.; *U.S. Public*, pg. 726
FERRO (BELGIUM) SPRL—See American Securities LLC; *U.S. Private*, pg. 251
FERRO COLORES SA DE CV—See American Securities LLC; *U.S. Private*, pg. 251
FERRO EGYPT FOR GLAZE (S.A.E.)—See American Securities LLC; *U.S. Private*, pg. 251
FERRO FAR EAST COMPANY SDN, BHD—See American Securities LLC; *U.S. Private*, pg. 252
FERRO INDIA PRIVATE LIMITED—See American Securities LLC; *U.S. Private*, pg. 251
FERRO SPAIN SA—See American Securities LLC; *U.S. Private*, pg. 252
FERRO TAIWAN LTD—See American Securities LLC; *U.S. Private*, pg. 252
FERROTEC GMBH—See Ferrotec Holdings Corporation; *Int'l*, pg. 2643
FIBON BERHAD; *Int'l*, pg. 2652

FIBRANT B.V.—See Highsun Holding Group Co., Ltd.; *Int'l*, pg. 3388
FIBRANT, LLC—See Highsun Holding Group Co., Ltd.; *Int'l*, pg. 3388
FIDELITY NATIONAL INFORMATION SERVICES, INC.; *U.S. Public*, pg. 831
FILL-MORE SEEDS INC.—See Seaboard Corporation; *U.S. Public*, pg. 1850
FINE ORGANICS CORPORATION; *U.S. Private*, pg. 1509
FINE ORGANICS INDUSTRIES LTD.; *Int'l*, pg. 2673
FINEOTEX CHEMICAL LTD.; *Int'l*, pg. 2674
FLAME GUARD B.V.—See AFG Group Nijmegen B.V.; *Int'l*, pg. 188
FLAUREA CHEMICALS S.A.—See Aurea, S.A.; *Int'l*, pg. 707
FLEXIBLE SOLUTIONS INTERNATIONAL, INC.; *Int'l*, pg. 2704
FLEXSYS CHEMICALS (M) SDN BHD—See Eastman Chemical Company; *U.S. Public*, pg. 706
FLEXSYS SA/NV—See Eastman Chemical Company; *U.S. Public*, pg. 705
FLEXSYS—See Eastman Chemical Company; *U.S. Public*, pg. 705
FLORALIFE INC.—See Smithers-Oasis Company; *U.S. Private*, pg. 3697
FLOTEK INDUSTRIES, INC.; *U.S. Public*, pg. 853
FLOWCHEM LLC—See Entegris, Inc.; *U.S. Public*, pg. 776
FMC CORP. - HEALTH & NUTRITION—See DuPont de Nemours, Inc.; *U.S. Public*, pg. 693
FMC CORP. - RESEARCH & TECHNOLOGY CENTER—See FMC Corporation; *U.S. Public*, pg. 862
FMC FRANCE S.A.—See FMC Corporation; *U.S. Public*, pg. 862
FMC KOREA LTD.—See FMC Corporation; *U.S. Public*, pg. 862
FMC PHILIPPINES INC.—See FMC Corporation; *U.S. Public*, pg. 861
FMC SHANGHAI COMMERCIAL ENTERPRISE—See FMC Corporation; *U.S. Public*, pg. 862
FORCHEM SP. Z O.O.—See BRENNTAG SE; *Int'l*, pg. 1149
FORMOSA CHEMICALS & FIBRE CORPORATION—See Formosa Petrochemical Corporation; *Int'l*, pg. 2735
FORMOSA PLASTICS CORPORATION - CHEMICALS DIVISION—See Formosa Plastics Corporation; *Int'l*, pg. 2735
FOSECO INDIA LIMITED; *Int'l*, pg. 2748
FOSHAN EFTEC AUTOMOTIVE MATERIALS CO., LTD.—See EMS-Chemie Holding AG; *Int'l*, pg. 2393
FRENS SPECIALTY CHEMICALS & EQUIPMENT LTD.—See Momar, Inc.; *U.S. Private*, pg. 2768
FRITZ INDUSTRIES INC.; *U.S. Private*, pg. 1613
FRONTIER SCIENTIFIC SERVICES, INC.—See Avista Capital Partners, L.P.; *U.S. Private*, pg. 409
FUJICHEMI CO., LTD.—See Fujibo Holdings, Inc.; *Int'l*, pg. 2820
FUJIFILM ELECTRONIC MATERIALS CO., LTD.—See FUJIFILM Holdings Corporation; *Int'l*, pg. 2824
FUJIFILM ELECTRONIC MATERIALS (SUZHOU) CO., LTD.—See FUJIFILM Holdings Corporation; *Int'l*, pg. 2824
FUJIFILM FINECHEMICALS CO., LTD. - HIRONO FACTORY—See FUJIFILM Holdings Corporation; *Int'l*, pg. 2824
FUJIFILM FINECHEMICALS CO., LTD.—See FUJIFILM Holdings Corporation; *Int'l*, pg. 2824
FUJIFILM FINECHEMICALS (WUXI) CO., LTD—See FUJIFILM Holdings Corporation; *Int'l*, pg. 2824
FUJIFILM HUNT PHOTOGRAPHIC CHEMICALS INC.—See FUJIFILM Holdings Corporation; *Int'l*, pg. 2823
FUJIFILM HUNT SMART SURFACE, LLC—See FUJIFILM Holdings Corporation; *Int'l*, pg. 2823
FUJIFILM PLANAR SOLUTIONS, LLC—See FUJIFILM Holdings Corporation; *Int'l*, pg. 2822
FUJIFILM ULTRA PURE SOLUTIONS INC.—See FUJIFILM Holdings Corporation; *Int'l*, pg. 2822
FUJI HUNT PHOTOGRAPHIC CHEMICALS, N.V.—See FUJIFILM Holdings Corporation; *Int'l*, pg. 2822
FUJIKURA KASEI COATING INDIA PRIVATE LTD.—See Fujikura Kasei Co., Ltd.; *Int'l*, pg. 2827
FUJIKURA KASEI COATING (TIANJIN) CO., LTD.—See Fujikura Kasei Co., Ltd.; *Int'l*, pg. 2827
FUJIKURA KASEI CO., LTD.; *Int'l*, pg. 2826
FUJIKURA KASEI (FOSHAN) COATING CO., LTD.—See Fujikura Kasei Co., Ltd.; *Int'l*, pg. 2826
FUJIKURA KASEI MALAYSIA SDN. BHD.—See Fujikura Kasei Co., Ltd.; *Int'l*, pg. 2827
FUJIKURA KASEI (THAILAND) CO., LTD.—See Fujikura Kasei Co., Ltd.; *Int'l*, pg. 2826
FUSO CHEMICAL CO., LTD.; *Int'l*, pg. 2849
FUSO CORPORATION CO LTD—See Fuso Chemical Co., Ltd.; *Int'l*, pg. 2850
FUTURE FOAM, INC. - HIGH POINT POURING PLANT—See Future Foam, Inc.; *U.S. Private*, pg. 1627
FUTURE FOAM, INC. - KANSAS CITY FABRICATION PLANT—See Future Foam, Inc.; *U.S. Private*, pg. 1627
FUTURE FOAM, INC. - MIDDLETON FABRICATION PLANT—See Future Foam, Inc.; *U.S. Private*, pg. 1627
FUTURE FOAM, INC. - NEWTON POURING PLANT—See Future Foam, Inc.; *U.S. Private*, pg. 1627

FUTURE FOAM, INC. - OKLAHOMA CITY FABRICATION PLANT—See Future Foam, Inc.; *U.S. Private*, pg. 1627
FUTURE FOAM, INC. - OMAHA FABRICATION PLANT—See Future Foam, Inc.; *U.S. Private*, pg. 1627
FUTURE FOAM, INC. - SPRINGFIELD FABRICATION PLANT—See Future Foam, Inc.; *U.S. Private*, pg. 1627
GAC CHEMICAL CORP—See GAC Chemical Corp.; *U.S. Private*, pg. 1633
GACL-NALCO ALKALIES & CHEMICALS PVT. LTD.—See Gujarat Alkalies & Chemicals Ltd; *Int'l*, pg. 3175
GADOT BIO-CHEM (EUROPE) B.V.—See Delek Group Ltd.; *Int'l*, pg. 2011
GADOT BIOCHEMICAL INDUSTRIES LTD.—See Delek Group Ltd.; *Int'l*, pg. 2011
GALAXY SURFACTANTS LIMITED; *Int'l*, pg. 2871
GALAXY SURFACTANTS LTD-ASIA PACIFIC—See Galaxy Surfactants Limited; *Int'l*, pg. 2872
GAMIDOR DIAGNOSTICS LTD.—See Gamida for Life B.V.; *Int'l*, pg. 2878
GAONA AERO MATERIAL CO., LTD.; *Int'l*, pg. 2882
GARDENIA-QUIMICA SA—See American Securities LLC; *U.S. Private*, pg. 252
GARGI HUTTENES-ALBERTUS PVT. LTD.—See Huettenes-Albertus Chemische Werke GmbH; *Int'l*, pg. 3522
GARRATT-CALLAHAN COMPANY; *U.S. Private*, pg. 1645
GAS TECHNOLOGY PRODUCTS LLC—See Merichem Company; *U.S. Private*, pg. 2672
GAYLORD CHEMICAL COMPANY LLC—See EagleTree Capital, LP; *U.S. Private*, pg. 1311
GCP APPLIED TECHNOLOGIES INC.—See Compagnie de Saint-Gobain SA; *Int'l*, pg. 1730
GEA ANDINA S.A.S.—See GEA Group Aktiengesellschaft; *Int'l*, pg. 2897
GEA ARABIA LTD.—See GEA Group Aktiengesellschaft; *Int'l*, pg. 2897
GEA AUSTRIA GMBH—See GEA Group Aktiengesellschaft; *Int'l*, pg. 2897
GEA BALTICS UAB—See GEA Group Aktiengesellschaft; *Int'l*, pg. 2897
GEA CZECH REPUBLIC S.R.O.—See GEA Group Aktiengesellschaft; *Int'l*, pg. 2898
GEA EEC BULGARIA EOOD—See GEA Group Aktiengesellschaft; *Int'l*, pg. 2898
GEA EEC SERBIA D.O.O.—See GEA Group Aktiengesellschaft; *Int'l*, pg. 2898
GEA EQUIPAMENTOS E SOLUCOES LTDA.—See GEA Group Aktiengesellschaft; *Int'l*, pg. 2898
GEA FARM TECHNOLOGIES CANADA INC.—See GEA Group Aktiengesellschaft; *Int'l*, pg. 2898
GEA FINLAND OY—See GEA Group Aktiengesellschaft; *Int'l*, pg. 2899
GEA GROUP HOLDING FRANCE SAS—See GEA Group Aktiengesellschaft; *Int'l*, pg. 2899
GEA KOREA LTD.—See GEA Group Aktiengesellschaft; *Int'l*, pg. 2899
GEA MECHANICAL EQUIPMENT ITALIA S.P.A.—See GEA Group Aktiengesellschaft; *Int'l*, pg. 2901
GEA MESSO GMBH—See GEA Group Aktiengesellschaft; *Int'l*, pg. 2901
GEA NORWAY AS—See GEA Group Aktiengesellschaft; *Int'l*, pg. 2901
GEA PERUANA SAC—See GEA Group Aktiengesellschaft; *Int'l*, pg. 2901
GEA PILIPINAS INC.—See GEA Group Aktiengesellschaft; *Int'l*, pg. 2901
GEA PROCESS ENGINEERING A/S—See GEA Group Aktiengesellschaft; *Int'l*, pg. 2901
GEA PROCESS ENGINEERING SP. Z O.O.—See GEA Group Aktiengesellschaft; *Int'l*, pg. 2902
GEA REFRIGERATION MALAYSIA SDN. BHD.—See GEA Group Aktiengesellschaft; *Int'l*, pg. 2902
GEA SUISSE AG—See GEA Group Aktiengesellschaft; *Int'l*, pg. 2903
GEA SWEDEN AB—See GEA Group Aktiengesellschaft; *Int'l*, pg. 2903
GEA (THAILAND) CO., LTD.—See GEA Group Aktiengesellschaft; *Int'l*, pg. 2897
GEA WEST AFRICA LTD.—See GEA Group Aktiengesellschaft; *Int'l*, pg. 2903
GEA WESTFALIA SEPARATOR HELLAS A.E.—See GEA Group Aktiengesellschaft; *Int'l*, pg. 2903
GEECEE VENTURES LTD. - CHEMICAL PLANT 2—See GeeCee Ventures Limited; *Int'l*, pg. 2911
GENERAL TRADING & CHEMICALS CO.—See Chemical Industries Holding Company; *Int'l*, pg. 1462
GENIUS ELECTRONIC OPTICAL (SHENZHEN) CO., LTD.—See Genius Electronic Optical Co., Ltd.; *Int'l*, pg. 2924
GENOFOCUS, INC.; *Int'l*, pg. 2925
GENOMATICA, INC.; *U.S. Private*, pg. 1673
GENPHARMASEC LIMITED; *Int'l*, pg. 2927
GEORG FISCHER GMBH—See Georg Fischer AG; *Int'l*, pg. 2935
GEORGIA-PACIFIC RESINS TAYLORSVILLE—See Koch Industries, Inc.; *U.S. Private*, pg. 2329
GEORGIA-PACIFIC RESINS VIENNA—See Koch Indus-

tries, Inc.; *U.S. Private*, pg. 2329
GEO SPECIALTY CHEMICALS - BASTROP—See Arsenal Capital Management LP; *U.S. Private*, pg. 337
GEO SPECIALTY CHEMICALS - CEDARTOWN—See Arsenal Capital Management LP; *U.S. Private*, pg. 337
GEO SPECIALTY CHEMICALS, INC.—See Arsenal Capital Management LP; *U.S. Private*, pg. 337
GEVO, INC.; *U.S. Public*, pg. 935
GIDA PAKETLEME VE SANAYI VE TICARET A.S.—See BIM Birlesik Magazalar A.S.; *Int'l*, pg. 1032
GLEASON CORPORATION; *U.S. Private*, pg. 1708
GLOBAL GREEN CHEMICALS PUBLIC COMPANY LIMITED; *Int'l*, pg. 2997
GODREJ HOUSEHOLD PRODUCTS LIMITED—See Godrej & Boyce Mfg. Co. Ltd.; *Int'l*, pg. 3021
GOLD EAGLE COMPANY; *U.S. Private*, pg. 1727
GOLDEN HARVEST MIDDLE EAST FZC—See Aries Agro Limited; *Int'l*, pg. 564
GOO CHEMICAL CO., LTD.; *Int'l*, pg. 3037
GRACE CATALYST AB—See Standard Industries Holdings Inc.; *U.S. Private*, pg. 3779
GRACE CATALYST AB—See Standard Industries Holdings Inc.; *U.S. Private*, pg. 3779
GRACE COLOMBIA S.A.—See Standard Industries Holdings Inc.; *U.S. Private*, pg. 3779
GRACE CONSTRUCTION PRODUCTS—See Standard Industries Holdings Inc.; *U.S. Private*, pg. 3779
GRACE DAVISON - CURTIS BAY (BALTIMORE) PLANT—See Standard Industries Holdings Inc.; *U.S. Private*, pg. 3779
GRACE DAVISON (PROPRIETARY) LIMITED—See Standard Industries Holdings Inc.; *U.S. Private*, pg. 3780
GRACE DAVISON—See Standard Industries Holdings Inc.; *U.S. Private*, pg. 3779
GRACE (NEW ZEALAND) LIMITED—See Standard Industries Holdings Inc.; *U.S. Private*, pg. 3779
GRACE SILICA GMBH—See Standard Industries Holdings Inc.; *U.S. Private*, pg. 3780
GRACE SP. Z O.O.—See Standard Industries Holdings Inc.; *U.S. Private*, pg. 3780
GRAFT POLYMER (UK) PLC; *Int'l*, pg. 3050
GRAPHENE NANOCHEM PLC; *Int'l*, pg. 3060
GREAT CHINASOFT TECHNOLOGY CO., LTD.; *Int'l*, pg. 3064
GREENFIELD SPECIALTY ALCOHOLS INC.; *Int'l*, pg. 3074
GREEN OLEO SPA; *Int'l*, pg. 3072
GREEN VIEW TECHNOLOGIES, INC.—See Clean Harbors, Inc.; *U.S. Public*, pg. 510
GREENWELL ENERGY SOLUTIONS LLC; *U.S. Private*, pg. 1781
GRODNO AZOT JSC—See Concern Belneftekhim; *Int'l*, pg. 1764
GROGENESIS, INC.; *U.S. Public*, pg. 970
GRUNAU ILLERTISSEN GMBH—See BASF SE; *Int'l*, pg. 884
GRUPA AZOTY ZAKIADY AZOTOWE PULAWY S. A.—See Grupa Azoty S.A.; *Int'l*, pg. 3115
GS ENTEC CORP.—See GS Holdings Corp.; *Int'l*, pg. 3142
GUANGDONG DELIAN GROUP CO., LTD.; *Int'l*, pg. 3153
GUANGDONG GUANGHUA SCI-TECH CO., LTD.; *Int'l*, pg. 3155
GUANGDONG ORIENT ZIRCONIC INDUSTRY SCIENCE & TECHNOLOGY CO., LTD.; *Int'l*, pg. 3158
GUANGXI HUAXI NONFERROUS METALS CO., LTD; *Int'l*, pg. 3163
GUANGZHOU APPLE FOODS TECH CO., LTD.—See Apple Flavor & Fragrance Group Co., Ltd.; *Int'l*, pg. 520
GUANGZHOU NATIONAL ADHESIVES CO. LTD.—See Henkel AG & Co. KGaA; *Int'l*, pg. 3348
GUANGZHOU TINCI MATERIALS TECHNOLOGY COMPANY LIMITED; *Int'l*, pg. 3168
GUANO-WERKE GMBH & CO. KG—See BASF SE; *Int'l*, pg. 884
GUARDIAN PROTECTION PRODUCTS, INC.—See OnPoint Warranty Solutions, LLC; *U.S. Private*, pg. 3027
GUJCHEM DISTILLERS INDIA LIMITED; *Int'l*, pg. 3177
GULF BAYPORT CHEMICALS L.P.—See Platte River Ventures, LLC; *U.S. Private*, pg. 3211
HABRINOL DECIN S.R.O. (GMBH)—See Huettenes-Albertus Chemische Werke GmbH; *Int'l*, pg. 3523
HA FRANCE S.A.R.L.—See Huettenes-Albertus Chemische Werke GmbH; *Int'l*, pg. 3522
HALOCARBON PRODUCTS CORPORATION; *U.S. Private*, pg. 1846
HALOTRON, INC.—See H.I.G. Capital, LLC; *U.S. Private*, pg. 1829
HANDYMAN—See Momar, Inc.; *U.S. Private*, pg. 2768
HANG JIN TECHNOLOGY CO., LTD.; *Int'l*, pg. 3244
HANGZHOU CAIZHIXIN TECHNOLOGY CO., LTD.—See Dalian Thermal Power Co., Ltd.; *Int'l*, pg. 1952
HANGZHOU HANGHUA-HARIMA CHEMICALS CO., LTD.—See Harima Chemicals Group, Inc.; *Int'l*, pg. 3276
HANGZHOU TIANSHUN FOOD CO., LTD.—See Apple Flavor & Fragrance Group Co., Ltd.; *Int'l*, pg. 520
HANSA CHEMIE HOLLAND BV—See Hansa Chemie International AG; *Int'l*, pg. 3259
HANWHA CHEMICAL MALAYSIA SDN. BHD.—See Hanwha Group; *Int'l*, pg. 3265

HANWHA CHEMICAL (NINGBO) CO., LTD.—See Hanwha Group; *Int'l*, pg. 3265
HANWHA CHEMICAL TRADING (SHANGHAI) CO., LTD.—See Hanwha Group; *Int'l*, pg. 3265
HANWHA EUROPE GMBH—See Hanwha Group; *Int'l*, pg. 3265
HANWHA GENERAL CHEMICAL CO., LTD.—See Hanwha Group; *Int'l*, pg. 3265
HARCROS CHEMICALS INC.; *U.S. Private*, pg. 1862
HARIMA CHEMICALS GROUP, INC.; *Int'l*, pg. 3276
HARIMA DO BRASIL INDUSTRIA QUIMICA LTDA.—See Harima Chemicals Group, Inc.; *Int'l*, pg. 3276
HARIMA KASEI POLYMER CO., LTD.—See Harima Chemicals Group, Inc.; *Int'l*, pg. 3276
HARIMATEC CZECH S.R.O.—See Harima Chemicals Group, Inc.; *Int'l*, pg. 3276
HARIMATEC HANGZHOU CO., LTD.—See Harima Chemicals Group, Inc.; *Int'l*, pg. 3276
HARIMATEC MALAYSIA SDN. BHD.—See Harima Chemicals Group, Inc.; *Int'l*, pg. 3276
HARIMA USA, INC.—See Harima Chemicals Group, Inc.; *Int'l*, pg. 3276
HA ROMANIA S.R.L.—See Huettenes-Albertus Chemische Werke GmbH; *Int'l*, pg. 3523
HARPURE ENTERPRISES INC.; *U.S. Private*, pg. 1868
HARYANA LEATHER CHEMICALS LTD.; *Int'l*, pg. 3282
HAVILAND ENTERPRISES INC.; *U.S. Private*, pg. 1880
HAYLEYS GROUP SERVICES LTD.—See Hayleys PLC; *Int'l*, pg. 3292
HAYMARK INC.—See Hayleys PLC; *Int'l*, pg. 3292
H.B. FULLER SOUTH AFRICA (PTY) LTD.—See H.B. Fuller Company; *U.S. Public*, pg. 978
HEBEI CHENGXIN CO., LTD.; *Int'l*, pg. 3305
HEBEI HEZHONG BUILDING MATERIALS CO., LTD.—See Beijing Hanjian Heshan Pipeline Co.,LTD.; *Int'l*, pg. 951
HEBEI JIANXIN CHEMICAL CO., LTD.; *Int'l*, pg. 3306
HEBRO CHEMIE ZWEIGNIEDERLASSUNG DER ROCK-WOOD SPECIALTIES GROUP GMBH—See Albemarle Corporation; *U.S. Public*, pg. 74
HEMOMAK HEM UROS DOOEL—See BASF SE; *Int'l*, pg. 884
HEMPRO A.D.; *Int'l*, pg. 3341
HENAN HUALONG AROMA CHEMICALS CO., LTD.—See Apple Flavor & Fragrance Group Co., Ltd.; *Int'l*, pg. 520
HENAN QINGSHUIYUAN TECHNOLOGY CO., LTD.; *Int'l*, pg. 3342
HENAN YICHENG NEW ENERGY CO., LTD.; *Int'l*, pg. 3343
HENGI CHEMICAL CO., LTD.—See Coremax Corp.; *Int'l*, pg. 1798
HENKEL ANAND INDIA PVT. LTD.—See Henkel AG & Co. KGaA; *Int'l*, pg. 3348
HENKEL BULGARIA EOOD—See Henkel AG & Co. KGaA; *Int'l*, pg. 3350
HENKEL CANADA CORPORATION—See Henkel AG & Co. KGaA; *Int'l*, pg. 3350
HENKEL CAPITAL S.A. DE C.V.—See Henkel AG & Co. KGaA; *Int'l*, pg. 3350
HENKEL COSTA RICA LTDA.—See Henkel AG & Co. KGaA; *Int'l*, pg. 3350
HENKEL DETERGENTS SAUDI ARABIA LTD.—See Henkel AG & Co. KGaA; *Int'l*, pg. 3350
HENKEL ECUATORIANA S.A.—See Henkel AG & Co. KGaA; *Int'l*, pg. 3350
HENKEL IBERICA PORTUGAL, UNIPESSOAL LDA.—See Henkel AG & Co. KGaA; *Int'l*, pg. 3351
HENKEL INDUSTRIE AG—See Henkel AG & Co. KGaA; *Int'l*, pg. 3351
HENKEL JAPAN LTD.—See Henkel AG & Co. KGaA; *Int'l*, pg. 3349
HENKEL KOREA LTD.—See Henkel AG & Co. KGaA; *Int'l*, pg. 3349
HENKEL LEBANON S.A.L.—See Henkel AG & Co. KGaA; *Int'l*, pg. 3351
HENKEL LTD.—See Henkel AG & Co. KGaA; *Int'l*, pg. 3351
HENKEL MERIMA A.D.—See Henkel AG & Co. KGaA; *Int'l*, pg. 3350
HENKEL NEW ZEALAND LTD.—See Henkel AG & Co. KGaA; *Int'l*, pg. 3349
HENKEL NORDEN OY—See Henkel AG & Co. KGaA; *Int'l*, pg. 3352
HENKEL OBERFLACHENTECHNIK GMBH—See Henkel AG & Co. KGaA; *Int'l*, pg. 3352
HENKEL PERUANA S.A.—See Henkel AG & Co. KGaA; *Int'l*, pg. 3352
HENKEL PHILIPPINES INC.—See Henkel AG & Co. KGaA; *Int'l*, pg. 3352
HENKEL SLOVENIJA D.O.O.—See Henkel AG & Co. KGaA; *Int'l*, pg. 3350
HENKEL SLOVENSKO SPOL. S.R.O.—See Henkel AG & Co. KGaA; *Int'l*, pg. 3350
HENKEL SOAD LTD.—See Henkel AG & Co. KGaA; *Int'l*, pg. 3352
HENKEL SOUTH AFRICA (PTY.) LTD.—See Henkel AG & Co. KGaA; *Int'l*, pg. 3352
HENKEL SURFACE TECHNOLOGIES GMBH—See Henkel AG & Co. KGaA; *Int'l*, pg. 3352
HENKEL SURFACE TECHNOLOGIES—See Henkel AG & Co. KGaA; *Int'l*, pg. 3352

HENKEL TAIWAN LTD.—See Henkel AG & Co. KGaA; *Int'l*, pg. 3349
HENKEL TRADING MAGHREB S.A.R.L.—See Henkel AG & Co. KGaA; *Int'l*, pg. 3352
HENKEL TUNISIE S.A.—See Henkel AG & Co. KGaA; *Int'l*, pg. 3352
HENKEL VIETNAM CO. LTD. - BINH DUONG COSMETICS PLANT—See Henkel AG & Co. KGaA; *Int'l*, pg. 3349
HERAEUS DEUTSCHLAND GMBH & CO. KG—See Heraeus Holding GmbH; *Int'l*, pg. 3357
HERAEUS ELECTRO-NITE MEXICANA S.A. DE C.V.—See Heraeus Holding GmbH; *Int'l*, pg. 3357
HERAEUS ELECTRO-NITE POLSKA SP. Z O.O.—See Heraeus Holding GmbH; *Int'l*, pg. 3357
HERAEUS ELECTRO-NITE SHENYANG CO. LTD.—See Heraeus Holding GmbH; *Int'l*, pg. 3357
HERAEUS ELECTRO-NITE TAIWAN LTD.—See Heraeus Holding GmbH; *Int'l*, pg. 3357
HERAEUS ELECTRO-NITE UKRAINA LLC—See Heraeus Holding GmbH; *Int'l*, pg. 3357
HERAEUS KULZER AUSTRALIA PTY. LTD.—See Heraeus Holding GmbH; *Int'l*, pg. 3357
HERAEUS LTD.—See Heraeus Holding GmbH; *Int'l*, pg. 3357
HERAEUS MATERIALS S.A.—See Heraeus Holding GmbH; *Int'l*, pg. 3357
HERAEUS MATERIALS TECHNOLOGY NORTH AMERICA LLC—See Heraeus Holding GmbH; *Int'l*, pg. 3357
HERAEUS MATERIALS TECHNOLOGY SHANGHAI LTD.—See Heraeus Holding GmbH; *Int'l*, pg. 3357
HERAEUS MATERIALS TECHNOLOGY TAIWAN LTD.—See Heraeus Holding GmbH; *Int'l*, pg. 3357
HERAEUS PRECIOUS METALS NORTH AMERICA CONSHOHOCKEN LLC—See Heraeus Holding GmbH; *Int'l*, pg. 3357
HERAEUS QUARTZ UK LTD.—See Heraeus Holding GmbH; *Int'l*, pg. 3358
HERAEUS RECYCLING TECHNOLOGY (TAICANG) CO., LTD.—See Heraeus Holding GmbH; *Int'l*, pg. 3358
HERAEUS SENSOR TECHNOLOGY GMBH—See Heraeus Holding GmbH; *Int'l*, pg. 3358
HERAEUS SHINETSU QUARTZ CHINA INC.—See Heraeus Holding GmbH; *Int'l*, pg. 3358
HERAEUS SOUTH AFRICA (PTY.) LTD.—See Heraeus Holding GmbH; *Int'l*, pg. 3358
HERAEUS ZHAOYUAN CHANGSHU LTD.—See Heraeus Holding GmbH; *Int'l*, pg. 3358
HERCULES CHEMICAL CO., INC.; *U.S. Private*, pg. 1921
HERCULES CHEMICALS SOLUTION PTE. LTD.—See Ashland Inc.; *U.S. Public*, pg. 212
HERCULES CHEMICALS (TAIWAN) CO., LTD.—See Ashland Inc.; *U.S. Public*, pg. 212
HERCULES CLOROBEN CORP.—See Hercules Chemical Co., Inc.; *U.S. Private*, pg. 1921
HERCULES DO BRASIL PRODUTOS QUIMICOS LTDA.—See Ashland Inc.; *U.S. Public*, pg. 212
HERCULES DOEL BVBA—See Ashland Inc.; *U.S. Public*, pg. 212
HEREAUS PRECIOUS METALS GMBH & CO. KG—See Heraeus Holding GmbH; *Int'l*, pg. 3358
HEXION B.V. - ROTTERDAM, BOTLEK—See American Securities LLC; *U.S. Private*, pg. 249
HEXION CANADA INC.—See American Securities LLC; *U.S. Private*, pg. 249
HEXION GMBH—See American Securities LLC; *U.S. Private*, pg. 249
HEXION UK LTD. - PETERLEE—See American Securities LLC; *U.S. Private*, pg. 249
HEXION UK LTD.—See American Securities LLC; *U.S. Private*, pg. 249
HEXION UK LTD. - STIRLING—See American Securities LLC; *U.S. Private*, pg. 249
HI-BIS GMBH—See Honshu Chemical Industry Co., Ltd.; *Int'l*, pg. 3472
HIKAL LIMITED; *Int'l*, pg. 3389
HILL BROTHERS CHEMICAL COMPANY INC. - CITY OF INDUSTRY—See Hill Brothers Chemical Company Inc.; *U.S. Private*, pg. 1944
HINDCON CHEMICALS LIMITED; *Int'l*, pg. 3397
HINDPRAKASH INDUSTRIES LTD.; *Int'l*, pg. 3397
H.K. WENTWORTH (INDIA) PRIVATE LIMITED—See Element Solutions Inc.; *U.S. Public*, pg. 726
HODOGAYA CHEMICAL CO., LTD. - NANYO PLANT—See Hodogaya Chemical Co., Ltd.; *Int'l*, pg. 3438
HODOGAYA CHEMICAL CO., LTD. - YOKOHAMA PLANT—See Hodogaya Chemical Co., Ltd.; *Int'l*, pg. 3438
HOGANAS INDIA LTD—See Hoganas AB; *Int'l*, pg. 3441
H-O-H WATER TECHNOLOGY, INC.; *U.S. Private*, pg. 1824
HOLLAND COLOURS EUROPE BV—See Holland Colours NV; *Int'l*, pg. 3451
HOLLIDAY CHEMICAL ESPANA S.A.—See Huntsman Corporation; *U.S. Public*, pg. 1073
HOME UPHOLSTERY INDUSTRIES SDN. BHD.—See Homeritz Corporation Berhad; *Int'l*, pg. 3455
HONEYWELL SAFETY PRODUCTS EMERGENCY EYEWASH—See Honeywell International Inc.; *U.S. Public*, pg. 1049

325998 — ALL OTHER MISCELLAN...   CORPORATE AFFILIATIONS

HONEYWELL SPECIALTY CHEMICALS SEELZE GMBH—See Honeywell International Inc.; *U.S. Public*, pg. 1051
HONGBAOLI GROUP CO., LTD; *Int'l*, pg. 3469
HONGLK CO., LTD—See AK Holdings, Inc.; *Int'l*, pg. 259
HONJO CHEMICAL CORPORATION - NAOSHIMA FACTORY—See Honjo Chemical Corporation; *Int'l*, pg. 3471
HONJO CHEMICAL CORPORATION; *Int'l*, pg. 3471
HONJO CHEMICAL (SINGAPORE) PTE LTD—See Honjo Chemical Corporation; *Int'l*, pg. 3471
HONSHU CHEMICAL INDUSTRY CO., LTD. - WAKAYAMA WORKS—See Honshu Chemical Industry Co., Ltd.; *Int'l*, pg. 3472
HOSOYA PYRO-ENGINEERING CO., LTD.; *Int'l*, pg. 3486
HOUGHTON AUSTRALIA PTY. LTD.—See Quaker Chemical Corporation; *U.S. Public*, pg. 1746
HOUGHTON BRAZIL LTDA.—See Quaker Chemical Corporation; *U.S. Public*, pg. 1746
HOUGHTON CHEMICAL CORPORATION - ALLSTON FACILITY—See Houghton Chemical Corporation; *U.S. Private*, pg. 1990
HOUGHTON DEUTSCHLAND GMBH—See Quaker Chemical Corporation; *U.S. Public*, pg. 1746
HOUGHTON IBERICA S.A.—See Quaker Chemical Corporation; *U.S. Public*, pg. 1746
HOUGHTON INTERNATIONAL INC.—See Quaker Chemical Corporation; *U.S. Public*, pg. 1745
HOUGHTON ITALIA S.P.A.—See Quaker Chemical Corporation; *U.S. Public*, pg. 1746
HOUGHTON PLC—See Quaker Chemical Corporation; *U.S. Public*, pg. 1746
HOUGHTON (SHANGHAI) SPECIALTY INDUSTRIAL FLUIDS CO. LTD.—See Quaker Chemical Corporation; *U.S. Public*, pg. 1745
HOUGHTON SINGAPORE—See Quaker Chemical Corporation; *U.S. Public*, pg. 1746
HPS TECHNOLOGIES, INC.; *U.S. Private*, pg. 1997
H&R CHEMPHARM (UK) LTD.—See H&R KGaA; *Int'l*, pg. 3193
H&R INTERNATIONAL GMBH—See H&R KGaA; *Int'l*, pg. 3193
H&R KGAA; *Int'l*, pg. 3193
HUANGSHAN HUAJIA SURFACE TECHNOLOGY CO., LTD.—See PPG Industries, Inc.; *U.S. Public*, pg. 1707
HUBEI DINGLONG CO., LTD.; *Int'l*, pg. 3517
HUBEI XINGFA CHEMICALS GROUP CO., LTD.; *Int'l*, pg. 3518
HUBER ENGINEERED MATERIALS, LLC—See J.M. Huber Corporation; *U.S. Private*, pg. 2168
HUETTENES-ALBERTUS CHEMISCHE WERKE GMBH; *Int'l*, pg. 3522
HUIXIN WASTE WATER SOLUTIONS, INC.; *Int'l*, pg. 3527
HUNAN HENGGUANG CHEMICAL CO., LTD.—See Hunan Hengguang Technology Co., Ltd.; *Int'l*, pg. 3532
HUNTSMAN (ARGENTINA) S.R.L.—See Huntsman Corporation; *U.S. Public*, pg. 1073
HUNTSMAN (COLOMBIA) LIMITADA—See Huntsman Corporation; *U.S. Public*, pg. 1073
HUNTSMAN CORPORATION HUNGARY RT.—See Huntsman Corporation; *U.S. Public*, pg. 1074
HUNTSMAN CORPORATION UK LIMITED—See Huntsman Corporation; *U.S. Public*, pg. 1074
HUNTSMAN (CZECH REPUBLIC) SPOL.SR.O—See Huntsman Corporation; *U.S. Public*, pg. 1073
HUNTSMAN (GERMANY) GMBH—See Huntsman Corporation; *U.S. Public*, pg. 1073
HUNTSMAN HOLLAND B.V.—See Huntsman Corporation; *U.S. Public*, pg. 1074
HUNTSMAN INTERNATIONAL LLC—See Huntsman Corporation; *U.S. Public*, pg. 1073
HUNTSMAN (POLAND) SP. Z O.O.—See Huntsman Corporation; *U.S. Public*, pg. 1073
HUNTSMAN POLYURETHANES (CHINA) LIMITED—See Huntsman Corporation; *U.S. Public*, pg. 1074
HUNTSMAN - POLYURETHANES DIVISION—See Huntsman Corporation; *U.S. Public*, pg. 1074
HUNTSMAN QUIMICA BRASIL LTDA.—See Huntsman Corporation; *U.S. Public*, pg. 1074
HUNTSMAN SAINT-MIHIEL SAS—See Huntsman Corporation; *U.S. Public*, pg. 1074
HUNTSMAN SOLUTIONS INDIA PRIVATE LIMITED—See Huntsman Corporation; *U.S. Public*, pg. 1075
HUNTSMAN SPECIALTY CHEMICALS KIMYA SANAYI VE TICARET ANONIM SIRKETI—See Huntsman Corporation; *U.S. Public*, pg. 1075
HUNTSMAN TEXTILE EFFECTS (MEXICO) S. DE R.L. DE C.V.—See Huntsman Corporation; *U.S. Public*, pg. 1074
HUNTSMAN (UAE) FZE—See Huntsman Corporation; *U.S. Public*, pg. 1072
HUTTENES ALBERTUS BELGIE N.V.—See Huettenes-Albertus Chemische Werke GmbH; *Int'l*, pg. 3523
HUTTENES ALBERTUS NEDERLAND B.V.—See Huettenes-Albertus Chemische Werke GmbH; *Int'l*, pg. 3523
HYDRITE CHEMICAL COMPANY - COTTAGE GROVE PLANT—See Hydrite Chemical Company; *U.S. Private*, pg. 2017
HYDRITE CHEMICAL COMPANY - LACROSSE PLANT—See Hydrite Chemical Company; *U.S. Private*, pg. 2017
HYDRITE CHEMICAL COMPANY - MILWAUKEE PLANT—See Hydrite Chemical Company; *U.S. Private*, pg. 2017
HYDRITE CHEMICAL COMPANY - OSHKOSH PLANT—See Hydrite Chemical Company; *U.S. Private*, pg. 2017
HYDRITE CHEMICAL COMPANY - TERRE HAUTE PLANT—See Hydrite Chemical Company; *U.S. Private*, pg. 2017
HYDRITE CHEMICAL COMPANY - WATERLOO PLANT—See Hydrite Chemical Company; *U.S. Private*, pg. 2017
HYDRITE CHEMICAL COMPANY - WAUSAU PLANT—See Hydrite Chemical Company; *U.S. Private*, pg. 2017
HYFLUX LTD; *Int'l*, pg. 3548
HYWAX GMBH—See AWAX S.p.A.; *Int'l*, pg. 752
IBC ADVANCED TECHNOLOGIES, INC.; *U.S. Private*, pg. 2028
ICHEMCO S.R.L.; *Int'l*, pg. 3579
ICM PRODUCTS, INC.—See Akoya Capital LLC; *U.S. Private*, pg. 146
ICM PRODUCTS, INC.—See Century Park Capital Partners, LLC; *U.S. Private*, pg. 833
ICS PENETRON INTERNATIONAL LTD.; *U.S. Private*, pg. 2033
IDEMITSU CHEMICALS (M) SDN. BHD.—See Idemitsu Kosan Co., Ltd.; *Int'l*, pg. 3590
IDEMITSU TECHNOFINE CO., LTD.—See Idemitsu Kosan Co., Ltd.; *Int'l*, pg. 3591
IGM RESINS B.V.—See Astorg Partners S.A.S.; *Int'l*, pg. 656
ILARDUYA PRODUCTOS DE FUNDICION—See Huettenes-Albertus Chemische Werke GmbH; *Int'l*, pg. 3523
IMCD POLSKA SP. Z.O.O.—See IMCD N.V.; *Int'l*, pg. 3622
IMMUNOTECH LABORATORIES, INC.—See Enzolytics, Inc.; *U.S. Public*, pg. 782
INCA BRONZE POWDERS LTD.—See BASF SE; *Int'l*, pg. 884
INDSPEC CHEMICAL CORPORATION—See Occidental Petroleum Corporation; *U.S. Public*, pg. 1561
INDUSTRIAL NANOTECH, INC.; *U.S. Public*, pg. 1117
INDUSTRIAL SPECIALTY CHEMICALS, INC.—See Element Solutions Inc.; *U.S. Public*, pg. 726
INDUSTRIA QUIMICA DEL ISTMO, S.A. DE C.V. - COATZACOALCOS PLANT—See Cydsa S.A.B. de C.V.; *Int'l*, pg. 1895
INDUSTRIA QUIMICA DEL ISTMO, S.A. DE C.V. - HERMOSILLO PLANT—See Cydsa S.A.B. de C.V.; *Int'l*, pg. 1895
INDUSTRIA QUIMICA DEL ISTMO, S.A. DE C.V.—See Cydsa S.A.B. de C.V.; *Int'l*, pg. 1895
INDUSTRIAS P. KAY DE MEXICO—See P. Kay Metal Supply Inc.; *U.S. Private*, pg. 3060
INEOS ENTERPRISES GROUP LIMITED—See One Rock Capital Partners, LLC; *U.S. Private*, pg. 3023
INEOS SOLVENTS GERMANY GMBH—See One Rock Capital Partners, LLC; *U.S. Private*, pg. 3023
INGEVITY SOUTH CAROLINA, LLC—See Ingevity Corporation; *U.S. Public*, pg. 1122
INGREDION CHINA LIMITED—See Ingredion Incorporated; *U.S. Public*, pg. 1123
INGREDION INDIA PRIVATE LIMITED—See Ingredion Incorporated; *U.S. Public*, pg. 1123
INGREDION MALAYSIA SDN. BHD.—See Ingredion Incorporated; *U.S. Public*, pg. 1123
INGREDION (THAILAND) LTD.—See Ingredion Incorporated; *U.S. Public*, pg. 1123
INKJET INC.; *U.S. Private*, pg. 2077
INNOSPEC ACTIVE CHEMICALS LLC—See Innospec Inc.; *U.S. Public*, pg. 1125
INNOSPEC DEVELOPMENTS LIMITED—See Innospec Inc.; *U.S. Public*, pg. 1125
INNOSPEC PERFORMANCE CHEMICALS ITALIA S.R.L—See Innospec Inc.; *U.S. Public*, pg. 1125
INNOSPEC PERFORMANCE CHEMICALS SPAIN S.L.—See Innospec Inc.; *U.S. Public*, pg. 1125
INNOSPEC SPECIALTY CHEMICALS—See Innospec Inc.; *U.S. Public*, pg. 1125
INNOSPEC SWEDEN AB—See Innospec Inc.; *U.S. Public*, pg. 1125
INNOVATION DIC CHIMITRONIQUES INC.—See DIC Corporation; *Int'l*, pg. 2109
INOCHEM S.A. DE C.V.—See Revvity, Inc.; *U.S. Public*, pg. 1794
INREOS SOLVENTS GERMANY GMBH—See One Rock Capital Partners, LLC; *U.S. Private*, pg. 3023
INSTITUTE OF SCRAP RECYCLING INDUSTRIES, INC.; *U.S. Private*, pg. 2093
INTERNATIONAL FLAVORS & FRAGRANCES INC.; *U.S. Public*, pg. 1151
INTERNATIONAL FLAVOURS & FRAGRANCES INDIA PRIVATE LIMITED—See International Flavors & Fragrances Inc.; *U.S. Public*, pg. 1153
INTERNATIONAL ISOTOPES INC.; *U.S. Public*, pg. 1154
INTERNATIONAL WATER-GUARD INDUSTRIES INC.—See Arcline Investment Management LP; *U.S. Private*, pg. 314
I.P. CALLISON & SONS INC.; *U.S. Private*, pg. 2027
ISP CHEMICALS LLC—See Ashland Inc.; *U.S. Public*, pg. 212
ISP TECHNOLOGIES INC.—See Ashland Inc.; *U.S. Public*, pg. 213
ITALMATCH CHEMICALS S.P.A.—See Bain Capital, LP; *U.S. Private*, pg. 441
ITALMATCH USA CORPORATION—See Bain Capital, LP; *U.S. Private*, pg. 441
ITW CHEMTRONICS—See Blackstone Inc.; *U.S. Public*, pg. 354
ITW DYMON—See Illinois Tool Works Inc.; *U.S. Public*, pg. 1105
ITW POLYMERS & FLUIDS PTY. LTD.—See Illinois Tool Works Inc.; *U.S. Public*, pg. 1107
JACAM CHEMICAL COMPANY, INC.; *U.S. Private*, pg. 2173
JACKSAM CORPORATION; *U.S. Public*, pg. 1183
JAMES AUSTIN CO. - DELAND PLANT—See James Austin Co.; *U.S. Private*, pg. 2183
JAMES AUSTIN CO. - LUDLOW PLANT—See James Austin Co.; *U.S. Private*, pg. 2183
JAMES AUSTIN CO. - STATESVILLE PLANT—See James Austin Co.; *U.S. Private*, pg. 2183
JAPAN ACRYLIC CHEMICAL CO., LTD.—See Dow Inc.; *U.S. Public*, pg. 685
JAPAN CARLIT CO., LTD.—See Carlit Co., Ltd.; *Int'l*, pg. 1338
JASMINAL S.A.R.L.—See Henkel AG & Co. KGaA; *Int'l*, pg. 3352
JBT FOODTECH FORT PIERCE—See John Bean Technologies Corporation; *U.S. Public*, pg. 1191
JBT FOODTECH LINDSAY—See John Bean Technologies Corporation; *U.S. Public*, pg. 1191
JET-LUBE OF CANADA LTD.—See CSW Industrials, Inc.; *U.S. Public*, pg. 601
JIANGSU BOSTIK ADHESIVE CO., LTD.—See Arkema S.A.; *Int'l*, pg. 571
JIANGSU GRAND XIANLE PHARMACEUTICAL CO., LTD.—See Grand Pharmaceutical Group Limited; *Int'l*, pg. 3056
JIANGSU ZEOCHEM TECHNOLOGY CO. LTD.—See CPH Chemie + Papier Holding AG; *Int'l*, pg. 1824
JIANGXI ALBEMARLE LITHIUM CO., LTD.—See Albemarle Corporation; *U.S. Public*, pg. 73
JIANGXI HUATE ELECTRONIC CHEMICAL CO., LTD.—See Guangdong Huate Gas Co., Ltd.; *Int'l*, pg. 3156
JILIN CHUANGYUAN CHEMICAL CO., LTD.—See Planet Green Holdings Corp.; *U.S. Public*, pg. 1697
JINAN HUAJIA SURFACE TECHNOLOGY CO., LTD.—See PPG Industries, Inc.; *U.S. Public*, pg. 1707
JINGMEN GEM NEW MATERIAL CO., LTD—See GEM Co., Ltd.; *Int'l*, pg. 2914
J.M. HUBER (INDIA) PVT. LTD.—See J.M. Huber Corporation; *U.S. Private*, pg. 2168
JOHANN HALTERMANN LTD.—See Heritage Group; *U.S. Private*, pg. 1923
JORDANIAN SWISS COMPANY FOR MANUFACTURING & MARKETING CONSTRUCTION CHEMICALS COMPANY LTD.—See BASF SE; *Int'l*, pg. 884
KALINGANAGAR SPECIAL STEEL PRIVATE LIMITED—See Balaji Amines Limited; *Int'l*, pg. 806
KANTO DAINICHISEIKA KOGYO CO., LTD.—See Dainichiseika Color & Chemicals Mfg. Co., Ltd.; *Int'l*, pg. 1939
KARTAL KIMYA SANAYI VE TICARET A.S.—See BASF SE; *Int'l*, pg. 884
KASHIMA CHEMICAL CO., LTD.—See AGC Inc.; *Int'l*, pg. 204
K.A. STEEL CHEMICALS INC.—See Olin Corporation; *U.S. Public*, pg. 1570
K. A. STEEL CHEMICALS INC.—See Olin Corporation; *U.S. Public*, pg. 1570
KB ALLOYS, INC.—See AMG Critical Materials N.V.; *Int'l*, pg. 425
KELKO QUAKER CHEMICAL, S.A.—See Quaker Chemical Corporation; *U.S. Public*, pg. 1746
KENDELL S.R.L.—See BASF SE; *Int'l*, pg. 884
KENTUCKY BERWIND LAND COMPANY—See Berwind Corporation; *U.S. Private*, pg. 540
KEUM JUNG AKZO NOBEL PEROXIDES LTD—See Akzo Nobel N.V.; *Int'l*, pg. 274
KEY POLYMER CORPORATION—See Dalfort Capital Partners, LLC; *U.S. Private*, pg. 1149
KEY RESIN CO.—See RPM International Inc.; *U.S. Public*, pg. 1817
KIK POOL ADDITIVES INC.; *U.S. Private*, pg. 2304
KING INDUSTRIES, INC.; *U.S. Private*, pg. 2309
K.K. KODAK INFORMATION SYSTEMS—See Eastman Kodak Company; *U.S. Public*, pg. 707
KL TEXAS L.P.—See Freudenberg SE; *Int'l*, pg. 2786
KLUBER LUBRICATION BELGIUM NETHERLANDS S.A.—See Freudenberg SE; *Int'l*, pg. 2785
KLUBER LUBRICATION DEUTSCHLAND SE & CO. KG—See Freudenberg SE; *Int'l*, pg. 2785
KLUBER LUBRICATION INDIA PVT. LTD. - MYSORE

325998 — ALL OTHER MISCELLAN...

FACTORY—See Freudenberg SE; *Int'l*, pg. 2785
KLUEBER LUBRICATION ROMANIA S.R.L.—See Freudenberg SE; *Int'l*, pg. 2789
KMCO, LLC—See BRENNTAG SE; *Int'l*, pg. 1148
KMG-BERNUTH, INC.—See Entegris, Inc.; *U.S. Public*, pg. 776
KMG CHEMICALS, INC.—See Entegris, Inc.; *U.S. Public*, pg. 776
KMG ULTRA PURE CHEMICALS LIMITED—See Entegris, Inc.; *U.S. Public*, pg. 776
KMG ULTRA PURE CHEMICALS SAS—See Entegris, Inc.; *U.S. Public*, pg. 776
KMTEX, LLC—See BRENNTAG SE; *Int'l*, pg. 1148
KOCH CHEMICAL TECHNOLOGY GROUP INDIA PVT. LTD. - KOCH-GLITSCH BARODA DIVISION—See Koch Industries, Inc.; *U.S. Private*, pg. 2331
KOCH CHEMICAL TECHNOLOGY GROUP S.A. DE C.V.—See Koch Industries, Inc.; *U.S. Private*, pg. 2331
KOCH CHEMICAL TECHNOLOGY GROUP S.L. KOCH-GLITSCH DIVISION—See Koch Industries, Inc.; *U.S. Private*, pg. 2331
KOCH KNIGHT LLC—See Koch Industries, Inc.; *U.S. Private*, pg. 2331
KOFFOLK LTD.—See Phibro Animal Health Corporation; *U.S. Public*, pg. 1685
KOREA ZERUST CO., LTD.—See Northern Technologies International Corporation; *U.S. Public*, pg. 1538
KORSNAS ROCKHAMMAR AB—See Billerud AB; *Int'l*, pg. 1030
KOYO SANGYO CO., LTD.—See Bando Chemical Industries, Ltd.; *Int'l*, pg. 830
KRATON CHEMICAL A.B.—See Daelim Industrial Co., Ltd.; *Int'l*, pg. 1908
KRATON CHEMICAL B.V.—See Daelim Industrial Co., Ltd.; *Int'l*, pg. 1908
KRATON CHEMICAL, LLC—See Daelim Industrial Co., Ltd.; *Int'l*, pg. 1908
KRATON POLYMERS JAPAN LTD.—See Daelim Industrial Co., Ltd.; *Int'l*, pg. 1908
KRONOS CHEMIE GMBH—See Contran Corporation; *U.S. Private*, pg. 1033
KRONOS EUROPE S.A./N.V.—See Contran Corporation; *U.S. Private*, pg. 1033
K-SOLV GROUP, LLC; *U.S. Private*, pg. 2251
KUNMING APPLE KAIXIN FOODS INGREDIENTS CO., LTD.—See Apple Flavor & Fragrance Group Co., Ltd.; *Int'l*, pg. 520
KUSTOM GROUP; *U.S. Private*, pg. 2358
KYOTO ELEX CO., LTD.—See DKS Co. Ltd.; *Int'l*, pg. 2140
KYZEN CORPORATION - NORTH AMERICAN OPERATIONS FACILITY—See Kyzen Corporation; *U.S. Private*, pg. 2361
LABSO CHIMIE FINE S.A.R.L.—See C.H. Boehringer Sohn AG & Co. KG; *Int'l*, pg. 1242
LA-CO INDUSTRIES MARKAL CO., INC.; *U.S. Private*, pg. 2370
LAMBENT TECHNOLOGIES—See H.I.G. Capital, LLC; *U.S. Private*, pg. 1832
LAMBSON LIMITED—See Arkema S.A.; *Int'l*, pg. 571
LANGLEY WIRE CLOTH PRODUCTS—See Graycliff Partners LP; *U.S. Private*, pg. 1760
LANXESS CISA (PTY) LIMITED—See Brother Enterprises Holding Co., Ltd.; *Int'l*, pg. 1196
LANZATECH GLOBAL, INC.; *U.S. Public*, pg. 1293
LAWTER ARGENTINA S.A.—See Harima Chemicals Group, Inc.; *Int'l*, pg. 3276
LAWTER BVBA—See Harima Chemicals Group, Inc.; *Int'l*, pg. 3276
LAWTER CHEMICALS (SHANGHAI) CO., LTD.—See Harima Chemicals Group, Inc.; *Int'l*, pg. 3276
LAWTER MAASTRICHT B.V.—See Harima Chemicals Group, Inc.; *Int'l*, pg. 3276
LAWTER (N.Z.) LTD.—See Harima Chemicals Group, Inc.; *Int'l*, pg. 3276
LCP LEUNA CARBOXYLATION PLANT GMBH—See Daicel Corporation; *Int'l*, pg. 1919
LCY CHEMICAL CORP.—See KKR & Co. Inc.; *U.S. Public*, pg. 1258
LEHIGH TECHNOLOGIES INC.—See Compagnie Generale des Etablissements Michelin SCA; *Int'l*, pg. 1743
LGC BIOSEARCH TECHNOLOGIES—See KKR & Co. Inc.; *U.S. Public*, pg. 1258
LIG ACE CO. LTD.—See BASF SE; *Int'l*, pg. 884
LIGHTWAVE LOGIC, INC.; *U.S. Public*, pg. 1315
LION AKZO CO., LTD.—See GIC Pte. Ltd.; *Int'l*, pg. 2968
LION AKZO CO., LTD.—See The Carlyle Group Inc.; *U.S. Public*, pg. 2051
LIQUID FENCE CO., INC.—See Spectrum Brands Holdings, Inc.; *U.S. Public*, pg. 1917
LITTLE SIOUX CORN PROCESSORS, L.L.C.; *U.S. Public*, pg. 1327
L&M CONSTRUCTION CHEMICALS, INC.—See LATICRETE International, Inc.; *U.S. Private*, pg. 2397
L.M. SCOFIELD COMPANY; *U.S. Private*, pg. 2366
L.M. SCOFIELD COMPANY—See L.M. Scofield Company; *U.S. Private*, pg. 2366
L.M. SCOFIELD COMPANY—See L.M. Scofield Company; *U.S. Private*, pg. 2366

LORD CHEMICAL (SHANGHAI) CO., LTD.—See Parker Hannifin Corporation; *U.S. Public*, pg. 1641
LORD CORPORATION SLOVAKIA S.R.O.—See Parker Hannifin Corporation; *U.S. Public*, pg. 1641
LORD INDIA PVT. LTD.—See Parker Hannifin Corporation; *U.S. Public*, pg. 1641
LORD INDUSTRIAL LTDA.—See Parker Hannifin Corporation; *U.S. Public*, pg. 1641
LORD KOREA, LTD.—See Parker Hannifin Corporation; *U.S. Public*, pg. 1641
LSB CHEMICAL LLC—See LSB Industries, Inc.; *U.S. Public*, pg. 1344
LUBEST—See Momar, Inc.; *U.S. Private*, pg. 2768
LUBRIZOL ADVANCED MATERIALS, INC.—See Berkshire Hathaway Inc.; *U.S. Public*, pg. 319
THE LUBRIZOL CORPORATION—See Berkshire Hathaway Inc.; *U.S. Public*, pg. 318
LUBRIZOL DO BRASIL ADITIVOS LTDA.—See Berkshire Hathaway Inc.; *U.S. Public*, pg. 319
LUBRIZOL INDIA PVT. LTD.—See Berkshire Hathaway Inc.; *U.S. Public*, pg. 319
LUSTER-ON PRODUCTS, INC.; *U.S. Private*, pg. 2516
MACDERMID CHEMICAL TAIWAN LTD—See Element Solutions Inc.; *U.S. Public*, pg. 727
MACDERMID DO BRASIL LTDA.—See Element Solutions Inc.; *U.S. Public*, pg. 727
MACDERMID, INCORPORATED—See Element Solutions Inc.; *U.S. Public*, pg. 726
MACDERMID OFFSHORE SOLUTIONS LLC—See Element Solutions Inc.; *U.S. Public*, pg. 727
MACDERMID PRINTING SOLUTIONS EUROPE—See Element Solutions Inc.; *U.S. Public*, pg. 727
MACDERMID SCANDINAVIA AB—See Element Solutions Inc.; *U.S. Public*, pg. 727
MACDERMID SUISSE SARL—See Element Solutions Inc.; *U.S. Public*, pg. 727
MAGENTA MASTER FIBERS CO., LTD.—See Avient Corporation; *U.S. Public*, pg. 247
MAGNI GROUP INC.; *U.S. Public*, pg. 2547
MAGNI-INDUSTRIES INC.—See Magni Group Inc.; *U.S. Private*, pg. 2548
MARTINSWERK GMBH—See Albemarle Corporation; *U.S. Public*, pg. 73
MASTER CHEMICALS OOO—See Ecolab Inc.; *U.S. Public*, pg. 714
MATECRA GMBH—See Berner SE; *Int'l*, pg. 988
MCBRIDE (CARIBBEAN) LIMITED—See Goddard Enterprises Limited; *Int'l*, pg. 3019
MCGEAN-ROHCO, INC.; *U.S. Private*, pg. 2634
MEDIZONE INTERNATIONAL, INC.; *U.S. Public*, pg. 1413
MEGLOBAL CANADA INC.—See Dow Inc.; *U.S. Public*, pg. 683
MEGUIAR'S, INC.—See 3M Company; *U.S. Public*, pg. 5
MERICHEM COMPANY - MERICHEM CATALYST PLANT—See Merichem Company; *U.S. Private*, pg. 2672
MERICHEM HONG KONG LTD.—See Merichem Company; *U.S. Private*, pg. 2672
MERISANT FRANCE SAS—See MacAndrews & Forbes Incorporated; *U.S. Private*, pg. 2532
METKO HUTTENES ALBERTUS KIMYA SANAYI VE TICARET A.S.—See Huettenes-Albertus Chemische Werke GmbH; *Int'l*, pg. 3523
MEXICHEM DERIVADOS, S.A. DE C.V.—See Grupo Empresarial Kaluz S.A. de C.V.; *Int'l*, pg. 3127
MEXICHEM FLUOR LTD.—See Grupo Empresarial Kaluz S.A. de C.V.; *Int'l*, pg. 3127
MEYER LABORATORY, INC.—See TruArc Partners, L.P.; *U.S. Private*, pg. 4245
MICHELMAN ASIA-PACIFIC PTE. LTD.—See Michelman Inc.; *U.S. Private*, pg. 2699
MICHELMAN (SHANGHAI) CHEMICAL TRADING CO., LTD.—See Michelman Inc.; *U.S. Private*, pg. 2699
MIDWEST INDUSTRIAL SUPPLY, INC.; *U.S. Private*, pg. 2722
MINERAL-RIGHT INC—See A. O. Smith Corporation; *U.S. Public*, pg. 12
MIRACHEM, LLC—See J.F. Lehman & Company, Inc.; *U.S. Private*, pg. 2163
MODERN MASTERS INC.—See RPM International Inc.; *U.S. Public*, pg. 1817
MOEHS IBERICA, S.L.—See PMC Capital Partners, LLC; *U.S. Private*, pg. 3217
MOHAMED ALI ABUDAWOOD FOR INDUSTRY AND PARTNERS FOR INDUSTRY COMPANY LTD.—See The Clorox Company; *U.S. Public*, pg. 2062
MOHAWK LABORATORIES DIVISION—See NCH Corporation; *U.S. Private*, pg. 2875
MOMAR AUSTRALIA PTY LTD—See Momar, Inc.; *U.S. Private*, pg. 2768
MONSANTO DO BRASIL LTDA.—See Bayer Aktiengesellschaft; *Int'l*, pg. 909
MONUMENT CHEMICAL BVBA—See Heritage Group; *U.S. Private*, pg. 1923
MORGRO, INC.; *U.S. Private*, pg. 2785
MULTISORB TECHNOLOGIES, INC.—See Summer Street Capital Partners LLC; *U.S. Private*, pg. 3853

MYCELX TECHNOLOGIES CORPORATION; *U.S. Public*, pg. 1487
NAGAHAMA CANON INC.—See Canon Inc.; *Int'l*, pg. 1298
NALCO ARGENTINA S.R.L.—See Ecolab Inc.; *U.S. Public*, pg. 715
NALCO AUSTRALIA PTY. LTD.—See Ecolab Inc.; *U.S. Public*, pg. 715
NALCO AZERBAIJAN LLC—See Ecolab Inc.; *U.S. Public*, pg. 715
NALCO CANADA COMPANY—See Ecolab Inc.; *U.S. Public*, pg. 715
NALCO DE COLOMBIA LTDA—See Ecolab Inc.; *U.S. Public*, pg. 715
NALCO DEUTSCHLAND MANUFACTURING GMBH UND CO. KG—See Ecolab Inc.; *U.S. Public*, pg. 715
NALCO ENERGY SERVICES, L.P.—See Ecolab Inc.; *U.S. Public*, pg. 715
NALCO EUROPE BV—See Ecolab Inc.; *U.S. Public*, pg. 715
NALCO FINLAND OY—See Ecolab Inc.; *U.S. Public*, pg. 715
NALCO ITALIANA MANUFACTURING S.R.L.—See Ecolab Inc.; *U.S. Public*, pg. 716
NALCO LATIN AMERICAN OPERATIONS—See Ecolab Inc.; *U.S. Public*, pg. 716
NALCO LIBYA—See Ecolab Inc.; *U.S. Public*, pg. 716
NALCO SAUDI CO. LTD.—See Ecolab Inc.; *U.S. Public*, pg. 716
NALCO WATER INDIA LIMITED—See Ecolab Inc.; *U.S. Public*, pg. 716
NANJING GUO ZHONG MAGNETIC MATERIAL CO., LTD.—See CEC International Holdings Limited; *Int'l*, pg. 1372
NANJING YANGZI EASTMAN CHEMICAL LTD.—See Eastman Chemical Company; *U.S. Public*, pg. 705
NANNING HARIMA CHEMICALS CO., LTD.—See Harima Chemicals Group, Inc.; *Int'l*, pg. 3276
NANOCHEM SOLUTIONS INC.—See Flexible Solutions International, Inc.; *Int'l*, pg. 2704
NANOFIL TECHNOLOGIES PVT. LTD.—See Flexituff Ventures International Limited; *Int'l*, pg. 2705
NANTONG XINGCHEN SYNTHETIC MATERIAL CO., LTD.—See Bluestar Adisseo Company Limited; *Int'l*, pg. 1074
NATIONAL CHEMSEARCH OF CANADA LTD.—See NCH Corporation; *U.S. Private*, pg. 2876
NATIONAL STARCH & CHEMICAL-LINCOLNSHIRE—See Ingredion Incorporated; *U.S. Public*, pg. 1124
NATIONAL STARCH COMPANY—See Ingredion Incorporated; *U.S. Public*, pg. 1124
NATIONAL STARCH SERVICIOS, S.A. DE C.V.—See Ingredion Incorporated; *U.S. Public*, pg. 1124
NCH CORPORATION KOREA—See NCH Corporation; *U.S. Private*, pg. 2875
NCH CZECHOSLOVAKIA SPOL S.R.O.—See NCH Corporation; *U.S. Private*, pg. 2875
N.E. CHEMCAT CORPORATION—See BASF SE; *Int'l*, pg. 875
NEOVIA SAS—See Archer-Daniels-Midland Company; *U.S. Public*, pg. 185
NESTLE WATERS NORTH AMERICA INC. - ROCHESTER—See Metropoulos & Co.; *U.S. Private*, pg. 2690
NESTLE WATERS NORTH AMERICA INC. - ROCHESTER—See One Rock Capital Partners, LLC; *U.S. Private*, pg. 3021
NICHINO INDIA PVT. LTD.—See Adeka Corporation; *Int'l*, pg. 142
NIGU CHEMIE GMBH—See BLUO SICAV-SIF; *Int'l*, pg. 1075
NIHON CHEMICAL COAT CO., LTD.—See Asahi Intecc Co., Ltd.; *Int'l*, pg. 594
NINGXIA BAOFENG ENERGY GROUP CO., LTD.—See China Baofeng (International) Ltd.; *Int'l*, pg. 1485
NIPPON FILLER METALS, LTD.—See Harima Chemicals Group, Inc.; *Int'l*, pg. 3276
NIPPON KETJEN CO., LTD.—See Albemarle Corporation; *U.S. Public*, pg. 73
NIPPON QUAKER CHEMICAL, LTD.—See Quaker Chemical Corporation; *U.S. Public*, pg. 1746
NOBIAN CHEMICALS B.V.—See GIC Pte. Ltd.; *Int'l*, pg. 2967
NOBIAN CHEMICALS B.V.—See The Carlyle Group Inc.; *U.S. Public*, pg. 2050
NOBIAN INDUSTRIAL CHEMICALS B.V.—See GIC Pte. Ltd.; *Int'l*, pg. 2967
NOBIAN INDUSTRIAL CHEMICALS B.V.—See The Carlyle Group Inc.; *U.S. Public*, pg. 2050
NOFIRE TECHNOLOGIES, INC.; *U.S. Public*, pg. 1532
NOF (THAILAND) LTD.—See BASF SE; *Int'l*, pg. 884
NOLUMA INTERNATIONAL, LLC—See The Chemours Company; *U.S. Public*, pg. 2059
NOURYON CHEMICALS GMBH—See GIC Pte. Ltd.; *Int'l*, pg. 2968
NOURYON CHEMICALS GMBH—See GIC Pte. Ltd.; *Int'l*, pg. 2968
NOURYON CHEMICALS GMBH—See The Carlyle Group Inc.; *U.S. Public*, pg. 2051
NOURYON CHEMICALS GMBH—See The Carlyle Group Inc.; *U.S. Public*, pg. 2051

3423

325998 — ALL OTHER MISCELLAN...

NOURYON CHEMICALS LIMITED—See GIC Pte. Ltd.; *Int'l*, pg. 2968
NOURYON CHEMICALS LIMITED—See The Carlyle Group Inc.; *U.S. Public*, pg. 2051
NOURYON CHEMICALS MCA (TAIXING) CO. LTD—See GIC Pte. Ltd.; *Int'l*, pg. 2968
NOURYON CHEMICALS MCA (TAIXING) CO. LTD—See The Carlyle Group Inc.; *U.S. Public*, pg. 2051
NOURYON FUNCTIONAL CHEMICALS B.V.—See GIC Pte. Ltd.; *Int'l*, pg. 2968
NOURYON FUNCTIONAL CHEMICALS B.V.—See The Carlyle Group Inc.; *U.S. Public*, pg. 2051
NOURYON FUNCTIONAL CHEMICALS GMBH—See GIC Pte. Ltd.; *Int'l*, pg. 2968
NOURYON FUNCTIONAL CHEMICALS GMBH—See The Carlyle Group Inc.; *U.S. Public*, pg. 2051
NOURYON PULP AND PAPER CHEMICALS B.V.—See GIC Pte. Ltd.; *Int'l*, pg. 2968
NOURYON PULP AND PAPER CHEMICALS B.V.—See The Carlyle Group Inc.; *U.S. Public*, pg. 2051
NOURYON PULP AND PERFORMANCE CHEMICALS (TAIWAN) CO. LTD—See GIC Pte. Ltd.; *Int'l*, pg. 2968
NOURYON PULP AND PERFORMANCE CHEMICALS (TAIWAN) CO. LTD—See The Carlyle Group Inc.; *U.S. Public*, pg. 2051
NOVA PRESSROOM PRODUCTS, LLC; *U.S. Private*, pg. 2966
NOVA TECHNOLOGY CORP.—See Acter Co., Ltd.; *Int'l*, pg. 117
NOVOMER, INC.—See Danimer Scientific, Inc.; *U.S. Public*, pg. 632
NOVUSTERRA INC.; *U.S. Private*, pg. 2968
NSI LAB SOLUTIONS, INC.; *U.S. Private*, pg. 2970
NTIA ZERUST PHILIPPINES, INC.—See Northern Technologies International Corporation; *U.S. Public*, pg. 1538
NTI FACILITIES, INC.—See Northern Technologies International Corporation; *U.S. Public*, pg. 1538
NULANDIS—See AECI Limited; *Int'l*, pg. 171
NUNHEMS TOHUMCULUK A.S.—See BASF SE; *Int'l*, pg. 884
NUNHEMS UKRAINE T.O.V.—See BASF SE; *Int'l*, pg. 884
OCTAGON PROCESS, L.L.C.—See Clariant AG; *Int'l*, pg. 1647
OIL-CHEM RESEARCH CORPORATION—See Sonic Financial Corporation; *U.S. Private*, pg. 3713
OIL CHEM TECHNOLOGIES; *U.S. Private*, pg. 3006
OIL-DRI CANADA ULC—See Oil-Dri Corporation of America; *U.S. Public*, pg. 1566
OIL-DRI CORPORATION OF AMERICA; *U.S. Public*, pg. 1565
OIL-DRI (U.K.) LTD.—See Oil-Dri Corporation of America; *U.S. Public*, pg. 1566
OITA CANON MATERIALS INC.—See Canon Inc.; *Int'l*, pg. 1298
OKANAGAN SPECIALTY FRUITS INC.—See Precigen, Inc.; *U.S. Public*, pg. 1713
OKS SPEZIALSCHMIERSTOFFE GMBH—See Freudenberg SE; *Int'l*, pg. 2790
OLD WORLD INDUSTRIES, LLC; *U.S. Private*, pg. 3009
OMG AMERICAS, INC.—See Apollo Global Management, Inc.; *U.S. Public*, pg. 166
OMI INDUSTRIES; *U.S. Private*, pg. 3016
OMNOVA NINGBO CO., LTD.—See OMNOVA Solutions Inc.; *U.S. Private*, pg. 3017
OMNOVA SOLUTIONS INC.; *U.S. Private*, pg. 3017
OMNOVA SOLUTIONS PORTUGAL S.A—See OMNOVA Solutions Inc.; *U.S. Private*, pg. 3017
ONE BIO, CORP.; *U.S. Public*, pg. 1602
O'NEIL COLOR & COMPOUNDING CORP. - NORTH FACILITY—See ICC Industries, Inc.; *U.S. Private*, pg. 2030
O'NEIL COLOR & COMPOUNDING CORP. - SOUTH FACILITY—See ICC Industries, Inc.; *U.S. Private*, pg. 2030
OOO AKZO NOBEL—See Akzo Nobel N.V.; *Int'l*, pg. 274
OOO ELASTOKAM—See BASF SE; *Int'l*, pg. 883
OOO WOLGODEMINOIL—See BASF SE; *Int'l*, pg. 885
OPTIMA CHEMICAL GROUP, LLC—See Charkit Chemical Company, LLC; *U.S. Private*, pg. 851
ORG CHEM GROUP, LLC; *U.S. Private*, pg. 3041
ORIENT-SALT CHEMICALS PTE. LTD.—See Abundance International Ltd.; *Int'l*, pg. 74
ORIENT-SALT CHEMICALS (SHANGHAI) CO., LTD.—See Abundance International Ltd.; *Int'l*, pg. 74
OY MERCANTILE AB—See BASF SE; *Int'l*, pg. 880
PADANAPLAST S.R.L.—See Finproject S.p.A.; *Int'l*, pg. 2676
PAG HOLDINGS, INC.—See Metals and Additives; *U.S. Private*, pg. 2682
PAINT OVER RUST PRODUCTS, INC.—See CapVest Limited; *Int'l*, pg. 1318
PARAMOUNT TECHNICAL PRODUCTS—See RPM International Inc.; *U.S. Public*, pg. 1818
PARKER HANNIFIN-HYDRAULICS DIVISION—See Parker Hannifin Corporation; *U.S. Public*, pg. 1646
PARKER HANNIFIN OY FILTER DIVISION EUROPE—See Parker Hannifin Corporation; *U.S. Public*, pg. 1645
PARO SERVICES CORP. - ROYAL CHEMICAL CHATTA-

NOOGA PLANT—See Paro Services Corp.; *U.S. Private*, pg. 3099
PARO SERVICES CORP. - ROYAL CHEMICAL DALLAS PLANT—See Paro Services Corp.; *U.S. Private*, pg. 3099
PARO SERVICES CORP. - ROYAL CHEMICAL EAST STROUDSBURG PLANT—See Paro Services Corp.; *U.S. Private*, pg. 3099
PARO SERVICES CORP. - ROYAL CHEMICAL MACEDONIA PLANT—See Paro Services Corp.; *U.S. Private*, pg. 3099
PARO SERVICES CORP.; *U.S. Private*, pg. 3099
PBBPOLISUR S.R.L.—See Dow Inc.; *U.S. Public*, pg. 685
PCAS FINLAND OY—See Eurazeo SE; *Int'l*, pg. 2530
PCAS GMBH—See Eurazeo SE; *Int'l*, pg. 2530
PCAS SA—See Eurazeo SE; *Int'l*, pg. 2530
THE PENRAY COMPANIES, INC.—See The Pritzker Group - Chicago, LLC; *U.S. Private*, pg. 4099
PENRECO—See Calumet, Inc.; *U.S. Public*, pg. 425
PERIMETER SOLUTIONS, SA; *U.S. Public*, pg. 1676
PERLA GREEK SALT LTD.—See Dem. Th. Bertzeletos & Bros. SA; *Int'l*, pg. 2022
PERLA GREEK SALT LTD.—See GIC Pte. Ltd.; *Int'l*, pg. 2968
PERLA GREEK SALT LTD.—See The Carlyle Group Inc.; *U.S. Public*, pg. 2051
PETROCEL - TEMEX, S.A. DE C.V.—See ALFA, S.A.B. de C.V.; *Int'l*, pg. 313
PETROFERM CLEANING PRODUCTS—See H.I.G. Capital, LLC; *U.S. Private*, pg. 1832
P&G DISTRIBUTION EAST AFRICA LIMITED—See The Procter & Gamble Company; *U.S. Public*, pg. 2121
PHIBRO-TECH, INC.—See Phibro Animal Health Corporation; *U.S. Public*, pg. 1685
PIEDMONT CHEMICAL INDUSTRIES I, LLC—See Piedmont Chemical Industries, Inc.; *U.S. Private*, pg. 3177
PILOT POLYMER TECHNOLOGIES, INC.—See Pilot Chemical Company; *U.S. Private*, pg. 3181
PLASMO INDUSTRIETECHNIK GMBH—See Berndorf AG; *Int'l*, pg. 987
PLASTIC2OIL, INC.; *U.S. Public*, pg. 1697
PLAZE, INC.—See The Pritzker Group - Chicago, LLC; *U.S. Private*, pg. 4099
PLZ CORP.—See The Pritzker Group - Chicago, LLC; *U.S. Private*, pg. 4099
PMC BIOGENIX KOREA LTD.—See PMC Group, Inc.; *U.S. Private*, pg. 3218
PMC GROUP - CINCINNATI—See PMC Group, Inc.; *U.S. Private*, pg. 3218
PMC ORGANOMETALLIX, INC.—See PMC Group, Inc.; *U.S. Private*, pg. 3218
PMC RUBBER CHEMICALS INDIA PRIVATE LIMITED—See PMC Group, Inc.; *U.S. Public*, pg. 3218
PMC SPECIALTIES GROUP, CO., INC.—See PMC Capital Partners, LLC; *U.S. Private*, pg. 3217
POLYAD SERVICES GMBH—See BASF SE; *Int'l*, pg. 884
POLYMER ADDITIVES, INC.—See H.I.G. Capital, LLC; *U.S. Private*, pg. 1831
POLYMER SOLUTIONS IBERICA S.L.U.—See Celanese Corporation; *U.S. Public*, pg. 465
POLYNT CHEMICAL (CHANGZHOU) CO. LTD.—See Reichhold, Inc.; *U.S. Private*, pg. 3390
POLYNT GMBH—See Reichhold, Inc.; *U.S. Public*, pg. 3390
POLYNT S.P.A. - BREMBATE DI SOPRA PLANT—See Reichhold, Inc.; *U.S. Private*, pg. 3391
POLYNT S.P.A. - CAVAGLIA PLANT—See Reichhold, Inc.; *U.S. Private*, pg. 3391
POLYNT S.P.A. - RAVENNA PLANT—See Reichhold, Inc.; *U.S. Private*, pg. 3391
POLYNT SP. Z O.O.—See Reichhold, Inc.; *U.S. Private*, pg. 3391
POLYNT UK LTD.—See Reichhold, Inc.; *U.S. Private*, pg. 3391
POLYONE CORPORATION UK LIMITED - TRADING COMPANY—See Avient Corporation; *U.S. Public*, pg. 248
POLYONE DSS CANADA INC.—See Avient Corporation; *U.S. Public*, pg. 248
POLYONE MANAGEMENT (SHANGHAI) CO. LTD.—See Avient Corporation; *U.S. Public*, pg. 248
POLYSCIENCES INC.; *U.S. Private*, pg. 3226
POLYXYLENOL SINGAPORE PTE. LTD.—See Asahi Kasei Corporation; *Int'l*, pg. 597
POTTERS BALLOTINI S.A.S.—See Ecovyst Inc.; *U.S. Public*, pg. 717
P. PAPAS & CO. O.E. TRADING COMPANY—See BASF SE; *Int'l*, pg. 884
PPG INDUSTRIES, INC. - MONROEVILLE CHEMICAL CENTER—See PPG Industries, Inc.; *U.S. Public*, pg. 1709
PQ CORPORATION—See Ecovyst Inc.; *U.S. Public*, pg. 717
PRAIRIE PETRO-CHEM LTD.—See Clariant AG; *Int'l*, pg. 1645
PRECIGEN, INC.; *U.S. Public*, pg. 1713
PRESERVATION TECHNOLOGIES L.P.; *U.S. Private*, pg. 3254

PRESERVE INTERNATIONAL—See Neogen Corporation; *U.S. Public*, pg. 1505
PRISTINE WATER SOLUTIONS INC.—See CECO Environmental Corp.; *U.S. Public*, pg. 464
PROCTER & GAMBLE MANUFACTURING MEXICO S. DE R.L. DE C.V.—See The Procter & Gamble Company; *U.S. Public*, pg. 2122
PRODUCTOS QUIMICOS NATURALES, S.A. DE C.V.—See Bayer Aktiengesellschaft; *Int'l*, pg. 910
PRODUITS CHIMIQUES AUXILIAIRES ET DE SYNTHESE SA - USINE DE BOURGOIN PLANT—See Eurazeo SE; *Int'l*, pg. 2530
PRODUITS CHIMIQUES DE LUCETTE S.A.S.—See AMG Critical Materials N.V.; *Int'l*, pg. 426
PROSOCO, INC.; *U.S. Public*, pg. 3287
PROTEOS BIOTECH, S.L.—See PMC Capital Partners, LLC; *U.S. Private*, pg. 3217
PROTEXA INDUSTRIAS S.A. DE C.V.—See Grupo Protexa S.A. de C.V.; *Int'l*, pg. 3134
PROTIM SOLIGNUM LTD.—See Koppers Holdings Inc.; *U.S. Public*, pg. 1272
PROXAN DICHTSTOFFE GMBH—See Dortmunder Gussasphalt GmbH & Co. KG; *Int'l*, pg. 2180
PT APPLE FLAVOR & FRAGRANCE INDONESIA—See Apple Flavor & Fragrance Group Co., Ltd.; *Int'l*, pg. 520
P.T. ASAHIMAS CHEMICAL - CILEGON FACTORY—See AGC Inc.; *Int'l*, pg. 204
P.T. ASAHIMAS CHEMICAL—See AGC Inc.; *Int'l*, pg. 204
P.T. BASF CARE CHEMICALS INDONESIA—See BASF SE; *Int'l*, pg. 884
P.T. BASF INDONESIA—See BASF SE; *Int'l*, pg. 884
PT CCM INDONESIA—See Batu Kawan Berhad; *Int'l*, pg. 891
PT CHEETHAM GARAM INDONESIA—See CK Hutchison Holdings Limited; *Int'l*, pg. 1637
PT. CLARIANT ADSORBENTS INDONESIA—See Clariant AG; *Int'l*, pg. 1648
P.T. COLORANTS SOLUTIONS INDONESIA—See Clariant AG; *Int'l*, pg. 1648
PT COVESTRO POLYMERS INDONESIA—See Bayer Aktiengesellschaft; *Int'l*, pg. 907
PT CRODA CIKARANG—See Croda International plc; *Int'l*, pg. 1853
PT CRODA INDONESIA LTD—See Croda International plc; *Int'l*, pg. 1853
PT DOW INDONESIA—See Dow Inc.; *U.S. Public*, pg. 684
PT EAC INDONESIA—See BRENNTAG SE; *Int'l*, pg. 1149
PT EKA CHEMICALS INDONESIA—See Akzo Nobel N.V.; *Int'l*, pg. 274
P.T. ETERNAL MATERIALS INDONESIA—See Eternal Materials Co., Ltd.; *Int'l*, pg. 2521
PT FERRO CERAMIC COLORS INDONESIA—See American Securities LLC; *U.S. Private*, pg. 252
PT FERRO MAS DINAMIKA—See American Securities LLC; *U.S. Private*, pg. 252
PT. FUJIKURA KASEI INDONESIA—See Fujikura Kasei Co., Ltd.; *Int'l*, pg. 2827
PT HENKEL INDONESIEN—See Henkel AG & Co. KGaA; *Int'l*, pg. 3349
PT MAPALUS MAKAWANUA CHARCOAL INDUSTRY—See Hayleys PLC; *Int'l*, pg. 3292
PT ROHM AND HAAS INDONESIA—See Dow Inc.; *U.S. Public*, pg. 685
PURITAN PRODUCTS, INC.—See Avantor, Inc.; *U.S. Public*, pg. 241
PVS CHEMICALS BELGIUM N.V.—See PVS Chemicals, Inc.; *U.S. Private*, pg. 3308
PVS CHEMICAL SOLUTIONS, INC.—See PVS Chemicals, Inc.; *U.S. Private*, pg. 3308
PVS TECHNOLOGIES, INC.—See PVS Chemicals, Inc.; *U.S. Private*, pg. 3308
QILU EASTMAN SPECIALTY CHEMICALS LTD.—See China Petrochemical Corporation; *Int'l*, pg. 1539
QILU EASTMAN SPECIALTY CHEMICALS LTD.—See Eastman Chemical Company; *U.S. Public*, pg. 705
QINGDAO APPLE FOODS TECH CO., LTD.—See Apple Flavor & Fragrance Group Co., Ltd.; *Int'l*, pg. 520
QINGQING ENVIRONMENTAL PROTECTION EQUIPMENT CO., LTD.—See Beijing Hanjian Heshan Pipeline Co.,LTD.; *Int'l*, pg. 951
QUAKER CHEMICAL B.V.—See Quaker Chemical Corporation; *U.S. Public*, pg. 1746
QUAKER CHEMICAL EUROPE B.V.—See Quaker Chemical Corporation; *U.S. Public*, pg. 1746
QUAKER CHEMICAL INDIA LTD.—See Quaker Chemical Corporation; *U.S. Public*, pg. 1746
QUAKER CHEMICAL INDUSTRIA E COMERCIO LTDA.—See Quaker Chemical Corporation; *U.S. Public*, pg. 1746
QUAKER CHEMICAL MEA FZE—See Quaker Chemical Corporation; *U.S. Public*, pg. 1746
QUAKER CHEMICAL PARTICIPACOES, LTDA.—See Quaker Chemical Corporation; *U.S. Public*, pg. 1746
QUAKER CHEMICAL SOUTH AFRICA (PTY.) LTD.—See Quaker Chemical Corporation; *U.S. Public*, pg. 1746
QUAKER RUSSIA B.V.—See Quaker Chemical Corporation; *U.S. Public*, pg. 1746
QUALITEK INTERNATIONAL INC.; *U.S. Private*, pg. 3317

N.A.I.C.S. INDEX

325998 — ALL OTHER MISCELLAN...

QUALTEK MOLECULAR LABORATORIES—See Discovery Life Sciences, LLC; *U.S. Private*, pg. 1238
QUANTUM SILICONES, INC.—See Akoya Capital LLC; *U.S. Private*, pg. 146
QUANTUM SILICONES, INC.—See Century Park Capital Partners, LLC; *U.S. Private*, pg. 834
QUES INDUSTRIES, INC.; *U.S. Private*, pg. 3325
QUIMICA HERCULES, S.A. DE C.V.—See Ashland Inc.; *U.S. Public*, pg. 212
QUIMICA REAL LTDA.—See Phibro Animal Health Corporation; *U.S. Public*, pg. 1685
RADIATOR SPECIALTY COMPANY - RSC CHEMICAL SOLUTIONS DIVISION—See Radiator Specialty Company; *U.S. Private*, pg. 3343
RADIATOR SPECIALTY COMPANY; *U.S. Private*, pg. 3343
RAINBOW TECHNOLOGY CORPORATION; *U.S. Private*, pg. 3347
RASCHIG UK LTD.—See PMC Capital Partners, LLC; *U.S. Private*, pg. 3217
RAYONIER ADVANCED MATERIALS INC.; *U.S. Public*, pg. 1765
RBP CHEMICAL TECHNOLOGY, INC.; *U.S. Private*, pg. 3360
RCS LTD—See Afarak Group SE; *Int'l*, pg. 185
RECOCHEM GROUP, INC.—See CapVest Limited; *Int'l*, pg. 1318
REG GERMANY GMBH—See Chevron Corporation; *U.S. Public*, pg. 487
REG LIFE SCIENCES, LLC—See Chevron Corporation; *U.S. Public*, pg. 488
REG MADISON, LLC—See Chevron Corporation; *U.S. Public*, pg. 488
REITZ COAL COMPANY LLC—See Berwind Corporation; *U.S. Private*, pg. 540
RENTECH, INC.; *U.S. Private*, pg. 3400
ROHM AND HAAS CANADA LP—See Dow Inc.; *U.S. Public*, pg. 685
ROHM AND HAAS CHEMICALS SINGAPORE PTE LTD.—See Dow Inc.; *U.S. Public*, pg. 686
ROHM AND HAAS CHEMICAL (THAILAND) LIMITED—See Dow Inc.; *U.S. Public*, pg. 686
ROHM AND HAAS CHILE LIMITADA.—See Dow Inc.; *U.S. Public*, pg. 686
ROHM AND HAAS ELECTRONIC MATERIALS LLC—See DuPont de Nemours, Inc.; *U.S. Public*, pg. 694
ROHM AND HAAS (FOSHAN) SPECIALTY MATERIALS CO., LTD.—See Dow Inc.; *U.S. Public*, pg. 686
ROHM AND HAAS MALAYSIA SDN. BHD.—See Dow Inc.; *U.S. Public*, pg. 686
ROHM AND HAAS SINGAPORE (PTE.) LTD.—See Dow Inc.; *U.S. Public*, pg. 686
ROHM AND HAAS TEXAS INCORPORATED—See Dow Inc.; *U.S. Public*, pg. 686
ROHM & HAAS COMPANY—See Dow Inc.; *U.S. Public*, pg. 685
RUSMAR INCORPORATED—See Palo Duro Capital, LLC; *U.S. Private*, pg. 3082
S.A. AJINOMOTO OMNICHEM N.V.—See Ajinomoto Company, Inc.; *Int'l*, pg. 257
SACHEM ASIA LTD.—See SACHEM Inc.; *U.S. Private*, pg. 3521
SACHEM EUROPE BV—See SACHEM Inc.; *U.S. Private*, pg. 3521
SAFETY-KLEEN CANADA, INC.—See Clean Harbors, Inc.; *U.S. Public*, pg. 510
SAINT-GOBAIN ADVANCED CERAMICS CORPORATION—See Compagnie de Saint-Gobain SA; *Int'l*, pg. 1730
SAINT-GOBAIN PPL KOREA CO LTD.—See Compagnie de Saint-Gobain SA; *Int'l*, pg. 1735
SAN-APRO LTD—See Air Products & Chemicals, Inc.; *U.S. Public*, pg. 67
SANGJI SHIPPING CO., LTD.—See GS Holdings Corp.; *Int'l*, pg. 3142
SANTOKU BASF PTE. LTD.—See BASF SE; *Int'l*, pg. 878
SARTOMER ASIA LIMITED—See Arkema S.A.; *Int'l*, pg. 569
SARTOMER (GUANGZHOU) CHEMICALS CO., LTD.—See Arkema S.A.; *Int'l*, pg. 571
SARTOMER USA, LLC—See Arkema S.A.; *Int'l*, pg. 569
SARTOMER USA, LLC—See Arkema S.A.; *Int'l*, pg. 569
SARTOMER USA, LLC—See Arkema S.A.; *Int'l*, pg. 569
SATEF HUETTENES ALBERTUS S.P.A.—See Huettenes-Albertus Chemische Werke GmbH; *Int'l*, pg. 3523
SAVANNA AG—See Hansa Chemie International AG; *Int'l*, pg. 3259
SAVONLINNA WORKS OY—See ANDRITZ AG; *Int'l*, pg. 454
SCANDIFLEX DO BRASIL LTDA.—See Eastman Chemical Company; *U.S. Public*, pg. 705
SCHERING BERLIN INC.—See Bayer Aktiengesellschaft; *Int'l*, pg. 902
SCIENTIFIC BOILER WATER CONDITIONING CO, INC.—See Nolan Capital, Inc.; *U.S. Private*, pg. 2934
S.C. JOHNSON MANUFACTURING (M) SDN BHD—See S.C. Johnson & Son, Inc.; *U.S. Private*, pg 3517
SCM METAL PRODUCTS, INC.—See Palladium Equity Partners, LLC; *U.S. Private*, pg. 3078
SEALIFE CORP.; *U.S. Public*, pg. 1855

SEASTAR CHEMICALS ULC—See Avantor, Inc.; *U.S. Public*, pg. 242
SEDERMA SA—See Croda International plc; *Int'l*, pg. 1853
SENMIN INTERNATIONAL (PTY) LIMITED—See AECI Limited; *Int'l*, pg. 171
SENSIENT IMAGING TECHNOLOGIES S.A. DE C.V.—See Sensient Technologies Corporation; *U.S. Public*, pg. 1867
SHANDONG DONGYUE POLYMER MATERIAL CO., LTD—See Dongyue Group Limited; *Int'l*, pg. 2172
SHANDONG HONGRI CHEMICAL JOINT STOCK COMPANY LIMITED—See Century Sunshine Group Holdings Limited; *Int'l*, pg. 1419
SHANGHAI APPLE AROMATECH FLAVORS TECHNOLOGY CO., LTD.—See Apple Flavor & Fragrance Group Co., Ltd.; *Int'l*, pg. 520
SHANGHAI APPLE AROMATIC PLANTATION CO., LTD.—See Apple Flavor & Fragrance Group Co., Ltd.; *Int'l*, pg. 520
SHANGHAI APPLE BOTANIC-TECH CO., LTD.—See Apple Flavor & Fragrance Group Co., Ltd.; *Int'l*, pg. 520
SHANGHAI APPLE FOODS INGREDIENTS CO., LTD.—See Apple Flavor & Fragrance Group Co., Ltd.; *Int'l*, pg. 520
SHANGHAI APPLE FOODS TECH (GROUP) CO., LTD.—See Apple Flavor & Fragrance Group Co., Ltd.; *Int'l*, pg. 520
SHANGHAI BAOSTEEL CHEMICAL CO., LTD.—See China Baowu Steel Group Corp., Ltd.; *Int'l*, pg. 1486
SHANGHAI DAICOLOR & FUJI CO., LTD.—See Dainichiseika Color & Chemicals Mfg. Co., Ltd.; *Int'l*, pg. 1939
SHANGHAI FINE CHEMICALS CO., LTD.—See EcoGreen International Group Limited; *Int'l*, pg. 2295
SHANGHAI FUJIKURA KASEI COATING CO., LTD.—See Fujikura Kasei Co., Ltd.; *Int'l*, pg. 2827
SHANGHAI KAIXIN BIOTECH CO., LTD.—See Apple Flavor & Fragrance Group Co., Ltd.; *Int'l*, pg. 520
SHANGHAI LANG CHEMICAL CO., LTD.—See CD International Enterprises, Inc.; *U.S. Public*, pg. 461
SHANGHAI MENGZE TRADING CO., LTD.—See Apple Flavor & Fragrance Group Co., Ltd.; *Int'l*, pg. 520
SHANGHAI PUJIA FOOD TECHNOLOGY CO., LTD.—See Apple Flavor & Fragrance Group Co., Ltd.; *Int'l*, pg. 520
SHANGHAI PUYANG BIOTECH CO., LTD.—See Apple Flavor & Fragrance Group Co., Ltd.; *Int'l*, pg. 520
SHANGHAI PUYI CHEMICAL CO., LTD.—See ABA Chemicals Corporation; *Int'l*, pg. 47
SHANGHAI SEPR ZIRCONIUM PRODUCTS CO., LTD—See Compagnie de Saint-Gobain SA; *Int'l*, pg. 1728
SHANGHAI SHIGE INDUSTRY CO., LTD.—See Anhui Deli Household Glass Co., Ltd.; *Int'l*, pg. 467
SHANGHIA DELIAN CHEMICAL CO., LTD.—See Guangdong Delian Group Co., Ltd.; *Int'l*, pg. 3153
SHINKO TECHNOSERVE CO., LTD.—See Fujitsu Limited; *Int'l*, pg. 2838
SHOWA KOSAN CO., LTD.—See Adeka Corporation; *Int'l*, pg. 142
SHRIEVE CHEMICAL PRODUCTS INC.—See Gemspring Capital Management, LLC; *U.S. Private*, pg. 1659
SIAM POLYSTYRENE CO., LTD.—See Dow Inc.; *U.S. Public*, pg. 686
SIAM PVS CHEMICALS COMPANY LIMITED (SPVS)—See PVS Chemicals, Inc.; *U.S. Private*, pg. 3643
SICHUAN APPLE FOODS CO., LTD.—See Apple Flavor & Fragrance Group Co., Ltd.; *Int'l*, pg. 520
SICHUAN GUORUN NEW MATERIAL CO., LTD.—See Albemarle Corporation; *U.S. Public*, pg. 73
SICHUAN MIANZHU NORWEST PHOSPHATE CHEMICAL CO., LTD.—See AsiaPhos Limited; *Int'l*, pg. 620
SICHUAN NITROCELL CORPORATION—See China North Industries Group Corporation; *Int'l*, pg. 1536
SI GROUP - BETHUNE SAS—See SK Capital Partners, LP; *U.S. Private*, pg. 3679
SI GROUP CRIOS - JUNDIAI - PLANT 2—See SK Capital Partners, LP; *U.S. Private*, pg. 3679
SI GROUP CRIOS - RIO CLARO - PLANT 1—See SK Capital Partners, LP; *U.S. Private*, pg. 3679
SI GROUP - INDIA LIMITED - LOTE UNIT—See SK Capital Partners, LP; *U.S. Private*, pg. 3680
SI GROUP - INDIA LIMITED - NAVI MUMBAI UNIT—See SK Capital Partners, LP; *U.S. Private*, pg. 3680
SI GROUP - INDIA LIMITED - RANJANGAON UNIT—See SK Capital Partners, LP; *U.S. Private*, pg. 3680
SI GROUP - INDIA LIMITED - RASAL UNIT—See SK Capital Partners, LP; *U.S. Private*, pg. 3680
SI GROUP KOREA LTD.—See SK Capital Partners, LP; *U.S. Private*, pg. 3680
SI-GROUP - SHANGHAI CO, LTD.—See SK Capital Partners, LP; *U.S. Private*, pg. 3680
SI GROUP - SINGAPORE PTD. LTD—See SK Capital Partners, LP; *U.S. Private*, pg. 3679
SI GROUP SOUTH AFRICA (PTD) LTD—See SK Capital Partners, LP; *U.S. Private*, pg. 3680
SIOVATION, LLC—See Akoya Capital LLC; *U.S. Private*, pg. 146
SIOVATION, LLC—See Century Park Capital Partners, LLC; *U.S. Private*, pg. 834

SLG CHEMICALS, INC.—See Scott's Liquid Gold-Inc.; *U.S. Public*, pg. 1849
SNAPPY MARINE INC.—See OneWater Marine Inc.; *U.S. Public*, pg. 1604
SOCIETE BEARNAISE DE SYNTHESE S.A.S.—See Firmenich International SA; *Int'l*, pg. 2681
SOCIETE FONCIERE ET INDUSTRIELLE S.A.S.—See BASF SE; *Int'l*, pg. 879
SOCIETE INDUSTRIELLE ET CHIMIQUE DE L'AISNE S.A.S.—See AMG Critical Materials N.V.; *Int'l*, pg. 426
SOLARIS CHEMTECH INDUSTRIES LIMITED—See Avantha Group; *Int'l*, pg. 736
SOLENIS INTERNATIONAL, L.P.—See Platinum Equity, LLC; *U.S. Private*, pg. 3204
SOLENIS LLC—See Platinum Equity, LLC; *U.S. Private*, pg. 3204
SOLENIS TECHNOLOGIES GERMANY GMBH—See Platinum Equity, LLC; *U.S. Private*, pg. 3205
SOLUTIA ARGENTINA S.R.L.—See Eastman Chemical Company; *U.S. Public*, pg. 705
SOLUTIA AUSTRALIA PTY. LTD.—See Eastman Chemical Company; *U.S. Public*, pg. 705
SOLUTIA EUROPE SPRL/BVBA—See Eastman Chemical Company; *U.S. Public*, pg. 706
SOLUTIA HONG KONG LIMITED—See Eastman Chemical Company; *U.S. Public*, pg. 705
SOLUTIA PERFORMANCE PRODUCTS (SUZHOU) CO., LTD.—See Eastman Chemical Company; *U.S. Public*, pg. 706
SOLUTIA (THAILAND) LTD.—See Eastman Chemical Company; *U.S. Public*, pg. 705
SOLUTIA U.K. LIMITED—See Eastman Chemical Company; *U.S. Public*, pg. 706
SOLUTIA VENEZUELA, S.R.L.—See Eastman Chemical Company; *U.S. Public*, pg. 706
SONNEBORN REFINED PRODUCTS B.V.—See Sonneborn, LLC; *U.S. Private*, pg. 3714
SOUTHWALL EUROPE GMBH—See Eastman Chemical Company; *U.S. Public*, pg. 706
SPECIAL DEVICES, INCORPORATED—See Daicel Corporation; *Int'l*, pg. 1918
SPECTRUM CHEMICAL MANUFACTURING CORPORATION; *U.S. Private*, pg. 3752
SPECTRUM CHEMICALS & LABORATORY PRODUCTS, INC.—See Spectrum Chemical Manufacturing Corporation; *U.S. Private*, pg. 3752
STANCHEM, INC.—See SK Capital Partners, LP; *U.S. Private*, pg. 3679
STANDARD FUSEE CORPORATION; *U.S. Private*, pg. 3778
STATE CONTRACT MANUFACTURING—See State Industrial Products Corporation; *U.S. Private*, pg. 3792
STEARNS PACKAGING CORPORATION; *U.S. Private*, pg. 3795
STEPAN ASIA PTE. LTD.—See Stepan Company; *U.S. Public*, pg. 1945
STEPAN COLOMBIA S.A.S.—See Stepan Company; *U.S. Public*, pg. 1945
STEPAN COMPANY; *U.S. Public*, pg. 1945
STEPAN EUROPE S.A.—See Stepan Company; *U.S. Public*, pg. 1945
STEPAN POLSKA SP. Z O.O.—See Stepan Company; *U.S. Public*, pg. 1945
ST. GABRIEL CC COMPANY, LLC—See Eastman Chemical Company; *U.S. Public*, pg. 706
STREM CHEMICALS, INC.—See Wind Point Advisors LLC; *U.S. Private*, pg. 4534
STYROLUTION MEXICANA S.A. DE C.V.—See BASF SE; *Int'l*, pg. 885
SUD-CHEMIE INDIA PVT. LTD.—See Clariant AG; *Int'l*, pg. 1648
SUMIKA STYRON POLYCARBONATE LIMITED—See Bain Capital, LP; *U.S. Private*, pg. 449
SUNBOSS CHEMICALS CORP.—See AirBoss of America Corp.; *Int'l*, pg. 241
SUNTEK EUROPE GMBH—See Eastman Chemical Company; *U.S. Public*, pg. 706
SUNTEK FILMS CANADA, INC.—See Eastman Chemical Company; *U.S. Public*, pg. 706
SUNTEK UK LIMITED—See Eastman Chemical Company; *U.S. Public*, pg. 706
SUPERIOR ADSORBENTS, INC.—See Oxbow Corporation; *U.S. Private*, pg. 3056
SUPERIOR OIL CO., INC. - CINCINNATI PLANT—See Superior Oil Co., Inc.; *U.S. Private*, pg. 3879
SUPERIOR OIL CO., INC. - COWPENS PLANT—See Superior Oil Co., Inc.; *U.S. Private*, pg. 3879
SUPERIOR OIL CO., INC. - EFFINGHAM PLANT—See Superior Oil Co., Inc.; *U.S. Private*, pg. 3879
SUPERIOR OIL CO., INC. - ELKHART PLANT—See Superior Oil Co., Inc.; *U.S. Private*, pg. 3879
SUPERIOR OIL CO., INC. - INDIANAPOLIS PLANT—See Superior Oil Co., Inc.; *U.S. Private*, pg. 3879
SUPERIOR OIL CO., INC. - LOUISVILLE PLANT—See Superior Oil Co., Inc.; *U.S. Private*, pg. 3879
SUPERIOR OIL CO., INC. - NASHVILLE PLANT—See Superior Oil Co., Inc.; *U.S. Private*, pg. 3879
SUPERIOR OIL CO., INC. - SPRINGFIELD PLANT—See

Superior Oil Co., Inc.; *U.S. Private*, pg. 3879
SUPERIOR OIL CO., INC. - ST. LOUIS PLANT—See Superior Oil Co., Inc.; *U.S. Private*, pg. 3879
SUPERIOR SYSTEMS & TECHNOLOGIES, LLP.—See Mission Critical Group; *U.S. Private*, pg. 2747
SURTEC, INC.—See Freudenberg SE; *Int'l*, pg. 2790
SURTEC INTERNATIONAL GMBH—See Freudenberg SE; *Int'l*, pg. 2790
SUSPA TEC AG—See Andlinger & Company, Inc.; *U.S. Private*, pg. 279
SYNERGY TECHNOLOGIES, INC.; *U.S. Private*, pg. 3904
SYNGENTA GRANGEMOUTH—See China National Chemical Corporation; *Int'l*, pg. 1530
TAMINCO ARGENTINA SA—See Eastman Chemical Company; *U.S. Public*, pg. 706
TAMINCO BVBA—See Eastman Chemical Company; *U.S. Public*, pg. 706
TAMINCO CHOLINE CHLORIDE (SHANGHAI) CO., LTD.—See Eastman Chemical Company; *U.S. Public*, pg. 706
TAMINCO DO BRAZIL PRODUTOS QUIMICOS LTDA.—See Eastman Chemical Company; *U.S. Public*, pg. 706
TAMINCO GERMANY GMBH—See Eastman Chemical Company; *U.S. Public*, pg. 706
TAMINCO GLOBAL CHEMICAL CORPORATION—See Eastman Chemical Company; *U.S. Public*, pg. 706
TAMINCO UK LIMITED—See Eastman Chemical Company; *U.S. Public*, pg. 706
TATEHO CHEMICAL INDUSTRIES CO., LTD.—See Air Water Inc.; *Int'l*, pg. 241
TECHNIC CANADA—See Technic Incorporated; *U.S. Private*, pg. 3953
TECHNIC INCORPORATED; *U.S. Private*, pg. 3953
TECHNIC JAPAN, INC.—See Technic Incorporated; *U.S. Private*, pg. 3953
TECHNIC UK—See Technic Incorporated; *U.S. Private*, pg. 3953
TECNIQUIMIA MEXICANA S.A. DE C.V.—See Quaker Chemical Corporation; *U.S. Public*, pg. 1747
TEKNEK (CHINA) LIMITED—See Illinois Tool Works Inc.; *U.S. Public*, pg. 1111
TEKNEK (JAPAN) LIMITED—See Illinois Tool Works Inc.; *U.S. Public*, pg. 1111
TEKNEK LIMITED—See Illinois Tool Works Inc.; *U.S. Public*, pg. 1111
TENCATE FRANCE SASU—See ABN AMRO Group N.V.; *Int'l*, pg. 64
TENCATE FRANCE SASU—See Gilde Buy Out Partners B.V.; *Int'l*, pg. 2974
TENCATE GEOSYNTHETICS FRANCE S.A.S.—See ABN AMRO Group N.V.; *Int'l*, pg. 64
TENCATE GEOSYNTHETICS FRANCE S.A.S.—See Gilde Buy Out Partners B.V.; *Int'l*, pg. 2975
TETRADYNE, LLC—See Neogen Corporation; *U.S. Public*, pg. 1505
THAI HOUGHTON 1993 CO., LTD.—See Quaker Chemical Corporation; *U.S. Public*, pg. 1746
THERMO FISHER (KANDEL) GMBH—See Thermo Fisher Scientific Inc.; *U.S. Public*, pg. 2152
THUNDERSHIRT, LLC—See Ceva Sante Animale SA; *Int'l*, pg. 1425
TIANJIN AKZO NOBEL PEROXIDES CO. LTD—See Akzo Nobel N.V.; *Int'l*, pg. 275
TIANJIN APPLE NORTHERN TECH CO., LTD.—See Apple Flavor & Fragrance Group Co., Ltd.; *Int'l*, pg. 520
TIANJIN TINCI MATERIALS TECHNOLOGY CO., LTD.—See Guangzhou Tinci Materials Technology Company Limited; *Int'l*, pg. 3168
TIANQI LITHIUM CORPORATION—See Chengdu Tianqi Industry (Group) Co., Ltd.; *Int'l*, pg. 1469
T & N, INC.; *U.S. Private*, pg. 3908
TOHOKU CHEMICAL INDUSTRIES, LTD.—See F.C.C. Co., Ltd.; *Int'l*, pg. 2596
TOHOKU CHEMICAL INDUSTRIES (VIETNAM), LTD—See F.C.C. Co., Ltd.; *Int'l*, pg. 2596
TONGSUH PETROCHEMICAL CORP., LTD.—See Asahi Kasei Corporation; *Int'l*, pg. 595
TONG SUH PETROCHEMICAL CORP., LTD.—See Asahi Kasei Corporation; *Int'l*, pg. 597
TOUEN JAPAN CO., LTD.—See Abundance International Ltd.; *Int'l*, pg. 74
TRANSFORMATIONAL SECURITY, LLC—See HEICO Corporation; *U.S. Public*, pg. 1021
TRASHCO INC.—See Waste Management, Inc.; *U.S. Public*, pg. 2332
TRECO S.R.L.—See Akoya Capital LLC; *U.S. Private*, pg. 146
TRECO S.R.L.—See Century Park Capital Partners, LLC; *U.S. Private*, pg. 834
TRION CHEMICALS PVT. LTD.—See Bodal Chemicals Ltd.; *Int'l*, pg. 1097
TRI-TEX CO INC—See SK Capital Partners, LP; *U.S. Private*, pg. 3680
TSI HOLDINGS, LLC; *U.S. Private*, pg. 4253
TUBEX LIMITED—See Berry Global Group, Inc; *U.S. Public*, pg. 326

TURCO PRODUKTEN B.V.—See Henkel AG & Co. KGaA; *Int'l*, pg. 3351
UENO CANON MATERIALS INC.—See Canon.; *Int'l*, pg. 1298
ULTRACHEM INC.—See FUCHS SE; *Int'l*, pg. 2804
UNBENCH B.V.—See BASF SE; *Int'l*, pg. 885
UNGERER AUSTRALIA—See Givaudan S.A.; *Int'l*, pg. 2982
UNGERER DE MEXICO S.A. DE C.V.—See Givaudan S.A.; *Int'l*, pg. 2982
UNGERER LIMITED—See Givaudan S.A.; *Int'l*, pg. 2982
UNITED ENERGY CORPORATION; *U.S. Public*, pg. 2230
UNIVATION TECHNOLOGIES, LLC—See Dow Inc.; *U.S. Public*, pg. 694
UNIVERSAL COOPERATIVES, INC - UCPA CHEMICAL PLANT—See Universal Cooperatives, Inc.; *U.S. Private*, pg. 4304
UNTERTAGE-SPEICHER-GESELLSCHAFT MBH (USG)—See BASF SE; *Int'l*, pg. 885
URALCHIMPLAST HUTTENES-ALBERTUS LTD.—See Huettenes-Albertus Chemische Werke GmbH; *Int'l*, pg. 3523
URANUS CHEMICALS CO., LTD.—See Coremax Corp.; *Int'l*, pg. 1799
USALCO ASHTABULA PLANT, LLC—See H.I.G. Capital, LLC; *U.S. Private*, pg. 1832
USALCO BALTIMORE PLANT, LLC—See H.I.G. Capital, LLC; *U.S. Private*, pg. 1832
USALCO FAIRFIELD PLANT, LLC—See H.I.G. Capital, LLC; *U.S. Private*, pg. 1832
USALCO GAHANNA PLANT, LLC—See H.I.G. Capital, LLC; *U.S. Private*, pg. 1832
USALCO, LLC—See H.I.G. Capital, LLC; *U.S. Private*, pg. 1832
USALCO MICHIGAN CITY PLANT, LLC—See H.I.G. Capital, LLC; *U.S. Private*, pg. 1832
USALCO PORT ALLEN PLANT, LLC—See H.I.G. Capital, LLC; *U.S. Private*, pg. 1832
U.S. SILICA HOLDINGS, INC.—See Apollo Global Management, Inc.; *U.S. Public*, pg. 164
US VANADIUM LLC; *U.S. Private*, pg. 4320
VANDERBILT CHEMICAL, LLC—See R.T. Vanderbilt Holding Company, Inc.; *U.S. Private*, pg. 3340
VANDERBILT INTERNATIONAL SARL—See R.T. Vanderbilt Holding Company, Inc.; *U.S. Private*, pg. 3340
VANDERBILT MINERALS, LLC—See R.T. Vanderbilt Holding Company, Inc.; *U.S. Private*, pg. 3340
VAN MANNEKUS & CO. B.V.—See Compagnie Financiere et de Participations Roullier SA; *Int'l*, pg. 1740
VAN MANNEKUS & CO. B.V.—See Grecian Magnesite S.A; *Int'l*, pg. 3068
VAN MANNEKUS UNIVERSAL V.O.F.—See Compagnie Financiere et de Participations Roullier SA; *Int'l*, pg. 1740
VAN MANNEKUS UNIVERSAL V.O.F.—See Grecian Magnesite S.A; *Int'l*, pg. 3068
VENANCO AG—See Hansa Chemie International AG; *Int'l*, pg. 3259
VENATOR MATERIALS PLC—See Huntsman Corporation; *U.S. Public*, pg. 1075
VENUS LABORATORIES INC. - EASTERN DIVISION—See Venus Laboratories Inc.; *U.S. Private*, pg. 4358
VENUS LABORATORIES INC. - SOUTH EASTERN DIVISION—See Venus Laboratories Inc.; *U.S. Private*, pg. 4358
VENUS LABORATORIES INC. - WESTERN DIVISION—See Venus Laboratories Inc.; *U.S. Private*, pg. 4358
VERICHEM LABORATORIES INC.; *U.S. Private*, pg. 4360
VERSALIS S.P.A.—See Eni S.p.A.; *Int'l*, pg. 2438
VERTELLUS AGRICULTURE & NUTRITION SPECIALTIES LLC—See Black Diamond Capital Holdings, LLC; *U.S. Private*, pg. 571
VERTELLUS AGRICULTURE & NUTRITION SPECIALTIES LLC—See Brightwood Capital Advisors, LLC; *U.S. Private*, pg. 653
VERTELLUS HEALTH & SPECIALTY PRODUCTS LLC—See Black Diamond Capital Holdings, LLC; *U.S. Private*, pg. 571
VERTELLUS HEALTH & SPECIALTY PRODUCTS LLC—See Brightwood Capital Advisors, LLC; *U.S. Private*, pg. 653
VERTELLUS HEALTH & SPECIALTY PRODUCTS LLC - ZEELAND—See Black Diamond Capital Holdings, LLC; *U.S. Private*, pg. 571
VERTELLUS HEALTH & SPECIALTY PRODUCTS LLC - ZEELAND—See Brightwood Capital Advisors, LLC; *U.S. Private*, pg. 654
VERTELLUS SPECIALTIES ASIA PACIFIC—See Black Diamond Capital Holdings, LLC; *U.S. Private*, pg. 571
VERTELLUS SPECIALTIES ASIA PACIFIC—See Brightwood Capital Advisors, LLC; *U.S. Private*, pg. 654
VETRICERAMICI SERAMIK MAMULLERI HIZMETLERI SANAYI VE TICARET LIMITED SIRKETI—See American Securities LLC; *U.S. Private*, pg. 252
VINYTHAI PUBLIC COMPANY LTD.—See AGC Inc.; *Int'l*, pg. 204
VITAS PORTUGAL, LDA.—See Compagnie Financiere et de Participations Roullier SA; *Int'l*, pg. 1740
VITIVA PROIZVODNJA IN STORITVE D.D.—See International Flavors & Fragrances Inc.; *U.S. Public*, pg. 1154
VIVOS, INC.; *U.S. Public*, pg. 2307
V-KOOL INTERNATIONAL PTE. LTD.—See Eastman Chemical Company; *U.S. Public*, pg. 706
VLG CHEM S.A.S.—See Eurazeo SE; *Int'l*, pg. 2530
VOLTAIX LLC; *U.S. Private*, pg. 4411
WARWICK INTERNATIONAL GROUP LIMITED—See Berkshire Hathaway Inc.; *U.S. Public*, pg. 319
WASHING SYSTEMS, LLC.; *U.S. Private*, pg. 4446
WD-40 COMPANY (CANADA) LTD.—See WD-40 Company; *U.S. Public*, pg. 2339
WD-40 COMPANY; *U.S. Public*, pg. 2338
WEATHERFORD ENGINEERED CHEMISTRY CANADA LTD.—See Weatherford International plc; *U.S. Public*, pg. 2340
WELD-AID PRODUCTS, INC.—See Berwind Corporation; *U.S. Private*, pg. 541
WESTLAKE CHEMICAL PARTNERS LP—See Westlake Corporation; *U.S. Public*, pg. 2360
WESTLAKE NATRIUM LLC—See Westlake Corporation; *U.S. Public*, pg. 2360
WESTLAKE VINNOLIT BENELUX-FRANCE B.V.—See Westlake Corporation; *U.S. Public*, pg. 2361
WESTLAKE VINNOLIT ITALIA S.R.L.—See Westlake Corporation; *U.S. Public*, pg. 2361
WESTLAKE VINNOLIT LIMITED—See Westlake Corporation; *U.S. Public*, pg. 2361
WHITFORD DO BRASIL LTDA.—See PPG Industries, Inc.; *U.S. Public*, pg. 1711
WILD FLAVORS AND SPECIALTY INGREDIENTS INC. - A.M. TODD DIVISION—See Archer-Daniels-Midland Company; *U.S. Public*, pg. 184
WILD FLAVORS, INC. - TARAPUR FACILITY—See Archer-Daniels-Midland Company; *U.S. Public*, pg. 184
WILFERT CHEMICAL DENMARK A/S—See Aspo Oyj; *Int'l*, pg. 631
WILHELM ROSENSTEIN LTD.—See BASF SE; *Int'l*, pg. 885
WILMORE COAL COMPANY—See Berwind Corporation; *U.S. Private*, pg. 540
WINTERSHALL AG DQHA—See BASF SE; *Int'l*, pg. 885
WINTERSHALL AG VERTRETUNG MOSKAU—See BASF SE; *Int'l*, pg. 885
WINTERSHALL ENERGIA S.A.—See BASF SE; *Int'l*, pg. 885
WINTERSHALL HOLDING GMBH—See BASF SE; *Int'l*, pg. 886
WIROM GAS S.A.—See BASF SE; *Int'l*, pg. 885
WITSVINA COMPANY LIMITED—See Chemtronics Co., Ltd.; *Int'l*, pg. 1464
WORWAG COATINGS (LANGFANG) CO., LTD.—See PPG Industries, Inc.; *U.S. Public*, pg. 1711
W. R. GRACE BRASIL INDUSTRIA E COMERCIO DE PRODUTOS QUIMICOS LTDA.—See Standard Industries Holdings Inc.; *U.S. Private*, pg. 3780
W. R. GRACE CANADA CORP.—See Standard Industries Holdings Inc.; *U.S. Private*, pg. 3780
W. R. GRACE & CO.-CONN.—See Standard Industries Holdings Inc.; *U.S. Private*, pg. 3779
W. R. GRACE (HONG KONG) LTD.—See Standard Industries Holdings Inc.; *U.S. Private*, pg. 3780
W. R. GRACE (PANAMA) S.A.—See Standard Industries Holdings Inc.; *U.S. Private*, pg. 3780
W. R. GRACE (THAILAND) LTD.—See Standard Industries Holdings Inc.; *U.S. Private*, pg. 3780
W. R. GRACE VIETNAM COMPANY LIMITED—See Standard Industries Holdings Inc.; *U.S. Private*, pg. 3780
W. R. MEADOWS, INC.; *U.S. Private*, pg. 4418
WUXI RAYON MEMBRANE TECHNOLOGY CO.,LTD.—See Beijing Origin Water Technology Co., Ltd.; *Int'l*, pg. 955
WYCHEM LTD.—See Aurelius Equity Opportunities SE & Co. KGaA; *Int'l*, pg. 710
WYNN OIL (SOUTH AFRICA) (PTY) LTD.—See Illinois Tool Works Inc.; *U.S. Public*, pg. 1111
WYNN'S AUTOMOTIVE FRANCE SAS—See Illinois Tool Works Inc.; *U.S. Public*, pg. 1111
XENOTECH, LLC—See BioIVT, LLC; *U.S. Private*, pg. 562
XIAMEN AMBER DAILY CHEMICAL TECHNOLOGY CO., LTD.—See Huabao International Holdings Limited; *Int'l*, pg. 3510
XIAMEN DOINGCOM CHEMICAL CO., LTD.—See EcoGreen International Group Limited; *Int'l*, pg. 2295
XIAMEN DOINGCOM FOOD CO., LTD.—See EcoGreen International Group Limited; *Int'l*, pg. 2295
XI'AN HAOTIAN BIO-ENGINEERING TECHNOLOGY CO. LIMITED—See Cathay International Holdings Limited; *Int'l*, pg. 1360
XINXIANG RUICHENG TECHNOLOGY CO., LTD.—See China XLX Fertiliser Ltd; *Int'l*, pg. 1564
XINYI RIHONG PLASTIC CHEMICAL CO., LTD.—See Harima Chemicals Group, Inc.; *Int'l*, pg. 3276
XINYI ZHONGLIN ROSIN CO., LTD.—See Harima Chemicals Group, Inc.; *Int'l*, pg. 3276
YANAI CHEMICAL INDUSTRY CO., LTD.—See Fujibo Holdings, Inc.; *Int'l*, pg. 2820
YANCHENG CITY CHUNZHU AROMA CO., LTD.—See Huabao International Holdings Limited; *Int'l*, pg. 3511
YOKKAICHI CHEMICAL CO., LTD. - ROKUROMI FACILITY—See DKS Co. Ltd.; *Int'l*, pg. 2140

326112 — PLASTICS PACKAGING ...

YOKKAICHI CHEMICAL CO., LTD.—See DKS Co. Ltd.; *Int'l*, pg. 2140
YOUNG LIVING ESSENTIAL OILS, LC; *U.S. Private*, pg. 4593
ZAO BASF—See BASF SE; *Int'l*, pg. 886
ZEIT O&M CO., LTD.—See GS Holdings Corp.; *Int'l*, pg. 3142
ZEOCHEM AG—See CPH Chemie + Papier Holding AG; *Int'l*, pg. 1824
ZEOCHEM D.O.O.—See CPH Chemie + Papier Holding AG; *Int'l*, pg. 1825
ZERUST AB—See Northern Technologies International Corporation; *U.S. Public*, pg. 1538
ZERUST-EXCOR MEXICO, S. DE R.L. DE C.V—See Northern Technologies International Corporation; *U.S. Public*, pg. 1538
ZERUST-NIC (TAIWAN) CORP.—See Northern Technologies International Corporation; *U.S. Public*, pg. 1538
ZERUST OY—See Northern Technologies International Corporation; *U.S. Public*, pg. 1538
ZERUST PREVENCOA DE CORROSAO S.A.—See Northern Technologies International Corporation; *U.S. Public*, pg. 1538
ZERUST SINGAPORE PTE. LTD.—See Northern Technologies International Corporation; *U.S. Public*, pg. 1538
ZERUST (U.K.) LIMITED—See Northern Technologies International Corporation; *U.S. Public*, pg. 1538
ZHAOQING PERFUMERY CO., LTD.—See Huabao International Holdings Limited; *Int'l*, pg. 3511
ZHEJIANG WANSHENG CO., LTD.—See 3SBio Inc.; *Int'l*, pg. 9
ZHENGZHOU APPLE FOODS TECH CO., LTD.—See Apple Flavor & Fragrance Group Co., Ltd.; *Int'l*, pg. 520
ZHENJIANG LEE CHANG YUNG GENERAL CHEMICAL CO., LTD.—See KKR & Co. Inc.; *U.S. Public*, pg. 1258
ZIBO FERRO PERFORMANCE MATERIALS COMPANY, LIMITED—See American Securities LLC; *U.S. Private*, pg. 253
ZINKAN ENTERPRISES INCORPORATED; *U.S. Private*, pg. 4605

326111 — PLASTICS BAG AND POUCH MANUFACTURING

ADVANCE POLYBAG INC.; *U.S. Private*, pg. 84
ALL AMERICAN-ARKANSAS POLY CORP.—See All American Poly Corp.; *U.S. Private*, pg. 170
ALPHA INDUSTRIES, INC.; *U.S. Private*, pg. 197
ALUF PLASTICS; *U.S. Private*, pg. 211
AMERICAN FUJI SEAL, INC.—See Fuji Seal International, Inc.; *Int'l*, pg. 2816
AMERIGLOBE FIBC SOLUTIONS; *U.S. Private*, pg. 259
A & M JUMBO BAGS LTD.; *Int'l*, pg. 17
AMPAC FLEXIBLES GMBH—See The Pritzker Group - Chicago, LLC; *U.S. Private*, pg. 4099
ANSA POLYMER—See ANSA McAL Limited; *Int'l*, pg. 477
API INDUSTRIES INC.; *U.S. Private*, pg. 294
AUTOMATED PACKAGING SYSTEMS COMERCIALE IMPORTACAO DO BRASIL LTDA.—See Sealed Air Corporation; *U.S. Public*, pg. 1852
AUTOMATED PACKAGING SYSTEMS EUROPE—See Sealed Air Corporation; *U.S. Public*, pg. 1852
AUTOMATED PACKAGING SYSTEMS GMBH & CO. KG—See Sealed Air Corporation; *U.S. Public*, pg. 1852
AUTOMATED PACKAGING SYSTEMS INC.—See Sealed Air Corporation; *U.S. Public*, pg. 1852
AUTOMATED PACKAGING SYSTEMS LIMITED—See Sealed Air Corporation; *U.S. Public*, pg. 1852
AVRO INDIA LIMITED; *Int'l*, pg. 750
BAOBAG SAS—See Caisse des Depots et Consignations; *Int'l*, pg. 1258
BAOBAG SAS—See EPIC Bpifrance; *Int'l*, pg. 2460
BETA PLASTICS CORPORATION—See Alpha Industries, Inc.; *U.S. Private*, pg. 197
CARROLL PRODUCTS, INC.; *U.S. Private*, pg. 773
CHEMPLAST INTERNATIONAL CORP.—See McNeel International Corporation; *U.S. Private*, pg. 2643
CONTINENTAL PRODUCTS; *U.S. Private*, pg. 1030
CORESA PERU S.A.—See Coresa S.A.; *Int'l*, pg. 1799
COVERIS FLEXIBLES US LLC—See Sun Capital Partners, Inc.; *U.S. Private*, pg. 3859
DALLAS PLASTICS CORPORATION—See Sole Source Capital LLC; *U.S. Private*, pg. 3708
DAM PHU MY PACKAGING JSC; *Int'l*, pg. 1955
D.C. PLASTICS INC.; *U.S. Private*, pg. 1141
DM NOVAFOAM LTD.—See Daicel Corporation; *Int'l*, pg. 1918
DURABAG COMPANY INC.; *U.S. Private*, pg. 1292
DYNISCO-VIATRAN INSTRUMENT SDN BI ID—See Roper Technologies, Inc.; *U.S. Public*, pg. 1811
ELECSTER (TIANJIN) ASEPTIC PACKAGING CO. LTD.—See Elecster Oyj; *Int'l*, pg. 2348
EMERALD PACKAGING, INC.; *U.S. Private*, pg. 1380
EMQTEC AG; *Int'l*, pg. 2392
ENVISION; *U.S. Private*, pg. 1410
EPSILON PLASTICS, INC.—See Alpha Industries, Inc.; *U.S. Private*, pg. 197
EWIFOAM E. WICKLEIN GMBH—See Decora S.A.; *Int'l*, pg. 2001
FABRICON PRODUCTS INC.; *U.S. Private*, pg. 1459
FLEXITUFF TECHNOLOGY INTERNATIONAL LIMITED—See Flexituff Ventures International Limited; *Int'l*, pg. 2705
FOSHAN CROWN EASY-OPENING END CO. LIMITED—See Crown Holdings, Inc.; *U.S. Public*, pg. 598
FREDMAN BAG COMPANY—See LongueVue Capital, LLC; *U.S. Private*, pg. 2493
FUJI SEAL ENGINEERING CO., LTD.—See Fuji Seal International, Inc.; *Int'l*, pg. 2816
FUJI SEAL INDIA PVT LTD.—See Fuji Seal International, Inc.; *Int'l*, pg. 2816
FUJI SEAL PACKAGING (THAILAND) CO., LTD.—See Fuji Seal International, Inc.; *Int'l*, pg. 2816
FUJI SEAL PERSONNEL SERVICES, S.A. DE C.V.—See Fuji Seal International, Inc.; *Int'l*, pg. 2816
FUJI SEAL VIETNAM CO., LTD.—See Fuji Seal International, Inc.; *Int'l*, pg. 2816
FUJI SEAL WEST, INC.—See Fuji Seal International, Inc.; *Int'l*, pg. 2816
FUJI TACK, INC.—See Fuji Seal International, Inc.; *Int'l*, pg. 2816
FUKUSHIMA PLASTICS CO., LTD.—See Gunze Limited; *Int'l*, pg. 3185
GLAD MANUFACTURING CO.—See The Clorox Company; *U.S. Public*, pg. 2062
GLAD MANUFACTURING—See The Clorox Company; *U.S. Public*, pg. 2062
GOGLIO S.P.A.; *Int'l*, pg. 3022
GRAYLING INDUSTRIES INC.; *U.S. Private*, pg. 1761
HERITAGE BAG COMPANY - FAIRFIELD—See Apollo Global Management, Inc.; *U.S. Public*, pg. 153
HERITAGE BAG COMPANY - LOGAN TOWNSHIP—See Apollo Global Management, Inc.; *U.S. Public*, pg. 153
HERITAGE BAG COMPANY - RANCHO CUCAMONGA—See Apollo Global Management, Inc.; *U.S. Public*, pg. 153
HERITAGE BAG COMPANY - VILLA RICA—See Apollo Global Management, Inc.; *U.S. Public*, pg. 154
HILEX POLY CO. LLC - NORTH VERNON—See Apollo Global Management, Inc.; *U.S. Public*, pg. 154
HILEX POLY CO. LLC—See Apollo Global Management, Inc.; *U.S. Public*, pg. 154
HUASHENG INTERNATIONAL HOLDING LIMITED; *Int'l*, pg. 3514
HUIZHOU JUNYANG PLASTIC CO., LTD.—See Huasheng International Holding Limited; *Int'l*, pg. 3514
IMAFLEX INC.; *Int'l*, pg. 3617
INTEPLAST GROUP, LTD. - INTEGRATED BAGGING SYSTEMS—See Inteplast Group, Ltd.; *U.S. Private*, pg. 2106
JAD CORPORATION—See Bain Capital, LP; *U.S. Private*, pg. 441
KRIS AUTOMATED PACKAGING SYSTEMS PRIVATE LIMITED—See Sealed Air Corporation; *U.S. Public*, pg. 1853
LADDAWN INC.—See Berry Global Group, Inc; *U.S. Public*, pg. 322
LIQUI-BOX CORPORATION—See Sealed Air Corporation; *U.S. Public*, pg. 1853
MERCURY PLASTICS INC.; *U.S. Private*, pg. 2671
MIDWEST POLY—See Custom-Pak, Inc.; *U.S. Private*, pg. 1130
MINIGRIP, LLC—See Illinois Tool Works Inc.; *U.S. Public*, pg. 1109
MONARCH SEPARATORS INC.—See Water Standard Management; *U.S. Private*, pg. 4451
OPW MALAYSIA SDN. BHD.—See Dover Corporation; *U.S. Public*, pg. 682
P3 PULLEN POLYURETHANE PRODUCTS B.V.—See Team, Inc.; *U.S. Public*, pg. 1988
PAGO AG—See Fuji Seal International, Inc.; *Int'l*, pg. 2816
P.H.I. DIVISION—See Tulip Corporation; *U.S. Private*, pg. 4257
POLYFIRST PACKAGING, INC.—See The Pritzker Group - Chicago, LLC; *U.S. Private*, pg. 4099
POLY-PAK INDUSTRIES, INC.; *U.S. Private*, pg. 3225
PPC FLEXIBLE PACKAGING LLC—See GTCR LLC; *U.S. Private*, pg. 1806
PRIMARY PACKAGING INCORPORATED; *U.S. Private*, pg. 3260
PRINTPACK INC.—See Printpack Inc.; *U.S. Private*, pg. 3266
PRO PLASTICS INC.; *U.S. Private*, pg. 3270
PT.FUJI SEAL PACKAGING INDONESIA—See Fuji Seal International, Inc.; *Int'l*, pg. 2817
PUTNAM PLASTICS, INC.; *U.S. Private*, pg. 3307
RAPAK, LLC - INDIANAPOLIS PLANT—See Sealed Air Corporation; *U.S. Public*, pg. 1853
ROLLPAK CORPORATION—See Berry Global Group, Inc; *U.S. Public*, pg. 321
SEALED AIR CORPORATION; *U.S. Public*, pg. 1852
SHANGHAI GUNZE NEW PACKAGING CO., LTD.—See Gunze Limited; *Int'l*, pg. 3186
SHARP PACKAGING SYSTEMS, LLC—See Warburg Pincus LLC; *U.S. Private*, pg. 4439
S.L. PACKAGING INDUSTRIES PTE LTD—See Dynamic Colours Limited; *Int'l*, pg. 2240
STAR PACKAGING CORP.—See Nicolet Capital Partners, LLC; *U.S. Private*, pg. 2926
SUNWAY KORDIS (SHANGHAI) LIMITED—See Hengan International Group Co. Ltd.; *Int'l*, pg. 3346
SUPERIOR PACKAGING INC.; *U.S. Private*, pg. 3879
TARA PLASTICS CORPORATION—See Alpha Industries, Inc.; *U.S. Private*, pg. 197
TRINITY PACKAGING CORPORATION—See The Pritzker Group - Chicago, LLC; *U.S. Private*, pg. 4099
TUFPAK, INC.—See The Jordan Company, L.P.; *U.S. Private*, pg. 4062
VALERON STRENGTH FILMS B.V.B.A.—See Illinois Tool Works Inc.; *U.S. Public*, pg. 1111
WISCONSIN FILM & BAG, INC.—See Apollo Global Management, Inc.; *U.S. Public*, pg. 154
X-L PLASTICS INC.; *U.S. Private*, pg. 4579

326112 — PLASTICS PACKAGING FILM AND SHEET (INCLUDING LAMINATED) MANUFACTURING

ACCUTECH FILMS, INC.—See Apollo Global Management, Inc.; *U.S. Public*, pg. 154
AC-FOLIEN GMBH—See CPH Chemie + Papier Holding AG; *Int'l*, pg. 1824
ACME PRINTING & PACKAGING PLC; *Int'l*, pg. 107
ACORN PACKAGING INC.—See Aga Khan Development Network; *Int'l*, pg. 199
ADVANTEK INC.—See Cornell Capital LLC; *U.S. Private*, pg. 1051
AGC POLYCARBONATE CO., LTD.—See AGC Inc.; *Int'l*, pg. 202
AGRIPLAS COMPANY—See Compagnie Financiere et de Participations Roullier SA; *Int'l*, pg. 1740
ALLIANCE PLASTICS, LLC; *U.S. Private*, pg. 184
ALTA COMPANY; *Int'l*, pg. 384
ALUFLEXPACK AG—See Global Equity Partners Beteiligungs-Management AG; *Int'l*, pg. 2996
ALUPOL PACKAGING KETY SP. Z O.O.—See Grupa Kety S.A.; *Int'l*, pg. 3116
ALUPOL PACKAGING S.A.—See Grupa Kety S.A.; *Int'l*, pg. 3116
ALUPROF BELGIUM N.V.—See Grupa Kety S.A.; *Int'l*, pg. 3116
ALUPROF HUNGARY KFT.—See Grupa Kety S.A.; *Int'l*, pg. 3116
ALUPROF NETHERLANDS B.V.—See Grupa Kety S.A.; *Int'l*, pg. 3116
AMARAY—See Atlas Holdings, LLC; *U.S. Private*, pg. 378
AMERICAN BILTRITE INC.; *U.S. Public*, pg. 97
AMERPLAST LTD.—See Chiltern Capital LLP; *Int'l*, pg. 1479
AMERPLAST SP. Z O.O.—See Chiltern Capital LLP; *Int'l*, pg. 1479
AMTOPP CORPORATION—See Inteplast Group, Ltd.; *U.S. Private*, pg. 2106
APTAR CSP TECHNOLOGIES, INC.—See AptarGroup, Inc.; *U.S. Public*, pg. 174
ARABIAN PACKAGING CO. LLC—See Al Ghurair Group; *Int'l*, pg. 277
ARLA PLAST AB; *Int'l*, pg. 573
ARROW COATED PRODUCTS (UK) LIMITED—See Arrow Greentech Limited; *Int'l*, pg. 579
ARROW GREENTECH LIMITED; *Int'l*, pg. 579
ASAHI PRINTING CO., LTD.; *Int'l*, pg. 598
ASENOVA KREPOST AD; *Int'l*, pg. 606
BAK AMBALAJ SANAYI VE TICARET A.S.; *Int'l*, pg. 804
BEIJING XINYANG TONGLI COMMERCIAL FACILITIES COMPANY LIMITED—See Beijing Jingkelong Company Limited; *Int'l*, pg. 953
BEMIS SAS—See Amcor plc; *Int'l*, pg. 418
BERKOSAN YALITIM VE TECRIT MADDELERI URETIM VE TICARET A.S.; *Int'l*, pg. 985
BERRY PLASTICS CORP. - FLEXIBLE PACKAGING, SCHAUMBERG PLANT—See Berry Global Group, Inc; *U.S. Public*, pg. 321
BERRY SUPERFOS DEVENTER B.V.—See Berry Global Group, Inc; *U.S. Public*, pg. 321
BERWICK OFFRAY, LLC—See IG Design Group Plc; *Int'l*, pg. 3600
BIEN HOA PACKAGING COMPANY; *Int'l*, pg. 1020
BORDEX PACKAGING B.V.; *Int'l*, pg. 1113
BOSCH PACKAGING SYSTEMS KFT.—See CVC Capital Partners SICAV-FIS S.A.; *Int'l*, pg. 1884
BOSCH PACKAGING TECHNOLOGY B.V.—See CVC Capital Partners SICAV-FIS S.A.; *Int'l*, pg. 1884
BOSCH PACKAGING TECHNOLOGY SA—See CVC Capital Partners SICAV-FIS S.A.; *Int'l*, pg. 1884
BOSCH PACKAGING TECHNOLOGY SAS—See CVC Capital Partners SICAV-FIS S.A.; *Int'l*, pg. 1884
BP PLASTICS HOLDING BHD.; *Int'l*, pg. 1125
BRADFORD DE MEXICO, S. DE R.L. DE C.V—See Bradford Company; *U.S. Private*, pg. 631
BRADFORD SYSTEMS MALAYSIA SDN. BHD.—See Bradford Company; *U.S. Private*, pg. 631

326112 — PLASTICS PACKAGING ...

BRITISH POLYTHENE INDUSTRIES LIMITED—See Berry Global Group, Inc; *U.S. Public*, pg. 322
BRITTON-DECOFLEX LTD.—See Sun Capital Partners, Inc.; *U.S. Private*, pg. 3861
BRITTON GROUP HOLDINGS LTD.—See Sun Capital Partners, Inc.; *U.S. Private*, pg. 3861
BRITTON TACO LTD.—See Sun Capital Partners, Inc.; *U.S. Private*, pg. 3861
BRYCE CORPORATION; *U.S. Private*, pg. 674
CANNON INDUSTRIES LTD.—See Whirlpool Corporation; *U.S. Public*, pg. 2367
CAPCO PLASTICS INC.; *U.S. Private*, pg. 737
CAREER TECHNOLOGY (MFG.) CO., LTD.; *Int'l*, pg. 1323
CF (NETHERLANDS) HOLDINGS LIMITED B.V.—See Cosmo First Limited; *Int'l*, pg. 1812
CHEMOS A.D.; *Int'l*, pg. 1463
CHINA FLEXIBLE PACKAGING HOLDINGS LIMITED; *Int'l*, pg. 1503
CLARA INDUSTRIES LIMITED; *Int'l*, pg. 1642
CLONDALKIN PHARMA & HEALTHCARE INC.—See Egeria Capital Management B.V.; *Int'l*, pg. 2323
COMMAND PLASTIC CORPORATION; *U.S. Private*, pg. 982
CONSTANTIA FLEXIBLES GROUP GMBH—See One Rock Capital Partners, LLC; *U.S. Private*, pg. 3021
CONVERFLEX S.A.—See Arcor Sociedad Anonima, Industrial y Comercial; *Int'l*, pg. 550
CONVERTIDORA INDUSTRIAL S.A.B. DE C.V; *Int'l*, pg. 1787
COOL-PAK, LLC—See Bunzl plc; *Int'l*, pg. 1218
COSET INC.; *Int'l*, pg. 1810
COSMO FILMS, INC.—See Cosmo First Limited; *Int'l*, pg. 1812
COSMO FILMS JAPAN, GK—See Cosmo First Limited; *Int'l*, pg. 1812
COSMO FILMS KOREA LIMITED—See Cosmo First Limited; *Int'l*, pg. 1812
COSMO FILMS LTD. - PLANT III—See Cosmo First Limited; *Int'l*, pg. 1812
COSMO FILMS LTD. - PLANT II—See Cosmo First Limited; *Int'l*, pg. 1812
COSMO FILMS LTD. - PLANT I—See Cosmo First Limited; *Int'l*, pg. 1812
COSMO FILMS LTD. - PLANT IV—See Cosmo First Limited; *Int'l*, pg. 1812
COSMO FILMS (NETHERLANDS) COOPERATIEF U.A—See Cosmo First Limited; *Int'l*, pg. 1812
COSMO FILMS (SINGAPORE) PTE LTD—See Cosmo First Limited; *Int'l*, pg. 1812
COVERIS FLEXIBLES US LLC - PERFORMANCE FILMS DIVISION—See Sun Capital Partners, Inc.; *U.S. Private*, pg. 3859
CYDSA S.A. DE C.V. - PACKAGING DIVISION—See Cydsa S.A.B. de C.V.; *Int'l*, pg. 1895
DAIO MILL SUPPORT TOKAI CORPORATION—See Daio Paper Corporation; *Int'l*, pg. 1939
DANAFILMS CORP.—See Inteplast Group, Ltd.; *U.S. Private*, pg. 2106
DANANG PLASTIC JOINT-STOCK COMPANY; *Int'l*, pg. 1958
DE NEEF SCANDINAVIA AB—See Standard Industries Holdings Inc.; *U.S. Private*, pg. 3779
DESTINY PACKAGING, LLC—See Bunzl plc; *Int'l*, pg. 1218
DIESSE SRL; *Int'l*, pg. 2116
DIRECT PLASTICS GROUP, LTD.—See Apollo Global Management, Inc.; *U.S. Public*, pg. 153
D&K COATING TECHNOLOGIES, INC.—See D&K Group, Inc.; *U.S. Private*, pg. 1138
DONGFANG DIGICOM TECHNOLOGY (GUANGDONG) CO., LTD.—See Guangdong Dongfang Science & Technology Co., Ltd.; *Int'l*, pg. 3153
DONGWON SYSTEMS CORP.—See Dongwon Enterprise Co., Ltd.; *Int'l*, pg. 2171
DUNMORE LLLP—See Enstar Group Limited; *Int'l*, pg. 2448
EASTMAN CHEMICAL HTF GMBH—See Eastman Chemical Company; *U.S. Public*, pg. 704
ELKAY PLASTICS COMPANY, INC.; *U.S. Private*, pg. 1363
ELSA SILGAN METAL PACKAGING S.A.—See Silgan Holdings, Inc.; *U.S. Public*, pg. 1878
EURO-M FLEXIBLE PACKAGING SA; *Int'l*, pg. 2531
FAERCH A/S—See Advent International Corporation; *U.S. Private*, pg. 101
FIBOPE PORTUGUESA-FILMES BIORIENTADOS, S.A.—See Clearlake Capital Group, L.P.; *U.S. Private*, pg. 935
FLEXIBLE INDUSTRIAL PACKAGES CO. SAOC; *Int'l*, pg. 2704
FLEXICON INC.; *U.S. Private*, pg. 1544
FLEXOPACK POLSKA SP. Z O.O.—See FLEXOPACK S.A.; *Int'l*, pg. 2705
FLEXOPACK S.A.; *Int'l*, pg. 2705
FPCO ALRIGHT CO. LTD.—See FP Corporation; *Int'l*, pg. 2756
GEORG FISCHER SAS—See Georg Fischer AG; *Int'l*, pg. 2937
GINEGAR PLASTIC PRODUCTS LTD.; *Int'l*, pg. 2976
GLOBOPLASTT S.R.O.—See Illinois Tool Works Inc.; *U.S. Public*, pg. 1103

GLORY FILMS LIMITED; *Int'l*, pg. 3009
GRACE GERMANY GMBH—See Standard Industries Holdings Inc.; *U.S. Private*, pg. 3780
GRACE GMBH & CO. KG—See Standard Industries Holdings Inc.; *U.S. Private*, pg. 3780
GRACE JAPAN KABUSHIKI KAISHA—See Standard Industries Holdings Inc.; *U.S. Private*, pg. 3780
GRACE NETHERLANDS B.V.—See Standard Industries Holdings Inc.; *U.S. Private*, pg. 3780
GREEN BUILD TECHNOLOGY LTD.; *Int'l*, pg. 3069
GREENLAM DECOLAN SA—See Greenlam Industries Limited; *Int'l*, pg. 3075
GREEN SEAL HOLDING LIMITED; *Int'l*, pg. 3072
GREIF FLEXIBLES GERMANY GMBH & CO.—See Greif Inc.; *U.S. Public*, pg. 967
GRUPO PHOENIX—See Genstar Capital, LLC; *U.S. Private*, pg. 1678
GUILLIN ROMANIA SRL—See Groupe Guillin SA; *Int'l*, pg. 3104
HAMPDEN PAPERS INC.—See LLFlex, LLC; *U.S. Private*, pg. 2475
HANG FUNG INTERNATIONAL INDUSTRIAL CO., LTD.; *Int'l*, pg. 3244
HANWHA POLYDREAMER CO., LTD.—See Hanwha Group; *Int'l*, pg. 3266
HARRIS INDUSTRIAL PRODUCTS & PACKAGING—See Jackson Paper Company; *U.S. Private*, pg. 2178
HERITAGE BAG COMPANY—See Apollo Global Management, Inc.; *U.S. Public*, pg. 153
HOOD PACKAGING CORPORATION - GRAPHICS FACILITY—See Hood Packaging Corporation; *U.S. Private*, pg. 1977
HOOD PACKAGING CORPORATION - PLASTIC PACKAGING - GLOPAK DIVISION—See Hood Packaging Corporation; *U.S. Private*, pg. 1977
HOSOKAWA ALPINE POLAND SP. Z O.O.—See Hosokawa Micron Corporation; *Int'l*, pg. 3486
HOSOKAWA MICRON INDIA PVT. LTD.—See Hosokawa Micron Corporation; *Int'l*, pg. 3486
HUATONG UNITED (NANTONG) PLASTIC INDUSTRY CO., LTD.—See Great China Metal Ind. Co., Ltd.; *Int'l*, pg. 3064
HUHTAMAKI PHILIPPINES, INC.—See Huhtamaki Oyj; *Int'l*, pg. 3525
HUNTINGTON FOAM, LLC—See Wynnchurch Capital, L.P.; *U.S. Private*, pg. 4577
HWASEUNG INDUSTRIES CO., LTD.; *Int'l*, pg. 3542
H. WETERINGS-PLASTICS B.V.—See Hexatronic Group AB; *Int'l*, pg. 3370
I-COMPONENTS CO., LTD.; *Int'l*, pg. 3563
INAPEL EMBALAGENS LTDA.—See Sonoco Products Company; *U.S. Public*, pg. 1904
INFIANA GERMANY GMBH & CO. KG—See Deutsche Beteiligungs AG; *Int'l*, pg. 2063
INFIANA (THAILAND) LIMITED—See Deutsche Beteiligungs AG; *Int'l*, pg. 2063
INFIANA USA, INC.—See Deutsche Beteiligungs AG; *Int'l*, pg. 2063
INNOVATIVE PLASTICS CORPORATION—See Global Supply LLC; *U.S. Public*, pg. 1718
INOVAR PACKAGING GROUP, LLC—See AEA Investors LP; *U.S. Private*, pg. 114
INTERTAPE POLYMER CORP.—See Clearlake Capital Group, L.P.; *U.S. Private*, pg. 935
INTERTAPE POLYMER EUROPE GMBH—See Clearlake Capital Group, L.P.; *U.S. Private*, pg. 935
ISO POLY FILMS, INC.—See Alpha Industries, Inc.; *U.S. Private*, pg. 197
ISTRAGRAFIKA D.D.—See CVC Capital Partners SICAV-FIS S.A.; *Int'l*, pg. 1881
JUBAIL INTEGRATED PACKAGING COMPANY LIMITED LLC—See Boubyan Petrochemical Co. KSC; *Int'l*, pg. 1119
KENYA LITHO LTD—See Aga Khan Development Network; *Int'l*, pg. 199
KIV VERPACKUNGEN GMBH—See Groupe Guillin SA; *Int'l*, pg. 3104
KOBUSCH-SENGEWALD GMBH - HALLE—See Sun Capital Partners, Inc.; *U.S. Private*, pg. 3862
KOBUSCH SENGEWALD GMBH—See Sun Capital Partners, Inc.; *U.S. Private*, pg. 3862
KOBUSCH UK LIMITED—See Sun Capital Partners, Inc.; *U.S. Private*, pg. 3862
LINPAC PACKAGING PONTIVY SAS—See Strategic Value Partners, LLC; *U.S. Private*, pg. 3836
LINPAC PACKAGING PRODUCTION SP Z.O.O.—See Strategic Value Partners, LLC; *U.S. Private*, pg. 3836
LINPAC PACKAGING RUSSIA OOO—See Strategic Value Partners, LLC; *U.S. Private*, pg. 3836
MACTAC POLSKA—See Avery Dennison Corporation; *U.S. Public*, pg. 244
MARTIN EMPLOYEES, INC.; *U.S. Private*, pg. 2594
MATERION UK LIMITED—See Materion Corporation; *U.S. Public*, pg. 1396
MAXCO SUPPLY INC., MACHINERY DIVISION—See Maxco Supply Inc.; *U.S. Private*, pg. 2617
MIPAC AB—See Berry Global Group, Inc; *U.S. Public*, pg. 323

MOLD-RITE PLASTICS LLC—See Irving Place Capital Management, L.P.; *U.S. Private*, pg. 2142
NESPAK IMBALLAGGI SPA—See Groupe Guillin SA; *Int'l*, pg. 3104
NEXT GENERATION FILMS, INC.; *U.S. Private*, pg. 2919
NIAFLEX CORPORATION—See Inteplast Group, Ltd.; *U.S. Private*, pg. 2106
NIKKO MATERIALS CO., LTD.—See Eternal Materials Co., Ltd.; *Int'l*, pg. 2521
NOVACEL KOREA LTD.—See Chargeurs SA; *Int'l*, pg. 1450
PACKAGING FIRST LTD.—See Bong AB; *Int'l*, pg. 1107
PAC WORLDWIDE MEXICO, S. DE R.L. DE C.V.—See PAC Worldwide Corporation; *U.S. Private*, pg. 3063
PARAGON FILMS, INC.—See Wellspring Capital Management LLC; *U.S. Private*, pg. 4477
PFLUEGER KOPERTY SP Z O.O.—See Bong AB; *Int'l*, pg. 1107
PHOENIX PACKAGING CARIBE S.A.S.—See Genstar Capital, LLC; *U.S. Private*, pg. 1679
PHOENIX PAPER PACKAGING COLOMBIA S.A.S.—See Genstar Capital, LLC; *U.S. Private*, pg. 1679
PHOENIX PAPER PACKAGING MEXICO, S. DE R.L. DE C.V.—See Genstar Capital, LLC; *U.S. Private*, pg. 1679
PI ADVANCED MATERIALS CO., LTD—See Arkema S.A.; *Int'l*, pg. 569
POLAR PAK INC.—See Apollo Global Management, Inc.; *U.S. Public*, pg. 154
POLYAIR INTER PACK, DALLAS—See Clearlake Capital Group, L.P.; *U.S. Private*, pg. 935
PPC INDUSTRIES INC.—See Kohlberg & Company, LLC; *U.S. Private*, pg. 2338
PREGIS LLC—See Warburg Pincus LLC; *U.S. Private*, pg. 4439
PROCHIMIR INC.—See Arkema S.A.; *Int'l*, pg. 571
PROCHIMIR SAS—See Arkema S.A.; *Int'l*, pg. 571
PT.HOKKAN DELTAPACK INDUSTRI—See Hokkan Holdings Limited; *Int'l*, pg. 3443
RAVEN INDUSTRIES, INC. - ENGINEERED FILMS DIVISION—See CNH Industrial N.V.; *Int'l*, pg. 1676
RAVEN INDUSTRIES, INC. - MADISON—See CNH Industrial N.V.; *Int'l*, pg. 1676
REEL SERVICE LIMITED—See ASTI Holdings Limited; *Int'l*, pg. 655
REEL SERVICE (PHILIPPINES), INC.—See ASTI Holdings Limited; *Int'l*, pg. 655
REYNOLDS FLEXIBLE PACKAGING—See Pactiv Evergreen Inc.; *U.S. Public*, pg. 1634
REYNOLDS PRESTO PRODUCTS INC.—See Pactiv Evergreen Inc.; *U.S. Public*, pg. 1634
RICHMOND TECHNOLOGY SDN. BHD.—See D'nonce Technology Bhd.; *Int'l*, pg. 1900
ROYAL INTER PACK CO., LTD.; *U.S. Private*, pg. 3492
RPC ASTRAPAK PROPRIETARY LIMITED—See Berry Global Group, Inc; *U.S. Public*, pg. 322
RPC BEBO FOOD PACKAGING GMBH—See Berry Global Group, Inc; *U.S. Public*, pg. 322
RPC BEBO NEDERLAND BV—See Berry Global Group, Inc; *U.S. Public*, pg. 324
RPC TEDECO-GIZEH TROYES SASU—See Berry Global Group, Inc; *U.S. Public*, pg. 325
RUMA INDUSTRIEVERPACKUNG LEIPZIG GMBH—See Silgan Holdings, Inc.; *U.S. Public*, pg. 1878
SAKURA BUSSAN CO., LTD.—See GSI Creos Corporation; *Int'l*, pg. 3145
SIGNATURE FLEXIBLE PACKAGING, INC.—See H.I.G. Capital, LLC; *U.S. Private*, pg. 1834
SIGNODE INDIA LIMITED—See Crown Holdings, Inc.; *U.S. Public*, pg. 599
SILGAN METAL PACKAGING ENEM O.O.O.—See Silgan Holdings, Inc.; *U.S. Public*, pg. 1879
SKC KOLON PI, INC. - GUMI PLANT—See Arkema S.A.; *Int'l*, pg. 569
SKC KOLON PI, INC. - JINCHEON PLANT—See Arkema S.A.; *Int'l*, pg. 569
SONOCO ALCORE GMBH—See Sonoco Products Company; *U.S. Public*, pg. 1905
SONOCO DISPLAY AND PACKAGING, LLC—See Sonoco Products Company; *U.S. Public*, pg. 1906
SONOCO FOR PLAS DO BRAZIL LTDA—See Sonoco Products Company; *U.S. Public*, pg. 1906
SPARTECH - LA MIRADA—See The Jordan Company, L.P.; *U.S. Private*, pg. 4062
STRETCH WRAP PACKAGING INDUSTRIES LLC; *U.S. Private*, pg. 3839
SUNDIC INC.—See DIC Corporation; *Int'l*, pg. 2109
SUPERIOR (CHENGDU) MULTI-PACKAGING CO., LTD.—See Crown Holdings, Inc.; *U.S. Public*, pg. 599
SUPERIOR (LANGFANG) MULTI-PACKAGING CO., LTD.—See Crown Holdings, Inc.; *U.S. Public*, pg. 599
SUPERIOR (TIANJIN) MULTI-PACKAGING CO., LTD.—See Crown Holdings, Inc.; *U.S. Public*, pg. 599
SYDEK HANG FUNG PRECISE PACKAGE (SHANGHAI) CO., LTD.—See Hang Fung International Industrial Co., Ltd.; *Int'l*, pg. 3244
SYDEK HANG FUNG PRECISION (SUZHOU) CO., LTD.—See Hang Fung International Industrial Co., Ltd.; *Int'l*, pg. 3244
SYFAN MANUFACTURING CORP.; *U.S. Private*, pg. 3898

N.A.I.C.S. INDEX

326113 — UNLAMINATED PLASTIC...

TAGHLEEF INDUSTRIES CANADA INC.—See Al Ghurair Group; *Int'l*, pg. 277
TAGHLEEF INDUSTRIES INC.—See Al Ghurair Group; *Int'l*, pg. 277
TAGHLEEF INDUSTRIES KFT—See Al Ghurair Group; *Int'l*, pg. 278
TAGHLEEF INDUSTRIES L.L.C.—See Al Ghurair Group; *Int'l*, pg. 277
TAGHLEEF INDUSTRIES PTY. LTD.—See Al Ghurair Group; *Int'l*, pg. 277
TAGHLEEF INDUSTRIES S.A.O.C.—See Al Ghurair Group; *Int'l*, pg. 278
TAGHLEEF INDUSTRIES S.L.U.—See Al Ghurair Group; *Int'l*, pg. 278
TAGHLEEF INDUSTRIES S.P.A.—See Al Ghurair Group; *Int'l*, pg. 278
TEGRANT ALLOYD BRANDS, INC.—See Sonoco Products Company; *U.S. Public*, pg. 1905
THAI POLY ACRYLIC PUBLIC COMPANY LTD.—See EAC Invest AS; *Int'l*, pg. 2262
TLL PRINTING & PACKAGING LTD—See Aga Khan Development Network; *Int'l*, pg. 199
TPC FZE - PROCESS PACKAGE DIVISION—See Bhatia Brothers Group; *Int'l*, pg. 1014
TRANSPAK CORPORATION—See Delos Capital, LLC; *U.S. Private*, pg. 1198
TREDEGAR FILM PRODUCTS COMPANY SHANGHAI, LIMITED—See Tredegar Corporation; *U.S. Public*, pg. 2187
TSIMIS S.A.—See Mondelez International, Inc.; *U.S. Public*, pg. 1464
UNIPLAST KNAUER VERWALTUNGS GMBH—See Blue Cap AG; *Int'l*, pg. 1067
VINCO VENTURES, INC.; *U.S. Public*, pg. 2298
VISIPAK—See Cameron Holdings Corporation; *U.S. Private*, pg. 729
VULCAN MATERIAL PLASTICO LTDA.—See Grupo Brasil Participacoes; *Int'l*, pg. 3123
WEIDENHAMMER CHILE LTDA.—See Sonoco Products Company; *U.S. Public*, pg. 1909
XIAMEN CHANGSU INDUSTRIAL CORPORATION LIMITED—See Green Seal Holding Limited; *Int'l*, pg. 3072
YEMEN COMPANY FOR PACKAGING MATERIAL INDUSTRY—See Hayel Saeed Anam Group of Companies; *Int'l*, pg. 3291
ZHEJIANG GAOTE METAL DECORATING CO., LTD.—See Crown Holdings, Inc.; *U.S. Public*, pg. 599

326113 — UNLAMINATED PLASTICS FILM AND SHEET (EXCEPT PACKAGING) MANUFACTURING

ABNOTE NORTH AMERICA—See American Banknote Corporation; *U.S. Private*, pg. 224
ACHILLES USA, INC.—See Achilles Corporation; *Int'l*, pg. 103
ACTON TECHNOLOGIES, INC.; *U.S. Private*, pg. 70
ADVANCED BARRIER EXTRUSIONS, LLC—See The Graham Group, Inc.; *U.S. Private*, pg. 4036
AKROTEX FILMS INC.—See Akrotex, Inc.; *U.S. Private*, pg. 146
ALL AMERICAN POLY CORP.; *U.S. Private*, pg. 169
ALROS PRODUCTS LIMITED; *Int'l*, pg. 377
ALTUGLAS INTERNATIONAL DENMARK A/S—See Arkema S.A.; *Int'l*, pg. 568
AMCOR FLEXIBLES (NEW ZEALAND) LTD—See Amcor plc; *Int'l*, pg. 416
AMERICAN DECORATIVE SURFACES, INC.—See Ares Management Corporation; *U.S. Public*, pg. 188
ASIMILAR GROUP PLC; *Int'l*, pg. 621
AT FILMS INC.—See Berry Global Group, Inc; *U.S. Public*, pg. 320
BAYER MATERIALSCIENCE (BEIJING) COMPANY LIMITED—See Bayer Aktiengesellschaft; *Int'l*, pg. 907
BEMIS CLYSAR, INC.—See Amcor plc; *Int'l*, pg. 418
BEMIS COMPANY—See Amcor plc; *Int'l*, pg. 418
BERKEMPLAST SAN. VE TIC. LTD. STI.—See Bischof + Klein GmbH & Co. KG; *Int'l*, pg. 1048
BERRY GLOBAL, INC—See Berry Global Group, Inc; *U.S. Public*, pg. 321
BJK INDUSTRIES INC.; *U.S. Private*, pg. 568
BLOOMER PLASTICS, INC.; *U.S. Private*, pg. 584
BLUERIDGE FILMS INC.—See Arkema S.A.; *Int'l*, pg. 570
BRITISH POLYTHENE LIMITED—See Berry Global Group, Inc; *U.S. Public*, pg. 322
CABOT NORIT JAPAN CO. LTD.—See Cabot Corporation; *U.S. Public*, pg. 417
CABOT SINGAPORE PTE. LTD.—See Cabot Corporation; *U.S. Public*, pg. 417
CAST FILM JAPAN CO., LTD.—See DIC Corporation; *Int'l*, pg. 2107
CDG PETCHEM LIMITED; *Int'l*, pg. 1370
CELLO-PACK CORPORATION; *U.S. Private*, pg. 807
C.E. SHEPHERD COMPANY LP; *U.S. Private*, pg. 706
CHARTER FILMS, INC.; *U.S. Private*, pg. 858
CHOKSI IMAGING LTD.; *Int'l*, pg. 1577

CLEAR VIEW BAG CO. INC.; *U.S. Private*, pg. 932
CLOPAY ASCHERSLEBEN GMBH—See Berry Global Group, Inc; *U.S. Public*, pg. 321
CLOPAY DO BRASIL LTDA.—See Berry Global Group, Inc; *U.S. Public*, pg. 321
COBURN JAPAN CORPORATION; *Int'l*, pg. 1683
COMCO PLASTICS INC.; *U.S. Public*, pg. 981
CONGOLEUM CORPORATION—See Congoleum Corporation; *U.S. Private*, pg. 1013
COPOL INTERNATIONAL LTD.; *Int'l*, pg. 1793
CORBI PLASTICS, LLC—See Menasha Corporation; *U.S. Private*, pg. 2665
CORPLAST PACKAGING INDUSTRIES SDN. BHD.—See CLPG Packaging Industries Sdn. Bhd.; *Int'l*, pg. 1663
CORTEC ADVANCED FILMS—See Cortec Corporation; *U.S. Private*, pg. 1060
COVESTRO LLC - SPECIALTY FILMS BUSINESS—See Bayer Aktiengesellschaft; *Int'l*, pg. 907
CPFILMS INC.—See Eastman Chemical Company; *U.S. Public*, pg. 705
DAUBERT CROMWELL, LLC—See Daubert Industries, Inc.; *U.S. Private*, pg. 1167
DELTA GLASS B.V.—See LCI Industries; *U.S. Public*, pg. 1295
DESIGN PACKAGING COMPANY INC.; *U.S. Private*, pg. 1214
DEWAL INDUSTRIES, INC.—See Rogers Corporation; *U.S. Public*, pg. 1808
DIAXON SA—See HELLENiQ ENERGY Holdings S.A.; *Int'l*, pg. 3334
DIC FILTEC, INC.—See DIC Corporation; *Int'l*, pg. 2108
DIELECTRICS INDUSTRIES INC.; *U.S. Private*, pg. 1228
DUNMORE CORPORATION—See Steel Partners Holdings L.P.; *U.S. Public*, pg. 1942
DUPONT DE NEMOURS (LUXEMBOURG) SARL—See DuPont de Nemours, Inc.; *U.S. Public*, pg. 693
DUPONT TEIJIN FILMS CHINA LTD.—See DuPont de Nemours, Inc.; *U.S. Public*, pg. 693
ECOMEMBRANE LLC—See Ecomembrane S.p.A.; *Int'l*, pg. 2296
ECOMEMBRANE S.P.A.; *Int'l*, pg. 2296
ECOPLAST LTD.; *Int'l*, pg. 2299
ERGIS S.A.; *Int'l*, pg. 2491
ES ROBBINS CORPORATION; *U.S. Private*, pg. 1424
ESTER INDUSTRIES LTD; *Int'l*, pg. 2518
EX-TECH PLASTICS, INC.—See Good Natured Products Inc.; *Int'l*, pg. 3038
EXXONMOBIL CHEMICAL COMPANY - FILM DIV.—See Exxon Mobil Corporation; *U.S. Public*, pg. 814
EXXONMOBIL CHEMICAL FILMS CANADA, LTD.—See Exxon Mobil Corporation; *U.S. Public*, pg. 814
FITESA FILM PRODUCTS LLC—See Tredegar Corporation; *U.S. Public*, pg. 2187
FLEXBARRIER PRODUCTS, LLC—See ShoreView Industries, LLC; *U.S. Private*, pg. 3642
FLEXIBLE PACKAGING & CO. INC.; *U.S. Private*, pg. 1544
FLEX-O-FILM PLASTIC DIV.—See Flex-O-Glass, Inc.; *U.S. Private*, pg. 1543
FLEX-O-GLASS, INC.; *U.S. Private*, pg. 1543
FLEXTECH S.R.L.—See Ginegar Plastic Products Ltd.; *Int'l*, pg. 2976
FLORACRAFT OF PHILADELPHIA INC.—See Floracraft Corporation; *U.S. Private*, pg. 1546
FUKUSHIMA GRAVURE CO., LTD.—See Gunze Limited; *Int'l*, pg. 3185
FUTUREX INDUSTRIES INC.; *U.S. Private*, pg. 1627
FUWEI FILMS (SHANDONG) CO., LTD.—See Baijiayun Group Ltd; *Int'l*, pg. 802
GARWARE HI-TECH FILMS LIMITED; *Int'l*, pg. 2886
GEDIZ AMBALAJ SANAYI VE TICARET A.S.; *Int'l*, pg. 2910
GENERAL FILMS, INC.; *U.S. Private*, pg. 1665
GLENROY INC.; *U.S. Private*, pg. 1711
GLOBAL PET FILMS INC.—See Garware Hi-Tech Films Limited; *Int'l*, pg. 2886
GOEX CORPORATION; *U.S. Private*, pg. 1726
GUILLIN PORTUGAL—See Groupe Guillin SA; *Int'l*, pg. 3104
GUNZE PLASTICS & ENGINEERING CORPORATION OF AMERICA—See Gunze Limited; *Int'l*, pg. 3185
GUNZE PLASTICS & ENGINEERING CORPORATION—See Gunze Limited; *Int'l*, pg. 3185
HILLSIDE PLASTICS CORPORATION; *U.S. Private*, pg. 1947
HORNSCHUCH FRANCE SARL—See Continental Aktiengesellschaft; *Int'l*, pg. 1780
HORNSCHUCH ITALIA S.R.L.—See Continental Aktiengesellschaft; *Int'l*, pg. 1780
HORNSCHUCH UK LTD.—See Continental Aktiengesellschaft; *Int'l*, pg. 1780
INNOVATIVE PLASTICS—See Global Supply LLC; *U.S. Private*, pg. 1718
INNOVIA FILMS AMERICA, INC.—See CCL Industries Inc.; *Int'l*, pg. 1369
INPRO CORPORATION; *U.S. Private*, pg. 2084
INTEPLAST CORPORATION; *U.S. Private*, pg. 2106
INTEPLAST GROUP, LTD. - WORLD-PAK—See Inteplast Group, Ltd.; *U.S. Private*, pg. 2106

INTERFILM HOLDINGS INC.—See Nicolet Capital Partners, LLC; *U.S. Private*, pg. 2926
ITW IMAGEDATA—See Illinois Tool Works Inc.; *U.S. Public*, pg. 1106
KLOCKNER PENTAPLAST GMBH—See Strategic Value Partners, LLC; *U.S. Private*, pg. 3836
KLOCKNER PENTAPLAST LTD.—See Strategic Value Partners, LLC; *U.S. Private*, pg. 3836
KLOCKNER PENTAPLAST OF AMERICA, INC.—See Strategic Value Partners, LLC; *U.S. Private*, pg. 3836
KLOECKNER PENTAPLAST (SHANGHAI) CO., LTD.—See Strategic Value Partners, LLC; *U.S. Private*, pg. 3836
KONRAD HORNSCHUCH AG—See Continental Aktiengesellschaft; *Int'l*, pg. 1780
KW PLASTICS; *U.S. Private*, pg. 2359
LIGHT IMPRESSIONS; *U.S. Private*, pg. 2452
LONE STAR PLASTICS, INC.—See Myers Industries, Inc.; *U.S. Public*, pg. 1488
LUCENT POLYMERS, INC.; *U.S. Private*, pg. 2510
MAIWEAVE LLC—See Clearlake Capital Group, L.P.; *U.S. Private*, pg. 935
MAXFORD TECHNOLOGY, LLC—See CN Innovations Holdings Limited; *Int'l*, pg. 1673
MULTI-PLASTICS EXTRUSIONS, INC.—See Multi-Plastics, Inc.; *U.S. Private*, pg. 2812
MULTI-PLASTICS, INC.—See Multi-Plastics, Inc.; *U.S. Private*, pg. 2812
NATIONWIDE TARPS INC.; *U.S. Private*, pg. 2866
NEW ENGLAND PLASTICS CORP; *U.S. Private*, pg. 2894
NEW HAMPSHIRE PLASTICS INC.; *U.S. Private*, pg. 2896
N.E.W. PLASTICS CORP.; *U.S. Private*, pg. 2828
NEX PERFORMANCE FILMS—See Mason Wells, Inc.; *U.S. Private*, pg. 2602
NEXUS PLASTICS, INC.; *U.S. Private*, pg. 2922
NIKE IHM, INC.—See NIKE, Inc.; *U.S. Public*, pg. 1529
NILEX INC.—See Fulcrum Capital Partners Inc.; *Int'l*, pg. 2841
NORFLEX, INC.—See Arsenal Capital Management LP; *U.S. Private*, pg. 339
OOO HORNSCHUCH RUS—See Continental Aktiengesellschaft; *Int'l*, pg. 1780
O'SULLIVAN FILMS, INC.—See Continental Aktiengesellschaft; *Int'l*, pg. 1780
PACE POLYETHYLENE MFG. CO. INC.; *U.S. Private*, pg. 3063
PERLEN CONVERTING AG—See CPH Chemie + Papier Holding AG; *Int'l*, pg. 1824
PETOSKEY PLASTICS INC.; *U.S. Private*, pg. 3161
PLACON CORPORATION; *U.S. Private*, pg. 3194
PLASCAL CORPORATION; *U.S. Private*, pg. 3198
PLASTIC SUPPLIERS, INC.; *U.S. Private*, pg. 3199
PLASTIMAYD CORPORATION; *U.S. Private*, pg. 3199
POLIGOF SPA—See 21 Investimenti Societa' di Gestione del Risparmio S.p.A.; *Int'l*, pg. 4
POLY-AMERICA LP; *U.S. Private*, pg. 3225
POLY PAK AMERICA, INC.; *U.S. Private*, pg. 3225
POLYVINYL FILMS, INC.; *U.S. Private*, pg. 3226
PRENT CORPORATION; *U.S. Private*, pg. 3252
PRIMEX PLASTICS CORP.—See ICC Industries, Inc.; *U.S. Private*, pg. 2030
PROFESSIONAL PACKAGE COMPANY; *U.S. Private*, pg. 3275
QINGDAO TRACON ELECTRONIC CO., LTD.—See Chonbang Co., Ltd.; *Int'l*, pg. 1578
RAYONIER PERFORMANCE FIBERS, LLC—See Rayonier Advanced Materials Inc.; *U.S. Public*, pg. 1765
RAYVEN, INC.—See OpenGate Capital Management, LLC; *U.S. Private*, pg. 3030
REDI-BAG, INC.—See Ardian SAS; *Int'l*, pg. 554
REYNOLDS FLEXIBLE PACKAGING-GROTTOES PLASTICS PLANT—See Pactiv Evergreen Inc.; *U.S. Public*, pg. 1634
REYNOLDS FOOD PACKAGING-CHICAGO—See Pactiv Evergreen Inc.; *U.S. Public*, pg. 1634
RJF INTERNATIONAL CORPORATION; *U.S. Private*, pg. 3449
RONALD MARK ASSOCIATES INC.; *U.S. Private*, pg. 3477
RPC BPI AGRICULTURE—See Berry Global Group, Inc; *U.S. Public*, pg. 322
RPC EMBALLAGES MONTPONT SA—See Berry Global Group, Inc; *U.S. Public*, pg. 324
RPC NEUTRAUBLING GMBH—See Berry Global Group, Inc; *U.S. Public*, pg. 324
SAINT-GOBAIN SOLAR GARD AUSTRALIA PTY LTD.—See Compagnie de Saint-Gobain SA; *Int'l*, pg. 1728
SAINT-GOBAIN SOLAR GARD, LLC—See Compagnie de Saint-Gobain SA; *Int'l*, pg. 1730
SAINT-GOBAIN SOLAR GARD NV—See Compagnie de Saint-Gobain SA; *Int'l*, pg. 1728
SAINT-GOBAIN SOLAR GARD UK, LTD—See Compagnie de Saint-Gobain SA; *Int'l*, pg. 1728
SCORPION PROTECTIVE COATINGS, INC.; *U.S. Private*, pg. 3575
SENTINEL PRODUCTS CORP.; *U.S. Private*, pg. 3609
SIDAPLAX V.O.F.—See Plastic Suppliers, Inc.; *U.S. Private*, pg. 3199

326113 — UNLAMINATED PLASTIC...

SOLAR GARD NORDIC AB—See Compagnie de Saint-Gobain SA; *Int'l*, pg. 1729
SOUTHERN FILM EXTRUDERS INC.; *U.S. Private*, pg. 3731
SOUTHWALL TECHNOLOGIES INC.—See Eastman Chemical Company; *U.S. Public*, pg. 706
SPARTECH - MCMINNVILLE—See The Jordan Company, L.P.; *U.S. Private*, pg. 4062
SPARTECH - STAMFORD—See The Jordan Company, L.P.; *U.S. Private*, pg. 4062
SPORT COURT INTERNATIONAL INC.—See The Riverside Company; *U.S. Private*, pg. 4110
SUN PROCESS CONVERTING COMPANY, INC.; *U.S. Private*, pg. 3864
SWM INTERNATIONAL - MASSACHUSETTS—See Mativ Holdings, Inc.; *U.S. Public*, pg. 1396
TC MANUFACTURING CO., INC.; *U.S. Private*, pg. 3942
TEE GROUP FILMS; *U.S. Private*, pg. 3957
TEIJIN DUPONT FILMS JAPAN LIMITED—See DuPont de Nemours, Inc.; *U.S. Public*, pg. 692
TEKRA, LLC—See Audax Group, Limited Partnership; *U.S. Private*, pg. 387
TEX-TRUDE LP; *U.S. Private*, pg. 3974
THERMWELL PRODUCTS CO., INC.; *U.S. Private*, pg. 4143
TIANJIN BOAI NKY INTERNATIONAL LTD—See Boai NKY Medical Holdings Ltd.; *Int'l*, pg. 1094
TOYOSHINA FILM CO., LTD.—See Daicel Corporation; *Int'l*, pg. 1920
TRANSILWRAP COMPANY, INC. - HEBRON PLANT—See Nicolet Capital Partners, LLC; *U.S. Private*, pg. 2926
TRANSILWRAP COMPANY, INC. - LAMINATION/ID SECURITIES DIVISION—See Nicolet Capital Partners, LLC; *U.S. Private*, pg. 2926
TRANSILWRAP COMPANY, INC. - NORTHEAST DIVISION—See Nicolet Capital Partners, LLC; *U.S. Private*, pg. 2926
TRANSILWRAP COMPANY, INC. - PRINTABLE PLASTICS DIVISION—See Nicolet Capital Partners, LLC; *U.S. Private*, pg. 2926
TRANSILWRAP COMPANY, INC.—See Nicolet Capital Partners, LLC; *U.S. Private*, pg. 2926
TRANSILWRAP COMPANY, INC. - SPECIALTY & INDUSTRIAL FILMS DIVISION—See Nicolet Capital Partners, LLC; *U.S. Private*, pg. 2926
TREDEGAR CORPORATION; *U.S. Private*, pg. 2186
TREDEGAR FILM PRODUCTS CORPORATION - TERRE HAUTE PLANT—See Tredegar Corporation; *U.S. Public*, pg. 2187
TREDEGAR FILM PRODUCTS - LAKE ZURICH, LLC—See Tredegar Corporation; *U.S. Public*, pg. 2187
TRI-SEAL, INC.—See Genstar Capital, LLC; *U.S. Private*, pg. 1679
TRI-SEAL, INC.—See Genstar Capital, LLC; *U.S. Private*, pg. 1679
UK POLYFILM LIMITED—See Berry Global Group, Inc; *U.S. Public*, pg. 326
UK POLYTHENE LIMITED—See Berry Global Group, Inc; *U.S. Public*, pg. 326
VALERON STRENGTH FILMS—See Illinois Tool Works Inc.; *U.S. Public*, pg. 1111
VCF FILMS, INC.—See PMC Capital Partners, LLC; *U.S. Private*, pg. 3218
VITA THERMOPLASTIC SHEET LIMITED—See TPG Capital, L.P.; *U.S. Public*, pg. 2175
WARP BROTHERS—See Flex-O-Glass, Inc.; *U.S. Private*, pg. 1543
WIMAN CORPORATION—See RTP Company; *U.S. Private*, pg. 3498

326121 — UNLAMINATED PLASTICS PROFILE SHAPE MANUFACTURING

ACCU TECH PLASTICS, INC.; *U.S. Private*, pg. 54
AMERICAN EXTRUDED PLASTICS, INC.—See Odyssey Investment Partners, LLC; *U.S. Private*, pg. 2995
APM PLASTICS SDN. BHD.—See APM Automotive Holdings Berhad; *Int'l*, pg. 516
ARMORCAST ROTATIONAL MOLDING—See Armorcast Products Company; *U.S. Private*, pg. 331
AYABE ENGINEERING PLASTICS CO., LTD.—See Gunze Limited; *Int'l*, pg. 3185
BASSO INDUSTRY CORPORATION - PLASTIC INJECTION PLANT—See Basso Industry Corporation; *Int'l*, pg. 888
BERRY PLASTICS CORPORATION—See Berry Global Group, Inc; *U.S. Public*, pg. 320
CENTROTHERM ECO SYSTEMS, LLC—See CENTROTEC SE; *Int'l*, pg. 1414
CONSUMERMETRICS, INC.; *U.S. Private*, pg. 1026
COSMO CORPORATION; *U.S. Private*, pg. 1062
COXON INDUSTRIAL LTD.—See COXON Precise Industrial Co., Ltd.; *Int'l*, pg. 1823
DECEUNINCK BALTIC UAB—See Deceuninck NV; *Int'l*, pg. 1999
DECEUNINCK BULGARIA EOOD—See Deceuninck NV; *Int'l*, pg. 2000

DECEUNINCK D.O.O.—See Deceuninck NV; *Int'l*, pg. 2000
DECEUNINCK D.O.O.—See Deceuninck NV; *Int'l*, pg. 2000
DECEUNINCK HOLDINGS UK LTD—See Deceuninck NV; *Int'l*, pg. 2000
DECEUNINCK ITALIA SRL—See Deceuninck NV; *Int'l*, pg. 1999
DECEUNINCK NORTH AMERICA INC.—See Deceuninck NV; *Int'l*, pg. 2000
DECEUNINCK RUS OOO—See Deceuninck NV; *Int'l*, pg. 2000
FISCHER SOLUTION (SUZHOU) CO., LTD.—See Platinum Equity, LLC; *U.S. Private*, pg. 3207
FISCHER-TECH MALAYSIA—See Platinum Equity, LLC; *U.S. Private*, pg. 3207
FISCHER TECH (SUZHOU) CO., LTD.—See Platinum Equity, LLC; *U.S. Private*, pg. 3207
GERRESHEIMER HORSOVSKY TYN SPOL. S R.O.—See Gerresheimer AG; *Int'l*, pg. 2943
HUIYE (VIETNAM) PLASTIC CO., LTD.—See Dynamic Colours Limited; *Int'l*, pg. 2240
INOUTIC DECEUNINCK GMBH—See Deceuninck NV; *Int'l*, pg. 2000
JUKEN MICRO-AIR (TIANJIN) TECHNOLOGY CO., LTD.—See Frencken Group Limited; *Int'l*, pg. 2773
JUKEN (THAILAND) CO., LTD.—See Frencken Group Limited; *Int'l*, pg. 2772
JUKEN UNIPRODUCTS PVT LTD—See Frencken Group Limited; *Int'l*, pg. 2773
JUKEN (ZHUHAI) CO., LTD.—See Frencken Group Limited; *Int'l*, pg. 2772
MEDIMONDI AG—See CENTROTEC SE; *Int'l*, pg. 1415
MYE CANADA OPERATIONS INC.—See Myers Industries, Inc.; *U.S. Public*, pg. 1488
MYERS DE EL SALVADOR S.A. DE C.V.—See Myers Industries, Inc.; *U.S. Public*, pg. 1488
MYERS DE PANAMA S.A.—See Myers Industries, Inc.; *U.S. Public*, pg. 1488
MYERS INDUSTRIES, INC.; *U.S. Public*, pg. 1488
NORDSON MEDICAL (NH), INC.—See Nordson Corporation; *U.S. Public*, pg. 1534
NORTHWEST POLYMERS LLC—See Clayton, Dubilier & Rice, LLC; *U.S. Public*, pg. 920
PLASTIC TECHNOLOGY INC.—See Hickory Springs Manufacturing Company; *U.S. Private*, pg. 1933
PLASTO-TECH CORPORATION—See Magni-Power Company Inc.; *U.S. Private*, pg. 2548
POLYGON COMPANY; *U.S. Private*, pg. 3225
POLY VISIONS, INC.—See Bemis Associates Inc.; *U.S. Private*, pg. 522
PREMIER CROWN CORP.—See Sirchie Fingerprint Labs; *U.S. Private*, pg. 3672
PT. ALTECH—See Altech Co., Ltd.; *Int'l*, pg. 388
QUALITY SCIENTIFIC PLASTICS, INC.—See Thermo Fisher Scientific Inc.; *U.S. Public*, pg. 2151
RANGE VALLEY EXTRUSIONS LTD—See Deceuninck NV; *Int'l*, pg. 2000
RPC ENVASES SA—See Berry Global Group, Inc; *U.S. Public*, pg. 324
RPC VERPACKUNGEN KUTENHOLZ GMBH—See Berry Global Group, Inc; *U.S. Public*, pg. 325
SKIFFY B.V.—See Essentra plc; *Int'l*, pg. 2511
SKIFFY S.A.S.—See Essentra plc; *Int'l*, pg. 2512
SUN CAN INTERNATIONAL LTD. - SINYON PLASTIC & MOULD FACTORY—See COXON Precise Industrial Co., Ltd.; *Int'l*, pg. 1823
TMDWEK NORTH, LLC—See Grammer AG; *Int'l*, pg. 3053
VASTECH PLASTIC (SHANGHAI) INDUSTRIAL CO., LTD.—See COXON Precise Industrial Co., Ltd.; *Int'l*, pg. 1823
VINYLEX CORPORATION; *U.S. Private*, pg. 4386
WESTLAKE PLASTICS COMPANY; *U.S. Private*, pg. 4499
WHITERIDGE PLASTICS, LLC—See Myers Industries, Inc.; *U.S. Public*, pg. 1488
ZEUS INDUSTRIAL PRODUCTS INC.; *U.S. Private*, pg. 4603

326122 — PLASTICS PIPE AND PIPE FITTING MANUFACTURING

ADS CANADA INC—See Advanced Drainage Systems, Inc.; *U.S. Public*, pg. 46
ADS MEXICANA, S.A DE C.V.—See Advanced Drainage Systems, Inc.; *U.S. Public*, pg. 46
ADVANCED DRAINAGE SYSTEMS, INC.; *U.S. Public*, pg. 46
ADVANCED PEDESTALS, INC.—See Petroflex North America, Ltd.; *U.S. Private*, pg. 3162
ADVANCED PIPES AND CASTS COMPANY W.L.L.—See Aamal Company Q.S.C.; *Int'l*, pg. 36
AKATHERM B.V.—See Aliaxis S.A./N.V.; *Int'l*, pg. 323
ALLWIRE INC.; *U.S. Private*, pg. 194
ALPHACAN B.V.—See OpenGate Capital Management, LLC; *U.S. Private*, pg. 3030
ALPHACAN D.O.O.—See OpenGate Capital Management, LLC; *U.S. Private*, pg. 3031
ALPHACAN OMNIPLAST GMBH—See OpenGate Capital Management, LLC; *U.S. Private*, pg. 3031

ALPHACAN S.P.A.—See OpenGate Capital Management, LLC; *U.S. Private*, pg. 3031
AMANCO MEXICO—See Bharti Enterprises Limited; *Int'l*, pg. 1012
AMERICAN PIPE & PLASTICS, INC.—See Clayton, Dubilier & Rice, LLC; *U.S. Private*, pg. 919
AMERICAN PLASTIC PIPE AND SUPPLY, L.L.C.—See The Shaw Group Inc.; *U.S. Private*, pg. 4117
APT PACKAGING LTD.; *Int'l*, pg. 523
AQUATHERM INTERNATIONAL; *U.S. Private*, pg. 303
ARABIAN PLASTIC MANUFACTURING COMPANY—See Georg Fischer AG; *Int'l*, pg. 2935
ARCEE INDUSTRIES LIMITED; *Int'l*, pg. 543
AROT POLSKA SP.Z.O.O.—See Bharti Enterprises Limited; *Int'l*, pg. 1012
ASAHI/AMERICA, INC.—See Asahi Yukizai Corporation; *Int'l*, pg. 598
ASAHI AV EUROPE GMBH—See Asahi Yukizai Corporation; *Int'l*, pg. 598
ASAHI YUKIZAI MEXICO S.A. DE C.V.—See Asahi Yukizai Corporation; *Int'l*, pg. 598
ASHIRVAD PIPES PVT. LTD.—See Aliaxis S.A./N.V.; *Int'l*, pg. 323
ASHWORTH—See Compagnie de Saint-Gobain SA; *Int'l*, pg. 1722
ASTRAL LIMITED; *Int'l*, pg. 658
ATCO RUBBER PRODUCTS INC.—See Mueller Industries, Inc.; *U.S. Public*, pg. 1484
AUSPLASTICS PTY LTD—See CTI Logistics Limited; *Int'l*, pg. 1871
AZIZ PIPES LIMITED; *Int'l*, pg. 780
BAUER CASINGS MAKINA SANAYI VE TICARET LIMITED SIRKETI—See BAUER Aktiengesellschaft; *Int'l*, pg. 892
BAUGHMAN TILE COMPANY, INC.; *U.S. Private*, pg. 490
BEETLE PLASTICS, LLC—See Midwest Towers Inc.; *U.S. Private*, pg. 2723
BERGEN PIPE SUPPORTS, INC.—See Hill & Smith PLC; *Int'l*, pg. 3391
BINH HIEP JOINT STOCK COMPANY—See DongNai Plastic JSC; *Int'l*, pg. 2169
BINH MINH PLASTICS JOINT STOCK COMPANY; *Int'l*, pg. 1034
BLOHM + VOSS OIL TOOLS GMBH—See Forum Energy Technologies, Inc.; *U.S. Public*, pg. 873
BOW PLANNING GROUP INC; *Int'l*, pg. 1123
CANGZHOU MINGZHU PLASTIC CO., LTD.—See China National Chemical Corporation; *Int'l*, pg. 1526
CANPLAS INDUSTRIES LTD.—See Aliaxis S.A./N.V.; *Int'l*, pg. 323
CANPLAS USA LLC—See Aliaxis S.A./N.V.; *Int'l*, pg. 323
CAPITOL PIPE & STEEL—See Canerector Inc.; *Int'l*, pg. 1290
CAPTAIN PIPES LTD.; *Int'l*, pg. 1317
CAPTAIN POLYPLAST LTD.; *Int'l*, pg. 1317
CENTRAL INDUSTRIES PLC—See Central Finance Company PLC; *Int'l*, pg. 1406
CHARLOTTE PIPE & FOUNDRY COMPANY; *U.S. Private*, pg. 857
CHINA LESSO GROUP HOLDINGS LIMITED; *Int'l*, pg. 1514
C.I. MEXICHEM COMPUESTOS COLOMBIA, S.A.S.—See Grupo Empresarial Kaluz S.A. de C.V.; *Int'l*, pg. 3127
COLONIAL ENGINEERING INC.; *U.S. Private*, pg. 970
COSMOFLEX, INC.—See The Goodyear Tire & Rubber Company; *U.S. Public*, pg. 2083
CRANE RESISTOFLEX/INDUSTRIAL—See Crane NXT, Co.; *U.S. Public*, pg. 590
CRESLINE PLASTIC PIPE CO., INC.; *U.S. Private*, pg. 1094
CRESLINE-WEST, INC.—See Cresline Plastic Pipe Co., Inc.; *U.S. Private*, pg. 1094
DECALU NV—See Deceuninck NV; *Int'l*, pg. 1999
DECEUNINCK D.O.O.—See Deceuninck NV; *Int'l*, pg. 2000
DECEUNINCK IMPORTADORA LIMITADA—See Deceuninck NV; *Int'l*, pg. 2000
DECEUNINCK PROFILES INDIA PRIVATE LIMITED—See Deceuninck NV; *Int'l*, pg. 2000
DECEUNINCK S.A.S.—See Deceuninck NV; *Int'l*, pg. 2000
DECEUNINCK SP. Z O.O.—See Deceuninck NV; *Int'l*, pg. 2000
DECEUNINCK (THAILAND) CO., LTD.—See Deceuninck NV; *Int'l*, pg. 1999
DIAMOND PLASTICS CORPORATION; *U.S. Private*, pg. 1223
DONGNAI PLASTIC JSC; *Int'l*, pg. 2169
DPI HOLDINGS (PROPRIETARY) LIMITED—See DISTRIBUTION AND WAREHOUSING NETWORK LIMITED; *Int'l*, pg. 2136
DPI PLASTICS (PROPRIETARY) LIMITED—See DISTRIBUTION AND WAREHOUSING NETWORK LIMITED; *Int'l*, pg. 2136
DURMAN COLOMBIA SAS—See Aliaxis S.A./N.V.; *Int'l*, pg. 323
DURMAN ESQUIVEL DE MEXICO S.A. DE CV—See Aliaxis S.A./N.V.; *Int'l*, pg. 324
DURMAN ESQUIVEL GUATEMALA S.A.—See Aliaxis S.A./N.V.; *Int'l*, pg. 324

N.A.I.C.S. INDEX

326122 — PLASTICS PIPE AND P...

DURMAN ESQUIVEL PUERTO RICO CORP.—See Aliaxis S.A./N.V.; *Int'l*, pg. 324
DURMAN ESQUIVEL S.A.—See Aliaxis S.A./N.V.; *Int'l*, pg. 324
DUTRON POLYMERS LIMITED; *Int'l*, pg. 2235
DUX INDUSTRIES LTD—See Aliaxis S.A./N.V.; *Int'l*, pg. 324
DYNEX EXTRUSIONS LTD—See Aliaxis S.A./N.V.; *Int'l*, pg. 324
EAST 74TH STREET HOLDINGS, INC.—See Steel Partners Holdings L.P.; *U.S. Public*, pg. 1942
EGEPLAST EGE PLASTIK SAN VE TIC. A.S.; *Int'l*, pg. 2322
EGE PROFIL TICARET VE SANAYI AS—See Deceuninck NV; *Int'l*, pg. 2000
EGE PROFIL TIC. VE SAN. A.S.—See Deceuninck NV; *Int'l*, pg. 2000
ELASTO VALVE RUBBER PRODUCTS INC.—See Devjo Industries, Inc.; *Int'l*, pg. 2089
THE ELCO CORP.—See Bain Capital, LP; *U.S. Private*, pg. 441
ERA CO., LTD.; *Int'l*, pg. 2488
FERGUSON PRODUCTION, INC.—See Ardian SAS; *Int'l*, pg. 554
FIBERGLASS SYSTEMS—See NOV, Inc.; *U.S. Public*, pg. 1544
FINOLEX INDUSTRIES LTD.—See Finolex Group; *Int'l*, pg. 2676
FLYING W PLASTICS INC.; *U.S. Private*, pg. 1553
FORMATURA INEZIONE POLIMERI SPA—See Aliaxis S.A./N.V.; *Int'l*, pg. 324
FORUM B+V OIL TOOLS GMBH—See Forum Energy Technologies, Inc.; *U.S. Public*, pg. 873
FORUM GLOBAL TUBING LLC—See Forum Energy Technologies, Inc.; *U.S. Public*, pg. 873
FUJIAN NEWCHOICE PIPE TECHNOLOGY CO., LTD.; *Int'l*, pg. 2819
FUJIAN ZHENYUN PLASTICS INDUSTRY CO., LTD.; *Int'l*, pg. 2820
GENOVA-NEVADA—See Genova Products, Inc.; *U.S. Private*, pg. 1673
GENOVA-PENNSYLVANIA, INC.—See Genova Products, Inc.; *U.S. Private*, pg. 1673
GENOVA PRODUCTS, INC. - GENOVA MINNESOTA FACTORY—See Genova Products, Inc.; *U.S. Private*, pg. 1673
GENOVA PRODUCTS, INC. - GENOVA NEVADA FACTORY—See Genova Products, Inc.; *U.S. Private*, pg. 1673
GENOVA PRODUCTS, INC. - RENSSELAER PLASTICS FACTORY—See Genova Products, Inc.; *U.S. Private*, pg. 1673
GEORGE FISCHER SLOANE, INC.—See Georg Fischer AG; *Int'l*, pg. 2936
GEORG FISCHER AB—See Georg Fischer AG; *Int'l*, pg. 2935
GEORG FISCHER A.S.—See Georg Fischer AG; *Int'l*, pg. 2935
GEORG FISCHER CENTRAL PLASTICS SUDAMERICA SRL—See Georg Fischer AG; *Int'l*, pg. 2936
GEORG FISCHER DEKA GMBH—See Georg Fischer AG; *Int'l*, pg. 2935
GEORG FISCHER FLUORPOLYMER PRODUCTS GMBH—See Georg Fischer AG; *Int'l*, pg. 2935
GEORG FISCHER GMBH—See Georg Fischer AG; *Int'l*, pg. 2936
GEORG FISCHER (GREAT BRITAIN) LTD.—See Georg Fischer AG; *Int'l*, pg. 2935
GEORG FISCHER HARVEL LLC - BAKERSFIELD PLANT—See Georg Fischer AG; *Int'l*, pg. 2936
GEORG FISCHER HARVEL LLC—See Georg Fischer AG; *Int'l*, pg. 2936
GEORG FISCHER KOREA CO. LTD—See Georg Fischer AG; *Int'l*, pg. 2936
GEORG FISCHER KUNSTSTOFFARMATUREN AG—See Georg Fischer AG; *Int'l*, pg. 2936
GEORG FISCHER LLC—See Georg Fischer AG; *Int'l*, pg. 2936
GEORG FISCHER LTD.—See Georg Fischer AG; *Int'l*, pg. 2936
GEORG FISCHER NV-SA—See Georg Fischer AG; *Int'l*, pg. 2936
GEORG FISCHER OMICRON SRL—See Georg Fischer AG; *Int'l*, pg. 2936
GEORG FISCHER PFCI SRL—See Georg Fischer AG; *Int'l*, pg. 2936
GEORG FISCHER PIPING SYSTEMS LTD.—See Georg Fischer AG; *Int'l*, pg. 2936
GEORG FISCHER PTY. LTD.—See Georg Fischer AG; *Int'l*, pg. 2936
GEORG FISCHER PTY. LTD.—See Georg Fischer AG; *Int'l*, pg. 2936
GEORG FISCHER ROHRLEITUNGSSYSTEMS GMBH—See Georg Fischer AG; *Int'l*, pg. 2937
GEORG FISCHER SALES LTD—See Georg Fischer AG; *Int'l*, pg. 2937
GEORG FISCHER, S.A.—See Georg Fischer AG; *Int'l*, pg. 2937
GEORG FISCHER S.P.A.—See Georg Fischer AG; *Int'l*, pg. 2937
GEORG FISCHER TRENTON LTD.—See Georg Fischer AG; *Int'l*, pg. 2937
GEORGIA PIPE COMPANY—See Clayton, Dubilier & Rice, LLC; *U.S. Private*, pg. 919
GOLAN PLASTIC PRODUCTS LTD.; *Int'l*, pg. 3023
GOODY SCIENCE & TECHNOLOGY CO., LTD.; *Int'l*, pg. 3042
GPT HOUSTON—See Enpro Inc.; *U.S. Public*, pg. 774
GROUPE ELYDAN; *Int'l*, pg. 3102
GUANGDONG XIONGSU TECHNOLOGY GROUP CO., LTD.; *Int'l*, pg. 3162
GWE POL-BUD SP.Z.O.O—See BAUER Aktiengesellschaft; *Int'l*, pg. 893
HAMILTON KENT INC—See Aliaxis S.A./N.V.; *Int'l*, pg. 324
HANWEI ENERGY SERVICES CORP.; *Int'l*, pg. 3264
HANWHA CHEMICAL (THAILAND) CO., LTD.—See Hanwha Group; *Int'l*, pg. 3265
HATTERSLY NEWMAN HENDER LTD.—See Crane NXT, Co.; *U.S. Public*, pg. 591
HEPWORTH PME LLC; *Int'l*, pg. 3356
HERITAGE PLASTICS, INC.—See Clayton, Dubilier & Rice, LLC; *U.S. Private*, pg. 919
HERITAGE PLASTICS, INC. - TAMPA—See Clayton, Dubilier & Rice, LLC; *U.S. Private*, pg. 919
HOA SEN PLASTICS JOINT STOCK COMPANY—See Hoa Sen Group; *Int'l*, pg. 3436
IDEAL PIPE—See Advanced Drainage Systems, Inc.; *U.S. Public*, pg. 46
IHARA SCIENCE CORPORATION - GIFU PLANT—See IHARA SCIENCE CORPORATION; *Int'l*, pg. 3603
IHARA SCIENCE CORPORATION - SHIZUOKA PLANT—See IHARA SCIENCE CORPORATION; *Int'l*, pg. 3603
INNOGE PE INDUSTRIES S.A.M.—See Aliaxis S.A./N.V.; *Int'l*, pg. 324
INNOVATIVE COMPONENTS, INC.—See Essentra plc; *Int'l*, pg. 2511
INOUTIC D.O.O.—See Deceuninck NV; *Int'l*, pg. 2000
INTERNATIONAL PRECISION COMPONENTS CORPORATION; *U.S. Private*, pg. 2119
IPEX BRANDING INC—See Aliaxis S.A./N.V.; *Int'l*, pg. 324
IPEX ELECTRICAL INC—See Aliaxis S.A./N.V.; *Int'l*, pg. 325
IPEX, INC.—See Aliaxis S.A./N.V.; *Int'l*, pg. 324
IPEX MANAGEMENT INC—See Aliaxis S.A./N.V.; *Int'l*, pg. 325
IPEX USA MANUFACTURING/DISTRIBUTION—See Aliaxis S.A./N.V.; *Int'l*, pg. 324
KENWAY CORPORATION—See Hill & Smith PLC; *Int'l*, pg. 3391
KEY PLASTICS PTY. LTD.—See Fletcher Building Limited; *Int'l*, pg. 2700
KING PLASTICS, INC.; *U.S. Private*, pg. 2310
KNET CO. LTD.—See Hexatronic Group AB; *Int'l*, pg. 3371
KZ HANDELS AB—See Addtech AB; *Int'l*, pg. 134
L.F. MANUFACTURING INC.; *U.S. Private*, pg. 2365
LIANYUNGANG ZHONGFU LIANZHONG COMPOSITES GROUP CO., LTD.—See China National Building Material Group Co., Ltd.; *Int'l*, pg. 1525
LUNDGRENS SVERIGE AB—See Beijer Alma AB; *Int'l*, pg. 943
MERCURY PLASTICS, INC.; *U.S. Private*, pg. 2671
MEXICHEM COSTA RICA, S.A.—See Grupo Empresarial Kaluz S.A. de C.V.; *Int'l*, pg. 3127
MIDLAND TECHNOLOGIES, INC.—See Innovance, Inc.; *U.S. Private*, pg. 2081
MPC SP.Z.O.O.—See Bharti Enterprises Limited; *Int'l*, pg. 1012
MULTI FITTINGS CORPORATION—See Aliaxis S.A./N.V.; *Int'l*, pg. 325
NEBRASKA PLASTICS, INC.; *U.S. Private*, pg. 2878
NICOLL INDUSTRIA PLASTICA LTDA—See Aliaxis S.A./N.V.; *Int'l*, pg. 325
NICOLL PERU S.A.—See Aliaxis S.A./N.V.; *Int'l*, pg. 325
NICOLL S.A.—See Aliaxis S.A./N.V.; *Int'l*, pg. 325
NICOLL URUGUAY S.A.—See Aliaxis S.A./N.V.; *Int'l*, pg. 325
NIPPON SWAGELOK FST INC.—See Swagelok Company; *U.S. Private*, pg. 3889
NORDISK WAVIN A/S—See Bharti Enterprises Limited; *Int'l*, pg. 1012
NORMANDY INDUSTRIES INC.; *U.S. Private*, pg. 2938
NORSK WAVIN A/S—See Bharti Enterprises Limited; *Int'l*, pg. 1012
NORTH AMERICAN PIPE CORPORATION—See Westlake Corporation; *U.S. Public*, pg. 2360
NORTHERN PIPE PRODUCT INC.—See Otter Tail Corporation; *U.S. Public*, pg. 1624
NOV FIBER GLASS SYSTEMS—See NOV, Inc.; *U.S. Public*, pg. 1544
NWPC DE SLRC, S DE RL DE CV—See Northwest Pipe Company; *U.S. Public*, pg. 1542
OCEANSIDE GLASSTILE COMPANY; *U.S. Private*, pg. 2990
ORION ENTERPRISES, INC.—See Watts Water Technologies, Inc.; *U.S. Public*, pg. 2337
ORION FITTINGS INC.—See Watts Water Technologies, Inc.; *U.S. Public*, pg. 2337
OSBURN ASSOCIATES INC.; *U.S. Private*, pg. 3046
PETROFLEX NORTH AMERICA, LTD.; *U.S. Private*, pg. 3162
PHILMAC PTY. LTD.—See Aliaxis S.A./N.V.; *Int'l*, pg. 325
POL-BUD TECHNOLOGIA WODY SP.Z.O.O—See BAUER Aktiengesellschaft; *Int'l*, pg. 893
POLYPIPE FRANCE SAS—See Groupe ELYDAN; *Int'l*, pg. 3102
POLYPIPE GULF FZ LLC—See Genuit Group plc; *Int'l*, pg. 2930
POLYPIPE GULF FZ LLC—See Genuit Group plc; *Int'l*, pg. 2930
POLYPIPE ITALIA S.R.L.—See Genuit Group plc; *Int'l*, pg. 2930
POLYPIPE LIMITED - POLYPIPE CIVILS DIVISION—See Genuit Group plc; *Int'l*, pg. 2930
POLYPIPE LIMITED - POLYPIPE TDI DIVISION—See Genuit Group plc; *Int'l*, pg. 2930
POLYPIPE LIMITED—See Genuit Group plc; *Int'l*, pg. 2930
POLYPIPE, LLC—See Grupo Empresarial Kaluz S.A. de C.V.; *Int'l*, pg. 3127
PRINSCO INC.; *U.S. Private*, pg. 3265
REISS CORPORATION INC.; *U.S. Private*, pg. 3392
REP. OFFICE DECEUNINCK NV—See Deceuninck NV; *Int'l*, pg. 2000
RS LINING SYSTEMS, LLC—See The Toro Company; *U.S. Public*, pg. 2135
RX PLASTICS LIMITED—See Aliaxis S.A./N.V.; *Int'l*, pg. 325
SAGAMI YOKI CO., LTD.—See Dai Nippon Printing Co., Ltd.; *Int'l*, pg. 1916
SHALE-INLAND HOLDINGS LLC; *U.S. Private*, pg. 3623
THE SHAW GROUP INC.; *U.S. Private*, pg. 4117
SHURJOINT PIPING PRODUCTS, INC.—See Aalberts N.V.; *Int'l*, pg. 35
SILVER-LINE PLASTICS CORP.; *U.S. Private*, pg. 3662
SMITH FIBERCAST—See NOV, Inc.; *U.S. Public*, pg. 1544
SOUTHERN PIPE, INC.; *U.S. Private*, pg. 3734
SPECIALTY PLASTICS, INC.—See Future Pipe Industries Group Ltd.; *Int'l*, pg. 2857
SWISSTEX INC.—See Bystronic AG; *Int'l*, pg. 1236
TECHNIPAQ, INC.; *U.S. Private*, pg. 3954
THOMSON PLASTICS, INC.; *U.S. Private*, pg. 4162
TIGRE-ADS COLOMBIA LIMITADA—See Advanced Drainage Systems, Inc.; *U.S. Public*, pg. 46
TIGRE-ADS PERU S.A.C.—See Advanced Drainage Systems, Inc.; *U.S. Public*, pg. 46
TOP-COMMENT RESOURCES COMPANY LIMITED—See Cleanaway Company Limited; *Int'l*, pg. 1654
TUBOS TIGRE-ADS DO BRASIL LIMITADA—See Advanced Drainage Systems, Inc.; *U.S. Public*, pg. 46
TUBOS Y PLASTICOS ADS CHILE LIMITADA—See Advanced Drainage Systems, Inc.; *U.S. Public*, pg. 46
TUBULAR & EQUIPMENT SERVICES, LLC; *U.S. Private*, pg. 4256
UTILITIES SUPPLY COMPANY—See F.W. Webb Company; *U.S. Private*, pg. 1457
VALUE PLASTICS, INC.—See Nordson Corporation; *U.S. Public*, pg. 1534
VASSALLO INTERNATIONAL GROUP, INC.; *U.S. Private*, pg. 4347
VICTAULIC COMPANY - VICTAULIC CONSTRUCTION PIPING SERVICES DIVISION—See Victaulic Company; *U.S. Private*, pg. 4377
VIKING JOHNSON LTD.—See Crane NXT, Co.; *U.S. Public*, pg. 591
VINIDEX PTY LTD.—See Aliaxis S.A./N.V.; *Int'l*, pg. 325
VINNOLIT LIMITED—See Westlake Corporation; *U.S. Public*, pg. 2360
VITAL PLASTICS, INC.—See Wolverine Capital Partners LLC; *U.S. Private*, pg. 4555
WASK LTD.—See Crane NXT, Co.; *U.S. Public*, pg. 591
WATTS WATER TECHNOLOGIES, INC.; *U.S. Public*, pg. 2337
WAVIN BALKAN D-O-O.—See Bharti Enterprises Limited; *Int'l*, pg. 1012
WAVIN DIENSTEN B.V.—See Bharti Enterprises Limited; *Int'l*, pg. 1012
WAVIN EKOPLASTIK S.R.O.—See Bharti Enterprises Limited; *Int'l*, pg. 1012
WAVIN HUNGARY KFT.—See Grupo Empresarial Kaluz S.A. de C.V.; *Int'l*, pg. 3128
WAVIN IRELAND LTD.—See Bharti Enterprises Limited; *Int'l*, pg. 1012
WAVIN N.V.—See Bharti Enterprises Limited; *Int'l*, pg. 1012
WAVIN PLASTICS LTD.—See Bharti Enterprises Limited; *Int'l*, pg. 1013
WAVIN PORTUGAL-PLASTICOS S.A.—See Bharti Enterprises Limited; *Int'l*, pg. 1013
WAVIN SLOVAKIA SPOL S.R.O.—See Bharti Enterprises Limited; *Int'l*, pg. 1013
WAVIN SWISSPIPE AG—See Bharti Enterprises Limited; *Int'l*, pg. 1013
WEFATHERM GMBH—See Aliaxis S.A./N.V.; *Int'l*, pg. 325
WELLSTREAM DO BRAZIL INDUSTRIA E SERVICOS LTDA—See General Electric Company; *U.S. Public*, pg. 920

326122 — PLASTICS PIPE AND P...

WELLSTREAM, INC.—See General Electric Company; *U.S. Public*, pg. 920
W FLYING PLASTICS, INC.; *U.S. Private*, pg. 4417
WIIK PUBLIC COMPANY LIMITED—See Georg Fischer AG; *Int'l*, pg. 2938
YAMAGATA-IHARA CORPORATION—See IHARA SCIENCE CORPORATION; *Int'l*, pg. 3603
ZHONGSHAN UNIVERSAL ENTERPRISES LTD—See Aliaxis S.A./N.V.; *Int'l*, pg. 325

326130 — LAMINATED PLASTICS PLATE, SHEET (EXCEPT PACKAGING), AND SHAPE MANUFACTURING

AICA ASIA LAMINATES HOLDING CO., LTD.—See AICA Kogyo Company, Limited; *Int'l*, pg. 228
AICA KOGYO CO., LTD.—See AICA Kogyo Company, Limited; *Int'l*, pg. 228
AICA LAMINATES INDIA PVT. LTD. - RUDRAPUR FACTORY—See AICA Kogyo Company, Limited; *Int'l*, pg. 228
AICA LAMINATES VIETNAM CO., LTD.—See AICA Kogyo Company, Limited; *Int'l*, pg. 228
AICA SINGAPORE PTE. LTD.—See AICA Kogyo Company, Limited; *Int'l*, pg. 228
ALCORE, INC.—See M.C. Gill Corporation; *U.S. Private*, pg. 2528
ALFA ICA (INDIA) LTD.; *Int'l*, pg. 308
ALTIUM HEALTHCARE—See Loews Corporation; *U.S. Public*, pg. 1339
ALTUGLAS INTERNATIONAL S.A.S.—See Arkema S.A.; *Int'l*, pg. 568
ALTUGLAS INTERNATIONAL—See Arkema S.A.; *Int'l*, pg. 568
ALTUGLAS INTERNATIONAL—See Arkema S.A.; *Int'l*, pg. 568
ALTUGLAS INTERNATIONAL—See Arkema S.A.; *Int'l*, pg. 568
AMBITION MICA LIMITED; *Int'l*, pg. 415
AMERICAN PACKAGING CORPORATION - EXTRUSION DIVISION—See American Packaging Corporation; *U.S. Private*, pg. 242
AMERISE BIOSCIENCES LTD; *Int'l*, pg. 423
APPLIED COMPOSITES AB—See GKN plc; *Int'l*, pg. 2986
ARBORITE; *Int'l*, pg. 539
AVERY DENNISON JAPAN MATERIALS COMPANY LTD.—See Avery Dennison Corporation; *U.S. Public*, pg. 243
AVERY DENNISON (KENYA) PRIVATE LIMITED—See Avery Dennison Corporation; *U.S. Public*, pg. 243
BECKMANN CONVERTING, INC.; *U.S. Private*, pg. 511
BEWI ASA; *Int'l*, pg. 1004
BIXBY INTERNATIONAL CORP.; *U.S. Private*, pg. 567
BLOOM DEKOR LIMITED; *Int'l*, pg. 1065
THE BOXBORO GROUP—See Bischof + Klein GmbH & Co. KG; *Int'l*, pg. 1049
CLAYENS NP GROUP—See OEP Capital Advisors, L.P.; *U.S. Private*, pg. 2998
CLPG PACKAGING INDUSTRIES SDN. BHD.; *Int'l*, pg. 1663
CROWN OPERATIONS INTERNATIONAL, LTD.—See Eastman Chemical Company; *U.S. Public*, pg. 706
CURRENT, INC.; *U.S. Private*, pg. 1125
DAIOS PLASTICS S.A; *Int'l*, pg. 1940
DECO-MICA LIMITED - RAJPUR FACTORY—See DECO-MICA LIMITED; *Int'l*, pg. 2001
DECO-MICA LIMITED; *Int'l*, pg. 2001
EIS FABRICO—See Audax Group, Limited Partnership; *U.S. Private*, pg. 387
ENSINGER GMBH; *Int'l*, pg. 2447
ENSINGER-HYDE—See Ensinger GmbH; *Int'l*, pg. 2448
ENSINGER, INC.—See Ensinger GmbH; *Int'l*, pg. 2448
EPUREX FILMS GMBH & CO.KG—See Bayer Aktiengesellschaft; *Int'l*, pg. 907
FIBERLINE COMPOSITES A/S—See Gurit Holding AG; *Int'l*, pg. 3187
FIBER-TECH INDUSTRIES, INC.—See Celstar Group Inc.; *U.S. Private*, pg. 808
FORMICA ASIA LTD.—See HAL Trust N.V.; *Int'l*, pg. 3223
FORMICA CORPORATION—See HAL Trust N.V.; *Int'l*, pg. 3223
FORMICA LTD.—See HAL Trust N.V.; *Int'l*, pg. 3223
FORMICA S.A.—See HAL Trust N.V.; *Int'l*, pg. 3223
FORMICA SOCIETE ANONYME—See HAL Trust N.V.; *Int'l*, pg. 3223
FORMICA SWITZERLAND AG—See HAL Trust N.V.; *Int'l*, pg. 3223
FORMICA TAIWAN—See HAL Trust N.V.; *Int'l*, pg. 3223
FRESH-PAK CORP—See ZL Star Inc.; *U.S. Private*, pg. 4606
GREENLAM ASIA PACIFIC PTE. LTD.—See Greenply Industries Limited; *Int'l*, pg. 3076
GREENLAM ASIA PACIFIC (THAILAND) CO LTD.—See Greenply Industries Limited; *Int'l*, pg. 3076
GURIT (KASSEL) GMBH—See Gurit Holding AG; *Int'l*, pg. 3187
HANWHA AZDEL, INC.—See Hanwha Group; *Int'l*, pg. 3265
HARTSON-KENNEDY CABINET TOP CO. INC. - LUKE AFB—See Hartson-Kennedy Cabinet Top Co. Inc.; *U.S. Private*, pg. 1874
HARTSON-KENNEDY CABINET TOP CO. INC. - MACON—See Hartson-Kennedy Cabinet Top Co. Inc.; *U.S. Private*, pg. 1874
HARTSON-KENNEDY CABINET TOP CO. INC.; *U.S. Private*, pg. 1874
HICKS & OTIS PRINTS INC.; *U.S. Private*, pg. 1934
JIANGYIN LITAI DECORATIVE MATERIALS CO., LTD.—See China Haida Ltd.; *Int'l*, pg. 1506
LEE CONTAINER CORPORATION, INC.—See Greif Inc.; *U.S. Public*, pg. 968
LEHIGH VALLEY PLASTICS INC.; *U.S. Private*, pg. 2419
MAICA LAMINATES SDN. BHD.—See AICA Kogyo Company, Limited; *Int'l*, pg. 229
MAQUILADORA GENERAL DE MATAMOROS S.A. DE C.V.—See Arkema S.A.; *Int'l*, pg. 568
MESA FULLY FORMED INC.; *U.S. Private*, pg. 2677
NALGE NUNC INTERNATIONAL CORPORATION—See Thermo Fisher Scientific Inc.; *U.S. Public*, pg. 2149
NAM HING INDUSTRIAL LAMINATE LIMITED—See China Environmental Energy Investment Limited; *Int'l*, pg. 1500
NELCO PRODUCTS, INC.—See AGC Inc.; *Int'l*, pg. 204
NEW ENGLAND LAMINATES CO., INC.—See AGC Inc.; *Int'l*, pg. 204
NUDO PRODUCTS INC.—See RFE Investment Partners; *U.S. Private*, pg. 3419
PARKER HANNIFIN PARFLEX DIV., RAVENNA PLANT—See Parker Hannifin Corporation; *U.S. Public*, pg. 1646
PERGO AB—See Mohawk Industries, Inc.; *U.S. Public*, pg. 1458
PILGRIM PLASTIC PRODUCTS COMPANY; *U.S. Private*, pg. 3180
PLASKOLITE, LLC—See The Pritzker Group - Chicago, LLC; *U.S. Private*, pg. 4099
PLITEK, LLC.; *U.S. Private*, pg. 3214
PT GREENLAM INDO PACIFIC—See Greenlam Industries Limited; *Int'l*, pg. 3075
RCCT TECHNOLOGY CO., LTD.—See ChangChun Group; *Int'l*, pg. 1442
REEF INDUSTRIES INCORPORATED; *U.S. Private*, pg. 3383
REMCON PLASTICS INCORPORATED; *U.S. Private*, pg. 3396
ROWMARK LLC—See Windjammer Capital Investors, LLC; *U.S. Private*, pg. 4538
SABERT CORPORATION; *U.S. Private*, pg. 3520
SCHNELLER FLORIDA—See TransDigm Group Incorporated; *U.S. Public*, pg. 2183
SCHNELLER LLC—See TransDigm Group Incorporated; *U.S. Public*, pg. 2183
SOIS MENDINNI INDUSTRIAL TECHNOLOGY (SHANGHAI) CO., LTD.—See AICA Kogyo Company, Limited; *Int'l*, pg. 229
SPARTECH LLC—See The Jordan Company, L.P.; *U.S. Private*, pg. 4062
SPAULDING COMPOSITES, INC.; *U.S. Private*, pg. 3747
SUNRISE FIBERGLASS LLC.—See North Central Equity LLC; *U.S. Private*, pg. 2943
TOTAL PLASTICS, INC. - GRAND RAPIDS—See Prophet Equity L.P.; *U.S. Private*, pg. 3286
TOTAL PLASTICS, INC.—See Prophet Equity L.P.; *U.S. Private*, pg. 3286
VYCOM PLASTICS—See The AZEK Company Inc.; *U.S. Public*, pg. 2035
WIN PLASTIC EXTRUSIONS, LLC—See ShoreView Industries, LLC; *U.S. Private*, pg. 3642
ZHONGSHAN NAM HING INSULATING MATERIAL LIMITED—See China Environmental Energy Investment Limited; *Int'l*, pg. 1500

326140 — POLYSTYRENE FOAM PRODUCT MANUFACTURING

ACH FOAM TECHNOLOGIES, LLC - FOND DULAC—See Atlas Roofing Corp.; *U.S. Private*, pg. 380
ACH FOAM TECHNOLOGIES, LLC - GEORGIA PLANT—See Atlas Roofing Corp.; *U.S. Private*, pg. 380
ACH FOAM TECHNOLOGIES, LLC - NEVADA PLANT—See Atlas Roofing Corp.; *U.S. Private*, pg. 380
ACH FOAM TECHNOLOGIES, LLC—See Atlas Roofing Corp.; *U.S. Private*, pg. 380
ACH FOAM TECHNOLOGIES, LLC—See Atlas Roofing Corp.; *U.S. Private*, pg. 380
ACH FOAM TECHNOLOGIES, LLC—See Atlas Roofing Corp.; *U.S. Private*, pg. 380
ACH FOAM TECHNOLOGIES, LLC - UTAH PLANT—See Atlas Roofing Corp.; *U.S. Private*, pg. 380
AL-BAGHLI SPONGE MANUFACTURING COMPANY; *Int'l*, pg. 284
ALLEN-BECK INDUSTRIES INC.—See Hickory Springs Manufacturing Company; *U.S. Private*, pg. 1933
ALLIED AEROFOAM PRODUCTS, LLC; *U.S. Private*, pg. 185
AL MUSAHA AL MUSHTARAKA CO.—See Fouad Alghanim & Sons Group of Companies; *Int'l*, pg. 2753
ALP GROUP; *Int'l*, pg. 365
ALP OVERSEAS PVT. LTD.—See ALP Group; *Int'l*, pg. 365
AMCOR RIGID PLASTICS DE VENEZUELA S.A.—See Amcor plc; *Int'l*, pg. 417
ARVIND INTERNATIONAL LTD.; *Int'l*, pg. 587
ASAHI KASEI CONSTRUCTION MATERIALS—See Asahi Kasei Corporation; *Int'l*, pg. 595
AUTINS GROUP PLC; *Int'l*, pg. 724
BASF PERFORMANCE POLYMERS GMBH—See BASF SE; *Int'l*, pg. 880
BASF POLIURETAN HUNGARIA KFT.—See BASF SE; *Int'l*, pg. 883
BASF POLYURETHANES (MALAYSIA) SDN. BHD.—See BASF SE; *Int'l*, pg. 878
BAY FABRICATION INC.—See Bay Industries Inc.; *U.S. Private*, pg. 493
BAY INDUSTRIES INC. - FABRICATED INSULATION DIVISION—See Bay Industries Inc.; *U.S. Private*, pg. 493
BAY INSULATION OF ILLINOIS INC.—See Bay Industries Inc.; *U.S. Private*, pg. 493
BC CHEMICAL CO., LTD.—See Grand Pacific Petrochemical Corporation; *Int'l*, pg. 3055
BIFIRE S.P.A.; *Int'l*, pg. 1020
CASCADES PLASTICS INC.—See Cascades Inc.; *Int'l*, pg. 1350
CELLOFOAM NORTH AMERICA INC.; *U.S. Private*, pg. 807
CEMEX SPECIALIST PRODUCTS—See CEMEX, S.A.B. de C.V.; *Int'l*, pg. 1399
CHONGQING BROADWAY FOAM APPLICATIONS & TOTAL PACKAGING CO., LTD.—See Platinum Equity, LLC; *U.S. Private*, pg. 3201
COVESTRO A/S - POLYURETHANES—See Bayer Aktiengesellschaft; *Int'l*, pg. 907
CTA ACOUSTICS, INC. - CORBIN MANUFACTURING FACILITY—See Cerberus Capital Management, L.P.; *U.S. Private*, pg. 837
CTA ACOUSTICS, INC.—See Cerberus Capital Management, L.P.; *U.S. Private*, pg. 837
CUSTOM CUTLERY, INC.—See PMC Capital Partners, LLC; *U.S. Private*, pg. 3217
DAICEL NOVAFOAM LTD.—See Daicel Corporation; *Int'l*, pg. 1973
DART CONTAINER CORPORATION; *U.S. Private*, pg. 1160
DIRECT PACK, INC.—See PMC Capital Partners, LLC; *U.S. Private*, pg. 3217
EASTERN INSULATION COMPANY—See A.H. Algosaibi & Bros.; *Int'l*, pg. 24
EBR SYSTEMS, INC.; *U.S. Private*, pg. 1324
EFP CORPORATION—See J.B. Poindexter & Co., Inc.; *U.S. Private*, pg. 2158
EUROFOAM BOHEMIA S.R.O.—See Greiner Holding AG; *Int'l*, pg. 3078
EUROFOAM GDANSK SP. Z O.O.—See Greiner Holding AG; *Int'l*, pg. 3078
EUROFOAM POLSKA SP. Z O.O.—See Greiner Holding AG; *Int'l*, pg. 3078
EUROFOAM POZNAN SP. Z O.O.—See Greiner Holding AG; *Int'l*, pg. 3078
FAGERDALA SINGAPORE PTE. LTD.—See Sealed Air Corporation; *U.S. Public*, pg. 1853
FLOWCARDIA, INC.—See Becton, Dickinson & Company; *U.S. Public*, pg. 291
FOAM FABRICATORS QUERETARO, S. DE R.L. DE C.V.—See Compass Diversified Holdings; *U.S. Public*, pg. 560
FOAMTASTIC PRODUCTS, INC.—See Berkshire Hathaway Inc.; *U.S. Public*, pg. 312
FORMAN MANUFACTURING LIMITED—See Fletcher Building Limited; *Int'l*, pg. 2700
FPCO FUKUYAMA CO.—See FP Corporation; *Int'l*, pg. 2756
FPCO YAMAGATA, LTD.—See FP Corporation; *Int'l*, pg. 2756
FRINA MOUSSE FRANCE S.A.R.L.—See Bystronic AG; *Int'l*, pg. 1236
FRITZ NAUER AG—See Bystronic AG; *Int'l*, pg. 1236
GPPC CHEMICAL CO., LTD.—See Grand Pacific Petrochemical Corporation; *Int'l*, pg. 3055
GREINER PURTEC GMBH—See Greiner Holding AG; *Int'l*, pg. 3079
GUALA CLOSURES TECHNOLOGIA UKRAINE LLC—See Guala Closures S.p.A.; *Int'l*, pg. 3152
GUSMER-EUROPE—See Graco, Inc.; *U.S. Public*, pg. 953
HANGZHOU TODAYTEC DIGITAL CO., LTD.; *Int'l*, pg. 3251
HUHTAMAKI CONSUMER PACKAGING—See Huhtamaki Oyj; *Int'l*, pg. 3526
HUNTSMAN BUILDING SOLUTIONS (CENTRAL EUROPE) A.S.—See Huntsman Corporation; *U.S. Public*, pg. 1072
HUNTSMAN BUILDING SOLUTIONS (EUROPE) BV—See Huntsman Corporation; *U.S. Public*, pg. 1072
ICYNENE, INC.—See Huntsman Corporation; *U.S. Public*, pg. 1075
IGLOO PRODUCTS CORPORATION—See Dometic Group AB; *Int'l*, pg. 2160
INSULFOAM, LLC—See Carlisle Companies Incorporated; *U.S. Public*, pg. 436

N.A.I.C.S. INDEX

326150 — URETHANE AND OTHER ...

INSULSPAN, LLC - DELTA PLANT—See The Riverside Company; *U.S. Private*, pg. 4109
ISO PANELS, INC.—See Ergon, Inc.; *U.S. Private*, pg. 1418
KAPLAMIN AMBALAJ SANAYI VE TICARET A.S.—See Cukurova Holding A.S.; *Int'l*, pg. 1876
KEVOTHERMAL LLC—See Sealed Air Corporation; *U.S. Public*, pg. 1853
KNAUF INDUSTRIES EST—See Gebr. Knauf KG; *Int'l*, pg. 2907
LIFOAM INDUSTRIES, LLC—See Newell Brands Inc.; *U.S. Public*, pg. 1514
MICROTHERM ENGINEERED SOLUTIONS N.V.—See Etex SA/NV; *Int'l*, pg. 2522
NEXKEMIA PETROCHEMICALS INC.—See Integreon Global; *U.S. Private*, pg. 2102
NIPPON MICROTHERM CO. LTD.—See Etex SA/NV; *Int'l*, pg. 2522
PACOR, INC. - FABRICATING DIVISION—See Pacor, Inc.; *U.S. Private*, pg. 3073
PEAK INTERNATIONAL, INC.—See Daewon Semiconductor Packaging Industrial Corporation; *Int'l*, pg. 1910
PHOENIX MANUFACTURING SERVICES PTY. LTD.—See Dart Container Corporation; *U.S. Private*, pg. 1160
PLYMOUTH FOAM, INC. - MINNESOTA—See Plymouth Foam Incorporated; *U.S. Private*, pg. 3216
POLYAIR INTER PACK, ATLANTA—See Clearlake Capital Group, L.P.; *U.S. Private*, pg. 935
POLYAIR INTER PACK, BARDSTOWN—See Clearlake Capital Group, L.P.; *U.S. Private*, pg. 935
POLYAIR INTER PACK, CHICAGO—See Clearlake Capital Group, L.P.; *U.S. Private*, pg. 935
POLYAIR INTER PACK, CORONA—See Clearlake Capital Group, L.P.; *U.S. Private*, pg. 935
POLYAIR INTER PACK INC.—See Clearlake Capital Group, L.P.; *U.S. Private*, pg. 935
POLYAIR INTER PACK, NEW JERSEY—See Clearlake Capital Group, L.P.; *U.S. Private*, pg. 935
POLYFORM S.R.O.—See Hirsch Servo AG; *Int'l*, pg. 3406
POLYMER COMPOSITE ASIA (SHANGHAI) CO. LTD—See Hexagon Holdings Berhad; *Int'l*, pg. 3406
POLYSTAR ASIA PRIVATE LTD.—See Elisa Corporation; *Int'l*, pg. 2361
POLYSTAR INSTRUMENTS INC.—See Elisa Corporation; *Int'l*, pg. 2361
POLYSTAR OSIX AB—See Elisa Corporation; *Int'l*, pg. 2361
POLYSTAR RYSSLAND LLC—See Elisa Corporation; *Int'l*, pg. 2361
PS JAPAN CORP.—See Asahi Kasei Corporation; *Int'l*, pg. 596
RADVA CORPORATION—See Wynnchurch Capital, L.P.; *U.S. Private*, pg. 4577
RICHMOND DENTAL—See Barnhardt Manufacturing Company; *U.S. Private*, pg. 478
SAINT-GOBAIN ISOVER—See Compagnie de Saint-Gobain SA; *Int'l*, pg. 1726
SAINT-GOBAIN PERFORMANCE PLASTICS BRASIL—See Compagnie de Saint-Gobain SA; *Int'l*, pg. 1732
SCHMITZ REINIGUNGSKUGELN GMBH—See BGR Energy Systems Limited; *Int'l*, pg. 1009
SEALED AIR B.V.—See Sealed Air Corporation; *U.S. Public*, pg. 1854
SEALED AIR CORPORATION - DANBURY—See Sealed Air Corporation; *U.S. Public*, pg. 1854
SEALED AIR LIMITED—See Sealed Air Corporation; *U.S. Public*, pg. 1854
SEALED AIR S.L.—See Sealed Air Corporation; *U.S. Public*, pg. 1855
SEALED AIR SVENSKA A.B.—See Sealed Air Corporation; *U.S. Public*, pg. 1855
SHANGHAI BROADWAY PACKAGING & INSULATION MATERIALS CO., LTD.—See Platinum Equity, LLC; *U.S. Private*, pg. 3201
SHENZHEN BROADWAY TOTAL PACKAGING SOLUTION CO., LTD.—See Platinum Equity, LLC; *U.S. Private*, pg. 3201
STYROPEK DO BRASIL LTD.—See ALFA, S.A.B. de C.V.; *Int'l*, pg. 314
STYROPEK MEXICO, S. A. DE C. V.—See ALFA, S.A.B. de C.V.; *Int'l*, pg. 314
STYROPEK S. A.—See ALFA, S.A.B. de C.V.; *Int'l*, pg. 314
SYNTHANE-TAYLOR (CANADA) LTD. - STE. THERESE FACILITY—See Dunes Point Capital, LLC; *U.S. Private*, pg. 1289
THERMOZELL ENTWICKLUNGS- UND VERTRIEBS GMBH—See Hirsch Servo AG; *Int'l*, pg. 3406
WM T. BURNETT & CO. - FOAM DIVISION—See Wm T. Burnett & Co.; *U.S. Private*, pg. 4552
YALOVA AMBALAJ SANAYI VE TICARET A.S.—See Cukurova Holding A.S.; *Int'l*, pg. 1876

326150 — URETHANE AND OTHER FOAM PRODUCT (EXCEPT POLYSTYRENE) MANUFACTURING

ADVANCED MEDICAL SOLUTIONS B.V.—See Advanced Medical Solutions Group plc; *Int'l*, pg. 161
ADVANCE PACKAGING LIMITED—See Alco Holdings Limited; *Int'l*, pg. 301
AL-KHAIR GADOON LIMITED; *Int'l*, pg. 286
ALTIUM PACKAGING LP—See Loews Corporation; *U.S. Public*, pg. 1339
ALTOR SOLUTIONS INC.—See Compass Diversified Holdings; *U.S. Public*, pg. 559
AMERICAN EXCELSIOR COMPANY; *U.S. Private*, pg. 232
AMERICAN POLY-FOAM CO. LTD—See Future Foam, Inc.; *U.S. Private*, pg. 1626
ARMACELL GMBH—See Blackstone Inc.; *U.S. Public*, pg. 360
ATLAS EPS—See Atlas Roofing Corp.; *U.S. Private*, pg. 380
ATLAS ROOFING CORP.; *U.S. Private*, pg. 380
AURORA PLASTICS, LLC—See Nautic Partners, LLC; *U.S. Private*, pg. 2868
BANDO IBERICA S.A.—See Bando Chemical Industries, Ltd.; *Int'l*, pg. 830
BANDO (SINGAPORE) PTE. LTD.—See Bando Chemical Industries, Ltd.; *Int'l*, pg. 830
BARNHARDT MANUFACTURING COMPANY; *U.S. Private*, pg. 477
BASF CORP. - WYANDOTTE PLANT—See BASF SE; *Int'l*, pg. 876
BASF FOAM ENTERPRISES—See BASF SE; *Int'l*, pg. 876
BASF INOAC POLYURETHANES LTD.—See BASF SE; *Int'l*, pg. 881
BASF POLIURETANY POLSKA SP. Z O.O.—See BASF SE; *Int'l*, pg. 881
BASF POLYURETHANES FRANCE S.A.S.—See BASF SE; *Int'l*, pg. 881
BASF POLYURETHANES GMBH—See BASF SE; *Int'l*, pg. 881
BASF POLYURETHANES PARS (PRIVATE JOINT STOCK) COMPANY—See BASF SE; *Int'l*, pg. 881
BASF POLYURETHANES U.K. LTD.—See BASF SE; *Int'l*, pg. 881
BRECO ANTRIEBSTECHNIK BREHER GMBH & CO. KG; *Int'l*, pg. 1144
BREMEN CORPORATION—See Industrial Opportunity Partners, LLC; *U.S. Private*, pg. 2067
BROOKDALE PLASTICS, INC.—See Placon Corporation; *U.S. Private*, pg. 3194
CAROLINA ABSORBENT COTTON COMPANY—See Barnhardt Manufacturing Company; *U.S. Private*, pg. 477
CARPENTER CO.; *U.S. Private*, pg. 770
CENTURY SERVICE AFFILIATES, INC.; *U.S. Private*, pg. 834
CFM CONSOLIDATED, INC.—See RPM International Inc.; *U.S. Public*, pg. 1816
CFOAM LIMITED; *Int'l*, pg. 1430
CHINA TECHNO FOAM CO LTD—See Gurit Holding AG; *Int'l*, pg. 3187
CHINYANG POLY URETHANE CO LTD; *Int'l*, pg. 1572
COLOMBIN BEL, S.A. DE C.V. - SANTA CATARINA PLANT—See ALFA, S.A.B. de C.V.; *Int'l*, pg. 313
COLOMBIN BEL, S.A. DE C.V.—See ALFA, S.A.B. de C.V.; *Int'l*, pg. 313
COLOMBIN BEL, S.A. DE C.V. - TLALNEPANTLA PLANT—See ALFA, S.A.B. de C.V.; *Int'l*, pg. 313
CONCEPT INDUSTRIES INC; *U.S. Private*, pg. 1008
CREATIVE FOAM CORPORATION—See Industrial Opportunity Partners, LLC; *U.S. Private*, pg. 2067
CREST-FOAM CORP.—See Leggett & Platt, Incorporated; *U.S. Public*, pg. 1301
CREST FOAM INDUSTRIES, INC.—See TPG Capital, L.P.; *U.S. Public*, pg. 2175
CRYOVAC, INC.—See Sealed Air Corporation; *U.S. Public*, pg. 1852
CUMING CORPORATION—See First Reserve Management, L.P.; *U.S. Private*, pg. 1525
CUMING INSULATION CORP.—See First Reserve Management, L.P.; *U.S. Private*, pg. 1525
CUMING MICROWAVE CORPORATION—See PPG Industries, Inc.; *U.S. Public*, pg. 1707
DEMILEC INC.—See Huntsman Corporation; *U.S. Public*, pg. 1072
DEMILEC (USA) INC.—See Huntsman Corporation; *U.S. Public*, pg. 1072
DIVERSIFIED PLASTICS CORPORATION; *U.S. Private*, pg. 1243
THE DOW CHEMICAL COMPANY-MIDLAND—See Dow Inc.; *U.S. Public*, pg. 686
DOW ITALIA S.R.L.—See Dow Inc.; *U.S. Public*, pg. 685
DREW FOAM COMPANIES, INC.—See Wynnchurch Capital, L.P.; *U.S. Private*, pg. 4577
EARTH SCIENCE DIVISION—See American Excelsior Company; *U.S. Private*, pg. 232
ECS CABLE PROTECTION SP. Z O.O.—See Illinois Tool Works Inc.; *U.S. Public*, pg. 1103
ELASTOGRAN GMBH—See BASF SE; *Int'l*, pg. 883
ELITE FOAM, LLC—See Leggett & Platt, Incorporated; *U.S. Public*, pg. 1302
ERNST DIEGEL GMBH—See American Securities LLC; *U.S. Private*, pg. 252
EUROFOAM GMBH—See Greiner Holding AG; *Int'l*, pg. 3078

EUROFOAM HUNGARY KFT—See Greiner Holding AG; *Int'l*, pg. 3078
FAGERDALA (CHENGDU) PACKAGING CO., LTD.—See Sealed Air Corporation; *U.S. Public*, pg. 1853
FAGERDALA (CHONGQING) PACKAGING CO., LTD.—See Sealed Air Corporation; *U.S. Public*, pg. 1853
FAGERDALA (LEAMCHABUNG) LTD.—See Sealed Air Corporation; *U.S. Public*, pg. 1853
FAGERDALA MEXICO S.A. DE C.V.—See Sealed Air Corporation; *U.S. Public*, pg. 1853
FAGERDALA (SHANGHAI) POLYMER CO. LTD.—See Sealed Air Corporation; *U.S. Public*, pg. 1853
FAGERDALA (SUZHOU) PACKAGING CO., LTD.—See Sealed Air Corporation; *U.S. Public*, pg. 1853
FAGERDALA (THAILAND) LTD.—See Sealed Air Corporation; *U.S. Public*, pg. 1853
FEDERAL FOAM TECHNOLOGIES, INC. - COKATO DIVISION—See Federal International Inc.; *U.S. Private*, pg. 1489
FEDERAL FOAM TECHNOLOGIES INC.—See Federal International Inc.; *U.S. Private*, pg. 1489
FEDERAL INTERNATIONAL INC.; *U.S. Private*, pg. 1489
FISHER CLINICAL SERVICES INC.—See Thermo Fisher Scientific Inc.; *U.S. Public*, pg. 2147
FLEX-A-LITE CONSOLIDATED INC.; *U.S. Private*, pg. 1543
FLORACRAFT CORPORATION; *U.S. Private*, pg. 1546
FOAM CONCEPTS INC.—See Compass Diversified Holdings; *U.S. Public*, pg. 559
FOAM DESIGN INCORPORATED; *U.S. Private*, pg. 1556
FOAM MOLDERS AND SPECIALTIES; *U.S. Private*, pg. 1556
FOAM RUBBER PRODUCTS COMPANY; *U.S. Private*, pg. 1556
FOARM FOLLOWING FUNCTION, INC.—See M-C Industries Inc.; *U.S. Private*, pg. 2525
FP INTERNATIONAL, INC.; *U.S. Private*, pg. 1585
FUTURE FOAM, INC. - COUNCIL BLUFFS POURING PLANT—See Future Foam, Inc.; *U.S. Private*, pg. 1627
FUTURE FOAM, INC. - DALLAS FABRICATION PLANT—See Future Foam, Inc.; *U.S. Private*, pg. 1627
FUTURE FOAM, INC. - DENVER FABRICATION PLANT—See Future Foam, Inc.; *U.S. Private*, pg. 1627
FUTURE FOAM, INC. - FULLERTON POURING PLANT—See Future Foam, Inc.; *U.S. Private*, pg. 1627
FUTURE FOAM, INC.; *U.S. Private*, pg. 1626
FXI HOLDINGS, INC.—See One Rock Capital Partners, LLC; *U.S. Private*, pg. 3022
FXI, INC.—See One Rock Capital Partners, LLC; *U.S. Private*, pg. 3022
GENERAL PLASTICS MANUFACTURING COMPANY; *U.S. Private*, pg. 1666
GRAND RAPIDS FOAM TECHNOLOGIES, INC.; *U.S. Private*, pg. 1753
GREAT AMERICAN INDUSTRIES, INC.; *U.S. Private*, pg. 1762
GREINER MULTIFOAM SP. Z O.O.—See Greiner Holding AG; *Int'l*, pg. 3079
G&T INDUSTRIES OF INDIANA INC.—See G&T Industries Inc.; *U.S. Private*, pg. 1629
HARDWARE IMAGINATION-TECH; *U.S. Private*, pg. 1863
HEBEI MEISHAN POLYSACCHARIDE & POLYPEPTIDE TECHNOLOGY CO., LTD.—See Hebei Changshan Biochemical Pharmaceutical Co. Ltd.; *Int'l*, pg. 3305
HENNECKE GMBH—See Capvis AG; *Int'l*, pg. 1318
HENNECKE INC. POLYURETHANE TECHNOLOGY—See Capvis AG; *Int'l*, pg. 1318
HERMANN COMPANIES INC.; *U.S. Private*, pg. 1925
HIBCO PLASTICS INCORPORATED; *U.S. Private*, pg. 1933
HICKORY SPRINGS OF CALIFORNIA, INC.—See Hickory Springs Manufacturing Company; *U.S. Private*, pg. 1933
HINKLE MANUFACTURING INC; *U.S. Private*, pg. 1949
HORIZON PLASTICS INTERNATIONAL INC.—See Core Molding Technologies, Inc.; *U.S. Public*, pg. 576
HUDSON INDUSTRIES INC.; *U.S. Private*, pg. 2002
HUNTSMAN BUILDING SOLUTIONS (USA) LLC—See Huntsman Corporation; *U.S. Public*, pg. 1072
HUNTSMAN IFS POLYURETHANES LIMITED—See Huntsman Corporation; *U.S. Public*, pg. 1072
HUNTSMAN INTERNATIONAL (CANADA) CORPORATION—See Huntsman Corporation; *U.S. Public*, pg. 1074
HUNTSMAN POLYURETHANES—See Huntsman Corporation; *U.S. Public*, pg. 1074
HYPERLAST LIMITED—See Dow Inc.; *U.S. Public*, pg. 686
IBC SHELL CONTAINERS INC.—See International Business Communications Inc.; *U.S. Private*, pg. 2115
ICYNENE ASIA PACIFIC INC.—See Huntsman Corporation; *U.S. Public*, pg. 1075
ILLBRUCK FOAM TEC—See Illbruck GmbH; *Int'l*, pg. 3615
INTERNATIONAL BUSINESS COMMUNICATIONS INC.; *U.S. Private*, pg. 2114
INTERNATIONAL TRAY PADS & PACKAGING, INC.—See Pactiv Evergreen Inc.; *U.S. Public*, pg. 1633
IRATHANE SYSTEMS, INC.—See Lime Rock Partners, LLC; *U.S. Private*, pg. 2456
IRATHANE SYSTEMS, INC.—See Thompson Street Capital Manager LLC; *U.S. Private*, pg. 4161

326150 — URETHANE AND OTHER ...

IR SPECIALTY FOAM, LLC; *U.S. Private*, pg. 2137
JANESVILLE ACOUSTICS—See Jason Industries, Inc.; *U.S. Private*, pg. 2189
KAY-METZELER LIMITED—See TPG Capital, L.P.; *U.S. Public*, pg. 2175
KEE FATT INDUSTRIES, SDN. BHD.—See Bando Chemical Industries, Ltd.; *Int'l*, pg. 830
KFM-SCHAUMSTOFF GMBH—See Greiner Holding AG; *Int'l*, pg. 3078
LANCE INDUSTRIES INC.; *U.S. Private*, pg. 2382
LE CLAIR INDUSTRIES INC.; *U.S. Private*, pg. 2405
MARKO FOAM PRODUCTS, INC.; *U.S. Private*, pg. 2582
MAXWELL CHASE TECHNOLOGIES, LLC.—See AptarGroup, Inc.; *U.S. Public*, pg. 174
MERRYWEATHER FOAM INC.; *U.S. Private*, pg. 2677
MOUKA LIMITED—See Abraaj Capital Limited; *Int'l*, pg. 67
NORTH CAROLINA FOAM INDUSTRIES, INC. - DALTON FOAM DIVISION—See Barnhardt Manufacturing Company; *U.S. Private*, pg. 478
OHIO DECORATIVE PRODUCTS INC.; *U.S. Private*, pg. 3004
PERMA R PRODUCTS INC.—See Le Clair Industries Inc.; *U.S. Private*, pg. 2405
PERRY CHEMICAL & MANUFACTURING CO. INC.; *U.S. Private*, pg. 3153
PERRY FOAM PRODUCTS INC.; *U.S. Private*, pg. 3154
PLASTOMER CORP.; *U.S. Private*, pg. 3200
PLYMOUTH FOAM INCORPORATED; *U.S. Private*, pg. 3215
PRESTIGE FABRICATORS INC.—See Monomoy Capital Partners LLC; *U.S. Private*, pg. 2772
PROTEXIC—See Sonoco Products Company; *U.S. Public*, pg. 1905
REPUBLIC PACKAGING CORP.; *U.S. Private*, pg. 3402
RMAX INC.; *U.S. Private*, pg. 3451
ROGERS FOAM CORPORATION; *U.S. Private*, pg. 3472
RUBICON LLC—See Huntsman Corporation; *U.S. Public*, pg. 1075
SEALED AIR ARGENTINA S.A.—See Sealed Air Corporation; *U.S. Public*, pg. 1854
SEALED AIR S.A.S.—See Sealed Air Corporation; *U.S. Public*, pg. 1855
SIGNODE INDIA LIMITED—See Illinois Tool Works Inc.; *U.S. Public*, pg. 1110
SMITHERS-OASIS COMPANY; *U.S. Private*, pg. 3697
SOLIMIDE—See The Goldman Sachs Group, Inc.; *U.S. Public*, pg. 2080
SONOCO-CORRFLEX—See Sonoco Products Company; *U.S. Public*, pg. 1909
SONOCO-CORRFLEX—See Sonoco Products Company; *U.S. Public*, pg. 1909
SOUTHWIND MANUFACTURING; *U.S. Private*, pg. 3742
SPC RESOURCES, INC.—See Sonoco Products Company; *U.S. Public*, pg. 1905
STELLANA U.S. INC.—See HEXPOL AB; *Int'l*, pg. 3372
STEPHEN GOULD PAPER CO., INC.—See Stephen Gould Corporation; *U.S. Private*, pg. 3802
TASLER INC.; *U.S. Private*, pg. 3935
TEXAS FOAM, INC.—See Wynnchurch Capital, L.P.; *U.S. Private*, pg. 4577
TEXAS RECREATION CORPORATION; *U.S. Private*, pg. 3977
THERMOSAFE BRANDS EUROPE LTD.—See Sonoco Products Company; *U.S. Public*, pg. 1909
TOTAL CONCEPTS OF DESIGN, INC.; *U.S. Private*, pg. 4190
TRIAD-FABCO INC.; *U.S. Private*, pg. 4225
UFP TECHNOLOGIES, INC. - GRAND RAPIDS—See UFP Technologies, Inc.; *U.S. Public*, pg. 2221
UFP TECHNOLOGIES, INC.; *U.S. Public*, pg. 2221
UNITED INDUSTRIES; *U.S. Private*, pg. 4293
VITAFOAM LIMITED—See TPG Capital, L.P.; *U.S. Public*, pg. 2175
VOLUNTEER FOAM AND SUPPLY CORPORATION—See Hickory Springs Manufacturing Company; *U.S. Private*, pg. 1934
WALTON INDUSTRIES, INC.; *U.S. Private*, pg. 4434
WELDOTRON 2000, INC.; *U.S. Private*, pg. 4474
WESTERN INDUSTRIES CORPORATION, CORRUGATED DIVISION—See Western Industries Corporation; *U.S. Private*, pg. 4494
WESTERN INDUSTRIES CORPORATION; *U.S. Private*, pg. 4493
WM T. BURNETT & CO.; *U.S. Private*, pg. 4552

326160 — PLASTICS BOTTLE MANUFACTURING

AHF INDUSTRIES, INC.; *U.S. Private*, pg. 130
ALPHA PACKAGING LLC—See Irving Place Capital Management, L.P.; *U.S. Private*, pg. 2141
ALPHA PACKAGING LLC—See Irving Place Capital Management, L.P.; *U.S. Private*, pg. 2141
ALPHAPOINTE ASSOCIATION FOR THE BLIND; *U.S. Private*, pg. 200
ALPLA INC.—See Alpla-Werke Alwin Lehner GmbH & Co. KG; *Int'l*, pg. 374
ALTIRA, INC.; *U.S. Private*, pg. 209
AMCOR RIGID PLASTICS USA, INC. - TUMWATER PLANT—See Amcor plc; *Int'l*, pg. 417
APEX PLASTICS INC.—See Container Services LLC; *U.S. Private*, pg. 1027
BERRY PLASTICS CORP. - ANAHEIM—See Berry Global Group, Inc; *U.S. Public*, pg. 321
BISIL PLAST LIMITED; *Int'l*, pg. 1049
C2 THERAPEUTICS, INC.—See Hoya Corporation; *Int'l*, pg. 3495
CKS PACKAGING, INC. - NAUGATUCK—See CKS Packaging, Inc.; *U.S. Private*, pg. 909
COCA-COLA BEVERAGES PAKISTAN LTD.—See Anadolu Efes Biracilik ve Malt Sanayii A.S.; *Int'l*, pg. 445
DRUG PLASTICS & GLASS CO. INC.; *U.S. Private*, pg. 1279
DS SMITH WORLDWIDE DISPENSERS—See Sealed Air Corporation; *U.S. Public*, pg. 1853
EFES DEUTSCHLAND GMBH—See Anadolu Efes Biracilik ve Malt Sanayii A.S.; *Int'l*, pg. 445
E. PAIRIS S.A.; *Int'l*, pg. 2250
ESTERFORM PACKAGING LTD.; *Int'l*, pg. 2518
FRANCISCO OLLER, S.A.—See CORTICEIRA AMORIM, S.G.P.S., S.A.; *Int'l*, pg. 1807
FULCRUM CONTAINER LLC—See N.E.W. Plastics Corp.; *U.S. Private*, pg. 2828
GEMATEK OOO—See B. Braun Melsungen AG; *Int'l*, pg. 787
GERRESHEIMER PEACHTREE CITY (USA), L.P.—See Gerresheimer AG; *Int'l*, pg. 2944
GERRESHEIMER PLASTICOS SAO PAULO LTDA.—See Gerresheimer AG; *Int'l*, pg. 2944
GIZEH VERPACKUNGEN GMBH & CO. KG; *Int'l*, pg. 2982
GLOBAL CLOSURE SYSTEMS FRANCE 1 SAS—See Berry Global Group, Inc; *U.S. Public*, pg. 322
HATO REY PLASTICS INC.—See Vaqueria Tres Monjitas Inc.; *U.S. Private*, pg. 4345
HILLSIDE PLASTICS INC.—See Behrman Brothers Management Corp.; *U.S. Private*, pg. 515
LEFKA ORI S.A.—See Attica Group; *Int'l*, pg. 696
LLFLEX, LLC; *U.S. Private*, pg. 2475
LUV 'N CARE LTD.; *U.S. Private*, pg. 2518
LUXPET A.G./S.A.—See Plastipak Holdings, Inc.; *U.S. Private*, pg. 3199
MILLIS INDUSTRIES, INC.—See Radius Recycling, Inc.; *U.S. Public*, pg. 1760
MUNCHKIN, INC.; *U.S. Private*, pg. 2813
O. BERK COMPANY - BOTTLESTORE DIVISION—See O. Berk Company L.L.C.; *U.S. Private*, pg. 2981
PACKAGING CONCEPTS ASSOC., LLC.; *U.S. Private*, pg. 3072
PJSC EFES UKRAINE—See Anadolu Efes Biracilik ve Malt Sanayii A.S.; *Int'l*, pg. 445
PLASTIPAK BELGIUM—See Plastipak Holdings, Inc.; *U.S. Private*, pg. 3199
PLASTIPAK DEUTSCHLAND GMBH—See Plastipak Holdings, Inc.; *U.S. Private*, pg. 3199
PLASTIPAK IBERIA—See Plastipak Holdings, Inc.; *U.S. Private*, pg. 3199
PLASTIPAK PACKAGING FRANCE—See Plastipak Holdings, Inc.; *U.S. Private*, pg. 3199
PLASTIPAK PACKAGING INC. - JACKSON CENTER—See Plastipak Holdings, Inc.; *U.S. Private*, pg. 3200
PLASTIPAK UK LTD.—See Plastipak Holdings, Inc.; *U.S. Private*, pg. 3200
PLASTIQUE MICRON INC.—See Loews Corporation; *U.S. Public*, pg. 1339
POLYCON INDUSTRIES INC.—See Crown Packaging International Inc.; *U.S. Private*, pg. 1111
POLY-TAINER INC.; *U.S. Private*, pg. 3225
PRETIUM PACKAGING CORPORATION—See Clearlake Capital Group, L.P.; *U.S. Private*, pg. 937
PRETIUM PACKAGING - MANCHESTER—See Clearlake Capital Group, L.P.; *U.S. Private*, pg. 937
PRETIUM PACKAGING - PHILMONT—See Clearlake Capital Group, L.P.; *U.S. Private*, pg. 937
PROMENS DEVENTER B.V.—See Berry Global Group, Inc; *U.S. Public*, pg. 323
PROMENS FIRENZE S.R.L.—See Berry Global Group, Inc; *U.S. Public*, pg. 323
PROMENS OY—See Berry Global Group, Inc; *U.S. Public*, pg. 323
PROMENS PACKAGING GMBH - NEUMUNSTER—See Berry Global Group, Inc; *U.S. Public*, pg. 323
PROTO LABS GMBH—See Proto Labs, Inc.; *U.S. Public*, pg. 1730
RING CONTAINER TECHNOLOGIES INC.—See MSD Capital, L.P.; *U.S. Private*, pg. 2807
RPC BRAMLAGE DIVISION GMBH & CO., KG—See Berry Global Group, Inc; *U.S. Public*, pg. 322
SAF-T-PAK INC.—See Kelso & Company, L.P.; *U.S. Private*, pg. 2278
SILGAN CLOSURES UK LIMITED—See Silgan Holdings, Inc.; *U.S. Public*, pg. 1878
SILGAN PLASTICS CORPORATION—See Silgan Holdings, Inc.; *U.S. Public*, pg. 1879
SOUTHEASTERN CONTAINER INC.; *U.S. Private*, pg. 3727
TAI RUNG DEVELOPMENT CO., LTD.—See China Chemical & Pharmaceutical Co., Ltd.; *Int'l*, pg. 1488
TECH GROUP PUERTO RICO—See West Pharmaceutical Services, Inc.; *U.S. Public*, pg. 2352
TECH LONG EUROPE GMBH—See Guangzhou Tech-Long Packaging Machinery Co., Ltd.; *Int'l*, pg. 3168
TERVIS TUMBLER COMPANY; *U.S. Private*, pg. 3972
UNITED GLASS GROUP LTD.—See O-I Glass, Inc.; *U.S. Public*, pg. 1560
WESTERN CONTAINER CORPORATION—See The Coca-Cola Company; *U.S. Public*, pg. 2065

326191 — PLASTICS PLUMBING FIXTURE MANUFACTURING

AGCO INC.; *U.S. Private*, pg. 126
AIRBATH GROUP PLC; *Int'l*, pg. 241
ALIAXIS S.A./N.V.; *Int'l*, pg. 323
AQUALISA PRODUCTS LIMITED; *Int'l*, pg. 527
AQUA MIZER INC.; *U.S. Private*, pg. 302
AQUATIC CO.—See The Sterling Group, L.P.; *U.S. Private*, pg. 4121
ASTORE VALVES & FITTINGS S.R.L.—See Aliaxis S.A./N.V.; *Int'l*, pg. 323
BRADLEY WASHROOM ACCESSORIES DIV—See Watts Water Technologies, Inc.; *U.S. Public*, pg. 2337
CAPITOL PLASTIC PRODUCTS, LLC—See AptarGroup, Inc.; *U.S. Public*, pg. 174
CARSTIN BRANDS, INC.—See The Wolf Organization, LLC; *U.S. Private*, pg. 4138
CENTRAL ALUMINIUM MANUFACTORY SDN. BHD.—See CAM Resources Berhad; *Int'l*, pg. 1267
CHARLOMA INC.; *U.S. Private*, pg. 857
CLARION BATHWARE INC.; *U.S. Private*, pg. 911
CRANE GROUP LIMITED—See Fletcher Building Limited; *Int'l*, pg. 2699
DAELIM B&CO., LTD. - JECHEON PLANT—See DAELIM B&Co., LTD.; *Int'l*, pg. 1907
DAMO WELLNESS ROMANIA SRL—See Harvia Oyj; *Int'l*, pg. 3281
DANSK GENERATIONSSKIFTE A/S; *Int'l*, pg. 1968
DUO-FORM PLASTICS; *U.S. Private*, pg. 1291
E.L. MUSTEE & SONS, INC.; *U.S. Private*, pg. 1306
FLORESTONE PRODUCTS CO.; *U.S. Private*, pg. 1547
FORMOSA PROSONIC MANUFACTURING SDN. BHD.—See Formosa Prosonic Industries Berhad; *Int'l*, pg. 2736
FRONTLINE MANUFACTURING INC.—See Patrick Industries, Inc.; *U.S. Public*, pg. 1652
GEBERIT PLUMBING TECHNOLOGY CO. LTD.—See Geberit AG; *Int'l*, pg. 2905
GENOVA-MINNESOTA, INC.—See Genova Products, Inc.; *U.S. Private*, pg. 1673
HARBIN FIBER GLASS—See NOV, Inc.; *U.S. Public*, pg. 1544
HENRY-TECHNOLOGIES GMBH—See Hendricks Holding Company, Inc.; *U.S. Private*, pg. 1915
HIDRA STIL D.D.; *Int'l*, pg. 3384
HOCHENG CORPORATION; *Int'l*, pg. 3437
J&B PRODUCTS, INC.—See Federal Process Corporation; *U.S. Private*, pg. 1489
JETTA CORPORATION; *U.S. Private*, pg. 2204
KAN S.P. Z O.O.—See Aalberts N.V.; *Int'l*, pg. 34
LASCO COMPOSITES, LP—See Crane NXT, Co.; *U.S. Public*, pg. 590
LYONS INDUSTRIES, INC.; *U.S. Private*, pg. 2522
MAAX BATH INC. - PLYMOUTH—See American Bath Group; *U.S. Private*, pg. 224
MAAX INC.-MINNEAPOLIS—See American Bath Group; *U.S. Private*, pg. 224
MAAX SPAS INDUSTRIES CORP.—See American Bath Group; *U.S. Private*, pg. 224
MASCO BATH CORPORATION—See Masco Corporation; *U.S. Public*, pg. 1390
MASCO BATH—See Masco Corporation; *U.S. Public*, pg. 1390
NIBCO INC. - LEBANON PLANT—See NIBCO Inc.; *U.S. Private*, pg. 2924
OLIVERI SOLUTIONS PTY LIMITED—See Fletcher Building Limited; *Int'l*, pg. 2700
POLYPIPE LIMITED - POLYPIPE BUILDING PRODUCTS DIVISION—See Genuit Group plc; *Int'l*, pg. 2930
THE PRAXIS COMPANIES, LLC—See Meridian Venture Partners; *U.S. Private*, pg. 2674
R.W. LYALL & COMPANY INC.—See Hubbell Incorporated; *U.S. Public*, pg. 1067
SAFETY TUBS LLC—See Sun Capital Partners, Inc.; *U.S. Private*, pg. 3858
SEELYE-EILER INDUSTRIAL PLASTIC PRODUCTS—See Activar, Inc.; *U.S. Private*, pg. 68
SINOMA JINJING FIBER GLASS CO., LTD.—See China National Materials; *Int'l*, pg. 1532
SPURLIN INDUSTRIES INC.; *U.S. Private*, pg. 3765
SWAN STONE CORPORATION; *U.S. Private*, pg. 3889
TRADELINK PTY LTD—See Fletcher Building Limited; *Int'l*, pg. 2701
VAINO KORPINEN OY—See AddLife AB; *Int'l*, pg. 130

N.A.I.C.S. INDEX

326199 — ALL OTHER PLASTICS ...

WATKINS MANUFACTURING CORPORATION—See Masco Corporation; *U.S. Public*, pg. 1392
WAVIN METALPLAST-BUK SP.Z.O.O.—See Bharti Enterprises Limited; *Int'l*, pg. 1013
WAVIN TECHNOLOGY & INNOVATION B.V.—See Bharti Enterprises Limited; *Int'l*, pg. 1012
ZURN INDUSTRIES, LLC—See Zurn Elkay Water Solutions Corporation; *U.S. Public*, pg. 2413

326199 — ALL OTHER PLASTICS PRODUCT MANUFACTURING

10 DAY PARTS, INC.—See BlackBern Partners LLC; *U.S. Private*, pg. 573
10 DAY PARTS, INC.—See Lee Equity Partners LLC; *U.S. Private*, pg. 2412
123PRINT, INC.—See Taylor Corporation; *U.S. Private*, pg. 3938
3C-CARBON GROUP AG; *Int'l*, pg. 7
3D PLASTICS, INC.—See Quantum Plastics, Inc.; *U.S. Private*, pg. 3323
3P GMBH—See Burelle S.A.; *Int'l*, pg. 1222
3P- PRODUCTOS PLASTICOS PERFORMANTES SA—See Burelle S.A.; *Int'l*, pg. 1222
3P SPA—See Burelle S.A.; *Int'l*, pg. 1222
600956 ONTARIO LTD; *Int'l*, pg. 14
AAC STRUCTURAL FOAM LTD.—See Madison Dearborn Partners, LLC; *U.S. Private*, pg. 2541
AAPICO PLASTICS PUBLIC CO., LTD.—See AAPICO Hitech plc; *Int'l*, pg. 37
AARGUS PLASTICS, INC.—See Alpha Industries, Inc.; *U.S. Private*, pg. 197
AB CERBO; *Int'l*, pg. 39
ABCO KOVEX LIMITED—See Bunzl plc; *Int'l*, pg. 1217
ABCO KOVEX (UK) LIMITED—See Bunzl plc; *Int'l*, pg. 1217
ABCORP USA—See American Banknote Corporation; *U.S. Private*, pg. 224
ABC POLYMER INDUSTRIES, LLC; *U.S. Private*, pg. 36
ABC TECHNOLOGIES INC.—See Cerberus Capital Management, L.P.; *U.S. Private*, pg. 835
ABNOTE NZ LTD—See American Banknote Corporation; *U.S. Private*, pg. 224
ACCENT PLASTICS INC.—See Syntech Development & Manufacturing, Inc.; *U.S. Private*, pg. 3904
ACCUMA CORPORATION; *U.S. Private*, pg. 55
ACCU-MOLD, LLC—See Pokagon Band of Potawatomi Indians; *U.S. Private*, pg. 3223
ACCURATE MOLDED PLASTICS INC.; *U.S. Private*, pg. 55
ACCURATE MOLD & PLASTICS CORP.—See Diversified Plastics Corporation; *U.S. Private*, pg. 1243
ACHILLES ADVANCED TECHNOLOGY CO., LTD.—See Achilles Corporation; *Int'l*, pg. 103
ACHILLES (SHANGHAI) INTERNATIONAL TRADING CO., LTD.—See Achilles Corporation; *Int'l*, pg. 103
ACIG TECHNOLOGY CORP.—See Identiv, Inc.; *U.S. Public*, pg. 1089
ACMA LTD.; *Int'l*, pg. 107
ACORN-GENCON PLASTICS—See Acorn Engineering Company, Inc.; *U.S. Private*, pg. 63
ACRYLON PLASTICS INC.; *Int'l*, pg. 109
ACTION TECHNOLOGY BELGIUM—See Genstar Capital, LLC; *U.S. Private*, pg. 1678
ADAC PLASTICS INC.; *U.S. Private*, pg. 72
ADAMS MFG CORP.—See BC Partners LLP; *Int'l*, pg. 925
ADAMWORKS, LLC—See Odyssey Investment Partners, LLC; *U.S. Private*, pg. 2994
ADEKA KOREA CORPORATION—See Adeka Corporation; *Int'l*, pg. 141
ADLAM FILMS—See Bryce Corporation; *U.S. Private*, pg. 674
ADON PRODUCTION AG; *Int'l*, pg. 152
ADP D.O.O.—See AD Plastik d.d.; *Int'l*, pg. 122
AD PLASTIK D.D.; *Int'l*, pg. 122
AD PLASTIK D.D. - ZAGREB PLANT 1—See AD Plastik d.d.; *Int'l*, pg. 122
AD PLASTIK D.D. - ZAGREB PLANT 2—See AD Plastik d.d.; *Int'l*, pg. 122
AD PLASTIK D.O.O.—See AD Plastik d.d.; *Int'l*, pg. 122
ADVANCED CONTAINER TECHNOLOGIES, INC.; *U.S. Public*, pg. 46
ADVANCE TOOLING CONCEPTS, LLC—See ARC Group Worldwide, Inc.; *U.S. Public*, pg. 179
ADWEST TECHNOLOGIES, INC.—See CECO Environmental Corp.; *U.S. Public*, pg. 463
AEROCON, LLC—See Berry Global Group, Inc; *U.S. Public*, pg. 321
AEROKLAS AUSTRALIA PTY LTD.—See Eastern Polymer Group Public Company Limited; *Int'l*, pg. 2273
AEROKLAS CO., LTD.—See Eastern Polymer Group Public Company Limited; *Int'l*, pg. 2273
AFCO INDUSTRIES, INC.; *U.S. Private*, pg. 121
THE AFFINIS GROUP; *U.S. Private*, pg. 3983
AGC MATEX CO., LTD.—See AGC Inc.; *Int'l*, pg. 202
AGIE CHARMILLES BV—See Georg Fischer AG; *Int'l*, pg. 2934
AGIE CHARMILLES S.A.R.L.—See Georg Fischer AG; *Int'l*, pg. 2934

AGIE LTD.—See Georg Fischer AG; *Int'l*, pg. 2934
AGRICULTURAL PLASTIC INDUSTRIAL COMPANY (APICO)—See Arab Supply & Trading Co.; *Int'l*, pg. 532
AIM PROCESSING, INC.—See Mcm Capital Partners, LP; *U.S. Private*, pg. 2642
AIRDEX INTERNATIONAL, INC.; *U.S. Private*, pg. 140
AIRLITE PLASTICS COMPANY; *U.S. Private*, pg. 141
AIRLITE PLASTICS CO.—See Airlite Plastics Company; *U.S. Private*, pg. 141
AIR LOGISTICS CORPORATION; *U.S. Private*, pg. 139
AIRMATE COMPANY; *U.S. Private*, pg. 141
AJAX COMB COMPANY—See Antonio's Manufacturing Inc.; *U.S. Private*, pg. 288
AJAX-UNITED PATTERNS & MOLDS, INC.—See Francisco Partners Management, LP; *U.S. Private*, pg. 1590
AKRO-MILS—See Myers Industries, Inc.; *U.S. Public*, pg. 1488
AKRON PORCELAIN & PLASTICS CO.; *U.S. Private*, pg. 146
AKUMPLAST JSC; *Int'l*, pg. 267
ALCO PLASTIC PRODUCTS LIMITED; *Int'l*, pg. 301
ALCO PLASTICS INC.; *U.S. Private*, pg. 154
ALIAXIS SERVICES S.A.—See Aliaxis S.A./N.V.; *Int'l*, pg. 323
ALIPLAST IBERIA SL—See Hera S.p.A.; *Int'l*, pg. 3356
ALIPLAST SPA—See Hera S.p.A.; *Int'l*, pg. 3356
ALL AMERICAN POLY CORP. - LAWRENCEVILLE PLANT—See All American Poly Corp.; *U.S. Private*, pg. 170
ALLAN PLASTIC MFG., LIMITED—See Allan International Holdings Limited; *Int'l*, pg. 332
ALLEGHENY PRINTED PLASTICS, LLC—See Allegheny Plastics Inc.; *U.S. Private*, pg. 176
ALLFLEX EUROPE SA—See BC Partners LLP; *Int'l*, pg. 923
ALLFLEX USA, INC.—See BC Partners LLP; *Int'l*, pg. 923
ALLIED PLASTICS HOLDINGS, LLC—See Alpha Industries, Inc.; *U.S. Private*, pg. 197
ALLIED PLASTIC SKYLIGHT; *Int'l*, pg. 358
ALLIED PLASTIC SUPPLY, INC.; *U.S. Private*, pg. 187
ALLOYD BRANDS CONSUMER PACKAGING—See Sonoco Products Company; *U.S. Public*, pg. 1905
ALLTRISTA PLASTICS LLC—See One Rock Capital Partners, LLC; *U.S. Private*, pg. 3023
ALMAAK INTERNATIONAL GMBH—See HEXPOL AB; *Int'l*, pg. 3371
ALPAR ARCHITECTURAL PRODUCTS, LLC—See Pawling Corporation; *U.S. Private*, pg. 3115
THE ALPHA CORPORATION OF TENNESSEE; *U.S. Private*, pg. 3984
ALPHA FRANCE SAS—See Element Solutions Inc.; *U.S. Public*, pg. 726
ALPHA PLASTICS INC.; *U.S. Private*, pg. 199
ALPLA-WERKE ALWIN LEHNER GMBH & CO. KG; *Int'l*, pg. 373
ALSIDE - BOTHELL PLANT—See Hellman & Friedman LLC; *U.S. Private*, pg. 1907
ALSIDE—See Hellman & Friedman LLC; *U.S. Private*, pg. 1907
ALTECH NEW MATERIAL CO., LTD.—See Altech Co., Ltd.; *Int'l*, pg. 388
ALTECH NEW MATERIALS (FUKUI) CO., LTD.—See Altech Co., Ltd.; *Int'l*, pg. 388
ALTIUM PACKAGING CANADA—See Loews Corporation; *U.S. Public*, pg. 1339
ALTO PLASTICS LTD.; *Int'l*, pg. 394
ALTOR INDUSTRIE—See Altor; *Int'l*, pg. 394
ALTOR; *Int'l*, pg. 394
ALUMILITE, INC.—See Arsenal Capital Management LP; *U.S. Private*, pg. 339
AMA PLASTICS; *U.S. Private*, pg. 215
AMARI PLASTICS PLC—See Blackfriars Corp.; *U.S. Private*, pg. 574
AMBER PLASTICS PTY. LIMITED—See Berry Global Group, Inc; *U.S. Public*, pg. 320
AMCOR FLEXIBLES DENMARK APS—See Amcor plc; *Int'l*, pg. 417
AMCOR FLEXIBLES TRANSPAC B.V.B.A—See Amcor plc; *Int'l*, pg. 417
AMERICAN BILTRITE LTD.—See American Biltrite Inc.; *U.S. Public*, pg. 97
AMERICAN CASTING & MANUFACTURING CORPORATION; *U.S. Private*, pg. 226
AMERICAN FABRICATION CORPORATION; *U.S. Private*, pg. 232
AMERICAN FLANGE & MANUFACTURING CO., INC.—See Greif Inc.; *U.S. Public*, pg. 965
AMERICAN INDUSTRIAL PLASTIC, LLC—See Compagnie Generale des Etablissements Michelin SCA; *Int'l*, pg. 1744
AMERICAN MADE LINER SYSTEMS—See American Made, LLC; *U.S. Private*, pg. 240
AMERICAN MADE, LLC; *U.S. Private*, pg. 240
AMERICAN METAL & PLASTICS INC.; *U.S. Private*, pg. 241
AMERICAN PLASTIC MOLDING CORP.; *U.S. Private*, pg. 244
AMERICAN PLAST S.A.—See Amcor plc; *Int'l*, pg. 418
AMERICAN SAFETY TECHNOLOGIES—See Illinois Tool Works Inc.; *U.S. Public*, pg. 1101
AMERICAN TECHNICAL MOLDING, INC.—See Integer Holdings Corporation; *U.S. Public*, pg. 1135
AMERICAN WINDOW & GLASS INC.; *U.S. Private*, pg. 258
AMERICA TAMPAS S/A—See Evora S.A.; *Int'l*, pg. 2573
AMERI-KART CORP.—See Myers Industries, Inc.; *U.S. Public*, pg. 1488
AMMEX PLASTICS, LLC—See Echo Engineering & Production Supplies, Inc.; *U.S. Private*, pg. 1327
AMPACET CORPORATION; *U.S. Private*, pg. 264
AMPACET EUROPE, S.A.—See Ampacet Corporation; *U.S. Private*, pg. 264
AMPACET (THAILAND) COMPANY, LTD.—See Ampacet Corporation; *U.S. Private*, pg. 264
AMS PLASTICS, INC.—See BlackBern Partners LLC; *U.S. Private*, pg. 573
AMS PLASTICS, INC.—See Lee Equity Partners LLC; *U.S. Private*, pg. 2412
AMTICO INTERNATIONAL LTD.—See Mannington Mills, Inc.; *U.S. Private*, pg. 2565
AMWAAL TRADE & ENGINEERING CO., LTD.—See BERICAP GmbH & Co. KG; *Int'l*, pg. 980
ANCO PRODUCTS, INC.—See APi Group Corporation; *Int'l*, pg. 513
ANDERSON TECHNOLOGIES INC.; *U.S. Private*, pg. 277
ANHUI GUOFENG NEW MATERIALS CO., LTD.; *Int'l*, pg. 467
AN PHAT BIOPLASTICS; *Int'l*, pg. 443
AN PHAT PLASTIC & GREEN ENVIRONMENT JOINT STOCK COMPANY - FACTORY NO 2—See An Phat Bioplastics; *Int'l*, pg. 443
ANTIEN INDUSTRIES JOINT STOCK COMPANY; *Int'l*, pg. 483
ANTONIO'S MANUFACTURING INC.; *U.S. Private*, pg. 288
AO AD PLASTIK TOGLIATTI—See AD Plastik d.d.; *Int'l*, pg. 122
APEX RESOURCE TECHNOLOGIES, INC.—See DuPont de Nemours, Inc.; *U.S. Public*, pg. 694
APM AUTO COMPONENTS (THAILAND) LTD.—See APM Automotive Holdings Berhad; *Int'l*, pg. 516
APOLLO PLASTICS CORP.—See Specialty Manufacturers, Inc.; *U.S. Private*, pg. 3750
A.P. PLASMAN, INC.—See Insight Equity Holdings LLC; *U.S. Private*, pg. 2086
ARCHITECTURAL PLASTICS LIMITED—See Allied Plastic Skylight; *Int'l*, pg. 358
ARISAWA JUSHI KOGYO CO., LTD.—See Arisawa Manufacturing Co., Ltd.; *Int'l*, pg. 565
ARISAWA SOGYO CO., LTD.—See Arisawa Manufacturing Co., Ltd.; *Int'l*, pg. 566
ARLON GRAPHICS, LLC—See FLEXcon Corporation; *U.S. Private*, pg. 1543
ARMALY SPONGE COMPANY, INC.; *U.S. Private*, pg. 330
ARMOUR PLASTICS LIMITED; *Int'l*, pg. 575
ARMSTRONG DLW AG—See Armstrong World Industries, Inc.; *U.S. Public*, pg. 194
ARMSTRONG WORLD INDUSTRIES (AUSTRALIA) PTY. LTD.—See Armstrong World Industries, Inc.; *U.S. Public*, pg. 194
ARMSTRONG WORLD INDUSTRIES CANADA LTD.—See Armstrong World Industries, Inc.; *U.S. Public*, pg. 194
ARMSTRONG WORLD INDUSTRIES, INC.; *U.S. Public*, pg. 193
ARO GRANITE INDUSTRIES LTD.; *Int'l*, pg. 577
ARROWHEAD PLASTIC ENGINEERING, INC.; *U.S. Private*, pg. 336
ARTUS CORPORATION; *U.S. Private*, pg. 344
ASAHI KASEI PLASTICS (GUANGZHOU) CO., LTD.—See Asahi Kasei Corporation; *Int'l*, pg. 596
ASAHI KASEI PLASTICS VIETNAM CO., LTD.—See Asahi Kasei Corporation; *Int'l*, pg. 596
ASAHI KASEI TECHNOPLUS CO., LTD.—See Asahi Kasei Corporation; *Int'l*, pg. 596
ASHLAND HARDWARE SYSTEMS—See Quanex Building Products Corp.; *U.S. Public*, pg. 1749
ASIA PLASTIC RECYCLING HOLDING LIMITED; *Int'l*, pg. 614
ASP PLASTICS PTY LIMITED—See Cleanaway Waste Management Limited; *Int'l*, pg. 1654
ASSOCIATED MATERIALS, LLC—See Hellman & Friedman LLC; *U.S. Private*, pg. 1907
ASTRAPAK GAUTENG (PTY) LTD—See Berry Global Group, Inc; *U.S. Public*, pg. 323
ASTRA POLYMER COMPOUNDING CO. LTD.—See ASTRA INDUSTRIAL GROUP COMPANY; *Int'l*, pg. 657
ASTROPLAST KUNSTSTOFFTECHNIK GMBH & CO. KG—See Gesco AG; *Int'l*, pg. 2945
ATC NYMOLD CORPORATION—See ATC Group, Inc.; *U.S. Private*, pg. 365
ATRION MEDICAL PRODUCTS, INC.—See Nordson Corporation; *U.S. Public*, pg. 1532
ATS PRODUCTS INC.; *U.S. Private*, pg. 382
ATTEMA B.V.—See ABN AMRO Group N.V.; *Int'l*, pg. 65
AURORA TECHNOLOGIES INC.; *U.S. Private*, pg. 395
AUTOPARTES DE PRECISION DE SANTANA, S.A. DE C.V.—See Equistone Partners Europe Limited; *Int'l*, pg. 2487
AUTRONIC PLASTICS INC.; *U.S. Private*, pg. 401

AUVITRONICS LIMITED - MANUFACTURING UNIT-2—See House of Habib; *Int'l*, pg. 3491
AVIENT COLORANTS BELGIUM SA—See Avient Corporation; *U.S. Public*, pg. 246
AVIENT COLORANTS SWITZERLAND AG—See Avient Corporation; *U.S. Public*, pg. 247
AVIENT FINLAND OY—See Avient Corporation; *U.S. Public*, pg. 247
AVIENT NEW ZEALAND LIMITED—See Avient Corporation; *U.S. Public*, pg. 247
AVIENT SAUDI INDUSTRIES CO., LTD.—See Avient Corporation; *U.S. Public*, pg. 247
AVON PLASTICS, INC.; *U.S. Private*, pg. 410
AVON RUBBER & PLASTICS INC.—See Avon Protection plc; *Int'l*, pg. 750
AV PLASTICS SDN. BHD.—See D'nonce Technology Bhd.; *Int'l*, pg. 1899
AWC HOLDING COMPANY—See Clayton, Dubilier & Rice, LLC; *U.S. Private*, pg. 921
AXALTA COATING SYSTEMS UK LIMITED—See Axalta Coating Systems Ltd.; *U.S. Public*, pg. 255
THE AZEK GROUP LLC—See The AZEK Company Inc.; *U.S. Public*, pg. 2035
BACPLAS INC.; *U.S. Private*, pg. 423
BADGER PLUG COMPANY; *U.S. Private*, pg. 424
BALMORAL ADVANCED COMPOSITES LIMITED—See Balmoral Group Ltd.; *Int'l*, pg. 810
BALMORAL GROUP LTD.; *Int'l*, pg. 810
BALMORAL WELLBEING LTD.—See Balmoral Group Ltd.; *Int'l*, pg. 810
BARPLAS LIMITED—See Berry Global Group, Inc; *U.S. Public*, pg. 322
BARRIERMED GLOVE CO. INC.—See Barriermed Inc.; *U.S. Private*, pg. 480
BASF COLORS & EFFECTS GMBH—See BASF SE; *Int'l*, pg. 874
BASF COMPANY LTD.—See BASF SE; *Int'l*, pg. 878
BASF CONSTRUCTION CHEMICALS (SCHWEIZ) AG—See BASF SE; *Int'l*, pg. 874
BASF PLASTIC ADDITIVES MIDDLE EAST S.P.C.—See BASF SE; *Int'l*, pg. 880
BASLER PLASTICS LLC—See Basler Electric Company; *U.S. Private*, pg. 485
BATIMETAL S.A.S.—See Owens Corning; *U.S. Public*, pg. 1626
BAXI FRANCE—See BDR Thermea Group B.V.; *Int'l*, pg. 930
BAYER MATERIALSCIENCE GMBH—See Bayer Aktiengesellschaft; *Int'l*, pg. 907
BAYER MATERIALSCIENCE LTD.—See Bayer Aktiengesellschaft; *Int'l*, pg. 907
BAYER MATERIALSCIENCE OLDENBURG VERWALTUNGS-GMBH—See Bayer Aktiengesellschaft; *Int'l*, pg. 907
BAYER MATERIALSCIENCE (SHANGHAI) MANAGEMENT COMPANY LIMITED—See Bayer Aktiengesellschaft; *Int'l*, pg. 907
BAYER MATERIALSCIENCE TRADING (SHANGHAI) CO. LTD.—See Bayer Aktiengesellschaft; *Int'l*, pg. 907
BAYER MIDDLE EAST FZE—See Bayer Aktiengesellschaft; *Int'l*, pg. 905
BAYER SA—See Bayer Aktiengesellschaft; *Int'l*, pg. 907
BCD POLYMERS SP. Z O.O.—See BRENNTAG SE; *Int'l*, pg. 1146
BEDFORD INDUSTRIES, INC.; *U.S. Private*, pg. 512
BEDFORD REINFORCED PLASTICS; *U.S. Private*, pg. 512
BEDFORD TECHNOLOGY, LLC—See Bedford Industries, Inc.; *U.S. Private*, pg. 512
BEEMAK PLASTICS, INC.—See Jordan Industries, Inc.; *U.S. Private*, pg. 2235
BEE WINDOW INCORPORATED; *U.S. Private*, pg. 513
BE GREEN PACKAGING LLC—See The Riverside Company; *U.S. Private*, pg. 4108
BE GREEN PACKAGING LLC - SOUTH CAROLINA MFG FACILITY—See The Riverside Company; *U.S. Private*, pg. 4108
BEIJING AGIE CHARMILLES INDUSTRIAL ELECTRONICS LTD.—See Georg Fischer AG; *Int'l*, pg. 2934
BEKOMOLD WERKZEUGBAU GMBH—See BERICAP GmbH & Co. KG; *Int'l*, pg. 980
BEL-ART PRODUCTS, INC.—See Harbour Group Industries, Inc.; *U.S. Private*, pg. 1861
BELCO, INC.—See NOV, Inc.; *U.S. Public*, pg. 1544
BELDEN CEKAN A/S—See Belden, Inc.; *U.S. Public*, pg. 293
BEMIS DEUTSCHLAND HOLDINGS GMBH—See Amcor plc; *Int'l*, pg. 418
BEMIS ELSHAM LIMITED—See Amcor plc; *Int'l*, pg. 418
BEMIS FLEXIBLE PACKAGING (SUZHOU) CO., LTD.—See Amcor plc; *Int'l*, pg. 418
BEMIS HEALTHCARE PACKAGING IRELAND LIMITED—See Kohlberg & Company, LLC; *U.S. Private*, pg. 2337
BEMIS MANUFACTURING COMPANY; *U.S. Private*, pg. 522
BEMIS MAYOR PACKAGING LIMITED—See Amcor plc; *Int'l*, pg. 418
BEMIS PACKAGING POLSKA SP. Z.O.O.—See Amcor plc; *Int'l*, pg. 418
BEMIS (SHANGHAI) TRADING CO., LTD.—See Amcor plc; *Int'l*, pg. 418
BENGAL WINDSOR THERMOPLASTICS LIMITED—See Bengal Group; *Int'l*, pg. 973
BENVIC EUROPE IBE SL—See BI-Invest Advisors S.A.; *Int'l*, pg. 1017
BENVIC EUROPE S.A.S.—See BI-Invest Advisors S.A.; *Int'l*, pg. 1017
BENVIC EUROPE S.P.A.—See BI-Invest Advisors S.A.; *Int'l*, pg. 1017
BERICAP ASIA PTE. LTD.—See BERICAP GmbH & Co. KG; *Int'l*, pg. 980
BERICAP ASIA PTE. LTD.—See BERICAP GmbH & Co. KG; *Int'l*, pg. 980
BERICAP BENELUX B.V.—See BERICAP GmbH & Co. KG; *Int'l*, pg. 980
BERICAP DO BRASIL LTDA.—See BERICAP GmbH & Co. KG; *Int'l*, pg. 981
BERICAP D.O.O.—See BERICAP GmbH & Co. KG; *Int'l*, pg. 981
BERICAP EAST AFRICA LTD.—See BERICAP GmbH & Co. KG; *Int'l*, pg. 980
BERICAP EGYPT JSC—See BERICAP GmbH & Co. KG; *Int'l*, pg. 980
BERICAP GMBH & CO. KG; *Int'l*, pg. 980
BERICAP INDIA PVT. LTD.—See BERICAP GmbH & Co. KG; *Int'l*, pg. 980
BERICAP KAPAK SANAYI A.S.—See BERICAP GmbH & Co. KG; *Int'l*, pg. 980
BERICAP KAZAKHSTAN LTD.—See BERICAP GmbH & Co. KG; *Int'l*, pg. 980
BERICAP (KUNSHAN) CO. LTD.—See BERICAP GmbH & Co. KG; *Int'l*, pg. 980
BERICAP, LLC—See Amcor plc; *Int'l*, pg. 417
BERICAP, LLC—See BERICAP GmbH & Co. KG; *Int'l*, pg. 981
BERICAP MALAYSIA SDN. BHD.—See BERICAP GmbH & Co. KG; *Int'l*, pg. 980
BERICAP MEXICO, S. DE R.L. DE C.V.—See BERICAP GmbH & Co. KG; *Int'l*, pg. 980
BERICAP MIDDLE EAST FZE—See BERICAP GmbH & Co. KG; *Int'l*, pg. 980
BERICAP NORTH AMERICA, INC.—See Amcor plc; *Int'l*, pg. 417
BERICAP NORTH AMERICA, INC.—See BERICAP GmbH & Co. KG; *Int'l*, pg. 981
BERICAP POLSKA SP. Z O.O.—See BERICAP GmbH & Co. KG; *Int'l*, pg. 981
BERICAP ROMANIA S.R.L.—See BERICAP GmbH & Co. KG; *Int'l*, pg. 981
BERICAP S.A. - BUENOS AIRES PLANT—See BERICAP GmbH & Co. KG; *Int'l*, pg. 981
BERICAP SARL—See BERICAP GmbH & Co. KG; *Int'l*, pg. 981
BERICAP S.A.—See BERICAP GmbH & Co. KG; *Int'l*, pg. 981
BERICAP S.A.U.—See BERICAP GmbH & Co. KG; *Int'l*, pg. 981
BERICAP SC LLC—See Amcor plc; *Int'l*, pg. 417
BERICAP SC LLC—See BERICAP GmbH & Co. KG; *Int'l*, pg. 981
BERICAP SINGAPORE PTE LTD—See BERICAP GmbH & Co. KG; *Int'l*, pg. 981
BERICAP S.R.L.—See BERICAP GmbH & Co. KG; *Int'l*, pg. 981
BERICAP UK LTD.—See BERICAP GmbH & Co. KG; *Int'l*, pg. 981
BERICAP ZARODASTECHNIKAI B.T.—See BERICAP GmbH & Co. KG; *Int'l*, pg. 981
BERICAP ZHUHAI CO., LTD.—See BERICAP GmbH & Co. KG; *Int'l*, pg. 981
BERRY GLOBAL, INC.—See Berry Global Group, Inc; *U.S. Public*, pg. 321
BERRY GLOBAL, INC.—See Berry Global Group, Inc; *U.S. Public*, pg. 321
BERRY GLOBAL INDIA PRIVATE LIMITED—See Berry Global Group, Inc; *U.S. Public*, pg. 320
BERRY IOWA, LLC—See Berry Global Group, Inc; *U.S. Public*, pg. 321
BERRY PLASTICS CORP. - BALTIMORE—See Berry Global Group, Inc; *U.S. Public*, pg. 321
BERRY PLASTICS CORP. - CHICAGO—See Berry Global Group, Inc; *U.S. Public*, pg. 321
BERRY PLASTICS CORP. - CRANBURY—See Berry Global Group, Inc; *U.S. Public*, pg. 321
BERRY PLASTICS CORP. - EVANSVILLE—See Berry Global Group, Inc; *U.S. Public*, pg. 321
BERRY PLASTICS CORP. - HENDERSON—See Berry Global Group, Inc; *U.S. Public*, pg. 321
BERRY PLASTICS CORP. - LANCASTER—See Berry Global Group, Inc; *U.S. Public*, pg. 321
BERRY PLASTICS CORP. - SARASOTA—See Berry Global Group, Inc; *U.S. Public*, pg. 321
BERRY PLASTICS CORP. - SUFFOLK—See Berry Global Group, Inc; *U.S. Public*, pg. 321
BERRY PLASTICS CORP. - TUBED PRODUCTS DIVISION—See Berry Global Group, Inc; *U.S. Public*, pg. 321
BERRY PLASTICS FILMCO, INC.—See Berry Global Group, Inc; *U.S. Public*, pg. 321
BERRY PLASTICS SP, INC.—See Berry Global Group, Inc; *U.S. Public*, pg. 321
BERRY SUPERFOS PAMPLONA SA—See Berry Global Group, Inc; *U.S. Public*, pg. 321
BETRAS USA, INC.; *U.S. Private*, pg. 546
BEVPAC COMPANY LIMITED—See BERICAP GmbH & Co. KG; *Int'l*, pg. 981
BEWI NORPLASTA AS—See BEWI Produkter AS; *Int'l*, pg. 1004
BEWI PRODUKTER AS; *Int'l*, pg. 1004
B.F. RICH CO. INC.; *U.S. Private*, pg. 420
BGF ECOMATERIALS, CO. LTD.—See BGF Co., Ltd.; *Int'l*, pg. 1007
B&G PLASTICS, INC; *U.S. Private*, pg. 418
BIOBE AS—See BEWi ASA; *Int'l*, pg. 1004
BIOME BIOPLASTICS LIMITED—See Biome Technologies plc; *Int'l*, pg. 1039
BIOMERICS, LLC—See Wasatch Advantage Group, LLC; *U.S. Private*, pg. 4445
BIOME TECHNOLOGIES PLC; *Int'l*, pg. 1039
BISCHOF & KLEIN (U.K.) LTD.—See Bischof + Klein GmbH & Co. KG; *Int'l*, pg. 1048
BK PLASTICS INDUSTRY, INC.; *U.S. Private*, pg. 568
BLACKHAWK MANUFACTURING, INC.—See Green Automotive Company; *U.S. Private*, pg. 1771
BLACKHAWK MOLDING CO. INC.; *U.S. Private*, pg. 575
BLUE DIAMOND INDUSTRIES LLC—See Hexatronic Group AB; *Int'l*, pg. 3370
BM POLYCO LTD.; *Int'l*, pg. 1075
BOLLORE PLASTIC FILM DIVISION—See Financiere de L'Odet; *Int'l*, pg. 2667
BONDSTRAND LTD.—See NOV, Inc.; *U.S. Public*, pg. 1544
BORAC EXPORT-IMPORT D.D.; *Int'l*, pg. 1112
BOREALMAGIC UNIPESSOAL, LDA.—See BERICAP GmbH & Co. KG; *Int'l*, pg. 981
BORG MANUFACTURING PTY LTD.; *Int'l*, pg. 1114
BORISOV PLASTIC PRODUCTS PLANT OPEN JOINT-STOCK COMPANY—See Concern Belneftekhim; *Int'l*, pg. 1764
BOSNAPLAST D.O.O.; *Int'l*, pg. 1116
BOSS CANADA, INC.—See Boss Holdings, Inc.; *U.S. Public*, pg. 371
BOWATER BUILDING PRODUCTS LTD.; *Int'l*, pg. 1123
BOWLER METCALF LIMITED; *Int'l*, pg. 1124
BPI PLC—See Berry Global Group, Inc; *U.S. Public*, pg. 322
BPREX CLOSURES, LLC—See Berry Global Group, Inc; *U.S. Public*, pg. 321
BPREX DELTA, INC.—See Berry Global Group, Inc; *U.S. Public*, pg. 321
BRADLEY HARDWARE INC.; *U.S. Private*, pg. 633
BRAM INDUSTRIES LTD.; *Int'l*, pg. 1138
BRENTWOOD INDUSTRIES INC. - NRG PRODUCTS DIVISION—See Brentwood Industries Inc.; *U.S. Private*, pg. 646
BRENTWOOD INDUSTRIES INC.; *U.S. Private*, pg. 646
BRIGHT PLASTICS, INC.—See Thunderbird LLC; *U.S. Private*, pg. 4166
BRISTOL FIBERLITE INDUSTRIES; *U.S. Private*, pg. 656
BUCKHORN INC.—See Myers Industries, Inc.; *U.S. Public*, pg. 1488
BUDDY'S CARPET AND FLOORING LLC; *U.S. Private*, pg. 679
BULL ENGINEERED PRODUCTS, INC.; *U.S. Private*, pg. 684
BUNZL ROMANIA SRL—See Bunzl plc; *Int'l*, pg. 1217
BURKE FLOORING PRODUCTS DIVISION—See Mannington Mills, Inc.; *U.S. Private*, pg. 2565
BURKE FLOORING PRODUCTS—See Mannington Mills, Inc.; *U.S. Private*, pg. 2565
BURKE INDUSTRIES, INC.—See Mannington Mills, Inc.; *U.S. Private*, pg. 2565
BURKE RUBBER CO.—See Mannington Mills, Inc.; *U.S. Private*, pg. 2566
BUTTIKOFER AG—See Bystronic AG; *Int'l*, pg. 1236
BWAY CORP. - ELK GROVE VILLAGE PLANT—See Stone Canyon Industries, LLC; *U.S. Private*, pg. 3817
BWAY CORP. - LAGRANGE PLANT—See Stone Canyon Industries, LLC; *U.S. Private*, pg. 3817
BWAY CORP. - LANGLEY PLANT—See Stone Canyon Industries, LLC; *U.S. Private*, pg. 3817
BWAY CORP. - MANSFIELD PLANT—See Stone Canyon Industries, LLC; *U.S. Private*, pg. 3817
BWAY CORP. - OAKVILLE PLANT—See Stone Canyon Industries, LLC; *U.S. Private*, pg. 3817
BWAY CORP. - SPRINGHILL PLANT—See Stone Canyon Industries, LLC; *U.S. Private*, pg. 3817
CABKA GMBH & CO. KG—See CABKA Group GmbH; *Int'l*, pg. 1245
CABKA NORTH AMERICA, INC.—See CABKA Group GmbH; *Int'l*, pg. 1245
CABKA N.V.; *Int'l*, pg. 1245
CABKA SPAIN S.L.U.—See CABKA Group GmbH; *Int'l*, pg. 1245
CABOT SPECIALTY CHEMICALS COORDINATION

326199 — ALL OTHER PLASTICS ...

CENTER—See Cabot Corporation; *U.S. Public*, pg. 417
CALICO PRECISION MOLDING, LLC; *U.S. Private*, pg. 717
CAMBRO MANUFACTURING COMPANY; *U.S. Private*, pg. 727
CAM PLASTIC INDUSTRY SDN. BHD.—See CAM Resources Berhad; *Int'l*, pg. 1267
CAM SPECIALTY PRODUCTS, INC.—See Riverstone Holdings LLC; *U.S. Private*, pg. 3448
CANADIAN THERMOS PRODUCTS, INC.—See Thermos L.L.C.; *U.S. Private*, pg. 4143
CANON MOLD CO., LTD.—See Canon Inc.; *Int'l*, pg. 1296
CAPITOL VIAL, INC.—See Thermo Fisher Scientific Inc.; *U.S. Public*, pg. 2145
CAPLUGS—See Windjammer Capital Investors, LLC; *U.S. Private*, pg. 4538
CAPRIHANS INDIA LIMITED—See Bilcare Limited; *Int'l*, pg. 1023
CAPROCK MANUFACTURING, INC.—See NN, Inc.; *U.S. Public*, pg. 1531
CAPSONIC GROUP LLC; *U.S. Private*, pg. 745
CAPTIVE PLASTICS, INC.—See Berry Global Group, Inc; *U.S. Public*, pg. 321
CAPTIVE PLASTICS, INC.—See Berry Global Group, Inc; *U.S. Public*, pg. 321
CARCLO PLC; *Int'l*, pg. 1321
CARCLO TECHNICAL PLASTICS (BRNO) S.R.O—See Carclo plc; *Int'l*, pg. 1321
CARCLO TECHNICAL PLASTICS LTD.—See Carclo plc; *Int'l*, pg. 1321
CARCLO TECHNICAL PLASTICS LTD—See Carclo plc; *Int'l*, pg. 1321
CARCLO TECHNICAL PLASTICS LTD—See Carclo plc; *Int'l*, pg. 1321
CARCLO TECHNICAL PLASTICS MITCHAM LTD.—See Carclo plc; *Int'l*, pg. 1321
CARCLO TECHNICAL PLASTICS—See Carclo plc; *Int'l*, pg. 1321
CARDINAL INDUSTRIES, INC.; *U.S. Private*, pg. 750
CARIBBEAN CAPS & CONTAINERS LTD.—See BERICAP GmbH & Co. KG; *Int'l*, pg. 981
CARLIER PLASTIQUES; *Int'l*, pg. 1337
CARLISLE FOODSERVICE PRODUCTS INCORPORATED—See The Jordan Company, L.P.; *U.S. Private*, pg. 4060
CAROLINA PRECISION PLASTICS LLC—See BlackBern Partners LLC; *U.S. Private*, pg. 573
CAROLINA PRECISION PLASTICS LLC—See Lee Equity Partners LLC; *U.S. Private*, pg. 2412
CAROMA INDUSTRIES LIMITED—See GWA Group Limited; *Int'l*, pg. 3190
CARSONITE—See Valmont Industries, Inc.; *U.S. Public*, pg. 2274
CARTON PLASTICO S.A.—See DS Smith Plc; *Int'l*, pg. 2207
CASCADE DESIGNS, INC. - MSR DIVISION—See Cascade Designs, Inc.; *U.S. Private*, pg. 779
CASCADE DESIGNS, INC.; *U.S. Private*, pg. 779
CCL TUBE, INC.—See CCL Industries Inc.; *Int'l*, pg. 1367
CCW PRODUCTS, INC.—See Priority Plastics, Inc.; *U.S. Private*, pg. 3267
CDF CORPORATION; *U.S. Private*, pg. 802
CDR SYSTEMS CORPORATION—See Hubbell Incorporated; *U.S. Public*, pg. 1067
CECO ENVIRONMENTAL NETHERLANDS B.V.—See CECO Environmental Corp.; *U.S. Public*, pg. 463
CELLECT LLC; *U.S. Private*, pg. 807
CELSTAR GROUP LLC; *U.S. Private*, pg. 808
CENTRAL PLASTICS & RUBBER CO., INC.; *U.S. Private*, pg. 824
CENTREX PLASTICS, LLC—See Highview Capital, LLC; *U.S. Private*, pg. 1942
CENTREX PLASTICS, LLC—See Victory Park Capital Advisors, LLC; *U.S. Private*, pg. 4379
CENTROTHERM SYSTEMTECHNIK GMBH—See CENTROTEC SE; *Int'l*, pg. 1414
CENTURY CONTAINER, LLC; *U.S. Private*, pg. 832
CENTURY MANUFACTURING, INC.; *U.S. Private*, pg. 833
CENTURY MOLD CO., INC; *U.S. Private*, pg. 833
CGL PACK ANNECY—See Advent International Corporation; *U.S. Private*, pg. 101
CGL PACK LORIENT—See Advent International Corporation; *U.S. Private*, pg. 101
CHAMPION WINDOWS MANUFACTURING INC.; *U.S. Private*, pg. 847
CHANGCHUN EFTEC CHEMICAL PRODUCTS LTD.—See EMS-Chemie Holding AG; *Int'l*, pg. 2393
CHANG CHUN PLASTICS CO., LTD.—See ChangChun Group; *Int'l*, pg. 1442
CHANGZHOU LANGBO SEALING TECHNOLOGY CO., LTD.; *Int'l*, pg. 1445
CHEE YUEN PLASTIC PRODUCTS (HUIZHOU) COMPANY LIMITED—See China Aerospace International Holdings Limited; *Int'l*, pg. 1481
CHEMIPLASTICA AB—See Chemiplastica S.p.A.; *Int'l*, pg. 1462
CHEMIPLASTICA INC.—See Chemiplastica S.p.A.; *Int'l*, pg. 1462
CHEM-TAINER INDUSTRIES, INC.; *U.S. Private*, pg. 871

CHEM-TAINER OF HAWAII—See Chem-Tainer Industries, Inc.; *U.S. Private*, pg. 871
CHI MEI CORPORATION—See Chi Mei Group; *Int'l*, pg. 1475
CHI MEI CORP - PRP TREE VALLEY PLANT—See Chi Mei Group; *Int'l*, pg. 1475
CHINA TREASURES NEW MATERIALS GROUP LTD.; *Int'l*, pg. 1560
CHINA XD PLASTICS COMPANY LTD.; *Int'l*, pg. 1563
CHIN YANG INDUSTRY CO., LTD.—See Chinyang Holdings Corporation; *Int'l*, pg. 1571
CHONG WAH PLASTICS SDN BHD; *Int'l*, pg. 1578
CITP SAS - LYON PLANT—See Carlier Plastiques; *Int'l*, pg. 1338
CITP SAS—See Carlier Plastiques; *Int'l*, pg. 1338
CKS PACKAGING, INC.; *U.S. Private*, pg. 909
CK TECHNOLOGIES, LLC—See Cascade Engineering, Inc.; *U.S. Private*, pg. 779
CLAIRSON PLASTICS LLC; *U.S. Private*, pg. 910
CLASSIC ADVANTAGE SDN BHD—See Fu Yu Corporation Limited; *Int'l*, pg. 2801
CLEAN TIDE CONTAINER, INC.—See IBC North America Inc.; *U.S. Private*, pg. 2028
CLEAR LAM PACKAGING, INC.—See Sonoco Products Company; *U.S. Public*, pg. 1904
CLEAR PACK COMPANY—See Sonoco Products Company; *U.S. Public*, pg. 1904
CLEAR PLASTICS LIMITED—See Hitech Corporation Ltd.; *Int'l*, pg. 3425
C-LINE PRODUCTS, INC.; *U.S. Private*, pg. 704
CLOSURE SYSTEMS INTERNATIONAL-KILGORE—See Cerberus Capital Management, L.P.; *U.S. Private*, pg. 837
COASTAL FILMS OF FLORIDA—See Alpha Industries, Inc.; *U.S. Private*, pg. 197
COASTAL INTEGRATED SERVICES, INC.; *U.S. Private*, pg. 956
COBELPLAST NV—See BAVARIA Industries Group AG; *Int'l*, pg. 899
COBRA PLASTICS, INC.—See Silgan Holdings, Inc.; *U.S. Public*, pg. 1878
COEXPAN MONTONATE S.R.L.—See Coexpan S.A.; *Int'l*, pg. 1690
COEXPAN S.A.; *Int'l*, pg. 1690
COLUMBIA DIE MOLD—See Precision Plastics, Inc.; *U.S. Private*, pg. 3246
COMAR, LLC; *U.S. Private*, pg. 980
COMPAGNIE PLASTIC OMNIUM S.A.—See Burelle S.A.; *Int'l*, pg. 1222
COMPOSITES TECHNOLOGY RESEARCH MALAYSIA SDN. BHD.—See DRB-HICOM Berhad; *Int'l*, pg. 2201
COMPTEK KUNSTSTOFFVERARBEITUNG GMBH—See Avient Corporation; *U.S. Public*, pg. 247
CONCEPT PLASTICS INC.; *U.S. Private*, pg. 1008
CONCH ANHUI ENERGY SAVING AND ENVIRONMENT PROTECTION NEW MATERIAL CO LTD; *Int'l*, pg. 1764
CONGOLEUM CORPORATION; *U.S. Private*, pg. 1013
CONNECTICUT PLASTICS LLC—See NN, Inc.; *U.S. Public*, pg. 1531
CONNOR CORPORATION; *U.S. Private*, pg. 1018
CON-PEARL NORTH AMERICA INC.—See Blue Cap AG; *Int'l*, pg. 1067
CONTAINER COMPONENTS INC.; *U.S. Private*, pg. 1026
CONTAINER SERVICES LLC; *U.S. Private*, pg. 1027
CONTINENTAL COMMERCIAL PRODUCTS, LLC—See Highview Capital, LLC; *U.S. Private*, pg. 1942
CONTINENTAL COMMERCIAL PRODUCTS, LLC—See Victory Park Capital Advisors, LLC; *U.S. Private*, pg. 4379
CONTINENTAL PLASTIC CARD COMPANY; *U.S. Private*, pg. 1030
CONTINENTAL PLASTICS CO. INC.; *U.S. Private*, pg. 1030
CONTINENTAL PRECISION CORP; *U.S. Private*, pg. 1030
CONWED PLASTICS LLC—See Mativ Holdings, Inc.; *U.S. Public*, pg. 1396
CONWED PLASTICS N.V.—See Mativ Holdings, Inc.; *U.S. Public*, pg. 1396
COOK POLYMER TECHNOLOGY—See Cook Group Incorporated; *U.S. Private*, pg. 1037
COOL GEAR INTERNATIONAL LLC—See Dometic Group AB; *Int'l*, pg. 2160
COPERION AB—See Hillenbrand, Inc.; *U.S. Public*, pg. 1036
COPERION CORP.—See Hillenbrand, Inc.; *U.S. Public*, pg. 1036
COPERION GMBH—See Hillenbrand, Inc.; *U.S. Public*, pg. 1036
COPERION IDEAL PVT LTD.—See Hillenbrand, Inc.; *U.S. Public*, pg. 1036
COPERION K.K.—See Hillenbrand, Inc.; *U.S. Public*, pg. 1036
COPERION LTD.—See Hillenbrand, Inc.; *U.S. Public*, pg. 1036
COPERION PTE LTD.—See Hillenbrand, Inc.; *U.S. Public*, pg. 1036
COPERION S.A.R.L.—See Hillenbrand, Inc.; *U.S. Public*, pg. 1036
CORAL PRODUCTS (MOULDINGS) LIMITED—See Coral

Products PLC; *Int'l*, pg. 1795
CORDSTRAP CANADA—See Cordstrap Netherlands B.V.; *Int'l*, pg. 1796
CORDSTRAP DEUTSCHLAND GMBH—See Cordstrap Netherlands B.V.; *Int'l*, pg. 1796
CORDSTRAP ESPANA S.L.U.—See Cordstrap Netherlands B.V.; *Int'l*, pg. 1796
CORDSTRAP FRANCE SARL—See Cordstrap Netherlands B.V.; *Int'l*, pg. 1796
CORDSTRAP INDIA PRIVATE LIMITED—See Cordstrap Netherlands B.V.; *Int'l*, pg. 1796
CORDSTRAP IRELAND LIMITED—See Cordstrap Netherlands B.V.; *Int'l*, pg. 1796
CORDSTRAP ITALIA S.R.L.—See Cordstrap Netherlands B.V.; *Int'l*, pg. 1796
CORDSTRAP LOAD SECURING SYSTEMS (WUXI) CO., LTD—See Cordstrap Netherlands B.V.; *Int'l*, pg. 1796
CORDSTRAP MALAYSIA SDN BHD—See Cordstrap Netherlands B.V.; *Int'l*, pg. 1796
CORDSTRAP MEXICO, S.A. DE C.V.—See Cordstrap Netherlands B.V.; *Int'l*, pg. 1797
CORDSTRAP NETHERLANDS B.V.; *Int'l*, pg. 1796
CORDSTRAP POLSKA SP. Z O.O.—See Cordstrap Netherlands B.V.; *Int'l*, pg. 1797
CORDSTRAP SA (PTY) LTD—See Cordstrap Netherlands B.V.; *Int'l*, pg. 1797
CORDSTRAP, S.R.O.—See Cordstrap Netherlands B.V.; *Int'l*, pg. 1797
CORDSTRAP UK LTD—See Cordstrap Netherlands B.V.; *Int'l*, pg. 1797
CORDSTRAP USA, INC.—See Cordstrap Netherlands B.V.; *Int'l*, pg. 1797
CORE MOLDING TECHNOLOGIES INC—See Core Molding Technologies, Inc.; *U.S. Public*, pg. 576
CORE SYSTEMS LLC; *U.S. Private*, pg. 1049
CORNERSTONE COMPOSITES INC.—See Wisconsin Thermoset Molding, Inc.; *U.S. Private*, pg. 4549
CORPORACION CORAL S. DE R.L. DE C.V.—See Illinois Tool Works Inc.; *U.S. Public*, pg. 1102
COVERIS FLEXIBLES (THOMASVILLE) US LLC—See Sun Capital Partners, Inc.; *U.S. Private*, pg. 3859
COVESTRO AG—See Bayer Aktiengesellschaft; *Int'l*, pg. 907
COVESTRO (INDIA) PRIVATE LIMITED—See Bayer Aktiengesellschaft; *Int'l*, pg. 907
COVESTRO LLC - AUTOMOTIVE PRODUCT CENTER—See Bayer Aktiengesellschaft; *Int'l*, pg. 907
COVESTRO LLC—See Bayer Aktiengesellschaft; *Int'l*, pg. 907
COVESTRO N.V.—See Bayer Aktiengesellschaft; *Int'l*, pg. 907
COVESTRO (TIELT) N.V.—See Bayer Aktiengesellschaft; *Int'l*, pg. 907
CPPC PUBLIC COMPANY LIMITED—See Charoen Pokphand Group Co., Ltd.; *Int'l*, pg. 1453
CPS CARDS; *U.S. Private*, pg. 1080
CPS GMBH; *Int'l*, pg. 1826
CPX INC.; *U.S. Private*, pg. 1081
CRAIG TECHNOLOGIES, INC.; *U.S. Private*, pg. 1083
CRANE COMPOSITES INC.—See Crane NXT, Co.; *U.S. Public*, pg. 590
CRANE PLASTICS HOLDING COMPANY; *U.S. Private*, pg. 1085
CRAWFORD INDUSTRIES, LLC—See The Jordan Company, L.P.; *U.S. Private*, pg. 4062
CREATIVE EXTRUDED PRODUCTS; *U.S. Private*, pg. 1088
CREATIVE MASTER L&W LIMITED—See Creative Master Bermuda Ltd.; *Int'l*, pg. 1833
CREATIVE PULTRUSIONS INC.—See Hill & Smith PLC; *Int'l*, pg. 3391
CROWN ASIA PACIFIC HOLDINGS, LTD.—See Crown Holdings, Inc.; *U.S. Public*, pg. 598
CROWN OBRIST AG—See Crown Holdings, Inc.; *U.S. Public*, pg. 598
CROWN VINALIMEX PACKAGING LTD.—See Crown Holdings, Inc.; *U.S. Public*, pg. 598
C/S DEUTSCHLAND GMBH—See Construction Specialties, Inc.; *U.S. Private*, pg. 1024
CSI JAPAN LTD.—See Cerberus Capital Management, L.P.; *U.S. Private*, pg. 837
CS MANUFACTURING, INC.; *U.S. Private*, pg. 1116
CTP ITALIA S.P.A.—See Information Services Group, Inc.; *U.S. Public*, pg. 1117
CULTEC, INC.—See Advanced Drainage Systems, Inc.; *U.S. Public*, pg. 46
CUSTOMISED PACKAGING LIMITED—See Coral Products PLC; *Int'l*, pg. 1795
CUSTOM-PAK DE MEXICO S. DE R.L. DE C.V.—See Custom-Pak, Inc.; *U.S. Private*, pg. 1130
CUSTOM-PAK, INC.; *U.S. Private*, pg. 1130
CUSTOM-PAK, INC. - WALNUT RIDGE PLANT—See Custom-Pak, Inc.; *U.S. Private*, pg. 1130
CUSTOM PLASTIC DEVELOPMENTS, INC.; *U.S. Private*, pg. 1129
CUSTOM PULTRUSIONS, INC.—See Andersen Corporation; *U.S. Private*, pg. 275
CV HOLDINGS, LLC.; *U.S. Private*, pg. 1132

326199 — ALL OTHER PLASTICS ...

CYDSA S.A. DE C.V. - ALTAMIRA PLANT—See Cydsa S.A.B. de C.V.; *Int'l*, pg. 1895
DACARTO BENVIC S.A.; *Int'l*, pg. 1903
DAEWON SEMICONDUCTOR PACKAGING INDUSTRIAL CORPORATION; *Int'l*, pg. 1910
DAICEL PACKSYSTEMS LTD.—See Daicel Corporation; *Int'l*, pg. 1919
DAICEL POLYMER, LTD.—See Daicel Corporation; *Int'l*, pg. 1919
DALIAN DATONG MACHINERY PRODUCTS CO., LTD.—See Hitachi Zosen Corporation; *Int'l*, pg. 3410
DAMAR PLASTICS MANUFACTURING, INC.—See Evome Medical Technologies Inc.; *U.S. Public*, pg. 805
DART DO BRASIL INDUSTRIA E COMERCIO LTDA.—See Tupperware Brands Corporation; *U.S. Public*, pg. 2204
DART S.A. DE C.V.—See Tupperware Brands Corporation; *U.S. Public*, pg. 2204
DART SUDAMERICANA S.A.—See Dart Container Corporation; *U.S. Private*, pg. 1160
DATACARD ASIA PACIFIC LIMITED—See DataCard Corporation; *U.S. Private*, pg. 1164
DATACARD ASIA PACIFIC LIMITED—See DataCard Corporation; *U.S. Private*, pg. 1164
DATACARD IBERICA, S.L.—See DataCard Corporation; *U.S. Private*, pg. 1164
DATACARD (SHANGHAI) TRADING CO., LTD.—See DataCard Corporation; *U.S. Private*, pg. 1164
DATACARD SOUTH PACIFIC (NZ) LTD.—See DataCard Corporation; *U.S. Private*, pg. 1164
DAVALOR MOLD COMPANY, LLC—See Blackford Capital LLC; *U.S. Private*, pg. 574
DAVID S. SMITH AMERICA INC—See Sealed Air Corporation; *U.S. Public*, pg. 1853
DAVIES MOLDING LLC—See The Heico Companies, L.L.C.; *U.S. Private*, pg. 4050
DBM TECHNOLOGIES LLC; *U.S. Private*, pg. 1179
DECEUNINCK BEHEER BV—See Deceuninck NV; *Int'l*, pg. 1999
DECEUNINCK KUNSTSTOF B.V.—See Deceuninck NV; *Int'l*, pg. 2000
DECEUNINCK LTD.—See Deceuninck NV; *Int'l*, pg. 2000
DECEUNINCK NV; *Int'l*, pg. 1999
DECEUNINCK NV SUCURSAL EM PORTUGAL—See Deceuninck NV; *Int'l*, pg. 2000
DECEUNINCK NV SUCURSAL EN ESPANA—See Deceuninck NV; *Int'l*, pg. 2000
DECEUNINCK PTY. LTD.—See Deceuninck NV; *Int'l*, pg. 2000
DECEUNINCK ROMANIA SRL—See Deceuninck NV; *Int'l*, pg. 2000
DECEUNINCK SA—See Deceuninck NV; *Int'l*, pg. 2000
DEDIENNE MULTIPLASTURGY GROUP SAS; *Int'l*, pg. 2002
DEEP RIVER PLASTICS, LLC—See Smith & Wesson Brands, Inc.; *U.S. Public*, pg. 1896
DEFLECT-O CORP.—See Jordan Industries, Inc.; *U.S. Private*, pg. 2235
DELFINGEN US, INC—See Delfingen Industry, S.A.; *Int'l*, pg. 2012
DELPHI RIMIR S.A. DE CV—See Aptiv PLC; *Int'l*, pg. 525
DELSTAR TECHNOLOGIES, INC.—See Mativ Holdings, Inc.; *U.S. Public*, pg. 1396
DELTAFORM LTD—See Apollo Global Management, Inc.; *U.S. Public*, pg. 154
DELTA PACIFIC PRODUCTS, INC.—See BlackBern Partners LLC; *U.S. Private*, pg. 573
DELTA PACIFIC PRODUCTS, INC.—See Lee Equity Partners LLC; *U.S. Private*, pg. 2412
DELTECH POLYMERS CORPORATION—See SK Capital Partners, LP; *U.S. Private*, pg. 3679
DENSO KATSUYAMA CO., LTD.—See Denso Corporation; *Int'l*, pg. 2029
DERBY FABRICATING SOLUTIONS, LLC—See Prophet Equity L.P.; *U.S. Private*, pg. 3286
DESIGN CENTER INC.; *U.S. Private*, pg. 1213
DESIGN DISPLAY GROUP INC.; *U.S. Private*, pg. 1213
DESIGNER SASH & DOOR SYSTEMS, INC.; *U.S. Private*, pg. 1215
DESIGN MOLDED PLASTICS INC.—See Big Shoulders Capital LLC; *U.S. Private*, pg. 554
DESIGN PLASTICS, INC.—See Coda Resources, Ltd.; *U.S. Private*, pg. 959
DESIGN TANKS LLC—See Aldine Capital Partners, Inc.; *U.S. Private*, pg. 159
DESWELL INDUSTRIES, INC.; *Int'l*, pg. 2047
DHABRIYA POLYWOOD LIMITED; *Int'l*, pg. 2097
DIC KAKO, INC.—See DIC Corporation; *Int'l*, pg. 2108
DICKTEN MASCH PLASTICS—See Techniplas, LLC; *U.S. Private*, pg. 3954
DIC MOLDING, INC.—See DIC Corporation; *Int'l*, pg. 2108
DIC PLASTICS, INC.—See DIC Corporation; *Int'l*, pg. 2108
DIELECTRIC CORPORATION; *U.S. Private*, pg. 1228
DIEMOLDING CORPORATION; *U.S. Private*, pg. 1228
DIE-MOLD TOOL LTD.—See Mueller Industries, Inc.; *U.S. Public*, pg. 1484
DIETZEL GMBH; *Int'l*, pg. 2117
DIMCO-GRAY CORP.; *U.S. Private*, pg. 1232

DIMEX LLC—See Westlake Corporation; *U.S. Public*, pg. 2360
DIPCRAFT MANUFACTURING COMPANY; *U.S. Private*, pg. 1234
DISA INDUSTRIES INC.—See Georg Fischer AG; *Int'l*, pg. 2935
DISPENSING DYNAMICS INTERNATIONAL; *U.S. Private*, pg. 1238
DISPLAY PACK INC.; *U.S. Private*, pg. 1239
DIXIE NUMERICS LLC; *U.S. Private*, pg. 1245
DLHBOWLES, INC.—See Apollo Global Management, Inc.; *U.S. Public*, pg. 146
D MARTONE INDUSTRIES INC.—See AJD Holding Co.; *U.S. Private*, pg. 144
DNP BUSINESS CONSULTING (SHANGHAI) CO., LTD.—See Dai Nippon Printing Co., Ltd.; *Int'l*, pg. 1914
DNP DATA TECHNO CO., LTD.—See Dai Nippon Printing Co., Ltd.; *Int'l*, pg. 1914
DNP PLASTIC MOLDING (SHANGHAI) CO., LTD.—See Dai Nippon Printing Co., Ltd.; *Int'l*, pg. 1915
DNP TAMURA PLASTIC CO., LTD.—See Dai Nippon Printing Co., Ltd.; *Int'l*, pg. 1915
DNP TECHNO POLYMER CO., LTD.—See Dai Nippon Printing Co., Ltd.; *Int'l*, pg. 1915
DO-IT CORPORATION; *U.S. Private*, pg. 1250
DOLBY LABORATORIES, INC.; *U.S. Public*, pg. 672
DOLCO PACKAGING—See Genstar Capital, LLC; *U.S. Private*, pg. 1678
DOLCO PACKAGING—See Genstar Capital, LLC; *U.S. Private*, pg. 1678
DONG A PLASTIC GROUP JSC; *Int'l*, pg. 2163
DONG GUAN CHENG DA METAL PRODUCT COMPANY LIMITED—See COXON Precise Industrial Co., Ltd.; *Int'l*, pg. 1823
DONG GUAN DAI-ICHI SEIKO MOLD & PLASTICS CO., LTD.—See I-PEX Inc.; *Int'l*, pg. 3563
DOPLA S.P.A.; *Int'l*, pg. 2174
DOREL JUVENILE GROUP, INC.—See Dorel Industries, Inc.; *Int'l*, pg. 2176
DOSKOCIL MANUFACTURING COMPANY INC.—See Platinum Equity, LLC; *U.S. Private*, pg. 3202
DO THANH TECHNOLOGY CORPORATION; *Int'l*, pg. 2152
DOUGLAS CORPORATION; *U.S. Private*, pg. 1267
DOUGLAS STEPHEN PLASTICS, INC.; *U.S. Private*, pg. 1267
DOW OLEFINVERBUND GMBH—See Dow Inc.; *U.S. Public*, pg. 684
D PLAST-EFTEC NN—See EMS-Chemie Holding AG; *Int'l*, pg. 2393
DROP STOP, LLC; *U.S. Private*, pg. 1279
DRUGASAR LTD.—See DRU Verwarming B.V.; *Int'l*, pg. 2206
DRUG PLASTICS CLOSURES—See Drug Plastics & Glass Co. Inc.; *U.S. Private*, pg. 1279
DS SMITH CORREX—See DS Smith Plc; *Int'l*, pg. 2207
DS SMITH DUCAPLAST—See DS Smith Plc; *Int'l*, pg. 2207
DS SMITH PLASTICS LTD.—See Sealed Air Corporation; *U.S. Public*, pg. 1853
DS SMITH REPLEN—See Sealed Air Corporation; *U.S. Public*, pg. 1853
DS SMITH RIVATEX—See DS Smith Plc; *Int'l*, pg. 2207
DS SMITH SLOVAKIA S.R.O.—See DS Smith Plc; *Int'l*, pg. 2207
DUPONT STYLO CORPORATION—See DuPont de Nemours, Inc.; *U.S. Public*, pg. 693
DUPONT WASHINGTON WORKS—See Corteva, Inc.; *U.S. Public*, pg. 584
DURANT PLASTICS & MANUFACTURING, INC.; *U.S. Private*, pg. 1292
DURCON COMPANY OF POLAND SP. Z O.O.—See Clayton, Dubilier & Rice, LLC; *U.S. Private*, pg. 930
DURCON, LLC—See Clayton, Dubilier & Rice, LLC; *U.S. Private*, pg. 930
DUVAPLAST A.D.; *Int'l*, pg. 2236
DWEWANG INTERNATIONAL CORP.—See BERICAP GmbH & Co. KG; *Int'l*, pg. 981
D&W FINE PACK LLC - FORT CALHOUN—See Mid Oaks Investments LLC; *U.S. Private*, pg. 2706
DW PLASTICS NV—See Sealed Air Corporation; *U.S. Public*, pg. 1853
DYNARIC, INC.; *U.S. Private*, pg. 1299
DYNISCO INSTRUMENTS S.A.R.L.—See Roper Technologies, Inc.; *U.S. Public*, pg. 1811
EAGLE AFFILIATES, INC.—See Injectron Corporation; *U.S. Private*, pg. 2077
EARTHMINDED FRANCE—See Greif Inc.; *U.S. Public*, pg. 969
EASTCOMPEACE (INDIA) CO., LTD.—See Eastcompeace Technology Co., Ltd.; *Int'l*, pg. 2271
EASTCOMPEACE (RUSSIA) CO., LTD.—See Eastcompeace Technology Co., Ltd.; *Int'l*, pg. 2271
EASTCOMPEACE SMART CARD (BANGLADESH) CO., LTD.—See Eastcompeace Technology Co., Ltd.; *Int'l*, pg. 2271
EASTERN POLYPACK CO., LTD.—See Eastern Polymer Group Public Company Limited; *Int'l*, pg. 2273
EFTEC ASIA PTE. LTD.—See EMS-Chemie Holding AG; *Int'l*, pg. 2393

EFTEC ENGINEERING AB—See EMS-Chemie Holding AG; *Int'l*, pg. 2393
EFTEC LTD.—See EMS-Chemie Holding AG; *Int'l*, pg. 2393
EFTEC MARKET GMBH—See EMS-Chemie Holding AG; *Int'l*, pg. 2393
EFTEC N.V.—See EMS-Chemie Holding AG; *Int'l*, pg. 2393
EFTEC S.A.R.L.—See EMS-Chemie Holding AG; *Int'l*, pg. 2394
EFTEC S.A.—See EMS-Chemie Holding AG; *Int'l*, pg. 2394
EFTEC (THAILAND) CO. LTD.—See EMS-Chemie Holding AG; *Int'l*, pg. 2393
EGE PROFIL AS—See Deceuninck NV; *Int'l*, pg. 2000
EGS AUTOMATION GMBH—See AMETEK, Inc.; *U.S. Public*, pg. 120
EHRLICH WERKZEUG & GERATEBAU GMBH—See Amphenol Corporation; *U.S. Public*, pg. 130
E-KART ELECTRONIC CARD SYSTEMS CO.—See Eczacibasi Holding A.S.; *Int'l*, pg. 2301
ELDRA KUNSTSTOFFTECHNIK GMBH—See Draexlmaier Gruppe; *Int'l*, pg. 2198
ELEKEM LTD.—See Ensinger GmbH; *Int'l*, pg. 2447
ELGIN MOLDED PLASTICS INC.; *U.S. Private*, pg. 1359
ELKHART PLASTICS, INC.; *U.S. Private*, pg. 1363
ELRINGKLINGER ENGINEERED PLASTICS NORTH AMERICA, INC.—See ElringKlinger AG; *Int'l*, pg. 2369
ELRINGKLINGER ENGINEERED PLASTICS (QINGDAO) CO., LTD.—See ElringKlinger AG; *Int'l*, pg. 2369
ELRINGKLINGER ENGINEERED PLASTICS (QINGDAO) COMMERCIAL CO., LTD.—See ElringKlinger AG; *Int'l*, pg. 2369
ELRING KLINGER, S.A.U.—See ElringKlinger AG; *Int'l*, pg. 2369
EMICO PENANG SDN. BHD.—See Emico Holdings Berhad; *Int'l*, pg. 2380
E'MOLD HOLDING PTE. LTD.—See Accrelist Ltd.; *Int'l*, pg. 93
EMPLAL NORDESTE EMBALAGENS PLASTICAS LTDA.—See Amcor plc; *Int'l*, pg. 418
EMPLAL PARTICIPACOES S.A.—See Amcor plc; *Int'l*, pg. 418
EMS-CHEMIE AG—See EMS-Chemie Holding AG; *Int'l*, pg. 2393
EMS-CHEMIE (CHINA) LTD.—See EMS-Chemie Holding AG; *Int'l*, pg. 2393
EMS-CHEMIE (DEUTSCHLAND) GMBH—See EMS-Chemie Holding AG; *Int'l*, pg. 2393
EMS-CHEMIE HOLDING AG; *Int'l*, pg. 2393
EMS-CHEMIE (KOREA) LTD.—See EMS-Chemie Holding AG; *Int'l*, pg. 2393
EMS-CHEMIE (NEUMUNSTER) GMBH CO. KG—See EMS-Chemie Holding AG; *Int'l*, pg. 2393
EMS-CHEMIE (SUZHOU) LTD.—See EMS-Chemie Holding AG; *Int'l*, pg. 2393
EMS-CHEMIE (TAIWAN) LTD.—See EMS-Chemie Holding AG; *Int'l*, pg. 2393
EMS-CHEMIE (UK) LTD.—See EMS-Chemie Holding AG; *Int'l*, pg. 2393
EMS-PATENT AG—See EMS-Chemie Holding AG; *Int'l*, pg. 2393
EMS-UBE LTD.—See EMS-Chemie Holding AG; *Int'l*, pg. 2393
ENDURANCE ENGINEERING S.R.L.—See Affirma Capital Limited; *Int'l*, pg. 187
ENDURA PLASTICS, INC.; *U.S. Private*, pg. 1392
ENDURO SYSTEMS, INC.; *U.S. Private*, pg. 1392
ENFLO LLC—See Odyssey Investment Partners, LLC; *U.S. Private*, pg. 2995
ENGINEERED PLASTIC COMPONENTS INC.; *U.S. Private*, pg. 1398
ENGINEERED PLASTICS COMPANY, LLC—See MacLean-Fogg Company; *U.S. Private*, pg. 2537
ENGINEERED PLASTICS INC.; *U.S. Private*, pg. 1398
ENGINEERED POLYMERS CORPORATION—See Imperial Plastics, Inc.; *U.S. Private*, pg. 2049
ENOR CORPORATION; *U.S. Private*, pg. 1401
ENPAC LLC; *U.S. Private*, pg. 1401
ENPLAS CORPORATION - ENGINEERING PLASTICS PRODUCTS DIVISION—See ENPLAS CORPORATION; *Int'l*, pg. 2445
ENPLAS CORPORATION - KANUMA PLANT—See ENPLAS CORPORATION; *Int'l*, pg. 2445
ENPLAS CORPORATION; *Int'l*, pg. 2444
ENPLAS LIFE TECH, INC.—See ENPLAS CORPORATION; *Int'l*, pg. 2445
ENPLAS PRECISION (MALAYSIA) SDN. BHD.—See ENPLAS CORPORATION; *Int'l*, pg. 2445
ENPLAS PRECISION (THAILAND) CO., LTD.—See ENPLAS CORPORATION; *Int'l*, pg. 2445
ENSINGER GROUP LIMITED—See Ensinger GmbH; *Int'l*, pg. 2447
ENSINGER KOREA LTD.—See Ensinger GmbH; *Int'l*, pg. 2447
ENSINGER PRECISION ENGINEERING LTD.—See Ensinger GmbH; *Int'l*, pg. 2448
ENSINGER (SHANGHAI) ENGINEERING PLASTICS CO., LTD.—See Ensinger GmbH; *Int'l*, pg. 2447
ENSINGER TECARIM GMBH—See Ensinger GmbH; *Int'l*, pg. 2448

N.A.I.C.S. INDEX

326199 — ALL OTHER PLASTICS ...

ENSINGER TURKEY TEKNIK DANISMANLIK LTD. STI.—See Ensinger GmbH; *Int'l*, pg. 2448
ENTEGRIS SINGAPORE PTE. LTD.—See Entegris, Inc.; *U.S. Public*, pg. 776
ENTEK HOLDING LLC; *U.S. Private*, pg. 1403
ENVASES CMF S.A.—See Embotelladora Andina S.A.; *Int'l*, pg. 2375
ENVASES MULTIPAC S.A. DE C.V.—See Illinois Tool Works Inc.; *U.S. Public*, pg. 1103
ENVISION PLASTICS INDUSTRIES, LLC—See Loews Corporation; *U.S. Public*, pg. 1339
EPC-COLUMBIA, INC.—See Engineered Plastic Components Inc.; *U.S. Private*, pg. 1398
EPC, INC.-EAST TROY—See Engineered Plastic Components Inc.; *U.S. Private*, pg. 1398
EPG INNOVATION CENTER CO., LTD.—See Eastern Polymer Group Public Company Limited; *Int'l*, pg. 2273
EPWIN GROUP PLC; *Int'l*, pg. 2466
ERCROS SA - PLASTICS DIVISION—See Ercros SA; *Int'l*, pg. 2490
ER&GE GMBH; *Int'l*, pg. 2488
ERGIS-RECYCLING SP. Z O.O.—See Ergis S.A.; *Int'l*, pg. 2491
ERG S.A.; *Int'l*, pg. 2490
ESE BV—See Berry Global Group, Inc; *U.S. Public*, pg. 321
ESE FRANCE SA—See Berry Global Group, Inc; *U.S. Public*, pg. 321
ESE GMBH—See Berry Global Group, Inc; *U.S. Public*, pg. 321
ESE KFT—See Berry Global Group, Inc; *U.S. Public*, pg. 321
ESE NV—See Berry Global Group, Inc; *U.S. Public*, pg. 321
ESE SP. Z O.O.—See Berry Global Group, Inc; *U.S. Public*, pg. 321
ESE WORLD BV—See Berry Global Group, Inc; *U.S. Public*, pg. 321
ESSENTRA (BANGOR) LTD.—See Essentra plc; *Int'l*, pg. 2511
ESSENTRA COMPONENTS KFT—See Essentra plc; *Int'l*, pg. 2511
ESSENTRA COMPONENTS LTD.—See Essentra plc; *Int'l*, pg. 2511
ESSENTRA COMPONENT SOLUTIONS—See Essentra plc; *Int'l*, pg. 2511
ESSENTRA COMPONENTS S.R.O.—See Essentra plc; *Int'l*, pg. 2511
ESSENTRA CORPORATION—See Essentra plc; *Int'l*, pg. 2511
ESSENTRA EXTRUSION B.V.—See Essentra plc; *Int'l*, pg. 2511
ESSENTRA LIMITED—See Essentra plc; *Int'l*, pg. 2511
ESSENTRA PACKAGING B.V.—See Essentra plc; *Int'l*, pg. 2511
ESSENTRA PACKAGING GMBH—See Essentra plc; *Int'l*, pg. 2511
ESSENTRA PLC; *Int'l*, pg. 2510
ESSENTRA PTY. LTD.—See Essentra plc; *Int'l*, pg. 2511
ESSENTRA SP. Z O.O.—See Essentra plc; *Int'l*, pg. 2511
ETERNIT ATLANTICO S.A.—See Grupo Empresarial Kaluz S.A. de C.V.; *Int'l*, pg. 3126
ETERNIT COLOMBIANA S.A.—See Grupo Empresarial Kaluz S.A. de C.V.; *Int'l*, pg. 3127
ETERNIT PACIFICO S.A.—See Grupo Empresarial Kaluz S.A. de C.V.; *Int'l*, pg. 3127
ETEX SA/NV; *Int'l*, pg. 2521
ETIMEX GMBH; *Int'l*, pg. 2523
ETIMEX TECHNICAL COMPONENTS GMBH—See Etimex GmbH; *Int'l*, pg. 2523
ETIMEX USA, INC.—See Etimex GmbH; *Int'l*, pg. 2523
E.T. MACKENZIE COMPANY INC.; *U.S. Private*, pg. 1307
E&T PLASTIC MANUFACTURING CO.; *U.S. Private*, pg. 1301
EUROFLACO COMPIEGNE SARL; *Int'l*, pg. 2552
EUROFOAM DEUTSCHLAND GMBH SCHAUMSTOFFE—See Greiner Holding AG; *Int'l*, pg. 3078
EURO PACKAGING EUROPE—See Europackaging Ltd.; *Int'l*, pg. 2555
EUROPACKAGING LTD. - EURO PACKAGING LUXURY DIVISION—See Europackaging Ltd.; *Int'l*, pg. 2555
EUROPACKAGING LTD.; *Int'l*, pg. 2555
EUROVITI S.R.L.; *Int'l*, pg. 2559
EVADIX LABELS S.R.L.—See Amcor plc; *Int'l*, pg. 418
EVANS MANUFACTURING INC.; *U.S. Private*, pg. 1435
EVCO PLASTICS INC.; *U.S. Private*, pg. 1436
EVER LOTUS ENTERPRISE CO., LTD.; *Int'l*, pg. 2562
EXCEET CARD AG—See H2APEX Group SCA; *Int'l*, pg. 3199
EXCEET CARD AUSTRIA GMBH—See H2APEX Group SCA; *Int'l*, pg. 3200
EXCEET CARD GROUP AG—See H2APEX Group SCA; *Int'l*, pg. 3199
EXEL COMPOSITES GMBH—See Exel Composites Oyj; *Int'l*, pg. 2581
EXEL COMPOSITES UK LTD.—See Exel Composites Oyj; *Int'l*, pg. 2581
EXLON EXTRUSION INC—See Odyssey Investment Partners, LLC; *U.S. Private*, pg. 2995
EXXARO TILES LIMITED; *Int'l*, pg. 2592

EXXONMOBIL CHEMICAL COMPANY—See Exxon Mobil Corporation; *U.S. Public*, pg. 814
EZZI VISION PTY LTD; *Int'l*, pg. 2594
THE FABRI-FORM COMPANY—See Kruger Brown Holdings, LLC; *U.S. Private*, pg. 2353
FABRI-KAL CORPORATION—See Pactiv Evergreen Inc.; *U.S. Public*, pg. 1633
FABRIK INDUSTRIES INC.; *U.S. Private*, pg. 1459
FAERCH FRANCE SAS—See Advent International Corporation; *U.S. Private*, pg. 101
FALCON PLASTICS INC.; *U.S. Private*, pg. 1466
FAST PLASTIC PARTS LLC—See COMSovereign Holding Corp.; *U.S. Public*, pg. 562
FAURECIA INTERIEUR INDUSTRIE—See FORVIA SE; *Int'l*, pg. 2746
FAWN INDUSTRIES, INC.; *U.S. Private*, pg. 1484
FDC INTERNATIONAL LIMITED—See FDC Ltd; *Int'l*, pg. 2628
FEDERAL-MOGUL WIESBADEN GMBH—See Apollo Global Management, Inc.; *U.S. Public*, pg. 162
FERRIOT, INC.; *U.S. Private*, pg. 1498
FEY INDUSTRIES, INC.; *U.S. Private*, pg. 1500
FIBERGLASS TECHNOLOGY INDUSTRIES—See Celstar Group Inc.; *U.S. Public*, pg. 808
FIBERGRATE COMPOSITE STRUCTURES, INC.—See RPM International Inc.; *U.S. Public*, pg. 1818
FILAMAT COMPOSITES INC.—See Zurn Elkay Water Solutions Corporation; *U.S. Public*, pg. 2412
FILMTECH CORP.—See Alpha Industries, Inc.; *U.S. Private*, pg. 197
FINELINE PROTOTYPING, INC.—See Proto Labs, Inc.; *U.S. Public*, pg. 1729
FISCHER MEDTECH PTE LTD.—See Platinum Equity, LLC; *U.S. Private*, pg. 3207
FISCHER TECHNOLOGY PTE LTD.—See Platinum Equity, LLC; *U.S. Private*, pg. 3207
FISCHER-TECH THAILAND—See Platinum Equity, LLC; *U.S. Private*, pg. 3207
FLAMBEAU, INC. - FLAMBEAU BLOW MOLDING FACILITY—See Nordic Group of Companies, Ltd.; *U.S. Private*, pg. 2937
FLAMBEAU, INC. - FLAMBEAU COLUMBUS FACILITY—See Nordic Group of Companies, Ltd.; *U.S. Private*, pg. 2937
FLAMBEAU, INC. - FLAMBEAU FLUID SYSTEMS DIVISION—See Nordic Group of Companies, Ltd.; *U.S. Private*, pg. 2937
FLAMBEAU, INC. - FLAMBEAU HARDWARE PRODUCTS DIVISION—See Nordic Group of Companies, Ltd.; *U.S. Private*, pg. 2937
FLAMBEAU, INC. - FLAMBEAU INJECTION MOLDING FACILITY—See Nordic Group of Companies, Ltd.; *U.S. Private*, pg. 2937
FLAMBEAU, INC. - FLAMBEAU MADISON FACILITY—See Nordic Group of Companies, Ltd.; *U.S. Private*, pg. 2937
FLAMBEAU, INC. - FLAMBEAU MIDDLEFIELD FACILITY—See Nordic Group of Companies, Ltd.; *U.S. Private*, pg. 2937
FLAMBEAU, INC. - FLAMBEAU PHOENIX FACILITY—See Nordic Group of Companies, Ltd.; *U.S. Private*, pg. 2937
FLAMBEAU, INC. - FLAMBEAU SHARON CENTER FACILITY—See Nordic Group of Companies, Ltd.; *U.S. Private*, pg. 2937
FLAMBEAU, INC. - FLAMBEAU WELDON FACILITY—See Nordic Group of Companies, Ltd.; *U.S. Private*, pg. 2937
FLAMBEAU, INC. - PLASTICOS FLAMBEAU FACILITY—See Nordic Group of Companies, Ltd.; *U.S. Private*, pg. 2937
FLAMBEAU, INC.—See Nordic Group of Companies, Ltd.; *U.S. Private*, pg. 2936
FLAMBEAU PLASTICS CO.—See Nordic Group of Companies, Ltd.; *U.S. Private*, pg. 2936
FLAMBEAU PRODUCTS-COLUMBUS—See Nordic Group of Companies, Ltd.; *U.S. Private*, pg. 2937
FLAMBEAU SOUTHEAST CO.—See Nordic Group of Companies, Ltd.; *U.S. Private*, pg. 2937
FLAMBEAU TECHNOLOGIES—See Nordic Group of Companies, Ltd.; *U.S. Private*, pg. 2937
FLAME TREE GROUP HOLDINGS LTD.; *Int'l*, pg. 2698
FLEX CONCEPTS INC.—See Entegris, Inc.; *U.S. Public*, pg. 777
FLEXERGIS SP. Z O.O.—See Ergis S.A.; *Int'l*, pg. 2491
FLEXOPACK PLASTICS S.A.—See FLEXOPACK S.A.; *Int'l*, pg. 2705
FLEXOPACK PTY LTD—See FLEXOPACK S.A.; *Int'l*, pg. 2705
FLEXPAK CORPORATION—See Kohlberg & Company, LLC; *U.S. Private*, pg. 2338
FLEXSOL PACKAGING CORP. - NORTH CAROLINA FACILITY—See Alpha Industries, Inc.; *U.S. Private*, pg. 197
FLEXSOL PACKAGING CORP. - TENNESSEE FACILITY—See Alpha Industries, Inc.; *U.S. Private*, pg. 197
FLEX TECHNOLOGIES INC.; *U.S. Private*, pg. 1543
FLEXTOR INC.—See CECO Environmental Corp.; *U.S. Public*, pg. 463

FLEXTRONICS PLASTICS, S.A. DE C.V.—See Flex Ltd.; *Int'l*, pg. 2704
FLEXTRONICS PLASTIC TECHNOLOGY (SHENZHEN) LTD.—See Flex Ltd.; *Int'l*, pg. 2704
FLEXTRONICS S.R.L—See Flex Ltd.; *Int'l*, pg. 2704
FLITETEC LTD—See ALA SpA; *Int'l*, pg. 289
FLO S.P.A.; *Int'l*, pg. 2706
FLOWCRETE GROUP LTD.—See RPM International Inc.; *U.S. Public*, pg. 1818
FLOWCRETE (HONG KONG) LTD—See RPM International Inc.; *U.S. Public*, pg. 1818
FLOWCRETE NORTH AMERICA INC.—See RPM International Inc.; *U.S. Public*, pg. 1819
FLOWCRETE POLSKA SP. Z O.O.—See RPM International Inc.; *U.S. Public*, pg. 1819
FLOWCRETE SA (PTY) LTD—See RPM International Inc.; *U.S. Public*, pg. 1819
FLOWCRETE SWEDEN AB—See RPM International Inc.; *U.S. Public*, pg. 1819
FLUORTEK, INC.—See Nordson Corporation; *U.S. Public*, pg. 1533
FM STRUCTURAL PLASTIC TECHNOLOGY INC.; *U.S. Private*, pg. 1553
FOAM FABRICATORS INC. - MOLDING PLANT—See Compass Diversified Holdings; *U.S. Public*, pg. 559
FOODHANDLER INC.—See Bunzl plc; *Int'l*, pg. 1218
FOOSUNG INDUSTRIAL CO., LTD. - EUMSUNG FACTORY—See Foosung Co., Ltd.; *Int'l*, pg. 2728
FOOSUNG INDUSTRIAL CO., LTD.—See Foosung Co., Ltd.; *Int'l*, pg. 2728
FORBO FLOORING, INC.—See Forbo Holding Ltd.; *Int'l*, pg. 2729
FORBO HOLDING LTD.; *Int'l*, pg. 2729
FORBO INTERNATIONAL HONG KONG LTD.—See Forbo Holding Ltd.; *Int'l*, pg. 2729
FORBO LINOLIUM B.V.—See Forbo Holding Ltd.; *Int'l*, pg. 2730
FORBO MANAGEMENT SA—See Forbo Holding Ltd.; *Int'l*, pg. 2730
FORBO-NAIRN LTD.—See Forbo Holding Ltd.; *Int'l*, pg. 2730
FORBO PARQUET AB—See Forbo Holding Ltd.; *Int'l*, pg. 2730
FORBO SARLINO SA—See Forbo Holding Ltd.; *Int'l*, pg. 2730
FORMED FIBER TECHNOLOGIES, INC.—See MPE Partners, LLC; *U.S. Private*, pg. 2803
FORMICA IKI OY—See HAL Trust N.V.; *Int'l*, pg. 3223
FORMOSA ASAHI SPANDEX CO., LTD.—See Asahi Kasei Corporation; *Int'l*, pg. 596
FORMOSA ASAHI SPANDEX CO., LTD.—See Formosa Plastics Corporation; *Int'l*, pg. 2735
FORMOSAN RUBBER GROUP INC.; *Int'l*, pg. 2736
FORMOSA PLASTICS CORPORATION - CARBIDE DIVISION—See Formosa Plastics Corporation; *Int'l*, pg. 2735
FORMOSA PLASTICS CORPORATION, DELAWARE—See Formosa Plastics Corporation; *Int'l*, pg. 2735
FORMOSA PLASTICS CORPORATION - LINYUAN PLANT—See Formosa Plastics Corporation; *Int'l*, pg. 2735
FORMOSA PLASTICS CORPORATION, LOUISIANA—See Formosa Plastics Corporation; *Int'l*, pg. 2736
FORMOSA PLASTICS CORPORATION - PLASTICS DIVISION—See Formosa Plastics Corporation; *Int'l*, pg. 2735
FORMOSA PLASTICS CORPORATION; *Int'l*, pg. 2735
FORMOSA PLASTICS CORPORATION - TAIRYLAN DIVISION—See Formosa Plastics Corporation; *Int'l*, pg. 2735
FORMOSA PLASTICS CORPORATION, TEXAS—See Formosa Plastics Corporation; *Int'l*, pg. 2736
FORMTECH ENTERPRISES, INC.; *U.S. Private*, pg. 1572
FORMTEX PLASTICS CORP.—See Good Natured Products Inc.; *Int'l*, pg. 3038
FORTEQ DERENDINGEN AG—See forteq Group; *Int'l*, pg. 2738
FORTEQ GROUP; *Int'l*, pg. 2738
FORTEQ ITALY S.P.A.—See forteq Group; *Int'l*, pg. 2738
FORTEQ NETHERLANDS BV—See forteq Group; *Int'l*, pg. 2738
FORTEQ NORTH AMERICA, INC.—See forteq Group; *Int'l*, pg. 2738
FORTEQ UK LTD.—See forteq Group; *Int'l*, pg. 2738
FORTIS PLASTICS LLC—See Monomoy Capital Partners LLC; *U.S. Private*, pg. 2772
FOSTER CORPORATION; *U.S. Private*, pg. 1578
FPCO SAGA CO, LTD.—See FP Corporation; *Int'l*, pg. 2756
FREUDENBERG NOK—See Freudenberg SE; *Int'l*, pg. 2788
FSPG HI-TECH CO., LTD.; *Int'l*, pg. 2800
FT. WAYNE PLASTICS INC.; *U.S. Private*, pg. 1618
FU CHUN SHIN MACHINERY MANUFACTURE CO., LTD.; *Int'l*, pg. 2800
FU HAO MANUFACTURING (M) SDN BHD—See Fu Yu Corporation Limited; *Int'l*, pg. 2801
FUJIKON PACKING MATERIAL COMPANY LIMITED—See Fujikon Industrial Holdings Ltd; *Int'l*, pg. 2826

326199 — ALL OTHER PLASTICS

FUKOKU CZECH S.R.O.—See Fukoku Co., Ltd.; *Int'l*, pg. 2839
FUKUVI CHEMICAL INDUSTRY CO., LTD. - AWARA FACTORY—See Fukuvi Chemical Industry Co., Ltd.; *Int'l*, pg. 2841
FUKUVI CHEMICAL INDUSTRY CO., LTD. - MIKATA FACTORY—See Fukuvi Chemical Industry Co., Ltd.; *Int'l*, pg. 2841
FUKUVI CHEMICAL INDUSTRY CO., LTD. - OSAKA FACTORY—See Fukuvi Chemical Industry Co., Ltd.; *Int'l*, pg. 2841
FUKUVI CHEMICAL INDUSTRY CO., LTD. - SAKAI FACTORY—See Fukuvi Chemical Industry Co., Ltd.; *Int'l*, pg. 2841
FUKUVI HOUSING CO., LTD.—See Fukuvi Chemical Industry Co., Ltd.; *Int'l*, pg. 2841
FUKUVI (THAILAND) CO., LTD.—See Fukuvi Chemical Industry Co., Ltd.; *Int'l*, pg. 2841
FUKUVI USA, INC.—See Fukuvi Chemical Industry Co., Ltd.; *Int'l*, pg. 2841
FUKUVI VIETNAM CO., LTD.—See Fukuvi Chemical Industry Co., Ltd.; *Int'l*, pg. 2841
FULING GLOBAL INC.; *Int'l*, pg. 2842
FU YU CORPORATION LIMITED; *Int'l*, pg. 2801
FU YU MOULDING & TOOLING (DONGGUAN) CO., LTD.—See Fu Yu Corporation Limited; *Int'l*, pg. 2801
FU YU MOULDING & TOOLING (SHANGHAI) CO., LTD.—See Fu Yu Corporation Limited; *Int'l*, pg. 2801
FU YU MOULDING & TOOLING (SUZHOU) CO., LTD.—See Fu Yu Corporation Limited; *Int'l*, pg. 2801
FU YU MOULDING & TOOLING (WUJIANG) CO., LTD.—See Fu Yu Corporation Limited; *Int'l*, pg. 2801
GAGAN POLYCOT INDIA LIMITED; *Int'l*, pg. 2868
GAGE INDUSTRIES INC.; *U.S. Private*, pg. 1634
GALION SA—See Berry Global Group, Inc; *U.S. Public*, pg. 322
GATEWAY PLASTICS, INC.—See Silgan Holdings, Inc.; *U.S. Public*, pg. 1878
GEBERIT SANITARNA TEHNIKA D.O.O.—See Geberit AG; *Int'l*, pg. 2905
GEDY S.P.A.; *Int'l*, pg. 2910
GEL-PAK LLC; *U.S. Private*, pg. 1656
GEMINI INCORPORATED; *U.S. Private*, pg. 1658
GENERAL PATTERN CO. INC.; *U.S. Private*, pg. 1666
GENEVA SCIENTIFIC, INC.—See Argosy Capital Group, LLC; *U.S. Private*, pg. 321
GENIUS ELECTRONIC OPTICAL CO., LTD.; *Int'l*, pg. 2924
GENMAB B.V.—See Genmab A/S; *Int'l*, pg. 2924
GENOVA PRODUCTS, INC.; *U.S. Private*, pg. 1673
GEORG FISCHER AG; *Int'l*, pg. 2934
GEORG FISCHER AUTOMOTIVE PRODUCTS INC.—See Georg Fischer AG; *Int'l*, pg. 2935
GEORG FISCHER GMBH & CO KG—See Georg Fischer AG; *Int'l*, pg. 2936
GEORG FISCHER IMMOBILIEN AG—See Georg Fischer AG; *Int'l*, pg. 2936
GEOTEK, INC.—See Granite Equity Partners LLC; *U.S. Private*, pg. 1755
GEPE-GEIMUPLAST GMBH—See Gepe Holding AG; *Int'l*, pg. 2942
GERFLOR SA—See Cobepa S.A.; *Int'l*, pg. 1683
GERMANOW-SIMON CORPORATION; *U.S. Private*, pg. 1687
GERRESHEIMER BOLESLAWIEC S.A.—See Gerresheimer AG; *Int'l*, pg. 2943
GERRESHEIMER DENMARK A/S—See Gerresheimer AG; *Int'l*, pg. 2943
GERRESHEIMER PEACHTREE CITY, INC.—See Gerresheimer AG; *Int'l*, pg. 2944
GERRESHEIMER REGENSBURG GMBH - PFREIMD PLANT—See Gerresheimer AG; *Int'l*, pg. 2944
GERRESHEIMER WILDEN ASIA MEDICAL AND TECHNICAL PLASTIC SYSTEMS CO. LTD.—See Gerresheimer AG; *Int'l*, pg. 2944
GE-SHEN PLASTIC (M) SDN. BHD.—See Ge-Shen Corporation Berhad; *Int'l*, pg. 2897
GESSNER PRODUCTS COMPANY, INC.—See New ThermoServ, Ltd.; *U.S. Private*, pg. 2907
GILKEY WINDOW COMPANY INC.; *U.S. Private*, pg. 1700
GINEGAR IBERICA S.L.—See Ginegar Plastic Products Ltd.; *Int'l*, pg. 2976
GINEGAR PLASTIC INC.—See Ginegar Plastic Products Ltd.; *Int'l*, pg. 2976
GINEGAR SPECIALTY PLASTIC PRIVATE LIMITED—See Ginegar Plastic Products Ltd.; *Int'l*, pg. 2976
GIORGIO FEDON & FIGLI SPA—See EssilorLuxottica SA; *Int'l*, pg. 2515
GIRPI S.A.—See Aliaxis S.A./N.V.; *Int'l*, pg. 324
GLEASON CORPORATION - GLEASON K2 PLASTICS PLANT—See Gleason Corporation; *U.S. Private*, pg. 1708
GLOBAL MANUFACTURING & ASSEMBLY; *U.S. Private*, pg. 1716
GLOBE COMPOSITE SOLUTIONS, LLC—See ESCO Technologies, Inc.; *U.S. Public*, pg. 794
GLS CORPORATION—See Avient Corporation; *U.S. Public*, pg. 247
GLS HONG KONG LIMITED—See Avient Corporation; *U.S. Public*, pg. 247
GLS THERMOPLASTIC ALLOYS SUZHOU CO., LTD.—See Avient Corporation; *U.S. Public*, pg. 247
GM POLYPLAST LIMITED; *Int'l*, pg. 3012
GOLDEN BRIGHT PLASTIC MANUFACTURING COMPANY LIMITED—See Highway Holdings Limited; *Int'l*, pg. 3389
GOLDEN FRONTIER PACKAGING SDN. BHD.—See Golden Frontier Berhad; *Int'l*, pg. 3029
GOLD KOGYO LAGUNA PHILIPPINES, INC.—See Air Water Inc.; *Int'l*, pg. 240
GOLDSHIELD FIBERGLASS, INC.—See AIP, LLC; *U.S. Private*, pg. 135
GOLETZ GMBH; *Int'l*, pg. 3035
GPI (SAS)—See 3M Company; *U.S. Public*, pg. 6
GRACO CHILDREN'S PRODUCTS, INC.—See Newell Brands Inc.; *U.S. Public*, pg. 1514
GRADUATE PLASTICS, INC.; *U.S. Private*, pg. 1750
GRAFCO INDUSTRIES LIMITED PARTNERSHIP—See Berry Global Group, Inc; *U.S. Public*, pg. 321
GRAPHIC PACKAGING INTERNATIONAL BREMEN GMBH—See Graphic Packaging Holding Company; *U.S. Public*, pg. 958
GRAPHIC PACKAGING INTERNATIONAL DO BRASIL - EMBALAGENS LTDA.—See Graphic Packaging Holding Company; *U.S. Public*, pg. 959
GRAPHIC PACKAGING INTERNATIONAL EUROPE CARTONS B.V.—See Graphic Packaging Holding Company; *U.S. Public*, pg. 959
GRAPHIC PACKAGING INTERNATIONAL FRANCE—See Graphic Packaging Holding Company; *U.S. Public*, pg. 959
GRAPHIC PACKAGING INTERNATIONAL JAPAN LTD.—See Graphic Packaging Holding Company; *U.S. Public*, pg. 959
GRAPHIC PACKAGING INTERNATIONAL LIMITED—See Graphic Packaging Holding Company; *U.S. Public*, pg. 959
GRAPHIC PACKAGING INTERNATIONAL, LLC CLARKSVILLE—See Graphic Packaging Holding Company; *U.S. Public*, pg. 959
GRAPHIC PACKAGING INTERNATIONAL, LLC PITTSTON—See Graphic Packaging Holding Company; *U.S. Public*, pg. 959
GRAPHIC PACKAGING INTERNATIONAL MEXICANA, S. DE R.L. DE C.V.—See Graphic Packaging Holding Company; *U.S. Public*, pg. 959
GRAPHIC PACKAGING INTERNATIONAL SPAIN, S.A.—See Graphic Packaging Holding Company; *U.S. Public*, pg. 959
GRAYLINE HOUSEWARES, INC.—See Panacea Products Corporation; *U.S. Private*, pg. 3084
GREAT LAKES WINDOW, INC.—See Clayton, Dubilier & Rice, LLC; *U.S. Private*, pg. 921
GREEN POINT PRECISION (M) SDN, BHD.—See Jabil Inc.; *U.S. Public*, pg. 1180
GREEN POINT (SUZHOU) TECHNOLOGY CO., LTD.—See Jabil Inc.; *U.S. Public*, pg. 1180
GREIF ARGENTINA S.A.—See Greif Inc.; *U.S. Public*, pg. 967
GREIF FLEXIBLES BENELUX B.V.—See Greif Inc.; *U.S. Public*, pg. 967
GREIF FLEXIBLES ROMANIA SRL—See Greif Inc.; *U.S. Public*, pg. 967
GREIF FLEXIBLES UK LTD.—See Greif Inc.; *U.S. Public*, pg. 968
GREIF PLASTICS ITALY SRL—See Greif Inc.; *U.S. Public*, pg. 968
GREIF POLAND SP. Z.O.O.—See Greif Inc.; *U.S. Public*, pg. 968
GREIF S.A. (PTY) LTD.—See Greif Inc.; *U.S. Public*, pg. 968
GREIF SWEDEN AB—See Greif Inc.; *U.S. Public*, pg. 968
GREIF VENEZUELA, C.A.—See Greif Inc.; *U.S. Public*, pg. 968
GREIF ZIMBABWE PRIVATE LTD.—See Greif Inc.; *U.S. Public*, pg. 968
GREINER ASSISTEC GMBH—See Greiner Holding AG; *Int'l*, pg. 3079
GREYSTONE LOGISTICS, INC.; *U.S. Public*, pg. 969
GRIFFON CORPORATION; *U.S. Public*, pg. 969
GROUP DEKKO - AVILLA—See Graham Holdings Company; *U.S. Public*, pg. 955
GROUP TOOL & DIE CO. INC.; *U.S. Private*, pg. 1794
GUANGDONG KIN LONG HARDWARE PRUDUCTS (HK) CO., LTD.—See Guangdong Kinlong Hardware Prdcts Co., Ltd.; *Int'l*, pg. 3157
GUANGDONG SILVER AGE SCI & TECH CO., LTD.; *Int'l*, pg. 3160
GUANGDONG SUNWILL PRECISING PLASTIC CO., LTD.; *Int'l*, pg. 3160
GUANGZHOU ENPLAS MECHATRONICS CO., LTD.—See ENPLAS CORPORATION; *Int'l*, pg. 2445
GUANGZHOU TREDEGAR FILM PRODUCTS COMPANY LIMITED—See Tredegar Corporation; *U.S. Public*, pg. 2187
GULF PLASTICS INDUSTRIES COMPANY SAOG; *Int'l*, pg. 3182
GUNZE KOBUNSHI CORPORATION—See Gunze Limited; *Int'l*, pg. 3185
GURIT (AUSTRALIA) PTY LTD—See Gurit Holding AG; *Int'l*, pg. 3187
GURIT (SPAIN) LTD—See Gurit Holding AG; *Int'l*, pg. 3188
GURIT (ZULLWIL) AG—See Gurit Holding AG; *Int'l*, pg. 3188
HABASIT AMERICA - READING—See Habasit AG; *Int'l*, pg. 3202
HAI PLASTIC LTD.—See Bram Industries Ltd.; *Int'l*, pg. 1138
HALLINK MOULDS, INC.—See The Eastern Company; *U.S. Public*, pg. 2069
HAMMERL GMBH & CO. KG—See CRH plc; *Int'l*, pg. 1844
HANDGARDS INC.—See Wind Point Advisors LLC; *U.S. Private*, pg. 4534
HARBISON CORPORATION; *U.S. Private*, pg. 1858
HARDIGG FRANCE SAS—See Platinum Equity, LLC; *U.S. Private*, pg. 3207
HARDIGG UK LIMITED—See Platinum Equity, LLC; *U.S. Private*, pg. 3207
HARTLAGE MANUFACTURING, INC.—See Maxey Logistics, Inc; *U.S. Private*, pg. 2617
HAYDOCK CASTER COMPANY—See E.R. Wagner Manufacturing Co.; *U.S. Private*, pg. 1307
HAYSITE REINFORCED PLASTICS, LLC—See Dunes Point Capital, LLC; *U.S. Private*, pg. 1288
HAYSITE REINFORCED PLASTICS LTD.—See Dunes Point Capital, LLC; *U.S. Private*, pg. 1288
HDC HYUNDAI ENGINEERING PLASTICS CO., LTD.; *Int'l*, pg. 3300
HD HOSPITAL DISPOSABLES INCORPORATED—See DeRoyal Industries Inc.; *U.S. Private*, pg. 1210
HEARTHMARK, LLC—See Newell Brands Inc.; *U.S. Public*, pg. 1514
HEINKE TECHNOLOGY INC.—See PCE, Inc.; *U.S. Private*, pg. 3120
HEINZE KUNSTSTOFFTECHNIK GMBH & CO. KG—See Heinze Gruppe GmbH; *Int'l*, pg. 3325
HELESI ITALIA S.R.L.—See Helesi Plc; *Int'l*, pg. 3329
HELESI PLC - KOMOTINI PLANT—See Helesi Plc; *Int'l*, pg. 3329
HELESI S.A.—See Helesi Plc; *Int'l*, pg. 3329
HEMIJSKA INDUSTRIJA VRANJE A.D.; *Int'l*, pg. 3341
HENGBAO CO., LTD.; *Int'l*, pg. 3346
HERTI GROUP INTERNATIONAL—See Herti AD; *Int'l*, pg. 3365
HEXION SPECIALTY CHEMICALS IBERICA, S.A.—See American Securities LLC; *U.S. Private*, pg. 249
HEXPOL TPE AB—See HEXPOL AB; *Int'l*, pg. 3372
HEXPOL TPE GMBH—See HEXPOL AB; *Int'l*, pg. 3372
HEXPOL TPE LTD—See HEXPOL AB; *Int'l*, pg. 3372
HICKS PLASTICS COMPANY, INC.—See New Water Capital, L.P.; *U.S. Private*, pg. 2908
HID GLOBAL GMBH—See ASSA ABLOY AB; *Int'l*, pg. 637
HID GLOBAL IRELAND TEORANTA LTD.—See ASSA ABLOY AB; *Int'l*, pg. 637
HID GLOBAL RASTEDE GMBH—See ASSA ABLOY AB; *Int'l*, pg. 637
HIEP QUANG TRADING CO., LTD—See DABACO Group Joint Stock Company; *Int'l*, pg. 1902
HIGHLAND PACKAGING SOLUTIONS, LLC—See Sonoco Products Company; *U.S. Public*, pg. 1904
HILFORT PLASTICS (PTY) LTD—See Berry Global Group, Inc; *U.S. Public*, pg. 324
HI-P (SHANGHAI) HOUSING APPLIANCE CO., LTD.—See Hi-P International Limited; *Int'l*, pg. 3381
HI-P (SHANGHAI) TECHNOLOGY CO., LTD.—See Hi-P International Limited; *Int'l*, pg. 3381
HI-P TIANJIN ELECTRONICS CO., LTD.—See Hi-P International Limited; *Int'l*, pg. 3381
HI-P (XIAMEN) PRECISION PLASTIC MANUFACTURING CO., LTD.—See Hi-P International Limited; *Int'l*, pg. 3381
HIRSCH ITALIA S.R.L.—See Hirsch Servo AG; *Int'l*, pg. 3405
HIRSCH POROZELL KFT—See Hirsch Servo AG; *Int'l*, pg. 3406
HIRSCH SERVO AG; *Int'l*, pg. 3405
HI-TECH COLOR (SHANGHAI) CO., LTD.—See Dainichiseika Color & Chemicals Mfg. Co., Ltd.; *Int'l*, pg. 1939
HL S.R.L.—See El.En. S.p.A.; *Int'l*, pg. 2342
HOFFER PLASTICS CORPORATION; *U.S. Private*, pg. 1959
HOLCOMB & HOKE MANUFACTURING COMPANY, INC.; *U.S. Private*, pg. 1961
HOLM KK EXTRUSIONS PVT. LTD.—See Ilpea Inc.; *U.S. Private*, pg. 2043
HOME CENTER HOLDINGS CO., LTD.; *Int'l*, pg. 3454
HOMERWOOD HARDWOOD FLOORING COMPANY—See Armstrong World Industries, Inc.; *U.S. Public*, pg. 194
HUF POLSKA SP. Z.O.O.—See Huf Hulsbeck & Furst GmbH & Co. KG; *Int'l*, pg. 3523
HUF U.K. LTD.—See Huf Hulsbeck & Furst GmbH & Co. KG; *Int'l*, pg. 3523
HUHTAMAKI AUSTRALIA PTY LTD—See Huhtamaki Oyj; *Int'l*, pg. 3524
HUHTAMAKI AUSTRALIA PTY LTD—See Huhtamaki Oyj; *Int'l*, pg. 3524
HUHTAMAKI CONSORCIO MEXICANA S.A. DE C.V.—See Huhtamaki Oyj; *Int'l*, pg. 3524

N.A.I.C.S. INDEX

326199 — ALL OTHER PLASTICS ...

HUHTAMAKI FINANCE BV—See Huhtamaki Oyj; *Int'l*, pg. 3524
HUHTAMAKI MALAYSIA SDN BHD—See Huhtamaki Oyj; *Int'l*, pg. 3525
HUHTAMAKI MOULDED FIBRE DO BRASIL LTDA.—See Huhtamaki Oyj; *Int'l*, pg. 3525
HUHTAMAKI NORWAY A/S—See Huhtamaki Oyj; *Int'l*, pg. 3525
HUHTAMAKI SINGAPORE PTE. LTD.—See Huhtamaki Oyj; *Int'l*, pg. 3525
HUHTAMAKI SOUTH AFRICA (PTY) LTD.—See Huhtamaki Oyj; *Int'l*, pg. 3525
HUHTAMAKI SOUTH AFRICA (PTY) LTD.—See Huhtamaki Oyj; *Int'l*, pg. 3525
HUHTAMAKI SWEDEN AB—See Huhtamaki Oyj; *Int'l*, pg. 3526
HUHTAMAKI (UK) LTD.—See Huhtamaki Oyj; *Int'l*, pg. 3524
HUHTAMAKI (UK) LTD.—See Huhtamaki Oyj; *Int'l*, pg. 3524
HUIYANG CCT PLASTIC PRODUCTS CO.,LTD—See CCT Fortis Holdings Limited; *Int'l*, pg. 1370
HUNTER DOUGLAS FABRICATION SP. Z.O.O. —See 3G Capital Partners L.P.; *U.S. Private*, pg. 12
HUNTSMAN ADVANCED MATERIALS (EUROPE) BVBA—See Huntsman Corporation; *U.S. Public*, pg. 1073
HYCOMP, LLC—See Compagnie de Saint-Gobain SA; *Int'l*, pg. 1731
HYUNDAI L&C CO., LTD.—See Hyundai Department Store Co., Ltd.; *Int'l*, pg. 3556
HZ FBZ FORMENBAU ZUTTLINGEN GMBH—See Huazhong In-Vehicle Holdings Company Limited; *Int'l*, pg. 3516
IDEAL WINDOW MANUFACTURING; *U.S. Private*, pg. 2036
IDEMIA SINGAPORE PTE LTD—See Advent International Corporation; *U.S. Private*, pg. 102
IDEMITSU UNITECH CO., LTD. - ENGINEERING MATERIAL PLANT—See Idemitsu Kosan Co., Ltd.; *Int'l*, pg. 3591
IDEMITSU UNITECH CO., LTD.—See Idemitsu Kosan Co., Ltd.; *Int'l*, pg. 3591
IDENTICARD SYSTEMS, INC.—See Brady Corporation; *U.S. Public*, pg. 379
IDI FABRICATION, INC.—See Industrial Dielectrics Holdings, Inc.; *U.S. Private*, pg. 2065
ILC DOVER LP—See New Mountain Capital, LLC; *U.S. Private*, pg. 2902
IMARK MOLDING, INC.—See Comar, LLC; *U.S. Private*, pg. 980
IMPERIAL PLASTICS, INC.; *U.S. Private*, pg. 2049
INCA PRODUCTS ACQUISITION CORP.—See Dometic Group AB; *Int'l*, pg. 2160
INDEPAK, INC.—See Cameron Holdings Corporation; *U.S. Private*, pg. 729
INDUSTRIAL CUSTOM PRODUCTS, INC. - ROSEVILLE PLANT—See Industrial Custom Products, Inc.; *U.S. Private*, pg. 2065
INDUSTRIAL CUSTOM PRODUCTS, INC.; *U.S. Private*, pg. 2065
INDUSTRIAL DE PLASTICOS DE CHIHUAHUA, S.A. DE C.V.—See Northern Technologies International Corporation; *U.S. Public*, pg. 1538
INDUSTRIAL LAMINATES/NORPLEX, INC.—See Hidden Harbor Capital Partners; *U.S. Private*, pg. 1934
INDUSTRIAL MOLDING CORPORATION—See Blackford Capital LLC; *U.S. Private*, pg. 574
INDUSTRIAL NETTING, INC.—See Frandsen Corporation; *U.S. Private*, pg. 1593
INEOS FILMS & COMPOUNDS—See One Rock Capital Partners, LLC; *U.S. Private*, pg. 3022
INEOS NORGE AS—See One Rock Capital Partners, LLC; *U.S. Private*, pg. 3023
INERGY AUTOMOTIVE SYSTEMS BELGIUM NV—See Burelle S.A.; *Int'l*, pg. 1222
INERGY AUTOMOTIVE SYSTEMS FRANCE—See Burelle S.A.; *Int'l*, pg. 1222
INERGY AUTOMOTIVE SYSTEMS GERMANY GMBH—See Burelle S.A.; *Int'l*, pg. 1222
INERGY AUTOMOTIVE SYSTEMS GERMANY GMBH—See Burelle S.A.; *Int'l*, pg. 1222
INERGY AUTOMOTIVE SYSTEMS GERMANY GMBH—See Burelle S.A.; *Int'l*, pg. 1222
INERGY AUTOMOTIVE SYSTEMS INC.—See Burelle S.A.; *Int'l*, pg. 1222
INERGY AUTOMOTIVE SYSTEMS MEXICO S.A. DE C.V.—See Burelle S.A.; *Int'l*, pg. 1222
INFILTRATOR SYSTEMS INC.—See The Graham Group, Inc.; *U.S. Private*, pg. 4037
INJECTRON CORPORATION; *U.S. Private*, pg. 2077
INJECTRONICS INC.; *U.S. Private*, pg. 2077
INLINE PLASTICS CORP. - SHUR-LOCK DIVISION—See Inline Plastics Corp.; *U.S. Private*, pg. 2079
INLINE PLASTICS CORP.; *U.S. Private*, pg. 2079
INLINE POL AND SP. Z O.O.—See Inline Plastics Corp.; *U.S. Private*, pg. 2079
INNOVATIVE MOLDING INC.—See TriMas Corporation; *U.S. Public*, pg. 2189

INOUTIC / DECEUNINCK, SPOL. S R.O.—See Deceuninck NV; *Int'l*, pg. 2000
INPLASTOR GRAPHISCHE PRODUKTE GESELLSCHAFT M.B.H.—See H2APEX Group SCA; *Int'l*, pg. 3199
INSERTECH, LLC; *U.S. Private*, pg. 2085
THE INTEC GROUP INC.; *U.S. Private*, pg. 4056
INTEK PLASTICS INC.; *U.S. Private*, pg. 2104
INTERPACK LIMITED—See Coral Products PLC; *Int'l*, pg. 1795
INTERPAK SN SA—See BERICAP GmbH & Co. KG; *Int'l*, pg. 981
INTERTAPE POLYMER INC.—See Clearlake Capital Group, L.P.; *U.S. Private*, pg. 935
INTERTECH PLASTICS INC.—See TriMas Corporation; *U.S. Public*, pg. 2189
INTERTRADE INDUSTRIES LTD.; *U.S. Private*, pg. 2127
INTRICON PTE. LTD.—See IntriCon Corporation; *U.S. Public*, pg. 1159
INVISAFLOW, LLC—See Omnimax Holdings, Inc.; *U.S. Private*, pg. 3017
IN ZONE, INC.; *U.S. Private*, pg. 2052
IP3 LYONS—See American Industrial Acquisition Corporation; *U.S. Private*, pg. 237
IPG (US) HOLDINGS INC.—See Clearlake Capital Group, L.P.; *U.S. Private*, pg. 935
IRONWOOD PLASTICS, INC.—See Berkshire Hathaway Inc.; *U.S. Public*, pg. 303
ISI DESIGN AND INSTALLATION SOLUTIONS, INC.—See The Home Depot, Inc.; *U.S. Public*, pg. 2089
ITEN INDUSTRIES INC.; *U.S. Private*, pg. 2149
ITT INDUSTRIES ENGINEERED PRODUCTS DIVISION—See ITT Inc.; *U.S. Public*, pg. 1178
ITW DE FRANCE S.A.S.—See Illinois Tool Works Inc.; *U.S. Public*, pg. 1108
ITW MOTION—See Illinois Tool Works Inc.; *U.S. Public*, pg. 1106
ITW NEXUS—See Illinois Tool Works Inc.; *U.S. Public*, pg. 1106
ITW SHAKEPROOF AUTOMOTIVE PRODUCTS—See Illinois Tool Works Inc.; *U.S. Public*, pg. 1107
ITW SVERIGE AB—See Illinois Tool Works Inc.; *U.S. Public*, pg. 1107
ITW TEKFAST—See Illinois Tool Works Inc.; *U.S. Public*, pg. 1107
IVC GROUP LIMITED—See Mohawk Industries, Inc.; *U.S. Public*, pg. 1457
IZOBLOK SA—See BEWi ASA; *Int'l*, pg. 1004
JACO MANUFACTURING CO. INC.; *U.S. Private*, pg. 2179
JAC PRODUCTS, INC. - JAC MOLDING PLANT—See Argonaut Private Equity, LLC; *U.S. Private*, pg. 321
JAC PRODUCTS, INC. - JAC MOLDING PLANT—See Hall Capital, LLC; *U.S. Private*, pg. 1843
JAC PRODUCTS, INC.—See Argonaut Private Equity, LLC; *U.S. Private*, pg. 321
JAC PRODUCTS, INC.—See Hall Capital, LLC; *U.S. Private*, pg. 1843
JAMESTOWN PLASTICS INC.; *U.S. Private*, pg. 2186
JAY INDUSTRIES INC.; *U.S. Private*, pg. 2192
JAY PLASTICS, INC.; *U.S. Private*, pg. 2192
JEDDAH BEVERAGE CAN MAKING CO. LTD.—See A.H. Algosaibi & Bros.; *Int'l*, pg. 24
JEDDAH BEVERAGE CAN MAKING CO. LTD.—See Crown Holdings, Inc.; *U.S. Public*, pg. 598
JETCROWN INDUSTRIAL (DONGGUAN) LIMITED—See Deswell Industries, Inc.; *Int'l*, pg. 2047
JETCROWN INDUSTRIAL (MACAO COMMERCIAL OFFSHORE) LIMITED—See Deswell Industries, Inc.; *Int'l*, pg. 2047
JIANGSU GINAR PLASTIC TECHNOLOGY CO., LTD.—See Ginar Technology Co., Ltd.; *Int'l*, pg. 2976
JONES PLASTIC & ENGINEERING COMPANY, LLC; *U.S. Private*, pg. 2233
JORDAN PLASTICS LIMITED—See Berry Global Group, Inc; *U.S. Public*, pg. 322
J P PLAST SLOVAKIA SPOL S R O—See Berry Global Group, Inc; *U.S. Public*, pg. 322
J P PLAST S R O—See Berry Global Group, Inc; *U.S. Public*, pg. 322
JUAREZ MEXICO DIVISION—See Jones Plastic & Engineering Company, LLC; *U.S. Private*, pg. 2234
JUKEN ENGINEERING TECHNOLOGY SDN BHD - JOHOR BAHRU FACTORY—See Frencken Group Limited; *Int'l*, pg. 2772
JUKEN ENGINEERING TECHNOLOGY SDN BHD - KUALA LUMPUR FACTORY—See Frencken Group Limited; *Int'l*, pg. 2772
JUKEN (H.K.) CO., LIMITED—See Frencken Group Limited; *Int'l*, pg. 2772
JUKEN MECPLAS TECHNOLOGY PTE LTD—See Frencken Group Limited; *Int'l*, pg. 2772
JUKEN TECHNOLOGY LIMITED—See Frencken Group Limited; *Int'l*, pg. 2772
JUNOPACIFIC, INC.—See The Cretex Companies, Inc.; *U.S. Private*, pg. 4016
JUSHI GROUP HONG KONG CO., LIMITED—See China Jushi Co., Ltd.; *Int'l*, pg. 1513
JUSHI SPAIN.S.A.—See China Jushi Co., Ltd.; *Int'l*, pg. 1514

JUTEKS D.D.—See Beaulieu International Group NV; *Int'l*, pg. 934
KALWALL CORPORATION; *U.S. Private*, pg. 2258
KAMAN COMPOSITES - VERMONT, INC.—See Arcline Investment Management LP; *U.S. Private*, pg. 314
KAM PLASTICS CORPORATION; *U.S. Private*, pg. 2258
KANAAK CORPORATION—See Sealaska Corporation; *U.S. Private*, pg. 3585
KASSON & KELLER—See Keymark Corporation; *U.S. Private*, pg. 2294
KAYSUN CORPORATION; *U.S. Private*, pg. 2267
KENNERLEY-SPRATLING INC.; *U.S. Private*, pg. 2286
KESTREL-BCE LIMITED—See Epwin Group Plc; *Int'l*, pg. 2466
KETER PLASTIC LTD.—See BC Partners LLP; *Int'l*, pg. 925
KIDS2, INC.; *U.S. Private*, pg. 2303
KING PLASTIC CORPORATION; *U.S. Private*, pg. 2310
KIN LONG HARDWARE (THAILAND) COMPANY LIMITED—See Guangdong Kinlong Hardware Prdcts Co., Ltd.; *Int'l*, pg. 3157
KITTRICH LLC—See Kittrich Corporation; *U.S. Private*, pg. 2316
KLW PLASTICS, INC.—See KODA Enterprises Group, LLC; *U.S. Private*, pg. 2335
KNAUF AMF GMBH & CO. KG—See Gebr. Knauf KG; *Int'l*, pg. 2906
KNAUF AQUAPANEL GMBH—See Gebr. Knauf KG; *Int'l*, pg. 2906
KNIGHT PLASTICS, LLC—See Berry Global Group, Inc; *U.S. Public*, pg. 321
KOEMMERLING TIANJIN KUNSTSTOFF CO. LTD.—See Arcapita Group Holdings Limited; *Int'l*, pg. 542
KOLLER ENTERPRISES, INC. - KOLLER-CRAFT SOUTH DIVISION—See Koller Enterprises, Inc.; *U.S. Private*, pg. 2341
KOLLER ENTERPRISES, INC.; *U.S. Private*, pg. 2341
KOMMERLING USA, INC.—See Arcapita Group Holdings Limited; *Int'l*, pg. 542
KRUGER PLASTIC PRODUCTS, LLC—See HC Private Investments LLC; *U.S. Private*, pg. 1888
KTS KUNSTSTOFF TECHNIK SCHMOLLN GMBH—See AdCapital AG; *Int'l*, pg. 126
KUBETECH CUSTOM MOLDING INC.—See Sun Capital Partners, Inc.; *U.S. Private*, pg. 3859
KUNSHAN ACHILLES NEW MATERIAL TECHNOLOGY CO., LTD.—See Achilles Corporation; *Int'l*, pg. 103
KWIK LOK CORP. - NEW HAVEN—See KLC Holdings, Ltd.; *U.S. Private*, pg. 2318
KWIK LOK CORPORATION—See KLC Holdings, Ltd.; *U.S. Private*, pg. 2318
KWIK LOK (IRELAND) LTD—See KLC Holdings, Ltd.; *U.S. Private*, pg. 2318
KYOWA CARTON CO., LTD.—See Asahi Printing Co., Ltd.; *Int'l*, pg. 598
LACERTA GROUP, INC.—See SK Capital Partners, LP; *U.S. Private*, pg. 3679
LACKS ENTERPRISES, INC.; *U.S. Private*, pg. 2371
LACKS TRIM SYSTEMS, INC.—See Lacks Enterprises, Inc.; *U.S. Private*, pg. 2371
LACKS WHEEL TRIM SYSTEMS, INC.—See Lacks Enterprises, Inc.; *U.S. Private*, pg. 2371
LAFRANCE CORPORATION - PACTEC CUSTOM DIVISION—See LaFrance Corporation; *U.S. Private*, pg. 2373
LAFRANCE CORPORATION - PACTEC STANDARD DIVISION—See LaFrance Corporation; *U.S. Private*, pg. 2373
LAFRANCE CORPORATION; *U.S. Private*, pg. 2373
LAMINEX (AUSTRALIA) PTY. LTD.—See Fletcher Building Limited; *Int'l*, pg. 2700
LANCER DISPERSIONS INC.; *U.S. Private*, pg. 2382
LANDMARK PLASTIC CORPORATION; *U.S. Private*, pg. 2385
LAUREN PLASTICS LLC—See Cooper-Standard Holdings Inc.; *U.S. Public*, pg. 574
LEAKTITE CORPORATION; *U.S. Private*, pg. 2407
LEAR MEXICAN SEATING CORPORATION—See Lear Corporation; *U.S. Public*, pg. 1297
LENCO, INC. - PMC—See PMC Group, Inc.; *U.S. Private*, pg. 3218
LETICA CORPORATION - LETICA OF ALABAMA FACILITY—See Berry Global Group, Inc; *U.S. Public*, pg. 322
LETICA CORPORATION - LETICA OF DELAWARE FACILITY—See Berry Global Group, Inc; *U.S. Public*, pg. 322
LETICA CORPORATION - LETICA OF GEORGIA FACILITY—See Berry Global Group, Inc; *U.S. Public*, pg. 322
LETICA CORPORATION - LETICA OF INDIANA FACILITY—See Berry Global Group, Inc; *U.S. Public*, pg. 322
LETICA CORPORATION - LETICA OF IOWA FACILITY—See Berry Global Group, Inc; *U.S. Public*, pg. 322
LETICA CORPORATION - LETICA OF KENTUCKY FACILITY—See Berry Global Group, Inc; *U.S. Public*, pg. 322

326199 — ALL OTHER PLASTICS ...

LETICA CORPORATION - LETICA OF NEVADA FACILITY—See Berry Global Group, Inc; *U.S. Public*, pg. 323
LETICA CORPORATION - LETICA OF OKLAHOMA FACILITY—See Berry Global Group, Inc; *U.S. Public*, pg. 323
LETICA CORPORATION - LETICA OF OREGON FACILITY—See Berry Global Group, Inc; *U.S. Public*, pg. 323
LETICA CORPORATION—See Berry Global Group, Inc; *U.S. Public*, pg. 322
LIBERTY POLYGLAS, INC.; *U.S. Private*, pg. 2447
LINCOLN CASTING LTD.—See Georg Fischer AG; *Int'l*, pg. 2937
LINCOLN INDUSTRIES, INC.—See Zoeller Co.; *U.S. Private*, pg. 4607
LINPAC PACKAGING GMBH—See Strategic Value Partners, LLC; *U.S. Private*, pg. 3836
LINPAC PACKAGING LIMITED—See Strategic Value Partners, LLC; *U.S. Private*, pg. 3836
LINPAC PACKAGING RIGID GMBH—See Strategic Value Partners, LLC; *U.S. Private*, pg. 3836
LIPLASTEC S.R.O.—See Denso Corporation; *Int'l*, pg. 2032
LIQUI-BOX CORP.—See Sealed Air Corporation; *U.S. Public*, pg. 1854
LLC ESE SOUTH AMERICA S.R.L.—See Berry Global Group, Inc; *U.S. Public*, pg. 322
THE L&L COMPANY-BALTIMORE/DELAWARE DIVISION—See The L&L Company; *U.S. Private*, pg. 4066
THE L&L COMPANY-CENTRAL VIRGINIA—See The L&L Company; *U.S. Private*, pg. 4066
THE L&L COMPANY-CERAMIC DIVISION—See The L&L Company; *U.S. Private*, pg. 4066
THE L&L COMPANY-CHARLOTTE DIVISION—See The L&L Company; *U.S. Private*, pg. 4066
THE L&L COMPANY-FRANKLIN DIVISION—See The L&L Company; *U.S. Private*, pg. 4066
THE L&L COMPANY-FREDERICK—See The L&L Company; *U.S. Private*, pg. 4066
THE L&L COMPANY-GREENVILLE DIVISION—See The L&L Company; *U.S. Private*, pg. 4066
THE L&L COMPANY-OWINGS MILLS—See The L&L Company; *U.S. Private*, pg. 4066
THE L&L COMPANY - PITTSBURGH DIVISION—See The L&L Company; *U.S. Private*, pg. 4066
THE L&L COMPANY-POINTER RIDGE & BLINDS DIVISIONS—See The L&L Company; *U.S. Private*, pg. 4066
THE L&L COMPANY-RICHMOND—See The L&L Company; *U.S. Private*, pg. 4066
THE L&L COMPANY-SALISBURY DIVISION—See The L&L Company; *U.S. Private*, pg. 4066
THE L&L COMPANY; *U.S. Private*, pg. 4066
THE L&L COMPANY - TIMONIUM DIVISION—See The L&L Company; *U.S. Private*, pg. 4066
LLC RPC BRAMLAGE YEKATERINBURG—See Berry Global Group, Inc; *U.S. Public*, pg. 324
LOMONT MOLDING LLC; *U.S. Private*, pg. 2483
LOOP-LOC LTD.; *U.S. Private*, pg. 2494
LOW & BONAR PLC—See Freudenberg SE; *Int'l*, pg. 2789
LSP PRODUCTS GROUP INC.—See NCH Corporation; *U.S. Private*, pg. 2875
L T HAMPEL CORP.; *U.S. Private*, pg. 2362
MACK GROUP INC.; *U.S. Private*, pg. 2536
MACK MOLDING COMPANY INC.; *U.S. Private*, pg. 2536
MAC MOLDING COMPANY, INC.—See Tacony Corporation; *U.S. Private*, pg. 3921
MAGMATIC LIMITED—See Heroes Technology Ltd.; *Int'l*, pg. 3364
MAGRI S.A.S.—See Owens Corning; *U.S. Public*, pg. 1627
M.A. INDUSTRIES, INC.; *U.S. Private*, pg. 2527
MAJORS PLASTICS INC.; *U.S. Private*, pg. 2555
MANAR, INC.; *U.S. Private*, pg. 2561
MANNINGTON MILLS, INC.; *U.S. Private*, pg. 2565
MANNINGTON RESILIENT FLOORS—See Mannington Mills, Inc.; *U.S. Private*, pg. 2566
MAPA GMBH—See Newell Brands Inc.; *U.S. Public*, pg. 1514
MAR-BAL INC.; *U.S. Private*, pg. 2569
MARIAH INDUSTRIES, INC.—See AEA Investors LP; *U.S. Private*, pg. 115
MARIAK INDUSTRIES, INC.—See British Columbia Investment Management Corp.; *Int'l*, pg. 1170
MARINA FOR INDUSTRIAL SOLUTIONS CO.—See BERICAP GmbH & Co. KG; *Int'l*, pg. 981
MARKEL INDUSTRIES, INC.—See Mativ Holdings, Inc.; *U.S. Public*, pg. 1397
MARVAL INDUSTRIES, INC.; *U.S. Private*, pg. 2597
MARYLAND PLASTICS, INC.—See Bio Medic Corporation; *U.S. Private*, pg. 561
MASTER MOLDED PRODUCTS CORPORATION; *U.S. Private*, pg. 2607
MASTERPAC CORP.—See Cameron Holdings Corporation; *U.S. Private*, pg. 729
MATRIX IV INC.; *U.S. Private*, pg. 2612
MAUSER USA, LLC—See Stone Canyon Industries, LLC; *U.S. Private*, pg. 3817

MAYFIELD PLASTICS, INC.—See Wembly Enterprises LLC; *U.S. Private*, pg. 4480
MAYNARD & HARRIS PLASTICS—See Berry Global Group, Inc; *U.S. Public*, pg. 324
MCCANN PLASTICS LLC—See HEXPOL AB; *Int'l*, pg. 3372
MCCLARIN PLASTICS, LLC; *U.S. Private*, pg. 2628
M.C. GILL CORPORATION; *U.S. Private*, pg. 2528
M-C INDUSTRIES INC.; *U.S. Private*, pg. 2525
MCKECHNIE TOOLING & ENGINEERING—See MVC Holdings LLC; *U.S. Private*, pg. 2821
MDI SDN. BHD.—See I-PEX Inc.; *Int'l*, pg. 3564
MEARTHANE PRODUCTS CORPORATION; *U.S. Private*, pg. 2647
MEDALLION PLASTICS INC.—See Patrick Industries, Inc.; *U.S. Public*, pg. 1652
MEESE INC.—See Olympus Partners; *U.S. Private*, pg. 3013
MEGA PAK ZIMBABWE (PVT) LTD—See Delta Corporation Limited; *Int'l*, pg. 2016
MENASHA CORP., TRAEX DIVISION—See Menasha Corporation; *U.S. Private*, pg. 2665
MERRICK ENGINEERING, INC.; *U.S. Private*, pg. 2675
MESAN KILIT A.S.—See Essentra plc; *Int'l*, pg. 2511
MET2PLASTIC LLC—See Dedienne Multiplasturgy Group SAS; *Int'l*, pg. 2002
METROLINA PLASTICS, INC.—See Falfurrias Capital Partners, LP; *U.S. Private*, pg. 1652
METRO MOLD & DESIGN - ICM PLASTICS—See Metro Mold & Design, Inc.; *U.S. Private*, pg. 2686
METROPLAST SA—See Burelle S.A.; *Int'l*, pg. 1222
METRO SIGN & AWNING; *U.S. Private*, pg. 2686
MEXICO KIN LONG S.A. DE C.A.—See Guangdong Kinlong Hardware Prdcts Co., Ltd.; *Int'l*, pg. 3157
MFG DE MEXICO—See Molded Fiber Glass Companies; *U.S. Private*, pg. 2766
MGB PLASTICS LTD.—See Madison Dearborn Partners, LLC; *U.S. Private*, pg. 2541
MGS MANUFACTURING GROUP, INC.; *U.S. Private*, pg. 2695
M&H PLASTICS INC.—See Berry Global Group, Inc; *U.S. Public*, pg. 324
MICRODYNE PLASTICS, INC.; *U.S. Private*, pg. 2703
MICROMOLD, INC.; *U.S. Private*, pg. 2704
MICRO PLASTICS, INC.—See Essentra plc; *Int'l*, pg. 2511
MICRO PLASTICS INTERNATIONAL LIMITED—See Essentra plc; *Int'l*, pg. 2511
MID-AMERICA PLASTICS—See Activar, Inc.; *U.S. Private*, pg. 68
MILGARD MANUFACTURING INCORPORATED—See Koch Industries, Inc.; *U.S. Private*, pg. 2332
MINERALI INDUSTRIALI EOOD, BULGARIA—See Gruppo Minerali Maffei S.p.A.; *Int'l*, pg. 3140
MINIATURE PRECISION COMPONENTS, INC.—See Equistone Partners Europe Limited; *Int'l*, pg. 2487
MIRAGE ENERGY CORPORATION; *U.S. Public*, pg. 1450
MIRSA MANUFACTURING LLC; *U.S. Private*, pg. 2746
MISSION PLASTICS OF ARKANSAS, INC.—See Peterson Manufacturing Company Inc.; *U.S. Private*, pg. 3160
MISSISSIPPI POLYMERS—See Mississippi Polymers, Inc.; *U.S. Private*, pg. 2748
MKF-ERGIS SP. Z O.O.—See Ergis S.A.; *Int'l*, pg. 2491
M & N PLASTICS, INC.—See Gibraltar Industries, Inc.; *U.S. Public*, pg. 936
MOCAP FRANCE—See MOCAP Inc.; *U.S. Private*, pg. 2758
MOCAP INC.; *U.S. Private*, pg. 2758
MOCAP LIMITED—See MOCAP Inc.; *U.S. Private*, pg. 2758
MOCAP SRL—See MOCAP Inc.; *U.S. Private*, pg. 2758
MODERN TRADING & SERVICES SARL—See BERICAP GmbH & Co. KG; *Int'l*, pg. 981
MOELLER MARINE PRODUCTS, INC.—See Dometic Group AB; *Int'l*, pg. 2160
MOLDAMATIC INC.; *U.S. Private*, pg. 2758
MOLDED DEVICES, INC.—See TruArc Partners, L.P.; *U.S. Private*, pg. 4245
MOLDED FIBER GLASS COMPANIES - MFG ALABAMA FACTORY—See Molded Fiber Glass Companies; *U.S. Private*, pg. 2766
MOLDED FIBER GLASS COMPANIES - MFG CONSTRUCTION PRODUCTS FACTORY—See Molded Fiber Glass Companies; *U.S. Private*, pg. 2766
MOLDED FIBER GLASS COMPANIES - MFG SOUTH DAKOTA FACTORY—See Molded Fiber Glass Companies; *U.S. Private*, pg. 2766
MOLDED FIBER GLASS COMPANIES - MFG SOUTHEAST FACTORY—See Molded Fiber Glass Companies; *U.S. Private*, pg. 2766
MOLDED FIBER GLASS COMPANIES; *U.S. Private*, pg. 2766
MOLDED FIBER GLASS COMPOSITE SYSTEMS CO.—See Molded Fiber Glass Companies; *U.S. Private*, pg. 2766
MOLDED FIBER GLASS NORTH CAROLINA—See Molded Fiber Glass Companies; *U.S. Private*, pg. 2766
MOLDED FIBER GLASS NORTHWEST—See Molded Fiber Glass Companies; *U.S. Private*, pg. 2766
MOLDED FIBER GLASS TRAY CO.—See Molded Fiber Glass Companies; *U.S. Private*, pg. 2766
MOLDED FIBER GLASS UNION CITY—See Molded Fiber

Glass Companies; *U.S. Private*, pg. 2766
MOLDED FIBER GLASS WEST—See Molded Fiber Glass Companies; *U.S. Private*, pg. 2766
MOLDING CORPORATION OF AMERICA—See Performance Engineered Products Inc.; *U.S. Private*, pg. 3149
MONROE, LLC—See Huizenga Manufacturing Group, Inc.; *U.S. Private*, pg. 2004
MORSE RUBBER, LLC—See FLSmidth & Co. A/S; *Int'l*, pg. 2711
MOS PLASTICS INC.—See Kennerley-Spratling Inc.; *U.S. Private*, pg. 2286
MOSS SUPPLY COMPANY; *U.S. Private*, pg. 2794
MPC INC.—See CECO Environmental Corp.; *U.S. Public*, pg. 464
MPR PLASTICS INC.—See Thunderbird LLC; *U.S. Private*, pg. 4166
M&Q PACKAGING CORPORATION—See M&Q Plastic Products, Inc.; *U.S. Private*, pg. 2525
M&Q PLASTIC PRODUCTS, INC.; *U.S. Private*, pg. 2525
MRC MANUFACTURING, INC.—See Lanzo Construction Company Inc.; *U.S. Private*, pg. 2391
MULLER KUNSTSTOFFE GMBH—See HEXPOL AB; *Int'l*, pg. 3372
MULLINIX PACKAGES INC.—See Sabert Corporation; *U.S. Private*, pg. 3520
MULTICARD AUSTRALIA PTY LTD—See Identiv, Inc.; *U.S. Public*, pg. 1089
MULTIDIMENSIONALES S.A.—See Genstar Capital, LLC; *U.S. Private*, pg. 1679
MULTI-PLASTICS, INC.—See Multi-Plastics, Inc.; *U.S. Private*, pg. 2812
MYRON MANUFACTURING CORPORATION; *U.S. Private*, pg. 2826
NAMPAK PLASTICS EUROPE LTD.—See Greybull Capital LLP; *Int'l*, pg. 3082
NANTONG DOCHARM AMPHENOL AUTOMOTIVE ELECTRONICS CO., LTD.—See Amphenol Corporation; *U.S. Public*, pg. 131
NAN YA PLASTICS CORPORATION—See Formosa Plastics Corporation; *Int'l*, pg. 2736
NARPLAST LLC—See Dohler GmbH; *Int'l*, pg. 2156
NATCO PRODUCTS CORPORATION; *U.S. Private*, pg. 2838
NATIONAL COMPANY FOR SPONGE AND PLASTIC INDUSTRY LTD.—See Hayel Saeed Anam Group of Companies; *Int'l*, pg. 3291
NATIONAL DIVERSIFIED SALES INC.; *U.S. Private*, pg. 2852
NATIONAL MOLDING CORPORATION; *U.S. Private*, pg. 2859
NATIONAL PLASTICS, INC.—See Cameron Holdings Corporation; *U.S. Private*, pg. 729
NATIONWIDE PLASTICS, INC.—See Curbell, Inc.; *U.S. Private*, pg. 1124
NATVAR TEKNI-PLEX, INC.—See Genstar Capital, LLC; *U.S. Private*, pg. 1679
NCG-ERC, LLC—See Stone Canyon Industries, LLC; *U.S. Private*, pg. 3817
THE NEAT NURSERY CO.—See Nordic Group of Companies, Ltd.; *U.S. Private*, pg. 2936
NEIL INTERNATIONAL INC.; *U.S. Private*, pg. 2882
NELIPAK CORPORATION, INC.—See Kohlberg & Company, LLC; *U.S. Private*, pg. 2338
NEQCON—See Exco Technologies Limited; *Int'l*, pg. 2580
NEWAGE INDUSTRIES, INC.; *U.S. Private*, pg. 2913
NEW BERLIN PLASTICS INC.; *U.S. Private*, pg. 2892
NEWBOLD CORPORATION - ADDRESSOGRAPH DIVISION—See Fort Point Capital, LLC; *U.S. Private*, pg. 1574
NEW DIMENSIONS RESEARCH CORP.—See Westminster Capital Inc.; *U.S. Private*, pg. 4499
NEWELL RUBBERMAID ASIA PACIFIC LIMITED—See Newell Brands Inc.; *U.S. Public*, pg. 1514
NEWELL RUBBERMAID COMMERCIAL PRODUCTS—See Newell Brands Inc.; *U.S. Public*, pg. 1514
NEWELL RUBBERMAID DE MEXICO S. DE R.L. DE C.V.—See Newell Brands Inc.; *U.S. Public*, pg. 1514
NEWELL RUBBERMAID INC.—See Newell Brands Inc.; *U.S. Public*, pg. 1514
NEWELL RUBBERMAID MIDDLE EAST FZE—See Newell Brands Inc.; *U.S. Public*, pg. 1514
NEWELL RUBBERMAID (THAILAND) CO., LTD.—See Newell Brands Inc.; *U.S. Public*, pg. 1514
NEW GLAZING INDUSTRIES, LTD.—See Clayton, Dubilier & Rice, LLC; *U.S. Private*, pg. 921
NEW THERMOSERV, LTD.; *U.S. Private*, pg. 2907
NEW WAY AIR BEARINGS; *U.S. Private*, pg. 2908
NEW YORK WIRE COMPANY—See Compagnie de Saint-Gobain SA; *Int'l*, pg. 1730
NICOLET PLASTICS, INC.; *U.S. Private*, pg. 2926
NICOLL POLSKA SP. Z O.O.—See Aliaxis S.A./N.V.; *Int'l*, pg. 325
NIDAPLAST-HONEYCOMBS S.A.S.—See Etex SA/NV; *Int'l*, pg. 2522
NID SA—See Advent International Corporation; *U.S. Private*, pg. 102
NIKKO HANSEN & CO., LTD.—See AS ONE Corporation; *Int'l*, pg. 591

N.A.I.C.S. INDEX

326199 — ALL OTHER PLASTICS ...

NIPPON MUKI CO., LTD.—See Daikin Industries, Ltd.; *Int'l*, pg. 1936
NOMACO, INC.—See Noel Group, LLC; *U.S. Private*, pg. 2933
NON-METALLIC COMPONENTS INC.; *U.S. Private*, pg. 2934
NORDFOLIEN GMBH—See Berry Global Group, Inc; *U.S. Public*, pg. 322
NORDON INC; *U.S. Private*, pg. 2937
NORDSON XALOY ITALIA S.R.L.—See Nordson Corporation; *U.S. Public*, pg. 1534
NORO AB—See BHG Group AB; *Int'l*, pg. 1015
NORTHLAND ALUMINUM PRODUCTS INC.; *U.S. Private*, pg. 2955
NORTH STATES INDUSTRIES INC.; *U.S. Private*, pg. 2948
NORTON INDUSTRIES; *U.S. Private*, pg. 2964
NORWESCO, INC. - HANFORD—See Olympus Partners; *U.S. Private*, pg. 3013
NORWESCO, INC.—See Olympus Partners; *U.S. Private*, pg. 3013
NOVARES US LLC - FELTON—See Equistone Partners Europe Limited; *Int'l*, pg. 2487
NOVARES US LLC—See Equistone Partners Europe Limited; *Int'l*, pg. 2487
NOVATION INDUSTRIES; *U.S. Private*, pg. 2967
NOVELEX AG—See Heitkamp & Thumann KG; *Int'l*, pg. 3326
NOV FIBER GLASS SYSTEMS—See NOV, Inc.; *U.S. Public*, pg. 1544
NOVIK INC.—See Clearview Capital, LLC; *U.S. Private*, pg. 939
NP MEDICAL INC.—See Jabil Inc.; *U.S. Public*, pg. 1181
NRH LIMITED—See Newell Brands Inc.; *U.S. Public*, pg. 1514
NUPIK-FLO UK LTD—See FLO S.p.A.; *Int'l*, pg. 2707
NUPIK INTERNACIONAL SL—See FLO S.p.A.; *Int'l*, pg. 2707
NURSERY SUPPLIES INC.—See Guggenheim Partners, LLC; *U.S. Private*, pg. 1812
NYLACARB CORPORATION; *U.S. Private*, pg. 2976
NYLONCRAFT, INC. - JONESVILLE—See Hammond, Kennedy, Whitney & Company, Inc.; *U.S. Private*, pg. 1850
NYLONCRAFT, INC.—See Hammond, Kennedy, Whitney & Company, Inc.; *U.S. Private*, pg. 1850
NYLONCRAFT, INC.—See Hammond, Kennedy, Whitney & Company, Inc.; *U.S. Private*, pg. 1850
NYPRO ASHEVILLE INC.—See Jabil Inc.; *U.S. Public*, pg. 1181
NYPRO CHICAGO—See Jabil Inc.; *U.S. Public*, pg. 1181
NYPRO DE LA FRONTERA, S DE RL DE CV—See Jabil Inc.; *U.S. Public*, pg. 1182
NYPRO FRANCE SAS—See Jabil Inc.; *U.S. Public*, pg. 1181
NYPRO GUADALAJARA—See Jabil Inc.; *U.S. Public*, pg. 1181
NYPRO KANAAK-ALABAMA LLC—See Jabil Inc.; *U.S. Public*, pg. 1182
NYPRO KANAAK IOWA INC.—See Jabil Inc.; *U.S. Public*, pg. 1181
NYPRO NAGYIGMAND VAGYONKEZELO KFT—See Jabil Inc.; *U.S. Public*, pg. 1182
NYPRO PUERTO RICO INC.—See Jabil Inc.; *U.S. Public*, pg. 1182
NYPRO SAN DIEGO INC.—See Jabil Inc.; *U.S. Public*, pg. 1182
NYTEF PLASTICS CORP.—See Nytef Plastics Ltd.; *U.S. Private*, pg. 2977
NYX FORT WAYNE—See NYX Inc.; *U.S. Private*, pg. 2977
OBERTHUR CARD SYSTEMS KFT.—See Advent International Corporation; *U.S. Private*, pg. 102
OCTEX LLC; *U.S. Private*, pg. 2993
OLBRICH GMBH—See Matthews International Corporation; *U.S. Public*, pg. 1400
OLCOTT PLASTICS, INC.—See Clearlake Capital Group, L.P.; *U.S. Private*, pg. 937
OMEGA PLASTICS, INC.—See TriMas Corporation; *U.S. Public*, pg. 2189
OMICO INC.; *U.S. Private*, pg. 3016
OMNI PLASTICS (THAILAND) CO. LTD—See Adval Tech Holding AG; *Int'l*, pg. 155
OMNI PLASTICS (XIAMEN) CO. LTD—See Adval Tech Holding AG; *Int'l*, pg. 155
ONEIDA MOLDED PLASTICS, LLC; *U.S. Private*, pg. 3025
O.O.O. BERICAP—See BERICAP GmbH & Co. KG; *Int'l*, pg. 981
O.O.O BERICAP—See BERICAP GmbH & Co. KG; *Int'l*, pg. 981
OPTICOLOR, INC.—See Techmer PM, LLC; *U.S. Private*, pg. 3953
ORBIS CORPORATION - LEWISBINS+ DIVISION—See Menasha Corporation; *U.S. Private*, pg. 2666
ORBIS CORPORATION—See Menasha Corporation; *U.S. Private*, pg. 2665
ORBIS (SHANGHAI) MATERIAL HANDLING CO., LTD.—See Menasha Corporation; *U.S. Private*, pg. 2665
OSCODA PLASTICS, INC.; *U.S. Private*, pg. 3047
OXXO SA—See Cevital S.p.A.; *Int'l*, pg. 1425
PACHAMA PACKAGING LTD—See Greif Inc.; *U.S. Public*, pg. 968
PACK2PACK ZWOLLE B.V.—See Greif Inc.; *U.S. Public*, pg. 969
PACKERWARE, LLC—See Berry Global Group, Inc; *U.S. Public*, pg. 321
PACKESTATE LIMITED—See ENL Limited; *Int'l*, pg. 2441
PACK PLASTICS LIMITED—See ENL Limited; *Int'l*, pg. 2441
PAC STRAPPING PRODUCTS INC.; *U.S. Private*, pg. 3063
PACTIV CORP. - BEECH ISLAND—See Pactiv Evergreen Inc.; *U.S. Public*, pg. 1633
PACTIV CORP. - BELVIDERE—See Pactiv Evergreen Inc.; *U.S. Public*, pg. 1633
PALESTINE PLASTIC INDUSTRIES CO. LTD.—See Arab Supply & Trading Co.; *Int'l*, pg. 532
PALL LIFE SCIENCES BELGIUM BVBA—See Danaher Corporation; *U.S. Public*, pg. 630
PARADIGM PACKAGING, INC.—See Linsalata Capital Partners, Inc.; *U.S. Private*, pg. 2463
PARAGON MEDICAL, INC.—See AMETEK, Inc.; *U.S. Public*, pg. 121
PARAGON PLASTICS, INC.; *U.S. Private*, pg. 3091
PARAMONT MACHINE COMPANY, INC.—See A. M. Castle & Co.; *U.S. Public*, pg. 11
PARAMOUNT MANUFACTURING LLC; *U.S. Private*, pg. 3093
PARKWAY PRODUCTS, LLC - ATLANTA FACILITY—See Heartwood Partners, LLC; *U.S. Private*, pg. 1901
PARKWAY PRODUCTS, LLC - MARIETTA FACILITY—See Heartwood Partners, LLC; *U.S. Private*, pg. 1901
PARKWAY PRODUCTS, LLC—See Heartwood Partners, LLC; *U.S. Private*, pg. 1901
PAULMAY CO., INC.; *U.S. Private*, pg. 3114
PCE, INC.; *U.S. Private*, pg. 3120
PEAK INTERNATIONAL, INC.—See Daewon Semiconductor Packaging Industrial Corporation; *Int'l*, pg. 1910
PEAK INTERNATIONAL SINGAPORE—See Daewon Semiconductor Packaging Industrial Corporation; *Int'l*, pg. 1910
PEDEX GMBH—See Global Equity Partners Beteiligungs-Management AG; *Int'l*, pg. 2996
PELICAN PRODUCTS, INC.—See Platinum Equity, LLC; *U.S. Private*, pg. 3207
PELICULAS PLASTICAS, S.A. DE C.V.—See Grupo La Moderna, S.A.B. de C.V.; *Int'l*, pg. 3131
PENDA CORPORATION—See Kruger Brown Holdings, LLC; *U.S. Private*, pg. 2353
PENINSULA PACKAGING, LLC—See Sonoco Products Company; *U.S. Public*, pg. 1904
PERFECT SHUTTERS INC.; *U.S. Private*, pg. 3148
PERFORMANCE ENGINEERED PRODUCTS INC.; *U.S. Private*, pg. 3149
PERFORMANCE PACKAGING INC.—See Alpha Industries, Inc.; *U.S. Private*, pg. 197
PERFORMANCE PLASTICS, LTD.—See Odyssey Investment Partners, LLC; *U.S. Private*, pg. 2995
PERFORMANCE SYSTEMATIX, INC.—See Henry Crown & Company; *U.S. Private*, pg. 1918
PERGO (FRANCE) S. A. S.—See Mohawk Industries, Inc.; *U.S. Public*, pg. 1458
PERGO INC.—See Mohawk Industries, Inc.; *U.S. Public*, pg. 1458
PERLIT THERMOPUTZ ERSEN GMBH—See Compagnie de Saint-Gobain SA; *Int'l*, pg. 1726
PERUSAHAAN JAYA PLASTIK (M) SDN. BHD.—See CYL Corporation Berhad; *Int'l*, pg. 1896
PET POWER BV—See Berry Global Group, Inc; *U.S. Public*, pg. 322
PEXCO AEROSPACE, INC.—See TransDigm Group Incorporated; *U.S. Public*, pg. 2183
PEXCO LLC - MONTERREY—See Odyssey Investment Partners, LLC; *U.S. Private*, pg. 2995
PEXCO LLC - MORRISVILLE—See Odyssey Investment Partners, LLC; *U.S. Private*, pg. 2995
PEXCO LLC—See Odyssey Investment Partners, LLC; *U.S. Private*, pg. 2995
PEXCO LLC - TACOMA—See Odyssey Investment Partners, LLC; *U.S. Private*, pg. 2995
PHIL-GOOD PRODUCTS INCORPORATED; *U.S. Public*, pg. 1685
PHILLIPS-MEDISIZE, LLC—See Koch Industries, Inc.; *U.S. Private*, pg. 2335
PHILSON, INC.—See AptarGroup, Inc.; *U.S. Public*, pg. 174
PHOENIX PACKAGING LLC—See Genstar Capital, LLC; *U.S. Private*, pg. 1679
PHOENIX PACKAGING MEXICO, S.A. DE C.V.—See Genstar Capital, LLC; *U.S. Private*, pg. 1679
PHOENIX TECHNOLOGY LTD; *U.S. Private*, pg. 3173
PICKHARDT & GERLACH GMBH & CO. KG—See Gesco AG; *Int'l*, pg. 2946
PIEDMONT MANUFACTURING GROUP LLC—See Berkshire Hathaway Inc.; *U.S. Public*, pg. 298
PIMAS PLASTIK INSAAT MALZEMELERI A.S.—See Deceuninck NV; *Int'l*, pg. 2000
PIONEER COVER-ALL—See H.I.G. Capital, LLC; *U.S. Private*, pg. 1832
PIONEER PAPER CORPORATION—See Vidya Brands Group LLC; *U.S. Private*, pg. 4381
PIONEER VENTURE PTE LTD—See Advanced Systems Automation Limited; *Int'l*, pg. 162
PLAFACTORY CO., LTD.—See Daiei Kankyo Co., Ltd.; *Int'l*, pg. 1924
PLAINFIELD MOLDING, INC.—See Plainfield Precision Companies; *U.S. Private*, pg. 3194
PLA-MA BELGIUM NV—See Arplama N.V.; *Int'l*, pg. 578
PLASCO INC.; *U.S. Private*, pg. 3198
PLASMOTECH PTE. LTD.—See Amphenol Corporation; *U.S. Public*, pg. 132
PLAS-PAK INDUSTRIES, INC.—See Nordson Corporation; *U.S. Public*, pg. 1534
PLASTECH MOULDERS (PTY) LTD—See Berry Global Group, Inc; *U.S. Public*, pg. 324
THE PLASTEK GROUP - ENGINEERED PLASTICS DIVISION—See The Plastek Group; *U.S. Private*, pg. 4096
THE PLASTEK GROUP; *U.S. Private*, pg. 4096
PLASTEK INDUSTRIES, INC.—See The Plastek Group; *U.S. Private*, pg. 4096
PLASTEK UK LTD—See The Plastek Group; *U.S. Private*, pg. 4096
PLASTI-APE S.P.A.—See Berry Global Group, Inc; *U.S. Public*, pg. 322
PLASTIBENACO SRL—See Camozzi Group; *Int'l*, pg. 1274
PLASTICARD - LOCKTECH INTERNATIONAL—See Platinum Equity, LLC; *U.S. Private*, pg. 3207
PLASTIC COMPONENTS, INC.; *U.S. Private*, pg. 3198
PLASTIC INGENUITY INC.; *U.S. Private*, pg. 3198
PLASTIC OMNIUM AB—See Burelle S.A.; *Int'l*, pg. 1222
PLASTIC OMNIUM AG—See Burelle S.A.; *Int'l*, pg. 1223
PLASTIC OMNIUM AUTO EXTERIEUR SA—See Burelle S.A.; *Int'l*, pg. 1223
PLASTIC OMNIUM AUTOMOTIVE LTD—See Burelle S.A.; *Int'l*, pg. 1223
PLASTIC OMNIUM BV—See Burelle S.A.; *Int'l*, pg. 1223
PLASTIC OMNIUM DO BRASIL LTDA—See Burelle S.A.; *Int'l*, pg. 1223
PLASTIC OMNIUM ENTSORGUNGSTECHNIK GMBH—See Burelle S.A.; *Int'l*, pg. 1223
PLASTIC OMNIUM EQUIPAMIENTOS EXTERIORES SA—See Burelle S.A.; *Int'l*, pg. 1223
PLASTIC OMNIUM, INC—See Burelle S.A.; *Int'l*, pg. 1223
PLASTIC OMNIUM MEDICAL SA—See Burelle S.A.; *Int'l*, pg. 1223
PLASTIC OMNIUM SA—See Burelle S.A.; *Int'l*, pg. 1223
PLASTIC OMNIUM SISTEMAS URBANOS SA—See Burelle S.A.; *Int'l*, pg. 1223
PLASTIC OMNIUM SYSTEMES URBAINS SA—See Burelle S.A.; *Int'l*, pg. 1223
PLASTICOMP, INC.—See Avient Corporation; *U.S. Public*, pg. 248
PLASTICOS AMC, DE MEXICO, S.A. DE C.V.—See Power-Sonic Corporation; *U.S. Private*, pg. 3239
PLASTICOS NOVEL DO PARANA S.A.—See Myers Industries, Inc.; *U.S. Public*, pg. 1488
PLASTIC PLATE, INC.—See Lacks Enterprises, Inc.; *U.S. Private*, pg. 2371
PLASTIC PRODUCTS COMPANY, INC. - GREENFIELD FACILITY—See Plastic Products Company, Inc.; *U.S. Private*, pg. 3199
PLASTIC PRODUCTS COMPANY, INC. - GREENVILLE FACILITY—See Plastic Products Company, Inc.; *U.S. Private*, pg. 3199
PLASTIC PRODUCTS COMPANY, INC. - LEBANON FACILITY—See Plastic Products Company, Inc.; *U.S. Private*, pg. 3199
PLASTIC PRODUCTS COMPANY, INC. - MOLINE FACILITY—See Plastic Products Company, Inc.; *U.S. Private*, pg. 3199
PLASTIC PRODUCTS COMPANY, INC. - PRINCETON FACILITY—See Plastic Products Company, Inc.; *U.S. Private*, pg. 3199
PLASTIC PRODUCTS COMPANY, INC.; *U.S. Private*, pg. 3199
PLASTIC PRODUCTS COMPANY, INC. - WEST BRANCH FACILITY—See Plastic Products Company, Inc.; *U.S. Private*, pg. 3199
PLASTICRAFT MANUFACTURING COMPANY, INC.; *U.S. Private*, pg. 3199
PLASTICS DECEUNINCK NV—See Deceuninck NV; *Int'l*, pg. 2000
PLASTICS DESIGN & MANUFACTURING, INC.—See Tide Rock Holdings, LLC; *U.S. Private*, pg. 4167
PLASTIC SERVICES, INC.—See Laser Excel, Inc.; *U.S. Private*, pg. 2395
PLASTICS GROUP INC.; *U.S. Private*, pg. 3199
PLASTICS RESEARCH CORPORATION; *U.S. Private*, pg. 3199
PLASTIC SYSTEMS, LLC.; *U.S. Private*, pg. 3199
PLASTI-FAB LTD.—See The Riverside Company; *U.S. Private*, pg. 4109
PLASTILITE CORPORATION; *U.S. Private*, pg. 3199
PLASTIPAK PACKAGING, INC.—See Plastipak Holdings, Inc.; *U.S. Private*, pg. 3199
PLASTOP KWAZULU-NATAL (PTY) LTD—See Berry Global Group, Inc; *U.S. Public*, pg. 324
PLAS-TOP (PTY) LTD—See Berry Global Group, Inc; *U.S. Public*, pg. 324
PLASTUBE INC.—See CAI Private Equity; *Int'l*, pg. 1252

326199 — ALL OTHER PLASTICS ...

PLAYLAND INC.—See Pfingsten Partners, LLC; *U.S. Private,* pg. 3165
PLY GEM INDUSTRIES, INC.—See Clayton, Dubilier & Rice, LLC; *U.S. Private,* pg. 921
PMC SMART SOLUTIONS, LLC; *U.S. Private,* pg. 3218
POLARIS PLASTICS LIMITED—See IG Design Group Plc; *Int'l,* pg. 3600
POLLEN GEAR LLC—See Greenlane Holdings, Inc.; *U.S. Public,* pg. 965
POLO CUSTOM PRODUCTS—See M-C Industries Inc.; *U.S. Private,* pg. 2525
POLYCEL STRUCTURAL FOAM, INC.—See Polycel Holdings Inc.; *U.S. Private,* pg. 3225
POLYCHEM SYSTEMS—See Brentwood Industries Inc.; *U.S. Private,* pg. 646
POLYDAKIS LTD.—See BERICAP GmbH & Co. KG; *Int'l,* pg. 981
POLYFAB CORPORATION; *U.S. Private,* pg. 3225
POLY FOAM, INC.—See The Riverside Company; *U.S. Private,* pg. 4109
POLYMER COMPOSITE ASIA SDN. BHD.—See Hexagon Holdings Berhad; *Int'l,* pg. 3370
POLYMER ENGINEERED PRODUCTS; *U.S. Private,* pg. 3226
POLYMER INDUSTRIES; *U.S. Private,* pg. 3226
POLYONE CORP. - LONG BEACH PLANT—See Avient Corporation; *U.S. Public,* pg. 248
POLYONE CORP. - WICHITA—See Avient Corporation; *U.S. Public,* pg. 248
POLYPLAS SDN. BHD.—See Ge-Shen Corporation Berhad; *Int'l,* pg. 2897
POLY PLASTIC PRODUCTS INC—See Alpha Industries, Inc.; *U.S. Private,* pg. 197
POLY PLASTIC PRODUCTS OF NORTH CAROLINA, INC—See Alpha Industries, Inc.; *U.S. Private,* pg. 198
POLYPLASTICS MARKETING (T) LTD.—See Daicel Corporation; *Int'l,* pg. 1920
POLYPLASTICS TRADING (SHANGHAI) LTD.—See Daicel Corporation; *Int'l,* pg. 1920
POLYPRINT LTD.—See BERICAP GmbH & Co. KG; *Int'l,* pg. 981
POLY VINYL CO.; *U.S. Private,* pg. 3225
POOL DISTRIBUTORS COLOMBIA S.A.S.—See Pool Corporation; *U.S. Public,* pg. 1701
POOL SYSTEMS PTY. LTD.—See Pool Corporation; *U.S. Public,* pg. 1701
POREX CORPORATION—See Madison Industries Holdings LLC; *U.S. Private,* pg. 2543
PORT ERIE PLASTICS, INC.; *U.S. Private,* pg. 3230
PORT PLASTIC INC.—See Blackfriars Corp.; *U.S. Private,* pg. 574
POSEDO CO., LTD.—See Burelle S.A.; *Int'l,* pg. 1223
POTEX INDUSTRIES SDN. BHD.—See C.I. Holdings Berhad; *Int'l,* pg. 1243
POWER DESIGN INC.; *U.S. Private,* pg. 3237
PPC B.V.—See H2APEX Group SCA; *Int'l,* pg. 3199
PRAIRIE PACKAGING, INC.—See Pactiv Evergreen Inc.; *U.S. Public,* pg. 1633
PRD INC.—See Specialty Manufacturers, Inc.; *U.S. Private,* pg. 3750
PRECISION COATINGS INC.; *U.S. Private,* pg. 3244
PRECISION PLASTICS, INC.; *U.S. Private,* pg. 3246
PRECISION SOUTHEAST INC.—See Gladstone Management Corporation; *U.S. Private,* pg. 1705
PREMIER TRADE FRAMES LTD.—See Masco Corporation; *U.S. Public,* pg. 1391
PREMIX, INC.; *U.S. Private,* pg. 3252
PRENTIUM PACKAGING LLC—See Harbison Corporation; *U.S. Private,* pg. 1858
PRESTAGON LLC; *U.S. Private,* pg. 3255
PRIDE SOLUTIONS, LLC—See Daggett Ventures, LLC; *U.S. Private,* pg. 1144
PRIMEX PLASTICS CORP.—See ICC Industries, Inc.; *U.S. Private,* pg. 2030
PRINCE RUBBER & PLASTICS CO., INC.; *U.S. Private,* pg. 3264
PRIORITY PLASTICS, INC.; *U.S. Private,* pg. 3267
PRISM PLASTICS, INC. - HARLINGEN PLANT—See Berkshire Hathaway Inc.; *U.S. Public,* pg. 311
PRISM PLASTICS, INC.—See Berkshire Hathaway Inc.; *U.S. Public,* pg. 311
PRISM PLASTICS PRODUCTS, INC.—See BlackBern Partners LLC; *U.S. Private,* pg. 573
PRISM PLASTICS PRODUCTS, INC.—See Lee Equity Partners LLC; *U.S. Private,* pg. 2412
PROCESS SYSTEMS, INC.—See Horizon Systems, Inc.; *U.S. Private,* pg. 1982
PRO DESIGNS—See Berkshire Hathaway Inc.; *U.S. Public,* pg. 305
PRODUCTOS MOCAP S. DE R.L. DE C.V.—See MOCAP Inc.; *U.S. Private,* pg. 2759
PRODUITS PLASTIQUES PERFORMANTS - 3P—See Burelle S.A.; *Int'l,* pg. 1223
PROFESSIONAL PROTECTION SYSTEMS LTD.—See Kingswood Capital Management LLC; *U.S. Private,* pg. 2312
PROFIALIS CLERVAL S.A.S.—See OpenGate Capital Management, LLC; *U.S. Private,* pg. 3031

PROFIALIS N.V.—See OpenGate Capital Management, LLC; *U.S. Private,* pg. 3031
PROFINE AUSTRIA GMBH—See Arcapita Group Holdings Limited; *Int'l,* pg. 542
PROFINE BH D.O.O.—See Arcapita Group Holdings Limited; *Int'l,* pg. 542
PROFINE CROATIA DOO—See Arcapita Group Holdings Limited; *Int'l,* pg. 542
PROFINE FRANCE SAS—See Arcapita Group Holdings Limited; *Int'l,* pg. 542
PROFINE GMBH—See Arcapita Group Holdings Limited; *Int'l,* pg. 542
PROFINE IBERIA S.A.—See Arcapita Group Holdings Limited; *Int'l,* pg. 542
PROFINE ITALIA SRL—See Arcapita Group Holdings Limited; *Int'l,* pg. 542
PROFINE ROMANIA SRL—See Arcapita Group Holdings Limited; *Int'l,* pg. 543
PROFINE UK LTD.—See Arcapita Group Holdings Limited; *Int'l,* pg. 543
PROFINE UKRAINE—See Arcapita Group Holdings Limited; *Int'l,* pg. 543
PROGRESS PLASTIC PRODUCTS INC.; *U.S. Private,* pg. 3278
PROMENS AS—See Berry Global Group, Inc; *U.S. Public,* pg. 323
PROMENS AS—See Berry Global Group, Inc; *U.S. Public,* pg. 323
PROMENS HOCKENHEIM GMBH—See Berry Global Group, Inc; *U.S. Public,* pg. 323
PROMENS MONASTIR SARL—See Berry Global Group, Inc; *U.S. Public,* pg. 323
PROMENS MUNCHEN GMBH—See Berry Global Group, Inc; *U.S. Public,* pg. 323
PROMENS NITRA S.R.O.—See Berry Global Group, Inc; *U.S. Public,* pg. 323
PROMENS PACKAGING GMBH - ETTLINGEN—See Berry Global Group, Inc; *U.S. Public,* pg. 323
PROMENS PACKAGING GMBH—See Berry Global Group, Inc; *U.S. Public,* pg. 323
PROMENS PACKAGING LTD.—See Berry Global Group, Inc; *U.S. Public,* pg. 323
PROMENS PACKAGING SAU—See Berry Global Group, Inc; *U.S. Public,* pg. 323
PROMENS RIJEN B.V.—See Berry Global Group, Inc; *U.S. Public,* pg. 323
PROMENS SA - GEOVREISSET—See Berry Global Group, Inc; *U.S. Public,* pg. 323
PROMENS SARL—See Berry Global Group, Inc; *U.S. Public,* pg. 323
PROMENS SA—See Berry Global Group, Inc; *U.S. Public,* pg. 323
PROMENS ZEVENAAR B.V.—See Berry Global Group, Inc; *U.S. Public,* pg. 323
PROTECTIVE INDUSTRIES, INC.—See Windjammer Capital Investors, LLC; *U.S. Private,* pg. 4538
PROTOGENIC, INC.—See CORE Industrial Partners, LLC; *U.S. Private,* pg. 1048
PROTO LABS, G.K.—See Proto Labs, Inc.; *U.S. Public,* pg. 1730
PROTO LABS, INC.; *U.S. Public,* pg. 1729
PROTO LABS, LTD.—See Proto Labs, Inc.; *U.S. Public,* pg. 1730
PROTO PLASTICS INC.—See Thogus Products Company; *U.S. Private,* pg. 4145
PROTOTYPE PLASTICS, LLC; *U.S. Private,* pg. 3290
PSI MOLDED PLASTICS NEW HAMPSHIRE, INC.—See Gladstone Management Corporation; *U.S. Private,* pg. 1705
PTA CORPORATION; *U.S. Private,* pg. 3298
PT AMTEK PLASTIC BATAM—See Blackstone Inc.; *U.S. Public,* pg. 355
PT ESSENTRA—See Essentra plc; *Int'l,* pg. 2511
PT HONFOONG PLASTIC INDUSTRIES—See Accrelist Ltd.; *Int'l,* pg. 93
PTI ENGINEERED PLASTICS INC.; *U.S. Private,* pg. 3298
PT JUKEN TECHNOLOGY INDONESIA—See Frencken Group Limited; *Int'l,* pg. 2773
PT. PERTAMA PRECISION BINTAN—See I-PEX Inc.; *Int'l,* pg. 3564
PT PLASMOTECH BATAM—See Amphenol Corporation; *U.S. Public,* pg. 132
PUTNAM PLASTICS COMPANY, LLC—See Foster Corporation; *U.S. Private,* pg. 1578
PWP INDUSTRIES, INC.—See Pactiv Evergreen Inc.; *U.S. Public,* pg. 1633
PWS NORDIC AB—See Berry Global Group, Inc; *U.S. Public,* pg. 322
Q3 INDUSTRIES—See Q3 Stamped Metal; *U.S. Private,* pg. 3312
QINGDAO VICTORY PLASTIC CO., LTD—See Flex Ltd.; *Int'l,* pg. 2704
QUADION LLC - RIVER FALLS PLANT—See KKR & Co. Inc.; *U.S. Public,* pg. 1263
QUAKER PLASTIC CORPORATION—See Wexco Incorporated; *U.S. Private,* pg. 4502
QUALITY INDUSTRIES, INC.—See Anchor Fabrication Ltd.; *U.S. Private,* pg. 273

QUANTUM PLASTICS, INC.; *U.S. Private,* pg. 3323
RAPIDWERKS LLC—See Emerson Electric Co.; *U.S. Public,* pg. 752
RAVEN INDUSTRIES AUSTRALIA PTY LTD—See CNH Industrial N.V.; *Int'l,* pg. 1676
RAVEN INDUSTRIES, INC.—See CNH Industrial N.V.; *Int'l,* pg. 1676
RBL PRODUCTS, INC.—See MPE Partners, LLC; *U.S. Private,* pg. 2803
R&D MOLDERS, INC.—See Lomont Molding LLC; *U.S. Private,* pg. 2483
READEREST; *U.S. Private,* pg. 3366
REBHAN FPS KUNSTSTOFF-VERPACKUNGEN GMBH—See Certina Holding AG; *Int'l,* pg. 1423
REESE ENTERPRISES, INC. - ASTRO PLASTICS DIVISION—See Reese Enterprises, Inc.; *U.S. Private,* pg. 3383
REESE ENTERPRISES, INC.; *U.S. Private,* pg. 3383
REESE ENTERPRISES, INC. - WEATHER STRIP DIVISION—See Reese Enterprises, Inc.; *U.S. Private,* pg. 3383
REFRESH PLASTICS PTY LTD—See Eneco Refresh Limited; *Int'l,* pg. 2411
REGENCY PLASTICS - UBLY INC.; *U.S. Private,* pg. 3386
REHRIG PACIFIC COMPANY - ATLANTA PLANT—See Rehrig Pacific Company; *U.S. Private,* pg. 3390
REHRIG PACIFIC COMPANY - DALLAS PLANT—See Rehrig Pacific Company; *U.S. Private,* pg. 3390
REHRIG PACIFIC COMPANY DE MEXICO S.A. DE C.V.—See Rehrig Pacific Company; *U.S. Private,* pg. 3390
REHRIG PACIFIC COMPANY - ERIE PLANT—See Rehrig Pacific Company; *U.S. Private,* pg. 3390
REHRIG PACIFIC COMPANY - KANSAS PLANT—See Rehrig Pacific Company; *U.S. Private,* pg. 3390
REHRIG PACIFIC COMPANY - KENOSHA PLANT—See Rehrig Pacific Company; *U.S. Private,* pg. 3390
REHRIG PACIFIC COMPANY - ORLANDO PLANT—See Rehrig Pacific Company; *U.S. Private,* pg. 3390
REHRIG PACIFIC COMPANY; *U.S. Private,* pg. 3389
REICHHOLD FINANCE BV—See Reichhold, Inc.; *U.S. Private,* pg. 3391
REICHHOLD INDIA PRIVATE LIMITED—See Reichhold, Inc.; *U.S. Private,* pg. 3391
REICHHOLD KIMYA SANAYI VE TICARET AS—See Reichhold, Inc.; *U.S. Private,* pg. 3391
REICHHOLD SRL—See Reichhold, Inc.; *U.S. Private,* pg. 3391
REINHOLD HOLDINGS, INC.—See HEICO Corporation; *U.S. Public,* pg. 1021
RELIANCE PRODUCTS, LTD.—See Greif Inc.; *U.S. Public,* pg. 968
RENOSOL CORPORATION; *U.S. Private,* pg. 3399
REO PLASTICS, INC.; *U.S. Public,* pg. 1784
REPUBLIC BAG INC.—See Alpha Industries, Inc.; *U.S. Private,* pg. 198
RESITECH GERMANY GMBH—See OpenGate Capital Management, LLC; *U.S. Private,* pg. 3031
REVERE PLASTICS SYSTEMS, LLC - POPLAR BLUFF—See Ardian SAS; *Int'l,* pg. 554
REVERE PLASTICS SYSTEMS, LLC—See Ardian SAS; *Int'l,* pg. 554
REYNOLDS FOOD PACKAGING—See Pactiv Evergreen Inc.; *U.S. Public,* pg. 1634
RHENUM METALL LTD.—See Georg Fischer AG; *Int'l,* pg. 2937
RHETECH ENGINEERED PLASTICS LTD.—See HEXPOL AB; *Int'l,* pg. 3372
RICHARDSON MOLDING, INC.—See Owner Resource Group, LLC; *U.S. Private,* pg. 3055
RICHARDSON MOLDING, LLC; *U.S. Private,* pg. 3429
RICHCO, INC.—See Essentra plc; *Int'l,* pg. 2511
RIVER BEND INDUSTRIES LLC; *U.S. Private,* pg. 3443
RIVER BEND INDUSTRIES-NORTH LIBERTY DIVISION—See River Bend Industries LLC; *U.S. Private,* pg. 3443
RIVER BEND INDUSTRIES-VICTOR DIVISION—See River Bend Industries LLC; *U.S. Private,* pg. 3443
RLR INDUSTRIES INC.; *U.S. Private,* pg. 3450
ROBERTS POLYPRO INC.—See Leonard Green & Partners, L.P.; *U.S. Private,* pg. 2428
ROBINSON INDUSTRIES INC.; *U.S. Private,* pg. 3462
ROGAN CORPORATION; *U.S. Private,* pg. 3471
ROHRER CORP. - HUNTLEY PLANT—See Wellspring Capital Management LLC; *U.S. Private,* pg. 4477
ROHRER CORPORATION OF PENNSYLVANIA—See Wellspring Capital Management LLC; *U.S. Private,* pg. 4477
ROHRER CORPORATION—See Wellspring Capital Management LLC; *U.S. Private,* pg. 4477
ROLITE PLASTICS INC—See Jordan Industries, Inc.; *U.S. Private,* pg. 2235
ROMEO RIM, INC.—See Reserve Group Management Company; *U.S. Private,* pg. 3404
ROTATIONAL MOLDING, INC.—See Olympus Partners; *U.S. Private,* pg. 3013
ROTEX GLOBAL, LLC—See Hillenbrand, Inc.; *U.S. Public,* pg. 1037
ROYALE COMFORT SEATING INC.; *U.S. Private,* pg. 3494

N.A.I.C.S. INDEX

326199 — ALL OTHER PLASTICS ...

ROYAL INDUSTRIES, INC.; *U.S. Private*, pg. 3492
ROYAL TECHNOLOGIES CORPORATION; *U.S. Private*, pg. 3493
ROYLE EXTRUSION SYSTEMS PVT. LTD.—See Royle Systems Group; *U.S. Private*, pg. 3494
RPC BEAUTE MAROLLES SAS—See Berry Global Group, Inc; *U.S. Public*, pg. 324
RPC BEBO FOOD PACKAGING - KRISTIANSAND—See Berry Global Group, Inc; *U.S. Public*, pg. 324
RPC BRAMLAGE ANTWERPEN NV—See Berry Global Group, Inc; *U.S. Public*, pg. 324
RPC BRAMLAGE GMBH—See Berry Global Group, Inc; *U.S. Public*, pg. 324
RPC BRAMLAGE WARSZAWA SP. Z.O.O.—See Berry Global Group, Inc; *U.S. Public*, pg. 324
RPC FORMATEC GMBH—See Berry Global Group, Inc; *U.S. Public*, pg. 324
RPC GROUP PLC—See Berry Global Group, Inc; *U.S. Public*, pg. 322
RPC KOLDING A/S—See Berry Global Group, Inc; *U.S. Public*, pg. 325
RPC PACKAGING GENT NV—See Berry Global Group, Inc; *U.S. Public*, pg. 324
RPC PROMENS EKE NV—See Berry Global Group, Inc; *U.S. Public*, pg. 325
RPC PROMENS INDUSTRIAL JAGTENBERG B.V—See Berry Global Group, Inc; *U.S. Public*, pg. 325
RPC SUPERFOS A/S—See Berry Global Group, Inc; *U.S. Public*, pg. 325
RPC SUPERFOS BESANCON SAS—See Berry Global Group, Inc; *U.S. Public*, pg. 325
RPC SUPERFOS - HAMBURG—See Berry Global Group, Inc; *U.S. Public*, pg. 325
RPC SUPERFOS LIDKOPING AB—See Berry Global Group, Inc; *U.S. Public*, pg. 325
RPC SUPERFOS MULLSJO AB—See Berry Global Group, Inc; *U.S. Public*, pg. 325
RPC SUPERFOS STILLING A/S—See Berry Global Group, Inc; *U.S. Public*, pg. 325
RPC SUPERFOS US INC.—See Berry Global Group, Inc; *U.S. Public*, pg. 325
RPC SUPERFOS WETTEREN NV—See Berry Global Group, Inc; *U.S. Public*, pg. 325
RPC TEDECO-GIZEH KFT—See Berry Global Group, Inc; *U.S. Public*, pg. 325
RPC TEDECO-GIZEH SAS—See Berry Global Group, Inc; *U.S. Public*, pg. 325
RPC TEDECO-GIZEH (UK) LIMITED—See Berry Global Group, Inc; *U.S. Public*, pg. 325
RPC WIKO GMBH—See Berry Global Group, Inc; *U.S. Public*, pg. 324
RPC ZELLER PLASTIK LIBERTYVILLE INC.—See Berry Global Group, Inc; *U.S. Public*, pg. 325
RPS COMPOSITES ONTARIO INC.—See RPS Composites, Inc.; *U.S. Private*, pg. 3496
R&R PLASTICS; *U.S. Private*, pg. 3333
RUBBERMAID COMMERCIAL PRODUCTS LLC—See Newell Brands Inc.; *U.S. Public*, pg. 1514
RUBBERMAID HOME PRODUCTS—See Newell Brands Inc.; *U.S. Public*, pg. 1514
RUTLAND INTERNATIONAL LIMITED—See Avient Corporation; *U.S. Public*, pg. 248
RYKO PLASTIC PRODUCTS INC.; *U.S. Private*, pg. 3511
RYMAC ENTERPRISES—See Q3 Stamped Metal; *U.S. Private*, pg. 3312
SACOPA, S.A.U.—See Fluidra SA; *Int'l*, pg. 2714
SA DETAJOINT NV—See Deceuninck NV; *Int'l*, pg. 2000
SAEPLAST AMERICAS INC.—See Berry Global Group, Inc; *U.S. Public*, pg. 325
SAEPLAST ICELAND EHF—See Berry Global Group, Inc; *U.S. Public*, pg. 325
SAEPLAST SPAIN SAU—See Berry Global Group, Inc; *U.S. Public*, pg. 325
SAFE-HIT CORPORATION—See Trinity Industries, Inc.; *U.S. Public*, pg. 2193
SAFETY TECHNOLOGY INTERNATIONAL, INC.; *U.S. Private*, pg. 3525
SAINT-GOBAIN ADFORS CANADA LTD—See Compagnie de Saint-Gobain SA; *Int'l*, pg. 1732
SAINT-GOBAIN NORPRO GMBH—See Compagnie de Saint-Gobain SA; *Int'l*, pg. 1735
SAINT-GOBAIN PERFORMANCE PLASTICS CHAINEUX SA—See Compagnie de Saint-Gobain SA; *Int'l*, pg. 1731
SAINT-GOBAIN PERFORMANCE PLASTICS CORP.—See Compagnie de Saint-Gobain SA; *Int'l*, pg. 1730
SAINT-GOBAIN PERFORMANCE PLASTICS CORP.—See Compagnie de Saint-Gobain SA; *Int'l*, pg. 1731
SAINT-GOBAIN PERFORMANCE PLASTICS ESPANA S.A.—See Compagnie de Saint-Gobain SA; *Int'l*, pg. 1735
SAINT-GOBAIN PERFORMANCE PLASTICS EUROPE, S.A.—See Compagnie de Saint-Gobain SA; *Int'l*, pg. 1735
SAINT-GOBAIN PERFORMANCE PLASTICS ISOFLUOR GMBH—See Compagnie de Saint-Gobain SA; *Int'l*, pg. 1728
SAINT-GOBAIN PERFORMANCE PLASTICS PAMPUS GMBH—See Compagnie de Saint-Gobain SA; *Int'l*, pg. 1732
SAINT-GOBAIN PERFORMANCE PLASTICS SHANGHAI—See Compagnie de Saint-Gobain SA; *Int'l*, pg. 1732
SAINT-GOBAIN PERFORMANCE PLASTICS SIPRO GMBH—See Compagnie de Saint-Gobain SA; *Int'l*, pg. 1735
SAJAR PLASTICS, LLC—See Wembly Enterprises LLC; *U.S. Private*, pg. 4480
SAKAMOTO PRINTING CO., LTD.—See Asahi Printing Co., Ltd.; *Int'l*, pg. 598
SANTA FE PACKAGING CORP.—See Alpha Industries, Inc.; *U.S. Private*, pg. 198
SANYPICK PLASTIC, S.A.—See ACS, Actividades de Construccion y Servicios, S.A.; *Int'l*, pg. 116
SAO PROFINE RUS—See Arcapita Group Holdings Limited; *Int'l*, pg. 542
SAS FABRICAUTO—See 3M Company; *U.S. Public*, pg. 6
SCAPA TAPES NORTH AMERICA INC.—See Mativ Holdings, Inc.; *U.S. Public*, pg. 1397
S.C. ARPLAMA ROMANIA S.R.L.—See Arplama N.V.; *Int'l*, pg. 578
SCEPTER CANADA INC.—See Myers Industries, Inc.; *U.S. Public*, pg. 1488
SCHIFFMAYER PLASTICS CORP; *U.S. Private*, pg. 3564
SCHOELLER ALLIBERT AB—See OEP Capital Advisors, L.P.; *U.S. Private*, pg. 3000
SCHOELLER ALLIBERT LIMITED—See OEP Capital Advisors, L.P.; *U.S. Private*, pg. 3000
SCHOELLER ALLIBERT—See OEP Capital Advisors, L.P.; *U.S. Private*, pg. 3000
SCHOELLER ARCA SYSTEMS BV—See OEP Capital Advisors, L.P.; *U.S. Private*, pg. 3000
SCHOELLER ARCA SYSTEMS GMBH—See OEP Capital Advisors, L.P.; *U.S. Private*, pg. 3000
SCHOELLER ARCA SYSTEMS GMBH—See OEP Capital Advisors, L.P.; *U.S. Private*, pg. 3000
SCHOELLER ARCA SYSTEMS INC.—See OEP Capital Advisors, L.P.; *U.S. Private*, pg. 3000
SCHOELLER ARCA SYSTEMS LIMITED—See OEP Capital Advisors, L.P.; *U.S. Private*, pg. 3000
SCHOELLER ARCA SYSTEMS OY—See OEP Capital Advisors, L.P.; *U.S. Private*, pg. 3000
SCHOELLER ARCA SYSTEMS S.A.—See OEP Capital Advisors, L.P.; *U.S. Private*, pg. 3000
SCHOELLER ARCA SYSTEMS S.L.—See OEP Capital Advisors, L.P.; *U.S. Private*, pg. 3000
SCHOELLER ARCA SYSTEMS, SPOL S.R.O.—See OEP Capital Advisors, L.P.; *U.S. Private*, pg. 3000
SCHOELLER ARCA SYSTEMS ZAO—See OEP Capital Advisors, L.P.; *U.S. Private*, pg. 3000
SCHUCO USA L.L.L.P.; *U.S. Private*, pg. 3570
SCIENTIFIC MOLDING CORPORATION; *U.S. Private*, pg. 3574
SCM MICROSYSTEMS LTD.—See Identiv, Inc.; *U.S. Public*, pg. 1089
SCOPUS-OMNIBADGES S.A.S.—See Amano Corporation; *Int'l*, pg. 411
SEA-LECT PLASTIC CORP.—See Patrick Industries, Inc.; *U.S. Public*, pg. 1653
SEALED AIR (CHINA) CO., LTD.—See Sealed Air Corporation; *U.S. Public*, pg. 1854
SEALED AIR DENMARK A/S—See Sealed Air Corporation; *U.S. Public*, pg. 1854
SEALED AIR GMBH—See Sealed Air Corporation; *U.S. Public*, pg. 1854
SEAPLAST (INDIA) PRIVATE LIMITED—See Berry Global Group, Inc; *U.S. Public*, pg. 325
SEASAFE INC.—See Gibraltar Industries, Inc.; *U.S. Public*, pg. 935
SEAWAY MANUFACTURING CORP.; *U.S. Private*, pg. 3592
SEBRO PLASTICS, INC.—See Sonoco Products Company; *U.S. Public*, pg. 1906
SECURITY PLASTICS DIVISION/NMC LLC—See National Molding Corporation; *U.S. Private*, pg. 2859
SERCO MOLD INC.; *U.S. Private*, pg. 3613
SETCO, LLC—See Berry Global Group, Inc; *U.S. Public*, pg. 321
S&G COMPANY, LTD.—See Daewon Semiconductor Packaging Industrial Corporation; *Int'l*, pg. 1910
SHANGHAI DAI-ICHI SEIKO MOULD & PLASTICS CO., LTD. - SHANGHAI PLANT 1—See I-PEX Inc.; *Int'l*, pg. 3564
SHANGHAI DAI-ICHI SEIKO MOULD & PLASTICS CO., LTD. - SHANGHAI PLANT 2—See I-PEX Inc.; *Int'l*, pg. 3564
SHANGHAI FORMICA DECORATIVE MATERIAL CO. LTD—See Fletcher Building Limited; *Int'l*, pg. 2701
SHANGHAI PINGUAN PLASTIC INDUSTRY COMPANY LIMITED—See CPMC Holdings Limited; *Int'l*, pg. 1826
SHENZHEN CHEE YUEN PLASTIC PRODUCTS COMPANY LIMITED—See China Aerospace International Holdings Limited; *Int'l*, pg. 1481
SHENZHEN KWAN WING TRADING COMPANY LIMITED—See Deswell Industries, Inc.; *Int'l*, pg. 2047
SHINKO ELECTRIC INDUSTRIES CO., LTD.—See Fujitsu Limited; *Int'l*, pg. 2837
SHUBEE CUSTOMER CARE WEAR; *U.S. Private*, pg. 3644
SIAM YACHIYO CO., LTD.—See Honda Motor Co., Ltd.; *Int'l*, pg. 3464
THE SIEMON COMPANY; *U.S. Private*, pg. 4118
SIGMA STRETCH FILM - CALIFORNIA PLANT—See Alpha Industries, Inc.; *U.S. Private*, pg. 198
SIGMA STRETCH FILM - CANADA PLANT—See Alpha Industries, Inc.; *U.S. Private*, pg. 198
SIGMA STRETCH FILM - KENTUCKY PLANT—See Alpha Industries, Inc.; *U.S. Private*, pg. 198
SIGMA STRETCH FILM - OKLAHOMA PLANT—See Alpha Industries, Inc.; *U.S. Private*, pg. 198
SIGNODE BVBA—See Crown Holdings, Inc.; *U.S. Public*, pg. 599
SILGAN CONTAINERS MANUFACTURING PUERTO RICO LLC—See Silgan Holdings, Inc.; *U.S. Public*, pg. 1878
SILGAN DISPENSING SYSTEMS CORPORATION—See Silgan Holdings, Inc.; *U.S. Public*, pg. 1879
SILGAN PLASTIC CLOSURE SOLUTIONS—See Silgan Holdings, Inc.; *U.S. Public*, pg. 1879
SIMONTON WINDOWS, INC.—See Clayton, Dubilier & Rice, LLC; *U.S. Private*, pg. 921
SIMTEK FENCE, INC.—See Compagnie de Saint-Gobain SA; *Int'l*, pg. 1730
SINCLAIR & RUSH, INC.—See Cameron Holdings Corporation; *U.S. Private*, pg. 729
SINCLAIR & RUSH LTD.—See Cameron Holdings Corporation; *U.S. Private*, pg. 729
SINGAPORE DAI-ICHI PTE. LTD. - WOODLANDS PLANT—See I-PEX Inc.; *Int'l*, pg. 3564
SKB CORPORATION; *U.S. Private*, pg. 3681
SKS STAKUSIT BAUTECHNIK GMBH—See GEI-Immo AG; *Int'l*, pg. 2912
SLG PLASTICS, INC.—See Scott's Liquid Gold-Inc.; *U.S. Public*, pg. 1849
SLOVAK DIRECT, SPOL. S.R.O.—See ANY Security Printing Company PLC; *Int'l*, pg. 486
SMARTTECH PRODUCTION LTD.—See Aisino Corporation; *Int'l*, pg. 254
SMITHS MEDICAL—See ICU Medical, Inc.; *U.S. Public*, pg. 1087
SNYDER INDUSTRIES, INC. - MARKED TREE—See Olympus Partners; *U.S. Private*, pg. 3013
SNYDER INDUSTRIES, INC. - PLASTIC SOLUTIONS DIVISION—See Olympus Partners; *U.S. Private*, pg. 3013
SOLAR PLASTICS LLC—See Olympus Partners; *U.S. Private*, pg. 3013
SOLO CUP COMPANY—See Dart Container Corporation; *U.S. Private*, pg. 1160
SOLO CUP COMPANY—See Dart Container Corporation; *U.S. Private*, pg. 1160
SOLO CUP OPERATING CORPORATION—See Dart Container Corporation; *U.S. Private*, pg. 1160
SONOCO BAKER—See Sonoco Products Company; *U.S. Public*, pg. 1908
SONOCO CLEAR PACK—See Sonoco Products Company; *U.S. Public*, pg. 1906
SONOCO FLEXIBLE PACKAGING CANADA CORPORATION—See Sonoco Products Company; *U.S. Public*, pg. 1906
SONOCO HICKORY, INC.—See Sonoco Products Company; *U.S. Public*, pg. 1906
SONOCO PLASTICS B.V.—See Sonoco Products Company; *U.S. Public*, pg. 1907
SONOCO PLASTICS GERMANY GMBH—See Sonoco Products Company; *U.S. Public*, pg. 1906
SONOCO PLASTICS GERMANY GMBH—See Sonoco Products Company; *U.S. Public*, pg. 1906
SONOCO PRODUCTS COMPANY—See Sonoco Products Company; *U.S. Public*, pg. 1908
SORENSON BIOSCIENCE, INC.—See Corning Incorporated; *U.S. Public*, pg. 579
SOREPLA SRL—See ERG S.p.A.; *Int'l*, pg. 2491
SOUTHEASTERN PLASTICS CORP.—See Alpha Industries, Inc.; *U.S. Private*, pg. 198
SOUTHERN DIVERSIFIED INDUSTRIES—See Liberty Diversified International Inc.; *U.S. Private*, pg. 2444
SPARTECH - PAULDING—See The Jordan Company, L.P.; *U.S. Private*, pg. 4062
SPEARS MANUFACTURING COMPANY; *U.S. Private*, pg. 3748
SPECIALTY MANUFACTURERS, INC.; *U.S. Private*, pg. 3750
SPECIALTY PLASTICS COMPANY—See Parrish Enterprises, Ltd.; *U.S. Private*, pg. 3100
SPECTRUM MOLDING—See The Plastek Group; *U.S. Private*, pg. 4096
THE SPECTRUM PLASTICS GROUP - ATHOL—See Odyssey Investment Partners, LLC; *U.S. Private*, pg. 2995
SPECTRUM PLASTICS GROUP, INC.—See DuPont de Nemours, Inc.; *U.S. Public*, pg. 694
THE SPECTRUM PLASTICS GROUP - MEXICALI PLANT—See The Odyssey Investment Partners, LLC; *U.S. Private*, pg. 2995
SPENCER INDUSTRIES INC.; *U.S. Private*, pg. 3755
SPERIAN PROTECTION CLOTHING S.A.—See Honeywell International Inc.; *U.S. Public*, pg. 1049

326199 — ALL OTHER PLASTICS ...

SPIN PRODUCTS, INC.—See Olympus Partners; *U.S. Private*, pg. 3013
SPIRATEX COMPANY INC.; *U.S. Private*, pg. 3757
SPIREX CORPORATION—See Nordson Corporation; *U.S. Public*, pg. 1534
SPONTEX S.A.S.—See Newell Brands Inc.; *U.S. Public*, pg. 1515
SPRAYING SYSTEMS DEUTSCHLAND GMBH—See Spraying Systems Co.; *U.S. Private*, pg. 3762
SPRAYING SYSTEMS JAPAN CO. LTD.—See Spraying Systems Co.; *U.S. Private*, pg. 3762
SRG GLOBAL AUTOMOTIVE, LLC—See Koch Industries, Inc.; *U.S. Private*, pg. 2329
SSI TECHNOLOGIES; *U.S. Private*, pg. 3769
STARC SYSTEMS, INC.; *U.S. Private*, pg. 3786
ST. CLAIRE PLASTICS CO.; *U.S. Private*, pg. 3771
STEEL CITY CORPORATION; *U.S. Private*, pg. 3795
STEINWALL INC.; *U.S. Private*, pg. 3798
THE STEP2 COMPANY LLC—See Aterian Investment Management, L.P.; *U.S. Private*, pg. 367
STERILITE CORPORATION; *U.S. Private*, pg. 3804
STOPAQ B.V.—See Berry Global Group, Inc; *U.S. Public*, pg. 325
STRAIGHT LTD—See Madison Dearborn Partners, LLC; *U.S. Private*, pg. 2541
STRATA PRODUCTS LIMITED—See Chiltern Capital LLP; *Int'l*, pg. 1479
STRIEBEL & JOHN FRANCE S.A.R.L.—See ABB Ltd.; *Int'l*, pg. 50
STRONGWELL CORPORATION; *U.S. Private*, pg. 3841
STRUCTURAL COMPOSITES OF INDIANA, INC.—See Patrick Industries, Inc.; *U.S. Public*, pg. 1653
STULL TECHNOLOGIES INC.—See Irving Place Capital Management, L.P.; *U.S. Private*, pg. 2142
STYLE CREST, INC.; *U.S. Private*, pg. 3846
STYRON LLC—See Bain Capital, LP; *U.S. Private*, pg. 449
SUBURBAN PLASTICS CO; *U.S. Private*, pg. 3848
SUMMIT PACKAGING SYSTEMS INC.; *U.S. Private*, pg. 3855
SUMMIT PLASTIC CO.; *U.S. Private*, pg. 3856
SUMMIT PLASTICS, INC.—See LongueVue Capital, LLC; *U.S. Private*, pg. 2493
SUMMIT POLYMERS INC.; *U.S. Private*, pg. 3856
SUN COAST INDUSTRIES, LLC—See Berry Global Group, Inc; *U.S. Public*, pg. 321
SUNDQUIST COMPONENTS AB—See Axel Johnson Gruppen AB; *Int'l*, pg. 763
SUNRISE PACKAGING INC.; *U.S. Private*, pg. 3870
SUPERIOR INTERNATIONAL INDUSTRIES INC.—See Pfingsten Partners, LLC; *U.S. Private*, pg. 3164
SUPER WIN ELECTRONICS LIMITED—See IDT International Limited; *Int'l*, pg. 3597
SUPREME CONCRETE LIMITED—See Ibstock plc; *Int'l*, pg. 3577
SUR-FLO PLASTICS & ENGINEERING INC.; *U.S. Private*, pg. 3883
SUZHOU ASIAN MICRO RECOVERY TECHNOLOGY CO LTD—See Asian Micro Holdings Ltd.; *Int'l*, pg. 618
SVE PORTABLE ROADWAY SYSTEMS, INC.—See Audax Group, Limited Partnership; *U.S. Private*, pg. 387
SWISH BUILDING PRODUCTS LIMITED—See Epwin Group Plc; *Int'l*, pg. 2466
SYLVIN TECHNOLOGIES, INC.—See Grupo Empresarial Kaluz S.A. de C.V.; *Int'l*, pg. 3128
SYNDICATE SALES INC.; *U.S. Private*, pg. 3903
SYNERGY PACKAGING PTY. LIMITED—See Berry Global Group, Inc; *U.S. Public*, pg. 325
SYNRES-ALMOCO B.V.—See PMC Capital Partners, LLC; *U.S. Private*, pg. 3217
SYNTECH DEVELOPMENT & MANUFACTURING, INC.; *U.S. Private*, pg. 3904
SYNTEC OPTICS, INC.—See Syntec Optics Holding, Inc.; *U.S. Public*, pg. 1972
SYNVENTIVE MOLDING SOLUTIONS LTDA—See Barnes Group Inc.; *U.S. Public*, pg. 278
SYSTEX JAPAN INC.—See Denso Corporation; *Int'l*, pg. 2032
SYSTEX PRODUCTS ARKANSAS COMPANY—See Denso Corporation; *Int'l*, pg. 2033
TABLE TRENDS INC.—See Lee's Curtain Co., Inc.; *U.S. Private*, pg. 2414
TAIAN HAOHUA PLASTIC CO., LTD—See China National Chemical Corporation; *Int'l*, pg. 1527
TAIWAN GREEN POINT ENTERPRISES CO., LTD—See Jabil Inc.; *U.S. Public*, pg. 1182
TANGENT TECHNOLOGIES, LLC; *U.S. Private*, pg. 3930
TATRA ROTALAC LIMITED—See Coral Products PLC; *Int'l*, pg. 1795
TCL HOFMANN PTY. LTD.—See BERICAP GmbH & Co. KG; *Int'l*, pg. 981
TEAM ONE PLASTICS INC.; *U.S. Private*, pg. 3950
TEC-AIR INC.; *U.S. Private*, pg. 3951
TECH GROUP NORTH AMERICA, INC.—See West Pharmaceutical Services, Inc.; *U.S. Public*, pg. 2352
TECH GROUP PHOENIX, INC.—See West Pharmaceutical Services, Inc.; *U.S. Public*, pg. 2352
TECH GROUP—See West Pharmaceutical Services, Inc.; *U.S. Public*, pg. 2352

TECH NH INC.; *U.S. Private*, pg. 3952
TECHNIMARK LLC—See The Pritzker Group - Chicago, LLC; *U.S. Private*, pg. 4099
TECHNIPLAS, LLC; *U.S. Private*, pg. 3954
TECKON INDUSTRIAL CORPORATION—See COXON Precise Industrial Co., Ltd.; *Int'l*, pg. 1823
TECSTAR MFG. GROUP, INC.—See MGS Manufacturing Group, Inc.; *U.S. Private*, pg. 2695
TEEL PLASTICS INC.—See JLS Investment Group LLC; *U.S. Private*, pg. 2213
TEIKA-PRECISION CO.—See FP Corporation; *Int'l*, pg. 2756
TEKNOR APEX B.V.—See Teknor Apex Company; *U.S. Private*, pg. 3958
TEMPRA EHF.—See Berry Global Group, Inc; *U.S. Public*, pg. 325
TENEX CORPORATION; *U.S. Private*, pg. 3966
TERRACON CORPORATION—See Chargepoint Technology Ltd.; *Int'l*, pg. 1448
TESSY PLASTICS CORP; *U.S. Private*, pg. 3973
TETRALENE, INC.—See Freudenberg SE; *Int'l*, pg. 2790
TEXON POLYMER GROUP, INC.—See Myers Industries, Inc.; *U.S. Public*, pg. 1488
THERMO FISHER SCIENTIFIC - NALGENE & NUNC—See Thermo Fisher Scientific, Inc.; *U.S. Public*, pg. 2153
THERMOSAFE BRANDS—See Sonoco Products Company; *U.S. Public*, pg. 1905
THOGUS PRODUCTS COMPANY; *U.S. Private*, pg. 4145
THOMPSON CREEK WINDOW COMPANY; *U.S. Private*, pg. 4159
THORMAC ENGINEERING LTD.—See Madison Dearborn Partners, LLC; *U.S. Private*, pg. 2541
TH PLASTICS INC.; *U.S. Private*, pg. 3979
THUMB PLASTICS INC.—See Gemini Group, Inc.; *U.S. Private*, pg. 1658
TICONA GMBH—See Celanese Corporation; *U.S. Public*, pg. 465
TMI INTERNATIONAL, LLC—See ShoreView Industries, LLC; *U.S. Private*, pg. 3642
TODD ENTERPRISES—See Chem-Tainer Industries, Inc.; *U.S. Private*, pg. 871
TOLEDO MOLDING & DIE INC.—See Grammer AG; *Int'l*, pg. 3053
TOMPKINS INDUSTRIES, INC.; *U.S. Private*, pg. 4184
TOPCRAFT PRECISION MOLDERS, INC.; *U.S. Private*, pg. 4187
T.O. PLASTICS, INC.—See Otter Tail Corporation; *U.S. Public*, pg. 1624
TOTER, LLC—See H.I.G. Capital, LLC; *U.S. Private*, pg. 1832
TOWER TAG & LABEL, LLC—See Do-It Corporation; *U.S. Private*, pg. 1250
TP COMPOSITES, INC.—See SK Capital Partners, LP; *U.S. Private*, pg. 3680
TRANSPARENT CONTAINER CO., INC.—See Wellspring Capital Management LLC; *U.S. Private*, pg. 4477
TRAY-PAK CORP.—See Archbrook Capital Management LLC; *U.S. Private*, pg. 310
TREDEGAR BRASIL INDUSTRIA DE PLASTICOS LTDA.—See Tredegar Corporation; *U.S. Public*, pg. 2187
TREDEGAR FILM PRODUCTS B.V.—See Tredegar Corporation; *U.S. Public*, pg. 2187
TREDEGAR FILM PRODUCTS KFT—See Tredegar Corporation; *U.S. Public*, pg. 2187
TRELLIS BIOPLASTICS—See Trellis Earth Products, Inc.; *U.S. Private*, pg. 4217
TRELLIS EARTH PRODUCTS, INC.; *U.S. Private*, pg. 4217
TREND TECHNOLOGIES, LLC; *U.S. Private*, pg. 4218
TRIENDA HOLDINGS, LLC—See Kruger Brown Holdings, LLC; *U.S. Private*, pg. 2353
TRIG ENGINEERING LIMITED—See Ensinger GmbH; *Int'l*, pg. 2448
TRINITY STERILE; *U.S. Private*, pg. 4235
TRI-PACK ENTERPRISES INC.—See Clearlake Capital Group, L.P.; *U.S. Private*, pg. 937
TRIPP ENTERPRISES INC.; *U.S. Private*, pg. 4238
TRI-STAR PLASTICS INC.; *U.S. Private*, pg. 4223
TRI-STATE WINDOW FACTORY, CORP.; *U.S. Private*, pg. 4224
TRI-SURE CLOSURES NETHERLANDS—See Greif Inc.; *U.S. Public*, pg. 968
TSE INDUSTRIES INC.; *U.S. Private*, pg. 4252
TUBE CLEAN GMBH—See Fouad Alghanim & Sons Group of Companies; *Int'l*, pg. 2753
TUBEX WASUNGEN GMBH—See CAG Holding GmbH; *Int'l*, pg. 1251
TULIP CORP., MILWAUKEE DIV.—See Tulip Corporation; *U.S. Private*, pg. 4257
TULIP CORPORATION; *U.S. Private*, pg. 4257
TULIP MOLDED PLASTICS CORP - NIAGARA FALLS DIV.—See Tulip Corporation; *U.S. Private*, pg. 4257
TU-PLAST TUBE PRODUCING LTD.—See Hoffmann Neopac; *Int'l*, pg. 3440
TUPPERWARE BELGIUM N.V.—See Tupperware Brands Corporation; *U.S. Public*, pg. 2204
TUPPERWARE BRANDS CORPORATION; *U.S. Public*, pg. 2204
TUPPERWARE GENERAL SERVICES N.V.—See Tupper-

CORPORATE AFFILIATIONS

ware Brands Corporation; *U.S. Public*, pg. 2204
TUPPERWARE TRADING LTD.—See Tupperware Brands Corporation; *U.S. Public*, pg. 2204
TUPPERWARE TURKEY, INC.—See Tupperware Brands Corporation; *U.S. Public*, pg. 2204
TUPPERWARE UNITED KINGDOM & IRELAND LIMITED—See Tupperware Brands Corporation; *U.S. Public*, pg. 2205
TUPPERWARE U.S., INC.—See Tupperware Brands Corporation; *U.S. Public*, pg. 2205
TUTHILL PLASTICS GROUP—See Tuthill Corporation; *U.S. Private*, pg. 4263
UNETTE CORPORATION; *U.S. Private*, pg. 4281
UNICASA PTY LTD—See Casa Holdings Ltd.; *Int'l*, pg. 1349
UNITED PLASTIC FABRICATING; *U.S. Private*, pg. 4295
UNITED STATES NAME PLATE—See LaFrance Corporation; *U.S. Private*, pg. 2373
UNIVERSAL PLASTICS CORP.—See Wembly Enterprises LLC; *U.S. Public*, pg. 4480
URGENT PLASTIC SERVICES INC.; *U.S. Private*, pg. 4315
US ACRYLIC INC.; *U.S. Private*, pg. 4317
U.S. FARATHANE, LLC—See The Gores Group, LLC; *U.S. Private*, pg. 4035
U.S. LINER COMPANY—See Transtex LLC; *U.S. Private*, pg. 4211
VAN BLARCOM CLOSURES INC.; *U.S. Private*, pg. 4338
VANTAGE VEHICLE INTERNATIONAL, INC.—See Salt Creek Capital Management, LLC; *U.S. Private*, pg. 3533
VBC-BRISTOL INC.—See Van Blarcom Closures Inc.; *U.S. Private*, pg. 4339
VENTANA USA; *U.S. Private*, pg. 4357
VEN-TEL PLASTICS CORPORATION; *U.S. Private*, pg. 4355
VENTION MEDICAL, INC. - KERRVILLE—See Viant Medical, LLC; *U.S. Private*, pg. 4375
VENTRA EVART, LLC—See Flex-N-Gate Corporation; *U.S. Private*, pg. 1543
VENTRA PLASTICS - PETERBOROUGH—See Flex-N-Gate Corporation; *U.S. Private*, pg. 1543
VENTRA SALEM, LLC; *U.S. Private*, pg. 4357
VERIPACK EMBALAJES SL—See Groupe Guillin SA; *Int'l*, pg. 3104
VICTORIA PACKAGE (SUZHOU) COMPANY LIMITED—See CPMC Holdings Limited; *Int'l*, pg. 1826
VIDEOLARM, INC.—See Moog Inc.; *U.S. Public*, pg. 1470
VIKING PLASTICS INC.—See The Hoffman Family of Companies; *U.S. Private*, pg. 4053
VINK A/S—See Blackfriars Corp.; *U.S. Private*, pg. 574
VINK FINLAND OY—See Blackfriars Corp.; *U.S. Private*, pg. 574
VINK KUNSTSTOFFE GMBH & CO. KG—See Blackfriars Corp.; *U.S. Private*, pg. 574
VINK KUNSTSTOFFEN B.V.—See Blackfriars Corp.; *U.S. Private*, pg. 574
VINK NORWAY AS—See Blackfriars Corp.; *U.S. Private*, pg. 574
VINK N.V.—See Blackfriars Corp.; *U.S. Private*, pg. 574
VIRGINIA INDUSTRIAL PLSTCS INC.; *U.S. Private*, pg. 4387
VISION PLASTICS, INC.; *U.S. Private*, pg. 4391
VISKASE COMPANIES, INC.—See Icahn Enterprises L.P.; *U.S. Public*, pg. 1085
VISKASE FILMS, INC.—See Icahn Enterprises L.P.; *U.S. Public*, pg. 1085
VISKASE POLSKA SP Z O.O.—See Icahn Enterprises L.P.; *U.S. Public*, pg. 1085
VISKASE S.A.S.—See Icahn Enterprises L.P.; *U.S. Public*, pg. 1085
VISKASE S.P.A.—See Icahn Enterprises L.P.; *U.S. Public*, pg. 1085
VITIS D.O.O.—See BERICAP GmbH & Co. KG; *Int'l*, pg. 981
VIXEN COMPOSITES, LLC—See Thor Industries, Inc.; *U.S. Public*, pg. 2157
VOLK ENTERPRISES, INC.; *U.S. Private*, pg. 4410
VULCAN PLASTICS INC—See Consolidated Pipe & Supply Company; *U.S. Private*, pg. 1021
WABASH PLASTICS INC.; *U.S. Private*, pg. 4423
WADDINGTON NORTH AMERICA, INC.—See Apollo Global Management, Inc.; *U.S. Public*, pg. 154
WANNER INTERNATIONAL LTD.—See Wanner Engineering Inc.; *U.S. Private*, pg. 4436
WARMINSTER FIBERGLASS, LLC; *U.S. Private*, pg. 4442
WEATHERCHEM CORP; *U.S. Private*, pg. 4462
WEST COAST VINYL, INC.; *U.S. Private*, pg. 4484
WESTECH BUILDING PRODUCTS, INC.—See Westlake Corporation; *U.S. Public*, pg. 2360
WESTERN BUILDING CENTER OF KALISPELL; *U.S. Private*, pg. 4491
WESTERN INDUSTRIES, INC. - PLASTIC PRODUCTS GROUP—See Western Industries, Inc.; *U.S. Private*, pg. 4494
WESTLAKE BUILDING PRODUCTS ULC—See Westlake Corporation; *U.S. Public*, pg. 2360
WEST PHARMACEUTICAL SERVICES, INC.—See West Pharmaceutical Services, Inc.; *U.S. Public*, pg. 2353
WEXCO INCORPORATED; *U.S. Private*, pg. 4502
W.F.C. COMPANY, INC.—See Warminster Fiberglass, LLC; *U.S. Private*, pg. 4442

N.A.I.C.S. INDEX

326211 — TIRE MANUFACTURING ...

WHIRLEY INDUSTRIES, INC.; *U.S. Private*, pg. 4507
WHITMAN PACKAGING CORP.—See The Estee Lauder Companies Inc.; *U.S. Public*, pg. 2073
WILBERT INC. - BELLEVUE FACILITY—See Berkshire Hathaway Inc.; *U.S. Public*, pg. 298
WILBERT INC. - BELMONT FACILITY—See Berkshire Hathaway Inc.; *U.S. Public*, pg. 298
WILBERT INC. - EASLEY FACILITY—See Berkshire Hathaway Inc.; *U.S. Public*, pg. 298
WILBERT INC. - FOREST CITY FACILITY—See Berkshire Hathaway Inc.; *U.S. Public*, pg. 298
WILBERT INC. - HARRISBURG FACILITY—See Berkshire Hathaway Inc.; *U.S. Public*, pg. 298
WILBERT INC. - LEBANON FACILITY—See Berkshire Hathaway Inc.; *U.S. Public*, pg. 298
WILBERT INC. - WHITE BEAR LAKE FACILITY—See Berkshire Hathaway Inc.; *U.S. Public*, pg. 298
WILBERT PLASTIC SERVICES, INC.—See Berkshire Hathaway Inc.; *U.S. Public*, pg. 298
WILTEC INDUSTRIES LIMITED—See CCT Fortis Holdings Limited; *Int'l*, pg. 1370
WINDOW MART, INC.; *U.S. Private*, pg. 4538
WINFAST TECHNOLOGY LTD.—See Achilles Corporation; *Int'l*, pg. 103
WING ENTERPRISES, INCORPORATED—See Industrial Opportunity Partners, LLC; *U.S. Private*, pg. 2067
WINSHENG PLASTIC INDUSTRY SDN. BHD.—See ATA IMS Berhad; *Int'l*, pg. 665
WINTECH POLYMER LTD.—See Daicel Corporation; *Int'l*, pg. 1920
WINZELER GEAR; *U.S. Private*, pg. 4546
WISCONSIN THERMOSET MOLDING, INC.; *U.S. Private*, pg. 4549
W. L. GORE & ASSOCIATES (AUSTRALIA) PTY, LTD.—See W.L. Gore & Associates, Inc.; *U.S. Private*, pg. 4421
W. L. GORE & ASSOCIATES, POLSKA SP.Z.O.O.—See W.L. Gore & Associates, Inc.; *U.S. Private*, pg. 4421
W-L MOLDING COMPANY; *U.S. Private*, pg. 4417
WORLD WIDE PACKAGING, LLC—See Bain Capital, LP; *U.S. Private*, pg. 452
WRIGHT ENGINEERED PLASTICS, INC.; *U.S. Private*, pg. 4573
WRIGHT PLASTIC PRODUCTS CO., LLC; *U.S. Private*, pg. 4573
XCENTRIC MOLD & ENGINEERING, LLC—See Trilantic Capital Management L.P.; *U.S. Private*, pg. 4231
XIAMEN CHANGTIAN ENTERPRISE CO., LTD.—See Changtian Plastic & Chemical Limited; *Int'l*, pg. 1444
YD PLASTICS CO., LTD.—See DIC Corporation; *Int'l*, pg. 2111
YETI COOLERS LLC; *U.S. Private*, pg. 4588
YICK KWAN TAT ENTERPRISES COMPANY LIMITED—See China Kunda Technology Holdings Limited; *Int'l*, pg. 1514
YIELD10 BIOSCIENCE, INC.; *U.S. Public*, pg. 2399
YOUNG'S CORPORATION—See BERICAP GmbH & Co. KG; *Int'l*, pg. 981
ZAO AD PLASTIK KALUGA—See AD Plastik d.d.; *Int'l*, pg. 122
ZENITH GLOBAL, INC.—See PMC Capital Partners, LLC; *U.S. Private*, pg. 3218
ZHONGSHAN SAITECH ENGINEERING PLASTICS CO., LTD.—See Guangdong Sunwill Precising Plastic Co., Ltd.; *Int'l*, pg. 3161
THE ZIPPERTUBING COMPANY; *U.S. Private*, pg. 4140

326211 — TIRE MANUFACTURING (EXCEPT RETREADING)

ACME AUTOMOTIVE—See Coilhose Pneumatics Inc.; *U.S. Private*, pg. 964
AEOLUS TYRE CO., LTD.; *Int'l*, pg. 176
AHLSELL NORWAY AS—See Ahlsell AB; *Int'l*, pg. 223
AHLSELL OY—See Ahlsell AB; *Int'l*, pg. 223
ALICE NEUMATICOS DE VENEZUELA, C.A.—See Corimon, C.A.; *Int'l*, pg. 1800
AME INTERNATIONAL; *U.S. Private*, pg. 218
AMERITYRE CORPORATION; *U.S. Public*, pg. 115
AMIN TYRE LTD.—See Bridgestone Corporation; *Int'l*, pg. 1155
APOLLO TIRES (US) INC.—See Apollo Tyres Ltd.; *Int'l*, pg. 518
APOLLO TYRES AG—See Apollo Tyres Ltd.; *Int'l*, pg. 518
APOLLO TYRES (AUSTRIA) GESELLSCHAFT M.B.H.—See Apollo Tyres Ltd.; *Int'l*, pg. 518
APOLLO TYRES (BELUX) S.A.—See Apollo Tyres Ltd.; *Int'l*, pg. 518
APOLLO TYRES (HUNGARY) SALES KFT.—See Apollo Tyres Ltd.; *Int'l*, pg. 518
APOLLO TYRES IBERICA S.A.U.—See Apollo Tyres Ltd.; *Int'l*, pg. 518
APOLLO TYRES LTD.; *Int'l*, pg. 518
APOLLO TYRES (R&D) GMBH—See Apollo Tyres Ltd.; *Int'l*, pg. 518
APOLLO TYRES (UK) HOLDINGS LTD.—See Apollo Tyres Ltd.; *Int'l*, pg. 518
APOLLO TYRES (UK) SALES LTD.—See Apollo Tyres Ltd.; *Int'l*, pg. 518
APOLLO VREDESTEIN B.V.—See Apollo Tyres Ltd.; *Int'l*, pg. 518
APOLLO VREDESTEIN OPONY POLSKA SP. ZO.O.—See Apollo Tyres Ltd.; *Int'l*, pg. 519
APOLLO VREDESTEIN TIRES INC.—See Apollo Tyres Ltd.; *Int'l*, pg. 519
APOLLO VREDESTEIN (UK) LTD.—See Apollo Tyres Ltd.; *Int'l*, pg. 518
AROS DEL PACIFICO S.A.—See Titan International, Inc.; *U.S. Public*, pg. 2160
ASA AUTOMOTIVE SYSTEMS, LLC—See Constellation Software Inc.; *Int'l*, pg. 1773
ASSOCIATED TYRE SPECIALISTS LIMITED—See Compagnie Generale des Etablissements Michelin SCA; *Int'l*, pg. 1744
BALKRISHNA INDUSTRIES LIMITED; *Int'l*, pg. 809
BARUM CONTINENTAL SPOL. S.R.O.—See Continental Aktiengesellschaft; *Int'l*, pg. 1782
BEARCAT TYRES PTY LTD—See Compagnie Generale des Etablissements Michelin SCA; *Int'l*, pg. 1741
B. GJERDE—See Bridgestone Corporation; *Int'l*, pg. 1158
BINTER & CO PTE. LTD.—See Bridgestone Corporation; *Int'l*, pg. 1155
BIRLA TYRES LIMITED; *Int'l*, pg. 1048
BRIDGESTONE AIRCRAFT TIRE COMPANY (ASIA) LIMITED—See Bridgestone Corporation; *Int'l*, pg. 1156
BRIDGESTONE AMERICAS, INC.—See Bridgestone Corporation; *Int'l*, pg. 1156
BRIDGESTONE AMERICAS TIRE OPERATIONS, LLC - AGRICULTURAL TIRE, U.S. & CANADA COMMERCIAL TIRE SALES DIVISION—See Cox Enterprises, Inc.; *U.S. Private*, pg. 1075
BRIDGESTONE AMERICAS TIRE OPERATIONS, LLC - AIKEN COUNTY MANUFACTURING FACILITY—See Cox Enterprises, Inc.; *U.S. Private*, pg. 1075
BRIDGESTONE AMERICAS TIRE OPERATIONS, LLC - AKRON MANUFACTURING FACILITY—See Cox Enterprises, Inc.; *U.S. Private*, pg. 1075
BRIDGESTONE AMERICAS TIRE OPERATIONS, LLC - BLOOMINGTON-NORMAL MANUFACTURING FACILITY—See Cox Enterprises, Inc.; *U.S. Private*, pg. 1075
BRIDGESTONE AMERICAS TIRE OPERATIONS, LLC - BRIDGESTONE BANDAG TIRE SOLUTIONS DIVISION—See Cox Enterprises, Inc.; *U.S. Private*, pg. 1075
BRIDGESTONE AMERICAS TIRE OPERATIONS, LLC - DES MOINES MANUFACTURING FACILITY—See Cox Enterprises, Inc.; *U.S. Private*, pg. 1075
BRIDGESTONE AMERICAS TIRE OPERATIONS, LLC - JOLIETTE MANUFACTURING FACILITY—See Cox Enterprises, Inc.; *U.S. Private*, pg. 1075
BRIDGESTONE AMERICAS TIRE OPERATIONS, LLC - LAVERGNE MANUFACTURING FACILITY—See Cox Enterprises, Inc.; *U.S. Private*, pg. 1075
BRIDGESTONE AMERICAS TIRE OPERATIONS, LLC - ORIGINAL EQUIPMENT, U.S. & CANADA CONSUMER TIRE SALES DIVISION—See Cox Enterprises, Inc.; *U.S. Private*, pg. 1075
BRIDGESTONE AMERICAS TIRE OPERATIONS, LLC - SAO PAULO FACILITY—See Cox Enterprises, Inc.; *U.S. Private*, pg. 1075
BRIDGESTONE AMERICAS TIRE OPERATIONS, LLC—See Cox Enterprises, Inc.; *U.S. Private*, pg. 1075
BRIDGESTONE AMERICAS TIRE OPERATIONS, LLC - WARREN COUNTY MANUFACTURING FACILITY—See Cox Enterprises, Inc.; *U.S. Private*, pg. 1075
BRIDGESTONE AMERICAS TIRE OPERATIONS, LLC - WILSON MANUFACTURING FACILITY—See Cox Enterprises, Inc.; *U.S. Private*, pg. 1075
BRIDGESTONE ARGENTINA S.A.I.C.—See Bridgestone Corporation; *Int'l*, pg. 1156
BRIDGESTONE ASIA PACIFIC PTE. LTD. - INDORE PLANT—See Bridgestone Corporation; *Int'l*, pg. 1157
BRIDGESTONE ASIA PACIFIC TECHNICAL CENTER CO., LTD.—See Bridgestone Corporation; *Int'l*, pg. 1157
BRIDGESTONE AUSTRALIA LTD.—See Bridgestone Corporation; *Int'l*, pg. 1158
BRIDGESTONE BALTICS, SIA—See Bridgestone Corporation; *Int'l*, pg. 1158
BRIDGESTONE BELUX NV/SA—See Bridgestone Corporation; *Int'l*, pg. 1158
BRIDGESTONE CANADA, INC.—See Bridgestone Corporation; *Int'l*, pg. 1156
BRIDGESTONE (CHINA) RESEARCH & DEVELOPMENT CO., LTD.—See Bridgestone Corporation; *Int'l*, pg. 1155
BRIDGESTONF (CHINA) TIRE ASSESSMENT & DEVELOPMENT CO., LTD.—See Bridgestone Corporation; *Int'l*, pg. 1155
BRIDGESTONE CORPORATION - AMAGI PLANT—See Bridgestone Corporation; *Int'l*, pg. 1158
BRIDGESTONE CORPORATION - HOFU PLANT—See Bridgestone Corporation; *Int'l*, pg. 1158
BRIDGESTONE CORPORATION - KUMAMOTO PLANT—See Bridgestone Corporation; *Int'l*, pg. 1158
BRIDGESTONE CORPORATION - KUROISO PLANT—See Bridgestone Corporation; *Int'l*, pg. 1158
BRIDGESTONE CORPORATION - KURUME PLANT—See Bridgestone Corporation; *Int'l*, pg. 1158
BRIDGESTONE CORPORATION - NASU PLANT—See Bridgestone Corporation; *Int'l*, pg. 1158
BRIDGESTONE CORPORATION - SEKI PLANT—See Bridgestone Corporation; *Int'l*, pg. 1158
BRIDGESTONE CORPORATION - SHIMONOSEKI PLANT—See Bridgestone Corporation; *Int'l*, pg. 1158
BRIDGESTONE CORPORATION - TOCHIGI PLANT—See Bridgestone Corporation; *Int'l*, pg. 1158
BRIDGESTONE CORPORATION - TOKYO PLANT—See Bridgestone Corporation; *Int'l*, pg. 1158
BRIDGESTONE CORPORATION - TOSU PLANT—See Bridgestone Corporation; *Int'l*, pg. 1158
BRIDGESTONE CORPORATION - YOKOHAMA PLANT—See Bridgestone Corporation; *Int'l*, pg. 1158
BRIDGESTONE CR, S.R.O.—See Bridgestone Corporation; *Int'l*, pg. 1158
BRIDGESTONE DE COLOMBIA, S.A.S—See Bridgestone Corporation; *Int'l*, pg. 1158
BRIDGESTONE DE COSTA RICA, S.A.—See Bridgestone Corporation; *Int'l*, pg. 1158
BRIDGESTONEDE MEXICO, S.A. DE C.V.—See Bridgestone Corporation; *Int'l*, pg. 1157
BRIDGESTONE DE MEXICO, S.A.DE C.V.—See Bridgestone Corporation; *Int'l*, pg. 1157
BRIDGESTONE DENMARK A/S—See Bridgestone Corporation; *Int'l*, pg. 1158
BRIDGESTONE DIVERSIFIED PRODUCTS WEST CO., LTD.—See Bridgestone Corporation; *Int'l*, pg. 1158
BRIDGESTONE DO BRASIL INDUSTRIA E COMERCIO LTDA. - SAO PAULO PLANT—See Bridgestone Corporation; *Int'l*, pg. 1157
BRIDGESTONE DO BRASIL INDUSTRIA E COMERCIO LTDA.—See Bridgestone Corporation; *Int'l*, pg. 1158
BRIDGESTONE FINLAND OY—See Bridgestone Corporation; *Int'l*, pg. 1158
BRIDGESTONE/FIRESTONE CANADA, INC.—See Bridgestone Corporation; *Int'l*, pg. 1157
BRIDGESTONE/FIRESTONE CHILE, S.A.—See Bridgestone Corporation; *Int'l*, pg. 1157
BRIDGESTONE/FIRESTONE DE COSTA RICA, S.A.—See Bridgestone Corporation; *Int'l*, pg. 1157
BRIDGESTONE/FIRESTONE DO BRASIL INDUSTRIA E COMERCIO LTDA—See Bridgestone Corporation; *Int'l*, pg. 1157
BRIDGESTONE FRANCE S.A.S - BETHUNE PLANT—See Bridgestone Corporation; *Int'l*, pg. 1158
BRIDGESTONE FRANCE S.A.—See Bridgestone Corporation; *Int'l*, pg. 1158
BRIDGESTONE HISPANIA S.A - BILBAO PLANT—See Bridgestone Corporation; *Int'l*, pg. 1159
BRIDGESTONE HISPANIA S.A - BURGOS PLANT—See Bridgestone Corporation; *Int'l*, pg. 1159
BRIDGESTONE HISPANIA S.A.—See Bridgestone Corporation; *Int'l*, pg. 1159
BRIDGESTONE (HUIZHOU) TIRE CO., LTD.—See Bridgestone Corporation; *Int'l*, pg. 1155
BRIDGESTONE INDIA PRIVATE LIMITED—See Bridgestone Corporation; *Int'l*, pg. 1159
BRIDGESTONE ITALIA SALES S.R.L.—See Bridgestone Corporation; *Int'l*, pg. 1159
BRIDGESTONE ITALIA S.P.A.—See Bridgestone Corporation; *Int'l*, pg. 1159
BRIDGESTONE MAGYARORSZAG KFT.—See Bridgestone Corporation; *Int'l*, pg. 1159
BRIDGESTONE NEDERLAND B.V.—See Bridgestone Corporation; *Int'l*, pg. 1159
BRIDGESTONE NEW ZEALAND LTD.—See Bridgestone Corporation; *Int'l*, pg. 1159
BRIDGESTONE OFF-THE-ROAD TIRE LATIN AMERICA S.A—See Bridgestone Corporation; *Int'l*, pg. 1156
BRIDGESTONE POZNAN SP. Z.O.O.—See Bridgestone Corporation; *Int'l*, pg. 1159
BRIDGESTONE RIHGA, LTD.—See Bridgestone Corporation; *Int'l*, pg. 1155
BRIDGESTONE ROMANIA S.R.L.—See Bridgestone Corporation; *Int'l*, pg. 1159
BRIDGESTONE SALES POLSKA SP. Z O.O.—See Bridgestone Corporation; *Int'l*, pg. 1159
BRIDGESTONE (SHENYANG) TIRE CO., LTD.—See Bridgestone Corporation; *Int'l*, pg. 1159
BRIDGESTONE SOUTH AFRICA HOLDINGS (PTY) LTD.—See Bridgestone Corporation; *Int'l*, pg. 1159
BRIDGESTONE SOUTH AFRICA (PTY) LTD.—See Bridgestone Corporation; *Int'l*, pg. 1159
BRIDGESTONE STARGARD SP. Z.O.O—See Bridgestone Corporation; *Int'l*, pg. 1159
BRIDGESTONE TAIWAN CO., LTD.—See Bridgestone Corporation; *Int'l*, pg. 1159
BRIDGESTONE (TIANJIN) TIRE CO., LTD.—See Bridgestone Corporation; *Int'l*, pg. 1157
BRIDGESTONE TIRE MANUFACTURING (THAILAND) CO., LTD.—See Bridgestone Corporation; *Int'l*, pg. 1159
BRIDGESTONE TIRE MANUFACTURING VIETNAM LIM-

ITED LIABILITY COMPANY—See Bridgestone Corporation; *Int'l*, pg. 1159
BRIDGESTONE TIRE SALES KOREA LTD.—See Bridgestone Corporation; *Int'l*, pg. 1159
BRIDGESTONE TYRE SALES (MALAYSIA) SDN. BHD.—See Bridgestone Corporation; *Int'l*, pg. 1159
BRIDGESTONE TYRE SALES VIETNAM LLC—See Bridgestone Corporation; *Int'l*, pg. 1159
BRIDGESTONE (WUXI) TIRE CO., LTD.—See Bridgestone Corporation; *Int'l*, pg. 1156
BRISA BRIDGESTONE SABANCI LASTIK SANAYI VE TICARET A.S.—See Bridgestone Corporation; *Int'l*, pg. 1159
BRISA BRIDGESTONE SABANCI LASTIK SANAYI VE TICARET A.S.—See Haci Omer Sabanci Holding A.S.; *Int'l*, pg. 3203
BUTLER ENGINEERING & MARKETING S.P.A.—See Dover Corporation; *U.S. Public*, pg. 678
BUWON MOTORS CO., LTD.—See Bridgestone Corporation; *Int'l*, pg. 1159
CARLISLE CANADA—See Carlisle Companies Incorporated; *U.S. Public*, pg. 436
THE CARLSTAR GROUP B.V.—See AIP, LLC; *U.S. Private*, pg. 137
CAYMAN GOLDEN CENTURY WHEEL GROUP LIMITED; *Int'l*, pg. 1364
CHEMCHINA GUILIN TIRE CO, LTD—See China National Chemical Corporation; *Int'l*, pg. 1526
CHENG SHIN HOLLAND BV.—See Cheng Shin Rubber (Xiamen) Ind., Ltd.; *Int'l*, pg. 1466
CHENG SHIN RUBBER IND. CO., LTD.—See Cheng Shin Rubber (Xiamen) Ind., Ltd.; *Int'l*, pg. 1466
CHENG SHIN RUBBER USA, INC.—See Cheng Shin Rubber (Xiamen) Ind., Ltd.; *Int'l*, pg. 1466
CHENG SHIN TIRE (XIAMEN) CO., LTD.—See Cheng Shin Rubber (Xiamen) Ind., Ltd.; *Int'l*, pg. 1466
CHINA SUNSINE CHEMICAL HOLDINGS LTD; *Int'l*, pg. 1556
COMERCIAL E IMPORTADORA DE PNEUS LTDA—See China National Chemical Corporation; *Int'l*, pg. 1528
COMPANHIA GOODYEAR DO BRASIL PRODUTOS DE BORRACHA—See The Goodyear Tire & Rubber Company; *U.S. Public*, pg. 2082
COMPANIA ANONIMA GOODYEAR DE VENEZUELA—See The Goodyear Tire & Rubber Company; *U.S. Public*, pg. 2082
COMPANIA GOODYEAR DEL PERU, S.A.—See The Goodyear Tire & Rubber Company; *U.S. Public*, pg. 2082
CONTINENTAL COMMERCIAL VEHICLE TIRES DIVISION—See Continental Aktiengesellschaft; *Int'l*, pg. 1782
CONTINENTAL DO BRASIL PRODUTOS AUTOMOTIVOS LTDA.—See Continental Aktiengesellschaft; *Int'l*, pg. 1781
CONTINENTAL GENERAL TIRE INC.—See Continental Aktiengesellschaft; *Int'l*, pg. 1782
CONTINENTAL MABOR—See Continental Aktiengesellschaft; *Int'l*, pg. 1782
CONTINENTAL MATADOR S.R.O.—See Continental Aktiengesellschaft; *Int'l*, pg. 1782
CONTINENTAL PASSENGER & LIGHT TRUCK TIRES DIVISION—See Continental Aktiengesellschaft; *Int'l*, pg. 1782
CONTINENTAL SIME TYRE MARKETING SDN. BHD.—See Continental Aktiengesellschaft; *Int'l*, pg. 1783
CONTINENTAL SIME TYRE SDN BHD—See Continental Aktiengesellschaft; *Int'l*, pg. 1783
CONTINENTAL TIRE NORTH AMERICA—See Continental Aktiengesellschaft; *Int'l*, pg. 1783
CONTINENTAL TIRE THE AMERICAS, LLC—See Continental Aktiengesellschaft; *Int'l*, pg. 1783
CONTINENTAL TYRE GROUP LTD.—See Continental Aktiengesellschaft; *Int'l*, pg. 1783
COOPER TIRE & RUBBER COMPANY, CLARKSDALE PLANT—See The Goodyear Tire & Rubber Company; *U.S. Public*, pg. 2083
COOPER TIRE & RUBBER COMPANY DEUTSCHLAND GMBH—See The Goodyear Tire & Rubber Company; *U.S. Public*, pg. 2083
COOPER TIRE & RUBBER COMPANY ESPANA S.L.—See The Goodyear Tire & Rubber Company; *U.S. Public*, pg. 2083
COOPER TIRE & RUBBER COMPANY EUROPE LTD.—See The Goodyear Tire & Rubber Company; *U.S. Public*, pg. 2082
COOPER TIRE & RUBBER COMPANY—See The Goodyear Tire & Rubber Company; *U.S. Public*, pg. 2082
COOPER TIRE & RUBBER COMPANY, TEXARKANA PLANT—See The Goodyear Tire & Rubber Company; *U.S. Public*, pg. 2083
COOPER TYRE & RUBBER COMPANY UK LIMITED—See The Goodyear Tire & Rubber Company; *U.S. Public*, pg. 2083
DEUTSCHE GOODYEAR GMBH—See The Goodyear Tire & Rubber Company; *U.S. Public*, pg. 2083
DEUTSCHE PIRELLI REIFEN HOLDING GMBH—See China National Chemical Corporation; *Int'l*, pg. 1528
DN AUTOMOTIVE CORPORATION; *Int'l*, pg. 2147
DOUBLE HAPPINESS TYRE INDUSTRIAL CO, LTD—See China National Chemical Corporation; *Int'l*, pg. 1527
DRIVER HELLAS C.S.A.—See China National Chemical Corporation; *Int'l*, pg. 1528
DRIVER ITALIA S.P.A.—See China National Chemical Corporation; *Int'l*, pg. 1528
DUNLOP AIRCRAFT TYRES LIMITED—See Liberty Hall Capital Partners, L.P.; *U.S. Private*, pg. 2444
DYNAMIC TIRE CORP.; *Int'l*, pg. 2241
EASTERN MOTORS LTD.—See Bridgestone Corporation; *Int'l*, pg. 1159
EASTERN TREADS LIMITED; *Int'l*, pg. 2274
EDC EUROPEAN EXCAVATOR DESIGN CENTER VERWALTUNGS GMBH—See Caterpillar, Inc.; *U.S. Public*, pg. 450
ELASTIKA PIRELLI C.S.A.—See China National Chemical Corporation; *Int'l*, pg. 1528
EUROMASTER AUTOMOCION Y SERVICIOS, S.A.—See Compagnie Generale des Etablissements Michelin SCA; *Int'l*, pg. 1742
EUROMASTER BANDENSERVICE B.V.—See Compagnie Generale des Etablissements Michelin SCA; *Int'l*, pg. 1742
EUROMASTER (SUISSE) S.A.—See Compagnie Generale des Etablissements Michelin SCA; *Int'l*, pg. 1742
EUROTRED (NZ) LTD.—See Bridgestone Corporation; *Int'l*, pg. 1159
FATE S.A.I.C.I.; *Int'l*, pg. 2622
FEDERAL CORPORATION; *Int'l*, pg. 2630
FEDERAL TIRE (JIANGXI) CO., LTD.—See Federal Corporation; *Int'l*, pg. 2630
FIRESTONE AGRICULTURAL-DES MOINES—See Cox Enterprises, Inc.; *U.S. Private*, pg. 1075
FIRESTONE TUBE DIVISION—See Cox Enterprises, Inc.; *U.S. Private*, pg. 1075
FIRST JAPAN TIRE SERVICES COMPANY LIMITED—See Bridgestone Corporation; *Int'l*, pg. 1160
FU-CHIAN TIRE CO., LTD.; *Int'l*, pg. 2801
GANDHI SPECIAL TUBES LTD.; *Int'l*, pg. 2880
GELIA INDUSTRI AB—See Ahlsell AB; *Int'l*, pg. 223
GENERAL TYRE EAST AFRICA LTD.—See Continental Aktiengesellschaft; *Int'l*, pg. 1783
GIANT TIRE & SERVICE COMPANY LIMITED—See Bridgestone Corporation; *Int'l*, pg. 1160
GITI TIRE CORPORATION—See Giti Tire Pte. Ltd.; *Int'l*, pg. 2979
GJERDE & BYHRING AS—See Bridgestone Corporation; *Int'l*, pg. 1160
GKN WHEELS (LIUZHOU) COMPANY LTD—See GKN plc; *Int'l*, pg. 2986
GOODWAY EUROPE (SWEDEN) AB—See GIIB HOLDINGS BERHAD; *Int'l*, pg. 2972
GOODWAY RUBBER INDUSTRIES SDN. BHD.—See GIIB HOLDINGS BERHAD; *Int'l*, pg. 2972
GOODYEAR BELGIUM N.V./SA—See The Goodyear Tire & Rubber Company; *U.S. Public*, pg. 2083
GOODYEAR CANADA INC.—See The Goodyear Tire & Rubber Company; *U.S. Public*, pg. 2083
GOODYEAR DE CHILE S.A.I.C.—See The Goodyear Tire & Rubber Company; *U.S. Public*, pg. 2082
GOODYEAR DE COLOMBIA S.A.—See The Goodyear Tire & Rubber Company; *U.S. Public*, pg. 2082
GOODYEAR DUNLOP SAVA TIRES D.O.O.—See The Goodyear Tire & Rubber Company; *U.S. Public*, pg. 2083
GOODYEAR DUNLOP TIRES AUSTRIA GMBH—See The Goodyear Tire & Rubber Company; *U.S. Public*, pg. 2083
GOODYEAR DUNLOP TIRES BELGIUM N.V.—See The Goodyear Tire & Rubber Company; *U.S. Public*, pg. 2083
GOODYEAR DUNLOP TIRES CZECH S.R.O.—See The Goodyear Tire & Rubber Company; *U.S. Public*, pg. 2083
GOODYEAR DUNLOP TIRES ESPANA S.A.—See The Goodyear Tire & Rubber Company; *U.S. Public*, pg. 2083
GOODYEAR DUNLOP TIRES IRELAND LTD—See The Goodyear Tire & Rubber Company; *U.S. Public*, pg. 2083
GOODYEAR DUNLOP TIRES OPERATIONS ROMANIA S.R.L.—See The Goodyear Tire & Rubber Company; *U.S. Public*, pg. 2083
GOODYEAR DUNLOP TIRES OPERATIONS S.A.—See The Goodyear Tire & Rubber Company; *U.S. Public*, pg. 2083
GOODYEAR DUNLOP TIRES PORTUGAL UNIPESSOAL, LTDA—See The Goodyear Tire & Rubber Company; *U.S. Public*, pg. 2083
GOODYEAR DUNLOP TIRES SUISSE SA—See The Goodyear Tire & Rubber Company; *U.S. Public*, pg. 2084
GOODYEAR & DUNLOP TYRES (AUSTRALIA) PTY LTD—See The Goodyear Tire & Rubber Company; *U.S. Public*, pg. 2083
GOODYEAR DUNLOP TYRES UK LTD.—See The Goodyear Tire & Rubber Company; *U.S. Public*, pg. 2084
GOODYEAR EARTHMOVER PTY LIMITED—See The Goodyear Tire & Rubber Company; *U.S. Public*, pg. 2083
GOODYEAR EUROPE B.V.—See The Goodyear Tire & Rubber Company; *U.S. Public*, pg. 2084
GOODYEAR FRANCE SAS—See The Goodyear Tire & Rubber Company; *U.S. Public*, pg. 2084
GOODYEAR HELLAS S.A.I.C.—See The Goodyear Tire & Rubber Company; *U.S. Public*, pg. 2084
GOODYEAR HRVATSKA D.O.O.—See The Goodyear Tire & Rubber Company; *U.S. Public*, pg. 2084
GOODYEAR INDIA LTD.—See The Goodyear Tire & Rubber Company; *U.S. Public*, pg. 2084
GOODYEAR INTERNATIONAL CORPORATION—See The Goodyear Tire & Rubber Company; *U.S. Public*, pg. 2084
GOODYEAR LASTIKLERI TURK ANONIM SIRKETI—See The Goodyear Tire & Rubber Company; *U.S. Public*, pg. 2084
GOODYEAR LUXEMBOURG TIRES SA—See The Goodyear Tire & Rubber Company; *U.S. Public*, pg. 2084
GOODYEAR MALAYSIA BHD—See The Goodyear Tire & Rubber Company; *U.S. Public*, pg. 2084
GOODYEAR ORIENT COMPANY PRIVATE LIMITED—See The Goodyear Tire & Rubber Company; *U.S. Public*, pg. 2084
GOODYEAR PHILIPPINES, INC.—See The Goodyear Tire & Rubber Company; *U.S. Public*, pg. 2084
GOODYEAR POLSKA SP. Z O.O.—See The Goodyear Tire & Rubber Company; *U.S. Public*, pg. 2084
GOODYEAR PORTUGAL UNIPESSOAL, LTDA—See The Goodyear Tire & Rubber Company; *U.S. Public*, pg. 2084
GOODYEAR SERVICIOS COMERCIALES S.A. DE C.V.—See The Goodyear Tire & Rubber Company; *U.S. Public*, pg. 2084
GOODYEAR SOUTH AFRICA (PTY) LTD—See The Goodyear Tire & Rubber Company; *U.S. Public*, pg. 2084
GOODYEAR SUISSE S.A.—See The Goodyear Tire & Rubber Company; *U.S. Public*, pg. 2084
GOODYEAR SVERIGE A.B.—See The Goodyear Tire & Rubber Company; *U.S. Public*, pg. 2084
GOODYEAR TAIWAN LIMITED—See The Goodyear Tire & Rubber Company; *U.S. Public*, pg. 2084
GOODYEAR TIRE MANAGEMENT COMPANY (SHANGHAI) LTD.—See The Goodyear Tire & Rubber Company; *U.S. Public*, pg. 2084
THE GOODYEAR TIRE & RUBBER COMPANY; *U.S. Public*, pg. 2082
GOODYEAR TYRES IRELAND LTD.—See The Goodyear Tire & Rubber Company; *U.S. Public*, pg. 2084
GOODYEAR TYRES UK LIMITED—See The Goodyear Tire & Rubber Company; *U.S. Public*, pg. 2084
GOODYEAR UKRAINE—See The Goodyear Tire & Rubber Company; *U.S. Public*, pg. 2084
GREATOO INTELLIGENT EQUIPMENT INC.; *Int'l*, pg. 3067
HABIB GULZAR MOTORS LTD.—See Bridgestone Corporation; *Int'l*, pg. 1160
HANKOOK CAR & LIFE CO., LTD.—See Hankook Tire & Technology Co.,Ltd.; *Int'l*, pg. 3253
HANKOOK DONGGEURAMI PARTNERS CO., LTD.—See Hankook Tire & Technology Co.,Ltd.; *Int'l*, pg. 3253
HANKOOK ESPANA S.A.—See Hankook Tire & Technology Co.,Ltd.; *Int'l*, pg. 3254
HANKOOK FRANCE SARL—See Hankook Tire & Technology Co.,Ltd.; *Int'l*, pg. 3253
HANKOOK TIRE AUSTRIA GMBH—See Hankook Tire & Technology Co.,Ltd.; *Int'l*, pg. 3253
HANKOOK TIRE BUDAPEST KERESKEDELMI KFT—See Hankook Tire & Technology Co.,Ltd.; *Int'l*, pg. 3253
HANKOOK TIRE CESKA REPUBLIKA S.R.O.—See Hankook Tire & Technology Co.,Ltd.; *Int'l*, pg. 3254
HANKOOK TIRE COLOMBIA LTDA.—See Hankook Tire & Technology Co.,Ltd.; *Int'l*, pg. 3254
HANKOOK TIRE CO., LTD.—See Hankook & Company Co., Ltd.; *Int'l*, pg. 3253
HANKOOK TIRE CO., LTD.—See Hankook Tire & Technology Co.,Ltd.; *Int'l*, pg. 3254
HANKOOK TIRE CO., LTD.—See Hankook Tire & Technology Co.,Ltd.; *Int'l*, pg. 3254
HANKOOK TIRE CO., LTD.—See Hankook Tire & Technology Co.,Ltd.; *Int'l*, pg. 3254
HANKOOK TIRE DE MEXICO, S.A. DE C.V—See Hankook Tire & Technology Co.,Ltd.; *Int'l*, pg. 3254
HANKOOK TIRE D.O.O—See Hankook Tire & Technology Co.,Ltd.; *Int'l*, pg. 3254
HANKOOK TIRE EUROPE GMBH—See Hankook Tire & Technology Co.,Ltd.; *Int'l*, pg. 3254
HANKOOK TIRE JAPAN CORP.—See Hankook Tire & Technology Co.,Ltd.; *Int'l*, pg. 3254
HANKOOK TIRE MALAYSIA SDN. BHD.—See Hankook Tire & Technology Co.,Ltd.; *Int'l*, pg. 3254
HANKOOK TIRE MIDDLE EAST & AFRICA FZE—See Hankook Tire & Technology Co.,Ltd.; *Int'l*, pg. 3254
HANKOOK TIRE NETHERLANDS B.V—See Hankook Tire & Technology Co.,Ltd.; *Int'l*, pg. 3254
HANKOOK TIRE PANAMA LTDA.—See Hankook Tire & Technology Co.,Ltd.; *Int'l*, pg. 3254
HANKOOK TIRE POLSKA SP. Z O.O.—See Hankook Tire & Technology Co.,Ltd.; *Int'l*, pg. 3254
HANKOOK TIRE RUS LLC—See Hankook Tire & Technology Co.,Ltd.; *Int'l*, pg. 3254
HANKOOK TIRES INDIA LLP—See Hankook Tire & Technology Co.,Ltd.; *Int'l*, pg. 3254
HANKOOK TIRE SWEDEN AB—See Hankook Tire & Technology Co.,Ltd.; *Int'l*, pg. 3254
HANKOOK TIRE & TECHNOLOGY CO.,LTD.; *Int'l*, pg. 3253
HANKOOK TIRE THAILAND CO., LTD.—See Hankook Tire

N.A.I.C.S. INDEX 326211 — TIRE MANUFACTURING ...

N.A.I.C.S. Index

& Technology Co.,Ltd.; *Int'l*, pg. 3254
HANKOOK TIRE UKRAINE LLC—See Hankook Tire & Technology Co.,Ltd.; *Int'l*, pg. 3254
HANKOOK TIRE VIETNAM CO., LTD.—See Hankook Tire & Technology Co.,Ltd.; *Int'l*, pg. 3254
HOCK THAI MOTOR CO.—See Bridgestone Corporation; *Int'l*, pg. 1160
HWA FONG RUBBER INDUSTRY CO., LTD.; *Int'l*, pg. 3541
ITC INTERNATIONAL TIRE NV—See Compagnie Generale des Etablissements Michelin SCA; *Int'l*, pg. 1742
ITW GLOBAL TIRE REPAIR EUROPE GMBH—See Illinois Tool Works Inc.; *U.S. Public*, pg. 1106
KLEBER PNEUMATIQUES SA—See Compagnie Generale des Etablissements Michelin SCA; *Int'l*, pg. 1743
KLEBER REIFEN GMBH—See Compagnie Generale des Etablissements Michelin SCA; *Int'l*, pg. 1743
KONG NUON GROUP CO., LTD.—See Bridgestone Corporation; *Int'l*, pg. 1160
KRAUSSMAFFEI COMPANY LIMITED—See China National Chemical Corporation; *Int'l*, pg. 1528
LAURENT REIFEN GMBH—See Compagnie Generale des Etablissements Michelin SCA; *Int'l*, pg. 1743
LI ANG TIMOR, LTDA.—See Bridgestone Corporation; *Int'l*, pg. 1160
LIBERTY TIRE RECYCLING, LLC—See The Carlyle Group Inc.; *U.S. Public*, pg. 2048
MANUFACTURE FRANCAISE DES PNEUMATIQUES MICHELIN—See Compagnie Generale des Etablissements Michelin SCA; *Int'l*, pg. 1743
MARASTAR LLC—See AIP, LLC; *U.S. Private*, pg. 137
MCLEOD ACCESSORIES PTY. LTD.—See Bridgestone Corporation; *Int'l*, pg. 1160
MICHELIN AIM FZCO—See Compagnie Generale des Etablissements Michelin SCA; *Int'l*, pg. 1743
MICHELIN AIRCRAFT TIRE CORPORATION—See Compagnie Generale des Etablissements Michelin SCA; *Int'l*, pg. 1743
MICHELIN AIR SERVICES—See Compagnie Generale des Etablissements Michelin SCA; *Int'l*, pg. 1743
MICHELIN ALGERIE SPA—See Compagnie Generale des Etablissements Michelin SCA; *Int'l*, pg. 1743
MICHELIN ARGENTINA SOCIEDAD ANONIMA, INDUSTRIAL, COMERCIAL Y FINANCIERA—See Compagnie Generale des Etablissements Michelin SCA; *Int'l*, pg. 1743
MICHELIN ASIA-PACIFIC PTE LTD—See Compagnie Generale des Etablissements Michelin SCA; *Int'l*, pg. 1743
MICHELIN CHILE LTDA.—See Compagnie Generale des Etablissements Michelin SCA; *Int'l*, pg. 1743
MICHELIN CHUN SHIN LTD.—See Compagnie Generale des Etablissements Michelin SCA; *Int'l*, pg. 1743
MICHELIN CORPORATION—See Compagnie Generale des Etablissements Michelin SCA; *Int'l*, pg. 1743
MICHELIN ESPANA PORTUGAL, S.A.—See Compagnie Generale des Etablissements Michelin SCA; *Int'l*, pg. 1744
MICHELIN FINANZ GESELLSCHAFT FUR BETEILIGUNGEN AG & CO. OHG—See Compagnie Generale des Etablissements Michelin SCA; *Int'l*, pg. 1744
MICHELIN HUNGARIA TYRE MANUFACTURE LTD.—See Compagnie Generale des Etablissements Michelin SCA; *Int'l*, pg. 1744
MICHELIN INDIA PRIVATE LIMITED—See Compagnie Generale des Etablissements Michelin SCA; *Int'l*, pg. 1744
MICHELIN INDIA TAMILNADU TYRES PRIVATE LIMITED—See Compagnie Generale des Etablissements Michelin SCA; *Int'l*, pg. 1744
MICHELIN INDIA TYRES PRIVATE LIMITED—See Compagnie Generale des Etablissements Michelin SCA; *Int'l*, pg. 1744
MICHELIN LASTIKLERI TICARET A.S.—See Compagnie Generale des Etablissements Michelin SCA; *Int'l*, pg. 1744
MICHELIN NEDERLAND N.V.—See Compagnie Generale des Etablissements Michelin SCA; *Int'l*, pg. 1744
MICHELIN NORTH AMERICA, INC.—See Compagnie Generale des Etablissements Michelin SCA; *Int'l*, pg. 1743
MICHELIN POLSKA S.A.—See Compagnie Generale des Etablissements Michelin SCA; *Int'l*, pg. 1744
MICHELIN RECHERCHE ET TECHNIQUE S.A.—See Compagnie Generale des Etablissements Michelin SCA; *Int'l*, pg. 1744
MICHELIN REIFENWERKE KGAA—See Compagnie Generale des Etablissements Michelin SCA; *Int'l*, pg. 1744
MICHELIN ROMANIA S.A.—See Compagnie Generale des Etablissements Michelin SCA; *Int'l*, pg. 1744
MICHELIN SIAM CO., LTD. - NONGKHAE PLANT—See Compagnie Generale des Etablissements Michelin SCA; *Int'l*, pg. 1743
MICHELIN SIAM CO., LTD. - SI RACHA PLANT—See Compagnie Generale des Etablissements Michelin SCA; *Int'l*, pg. 1743
MICHELIN SIAM CO., LTD.—See Compagnie Generale des Etablissements Michelin SCA; *Int'l*, pg. 1743
MICHELIN SUISSE S.A.—See Compagnie Generale des Etablissements Michelin SCA; *Int'l*, pg. 1744
MICHELIN TYRE COMPANY SOUTH AFRICA (PROPRIETARY) LIMITED—See Compagnie Generale des Etablissements Michelin SCA; *Int'l*, pg. 1744
MICHELIN TYRE P.L.C.—See Compagnie Generale des Etablissements Michelin SCA; *Int'l*, pg. 1744
MICHELIN TYRE SERVICES COMPANY LTD.—See Compagnie Generale des Etablissements Michelin SCA; *Int'l*, pg. 1745
MICHELIN UKRAINE LLC—See Compagnie Generale des Etablissements Michelin SCA; *Int'l*, pg. 1745
MICHELIN VIETNAM COMPANY LIMITED—See Compagnie Generale des Etablissements Michelin SCA; *Int'l*, pg. 1743
MILLENNIUM INDUSTRIAL TIRES LLC.; *U.S. Private*, pg. 2731
NEUMATICOS GOODYEAR S.R.L.—See The Goodyear Tire & Rubber Company; *U.S. Public*, pg. 2082
NEXTRAQ LLC—See Compagnie Generale des Etablissements Michelin SCA; *Int'l*, pg. 1745
NIHON MICHELIN TIRE CO., LTD.—See Compagnie Generale des Etablissements Michelin SCA; *Int'l*, pg. 1743
OFFICINE MECCANICHE SIRIO S.R.L.—See Dover Corporation; *U.S. Public*, pg. 682
OLYMPIC RETREADS (M) SDN BHD—See Eversafe Rubber Berhad; *Int'l*, pg. 2568
OMNIA MOTOR S.A.—See China National Chemical Corporation; *Int'l*, pg. 1528
PAKISTAN RAHMAN TYRES INTERNATIONAL PVT. LTD.—See Bridgestone Corporation; *Int'l*, pg. 1160
PAKISTAN RUBBER & TYRE CO.—See Bridgestone Corporation; *Int'l*, pg. 1160
PENSLER CAPITAL CORPORATION; *U.S. Private*, pg. 3139
PHILIPPINE ALLIED ENTERPRISES CORPORATION—See Bridgestone Corporation; *Int'l*, pg. 1160
PIRELLI AMBIENTE S.R.L.—See China National Chemical Corporation; *Int'l*, pg. 1528
PIRELLI ASIA PTE. LIMITED—See China National Chemical Corporation; *Int'l*, pg. 1529
PIRELLI CHINA TYRE N.V.—See China National Chemical Corporation; *Int'l*, pg. 1528
PIRELLI COMERCIAL DE PNEUS BRASIL LTDA—See China National Chemical Corporation; *Int'l*, pg. 1528
PIRELLI & C. S.P.A.—See China National Chemical Corporation; *Int'l*, pg. 1528
PIRELLI DEUTSCHLAND GMBH—See China National Chemical Corporation; *Int'l*, pg. 1528
PIRELLI GMBH—See China National Chemical Corporation; *Int'l*, pg. 1529
PIRELLI INDUSTRIE PNEUMATICI S.R.L.—See China National Chemical Corporation; *Int'l*, pg. 1528
PIRELLI JAPAN K.K.—See China National Chemical Corporation; *Int'l*, pg. 1528
PIRELLI MOTORSPORT SERVICES LTD—See China National Chemical Corporation; *Int'l*, pg. 1528
PIRELLI NEUMATICOS DE MEXICO S.A. DE C.V.—See China National Chemical Corporation; *Int'l*, pg. 1528
PIRELLI NEUMATICOS S.A. DE C.V.—See China National Chemical Corporation; *Int'l*, pg. 1528
PIRELLI NEUMATICOS S.A.I.C—See China National Chemical Corporation; *Int'l*, pg. 1528
PIRELLI NEUMATICOS S.A.—See China National Chemical Corporation; *Int'l*, pg. 1528
PIRELLI PNEUS LTDA—See China National Chemical Corporation; *Int'l*, pg. 1528
PIRELLI POLSKA SP. Z.O.O.—See China National Chemical Corporation; *Int'l*, pg. 1528
PIRELLI SLOVAKIA S.R.O.—See China National Chemical Corporation; *Int'l*, pg. 1529
PIRELLI TIRE LLC—See China National Chemical Corporation; *Int'l*, pg. 1528
PIRELLI TYRE CO., LTD—See China National Chemical Corporation; *Int'l*, pg. 1528
PIRELLI TYRE NORDIC AB—See China National Chemical Corporation; *Int'l*, pg. 1529
PIRELLI TYRE (PTY) LTD—See China National Chemical Corporation; *Int'l*, pg. 1529
PIRELLI TYRES ALEXANDRIA CO.—See China National Chemical Corporation; *Int'l*, pg. 1529
PIRELLI TYRES AUSTRALIA PTY. LTD.—See China National Chemical Corporation; *Int'l*, pg. 1529
PIRELLI TYRES BELUX S.A.—See China National Chemical Corporation; *Int'l*, pg. 1529
PIRELLI TYRES LTD—See China National Chemical Corporation; *Int'l*, pg. 1529
PIRELLI TYRES NEDERLAND B.V.—See China National Chemical Corporation; *Int'l*, pg. 1529
PIRELLI TYRE S.P.A.—See China National Chemical Corporation; *Int'l*, pg. 1528
PIRELLI TYRE (SUISSE) S.A. - CZECH—See China National Chemical Corporation; *Int'l*, pg. 1529
PIRELLI TYRE (SUISSE) SA—See China National Chemical Corporation; *Int'l*, pg. 1529
PIRELLI UK TYRES LIMITED—See China National Chemical Corporation; *Int'l*, pg. 1529
PNEUMATIQUES KLEBER S.A—See Compagnie Generale des Etablissements Michelin SCA; *Int'l*, pg. 1745
PNEUS PIRELLI SAS—See China National Chemical Corporation; *Int'l*, pg. 1529
POLYMER ENTERPRISES INC.; *U.S. Private*, pg. 3226
PROMETEON TYRE GROUP S.R.L.—See China National Chemical Corporation; *Int'l*, pg. 1529
PT. BRIDGESTONE TIRE INDONESIA - BEKASI PLANT—See Bridgestone Corporation; *Int'l*, pg. 1160
PT BRIDGESTONE TIRE INDONESIA - KARAWANG PLANT—See Bridgestone Corporation; *Int'l*, pg. 1160
P.T. BRIDGESTONE TIRE INDONESIA—See Bridgestone Corporation; *Int'l*, pg. 1160
PT GAJAH TUNGGAL TBK—See Giti Tire Pte. Ltd.; *Int'l*, pg. 2979
P.T. GOODYEAR INDONESIA TBK—See The Goodyear Tire & Rubber Company; *U.S. Public*, pg. 2084
PT. HANKOOK TIRE SALES INDONESIA—See Hankook Tire & Technology Co.,Ltd.; *Int'l*, pg. 3254
QUALITY & WINNER MOTORS IMP EXP EIRELI—See Bridgestone Corporation; *Int'l*, pg. 1160
RA S.A.—See Bridgestone Corporation; *Int'l*, pg. 1160
RENNEN INTERNATIONAL; *U.S. Private*, pg. 3398
RM MART SDN. BHD.—See Bridgestone Corporation; *Int'l*, pg. 1160
S.A.R.L. PACIFIQUE PNEUS—See Bridgestone Corporation; *Int'l*, pg. 1160
SASCAR TECNOLOGIA E SEGURANGA AUTOMOTIVA S.A.—See Compagnie Generale des Etablissements Michelin SCA; *Int'l*, pg. 1745
SCHMID & WEZEL GMBH—See Fukuda Corporation; *Int'l*, pg. 2839
S.C. PIRELLI TYRES ROMANIA S.R.L.—See China National Chemical Corporation; *Int'l*, pg. 1529
SEMPERIT REIFEN GESMBH—See Continental Aktiengesellschaft; *Int'l*, pg. 1783
SERVCO TIRE COMPANY—See Bridgestone Corporation; *Int'l*, pg. 1160
SEVA ENGENHARIA ELETRONICA S.A.—See Compagnie Generale des Etablissements Michelin SCA; *Int'l*, pg. 1745
SHANGHAI MICHELIN WARRIOR TIRE CO., LTD.—See Compagnie Generale des Etablissements Michelin SCA; *Int'l*, pg. 1743
SOCIETE DES MATIERES PREMIERES TROPICALES PTE. LTD.—See Compagnie Generale des Etablissements Michelin SCA; *Int'l*, pg. 1743
SOCIETE MODERNE DU PNEUMATIQUE CAMEROUNAIS—See Compagnie Generale des Etablissements Michelin SCA; *Int'l*, pg. 1745
S.O.D.G.—See Compagnie Generale des Etablissements Michelin SCA; *Int'l*, pg. 1745
SPECIALTY TIRES OF AMERICA INC.—See Polymer Enterprises Inc.; *U.S. Private*, pg. 3226
STATE TRADING CORPORATION OF BHUTAN LTD.—See Bridgestone Corporation; *Int'l*, pg. 1160
SUNRICH INTEGRATED SDN. BHD—See ecoWise Holdings Limited; *Int'l*, pg. 2300
SUN RUBBER INDUSTRY SDN. BHD—See ecoWise Holdings Limited; *Int'l*, pg. 2300
TECHNICAL RUBBER COMPANY, INC.; *U.S. Private*, pg. 3954
THAI BRIDGESTONE CO., LTD. - NONG KHAE PLANT—See Bridgestone Corporation; *Int'l*, pg. 1160
THAI BRIDGESTONE CO., LTD. - RANGSIT PLANT—See Bridgestone Corporation; *Int'l*, pg. 1160
THAI BRIDGESTONE CO., LTD.—See Bridgestone Corporation; *Int'l*, pg. 1160
TIGAR TYRES D.O.O.—See Compagnie Generale des Etablissements Michelin SCA; *Int'l*, pg. 1745
TIRE CENTERS WEST, LLC—See Compagnie Generale des Etablissements Michelin SCA; *Int'l*, pg. 1745
TIRE COMPANY DEBICA S.A.—See The Goodyear Tire & Rubber Company; *U.S. Public*, pg. 2084
TITAN TIRE CORPORATION OF BRYAN—See Titan International, Inc.; *U.S. Public*, pg. 2160
TITAN TIRE CORPORATION—See Titan International, Inc.; *U.S. Public*, pg. 2160
TONG SENG CO. LTD.—See Bridgestone Corporation; *Int'l*, pg. 1160
TRANSITYRE B.V.—See Compagnie Generale des Etablissements Michelin SCA; *Int'l*, pg. 1745
TRANSPORT & ENGINEERING CO—See Chemical Industries Holding Company; *Int'l*, pg. 1462
TREDCOR KENYA LIMITED—See The Goodyear Tire & Rubber Company; *U.S. Public*, pg. 2085
UNIROYAL GOODRICH CANADA, INC.—See Compagnie Generale des Etablissements Michelin SCA; *Int'l*, pg. 1744
UNIROYAL GOODRICH INTELLECTUAL—See Compagnie Generale des Etablissements Michelin SCA; *Int'l*, pg. 1744
U.S., CANADA AND MONTERREY MANUFACTURING GROUP—See Cox Enterprises, Inc.; *U.S. Private*, pg. 1075
VEYANCE TECHNOLOGIES EUROPE, D.O.O.—See Continental Aktiengesellschaft; *Int'l*, pg. 1780
VVS TRADING A/S—See Ahlsell AB; *Int'l*, pg. 223
WAH SENG FAR EAST LTD.—See Bridgestone Corporation; *Int'l*, pg. 1160

326211 — TIRE MANUFACTURING ...

WINGFOOT AUSTRALIA PARTNER PTY LTD—See The Goodyear Tire & Rubber Company; *U.S. Public*, pg. 2085
XIAMEN CHENG SHIN ENTERPRISE CO., LTD.—See Cheng Shin Rubber (Xiamen) Ind., Ltd.; *Int'l*, pg. 1466
ZAO AHLSELL SPB—See Ahlsell AB; *Int'l*, pg. 223

326212 — TIRE RETREADING

BANDAG INCORPORATED—See Bridgestone Corporation; *Int'l*, pg. 1155
BANDVULC TYRES LTD.; *Int'l*, pg. 831
ELGITREAD (USA) LLC—See ELGI Equipments Limited; *Int'l*, pg. 2360
GOODYEAR NEDERLAND BV—See The Goodyear Tire & Rubber Company; *U.S. Public*, pg. 2084
GOODYEAR THAILAND PUBLIC CO. LTD.—See The Goodyear Tire & Rubber Company; *U.S. Public*, pg. 2084
HILL TIRE COMPANY—See Continental Aktiengesellschaft; *Int'l*, pg. 1783
INDUSTRIAL LEVORIN S.A.—See Compagnie Generale des Etablissements Michelin SCA; *Int'l*, pg. 1743
ISAAC TIRE INC.; *U.S. Private*, pg. 2142
KLINGE HOLDINGS PTY LTD—See Compagnie Generale des Etablissements Michelin SCA; *Int'l*, pg. 1743
MCGRIFF INDUSTRIES INC.; *U.S. Private*, pg. 2635
PNEU LAURENT S.N.C—See Compagnie Generale des Etablissements Michelin SCA; *Int'l*, pg. 1745
ROBBINS LLC—See HEXPOL AB; *Int'l*, pg. 3372
SUNRICH MARKETING SDN. BHD—See ecoWise Holdings Limited; *Int'l*, pg. 2300
SUN TYRE INDUSTRIES SDN. BHD—See ecoWise Holdings Limited; *Int'l*, pg. 2300
VIAMICHELIN NORTH AMERICA LLC—See Compagnie Generale des Etablissements Michelin SCA; *Int'l*, pg. 1745
WHITE TIRE—See Cox Enterprises, Inc.; *U.S. Private*, pg. 1076
WINGFOOT COMMERCIAL TIRE SYSTEMS, LLC—See The Goodyear Tire & Rubber Company; *U.S. Public*, pg. 2085

326220 — RUBBER AND PLASTICS HOSES AND BELTING MANUFACTURING

AA INDUSTRIAL BELTING (SHANGHAI) CO., LTD.; *Int'l*, pg. 30
AEROFLEX USA INC.—See Eastern Polymer Group Public Company Limited; *Int'l*, pg. 2273
AG BELT, INC,—See Genuine Parts Company; *U.S. Public*, pg. 933
ALL-STATE BELTING COMPANY; *U.S. Private*, pg. 173
A.M. ANDREWS CO.; *U.S. Private*, pg. 27
AMMERAAL BELTECH HOLDING BV—See Advent International Corporation; *U.S. Private*, pg. 98
AMMERAAL BELTECH INC.—See Advent International Corporation; *U.S. Private*, pg. 98
AMMERAAL BELTECH SA—See Advent International Corporation; *U.S. Private*, pg. 98
APS CO., LTD.—See Eastern Polymer Group Public Company Limited; *Int'l*, pg. 2273
AUTOLIV BEIJING SAFETY SYSTEMS—See Autoliv, Inc.; *Int'l*, pg. 728
AUTOLIV KFT.—See Autoliv, Inc.; *Int'l*, pg. 729
AVON ENGINEERED FABRICATIONS, INC—See Avon Protection plc; *Int'l*, pg. 750
AVON POLYMER PRODUCTS LIMITED—See Avon Protection plc; *Int'l*, pg. 750
AVON RUBBER OVERSEAS LIMITED—See Avon Protection plc; *Int'l*, pg. 750
BANDO CHEMICAL INDUSTRIES, LTD. - ASHIKAGA PLANT—See Bando Chemical Industries, Ltd.; *Int'l*, pg. 830
BANDO CHEMICAL INDUSTRIES, LTD. - KAKOGAWA PLANT—See Bando Chemical Industries, Ltd.; *Int'l*, pg. 830
BANDO CHEMICAL INDUSTRIES, LTD. - NANKAI PLANT—See Bando Chemical Industries, Ltd.; *Int'l*, pg. 830
BANDO CHEMICAL INDUSTRIES, LTD.; *Int'l*, pg. 830
BANDO CHEMICAL INDUSTRIES, LTD. - WAKAYAMA PLANT—See Bando Chemical Industries, Ltd.; *Int'l*, pg. 830
BANDO EUROPE GMBH—See Bando Chemical Industries, Ltd.; *Int'l*, pg. 830
BANDO (INDIA) PVT. LTD.—See Bando Chemical Industries, Ltd.; *Int'l*, pg. 830
BANDO MANUFACTURING (DONGGUAN) CO., LTD,—See Bando Chemical Industries, Ltd.; *Int'l*, pg. 830
BANDO SIIX LTD.—See Bando Chemical Industries, Ltd.; *Int'l*, pg. 830
BANDO USA, INC.—See Bando Chemical Industries, Ltd.; *Int'l*, pg. 830
BANDO USA, INC.—See Bando Chemical Industries, Ltd.; *Int'l*, pg. 830
BANNER STAKES LLC—See Bunzl plc; *Int'l*, pg. 1217
BELTING SUPPLY SERVICES (PTY) LTD—See Hudaco Industries Limited; *Int'l*, pg. 3521
BELT TECHNOLOGIES, INC.—See Peter Pan Bus Lines, Inc.; *U.S. Private*, pg. 3159
BEN THANH RUBBER JOINT STOCK COMPANY; *Int'l*, pg. 969
BRAKEQUIP, LLC; *U.S. Private*, pg. 635
BRIDGESTONE FLOWTECH CORPORATION—See Bridgestone Corporation; *Int'l*, pg. 1159
THE CARLSTAR GROUP LLC—See AIP, LLC; *U.S. Private*, pg. 137
CHENGDU SHENGBANG SEALS CO., LTD.; *Int'l*, pg. 1469
CHIORINO S.P.A.; *Int'l*, pg. 1572
CHONCHE GROUP NANJING NO.7425 FACTORY—See China National Chemical Corporation; *Int'l*, pg. 1527
COLORITE POLYMERS—See Genstar Capital, LLC; *U.S. Private*, pg. 1678
COMERCIAL GASSO SA; *Int'l*, pg. 1710
CONTITECH AG—See Continental Aktiengesellschaft; *Int'l*, pg. 1780
CONTITECH ANOFLEX S.A.S.—See Continental Aktiengesellschaft; *Int'l*, pg. 1780
CONTITECH ANTRIEBSSYSTEME GMBH—See Continental Aktiengesellschaft; *Int'l*, pg. 1780
CONTITECH BEATTIE CORP.—See Continental Aktiengesellschaft; *Int'l*, pg. 1780
CONTITECH FLUID AUTOMOTIVE HUNGARIA KFT.—See Continental Aktiengesellschaft; *Int'l*, pg. 1780
CONTITECH MGW GMBH—See Continental Aktiengesellschaft; *Int'l*, pg. 1781
CONTITECH ROULUNDS RUBBER A/S—See Continental Aktiengesellschaft; *Int'l*, pg. 1780
CONTITECH SCHLAUCH GMBH—See Continental Aktiengesellschaft; *Int'l*, pg. 1781
CONTITECH THERMOPOL LLC—See Continental Aktiengesellschaft; *Int'l*, pg. 1781
COOPER-STANDARD AUTOMOTIVE INC. - BOWLING GREEN PLANT—See Cooper-Standard Holdings Inc.; *U.S. Public*, pg. 574
COURANT SAS; *Int'l*, pg. 1819
DANA SPICER AXLE SOUTH AFRICA (PTY) LTD.—See Dana Incorporated; *U.S. Public*, pg. 623
DAYCO LLC; *U.S. Private*, pg. 1177
DKS DRAXLMAIER KUNSTSTOFFSYSTEME GMBH—See Draexlmaier Gruppe; *Int'l*, pg. 2198
DONGIL RUBBER BELT AMERICA, INC.—See DRB Holding Co., Ltd.; *Int'l*, pg. 2201
DONGIL RUBBER BELT JAPAN CO., LTD.—See DRB Holding Co., Ltd.; *Int'l*, pg. 2201
DONGIL RUBBER BELT SLOVAKIA, S.R.O.—See DRB Holding Co., Ltd.; *Int'l*, pg. 2201
DONGIL RUBBER BELT VIETNAM CO., LTD.—See DRB Holding Co., Ltd.; *Int'l*, pg. 2201
DRB INDUSTRIAL CO., LTD.—See DRB Holding Co., Ltd.; *Int'l*, pg. 2201
DUNLOP OIL & MARINE LTD.—See Continental Aktiengesellschaft; *Int'l*, pg. 1781
EATON CORP. - FLUID CONNECTORS—See Eaton Corporation plc; *Int'l*, pg. 2280
EKB ELEKTRO UND KUNSTSTOFFTECHNIK GMBH—See Draexlmaier Gruppe; *Int'l*, pg. 2198
EL NASSR COMPANY FOR RUBBER PRODUCTS (NARUBEEN)—See Chemical Industries Holding Company; *Int'l*, pg. 1461
ENPLAS HY-CAD ELECTRONIC (SHANGHAI) CO., LTD.—See ENPLAS CORPORATION; *Int'l*, pg. 2445
ERICKSON FRAMING OPERATIONS LLC—See Asahi Kasei Corporation; *Int'l*, pg. 596
ERRECINQUE S.R.L. - BOLOGNA PLANT—See Errecinque S.r.l.; *Int'l*, pg. 2497
ERRECINQUE S.R.L. - COSENZA PLANT—See Errecinque S.r.l.; *Int'l*, pg. 2497
ERRECINQUE S.R.L.; *Int'l*, pg. 2497
ERRECINQUE S.R.L. - VOLPIANO PLANT—See Errecinque S.r.l.; *Int'l*, pg. 2497
FIBERGRATE COMPOSITE STRUCTURES LIMITED—See RPM International Inc.; *U.S. Public*, pg. 1818
FISKARS BRANDS, INC. - NELSON—See Fiskars Oyj Abp; *Int'l*, pg. 2693
FLEXFAB EUROPE LTD.—See Flexfab Horizons International, LLC; *U.S. Private*, pg. 1544
FLEXFIT HOSE LLC—See Audax Group, Limited Partnership; *U.S. Private*, pg. 388
FLUID ROUTING SOLUTIONS, LLC—See Park-Ohio Holdings Corp.; *U.S. Public*, pg. 1639
FORBO SIEGLING AUSTRIA GMBH—See Forbo Holding Ltd.; *Int'l*, pg. 2730
FORBO SIEGLING CANADA CORP.—See Forbo Holding Ltd.; *Int'l*, pg. 2730
FORBO SIEGLING LLC—See Forbo Holding Ltd.; *Int'l*, pg. 2729
FUJI MICRO ELECTRONICS CO., LTD.—See Advanex Inc.; *Int'l*, pg. 163
GAMMA HOLDING NEDERLAND N.V.—See Gilde Buy Out Partners B.V.; *Int'l*, pg. 2974
GATES ARGENTINA S.A.—See Blackstone Inc.; *U.S. Public*, pg. 353
GATES CANADA INC.—See Blackstone Inc.; *U.S. Public*, pg. 353
GATES CORPORATION—See Blackstone Inc.; *U.S. Public*, pg. 353
GATES CORP—See Blackstone Inc.; *U.S. Public*, pg. 354
GATES DE MEXICO S.A. DE C.V.—See Blackstone Inc.; *U.S. Public*, pg. 354
GATES DO BRASIL INDUSTRIA E COMERICO LIMITED—See Blackstone Inc.; *U.S. Public*, pg. 354
GATES EUROPE B.V.B.A—See Blackstone Inc.; *U.S. Public*, pg. 354
GATES HYDRAULICS LTD.—See Blackstone Inc.; *U.S. Public*, pg. 354
GATES PT SPAIN S.A.—See Blackstone Inc.; *U.S. Public*, pg. 354
GATES RUBBER CO. INC.—See Blackstone Inc.; *U.S. Public*, pg. 354
THE GATES RUBBER COMPANY—See Blackstone Inc.; *U.S. Public*, pg. 354
HABASIT AB—See Habasit AG; *Int'l*, pg. 3201
HABASIT AB—See Habasit AG; *Int'l*, pg. 3201
HABASIT AG; *Int'l*, pg. 3201
HABASIT (AUSTRALIA) PTY LIMITED—See Habasit AG; *Int'l*, pg. 3201
HABASIT BELGIUM N.V.—See Habasit AG; *Int'l*, pg. 3202
HABASIT BULGARIA—See Habasit AG; *Int'l*, pg. 3202
HABASIT CANADA LIMITED—See Habasit AG; *Int'l*, pg. 3202
HABASIT DO BRASIL IND. E COM. DE CORREIAS LTDA.—See Habasit AG; *Int'l*, pg. 3202
HABASIT FAR EAST PTE. LTD.—See Habasit AG; *Int'l*, pg. 3202
HABASIT FRANCE S.A.S.—See Habasit AG; *Int'l*, pg. 3202
HABASIT GMBH—See Habasit AG; *Int'l*, pg. 3201
HABASIT GMBH—See Habasit AG; *Int'l*, pg. 3202
HABASIT HUNGARIA KFT.—See Habasit AG; *Int'l*, pg. 3202
HABASIT MOSCOW—See Habasit AG; *Int'l*, pg. 3202
HABASIT NETHERLANDS BV—See Habasit AG; *Int'l*, pg. 3202
HABASIT NORGE A/S—See Habasit AG; *Int'l*, pg. 3201
HABASIT POLSKA SP. Z O.O.—See Habasit AG; *Int'l*, pg. 3202
HABASIT (UK) LIMITED—See Habasit AG; *Int'l*, pg. 3201
HBD INDUSTRIES, INC.; *U.S. Private*, pg. 1887
HIDONG ESTATE PLC; *Int'l*, pg. 3384
HIFLEX DENMARK A/S—See Alfagomma S.p.A.; *Int'l*, pg. 315
HL RUBBER INDUSTRIES SDN. BHD.—See HLT Global Berhad; *Int'l*, pg. 3431
HSIN YUNG CHIEN CO., LTD.; *Int'l*, pg. 3507
HSIN YUNG CHIEN RUBBER CO.,LTD.—See Hsin Yung Chien Co., Ltd.; *Int'l*, pg. 3507
HSIN YUNG CHIEN (TIANJIN) CO.,LTD.—See Hsin Yung Chien Co., Ltd.; *Int'l*, pg. 3507
INTRALOX LLC—See The Laitram LLC; *U.S. Private*, pg. 4067
INTRALOX LTD.—See The Laitram LLC; *U.S. Private*, pg. 4067
JAMES DAWSON & SON LTD.—See Compagnie Generale des Etablissements Michelin SCA; *Int'l*, pg. 1745
JGB ENTERPRISES INC.—See HCI Equity Management, L.P.; *U.S. Private*, pg. 1889
J.JUAN S.A.U.—See Brembo S.p.A.; *Int'l*, pg. 1145
KURT MANUFACTURING CO. INC. - KURT HYDRAULICS DIVISION—See Kurt Manufacturing Co. Inc.; *U.S. Private*, pg. 2358
LUDOWICI (BEIJING) CO., LTD—See FLSmidth & Co. A/S; *Int'l*, pg. 2711
LUDOWICI TECHNOLOGIES PTY LTD—See FLSmidth & Co. A/S; *Int'l*, pg. 2711
MAGICGRAND DEVELOPMENT LIMITED—See China Automobile New Retail (Holdings) Limited; *Int'l*, pg. 1484
MARINE PRODUCTS INTERNATIONAL LLC—See Crawford United Corporation; *U.S. Public*, pg. 592
MULHERN BELTING, INC.; *U.S. Private*, pg. 2811
NEPHI RUBBER PRODUCTS; *U.S. Private*, pg. 2885
NIEDNER INC.—See Blue Wolf Capital Partners LLC; *U.S. Private*, pg. 595
NILOS GMBH & CO. KG—See Fukuda Corporation; *Int'l*, pg. 2839
OCEANEERING UMBILICAL SOLUTIONS—See Oceaneering International, Inc.; *U.S. Public*, pg. 1563
PARKER HANNIFIN INDUSTRIAL HOSE PRODUCTS DIVISION—See Parker Hannifin Corporation; *U.S. Public*, pg. 1646
PARKER HANNIFIN PARFLEX DIVISION - PARKER-TEXLOC—See Parker Hannifin Corporation; *U.S. Public*, pg. 1646
PHILIPPINE BELT MANUFACTURING CORP.—See Bando Chemical Industries, Ltd.; *Int'l*, pg. 830
PHILIPPINE BELT MFG. CORP.—See Bando Chemical Industries, Ltd.; *Int'l*, pg. 831
PRICE RUBBER CORP.; *U.S. Private*, pg. 3258
PROMED MOLDED PRODUCTS, INC.; *U.S. Private*, pg. 3282
PT. DONGIL RUBBER BELT INDONESIA—See DRB Holding Co., Ltd.; *Int'l*, pg. 2201
REGENT HOSE & HYDRAULICS LIMITED—See Illinois Tool Works Inc.; *U.S. Public*, pg. 1110

N.A.I.C.S. INDEX
326299 — ALL OTHER RUBBER PR...

SANWU BANDO INC.—See Bando Chemical Industries, Ltd.; *Int'l*, pg. 831
SHANGHAI DONGIL RUBBER BELT CO., LTD.—See DRB Holding Co., Ltd.; *Int'l*, pg. 2201
SHENYANG SPICER DRIVESHAFT CO. LTD.—See Dana Incorporated; *U.S. Public*, pg. 623
SUMMERS RUBBER CO. INC.—See AEA Investors LP; *U.S. Private*, pg. 115
SWAN HOSE—See Jacobson Partners; *U.S. Private*, pg. 2180
TOYO RUBBER CHIP CO., LTD.—See Envipro Holdings Inc.; *Int'l*, pg. 2454
TRICOFLEX SA—See Exel Industries SA; *Int'l*, pg. 2583
TRI-STATE HOSE & FITTING, INC.—See Frontenac Company LLC; *U.S. Private*, pg. 1614
VAN OERLE ALBERTON B.V.—See Autoliv, Inc.; *Int'l*, pg. 730
WOLVERINE ADVANCE MATERIALS GMBH—See ITT Inc.; *U.S. Public*, pg. 1179

326291 — RUBBER PRODUCT MANUFACTURING FOR MECHANICAL USE

3A MCOM SRL—See HEXPOL AB; *Int'l*, pg. 3372
ABS MANUFACTURING & DISTRIBUTING LIMITED; *Int'l*, pg. 69
ACOT PLASTICS (XIAMEN) CO., LTD.—See Acma Ltd.; *Int'l*, pg. 107
AIA CO., LTD.—See Ecoplastic Corporation; *Int'l*, pg. 2299
AIR WATER MACH INC.—See Air Water Inc.; *Int'l*, pg. 239
AIR WATER MACH RUBBER PRODUCTS (FUJIAN) CO., LTD.—See Air Water Inc.; *Int'l*, pg. 239
ALLAN MASKEW (PTY) LTD—See ARGENT INDUSTRIAL LIMITED; *Int'l*, pg. 560
APAC RUBBER, INC.; *U.S. Private*, pg. 290
ARMSTRONG RUBBER MANUFACTURING PTE LTD—See Armstrong Industrial Corporation Ltd.; *Int'l*, pg. 575
BANDO ELASTOMER CO., LTD.—See Bando Chemical Industries, Ltd.; *Int'l*, pg. 830
BANDO INDUSTRIAL COMPONENTS & SERVICES, LTD.—See Bando Chemical Industries, Ltd.; *Int'l*, pg. 830
BANDO KOSAN CO., LTD.—See Bando Chemical Industries, Ltd.; *Int'l*, pg. 830
BANDO-SCHOLTZ CORPORATION—See Bando Chemical Industries, Ltd.; *Int'l*, pg. 830
BERWIN INDUSTRIAL POLYMERS LIMITED—See HEXPOL AB; *Int'l*, pg. 3371
BRC RUBBER & PLASTICS INC.; *U.S. Private*, pg. 642
BRIDGESTONE DIVERSIFIED PRODUCTS EAST CO., LTD.—See Bridgestone Corporation; *Int'l*, pg. 1158
BURKE INDUSTRIES, INC. - CUSTOM PROCESS—See Mannington Mills, Inc.; *U.S. Private*, pg. 2565
COOPER-STANDARD AUTOMOTIVE BRASIL SEALING LTDA. - CAMACARI PLANT—See Cooper-Standard Holdings Inc.; *U.S. Public*, pg. 574
COOPER-STANDARD AUTOMOTIVE BRASIL SEALING LTDA.—See Cooper-Standard Holdings Inc.; *U.S. Public*, pg. 574
COOPER-STANDARD AUTOMOTIVE KOREA INC.—See Cooper-Standard Holdings Inc.; *U.S. Public*, pg. 574
COOPER-STANDARD AUTOMOTIVE UK LIMITED—See Cooper-Standard Holdings Inc.; *U.S. Public*, pg. 574
DAWSON MANUFACTURING COMPANY; *U.S. Private*, pg. 1176
DONG GUAN CHENSONG PLASTIC & MOULD—See COXON Precise Industrial Co., Ltd.; *Int'l*, pg. 1823
THE D.S. BROWN COMPANY—See Gibraltar Industries, Inc.; *U.S. Public*, pg. 936
EAST JAPAN BELT PRODUCTS, INC.—See Bando Chemical Industries, Ltd.; *Int'l*, pg. 830
ECORUB AB; *Int'l*, pg. 2299
EIDAI KAKO CO., LTD.; *Int'l*, pg. 2328
ELEKTROMETAL AD; *Int'l*, pg. 2357
ELGI RUBBER COMPANY LIMITED; *Int'l*, pg. 2360
EVERSAFE RUBBER WORKS SDN BHD—See Eversafe Rubber Berhad; *Int'l*, pg. 2568
FIRESTONE BUILDING PRODUCTS DIVISION—See Bridgestone Corporation; *Int'l*, pg. 1156
FIRESTONE NATURAL RUBBER COMPANY, LLC—See Bridgestone Corporation; *Int'l*, pg. 1157
FLEXI-CELL (UK) LTD.—See HEXPOL AB; *Int'l*, pg. 3371
FREUDENBERG NOK—See Freudenberg SE; *Int'l*, pg. 2788
FREUDENBERG NORTH AMERICA LIMITED PARTNERSHIP—See Freudenberg SE; *Int'l*, pg. 2787
FREUDENBERG SCHWAB VIBRATION CONTROL AG—See Freudenberg SE; *Int'l*, pg. 2788
FUJI LATEX CO., LTD.; *Int'l*, pg. 2813
FUKOKU CO., LTD.; *Int'l*, pg. 2838
FUKUIBELT. INDUSTRIES, LTD.—See Bando Chemical Industries, Ltd.; *Int'l*, pg. 830
GIIB HEALTHCARE PRODUCTS SDN. BHD.—See GIIB HOLDINGS BERHAD; *Int'l*, pg. 2972
GRIFFITH RUBBER MILLS INC.; *U.S. Private*, pg. 1789
GRIFFITH RUBBER MILLS OF GARRETT, INC.—See Griffith Rubber Mills Inc.; *U.S. Private*, pg. 1789

HANNA RUBBER CO., INC.—See AEA Investors LP; *U.S. Private*, pg. 115
HARDYFLEX INDUSTRIES SDN BHD—See Armstrong Industrial Corporation Ltd.; *Int'l*, pg. 575
HEXPOL AB; *Int'l*, pg. 3371
HEXPOL COMPOUNDING CA INC.—See HEXPOL AB; *Int'l*, pg. 3372
HEXPOL COMPOUNDING HQ SA—See HEXPOL AB; *Int'l*, pg. 3372
HEXPOL COMPOUNDING HQ SPRL—See HEXPOL AB; *Int'l*, pg. 3372
HEXPOL COMPOUNDING (QINGDAO) CO., LTD.—See HEXPOL AB; *Int'l*, pg. 3371
HEXPOL COMPOUNDING S.L.U.—See HEXPOL AB; *Int'l*, pg. 3372
HEXPOL COMPOUNDING (UK) LTD.—See HEXPOL AB; *Int'l*, pg. 3372
HEXPOL SERVICES COMPOUNDING S.A DE C.V—See HEXPOL AB; *Int'l*, pg. 3372
HLN RUBBER PRODUCTS PTE. LTD.; *Int'l*, pg. 3431
ICHIA RUBBER IND. (M) SDN. BHD.—See Ichia Technologies Inc.; *Int'l*, pg. 3580
IMAS A.E.—See Continental Aktiengesellschaft; *Int'l*, pg. 1781
INNOVATIVE ELASTOMERS, INC.—See AirBoss of America Corp.; *Int'l*, pg. 241
JAMAK FABRICATION-TEX LTD.—See JMK International, Inc.; *U.S. Private*, pg. 2216
JASPER RUBBER PRODUCTS INC.; *U.S. Private*, pg. 2190
JMK INTERNATIONAL, INC.; *U.S. Private*, pg. 2216
KINUGAWA RUBBER INDUSTRIAL CO., LTD.—See Development Bank of Japan, Inc.; *Int'l*, pg. 2088
KIRKHILL MANUFACTURING COMPANY INC.—See HEXPOL AB; *Int'l*, pg. 3372
KISMET RUBBER PRODUCTS INC.; *U.S. Private*, pg. 2315
MIDWEST RUBBER COMPANY; *U.S. Private*, pg. 2723
MINOR RUBBER CO., INC.; *U.S. Private*, pg. 2744
MOLD-TECH (SUZHOU) CO. LTD.—See Standex International; *U.S. Public*, pg. 1930
OLIVER RUBBER COMPANY—See Compagnie Generale des Etablissements Michelin SCA; *Int'l*, pg. 1744
OTTAWA RUBBER COMPANY; *U.S. Private*, pg. 3049
PARKER HANNIFIN CORPORATION, ENGINEERED SEALS DIVISION, SYRACUSE—See Parker Hannifin Corporation; *U.S. Public*, pg. 1643
PARKER HANNIFIN ENGINEERED SEALS DIVISION—See Parker Hannifin Corporation; *U.S. Public*, pg. 1649
PAWLING CORPORATION-ARCHITECTURAL PRODUCTS DIVISION—See Pawling Corporation; *U.S. Private*, pg. 3115
P.I. COMPONENTS CORP.; *U.S. Private*, pg. 3060
PRECISION POLYMER ENGINEERING LIMITED—See IDEX Corp; *U.S. Public*, pg. 1091
PRELAST, S.A.—See Fluidra SA; *Int'l*, pg. 2714
REX-HIDE INC.; *U.S. Private*, pg. 3417
SINGER EQUITIES INC.—See AEA Investors LP; *U.S. Private*, pg. 115
STELLANA (QINGDAO) CO., LTD.—See HEXPOL AB; *Int'l*, pg. 3372
TRELLEBORG AUTOMOTIVE TOLUCA SA DE CV—See Freudenberg SE; *Int'l*, pg. 2790
VERNAY LABORATORIES, INC.; *U.S. Private*, pg. 4368
VEYANCE TECHNOLOGIES, INC.—See Continental Aktiengesellschaft; *Int'l*, pg. 1780
VICEROY RUBBER LIMITED—See Allied Plastic Skylight; *Int'l*, pg. 358
WABTEC RUBBER PRODUCTS—See Westinghouse Air Brake Technologies Corporation; *U.S. Public*, pg. 2360

326299 — ALL OTHER RUBBER PRODUCT MANUFACTURING

A.B. BOYD CO.—See The Goldman Sachs Group, Inc.; *U.S. Public*, pg. 2080
ABITALIA, INC.—See American Biltrite Inc.; *U.S. Public*, pg. 97
ABTRE, INC.—See American Biltrite Inc.; *U.S. Public*, pg. 97
ACCURATE ELASTOMER PRODUCTS; *U.S. Private*, pg. 55
AE RUBBER SDN. BHD.—See Blackstone Inc.; *U.S. Public*, pg. 354
AIRBOSS-DEFENSE INC.—See AirBoss of America Corp.; *Int'l*, pg. 241
AIRBOSS-DEFENSE—See AirBoss of America Corp.; *Int'l*, pg. 241
AIRBOSS FLEXIBLE PRODUCTS LLC—See AirBoss of America Corp.; *Int'l*, pg. 241
AIRBOSS OF AMERICA CORP.; *Int'l*, pg. 241
AIRBOSS RUBBER COMPOUNDING (NC) INC.—See AirBoss of America Corp.; *Int'l*, pg. 241
AIRBOSS RUBBER COMPOUNDING—See AirBoss of America Corp.; *Int'l*, pg. 241
ALFAGOMMA AUSTRALIA PTY LTD—See Alfagomma S.p.A.; *Int'l*, pg. 315
ALFAGOMMA CANADA, INC.—See Alfagomma S.p.A.; *Int'l*, pg. 315

ALFAGOMMA FRACNE PARIS IDF—See Alfagomma S.p.A.; *Int'l*, pg. 315
ALFAGOMMA GERMANY GMBH—See Alfagomma S.p.A.; *Int'l*, pg. 315
ALFAGOMMA HELLAS S.A.—See Alfagomma S.p.A.; *Int'l*, pg. 315
ALFAGOMMA INTERNATIONAL BV—See Alfagomma S.p.A.; *Int'l*, pg. 315
ALFAGOMMA KOREA CO. LTD.—See Alfagomma S.p.A.; *Int'l*, pg. 315
ALFAGOMMA (NINGBO) CO LTD—See Alfagomma S.p.A.; *Int'l*, pg. 315
ALFAGOMMA PACIFIC PTE LTD—See Alfagomma S.p.A.; *Int'l*, pg. 315
ALFAGOMMA SOUTH AFRICA PTY LTD—See Alfagomma S.p.A.; *Int'l*, pg. 315
ALFAGOMMA UK LTD.—See Alfagomma S.p.A.; *Int'l*, pg. 315
ALLIANCE RUBBER COMPANY; *U.S. Private*, pg. 184
ALLIED-BALTIC RUBBER, INC.—See Anhui Zhongding Holding (Group) Co., Ltd.; *Int'l*, pg. 470
ALP USA, INC.—See ALP Group; *Int'l*, pg. 365
AMERICAN CONSOLIDATED INDUSTRIES; *U.S. Private*, pg. 228
AMERICAN PHOENIX INC.; *U.S. Private*, pg. 243
ANAGRAM INTERNATIONAL, INC.—See Thomas H. Lee Partners, L.P.; *U.S. Private*, pg. 4156
ANHUI ZHONGDING SEALING PARTS CO., LTD.—See Anhui Zhongding Holding (Group) Co., Ltd.; *Int'l*, pg. 470
ANJI FUJIKURA RUBBER CO., LTD.—See Fujikura Composites Inc.; *Int'l*, pg. 2826
ANSELL HEALTHCARE EUROPE N.V.—See Ansell Limited; *Int'l*, pg. 478
ANSELL HEALTHCARE LLC—See Ansell Limited; *Int'l*, pg. 478
ANSELL (HONG KONG) LIMITED—See Ansell Limited; *Int'l*, pg. 478
ANTIPHON AB; *Int'l*, pg. 483
APPLE RUBBER PRODUCTS INC.; *U.S. Private*, pg. 297
ASSEM-PAK, INC.—See OEP Capital Advisors, L.P.; *U.S. Private*, pg. 2999
AVK GUMMI A/S—See AVK Holding A/S; *Int'l*, pg. 746
AVON HI-LIFE INC.—See Avon Protection plc; *Int'l*, pg. 750
AVON MILK-RITE USA INC.—See Avon Protection plc; *Int'l*, pg. 750
AVON PROTECTION PLC; *Int'l*, pg. 749
BANDO KOREA CO., LTD.—See Bando Chemical Industries, Ltd.; *Int'l*, pg. 830
BAODING NUOBO RUBBER PRODUCTION COMPANY LIMITED—See Great Wall Motor Company Limited; *Int'l*, pg. 3066
BEIJER TECH AB—See Beijer Alma AB; *Int'l*, pg. 942
BESTWAY GLOBAL HOLDING INC.; *Int'l*, pg. 1001
BETALLIC LLC—See Centric Group LLC; *U.S. Private*, pg. 830
BILLIONS CO., LTD.; *Int'l*, pg. 1031
BIOMAX RUBBER INDUSTRIES LIMITED; *Int'l*, pg. 1039
BLUE SAIL MEDICAL CO., LTD.; *Int'l*, pg. 1069
BODE GRAVEL CO.—See Vulcan Materials Company; *U.S. Public*, pg. 2313
BORRACHAS VIPAL SA; *Int'l*, pg. 1114
BOSS BALLOON COMPANY—See Boss Holdings, Inc.; *U.S. Public*, pg. 371
BRIDGESTONE AMERICAS TIRE OPERATIONS, LLC - ABILENE MANUFACTURING FACILITY—See Cox Enterprises, Inc.; *U.S. Private*, pg. 1075
BRIDGESTONE AMERICAS TIRE OPERATIONS, LLC - GRIFFIN MANUFACTURING FACILITY—See Cox Enterprises, Inc.; *U.S. Private*, pg. 1075
BRIDGESTONE AMERICAS TIRE OPERATIONS, LLC - LONG BEACH MANUFACTURING FACILITY—See Cox Enterprises, Inc.; *U.S. Private*, pg. 1075
BRIDGESTONE AMERICAS TIRE OPERATIONS, LLC - OXFORD MANUFACTURING FACILITY—See Cox Enterprises, Inc.; *U.S. Private*, pg. 1075
BRIDGESTONE CORPORATION; *Int'l*, pg. 1155
BRIDGESTONE NATURAL RUBBER (THAILAND) CO., LTD.—See Bridgestone Corporation; *Int'l*, pg. 1159
BRP HANNIBAL, INC.—See Anhui Zhongding Holding (Group) Co., Ltd.; *Int'l*, pg. 471
BRYANT RUBBER CORP; *U.S. Private*, pg. 673
CALIFORNIA MEDICAL INNOVATIONS—See Arsenal Capital Management LP; *U.S. Private*, pg. 339
CAROLINA RUBBER ROLLS—See HBD Industries, Inc.; *U.S. Private*, pg. 1887
CENTRAL RUBBER COMPANY—See Koch Industries, Inc.; *U.S. Private*, pg. 2335
CHASE ELASTOMER (UK) LTD.—See HEXPOL AB; *Int'l*, pg. 3372
CHEMIONICS CORPORATION—See Chessco Industries, Inc.; *U.S. Private*, pg. 875
CHESTNUT RIDGE FOAM INC.; *U.S. Private*, pg. 875
CHINA HAINAN RUBBER INDUSTRY GROUP CO., LTD.; *Int'l*, pg. 1506
CHINA ORAL INDUSTRY GROUP HOLDINGS LIMITED; *Int'l*, pg. 1538
CODAN TECH QINGDAO RUBBER & PLASTIC PARTS CO., LTD.—See Addtech AB; *Int'l*, pg. 132

326299 — ALL OTHER RUBBER PR...

COLOR RUBBER NUGGETS, INC.—See Allen County Recyclers Inc.; *U.S. Private*, pg. 178
COMFORT RUBBER GLOVES INDUSTRIES SDN. BHD.—See Comfort Gloves Berhad; *Int'l*, pg. 1711
COMITAL S.P.A.; *Int'l*, pg. 1714
CONTINENTAL AMERICAN CORPORATION; *U.S. Private*, pg. 1028
CONTITECH BELGIUM BVBA—See Continental Aktiengesellschaft; *Int'l*, pg. 1780
CONTITECH FRANCE SNC—See Continental Aktiengesellschaft; *Int'l*, pg. 1780
CONTITECH KUHNER GMBH & CIE. KG—See Continental Aktiengesellschaft; *Int'l*, pg. 1781
CONTITECH TECHNO-CHEMIE GMBH—See Continental Aktiengesellschaft; *Int'l*, pg. 1780
CONTITECH UNITED KINGDOM LTD.—See Continental Aktiengesellschaft; *Int'l*, pg. 1781
CORCOS INDUSTRIALE S.P.A.—See Freudenberg SE; *Int'l*, pg. 2782
CTI BALLOONS LTD.—See Yunhong Green CTI Ltd.; *U.S. Public*, pg. 2400
CUSTOM RUBBER PRODUCTS, INC.—See Bridgepoint Group Plc; *Int'l*, pg. 1154
DA-PRO RUBBER INC.; *U.S. Private*, pg. 1143
D.A RUS., LLC—See Dong-A Hwasung Co., Ltd.; *Int'l*, pg. 2164
DENKA ELASTLUTION CO., LTD.—See Denki Company Limited; *Int'l*, pg. 2027
DIAM INTERNATIONAL SAS—See Ardian SAS; *Int'l*, pg. 555
DISCO, INC.—See Cellucap Manufacturing Co.; *U.S. Private*, pg. 807
DIVERSIFIED SILICONE PRODUCTS, INC.—See Rogers Corporation; *U.S. Public*, pg. 1808
DOLFIN RUBBERS LTD.; *Int'l*, pg. 2158
DONG-A HWASUNG CO., LTD.; *Int'l*, pg. 2164
DONGA HWASUNG MEXICO, S.A. DE C.V.—See Dong-A Hwasung Co., Ltd.; *Int'l*, pg. 2164
DONG-A HWA SUNG TECHNOLOGY(WUXI) CO., LTD.—See Dong-A Hwasung Co., Ltd.; *Int'l*, pg. 2164
DONG-A INDIA AUTOMOTIVE PVT. LTD.—See Dong-A Hwasung Co., Ltd.; *Int'l*, pg. 2164
DONG-A POLAND SP.Z O.O—See Dong-A Hwasung Co., Ltd.; *Int'l*, pg. 2164
DONG PHU RUBBER JOINT STOCK COMPANY; *Int'l*, pg. 2164
DSP SINGAPORE HOLDINGS PTE. LTD.—See DuPont de Nemours, Inc.; *U.S. Public*, pg. 692
DUCATEX S.A.; *Int'l*, pg. 2223
DUKSAN TECHOPIA CO., LTD.; *Int'l*, pg. 2224
EASTERN AERO MARINE INC.; *U.S. Private*, pg. 1319
EASTERN MERCHANTS PLC; *Int'l*, pg. 2273
EASY SUN SDN. BHD.—See ES Ceramics Technology Bhd; *Int'l*, pg. 2500
EATON CORP. - GOLF GRIP—See Eaton Corporation plc; *Int'l*, pg. 2280
ELASTOMERIC ENGINEERING CO. LTD.—See HEXPOL AB; *Int'l*, pg. 3372
ELASTOMEROS TECNICOS MOLDEADOS, INC.—See Park-Ohio Holdings Corp.; *U.S. Public*, pg. 1639
ELASTOMEROS TECNICOS MOLDEADOS, S. DE R. L. DE C.V.—See Park-Ohio Holdings Corp.; *U.S. Public*, pg. 1638
EMERSON PROCESS MANAGEMENT (SOUTH AFRICA) (PROPRIETARY) LTD.—See Emerson Electric Co.; *U.S. Public*, pg. 745
EUROCERAMIC TECHNOLOGIES CO., LTD.—See ES Ceramics Technology Bhd; *Int'l*, pg. 2500
EUROPOWER CR S.R.O.—See Park-Ohio Holdings Corp.; *U.S. Public*, pg. 1638
EXPEDIENT RESOURCES SDN BHD—See IJM Corporation Berhad; *Int'l*, pg. 3608
EXTERNA HANDELS- UND BETEILIGUNGSGESELLSCHAFT MBH—See Freudenberg SE; *Int'l*, pg. 2785
FABSOL, LLC—See Prophet Equity L.P.; *U.S. Private*, pg. 3286
FDT FLACHDACH TECHNOLOGIE GMBH & CO. KG—See Holcim Ltd.; *Int'l*, pg. 3446
THE FEMALE HEALTH COMPANY LIMITED—See Veru Inc.; *U.S. Public*, pg. 2290
THE FEMALE HEALTH COMPANY (M) SDN BHD—See Veru Inc.; *U.S. Public*, pg. 2289
THE FEMALE HEALTH COMPANY (UK) PLC—See Veru Inc.; *U.S. Public*, pg. 2290
FIDELITY INDUSTRIES INC.; *U.S. Private*, pg. 1503
FIRESTONE BUILDING PRODUCTS-PRESCOTT—See Bridgestone Corporation; *Int'l*, pg. 1156
FIRESTONE DIVERSIFIED PRODUCTS, LLC—See Bridgestone Corporation; *Int'l*, pg. 1157
FLEXAN, LLC—See New Mountain Capital, LLC; *U.S. Private*, pg. 2902
FLEXO UNIVERSAL SA DE CV—See Yunhong Green CTI Ltd.; *U.S. Public*, pg. 2400
FLEXSYS AMERICA L.P.—See Eastman Chemical Company; *U.S. Public*, pg. 706
FOAMCRAFT INC.; *U.S. Private*, pg. 1556
FORMOSAN RUBBER GROUP INC. - TAOYUAN PLANT—See Formosan Rubber Group Inc.; *Int'l*, pg. 2736
FRC HOLDING CORP.; *U.S. Private*, pg. 1600
FREUDENBERG BETEILIGUNGSGESELLSCHAFT MBH—See Freudenberg SE; *Int'l*, pg. 2785
FREUDENBERG & CO. LTD. PARTNERSHIP—See Freudenberg SE; *Int'l*, pg. 2785
FREUDENBERG ESPANA S.A.—See Freudenberg SE; *Int'l*, pg. 2786
FREUDENBERG HOUSEHOLD PRODUCTS AB—See Freudenberg SE; *Int'l*, pg. 2786
FREUDENBERG HOUSEHOLD PRODUCTS OY AB—See Freudenberg SE; *Int'l*, pg. 2787
FREUDENBERG IBERICA S.A., S.EN C.—See Freudenberg SE; *Int'l*, pg. 2787
FREUDENBERG NAO-TECIDOS LTDA. & CIA.—See Freudenberg SE; *Int'l*, pg. 2787
FREUDENBERG S.A.S.—See Freudenberg SE; *Int'l*, pg. 2788
FREUDENBERG SEALING TECHNOLOGIES—See Freudenberg SE; *Int'l*, pg. 2788
FREUDENBERG SIMRIT AG—See Freudenberg SE; *Int'l*, pg. 2788
FREUDENBERG TECHNICAL PRODUCTS LP—See Freudenberg SE; *Int'l*, pg. 2788
FREUDENBERG TELAS SIN TEJER S.A.—See Freudenberg SE; *Int'l*, pg. 2788
FREUDENBERG UCHIYAMA EUROPE S.A.S.—See Freudenberg SE; *Int'l*, pg. 2788
FREUDENBERG VERSICHERUNGSVERMITTLUNGS-GMBH—See Freudenberg SE; *Int'l*, pg. 2788
FUJIKURA COMPOSITE HAIPHONG, INC.—See Fujikura Composites Inc.; *Int'l*, pg. 2826
FUJIKURA COMPOSITE KOREA, LTD.—See Fujikura Composites Inc.; *Int'l*, pg. 2826
FUJIKURA COMPOSITES INC.; *Int'l*, pg. 2826
FUKOKU CO., LTD. - NISHIO PLANT—See Fukoku Co., Ltd.; *Int'l*, pg. 2838
GAYLA INDUSTRIES, INC.; *U.S. Private*, pg. 1652
GD HANDELSSYSTEME GMBH—See The Goodyear Tire & Rubber Company; *U.S. Public*, pg. 2083
G.I.E. GOODYEAR MIREVAL—See The Goodyear Tire & Rubber Company; *U.S. Public*, pg. 2083
GISLAVED GUMMI AB—See HEXPOL AB; *Int'l*, pg. 3371
GLOBOS QUALATEX DE PIONEER, S.A. DE C.V.—See Continental American Corporation; *U.S. Private*, pg. 1028
GOLDKEY PROCESSING, INC.—See HEXPOL AB; *Int'l*, pg. 3372
GOODYEAR DUNLOP TIRES FRANCE—See The Goodyear Tire & Rubber Company; *U.S. Public*, pg. 2083
GOOD YEAR LASTIKLERI TAS; *Int'l*, pg. 3039
GOVIND RUBBER LTD.; *Int'l*, pg. 3044
GRAB ON GRIPS LLC—See Columbia Ventures Corporation; *U.S. Private*, pg. 978
GREAT LAKES RUBBER CO. INC.—See MAC Valves, Inc.; *U.S. Private*, pg. 2531
GRISWOLD, LLC—See Rogers Corporation; *U.S. Public*, pg. 1808
GRP LIMITED; *Int'l*, pg. 3113
GUKO TECH GMBH—See Greiner Holding AG; *Int'l*, pg. 3079
HALCYON AGRI CORPORATION LTD.—See China Hainan Rubber Industry Group Co., Ltd.; *Int'l*, pg. 1506
HANNS GLASS GMBH & CO. KG—See Freudenberg SE; *Int'l*, pg. 2789
HARRISONS MALAYALAM LIMITED; *Int'l*, pg. 3279
HEXPOL COMPOUNDING (FOSHAN) CO., LTD.—See HEXPOL AB; *Int'l*, pg. 3372
HEXPOL COMPOUNDING GMBH—See HEXPOL AB; *Int'l*, pg. 3372
HEXPOL COMPOUNDING LESINA S.R.O—See HEXPOL AB; *Int'l*, pg. 3372
HEXPOL COMPOUNDING LLC—See HEXPOL AB; *Int'l*, pg. 3372
HEXPOL COMPOUNDING NC INC.—See HEXPOL AB; *Int'l*, pg. 3372
HEXPOL COMPOUNDING QUERETARO S.A. DE C.V.—See HEXPOL AB; *Int'l*, pg. 3372
HEXPOL COMPOUNDING S.A. DE C.V.—See HEXPOL AB; *Int'l*, pg. 3372
HEXPOL COMPOUNDING SPRL—See HEXPOL AB; *Int'l*, pg. 3372
HEXPOL COMPOUNDING S.R.O.—See HEXPOL AB; *Int'l*, pg. 3372
HICKORY SPRINGS MANUFACTURING COMPANY; *U.S. Private*, pg. 1933
HICKORY SPRINGS MANUFACTURING COMPANY—See Hickory Springs Manufacturing Company; *U.S. Private*, pg. 1933
HICKORY SPRINGS MANUFACTURING COMPANY—See Hickory Springs Manufacturing Company; *U.S. Private*, pg. 1933
HLN (SUZHOU) RUBBER PRODUCTS CO., LTD.—See HLN Rubber Products Pte. Ltd.; *Int'l*, pg. 3431
HONEYWELL SALISBURY ELECTRICAL SAFETY—See Honeywell International Inc.; *U.S. Public*, pg. 1049
HONG SENG GLOVES SDN. BHD.—See Hong Seng Consolidated Berhad; *Int'l*, pg. 3469
HORDAGRUPPEN AB; *Int'l*, pg. 3474
HSLS RUBBER INDUSTRIES SDA. BHD.—See Hwaseung Industries Co., Ltd.; *Int'l*, pg. 3542
HS NETWORKS INDIA PVT LTD—See Hwaseung Industries Co., Ltd.; *Int'l*, pg. 3542
HUMANE MANUFACTURING COMPANY, LLC—See Hendricks Holding Company, Inc.; *U.S. Private*, pg. 1915
HWA FONG RUBBER (CHINA) CO., LTD.—See Hwa Fong Rubber Industry Co., Ltd.; *Int'l*, pg. 3541
HWA FONG RUBBER (SUZHOU) CO., LTD.—See Hwa Fong Rubber Industry Co., Ltd.; *Int'l*, pg. 3541
HWA FONG RUBBER (U.S.A.) INC.—See Hwa Fong Rubber Industry Co., Ltd.; *Int'l*, pg. 3541
THE HYGENIC CORPORATION—See Madison Dearborn Partners, LLC; *U.S. Private*, pg. 2542
IAC CANTON LLC—See Invesco Ltd.; *U.S. Public*, pg. 1164
IER FUJIKURA INC.—See Fujikura Ltd.; *Int'l*, pg. 2829
INDUSTRIAL RUBBER APPLICATORS, INC.—See Lime Rock Partners, LLC; *U.S. Private*, pg. 2456
INDUSTRIAL RUBBER APPLICATORS, INC.—See Thompson Street Capital Manager LLC; *U.S. Private*, pg. 4161
INTERPLASTIC CORPORATION MOLDING PRODUCTS DIV.—See Interplastic Corporation; *U.S. Private*, pg. 2123
IRACORE INTERNATIONAL, INC.—See Lime Rock Partners, LLC; *U.S. Private*, pg. 2456
IRACORE INTERNATIONAL, INC.—See Thompson Street Capital Manager LLC; *U.S. Private*, pg. 4161
KIBARU MANUFACTURING SDN BHD—See Ge-Shen Corporation Berhad; *Int'l*, pg. 2897
KIRKHILL-TA COMPANY—See TransDigm Group Incorporated; *U.S. Public*, pg. 2181
KLEEN-TEX THAILAND CO. LTD.—See Kleen-Tex Industries, Inc.; *U.S. Private*, pg. 2318
KLUBER LUBRICATION ARGENTINA S.A.—See Freudenberg SE; *Int'l*, pg. 2785
KOLUBARA UNIVERZAL D.O.O.—See Continental Aktiengesellschaft; *Int'l*, pg. 1781
KONETA, INC.—See Kinderhook Industries, LLC; *U.S. Private*, pg. 2307
KRACO ENTERPRISES, LLC—See Sun Capital Partners, Inc.; *U.S. Private*, pg. 3860
KURTZ GRAVEL COMPANY, INC.—See Vulcan Materials Company; *U.S. Public*, pg. 2314
LAMKIN CORPORATION; *U.S. Private*, pg. 2380
LANKEM TEA & RUBBER PLANTATIONS (PVT) LTD.—See E.B. Creasy & Company PLC; *Int'l*, pg. 2251
LAUREN INTERNATIONAL INC.; *U.S. Private*, pg. 2399
LAVELLE INDUSTRIES INC.; *U.S. Private*, pg. 2400
LEXINGTON PRECISION CORPORATION—See Aurora Capital Group, LLC; *U.S. Private*, pg. 393
LIFESTYLE FOOTWEAR, INC.—See Rocky Brands, Inc.; *U.S. Public*, pg. 1807
LIFETIME INDUSTRIES, INC.—See The Goldman Sachs Group, Inc.; *U.S. Public*, pg. 2080
LMS, INC.—See AptarGroup, Inc.; *U.S. Public*, pg. 174
LONGWOOD ELASTOMERS, INC.—See Longwood Industries Holdings, LLC; *U.S. Private*, pg. 2493
LONGWOOD ELASTOMERS, S.A.—See Westinghouse Air Brake Technologies Corporation; *U.S. Public*, pg. 2358
LUDLOW COMPOSITES CORPORATION; *U.S. Private*, pg. 2512
LYDALL THERMAL/ACOUSTICAL—See Lydall, Inc.; *U.S. Public*, pg. 1350
MALONEY TECHNICAL PRODUCTS, INC.—See S&B Technical Products, Inc.; *U.S. Private*, pg. 3512
MAPLE CITY RUBBER COMPANY; *U.S. Private*, pg. 2568
MCP INDUSTRIES INC.; *U.S. Private*, pg. 2644
THE MERCER RUBBER COMPANY—See Mason Industries; *U.S. Private*, pg. 2602
MERIDIAN INDUSTRIES, INC.; *U.S. Private*, pg. 2673
MESGO ASIA KAUCUK A.S.—See HEXPOL AB; *Int'l*, pg. 3372
METALLFORM, S.R.O.—See Enco spol. s r.o.; *Int'l*, pg. 2401
MICRODYN-NADIR (XIAMEN) CO., LTD.—See CDH China Management Company Limited; *Int'l*, pg. 1370
MICROPOROUS PRODUCTS, LLC—See Seven Mile Capital Partners, LLC; *U.S. Private*, pg. 3618
MILLER PRODUCTS COMPANY, INC.; *U.S. Private*, pg. 2735
MILLER RUBBER PRODUCTS COMPANY—See Miller Products Company, Inc.; *U.S. Private*, pg. 2735
MITCHELL RUBBER PRODUCTS INC.; *U.S. Private*, pg. 2751
MOLDED DIMENSIONS INC.; *U.S. Private*, pg. 2766
MOUNTVILLE MILLS CHINA CO.—See Mountville Mills Inc.; *U.S. Private*, pg. 2801
MOUNTVILLE MILLS EUROPE BVBA—See Mountville Mills Inc.; *U.S. Private*, pg. 2801
MOUNTVILLE RUBBER COMPANY, LLC—See Mountville Mills Inc.; *U.S. Private*, pg. 2801
NANTONG SHIBAKE RUBBER PRODUCT CO. LTD.—See GIIB HOLDINGS BERHAD; *Int'l*, pg. 2972
NATIONAL RUBBER TECHNOLOGIES—See Kinderhook Industries, LLC; *U.S. Private*, pg. 2307
NEFF-PERKINS COMPANY INC.; *U.S. Private*, pg. 2880
NISHIKAWA COOPER LLC—See Cooper-Standard Holdings Inc.; *U.S. Public*, pg. 574

N.A.I.C.S. INDEX

NORA SYSTEMS GMBH—See Interface, Inc.; *U.S. Public*, pg. 1144
NORA SYSTEMS, INC.—See Interface, Inc.; *U.S. Public*, pg. 1144
NOTRAX - MATS FOR PROFESSIONAL USE—See Audax Group, Limited Partnership; *U.S. Private*, pg. 387
OMNI PRODUCTS, INC.; *U.S. Private*, pg. 3016
O'NEILL INC.; *U.S. Private*, pg. 2980
PACESETTER GRAPHIC SERVICE; *U.S. Private*, pg. 3065
PARKER HANNIFIN CORP., TECHSEAL DIV.—See Parker Hannifin Corporation; *U.S. Public*, pg. 1643
PARKER TECH SEAL DIVISION—See Parker Hannifin Corporation; *U.S. Public*, pg. 1643
PARK-OHIO INDUSTRIES (SHANGHAI) CO. LTD.—See Park-Ohio Holdings Corp.; *U.S. Public*, pg. 1639
PARK-OHIO PRODUCTS, INC.—See Park-Ohio Holdings Corp.; *U.S. Public*, pg. 1640
PATCH RUBBER COMPANY—See Myers Industries, Inc.; *U.S. Public*, pg. 1488
PAWLING CORPORATION; *U.S. Private*, pg. 3115
PERMA-FLEX/ESI—See Perma-Flex Roller Technology LLC; *U.S. Private*, pg. 3152
PERMA-FLEX ROLLER TECHNOLOGY LLC; *U.S. Private*, pg. 3152
PHOENIX COMPOUNDING TECHNOLOGY GMBH—See Continental Aktiengesellschaft; *Int'l*, pg. 1781
PIONEER NATIONAL LATEX COMPANY—See Continental American Corporation; *Int'l*, pg. 1028
POLITEX S.A.S. DI FREUDENBERG POLITEX S.R.L.—See Freudenberg SE; *Int'l*, pg. 2790
POLYCORP LTD.—See Arsenal Capital Management LP; *U.S. Private*, pg. 339
POLYMER GIKEN CO., LTD.—See Fukoku Co., Ltd.; *Int'l*, pg. 2839
POLYMERICS, INC.; *U.S. Private*, pg. 3226
PORTAGE PRECISION POLYMERS, INC.—See HEXPOL AB; *Int'l*, pg. 3372
PRECISION POLYMER ENGINEERING INTERNATIONAL LIMITED—See IDEX Corp; *U.S. Public*, pg. 1091
PRECISION RUBBER SEALINGS S.R.L.—See Freudenberg SE; *Int'l*, pg. 2790
PREFERRED COMPOUNDING CORP.—See HEXPOL AB; *Int'l*, pg. 3372
PREFERRED COMPOUNDING CORP. - TALLAPOOSA—See HEXPOL AB; *Int'l*, pg. 3372
PRESRAY CORP.—See Pawling Corporation; *U.S. Private*, pg. 3115
PROCAL GMBH—See Freudenberg SE; *Int'l*, pg. 2790
PROCO PRODUCTS INC.; *U.S. Private*, pg. 3272
PT. FUKOKU TOKAI RUBBER INDONESIA - FACTORY 1—See Fukoku Co., Ltd.; *Int'l*, pg. 2839
PT. FUKOKU TOKAI RUBBER INDONESIA - FACTORY 3—See Fukoku Co., Ltd.; *Int'l*, pg. 2839
PT. FUKOKU TOKAI RUBBER INDONESIA—See Fukoku Co., Ltd.; *Int'l*, pg. 2839
PT HLN BATAM—See HLN Rubber Products Pte. Ltd.; *Int'l*, pg. 3431
PTS S.A.—See Bridgestone Corporation; *Int'l*, pg. 1160
PT.TRIM RUBBER CO., LTD.—See Fukoku Co., Ltd.; *Int'l*, pg. 2839
PULASKI RUBBER CO.—See R.C.A. Rubber Company; *U.S. Private*, pg. 3335
QINGDAO FUKOKU AUTO FITTINGS CO., LTD.—See Fukoku Co., Ltd.; *Int'l*, pg. 2839
QINGDAO RUBBER SIX CONVEYOR BELT CO, LTD—See China National Chemical Corporation; *Int'l*, pg. 1529
QUABAUG CORPORATION; *U.S. Private*, pg. 3314
QUADION LLC—See KKR & Co. Inc.; *U.S. Public*, pg. 1263
QUALATEX BALLOON PTY. LTD.—See Continental American Corporation; *U.S. Private*, pg. 1028
QUALITY SYNTHETIC RUBBER INCORPORATED; *U.S. Private*, pg. 3321
QUINTANA ROO WETSUITS INC.—See The American Bicycle Group LLC; *U.S. Private*, pg. 3986
R.C.A. RUBBER COMPANY; *U.S. Private*, pg. 3335
REISGIES SCHAUMSTOFF E GMBH—See Bystronic AG; *Int'l*, pg. 1236
REMINGTON PRODUCTS COMPANY; *U.S. Private*, pg. 3396
RITUS CORP.—See Blue Point Capital Partners, LLC; *U.S. Private*, pg. 590
ROBIN INDUSTRIES, INC.; *U.S. Private*, pg. 3460
ROPPE CORPORATION; *U.S. Private*, pg. 3480
R&R FUJIKURA LTD.—See Fujikura Composites Inc.; *Int'l*, pg. 2826
RUBBER ASSOCIATES, INC.; *U.S. Private*, pg. 3499
RUBBER ENTERPRISES INC.; *U.S. Private*, pg. 3499
RUBBER ROLLS INC.; *U.S. Private*, pg. 3499
RUBBER TECHNOLOGY INC.—See Polymer Enterprises Inc.; *U.S. Private*, pg. 3226
SANDBOX MEDICAL LLC—See Canadian Hospital Specialties Limited; *Int'l*, pg. 1283
S&B TECHNICAL PRODUCTS, INC.; *U.S. Private*, pg. 3512
SCHLEGEL SYSTEMS, INC.—See Quanex Building Products Corp.; *U.S. Public*, pg. 1749
SCT SUNTAR CERAMIC TECHNOLOGY (XIAMEN) CO., LTD.—See CDH China Management Company Limited; *Int'l*, pg. 1370

SEALEX, INC.; *U.S. Private*, pg. 3585
SEALS UNLIMITED, INC.—See Genuine Parts Company; *U.S. Public*, pg. 933
SEMYUNG INDUSTRIAL CO., LTD.—See Cheil Grinding Wheel Ind. Co., Ltd.; *Int'l*, pg. 1460
SHANGHAI FUKOKU RUBBER & PLASTICS INDUSTRY CO., LTD.—See Fukoku Co., Ltd.; *Int'l*, pg. 2839
SHERCON, INC.—See Windjammer Capital Investors, LLC; *U.S. Private*, pg. 4538
SIAM FUKOKU CO., LTD. - KORAT FACTORY 1—See Fukoku Co., Ltd.; *Int'l*, pg. 2839
SIAM FUKOKU CO., LTD. - KORAT FACTORY 2—See Fukoku Co., Ltd.; *Int'l*, pg. 2839
SIAM FUKOKU CO., LTD.—See Fukoku Co., Ltd.; *Int'l*, pg. 2839
SINGLE SOURCE ROOFING CORP; *U.S. Private*, pg. 3670
SOFFSEAL, INC.—See ALP Group; *Int'l*, pg. 365
SPECTRATURF INC.—See Ecore International Inc.; *U.S. Private*, pg. 1330
SPERRY & RICE LLC; *U.S. Private*, pg. 3756
SPONGE-CUSHION, INC.—See Leggett & Platt, Incorporated; *U.S. Public*, pg. 1303
STAR-GLO INDUSTRIES LLC; *U.S. Private*, pg. 3786
STELLANA AB—See HEXPOL AB; *Int'l*, pg. 3372
SUNRISE MEDICAL LTD.—See Vestar Capital Partners, LLC; *U.S. Private*, pg. 4372
SUNTAR MEMBRANE TECHNOLOGY (SINGAPORE) PTE LTD—See CDH China Management Company Limited; *Int'l*, pg. 1370
SUNTAR MEMBRANE TECHNOLOGY (XIAMEN) CO., LTD.—See CDH China Management Company Limited; *Int'l*, pg. 1370
SUPERIOR MANUFACTURING GROUP EUROPE BV—See Audax Group, Limited Partnership; *U.S. Private*, pg. 387
SWIFTECH COMPANY LIMITED—See China Oral Industry Group Holdings Limited; *Int'l*, pg. 1538
SWITLIK PARACHUTE COMPANY INC.; *U.S. Private*, pg. 3894
TEXNIL LIMITED—See Hayleys PLC; *Int'l*, pg. 3291
TEXTILE RUBBER & CHEMICAL CO., INC. - COATINGS & ADHESIVES DIVISION—See Textile Rubber & Chemical Co., Inc.; *U.S. Private*, pg. 3978
THAI FUKOKU CO., LTD.—See Fukoku Co., Ltd.; *Int'l*, pg. 2839
THAI NIPPON RUBBER INDUSTRY CO., LTD. - SI RACHA FACTORY—See Charoen Aksorn Holding Group Co. Ltd.; *Int'l*, pg. 1451
TOKYO RUBBER MFG. CO., LTD.—See Fukoku Co., Ltd.; *Int'l*, pg. 2839
ULTIMATE RB, INC.—See Carlisle Companies Incorporated; *U.S. Public*, pg. 436
UNION DE INDUSTRIAS C.A., S.A.—See HEXPOL AB; *Int'l*, pg. 3373
UNIVERSAL POLYMER & RUBBER LTD.; *U.S. Private*, pg. 4306
VAIL RUBBER WORKS, INC.; *U.S. Private*, pg. 4329
VALLEY RUBBER, LLC; *U.S. Private*, pg. 4335
VELOX GMBH—See IMCD N.V.; *Int'l*, pg. 3622
VENIGROS LIMITED—See Hayleys PLC; *Int'l*, pg. 3291
VERNAY ITALIA, S.R.L.—See Vernay Laboratories, Inc.; *U.S. Private*, pg. 4368
VERNAY MANUFACTURING, INC.—See Vernay Laboratories, Inc.; *U.S. Private*, pg. 4368
VESTA INC.—See Sientra, Inc.; *U.S. Public*, pg. 1876
VIBRATION MOUNTINGS & CONTROLS, INC.; *U.S. Private*, pg. 4376
VIKING INDUSTRIES LLC; *U.S. Private*, pg. 4382
VULCAN CORPORATION—See Vulcan International Corporation; *U.S. Private*, pg. 4416
VULCAN INTERNATIONAL CORPORATION; *U.S. Private*, pg. 4416
WEST AMERICAN RUBBER CO., LLC; *U.S. Private*, pg. 4483
WESTLAND TECHNOLOGIES INC.—See ESCO Technologies, Inc.; *U.S. Public*, pg. 794
WEST PHARMACEUTICAL SERVICES DANMARK A/S—See West Pharmaceutical Services, Inc.; *U.S. Public*, pg. 2353
WEST PHARMACEUTICAL SERVICES DEUTSCHLAND GMBH & CO. KG—See West Pharmaceutical Services, Inc.; *U.S. Public*, pg. 2353
WEST PHARMACEUTICAL SERVICES FINANCE DANMARK APS—See West Pharmaceutical Services, Inc.; *U.S. Public*, pg. 2353
WEST PHARMACEUTICAL SERVICES FRANCE S.A.—See West Pharmaceutical Services, Inc.; *U.S. Public*, pg. 2353
WEST PHARMACEUTICAL SERVICES, INC.—See West Pharmaceutical Services, Inc.; *U.S. Public*, pg. 2353
WEST PHARMACEUTICAL SERVICES, INC.—See West Pharmaceutical Services, Inc.; *U.S. Public*, pg. 2353
WEST PHARMACEUTICAL SERVICES, INC.—See West Pharmaceutical Services, Inc.; *U.S. Public*, pg. 2353
WEST PHARMACEUTICAL SERVICES, INC.—See West Pharmaceutical Services, Inc.; *U.S. Public*, pg. 2353
WEST PHARMACEUTICAL SERVICES, INC.—See West Pharmaceutical Services, Inc.; *U.S. Public*, pg. 2353
WEST PHARMACEUTICAL SERVICES, INC.—See West Pharmaceutical Services, Inc.; *U.S. Public*, pg. 2353

327110 — POTTERY, CERAMICS, ...

WING INFLATABLES, INC.; *U.S. Private*, pg. 4541
WINSLOW MARINE PRODUCTS CORPORATION—See RTX Corporation; *U.S. Public*, pg. 1822

327110 — POTTERY, CERAMICS, AND PLUMBING FIXTURE MANUFACTURING

ACCURATE PARTITIONS CORP.—See ITR Industries Inc.; *U.S. Private*, pg. 2150
ACME ELECTRONICS (GUANGZHOU) CO. LTD.—See Acme Electronics Corporation; *Int'l*, pg. 107
ACME ELECTRONICS (KUNSHAN) CO. LTD.—See Acme Electronics Corporation; *Int'l*, pg. 107
ACME FERRITE PRODUCTS SDN. BHD.—See Acme Electronics Corporation; *Int'l*, pg. 107
AFG WARENDORFER IMMOBILIEN GMBH.—See Arbonia AG; *Int'l*, pg. 537
AGNORA LTD; *Int'l*, pg. 212
ALVAND TILE & CERAMIC COMPANY; *Int'l*, pg. 401
ALVAND TILE & CERAMIC INDUSTRIES CO.; *Int'l*, pg. 401
AMAZOONE CERAMICS LIMITED—See Asian Granito India Limited; *Int'l*, pg. 617
AMERICAN STANDARD B&K MEXICO, S. DE R.L. DE C.V.—See Sun Capital Partners, Inc.; *U.S. Private*, pg. 3858
ANDREW SHERET LIMITED; *Int'l*, pg. 452
ANHUI EARTH-PANDA ADVANCED MAGNETIC MATERIAL CO., LTD.—See Earth-Panda Advance Magnetic Material Co., Ltd.; *Int'l*, pg. 2268
ARDAKAN INDUSTRIAL CERAMICS CO.; *Int'l*, pg. 553
A.R.T. STUDIO CLAY COMPANY, INC.—See T.J. Haggerty, Inc.; *U.S. Private*, pg. 3912
AS AMERICA, INC.—See Sun Capital Partners, Inc.; *U.S. Private*, pg. 3858
ASHAPURA PERFOCLAY LIMITED—See Ashapura Minechem Limited; *Int'l*, pg. 606
ASIA FILE CORPORATION BHD.; *Int'l*, pg. 612
ASIAN POTTERY (PENANG) SDN. BHD.—See CSH Alliance Berhad; *Int'l*, pg. 1865
ATLAS HOMEWARES, INC.—See The Jordan Company, L.P.; *U.S. Private*, pg. 4062
BAINULTRA INC.; *Int'l*, pg. 803
BELLEEK POTTERY LTD.; *Int'l*, pg. 967
BERNARDAUD S.A.; *Int'l*, pg. 986
BRIGGS INDUSTRIES, INC.—See Ceramica Lima S.A.; *Int'l*, pg. 1421
BRISTAN GROUP LTD.—See Masco Corporation; *U.S. Public*, pg. 1391
BUFFALO CHINA, INC.—See EveryWare Global, Inc.; *U.S. Private*, pg. 1441
BUNTING MAGNETICS CO.; *U.S. Private*, pg. 686
BURGBAD AKTIENGESELLSCHAFT; *Int'l*, pg. 1223
CAP PARTS AG; *Int'l*, pg. 1300
CAROMA INDUSTRIES (NZ) LIMITED—See GWA Group Limited; *Int'l*, pg. 3190
CASEY POTTERY COMPANY LLP; *U.S. Private*, pg. 782
CEMACON S.A.; *Int'l*, pg. 1396
CERAMICA LIMA S.A.; *Int'l*, pg. 1421
CERAMIC INDUSTRIES LIMITED; *Int'l*, pg. 1421
CERAMIC MAGNETICS, INC.—See Thomas & Skinner, Inc.; *U.S. Private*, pg. 4154
CERAVID GMBH—See Geberit AG; *Int'l*, pg. 2904
CERSANIT S.A.; *Int'l*, pg. 1423
CERTECH SPA; *Int'l*, pg. 1423
CERTINA CONSTRUCTION AG—See Certina Holding AG; *Int'l*, pg. 1423
CHEE WAH CORPORATION BERHAD; *Int'l*, pg. 1459
CHINA ELECTRONICS HUADA TECHNOLOGY COMPANY LIMITED—See China Electronics Corporation; *Int'l*, pg. 1499
CHURCHILL CHINA PLC; *Int'l*, pg. 1600
CLAFFEY POOLS; *U.S. Private*, pg. 909
COLE + CO.—See C3G, L.P.; *U.S. Private*, pg. 710
COLUMBIA GLAZING SYSTEMS INC.—See Columbia Manufacturing Co Ltd.; *Int'l*, pg. 1706
COORSTEK, INC. - COORSTEK LAUF FACILITY—See CoorsTek, Inc.; *U.S. Private*, pg. 1043
COORSTEK, INC. - COORSTEK PARIS FACILITY—See CoorsTek, Inc.; *U.S. Private*, pg. 1044
COORSTEK, INC. - COORSTEK SAN LUIS POTOSI FACILITY—See CoorsTek, Inc.; *U.S. Private*, pg. 1044
COORSTEK, INC. - COORSTEK SWEDEN FACILITY—See CoorsTek, Inc.; *U.S. Private*, pg. 1044
COORSTEK, INC.; *U.S. Private*, pg. 1043
COORSTEK KK—See CoorsTek, Inc.; *U.S. Private*, pg. 1043
COORSTEK TAIWAN CORP.—See CoorsTek, Inc.; *U.S. Private*, pg. 1043
COTON COLORS EXPRESS, LLC; *U.S. Private*, pg. 1063
CRANE PLUMBING, L.L.C.—See Sun Capital Partners, Inc.; *U.S. Private*, pg. 3858
CREATIVE BATH PRODUCTS INC.; *U.S. Private*, pg. 1087
CROSSVILLE, INC.—See Paceline Equity Partners LLC; *U.S. Private*, pg. 3064
CRYSTAL CERAMIC INDUSTRIES PRIVATE LIMITED—See Asian Granito India Limited; *Int'l*, pg. 617
CSH ALLIANCE BERHAD; *Int'l*, pg. 1865
DAELIM B&CO., LTD.; *Int'l*, pg. 1907

327110 — POTTERY, CERAMICS, ...

DAELIM TRADING CO., LTD. - DOBIDOS PLANT—See DAELIM TRADING Co., Ltd.; *Int'l*, pg. 1908
DAELIM TRADING CO., LTD. - FAUCET PLANT—See DAELIM TRADING Co., Ltd.; *Int'l*, pg. 1908
DAELIM TRADING CO., LTD. - JEUNGPYEONG PLANT—See DAELIM TRADING Co., Ltd.; *Int'l*, pg. 1908
DALIAN INSULATOR (FUJIAN) CO., LTD.—See Dalian Insulator Group Co., Ltd.; *Int'l*, pg. 1952
DALIAN INSULATOR GROUP CO., LTD.; *Int'l*, pg. 1952
DANKOTUWA PORCELAIN PLC; *Int'l*, pg. 1965
DD TRADERS, INC.; *U.S. Private*, pg. 1180
DECOR INC.; *U.S. Private*, pg. 1187
DEUTSCHE STEINZEUG CREMER & BREUER AG; *Int'l*, pg. 2083
DUAL ENGRAVING PTY. LTD.—See Dewhurst Group plc; *Int'l*, pg. 2091
EARTH-PANDA JAPAN CO., LTD.—See Earth-Panda Advance Magnetic Material Co., Ltd.; *Int'l*, pg. 2268
EARTH-PANDA (SUZHOU) CO., LTD.—See Earth-Panda Advance Magnetic Material Co., Ltd.; *Int'l*, pg. 2268
ELEKTROPORCELAN ARANDELOVAC A.D.; *Int'l*, pg. 2357
ELHO BV; *Int'l*, pg. 2360
ENESCO, LLC; *U.S. Private*, pg. 1397
ES CERAMICS TECHNOLOGY BHD; *Int'l*, pg. 2500
EUNISELL INTERLINKED PLC; *Int'l*, pg. 2526
FERRITE INTERNATIONAL COMPANY; *U.S. Private*, pg. 1498
FIBON UK LIMITED—See Fibon Berhad; *Int'l*, pg. 2652
FISKARS OYJ ABP - ARABIA PORCELAIN FACTORY—See Fiskars Oyj Abp; *Int'l*, pg. 2694
FOXCONN CZ S.R.O.—See Hon Hai Precision Industry Co., Ltd.; *Int'l*, pg. 3456
FUJAIRAH BUILDING INDUSTRIES COMPANY P.S.C. - EMIRATES CERAMIC FACTORY—See Fujairah Building Industries Company P.S.C.; *Int'l*, pg. 2808
FU-WANG CERAMIC LIMITED; *Int'l*, pg. 2801
GEBERIT PRODUKTIONS GMBH—See Geberit AG; *Int'l*, pg. 2905
GEBERIT SPOL. S.R.O.—See Geberit AG; *Int'l*, pg. 2905
GEBERIT VERTRIEBS GMBH—See Geberit AG; *Int'l*, pg. 2905
GEBERIT VERWALTUNGS GMBH—See Geberit AG; *Int'l*, pg. 2905
GENERAL ACCESSORY MANUFACTURING COMPANY—See Masco Corporation; *U.S. Public*, pg. 1390
GENERAL CERAMICS LTD.; *Int'l*, pg. 2918
GENERAL COMPANY FOR CERAMIC & PORCELAIN PRODUCTS; *Int'l*, pg. 2918
GRAFF—See Meridian International Group, Inc.; *U.S. Private*, pg. 2673
GRANITIFIANDRE S.P.A.; *Int'l*, pg. 3059
GRID SOLTUIONS OY—See General Electric Company; *U.S. Public*, pg. 918
GRUPO INDUSTRIAL SALTILLO S.A. DE C.V.; *Int'l*, pg. 3130
GUANGDONG SITONG GROUP CO., LTD.; *Int'l*, pg. 3160
GUANGDONG SONGFA CERAMICS CO., LTD.; *Int'l*, pg. 3160
GUANGZHOU SONGFA HOTEL EQUIPMENT SUPPLIERS CO., LTD.—See Guangdong Songfa Ceramics Co., Ltd.; *Int'l*, pg. 3160
HAEGER POTTERIES, INC.—See Haeger Industries, Inc.; *U.S. Private*, pg. 1839
HAEGER POTTERIES OF MACOMB INC.—See Haeger Industries, Inc.; *U.S. Private*, pg. 1839
THE HALL CHINA COMPANY; *U.S. Private*, pg. 4042
HANSGROHE N.V.—See Masco Corporation; *U.S. Public*, pg. 1390
HANSGROHE SE7—See Masco Corporation; *U.S. Public*, pg. 1390
HIMAG MAGNETIC CORPORATION—See China Steel Corporation; *Int'l*, pg. 1555
HOME POTTERY PUBLIC COMPANY LIMITED; *Int'l*, pg. 3455
THE HOMER LAUGHLIN CHINA COMPANY; *U.S. Private*, pg. 4054
HOOSIER MAGNETICS INC.; *U.S. Private*, pg. 1978
HUNAN HUALIAN CHINA INDUSTRY CO., LTD.; *Int'l*, pg. 3532
HUPPE GMBH—See Masco Corporation; *U.S. Public*, pg. 1391
HUPPE SARL—See Masco Corporation; *U.S. Public*, pg. 1391
IBIDEN CERAM GMBH—See Ibiden Co., Ltd.; *Int'l*, pg. 3575
IBIDEN DPF FRANCE S.A.S.—See Ibiden Co., Ltd.; *Int'l*, pg. 3575
IBIDEN HUNGARY KFT.—See Ibiden Co., Ltd.; *Int'l*, pg. 3575
IBIDEN MEXICO, S.A. DE C.V.—See Ibiden Co., Ltd.; *Int'l*, pg. 3575
IDEAL STANDARD FRANCE—See Anchorage Capital Group, L.L.C.; *U.S. Private*, pg. 274
IDEAL STANDARD FRANCE—See CVC Capital Partners SICAV-FIS S.A.; *Int'l*, pg. 1888
IDEAL STANDARD GMBH—See Anchorage Capital Group, L.L.C.; *U.S. Private*, pg. 274

IDEAL STANDARD GMBH—See CVC Capital Partners SICAV-FIS S.A.; *Int'l*, pg. 1888
IDEAL STANDARD GMBH ZWEIGNIEDERLASSUNG OSTERREICH—See Anchorage Capital Group, L.L.C.; *U.S. Private*, pg. 274
IDEAL STANDARD GMBH ZWEIGNIEDERLASSUNG OSTERREICH—See CVC Capital Partners SICAV-FIS S.A.; *Int'l*, pg. 1888
IDEAL STANDARD ITALIA S.R.L.—See Anchorage Capital Group, L.L.C.; *U.S. Private*, pg. 274
IDEAL STANDARD ITALIA S.R.L.—See CVC Capital Partners SICAV-FIS S.A.; *Int'l*, pg. 1888
IDEAL STANDARD S.A.I.—See Anchorage Capital Group, L.L.C.; *U.S. Private*, pg. 274
IDEAL STANDARD S.A.I.—See CVC Capital Partners SICAV-FIS S.A.; *Int'l*, pg. 1888
IDEAL STANDARD (UK) LTD.—See Anchorage Capital Group, L.L.C.; *U.S. Private*, pg. 274
IDEAL STANDARD (UK) LTD.—See CVC Capital Partners SICAV-FIS S.A.; *Int'l*, pg. 1888
KAI GROUP—See Mohawk Industries, Inc.; *U.S. Public*, pg. 1457
KENNAMETAL SINTEC KERAMIK GMBH—See Kennametal Inc.; *U.S. Public*, pg. 1222
KOHLER CANADA CO. - HYTEC PLUMBING PRODUCTS DIVISION—See Kohler Company; *U.S. Private*, pg. 2339
KRAUS USA PLUMBING LLC—See Masco Corporation; *U.S. Public*, pg. 1390
LAPP INSULATOR COMPANY, LLC; *U.S. Private*, pg. 2391
LENOX CORPORATION—See Centre Lane Partners, LLC; *U.S. Private*, pg. 827
LENOX - KINSTON PLANT—See Centre Lane Partners, LLC; *U.S. Private*, pg. 827
LIBBEY, INC.; *U.S. Private*, pg. 2442
MACKENZIE-CHILDS LLC—See EagleTree Capital, LP; *U.S. Private*, pg. 1311
MANSFIELD PLUMBING PRODUCTS LLC; *U.S. Private*, pg. 2566
MCDANEL ADVANCED MATERIAL TECHNOLOGIES LLC—See Artemis Capital Partners Management Co., LLC; *U.S. Private*, pg. 341
MMR OFFSHORE SERVICES, INC.—See MMR Group Inc.; *U.S. Private*, pg. 2755
NANCHONG THREE CIRCLE ELECTRONIC CO. LTD.—See Chaozhou Three-Circle Group Co., Ltd.; *Int'l*, pg. 1447
NATIONAL CERAMIC INDUSTRIES PTY LTD—See Ceramic Industries Limited; *Int'l*, pg. 1421
NATIONAL MAGNETICS GROUP, INC.; *U.S. Private*, pg. 2859
NINGBO KONIT INDUSTRIAL INC. LTD.—See Beijing Zhong Ke San Huan High-tech Co., Ltd.; *Int'l*, pg. 961
ORIWINA SDN. BHD.—See CSH Alliance Berhad; *Int'l*, pg. 1865
OXIMET S.R.L.—See American Securities LLC; *U.S. Private*, pg. 252
PORCELAIN PRODUCTS CO., LTD—See The Riverside Company; *U.S. Private*, pg. 4110
P&R LIFTCARS PTY. LTD.—See Dewhurst Group plc; *Int'l*, pg. 2091
PROCOPLAST S.A.—See Methode Electronics, Inc.; *U.S. Public*, pg. 1429
PT DAELIM INDONESIA—See DAELIM TRADING Co., Ltd.; *Int'l*, pg. 1908
PT. HITACHI METALS INDONESIA—See Hitachi, Ltd.; *Int'l*, pg. 3424
QUAKER CHEMICAL, S.R.L.—See Quaker Chemical Corporation; *U.S. Public*, pg. 1746
QUALITY CERAMIC (ARKLOW) LIMITED—See Anchorage Capital Group, L.L.C.; *U.S. Private*, pg. 274
QUALITY CERAMIC (ARKLOW) LIMITED—See CVC Capital Partners SICAV-FIS S.A.; *Int'l*, pg. 1888
QUAY BATHROOMS LIMITED—See Anchorage Capital Group, L.L.C.; *U.S. Private*, pg. 274
QUAY BATHROOMS LIMITED—See CVC Capital Partners SICAV-FIS S.A.; *Int'l*, pg. 1888
RDI TECHNOLOGIES, INC.—See SFW Capital Partners LLC; *U.S. Private*, pg. 3622
REHT (ANHUI) PERMANENT MAGNET TECHNOLOGY CO., LTD.—See Earth-Panda Advance Magnetic Material Co., Ltd.; *Int'l*, pg. 2268
ROBINSON-RANSBOTTOM POTTERY COMPANY—See Brittany Stamping, LLC; *U.S. Private*, pg. 657
ROMB S.A.—See Grupa Kety S.A.; *Int'l*, pg. 3116
ROYAL BATHS MANUFACTURING CO. LTD.—See Cotton Creek Capital Management LLC; *U.S. Private*, pg. 1063
ROYAL COPENHAGEN A/S—See Fiskars Oyj Abp; *Int'l*, pg. 2694
SAINT-GOBAIN CERAMICS—See Compagnie de Saint-Gobain SA; *Int'l*, pg. 1732
SANITARIOS DOMINICANOS, S.A.—See Sun Capital Partners, Inc.; *U.S. Private*, pg. 3858
SANITEC CORPORATION—See Geberit AG; *Int'l*, pg. 2905
SANVAC (BEIJING) MAGNETICS CO., LTD.—See Beijing Zhong Ke San Huan High-tech Co., Ltd.; *Int'l*, pg. 961
SEATEK COMPANY INC.—See Southwire Company, LLC; *U.S. Private*, pg. 3742
SHANGHAI EARTH-PANDA PERMANENT MAGNET TECH-

NOLOGY CO., LTD.—See Earth-Panda Advance Magnetic Material Co., Ltd.; *Int'l*, pg. 2268
SHENZHEN THREE-CIRCLE ELECTRONIC CO., LTD.—See Chaozhou Three-Circle Group Co., Ltd.; *Int'l*, pg. 1447
SINTEC KERAMIK USA INC.—See Kennametal Inc.; *U.S. Public*, pg. 1222
SLOAN VALVE WATER TECHNOLOGIES (SUZHOU) CO., LTD—See Sloan Valve Company; *U.S. Private*, pg. 3689
STERLING PLUMBING, INC.—See Kohler Company; *U.S. Private*, pg. 2340
SWEET FLAVOR OF FLORIDA LLC; *U.S. Private*, pg. 3892
TAM CERAMICS LLC—See TAM Ceramics Group of NY, LLC; *U.S. Private*, pg. 3927
TATEHO OZARK TECHNICAL CERAMICS, INC.—See Air Water Inc.; *Int'l*, pg. 241
TIANJIN SANHUAN LUCKY NEW MATERIAL INC.—See Beijing Zhong Ke San Huan High-tech Co., Ltd.; *Int'l*, pg. 961
TRAEGER, INC.; *U.S. Public*, pg. 2179
TRANSPAC IMPORTS INC.; *U.S. Private*, pg. 4210
VALVEX S.A.—See Meridian International Group, Inc.; *U.S. Private*, pg. 2673
VITAVIVA ITALIA SRL—See Certina Holding AG; *Int'l*, pg. 1423
ZHAOQING SAN HUAN JINGYUE MAGNETIC MATERIALS INC. LTD—See Beijing Zhong Ke San Huan High-tech Co., Ltd.; *Int'l*, pg. 961
ZHONG KE SAN HUAN YU XIAN JINGXIU MAGNETIC MATERIALS INC., LTD—See Beijing Zhong Ke San Huan High-tech Co., Ltd.; *Int'l*, pg. 961

327120 — CLAY BUILDING MATERIAL AND REFRACTORIES MANUFACTURING

AALBORG PORTLAND A/S—See Cementir Holding N.V.; *Int'l*, pg. 1397
A&A MATERIAL CORPORATION; *Int'l*, pg. 18
ACME BRICK COMPANY—See Berkshire Hathaway Inc.; *U.S. Public*, pg. 297
ACME-OCHS BRICK AND STONE, INC.—See Berkshire Hathaway Inc.; *U.S. Public*, pg. 298
AFARAK DOO—See Afarak Group SE; *Int'l*, pg. 185
AGC PLIBRICO CO., LTD.—See AGC Inc.; *Int'l*, pg. 203
AIR WATER ECOROCA INC.—See Air Water Inc.; *Int'l*, pg. 239
AL ANWAR CERAMIC TILES CO. SAOG; *Int'l*, pg. 275
ALCERA (SUZHOU) CO., LTD.—See Almedio, Inc.; *Int'l*, pg. 364
ALFA; *Int'l*, pg. 307
AL GHURAIR CONSTRUCTION ALUMINUM QATAR—See Al Ghurair Investment LLC; *Int'l*, pg. 278
ALLIED MINERAL PRODUCTS, ASIA—See Allied Mineral Products, Inc.; *U.S. Private*, pg. 187
ALLIED MINERAL PRODUCTS EUROPE BV—See Allied Mineral Products, Inc.; *U.S. Private*, pg. 187
ALLIED MINERAL PRODUCTS, INC.; *U.S. Private*, pg. 186
ALLIED MINERAL PRODUCTS, LATIN AMERICA—See Allied Mineral Products, Inc.; *U.S. Private*, pg. 187
ALLIED MINERAL PRODUCTS (TIANJIN) CO., LTD. (AMT)—See Allied Mineral Products, Inc.; *U.S. Private*, pg. 187
ALLIED REFRACTORY PRODUCTS INDIA PRIVATE, LTD.—See Allied Mineral Products, Inc.; *U.S. Private*, pg. 187
AMBUJA CEMENTS LTD—See Adani Enterprises Limited; *Int'l*, pg. 125
AMERICAN MARAZZI TILE, INC.—See Mohawk Industries, Inc.; *U.S. Public*, pg. 1457
ANH REFRACTORIES EUROPE LIMITED—See Platinum Equity, LLC; *U.S. Private*, pg. 3203
ANKER INDUSTRIES—See Speyside Equity LLC; *U.S. Private*, pg. 3756
ANNEC GREEN REFRACTORIES CORPORATION; *Int'l*, pg. 473
AP GREEN DE MEXICO, S.A. DE C.V.—See Platinum Equity, LLC; *U.S. Private*, pg. 3203
A.P. GREEN REFRACTORIES, INC.—See Platinum Equity, LLC; *U.S. Private*, pg. 3203
APPLIED MINERALS, INC.; *U.S. Public*, pg. 173
ARAMIT CEMENT LTD.; *Int'l*, pg. 535
ARCHI-RO KFT.—See Deutsche Steinzeug Cremer & Breuer AG; *Int'l*, pg. 2083
ARDOISIERES D'ANGERS—See Groupe Bruxelles Lambert SA; *Int'l*, pg. 3099
ARKAN HOLDING COMPANY K.S.C.—See Bayan Investment Holding Company K.S.C.C.; *Int'l*, pg. 901
AS BYGGFORM—See Byggma ASA; *Int'l*, pg. 1235
ASIAN GRANITO INDIA LIMITED - GUJARAT UNIT—See Asian Granito India Limited; *Int'l*, pg. 617
ASIAN GRANITO INDIA LIMITED; *Int'l*, pg. 617
ASK SANSHIN ENGINEERING CORPORATION—See A&A Material Corporation; *Int'l*, pg. 18
ASSOCIATED CERAMICS LIMITED; *Int'l*, pg. 648
ATTOCK CEMENT PAKISTAN LIMITED; *Int'l*, pg. 697
AUSTRAL BRICKS (TASMANIA) PTY LTD.—See Brickworks Limited; *Int'l*, pg. 1152

N.A.I.C.S. INDEX

327120 — CLAY BUILDING MATER...

AUSWEST TIMBERS PTY LTD.—See Brickworks Limited; *Int'l*, pg. 1152

BASANITE INDUSTRIES, LLC—See Basanite, Inc.; *U.S. Public*, pg. 279

BEHCERAM COMPANY; *Int'l*, pg. 941

BEIJING TONGDA REFRACTORY ENGINEERING TECHNOLOGY CO., LTD.—See BBMG Corporation; *Int'l*, pg. 921

THE BELDEN BRICK COMPANY INC.; *U.S. Private*, pg. 3993

BESTCRETE AGGREGATES LIMITED—See ANSA McAL Limited; *Int'l*, pg. 477

BNZ MATERIALS, INC. - INSULATING FIRE BRICK PLANT—See BNZ Materials, Inc.; *U.S. Private*, pg. 602

BNZ MATERIALS, INC.; *U.S. Private*, pg. 602

BNZ S.A.—See BNZ Materials, Inc.; *U.S. Private*, pg. 602

BOSTA BETON SP. Z O.O.—See CRH plc; *Int'l*, pg. 1843

BOUYER LEROUX SA; *Int'l*, pg. 1121

THE BOWERSTON SHALE COMPANY; *U.S. Private*, pg. 3998

BRAMPTON BRICK INC—See Brampton Brick Limited; *Int'l*, pg. 1139

BRICK AND TILE CORP. OF LAWRENCEVILLE; *U.S. Private*, pg. 648

BRICKWORKS BUILDING PRODUCTS PTY LTD—See Brickworks Limited; *Int'l*, pg. 1152

BRICKWORKS LIMITED; *Int'l*, pg. 1151

BRISTILE GUARDIANS PTY LTD.—See Brickworks Limited; *Int'l*, pg. 1152

BRISTILE OPERATIONS PTY LTD.—See Brickworks Limited; *Int'l*, pg. 1152

BROCKS PLYWOOD SALES, INC.—See Hammond Lumber Company; *U.S. Private*, pg. 1850

BUILDERS ALLIANCE LLC—See The Sterling Group, L.P.; *U.S. Private*, pg. 4122

BURLINGAME INDUSTRIES, INCORPORATED; *U.S. Private*, pg. 688

BX OKINAWA BUNKA SHUTTER CO., LTD.—See Bunka Shutter Co., Ltd.; *Int'l*, pg. 1216

CALDERYS ITALIA SRL—See Groupe Bruxelles Lambert SA; *Int'l*, pg. 3099

CALDURAN KALKZANDSTEEN B.V.—See CRH plc; *Int'l*, pg. 1844

CANADIAN FERRO REFRACTORIES; *Int'l*, pg. 1283

CANTERAS CERRO NEGRO S.A.—See CRH plc; *Int'l*, pg. 1844

CANTILLANA B.V.—See Cantillana SA/NV; *Int'l*, pg. 1299

CANTILLANA SA/NV; *Int'l*, pg. 1299

CANTILLANA SAS—See Cantillana SA/NV; *Int'l*, pg. 1299

CAROLINA CERAMICS BRICK COMPANY; *U.S. Private*, pg. 767

CASTEC, INC. & ONA CORPORATION—See CFS Group, Inc.; *Int'l*, pg. 1430

CEDAR HEIGHTS CLAY—See Balmoral Funds LLC; *U.S. Private*, pg. 461

CEMENTO BAYANO, S.A.—See CEMEX, S.A.B. de C.V.; *Int'l*, pg. 1398

CEMEX NICARAGUA, S.A.—See CEMEX, S.A.B. de C.V.; *Int'l*, pg. 1398

CERADEL - SOCOR—See Groupe Bruxelles Lambert SA; *Int'l*, pg. 3100

CERADYNE THERMO MATERIALS—See 3M Company; *U.S. Public*, pg. 8

CERAMAX INC.; *Int'l*, pg. 1421

CERAMICA CARABOBO SACA; *Int'l*, pg. 1421

CERAMICA CHIARELLI S.A.; *Int'l*, pg. 1421

CERAMICA SANTA ANITA, S.A. DE C.V.—See Grupo Industrial Saltillo S.A. de C.V.; *Int'l*, pg. 3130

CERAMIKA GRES SA—See Ceramika Nowa Gala S.A.; *Int'l*, pg. 1421

CERAM LIEGENSCHAFTSVERWALTUNG GMBH—See Ibiden Co., Ltd.; *Int'l*, pg. 3575

CG TEC SERVICE GMBH—See Consus Real Estate AG; *Int'l*, pg. 1778

CHAMPION BUILDING MATERIALS CO., LTD.; *Int'l*, pg. 1440

CHANG YIH CERAMIC JOINT STOCK COMPANY; *Int'l*, pg. 1441

CHENGDU BUILDING MATERIALS COMPANY—See Dalian Shide Group Co., Ltd.; *Int'l*, pg. 1952

CHEROKEE BRICK & TILE COMPANY; *U.S. Private*, pg. 873

CHIYODA UTE CO., LTD.; *Int'l*, pg. 1575

CHOSUN REFRACTORIES ENG CO., LTD.—See CR Holdings Co., Ltd.; *Int'l*, pg. 1827

CKM APPLIED MATERIALS CORP.; *Int'l*, pg. 1639

CLIFTON BRICK MANUFACTURERS PTY LTD.—See Brickworks Limited; *Int'l*, pg. 1152

CMC JOINT STOCK COMPANY; *Int'l*, pg. 1669

CONCRETE SUPPLY OF TOPEKA, LLC—See Summit Materials, Inc.; *U.S. Public*, pg. 1959

COORSTEK NAGASAKI CORPORATION—See CoorsTek, Inc.; *U.S. Public*, pg. 1043

CORHART REFRACTORIES CORP.—See Compagnie de Saint-Gobain SA; *Int'l*, pg. 1730

CORMELA S.A.—See CRH plc; *Int'l*, pg. 1844

CPI LIMITED—See Grafton Group plc; *Int'l*, pg. 3050

CPI MORTARS LIMITED—See Grafton Group plc; *Int'l*, pg. 3050

CRADLEY SPECIAL BRICK COMPANY LIMITED—See Heidelberg Materials AG; *Int'l*, pg. 3310

CREATON AG—See Etex SA/NV; *Int'l*, pg. 2521

CREATON & ETERNIT S.R.L.—See Etex SA/NV; *Int'l*, pg. 2521

CRH FENCING LIMITED—See CRH plc; *Int'l*, pg. 1843

CRH KLEIWAREN BEHEER B.V.—See CRH plc; *Int'l*, pg. 1844

CR HOLDINGS CO., LTD.; *Int'l*, pg. 1827

CURRAN GROUP, INC.; *U.S. Private*, pg. 1125

DAIKEN (SHANGHAI) CORPORATION—See Daiken Corporation; *Int'l*, pg. 1931

DALIAN BUILDING MATERIALS COMPANY—See Dalian Shide Group Co., Ltd.; *Int'l*, pg. 1952

DAL-TILE CORPORATION—See Mohawk Industries, Inc.; *U.S. Public*, pg. 1457

DAL-TILE DISTRIBUTION, INC.—See Mohawk Industries, Inc.; *U.S. Public*, pg. 1457

DAL-TILE GROUP, INC—See Mohawk Industries, Inc.; *U.S. Public*, pg. 1457

DAL-TILE MEXICO S.A. DE C.V.—See Mohawk Industries, Inc.; *U.S. Public*, pg. 1457

DAL-TILE SERVICES, INC.—See Mohawk Industries, Inc.; *U.S. Public*, pg. 1457

DEUTSCHE STEINZEUG AMERICA INC.—See Deutsche Steinzeug Cremer & Breuer AG; *Int'l*, pg. 2083

DEUTSCHE STEINZEUG ITALIA S.R.L.—See Deutsche Steinzeug Cremer & Breuer AG; *Int'l*, pg. 2083

DIAMOND BUILDING PRODUCTS PUBLIC COMPANY LIMITED; *Int'l*, pg. 2105

DIC DA LAT INVESTMENT & TRADING JOINT STOCK COMPANY—See DIC Investment and Trading Joint Stock Company; *Int'l*, pg. 2111

DIC DA NANG INVESTMENT & TRADING JOINT STOCK COMPANY—See DIC Investment and Trading Joint Stock Company; *Int'l*, pg. 2111

DONG NAI ROOFSHEET & CONSTRUCTION MATERIAL JOINT STOCK COMPANY; *Int'l*, pg. 2164

DONSKOY FACTORY OF RADIOCOMPONENTS OJSC; *Int'l*, pg. 2172

DU-CO CERAMICS COMPANY; *U.S. Private*, pg. 1282

DUPONT DE NEMOURS KENYA LIMITED—See International Flavors & Fragrances Inc.; *U.S. Public*, pg. 1151

DYNASTY CERAMIC PUBLIC COMPANY LIMITED; *Int'l*, pg. 2242

ECZACIBASI YAPI GERECLERI SANAYI VE TICARET A.S.—See Eczacibasi Holding A.S.; *Int'l*, pg. 2301

EDILIANS SASU—See Groupe Bruxelles Lambert SA; *Int'l*, pg. 3100

EGE SERAMIK IC VE DIS TICARET A.S.—See Ege Seramik Sanayi ve Ticaret A.S.; *Int'l*, pg. 2322

EGE SERAMIK SANAYI VE TICARET A.S.; *Int'l*, pg. 2322

EGYPTIAN FOR DEVELOPING BUILDING MATERIALS; *Int'l*, pg. 2327

ELEGANZA TILES, INC.; *U.S. Private*, pg. 1356

ELENICA AD; *Int'l*, pg. 2359

ELGIN-BUTLER BRICK COMPANY; *U.S. Private*, pg. 1359

ELIANE S/A - REVESTIMENTOS CERAMICOS—See Mohawk Industries, Inc.; *U.S. Public*, pg. 1457

ELPRECO SA—See CRH plc; *Int'l*, pg. 1844

EMPRESA DE REFRACTARIOS COLOMBIANOS S.A.—See Platinum Equity, LLC; *U.S. Private*, pg. 3203

ENDEKA CERAMICS SPA—See American Securities LLC; *U.S. Private*, pg. 251

ENDICOTT CLAY PRODUCTS CO.; *U.S. Private*, pg. 1391

ERICKSON BUILDING COMPONENTS, LLC—See Masco Corporation; *U.S. Public*, pg. 1390

EURO CERAMICS LTD; *Int'l*, pg. 2530

EURO MERCHANDISE (INDIA) LIMITED—See Euro Ceramics Ltd; *Int'l*, pg. 2531

FAYENCERIES DE SARREGUEMINES DIGOIN VITRY-LE-FRANCOIS SA; *Int'l*, pg. 2626

FLEXCO CORPORATION—See Roppe Corporation; *U.S. Private*, pg. 3480

FLORIM CERAMICHE S.P.A.; *Int'l*, pg. 2708

FLORIM USA, INC.—See Florim Ceramiche S.p.A.; *Int'l*, pg. 2708

FRAUENTHAL OST BETEILIGUNGS-GMBH—See Frauenthal Holding AG; *Int'l*, pg. 2767

FREEBORN LUMBER COMPANY—See Bain Capital, LP; *U.S. Private*, pg. 450

FRONTIER CERAMICS LIMITED; *Int'l*, pg. 2795

FSILON HOME BUILDING MATERIALS CO., LTD.; *Int'l*, pg. 2798

FUJAIRAH BUILDING INDUSTRIES COMPANY P.S.C.; *Int'l*, pg. 2808

FUJIAN YUANXIANG NEW MATERIALS CO., LTD.; *Int'l*, pg. 2820

FULTON HOGAN LIMITED - ALLIED ASPHALT PLANT—See Fulton Hogan Limited; *Int'l*, pg. 2843

FULTON HOGAN LIMITED - BAY OF PLENTY PLANT—See Fulton Hogan Limited; *Int'l*, pg. 2843

FULTON HOGAN LIMITED - BURNHAM FACILITY—See Fulton Hogan Limited; *Int'l*, pg. 2843

FULTON HOGAN LIMITED - CANTERBURY BAGGING PLANT—See Fulton Hogan Limited; *Int'l*, pg. 2843

FULTON HOGAN LIMITED - MINERS ROAD ASPHALT PLANT—See Fulton Hogan Limited; *Int'l*, pg. 2843

FULTON HOGAN LIMITED - NELSON BITUMEN PLANT—See Fulton Hogan Limited; *Int'l*, pg. 2843

FULTON HOGAN LIMITED - NORTHLAND PLANT—See Fulton Hogan Limited; *Int'l*, pg. 2843

FULTON HOGAN LIMITED - PAPAKURA FACILITY—See Fulton Hogan Limited; *Int'l*, pg. 2843

FULTON HOGAN LIMITED - RENWICK PLANT—See Fulton Hogan Limited; *Int'l*, pg. 2843

FULTON HOGAN LIMITED - SOUTHLAND PLANT—See Fulton Hogan Limited; *Int'l*, pg. 2843

FULTON HOGAN LIMITED - WARRNAMBOOL PLANT—See Fulton Hogan Limited; *Int'l*, pg. 2843

FULTON HOGAN LIMITED - WELLINGTON PLANT—See Fulton Hogan Limited; *Int'l*, pg. 2843

FURLONG MILLS LIMITED—See Churchill China plc; *Int'l*, pg. 1600

GHANI GLASS LIMITED; *Int'l*, pg. 2958

GKM HOLDINGS JOINT STOCK COMPANY; *Int'l*, pg. 2983

GLASS & SILICE, S.A. DE C.V.—See Crown Holdings, Inc.; *U.S. Public*, pg. 598

GLEN-GERY CORPORATION—See Brickworks Limited; *Int'l*, pg. 1152

GODO CERAMICS LTD.—See Godo Steel, Ltd.; *Int'l*, pg. 3020

GORISKE OPEKARNE D.D.; *Int'l*, pg. 3043

GPD DRINA D.D.; *Int'l*, pg. 3046

GRADEVINAR A.D.; *Int'l*, pg. 3049

GRANDECO WALLFASHION GROUP - BELGIUM NV—See Down2Earth Capital NV; *Int'l*, pg. 2185

GUANGDONG SANHE PILE CO., LTD.; *Int'l*, pg. 3160

HAFARY HOLDINGS LIMITED—See Hap Seng Consolidated Berhad; *Int'l*, pg. 3268

HAMILTON MATERIALS INC.; *U.S. Private*, pg. 1848

HANSON BRICK EAST, LLC—See Heidelberg Materials AG; *Int'l*, pg. 3313

HANSON THERMALITE LIMITED—See Heidelberg Materials AG; *Int'l*, pg. 3313

HARBISON-WALKER REFRACTORIES COMPANY—See Platinum Equity, LLC; *U.S. Private*, pg. 3203

HAZNEDAR REFRAKTER SANAYII A.S.—See Groupe Bruxelles Lambert SA; *Int'l*, pg. 3100

HEATER SPECIALISTS LLC; *U.S. Private*, pg. 1902

HEIDELBERG MATERIALS ALKMAAR BETON B.V.—See Heidelberg Materials AG; *Int'l*, pg. 3314

HEIDELBERG MATERIALS BETONG NORGE AS—See Heidelberg Materials AG; *Int'l*, pg. 3314

HEIDELBERG MATERIALS BETONG SVERIGE AB—See Heidelberg Materials AG; *Int'l*, pg. 3314

HEIDELBERG MATERIALS BETOON AS—See Heidelberg Materials AG; *Int'l*, pg. 3314

HEIDELBERG MATERIALS CEMENT SVERIGE AB—See Heidelberg Materials AG; *Int'l*, pg. 3314

HEIDELBERG MATERIALS DIGITAL HUB VARNA EAD—See Heidelberg Materials AG; *Int'l*, pg. 3314

HEIDELBERG MATERIALS FRANCE S.A.S.—See Heidelberg Materials AG; *Int'l*, pg. 3314

HEIDELBERG MATERIALS- HELWAN CEMENT S.A.E.—See Heidelberg Materials AG; *Int'l*, pg. 3314

HEIDELBERG MATERIALS HISPANIA CEMENTOS, S.A.—See Heidelberg Materials AG; *Int'l*, pg. 3314

HEIDELBERG MATERIALS KAZAKHSTAN LLP—See Heidelberg Materials AG; *Int'l*, pg. 3314

HEIDELBERG MATERIALS LATVIJA SSC SIA—See Heidelberg Materials AG; *Int'l*, pg. 3314

HEIDELBERG MATERIALS LIETUVA CEMENTAS UAB—See Heidelberg Materials AG; *Int'l*, pg. 3314

HEIDELBERG MATERIALS MILJO AS—See Heidelberg Materials AG; *Int'l*, pg. 3314

HEIDELBERG MATERIALS NEDERLAND BETON B.V.—See Heidelberg Materials AG; *Int'l*, pg. 3314

HEIDELBERG MATERIALS PREFAB NORGE AS—See Heidelberg Materials AG; *Int'l*, pg. 3314

HEIDELBERG MATERIALS ROMANIA S.A.—See Heidelberg Materials AG; *Int'l*, pg. 3314

HEIDELBERG MATERIALS- TOURAH CEMENT S.A.E.—See Heidelberg Materials AG; *Int'l*, pg. 3314

HEIDELBERG MATERIALS UK LIMITED—See Heidelberg Materials AG; *Int'l*, pg. 3314

HEPWORTH BUILDING PRODUCTS LIMITED—See Bharti Enterprises Limited; *Int'l*, pg. 1012

H+H KALKSANDSTEIN GMBH—See H+H International A/S; *Int'l*, pg. 3193

HOA CAM CONCRETE JSC; *Int'l*, pg. 3435

H.R. CURRY COMPANY, INC.; *U.S. Private*, pg. 1835

HUARONG CHEMICAL CO., LTD.; *Int'l*, pg. 3514

HUNAN HENGGUANG TECHNOLOGY CO., LTD.; *Int'l*, pg. 3532

HUNG LONG MINERAL & BUILDING MATERIALS JSC; *Int'l*, pg. 3535

HUONG VIET REAL ESTATE INVESTMENT JOINT STOCK COMPANY; *Int'l*, pg. 3537

IBERIA TILE CORP.; *U.S. Private*, pg. 2028

IBIDEN CERAM ENVIRONMENTAL INC.—See Ibiden Co., Ltd.; *Int'l*, pg. 3575

IBIDEN CO., LTD. - OGAKI-KITA PLANT—See Ibiden Co., Ltd.; *Int'l*, pg. 3575

327120 — CLAY BUILDING MATER...

IBIDEN PORZELLANFABRIK FRAUENTHAL GMBH—See Ibiden Co., Ltd.; *Int'l*, pg. 3575
IFS INDUSTRIES, INC.—See CFS Group, Inc.; *Int'l*, pg. 1430
IGM DRINA AD; *Int'l*, pg. 3602
IMERYS CERAMICS FRANCE—See Groupe Bruxelles Lambert SA; *Int'l*, pg. 3100
IMERYS KILN FURNITURE ESPANA, S.A.—See Groupe Bruxelles Lambert SA; *Int'l*, pg. 3100
IMERYS KILN FURNITURE FRANCE—See Groupe Bruxelles Lambert SA; *Int'l*, pg. 3100
IMERYS KILN FURNITURE THAILAND LTD.—See Groupe Bruxelles Lambert SA; *Int'l*, pg. 3100
IMERYS REFRACTORY MINERALS GLOMEL SAS—See Groupe Bruxelles Lambert SA; *Int'l*, pg. 3100
INTERFACE AUST. PTY LIMITED—See Interface, Inc.; *U.S. Public*, pg. 1144
INTERFACE SINGAPORE PTE. LTD.—See Interface, Inc.; *U.S. Public*, pg. 1144
INTERNATIONAL BRICK & TILE PTY LTD—See Brickworks Limited; *Int'l*, pg. 1152
INTERSTATE BRICK COMPANY—See Pacific Coast Building Products, Inc.; *U.S. Private*, pg. 3065
ISOBOUW SYSTEMS BV—See BEWi ASA; *Int'l*, pg. 1004
ISTAV MEDIA, S.R.O.—See Byggfakta Group Nordic HoldCo AB; *Int'l*, pg. 1234
ITALAISE, S.A. DE C.V.—See Grupo Lamosa S.A. de C.V.; *Int'l*, pg. 3132
JASBA MOSAIK GMBH—See Deutsche Steinzeug Cremer & Breuer AG; *Int'l*, pg. 2083
JIANGXI BUILDING MATERIALS COMPANY—See Dalian Shide Group Co., Ltd.; *Int'l*, pg. 1952
JIANGXI SINOMA NEW SOLAR MATERIALS CO., LTD.—See China National Materials; *Int'l*, pg. 1532
JIAXING BUILDING MATERIALS COMPANY—See Dalian Shide Group Co., Ltd.; *Int'l*, pg. 1952
J.L. ANDERSON COMPANY INC.; *U.S. Private*, pg. 2167
JOSEPH DAIJI TAYLOR JR. ENTERPRISES, LLC—See J.F. Lehman & Company, *Int'l*, pg. 2163
KEENE BUILDING PRODUCTS COMPANY, INC.; *U.S. Private*, pg. 2272
KERAMA MARAZZI—See Mohawk Industries, Inc.; *U.S. Public*, pg. 1457
KERAMA MARAZZI UKRAINE OOO—See Mohawk Industries, Inc.; *U.S. Public*, pg. 1457
KIN LONG CONSTRUCTION MATERIALS TRADING L.L.C—See Guangdong Kinlong Hardware Prdcts Co., Ltd.; *Int'l*, pg. 3157
KIN LONG INDUSTRIAL (PHILIPPINES) INC.—See Guangdong Kinlong Hardware Prdcts Co., Ltd., *Int'l*, pg. 3157
KNAUF GES.M.B.H.—See Gebr. Knauf KG; *Int'l*, pg. 2906
KNAUF INSULATION OPERATION GMBH—See Gebr. Knauf KG; *Int'l*, pg. 2907
KNAUF LLC—See Gebr. Knauf KG; *Int'l*, pg. 2907
KNAUF TRANS GMBH—See Gebr. Knauf KG; *Int'l*, pg. 2908
KUMAS MANYEZIT SANAYI A.S.—See Eregli Demir Ve Celik Fabrikalari T.A.S.; *Int'l*, pg. 2490
KUREHA CERAMIC CO., LTD.—See Hokuriku Electric Industry Co., Ltd.; *Int'l*, pg. 3445
LOGAN CLAY PRODUCTS CO.; *U.S. Public*, pg. 1340
LUOHE BUILDING MATERIALS COMPANY—See Dalian Shide Group Co., Ltd.; *Int'l*, pg. 1952
MAGNECO/METREL, INC.; *U.S. Private*, pg. 2547
MALAYSIAN MOSAICS SDN BHD.—See Hap Seng Consolidated Berhad; *Int'l*, pg. 3268
MANUFACTURAS VITROMEX, S.A. DE C.V.—See Grupo Industrial Saltillo S.A. de C.V.; *Int'l*, pg. 3130
MARAZZI GROUP S.R.L.—See Mohawk Industries, Inc.; *U.S. Public*, pg. 1457
MARAZZI IBERIA S.A.—See Mohawk Industries, Inc.; *U.S. Public*, pg. 1457
MARLEY ALUTEC LTD.—See Aliaxis S.A./N.V.; *Int'l*, pg. 325
MARLEY DEUTSCHLAND GMBH—See Aliaxis S.A./N.V.; *Int'l*, pg. 325
MARLEY LTD.—See Etex SA/NV; *Int'l*, pg. 2522
MARLEY MAGYARORSZAG RT—See Aliaxis S.A./N.V.; *Int'l*, pg. 325
MARLEY NEW ZEALAND—See Aliaxis S.A./N.V.; *Int'l*, pg. 325
MARLEY PIPE SYSTEMS PTY LTD—See Aliaxis S.A./N.V.; *Int'l*, pg. 325
MARLEY POLSKA SP. Z.O.O.—See Aliaxis S.A./N.V.; *Int'l*, pg. 325
MASFALT SP. Z O.O.—See CRH plc; *Int'l*, pg. 1845
MASONITE BEAMS AB—See Byggma ASA; *Int'l*, pg. 1235
MAVOTRANS B.V.—See CRH plc; *Int'l*, pg. 1845
MCINTYRE TILE COMPANY INC.—See Elgin-Butler Brick Company; *U.S. Private*, pg. 1359
MEISSEN KERAMIK VERTRIEBS GMBH & CO. KG—See Deutsche Steinzeug Cremer & Breuer AG; *Int'l*, pg. 2083
MERCANTIL DE PISOS Y BANOS, S.A. DE C.V.—See Grupo Lamosa S.A. de C.V.; *Int'l*, pg. 3132
MERCURY MOSAICS & TILE, INC.; *U.S. Private*, pg. 2671
MILLWORK 360 LLC—See Validor Capital LLC; *U.S. Private*, pg. 4332
MINCO, INC.—See 3M Company; *U.S. Public*, pg. 8
MINTEQ AUSTRALIA PTY LTD.—See Minerals Technologies, Inc.; *U.S. Public*, pg. 1449

MINTEQ B.V.—See Minerals Technologies, Inc.; *U.S. Public*, pg. 1449
MINTEQ EUROPE LIMITED.—See Minerals Technologies, Inc.; *U.S. Public*, pg. 1449
MINTEQ INTERNATIONAL GMBH—See Minerals Technologies, Inc.; *U.S. Public*, pg. 1449
MINTEQ ITALIANA S.P.A.—See Minerals Technologies, Inc.; *U.S. Public*, pg. 1449
MINTEQ SHAPES AND SERVICES INC.—See Minerals Technologies, Inc.; *U.S. Public*, pg. 1449
MINTEQ UK LIMITED.—See Minerals Technologies, Inc.; *U.S. Public*, pg. 1449
MML MARKETING PTE. LTD.—See Hap Seng Consolidated Berhad; *Int'l*, pg. 3268
MML (SHANGHAI) TRADING CO., LTD.—See Hap Seng Consolidated Berhad; *Int'l*, pg. 3268
MONARCH CERAMIC TILES—See Mohawk Industries, Inc.; *U.S. Public*, pg. 1457
MOTAWI TILEWORKS, INC.; *U.S. Private*, pg. 2795
MUANGTHONG CERAMIC CO., LTD.—See Dynasty Ceramic Public Company Limited; *Int'l*, pg. 2242
MULLINS BUILDING PRODUCTS, INC.—See Platinum Equity, LLC; *U.S. Private*, pg. 3209
MUTUAL MATERIALS COMPANY; *U.S. Private*, pg. 2820
NEORIS N.V.—See CEMEX, S.A.B. de C.V.; *Int'l*, pg. 1400
NIHONKAI CONCRETE INDUSTRIES CO.—See Hokuriku Electric Power Co.; *Int'l*, pg. 3445
NORRISTOWN BRICK INC.—See Trilantic Capital Management L.P.; *U.S. Private*, pg. 4231
OAKS CONCRETE PRODUCTS INC—See Brampton Brick Limited; *Int'l*, pg. 1139
OCL CHINA LIMITED—See Dalmia Bharat Limited; *Int'l*, pg. 1954
OLDCASTLE APG SOUTH, INC.—See CRH plc; *Int'l*, pg. 1846
OLDCASTLE APG WEST, INC.—See CRH plc; *Int'l*, pg. 1846
ORCON CORPORATION; *U.S. Private*, pg. 3039
PACIFIC CLAY PRODUCTS, INC.—See Murdock Holdings, LLC; *U.S. Private*, pg. 2814
PAVILLION, S.A. DE C.V.—See Grupo Lamosa S.A. de C.V.; *Int'l*, pg. 3132
P.C. HENDERSON (IRELAND) LTD.—See ASSA ABLOY AB; *Int'l*, pg. 635
PEI WORLDWIDE HOLDINGS, INC.; *U.S. Public*, pg. 1661
PERGO GMBH—See Mohawk Industries, Inc.; *U.S. Public*, pg. 1458
PERMATECH, INC.; *U.S. Private*, pg. 3152
PGH BRICKS & PAVERS PTY LIMITED—See CSR Limited; *Int'l*, pg. 1867
P-G INDUSTRIES INC.; *U.S. Private*, pg. 3059
PIEDMONT MINERALS DIVISION—See Balmoral Funds LLC; *U.S. Private*, pg. 461
PINE HALL BRICK CO. INC.; *U.S. Private*, pg. 3182
PLANTA MONTERREY, S.A. DE C.V.—See Grupo Lamosa S.A. de C.V.; *Int'l*, pg. 3132
POMEL (ETABLISSEMENTS)—See Groupe Bruxelles Lambert SA; *Int'l*, pg. 3100
PORCELANITE LAMOSA, S.A. DE C.V.—See Grupo Lamosa S.A. de C.V.; *Int'l*, pg. 3132
PORCELANITE SA DE CV—See Grupo Lamosa S.A. de C.V.; *Int'l*, pg. 3132
PROJECT FROG, INC.; *U.S. Private*, pg. 3280
PRYOR GIGGEY CO., INC.; *U.S. Private*, pg. 3296
PT. CHINA GLAZE INDONESIA—See China Glaze Co., Ltd.; *Int'l*, pg. 1504
P.T. DYSON ZEDMARK INDONESIA LIMITED—See Dyson Group plc; *Int'l*, pg. 2243
P.T. HARBISON-WALKER REFRACTORIES—See Platinum Equity, LLC; *U.S. Private*, pg. 3203
PT. KIN LONG HARDWARE INDONESIA—See Guangdong Kinlong Hardware Prdcts Co., Ltd.; *Int'l*, pg. 3157
PYROTEK INCORPORATED; *U.S. Private*, pg. 3310
PYROTEK LTD.—See Pyrotek Incorporated; *U.S. Private*, pg. 3311
PYROTEK SCANDINAVIA AB—See Pyrotek Incorporated; *U.S. Private*, pg. 3311
QUIGLEY COMPANY, INC.—See Pfizer Inc.; *U.S. Public*, pg. 1683
RAAB KARCHER BOUWSTOFFEN B.V.—See Compagnie de Saint-Gobain SA; *Int'l*, pg. 1733
RAAB KARCHER HAMM—See Compagnie de Saint-Gobain SA; *Int'l*, pg. 1733
RECON ENGINEERING & CONSTRUCTION, INC.; *U.S. Private*, pg. 3371
REDLAND BRICK INC.—See The Belden Brick Company Inc.; *U.S. Public*, pg. 3993
REFRACTORY SALES & SERVICE CO., INCORPORATED—See CFS Group, Inc.; *Int'l*, pg. 1430
RESCO PRODUCTS ENGINEERING DIVISION—See Balmoral Funds LLC; *U.S. Private*, pg. 461
RESCO PRODUCTS INC—See Balmoral Funds LLC; *U.S. Private*, pg. 461
RESCO PRODUCTS, INC.—See Balmoral Funds LLC; *U.S. Private*, pg. 461
RESCO PRODUCTS UK—See Balmoral Funds LLC; *U.S. Private*, pg. 461
REVESTIMIENTOS PORCELANITE LAMOSA, S.A. DE

CORPORATE AFFILIATIONS

C.V.—See Grupo Lamosa S.A. de C.V.; *Int'l*, pg. 3132
RICHARD'S BRICK CO.; *U.S. Private*, pg. 3428
RIVERSIDE REFRACTORIES, INC.; *U.S. Private*, pg. 3446
ROADSTONE LIMITED—See CRH plc; *Int'l*, pg. 1848
ROJAN ADVANCED CERAMICS PTY LTD—See FLSmidth & Co. A/S; *Int'l*, pg. 2711
ROMCIM S.A.—See CRH plc; *Int'l*, pg. 1848
ROMPO PRODUCTS CO. LTD.—See DCON Products Public Company Limited; *Int'l*, pg. 1993
SAINT-GOBAIN ADVANCED CERAMICS (SHANGHAI) CO. LTD—See Compagnie de Saint-Gobain SA; *Int'l*, pg. 1729
SAINT-GOBAIN BYGGEVARER AS—See Compagnie de Saint-Gobain SA; *Int'l*, pg. 1726
SAINT-GOBAIN BYGGPRODUKTER AB—See Compagnie de Saint-Gobain SA; *Int'l*, pg. 1727
SAINT-GOBAIN CERAMICS STRUCTURAL CERAMICS INC—See Compagnie de Saint-Gobain SA; *Int'l*, pg. 1732
SAINT-GOBAIN CONSTRUCTION PRODUCTS CZ A.S.—See Compagnie de Saint-Gobain SA; *Int'l*, pg. 1726
SAINT-GOBAIN ECOPHON BV—See Compagnie de Saint-Gobain SA; *Int'l*, pg. 1733
SAINT-GOBAIN GYPROC SOUTH AFRICA (PTY) LTD—See Compagnie de Saint-Gobain SA; *Int'l*, pg. 1734
SAINT-GOBAIN INDUSTRIAL CERAMICS LTD.—See Compagnie de Saint-Gobain SA; *Int'l*, pg. 1731
SAINT-GOBAIN INDUSTRIAL CERAMICS PTY LTD—See Compagnie de Saint-Gobain SA; *Int'l*, pg. 1728
SAINT-GOBAIN INDUSTRIEKERAMIK ROEDENTAL GMBH—See Compagnie de Saint-Gobain SA; *Int'l*, pg. 1728
SAINT-GOBAIN MATERIAUX CERAMIQUES SA—See Compagnie de Saint-Gobain SA; *Int'l*, pg. 1732
SAINT-GOBAIN PRODUITS POUR LA CONSTRUCTION SAS—See Compagnie de Saint-Gobain SA; *Int'l*, pg. 1728
SAINT-GOBAIN STATYBOS GAMINIAI UAB—See Compagnie de Saint-Gobain SA; *Int'l*, pg. 1727
SAINT-GOBAIN TM K.K.—See Compagnie de Saint-Gobain SA; *Int'l*, pg. 1736
SAINT-GOBAIN WEBER AG—See Compagnie de Saint-Gobain SA; *Int'l*, pg. 1727
SAINT-GOBAIN WEBER A/S—See Compagnie de Saint-Gobain SA; *Int'l*, pg. 1727
SAINT-GOBAIN WEBER BEAMIX B.V.—See Compagnie de Saint-Gobain SA; *Int'l*, pg. 1727
SAINT-GOBAIN WEBER BELGIUM NV/SA—See Compagnie de Saint-Gobain SA; *Int'l*, pg. 1727
SAINT-GOBAIN WEBER FRANCE—See Compagnie de Saint-Gobain SA; *Int'l*, pg. 1727
SAINT-GOBAIN WEBER GMBH—See Compagnie de Saint-Gobain SA; *Int'l*, pg. 1727
SAINT-GOBAIN WEBER LUJIAN BUILDING MATERIALS (SHANGHAI) CO., LTD.—See Compagnie de Saint-Gobain SA; *Int'l*, pg. 1727
SAINT-GOBAIN WEBER OY AB—See Compagnie de Saint-Gobain SA; *Int'l*, pg. 1727
SAINT-GOBAIN WEBER SOUTH AFRICA (PTY) LTD. - CAPE TOWN FACTORY—See Compagnie de Saint-Gobain SA; *Int'l*, pg. 1727
SAINT-GOBAIN WEBER SOUTH AFRICA (PTY) LTD. - KWAZULU NATAL FACTORY—See Compagnie de Saint-Gobain SA; *Int'l*, pg. 1727
SAINT-GOBAIN WEBER SOUTH AFRICA (PTY) LTD. - PORT ELIZABETH FACTORY—See Compagnie de Saint-Gobain SA; *Int'l*, pg. 1727
SAINT-GOBAIN WEBER SOUTH AFRICA (PTY) LTD.—See Compagnie de Saint-Gobain SA; *Int'l*, pg. 1727
SAINT-GOBAIN WEBER YAPI KIMYASALLARI SAN. VE TIC. A.S—See Compagnie de Saint-Gobain SA; *Int'l*, pg. 1727
SAVOIE REFRACTAIRES—See Compagnie de Saint-Gobain SA; *Int'l*, pg. 1732
SCOTASH LIMITED—See CRH plc; *Int'l*, pg. 1848
SCOTASH LIMITED—See Iberdrola, S.A.; *Int'l*, pg. 3573
SEPR INDIA LIMITED—See Compagnie de Saint-Gobain SA; *Int'l*, pg. 1728
SEPR ITALIA S.P.A.—See Compagnie de Saint-Gobain SA; *Int'l*, pg. 1732
SERVICIOS COMERCIALES LAMOSA, S.A. DE C.V.—See Grupo Lamosa S.A. de C.V.; *Int'l*, pg. 3132
S.G. MATERIAUX DE CONSTRUCTION—See Compagnie de Saint-Gobain SA; *Int'l*, pg. 1725
SIOUX CITY BRICK & TILE CO—See Brickworks Limited; *Int'l*, pg. 1152
SKAMOL A/S - CALCIUM SILICATE PLANT—See FSN Capital Partners AS; *Int'l*, pg. 2799
SKAMOL A/S - MOLER BRICK PLANT—See FSN Capital Partners AS; *Int'l*, pg. 2799
SKAMOL A/S—See FSN Capital Partners AS; *Int'l*, pg. 2799
SKAMOL A/S - VERMICULITE PLANT—See FSN Capital Partners AS; *Int'l*, pg. 2800
SMALTI PER CERAMICA S.R.L.—See American Securities LLC; *U.S. Private*, pg. 252
SOCIETE EUROPEENNE DES PRODUITS

N.A.I.C.S. INDEX

REFRACTAIRES—See Compagnie de Saint-Gobain SA; *Int'l*, pg. 1732
SOLTHERM EXTERNAL INSULATIONS LIMITED—See Berger Paints India Limited; *Int'l*, pg. 980
SOUTH CYPRESS; *U.S. Private*, pg. 3721
SOUTHERN SAMPLE COMPANY—See Sampco Inc.; *U.S. Private*, pg. 3537
SUMMITVILLE TILES, INC.; *U.S. Private*, pg. 3857
TANNER MATERIALS COMPANY LLC; *U.S. Private*, pg. 3932
TILE IMPORTS LLC; *U.S. Private*, pg. 4170
TILE TOP INDUSTRY CO., LTD.—See Dynasty Ceramic Public Company Limited; *Int'l*, pg. 2242
TOGAMA S.A.—See Fluidra SA; *Int'l*, pg. 2714
TRIFFID INVESTMENTS PTY LTD.—See Brickworks Limited; *Int'l*, pg. 1152
VANDE HEY RALEIGH ROOF TILE MANUFACTURING, INC.—See Hendricks Holding Company, Inc.; *U.S. Private*, pg. 1915
V&B FLIESEN GMBH—See Eczacibasi Holding A.S.; *Int'l*, pg. 2301
VIET NAM KIN LONG COMPANY LIMITED—See Guangdong Kinlong Hardware Prdcts Co., Ltd.; *Int'l*, pg. 3158
VITROMEX, S.A. DE C.V.—See Grupo Industrial Saltillo S.A. de C.V.; *Int'l*, pg. 3130
V&S NEW YORK GALVANIZING LLC—See Hill & Smith PLC; *Int'l*, pg. 3392
WAHL REFRACTORY SOLUTIONS, LLC; *U.S. Private*, pg. 4426
WESTLAKE CANADA INC.—See Westlake Corporation; *U.S. Public*, pg. 2360
WESTLAKE DAVINCI ROOFSCAPES, LLC—See Westlake Corporation; *U.S. Public*, pg. 2360
WHITACRE GREER COMPANY; *U.S. Private*, pg. 4507
YANKEE HILL BRICK & TILE - OMAHA BRICK YARD—See Murdock Holdings, LLC; *U.S. Private*, pg. 2815
YANKEE HILL BRICK & TILE—See Murdock Holdings, LLC; *U.S. Private*, pg. 2814
YINCHUAN BUILDING MATERIALS COMPANY—See Dalian Shide Group Co., Ltd.; *Int'l*, pg. 1952
YIXING XINWEI LEESHING RARE EARTH COMPANY LIMITED—See China Rare Earth Holdings Limited; *Int'l*, pg. 1544

327211 — FLAT GLASS MANUFACTURING

ABRISA TECHNOLOGIES—See The Graham Group, Inc.; *U.S. Private*, pg. 4036
AGC CHEMICALS AMERICAS, INC.—See AGC Inc.; *Int'l*, pg. 202
AGC CHEMICALS EUROPE, LTD.—See AGC Inc.; *Int'l*, pg. 202
AGC DISPLAY GLASS YONEZAWA CO., LTD.—See AGC Inc.; *Int'l*, pg. 201
AGC FLAT GLASS ASIA PACIFIC PTE. LTD.—See AGC Inc.; *Int'l*, pg. 202
AGC FLAT GLASS EUROPE—See AGC Inc.; *Int'l*, pg. 202
AGC FLAT GLASS ITALIA S.R.L—See AGC Inc.; *Int'l*, pg. 202
AGC FLAT GLASS NEDERLAND B.V.—See AGC Inc.; *Int'l*, pg. 202
AGC FLAT GLASS NORTH AMERICA, INC. - AGC-CALGARY PLANT—See AGC Inc.; *Int'l*, pg. 200
AGC FLAT GLASS NORTH AMERICA, INC. - AGC-EDMONTON PLANT—See AGC Inc.; *Int'l*, pg. 200
AGC FLAT GLASS NORTH AMERICA, INC. - AGC-FALL RIVER PLANT—See AGC Inc.; *Int'l*, pg. 200
AGC FLAT GLASS NORTH AMERICA, INC. - AGC-JACKSONVILLE PLANT—See AGC Inc.; *Int'l*, pg. 200
AGC FLAT GLASS NORTH AMERICA, INC. - AGC-REGINA PLANT—See AGC Inc.; *Int'l*, pg. 201
AGC FLAT GLASS NORTH AMERICA, INC. - BLUE RIDGE PLANT—See AGC Inc.; *Int'l*, pg. 201
AGC FLAT GLASS NORTH AMERICA, INC. - GREENLAND PLANT—See AGC Inc.; *Int'l*, pg. 201
AGC FLAT GLASS NORTH AMERICA, INC. - MARIETTA—See AGC Inc.; *Int'l*, pg. 201
AGC FLAT GLASS NORTH AMERICA, INC. - QUAKERTOWN PLANT—See AGC Inc.; *Int'l*, pg. 201
AGC FLAT GLASS NORTH AMERICA, INC. - RICHMOND PLANT—See AGC Inc.; *Int'l*, pg. 201
AGC FLAT GLASS NORTH AMERICA, INC.—See AGC Inc.; *Int'l*, pg. 200
AGC FLAT GLASS NORTH AMERICA, INC. - SPRING HILL PLANT—See AGC Inc.; *Int'l*, pg. 201
AGC FLAT GLASS (SUZHOU) CO., LTD.—See AGC Inc.; *Int'l*, pg. 202
AGC FLAT GLASS (THAILAND) PUBLIC CO., LTD.—See AGC Inc.; *Int'l*, pg. 202
AGC GLASS EUROPE S.A.—See AGC Inc.; *Int'l*, pg. 202
AGC GLASS PRODUCTS CO., LTD—See AGC Inc.; *Int'l*, pg. 202
AGC MULTI MATERIAL SINGAPORE PTE. LTD.—See AGC Inc.; *Int'l*, pg. 202
AGC MULTI MATERIAL (SUZHOU) INC.—See AGC Inc.; *Int'l*, pg. 202

AGC TECHNOLOGY SOLUTIONS TAIWAN INC.—See AGC Inc.; *Int'l*, pg. 203
ALP'VERRE—See Compagnie de Saint-Gobain SA; *Int'l*, pg. 1722
AL RUSHAID EASTMAN ARABIA LIMITED—See Compagnie de Saint-Gobain SA; *Int'l*, pg. 1730
AMERICAN INSULATED GLASS, LLC—See Trulite Glass & Aluminum Solutions, LLC; *U.S. Private*, pg. 4249
AMERICAN SPECIALTY GLASS, INC.—See Littlejohn & Co., LLC; *U.S. Private*, pg. 2471
ANLIN INDUSTRIES; *U.S. Private*, pg. 284
APOGEE ENTERPRISES, INC.; *U.S. Public*, pg. 145
ARCH OHIO, INC.—See Trulite Glass & Aluminum Solutions, LLC; *U.S. Private*, pg. 4249
ASAHI GLASS CO., LTD. - AICHI PLANT (TAKETOYO)—See AGC Inc.; *Int'l*, pg. 203
ASAHI GLASS CO., LTD. - AICHI PLANT (TOYOTA)—See AGC Inc.; *Int'l*, pg. 203
ASAHI INDIA GLASS LTD.—See AGC Inc.; *Int'l*, pg. 203
ATLANTIQUE MENUISERIES FERMETURES (A.M.F.)—See Compagnie de Saint-Gobain SA; *Int'l*, pg. 1722
AUVERGNE ISOLATION—See Compagnie de Saint-Gobain SA; *Int'l*, pg. 1722
BAVELLONI S.P.A.; *Int'l*, pg. 900
BEIJING CNG SINGYES GREEN BUILDING TECHNOLOGY CO., LTD.—See China Glass Holdings Limited; *Int'l*, pg. 1504
BRIN NORTHWESTERN GLASS COMPANY INC.; *U.S. Private*, pg. 654
BURNBRIDGE GLASS PTY LIMITED—See CSR Limited; *Int'l*, pg. 1867
BYSTRONIC INC.—See Bystronic AG; *Int'l*, pg. 1236
CARLEX GLASS COMPANY, LLC - LIGONIER—See Central Glass Co., Ltd.; *Int'l*, pg. 1406
CENTRAL GLASS CHUBU CO., LTD.—See Central Glass Co., Ltd.; *Int'l*, pg. 1406
CENTRAL GLASS CO., LTD.; *Int'l*, pg. 1406
CENTRAL GLASS GERMANY GMBH—See Central Glass Co., Ltd.; *Int'l*, pg. 1406
CENTRAL GLASS HOKKAIDO CO., LTD.—See Central Glass Co., Ltd.; *Int'l*, pg. 1406
CENTRAL GLASS KYUSHU CO., LTD.—See Central Glass Co., Ltd.; *Int'l*, pg. 1406
CENTRAL GLASS TOHOKU CO., LTD.—See Central Glass Co., Ltd.; *Int'l*, pg. 1406
CENTRAL GLASS TOKYO CO., LTD.—See Central Glass Co., Ltd.; *Int'l*, pg. 1406
CENTRE EST VITRAGE—See Compagnie de Saint-Gobain SA; *Int'l*, pg. 1722
CERAMIDI—See Compagnie de Saint-Gobain SA; *Int'l*, pg. 1722
CHANGZHOU ALMADEN STOCK CO., LTD.; *Int'l*, pg. 1445
COLUMBIA MANUFACTURING CO LTD.; *Int'l*, pg. 1706
COMPANHIA BRASILEIRA DE CRISTAL—See Compagnie de Saint-Gobain SA; *Int'l*, pg. 1723
COMPLETE CRYOGENIC SERVICES, INC.—See ITT Inc.; *U.S. Public*, pg. 1179
CORAGLASS, INC.—See Coral Industries, Inc.; *U.S. Private*, pg. 1046
CORNING CABLE SYSTEMS PTY. LTD.—See Corning Incorporated; *U.S. Public*, pg. 578
COURBU VITRAGES—See Compagnie de Saint-Gobain SA; *Int'l*, pg. 1723
COVIPOR-CIA VIDREIRA DO NORTE LTDA.—See Compagnie de Saint-Gobain SA; *Int'l*, pg. 1734
CRISTALERIA DEL ECUADOR, S.A.—See O-I Glass, Inc.; *U.S. Public*, pg. 1559
CRYSTAL WINDOW & DOOR SYSTEMS; *U.S. Private*, pg. 1116
CSR BUILDING PRODUCTS LTD.—See Crescent Capital Partners Ltd.; *Int'l*, pg. 1839
CTKC CORPORATION—See Compagnie de Saint-Gobain SA; *Int'l*, pg. 1729
CUMBERLAND COUNTY GLASS—See Harvest Partners L.P.; *U.S. Private*, pg. 1877
DATA MODUL FZE—See Arrow Electronics, Inc.; *U.S. Public*, pg. 199
DE CEUNYNCK & CO NV—See EssilorLuxottica SA; *Int'l*, pg. 2512
DECOUPAGE ET MECANIQUE DE L'OUEST—See Compagnie de Saint-Gobain SA; *Int'l*, pg. 1723
DEUTSCHE TERRANOVA INDUSTRIE—See Compagnie de Saint-Gobain SA; *Int'l*, pg. 1723
DISPANO—See Compagnie de Saint-Gobain SA; *Int'l*, pg. 1723
DORMA DOOR SYSTEMS D.O.O.—See dormakaba Holding AG; *Int'l*, pg. 2178
DORMA GULF DOOR CONTROLS FZE—See dormakaba Holding AG; *Int'l*, pg. 2178
DORMA HUPPE AUSTRIA GMBH—See dormakaba Holding AG; *Int'l*, pg. 2178
DORMA HUPPE RAUMTRENNSYSTEME GMBH + CO. KG—See dormakaba Holding AG; *Int'l*, pg. 2178
DORMA INDIA PRIVATE LIMITED—See dormakaba Holding AG; *Int'l*, pg. 2178
DORMA ITALIANA S.R.L.—See dormakaba Holding AG; *Int'l*, pg. 2178

DORMAKABA KAPI VE GUVENLIK SISTEMLERI SANAYI VE TICARET A.S.—See dormakaba Holding AG; *Int'l*, pg. 2178
DORMAKABA MIDDLE EAST LLC—See dormakaba Holding AG; *Int'l*, pg. 2178
DORMAKABA SLOVENSKO S.R.O.—See dormakaba Holding AG; *Int'l*, pg. 2178
DORMA ROMANIA S.R.L.—See dormakaba Holding AG; *Int'l*, pg. 2178
DORMA UKRAINE LLC—See dormakaba Holding AG; *Int'l*, pg. 2178
ECKELT GLAS GMBH—See Compagnie de Saint-Gobain SA; *Int'l*, pg. 1723
EDGETECH (UK) LTD—See Quanex Building Products Corp.; *U.S. Public*, pg. 1749
EFESIS SCHLEIFTECHNIK GMBH—See Compagnie de Saint-Gobain SA; *Int'l*, pg. 1730
EUROFLOAT SAS—See Compagnie de Saint-Gobain SA; *Int'l*, pg. 1736
EUROKERA GUANGZHOU CO., LTD.—See Corning Incorporated; *U.S. Public*, pg. 579
EUROKERA NORTH AMERICA, INC.—See Compagnie de Saint-Gobain SA; *Int'l*, pg. 1730
EUROKERA NORTH AMERICA, INC.—See Corning Incorporated; *U.S. Public*, pg. 579
EXA E&C INC. - KIMPO FACTORY—See EXA E&C Inc.; *Int'l*, pg. 2576
EXPOBOIS—See Compagnie de Saint-Gobain SA; *Int'l*, pg. 1723
FABA AUTOGLAS TECHNIK GMBH—See Compagnie de Saint-Gobain SA; *Int'l*, pg. 1723
FLABEG DEUTSCHLAND GMBH—See CORDET Capital Partners LLP; *Int'l*, pg. 1796
FLABEG TECHNICAL GLASS CORP.—See CORDET Capital Partners LLP; *Int'l*, pg. 1796
FLACHGLAS TORGAU GMBH—See Compagnie de Saint-Gobain SA; *Int'l*, pg. 1723
FUYAO GLASS ILLINOIS, INC.—See Fuyao Glass Industry Group Co., Ltd.; *Int'l*, pg. 2858
GHANI GLASS LIMITED - HATTAR PLANT—See Ghani Glass Limited; *Int'l*, pg. 2958
GHANI GLASS LIMITED - SHEIKHUPURA (FLOAT GLASS PLANT)—See Ghani Glass Limited; *Int'l*, pg. 2958
GLACERIES DE SAINT-ROCH GERMANIA—See Compagnie de Saint-Gobain SA; *Int'l*, pg. 1723
GLACERIES DE SAINT-ROCH SA—See Compagnie de Saint-Gobain SA; *Int'l*, pg. 1723
GLASFABRIEK SAS VAN GENT B.V.—See Compagnie de Saint-Gobain SA; *Int'l*, pg. 1723
GLASHUSET I SVERIGE AB—See Compagnie de Saint-Gobain SA; *Int'l*, pg. 1723
GLASSEC VIDROS DE SEGURANCA LTD.—See Apogee Enterprises, Inc.; *U.S. Public*, pg. 145
GLASSOLUTIONS BV—See Aequita SE & Co. KGaA; *Int'l*, pg. 179
GLASSWERKS LA CO.; *U.S. Private*, pg. 1707
GLAS ZIEGLER GESMBH—See Compagnie de Saint-Gobain SA; *Int'l*, pg. 1723
GLOBAL SECURITY GLAZING LLC—See Grey Mountain Partners, LLC; *U.S. Private*, pg. 1784
GOBBA VITRAGE—See Compagnie de Saint-Gobain SA; *Int'l*, pg. 1723
GOLDEN PHAROS GLASS SDN BHD—See Golden Pharos Berhad; *Int'l*, pg. 3030
G-SMATT EUROPE MEDIA LIMITED—See G-Smatt Global Co., Ltd.; *Int'l*, pg. 2863
GUARDIAN GLASS CO. - CORSICANA PLANT—See Koch Industries, Inc.; *U.S. Private*, pg. 2329
GUARDIAN GLASS CO. - KINGSBURY PLANT—See Koch Industries, Inc.; *U.S. Private*, pg. 2329
GUARDIAN GLASS CO. - MILLBURY PLANT—See Koch Industries, Inc.; *U.S. Private*, pg. 2329
GUARDIAN GLASS COMPANY—See Koch Industries, Inc.; *U.S. Private*, pg. 2329
GUARDIAN INDUSTRIES CORP - RICHBURG PLANT—See Koch Industries, Inc.; *U.S. Private*, pg. 2329
GUARDIAN INDUSTRIES CORP.—See Koch Industries, Inc.; *U.S. Private*, pg. 2329
GUARDIAN INDUSTRIES UK LTD—See Koch Industries, Inc.; *U.S. Private*, pg. 2329
GUARDIAN INDUSTRIES VP, S. DE R.L. DE C.V.—See Koch Industries, Inc.; *U.S. Private*, pg. 2329
GUARDIAN LLODIO UNO, S.L.—See Koch Industries, Inc.; *U.S. Private*, pg. 2329
HANKUK GLASS INDUSTRIES INC.; *Int'l*, pg. 3254
HARTUNG GLASS INDUSTRIES, INC.; *U.S. Private*, pg. 1874
HNG FLOAT GLASS LIMITED—See Hindusthan National Glass & Industries Limited; *Int'l*, pg. 3400
HUBEI SANXIA NEW BUILDING MATERIALS CO., LTD.; *Int'l*, pg. 3518
JAPAN TEMPERED & LAMINATED GLASS CO., LTD.—See Central Glass Co., Ltd.; *Int'l*, pg. 1407
JIANGSU DONGHAI SAINT-GOBAIN CO. LTD.—See Compagnie de Saint-Gobain SA; *Int'l*, pg. 1723
KERAGLASS SNC—See Compagnie de Saint-Gobain SA; *Int'l*, pg. 1724

327211 — FLAT GLASS MANUFACT...

KERAGLASS SNC—See Corning Incorporated; *U.S. Public*, pg. 579
LA BASQUAISE DE CD—See Compagnie de Saint-Gobain SA; *Int'l*, pg. 1724
LAGRANGE PRODUCTION—See Compagnie de Saint-Gobain SA; *Int'l*, pg. 1724
LA SAVOISIENNE DE CD—See Compagnie de Saint-Gobain SA; *Int'l*, pg. 1724
LA VENECIA IBERIAGLASS S.L.—See Compagnie de Saint-Gobain SA; *Int'l*, pg. 1724
LA VENECIANA CENTRO S.A.—See Compagnie de Saint-Gobain SA; *Int'l*, pg. 1724
MABETOC—See Compagnie de Saint-Gobain SA; *Int'l*, pg. 1724
MATSUSAKA PLANT SAKAI MANUFACTURING—See Central Glass Co., Ltd.; *Int'l*, pg. 1407
MEDEX MEDICAL GMBH—See ICU Medical, Inc.; *U.S. Public*, pg. 1087
M.F.G. EUROPE S.R.L.—See Cevital S.p.A.; *Int'l*, pg. 1425
MFG SPA—See Cevital S.p.A.; *Int'l*, pg. 1425
MFG TUNISIA—See Cevital S.p.A.; *Int'l*, pg. 1425
MIDWEST GLASS FABRICATORS, INC.—See KPS Capital Partners, LP; *U.S. Private*, pg. 2348
MIROITERIE DU RHIN—See Compagnie de Saint-Gobain SA; *Int'l*, pg. 1724
MIROITERIES DE L'OUEST ATLANTIQUE—See Compagnie de Saint-Gobain SA; *Int'l*, pg. 1724
MODENFIX ITALIA SRL—See Compagnie de Saint-Gobain SA; *Int'l*, pg. 1724
MODERNFOLD OF NEVADA, LLC—See dormakaba Holding AG; *Int'l*, pg. 2179
MOVETRO S.R.L.—See Biesse S.p.A.; *Int'l*, pg. 1020
MR. SHOWER DOOR INC.; *U.S. Private*, pg. 2805
NATEC—See Compagnie de Saint-Gobain SA; *Int'l*, pg. 1724
NORTHWESTERN INDUSTRIES-ARIZONA, INC.—See GlassWerks LA Co.; *U.S. Private*, pg. 1707
OWENS CORNING MEXICO S. DE RL DE C.V.—See Owens Corning; *U.S. Public*, pg. 1628
PARTICIPATIONS DES ARDENNES—See Compagnie de Saint-Gobain SA; *Int'l*, pg. 1724
PENSACOLA GLASS COMPANY—See Dothan Glass Co. Inc.; *U.S. Private*, pg. 1265
PITTSBURGH CORNING EUROPE, N.V.—See Owens Corning; *U.S. Public*, pg. 1628
PPG CANADA INC.—See PPG Industries, Inc.; *U.S. Public*, pg. 1708
PRO-GLASS LTD—See Bronsstadet AB; *Int'l*, pg. 1174
QUANEX SCREENS LLC—See Quanex Building Products Corp.; *U.S. Public*, pg. 1749
QUINCAILLERIE LORRAINE—See Compagnie de Saint-Gobain SA; *Int'l*, pg. 1725
ROYAL COPENHAGEN FLAGSHIP STORE—See Fiskars Oyj Abp; *Int'l*, pg. 2694
SAE ASTI—See Compagnie de Saint-Gobain SA; *Int'l*, pg. 1727
SAGE ELECTROCHROMICS, INC.—See Compagnie de Saint-Gobain SA; *Int'l*, pg. 1730
SAINT-GOBAIN ASSESSORIA E ADMINISTRACAO LTDA.—See Compagnie de Saint-Gobain SA; *Int'l*, pg. 1727
SAINT GOBAIN AUTOVER FRANCE S.A.S.—See Compagnie de Saint-Gobain SA; *Int'l*, pg. 1729
SAINT-GOBAIN AUTOVER FRANCE—See Compagnie de Saint-Gobain SA; *Int'l*, pg. 1729
SAINT-GOBAIN CERAMICAS INDUSTRIALES S.A.—See Compagnie de Saint-Gobain SA; *Int'l*, pg. 1731
SAINT-GOBAIN CONDOTTE S.P.A.—See Compagnie de Saint-Gobain SA; *Int'l*, pg. 1729
SAINT-GOBAIN DE COLOMBIA SA—See Compagnie de Saint-Gobain SA; *Int'l*, pg. 1727
SAINT-GOBAIN DEVELOPPEMENT MAROC—See Compagnie de Saint-Gobain SA; *Int'l*, pg. 1727
SAINT-GOBAIN DEVISA S.A.—See Compagnie de Saint-Gobain SA; *Int'l*, pg. 1727
SAINT-GOBAIN GLASS BENELUX SA—See Compagnie de Saint-Gobain SA; *Int'l*, pg. 1733
SAINT-GOBAIN GLASS EXPROVER NORTH AMERICA CORP.—See Compagnie de Saint-Gobain SA; *Int'l*, pg. 1730
SAINT-GOBAIN GLASS INDIA LTD.—See Compagnie de Saint-Gobain SA; *Int'l*, pg. 1734
SAINT-GOBAIN GLASS ITALIA LOGISTICA SERVIZI S.R.L.—See Compagnie de Saint-Gobain SA; *Int'l*, pg. 1734
SAINT-GOBAIN GLASS MEXICO, S.A. DE C.V—See Compagnie de Saint-Gobain SA; *Int'l*, pg. 1734
SAINT-GOBAIN GLASS NORDIC A/S—See Compagnie de Saint-Gobain SA; *Int'l*, pg. 1734
SAINT-GOBAIN GLASSOLUTIONS NITRASKLO, S.R.O.—See Compagnie de Saint-Gobain SA; *Int'l*, pg. 1728
SAINT GOBAIN GLASS OPERADORA S.A. DE C.V.—See Compagnie de Saint-Gobain SA; *Int'l*, pg. 1727
SAINT-GOBAIN GLASS POLSKA—See Compagnie de Saint-Gobain SA; *Int'l*, pg. 1734
SAINT-GOBAIN GLASS PORTUGAL VIDRO PLANO SA—See Compagnie de Saint-Gobain SA; *Int'l*, pg. 1734
SAINT-GOBAIN GLASS SOLUTION BURNIAT—See Compagnie de Saint-Gobain SA; *Int'l*, pg. 1734
SAINT-GOBAIN GLASS SOLUTION FRANKENGLAS NV—See Compagnie de Saint-Gobain SA; *Int'l*, pg. 1734
SAINT-GOBAIN GLASS SOLUTION GLORIOUS NV—See Compagnie de Saint-Gobain SA; *Int'l*, pg. 1734
SAINT-GOBAIN GLASS SOLUTION MIROVER NV—See Compagnie de Saint-Gobain SA; *Int'l*, pg. 1734
SAINT-GOBAIN GLASS SOLUTIONS MENUISIERS INDUSTRIEL—See Compagnie de Saint-Gobain SA; *Int'l*, pg. 1728
SAINT-GOBAIN GLASS SOLUTIONS PARIS NORMANDIE—See Compagnie de Saint-Gobain SA; *Int'l*, pg. 1728
SAINT-GOBAIN GLASSSOLUTIONS—See Compagnie de Saint-Gobain SA; *Int'l*, pg. 1734
SAINT-GOBAIN GLASS SOLUTIONS SUD-OUEST—See Compagnie de Saint-Gobain SA; *Int'l*, pg. 1728
SAINT-GOBAIN GLASS SOLUTION WAGENER-JOWACO EUPEN—See Compagnie de Saint-Gobain SA; *Int'l*, pg. 1734
SAINT-GOBAIN ISOVER ARGENTINA S.A.—See Compagnie de Saint-Gobain SA; *Int'l*, pg. 1726
SAINT-GOBAIN ISOVER ESPANA—See Compagnie de Saint-Gobain SA; *Int'l*, pg. 1734
SAINT-GOBAIN MONDEGO S.A.—See Compagnie de Saint-Gobain SA; *Int'l*, pg. 1734
SAINT-GOBAIN NEDERLAND BEHEER BV—See Compagnie de Saint-Gobain SA; *Int'l*, pg. 1734
SAINT-GOBAIN PAM UK—See Compagnie de Saint-Gobain SA; *Int'l*, pg. 1735
SAINT GOBAIN PERU SA—See Compagnie de Saint-Gobain SA; *Int'l*, pg. 1727
SAINT-GOBAIN PRODUITS INDUSTRIELS—See Compagnie de Saint-Gobain SA; *Int'l*, pg. 1735
SAINT-GOBAIN PROPPANTS (GUANGHAN) CO., LTD.—See Compagnie de Saint-Gobain SA; *Int'l*, pg. 1735
SAINT-GOBAIN RAKENNUSTUOTTEET OY—See Compagnie de Saint-Gobain SA; *Int'l*, pg. 1726
SAINT-GOBAIN SEKURIT BENELUX S.A.—See Compagnie de Saint-Gobain SA; *Int'l*, pg. 1736
SAINT-GOBAIN SEKURIT DEUTSCHLAND BETEILIGUNGEN GMBH—See Compagnie de Saint-Gobain SA; *Int'l*, pg. 1736
SAINT-GOBAIN SEKURIT FRANCE—See Compagnie de Saint-Gobain SA; *Int'l*, pg. 1736
SAINT-GOBAIN SEKURIT MAROC—See Compagnie de Saint-Gobain SA; *Int'l*, pg. 1736
SAINT-GOBAIN SEKURIT MEXICO, S.A. DE C.V.—See Compagnie de Saint-Gobain SA; *Int'l*, pg. 1736
SAINT-GOBAIN SEKURIT USA—See Compagnie de Saint-Gobain SA; *Int'l*, pg. 1732
SAINT-GOBAIN SERVICES AUSTRIA GMBH—See Compagnie de Saint-Gobain SA; *Int'l*, pg. 1728
SAINT-GOBAIN VETROTEX (THAILAND) LTD.—See Compagnie de Saint-Gobain SA; *Int'l*, pg. 1736
SAINT-GOBAIN VICASA SA—See Compagnie de Saint-Gobain SA; *Int'l*, pg. 1736
SAINT-GOBAIN VIDROS S.A.—See Compagnie de Saint-Gobain SA; *Int'l*, pg. 1736
SAINT-GOBAIN VITRAGE—See Compagnie de Saint-Gobain SA; *Int'l*, pg. 1736
SAINT-GOBAIN WEBER STAHEL-KELLER AG—See Compagnie de Saint-Gobain SA; *Int'l*, pg. 1727
SANITAIRE COMTOIS—See Compagnie de Saint-Gobain SA; *Int'l*, pg. 1736
SCANDI-GLASS A/S—See Compagnie de Saint-Gobain SA; *Int'l*, pg. 1736
SCHOTT GEMTRON CORPORATION—See AGC Inc.; *Int'l*, pg. 201
SCHOTT GEMTRON CORPORATION—See Carl-Zeiss-Stiftung; *Int'l*, pg. 1337
SCHOTT IBERICA, S.A. COMMERCIAL DIVISION—See Carl-Zeiss-Stiftung; *Int'l*, pg. 1337
SCHOTT NORTH AMERICA INC—See Carl-Zeiss-Stiftung; *Int'l*, pg. 1337
SEKURIT SAINT-GOBAIN DEUTSCHLAND GMBH & CO. KG—See Compagnie de Saint-Gobain SA; *Int'l*, pg. 1736
SEKURIT SAINT-GOBAIN ITALIA S.R.L.—See Compagnie de Saint-Gobain SA; *Int'l*, pg. 1736
SEKURIT SAINT-GOBAIN SCANDINAVIA AB—See Compagnie de Saint-Gobain SA; *Int'l*, pg. 1737
SEKURIT SAINT-GOBAIN TORGAU GMBH—See Compagnie de Saint-Gobain SA; *Int'l*, pg. 1737
SELECT GLASS INDUSTRIES LLC—See Al Hamad Contracting Company LLC; *Int'l*, pg. 278
SERVILOG—See Compagnie de Saint-Gobain SA; *Int'l*, pg. 1737
S.G. AUTOVER ITALIA S.R.L.—See Compagnie de Saint-Gobain SA; *Int'l*, pg. 1737
SGGS BELGIUM SA—See Compagnie de Saint-Gobain SA; *Int'l*, pg. 1728
SGGS GLASINDUSTRIE BOERMANS—See Compagnie de Saint-Gobain SA; *Int'l*, pg. 1728
SHANGHAI FLAT GLASS CO., LTD.—See Flat Glass Group Co., Ltd.; *Int'l*, pg. 2698
SOCIETE ATLANTIQUE DE PREFABRICATION—See Compagnie de Saint-Gobain SA; *Int'l*, pg. 1737
SOCIETE VERRIERE D'ENCAPSULATION—See Compagnie de Saint-Gobain SA; *Int'l*, pg. 1737
SOLAR INDUSTRIES INC.; *U.S. Private*, pg. 3707
SOLAR INNOVATIONS, INC.; *U.S. Private*, pg. 3707
SOTAWALL LIMITED—See Apogee Enterprises, Inc.; *U.S. Public*, pg. 145
SOVEDYS—See Compagnie de Saint-Gobain SA; *Int'l*, pg. 1737
SUPER SKY PRODUCTS ENTERPRISES, LLC—See Trulite Glass & Aluminum Solutions, LLC; *U.S. Private*, pg. 4249
SUQIAN CNG ELECTRONIC GLASS COMPANY LIMITED—See China Glass Holdings Limited; *Int'l*, pg. 1504
TBF MALAISIE—See Compagnie de Saint-Gobain SA; *Int'l*, pg. 1737
TECHNICAL GLASS PRODUCTS, INC.—See Allegion Public Limited Company; *Int'l*, pg. 335
THALETEC GMBH—See HLE Glascoat Limited; *Int'l*, pg. 3431
TRULITE GLASS & ALUMINUM SOLUTIONS, LLC - ATLANTA—See Trulite Glass & Aluminum Solutions, LLC; *U.S. Private*, pg. 4249
TRULITE GLASS & ALUMINUM SOLUTIONS, LLC - GRENADA—See Trulite Glass & Aluminum Solutions, LLC; *U.S. Private*, pg. 4249
TRULITE GLASS & ALUMINUM SOLUTIONS, LLC - NEW BERLIN—See Trulite Glass & Aluminum Solutions, LLC; *U.S. Private*, pg. 4250
TUBELITE INC.—See Apogee Enterprises, Inc.; *U.S. Public*, pg. 145
UNICORN PRECIDIA SA—See Compagnie de Saint-Gobain SA; *Int'l*, pg. 1737
VAL GLASS US LLC—See Dover Corporation; *U.S. Public*, pg. 683
VANGUARD PROPERTIES CO.; *U.S. Private*, pg. 4344
VERRERIE AURYS—See Compagnie de Saint-Gobain SA; *Int'l*, pg. 1737
VERRERIE DE SAINT-JUST—See Compagnie de Saint-Gobain SA; *Int'l*, pg. 1737
VETROTECH SAINT-GOBAIN ATLANTIQUE SARL—See Compagnie de Saint-Gobain SA; *Int'l*, pg. 1737
VETROTECH SAINT-GOBAIN NORTH AMERICA INC.—See Compagnie de Saint-Gobain SA; *Int'l*, pg. 1732
VETROTECH SAINT-GOBAIN UK LTD—See Compagnie de Saint-Gobain SA; *Int'l*, pg. 1737
VETROTEX ITALIA S.P.A.—See Compagnie de Saint-Gobain SA; *Int'l*, pg. 1737
VIRACON GEORGIA, INC.—See Apogee Enterprises, Inc.; *U.S. Public*, pg. 145
VIRGINIA GLASS PRODUCTS CORPORATION—See Virginia Mirror Company Incorporated; *U.S. Private*, pg. 4388
VIRIDIAN—See Crescent Capital Partners Ltd.; *Int'l*, pg. 1839
VITRULAN HOLDING GMBH—See ADCURAM Group AG; *Int'l*, pg. 128
W.A. WILSON & SONS, INC.; *U.S. Private*, pg. 4419
W C P, INC.—See AGNORA Ltd; *Int'l*, pg. 212
ZHEJIANG FLAT GLASS CO., LTD.—See Flat Glass Group Co., Ltd.; *Int'l*, pg. 2698
ZHEJIANG JIAFU GLASS CO., LTD.—See Flat Glass Group Co., Ltd.; *Int'l*, pg. 2698

327212 — OTHER PRESSED AND BLOWN GLASS AND GLASSWARE MANUFACTURING

AFORA S.A.U.—See Thermo Fisher Scientific Inc.; *U.S. Public*, pg. 2145
AJIYA SAFETY GLASS SDN. BHD.—See Ajiya Berhad; *Int'l*, pg. 258
ALEMBIC GLASS INDUSTRIES LTD.—See Alembic Limited; *Int'l*, pg. 306
ANCHOR HOCKING, CANADA, INC.—See EveryWare Global, Inc.; *U.S. Private*, pg. 1441
ANCHOR HOCKING, LLC—See EveryWare Global, Inc.; *U.S. Private*, pg. 1441
AQUA ART CO., LTD.—See Fuyo General Lease Co., Ltd.; *Int'l*, pg. 2859
ARCH PROMO GROUP LLC; *U.S. Private*, pg. 310
ARISAWA FIBER GLASS CO., LTD.—See Arisawa Manufacturing Co., Ltd.; *Int'l*, pg. 565
AUSTRALIAN FIBRE GLASS PTY LIMITED—See Fletcher Building Limited; *Int'l*, pg. 2699
AVIC (HAINAN) SPECIAL GLASS MATERIAL CO., LTD.—See Hainan Development Holdings Nanhai Co., Ltd.; *Int'l*, pg. 3211
AVIC SANXIN SOLAR GLASS CO., LTD.—See Hainan Development Holdings Nanhai Co., Ltd.; *Int'l*, pg. 3211
BARTLETT-COLLINS CO., INC.—See EveryWare Global, Inc.; *U.S. Private*, pg. 1441
BERLI JUCKER PUBLIC CO, LTD.; *Int'l*, pg. 985
BLENKO GLASS COMPANY INC.; *U.S. Private*, pg. 580
BMAC LIMITED—See Methode Electronics, Inc.; *U.S. Public*, pg. 1428

N.A.I.C.S. INDEX

327213 — GLASS CONTAINER MAN...

BORMIOLI ROCCO GLASS CO. INC.—See Banco BPM S.p.A.; *Int'l*, pg. 819
BOROSIL RENEWABLES LIMITED; *Int'l*, pg. 1114
CARLEY LAMPS INC.; *U.S. Private*, pg. 763
CENTRAL GLASS FIBER CO., LTD.—See Central Glass Co., Ltd.; *Int'l*, pg. 1406
CENTRAL GLASS SALES CO., LTD.—See Central Glass Co., Ltd.; *Int'l*, pg. 1406
CHIHULY INC.; *U.S. Private*, pg. 881
CHINA COMPOSITES GROUP CORPORATION LTD.—See China National Building Material Group Co., Ltd.; *Int'l*, pg. 1525
CHINA GLAZE CO., LTD.; *Int'l*, pg. 1504
CHINA JUSHI CO., LTD.; *Int'l*, pg. 1513
CORELLE BRANDS MANUFACTURING (M) SDN. BHD.—See Cornell Capital Management LLC; *U.S. Private*, pg. 1051
CORNING GMBH—See Corning Incorporated; *U.S. Public*, pg. 578
CORNING INCORPORATED; *U.S. Public*, pg. 578
CORNING INDIA—See Corning Incorporated; *U.S. Public*, pg. 578
CORNING PHARMACEUTICAL GLASS S.P.A.—See Corning Incorporated; *U.S. Public*, pg. 578
CORNING PRECISION MATERIALS COMPANY LTD.—See Corning Incorporated; *U.S. Public*, pg. 578
CRISAL - CRISTALARIA AUTOMATICA, S.A.—See Libbey, Inc.; *U.S. Private*, pg. 2442
CRISA LIBBEY MEXICO S. DE R.L. DE C.V.—See Libbey, Inc.; *U.S. Private*, pg. 2442
CRISTALLERIA ARTISTICA LA PIANA S.P.A.; *Int'l*, pg. 1850
CRISTIRO S.A.; *Int'l*, pg. 1850
CTG INTERNATIONAL INC.—See China National Materials; *Int'l*, pg. 1532
CUSTOM DECO, LLC—See The Boelter Companies Inc.; *U.S. Private*, pg. 3995
DARBY GLASS LTD.—See Bronsstadet AB; *Int'l*, pg. 1174
DOW CORNING AUSTRALIA PTY LTD—See Dow Inc.; *U.S. Public*, pg. 684
DUCATT NV; *Int'l*, pg. 2223
ENVIRATRENDS, INC.; *U.S. Private*, pg. 1406
EXEL GMBH—See Exel Composites Oyj; *Int'l*, pg. 2581
THE FENTON ART GLASS COMPANY; *U.S. Private*, pg. 4028
FORMICA S.A.S—See HAL Trust N.V.; *Int'l*, pg. 3223
FULLTECH FIBER GLASS CORP.; *Int'l*, pg. 2843
GED INTEGRATED SOLUTIONS, INC.—See The Beekman Group, LLC; *U.S. Private*, pg. 3993
GEROM SA; *Int'l*, pg. 2943
GERRESHEIMER GLASS INC. - CHICAGO HEIGHTS PLANT—See Gerresheimer AG; *Int'l*, pg. 2943
GERRESHEIMER GLASS INC. - MILLVILLE PLANT—See Gerresheimer AG; *Int'l*, pg. 2943
GERRESHEIMER GLASS INC. - MORGANTON PLANT—See Gerresheimer AG; *Int'l*, pg. 2943
GERRESHEIMER SHUANGFENG PHARMACEUTICAL GLASS (DANYANG) CO. LTD. - NEW PLANT—See Gerresheimer AG; *Int'l*, pg. 2944
GERRESHEIMER SHUANGFENG PHARMACEUTICAL GLASS (DANYANG) CO. LTD.—See Gerresheimer AG; *Int'l*, pg. 2944
THE GLASS BARON INC.; *U.S. Private*, pg. 4033
THE GLASSHOUSE L.L.C—See GIBCA Limited; *Int'l*, pg. 2963
G-TECH OPTOELECTRONICS CORPORATION; *Int'l*, pg. 2863
GUANGDONG AVIC SPECIAL GLASS TECHNOLOGY CO., LTD.—See Hainan Development Holdings Nanhai Co., Ltd.; *Int'l*, pg. 3211
GUARDIAN INDUSTRIES CORP. LTD.—See Koch Industries, Inc.; *U.S. Private*, pg. 2329
GULF GLASS FIBER TECHNOLOGICAL INDUSTRIES COMPANY; *Int'l*, pg. 3180
GXC COATINGS GMBH; *Int'l*, pg. 3190
HAINAN DEVELOPMENT HOLDINGS NANHAI CO., LTD.; *Int'l*, pg. 3211
HENAN ANCAI HI-TECH CO., LTD.; *Int'l*, pg. 3342
HUTA SZKLA GOSPODARCZEGO IRENA S.A.; *Int'l*, pg. 3540
IDI COMPOSITES INTERNATIONAL EUROPE (FR) SAS—See Industrial Dielectrics Holdings, Inc.; *U.S. Private*, pg. 2065
INDUSTRIAL DIELECTRICS, INC.—See Industrial Dielectrics Holdings, Inc.; *U.S. Private*, pg. 2065
JOHNS MANVILLE SLOVAKIA, A.S.—See Berkshire Hathaway Inc.; *U.S. Public*, pg. 308
JUSHI CANADA CO., LTD.—See China National Building Material Group Co., Ltd.; *Int'l*, pg. 1525
JUSHI GROUP CO., LTD.—See China National Building Material Group Co., Ltd.; *Int'l*, pg. 1525
JUSHI GROUP JIUJIANG CO., LTD.—See China Jushi Co., Ltd.; *Int'l*, pg. 1514
JUSHI SINGAPORE PTE. LTD.—See China National Building Material Group Co., Ltd.; *Int'l*, pg. 1526
KIMBLE BOMEX (BEIJING) GLASS CO. LTD.—See Gerresheimer AG; *Int'l*, pg. 2944

LE VITRAGE DU MIDI—See Compagnie de Saint-Gobain SA; *Int'l*, pg. 1736
LIBBEY EUROPE B.V.—See Libbey, Inc.; *U.S. Private*, pg. 2442
LIULIGONGFANG HONG KONG CO., LTD.—See Coretronic Corporation; *Int'l*, pg. 1800
LIULIGONGFANG SHANGHAI CO., LTD—See Coretronic Corporation; *Int'l*, pg. 1800
LIULI GONG FANG (U.S.A), INC.—See Coretronic Corporation; *Int'l*, pg. 1800
LOOS & COMPANY, INC.; *U.S. Private*, pg. 2494
MIE GLASS INDUSTRY CO., LTD.—See Central Glass Co., Ltd.; *Int'l*, pg. 1407
MILES FIBERGLASS & COMPOSITES, INC.; *U.S. Private*, pg. 2727
NBI, INC.; *U.S. Private*, pg. 2875
OWENS CORNING KOREA—See Owens Corning; *U.S. Public*, pg. 1628
PITTSBURGH CORNING, LLC—See Owens Corning; *U.S. Public*, pg. 1628
PYROTEK INC.—See Pyrotek Incorporated; *U.S. Private*, pg. 3311
RADIANT COMMUNICATIONS CORP.; *U.S. Private*, pg. 3343
RESEARCH FRONTIERS INCORPORATED; *U.S. Public*, pg. 1789
SAINT-GOBAIN CENTRAL SEKURIT (QINGDAO) CO., LTD.—See Central Glass Co., Ltd.; *Int'l*, pg. 1407
SAINT-GOBAIN CERAMIC MATERIALS (ZHENGZHOU) CO., LTD.—See Compagnie de Saint-Gobain SA; *Int'l*, pg. 1729
SAINT-GOBAIN CERAMICS & PLASTICS PLC—See Compagnie de Saint-Gobain SA; *Int'l*, pg. 1729
SAINT-GOBAIN CERAMICS SC—See Compagnie de Saint-Gobain SA; *Int'l*, pg. 1732
SAINT-GOBAIN DESJONQUERES—See Compagnie de Saint-Gobain SA; *Int'l*, pg. 1733
SAINT-GOBAIN EMBALLAGE—See Compagnie de Saint-Gobain SA; *Int'l*, pg. 1733
SCHERF-PRAZISION EUROPA GMBH—See Gerresheimer AG; *Int'l*, pg. 2944
SCHOTT AG—See Carl-Zeiss-Stiftung; *Int'l*, pg. 1336
SHANGHAI CORNING ENGINEERING CORPORATION—See Corning Incorporated; *U.S. Public*, pg. 579
SHOWA KDE CO., LTD.—See The Carlyle Group Inc.; *U.S. Public*, pg. 2048
SHRENO LTD—See Alembic Limited; *Int'l*, pg. 306
SIMON PEARCE US INC.; *U.S. Private*, pg. 3666
SMOKE CARTEL, INC.—See High Tide, Inc.; *Int'l*, pg. 3386
SOCIETE VERRIERE DE L'ATLANTIQUE—See Compagnie de Saint-Gobain SA; *Int'l*, pg. 1737
SOUND SEAL, INC.; *U.S. Private*, pg. 3717
TAISHAN FIBERGLASS ZOUCHENG CO., LTD.—See China National Materials; *Int'l*, pg. 1532
TAIWAN CENTRAL GLASS CO., LTD.—See Central Glass Co., Ltd.; *Int'l*, pg. 1407
THERMO FISHER SCIENTIFIC—See Thermo Fisher Scientific Inc.; *U.S. Public*, pg. 2153
TOSHO CENTRAL CO., LTD.—See Central Glass Co., Ltd.; *Int'l*, pg. 1407
TRANSLEC LIMITED—See Methode Electronics, Inc.; *U.S. Public*, pg. 1429
TRIMLITE LLC—See Wynnchurch Capital, L.P.; *U.S. Private*, pg. 4578
VIRIDOR GLASS RECYCLING LIMITED—See KKR & Co. Inc.; *U.S. Public*, pg. 1266
VLC PHOTONICS SOCIEDAD LIMITADA—See Hitachi, Ltd.; *Int'l*, pg. 3424
X-CEL OPTICAL CO.; *U.S. Private*, pg. 4579
YUE SHENG INDUSTRIAL CO., LTD.—See Central Glass Co., Ltd.; *Int'l*, pg. 1407

327213 — GLASS CONTAINER MANUFACTURING

ACI GUANGDONG GLASS COMPANY LTD.—See O-I Glass, Inc.; *U.S. Public*, pg. 1559
ACI OPERATIONS NZ LIMITED—See O-I Glass, Inc.; *U.S. Public*, pg. 1559
ACI TIANJIN MOULD COMPANY LIMITED—See O-I Glass, Inc.; *U.S. Public*, pg. 1559
ADVANCED PACKAGING TECHNOLOGY (M) BHD; *Int'l*, pg. 161
ADVANCED PHARMACEUTICAL PACKAGING CO.; *Int'l*, pg. 161
AHLSTROM GLASSFIBRE OY - MIKKELI PLANT—See ADCURAM Group AG; *Int'l*, pg. 128
ALL AMERICAN CONTAINERS, LLC—See Clayton, Dubilier & Rice, LLC; *U.S. Private*, pg. 928
ANCHOR GLASS CONTAINER CORPORATION—See BA Glass B.V.; *Int'l*, pg. 791
ANCHOR GLASS CONTAINER CORPORATION—See CVC Capital Partners SICAV-FIS S.A.; *Int'l*, pg. 1884
ANHUI DELI HOUSEHOLD GLASS CO., LTD.; *Int'l*, pg. 467
ARDAGH GLASS INC. - BRIDGETON—See Ardagh Group S.A.; *Int'l*, pg. 553

ARDAGH GLASS INC. - DUNKIRK—See Ardagh Group S.A.; *Int'l*, pg. 553
ARDAGH GLASS INC. - MADERA—See Ardagh Group S.A.; *Int'l*, pg. 553
ARDAGH GLASS INC.—See Ardagh Group S.A.; *Int'l*, pg. 553
ARDAGH GLASS LIMITED—See Ardagh Group S.A.; *Int'l*, pg. 553
ARDAGH METAL PACKAGING S.A.; *Int'l*, pg. 553
ARDAGH PACKAGING GROUP LIMITED—See Ardagh Group S.A.; *Int'l*, pg. 553
ARKANSAS GLASS CONTAINER CORP.; *U.S. Private*, pg. 326
A/S JARVAKANDI KLAAS—See O-I Glass, Inc.; *U.S. Public*, pg. 1560
AYUTTHAYA GLASS INDUSTRY CO., LTD.—See BG Container Glass Public Company Limited; *Int'l*, pg. 1006
BA GLASS BULGARIA S.A.—See BA Glass B.V.; *Int'l*, pg. 791
BA GLASS GERMANY GMBH—See BA Glass B.V.; *Int'l*, pg. 791
BA GLASS GREECE , S.A.—See BA Glass B.V.; *Int'l*, pg. 791
BA GLASS I - SERVICOS DE GESTAO E INVESTIMENTOS, S.A.—See BA Glass B.V.; *Int'l*, pg. 791
BA GLASS POLAND SP.Z.O.O.—See BA Glass B.V.; *Int'l*, pg. 791
BA GLASS PORTUGAL S.A.—See BA Glass B.V.; *Int'l*, pg. 791
BGC GLASS SOLUTION CO., LTD.—See BG Container Glass Public Company Limited; *Int'l*, pg. 1006
BGC PACKAGING CO., LTD.—See BG Container Glass Public Company Limited; *Int'l*, pg. 1006
BIG C FAIRY LIMITED—See Berli Jucker Public Co. Ltd.; *Int'l*, pg. 985
BJC INTERNATIONAL CO., LTD.—See Berli Jucker Public Co. Ltd.; *Int'l*, pg. 985
BJC INTERNATIONAL HOLDING PTE. LTD.—See Berli Jucker Public Co. Ltd.; *Int'l*, pg. 985
BSN GASSPACK FRANCE—See O-I Glass, Inc.; *U.S. Public*, pg. 1559
BSN GLASSPACK SPAIN—See O-I Glass, Inc.; *U.S. Public*, pg. 1559
CARIB GLASSWORKS LIMITED—See ANSA McAL Limited; *Int'l*, pg. 477
CATTORINI HNOS. S.A.; *Int'l*, pg. 1361
CCL CONTAINER MEXICO—See CCL Industries Inc.; *Int'l*, pg. 1367
CENTRAL GLASS INDUSTRIES LTD—See Diageo plc; *Int'l*, pg. 2102
CERTAINTEED CORPORATION FOUNDATION—See Compagnie de Saint-Gobain SA; *Int'l*, pg. 1729
CERTAINTEED CORPORATION—See Compagnie de Saint-Gobain SA; *Int'l*, pg. 1729
CERTAINTEED CORPORATION TECHNICAL CENTER—See Compagnie de Saint-Gobain SA; *Int'l*, pg. 1729
CERTAINTEED FOREIGN SALES CORP.—See Compagnie de Saint-Gobain SA; *Int'l*, pg. 1729
CHONGQING STORSACK JIANFENG—See Greif Inc.; *U.S. Public*, pg. 967
CHONGQING ZHENGCHUAN YONGCHENG PHARMACEUTICAL MATERIAL CO., LTD.—See Chongqing Zhengchuan Pharmaceutical Packaging Co., Ltd.; *Int'l*, pg. 1582
CONSUMERS SKLO ZORYA—See Compagnie de Saint-Gobain SA; *Int'l*, pg. 1723
CRISTALERIAS DE CHILE S.A.; *Int'l*, pg. 1850
CROWN UK HOLDINGS LTD—See Crown Holdings, Inc.; *U.S. Public*, pg. 598
C SMART SOLUTION COMPANY LIMITED—See Berli Jucker Public Co. Ltd.; *Int'l*, pg. 985
DEMPTOS GLASS COMPANY—See Atlas Holdings, LLC; *U.S. Private*, pg. 378
DONG WHA G&P CORPORATION—See DONG WHA PHARM CO., LTD.; *Int'l*, pg. 2164
DWK LIFE SCIENCES GMBH—See OEP Capital Advisors, L.P.; *U.S. Private*, pg. 2999
EMHART GLASS MANUFACTURING INC.—See Bucher Industries AG; *Int'l*, pg. 1208
EMHART GLASS SDN BHD—See Bucher Industries AG; *Int'l*, pg. 1208
EMMABODA GLAS AB—See Compagnie de Saint-Gobain SA; *Int'l*, pg. 1734
FERGUSON CONTAINERS, INC.—See Vinco Ventures, Inc.; *U.S. Public*, pg. 2298
FUJI GLASS CO., LTD.; *Int'l*, pg. 2813
GEBR. WILLACH GMBH; *Int'l*, pg. 2909
GERRESHEIMER AG; *Int'l*, pg. 2943
GERRESHEIMER GLAS GMBH—See Gerresheimer AG; *Int'l*, pg. 2943
GERRESHEIMER LOHR GMBH—See Gerresheimer AG; *Int'l*, pg. 2943
GERRESHEIMER MOMIGNIES S.A.—See Gerresheimer AG; *Int'l*, pg. 2943
GERRESHEIMER MOULDED GLASS GMBH.—See Gerresheimer AG; *Int'l*, pg. 2943
GERRESHEIMER PHARMACEUTICAL PACKAGING MUM-

327213 — GLASS CONTAINER MAN...

BAI PRIVATE LTD.—See Gerresheimer, AG; *Int'l*, pg. 2944
GERRESHEIMER REGENSBURG GMBH—See Gerresheimer AG; *Int'l*, pg. 2944
GERRESHEIMER TETTAU GMBH—See Gerresheimer AG; *Int'l*, pg. 2944
GERRESHEIMER WERTHEIM GMBH—See Gerresheimer AG; *Int'l*, pg. 2944
GERRESHEIMER WILDEN CZECH SPOL. S R.O.—See Gerresheimer AG; *Int'l*, pg. 2944
GERRESHEIMER ZARAGOZA S.A.—See Gerresheimer AG; *Int'l*, pg. 2944
GLASS EQUIPMENT (INDIA) LTD—See Hindusthan National Glass & Industries Limited; *Int'l*, pg. 3400
GREIF - CHILE—See Greif Inc.; *U.S. Public*, pg. 967
GREIF FLEXIBLES BELGIUM N.V.—See Greif Inc.; *U.S. Public*, pg. 967
GREIF FLEXIBLES FINLAND OY—See Greif Inc.; *U.S. Public*, pg. 967
GREIF PORTUGAL LTDA.—See Greif Inc.; *U.S. Public*, pg. 968
HALDYN GLASS LTD.; *Int'l*, pg. 3228
H&A PRESTIGE BOTTLING LTD.—See Halewood International Ltd.; *Int'l*, pg. 3229
HINDUSTHAN NATIONAL GLASS & INDUSTRIES LIMITED; *Int'l*, pg. 3400
HINDUSTHAN NATIONAL GLASS & INDUSTRIES LTD. - BAHADURGARH PLANT—See Hindusthan National Glass & Industries Limited; *Int'l*, pg. 3400
HINDUSTHAN NATIONAL GLASS & INDUSTRIES LTD. - RISHIKESH PLANT—See Hindusthan National Glass & Industries Limited; *Int'l*, pg. 3400
HINDUSTHAN NATIONAL GLASS & INDUSTRIES LTD. - RISHRA PLANT—See Hindusthan National Glass & Industries Limited; *Int'l*, pg. 3400
HUHTAMAKI CESKA REPUBLIKA A/S—See Huhtamaki Oyj; *Int'l*, pg. 3524
HUHTAMAKI EGYPT—See Huhtamaki Oyj; *Int'l*, pg. 3524
HUHTAMAKI ISTANBUL AMBALAJ SANAYI A.S.—See Huhtamaki Oyj; *Int'l*, pg. 3525
HUHTAMAKI LA ROCHELLE SNC—See Huhtamaki Oyj; *Int'l*, pg. 3525
HUHTAMAKI LTD.—See Huhtamaki Oyj; *Int'l*, pg. 3525
HUHTAMAKI (LURGAN) LIMITED—See Huhtamaki Oyj; *Int'l*, pg. 3525
HUHTAMAKI NEDERLAND B.V.—See Huhtamaki Oyj; *Int'l*, pg. 3525
HUHTAMAKI PAPER RECYCLING B.V.—See Huhtamaki Oyj; *Int'l*, pg. 3525
HUHTAMAKI PROTECTIVE PACKAGING B.V.—See Huhtamaki Oyj; *Int'l*, pg. 3525
HUHTAMAKI SOUTH AFRICA (PTY) LTD.—See Huhtamaki Oyj; *Int'l*, pg. 3525
HUHTAMAKI SPAIN S.L.—See Huhtamaki Oyj; *Int'l*, pg. 3526
HUHTAMAKI SVENSKA AB—See Huhtamaki Oyj; *Int'l*, pg. 3526
HUHTAMAKI (TIANJIN) LTD.—See Huhtamaki Oyj; *Int'l*, pg. 3524
INDUSTRIA VIDRIERA DE COAHUILA, S. DE R.L. DE C.V.—See Constellation Brands, Inc.; *U.S. Public*, pg. 571
KARAT PACKAGING INC.; *U.S. Public*, pg. 1214
KARHULAN LASI OY—See O-I Glass, Inc.; *U.S. Public*, pg. 1560
KIMBLE CHASE LIFE SCIENCE & RESEARCH PRODUCTS LLC - ROCHESTER PLANT—See OEP Capital Advisors, L.P.; *U.S. Private*, pg. 2999
KUSH SUPPLY CO. LLC—See Greenlane Holdings, Inc.; *U.S. Public*, pg. 965
LIFEFACTORY, INC.—See Thermos L.L.C.; *U.S. Private*, pg. 4143
LONGHORN GLASS INC.—See Anheuser-Busch InBev SA/NV; *Int'l*, pg. 465
MULOX DE MEXICO C. V.—See Greif Inc.; *U.S. Public*, pg. 967
O-I ASIA PACIFIC—See O-I Glass, Inc.; *U.S. Public*, pg. 1559
O-I CHINA—See O-I Glass, Inc.; *U.S. Public*, pg. 1559
O-I CZECH REPUBLIC A.S.—See O-I Glass, Inc.; *U.S. Public*, pg. 1559
OI FINNISH HOLDINGS OY—See O-I Glass, Inc.; *U.S. Public*, pg. 1560
O-I FRANCE SAS—See O-I Glass, Inc.; *U.S. Public*, pg. 1559
O-I GERMANY GMBH & CO. KG—See O-I Glass, Inc.; *U.S. Public*, pg. 1559
O-I GLASS, INC.; *U.S. Public*, pg. 1559
O-I GLASS LIMITED—See O-I Glass, Inc.; *U.S. Public*, pg. 1559
O-I GLASS LIMITED—See O-I Glass, Inc.; *U.S. Public*, pg. 1560
O-I GLASSPACK BETEILIGUNGS & VERWALTUNGSGESELLSCHAFT GMBH—See O-I Glass, Inc.; *U.S. Public*, pg. 1559
O-I MANUFACTURING CZECH REPUBLIC A.S.—See O-I Glass, Inc.; *U.S. Public*, pg. 1559
O-I MANUFACTURING ITALY S.P.A.—See O-I Glass, Inc.; *U.S. Public*, pg. 1559
O-I MANUFACTURING LTD.—See O-I Glass, Inc.; *U.S. Public*, pg. 1560
O-I NETHERLANDS B.V.—See O-I Glass, Inc.; *U.S. Public*, pg. 1559
O-I NETHERLANDS B.V.—See O-I Glass, Inc.; *U.S. Public*, pg. 1560
O-I PACKAGING SOLUTIONS, LLC—See O-I Glass, Inc.; *U.S. Public*, pg. 1560
O-I SALES AND DISTRIBUTION LT—See O-I Glass, Inc.; *U.S. Public*, pg. 1560
OWENS-ILLINOIS GROUP, INC.—See O-I Glass, Inc.; *U.S. Public*, pg. 1559
OWENS-ILLINOIS PERU S.A.—See O-I Glass, Inc.; *U.S. Public*, pg. 1560
OWENS-ILLINOIS POLSKA S.A.—See O-I Glass, Inc.; *U.S. Public*, pg. 1560
PACIFIC CONTAINERBAG CO. LTD.—See Greif Inc.; *U.S. Public*, pg. 967
PATHUMTHANI GLASS INDUSTRY CO., LTD.—See BG Container Glass Public Company Limited; *Int'l*, pg. 1006
PLASTICS NEW ZEALAND—See O-I Glass, Inc.; *U.S. Public*, pg. 1559
PRACHINBURI GLASS INDUSTRY CO., LTD.—See BG Container Glass Public Company Limited; *Int'l*, pg. 1007
PT KANGAR CONSOLIDATED INDUSTRIES—See O-I Glass, Inc.; *U.S. Public*, pg. 1560
RAK GHANI GLASS LLC—See Ghani Glass Limited; *Int'l*, pg. 2958
RATCHABURI GLASS INDUSTRY CO., LTD.—See BG Container Glass Public Company Limited; *Int'l*, pg. 1007
RAYEN CURA, S.A.I.C.—See Compagnie de Saint-Gobain SA; *Int'l*, pg. 1725
SAGA DECOR S.A.S.—See Compagnie de Saint-Gobain SA; *Int'l*, pg. 1733
SAINT-GOBAIN DESJONQUERES MANUFACTURING, INC—See Compagnie de Saint-Gobain SA; *Int'l*, pg. 1732
SAINT-GOBAIN ENVASES SA—See Compagnie de Saint-Gobain SA; *Int'l*, pg. 1733
SAINT-GOBAIN OBERLAND AG—See Compagnie de Saint-Gobain SA; *Int'l*, pg. 1735
SAINT-GOBAIN VETRERIE SPA—See Compagnie de Saint-Gobain SA; *Int'l*, pg. 1736
SAN DOMENICO VETRARIA S.R.L.—See O-I Glass, Inc.; *U.S. Public*, pg. 1560
SAXCO INTERNATIONAL, LLC—See Atlas Holdings, LLC; *U.S. Private*, pg. 378
SGD KIPFENBERG GMBH—See China Investment Corporation; *Int'l*, pg. 1513
SGD S.A.—See China Investment Corporation; *Int'l*, pg. 1513
SOMA WATER, INC.—See Full Circle Home LLC; *U.S. Private*, pg. 1620
SOOSEOK CO., LTD.—See Dong-A Socio Holdings Co., Ltd.; *Int'l*, pg. 2165
SPECIALTY BOTTLE LLC; *U.S. Private*, pg. 3749
SP INDUSTRIES INC.—See Harbour Group Industries, Inc.; *U.S. Private*, pg. 1861
STOELZLE GLASS LLC—See CAG Holding GmbH; *Int'l*, pg. 1250
STOELZLE MASNIERES SAS—See CAG Holding GmbH; *Int'l*, pg. 1250
STORSACK PVT LTD.—See Greif Inc.; *U.S. Public*, pg. 967
STORSACK SHENZEN CO., LTD.—See Greif Inc.; *U.S. Public*, pg. 967
STORSACK VIETNAM LTD.—See Greif Inc.; *U.S. Public*, pg. 967
STRATHMANN GMBH & CO. KG—See Dermapharm Holding SE; *Int'l*, pg. 2043
THAI MALAYA GLASS CO., LTD.—See Berli Jucker Public Co. Ltd.; *Int'l*, pg. 985
VERALLIA ARGENTINA—See Apollo Global Management, Inc.; *U.S. Public*, pg. 167
VERALLIA CHILE—See Apollo Global Management, Inc.; *U.S. Public*, pg. 167
VERALLIA FRANCE—See Apollo Global Management, Inc.; *U.S. Public*, pg. 167
VERDOME EXPLOITATION SA—See O-I Glass, Inc.; *U.S. Public*, pg. 1559
VETRERIE MERIDIONALI S.P.A.—See O-I Glass, Inc.; *U.S. Public*, pg. 1560
VIDRIERIA ROVIRA, S.A.—See O-I Glass, Inc.; *U.S. Public*, pg. 1560
VINTNERS GLOBAL RESOURCE LLC; *U.S. Private*, pg. 4386
VMC—See Danone; *Int'l*, pg. 1968
VOA VERRERIE D'ALBI SA—See Compagnie de Saint-Gobain SA; *Int'l*, pg. 1733
WUHAN OWENS GLASS CONTAINER COMPANY LIMITED—See O-I Glass, Inc.; *U.S. Public*, pg. 1559
ZAO "SAINT-GOBAIN KAVMINSTEKLO"—See Compagnie de Saint-Gobain SA; *Int'l*, pg. 1737

327215 — GLASS PRODUCT MANUFACTURING MADE OF PURCHASED GLASS

ACE GLASS INCORPORATED; *U.S. Private*, pg. 56
AGC ADVANCED BUSINESS EXPERTS (THAILAND) LTD.—See AGC Inc.; *Int'l*, pg. 200
AGC ADVANCED ELECTRONICS DISPLAY GLASS (SHENZHEN) CO., LTD.—See AGC Inc.; *Int'l*, pg. 203
AGC ASIA PACIFIC (VIETNAM) CO., LTD.—See AGC Inc.; *Int'l*, pg. 201
AGC AUTOMOTIVE AMERICAS CO.—See AGC Inc.; *Int'l*, pg. 200
AGC AUTOMOTIVE AMERICAS R&D, INC.—See AGC Inc.; *Int'l*, pg. 200
AGC AUTOMOTIVE CANADA, INC.—See AGC Inc.; *Int'l*, pg. 201
AGC AUTOMOTIVE EUROPE S.A—See AGC Inc.; *Int'l*, pg. 201
AGC AUTOMOTIVE GLASS MEXICO S.A. DE C.V.—See AGC Inc.; *Int'l*, pg. 203
AGC AUTOMOTIVE ITALY S.R.L—See AGC Inc.; *Int'l*, pg. 202
AGC AUTOMOTIVE MEXICO S.DE R.L. DE C.V—See AGC Inc.; *Int'l*, pg. 203
AGC AUTOMOTIVE (QINHUANGDAO) INC.—See AGC Inc.; *Int'l*, pg. 201
AGC AUTOMOTIVE—See AGC Inc.; *Int'l*, pg. 200
AGC AUTOMOTIVE (SUZHOU) INC.—See AGC Inc.; *Int'l*, pg. 203
AGC AUTOMOTIVE U.K. LTD.—See AGC Inc.; *Int'l*, pg. 202
AGC AUTOMOTIVE WINDOW SYSTEMS CO., LTD.—See AGC Inc.; *Int'l*, pg. 201
AGC BOR GLASSWORKS OOO—See AGC Inc.; *Int'l*, pg. 203
AGC DISPLAY GLASS (CHONGQING) INC.—See AGC Inc.; *Int'l*, pg. 203
AGC DISPLAY GLASS (HUIZHOU) CO., LTD.—See AGC Inc.; *Int'l*, pg. 203
AGC DISPLAY GLASS (KUNSHAN) INC.—See AGC Inc.; *Int'l*, pg. 203
AGC DISPLAY GLASS OCHANG CO., LTD.—See AGC Inc.; *Int'l*, pg. 203
AGC DISPLAY GLASS (SHENZHEN) INC.—See AGC Inc.; *Int'l*, pg. 203
AGC DISPLAY GLASS TAIWAN INC.—See AGC Inc.; *Int'l*, pg. 203
AGC EUROPE S.A.—See AGC Inc.; *Int'l*, pg. 201
AGC FINE TECHNO KOREA CO., LTD.—See AGC Inc.; *Int'l*, pg. 202
AGC FLAT GLASS CZECH A.S.—See AGC Inc.; *Int'l*, pg. 202
AGC FLAT GLASS NORTH AMERICA, INC. - ABINGDON PLANT—See AGC Inc.; *Int'l*, pg. 201
AGC FLAT GLASS NORTH AMERICA, INC. - AGC-ALVARADO PLANT—See AGC Inc.; *Int'l*, pg. 200
AGC FLAT GLASS NORTH AMERICA, INC. - AGC-BATON ROUGE PLANT—See AGC Inc.; *Int'l*, pg. 200
AGC FLAT GLASS NORTH AMERICA, INC. - AGC-CARBONDALE PLANT—See AGC Inc.; *Int'l*, pg. 200
AGC FLAT GLASS NORTH AMERICA, INC. - AGC-HOUSTON PLANT—See AGC Inc.; *Int'l*, pg. 200
AGC FLAT GLASS NORTH AMERICA, INC. - AGC-KNOXVILLE PLANT—See AGC Inc.; *Int'l*, pg. 200
AGC FLAT GLASS NORTH AMERICA, INC. - AGC-OPELOUSAS PLANT—See AGC Inc.; *Int'l*, pg. 200
AGC FLAT GLASS NORTH AMERICA, INC. - AGC-RICHMOND PLANT—See AGC Inc.; *Int'l*, pg. 201
AGC FLAT GLASS NORTH AMERICA, INC. - AGC-SALT LAKE CITY PLANT—See AGC Inc.; *Int'l*, pg. 201
AGC FLAT GLASS NORTH AMERICA, INC. - AGC-SAN ANTONIO PLANT—See AGC Inc.; *Int'l*, pg. 201
AGC FLAT GLASS NORTH AMERICA, INC. - AGC-WINNIPEG PLANT—See AGC Inc.; *Int'l*, pg. 201
AGC FLAT GLASS NORTH AMERICA, INC. - BOARDMAN PLANT—See AGC Inc.; *Int'l*, pg. 201
AGC FLAT GLASS NORTH AMERICA, INC. - CARBONDALE—See AGC Inc.; *Int'l*, pg. 201
AGC FLAT GLASS PROTECH (SHENZHEN) CO., LTD.—See AGC Inc.; *Int'l*, pg. 202
AGC FRANCE S.A.—See AGC Inc.; *Int'l*, pg. 203
AGC GLASS FRANCE S.A.—See AGC Inc.; *Int'l*, pg. 202
AGC GLASS UK LTD.—See AGC Inc.; *Int'l*, pg. 203
AGC MICRO GLASS CO., LTD.—See AGC Inc.; *Int'l*, pg. 202
AGC MICRO GLASS (THAILAND) CO., LTD—See AGC Inc.; *Int'l*, pg. 202
AGC MIDDLE EAST & AFRICA FZCO—See AGC Inc.; *Int'l*, pg. 203
AGC PRECISION GLASS (SHENZHEN) INC.—See AGC Inc.; *Int'l*, pg. 203
AGC TECHNO GLASS CO., LTD.—See AGC Inc.; *Int'l*, pg. 203
AGC TECHNO GLASS CORPORATION—See AGC Inc.; *Int'l*, pg. 203
AGC TECHNO GLASS (THAILAND) CO., LTD.—See AGC Inc.; *Int'l*, pg. 203
AGC VIDROS DO BRASIL LTDA.—See AGC Inc.; *Int'l*, pg. 203
AHLSTROM-MUNKSJO GLASSFIBRE OY—See Ahlstrom Capital Oy; *Int'l*, pg. 224
AHLSTROM-MUNKSJO GLASSFIBRE OY—See Bain Capital, LP; *U.S. Private*, pg. 429

N.A.I.C.S. INDEX

327215 — GLASS PRODUCT MANUF...

AHLSTROM-MUNKSJO TVER LLC—See Ahlstrom Capital Oy; *Int'l*, pg. 224
AHLSTROM-MUNKSJO TVER LLC—See Bain Capital, LP; *U.S. Private*, pg. 429
AIMCORE TECHNOLOGY CO., LTD.; *Int'l*, pg. 232
ALDORA ALUMINUM & GLASS PRODUCTS, INC.; *U.S. Private*, pg. 160
ALLERGAN INDIA LIMITED—See AbbVie Inc.; *U.S. Public*, pg. 23
AMPAC ENTERPRISES INC.; *U.S. Private*, pg. 264
ANH VIET MECHANICAL & ALUMINUM GLASS CORPORATION—See Hoa Binh Construction Group JSC; *Int'l*, pg. 3435
ANTHONY, INC.; *U.S. Private*, pg. 288
ANTHONY INTERNATIONAL, INC.—See Avista Capital Partners, L.P.; *U.S. Public*, pg. 408
ANTHONY REFRESH GROUP, LLC—See Dover Corporation; *U.S. Public*, pg. 678
ANTHONY TECHNICAL GLASS (SHANGHAI) CO. LTD—See Dover Corporation; *U.S. Public*, pg. 678
ASAHI GLASS CO., LTD. - KANSAI PLANT—See AGC Inc.; *Int'l*, pg. 203
ASAHI GLASS CO., LTD. - KASHIMA PLANT—See AGC Inc.; *Int'l*, pg. 203
ASAHI GLASS CO., LTD. - KEIHIN PLANT—See AGC Inc.; *Int'l*, pg. 203
ASAHI GLASS CO., LTD. - KITAKYUSHU PLANT—See AGC Inc.; *Int'l*, pg. 203
ASAHI GLASS CO., LTD. - SAGAMI PLANT—See AGC Inc.; *Int'l*, pg. 203
ASAHI GLASS CO., LTD. - TAKASAGO PLANT—See AGC Inc.; *Int'l*, pg. 203
ASAHI GLASS FINE TECHNO KOREA CO., LTD.—See Asahi Kasei Corporation; *Int'l*, pg. 594
ASAHI INDIA GLASS, LTD. - AIS (AUTO) HARYANA WORKS.—See AGC Inc.; *Int'l*, pg. 204
ASAHI INDIA GLASS, LTD. - AIS (FLOAT) WORKS—See AGC Inc.; *Int'l*, pg. 204
ASAHI PD GLASS KOREA CO., LTD.—See AGC Inc.; *Int'l*, pg. 204
ASLAN CEMENT A.S.; *Int'l*, pg. 625
ASTRO-TEC MANUFACTURING, INC.; *U.S. Private*, pg. 362
AUTO TEMP, INC.; *U.S. Private*, pg. 397
AVALON GLASS & MIRROR COMPANY; *U.S. Private*, pg. 403
BALOCHISTAN GLASS LIMITED; *Int'l*, pg. 810
BASCO MANUFACTURING COMPANY; *U.S. Private*, pg. 484
BEIJING SANCHONG MIRRORS CO., LTD—See BBMG Corporation; *Int'l*, pg. 921
BELLETECH CORP.—See AGC Inc.; *Int'l*, pg. 201
BELLETECH CORP.—See PPG Industries, Inc.; *U.S. Public*, pg. 1707
BEL SHOWER DOOR CORP.—See Baymark Partners; *U.S. Private*, pg. 496
BICRON PRODUCTS PPL—See Compagnie de Saint-Gobain SA; *Int'l*, pg. 1730
BOHLE AG; *Int'l*, pg. 1100
BYSTRONIC GLASS UK LTD.—See Bystronic AG; *Int'l*, pg. 1236
CALUMITE LIMITED—See Heidelberg Materials AG; *Int'l*, pg. 3309
CAPILLARY SOLUTIONS GMBH—See Geratherm Medical AG; *Int'l*, pg. 2942
CAPTIVISION INC.; *Int'l*, pg. 1317
CARLEX GLASS COMPANY, LLC—See Central Glass Co., Ltd.; *Int'l*, pg. 1406
CARLEX GLASS LUXEMBOURG, S.A.—See Central Glass Co., Ltd.; *Int'l*, pg. 1406
CARL ZEISS S.P.A.—See Carl-Zeiss-Stiftung; *Int'l*, pg. 1335
CARL ZEISS SPOL. S.R.O.—See Carl-Zeiss-Stiftung; *Int'l*, pg. 1336
CENTRAL GLASS WOOL CO., LTD.—See Central Glass Co., Ltd.; *Int'l*, pg. 1407
CENTRAL INSULATION CO., LTD.—See Central Glass Co., Ltd.; *Int'l*, pg. 1407
CENTURY BATHWORKS, INC.; *U.S. Private*, pg. 832
CERTAINTEED INSULATION—See Compagnie de Saint-Gobain SA; *Int'l*, pg. 1730
CHINA GLASS HOLDINGS LIMITED; *Int'l*, pg. 1504
CHINA YUTIAN HOLDINGS LIMITED; *Int'l*, pg. 1566
CHONGQING ZHENGCHUAN PHARMACEUTICAL PACKAGING CO., LTD.; *Int'l*, pg. 1581
CHRISTMAS BY KREBS CORPORATION; *U.S. Private*, pg. 891
CHROMOGENICS AB; *Int'l*, pg. 1588
CLAYTON GLASS LTD.; *Int'l*, pg. 1653
CLEER VISION TEMPERED GLASS, LLC—See Thor Industries, Inc.; *U.S. Public*, pg. 2156
CORAL INDUSTRIES, INC.; *U.S. Private*, pg. 1046
CORNING CHINA (SHANGHAI) REGIONAL HEADQUARTER—See Corning Incorporated; *U.S. Public*, pg. 578
CORNING DISPLAY TECHNOLOGIES (CHINA) CO., LTD.—See Corning Incorporated; *U.S. Public*, pg. 578
CORNING OPTICAL COMMUNICATIONS S. DE R.L. DE C.V.—See Corning Incorporated; *U.S. Public*, pg. 578

CORNING PHARMACEUTICAL GLASS, LLC—See Corning Incorporated; *U.S. Public*, pg. 578
CROWN ELECTROKINETICS CORP.; *U.S. Public*, pg. 596
CRYSTAL—See Ligand Pharmaceuticals Incorporated; *U.S. Public*, pg. 1314
CUSTOM GLASS & DOORS, INC.—See Installed Building Products, Inc.; *U.S. Public*, pg. 1132
DELBAR PRODUCTS INCORPORATED; *U.S. Private*, pg. 1196
DENIZLI CAM SANAYII VE TICARET A.S.; *Int'l*, pg. 2027
DESIGN SPECIALTIES, INC.—See Blackthorne Partners Ltd.; *U.S. Private*, pg. 577
DIEN QUANG LAMP JSC; *Int'l*, pg. 2115
DILWORTH MANUFACTURING COMPANY; *U.S. Private*, pg. 1232
DLUBAK SPECIALTY GLASS CORPORATION—See Grey Mountain Partners, LLC; *U.S. Private*, pg. 1784
DOCTER OPTICS SE—See Hella GmbH & Co. KGaA; *Int'l*, pg. 3331
DONGTAI CHINA GLASS SPECIAL GLASS COMPANY LIMITED—See China Glass Holdings Limited; *Int'l*, pg. 1504
ECO GLASS PRODUCTION, LLC—See Koch Industries, Inc.; *U.S. Private*, pg. 2332
EMHART GLASS INC—See Bucher Industries AG; *Int'l*, pg. 1208
EMIRATES FLOAT GLASS LLC—See Dubai Investments PJSC; *Int'l*, pg. 2219
EMIRATES GLASS LLC—See Dubai Investments PJSC; *Int'l*, pg. 2219
ENGINEERED GLASS PRODUCTS LLC; *U.S. Private*, pg. 1398
ERIE-WATALA GLASS COMPANY LIMITED—See Thermo Fisher Scientific Inc.; *U.S. Public*, pg. 2146
EUROKERA S.N.C.—See Corning Incorporated; *U.S. Public*, pg. 579
EYE CARE EXPRESS LAB INC.—See EssilorLuxottica SA; *Int'l*, pg. 2513
FGP LTD.; *Int'l*, pg. 2649
FIBERGLASS COLOMBIA S.A.—See Compagnie de Saint-Gobain SA; *Int'l*, pg. 1723
FINNMIRROR OY; *Int'l*, pg. 2676
FISKARS OYJ ABP - IITTALA GLASS FACTORY—See Fiskars Oyj Abp; *Int'l*, pg. 2694
FISKARS OYJ ABP - NUUTAJARVI GLASS FACTORY—See Fiskars Oyj Abp; *Int'l*, pg. 2694
FISKARS (THAILAND) CO., LIMITED—See Fiskars Oyj Abp; *Int'l*, pg. 2693
FORMGLAS PRODUCTS LTD.; *Int'l*, pg. 2734
FREUDENBERGER AUTOGLAS GMBH—See Compagnie de Saint-Gobain SA; *Int'l*, pg. 1736
FUYAO EUROPE GMBH—See Fuyao Glass Industry Group Co., Ltd.; *Int'l*, pg. 2858
FUYAO GLASS AMERICA INC.—See Fuyao Glass Industry Group Co., Ltd.; *Int'l*, pg. 2858
FUYAO NORTH AMERICA INCORPORATED—See Fuyao Glass Industry Group Co., Ltd.; *Int'l*, pg. 2858
GARDNER GLASS PRODUCTS INC.; *U.S. Private*, pg. 1643
GAUZY LTD.—See Hamilton Global Opportunities Plc; *Int'l*, pg. 3238
GEMTECH OPTOELECTRONICS CORP.—See Cheng Loong Corp.; *Int'l*, pg. 1466
GENTEX HOLDINGS, INC.—See Gentex Corporation; *U.S. Public*, pg. 931
GERRESHEIMER CHALON S.A.—See Gerresheimer AG; *Int'l*, pg. 2943
GERRESHEIMER GLASS INC.—See Gerresheimer AG; *Int'l*, pg. 2943
GERRESHEIMER VAERLOESE A/S—See Gerresheimer AG; *Int'l*, pg. 2944
GHANI GLOBAL GLASS LIMITED—See Ghani Global Holdings Limited; *Int'l*, pg. 2958
GHANI VALUE GLASS LIMITED; *Int'l*, pg. 2958
GLASSCRAFT DECORATIVE LIMITED—See CorpAcq Holdings Limited; *Int'l*, pg. 1802
GLASTON AMERICA INC—See Glaston Oyj Abp; *Int'l*, pg. 2989
GLASTON MANAGEMENT (SHANGHAI) CO. LTD—See Glaston Oyj Abp; *Int'l*, pg. 2989
GLASTON SHANGHAI CO., LTD.—See Glaston Oyj Abp; *Int'l*, pg. 2989
GLASTON TIANJIN CO. LTD.—See Glaston Oyj Abp; *Int'l*, pg. 2989
GRACE FABRIC TECHNOLOGY CO., LTD.; *Int'l*, pg. 3048
G-SMATT AMERICA CO., LTD.—See G-Smatt Global Co., Ltd.; *Int'l*, pg. 2863
G-SMATT HONG KONG LTD.—See G-Smatt Global Co., Ltd.; *Int'l*, pg. 2863
GUARDIAN AFRICA CORP (PTY) LTD.—See Koch Industries, Inc.; *U.S. Private*, pg. 2329
GUARDIAN DO BRASIL VIDROS PLANOS LTDA—See Koch Industries, Inc.; *U.S. Private*, pg. 2329
GUARDIAN EUROPE S.A.R.L.—See Koch Industries, Inc.; *U.S. Private*, pg. 2329
GUARDIAN FLACHGLAS GMBH—See Koch Industries, Inc.; *U.S. Private*, pg. 2329
GUARDIAN GLASS ESPANA CENTRAL VIDRIERA

S.L.—See Koch Industries, Inc.; *U.S. Private*, pg. 2329
GUARDIAN INDUSTRIES POLAND SP.Z.O.O.—See Koch Industries, Inc.; *U.S. Private*, pg. 2329
GUARDIAN LUXGUARD I S.A.—See Koch Industries, Inc.; *U.S. Private*, pg. 2329
GUARDIAN NAVARRA S.L.—See Koch Industries, Inc.; *U.S. Private*, pg. 2329
GUARDIAN OROSHAZA CO. LTD.—See Koch Industries, Inc.; *U.S. Private*, pg. 2329
GUARDIAN STEKLO ROSTOV LLC—See Koch Industries, Inc.; *U.S. Private*, pg. 2329
GUARDIAN STEKLO RYAZAN LLC—See Koch Industries, Inc.; *U.S. Private*, pg. 2329
GUARDIAN ZOUJAJ INTERNATIONAL FLOAT GLASS CO. LLC—See Koch Industries, Inc.; *U.S. Private*, pg. 2329
GUJARAT GUARDIAN LTD.—See Koch Industries, Inc.; *U.S. Private*, pg. 2329
GULF GLASS MANUFACTURING CO. K.S.C.; *Int'l*, pg. 3180
HAMADAN GLASS COMPANY LLP; *Int'l*, pg. 3234
HANKUK ELECTRIC GLASS CO., LTD.—See AGC Inc.; *Int'l*, pg. 204
HANKYU EYEWEAR CO LTD—See H2O Retailing Corp.; *Int'l*, pg. 3200
HANWOOK TECHNO GLASS CO., LTD.—See AGC Inc.; *Int'l*, pg. 204
HCS CORPORATION—See Compagnie de Saint-Gobain SA; *Int'l*, pg. 1730
HEHR GLASS COMPANY INC.—See LCI Industries; *U.S. Public*, pg. 1295
HEHR INTERNATIONAL INC. - KANSAS GLASS PLANT—See LCI Industries; *U.S. Public*, pg. 1295
HOYA GLASS DISK (THAILAND) LTD.—See Hoya Corporation; *Int'l*, pg. 3495
IAG GLASS COMPANY LIMITED; *Int'l*, pg. 3568
ICC UKRAINE LTD.—See Carl-Zeiss-Stiftung; *Int'l*, pg. 1336
IG WINDOWS CO., LTD.—See Iida Group Holdings Co., Ltd.; *Int'l*, pg. 3607
IITTALA GROUP OY AB—See Fiskars Oyj Abp; *Int'l*, pg. 2694
INTERGLASS CORP.; *U.S. Private*, pg. 2110
INTIGRAL INC; *U.S. Private*, pg. 2128
J.E. BERKOWITZ, LP; *U.S. Private*, pg. 2161
JENAER GLASWERK GMBH—See Carl-Zeiss-Stiftung; *Int'l*, pg. 1336
KERAGLASS INDUSTRIES S.R.L.—See Cifin S.r.l.; *Int'l*, pg. 1606
KIMBLE CHASE LIFE SCIENCE & RESEARCH PRODUCTS LLC - ROCKWOOD PLANT—See OEP Capital Advisors, L.P.; *U.S. Private*, pg. 2999
KLASS PACK LIMITED—See Borosil Renewables Limited; *Int'l*, pg. 1114
KOPP GLASS, INC.; *U.S. Public*, pg. 1271
LARRY METHVIN INSTALLATION; *U.S. Private*, pg. 2393
LAVET S.R.L.—See LCI Industries; *U.S. Public*, pg. 1295
LAWSON INDUSTRIES INC.—See Pella Corporation; *U.S. Private*, pg. 3131
LINYI CNG GLASS COMPANY LIMITED—See China Glass Holdings Limited; *Int'l*, pg. 1504
LOUWERSHANIQUE B.V.—See IDEX Corp; *U.S. Public*, pg. 1091
M3 GLASS TECHNOLOGIES; *U.S. Private*, pg. 2530
METAPACK FRANCE SAS—See Thoma Bravo, L.P.; *U.S. Private*, pg. 4154
MORITEX TECHNOLOGIES (SHENZHEN) CO., LTD.—See Cognex Corporation; *U.S. Public*, pg. 523
MUNN WORKS LLC—See Applied UV, Inc.; *U.S. Public*, pg. 173
NEKSVISION CO., LTD.—See Honda Motor Co., Ltd.; *Int'l*, pg. 3463
NEUMAN ALUMINIUM FLIESSPRESSWERK GMBH—See CAG Holding GmbH; *Int'l*, pg. 1250
NEUTRAL GLASS & ALLIED INDUSTRIES PRIVATE LTD.—See Gerresheimer AG; *Int'l*, pg. 2944
NEXTGLASS TECHNOLOGIES CORPORATION; *U.S. Private*, pg. 2921
NORTH AMERICAN SPECIALTY GLASS LLC—See Stellex Capital Management LP; *U.S. Private*, pg. 3800
OCV REINFORCEMENTS ALCALA SPAIN, S.L.—See Owens Corning; *U.S. Public*, pg. 1627
OCV REINFORCEMENTS (HANGZHOU) CO., LTD.—See Owens Corning; *U.S. Public*, pg. 1627
ODL EUROPE B.V.—See ODL Incorporated; *U.S. Private*, pg. 2993
O-I MANUFACTURING FRANCE SAS—See O-I Glass, Inc.; *U.S. Public*, pg. 1559
OLDCASTLE BUILDINGENVELOPE, INC.—See KPS Capital Partners, LP; *U.S. Private*, pg. 2348
OOO CARL ZEISS—See Carl-Zeiss-Stiftung; *Int'l*, pg. 1336
PHOENICIA LTD.—See Fortissimo Capital Management Ltd.; *Int'l*, pg. 2740
PLASTPRO, INC.; *U.S. Private*, pg. 3200
POTTERS INDUSTRIES, LLC—See The Jordan Company, L.P.; *U.S. Private*, pg. 4061
PYRAMID SPECIALITIES PRODUCTS LTD.—See Compagnie de Saint-Gobain SA; *Int'l*, pg. 1730
RAUCH INDUSTRIES, INC.—See Blackstreet Capital Management, LLC; *U.S. Private*, pg. 577

327215 — GLASS PRODUCT MANUF...

RENOVATE BY BERKOWITZ LLC—See J.E. Berkowitz, LP; *U.S. Private*, pg. 2161
RODENSTOCK AUSTRALIA PTY. LTD.—See Compass Advisers Group LLC; *U.S. Private*, pg. 999
RODENSTOCK OSTERREICH GMBH—See Compass Advisers Group LLC; *U.S. Private*, pg. 999
SAINT-GOBAIN ACHATS—See Compagnie de Saint-Gobain SA; *Int'l*, pg. 1727
SAINT-GOBAIN ADFORS AUSTRIA GMBH—See Compagnie de Saint-Gobain SA; *Int'l*, pg. 1729
SAINT-GOBAIN ADFORS CZ GLASS MAT S.R.O.—See Compagnie de Saint-Gobain SA; *Int'l*, pg. 1727
SAINT-GOBAIN ADFORS CZ S.R.O.—See Compagnie de Saint-Gobain SA; *Int'l*, pg. 1729
SAINT-GOBAIN ADFORS ITALIA S.P.A.—See Compagnie de Saint-Gobain SA; *Int'l*, pg. 1729
SAINT-GOBAIN AUTOVER DIREKTGLAS AB—See Compagnie de Saint-Gobain SA; *Int'l*, pg. 1729
SAINT-GOBAIN AUTOVER HELLAS S.A.—See Compagnie de Saint-Gobain SA; *Int'l*, pg. 1729
SAINT-GOBAIN AUTOVER INC—See Compagnie de Saint-Gobain SA; *Int'l*, pg. 1732
SAINT-GOBAIN AUTOVER—See Compagnie de Saint-Gobain SA; *Int'l*, pg. 1729
SAINT-GOBAIN CONCEPTIONS VERRIERES—See Compagnie de Saint-Gobain SA; *Int'l*, pg. 1727
SAINT-GOBAIN CRYSTALS NV—See Compagnie de Saint-Gobain SA; *Int'l*, pg. 1732
SAINT-GOBAIN EUROVEDER ITALIA SPA—See Compagnie de Saint-Gobain SA; *Int'l*, pg. 1733
SAINT-GOBAIN FACILITAS PORTUGAL, SOCIEDADE UNIPESS—See Compagnie de Saint-Gobain SA; *Int'l*, pg. 1728
SAINT-GOBAIN GLASS ESTONIA SE—See Compagnie de Saint-Gobain SA; *Int'l*, pg. 1728
SAINT-GOBAIN GLASS FINLAND OY—See Compagnie de Saint-Gobain SA; *Int'l*, pg. 1733
SAINT-GOBAIN GLASS FRANCE SA—See Compagnie de Saint-Gobain SA; *Int'l*, pg. 1733
SAINT-GOBAIN GLASS HELLAS—See Compagnie de Saint-Gobain SA; *Int'l*, pg. 1728
SAINT-GOBAIN GLASS ITALIA SPA—See Compagnie de Saint-Gobain SA; *Int'l*, pg. 1734
SAINT-GOBAIN GLASS ROMANIA SRL—See Compagnie de Saint-Gobain SA; *Int'l*, pg. 1734
SAINT-GOBAIN GLASS SOLUTION SAS GLAS—See Compagnie de Saint-Gobain SA; *Int'l*, pg. 1734
SAINT-GOBAIN GLASS SOLUTIONS CZ, S.R.O.—See Compagnie de Saint-Gobain SA; *Int'l*, pg. 1728
SAINT-GOBAIN GLASS UK LTD—See Compagnie de Saint-Gobain SA; *Int'l*, pg. 1734
SAINT-GOBAIN HANGLAS JAPAN K.K.—See Compagnie de Saint-Gobain SA; *Int'l*, pg. 1734
SAINT-GOBAIN HORNSTEIN GLASTEXTIL GMBH—See Compagnie de Saint-Gobain SA; *Int'l*, pg. 1734
SAINT-GOBAIN INTERSERVICES S.A.—See Compagnie de Saint-Gobain SA; *Int'l*, pg. 1728
SAINT-GOBAIN MEXICO S.A. DE C.V.—See Compagnie de Saint-Gobain SA; *Int'l*, pg. 1734
SAINT-GOBAIN PARTICIPACOES LTDA—See Compagnie de Saint-Gobain SA; *Int'l*, pg. 1728
SAINT-GOBAIN POLSKA SP. Z O.O.—See Compagnie de Saint-Gobain SA; *Int'l*, pg. 1728
SAINT-GOBAIN SEKURIT DE COLOMBIA S.A.—See Compagnie de Saint-Gobain SA; *Int'l*, pg. 1736
SAINT-GOBAIN SEKURIT PORTUGAL VIDRO AUTOMOVEL SA—See Compagnie de Saint-Gobain SA; *Int'l*, pg. 1736
SAINT-GOBAIN SEKURIT (SHANGHAI) CO., LTD.—See Compagnie de Saint-Gobain SA; *Int'l*, pg. 1736
SAINT-GOBAIN SEKURIT THAILAND CO., LTD.—See Compagnie de Saint-Gobain SA; *Int'l*, pg. 1736
SAINT-GOBAIN SOVIS SAS—See Compagnie de Saint-Gobain SA; *Int'l*, pg. 1733
SAINT-GOBAIN SULLY S.A.S.—See Compagnie de Saint-Gobain SA; *Int'l*, pg. 1733
SCANGLAS A/S—See Compagnie de Saint-Gobain SA; *Int'l*, pg. 1734
SCHOTT BRASIL LTDA.—See Carl-Zeiss-Stiftung; *Int'l*, pg. 1336
SCHOTT BRAZIL—See Carl-Zeiss-Stiftung; *Int'l*, pg. 1336
SCHOTT DE MEXICO, S.A. DE C.V.—See Carl-Zeiss-Stiftung; *Int'l*, pg. 1337
SCHOTT DIAMONDVIEW ARMOR PRODUCTS, LLC—See Carl-Zeiss-Stiftung; *Int'l*, pg. 1337
SCHOTT ENVASES ARGENTINA S.A.—See Carl-Zeiss-Stiftung; *Int'l*, pg. 1337
SCHOTT ENVASES FARMACEUTICOS S.A.—See Carl-Zeiss-Stiftung; *Int'l*, pg. 1337
SCHOTT FLAT GLASS DO BRASIL LTDA.—See Carl-Zeiss-Stiftung; *Int'l*, pg. 1337
SCHOTT GEMTRON CANADA CORPORATION—See Carl-Zeiss-Stiftung; *Int'l*, pg. 1337
SCHOTT GEMTRON CORPORATION—See AGC Inc.; *Int'l*, pg. 201
SCHOTT GEMTRON CORPORATION—See Carl-Zeiss-Stiftung; *Int'l*, pg. 1337

SCHOTT GLAS EXPORT GMBH—See Carl-Zeiss-Stiftung; *Int'l*, pg. 1337
SCHOTT GLASS INDIA PVT. LTD.—See Carl-Zeiss-Stiftung; *Int'l*, pg. 1337
SCHOTT GLASS (MALAYSIA) SDN. BHD.—See Carl-Zeiss-Stiftung; *Int'l*, pg. 1337
SCHOTT GLASS TECHNOLOGIES (SUZHOU) CO., LTD.—See Carl-Zeiss-Stiftung; *Int'l*, pg. 1337
SCHOTT GOVERNMENT SERVICES, LLC—See Carl-Zeiss-Stiftung; *Int'l*, pg. 1337
SCHOTT ITALVETRO S.P.A.—See Carl-Zeiss-Stiftung; *Int'l*, pg. 1337
SCHOTT NIPPON K.K.—See Carl-Zeiss-Stiftung; *Int'l*, pg. 1337
SCHOTT NORTH AMERICA, INC. - FLAT GLASS DIVISION—See Carl-Zeiss-Stiftung; *Int'l*, pg. 1337
SCHOTT ORIM CAM SANAYI VE TICARET A.S.—See Carl-Zeiss-Stiftung; *Int'l*, pg. 1337
SCHOTT SCHWEIZ AG—See Carl-Zeiss-Stiftung; *Int'l*, pg. 1337
SCHOTT TECHNICAL GLASS SOLUTIONS GMBH—See Carl-Zeiss-Stiftung; *Int'l*, pg. 1337
SCHOTT TERMOFROST AB—See Carl-Zeiss-Stiftung; *Int'l*, pg. 1337
SCHOTT TERMOFROST AS—See Carl-Zeiss-Stiftung; *Int'l*, pg. 1337
SCHOTT UK LTD.—See Carl-Zeiss-Stiftung; *Int'l*, pg. 1337
SCILAB KOREA CO., LTD.—See Daihan Scientific Co., Ltd.; *Int'l*, pg. 1926
SCOPRO OPTICAL CO., INC.—See Asia Optical Co., Inc.; *Int'l*, pg. 613
SEPR REFRACTORIES INDIA LTD—See Compagnie de Saint-Gobain SA; *Int'l*, pg. 1728
SHAANXI CNG NEW TECHNOLOGY CO., LTD.—See China Glass Holdings Limited; *Int'l*, pg. 1504
SHINKO PARTS CO., LTD.—See Fujitsu Limited; *Int'l*, pg. 2838
SICURGLASS SUD SRL—See Compagnie de Saint-Gobain SA; *Int'l*, pg. 1737
SIEGEL-ROBERT AUTOMOTIVE (SUZHOU) CO., LTD.—See Koch Industries, Inc.; *U.S. Private*, pg. 2330
SOCIETE INDUSTRIELLE DES VITRAGES D'AQUITAINE—See Compagnie de Saint-Gobain SA; *Int'l*, pg. 1736
SOLUTIA EUROPE BVBA/SPRL—See Eastman Chemical Company; *U.S. Public*, pg. 705
SPECTRUM GLASS COMPANY INC.; *U.S. Private*, pg. 3752
STOLZLE CZESTOCHOWA SP. Z O.O.—See CAG Holding GmbH; *Int'l*, pg. 1250
STOLZLE FLACONNAGE LTD.—See CAG Holding GmbH; *Int'l*, pg. 1250
STOLZLE FRANCE SAS—See CAG Holding GmbH; *Int'l*, pg. 1251
STOLZLE GLASS USA, INC.—See CAG Holding GmbH; *Int'l*, pg. 1251
STOLZLE LAUSITZ GMBH—See CAG Holding GmbH; *Int'l*, pg. 1250
STOLZLE-OBERGLAS GMBH—See CAG Holding GmbH; *Int'l*, pg. 1250
STOLZLE-UNION S.R.O—See CAG Holding GmbH; *Int'l*, pg. 1251
SUEZ COMPANY FOR MINERALS—See Gruppo Minerali Maffei S.p.A; *Int'l*, pg. 3140
SUPERGLASS S.A.—See CRH plc; *Int'l*, pg. 1848
SUQIAN CNG NEW MATERIALS COMPANY LIMITED—See China Glass Holdings Limited; *Int'l*, pg. 1504
TAYLOR MADE GLASS OHIO, INC.—See LCI Industries; *U.S. Public*, pg. 1295
TAYLOR MADE GLASS & SYSTEMS LIMITED—See LCI Industries; *U.S. Public*, pg. 1295
THALETEC INC.—See HLE Glascoat Limited; *Int'l*, pg. 3431
THERMO FISHER SCIENTIFIC GERMANY BV & CO. KG—See Thermo Fisher Scientific Inc.; *U.S. Public*, pg. 2153
THERMOSEAL INDUSTRIES, LLC—See Audax Group, Limited Partnership; *U.S. Public*, pg. 386
TREND MARINE PRODUCTS LIMITED—See LCI Industries; *U.S. Public*, pg. 1295
TRINITY GLASS INTERNATIONAL INC.; *U.S. Private*, pg. 4233
TRUDECO—See Trulite Glass & Aluminum Solutions, LLC; *U.S. Private*, pg. 4249
TRU VUE, INC.—See Apogee Enterprises, Inc.; *U.S. Public*, pg. 145
TUBEX ZAO—See CAG Holding GmbH; *Int'l*, pg. 1251
VANCE INDUSTRIES, INC.; *U.S. Private*, pg. 4342
VERRERIES DE L'ORNE SAS—See Compagnie de Saint-Gobain SA; *Int'l*, pg. 1733
VETROTECH SAINT-GOBAIN BENELUX NV—See Compagnie de Saint-Gobain SA; *Int'l*, pg. 1737
VETROTECH SAINT-GOBAIN CENTRAL & EASTERN EUROPE AG—See Compagnie de Saint-Gobain SA; *Int'l*, pg. 1737
VETROTECH SAINT-GOBAIN FRANCE—See Compagnie de Saint-Gobain SA; *Int'l*, pg. 1737
VETROTECH SAINT-GOBAIN INTERNATIONAL AG—See Compagnie de Saint-Gobain SA; *Int'l*, pg. 1737
VIDRIOS DELL ORTO, S.A.—See CRH plc; *Int'l*, pg. 1849
VIEW, INC.; *U.S. Public*, pg. 2297
VIRGINIA MIRROR COMPANY INCORPORATED; *U.S. Private*, pg. 4387
VITRERIE NOVY GLASS—See Koch Industries, Inc.; *U.S. Private*, pg. 2330
VITROCOM INC.—See H&Q Asia Pacific, Ltd.; *U.S. Private*, pg. 1823
WEIHAI CNG COATED GLASS COMPANY LIMITED—See China Glass Holdings Limited; *Int'l*, pg. 1504
WEST CAPE SAFETY GLASS (PTY) LIMITED—See AG Industries Limited; *Int'l*, pg. 198
WINDOOR, INC.—See Koch Industries, Inc.; *U.S. Private*, pg. 2333
WUHAI CNG SPECIAL GLASS COMPANY LIMITED—See China Glass Holdings Limited; *Int'l*, pg. 1504
ZAO ZAVOD MINPLITA—See Compagnie de Saint-Gobain SA; *Int'l*, pg. 1737
Z. BAVELLONI SOUTH AMERICA LTDA—See Glaston Oyj Abp; *Int'l*, pg. 2989

327310 — CEMENT MANUFACTURING

AALBORG PORTLAND HOLDING A/S—See Cementir Holding N.V.; *Int'l*, pg. 1397
AAMAL CEMENT INDUSTRIES W.L.L.—See Aamal Company Q.S.C.; *Int'l*, pg. 36
ABETONG TEKNIK AB—See Heidelberg Materials AG; *Int'l*, pg. 3315
ACC CONCRETE LIMITED—See ACC Limited; *Int'l*, pg. 78
ACC LIMITED - BARGARH CEMENT WORKS—See ACC Limited; *Int'l*, pg. 78
ACC LIMITED - CHANDA CEMENT WORKS—See ACC Limited; *Int'l*, pg. 78
ACC LIMITED - DAMODHAR CEMENT WORKS—See ACC Limited; *Int'l*, pg. 78
ACC LIMITED - JAMUL CEMENT WORKS—See ACC Limited; *Int'l*, pg. 79
ACC LIMITED - KUNDALI PLANT—See ACC Limited; *Int'l*, pg. 79
ACC LIMITED - KYMORE CEMENT WORKS—See ACC Limited; *Int'l*, pg. 79
ACC LIMITED - LAKHERI CEMENT WORKS—See ACC Limited; *Int'l*, pg. 79
ACC LIMITED; *Int'l*, pg. 78
ACC LIMITED - VADODARA FRANCHISEE PLANT—See ACC Limited; *Int'l*, pg. 79
ADBRI LIMITED—See CRH plc; *Int'l*, pg. 1842
ADELAIDE BRIGHTON CEMENT, (FLORIDA) INC.—See CRH plc; *Int'l*, pg. 1842
ADELAIDE BRIGHTON CEMENT LTD.—See CRH plc; *Int'l*, pg. 1842
AFRISAM (SOUTH AFRICA) (PTY) LTD.; *Int'l*, pg. 193
AFYON CIMENTO SANAYI TURK A.S.—See Haci Omer Sabanci Holding A.S.; *Int'l*, pg. 3203
AGGREGATE INDUSTRIES MANAGEMENT, INC.—See Holcim Ltd.; *Int'l*, pg. 3446
AKCANSA CIMENTO SANAYI VE TICARET A.S.—See Haci Omer Sabanci Holding A.S.; *Int'l*, pg. 3203
AKCANSA CIMENTO SANAYI VE TICARET A.S.—See Heidelberg Materials AG; *Int'l*, pg. 3308
ALAMO CEMENT COMPANY; *U.S. Private*, pg. 149
AL JOUF CEMENT COMPANY; *Int'l*, pg. 280
ALLIED OIL & GAS SERVICES LLC—See Intervale Capital, LLC; *U.S. Private*, pg. 2127
ALLURA—See Grupo Empresarial Kaluz S.A. de C.V.; *Int'l*, pg. 3126
AMBUJA CEMENT RAJASTHAN LTD.—See Adani Enterprises Limited; *Int'l*, pg. 125
AMREYAH CEMENT COMPAMY S.A.E.—See Camargo Correa S.A.; *Int'l*, pg. 1267
ANHUI CHANGFENG CONCH CEMENT CO., LTD.—See Anhui Conch Cement Company Limited; *Int'l*, pg. 466
ANHUI CONCH CEMENT COMPANY LIMITED; *Int'l*, pg. 466
ANJANI PORTLAND CEMENT LTD. - NALGONDA WORKS—See Anjani Portland Cement Ltd.; *Int'l*, pg. 472
ANJANI PORTLAND CEMENT LTD.; *Int'l*, pg. 472
APO CEMENT CORPORATION—See CEMEX, S.A.B. de C.V.; *Int'l*, pg. 1398
ARABIAN CEMENT COMPANY LTD.; *Int'l*, pg. 533
ARABIAN CEMENT COMPANY; *Int'l*, pg. 533
ARABIAN CEMENT CO.—See Arabian Cement Company Ltd.; *Int'l*, pg. 533
ARAWAK CEMENT COMPANY LIMITED—See CEMEX, S.A.B. de C.V.; *Int'l*, pg. 1400
ARES CIMENTO INSAAT SAN. VE TIC. A.S.—See Bursa Cimento Fabrikaci A.S.; *Int'l*, pg. 1226
ARGOS GUATEMALA S.A.—See Grupo Argos S.A.; *Int'l*, pg. 3120
ARGOS USA LLC—See Grupo Argos S.A.; *Int'l*, pg. 3120
ARIDOS VELILLA, S.A.—See Heidelberg Materials AG; *Int'l*, pg. 3308
ARM CEMENT LIMITED; *Int'l*, pg. 573
ASAMER BAUSTOFFE AG; *Int'l*, pg. 599

N.A.I.C.S. INDEX   327310 — CEMENT MANUFACTURIN...

ASEC CEMENT CO.—See Citadel Capital S.A.E.; *Int'l*, pg. 1619
ASHAKACEM PLC—See Holcim Ltd.; *Int'l*, pg. 3448
ASH GROVE CEMENT PLANT—See CRH plc; *Int'l*, pg. 1842
ASH GROVE MATERIALS CORP.—See CRH plc; *Int'l*, pg. 1842
ASH GROVE TEXAS—See CRH plc; *Int'l*, pg. 1843
ASIA CEMENT CO., LTD.—See Asia Holdings Co., Ltd.; *Int'l*, pg. 612
ASIA CEMENT CORPORATION - HSINCHU PLANT—See Asia Cement Corporation; *Int'l*, pg. 611
ASIA CEMENT CORPORATION - HUALIEN PLANT—See Asia Cement Corporation; *Int'l*, pg. 611
ASIA CEMENT (SINGAPORE) PTE. LTD.—See Asia Cement Corporation; *Int'l*, pg. 611
ASMENT DE TEMARA S.A.—See Camargo Correa S.A.; *Int'l*, pg. 1267
A/S SCANCEM CHEMICALS—See Heidelberg Materials AG; *Int'l*, pg. 3315
ASSIUT CEMENT COMPANY—See CEMEX, S.A.B. de C.V.; *Int'l*, pg. 1398
AZARIT COMPANY; *Int'l*, pg. 776
BAMBURI CEMENT PLC—See Amsons Group; *Int'l*, pg. 441
BARAK VALLEY CEMENTS LIMITED; *Int'l*, pg. 858
BATICIM BATI ANADOLU CIMENTO SANAYII A.S.; *Int'l*, pg. 889
BATISOKE SOKE CIMENTO SANAYII TAS; *Int'l*, pg. 889
BAZIAN CEMENT COMPANY LTD.—See Holcim Ltd.; *Int'l*, pg. 3446
BBMG CORPORATION; *Int'l*, pg. 920
BEHBAHAN CEMENT COMPANY; *Int'l*, pg. 941
BEIJING LIULIHE CEMENT CO., LTD—See BBMG Corporation; *Int'l*, pg. 920
BENCHMARK COMPLETIONS, LLC—See Intervale Capital, LLC; *U.S. Private*, pg. 2127
BETOCIM SA—See Camargo Correa S.A.; *Int'l*, pg. 1267
BETONG SOR AS—See Heidelberg Materials AG; *Int'l*, pg. 3309
BHEEMA CEMENTS LTD.; *Int'l*, pg. 1014
BILDCO CEMENT PRODUCTS LLC—See Abu Dhabi National Company for Building Material; *Int'l*, pg. 72
BIMSON CEMENT JOINT STOCK COMPANY; *Int'l*, pg. 1032
BINA READY-MIX CONCRETE PRODUCTS COMPANY—See Bawan Company; *Int'l*, pg. 900
BIRCHWOOD OMNIA LIMITED—See Heidelberg Materials AG; *Int'l*, pg. 3309
BIRLA CORPORATION LTD. - DURGAPUR CEMENT WORKS—See Birla Corporation Ltd.; *Int'l*, pg. 1047
BIRLA CORPORATION LTD. - JUTE DIVISION—See Birla Corporation Ltd.; *Int'l*, pg. 1047
BIRLA CORPORATION LTD. - RAEBARELI CEMENT WORKS—See Birla Corporation Ltd.; *Int'l*, pg. 1047
BIRLA CORPORATION LTD. - SATNA CEMENT WORKS—See Birla Corporation Ltd.; *Int'l*, pg. 1047
BIRLA VIKAS CEMENT—See Birla Corporation Ltd.; *Int'l*, pg. 1047
BOGAZ ENDUSTRI VE MADENCILIK LTD.—See Holcim Ltd.; *Int'l*, pg. 3446
BOJNOURD CEMENT CO.—See Fars & Khuzestan Cement Co.; *Int'l*, pg. 2620
BOLU CIMENTO SANAYII A.S.; *Int'l*, pg. 1103
BT POZNAN SP. Z.O.O.—See Heidelberg Materials AG; *Int'l*, pg. 3308
BUA CEMENT PLC; *Int'l*, pg. 1206
BULK MATERIALS INTERNATIONAL CO.; *U.S. Private*, pg. 684
BURNPUR CEMENT LIMITED; *Int'l*, pg. 1226
BURSA CIMENTO FABRIKASI A.S.; *Int'l*, pg. 1226
BUZZI UNICEM USA—See Buzzi SpA; *Int'l*, pg. 1230
B.V. BETONCENTRALE BEMA—See Heidelberg Materials AG; *Int'l*, pg. 3308
B.V. BETONCENTRALE DE SCHELDE—See Heidelberg Materials AG; *Int'l*, pg. 3308
CABI S.A.—See CRH plc; *Int'l*, pg. 1844
C.A. FABRICA NACIONAL DE CEMENTOS, S.A.C.A.; *Int'l*, pg. 1240
CAHYA MATA CEMENT SDN. BHD.—See Cahya Mata Sarawak Berhad; *Int'l*, pg. 1251
CAN THO MINERAL & CEMENT JSC; *Int'l*, pg. 1276
CARIBBEAN CEMENT CO., LTD.—See CEMEX, S.A.B. de C.V.; *Int'l*, pg. 1400
CARICEMENT ANTIGUA LIMITED—See Grupo Argos S.A.; *Int'l*, pg. 3121
CASTLE CEMENT (CHATBURN) LIMITED—See Heidelberg Materials AG; *Int'l*, pg. 3309
CASTLE CEMENT LIMITED—See Heidelberg Materials AG; *Int'l*, pg. 3309
CASTLE CEMENT LTD. - PADESWOOD WORKS—See Heidelberg Materials AG; *Int'l*, pg. 3308
CASTLE CEMENT (RIBBLESDALE) LIMITED—See Heidelberg Materials AG; *Int'l*, pg. 3309
CAVA DELLE CAPANNELLE S.R.L.—See Heidelberg Materials AG; *Int'l*, pg. 3309
CEMENTA AB (MALMO)—See Heidelberg Materials AG; *Int'l*, pg. 3315

CEMENTA AB (STOCKHOLM)—See Heidelberg Materials AG; *Int'l*, pg. 3315
CEMENTA RESEARCH AB—See Heidelberg Materials AG; *Int'l*, pg. 3315
CEMENT AUSTRALIA HOLDINGS PTY LTD - BULWER ISLAND PLANT—See Heidelberg Materials AG; *Int'l*, pg. 3311
CEMENT AUSTRALIA HOLDINGS PTY LTD - BULWER ISLAND PLANT—See Holcim Ltd.; *Int'l*, pg. 3446
CEMENT AUSTRALIA HOLDINGS PTY LTD - GLADSTONE PLANT—See Heidelberg Materials AG; *Int'l*, pg. 3311
CEMENT AUSTRALIA HOLDINGS PTY LTD - GLADSTONE PLANT—See Holcim Ltd.; *Int'l*, pg. 3446
CEMENT AUSTRALIA HOLDINGS PTY LTD - RAILTON PLANT—See Heidelberg Materials AG; *Int'l*, pg. 3311
CEMENT AUSTRALIA HOLDINGS PTY LTD - RAILTON PLANT—See Holcim Ltd.; *Int'l*, pg. 3446
CEMENT AUSTRALIA HOLDINGS PTY. LTD.—See Heidelberg Materials AG; *Int'l*, pg. 3311
CEMENT AUSTRALIA HOLDINGS PTY. LTD.—See Holcim Ltd.; *Int'l*, pg. 3446
CEMENT HRANICE A.S.—See Buzzi SpA; *Int'l*, pg. 1230
CEMENT MANUFACTURING CO. LTD—See Century Plyboards (I) Ltd.; *Int'l*, pg. 1419
CEMENTOS ARGOS S.A.—See Grupo Argos S.A.; *Int'l*, pg. 3120
CEMENTOS ARTIGAS S.A—See Cementos Molins S.A.; *Int'l*, pg. 1397
CEMENTOS AVELLANEDA S.A.—See Cementos Molins S.A.; *Int'l*, pg. 1397
CEMENTOS BIO-BIO S.A.; *Int'l*, pg. 1397
CEMENTOS COSMOS S.A.—See Camargo Correa S.A.; *Int'l*, pg. 1267
CEMENTOS FORTALEZA, S.A. DE C.V. - EL PALMAR PLANT—See Grupo Empresarial Kaluz S.A. de C.V.; *Int'l*, pg. 3126
CEMENTOS FORTALEZA, S.A. DE C.V. - TULA PLANT—See Grupo Empresarial Kaluz S.A. de C.V.; *Int'l*, pg. 3126
CEMENTOS FORTALEZA, S.A. DE C.V. - VITO PLANT—See Grupo Empresarial Kaluz S.A. de C.V.; *Int'l*, pg. 3126
CEMENTOS HISPANIA S.A.—See Buzzi SpA; *Int'l*, pg. 1230
CEMENTOS MOLINS INDUSTRIAL, S.A.—See Cementos Molins S.A.; *Int'l*, pg. 1397
CEMENTOS MOLINS S.A.; *Int'l*, pg. 1397
CEMENTOS PACASMAYO S.A.A.; *Int'l*, pg. 1398
CEMENTOS PORTLAND VALDERRIVAS, S.A.—See Fomento de Construcciones y Contratas, S.A.; *Int'l*, pg. 2722
CEMENT OZAROW S.A.—See CRH plc; *Int'l*, pg. 1844
CEMENTRUM I B.V.—See Heidelberg Materials AG; *Int'l*, pg. 3309
CEMENTRUM II B.V.—See Heidelberg Materials AG; *Int'l*, pg. 3309
CEMEX AS—See CEMEX, S.A.B. de C.V.; *Int'l*, pg. 1398
CEMEX BRAZIL—See CEMEX, S.A.B. de C.V.; *Int'l*, pg. 1398
CEMEX COLOMBIA, S.A.—See CEMEX, S.A.B. de C.V.; *Int'l*, pg. 1398
CEMEX CORP.—See CEMEX, S.A.B. de C.V.; *Int'l*, pg. 1399
CEMEX COSTA RICA S.A.—See CEMEX, S.A.B. de C.V.; *Int'l*, pg. 1398
CEMEX DE PUERTO RICO INC.—See CEMEX, S.A.B. de C.V.; *Int'l*, pg. 1399
CEMEX DOMINICANA, S.A.—See CEMEX, S.A.B. de C.V.; *Int'l*, pg. 1398
CEMEX EGYPT—See CEMEX, S.A.B. de C.V.; *Int'l*, pg. 1398
CEMEX EL SALVADOR S.A DE C.V.—See CEMEX, S.A.B. de C.V.; *Int'l*, pg. 1399
CEMEX ESPANA S.A. - GADOR PLANT—See CEMEX, S.A.B. de C.V.; *Int'l*, pg. 1398
CEMEX ESPANA S.A.—See CEMEX, S.A.B. de C.V.; *Int'l*, pg. 1398
CEMEX FALCON LLC—See CEMEX, S.A.B. de C.V.; pg. 1400
CEMEX FRANCE S.A.—See CEMEX, S.A.B. de C.V.; *Int'l*, pg. 1398
CEMEX GUATEMALA—See CEMEX, S.A.B. de C.V.; *Int'l*, pg. 1398
CEMEX HOLDINGS PHILIPPINES, INC.—See CEMEX, S.A.B. de C.V.; *Int'l*, pg. 1398
CEMEX MEXICO, S.A. DE C.V.—See CEMEX, S.A.B. de C.V.; *Int'l*, pg. 1399
CEMEX NETHERLANDS B.V.—See CEMEX, S.A.B. de C.V.; *Int'l*, pg. 1399
CEMEX POLSKA SP.Z.O.O.—See CEMEX, S.A.B. de C.V.; *Int'l*, pg. 1399
CEMFX SIA—See CEMEX, S.A.B. de C.V.; *Int'l*, pg. 1399
CEMEX SUPERMIX LLC—See CEMEX, S.A.B. de C.V.; pg. 1400
CEMEX TOPMIX LLC—See CEMEX, S.A.B. de C.V.; *Int'l*, pg. 1400
CEMEX UK—See CEMEX, S.A.B. de C.V.; *Int'l*, pg. 1399
CEMMAC AS; *Int'l*, pg. 1400
CESKOMORAVSKY CEMENT, A.S.—See Heidelberg Materials AG; *Int'l*, pg. 3309

CHC RESOURCES CORPORATION—See China Steel Corporation; *Int'l*, pg. 1555
CHETTINAD CEMENTS CORP. LTD. - KARIKKALI PLANT—See Chettinad Group of Companies; *Int'l*, pg. 1473
CHETTINAD CEMENTS CORP. LTD. - PULIYUR PLANT—See Chettinad Group of Companies; *Int'l*, pg. 1473
CHETTINAD CEMENTS CORPORATION LIMITED—See Chettinad Group of Companies; *Int'l*, pg. 1473
CHIA HSIN CEMENT CORP.; *Int'l*, pg. 1475
CHINA CENTURY CEMENT LTD.—See Heidelberg Materials AG; *Int'l*, pg. 3309
CHINA HI-MENT CORP.—See China Steel Corporation; *Int'l*, pg. 1555
CHINA NATIONAL BUILDING MATERIAL COMPANY LIMITED—See China National Building Material Group Co., Ltd.; *Int'l*, pg. 1525
CHINA RESOURCES BUILDING MATERIALS TECHNOLOGY HOLDINGS LIMITED; *Int'l*, pg. 1548
CHINA RESOURCES CEMENT (FENGKAI) LIMITED—See China Resources Building Materials Technology Holdings Limited; *Int'l*, pg. 1548
CHINA RESOURCES CEMENT (SHANGSI) LIMITED—See China Resources Building Materials Technology Holdings Limited; *Int'l*, pg. 1548
CHINA SHANSHUI CEMENT GROUP LTD.; *Int'l*, pg. 1550
CHINA TIANRUI GROUP CEMENT COMPANY LIMITED; *Int'l*, pg. 1559
CHINA TUNGSTEN & HIGHTECH MATERIALS CO., LTD.—See Hunan Nonferrous Metals Corporation Ltd.; *Int'l*, pg. 3533
CHONGQING SIFANG NEW MATERIAL CO., LTD.; *Int'l*, pg. 1581
CIMENTACOR - CIMENTOS DOS ACORES LDA—See Camargo Correa S.A.; *Int'l*, pg. 1267
CIMENTAS IZMIR CIMENTO FABRIKASI TURK A.S.; *Int'l*, pg. 1609
CIMENTOS VENCEMOS DO AMAZONAS, LTDA.—See CEMEX, S.A.B. de C.V.; *Int'l*, pg. 1398
CIMENTS CALCIA S.A.S.—See Heidelberg Materials AG; *Int'l*, pg. 3316
CIMENTS DU MAROC SA—See Heidelberg Materials AG; *Int'l*, pg. 3310
CIMENTS DU TOGO, S.A.—See Heidelberg Materials AG; *Int'l*, pg. 3310
CIMENTS FRANCAIS S.A.—See Heidelberg Materials AG; *Int'l*, pg. 3316
CIMENTS LUXEMBOURGEOIS S.A.—See Buzzi SpA; *Int'l*, pg. 1230
CIMPOR BETAO MOCAMBIQUE, S.A.—See Camargo Correa S.A.; *Int'l*, pg. 1267
CIMPOR - CIMENTOS DE PORTUGAL, SGPS, S.A.—See Camargo Correa S.A.; *Int'l*, pg. 1267
CIMPOR - INDUSTRIA DE CIMENTOS S.A.—See Camargo Correa S.A.; *Int'l*, pg. 1267
CIMSA CIMENTO SANAYI VE TICARET A.S.—See Haci Omer Sabanci Holding A.S.; *Int'l*, pg. 3203
CITY CEMENT COMPANY; *Int'l*, pg. 1626
CITY DEVELOPMENT ENVIRONMENT CO., LTD.; *Int'l*, pg. 1626
C.J.O.-SOCIETE LES CIMENTS DE JBEL OUST—See Camargo Correa S.A.; *Int'l*, pg. 1267
CLOSED JOINED STOCK COMPANY CONSTRUCTION MATERIALS—See Heidelberg Materials AG; *Int'l*, pg. 3310
CMS CLINKER SDN. BHD.—See Cahya Mata Sarawak Berhad; *Int'l*, pg. 1251
COASTAL CEMENT CORPORATION—See Grupo Empresarial Kaluz S.A. de C.V.; *Int'l*, pg. 3127
COCKBURN CEMENT—See CRH plc; *Int'l*, pg. 1842
COMPANHIA DE CIMENTOS DO BRASIL LTDA—See Camargo Correa S.A.; *Int'l*, pg. 1268
CONFIDENCE CEMENT PLC; *Int'l*, pg. 1767
CONTINENTAL CEMENT COMPANY, LLC—See Summit Materials, Inc.; *U.S. Public*, pg. 1960
CRH CANADA GROUP INC.—See CRH plc; *Int'l*, pg. 1843
CRH CEMENT - JOLIETTE PLANT—See CRH plc; *Int'l*, pg. 1843
CRH CIMENT (ROMANIA) S.A.—See CRH plc; *Int'l*, pg. 1843
CRH (SRBIJA) D.O.O.—See CRH plc; *Int'l*, pg. 1843
CRH (WIEN) GMBH—See CRH plc; *Int'l*, pg. 1843
CUBIC DIGITAL TECHNOLOGY CO., LTD.; *Int'l*, pg. 1875
THE CYPRUS CEMENT PUBLIC COMPANY LIMITED—See G.S. Galatariotis & Sons Ltd.; *Int'l*, pg. 2866
DADEX ETERNIT LIMITED; *Int'l*, pg. 1904
DALMIA BHARAT LIMITED; *Int'l*, pg. 1954
DALMIA BHARAT SUGAR AND INDUSTRIES LTD—See Dalmia Bharat Limited; *Int'l*, pg. 1954
DALMIA CEMENT (BHARAT) LIMITED—See Dalmia Bharat Limited; *Int'l*, pg. 1954
DALMIA REFRACTORIES LIMITED—See Dalmia Bharat Limited; *Int'l*, pg. 1954
DANDOT CEMENT CO., LTD.; *Int'l*, pg. 1959
DANGOTE BAIL LIMITED—See Dangote Group Limited; *Int'l*, pg. 1962

327310 — CEMENT MANUFACTURIN...

DANGOTE CEMENT PLC—See Dangote Group Limited; *Int'l*, pg. 1962
DANGOTE GLOBAL SERVICES LIMITED—See Dangote Group Limited; *Int'l*, pg. 1962
DARAB CEMENT COMPANY; *Int'l*, pg. 1972
DASHTESTAN CEMENT INDUSTRIES COMPANY; *Int'l*, pg. 1974
DECCAN CEMENTS LIMITED; *Int'l*, pg. 1999
DEMIX BETON - QUEBEC—See CRH plc; *Int'l*, pg. 1843
DEUNA ZEMENT GMBH—See Buzzi SpA; *Int'l*, pg. 1230
DEVNYA CEMENT JSC—See Heidelberg Materials AG; *Int'l*, pg. 3316
DIC INVESTMENT AND TRADING JOINT STOCK COMPANY; *Int'l*, pg. 2111
DIRK INDIA PRIVATE LIMITED—See Adani Enterprises Limited; *Int'l*, pg. 125
DK CEMENT A/S—See Heidelberg Materials AG; *Int'l*, pg. 3310
DOROUD CEMENT COMPANY—See Fars & Khuzestan Cement Co.; *Int'l*, pg. 2620
DRAGON ALFA CEMENT LIMITED—See Fomento de Construcciones y Contratas, S.A.; *Int'l*, pg. 2722
DRAGON PORTLAND LIMITED—See Fomento de Construcciones y Contratas, S.A.; *Int'l*, pg. 2722
DRAGON PRODUCTS COMPANY, LLC—See Grupo Empresarial Kaluz S.A. de C.V.; *Int'l*, pg. 3127
DUNA-DRAVA CEMENT KFT.—See Heidelberg Materials AG; *Int'l*, pg. 3310
DURALIT—See Grupo Empresarial Kaluz S.A. de C.V.; *Int'l*, pg. 3126
EASTERN PROVINCE CEMENT COMPANY; *Int'l*, pg. 2273
ELKEM ASA - MATERIALS DIVISION—See China National Chemical Corporation; *Int'l*, pg. 1527
EMIRATES CEMENT LLC; *Int'l*, pg. 2615
ENCI B.V.—See Heidelberg Materials AG; *Int'l*, pg. 3310
ENCI-MAASBRICHT B.V.—See Heidelberg Materials AG; *Int'l*, pg. 3309
ENGRO CORPORATION LIMITED; *Int'l*, pg. 2435
EQIOM S.A.S. - GRAND-COURONNE GRINDING PLANT—See CRH plc; *Int'l*, pg. 1843
EQIOM S.A.S. - HEMING PLANT—See CRH plc; *Int'l*, pg. 1843
EQIOM S.A.S. - LA ROCHELLE GRINDING CENTER—See CRH plc; *Int'l*, pg. 1843
EQIOM S.A.S. - LUMBRES PLANT—See CRH plc; *Int'l*, pg. 1843
EQIOM S.A.S.—See CRH plc; *Int'l*, pg. 1843
ESSROC SAN JUAN INC.—See Grupo Argos S.A.; *Int'l*, pg. 3121
ETABLISSEMENT F.S. BIVOIS SARL—See Heidelberg Materials AG; *Int'l*, pg. 3310
ETERNIT GUANGZHOU BUILDING SYSTEMS CO. LTD.—See Etex SA/NV; *Int'l*, pg. 2521
ETERNIT S.A.S.—See Etex SA/NV; *Int'l*, pg. 2522
EURARCO FRANCE S.A.—See Heidelberg Materials AG; *Int'l*, pg. 3316
FABRIKA CEMENTA LUKAVAC D.D.; *Int'l*, pg. 2599
FARS CEMENT COMPANY; *Int'l*, pg. 2620
FARS & KHUZESTAN CEMENT CO.; *Int'l*, pg. 2620
FARSNOV CEMENT CO.—See Fars & Khuzestan Cement Co.; *Int'l*, pg. 2620
FAUJI CEMENT COMPANY LIMITED—See Fauji Foundation; *Int'l*, pg. 2623
FECTO CEMENT LIMITED—See Fecto Group of Companies; *Int'l*, pg. 2629
FEDERAL WHITE CEMENT; *Int'l*, pg. 2630
FINNSEMENTTI OY—See CRH plc; *Int'l*, pg. 1844
FLS MAROC S.A.—See FLSmidth & Co. A/S; *Int'l*, pg. 2710
FLSMIDTH A/S (JORDAN) LTD.—See FLSmidth & Co. A/S; *Int'l*, pg. 2710
FLSMIDTH (BEIJING) LTD.—See FLSmidth & Co. A/S; *Int'l*, pg. 2710
FLSMIDTH CAUCASUS LIMITED LIABILITY COMPANY—See FLSmidth & Co. A/S; *Int'l*, pg. 2710
FLSMIDTH & CO. A/S; *Int'l*, pg. 2710
FLSMIDTH CO., LTD.—See FLSmidth & Co. A/S; *Int'l*, pg. 2710
FLSMIDTH LTDA.—See FLSmidth & Co. A/S; *Int'l*, pg. 2710
FLSMIDTH MOZAMBIQUE LIMITADA—See FLSmidth & Co. A/S; *Int'l*, pg. 2711
FLSMIDTH PHILIPPINES, INC.—See FLSmidth & Co. A/S; *Int'l*, pg. 2711
FLSMIDTH QINGDAO LTD.—See FLSmidth & Co. A/S; *Int'l*, pg. 2711
FLSMIDTH SAS—See FLSmidth & Co. A/S; *Int'l*, pg. 2711
FLSMIDTH SPOL. S.R.O.—See FLSmidth & Co. A/S; *Int'l*, pg. 2711
FLSMIDTH (THAILAND) CO., LTD.—See FLSmidth & Co. A/S; *Int'l*, pg. 2710
FUJAIRAH CEMENT INDUSTRIES COMPANY PSC; *Int'l*, pg. 2808
FUJIAN CEMENT INC.; *Int'l*, pg. 2817
GANSU QILIANSHAN CEMENT GROUP CO., LTD.; *Int'l*, pg. 2881
GANSU SHANGFENG CEMENT CO LTD; *Int'l*, pg. 2881
GCC DACOTAH INC.; *U.S. Private*, pg. 1653
GCC, S.A.B. DE C.V.; *Int'l*, pg. 2894
GEOFER - PRODUCAO E COMERCIALIZACAO DE BENS E EQUIPAMENTOS, S.A.—See Camargo Correa S.A.; *Int'l*, pg. 1268
GHARIBWAL CEMENT LTD. - FACTORY—See GHARIBWAL CEMENT LIMITED; *Int'l*, pg. 2959
GIANT CEMENT COMPANY—See Grupo Empresarial Kaluz S.A. de C.V.; *Int'l*, pg. 3127
GIANT CEMENT NC, INC.—See Grupo Empresarial Kaluz S.A. de C.V.; *Int'l*, pg. 3127
GOLTAS CIMENTO A.S.; *Int'l*, pg. 3037
GORAZDZE CEMENT S.A.—See Heidelberg Materials AG; *Int'l*, pg. 3310
GRANOR S.A.S.—See Heidelberg Materials AG; *Int'l*, pg. 3310
GRANULATS BOURGOGNE AUVERGNE—See Holcim Ltd.; *Int'l*, pg. 3449
GROUPE CIMENT QUEBEC, INC.; *Int'l*, pg. 3101
GRUPA OZAROW S.A.—See CRH plc; *Int'l*, pg. 1844
GS GLOBAL AUSTRALIA PTY., LTD.—See GS Holdings Corp.; *Int'l*, pg. 3142
GUANGDONG TAPAI GROUP CO., LTD.; *Int'l*, pg. 3161
GUIZHOU NEW SHUANGLONG CEMENT CO., LTD.—See Anhui Conch Cement Company Limited; *Int'l*, pg. 467
GUJARAT SIDHEE CEMENT LIMITED; *Int'l*, pg. 3177
GULF CEMENT COMPANY P.S.C.; *Int'l*, pg. 3180
HAINAN RUIZE NEW BUILDING MATERIAL CO.; *Int'l*, pg. 3212
HANIL HYUNDAI CEMENT CO., LTD.—See Hanil Holdings Co., Ltd; *Int'l*, pg. 3252
HANSON AUSTRALIA CEMENT PTY LIMITED—See Heidelberg Materials AG; *Int'l*, pg. 3311
HANSON CEMENT LTD.—See Heidelberg Materials AG; *Int'l*, pg. 3308
HANSON CEMENT - RIBBLESDALE WORKS—See Heidelberg Materials AG; *Int'l*, pg. 3308
HANSON PEABODY LIMITED—See Heidelberg Materials AG; *Int'l*, pg. 3312
HAWAIIAN CEMENT; *U.S. Private*, pg. 1881
HAWAIIAN CEMENT—See MDU Resources Group, Inc.; *U.S. Public*, pg. 1410
HCT SERVICES ASIA PTE. LTD.—See Heidelberg Materials AG; *Int'l*, pg. 3311
HEIDELBERGCEMENT ASIA PTE LTD—See Heidelberg Materials AG; *Int'l*, pg. 3314
HEIDELBERGCEMENT BANGLADESH LIMITED—See Heidelberg Materials AG; *Int'l*, pg. 3314
HEIDELBERGCEMENT CHINA—See Heidelberg Materials AG; *Int'l*, pg. 3310
HEIDELBERGCEMENT INDIA LTD.—See Heidelberg Materials AG; *Int'l*, pg. 3314
HEIDELBERGCEMENT MILJO AB - PRODUCTION PLANT—See Heidelberg Materials AG; *Int'l*, pg. 3315
HEIDELBERGCEMENT NORTHERN EUROPE AB—See Heidelberg Materials AG; *Int'l*, pg. 3315
HEIDELBERGCEMENT NORWAY A.S.—See Heidelberg Materials AG; *Int'l*, pg. 3315
HEIDELBERGCEMENT ROMANIA SA—See Heidelberg Materials AG; *Int'l*, pg. 3315
HEIDELBERGCEMENT SHARED SERVICE CENTRE AB—See Heidelberg Materials AG; *Int'l*, pg. 3315
HEIDELBERGER BETON RHEIN-NAHE GMBH & CO.KG—See Heidelberg Materials AG; *Int'l*, pg. 3316
HEIDELBERG MATERIALS AG; *Int'l*, pg. 3308
HEIDELBERG MATERIALS BETON DE GMBH—See Heidelberg Materials AG; *Int'l*, pg. 3314
HEIDELBERG MATERIALS DIGITAL HUB BRNO, S.R.O.—See Heidelberg Materials AG; *Int'l*, pg. 3314
HEIDELBERG MATERIALS MINERALIK DE GMBH—See Heidelberg Materials AG; *Int'l*, pg. 3314
HEIDELBERG MATERIALS NORWAY AS—See Heidelberg Materials AG; *Int'l*, pg. 3314
HEIDELBERG MATERIALS PRECAST ABETONG AB—See Heidelberg Materials AG; *Int'l*, pg. 3314
HEIDELBERG MATERIALS PRECAST CONTIGA AB—See Heidelberg Materials AG; *Int'l*, pg. 3314
HELWAN CEMENT COMPANY S.A.E.—See Heidelberg Materials AG; *Int'l*, pg. 3316
HENKEL BAUTECHNIK (UKRAINA) TOB—See Henkel AG & Co. KGaA; *Int'l*, pg. 3349
HERACLES GENERAL CEMENT COMPANY S.A.—See Holcim Ltd.; *Int'l*, pg. 3446
HILAL CEMENT COMPANY K.S.C.C.; *Int'l*, pg. 3390
HIL LIMITED—See CK Birla Group; *Int'l*, pg. 1636
HIMA CEMENT LTD.—See Holcim Ltd.; *Int'l*, pg. 3446
HM GORAZDZE PREFABRYKACJA SP.Z.O.O.—See Heidelberg Materials AG; *Int'l*, pg. 3311
HOFFMANN GREEN CEMENT TECHNOLOGIES SAS; *Int'l*, pg. 3440
HOLCIBEL S.A.—See Holcim Ltd.; *Int'l*, pg. 3446
HOLCIM AGGREGATI CALCESTRUZZI S.R.L.—See Holcim Ltd.; *Int'l*, pg. 3448
HOLCIM (AZERBAIJAN) O.J.S.C.—See Holcim Ltd.; *Int'l*, pg. 3446
HOLCIM (BELGIQUE) S.A.—See Holcim Ltd.; *Int'l*, pg. 3446
HOLCIM (BULGARIA) AD—See Holcim Ltd.; *Int'l*, pg. 3447
HOLCIM CEMENTS (BANGLADESH) LTD.—See Holcim Ltd.; *Int'l*, pg. 3448
HOLCIM COLOMBIA S.A.—See Holcim Ltd.; *Int'l*, pg. 3448
HOLCIM (COSTA RICA) S.A. - CARTAGO PLANT—See Holcim Ltd.; *Int'l*, pg. 3448
HOLCIM COSTA RICA S.A.—See Holcim Ltd.; *Int'l*, pg. 3448
HOLCIM (DEUTSCHLAND) GMBH - BREMEN GRINDING PLANT—See Holcim Ltd.; *Int'l*, pg. 3447
HOLCIM (DEUTSCHLAND) GMBH - LAGERDORF PLANT—See Holcim Ltd.; *Int'l*, pg. 3447
HOLCIM (DEUTSCHLAND) GMBH—See Holcim Ltd.; *Int'l*, pg. 3447
HOLCIM EL SALVADOR S.A. DE C.V. - EL RONCO PLANT—See Holcim Ltd.; *Int'l*, pg. 3448
HOLCIM EL SALVADOR S.A. DE C.V. - MAYA PLANT—See Holcim Ltd.; *Int'l*, pg. 3448
HOLCIM EL SALVADOR S.A. DE C.V.—See Holcim Ltd.; *Int'l*, pg. 3448
HOLCIM (ESPANA) S.A. - JEREZ PLANT—See Holcim Ltd.; *Int'l*, pg. 3449
HOLCIM GRUPPO (ITALIA) S.P.A. - TERNATE PLANT—See Holcim Ltd.; *Int'l*, pg. 3448
HOLCIM (HRVATSKA) D.O.O.—See Holcim Ltd.; *Int'l*, pg. 3447
HOLCIM (LIBAN) S.A.L.—See Holcim Ltd.; *Int'l*, pg. 3447
HOLCIM LTD.; *Int'l*, pg. 3446
HOLCIM (MALAYSIA) SDN BHD. - PASIR GUDANG PLANT—See Holcim Ltd.; *Int'l*, pg. 3447
HOLCIM MEXICO S.A. DE C.V.—See Holcim Ltd.; *Int'l*, pg. 3448
HOLCIM (NICARAGUA) S.A.—See Holcim Ltd.; *Int'l*, pg. 3447
HOLCIM (PHILIPPINES) INC.—See Holcim Ltd.; *Int'l*, pg. 3447
HOLCIM (ROMANIA) S.A. - ALESD PLANT—See Holcim Ltd.; *Int'l*, pg. 3447
HOLCIM (ROMANIA) S.A. - CAMPULUNG PLANT—See Holcim Ltd.; *Int'l*, pg. 3447
HOLCIM (ROMANIA) S.A.—See Holcim Ltd.; *Int'l*, pg. 3447
HOLCIM (ROMANIA) S.A. - TURDA GRINDING PLANT—See Holcim Ltd.; *Int'l*, pg. 3447
HOLCIM (RUS) CM LTD. - SHUROVO PLANT—See Holcim Ltd.; *Int'l*, pg. 3449
HOLCIM (RUS) OOO- VOLSK PLANT—See Holcim Ltd.; *Int'l*, pg. 3449
HOLCIM (SINGAPORE) LIMITED—See Holcim Ltd.; *Int'l*, pg. 3447
HOLCIM (SUDDEUTSCHLAND) GMBH - DOTTERNHAUSEN PLANT—See Holcim Ltd.; *Int'l*, pg. 3447
HOLCIM (US) INC. - ADA PLANT—See Holcim Ltd.; *Int'l*, pg. 3447
HOLCIM (US) INC. - ARTESIA PLANT—See Holcim Ltd.; *Int'l*, pg. 3447
HOLCIM (US) INC. - BIRMINGHAM PLANT—See Holcim Ltd.; *Int'l*, pg. 3447
HOLCIM (US) INC. - HAGERSTOWN PLANT—See Holcim Ltd.; *Int'l*, pg. 3447
HOLCIM (US) INC. - HOLLY HILL PLANT—See Holcim Ltd.; *Int'l*, pg. 3447
HOLCIM (US) INC. - MIDLOTHIAN PLANT—See Holcim Ltd.; *Int'l*, pg. 3447
HOLCIM (US) INC. - PORTLAND PLANT—See Holcim Ltd.; *Int'l*, pg. 3447
HOLCIM (US) INC.—See Holcim Ltd.; *Int'l*, pg. 3447
HOLCIM (US) INC. - STE. GENEVIEVE PLANT—See Holcim Ltd.; *Int'l*, pg. 3447
HOLCIM (US) INC. - THEODORE PLANT—See Holcim Ltd.; *Int'l*, pg. 3447
HOLCIM (VENEZUELA) C.A.; *Int'l*, pg. 3446
HORMIGONES Y MINAS—See Heidelberg Materials AG; *Int'l*, pg. 3317
HORMOZGAN CEMENT CO.; *Int'l*, pg. 3481
HP ADHESIVES LIMITED; *Int'l*, pg. 3499
HSING TA CEMENT CO., LTD.; *Int'l*, pg. 3507
HUAXIN CEMENT CO., LTD.; *Int'l*, pg. 3515
HUU NGHI VINH SINH MINING & MECHANIC JSC; *Int'l*, pg. 3540
ILAM CEMENT CO.; *Int'l*, pg. 3613
ILLINOIS CEMENT COMPANY LLC—See Eagle Materials Inc.; *U.S. Public*, pg. 702
IMERYS ALUMINATES S.A.—See Groupe Bruxelles Lambert SA; *Int'l*, pg. 3100
INTERCEMENT BRASIL S.A.—See Camargo Correa S.A.; *Int'l*, pg. 1268
IRISH CEMENT LTD.—See CRH plc; *Int'l*, pg. 1844
ITACAMBA CEMENTO S.A.—See Cementos Molins S.A.; *Int'l*, pg. 1397
JALAPRATHAN CEMENT PUBLIC COMPANY LIMITED—See Heidelberg Materials AG; *Int'l*, pg. 3317
JIANGXI YADONG CEMENT CO., LTD.—See Asia Cement Corporation; *Int'l*, pg. 611
KERNEOS DO BRAZIL PRODUCAO E COMERCIO DE ALUMINOSOS LTDA—See Groupe Bruxelles Lambert SA; *Int'l*, pg. 3100
KERNEOS INC.—See Groupe Bruxelles Lambert SA; *Int'l*, pg. 3100
KERNEOS LTD.—See Groupe Bruxelles Lambert SA; *Int'l*, pg. 3100
KERNEOS SOUTHERN AFRICA (PTY) LTD.—See Groupe Bruxelles Lambert SA; *Int'l*, pg. 3100
KEYSTONE CEMENT COMPANY—See Grupo Empresarial

N.A.I.C.S. INDEX

327310 — CEMENT MANUFACTURIN...

Kaluz S.A. de C.V.; *Int'l*, pg. 3127
KOMMANDITBOLAGET CEMENTEN—See Heidelberg Materials AG; *Int'l*, pg. 3318
KOREA CEMENT CO., LTD.—See Gangdong Industry Co., Ltd.; *Int'l*, pg. 2880
KUNDA NORDIC CEMENT CORP.—See Heidelberg Materials AG; *Int'l*, pg. 3318
LA CIMENTERIE DE LUKALA S.A.R.L.—See Heidelberg Materials AG; *Int'l*, pg. 3318
LAFARGE ALGERIE—See Holcim Ltd.; *Int'l*, pg. 3448
LAFARGE BEOCINSKA FABRIKA CEMENTA D.O.O.—See Holcim Ltd.; *Int'l*, pg. 3448
LAFARGE CANADA INC.—See Holcim Ltd.; *Int'l*, pg. 3449
LAFARGE CANADA INC.—See Holcim Ltd.; *Int'l*, pg. 3449
LAFARGE CEMENT AS—See Holcim Ltd.; *Int'l*, pg. 3448
LAFARGE CEMENT D.O.O.—See Holcim Ltd.; *Int'l*, pg. 3448
LAFARGE CEMENT MALAWI LTD.—See Holcim Ltd.; *Int'l*, pg. 3448
LAFARGE CEMENT S.A.—See Holcim Ltd.; *Int'l*, pg. 3448
LAFARGE CEMENT SYRIA—See Holcim Ltd.; *Int'l*, pg. 3448
LAFARGE CEMENT ZIMBABWE LIMITED—See Holcim Ltd.; *Int'l*, pg. 3448
LAFARGE CIMENTS ANTILLES—See Holcim Ltd.; *Int'l*, pg. 3448
LAFARGEHOLCIM (BRASIL) S.A. - BARROSO PLANT—See Companhia Siderurgica Nacional; *Int'l*, pg. 1748
LAFARGEHOLCIM (BRASIL) S.A. - CANTAGALO PLANT—See Companhia Siderurgica Nacional; *Int'l*, pg. 1748
LAFARGEHOLCIM (BRASIL) S.A.—See Companhia Siderurgica Nacional; *Int'l*, pg. 1748
LAFARGEHOLCIM ESPANA S.A.—See Holcim Ltd.; *Int'l*, pg. 3449
LAFARGEHOLCIM FRANCE SAS—See Holcim Ltd.; *Int'l*, pg. 3449
LAFARGEHOLCIM GUINEE—See Holcim Ltd.; *Int'l*, pg. 3449
LAFARGEHOLCIM MAROC—See Holcim Ltd.; *Int'l*, pg. 3448
LAFARGEHOLCIM RUSSIA—See Holcim Ltd.; *Int'l*, pg. 3449
LAFARGE INDUSTRIES SOUTH AFRICA (PTY) LTD.—See Holcim Ltd.; *Int'l*, pg. 3448
LAFARGE KRUSZYWA I BETON SP. Z O.O.—See Holcim Ltd.; *Int'l*, pg. 3448
LAFARGE (MAURITIUS) CEMENT LTD—See Holcim Ltd.; *Int'l*, pg. 3448
LAFARGE NORTH AMERICA INC. - WHITEHALL CEMENT PLANT—See Holcim Ltd.; *Int'l*, pg. 3449
LAFARGE READYMIX NIGERIA LIMITED—See Holcim Ltd.; *Int'l*, pg. 3448
LAFARGE ZEMENTWERKE GMBH—See Holcim Ltd.; *Int'l*, pg. 3449
LEHIGH CEMENT COMPANY LLC—See Heidelberg Materials AG; *Int'l*, pg. 3313
LEHIGH CEMENT CO.—See Heidelberg Materials AG; *Int'l*, pg. 3313
LEHIGH CEMENT - INDIANA PLANT—See Heidelberg Materials AG; *Int'l*, pg. 3317
LEHIGH CEMENT—See Heidelberg Materials AG; *Int'l*, pg. 3313
LEHIGH HANSON CANADA—See Heidelberg Materials AG; *Int'l*, pg. 3313
LEHIGH HANSON ECC, INC.—See Heidelberg Materials AG; *Int'l*, pg. 3317
LEHIGH NORTHEAST CEMENT CO.—See Heidelberg Materials AG; *Int'l*, pg. 3313
LEHIGH NORTHWEST CEMENT COMPANY—See Heidelberg Materials AG; *Int'l*, pg. 3314
LEHIGH SOUTHWEST CEMENT COMPANY—See Heidelberg Materials AG; *Int'l*, pg. 3313
LEHIGH WHITE CEMENT COMPANY—See Cementir Holding N.V.; *Int'l*, pg. 1397
LEHIGH WHITE CEMENT COMPANY - WACO PLANT—See Cementir Holding N.V.; *Int'l*, pg. 1397
LESCHUPLAT GMBH—See Buzzi SpA; *Int'l*, pg. 1230
LIBERIA CEMENT CORPORATION LTD.—See Heidelberg Materials AG; *Int'l*, pg. 3318
LIMAY GRINDING MILL CORPORATION CO. LTD.—See Heidelberg Materials AG; *Int'l*, pg. 3310
LLC HEIDELBERGCEMENT RUS—See Heidelberg Materials AG; *Int'l*, pg. 3318
LOMA NEGRA CIA INDUSTRIA ARGENTINA SA—See Camargo Correa S.A.; *Int'l*, pg. 1268
LOWDENS—See Grafton Group plc; *Int'l*, pg. 3051
LUCKY MINMAT LIMITED—See Adani Enterprises Limited; *Int'l*, pg. 125
LUQUAN DONGFANG DINGXIN CEMENT CO., LTD—See BBMG Corporation; *Int'l*, pg. 921
MACAO CEMENT MANUFACTURING CO., LTD.—See CITIC Group Corporation; *Int'l*, pg. 1621
MARINE CEMENT AG—See Holcim Ltd.; *Int'l*, pg. 3449
MATERIAUX S.A.—See Buzzi SpA; *Int'l*, pg. 1230
MBEYA CEMENT COMPANY LIMITED—See Holcim Ltd.; *Int'l*, pg. 3449

MEAG VA-SYSTEM AB—See Heidelberg Materials AG; *Int'l*, pg. 3315
MEBIN LEEUWARDEN B.V.—See Heidelberg Materials AG; *Int'l*, pg. 3318
MORAVACEM D.O.O.—See CRH plc; *Int'l*, pg. 1845
MOUNTAIN CEMENT COMPANY—See Eagle Materials Inc.; *U.S. Public*, pg. 702
NANCHANG YALI CONCRETE PRODUCE LTD.—See Asia Cement Corporation; *Int'l*, pg. 611
NATAL PORTLAND CEMENT COMPANY (PTY) LTD.—See Camargo Correa S.A.; *Int'l*, pg. 1268
NATIONAL CEMENT HOLDINGS LIMITED—See Devki Group of Companies; *Int'l*, pg. 2089
NESHER ISRAEL CEMENT ENTERPRISES LTD.—See Access Industries, Inc.; *U.S. Private*, pg. 51
NEVADA CEMENT COMPANY—See Eagle Materials Inc.; *U.S. Public*, pg. 702
NINGXIA BUILDING MATERIALS GROUP CO., LTD.—See China National Materials; *Int'l*, pg. 1532
NLSUPERVISION COMPANY ANGOLA, LTDA.—See FLSmidth & Co. A/S; *Int'l*, pg. 2711
NL SUPERVISION COMPANY TUNISIA SARL—See FLSmidth & Co. A/S; *Int'l*, pg. 2711
NORCEM A.S.—See Heidelberg Materials AG; *Int'l*, pg. 3318
NORTHERN CEMENT LTD.—See CRH plc; *Int'l*, pg. 1842
NOVA CIMANGOLA S.A.R.L.—See Heidelberg Materials AG; *Int'l*, pg. 3315
OAO SUCHOLOSHSKZEMENT—See Buzzi SpA; *Int'l*, pg. 1230
OCL INDIA LIMITED—See Dalmia Bharat Limited; *Int'l*, pg. 1954
OJSC CESLA—See Heidelberg Materials AG; *Int'l*, pg. 3318
OMAN CEMENT COMPANY SAOG—See HUAXIN CEMENT CO., LTD.; *Int'l*, pg. 3515
ONEINDIA BSC PRIVATE LIMITED—See Adani Enterprises Limited; *Int'l*, pg. 125
OPEN JOINT-STOCK COMPANY SLANTSY CEMENT PLANT CESLA—See Heidelberg Materials AG; *Int'l*, pg. 3318
OPTERRA GMBH—See CRH plc; *Int'l*, pg. 1845
OPTERRA ZEMENT GMBH—See CRH plc; *Int'l*, pg. 1845
OSWALD TILLOTSON LIMITED—See Heidelberg Materials AG; *Int'l*, pg. 3318
OYSA CIMENTO SANAYII A.S.—See Haci Omer Sabanci Holding A.S.; *Int'l*, pg. 3203
PACIFIC CEMENT PTE LIMITED—See Fijian Holdings Limited; *Int'l*, pg. 2662
PAKCEM LIMITED—See Bestway (Holdings) Limited; *Int'l*, pg. 1001
PJSC MYKOLAIVCEMENT—See CRH plc; *Int'l*, pg. 1848
PODILSKY CEMENT PJSC—See CRH plc; *Int'l*, pg. 1848
POVAZSKA CEMENTAREN A.S.—See BERGER Holding GmbH; *Int'l*, pg. 979
PREMIER CEMENT LIMITED—See CRH plc; *Int'l*, pg. 1848
PRETORIA PORTLAND CEMENT CO. LTD.—See Barloworld Ltd.; *Int'l*, pg. 866
PROMSA—See Cementos Molins S.A.; *Int'l*, pg. 1397
PT CONCH NORTH SULAWESI CEMENT—See Anhui Conch Cement Company Limited; *Int'l*, pg. 467
PT CONCH SOUTH KALIMANTAN CEMENT—See Anhui Conch Cement Company Limited; *Int'l*, pg. 467
P.T. SEMEN GROBOGAN—See Heidelberg Materials AG; *Int'l*, pg. 3318
REPUBLIC CEMENT & BUILDING MATERIALS INC.—See Aboitiz Equity Ventures, Inc.; *Int'l*, pg. 66
REPUBLIC CEMENT & BUILDING MATERIALS INC.—See CRH plc; *Int'l*, pg. 1842
REPUBLIC CEMENT SERVICES, INC. - BATANGAS PLANT—See Aboitiz Equity Ventures, Inc.; *Int'l*, pg. 66
REPUBLIC CEMENT SERVICES, INC. - BATANGAS PLANT—See CRH plc; *Int'l*, pg. 1842
REPUBLIC CEMENT SERVICES, INC. - BULACAN CEMENT PLANT—See Aboitiz Equity Ventures, Inc.; *Int'l*, pg. 66
REPUBLIC CEMENT SERVICES, INC. - BULACAN CEMENT PLANT—See CRH plc; *Int'l*, pg. 1842
REPUBLIC CEMENT SERVICES, INC. - NORZAGARAY PLANT—See Aboitiz Equity Ventures, Inc.; *Int'l*, pg. 66
REPUBLIC CEMENT SERVICES, INC. - NORZAGARAY PLANT—See CRH plc; *Int'l*, pg. 1842
REPUBLIC CEMENT SERVICES, INC.—See Aboitiz Equity Ventures, Inc.; *Int'l*, pg. 66
REPUBLIC CEMENT SERVICES, INC.—See CRH plc; *Int'l*, pg. 1842
REPUBLIC CEMENT SERVICES, INC. - TERESA PLANT—See Aboitiz Equity Ventures, Inc.; *Int'l*, pg. 66
REPUBLIC CEMENT SERVICES, INC. - TERESA PLANT—See CRH plc; *Int'l*, pg. 1842
RHEBAU RHEINISCHE BETON- UND BAUINDUSTRIE GMBH & CO. KG—See Buzzi SpA; *Int'l*, pg. 1230
SAARLANDISCHE ZEMENT GESELLSCHAFT GMBH—See Heidelberg Materials AG; *Int'l*, pg. 3317
SAUDI FLSMIDTH CO.—See FLSmidth & Co. A/S; *Int'l*, pg. 2712
SA VICTIRIA INTERNATIONAL TECHNOLOGY PTY. LTD.—See Eastern Platinum Limited; *Int'l*, pg. 2273
SCANCEM INTERNATIONAL ANS—See Heidelberg Materials AG; *Int'l*, pg. 3315

SCANCEM INTERNATIONAL DA—See Heidelberg Materials AG; *Int'l*, pg. 3319
SEMENTSVERKSMIDJAN EHF—See Heidelberg Materials AG; *Int'l*, pg. 3319
SEPHAKU CEMENT (PTY) LIMITED—See Dangote Group Limited; *Int'l*, pg. 1962
SHANDONG SHANSHUI CEMENT GROUP LTD. (SUNNSY)—See China Shanshui Cement Group Ltd.; *Int'l*, pg. 1550
SHANGHAI CONCH CEMENT CO., LTD.—See Anhui Conch Cement Company Limited; *Int'l*, pg. 467
SHANGHAI CONCH CONSTRUCTION MATERIAL INTERNATIONAL TRADING CO., LTD.—See Anhui Conch Cement Company Limited; *Int'l*, pg. 467
SICHUAN YADONG CEMENT CO., LTD.—See Asia Cement Corporation; *Int'l*, pg. 611
SIERRA LEONE CEMENT CORP. LTD.—See Heidelberg Materials AG; *Int'l*, pg. 3315
SKYWAY CEMENT COMPANY LLC—See Eagle Materials Inc.; *U.S. Public*, pg. 702
SOCIEDAD DE CEMENTOS Y MATERIALES DE CONSTRUCCION DE ANDALUCIA S.A.—See Camargo Correa S.A.; *Int'l*, pg. 1268
SOCIEDAD FINANCIERA Y MINERA S.A. - ANORGA CEMENT FACTORY—See Heidelberg Materials AG; *Int'l*, pg. 3317
SOCIEDAD FINANCIERA Y MINERA S.A. - ARRIGORRIAGA CEMENT FACTORY—See Heidelberg Materials AG; *Int'l*, pg. 3317
SOCIEDAD FINANCIERA Y MINERA S.A. - MALAGA CEMENT FACTORY—See Heidelberg Materials AG; *Int'l*, pg. 3317
SOCIEDAD FINANCIERA Y MINERA, SA—See Heidelberg Materials AG; *Int'l*, pg. 3317
SOCIETE TUNISO-ANDALOUSE DE CIMENT BLANC—See Cementos Molins S.A.; *Int'l*, pg. 1397
SOLA BETONG AS—See Heidelberg Materials AG; *Int'l*, pg. 3319
SOLID CEMENT CORP.—See CEMEX, S.A.B. de C.V.; *Int'l*, pg. 1398
SOUTH COAST STONE CRUSHERS (PTY) LTD.—See Camargo Correa S.A.; *Int'l*, pg. 1268
SSANGYONG CEMENT INDUSTRIAL CO., LTD. - DONGHAE PLANT—See Hahn & Company; *Int'l*, pg. 3208
SSANGYONG CEMENT INDUSTRIAL CO., LTD.—See Hahn & Company; *Int'l*, pg. 3208
SSANGYONG CEMENT INDUSTRIAL CO., LTD. - YEONGWOL PLANT—See Hahn & Company; *Int'l*, pg. 3208
SSANGYONG CEMENT SINGAPORE (CHINA) PTE LTD—See EnGro Corporation Limited; *Int'l*, pg. 2436
STARKEN DRYMIX SOLUTIONS SDN BHD—See Chin Hin Group Berhad; *Int'l*, pg. 1480
SUEZ CEMENT COMPANY (S.A.E.)—See Heidelberg Materials AG; *Int'l*, pg. 3320
SUWANNEE AMERICAN CEMENT CO INC—See Anderson Columbia Co. Inc.; *U.S. Private*, pg. 276
SUZHOU TIANSHAN CEMENT CO.,LTD.—See China National Materials; *Int'l*, pg. 1532
TANZANIA PORTLAND CEMENT COMPANY LTD.—See Heidelberg Materials AG; *Int'l*, pg. 3315
TARMAC CEMENT & LIME LIMITED—See CRH plc; *Int'l*, pg. 1848
TASEK CORPORATION BERHAD - IPOH FACTORY—See Hong Leong Investment Holdings Pte. Ltd.; *Int'l*, pg. 3469
TEXAS LEHIGH CEMENT COMPANY LP—See Eagle Materials Inc.; *U.S. Public*, pg. 702
TEXAS LEHIGH CEMENT COMPANY LP—See Heidelberg Materials AG; *Int'l*, pg. 3313
TIANRUI GROUP NANZHAO CEMENT COMPANY LIMITED—See China Tianrui Group Cement Company Limited; *Int'l*, pg. 1559
TIANRUI GROUP ZHOUKOU CEMENT COMPANY LIMITED—See China Tianrui Group Cement Company Limited; *Int'l*, pg. 1559
TIANRUI XINDENG ZHENGZHOU CEMENT COMPANY LIMITED—See China Tianrui Group Cement Company Limited; *Int'l*, pg. 1559
TOURAH PORTLAND CEMENT COMPANY—See Heidelberg Materials AG; *Int'l*, pg. 3320
TRINIDAD CEMENT LIMITED—See CEMEX, S.A.B. de C.V.; *Int'l*, pg. 1400
TUBAG TRASS-ZEMENT-STEINWERKE GMBH—See Buzzi SpA; *Int'l*, pg. 1231
TULACEMENT LIMITED LIABILITY COMPANY—See Heidelberg Materials AG; *Int'l*, pg. 3320
TXI RIVERSIDE INC.—See Martin Marietta Materials, Inc.; *U.S. Public*, pg. 1389
VALLEY STRONG CEMENTS (ASSAM) LIMITED—See Barak Valley Cements Limited; *Int'l*, pg. 858
VEGA INDUSTRIES (MIDDLE EAST) F.Z.C.—See AIA Engineering Ltd.; *Int'l*, pg. 227
YA LI PRECAST & PRESTRESSED CONCRETE INDUSTRIES CORP.—See Asia Cement Corporation; *Int'l*, pg. 611
YANTAI SHANSHUI CEMENT CO.,LTD—See China Shanshui Cement Group Ltd.; *Int'l*, pg. 1550
YURA CHILE SA—See Consorcio Cementero del Sur SA; *Int'l*, pg. 1772

327310 — CEMENT MANUFACTURIN...

ZUARI CEMENT—See Heidelberg Materials AG; *Int'l*, pg. 3317

327320 — READY-MIX CONCRETE MANUFACTURING

AAMAL READYMIX—See Aamal Company Q.S.C.; *Int'l*, pg. 36
A&A READY MIXED CONCRETE INC.; *U.S. Private*, pg. 19
ABUNDANTE LIMITED; *Int'l*, pg. 74
ACC LIMITED - BACHUPALLY PLANT—See ACC Limited; *Int'l*, pg. 78
ACC LIMITED - CHANGODAR PLANT—See ACC Limited; *Int'l*, pg. 78
ACC LIMITED - GHAZIABAD CONCRETE PLANT—See ACC Limited; *Int'l*, pg. 78
ACC LIMITED - GREATER NOIDA CONCRETE PLANT—See ACC Limited; *Int'l*, pg. 79
ACC LIMITED - JAIPUR PLANT—See ACC Limited; *Int'l*, pg. 79
ACC LIMITED - LUDHIANA PLANT—See ACC Limited; *Int'l*, pg. 79
ACC LIMITED - MANDOLI PLANT—See ACC Limited; *Int'l*, pg. 79
ACC LIMITED - MOHALI PLANT—See ACC Limited; *Int'l*, pg. 79
ACC LIMITED - PATANCHERU PLANT—See ACC Limited; *Int'l*, pg. 79
ACC LIMITED - RAJARHAT PLANT—See ACC Limited; *Int'l*, pg. 79
ACHESON & GLOVER LTD.; *Int'l*, pg. 103
AFRIMAT READYMIX (CAPE) (PTY) LIMITED—See Afrimat Limited; *Int'l*, pg. 192
AFRIMIX READY MIXED CONCRETE (PROPRIETARY) LIMITED - BENONI PLANT—See Group Five Limited; *Int'l*, pg. 3089
AFRIMIX READY MIXED CONCRETE (PROPRIETARY) LIMITED - BLUE HILLS PLANT—See Group Five Limited; *Int'l*, pg. 3089
AFRIMIX READY MIXED CONCRETE (PROPRIETARY) LIMITED—See Group Five Limited; *Int'l*, pg. 3089
AGGREGATE INDUSTRIES - SOUTHWEST REGION—See Holcim Ltd.; *Int'l*, pg. 3446
AHLCON READY MIX CONCRETE PVT. LTD. - BOMMENHALLI PLANT—See Ahluwalia Contracts (India) Limited; *Int'l*, pg. 225
AHLCON READY MIX CONCRETE PVT. LTD.—See Ahluwalia Contracts (India) Limited; *Int'l*, pg. 225
ALABAMA CONCRETE CO., INC.; *U.S. Private*, pg. 148
ALEX FRASER ASPHALT PTY. LTD.—See Heidelberg Materials AG; *Int'l*, pg. 3308
AL GHURAIR CONSTRUCTION - READYMIX LLC—See Al Ghurair Investment LLC; *Int'l*, pg. 278
AL GHURAIR CONSTRUCTION & READYMIX SAUDI LLC—See Al Ghurair Investment LLC; *Int'l*, pg. 278
AL GHURAIR CONSTRUCTION - READYMIX WLL—See Al Ghurair Investment LLC; *Int'l*, pg. 278
ALLIED READY MIX CONCRETE LIMITED—See Heidelberg Materials AG; *Int'l*, pg. 3308
ALL OHIO READY MIX—See CRH plc; *Int'l*, pg. 1847
AL QUDS READYMIX; *Int'l*, pg. 282
ALRASHID-ABETONG CO. LTD.—See Heidelberg Materials AG; *Int'l*, pg. 3315
AMATEK INDUSTRIES PTY LIMITED—See Fletcher Building Limited; *Int'l*, pg. 2699
AMERICAN CONCRETE PRODUCTS—See CRH plc; *Int'l*, pg. 1847
AMERICAN READY MIX INC.; *U.S. Private*, pg. 245
AMERICAN TRANSIT MIX CEMEX—See CEMEX, S.A.B. de C.V.; *Int'l*, pg. 1399
AMES SAND & GRAVEL, INC.—See MDU Resources Group, Inc.; *U.S. Public*, pg. 1409
ANDERSON CONCRETE CORP.; *U.S. Private*, pg. 276
ANGELLE CONCRETE GROUP, LLC; *U.S. Private*, pg. 282
ARGOS USA CORPORATION - GAINESVILLE BLOCK/READY-MIX—See Grupo Argos S.A.; *Int'l*, pg. 3120
ARGOS USA CORPORATION - LINEBAUGH READY-MIX—See Grupo Argos S.A.; *Int'l*, pg. 3120
ARGOS USA CORPORATION - PALMETTO READY-MIX—See Grupo Argos S.A.; *Int'l*, pg. 3120
ARROW CONCRETE COMPANY; *U.S. Private*, pg. 335
ASH GROVE CEMENT COMPANY, CEMENT PLT—See CRH plc; *Int'l*, pg. 1842
ASH VENTURE LLC—See SER Capital Partners LLC; *U.S. Private*, pg. 3612
ASIA CEMENT CORPORATION; *Int'l*, pg. 611
ASIA HOLDINGS CO., LTD. - DAEJEON PLANT—See Asia Holdings Co., Ltd.; *Int'l*, pg. 612
ASIA HOLDINGS CO., LTD. - HONGSEONG PLANT—See Asia Holdings Co., Ltd.; *Int'l*, pg. 612
ASIA HOLDINGS CO., LTD. - JECHEON PLANT—See Asia Holdings Co., Ltd.; *Int'l*, pg. 612
ASIA HOLDINGS CO., LTD. - JUNGBU PLANT—See Asia Holdings Co., Ltd.; *Int'l*, pg. 612
ASSOCIATED READY MIX CONCRETE; *U.S. Private*, pg. 357

ASTEC INDUSTRIES AFRICA MIDDLE EAST (PTY) LTD.—See Astec Industries, Inc.; *U.S. Public*, pg. 216
ATLAS-TUCK CONCRETE, INC.—See Vulcan Materials Company; *U.S. Public*, pg. 2313
AUSTRAL PRECAST PTY LTD—See Brickworks Limited; *Int'l*, pg. 1152
AZTEC MATERIAL SERVICE CORP.; *U.S. Private*, pg. 416
BALDWIN REDI-MIX CO. INC.; *U.S. Private*, pg. 459
BAMA CONCRETE BIRMINGHAM, INC.—See Bama Concrete Products Co., Inc.; *U.S. Private*, pg. 463
BAMA CONCRETE PRODUCTS CO., INC.; *U.S. Private*, pg. 463
BASIC MATERIALS; *U.S. Private*, pg. 485
BAYKAZ BETON LLP—See Heidelberg Materials AG; *Int'l*, pg. 3309
BAYOU CONCRETE COMPANY INC.—See Ready Mix USA, Inc.; *U.S. Private*, pg. 3367
B&B CONCRETE COMPANY INC.; *U.S. Private*, pg. 417
BEATRICE CONCRETE COMPANY INC.—See Nebco Inc.; *U.S. Private*, pg. 2878
BEELMAN TRUCK CO. INC.; *U.S. Private*, pg. 514
BEKTAS GROUP LLP—See Heidelberg Materials AG; *Int'l*, pg. 3308
BELHASA FOR QUARRIES & CRUSHERS MANAGEMENT L.L.C—See Belhasa Group of Companies; *Int'l*, pg. 964
BERGER BETON GMBH—See BERGER Holding GmbH; *Int'l*, pg. 979
BETABEIRAS - BETOES DA BEIRA S.A.—See Camargo Correa S.A.; *Int'l*, pg. 1267
BETON CATALAN S.A.—See CRH plc; *Int'l*, pg. 1843
BETON DE LIEGE SA—See Heidelberg Materials AG; *Int'l*, pg. 3309
BETON DU RIED S.A.S.—See Buzzi SpA; *Int'l*, pg. 1230
BETON MANUFACTURE DE VITRE—See Compagnie de Saint-Gobain SA; *Int'l*, pg. 1722
BETONMORTEL CENTRALE GRONINGEN (B.C.G.) B.V.—See Buzzi SpA; *Int'l*, pg. 1230
BETOTECH BAUSTOFFLABOR GMBH—See Heidelberg Materials AG; *Int'l*, pg. 3309
BETOTECH GMBH—See Heidelberg Materials AG; *Int'l*, pg. 3309
BLINKBONNY QUARRY (BORDERS) LIMITED—See Breedon Group plc; *Int'l*, pg. 1144
BMC ENTERPRISES, INC—See Breedon Group plc; *Int'l*, pg. 1144
B.M.H. SYSTEMS INC.—See Astec Industries, Inc.; *U.S. Public*, pg. 216
BODIN CONCRETE LP; *U.S. Private*, pg. 608
BOGER CONCRETE; *U.S. Private*, pg. 609
BOLIVAR READY MIX & MATERIAL, INC.; *U.S. Private*, pg. 610
BOSTON SAND & GRAVEL COMPANY; *U.S. Public*, pg. 373
BOUBLOK (PTY) LIMITED—See Afrimat Limited; *Int'l*, pg. 192
BRECKENRIDGE MATERIAL COMPANY—See Breedon Group plc; *Int'l*, pg. 1144
BROADWAY & FRAME PREMIX CONCRETE PTY LTD—See Holcim Ltd.; *Int'l*, pg. 3446
BUCKEYE READY-MIX LLC; *U.S. Private*, pg. 677
BUILDERS SAND & CEMENT CO., INC.; *U.S. Private*, pg. 682
BULK CEMENT CORPORATION (INDIA) LIMITED—See ACC Limited; *Int'l*, pg. 79
BURNCO ROCK PRODUCTS LTD; *Int'l*, pg. 1226
BURSA BETON A.S.—See Bursa Cimento Fabrikasi A.S.; *Int'l*, pg. 1226
BURSA BETON SANAYI TICARET A.S.—See Bursa Cimento Fabrikasi A.S.; *Int'l*, pg. 1226
BUSAN INDUSTRIAL CO., LTD.; *Int'l*, pg. 1227
BUTRA HEIDELBERGCEMENT SDN. BHD.—See Heidelberg Materials AG; *Int'l*, pg. 3308
B.V. MORTEL INSTALLATIE ASSEN—See Heidelberg Materials AG; *Int'l*, pg. 3308
BYRAM CONCRETE & SUPPLY LLC—See Peckham Industries, Inc.; *U.S. Private*, pg. 3127
CADMAN (BLACK DIAMOND), INC.—See Heidelberg Materials AG; *Int'l*, pg. 3309
CADMAN, INC.—See Heidelberg Materials AG; *Int'l*, pg. 3313
CADMAN (SEATTLE), INC.—See Heidelberg Materials AG; *Int'l*, pg. 3309
CALAVERAS MATERIALS INC. - CENTRAL AVENUE PLANT—See Heidelberg Materials AG; *Int'l*, pg. 3313
CALAVERAS MATERIALS INC. - LATHROP PLANT—See Heidelberg Materials AG; *Int'l*, pg. 3313
CALAVERAS MATERIALS INC. - RIVER ROCK PLANT—See Heidelberg Materials AG; *Int'l*, pg. 3314
CALAVERAS MATERIALS INC. - SAN ANDREAS PLANT—See Heidelberg Materials AG; *Int'l*, pg. 3314
CALAVERAS MATERIALS INC.—See Heidelberg Materials AG; *Int'l*, pg. 3313
CALAVERAS MATERIALS INC. - THORNE AVENUE PLANT—See Heidelberg Materials AG; *Int'l*, pg. 3314
CALAVERAS STANDARD MATERIALS—See Heidelberg Materials AG; *Int'l*, pg. 3309
CALCESTRUZZI S.P.A—See Heidelberg Materials AG; *Int'l*, pg. 3316

CALIFORNIA NANOTECHNOLOGIES CORP.; *U.S. Private*, pg. 719
CAMPBELL CONCRETE & MATERIALS, L.P.—See Heidelberg Materials AG; *Int'l*, pg. 3313
CANTON AGGREGATE DIVISION—See Central Allied Enterprises; *U.S. Private*, pg. 818
CAPITAL CONCRETE, INC.; *U.S. Private*, pg. 739
CAREW CONCRETE & SUPPLY CO. INC.; *U.S. Private*, pg. 754
CARPAT BETON S.R.L.—See Heidelberg Materials AG; *Int'l*, pg. 3309
CCI MANUFACTURING INC.; *U.S. Private*, pg. 799
CDN-USA, INC.—See Fomento de Construcciones y Contratas, S.A.; *Int'l*, pg. 2722
CEMENTBOUW B.V.—See CRH plc; *Int'l*, pg. 1844
CEMENTOS OTORONGO, S.A.C.—See Consorcio Cementero del Sur SA; *Int'l*, pg. 1772
CEMEX CZECH REPUBLIC K.S.—See CEMEX, S.A.B. de C.V.; *Int'l*, pg. 1398
CEMEX, INC. - LAKELAND—See CEMEX, S.A.B. de C.V.; *Int'l*, pg. 1399
CEMEX, INC. - MCKELLINGTON CANYON—See CEMEX, S.A.B. de C.V.; *Int'l*, pg. 1399
CEMEX, INC. - MESA—See CEMEX, S.A.B. de C.V.; *Int'l*, pg. 1399
CEMEX, INC. - NAPLES—See CEMEX, S.A.B. de C.V.; *Int'l*, pg. 1399
CEMEX, INC.—See CEMEX, S.A.B. de C.V.; *Int'l*, pg. 1399
CEMEX READY MIXED CONCRETE (EAST MIDLANDS) LTD.—See CEMEX, S.A.B. de C.V.; *Int'l*, pg. 1399
CEMITALY S.P.A.—See Heidelberg Materials AG; *Int'l*, pg. 3309
CEMSTONE PRODUCTS COMPANY INC.; *U.S. Private*, pg. 808
CEMSTONE READY MIX, INC.—See Cemstone Products Company Inc.; *U.S. Private*, pg. 808
CENTRAL ALLIED ENTERPRISES; *U.S. Private*, pg. 818
CENTRAL CONCRETE SUPPLY CO., INC.—See Vulcan Materials Company; *U.S. Public*, pg. 2313
CENTRAL OREGON REDI-MIX, LLC—See MDU Resources Group, Inc.; *U.S. Public*, pg. 1410
CENTURY READY MIX CORPORATION; *U.S. Private*, pg. 834
CHANDLER CONCRETE COMPANY INC.—See Chandler Concrete Inc.; *U.S. Private*, pg. 848
CHANDLER CONCRETE INC.; *U.S. Private*, pg. 848
CHANEY ENTERPRISES LP; *U.S. Private*, pg. 848
CHARLEYS CONCRETE CO.; *U.S. Private*, pg. 857
CHINA INFRASTRUCTURE CONSTRUCTION CORPORATION; *Int'l*, pg. 1510
CHINA RESOURCES CONCRETE (NANNING) LIMITED—See China Resources Building Materials Technology Holdings Limited; *Int'l*, pg. 1548
CHIN HIN CONCRETE (KL) SDN BHD—See Chin Hin Group Berhad; *Int'l*, pg. 1480
CHIN HIN CONCRETE (NORTH) SDN BHD—See Chin Hin Group Berhad; *Int'l*, pg. 1480
CIMALUX S.A.—See Buzzi SpA; *Int'l*, pg. 1230
CIMPOR HORMIGON ESPANA, S.A.—See Camargo Correa S.A.; *Int'l*, pg. 1267
CJ HORNER COMPANY INC.; *U.S. Private*, pg. 908
CLEMENTS CONCRETE CO—See Clyde Companies Inc.; *U.S. Private*, pg. 949
CMS CEMENT INDUSTRIES SDN. BHD.—See Cahya Mata Sarawak Berhad; *Int'l*, pg. 1251
CMS CONCRETE PRODUCTS SDN. BHD.—See Cahya Mata Sarawak Berhad; *Int'l*, pg. 1251
CMS PREMIX SDN. BHD.—See Cahya Mata Sarawak Berhad; *Int'l*, pg. 1251
COLOR STAR TECHNOLOGY CO., LTD.; *U.S. Public*, pg. 533
CON-AGG OF MO, LLC—See Summit Materials, Inc.; *U.S. Public*, pg. 1960
CONCRETE COMPANY SPRINGFIELD; *U.S. Private*, pg. 1011
CONCRETE, INC.—See MDU Resources Group, Inc.; *U.S. Public*, pg. 1410
CONCRETE INDUSTRY DIV—See CEMEX, S.A.B. de C.V.; *Int'l*, pg. 1398
CONCRETE RECYCLERS AUSTRALIA PTY. LTD.—See Heidelberg Materials AG; *Int'l*, pg. 3310
CONCRETE SUPPLY CO.; *U.S. Private*, pg. 1011
CONCRETE SUPPLY OF TOPEKA, INC.—See Summit Materials, Inc.; *U.S. Public*, pg. 1960
CONSUMER ACQUISITIONS, INC.; *U.S. Private*, pg. 1025
CONSUMERS CONCRETE CORPORATION; *U.S. Private*, pg. 1026
CONTRACTOR'S SUPPLIES, INC. - LONGVIEW PLANT—See Contractor's Supplies, Inc.; *U.S. Private*, pg. 1032
CONTRACTOR'S SUPPLIES, INC. - LUFKIN PLANT—See Contractor's Supplies, Inc.; *U.S. Private*, pg. 1032
CONTRACTOR'S SUPPLIES, INC. - MARSHALL PLANT—See Contractor's Supplies, Inc.; *U.S. Private*, pg. 1032
CONTRACTOR'S SUPPLIES, INC.; *U.S. Private*, pg. 1032
CONTRACTOR'S SUPPLIES, INC. - TYLER PLANT—See Contractor's Supplies, Inc.; *U.S. Private*, pg. 1032

N.A.I.C.S. INDEX

327320 — READY-MIX CONCRETE ...

CORDOVA CONCRETE INC.; *U.S. Private*, pg. 1048
CORPORACION MOCTEZUMA S.A.B. DE C.V.; *Int'l*, pg. 1804
COUNTY CONCRETE CORPORATION; *U.S. Private*, pg. 1068
COYOTE GRAVEL PRODUCTS, INC.; *U.S. Private*, pg. 1079
CPM DEVELOPMENT CORPORATION—See CRH plc; *Int'l*, pg. 1843
CUSTOM-CRETE, LLC—See Vulcan Materials Company; *U.S. Public*, pg. 2314
CUSTOM-CRETE REDI-MIX, LLC—See Vulcan Materials Company; *U.S. Public*, pg. 2314
DANUCEM MAGYARORSZAG KFT.—See CRH plc; *Int'l*, pg. 1844
DELANEY CRUSHED STONE PRODUCTS, INC.—See Tetra Tech, Inc.; *U.S. Public*, pg. 2023
DELAWARE VALLEY CONCRETE CO.; *U.S. Private*, pg. 1196
DELMON READY MIXED CONCRETE & PRODUCTS CO. WLL—See Abdulla Ahmed Nass Group WLL; *Int'l*, pg. 58
DELTA INDUSTRIES INC.; *U.S. Private*, pg. 1200
D & G BRICE CONTRACTORS, INC.; *U.S. Private*, pg. 1136
DIC - DONG TIEN JOINT STOCK COMPANY; *Int'l*, pg. 2107
DIE ALPENPUMPE GMBH—See BERGER Holding GmbH; *Int'l*, pg. 979
DK BETON A/S—See Heidelberg Materials AG; *Int'l*, pg. 3310
DOLESE BROS. CO.; *U.S. Private*, pg. 1254
DOLOMITE READYMIXED CONCRETE SDN. BHD.—See Dolomite Corporation Berhad; *Int'l*, pg. 2159
DONAU-MORTEL GMBH & CO. KG—See BERGER Holding GmbH; *Int'l*, pg. 979
DORSETT BROS CONCRETE SUPPLY, INC.; *U.S. Private*, pg. 1263
DUFFERIN CONCRETE—See CRH plc; *Int'l*, pg. 1843
DUNBAR STONE COMPANY; *U.S. Private*, pg. 1287
DUNHAM-PRICE INC.; *U.S. Private*, pg. 1289
DYCKERHOFF BASAL BETONMORTEL B.V.—See Buzzi SpA; *Int'l*, pg. 1230
DYCKERHOFF BASAL NEDERLAND B.V.—See Buzzi SpA; *Int'l*, pg. 1230
DYCKERHOFF GMBH—See Buzzi SpA; *Int'l*, pg. 1230
DYCKERHOFF POLSKA SP. Z O.O.—See Buzzi SpA; *Int'l*, pg. 1230
DYNAMIC FLUID CONTROL (PTY) LTD.—See Aveng Limited; *Int'l*, pg. 738
EASTERN CONCRETE MATERIALS, INC.—See Vulcan Materials Company; *U.S. Public*, pg. 2314
EDWARD B. HOWLIN INC.; *U.S. Private*, pg. 1340
EDWARD C. LEVY CO.; *U.S. Private*, pg. 1340
ELLIS BROTHERS INC.; *U.S. Private*, pg. 1374
ELSINORE READY MIX CO. INC.; *U.S. Private*, pg. 1377
ENTREPRISE PAUL CALIN; *Int'l*, pg. 2453
ERIE-HAVEN INC.; *U.S. Private*, pg. 1420
ERNST ENTERPRISES, INC.; *U.S. Private*, pg. 1423
ESPANOLA MERCANTILE CO.; *U.S. Private*, pg. 1426
EVANS CONCRETE LLC; *U.S. Private*, pg. 1434
EVERMIX CONCRETE SDN. BHD.—See ES Ceramics Technology Bhd; *Int'l*, pg. 2500
EXCEL CONCRETE PTY LTD—See Holcim Ltd.; *Int'l*, pg. 3446
FAIRBURN READY-MIX, INC.; *U.S. Private*, pg. 1462
FAIRFAX HOLDING COMPANY INC.; *U.S. Private*, pg. 1463
FERNDALE READY MIX & GRAVEL; *U.S. Private*, pg. 1497
FERRARA BROS. BUILDING MATERIALS CORP.; *U.S. Private*, pg. 1498
F.F. PHILLIPS INC.; *U.S. Private*, pg. 1456
FIRMES Y HORMIGONES SANI S.L.—See Camargo Correa S.A.; *Int'l*, pg. 1268
FORDYCE CONCRETE COMPANY, INC.—See CRH plc; *Int'l*, pg. 1843
FORT MCDOWELL YAVAPAI MATERIALS; *U.S. Private*, pg. 1574
FOUNDAMENTAL GMBH—See Heidelberg Materials AG; *Int'l*, pg. 3310
FOWLER-FLEMISTER CONCRETE INC.; *U.S. Private*, pg. 1583
FRANK BRYAN INC.; *U.S. Private*, pg. 1594
FRIESLAND BETON HEERENVEEN B.V.—See Buzzi SpA; *Int'l*, pg. 1230
FUJAIRAH CEMENT INDUSTRIES PJSC FZ—See Fujairah Cement Industries Company PSC; *Int'l*, pg. 2808
GANGDONG CO., LTD.—See Gangdong Industry Co., Ltd.; *Int'l*, pg. 2880
GARROTT BROTHERS CONTINUOUS MIX, INC.; *U.S. Private*, pg. 1646
G-CAST CONCRETE SDN BHD—See Chin Hin Group Berhad; *Int'l*, pg. 1480
G-CAST UHPC SDN BHD—See Chin Hin Group Berhad; *Int'l*, pg. 1480
GCC ALLIANCE CONCRETE INC.—See GCC, S.A.B. de C.V.; *Int'l*, pg. 2894
GEIGER READY MIX COMPANY INCORPORATED; *U.S. Private*, pg. 1656
GEIRHOS-BETON GMBH—See BERGER Holding GmbH; *Int'l*, pg. 979

GOLDSUN BUILDING MATERIALS CO., LTD.; *Int'l*, pg. 3035
GOLIK CONCRETE LIMITED—See Golik Holdings Limited; *Int'l*, pg. 3036
GORAZDZE BETON SP. Z O.O.—See Heidelberg Materials AG; *Int'l*, pg. 3310
GRAFTON READY MIX CONCRETE—See Consumer Acquisitions, Inc.; *U.S. Private*, pg. 1025
GRAND RAPIDS GRAVEL CO.; *U.S. Private*, pg. 1753
GUANGDONG REDWALL NEW MATERIALS LIMITED; *Int'l*, pg. 3159
GULF COAST STABILIZED MATERIALS LLC—See Heidelberg Materials AG; *Int'l*, pg. 3310
HALYPS BUILDING MATERIALS S.A.—See Heidelberg Materials AG; *Int'l*, pg. 3316
HANSON AGGREGATES DAVON LLC—See Heidelberg Materials AG; *Int'l*, pg. 3313
HANSON AGGREGATES LLC—See Heidelberg Materials AG; *Int'l*, pg. 3313
HANSON AGGREGATES NORTH AMERICA—See Heidelberg Materials AG; *Int'l*, pg. 3313
HANSON AGGREGATES (NORTH) LIMITED—See Heidelberg Materials AG; *Int'l*, pg. 3311
HANSON AGGREGATES PACIFIC SOUTHWEST, INC.—See Heidelberg Materials AG; *Int'l*, pg. 3313
HANSON AGGREGATES SOUTHEAST LLC—See Heidelberg Materials AG; *Int'l*, pg. 3313
HANSON AUSTRALIA PTY LIMITED—See Heidelberg Materials AG; *Int'l*, pg. 3311
HANSON BETON NEDERLAND B.V.—See Heidelberg Materials AG; *Int'l*, pg. 3311
HANSON BUILDING MATERIALS-KTPC SDN BHD—See Heidelberg Materials AG; *Int'l*, pg. 3312
HANSON BUILDING MATERIALS MALAYSIA SDN BHD—See Heidelberg Materials AG; *Int'l*, pg. 3312
HANSON BUILDING MATERIALS MANUFACTURING SDN BHD—See Heidelberg Materials AG; *Int'l*, pg. 3312
HANSON BUILDING MATERIALS PRODUCTION SDN BHD—See Heidelberg Materials AG; *Int'l*, pg. 3312
HANSON CONCRETE (M) SDN BHD—See Heidelberg Materials AG; *Int'l*, pg. 3312
HANSON (ISRAEL) LTD.—See Heidelberg Materials AG; *Int'l*, pg. 3311
HANSON PTY LIMITED—See Heidelberg Materials AG; *Int'l*, pg. 3312
HANSON READY MIX, INC. - ARNPRIOR PLANT—See Heidelberg Materials AG; *Int'l*, pg. 3317
HANSON READY MIX, INC. - ASHTON PLANT—See Heidelberg Materials AG; *Int'l*, pg. 3317
HANSON READY MIX, INC. - AYLMER PLANT—See Heidelberg Materials AG; *Int'l*, pg. 3317
HANSON READY MIX, INC. - BRADDOCK PLANT—See Heidelberg Materials AG; *Int'l*, pg. 3317
HANSON READY MIX, INC. - CHARLESTON PLANT—See Heidelberg Materials AG; *Int'l*, pg. 3317
HANSON READY MIX, INC. - HUNTINGTON PLANT—See Heidelberg Materials AG; *Int'l*, pg. 3317
HANSON READY MIX, INC. - OTTAWA PLANT—See Heidelberg Materials AG; *Int'l*, pg. 3317
HANSON READY MIX, INC. - OTTAWA—See Heidelberg Materials AG; *Int'l*, pg. 3317
HANSON READY MIX, INC. - PARKERSBURG PLANT—See Heidelberg Materials AG; *Int'l*, pg. 3317
HANSON READY MIX, INC. - PEMBROKE PLANT—See Heidelberg Materials AG; *Int'l*, pg. 3317
HANSON READY MIX, INC. - PITTSBURGH PLANT—See Heidelberg Materials AG; *Int'l*, pg. 3317
HANSON READY MIX, INC. - STATE COLLEGE—See Heidelberg Materials AG; *Int'l*, pg. 3317
HANSON READY MIX, INC. - THURSO PLANT—See Heidelberg Materials AG; *Int'l*, pg. 3317
HANSON READY MIX, INC.- WHEELING PLANT—See Heidelberg Materials AG; *Int'l*, pg. 3317
HANSON READY MIX, INC. - WINFIELD PLANT—See Heidelberg Materials AG; *Int'l*, pg. 3317
HARPER INDUSTRIES INC.; *U.S. Private*, pg. 1867
HC BETOON AS—See Heidelberg Materials AG; *Int'l*, pg. 3310
H. C. RUSTIN CORPORATION; *U.S. Private*, pg. 1824
HECK ENTERPRISES INC.; *U.S. Private*, pg. 1903
HEIDELBERGCEMENT SHARED SERVICES GMBH—See Heidelberg Materials AG; *Int'l*, pg. 3315
HEIDELBERGCEMENT UK LIMITED—See Heidelberg Materials AG; *Int'l*, pg. 3315
HEIDELBERGER BETON ASCHAFFENBURG VERWALTUNGS-GMBH—See Heidelberg Materials AG; *Int'l*, pg. 3315
HEIDELBERGER BETON DONAU-NAAB GMBH & CO. KG—See Heidelberg Materials AG; *Int'l*, pg. 3315
HEIDELBERGER BETON ELSTER-SPREE GMBH & CO. KG—See Heidelberg Materials AG; *Int'l*, pg. 3316
HEIDELBERGER BETON GMBH—See Heidelberg Materials AG; *Int'l*, pg. 3316
HEIDELBERGER BETON INNTAL GMBH & CO. KG—See Heidelberg Materials AG; *Int'l*, pg. 3316
HEIDELBERGER BETON KURPFALZ GMBH & CO. KG—See Heidelberg Materials AG; *Int'l*, pg. 3316
HEIDELBERGER BETONPUMPEN RHEIN-MAIN-NAHE

GMBH & CO. KG—See Heidelberg Materials AG; *Int'l*, pg. 3316
HEIDELBERGER BETONPUMPEN SIMONIS GMBH & CO. KG—See Heidelberg Materials AG; *Int'l*, pg. 3316
HEIDELBERGER BETON ZWICKAU GMBH & CO. KG—See Heidelberg Materials AG; *Int'l*, pg. 3316
HEIDELBERGER BETON ZWICKAU VERWALTUNGS-GMBH—See Heidelberg Materials AG; *Int'l*, pg. 3316
HEIDELBERGER FLIESSESTRICH SUDWEST GMBH—See Heidelberg Materials AG; *Int'l*, pg. 3316
HEIDELBERG MATERIALS US, INC.—See Heidelberg Materials AG; *Int'l*, pg. 3313
HERIGE SA; *Int'l*, pg. 3361
HIGH GRADE MATERIALS COMPANY; *U.S. Private*, pg. 1935
HOLCIM (AUSTRALIA) PTY., LTD.—See Holcim Ltd.; *Int'l*, pg. 3446
HOLCIM BETON UND ZUSCHLAGSTOFFE GMBH—See Holcim Ltd.; *Int'l*, pg. 3447
HOLCIM (DEUTSCHLAND) GMBH - HOVER PLANT—See Holcim Ltd.; *Int'l*, pg. 3447
HOLCIM (MADAGASCAR) S.A.—See Holcim Ltd.; *Int'l*, pg. 3447
HOLCIM (MALAYSIA) SDN. BHD.—See Holcim Ltd.; *Int'l*, pg. 3447
HOLCIM (SCHWEIZ) AG—See Holcim Ltd.; *Int'l*, pg. 3447
HOLCIM (SUDDEUTSCHLAND) GMBH—See Holcim Ltd.; *Int'l*, pg. 3447
HOLCIM TRADING INC.—See Holcim Ltd.; *Int'l*, pg. 3448
HOLLISTER LANDSCAPE SUPPLY—See Assured Aggregates Company; *U.S. Private*, pg. 359
HONG HA LONG AN JOINT STOCK COMPANY; *Int'l*, pg. 3465
HOOVER INC.; *U.S. Private*, pg. 1978
HORMIGONES HERCULES S.L.—See Camargo Correa S.A.; *Int'l*, pg. 1268
HORMIGONES Y ARIDOS, S.A.—See Heidelberg Materials AG; *Int'l*, pg. 3316
HYMIX AUSTRALIA PTY. LTD.—See Heidelberg Materials AG; *Int'l*, pg. 3311
HY-TEC INDUSTRIES (QUEENSLAND) PTY. LTD.—See CRH plc; *Int'l*, pg. 1842
IBERA - INDUSTRIA DE BETAO S.A.—See Camargo Correa S.A.; *Int'l*, pg. 1268
IDEAL READY-MIX COMPANY INC.—See Rasmussen Group Inc.; *U.S. Private*, pg. 3357
INGRAM READYMIX, INC.; *U.S. Private*, pg. 2077
INTER-BETON S.A.—See Heidelberg Materials AG; *Int'l*, pg. 3310
IRVING MATERIALS INC.; *U.S. Private*, pg. 2141
ISAR-DONAU-MORTEL GMBH & CO. KG—See BERGER Holding GmbH; *Int'l*, pg. 979
ISLAND READY-MIX CONCRETE, INC.—See NOV, Inc.; *U.S. Public*, pg. 1544
JANESVILLE SAND & GRAVEL CO; *U.S. Private*, pg. 2186
JDM MATERIALS COMPANY INCORPORATED; *U.S. Private*, pg. 2195
JG MACLELLAN CONCRETE CO.; *U.S. Private*, pg. 2206
JOE BROWN COMPANY INC.; *U.S. Private*, pg. 2218
JOE MCCLELLAND INC.; *U.S. Private*, pg. 2218
KAY CONCRETE MATERIALS, CO.—See Monarch Cement Company; *U.S. Public*, pg. 1460
KINGS READY MIX, INC.—See Vulcan Materials Company; *U.S. Public*, pg. 2314
KNIFE RIVER CORPORATION - NORTH CENTRAL—See MDU Resources Group, Inc.; *U.S. Public*, pg. 1410
KNIFE RIVER - EAST TEXAS DIVISION—See MDU Resources Group, Inc.; *U.S. Public*, pg. 1410
KNIFE RIVER HAWAII, INC.—See MDU Resources Group, Inc.; *U.S. Public*, pg. 1411
KNIFE RIVER MATERIALS - MEDFORD—See MDU Resources Group, Inc.; *U.S. Public*, pg. 1410
KNIFE RIVER MATERIALS—See MDU Resources Group, Inc.; *U.S. Public*, pg. 1410
KOENIG COMPANY INC.; *U.S. Private*, pg. 2336
KOENIG FUEL & SUPPLY CO. INC.—See Koenig Company Inc.; *U.S. Private*, pg. 2336
KUERT CONCRETE INCORPORATED; *U.S. Private*, pg. 2356
KUHLMAN CONCRETE LLC—See Kuhlman Corporation; *U.S. Private*, pg. 2356
KUHLMAN CORPORATION; *U.S. Private*, pg. 2356
LADCE BETON S.R.O.—See BERGER Holding GmbH; *Int'l*, pg. 979
LAFARGE BETONS - AGENCE—See Holcim Ltd.; *Int'l*, pg. 3449
LAFARGE CEMENT HUNGARY LTD.—See Holcim Ltd.; *Int'l*, pg. 3448
LANCASTER PRE-CAST (PTY) LIMITED—See Afrimat Limited; *Int'l*, pg. 193
LEES READY MIX & TRUCKING, INC.; *U.S. Private*, pg. 2415
LIVINGSTON'S CONCRETE SERVICE, INC.; *U.S. Private*, pg. 2474
LOCAL CONCRETE SUPPLY & EQUIPMENT, LLC—See Vulcan Materials Company; *U.S. Public*, pg. 2314
LONDON CONCRETE LTD.—See Holcim Ltd.; *Int'l*, pg. 3446

327320 — READY-MIX CONCRETE

L. SUZIO CONCRETE COMPANY INC.; *U.S. Private*, pg. 2364
LYCON, INC.; *U.S. Private*, pg. 2519
MASTER MIX, LLC—See Vulcan Materials Company; *U.S. Public*, pg. 2314
MATHEWS READYMIX LLC—See Teichert, Inc.; *U.S. Private*, pg. 3958
MAYCO MIX LTD.—See Heidelberg Materials AG; *Int'l*, pg. 3318
MCC INCORPORATED; *U.S. Private*, pg. 2626
MCGEE BROTHERS CO. INC. - CONCRETE PLANT—See McGee Brothers Co. Inc.; *U.S. Private*, pg. 2634
MCLEAN COUNTY ASPHALT & CONCRETE COMPANY, INC.; *U.S. Private*, pg. 2641
MEBIN B.V.—See Heidelberg Materials AG; *Int'l*, pg. 3309
MEGAMIX (PROPRIETARY) LIMITED—See ARGENT INDUSTRIAL LIMITED; *Int'l*, pg. 560
MELBOURNE CONCRETE PTY. LTD.—See Heidelberg Materials AG; *Int'l*, pg. 3318
MEPPELER BETONCENTRALE B.V.—See Heidelberg Materials AG; *Int'l*, pg. 3318
METHENY CONCRETE PRODUCTS INC.; *U.S. Private*, pg. 2683
MEYER MATERIAL COMPANY, LLC—See Holcim Ltd.; *Int'l*, pg. 3446
MID-CONTINENT CONCRETE CO.—See GCC, S.A.B. de C.V.; *Int'l*, pg. 2895
MILES SAND & GRAVEL COMPANY; *U.S. Private*, pg. 2727
M. KINGSBURY CONCRETE INC.; *U.S. Private*, pg. 2526
MM MAIN-MORTEL GMBH & CO.KG—See Heidelberg Materials AG; *Int'l*, pg. 3318
MONARCH CEMENT COMPANY; *U.S. Public*, pg. 1460
MONROE READY MIX—See Martin Marietta Materials, Inc.; *U.S. Public*, pg. 1389
MORGAN CONCRETE COMPANY INC; *U.S. Private*, pg. 2783
MUNCHNER MORTEL GMBH & CO. KG—See BERGER Holding GmbH; *Int'l*, pg. 979
NASHVILLE READY MIX INC.; *U.S. Private*, pg. 2836
NEWPORT SAND & GRAVEL CO. INC.; *U.S. Private*, pg. 2916
NORBETONG A.S.—See Heidelberg Materials AG; *Int'l*, pg. 3315
NORDENHAMER TRANSPORTBETON GMBH & CO. KG—See Buzzi SpA; *Int'l*, pg. 1230
NORTHGATE READY MIX, LLC—See CRH plc; *Int'l*, pg. 1845
NORWALK READY-MIXED CONCRETE, INC.; *U.S. Private*, pg. 2964
NYC CONCRETE MATERIALS, LLC—See Vulcan Materials Company; *U.S. Public*, pg. 2314
OCCIDENTAL DE HORMIGONES S.L.—See Camargo Correa S.A.; *Int'l*, pg. 1268
OLDCASTLE, INC.—See CRH plc; *Int'l*, pg. 1845
OLDCASTLE MATERIALS, INC.-MID-ATLANTIC GROUP—See CRH plc; *Int'l*, pg. 1847
OLDCASTLE SW GROUP, INC.—See CRH plc; *Int'l*, pg. 1848
OOO DYCKERHOFF KORKINO CEMENT—See Buzzi SpA; *Int'l*, pg. 1230
ORCO BLENDED PRODUCTS, INC.—See Orco Block Company Inc.; *U.S. Private*, pg. 3039
OZINGA BROS., INC.; *U.S. Private*, pg. 3058
OZINGA CHICAGO RMC, INC.—See Ozinga Bros., Inc.; *U.S. Private*, pg. 3058
OZINGA SOUTH SUBURBAN RMC, INC.—See Ozinga Bros., Inc.; *U.S. Private*, pg. 3058
PADERBORNER TRANSPORT-BETON-GESELLSCHAFT MIT BESCHRANKTER HAFTUNG—See Heidelberg Materials AG; *Int'l*, pg. 3318
PAMPA CONCRETE CO; *U.S. Private*, pg. 3083
PENNY'S CONCRETE INC.; *U.S. Private*, pg. 3137
PENSACOLA READY MIX, LLC.; *U.S. Private*, pg. 3138
PETE LIEN & SONS INC.; *U.S. Private*, pg. 3157
PETERS CONCRETE; *U.S. Private*, pg. 3159
POLBRUK S.A.—See CRH plc; *Int'l*, pg. 1848
PPES CONCRETE PRODUCT SDN. BHD.—See Cahya Mata Sarawak Berhad; *Int'l*, pg. 1251
PRAIRIE MATERIAL; *U.S. Private*, pg. 3243
PREBETONG GALICIA S.A.—See Camargo Correa S.A.; *Int'l*, pg. 1268
PREBETONG LUGO HORMIGONES S.A.—See Camargo Correa S.A.; *Int'l*, pg. 1268
PREBETONG LUGO S.A.—See Camargo Correa S.A.; *Int'l*, pg. 1268
PT PIONIRBETON INDUSTRI—See Heidelberg Materials AG; *Int'l*, pg. 3318
QUAD-COUNTY READY MIX CORP; *U.S. Private*, pg. 3315
THE QUIKRETE COMPANIES, LLC; *U.S. Private*, pg. 4101
RAHNS CONSTRUCTION MATERIAL CO.—See Haines & Kibblehouse Inc.; *U.S. Private*, pg. 1841
RAINERI BUILDING MATERIALS, INC.—See Breedon Group plc; *Int'l*, pg. 1144
RAPTOR MATERIALS LLC—See Eagle Materials Inc.; *U.S. Public*, pg. 702
RAZORBACK CONCRETE CO.; *U.S. Private*, pg. 3360

READY MIX CONCRETE, INC.—See CEMEX, S.A.B. de C.V.; *Int'l*, pg. 1399
READY MIX CONCRETE SOMERSET INC.; *U.S. Private*, pg. 3367
READY MIX CONCRETE; *U.S. Private*, pg. 3367
READY MIXED CONCRETE CO.—See Brannan Sand & Gravel Co. LLC; *U.S. Private*, pg. 639
READYMIX INDUSTRIES (ISRAEL) LIMITED—See CEMEX, S.A.B. de C.V.; *Int'l*, pg. 1398
READYMIX LIMITED—See CEMEX, S.A.B. de C.V.; *Int'l*, pg. 1400
READYMIX (ROI) LTD—See CEMEX, S.A.B. de C.V.; *Int'l*, pg. 1400
READY MIX USA - TRI-STATES DIV—See Ready Mix USA, Inc.; *U.S. Private*, pg. 3367
READYMIX (WEST INDIES) LIMITED—See CEMEX, S.A.B. de C.V.; *Int'l*, pg. 1400
REGENSBURGER FRISCHMORTEL GMBH & CO.KG—See BERGER Holding GmbH; *Int'l*, pg. 979
REMPEL BROS. CONCRETE LTD.—See Heidelberg Materials AG; *Int'l*, pg. 3319
REYNOLDS READY MIX LLC; *U.S. Private*, pg. 3418
RIGHT AWAY REDY MIX INCORPORATED—See Vulcan Materials Company; *U.S. Public*, pg. 2314
RIVERBEND INDUSTRIES INC.—See Bee Street Holdings LLC; *U.S. Private*, pg. 513
ROBAR ENTERPRISES INC.; *U.S. Private*, pg. 3456
ROCKVILLE FUEL & FEED COMPANY; *U.S. Private*, pg. 3467
ROGERS READY MIX & MATERIALS; *U.S. Private*, pg. 3472
ROSENFELD CONCRETE CORP.—See Boston Sand & Gravel Company; *U.S. Private*, pg. 373
ROSS ISLAND SAND & GRAVEL CO., INC.—See R.B. Pamplin Corporation; *U.S. Private*, pg. 3334
SAGAMORE READY MIX, LLC; *U.S. Private*, pg. 3526
SAKRETE OF NORTH AMERICA, LLC—See CRH plc; *Int'l*, pg. 1845
SARDINIA CONCRETE COMPANY; *U.S. Private*, pg. 3550
SCANPAC AB—See Compagnie de Saint-Gobain SA; *Int'l*, pg. 1736
SCHMITZ READY MIX INC.; *U.S. Private*, pg. 3566
SCOTT COUNTY READY MIX INC.—See WG Block Co.; *U.S. Private*, pg. 4503
SCRUGGS CONCRETE COMPANY; *U.S. Private*, pg. 3580
SEAGOE CONCRETE PRODUCTS LIMITED—See Heidelberg Materials AG; *Int'l*, pg. 3319
SEVILLE CENTRAL MIX CORPORATION; *U.S. Private*, pg. 3619
SHAMROCK CONCRETE COMPANY—See Lyman-Richey Corporation; *U.S. Private*, pg. 2520
SHAMROCK MATERIALS INC.—See Vulcan Materials Company; *U.S. Public*, pg. 2313
SHAMROCK MATERIALS OF NOVATO INC.—See Vulcan Materials Company; *U.S. Public*, pg. 2313
SHELBY GRAVEL INC.; *U.S. Private*, pg. 3630
SHERMAN INDUSTRIES LLC—See Heidelberg Materials AG; *Int'l*, pg. 3319
SHYMKENT CEMENT JSC—See Heidelberg Materials AG; *Int'l*, pg. 3317
SIBOBETON EMS GMBH & CO. KG—See Buzzi SpA; *Int'l*, pg. 1231
SIBOBETON ENGER GMBH & CO. KG—See Buzzi SpA; *Int'l*, pg. 1231
SIBOBETON OSNABRUCK GMBH & CO. KG—See Buzzi SpA; *Int'l*, pg. 1231
SIBOBETON WILHELMSHAVEN GMBH & CO. KG—See Buzzi SpA; *Int'l*, pg. 1231
SIBO-GRUPPE GMBH & CO. KG—See Buzzi SpA; *Int'l*, pg. 1231
SIMON CONTRACTORS OF SOUTH DAKOTA INC.—See CRH plc; *Int'l*, pg. 1847
SMITH CONCRETE—See CRH plc; *Int'l*, pg. 1847
SMITH READY MIX INC.; *U.S. Private*, pg. 3695
SONAG READY MIX, LLC—See Sonag Company, Inc.; *U.S. Private*, pg. 3712
SOUTHERN CONCRETE MATERIALS INC.—See Hedrick Industries Inc.; *U.S. Private*, pg. 1903
SOUTHERN CRUSHED CONCRETE LLC—See Ferrovial S.A.; *Int'l*, pg. 2645
SOUTHERN EQUIPMENT CO. INC.; *U.S. Private*, pg. 3731
SOUTHERN STAR CONCRETE, INC.—See Grupo Argos S.A.; *Int'l*, pg. 3121
SOUTH VALLEY MATERIALS, INC. - COALINGA PLANT—See Heidelberg Materials AG; *Int'l*, pg. 3319
SOUTH VALLEY MATERIALS, INC. - EXETER PLANT—See Heidelberg Materials AG; *Int'l*, pg. 3319
SOUTH VALLEY MATERIALS, INC. - PORTERVILLE PLANT—See Heidelberg Materials AG; *Int'l*, pg. 3319
SOUTH VALLEY MATERIALS, INC. - TULARE PLANT—See Heidelberg Materials AG; *Int'l*, pg. 3319
SPRAGUES' ROCK & SAND CO.; *U.S. Private*, pg. 3762
STAHLSAITEN BETONWERKE GMBH—See Heidelberg Materials AG; *Int'l*, pg. 3319
STANDARD CONCRETE PRODUCTS, INC.—See Heidelberg Materials AG; *Int'l*, pg. 3313
STANDARD READY MIX CONCRETE CO.—See Lyman-Richey Corporation; *U.S. Private*, pg. 2520

STARKEN AAC SDN BHD—See Chin Hin Group Berhad; *Int'l*, pg. 1480
STAR READY MIX INC.; *U.S. Private*, pg. 3785
STARVAGGI INDUSTRIES, INC.; *U.S. Private*, pg. 3788
ST. HENRY TILE CO. INC.; *U.S. Private*, pg. 3770
STONE & COMPANY; *U.S. Private*, pg. 3816
STRONG MIXED CONCRETE SDN BHD—See IJM Corporation Berhad; *Int'l*, pg. 3609
SUMMIT MATERIALS FINANCE CORP.—See Summit Materials, Inc.; *U.S. Public*, pg. 1959
SUNCOAST ASPHALT PTY. LTD.—See Heidelberg Materials AG; *Int'l*, pg. 3320
SUNROC CORPORATION—See Clyde Companies Inc.; *U.S. Private*, pg. 949
SUPERIOR CONCRETE MATERIALS, INC.—See Vulcan Materials Company; *U.S. Public*, pg. 2314
SUPERIOR READY MIX CONCRETE LP ; AGUANGA PLANT—See Superior Ready Mix Concrete LP; *U.S. Private*, pg. 3880
SUPERIOR READY MIX CONCRETE LP - CARROLL CANYON PLANT—See Superior Ready Mix Concrete LP; *U.S. Private*, pg. 3880
SUPERIOR READY MIX CONCRETE LP - COACHELLA PLANT—See Superior Ready Mix Concrete LP; *U.S. Private*, pg. 3880
SUPERIOR READY MIX CONCRETE LP - EL CENTRO PLANT—See Superior Ready Mix Concrete LP; *U.S. Private*, pg. 3880
SUPERIOR READY MIX CONCRETE LP - FALLBROOK PLANT—See Superior Ready Mix Concrete LP; *U.S. Private*, pg. 3880
SUPERIOR READY MIX CONCRETE LP - HEMET (BCC) PLANT—See Superior Ready Mix Concrete LP; *U.S. Private*, pg. 3880
SUPERIOR READY MIX CONCRETE LP - OCEANSIDE PLANT—See Superior Ready Mix Concrete LP; *U.S. Private*, pg. 3880
SUPERIOR READY MIX CONCRETE LP - RAMONA PLANT—See Superior Ready Mix Concrete LP; *U.S. Private*, pg. 3880
SUPERIOR READY MIX CONCRETE LP; *U.S. Private*, pg. 3880
SUPERIOR READY MIX CONCRETE LP - SOUTHLAND PLANT—See Superior Ready Mix Concrete LP; *U.S. Private*, pg. 3880
SUPERMIX, INC.; *U.S. Private*, pg. 3881
TARRANT CONCRETE COMPANY, INC.—See Holcim Ltd.; *Int'l*, pg. 3449
TASEK CONCRETE SDN. BHD.—See Hong Leong Investment Holdings Pte. Ltd.; *Int'l*, pg. 3469
TBG BETONMIX A. S.—See Heidelberg Materials AG; *Int'l*, pg. 3320
TBG BETONPUMPY MORAVA S.R.O.—See Heidelberg Materials AG; *Int'l*, pg. 3320
TBG ILM-BETON GMBH & CO. KG—See Heidelberg Materials AG; *Int'l*, pg. 3320
TBG TRANSPORTBETON FRANKEN GESCHAFTSFUHRUNG GMBH—See Heidelberg Materials AG; *Int'l*, pg. 3320
TBG TRANSPORTBETON KURPFALZ GMBH & CO. KG—See Heidelberg Materials AG; *Int'l*, pg. 3320
TBG TRANSPORTBETON MAINFRANKEN GESCHAFTSFUHRUNGS GMBH—See Heidelberg Materials AG; *Int'l*, pg. 3320
TBG TRANSPORTBETON REICHENBACH GMBH & CO. KG—See Heidelberg Materials AG; *Int'l*, pg. 3320
TBG TRANSPORTBETON SCHWARZENBERG VERWALTUNGS-GMBH—See Heidelberg Materials AG; *Int'l*, pg. 3320
TBH TRANSPORTBETON HAMBURG VERWALTUNGSGMBH—See Heidelberg Materials AG; *Int'l*, pg. 3320
TERALTA—See CRH plc; *Int'l*, pg. 1849
THOMAS BENNETT & HUNTER INC.; *U.S. Private*, pg. 4154
TMOP LEGACY COMPANY—See Bee Street Holdings LLC; *U.S. Private*, pg. 513
TOB DYCKERHOFF UKRAINA—See Buzzi SpA; *Int'l*, pg. 1230
TOKAI CONCRETE INDUSTRIES CO., LTD.—See Chubu Electric Power Co., Inc.; *Int'l*, pg. 1593
TOP MIX CONCRETE PTE LTD—See EnGro Corporation Limited; *Int'l*, pg. 2436
TRANSIT MIX CONCRETE CO.—See Holcim Ltd.; *Int'l*, pg. 3446
TRANSPORTBETON BAD WALDSEE GESCHAFTSFUHRUNGS GMBH—See Heidelberg Materials AG; *Int'l*, pg. 3320
TROY VINES, INC.—See Summit Materials, Inc.; *U.S. Public*, pg. 1960
UAB GERDUKAS—See Heidelberg Materials AG; *Int'l*, pg. 3320
UNIBETON EST—See Heidelberg Materials AG; *Int'l*, pg. 3316
UNIBETON ILE DE FRANCE—See Heidelberg Materials AG; *Int'l*, pg. 3316
UNIBETON MEDITERRANEE—See Heidelberg Materials AG; *Int'l*, pg. 3316

N.A.I.C.S. INDEX

327331 — CONCRETE BLOCK AND ...

UNIBETON OUEST PAYS DE LOIRE—See Heidelberg Materials AG; *Int'l*, pg. 3316
UNIBETON S.A.S.—See Heidelberg Materials AG; *Int'l*, pg. 3316
UNIBETON SUD OUEST—See Heidelberg Materials AG; *Int'l*, pg. 3316
UNI-MIX SDN. BHD.—See B.I.G. Industries Berhad; *Int'l*, pg. 790
USC ATLANTIC, INC.—See Vulcan Materials Company; *U.S. Public*, pg. 2314
U.S. CONCRETE, INC.—See Vulcan Materials Company; *U.S. Public*, pg. 2313
U.S. CONCRETE ON-SITE, INC.—See Vulcan Materials Company; *U.S. Public*, pg. 2314
VALLEY QUARRIES INC.—See New Enterprise Stone & Lime Co., Inc.; *U.S. Private*, pg. 2895
VAN HORN BROS INC.; *U.S. Private*, pg. 4340
VULCAN MATERIALS CO. - FRESNO—See Vulcan Materials Company; *U.S. Public*, pg. 2314
VVM N.V.—See CRH plc; *Int'l*, pg. 1849
WALKER CONCRETE COMPANY INC.; *U.S. Private*, pg. 4428
WAMEGO SAND COMPANY, INC.; *U.S. Private*, pg. 4435
WAYNE DAVIS CONCRETE CO.; *U.S. Private*, pg. 4459
WEBB CONCRETE COMPANY INC.; *U.S. Private*, pg. 4464
WELLINGTON HAMRICK, INC. - SHELBY—See Wellington Hamrick, Inc.; *U.S. Private*, pg. 4475
WELLINGTON HAMRICK, INC.; *U.S. Private*, pg. 4475
WELLS GROUP LLC; *U.S. Private*, pg. 4476
WESCON CORP OF CONN.—See J.H. Lynch & Sons Inc.; *U.S. Private*, pg. 2166
WESTERN AGGREGATES LLC—See Teichert, Inc.; *U.S. Private*, pg. 3958
WESTROC, INC.—See Summit Materials, Inc.; *U.S. Public*, pg. 1960
WG BLOCK CO.; *U.S. Private*, pg. 4503
WILDISH SAND & GRAVEL CO.—See Wildish Land Company; *U.S. Private*, pg. 4519
WILLCAN INC.—See Sequatchie Concrete Service Inc.; *U.S. Private*, pg. 3612
WILLIAM E. DAILEY INC.—See Peckham Industries, Inc.; *U.S. Private*, pg. 3127
WIND RIVER MATERIALS, LLC—See Summit Materials, Inc.; *U.S. Public*, pg. 1960
WINGRA STONE COMPANY; *U.S. Private*, pg. 4541
XTRAMIX CONCRETE SOLUTION MIX LLC—See Al Jaber Group; *Int'l*, pg. 280
YA TUNG READY-MIXED CONCRETE CORP.—See Asia Cement Corporation; *Int'l*, pg. 611
ZAPA BETON A.S.—See Buzzi SpA; *Int'l*, pg. 1230
ZAPA BETON SK S.R.O.—See Buzzi SpA; *Int'l*, pg. 1230
ZIGNEGO READY MIX INC.; *U.S. Private*, pg. 4604

327331 — CONCRETE BLOCK AND BRICK MANUFACTURING

5. OKTOBAR A.D.; *Int'l*, pg. 12
ACICO INDUSTRIES CO. K.S.C.C.; *Int'l*, pg. 104
ADBRI MASONRY GROUP PTY. LTD.—See CRH plc; *Int'l*, pg. 1842
ADBRI MASONRY PTY. LTD.—See CRH plc; *Int'l*, pg. 1842
A. DUCHINI INCORPORATED; *U.S. Private*, pg. 23
AGGREGATES USA (AUGUSTA), LLC—See Vulcan Materials Company; *U.S. Public*, pg. 2313
AGGREGATES USA (MACON), LLC—See Vulcan Materials Company; *U.S. Public*, pg. 2313
AGGREGATES USA (SAVANNAH), LLC—See Vulcan Materials Company; *U.S. Public*, pg. 2313
AGGREGATES USA (SPARTA), LLC—See Vulcan Materials Company; *U.S. Public*, pg. 2313
AJIYA STI SDN. BHD.—See Ajiya Berhad; *Int'l*, pg. 258
ALLAN BLOCK CORPORATION; *U.S. Private*, pg. 174
ALLEY-CASSETTY BRICK GALLATIN DIV.—See Alley-Cassetty Companies; *U.S. Private*, pg. 180
ALLIED CONCRETE COMPANY—See CRH plc; *Int'l*, pg. 1845
AMCON BLOCK & PRECAST INCORPORATED; *U.S. Private*, pg. 218
AMREYAH CIMPOR CEMENT COMPANY S.A.E.—See Camargo Correa S.A.; *Int'l*, pg. 1267
ANCHOR BLOCK COMPANY—See CRH plc; *Int'l*, pg. 1845
ANCHOR CONCRETE PRODUCTS INC.—See CRH plc; *Int'l*, pg. 1845
APG CANADA—See CRH plc; *Int'l*, pg. 1845
ARMTEC LP—See Brookfield Corporation; *Int'l*, pg. 1175
ASANUMA CORPORATION - PRECAST CONCRETE PLANT—See Asanuma Corporation; *Int'l*, pg. 599
ASIA PILE HOLDINGS CORPORATION; *Int'l*, pg. 614
THE AUSTRAL BRICK COMPANY PTY. LIMITED—See Brickworks Limited; *Int'l*, pg. 1152
AUSTRAL BRICKS (QLD) PTY LTD—See Brickworks Limited; *Int'l*, pg. 1151
AUSTRAL BRICKS (SA) PTY LTD—See Brickworks Limited; *Int'l*, pg. 1151
AUSTRAL BRICKS (VIC) PTY LTD—See Brickworks Limited; *Int'l*, pg. 1152
AUSTRAL BRICKS (WA) PTY LTD—See Brickworks Limited; *Int'l*, pg. 1152
AUSTRAL MASONRY (NSW) PTY LTD—See Brickworks Limited; *Int'l*, pg. 1152
AUSTRAL MASONRY (QLD) PTY LTD—See Brickworks Limited; *Int'l*, pg. 1152
AUSTRAL MASONRY (VIC) PTY LTD—See Brickworks Limited; *Int'l*, pg. 1152
BARKMAN CONCRETE LTD.; *Int'l*, pg. 865
BASALITE CONCRETE PRODUCTS, LLC—See Pacific Coast Building Products, Inc.; *U.S. Private*, pg. 3065
THE BAUER COMPANY, INC.—See The Snyder Group, Inc.; *U.S. Private*, pg. 4119
BEACON REDEVELOPMENT INDUSTRIAL CORP.; *U.S. Public*, pg. 285
BEAVERTOWN BLOCK CO. INC.; *U.S. Private*, pg. 509
BEN TRE BUILDING MATERIAL JOINT STOCK COMPANY; *Int'l*, pg. 969
BETON 06 SA—See Chequers SA; *Int'l*, pg. 1471
BETON 6 CORPORATION; *Int'l*, pg. 1002
BETON CHANTIERS DE BRETAGNE S.A.S.—See Holcim Ltd.; *Int'l*, pg. 3449
BETON MOULE INDUSTRIEL S.A.—See CRH plc; *Int'l*, pg. 1843
BIGBLOC CONSTRUCTION LIMITED; *Int'l*, pg. 1022
BINKLEY & OBER INC.—See CRH plc; *Int'l*, pg. 1847
BLOCK USA ALABAMA DIVISION LLC—See Ready Mix USA, Inc.; *U.S. Private*, pg. 3367
BORAL CONSTRUCTION MATERIALS LLC—See Brannan Sand & Gravel Co. LLC; *U.S. Private*, pg. 639
BRAMPTON BRICK LIMITED; *Int'l*, pg. 1139
BRICKABILITY GROUP PLC; *Int'l*, pg. 1151
BUILDING PRODUCTS CORP.; *U.S. Private*, pg. 683
CALSTONE, CO.—See CRH plc; *Int'l*, pg. 1845
CELEKULA A.D.; *Int'l*, pg. 1392
CEMEX CONCRETE PRODUCTS—See CEMEX, S.A.B. de C.V.; *Int'l*, pg. 1399
CEMEX CONSTRUCTION MATERIALS FLORIDA, LLC—See CEMEX, S.A.B. de C.V.; *Int'l*, pg. 1399
CEMEX MATERIALS LLC—See CEMEX, S.A.B. de C.V.; *Int'l*, pg. 1399
CHEMROCK CORPORATION—See RGP Holding, Inc.; *U.S. Private*, pg. 3420
CIGLANA A.D.; *Int'l*, pg. 1607
CLARK PACIFIC - FONTANA PLANT—See Clark Pacific; *U.S. Private*, pg. 913
CLARK PACIFIC - IRWINDALE PLANT—See Clark Pacific; *U.S. Private*, pg. 913
CLARK PACIFIC - WOODLAND PLANT—See Clark Pacific; *U.S. Private*, pg. 913
COLUMBIA DBL (PTY) LIMITED; *Int'l*, pg. 1706
CRANESVILLE BLOCK CO., INC.; *U.S. Private*, pg. 1085
CRH EUROPE - PRODUCTS & DISTRIBUTION—See CRH plc; *Int'l*, pg. 1843
CRH GETAZ HOLDING AG—See CRH plc; *Int'l*, pg. 1844
CUONGTHUAN INVESTMENT CORPORATION; *Int'l*, pg. 1878
DAYTON SUPERIOR CANADA LTD.—See Dayton Superior Corporation; *U.S. Private*, pg. 1178
DOLOMITE BERHAD—See Dolomite Corporation Berhad; *Int'l*, pg. 2159
DUKE CONCRETE PRODUCTS INC.—See The Fort Miller Group Inc.; *U.S. Private*, pg. 4029
D.W. DICKEY & SONS INC. - COLUMBIANA PLANT—See D.W. Dickey & Sons Inc.; *U.S. Private*, pg. 1143
D.W. DICKEY & SONS INC. - EAST LIVERPOOL CONCRETE PLANT—See D.W. Dickey & Sons Inc.; *U.S. Private*, pg. 1143
D.W. DICKEY & SONS INC. - LISBON CONCRETE PLANT—See D.W. Dickey & Sons Inc.; *U.S. Private*, pg. 1143
D.W. DICKEY & SONS INC. - STEUBENVILLE PLANT—See D.W. Dickey & Sons Inc.; *U.S. Private*, pg. 1143
EHL AG—See CRH plc; *Int'l*, pg. 1844
ELITE CRETE SYSTEMS INC.; *U.S. Private*, pg. 1360
E.P. HENRY CORPORATION; *U.S. Private*, pg. 1306
ERNEST MAIER, INC.; *U.S. Private*, pg. 1421
ETERNIT S.A.; *Int'l*, pg. 2521
FABRICA DE BLOQUES MASSO INC.—See Masso Enterprises; *U.S. Private*, pg. 2607
FEATHERLITE BUILDING PRODUCTS—See Berkshire Hathaway Inc.; *U.S. Public*, pg. 298
FENDT BUILDERS SUPPLY INC.; *U.S. Private*, pg. 1494
FERROBETON CONCRETE AND REINFORCED CONCRETE PRODUCER PUBLIC LIMITED COMPANY—See CRH plc; *Int'l*, pg. 1844
FIRESTONE BUILDING PRODUCTS COMPANY, LLC - WELLFORD MANUFACTURING FACILITY—See Bridgestone Corporation; *Int'l*, pg. 1157
FLETCHER CONSTRUCTION AUSTRALIA PTY LIMITED—See Fletcher Building Limited; *Int'l*, pg. 2700
FORMICA (THAILAND) CO., LTD. - PHRAPRADAENG FACTORY—See HAL Trust N.V.; *Int'l*, pg. 3223
FORMICA (THAILAND) CO., LTD.—See HAL Trust N.V.; *Int'l*, pg. 3223
FORMPAVE LIMITED—See Heidelberg Materials AG; *Int'l*, pg. 3310
FORTERRA BUILDING PRODUCTS LIMITED—See Lone Star Global Acquisitions, LLC; *U.S. Private*, pg. 2487
FORTICRETE LTD—See Ibstock plc; *Int'l*, pg. 3577
GENEST CONCRETE WORKS INC.; *U.S. Private*, pg. 1670
GRAND BLANC CEMENT PRODUCTS; *U.S. Private*, pg. 1752
GS GLOBAL CORPORATION-KUALA LUMPUR—See GS Holdings Corp.; *Int'l*, pg. 3142
GS GLOBAL CORPORATION-NEW DELHI—See GS Holdings Corp.; *Int'l*, pg. 3142
HANSON BRICK LIMITED—See Heidelberg Materials AG; *Int'l*, pg. 3311
HEIDELBERGCEMENT MILJO AB—See Heidelberg Materials AG; *Int'l*, pg. 3314
HEIDELBERGER WESERKIES VERWALTUNGS-GMBH—See Heidelberg Materials AG; *Int'l*, pg. 3316
HERAS SKS GMBH—See CRH plc; *Int'l*, pg. 1844
H+H DANMARK A/S—See H+H International A/S; *Int'l*, pg. 3193
H+H DEUTSCHLAND GMBH—See H+H International A/S; *Int'l*, pg. 3193
H+H FINLAND OY—See H+H International A/S; *Int'l*, pg. 3194
H+H INTERNATIONAL A/S; *Int'l*, pg. 3193
H+H NEDERLAND B.V.—See H+H International A/S; *Int'l*, pg. 3194
H+H NORGE AS—See H+H International A/S; *Int'l*, pg. 3194
H+H POLSKA SP. Z O.O.—See H+H International A/S; *Int'l*, pg. 3194
H+H SLOVENSKA REPUBLIKA S.R.O.—See H+H International A/S; *Int'l*, pg. 3194
H+H SVERIGE AB—See H+H International A/S; *Int'l*, pg. 3194
HIGH-GRADE BRICK-TILE JOINT STOCK COMPANY; *Int'l*, pg. 3386
HINKLE BLOCK & MASONRY—See Summit Materials, Inc.; *U.S. Public*, pg. 1960
HUNZIKER KALKSANDSTEIN AG—See H+H International A/S; *Int'l*, pg. 3194
IBSTOCK BRICK LIMITED—See Ibstock plc; *Int'l*, pg. 3577
JOHNSON CONCRETE CO.; *U.S. Private*, pg. 2227
KEVINGTON BUILDING PRODUCTS LIMITED—See Ibstock plc; *Int'l*, pg. 3577
KS-QUADRO BAUSYSTEME GMBH—See H+H International A/S; *Int'l*, pg. 3194
KWENA CONCRETE PRODUCTS (PTY) LTD—See Botswana Development Corporation Limited; *Int'l*, pg. 1118
LAKESIDE INDUSTRIES - ABERDEEN PLANT—See Lakeside Industries; *U.S. Private*, pg. 2378
LAKESIDE INDUSTRIES - CENTRALIA PLANT—See Lakeside Industries; *U.S. Private*, pg. 2378
LAKESIDE INDUSTRIES - FOSTER ROAD PLANT—See Lakeside Industries; *U.S. Private*, pg. 2378
LAKESIDE INDUSTRIES - FREMONT PLANT—See Lakeside Industries; *U.S. Private*, pg. 2378
LAKESIDE INDUSTRIES - HILLSBORO PLANT—See Lakeside Industries; *U.S. Private*, pg. 2378
LAKESIDE INDUSTRIES - ISSAQUAH PLANT—See Lakeside Industries; *U.S. Private*, pg. 2378
LAKESIDE INDUSTRIES - KENT PLANT—See Lakeside Industries; *U.S. Private*, pg. 2378
LAKESIDE INDUSTRIES - LONGVIEW PLANT—See Lakeside Industries; *U.S. Private*, pg. 2378
LAKESIDE INDUSTRIES - PORT ANGELES PLANT—See Lakeside Industries; *U.S. Private*, pg. 2378
LAKESIDE INDUSTRIES - PORTLAND PLANT—See Lakeside Industries; *U.S. Private*, pg. 2378
LAKESIDE INDUSTRIES - VALLEY PAVING PLANT—See Lakeside Industries; *U.S. Private*, pg. 2378
LEE MASONRY PRODUCTS, LLC; *U.S. Private*, pg. 2413
LEMMINKAINEN RAKENNUSTUOTTEET OY—See CRH plc; *Int'l*, pg. 1848
LENTINE MANAGEMENT INC.; *U.S. Private*, pg. 2422
LH TRADING PTE. LTD.—See Holcim Ltd.; *Int'l*, pg. 3448
LIME & STONE PRODUCTION CO LTD—See CEMEX, S.A.B. de C.V.; *Int'l*, pg. 1398
LITHONPLUS GMBH & CO. KG—See Heidelberg Materials AG; *Int'l*, pg. 3318
LOBATSE CLAY WORKS (PTY) LTD—See Botswana Development Corporation Limited; *Int'l*, pg. 1118
LONDON BRICK ENGINEERING LIMITED—See Heidelberg Materials AG; *Int'l*, pg. 3318
LONGLEY CONCRETE LTD.—See Ibstock plc; *Int'l*, pg. 3577
MARVIL PACKAGE COMPANY; *U.S. Private*, pg. 2597
MIDLOTHIAN CEMENT PLANT—See Martin Marietta Materials, Inc.; *U.S. Public*, pg. 1389
MOHAVE BLOCK INC.—See Paragon Building Products Inc.; *U.S. Private*, pg. 3090
MORIN BRICK CO.; *U.S. Private*, pg. 2785
NATIONAL BRICK COMPANY LIMITED—See Heidelberg Materials AG; *Int'l*, pg. 3318
NORTHFIELD BLOCK CO.—See CRH plc; *Int'l*, pg. 1845
NOVADAL PRIVAT SAS—See Chequers SA; *Int'l*, pg. 1471
NUBRIK PTY LTD—See Brickworks Limited; *Int'l*, pg. 1152
N.V. SILICAATSTEEN—See Heidelberg Materials AG; *Int'l*, pg. 3318

327331 — CONCRETE BLOCK AND ...

OBERFIELDS LLC—See Graycliff Partners LP; *U.S. Private*, pg. 1761
OLDCASTLE ADAMS PRODUCTS COMPANY—See CRH plc; *Int'l*, pg. 1845
OLDCASTLE ARCHITECTURAL, INC.—See CRH plc; *Int'l*, pg. 1845
OLDCASTLE BUILDING PRODUCTS CANADA, INC.—See CRH plc; *Int'l*, pg. 1846
OLDCASTLE BUILDING PRODUCTS, INC—See CRH plc; *Int'l*, pg. 1846
OLD CASTLE COASTAL INC.; *U.S. Private*, pg. 3008
ORCO BLOCK COMPANY INC. - ORCO PAVINGSTONES DIVISION—See Orco Block Company Inc.; *U.S. Private*, pg. 3039
ORCO BLOCK COMPANY INC.; *U.S. Private*, pg. 3039
ORCO PAVINGSTONES - COACHELLA / IMPERIAL PLANT—See Orco Block Company Inc.; *U.S. Private*, pg. 3039
ORCO PAVINGSTONES - INLAND EMPIRE PLANT—See Orco Block Company Inc.; *U.S. Private*, pg. 3039
ORCO PAVINGSTONES - ORANGE / LOS ANGELES PLANT—See Orco Block Company Inc.; *U.S. Private*, pg. 3039
ORCO PAVINGSTONES - TEMECULA VALLEY PLANT—See Orco Block Company Inc.; *U.S. Private*, pg. 3039
OSKALOOSA CONCRETE PRODUCTS—See Johnson Holding Co.; *U.S. Private*, pg. 2228
PABCO BUILDING PRODUCTS, LLC - H.C. MUDDOX DIVISION—See Pacific Coast Building Products, Inc.; *U.S. Private*, pg. 3066
PABCO BUILDING PRODUCTS, LLC - INTERSTATE BRICK DIVISION—See Pacific Coast Building Products, Inc.; *U.S. Private*, pg. 3066
PARAGON AGGREGATE PRODUCTS INC.—See Paragon Building Products Inc.; *U.S. Private*, pg. 3090
PARAGON BUILDING PRODUCTS INC. - NEVADA PREMIX DIVISION—See Paragon Building Products Inc.; *U.S. Private*, pg. 3090
PARAGON BUILDING PRODUCTS INC. - PARAGON CONCRETE PRODUCTS DIVISION—See Paragon Building Products Inc.; *U.S. Private*, pg. 3090
PETRICCA INDUSTRIES, INC.; *U.S. Private*, pg. 3161
PREFACO N.V.—See CRH plc; *Int'l*, pg. 1848
RCP BLOCK & BRICK, INC.; *U.S. Private*, pg. 3362
READING ROCK INCORPORATED; *U.S. Private*, pg. 3367
RINKER MATERIALS-ENVIRONMENTAL SERVICES—See CEMEX, S.A.B. de C.V.; *Int'l*, pg. 1399
ROYALE HOUSE INC.—See Seater Construction Co. Inc.; *U.S. Private*, pg. 3591
SABLE CLASSIFIE ET EQUIPEMENT DE WILSON LTEE—See Heidelberg Materials AG; *Int'l*, pg. 3317
SC CERAMICA SA—See Advent International Corporation; *U.S. Private*, pg. 105
SEQUATCHIE CONCRETE SERVICE INC.; *U.S. Private*, pg. 3612
SEQUATCHIE CONCRETE SERVICE INC.—See Sequatchie Concrete Service Inc.; *U.S. Private*, pg. 3612
SOUTHERN CONCRETE PRODUCTS INC.; *U.S. Private*, pg. 3730
STEPSTONE, INC.; *U.S. Private*, pg. 3804
SUNCOKE LOGISTICS LLC—See SunCoke Energy, Inc.; *U.S. Public*; pg. 1964
TERRASSA CONCRETE INDUSTRIES; *U.S. Private*, pg. 3972
TRANSPAVE, INC.—See CRH plc; *Int'l*, pg. 1849
TRENDSET CONCRETE PRODUCTS INC.—See SiteOne Landscape Supply, Inc.; *U.S. Public*, pg. 1889
UPSTONE MATERIALS INC.—See Barrett Industries, Inc.; *U.S. Private*, pg. 480
VAPIS STAVEBNI HMOTY S.R.O.—See Heidelberg Materials AG; *Int'l*, pg. 3320
WESTERN STATES WHOLESALE INC.; *U.S. Private*, pg. 4497
XELLA KALKZANDSTEENFABRIEK HOOGDONK B.V.—See Lone Star Global Acquisitions, LLC; *U.S. Private*, pg. 2489
XELLA NEDERLAND B.V.—See Lone Star Global Acquisitions, LLC; *U.S. Private*, pg. 2489
YORK BUILDING PRODUCTS CO., INC.; *U.S. Private*, pg. 4590

327332 — CONCRETE PIPE MANUFACTURING

ABETONG AB—See Heidelberg Materials AG; *Int'l*, pg. 3315
ABETONG AB—See Heidelberg Materials AG; *Int'l*, pg. 3315
AMERICAN PIPE & CONSTRUCTION INTERNATIONAL—See NOV, Inc.; *U.S. Public*, pg. 1543
ANHUI JIANHUAI PIPELINE ENGINEERING CO., LTD.—See Beijing Hanjian Heshan Pipeline Co.,LTD.; *Int'l*, pg. 951
ASAHI CONCRETE WORKS CO., LTD.; *Int'l*, pg. 592
BEIJING HANJIAN HESHAN PIPELINE CO.,LTD.; *Int'l*, pg. 951
BEIJING HANJIAN HESHAN TECHNOLOGY CO., LTD.—See Beijing Hanjian Heshan Pipeline Co.,LTD.; *Int'l*, pg. 951
BETONGINDUSTRI AB—See Heidelberg Materials AG; *Int'l*, pg. 3315
BETONJERKA A.D.; *Int'l*, pg. 1003
BONNA TUNISIA—See Bain Capital, LP; *U.S. Private*, pg. 438
CEMENTO POLPAICO S.A.; *Int'l*, pg. 1397
CEMEX CANADA—See CEMEX, S.A.B. de C.V.; *Int'l*, pg. 1399
CONCRETE TECHNOLOGIES WORLDWIDE, INC.—See Kohlberg & Company, LLC; *U.S. Private*, pg. 2337
CRETEX CONCRETE PRODUCTS MIDWEST, INC.—See The Cretex Companies, Inc.; *U.S. Private*, pg. 4016
CSR LIMITED; *Int'l*, pg. 1867
DAELIM CONCRETE PRODUCTS CO., LTD.—See Daelim Industrial Co., Ltd.; *Int'l*, pg. 1908
DOGUSAN BORU SANAYII VE TICARET A.S.; *Int'l*, pg. 2155
THE EGYPTIAN COMPANY FOR PIPES & CEMENT PRODUCTS CO. (SIEGWART)—See Chemical Industries Holding Company; *Int'l*, pg. 1462
FLEXHEAD INDUSTRIES, INC.—See Tailwind Capital Group, LLC; *U.S. Private*, pg. 3923
FOLEY PRODUCTS COMPANY, LLC; *U.S. Private*, pg. 1558
FRAMO HOLSNOY AS—See Alfa Laval AB; *Int'l*, pg. 312
GENEVA PIPE COMPANY—See Northwest Pipe Company; *U.S. Public*, pg. 1542
GRAND JUNCTION CONCRETE PIPE CO.—See Ferguson plc; *Int'l*, pg. 2638
HANCOCK CONCRETE PRODUCTS INC.—See CRH plc; *Int'l*, pg. 1846
HANSON PIPE & PRECAST QUEBEC LTD.—See Heidelberg Materials AG; *Int'l*, pg. 3312
HEIDELBERGER BETONPUMPEN RHEIN-MAIN-NAHE VERWALTUNGS-GMBH—See Heidelberg Materials AG; *Int'l*, pg. 3316
HOLCIM GROUP SERVICES LTD—See Holcim Ltd.; *Int'l*, pg. 3448
HUATRACO INDUSTRIES SDN BHD—See Hiap Teck Venture Berhad; *Int'l*, pg. 3382
LEEP INC; *U.S. Public*, pg. 1301
LEHIGH HANSON MATERIALS LIMITED—See Heidelberg Materials AG; *Int'l*, pg. 3318
THE MACHINES YVONAND SA—See CAPCELLENCE Mittelstandspartner GmbH; *Int'l*, pg. 1302
MI POLYMER CONCRETE PIPES SDN BHD—See Chin Hin Group Berhad; *Int'l*, pg. 1480
NATIONAL CONCRETE PRODUCTS COMPANY; *U.S. Private*, pg. 2851
OLDCASTLE PRECAST, INC. - PORTLAND—See CRH plc; *Int'l*, pg. 1846
OLSON PRECAST COMPANY; *U.S. Private*, pg. 3011
PEDERSHAAB CONCRETE TECHNOLOGIES A/S—See Kohlberg & Company, LLC; *U.S. Private*, pg. 2337
PHAN VU INVESTMENT CORPORATION—See ASIA PILE HOLDINGS CORPORATION; *Int'l*, pg. 614
PRE-CON PRODUCTS; *U.S. Private*, pg. 3243
PREMARC—See Premarc Corporation; *U.S. Private*, pg. 3249
P.T. BONNA INDONESIA—See Bain Capital, LP; *U.S. Private*, pg. 438
READYMIX CONCRETE PRODUCTS (ISRAEL) LTD—See CEMEX, S.A.B. de C.V.; *Int'l*, pg. 1398
READYMIX—See CEMEX, S.A.B. de C.V.; *Int'l*, pg. 1400
RINKER MATERIALS-CONCRETE PIPE & STORMWATER TREATMENT—See CEMEX, S.A.B. de C.V.; *Int'l*, pg. 1399
RINKER MATERIALS-HARRISBURG—See CEMEX, S.A.B. de C.V.; *Int'l*, pg. 1399
SAUDI ARABIA CONCRETE PRODUCTS LTD.—See NOV, Inc.; *U.S. Public*, pg. 1544
SOCIETE DES TUYAUX ARMES DE LA CHARENTE—See Compagnie de Saint-Gobain SA; *Int'l*, pg. 1737
SUPREME CONCRETE BLOCK INC.—See CRH plc; *Int'l*, pg. 1844
THERMOGENICS INC.—See Audax Group, Limited Partnership; *U.S. Private*, pg. 390
TUYAUX ET AGGLOMERES VENDEENS—See Compagnie de Saint-Gobain SA; *Int'l*, pg. 1737
UNICON A/S—See Cementir Holding N.V.; *Int'l*, pg. 1397
UNION CEMENT CORPORATION—See FLSmidth & Co. A/S; *Int'l*, pg. 2712
UNITED CONCRETE PRODUCTS, LLC—See Eagle Manufacturing Group; *U.S. Private*, pg. 1309
VIANINI PIPE INC.—See Cementir Holding N.V.; *Int'l*, pg. 1397

327390 — OTHER CONCRETE PRODUCT MANUFACTURING

3BETONY LTD.—See Bain Capital, LP; *U.S. Private*, pg. 438
ACC LIMITED - RAVIRALA PLANT—See ACC Limited; *Int'l*, pg. 79
A.C. MILLER CONCRETE PRODUCTS INC.; *U.S. Private*, pg. 24
ADHORNA PREFABRICACION, SA—See Elecnor, S.A.; *Int'l*, pg. 2347
AEROC INTERNATIONAL AS; *Int'l*, pg. 180
AEROC JAMERA AS—See Aeroc International AS; *Int'l*, pg. 180
AGGLITE OF VIRGINIA INC.—See Eagle Corporation; *U.S. Private*, pg. 1309
ALAMO CONCRETE PRODUCTS LTD.—See Alamo Cement Company; *U.S. Private*, pg. 149
AL JABER FUSION-BONDED EPOXY COATING PLANT—See Al Jaber Group; *Int'l*, pg. 279
ALKERN SAS—See Chequers SA; *Int'l*, pg. 1471
AMERON HAWAII—See NOV, Inc.; *U.S. Public*, pg. 1543
AMERON INTERNATIONAL CORPORATION—See NOV, Inc.; *U.S. Public*, pg. 1543
AMERON POLE PRODUCTS LLC—See Arcosa, Inc.; *U.S. Public*, pg. 186
ANDERTON CONCRETE PRODUCTS LTD.—See Ibstock plc; *Int'l*, pg. 3577
ARAMIT GROUP; *Int'l*, pg. 535
ARNOLD-WILBERT CORP.; *U.S. Private*, pg. 333
ASA CONS ROMANIA S.R.L.—See Bain Capital, LP; *U.S. Private*, pg. 438
ASA EPITOIPARI KFT.—See Bain Capital, LP; *U.S. Private*, pg. 438
ATLANTIC CONCRETE PRODUCTS, INC. - COCKEYSVILLE PLANT—See Atlantic Concrete Products, Inc.; *U.S. Private*, pg. 372
ATLANTIC CONCRETE PRODUCTS, INC.; *U.S. Private*, pg. 372
ATMI DYNACORE LLC; *U.S. Private*, pg. 381
ATMI PRECAST INC.; *U.S. Private*, pg. 381
AUSCRETE CORPORATION; *U.S. Public*, pg. 228
AUSTIN PRESTRESS CO—See Abrams International LLP; *U.S. Private*, pg. 40
AUSTRAL BRICKS (NSW) PTY LTD—See Brickworks Limited; *Int'l*, pg. 1151
AUSTRAL PRECAST (QLD) PTY LTD—See Brickworks Limited; *Int'l*, pg. 1152
AUTOMATIC TERRAZZO TILES FACTORY LLC—See Badr Investment Group LLC; *Int'l*, pg. 796
AVILA'S GARDEN ART; *U.S. Private*, pg. 407
BASF ADMIXTURE SYSTEMS EUROPE—See BASF SE; *Int'l*, pg. 874
BASF CONSTRUCTION CHEMICALS ASIA/PACIFIC—See BASF SE; *Int'l*, pg. 874
BASF CONSTRUCTION CHEMICALS CANADA LTD.—See BASF SE; *Int'l*, pg. 874
BASF EAST AFRICA LTD.—See BASF SE; *Int'l*, pg. 877
BASF MIDDLE EAST CHEMICALS LLC—See BASF SE; *Int'l*, pg. 880
BAUSTOFFWERKE DRESDEN GMBH & CO. KG—See Heidelberg Materials AG; *Int'l*, pg. 3316
BEPRONOR - SOCIEDADE DE BETAO PRONTO DO NORDESTE S.A.—See Camargo Correa S.A.; *Int'l*, pg. 1267
BETONIKA UAB—See Bain Capital, LP; *U.S. Private*, pg. 438
BETONJERKA A.D; *Int'l*, pg. 1003
BETON PROVINCIAL LTEE; *Int'l*, pg. 1002
BETONSKI PROIZVODI A.D.; *Int'l*, pg. 1003
B+F BETON- UND FERTIGTEILGESELLSCHAFT MBH LAUCHHAMMER—See General Atomics; *U.S. Private*, pg. 1663
BILTECH BUILDING ELEMENTS LIMITED—See Avantha Group; *Int'l*, pg. 735
BINA ADVANCED CONCRETE PRODUCTS COMPANY—See Bawan Company; *Int'l*, pg. 900
BLAKESLEE PRESTRESS INC.; *U.S. Private*, pg. 578
BODON INDUSTRIES INC.; *U.S. Private*, pg. 608
BOMAT, INC.—See RPM International Inc.; *U.S. Public*, pg. 1816
BONSAL AMERICAN, INC.—See CRH plc; *Int'l*, pg. 1845
BRADLEY CORPORATION—See Watts Water Technologies, Inc.; *U.S. Public*, pg. 2337
BREEDON GROUP PLC; *Int'l*, pg. 1144
BRISTILE ROOFING (EAST COAST) PTY LTD.—See Brickworks Limited; *Int'l*, pg. 1152
BROWN-WILBERT INC.; *U.S. Private*, pg. 669
BUFFALO CRUSHED STONE, INC. - BARTON ROAD BLACKTOP PLANT—See New Enterprise Stone & Lime Co., Inc.; *U.S. Private*, pg. 2895
BUFFALO CRUSHED STONE, INC. - COMO PARK BLACKTOP PLANT—See New Enterprise Stone & Lime Co., Inc.; *U.S. Private*, pg. 2895
BUFFALO CRUSHED STONE, INC. - OLEAN BLACKTOP PLANT—See New Enterprise Stone & Lime Co., Inc.; *U.S. Private*, pg. 2895
BUILDEX, LLC—See Summit Materials, Inc.; *U.S. Public*, pg. 1959
CALLANAN INDUSTRIES, INC.—See CRH plc; *Int'l*, pg. 1847
CARPAT BETON SERVICII POMPE SRL—See Heidelberg Materials AG; *Int'l*, pg. 3309
CARR CONCRETE CORP.—See R.W. Sidley, Incorporated; *U.S. Private*, pg. 3340
CAST-CRETE USA, LLC—See Stonebridge Partners, LLC; *U.S. Private*, pg. 3827
CEMATRIX (CANADA) INC.—See Cematrix Corporation; *Int'l*, pg. 1396
CEMATRIX CORPORATION; *Int'l*, pg. 1396

N.A.I.C.S. INDEX — 327390 — OTHER CONCRETE PROD...

CEMATRIX (USA) INC.—See Cematrix Corporation; *Int'l*, pg. 1396
CEMENT INDUSTRIES, INC.; *U.S. Private*, pg. 808
CEMEX FRANCE GESTION (S.A.S.)—See CEMEX, S.A.B. de C.V.; *Int'l*, pg. 1398
CEMEX HRVATSKA D.D.—See CEMEX, S.A.B. de C.V.; *Int'l*, pg. 1399
CENTURY GROUP INC.; *U.S. Private*, pg. 833
CENTURY PRECAST PRODUCTS, LLC; *U.S. Private*, pg. 834
CES-PRECAST PTE. LTD.—See Chip Eng Seng Corporation Ltd.; *Int'l*, pg. 1572
CHONBURI CONCRETE PRODUCT PUBLIC COMPANY LIMITED; *Int'l*, pg. 1578
CIC39 CORP.; *Int'l*, pg. 1602
CIMBETON HAZIRBETON VE PREFABRIK YAPI ELEMANLARI SANAYI VE TICARET A.S.—See Cementir Holding N.V.; *Int'l*, pg. 1397
CITY CONCRETE, INC.—See Vulcan Materials Company; *U.S. Public*, pg. 2314
CLARK PACIFIC; *U.S. Private*, pg. 913
COASTAL PRECAST OF FLORIDA, INC.—See Foley Products Company, LLC; *U.S. Private*, pg. 1558
COMPLETE HOME CONCEPTS INC.; *U.S. Private*, pg. 1000
COMPTOIR DU BATIMENT NV—See Etex SA/NV; *Int'l*, pg. 2521
CONCRETE ENGINEERING PRODUCTS BERHAD - BATANG KALI FACTORY—See Concrete Engineering Products Berhad; *Int'l*, pg. 1765
CONCRETE ENGINEERING PRODUCTS BERHAD - NILAI FACTORY—See Concrete Engineering Products Berhad; *Int'l*, pg. 1765
CONCRETE ENGINEERING PRODUCTS BERHAD - PASIR GUDANG FACTORY—See Concrete Engineering Products Berhad; *Int'l*, pg. 1765
CONCRETE ENGINEERING PRODUCTS BERHAD - RAWANG FACTORY—See Concrete Engineering Products Berhad; *Int'l*, pg. 1765
CONCRETE ENGINEERING PRODUCTS BERHAD - SUNGAI PETANI FACTORY—See Concrete Engineering Products Berhad; *Int'l*, pg. 1766
CONCRETE EQUIPMENT COMPANY,INC.—See Astec Industries, Inc.; *U.S. Public*, pg. 216
CONCRETE SPECIALTIES COMPANY—See CRH plc; *Int'l*, pg. 1844
CONCRETE TECHNOLOGY CORP.; *U.S. Private*, pg. 1011
CONCRETE TECHNOLOGY INCORPORATED; *U.S. Private*, pg. 1011
CONCRETE VALLEY GROUP BV; *Int'l*, pg. 1766
CONSOLIS POLSKA SP. Z O.O.—See Bain Capital, LP; *U.S. Private*, pg. 438
CORESLAB STRUCTURES (ALBUQUERQUE) INC.—See Coreslab International, Inc.; *Int'l*, pg. 1799
CORESLAB STRUCTURES (ARK) INC.—See Coreslab International, Inc.; *Int'l*, pg. 1799
CORESLAB STRUCTURES (ATLANTA) INC.—See Coreslab International, Inc.; *Int'l*, pg. 1799
CORESLAB STRUCTURES (CONN) INC.—See Coreslab International, Inc.; *Int'l*, pg. 1799
CORESLAB STRUCTURES, INC.—See Coreslab International, Inc.; *Int'l*, pg. 1799
CORESLAB STRUCTURES, INC.—See Coreslab International, Inc.; *Int'l*, pg. 1799
CORESLAB STRUCTURES, INC.—See Coreslab International, Inc.; *Int'l*, pg. 1799
CORESLAB STRUCTURES (LA) INC.—See Coreslab International, Inc.; *Int'l*, pg. 1799
CORESLAB STRUCTURES (ONT) INC.—See Coreslab International, Inc.; *Int'l*, pg. 1799
CORESLAB STRUCTURES (ORLANDO) INC.—See Coreslab International, Inc.; *Int'l*, pg. 1799
CORESLAB STRUCTURES (TAMPA) INC.—See Coreslab International, Inc.; *Int'l*, pg. 1799
CORESLAB STRUCTURES (TULSA) INC.—See Coreslab International, Inc.; *Int'l*, pg. 1799
COUNTY MATERIALS CORP.; *U.S. Private*, pg. 1068
CREATIVE MANUFACTURING INC.; *U.S. Private*, pg. 1089
THE CRETEX COMPANIES, INC.; *U.S. Private*, pg. 4016
CRETEX CONCRETE PRODUCTS NORTH, INC.—See The Cretex Companies, Inc.; *U.S. Private*, pg. 4016
CRETEX CONCRETE PRODUCTS NORTH, INC.—See The Cretex Companies, Inc.; *U.S. Private*, pg. 4016
CRH AGREGATE BETOANE S.A.—See CRH plc; *Int'l*, pg. 1843
C/S CONSTRUCTION SPECIALTIES COMPANY—See Construction Specialties, Inc.; *U.S. Private*, pg. 1024
CXT, INC.—See L.B. Foster Company; *U.S. Public*, pg. 1278
DAN'S CEMENT, INC.; *U.S. Private*, pg. 1152
DAYTON SUPERIOR CORPORATION—See Dayton Superior Corporation; *U.S. Private*, pg. 1178
DCON PRODUCTS PUBLIC COMPANY LIMITED - LOPBURI FACTORY 1—See DCON Products Public Company Limited; *Int'l*, pg. 1993
DCON PRODUCTS PUBLIC COMPANY LIMITED - LOPBURI FACTORY 2—See DCON Products Public Company Limited; *Int'l*, pg. 1993
DCON PRODUCTS PUBLIC COMPANY LIMITED - SURAT THANI FACTORY—See DCON Products Public Company Limited; *Int'l*, pg. 1993
DELMON PRECAST COMPANY WLL—See Abdulla Ahmed Nass Group WLL; *Int'l*, pg. 58
DKLS PRECAST SYSTEM SDN BHD—See DKLS Industries Berhad; *Int'l*, pg. 2139
DMG EQUIPMENT COMPANY, LLC—See Vulcan Materials Company; *U.S. Public*, pg. 2313
DULHUNTY POLES PTY LTD—See Energy Technologies Limited; *Int'l*, pg. 2423
DUNAPREF SA; *Int'l*, pg. 2225
DURA ART STONE INC.; *U.S. Private*, pg. 1291
DURISOL RAALTE B.V.; *Int'l*, pg. 2228
DW SCHWELLEN GMBH—See Bain Capital, LP; *U.S. Private*, pg. 438
DW SYSTEMBAU GMBH—See Bain Capital, LP; *U.S. Private*, pg. 438
DYCORE B.V.—See CRH plc; *Int'l*, pg. 1844
EAGLE CORPORATION; *U.S. Private*, pg. 1309
EASTERN INDUSTRIES, INC. - BETHLEHEM PLANT—See New Enterprise Stone & Lime Co., Inc.; *U.S. Private*, pg. 2895
EB MAWSON & SONS PTY LTD.; *Int'l*, pg. 2282
ECHO ROCK VENTURES INC.; *U.S. Private*, pg. 1327
EKOTON+ JSC; *Int'l*, pg. 2339
ELITE ALUMINUM CORPORATION; *U.S. Private*, pg. 1360
EMIRATES THERMOSTONE FACTORY LLC—See Dubai Investments PJSC; *Int'l*, pg. 2219
ENTEGRA ROOF TILE CORP-POMPANO; *U.S. Private*, pg. 1403
ENTERPRISE PROPERTIES INC.; *U.S. Private*, pg. 1404
ERECT-A-LINE INC.—See Georgeco Inc.; *U.S. Private*, pg. 1684
ETERNIT LTD.—See Etex SA/NV; *Int'l*, pg. 2521
ETERNIT NV—See Etex SA/NV; *Int'l*, pg. 2522
ETEX BUILDING MATERIALS POLSKA SP. Z O.O.—See Etex SA/NV; *Int'l*, pg. 2522
EURONIT FACHADAS Y CUBIERTAS S.L.—See Etex SA/NV; *Int'l*, pg. 2522
EURO PANELS OVERSEAS NV—See Etex SA/NV; *Int'l*, pg. 2522
EXPOCRETE CONCRETE PRODUCTS LTD.—See CRH plc; *Int'l*, pg. 1846
EZ GROUT CORPORATION, INC.; *U.S. Private*, pg. 1454
FABCON PRECAST LLC—See Solace Capital Partners, LLC; *U.S. Private*, pg. 3706
FAB-FORM INDUSTRIES (1986) LTD.—See Fab-Form Industries Ltd.; *Int'l*, pg. 2598
FABRICA PERUANA ETERNIT S.A.—See Etex SA/NV; *Int'l*, pg. 2522
FABRIKA KARPOS AD—See Gradezen Institut Makedonija; *Int'l*, pg. 3049
FAIRBANKS MATERIALS, INC.—See MDU Resources Group, Inc.; *U.S. Public*, pg. 1410
FECON MINING JOINT STOCK COMPANY—See ASIA PILE HOLDINGS CORPORATION; *Int'l*, pg. 614
FIBREBOND CORPORATION; *U.S. Private*, pg. 1502
FLETCHER BUILDING AUSTRALIA—See Fletcher Building Limited; *Int'l*, pg. 2700
FLEXICORE OF TEXAS, L.P.; *U.S. Private*, pg. 1544
FLORENCE CONCRETE PRODUCTS CO. INC; *U.S. Private*, pg. 1547
FORMING CONCEPTS, INC.—See Brand Industrial Services, Inc.; *U.S. Private*, pg. 636
THE FORT MILLER COMPANY INC.—See The Fort Miller Group Inc.; *U.S. Private*, pg. 4030
THE FORT MILLER GROUP INC.; *U.S. Private*, pg. 4029
FOUR CORNERS MATERIALS—See CRH plc; *Int'l*, pg. 1847
FOX SERVICES, INC.—See Fox Corporation; *U.S. Public*, pg. 876
GAMUDA INDUSTRIAL BUILDING SYSTEM SDN. BHD.—See Gamuda Berhad; *Int'l*, pg. 2879
GAMUDA TRADING SDN. BHD.—See Gamuda Berhad; *Int'l*, pg. 2879
GAS BETON CELKON A.D.; *Int'l*, pg. 2887
GATE PRECAST COMPANY - JACKSONVILLE—See Gate Petroleum Company; *U.S. Private*, pg. 1649
GATE PRECAST COMPANY—See Gate Petroleum Company; *U.S. Private*, pg. 1649
GATE PRECAST CO.—See Gate Petroleum Company; *U.S. Private*, pg. 1649
GATE PRECAST CO.—See Gate Petroleum Company; *U.S. Private*, pg. 1649
GATE PRECAST CO.—See Gate Petroleum Company; *U.S. Private*, pg. 1649
GATE PRECAST CO.—See Gate Petroleum Company; *U.S. Private*, pg. 1649
GATE PRECAST CO.—See Gate Petroleum Company; *U.S. Private*, pg. 1649
G.B. KUARI SDN. BHD.—See Gamuda Berhad; *Int'l*, pg. 2879
GENERAL NIPPON CONCRETE INDUSTRIES LIMITED—See General Engineering Public Company Limited; *Int'l*, pg. 2918
GFRC SHELTERS, INC.; *U.S. Private*, pg. 1690
GIWARITE LTD.—See Etex SA/NV; *Int'l*, pg. 2522
GORGE ROCK PRODUCTS, INC.—See Clyde Companies Inc.; *U.S. Private*, pg. 949
GP/RM PRESTRESS, LLC—See Alexander & Baldwin, Inc.; *U.S. Public*, pg. 75
GRAND RIVER INFRASTRUCTURE—See Premarc Corporation; *U.S. Private*, pg. 3249
GRANITUL SA; *Int'l*, pg. 3059
GROUP DE CLOEDT SA; *Int'l*, pg. 3088
GROUPE PLAFOLIFT INC.; *Int'l*, pg. 3109
GULF COAST PRE-STRESS, INC.; *U.S. Private*, pg. 1815
HAMILTON FORM CO., LTD.; *U.S. Private*, pg. 1847
HANSON HISPANIA S.A.—See Heidelberg Materials AG; *Int'l*, pg. 3312
H.A.N.S. PREFA A.S.—See Bain Capital, LP; *U.S. Private*, pg. 438
HARRIS REBAR BOISE, INC—See Nucor Corporation; *U.S. Public*, pg. 1553
HEIDELBERGER BETONELEMENTE VERWALTUNGS-GMBH—See Heidelberg Materials AG; *Int'l*, pg. 3316
HEIDELBERG MATERIALS KUNDA AS—See Heidelberg Materials AG; *Int'l*, pg. 3314
HEIDELBERG MATERIALS LATVIJA BETONS SIA—See Heidelberg Materials AG; *Int'l*, pg. 3314
HEIDELBERG MATERIALS PRECAST DENMARK A/S—See Heidelberg Materials AG; *Int'l*, pg. 3314
HEIJMANS BESTCON B.V.—See Heijmans N.V.; *Int'l*, pg. 3322
HELDENFELS ENTERPRISES INC.; *U.S. Private*, pg. 1905
HIGH CONCRETE GROUP LLC—See High Industries, Inc.; *U.S. Private*, pg. 1935
HIGH CONCRETE TECHNOLOGY LLC—See High Industries, Inc.; *U.S. Private*, pg. 1935
HILL & SMITH PTY LIMITED—See Hill & Smith PLC; *Int'l*, pg. 3391
HM TRADING GLOBAL GMBH—See Heidelberg Materials AG; *Int'l*, pg. 3311
HUME CEMENT SDN. BHD.—See Hume Cement Industries Berhad; *Int'l*, pg. 3530
HUME CONCRETE SDN. BHD.—See Hume Cement Industries Berhad; *Int'l*, pg. 3530
HUNTONIT AS—See Byggma ASA; *Int'l*, pg. 1235
ICP JIANGMEN CO. LTD.—See IJM Corporation Berhad; *Int'l*, pg. 3609
ICP MARKETING SDN BHD—See IJM Corporation Berhad; *Int'l*, pg. 3608
IHI CONSTRUCTION MATERIALS CO., LTD.—See IHI Corporation; *Int'l*, pg. 3604
INCRETE SYSTEMS INC.—See RPM International Inc.; *U.S. Public*, pg. 1818
INDUSTRIAL CONCRETE PRODUCTS BERHAD—See IJM Corporation Berhad; *Int'l*, pg. 3609
INNOVATIVE HEARTH PRODUCTS LLC—See TRM Equity LLC; *U.S. Private*, pg. 4241
ISABEL BLOOM LLC; *U.S. Private*, pg. 2142
JENNA CONCRETE CORP.—See Vulcan Materials Company; *U.S. Public*, pg. 2314
JENSEN ENTERPRISES INC.; *U.S. Private*, pg. 2200
JOBE MATERIALS, L.P.; *U.S. Private*, pg. 2217
JOSEPH P. CARRARA & SONS INC.; *U.S. Private*, pg. 2237
KAM-CRETE LTD.—See Bird Construction Inc.; *Int'l*, pg. 1047
KEMENA INDUSTRIES SDN BHD—See IJM Corporation Berhad; *Int'l*, pg. 3609
KESAS SDN. BHD.—See Gamuda Berhad; *Int'l*, pg. 2879
KIESWERKE FLEMMINGEN GMBH—See Heidelberg Materials AG; *Int'l*, pg. 3317
KNAUER'S WILBERT VAULT INC.—See Berkshire Hathaway Inc.; *U.S. Public*, pg. 298
KNIFE RIVER-WACO READY MIX PLANT—See MDU Resources Group, Inc.; *U.S. Public*, pg. 1410
LATICRETE INTERNATIONAL, INC.; *U.S. Private*, pg. 2396
LOMBARD ARCHITECTURAL PRECAST PRODUCTS CO., INC.—See The Lombard Investment Co.; *U.S. Private*, pg. 4072
LYTAG LTD—See Holcim Ltd.; *Int'l*, pg. 3446
MACK INDUSTRIES INC.; *U.S. Private*, pg. 2536
MACON SRL—See Lone Star Global Acquisitions, LLC; *U.S. Private*, pg. 2489
MANHATTAN AMERICAN TERRAZZO STRIP COMPANY INC.—See The Platt Brothers & Company, Inc.; *U.S. Private*, pg. 4096
MARLEY ROOFING (PTY) LTD—See Etex SA/NV; *Int'l*, pg. 2522
MASTERPAVE SDN. BHD.—See Gamuda Berhad; *Int'l*, pg. 2879
METROMONT CORPORATION; *U.S. Private*, pg. 2687
MID-ILLINOIS CONCRETE INC.; *U.S. Private*, pg. 2708
MILBURY SYSTEMS LIMITED—See Eleco Plc; *Int'l*, pg. 2348
NEWBASIS—See Echo Rock Ventures Inc.; *U.S. Private*, pg. 1327
NITTERHOUSE CONCRETE PRODUCTS INC.; *U.S. Private*, pg. 2930
NMB CO., LTD.—See BASF SE; *Int'l*, pg. 874
NORTH AMERICAN RECYCLING AND CRUSHING, LLC—See Vulcan Materials Company; *U.S. Public*, pg. 2313

327390 — OTHER CONCRETE PROD...

OETERBETON N.V.—See CRH plc; *Int'l*, pg. 1845
OLDCASTLE APG, INC.—See CRH plc; *Int'l*, pg. 1845
OLDCASTLE BUILDING PRODUCTS CANADA, INC. - PERMACON DIVISION—See CRH plc; *Int'l*, pg. 1846
OLDCASTLE COASTAL, INC.; *U.S. Private*, pg. 3009
OLDCASTLE INFRASTRUCTURE, INC,—See CRH plc; *Int'l*, pg. 1846
OLDCASTLE PRECAST BUILDING SYSTEMS—See CRH plc; *Int'l*, pg. 1846
OPTERRA BETON GMBH—See CRH plc; *Int'l*, pg. 1845
OPTIROC SA—See Compagnie de Saint-Gobain SA; *Int'l*, pg. 1727
PALPLINTAR I SVERIGE AB—See AF Gruppen ASA; *Int'l*, pg. 184
PARASTEK OY AB—See Bain Capital, LP; *U.S. Private*, pg. 438
PARMA OY—See Bain Capital, LP; *U.S. Private*, pg. 438
PDM PRECAST, INC.; *U.S. Private*, pg. 3122
PHELPS TOINTON INC.; *U.S. Private*, pg. 3167
THE PINDEN PLANT & PROCESSING CO. LIMITED—See Heidelberg Materials AG; *Int'l*, pg. 3320
PRECON POLSKA SP.Z.O.O.—See Heidelberg Materials AG; *Int'l*, pg. 3319
PREFABRICACIONES Y CONTRATAS, S.A.U.—See Cementos Molins S.A.; *Int'l*, pg. 1397
PREMARC CORPORATION; *U.S. Private*, pg. 3249
PREMARC/MARSH PRODUCTS—See Premarc Corporation; *U.S. Private*, pg. 3249
PREMIX & PRECAST CONCRETE INCORPORATED—See CEMEX, S.A.B. de C.V.; *Int'l*, pg. 1400
PRESTRESS SERVICES INDUSTRIES LLC; *U.S. Private*, pg. 3257
PROMOTORA MEDITERRANEA-2, S.A.—See Cementos Molins S.A.; *Int'l*, pg. 1397
PT. ESTOP INDONESIA—See Denki Company Limited; *Int'l*, pg. 2027
PUERTO RICO PRECAST CONCRETE, INC.—See Atlantic Concrete Products, Inc.; *U.S. Private*, pg. 372
QUALITY CONCRETE PRODUCTS, INC.—See CRH plc; *Int'l*, pg. 1846
QUIKRETE—See The Quikrete Companies, LLC; *U.S. Private*, pg. 4101
R. C. SMITH COMPANIES, LLC—See Vulcan Materials Company; *U.S. Public*, pg. 2313
REDBANK MANUFACTURING COMPANY LIMITED—See Heidelberg Materials AG; *Int'l*, pg. 3319
REX PRECAST SYSTEMS, INC.—See Superior Products Distributors Inc.; *U.S. Private*, pg. 3880
ROCKY MOUNTAIN PRESTRESS, LLC—See Phelps Tointon Inc.; *U.S. Private*, pg. 3167
ROCLA PTY LIMITED—See Heidelberg Materials AG; *Int'l*, pg. 3314
RUDUS OY AB—See CRH plc; *Int'l*, pg. 1848
SABREFIX (UK) LIMITED—See Simpson Manufacturing Company, Inc.; *U.S. Public*, pg. 1883
SAINT-GOBAIN WEBER CEMARKSA SA—See Compagnie de Saint-Gobain SA; *Int'l*, pg. 1727
SAINT-GOBAIN WEBER CO., LTD.—See Compagnie de Saint-Gobain SA; *Int'l*, pg. 1727
SAINT-GOBAIN WEBER PORTUGAL S.A.—See Compagnie de Saint-Gobain SA; *Int'l*, pg. 1727
SAN-CON INDUSTRIES, INC.—See Marietta Silos LLC; *U.S. Private*, pg. 2574
SCHELFHOUT N.V.—See CRH plc; *Int'l*, pg. 1848
SCURLOCK INDUSTRIES; *U.S. Private*, pg. 3581
SELKIRK CANADA CORPORATION—See Canada Pension Plan Investment Board; *Int'l*, pg. 1282
SEMINOLE PRECAST MANUFACTURING, INC.; *U.S. Private*, pg. 3604
SER SANIERUNG IM ERD- UND RUCKBAU GMBH—See Heidelberg Materials AG; *Int'l*, pg. 3319
SHAMROCK MATERIALS INC. - BUILDING MATERIALS DIVISION—See Vulcan Materials Company; *U.S. Public*, pg. 2313
THE SHOCKEY PRECAST GROUP—See Metromont Corporation; *U.S. Private*, pg. 2687
SIA AEROC—See Aeroc International AS; *Int'l*, pg. 180
SIA CONSOLIS LATVIJA—See Bain Capital, LP; *U.S. Private*, pg. 438
SIERRA PRECAST, INC.—See Vulcan Materials Company; *U.S. Public*, pg. 2314
SMARTPANEL AS—See Byggma ASA; *Int'l*, pg. 1235
SMITH-MIDLAND CORPORATION; *U.S. Public*, pg. 1896
SOCIEDAD FINANCIERA Y MINERA S.A. - KUKULARRA PLANT—See Heidelberg Materials AG; *Int'l*, pg. 3317
SOCIEDAD FINANCIERA Y MINERA S.A.—See Heidelberg Materials AG; *Int'l*, pg. 3317
SOCLI S.A.S.—See Heidelberg Materials AG; *Int'l*, pg. 3316
SOUTHERN FRAC, LLC—See United Rentals, Inc.; *U.S. Public*, pg. 2235
SPAENCOM A/S—See Bain Capital, LP; *U.S. Private*, pg. 438
SPANBETON B.V.—See Bain Capital, LP; *U.S. Private*, pg. 438
SPANCRETE INC.—See Wells Concrete Products Company Inc.; *U.S. Private*, pg. 4476
SPANCRETE OF ILLINOIS INC.—See Wells Concrete Products Company Inc.; *U.S. Private*, pg. 4476

SPENNCON AS—See Bain Capital, LP; *U.S. Private*, pg. 438
S & S PRECAST, INC.; *U.S. Private*, pg. 3512
STANDARD CONCRETE PRODUCTS INC.; *U.S. Private*, pg. 3778
STARFIRE DIRECT, INC.—See Blackford Capital LLC; *U.S. Private*, pg. 574
STRADAL SAS—See CRH plc; *Int'l*, pg. 1844
STRAITFLEX CORPORATION—See Worthington Industries, Inc.; *U.S. Public*, pg. 2382
STRANGBETONG AB—See Bain Capital, LP; *U.S. Private*, pg. 438
STRESSCON CORPORATION; *U.S. Private*, pg. 3839
STRESS CON INDUSTRIES INC.; *U.S. Private*, pg. 3839
SUPERIOR CONCRETE FENCE OF TEXAS; *U.S. Private*, pg. 3876
SUPERIOR MATERIALS, INC.—See Vulcan Materials Company; *U.S. Public*, pg. 2314
SUPER-KRETE PRODUCTS—See Audax Group, Limited Partnership; *U.S. Private*, pg. 388
TBG ZNOJMO S. R. O.—See Heidelberg Materials AG; *Int'l*, pg. 3320
TBH TRANSPORTBETON HAMBURG GMBH & CO. KG—See Heidelberg Materials AG; *Int'l*, pg. 3320
TECHNOMATERIAL CORPORATION—See Daiwa House Industry Co., Ltd.; *Int'l*, pg. 1946
TERRE HILL CONCRETE PRODUCTS, INC.; *U.S. Private*, pg. 3972
TINDALL CORPORATION; *U.S. Private*, pg. 4173
TINGLEV ELEMENTFABRIK GMBH—See Heidelberg Materials AG; *Int'l*, pg. 3320
TRANS-SERVIS, SPOL. S R.O.—See Heidelberg Materials AG; *Int'l*, pg. 3320
TRAP ROCK INDUSTRIES, INC.; *U.S. Private*, pg. 4212
TRENWA; *U.S. Private*, pg. 4218
TRESPA INTERNATIONAL B.V.—See HAL Trust N.V.; *Int'l*, pg. 3224
UAB HC BETONAS—See Heidelberg Materials AG; *Int'l*, pg. 3320
UAB HEIDELBERG CEMENT KLAIPEDA—See Heidelberg Materials AG; *Int'l*, pg. 3320
UNITED CONCRETE PRODUCTS, LLC—See Eagle Manufacturing Group; *U.S. Private*, pg. 1309
UNITED PRECAST, INC.; *U.S. Private*, pg. 4295
UNIVERSAL CONCRETE PRODUCTS CORPORATION—See Bodon Industries Inc.; *U.S. Private*, pg. 608
UNIVERSAL CONCRETE PRODUCTS OF NEW JERSEY INC.—See Bodon Industries Inc.; *U.S. Private*, pg. 608
USM-RGC, INC.—See CRH plc; *Int'l*, pg. 1845
US PRECAST CORP.—See Eagle Manufacturing Group; *U.S. Private*, pg. 1309
UTILITY VAULT CO., INC.—See CRH plc; *Int'l*, pg. 1846
VALLEY BUILDING SUPPLY INC.—See Eagle Corporation; *U.S. Private*, pg. 1309
VALLEY QUARRIES INC. - SHIPPENSBURG PLANT—See New Enterprise Stone & Lime Co., Inc.; *U.S. Private*, pg. 2895
VBI VERENIGDE BOUWPRODUKTEN INDUSTRIE B.V.—See Bain Capital, LP; *U.S. Private*, pg. 438
WACO BV—See Concrete Valley Group BV; *Int'l*, pg. 1766
WALTERS & WOLF PRECAST—See Walters & Wolf; *U.S. Private*, pg. 4434
WEHRUNG'S LUMBER & HOME CENTER—See Modern Precast Concrete; *U.S. Private*, pg. 2762
WELLS CONCRETE PRODUCTS COMPANY INC.; *U.S. Private*, pg. 4476
WIESER CONCRETE PRODUCTS INC.; *U.S. Private*, pg. 4517
WILBERT FUNERAL SERVICES, INC.—See Berkshire Hathaway Inc.; *U.S. Public*, pg. 298
WYTWORNIA PODKLADOW STRUNOBETONOWYCH S.A.—See Bain Capital, LP; *U.S. Private*, pg. 438

327410 — LIME MANUFACTURING

AUSTIN WHITE LIME COMPANY; *U.S. Private*, pg. 396
AZAR REFRACTORIES CO.; *Int'l*, pg. 776
CARMEUSE HOLDING SA; *Int'l*, pg. 1341
CARMEUSE N.A.—See Carmeuse Holding SA; *Int'l*, pg. 1341
CARMEUSE NORTH AMERICA—See Carmeuse Holding SA; *Int'l*, pg. 1341
CEMEX DE PUERTO RICO INC. - LIME DIVISION—See CEMEX, S.A.B. de C.V.; *Int'l*, pg. 1399
CHEMEMAN PUBLIC COMPANY LIMITED; *Int'l*, pg. 1461
CHENEY LIME & CEMENT CO. INC.; *U.S. Private*, pg. 872
FALCO LIME COMPANY—See HBM Holdings Company; *U.S. Private*, pg. 1887
GOLDEN LIME PUBLIC COMPANY LIMITED; *Int'l*, pg. 3030
GRAYMONT DOLIME (OH) INC.—See Graymont Limited; *Int'l*, pg. 3062
GRAYMONT INC.—See Graymont Limited; *Int'l*, pg. 3062
GRAYMONT LIMITED BEDFORD PLANT—See Graymont Limited; *Int'l*, pg. 3063
GRAYMONT LIMITED CRICKET MOUNTAIN PLANT—See Graymont Limited; *Int'l*, pg. 3063

GRAYMONT LIMITED EDEN PLANT—See Graymont Limited; *Int'l*, pg. 3063
GRAYMONT LIMITED EXSHAW PLANT—See Graymont Limited; *Int'l*, pg. 3063
GRAYMONT LIMITED FAULKNER PLANT—See Graymont Limited; *Int'l*, pg. 3063
GRAYMONT LIMITED GREEN BAY PLANT—See Graymont Limited; *Int'l*, pg. 3063
GRAYMONT LIMITED HAVELOCK PLANT—See Graymont Limited; *Int'l*, pg. 3063
GRAYMONT LIMITED INDIAN CREEK PLANT—See Graymont Limited; *Int'l*, pg. 3063
GRAYMONT LIMITED JOLIETTE PLANT—See Graymont Limited; *Int'l*, pg. 3063
GRAYMONT LIMITED - LAMONT COUNTY FACILITY—See Graymont Limited; *Int'l*, pg. 3062
GRAYMONT LIMITED MAKAREAO PLANT—See Graymont Limited; *Int'l*, pg. 3063
GRAYMONT LIMITED MARBLETON PLANT—See Graymont Limited; *Int'l*, pg. 3063
GRAYMONT LIMITED PAVILION PLANT—See Graymont Limited; *Int'l*, pg. 3063
GRAYMONT LIMITED PILOT PEAK PLANT—See Graymont Limited; *Int'l*, pg. 3063
GRAYMONT LIMITED PORT INLAND PLANT—See Graymont Limited; *Int'l*, pg. 3063
GRAYMONT LIMITED - RIVERGATE FACILITY—See Graymont Limited; *Int'l*, pg. 3062
GRAYMONT LIMITED SCHUYLER FALLS PLANT—See Graymont Limited; *Int'l*, pg. 3063
GRAYMONT LIMITED; *Int'l*, pg. 3062
GRAYMONT LIMITED SUMMIT PLANT—See Graymont Limited; *Int'l*, pg. 3063
GRAYMONT LIMITED SUPERIOR PLANT—See Graymont Limited; *Int'l*, pg. 3063
GRAYMONT LIMITED TE KUITI PLANT—See Graymont Limited; *Int'l*, pg. 3063
GRAYMONT WESTERN LIME INC. - GREEN BAY—See Graymont Limited; *Int'l*, pg. 3063
GRAYMONT WESTERN LIME INC.—See Graymont Limited; *Int'l*, pg. 3063
GREER INDUSTRIES INC.; *U.S. Private*, pg. 1782
MINERAL PROCESSING COMPANY—See The Andersons Incorporated; *U.S. Public*, pg. 2034
MISSISSIPPI LIME COMPANY—See HBM Holdings Company; *U.S. Private*, pg. 1887
WALHALLA KALK GMBH & CO. KG—See Heidelberg Materials AG; *Int'l*, pg. 3320

327420 — GYPSUM PRODUCT MANUFACTURING

AG SOUTH CAROLINA LLC—See Eagle Materials Inc.; *U.S. Public*, pg. 702
AMERICAN GYPSUM CO. LLC - DUKE PLANT—See Eagle Materials Inc.; *U.S. Public*, pg. 702
AMERICAN GYPSUM COMPANY LLC—See Eagle Materials Inc.; *U.S. Public*, pg. 702
BPB GYPROC—See Compagnie de Saint-Gobain SA; *Int'l*, pg. 1725
BPB GYPSUM BV—See Compagnie de Saint-Gobain SA; *Int'l*, pg. 1722
BPB GYPSUM (PTY) LTD.—See Compagnie de Saint-Gobain SA; *Int'l*, pg. 1725
BPB GYPSUM URETIM VE TICARET LTD. STI (TRADING)—See Compagnie de Saint-Gobain SA; *Int'l*, pg. 1725
BPB IBERPLACO SA—See Compagnie de Saint-Gobain SA; *Int'l*, pg. 1725
BPB ITALIA SPA—See Compagnie de Saint-Gobain SA; *Int'l*, pg. 1725
BPB LIMITADA—See Compagnie de Saint-Gobain SA; *Int'l*, pg. 1725
BPB PLACO S.A.—See Compagnie de Saint-Gobain SA; *Int'l*, pg. 1725
BRITISH GYPSUM LTD.—See Compagnie de Saint-Gobain SA; *Int'l*, pg. 1725
CALTAGIRONE EDITORE S.P.A.; *Int'l*, pg. 1265
CELFA - SOCEDADE INDUSTRIAL DE TRANSFORMACAO DE GESSOS S.A.—See Camargo Correa S.A.; *Int'l*, pg. 1267
CERTAINTEED GYPSUM AND CEILING MANUFACTURING, INC.—See Compagnie de Saint-Gobain SA; *Int'l*, pg. 1729
CERTAINTEED GYPSUM CANADA, INC.—See Compagnie de Saint-Gobain SA; *Int'l*, pg. 1730
CERTAINTEED GYPSUM, INC.—See Compagnie de Saint-Gobain SA; *Int'l*, pg. 1729
CERTAINTEED GYPSUM MANUFACTURING, INC—See Compagnie de Saint-Gobain SA; *Int'l*, pg. 1729
CERTAINTEED GYPSUM NORTH AMERICAN SERVICES, INC.—See Compagnie de Saint-Gobain SA; *Int'l*, pg. 1729
CERTAINTEED GYPSUM WEST VRGINIA, INC.—See Compagnie de Saint-Gobain SA; *Int'l*, pg. 1729

N.A.I.C.S. INDEX

CHINA RAILWAY PREFABRICATED CONSTRUCTION CO., LTD.; *Int'l*, pg. 1544
CHIYODA UTE CO., LTD. - CHIBA PLANT—See Chiyoda Ute Co., Ltd.; *Int'l*, pg. 1575
CHIYODA UTE CO., LTD. - KAIZUKA PLANT—See Chiyoda Ute Co., Ltd.; *Int'l*, pg. 1575
CHIYODA UTE CO., LTD. - MURORAN PLANT—See Chiyoda Ute Co., Ltd.; *Int'l*, pg. 1575
CHIYODA UTE CO., LTD. - OKAYAMA PLANT—See Chiyoda Ute Co., Ltd.; *Int'l*, pg. 1575
CHIYODA UTE CO., LTD. - SHIMONOSEKI PLANT—See Chiyoda Ute Co., Ltd.; *Int'l*, pg. 1575
CIA INDUSTRIAL EL VOLCAN SA—See Compagnie de Saint-Gobain SA; *Int'l*, pg. 1725
CONTINENTAL BUILDING PRODUCTS, INC.—See Compagnie de Saint-Gobain SA; *Int'l*, pg. 1730
CORAMINE S.A.S.—See Compagnie de Saint-Gobain SA; *Int'l*, pg. 1723
DOGANER ALCI MADENCILIK ENERJI ITHALAT IHRACAT PAZARLAMA TICARET VE SANAYI A.S.—See Compagnie de Saint-Gobain SA; *Int'l*, pg. 1723
DONN PRODUCTS (PTY) LTD.—See Compagnie de Saint-Gobain SA; *Int'l*, pg. 1725
DONN SOUTH AFRICA (PTY) LTD.—See Compagnie de Saint-Gobain SA; *Int'l*, pg. 1725
DUNCAN FINANCIAL CORPORATION; *U.S. Private*, pg. 1287
DURLOCK S.A.—See Etex SA/NV; *Int'l*, pg. 2521
ESCO INDUSTRIES INCORPORATED; *U.S. Private*, pg. 1425
GEORGIA-PACIFIC CANADA, INC.—See Koch Industries, Inc.; *U.S. Private*, pg. 2328
GEORGIA-PACIFIC CORPORATION PRYOR—See Koch Industries, Inc.; *U.S. Private*, pg. 2328
GEORGIA-PACIFIC GYPSUM LLC - LAS VEGAS TOUGH-ROCK PLANT—See Koch Industries, Inc.; *U.S. Private*, pg. 2328
GEORGIA-PACIFIC GYPSUM LLC—See Koch Industries, Inc.; *U.S. Private*, pg. 2328
GMS STRATEGIC SOLUTIONS, INC.—See GMS Inc.; *U.S. Public*, pg. 948
G-P GYPSUM CORP. - ACME—See Koch Industries, Inc.; *U.S. Private*, pg. 2327
G-P GYPSUM CORP. - ANTIOCH—See Koch Industries, Inc.; *U.S. Private*, pg. 2327
G-P GYPSUM CORP. - BLUE RAPIDS—See Koch Industries, Inc.; *U.S. Private*, pg. 2327
G-P GYPSUM CORP. - CAMDEN—See Koch Industries, Inc.; *U.S. Private*, pg. 2327
G-P GYPSUM CORP. - NEWINGTON—See Koch Industries, Inc.; *U.S. Private*, pg. 2327
G-P GYPSUM CORPORATION—See Koch Industries, Inc.; *U.S. Private*, pg. 2327
G-P GYPSUM CORP. - SAN LEANDRO—See Koch Industries, Inc.; *U.S. Private*, pg. 2327
G-P GYPSUM CORP. - SAVANNAH—See Koch Industries, Inc.; *U.S. Private*, pg. 2327
G-P GYPSUM CORP. - WHEATFIELD—See Koch Industries, Inc.; *U.S. Private*, pg. 2327
GRANIT PESACAR A.D.; *Int'l*, pg. 3059
GYPCO SHANGHAI—See Compagnie de Saint-Gobain SA; *Int'l*, pg. 1725
GYPROC AB—See Compagnie de Saint-Gobain SA; *Int'l*, pg. 1725
GYPROC OY—See Heidelberg Materials AG; *Int'l*, pg. 3315
GYPSUM INDUSTRIES (IRELAND) LIMITED—See Compagnie de Saint-Gobain SA; *Int'l*, pg. 1725
GYPSUM INDUSTRIES (PVT) LTD.—See Compagnie de Saint-Gobain SA; *Int'l*, pg. 1725
GYPSUM INDUSTRIES (UK) LTD.—See Compagnie de Saint-Gobain SA; *Int'l*, pg. 1725
KNAUF GIPS S.R.L.—See Gebr. Knauf KG; *Int'l*, pg. 2906
KNAUF INTEGRAL M—See Gebr. Knauf KG; *Int'l*, pg. 2907
KNAUF PLASTERBOARD PTY LTD—See Gebr. Knauf KG; *Int'l*, pg. 2908
KNAUF RIESSLER GMBH & CO. KG—See Gebr. Knauf KG; *Int'l*, pg. 2906
KNAUF SH.P.K.—See Gebr. Knauf KG; *Int'l*, pg. 2908
LAFARGE GIPS BV—See Holcim Ltd.; *Int'l*, pg. 3448
LIN YI SAINT-GOBAIN REFRACTORY CO., LTD—See Compagnie de Saint-Gobain SA; *Int'l*, pg. 1724
LM MATERIAUX SA—See Compagnie de Saint-Gobain SA; *Int'l*, pg. 1725
NATIONAL CEMENT COMPANY—See Chemical Industries Holding Company; *Int'l*, pg. 1462
NATIONAL GYPSUM SERVICES COMPANY—See Spangler Companies, Inc.; *U.S. Private*, pg. 3745
NEW ENGLAND GYPSUM SUPPLY, INC.—See GMS Inc.; *U.S. Public*, pg. 948
NIIGATA YOSHINO GYPSUM CO., LTD.—See Central Glass Co., Ltd.; *Int'l*, pg. 1407
NRP STONE, INC.; *U.S. Public*, pg. 1551
PABCO BUILDING PRODUCTS, LLC - PABCO GYPSUM DIVISION—See Pacific Coast Building Products, Inc.; *U.S. Private*, pg. 3066
PACIFIC COAST BUILDING PRODUCTS, INC.; *U.S. Private*, pg. 3065
PATRICK ADORN MANUFACTURING—See Patrick Industries, Inc.; *U.S. Public*, pg. 1653
PLACO ARGENTINA S.A.—See Compagnie de Saint-Gobain SA; *Int'l*, pg. 1725
PLACO DO BRASIL LTDA.—See Compagnie de Saint-Gobain SA; *Int'l*, pg. 1725
PROFORM FINISHING PRODUCTS, LLC—See Spangler Companies, Inc.; *U.S. Private*, pg. 3745
PT KNAUF GYPSUM INDONESIA—See Gebr. Knauf KG; *Int'l*, pg. 2908
PT PRIMA REZEKI PERTIWI—See Compagnie de Saint-Gobain SA; *Int'l*, pg. 1724
RIGIPS AUSTRIA GMBH—See Compagnie de Saint-Gobain SA; *Int'l*, pg. 1725
RIGIPS HUNGARIA GIPSZKARTON KFT—See Compagnie de Saint-Gobain SA; *Int'l*, pg. 1725
RIGIPS POLSKA-STAWIANY SP. Z O.O.—See Compagnie de Saint-Gobain SA; *Int'l*, pg. 1725
RIGIPS SLOVAKIA SRO—See Compagnie de Saint-Gobain SA; *Int'l*, pg. 1725
RIGIPS SLOVENIA—See Compagnie de Saint-Gobain SA; *Int'l*, pg. 1726
RIGIPS VERWALTUNGS GMBH—See Compagnie de Saint-Gobain SA; *Int'l*, pg. 1726
SAINT-GOBAIN CONSTRUCTION PRODUCTS CZ A.S.—See Compagnie de Saint-Gobain SA; *Int'l*, pg. 1726
SAINT-GOBAIN CONSTRUCTION PRODUCTS ROMANIA SRL—See Compagnie de Saint-Gobain SA; *Int'l*, pg. 1726
SAINT-GOBAIN CONSTRUCTION PRODUCTS SOUTH AFRICA LTD.—See Compagnie de Saint-Gobain SA; *Int'l*, pg. 1726
SAINT-GOBAIN CONSTRUCTION PRODUCTS UKRAINE—See Compagnie de Saint-Gobain SA; *Int'l*, pg. 1726
SAINT-GOBAIN CONSTRUCTION PRODUCTS VIETNAM LIMITED—See Compagnie de Saint-Gobain SA; *Int'l*, pg. 1726
SAINT-GOBAIN EUROVEDER POLSKA SP. Z O.O.—See Compagnie de Saint-Gobain SA; *Int'l*, pg. 1734
SAINT-GOBAIN FORMULA GMBH—See Compagnie de Saint-Gobain SA; *Int'l*, pg. 1728
SAINT-GOBAIN GYPROC INDIA LTD - BENGALURU PLANT—See Compagnie de Saint-Gobain SA; *Int'l*, pg. 1734
SAINT-GOBAIN GYPROC INDIA LTD—See Compagnie de Saint-Gobain SA; *Int'l*, pg. 1734
SAINT-GOBAIN GYPSUM (CHANGZHOU) CO., LTD.—See Compagnie de Saint-Gobain SA; *Int'l*, pg. 1734
SAINT-GOBAIN GYPSUM CHINA (SHANGHAI)—See Compagnie de Saint-Gobain SA; *Int'l*, pg. 1734
SAINT-GOBAIN GYPSUM MATERIALS SHANGHAI—See Compagnie de Saint-Gobain SA; *Int'l*, pg. 1734
SAINT GOBAIN GYPSUM OPERADORA SA DE CV—See Compagnie de Saint-Gobain SA; *Int'l*, pg. 1727
SAINT-GOBAIN GYPSUM SA DE CV—See Compagnie de Saint-Gobain SA; *Int'l*, pg. 1734
SAINT-GOBAIN HELLAS ABEE—See Compagnie de Saint-Gobain SA; *Int'l*, pg. 1726
SAINT-GOBAIN ISOVER (GU'AN) GLASS WOOL CO., LTD.—See Compagnie de Saint-Gobain SA; *Int'l*, pg. 1734
SAINT-GOBAIN MALAYSIA SDN BHD.—See Compagnie de Saint-Gobain SA; *Int'l*, pg. 1728
SAINT-GOBAIN PLACO SAS—See Compagnie de Saint-Gobain SA; *Int'l*, pg. 1728
SAINT-GOBAIN PPC ITALIA SPA—See Compagnie de Saint-Gobain SA; *Int'l*, pg. 1735
SAINT-GOBAIN RIGIPS ALCI SANAYI VE TICARET ANONIM A.S—See Compagnie de Saint-Gobain SA; *Int'l*, pg. 1735
SAINT-GOBAIN RIGIPS GMBH—See Compagnie de Saint-Gobain SA; *Int'l*, pg. 1726
SHANDONG SANJIN GLASS MACHINERY CO., LTD.—See Bucher Industries AG; *Int'l*, pg. 1209
SIA GYPROC—See Compagnie de Saint-Gobain SA; *Int'l*, pg. 1726
SINAI MANGANESE COMPANY—See Chemical Industries Holding Company; *Int'l*, pg. 1462
SINIAT GMBH—See Etex SA/NV; *Int'l*, pg. 2522
SINIAT LIMITED—See Etex SA/NV; *Int'l*, pg. 2522
SINIAT SA—See Etex SA/NV; *Int'l*, pg. 2522
SINIAT S.P.A—See Etex SA/NV; *Int'l*, pg. 2522
SOUTHERN WALL PRODUCTS INC.—See GMS Inc.; *U.S. Public*, pg. 948
THAI GYPSUM PRODUCTS PCL.—See Compagnie de Saint-Gobain SA; *Int'l*, pg. 1727
TOO KNAUF GIPS KAPTSCHAGAJ—See Gebr. Knauf KG; *Int'l*, pg. 2908
TRANS GLOBAL GROUP, INC.; *U.S. Public*, pg. 2179
UBE YOSHINO GYPSUM CO., LTD.—See Central Glass Co., Ltd.; *Int'l*, pg. 1407
USG CORP.—See Gebr. Knauf KG; *Int'l*, pg. 2908
WINSTONE WALLBOARDS LIMITED—See Fletcher Building Limited; *Int'l*, pg. 2701

327910 — ABRASIVE PRODUCT MANUFACTURING

3M ABRASIVE SYSTEMS DIVISION—See 3M Company; *U.S. Public*, pg. 5
3M ABRASIVE SYSTEMS—See 3M Company; *U.S. Public*, pg. 5
3M COMPANY - ROYERSFORD—See 3M Company; *U.S. Public*, pg. 5
3M TOUCH SYSTEMS, INC.—See 3M Company; *U.S. Public*, pg. 7
ABC SUPERABRASIVES—See Compagnie de Saint-Gobain SA; *Int'l*, pg. 1730
ABRASIVE TECHNOLOGY INCORPORATED; *U.S. Private*, pg. 40
AHLSTROM-MUNKSJO ARCHES S.A.S.—See Ahlstrom Capital Oy; *Int'l*, pg. 224
AHLSTROM-MUNKSJO ARCHES S.A.S.—See Bain Capital, LP; *U.S. Private*, pg. 429
AHLSTROM-MUNKSJO BRASIL INDUSTRIA E COMERCIO DE PAPEIS ESPECIAIS LTDA.—See Ahlstrom Capital Oy; *Int'l*, pg. 224
AHLSTROM-MUNKSJO BRASIL INDUSTRIA E COMERCIO DE PAPEIS ESPECIAIS LTDA.—See Bain Capital, LP; *U.S. Private*, pg. 429
AIDS HEALTHCARE FOUNDATION; *U.S. Private*, pg. 131
ALI INDUSTRIES, INC.—See RPM International Inc.; *U.S. Public*, pg. 1817
AMERICO MANUFACTURING CO., INC.—See Branford Castle, Inc.; *U.S. Private*, pg. 639
ANALYTICON DISCOVERY GMBH—See BRAIN Biotech AG; *Int'l*, pg. 1137
ARJOHUNTLEIGH (HONG KONG) LTD—See Getinge AB; *Int'l*, pg. 2948
ARTNET WORLDWIDE CORPORATION—See artnet AG; *Int'l*, pg. 585
ASKEY COMPUTER CORP.—See ASUSTeK Computer Inc.; *Int'l*, pg. 663
ATI GARRYSON LTD.—See ATI Inc.; *U.S. Public*, pg. 221
AVERY OFFICE PRODUCTS PUERTO RICO L.L.C.—See CCL Industries Inc.; *Int'l*, pg. 1367
AVOCENT DO BRASIL INFORMATICA S.A.—See Vertiv Holdings Co; *U.S. Public*, pg. 2288
AXA D.D.S., A.S.—See AXA S.A.; *Int'l*, pg. 759
BAO-TRANS ENTERPRISES LTD.—See China Baowu Steel Group Corp., Ltd.; *Int'l*, pg. 1485
BARRDAY COMPOSITE SOLUTIONS—See Barrday, Inc.; *Int'l*, pg. 869
BASIC CARBIDE CORP; *U.S. Private*, pg. 485
BELGIAN VOLITION SA—See VolitionRX Limited; *U.S. Public*, pg. 2308
BELL BUCKLE HOLDINGS, INC.; *U.S. Public*, pg. 294
BNPP REAL ESTATE ADVISORY NETHERLANDS BV—See BNP Paribas SA; *Int'l*, pg. 1088
BNPP REAL ESTATE APM CR SRO—See BNP Paribas SA; *Int'l*, pg. 1088
BNPP RENTAL SOLUTIONS LTD.—See BNP Paribas SA; *Int'l*, pg. 1088
BOMBARDIER EUROPEAN HOLDINGS, S.L.U.—See Bombardier Inc.; *Int'l*, pg. 1104
BOMBARDIER TRANSPORTATION (SIGNAL) GERMANY GMBH—See Alstom S.A.; *Int'l*, pg. 382
CALDER URGENT CARE, PLLC—See HCA Healthcare, Inc.; *U.S. Public*, pg. 992
CAMPBELL SUPPLY CO.—See Campbell Supply Company; *U.S. Private*, pg. 730
CANFOR CORPORATION - FORT ST JOHN SAWMILL FACILITY—See Canfor Corporation; *Int'l*, pg. 1290
CARBO CERAMICS—See CARBO Ceramics Inc.; *U.S. Private*, pg. 748
CARBO CERAMICS—See CARBO Ceramics Inc.; *U.S. Private*, pg. 748
CARDIF EL DJAZAIR, SPA—See BNP Paribas SA; *Int'l*, pg. 1083
CARRIERS INSURANCE BROKERS PTY. LTD.—See AUB Group Limited; *Int'l*, pg. 698
CENTRIC DIGITAL LLC.; *U.S. Private*, pg. 829
CERATERA S A—See Groupe Bruxelles Lambert SA; *Int'l*, pg. 3100
CHEIL GRINDING WHEEL IND. CO., LTD.; *Int'l*, pg. 1460
CHESSCO INDUSTRIES, INC.; *U.S. Private*, pg. 875
CHUGOKU PAINTS (GERMANY) GMBH—See Chugoku Marine Paints, Ltd.; *Int'l*, pg. 1595
COBRA GMBH—See Comet Umetni brusi in nekovine, d.d.; *Int'l*, pg. 1711
COLUMBIA PRIMARY CARE, LLC—See HCA Healthcare, Inc.; *U.S. Public*, pg. 994
COMERICIALIZADORA KENNAMETAL BOLIVIA S.R.L.—See Kennametal Inc.; *U.S. Public*, pg. 1221
COMET UMETNI BRUSI IN NEKOVINE, D.D.; *Int'l*, pg. 1711
COMPLETE OFFICE, LLC.—See The ODP Corporation; *U.S. Public*, pg. 2117
COORSTEK, INC. - COORSTEK VINHEDO FACILITY—See CoorsTek, Inc.; *U.S. Private*, pg. 1044
CORNING B.V.—See Corning Incorporated; *U.S. Public*, pg. 578

327910 — ABRASIVE PRODUCT MA...

CRATEX MANUFACTURING CO., INC.; *U.S. Private*, pg. 1086
DAIDO STEEL CO., LTD. - CHITA PLANT—See Daido Steel Co., Ltd.; *Int'l*, pg. 1923
DAKO NORTH AMERICA, INC.—See Agilent Technologies, Inc.; *U.S. Public*, pg. 61
DBRS LIMITED—See Morningstar, Inc.; *U.S. Public*, pg. 1476
DENTSPLY (THAILAND) LTD.—See DENTSPLY SIRONA Inc.; *U.S. Public*, pg. 654
DETROIT TELEVISION STATION WKBD INC.—See National Amusements, Inc.; *U.S. Private*, pg. 2841
DIAMOND INNOVATIONS, INC.—See KKR & Co. Inc.; *U.S. Public*, pg. 1252
DIGONEX TECHNOLOGIES, INC.—See Emmis Communications Corporation; *U.S. Public*, pg. 753
DOCTORS SAME DAY SURGERY CENTER, LTD.—See HCA Healthcare, Inc.; *U.S. Public*, pg. 995
DONGGUAN GOLDEN SUN ABRASIVES CO., LTD.; *Int'l*, pg. 2167
DRONCO GMBH—See Jason Industries, Inc.; *U.S. Private*, pg. 2189
ECONOMIC INVESTMENT TRUST LIMITED; *Int'l*, pg. 2298
ECUTEC BARCELONA S.L.—See Erich Netzsch GmbH & Co. Holding KG; *Int'l*, pg. 2491
EDELMAN—See Daniel J. Edelman, Inc.; *U.S. Private*, pg. 1154
ERVIN AMASTEEL DIVISION OF ERVIN INDUSTRIES INC.—See Ervin Industries, Inc.; *U.S. Private*, pg. 1423
ERVIN AMASTEEL DIV.—See Ervin Industries, Inc.; *U.S. Private*, pg. 1423
ERVIN AMASTEEL UK LP—See Ervin Industries, Inc.; *U.S. Private*, pg. 1423
ERVIN GERMANY GMBH—See Ervin Industries, Inc.; *U.S. Private*, pg. 1423
ERVIN INDUSTRIES, INC.; *U.S. Private*, pg. 1423
ESSECO DO BRASIL INDUSTRIA E COMERCIO DE PRODUTOS QUIMICOS LTDA—See Esseco Group SRL; *Int'l*, pg. 2509
EURO BROKERS MEXICO S.A. DE C.V.—See BGC Group, Inc.; *U.S. Public*, pg. 328
EUROPROJECT LLC; *Int'l*, pg. 2557
EXPEDIA PARTNER SERVICES GROUP SARL—See Expedia Group, Inc.; *U.S. Public*, pg. 809
FACTORING.PLUS.GMBH—See flatexDEGIRO AG; *Int'l*, pg. 2698
FKP SCORPIO KONZERTPRODUKTIONEN GMBH—See CTS Eventim AG & Co. KGAA; *Int'l*, pg. 1873
FLOW EASTERN EUROPE, S.R.O.—See AIP, LLC; *U.S. Private*, pg. 137
FLOW INTERNATIONAL CORPORATION—See AIP, LLC; *U.S. Private*, pg. 137
FRIENDS & PARTNERS S.P.A.—See CTS Eventim AG & Co. KGAA; *Int'l*, pg. 1873
FTI CONSULTING SERVICES LIMITED—See FTI Consulting, Inc.; *U.S. Public*, pg. 890
FUJIMI CORPORATION—See Fujimi Incorporated; *Int'l*, pg. 2829
FUJIMI INCORPORATED; *Int'l*, pg. 2829
FUJIMI-MICRO TECHNOLOGY SDN. BHD—See Fujimi Incorporated; *Int'l*, pg. 2829
FUKOKU CO., LTD. - GUNMA PLANT—See Fukoku Co., Ltd.; *Int'l*, pg. 2838
GATES INDUSTRIAL CORPORATION PLC—See Blackstone Inc.; *U.S. Public*, pg. 353
GENESIS LOGISTICS INC.—See Deutsche Post AG; *Int'l*, pg. 2079
GLOBALWINE AG—See Hawesko Holding AG; *Int'l*, pg. 3288
GREAT LAKES EDUCATIONAL LOAN SERVICES INC—See Nelnet, Inc.; *U.S. Public*, pg. 1504
GREEN ECONOMY DEVELOPMENT LIMITED; *Int'l*, pg. 3070
GREYSTON BAKERY INC.; *U.S. Private*, pg. 1785
GRINDWELL NORTON LTD.—See Compagnie de Saint-Gobain SA; *Int'l*, pg. 1730
GUANGDONG KINGSTRONG TECHNOLOGY CO., LTD.; *Int'l*, pg. 3157
HACH LANGE S.L.—See Danaher Corporation; *U.S. Public*, pg. 627
HANOVER HOUSE—See Communicare, Inc.; *U.S. Private*, pg. 988
HARSCO MINERAIS LIMITADA—See Enviri Corporation; *U.S. Public*, pg. 781
HARSCO MINERALS DEUTSCHLAND GMBH—See Enviri Corporation; *U.S. Public*, pg. 781
HARTE-HANKS BELGIUM NV—See Harte Hanks, Inc.; *U.S. Public*, pg. 986
HEIDELBERGCEMENT INTERNATIONAL HOLDING GMBH—See Heidelberg Materials AG; *Int'l*, pg. 3315
HENKEL TECHNOLOGIES (KOREA) LTD. - EUMSUNG PLANT—See Henkel AG & Co. KGaA; *Int'l*, pg. 3349
HERMES ABRASIVES LTD.—See Hermes Schleifmittel GmbH & Co. KG; *Int'l*, pg. 3363
HERMES SCHLEIFKORPER GMBH—See Hermes Schleifmittel GmbH & Co. KG; *Int'l*, pg. 3363
HERMES SCHLEIFMITTEL GMBH & CO. KG; *Int'l*, pg. 3363

HERREN ENTERPRISES, INC.—See KKR & Co. Inc.; *U.S. Public*, pg. 1249
HIGH ARCTIC ENERGY SERVICES PNG LIMITED—See High Arctic Energy Services Inc.; *Int'l*, pg. 3385
HUF MEXICO S. DE R.L. DE C.V.—See Huf Hulsbeck & Furst GmbH & Co. KG; *Int'l*, pg. 3523
IM 40 SP. Z O.O—See Agora S.A.; *Int'l*, pg. 212
IMERYS MARBLE INC.—See Groupe Bruxelles Lambert SA; *Int'l*, pg. 3100
IMERYS TABLEWARE—See Groupe Bruxelles Lambert SA; *Int'l*, pg. 3100
IMMOSOLVE GMBH—See Axel Springer SE; *Int'l*, pg. 766
IMPERIAL INDUSTRIES, INC.—See Q.E.P. Co., Inc.; *U.S. Public*, pg. 1741
INTEGRA PORT SERVICES N.V.—See Dubai World Corporation; *Int'l*, pg. 2221
INTERNATIONAL STEEL WOOL CORPORATION—See F.H. Bonn Company; *U.S. Private*, pg. 1456
IREP CO., LTD.—See Hakuhodo DY Holdings Incorporated; *Int'l*, pg. 3221
ISCAR FINLAND OY—See Berkshire Hathaway Inc.; *U.S. Public*, pg. 307
JACOBS ENGINEERING INDIA PRIVATE LIMITED—See Jacobs Engineering Group, Inc.; *U.S. Public*, pg. 1184
JAPAN ABRASIVE GRAIN, LTD.—See Carlit Co., Ltd.; *Int'l*, pg. 1338
JASON OHIO CORPORATION—See Jason Industries, Inc.; *U.S. Private*, pg. 2190
JH RHODES COMPANY, INC. - CLINTON MANUFACTURING FACILITY—See Universal Photonics, Inc.; *U.S. Private*, pg. 4306
JH RHODES COMPANY, INC.—See Universal Photonics, Inc.; *U.S. Private*, pg. 4306
KAMIC COMPONENTS AB—See Amplex AB; *Int'l*, pg. 434
KEENELAND ASSOCIATION INC. - THE THOROUGHBRED CENTER DIVISION—See Keeneland Association Inc.; *U.S. Private*, pg. 2272
KENNAMETAL STELLITE COATINGS S.R.L.—See Kennametal Inc.; *U.S. Public*, pg. 1222
KENNAMETAL STELLITE, L.P.—See Kennametal Inc.; *U.S. Public*, pg. 1223
KEUM SUNG GRINDING WHEEL CO., LTD.—See Cheil Grinding Wheel Ind. Co., Ltd.; *Int'l*, pg. 1460
KLINIK FUR HERZCHIRURGIE KARLSRUHE GMBH—See Fresenius SE & Co. KGaA; *Int'l*, pg. 2779
KLINIK KIPFENBERG GMBH—See Fresenius SE & Co. KGaA; *Int'l*, pg. 2779
KLINIKUM HILDESHEIM GMBH—See Fresenius SE & Co. KGaA; *Int'l*, pg. 2779
K-SWISS DIRECT, INC—See E-Land World Ltd.; *Int'l*, pg. 2248
LANITIS BROS LTD.—See Coca-Cola HBC AG; *Int'l*, pg. 1686
LEAF TRADING COMPANY LTD.—See Pyxus International, Inc.; *U.S. Public*, pg. 1740
LENNAR MARE ISLAND, LLC—See Lennar Corporation; *U.S. Public*, pg. 1306
LEVI STRAUSS SA (PTY) LTD.—See Levi Strauss & Co.; *U.S. Public*, pg. 1309
LORENTZEN & WETTRE LTDA—See ABB Ltd.; *Int'l*, pg. 50
MAJIQ INC.—See Constellation Software Inc.; *Int'l*, pg. 1772
MANUS ABRASIVE SYSTEMS, INC—See Ridgemont Partners Management LLC; *U.S. Private*, pg. 3432
MARCO GROUP INTERNATIONAL, INC.—See Ridgemont Partners Management LLC; *U.S. Private*, pg. 3432
MARSH MANAGEMENT SERVICES (LABUAN) LIMITED—See Marsh & McLennan Companies, Inc.; *U.S. Public*, pg. 1383
MARTIN-LOGAN, LTD.—See ShoreView Industries, LLC; *U.S. Private*, pg. 3642
MARUBUN/ARROW (PHILIPPINES) INC.—See Arrow Electronics, Inc.; *U.S. Public*, pg. 199
MICHIGAN WIRE DIE COMPANY—See MNP Corporation; *U.S. Private*, pg. 2756
MINERALTECH GULF COAST ABRASIVES, LLC; *U.S. Private*, pg. 2741
MONO PUMPS NEW ZEALAND COMPANY—See NOV, Inc.; *U.S. Public*, pg. 1545
MORRISON CONSTRUCTION SCOTLAND—See Galliford Try Holdings plc; *Int'l*, pg. 2874
MOTION CONTROL INDUSTRIES, INC.—See Carlisle Companies Incorporated; *U.S. Public*, pg. 437
MT ATLANTIC INC.—See Hojgaard Holding A/S; *Int'l*, pg. 3442
OPA INTERNATIONAL CORPORATION—See Alfa; *Int'l*, pg. 307
OVERHEAD DOOR COMPANY OF KANSAS CITY—See E.E. Newcomer Enterprises Inc.; *U.S. Private*, pg. 1305
OVERLAND STORAGE (EUROPE) LTD.—See Overland Storage, Inc.; *U.S. Public*, pg. 3053
PEARL ABRASIVE COMPANY—See Harbour Group Industries, Inc.; *U.S. Private*, pg. 1860
PETROCHINA INTERNATIONAL (KAZAKHSTAN) CO., LTD—See China National Petroleum Corporation; *Int'l*, pg. 1533
PETROCHINA INTERNATIONAL (TURKMENISTAN) LTD.—See China National Petroleum Corporation; *Int'l*, pg. 1533

PFERD CANADA INC.—See August Rueggeberg GmbH & Co. KG PFERD-Werkzeuge; *Int'l*, pg. 703
PIEZO KINETICS INC.—See Crest Group Inc.; *U.S. Private*, pg. 1096
PIEZOTECH, LLC—See Amphenol Corporation; *U.S. Public*, pg. 132
POYRY SAS—See AFRY AB; *Int'l*, pg. 196
PPG COATINGS (THAILAND) CO., LTD.—See PPG Industries, Inc.; *U.S. Public*, pg. 1708
PRODUCTORA DE ABRASIVOS LTDA.—See Compagnie de Saint-Gobain SA; *Int'l*, pg. 1725
PRODUCTORA DE ABRASIVOS PABSA LTDA—See Compagnie de Saint-Gobain SA; *Int'l*, pg. 1725
PT. SAINT-GOBAIN ABRASIVES INDONESIA—See Compagnie de Saint-Gobain SA; *Int'l*, pg. 1724
PT SAINT-GOBAIN WINTER DIAMAS—See Compagnie de Saint-Gobain SA; *Int'l*, pg. 1724
PULPO MEDIA, INC.—See Entravision Communications Corporation; *U.S. Public*, pg. 779
PYROTEK PRODUCTS LTD.—See Pyrotek Incorporated; *U.S. Private*, pg. 3311
RANSOM & RANDOLPH COMPANY—See PMC Capital Partners, LLC; *U.S. Private*, pg. 3218
SAINT-GOBAIN ABRASIFS SA—See Compagnie de Saint-Gobain SA; *Int'l*, pg. 1731
SAINT-GOBAIN ABRASIFS—See Compagnie de Saint-Gobain SA; *Int'l*, pg. 1729
SAINT-GOBAIN ABRASIVES AB—See Compagnie de Saint-Gobain SA; *Int'l*, pg. 1731
SAINT-GOBAIN ABRASIVES A/S—See Compagnie de Saint-Gobain SA; *Int'l*, pg. 1731
SAINT-GOBAIN ABRASIVES BV—See Compagnie de Saint-Gobain SA; *Int'l*, pg. 1731
SAINT-GOBAIN ABRASIVES CANADA INC—See Compagnie de Saint-Gobain SA; *Int'l*, pg. 1731
SAINT-GOBAIN ABRASIVES GMBH—See Compagnie de Saint-Gobain SA; *Int'l*, pg. 1731
SAINT-GOBAIN ABRASIVES, INC. - PHILADELPHIA—See Compagnie de Saint-Gobain SA; *Int'l*, pg. 1732
SAINT-GOBAIN ABRASIVES, INC—See Compagnie de Saint-Gobain SA; *Int'l*, pg. 1730
SAINT-GOBAIN ABRASIVES LIMITED—See Compagnie de Saint-Gobain SA; *Int'l*, pg. 1731
SAINT-GOBAIN ABRASIVES LTD—See Compagnie de Saint-Gobain SA; *Int'l*, pg. 1731
SAINT-GOBAIN ABRASIVES MALAYSIA—See Compagnie de Saint-Gobain SA; *Int'l*, pg. 1731
SAINT-GOBAIN ABRASIVES NEDERLAND B.V.—See Compagnie de Saint-Gobain SA; *Int'l*, pg. 1729
SAINT GOBAIN ABRASIVES PTY. LTD.—See Compagnie de Saint-Gobain SA; *Int'l*, pg. 1731
SAINT-GOBAIN ABRASIVES (PTY.) LTD.—See Compagnie de Saint-Gobain SA; *Int'l*, pg. 1731
SAINT-GOBAIN ABRASIVES SA/NV—See Compagnie de Saint-Gobain SA; *Int'l*, pg. 1731
SAINT-GOBAIN ABRASIVES S.A.—See Compagnie de Saint-Gobain SA; *Int'l*, pg. 1731
SAINT GOBAIN ABRASIVES—See Compagnie de Saint-Gobain SA; *Int'l*, pg. 1729
SAINT-GOBAIN ABRASIVES S.R.O.—See Compagnie de Saint-Gobain SA; *Int'l*, pg. 1731
SAINT-GOBAIN ABRASIVES (SUZHOU) CO., LTD.—See Compagnie de Saint-Gobain SA; *Int'l*, pg. 1731
SAINT-GOBAIN ABRASIVES THAILAND LTD.—See Compagnie de Saint-Gobain SA; *Int'l*, pg. 1731
SAINT-GOBAIN ABRASIVI S.P.A—See Compagnie de Saint-Gobain SA; *Int'l*, pg. 1731
SAINT-GOBAIN ABRASIVI S.P.A.—See Compagnie de Saint-Gobain SA; *Int'l*, pg. 1731
SAINT-GOBAIN ABRASIVOS ARGENTINA SA—See Compagnie de Saint-Gobain SA; *Int'l*, pg. 1729
SAINT-GOBAIN ABRASIVOS BRASIL LTDA—See Compagnie de Saint-Gobain SA; *Int'l*, pg. 1729
SAINT-GOBAIN ABRASIVOS CA—See Compagnie de Saint-Gobain SA; *Int'l*, pg. 1731
SAINT-GOBAIN ABRASIVOS COLOMBIA LTDA—See Compagnie de Saint-Gobain SA; *Int'l*, pg. 1731
SAINT-GOBAIN ABRASIVOS LDA—See Compagnie de Saint-Gobain SA; *Int'l*, pg. 1731
SAINT-GOBAIN ABRASIVOS LIMITADA—See Compagnie de Saint-Gobain SA; *Int'l*, pg. 1731
SAINT-GOBAIN ABRASIVOS, S.A. DE C.V.—See Compagnie de Saint-Gobain SA; *Int'l*, pg. 1731
SAINT-GOBAIN ABRASIVOS SA—See Compagnie de Saint-Gobain SA; *Int'l*, pg. 1731
SAINT GOBAIN AMERICA S.A. DE C.V.—See Compagnie de Saint-Gobain SA; *Int'l*, pg. 1727
SAINT-GOBAIN CANALIZACION CHILE SA—See Compagnie de Saint-Gobain SA; *Int'l*, pg. 1727
SAINT-GOBAIN CERAMIC MATERIALS AS—See Compagnie de Saint-Gobain SA; *Int'l*, pg. 1731
SAINT-GOBAIN COATING SOLUTIONS—See Compagnie de Saint-Gobain SA; *Int'l*, pg. 1727
SAINT-GOBAIN DIAMANTWERKZEUGE GMBH & CO. KG—See Compagnie de Saint-Gobain SA; *Int'l*, pg. 1727
SAINT-GOBAIN HPM POLSKA SP ZOO—See Compagnie de Saint-Gobain SA; *Int'l*, pg. 1734
SAINT-GOBAIN HPM RUS. OOO—See Compagnie de

N.A.I.C.S. INDEX

327992 — GROUND OR TREATED M...

Saint-Gobain SA; *Int'l*, pg. 1728
SAINT-GOBAIN INDUSTRIAL CERAMICS INC.—See Compagnie de Saint-Gobain SA; *Int'l*, pg. 1730
SAINT-GOBAIN MATERIAUX CERAMIQUES BENELUX SA—See Compagnie de Saint-Gobain SA; *Int'l*, pg. 1734
SAINT-GOBAIN SCHLEIFMITTEL GMBH—See Compagnie de Saint-Gobain SA; *Int'l*, pg. 1735
SAINT-GOBAIN—See Compagnie de Saint-Gobain SA; *Int'l*, pg. 1730
SAINT-GOBAIN WINTER INC—See Compagnie de Saint-Gobain SA; *Int'l*, pg. 1732
SCHENKER AMERICAS, INC.—See Deutsche Bahn AG; *Int'l*, pg. 2054
SCIE-PLAS LTD.—See Harvard Bioscience, Inc.; *U.S. Public*, pg. 987
SG CERAMICS MATERIALS CANADA INC.—See Compagnie de Saint-Gobain SA; *Int'l*, pg. 1730
SHARK INDUSTRIES, LTD.; *U.S. Private*, pg. 3626
SHENZHEN CIMC VEHICLE SALES CO., LTD.—See CIMC Vehicle (Group) Co., Ltd.; *Int'l*, pg. 1608
SOPHEON NV—See Wellspring Worldwide, LLC; *U.S. Private*, pg. 4478
SPOETZL BREWERY—See The Gambrinus Company; *U.S. Private*, pg. 4032
STADTISCHES KRANKENHAUS WITTINGEN GMBH—See Fresenius SE & Co. KGaA; *Int'l*, pg. 2779
SURGERY CENTER OF FORT COLLINS, LLC—See UnitedHealth Group Incorporated; *U.S. Public*, pg. 2250
TAIWAN ASAHI DIAMOND INDUSTRIAL CO., LTD.—See Asahi Diamond Industrial Co. Ltd.; *Int'l*, pg. 593
TEXAS PIPE WORKS INC; *U.S. Private*, pg. 3976
THEORY, LLC—See Fast Retailing Co., Ltd.; *Int'l*, pg. 2621
THERMO FISHER SCIENTIFIC MILANO SRL—See Thermo Fisher Scientific Inc.; *U.S. Public*, pg. 2152
TIBERIUS ACQUISITION CORPORATION; *U.S. Public*, pg. 2158
TICKETONE S.P.A.—See CTS Eventim AG & Co. KGAA; *Int'l*, pg. 1874
TOROFLEX GMBH—See Comet Umetni brusi in nekovine, d.d.; *Int'l*, pg. 1711
TREIBACHER SCHLEIFMITTEL AG—See Groupe Bruxelles Lambert SA; *Int'l*, pg. 3100
TREIBACHER SCHLEIFMITTEL NORTH AMERICA, INC.—See Groupe Bruxelles Lambert SA; *Int'l*, pg. 3100
TSYS MERCHANT SOLUTIONS, LLC—See Global Payments Inc.; *U.S. Public*, pg. 944
UNITED ABRASIVES INC.; *U.S. Private*, pg. 4287
UNIVERSAL PHOTONICS FAR EAST, INC—See Universal Photonics, Inc.; *U.S. Private*, pg. 4306
UNIVERSAL PHOTONICS HONG KONG LIMITED—See Universal Photonics, Inc.; *U.S. Private*, pg. 4306
UNIVERSAL PHOTONICS (SHENZHEN) CO., LTD.—See Universal Photonics, Inc.; *U.S. Private*, pg. 4306
VIRGINIA ABRASIVES CORPORATION—See Barton Mines Company LLC; *U.S. Private*, pg. 483
VOLVO BUS CORPORATION—See AB Volvo; *Int'l*, pg. 42
VOLVO CONSTRUCTION EQUIPMENT KOREA LTD.—See AB Volvo; *Int'l*, pg. 43
VOLVO EAST ASIA (PTE.) LTD.—See AB Volvo; *Int'l*, pg. 43
WARREN DIAMOND POWDER COMPANY, INC.—See Compagnie de Saint-Gobain SA; *Int'l*, pg. 1732
WASHINGTON MILLS CERAMICS CORPORATION—See Washington Mills Company Inc.; *U.S. Private*, pg. 4447
WASHINGTON MILLS COMPANY INC.; *U.S. Private*, pg. 4447
WASHINGTON MILLS COMPANY INC.—See Washington Mills Company Inc.; *U.S. Private*, pg. 4447
WASHINGTON MILLS ELECTRO MINERALS CORPORATION—See Washington Mills Company Inc.; *U.S. Private*, pg. 4447
WASHINGTON MILLS TONAWANDA, INC.—See Washington Mills Company Inc.; *U.S. Private*, pg. 4447
WELCAST STEELS LTD.—See AIA Engineering Ltd.; *Int'l*, pg. 227
WINTERTHUR TECHNOLOGY (FRANCE) S.A.R.L.—See 3M Company; *U.S. Public*, pg. 9
WINTERTHUR TECHNOLOGY KOREA LTD.—See 3M Company; *U.S. Public*, pg. 9
YAMAGUCHI SEIKEN KOGYO CO., LTD.—See Arakawa Chemical Industries, Ltd.; *Int'l*, pg. 535
YEAGER ENTERPRISES CORP.; *U.S. Private*, pg. 4587
THE YUMA AZ ENDOSCOPY ASC, LLC—See KKR & Co. Inc.; *U.S. Private*, pg. 1249

327991 — CUT STONE AND STONE PRODUCT MANUFACTURING

209 ENTERPRISES—See Haines & Kibblehouse Inc.; *U.S. Private*, pg. 1840
ABLEGROUP BERHAD; *Int'l*, pg. 63
ADO PRODUCTS LLC—See TopBuild Corp.; *U.S. Public*, pg. 2163
ALLIED MARBLE, INC.; *U.S. Private*, pg. 186
AMERICAN SLATE COMPANY—See Hendricks Holding Company, Inc.; *U.S. Private*, pg. 1914
APAC-ARKANSAS - ARKHOLA DIVISION—See CRH plc; *Int'l*, pg. 1846
ARCHITECTURAL STONE—See Haines & Kibblehouse Inc.; *U.S. Private*, pg. 1840
ARO GRANITE INDUSTRIES LTD. - UNIT II—See Aro Granite Industries Ltd.; *Int'l*, pg. 577
ARO GRANITE INDUSTRIES LTD. - UNIT I—See Aro Granite Industries Ltd.; *Int'l*, pg. 577
ARTISTIC COUNTERS, INC.; *U.S. Private*, pg. 343
ATLAS RHYTHM SDN. BHD.—See AbleGroup Berhad; *Int'l*, pg. 63
BEDROCK QUARRIES, INC.—See Haines & Kibblehouse Inc.; *U.S. Private*, pg. 1840
BIRDSBORO MATERIALS—See Haines & Kibblehouse Inc.; *U.S. Private*, pg. 1840
BRICKWORKS SUPPLY LLC—See Brickworks Limited; *Int'l*, pg. 1152
BUFFALO CRUSHED STONE, INC. - ALFRED SAND AND GRAVEL PLANT—See New Enterprise Stone & Lime Co., Inc.; *U.S. Private*, pg. 2895
BUFFALO CRUSHED STONE, INC. - FRANKLINVILLE SAND, AND GRAVEL PLANT—See New Enterprise Stone & Lime Co., Inc.; *U.S. Private*, pg. 2895
CAESARSTONE AUSTRALIA PTY LTD—See Caesarstone Ltd.; *Int'l*, pg. 1249
CAESARSTONE CANADA INC.—See Caesarstone Ltd.; *Int'l*, pg. 1249
CAESARSTONE LTD.; *Int'l*, pg. 1249
CAESARSTONE SOUTH EAST ASIA PTE LTD—See Caesarstone Ltd.; *Int'l*, pg. 1249
CAESARSTONE US—See Caesarstone Ltd.; *Int'l*, pg. 1249
CAGGIATI FRANCE SARL—See Matthews International Corporation; *U.S. Public*, pg. 1400
CANTON CUT STONE CO. INC.—See Sims-Lohman, Inc.; *U.S. Private*, pg. 3669
CEETA INDUSTRIES LIMITED; *Int'l*, pg. 1389
CHESTERFIELD MACADAM—See CEMEX, S.A.B. de C.V.; *Int'l*, pg. 1399
COLD SPRING GRANITE COMPANY; *U.S. Private*, pg. 965
CONSTRUCTION RESOURCES LLC—See Guggenheim Partners, LLC; *U.S. Private*, pg. 1811
COSENTINO USA; *U.S. Private*, pg. 1061
CRH EUROPE-MATERIALS—See CRH plc; *Int'l*, pg. 1843
CRH EUROPE—See CRH plc; *Int'l*, pg. 1843
CRH SUDAMERICANA S.A—See CRH plc; *Int'l*, pg. 1844
DAKOTA GRANITE COMPANY; *U.S. Private*, pg. 1147
DALE TILE COMPANY; *U.S. Private*, pg. 1149
DELAWARE VALLEY RECYCLING, INC.—See Haines & Kibblehouse Inc.; *U.S. Private*, pg. 1841
DFCITY GROUP BERHAD; *Int'l*, pg. 2094
DIVYASHAKTI LIMITED; *Int'l*, pg. 2138
ELEGANT MARBLES & GRANI INDUSTRIES LTD.; *Int'l*, pg. 2355
EMILGERMANY GMBH—See Mohawk Industries, Inc.; *U.S. Public*, pg. 1457
ENVIRONMENTAL MATERIALS LLC—See Clayton, Dubilier & Rice, LLC; *U.S. Private*, pg. 920
FERROTEC ALION CORPORATION—See Ferrotec Holdings Corporation; *Int'l*, pg. 2643
FORMS & SURFACES, INC.; *U.S. Private*, pg. 1572
FUJAIRAH BUILDING INDUSTRIES COMPANY P.S.C. - FUJAIRAH MARBLE & TILES FACTORY—See Fujairah Building Industries Company P.S.C.; *Int'l*, pg. 2808
FUNKSJONSUTSTYR AS—See AddLife AB; *Int'l*, pg. 129
GLITTEK GRANITES LTD.; *Int'l*, pg. 2992
GULF STONE COMPANY SAOG; *Int'l*, pg. 3182
HALABI INC.; *U.S. Private*, pg. 1841
HAL MANN VELLA GROUP PLC; *Int'l*, pg. 3222
HAZLETON MATERIALS, L.L.C.—See Haines & Kibblehouse Inc.; *U.S. Private*, pg. 1841
HG INDUSTRIES LIMITED—See Greenlam Industries Limited; *Int'l*, pg. 3075
H&K MATERIALS—See Haines & Kibblehouse Inc.; *U.S. Private*, pg. 1841
HOCK HENG MARKETING (KL) SDN. BHD.—See DFCITY Group Berhad; *Int'l*, pg. 2094
HOCK HENG STONE (EAST COAST) SDN BHD—See DFCITY Group Berhad; *Int'l*, pg. 2094
IKTINOS HELLAS SA; *Int'l*, pg. 3612
ITALIAN CAST STONE; *U.S. Private*, pg. 2149
JASPER STONE COMPANY—See L.G. Everist Inc.; *U.S. Private*, pg. 2366
L.G. EVERIST INC. - MOUNTAIN DIVISION—See L.G. Everist Inc.; *U.S. Private*, pg. 2366
LOCUST RIDGE QUARRY—See Haines & Kibblehouse Inc.; *U.S. Private*, pg. 1841
L.S. STARRETT COMPANY - SAW DIVISION—See MiddleGround Management, LP; *U.S. Private*, pg. 2713
MADISON BLOCK & STONE LLC—See SiteOne Landscape Supply, Inc.; *U.S. Public*, pg. 1889
MAJESTIC MARBLE AND GLASS CO.; *U.S. Private*, pg. 2554
NATURAL STONE CONCEPTS LLC; *U.S. Private*, pg. 2867
NORTH CAROLINA GRANITE CORP.; *U.S. Private*, pg. 2943
PALLETTE STONE CORPORATION—See The D.A. Collins Construction Co., Inc.; *U.S. Private*, pg. 4017
PENN/MD MATERIALS—See Haines & Kibblehouse Inc.; *U.S. Private*, pg. 1841
PEUTE BAUSTOFF GMBH—See Aurubis AG; *Int'l*, pg. 715
POLLUX MANUFACTURING, INC.—See Dale Tile Company; *U.S. Private*, pg. 1149
POWERGRACE INDUSTRIES LIMITED—See Asian Granito India Limited; *Int'l*, pg. 617
PRECISION GROUND FLAT STOCK DIVISION—See MiddleGround Management, LP; *U.S. Private*, pg. 2713
QUARRIES DIRECT INTERNATIONAL LLC; *U.S. Private*, pg. 3324
RAYMOND GRANITE CO.—See Cold Spring Granite Company; *U.S. Private*, pg. 966
REAL VALUE, INC.; *U.S. Private*, pg. 3368
ROTTENECKER-CAGGIATI GMBH—See Matthews International Corporation; *U.S. Public*, pg. 1400
R.W. SIDLEY, INCORPORATED; *U.S. Private*, pg. 3340
RYNONE MANUFACTURING CORPORATION; *U.S. Private*, pg. 3511
SAUNA-EUROX OY—See Harvia Oyj; *Int'l*, pg. 3281
SILVER HILL QUARRY—See Haines & Kibblehouse Inc.; *U.S. Private*, pg. 1841
STAR GRANITE CO., INC.—See Matthews International Corporation; *U.S. Public*, pg. 1401
STARRETT GRANITE SURFACE PLATE DIVISION—See MiddleGround Management, LP; *U.S. Private*, pg. 2713
STOCKERTOWN CONSTRUCTION MATERIALS—See Haines & Kibblehouse Inc.; *U.S. Private*, pg. 1841
STONE CENTER—See SiteOne Landscape Supply, Inc.; *U.S. Public*, pg. 1889
STONE PANELS, INC.—See Thompson Street Capital Manager LLC; *U.S. Private*, pg. 4161
TANDO BUILDING PRODUCTS—See Clearview Capital, LLC; *U.S. Private*, pg. 939
TENAX USA; *U.S. Private*, pg. 3965
TRANSPACIFIC BITUMINOUS PRODUCTS PTY LTD—See Cleanaway Waste Management Limited; *Int'l*, pg. 1655
TUSCANY PAVERS; *U.S. Private*, pg. 4262
UNITED STATES MARBLE, INC.—See O2 Investment Partners, LLC; *U.S. Private*, pg. 2982
UNITED STATES MARBLE, INC.—See Oakland Standard Co., LLC; *U.S. Private*, pg. 2985
UTELITE CORP.—See Holcim Ltd.; *Int'l*, pg. 3449
VALLEY QUARRIES INC. - CHAMBERSBURG PLANT—See New Enterprise Stone & Lime Co., Inc.; *U.S. Private*, pg. 2895
VALLEY QUARRIES INC. - GETTYSBURG PLANT—See New Enterprise Stone & Lime Co., Inc.; *U.S. Private*, pg. 2895
VETTER STONE COMPANY; *U.S. Private*, pg. 4374
WM. HILGERS GMBH & CO. KG—See Dortmunder Gussasphalt GmbH & Co. KG; *Int'l*, pg. 2180

327992 — GROUND OR TREATED MINERAL AND EARTH MANUFACTURING

AKTOBE-TEMIR-VS JSC; *Int'l*, pg. 267
ALUCHEM INC.; *U.S. Private*, pg. 211
AMERICAN ART CLAY CO., INC.; *U.S. Private*, pg. 222
ASBURY EQUIPMENT—See Great Mill Rock LLC; *U.S. Private*, pg. 1765
ASBURY GRAPHITE MILLS, INC—See Great Mill Rock LLC; *U.S. Private*, pg. 1766
ASBURY GRAPHITE—See Great Mill Rock LLC; *U.S. Private*, pg. 1765
BGRIMM SCIENCE & TECHNOLOGY CO., LTD.; *Int'l*, pg. 1009
BIG RIVER INDUSTRIES, INC.—See CRH plc; *Int'l*, pg. 1845
BLOOMING GLEN QUARRY—See Haines & Kibblehouse Inc.; *U.S. Private*, pg. 1840
BLUE MOUNTAIN PRODUCTION CO.—See Oil-Dri Corporation of America; *U.S. Public*, pg. 1565
BUFFALO CRUSHED STONE, INC.—See New Enterprise Stone & Lime Co., Inc.; *U.S. Private*, pg. 2895
BURGESS PIGMENT COMPANY; *U.S. Private*, pg. 687
CALUMITE S.R.O.—See Heidelberg Materials AG; *Int'l*, pg. 3309
CARMEUSE LIME & STONE—See Carmeuse Holding SA; *Int'l*, pg. 1341
CESKOMORAVSKY STERK, A.S.—See Heidelberg Materials AG; *Int'l*, pg. 3309
CUMMINGS-MOORE GRAPHITE CO.—See Great Mill Rock LLC; *U.S. Private*, pg. 1766
DESICCARE, INC.; *U.S. Private*, pg. 1213
HANSON AGGREGATES BMC, INC.—See Heidelberg Materials AG; *Int'l*, pg. 3313
HANSON AGGREGATES EAST LLC—See Heidelberg Materials AG; *Int'l*, pg. 3313
HILL & GRIFFITH COMPANY; *U.S. Private*, pg. 1944
HILLTOP QUARRY—See Haines & Kibblehouse Inc.; *U.S. Private*, pg. 1841
MARTIN MARIETTA MAGNESIA SPECIALTIES, INC.—See Martin Marietta Materials, Inc.; *U.S. Public*, pg. 1389
MILL CREEK DOLOMITE LLC—See United States Lime & Minerals, Inc.; *U.S. Public*, pg. 2236
MONDO MINERALS B.V.—See Elementis plc; *Int'l*, pg. 2359
NAN HWA CEMENT CORP.—See Asia Cement Corporation; *Int'l*, pg. 611

327992 — GROUND OR TREATED M...

NORTHEAST SOLITE CORPORATION; *U.S. Private*, pg. 2951
OIL-DRI CORPORATION OF GEORGIA—See Oil-Dri Corporation of America; *U.S. Public*, pg. 1566
OIL-DRI PRODUCTION COMPANY—See Oil-Dri Corporation of America; *U.S. Public*, pg. 1566
PIONEER AGGREGATES (UK) LIMITED—See Heidelberg Materials AG; *Int'l*, pg. 3318
POCO GRAPHITE SARL—See Entegris, Inc.; *U.S. Public*, pg. 777
PREMIER MAGNESIA, LLC.; *U.S. Private*, pg. 3250
RESCO PRODUCTS GREENSBORO—See Balmoral Funds LLC; *U.S. Private*, pg. 461
SILBRICO CORPORATION; *U.S. Private*, pg. 3652
SOUTHWESTERN GRAPHITE CO.—See Great Mill Rock LLC; *U.S. Private*, pg. 1766
SPECIALTY GRANULES INC.—See Specialty Granules Inc.; *U.S. Private*, pg. 3749
SUPERIOR GRAPHITE CO.; *U.S. Private*, pg. 3878
SUPERIOR MINERALS COMPANY—See Carmeuse Holding SA; *Int'l*, pg. 1342
TERNA MAG SA—See Gek Terna Societe Anonyme Holdings Real Estate Constructions; *Int'l*, pg. 2913
TMC PIONEER AGGREGATES LIMITED—See Heidelberg Materials AG; *Int'l*, pg. 3320

327993 — MINERAL WOOL MANUFACTURING

ACOUSTIC INNOVATIONS INC.; *U.S. Private*, pg. 64
ADVANCE THERMAL CORP.—See Transco Inc.; *U.S. Private*, pg. 4207
AMIANTIT FIBERGLASS INDUSTRIAL, LTD.—See Owens Corning; *U.S. Public*, pg. 1626
ARABIAN FIBERGLASS INSULATION CO.—See Owens Corning; *U.S. Public*, pg. 1626
ASCENT DEVELOPMENT CO., LTD; *Int'l*, pg. 602
BARON INSULATION PTY LTD—See Fletcher Building Limited; *Int'l*, pg. 2700
BEIJING STAR BUILDING MATERIALS CO., LTD—See BBMG Corporation; *Int'l*, pg. 921
BRITISH GYPSUM-ISOVER LTD.—See Compagnie de Saint-Gobain SA; *Int'l*, pg. 1725
BYUCKSAN CORPORATION; *Int'l*, pg. 1237
C.A. SCHROEDER COMPANY, INC.; *U.S. Private*, pg. 706
CONSOLIDATED FIBERGLASS PRODUCTS CO.; *U.S. Private*, pg. 1020
ECKEL INDUSTRIES INC.; *U.S. Private*, pg. 1327
EUROACOUSTIC—See Compagnie de Saint-Gobain SA; *Int'l*, pg. 1723
FIBERTEK INSULATION LLC—See Owens Corning; *U.S. Public*, pg. 1626
FLIGHT ENVIRONMENTS INC.; *U.S. Private*, pg. 1545
FUJAIRAH BUILDING INDUSTRIES COMPANY P.S.C. - FUJAIRAH ROCKWOOL FACTORY—See Fujairah Building Industries Company P.S.C.; *Int'l*, pg. 2808
GDP SILVERCOTE INC.—See Pacific Avenue Capital Partners, LLC; *U.S. Private*, pg. 3065
GLASSROCK INSULATION COMPANY—See ASEC Company for Mining; *Int'l*, pg. 605
HI TEMP INSULATION INC.; *U.S. Private*, pg. 1931
H&R BENELUX B.V.—See H&R KGaA; *Int'l*, pg. 3193
INDUSTRIAL INSULATION GROUP, LLC—See Berkshire Hathaway Inc.; *U.S. Public*, pg. 308
JOHNS MANVILLE CORP. - ENGINEERED PRODUCTS, WATERVILLE—See Berkshire Hathaway Inc.; *U.S. Public*, pg. 308
JUSHI CANADA FIBERGLASS CO. LTD.—See China Jushi Co., Ltd.; *Int'l*, pg. 1513
JUSHI GROUP (BZ) SINOSIA COMPOSITE MATERIALS CO., LTD—See China Jushi Co., Ltd.; *Int'l*, pg. 1513
JUSHI GROUP CHENGDU CO., LTD.—See China Jushi Co., Ltd.; *Int'l*, pg. 1513
JUSHI GROUP (SA) SINOSIA COMPOSITE MATERIALS CO., LTD.—See China Jushi Co., Ltd.; *Int'l*, pg. 1513
JUSHI INDIA FIBERGLASS PVT LTD.—See China Jushi Co., Ltd.; *Int'l*, pg. 1514
JUSHI ITALY SRL—See China Jushi Co., Ltd.; *Int'l*, pg. 1514
JUSHI KOREA CO., LTD.—See China Jushi Co., Ltd.; *Int'l*, pg. 1514
KNAUF ALCOPOR ITALIA S.P.A.—See Gebr. Knauf KG; *Int'l*, pg. 2906
KNAUF INSULATION D.O.O.—See Gebr. Knauf KG; *Int'l*, pg. 2907
KNAUF INSULATION, D.O.O.—See Gebr. Knauf KG; *Int'l*, pg. 2907
KNAUF INSULATION GMBH—See Gebr. Knauf KG; *Int'l*, pg. 2907
KNAUF INSULATION GMBH—See Gebr. Knauf KG; *Int'l*, pg. 2907
KNAUF INSULATION LTD—See Gebr. Knauf KG; *Int'l*, pg. 2907
KNAUF INSULATION - SHELBYVILLE—See Gebr. Knauf KG; *Int'l*, pg. 2907
KNAUF INSULATION, S.R.O.—See Gebr. Knauf KG; *Int'l*, pg. 2907
LYNCH INSULATION OF MONTANA, LLC—See Installed Building Products, Inc.; *U.S. Public*, pg. 1133

MAG ISOVER K.K.—See Compagnie de Saint-Gobain SA; *Int'l*, pg. 1724
MIDWEST ACOUST-A-FIBER INC.; *U.S. Private*, pg. 2719
MOY-ISOVER LTD.—See Compagnie de Saint-Gobain SA; *Int'l*, pg. 1725
N.V. OWENS-CORNING S.A.—See Owens Corning; *U.S. Public*, pg. 1627
OCV DISTRIBUTION ANZ PTY LTD—See Owens Corning; *U.S. Public*, pg. 1627
OCV FABRICS US, INC.—See Owens Corning; *U.S. Public*, pg. 1627
OEM SOLUTIONS—See Owens Corning; *U.S. Public*, pg. 1627
ORR INDUSTRIES OF PENNSYLVANIA, LLC—See Installed Building Products, Inc.; *U.S. Public*, pg. 1133
OWENS CORNING AUSTRALIA PTY LTD—See Owens Corning; *U.S. Public*, pg. 1627
OWENS CORNING NETHERLAND—See Owens Corning; *U.S. Public*, pg. 1628
OWENS-CORNING VEIL U.K. LIMITED—See Owens Corning; *U.S. Public*, pg. 1628
PAROC AB—See Owens Corning; *U.S. Public*, pg. 1628
PAROC GMBH—See Owens Corning; *U.S. Public*, pg. 1628
PAROC GROUP OY—See Owens Corning; *U.S. Public*, pg. 1628
PAROC LIMITED—See Owens Corning; *U.S. Public*, pg. 1628
PAROC POLSKA SP. Z O.O.—See Owens Corning; *U.S. Public*, pg. 1628
PITTSBURGH CORNING CR, S.R.O.—See Owens Corning; *U.S. Public*, pg. 1628
SAINT-GOBAIN ISOVER AB—See Compagnie de Saint-Gobain SA; *Int'l*, pg. 1726
SAINT-GOBAIN ISOVER A/S—See Compagnie de Saint-Gobain SA; *Int'l*, pg. 1726
SAINT-GOBAIN ISOVER AUSTRIA AG—See Compagnie de Saint-Gobain SA; *Int'l*, pg. 1726
SAINT-GOBAIN ISOVER BENELUX—See Compagnie de Saint-Gobain SA; *Int'l*, pg. 1726
SAINT-GOBAIN ISOVER ITALIA S.P.A.—See Compagnie de Saint-Gobain SA; *Int'l*, pg. 1726
SAINT-GOBAIN ISOVER SA—See Compagnie de Saint-Gobain SA; *Int'l*, pg. 1726
SAINT-GOBAIN ORSIL S.R.O.—See Compagnie de Saint-Gobain SA; *Int'l*, pg. 1735
SAINT-GOBAIN SOUTH AFRICA PTY. LTD.—See Compagnie de Saint-Gobain SA; *Int'l*, pg. 1735
SAINT-GOBAIN WANNER SA—See Compagnie de Saint-Gobain SA; *Int'l*, pg. 1736
SCOTT INDUSTRIES LLC; *U.S. Private*, pg. 3577
SIA PAROC—See Owens Corning; *U.S. Public*, pg. 1628
THERMAFIBER, INC.—See Owens Corning; *U.S. Public*, pg. 1628
UNITED STATES MINERAL PRODUCTS COMPANY—See SK Capital Partners, LP; *U.S. Private*, pg. 3680
WARMINSTER FIBERGLASS CO.—See Warminster Fiberglass, LLC; *U.S. Private*, pg. 4442
XTRATHERM LIMITED—See Mohawk Industries, Inc.; *U.S. Public*, pg. 1458

327999 — ALL OTHER MISCELLANEOUS NONMETALLIC MINERAL PRODUCT MANUFACTURING

20 MICRONS LIMITED; *Int'l*, pg. 3
AFRICO RESOURCES LTD.—See Eurasian Natural Resources Corporation Limited; *Int'l*, pg. 2527
AGNICO-EAGLE MINES LIMITED-MEADOWBANK—See Agnico Eagle Mines Limited; *Int'l*, pg. 212
ALBION LABORATORIES, INC.—See Balchem Corporation; *U.S. Public*, pg. 265
ALEMPEDRAS - SOCIEDADE DE BRITAS LDA—See Camargo Correa S.A.; *Int'l*, pg. 1267
AOYUAN MEIGU TECHNOLOGY CO., LTD.; *Int'l*, pg. 499
AR METALLIZING LTD.—See H.I.G. Capital, LLC; *U.S. Private*, pg. 1828
ARMETALLIZING N.V.—See H.I.G. Capital, LLC; *U.S. Private*, pg. 1828
AR METALLIZING SRL—See H.I.G. Capital, LLC; *U.S. Private*, pg. 1828
ARMSTRONG BUILDING PRODUCTS B.V.—See Armstrong World Industries, Inc.; *U.S. Public*, pg. 194
ARMSTRONG WORLD INDUSTRIES LTD.—See Aurelius Equity Opportunities SE & Co. KGaA; *Int'l*, pg. 707
ASAHI MODI MATERIALS PVT., LTD.—See Asahi Yukizai Corporation; *Int'l*, pg. 598
AS CHILE ENERGY GROUP SA—See Edenred S.A.; *Int'l*, pg. 2307
ATLAS CORPORATION S.R.L.; *Int'l*, pg. 684
THE BEN SILVER CORPORATION; *U.S. Private*, pg. 3993
BIG BELL GOLD OPERATIONS PTY LTD—See Harmony Gold Mining Company Limited; *Int'l*, pg. 3278
BONANZA RESOURCES CORP.; *Int'l*, pg. 1105
CARRARA MID-EAST INDUSTRIAL CO. LLC—See Depa PLC; *Int'l*, pg. 2040
CATAI S.R.L.—See Apollo Global Management, Inc.; *U.S. Public*, pg. 160

CERADYNE ESK, LLC—See 3M Company; *U.S. Public*, pg. 8
CERADYNE (TIANJIN) TECHNICAL CERAMICS CO., LTD.—See 3M Company; *U.S. Public*, pg. 8
CERAMTEC NORTH AMERICA CORP.—See BC Partners LLP; *Int'l*, pg. 923
CHEETHAM SALT LIMITED—See CK Hutchison Holdings Limited; *Int'l*, pg. 1637
CHEMSERVE PERLITE (PTY) LIMITED—See AECI Limited; *Int'l*, pg. 171
CHINA GENGSHENG MINERALS, INC.; *Int'l*, pg. 1504
CHINA STEEL RESOURCES CORPORATION—See China Steel Corporation; *Int'l*, pg. 1555
CHINA WEST CONSTRUCTION CO., LTD.; *Int'l*, pg. 1563
CHONGQING CHANGJIANG RIVER MOULDING MATERIAL CHANGZHOU CO., LTD.—See Chongqing Changjiang River Moulding Material (Group) Co., Ltd.; *Int'l*, pg. 1579
CHONGQING CHANGJIANG RIVER MOULDING MATERIAL CHENGDU CO., LTD.—See Chongqing Changjiang River Moulding Material (Group) Co., Ltd.; *Int'l*, pg. 1579
CHONGQING CHANGJIANG RIVER MOULDING MATERIAL KUNSHAN CO., LTD.—See Chongqing Changjiang River Moulding Material (Group) Co., Ltd.; *Int'l*, pg. 1579
CHONGQING CHANGJIANG RIVER MOULDING MATERIAL SHIYAN CO., LTD.—See Chongqing Changjiang River Moulding Material (Group) Co., Ltd.; *Int'l*, pg. 1579
CHONGQING CHANGJIANG RIVER MOULDING MATERIAL XIANTAO CO., LTD.—See Chongqing Changjiang River Moulding Material (Group) Co., Ltd.; *Int'l*, pg. 1579
CHOWGULE & COMPANY (SALT) PRIVATE LIMITED—See Chowgule & Company Pvt. Ltd.; *Int'l*, pg. 1585
CIMC VEHICLE (SHANDONG) CO., LTD.—See China International Marine Containers (Group) Co., Ltd.; *Int'l*, pg. 1511
COORSTEK, INC. - COORSTEK MONCHENGLADBACH FACILITY—See CoorsTek, Inc.; *U.S. Private*, pg. 1043
CUSTOM VAULT CORP; *U.S. Private*, pg. 1130
DK AZTEC CO., LTD.; *Int'l*, pg. 2138
DONGSUNG FINETEC INTERNATIONAL, INC.—See Dongsung Finetec Co., Ltd.; *Int'l*, pg. 2170
DR. PAUL LOHMANN GMBH KG; *Int'l*, pg. 2194
DYNASIL CORPORATION OF AMERICA; *U.S. Private*, pg. 1299
DYNASIL - SYNTHETIC FUSED SILICA—See Dynasil Corporation of America; *U.S. Private*, pg. 1299
EARTH CONTACT PRODUCTS, LLC.; *U.S. Private*, pg. 1314
ECKA GRANULES AUSTRALIA PTY. LTD.—See Palladium Equity Partners, LLC; *U.S. Private*, pg. 3078
EP ENGINEERED CLAYS CORPORATION—See Apollo Global Management, Inc.; *U.S. Public*, pg. 164
EURO SUN MINING INC.; *Int'l*, pg. 2531
FEREBEE ASPHALT CORPORATION—See Construction Partners, Inc.; *U.S. Public*, pg. 572
FIORE STONE, INC.; *U.S. Private*, pg. 1511
FRE COMPOSITES INC.—See Clayton, Dubilier & Rice, LLC; *U.S. Private*, pg. 920
GLOBAL PIONEER ALUMINIUM INDUSTRIAL FZE—See Al Hamad Contracting Company LLC; *Int'l*, pg. 278
GMH AKADEMIE GMBH—See Georgsmarienhutte Holding GmbH; *Int'l*, pg. 2940
GMH EAST EUROPE GMBH—See Georgsmarienhutte Holding GmbH; *Int'l*, pg. 2940
GMH FRANCE S.A.R.L.—See Georgsmarienhutte Holding GmbH; *Int'l*, pg. 2940
GMH INTERNATIONAL S.R.L.—See Georgsmarienhutte Holding GmbH; *Int'l*, pg. 2940
GMH INTERNATIONAL S.R.L.—See Georgsmarienhutte Holding GmbH; *Int'l*, pg. 2940
GMH UK LTD.—See Georgsmarienhutte Holding GmbH; *Int'l*, pg. 2940
GRODITZ CELIK ENDUSTRI MALZ. SAN.VE TIC. A.S.—See Georgsmarienhutte Holding GmbH; *Int'l*, pg. 2940
GUALA CLOSURES (CHENGDU) CO., LTD.—See Guala Closures S.p.A.; *Int'l*, pg. 3152
GUALA CLOSURES DEUTSCHLAND GMBH—See Guala Closures S.p.A.; *Int'l*, pg. 3152
HANCHANG INDUSTRY CO., LTD.; *Int'l*, pg. 3242
HEANY INDUSTRIES, INC.—See Crawford United Corporation; *U.S. Public*, pg. 592
HILGER CRYSTALS LTD.—See Dynasil Corporation of America; *U.S. Private*, pg. 1299
HUAXUN FANGZHOU CO., LTD.; *Int'l*, pg. 3515
IGC-INDUSTRIAL GALVANIZERS CORPORATION (M) SDN. BHD.—See Valmont Industries, Inc.; *U.S. Public*, pg. 2273
INNOVATIVE CONCRETE TECHNOLOGY CORP.—See Elvisridge Capital, LLC; *U.S. Private*, pg. 1377
JSW ISPAT SPECIAL PRODUCTS LIMITED—See Apollo Global Management, Inc.; *U.S. Public*, pg. 152
METALLURG SERVICIOS S.A. DE R.L. DE C.V.—See AMG Critical Materials N.V.; *Int'l*, pg. 426
MINERALS TECHNOLOGIES, INC.; *U.S. Public*, pg. 1448
MINMETALS CAPITAL CO., LTD.—See China Rare Earth Resources And Technology Co., Ltd.; *Int'l*, pg. 1546

N.A.I.C.S. INDEX

331110 — IRON AND STEEL MILL...

NANTONG CIMC TANK EQUIPMENT CO., LTD.—See China International Marine Containers (Group) Co., Ltd.; *Int'l*, pg. 1512
NON-METALLIC SOLUTIONS, INC.—See Repligen Corporation; *U.S. Public*, pg. 1784
PARAGON BUILDING PRODUCTS INC.; *U.S. Private*, pg. 3090
PQ CORPORATION—See The Carlyle Group Inc.; *U.S. Public*, pg. 2052
PRECON GOIAS INDUSTRIAL LTDA.—See Eternit S.A.; *Int'l*, pg. 2521
PST PRESS SINTERTECNICA BRASIL LTDA—See BC Partners LLP; *Int'l*, pg. 923
QC CORP.—See AEA Investors LP; *U.S. Private*, pg. 116
QINGDAO CIMC SPECIAL REEFER CO., LTD.—See China International Marine Containers (Group) Co., Ltd.; *Int'l*, pg. 1512
QINGDAO DIC LIQUID CRYSTAL CO., LTD.—See DIC Corporation; *Int'l*, pg. 2109
QUIKRETE OF VIRGINIA—See The Quikrete Companies, LLC; *U.S. Private*, pg. 4101
R. D. WING CO., INC.; *U.S. Private*, pg. 3333
RED BUTTERFLY STRONTIUM INDUSTRY CO., LTD.—See Chori Co., Ltd.; *Int'l*, pg. 1583
ROCKY MOUNTAIN INDUSTRIALS, INC.; *U.S. Public*, pg. 1807
SAFFIL AUTOMOTIVE LIMITED—See Clearlake Capital Group, L.P.; *U.S. Private*, pg. 937
SAFFIL AUTOMOTIVE SOUTH AFRICA (PTY) LIMITED—See Clearlake Capital Group, L.P.; *U.S. Private*, pg. 937
SEMICON ASSOCIATES—See 3M Company; *U.S. Public*, pg. 8
SHENZHEN CIMC YANTIAN PORT CONTAINER SERVICE CO., LTD—See China International Marine Containers (Group) Co., Ltd.; *Int'l*, pg. 1512
SIVOMATIC B.V.—See Minerals Technologies, Inc.; *U.S. Public*, pg. 1449
SMB SCHWERMECHANIK GMBH—See Georgsmarienhutte Holding GmbH; *Int'l*, pg. 2941
STRUXURE OUTDOOR, INC.; *U.S. Private*, pg. 3842
THERMAL STRUCTURES, INC.—See HEICO Corporation; *U.S. Public*, pg. 1021
UNIFRAX I LLC—See Clearlake Capital Group, L.P.; *U.S. Private*, pg. 937
VETRICERAMICI POLSKA SPOKA Z OGRANICZONA ODPOWIEDZIALNOSCIA—See American Securities LLC; *U.S. Private*, pg. 252
VETRICERAMICI S.P.A.—See American Securities LLC; *U.S. Private*, pg. 252
WESTERN INDUSTRIAL CERAMICS; *U.S. Private*, pg. 4493
XELLA INTERNATIONAL GMBH—See Lone Star Global Acquisitions, LLC; *U.S. Private*, pg. 2489
YANGZHOU TONGLEE REEFER CONTAINER CO., LTD.—See China International Marine Containers (Group) Co., Ltd.; *Int'l*, pg. 1512
YANGZHOU TONGLEE REEFER EQUIPMENT CO.,LTD—See China International Marine Containers (Group) Co., Ltd.; *Int'l*, pg. 1512
ZHUMADIAN CIMC HUAJUN VEHICLE CO.,LTD—See China International Marine Containers (Group) Co., Ltd.; *Int'l*, pg. 1513

331110 — IRON AND STEEL MILLS AND FERROALLOY MANUFACTURING

24 IANUARIE S.A.; *Int'l*, pg. 4
2S METAL PUBLIC COMPANY LIMITED; *Int'l*, pg. 5
AAA GALVANIZING - CHELSEA, INC.—See AZZ, Inc.; *U.S. Public*, pg. 258
AAA GALVANIZING - DIXON, INC.—See AZZ, Inc.; *U.S. Public*, pg. 258
AAA GALVANIZING - HAMILTON, INC.—See AZZ, Inc.; *U.S. Public*, pg. 258
AAA GALVANIZING - JOLIET, INC.—See AZZ, Inc.; *U.S. Public*, pg. 258
AAA GALVANIZING - PEORIA, INC.—See AZZ, Inc.; *U.S. Public*, pg. 258
AAA GALVANIZING - WINSTED, INC.—See AZZ, Inc.; *U.S. Public*, pg. 258
AACOA EXTRUSIONS, INC.—See Tredegar Corporation; *U.S. Public*, pg. 2186
A&A GLOBAL INDUSTRIES INC.; *U.S. Private*, pg. 19
AANCHAL ISPAT LTD.; *Int'l*, pg. 36
ABS CENTRE METALLURGIQUE SARL—See Danieli & C. Officine Meccaniche S.p.A.; *Int'l*, pg. 1962
ABS SISAK DOO—See Danieli & C. Officine Meccaniche S.p.A.; *Int'l*, pg. 1962
ABS SPA—See Danieli & C. Officine Meccaniche S.p.A.; *Int'l*, pg. 1962
ACCIAIERIE VALBRUNA S.P.A. - BOLZANO PLANT—See Acciaierie Valbruna S.p.A.; *Int'l*, pg. 89
ACCIAIERIE VALBRUNA S.P.A.; *Int'l*, pg. 89
ACERINOX EUROPA, S.A.U.—See Acerinox, S.A.; *Int'l*, pg. 100

ACERINOX SOUTH EAST ASIA, PTE. LTD.—See Acerinox, S.A.; *Int'l*, pg. 100
ACML—See FAYAT SAS; *Int'l*, pg. 2624
ADHUNIK METALIKS LIMITED—See GFG Alliance Limited; *Int'l*, pg. 2956
ADITYA FORGE LIMITED; *Int'l*, pg. 149
ADITYA ISPAT LTD.; *Int'l*, pg. 149
ADVANCED FORMING TECHNOLOGY, INC.—See ARC Group Worldwide, Inc.; *U.S. Public*, pg. 179
AICHI FORGING COMPANY OF ASIA, INC.—See Aichi Steel Corporation; *Int'l*, pg. 230
AISHA STEEL MILLS LIMITED; *Int'l*, pg. 251
AJU STEEL CO., LTD.; *Int'l*, pg. 258
AKANKSHA POWER & INFRASTRUCTURE LIMITED; *Int'l*, pg. 259
AK STEEL BV—See Cleveland-Cliffs, Inc.; *U.S. Public*, pg. 513
AK STEEL CORP.—See Cleveland-Cliffs, Inc.; *U.S. Public*, pg. 513
AK STEEL GMBH—See Cleveland-Cliffs, Inc.; *U.S. Public*, pg. 513
AK STEEL HOLDING CORPORATION—See Cleveland-Cliffs, Inc.; *U.S. Public*, pg. 513
AK STEEL INTERNATIONAL BV—See Cleveland-Cliffs, Inc.; *U.S. Public*, pg. 513
AK STEEL LIMITED—See Cleveland-Cliffs, Inc.; *U.S. Public*, pg. 513
AK STEEL MERCHANDISING S.A.—See Cleveland-Cliffs, Inc.; *U.S. Public*, pg. 514
AK STEEL NV—See Cleveland-Cliffs, Inc.; *U.S. Public*, pg. 514
AK STEEL SRL—See Cleveland-Cliffs, Inc.; *U.S. Public*, pg. 514
ALCECAP S.A.S.—See Hanwa Co., Ltd.; *Int'l*, pg. 3261
AL EZZ DEKHEILA STEEL COMPANY ALEXANDRIA SAE—See Ezz Steel Co. S.A.E.; *Int'l*, pg. 2594
AL EZZ FLAT STEEL COMPANY—See Ezz Steel Co. S.A.E.; *Int'l*, pg. 2594
ALFA ACCIAI SPA; *Int'l*, pg. 307
AL ITTEFAQ STEEL PRODUCTS COMPANY—See Al-Tuwairqi Group; *Int'l*, pg. 289
ALLIED TUBE & CONDUIT—See Clayton, Dubilier & Rice, LLC; *U.S. Private*, pg. 919
ALL ORE MINERACAO PARTICIPACOES S.A.; *Int'l*, pg. 332
ALLOY STEEL INTERNATIONAL, INC.; *Int'l*, pg. 360
ALPINE PIPE MANUFACTURING SDN BHD—See Hiap Teck Venture Berhad; *Int'l*, pg. 3382
ALTON STEEL INC.; *U.S. Private*, pg. 210
ALTOS HORNOS DE MEXICO, S.A. DE C.V.—See Grupo Acerero del Norte S.A. de C.V.; *Int'l*, pg. 3118
AL YAMAMAH STEEL INDUSTRIES COMPANY; *Int'l*, pg. 283
AMERICAN APPLIANCE PRODUCTS, INC.—See Trive Capital Inc.; *U.S. Private*, pg. 4240
AMERICAN GARDENWORKS; *U.S. Private*, pg. 235
AMERICAN STEEL PIPE DIV.—See American Cast Iron Pipe Company; *U.S. Private*, pg. 226
AMER INTERNATIONAL GROUP CO., LTD.; *Int'l*, pg. 420
AMG ALUMINUM MEXICO, S.A. DE CV—See AMG Critical Materials N.V.; *Int'l*, pg. 426
AMG RESOURCES CORP. - BALTIMORE FACILITY—See AMG Resources Corp.; *U.S. Private*, pg. 262
AMG RESOURCES CORP. - GARY FACILITY—See AMG Resources Corp.; *U.S. Private*, pg. 262
AMG RESOURCES CORP. - MILWAUKEE FACILITY—See AMG Resources Corp.; *U.S. Private*, pg. 262
AMG RESOURCES CORP. - NEWARK FACILITY—See AMG Resources Corp.; *U.S. Private*, pg. 262
AMG RESOURCES CORP.; *U.S. Private*, pg. 262
AMG RESOURCES CORP. - ST. JOSEPH FACILITY—See AMG Resources Corp.; *U.S. Private*, pg. 262
AMG RESOURCES CORP. - ST. PAUL FACILITY—See AMG Resources Corp.; *U.S. Private*, pg. 262
AMG SUPERALLOYS UK LIMITED—See AMG Critical Materials N.V.; *Int'l*, pg. 426
ANCOFERWALDRAM STEELPLATES B.V.—See AG der Dillinger Huttenwerke; *Int'l*, pg. 197
ANDRESEN TOWERS A/S—See IAI Holding A/S; *Int'l*, pg. 3568
ANDRITZ METALS FRANCE S.A.S.—See ANDRITZ AG; *Int'l*, pg. 454
ANDRITZ METALS GERMANY GMBH—See ANDRITZ AG; *Int'l*, pg. 454
ANDRITZ METALS NETHERLANDS B.V.—See ANDRITZ AG; *Int'l*, pg. 454
ANHUI BRC & MA STEEL WELDMESH CO. LTD.—See China Baowu Steel Group Corp., Ltd.; *Int'l*, pg. 1486
ANHUI FUHUANG STEEL STRUCTURE CO., LTD.; *Int'l*, pg. 467
ANIK FERRO-ALLOYS PVT. LTD—See Anik Industries Ltd.; *Int'l*, pg. 471
ANJANEY ALLOYS LTD.—See Bhagwati Syndicate Pvt. Ltd.; *Int'l*, pg. 1010
ANKIT METAL & POWER LTD.; *Int'l*, pg. 472
ANSHAN IRON & STEEL GROUP CORPORATION; *Int'l*, pg. 479

ANVA KSG AB—See AnVa Tubes & Components AB; *Int'l*, pg. 486
ANVA ROSTFRITT & SMIDE AB—See AnVa Tubes & Components AB; *Int'l*, pg. 486
ANYANG IRON & STEEL INC.—See Anyang Iron & Steel Group Co., Ltd.; *Int'l*, pg. 487
APERAM ISTANBUL PASLANMAZ CELIK SANAYI VE TICARET A.S.—See Aperam SA; *Int'l*, pg. 508
APERAM SA - MONTEVIDEO UNIT—See Aperam SA; *Int'l*, pg. 508
APERAM SA - RIBEIRAO PIRES UNIT—See Aperam SA; *Int'l*, pg. 508
APERAM SA; *Int'l*, pg. 508
APERAM SA - SUMARE UNIT—See Aperam SA; *Int'l*, pg. 508
APERAM STAINLESS BELGIUM N.V.—See Aperam SA; *Int'l*, pg. 508
APERAM STAINLESS SERVICES & SOLUTIONS ARGENTINA S.A.—See Aperam SA; *Int'l*, pg. 508
APERAM STAINLESS SERVICES & SOLUTIONS BRAZIL—See Aperam SA; *Int'l*, pg. 508
APERAM STAINLESS SERVICES & SOLUTIONS GERMANY GMBH—See Aperam SA; *Int'l*, pg. 508
APERAM STAINLESS SERVICES & SOLUTIONS LUXEMBOURG SA—See Aperam SA; *Int'l*, pg. 508
APERAM STAINLESS SERVICES & SOLUTIONS TUBES BRAZIL—See Aperam SA; *Int'l*, pg. 508
APERAM STAINLESS SERVICES & SOLUTIONS TUBES CZECH REPUBLIC—See Aperam SA; *Int'l*, pg. 508
APERAM STAINLESS SERVICES & SOLUTIONS UK LTD—See Aperam SA; *Int'l*, pg. 508
APL APOLLO TUBES LTD.; *Int'l*, pg. 515
APOLLO TRICOAT TUBES LIMITED—See Apl Apollo Tubes Ltd.; *Int'l*, pg. 515
ARABIAN PIPES COMPANY; *Int'l*, pg. 533
ARABIAN STEEL PIPES MFG CO. LTD; *Int'l*, pg. 533
ARCELORMITTAL ANNABA SPA—See ArcelorMittal S.A.; *Int'l*, pg. 543
ARCELORMITTAL - ARCELORMITTAL DESVRES MILL—See ArcelorMittal S.A.; *Int'l*, pg. 543
ARCELORMITTAL - ARCELORMITTAL MONTATAIRE MILL—See ArcelorMittal S.A.; *Int'l*, pg. 543
ARCELORMITTAL ASTURIAS S.A.—See ArcelorMittal S.A.; *Int'l*, pg. 545
ARCELORMITTAL CELAYA S.A. DE C.V.—See ArcelorMittal S.A.; *Int'l*, pg. 545
ARCELORMITTAL DOFASCO INC.—See ArcelorMittal S.A.; *Int'l*, pg. 544
ARCELORMITTAL GALATI S.A.—See GFG Alliance Limited; *Int'l*, pg. 2956
ARCELORMITTAL HAUTMONT—See ArcelorMittal S.A.; *Int'l*, pg. 544
ARCELORMITTAL HUNEDOARA S.A.—See ArcelorMittal S.A.; *Int'l*, pg. 544
ARCELORMITTAL JUBAIL—See ArcelorMittal S.A.; *Int'l*, pg. 544
ARCELORMITTAL KRYVIY RIH—See ArcelorMittal S.A.; *Int'l*, pg. 544
ARCELORMITTAL LESAKA S.A.—See ArcelorMittal S.A.; *Int'l*, pg. 543
ARCELORMITTAL LONG PRODUCTS CANADA G.P.—See ArcelorMittal S.A.; *Int'l*, pg. 544
ARCELORMITTAL MEXICO S.A. DE C.V.—See ArcelorMittal S.A.; *Int'l*, pg. 545
ARCELORMITTAL OSTRAVA A.S.—See GFG Alliance Limited; *Int'l*, pg. 2956
ARCELORMITTAL POLAND S.A.—See ArcelorMittal S.A.; *Int'l*, pg. 545
ARCELORMITTAL ST. CHELY D'APCHER MILL—See ArcelorMittal S.A.; *Int'l*, pg. 545
ARCELORMITTAL STEEL USA INC.—See Cleveland-Cliffs, Inc.; *U.S. Public*, pg. 514
ARCELORMITTAL TUBULAR PRODUCTS IASI SA—See ArcelorMittal S.A.; *Int'l*, pg. 545
ARCELORMITTAL TUBULAR PRODUCTS ROMAN S.A.—See ArcelorMittal S.A.; *Int'l*, pg. 545
ARCELORMITTAL VINTON, INC—See Cleveland-Cliffs, Inc.; *U.S. Public*, pg. 514
ARCELORMITTAL WARSZAWA SP. Z.O.O.—See ArcelorMittal S.A.; *Int'l*, pg. 545
ARGENT INDUSTRIAL LIMITED; *Int'l*, pg. 560
ARMACERO INDUSTRIAL Y COMERCIAL LTDA—See CAP S.A.; *Int'l*, pg. 1300
ASHIRWAD STEELS & INDUSTRIES LIMITED; *Int'l*, pg. 607
ASHNISHA INDUSTRIES LTD.; *Int'l*, pg. 608
ASIA-BENI STEEL INDUSTRIES (PTE) LTD—See Asia Enterprises Holding Limited; *Int'l*, pg. 612
ASIA ENTERPRISES HOLDING LIMITED; *Int'l*, pg. 612
ASIL CELIK SANAYI VE TICARET A.S.; *Int'l*, pg. 621
ASTURIANA DE LAMINADOS SA; *Int'l*, pg. 663
ATC ALLOYS LTD.; *Int'l*, pg. 666
ATLANTIC SERVICE CO. LTD.—See Steel Partners Holdings L.P.; *U.S. Public*, pg. 1943
AUBERT & DUVAL SAS - FIRMINY PLANT—See Eramet SA; *Int'l*, pg. 2489
AUBERT & DUVAL SAS - GENNEVILLIERS PLANT—See Eramet SA; *Int'l*, pg. 2489

331110 — IRON AND STEEL MILL...

AUBERT & DUVAL SAS - IMPHY PLANT—See Eramet SA; *Int'l*, pg. 2489
AUBERT & DUVAL SAS - ISSOIRE INTERFORGE PLANT—See Eramet SA; *Int'l*, pg. 2489
AUBERT & DUVAL SAS - LES ANCIZES PLANT—See Eramet SA; *Int'l*, pg. 2489
AVARUS AG—See CRONIMET Holding GmbH; *Int'l*, pg. 1854
AYES CELIK HASIR VE CIT SANAYI A.S.; *Int'l*, pg. 775
AZTEC MANUFACTURING PARTNERSHIP, LTD.—See AZZ, Inc.; *U.S. Public*, pg. 259
BACVIET STEEL JSC; *Int'l*, pg. 795
BALLI KLOCKNER MIDDLE EAST FZE—See Balli Group plc; *Int'l*, pg. 809
BANGKOK STEEL INDUSTRY PUBLIC COMPANY LIMITED; *Int'l*, pg. 835
BANGLADESH STEEL RE-ROLLING MILLS LTD.; *Int'l*, pg. 836
BAO ISLAND ENTERPRISES LIMITED—See China Baowu Steel Group Corp., Ltd.; *Int'l*, pg. 1485
BAOSHAN IRON & STEEL CO., LTD.—See China Baowu Steel Group Corp., Ltd.; *Int'l*, pg. 1485
BAOSTEEL AMERICA INC.—See China Baowu Steel Group Corp., Ltd.; *Int'l*, pg. 1485
BAOSTEEL DO BRASIL LTDA.—See China Baowu Steel Group Corp., Ltd.; *Int'l*, pg. 1485
BAOSTEEL EUROPE GMBH—See China Baowu Steel Group Corp., Ltd.; *Int'l*, pg. 1485
BAOSTEEL ITALIA DISTRIBUTION CENTER S.P.A.—See China Baowu Steel Group Corp., Ltd.; *Int'l*, pg. 1485
BAOSTEEL SINGAPORE PTE. LTD.—See China Baowu Steel Group Corp., Ltd.; *Int'l*, pg. 1485
BAOSTEEL TRADING EUROPE GMBH—See China Baowu Steel Group Corp., Ltd.; *Int'l*, pg. 1485
BARBOT CM—See FAYAT SAS; *Int'l*, pg. 2624
BARNA STEEL SA—See Celsa Group; *Int'l*, pg. 1395
BAR PROCESSING - WICKLIFFE—See Bar Proccessing Corp.; *U.S. Private*, pg. 471
BARRETT STEEL LIMITED; *Int'l*, pg. 869
BARRETT TUBES DIVISION—See Barrett Steel Limited; *Int'l*, pg. 869
BEDMUTHA INDUSTRIES LIMITED; *Int'l*, pg. 938
BEEKAY STEEL INDUSTRIES LTD.; *Int'l*, pg. 939
BEHLEN CUSTOM FABRICATION—See Behlen Mfg. Co.; *U.S. Private*, pg. 515
BEHLEN MFG. CO. - EAST COAST DISTRIBUTION CENTER—See Behlen Mfg. Co.; *U.S. Private*, pg. 515
BEHLEN MFG. CO. - WEST COAST PLANT—See Behlen Mfg. Co.; *U.S. Private*, pg. 515
BEML LIMITED - TRADING DIVISION—See BEML Limited; *Int'l*, pg. 969
BENGANG STEEL PLATES COMPANY LTD.; *Int'l*, pg. 974
BIHAR SPONGE IRON LIMITED; *Int'l*, pg. 1022
BIRCH BRANCH ACQUISITION CORP.; *Int'l*, pg. 1046
BITROS HOLDING S.A.; *Int'l*, pg. 1050
BITROS REBAR CENTER S.A.—See Bitros Holding S.A.; *Int'l*, pg. 1050
BITROS STEEL S.A.—See Bitros Holding S.A.; *Int'l*, pg. 1050
BLUCHER SWEDEN AB—See Watts Water Technologies, Inc.; *U.S. Public*, pg. 2337
BLUCHER UK LTD—See Watts Water Technologies, Inc.; *U.S. Public*, pg. 2337
BLUESCOPE ACIER NOUVELLE CALEDONIE SA—See BlueScope Steel Limited; *Int'l*, pg. 1072
BLUESCOPE BUILDINGS (GUANGZHOU) LTD.—See BlueScope Steel Limited; *Int'l*, pg. 1072
BLUESCOPE BUILDINGS (VIETNAM) LIMITED—See BlueScope Steel Limited; *Int'l*, pg. 1072
BLUESCOPE BUILDING SYSTEMS (XI'AN) CO., LTD.—See BlueScope Steel Limited; *Int'l*, pg. 1072
BLUESCOPE DISTRIBUTION PTY LTD.—See BlueScope Steel Limited; *Int'l*, pg. 1072
BLUESCOPE LYSAGHT (CHENGDU) LTD.—See BlueScope Steel Limited; *Int'l*, pg. 1072
BLUESCOPE LYSAGHT FIJI LTD.—See BlueScope Steel Limited; *Int'l*, pg. 1073
BLUESCOPE LYSAGHT (SABAH) SDN BHD—See BlueScope Steel Limited; *Int'l*, pg. 1072
BLUESCOPE LYSAGHT (SHANGHAI) LTD.—See BlueScope Steel Limited; *Int'l*, pg. 1072
BLUESCOPE LYSAGHT SINGAPORE PTE. LTD.—See BlueScope Steel Limited; *Int'l*, pg. 1073
BLUESCOPE LYSAGHT TAIWAN LTD.—See BlueScope Steel Limited; *Int'l*, pg. 1073
BLUESCOPE LYSAGHT (THAILAND) LTD.—See BlueScope Steel Limited; *Int'l*, pg. 1073
BLUESCOPE LYSAGHT (VANUATU) LTD.—See BlueScope Steel Limited; *Int'l*, pg. 1073
BLUESCOPE PTY LTD.—See BlueScope Steel Limited; *Int'l*, pg. 1073
BLUESCOPE STEEL (AIS) PTY LTD—See BlueScope Steel Limited; *Int'l*, pg. 1073
BLUESCOPE STEEL ASIA HOLDINGS PTY LTD.—See BlueScope Steel Limited; *Int'l*, pg. 1073
BLUESCOPE STEEL ASIA PTE LTD.—See BlueScope Steel Limited; *Int'l*, pg. 1073
BLUESCOPE STEEL (FINANCE) LTD.—See BlueScope Steel Limited; *Int'l*, pg. 1073
BLUESCOPE STEEL INTERNATIONAL TRADING (SHANGHAI) CO.,LTD.—See BlueScope Steel Limited; *Int'l*, pg. 1073
BLUESCOPE STEEL INVESTMENT MANAGEMENT (SHANGHAI) LTD.—See BlueScope Steel Limited; *Int'l*, pg. 1073
BLUESCOPE STEEL LIMITED; *Int'l*, pg. 1072
BLUESCOPE STEEL NORTH ASIA LTD—See BlueScope Steel Limited; *Int'l*, pg. 1073
BLUESCOPE STEEL PHILIPPINES INC—See BlueScope Steel Limited; *Int'l*, pg. 1073
BLUESCOPE STEEL (SUZHOU) LTD—See BlueScope Steel Limited; *Int'l*, pg. 1073
BLUESCOPE STEEL (THAILAND) LTD.—See BlueScope Steel Limited; *Int'l*, pg. 1073
BLUESCOPE STEEL TRADING NZ LTD—See BlueScope Steel Limited; *Int'l*, pg. 1073
BLUESCOPE STEEL VIETNAM LIMITED.—See BlueScope Steel Limited; *Int'l*, pg. 1073
BOHAI STEEL GROUP CO., LTD.; *Int'l*, pg. 1100
BOMBAY WIRE ROPES LIMITED; *Int'l*, pg. 1104
BOOKOOK STEEL CO., LTD.; *Int'l*, pg. 1110
BORBET SACHSEN GMBH—See BORBET GmbH; *Int'l*, pg. 1112
BOURQUE INDUSTRIES, INC.; *U.S. Public*, pg. 375
BRAEBURN ALLOY STEEL—See Compagnie de Saint-Gobain SA; *Int'l*, pg. 1730
BRC ASIA LIMITED; *Int'l*, pg. 1143
BRC PREFAB HOLDINGS SDN. BHD.—See BRC Asia Limited; *Int'l*, pg. 1143
BRECKNELL WILLIS (TIANJIN) ELECTRIFICATION SYSTEMS, CO., LTD—See Westinghouse Air Brake Technologies Corporation; *U.S. Public*, pg. 2357
BROWN EUROPE SAS—See Eramet SA; *Int'l*, pg. 2488
BSRM STEELS LIMITED; *Int'l*, pg. 1202
BUTLER (TIANJIN) INC.—See BlueScope Steel Limited; *Int'l*, pg. 1073
CALCIMIN COMPANY; *Int'l*, pg. 1262
CALENTADORES CINSA, S.A. DE C.V.—See Grupo Industrial Saltillo S.A. de C.V.; *Int'l*, pg. 3130
CANAM STEEL CORPORATION—See AIP, LLC; *U.S. Private*, pg. 134
CAPITOL STEEL & IRON COMPANY—See Rasmussen Group Inc.; *U.S. Private*, pg. 3356
CAP S.A.; *Int'l*, pg. 1300
CARPENTER SPECIALTY WIRE PRODUCTS—See Carpenter Technology Corporation; *U.S. Public*, pg. 439
CASCADE STEEL ROLLING MILLS, INC.—See Radius Recycling, Inc.; *U.S. Public*, pg. 1760
CELSA ARMERINGSSTAL AS—See Celsa Group; *Int'l*, pg. 1395
CELSA ATLANTIC S.A.—See Celsa Group; *Int'l*, pg. 1395
CELSA FRANCE S.A.S.—See Celsa Group; *Int'l*, pg. 1395
CELSA GERMANY—See Celsa Group; *Int'l*, pg. 1395
CELSA GROUP; *Int'l*, pg. 1395
CELSA HUTA OSTROWIEC SP. Z O.O.—See Celsa Group; *Int'l*, pg. 1395
CELSA STEEL SERVICE AB—See Celsa Group; *Int'l*, pg. 1395
CELSA STEEL SERVICE AS—See Celsa Group; *Int'l*, pg. 1395
CELSA STEEL SERVICE A/S—See Celsa Group; *Int'l*, pg. 1395
CELSA STEEL SERVICE OY—See Celsa Group; *Int'l*, pg. 1395
CELSA STEEL (UK) LTD.—See Celsa Group; *Int'l*, pg. 1395
CEMTAS CELIK MAKINA SANAYI TICARET A.S.—See Bursa Cimento Fabrikasi A.S.; *Int'l*, pg. 1227
CENIT CO., LTD.; *Int'l*, pg. 1401
CENTAUR, INC.; *U.S. Private*, pg. 809
CENTRAL LAKE ARMOR EXPRESS, INC.—See Spanos Barber Jesse & Co.; *U.S. Private*, pg. 3745
CHANGSHU FENGFAN POWER EQUIPMENT CO., LTD.; *Int'l*, pg. 1444
CHARIGNON—See FAYAT SAS; *Int'l*, pg. 2625
CHASE BRIGHT STEEL LTD.; *Int'l*, pg. 1456
CHELYABINSK FORGE & PRESS PLANT PJSC; *Int'l*, pg. 1460
CHELYABINSK PLANT OF THE PROFILED STEEL DECKING PJSC; *Int'l*, pg. 1460
CHENNAI FERROUS INDUSTRIES LIMITED; *Int'l*, pg. 1470
CHIA TA WORLD CO., LTD.; *Int'l*, pg. 1475
CHICAGO HEIGHTS STEEL; *U.S. Private*, pg. 878
CHIEN SHING STAINLESS STEEL CO., LTD.; *Int'l*, pg. 1477
CHIH LIEN INDUSTRIAL CO., LTD. - DONG GUAN FACTORY—See Chih Lien Industrial Co., Ltd.; *Int'l*, pg. 1478
CHIH LIEN INDUSTRIAL CO., LTD. - SHIN WU FACTORY—See Chih Lien Industrial Co., Ltd.; *Int'l*, pg. 1478
CHIH LIEN INDUSTRIAL CO., LTD.; *Int'l*, pg. 1478
CHINA ORIENTAL GROUP COMPANY LIMITED; *Int'l*, pg. 1538
CHINA STEEL CORPORATION INDIA PVT. LTD.—See China Steel Corporation; *Int'l*, pg. 1555
CHINA STEEL CORPORATION; *Int'l*, pg. 1555

CORPORATE AFFILIATIONS

CHINA STEEL STRUCTURE CO., LTD.; *Int'l*, pg. 1556
CHIN HERR INDUSTRIES (M) SDN. BHD.—See Chin Well Holdings Berhad; *Int'l*, pg. 1480
CHOO BEE METAL INDUSTRIES BERHAD; *Int'l*, pg. 1582
CHOW STEEL INDUSTRIES PUBLIC COMPANY LIMITED; *Int'l*, pg. 1584
CHUNG HUNG STEEL CORPORATION—See China Steel Corporation; *Int'l*, pg. 1555
CHUN YUAN STEEL INDUSTRY CO., LTD. - SPECIAL STEEL STRIP DIVISION—See Chun Yuan Steel Industry Co., Ltd.; *Int'l*, pg. 1596
CHUN YUAN STEEL INDUSTRY CO., LTD. - SPECIAL STEEL TAI CHUNG PLANT—See Chun Yuan Steel Industry Co., Ltd.; *Int'l*, pg. 1596
CHUN YU WORKS & CO., LTD. - KANGSHAN PLANT—See Chun Yu Works & Co., Ltd.; *Int'l*, pg. 1596
CIVES CORPORATION - MID-SOUTH DIVISION—See Cives Corporation; *U.S. Private*, pg. 908
CIVES CORPORATION - MID-WEST DIVISION—See Cives Corporation; *U.S. Private*, pg. 908
CIVES CORPORATION - NEW ENGLAND DIVISION—See Cives Corporation; *U.S. Private*, pg. 908
CJSC DONETSKSTEEL METALLURGICAL PLANT; *Int'l*, pg. 1634
CLEVELAND-CLIFFS PLATE LLC—See Cleveland-Cliffs, Inc.; *U.S. Public*, pg. 514
CLEVELAND-CLIFFS WEIRTON LLC—See Cleveland-Cliffs, Inc.; *U.S. Public*, pg. 514
CMC (AUSTRALIA) PTY LIMITED—See Commercial Metals Company; *U.S. Public*, pg. 545
CMC (AUSTRALIA) PTY LIMITED—See Commercial Metals Company; *U.S. Public*, pg. 545
CMC (BEIJING) INTERNATIONAL TRADE COMPANY LTD.—See Commercial Metals Company; *U.S. Public*, pg. 545
CMC STEEL ALABAMA—See Commercial Metals Company; *U.S. Public*, pg. 546
CMC STEEL SOUTH CAROLINA—See Commercial Metals Company; *U.S. Public*, pg. 546
CMC STEEL TEXAS—See Commercial Metals Company; *U.S. Public*, pg. 546
COAL INNOVATIONS, LLC—See Cleveland-Cliffs, Inc.; *U.S. Public*, pg. 514
COCKERILL MECANIQUE PRESTATIONS—See ArcelorMittal S.A.; *Int'l*, pg. 545
COCKERILL SAMBRE S.A.—See ArcelorMittal S.A.; *Int'l*, pg. 545
COMMERCIAL STEEL PRODUCTS LLC; *U.S. Private*, pg. 984
COMPANHIA DE FERRO LIGAS DA BAHIA - FERBASA; *Int'l*, pg. 1746
COMPANHIA DE FERRO LIGAS DA BAHIA - FERBASA - THE POJUCA FACTORY—See Companhia de Ferro Ligas da Bahia - Ferbasa; *Int'l*, pg. 1746
COMPANHIA SIDERURGICA NACIONAL; *Int'l*, pg. 1748
COMPANIA MINERA AUTLAN S.A. DE C.V.—See Grupo Ferrominero, S.A. de C.V.; *Int'l*, pg. 3129
COMPONENTA FINLAND OY—See Componenta Corporation; *Int'l*, pg. 1753
CONCEPT LASER GMBH—See General Electric Company; *U.S. Public*, pg. 916
CONG TY TNHH FILTRAFINE CO., LTD.—See Bright Sheland International Co., Ltd.; *Int'l*, pg. 1162
CREST STEEL CORP.—See Reliance Steel & Aluminum Co.; *U.S. Public*, pg. 1779
CRIMSON METAL ENGINEERING COMPANY LIMITED; *Int'l*, pg. 1849
CRONIMET FERROLEGIERUNGEN HANDELSGES. MBH—See CRONIMET Holding GmbH; *Int'l*, pg. 1854
CRUCIBLE INDUSTRIES LLC; *U.S. Private*, pg. 1113
CSC STEEL HOLDINGS BERHAD; *Int'l*, pg. 1863
CSP CHINA STEEL PLC; *Int'l*, pg. 1867
DAEHAN STEEL CO., LTD. - NOKSAN PLANT—See Daehan Steel Co., Ltd.; *Int'l*, pg. 1907
DAEHAN STEEL CO., LTD. - PYEONGTAEK PLANT—See Daehan Steel Co., Ltd.; *Int'l*, pg. 1907
DAEHAN STEEL CO., LTD.; *Int'l*, pg. 1907
DAIDO AMISTAR (M) SDN. BHD.—See Daido Steel Co., Ltd.; *Int'l*, pg. 1922
DAIDO STEEL CO., LTD. - KAWASAKI PLANT—See Daido Steel Co., Ltd.; *Int'l*, pg. 1923
DAIDO STEEL CO., LTD. - KIMITSU PLANT—See Daido Steel Co., Ltd.; *Int'l*, pg. 1923
DAIDO STEEL CO., LTD. - OJI PLANT—See Daido Steel Co., Ltd.; *Int'l*, pg. 1923
DAIDO TECHNICA CO., LTD.—See Daido Steel Co., Ltd.; *Int'l*, pg. 1923
DAIDO TIENWEN STEEL CO., LTD.—See Daido Steel Co., Ltd.; *Int'l*, pg. 1923
DAI-ICHI JITSUGYO (THAILAND) CO., LTD.—See Daiichi Jitsugyo Co. Ltd.; *Int'l*, pg. 1927
DAIKOH OWANO CO.,LTD.—See Hanwa Co., Ltd.; *Int'l*, pg. 3261
DAIKOH STEEL CO., LTD.—See Hanwa Co., Ltd.; *Int'l*, pg. 3261
DAI THIEN LOC CORPORATION; *Int'l*, pg. 1917
DAIYANG METAL CO., LTD.; *Int'l*, pg. 1950
DAJIN HEAVY INDUSTRY CORPORATION; *Int'l*, pg. 1950

N.A.I.C.S. INDEX

331110 — IRON AND STEEL MILL...

DALEKOVOD-CINCAONICA D.O.O.,—See Dalekovod d.d.; *Int'l*, pg. 1951
DA MING INTERNATIONAL HOLDINGS LIMITED; *Int'l*, pg. 1901
DANA-Y STEEL JOINT STOCK COMPANY; *Int'l*, pg. 1958
DANIELI AUTOMATION SPA—See Danieli & C. Officine Meccaniche S.p.A.; *Int'l*, pg. 1962
DANIELI CO., LTD.—See Danieli & C. Officine Meccaniche S.p.A.; *Int'l*, pg. 1962
DANIELI CONSTR INTERNATIONAL SPA—See Danieli & C. Officine Meccaniche S.p.A.; *Int'l*, pg. 1962
DANIELI DO BRAZIL SA—See Danieli & C. Officine Meccaniche S.p.A.; *Int'l*, pg. 1963
DANIELI ENGINEERING JAPAN LTD.—See Danieli & C. Officine Meccaniche S.p.A.; *Int'l*, pg. 1963
DANIELI ENGINEERING & SERVICE GMBH—See Danieli & C. Officine Meccaniche S.p.A.; *Int'l*, pg. 1963
DANIELI GERMANY GMBH—See Danieli & C. Officine Meccaniche S.p.A.; *Int'l*, pg. 1963
DANIELI HENSCHEL SAS—See Danieli & C. Officine Meccaniche S.p.A.; *Int'l*, pg. 1963
DANIELI METALL EQUIPMENT & SERVICE CO., LTD.—See Danieli & C. Officine Meccaniche S.p.A.; *Int'l*, pg. 1963
DANIELI MIDDLE EAST ENG. & SERV.CO.—See Danieli & C. Officine Meccaniche S.p.A.; *Int'l*, pg. 1963
DANIELI PROCOME IBERICA SA—See Danieli & C. Officine Meccaniche S.p.A.; *Int'l*, pg. 1963
DANIELI SYSTEC DOO—See Danieli & C. Officine Meccaniche S.p.A.; *Int'l*, pg. 1963
DANIELI UK HOLDING LTD.—See Danieli & C. Officine Meccaniche S.p.A.; *Int'l*, pg. 1963
DANIELI VOLGA LLC—See Danieli & C. Officine Meccaniche S.p.A.; *Int'l*, pg. 1963
DCM CORP.; *Int'l*, pg. 1991
DELACO KASLE LLC—See Delaco Steel Corp.; *U.S. Private*, pg. 1193
DELACO STEEL CORP.; *U.S. Private*, pg. 1193
DELAWARE USS CORPORATION—See United States Steel Corporation; *U.S. Public*, pg. 2236
DELTA MANUFACTURING LTD; *Int'l*, pg. 2019
DILLINGER NORGE AS—See AG der Dillinger Huttenwerke; *Int'l*, pg. 197
DINA IRON & STEEL LIMITED; *Int'l*, pg. 2126
DIS-TRAN STEEL POLE, LLC—See Crest Industries, LLC; *U.S. Private*, pg. 1096
DMC GLOBAL INC.; *U.S. Public*, pg. 671
DONGBU STEEL CO.,LTD.—See Dongbu Group; *Int'l*, pg. 2166
DONGGUAN CHITWING TECHNOLOGY CO LTD; *Int'l*, pg. 2167
DONGIL STEEL CO., LTD.; *Int'l*, pg. 2168
DONG IL STEEL MFG CO., LTD.; *Int'l*, pg. 2163
DONGKUK CORPORATION—See Dongkuk Steel Mill Co., Ltd.; *Int'l*, pg. 2169
DONGKUK INTERNATIONAL, INC.—See Dongkuk Steel Mill Co., Ltd.; *Int'l*, pg. 2169
DONGKUK STEEL CHINA CO., LTD.—See Dongkuk Steel Mill Co., Ltd.; *Int'l*, pg. 2169
DONGKUK STEEL INDIA PRIVATE LIMITED—See Dongkuk Steel Mill Co., Ltd.; *Int'l*, pg. 2169
DONGKUK STEEL MEXICO, S.A. DE C.V.—See Dongkuk Steel Mill Co., Ltd.; *Int'l*, pg. 2169
DONGKUK STEEL MILL CO., LTD. - BUSAN WORKS—See Dongkuk Steel Mill Co., Ltd.; *Int'l*, pg. 2169
DONGKUK STEEL MILL CO., LTD. - DANGJIN WORKS—See Dongkuk Steel Mill Co., Ltd.; *Int'l*, pg. 2169
DONGKUK STEEL MILL CO., LTD. - INCHEON WORKS—See Dongkuk Steel Mill Co., Ltd.; *Int'l*, pg. 2169
DONGKUK STEEL MILL CO., LTD. - POHANG WORKS—See Dongkuk Steel Mill Co., Ltd.; *Int'l*, pg. 2169
DONGKUK STEEL MILL CO., LTD.; *Int'l*, pg. 2169
DONGKUK STEEL THAILAND LTD.—See Dongkuk Steel Mill Co., Ltd.; *Int'l*, pg. 2169
DOST STEELS LIMITED; *Int'l*, pg. 2180
DOUBLE EAGLE STEEL COATING COMPANY—See United States Steel Corporation; *U.S. Public*, pg. 2236
DRAGON STEEL CORPORATION—See China Steel Corporation; *Int'l*, pg. 1555
DUFERCO S.A.; *Int'l*, pg. 2223
DUFERCOSTEEL PROCESSING (PTY) LTD—See HBIS Group Co., Ltd.; *Int'l*, pg. 3295
DZERZHYNSKY PJSC; *Int'l*, pg. 2245
EATON METAL PRODUCTS COMPANY; *U.S. Private*, pg. 1323
EFESAN DEMIR SANAYI VE TICARET A.S.—See Efesan Group; *Int'l*, pg. 2319
EFESAN GROUP; *Int'l*, pg. 2319
E&H STEEL CORPORATION; *U.S. Private*, pg. 1301
ELEKTROWERK WEISWEILER GMBH—See Afarak Group SE; *Int'l*, pg. 185
ELKEM ICELAND—See China National Chemical Corporation; *Int'l*, pg. 1527
ELKEM METAL CANADA INC.—See China National Chemical Corporation; *Int'l*, pg. 1527

ELKEM THAMSHAVN—See China National Chemical Corporation; *Int'l*, pg. 1527
ELLWOOD MILL PRODUCTS—See Ellwood Group, Inc.; *U.S. Private*, pg. 1375
ELLWOOD QUALITY STEELS COMPANY—See Ellwood Group, Inc.; *U.S. Private*, pg. 1375
ENDO STAINLESS STEEL (VIETNAM) CO., LTD.—See Endo Manufacturing Co., Ltd.; *Int'l*, pg. 2405
ENNIS STEEL INDUSTRIES INC.; *U.S. Private*, pg. 1401
EONMETALL GROUP BERHAD; *Int'l*, pg. 2458
EONMETALL INDUSTRIES SDN. BHD.—See Eonmetall Group Berhad; *Int'l*, pg. 2458
ERAMET NORWAY A/S—See Eramet SA; *Int'l*, pg. 2489
ERDEMIR MADENCILIK SANAYI VE TICARET A.S.—See Eregli Demir Ve Celik Fabrikalari T.A.S.; *Int'l*, pg. 2490
ERDEMIR ROMANIA S.R.L.—See Eregli Demir Ve Celik Fabrikalari T.A.S.; *Int'l*, pg. 2490
ESAN ECZACIBASI INDUSTRIAL RAW MATERIALS CO.—See Eczacibasi Holding A.S.; *Int'l*, pg. 2301
ESFAHAN'S MOBARAKEH STEEL COMPANY; *Int'l*, pg. 2503
EURODECOUPE S.A.S.—See AG der Dillinger Huttenwerke; *Int'l*, pg. 197
EUROKONSTRUKCJE SP. Z O.O.—See Huta Pokoj S.A.; *Int'l*, pg. 3540
EUROMISI HIGH TECH, JIAXING CO., LTD.—See EuroGroup Laminations S.p.A.; *Int'l*, pg. 2552
EUROSERWIS SP. Z O.O.—See Huta Pokoj S.A.; *Int'l*, pg. 3540
EUROSLOT TOOLS S.R.L.—See EuroGroup Laminations S.p.A.; *Int'l*, pg. 2552
EUROTRANCIATURA MEXICO S.A. DE C.V.—See EuroGroup Laminations S.p.A.; *Int'l*, pg. 2552
EUROTRANCIATURA S.P.A.—See EuroGroup Laminations S.p.A.; *Int'l*, pg. 2552
EUROTRANCIATURA TUNISIE S.A.R.L.—See EuroGroup Laminations S.p.A.; *Int'l*, pg. 2552
EVRAZ INC. NA - PUEBLO—See Evraz plc; *Int'l*, pg. 2574
EVRAZ NIKOM A.S.—See Evraz plc; *Int'l*, pg. 2574
EVRAZ NORTH AMERICA LIMITED—See Evraz plc; *Int'l*, pg. 2574
EVRAZ NORTH AMERICA PLC—See Evraz plc; *Int'l*, pg. 2574
EVRAZ STRATCOR, INC.—See US Vanadium LLC; *U.S. Private*, pg. 4320
EXPRESS REINFORCEMENTS LTD.—See Celsa Group; *Int'l*, pg. 1395
EZZ STEEL CO. S.A.E.; *Int'l*, pg. 2594
FAB TECH INC.; *U.S. Private*, pg. 1458
FACB INDUSTRIES INCORPORATED BERHAD; *Int'l*, pg. 2600
FACOR ALLOYS LIMITED; *Int'l*, pg. 2601
FALCI S.R.L.—See Calvi Holding S.r.l.; *Int'l*, pg. 1266
FALCK ACCIAI-CNS SPA—See Falck S.p.A.; *Int'l*, pg. 2610
FALCK S.P.A.; *Int'l*, pg. 2610
FANGDA SPECIAL STEEL TECHNOLOGY CO., LTD.; *Int'l*, pg. 2613
FENG HSIN STEEL CO., LTD.; *Int'l*, pg. 2634
FERROATLANTICA, S.A.U.—See Sixth Street Partners LLC; *U.S. Private*, pg. 3677
FERROUS85″ CO.—See Ferragon Corporation; *U.S. Private*, pg. 1498
FERROUSOUTH—See Ferragon Corporation; *U.S. Private*, pg. 1498
FIAV L. MAZZACCHERA S.P.A.—See Calvi Holding S.r.l.; *Int'l*, pg. 1266
FIBERCON INTERNATIONAL INC.; *U.S. Private*, pg. 1501
FLAMCO IMZ B.V.—See Aalberts N.V.; *Int'l*, pg. 34
FLETCHER PACIFIC STEEL (FIJI) LIMITED—See Fletcher Building Limited; *Int'l*, pg. 2700
FLETCHER STEEL LIMITED—See Fletcher Building Limited; *Int'l*, pg. 2700
FLUIDA, S.A. DE C.V.—See Grupo Industrial Saltillo S.A. de C.V.; *Int'l*, pg. 3130
FORMOSA HA TINH STEEL CORPORATION—See China Steel Corporation; *Int'l*, pg. 1555
FOUNDRY FUEL PRODUCTS LTD.; *Int'l*, pg. 2754
FTT MANUFACTURING, INC.—See Fairchild Capital Partners, LLC; *U.S. Private*, pg. 1462
FUJIAN FUXIN SPECIAL STEEL CO., LTD.—See Formosa Plastics Corporation; *Int'l*, pg. 2735
FUSHUN SPECIAL STEEL CO., LTD.; *Int'l*, pg. 2849
GALLANTT ISPAT LIMITED; *Int'l*, pg. 2874
GANSU JIU STEEL GROUP HONGXING IRON & STEEL CO., LTD.; *Int'l*, pg. 2881
GANTRAIL (MIDDLE EAST) LTD—See Gantry Railing Limited; *Int'l*, pg. 2882
GAUTIER STEEL, LTD.—See Reserve Group Management Company; *U.S. Private*, pg. 3404
GDH GUANGNAN (HOLDINGS) LIMITED—See GDH Limited; *Int'l*, pg. 2896
GENERAL STEEL HOLDINGS, INC.; *Int'l*, pg. 2920
GERDAU KNOXVILLE STEEL MILL—See Commercial Metals Company; *U.S. Public*, pg. 546
GERDAU RANCHO CUCAMONGA STEEL MILL—See Commercial Metals Company; *U.S. Public*, pg. 546
GERDAU SA (CHILE); *Int'l*, pg. 2942
GERDAU SAYREVILLE STEEL MILL—See Commercial Metals Company; *U.S. Public*, pg. 546
GFE FREMAT GMBH—See AMG Critical Materials N.V.; *Int'l*, pg. 426
GFE METALLE UND MATERIALIEN GMBH—See AMG Critical Materials N.V.; *Int'l*, pg. 426
GFE-MIR ALLOYS AND MINERALS SA (PTY) LTD—See GFE-MIR Holdings AG; *Int'l*, pg. 2956
GFE-MIR BERLIN—See GFE-MIR Holdings AG; *Int'l*, pg. 2956
GFE-MIR POLAND SP—See GFE-MIR Holdings AG; *Int'l*, pg. 2956
GFE-MIR (SHANGHAI) LTD—See GFE-MIR Holdings AG; *Int'l*, pg. 2956
GH METAL SOLUTIONS, INC.—See Reliance Steel & Aluminum Co.; *U.S. Public*, pg. 1780
GIBRALTAR STEEL CORPORATION OF NEW YORK—See Gibraltar Industries, Inc.; *U.S. Public*, pg. 936
GJ STEEL PUBLIC COMPANY LIMITED; *Int'l*, pg. 2982
GKD (UK) LTD.—See GKD - Gebr. Kufferath AG; *Int'l*, pg. 2983
GKN GEPLASMETAL SA—See GKN plc; *Int'l*, pg. 2985
GKN SINTER METALS SPA—See GKN plc; *Int'l*, pg. 2985
GKW LIMITED - POWMEX STEELS DIVISION—See GKW Limited; *Int'l*, pg. 2986
GLOBAL STEEL WIRE, S.A.—See Celsa Group; *Int'l*, pg. 1395
GLOBAL TITANIUM INC.—See Palladium Equity Partners, LLC; *U.S. Private*, pg. 3078
GLORIA MATERIAL TECHNOLOGY CORP.; *Int'l*, pg. 3008
G.O. CARLSON, INC.; *U.S. Private*, pg. 1631
GODO STEEL, LTD. - FUNABASHI WORKS—See Godo Steel, Ltd.; *Int'l*, pg. 3020
GODO STEEL, LTD. - HIMEJI WORKS—See Godo Steel, Ltd.; *Int'l*, pg. 3020
GODO STEEL, LTD. - OSAKA WORKS—See Godo Steel, Ltd.; *Int'l*, pg. 3020
GODO STEEL, LTD.; *Int'l*, pg. 3020
GOLIK CONCRETE (HK) LIMITED—See Golik Holdings Limited; *Int'l*, pg. 3036
GOLIK STEEL (HK) LIMITED—See Golik Holdings Limited; *Int'l*, pg. 3036
GOLIK WIRE ROPE HONG KONG LIMITED—See Golik Holdings Limited; *Int'l*, pg. 3036
GOODLUCK INDIA LIMITED; *Int'l*, pg. 3040
GOPAL IRON & STEELS CO. (GUJARAT) LIMITED; *Int'l*, pg. 3042
GOTETSU SANGYO CO., LTD.—See Godo Steel, Ltd.; *Int'l*, pg. 3020
GOYAL ALUMINIUMS LIMITED; *Int'l*, pg. 3045
GPH ISPAT LIMITED; *Int'l*, pg. 3046
GRAND FOUNDRY LIMITED; *Int'l*, pg. 3054
GRAY AMERICA CORP.; *U.S. Private*, pg. 1759
GROUP STEEL CORPORATION (M) SDN. BHD.—See China Steel Corporation; *Int'l*, pg. 1555
GRUPO COLLADO S.A. DE C.V.; *Int'l*, pg. 3125
GRUPO GONVARRI—See Corporacion Gestamp SL; *Int'l*, pg. 1804
GUANGXI IRON & STEEL GROUP CO., LTD.—See China Baowu Steel Group Corp., Ltd.; *Int'l*, pg. 1485
GUANGZHENG EYE HOSPITAL GROUP CO., LTD.; *Int'l*, pg. 3164
GUIZHOU WIRE ROPE INCORPORATED COMPANY; *Int'l*, pg. 3175
GULF CHEMICAL & METALLURGICAL CORPORATION—See Eramet SA; *Int'l*, pg. 2489
HAMILTON SPECIALTY BAR CORP.—See Woodside Capital Partners; *U.S. Private*, pg. 4560
HANDY & HARMAN GROUP, LTD.—See Steel Partners Holdings L.P.; *U.S. Public*, pg. 1942
HANGZHOU IRON & STEEL CO., LTD.; *Int'l*, pg. 3248
HANIL IRON & STEEL CO., LTD.; *Int'l*, pg. 3252
HANKUK STEEL WIRE CO., LTD.; *Int'l*, pg. 3254
HANWA ECO STEEL CO., LTD.—See Hanwa Co., Ltd.; *Int'l*, pg. 3262
HANWA (KOREA) CO., LTD.—See Hanwa Co., Ltd.; *Int'l*, pg. 3262
HANWA SINGAPORE (PRIVATE) LTD.—See Hanwa Co., Ltd.; *Int'l*, pg. 3262
HANWA STEEL CENTRE (M) SDN. BHD.—See Hanwa Co., Ltd.; *Int'l*, pg. 3262
HANWA STEEL SERVICE (THAILAND) CO., LTD.—See Hanwa Co., Ltd.; *Int'l*, pg. 3262
HANZA LEVYPROFIILI OY—See Hanza AB; *Int'l*, pg. 3267
HANZA MECHANICS KUNOVICE S.R.O—See Hanza AB; *Int'l*, pg. 3267
HANZA TECH SOLUTIONS GMBH—See Hanza AB; *Int'l*, pg. 3267
HAYNES INTERNATIONAL K. K.—See Acerinox, S.A.; *Int'l*, pg. 101
HBIS GROUP HANDAN IRON & STEEL COMPANY—See HBIS Group Co., Ltd.; *Int'l*, pg. 3296
HBIS GROUP HENGSTRIP COMPANY—See HBIS Group Co., Ltd.; *Int'l*, pg. 3296
HBIS GROUP SHIJIAZHUANG IRON & STEEL COMPANY—See HBIS Group Co., Ltd.; *Int'l*, pg. 3296
HBIS GROUP TANGSHAN IRON & STEEL COMPANY—See HBIS Group Co., Ltd.; *Int'l*, pg. 3296
HBIS GROUP XUANHUA IRON & STEEL COMPANY—See

331110 — IRON AND STEEL MILL...

HBIS Group Co., Ltd.; *Int'l*, pg. 3296
HBIS INDUSTRIAL TECHNOLOGY SERVICE CO., LTD.—See HBIS Group Co., Ltd.; *Int'l*, pg. 3296
HBIS LIMITED—See HBIS Group Co., Ltd.; *Int'l*, pg. 3296
HBIS SALES CO. LTD.—See HBIS Group Co., Ltd.; *Int'l*, pg. 3296
HBIS SERBIA IRON & STEEL D.O.O.—See HBIS Group Co., Ltd.; *Int'l*, pg. 3296
HEBEI JINXI IRON & STEEL GROUP CO., LTD.—See China Oriental Group Company Limited; *Int'l*, pg. 1538
HEBEI YICHEN INDUSTRIAL GROUP CORPORATION LIMITED; *Int'l*, pg. 3306
HEERA ISPAT LTD.; *Int'l*, pg. 3307
HEIDTMAN STEEL PRODUCTS, INC.; *U.S. Private*, pg. 1904
HERAEUS METAL PROCESSING, LTD.—See Heraeus Holding GmbH; *Int'l*, pg. 3358
HERAEUS METALS HONG KONG LTD.—See Heraeus Holding GmbH; *Int'l*, pg. 3358
HERAEUS METALS NEW YORK LLC—See Heraeus Holding GmbH; *Int'l*, pg. 3357
HERAEUS METALS (SHANGHAI) CO., LTD.—See Heraeus Holding GmbH; *Int'l*, pg. 3358
HG CONSTRUCTION STEEL PTE LTD.—See HG Metal Manufacturing Limited; *Int'l*, pg. 3375
HG METAL MANUFACTURING LIMITED; *Int'l*, pg. 3375
HG METAL MANUFACTURING SDN. BHD.—See HG Metal Manufacturing Limited; *Int'l*, pg. 3375
HIGH STEEL STRUCTURES INC.—See High Industries, Inc.; *U.S. Private*, pg. 1936
HINDUSTHAN UDYOG LIMITED; *Int'l*, pg. 3400
HIRA FERRO ALLOYS LTD.; *Int'l*, pg. 3402
HIROUCHI STEEL CO., LTD.—See Hanwa Co., Ltd.; *Int'l*, pg. 3263
HISAR MADEN A.S.—See Bera Holding A.S.; *Int'l*, pg. 978
HISAR METAL INDUSTRIES LIMITED; *Int'l*, pg. 3406
HITACHI METALS TRADING, LTD.—See Hitachi, Ltd.; *Int'l*, pg. 3420
HI-TECH PIPES LTD.; *Int'l*, pg. 3382
HMY, LTD.—See Hitachi, Ltd.; *Int'l*, pg. 3413
HOA PHAT STEEL JSC—See Hoa Phat Group Joint Stock Company; *Int'l*, pg. 3435
HOD-ASSAF INDUSTRIES LTD.; *Int'l*, pg. 3438
HOESCH SCHWERTER PROFIL GMBH—See Calvi Holding S.r.l.; *Int'l*, pg. 1266
HOE SENG HUAT PTE LTD—See HupSteel Limited; *Int'l*, pg. 3538
HOGANAS (CHINA) LTD—See Hoganas AB; *Int'l*, pg. 3441
HOGANAS KOREA LTD.—See Hoganas AB; *Int'l*, pg. 3441
HOGANAS TAIWAN LTD.—See Hoganas AB; *Int'l*, pg. 3441
HOKUETSU METAL CO., LTD.; *Int'l*, pg. 3444
HOMOGENEOUS METALS INC.—See RTX Corporation; *U.S. Public*, pg. 1823
HOSHINE SILICON (JIAXING) INDUSTRY CO., LTD.—See Hoshine Silicon Industry Co., Ltd.; *Int'l*, pg. 3482
HOWCO GROUP PLC; *Int'l*, pg. 3493
HOWMET CASTINGS & SERVICES, INC. - WICHITA FALLS—See Howmet Aerospace Inc.; *U.S. Public*, pg. 1061
HUNAN VALIN STEEL CO., LTD.; *Int'l*, pg. 3534
HUP LIAN ENGINEERING PTE LTD—See Chasen Holdings Limited; *Int'l*, pg. 1457
HWANG KUM STEEL & TECHNOLOGY CO., LTD.; *Int'l*, pg. 3542
HYUNDAI STEEL RUS LLC—See Hyundai Steel Company; *Int'l*, pg. 3560
IAT LTDA—See CVC Capital Partners SICAV-FIS S.A.; *Int'l*, pg. 1887
INAL NORDESTE S.A.—See Companhia Siderurgica Nacional; *Int'l*, pg. 1748
INDUSTEEL BELGIUM S.A.—See ArcelorMittal S.A.; *Int'l*, pg. 545
INDUSTRIELLE BETEILIGUNG CO., LTD.—See Danieli & C. Officine Meccaniche S.p.A.; *Int'l*, pg. 1963
INSTEEL INDUSTRIES, INC.; *U.S. Public*, pg. 1134
INTEGRATE PTE LTD—See Compact Metal Industries Ltd.; *Int'l*, pg. 1721
IRON DYNAMICS—See Steel Dynamics, Inc.; *U.S. Public*, pg. 1942
I-SOLUTIONS DIRECT, INC.—See Reliance Steel & Aluminum, Co.; *U.S. Public*, pg. 1780
ITLA S.P.A.—See Falck S.p.A.; *Int'l*, pg. 2610
IZUMI DENKI KOGYO CO., LTD.—See Daido Steel Co., Ltd.; *Int'l*, pg. 1923
J. ADOLF BAEUERLE GMBH & CO. KG—See Georgsmarienhutte Holding GmbH; *Int'l*, pg. 2940
JEBENS GMBH—See AG der Dillinger Huttenwerke; *Int'l*, pg. 197
JERSEY SHORE STEEL CO.; *U.S. Private*, pg. 2203
JIANGSU ATLANTIC WELDING CONSUMABLES LIMITED LIABILITY COMPANY—See Atlantic China Welding Consumables, Inc.; *Int'l*, pg. 674
JIANGYIN XINGCHENG SPECIAL STEEL WORKS CO., LTD.—See CITIC Group Corporation; *Int'l*, pg. 1621
KINDLIMANN AG—See Benteler International AG; *Int'l*, pg. 977
KRAMZ—See En+ Group Ltd.; *Int'l*, pg. 2395
KUNSHAN CHAITAI-XINCHENG PRECISION FORGING CO., LTD.—See AAPICO Hitech plc; *Int'l*, pg. 37
KWIKOT (PTY) LTD.—See AB Electrolux; *Int'l*, pg. 41
LAPORTE CUSTOM METAL PROCESSING, LLC—See Acerinox, S.A.; *Int'l*, pg. 101
LASER DYNAMICS AUSTRALIA PTY LTD.—See BlueScope Steel Limited; *Int'l*, pg. 1073
LATROBE SPECIALTY METALS COMPANY, LLC—See Carpenter Technology Corporation; *U.S. Public*, pg. 439
LEHIGH HEAVY FORGE CORP—See Park Corp.; *U.S. Private*, pg. 3096
L&H THREADED RODS CORP.—See Gray America Corp.; *U.S. Private*, pg. 1759
LIBERTY IRON & METAL, INC.; *U.S. Private*, pg. 2444
LITHIONICS BATTERY, LLC—See Winnebago Industries, Inc.; *U.S. Public*, pg. 2374
LIVERPOOL COIL PROCESSING, INCORPORATED—See Shiloh Industries, Inc.; *U.S. Private*, pg. 3636
LSM (JIAXING) CO., LTD.—See AMG Critical Materials N.V.; *Int'l*, pg. 426
MAKSTEEL—See UPG Enterprises LLC; *U.S. Private*, pg. 4311
MANGANESOS ATACAMA S.A.—See CAP S.A.; *Int'l*, pg. 1300
MCDONALD STEEL CORPORATION; *U.S. Private*, pg. 2632
MEGASA SIDERURGICA S.L.—See Bipadosa SA; *Int'l*, pg. 1045
MERCER COMPANY—See Columbia National Group Inc; *U.S. Private*, pg. 977
MERCURY TUBE PRODUCTS LLC—See Washington Equity Partners L.L.C.; *U.S. Private*, pg. 4447
MESABI NUGGET DELAWARE, LLC—See Steel Dynamics, Inc.; *U.S. Public*, pg. 1942
METALNO D.D.—See Almy d.o.o.; *Int'l*, pg. 364
METALS USA BUILDING PRODUCTS, CANADA INC.—See Reliance Steel & Aluminum Co.; *U.S. Public*, pg. 1780
METALS USA CARBON FLAT ROLLED, INC.—See Reliance Steel & Aluminum Co.; *U.S. Public*, pg. 1780
METALS USA PLATE PROCESSING L.L.C.—See Reliance Steel & Aluminum Co.; *U.S. Public*, pg. 1780
METALS USA SPECIALTY METALS NORTHCENTRAL, INC.—See Reliance Steel & Aluminum Co.; *U.S. Public*, pg. 1781
METAL WANG PTE LTD—See AnnAik Limited; *Int'l*, pg. 473
METEX STEEL SDN BHD—See Chin Hin Group Berhad; *Int'l*, pg. 1480
MIDWEST CONTROL PRODUCTS CORP.; *U.S. Private*, pg. 2720
MID-WEST MATERIALS, INC.; *U.S. Private*, pg. 2710
MILLERBERND MANUFACTURING CO.; *U.S. Private*, pg. 2736
MK KAZSILICON LLP—See Canadian Solar Inc.; *Int'l*, pg. 1286
MK KAZSILICON LLP—See ECM Technologies SAS; *Int'l*, pg. 2292
M LEGO—See Aurea, S.A.; *Int'l*, pg. 707
MMK METALURJI SANAYI TICARET VE LIMAN ISLETMECILIGI ANONIM SIRKETI—See Fraport AG; *Int'l*, pg. 2764
MOLD-TECH PORTUGAL LDA.—See Standex International; *U.S. Public*, pg. 1930
MONNET INDUSTRIES LTD.—See Apollo Global Management, Inc.; *U.S. Public*, pg. 153
MONOTUBE PILE CORPORATION—See Ferguson plc; *Int'l*, pg. 2637
MOREDA RIVIERE TREFILERIAS, SA—See Celsa Group; *Int'l*, pg. 1395
MORE SRL—See Danieli & C. Officine Meccaniche S.p.A.; *Int'l*, pg. 1963
MSP METALL SERVICE PEDACK GMBH—See CRONIMET Holding GmbH; *Int'l*, pg. 1855
MUKAND LTD.—See Bajaj Auto Ltd.; *Int'l*, pg. 804
MYANMAR CENTURY STEEL STURCTURE LIMITED—See Century Iron & Steel Industrial Co., Ltd.; *Int'l*, pg. 1418
NACIONAL DE ACERO—See Grupo Acerero del Norte S.A. de C.V.; *Int'l*, pg. 3118
NANJING IRON & STEEL CO., LTD.—See CITIC Group Corporation; *Int'l*, pg. 1621
NATIONAL GALVANIZING LP—See Heidtman Steel Products, Inc.; *U.S. Private*, pg. 1904
NERVACERO, S.A.—See Celsa Group; *Int'l*, pg. 1395
NEW STEEL INC.—See American Agencies Co, Inc.; *U.S. Private*, pg. 222
NEW ZEALAND STEEL (AUST) PTY LTD.—See BlueScope Steel Limited; *Int'l*, pg. 1074
NEW ZEALAND STEEL DEVELOPMENT LTD.—See BlueScope Steel Limited; *Int'l*, pg. 1074
NEW ZEALAND STEEL HOLDINGS LTD.—See BlueScope Steel Limited; *Int'l*, pg. 1074
NINGBO BAOXIN STAINLESS STEEL CO., LTD.—See China Baowu Steel Group Corp., Ltd.; *Int'l*, pg. 1486
NIPPON SEISEN CO., LTD. - HIRAKATA FACTORY—See Daido Steel Co., Ltd.; *Int'l*, pg. 1923
NIPPON SEISEN CO., LTD. - NAGOYA FACTORY—See Daido Steel Co., Ltd.; *Int'l*, pg. 1923
NIPPON SEISEN CO., LTD. - OSAKA FACTORY—See Daido Steel Co., Ltd.; *Int'l*, pg. 1923

CORPORATE AFFILIATIONS

NIPPON SEISEN CO., LTD.—See Daido Steel Co., Ltd.; *Int'l*, pg. 1923
NOVACERO S.A.—See CAP S.A.; *Int'l*, pg. 1301
NS BLUESCOPE (MALAYSIA) SDN BHD—See BlueScope Steel Limited; *Int'l*, pg. 1073
NUCOR CASTRIP ARKANSAS LLC—See Nucor Corporation; *U.S. Public*, pg. 1553
NUCOR CORPORATION; *U.S. Public*, pg. 1553
NUCOR ENERGY HOLDINGS INC—See Nucor Corporation; *U.S. Public*, pg. 1554
NUCOR STEEL AUBURN, INC.—See Nucor Corporation; *U.S. Public*, pg. 1554
NUCOR STEEL-BERKELEY—See Nucor Corporation; *U.S. Public*, pg. 1554
NUCOR STEEL BIRMINGHAM, INC.—See Nucor Corporation; *U.S. Public*, pg. 1554
NUCOR STEEL-INDIANA—See Nucor Corporation; *U.S. Public*, pg. 1554
NUCOR STEEL KANKAKEE, INC.—See Nucor Corporation; *U.S. Public*, pg. 1554
NUCOR STEEL KINGMAN, LLC—See Nucor Corporation; *U.S. Public*, pg. 1554
NUCOR STEEL MARION, INC.—See Nucor Corporation; *U.S. Public*, pg. 1554
NUCOR STEEL MEMPHIS, INC.—See Nucor Corporation; *U.S. Public*, pg. 1554
NUCOR STEEL-NEBRASKA—See Nucor Corporation; *U.S. Public*, pg. 1554
NUCOR STEEL SEATTLE, INC.—See Nucor Corporation; *U.S. Public*, pg. 1554
NUCOR STEEL-TEXAS—See Nucor Corporation; *U.S. Public*, pg. 1554
NUCOR STEEL TUSCALOOSA, INC.—See Nucor Corporation; *U.S. Public*, pg. 1554
NUCOR STEEL-UTAH—See Nucor Corporation; *U.S. Public*, pg. 1554
NUCOR TUBULAR PRODUCTS, INC.—See Nucor Corporation; *U.S. Public*, pg. 1554
NUCOR-YAMATO STEEL COMPANY—See Nucor Corporation; *U.S. Public*, pg. 1554
OAKLEY INDUSTRIES INCORPORATED; *U.S. Private*, pg. 2985
OMZ-SPECIAL STEELS LLC—See Gazprombank JSC; *Int'l*, pg. 2892
OWEN ELECTRIC STEEL COMPANY OF SOUTH CAROLINA—See Commercial Metals Company; *U.S. Public*, pg. 547
PACAL INDUSTRIES, LLC—See Pacal LLC; *U.S. Private*, pg. 3063
PACIFIC STATES CAST IRON PIPE COMPANY—See McWane, Inc.; *U.S. Private*, pg. 2645
PALMYRA DO BRASIL INDUSTRIA E COMERCIO DE SILICIO METALICO E RECURSOS NATURAIS LTDA—See Dow Inc.; *U.S. Public*, pg. 685
PATSY STROCCHIA & SONS IRON WORKS, INC.; *U.S. Private*, pg. 3111
P.C. CAMPANA INC.; *U.S. Private*, pg. 3060
PEGASUS STEEL, LLC—See Arlington Capital Partners LLC; *U.S. Private*, pg. 328
PELCO STRUCTURAL, LLC.; *U.S. Private*, pg. 3130
PJSC ARCELORMITTAL KRYVYI RIH—See ArcelorMittal S.A.; *Int'l*, pg. 546
PRECISION SPECIALTY METALS, INC.—See Worthington Industries, Inc.; *U.S. Public*, pg. 2382
PROCOIL COMPANY, LLC—See United States Steel Corporation; *U.S. Public*, pg. 2237
PROCOIL COMPANY, LLC—See Worthington Industries, Inc.; *U.S. Public*, pg. 2383
PROGRESSIVE MARKETING PRODUCTS, INC.—See Main Street Capital Corporation; *U.S. Public*, pg. 1355
PROGRESS RAIL SERVICES UK LIMITED—See Caterpillar, Inc.; *U.S. Public*, pg. 453
PT BLUESCOPE LYSAGHT INDONESIA—See BlueScope Steel Limited; *Int'l*, pg. 1074
P.T. CHICAGO BRIDGE & IRON—See McDermott International, Inc.; *U.S. Public*, pg. 1405
PT HANWA STEEL SERVICE INDONESIA—See Hanwa Co., Ltd.; *Int'l*, pg. 3263
PT PANDROL INDONESIA—See CVC Capital Partners SICAV-FIS S.A.; *Int'l*, pg. 1887
QINGDAO HBIS NEW MATERIAL TECHNOLOGY CO., LTD.—See HBIS Group Co., Ltd.; *Int'l*, pg. 3296
QUALITEK EUROPE LTD.—See Qualitek International Inc.; *U.S. Private*, pg. 3317
RAILTECH ALU SINGEN SAS—See CVC Capital Partners SICAV-FIS S.A.; *Int'l*, pg. 1887
RAILTECH DEUTSCHLAND GMBH—See CVC Capital Partners SICAV-FIS S.A.; *Int'l*, pg. 1887
RAILTECH PANDROL CHINA LTD.—See CVC Capital Partners SICAV-FIS S.A.; *Int'l*, pg. 1887
RAILTECH PANDROL ITALIA SRL—See CVC Capital Partners SICAV-FIS S.A.; *Int'l*, pg. 1887
RAILTECH PORSOL LTDA.—See CVC Capital Partners SICAV-FIS S.A.; *Int'l*, pg. 1887
RAILTECH STEDEF LTD—See CVC Capital Partners SICAV-FIS S.A.; *Int'l*, pg. 1887
RAILTECH UK LTD—See CVC Capital Partners SICAV-FIS S.A.; *Int'l*, pg. 1887

N.A.I.C.S. INDEX

331210 — IRON AND STEEL PIPE...

RAMESHWARAM STEEL & POWER PVT. LTD.—See Apollo Global Management, Inc.; *U.S. Public*, pg. 153
REGUM GMBH—See Bermuller & Co. GmbH; *Int'l*, pg. 986
REPUBLIC STEEL; *U.S. Private*, pg. 3402
REPUBLIC TECHNOLOGIES INTERNATIONAL LLC—See Republic Steel; *U.S. Private*, pg. 3402
RG STEEL WHEELING, LLC—See Esmark Incorporated; *U.S. Private*, pg. 1426
RHETAN ROLLING MILLS PRIVATE LIMITED—See Ashoka Metcast Limited; *Int'l*, pg. 608
RIDGID, INC.—See Emerson Electric Co.; *U.S. Public*, pg. 749
RIO GRANDE HOLDINGS—See General Atomics; *U.S. Private*, pg. 1663
RIO GRANDE RESOURCES CORPORATION—See General Atomics; *U.S. Private*, pg. 1663
RK TEKNIK I GUSUM AB—See Balco Group AB; *Int'l*, pg. 807
RMS, A.S. KOSICE—See United States Steel Corporation; *U.S. Public*, pg. 2237
ROEHLEN INDUSTRIES PTY. LIMITED—See Standex International; *U.S. Public*, pg. 1930
ROLDAN S.A.—See Acerinox, S.A.; *Int'l*, pg. 101
ROLF PLOTZ GMBH & CO. KG—See CVC Capital Partners SICAV-FIS S.A.; *Int'l*, pg. 1887
ROTELEC SA—See Danieli & C. Officine Meccaniche S.p.A.; *Int'l*, pg. 1963
RT CONTRACTING CORP.—See CVC Capital Partners SICAV-FIS S.A.; *Int'l*, pg. 1887
RTG RAMMTECHNIK GMBH.—See BAUER Aktiengesellschaft; *Int'l*, pg. 893
SAKURAI KOSAN CO., LTD.—See Daido Steel Co., Ltd.; *Int'l*, pg. 1923
SANTO STEEL CO., LTD.—See Hanwa Co., Ltd.; *Int'l*, pg. 3263
SCAFFOLD MASTER SDN BHD—See IJM Corporation Berhad; *Int'l*, pg. 3609
S.C. BOG'ART STEEL S.R.L.—See Bog'Art S.R.L.; *Int'l*, pg. 1100
SEGAL S.C.—See ArcelorMittal S.A.; *Int'l*, pg. 546
SHAANXI LONGMEN IRON AND STEEL CO., LTD.—See General Steel Holdings, Inc.; *Int'l*, pg. 2920
SHINNICHI KOGYO CO., LTD.—See Honda Motor Co.; *Int'l*, pg. 3464
SHINSEI INDUSTRY SDN BHD—See AnnAik Limited; *Int'l*, pg. 473
SHINSEI KOGYO., LTD.—See Daido Kogyo Co., Ltd.; *Int'l*, pg. 1921
SIMCOTE INC.; *U.S. Private*, pg. 3665
SINECO S.P.A.—See Argo Finanziaria S.p.A.; *Int'l*, pg. 562
SIPA S.P.A.—See Calvi Holding S.r.l.; *Int'l*, pg. 1266
SMI STEEL INC.—See Commercial Metals Company; *U.S. Public*, pg. 547
SOMMER & STRASSBURGER EDELSTAHLANLAGENBAU GMBH & CO. KG—See Gesco AG; *Int'l*, pg. 2946
SONORAN LLC—See Big Lots, Inc.; *U.S. Public*, pg. 331
SOUTHERN POST COMPANY-TEXAS—See Commercial Metals Company; *U.S. Public*, pg. 546
SOUTHERN POST COMPANY-UTAH—See Commercial Metals Company; *U.S. Public*, pg. 546
SOUTHLAND TUBE, INC.—See Nucor Corporation; *U.S. Public*, pg. 1554
SOUTHWEST GROWTH CORPORATION—See Kasco Corporation; *U.S. Private*, pg. 2264
THE SPACERS & BAR CHAIRS MANUFACTURER COMPANY LIMITED—See Golik Holdings Limited; *Int'l*, pg. 3036
SPARTANBURG STAINLESS PRODUCTS INC.—See Reserve Group Management Company; *U.S. Private*, pg. 3405
STAHLHAMMER BOMMERN GMBH—See Columbus McKinnon Corporation; *U.S. Public*, pg. 536
STAHL JUDENBURG GMBH— See Georgsmarienhutte Holding GmbH; *Int'l*, pg. 2941
STAINLESS FABRICATION, INC—See Exchange Income Corporation; *Int'l*, pg. 2579
STAINLESS SERVICE ANDINO S/A—See Aperam SA; *Int'l*, pg. 508
STANLEY ENGINEERED FASTENING BENELUX B.V.—See Stanley Black & Decker, Inc.; *U.S. Public*, pg. 1935
STANLEY ENGINEERED FASTENING EASTERN EUROPE SP. Z O.O.—See Stanley Black & Decker, Inc.; *U.S. Public*, pg. 1935
STANLEY ENGINEERED FASTENING FRANCE SAS—See Stanley Black & Decker, Inc.; *U.S. Public*, pg. 1935
STANLEY ENGINEERED FASTENING INDUSTRIAL DEUTSCHLAND GMBH—See Stanley Black & Decker, Inc.; *U.S. Public*, pg. 1935
STANLEY ENGINEERED FASTENING ITALY S.R.L.—See Stanley Black & Decker, Inc.; *U.S. Public*, pg. 1935
STANLEY ENGINEERED FASTENING SPAIN, S.L.U.—See Stanley Black & Decker, Inc.; *U.S. Public*, pg. 1935
STAZ SINGAPORE PTE. LTD.—See Daehan Steel Co., Ltd.; *Int'l*, pg. 1907
STAZ USA INC.—See Daehan Steel Co., Ltd.; *Int'l*, pg. 1907
STAZ VIETNAM CO. LTD.—See Daehan Steel Co., Ltd.; *Int'l*, pg. 1907

STEEL DYNAMICS COLUMBUS, LLC—See Steel Dynamics, Inc.; *U.S. Public*, pg. 1942
STEEL DYNAMICS HEARTLAND, LLC—See Steel Dynamics, Inc.; *U.S. Public*, pg. 1942
STEEL DYNAMICS, INC.; *U.S. Public*, pg. 1942
STEEL DYNAMICS ROANOKE BAR DIVISION—See Steel Dynamics, Inc.; *U.S. Public*, pg. 1942
STEEL OF WEST VIRGINIA, INC.—See Steel Dynamics, Inc.; *U.S. Public*, pg. 1942
STEIN, LLC—See The Pritzker Organization, LLC; *U.S. Private*, pg. 4100
SUBURBAN STEEL SUPPLY CO.; *U.S. Private*, pg. 3848
SYNTRANS, LLC—See Ascent Industries Co.; *U.S. Public*, pg. 210
TALLEY METALS TECHNOLOGY, INC.—See Carpenter Technology Corporation; *U.S. Public*, pg. 439
TANGSTEEL COMPANY LTD.—See HBIS Group Co., Ltd.; *Int'l*, pg. 3296
TEMPEL (CHANGZHOU) PRECISION METAL PRODUCTS CO. LTD.—See Worthington Industries, Inc.; *U.S. Public*, pg. 2383
TETON STEEL CO.—See Dalco Industries Inc.; *U.S. Private*, pg. 1148
THAI SEISEN CO., LTD.—See Daido Steel Co., Ltd.; *Int'l*, pg. 1923
TIANJIN HERONG TITANIUM INDUSTRY CO., LTD.—See Atlantic China Welding Consumables, Inc.; *Int'l*, pg. 674
TIANJIN SAINTEAGLE WELDING CO., LTD.—See Advanced Technology & Materials Co., Ltd.; *Int'l*, pg. 162
TMS INTERNATIONAL CORPORATION—See The Pritzker Organization, LLC; *U.S. Private*, pg. 4100
TMS INTERNATIONAL, LLC—See The Pritzker Organization, LLC; *U.S. Private*, pg. 4100
TOKAI SPECIALTY STEEL CO. LTD.—See Aichi Steel Corporation; *Int'l*, pg. 230
TRANS-OVERSEAS B.V.—See AG der Dillinger Huttenwerke; *Int'l*, pg. 197
TRANS-TEX FABRICATING CO., INC.; *U.S. Private*, pg. 4206
TREFILERIAS QUIJANO, S.A.—See Celsa Group; *Int'l*, pg. 1395
TREFILKIN SPRL—See Aga Khan Development Network; *Int'l*, pg. 199
TRIDENT STEEL (PTY) LIMITED—See Aveng Limited; *Int'l*, pg. 738
TRINITY PRODUCTS INC.; *U.S. Private*, pg. 4235
TRIPLE S&P, INC.; *U.S. Private*, pg. 4237
TSA PROCESSING DALLAS, LLC—See Ryerson Holding Corporation; *U.S. Public*, pg. 1829
TUBE CITY IMS DE MEXICO S. DE R.L. DE C.V.—See The Pritzker Organization, LLC; *U.S. Private*, pg. 4100
TUBE CITY IMS KOSICE S.R.O.—See The Pritzker Organization, LLC; *U.S. Private*, pg. 4100
TUBE CITY IMS SOUTH AFRICA (PTY) LTD.—See The Pritzker Organization, LLC; *U.S. Private*, pg. 4100
UMFORMTECHNIK BAEUERLE GMBH—See Georgsmarienhutte Holding GmbH; *Int'l*, pg. 2941
UNITED PERFORMANCE METALS, INC.—See O'Neal Industries, Inc.; *U.S. Public*, pg. 2979
UNITED STATES STEEL, AIRCRAFT DIVISION—See United States Steel Corporation; *U.S. Public*, pg. 2237
UNITED STATES STEEL CORP. - BRADDOCK—See United States Steel Corporation; *U.S. Public*, pg. 2237
UNITED STATES STEEL CORPORATION; *U.S. Public*, pg. 2236
UNITED STATES STEEL CORP.—See United States Steel Corporation; *U.S. Public*, pg. 2237
UNITED STATES STEEL GREAT LAKES WORKS—See United States Steel Corporation; *U.S. Public*, pg. 2237
UNITED STATES STEEL MIDWEST—See United States Steel Corporation; *U.S. Public*, pg. 2237
USS GALVANIZING, INC.—See United States Steel Corporation; *U.S. Public*, pg. 2237
USS-POSCO INDUSTRIES—See United States Steel Corporation; *U.S. Public*, pg. 2237
USS REAL ESTATE—See United States Steel Corporation; *U.S. Public*, pg. 2237
U. S. STEEL EUROPE - BOHEMIA A.S.—See United States Steel Corporation; *U.S. Public*, pg. 2237
U. S. STEEL EUROPE - ITALY S.R.L.—See United States Steel Corporation; *U.S. Public*, pg. 2237
U.S. STEEL RECEIVABLES LLC—See United States Steel Corporation; *U.S. Public*, pg. 2237
VACUUMSCHMELZE GMBH & CO., KG—See Ara Partners Group; *U.S. Private*, pg. 306
VALBRUNA ASIA LIMITED—See Acciaierie Valbruna S.p.A.; *Int'l*, pg. 89
VALBRUNA AUSTRALIA PTY LTD—See Acciaierie Valbruna S.p.A.; *Int'l*, pg. 89
VALBRUNA EDEL INOX GMBH—See Acciaierie Valbruna S.p.A.; *Int'l*, pg. 89
VALBRUNA SLATER STAINLESS, INC.—See Acciaierie Valbruna S.p.A.; *Int'l*, pg. 89
VDM METALS AUSTRALIA PTY. LTD.—See Acerinox, S.A.; *Int'l*, pg. 101
VDM METALS AUSTRIA GMBH—See Acerinox, S.A.; *Int'l*, pg. 101

VDM METALS CANADA LIMITED—See Acerinox, S.A.; *Int'l*, pg. 101
VDM METALS DE MEXICO S.A. DE C.V.—See Acerinox, S.A.; *Int'l*, pg. 101
VDM METALS FRANCE S.A.S.—See Acerinox, S.A.; *Int'l*, pg. 101
VDM METALS ITALIA S.R.L.—See Acerinox, S.A.; *Int'l*, pg. 101
VDM METALS JAPAN K.K.—See Acerinox, S.A.; *Int'l*, pg. 101
VDM METALS SCHWEIZ AG—See Acerinox, S.A.; *Int'l*, pg. 101
VDM METALS U.K. LTD.—See Acerinox, S.A.; *Int'l*, pg. 101
VDM METALS USA, LLC—See Acerinox, S.A.; *Int'l*, pg. 101
VEREDELUNGSTECHNIK KRIEGLACH GMBH—See Georgsmarienhutte Holding GmbH; *Int'l*, pg. 2941
VSMA INC—See BlueScope Steel Limited; *Int'l*, pg. 1073
WEARTECH INTERNATIONAL, INC.—See Lincoln Electric Holdings, Inc.; *U.S. Public*, pg. 1318
WESTERMAN ACQUISITION CO., LLC—See Worthington Industries, Inc.; *U.S. Public*, pg. 2383
WESTERMAN, INC.—See Ten Oaks Group; *U.S. Private*, pg. 3964
WHITEFAB INC.; *U.S. Private*, pg. 4511
WIRE TECHNO, LTD.—See Godo Steel, Ltd.; *Int'l*, pg. 3020
WISCO ECHENG IRON & STEEL CO., LTD.—See China Baowu Steel Group Corp., Ltd.; *Int'l*, pg. 1485
WITT GALVANIZING - MUNCIE, LLC—See AZZ, Inc.; *U.S. Public*, pg. 260
XINJIANG BA YI IRON & STEEL CO., LTD.—See China Baowu Steel Group Corp., Ltd.; *Int'l*, pg. 1486
XINJIANG MIDDLE HOSHINE SILICON INDUSTRY CO., LTD.—See Hoshine Silicon Industry Co., Ltd.; *Int'l*, pg. 3483
YK STEEL CORP.—See Daehan Steel Co., Ltd.; *Int'l*, pg. 1907
ZALK STEEL & SUPPLY CO.—See AZZ, Inc.; *U.S. Public*, pg. 260
ZHONGSHAN ZHONGYUE TINPLATE INDUSTRIAL CO. LTD—See GDH Limited; *Int'l*, pg. 2896

331210 — IRON AND STEEL PIPE AND TUBE MANUFACTURING FROM PURCHASED STEEL

101 VERTICAL FABRICATION, INC.—See 101 Pipe & Casing Inc.; *U.S. Private*, pg. 2
ACCU-TUBE CORP.—See Washington Equity Partners L.L.C.; *U.S. Private*, pg. 4447
ACERINOX, S.A.; *Int'l*, pg. 100
ACME/ROMAC INC.—See Nusser Industries Inc.; *U.S. Private*, pg. 2974
A.G. UNIVERSAL LIMITED; *Int'l*, pg. 24
AHMEDABAD STEELCRAFT LTD.; *Int'l*, pg. 225
AHWAZ PIPE MILLS COMPANY; *Int'l*, pg. 226
AHWAZ ROLLING & PIPE MILLS CO.; *Int'l*, pg. 226
AK TUBE LLC—See Cleveland-Cliffs, Inc.; *U.S. Public*, pg. 513
ALCHEMIA S.A.; *Int'l*, pg. 300
AL EZZ DEKHEILA STEEL CO.—See Ezz Steel Co. S.A.E.; *Int'l*, pg. 2594
AL EZZ ROLLING MILLS COMPANY—See Ezz Steel Co. S.A.E.; *Int'l*, pg. 2594
AL JAZEERA STEEL PRODUCTS COMPANY S.A.O.G.; *Int'l*, pg. 280
ALL METAL SERVICES LTD.; *Int'l*, pg. 332
ALMACENES METALURGICOS, S.A.U; *Int'l*, pg. 363
ALPOS, D.D.; *Int'l*, pg. 374
ALPOS, INDUSTRIJA KOVINSKLH IZDELKOV ON OPREME, D.D.—See ALPOS, d.d.; *Int'l*, pg. 375
ALPOS OPREMA TRGOVIN D.O.O.—See ALPOS, d.d.; *Int'l*, pg. 374
AMCOR INC.—See CRH plc; *Int'l*, pg. 1846
AMERICAN SPIRALWELD PIPE COMPANY, LLC—See American Cast Iron Pipe Company; *U.S. Private*, pg. 226
AMERICAN STAINLESS TUBING, INC.—See Ascent Industries Co.; *U.S. Public*, pg. 210
AMERICAN TUBE CORP.; *U.S. Private*, pg. 257
AMIYA CORPORATION; *Int'l*, pg. 428
ANIL SPECIAL STEEL INDUSTRIES LTD.; *Int'l*, pg. 471
ANNAIK LIMITED; *Int'l*, pg. 473
ANN JOO INTEGRATED STEEL SDN. BHD.—See Ann Joo Resources Berhad; *Int'l*, pg. 473
ANN JOO MANAGEMENT SERVICES SDN. BHD.—See Ann Joo Resources Berhad; *Int'l*, pg. 473
ANN JOO METAL SDN. BHD.—See Ann Joo Resources Berhad; *Int'l*, pg. 473
ANSHIN STEEL INDUSTRIES SDN. BHD.—See Ann Joo Resources Berhad; *Int'l*, pg. 473
ANSHIN STEEL PROCESSOR SDN. BHD.—See Ann Joo Resources Berhad; *Int'l*, pg. 473
ANVA TUBES & COMPONENTS AB; *Int'l*, pg. 486
ARCELORMITTAL BRAMPTON—See ArcelorMittal S.A.; *Int'l*, pg. 544
ARCELORMITTAL MONTERREY—See ArcelorMittal S.A.; *Int'l*, pg. 545
ARCELORMITTAL WOODSTOCK—See ArcelorMittal S.A.; *Int'l*, pg. 544

331210 — IRON AND STEEL PIPE...

ARGPEX S.A.—See Golan Plastic Products Ltd.; *Int'l*, pg. 3023
ARZON LIMITED; *Int'l*, pg. 589
ASCENT INDUSTRIES CO.; *U.S. Public*, pg. 210
ATKORE INTERNATIONAL, INC.—See Clayton, Dubilier & Rice, LLC; *U.S. Private*, pg. 919
ATLANTIC STATES CAST IRON PIPE COMPANY—See McWane, Inc.; *U.S. Private*, pg. 2645
ATLAS TUBE INC. - CHICAGO—See Zekelman Industries Inc.; *U.S. Private*, pg. 4600
ATLAS TUBE INC. - PLYMOUTH—See Zekelman Industries Inc.; *U.S. Private*, pg. 4600
ATLAS TUBE INC.—See Zekelman Industries Inc.; *U.S. Private*, pg. 4600
AUSTRALIAN CONSTRUCTION PRODUCTS PTY LIMITED—See Fletcher Building Limited; *Int'l*, pg. 2699
AUSTRALIAN TUBE MILLS PTY. LIMITED—See GFG Alliance Limited; *Int'l*, pg. 2956
AZTEC TUBULAR PRODUCTS—See AZZ, Inc.; *U.S. Public*, pg. 258
BALLI STEEL PIPE LLC—See Balli Group plc; *Int'l*, pg. 809
BENTELER FRANCE S.A.S—See Benteler International AG; *Int'l*, pg. 975
BENTELER INTERNATIONAL AG; *Int'l*, pg. 975
BENTELER ROTHRIST AG—See Benteler International AG; *Int'l*, pg. 977
BENTELER STEEL & TUBE CORPORATION—See Benteler International AG; *Int'l*, pg. 977
BENTELER STEEL/TUBE MANUFACTURING CORPORATION—See Benteler International AG; *Int'l*, pg. 977
BENTELER STEEL/TUBE (NANTONG) CO., LTD.—See Benteler International AG; *Int'l*, pg. 976
BENTELER TUBOS Y MAQUINARIA S.A.—See Benteler International AG; *Int'l*, pg. 977
BHR PIPING SYSTEMS (PTY) LTD.—See Bilfinger SE; *Int'l*, pg. 1027
BRI-STEEL CORPORATION—See Bri-Chem Corp.; *Int'l*, pg. 1151
BRISTOL METALS, LLC—See Ascent Industries Co.; *U.S. Public*, pg. 210
BRUDER MANNESMANN AG; *Int'l*, pg. 1199
BSI STEEL LIMITED; *Int'l*, pg. 1202
BULL MOOSE TUBE COMPANY - CASA GRANDE PLANT—See Caparo Group Ltd.; *Int'l*, pg. 1301
BULL MOOSE TUBE COMPANY - CHICAGO HEIGHTS PLANT—See Caparo Group Ltd.; *Int'l*, pg. 1301
BULL MOOSE TUBE COMPANY - GERALD PLANT—See Caparo Group Ltd.; *Int'l*, pg. 1301
BULL MOOSE TUBE COMPANY - MASURY PLANT—See Caparo Group Ltd.; *Int'l*, pg. 1301
BULL MOOSE TUBE COMPANY—See Caparo Group Ltd.; *Int'l*, pg. 1301
BULL MOOSE TUBE COMPANY - TRENTON PLANT—See Caparo Group Ltd.; *Int'l*, pg. 1301
BULL MOOSE TUBES LTD.—See Caparo Group Ltd.; *Int'l*, pg. 1301
BULL MOOSE TUBES—See Caparo Group Ltd.; *Int'l*, pg. 1301
BURG SERVICE B.V.—See China International Marine Containers (Group) Co., Ltd.; *Int'l*, pg. 1511
BWL LIMITED; *Int'l*, pg. 1232
CAPARO ENGINEERING LTD. - CLYDESDALE JONES DIVISION—See Caparo Group Ltd.; *Int'l*, pg. 1302
CAPARO PRECISION TUBES LTD. - CAPARO DRAWN PRODUCTS DIVISION—See Caparo Group Ltd.; *Int'l*, pg. 1302
CAPARO PRECISION TUBES LTD.—See Caparo Group Ltd.; *Int'l*, pg. 1302
CAPARO STEEL PRODUCTS LTD. - HUB LE BAS DIVISION—See Caparo Group Ltd.; *Int'l*, pg. 1302
CAPARO TUBE COMPONENTS LTD.—See Caparo Group Ltd.; *Int'l*, pg. 1302
CAPARO TUBES LIMITED—See Caparo Group Ltd.; *Int'l*, pg. 1301
CARDINAL UHP LLC—See AMETEK, Inc.; *U.S. Public*, pg. 118
CARL FROH GMBH; *Int'l*, pg. 1302
CELBOR CELIK CEKME BORU SANAYI VE TICARET A.S.—See Eregli Demir Ve Celik Fabrikalari T.A.S.; *Int'l*, pg. 2490
CF&I STEEL LP—See Evraz plc; *Int'l*, pg. 2573
CHANGZHOU CHINA STEEL PRECISION MATERIALS CO., LTD.—See China Steel Corporation; *Int'l*, pg. 1555
CHINA STEEL PRECISION METALS QINGDAO, CO., LTD.—See China Steel Corporation; *Int'l*, pg. 1555
CHOO BEE HARDWARE (SABAH) SDN. BHD.—See Choo Bee Metal Industries Berhad; *Int'l*, pg. 1582
CHOO BEE HARDWARES SDN. BERHAD—See Choo Bee Metal Industries Berhad; *Int'l*, pg. 1582
CHROME DEPOSIT CORPORATION—See United States Steel Corporation; *U.S. Public*, pg. 2236
CHU KONG PETROLEUM AND NATURAL GAS STEEL PIPE HOLDINGS LIMITED; *Int'l*, pg. 1589
CIMTAS (NINGBO) STEEL PROCESSING COMPANY LTD.—See Enka Insaat ve Sanayi A.S.; *Int'l*, pg. 2440
CLOCK SPRING COMPANY, INC.—See Wind Point Advisors LLC; *U.S. Private*, pg. 4534

COMAP POLSKA SP. Z.O.O.—See Aalberts N.V.; *Int'l*, pg. 33
COMECOP—See Grupo Empresarial Kaluz S.A. de C.V.; *Int'l*, pg. 3126
CONTINENTAL ALLOYS & SERVICES (DELAWARE) LLC—See Reliance Steel & Aluminum Co.; *U.S. Public*, pg. 1779
COSMIC CRF LIMITED; *Int'l*, pg. 1811
CRESCENT STEEL AND ALLIED PRODUCTS LIMITED; *Int'l*, pg. 1839
CSGT (SINGAPORE) PTE. LTD.—See China Steel Corporation; *Int'l*, pg. 1555
DAEJOO ENERGY INNOVATION TECHNOLOGY CO LTD; *Int'l*, pg. 1907
DAIDO D.M.S. INDIA PVT. LTD.—See Daido Steel Co., Ltd.; *Int'l*, pg. 1922
DAIDO KOGYO (THAILAND) CO., LTD.—See Daido Steel Co., Ltd.; *Int'l*, pg. 1922
DAYTON SUPERIOR CORPORATION; *U.S. Private*, pg. 1178
DDG INC.; *U.S. Private*, pg. 1181
DELATTRE LEVIVIER MAROC; *Int'l*, pg. 2010
DIEHL METALL STIFTUNG & CO. KG—See Diehl Stiftung & Co. KG; *Int'l*, pg. 2115
DOFASCO TUBULAR PRODUCTS—See ArcelorMittal S.A.; *Int'l*, pg. 544
DONG YANG STEEL PIPE CO., LTD. - CHUNGJU FACTORY—See Dong Yang Steel Pipe Co., Ltd.; *Int'l*, pg. 2164
DONG YANG STEEL PIPE CO., LTD.; *Int'l*, pg. 2164
DOUGLAS BARWICK INC.—See Canerector Inc.; *Int'l*, pg. 1290
DOUGLAS BARWICK—See Canerector Inc.; *Int'l*, pg. 1290
DUFFIN MANUFACTURING COMPANY—See Geberit AG; *Int'l*, pg. 2904
DYFED STEELS LIMITED; *Int'l*, pg. 2238
E.A. PATTEN CO., LLC—See Stanley Black & Decker, Inc.; *U.S. Public*, pg. 1932
EAST PIPES INTEGRATED COMPANY FOR INDUSTRY; *Int'l*, pg. 2270
EISENBAU KRAMER GMBH - LITTFELD PLANT—See Eisenbau Kramer GmbH; *Int'l*, pg. 2336
EISENBAU KRAMER GMBH - RECKLINGHAUSEN PLANT—See Eisenbau Kramer GmbH; *Int'l*, pg. 2336
ELG HANIEL GMBH—See Franz Haniel & Cie. GmbH; *Int'l*, pg. 2762
ENCORE METALS—See Reliance Steel & Aluminum Co.; *U.S. Public*, pg. 1781
ENCORE METALS—See Reliance Steel & Aluminum Co.; *U.S. Public*, pg. 1781
ENCORE METALS—See Reliance Steel & Aluminum Co.; *U.S. Public*, pg. 1781
ENG LIAN HUP TRADING SDN. BHD.—See Engtex Group Berhad; *Int'l*, pg. 2436
ENGTEX METALS SDN. BHD.—See Engtex Group Berhad; *Int'l*, pg. 2436
EONMETALL SYSTEMS SDN. BHD.—See Eonmetall Group Berhad; *Int'l*, pg. 2458
ERBOSAN ERCIYAS BORU SANAYII VE TICARET A.S.; *Int'l*, pg. 2489
EVRAZ INC. NA CANADA - CAMROSE—See Evraz plc; *Int'l*, pg. 2574
EZZ FLAT STEEL COMPANY—See Ezz Steel Co. S.A.E.; *Int'l*, pg. 2594
FELKER BROTHERS CORPORATION; *U.S. Private*, pg. 1493
FERRUM S.A.; *Int'l*, pg. 2645
FINE TUBES LIMITED—See Superior Group, Inc.; *U.S. Private*, pg. 3878
FINOW ROHRSYSTEME GMBH—See Alpiq Holding AG; *Int'l*, pg. 372
FRANCE GALVA SA; *Int'l*, pg. 2759
FUJI SHAFT CO., LTD.—See Fuji Die Co., Ltd.; *Int'l*, pg. 2810
GANGOTRI IRON & STEEL COMPANY LTD.; *Int'l*, pg. 2880
GATIC PTY LIMITED—See Fletcher Building Limited; *Int'l*, pg. 2700
GEBERIT MAPRESS GMBH—See Geberit AG; *Int'l*, pg. 2904
GEBERIT RLS BETEILIGUNGS GMBH—See Geberit AG; *Int'l*, pg. 2904
GKN SINTER METALS CAPE TOWN (PTY) LTD—See GKN plc; *Int'l*, pg. 2985
GLOBAL TUBING, LLC—See Forum Energy Technologies, Inc.; *U.S. Public*, pg. 874
GREENVILLE TUBE COMPANY, LLC—See Berkshire Hathaway Inc.; *U.S. Public*, pg. 314
GRUPO CINTAC S.A.—See CAP S.A.; *Int'l*, pg. 1300
GUANGZHOU UNITED STEEL STRUCTURES LIMITED—See CSSC Offshore & Marine Engineering Company Ltd.; *Int'l*, pg. 1868
GWE TUBOMIN S.A.—See BAUER Aktiengesellschaft; *Int'l*, pg. 893
HAIBO HEAVY ENGINERNG SCNC & TECH CO LTD; *Int'l*, pg. 3209
HALL LONGMORE (PROPRIETARY) LIMITED; *Int'l*, pg. 3229
HANDY & HARMAN TUBE CO., INC.—See Steel Partners

Holdings L.P.; *U.S. Public*, pg. 1942
HANDYTUBE CORPORATION—See Steel Partners Holdings L.P.; *U.S. Public*, pg. 1943
HANNA STEEL CORPORATION; *U.S. Private*, pg. 1855
HARIOM PIPE INDUSTRIES LIMITED; *Int'l*, pg. 3276
HARIYANA SHIP BREAKERS LTD.; *Int'l*, pg. 3277
HBIS SERBIA LTD.—See HBIS Group Co., Ltd.; *Int'l*, pg. 3296
HIAP TECK VENTURE BERHAD; *Int'l*, pg. 3382
HOFMANN INDUSTRIES, INC. - EAU CLAIRE DIVISION—See Hofmann Industries, Inc.; *U.S. Private*, pg. 1961
HOFMANN INDUSTRIES, INC.; *U.S. Private*, pg. 1960
HUSTEEL CO., LTD. - DANGJIN PLANT—See HUSTEEL CO., Ltd.; *Int'l*, pg. 3540
HUSTEEL CO., LTD.; *Int'l*, pg. 3540
HUU LIEN ASIA CORPORATION; *Int'l*, pg. 3540
ICHINOSE EMICO VALVES (S) PTE LTD.—See AnnAik Limited; *Int'l*, pg. 473
ILJIN STEEL CORPORATION—See Iijin Display Co., Ltd.; *Int'l*, pg. 3614
INDEPENDENCE TUBE CORPORATION—See Nucor Corporation; *U.S. Public*, pg. 1553
INDIANA TUBE CORP.—See Steel Partners Holdings L.P.; *U.S. Public*, pg. 1943
INOXFIL S.A.—See Acerinox, S.A.; *Int'l*, pg. 101
INSULTAB, INC.—See Odyssey Investment Partners, LLC; *U.S. Private*, pg. 2995
JACKSON TUBE SERVICE INC.; *U.S. Private*, pg. 2178
JAMES STEEL & TUBE COMPANY—See Avis Industrial Corporation; *U.S. Private*, pg. 407
JIANGMEN HUAJIN METAL PRODUCT COMPANY LIMITED—See Huajin International Holdings Limited; *Int'l*, pg. 3512
JIANGYIN HANIL STEEL CO., LTD.—See HISTEEL Co., Ltd.; *Int'l*, pg. 3408
JOHN MANEELY COMPANY—See Zekelman Industries Inc.; *U.S. Private*, pg. 4600
KE TUBE INC.; *U.S. Private*, pg. 2270
KLAD MANUFACTURING COMPANY, LTD.—See Berkshire Hathaway Inc.; *U.S. Public*, pg. 314
K-TUBE CORPORATION—See Cook Group Incorporated; *U.S. Private*, pg. 1037
LALLY PIPE & TUBE—See L B Industries, Inc.; *U.S. Private*, pg. 2361
L B PIPE & COUPLING PRODUCTS, LLC—See L.B. Foster Company; *U.S. Public*, pg. 1278
L B PIPE & COUPLING PRODUCTS, LLC—See L B Industries, Inc.; *U.S. Private*, pg. 2361
LIFETIME METALS, INC.—See Lifetime Products Inc.; *U.S. Private*, pg. 2451
LOCK JOINT TUBE INC.; *U.S. Private*, pg. 2478
MARKIN TUBING, INC.; *U.S. Private*, pg. 2582
MARMON FLOW PRODUCTS—See Berkshire Hathaway Inc.; *U.S. Public*, pg. 310
MARMON/KEYSTONE CANADA, INC.—See Berkshire Hathaway Inc.; *U.S. Public*, pg. 309
MAYVILLE ENGINEERING COMPANY, INC. - BYRON CENTER—See Mayville Engineering Company, Inc.; *U.S. Public*, pg. 1403
MCWANE, INC. - MCWANE POLES DIVISION—See McWane, Inc.; *U.S. Private*, pg. 2645
MCWANE, INC. - TYLER PIPE & COUPLING DIVISION—See McWane, Inc.; *U.S. Private*, pg. 2645
MERCER STAINLESS LIMITED—See KKR & Co. Inc.; *U.S. Public*, pg. 1241
METAL-MATIC, INC. - BEDFORD PARK PLANT—See Metal-Matic, Inc.; *U.S. Private*, pg. 2680
METAL-MATIC, INC. - OHIO PLANT—See Metal-Matic, Inc.; *U.S. Private*, pg. 2680
METAL-MATIC, INC.; *U.S. Private*, pg. 2680
MICHIGAN SEAMLESS TUBE LLC—See Optima Specialty Steel, Inc.; *U.S. Private*, pg. 3034
MICRO-TUBE FABRICATORS INC.—See Steel Partners Holdings L.P.; *U.S. Public*, pg. 1943
THE MIDDLE EAST TUBE COMPANY LTD.—See Gaon Group Ltd; *Int'l*, pg. 2882
MOHAWK ENERGY LTD.; *U.S. Private*, pg. 2765
MONIND LTD.—See Apollo Global Management, Inc.; *U.S. Public*, pg. 152
MORRIS INDUSTRIES INC.; *U.S. Private*, pg. 2788
NANTONG HILONG STEEL PIPE CO., LTD.—See Hilong Holding Limited; *Int'l*, pg. 3393
NAYLOR PIPE COMPANY; *U.S. Private*, pg. 2874
NINGBO SANHE STEEL PIPE CO., LTD.—See Chu Kong Petroleum and Natural Gas Steel Pipe Holdings Limited; *Int'l*, pg. 1589
NOKSEL A.S.—See Cukurova Holding A.S.; *Int'l*, pg. 1876
NOKSEL ESPANA S.A.—See Cukurova Holding A.S.; *Int'l*, pg. 1876
NORTHSHORE MINING COMPANY—See Cleveland-Cliffs, Inc.; *U.S. Public*, pg. 514
NORTHWEST PIPE COMPANY; *U.S. Public*, pg. 1542
NUSSER INDUSTRIES INC.; *U.S. Private*, pg. 2974
NW TOTAL ENGINEERED SOLUTIONS LTD.—See Carr's Group PLC; *Int'l*, pg. 1343
ORIENTAL SHIMOMURA DRAWING (M) SDN. BHD.—See Daido Steel Co., Ltd.; *Int'l*, pg. 1923

N.A.I.C.S. INDEX

331221 — ROLLED STEEL SHAPE ...

ORRCON OPERATIONS PTY. LTD.—See BlueScope Steel Limited; *Int'l*, pg. 1074
PALADEX LTD.—See Avrot Industries Ltd.; *Int'l*, pg. 750
PAM COLOMBIA SA—See Compagnie de Saint-Gobain SA; *Int'l*, pg. 1724
PANYU CHU KONG STEEL PIPE (LIANYUNGANG) CO., LTD.—See Chu Kong Petroleum and Natural Gas Steel Pipe Holdings Limited; *Int'l*, pg. 1589
PANYU CHU KONG STEEL PIPE (ZHUHAI) CO., LTD.—See Chu Kong Petroleum and Natural Gas Steel Pipe Holdings Limited; *Int'l*, pg. 1589
PARAGON INDUSTRIES, INC.; *U.S. Private*, pg. 3091
PARAGON STEEL INC—See Midwest Pipe & Steel Inc.; *U.S. Private*, pg. 2722
PARAGON TUBE CORP.—See Midwest Pipe & Steel Inc.; *U.S. Private*, pg. 2722
PARTHENON METAL WORKS, INC.—See Crowne Group LLC; *U.S. Private*, pg. 1112
PERMALOK CORPORATION—See Northwest Pipe Company; *U.S. Public*, pg. 1542
PICA CO., LTD.—See Fuji Kyuko Co., Ltd.; *Int'l*, pg. 2813
PITTSBURGH PIPE & SUPPLY CORP; *U.S. Private*, pg. 3191
PLYMOUTH TUBE COMPANY - EAST TROY MILL—See Plymouth Tube Company; *U.S. Private*, pg. 3216
PLYMOUTH TUBE COMPANY - EUPORA MILL—See Plymouth Tube Company; *U.S. Private*, pg. 3216
PLYMOUTH TUBE COMPANY - SALISBURY MILL—See Plymouth Tube Company; *U.S. Private*, pg. 3216
PLYMOUTH TUBE COMPANY; *U.S. Private*, pg. 3216
PLYMOUTH TUBE COMPANY - STREATOR MILL—See Plymouth Tube Company; *U.S. Private*, pg. 3216
PLYMOUTH TUBE COMPANY - THE WINAMAC COLD DRAW MILL—See Plymouth Tube Company; *U.S. Private*, pg. 3216
PTC ALLIANCE CORP.—See Black Diamond Capital Holdings, LLC; *U.S. Private*, pg. 570
PT. CHU KONG STEEL INDONESIA—See Chu Kong Petroleum and Natural Gas Steel Pipe Holdings Limited; *Int'l*, pg. 1589
RATHGIBSON NORTH BRANCH LLC—See Berkshire Hathaway Inc.; *U.S. Public*, pg. 314
THE REINFORCED EARTH COMPANY—See The Reinforced Earth Company; *U.S. Private*, pg. 4103
RELIANCE METALS CANADA LIMITED—See Reliance Steel & Aluminum Co.; *U.S. Public*, pg. 1781
REPUBLIC CONDUIT INC.—See Nucor Corporation; *U.S. Public*, pg. 1554
ROBOR INDUSTRIAL (PTY) LIMITED—See Barloworld Ltd.; *Int'l*, pg. 866
ROSCOE MOSS COMPANY; *U.S. Private*, pg. 3481
SAGA MAKMUR INDUSTRI SDN. BHD.—See Ann Joo Resources Berhad; *Int'l*, pg. 473
SAINT-GOBAIN FOUNDRY (MA'ANSHAN) CO., LTD.—See Compagnie de Saint-Gobain SA; *Int'l*, pg. 1733
SAINT-GOBAIN GUSSROHRVERTIEB OSTERREICH GMBH—See Compagnie de Saint-Gobain SA; *Int'l*, pg. 1728
SAINT-GOBAIN PAM CZ S.R.O—See Compagnie de Saint-Gobain SA; *Int'l*, pg. 1735
SAINT-GOBAIN PAM ITALIA SPA—See Compagnie de Saint-Gobain SA; *Int'l*, pg. 1735
SAINT-GOBAIN PAM PORTUGAL SA—See Compagnie de Saint-Gobain SA; *Int'l*, pg. 1735
SAINT-GOBAIN PAM S.A.—See Compagnie de Saint-Gobain SA; *Int'l*, pg. 1735
SAINT-GOBAIN PIPELINE HONG KONG LTD.—See Compagnie de Saint-Gobain SA; *Int'l*, pg. 1735
SAINT-GOBAIN PIPELINES CO. LTD.—See Compagnie de Saint-Gobain SA; *Int'l*, pg. 1735
SAINT-GOBAIN PIPELINES SOUTH AFRICA (PTY) LIMITED—See Compagnie de Saint-Gobain SA; *Int'l*, pg. 1735
SAINT-GOBAIN PIPE SYSTEMS BELGIUM SA/NV—See Compagnie de Saint-Gobain SA; *Int'l*, pg. 1735
SAINT-GOBAIN PIPE SYSTEMS BV—See Compagnie de Saint-Gobain SA; *Int'l*, pg. 1728
SAINT-GOBAIN PIPE SYSTEMS OY—See Compagnie de Saint-Gobain SA; *Int'l*, pg. 1735
SCHOTT BRASIL LTDA. DIVISAO VITROFARMA—See Carl-Zeiss-Stiftung; *Int'l*, pg. 1336
SHRI LAKSHMI METAL UDYOG LIMITED—See Apl Apollo Tubes Ltd.; *Int'l*, pg. 515
SONOCO ALCORE GMBH—See Sonoco Products Company; *U.S. Public*, pg. 1906
SONOCO AUSTRALIA PTY. LTD. - WODONGA—See Sonoco Products Company; *U.S. Public*, pg. 1905
SOUTHERN ANCHOR BOLT CO.—See Portland Bolt & Manufacturing Co., LLC; *U.S. Private*, pg. 3232
SPECIALTY BAR PRODUCTS COMPANY—See Dubai Holding LLC; *Int'l*, pg. 2218
SPECITUBES SAS—See Leggett & Platt, Incorporated; *U.S. Public*, pg. 1303
STAINLESS PIPING SYSTEMS, INC.—See Alco Investment Co., Inc.; *U.S. Private*, pg. 154
STEELASTIC COMPANY, LLC—See The Heico Companies, L.L.C.; *U.S. Private*, pg. 4051
STEEL FABRICATION DIVISION—See NOV, Inc.; *U.S. Public*, pg. 1544
STERLING PIPE & TUBE INC.; *U.S. Private*, pg. 3807
STUPP CORPORATION—See Stupp Bros., Inc.; *U.S. Private*, pg. 3844
SUMMIT STEEL & MANUFACTURING INC.—See Lorraine Capital LLC; *U.S. Private*, pg. 2496
SUPERIOR TUBE COMPANY INC.—See AMETEK, Inc.; *U.S. Public*, pg. 116
T & B TUBE COMPANY; *U.S. Private*, pg. 3908
TEAM TUBE—See Reliance Steel & Aluminum Co.; *U.S. Public*, pg. 1781
TEXAS STEEL CONVERSION, INC.; *U.S. Private*, pg. 3977
TEXAS TUBULAR PRODUCTS—See Friedman Industries, Inc.; *U.S. Public*, pg. 886
TOOLPUSHER SUPPLY CO.—See True Companies; *U.S. Private*, pg. 4247
THE TROXEL COMPANY; *U.S. Private*, pg. 4128
TUBETECH INC.; *U.S. Private*, pg. 4256
TUBOS ARGENTINOS S.A.—See CAP S.A.; *Int'l*, pg. 1301
TUBULAR INSTRUMENTATION & CONTROLS LP; *U.S. Private*, pg. 4256
UNITED INDUSTRIES, INC.—See United Stars Inc.; *U.S. Private*, pg. 4298
UNITED STAINLESS, INC.—See United Stars Inc.; *U.S. Private*, pg. 4298
UNITED STARS INC.; *U.S. Private*, pg. 4298
UNITED STARS INDUSTRIES, INC.—See United Stars Inc.; *U.S. Private*, pg. 4298
UNITED TUBE CORPORATION; *U.S. Private*, pg. 4301
U. S. STEEL OILWELL SERVICES, LLC—See United States Steel Corporation; *U.S. Public*, pg. 2237
VALINOX NUCLEAIRE S.A.S.—See Electricite de France S.A.; *Int'l*, pg. 2351
VALIN TUBE—See Hunan Valin Steel Co., Ltd.; *Int'l*, pg. 3534
VALLEY VIEW TUBE, INC.; *U.S. Private*, pg. 4336
VALMONT INTERNATIONAL CORP—See Valmont Industries, Inc.; *U.S. Public*, pg. 2274
VDM METALS HOLDING GMBH—See Acerinox, S.A.; *Int'l*, pg. 101
VDM METALS INTERNATIONAL GMBH—See Acerinox, S.A.; *Int'l*, pg. 101
VERIDIAM, INC.—See William Harris Investors Inc.; *U.S. Private*, pg. 4523
WELDED TUBES INC.; *U.S. Private*, pg. 4474
WELDING OUTLETS, INC.; *U.S. Private*, pg. 4474
WHEATLAND TUBE COMPANY - MILL STREET PLANT—See Zekelman Industries Inc.; *U.S. Private*, pg. 4600
WHEATLAND TUBE COMPANY—See Zekelman Industries Inc.; *U.S. Private*, pg. 4600
WIEDERHOLT GMBH—See Black Diamond Capital Holdings, LLC; *U.S. Private*, pg. 571
WOODSAGE INDUSTRIES—See Woodsage Holdings, LLC; *U.S. Private*, pg. 4560
YANTAI LUBAO STEEL PIPE CO., LTD.—See China Baowu Steel Group Corp., Ltd.; *Int'l*, pg. 1486
ZEKELMAN INDUSTRIES INC.; *U.S. Private*, pg. 4599
ZIEMANN HOLVRIEKA B.V.—See China International Marine Containers (Group) Co., Ltd.; *Int'l*, pg. 1511
ZIEMANN HOLVRIEKA INTERNATIONAL B.V.—See China International Marine Containers (Group) Co., Ltd.; *Int'l*, pg. 1511

331221 — ROLLED STEEL SHAPE MANUFACTURING

ACENTA STEEL LIMITED - HOT ROLLED DIVISION—See Acenta Steel Limited; *Int'l*, pg. 98
ACERINOX BENELUX, S.A./NV—See Acerinox, S.A.; *Int'l*, pg. 100
ACERINOX DEUTSCHLAND GMBH—See Acerinox, S.A.; *Int'l*, pg. 100
ACERINOX DEUTSCHLAND GMBH—See Acerinox, S.A.; *Int'l*, pg. 100
ACERINOX ITALIA SRL—See Acerinox, S.A.; *Int'l*, pg. 100
ACERINOX MALAYSIA SDN. BHD.—See Acerinox, S.A.; *Int'l*, pg. 100
ACERINOX NORWAY A.S.—See Acerinox, S.A.; *Int'l*, pg. 100
ACERINOX POLSKA SP.ZO.O.—See Acerinox, S.A.; *Int'l*, pg. 100
ACERINOX SCANDINAVIA A.B.—See Acerinox, S.A.; *Int'l*, pg. 100
ACERINOX (SCHWEIZ) A.G.—See Acerinox, S.A.; *Int'l*, pg. 100
ACERINOX SEA PTE LTD—See Acerinox, S.A.; *Int'l*, pg. 100
ACERINOX UK LTD—See Acerinox, S.A.; *Int'l*, pg. 100
ACERTEC PLC; *Int'l*, pg. 102
ACUPOWDER INTERNATIONAL LLC—See Palladium Equity Partners, LLC; *U.S. Private*, pg. 3078
ACUPOWDER TENNESSEE LLC—See Palladium Equity Partners, LLC; *U.S. Private*, pg. 3078
ADF INTERNATIONAL INC.—See ADF Group Inc.; *Int'l*, pg. 145
AG DER DILLINGER HUTTENWERKE; *Int'l*, pg. 197
AK COATINGS INC.—See Cleveland-Cliffs, Inc.; *U.S. Public*, pg. 513
ALGOMA INC.; *Int'l*, pg. 318
ALLEGHENY LUDLUM-VANDERGRIFT—See ATI Inc.; *U.S. Public*, pg. 222
ALLEGHENY RODNEY—See ATI Inc.; *U.S. Public*, pg. 221
AMRELI STEELS LTD.; *Int'l*, pg. 437
APERAM STAINLESS EUROPE S.A.—See Aperam SA; *Int'l*, pg. 508
APERAM STAINLESS PRECISION EUROPE—See Aperam SA; *Int'l*, pg. 508
APPOLLO ISPAT COMPLEX LIMITED; *Int'l*, pg. 522
ARCELORMITTAL AMBALAJ CELIGI SANAYI VE TICARET A.S.—See ArcelorMittal S.A.; *Int'l*, pg. 543
ARCELORMITTAL - ARCELORMITTAL DUNKERQUE MILL—See ArcelorMittal S.A.; *Int'l*, pg. 543
ARCELORMITTAL - ARCELORMITTAL ETXEBARRI MILL—See ArcelorMittal S.A.; *Int'l*, pg. 543
ARCELORMITTAL - ARCELORMITTAL MARDYCK MILL—See ArcelorMittal S.A.; *Int'l*, pg. 543
ARCELORMITTAL - ARCELORMITTAL MOUZON MILL—See ArcelorMittal S.A.; *Int'l*, pg. 543
ARCELORMITTAL ATLANTIQUE ET LORRAINE S.A.S.—See ArcelorMittal S.A.; *Int'l*, pg. 543
ARCELORMITTAL BELVAL & DIFFERDANGE S.A.—See ArcelorMittal S.A.; *Int'l*, pg. 543
ARCELORMITTAL BREMEN GMBH—See ArcelorMittal S.A.; *Int'l*, pg. 543
ARCELORMITTAL CARIACICA—See ArcelorMittal S.A.; *Int'l*, pg. 544
ARCELORMITTAL - COTEAU DU LAC—See ArcelorMittal S.A.; *Int'l*, pg. 543
ARCELORMITTAL DUISBURG GMBH—See ArcelorMittal S.A.; *Int'l*, pg. 543
ARCELORMITTAL EISENHUTTENSTADT GMBH—See ArcelorMittal S.A.; *Int'l*, pg. 544
ARCELORMITTAL ESPANA S.A.—See ArcelorMittal S.A.; *Int'l*, pg. 544
ARCELORMITTAL FLAT CARBON EUROPE S.A.—See ArcelorMittal S.A.; *Int'l*, pg. 544
ARCELORMITTAL GANDRANGE S.A—See ArcelorMittal S.A.; *Int'l*, pg. 544
ARCELORMITTAL GENK N.V.—See ArcelorMittal S.A.; *Int'l*, pg. 543
ARCELORMITTAL GENK STAINLESS SERVICE BELGIUM N.V.—See ArcelorMittal S.A.; *Int'l*, pg. 544
ARCELORMITTAL GENT N.V.—See ArcelorMittal S.A.; *Int'l*, pg. 544
ARCELORMITTAL GIPUZKOA S.L.—See ArcelorMittal S.A.; *Int'l*, pg. 544
ARCELORMITTAL GUAPILES—See ArcelorMittal S.A.; *Int'l*, pg. 545
ARCELORMITTAL HAMILTON INC.—See ArcelorMittal S.A.; *Int'l*, pg. 543
ARCELORMITTAL ITAUNA—See ArcelorMittal S.A.; *Int'l*, pg. 544
ARCELORMITTAL JUIZ DE FORA.—See ArcelorMittal S.A.; *Int'l*, pg. 544
ARCELORMITTAL LAPLACE—See Cleveland-Cliffs, Inc.; *U.S. Public*, pg. 514
ARCELORMITTAL LIEGE SA—See GFG Alliance Limited; *Int'l*, pg. 2956
ARCELORMITTAL LONDON—See ArcelorMittal S.A.; *Int'l*, pg. 544
ARCELORMITTAL MADRID S.L.—See ArcelorMittal S.A.; *Int'l*, pg. 544
ARCELORMITTAL MEDITERRANEE S.A.S.—See ArcelorMittal S.A.; *Int'l*, pg. 544
ARCELORMITTAL MONLEVADE S.A.—See ArcelorMittal S.A.; *Int'l*, pg. 545
ARCELORMITTAL MONTREAL INC.—See ArcelorMittal S.A.; *Int'l*, pg. 545
ARCELORMITTAL PIOMBINO S.P.A.—See GFG Alliance Limited; *Int'l*, pg. 2956
ARCELORMITTAL PROJECTS BELGIUM NV—See ArcelorMittal S.A.; *Int'l*, pg. 545
ARCELORMITTAL PROJECTS NETHERLANDS BV—See ArcelorMittal S.A.; *Int'l*, pg. 545
ARCELORMITTAL RONGCHENG—See ArcelorMittal S.A.; *Int'l*, pg. 545
ARCELORMITTAL SESTAO S.L.U—See ArcelorMittal S.A.; *Int'l*, pg. 543
ARCELORMITTAL SKOPJE (CRM) AD—See GFG Alliance Limited; *Int'l*, pg. 2956
ARCELORMITTAL SOUTH AFRICA LTD. - NEWCASTLE WORKS—See ArcelorMittal S.A.; *Int'l*, pg. 545
ARCELORMITTAL SOUTH AFRICA LTD. - PRETORIA WORKS—See ArcelorMittal S.A.; *Int'l*, pg. 545
ARCELORMITTAL SOUTH AFRICA LTD. - SALDANHA WORKS—See ArcelorMittal S.A.; *Int'l*, pg. 545
ARCELORMITTAL SOUTH AFRICA LTD. - VANDERBIJLPARK WORKS—See ArcelorMittal S.A.; *Int'l*, pg. 545
ARCELORMITTAL SOUTH AFRICA LTD. - VEREENIGING WORKS—See ArcelorMittal S.A.; *Int'l*, pg. 545
ARCELORMITTAL TUBARAO—See ArcelorMittal S.A.; *Int'l*, pg. 543
ARCELORMITTAL TUBULAR PRODUCTS KARVINA A.S.—See ArcelorMittal S.A.; *Int'l*, pg. 545

331221 — ROLLED STEEL SHAPE ...

ASHINCKIY METZAVOD PAO; *Int'l*, pg. 607
ATI OPERATING HOLDINGS, LLC—See ATI Inc.; *U.S. Public*, pg. 221
AZCO STEEL COMPANY—See Berkshire Hathaway Inc.; *U.S. Public*, pg. 309
BALKANCAR ZARYA PLC; *Int'l*, pg. 809
BAMESA ACEROS; *Int'l*, pg. 813
BANGSAPHAN BARMILL PUBLIC COMPANY LIMITED; *Int'l*, pg. 836
BARON DRAWN STEEL CORP.—See The Renco Group Inc.; *U.S. Private*, pg. 4104
BAYOU STEEL CORPORATION (TENNESSEE)—See Cleveland-Cliffs, Inc.; *U.S. Public*, pg. 514
BISALLOY STEEL GROUP LTD.; *Int'l*, pg. 1048
BISALLOY STEELS PTY LIMITED—See Bisalloy Steel Group Ltd.; *Int'l*, pg. 1048
BLUESCOPE STEEL AMERICAS LLC—See BlueScope Steel Limited; *Int'l*, pg. 1073
BSI LLC—See Levine Leichtman Capital Partners, LLC; *U.S. Private*, pg. 2435
BURWILL STEEL PIPES LIMITED—See Burwill Holdings Limited; *Int'l*, pg. 1227
CALIFORNIA STEEL INDUSTRIES, INC.—See Nucor Corporation; *U.S. Public*, pg. 1553
CALSTRIP INDUSTRIES INC.; *U.S. Private*, pg. 723
CALSTRIP STEEL CORPORATION—See Calstrip Industries Inc.; *U.S. Private*, pg. 723
CAPARO MERCHANT BAR PLC—See Caparo Group Ltd.; *Int'l*, pg. 1302
CAPARO PRECISION STRIP LIMITED—See Caparo Group Ltd.; *Int'l*, pg. 1302
CAPARO PRECISION STRIP LTD. - DUCTILE STOURBRIDGE COLD MILLS DIVISION—See Caparo Group Ltd.; *Int'l*, pg. 1302
CARDINAL MANUFACTURING COMPANY, INC.; *U.S. Private*, pg. 750
CHARTER STEEL, INC.—See Charter Manufacturing Company, Inc.; *U.S. Private*, pg. 858
CHARTER WIRE—See Charter Manufacturing Company, Inc.; *U.S. Private*, pg. 858
CHINA GERUI ADVANCED MATERIALS GROUP LIMITED; *Int'l*, pg. 1504
CHINA PRECISION STEEL, INC.; *Int'l*, pg. 1542
CHINA STEEL AND NIPPON STEEL VIETNAM JOINT STOCK COMPANY—See China Steel Corporation; *Int'l*, pg. 1555
CHUN YU (DONGGUAN) METAL PRODUCTS CO., LTD.—See Chun Yu Works & Co., Ltd.; *Int'l*, pg. 1596
CITIC PACIFIC SPECIAL STEEL GROUP CO., LTD.; *Int'l*, pg. 1621
CJT KOOLCARB, INC.—See L Squared Capital Management LP; *U.S. Private*, pg. 2361
CLEVELAND-CLIFFS CLEVELAND WORKS LLC—See Cleveland-Cliffs, Inc.; *U.S. Public*, pg. 514
CMC STEEL GROUP—See Commercial Metals Company; *U.S. Public*, pg. 546
COLLINS INDUSTRIES, LTD.; *Int'l*, pg. 1702
COMERCIAL DEL ACERO S.A.—See Corporacion Aceros Arequipa S.A.; *Int'l*, pg. 1803
COMMERCIAL METALS DEUTSCHLAND GMBH—See Commercial Metals Company; *U.S. Public*, pg. 545
CONSOLIDATED METAL PRODUCTS, INC.-GERMANY—See Consolidated Metal Products, Inc.; *U.S. Private*, pg. 1021
CONSOLIDATED METAL PRODUCTS, INC.-SOUTH AMERICA—See Consolidated Metal Products, Inc.; *U.S. Private*, pg. 1021
CORPORACION ACEROS AREQUIPA S.A.; *Int'l*, pg. 1802
CSC STEEL SDN. BHD.—See China Steel Corporation; *Int'l*, pg. 1555
CSN CIMENTOS—See Companhia Siderurgica Nacional; *Int'l*, pg. 1748
CSP STEEL CENTER PUBLIC COMPANY LIMITED; *Int'l*, pg. 1867
CTL STEEL CO.—See Clark Grave Vault Company; *U.S. Private*, pg. 913
DAECHANG STEEL CO., LTD.; *Int'l*, pg. 1906
DAEDONG STEEL CO., LTD.; *Int'l*, pg. 1906
DELONG HOLDINGS LIMITED; *Int'l*, pg. 2015
DHATRE UDYOG LIMITED; *Int'l*, pg. 2099
DJ GALVANIZING—See ArcelorMittal S.A.; *Int'l*, pg. 544
DONGKUK INDUSTRIES CO., LTD.; *Int'l*, pg. 2168
DONG YANG S.TEC CO., LTD.; *Int'l*, pg. 2164
DORRENBERG EDELSTAHL GMBH—See Gesco AG; *Int'l*, pg. 2945
DUNKIRK SPECIALTY STEEL, LLC—See Universal Stainless & Alloy Products, Inc.; *U.S. Public*, pg. 2262
EAST COAST MANUFACTURING SDN. BHD.—See Engtex Group Berhad; *Int'l*, pg. 2436
EISENBAU KRAMER GMBH; *Int'l*, pg. 2336
ELEKTRODIZALICA A.D.; *Int'l*, pg. 2357
ELME METALL OU—See BLRT Grupp AS; *Int'l*, pg. 1065
ENGINEERING STEEL BELGIUM SPRL—See Georgsmarienhutte Holding GmbH; *Int'l*, pg. 2940
ETILAM S.A.—See ArcelorMittal S.A.; *Int'l*, pg. 545
EUROLLS DE MEXICO S. DE R.L. DE C.V.—See EUROLLS S.p.A.; *Int'l*, pg. 2553
EUROPROFIL AB—See IAI Holding A/S; *Int'l*, pg. 3568

EURO STEEL DANMARK A/S; *Int'l*, pg. 2531
EVRAZ INC. NA—See Evraz plc; *Int'l*, pg. 2574
EVRAZ PALINI E BERTOLI S.R.L—See Evraz plc; *Int'l*, pg. 2574
EXXELLIN GMBH; *Int'l*, pg. 2592
FBHS (AUST) PTY LIMITED—See Fletcher Building Limited; *Int'l*, pg. 2699
FERRALCA, S.A.—See Alfonso Gallardo S.A.; *Int'l*, pg. 316
FERROLUX METALS CO. LLC—See Ferragon Corporation; *U.S. Private*, pg. 1498
FOSHAN JINXI JINLAN COLD ROLLED SHEETS CO., LTD.—See China Oriental Group Company Limited; *Int'l*, pg. 1538
FRIEDMAN INDUSTRIES, INC.; *U.S. Public*, pg. 886
GCW/USS ENERGY, LLC—See United States Steel Corporation; *U.S. Public*, pg. 2236
GODHA CABCON & INSULATION LTD.; *Int'l*, pg. 3020
GOSS STEEL CO.—See Olympic Steel Inc.; *U.S. Public*, pg. 1570
GRANGES FINSPANG AB—See Granges AB; *Int'l*, pg. 3058
GRANGES KONIN S.A.—See Granges AB; *Int'l*, pg. 3058
GREER LIMESTONE COMPANY—See Greer Industries Inc.; *U.S. Private*, pg. 1782
GREER STEEL COMPANY—See Greer Industries Inc.; *U.S. Private*, pg. 1782
GREIF SOUTH AFRICA (PTY) LTD.—See Greif Inc.; *U.S. Public*, pg. 968
G STEEL PUBLIC COMPANY LIMITED; *Int'l*, pg. 2861
GUANGDONG HANGXIAO STEEL STRUCTURE CO., LTD.—See Hangxiao Steel Structure Co., Ltd.; *Int'l*, pg. 3246
HADLEY INDUSTRIES PLC; *Int'l*, pg. 3205
HAI KWANG ENTERPRISE CORPORATION; *Int'l*, pg. 3208
HAMILTON PRECISION METALS, INC.—See AMETEK, Inc.; *U.S. Public*, pg. 116
HANGXIAO STEEL STRUCTURE CO., LTD.; *Int'l*, pg. 3246
HANGZHOU HANGXIAO STEEL STRUCTURE CO., LTD.—See Hangxiao Steel Structure Co., Ltd.; *Int'l*, pg. 3246
HANWA LOGISTICS TOKYO CO., LTD. - SENDAI FACTORY—See Hanwa Co., Ltd.; *Int'l*, pg. 3262
HARRIS REBAR CARSON CITY, INC—See Nucor Corporation; *U.S. Public*, pg. 1553
HASCALL STEEL COMPANY INC. - BENTON PLANT—See Hascall Steel Company Inc.; *U.S. Private*, pg. 1878
HASCALL STEEL COMPANY INC. - NASHVILLE PLANT—See Hascall Steel Company Inc.; *U.S. Private*, pg. 1878
HASCALL STEEL COMPANY INC. - STRONG STREET PLANT—See Hascall Steel Company Inc.; *U.S. Private*, pg. 1878
HEBEI HANGXIAO STEEL STRUCTURE CO., LTD.—See Hangxiao Steel Structure Co., Ltd.; *Int'l*, pg. 3246
HENAN HANGXIAO STEEL STRUCTURE CO., LTD.—See Hangxiao Steel Structure Co., Ltd.; *Int'l*, pg. 3246
HERAEUS INC.—See Heraeus Holding GmbH; *Int'l*, pg. 3357
HI-TECH STEEL SERVICES LTD.; *Int'l*, pg. 3382
HOA PHAT DUNG QUAT STEEL JSC—See Hoa Phat Group Joint Stock Company; *Int'l*, pg. 3435
HOA PHAT HAI DUONG STEEL JSC—See Hoa Phat Group Joint Stock Company; *Int'l*, pg. 3435
HOA PHAT STEEL SHEET CO., LTD.—See Hoa Phat Group Joint Stock Company; *Int'l*, pg. 3435
HOA SEN BINHDINH ONE MEMBER CO., LTD.—See Hoa Sen Group; *Int'l*, pg. 3436
HOA SEN NGHE AN ONE MEMBER LIMITED LIABILITIES COMPANY—See Hoa Sen Group; *Int'l*, pg. 3436
HOA SEN NHON HOI - BINH DINH ONE MEMBER LIMITED LIABILITIES COMPANY—See Hoa Sen Group; *Int'l*, pg. 3436
HOA SEN STEEL SHEET ONE MEMBER LIMITED LIABILITIES COMPANY—See Hoa Sen Group; *Int'l*, pg. 3436
HOA SEN YEN BAI BUILDING MATERIAL CO., LTD.—See Hoa Sen Group; *Int'l*, pg. 3436
HOEGANAES CORP.—See GKN plc; *Int'l*, pg. 2986
HOJALATA MEXICANA, S.A. DE C.V.—See Grupo Acerero del Norte S.A. de C.V.; *Int'l*, pg. 3118
HORMANN AUTOMOTIVE SLOVAKIA S.R.O.—See Hormann Holding GmbH & Co. KG; *Int'l*, pg. 3480
HSIN KUANG STEEL CO., LTD.; *Int'l*, pg. 3507
HYUNDAI BNG STEEL CO., LTD.—See Hyundai Motor Company; *Int'l*, pg. 3559
HYUNDAI SPECIAL STEEL CO., LTD.—See Hyundai Steel Company; *Int'l*, pg. 3560
HYUNDAI STEEL CHONGQING CO., LTD.—See Hyundai Steel Company; *Int'l*, pg. 3560
HYUNDAI STEEL COMPANY; *Int'l*, pg. 3560
HYUNDAI STEEL COMPANY - ULSAN PLANT—See Hyundai Steel Company; *Int'l*, pg. 3560
HYUNDAI STEEL COMPANY - YESAN PLANT—See Hyundai Steel Company; *Int'l*, pg. 3560
HYUNDAI STEEL CZECH S.R.O—See Hyundai Steel Company; *Int'l*, pg. 3560
HYUNDAI STEEL INDIA PRIVATE, LTD.—See Hyundai Steel Company; *Int'l*, pg. 3560
HYUNDAI STEEL INDUSTRY & TRADE BRAZIL LLC—See Hyundai Steel Company; *Int'l*, pg. 3560

HYUNDAI STEEL INVESTMENT (CHINA) CO., LTD.—See Hyundai Steel Company; *Int'l*, pg. 3560
HYUNDAI STEEL JIANGSU PROCESS CO., LTD.—See Hyundai Steel Company; *Int'l*, pg. 3560
HYUNDAI STEEL MEXICO S DE R. L. DE C. V—See Hyundai Steel Company; *Int'l*, pg. 3560
HYUNDAI STEEL PIPE INDIA PRIVATE, LTD.—See Hyundai Steel Company; *Int'l*, pg. 3560
HYUNDAI STEEL SUZHOU PROCESS CO., LTD.—See Hyundai Steel Company; *Int'l*, pg. 3560
HYUNDAI STEEL TIANJIN CO., LTD.—See Hyundai Steel Company; *Int'l*, pg. 3561
HYUNDAI STEEL TR AUTOMOTIVE STEEL PARTS CO., LTD.—See Hyundai Steel Company; *Int'l*, pg. 3561
IAI HOLDING A/S; *Int'l*, pg. 3568
IB ANDRESEN INDUSTRI A/S-FREDERICIA—See IAI Holding A/S; *Int'l*, pg. 3568
IB ANDRESEN INDUSTRI A/S—See IAI Holding A/S; *Int'l*, pg. 3568
IB ANDRESEN INDUSTRY (THAILAND) CO. LTD—See IAI Holding A/S; *Int'l*, pg. 3568
IPCO AB—See FAM AB; *Int'l*, pg. 2611
IPCO US, LLC—See FAM AB; *Int'l*, pg. 2611
ITEC CORPORATION—See KKR & Co. Inc.; *U.S. Public*, pg. 1260
IVACO ROLLING MILLS, LP—See The Heico Companies, L.L.C.; *U.S. Private*, pg. 4050
JAMCO PRODUCTS, INC.—See Myers Industries, Inc.; *U.S. Public*, pg. 1488
JM STEEL CORP.—See Frank Calandra, Inc.; *U.S. Private*, pg. 1594
KEYSTONE STEEL & WIRE CO.—See Contran Corporation; *U.S. Private*, pg. 1033
KISWIRE ARCELORMITTAL LTD.—See ArcelorMittal S.A.; *Int'l*, pg. 545
KOIL METALS L.L.C.—See Cleveland-Cliffs, Inc.; *U.S. Public*, pg. 514
M.C.M. TECHNOLOGIES, INC.; *U.S. Private*, pg. 2528
MEDIKOMP GMBH—See Getinge AB; *Int'l*, pg. 2952
MEGASIDER ZARAGOZA S.A.U.—See Bipadosa SA; *Int'l*, pg. 1045
METAL MASTER SALES CORPORATION; *U.S. Private*, pg. 2680
MEXICHEM CID, S.A. DE C.V.—See Grupo Empresarial Kaluz S.A. de C.V.; *Int'l*, pg. 3127
MEXICHEM COLOMBIA, S.A.—See Grupo Empresarial Kaluz S.A. de C.V.; *Int'l*, pg. 3127
MEXICHEM SERVICIOS ADMINISTRATIVOS, S.A. DE C.V.—See Grupo Empresarial Kaluz S.A. de C.V.; *Int'l*, pg. 3128
MHM AUTOMATION LIMITED—See KKR & Co. Inc.; *U.S. Public*, pg. 1241
MIAMI VALLEY STEEL SERVICE INC.—See Polen Capital Management, Inc.; *U.S. Private*, pg. 3224
MINMETALS MATERIALS (CHANGSHU) MANAGEMENT CO., LTD.—See China Rare Earth Resources And Technology Co., Ltd.; *Int'l*, pg. 1546
MINMETALS YINGKOU MEDIUM-HEAVY PLATE CO., LTD.—See China Rare Earth Resources And Technology Co., Ltd.; *Int'l*, pg. 1546
MITSUBOSHI METAL INDUSTRY CO., LTD.—See Godo Steel, Ltd.; *Int'l*, pg. 3020
NELSEN STEEL & WIRE CO.; *U.S. Private*, pg. 2882
NEW DIMENSION METALS CORP.—See Gray America Corp.; *U.S. Private*, pg. 1759
NEW ZEALAND STEEL LIMITED—See BlueScope Steel Limited; *Int'l*, pg. 1074
NIAGARA LASALLE CORPORATION - BUFFALO PLANT—See Optima Specialty Steel, Inc.; *U.S. Private*, pg. 3034
NIAGARA LASALLE CORPORATION—See Optima Specialty Steel, Inc.; *U.S. Private*, pg. 3034
NIAGARA LASALLE CORPORATION - WARREN PLANT—See Optima Specialty Steel, Inc.; *U.S. Private*, pg. 3034
NORTH AMERICAN HOGANAS HIGH ALLOYS LLC—See Hoganas AB; *Int'l*, pg. 3441
NORTH AMERICAN HOGANAS-PYRON PLANT—See Hoganas AB; *Int'l*, pg. 3441
NORTH AMERICAN STAINLESS, INC.—See Acerinox, S.A.; *Int'l*, pg. 101
NORWALK POWDERED METALS, INC.; *U.S. Private*, pg. 2964
NUCOR COLD FINISH-NEBRASKA—See Nucor Corporation; *U.S. Public*, pg. 1553
NUCOR COLD FINISH-SOUTH CAROLINA—See Nucor Corporation; *U.S. Public*, pg. 1553
NUCOR STEEL - ARKANSAS—See Nucor Corporation; *U.S. Public*, pg. 1554
NUCOR STEEL DECATUR, LLC—See Nucor Corporation; *U.S. Public*, pg. 1554
NUCOR STEEL GALLATIN, LLC—See Nucor Corporation; *U.S. Public*, pg. 1554
OHIO GRATINGS, INC.; *U.S. Private*, pg. 3004
OHIO RIVER METAL SERVICES, INC.—See Reliance Steel & Aluminum Co.; *U.S. Public*, pg. 1781
OMEGA STEEL INC.—See Calstrip Industries Inc.; *U.S. Private*, pg. 723

N.A.I.C.S. INDEX

331313 — ALUMINA REFINING AN...

PARMATECH CORPORATION—See ATW Companies Inc.; *U.S. Private*, pg. 384
PCC STRUCTURALS (FRANCE)—See Berkshire Hathaway Inc.; *U.S. Public*, pg. 314
PEACHTREE METALS CO.—See Ta Chen International Inc; *U.S. Private*, pg. 3919
PERELLI ENTERPRISES, INC.; *U.S. Private*, pg. 3147
PHU MY ONE MEMBER LIMITED LIABILITIES COMPANY—See Hoa Sen Group; *Int'l*, pg. 3436
PLYMOUTH TUBE COMPANY - CHICAGO PROCESSING MILL—See Plymouth Tube Company; *U.S. Private*, pg. 3216
POWDER PROCESSING AND TECHNOLOGY, LLC—See E.J. Vestco Industries, LLC; *U.S. Private*, pg. 1306
PRECISION INDUSTRIES INC.—See Live Ventures Incorporated; *U.S. Public*, pg. 1332
PRECISION KIDD STEEL CO. INC.—See Jade Steel Group, Ltd.; *U.S. Private*, pg. 2181
PRECISION KIDD STEEL CO. INC.—See Standard Horse Nail Company, LLC; *U.S. Private*, pg. 3778
PREFAB TECHNOLOGY PTE LTD—See Hor Kew Corporation Limited; *Int'l*, pg. 3474
PROFILE STEEL & WIRE—See Whitesell Corporation; *U.S. Private*, pg. 4512
P.T. BIMA BISALLOY—See Bisalloy Steel Group Ltd.; *Int'l*, pg. 1048
PT ESSAR INDONESIA—See Essar Global Limited; *Int'l*, pg. 2508
QINGDAO HYUNDAI MACHINERY CO., LTD.—See Hyundai Steel Company; *Int'l*, pg. 3561
RATHBONE PRECISION METALS, INC.—See Calvi Holding S.r.l.; *Int'l*, pg. 1266
THE REMBAR COMPANY, LLC; *U.S. Private*, pg. 4104
ROME STRIP STEEL CO., INC.—See Worthington Industries, Inc.; *U.S. Public*, pg. 2382
SCHUFF STEEL MANAGEMENT COMPANY SE, LLC—See INNOVATE Corp.; *U.S. Public*, pg. 1126
SCHUFF STEEL MANAGEMENT COMPANY SW, INC.—See INNOVATE Corp.; *U.S. Public*, pg. 1126
SHANDONG HANGXIAO STEEL STRUCTURE CO., LTD.—See Hangxiao Steel Structure Co., Ltd.; *Int'l*, pg. 3246
SHANGHAI KRUPP STAINLESS CO., LTD.—See China Baowu Steel Group Corp., Ltd.; *Int'l*, pg. 1486
SHANGHAI STAL PRECISION STAINLESS STEEL COMPANY LIMITED—See ATI Inc.; *U.S. Public*, pg. 222
SIDERURGICA BALBOA, S.A.—See Alfonso Gallardo S.A.; *Int'l*, pg. 316
SIVACO WIRE GROUP L.P. - ONTARIO PLANT—See The Heico Companies, L.L.C.; *U.S. Private*, pg. 4051
SIVACO WIRE GROUP L.P.—See The Heico Companies, L.L.C.; *U.S. Private*, pg. 4051
SOCIETE NATIONALE DE SIDERURGIE S.A.—See ArcelorMittal S.A.; *Int'l*, pg. 546
STAHLWERK THURINGEN GMBH—See Companhia Siderurgica Nacional; *Int'l*, pg. 1748
STAKO SP. Z.O.O.—See Worthington Industries, Inc.; *U.S. Public*, pg. 2382
STEELSCAPE INC.—See BlueScope Steel Limited; *Int'l*, pg. 1073
STELCO INC.—See Bedrock Industries GP, LLC; *U.S. Private*, pg. 512
SWAN POINT YACHT & COUNTRY CLUB INC—See United States Steel Corporation; *U.S. Public*, pg. 2236
SYMMCO GROUP INC.; *U.S. Private*, pg. 3899
THEIS PRECISION STEEL INC.; *U.S. Private*, pg. 4141
THE THOMPSON COMPANIES; *U.S. Private*, pg. 4126
THOMPSON DAYTON STEEL SERVICE - PAULDING—See The Thompson Companies; *U.S. Private*, pg. 4126
THOMPSON DAYTON STEEL SERVICE - ROSEVILLE—See The Thompson Companies; *U.S. Private*, pg. 4126
THOMPSON DAYTON STEEL SERVICE—See The Thompson Companies; *U.S. Private*, pg. 4126
THREE D METALS CANADA, INC.—See Three D Metals Inc.; *U.S. Private*, pg. 4164
TIRUNA AMERICA INC.—See Guangdong Dongfang Science & Technology Co., Ltd.; *Int'l*, pg. 3153
ULBRICH PRECISION FLAT WIRE, INC.—See Ulbrich Stainless Steel & Special Metals, Inc.; *U.S. Private*, pg. 4275
ULBRICH SPECIALTY STRIP MILL—See Ulbrich Stainless Steel & Special Metals, Inc.; *U.S. Private*, pg. 4276
ULBRICH STAINLESS STEEL & SPECIAL METALS, INC.; *U.S. Private*, pg. 4275
U. S. STEEL EUROPE - FRANCE S.A.—See United States Steel Corporation; *U.S. Public*, pg. 2236
U. S. STEEL KOSICE - LABORTEST, S.R.O.—See United States Steel Corporation; *U.S. Public*, pg. 2236
U.S. STEEL KOSICE - SBS, S.R.O.—See United States Steel Corporation; *U.S. Public*, pg. 2237
VALIMET INC.; *U.S. Private*, pg. 4332
WESTERN TUBE & CONDUIT CORPORATION—See Zekelman Industries Inc.; *U.S. Private*, pg. 4600
WILCOX STEEL, LLC—See Ryerson Holding Corporation; *U.S. Public*, pg. 1829
WORLD RESOURCES COMPANY; *U.S. Private*, pg. 4567
WORTHINGTON CYLINDERS-EMBALAGENS INDUSTRIAIS DE GAS, S.A.—See Worthington Industries, Inc.; *U.S. Public*, pg. 2383
WORTHINGTON CYLINDERS GMBH—See Worthington Industries, Inc.; *U.S. Public*, pg. 2383
THE WORTHINGTON STEEL COMPANY—See Worthington Industries, Inc.; *U.S. Public*, pg. 2383
WORTHINGTON STEEL OF MICHIGAN, INC.—See Worthington Industries, Inc.; *U.S. Public*, pg. 2383
WORTHINGTON STEELPAC SYSTEMS, LLC—See Worthington Industries, Inc.; *U.S. Public*, pg. 2383
ZHANGJIAGANG XIAO-SHA COIL SERVICE CO., LTD.—See Hyosung Corporation; *Int'l*, pg. 3552
ZHEJIANG HEADERBOARD BUILDING MATERIALS CO., LTD.—See Hangxiao Steel Structure Co., Ltd.; *Int'l*, pg. 3246

331222 — STEEL WIRE DRAWING

ADVANEX AMERICAS, INC.—See Advanex Inc.; *Int'l*, pg. 163
ADVANEX EUROPE LTD—See Advanex Inc.; *Int'l*, pg. 163
AKVA GROUP ASA—See Egersund Group AS; *Int'l*, pg. 2323
AMERICAN SPRING WIRE CORP.; *U.S. Private*, pg. 255
AWP INDUSTRIES INC.; *U.S. Private*, pg. 411
AXEL JOHNSON INTERNATIONAL AB—See Axel Johnson Gruppen AB; *Int'l*, pg. 762
AXEL JOHNSON INTERNATIONAL AS—See Axel Johnson Gruppen AB; *Int'l*, pg. 764
AXFLOW OY—See Axel Johnson Gruppen AB; *Int'l*, pg. 763
AXFLOW S.R.O.—See Axel Johnson Gruppen AB; *Int'l*, pg. 763
BERGEN CABLE TECHNOLOGY, LLC—See Leggett & Platt, Incorporated; *U.S. Public*, pg. 1301
BLAST DEFLECTORS, INC.—See Hanover Partners, Inc.; *U.S. Private*, pg. 1855
CABLES Y ESLINGAS, S.A.—See Axel Johnson Gruppen AB; *Int'l*, pg. 763
CAPITAL ENGINEERING NETWORK PUBLIC COMPANY LIMITED; *Int'l*, pg. 1310
CHEROKEE MANUFACTURING INC.; *U.S. Private*, pg. 873
CHONGQING IRON & STEEL CO LTD; *Int'l*, pg. 1579
CMC STEEL FABRICATORS, INC.—See Commercial Metals Company; *U.S. Public*, pg. 545
DAVIS WIRE CORPORATION—See HEICO Corporation; *U.S. Public*, pg. 1019
EH BAARE CORPORATION; *U.S. Private*, pg. 1346
ENGTEX METALS (UTARA) SDN. BHD.—See Engtex Group Berhad; *Int'l*, pg. 2436
EUROLLS CARBIDE S.R.L.—See EUROLLS S.p.A.; *Int'l*, pg. 2553
EUROLLS DO BRASIL LTDA—See EUROLLS S.p.A.; *Int'l*, pg. 2553
EUROLLS S.P.A.; *Int'l*, pg. 2553
FORT WAYNE METALS IRELAND LTD—See Fort Wayne Metals Research Products Corp.; *U.S. Private*, pg. 1575
FORT WAYNE METALS RESEARCH PRODUCTS CORP.; *U.S. Private*, pg. 1575
FUJIKURA (MALAYSIA) SDN. BHD.—See Fujikura Ltd.; *Int'l*, pg. 2827
GEHR INDUSTRIES INC.—See The Gehr Group; *U.S. Private*, pg. 4032
GOLIK METAL MANUFACTURING CO. LIMITED—See Golik Holdings Limited; *Int'l*, pg. 3036
HAMPTON STEEL LTD.; *Int'l*, pg. 3240
HARSHA ENGINEERS EUROPE SRL—See Harsha Engineers International Limited; *Int'l*, pg. 3279
HARSHA PRECISION BEARING COMPONENTS (CHINA) CO. LTD.—See Harsha Engineers International Limited; *Int'l*, pg. 3279
HAYNES WIRE COMPANY—See Acerinox, S.A.; *Int'l*, pg. 101
HEICO WIRE GROUP—See HEICO Corporation; *U.S. Public*, pg. 1019
HENAN HENGXING SCIENCE & TECHNOLOGY CO., LTD.; *Int'l*, pg. 3342
HERAS-ADRONIT GMBH—See CRH plc; *Int'l*, pg. 1844
HERAS B.V.—See Equistone Partners Europe Limited; *Int'l*, pg. 2486
HEXONIA GMBH; *Int'l*, pg. 3371
HOLD KEY ELECTRIC WIRE & CABLE, CO. LTD. - TAIWAN FACTORY1—See Hold Key Electric Wire & Cable, Co. Ltd.; *Int'l*, pg. 3449
HOLD KEY ELECTRIC WIRE & CABLE, CO. LTD. - TAIWAN FACTORY2—See Hold Key Electric Wire & Cable, Co. Ltd.; *Int'l*, pg. 3449
HOLD KEY ELECTRIC WIRE & CABLE, CO. LTD. - TAIWAN FACTORY3—See Hold Key Electric Wire & Cable, Co. Ltd.; *Int'l*, pg. 3449
HYOSUNG STEEL CORD (QINGDAO) CO., LTD.—See Hyosung Corporation; *Int'l*, pg. 3551
ILSHINWELLS CO., LTD.; *Int'l*, pg. 3616
JOHNSTOWN WIRE TECHNOLOGIES, INC.—See GFG Alliance Limited; *Int'l*, pg. 2956
LAPHAM HICKEY STEEL (WI)—See Lapham-Hickey Steel Corp.; *U.S. Private*, pg. 2391
LIBERTY STEEL GEORGETOWN, INC.—See GFG Alliance Limited; *Int'l*, pg. 2956
LIFT-ALL CO., INC.; *U.S. Private*, pg. 2452
MAOMING HENGDA STEEL CO., LTD.—See General Steel Holdings, Inc.; *Int'l*, pg. 2920
MARLIN STEEL WIRE PRODUCTS LLC; *U.S. Private*, pg. 2585
MEADOW BURKE—See CRH plc; *Int'l*, pg. 1845
NESTAWAY—See Aurora Capital Group, LLC; *U.S. Private*, pg. 394
NUCOR STEEL CONNECTICUT INC.—See Nucor Corporation; *U.S. Public*, pg. 1554
OPTIMUS STEEL, LLC - BEAUMONT STEEL MILL—See Optimus Steel, LLC; *U.S. Private*, pg. 3365
REA MAGNET WIRE COMPANY, INC. - ASHLAND—See REA Magnet Wire Company, Inc.; *U.S. Private*, pg. 3365
ROLL ENG S.R.L.—See EUROLLS S.p.A.; *Int'l*, pg. 2553
SENECA WIRE & MANUFACTURING COMPANY; *U.S. Private*, pg. 3606
SHANDONG BAOSHIDA CABLE CO., LTD.—See Baoshida International Holding Group Co., Ltd.; *Int'l*, pg. 856
SONCO WORLDWIDE, INC.; *U.S. Private*, pg. 3712
ST. LOUIS COLD DRAWN LLC—See Nucor Corporation; *U.S. Public*, pg. 1554
TAUBENSEE STEEL & WIRE COMPANY INC.; *U.S. Private*, pg. 3936
TECHALLOY CO., INC.—See Lincoln Electric Holdings, Inc.; *U.S. Public*, pg. 1318
THAI-SCANDIC STEEL COMPANY LIMITED—See Berli Jucker Public Co. Ltd.; *Int'l*, pg. 985
TORPEDO SPECIALTY WIRE INC.; *U.S. Private*, pg. 4189
ULBRICH SHAPED WIRE, INC.—See Ulbrich Stainless Steel & Special Metals, Inc.; *U.S. Private*, pg. 4275
WALKER WIRE & STEEL COMPANY—See ArcelorMittal S.A.; *Int'l*, pg. 545

331313 — ALUMINA REFINING AND PRIMARY ALUMINUM PRODUCTION

AA METALS, INC; *U.S. Private*, pg. 29
AD SOLUTIONS S.R.L.—See Altair Engineering, Inc.; *U.S. Public*, pg. 86
AGES INDUSTRI AB; *Int'l*, pg. 206
ALCOA ALUMINIO S.A.—See Alcoa Corporation; *U.S. Public*, pg. 74
ALCOA CANADA LTD.—See Alcoa Corporation; *U.S. Public*, pg. 74
ALCOA INTALCO WORKS—See Alcoa Corporation; *U.S. Public*, pg. 74
ALCOA LTD.—See Alcoa Corporation; *U.S. Public*, pg. 74
ALCOA OF AUSTRALIA LIMITED—See Alcoa Corporation; *U.S. Public*, pg. 74
ALCOA WORLD ALUMINA LLC—See Alcoa Corporation; *U.S. Public*, pg. 74
ALCO HELLAS S.A.; *Int'l*, pg. 301
ALIBERICO, S.L.; *Int'l*, pg. 326
ALU-FORGE, INC.—See Berkshire Hathaway Inc.; *U.S. Public*, pg. 313
ALUMINERIE DE BECANCOUR INC.—See Alcoa Corporation; *U.S. Public*, pg. 74
ALUMINIUM DU MAROC SA; *Int'l*, pg. 401
ALUMINIUM OXID STADE GMBH—See Dadco Alumina & Chemicals Ltd.; *Int'l*, pg. 1904
ALUMINUM CORPORATION OF CHINA LIMITED; *Int'l*, pg. 401
ALUM S.A.; *Int'l*, pg. 400
ALUPROF DEUTSCHLAND GMBH—See Grupa Kety S.A.; *Int'l*, pg. 3116
ALUPROF S.A.—See Grupa Kety S.A.; *Int'l*, pg. 3116
ALUPROF SYSTEM CZECH, S.R.O.—See Grupa Kety S.A.; *Int'l*, pg. 3117
ALUPROF SYSTEM - ROMANIA SRL—See Grupa Kety S.A.; *Int'l*, pg. 3116
ALUPROF UK LTD.—See Grupa Kety S.A.; *Int'l*, pg. 3116
AMAG METAL GMBH—See AMAG Austria Metall AG; *Int'l*, pg. 408
AMARI AUSTRIA GMBH—See Henley Management Company; *U.S. Private*, pg. 1916
AMARI METALS IBERICA SLU—See Henley Management Company; *U.S. Private*, pg. 1916
ANHUI XINBO ALUMINUM CO., LTD.; *Int'l*, pg. 470
ARAMIT THAI ALUMINIUM LIMITED—See Aramit Group; *Int'l*, pg. 535
ASAHI SEIREN CO., LTD.; *Int'l*, pg. 598
AUSTEX DIES PTY LIMITED—See Capral Limited; *Int'l*, pg. 1315
BAHRAIN ATOMISERS INTERNATIONAL BSC—See Palladium Equity Partners, LLC; *U.S. Private*, pg. 3078
BANGLADESH THAI ALUMINIUM LIMITED; *Int'l*, pg. 836
BOHAI ALUMINIUM INDUSTRIES LTD.—See CITIC Group Corporation; *Int'l*, pg. 1619
BONNELL ALUMINUM (CLEARFIELD), INC.—See Tredegar Corporation; *U.S. Public*, pg. 2187
BONNELL ALUMINUM (ELKHART), INC.—See Tredegar Corporation; *U.S. Public*, pg. 2187
BONNELL ALUMINUM (NILES), LLC—See Tredegar Corporation; *U.S. Public*, pg. 2187

331313 — ALUMINA REFINING AN...

CENTURY ALUMINUM COMPANY; *U.S. Public,* pg. 474
CENTURY ALUMINUM OF KENTUCKY—See Century Aluminum Company; *U.S. Public,* pg. 474
CENTURY ALUMINUM OF SOUTH CAROLINA, INC.—See Century Aluminum Company; *U.S. Public,* pg. 474
CENTURY ALUMINUM OF WEST VIRGINIA, INC.—See Century Aluminum Company; *U.S. Public,* pg. 474
CENTURY ALUMINUM SEBREE, LLC—See Century Aluminum Company; *U.S. Public,* pg. 474
CHONGQING SHUNBO ALUMINUM CO., LTD.; *Int'l,* pg. 1581
CITIC AUSTRALIA TRADING LIMITED—See CITIC Group Corporation; *Int'l,* pg. 1620
CONNELL LIMITED PARTNERSHIP; *U.S. Private,* pg. 1017
CROFT LLC; *U.S. Private,* pg. 1103
DAIKI ALUMINIUM INDUSTRY CO., LTD.; *Int'l,* pg. 1931
DAIKI ALUMINIUM INDUSTRY (MALAYSIA) SDN. BHD.—See Daiki Aluminium Industry Co., Ltd.; *Int'l,* pg. 1931
DAIKI ALUMINIUM INDUSTRY THAILAND CO., LTD. - AMATA CITY FACTORY—See Daiki Aluminium Industry Co., Ltd.; *Int'l,* pg. 1931
DAIKI ALUMINIUM INDUSTRY THAILAND CO., LTD.—See Daiki Aluminium Industry Co., Ltd.; *Int'l,* pg. 1931
DAIKI MATERIAL CO., LTD.—See Daiki Aluminium Industry Co., Ltd.; *Int'l,* pg. 1931
EGYPT ALUMINUM COMPANY; *Int'l,* pg. 2327
ELIXIR INDUSTRIES - DIVISION 27—See Elixir Industries; *U.S. Private,* pg. 1362
FIRST ALUMINIUM NIGERIA PLC; *Int'l,* pg. 2681
GAC CHEMICAL CORP.; *U.S. Private,* pg. 1633
GARTNER EXTRUSION GMBH—See ALCO Hellas S.A.; *Int'l,* pg. 301
GUANGDONG HAOMEI NEW MATERIAL CO., LTD.; *Int'l,* pg. 3155
GUTMANN AG—See ALCO Hellas S.A.; *Int'l,* pg. 301
HIND ALUMINIUM INDUSTRIES LIMITED; *Int'l,* pg. 3397
HULAMIN EXTRUSIONS (PTY) LIMITED - CAPE TOWN PLANT—See Hulamin Limited; *Int'l,* pg. 3527
HULAMIN EXTRUSIONS (PTY) LIMITED - PIETERMARITZBURG PLANT—See Hulamin Limited; *Int'l,* pg. 3527
HULAMIN EXTRUSIONS (PTY) LIMITED—See Hulamin Limited; *Int'l,* pg. 3527
HULAMIN NORTH AMERICA LLC—See Hulamin Limited; *Int'l,* pg. 3528
HULAMIN OPERATIONS (PTY) LIMITED—See Hulamin Limited; *Int'l,* pg. 3527
HULAMIN ROLLED PRODUCTS (PTY) LIMITED—See Hulamin Limited; *Int'l,* pg. 3528
HULAMIN SYSTEMS (PTY) LIMITED—See Hulamin Limited; *Int'l,* pg. 3528
KAISER ALUMINUM CORPORATION; *U.S. Public,* pg. 1213
KYUSHU DAIKI ALUMINIUM CO., LTD.—See Daiki Aluminium Industry Co., Ltd.; *Int'l,* pg. 1931
LIONWELD KENNEDY FLOORING LTD—See Hill & Smith PLC; *Int'l,* pg. 3391
MEPURA METALLPULVERGESELLSCHAFT M. B. H.—See Palladium Equity Partners, LLC; *U.S. Private,* pg. 3078
NINGBO HUAYANG ALUMINIUM-TECH CO., LTD.—See China Steel Corporation; *Int'l,* pg. 1556
NON FERRUM KRANJ D.O.O.—See Palladium Equity Partners, LLC; *U.S. Private,* pg. 3078
NORDALU GMBH—See ALCO Hellas S.A.; *Int'l,* pg. 301
NORDURAL EHF—See Century Aluminum Company; *U.S. Public,* pg. 474
ONE UP INNOVATIONS, INC.—See Luvu Brands, Inc.; *U.S. Public,* pg. 1349
ORIENT ABRASIVES LIMITED—See Amergeris Wealth Management Group GmbH; *Int'l,* pg. 421
ORIENT ABRASIVES LIMITED—See Ashapura Minechem Limited; *Int'l,* pg. 606
PT. DAIKI ALUMINIUM INDUSTRY INDONESIA—See Daiki Aluminium Industry Co., Ltd.; *Int'l,* pg. 1931
PT WELL HARVEST WINNING ALUMINA REFINERY—See China Hongqiao Group Limited; *Int'l,* pg. 1508
PVS CHEMICALS SOLUTIONS, INC. - CHICAGO—See PVS Chemicals, Inc.; *U.S. Private,* pg. 3308
SEISHIN SEISAKUSYO CO., LTD.—See Daiki Aluminium Industry Co., Ltd.; *Int'l,* pg. 1932
SIGNATURE ALUMINUM CANADA, INC.—See H.I.G. Capital, LLC; *U.S. Private,* pg. 1831
SNIF SYSTEMS—See Pyrotek Incorporated; *U.S. Private,* pg. 3311
TALUM D.D.—See Elektro Slovenia d.o.o.; *Int'l,* pg. 2357
TENNESSEE ALUMINUM PROCESSORS; *U.S. Private,* pg. 3967
TRI-CITY EXTRUSION, INC.—See The Dyson-Kissner-Moran Corporation; *U.S. Private,* pg. 4024
ZIBO AGC ALUMINA MATERIALS CO., LTD.—See AGC Inc.; *Int'l,* pg. 204

331314 — SECONDARY SMELTING AND ALLOYING OF ALUMINUM

AFAI SOUTHERN SHIPYARD (PANYU GUANGZHOU) LTD.—See China Shipbuilding Industry Company Limited; *Int'l,* pg. 1551
AHRESTY CORPORATION - KUMAGAYA PLANT—See Ahresty Corporation; *Int'l,* pg. 225
ALCERECO INC.—See Grafoid, Inc.; *Int'l,* pg. 3050
ALLIED METAL COMPANY; *U.S. Private,* pg. 186
ALUMINIUM BAHRAIN B.S.C.; *Int'l,* pg. 401
ALUMINIUM REGEAL AFFIMET—See Aurea, S.A.; *Int'l,* pg. 707
AMG ALPOCO UK LIMITED—See AMG Critical Materials N.V.; *Int'l,* pg. 425
AMG ALUMINUM CHINA LIMITED—See AMG Critical Materials N.V.; *Int'l,* pg. 425
AMG ALUMINUM NORTH AMERICA, LLC - HENDERSON PLANT—See AMG Critical Materials N.V.; *Int'l,* pg. 425
AMG ALUMINUM NORTH AMERICA, LLC—See AMG Critical Materials N.V.; *Int'l,* pg. 425
AMG ALUMINUM NORTH AMERICA, LLC - WENATCHEE PLANT—See AMG Critical Materials N.V.; *Int'l,* pg. 425
AMG ALUMINUM UK LIMITED—See AMG Critical Materials N.V.; *Int'l,* pg. 425
AMG ANALYTICAL SERVICES LIMITED—See AMG Critical Materials N.V.; *Int'l,* pg. 425
AMG BRAZIL S.A.—See AMG Critical Materials N.V.; *Int'l,* pg. 426
A-RANK BERHAD; *Int'l,* pg. 20
ARORA-MATTHEY LIMITED; *Int'l,* pg. 577
AUDUBON METALS LLC—See Koch Enterprises, Inc.; *U.S. Private,* pg. 2326
AVY CO., LTD.—See AVY Precision Technology, Inc.; *Int'l,* pg. 751
A.W. FRASER LTD.; *Int'l,* pg. 28
BEIJER AS—See Beijer Alma AB; *Int'l,* pg. 942
BNC COMPANY CO., LTD.; *Int'l,* pg. 1078
CANNON-MUSKEGON CORPORATION—See Berkshire Hathaway Inc.; *U.S. Public,* pg. 314
CHINA RARE EARTH RESOURCES & TECHNOLOGY CO., LTD.—See China Rare Earth Resources And Technology Co., Ltd.; *Int'l,* pg. 1545
COMPX INTERNATIONAL INC.—See Contran Corporation; *U.S. Private,* pg. 1033
D. MAG (KUNSHAN) NEW MATERIAL TECHNOLOGY CO., LTD.—See Giant Manufacturing Co., Ltd.; *Int'l,* pg. 2961
DONG GUAN CHENG GUANG METAL PRODUCTS CO., LTD.—See AVY Precision Technology, Inc.; *Int'l,* pg. 751
DONG GUANG YING HUA PRECISION METAL CO., LTD.—See AVY Precision Technology, Inc.; *Int'l,* pg. 751
GRAVITA TANZANIA LIMITED—See Gravita India Limited; *Int'l,* pg. 3062
HAYNES INTERNATIONAL (CHINA) LTD.—See Acerinox, S.A.; *Int'l,* pg. 101
HAYNES INTERNATIONAL, INC.—See Acerinox, S.A.; *Int'l,* pg. 100
HAYNES INTERNATIONAL, LTD.—See Acerinox, S.A.; *Int'l,* pg. 100
HAYNES INTERNATIONAL SARL—See Acerinox, S.A.; *Int'l,* pg. 100
HAYNES INTERNATIONAL S.R.L.—See Acerinox, S.A.; *Int'l,* pg. 100
HAYNES PACIFIC PTE LTD—See Acerinox, S.A.; *Int'l,* pg. 101
HBIS GROUP CO., LTD.; *Int'l,* pg. 3295
HEYWOOD METAL FINISHERS LTD.—See Coil S.A./N.V.; *Int'l,* pg. 1696
IKD CO., LTD.; *Int'l,* pg. 3610
KAISER ALUMINUM CANADA LIMITED—See Kaiser Aluminum Corporation; *U.S. Public,* pg. 1213
KAISER ALUMINUM FABRICATED PRODUCTS—See Kaiser Aluminum Corporation; *U.S. Public,* pg. 1213
LISTON BRICK COMPANY OF CORONA INC.; *U.S. Private,* pg. 2467
NEMAK, S.A. DE C.V.—See ALFA, S.A.B. de C.V.; *Int'l,* pg. 313
OHIO VALLEY ALUMINUM COMPANY LLC—See Interlock Industries, Inc.; *U.S. Private,* pg. 2112
REAL ALLOY RECYCLING, INC. - MORGANTOWN—See Elah Holdings, Inc.; *U.S. Public,* pg. 722
REAL ALLOY RECYCLING, INC. - SAPULPA—See Elah Holdings, Inc.; *U.S. Public,* pg. 722
REAL ALLOY SPECIFICATION, INC.—See Elah Holdings, Inc.; *U.S. Public,* pg. 722
SCEPTER INC.; *U.S. Public,* pg. 3562
SIMS MANUFACTURING PTY. LTD.—See Sims Limited; *U.S. Public,* pg. 1884
TRG HOT SPRINGS, LLC—See Alter Trading Corporation; *U.S. Private,* pg. 207
TRIALCO INC.; *U.S. Private,* pg. 4225
TST INC.; *U.S. Private,* pg. 4254
UNITED ANODISERS UK LIMITED—See Coil S.A./N.V.; *Int'l,* pg. 1696

331315 — ALUMINUM SHEET, PLATE, AND FOIL MANUFACTURING

AEROLITE EXTRUSION COMPANY, INC.; *U.S. Private,* pg. 119
AGRA STAHLHANDELS-GMBH; *Int'l,* pg. 213

AHRESTY DIE MOLD KUMAMOTO CORPORATION—See Ahresty Corporation; *Int'l,* pg. 225
AHRESTY DIE MOLD TOCHIGI CORPORATION—See Ahresty Corporation; *Int'l,* pg. 225
AHRESTY INDIA PRIVATE LIMITED—See Ahresty Corporation; *Int'l,* pg. 226
AHRESTY PRECISION DIE MOLD (GUANGZHOU) CO., LTD.—See Ahresty Corporation; *Int'l,* pg. 226
AISIN AUTOMOTIVE CASTING TENNESSEE, INC.—See AISIN Corporation; *Int'l,* pg. 251
AISIN LIGHT METALS, LLC—See AISIN Corporation; *Int'l,* pg. 252
ALCAN PACKAGING RORSCHACH AG—See Amcor plc; *Int'l,* pg. 417
ALUCOAT CONVERSION, S.A.—See Aliberico, S.L.; *Int'l,* pg. 326
ALUKO CO., LTD; *Int'l,* pg. 400
ALUMIL ALBANIA SHPK.—See Alumil Aluminium Industry S.A.; *Int'l,* pg. 400
ALUMIL CY LTD.—See Alumil Aluminium Industry S.A.; *Int'l,* pg. 400
ALUMIL ITALIA S.R.L.—See Alumil Aluminium Industry S.A.; *Int'l,* pg. 400
ALUMIL OCEANIA PTY LTD—See Alumil Aluminium Industry S.A.; *Int'l,* pg. 400
ALUMIL S.A.—See Alumil Aluminium Industry S.A.; *Int'l,* pg. 400
ALUMIL SYSTEMS UK LIMITED—See Alumil Aluminium Industry S.A.; *Int'l,* pg. 400
ALUMINA A.D.; *Int'l,* pg. 400
ALUMINIUM COMPANY OF MALAYSIA BERHAD; *Int'l,* pg. 401
ALUMINIUMWERK UNNA AG—See China Zhongwang Holdings Limited; *Int'l,* pg. 1567
AMCOR FLEXIBLES SINGEN GMBH—See Amcor plc; *Int'l,* pg. 417
AMERICAN ALUMINUM EXTRUSION COMPANY, LLC.; *U.S. Private,* pg. 222
API FOILMAKERS LIMITED—See Aldus Pty. Ltd.; *Int'l,* pg. 305
ARAB ALUMINIUM INDUSTRY CO. LTD.; *Int'l,* pg. 529
ARCONIC (CHINA) INVESTMENT COMPANY LTD.—See Howmet Aerospace Inc.; *U.S. Public,* pg. 1062
ARFIN INDIA LIMITED; *Int'l,* pg. 560
AUTOLUM PROCESSING CO.—See Ferragon Corporation; *U.S. Private,* pg. 1498
BALL ADVANCED ALUMINUM TECHNOLOGIES CORP.—See Ball Corporation; *U.S. Public,* pg. 266
BALL AEROCAN CZ S.R.O.—See Ball Corporation; *U.S. Public,* pg. 266
BALL AEROCAN EUROPE S.A.S.—See Ball Corporation; *U.S. Public,* pg. 266
BALL AEROCAN FRANCE S.A.S—See Ball Corporation; *U.S. Public,* pg. 266
BALL AEROCAN MEXICO S.A. DE C.V.—See Ball Corporation; *U.S. Public,* pg. 266
BALL AEROCAN UK LTD.—See Ball Corporation; *U.S. Public,* pg. 266
BALL METAL FOOD CONTAINER (OAKDALE), LLC—See Ball Corporation; *U.S. Public,* pg. 267
BALL PACKAGING EUROPE FRANCE S.A.S.—See Ball Corporation; *U.S. Public,* pg. 267
BREMER STAHL SERVICE GMBH; *Int'l,* pg. 1145
BRIGHT PACKAGING INDUSTRY BERHAD; *Int'l,* pg. 1161
CAMCASTING SRL—See Camozzi Group; *Int'l,* pg. 1273
CCL CONTAINER—See CCL Industries Inc.; *Int'l,* pg. 1367
CENTURY ALUMINUM OF KENTUCKY GENERAL PARTNERSHIP—See Century Aluminum Company; *U.S. Public,* pg. 474
CENTURY KENTUCKY, INC.—See Century Aluminum Company; *U.S. Public,* pg. 474
CHOIL ALUMINUM CO., LTD.; *Int'l,* pg. 1577
CHUNG HSIN POWER SYSTEMS (SHENYANG) INC.—See Chung-Hsin Electric & Machinery Manufacturing Corp.; *Int'l,* pg. 1597
CITIC BOHAI ALUMINIUM INDUSTRIES HOLDING COMPANY LTD.—See CITIC Group Corporation; *Int'l,* pg. 1619
CLIMCO COILS COMPANY; *U.S. Private,* pg. 943
COMITAL SKULTUNA AB—See Comital S.p.A.; *Int'l,* pg. 1714
DAEHO AL CO., LTD.; *Int'l,* pg. 1907
DEXMET CORPORATION—See PPG Industries, Inc.; *U.S. Public,* pg. 1707
DOKTAS METAL SANAYI VE TICARTE A.S.; *Int'l,* pg. 2156
DONGYANG GANGCHUL CO., LTD - 1ST FACTORY—See Aluko Co., Ltd; *Int'l,* pg. 400
DONGYANG GANGCHUL CO., LTD - 2ND FACTORY—See Aluko Co., Ltd; *Int'l,* pg. 400
DONGYANG GANGCHUL CO., LTD - 5TH FACTORY—See Aluko Co., Ltd; *Int'l,* pg. 400
EBARA MATERIAL CO., LTD.—See Ebara Corporation; *Int'l,* pg. 2283
ENSAR CORP.; *U.S. Private,* pg. 1401
EUROFOIL LUXEMBOURG S.A.—See American Industrial Acquisition Corporation; *U.S. Public,* pg. 237
FEDCHEM LLC—See Federal Process Corporation; *U.S. Private,* pg. 1489

N.A.I.C.S. INDEX

331318 — OTHER ALUMINUM ROLL...

FRITZ LANGE GMBH; *Int'l*, pg. 2794
FUJI OFFSET PLATES MANUFACTURING LTD; *Int'l*, pg. 2814
GEREMARIE CORPORATION—See Patrick Industries, Inc.; *U.S. Public*, pg. 1652
GRUPA KETY S.A.; *Int'l*, pg. 3116
GRUPO VASCONIA, S.A.B.; *Int'l*, pg. 3138
GSC FOUNDRIES, INC.—See Berkshire Hathaway Inc.; *U.S. Public*, pg. 314
GUANGDONG HOSHION INDUSTRIAL ALUMINIUM CO.,LTD.; *Int'l*, pg. 3156
GUANGDONG HUAFENG NEW ENERGY TECHNOLOGY CO., LTD; *Int'l*, pg. 3156
GUANGZHOU AHRESTY CASTING CO., LTD.—See Ahresty Corporation; *Int'l*, pg. 226
HAKUDO CO., LTD. - FUKUSHIMA PLANT—See Hakudo Co., Ltd.; *Int'l*, pg. 3219
HAKUDO CO., LTD. - KANAGAWA PLANT—See Hakudo Co., Ltd.; *Int'l*, pg. 3220
HAKUDO CO., LTD. - KYUSHU PLANT—See Hakudo Co., Ltd.; *Int'l*, pg. 3220
HAKUDO CO., LTD. - SHIGA PLANT—See Hakudo Co., Ltd.; *Int'l*, pg. 3220
HAKUDO CO., LTD.; *Int'l*, pg. 3219
HEFEI AHRESTY CASTING CO., LTD.—See Ahresty Corporation; *Int'l*, pg. 226
HENAN MINGTAI ALUMINUM CO., LTD.; *Int'l*, pg. 3342
HENAN ZHONGFU INDUSTRY CO., LTD.; *Int'l*, pg. 3344
HENDRY ALUMINUM, INC.; *U.S. Private*, pg. 1916
HOEI SHOJI CO., LTD.—See Dowa Holdings Co., Ltd.; *Int'l*, pg. 2184
HOWARD PRECISION METALS, INC.—See Ryerson Holding Corporation; *U.S. Public*, pg. 1829
HUNTER DOUGLAS SOUTH AFRICA PTY LTD—See 3G Capital Partners L.P.; *U.S. Private*, pg. 12
IBERFOIL ARAGON S.L.U.—See Aliberico, S.L.; *Int'l*, pg. 326
IMPEXMETAL S.A.—See Boryszew S.A.; *Int'l*, pg. 1115
JIANGYIN LITAI ORNAMENTAL MATERIALS CO., LTD.—See China Haida Ltd.; *Int'l*, pg. 1506
JW ALUMINUM CO.—See Wellspring Capital Management LLC; *U.S. Private*, pg. 4477
JW ALUMINUM CO.—See Wellspring Capital Management LLC; *U.S. Private*, pg. 4477
KAISER ALUMINUM WASHINGTON, LLC—See Kaiser Aluminum Corporation; *U.S. Public*, pg. 1213
KROY INDUSTRIES, INC.; *U.S. Private*, pg. 2353
MAGIC TILT TRAILERS, INC.; *U.S. Private*, pg. 2546
METALES INTERAMERICANOS S.A. DE C.V.—See Endeavour Silver Corp.; *Int'l*, pg. 2403
NATIONAL ALUMINUM & PROFILES COMPANY PLC—See Arab Palestinian Investment Company; *Int'l*, pg. 531
NIKKEI HEAT EXCHANGER CO., LTD—See Modine Manufacturing Company; *U.S. Public*, pg. 1455
PETERSEN ALUMINUM CORPORATION—See Carlisle Companies Incorporated; *U.S. Public*, pg. 437
Q SALES, LLC—See Lanco International Inc.; *U.S. Private*, pg. 2382
QUANEX BUILDING PRODUCTS CORP.; *U.S. Public*, pg. 1749
RAYLIGHT ALUMINIUM LIMITED—See Fletcher Building Limited; *Int'l*, pg. 2701
REAL ALLOY CANADA LTD.—See Elah Holdings, Inc.; *U.S. Public*, pg. 722
REYNOLDS CONSUMER PRODUCTS CANADA INC.—See Pactiv Evergreen Inc.; *U.S. Public*, pg. 1633
RIALCA—See Corporacion Venezolana de Guayana; *Int'l*, pg. 1805
SARIO GRUNDSTUCKS-VERMIETUNGSGESELLSCHAFT MBH & CO. OBJEKT ELFI—See Ball Corporation; *U.S. Public*, pg. 268
SEIKI CO., LTD.—See Hanwa Co., Ltd.; *Int'l*, pg. 3263
SHEFFIELD METALS INTERNATIONAL, INC.; *U.S. Private*, pg. 3630
THAI AHRESTY ENGINEERING CO., LTD.—See Ahresty Corporation; *Int'l*, pg. 226
TIANJIN ZHONGWANG ALUMINIUM COMPANY LIMITED—See China Zhongwang Holdings Limited; *Int'l*, pg. 1567
UNITED ALUMINUM CORPORATION; *U.S. Private*, pg. 4287
UNITY ALUMINUM, INC.; *U.S. Private*, pg. 4302
VULCAN, INC. - VULCAN ALUMINUM DIVISION—See Vulcan, Inc.; *U.S. Private*, pg. 4416
WISE ALLOYS LLC; *U.S. Private*, pg. 4549
WRISCO INDUSTRIES INC. - ATLANTA DIVISION—See Wrisco Industries Inc.; *U.S. Private*, pg. 4574
WRISCO INDUSTRIES INC. - CHICAGO DIVISION—See Wrisco Industries Inc.; *U.S. Private*, pg. 4574
WRISCO INDUSTRIES INC. - DALLAS DIVISION—See Wrisco Industries Inc.; *U.S. Private*, pg. 4574
WRISCO INDUSTRIES INC. - EDISON DIVISION—See Wrisco Industries Inc.; *U.S. Private*, pg. 4574
ZERO HALLIBURTON, INC.; *U.S. Private*, pg. 4602

331318 — OTHER ALUMINUM ROLLING, DRAWING, AND EXTRUDING

ACS INTERNACIONAL S.A. DE C.V.—See ACS Industries, Inc.; *U.S. Private*, pg. 66
AIRGUIDE CORPORATION; *U.S. Private*, pg. 141
ALARI AUSTRIA GMBH—See Henley Management Company; *U.S. Private*, pg. 1916
ALCONEX SPECIALTY PRODUCTS, INC.; *U.S. Private*, pg. 154
ALCO ROM TRADE SRL—See ALCO Hellas S.A.; *Int'l*, pg. 301
ALEXANDRIA EXTRUSION COMPANY INC.; *U.S. Private*, pg. 164
ALGONQUIN INDUSTRIES DIVISION—See REA Magnet Wire Company, Inc.; *U.S. Private*, pg. 3365
AL JABER ALUMINUM EXTRUSION L.L.C.—See Al Jaber Group; *Int'l*, pg. 279
ALLTUB BV—See OEP Capital Advisors, L.P.; *U.S. Private*, pg. 2997
ALLTUB CENTRAL EUROPE A.S.—See OEP Capital Advisors, L.P.; *U.S. Private*, pg. 2997
ALLTUB DEUTSCHLAND GMBH—See OEP Capital Advisors, L.P.; *U.S. Private*, pg. 2998
ALLTUB ITALIA SRL—See OEP Capital Advisors, L.P.; *U.S. Private*, pg. 2998
ALUCOIL S.A.—See Aliberico, S.L.; *Int'l*, pg. 326
ALUMIL ALUMINIUM INDUSTRY S.A.; *Int'l*, pg. 400
ALUMIL BULGARIA LTD.—See Alumil Aluminium Industry S.A.; *Int'l*, pg. 400
ALUMIL DEUTSCHLAND GMBH—See Alumil Aluminium Industry S.A.; *Int'l*, pg. 400
ALUMIL GULF FZC—See Alumil Aluminium Industry S.A.; *Int'l*, pg. 400
ALUMIL HUNGARY K.T.F.—See Alumil Aluminium Industry S.A.; *Int'l*, pg. 400
ALUMIL KOSOVA SHPK—See Alumil Aluminium Industry S.A.; *Int'l*, pg. 400
ALUMIL LLC—See Alumil Aluminium Industry S.A.; *Int'l*, pg. 400
ALUMIL MOLDAVIA—See Alumil Aluminium Industry S.A.; *Int'l*, pg. 400
ALUMIL POLSKA SP. Z O.O.—See Alumil Aluminium Industry S.A.; *Int'l*, pg. 400
ALUMIL ROM INDUSTRY S.A.—See Alumil Aluminium Industry S.A.; *Int'l*, pg. 400
ALUMIL SKOPJE D.O.O.—See Alumil Aluminium Industry S.A.; *Int'l*, pg. 400
ALUMIL SRB D.O.O.—See Alumil Aluminium Industry S.A.; *Int'l*, pg. 400
ALUMIL TECHNIC D.O.O.—See Alumil Aluminium Industry S.A.; *Int'l*, pg. 400
ALUMIL UKRAINE LTD.—See Alumil Aluminium Industry S.A.; *Int'l*, pg. 400
ALUMIL VARNA LTD.—See Alumil Aluminium Industry S.A.; *Int'l*, pg. 400
ALUMIL YU INDUSTRY A.D.—See Alumil Aluminium Industry S.A.; *Int'l*, pg. 400
ALUMINA ESPANOLA, S.A.—See Alcoa Corporation; *U.S. Public*, pg. 74
THE ALUMINIUM POWDER COMPANY LIMITED—See AMG Critical Materials N.V.; *Int'l*, pg. 426
ALUMINUM PRODUCTS COMPANY LTD.; *Int'l*, pg. 401
ALUMINUM SHAPES, LLC—See H.I.G. Capital, LLC; *U.S. Private*, pg. 1831
ALUTEC ANODISING & MACHINE TOOLS (PVT) LTD.—See Hayleys PLC; *Int'l*, pg. 3291
ALUWORKS LIMITED; *Int'l*, pg. 401
AMAG AUSTRIA METALL AG; *Int'l*, pg. 407
AMAG ROLLING GMBH—See AMAG Austria Metall AG; *Int'l*, pg. 408
AMARI HUNGARIA KFT.—See Henley Management Company; *U.S. Private*, pg. 1916
ANAHEIM EXTRUSION CO. INC.—See UMC Acquisition Corp.; *U.S. Private*, pg. 4278
APOLO TOOL & DIE MANUFACTURING INC.—See TEOCO Corporation; *U.S. Private*, pg. 3969
ARCADIA INC.—See DMC Global Inc.; *U.S. Public*, pg. 671
ARCONIC ARCHITECTURAL PRODUCTS SAS—See Howmet Aerospace Inc.; *U.S. Public*, pg. 1062
ARCONIC DOMESTIC LLC—See Howmet Aerospace Inc.; *U.S. Public*, pg. 1061
ASCENT BRIDGE LIMITED; *Int'l*, pg. 602
ASIA ALUMINIUM HOLDINGS LIMITED; *Int'l*, pg. 610
ASIA PACIFIC WIRE & CABLE CORPORATION LIMITED; *Int'l*, pg. 614
ATLANTIC ALUMINUM, LLC—See H.I.G. Capital, LLC; *U.S. Private*, pg. 1829
BACO CONSUMER PRODUCTS LTD.—See Pactiv Evergreen Inc.; *U.S. Public*, pg. 1633
BELDEN CDT (CANADA) INC.—See Belden, Inc.; *U.S. Public*, pg. 293
BENTELER ALUMINIUM SYSTEMS SWEDEN AB—See Benteler International AG; *Int'l*, pg. 976
BHORUKA FABCONS PRIVATE LIMITED—See Bhoruka Aluminium Ltd.; *Int'l*, pg. 1015
BOLUO FENG CHING MAGNET WIRE MANUFACTURING CO., LTD.—See Feng Ching Metal Corp.; *Int'l*, pg. 2634
B&P MANUFACTURING; *U.S. Private*, pg. 419
BRAZEWAY INC.; *U.S. Private*, pg. 642

BRAZONICS, INC.—See RTX Corporation; *U.S. Public*, pg. 1822
BUTLER (SHANGHAI), INC.—See BlueScope Steel Limited; *Int'l*, pg. 1073
CALIFORNIA CUSTOM SHAPES INC.; *U.S. Private*, pg. 718
CAPRAL ALUMINIUM-SHEETS—See Capral Limited; *Int'l*, pg. 1315
CAPRAL LIMITED; *Int'l*, pg. 1315
CARDINAL ALUMINUM CO.; *U.S. Private*, pg. 749
CASTLE METALS AEROSPACE—See A. M. Castle & Co.; *U.S. Public*, pg. 11
CBT TECHNOLOGY INC.—See AbelConn LLC; *U.S. Private*, pg. 37
CENTURY EXTRUSIONS LIMITED; *Int'l*, pg. 1418
CHINA HAIDA LTD.; *Int'l*, pg. 1506
CHINA HONGQIAO GROUP LIMITED; *Int'l*, pg. 1508
CHINA ZHONGWANG HOLDINGS LIMITED; *Int'l*, pg. 1567
CHONGQING HI-LEX CABLE SYSTEM GROUP CO., LTD—See Hi-Lex Corporation; *Int'l*, pg. 3380
CMI ARCHITECTURAL PRODUCTS, INC.; *U.S. Private*, pg. 951
COIL S.A./N.V.; *Int'l*, pg. 1696
COMPONEX CORPORATION—See Berwind Corporation; *U.S. Private*, pg. 541
CONSTELLIUM AVIATUBE SAS—See Constellium SE; *Int'l*, pg. 1776
CONSTELLIUM EXTRUSIONS DECIN S.R.O.—See Constellium SE; *Int'l*, pg. 1776
CONSTELLIUM EXTRUSIONS LANDAU GMBH—See Constellium SE; *Int'l*, pg. 1776
CONSTELLIUM SABART SAS—See Constellium SE; *Int'l*, pg. 1776
CONSTRUCTION SPECIALTIES, INC.—See Construction Specialties, Inc.; *U.S. Private*, pg. 1024
COPARTNER WIRE & CABLE (SHENZHEN) CO LTD—See Copartner Technology Corporation; *Int'l*, pg. 1793
COPERION LTDA.—See Hillenbrand, Inc.; *U.S. Public*, pg. 1036
COPERION MIDDLE EAST CO. LTD.—See Hillenbrand, Inc.; *U.S. Public*, pg. 1036
COPERION N.V.—See Hillenbrand, Inc.; *U.S. Public*, pg. 1036
COPERION S.L.—See Hillenbrand, Inc.; *U.S. Public*, pg. 1036
CRANE ENFIELD METALS PTY LIMITED—See Fletcher Building Limited; *Int'l*, pg. 2699
CUPRUM S.A. DE C.V.; *Int'l*, pg. 1878
CUSTOM ALUMINUM PRODUCTS INC.; *U.S. Private*, pg. 1128
DAH SAN ELECTRIC WIRE & CABLE CO., LTD. - SECOND FACTORY—See Dah San Electric Wire & Cable Co., Ltd.; *Int'l*, pg. 1912
DDB UNLIMITED, INC.; *U.S. Private*, pg. 1180
DELAIR GROUP, LLC—See H.I.G. Capital, LLC; *U.S. Private*, pg. 1831
ELEKTRISOLA ATESINA S.R.L.—See Elektrisola Dr. Gerd Schildbach GmbH & Co. KG; *Int'l*, pg. 2356
ELEKTRISOLA DR. GERD SCHILDBACH GMBH & CO. KG; *Int'l*, pg. 2356
ELEKTRISOLA FEINDRAHT AG—See Elektrisola Dr. Gerd Schildbach GmbH & Co. KG; *Int'l*, pg. 2356
ELEKTRISOLA (HANGZHOU) CO., LTD.—See Elektrisola Dr. Gerd Schildbach GmbH & Co. KG; *Int'l*, pg. 2356
ELEKTRISOLA (M) SDN. BHD.—See Elektrisola Dr. Gerd Schildbach GmbH & Co. KG; *Int'l*, pg. 2356
ELEKTRISOLA S.A. DE C.V.—See Elektrisola Dr. Gerd Schildbach GmbH & Co. KG; *Int'l*, pg. 2356
ELIXIR INDUSTRIES—See Elixir Industries; *U.S. Private*, pg. 1362
EMIRATES EXTRUSIONS FACTORY LLC—See Dubai Investments PJSC; *Int'l*, pg. 2219
EWS (MANUFACTURING) LIMITED—See Hadley Industries PLC; *Int'l*, pg. 3205
EXALCO BULGARIA A.D.—See Biokarpet S.A.; *Int'l*, pg. 1038
EXALCO ROMANIA SRL—See Biokarpet S.A.; *Int'l*, pg. 1038
EXALCO S.A.—See Biokarpet S.A.; *Int'l*, pg. 1038
EXTRUSIONS INC.; *U.S. Private*, pg. 1453
FLETCHER ALUMINIUM—See Fletcher Building Limited; *Int'l*, pg. 2700
FOOSUNG PRECISION INDUSTRY CO., LTD.—See Foosung Co., Ltd.; *Int'l*, pg. 2728
FORGED SOLUTIONS GROUP, LTD—See Arlington Capital Partners LLC; *U.S. Private*, pg. 327
FRY REGLET CORPORATION; *U.S. Private*, pg. 1618
FUJIAN MINFA ALUMINIUM CO., LTD; *Int'l*, pg. 2818
FUTURA CORPORATION; *U.S. Private*, pg. 1626
FUTURA INDUSTRIES CORPORATION—See Tredegar Corporation; *U.S. Public*, pg. 2187
GALADA POWER & TELECOMMUNICATION LTD.; *Int'l*, pg. 2870
GAMMA INDUSTRIES INC.—See RED Holdings Group Inc.; *U.S. Private*, pg. 3374
GAMMA USA, INC.—See RED Holdings Group Inc.; *U.S. Private*, pg. 3375
GAMMID TRADING (PTY) LTD—See ARGENT INDUS-

331318 — OTHER ALUMINUM ROLL...

TRIAL LIMITED; *Int'l*, pg. 560
GEMINI ALUMINUM CORPORATION; *U.S. Private*, pg. 1657
GENERAL EXTRUSIONS INC.; *U.S. Private*, pg. 1665
GLOBAL MARINE SYSTEMS (AMERICAS) INC.—See J.F. Lehman & Company, Inc.; *U.S. Private*, pg. 2163
GOLKONDA ALUMINIUM EXTRUSIONS LTD.; *Int'l*, pg. 3036
GORDON ALUMINUM INDUSTRIES, INC.; *U.S. Private*, pg. 1741
GRANGES AMERICAS INC. - NEWPORT PLANT—See Granges AB; *Int'l*, pg. 3058
GRANGES AMERICAS INC.—See Granges AB; *Int'l*, pg. 3058
GULF CLOSURES W.L.L.—See AptarGroup, Inc.; *U.S. Public*, pg. 174
HEAVY DUTY RAMPS, LLC—See Rotunda Capital Partners LLC; *U.S. Private*, pg. 3488
HERTI AD; *Int'l*, pg. 3365
HUISHENG PLASTICS (SHEN ZHEN) CO LTD—See Copartner Technology Corporation; *Int'l*, pg. 1793
HYGRADE ACQUISITION METAL MOLDING; *U.S. Private*, pg. 2018
HYGRADE METAL MOULDING MANUFACTURING CORP.—See Hygrade Acquisition Metal Molding; *U.S. Private*, pg. 2018
IDEAL DEALS, LLC; *U.S. Private*, pg. 2036
INTERCONNECT SOLUTIONS INC.; *U.S. Private*, pg. 2109
INTERNATIONAL EXTRUSION CORP.—See UMC Acquisition Corp.; *U.S. Private*, pg. 4278
INTERNATIONAL EXTRUSIONS, INC.; *U.S. Private*, pg. 2116
INTERTECHSERVICE LTD.—See Herti AD; *Int'l*, pg. 3365
JIANGMEN COSCO SHIPPING ALUMINIUM CO., LTD.—See China COSCO Shipping Corporation Limited; *Int'l*, pg. 1495
JUPITER ALUMINUM CORPORATION; *U.S. Private*, pg. 2245
KAISER ALUMINUM ALEXCO LLC—See Kaiser Aluminum Corporation; *U.S. Public*, pg. 1213
KAISER ALUMINUM FABRICATED PRODUCTS, LLC—See Kaiser Aluminum Corporation; *U.S. Public*, pg. 1213
KAISER ALUMINUM FABRICATED PRODUCTS—See Kaiser Aluminum Corporation; *U.S. Public*, pg. 1213
KEYMARK CORPORATION; *U.S. Private*, pg. 2294
KYMERA INTERNATIONAL—See Palladium Equity Partners, LLC; *U.S. Private*, pg. 3077
LINN PRODUCTS, INC.; *U.S. Private*, pg. 2462
THE LOXCREEN COMPANY, INC.; *U.S. Private*, pg. 4073
LSM BRASIL S.A.—See AMG Critical Materials N.V.; *Int'l*, pg. 426
MAGNODE CORPORATION; *U.S. Private*, pg. 2548
METAL IMPACT LLC—See Thunderbird LLC; *U.S. Private*, pg. 4166
MID-STATES ALUMINUM CORP.—See Mayville Engineering Company, Inc.; *U.S. Public*, pg. 1403
NATIONAL ALUMINIUM LIMITED—See Capral Limited; *Int'l*, pg. 1315
NEDAL—See 3G Capital Partners L.P.; *U.S. Private*, pg. 13
OLYMPIC STEEL-SOUTHERN DIVISION—See Olympic Steel Inc.; *U.S. Public*, pg. 1571
OOO "COPERION"—See Hillenbrand, Inc.; *U.S. Public*, pg. 1036
PCC AIRFOILS S.A. DE C.V.—See Berkshire Hathaway Inc.; *U.S. Public*, pg. 314
PENN ALUMINUM INTERNATIONAL, INC.—See Berkshire Hathaway Inc.; *U.S. Public*, pg. 310
PREFORMADOS DE MEXICO SA—See Preformed Line Products Company; *U.S. Public*, pg. 1714
PROFILE CUSTOM EXTRUSION, LLC—See Highlander Partners, L.P.; *U.S. Private*, pg. 1939
PROFILE EXTRUSION COMPANY INC.; *U.S. Private*, pg. 3277
PROFILE PRECISION EXTRUSIONS—See Profile Extrusion Company Inc.; *U.S. Private*, pg. 3277
RICHARDSON METALS, INC.; *U.S. Private*, pg. 3429
SHEN ZHEN COPARTNER COMMUNICATION CO LTD—See Copartner Technology Corporation; *Int'l*, pg. 1793
SICOAC—See Aliaxis S.A./N.V.; *Int'l*, pg. 325
SOUTHEASTERN EXTRUSION & TOOL, INC.; *U.S. Private*, pg. 3727
SOUTHERN METALS CO INC.; *U.S. Private*, pg. 3733
SOUTHWIRE COMPANY, LLC; *U.S. Private*, pg. 3742
STRENGTH CAPITAL PARTNERS, LLC; *U.S. Private*, pg. 3839
TABER EXTRUSIONS LP—See Tang Industries Inc.; *U.S. Private*, pg. 3930
TAILOR WELDED BLANKS OF CANADA, INC.—See Worthington Industries, Inc.; *U.S. Public*, pg. 2382
TONER CABLE EQUIPMENT UK LTD—See Toner Cable Equipment Inc.; *U.S. Private*, pg. 4184
TULSA POWER, INC; *U.S. Private*, pg. 4258
UNION ELECTRIC STEEL UK LIMITED—See Ampco-Pittsburgh Corporation; *U.S. Public*, pg. 126
UNIVERSAL ALLOY CORPORATION—See Global Equity Partners Beteiligungs-Management AG; *Int'l*, pg. 2996
UNIVERSAL MOLDING EXTRUSION CO.—See UMC Acquisition Corp.; *U.S. Private*, pg. 4278
US POLYMERS INC.; *U.S. Private*, pg. 4319
VITEX EXTRUSION, LLC—See OEP Capital Advisors, L.P.; *U.S. Private*, pg. 2999
WESTERN EXTRUSIONS; *U.S. Private*, pg. 4493
WHITE ALUMINUM EXTRUSION LLC—See Dubai Investments PJSC; *Int'l*, pg. 2219
THE WILLIAM L. BONNELL CO., INC.—See Tredegar Corporation; *U.S. Public*, pg. 2187
YANFU COPARTNER TECHNOLOGY (SHENZHEN) CO., LTD—See Copartner Technology Corporation; *Int'l*, pg. 1793
ZEPHYR ALUMINUM INC.; *U.S. Private*, pg. 4602

331410 — NONFERROUS METAL (EXCEPT ALUMINUM) SMELTING AND REFINING

AKITA ZINC SOLUTIONS CO., LTD.—See Dowa Holdings Co., Ltd.; *Int'l*, pg. 2182
ALLOYWORKS, LLC—See Berkshire Hathaway Inc.; *U.S. Public*, pg. 313
ANHUI TRUCHUM ADVANCED MATERIALS AND TECHNOLOGY CO.; *Int'l*, pg. 470
ANHUI ZHONGYUAN NEW MATERIALS CO., LTD.; *Int'l*, pg. 471
ANSAM METALS LLC—See Audax Group, Limited Partnership; *U.S. Private*, pg. 390
ARCOTECH LTD.; *Int'l*, pg. 551
ARE HOLDINGS, INC.; *Int'l*, pg. 557
ARGEN CORPORATION; *U.S. Private*, pg. 319
ASAHI REFINING FLORIDA, LLC—See ARE Holdings, Inc.; *Int'l*, pg. 557
ASAKA RIKEN CO., LTD. - FUKUYAMA PLANT—See Asaka Riken Co., Ltd.; *Int'l*, pg. 599
ASAKA RIKEN CO., LTD. - IWAKI PLANT—See Asaka Riken Co., Ltd.; *Int'l*, pg. 599
ASTURIANA DE ZINC S.A.—See Glencore plc; *Int'l*, pg. 2990
ATI SPECIALTY ALLOYS AND COMPONENTS—See ATI Inc.; *U.S. Public*, pg. 221
ATLANTIC COPPER, S.A.—See Freeport-McMoRan Inc.; *U.S. Public*, pg. 884
AURUBIS BULGARIA AD—See Aurubis AG; *Int'l*, pg. 715
AURUBIS ITALIA SRL—See Aurubis AG; *Int'l*, pg. 715
AURUBIS NV/SA - OLEN—See Aurubis AG; *Int'l*, pg. 715
AURUBIS STOLBERG VERWALTUNGS GMBH—See Aurubis AG; *Int'l*, pg. 714
AVINS USA, INC.—See Baoshida International Holding Group Co., Ltd.; *Int'l*, pg. 856
BAOWU MAGNESIUM TECHNOLOGY CO., LTD.; *Int'l*, pg. 857
BARODA EXTRUSION LIMITED; *Int'l*, pg. 866
BASF CATALYSTS LLC - MATERIAL SERVICES—See BASF SE; *Int'l*, pg. 875
BEIJING SHOUGANG CO., LTD.; *Int'l*, pg. 956
BELMONT METALS, INC.; *U.S. Public*, pg. 520
BHORUKA ALUMINIUM LTD.; *Int'l*, pg. 1015
BOLIDEN HARJAVALTA OY - COPPER REFINERY—See Boliden AB; *Int'l*, pg. 1102
BOLIDEN HARJAVALTA OY—See Boliden AB; *Int'l*, pg. 1102
CHENGDU HUAZE COBALT & NICKEL MATERIAL CO., LTD.; *Int'l*, pg. 1468
CHENZHOU CITY JINGUI SILVER INDUSTRY CO., LTD.; *Int'l*, pg. 1470
CHINA NON-FERROUS METAL INDUSTRY'S FOREIGN ENGINEERING & CONSTRUCTION CO., LTD.—See China Nonferrous Metal Mining (Group) Co., Ltd.; *Int'l*, pg. 1535
CHUGAI MINING CO. LTD.; *Int'l*, pg. 1594
COLT REFINING INC.; *U.S. Private*, pg. 976
COMMODITY RESOURCE & ENVIRONMENTAL INC; *U.S. Private*, pg. 985
CONDOR GOLD PLC; *Int'l*, pg. 1766
DAECHANG CO., LTD.; *Int'l*, pg. 1906
DOWA METALS & MINING CO., LTD.—See Dowa Holdings Co., Ltd.; *Int'l*, pg. 2183
ELM CITY SALES INC.; *U.S. Private*, pg. 1375
EMIRATES GLOBAL ALUMINIUM PJSC; *Int'l*, pg. 2381
FLORET TRADELINK PRIVATE LIMITED—See Gravita India Limited; *Int'l*, pg. 3062
FREEPORT-MCMORAN INC. - ELIZABETH—See Freeport-McMoRan Inc.; *U.S. Public*, pg. 884
FURUKAWA METALS & RESOURCES CO., LTD.—See Furukawa Co., Ltd.; *Int'l*, pg. 2847
GEM (JIANGSU) COBALT INDUSTRY CO., LTD.—See GEM Co., Ltd.; *Int'l*, pg. 2914
GLENCORE NIKKELVERK AS—See Glencore plc; *Int'l*, pg. 2991
GLINES & RHODES, INC.; *U.S. Private*, pg. 1711
GLOBAL ADVANCED METALS USA INC.—See Global Advanced Metals Pty. Ltd.; *Int'l*, pg. 2993
GLOBE METALLURGICAL, INC.—See Grupo Villar Mir, S.A.U.; *Int'l*, pg. 3138
GRAVITA EXIM LTD—See Gravita India Limited; *Int'l*, pg. 3062
GRAVITA HONDURAS SA—See Gravita India Limited; *Int'l*, pg. 3062

GREEN PLUS CO., LTD.; *Int'l*, pg. 3072
GREENSTONE RESOURCES LTD.—See Horizon Minerals Limited; *Int'l*, pg. 3479
GROSSMAN IRON & STEEL COMPANY; *U.S. Private*, pg. 1792
GUOCHENG MINING CO., LTD.; *Int'l*, pg. 3186
HANDY & HARMAN MANUFACTURING (SINGAPORE) PTE. LTD.—See Steel Partners Holdings L.P.; *U.S. Public*, pg. 1942
H.C. STARCK INC—See Advent International Corporation; *U.S. Private*, pg. 102
H.C. STARCK INC—See The Carlyle Group Inc.; *U.S. Public*, pg. 2047
HENAN YUGUANG GOLD & LEAD CO., LTD; *Int'l*, pg. 3344
HULUDAO ZINC INDUSTRY CO., LTD; *Int'l*, pg. 3528
HUNAN GOLD CORPORATION LIMITED; *Int'l*, pg. 3532
HUNAN NONFERROUS METALS CORPORATION LTD.; *Int'l*, pg. 3533
HUTMEN S.A.—See Boryszew S.A.; *Int'l*, pg. 1115
JX ADVANCED METALS CORPORATION—See ENEOS Holdings, Inc.; *Int'l*, pg. 2415
KESTER, INC.—See Element Solutions Inc.; *U.S. Public*, pg. 726
KOSAKA SMELTING & REFINING CO.—See Dowa Holdings Co., Ltd.; *Int'l*, pg. 2183
LINCOLN BRASS WORKS, INC.—See Mueller Industries, Inc.; *U.S. Public*, pg. 1484
MARQUETTE COPPERSMITHING-PIPING DESIGN DIVISION—See Marquette Coppersmithing Co., Inc.; *U.S. Private*, pg. 2587
MATERION ADVANCED MATERIALS TECHNOLOGIES AND SERVICES (SUZHOU) LTD.—See Materion Corporation; *U.S. Public*, pg. 1395
METALLIX INC.; *U.S. Private*, pg. 2681
METALLURG, INC.—See AMG Critical Materials N.V.; *Int'l*, pg. 426
MICRO GAUGE INC.—See Mueller Industries, Inc.; *U.S. Public*, pg. 1484
MUELLER BRASS CO.—See Mueller Industries, Inc.; *U.S. Public*, pg. 1484
MUELLER BRASS FORGING COMPANY, INC.—See Mueller Industries, Inc.; *U.S. Public*, pg. 1484
MUELLER COPPER FITTINGS COMPANY, INC.—See Mueller Industries, Inc.; *U.S. Public*, pg. 1485
MUELLER COPPER TUBE COMPANY, INC.—See Mueller Industries, Inc.; *U.S. Public*, pg. 1484
MUELLER EUROPE LTD.—See Mueller Industries, Inc.; *U.S. Public*, pg. 1485
MUELLER FITTINGS COMPANY—See Mueller Industries, Inc.; *U.S. Public*, pg. 1484
MUELLER FORMED TUBE COMPANY, INC.—See Mueller Industries, Inc.; *U.S. Public*, pg. 1484
MUELLER IMPACTS COMPANY, INC.—See Mueller Industries, Inc.; *U.S. Public*, pg. 1484
MUELLER PLASTICS CORPORATION, INC.—See Mueller Industries, Inc.; *U.S. Public*, pg. 1484
MUELLER PLASTICS CORPORATION, INC.—See Mueller Industries, Inc.; *U.S. Public*, pg. 1484
MUELLER PLASTICS CORPORATION, INC.—See Mueller Industries, Inc.; *U.S. Public*, pg. 1484
MUELLER REFRIGERATION PRODUCTS COMPANY, INC.—See Mueller Industries, Inc.; *U.S. Public*, pg. 1484
MUELLER STREAMLINE COPPER AND BRASS LTD.—See Mueller Industries, Inc.; *U.S. Public*, pg. 1485
NANOPHASE TECHNOLOGIES CORPORATION; *U.S. Public*, pg. 1490
NIPPON PGM CO., LTD.—See Dowa Holdings Co., Ltd.; *Int'l*, pg. 2184
NIPPON PGM CO., LTD.—See Dowa Holdings Co., Ltd.; *Int'l*, pg. 2184
NORANDA INC.—See Glencore plc; *Int'l*, pg. 2991
NORDENHAMER ZINKHUTTE GMBH—See Glencore plc; *Int'l*, pg. 2991
OOO IRIDIUM COMMUNICATIONS—See Iridium Communications Inc.; *U.S. Public*, pg. 1171
OVERSTREET-HUGHES CO., INC.—See Lincoln Electric Holdings, Inc.; *U.S. Public*, pg. 1318
PENTA EXIM PVT. LTD—See Gravita India Limited; *Int'l*, pg. 3062
PRECIOUS METAL REFINING SERVICES INC.; *U.S. Private*, pg. 3244
PRECISION TUBE COMPANY—See Mueller Industries, Inc.; *U.S. Public*, pg. 1485
PREMIER METAL RECYCLERS LTD—See HL Thorne & Co., Ltd.; *Int'l*, pg. 3430
PROPIPE TECHNOLOGIES, INC.—See Mueller Industries, Inc.; *U.S. Public*, pg. 1485
PYROPURE, INC.; *U.S. Private*, pg. 3310
QUZHOU HUAYOU COBALT NEW MATERIAL CO., LTD.—See Huayou Cobalt Co., Ltd.; *Int'l*, pg. 3516
RELIABLE SILVER, INC.; *U.S. Private*, pg. 3394
REPUBLIC METALS CORP.—See ARE Holdings, Inc.; *Int'l*, pg. 557
RISING NONFERROUS METALS CO., LTD.—See Guangdong Rising Assets Management Co., Ltd.; *Int'l*, pg. 3159
ROYAL METAL POWDERS INC.—See American Chemet Corporation; *U.S. Private*, pg. 227
SOUTH AFRICA PALABORA COPPER (PTY)

331491 — NONFERROUS METAL (E...

LIMITED—See HBIS Group Co., Ltd.; *Int'l*, pg. 3296
TECHNICAL MATERIALS, INC.—See Materion Corporation; *U.S. Public*, pg. 1396
THAILAND SMELTING & REFINING CO LTD—See Amalgamated Metal Corporation PLC; *Int'l*, pg. 409
THERMOX ZINNOXIDE GMBH—See Amalgamated Metal Corporation PLC; *Int'l*, pg. 408
UNITED STATES ANTIMONY CORPORATION; *U.S. Public*, pg. 2235
UNITED STATES ENRICHMENT CORPORATION—See Centrus Energy Corp.; *U.S. Public*, pg. 474
VENNERBECK, STERN, LEACH; *U.S. Private*, pg. 4356
WESTERN MESQUITE MINES, INC.—See Equinox Gold Corp.; *Int'l*, pg. 2485

331420 — COPPER ROLLING, DRAWING, EXTRUDING, AND ALLOYING

ABC GAS (INTERNATIONAL) LTD.; *Int'l*, pg. 57
ACS INDUSTRIES (SHANGHAI) CO.—See ACS Industries, Inc.; *U.S. Private*, pg. 66
ALASKAN COPPER WORKS—See Alco Investment Co., Inc.; *U.S. Private*, pg. 154
ALPHA WIRE COMPANY—See Belden, Inc.; *U.S. Public*, pg. 293
AMERICAN TUBING INC.—See National Tube Holding Company Inc.; *U.S. Private*, pg. 2864
AMROD CORP.; *U.S. Private*, pg. 266
ANHUI TONGGUAN COPPER FOIL GROUP CO., LTD.; *Int'l*, pg. 470
ANSONIA COPPER & BRASS INC.; *U.S. Private*, pg. 286
APOLLO SOLAR ENERGY, INC.; *Int'l*, pg. 518
ARORA-MATTHEY LIMITED VISAKHAPATNAM UNIT—See Arora-Matthey Limited; *Int'l*, pg. 577
ATLANTIC COPPER, S.L.U.—See Freeport-McMoRan Inc.; *U.S. Public*, pg. 884
ATLANTIC SPECIALTY WIRE INC.—See AEB International Inc.; *U.S. Private*, pg. 116
AURUBIS NETHERLANDS B.V.—See Aurubis AG; *Int'l*, pg. 714
AURUBIS SLOVAKIA S.R.O.—See Aurubis AG; *Int'l*, pg. 714
AURUBIS SWEDEN AB—See Aurubis AG; *Int'l*, pg. 714
AURUBIS UK LIMITED—See Aurubis AG; *Int'l*, pg. 715
BADGER WIRE INC.; *U.S. Private*, pg. 424
BONLON INDUSTRIES LIMITED; *Int'l*, pg. 1107
CERRO FLOW PRODUCTS, INC.—See Berkshire Hathaway Inc.; *U.S. Public*, pg. 310
CERRO FLOW PRODUCTS, INC.—See Berkshire Hathaway Inc.; *U.S. Public*, pg. 310
CERRO WIRE LLC—See Berkshire Hathaway Inc.; *U.S. Public*, pg. 309
CHANGZHOU JINYUAN COPPER CO., LTD.—See Baosheng Science & Technology Innovation Co., Ltd; *Int'l*, pg. 856
CIRCUIT FOIL LUXEMBOURG S.A.R.L.—See ArcelorMittal S.A.; *Int'l*, pg. 545
CIRCUIT FOIL SERVICE S.A.—See ArcelorMittal S.A.; *Int'l*, pg. 545
CK SAN-ETSU CO., LTD.; *Int'l*, pg. 1638
CNMC ALBETTER ALBRONZE CO., LTD.—See China Nonferrous Metal Mining (Group) Co., Ltd.; *Int'l*, pg. 1535
COLEMAN CABLE, INC. - BREMEN—See Southwire Company, LLC; *U.S. Private*, pg. 3742
COPPERWELD TUBING EUROPE SPRL—See Fushi Copperweld, Inc.; *Int'l*, pg. 2849
CO-TECH DEVELOPMENT CORP.; *Int'l*, pg. 1680
CRANE COPPER TUBE—See Fletcher Building Limited; *Int'l*, pg. 2699
CUBEX TUBINGS LIMITED; *Int'l*, pg. 1875
CURAMIK ELECTRONICS GMBH—See Rogers Corporation; *U.S. Public*, pg. 1808
CXM INC.; *U.S. Private*, pg. 1133
DALIAN JINCHUAN ELECTRIC CABLE CO. LTD.—See Fushi Copperweld, Inc.; *Int'l*, pg. 2849
DEUTSCHE GIESSDRAHT GMBH—See Aurubis AG; *Int'l*, pg. 715
DIEHL AIRCABIN GMBH—See Diehl Stiftung & Co. KG; *Int'l*, pg. 2114
DIEHL AUGE DECOUPAGE SAS—See Diehl Stiftung & Co. KG; *Int'l*, pg. 2114
DIEHL COMFORT MODULES GMBH—See Diehl Stiftung & Co. KG; *Int'l*, pg. 2115
DIEHL & EAGLE-PICHER GESELLSCHAFT MIT BESCHRANKTER HAFTUNG—See Diehl Stiftung & Co. KG; *Int'l*, pg. 2114
DIEHL METALL (SHENZHEN) CO. LTD.—See Diehl Stiftung & Co. KG; *Int'l*, pg. 2115
DIEHL POWER ELECTRONIC SAS—See Diehl Stiftung & Co. KG; *Int'l*, pg. 2114
DOWA ADVANCED MATERIALS (SHANGHAI) CO., LTD.—See Dowa Holdings Co., Ltd.; *Int'l*, pg. 2183
DOWA METAL CO., LTD.—See Dowa Holdings Co., Ltd.; *Int'l*, pg. 2183
DOWA METALTECH CO., LTD.—See Dowa Holdings Co., Ltd.; *Int'l*, pg. 2183
DOWA METALTECH (THAILAND) CO., LTD.—See Dowa Holdings Co., Ltd.; *Int'l*, pg. 2183
DOWA METANIX CO., LTD.—See Dowa Holdings Co., Ltd.; *Int'l*, pg. 2183
DRAHTWERK FRIEDR. LOTTERS GMBH & CO. KG; *Int'l*, pg. 2200
THE ELECTRIC MATERIALS COMPANY INC.—See United Stars Inc.; *U.S. Private*, pg. 4298
ETERNAL (CHINA) INVESTMENT CO., LTD.—See Eternal Materials Co., Ltd.; *Int'l*, pg. 2520
EVERTOP WIRE CABLE CORPORATION - CHUNGLI PLANT—See Evertop Wire Cable Corporation; *Int'l*, pg. 2569
EXTRUDED METALS, INC.—See Mueller Industries, Inc.; *U.S. Public*, pg. 1484
FABRIKA BAKARNIH CEVI A.D.; *Int'l*, pg. 2599
FENG CHING METAL CORP.; *Int'l*, pg. 2633
FINE METAL TECHNOLOGIES PUBLIC COMPANY LIMITED; *Int'l*, pg. 2673
FIRST COPPER TECHNOLOGY CO., LTD.; *Int'l*, pg. 2683
FUSHI COPPERWELD EUROPE—See Fushi Copperweld, Inc.; *Int'l*, pg. 2849
FUSHI COPPERWELD, INC.; *Int'l*, pg. 2849
GOULD ELECTRONICS GMBH—See ENEOS Holdings, Inc.; *Int'l*, pg. 2416
GREAT LAKES COPPER LTD.—See Mueller Industries, Inc.; *U.S. Public*, pg. 1484
GUANGDONG JIA YUAN TECHNOLOGY SHARES CO., LTD.; *Int'l*, pg. 3156
HELLERMANNTYTON LTDA.—See Aptiv PLC; *Int'l*, pg. 526
HERAEUS ORIENTAL HITEC CO. LTD.—See Heraeus Holding GmbH; *Int'l*, pg. 3358
HEYCO INC.; *U.S. Private*, pg. 1928
HIGH PERFORMANCE COPPER FOIL, INC.—See ENEOS Holdings, Inc.; *Int'l*, pg. 2416
HNG CAPITAL SDN BHD; *Int'l*, pg. 3434
HONG TAI ELECTRIC INDUSTRIAL CO., LTD.; *Int'l*, pg. 3469
HOWELL METAL COMPANY—See Mueller Industries, Inc.; *U.S. Public*, pg. 1485
INTERNATIONAL WIRE GROUP, INC.—See Atlas Holdings, LLC; *U.S. Private*, pg. 376
INTERNATIONAL WIRE GROUP-WYRE WYND—See Atlas Holdings, LLC; *U.S. Private*, pg. 376
JEDDAH CABLE COMPANY—See El Sewedy Electric Company; *Int'l*, pg. 2341
JX METALS PHILIPPINES, INC.—See ENEOS Holdings, Inc.; *Int'l*, pg. 2416
KIRAMI OY—See Harvia Oyj; *Int'l*, pg. 3281
KUPFER COPPER GERMANY GMBH—See Anglo American PLC; *Int'l*, pg. 462
LIBERTAS COPPER, LLC—See Patriarch Partners, LLC; *U.S. Private*, pg. 3109
LINESETS, INC.—See Mueller Industries, Inc.; *U.S. Public*, pg. 1484
LITTLE FALLS ALLOYS, INC.; *U.S. Private*, pg. 2468
LUVATA FRANKLIN, INC.—See Waybill USA Inc.; *U.S. Private*, pg. 4459
MARMON BUILDING WIRE—See Berkshire Hathaway Inc.; *U.S. Public*, pg. 310
MATERION BRUSH (JAPAN) LTD.—See Materion Corporation; *U.S. Public*, pg. 1395
MATERION BRUSH PERFORMANCE ALLOYS—See Materion Corporation; *U.S. Public*, pg. 1395
MT OWEN PTY LIMITED—See Glencore plc; *Int'l*, pg. 2991
MUELLER COPPER TUBE PRODUCTS, INC.—See Mueller Industries, Inc.; *U.S. Public*, pg. 1485
NATIONAL COPPER & SMELTING COMPANY INC.—See National Tube Holding Company Inc.; *U.S. Private*, pg. 2864
NATIONAL TUBE HOLDING COMPANY INC.; *U.S. Private*, pg. 2864
NELCO PRODUCTS PTE. LTD.—See AGC Inc.; *Int'l*, pg. 204
NEW FRONTIER INDUSTRIES INC.—See U.S. Bronze Foundry & Machine, Inc.; *U.S. Private*, pg. 4270
NEW NIPPON BRASS CO., LTD.—See Dowa Holdings Co., Ltd.; *Int'l*, pg. 2183
NUMAZU COPPER REFINING & ROLLING CO., LTD.—See Fujikura Ltd.; *Int'l*, pg. 2829
OWL WIRE & CABLE, LLC—See Atlas Holdings, LLC; *U.S. Private*, pg. 376
PCC ENERGY GROUP—See Berkshire Hathaway Inc.; *U.S. Public*, pg. 314
PRESTORAC SAS—See Aalberts N.V.; *Int'l*, pg. 35
READING TUBE DIVISION—See Cambridge-Lee Industries, Inc.; *U.S. Public*, pg. 727
REA MAGNET WIRE COMPANY, INC. - AR PLANT—See REA Magnet Wire Company, Inc.; *U.S. Private*, pg. 3365
REA MAGNET WIRE COMPANY, INC. - INDIANA PLANT—See REA Magnet Wire Company, Inc.; *U.S. Private*, pg. 3365
REA MAGNET WIRE COMPANY, INC. - NEW HAVEN AVENUE PLANT—See REA Magnet Wire Company, Inc.; *U.S. Private*, pg. 3365
REPUBLIC WIRE, INC.; *U.S. Private*, pg. 3402
REVERE COPPER PRODUCTS INC.; *U.S. Private*, pg. 3414
SCHWERMETALL HALBZEUGWERK GMBH & CO. KG—See Aurubis AG; *Int'l*, pg. 715
SCOTT BRASS, INC.—See Sun Capital Partners, Inc.; *U.S. Private*, pg. 3860
SHANGHAI YAYANG ELECTRIC CO., LTD.—See Asia Pacific Wire & Cable Corporation Limited; *Int'l*, pg. 614
SUNDWIGER MESSINGWERK GMBH & CO. KG—See Deutsche Invest Capital Partners GmbH; *Int'l*, pg. 2066
SUPERIOR CABLES USA LTD.—See The Alpine Group, Inc.; *U.S. Private*, pg. 3984
SYNERGY CABLES LTD.—See The Alpine Group, Inc.; *U.S. Private*, pg. 3984
U.S. BRONZE FOUNDRY & MACHINE, INC.; *U.S. Private*, pg. 4270
U.S. ZINC CORPORATION—See Aterian Investment Management, L.P.; *U.S. Private*, pg. 367
YORKSHIRE COPPER TUBE—See Mueller Industries, Inc.; *U.S. Public*, pg. 1485
ZEHDENICK INNOVATIVE METALL- UND KUNSTSTOFFTECHNIK GMBH—See Diehl Stiftung & Co. KG; *Int'l*, pg. 2115

331491 — NONFERROUS METAL (EXCEPT COPPER AND ALUMINUM) ROLLING, DRAWING, AND EXTRUDING

3M ECC EUROPA B.V.—See 3M Company; *U.S. Public*, pg. 5
ACS INTERNACIONAL S. DE R.L. DE C.V.—See ACS Industries, Inc.; *U.S. Private*, pg. 66
ADVANCED MAGNETIC MATERIALS (THAILAND) CO., LTD.—See Brookfield Corporation; *Int'l*, pg. 1181
ADVANCED MATERIAL TRADING PTE LTD.—See Alconix Corporation; *Int'l*, pg. 302
A.E. PETSCHE COMPANY INC.—See Arrow Electronics, Inc.; *U.S. Public*, pg. 194
ALCONIX KOREA CORPORATION—See Alconix Corporation; *Int'l*, pg. 302
ALCONIX MITAKA CORPORATION—See Alconix Corporation; *Int'l*, pg. 302
ALCONIX USA, INC.—See Alconix Corporation; *Int'l*, pg. 302
ALCONIX VIETNAM CO., LTD.—See Alconix Corporation; *Int'l*, pg. 302
ALENT ALPHA METALS (SHENZEN) CO. LTD.—See Element Solutions Inc.; *U.S. Public*, pg. 726
ALLEGHENY LUDLUM, LLC—See ATI Inc.; *U.S. Public*, pg. 221
ALLMETAL RECYCLING, LLC; *U.S. Private*, pg. 192
ANFU CE LINK LIMITED; *Int'l*, pg. 459
ASAKA KOUUN CO., LTD.—See Asaka Riken Co., Ltd.; *Int'l*, pg. 599
AURUBIS MIDDLE EAST FZE—See Aurubis AG; *Int'l*, pg. 714
BAOJI TITANIUM INDUSTRY CO., LTD.; *Int'l*, pg. 856
BELDEN, INC.; *U.S. Public*, pg. 293
CUHADAROGLU METAL SANAYI VE PAZARLAMA AS; *Int'l*, pg. 1876
DAEWON CABLE CO., LTD.; *Int'l*, pg. 1909
DONG GUAN E-RUN ELECTRONIC PRODUCT LTD.—See Bright Led Electronics Corp.; *Int'l*, pg. 1161
ECO-SYSTEM OKAYAMA CO., LTD.—See Dowa Holdings Co., Ltd.; *Int'l*, pg. 2184
ERAMET SA; *Int'l*, pg. 2488
GIFU TOKODEN CO., LTD.—See Imasen Electric Industrial Co., Ltd.; *Int'l*, pg. 3620
GLENCORE AUSTRALIA HOLDINGS PTY LTD—See Glencore plc; *Int'l*, pg. 2990
GROT A.D.; *Int'l*, pg. 3088
GUANGDONG RIFENG ELECTRIC CABLE CO., LTD.; *Int'l*, pg. 3159
GUANGZHOU ALCONIX (SHANGHAI) CORP.—See Alconix Corporation; *Int'l*, pg. 302
HAMMOND LEAD PRODUCTS DIVISION - POTTSTOWN PLANT—See Hammond Group, Inc.; *U.S. Private*, pg. 1850
HANDY & HARMAN LTD.—See Steel Partners Holdings L.P.; *U.S. Public*, pg. 1942
H.C. STARCK, INC.—See Advent International Corporation; *U.S. Private*, pg. 102
H.C. STARCK, INC.—See The Carlyle Group Inc.; *U.S. Public*, pg. 2047
HEBEI HUATONG WIRES & CABLES GROUP CO., LTD.; *Int'l*, pg. 3306
HEIWA KINZOKU CO., LTD.—See Alconix Corporation; *Int'l*, pg. 302
HIRSCH METALS CORPORATION; *U.S. Private*, pg. 1951
HORSEHEAD METALS DEVELOPMENT, LLC—See Befesa S.A.; *Int'l*, pg. 939
HOWMET CORPORATION—See Howmet Aerospace Inc.; *U.S. Public*, pg. 1061
INDIUM CORPORATION OF AMERICA; *U.S. Private*, pg. 2064
INTERNATIONAL MAGNESIUM GROUP, INC.—See CD International Enterprises, Inc.; *U.S. Public*, pg. 461
INTERNATIONAL ROLLFORMS INC.; *U.S. Private*, pg. 2120
JARDEN ZINC PRODUCTS, LLC—See Newell Brands Inc.; *U.S. Public*, pg. 1514
JIANGYIN JIA HUA ADVANCED MATERIAL RESOURCES

331491 — NONFERROUS METAL (E...

CO., LTD.—See Brookfield Corporation; *Int'l*, pg. 1181
LUCAS-MILHAUPT, INC.—See Steel Partners Holdings L.P.; *U.S. Public*, pg. 1943
MAYCO INDUSTRIES—See Metalico Inc.; *U.S. Private*, pg. 2681
MEDWIRE—See Sigmund Cohn Corp.; *U.S. Private*, pg. 3649
METAL ARTS COMPANY, INC.; *U.S. Public*, pg. 1427
MULTICORE SOLDERS LTD.—See Henkel AG & Co. KGaA; *Int'l*, pg. 3351
MURRIN MURRIN OPERATIONS PTY LTD—See Glencore plc; *Int'l*, pg. 2991
NEVADA GOLD MINES LLC—See Barrick Gold Corporation; *Int'l*, pg. 869
THE PLATT BROTHERS & COMPANY, INC.; *U.S. Private*, pg. 4096
PSC METALS - AKRON, LLC—See Icahn Enterprises L.P.; *U.S. Public*, pg. 1084
PSC METALS - ALIQUIPPA, LLC—See Icahn Enterprises L.P.; *U.S. Public*, pg. 1084
PSC METALS - CAW, LLC—See Icahn Enterprises L.P.; *U.S. Public*, pg. 1085
PSC METALS - ELYRIA, LLC—See Icahn Enterprises L.P.; *U.S. Public*, pg. 1085
PSC METALS - JOYCE, LLC—See Icahn Enterprises L.P.; *U.S. Public*, pg. 1085
PSC METALS - KNOXVILLE, LLC—See Icahn Enterprises L.P.; *U.S. Public*, pg. 1085
PSC METALS - WOOSTER, LLC—See Icahn Enterprises L.P.; *U.S. Public*, pg. 1085
SAINT-GOBAIN CRISTAUX—See Compagnie de Saint-Gobain SA; *Int'l*, pg. 1732
SCHNITZER STEEL BC, INC.—See Radius Recycling, Inc.; *U.S. Public*, pg. 1760
SELECTRODE INDUSTRIES INC.; *U.S. Private*, pg. 3601
SHENZHEN ALCONIX (SHANGHAI) CORP.—See Alconix Corporation; *Int'l*, pg. 302
SIGMUND COHN CORP.; *U.S. Private*, pg. 3649
SPECIAL METALS CORPORATION—See Berkshire Hathaway Inc.; *U.S. Public*, pg. 315
STERN METALS, INC.—See Berkshire Hathaway Inc.; *U.S. Public*, pg. 316
SWEPCO TUBE CORPORATION; *U.S. Private*, pg. 3892
TECHNOLOGY GENERAL CORP.; *U.S. Public*, pg. 1988
TIMET SAVOIE, SA—See Berkshire Hathaway Inc.; *U.S. Public*, pg. 315
TIMET UK LIMITED—See Berkshire Hathaway Inc.; *U.S. Public*, pg. 315
TITANIUM FABRICATION CORPORATION - PHOENIX GROUP DIVISION—See Titanium Fabrication Corporation; *U.S. Private*, pg. 4177
TITANIUM INDUSTRIES, INC.; *U.S. Private*, pg. 4177
TITANIUM METALS CORPORATION—See Berkshire Hathaway Inc.; *U.S. Public*, pg. 315
TOYO KOKU DENSHI CO., LTD.—See Imasen Electric Industrial Co., Ltd.; *Int'l*, pg. 3620
UMC ACQUISITION CORP.; *U.S. Private*, pg. 4278
UMICORE BUILDING PRODUCTS FRANCE S.A.S.—See Fedrus International NV; *Int'l*, pg. 2631
UNIVERSAL MOLDING COMPANY INC—See UMC Acquisition Corp.; *U.S. Private*, pg. 4278
VALCAMBI S.A.—See Newmont Corporation; *U.S. Public*, pg. 1516
VESTED METALS INTERNATIONAL, LLC; *U.S. Private*, pg. 4373

331492 — SECONDARY SMELTING, REFINING, AND ALLOYING OF NONFERROUS METAL (EXCEPT COPPER AND ALUMINUM)

ACADEMY CORPORATION—See Materion Corporation; *U.S. Public*, pg. 1396
ALLOY HOLDINGS, LLC—See Trent Capital Partners, LLC; *U.S. Private*, pg. 4218
ALUMINUM & COPPER RECYCLING CENTER CORPORATION—See Alconix Corporation; *Int'l*, pg. 302
AMERICAN CATCON, INC.—See Metalico Inc.; *U.S. Private*, pg. 2681
AMES GOLDSMITH CORP.; *U.S. Private*, pg. 261
AMG ALLIANCE LLC—See AMG Resources Corp.; *U.S. Private*, pg. 262
APERAM ALLOYS IMPHY—See Aperam SA; *Int'l*, pg. 508
AQUA METALS, INC.; *U.S. Public*, pg. 175
ARNO FRIEDRICHS HARTMETALL GMBH & CO. KG—See KKR & Co. Inc.; *U.S. Public*, pg. 1253
BON L ALUMINUM LLC—See Tredegar Corporation; *U.S. Public*, pg. 2187
CALLICO METALS, INC.; *U.S. Private*, pg. 722
CANFIELD TECHNOLOGIES, LLC—See Gen Cap America, Inc.; *U.S. Private*, pg. 1659
CERTIFIED ALLOY PRODUCTS, INC.—See Dubai Holding LLC; *Int'l*, pg. 2218
CHARLESTON STEEL & METAL CO.; *U.S. Private*, pg. 857
CHONGQING CHUANYI METALLIC FUNCTIONAL MATERIALS CO., LTD.—See Chongqing Chuanyi Automation Co., Ltd.; *Int'l*, pg. 1579
CHUNG YO MATERIALS CO., LTD.—See Chia Yi Steel Co., Ltd.; *Int'l*, pg. 1475
CMC CENTROZŁOM SP. Z O.O.—See Commercial Metals Company; *U.S. Public*, pg. 545
CMI, INC.; *U.S. Private*, pg. 951
COLONIAL METALS CO.; *U.S. Private*, pg. 971
CRONIMET HOLDING GMBH; *Int'l*, pg. 1854
DAVID H. FELL & COMPANY INCORPORATED; *U.S. Private*, pg. 1170
DUROC AB; *Int'l*, pg. 2229
ELEMETAL REFINING, LLC; *U.S. Private*, pg. 1357
ELG UTICA ALLOYS, INC.; *U.S. Private*, pg. 1359
THE FEDERAL METAL COMPANY—See Oakwood Industries Inc.; *U.S. Private*, pg. 2985
F.W. HEMPEL METALLURGICAL GMBH—See Campine N.V.; *Int'l*, pg. 1275
THE G.A. AVRIL CO.; *U.S. Private*, pg. 4031
GEM CO., LTD.; *Int'l*, pg. 2914
GUANGDONG XIANGLU TUNGSTEN CO. LTD; *Int'l*, pg. 3162
HARDIDE COATINGS LIMITED—See Hardide Plc; *Int'l*, pg. 3273
HERAEUS METAL PROCESSING, LLC—See Heraeus Holding GmbH; *Int'l*, pg. 3357
HOGANAS BRASIL LTDA.—See Hoganas AB; *Int'l*, pg. 3441
HOOTECH INC.; *Int'l*, pg. 3472
HORSEHEAD CORP.—See Befesa S.A.; *Int'l*, pg. 939
HOSOKAWA MICRON CORPORATION; *Int'l*, pg. 3485
HYPERION MATERIALS & TECHNOLOGIES, INC.—See KKR & Co. Inc.; *U.S. Public*, pg. 1252
HYPERION MATERIALS & TECHNOLOGIES (SWEDEN) AB—See KKR & Co. Inc.; *U.S. Public*, pg. 1252
IMPERIAL ZINC CORP.; *U.S. Private*, pg. 2050
I. SCHUMANN & COMPANY; *U.S. Private*, pg. 2026
JANSEN RECYCLING GROUP—See The Jansen Group Inc.; *U.S. Private*, pg. 4058
LEADAGE ALLOYS INDIA LIMITED—See EXIDE INDUSTRIES LIMITED; *Int'l*, pg. 2585
MAYCO INDUSTRIES, LLC; *U.S. Private*, pg. 2620
METALICO ALUMINUM RECOVERY, INC.—See Metalico Inc.; *U.S. Private*, pg. 2681
METALICO BUFFALO, INC.—See Metalico Inc.; *U.S. Private*, pg. 2681
METALICO INC.; *U.S. Private*, pg. 2681
METALICO ROCHESTER, INC.—See Metalico Inc.; *U.S. Private*, pg. 2681
MIDWEST STEEL & ALLOY, INC.—See AMG Resources Corp.; *U.S. Private*, pg. 262
MIL-VER METAL COMPANY LTD—See Amalgamated Metal Corporation PLC; *Int'l*, pg. 408
NINGXIA ORIENT TANTALUM INDUSTRY CO., LTD.—See China Nonferrous Metal Mining (Group) Co., Ltd.; *Int'l*, pg. 1535
NORTH STAR BLUESCOPE STEEL LLC—See BlueScope Steel Limited; *Int'l*, pg. 1074
OAKWOOD INDUSTRIES INC.; *U.S. Private*, pg. 2985
PASAR GROUP—See Glencore plc; *Int'l*, pg. 2991
PEASE & CURREN INCORPORATED; *U.S. Private*, pg. 3126
QUEMETCO, INC.—See Quexco Incorporated; *U.S. Private*, pg. 3326
QUEMETCO METALS LIMITED, INC.—See Quexco Incorporated; *U.S. Private*, pg. 3326
ROLLED ALLOYS, INC. - LOS ANGELES—See Rolled Alloys, Inc.; *U.S. Private*, pg. 3474
ROSS CATHERALL AEROSPACE LIMITED—See Dubai Holding LLC; *Int'l*, pg. 2218
RSR CORPORATION—See Quexco Incorporated; *U.S. Private*, pg. 3326
SABIN METAL CORPORATION; *U.S. Private*, pg. 3520
SHOWA METAL CO., LTD.—See Hanwa Co., Ltd.; *Int'l*, pg. 3263
VELOSI INDUSTRIES SDN BHD—See I Squared Capital Advisors (US) LLC; *U.S. Private*, pg. 2024
ZODIAC ENTERPRISES, LLC—See BASF SE; *Int'l*, pg. 886
ZURN INDUSTRIES CAST METALS OPERATIONS—See Zurn Elkay Water Solutions Corporation; *U.S. Public*, pg. 2413

331511 — IRON FOUNDRIES

AB&I; *U.S. Private*, pg. 33
ACME FOUNDRY, INC.; *U.S. Private*, pg. 61
ADVANCED CAST PRODUCTS, INC.—See Gamut Capital Management, L.P.; *U.S. Private*, pg. 1641
AIRAM PRESS CO. LTD—See Industrial Machining Services, Inc.; *U.S. Private*, pg. 2067
ALIMACH HOLDINGS SDN. BHD.—See Engtex Group Berhad; *Int'l*, pg. 2436
ALLPIPES TECHNOLOGY SDN. BHD.—See Engtex Group Berhad; *Int'l*, pg. 2436
AMERICAN CASTINGS—See American Cast Iron Pipe Company; *U.S. Private*, pg. 226
AMERICAN CAST IRON PIPE COMPANY; *U.S. Private*, pg. 226
AMERICAN DUCTILE IRON PIPE DIV.—See American Cast Iron Pipe Company; *U.S. Private*, pg. 226
AMERICAN FLOW CONTROL—See American Cast Iron Pipe Company; *U.S. Private*, pg. 226
ATI CASTING SERVICE—See ATI Inc.; *U.S. Public*, pg. 221
BARBER STEEL FOUNDRY CORP.—See Westinghouse Air Brake Technologies Corporation; *U.S. Public*, pg. 2357
BAS CASTINGS LIMITED; *Int'l*, pg. 871
BENTON CORPORATION SDN. BHD.—See Engtex Group Berhad; *Int'l*, pg. 2436
BETSTAL SP. Z O.O.—See Bowim S.A.; *Int'l*, pg. 1124
BIRLA CORPORATION LTD. - VINDHYACHAL STEEL FOUNDRY—See Birla Corporation Ltd.; *Int'l*, pg. 1047
BOWIM-PODKARPACIE SP. Z O.O.—See Bowim S.A.; *Int'l*, pg. 1124
BRIDGESTATE FOUNDRY CORPORATION—See Campbell Foundry Company; *U.S. Private*, pg. 730
CAMPBELL FOUNDRY COMPANY; *U.S. Private*, pg. 730
CANOVA MANUFACTURING SDN. BHD.—See Engtex Group Berhad; *Int'l*, pg. 2436
CARLTON CREEK IRONWORKS INC.—See Monomoy Capital Partners LLC; *U.S. Private*, pg. 2772
CARLTON CREEK IRONWORKS—See Monomoy Capital Partners LLC; *U.S. Private*, pg. 2772
CARNATION INDUSTRIES LTD.; *Int'l*, pg. 1342
CAST-FAB TECHNOLOGIES, INC.; *U.S. Private*, pg. 784
CASTING SOLUTIONS, LLC—See Burnham Holdings, Inc.; *U.S. Public*, pg. 412
CHARTER DURA-BAR—See Charter Manufacturing Company, Inc.; *U.S. Private*, pg. 858
CHINA METAL AUTOMOTIVE INTERNATIONAL CO.—See China Metal Products Co., Ltd.; *Int'l*, pg. 1523
CHINA METAL INTERNATIONAL HOLDINGS INC.—See China Metal Products Co., Ltd.; *Int'l*, pg. 1523
CHINA METAL PRODUCTS CO., LTD. - HSINCHU PLANT—See China Metal Products Co., Ltd.; *Int'l*, pg. 1523
CHINA METAL PRODUCTS CO., LTD. - PINGZHEN PLANT—See China Metal Products Co., Ltd.; *Int'l*, pg. 1523
CHINA METAL PRODUCTS CO., LTD. - PLYMOUTH BRANCH—See China Metal Products Co., Ltd.; *Int'l*, pg. 1523
CHINA STEEL STRUCTURE CO., LTD. - TAINAN GUANTIAN FACTORY—See China Steel Structure Co., Ltd.; *Int'l*, pg. 1556
CHUNG-KANG STEEL STRUCTURE (KUNSHAN) CO., LTD.; *Int'l*, pg. 1597
CLOW WATER SYSTEMS CO.—See McWane, Inc.; *U.S. Private*, pg. 2645
CMW (TIANJIN) INDUSTRY CO., LTD.—See China Metal Products Co., Ltd.; *Int'l*, pg. 1523
CNC SPEEDWELL LIMITED—See Castings PLC; *Int'l*, pg. 1357
COMPONENTA FRANCE S.A.S.—See Componenta Corporation; *Int'l*, pg. 1753
DAEDONG METALS CO., LTD.; *Int'l*, pg. 1906
DAKOTA FOUNDRY, INC.—See Anderson Industries LLC; *U.S. Private*, pg. 277
DALTON CORPORATION—See Speyside Equity LLC; *U.S. Private*, pg. 3756
DEMISAS DOKUM EMAYE MAMULLERI SANAYI AS; *Int'l*, pg. 2025
DGS (CHINA) CO LTD.—See DGS Druckguss Systeme AG; *Int'l*, pg. 2097
DGS DRUCKGUSS SYSTEME AG; *Int'l*, pg. 2097
D&L FOUNDRY, INC.; *U.S. Private*, pg. 1138
DOMESTIC CASTING COMPANY, LLC; *U.S. Private*, pg. 1255
DONSCO, INC.; *U.S. Private*, pg. 1261
EAGLE MANUFACTURING GROUP; *U.S. Private*, pg. 1309
EBAA IRON, INC.; *U.S. Private*, pg. 1323
EJ GROUP, INC.; *U.S. Private*, pg. 1348
ELECTRO ACO ALTONA S.A.; *Int'l*, pg. 2352
ELECTROSTEEL ALGERIE SPA—See Electrosteel Castings Ltd; *Int'l*, pg. 2354
ELECTROSTEEL CASTINGS GULF FZE—See Electrosteel Castings Ltd; *Int'l*, pg. 2354
ELECTROSTEEL CASTINGS (UK) LIMITED—See Electrosteel Castings Ltd; *Int'l*, pg. 2354
ELECTROSTEEL EUROPE S.A.—See Electrosteel Castings Ltd; *Int'l*, pg. 2354
ELECTROSTEEL USA, LLC—See Electrosteel Castings Ltd; *Int'l*, pg. 2354
ELYRIA FOUNDRY COMPANY LLC—See Silverhawk Capital Partners, LLC; *U.S. Private*, pg. 3663
EMPORIA FOUNDRY INC.—See Campbell Foundry Company; *U.S. Private*, pg. 730
ENGLEN MANUFACTURING SDN. BHD.—See Engtex Group Berhad; *Int'l*, pg. 2436
ENG LIAN HUP MANUFACTURING SDN. BHD.—See Engtex Group Berhad; *Int'l*, pg. 2436
ENGTEX DUCTILE IRON MARKETING SDN. BHD.—See Engtex Group Berhad; *Int'l*, pg. 2436
ENGTEX MARKETING SDN. BHD.—See Engtex Group Berhad; *Int'l*, pg. 2436
ENGTEX PIPE INDUSTRY SDN. BHD.—See Engtex Group Berhad; *Int'l*, pg. 2436
ENGTEX SDN BERHAD—See Engtex Group Berhad; *Int'l*, pg. 2436

N.A.I.C.S. INDEX

331513 — STEEL FOUNDRIES (EX...

ENGTEX STEEL INDUSTRIES SDN. BHD.—See Engtex Group Berhad; *Int'l*, pg. 2436
FARRAR CORPORATION; *U.S. Private*, pg. 1480
FASTER INC.—See Helios Technologies, Inc.; *U.S. Public*, pg. 1023
FEDERAL-MOGUL POWERTRAIN, LLC—See Apollo Global Management, Inc.; *U.S. Public*, pg. 161
FIBRELITE COMPOSITES LIMITED.; *Int'l*, pg. 2653
FONDERIE GIROUD INDUSTRIE SAS; *Int'l*, pg. 2725
FONDERIE VRIGNAUD SA—See Beneteau S.A; *Int'l*, pg. 972
FRAZER & JONES DIVISION—See The Eastern Company; *U.S. Public*, pg. 2069
FRAZIER & FRAZIER INDUSTRIES; *U.S. Private*, pg. 1600
GEORG FISCHER AUTOMOBILGUSS GMBH—See Georg Fischer AG; *Int'l*, pg. 2935
GEORG FISCHER AUTOMOTIVE (SUZHOU) CO LTD—See Georg Fischer AG; *Int'l*, pg. 2935
GEORG FISCHER CENTRAL PLASTICS CO.—See Georg Fischer AG; *Int'l*, pg. 2936
GEORG FISCHER EISENGUSS GMBH—See Georg Fischer AG; *Int'l*, pg. 2935
GRAINGER & WORRALL LIMITED; *Int'l*, pg. 3052
GRANDOR CORPORATION; *U.S. Private*, pg. 1754
GREAT LAKES CASTINGS CORPORATION—See Brittany Stamping, LLC; *U.S. Public*, pg. 657
GREGG INDUSTRIES, INC.—See Charlotte Pipe & Foundry Company; *U.S. Public*, pg. 857
GRUPO HIDROAPLICACIONES Y GAS, SL—See Aalberts N.V.; *Int'l*, pg. 34
HACHITA ENTERPRISE SDN. BHD.—See Engtex Group Berhad; *Int'l*, pg. 2436
HINDUJA FOUNDRIES LTD—See Hinduja Group Ltd.; *Int'l*, pg. 3398
HODGE FOUNDRY, INC.—See Silverhawk Capital Partners, LLC; *U.S. Private*, pg. 3663
HUNAN HUAMIN HOLDINGS CO., LTD.; *Int'l*, pg. 3532
HYDRO CARBIDE INC.—See HBD Industries, Inc.; *U.S. Private*, pg. 1887
INTAT PRECISION, INC.—See AISIN Corporation; *Int'l*, pg. 253
INTERCAST SA—See American Cast Iron Pipe Company; *U.S. Private*, pg. 226
JACKSON PLASTICS OPERATIONS INC—See Lancaster Colony Corporation; *U.S. Public*, pg. 1291
JDH PACIFIC, INC.; *U.S. Private*, pg. 2195
JENSEN INTERNATIONAL INC.; *U.S. Private*, pg. 2200
JOHN BOUCHARD & SONS COMPANY; *U.S. Private*, pg. 2220
LUFKIN INDUSTRIES LLC - FOUNDRY DIVISION—See KPS Capital Partners, LP; *U.S. Private*, pg. 2347
LYE MANUFACTURING SDN. BHD.—See Engtex Group Berhad; *Int'l*, pg. 2436
MABRY IRON CASTINGS, LLC—See Advanced Metals Group, LLC; *U.S. Private*, pg. 91
MCWANE, INC. - AB&I FOUNDRY DIVISION—See McWane, Inc.; *U.S. Private*, pg. 2645
MCWANE, INC.; *U.S. Private*, pg. 2645
MCWANE, INC. - TYLER UNION COMPANY DIVISION—See McWane, Inc.; *U.S. Private*, pg. 2645
MEGA ALLIANCE BUILDER SUPPLIES SDN. BHD.—See Engtex Group Berhad; *Int'l*, pg. 2436
METAL TECHNOLOGIES THREE RIVERS—See Metal Technologies, Inc.; *U.S. Private*, pg. 2680
METAL TECHNOLOGIES WEST ALLIS DUCTILE IRON—See Metal Technologies, Inc.; *U.S. Private*, pg. 2680
METALTEK INTERNATIONAL; *U.S. Private*, pg. 2682
MID CITY FOUNDRY CO.; *U.S. Private*, pg. 2705
NAGASARI BITUMEN PRODUCTS SDN. BHD.—See Engtex Group Berhad; *Int'l*, pg. 2436
NEENAH FOUNDRY COMPANY—See Charlotte Pipe & Foundry Company; *U.S. Public*, pg. 857
NORTHERN ILLINOIS STEEL SUPPLY COMPANY—See Reliance Steel & Aluminum Co.; *U.S. Public*, pg. 1781
NORTHERN IRON AND BRASS FOUNDRY PTY. LTD.—See Fletcher Building Limited; *Int'l*, pg. 2699
NOVOCAST, S. DE R.L. DE C.V.—See Gamut Capital Management, L.P.; *U.S. Private*, pg. 1641
ODLEWNIA ZELIWA BYDGOSZCZ SP. Z O.O.—See DIHAG Holding GmbH; *Int'l*, pg. 2124
OLBERSDORFER GUB GMBH.—See BAUER Aktiengesellschaft; *Int'l*, pg. 893
OSCO INDUSTRIES INC.; *U.S. Private*, pg. 3047
PARAGON METALS—See Stellex Capital Management LP; *U.S. Private*, pg. 3800
PAXTON-MITCHELL COMPANY; *U.S. Private*, pg. 3116
PCB-PRECICAST BILBAO S.A.—See Bain Capital, LP; *U.S. Private*, pg. 433
PRESSURE PRODUCTS SDN. BHD.—See HupSteel Limited; *Int'l*, pg. 3538
PROSPECT FOUNDRY, LLC—See TMB Industries Inc.; *U.S. Private*, pg. 4179
QUALITY CASTINGS COMPANY; *U.S. Private*, pg. 3318
RAVENNA CASTING CENTER, INC.—See Metal Technologies, Inc.; *U.S. Private*, pg. 2680
RUSSELL DUCTILE CASTINGS LIMITED—See Chamberlin plc; *Int'l*, pg. 1439
SACHSEN GUSS GMBH—See The Carlyle Group Inc.; *U.S. Public*, pg. 2047
SAINT-GOBAIN FOUNDRY CO. LTD.—See Compagnie de Saint-Gobain SA; *Int'l*, pg. 1733
SAINT-GOBAIN GUSSROHR GMBH & CO. KG—See Compagnie de Saint-Gobain SA; *Int'l*, pg. 1734
SAINT-GOBAIN PAM UK—See Compagnie de Saint-Gobain SA; *Int'l*, pg. 1735
SAINT GOBAIN SA—See Compagnie de Saint-Gobain SA; *Int'l*, pg. 1729
SHANXI AKERS TISCO ROLL CO. LTD.—See Ampco-Pittsburgh Corporation; *U.S. Public*, pg. 126
SHELCO FOUNDRY—See Gnutti Carlo S.p.A.; *Int'l*, pg. 3017
SHINKO SEIKI CO., LTD.—See AISIN Corporation; *Int'l*, pg. 253
SIEMPELKAMP GIESSEREI GMBH—See G. Siempelkamp GmbH & Co. KG; *Int'l*, pg. 2865
SINGARDO INTERNATIONAL PTE LTD—See Electrosteel Castings Ltd; *Int'l*, pg. 2354
SLINGER MANUFACTURING CO., INC.; *U.S. Private*, pg. 3688
SPECIALTY CASTINGS, INC.—See Bahr Bros Mfg, Inc.; *U.S. Private*, pg. 425
STURGIS FOUNDRY CORP.—See Armstrong International, Inc.; *U.S. Private*, pg. 332
SUZHOU CMB MACHINERY CO., LTD.—See China Metal Products Co., Ltd.; *Int'l*, pg. 1523
SUZHOU CMS MACHINERY CO., LTD.—See China Metal Products Co., Ltd.; *Int'l*, pg. 1523
THAIFUKOKU PANAPLUS FOUNDRY CO., LTD.—See Fukoku Co., Ltd.; *Int'l*, pg. 2839
TIANJIN CMT INDUSTRY CO., LTD.—See China Metal Products Co., Ltd.; *Int'l*, pg. 1523
TRICKS WROUGHT IRON SERVICES PROPRIETARY LIMITED—See ARGENT INDUSTRIAL LIMITED; *Int'l*, pg. 561
TYLER (XIANXIAN) FOUNDRY CO., LTD.—See McWane, Inc.; *U.S. Private*, pg. 2645
UNITED STATES FOUNDRY MANUFACTURING INC.—See Eagle Manufacturing Group; *U.S. Private*, pg. 1309
VESTAL MANUFACTURING ENTERPRISES, INC.; *U.S. Private*, pg. 4371
WABTEC FOUNDRY—See Westinghouse Air Brake Technologies Corporation; *U.S. Public*, pg. 2359
WARD MANUFACTURING, INC.—See Tailwind Capital Group, LLC; *U.S. Private*, pg. 3923
WAUPACA FOUNDRY, INC.—See Monomoy Capital Partners LLC; *U.S. Private*, pg. 2772
WHITMAN CASTINGS, INC.; *U.S. Private*, pg. 4513
WILLIAM LEE LIMITED—See Castings PLC; *Int'l*, pg. 1357

331512 — STEEL INVESTMENT FOUNDRIES

ACCU-CAST INC.—See UCA Group Component Specialty Inc.; *U.S. Private*, pg. 4273
AERO METALS INC.; *U.S. Private*, pg. 118
AF AEROSPACE LIMITED—See Berkshire Hathaway Inc.; *U.S. Public*, pg. 313
AL-FAISAL STEEL PRODUCTS COMPANY—See Al-Tuwairqi Group; *Int'l*, pg. 289
ALSTONS BUILDING ENTERPRISES LIMITED—See ANSA McAL Limited; *Int'l*, pg. 477
AVALON PRECISION CASTING COMPANY, LLC—See Argand Partners, LP; *U.S. Private*, pg. 319
AVALON PRECISION METALSMITHS—See Argand Partners, LP; *U.S. Private*, pg. 319
BESCAST, INC.; *U.S. Private*, pg. 541
BURWILL HOLDINGS LIMITED; *Int'l*, pg. 1227
CALEDONIAN ALLOYS GROUP LIMITED—See Berkshire Hathaway Inc.; *U.S. Public*, pg. 313
CALEDONIAN ALLOYS LIMITED—See Berkshire Hathaway Inc.; *U.S. Public*, pg. 314
CAPTAIN TECHNOCAST LIMITED; *Int'l*, pg. 1317
CASTALLOY INC.—See Alcon Industries Inc.; *U.S. Private*, pg. 154
CONSOLIDATED PRECISION PRODUCTS CORP. - RANCHO CUCAMOUNGA—See Warburg Pincus LLC; *U.S. Private*, pg. 4437
DAMERON ALLOY FOUNDRIES; *U.S. Private*, pg. 1151
DASHENG TIMES CULTURAL INVESTMENT CO., LTD.; *Int'l*, pg. 1973
DOERRENBERG SPECIAL STEELS TAIWAN LTD.—See Gesco AG; *Int'l*, pg. 2945
FUNDICON, TALLERES S.A.—See Corporacion Nacional del Cobre de Chile; *Int'l*, pg. 1805
HITCHINER MANUFACTURING COMPANY INC.; *U.S. Private*, pg. 1953
HOA PHAT STEEL ONE MEMBER CO. LTD.—See Hoa Phat Group Joint Stock Company; *Int'l*, pg. 3435
HOWMET CASTINGS & SERVICES, INC. - DOVER ALLOY—See Howmet Aerospace Inc.; *U.S. Public*, pg. 1061
HOWMET CASTINGS & SERVICES, INC. - DOVER—See Howmet Aerospace Inc.; *U.S. Public*, pg. 1061
HOWMET CASTINGS & SERVICES, INC. - HAMPTON—See Howmet Aerospace Inc.; *U.S. Public*, pg. 1061
HOWMET CASTINGS & SERVICES, INC. - LA PORTE—See Howmet Aerospace Inc.; *U.S. Public*, pg. 1061
HOWMET CASTINGS & SERVICES, INC. - MORRISTOWN—See Howmet Aerospace Inc.; *U.S. Public*, pg. 1061
HOWMET CASTINGS & SERVICES, INC.—See Howmet Aerospace Inc.; *U.S. Public*, pg. 1061
HOWMET CASTINGS & SERVICES, INC. - STRUCTURAL CASTING—See Howmet Aerospace Inc.; *U.S. Public*, pg. 1061
LAPHAM-HICKEY STEEL CORP.—See Lapham-Hickey Steel Corp.; *U.S. Private*, pg. 2391
MINMETALS CAPITALS & SECURITIES, INC.—See China Rare Earth Resources And Technology Co., Ltd.; *Int'l*, pg. 1546
MISSISSIPPI PRECISION CAST PARTS—See Parrish Enterprises, Ltd.; *U.S. Private*, pg. 3100
O'FALLON CASTING, LLC; *U.S. Private*, pg. 2978
OKLAHOMA INVESTMENTS CASTING COMPANY—See Parrish Enterprises, Ltd.; *U.S. Private*, pg. 3100
OTTOWAY ENGINEERING PTY. LTD.—See E&A Limited; *Int'l*, pg. 2247
PURE CASTING COMPANY—See Lone Star Foundries, Inc.; *U.S. Private*, pg. 2484
R2 QUALITY CASTINGS, LLC; *U.S. Private*, pg. 3340
SEACAST AIC—See SeaCast, Inc.; *U.S. Private*, pg. 3583
SEACAST, INC.; *U.S. Private*, pg. 3583
SYNECTIC RESEARCH & ANALYSIS, INC.—See Avion Solutions, Inc.; *U.S. Private*, pg. 407
TRIUMPH ENGINEERED SOLUTIONS, INC.—See Triumph Group, Inc.; *U.S. Public*, pg. 2069
WILLIAM ROWLAND LTD—See Amalgamated Metal Corporation PLC; *Int'l*, pg. 409
WYMAN-GORDON CO. - BRIGHTON—See Berkshire Hathaway Inc.; *U.S. Public*, pg. 315

331513 — STEEL FOUNDRIES (EXCEPT INVESTMENT)

ACCURATE BUSHING COMPANY, INC.; *U.S. Private*, pg. 55
ACEROS FORTUNA, S.A. DE C.V.—See Carpenter Technology Corporation; *U.S. Public*, pg. 439
ACESIAN PARTNERS LIMITED; *Int'l*, pg. 102
AEROSPACE METAL COMPOSITES LIMITED—See Materion Corporation; *U.S. Public*, pg. 1395
AG AJIKAWA CORPORATION; *Int'l*, pg. 196
AICHI STEEL CORPORATION; *Int'l*, pg. 229
AKER EGERSUND AS—See Aker Solutions ASA; *Int'l*, pg. 262
ALASKA STEEL CO.—See Reliance Steel & Aluminum Co.; *U.S. Public*, pg. 1779
ALCON INDUSTRIES INC.; *U.S. Private*, pg. 154
ALGOMA STEEL INC.—See Algoma Steel Group Inc.; *Int'l*, pg. 318
AL JABER IRON & STEEL FOUNDRY LLC—See Al Jaber Group; *Int'l*, pg. 279
ALLOY CAST PRODUCTS, INC.—See Altus Capital Partners, Inc.; *U.S. Private*, pg. 211
ALPINE HOUSING DEVELOPMENT CORPORATION LTD. - ALPINE ALLOYS DIVISION—See Alpine Housing Development Corporation Ltd.; *Int'l*, pg. 371
AMITEC OY; *Int'l*, pg. 428
AMSCO CAST PRODUCTS (CANADA) INC.—See Black Cat Blades Ltd.; *U.S. Public*, pg. 1059
AMSTED CANADA INC.—See AMSTED Industries Incorporated; *U.S. Private*, pg. 267
AMSTED INDUSTRIES INCORPORATED; *U.S. Private*, pg. 267
ARCELORMITTAL FRANCE S.A.—See ArcelorMittal S.A.; *Int'l*, pg. 544
ARCELORMITTAL INTERNATIONAL ANTWERP SA—See ArcelorMittal S.A.; *Int'l*, pg. 543
ARCELORMITTAL SOUTH AFRICA LTD.—See ArcelorMittal S.A.; *Int'l*, pg. 545
ATLAS COPCO ASSISTANCE TECHNIQUE—See Atlas Copco AB; *Int'l*, pg. 677
ATLAS COPCO CONSTRUCTION TOOLS GMBH—See Atlas Copco AB; *Int'l*, pg. 678
ATLAS COPCO CONSTRUCTION TOOLS SARL—See Atlas Copco AB; *Int'l*, pg. 678
AXOS CLEARING LLC—See Axos Financial, Inc.; *U.S. Public*, pg. 256
BAHR BROS MFG, INC.; *U.S. Private*, pg. 425
BAILEY METAL PROCESSING LIMITED—See Bailey Metal Products Limited; *Int'l*, pg. 802
BAILEY METAL PRODUCTS LIMITED; *Int'l*, pg. 802
BAILEY WEST INC.—See Bailey Metal Products Limited; *Int'l*, pg. 802
BBC STEEL CORP.; *U.S. Private*, pg. 498
BENSON STEEL LIMITED; *Int'l*, pg. 975
BENXI IRON & STEEL GROUP CO. LTD.—See Anshan Iron & Steel Group Corporation; *Int'l*, pg. 479

331513 — STEEL FOUNDRIES (EX...)

BIG RIVER STEEL LLC—See United States Steel Corporation; *U.S. Public*, pg. 2236
BRADKEN-ENGINEERED PRODUCTS—See Hitachi, Ltd.; *Int'l*, pg. 3415
BRADKEN, INC.—See Hitachi, Ltd.; *Int'l*, pg. 3415
CAM RESOURCES BERHAD; *Int'l*, pg. 1267
CARL SCHAEFER (CASTING) GMBH & CO. KG—See Carl Schaefer GmbH & Co. KG; *Int'l*, pg. 1333
CARONDELET CORPORATION—See MetalTek International; *U.S. Private*, pg. 2682
CARPENTER TECHNOLOGY CORPORATION; *U.S. Public*, pg. 439
C. BROWN & SONS (STEEL) LTD; *Int'l*, pg. 1240
C. BROWN & SONS (STEEL) LTD—See C. Brown & Sons (Steel) Ltd; *Int'l*, pg. 1240
CEMTAS CELIK MAKINA SANAYI VE TICARET A.S.; *Int'l*, pg. 1400
CHAIN CHON INDUSTRIAL CO., LTD.; *Int'l*, pg. 1437
CHENGDE VANADIUM & TITANIUM NEW MATERIALS CO., LTD.—See HBIS Group Co., Ltd.; *Int'l*, pg. 3295
CHIA YI STEEL (YAN CHENG) CO., LTD.—See Chia Yi Steel Co., Ltd.; *Int'l*, pg. 1475
COLUMBIA STEEL CASTING CO., INC.; *U.S. Private*, pg. 977
COMPANIA ELECTRO METALURGICA S.A.; *Int'l*, pg. 1749
COPERION GMBH—See Hillenbrand, Inc.; *U.S. Public*, pg. 1035
CREATIVE CASTINGS LTD.; *Int'l*, pg. 1832
CYPRIUM, INC.—See Fortress Biotech, Inc.; *U.S. Public*, pg. 872
DAIDO CASTINGS CO., LTD.—See Daido Steel Co., Ltd.; *Int'l*, pg. 1922
DAIDO PRECISION INDUSTRIES LTD.—See Daido Steel Co., Ltd.; *Int'l*, pg. 1923
DAIDO STAR TECHNO CO., LTD.—See Daido Steel Co., Ltd.; *Int'l*, pg. 1923
DAIDO STEEL CO., LTD.; *Int'l*, pg. 1922
DGS DRUCKGUSS SYSTEME S.R.O—See DGS Druckguss Systeme AG; *Int'l*, pg. 2097
DONGIL INDUSTRIES CO., LTD.—See Dongil Metal Co., Ltd.; *Int'l*, pg. 2167
DONGIL METAL CO., LTD. - OGYE FACTORY—See Dongil Metal Co., Ltd.; *Int'l*, pg. 2167
DONGIL METAL CO., LTD.; *Int'l*, pg. 2167
DURALOY TECHNOLOGY—See Park Corp.; *U.S. Private*, pg. 3096
EIFFEL DEUTSCHLAND STAHLTECHNOLOGIE GMBH - DUISBURG—See Certina Holding AG; *Int'l*, pg. 1423
EIFFEL DEUTSCHLAND STAHLTECHNOLOGIE GMBH—See Certina Holding AG; *Int'l*, pg. 1423
ELG CARRS STAINLESS STEELS—See Franz Haniel & Cie. GmbH; *Int'l*, pg. 2763
ENERGY STEEL PRODUCTS—See Lone Star New Markets LP; *U.S. Private*, pg. 2489
EVRAZ HIGHVELD STEEL & VANADIUM LIMITED—See Evraz plc; *Int'l*, pg. 2574
EVRAZ INC. NA CANADA—See Evraz plc; *Int'l*, pg. 2574
FASTEEL INDUSTRIES LTD; *Int'l*, pg. 2622
FINE BESTEEL CO., LTD.; *Int'l*, pg. 2673
FRANK-HUNGARIA KFT.—See Gesco AG; *Int'l*, pg. 2945
THE FROG, SWITCH & MANUFACTURING COMPANY; *U.S. Private*, pg. 4031
FULWEALTH METAL FACTORY LIMITED—See Golik Holdings Limited; *Int'l*, pg. 3036
GEORG FISCHER AUTOMOTIVE AG—See Georg Fischer AG; *Int'l*, pg. 2935
GEORGSMARIENHUTTE GMBH—See Georgsmarienhutte Holding GmbH; *Int'l*, pg. 2940
GUJARAT INTRUX LIMITED; *Int'l*, pg. 3176
HAMPTON HYDRAULICS, LLC—See Ligon Industries LLC; *U.S. Private*, pg. 2455
HANKOOK STEEL CO., LTD.—See Hankook Tire & Technology Co.,Ltd.; *Int'l*, pg. 3253
HARRISON STEEL CASTINGS CO.; *U.S. Private*, pg. 1870
HIGHLAND FOUNDRY LTD.; *Int'l*, pg. 3387
HOGANAS GREAT BRITAIN UK—See Hoganas AB; *Int'l*, pg. 3441
HURON CASTING, INC.; *U.S. Private*, pg. 2012
INFRABUILD STEEL (MANUFACTURING) PTY LIMITED—See GFG Alliance Limited; *Int'l*, pg. 2956
ISKENDERUN DEMIR VE CELIK A.S.—See Eregli Demir Ve Celik Fabrikalari T.A.S.; *Int'l*, pg. 2490
JIASHAN DOERRENBERG MOULD & DIE TRADING CO.—See Gesco AG; *Int'l*, pg. 2945
JMAC INC.; *U.S. Private*, pg. 2214
KEYCAST KOHLSWA AB—See The Riverside Company; *U.S. Private*, pg. 4109
KEYCAST MEKO AB—See The Riverside Company; *U.S. Private*, pg. 4109
LANKA SPECIAL STEELS LTD—See E.B. Creasy & Company PLC; *Int'l*, pg. 2251
LAPHAM-HICKEY STEEL CORP. - FAIRFIELD DIVISION—See Lapham-Hickey Steel Corp.; *U.S. Private*, pg. 2391
LAPHAM-HICKEY STEEL CORP. - LITTLE CANADA DIVISION—See Lapham-Hickey Steel Corp.; *U.S. Private*, pg. 2391
LASERFLASH S.A.—See ArcelorMittal S.A.; *Int'l*, pg. 546

LIEBOVICH BROS., INC.—See Reliance Steel & Aluminum Co.; *U.S. Public*, pg. 1780
MANNSTAEDT-WERKE GMBH & CO. KG—See Georgsmarienhutte Holding GmbH; *Int'l*, pg. 2940
MANS-STEEL DIVISION—See Hutchens Industries Inc.; *U.S. Private*, pg. 2014
MANS-STEEL FOUNDRY—See Hutchens Industries Inc.; *U.S. Private*, pg. 2014
MAYNARD STEEL CASTING COMPANY; *U.S. Private*, pg. 2622
MCCONWAY & TORLEY, LLC—See Arcosa, Inc.; *U.S. Public*, pg. 186
MEDINA BLANKING, INC.—See Shiloh Industries, Inc.; *U.S. Private*, pg. 3636
MIDWEST ROLL FORMING & MANUFACTURING, INC.—See The Ohio Moulding Corporation; *U.S. Private*, pg. 4088
MMFX TECHNOLOGIES CORP.—See Commercial Metals Company; *U.S. Public*, pg. 545
MONARCH STEEL ALABAMA INC.—See American Consolidated Industries; *U.S. Private*, pg. 228
MUKAND ENGINEERS LTD—See Bajaj Auto Ltd.; *Int'l*, pg. 804
NORTHERN MANUFACTURING CO, INC.; *U.S. Private*, pg. 2953
OLBERSDORFER GUSS GMBH—See BAUER Aktiengesellschaft; *Int'l*, pg. 893
OMZ FOUNDRY MANUFACTURE LLC—See Gazprombank JSC; *Int'l*, pg. 2892
PACIFIC STEEL CASTING COMPANY; *U.S. Private*, pg. 3071
PRECISION CASTPARTS CORP.—See Berkshire Hathaway Inc.; *U.S. Public*, pg. 313
PRIME-LINE, INC.; *U.S. Private*, pg. 3262
PT. DONGIL METAL INDONESIA—See Dongil Metal Co., Ltd.; *Int'l*, pg. 2168
REGAL CAST INC—See PRL Inc.; *U.S. Private*, pg. 3269
ROBERTSON BUILDING SYSTEMS LIMITED—See Clayton, Dubilier & Rice, LLC; *U.S. Private*, pg. 921
RUHRPUMPEN METALS, S.A. DE C.V.—See Corporacion EG S.A.; *Int'l*, pg. 1803
SAWBROOK STEEL CASTINGS CO.; *U.S. Private*, pg. 3557
SHIMOMURA TOKUSHU SEIKO CO., LTD.—See Daido Steel Co., Ltd.; *Int'l*, pg. 1923
SIVYER STEEL CORPORATION RIVERSIDE PRODUCTS DIV.—See Sivyer Steel Corporation; *U.S. Private*, pg. 3677
SIVYER STEEL CORPORATION; *U.S. Private*, pg. 3677
SOUTHWEST STEEL COIL INC.—See Calstrip Industries Inc.; *U.S. Private*, pg. 723
SPOKANE INDUSTRIES INC.; *U.S. Private*, pg. 3759
STAINLESS FOUNDRY & ENGINEERING INC.—See TMB Industries Inc.; *U.S. Private*, pg. 4179
STEEL ROLLING MILLS LTD—See Alam Group of Companies; *Int'l*, pg. 289
TANG ENG IRON WORKS CO., LTD.—See China Steel Corporation; *Int'l*, pg. 1556
TEMPERFORM, LLC—See Oakland Standard Co., LLC; *U.S. Private*, pg. 2985
THYSSENKRUPP AUFZUGE GMBH—See Advent International Corporation; *U.S. Private*, pg. 106
THYSSENKRUPP AUFZUGE GMBH—See Cinven Limited; *Int'l*, pg. 1614
TUBE CITY IMS FRANCE CENTRE S.A.S.—See The Pritzker Organization, LLC; *U.S. Private*, pg. 4100
TUBE CITY IMS SERVICIOS DE MEXICO S. DE R.L. DE C.V.—See The Pritzker Organization, LLC; *U.S. Private*, pg. 4100
TUBE CITY IMS TRINIDAD LIMITED—See The Pritzker Organization, LLC; *U.S. Private*, pg. 4100
UNION ELECTRIC STEEL CORP.—See Ampco-Pittsburgh Corporation; *U.S. Public*, pg. 126
UNION ELECTRIC STEEL CORP.—See Ampco-Pittsburgh Corporation; *U.S. Public*, pg. 126
UNITED CASTINGS LIMITED—See Sims Limited; *U.S. Public*, pg. 1884
UNITED STATES STEEL CORP. - GARY—See United States Steel Corporation; *U.S. Public*, pg. 2237
U.S. STEEL KOSICE, S.R.O.—See United States Steel Corporation; *U.S. Public*, pg. 2237
VICTORY 1 PERFORMANCE, INC.—See MiddleGround Management, LP; *U.S. Private*, pg. 2712
VIGNYAN INDUSTRIES LIMITED—See BEML Limited; *Int'l*, pg. 969
VISHAY SANMAR LTD.—See Vishay Intertechnology, Inc.; *U.S. Public*, pg. 2303
WAUKESHA FOUNDRY INC.; *U.S. Private*, pg. 4457
WINSERT, INC.—See Altus Capital Partners, Inc.; *U.S. Private*, pg. 211
WYMAN-GORDON (LINCOLN) LIMITED—See Berkshire Hathaway Inc.; *U.S. Public*, pg. 315
YOUNG CORPORATION; *U.S. Private*, pg. 4592

331523 — NONFERROUS METAL DIE-CASTING FOUNDRIES

11. MART A.D.; *Int'l*, pg. 1
AALLIED DIE CASTING MANUFACTURING, INC.—See RCM Industries, Inc.; *U.S. Private*, pg. 3362
AALLIED DIE CASTING MANUFACTURING, INC.—See RCM Industries, Inc.; *U.S. Private*, pg. 3362
AAVID ALLCAST, LLC—See The Goldman Sachs Group, Inc.; *U.S. Public*, pg. 2080
ACCURATE CASTINGS INC.—See Hiler Industries; *U.S. Private*, pg. 1944
ACME DIE CASTING CORPORATION; *U.S. Private*, pg. 60
ADC L.P.; *U.S. Private*, pg. 76
AEROCAST, INC.; *U.S. Private*, pg. 118
AHRESTY CORPORATION - HIGASHIMATSUYAMA PLANT—See Ahresty Corporation; *Int'l*, pg. 225
AHRESTY CORPORATION; *Int'l*, pg. 225
AHRESTY DIE MOLD HAMAMATSU CORPORATION—See Ahresty Corporation; *Int'l*, pg. 225
AHRESTY MEXICANA, S.A. DE C.V.—See Ahresty Corporation; *Int'l*, pg. 226
AHRESTY WILMINGTON CORPORATION—See Ahresty Corporation; *Int'l*, pg. 226
AHRESTY YAMAGATA CORPORATION—See Ahresty Corporation; *Int'l*, pg. 226
AISIN AUTOMOTIVE CASTING, LLC—See AISIN Corporation; *Int'l*, pg. 252
AISIN HOKKAIDO CO., LTD.—See AISIN Corporation; *Int'l*, pg. 252
AISIN KEIKINZOKU CO., LTD.—See AISIN Corporation; *Int'l*, pg. 252
AISIN KYUSHU CASTING CO., LTD—See AISIN Corporation; *Int'l*, pg. 252
ALBANY CHICAGO COMPANY, LLC—See Shiloh Industries, Inc.; *U.S. Private*, pg. 3636
ALCONIX LOGISTICS (THAILAND) LTD.—See Alconix Corporation; *Int'l*, pg. 302
ALLOY DIE CASTING COMPANY—See Perella Weinberg Partners LP; *U.S. Public*, pg. 1674
ALLPER AG—See Exco Technologies Limited; *Int'l*, pg. 2580
ALTUM PRECISION SDN. BHD.—See Giovanni Agnelli B.V.; *Int'l*, pg. 2978
AMANO CORPORATION - MIYAKODA FACILITY—See Amano Corporation; *Int'l*, pg. 410
AMERICAN FOUNDRY GROUP, INC.; *U.S. Private*, pg. 234
AMERICAN METAL & TECHNOLOGY, INC.; *Int'l*, pg. 422
ANUP MALLEABLES LIMITED; *Int'l*, pg. 485
ATEK METAL TECHNOLOGIES, LLC—See ATEK Companies, Inc.; *U.S. Private*, pg. 365
ATI LADISH DIECAST TOOLING—See ATI Inc.; *U.S. Public*, pg. 221
BEST CAST IT LTD; *Int'l*, pg. 998
BLASER DIE CASTING CO.; *U.S. Private*, pg. 579
BLUE RIDGE PRESSURE CASTINGS, INC.; *U.S. Private*, pg. 592
BRABANT ALUCAST INTERNATIONAL B.V.—See Endless LLP; *Int'l*, pg. 2403
BREMEN CASTINGS, INC.; *U.S. Private*, pg. 645
BRILLCAST INC.—See Decorative Castings Inc.; *U.S. Private*, pg. 1188
CALLEN DIE CASTING LLC—See Callen Manufacturing Corporation; *U.S. Private*, pg. 722
CALLEN MANUFACTURING CORPORATION; *U.S. Private*, pg. 722
CAST ALUMINUM SOLUTIONS, LLC; *U.S. Private*, pg. 784
CHAMBERLIN & HILL CASTINGS LIMITED—See Chamberlin plc; *Int'l*, pg. 1439
CHANGCHUN FAWSN SWELL AUTOMOTIVE PARTS CO.,LTD.—See Guangdong Hongtu Technology (Holdings) Co., Ltd.; *Int'l*, pg. 3156
CHENGDU FUYI SWELL AUTO PARTS CO., LTD.—See Guangdong Hongtu Technology (Holdings) Co., Ltd.; *Int'l*, pg. 3156
CHICAGO WHITE METAL CASTING, INC.; *U.S. Private*, pg. 879
CHUNG MING CO., LTD.—See Chailease Holding Company Limited; *Int'l*, pg. 1437
CONSOLIDATED INDUSTRIES, INC.; *U.S. Private*, pg. 1021
CONSTELLIUM USSEL SAS—See Constellium SE; *Int'l*, pg. 1776
CONWAY MARSH GARRETT TECHNOLOGIES LIMITED; *Int'l*, pg. 1788
CREATIVE MASTER NORTHCORD LIMITED—See Creative Master Bermuda Ltd.; *Int'l*, pg. 1833
CREATIVE MASTER OVERSEAS HOLDINGS LIMITED—See Creative Master Bermuda Ltd.; *Int'l*, pg. 1833
CUSTOM METAL CRAFTERS, INC.; *U.S. Private*, pg. 1129
DECO PRODUCTS CO.; *U.S. Private*, pg. 1187
DEKSON CASTINGS LIMITED; *Int'l*, pg. 2010
DEL MAR INDUSTRIES INC.; *U.S. Private*, pg. 1192
DIEHL DO BRASIL METALURGICA LIMITADA—See Diehl Stiftung & Co. KG; *Int'l*, pg. 2115
DIEHL METAL INDIA PRIVATE LIMITED—See Diehl Stiftung & Co. KG; *Int'l*, pg. 2115
DIEHL SYNCHROTEC MANUFACTURING (WUXI) CO., LTD.—See Diehl Stiftung & Co. KG; *Int'l*, pg. 2115
DMG MORI CASTECH CO., LTD.—See DMG MORI Co., Ltd.; *Int'l*, pg. 2144

N.A.I.C.S. INDEX

331524 — ALUMINUM FOUNDRIES ...

DONGGUAN EONTEC CO., LTD.; *Int'l*, pg. 2167
DONGGUAN SWELL AUTO PARTS CO., LTD.—See Guangdong Hongtu Technology (Holdings) Co., Ltd.; *Int'l*, pg. 3156
DYERSVILLE DIE CAST—See Joseph L. Ertl, Inc.; *U.S. Private*, pg. 2237
DYNAFOND SA; *Int'l*, pg. 2239
EBARA-BENGUET, INC.—See Benguet Corporation; *Int'l*, pg. 974
EBARA-BENGUET, INC.—See Ebara Corporation; *Int'l*, pg. 2283
ECK INDUSTRIES, INC.; *U.S. Private*, pg. 1327
EDELBROCK FOUNDRY CORP.—See Edelbrock Corporation; *U.S. Private*, pg. 1332
EGS ENCLOSURES & CONTROLS—See Emerson Electric Co.; *U.S. Public*, pg. 740
ELKEM LTD.—See China National Chemical Corporation; *Int'l*, pg. 1527
EMPIRE DIE CASTING CO., INC.; *U.S. Private*, pg. 1384
ENDURANCE AMANN GMBH—See Affirma Capital Limited; *Int'l*, pg. 187
ENDURANCE F.O.A. S.P.A.—See Affirma Capital Limited; *Int'l*, pg. 187
EXCEL MASTER LIMITED—See Creative Master Bermuda Ltd.; *Int'l*, pg. 1833
FM PBW BEARINGS PRIVATE LIMITED—See Apollo Global Management, Inc.; *U.S. Public*, pg. 160
FOSHAN FUYI SWELL AUTO PARTS CO., LTD.—See Guangdong Hongtu Technology (Holdings) Co., Ltd.; *Int'l*, pg. 3156
FRANCIS MANUFACTURING CO.; *U.S. Private*, pg. 1587
FRANCONIA INDUSTRIES, INC.—See Diehl Stiftung & Co. KG; *Int'l*, pg. 2115
FUJI ALCONIX MEXICO S.A. DE C.V.—See Alconix Corporation; *Int'l*, pg. 302
GENERAL DIE CASTERS INC.; *U.S. Private*, pg. 1664
GEORG FISCHER AUTOMOBILGUSS GMBH—See Georg Fischer AG; *Int'l*, pg. 2935
GEORG FISCHER DRUCKGUSS GMBH & CO KG; *Int'l*, pg. 2938
GEORG FISCHER GMBH & CO KG—See Georg Fischer AG; *Int'l*, pg. 2936
GEORG FISCHER KOKILLENGUSS GMBH—See Georg Fischer AG; *Int'l*, pg. 2936
GIBBS DIE CASTING CORP.—See Koch Enterprises, Inc.; *U.S. Private*, pg. 2326
GOLD STAR BRAZIL LIMITED—See Goodwin PLC; *Int'l*, pg. 3042
GREAT LAKES DIE CAST CORPORATION; *U.S. Private*, pg. 1764
GRUBER & KAJA HIGH TECH METALS GMBH—See HTI High Tech Industries AG; *Int'l*, pg. 3508
GUANGDONG PAISHENG INTELLIGENT TECHNOLOGY CO., LTD.; *Int'l*, pg. 3158
HANJOO METAL CO., LTD.; *Int'l*, pg. 3253
HARRIS METALS COMPANY, LLC; *U.S. Private*, pg. 1869
HARZ GUSS ZORGE GMBH—See Georgsmarienhutte Holding GmbH; *Int'l*, pg. 2940
HDM HYDRAULICS, LLC—See Ligon Industries LLC; *U.S. Private*, pg. 2455
HICOM DIECASTINGS SDN. BHD.—See DRB-HICOM Berhad; *Int'l*, pg. 2201
HILER INDUSTRIES; *U.S. Private*, pg. 1944
HOFFMANN DIE CAST CORPORATION; *U.S. Private*, pg. 1960
HOWMET CASTINGS & SERVICES, INC. - TITANIUM CASTINGS—See Howmet Aerospace Inc.; *U.S. Public*, pg. 1061
HYATT DIE CAST & ENGINEERING CORP.; *U.S. Private*, pg. 2016
IBC ADVANCED ALLOYS CORP.; *U.S. Public*, pg. 1083
IMPERIAL DIE CASTING—See RCM Industries, Inc.; *U.S. Private*, pg. 3362
INLAND DIE CASTING—See RCM Industries, Inc.; *U.S. Private*, pg. 3362
JOSEPH L. ERTL, INC.; *U.S. Private*, pg. 2237
KITCHEN-QUIP, INC.; *U.S. Private*, pg. 2316
KOCH ENTERPRISES, INC.; *U.S. Private*, pg. 2326
LE SUEUR INCORPORATED—See Delos Capital, LLC; *U.S. Private*, pg. 1198
LE SUEUR INCORPORATED—See Silverfern Capital Management, LLC; *U.S. Private*, pg. 3663
LME CLEAR LIMITED—See Hong Kong Exchanges & Clearing Limited; *Int'l*, pg. 3466
LOVEJOY INDUSTRIES INC.; *U.S. Private*, pg. 2501
MAC CASTINGS INC.—See Mac Group Incorporated; *U.S. Private*, pg. 2531
MADISON-KIPP CORPORATION; *U.S. Private*, pg. 2544
MATTHEWS INTERNATIONAL CORPORATION; *U.S. Public*, pg. 1399
METAL TECHNOLOGIES WOODSTOCK—See Metal Technologies, Inc.; *U.S. Private*, pg. 2680
MICROCAST TECHNOLOGIES INC.; *U.S. Private*, pg. 2703
MIFA ALUMINIUM B V—See Aalberts N.V.; *Int'l*, pg. 35
MOULTRIE DIE CAST—See Joseph L. Ertl, Inc.; *U.S. Private*, pg. 2237
MUSKEGON CASTINGS CORP; *U.S. Private*, pg. 2818

NEBRASKA ALUMINUM CASTINGS, INC.; *U.S. Private*, pg. 2878
NEMAK GYOR KFT—See ALFA, S.A.B. de C.V.; *Int'l*, pg. 313
NEMAK POLAND SP. Z.O.O.—See ALFA, S.A.B. de C.V.; *Int'l*, pg. 313
NEMAK, S.A.—See ALFA, S.A.B. de C.V.; *Int'l*, pg. 313
NORSK ALCOA AS—See Alcoa Corporation; *U.S. Public*, pg. 74
NORTHWEST ALUMINUM SPECIALTIES, INC.; *U.S. Private*, pg. 2958
PACE INDUSTRIES DE CHIHUAHUA, S.A. DE C.V.—See Kenner & Company, Inc.; *U.S. Private*, pg. 2286
PACE INDUSTRIES, INC.—See Kenner & Company, Inc.; *U.S. Private*, pg. 2286
PACE INDUSTRIES - ST. PAUL DIVISION—See Kenner & Company, Inc.; *U.S. Private*, pg. 2286
PHB INC.; *U.S. Private*, pg. 3166
PHB MOLDING DIVISION—See PHB Inc.; *U.S. Private*, pg. 3167
PREMIER ALUMINUM, LLC; *U.S. Private*, pg. 3249
PRODUCTION CASTINGS INC.; *U.S. Private*, pg. 3273
RCM INDUSTRIES, INC.; *U.S. Private*, pg. 3362
ROSS ALUMINUM CASTINGS, LLC—See Advanced Metals Group, LLC; *U.S. Private*, pg. 91
ROSS CASTING & INNOVATION, LLC—See Revere Industries, LLC; *U.S. Private*, pg. 3414
SANCAST, INC.—See Westinghouse Air Brake Technologies Corporation; *U.S. Public*, pg. 2359
SAN-ETSU METALS CO., LTD. - SHIN NITTO PLANT—See CK SAN-ETSU Co., Ltd.; *Int'l*, pg. 1639
SAN-ETSU METALS CO., LTD.—See CK SAN-ETSU Co., Ltd.; *Int'l*, pg. 1639
SAN-ETSU METALS CO., LTD. - TAKAOKA PLANT—See CK SAN-ETSU Co., Ltd.; *Int'l*, pg. 1639
SHILOH INDUSTRIES ITALIA SRL—See Shiloh Industries, Inc.; *U.S. Private*, pg. 3636
SOUTHWESTERN DIE CASTING, INC.—See ABB Ltd.; *Int'l*, pg. 52
SPARTAN LIGHT METAL PRODUCTS; *U.S. Private*, pg. 3746
SPECIAL METALS WIGGIN TRUSTEES LIMITED—See Berkshire Hathaway Inc.; *U.S. Public*, pg. 315
STROHWIG INDUSTRIES, INC.; *U.S. Private*, pg. 3840
SUMMIT SHOWA ALUMINUM LTD.—See Asahi Seiren Co., Ltd.; *Int'l*, pg. 598
TCDC, INC.—See Target Corporation; *U.S. Public*, pg. 1982
TCH INDUSTRIES INC.; *U.S. Private*, pg. 3942
TEAM INDUSTRIES - DETROIT LAKES—See TEAM Industries, Inc.; *U.S. Private*, pg. 3949
THAI AHRESTY DIE CO., LTD.—See Ahresty Corporation; *Int'l*, pg. 225
THERMALCAST, LLC; *U.S. Private*, pg. 4142
THE TOP DIE CASTING CO. INC.; *U.S. Private*, pg. 4127
TST INC. - STANDARD METALS DIVISION—See TST Inc.; *U.S. Private*, pg. 4254
TWIN CITY DIE CASTINGS CO.; *U.S. Private*, pg. 4264
TWIN CITY DIE CASTINGS CO.—See Twin City Die Castings Co.; *U.S. Private*, pg. 4265
TWIN CITY DIE CASTINGS CO. - WATERTOWN FACILITY—See Twin City Die Castings Co.; *U.S. Private*, pg. 4265
TWIN CITY HOLLAND INDUSTRIES—See Twin City Fan Companies, Ltd.; *U.S. Private*, pg. 4265
UB VERKTYG AB—See AGES Industri AB; *Int'l*, pg. 206
UNI-CAST, INC.; *U.S. Private*, pg. 4281
WALKER DIE CASTING, INC.—See Allison Transmission Holdings, Inc.; *U.S. Public*, pg. 81
WDC ACQUISITION LLC—See TRM Equity LLC; *U.S. Private*, pg. 4241
WETZEL ACADEMY GMBH—See Matthews International Corporation; *U.S. Public*, pg. 1401
WETZEL SERVICE AG—See Matthews International Corporation; *U.S. Public*, pg. 1401
YODER INDUSTRIES INC.; *U.S. Private*, pg. 4589

331524 — ALUMINUM FOUNDRIES (EXCEPT DIE-CASTING)

AEROBOTIX, INC.; *U.S. Private*, pg. 118
AEROFOAM METALS, INC.; *Int'l*, pg. 181
AGES FALKENBERG AB—See AGES Industri AB; *Int'l*, pg. 206
AGES HORLE AB—See AGES Industri AB; *Int'l*, pg. 206
AGES KULLTORP AB—See AGES Industri AB; *Int'l*, pg. 206
AGES VARNAMO AB—See AGES Industri AB; *Int'l*, pg. 206
ALCOA LISTA-NORWAY—See Alcoa Corporation; *U.S. Public*, pg. 74
ALCOA MOSJOEN—See Alcoa Corporation; *U.S. Public*, pg. 74
ALCOA NORWAY ANS—See Alcoa Corporation; *U.S. Public*, pg. 74
ALICON CASTALLOY LIMITED; *Int'l*, pg. 327
ALTRAD ALUCON—See Altrad Investment Authority SAS; *Int'l*, pg. 397
ALUMINIUM KETY EMMI D.O.O.—See Grupa Kety S.A.; *Int'l*, pg. 3116

ALUTEC CO., LTD.; *Int'l*, pg. 401
APM ALUMINIUM CASTINGS SDN. BHD.—See APM Automotive Holdings Berhad; *Int'l*, pg. 516
APPALACHIAN CAST PRODUCTS, INC.; *U.S. Private*, pg. 295
ATA CASTING TECHNOLOGY CO., LTD.—See Daido Metal Corporation; *Int'l*, pg. 1921
ATLANTIC CASTING & ENGINEERING CORPORATION; *U.S. Private*, pg. 372
BRIDGE ALUMINIUM LIMITED—See Caparo Group Ltd.; *Int'l*, pg. 1301
CARLEY FOUNDRY, INC.; *U.S. Private*, pg. 763
CASTING TECHNOLOGY COMPANY—See Monomoy Capital Partners LLC; *U.S. Private*, pg. 2772
CERA-MET, LLC; *U.S. Private*, pg. 835
CONMET DE MEXICO—See AMSTED Industries Incorporated; *U.S. Private*, pg. 268
CONSOLIDATED METCO INC.—See AMSTED Industries Incorporated; *U.S. Private*, pg. 268
CONSOLIDATED PRECISION PRODUCTS CORP. - BLOOMINGTON—See Warburg Pincus LLC; *U.S. Private*, pg. 4437
CONSOLIDATED PRECISION PRODUCTS CORP. - CUDAHY—See Warburg Pincus LLC; *U.S. Private*, pg. 4437
CONSOLIDATED PRECISION PRODUCTS CORP. - POMONA—See Warburg Pincus LLC; *U.S. Private*, pg. 4437
CONSOLIDATED PRECISION PRODUCTS CORP.—See Warburg Pincus LLC; *U.S. Private*, pg. 4437
C.S. ALUMINIUM CORPORATION—See China Steel Corporation; *Int'l*, pg. 1555
DCX-CHOL ENTERPRISES, INC.; *U.S. Private*, pg. 1180
DCX-CHOL, INC.—See DCX-CHOL Enterprises, Inc.; *U.S. Private*, pg. 1180
DM CASTING TECHNOLOGY (THAILAND) CO., LTD.—See Daido Metal Corporation; *Int'l*, pg. 1921
DOLPHIN, INC.—See Karsten Manufacturing Corporation; *U.S. Private*, pg. 2263
ELKEM ASA - SILICON DIVISION—See China National Chemical Corporation; *Int'l*, pg. 1527
ELKEM ASA—See China National Chemical Corporation; *Int'l*, pg. 1527
ELKEM BJOLVEFOSSEN—See China National Chemical Corporation; *Int'l*, pg. 1527
ELKEM MARNES KVARTSITTBRUDD—See China National Chemical Corporation; *Int'l*, pg. 1527
ELKEM SILICON MATERIALS USA—See China National Chemical Corporation; *Int'l*, pg. 1527
GUPTA PERMOLD CORPORATION; *U.S. Private*, pg. 1819
HARMONY CASTINGS, LLC—See Ligon Industries LLC; *U.S. Private*, pg. 2455
HOWMET ALUMINUM CASTING LTD.—See Howmet Aerospace Inc.; *U.S. Public*, pg. 1061
HOWMET CIRAL S.N.C—See Howmet Aerospace Inc.; *U.S. Public*, pg. 1061
IKD FAEZA S.A. DE C.V.—See IKD Co., Ltd.; *Int'l*, pg. 3610
ILLICHMANN CASTALLOY GMBH—See Alicon Castalloy Limited; *Int'l*, pg. 327
ILLICHMANN CASTALLOY S.R.O—See Alicon Castalloy Limited; *Int'l*, pg. 327
LIGON INDUSTRIES LLC; *U.S. Private*, pg. 2455
MELLING TOOL COMPANY INC. - AC FOUNDRY DIVISION—See Melling Tool Company Inc.; *U.S. Private*, pg. 2662
MILLION HOPE INDUSTRIES LIMITED—See Hanison Construction Holdings Limited; *Int'l*, pg. 3252
MORRIS BEAN & COMPANY; *U.S. Private*, pg. 2786
NEMAK EUROPE GMBH—See ALFA, S.A.B. de C.V.; *Int'l*, pg. 313
OBERDORFER, LLC—See Advanced Metals Group, LLC; *U.S. Private*, pg. 91
RELIABLE CASTINGS CORPORATION - SIDNEY PLANT—See Reliable Castings Corporation; *U.S. Private*, pg. 3393
RELIABLE CASTINGS CORPORATION; *U.S. Private*, pg. 3393
RIEGER GMBH & CO. KG—See EnBW Energie Baden-Wurttemberg AG; *Int'l*, pg. 2400
SCHOTT IBERICA, S.A.—See Carl-Zeiss-Stiftung; *Int'l*, pg. 1337
SCOVILL HOLDINGS INC.; *U.S. Private*, pg. 3579
SHILOH INDUSTRIES NETHERLANDS B.V.—See Shiloh Industries, Inc.; *U.S. Private*, pg. 3636
S&H PRODUCTS, LLC—See B12 Capital Partners LLC; *U.S. Private*, pg. 421
SUPERIOR INDUSTRIES-FAYETTEVILLE—See SUPERIOR INDUSTRIES INTERNATIONAL INC; *U.S. Public*, pg. 1967
TC ALUMINIUM CASTINGS SDN. BHD.—See APM Automotive Holdings Berhad; *Int'l*, pg. 516
THRESHER INDUSTRIES, INC.; *U.S. Private*, pg. 2157
TPI-ARCADE, INC.—See Ligon Industries LLC; *U.S. Private*, pg. 2455
U.S. CASTINGS, LLC—See Advanced Metals Group, LLC; *U.S. Private*, pg. 91
WABASH CASTINGS INC.—See Callidus Capital Corporation; *U.S. Private*, pg. 1265

331524 — ALUMINUM FOUNDRIES ...

WARD CORPORATION; *U.S. Private*, pg. 4440
WATRY INDUSTRIES LLC—See Ligon Industries LLC; *U.S. Private*, pg. 2455

331529 — OTHER NONFERROUS METAL FOUNDRIES (EXCEPT DIE-CASTING)

A. B. C. RECYCLING LTD; *Int'l*, pg. 21
AETC LIMITED—See Berkshire Hathaway Inc.; *U.S. Public*, pg. 314
AKRON FOUNDRY CO.; *U.S. Private*, pg. 146
A.L. JOHNSON COMPANY; *U.S. Public*, pg. 12
AMERICAN BICYCLE GROUP—See The American Bicycle Group LLC; *U.S. Private*, pg. 3985
AMERICAN FOUNDRY—See American Foundry Group, Inc.; *U.S. Private*, pg. 234
AMERICAN METALCAST TECHNOLOGIES—See Meridian International Group, Inc.; *U.S. Private*, pg. 2673
AMPCO METAL, INC—See Ampco Metal SA; *Int'l*, pg. 433
AMPCO METAL LTD.—See Ampco Metal SA; *Int'l*, pg. 433
AMPCO METAL PORTUGAL LTDA.—See Ampco Metal SA; *Int'l*, pg. 433
AMPCO METAL SA; *Int'l*, pg. 433
AMPCO METAL SAS—See Ampco Metal SA; *Int'l*, pg. 433
AURORA METALS DIVISION LLC—See Hiler Industries; *U.S. Private*, pg. 1944
AURUBIS FINLAND OY—See Aurubis AG; *Int'l*, pg. 714
AURUBIS STOLBERG GMBH & CO. KG—See Aurubis AG; *Int'l*, pg. 714
BERNTSEN BRASS & ALUMINUM FOUNDRY INC.; *U.S. Private*, pg. 538
BOLIDEN KOKKOLA OY—See Boliden AB; *Int'l*, pg. 1102
BOMBARDIER MOTOR CORPORATION OF AMERICA—See Bain Capital, LP; *U.S. Private*, pg. 431
BRADKEN RESOURCES WUNDOWIE FOUNDRY PTY. LTD.—See Hitachi, Ltd.; *Int'l*, pg. 3415
BUNTING BEARINGS CORP.; *U.S. Private*, pg. 686
CAST-RITE INTERNATIONAL INC.—See Perella Weinberg Partners LP; *U.S. Public*, pg. 1674
CAST TECHNOLOGIES INCORPORATED; *U.S. Private*, pg. 784
CATCHER TECHNOLOGY (SUQIAN) CO., LTD.—See Catcher Technology Co., Ltd.; *Int'l*, pg. 1359
CHINA ALUMINUM GREAT WALL CONSTRUCTION CO., LTD.—See China Aluminum International Engineering Corporation Limited; *Int'l*, pg. 1482
CHINA ALUMINUM INTERNATIONAL ENGINEERING CORPORATION LIMITED; *Int'l*, pg. 1482
CHINA METAL RESOURCES UTILIZATION LTD.; *Int'l*, pg. 1524
CHINA NONFERROUS METALS INDUSTRY'S TWELFTH METALLURGICAL CONSTRUCTION CO., LTD.—See China Aluminum International Engineering Corporation Limited; *Int'l*, pg. 1482
CHINA NONFERROUS METALS PROCESSING TECHNOLOGY CO., LTD.—See China Aluminum International Engineering Corporation Limited; *Int'l*, pg. 1482
CHROMALLOY CASTINGS TAMPA CORPORATION—See Veritas Capital Fund Management, LLC; *U.S. Private*, pg. 4364
CONCAST METAL PRODUCTS CO. - OHIO PRODUCTION FACILITY—See Concast Metal Products Co.; *U.S. Private*, pg. 1008
CONCAST METAL PRODUCTS CO. - PENNSYLVANIA PRODUCTION FACILITY—See Concast Metal Products Co.; *U.S. Private*, pg. 1008
CONCAST METAL PRODUCTS CO.; *U.S. Private*, pg. 1008
DURAMOLD CASTINGS INC.; *U.S. Private*, pg. 1292
ENVIO TECHNOLOGY (SUQIAN) CO., LTD.—See Catcher Technology Co., Ltd.; *Int'l*, pg. 1359
FALCON FOUNDRY COMPANY; *U.S. Private*, pg. 1466
THE FALL RIVER GROUP, INC.; *U.S. Private*, pg. 4027
FANDSTAN ELECTRIC, INC.—See Westinghouse Air Brake Technologies Corporation; *U.S. Public*, pg. 2358
FRANKLIN BRONZE & ALLOY COMPANY, INVESTMENT CASTING DIVISION—See Franklin Bronze & Alloy Co.; *U.S. Private*, pg. 1596
FRANKLIN BRONZE & ALLOY CO., SAND CASTING DIVISION—See Franklin Bronze & Alloy Co.; *U.S. Private*, pg. 1596
FRANKLIN BRONZE & ALLOY CO.; *U.S. Private*, pg. 1596
FREEMAN MARINE EQUIPMENT, INC.; *U.S. Private*, pg. 1605
FRESNO VALVES & CASTINGS INC.; *U.S. Private*, pg. 1610
GOLIK METAL INDUSTRIAL COMPANY LIMITED—See Golik Holdings Limited; *Int'l*, pg. 3036
GREENWAY MINING GROUP LIMITED; *Int'l*, pg. 3077
GUANGDONG JINGYI METAL CO., LTD.; *Int'l*, pg. 3157
HARRIS SOLDAS ESPECIAIS S.A.—See Lincoln Electric Holdings, Inc.; *U.S. Public*, pg. 1317
HELMICK CORPORATION; *U.S. Private*, pg. 1912
HENAN NINTH METALLURGICAL CONSTRUCTION CO., LTD.—See China Aluminum International Engineering Corporation Limited; *Int'l*, pg. 1482
HITCHINER FRANCE—See Hitchiner Manufacturing Company Inc.; *U.S. Private*, pg. 1953

HITCHINER MANUFACTURING COMPANY DE MEXICO S. DE R.L. DE C.V.—See Hitchiner Manufacturing Company Inc.; *U.S. Private*, pg. 1953
HITCHINER S.A. DE C.V.—See Hitchiner Manufacturing Company Inc.; *U.S. Private*, pg. 1953
H. KRAMER & CO.; *U.S. Private*, pg. 1824
JIANGXI SOUTH RARE-EARTH HIGH-TECH CO., LTD.—See Beijing Zhong Ke San Huan High-tech Co., Ltd.; *Int'l*, pg. 961
JX NIPPON FOUNDRY CO., LTD.—See ENEOS Holdings, Inc.; *Int'l*, pg. 2416
LIVERS BRONZE CO., INC.—See Sage Capital LLC; *U.S. Private*, pg. 3526
LONE STAR FOUNDRIES, INC.; *U.S. Private*, pg. 2484
MAGNOLIA METAL CORPORATION; *U.S. Private*, pg. 2548
MATTHEWS INTERNATIONAL CORP. - BRONZE—See Matthews International Corporation; *U.S. Public*, pg. 1400
MCC INTERNATIONAL, INC.; *U.S. Private*, pg. 2626
MEECA TECHNOLOGY (SUZHOU INDUSTRIAL PARK) CO., LTD.—See Catcher Technology Co., Ltd.; *Int'l*, pg. 1359
MEECA TECHNOLOGY (TAIZHOU) CO., LTD.—See Catcher Technology Co., Ltd.; *Int'l*, pg. 1359
MEIGHS CASTINGS LTD—See MetalTek International; *U.S. Private*, pg. 2682
MG PRODUCTS COMPANY; *U.S. Private*, pg. 2694
MG ROHSTOFFHANDEL GMBH—See GEA Group Aktiengesellschaft; *Int'l*, pg. 2903
ORLANDINI ENTERPRISES; *U.S. Private*, pg. 3043
PACE INDUSTRIES - B & C DIVISION—See Kenner & Company, Inc.; *U.S. Private*, pg. 2286
PACIFIC CAST TECHNOLOGIES, INC.—See Warburg Pincus LLC; *U.S. Private*, pg. 4437
PARKER HANNIFIN BRASS PRODUCTS DIV.—See Parker Hannifin Corporation; *U.S. Public*, pg. 1645
PARKER HANNIFIN REFRIGERATION & AIR CONDITIONING DIV.—See Parker Hannifin Corporation; *U.S. Public*, pg. 1644
PCC AIRFOILS, LLC—See Berkshire Hathaway Inc.; *U.S. Public*, pg. 314
POLISHED METALS LTD INC.—See Sky Island Capital LLC; *U.S. Private*, pg. 3684
PT. DAIDO METAL INDONESIA—See Daido Metal Corporation; *Int'l*, pg. 1922
QINGDAO NPA INDUSTRY CO., LTD.—See Gaona Aero Material Co., Ltd.; *Int'l*, pg. 2882
RITCHEY METALS COMPANY INC.; *U.S. Private*, pg. 3441
ROSS CERAMICS LIMITED—See Dubai Holding LLC; *Int'l*, pg. 2218
SELMET, INC.—See Warburg Pincus LLC; *U.S. Private*, pg. 4437
SHENANGO LLC; *U.S. Private*, pg. 3632
SINTERMET LLC—See Vergani & Associates, LLC; *U.S. Private*, pg. 4359
SIXTH METALLURGICAL CONSTRUCTION COMPANY OF CHINA NONFERROUS METALS INDUSTRY CO., LTD.—See China Aluminum International Engineering Corporation Limited; *Int'l*, pg. 1482
SOUNDCAST COMPANY—See Griswold Industries, Inc.; *U.S. Private*, pg. 1791
ST. CLAIR DIE CASTING, LLC; *U.S. Private*, pg. 3771
ST. LAWRENCE ZINC COMPANY LLC—See HudBay Minerals Inc.; *Int'l*, pg. 3521
STURM, RUGER & CO., INC.-PRESCOTT FIREARMS DIVISION—See Sturm, Ruger & Company, Inc.; *U.S. Public*, pg. 1958
STURM, RUGER & CO., INC.—See Sturm, Ruger & Company, Inc.; *U.S. Public*, pg. 1958
SUDANESE EGYPTIAN ELECTRIC INDUSTRIES COMPANY LTD—See El Sewedy Electric Company; *Int'l*, pg. 2341
TAMPA BRASS & ALUMINUM CORP.; *U.S. Private*, pg. 3929
TOPO TECHNOLOGY (SUZHOU) CO., LTD.—See Catcher Technology Co., Ltd.; *Int'l*, pg. 1359
TOPO TECHNOLOGY (TAIZHOU) CO., LTD.—See Catcher Technology Co., Ltd.; *Int'l*, pg. 1359
VITO TECHNOLOGY (SUQIAN) CO., LTD.—See Catcher Technology Co., Ltd.; *Int'l*, pg. 1359
WISCONSIN ALUMINUM FOUNDRY COMPANY, INC.; *U.S. Private*, pg. 4547
ZHENJIANG TONGZHOU PROPELLER CO., LTD.—See Fullshare Holdings Limited; *Int'l*, pg. 2843

332111 — IRON AND STEEL FORGING

AAM GERMANY GMBH—See American Axle & Manufacturing Holdings, Inc.; *U.S. Public*, pg. 96
AAM PANTNAGAR AXLE PRIVATE LIMITED—See American Axle & Manufacturing Holdings, Inc.; *U.S. Public*, pg. 96
AAM POLAND SP. Z O. O.—See American Axle & Manufacturing Holdings, Inc.; *U.S. Public*, pg. 96
ABBEY FORGED PRODUCTS LIMITED; *Int'l*, pg. 56

ACCIAIERIE DI SICILIA S.P.A.—See Alfa Acciai SpA; *Int'l*, pg. 307
ACCUGEAR, INC.—See American Axle & Manufacturing Holdings, Inc.; *U.S. Public*, pg. 96
ACERINOX AUSTRALASIA PTY LTD—See Acerinox, S.A.; *Int'l*, pg. 100
ACEROS CHAPA INDUSTRIAL S.L.—See BAMESA Aceros; *Int'l*, pg. 813
ACINDAR INDUSTRIA ARGENTINA DE ACEROS S.A.—See ArcelorMittal S.A.; *Int'l*, pg. 543
ADVANTAGE STEEL SERVICE, INC.—See JM Walker LP; *U.S. Private*, pg. 2214
AFCO STEEL—See W&W Steel Company Inc.; *U.S. Private*, pg. 4417
AICHI FORGE & GEAR WORKS, LLC—See Aichi Steel Corporation; *Int'l*, pg. 230
AICHI FORGE PHILIPPINES, INC.—See Aichi Steel Corporation; *Int'l*, pg. 230
AICHI FORGE (THAILAND) CO., LTD.—See Aichi Steel Corporation; *Int'l*, pg. 230
ALFONSO GALLARDO S.A.; *Int'l*, pg. 316
AL JABER STEEL PRODUCTS L.L.C.—See Al Jaber Group; *Int'l*, pg. 279
ALLIED-LOCKE INDUSTRIES INCORPORATED; *U.S. Private*, pg. 191
AMFORGE INDUSTRIES LTD.; *Int'l*, pg. 424
AM/NS CALVERT—See ArcelorMittal S.A.; *Int'l*, pg. 543
AMPCO-PITTSBURGH CORPORATION; *U.S. Public*, pg. 126
ANGANG STEEL COMPANY LTD.—See Anshan Iron & Steel Group Corporation; *Int'l*, pg. 479
ANYANG IRON & STEEL GROUP CO., LTD.; *Int'l*, pg. 486
ARCELORMITTAL BRASIL S.A.—See ArcelorMittal S.A.; *Int'l*, pg. 543
ASHLAND FOUNDRY & MACHINE WORKS, LLC—See Speyside Equity LLC; *U.S. Private*, pg. 3756
ASW STEEL INC.—See Acciaierie Valbruna S.p.A.; *Int'l*, pg. 89
ATI FORGED PRODUCTS—See ATI Inc.; *U.S. Public*, pg. 221
ATI TITANIUM, LLC—See ATI Inc.; *U.S. Public*, pg. 221
ATI ZKM FORGING SP. Z O.O.—See ATI Inc.; *U.S. Public*, pg. 221
AUBERT & DUVAL—See Eramet SA; *Int'l*, pg. 2489
AUTOCAST AND FORGE PTY LTD—See KPS Capital Partners, LP; *U.S. Private*, pg. 2346
BALL CHAIN MFG CO, INC.; *U.S. Private*, pg. 459
BALO-MOTORTEX GMBH—See Georgsmarienhutte Holding GmbH; *Int'l*, pg. 2940
BAODING TECHNOLOGY CO., LTD.; *Int'l*, pg. 855
BAOTOU IRON & STEEL (GROUP) COMPANY LIMITED; *Int'l*, pg. 856
BARCELONESA DE METALES, S.A.—See BAMESA Aceros; *Int'l*, pg. 813
BAR PROCCESSING CORP.; *U.S. Private*, pg. 471
BERKELEY FORGE & TOOL INC.; *U.S. Private*, pg. 532
BERNDORF BADERBAU SK S.R.O.—See Berndorf AG; *Int'l*, pg. 987
BERNDORF BADERBAU SP. Z O.O.—See Berndorf AG; *Int'l*, pg. 987
BERNDORF BADERBAU SRL—See Berndorf AG; *Int'l*, pg. 987
BERNDORF BADERBAU S.R.O.—See Berndorf AG; *Int'l*, pg. 987
BERNDORF BELT TECHNOLOGY INC.—See Berndorf AG; *Int'l*, pg. 987
BERNDORF METALL- UND BADERBAU AG—See Berndorf AG; *Int'l*, pg. 987
BERNDORF METALLWAREN GMBH—See Berndorf AG; *Int'l*, pg. 987
BETONSTAHL LEIPZIG GMBH; *Int'l*, pg. 1003
BONNEY FORGE CORPORATION; *U.S. Private*, pg. 615
BRADKEN, INC.—See Hitachi, Ltd.; *Int'l*, pg. 3415
BROCKMAN ENGINEERING PTY LTD—See EVZ Limited; *Int'l*, pg. 2574
CALIFORNIA AMFORGE CORP.—See Wynnchurch Capital, L.P.; *U.S. Private*, pg. 4578
CALIFORNIA DROP FORGE, INC.—See HBD Industries, Inc.; *U.S. Private*, pg. 1887
CAMPRESS SRL—See Camozzi Group; *Int'l*, pg. 1274
CANADA FORGINGS INC.; *Int'l*, pg. 1278
CANTON DROP FORGE, INC.—See Park-Ohio Holdings Corp.; *U.S. Public*, pg. 1639
CARMESIN SA; *Int'l*, pg. 1341
CASTING & FORGING CO., LTD.—See Hitachi Zosen Corporation; *Int'l*, pg. 3410
CM CHAIN DIVISION—See Columbus McKinnon Corporation; *U.S. Public*, pg. 535
CM MECHANICAL HANDLING SYSTEMS—See Columbus McKinnon Corporation; *U.S. Public*, pg. 535
COIL STEELS (AUST) PTY LIMITED—See Commercial Metals Company; *U.S. Public*, pg. 546
COIL STEELS LONG PRODUCTS—See Commercial Metals Company; *U.S. Public*, pg. 546
COIL STEELS PROCESSING—See Commercial Metals Company; *U.S. Public*, pg. 546
COIL STEELS TRADING PTY LTD—See Commercial Metals Company; *U.S. Public*, pg. 546

N.A.I.C.S. INDEX

332112 — NONFERROUS FORGING

COLFOR MANUFACTURING, INC.—See American Axle & Manufacturing Holdings, Inc.; *U.S. Public*, pg. 96
COLUMBUS STAINLESS (PTY) LTD—See Acerinox, S.A.; *Int'l*, pg. 100
COMETALS FAR EAST, INC.—See Commercial Metals Company; *U.S. Public*, pg. 546
COMMERCIAL FORGED PRODUCTS—See Wozniak Industries, Inc.; *U.S. Private*, pg. 4571
COMPLEJO SIDERURGICO DE GUAYANA, C.A.—See Corporacion Venezolana de Guayana; *Int'l*, pg. 1805
CONLEY FROG/SWITCH & FORGE COMPANY; *U.S. Private*, pg. 1014
CORE PIPE INC.; *U.S. Private*, pg. 1049
CORNELL FORGE COMPANY; *U.S. Private*, pg. 1051
CORRY FORGE COMPANY—See Ellwood Group, Inc.; *U.S. Private*, pg. 1375
CSN PARANA—See Companhia Siderurgica Nacional; *Int'l*, pg. 1748
DAECHANG FORGING CO., LTD.; *Int'l*, pg. 1906
DAEDONG STEEL CO., LTD. - INCHOEN PLANT—See Daedong Steel Co., Ltd.; *Int'l*, pg. 1906
DAEDONG STEEL CO., LTD. - POHANG PLANT—See Daedong Steel Co., Ltd.; *Int'l*, pg. 1906
DAIDO STEEL CO., LTD. - SHIBUKAWA PLANT—See Daido Steel Co., Ltd.; *Int'l*, pg. 1923
DAIDO STEEL (SHANGHAI) CO., LTD.—See Daido Steel Co., Ltd.; *Int'l*, pg. 1923
DAYTON FORGING & HEAT TREATING COMPANY; *U.S. Private*, pg. 1177
DELTA (VANCOUVER), B.C.—See Daechang Forging Co., Ltd.; *Int'l*, pg. 1906
DIECKERHOFF GUSS GMBH—See Georgsmarienhutte Holding GmbH; *Int'l*, pg. 2940
DIRECT REDUCTION IRON COMPANY—See Al-Tuwairqi Group; *Int'l*, pg. 289
DOLD KALTFLIESSPRESSTEILE GMBH—See Gevelot S.A.; *Int'l*, pg. 2954
DUPRE MINERALS LIMITED—See Goodwin PLC; *Int'l*, pg. 3041
EASTHAM FORGE INC.—See Eastham Enterprises, Inc.; *U.S. Private*, pg. 1322
EDGERTON FORGE, INC.—See Avis Industrial Corporation; *U.S. Private*, pg. 407
ELLWOOD CITY FORGE—See Ellwood Group, Inc.; *U.S. Private*, pg. 1375
ELLWOOD GROUP, INC.; *U.S. Private*, pg. 1375
ELLWOOD SPECIALTY STEEL COMPANY, LLC—See Ellwood Group, Inc.; *U.S. Private*, pg. 1375
ELLWOOD TEXAS FORGE—See Ellwood Group, Inc.; *U.S. Private*, pg. 1375
ENERGIETECHNIK ESSEN GMBH—See Georgsmarienhutte Holding GmbH; *Int'l*, pg. 2940
ERAMET ALLOYS—See Eramet SA; *Int'l*, pg. 2488
EREGLI DEMIR VE CELIK FABRIKALARI T.A.S.; *Int'l*, pg. 2490
ERVIN INDUSTRIES, INC. - ERVIN TECHNOLOGIES DIVISION—See Ervin Industries, Inc.; *U.S. Private*, pg. 1423
ESSAR STEEL LTD.—See Essar Global Limited; *Int'l*, pg. 2508
ESSAR STEEL MINNESOTA LLC—See Essar Global Limited; *Int'l*, pg. 2508
FISKARS POLSKA SP. Z O.O.—See Fiskars Oyj Abp; *Int'l*, pg. 2694
FLOCAST AUSTRALIA PTY LTD—See Arrowcrest Group Pty. Ltd.; *Int'l*, pg. 580
FORGED COMPONENTS, INC.—See L.E. Simmons & Associates, Inc.; *U.S. Private*, pg. 2365
FORMETAL, INC.; *Int'l*, pg. 2734
FRIEDRICH WILHELMS - HUETTE GMBH—See Georgsmarienhutte Holding GmbH; *Int'l*, pg. 2940
GEAR COMPANY OF AMERICA, INC.; *U.S. Private*, pg. 1654
GEAR HEADQUARTERS INC.—See Headco Industries; *U.S. Private*, pg. 1891
GEAR PRODUCTS INC.—See Dover Corporation; *U.S. Public*, pg. 679
GENERAL FLANGE & FORGE LLC—See Quadrant Management, Inc.; *U.S. Private*, pg. 3316
GEVELOT EXTRUSION—See Gevelot S.A.; *Int'l*, pg. 2954
GKN DRIVELINE TRIER—See GKN plc; *Int'l*, pg. 2985
GLOBAL STEEL HOLDINGS LTD.; *Int'l*, pg. 3001
GOODWIN STEEL CASTINGS LTD.—See Goodwin PLC; *Int'l*, pg. 3042
GROEDITZER WERKZEUGSTAHL BURG GMBH—See Georgsmarienhutte Holding GmbH; *Int'l*, pg. 2940
HEARTLAND STEEL PRODUCTS, LLC—See LFM Capital LLC; *U.S. Private*, pg. 2441
HHI FORMTECH, LLC—See American Axle & Manufacturing Holdings, Inc.; *U.S. Public*, pg. 96
HILTON METAL FORGING LTD.; *Int'l*, pg. 3395
HUDACO INDUSTRIES LIMITED - BOSWORTH DIVISION—See Hudaco Industries Limited; *Int'l*, pg. 3521
IMPACT FORGE GROUP, LLC—See American Axle & Manufacturing Holdings, Inc.; *U.S. Public*, pg. 96
INNER MONGOLIA BAOTOU STEEL UNION COMPANY LIMITED—See Baotou Iron & Steel (Group) Company Limited; *Int'l*, pg. 857
INTASA S.A.—See CAP S.A.; *Int'l*, pg. 1300
INTERNATIONAL HEARTH MELTING, LLC—See ATI Inc.; *U.S. Public*, pg. 222
JAPAN DROP FORGE CO., LTD.—See Daido Steel Co., Ltd.; *Int'l*, pg. 1923
JERNBERG INDUSTRIES, LLC—See American Axle & Manufacturing Holdings, Inc.; *U.S. Public*, pg. 96
JERVIS B. WEBB COMPANY—See Daifuku Co., Ltd.; *Int'l*, pg. 1925
KELLER GROUP INC.; *U.S. Private*, pg. 2275
KES ACQUISITION COMPANY—See Steel Dynamics, Inc.; *U.S. Public*, pg. 1942
KT ACQUISITION LLC—See Crawford United Corporation; *U.S. Private*, pg. 592
L.B. FOSTER COMPANY; *U.S. Public*, pg. 1278
LEBUS MANUFACTURING CO.—See KKR & Co. Inc.; *U.S. Public*, pg. 1264
LE MIN INDUSTRIAL CO., LTD.—See Allis Electric Co., Ltd.; *Int'l*, pg. 359
MAANSHAN IRON & STEEL COMPANY LIMITED—See China Baowu Steel Group Corp., Ltd.; *Int'l*, pg. 1485
MA STEEL (WUHU) PROCESSING AND DISTRIBUTION CO., LTD.—See China Baowu Steel Group Corp., Ltd.; *Int'l*, pg. 1486
MCINNES ROLLED RINGS—See TSK Partners, Inc.; *U.S. Private*, pg. 4253
MCWILLIAMS FORGE CO.; *U.S. Private*, pg. 2645
MEADVILLE FORGING COMPANY INC.—See Keller Group Inc.; *U.S. Private*, pg. 2275
MERCER FORGE CORPORATION; *U.S. Private*, pg. 2669
METALDYNE NURNBERG GMBH—See American Axle & Manufacturing Holdings, Inc.; *U.S. Public*, pg. 97
METALDYNE OSLAVANY, SPOL. S.R.O.—See American Axle & Manufacturing Holdings, Inc.; *U.S. Public*, pg. 97
METALDYNE SINTERED RIDGWAY, LLC—See American Axle & Manufacturing Holdings, Inc.; *U.S. Public*, pg. 97
METALYST FORGINGS LTD.—See Amtek Auto Limited; *Int'l*, pg. 441
METFORM, LLC—See MacLean-Fogg Company; *U.S. Private*, pg. 2537
MID-WEST FORGE CORPORATION; *U.S. Private*, pg. 2709
MILWAUKEE FORGE, INC.; *U.S. Private*, pg. 2739
MODERN DROP FORGE CO.; *U.S. Private*, pg. 2760
MODERN FORGE/TENNESSEE—See Modern Drop Forge Co.; *U.S. Private*, pg. 2760
MSP INDUSTRIES CORPORATION—See American Axle & Manufacturing Holdings, Inc.; *U.S. Public*, pg. 96
MW UNIVERSAL INC.; *U.S. Private*, pg. 2822
NEW MILLENNIUM BUILDING SYSTEMS, LLC—See Steel Dynamics, Inc.; *U.S. Public*, pg. 1942
NOVA FORGE CORP.—See Reserve Group Management Company; *U.S. Private*, pg. 3404
OHIO METAL TECHNOLOGIES, INC.; *U.S. Private*, pg. 3004
OKLAHOMA FORGE INC.; *U.S. Private*, pg. 3007
OLYMPIC LASER PROCESSING, LLC—See Olympic Steel Inc.; *U.S. Public*, pg. 1570
OLYMPIC LASER PROCESSING, LLC—See United States Steel Corporation; *U.S. Public*, pg. 2236
OMNI-LITE INDUSTRIES CANADA INC.; *U.S. Public*, pg. 1572
OMZ-SPETSSTAL OOO—See Gazprombank JSC; *Int'l*, pg. 2892
OXFORD FORGE, INC.—See American Axle & Manufacturing Holdings, Inc.; *U.S. Public*, pg. 97
PACIFIC FORGE, INC.—See Avis Industrial Corporation; *U.S. Private*, pg. 407
PARKER HANNIFIN HYDRAULIC PUMP & MOTOR DIV.—See Parker Hannifin Corporation; *U.S. Public*, pg. 1647
PENNG AUSTRIA GMBH—See Berndorf AG; *Int'l*, pg. 987
PENNSYLVANIA MACHINE WORKS, LLC—See Wynnchurch Capital, L.P.; *U.S. Private*, pg. 4577
PERFORMANCE STAMPING CO., INC.—See Willis & Smith Capital, LLC; *U.S. Private*, pg. 4527
THE PERRYMAN CO. - PITTSBURGH PLANT—See The Perryman Company; *U.S. Private*, pg. 4093
PHOENIX FORGING COMPANY, INC.; *U.S. Private*, pg. 3172
PIONEER FORGE DIVISION—See Letts Industries, Inc.; *U.S. Private*, pg. 2433
PLYMOUTH TUBE COMPANY - TRENT MILL—See Plymouth Tube Company; *U.S. Private*, pg. 3216
PLYMOUTH TUBE COMPANY - WEST MONROE MILL—See Plymouth Tube Company; *U.S. Private*, pg. 3216
PORT COLBORNE DROP FORGE—See Mission Essential Personnel, LLC; *U.S. Public*, pg. 2747
PORTLAND CHAIN MANUFACTURING CO.—See MPE Partners, LLC; *U.S. Private*, pg. 2804
PRECISION CASTPARTS CZ S.R.O.—See Berkshiro Hathaway Inc.; *U.S. Public*, pg. 315
PRESRITE CORPORATION; *U.S. Private*, pg. 3255
PT. AICHI FORGING INDONESIA—See Aichi Steel Corporation; *Int'l*, pg. 230
PURECOAT INTERNATIONAL, LLC; *U.S. Private*, pg. 3306
RECTUS AG—See Parker Hannifin Corporation; *U.S. Public*, pg. 1646
RG STEEL WARREN, INC.—See Hilco Trading, LLC; *U.S. Private*, pg. 1944
RILEY GEAR CORPORATION; *U.S. Private*, pg. 3437
SAFESPAN PLATFORM SYSTEMS INC.; *U.S. Private*, pg. 3524
SBF-HAGUSTA GMBH.—See BAUER Aktiengesellschaft; *Int'l*, pg. 893
SCHAEFFER INDUSTRIES; *U.S. Private*, pg. 3563
SCHILLING FORGE, INC.—See CUTCO Corporation; *U.S. Private*, pg. 1131
SCHMIEDAG GMBH—See Georgsmarienhutte Holding GmbH; *Int'l*, pg. 2941
SCHMIEDEWERKE GROEDITZ GMBH—See Georgsmarienhutte Holding GmbH; *Int'l*, pg. 2941
SCOT FORGE COMPANY INC.; *U.S. Private*, pg. 3575
SHANGHAI AICHI FORGING CO., LTD.—See Aichi Steel Corporation; *Int'l*, pg. 230
SIFCO FORGE GROUP—See SIFCO Industries, Inc.; *U.S. Public*, pg. 1877
SOUTHWEST STEEL PROCESSING LLC—See Park-Ohio Holdings Corp.; *U.S. Public*, pg. 1640
STAHLGUSS GRODITZ GMBH—See Georgsmarienhutte Holding GmbH; *Int'l*, pg. 2941
STEEL INDUSTRIES INC.—See Arlington Capital Partners LLC; *U.S. Private*, pg. 327
SUPERIOR FORGE & STEEL CORPORATION - NEW CASTLE—See Superior Forge & Steel Corporation; *U.S. Private*, pg. 3878
SUPERIOR FORGE & STEEL CORPORATION; *U.S. Private*, pg. 3878
SYPRIS TECHNOLOGIES, INC. - TUBE TURNS FACILITY—See Sypris Solutions, Inc.; *U.S. Public*, pg. 1972
TEXAS HONING, INC.—See Berkshire Hathaway Inc.; *U.S. Public*, pg. 314
TEXAS METAL WORKS—See First Reserve Management, L.P.; *U.S. Private*, pg. 1525
TIMKEN DRIVES LLC—See The Timken Company; *U.S. Public*, pg. 2133
TOHAN STEEL CO., LTD.—See Hanwa Co., Ltd.; *Int'l*, pg. 3263
TRU-FORM INC.—See General Electric Company; *U.S. Public*, pg. 919
TSK PARTNERS, INC.; *U.S. Private*, pg. 4253
UNIT DROP FORGE CO., INC.; *U.S. Private*, pg. 4287
UNIVERSAL STAINLESS & ALLOY PRODUCTS, INC.; *U.S. Public*, pg. 2262
WALKER FORGE INC.; *U.S. Private*, pg. 4429
WALLACE FORGE COMPANY INC.; *U.S. Private*, pg. 4430
WALTER HUNDHAUSEN GMBH—See CE Capital Partner GmbH; *Int'l*, pg. 1372
WALZWERK BURG GMBH—See Georgsmarienhutte Holding GmbH; *Int'l*, pg. 2941
WESTERN AUSTRALIAN SPECIALTY ALLOYS, PTY. LTD.—See Berkshire Hathaway Inc.; *U.S. Public*, pg. 315
WESTERN FORGE & FLANGE CO.—See Wynnchurch Capital, L.P.; *U.S. Private*, pg. 4578
WILDAUER SCHMIEDEWERKE GMBH & CO. KG—See Georgsmarienhutte Holding GmbH; *Int'l*, pg. 2941
WORTHINGTON SAMUEL COIL PROCESSING, LLC—See United States Steel Corporation; *U.S. Public*, pg. 2237
WORTHINGTON SAMUEL COIL PROCESSING, LLC—See Worthington Industries, Inc.; *U.S. Public*, pg. 2383
WUHAN IRON & STEEL CO., LTD.—See China Baowu Steel Group Corp., Ltd.; *Int'l*, pg. 1485
WYMAN-GORDON DE MONTERREY S. DE R.L. DE C.V.—See Berkshire Hathaway Inc.; *U.S. Public*, pg. 315
WYMAN GORDON FORGINGS (CLEVELAND), INC.—See Berkshire Hathaway Inc.; *U.S. Public*, pg. 315
WYMAN-GORDON FORGINGS, INC.—See Berkshire Hathaway Inc.; *U.S. Public*, pg. 315
WYMAN-GORDON LIMITED—See Berkshire Hathaway Inc.; *U.S. Public*, pg. 315
XINYANG IRON & STEEL CO., LTD.—See Anyang Iron & Steel Group Co., Ltd.; *Int'l*, pg. 487

332112 — NONFERROUS FORGING

AAPICO FORGING PLC—See AAPICO Hitech plc; *Int'l*, pg. 37
ALFOT TECHNOLOGIES CO., LTD.; *Int'l*, pg. 316
ALUMINUM PRECISION PRODUCTS INC.; *U.S. Private*, pg. 211
BOLER VENTURES LLC; *U.S. Private*, pg. 610
CARLTON FORGE WORKS—See Berkshire Hathaway Inc.; *U.S. Public*, pg. 314
CERRO FABRICATED PRODUCTS, INC.—See Berkshire Hathaway Inc.; *U.S. Public*, pg. 310
CONTINENTAL FORGE COMPANY—See Arlington Capital Partners LLC; *U.S. Private*, pg. 327
DENDRIT HAUSTECHNIK-SOFTWARE GMBH—See Gebr. Kemper GmbH & Co. KG; *Int'l*, pg. 2906
FAR EAST ALUMINUM WORKS (U.S.) CORPORATION—See China State Construction International Holdings Limited; *Int'l*, pg. 1554

332112 — NONFERROUS FORGING

GENERAL ALUMINUM FORGINGS, LLC—See SIFCO Industries, Inc.; *U.S. Public*, pg. 1877
GUARANTEE SPECIALTIES INC.; *U.S. Private*, pg. 1809
LENAPE FORGE, INC.; *U.S. Private*, pg. 2421
MATTCO FORGE, INC.—See Blue Point Capital Partners, LLC; *U.S. Private*, pg. 590
OHIO STAR FORGE CO.—See Daido Steel Co., Ltd.; *Int'l*, pg. 1923
PREMIER FORGE GROUP, LLC—See Wynnchurch Capital, L.P.; *U.S. Private*, pg. 4578
PROFILTECH STUFENBANDPROFILE GMBH—See Gebr. Kemper GmbH & Co. KG; *Int'l*, pg. 2906
QUALITY ALUMINUM FORGE, LLC—See SIFCO Industries, Inc.; *U.S. Public*, pg. 1877
SCHULER ITALIA S.R.L.—See ANDRITZ AG; *Int'l*, pg. 456
SCHULTZ STEEL COMPANY; *U.S. Private*, pg. 3570
SIERRA ALLOYS COMPANY—See Platte River Ventures, LLC; *U.S. Private*, pg. 3211
STAR FORGE, LLC—See CE Star Holdings, LLC; *U.S. Private*, pg. 803
STAR FORMING MANUFACTURING, LLC - ORANGE PLANT—See CE Star Holdings, LLC; *U.S. Private*, pg. 803
WYMAN-GORDON COMPANY—See Berkshire Hathaway Inc.; *U.S. Public*, pg. 315

332114 — CUSTOM ROLL FORMING

OVEREEM B.V.—See Hadley Industries PLC; *Int'l*, pg. 3205
PYRAMID MOULDINGS - GEORGIA PLANT—See Roller Die & Forming Company, Inc.; *U.S. Private*, pg. 3474
PYRAMID MOULDINGS, INC.—See Roller Die & Forming Company, Inc.; *U.S. Private*, pg. 3474
PYRAMID MOULDINGS - MEXICO PLANT—See Roller Die & Forming Company, Inc.; *U.S. Private*, pg. 3474
ROLLER DIE & FORMING COMPANY, INC.; *U.S. Private*, pg. 3474
S & S STEEL SERVICES—See The Mill Steel Co., Inc.; *U.S. Private*, pg. 4079
U.S. CUSTOM MANUFACTURING—See U.S. Venture, Inc.; *U.S. Private*, pg. 4272
WEBEX, INC.—See Bertram Capital Management, LLC; *U.S. Private*, pg. 540

332117 — POWDER METALLURGY PART MANUFACTURING

ACME ELECTRONICS CORPORATION; *Int'l*, pg. 107
ALPHA SINTERED METALS, INC.—See O2 Investment Partners, LLC; *U.S. Private*, pg. 2982
THE ALUMINUM POWDER COMPANY LIMITED—See AMG Critical Materials N.V.; *Int'l*, pg. 426
AMERICAN FINE SINTER CO., LTD.—See Fine Sinter Co., Ltd.; *Int'l*, pg. 2673
AMERICAN SINTERED TECHNOLOGIES, INC.—See Fansteel, Inc.; *U.S. Private*, pg. 1472
BODYCOTE HEISS-ISOSTATISCHES PRESSEN GMBH—See Bodycote plc; *Int'l*, pg. 1098
BROOKSIDE METAL COMPANY LTD—See Amalgamated Metal Corporation PLC; *Int'l*, pg. 408
CALRAM, INC.—See Insight Equity Holdings LLC; *U.S. Private*, pg. 2086
CAPSTAN INC.; *U.S. Private*, pg. 746
CNMC (NINGXIA) ORIENT GROUP CO., LTD.—See China Nonferrous Metal Mining (Group) Co., Ltd.; *Int'l*, pg. 1535
COMILOG SA—See Eramet SA; *Int'l*, pg. 2488
CONFORMA CLAD, INC.—See Kennametal Inc.; *U.S. Public*, pg. 1221
DOWA ELECTRONICS MATERIALS OKAYAMA CO., LTD.—See Dowa Holdings Co., Ltd.; *Int'l*, pg. 2183
DOWA F-TEC (SINGAPORE) PTE. LTD.—See Dowa Holdings Co., Ltd.; *Int'l*, pg. 2183
DOWA IP CREATION CO., LTD.—See Dowa Holdings Co., Ltd.; *Int'l*, pg. 2183
ECKA GRANULES INTL. TRADING (SHANGHAI) CO. LTD.—See Palladium Equity Partners, LLC; *U.S. Private*, pg. 3078
FINE SINTER CO., LTD. - KASUGAI PLANT—See Fine Sinter Co., Ltd.; *Int'l*, pg. 2673
FINE SINTER CO., LTD. - SHIGA PLANT—See Fine Sinter Co., Ltd.; *Int'l*, pg. 2673
FINE SINTER CO., LTD.; *Int'l*, pg. 2673
FINE SINTER CO., LTD. - TAMAGAWA PLANT—See Fine Sinter Co., Ltd.; *Int'l*, pg. 2673
FINE SINTER CO., LTD. - YAMASHINA PLANT—See Fine Sinter Co., Ltd.; *Int'l*, pg. 2673
FINE SINTER SANSHIN CO., LTD.—See Fine Sinter Co., Ltd.; *Int'l*, pg. 2673
FINE SINTER TOHOKU CO., LTD.—See Fine Sinter Co., Ltd.; *Int'l*, pg. 2673
FORTUS SA; *Int'l*, pg. 2744
GEA CANADA INC.—See GEA Group Aktiengesellschaft; *Int'l*, pg. 2898
GKN DANYANG INDUSTRIES COMPANY LTD—See GKN plc; *Int'l*, pg. 2984
GKN SINTER METALS—See GKN plc; *Int'l*, pg. 2985
HANGZHOU ADVANCE FOUNDRY CO., LTD.—See Hangzhou Advance Gearbox Group Co., Ltd.; *Int'l*, pg. 3246
HANGZHOU ADVANCE GEARBOX GROUP CO., LTD.; *Int'l*, pg. 3246
HANGZHOU ADVANCE GENERAL MACHINERY CO., LTD.—See Hangzhou Advance Gearbox Group Co., Ltd.; *Int'l*, pg. 3246
H.B. FULLER CONSTRUCTION PRODUCTS INC. - LA MIRADA—See H.B. Fuller Company; *U.S. Public*, pg. 977
HOWELL METAL COMPANY—See Commercial Metals Company; *U.S. Public*, pg. 546
HUNAN BOYUN NEW MATERIALS CO., LTD.; *Int'l*, pg. 3531
KENNAMETAL, INC. - INTERNATIONAL SPECIALTY ALLOYS—See AMG Critical Materials N.V.; *Int'l*, pg. 426
MAGNPOWER CORPORATION—See China Steel Corporation; *Int'l*, pg. 1556
METAL POWDER PRODUCTS - FORD ROAD DIVISION—See Guggenheim Partners, LLC; *U.S. Private*, pg. 1812
METAL POWDER PRODUCTS, LLC—See Guggenheim Partners, LLC; *U.S. Private*, pg. 1812
MILLER POWDER COATING—See Miller Manufacturing, Inc.; *U.S. Private*, pg. 2735
MINTEQ INTERNATIONAL, INC.—See Minerals Technologies, Inc.; *U.S. Public*, pg. 1449
NETSHAPE TECHNOLOGIES, INC.—See Guggenheim Partners, LLC; *U.S. Private*, pg. 1812
PRECISION SINTERED PRODUCTS (WUXI) CO., LTD.—See Fine Sinter Co., Ltd.; *Int'l*, pg. 2673
PT. FINE SINTER INDONESIA—See Fine Sinter Co., Ltd.; *Int'l*, pg. 2673
SIDECH S.A.—See Floridienne SA; *Int'l*, pg. 2708
THAI FINE SINTER CO., LTD.—See Fine Sinter Co., Ltd.; *Int'l*, pg. 2673
THERMOSET INC.; *U.S. Private*, pg. 4143
U.S. METALS POWDERS INC.; *U.S. Private*, pg. 4271
WELLMAN PRODUCTS GROUP—See Lone Star Funds; *U.S. Private*, pg. 2485

332119 — METAL CROWN, CLOSURE, AND OTHER METAL STAMPING (EXCEPT AUTOMOTIVE)

AAP METALS, LLC—See Triple-S Steel Holdings Inc.; *U.S. Private*, pg. 4237
ACCURATE FORMING LLC; *U.S. Private*, pg. 55
ACCURATE PERFORATING COMPANY, INC.; *U.S. Private*, pg. 55
ACCUTREX PRODUCTS INC.; *U.S. Private*, pg. 55
ACE STAMPING & MACHINE CO, INC.; *U.S. Private*, pg. 57
ACME METAL CAP CO., INC.; *U.S. Private*, pg. 61
ADMIRAL TOOL & MANUFACTURING COMPANY INC.; *U.S. Private*, pg. 81
ADVAL TECH MANAGEMENT LTD—See Adval Tech Holding AG; *Int'l*, pg. 155
AFC STAMPING & PRODUCTION INC.—See F.C. Industries Inc.; *U.S. Private*, pg. 1456
AF HOLDING COMPANY; *U.S. Private*, pg. 121
AGRI-FAB INC.—See AF Holding Company; *U.S. Private*, pg. 121
AIDA CANADA INC.—See AIDA Engineering, Ltd.; *Int'l*, pg. 231
AJD HOLDING CO.; *U.S. Private*, pg. 144
ALBEST METAL STAMPING, CORP.; *U.S. Private*, pg. 153
ALINABAL INC.—See Alinabal Holdings Corporation; *U.S. Private*, pg. 168
ALLIED PRECISION (THAILAND) CO., LTD.—See Allied Technologies Ltd.; *Int'l*, pg. 358
ALLIED TECHNOLOGIES (SAIGON) CO., LTD.—See Allied Technologies Ltd.; *Int'l*, pg. 358
AMERICAN TRIM LLC; *U.S. Private*, pg. 257
AMTEK PRECISION ENGINEERING (SHANGHAI) CO., LTD.—See Blackstone Inc.; *U.S. Public*, pg. 354
API FOILS HOLDINGS LIMITED—See Aldus Pty. Ltd.; *Int'l*, pg. 305
APTAR LEEDS—See AptarGroup, Inc.; *U.S. Public*, pg. 175
ARUNDEL MACHINE TOOL CO.—See The Jordan Company, L.P.; *U.S. Private*, pg. 4060
ASK PRODUCTS, INC.—See Equistone Partners Europe Limited; *Int'l*, pg. 2487
ATLANTIC-DURANT TECHNOLOGY INC.—See Atlantic Tool & Die Company Inc.; *U.S. Private*, pg. 375
ATLANTIC TOOL & DIE COMPANY INC.; *U.S. Private*, pg. 374
AUBERT & DUVAL SAS - PAMIERS PLANT—See Eramet SA; *Int'l*, pg. 2489
AUL BROTHERS TOOL & DIE INC.—See Mursix Corporation; *U.S. Private*, pg. 2816
AUTO STYLING TRUCKMAN GROUP LIMITED—See ARB Corporation Limited; *Int'l*, pg. 536
AUTO TREND PRODUCTS—See Punch Press Products, Inc.; *U.S. Private*, pg. 3304
BARCO STAMPING CO; *U.S. Private*, pg. 473
BATESVILLE TOOL & DIE INC.; *U.S. Private*, pg. 487
BCN TECHNICAL SERVICES, INC.—See ANDRITZ AG; *Int'l*, pg. 456
BERMO INCORPORATED; *U.S. Private*, pg. 535
BERMO SCOTLAND, LTD—See Bermo Incorporated; *U.S. Private*, pg. 535
BERNARDAUD—See Bernardaud S.A.; *Int'l*, pg. 986
BILIA BMU AB—See Bilia AB; *Int'l*, pg. 1029
BI-LINK METAL SPECIALTIES INC.; *U.S. Private*, pg. 550
BLASE MANUFACTURING COMPANY; *U.S. Private*, pg. 579
BLOCK & COMPANY, INC.; *U.S. Private*, pg. 582
THE BOEHM PRESSED STEEL CO.—See Validor Capital LLC; *U.S. Private*, pg. 4332
BRITTANY STAMPING, LLC; *U.S. Private*, pg. 657
BRUNK INDUSTRIES, INC.; *U.S. Private*, pg. 672
BUD INDUSTRIES, INC.; *U.S. Private*, pg. 679
CAPARO INDIA PVT. LTD.—See Caparo Group Ltd.; *Int'l*, pg. 1301
CAPITAL INDUSTRIES, INC.; *U.S. Private*, pg. 740
CARAN PRECISION ENGINEERING & MANUFACTURING; *U.S. Private*, pg. 748
CARPENTER ADDITIVE U.S., LLC—See Carpenter Technology Corporation; *U.S. Public*, pg. 439
CARPIN MANUFACTURING INC.; *U.S. Private*, pg. 770
CFM SLOVAKIA S.R.O.—See CFM Holdings Limited; *Int'l*, pg. 1430
CFT, INC.—See Babcock & Wilcox Enterprises, Inc.; *U.S. Public*, pg. 263
CHANGZHOU RANTO METALWORK CO., LTD.; *Int'l*, pg. 1445
CHENMING MOLD IND. CORP. - KEELUNG PLANT—See Chenming Electronic Tech. Corp.; *Int'l*, pg. 1470
CHEONG FATT METAL FACTORY PTE LTD—See CFM Holdings Limited; *Int'l*, pg. 1430
CHIA CHANG CO., LTD.; *Int'l*, pg. 1475
CHIA CHANG TECHNOLOGY (CHONG QING) CO., LTD.—See Chia Chang Co., Ltd.; *Int'l*, pg. 1475
CHIA CHANG TECHNOLOGY (SUZHOU) CO., LTD.—See Chia Chang Co., Ltd.; *Int'l*, pg. 1475
CHICAGO METAL FABRICATORS, INC.; *U.S. Private*, pg. 878
CHONGQING HAONENG XINGFU SYNCHRONIZER CO., LTD.—See Chengdu Haoneng Technology Co., Ltd.; *Int'l*, pg. 1468
CHRISTOPHER TOOL & MFG CO.; *U.S. Private*, pg. 892
CHUN YUAN STEEL INDUSTRY CO., LTD. - SHI TSU PLANT—See Chun Yuan Steel Industry Co., Ltd.; *Int'l*, pg. 1596
CHUN YUAN STEEL INDUSTRY CO., LTD. - SPECIAL STEEL KAO HSIUNG PLANT—See Chun Yuan Steel Industry Co., Ltd.; *Int'l*, pg. 1596
CLAIRON METALS CORPORATION; *U.S. Private*, pg. 910
CLEVELAND DIE & MANUFACTURING, CO.; *U.S. Private*, pg. 941
CLOSURELOGIC GMBH—See Guala Closures S.p.A.; *Int'l*, pg. 3152
CLOW STAMPING COMPANY; *U.S. Private*, pg. 948
THE CLY-DEL MANUFACTURING COMPANY; *U.S. Private*, pg. 4011
COINING, INC.—See AMETEK, Inc.; *U.S. Public*, pg. 116
COMPAC DEVELOPMENT CORPORATION—See CPI Aerostructures, Inc.; *U.S. Public*, pg. 588
CONNECTICUT SPRING & STAMPING CORPORATION; *U.S. Private*, pg. 1016
CROWN, CORK & SEAL AVERY TECHNICAL CENTER—See Crown Holdings, Inc.; *U.S. Public*, pg. 597
CX TECHNOLOGY (SHANGHAI) CORP.—See CX Technology Corporation; *Int'l*, pg. 1891
CYGNET STAMPING & FABRICATING, INC.; *U.S. Private*, pg. 1134
DAIDO AMISTAR CO., LTD.—See Daido Steel Co., Ltd.; *Int'l*, pg. 1922
DAWS MANUFACTURING INC.; *U.S. Private*, pg. 1175
DAYTON ROGERS MFG. CO.; *U.S. Private*, pg. 1178
DAYTON ROGERS OF CALIFORNIA—See Dayton Rogers Mfg. Co.; *U.S. Private*, pg. 1178
DAYTON ROGERS OF MINNESOTA—See Dayton Rogers Mfg. Co.; *U.S. Private*, pg. 1178
DAYTON ROGERS OF NEW YORK—See Dayton Rogers Mfg. Co.; *U.S. Private*, pg. 1178
DAYTON ROGERS OF OHIO—See Dayton Rogers Mfg. Co.; *U.S. Private*, pg. 1178
DAYTON ROGERS OF TEXAS—See Dayton Rogers Mfg. Co.; *U.S. Private*, pg. 1178
D&D TOOLING MANUFACTURING, INC.; *U.S. Private*, pg. 1137
DEERFIELD MANUFACTURING, INC.—See Ice Industries Inc.; *U.S. Private*, pg. 2030
DEFIANCE METAL PRODUCTS, INC.—See Mayville Engineering Company, Inc.; *U.S. Public*, pg. 1403
DIAMOND MANUFACTURING COMPANY; *U.S. Private*, pg. 1223
DLSM INCORPORATED; *U.S. Private*, pg. 1247
DUBUQUE STAMPING & MANUFACTURING INC.; *U.S. Private*, pg. 1283
DUREX INC.; *U.S. Private*, pg. 1293

N.A.I.C.S. INDEX

332119 — METAL CROWN, CLOSUR...

EAST MOLINE METAL PRODUCTS COMPANY; *U.S. Private*, pg. 1316
ELIXIR INDUSTRIES; *U.S. Private*, pg. 1362
ENOPLASTIC SPA—See Cobepa S.A.; *Int'l*, pg. 1683
EQUIPTO ELECTRONICS CORP.; *U.S. Private*, pg. 1415
ERDLE PERFORATING COMPANY; *U.S. Private*, pg. 1417
E.S. INVESTMENTS, LLC; *U.S. Private*, pg. 1307
ETCO INCORPORATED; *U.S. Private*, pg. 1431
ETS RAYMOND BARRE; *Int'l*, pg. 2524
EVANS CAPACITOR COMPANY—See Arcline Investment Management LP; *U.S. Private*, pg. 313
EXPERI-METAL INC.—See HMK Enterprises, Inc.; *U.S. Private*, pg. 1955
FALCON STAMPING INC.; *U.S. Private*, pg. 1466
FANELLO INDUSTRIES, INC.—See Ryerson Holding Corporation; *U.S. Public*, pg. 1829
FERGUSON PERFORATING COMPANY—See Reliance Steel & Aluminum Co.; *U.S. Public*, pg. 1780
FINNVEDEN METAL STRUCTURES AB—See Shiloh Industries, Inc.; *U.S. Private*, pg. 3636
FLEX-N-GATE CANADA COMPANY—See Flex-N-Gate Corporation; *U.S. Private*, pg. 1543
FPI AUTO PARTS INDIA PRIVATE LIMITED—See Fortune Parts Industry Public Company Limited; *Int'l*, pg. 2744
FREEWON CHINA CO., LTD.; *Int'l*, pg. 2771
FULTON INDUSTRIES INC.; *U.S. Private*, pg. 1622
GANZHOU TENG YUAN COBALT NEW MATERIAL CO., LTD.; *Int'l*, pg. 2882
GARRETT MOTION JAPAN INC.—See Garrett Motion Inc.; *Int'l*, pg. 2886
GASSER & SONS, INC.; *U.S. Private*, pg. 1648
GENERAL MACHINE CORPORATION—See JEP Management, Inc.; *U.S. Private*, pg. 2201
GENESEE GLOBAL GROUP, INC.—See Genesee Group, Inc.; *U.S. Private*, pg. 1669
GENESEE GROUP, INC.; *U.S. Private*, pg. 1669
GH AUTO PARTS INDUSTRIES INC—See H-One Co., Ltd.; *Int'l*, pg. 3194
GMP METAL PRODUCTS—See Wozniak Industries, Inc.; *U.S. Private*, pg. 4571
GREATBATCH-GLOBE TOOL, INC.—See Integer Holdings Corporation; *U.S. Public*, pg. 1135
GR SPRING & STAMPING INC.—See Gill Industries Inc.; *U.S. Private*, pg. 1700
G-SHANK ENTERPRISE CO., LTD. - CHINA-SHANGHAI FACTORY—See G-Shank Enterprise Co., Ltd.; *Int'l*, pg. 2863
G-SHANK ENTERPRISE CO., LTD. - CHINA-SHENZHEN FACTORY—See G-Shank Enterprise Co., Ltd.; *Int'l*, pg. 2863
G-SHANK ENTERPRISE CO., LTD. - CHINA-SUZHOU FACTORY—See G-Shank Enterprise Co., Ltd.; *Int'l*, pg. 2863
G-SHANK ENTERPRISE CO., LTD. - DONGGUAN FACTORY—See G-Shank Enterprise Co., Ltd.; *Int'l*, pg. 2863
G-SHANK ENTERPRISE CO., LTD. - INDONESIA FACTORY—See G-Shank Enterprise Co., Ltd.; *Int'l*, pg. 2863
G-SHANK ENTERPRISE CO., LTD. - MALAYSIA FACTORY—See G-Shank Enterprise Co., Ltd.; *Int'l*, pg. 2863
G-SHANK ENTERPRISE CO., LTD. - MEXICO FACTORY—See G-Shank Enterprise Co., Ltd.; *Int'l*, pg. 2863
G-SHANK ENTERPRISE CO., LTD. - THAILAND FACTORY—See G-Shank Enterprise Co., Ltd.; *Int'l*, pg. 2863
HAMLIN NEWCO, LLC; *U.S. Private*, pg. 1848
HANG ZHOU YITONG NEW MATERIALS CO., LTD.; *Int'l*, pg. 3246
HANTONG METAL COMPONENT (KL) SDN BHD—See CFM Holdings Limited; *Int'l*, pg. 1430
HANTONG METAL COMPONENT (PENANG) SDN. BHD.—See EasyIO Engineering Pte Ltd.; *Int'l*, pg. 2276
HANTONG METAL COMPONENT SDN BHD—See CFM Holdings Limited; *Int'l*, pg. 1430
HAN TONG METAL COMPONENT SDN BHD—See CFM Holdings Limited; *Int'l*, pg. 1430
HARRINGTON & KING PERFORATING COMPANY, INC.; *U.S. Private*, pg. 1868
HARRINGTON & KING SOUTH, INC.—See Harrington & King Perforating Company, Inc.; *U.S. Private*, pg. 1868
HEINRICH HUHN GMBH + CO.KG; *Int'l*, pg. 3324
HEINZ HANGGI GMBH—See OEP Capital Advisors, L.P.; *U.S. Private*, pg. 2999
HENDRICK MANUFACTURING COMPANY; *U.S. Private*, pg. 1914
HIGHAIM (KUNSHAN) TECHNOLOGY INC.—See Ennoconn Corporation; *Int'l*, pg. 2443
HILL AEROSYSTEMS INC.—See Acorn Growth Companies, LC; *U.S. Private*, pg. 63
HI-TECH FABRICATION INC.; *U.S. Private*, pg. 1932
HI TECH HONEYCOMB INC.; *U.S. Private*, pg. 1931
HPL STAMPINGS INC.; *U.S. Private*, pg. 1997
HTT; *U.S. Private*, pg. 1999
HUDSON TECHNOLOGIES—See JSJ Corporation; *U.S. Private*, pg. 2241

HUGHES PARKER INDUSTRIES LLC—See JMAC Inc.; *U.S. Private*, pg. 2214
HUHN PRESSTECH, SPOL. S R O.—See HEINRICH HUHN GmbH + Co.KG; *Int'l*, pg. 3324
HUIZHOU INTERPLEX TECHNOLOGY, LTD.—See Blackstone Inc.; *U.S. Public*, pg. 354
ICE INDUSTRIES INC.; *U.S. Private*, pg. 2030
I.KELA COMPANY—See Illinois Tool Works Inc.; *U.S. Public*, pg. 1104
IMS BUHRKE-OLSON—See Innovative Manufacturing Solutions Corp.; *U.S. Private*, pg. 2083
INNOTEC, CORP.; *U.S. Private*, pg. 2080
INNOVATIVE MANUFACTURING SOLUTIONS CORP.; *U.S. Private*, pg. 2082
INTERPLEX DAYSTAR, INC.—See Blackstone Inc.; *U.S. Public*, pg. 355
INTERPLEX ELECTRONICS INDIA PVT LIMITED—See Blackstone Inc.; *U.S. Public*, pg. 355
INTERPLEX HUIZHOU (HK) INDUSTRIES LTD.—See Blackstone Inc.; *U.S. Public*, pg. 355
INTERPLEX (HUIZHOU) INDUSTRIES LTD.—See Blackstone Inc.; *U.S. Public*, pg. 354
INTERPLEXICO MANUFACTURING COMPANY, S.A. DE C.V.—See Blackstone Inc.; *U.S. Public*, pg. 355
INTERPLEX METALFORMING (SHANGHAI) LTD.—See Blackstone Inc.; *U.S. Public*, pg. 355
INTERPLEX NASCAL, INC.—See Blackstone Inc.; *U.S. Public*, pg. 355
INTERPLEX NAS INC.—See Blackstone Inc.; *U.S. Public*, pg. 355
INTERPLEX PMP LIMITED—See Blackstone Inc.; *U.S. Public*, pg. 355
INTERPLEX PRECISION ENGINEERING CZECH REPUBLIC S.R.O.—See Blackstone Inc.; *U.S. Public*, pg. 355
INTERPLEX PRECISION TECHNOLOGY (HANOI) CO., LTD.—See Blackstone Inc.; *U.S. Public*, pg. 355
INTERPLEX PRECISION TECHNOLOGY (SINGAPORE) PTE. LTD.—See Blackstone Inc.; *U.S. Public*, pg. 355
INTERPLEX SINGAPORE PTE. LTD.—See Blackstone Inc.; *U.S. Public*, pg. 355
INTERPLEX SOPREC SAS—See Blackstone Inc.; *U.S. Public*, pg. 355
INTERPLEX SUNBELT, INC.—See Blackstone Inc.; *U.S. Public*, pg. 355
INTERPLEX (SUZHOU) PRECISION ENGINEERING LTD.—See Blackstone Inc.; *U.S. Public*, pg. 354
INTO METAL INC.; *U.S. Private*, pg. 2129
INTRI-PLEX TECHNOLOGIES INC.; *U.S. Private*, pg. 2129
ITW DRAWFORM—See Illinois Tool Works Inc.; *U.S. Public*, pg. 1106
ITW METAL FASTENERS, S.L.—See Illinois Tool Works Inc.; *U.S. Public*, pg. 1106
JACOB HOLTZ COMPANY—See Dominus Capital, L.P.; *U.S. Private*, pg. 1256
JAGEMANN STAMPING COMPANY; *U.S. Private*, pg. 2181
JMR ELECTRONICS INC.; *U.S. Private*, pg. 2216
JOHNSON & HOFFMAN, LLC; *U.S. Private*, pg. 2226
JOHNSON/V.B.C. INC.—See Van Blarcom Closures Inc.; *U.S. Private*, pg. 4339
KAPCO INCORPORATED; *U.S. Private*, pg. 2261
KASPAR DIE & TOOL, INC.—See The Kaspar Companies; *U.S. Private*, pg. 4064
KENNEDY MANUFACTURING COMPANY; *U.S. Private*, pg. 2285
KEN-TRON MANUFACTURING INC.; *U.S. Private*, pg. 2283
KEYSTONE FRICTION HINGE CO.; *U.S. Private*, pg. 2296
KICKHAEFER MANUFACTURING COMPANY INC.; *U.S. Private*, pg. 2302
KING MANUFACTURING CO. INC.; *U.S. Private*, pg. 2309
LACEY MANUFACTURING COMPANY LLC—See NN, Inc.; *U.S. Public*, pg. 1531
LAIRD TECHNOLOGIES LTD—See DuPont de Nemours, Inc.; *U.S. Public*, pg. 693
LAIRD TECHONOLGIES (SEA) PTE., LTD.—See DuPont de Nemours, Inc.; *U.S. Public*, pg. 693
LAMINATION SPECIALTIES CORP.—See UPG Enterprises LLC; *U.S. Private*, pg. 4311
L.H. INDUSTRIES CORP.; *U.S. Private*, pg. 2366
L.H. STAMPING CORP.—See L.H. Industries Corp.; *U.S. Private*, pg. 2366
LONGWALL SERVICES INC.; *U.S. Private*, pg. 2493
LSI KENTUCKY LLC—See LSI Industries Inc.; *U.S. Public*, pg. 1344
LUZHOU CHANGJIANG MACHINERY CO., LTD.—See Chengdu Haoneng Technology Co., Ltd.; *Int'l*, pg. 1468
MARQUETTE TOOL & DIE COMPANY; *U.S. Private*, pg. 2587
MAYVILLE ENGINEERING COMPANY, INC.; *U.S. Public*, pg. 1403
MCKEY PERFORATING CO., INC.—See Reliance Steel & Aluminum Co.; *U.S. Public*, pg. 1780
MECO CORPORATION; *U.S. Private*, pg. 2649
METALCRAFT INDUSTRIES, INC.; *U.S. Private*, pg. 2680
METALIS S.A.S.—See Aalberts N.V.; *Int'l*, pg. 35
METALIS USA, INC.—See Aalberts N.V.; *Int'l*, pg. 35
METAL SPINNERS INC.; *U.S. Private*, pg. 2680
MICRO STAMPING CORP.; *U.S. Private*, pg. 2702

MILTON MANUFACTURING, INC.; *U.S. Private*, pg. 2738
THE MINCO GROUP; *U.S. Private*, pg. 4079
MODINEER COMPANY INC.; *U.S. Private*, pg. 2763
MORGAL MACHINE TOOL COMPANY, INC.; *U.S. Private*, pg. 2783
MOTION ASIA PACIFIC PTY LTD—See Genuine Parts Company; *U.S. Public*, pg. 933
MURSIX CORPORATION; *U.S. Private*, pg. 2816
MUTHIG INDUSTRIES, INC.—See LFM Capital LLC; *U.S. Private*, pg. 2441
NANJING CHIA-CHAN PRECIOUS ELECTRONICS CO., LTD.—See Chia Chang Co., Ltd.; *Int'l*, pg. 1475
NATIONAL BAND & TAG CO.; *U.S. Private*, pg. 2847
NEW STANDARD CORPORATION; *U.S. Private*, pg. 2906
NING BO CHIA CHANG ELECTROINC HARDWARE CO., LTD.—See Chia Chang Co., Ltd.; *Int'l*, pg. 1475
NINGBO CHIA CHANG ELECTRONICS HARDWARE CO., LTD.—See Chia Chang Co., Ltd.; *Int'l*, pg. 1475
NORDIC LIGHTS OY—See Methode Electronics, Inc.; *U.S. Public*, pg. 1429
NORTHERN ENGRAVING CORPORATION; *U.S. Private*, pg. 2952
NUPAR MANUFACTURING—See ABB Ltd.; *Int'l*, pg. 51
OBERG INDUSTRIES CORP.; *U.S. Private*, pg. 2986
OBERG INDUSTRIES—See Oberg Industries Corp.; *U.S. Private*, pg. 2986
OBERG MEXICO—See Oberg Industries Corp.; *U.S. Private*, pg. 2987
OHIO VALLEY MANUFACTURING INC.; *U.S. Private*, pg. 3005
OMNI MANUFACTURING INC.; *U.S. Private*, pg. 3016
OVERLAND PRODUCTS COMPANY, INC.—See Quanex Building Products Corp.; *U.S. Public*, pg. 1749
PACIFIC PRECISION METALS, INC.; *U.S. Private*, pg. 3070
PAX MACHINE WORKS INC.; *U.S. Private*, pg. 3115
PEKO PRECISION PRODUCTS INC.; *U.S. Private*, pg. 3130
PINNACLE PRECISION SHEET METAL; *U.S. Private*, pg. 3185
PITTCON INDUSTRIES; *U.S. Private*, pg. 3191
P-K TOOL & MANUFACTURING CO.; *U.S. Private*, pg. 3059
PLAINFIELD PRECISION COMPANIES; *U.S. Private*, pg. 3194
PLAINFIELD STAMPING TEXAS, INC.—See Plainfield Precision Companies; *U.S. Private*, pg. 3194
POLAR WARE COMPANY; *U.S. Private*, pg. 3223
PRECISION CONCEPTS GROUP LLC—See Wasatch Advantage Group, LLC; *U.S. Private*, pg. 4445
PRECISION ENGINEERED PRODUCTS LLC - WAUCONDA—See NN, Inc.; *U.S. Public*, pg. 1531
PRECISION ENGINEERING, INC—See The Heico Companies, L.L.C.; *U.S. Private*, pg. 4051
PRECISION INDUSTRIES, INC.; *U.S. Private*, pg. 3245
PRECISION PRESS INDUSTRIES SDN BHD (PPISB)—See Ewein Berhad; *Int'l*, pg. 2576
PRECISION RESOURCE - CALIFORNIA—See Precision Resource Inc.; *U.S. Private*, pg. 3246
PRECISION RESOURCE CANADA LTD.—See Precision Resource Inc.; *U.S. Private*, pg. 3246
PRECISION RESOURCE - ILLINOIS—See Precision Resource Inc.; *U.S. Private*, pg. 3246
PRECISION RESOURCE INC.; *U.S. Private*, pg. 3246
PRECISION RESOURCE - KENTUCKY—See Precision Resource Inc.; *U.S. Private*, pg. 3246
PREMIUM ALLIED TOOL INC.—See The Hines Group, Inc.; *U.S. Private*, pg. 4053
PRESSPART MANUFACTURING LTD.—See Heitkamp & Thumann KG; *Int'l*, pg. 3326
PRESSPART MANUFACTURING S.A.—See Heitkamp & Thumann KG; *Int'l*, pg. 3326
PRIDGEON & CLAY, KFT—See Pridgeon & Clay, Inc.; *U.S. Private*, pg. 3260
PRIDGEON & CLAY, S.DE R.L. DE C.V.—See Pridgeon & Clay, Inc.; *U.S. Private*, pg. 3260
PT AMTEK ENGINEERING BATAM—See Blackstone Inc.; *U.S. Public*, pg. 355
PT HANTONG PRECISION MANUFACTURING BATAM—See CFM Holdings Limited; *Int'l*, pg. 1430
PUNCH PRESS PRODUCTS, INC.; *U.S. Private*, pg. 3304
QSCH TERMELO ES KERESKEDELMI KFT—See Adval Tech Holding AG; *Int'l*, pg. 155
QUAKER MFG. CORP.; *U.S. Private*, pg. 3317
QUALITY PERFORATING, INC.; *U.S. Private*, pg. 3320
QUAN RUI (DONGGUAN) INDUSTRIAL CO., LTD.—See Chia Chang Co., Ltd.; *Int'l*, pg. 1475
QUICKWORK DIV.—See Beatty Machine & Mfg. Company; *U.S. Private*, pg. 507
QUIGLEY MANUFACTURING INC.; *U.S. Private*, pg. 3327
RAGO & SON, INC.; *U.S. Private*, pg. 3346
THE RALPH J. STOLLE COMPANY; *U.S. Private*, pg. 4102
REGAL METAL PRODUCTS CO.; *U.S. Private*, pg. 3385
RES MANUFACTURING COMPANY; *U.S. Private*, pg. 3403
RIDGEVIEW INDUSTRIES; *U.S. Private*, pg. 3433
RIGIDIZED METALS CORP.; *U.S. Private*, pg. 3436
ROLLOFFS USA INC.; *U.S. Private*, pg. 3475
SACO LOWELL PARTS LLC—See Hercules Engine Components LLC; *U.S. Private*, pg. 1921

332119 — METAL CROWN, CLOSUR...

SALSBURY INDUSTRIES; *U.S. Private*, pg. 3533
SATURNO DE MEXICO, SA DE CV—See Industrial Dielectrics Holdings, Inc.; *U.S. Private*, pg. 2065
SCHALLER CORPORATION; *U.S. Private*, pg. 3563
SCHULER FRANCE S.A.—See ANDRITZ AG; *Int'l*, pg. 456
SCHULER SLOVAKIA SERVICES S.R.O.—See ANDRITZ AG; *Int'l*, pg. 456
SCOTLAND MANUFACTURING CO., INC.—See Reserve Group Management Company; *U.S. Private*, pg. 3404
SECTIONAL STAMPING, INC.—See Shiloh Industries, Inc.; *U.S. Private*, pg. 3636
SEI METALFORMS INC.—See SEI MetalTek; *U.S. Private*, pg. 3599
SHEETS MANUFACTURING CO. INC.—See Hi Temp Insulation Inc.; *U.S. Private*, pg. 1931
SHILOH INDUSTRIES, INC.; *U.S. Private*, pg. 3636
SHILOH MANUFACTURING DIVISION-LIVERPOOL—See Shiloh Industries, Inc.; *U.S. Private*, pg. 3636
SHORT RUN STAMPING CO.; *U.S. Private*, pg. 3643
SILGAN CLOSURES GMBH—See Silgan Holdings, Inc.; *U.S. Public*, pg. 1878
SILGAN HOLDINGS AUSTRIA GMBH—See Silgan Holdings, Inc.; *U.S. Public*, pg. 1879
SILGAN WHITE CAP BELGIUM N.V.—See Silgan Holdings, Inc.; *U.S. Public*, pg. 1879
SILGAN WHITE CAP DEUTSCHLAND GMBH—See Silgan Holdings, Inc.; *U.S. Public*, pg. 1879
SILGAN WHITE CAP FRANCE S.A.S.—See Silgan Holdings, Inc.; *U.S. Public*, pg. 1879
SILGAN WHITE CAP HOLDINGS SPAIN, S.L.—See Silgan Holdings, Inc.; *U.S. Public*, pg. 1879
SILGAN WHITE CAP ITALIA S.R.L.—See Silgan Holdings, Inc.; *U.S. Public*, pg. 1879
SILGAN WHITE CAP NEDERLAND N.V.—See Silgan Holdings, Inc.; *U.S. Public*, pg. 1879
SILGAN WHITE CAP POLSKA SP. Z O.O.—See Silgan Holdings, Inc.; *U.S. Public*, pg. 1879
SILGAN WHITE CAP (SHANGHAI) CO., LTD.—See Silgan Holdings, Inc.; *U.S. Public*, pg. 1879
SILGAN WHITE CAP UK LTD.—See Silgan Holdings, Inc.; *U.S. Public*, pg. 1879
SONOCO, INC.—See Sonoco Products Company; *U.S. Public*, pg. 1908
SOUTHEASTERN METAL PRODUCTS LLC—See Juno Investments LLC; *U.S. Private*, pg. 2244
S-P COMPANY INC.; *U.S. Private*, pg. 3514
SPINCRAFT WISCONSIN—See Standex International; *U.S. Public*, pg. 1930
SPIROL INTERNATIONAL CORPORATION - STOW—See Spirol International Corporation; *U.S. Private*, pg. 3758
SPIROL WEST, INC.—See Spirol International Corporation; *U.S. Private*, pg. 3758
STACK-ON PRODUCTS CO. INC.; *U.S. Private*, pg. 3774
STEVENIN NOLLEVAUX FORGES ET ESTAMPAGE—See Capital Grand Est SAS; *Int'l*, pg. 1311
SUN MICROSTAMPING TECHNOLOGIES—See E.S. Investments, LLC; *U.S. Private*, pg. 1307
SUPERIOR PRODUCTION LLC - STAMPING DIVISION—See Superior Production LLC; *U.S. Private*, pg. 3880
TALAN PRODUCTS, INC.; *U.S. Private*, pg. 3925
T&C STAMPING INC.; *U.S. Private*, pg. 3909
TECH-ETCH INC.; *U.S. Private*, pg. 3952
TEMPEL BURLINGTON—See Worthington Industries, Inc.; *U.S. Public*, pg. 2383
TENIBAC-GRAPHION INC.; *U.S. Private*, pg. 3967
THOMAS ENGINEERING COMPANY; *U.S. Private*, pg. 4155
THOMAS INDUSTRIAL ROLLS, INC.—See Talon Group LLC; *U.S. Private*, pg. 3927
TORRMETAL CORPORATION; *U.S. Private*, pg. 4190
TRIAD METAL PRODUCTS COMPANY INC.; *U.S. Private*, pg. 4225
TRIDENT PRECISION MANUFACTURING INC.; *U.S. Private*, pg. 4230
TRITON INDUSTRIES, INC.; *U.S. Private*, pg. 4239
TRUELOVE & MACLEAN INC.; *U.S. Private*, pg. 4248
TUBING SEAL CAP—See Pacific Precision Metals, Inc.; *U.S. Private*, pg. 3070
ULTIMATE PRECISION METAL PRODUCTS; *U.S. Private*, pg. 4277
UMI COMPANY, INC.; *U.S. Private*, pg. 4278
UNIVERSAL INDUSTRIAL PRODUCTS CO.; *U.S. Private*, pg. 4305
UNIVERSAL METAL PRODUCTS INC.; *U.S. Private*, pg. 4305
VARBROS CORPORATION; *U.S. Private*, pg. 4345
VIRGINIA INDUSTRIES INC.; *U.S. Private*, pg. 4387
VOISARD MANUFACTURING INC.; *U.S. Private*, pg. 4409
VULCAN, INC.; *U.S. Private*, pg. 4416
WASHINGTON PRODUCTS INC.; *U.S. Private*, pg. 4449
WAUKESHA METAL PRODUCTS; *U.S. Private*, pg. 4457
WAVERLY PARTNERS INC.; *U.S. Private*, pg. 4458
WEBBER METAL PRODUCTS INC.; *U.S. Private*, pg. 4464
WEDGE PRODUCTS, INC.—See AJD Holding Co.; *U.S. Private*, pg. 144
WENZEL METAL SPINNING INC.; *U.S. Private*, pg. 4481
WISCO INDUSTRIES INC.; *U.S. Private*, pg. 4547

WISCONSIN METAL PRODUCTS CO.; *U.S. Private*, pg. 4548
WISCO PRODUCTS, INC.; *U.S. Private*, pg. 4547
WLS STAMPING & FABRICATING CO.; *U.S. Private*, pg. 4551
WOLFE INDUSTRIES, INC.; *U.S. Private*, pg. 4554
WOZNIAK INDUSTRIES, INC.; *U.S. Private*, pg. 4571
WRICO STAMPING OF ARIZONA—See Griffiths Corporation; *U.S. Private*, pg. 1789
WRICO STAMPING OF FLORIDA—See Griffiths Corporation; *U.S. Private*, pg. 1789
WRICO STAMPING OF MINNESOTA—See Griffiths Corporation; *U.S. Private*, pg. 1789
WRICO STAMPING OF NORTH CAROLINA—See Griffiths Corporation; *U.S. Private*, pg. 1789
WRICO STAMPING OF TEXAS—See Griffiths Corporation; *U.S. Private*, pg. 1789
WRICO STAMPING OF WISCONSIN—See Griffiths Corporation; *U.S. Private*, pg. 1789
WROUGHT WASHER MFG., INC.; *U.S. Private*, pg. 4574

332215 — METAL KITCHEN COOKWARE, UTENSIL, CUTLERY, AND FLATWARE (EXCEPT PRECIOUS) MANUFACTURING

ACECO PRECISION MANUFACTURING; *U.S. Private*, pg. 57
ACME UNITED EUROPE GMBH—See Acme United Corporation; *U.S. Public*, pg. 35
AISHIDA CO., LTD.; *Int'l*, pg. 251
AMBROSI CUTLERY LTD.—See Birch Hill Equity Partners Management Inc.; *Int'l*, pg. 1046
ANKARSRUM ASSISTENT AB—See Duroc AB; *Int'l*, pg. 2229
ANLI INTERNATIONAL CO., LTD.; *Int'l*, pg. 473
ATLANTIC SERVICE CO. (U.K.) LTD.—See Steel Partners Holdings L.P.; *U.S. Public*, pg. 1943
BARTSCHER GMBH; *Int'l*, pg. 870
BEAR & SON CUTLERY, INC.; *U.S. Private*, pg. 506
BNT POSLOVNI SUSTAV D.D.; *Int'l*, pg. 1094
BROWNE & CO.; *Int'l*, pg. 1198
BUCK KNIVES, INC.; *U.S. Private*, pg. 676
CARYSIL LIMITED; *Int'l*, pg. 1349
CENTRAL MELAMINEWARE SDN. BHD.—See CAM Resources Berhad; *Int'l*, pg. 1267
CHEM-TREND (DEUTSCHLAND) GMBH—See Freudenberg SE; *Int'l*, pg. 2782
CORELLE BRANDS LLC—See Cornell Capital Management LLC; *U.S. Private*, pg. 1051
CREATIVE TOPS LIMITED—See Lifetime Brands, Inc.; *U.S. Public*, pg. 1313
CUTCO CORPORATION; *U.S. Private*, pg. 1131
CUTCO CUTLERY CORPORATION—See CUTCO Corporation; *U.S. Private*, pg. 1131
DANIELS FAMILY CUTLERY CORPORATION; *U.S. Private*, pg. 1156
DEXTER-RUSSELL INC.—See Hyde Manufacturing Company; *U.S. Private*, pg. 2016
DIETHELM KELLER BRANDS AG—See Diethelm Keller Holding Limited; *Int'l*, pg. 2117
DKB HOUSEHOLD SWITZERLAND AG—See Diethelm Keller Holding Limited; *Int'l*, pg. 2116
DOUGLAS/QUIKUT—See Berkshire Hathaway Inc.; *U.S. Public*, pg. 300
DUNCAN KITCHEN GRIPS INC.—See Browne & Co.; *Int'l*, pg. 1198
DURA SUPREME LLC—See GHK Capital Partners LP; *U.S. Private*, pg. 1690
DYNAMIC LIVING, INC.; *U.S. Private*, pg. 1298
EATWARE INC.; *Int'l*, pg. 2282
ELRO GROSSKUCHEN GMBH—See Illinois Tool Works Inc.; *U.S. Public*, pg. 1103
ELRO-WERKE AG—See Illinois Tool Works Inc.; *U.S. Public*, pg. 1103
FABRISTEEL PRIVATE LIMITED—See The Manitowoc Company, Inc.; *U.S. Public*, pg. 2111
FGI INDUSTRIES LTD.; *U.S. Public*, pg. 830
FISKARS BRANDS, INC. - GERBER GEAR—See Fiskars Oyj Abp; *Int'l*, pg. 2693
FISKARS BRANDS, INC.—See Fiskars Oyj Abp; *Int'l*, pg. 2693
FISKARS CANADA INC.—See Fiskars Oyj Abp; *Int'l*, pg. 2693
FRESHSTOR INC.—See Boveda Inc.; *U.S. Private*, pg. 625
FREUDENBERG PERFORMANCE MATERIALS APPAREL SE & CO. KG—See Freudenberg SE; *Int'l*, pg. 2787
FREUDENBERG PERFORMANCE MATERIALS HOLDING SE & CO. KG—See Freudenberg SE; *Int'l*, pg. 2787
FREUDENBERG PERFORMANCE MATERIALS LOGISTICS SE & CO. KG—See Freudenberg SE; *Int'l*, pg. 2787
FREUDENBERG SEALING TECHNOLOGIES S.A.S. DI EXTERNA ITALIA S.R.L.U.—See Freudenberg SE; *Int'l*, pg. 2788
FUJIMAK FOOD SERVICE EQUIPMENT SINGAPORE PTE., LTD.—See Fujimak Corporation; *Int'l*, pg. 2829

FUXI SHANGHAI CORPORATION—See Fujimak Corporation; *Int'l*, pg. 2829
GILLETTE DEL PERU S.C.—See The Procter & Gamble Company; *U.S. Public*, pg. 2124
GILLETTE DEUTSCHLAND GMBH & CO. OHG—See The Procter & Gamble Company; *U.S. Public*, pg. 2124
GORANI INDUSTRIES LIMITED; *Int'l*, pg. 3042
GORENJE TIKI D.O.O.—See Hisense Co., Ltd.; *Int'l*, pg. 3407
HAMILTON BEACH, INC.—See Hamilton Beach Brands Holding Company; *U.S. Public*, pg. 981
HOBART DAYTON MEXICANA, S. DE R.L. DE C.V.—See Illinois Tool Works Inc.; *U.S. Public*, pg. 1104
HOBART FOOD EQUIPMENT CO., LTD.—See Illinois Tool Works Inc.; *U.S. Public*, pg. 1104
HOBART INTERNATIONAL (SINGAPORE) PTE. LTD.—See Illinois Tool Works Inc.; *U.S. Public*, pg. 1104
ILLA S.P.A.; *Int'l*, pg. 3615
INDUSTRIAL GALVANIZERS CORPORATION OF THE PHILIPPINES INC.—See Valmont Industries, Inc.; *U.S. Public*, pg. 2273
ITW FEG HONG KONG LIMITED—See Illinois Tool Works Inc.; *U.S. Public*, pg. 1105
JOYCE CHEN DIVISION—See Columbian Home Products; *U.S. Private*, pg. 978
KASCO LLC—See Steel Partners Holdings L.P.; *U.S. Public*, pg. 1943
KLEIN CUTLERY, LLC—See Klein Tools Inc.; *U.S. Private*, pg. 2319
LAMSON & GOODNOW MANUFACTURING CO.; *U.S. Private*, pg. 2381
LEGION INDUSTRIES, INC.—See The Legacy Companies; *U.S. Private*, pg. 4069
LEKUE, S.L.—See Espiga Capital Gestion S.G.E.C.R, S.A.; *Int'l*, pg. 2506
LEKUE USA, INC.—See Espiga Capital Gestion S.G.E.C.R, S.A.; *Int'l*, pg. 2506
LIFETIME BRANDS, INC.; *U.S. Public*, pg. 1313
MERRYCHEF LIMITED—See Ali Holding S.r.l.; *Int'l*, pg. 323
MIDWEST TOOL AND CUTLERY CO.; *U.S. Private*, pg. 2723
MODERNA FRANCE—See Moderna, Inc.; *U.S. Public*, pg. 1454
ONEIDA CANADA LTD.—See EveryWare Global, Inc.; *U.S. Private*, pg. 1441
ONEIDA LTD.—See EveryWare Global, Inc.; *U.S. Private*, pg. 1441
ONEIDA, S.A. DE C.V.—See EveryWare Global, Inc.; *U.S. Private*, pg. 1441
ONEIDA SILVERSMITHS INC.—See EveryWare Global, Inc.; *U.S. Private*, pg. 1441
ONTARIO KNIFE COMPANY—See Blue Ridge Knives, Inc.; *U.S. Private*, pg. 592
ORTHOBAND CO., INC.—See Barnhart Industries, Inc.; *U.S. Private*, pg. 478
OZTIRYAKILER MADENI ESYA SANAYI VE TICARET ANONIM SIRKETI—See Hoshizaki Corporation; *Int'l*, pg. 3484
PACIFIC HANDY CUTTER, INC.—See Levine Leichtman Capital Partners, LLC; *U.S. Private*, pg. 2436
THE PAMPERED CHEF, LTD.—See Berkshire Hathaway Inc.; *U.S. Public*, pg. 319
PERFECT FRY COMPANY LCC—See The Middleby Corporation; *U.S. Public*, pg. 2115
PERSONNA INTERNATIONAL DE MEXICO, S.A. DE C.V.—See Edgewell Personal Care Company; *U.S. Public*, pg. 718
PERSONNA INTERNATIONAL UK LIMITED—See Edgewell Personal Care Company; *U.S. Public*, pg. 718
PLEASANT HILL GRAIN LLC; *U.S. Private*, pg. 3213
PROCESSIA SOLUTIONS INC.—See Atos SE; *Int'l*, pg. 692
PROFESSIONAL BAKEWARE CO., INC.—See Tablecraft Products Co., Inc.; *U.S. Private*, pg. 3920
RANGE KLEEN MFG., INC.; *U.S. Private*, pg. 3354
ROYAL PRESTIGE OF NEW YORK—See Hy Cite Corporation; *U.S. Public*, pg. 2015
SAMUEL GROVES LIMITED—See EveryWare Global, Inc.; *U.S. Private*, pg. 1441
SCHICK ASIA LIMITED—See Edgewell Personal Care Company; *U.S. Public*, pg. 718
SCHICK (GUANGZHOU) COMPANY LTD.—See Edgewell Personal Care Company; *U.S. Public*, pg. 718
SODASTREAM INTERNATIONAL B.V.—See PepsiCo, Inc.; *U.S. Public*, pg. 1672
SODASTREAM ISRAEL LTD.—See PepsiCo, Inc.; *U.S. Public*, pg. 1672
SODASTREAM NORDICS AB—See PepsiCo, Inc.; *U.S. Public*, pg. 1672
SODASTREAM (SWITZERLAND) AG—See PepsiCo, Inc.; *U.S. Public*, pg. 1672
SUB-ZERO WOLF SOUTHEAST, INC.—See Sub-Zero Freezer Co., Inc.; *U.S. Private*, pg. 3847
TABLECRAFT PRODUCTS CO., INC.; *U.S. Private*, pg. 3920
TAYLOR CUTLERY CO. LLC; *U.S. Private*, pg. 3939
THOMAS PLANT (BIRMINGHAM) LIMITED—See Lifetime Brands, Inc.; *U.S. Public*, pg. 1313
TOWNECRAFT HOMEWARES, LLC; *U.S. Private*, pg. 4198

N.A.I.C.S. INDEX

VESTA GLOBAL LIMITED—See Illinois Tool Works Inc.; *U.S. Public*, pg. 1111
VESTA (GUANGZHOU) CATERING EQUIPMENT CO. LTD—See Illinois Tool Works Inc.; *U.S. Public*, pg. 1111
WEBER-STEPHEN NORDIC APS—See BDT Capital Partners, LLC; *U.S. Private*, pg. 503
WEBER-STEPHEN OSTERREICH GMBH—See BDT Capital Partners, LLC; *U.S. Private*, pg. 503
WEBER-STEPHEN PRODUCTS BELGIUM BVBA—See BDT Capital Partners, LLC; *U.S. Private*, pg. 503
WILKINSON SWORD GMBH—See Edgewell Personal Care Company; *U.S. Public*, pg. 718
WILKINSON SWORD LIMITED—See Edgewell Personal Care Company; *U.S. Public*, pg. 718
WINDWAY CAPITAL CORP.; *U.S. Private*, pg. 4539
WOLF APPLIANCE CO., LLC—See Sub-Zero Freezer Co., Inc.; *U.S. Private*, pg. 3847
W.R. CASE & SONS CUTLERY COMPANY—See Zippo Manufacturing Company, Inc.; *U.S. Private*, pg. 4606
ZHEJIANG ASD HOUSEHOLD EQUIPMENT CO., LTD—See Aishida Co., Ltd.; *Int'l*, pg. 251

332216 — SAW BLADE AND HANDTOOL MANUFACTURING

ACME UNITED LIMITED—See Acme United Corporation; *U.S. Public*, pg. 35
AKAR AUTO INDUSTRIES LTD.; *Int'l*, pg. 259
ALGOQUANT FINTECH LIMITED; *Int'l*, pg. 319
ALPS TOOL CO., LTD.—See Citizen Watch Co., Ltd.; *Int'l*, pg. 1624
AMADA AUSTRIA GMBH—See Amada Holdings Co., Ltd.; *Int'l*, pg. 403
AMADA CO., LTD. - ONO PLANT—See Amada Holdings Co., Ltd.; *Int'l*, pg. 403
AMADA EUROPE S.A.—See Amada Holdings Co., Ltd.; *Int'l*, pg. 403
AMADA KOREA CO., LTD.—See Amada Holdings Co., Ltd.; *Int'l*, pg. 404
AMADA TOOL AMERICA, INC.—See Amada Holdings Co., Ltd.; *Int'l*, pg. 404
AMERICAN TURNED PRODUCTS, INC.; *U.S. Private*, pg. 257
THE AMES COMPANIES, INC.—See Griffon Corporation; *U.S. Public*, pg. 969
AMES TAPING TOOLS CO. OF CANADA LIMITED—See Aurora Capital Group, LLC; *U.S. Private*, pg. 394
APEX TOOL GROUP GERMANY GMBH—See Bain Capital, LP; *U.S. Private*, pg. 430
APEX TOOL GROUP, LLC—See Bain Capital, LP; *U.S. Private*, pg. 430
APEX TOOL GROUP PTY. LTD.—See Bain Capital, LP; *U.S. Private*, pg. 430
APPLIED SCIENCES DIVISION—See Caddock Electronics, Inc.; *U.S. Private*, pg. 712
ASAKA INDUSTRIAL CO., LTD.; *Int'l*, pg. 599
ATLAS DIE, LLC - CHICAGO PLANT—See Auxo Investment Partners, LLC; *U.S. Private*, pg. 402
AUGUST RUEGGEBERG GMBH & CO. KG PFERD-WERKZEUGE; *Int'l*, pg. 703
AUROTEK (JAPAN) INC.—See Aurotek Corporation; *Int'l*, pg. 714
BEIJING AMADA MACHINE & TOOLING CO., LTD.—See Amada Holdings Co., Ltd.; *Int'l*, pg. 404
BERNZOMATIC—See Worthington Industries, Inc.; *U.S. Public*, pg. 2382
BICHAMP CUTTING TECHNOLOGY (HUNAN) CO., LTD; *Int'l*, pg. 1018
THE BLACK & DECKER CORPORATION—See Stanley Black & Decker, Inc.; *U.S. Public*, pg. 1936
BLACK & DECKER DE ESPANA S.A.—See Stanley Black & Decker, Inc.; *U.S. Public*, pg. 1936
BLACK & DECKER EUROPE—See Stanley Black & Decker, Inc.; *U.S. Public*, pg. 1932
BLACK & DECKER GMBH—See Stanley Black & Decker, Inc.; *U.S. Public*, pg. 1936
BLACK & DECKER ITALY S.P.A.—See Stanley Black & Decker, Inc.; *U.S. Public*, pg. 1936
THE BLOOMFIELD MANUFACTURING CO., INC.; *U.S. Private*, pg. 3995
BLOUNT CANADA LTD.—See American Securities LLC; *U.S. Private*, pg. 247
BLOUNT CANADA LTD.—See P2 Capital Partners, LLC; *U.S. Private*, pg. 3062
BLOUNT INDUSTRIAL LTDA.—See American Securities LLC; *U.S. Private*, pg. 247
BLOUNT INDUSTRIAL LTDA.—See P2 Capital Partners, LLC; *U.S. Private*, pg. 3061
BON TOOL COMPANY; *U.S. Private*, pg. 612
BRADY WORLDWIDE, INC.—See Brady Corporation; *U.S. Public*, pg. 379
CB MANUFACTURING & SALES CO., INC.; *U.S. Private*, pg. 796
CHANNELLOCK, INC.; *U.S. Private*, pg. 848
CHEUNG WOH PRECISION (ZHUHAI) CO., LTD—See Cheung Woh Technologies Ltd.; *Int'l*, pg. 1473
CHEUNG WOH TECHNOLOGIES (ZHUHAI) CO., LTD—See Cheung Woh Technologies Ltd.; *Int'l*, pg. 1473
CHUN YUAN STEEL INDUSTRY CO., LTD. - TAICHUNG PLANT—See Chun Yuan Steel Industry Co., Ltd.; *Int'l*, pg. 1596
CIRCLE MACHINE CO.—See Kennametal Inc.; *U.S. Public*, pg. 1222
COE ORCHARD EQUIPMENT, INC.—See Flory Industries, Inc.; *U.S. Private*, pg. 1551
COGSDILL-NUNEATON, LTD.—See Cogsdill Tool Products, Inc.; *U.S. Private*, pg. 962
COOPER TOOLS, LLC—See Bain Capital, LP; *U.S. Private*, pg. 430
COOPER TOOLS, LLC - SUMTER PLANT—See Bain Capital, LP; *U.S. Private*, pg. 430
CRESCENT MANUFACTURING COMPANY; *U.S. Private*, pg. 1094
CYCLONE INDUSTRIES PTY LTD—See Illinois Tool Works Inc.; *U.S. Public*, pg. 1104
DANIELS MANUFACTURING CORPORATION; *U.S. Private*, pg. 1156
DAUPHIN PRECISION TOOL, LLC—See Talbot Holdings LLC; *U.S. Private*, pg. 3925
DIXIE DIAMOND MANUFACTURING, INC.; *U.S. Private*, pg. 1245
DK-SPEC INC.; *Int'l*, pg. 2139
DUO-FAST CORPORATION—See Illinois Tool Works Inc.; *U.S. Public*, pg. 1102
EDLUND COMPANY, INC.; *U.S. Private*, pg. 1337
EDSBYNS INDUSTRI AB—See Snap-on Incorporated; *U.S. Public*, pg. 1897
EMERSON TOOL COMPANY—See Emerson Electric Co.; *U.S. Public*, pg. 749
ENERPRO DE MEXICO, S.A. DE C.V.—See NOV, Inc.; *U.S. Public*, pg. 1544
ETLA LIMITED—See Frencken Group Limited; *Int'l*, pg. 2772
EUROP USINAGE—See Hiolle Industries S.A.; *Int'l*, pg. 3401
EVANS RULE COMPANY, INC.—See MiddleGround Management, LP; *U.S. Private*, pg. 2713
FACOM S.A.—See Stanley Black & Decker, Inc.; *U.S. Public*, pg. 1932
FACOM UK LTD.—See Stanley Black & Decker, Inc.; *U.S. Public*, pg. 1932
FEINTECHNIK GMBH—See ADKM, Inc.; *U.S. Private*, pg. 80
FIRST TECHNOLOGY SHANGHAI LTD.—See Fuji Corporation; *Int'l*, pg. 2809
FISCHER PRECISE USA, INC.—See Fischer AG Prazissionsspindeln; *Int'l*, pg. 2692
FISKARS OYJ ABP; *Int'l*, pg. 2693
FOXCONN INDUSTRIAL INTERNET CO., LTD.—See Hon Hai Precision Industry Co., Ltd.; *Int'l*, pg. 3456
FRENCKEN MECHATRONICS (M) SDN BHD—See Frencken Group Limited; *Int'l*, pg. 2772
FUJIAN WIDE PLUS PRECISION INSTRUMENTS CO., LTD.—See China High Precision Automation Group Limited; *Int'l*, pg. 1508
GALAXY AGRICO EXPORTS LIMITED; *Int'l*, pg. 2871
GEA HOULE, INC.—See GEA Group Aktiengesellschaft; *Int'l*, pg. 2899
GEBR. LENNARTZ GMBH & CO.KG; *Int'l*, pg. 2908
GENERAL TOOLS & INSTRUMENTS COMPANY LLC—See Worthington Industries, Inc.; *U.S. Public*, pg. 2382
GLEASON WORKS (INDIA) PRIVATE LTD.—See Gleason Corporation; *U.S. Public*, pg. 1708
GORILLA GLUE CO.; *U.S. Private*, pg. 1743
GREEN BAY PACKAGING INC. - CALIFORNIA DIVISION—See Green Bay Packaging Inc.; *U.S. Private*, pg. 1771
HALEX CORPORATION—See Standard Industries Holdings Inc.; *U.S. Private*, pg. 3779
HAMAI OTAKI FACTORY LTD.—See HAMAI INDUSTRIES LIMITED; *Int'l*, pg. 3235
HANGZHOU GREAT STAR INDUSTRIAL CO., LTD.—See GreatStar Group Co., Ltd.; *Int'l*, pg. 3067
HARRAH MFG. CO.—See The Bloomfield Manufacturing Co., Inc.; *U.S. Private*, pg. 3995
HARRAMIENTAS TULTITLIN S.A.—See Klein Tools Inc.; *U.S. Private*, pg. 2319
HASSAS BAGLAMA EKIPMANLARI TIC LTD. STI—See Georg Fischer AG; *Int'l*, pg. 2935
H.C. MILLER COMPANY; *U.S. Private*, pg. 1825
HENDON MINING SUPPLIES (PTY) LTD—See ARGENT INDUSTRIAL LIMITED; *Int'l*, pg. 560
HISCO, INC.—See Q.E.P. Co., Inc.; *U.S. Public*, pg. 1741
HOLD-E-ZEE, LTD.—See Channellock, Inc.; *U.S. Private*, pg. 848
HOWESTEMCO, LLC—See NN, Inc.; *U.S. Public*, pg. 1531
HUACHEN PRECISION EQUIPMENT (KUNSHAN) CO., LTD.; *Int'l*, pg. 3511
HYDE MANUFACTURING COMPANY; *U.S. Private*, pg. 2016
HYDE TOOLS, INC.; *U.S. Private*, pg. 2017
IPE GROUP LIMITED—See China Baoan Group Co., Ltd.; *Int'l*, pg. 1485
JAMESON, LLC—See Platte River Ventures, LLC; *U.S. Private*, pg. 3211
JCSC SNA EUROPE INDUSTRIES BISOV—See Snap-on Incorporated; *U.S. Public*, pg. 1897
JS TECHNOLOGY INC.—See Danaher Corporation; *U.S. Public*, pg. 627
K2 DIAMOND COMPANY; *U.S. Public*, pg. 2253
KASSOY, LLC; *U.S. Private*, pg. 2264
KENNAMETAL DEUTSCHLAND GMBH—See Kennametal Inc.; *U.S. Public*, pg. 1222
KENNAMETAL IPG—See Kennametal Inc.; *U.S. Public*, pg. 1222
KENNAMETAL ITALIA S.P.A.—See Kennametal Inc.; *U.S. Public*, pg. 1222
KENNAMETAL JAPAN LTD.—See Kennametal Inc.; *U.S. Public*, pg. 1222
KENNAMETAL PRODUKTIONS GMBH & CO. KG—See Kennametal Inc.; *U.S. Public*, pg. 1222
KENNAMETAL STELLRAM LIMITED—See Kennametal Inc.; *U.S. Public*, pg. 1223
KENNAMETAL UK LIMITED—See Kennametal Inc.; *U.S. Public*, pg. 1222
KENNAMETAL XUZHOU CO., LTD.—See Kennametal Inc.; *U.S. Public*, pg. 1223
KEN-TOOL—See Summit Tool Company; *U.S. Private*, pg. 3857
KEY KNIFE INC.—See Kadant Inc.; *U.S. Public*, pg. 1212
THE KINETIC CO., INC.—See Live Ventures Incorporated; *U.S. Public*, pg. 1332
KLEIN TOOLS DE MEXICO S DE R.L DE C.V.—See Klein Tools Inc.; *U.S. Private*, pg. 2319
KLEIN TOOLS INC.; *U.S. Private*, pg. 2319
KRAFT TOOL COMPANY INC.; *U.S. Private*, pg. 2349
KWB GERMANY GMBH—See Einhell Germany AG; *Int'l*, pg. 2334
LAM RESEARCH CORPORATION—See Lam Research Corporation; *U.S. Public*, pg. 1289
LEATHERMAN TOOL GROUP, INC.; *U.S. Private*, pg. 2409
LENOX—See Stanley Black & Decker, Inc.; *U.S. Public*, pg. 1933
LISLE CORPORATION; *U.S. Private*, pg. 2466
LOADPOINT LIMITED—See GL Tech Co., Ltd.; *Int'l*, pg. 2986
THE L.S. STARRETT COMPANY LIMITED—See MiddleGround Management, LP; *U.S. Private*, pg. 2713
THE L.S. STARRETT COMPANY—See MiddleGround Management, LP; *U.S. Private*, pg. 2713
MALCO PRODUCTS, INC.; *U.S. Private*, pg. 2556
MALCO PRODUCTS—See Malco Products, Inc.; *U.S. Private*, pg. 2557
MARSHALLTOWN TROWEL COMPANY; *U.S. Private*, pg. 2593
MARTIN SPROCKET & GEAR, INC. - MARTIN TOOLS DIVISION—See Martin Sprocket & Gear, Inc.; *U.S. Private*, pg. 2596
MATCO TOOLS CORPORATION—See Vontier Corporation; *U.S. Public*, pg. 2309
MAYHEW STEEL PRODUCTS INC.; *U.S. Private*, pg. 2622
M&C SPECIALTIES (IRELAND) LIMITED—See Illinois Tool Works Inc.; *U.S. Public*, pg. 1109
MECATOOL AG—See Georg Fischer AG; *Int'l*, pg. 2935
MECTRON JAPAN, INC.—See Citizen Watch Co., Ltd.; *Int'l*, pg. 1624
MIDWEST INDUSTRIAL PACKAGING, INC.—See Illinois Tool Works Inc.; *U.S. Public*, pg. 1109
MK DIAMOND PRODUCTS, INC.; *U.S. Private*, pg. 2753
MOORE NANOTECHNOLOGY SYSTEMS LLC—See PMT Group Inc; *U.S. Private*, pg. 3219
MTD AUSTRIA HANDELSGESELLSCHAFT M.B.H.—See Stanley Black & Decker, Inc.; *U.S. Public*, pg. 1933
M.T.D. FRANCE SAS—See Stanley Black & Decker, Inc.; *U.S. Public*, pg. 1933
MTD HUNGARIA KFT.—See Stanley Black & Decker, Inc.; *U.S. Public*, pg. 1933
NATIONAL STEEL RULE CO. INC.; *U.S. Private*, pg. 2863
NEDERLANDSE HARDMETAAL FABRIEKEN B.V.—See Kennametal Inc.; *U.S. Public*, pg. 1222
NICHOLSON MEXICANA, S.A. DE C.V.—See Bain Capital, LP; *U.S. Private*, pg. 430
NICOTEC CO., LTD.—See Amada Holdings Co., Ltd.; *Int'l*, pg. 404
NORBAR TORQUE TOOLS, INC.—See Snap-on Incorporated; *U.S. Public*, pg. 1898
NORBAR TORQUE TOOLS LIMITED—See Snap-on Incorporated; *U.S. Public*, pg. 1898
NUPLA CORPORATION—See Q.E.P. Co., Inc.; *U.S. Public*, pg. 1741
OLFA NORTH AMERICA—See Cornell Capital Management LLC; *U.S. Private*, pg. 1051
OPTIWA B.V.—See Frencken Group Limited; *Int'l*, pg. 2773
PEERLESS SAW CO.; *U.S. Private*, pg. 3128
PENNFIELD PRECISION INCORPORATED; *U.S. Private*, pg. 3136
PIH SERVICES ME LLC—See Stanley Black & Decker, Inc.; *U.S. Public*, pg. 1933
PIH SERVICES ME LTD.—See Stanley Black & Decker, Inc.; *U.S. Public*, pg. 1933
POWER HAWK TECHNOLOGIES, INC.—See Snap-on Incorporated; *U.S. Public*, pg. 1898
PRECITECH, INC.—See AMETEK, Inc.; *U.S. Public*, pg. 118
PREMCO, INC.—See NN, Inc.; *U.S. Public*, pg. 1531

332216 — SAW BLADE AND HANDT...

PRODUCTS ENGINEERING CORP; *U.S. Private*, pg. 3274
Q.E.P. CO., INC.; *U.S. Public*, pg. 1741
RAYCO MANUFACTURING, INC.—See Alamo Group Inc.; *U.S. Public*, pg. 71
RIDGE TOOL EUROPE N.V.—See Emerson Electric Co.; *U.S. Public*, pg. 749
RIDGID PRODUCTS—See Emerson Electric Co.; *U.S. Public*, pg. 749
RIDGID SCANDINAVIA A/S—See Emerson Electric Co.; *U.S. Public*, pg. 749
RIDGID WERKZEUGE AG—See Emerson Electric Co.; *U.S. Public*, pg. 740
ROBERTS CONSOLIDATED INDUSTRIES INC.—See Q.E.P. Co., Inc.; *U.S. Public*, pg. 1741
ROMAG LTD.—See Clayton Glass Ltd.; *Int'l*, pg. 1653
ROSEBURG MANUFACTURING DIVISION—See Caddock Electronics, Inc.; *U.S. Private*, pg. 712
RUGG MANUFACTURING COMPANY; *U.S. Private*, pg. 3502
RUKO GMBH PRAZISIONSWERKZEUGE—See Dr. Helmut Rothenberger Holding GmbH; *Int'l*, pg. 2191
RYESON CORPORATION—See Snap-on Incorporated; *U.S. Public*, pg. 1898
SABART SRL—See Emak S.p.A.; *Int'l*, pg. 2373
SAINT-GOBAIN ABRASIVES, INC. - CHICAGO—See Compagnie de Saint-Gobain SA; *Int'l*, pg. 1732
SEYMOUR MANUFACTURING CO., INC.—See Seymour Midwest LLC; *U.S. Private*, pg. 3621
SEYMOUR MIDWEST LLC; *U.S. Private*, pg. 3621
SK HAND TOOL, LLC; *U.S. Private*, pg. 3680
SNAP-ON DIAGNOSTICS—See Snap-on Incorporated; *U.S. Public*, pg. 1898
SNAP-ON INDUSTRIAL—See Snap-on Incorporated; *U.S. Public*, pg. 1898
SNAP-ON POWER TOOLS INC.—See Snap-on Incorporated; *U.S. Public*, pg. 1898
SNAP-ON TOOLS (AUSTRALIA) PTY. LTD.—See Snap-on Incorporated; *U.S. Public*, pg. 1898
SNAP-ON TOOLS JAPAN K.K.—See Snap-on Incorporated; *U.S. Public*, pg. 1898
SPEED NORTH AMERICA INC.—See Emak S.p.A.; *Int'l*, pg. 2373
SPLINE GAUGES LTD.—See Danaher Corporation; *U.S. Public*, pg. 631
STANLEY ASSEMBLY TECHNOLOGIES—See Stanley Black & Decker, Inc.; *U.S. Public*, pg. 1934
STANLEY INFRASTRUCTURE, LLC—See Epiroc AB; *Int'l*, pg. 2463
STARRETT INDUSTRIA E COMERCIO LTDA.—See MiddleGround Management, LP; *U.S. Private*, pg. 2713
STARRETT TOOLS (SUZHOU) CO. LTD.—See MiddleGround Management, LP; *U.S. Private*, pg. 2713
STF PRECISION TECHNOLOGIES & TOOLS, INC.—See L Squared Capital Management LP; *U.S. Private*, pg. 2362
S-T INDUSTRIES, INC.; *U.S. Private*, pg. 3514
SUMMIT TOOL COMPANY; *U.S. Private*, pg. 3857
SUPERIOR TOOL CORPORATION; *U.S. Private*, pg. 3880
SWEDISH SAW BLADES AB—See Duroc AB; *Int'l*, pg. 2230
SYSTEM 3R AG—See Georg Fischer AG; *Int'l*, pg. 2935
SYSTEM 3R CZECH S.R.O.—See Georg Fischer AG; *Int'l*, pg. 2935
SYSTEM 3R FAR EAST PTE LTD.—See Georg Fischer AG; *Int'l*, pg. 2935
SYSTEM 3R FRANCE S.A.S.—See Georg Fischer AG; *Int'l*, pg. 2935
SYSTEM 3R INTERNATIONAL AB—See Georg Fischer AG; *Int'l*, pg. 2935
SYSTEM 3R JAPAN CO., LTD.—See Georg Fischer AG; *Int'l*, pg. 2935
SYSTEM 3R (UK) LTD.—See Georg Fischer AG; *Int'l*, pg. 2935
THEXTON MANUFACTURING COMPANY, INC.; *U.S. Private*, pg. 4144
TK SIMPLEX—See Enerpac Tool Group Corp.; *U.S. Public*, pg. 766
TOMOIKE INDUSTRIAL CO., LTD.—See CDW Holding Ltd.; *Int'l*, pg. 1372
ULLMAN DEVICES CORPORATION; *U.S. Private*, pg. 4276
VAUGHAN & BUSHNELL MANUFACTURING COMPANY, INC.; *U.S. Private*, pg. 4348
V & B MANUFACTURING CO.—See Vaughan & Bushnell Manufacturing Company, Inc.; *U.S. Private*, pg. 4348
VITREX LIMITED—See Q.E.P. Co., Inc.; *U.S. Public*, pg. 1741
WARNER MANUFACTURING COMPANY; *U.S. Private*, pg. 4442
WEBBER GAUGE DIVISION—See MiddleGround Management, LP; *U.S. Private*, pg. 2713
WESTCO IRON WORKS, INC.; *U.S. Private*, pg. 4489
WESTERN FORGE CORPORATION—See MW Universal Inc.; *U.S. Private*, pg. 2822
WILSON MACHINE KNIFE CO., INC.—See Hyde Manufacturing Company; *U.S. Private*, pg. 2016
WRIGHT TOOL COMPANY, INC.; *U.S. Private*, pg. 4573
YAMA SEIKI USA INC.—See GOODWAY MACHINE CORP.; *Int'l*, pg. 3041
YOST VISES, LLC—See Kian Capital Partners, LLC; *U.S. Private*, pg. 2302

332311 — PREFABRICATED METAL BUILDING AND COMPONENT MANUFACTURING

4FRONT ENGINEERED SOLUTIONS - MUSKEGO—See ASSA ABLOY AB; *Int'l*, pg. 633
957447 ALBERTA LTD; *Int'l*, pg. 16
ABU DHABI NATIONAL COMPANY FOR BUILDING MATERIAL; *Int'l*, pg. 72
ACI BUILDING SYSTEMS, LLC—See Promus Holdings, LLC; *U.S. Private*, pg. 3284
ACOUSTIBLOK INC.; *U.S. Private*, pg. 64
AIM METALS, LLC—See Promus Holdings, LLC; *U.S. Private*, pg. 3284
AJECOBOND - AL JABER ALUMINIUM COMPOSITE LLC—See Al Jaber Group; *Int'l*, pg. 279
ALGECO SAS—See Brookfield Corporation; *Int'l*, pg. 1176
ALGECO UK LIMITED—See Brookfield Corporation; *Int'l*, pg. 1176
ALTA-FAB STRUCTURES LTD.; *Int'l*, pg. 384
ALUTIIQ INTERNATIONAL SOLUTIONS, LLC; *U.S. Private*, pg. 211
AMERICAN BUILDING COMPONENTS—See Clayton, Dubilier & Rice, LLC; *U.S. Private*, pg. 920
AMERICAN BUILDINGS COMPANY—See Nucor Corporation; *U.S. Public*, pg. 1553
APPLY LEIRVIK AS—See Apply ASA; *Int'l*, pg. 522
APPLY LQ PARTNER AS—See Apply ASA; *Int'l*, pg. 521
ARCELORMITTAL TAILORED BLANKS—See Cleveland-Cliffs, Inc.; *U.S. Public*, pg. 514
ARMSTRONG METALLDECKEN GMBH—See Aurelius Equity Opportunities SE & Co. KGaA; *Int'l*, pg. 707
ARROW GROUP INDUSTRIES, INC.—See Leonard Green & Partners, L.P.; *U.S. Private*, pg. 2424
A&S BUILDING SYSTEMS, INC.—See Clayton, Dubilier & Rice, LLC; *U.S. Private*, pg. 920
ASC PROFILES INC.—See BlueScope Steel Limited; *Int'l*, pg. 1073
ASTINO BERHAD; *Int'l*, pg. 655
ATCO FRONTEC EUROPA KFT-SUCURSAL EM PORTUGAL—See ATCO Ltd.; *Int'l*, pg. 666
ATCO FRONTEC EUROPE LTD.—See ATCO Ltd.; *Int'l*, pg. 666
ATCO STRUCTURES & LOGISTICS LTD.—See ATCO Ltd.; *Int'l*, pg. 666
ATCO STRUCTURES & LOGISTICS PTY LTD.—See ATCO Ltd.; *Int'l*, pg. 666
ATCO STRUCTURES & LOGISTICS UK LTD.—See ATCO Ltd.; *Int'l*, pg. 666
ATCO STRUCTURES & LOGISTICS (USA) INC. - ALASKA—See ATCO Ltd.; *Int'l*, pg. 666
ATCO STRUCTURES & LOGISTICS (USA) INC.—See ATCO Ltd.; *Int'l*, pg. 666
ATEC, INC.; *U.S. Private*, pg. 365
AZAD ENGINEERING LIMITED; *Int'l*, pg. 776
BANGLADESH BUILDING SYSTEM LTD.; *Int'l*, pg. 835
BARNMASTER INC.; *U.S. Private*, pg. 478
BAY INSULATION OF TENNESSEE INC.—See Bay Industries Inc.; *U.S. Private*, pg. 493
BEHLEN MFG. CO. - BEHLEN BUILDING SYSTEMS UNIT—See Behlen Mfg. Co.; *U.S. Private*, pg. 515
BENNETT BUILDING SYSTEMS, LLC—See Bennett International Group, Inc.; *U.S. Private*, pg. 527
BETCO INC.; *U.S. Private*, pg. 545
BETPREF SP. Z O.O.—See Dekpol S.A.; *Int'l*, pg. 2006
B+F DORSTEN GMBH; *Int'l*, pg. 784
BLUESCOPE BUILDINGS NORTH AMERICA ENGINEERING (MICHIGAN) LLC—See BlueScope Steel Limited; *Int'l*, pg. 1072
BLUESCOPE STEEL NORTH AMERICA CORPORATION—See BlueScope Steel Limited; *Int'l*, pg. 1073
BLUFF MANUFACTURING, INC.—See Wincove Private Holdings, LP; *U.S. Private*, pg. 4533
BOG'ART STEEL SRL—See Bog'Art S.R.L.; *Int'l*, pg. 1100
BROADWIND, INC.; *U.S. Public*, pg. 392
BRYTEX BUILDING SYSTEMS INC.; *Int'l*, pg. 1201
BUIMA GROUP, INC.; *Int'l*, pg. 1212
BUTLER MANUFACTURING COMPANY—See BlueScope Steel Limited; *Int'l*, pg. 1073
CALIFORNIA EXPANDED METAL PRODUCTS COMPANY; *U.S. Private*, pg. 719
CBC STEEL BUILDINGS—See Nucor Corporation; *U.S. Public*, pg. 1553
CECO BUILDING SYSTEMS-EASTERN REGION—See Clayton, Dubilier & Rice, LLC; *U.S. Private*, pg. 920
CECO BUILDING SYSTEMS—See Clayton, Dubilier & Rice, LLC; *U.S. Private*, pg. 920
CELTECH CORP.—See Atec, Inc.; *U.S. Private*, pg. 365
CENTRAL STATES MANUFACTURING INC.; *U.S. Private*, pg. 825
CENTURION INDUSTRIES INC. - A-LERT BUILDING SYSTEMS DIVISION—See Centurion Industries, Inc.; *U.S. Private*, pg. 831
CHANGSHA BROAD HOMES INDUSTRIAL GROUP CO., LTD.; *Int'l*, pg. 1444
CHIEF INDUSTRIES, INC.; *U.S. Private*, pg. 881

COAST TO COAST CARPORTS, INC.; *U.S. Private*, pg. 954
CONSTRUCTION SPECIALITES (UK) LTD.—See Construction Specialties, Inc.; *U.S. Private*, pg. 1024
CONSTRUCTION SPECIALTIES (GULF) LLC—See Construction Specialties, Inc.; *U.S. Private*, pg. 1024
CONTRACTORS TRUSS SYSTEMS, INC.—See Bain Capital, LP; *U.S. Private*, pg. 450
CORLE BUILDING SYSTEMS; *U.S. Private*, pg. 1050
CRAIG INDUSTRIES INC.; *U.S. Private*, pg. 1083
C/S FRANCE—See Construction Specialties, Inc.; *U.S. Private*, pg. 1024
C/S POLSKA SP. ZO.O—See Construction Specialties, Inc.; *U.S. Private*, pg. 1024
CSR BUILDING PRODUCTS (NZ) LTD.—See CSR Limited; *Int'l*, pg. 1867
DACRO INDUSTRIES INC.; *Int'l*, pg. 1904
DEAN STEEL BUILDINGS INC.; *U.S. Private*, pg. 1184
DECLOET GREENHOUSE MANUFACTURING LTD.; *Int'l*, pg. 2001
DEKOMTE DE TEMPLE KOMPENSATOR-TECHNIK GMBH; *Int'l*, pg. 2006
DELUXE BUILDING SYSTEMS, INC.; *U.S. Private*, pg. 1202
ENERGY PANEL STRUCTURES, INC.—See MacArthur Co.; *U.S. Private*, pg. 2534
ENGINEERED METALS & COMPOSITES, INC.—See Patrick Industries, Inc.; *U.S. Public*, pg. 1652
ENVIROPLEX, INC—See McGrath RentCorp.; *U.S. Public*, pg. 1407
EUROPERFIL S.A.—See ArcelorMittal S.A.; *Int'l*, pg. 544
FACADEMASTER PTE LTD.—See Compact Metal Industries Ltd.; *Int'l*, pg. 1721
FAIRBORN USA, INC.; *U.S. Private*, pg. 1462
FALK BUILDING SYSTEMS BV; *Int'l*, pg. 2611
F&D SCENE CHANGES LTD.; *Int'l*, pg. 2595
FISHER SKYLIGHTS, INC.—See Epwin Group Plc; *Int'l*, pg. 2466
FORMICA DE MEXICO SA DE CV—See HAL Trust N.V.; *Int'l*, pg. 3223
FOUR SEASONS SUNROOM—See Epwin Group Plc; *Int'l*, pg. 2466
GARCO BUILDING SYSTEMS, INC.—See Clayton, Dubilier & Rice, LLC; *U.S. Private*, pg. 920
GCM HOLDING CORPORATION—See Avista Capital Partners, L.P.; *U.S. Private*, pg. 408
GICHNER SYSTEMS GROUP INC.—See Kratos Defense & Security Solutions, Inc.; *U.S. Public*, pg. 1276
GICHNER SYSTEMS INTERNATIONAL, INC.—See Kratos Defense & Security Solutions, Inc.; *U.S. Public*, pg. 1276
GLOBAL ARCHITECTURAL PANELS—See Weiss Sheet Metal Company; *U.S. Private*, pg. 4473
GREAT DAY IMPROVEMENTS LLC; *U.S. Private*, pg. 1762
HANDI-HOUSE MANUFACTURING CO.; *U.S. Private*, pg. 1852
HAWKEYE STEEL PRODUCTS, INC. - SPAN-TECH DIVISION—See Hawkeye Steel Products, Inc.; *U.S. Private*, pg. 1883
HILLTOP SERVICES LLC—See Comcast Corporation; *U.S. Public*, pg. 538
HORMANN LEGNICA SP. ZO.O—See Hormann KG Verkaufsgesellschaf; *Int'l*, pg. 3481
HUENNEBECK GMBH—See Brand Industrial Services, Inc.; *U.S. Private*, pg. 636
HUNNEBECK ROMANIA SRL—See Brand Industrial Services, Inc.; *U.S. Private*, pg. 636
IBOX S.R.L.—See Giglio Group S.p.A.; *Int'l*, pg. 2972
INDACO METALS, LLC; *U.S. Private*, pg. 2054
INTERNATIONAL BUILDING SYSTEMS FACTORY CO. LTD.—See ASTRA INDUSTRIAL GROUP COMPANY; *Int'l*, pg. 657
JACK WALTERS & SONS CORP.; *U.S. Private*, pg. 2175
JOBSITE TRAILER CORP.—See Reliant Asset Management LLC; *U.S. Private*, pg. 3395
JOHN L. CONLEY INC.; *U.S. Private*, pg. 2222
JOYCE MANUFACTURING CO.; *U.S. Private*, pg. 2239
KIRBY BUILDING SYSTEMS, INC.—See Nucor Corporation; *U.S. Public*, pg. 1553
LABTECH SERVICES LTD.—See Global Energy (Holdings) Ltd.; *Int'l*, pg. 2995
LIAONING HANKING GREEN BUILDING MATERIALS CO., LTD.—See China Hanking Holdings Limited; *Int'l*, pg. 1506
LOSBERGER FRANCE SAS—See Gilde Buy Out Partners B.V.; *Int'l*, pg. 2975
LOSBERGER GMBH—See Gilde Buy Out Partners B.V.; *Int'l*, pg. 2975
LOSBERGER RAPID DEPLOYMENT SYSTEMS SAS—See Gilde Buy Out Partners B.V.; *Int'l*, pg. 2975
MASCO UK WINDOW GROUP LIMITED—See Masco Corporation; *U.S. Public*, pg. 1391
MCELROY METAL MILL, INC.; *U.S. Private*, pg. 2633
MD ENTERPRISES INC.; *U.S. Private*, pg. 2646
METAL BUILDING COMPONENTS INC.—See Clayton, Dubilier & Rice, LLC; *U.S. Private*, pg. 921
METALLIC BUILDING COMPANY—See Clayton, Dubilier & Rice, LLC; *U.S. Private*, pg. 921

N.A.I.C.S. INDEX

332312 — FABRICATED STRUCTUR...

METAL MOULDING CORP.—See Patrick Industries, Inc.; *U.S. Public*, pg. 1653
METL-SPAN LLC—See Clayton, Dubilier & Rice, LLC; *U.S. Private*, pg. 921
MILLER BUILDINGS INC.; *U.S. Private*, pg. 2733
MORTON BUILDINGS INC.; *U.S. Private*, pg. 2791
MUELLER INC.; *U.S. Private*, pg. 2810
NEXUS CORPORATION—See Gibraltar Industries, Inc.; *U.S. Public*, pg. 936
NOLL/NORWESCO, LLC—See Gibraltar Industries, Inc.; *U.S. Public*, pg. 936
NORSHIELD SECURITY PRODUCTS LLC—See Spell Capital Partners, LLC; *U.S. Private*, pg. 3754
NORTHSTAR INDUSTRIES INC.; *U.S. Private*, pg. 2958
NRB INC.—See Dexterra Group Inc.; *Int'l*, pg. 2093
NUCOR BUILDING SYSTEMS UTAH LLC—See Nucor Corporation; *U.S. Public*, pg. 1553
OAKLAND METAL BUILDINGS, INC.—See Clayton, Dubilier & Rice, LLC; *U.S. Private*, pg. 921
OEM FABRICATORS, INC.; *U.S. Private*, pg. 2997
OPW FUELING COMPONENTS (SUZHOU) CO., LTD.—See Dover Corporation; *U.S. Public*, pg. 679
PACIFIC AWARDS METALS, INC.—See Gibraltar Industries, Inc.; *U.S. Public*, pg. 936
PCX CORP.—See Hubbell Incorporated; *U.S. Public*, pg. 1067
QC INDUSTRIES INC.—See Guardian Fall Protection, Inc.; *U.S. Private*, pg. 1810
ROOF MART, LLC—See Trachte Building Systems Inc.; *U.S. Private*, pg. 4200
ROUGH BROTHERS GREENHOUSE MANUFACTURING (SHANGHAI) CO., LTD—See Gibraltar Industries, Inc.; *U.S. Public*, pg. 936
ROUGH BROTHERS, INC.—See Gibraltar Industries, Inc.; *U.S. Public*, pg. 936
SAFETY STORAGE INC.; *U.S. Private*, pg. 3525
SAUDI BUILDING SYSTEMS, LTD.—See BlueScope Steel Limited; *Int'l*, pg. 1073
SCHULTE BUILDING SYSTEMS, INC.; *U.S. Private*, pg. 3570
SENQCIA CORPORATION—See The Carlyle Group Inc.; *U.S. Public*, pg. 2052
SENTINEL BUILDING SYSTEMS INC.; *U.S. Private*, pg. 3608
SHELTERLOGIC CORP.; *U.S. Private*, pg. 3631
SMITHBILT INDUSTRIES INC.; *U.S. Private*, pg. 3696
SOLAR GROUP, INC.—See Gibraltar Industries, Inc.; *U.S. Public*, pg. 936
STAR BUILDING SYSTEMS—See Clayton, Dubilier & Rice, LLC; *U.S. Private*, pg. 921
STARRCO COMPANY INC.; *U.S. Private*, pg. 3787
STEEL CONSTRUCTION SYSTEMS—See CEMEX, S.A.B. de C.V.; *Int'l*, pg. 1399
SUNBILT SOLAR PRODUCTS BY SUSSMAN, INC.—See J. Sussman, Inc.; *U.S. Private*, pg. 2157
SUNPORCH STRUCTURES INC.; *U.S. Private*, pg. 3869
SUNROOM CONCEPTS—See MacArthur Co.; *U.S. Private*, pg. 2534
SUNSHINE ROOMS, INC.; *U.S. Private*, pg. 3872
TASMAN BUILDING PRODUCTS PTY LIMITED—See Fletcher Building Limited; *Int'l*, pg. 2701
TEMO INC.; *U.S. Private*, pg. 3963
TRACHTE BUILDING SYSTEMS INC.; *U.S. Private*, pg. 4200
TRIDENT BUILDING SYSTEMS, INC.—See Behlen Mfg. Co.; *U.S. Private*, pg. 515
TRISTAR ELECTRONICS SA—See Carlisle Companies Incorporated; *U.S. Public*, pg. 437
TRUECORE, LLC—See Nucor Corporation; *U.S. Public*, pg. 1554
TRUSS-T STRUCTURES, INC.—See Roots Equity Group LLC; *U.S. Private*, pg. 3480
TYLER BUILDING SYSTEMS, L.P.; *U.S. Private*, pg. 4267
UNISTRUT CORPORATION—See Clayton, Dubilier & Rice, LLC; *U.S. Private*, pg. 920
UNISTRUT CORPORATION—See Clayton, Dubilier & Rice, LLC; *U.S. Private*, pg. 920
UNITED STRUCTURES OF AMERICA INC.; *U.S. Private*, pg. 4300
VANDENDORPE NV—See Ackermans & van Haaren NV; *Int'l*, pg. 106
VARCO PRUDEN BUILDINGS, INC.—See BlueScope Steel Limited; *Int'l*, pg. 1073
VITAL LINK, INC.—See Atec, Inc.; *U.S. Private*, pg. 365
VULCAN STEEL STRUCTURES, INC.; *U.S. Private*, pg. 4416
WEDGCOR INC.; *U.S. Private*, pg. 4468
WHIRLWIND BUILDING SYSTEM; *U.S. Private*, pg. 4507
WHIRLWIND STEEL; *U.S. Private*, pg. 4507
WILLIAMS SCOTSMAN, INC.—See WillScot Mobile Mini Holdings Corp.; *U.S. Public*, pg. 2372
WILLIAMS SCOTSMAN INTERNATIONAL, INC.—See WillScot Mobile Mini Holdings Corp.; *U.S. Public*, pg. 2372
WORTHINGTON ARMSTRONG VENTURE—See Armstrong World Industries, Inc.; *U.S. Public*, pg. 194
WORTHINGTON ARMSTRONG VENTURE—See Worthington Industries, Inc.; *U.S. Public*, pg. 2383

332312 — FABRICATED STRUCTURAL METAL MANUFACTURING

101 VERTICAL FABRICATION INC.—See 101 Pipe & Casing Inc.; *U.S. Private*, pg. 2
101 VERTICAL FABRICATION, MANUFACTURING FACILITY—See 101 Pipe & Casing Inc.; *U.S. Private*, pg. 2
80/20 INC.; *U.S. Private*, pg. 17
9083-7436 QUEBEC INC.; *Int'l*, pg. 16
A & B WELDING, INC.—See Precision Tank & Equip Co.; *U.S. Private*, pg. 3247
ACCURATE METAL FABRICATING—See Accurate Perforating Company, Inc.; *U.S. Private*, pg. 55
ACROW MISR FOR SCAFFOLDING & FORMWORK; *Int'l*, pg. 109
AEGIS METAL FRAMING, LLC—See Berkshire Hathaway Inc.; *U.S. Public*, pg. 312
AEREX INDUSTRIES, INC.—See Consolidated Water Co. Ltd.; *Int'l*, pg. 1771
AEROSEAL, LLC; *U.S. Private*, pg. 119
AFCO STEEL INC.; *U.S. Private*, pg. 121
AIRCON GUARDRAILS PRIVATE LIMITED—See Valmont Industries, Inc.; *U.S. Public*, pg. 2273
AIR WATER MACH (DALIAN) CO., LTD.—See Air Water Inc.; *Int'l*, pg. 239
A.J. WELLER CORP.; *U.S. Private*, pg. 26
AKRON REBAR CO.; *U.S. Private*, pg. 146
AL ARABI STEEL STRUCTURE MANUFACTURING CO.—See Al-Osais International Holding Company; *Int'l*, pg. 287
A-LERT CONSTRUCTION SERVICES INC. - FABRICATION FACILITY—See Centurion Industries Inc.; *U.S. Private*, pg. 831
ALLIANCE STEEL, INC.—See Promus Holdings, LLC; *U.S. Private*, pg. 3284
ALLOYS UNLIMITED PROCESSING—See Ampco-Pittsburgh Corporation; *U.S. Public*, pg. 126
AL MAHA MODULAR INDUSTRIES LLC—See Alpha Dhabi Holding PJSC; *Int'l*, pg. 367
ALNC, INC.; *U.S. Private*, pg. 195
ALSTOM FLERTEX S.A.S—See Alstom S.A.; *Int'l*, pg. 379
ALUMINIJ D.D.; *Int'l*, pg. 401
ALUMINIUM EXTRUSION INDUSTRIES PLC; *Int'l*, pg. 401
ALUMINIUM TECHNOLOGIES SDN BHD—See Apply ASA; *Int'l*, pg. 521
AMBASSADOR STEEL CORPORATION—See Nucor Corporation; *U.S. Public*, pg. 1553
AME ENGINEERING INDUSTRIES SDN. BHD.—See AME Elite Consortium Berhad; *Int'l*, pg. 420
AMERICAN GALVANIZING—See Valmont Industries, Inc.; *U.S. Public*, pg. 2273
ANCON LIMITED—See CRH plc; *Int'l*, pg. 1843
ANDERSON STEEL SUPPLY, INC.; *U.S. Private*, pg. 277
ANHUI HONGLU STEEL CONSTRUCTION (GROUP) CO., LTD.; *Int'l*, pg. 468
ANHUI TEC TOWER CO., LTD.—See Telidyne Inc.; *U.S. Public*, pg. 1998
APPLY EMTUNGA AB—See Apply ASA; *Int'l*, pg. 521
ARCELORMITTAL COMMERCIAL RPS DEUTSCHLAND GMBH—See ArcelorMittal S.A.; *Int'l*, pg. 544
ARCHITECTURAL ART MFG. INC.—See Pittcon Industries; *U.S. Private*, pg. 3191
ARCOSA WIND TOWERS, INC.—See Arcosa, Inc.; *U.S. Public*, pg. 186
ARMETAL METAL INDUSTRIES COMPANY LTD.—See Al-Hejailan Group; *Int'l*, pg. 286
ARROWHEAD STEEL FABRICATORS—See Chief Industries, Inc.; *U.S. Private*, pg. 881
ASHOKA METCAST LIMITED; *Int'l*, pg. 608
ASSET INTERNATIONAL LTD—See Hill & Smith PLC; *Int'l*, pg. 3391
ATA BYGG-OCH MARKPRODUKTER AB; *Int'l*, pg. 665
ATELIERS D ORVAL SA—See Ermewa Interservices Sarl; *Int'l*, pg. 2494
AT&F ADVANCED METALS LLC—See American Tank & Fabricating Company; *U.S. Private*, pg. 256
AT&F INDIA FABRICATION PVT. LTD.—See American Tank & Fabricating Company; *U.S. Private*, pg. 256
ATI INC.; *U.S. Public*, pg. 221
ATLANTIC CENTRAL ENTERPRISES, INC.; *U.S. Private*, pg. 372
AYS (FZ) SDN. BHD.—See AYS Ventures Berhad; *Int'l*, pg. 775
AYS WIRE PRODUCTS SDN. BHD.—See AYS Ventures Berhad; *Int'l*, pg. 776
AZUR INDUSTRIES; *Int'l*, pg. 782
BACKER ROD MANUFACTURING INC.—See Bay Industries Inc.; *U.S. Private*, pg. 493
BAILEY METAL PRODUCTS LIMITED—See Bailey Metal Products Limited; *Int'l*, pg. 802
BANGKOK SHEET METAL PUBLIC COMPANY LTD.; *Int'l*, pg. 835
BANKER STEEL CO., LLC—See Atlas Holdings, LLC; *U.S. Private*, pg. 376
BARKER STEEL MID-ATLANTIC LLC—See Nucor Corporation; *U.S. Public*, pg. 1553
BATTS INC.; *U.S. Private*, pg. 490
BAUDOUX CONSTRUCTION METALLIQUES; *Int'l*, pg. 891
BC STEEL BUILDINGS, INC.; *U.S. Private*, pg. 498
BEARIUM METALS CORPORATION—See MetalTek International; *U.S. Private*, pg. 2682
BENARA BEARINGS & PISTONS LTD.; *Int'l*, pg. 969
BENGAL STEEL INDUSTRIES LTD.; *Int'l*, pg. 973
THE BERLIN STEEL CONSTRUCTION COMPANY - BERLIN STEEL BALTIMORE/WASHINGTON DIVISION—See The Berlin Steel Construction Company; *U.S. Private*, pg. 3994
THE BERLIN STEEL CONSTRUCTION COMPANY - BERLIN STEEL MID-ATLANTIC DIVISION—See The Berlin Steel Construction Company; *U.S. Private*, pg. 3994
THE BERLIN STEEL CONSTRUCTION COMPANY - MA DIVISION—See The Berlin Steel Construction Company; *U.S. Private*, pg. 3994
THE BERLIN STEEL CONSTRUCTION COMPANY; *U.S. Private*, pg. 3993
BERRY SYSTEMS—See Hill & Smith PLC; *Int'l*, pg. 3391
BEST MANUFACTURING, INC.—See Reliance Steel & Aluminum Co.; *U.S. Public*, pg. 1779
BETA INTERNATIONAL & AFFILIATES; *U.S. Private*, pg. 544
BIRTLEY BUILDING PRODUCTS LTD—See Hill & Smith PLC; *Int'l*, pg. 3391
BITUMA-STOR, INC.—See Gencor Industries, Inc.; *U.S. Public*, pg. 911
BIZCONN INT'L CORP.—See BizLink Holding Inc.; *Int'l*, pg. 1053
BLICKMAN HEALTH INDUSTRIES, INC.; *U.S. Private*, pg. 581
BLUDAU FABRICATION INC.; *U.S. Private*, pg. 585
BODARD CONSTRUCTION MODULAIRE; *Int'l*, pg. 1097
BOMAN KEMP BASEMENT WINDOW SYSTEMS; *U.S. Private*, pg. 611
BOSA TECHNOLOGY HOLDINGS LTD.; *Int'l*, pg. 1116
BOSNAMONTAZA A.D.; *Int'l*, pg. 1116
BOWMAN & KEMP REBAR—See Boman Kemp Basement Window Systems; *U.S. Private*, pg. 611
BOWMAN & KEMP STEEL & SUPPLY COMPANY—See Boman Kemp Basement Window Systems; *U.S. Private*, pg. 611
BT WEALTH INDUSTRIES PUBLIC COMPANY LTD.; *Int'l*, pg. 1204
CANAM GROUP INC.—See AIP, LLC; *U.S. Public*, pg. 134
CAPARO ENGINEERING INDIA LTD.—See Caparo Group Ltd.; *Int'l*, pg. 1301
CAPITAL MACHINE TECHNOLOGIES, INC.; *U.S. Private*, pg. 741
CAPITAL STEEL SERVICE, LLC.—See Hill & Smith PLC; *Int'l*, pg. 3391
CAPITAL WELDING, INC.; *U.S. Private*, pg. 742
CARMEL FORGE LTD.—See Bet Shemesh Engines Holdings (1997) Ltd.; *Int'l*, pg. 1001
CAUTTRELL ENTERPRISES INC.; *U.S. Private*, pg. 794
CB&I - CLIVE—See McDermott International, Inc.; *U.S. Public*, pg. 1405
CDA METALS; *U.S. Private*, pg. 802
CENTRAL ILLINOIS STEEL COMPANY; *U.S. Private*, pg. 821
CENTRAL MINNESOTA FABRICATING INC.; *U.S. Private*, pg. 822
CENTRAL TEXAS IRON WORKS INC.—See The Herrick Corporation; *U.S. Private*, pg. 4052
CENTURY IRON & STEEL INDUSTRIAL CO., LTD. - TAOYUAN PLANT—See Century Iron & Steel Industrial Co., Ltd.; *Int'l*, pg. 1418
CENTURY WIND POWER CO., LTD.—See Century Iron & Steel Industrial Co., Ltd.; *Int'l*, pg. 1418
CHICAGO METAL ROLLED PRODUCTS CO.; *U.S. Private*, pg. 878
CHIEF INDUSTRIES, INC. - FABRICATION DIVISION—See Chief Industries, Inc.; *U.S. Private*, pg. 881
CHIEF TRANSPORTATION PRODUCTS, INC.—See Chief Industries, Inc.; *U.S. Private*, pg. 881
CHINA RAILWAY SHANHAIGUAN BRIDGE GROUP CO., LTD.—See China Railway Group Limited; *Int'l*, pg. 1543
CHINA STEEL STRUCTURE CO., LTD.—See China Steel Corporation; *Int'l*, pg. 1555
CIANBRO CORPORATION - GEORGETOWN FABRICATION FACILITY—See Cianbro Corporation; *U.S. Private*, pg. 896
CIE PRAGA LOUNY, A.S.—See Cie Automotive S.A.; *Int'l*, pg. 1604
CIMTAS CELIK IMALAT MONTAJ VE TESISAT A.S.—See Enka Insaat ve Sanayi A.S.; *Int'l*, pg. 2440
CIRCA METALS INC.—See Equistone Partners Europe Limited; *Int'l*, pg. 2487
C.I.S. CO. OF ALABAMA—See Central Illinois Steel Company; *U.S. Private*, pg. 821
CITIZEN SEIMITSU (THAILAND) CO., LTD.—See Citizen Watch Co., Ltd.; *Int'l*, pg. 1624
CITY STEEL PRODUCTS COMPANY LIMITED—See City Steel Public Company Limited; *Int'l*, pg. 1628
CIVES CORPORATION - MID-ATLANTIC DIVISION—See Cives Corporation; *U.S. Private*, pg. 908
CIVES CORPORATION; *U.S. Private*, pg. 908

332312 — FABRICATED STRUCTUR...

CIVES CORPORATION - SOUTHERN DIVISION—See Cives Corporation; *U.S. Private*, pg. 908
C & J GULF PIPE COATING EST.—See Bhatia Brothers Group; *Int'l*, pg. 1013
CLARK METAL WORKS—See Clark Pacific; *U.S. Private*, pg. 913
CLEANUP HEARTFUL CO., LTD.—See Cleanup Corporation; *Int'l*, pg. 1656
CLEANUP STEEL PROCESSING CO., LTD. - NODA FACTORY—See Cleanup Corporation; *Int'l*, pg. 1656
CLIFTON STEEL COMPANY; *U.S. Private*, pg. 943
CLINCH RIVER CORPORATION—See KBR, Inc.; *U.S. Public*, pg. 1216
CMC ALAMO STEEL—See Commercial Metals Company; *U.S. Public*, pg. 546
CMC REBAR CAROLINAS—See Commercial Metals Company; *U.S. Public*, pg. 546
CMC REBAR FLORIDA—See Commercial Metals Company; *U.S. Public*, pg. 546
CMC REBAR GEORGIA—See Commercial Metals Company; *U.S. Public*, pg. 546
CMC REBAR NORTH CAROLINA—See Commercial Metals Company; *U.S. Public*, pg. 546
CMC REBAR VIRGINIA—See Commercial Metals Company; *U.S. Public*, pg. 546
CMC STEEL ARKANSAS—See Commercial Metals Company; *U.S. Public*, pg. 546
CMC STERLING STEEL—See Commercial Metals Company; *U.S. Public*, pg. 546
CMC TEXAS COLD FINISHED STEEL, INC.—See Commercial Metals Company; *U.S. Public*, pg. 546
CN PRECISION CASING (SHENZHEN) CO., LTD-PINGHU—See CN Innovations Holdings Limited; *Int'l*, pg. 1672
COMPENTEK OY—See Freudenberg SE; *Int'l*, pg. 2783
CONDUCTIX-WAMPFLER LTD.—See CVC Capital Partners SICAV-FIS S.A.; *Int'l*, pg. 1887
CONIMAST INTERNATIONAL SAS—See Hill & Smith PLC; *Int'l*, pg. 3391
CONSTRUCTION MATERIALS INC.; *U.S. Private*, pg. 1024
CONSTRUCTIONS METALLIQUES D'OBERNAI; *Int'l*, pg. 1778
CONTRACT STEEL SALES INC.; *U.S. Private*, pg. 1032
CONXTECH, INC.; *U.S. Private*, pg. 1037
COSMOS TECHNOLOGY INTERNATIONAL BERHAD; *Int'l*, pg. 1814
CPI PRODUCTS, INC.—See Stabilus; *U.S. Private*, pg. 3774
CPS CONVERTIBLE POWER SYSTEMS GMBH—See Enerpac Tool Group Corp.; *U.S. Public*, pg. 765
CROSNO CONSTRUCTION, INC.; *U.S. Private*, pg. 1104
CSSC SCIENCE AND TECHNOLOGY CO., LTD—See China State Shipbuilding Corporation; *Int'l*, pg. 1554
CST MANUFACTURING FACILITY CONROE (CST COVERS)—See Solace Capital Partners, LLC; *U.S. Private*, pg. 3706
DAIDO DMS MALAYSIA SDN. BHD.—See Daido Steel Co., Ltd.; *Int'l*, pg. 1922
DAIDO STAR TEKUNO CO., LTD.—See Daido Steel Co., Ltd.; *Int'l*, pg. 1923
DAINICHI CO., LTD.; *Int'l*, pg. 1938
DAISUN CO., LTD.—See Hanwa Co., Ltd.; *Int'l*, pg. 3262
DALCO INDUSTRIES INC.; *U.S. Private*, pg. 1148
DANSER, INC.; *U.S. Private*, pg. 1157
DAVE STEEL COMPANY INC.; *U.S. Private*, pg. 1168
DEFIANCE METAL PRODUCTS CO. INC. - CHINA PLANT—See Mayville Engineering Company, Inc.; *U.S. Public*, pg. 1403
DEFIANCE METAL PRODUCTS CO. INC. - DEFIANCE NORTH PLANT—See Mayville Engineering Company, Inc.; *U.S. Public*, pg. 1403
DEFIANCE METAL PRODUCTS CO. INC. - OSHKOSH PLANT—See Mayville Engineering Company, Inc.; *U.S. Public*, pg. 1403
DEKALB STEEL & COWART IRON; *U.S. Private*, pg. 1192
DEMEDCO INC.—See DeRoyal Industries Inc.; *U.S. Private*, pg. 1210
DENKI KOGYO CO., LTD. - KAWAGOE PLANT—See DKK Co., Ltd.; *Int'l*, pg. 2139
DENKO CO., LTD.—See DKK Co., Ltd.; *Int'l*, pg. 2139
DILLINGER INTERNATIONAL S.A.—See AG der Dillinger Huttenwerke; *Int'l*, pg. 197
DILLINGER ITALIA S.R.L.—See AG der Dillinger Huttenwerke; *Int'l*, pg. 197
DIMOND FABRICATORS—See MDU Resources Group, Inc.; *U.S. Public*, pg. 1409
DIS-TRAN STEEL FABRICATION, LLC—See Crest Industries, LLC; *U.S. Private*, pg. 1096
DIVISION 5 LLC—See Rodgers Metal Craft, Inc.; *U.S. Private*, pg. 3470
DIXIE MACHINE & FABRICATING CO.—See Dallas Industries, Inc.; *U.S. Private*, pg. 1149
DMW CORPORATION; *Int'l*, pg. 2146
DRAKE-WILLIAMS STEEL INC.; *U.S. Private*, pg. 1272
DUKSHINEPC CO., LTD.; *Int'l*, pg. 2224
DUNNAGE ENGINEERING INC.; *U.S. Private*, pg. 1290
DURA-BOND INDUSTRIES INC.; *U.S. Private*, pg. 1292
EAGLE FAB; *U.S. Private*, pg. 1309

EASI-EDGE LIMITED—See Billington Holdings Plc; *Int'l*, pg. 1031
ELECTRO OPTICAL SYSTEMS NORDIC AB—See EOS GmbH Electro Optical Systems; *Int'l*, pg. 2458
ELITE STORAGE SOLUTIONS—See Nucor Corporation; *U.S. Public*, pg. 1553
ELIXIR DOOR COMPANY - DIVISION 81—See Elixir Industries; *U.S. Private*, pg. 1362
ELIXIR INDUSTRIES—See Elixir Industries; *U.S. Private*, pg. 1362
ELIXIR INDUSTRIES—See Elixir Industries; *U.S. Private*, pg. 1362
ELIXIR INDUSTRIES, WACO DIV—See Elixir Industries; *U.S. Private*, pg. 1362
ELLIS STEEL COMPANY INC.; *U.S. Private*, pg. 1374
EMIL VON DUNGEN INC.; *U.S. Private*, pg. 1382
EMPIRE DYNAMIC STRUCTURES LTD.—See Dynamic Technologies Group Inc.; *Int'l*, pg. 2241
EMPIRE IRON WORKS LTD.—See Dynamic Technologies Group Inc.; *Int'l*, pg. 2241
ENDRES MANUFACTURING CO, INC.; *U.S. Private*, pg. 1392
ENERGOINVEST TVORNICA DALEKOVODNIH STUBOVA D.D.; *Int'l*, pg. 2421
ENERGOMONTAJ S.A. - FEE—See Energomontaj S.A.; *Int'l*, pg. 2421
ENGINETICS AEROSPACE CORPORATION—See Standex International; *U.S. Public*, pg. 1930
EOS ELECTRO OPTICAL SYSTEMS LTD.—See EOS GmbH Electro Optical Systems; *Int'l*, pg. 2458
EOS OF NORTH AMERICA, INC.—See EOS GmbH Electro Optical Systems; *Int'l*, pg. 2458
EOS SINGAPORE PTE LTD—See EOS GmbH Electro Optical Systems; *Int'l*, pg. 2458
EOS S.R.L. ELECTRO OPTICAL SYSTEMS—See EOS GmbH Electro Optical Systems; *Int'l*, pg. 2458
EPI/CLEVELAND—See Engineered Products, Inc.; *U.S. Private*, pg. 1398
ERAM EILIA, INC.—See Atlantic China Welding Consumables, Inc.; *Int'l*, pg. 674
ESAB CORPORATION; *U.S. Public*, pg. 793
EUROPICKLING NV—See Commercial Metals Company; *U.S. Public*, pg. 546
EXACTECH, INC.—See Marine Travelift, Inc.; *U.S. Private*, pg. 2575
EXCELSIOR METALS, INC.—See Ryerson Holding Corporation; *U.S. Public*, pg. 1829
EXTREME STEEL, INC; *U.S. Private*, pg. 1452
FABCON KYUSHU CORPORATION—See Hanwa Co., Ltd.; *Int'l*, pg. 3262
FABRICATED STEEL PRODUCTS, INC.; *U.S. Private*, pg. 1458
FABRICATING SPECIALISTS, LLC—See Mayville Engineering Company, Inc.; *U.S. Public*, pg. 1403
FABRI-TECH INC.—See Hader Industries Inc.; *U.S. Private*, pg. 1839
FALCON STEEL CO.; *U.S. Private*, pg. 1466
FAM GRUPA KAPITALOWA S.A.; *Int'l*, pg. 2611
FERLAT ACCIAI S.P.A.—See Acciaierie Valbruna S.p.A.; *Int'l*, pg. 89
FINCANTIERI INFRASTRUCTURE S.P.A.—See Fincantieri S.p.A.; *Int'l*, pg. 2671
FINCANTIERI INFRASTRUCTURE S.P.A—See Fincantieri S.p.A.; *Int'l*, pg. 2671
FIRST FORTUNE INTERNATIONAL COMPANY LIMITED; *Int'l*, pg. 2683
FISHER & LUDLOW—See Nucor Corporation; *U.S. Public*, pg. 1553
FISHER & LUDLOW—See Nucor Corporation; *U.S. Public*, pg. 1553
FISHER & LUDLOW—See Nucor Corporation; *U.S. Public*, pg. 1553
FLACK STEEL LLC; *U.S. Private*, pg. 1538
FORD STEEL CHILE INDUSTRIAL SA—See North Shore Supply Company Inc.; *U.S. Private*, pg. 2947
FRANK H DALE LTD.; *Int'l*, pg. 2761
FUJIM DIGITAL SDN. BHD.—See ARTRONIQ BERHAD; *Int'l*, pg. 585
GANTRY RAILING LIMITED; *Int'l*, pg. 2882
GAYLE MANUFACTURING CO. INC.; *U.S. Private*, pg. 1652
GENZINK STEEL SUPPLY & WELDING CO.; *U.S. Private*, pg. 1680
GIESSE GROUP HELLAS S.A.—See Quanex Building Products Corp.; *U.S. Public*, pg. 1749
GIESSE S.P.A.—See Quanex Building Products Corp.; *U.S. Public*, pg. 1749
GLADWIN MACHINERY & SUPPLY CO; *U.S. Private*, pg. 1705
GOSA MONTAZA A.D.; *Int'l*, pg. 3043
GREGOR TECHNOLOGIES LLC—See Reliance Steel & Aluminum Co.; *U.S. Public*, pg. 1780
GREINER INDUSTRIES, INC.—See IES Holdings, Inc.; *U.S. Public*, pg. 1094
GRUPO OXYCHEM DE MEXICO, S.A. DE C.V.—See Occidental Petroleum Corporation; *U.S. Public*, pg. 1561
G-TECH METAL PTE. LTD.—See GT Steel Construction Group Limited; *Int'l*, pg. 3151

CORPORATE AFFILIATIONS

GT STEEL CONSTRUCTION GROUP LIMITED - SINGAPORE FACTORY—See GT Steel Construction Group Limited; *Int'l*, pg. 3151
GT STEEL CONSTRUCTION GROUP LIMITED; *Int'l*, pg. 3151
GURIT (CANADA) INC—See Gurit Holding AG; *Int'l*, pg. 3187
HANSTEEL COMPANY LTD.—See HBIS Group Co., Ltd.; *Int'l*, pg. 3296
HARRIS REBAR - ATLANTIC—See Nucor Corporation; *U.S. Public*, pg. 1553
HARRIS REBAR—See Nucor Corporation; *U.S. Public*, pg. 1553
HARRIS STEEL ULC—See Nucor Corporation; *U.S. Public*, pg. 1553
HARRIS STEEL ULC—See Nucor Corporation; *U.S. Public*, pg. 1553
HARSCO ASEAN—See Enviri Corporation; *U.S. Public*, pg. 780
HARSCO METALS FRANCE S.A.S.—See Enviri Corporation; *U.S. Public*, pg. 780
HARSCO METALS INDIA—See Enviri Corporation; *U.S. Public*, pg. 781
HARSCO METALS LUXEMBOURG S.A.—See Enviri Corporation; *U.S. Public*, pg. 780
HARSCO RAIL PTY. LTD.—See Enviri Corporation; *U.S. Public*, pg. 781
HBIS GROUP WUYANG IRON & STEEL COMPANY—See HBIS Group Co., Ltd.; *Int'l*, pg. 3296
HEARTLAND ENGINEERED PRODUCTS, LLC; *U.S. Private*, pg. 1900
HELMARK STEEL, INC.; *U.S. Private*, pg. 1911
THE HERRICK CORPORATION; *U.S. Private*, pg. 4052
HH ROBERTSON FLOOR SYSTEMS—See Clayton, Dubilier & Rice, LLC; *U.S. Private*, pg. 920
HIGH INDUSTRIES, INC.; *U.S. Private*, pg. 1935
HILL & SMITH LTD—See Hill & Smith PLC; *Int'l*, pg. 3391
HIROUCHI ATSUEN KOGYO CO., LTD.—See Hanwa Co., Ltd.; *Int'l*, pg. 3263
HIRSCHFELD INDUSTRIES, INC.—See Berkshire Hathaway Inc.; *U.S. Public*, pg. 298
H & M METALS, LLC—See OEP Capital Advisors, L.P.; *U.S. Private*, pg. 2999
HOKURIKU COLUMN CO., LTD.—See Hanwa Co., Ltd.; *Int'l*, pg. 3263
HORIZAL; *Int'l*, pg. 3478
HUTTER & SCHRANTZ AG—See Hutter & Schrantz PMS Ges.m.b.H; *Int'l*, pg. 3540
ICSN INC.; *U.S. Private*, pg. 2033
IHI MASTER METAL CO., LTD.—See IHI Corporation; *Int'l*, pg. 3605
ILSERV S.R.L.—See Enviri Corporation; *U.S. Public*, pg. 781
INDIANA STEEL FABRICATING INC.; *U.S. Private*, pg. 2063
INDUSTRIAL FABRICATORS, INC.; *U.S. Private*, pg. 2066
INOVATECH ENGINEERING CORPORATION—See Lincoln Electric Holdings, Inc.; *U.S. Public*, pg. 1317
INSTRUMENT CASES LLC—See Reliance Steel & Aluminum Co.; *U.S. Public*, pg. 1780
INTERLAKE MECALUX, INC.—See Acerolux SL; *Int'l*, pg. 101
IRONRIDGE INC.—See Esdec BV; *Int'l*, pg. 2502
JATEC GMBH—See Quanex Building Products Corp.; *U.S. Public*, pg. 1749
JCI METAL PRODUCTS, INC.—See J.F. Lehman & Company, Inc.; *U.S. Private*, pg. 2164
J.C. MACELROY CO. INC.; *U.S. Private*, pg. 2160
JESSE ENGINEERING COMPANY; *U.S. Private*, pg. 2203
JOHNSON MACHINE WORKS INC.; *U.S. Private*, pg. 2228
JOHNSTOWN WELDING & FABRICATION; *U.S. Private*, pg. 2230
KANEKI CO., LTD.—See Hanwa Co., Ltd.; *Int'l*, pg. 3263
KAWNEER COMPANY, INC. - SPRINGDALE—See Howmet Aerospace Inc.; *U.S. Public*, pg. 1062
KELAIR PRODUCTS INC.—See Matot Inc.; *U.S. Private*, pg. 2611
KELLER MANUFACTURING COMPANY, INC.; *U.S. Public*, pg. 1218
KEMCO INDUSTRIES INC.; *U.S. Private*, pg. 2281
KEWAUNEE FABRICATIONS, LLC—See Oshkosh Corporation; *U.S. Public*, pg. 1620
KING STEEL, INC.; *U.S. Private*, pg. 2310
K&K IRON WORKS INC.; *U.S. Private*, pg. 2249
KNIGHTS' MARINE & INDUSTRIAL SERVICES, INC.; *U.S. Private*, pg. 2322
L.B. FOSTER CO. - BEDFORD—See L.B. Foster Company; *U.S. Public*, pg. 1278
LEJEUNE STEEL COMPANY—See APi Group Corporation; *Int'l*, pg. 514
LEWIS INDUSTRIAL SERVICES, INC.; *U.S. Private*, pg. 2439
LILJENDALS BRUK AB—See Illinois Tool Works Inc.; *U.S. Public*, pg. 1109
LINCOLN CONTRACTING & EQUIPMENT CO. INC—See Riggs Industries, Inc.; *U.S. Private*, pg. 3435
LIPHART STEEL COMPANY INC.; *U.S. Private*, pg. 2464
LLOYDS ENGINEERING CO. L.L.C—See Gulf General Investment Company PSC; *Int'l*, pg. 3180

N.A.I.C.S. INDEX

332312 — FABRICATED STRUCTUR...

LONESTAR MARINE SHELTERS; *U.S. Private*, pg. 2489
LYNCHBURG STEEL & SPECIALTY CO.—See Beta International & Affiliates; *U.S. Private*, pg. 544
LYNDON STEEL COMPANY LLC; *U.S. Private*, pg. 2521
MADISON INDUSTRIES INC. OF ARIZONA—See John S. Frey Enterprises; *U.S. Private*, pg. 2224
MAGNI-FAB SOUTHWEST CO. INC.—See Magni-Power Company Inc.; *U.S. Private*, pg. 2548
MAGNI-POWER COMPANY INC.; *U.S. Private*, pg. 2548
MALDANER GMBH—See Quaker Chemical Corporation; *U.S. Public*, pg. 1746
MARKS METAL TECHNOLOGY INC.—See Environmental Containment Corporation; *U.S. Private*, pg. 1407
MARK WORLDWIDE COMPANY LIMITED—See City Steel Public Company Limited; *Int'l*, pg. 1628
MARSHALL STEEL, INC.—See Steel Dynamics, Inc.; *U.S. Public*, pg. 1942
MASON CORPORATION; *U.S. Private*, pg. 2602
MASON STRUCTURAL STEEL, INC.; *U.S. Private*, pg. 2602
MATHIS-KELLEY CONSTRUCTION SUPPLY CO.; *U.S. Private*, pg. 2611
MATRIX SERVICE COMPANY - FABRICATION DIVISION—See Matrix Service Company; *U.S. Public*, pg. 1397
MAYA STEELS FABRICATION, INC.; *U.S. Private*, pg. 2620
MCCUNE TECHNOLOGY; *U.S. Private*, pg. 2631
MCFARLANE MANUFACTURING COMPANY INC.; *U.S. Private*, pg. 2633
MECALUX ARGENTINA, S.A.—See Acerolux SL; *Int'l*, pg. 101
MECALUX DO BRASIL SISTEMAS DE ARMAZENAGEM LTDA.—See Acerolux SL; *Int'l*, pg. 102
MECALUX ESMENA—See Acerolux SL; *Int'l*, pg. 101
MEGA MANUFACTURING INC. - WHITNEY DIVISION—See Mega Manufacturing Inc.; *U.S. Private*, pg. 2660
METALTEK INTERNATIONAL - METALTEK - EUROPE DIVISION—See MetalTek International; *U.S. Private*, pg. 2682
METROPOLITAN STEEL INDUSTRIES INC.; *U.S. Private*, pg. 2689
METWOOD, INC.; *U.S. Public*, pg. 1433
MICHELMAN-CANCELLIERE IRON WORKS, INC.; *U.S. Private*, pg. 2699
MID AMERICA STEEL, INC.; *U.S. Private*, pg. 2705
MIDLAND STEEL COMPANY; *U.S. Private*, pg. 2715
MID-SOUTH STEEL INC.; *U.S. Private*, pg. 2709
M&I ELECTRIC FAR EAST PTE LTD—See STABILIS SOLUTIONS, INC.; *U.S. Public*, pg. 1924
MMI PRODUCTS, INC.—See CRH plc; *Int'l*, pg. 1845
MMW FABRICATION, LTD.; *U.S. Private*, pg. 2755
MODERN GROUP, LTD.; *U.S. Private*, pg. 2761
MODERN WELDING COMPANY OF CALIFORNIA, INC.—See Modern Welding Company, Inc.; *U.S. Private*, pg. 2762
MODERN WELDING COMPANY OF KENTUCKY, INC.—See Modern Welding Company, Inc.; *U.S. Private*, pg. 2762
MONLANGROUP—See Prab, Inc.; *U.S. Private*, pg. 3241
MORO CORP.; *U.S. Public*, pg. 1477
MORRISON TEXTILE MACHINERY CO. - MORRISON CONTRACT MANUFACTURING DIVISION—See Morrison Textile Machinery Co.; *U.S. Private*, pg. 2790
MOUND TECHNOLOGIES, INC.—See Heartland, Inc.; *U.S. Private*, pg. 1901
MOUNTAIN STATES STEEL, INC.—See INNOVATE Corp.; *U.S. Public*, pg. 1125
MRK INDUSTRIES, INC.—See Armstrong World Industries, Inc.; *U.S. Public*, pg. 194
MS HIYOSHI KOUZAI CO., LTD.—See Hanwa Co., Ltd.; *Int'l*, pg. 3263
MYREX INDUSTRIES; *U.S. Private*, pg. 2825
NEW MILLENNIUM BUILDING SYSTEMS—See Steel Dynamics, Inc.; *U.S. Public*, pg. 1942
NEW STANDARD CORPORATION - ROCKY MOUNT PLANT—See New Standard Corporation; *U.S. Private*, pg. 2906
NORTH ALABAMA FABRICATING CO.; *U.S. Private*, pg. 2939
NORTH STATE STEEL INC.; *U.S. Private*, pg. 2948
NORTH TEXAS STEEL COMPANY, INC.—See Laurus Capital Management, LLC; *U.S. Private*, pg. 2400
NOVEL IRON WORKS INC.; *U.S. Private*, pg. 2967
NUCOR STEEL LOUISIANA LLC—See Nucor Corporation; *U.S. Public*, pg. 1554
THE OHIO MOULDING CORPORATION; *U.S. Private*, pg. 4088
OLSON & CO. STEEL; *U.S. Private*, pg. 3011
OPTIMUS INDUSTRIES, LLC—See Babcock & Wilcox Enterprises, Inc.; *U.S. Public*, pg. 263
ORION CUSTOM METAL FABRICATION CORPORATION—See Lincoln Electric Holdings, Inc.; *U.S. Public*, pg. 1318
OVERLANDERS MANUFACTURING LP—See Exchange Income Corporation; *Int'l*, pg. 2579
OZARK STEEL, LLC.—See International Chemical Company; *U.S. Private*, pg. 2115
PACIFIC EMBEDDED PRODUCTS—See Clark Pacific; *U.S. Private*, pg. 913
PACIFIC STEEL (NZ) LIMITED—See BlueScope Steel Limited; *Int'l*, pg. 1074
PAGE STEEL, INC.; *U.S. Private*, pg. 3074
PAINTER BROTHERS LTD.—See Balfour Beatty plc; *Int'l*, pg. 808
PCM PROCESSING (THAILAND) LTD.—See Hanwa Co., Ltd.; *Int'l*, pg. 3263
PENNSYLVANIA STEEL COMPANY - ALLENTOWN DIVISION—See Pennsylvania Steel Company, Inc; *U.S. Private*, pg. 3137
PENNSYLVANIA STEEL COMPANY - CONNECTICUT DIVISION—See Pennsylvania Steel Company, Inc; *U.S. Private*, pg. 3137
PENNSYLVANIA STEEL COMPANY - LONG ISLAND DIVISION—See Pennsylvania Steel Company, Inc; *U.S. Private*, pg. 3137
PENNSYLVANIA STEEL COMPANY - RICHMOND DIVISION—See Pennsylvania Steel Company, Inc; *U.S. Private*, pg. 3137
PIEDMONT METAL PRODUCTS, INC.—See Williams Industries, Inc.; *U.S. Private*, pg. 4526
PILLAR ENTERPRISE LTD.—See The Berlin Steel Construction Company; *U.S. Private*, pg. 3994
PIPE WELDERS INC.; *U.S. Private*, pg. 3189
POLYMETALLURGICAL LLC—See NN, Inc.; *U.S. Public*, pg. 1531
PORTER CORP.—See Court Square Capital Partners, L.P.; *U.S. Private*, pg. 1070
PRECISION ENGINEERED PRODUCTS LLC - MICROPEP—See NN, Inc.; *U.S. Public*, pg. 1531
PROTOTEK HOLDINGS LLC—See TruArc Partners, L.P.; *U.S. Private*, pg. 4245
QSR STEEL CORPORATION, LLC; *U.S. Private*, pg. 3314
QUALICO STEEL COMPANY INC.; *U.S. Private*, pg. 3317
QUALITY MANUFACTURING CORP.; *U.S. Private*, pg. 3319
QUALITY STEEL FABRICATION; *U.S. Private*, pg. 3321
QUESTRON TECHNOLOGIES CORP.—See HORIBA Ltd; *Int'l*, pg. 3478
RANOR, INC.—See TechPrecision Corporation; *U.S. Public*, pg. 1988
RAULLI & SONS INC.; *U.S. Private*, pg. 3357
REGIUTTI S.P.A.—See Quanex Building Products Corp.; *U.S. Public*, pg. 1749
RE STEEL SUPPLY COMPANY INC.; *U.S. Private*, pg. 3364
RICHLAND TOWERS INC.—See Richland Properties Inc.; *U.S. Private*, pg. 3430
RICHLAND TOWERS MANAGEMENT, LLC—See American Tower Corporation; *U.S. Public*, pg. 111
RK SPECIALTIES, INC.—See RK Mechanical, Inc.; *U.S. Private*, pg. 3450
ROCKINGHAM STEEL; *U.S. Private*, pg. 3467
ROCKINGHAM STEEL—See Rockingham Steel; *U.S. Private*, pg. 3467
RODGERS METAL CRAFT, INC.; *U.S. Private*, pg. 3470
RODNEY HUNT COMPANY—See Zurn Elkay Water Solutions Corporation; *U.S. Public*, pg. 2414
RONANE INTERNATIONAL PTY LTD—See Grove International Pty Limited; *Int'l*, pg. 3112
SABRE TOWERS AND POLES—See The Jordan Company, L.P.; *U.S. Private*, pg. 4061
SABRE TUBULAR STRUCTURES - ELLWOOD CITY FACILITY—See The Jordan Company, L.P.; *U.S. Private*, pg. 4061
SABRE TUBULAR STRUCTURES - SIOUX CITY FACILITY—See The Jordan Company, L.P.; *U.S. Private*, pg. 4062
SABRE TUBULAR STRUCTURES—See The Jordan Company, L.P.; *U.S. Private*, pg. 4061
SANYO KOUZAI CO., LTD.—See Hanwa Co., Ltd.; *Int'l*, pg. 3263
SARGENT METAL FABRICATING—See Todd & Sargent, Inc.; *U.S. Private*, pg. 4181
SCHMIDT STRUCTURAL PRODUCTS, INC.—See Summa Holdings, Inc.; *U.S. Private*, pg. 3853
SCHMUESER & ASSOCIATES INC.—See Schmueser & Associates Inc.; *U.S. Private*, pg. 3566
SCHUFF STEEL-ATLANTIC, LLC—See INNOVATE Corp.; *U.S. Public*, pg. 1126
SEA SAFE, INC.—See Gibraltar Industries, Inc.; *U.S. Public*, pg. 936
SEISMIC ENERGY PRODUCTS LP; *U.S. Private*, pg. 3599
SHANGHAI CIMC REEFER CONTAINERS CO., LTD.—See China International Marine Containers (Group) Co., Ltd.; *Int'l*, pg. 1512
SHAW SSS FABRICATORS, INC.—See The Shaw Group Inc.; *U.S. Private*, pg. 4117
SHEPARD STEEL CO. INC.; *U.S. Private*, pg. 3632
SIA SBC—See Heidelberg Materials AG; *Int'l*, pg. 3319
SIGNAL METAL INDUSTRIES INC.; *U.S. Private*, pg. 3649
SIMPSON STRONG-TIE CO., INC.—See Simpson Manufacturing Company, Inc.; *U.S. Public*, pg. 1883
S.I.P. INC. OF DELAWARE—See Williams Industries, Inc.; *U.S. Private*, pg. 4526
SKYLINE STEEL, INC.—See Endres Manufacturing Co, Inc.; *U.S. Private*, pg. 1392
SKYLINE STEEL, LLC—See Nucor Corporation; *U.S. Public*, pg. 1554
SMCI INC.—See MetalTek International; *U.S. Private*, pg. 2682
SME INDUSTRIES INC.; *U.S. Private*, pg. 3693
SMF INC.; *U.S. Private*, pg. 3693
SMITH IRONWORKS INC.; *U.S. Private*, pg. 3695
SMITH METAL PRODUCTS INC—See Plastic Products Company, Inc.; *U.S. Private*, pg. 3199
SOUTH CAROLINA STEEL—See Commercial Metals Company; *U.S. Public*, pg. 546
SOUTHEAST TEXAS INDUSTRIES; *U.S. Private*, pg. 3726
SOUTHERN POST SOUTH CAROLINA—See Commercial Metals Company; *U.S. Public*, pg. 546
SOUTHERN STEEL COMPANY LLC—See Beta International & Affiliates; *U.S. Private*, pg. 545
SOUTHWEST STAIR INC—See SME Industries Inc.; *U.S. Private*, pg. 3693
SOUTHWEST STEEL FABRICATORS, INC.; *U.S. Private*, pg. 3741
SPECIAL APPLICATIONS TECHNOLOGY INC.—See Hammond, Kennedy, Whitney & Company, Inc.; *U.S. Private*, pg. 1850
SPEEDY INDUSTRIAL SUPPLIES PTE. LTD.—See BizLink Holding Inc.; *Int'l*, pg. 1053
SPIRIT FABS INC.—See VHC Inc.; *U.S. Private*, pg. 4375
SPX INTERNATIONAL LIMITED—See Lone Star Funds; *U.S. Private*, pg. 2487
SSM INDUSTRIES INC.; *U.S. Private*, pg. 3769
STAINLESS PIPE KOGYO CO., LTD.—See Hanwa Co., Ltd.; *Int'l*, pg. 3263
STAR FABRICATORS—See The Stellar Group Inc.; *U.S. Private*, pg. 4121
STATIONONE S.A.S.—See Alstom S.A.; *Int'l*, pg. 383
STEELCOM FITTINGS S.R.L.—See Acciaierie Valbruna S.p.A.; *Int'l*, pg. 89
STEELE SOLUTIONS, INC.—See Wellspring Capital Management LLC; *U.S. Private*, pg. 4477
STEELFAB INC. OF SOUTH CAROLINA—See Steelfab Inc.; *U.S. Private*, pg. 3797
STEELFAB INC. OF VIRGINIA—See Steelfab Inc.; *U.S. Private*, pg. 3797
STEELFAB INC.; *U.S. Private*, pg. 3796
STEELFAB TEXAS, INC.; *U.S. Private*, pg. 3797
STEEL KING INDUSTRIES INC.; *U.S. Private*, pg. 3796
STEEL, LLC; *U.S. Private*, pg. 3796
STEEL PLUS LIMITED—See AIP, LLC; *U.S. Private*, pg. 134
STEEL SERVICE CORPORATION; *U.S. Private*, pg. 3796
S&T MANUFACTURING CO.; *U.S. Private*, pg. 3514
STOBA PRAZISIONSTECHNIK GMBH & CO. KG—See Berndorf AG; *Int'l*, pg. 987
STOBA PRAZISIONSTECHNIK UK LTD.—See Berndorf AG; *Int'l*, pg. 987
STRAMIT CORPORATION PTY LIMITED—See Fletcher Building Limited; *Int'l*, pg. 2701
STRUCTURAL COMPOSITES, INC.—See Patrick Industries, Inc.; *U.S. Public*, pg. 1653
STRUCTURAL STEEL HOLDING INC.; *U.S. Private*, pg. 3842
STRUCTURAL STEEL OF CAROLINA, LLC—See Rodgers Metal Craft, Inc.; *U.S. Private*, pg. 3470
STRUCTURAL & STEEL PRODUCTS, INC.—See Race Rock GP, L.L.C; *U.S. Private*, pg. 3341
STRUCTURAL STEEL SERVICES INC.—See Structural Steel Holding Inc.; *U.S. Private*, pg. 3842
STUPP BRIDGE COMPANY—See Stupp Bros., Inc.; *U.S. Private*, pg. 3844
SUBARU STEEL CO., LTD.—See Hanwa Co., Ltd.; *Int'l*, pg. 3263
SUMMIT UTILITY STRUCTURES, LLC—See Nucor Corporation; *U.S. Public*, pg. 1554
SUPERIOR FABRICATION, INC.; *U.S. Private*, pg. 3878
SUPERIOR IRON WORKS INC.; *U.S. Private*, pg. 3878
SUPERIOR STEEL INC.; *U.S. Private*, pg. 3880
TAG MANUFACTURING, INC.; *U.S. Private*, pg. 3922
T. BRUCE SALES, INC.; *U.S. Private*, pg. 3911
TECHNYX EURO SERVICES S.R.L.—See AIP, LLC; *U.S. Private*, pg. 134
TECHPRECISION CORPORATION; *U.S. Public*, pg. 1988
TEGREL LIMITED—See Hill & Smith PLC; *Int'l*, pg. 3392
TEKKEN INDUSTRY COMPANY—See Hanwa Co., Ltd.; *Int'l*, pg. 3263
THAI HERRICK CO., LTD.—See The Herrick Corporation; *U.S. Private*, pg. 4052
THAI HERRICK CO., LTD. - THAI HERRICK PRACHINBURI PLANT—See The Herrick Corporation; *U.S. Private*, pg. 4052
THAI HERRICK CO., LTD. - THAI HERRICK RAYONG PLANT—See The Herrick Corporation; *U.S. Private*, pg. 4052
TIE DOWN ENGINEERING, INC.; *U.S. Private*, pg. 4168
TOKAI STEEL CORPORATION—See Godo Steel, Ltd.; *Int'l*, pg. 3020
TOPPER INDUSTRIAL INC.; *U.S. Private*, pg. 4187
TOWER AUTOMOTIVE AUSLANDSBETEILIGUNGEN GMBH—See Financiere SNOP Dunois SA; *Int'l*, pg. 2669
TOWER AUTOMOTIVE BELGIUM B.V.B.A.—See Financiere SNOP Dunois SA; *Int'l*, pg. 2669

332312 — FABRICATED STRUCTUR...

TOWER AUTOMOTIVE DO BRASIL, LTDA.—See KPS Capital Partners, LP; *U.S. Private*, pg. 2347
TOWER AUTOMOTIVE (WUHU) CO. LTD—See KPS Capital Partners, LP; *U.S. Private*, pg. 2347
TOWER DEFENSE & AEROSPACE, LLC—See KPS Capital Partners, LP; *U.S. Private*, pg. 2347
TOWER ITALIA S.R.L.—See Financiere SNOP Dunois SA; *Int'l*, pg. 2669
TOWER (SHANGHAI) AUTOMOTIVE TECH SERVICE CO. LTD.—See KPS Capital Partners, LP; *U.S. Private*, pg. 2347
TRANSPORTATION & TRANSIT ASSOCIATES, LLC; *U.S. Private*, pg. 4211
TRIANGLE METALS INC.—See Thomas Engineering Inc.; *U.S. Private*, pg. 4155
TRINITY HIGHWAY PRODUCTS, LLC—See Trinity Industries, Inc.; *U.S. Public*, pg. 2194
TRINITY HIGHWAY RENTALS, INC.—See Trinity Industries, Inc.; *U.S. Public*, pg. 2194
TRINITY INDUSTRIES—See Trinity Industries, Inc.; *U.S. Public*, pg. 2194
TRINITY STEEL FABRICATORS, INC.—See The CapStreet Group LLC; *U.S. Private*, pg. 4005
TRUENORTH STEEL - BILLINGS—See TrueNorth Steel Inc.; *U.S. Private*, pg. 4249
TRUENORTH STEEL - MANDAN—See TrueNorth Steel Inc.; *U.S. Private*, pg. 4249
T & T MANUFACTURING, LLC—See C. G. Bretting Manufacturing Co., Inc.; *U.S. Private*, pg. 705
TURNER INDUSTRIES GROUP, L.L.C. - CORPUS CHRISTI FACILITY—See Turner Industries Group, L.L.C.; *U.S. Private*, pg. 4261
TURNER INDUSTRIES GROUP, L.L.C. - DECATUR FACILITY—See Turner Industries Group, L.L.C.; *U.S. Private*, pg. 4261
TURNER INDUSTRIES GROUP, L.L.C. - PORT ALLEN FACILITY—See Turner Industries Group, L.L.C.; *U.S. Private*, pg. 4261
UGIVIS S.A.S.—See Acciaierie Valbruna S.p.A.; *Int'l*, pg. 89
ULTRA ALUMINUM MANUFACTURING INC.—See UFP Industries, Inc.; *U.S. Public*, pg. 2219
UMI COMPANY, INC. - MINNEAPOLIS PLANT—See UMI Company, Inc.; *U.S. Private*, pg. 4278
UMI COMPANY, INC. - SPANTEK DIVISION—See UMI Company, Inc.; *U.S. Private*, pg. 4278
UNION METAL CORPORATION; *U.S. Private*, pg. 4284
UNITED ALLOY, INC.; *U.S. Private*, pg. 4287
UNITED STEEL INC.; *U.S. Private*, pg. 4300
UNIVERSAL INDUSTRIAL SALES, INC.; *U.S. Private*, pg. 4305
UNIVERSAL METAL HOSE—See Hyspan Precision Products, Inc.; *U.S. Private*, pg. 2020
U.S. BELLOWS, INC.—See Piping Technology & Products Inc.; *U.S. Private*, pg. 3190
USF FABRICATION, INC.—See Eagle Manufacturing Group; *U.S. Private*, pg. 1309
USF FABRICATION, INC. - UTAH FACILITY—See Eagle Manufacturing Group; *U.S. Private*, pg. 1309
UTILITY COATINGS & FABRICATION, LLC—See Victaulic Company; *U.S. Private*, pg. 4377
VALLEY JOIST, LLC—See Black Diamond Capital Holdings, LLC; *U.S. Private*, pg. 571
VALMONT—See Valmont Industries, Inc.; *U.S. Public*, pg. 2274
VARLEY AND GULLIVER LTD—See Hill & Smith PLC; *Int'l*, pg. 3392
VERITAS STEEL LLC - EAU CLAIRE PLANT—See Atlas Holdings, LLC; *U.S. Private*, pg. 378
VERITAS STEEL LLC—See Atlas Holdings, LLC; *U.S. Private*, pg. 378
VIGOR WORKS LLC—See Stellex Capital Management LP; *U.S. Private*, pg. 3801
VIGOR WORKS LLC—See The Carlyle Group Inc.; *U.S. Public*, pg. 2056
VISTA STEEL COMPANY, INC.; *U.S. Private*, pg. 4403
VOTORANTIM SIDERURGIA S.A.—See ArcelorMittal S.A.; *Int'l*, pg. 543
V&S SCHULER ENGINEERING INC.—See Hill & Smith PLC; *Int'l*, pg. 3392
V&S SCHULER TUBULAR PRODUCTS LLC—See Hill & Smith PLC; *Int'l*, pg. 3392
VULCRAFT-ALABAMA—See Nucor Corporation; *U.S. Public*, pg. 1555
VULCRAFT-INDIANA—See Nucor Corporation; *U.S. Public*, pg. 1555
VULCRAFT-NEBRASKA—See Nucor Corporation; *U.S. Public*, pg. 1555
VULCRAFT-SOUTH CAROLINA—See Nucor Corporation; *U.S. Public*, pg. 1555
VULCRAFT-TEXAS—See Nucor Corporation; *U.S. Public*, pg. 1555
VULCRAFT-UTAH—See Nucor Corporation; *U.S. Public*, pg. 1555
WABASH STEEL COMPANY, LLC; *U.S. Private*, pg. 4424
WALPAR LLC—See Rock Gate Partners LLC; *U.S. Private*, pg. 3464
WARREN FABRICATING CORPORATION - NILES—See Warren Fabricating Corporation; *U.S. Private*, pg. 4444

WARREN FABRICATING CORPORATION; *U.S. Private*, pg. 4444
WATSON BOWMAN ACME CORP.—See BASF SE; *Int'l*, pg. 876
WESTERN INDUSTRIES, INC.—See Western Industries, Inc.; *U.S. Private*, pg. 4494
WESTERN TECHNOLOGY SERVICES INTERNATIONAL, INC.; *U.S. Private*, pg. 4497
WEST VIRGINIA STEEL CORPORATION—See Raleigh Mine & Industrial Supply, Inc.; *U.S. Private*, pg. 3350
WILLIAMS BRIDGE CO.—See Williams Industries, Inc.; *U.S. Private*, pg. 4526
WILLIAMS STEEL COMPANY INC.; *U.S. Private*, pg. 4526
WILTON ARMETALE INC.—See Lifetime Brands, Inc.; *U.S. Public*, pg. 1313
WING CO., LTD.—See Hanwa Co., Ltd.; *Int'l*, pg. 3263
WISCONSIN INVESTCAST INC.—See MetalTek International; *U.S. Private*, pg. 2682
WISCONSIN STRUCTURAL STEEL COMPANY—See APi Group Corporation; *Int'l*, pg. 514
WORTHINGTON INDUSTRIES CONSUMER PRODUCTS, LLC—See Worthington Industries, Inc.; *U.S. Public*, pg. 2383
WOTCO, INC.—See Western Technology Services International, Inc.; *U.S. Private*, pg. 4497
W&W STEEL COMPANY INC.; *U.S. Private*, pg. 4417
ZALK JOSEPHS FABRICATORS, LLC—See The Heico Companies, L.L.C.; *U.S. Private*, pg. 4051
ZEGERS, INC.—See Vorteq Coil Finishers, LLC; *U.S. Private*, pg. 4413
ZELLWOOD INT'L CORP.—See BizLink Holding Inc.; *Int'l*, pg. 1053
ZVS ENCO A.S.—See Enco spol. s r.o.; *Int'l*, pg. 2401

332313 — PLATE WORK MANUFACTURING

ACCESS DESIGN & ENGINEERING LIMITED—See Hill & Smith PLC; *Int'l*, pg. 3391
AC INC.; *U.S. Private*, pg. 45
ADVANCE BOILER & TANK CO.; *U.S. Private*, pg. 83
ALFA LAVAL PACKINOX—See Alfa Laval AB; *Int'l*, pg. 310
ALLOY ENGINEERING COMPANY; *U.S. Private*, pg. 193
ALLOY PRODUCTS CORP.; *U.S. Private*, pg. 193
AMERICAN INVESTMENT LLC—See CenterOak Partners LLC; *U.S. Private*, pg. 816
AMERICAN TANK & FABRICATING COMPANY; *U.S. Private*, pg. 256
AMTROL INC.—See Worthington Industries, Inc.; *U.S. Public*, pg. 2382
ARNTZEN CORPORATION; *U.S. Private*, pg. 333
BERGEN PIPE SUPPORTS (INDIA) PRIVATE LIMITED—See Hill & Smith PLC; *Int'l*, pg. 3391
BERGMANN AUTOMOTIVE GMBH—See ECM Equity Capital Management GmbH; *Int'l*, pg. 2291
BOILER TUBE COMPANY OF AMERICA—See Babcock Power, Inc.; *U.S. Private*, pg. 422
CAPITAL WELDING INC.—See Futuramic Tool & Engineering Company Inc.; *U.S. Private*, pg. 1626
CARBON PLATE STEEL PRODUCTS, LLC—See Icahn Enterprises L.P.; *U.S. Public*, pg. 1084
CELLXION LIGHTWEIGHT DIVISION LLC—See The Jordan Company, L.P.; *U.S. Private*, pg. 4061
CEMBELL INDUSTRIES INC.; *U.S. Private*, pg. 808
CHART INDUSTRIES INC.- DISTRIBUTION & STORAGE - HOUSTON—See Chart Industries, Inc.; *U.S. Public*, pg. 481
CHAUDRONNERIE DE L'EST; *Int'l*, pg. 1457
CHUBU STEEL PLATE CO., LTD.; *Int'l*, pg. 1593
CHUN YUAN STEEL INDUSTRY CO., LTD. - KAOHSIUNG PLANT—See Chun Yuan Steel Industry Co., Ltd.; *Int'l*, pg. 1596
CITAT AB—See Bure Equity AB; *Int'l*, pg. 1221
CK CLEAN AD CO., LTD.—See Chubu Steel Plate Co., Ltd.; *Int'l*, pg. 1594
CONQUEST MANUFACTURING, LLC; *U.S. Private*, pg. 1018
CONSOLIDATED ALLOYS PTY LTD—See Amalgamated Metal Corporation PLC; *Int'l*, pg. 408
CP INDUSTRIES HOLDINGS, INC.—See Everest Kanto Cylinder Limited; *Int'l*, pg. 2564
CSW, INC.; *U.S. Private*, pg. 1118
CUST-O-FAB, INC.; *U.S. Private*, pg. 1127
DAIDO DMS MEXICO, S.A. DE C.V.—See Daido Steel Co., Ltd.; *Int'l*, pg. 1922
DAIDO DMS PHILS., INC.—See Daido Steel Co., Ltd.; *Int'l*, pg. 1922
DAIDO DMS SINGAPORE PTE. LTD.—See Daido Steel Co., Ltd.; *Int'l*, pg. 1922
DAIDO DMS VIETNAM CO., LTD.—See Daido Steel Co., Ltd.; *Int'l*, pg. 1922
DAIDO KOGYO INDIA PVT. LTD.—See Daido Steel Co., Ltd.; *Int'l*, pg. 1922
DAIDO STEEL GROUP EUROPE GMBH—See Daido Steel Co., Ltd.; *Int'l*, pg. 1922
DCI, INC.; *U.S. Private*, pg. 1180
DEBRO STEEL LTD.—See Amalgamated Metal Corporation PLC; *Int'l*, pg. 408

DEIST INDUSTRIES, INC.—See Federal Signal Corporation; *U.S. Public*, pg. 826
DIXIE POLY DRUM CORPORATION; *U.S. Private*, pg. 1245
DMS MOLDES MEXICO S.A. DE C.V.—See Daido Steel Co., Ltd.; *Int'l*, pg. 1922
EESTI ENERGIA TEHNOLOOGIATOOSTUS AS—See Eesti Energia AS; *Int'l*, pg. 2317
EFFOX, INC.—See CECO Environmental Corp.; *U.S. Public*, pg. 463
ELECTROL SPECIALTIES, INC.; *U.S. Private*, pg. 1354
THE ENTWISTLE CO.—See The Entwistle Co.; *U.S. Private*, pg. 4026
ERICH UTSCH AG; *Int'l*, pg. 2493
FORMWELD FITTINGS—See Canerector Inc.; *Int'l*, pg. 1290
FREEPORT WELDING & FABRICATION INC; *U.S. Private*, pg. 1607
FRONT RUNNER GMBH—See Dometic Group AB; *Int'l*, pg. 2160
FUJI OOZX MEXICO, S.A. DE C.V.—See Daido Steel Co., Ltd.; *Int'l*, pg. 1923
GENERAL WELDING WORKS INC.; *U.S. Private*, pg. 1668
GERETT PRODUCTS—See Western Industries, Inc.; *U.S. Private*, pg. 4494
GUYAN INTERNATIONAL INC.; *U.S. Private*, pg. 1820
HANNA CYLINDERS; *U.S. Private*, pg. 1854
HARSCO MINERALS PA LLC—See Enviri Corporation; *U.S. Public*, pg. 781
HEAT-FLO, INC.—See Bradford-White Corporation; *U.S. Private*, pg. 632
HELSER INDUSTRIES INC.; *U.S. Private*, pg. 1912
HIGHWAY HOLDINGS LIMITED; *Int'l*, pg. 3389
HOSTETLERS SALES & CONSTRUCTION LLC; *U.S. Private*, pg. 1988
INTERNATIONAL MEZZO TECHNOLOGIES, INC.—See Arcline Investment Management LP; *U.S. Private*, pg. 314
JOHN WOOD COMPANY, LLC—See Dunes Point Capital, LLC; *U.S. Private*, pg. 1288
JUSTRITE MANUFACTURING COMPANY, LLC—See The Riverside Company; *U.S. Private*, pg. 4109
KAISER ALUMINUM WARRICK, LLC—See Kaiser Aluminum Corporation; *U.S. Public*, pg. 1213
KANAWHA MANUFACTURING COMPANY; *U.S. Private*, pg. 2259
KATALOGER I NORR AB—See Eniro Group AB; *Int'l*, pg. 2439
KENNEDY TANK & MANUFACTURING COMPANY, INC.; *U.S. Private*, pg. 2285
KOCH-GLITSCH, LP—See Koch Industries, Inc.; *U.S. Private*, pg. 2331
KOUNRAD COPPER COMPANY LLP—See Central Asia Metals plc; *Int'l*, pg. 1404
LAN HANDLING TECHNOLOGIES BV - HALFWEG FACTORY—See Hydratec Industries NV; *Int'l*, pg. 3546
LAN HANDLING TECHNOLOGIES BV—See Hydratec Industries NV; *Int'l*, pg. 3546
MANCHESTER TANK & EQUIPMENT COMPANY—See McWane, Inc.; *U.S. Private*, pg. 2645
MARK STEEL CORPORATION; *U.S. Private*, pg. 2578
MCNICHOLS COMPANY; *U.S. Private*, pg. 2644
MECO EQUIPMENT ENGINEERS B.V—See BE Semiconductor Industries N.V.; *Int'l*, pg. 931
MERRILL TOOL & MACHINE INC.; *U.S. Private*, pg. 2676
MINNOTTE MANUFACTURING CORPORATION; *U.S. Private*, pg. 2744
MITTERNIGHT, INC.; *U.S. Private*, pg. 2752
MODERN WELDING COMPANY OF FLORIDA, INC.—See Modern Welding Company, Inc.; *U.S. Private*, pg. 2762
MODERN WELDING COMPANY OF GEORGIA, INC.—See Modern Welding Company, Inc.; *U.S. Private*, pg. 2762
MODERN WELDING COMPANY OF OHIO, INC.—See Modern Welding Company, Inc.; *U.S. Private*, pg. 2762
MODERN WELDING COMPANY OF TEXAS, INC.—See Modern Welding Company, Inc.; *U.S. Private*, pg. 2763
MONO-SYSTEMS, INC.; *U.S. Private*, pg. 2771
MP HUSKY CORPORATION—See Gower Corporation; *U.S. Private*, pg. 1747
NORLEN, INC.—See Ryerson Holding Corporation; *U.S. Public*, pg. 1829
NUZINC ENTERPRISES, LLC—See AZZ, Inc.; *U.S. Public*, pg. 259
OFFENHAUSER COMPANY; *U.S. Private*, pg. 3001
OMNIFAB LLC; *U.S. Private*, pg. 3017
PACIFIC STAINLESS PRODUCTS; *U.S. Private*, pg. 3070
PAUL MUELLER COMPANY; *U.S. Public*, pg. 1655
PERIDOT CORPORATION—See Genstar Capital, LLC; *U.S. Private*, pg. 1679
PIAZZO ROSA S.R.L.—See Standex International; *U.S. Public*, pg. 1930
PLANT MAINTENANCE SERVICE CORPORATION; *U.S. Private*, pg. 3197
PRECISION COMPONENTS CORPORATION; *U.S. Private*, pg. 3244
PREFABRICADOS DELTA, S.A.—See Fomento de Construcciones y Contratas, S.A.; *Int'l*, pg. 2723
PSF INDUSTRIES INC.; *U.S. Private*, pg. 3297
PT. FUJI OOZX INDONESIA—See Daido Steel Co., Ltd.; *Int'l*, pg. 1923

N.A.I.C.S. INDEX

332321 — METAL WINDOW AND DO...

RAINIER WELDING, INC.—See Ranch Creek Partners, LLC; *U.S. Private*, pg. 3352
RECO CONSTRUCTORS, INC.; *U.S. Private*, pg. 3371
REYNOLDS INDUSTRIAL CONTRACTORS, INC.—See Catamaran Solutions, LLC; *U.S. Private*, pg. 787
ROYAL ENGINEERING FABRICATION COMPANY LLC—See Al Ghurair Group; *Int'l*, pg. 277
RPI OF INDIANA INC.—See JMAC Inc.; *U.S. Private*, pg. 2214
RUDCO PRODUCTS INC.; *U.S. Private*, pg. 3500
SARY KAZNA LLP—See Central Asia Metals plc; *Int'l*, pg. 1404
SAS GLOBAL; *U.S. Private*, pg. 3551
SHELBURNE CORP.; *U.S. Private*, pg. 3630
SIVALLS, INC.; *U.S. Private*, pg. 3677
SMALL PARTS, INC.; *U.S. Private*, pg. 3690
SOUTHERN TANK & MANUFACTURING INC—See Kennedy Tank & Manufacturing Company, Inc.; *U.S. Private*, pg. 2285
SOUTH GATE ENGINEERING, LLC.; *U.S. Private*, pg. 3722
SPENCER FABRICATIONS, INC.; *U.S. Private*, pg. 3755
STAKU STANZ UND KUNSSTOFF TECHNIK GMBH—See Amphenol Corporation; *U.S. Public*, pg. 132
STEEL TANK & FABRICATING CORPORATION—See Kennedy Tank & Manufacturing Company, Inc.; *U.S. Private*, pg. 2285
SUPERIOR MACHINE COMPANY OF SOUTH CAROLINA, INC.—See Woodings Industrial Corporation; *U.S. Private*, pg. 4558
SUPER STEEL LLC; *U.S. Private*, pg. 3875
TAYLOR FORGE ENGINEERED SYSTEMS INC.; *U.S. Private*, pg. 3939
TITANIUM FABRICATION CORPORATION; *U.S. Private*, pg. 4177
TOBUL ACCUMULATOR INCORPORATED—See Freudenberg SE; *Int'l*, pg. 2790
TOMCO2 EQUIPMENT COMPANY; *U.S. Private*, pg. 4183
TRANSCO PRODUCTS INC. - TPI FABRICATION FACILITY—See Transco Products Inc.; *U.S. Private*, pg. 4207
TRINITY INDUSTRIES DE MEXICO—See Trinity Industries, Inc.; *U.S. Public*, pg. 2194
TRINITY INDUSTRIES, INC. - FORT WORTH—See Trinity Industries, Inc.; *U.S. Public*, pg. 2194
TRINITY INDUSTRIES—See Trinity Industries, Inc.; *U.S. Public*, pg. 2194
TRINITY INDUSTRIES—See Trinity Industries, Inc.; *U.S. Public*, pg. 2194
ULTRATECH INTERNATIONAL, INC.—See Veeco Instruments Inc.; *U.S. Public*, pg. 2276
UNITED CONVEYOR CORPORATION; *U.S. Private*, pg. 4290
VAPOR POWER INTERNATIONAL, LLC—See Thermon Group Holdings, Inc.; *U.S. Public*, pg. 2155
VIRGINIA AMERICAN INDUSTRIES, LLC—See CenterOak Partners LLC; *U.S. Private*, pg. 816
WENDLAND MANUFACTURING CORPORATION—See Burnham Holdings, Inc.; *U.S. Public*, pg. 412
WESTERN INDUSTRIES, INC.; *U.S. Private*, pg. 4494
X-CEL STEEL FABRICATING, INC.—See Hess Industries, Inc.; *U.S. Private*, pg. 1927
YOUNGBERG INDUSTRIES, INC.; *U.S. Private*, pg. 4593
YUAN LONG STAINLESS STEEL CORP.—See Asia Cement Corporation; *Int'l*, pg. 611

332321 — METAL WINDOW AND DOOR MANUFACTURING

AADG, INC.—See ASSA ABLOY AB; *Int'l*, pg. 636
AAP WINDOWS LTD; *Int'l*, pg. 36
ABSOLUTE WINDOW & SHUTTER, INC.; *U.S. Private*, pg. 44
ACCENT WINDOWS INC.; *U.S. Private*, pg. 50
ACME ARCHITECTURAL PRODUCTS INC.; *U.S. Private*, pg. 60
ACME STEEL DOOR CORP.—See Acme Architectural Products Inc.; *U.S. Private*, pg. 60
ADPOL SP. Z O.O.—See Agora S.A.; *Int'l*, pg. 212
ADVANCED WINDOW, INC.—See Exchange Income Corporation; *Int'l*, pg. 2579
AGI MANUFACTURING (PTY) LIMITED—See AG Industries Limited; *Int'l*, pg. 198
AGTA RECORD AG—See ASSA ABLOY AB; *Int'l*, pg. 638
AGTATEC AG—See ASSA ABLOY AB; *Int'l*, pg. 638
AHLADA ENGINEERS LIMITED; *Int'l*, pg. 223
AIR LOUVERS, INC.—See Activar, Inc.; *U.S. Private*, pg. 68
AJIYA BERHAD; *Int'l*, pg. 258
AJ MANUFACTURING INC.; *U.S. Private*, pg. 143
ALBANY DOOR SYSTEMS, INC.—See ASSA ABLOY AB; *Int'l*, pg. 634
ALENCO WINDOW HOLDING CORP.; *U.S. Private*, pg. 160
AL KUHAIMI METAL INDUSTRIES LTD.; *Int'l*, pg. 281
ALLAN WINDOW TECHNOLOGIES LTD.; *Int'l*, pg. 332
ALLMETAL, INC.; *U.S. Private*, pg. 192
ALUKON KG—See Hormann KG Verkaufsgesellschaf; *Int'l*, pg. 3480
ALUMAROLL SPECIALTY CO. INC.; *U.S. Private*, pg. 211

ALUMINUM ROOFING SPECIALISTS INC.; *U.S. Private*, pg. 211
ALUMINUM SCREEN MANUFACTURING CO.—See Kenner & Company, Inc.; *U.S. Private*, pg. 2285
ALUMINUM SCREEN MANUFACTURING CO.—See North Cove Partners; *U.S. Private*, pg. 2944
ALUPLAST GMBH; *Int'l*, pg. 401
ALUSCAND AB—See Foga System International AB; *Int'l*, pg. 2720
AMERIMAX HOME PRODUCTS—See Omnimax Holdings, Inc.; *U.S. Private*, pg. 3017
AMWELD BUILDING PRODUCTS INC.; *U.S. Private*, pg. 269
AO, INC.—See Kodiak Building Partners LLC; *U.S. Private*, pg. 2336
ASSA ABLOY ENTRANCE SYSTEMS AUSTRALIA PTY LTD—See ASSA ABLOY AB; *Int'l*, pg. 634
ASSA ABLOY ENTRANCE SYSTEMS AUSTRIA GMBH—See ASSA ABLOY AB; *Int'l*, pg. 635
ASSA ABLOY ENTRANCE SYSTEMS FINLAND OY—See ASSA ABLOY AB; *Int'l*, pg. 633
ASSA ABLOY ENTRANCE SYSTEMS IDDS AB—See ASSA ABLOY AB; *Int'l*, pg. 635
ASSA ABLOY ENTRANCE SYSTEMS KFT.—See ASSA ABLOY AB; *Int'l*, pg. 633
ASSA ABLOY ENTRANCE SYSTEMS (PORTO)—See ASSA ABLOY AB; *Int'l*, pg. 634
ASSA ABLOY ENTRANCE SYSTEMS SWEDEN AB—See ASSA ABLOY AB; *Int'l*, pg. 633
ASSA ABLOY INDUSTRIETORE GMBH—See ASSA ABLOY AB; *Int'l*, pg. 635
ASSA ABLOY MERCOR DOORS SP. Z O.O.—See ASSA ABLOY AB; *Int'l*, pg. 633
ATIS GROUP INC.—See Fonciere Volta SA; *Int'l*, pg. 2725
ATIS GROUP INC.—See Fonds de Solidarite des Travailleurs du Quebec; *Int'l*, pg. 2725
ATI WINDOWS; *U.S. Private*, pg. 369
ATRIUM COMPANIES, INC.—See Kenner & Company, Inc.; *U.S. Private*, pg. 2285
ATRIUM COMPANIES, INC.—See North Cove Partners; *U.S. Private*, pg. 2944
ATRIUM DOOR & WINDOW CO.—See Kenner & Company, Inc.; *U.S. Private*, pg. 2285
ATRIUM DOOR & WINDOW CO.—See North Cove Partners; *U.S. Private*, pg. 2944
ATRYA SAS; *Int'l*, pg. 694
AWP LLC; *U.S. Private*, pg. 411
BAKER METAL PRODUCTS INC.; *U.S. Private*, pg. 456
BARON METAL INDUSTRIES INC.—See ASSA ABLOY AB; *Int'l*, pg. 639
BEKON-KORALLE AG—See Arbonia AG; *Int'l*, pg. 538
BEM SP. Z O.O.—See ASSA ABLOY AB; *Int'l*, pg. 633
BENBILT BUILDING SYSTEMS LP—See Woodgrain, Inc.; *U.S. Private*, pg. 4558
BERNER TORANTRIEBE KG—See Hormann KG Verkaufsgesellschaf; *Int'l*, pg. 3480
BESAM BELGIE N.V.—See ASSA ABLOY AB; *Int'l*, pg. 634
BESAM GMBH—See ASSA ABLOY AB; *Int'l*, pg. 634
BESAM IBERICA SA—See ASSA ABLOY AB; *Int'l*, pg. 634
BESAM LIMITED—See ASSA ABLOY AB; *Int'l*, pg. 634
BESAM (MANUFACTURING) PTE. LTD.—See ASSA ABLOY AB; *Int'l*, pg. 634
BESAM MASCHINENHANDELS GMBH—See ASSA ABLOY AB; *Int'l*, pg. 634
BESAM NEDERLAND BV—See ASSA ABLOY AB; *Int'l*, pg. 634
BESAM OY—See ASSA ABLOY AB; *Int'l*, pg. 634
BESAM POLSKA SP. Z O.O.—See ASSA ABLOY AB; *Int'l*, pg. 634
BESAM SA—See ASSA ABLOY AB; *Int'l*, pg. 634
BESAM S.P.A.—See ASSA ABLOY AB; *Int'l*, pg. 634
BESAM SPOL.S.R.O.—See ASSA ABLOY AB; *Int'l*, pg. 634
BESAM US INC.—See ASSA ABLOY AB; *Int'l*, pg. 634
BIK BOUWPRODUKTEN B.V.—See H2 Equity Partners B.V.; *Int'l*, pg. 3199
THE BILCO COMPANY—See Quanex Building Products Corp.; *U.S. Public*, pg. 1750
BLASI GMBH—See ASSA ABLOY AB; *Int'l*, pg. 638
BONELLI ENTERPRISES—See Pella Corporation; *U.S. Private*, pg. 3131
BOON EDAM B.V.; *Int'l*, pg. 1111
BOON EDAM THOMPSON INC—See Boon Edam B.V.; *Int'l*, pg. 1111
BUDVAR CENTRUM SA; *Int'l*, pg. 1211
BUNKA PANEL KOGYO CO., LTD.—See Bunka Shutter Co., Ltd.; *Int'l*, pg. 1216
BUNKA SHUTTER CO., LTD.; *Int'l*, pg. 1216
BX BUNKA VIETNAM CO., LTD.—See Bunka Shutter Co., Ltd.; *Int'l*, pg. 1216
CARDO AB—See ASSA ABLOY AB; *Int'l*, pg. 634
CARMEL STEEL PRODUCTS INC—See Engineered Glass Walls; *U.S. Private*, pg. 1398
CECO DOOR PRODUCTS—See ASSA ABLOY AB; *Int'l*, pg. 636
CENTENNIAL WINDOWS & DOORS; *Int'l*, pg. 1402
CGF INDUSTRIES, INC.; *U.S. Private*, pg. 844
CGI COMMERCIAL, INC.—See Koch Industries, Inc.; *U.S. Private*, pg. 2333

CGI WINDOWS AND DOORS, INC.—See Koch Industries, Inc.; *U.S. Private*, pg. 2333
CHAMPION ALUMINUM WINDOW CORPORATION; *U.S. Private*, pg. 846
CHASE INDUSTRIES, INC.—See Audax Group, Limited Partnership; *U.S. Private*, pg. 386
CHIEF INDUSTRIES, INC. - CHIEF CUSTOM PRODUCTS DIVISION—See Chief Industries, Inc.; *U.S. Private*, pg. 881
C.H.I. OVERHEAD DOORS, INC.—See Nucor Corporation; *U.S. Public*, pg. 1553
CITIC QINHUANGDAO CO., LTD.—See CITIC Group Corporation; *Int'l*, pg. 1621
CIW ENTERPRISES, INC.; *U.S. Private*, pg. 908
COASTAL WINDOWS LTD.—See Atlas Engineered Products Ltd.; *Int'l*, pg. 685
COLUMBIA COMMERCIAL BUILDING PRODUCTS LLC—See Grey Mountain Partners, LLC; *U.S. Private*, pg. 1784
COMFORT BILT LLC; *U.S. Private*, pg. 981
COMPACT METAL INDUSTRIES LTD.; *Int'l*, pg. 1721
COMPACT METAL INDUSTRIES SDN BHD—See Compact Metal Industries Ltd.; *Int'l*, pg. 1721
COMPREHENSIVE MANUFACTURING SERVICES, LLC—See Golden Gate Capital Management II, LLC; *U.S. Private*, pg. 1732
THE COOKSON COMPANY; *U.S. Private*, pg. 4014
CORDVER S.A.—See ASSA ABLOY AB; *Int'l*, pg. 638
CORNELLCOOKSON, INC.—See Griffon Corporation; *U.S. Public*, pg. 969
COX BUILDING PRODUCTS LIMITED—See H2 Equity Partners B.V.; *Int'l*, pg. 3199
CRAWFORD DOOR (KUNSHAN) CO., LTD.—See ASSA ABLOY AB; *Int'l*, pg. 634
CRITTALL WINDOWS LTD.; *Int'l*, pg. 1851
CRL US ALUMINUM OF CANADA - VANCOUVER—See KPS Capital Partners, LP; *U.S. Private*, pg. 2348
CROWN DIVERSIFIED INDUSTRIES; *U.S. Private*, pg. 1110
DALCO INDUSTRIES INC.—See Dalco Industries Inc.; *U.S. Private*, pg. 1148
DECEUNINCK DE MEXICO S.A. DE C.V.—See Deceuninck NV; *Int'l*, pg. 2000
DECEUNINCK DO BRAZIL LTDA.—See Deceuninck NV; *Int'l*, pg. 2000
DECEUNINCK GERMANY PRODUKTIONS GMBH & CO. KG—See Deceuninck NV; *Int'l*, pg. 2000
DECEUNINCK NORTH AMERICA LLC—See Deceuninck NV; *Int'l*, pg. 2000
DECEUNINCK POLAND SP. Z O.O.—See Deceuninck NV; *Int'l*, pg. 2000
DESCO CORPORATION; *U.S. Private*, pg. 1211
DITEC ENTREMATIC US INC—See ASSA ABLOY AB; *Int'l*, pg. 639
D & M INDUSTRIES, INC.; *U.S. Private*, pg. 1136
DOBROPLAST FABRYKA OKIEN SP. Z O.O.—See Arbonia AG; *Int'l*, pg. 538
DOERS WINDOW MANUFACTURING, LLC—See Koch Industries, Inc.; *U.S. Private*, pg. 2332
DON YOUNG COMPANY INCORPORATED; *U.S. Private*, pg. 1259
DOOR COMPONENTS, INC.; *U.S. Private*, pg. 1261
DOOR COMPONENTS, L.P.—See Platinum Equity, LLC; *U.S. Private*, pg. 3208
DOOR ENGINEERING AND MANUFACTURING LLC—See Audax Group, Limited Partnership; *U.S. Private*, pg. 386
DOOR GALLERY MFG. INC.; *U.S. Private*, pg. 1262
DOORLINK MANUFACTURING, INC.; *U.S. Private*, pg. 1262
DOOR-STOP INTERNATIONAL LIMITED—See Owens Corning; *U.S. Public*, pg. 1626
DOORWAYS PTY. LTD.—See ASSA ABLOY AB; *Int'l*, pg. 638
DUNBARTON CORPORATION—See CGF Industries, Inc.; *U.S. Private*, pg. 844
DURAFLEX LTD.—See Masco Corporation; *U.S. Public*, pg. 1391
DYNACO EUROPE NV—See ASSA ABLOY AB; *Int'l*, pg. 639
EASTERN METAL SUPPLY INC. - EASTERN ARCHITECTURAL SYSTEMS DIVISION—See Clayton, Dubilier & Rice, LLC; *U.S. Private*, pg. 920
ECONFRAME BERHAD; *Int'l*, pg. 2297
EFCO CORPORATION—See Apogee Enterprises, Inc.; *U.S. Public*, pg. 145
ELIXIR INDUSTRIES, CARGO TRAILER INDUSTRY—See Elixir Industries; *U.S. Private*, pg. 1362
ELIXIR INDUSTRIES—See Elixir Industries; *U.S. Private*, pg. 1362
ELIXIR INDUSTRIES—See Elixir Industries; *U.S. Private*, pg. 1362
EMCO ENTERPRISES, INC.—See Andersen Corporation; *U.S. Private*, pg. 275
ENDURA PRODUCTS INC.—See Owens Corning; *U.S. Public*, pg. 1626
ENSINGER BUILDING PRODUCTS LTD.—See Ensinger GmbH; *Int'l*, pg. 2447
E PLUS BUILDING PRODUCTS PTY. LTD.—See dormakaba Holding AG; *Int'l*, pg. 2177

332321 — METAL WINDOW AND DO...

ERA PRODUCTS LIMITED—See Quanex Building Products Corp.; *U.S. Public*, pg. 1749
ESI COMPANIES INC.—See Mainco Investments Inc.; *U.S. Private*, pg. 2552
FAIVELEY TRANSPORT AMIENS S.A.S.—See Westinghouse Air Brake Technologies Corporation; *U.S. Public*, pg. 2357
FAIVELEY TRANSPORT BIRKENHEAD LTD.—See Westinghouse Air Brake Technologies Corporation; *U.S. Public*, pg. 2357
FAIVELEY TRANSPORT DO BRASIL LTDA.—See Westinghouse Air Brake Technologies Corporation; *U.S. Public*, pg. 2358
FAIVELEY TRANSPORT IBERICA SA—See Westinghouse Air Brake Technologies Corporation; *U.S. Public*, pg. 2357
FAIVELEY TRANSPORT ITALIA S.P.A.—See Westinghouse Air Brake Technologies Corporation; *U.S. Public*, pg. 2357
FAIVELEY TRANSPORT METRO TECHNOLOGY TAIWAN LTD.—See Westinghouse Air Brake Technologies Corporation; *U.S. Public*, pg. 2357
FENPLAST; *Int'l*, pg. 2634
FIMBEL DOOR COMPANY—See ASSA ABLOY AB; *Int'l*, pg. 634
FINISHLINE INDUSTRIES INC. OF GEORGIA—See John S. Frey Enterprises; *U.S. Private*, pg. 2224
FLEMING DOOR PRODUCTS LTD—See ASSA ABLOY AB; *Int'l*, pg. 637
FOGA SYSTEM ETHIOPIA—See Foga System International AB; *Int'l*, pg. 2720
FOGA SYSTEMS AUSTRALIA PTY LTD—See Foga System International AB; *Int'l*, pg. 2720
FORMET CELIK KAPI SANAYI VE TICARET AS; *Int'l*, pg. 2734
FORTUNE BRANDS DOORS, INC.—See Fortune Brands Innovations, Inc.; *U.S. Public*, pg. 873
FRAMEWORKS MANUFACTURING INC.—See ASSA ABLOY AB; *Int'l*, pg. 639
FSW SECURITY PRODUCTS LTD.; *Int'l*, pg. 2800
FUJISASH CO., LTD.; *Int'l*, pg. 2830
GAINSBOROUGH HARDWARE INDUSTRIES LIMITED—See GWA Group Limited; *Int'l*, pg. 3190
GARADOR LTD.—See Hormann KG Verkaufsgesellschaf; *Int'l*, pg. 3480
GARAGA INC.; *Int'l*, pg. 2883
GDS GLOBAL LIMITED; *Int'l*, pg. 2896
GIRAUD—See Compagnie de Saint-Gobain SA; *Int'l*, pg. 1723
GRAHAM ARCHITECTURAL PRODUCTS CORPORATION—See The Graham Group, Inc.; *U.S. Private*, pg. 4036
HAAS DOOR COMPANY; *U.S. Private*, pg. 1837
HARMON, INC.—See Apogee Enterprises, Inc.; *U.S. Public*, pg. 145
HASIL A.S.—See ASSA ABLOY AB; *Int'l*, pg. 633
HASIL S.R.O.—See ASSA ABLOY AB; *Int'l*, pg. 633
HC HOODCO, INC.—See Platinum Equity, LLC; *U.S. Private*, pg. 3208
HEHR INTERNATIONAL INC.—See LCI Industries; *U.S. Public*, pg. 1295
HENDERSON NEDERLAND BV—See ASSA ABLOY AB; *Int'l*, pg. 635
HIAP TECK HARDWARE SDN BHD—See Hiap Teck Venture Berhad; *Int'l*, pg. 3382
HICKORY HERITAGE OF FALLING CREEK, INC.; *U.S. Private*, pg. 1933
HOA PHAT DOOR JSC—See Hoa Phat Group Joint Stock Company; *Int'l*, pg. 3435
HOERMANN (HK) LIMITED—See Hormann KG Verkaufsgesellschaf; *Int'l*, pg. 3480
HOPE'S WINDOWS, INC.; *U.S. Private*, pg. 1979
HORMANN ALKMAAR B.V.—See Hormann KG Verkaufsgesellschaf; *Int'l*, pg. 3480
HORMANN BALTIC, UAB—See Hormann KG Verkaufsgesellschaf; *Int'l*, pg. 3480
HORMANN BEIJING DOOR PRODUCTION CO. LTD.—See Hormann KG Verkaufsgesellschaf; *Int'l*, pg. 3480
HORMANN BELGIUM NV/SA—See Hormann KG Verkaufsgesellschaf; *Int'l*, pg. 3480
HORMANN BRASIL PORTAS LTDA—See Hormann KG Verkaufsgesellschaf; *Int'l*, pg. 3480
HORMANN CESKA REPUBLIKA S.R.O.—See Hormann KG Verkaufsgesellschaf; *Int'l*, pg. 3480
HORMANN DANMARK AS—See Hormann KG Verkaufsgesellschaf; *Int'l*, pg. 3480
HORMANN DOORS MALAYSIA SDN BHD—See Hormann KG Verkaufsgesellschaf; *Int'l*, pg. 3480
HORMANN EESTI OU—See Hormann KG Verkaufsgesellschaf; *Int'l*, pg. 3480
HORMANN ESPANA, S.A.—See Hormann KG Verkaufsgesellschaf; *Int'l*, pg. 3480
HORMANN FLEXON, LLC—See Hormann KG Verkaufsgesellschaf; *Int'l*, pg. 3481
HORMANN FRANCE S.A.—See Hormann KG Verkaufsgesellschaf; *Int'l*, pg. 3481
HORMANN HELLAS LTD—See Hormann KG Verkaufsgesellschaf; *Int'l*, pg. 3481
HORMANN HRVATSKA D.O.O.—See Hormann KG Verkaufsgesellschaf; *Int'l*, pg. 3481
HORMANN HUNGARIA KFT.—See Hormann KG Verkaufsgesellschaf; *Int'l*, pg. 3481
HORMANN ITALIA S.R.L.—See Hormann KG Verkaufsgesellschaf; *Int'l*, pg. 3481
HORMANN KAZAKHSTAN LLP—See Hormann KG Verkaufsgesellschaf; *Int'l*, pg. 3480
HORMANN KG VERKAUFSGESELLSCHAFT; *Int'l*, pg. 3480
HORMANN LLC—See Hormann KG Verkaufsgesellschaf; *Int'l*, pg. 3481
HORMANN MAROC SARL—See Hormann KG Verkaufsgesellschaf; *Int'l*, pg. 3481
HORMANN MEXICO, S.A DE C.V.—See Hormann KG Verkaufsgesellschaf; *Int'l*, pg. 3480
HORMANN MIDDLE EAST FZE—See Hormann KG Verkaufsgesellschaf; *Int'l*, pg. 3481
HORMANN NEDERLAND B.V.—See Hormann KG Verkaufsgesellschaf; *Int'l*, pg. 3481
HORMANN NORGE AS—See Hormann KG Verkaufsgesellschaf; *Int'l*, pg. 3481
HORMANN POLSKA SP. Z O.O.—See Hormann KG Verkaufsgesellschaf; *Int'l*, pg. 3481
HORMANN PORTUGAL, LDA.—See Hormann KG Verkaufsgesellschaf; *Int'l*, pg. 3481
HORMANN ROMANIA SRL—See Hormann KG Verkaufsgesellschaf; *Int'l*, pg. 3481
HORMANN SCHWEIZ AG—See Hormann KG Verkaufsgesellschaf; *Int'l*, pg. 3481
HORMANN SERBIA—See Hormann KG Verkaufsgesellschaf; *Int'l*, pg. 3480
HORMANN SLOVENSKA REPUBLIKA S.R.O.—See Hormann KG Verkaufsgesellschaf; *Int'l*, pg. 3481
HORMANN SVENSKA AB—See Hormann KG Verkaufsgesellschaf; *Int'l*, pg. 3481
HORMANN (UK) LIMITED—See Hormann KG Verkaufsgesellschaf; *Int'l*, pg. 3480
HORMANN YAPI ELEMANLARI TIC. LTD. STI.—See Hormann KG Verkaufsgesellschaf; *Int'l*, pg. 3481
IG DOORS LTD.—See Hormann KG Verkaufsgesellschaf; *Int'l*, pg. 3481
IKKA TECHNOLOGY (VIETNAM) CO., LTD.—See Abico Group; *Int'l*, pg. 61
INSULPANE OF CONNECTICUT, INC.—See Grey Mountain Partners, LLC; *U.S. Private*, pg. 1784
INTERNATIONAL IMPACT BUILDING PRODUCTS, LLC; *U.S. Private*, pg. 2117
INTERNATIONAL REVOLVING DOOR COMPANY; *U.S. Private*, pg. 2120
INTERNATIONAL WINDOW CORP. - NORTHERN CALIFORNIA—See UMC Acquisition Corp.; *U.S. Private*, pg. 4278
INTERNATIONAL WINDOW CORP.—See UMC Acquisition Corp.; *U.S. Private*, pg. 4278
THE IRON DOOR COMPANY LLC; *U.S. Private*, pg. 4057
JAMISON DOOR COMPANY; *U.S. Private*, pg. 2186
JANUS INTERNATIONAL GROUP, INC.—See Clearlake Capital Group, L.P.; *U.S. Private*, pg. 935
JET BRAKEL AERO GMBH—See H2 Equity Partners B.V.; *Int'l*, pg. 3199
JET TAGESLICHT & RWA GMBH—See H2 Equity Partners B.V.; *Int'l*, pg. 3199
JOHNSON EQUIPMENT COMPANY S. DE R. L. DE C.V.—See Johnson Equipment Company Inc.; *U.S. Private*, pg. 2227
JONES PAINT & GLASS INC.; *U.S. Private*, pg. 2233
J. SUSSMAN, INC.; *U.S. Private*, pg. 2157
J.T. WALKER INDUSTRIES, INC.; *U.S. Private*, pg. 2171
KATEKS SISUSTUS—See Foga System International AB; *Int'l*, pg. 2721
KAWNEER COMPANY CANADA LTD.—See Howmet Aerospace Inc.; *U.S. Public*, pg. 1062
KAWNEER COMPANY, INC.—See Howmet Aerospace Inc.; *U.S. Public*, pg. 1062
KAWNEER COMPANY, INC.—See Howmet Aerospace Inc.; *U.S. Public*, pg. 1062
KAWNEER COMPANY, INC.—See Howmet Aerospace Inc.; *U.S. Public*, pg. 1062
KAWNEER FRANCE SA—See Howmet Aerospace Inc.; *U.S. Public*, pg. 1062
KAWNEER MAROC SA—See Howmet Aerospace Inc.; *U.S. Public*, pg. 1062
KLS DOORS, LLC—See Patrick Industries, Inc.; *U.S. Public*, pg. 1652
KORALLE SANITARPRODUKTE GMBH—See Arbonia AG; *Int'l*, pg. 538
KOS SPEZIALTUREN GMBH—See ASSA ABLOY AB; *Int'l*, pg. 638
LAUSELL INC.; *U.S. Private*, pg. 2400
LECO PRODUCTS B.V.—See Aalberts N.V.; *Int'l*, pg. 35
LEGG INC.; *U.S. Private*, pg. 2418
LES ZELLES—See Compagnie de Saint-Gobain SA; *Int'l*, pg. 1724
LINETEC—See Apogee Enterprises, Inc.; *U.S. Public*, pg. 145
LOGAN SQUARE ALUMINUM SUPPLY, INC.; *U.S. Private*, pg. 2480
LOWLAND DOORS LIMITED—See BID Group Ltd; *Int'l*, pg. 1019
MANKO WINDOW SYSTEMS INC.; *U.S. Private*, pg. 2564
MARTIN DOOR MANUFACTURING, INC.; *U.S. Private*, pg. 2594
MARTIN SUPPLY COMPANY INC.—See Martin Supply Company Inc.; *U.S. Private*, pg. 2596
MCKEON DOOR OF NEVADA, INC.—See McKeon Rolling Steel Door Company, Inc.; *U.S. Private*, pg. 2638
MCKEON DOOR OF WASHINGTON DC—See McKeon Rolling Steel Door Company, Inc.; *U.S. Private*, pg. 2638
MCKEON DOOR WEST, INC.—See McKeon Rolling Steel Door Company, Inc.; *U.S. Private*, pg. 2638
MCKEON ROLLING STEEL DOOR COMPANY, INC.; *U.S. Private*, pg. 2638
MCKINNEY DOOR AND HARDWARE, INC.—See Bee Street Holdings LLC; *U.S. Private*, pg. 513
MEGAMET INDUSTRIES, INC.—See ASSA ABLOY AB; *Int'l*, pg. 640
MESKER DOOR, LLC—See dormakaba Holding AG; *Int'l*, pg. 2177
MESKER SOUTHEAST—See dormakaba Holding AG; *Int'l*, pg. 2177
MGM INDUSTRIES, INC.; *U.S. Private*, pg. 2694
MIRTEC CORP; *U.S. Private*, pg. 2746
MONARCH MATERIALS GROUP INC.; *U.S. Private*, pg. 2769
NEISEWANDER ENTERPRISES INC.; *U.S. Private*, pg. 2882
NEWSOUTH WINDOW SOLUTIONS OF BONITA SPRINGS, LLC—See Koch Industries, Inc.; *U.S. Private*, pg. 2332
NEWSOUTH WINDOW SOLUTIONS OF CHARLESTON, LLC—See Koch Industries, Inc.; *U.S. Private*, pg. 2332
NEWSOUTH WINDOW SOLUTIONS OF FT. LAUDERDALE, LLC—See Koch Industries, Inc.; *U.S. Private*, pg. 2332
NEWSOUTH WINDOW SOLUTIONS OF JACKSONVILLE, LLC—See Koch Industries, Inc.; *U.S. Private*, pg. 2332
NEWSOUTH WINDOW SOLUTIONS OF ORLANDO, LLC—See Koch Industries, Inc.; *U.S. Private*, pg. 2332
NEWSOUTH WINDOW SOLUTIONS OF WEST PALM BEACH, LLC—See Koch Industries, Inc.; *U.S. Private*, pg. 2333
NORTHEAST BUILDING PRODUCTS CORP.—See Clayton, Dubilier & Rice, LLC; *U.S. Private*, pg. 920
NORTHERN BUILDING PRODUCTS; *U.S. Private*, pg. 2952
NORTHWEST DOOR INC.; *U.S. Private*, pg. 2959
NOVATECH PATIO DOORS ONTARIO INC.—See Garaga Inc.; *Int'l*, pg. 2883
OLDCASTLE BUILDINGENVELOPE, INC. - CHANDLER—See KPS Capital Partners, LP; *U.S. Private*, pg. 2348
OSA DOOR PARTS LIMITED—See ARGENT INDUSTRIAL LIMITED; *Int'l*, pg. 561
OVERLY DOOR COMPANY; *U.S. Private*, pg. 3053
OVERLY MANUFACTURING COMPANY—See Overly Door Company; *U.S. Private*, pg. 3053
PAN PAN DOOR CO LTD—See ASSA ABLOY AB; *Int'l*, pg. 640
PARAGON DOOR DESIGNS, INC.—See True Home Value, Inc.; *U.S. Private*, pg. 4247
PAXTER SECURITY & AUTOMATION SDN BHD—See ASSA ABLOY AB; *Int'l*, pg. 638
P C HENDERSON LTD.—See ASSA ABLOY AB; *Int'l*, pg. 635
PEMKO MANUFACTURING COMPANY; *U.S. Private*, pg. 3132
PEMKO MANUFACTURING COMPANY—See Pemko Manufacturing Company; *U.S. Private*, pg. 3132
PERMASTEELISA S.P.A.—See Atlas Holdings, LLC; *U.S. Private*, pg. 377
PGT INDUSTRIES, INC.—See Koch Industries, Inc.; *U.S. Private*, pg. 2333
PHILLIPS MANUFACTURING INC.; *U.S. Private*, pg. 3171
PIONEER WINDOW & DOOR MFG. LTD.—See Pioneer Window Holdings Inc.; *U.S. Private*, pg. 3189
PIONEER WINDOW HOLDINGS INC.; *U.S. Private*, pg. 3189
PLYCO CORPORATION; *U.S. Private*, pg. 3215
POLYWOOD PROFILES PRIVATE LIMITED—See Dhabriya Polywood Limited; *Int'l*, pg. 2097
PRECISION SWISS PRODUCTS, INC.; *U.S. Private*, pg. 3247
PREMDOR CROSBY LIMITED—See Owens Corning; *U.S. Public*, pg. 1627
PRODUCTOS METALICOS DE SEGURIDAD, S.A. DE C.V.—See ASSA ABLOY AB; *Int'l*, pg. 640
PROTECTIVE DOOR INDUSTRIES—See L B Industries, Inc.; *U.S. Private*, pg. 2361
PT CAKRA COMPACT ALUMINIUM INDUSTRIES—See Compact Metal Industries Ltd.; *Int'l*, pg. 1721
PUBLIC SUPPLY COMPANY; *U.S. Private*, pg. 3300
PYROPANEL DEVELOPMENTS PTY LTD—See ASSA ABLOY AB; *Int'l*, pg. 640
QMI SECURITY SOLUTIONS; *U.S. Private*, pg. 3313
QUANEX HOMESHIELD LLC - RICE LAKE SCREENS

N.A.I.C.S. INDEX

332322 — SHEET METAL WORK MA...

PLANT—See Quanex Building Products Corp.; *U.S. Public*, pg. 1749
QUANEX HOMESHIELD LLC - RICHMOND PLANT—See Quanex Building Products Corp.; *U.S. Public*, pg. 1749
QUANEX HOMESHIELD, LLC—See Quanex Building Products Corp.; *U.S. Public*, pg. 1749
QUEST WINDOW SYSTEMS INC.—See Exchange Income Corporation; *Int'l*, pg. 2579
RACO INTERIOR PRODUCTS, INC.—See UMC Acquisition Corp.; *U.S. Private*, pg. 4278
RAYNOR DISTRIBUTION CENTER—See Neisewander Enterprises Inc.; *U.S. Private*, pg. 2882
RAYNOR GARAGE DOORS—See Neisewander Enterprises Inc.; *U.S. Private*, pg. 2882
RAYNOR MANUFACTURING. CO., INC.—See Neisewander Enterprises Inc.; *U.S. Private*, pg. 2882
RDL LL, LTD.—See Platinum Equity, LLC; *U.S. Private*, pg. 3209
RECORD AJTO KFT—See ASSA ABLOY AB; *Int'l*, pg. 638
RECORD AUSTRIA GMBH—See ASSA ABLOY AB; *Int'l*, pg. 638
RECORD AUTOMATIC DOORS (AUSTRALIA) PTY. LTD.—See ASSA ABLOY AB; *Int'l*, pg. 638
RECORD AUTOMATIC DOORS (CANADA), INC.—See ASSA ABLOY AB; *Int'l*, pg. 638
RECORD AUTOMATIC DOOR (SHANGHAI) CO., LTD.—See ASSA ABLOY AB; *Int'l*, pg. 638
RECORD AUTOMATIC DOORS (M) SDN BHD—See ASSA ABLOY AB; *Int'l*, pg. 638
RECORD AUTOMATISCHE DEUREN B.V.—See ASSA ABLOY AB; *Int'l*, pg. 638
RECORD AVTOMATSKA VRATA D.O.O.—See ASSA ABLOY AB; *Int'l*, pg. 638
RECORD BMT AS—See ASSA ABLOY AB; *Int'l*, pg. 638
RECORD DORRAUTOMATIK SWEDEN AB—See ASSA ABLOY AB; *Int'l*, pg. 638
RECORD DRZWI AUTOMATYCZNE SP.ZO.O—See ASSA ABLOY AB; *Int'l*, pg. 638
RECORD ELEMAT, S.A.—See ASSA ABLOY AB; *Int'l*, pg. 638
RECORD HOLDING NEDERLAND B.V.—See ASSA ABLOY AB; *Int'l*, pg. 638
RECORD INDIANA—See ASSA ABLOY AB; *Int'l*, pg. 638
RECORD INDUSTRY—See ASSA ABLOY AB; *Int'l*, pg. 638
RECORD INTERNATIONAL LTD—See ASSA ABLOY AB; *Int'l*, pg. 638
RECORD PORTES AUTOMATIQUES S.A—See ASSA ABLOY AB; *Int'l*, pg. 638
RECORD PUERTAS AUTOMATICAS SA—See ASSA ABLOY AB; *Int'l*, pg. 638
RECORD SVERIGE AB—See ASSA ABLOY AB; *Int'l*, pg. 638
RECORD TURAUTOMATION AG—See ASSA ABLOY AB; *Int'l*, pg. 638
RECORD TURAUTOMATION GMBH—See ASSA ABLOY AB; *Int'l*, pg. 638
RECORD UK LTD—See ASSA ABLOY AB; *Int'l*, pg. 638
RECORD - USA INC—See ASSA ABLOY AB; *Int'l*, pg. 638
REEM EMIRATES ALUMINUM LLC—See Alpha Dhabi Holding PJSC; *Int'l*, pg. 367
REPUBLIC DOORS AND FRAMES, LLC—See Allegion Public Limited Company; *Int'l*, pg. 335
RITE-HITE DOOR DIVISION—See Rite-Hite Holding Corporation; *U.S. Private*, pg. 3442
THE R. LANG COMPANY; *U.S. Private*, pg. 4101
ROLLADEN INC.; *U.S. Private*, pg. 3474
ROLLING SHIELD, INC.; *U.S. Private*, pg. 3475
ROLOX INC.—See True Home Value, Inc.; *U.S. Private*, pg. 4247
ROSATI WINDOWS; *U.S. Private*, pg. 3480
RV ACQUISITION CORP.; *U.S. Private*, pg. 3508
RWD SCHLATTER AG—See Arbonia AG; *Int'l*, pg. 538
SAMHWA PRECISION CO., LTD.—See ASSA ABLOY AB; *Int'l*, pg. 640
SANO ASSOCIATES, INC.; *U.S. Private*, pg. 3546
SCENOGRAFIE S.R.O—See Foga System International AB; *Int'l*, pg. 2721
SCHLEGEL AUSTRALIA PTY LIMITED—See Quanex Building Products Corp.; *U.S. Public*, pg. 1749
SCHLEGEL BELGIUM BVBA—See Quanex Building Products Corp.; *U.S. Public*, pg. 1749
SDS INDUSTRIES INC.; *U.S. Private*, pg. 3582
SECURITY METAL PRODUCTS CORP—See ASSA ABLOY AB; *Int'l*, pg. 636
SELACO ALUMINIUM BERHAD—See Compact Metal Industries Ltd.; *Int'l*, pg. 1721
SESSA KLEIN S.P.A.—See LCI Industrioc; *U.S. Public*, pg. 1296
SHAKTI HORMANN PRIVATE LIMITED—See Hormann KG Verkaufsgesellschaf; *Int'l*, pg. 3481
SHENZHEN LONGDIAN SCIENCE TECHNOLOGY INDUSTRIAL CO., LTD.—See ASSA ABLOY AB; *Int'l*, pg. 640
SICURA S.R.L.—See A2A S.p.A.; *Int'l*, pg. 29
SKYFENS SP. Z O.O.—See Arbonia AG; *Int'l*, pg. 538
SLAGELSE LASESERVICE A/S—See ASSA ABLOY AB; *Int'l*, pg. 640
THE SMART COMPANIES, INC.—See Rotunda Capital Partners LLC; *U.S. Private*, pg. 3488

SOPROFEN INDUSTRIE SAS—See Bouyer Leroux SA; *Int'l*, pg. 1121
SOPROFEN SAS—See Bouyer Leroux SA; *Int'l*, pg. 1121
SOUTHEASTERN ALUMINUM PRODUCTS, INC.; *U.S. Private*, pg. 3727
STEELCRAFT MANUFACTURING COMPANY—See Ingersoll Rand Inc.; *U.S. Public*, pg. 1122
STEEL-LINE GARAGE DOORS—See Crescent Capital Partners Ltd.; *Int'l*, pg. 1839
STILES CUSTOM METAL, INC.—See ASSA ABLOY AB; *Int'l*, pg. 640
STORM SMART BUILDING SYSTEMS, INC.; *U.S. Private*, pg. 3831
SUPERIOR ENGINEERED PRODUCTS CORP.—See Kenner & Company, Inc.; *U.S. Private*, pg. 2285
SUPERIOR ENGINEERED PRODUCTS CORP.—See North Cove Partners; *U.S. Private*, pg. 2944
SVATON SA—See ASSA ABLOY AB; *Int'l*, pg. 638
TASHCO INDUSTRIES, INC.—See Andersen Corporation; *U.S. Private*, pg. 275
THERMAL INDUSTRIES, INC.—See Kenner & Company, Inc.; *U.S. Private*, pg. 2285
THERMAL INDUSTRIES, INC.—See North Cove Partners; *U.S. Private*, pg. 2944
THERMAL WINDOWS INC.; *U.S. Private*, pg. 4142
THERMA-TRU CORP.—See Fortune Brands Innovations, Inc.; *U.S. Public*, pg. 873
THERMA-TRU CORP.—See Fortune Brands Innovations, Inc.; *U.S. Public*, pg. 873
THERMO-TECH PREMIUM WINDOWS & DOORS, INC.; *U.S. Private*, pg. 4143
THERMO-TWIN INDUSTRIES INC.; *U.S. Private*, pg. 4143
THV COMPOZIT WINDOWS & DOORS—See True Home Value, Inc.; *U.S. Private*, pg. 4247
TKO DOORS—See ASSA ABLOY AB; *Int'l*, pg. 633
TORTEC BRANDSCHUTZTOR GMBH—See Hormann KG Verkaufsgesellschaf; *Int'l*, pg. 3481
TRACO INC.—See Howmet Aerospace Inc.; *U.S. Public*, pg. 1062
TRAC-RITE DOOR INC.—See Trachte Building Systems Inc.; *U.S. Private*, pg. 4200
TRULITE GLASS & ALUMINUM SOLUTIONS, LLC; *U.S. Private*, pg. 4249
TUBAUTO S.A.S.—See Hormann KG Verkaufsgesellschaf; *Int'l*, pg. 3481
UNIQUE BALANCE, INC.; *U.S. Private*, pg. 4286
UNITED WINDOW & DOOR MANUFACTURING; *U.S. Private*, pg. 4302
VACULUX B.V.—See H2 Equity Partners B.V.; *Int'l*, pg. 3199
VAN NELFEN DEURTECHNIEK B.V.—See ASSA ABLOY AB; *Int'l*, pg. 638
VIGOR GROUP, LLC—See On-Point Group, LLC; *U.S. Private*, pg. 3019
VIKING ALUMINUM PRODUCTS INC.; *U.S. Private*, pg. 4382
WAUSAU WINDOW & WALL SYSTEMS—See Apogee Enterprises, Inc.; *U.S. Public*, pg. 145
WEILAND SLIDING DOORS & WINDOWS, INC.—See Andersen Corporation; *U.S. Private*, pg. 275
WERTBAU GMBH—See Arbonia AG; *Int'l*, pg. 538
WINDOW PRODUCTS, INC.—See Clayton, Dubilier & Rice, LLC; *U.S. Private*, pg. 921
WINDOW TECHNOLOGY, INC.; *U.S. Private*, pg. 4538
WOJAN WINDOW & DOOR CORPORATION; *U.S. Private*, pg. 4553
WWS ACQUISITION LLC—See Koch Industries, Inc.; *U.S. Private*, pg. 2333

332322 — SHEET METAL WORK MANUFACTURING

7 C'S MANUFACTURING, INC.; *U.S. Private*, pg. 16
AB HOORS PLAT—See AB Electrolux; *Int'l*, pg. 39
ABRISUD SAS—See Andera Partners SCA; *Int'l*, pg. 449
ACCRA-FAB INC.; *U.S. Private*, pg. 54
ACCUDUCT MANUFACTURING INC.; *U.S. Private*, pg. 54
ACCURATE METAL FABRICATORS, LLC.; *U.S. Private*, pg. 55
A.C. HORN & COMPANY; *U.S. Private*, pg. 24
ACOUSTICAL SHEETMETAL INCORPORATED; *U.S. Private*, pg. 64
ACTRON ENGINEERING, INC.; *U.S. Private*, pg. 70
ADAMS CAMPBELL COMPANY LTD.; *U.S. Private*, pg. 74
ADVANCED MANUFACTURING & DEVELOPMENT, INC.—See Montage Partners, Inc.; *U.S. Private*, pg. 2774
AERO-DATA METAL CRAFTERS, INC.; *U.S. Private*, pg. 118
AERO TECH MANUFACTURING INC.; *U.S. Private*, pg. 118
AES INDUSTRIES, INC.—See Lennox International Inc.; *U.S. Public*, pg. 1307
AHI ROOFING (MALAYSIA) SDN BHD—See Fletcher Building Limited; *Int'l*, pg. 2699
AIREDALE SHEET METAL LIMITED—See Modine Manufacturing Company; *U.S. Public*, pg. 1455
AIR VENT INC.—See Gibraltar Industries, Inc.; *U.S. Public*, pg. 935

AJU MCM CO., LTD.—See AJU Steel Co., Ltd.; *Int'l*, pg. 258
ALADDIN METAL PRODUCTS INC.—See Dealers Supply Company Inc.; *U.S. Private*, pg. 1182
ALLENTOWN, INC.—See Aterian Investment Management, L.P.; *U.S. Private*, pg. 366
ALPOS D.O.O. ALEKSINAC—See ALPOS, d.d.; *Int'l*, pg. 375
ALPOS ROHR UND METALLHANDEL DEUTSCHLAND GMBH—See ALPOS, d.d.; *Int'l*, pg. 375
ALTECO TECHNIK GMBH—See RPM International Inc.; *U.S. Public*, pg. 1819
AMCO ENGINEERING CO; *U.S. Private*, pg. 218
AMD FABRICATORS, INC.—See Astro Manufacturing & Design, Inc.; *U.S. Private*, pg. 362
AMERICAN FABRICATORS, INC.; *U.S. Private*, pg. 232
AMERICAN PRODUCTS, L.L.C.; *U.S. Private*, pg. 244
AMETEK AEGIS, INC.—See AMETEK, Inc.; *U.S. Public*, pg. 116
AMUNEAL MANUFACTURING CORPORATION; *U.S. Private*, pg. 269
ANDERSON & DAHLEN INC.—See Gray Inc.; *U.S. Private*, pg. 1759
ANDERSON INDUSTRIES LLC; *U.S. Private*, pg. 277
APOLLO ROOFING SOLUTIONS LIMITED—See H.B. Fuller Company; *U.S. Public*, pg. 977
AQ COMPONENTS SUZHOU CO., LTD.—See AQ Group AB; *Int'l*, pg. 526
AQ COMPONENTS VASTERAS AB—See AQ Group AB; *Int'l*, pg. 526
AQ ELECTRIC AD—See AQ Group AB; *Int'l*, pg. 526
AQ ELECTRIC & ENCLOSURES SUZHOU CO., LTD.—See AQ Group AB; *Int'l*, pg. 526
AQ ENCLOSURE SOLLEFTEA AB—See AQ Group AB; *Int'l*, pg. 526
ARCELORMITTAL TALLINN OU—See ArcelorMittal S.A.; *Int'l*, pg. 545
ARCELOR RPS—See ArcelorMittal S.A.; *Int'l*, pg. 543
ARKU MASCHINENBAU GMBH; *Int'l*, pg. 572
AS HARJU ELEKTER TELETEHNIKA—See Harju Elekter AS; *Int'l*, pg. 3277
ASL INDUSTRIES LIMITED; *Int'l*, pg. 625
ASTINO (MALAYSIA) COLOUR STEEL SHEET SDN. BHD.—See Astino Berhad; *Int'l*, pg. 655
ATI SPECIALTY MATERIALS—See ATI Inc.; *U.S. Public*, pg. 221
AUTOMOBILE CORPORATION OF GOA LTD; *Int'l*, pg. 730
AWARD METALS INC.; *U.S. Private*, pg. 410
BADGER SHEET METAL WORKS OF GREEN BAY, INC.; *U.S. Private*, pg. 424
BAOSTEEL-NIPPON STEEL AUTOMOTIVE STEEL SHEETS CO., LTD.—See China Baowu Steel Group Corp., Ltd.; *Int'l*, pg. 1485
BASMAT INC.; *U.S. Private*, pg. 485
BATICOMPOS SPA—See Cevital S.p.A.; *Int'l*, pg. 1425
BATIROC S.A.S.—See Etex SA/NV; *Int'l*, pg. 2521
BELDEN, INC. - PENNSYLVANIA PLANT—See Belden, Inc.; *U.S. Public*, pg. 294
BEN MACHINE PRODUCTS CO. INC.—See Exchange Income Corporation; *Int'l*, pg. 2579
BERGER BUILDING PRODUCTS, INC.—See Omnimax Holdings, Inc.; *U.S. Private*, pg. 3017
BERRIDGE MANUFACTURING COMPANY INC.; *U.S. Private*, pg. 538
BERT R HUNCILMAN & SON INC.; *U.S. Private*, pg. 539
BEYELER MASCHINENBAU GMBH—See Bystronic AG; *Int'l*, pg. 1236
CALVI HOLDING S.R.L.; *Int'l*, pg. 1266
CAL-X INCORPORATED—See CORE Industrial Partners, LLC; *U.S. Private*, pg. 1049
CANTRELL INTERNATIONAL—See A.C. Horn & Company; *U.S. Private*, pg. 24
CAPITOL STAMPINGS CORP.—See MiddleGround Management, LP; *U.S. Private*, pg. 2711
CAPPS MANUFACTURING, INC.; *U.S. Private*, pg. 745
CAPTIVE-AIRE SYSTEMS, INC.; *U.S. Private*, pg. 747
CASTLE INDUSTRIES—See M.C. Gill Corporation; *U.S. Private*, pg. 2528
CELIK D.O.O.; *Int'l*, pg. 1392
CELMET COMPANY, INC.—See Goldberg Lindsay & Co., LLC; *U.S. Private*, pg. 1729
CENTRAL STEEL FABRICATORS INC.—See Live Ventures Incorporated; *U.S. Public*, pg. 1332
CENTRIA ARCHITECTURAL SYSTEMS—See Clayton, Dubilier & Rice, LLC; *U.S. Private*, pg. 920
CENTRIA, INC.—See Clayton, Dubilier & Rice, LLC; *U.S. Private*, pg. 920
CENTURY IRRIGATION STATION—See Century Equipment Inc.; *U.S. Private*, pg. 832
CHINA MACHINERY INDUSTRIAL PRODUCTS CO., LTD.—See China Machinery Engineering Corporation; *Int'l*, pg. 1516
CHUN YUAN STEEL INDUSTRY CO., LTD.; *Int'l*, pg. 1596
CLARK STEEL FRAMING SYSTEMS—See Clark Steel Fabricators, Inc.; *U.S. Private*, pg. 914
CLIMATE CONTROL MECHANICAL SERVICES, INC.; *U.S. Private*, pg. 943
CLIMATE ENGINEERS INC.; *U.S. Private*, pg. 943
CL RIECKHOFF COMPANY; *U.S. Private*, pg. 909

332322 — SHEET METAL WORK MA...

CMC REBAR—See Commercial Metals Company; *U.S. Public*, pg. 545
COCHRAN EXTERIORS, LLC; *U.S. Private*, pg. 959
CODY COMPANY INC.; *U.S. Private*, pg. 960
COPPERFIELD CHIMNEY SUPPLY, INC.—See Olympia Chimney Supply Holdings, LLC; *U.S. Private*, pg. 3012
CORAZA INTEGRATED TECHNOLOGY BERHAD; *Int'l*, pg. 1795
CORRUGATED METALS, INC.; *U.S. Private*, pg. 1059
CORTEC PRECISION SHEET METAL, INC.; *U.S. Private*, pg. 1060
COSTAMP S.R.L; *Int'l*, pg. 1815
CRAFTSMAN CUSTOM METALS LLC—See Speyside Equity LLC; *U.S. Private*, pg. 3756
CRANE COMPOSITES, INC.—See Crane NXT, Co.; *U.S. Public*, pg. 590
CR METAL PRODUCTS INC.; *U.S. Private*, pg. 1081
CROWN PRODUCTS COMPANY INC.; *U.S. Private*, pg. 1112
CUMMINS KOREA LTD.—See Cummins Inc.; *U.S. Public*, pg. 606
CURBS PLUS, INC.; *U.S. Private*, pg. 1124
DANE MANUFACTURING COMPANY; *U.S. Private*, pg. 1153
DAVIS INDUSTRIES II, LLC; *U.S. Private*, pg. 1173
DAYTON T. BROWN INC.; *U.S. Private*, pg. 1178
DECRA ROOFING SYSTEMS INC.—See Fletcher Building Limited; *Int'l*, pg. 2699
DEXTER CHASSIS GROUP—See Brookfield Corporation; *Int'l*, pg. 1176
DHANADA ENGINEERING PVT. LTD.—See DHANADA CORPORATION LIMITED; *Int'l*, pg. 2098
DILLINGER FRANCE S.A.—See AG der Dillinger Huttenwerke; *Int'l*, pg. 197
DNP ELLIO CO., LTD.—See Dai Nippon Printing Co., Ltd.; *Int'l*, pg. 1914
DREXEL METALS CORPORATION; *U.S. Private*, pg. 1276
DUCOMMUN AEROSTRUCTURES NEW YORK, INC.—See Ducommun Incorporated; *U.S. Public*, pg. 690
DUCTMATE INDUSTRIES INC.; *U.S. Private*, pg. 1284
DU-MONT COMPANY INCORPORATED; *U.S. Private*, pg. 1282
DURAVENT, INC.—See Egeria Capital Management B.V.; *Int'l*, pg. 2323
ECB CORP.; *U.S. Private*, pg. 1326
E.K. MACHINE CO., INC.; *U.S. Private*, pg. 1306
ELDERLEE, INC.—See REH Holdings Inc.; *U.S. Private*, pg. 3389
ELECTROMET CORPORATION; *U.S. Private*, pg. 1354
ELITE MANUFACTURING TECHNOLOGIES, INC.—See CORE Industrial Partners, LLC; *U.S. Private*, pg. 1048
ENCO SPOL. S R.O.; *Int'l*, pg. 2401
ENGLERT INC.; *U.S. Private*, pg. 1400
ENVIRODYNE TECHNOLOGIES, INC.—See Prab, Inc.; *U.S. Private*, pg. 3241
ESJOT GOLDENBERG; *Int'l*, pg. 2503
ETM MANUFACTURING; *U.S. Private*, pg. 1432
EXACT, INC.—See Indigo South Capital, Inc.; *U.S. Private*, pg. 2063
FABRAL, INC.—See Flack Steel LLC; *U.S. Private*, pg. 1538
FABRICAS MONTERREY, S.A. DE C.V.—See Crown Holdings, Inc.; *U.S. Public*, pg. 598
FABRICATED METALS LLC; *U.S. Private*, pg. 1458
FAKOM AD; *Int'l*, pg. 2610
FALLS FABRICATING, INC.—See Spell Capital Partners, LLC; *U.S. Private*, pg. 3754
FEPER SA; *Int'l*, pg. 2635
FINE SHEETMETAL TECHNOLOGIES PTE. LTD.—See FSM Holdings Limited; *Int'l*, pg. 2798
FIRESTONE BUILDING PRODUCTS COMPANY, LLC - BRISTOL MANUFACTURING FACILITY—See Bridgestone Corporation; *Int'l*, pg. 1157
FIRESTONE BUILDING PRODUCTS COMPANY, LLC - DEFOREST MANUFACTURING FACILITY—See Bridgestone Corporation; *Int'l*, pg. 1157
FIRESTONE BUILDING PRODUCTS COMPANY, LLC - INDIANAPOLIS MANUFACTURING FACILITY—See Bridgestone Corporation; *Int'l*, pg. 1157
FIRESTONE BUILDING PRODUCTS COMPANY, LLC - PRESCOTT MANUFACTURING FACILITY—See Bridgestone Corporation; *Int'l*, pg. 1157
FIRESTONE BUILDING PRODUCTS COMPANY, LLC - YOUNGWOOD MANUFACTURING FACILITY—See Bridgestone Corporation; *Int'l*, pg. 1157
FIRESTONE GENFLEX ROOFING SYSTEMS, LLC—See Bridgestone Corporation; *Int'l*, pg. 1157
FIRESTONE METAL PRODUCTS COMPANY, LLC - COLLEGE PARK MANUFACTURING FACILITY—See Bridgestone Corporation; *Int'l*, pg. 1160
FIRESTONE METAL PRODUCTS COMPANY, LLC - WARREN MANUFACTURING FACILITY—See Bridgestone Corporation; *Int'l*, pg. 1160
FLEXIGLASS CHALLENGE PTY LTD—See Eastern Polymer Group Public Company Limited; *Int'l*, pg. 2273
FLORENCE CORPORATION OF KANSAS—See Gibraltar Industries, Inc.; *U.S. Public*, pg. 936

FLORIDA METAL PRODUCTS INC.; *U.S. Private*, pg. 1550
FLOWCRETE ASIA SDN. BHD.—See RPM International Inc.; *U.S. Public*, pg. 1818
FLOWCRETE AUSTRALIA PTY. LIMITED—See RPM International Inc.; *U.S. Public*, pg. 1818
FLOWCRETE FRANCE S.A.S.—See RPM International Inc.; *U.S. Public*, pg. 1819
FLOWCRETE INDIA PRIVATE LIMITED—See RPM International Inc.; *U.S. Public*, pg. 1819
FLOWCRETE MIDDLE EAST FZCO—See RPM International Inc.; *U.S. Public*, pg. 1819
FLOWCRETE NORWAY AS—See RPM International Inc.; *U.S. Public*, pg. 1819
FLOWCRETE UK LIMITED—See RPM International Inc.; *U.S. Public*, pg. 1819
FORMACH ASIA SDN. BHD.—See Grand Venture Technology Limited; *Int'l*, pg. 3057
FOX VALLEY METAL TECH, LLC—See Littlejohn & Co., LLC; *U.S. Private*, pg. 2470
FUJI LATEX SHANGHAI CO., LTD.—See Fuji Latex Co., Ltd.; *Int'l*, pg. 2813
FURUYA METAL CO., LTD.; *Int'l*, pg. 2848
GALLAGHER-KAISER CORPORATION; *U.S. Private*, pg. 1638
GANTAN BEAUTY INDUSTRY CO. LTD; *Int'l*, pg. 2882
GARY METALS MANUFACTURING LLC; *U.S. Private*, pg. 1646
GAVEN INDUSTRIES, INC.—See 3 Rivers Capital, LLC; *U.S. Private*, pg. 7
GENESEE STAMPING & FABRICATING, INC.—See Genesee Group, Inc.; *U.S. Private*, pg. 1669
GENTEK BUILDING PRODUCTS, INC.—See Hellman & Friedman LLC; *U.S. Private*, pg. 1907
GEROME MANUFACTURING COMPANY, INC.; *U.S. Private*, pg. 1687
G&G STEEL; *U.S. Private*, pg. 1629
GIDDENS INDUSTRIES—See Arlington Capital Partners LLC; *U.S. Private*, pg. 327
GKI ELECTRONIC ENCLOSURES—See Electromet Corporation; *U.S. Private*, pg. 1354
GREAT WESTERN METALS INC.—See Four Winds Investment Corp.; *U.S. Private*, pg. 1583
GROUP MANUFACTURING SERVICES OF ARIZONA; *U.S. Private*, pg. 1793
GROUP MANUFACTURING SERVICES; *U.S. Private*, pg. 1793
HALLETT ROOFING SERVICES PTY LTD—See Brickworks Limited; *Int'l*, pg. 1152
HARFORD SYSTEMS, INC.—See Bio Medic Corporation; *U.S. Private*, pg. 561
HARRINGTON ENGINEERING, INC.; *U.S. Private*, pg. 1868
HIGHWAY SAFETY LLC—See Race Rock GP, L.L.C.; *U.S. Private*, pg. 3341
HMT, LLC—See Tailwind Capital Group, LLC; *U.S. Private*, pg. 3924
H.M. WHITE LLC; *U.S. Private*, pg. 1835
HOWARD FINISHING LLC; *U.S. Private*, pg. 1994
HUNTINGTON SHEET METAL, INC.; *U.S. Private*, pg. 2010
ICF INDUSTRIES, INC.; *U.S. Private*, pg. 2031
ICOPAL DANMARK APS—See GAF Materials Corporation; *U.S. Private*, pg. 1633
ICOPAL S.A.—See GAF Materials Corporation; *U.S. Private*, pg. 1634
IDEAL ROOFING COMPANY LTD.; *Int'l*, pg. 3589
IKM HAALAND AS—See IKM Gruppen AS; *Int'l*, pg. 3611
IMAGINETICS LLC—See Centerfield Capital Partners, LLC; *U.S. Private*, pg. 816
IMAGINETICS LLC—See Kidd & Company LLC; *U.S. Private*, pg. 2302
INCODEMA HOLDINGS LLC—See CORE Industrial Partners, LLC; *U.S. Private*, pg. 1048
INDUSTRIAL VENTILATION, INC.; *U.S. Private*, pg. 2069
INTERACTIVE TECHNOLOGIES—See Montage Partners, Inc.; *U.S. Private*, pg. 2774
INTERLOCK INDUSTRIES, INC.; *U.S. Private*, pg. 2111
IPE BV—See Aviva plc; *Int'l*, pg. 746
JBM INCORPORATED; *U.S. Private*, pg. 2194
JENSEN BRIDGE & SUPPLY COMPANY; *U.S. Private*, pg. 2200
JERYCO INDUSTRIES INC.; *U.S. Private*, pg. 2203
JOHN W. MCDOUGALL CO. INC.; *U.S. Private*, pg. 2225
JOHN ZINK COMPANY LLC—See Koch Industries, Inc.; *U.S. Private*, pg. 2331
JONES METAL PRODUCTS CO.; *U.S. Private*, pg. 2233
JUNIPER ELBOW CO. INC.; *U.S. Private*, pg. 2244
KALAMAZOO FABRICATING—See Prab, Inc.; *U.S. Private*, pg. 3241
KARLEE CO.—See Littlejohn & Co., LLC; *U.S. Private*, pg. 2471
KICE INDUSTRIES INC.; *U.S. Private*, pg. 2302
KLAUER MANUFACTURING COMPANY; *U.S. Private*, pg. 2318
KOGOK CORPORATION; *U.S. Private*, pg. 2337
KOUEI INDUSTRY CO., LTD.—See Freesia Macross Corporation; *Int'l*, pg. 2771
KUSTOM US, INC.; *U.S. Private*, pg. 2358
LAKE AIR METAL PRODUCTS LLC; *U.S. Private*, pg. 2374

LAMBRO INDUSTRIES INC.; *U.S. Private*, pg. 2380
LANE ENTERPRISES INC.; *U.S. Private*, pg. 2388
LECTRUS, INC.—See RFE Investment Partners; *U.S. Private*, pg. 3419
LINX INDUSTRIES, INC.—See Ductmate Industries Inc.; *U.S. Private*, pg. 1284
LOMANCO INC.; *U.S. Private*, pg. 2483
MAJESTIC METALS, INC.—See CORE Industrial Partners, LLC; *U.S. Private*, pg. 1048
MAPP TECHONOLOGIES, LLC—See TGP Investments, LLC; *U.S. Private*, pg. 3979
MASS PRECISION SHEETMETAL; *U.S. Private*, pg. 2603
MATERION ADVANCED MATERIALS TECHNOLOGIES & SERVICES FAR EAST PHILIPPINES PTD LTD.—See Materion Corporation; *U.S. Public*, pg. 1395
MATERION SINGAPORE PTE. LTD.—See Materion Corporation; *U.S. Public*, pg. 1395
MATERION TAIWAN CO. LTD.—See Materion Corporation; *U.S. Public*, pg. 1395
MATTEO ALUMINUM, INC.; *U.S. Private*, pg. 2613
MAYSTEEL INDUSTRIES, LLC—See Littlejohn & Co., LLC; *U.S. Private*, pg. 2471
MCGILL AIRFLOW CORP.—See The McGill Corporation; *U.S. Private*, pg. 4076
THE MCGILL CORPORATION; *U.S. Private*, pg. 4076
MEDFORD FABRICATION, CSC INC.; *U.S. Private*, pg. 2651
MERCURY AIRCRAFT INC.; *U.S. Private*, pg. 2670
MERCURY MINNESOTA INC.—See Mercury Aircraft Inc.; *U.S. Private*, pg. 2670
MERIT ENDS INC—See Viking Processing Corporation; *U.S. Private*, pg. 4382
METALADE N.Y., INC.; *U.S. Private*, pg. 2680
METAL COMPONENTS LLC.; *U.S. Private*, pg. 2680
METALFAB, INC.; *U.S. Private*, pg. 2681
METAL FX—See Montage Partners, Inc.; *U.S. Private*, pg. 2774
METAL PRODUCTS COMPANY; *U.S. Private*, pg. 2680
METAL SALES MANUFACTURING CORPORATION—See Interlock Industries, Inc.; *U.S. Private*, pg. 2111
METAL TRADES, LLC—See Arlington Capital Partners LLC; *U.S. Private*, pg. 328
METALWORKING GROUP HOLDINGS, INC.; *U.S. Private*, pg. 2682
METAL WORKS INC.; *U.S. Private*, pg. 2680
MICROMETL CORP.; *U.S. Private*, pg. 2704
MID-PARK INC.; *U.S. Private*, pg. 2708
MIKA METAL FABRICATING, CO.—See Weybridge, LLC; *U.S. Private*, pg. 4503
MILBANK MANUFACTURING COMPANY INC.—See Milbank Manufacturing Company Inc.; *U.S. Private*, pg. 2726
MISHAWAKA SHEET METAL, INC.—See Patrick Industries, Inc.; *U.S. Public*, pg. 1653
M&M MANUFACTURING, LLC - DALLAS PLANT—See Berkshire Hathaway Inc.; *U.S. Public*, pg. 312
M&M MANUFACTURING, LLC - FORT WORTH (ADOLPH STREET) PLANT—See Berkshire Hathaway Inc.; *U.S. Public*, pg. 312
M&M MANUFACTURING, LLC - HOUSTON PLANT—See Berkshire Hathaway Inc.; *U.S. Public*, pg. 312
M&M MANUFACTURING, LLC—See Berkshire Hathaway Inc.; *U.S. Public*, pg. 312
MM SYSTEMS CORPORATION; *U.S. Private*, pg. 2754
MNDUSTRIES, INC.; *U.S. Private*, pg. 2755
MODERN FABRICATING INC.—See Modern Ice Equipment & Supply Co.; *U.S. Private*, pg. 2761
MOMENTUM MANUFACTURING GROUP, LLC—See OEP Capital Advisors, L.P.; *U.S. Private*, pg. 2999
MONTANA METAL PRODUCTS LLC; *U.S. Private*, pg. 2775
MOTEK-TEAM INDUSTRIES, INC.—See TEAM Industries, Inc.; *U.S. Private*, pg. 3949
MOUNTPAC AB—See Beijer Alma AB; *Int'l*, pg. 943
MSM MANUFACTURING DE MEXICO, S.A. DE C.V.—See Littlejohn & Co., LLC; *U.S. Private*, pg. 2471
NITRAM METAL FABRICATORS INC.; *U.S. Private*, pg. 2929
NOLL/NORWESCO LLC—See Gibraltar Industries, Inc.; *U.S. Public*, pg. 936
NOLL/NORWESCO LLC—See Gibraltar Industries, Inc.; *U.S. Public*, pg. 936
NU-WAY INDUSTRIES, INC.; *U.S. Private*, pg. 2972
NYSTROM, INC.; *U.S. Private*, pg. 2977
OERTEL SHEET METAL, INC.—See McCarthy Bush Corporation; *U.S. Private*, pg. 2626
OLYMPIA CHIMNEY SUPPLY HOLDINGS, LLC; *U.S. Private*, pg. 3012
OMEGA METALS—See STABILIS SOLUTIONS, INC.; *U.S. Public*, pg. 1924
OPTIMAL STEEL SERVICE LLC—See The Thompson Companies; *U.S. Private*, pg. 4126
OTARI GAC CO., LTD.—See Denso Corporation; *Int'l*, pg. 2032
PENNE INTERNATIONAL NV—See BNP Paribas SA; *Int'l*, pg. 1092
PHOENIX METALLICS, INC.—See John S. Frey Enterprises; *U.S. Private*, pg. 2224

N.A.I.C.S. INDEX

332323 — ORNAMENTAL AND ARCH...

PICKWICK COMPANY INC.; *U.S. Private*, pg. 3176
PLASTIQUE LIMITED—See Sonoco Products Company; *U.S. Public*, pg. 1904
PLASTIQUE SP. Z O.O.—See Sonoco Products Company; *U.S. Public*, pg. 1904
PRECISION METAL FABRICATION, INC.; *U.S. Private*, pg. 3245
PRECISION METAL INDUSTRIES, INC.; *U.S. Private*, pg. 3245
PREFCO, INC.—See J.T. Walker Industries, Inc.; *U.S. Private*, pg. 2171
PREMIER MANUFACTURING, INC.; *U.S. Private*, pg. 3250
PRINCE INDUSTRIES, LLC—See HC Private Investments LLC; *U.S. Private*, pg. 1888
PROGRESSIVE MANUFACTURING LTD.—See ASKO Holding A.S.; *Int'l*, pg. 625
PRO ROOF STEEL MERCHANTS PROPRIETARY LIMITED—See Andulela Investment Holdings Limited; *Int'l*, pg. 457
PROTOTEK SHEETMETAL FABRICATION, LLC—See CORE Industrial Partners, LLC; *U.S. Private*, pg. 1049
PUGLIA ENGINEERING INC.; *U.S. Private*, pg. 3303
QUALITY ALUMINUM PRODUCTS INC.—See Gibraltar Industries, Inc.; *U.S. Public*, pg. 936
QUALITY FABRICATION, INC.—See Canerector Inc.; *Int'l*, pg. 1290
QUALITY FABRICATORS INC.; *U.S. Private*, pg. 3319
QUALITY FORMING, LLC—See Arlington Capital Partners LLC; *U.S. Private*, pg. 327
QUALITY METAL WORKS, INC.; *U.S. Private*, pg. 3319
RADIANT POOLS—See Latham Group, Inc.; *U.S. Public*, pg. 1294
RAH INDUSTRIES; *U.S. Private*, pg. 3346
RANGAIRE MANUFACTURING COMPANY, LP; *U.S. Private*, pg. 3354
RBM PRECISION METAL PRODUCTS INC.—See 13i Capital Corporation; *U.S. Private*, pg. 3
REDMAN FISHER ENGINEERING LTD—See Hill & Smith PLC; *Int'l*, pg. 3392
RHOADS METAL FABRICATIONS INC.; *U.S. Private*, pg. 3421
ROBINSON METAL, INC.; *U.S. Private*, pg. 3462
ROBROY INDUSTRIES TEXAS INC.—See Robroy Industries Inc.; *U.S. Private*, pg. 3463
ROLLEX CORPORATION; *U.S. Private*, pg. 3474
ROURA IRON WORKS, INC.; *U.S. Private*, pg. 3489
RTI ADVANCED FORMING, LTD.—See Endless LLP; *Int'l*, pg. 2403
RUST-OLEUM FRANCE S.A.S.—See RPM International Inc.; *U.S. Public*, pg. 1820
SAGINAW CONTROL & ENGINEERING INC.; *U.S. Private*, pg. 3528
SAMMET DAMPERS OY—See Addtech AB; *Int'l*, pg. 135
SCHULER POLAND SERVICE SP. Z O.O.—See ANDRITZ AG; *Int'l*, pg. 456
SCHULER PRESSEN GMBH—See ANDRITZ AG; *Int'l*, pg. 456
SEGUNDO METAL PRODUCTS, INC.—See MiddleGround Management, LP; *U.S. Private*, pg. 2712
SHAPE CORP.; *U.S. Private*, pg. 3625
SHEET METAL PRECISION LIMITED—See Comtech Telecommunications Corp.; *U.S. Public*, pg. 563
SIGNATURE SKYLIGHTS, LLC.; *U.S. Private*, pg. 3650
S&J SHEET METAL SUPPLY INC.; *U.S. Private*, pg. 3513
SKILCRAFT LLC.; *U.S. Private*, pg. 3682
SOUTHEASTERN METALS MANUFACTURING CO. INC.—See Gibraltar Industries, Inc.; *U.S. Public*, pg. 936
SOUTHWARK METAL MANUFACTURING COMPANY - GREENVILLE DIVISION—See Southwark Metal Manufacturing Company; *U.S. Private*, pg. 3738
SOUTHWARK METAL MANUFACTURING COMPANY - IDAHO DIVISION—See Southwark Metal Manufacturing Company; *U.S. Private*, pg. 3738
SOUTHWARK METAL MANUFACTURING COMPANY - INDIANAPOLIS DIVISION—See Southwark Metal Manufacturing Company; *U.S. Private*, pg. 3738
SOUTHWARK METAL MANUFACTURING COMPANY - MISSISSIPPI DIVISION—See Southwark Metal Manufacturing Company; *U.S. Private*, pg. 3738
SOUTHWARK METAL MANUFACTURING COMPANY - NEBRASKA DIVISION—See Southwark Metal Manufacturing Company; *U.S. Private*, pg. 3738
SOUTHWARK METAL MANUFACTURING COMPANY; *U.S. Private*, pg. 3738
SPECIAL PRODUCTS & MANUFACTURING, INC.; *U.S. Private*, pg. 3748
SPEC WEST, INC.—See The Sterling Group, L.P.; *U.S. Private*, pg. 4122
SPEEDRACK PRODUCTS GROUP, LTD.; *U.S. Private*, pg. 3/54
STANDARD IRON & WIRE WORKS INC.; *U.S. Private*, pg. 3780
STEEL CRAFT CORP—See MiddleGround Management, LP; *U.S. Private*, pg. 2712
STEELER INC.; *U.S. Private*, pg. 3796
STEFFES CORPORATION; *U.S. Private*, pg. 3797
STONHARD S.A.S.—See RPM International Inc.; *U.S. Public*, pg. 1819
STONHARD (U.K.) LIMITED—See RPM International Inc.; *U.S. Public*, pg. 1819
SUN PORTS INTERNATIONAL INC.; *U.S. Private*, pg. 3863
SUPERIOR ROLL FORMING CO., INC.; *U.S. Private*, pg. 3880
SUPREME BUILDING PRODUCTS, INC.—See Beacon Roofing Supply, Inc.; *U.S. Public*, pg. 286
SYMONS CORPORATION—See Dayton Superior Corporation; *U.S. Private*, pg. 1178
TA CHEN INTERNATIONAL INC; *U.S. Private*, pg. 3919
TAIYOKOZAI CO., LTD.—See Hanwa Co., Ltd.; *Int'l*, pg. 3263
TEKUN ASAS SDN. BHD.—See Ewein Berhad; *Int'l*, pg. 2576
TENERE INC.—See CORE Industrial Partners, LLC; *U.S. Private*, pg. 1048
TIETEK, INC.—See North American Technologies Group, Inc. (NAMC); *U.S. Private*, pg. 2941
TRINITY HIGHWAY PRODUCTS—See Trinity Industries, Inc.; *U.S. Public*, pg. 2194
TRINITY INDUSTRIES—See Trinity Industries, Inc.; *U.S. Public*, pg. 2194
TROPAR MFG. CO., INC.—See Tropar Mfg. Co., Inc.; *U.S. Private*, pg. 4242
TRUENORTH STEEL - HURON—See TrueNorth Steel Inc.; *U.S. Private*, pg. 4249
UNITED MCGILL CORPORATION - BENNINGTON PLANT—See The McGill Corporation; *U.S. Private*, pg. 4076
UNITED MCGILL CORPORATION - FOUNTAIN INN PLANT—See The McGill Corporation; *U.S. Private*, pg. 4076
UNITED MCGILL CORPORATION - GRAND PRAIRIE PLANT—See The McGill Corporation; *U.S. Private*, pg. 4076
UNITED MCGILL CORPORATION - GRINNELL PLANT—See The McGill Corporation; *U.S. Private*, pg. 4076
UNITED MCGILL CORPORATION - HILLSBORO PLANT—See The McGill Corporation; *U.S. Private*, pg. 4076
UNITED MCGILL CORPORATION - SAN ANTONIO PLANT—See The McGill Corporation; *U.S. Private*, pg. 4076
UNITED MCGILL CORPORATION—See The McGill Corporation; *U.S. Private*, pg. 4076
UNITED MCGILL CORPORATION - STOCKTON PLANT—See The McGill Corporation; *U.S. Private*, pg. 4076
THE UNIVERSAL STEEL CO.—See Columbia National Group Inc; *U.S. Private*, pg. 977
VALLEY SHEET METAL COMPANY—See Frank M. Booth Inc.; *U.S. Private*, pg. 1595
VICON MACHINERY, LLC—See Plasma Automation, Inc.; *U.S. Private*, pg. 3198
VOGTLE SERVICE GMBH & CO. KG—See ANDRITZ AG; *Int'l*, pg. 456
WEBCO INTERNATIONAL LLC—See Balli Group plc; *Int'l*, pg. 809
WELDING METALLURGY, INC.—See CPI Aerostructures, Inc.; *U.S. Public*, pg. 588
WESTERN FORMS INC.; *U.S. Private*, pg. 4493
WEYBRIDGE, LLC; *U.S. Private*, pg. 4503
WHITACRE ENGINEERING CO. INC.; *U.S. Private*, pg. 4507
WILEY METAL FABRICATING, INC.; *U.S. Private*, pg. 4519
WLMD; *U.S. Private*, pg. 4551
WSB TITAN INC.—See GMS Inc.; *U.S. Public*, pg. 948
YG TECH CO., LTD.—See Honda Motor Co., Ltd.; *Int'l*, pg. 3464
ZENITH R.S.—See Cefla S.C.; *Int'l*, pg. 1390

332323 — ORNAMENTAL AND ARCHITECTURAL METAL WORK MANUFACTURING

3FORM LLC—See Armstrong World Industries, Inc.; *U.S. Public*, pg. 193
ACTION EQUIPMENT & SCAFFOLD CO. INC.; *U.S. Private*, pg. 67
AGCO CORPORATION-JACKSON OPERATIONS—See AGCO Corporation; *U.S. Public*, pg. 58
THE AIROLITE COMPANY; *U.S. Private*, pg. 3983
ALABAMA METAL INDUSTRIES CORPORATION—See Gibraltar Industries, Inc.; *U.S. Public*, pg. 935
ALFA LAVAL MID EUROPE GMBH—See Alfa Laval AB; *Int'l*, pg. 309
ALUMICOR LIMITED—See Apogee Enterprises, Inc.; *U.S. Public*, pg. 145
AMERICAN IRON WORKS; *U.S. Private*, pg. 238
AMERICAN STAIR CORPORATION; *U.S. Private*, pg. 255
AMICO FONTANA—See Gibraltar Industries, Inc.; *U.S. Public*, pg. 935
AMICO HOUSTON—See Gibraltar Industries, Inc.; *U.S. Public*, pg. 935
AMICO LAKELAND—See Gibraltar Industries, Inc.; *U.S. Public*, pg. 935
AMICO OREM—See Gibraltar Industries, Inc.; *U.S. Public*, pg. 935
AMICO—See Gibraltar Industries, Inc.; *U.S. Public*, pg. 935
ARIZONA STAIRS, INC.—See McDonough Corporation; *U.S. Private*, pg. 2632
AUTOMATED EQUIPMENT COMPANY INC.—See Diamond Parking Services LLC; *U.S. Private*, pg. 1223
BARKERS ENGINEERING LTD—See Hill & Smith PLC; *Int'l*, pg. 3391
BBQ GUY'S MANUFACTURING, LLC; *U.S. Private*, pg. 498
BEAD INDUSTRIES INC - BEAD CHAIN DIVISION—See Bead Industries Inc.; *U.S. Private*, pg. 505
B. GRIMM MBM METALWORKS LIMITED—See B. Grimm Group; *Int'l*, pg. 788
BIL-JAX, INC.—See Haulotte Group SA; *Int'l*, pg. 3285
BOSTON METAL PRODUCTS CORPORATION, HOME CENTER MERCHANDISING DIVISION—See Boston Metal Products Corporation; *U.S. Private*, pg. 622
BOSTON METAL PRODUCTS CORPORATION; *U.S. Private*, pg. 621
BURBAGE IRON CRAFT LTD.—See ARGENT INDUSTRIAL LIMITED; *Int'l*, pg. 560
BURGESS ARCHITECTURAL PRODUCTS LIMITED; *Int'l*, pg. 1223
CANNOCK GATES LTD.—See ARGENT INDUSTRIAL LIMITED; *Int'l*, pg. 560
CAPITOL WHOLESALE FENCE COMPANY, INC.—See The Sterling Group, L.P.; *U.S. Private*, pg. 4122
CHINA FANGDA GROUP CO., LTD.; *Int'l*, pg. 1501
CH YODOFORM SDN. BHD.—See AYS Ventures Berhad; *Int'l*, pg. 776
CONSPEC INTERNATIONAL (HONG KONG) LTD.—See Construction Specialties, Inc.; *U.S. Private*, pg. 1024
CONSTRUCTION SPECIALITIES, INC. - DECCOLINK PRODUCTS DIVISION—See Construction Specialties, Inc.; *U.S. Private*, pg. 1024
CONSTRUCTION SPECIALTIES, INC.; *U.S. Private*, pg. 1024
CONSTRUCTION SPECIALTIES LTD.—See Construction Specialties, Inc.; *U.S. Private*, pg. 1024
C.R. LAURENCE OF AUSTRALIA PTY LTD.—See KPS Capital Partners, LP; *U.S. Private*, pg. 2348
C.R. LAURENCE OF CANADA—See KPS Capital Partners, LP; *U.S. Private*, pg. 2348
C.R. LAURENCE OF EUROPE GMBH—See KPS Capital Partners, LP; *U.S. Private*, pg. 2348
C.R. LAURENCE OF EUROPE LTD.—See KPS Capital Partners, LP; *U.S. Private*, pg. 2348
CRL US ALUMINUM - CAROLINA—See KPS Capital Partners, LP; *U.S. Private*, pg. 2348
CRL US ALUMINUM - ILLINOIS—See KPS Capital Partners, LP; *U.S. Private*, pg. 2348
CRL US ALUMINUM—See KPS Capital Partners, LP; *U.S. Private*, pg. 2348
CROCODILE TOOL COMPANY (UGANDA) LTD.—See Alam Group of Companies; *Int'l*, pg. 289
C/S CONSTRUCTION SPECIALTIES MIDDLE EAST LLC—See Construction Specialties, Inc.; *U.S. Private*, pg. 1024
CSR MARTINI PTY LIMITED—See CSR Limited; *Int'l*, pg. 1867
DEAN FENCE & GATE, INC.; *U.S. Private*, pg. 1183
DIAMOND PERFORATED METALS, INC.—See Gibraltar Industries, Inc.; *U.S. Public*, pg. 935
DIXIE METAL PRODUCTS INC.; *U.S. Private*, pg. 1245
EAST & WEST ALUM CRAFT LTD.; *Int'l*, pg. 2269
ECOLITE MANUFACTURING CO. INC.; *U.S. Private*, pg. 1329
EMPIRE CITY IRON WORKS; *U.S. Private*, pg. 1384
ETOBICOKE IRONWORKS LIMITED; *Int'l*, pg. 2524
FABENCO, INC.—See Akoya Capital LLC; *U.S. Private*, pg. 146
FABENCO, INC.—See Gemini Investors LLC; *U.S. Private*, pg. 1658
FABENCO, INC.—See TMW Enterprises Inc.; *U.S. Private*, pg. 4180
FABRYKI SPRZETU I NARZEDZI GORNICZYCH GRUPA KAPITALOWA FASING S.A.; *Int'l*, pg. 2600
FENCING AND GATES—See ARGENT INDUSTRIAL LIMITED; *Int'l*, pg. 560
F.J. ASCHWANDEN AG—See CRH plc; *Int'l*, pg. 1844
FLORIDA MISCELLANEOUS STRUCTURAL PRODUCTS—See TTI Holdings Inc.; *U.S. Private*, pg. 4254
GLOBAL ARCHITECTURAL METALS INC—See Allan Window Technologies Ltd.; *Int'l*, pg. 333
GRECO ALUMINUM RAILINGS, LTD.—See CSW Industrials, Inc.; *U.S. Public*, pg. 601
GRECO ALUMINUM RAILINGS (U.S.A.) INC.—See CSW Industrials, Inc.; *U.S. Public*, pg. 601
HAPCO—See The Dyson-Kissner-Moran Corporation; *U.S. Private*, pg. 4024
HARSCO IKG, LLC—See KPS Capital Partners, LP; *U.S. Private*, pg. 2347
HARSCO METALS & MINERALS—See Enviri Corporation; *U.S. Public*, pg. 780
HARSCO METALS SWEDEN A.B.—See Enviri Corporation; *U.S. Public*, pg. 780

332323 — ORNAMENTAL AND ARCH...

HAULOTTE CHILE SPA—See Haulotte Group SA; *Int'l*, pg. 3285
HAULOTTE NORTH AMERICA MANUFACTURING L.L.C—See Haulotte Group SA; *Int'l*, pg. 3285
HUNTER DOUGLAS ARCHITECTURAL PRODUCTS INC.—See 3G Capital Partners L.P.; *U.S. Private*, pg. 13
HUNTER DOUGLAS MANAGEMENT AG—See 3G Capital Partners L.P.; *U.S. Private*, pg. 12
IDEX SAS—See IDEX Corp; *U.S. Public*, pg. 1091
INDUSTRIAL SERVICES PTE LTD—See Hai Leck Holdings Limited; *Int'l*, pg. 3208
JERITH MANUFACTURING LLC—See ASSA ABLOY AB; *Int'l*, pg. 639
JOSEF GARTNER & CO. UK LTD—See Atlas Holdings, LLC; *U.S. Private*, pg. 377
JOSEF GARTNER CURTAIN WALL (SHANGHAI) CO. LTD.—See Atlas Holdings, LLC; *U.S. Private*, pg. 377
JOSEF GARTNER GMBH—See Atlas Holdings, LLC; *U.S. Private*, pg. 377
JOSEF GARTNER SWITZERLAND AG—See Atlas Holdings, LLC; *U.S. Private*, pg. 377
LANE SUPPLY INC.; *U.S. Private*, pg. 2388
LAUBEUF SAS—See CRH plc; *Int'l*, pg. 1844
LAVI INDUSTRIES INC.; *U.S. Private*, pg. 2400
LOGTHAI-HAI LECK ENGINEERING CO., LTD.—See Hai Leck Holdings Limited; *Int'l*, pg. 3208
MCGREGOR INDUSTRIES INC.; *U.S. Private*, pg. 2635
M. COHEN & SONS INC.; *U.S. Private*, pg. 2526
MERCHANT & EVANS, INC.; *U.S. Private*, pg. 2669
MESH ARCHITECTURE + FABRICATION; *U.S. Private*, pg. 2678
MICHIGAN ORNAMENTAL METALS—See Western Construction Group; *U.S. Private*, pg. 4492
MISCELLANEOUS METALS INC.; *U.S. Private*, pg. 2746
O'KEEFFE'S, INC.; *U.S. Private*, pg. 2978
OLDCASTLE BUILDINGENVELOPE, INC. - DALLAS—See KPS Capital Partners, LP; *U.S. Private*, pg. 2348
OOO JOSEF GARTNER—See Atlas Holdings, LLC; *U.S. Private*, pg. 377
ORIENTAL METALS PTE LTD—See HG Metal Manufacturing Limited; *Int'l*, pg. 3375
OSRAM SYLVANIA PUERTO RICO—See ams AG; *Int'l*, pg. 440
PERMASTEELISA HONG KONG LTD.—See Atlas Holdings, LLC; *U.S. Private*, pg. 378
PERMASTEELISA PTY LTD—See Atlas Holdings, LLC; *U.S. Private*, pg. 378
PLASTIVAL INC.—See Cyprium Investment Partners LLC; *U.S. Private*, pg. 1135
PREFAB TECHNOLOGY 3 PTE LTD—See Hor Kew Corporation Limited; *Int'l*, pg. 3474
RAILTECH CALOMEX S. DE R. L. DE C. V.—See CVC Capital Partners SICAV-FIS S.A.; *Int'l*, pg. 1887
SAINT-GOBAIN ECOPHON A/S—See Compagnie de Saint-Gobain SA; *Int'l*, pg. 1733
SAINT-GOBAIN ECOPHON LTD—See Compagnie de Saint-Gobain SA; *Int'l*, pg. 1733
SAINT-GOBAIN ECOPHON PRODUCTION A/S—See Compagnie de Saint-Gobain SA; *Int'l*, pg. 1733
SAINT-GOBAIN GYPROC NEDERLAND BV—See Compagnie de Saint-Gobain SA; *Int'l*, pg. 1734
SAINT-GOBAIN MATERIAUX INNOVANTS—See Compagnie de Saint-Gobain SA; *Int'l*, pg. 1735
SFC KOENIG LLC—See IDEX Corp; *U.S. Public*, pg. 1092
SHENZHEN SANXIN FACADE ENGINEERING CO., LTD.—See Hainan Development Holdings Nanhai Co., Ltd.; *Int'l*, pg. 3212
SHOEMAKER MANUFACTURING, CO.—See CSW Industrials, Inc.; *U.S. Public*, pg. 602
SIAMMCO LTD.—See Alam Group of Companies; *Int'l*, pg. 289
SIGHTLINE COMMERCIAL SOLUTIONS LLC; *U.S. Private*, pg. 3648
SOUCY INDUSTRIES INC.; *U.S. Private*, pg. 3716
STENI AS—See Accent Equity Partners AB; *Int'l*, pg. 81
SUNSETTER PRODUCTS, LP—See AEA Investors LP; *U.S. Private*, pg. 115
SUNSETTER PRODUCTS, LP—See British Columbia Investment Management Corp.; *Int'l*, pg. 1170
SWANTON WELDING & MACHINING CO, INC.; *U.S. Private*, pg. 3891
TARTER GATE COMPANY, LLC—See Platinum Equity, LLC; *U.S. Private*, pg. 3208
TAYLOR MADE CUSTOM PRODUCTS—See LCI Industries; *U.S. Public*, pg. 1295
TECHNIFORM METAL CURVING OF TEXAS—See Techniform Metal Curving Inc.; *U.S. Private*, pg. 3954
THINXXS MICROTECHNOLOGY AG—See IDEX Corp; *U.S. Public*, pg. 1092
TITAN STAIRS INC.—See McDonough Corporation; *U.S. Private*, pg. 2633
TREX COMMERCIAL PRODUCTS, INC.—See Sightline Commercial Solutions LLC; *U.S. Private*, pg. 3648
TRUENORTH STEEL INC.; *U.S. Private*, pg. 4249
THE TYMETAL CORP.—See The Fort Miller Group Inc.; *U.S. Private*, pg. 4030
ULTRALOX TECHNOLOGY, LLC—See The AZEK Company Inc.; *U.S. Public*, pg. 2035

USG INTERIORS, INC.—See Gebr. Knauf KG; *Int'l*, pg. 2908
WASHINGTON ORNAMENTAL IRON WORKS; *U.S. Private*, pg. 4448
WESCO FOUNTAINS, INC.; *U.S. Private*, pg. 4482
WILDECK, INC.—See Holden Industries, Inc.; *U.S. Private*, pg. 1962
WON-DOOR CORPORATION; *U.S. Private*, pg. 4556
WOOSTER PRODUCTS, INC.; *U.S. Private*, pg. 4562
XPANDA SECURITY PROPRIETARY LIMITED—See ARGENT INDUSTRIAL LIMITED; *Int'l*, pg. 561

332410 — POWER BOILER AND HEAT EXCHANGER MANUFACTURING

AALBORG INDUSTRIES D.O.O.—See Alfa Laval AB; *Int'l*, pg. 308
ADVANCE BOILERS SDN. BHD.—See CB Industrial Product Holding Berhad; *Int'l*, pg. 1364
AE&E LENTJES PRAHA S.R.O.—See Doosan Corporation; *Int'l*, pg. 2173
AE&E NANJING BOILER CO. LTD.—See A-TEC Industries AG; *Int'l*, pg. 21
AERCO INTERNATIONAL, INC.—See Watts Water Technologies, Inc.; *U.S. Public*, pg. 2337
AESYS TECHNOLOGIES, LLC; *U.S. Private*, pg. 120
AGC HEAT TRANSFER INC.—See Alfa Laval AB; *Int'l*, pg. 309
AGC HEAT TRANSFER INC. - WESTERN FACTORY—See Alfa Laval AB; *Int'l*, pg. 309
AIXTRON INC.—See Aixtron SE; *Int'l*, pg. 255
AKG INDIA PRIVATE LTD.—See Autokuhler GmbH & Co. KG; *Int'l*, pg. 727
AKG THERMAL SYSTEMS (TAICANG) CO., LTD.—See Autokuhler GmbH & Co. KG; *Int'l*, pg. 727
AKG THERMOTECHNIK GMBH & CO. KG—See Autokuhler GmbH & Co. KG; *Int'l*, pg. 727
AKG VERWALTUNGSGESELLSCHAFT MBH—See Autokuhler GmbH & Co. KG; *Int'l*, pg. 727
A.L. EASTMOND & SONS INC.; *U.S. Private*, pg. 26
ALFA LAVAL AALBORG A/S—See Alfa Laval AB; *Int'l*, pg. 308
ALFA LAVAL AALBORG (FPS) PTE LTD—See Alfa Laval AB; *Int'l*, pg. 308
ALFA LAVAL AALBORG LTD—See Alfa Laval AB; *Int'l*, pg. 308
ALFA LAVAL AALBORG OY—See Alfa Laval AB; *Int'l*, pg. 308
ALFA LAVAL AALBORG PTY LTD—See Alfa Laval AB; *Int'l*, pg. 309
ALFA LAVAL CORPORATE AB—See Alfa Laval AB; *Int'l*, pg. 309
ALFA LAVAL D.O.O.—See Alfa Laval AB; *Int'l*, pg. 312
ALFA LAVAL EUROPE AB—See Alfa Laval AB; *Int'l*, pg. 309
ALFA LAVAL GRONINGEN BV—See Alfa Laval AB; *Int'l*, pg. 309
ALFA LAVAL HAIPHONG CO. LTD—See Alfa Laval AB; *Int'l*, pg. 308
ALFA LAVAL HOLDING GMBH—See Alfa Laval AB; *Int'l*, pg. 309
ALFA LAVAL (JIANGYIN) MANUFACTURING CO LTD—See Alfa Laval AB; *Int'l*, pg. 308
ALFA LAVAL KFT.—See Alfa Laval AB; *Int'l*, pg. 310
ALFA LAVAL KRAKOW SP.Z.O.O.—See Alfa Laval AB; *Int'l*, pg. 310
ALFA LAVAL (KUNSHAN) MANUFACTURING CO LTD—See Alfa Laval AB; *Int'l*, pg. 308
ALFA LAVAL LTD—See Alfa Laval AB; *Int'l*, pg. 310
ALFA LAVAL LUND AB—See Alfa Laval AB; *Int'l*, pg. 310
ALFA LAVAL MAKINE SANAYII VE TICARET LTD STI—See Alfa Laval AB; *Int'l*, pg. 310
ALFA LAVAL MIDDLE EAST LTD—See Alfa Laval AB; *Int'l*, pg. 310
ALFA LAVAL NIJMEGEN B.V.—See Alfa Laval AB; *Int'l*, pg. 312
ALFA LAVAL OLMI SPA—See Alfa Laval AB; *Int'l*, pg. 310
ALFA LAVAL (PTY) LTD—See Alfa Laval AB; *Int'l*, pg. 308
ALFA LAVAL (QINGDAO) CO. LTD—See Alfa Laval AB; *Int'l*, pg. 308
ALFA LAVAL S.A.—See Alfa Laval AB; *Int'l*, pg. 311
ALFA LAVAL SPIRAL SAS—See Alfa Laval AB; *Int'l*, pg. 309
ALFA LAVAL THERMAL A/S—See Alfa Laval AB; *Int'l*, pg. 311
ALFA LAVAL UKRAINE—See Alfa Laval AB; *Int'l*, pg. 311
ALFA LAVAL USA INC.—See Alfa Laval AB; *Int'l*, pg. 309
ALFA LAVAL VICARB SAS—See Alfa Laval AB; *Int'l*, pg. 309
ALL STATE TANK MANUFACTURING, LLC—See Cameron Holdings Corporation; *U.S. Private*, pg. 729
AMI EXCHANGERS LTD.—See DMI UK Ltd.; *Int'l*, pg. 2145
ANSALDOCALDAI BOILERS INDIA PRIVATE LIMITED—See Gammon India Limited; *Int'l*, pg. 2879
AO ALFA LAVAL POTOK—See Alfa Laval AB; *Int'l*, pg. 308
A. O. SMITH CORPORATION; *U.S. Public*, pg. 11
API HEAT TRANSFER, INC.—See Guggenheim Partners, LLC; *U.S. Private*, pg. 1811
API HEAT TRANSFER, INC.—See Littlejohn & Co., LLC; *U.S. Private*, pg. 2469

ARABIAN CBI LTD.—See McDermott International, Inc.; *U.S. Public*, pg. 1405
ARISTON DEUTSCHLAND GMBH—See Ariston Holding N.V.; *Int'l*, pg. 567
ARISTON THERMO CZ S.R.O.—See Ariston Holding N.V.; *Int'l*, pg. 567
ARISTON THERMO MAROC S.A.—See Ariston Holding N.V.; *Int'l*, pg. 567
ARISTON THERMO ROMANIA S.R.L.—See Ariston Holding N.V.; *Int'l*, pg. 567
ARISTON THERMO UK LTD.—See Ariston Holding N.V.; *Int'l*, pg. 567
ARMSTRONG-YOSHITAKE, INC.—See Armstrong International, Inc.; *U.S. Private*, pg. 332
ASM FAR EAST MARKETING LTD.—See ASM INTERNATIONAL N.V.; *Int'l*, pg. 626
ATAG VERWARMING BELGIE B.V.B.A.—See Ariston Holding N.V.; *Int'l*, pg. 567
ATLANTIC FRANCO BELGE—See Atlantic Societe Francaise Develop Thermique S.A.; *Int'l*, pg. 675
ATLANTIC GUILLOT—See Atlantic Societe Francaise Develop Thermique S.A.; *Int'l*, pg. 675
AUTOKUHLER GMBH & CO. KG; *Int'l*, pg. 727
AZENTA, INC.; *U.S. Public*, pg. 257
BABCOCK-HITACHI (PHILIPPINES) INC.—See Hitachi, Ltd.; *Int'l*, pg. 3423
BABCOCK WANSON SA - MANUFACTURING FACILITY—See Fonds de Consolidation et de Developpement des Entreprises; *Int'l*, pg. 2725
BABCOCK & WILCOX VOLUND A/S—See Babcock & Wilcox Enterprises, Inc.; *U.S. Public*, pg. 262
BARRIQUAND TECHNOLOGIES THERMIQUES SAS - ASET PRODUCTION FACILITY—See Groupe SFPI SA; *Int'l*, pg. 3111
BARRIQUAND TECHNOLOGIES THERMIQUES SAS—See Groupe SFPI SA; *Int'l*, pg. 3111
BDR THERMEA GROUP B.V.; *Int'l*, pg. 930
BHARAT HEAVY PLATES & VESSELS LIMITED—See Bharat Heavy Electricals Limited; *Int'l*, pg. 1011
BHI CO., LTD.; *Int'l*, pg. 1015
BLOOMFIELD ENGINEERING COMPANY INC.—See Caledonia Investments plc; *Int'l*, pg. 1262
BM GREENTECH BHD; *Int'l*, pg. 1075
BOILERMECH SDN BHD—See BM GreenTech Bhd; *Int'l*, pg. 1075
BOOSTER CO., LTD.; *Int'l*, pg. 1111
BRYAN STEAM LLC—See Burnham Holdings, Inc.; *U.S. Public*, pg. 412
BWXT CANADA LTD.—See BWX Technologies, Inc.; *U.S. Public*, pg. 413
BWXT NUCLEAR ENERGY CANADA INC.—See BWX Technologies, Inc.; *U.S. Public*, pg. 413
BWXT NUCLEAR ENERGY, INC.—See Electricite de France S.A.; *Int'l*, pg. 2351
BWXT NUCLEAR OPERATIONS GROUP, INC.—See Electricite de France S.A.; *Int'l*, pg. 2351
CANDU ENERGY INC.—See AtkinsRealis Group Inc.; *Int'l*, pg. 671
CB&I - ALPHARETTA—See McDermott International, Inc.; *U.S. Public*, pg. 1405
CEMM CO., LTD.—See Dowa Holdings Co., Ltd.; *Int'l*, pg. 2182
CHANUTE MANUFACTURING COMPANY—See Babcock & Wilcox Enterprises, Inc.; *U.S. Public*, pg. 263
CHART ENERGY & CHEMICALS INC.—See Chart Industries, Inc.; *U.S. Public*, pg. 481
CHART INDUSTRIES, INC.; *U.S. Public*, pg. 481
CHINA WESTERN POWER INDUSTRIAL CO., LTD.; *Int'l*, pg. 1563
C.I. GROUP PUBLIC COMPANY LIMITED - FACTORY 2—See C.I. Group Public Company Limited; *Int'l*, pg. 1243
C.I. GROUP PUBLIC COMPANY LIMITED - FACTORY 3—See C.I. Group Public Company Limited; *Int'l*, pg. 1243
CLEAVER-BROOKS INC.—See Harbour Group Industries, Inc.; *U.S. Private*, pg. 1860
CLYDE BERGEMANN DRYCON GMBH—See Clyde Blowers Capital IM LLP; *Int'l*, pg. 1665
COMELF SA; *Int'l*, pg. 1710
CORE WORKS, LLC—See Compass Group PLC; *Int'l*, pg. 1751
CTR S.R.L.—See Denso Corporation; *Int'l*, pg. 2028
CURO CO., LTD.; *Int'l*, pg. 1879
DALIAN CIMC CONTAINER CO., LTD—See China International Marine Containers (Group) Co., Ltd.; *Int'l*, pg. 1511
DELTA CHEMICAL CORP.—See Nolan Capital, Inc.; *U.S. Private*, pg. 2934
DELTA ENERGY SYSTEMS (GERMANY) GMBH—See Delta Electronics, Inc.; *Int'l*, pg. 2018
DIVERSE ENERGY SYSTEMS LLC—See Turnbridge Capital, LLC; *U.S. Private*, pg. 4260
DOOSAN VINA HAIPHONG CO., LTD.—See Doosan Corporation; *Int'l*, pg. 2173
ECOFLAM BRUCIATORI S.P.A.—See Ariston Holding N.V.; *Int'l*, pg. 567
ELCO AUSTRIA GMBH—See Ariston Holding N.V.; *Int'l*, pg. 567

N.A.I.C.S. INDEX

ELCO BURNERS B.V.—See Ariston Holding N.V.; *Int'l*, pg. 567
ELCO BURNERS GMBH—See Ariston Holding N.V.; *Int'l*, pg. 567
ELCO HEATING SOLUTIONS LIMITED—See Ariston Holding N.V.; *Int'l*, pg. 567
ENERGOINSTAL S.A.; *Int'l*, pg. 2421
FANELLI HAAG KILGER PLLC—See Seyfarth Shaw; *U.S. Private*, pg. 3620
FIBRO CHEM LLC.—See Polyventive LLC; *U.S. Private*, pg. 3226
FINTUBE, LLC—See Heartwood Partners, LLC; *U.S. Private*, pg. 1901
FRAMATOME SAS—See Electricite de France S.A.; *Int'l*, pg. 2351
FRANCO TOSI MECCANICA S.P.A.—See Gammon India Limited; *Int'l*, pg. 2879
FURNACE AND TUBE SERVICE INC.; *U.S. Private*, pg. 1624
FURUKAWA AVC ELECTRONICS (SUZHOU) CO., LTD.—See Asia Vital Components Co., Ltd.; *Int'l*, pg. 616
GANGWON CO., LTD.; *Int'l*, pg. 2881
GEA CALDEMON, S.A.—See GEA Group Aktiengesellschaft; *Int'l*, pg. 2898
GEA INDUSTRIAL HEAT EXCHANGER SYSTEMS (CHINA) LTD.—See GEA Group Aktiengesellschaft; *Int'l*, pg. 2899
GEA IRELAND LIMITED—See GEA Group Aktiengesellschaft; *Int'l*, pg. 2899
GETABEC PUBLIC COMPANY LIMITED; *Int'l*, pg. 2947
GRAFF—See Hiolle Industries S.A.; *Int'l*, pg. 3401
GRANGES AB; *Int'l*, pg. 3058
HAMON & CIE S.A.; *Int'l*, pg. 3239
HAMON DELTAK, INC.—See Hamon & Cie S.A.; *Int'l*, pg. 3239
HAMWORTHY HEATING LIMITED—See Atlantic Societe Francaise Develop Thermique S.A.; *Int'l*, pg. 675
HANGZHOU HONGSHENG ZHONGHONG NEW ENERGY CO., LTD.—See Hongsheng Heat Exchanger Manufacturing Co.,ltd; *Int'l*, pg. 3471
HARBIN ELECTRIC CORPORATION; *Int'l*, pg. 3270
HEATEC GUANGZHOU CO., LTD.—See Heatec JieTong Holdings Ltd; *Int'l*, pg. 3305
HEATEC JIETONG PTE. LTD.—See Heatec JieTong Holdings Ltd; *Int'l*, pg. 3305
HEATEC SHANGHAI CO., LTD.—See Heatec JieTong Holdings Ltd; *Int'l*, pg. 3305
HEATRIC—See Parker Hannifin Corporation; *U.S. Public*, pg. 1641
HERING AG—See BAVARIA Industries Group AG; *Int'l*, pg. 899
HISAKA MIDDLE EAST CO., LTD—See Hisaka Works, Ltd.; *Int'l*, pg. 3406
HISAKAWORKS S.E.A. SDN. BHD.—See Hisaka Works, Ltd.; *Int'l*, pg. 3406
HITACHI-GE NUCLEAR ENERGY, LTD.—See Hitachi, Ltd.; *Int'l*, pg. 3422
HLE GLASCOAT LIMITED; *Int'l*, pg. 3431
HUGHES-ANDERSON HEAT EXCHANGERS; *U.S. Private*, pg. 2004
INDUSTRIAL HEAT TRANSFER INC.; *U.S. Private*, pg. 2066
INTEVAC, INC.; *U.S. Public*, pg. 1159
JACKSON & CHURCH HVAC GLOBAL—See AESYS Technologies, LLC; *U.S. Private*, pg. 120
JOHNSTON BOILER COMPANY INC.—See Hines Corporation; *U.S. Private*, pg. 1949
JOSEPH OAT CORPORATION; *U.S. Private*, pg. 2237
KLINGENBURG GMBH—See Carel Industries S.p.A.; *Int'l*, pg. 1324
KLINGENBURG INTERNATIONAL SP. Z O.O.—See Carel Industries S.p.A.; *Int'l*, pg. 1324
KLINGENBURG USA, LLC—See Carel Industries S.p.A.; *Int'l*, pg. 1324
LAARS HEATING SYSTEMS CO.—See Bradford-White Corporation; *U.S. Private*, pg. 632
LEROUX & LOTZ MAINTYS SAS—See Altawest Group; *Int'l*, pg. 388
LEROUX & LOTZ TECHNOLOGIES SA—See Altawest Group; *Int'l*, pg. 388
LHE CO. LTD.—See Alfa Laval AB; *Int'l*, pg. 312
LOCHINVAR, LLC—See A. O. Smith Corporation; *U.S. Public*, pg. 12
MANNING & LEWIS ENGINEERING COMPANY; *U.S. Private*, pg. 2565
MCDERMOTT INTERNATIONAL, INC.; *U.S. Public*, pg. 1404
MITSUBISHI POWER, LTD.—See Hitachi, Ltd.; *Int'l*, pg. 3423
MONITOR PRODUCTS INC.; *U.S. Private*, pg. 2771
MUNROE, INC.—See Woodings Industrial Corporation; *U.S. Private*, pg. 4558
NOOTER/ERIKSEN, INC.—See CIC Group, Inc.; *U.S. Private*, pg. 896
NOOTER/ERIKSEN SRL—See CIC Group, Inc.; *U.S. Private*, pg. 896
NRF DEUTSCHLAND GMBH—See Banco Products (I) Ltd.; *Int'l*, pg. 824
NTI BOILERS INC.—See Ariston Holding N.V.; *Int'l*, pg. 567

OAO ALFA LAVAL POTOK—See Alfa Laval AB; *Int'l*, pg. 312
OJSC IZHORSKIYE ZAVODY—See Gazprombank JSC; *Int'l*, pg. 2892
PERRY PRODUCTS CORPORATION—See Perry Videx LLC; *U.S. Private*, pg. 3154
PRECISION BOILERS, INC.—See Source Capital, LLC; *U.S. Private*, pg. 3718
PROGEN SYSTEMS AND TECHNOLOGIES LIMITED—See BGR Energy Systems Limited; *Int'l*, pg. 1009
P.T. ARISTON THERMO INDONESIA—See Ariston Holding N.V.; *Int'l*, pg. 567
PT BOILERMECH MANUFACTURING INDONESIA—See BM GreenTech Bhd; *Int'l*, pg. 1075
R & D ENTERPRISES, INC.—See Resilience Capital Partners, LLC; *U.S. Private*, pg. 3405
SCHELDE EXOTECH B.V.—See BENCIS Capital Partners B.V.; *Int'l*, pg. 970
SCHWANK BE—See Schwank Inc.; *U.S. Private*, pg. 3572
SCHWANK BV—See Schwank Inc.; *U.S. Private*, pg. 3572
SCHWANK GMBH—See Schwank Inc.; *U.S. Private*, pg. 3572
SCHWANK LTD—See Schwank Inc.; *U.S. Private*, pg. 3572
SCHWANK S.A.R.L.—See Schwank Inc.; *U.S. Private*, pg. 3572
SCHWANK—See Schwank Inc.; *U.S. Private*, pg. 3572
SCHWANK SRL—See Schwank Inc.; *U.S. Private*, pg. 3572
SIA ALFA LAVAL EESTI FILIAAL—See Alfa Laval AB; *Int'l*, pg. 312
SIEMPELKAMP TENSIONING SYSTEMS GMBH—See G. Siempelkamp GmbH & Co. KG; *Int'l*, pg. 2865
SNOW DRAGON LLC—See Park-Ohio Holdings Corp.; *U.S. Public*, pg. 1640
SPX HEAT TRANSFER INC.—See SPX Technologies, Inc.; *U.S. Public*, pg. 1921
SPX HEAT TRANSFER—See SPX Technologies, Inc.; *U.S. Public*, pg. 1921
STERLING THERMAL TECHNOLOGY LIMITED—See Caledonia Investments plc; *Int'l*, pg. 1262
STORK - THERMEQ - HENGELO—See Fluor Corporation; *U.S. Public*, pg. 860
SWEP INTERNATIONAL AB—See Dover Corporation; *U.S. Public*, pg. 679
TEPLOPROGRESS OJSC—See Enel S.p.A.; *Int'l*, pg. 2414
THERMAL ENGINEERING INTERNATIONAL (USA) INC. - MSR DIVISION—See Babcock Power, Inc.; *U.S. Private*, pg. 422
TRANSISTOR DEVICES EUROPE LTD.—See TDI Power Systems; *U.S. Private*, pg. 3944
TRANTER HEAT EXCHANGERS (BEIJING) CO LTD—See Alfa Laval AB; *Int'l*, pg. 308
TRANTER HEAT EXCHANGERS CANADA INC.—See Alfa Laval AB; *Int'l*, pg. 310
TRANTER HES GMBH—See Alfa Laval AB; *Int'l*, pg. 310
TRANTER INC.—See Alfa Laval AB; *Int'l*, pg. 309
TRANTER INDIA PVT LTD—See Alfa Laval AB; *Int'l*, pg. 310
TRANTER INTERNATIONAL AB—See Alfa Laval AB; *Int'l*, pg. 310
TRANTER PHE, INC.—See Alfa Laval AB; *Int'l*, pg. 310
TRANTER SAS—See Alfa Laval AB; *Int'l*, pg. 310
TRANTER SRL—See Alfa Laval AB; *Int'l*, pg. 311
TRANTER WARMETAUSCHER GMBH—See Alfa Laval AB; *Int'l*, pg. 309
TSM CHAMP, LLC—See Altus Capital Partners, Inc.; *U.S. Private*, pg. 211
TTC NORGE AS—See Beijer Ref AB; *Int'l*, pg. 945
TURBOTEC PRODUCTS, INC.; *U.S. Private*, pg. 4259
VENT-RITE VALVE CORPORATION; *U.S. Private*, pg. 4357
VEROLME SPECIAL EQUIPMENT B.V.—See BENCIS Capital Partners B.V.; *Int'l*, pg. 970
VOGT POWER INTERNATIONAL INC.—See Babcock Power, Inc.; *U.S. Private*, pg. 422
WAKEFIELD THERMAL SOLUTIONS—See The Heico Companies, L.L.C.; *U.S. Private*, pg. 4051
WAKEFIELD-VETTE, INC. - COOLCENTRIC DIVISION—See The Heico Companies, L.L.C.; *U.S. Private*, pg. 4051
WAKEFIELD-VETTE, INC.—See The Heico Companies, L.L.C.; *U.S. Private*, pg. 4051
WEBSTER ENGINEERING & MANUFACTURING CO., L.L.C.—See Lionheart Ventures; *U.S. Private*, pg. 2464
WEISS FRANCE SAS—See Compagnie Financiere et de Participations Roullier SA; *Int'l*, pg. 1740
WUHAN BOILER COMPANY LIMITED—See General Electric Company; *U.S. Public*, pg. 918
WUXI GUANYUN HEAT EXCHANGER CO., LTD.—See Hongsheng Heat Exchanger Manufacturing Co.,ltd; *Int'l*, pg. 3471
YGNIS INDUSTRIE—See Atlantic Societe Francaise Devolop Thermique S.A.; *Int'l*, pg. 675
YORK SHIPLEY GLOBAL—See AESYS Technologies, LLC; *U.S. Private*, pg. 120
YOUNG TOUCHSTONE COMPANY—See Westinghouse Air Brake Technologies Corporation; *U.S. Public*, pg. 2360

332420 — METAL TANK (HEAVY G...

332420 — METAL TANK (HEAVY GAUGE) MANUFACTURING

ALFA-LAVAL BENELUX B.V.—See Alfa Laval AB; *Int'l*, pg. 311
ALFA LAVAL LKM A/S—See Alfa Laval AB; *Int'l*, pg. 310
ALFA LAVAL TANK EQUIPMENT A/S—See Alfa Laval AB; *Int'l*, pg. 310
A & M FEBCON LIMITED; *Int'l*, pg. 17
AMTROL-ALFA METALOMECANICA, S.A.—See Worthington Industries, Inc.; *U.S. Public*, pg. 2382
A. O. SMITH WATER PRODUCTS CO. - CHARLOTTE PLANT—See A. O. Smith Corporation; *U.S. Public*, pg. 11
APACHE STAINLESS EQUIPMENT CORP.; *U.S. Private*, pg. 290
APPLIED CRYO TECHNOLOGIES, INC.—See Plug Power Inc.; *U.S. Public*, pg. 1699
ARROW TANK & ENGINEERING CO.; *U.S. Private*, pg. 336
ARROW TECH HIGH PURITY DIVISION—See Arrow Tank & Engineering Co.; *U.S. Private*, pg. 336
ATS GROUP, LLC; *U.S. Private*, pg. 382
AYS METAL PRODUCTS & ENGINEERING SDN. BHD.—See AYS Ventures Berhad; *Int'l*, pg. 775
BAKER/ALTECH—See Justiss Oil Company, Inc.; *U.S. Private*, pg. 2246
BALMORAL TANKS LIMITED—See Balmoral Group Ltd.; *Int'l*, pg. 810
BEIJING COMPOSITE MATERIAL CO., LTD.—See China National Materials; *Int'l*, pg. 1532
BEIJING TIANHAI CRYOGENIC EQUIPMENT CO., LTD.—See Beijing Jingcheng Machinery Electric Co., Ltd.; *Int'l*, pg. 952
BEIJING TIANHAI INDUSTRY CO., LTD—See Beijing Jingcheng Machinery Electric Co., Ltd.; *Int'l*, pg. 952
BIGBEE STEEL & TANK COMPANY; *U.S. Private*, pg. 555
BLUESCOPE WATER PTY LTD.—See BlueScope Steel Limited; *Int'l*, pg. 1073
BROWN-MINNEAPOLIS-ROCKY MOUNTAIN, LLC—See Brown-Minneapolis Tank, Co.; *U.S. Private*, pg. 669
BROWN-MINNEAPOLIS TANK, CO.; *U.S. Private*, pg. 669
BTIC AMERICA CORPORATION—See Beijing Jingcheng Machinery Electric Co., Ltd.; *Int'l*, pg. 952
CALDWELL TANKS, INC. - ATLANTA—See Caldwell Tanks, Inc.; *U.S. Private*, pg. 716
CALDWELL TANKS, INC.; *U.S. Private*, pg. 716
CATALYST & CHEMICAL CONTAINERS—See First Reserve Management, L.P.; *U.S. Private*, pg. 1526
CC AMERICAN OILFIELD, LLC—See CSE Global Ltd.; *Int'l*, pg. 1863
CERTIFIED STAINLESS SERVICE INC.; *U.S. Private*, pg. 842
CHARLATTE RESERVOIRS—See FAYAT SAS; *Int'l*, pg. 2625
CHILTON PRODUCTS—See Western Industries, Inc.; *U.S. Private*, pg. 4494
CHIP NGAI ENGINEERING WORKS SDN. BHD.—See CN ASIA Corporation Bhd.; *Int'l*, pg. 1672
CONVAIR ENGINEERING PTY. LTD.—See Engenco Limited; *Int'l*, pg. 2426
CRYO DIFFUSION S.A.S.—See Chart Industries, Inc.; *U.S. Public*, pg. 481
CRYOGENIC VESSEL ALTERNATIVES; *U.S. Private*, pg. 1115
CST INDUSTRIES, INC.—See Solace Capital Partners, LLC; *U.S. Private*, pg. 3706
CST INDUSTRIES (MANUFACTURING FACILITY), INC. - UK—See Solace Capital Partners, LLC; *U.S. Private*, pg. 3706
CUSTOM BIOGENIC SYSTEMS, INC.—See Standex International; *U.S. Public*, pg. 1930
CYLINGAS COMPANY LLC—See Emirates National Oil Company Limited; *Int'l*, pg. 2381
DCI, INC. - SPRINGFIELD DIVISION—See DCI, Inc.; *U.S. Private*, pg. 1180
DEKALB MANUFACTURING FACILITY (CST STORAGE)—See Solace Capital Partners, LLC; *U.S. Private*, pg. 3706
DELAHAYE INDUSTRIES S.A.S.—See Empteezy Ltd; *Int'l*, pg. 2392
DURO FELGUERA OIL & GAS S.A.—See Duro Felguera, S.A.; *Int'l*, pg. 2228
EDEN CRYOGENICS LLC; *U.S. Private*, pg. 1333
EEW HOLDING GMBH—See Beijing Enterprises Holdings Limited; *Int'l*, pg. 950
EMERSON PROCESS MANAGEMENT—See Emerson Electric Co.; *U.S. Public*, pg. 747
EMPTEEZY BENELUX BVBA—See Empteezy Ltd; *Int'l*, pg. 2392
EMPTEEZY HOLLAND BV—See Empteezy Ltd; *Int'l*, pg. 2392
EMPTEEZY IBERICA S.L.—See Empteezy Ltd; *Int'l*, pg. 2392
EMPTEEZY ITALIA S.R.L.—See Empteezy Ltd; *Int'l*, pg. 2392
EMPTEEZY UAE FZE—See Empteezy Ltd; *Int'l*, pg. 2392
ENVASES DE ACERO, S.A. DE C.V.—See Air Products &

332420 — METAL TANK (HEAVY G...

Chemicals, Inc.; *U.S. Public*, pg. 66
EVEREST KANTO CYLINDER LIMITED; *Int'l*, pg. 2564
FELGUERA CALDERERIA PESADA, S.A.U.—See Duro Felguera, S.A.; *Int'l*, pg. 2228
FISHER TANK COMPANY; *U.S. Private*, pg. 1534
FLEXCON INDUSTRIES, INC.; *U.S. Private*, pg. 1543
FLORIDA MARINE TANKS, INC.; *U.S. Private*, pg. 1549
FORT WORTH F & D HEAD COMPANY; *U.S. Private*, pg. 1575
FUEL PROOF LIMITED—See ARGENT INDUSTRIAL LIMITED; *Int'l*, pg. 560
GCM PACKAGING (VIETNAM) CO., LTD.—See Great China Metal Ind. Co., Ltd.; *Int'l*, pg. 3064
GUANGDONG SOUTHERN-CHINA SPECIALTY GASES INSTITUTE CO., LTD.—See Guangdong Huate Gas Co., Ltd.; *Int'l*, pg. 3156
HEIL ASIA LIMITED—See Terex Corporation; *U.S. Public*, pg. 2019
HELGESEN INDUSTRIES INC.—See Standard Iron & Wire Works Inc.; *U.S. Private*, pg. 3780
HIGHLAND TANK & MANUFACTURING CO.; *U.S. Private*, pg. 1939
HMT AUSTRALIA PTY LTD—See Tailwind Capital Group, LLC; *U.S. Private*, pg. 3924
HMT PTE LTD.—See Tailwind Capital Group, LLC; *U.S. Private*, pg. 3924
HMT RUBBAGLAS, LTD.—See Tailwind Capital Group, LLC; *U.S. Private*, pg. 3924
HOOVER MATERIALS HANDLING GROUP, INC.—See First Reserve Management, L.P.; *U.S. Private*, pg. 1526
IMPCO TECHNOLOGIES B.V.—See Genisys Controls, LLC; *U.S. Private*, pg. 1671
IMPERIAL INDUSTRIES INC.—See Wausau Tile, Inc.; *U.S. Private*, pg. 4457
JAMES MACHINE WORKS, LLC; *U.S. Private*, pg. 2184
JET TANK SERVICE, LLC—See Quanta Services, Inc.; *U.S. Public*, pg. 1751
JINAN UNITED CAN CO., LTD.—See Great China Metal Ind. Co., Ltd.; *Int'l*, pg. 3064
LE RESERVOIR—See FAYAT SAS; *Int'l*, pg. 2625
LOCKHEED MARTIN SPACE SYSTEMS CO. - NEW ORLEANS—See Lockheed Martin Corporation; *U.S. Public*, pg. 1339
MAC CORPORATION; *U.S. Private*, pg. 2531
MANCHESTER TANK & EQUIPMENT COMPANY - CHILE PLANT—See McWane, Inc.; *U.S. Private*, pg. 2645
MANCHESTER TANK & EQUIPMENT—See McWane, Inc.; *U.S. Private*, pg. 2645
MATRIX SERVICE COMPANY - TANK CONSTRUCTION DIVISION—See Matrix Service Company; *U.S. Public*, pg. 1397
MODERN CUSTOM FABRICATION, INC.—See Modern Welding Company, Inc.; *U.S. Private*, pg. 2762
MODERN WELDING COMPANY, INC.; *U.S. Private*, pg. 2762
MODERN WELDING COMPANY, INC.—See Modern Welding Company, Inc.; *U.S. Private*, pg. 2763
MODERN WELDING COMPANY OF KENTUCKY, INC.—See Modern Welding Company, Inc.; *U.S. Private*, pg. 2762
MODERN WELDING COMPANY OF OWENSBORO, INC.—See Modern Welding Company, Inc.; *U.S. Private*, pg. 2762
MODERN WELDING COMPANY OF TEXAS, INC.—See Modern Welding Company, Inc.; *U.S. Private*, pg. 2763
MUELLER TRANSPORTATION, INC.—See Paul Mueller Company; *U.S. Public*, pg. 1655
NOOTER CORPORATION—See CIC Group, Inc.; *U.S. Private*, pg. 896
NORRIS CYLINDER COMPANY—See TriMas Corporation; *U.S. Public*, pg. 2189
ONTIC ENGINEERING & MANUFACTURING UK LIMITED—See CVC Capital Partners SICAV-FIS S.A.; *Int'l*, pg. 1884
OPW FUEL MANAGEMENT SYSTEMS, INC.—See Dover Corporation; *U.S. Public*, pg. 679
PAC-VAN, INC.—See United Rentals, Inc.; *U.S. Public*, pg. 2235
PALMER OF TEXAS TANKS, INC.—See Ascent Industries Co.; *U.S. Public*, pg. 210
PARR METAL FABRICATORS LTD—See Dynamic Technologies Group Inc.; *Int'l*, pg. 2241
PERMIAN TANK & MANUFACTURING, INC.; *U.S. Private*, pg. 3152
PETROFIELD INDUSTRIES INC—See Dynamic Technologies Group Inc.; *Int'l*, pg. 2241
PETROLEUM SEALS & SYSTEMS LTD.—See Tailwind Capital Group, LLC; *U.S. Private*, pg. 3924
PHOENIX FABRICATORS & ERECTORS INC.; *U.S. Private*, pg. 3172
PIONEER WATER TANKS (AUSTRALIA) PTY LTD—See BlueScope Steel Limited; *Int'l*, pg. 1074
PITTSBURG TANK & TOWER CO., INC.; *U.S. Private*, pg. 3191
POLAR CORPORATION—See Questor Management Company, LLC; *U.S. Private*, pg. 3326
PRECISION TANK & EQUIP CO.; *U.S. Private*, pg. 3247
PROTEC ARISAWA AMERICA, INC.—See Arisawa Manufacturing Co., Ltd.; *Int'l*, pg. 566
QINGDAO PACIFIC CONTAINER CO., LTD.—See China COSCO Shipping Corporation Limited; *Int'l*, pg. 1493
ROMOLD LTD—See Empteezy Ltd; *Int'l*, pg. 2392
ROSEMOUNT TANK RADAR PROPERTIES AB—See Emerson Electric Co.; *U.S. Public*, pg. 748
ROTO MOULDERS LIMITED—See Flame Tree Group Holdings Ltd.; *Int'l*, pg. 2698
SABRE MANUFACTURING LLC—See Super Steel LLC; *U.S. Private*, pg. 3875
SCHOELLER-BLECKMANN NITEC GMBH—See Christof Holding AG; *Int'l*, pg. 1587
SHANDONG TIANHAI HIGH PRESSURE CONTAINER CO., LTD.—See Beijing Jingcheng Machinery Electric Co., Ltd.; *Int'l*, pg. 952
SHANGHAI UNITED CAN CO., LTD.—See Great China Metal Ind. Co., Ltd.; *Int'l*, pg. 3064
SHARPSVILLE CONTAINER CORPORATION—See SSP Industrial Group, Inc.; *U.S. Private*, pg. 3769
SHIJIAZHUANG ENRIC GAS EQUIPMENT CO., LTD.—See China International Marine Containers (Group) Co., Ltd.; *Int'l*, pg. 1512
SNYDER INDUSTRIES, INC. - MANCELONA—See Olympus Partners; *U.S. Private*, pg. 3013
SNYDER INDUSTRIES, INC.—See Olympus Partners; *U.S. Private*, pg. 3013
SPRINGS FABRICATION, INC.; *U.S. Private*, pg. 3764
STAINLESS TANK & EQUIPMENT CO., LLC—See Hendricks Holding Company, Inc.; *U.S. Private*, pg. 1915
STAR FORMING MANUFACTURING, LLC—See CE Star Holdings, LLC; *U.S. Private*, pg. 803
STERIFLOW SAS—See Groupe SFPI SA; *Int'l*, pg. 3111
SUPERIOR TANK CO., INC.; *U.S. Private*, pg. 3880
TAMPA TANK & WELDING INC.—See TTI Holdings Inc.; *U.S. Private*, pg. 4254
TANK SYSTEMS BV—See Tailwind Capital Group, LLC; *U.S. Private*, pg. 3924
TAYLOR-WHARTON (BEIJING) CRYOGENIC EQUIPMENT CO.,LTD.—See Wind Point Advisors LLC; *U.S. Private*, pg. 4536
TAYLOR-WHARTON CRYOGENICS, LLC—See Wind Point Advisors LLC; *U.S. Private*, pg. 4536
TAYLOR-WHARTON GERMANY GMBH—See Wind Point Advisors LLC; *U.S. Private*, pg. 4536
TAYLOR-WHARTON SLOVAKIA S.R.O.—See Wind Point Advisors LLC; *U.S. Private*, pg. 4536
TECHNODYNE INTERNATIONAL LIMITED—See China International Marine Containers (Group) Co., Ltd.; *Int'l*, pg. 1512
TEXAS TRAILER CORP.—See Markel Group Inc.; *U.S. Public*, pg. 1369
TIANJIN CIMC NORTH OCEAN CONTAINER CO., LTD.—See China International Marine Containers (Group) Co., Ltd.; *Int'l*, pg. 1512
TITANLINER, INC.—See Capital Southwest Corporation; *U.S. Public*, pg. 432
TRINITY CONTAINERS, LLC—See Trinity Industries, Inc.; *U.S. Public*, pg. 2194
TRINITY HEADS, INC.—See Trinity Industries, Inc.; *U.S. Public*, pg. 2194
TTI HOLDINGS INC.; *U.S. Private*, pg. 4254
UNITED TANK TECHNOLOGY INC.—See Tailwind Capital Group, LLC; *U.S. Private*, pg. 3924
WESSELS COMPANY; *U.S. Private*, pg. 4483
WINBCO TANK COMPANY; *U.S. Private*, pg. 4533
ZHANGJIAGANG CIMC SANCTUM CRYOGENIC EQUIPMENT MACHINERY CO., LTD.—See China International Marine Containers (Group) Co., Ltd.; *Int'l*, pg. 1513
ZIEMANN HOLVRIEKA A/S—See China International Marine Containers (Group) Co., Ltd.; *Int'l*, pg. 1511
ZIEMANN HOLVRIEKA GMBH—See China International Marine Containers (Group) Co., Ltd.; *Int'l*, pg. 1511

332431 — METAL CAN MANUFACTURING

ABLE GLOBAL BERHAD; *Int'l*, pg. 62
AIR WATER SOL INC.—See Air Water Inc.; *Int'l*, pg. 239
AIR WATER SOL (SHANGHAI) TRADING CO. LTD.—See Air Water Inc.; *Int'l*, pg. 239
ALLSTATE CAN CORPORATION—See The Ohio Art Company, Inc.; *U.S. Public*, pg. 2118
ANN JOO RESOURCES BERHAD; *Int'l*, pg. 473
AQ LASERTOOL OU—See AQ Group AB; *Int'l*, pg. 526
ARDAGH METAL PACKAGING NETHERLANDS B.V.—See Ardagh Group S.A.; *Int'l*, pg. 553
ARDAGH METAL PACKAGING UK LIMITED—See Ardagh Group S.A.; *Int'l*, pg. 553
ARDAGH METAL PACKAGING UK LTD. - SUTTON-IN-ASHFIELD PLANT—See Ardagh Group S.A.; *Int'l*, pg. 553
ASA ITALIA SARL—See ASA San Marino S.p.A.; *Int'l*, pg. 592
ASA SAN MARINO S.P.A.; *Int'l*, pg. 592
BALL BEVERAGE CAN AMERICAS, S.A. DE C.V.—See Ball Corporation; *U.S. Public*, pg. 267
BALL BEVERAGE CAN SOUTH AMERICA SA—See Ball Corporation; *U.S. Public*, pg. 267
BALL BEVERAGE PACKAGING CZECH REPUBLIC SRO—See Ball Corporation; *U.S. Public*, pg. 267
BALL BEVERAGE PACKAGING EUROPE LIMITED—See Ball Corporation; *U.S. Public*, pg. 267
BALL BEVERAGE PACKAGING FOSIE AB—See Ball Corporation; *U.S. Public*, pg. 267
BALL BEVERAGE PACKAGING FRANCE SAS—See Ball Corporation; *U.S. Public*, pg. 267
BALL BEVERAGE PACKAGING IBERICA SL—See Ball Corporation; *U.S. Public*, pg. 267
BALL BEVERAGE PACKAGING IRELAND LIMITED—See Ball Corporation; *U.S. Public*, pg. 267
BALL BEVERAGE PACKAGING ITALIA SRL - SAN MARTINO—See Ball Corporation; *U.S. Public*, pg. 267
BALL BEVERAGE PACKAGING ITALIA SRL—See Ball Corporation; *U.S. Public*, pg. 267
BALL BEVERAGE PACKAGING UK LTD.—See Ball Corporation; *U.S. Public*, pg. 267
BALL BEVERAGE TURKEY PAKETLEME SANAYI VE TICARET AS—See Ball Corporation; *U.S. Public*, pg. 267
BALL METAL BEVERAGE CONTAINER CORP.—See Ball Corporation; *U.S. Public*, pg. 266
BALL METAL BEVERAGE CONTAINER CORP.—See Ball Corporation; *U.S. Public*, pg. 266
BALL METAL BEVERAGE CONTAINER CORP.—See Ball Corporation; *U.S. Public*, pg. 266
BALL METAL BEVERAGE CONTAINER CORP.—See Ball Corporation; *U.S. Public*, pg. 266
BALL METAL BEVERAGE CONTAINER CORP.—See Ball Corporation; *U.S. Public*, pg. 266
BALL PACKAGING CORP.—See Ball Corporation; *U.S. Public*, pg. 267
BALL PACKAGING EUROPE BIERNE S.A.S.—See Ball Corporation; *U.S. Public*, pg. 267
BALL PACKAGING EUROPE GMBH - BRAUNSCHWEIG—See Ball Corporation; *U.S. Public*, pg. 267
BALL PACKAGING EUROPE GMBH—See Ball Corporation; *U.S. Public*, pg. 267
BALL PACKAGING EUROPE HOLDING B.V.—See Ball Corporation; *U.S. Public*, pg. 267
BALL PACKAGING EUROPE LA CIOTAT S.A.S.—See Ball Corporation; *U.S. Public*, pg. 267
BALL PACKAGING PRODUCTS CANADA CORP.—See Ball Corporation; *U.S. Public*, pg. 267
BALL (UK) HOLDINGS, LTD.—See Ball Corporation; *U.S. Public*, pg. 266
BUTIMOVE—See Crown Holdings, Inc.; *U.S. Public*, pg. 597
BWAY CORP. - CINCINNATI PLANT—See Stone Canyon Industries, LLC; *U.S. Private*, pg. 3817
BWAY CORP. - YORK PLANT—See Stone Canyon Industries, LLC; *U.S. Private*, pg. 3817
CAN CORPORATION OF AMERICA; *U.S. Private*, pg. 732
CAN-ONE BERHAD; *Int'l*, pg. 1276
CARNAUDMETALBOX ENGINEERING LTD—See Crown Holdings, Inc.; *U.S. Public*, pg. 598
CARNAUDMETALBOX FINANCE SA—See Crown Holdings, Inc.; *U.S. Public*, pg. 598
CARNAUDMETALBOX FOOD SOUTH AFRICA (PTY) LIMITED—See Crown Holdings, Inc.; *U.S. Public*, pg. 598
CCL CONTAINER (HERMITAGE), INC.—See CCL Industries Inc.; *Int'l*, pg. 1367
CENTENNIAL STEEL—See Consolidated Fabricators Corp; *U.S. Private*, pg. 1020
CHINA ALUMINUM CANS HOLDINGS LIMITED; *Int'l*, pg. 1482
CHINA FOOD PACKING INC., LTD.; *Int'l*, pg. 1503
CLEVELAND STEEL CONTAINER CORPORATION; *U.S. Private*, pg. 941
CMP ADVANCED MECHANICAL SOLUTIONS LTD.; *Int'l*, pg. 1671
CONSOLIDATED FABRICATORS CORP; *U.S. Private*, pg. 1020
CPMC (CHENGDU) COMPANY LIMITED—See CPMC Holdings Limited; *Int'l*, pg. 1825
CPMC (KUNSHAN) COMPANY LIMITED—See CPMC Holdings Limited; *Int'l*, pg. 1825
CPMC (TIANJIN) COMPANY LIMITED—See CPMC Holdings Limited; *Int'l*, pg. 1825
CPMC (WUHAN) COMPANY LIMITED—See CPMC Holdings Limited; *Int'l*, pg. 1825
CPMC (ZHENJIANG) COMPANY LIMITED—See CPMC Holdings Limited; *Int'l*, pg. 1826
CROWN AEROSOLS NEDERLAND BV—See Crown Holdings, Inc.; *U.S. Public*, pg. 597
CROWN AEROSOLS UK LIMITED—See Crown Holdings, Inc.; *U.S. Public*, pg. 597
CROWN BEVCAN ESPANA S.L.—See Crown Holdings, Inc.; *U.S. Public*, pg. 597
CROWN BEVCAN FRANCE SAS—See Crown Holdings, Inc.; *U.S. Public*, pg. 597
CROWN BEVCAN TURKIYE AMBALAJ SANAYI VE TICARET—See Crown Holdings, Inc.; *U.S. Public*, pg. 597
CROWN BEVERAGE CANS BEIJING LIMITED—See Crown Holdings, Inc.; *U.S. Public*, pg. 597
CROWN BEVERAGE CANS (CAMBODIA) LIMITED—See

332439 — OTHER METAL CONTAIN...

Crown Holdings, Inc.; *U.S. Public*, pg. 597
CROWN BEVERAGE CANS HK LTD.—See Crown Holdings, Inc.; *U.S. Public*, pg. 598
CROWN BEVERAGE CANS MALAYSIA SDN BHD—See Crown Holdings, Inc.; *U.S. Public*, pg. 597
CROWN BEVERAGE CANS SINGAPORE PTE. LTD.—See Crown Holdings, Inc.; *U.S. Public*, pg. 597
CROWN COLOMBIANA, S.A.—See Crown Holdings, Inc.; *U.S. Public*, pg. 598
CROWN COMERCIAL DE ENVASES, S.L.—See Crown Holdings, Inc.; *U.S. Public*, pg. 598
CROWN CORK & SEAL CO., INC.—See Crown Holdings, Inc.; *U.S. Public*, pg. 597
CROWN CORK & SEAL CO INC. -SUGAR LAND—See Crown Holdings, Inc.; *U.S. Public*, pg. 597
CROWN CORK & SEAL DE PORTUGAL EMBALAGENS S.A.—See Crown Holdings, Inc.; *U.S. Public*, pg. 598
CROWN CORK & SEAL DEUTSCHLAND HOLDINGS GMBH—See Crown Holdings, Inc.; *U.S. Public*, pg. 598
CROWN CORK & SEAL USA, INC. - MASSILLON—See Crown Holdings, Inc.; *U.S. Public*, pg. 597
CROWN EMBALAGENS METALICAS DA AMAZONIA S.A.—See Crown Holdings, Inc.; *U.S. Public*, pg. 597
CROWN EMBALAGENS METALICAS DA AMAZONIA S.A.—See Evora S.A.; *Int'l*, pg. 2573
CROWN EMBALLAGE FRANCE SAS—See Crown Holdings, Inc.; *U.S. Public*, pg. 597
CROWN EMIRATES COMPANY LIMITED—See Crown Holdings, Inc.; *U.S. Public*, pg. 597
CROWN ENVASES MEXICO, S.A. DE C.V.—See Crown Holdings, Inc.; *U.S. Public*, pg. 598
CROWN EUROPEAN HOLDINGS SA—See Crown Holdings, Inc.; *U.S. Public*, pg. 598
CROWN HELLAS CAN PACKAGING SA—See Crown Holdings, Inc.; *U.S. Public*, pg. 597
CROWN HOLDINGS ITALIA SRL—See Crown Holdings, Inc.; *U.S. Public*, pg. 598
CROWN IMGALLAGGI ITALIA SRL—See Crown Holdings, Inc.; *U.S. Public*, pg. 598
CROWN METAL PACKAGING CANADA LTEE.—See Crown Holdings, Inc.; *U.S. Public*, pg. 598
CROWN MIDDLE EAST CAN CO. LTD.—See Crown Holdings, Inc.; *U.S. Public*, pg. 597
CROWN PACKAGING EUROPE GMBH—See Crown Holdings, Inc.; *U.S. Public*, pg. 598
CROWN PACKAGING IRELAND LTD.—See Crown Holdings, Inc.; *U.S. Public*, pg. 598
CROWN PACKAGING MAROC—See Crown Holdings, Inc.; *U.S. Public*, pg. 598
CROWN SENEGAL—See Crown Holdings, Inc.; *U.S. Public*, pg. 598
CROWN SIEM—See Crown Holdings, Inc.; *U.S. Public*, pg. 597
CROWN SPECIALITY PACKAGING BELGIE NV—See Crown Holdings, Inc.; *U.S. Public*, pg. 598
CROWN SPECIALITY PACKAGING B.V.—See Crown Holdings, Inc.; *U.S. Public*, pg. 598
CROWN SPECIALITY PACKAGING UK PLC—See Crown Holdings, Inc.; *U.S. Public*, pg. 598
CROWN SPECIALTY PACKAGING USA, INC.—See Crown Holdings, Inc.; *U.S. Public*, pg. 597
CROWN VOGEL AG—See Crown Holdings, Inc.; *U.S. Public*, pg. 598
DAIWA CAN COMPANY; *Int'l*, pg. 1944
DS CONTAINERS INC.—See Daiwa Can Company; *Int'l*, pg. 1944
EAGLE MANUFACTURING COMPANY; *U.S. Private*, pg. 1309
ENVASES CENTRAL S.A.—See Embotelladora Andina S.A.; *Int'l*, pg. 2375
EURO ASIA PACKAGING (GUANGDONG) CO., LTD.—See China Aluminum Cans Holdings Limited; *Int'l*, pg. 1482
FC PACKAGING (HARBIN) LIMITED—See CPMC Holdings Limited; *Int'l*, pg. 1826
FOSHAN CONTINENTAL CAN CO. LIMITED—See Crown Holdings, Inc.; *U.S. Public*, pg. 598
FOUNTAIN CAN CORPORATION TAINAN FACTORY—See Daiwa Can Company; *Int'l*, pg. 1944
FUJIAN FC PACKAGING LIMITED—See CPMC Holdings Limited; *Int'l*, pg. 1826
GLUD & MARSTRAND A/S—See AAC Capital Partners Holding B.V.; *Int'l*, pg. 31
GREAT CHINA METAL IND. CO., LTD.; *Int'l*, pg. 3064
GREIF FRANCE S.A.S.—See Greif Inc.; *U.S. Public*, pg. 968
GREIF HUA I TAIWAN CO., LTD.—See Greif Inc.; *U.S. Public*, pg. 968
GREIF MIMAYSAN AMBALAJ SANAYI AS—See Greif Inc.; *U.S. Public*, pg. 968
GREIF PACKAGING SPAIN SA—See Greif Inc.; *U.S. Public*, pg. 968
G&S METAL PRODUCTS CO. INC.; *U.S. Private*, pg. 1629
GUANGDONG ENPACK PACKAGING CO.; *Int'l*, pg. 3154
GUANGZHOU PANYU MCP INDUSTRIES LIMITED—See CPMC Holdings Limited; *Int'l*, pg. 1826
HASHIMI CAN COMPANY LIMITED; *Int'l*, pg. 3283
HINDUSTAN TIN WORKS LTD.; *Int'l*, pg. 3400

HOCKENHEIM RIGID PAPER—See Sonoco Products Company; *U.S. Public*, pg. 1904
INDASTRI KIAN JOO SDN. BHD.—See Can-One Berhad; *Int'l*, pg. 1276
INDEPENDENT CAN COMPANY; *U.S. Private*, pg. 2058
J.L. CLARK, INC. - LANCASTER—See Henry Crown & Company; *U.S. Private*, pg. 1917
J.L. CLARK, INC.—See Henry Crown & Company; *U.S. Private*, pg. 1917
JUSTRITE MANUFACTURING COMPANY—See The Riverside Company; *U.S. Private*, pg. 4109
KIAN JOO CAN FACTORY BERHAD—See Can-One Berhad; *Int'l*, pg. 1276
KIAN JOO CAN (VIETNAM) CO., LTD.—See Can-One Berhad; *Int'l*, pg. 1276
KIAN JOO PACKAGING SDN BHD—See Can-One Berhad; *Int'l*, pg. 1277
KJ CAN (JOHORE) SDN. BHD.—See Can-One Berhad; *Int'l*, pg. 1276
KJO INTERNATIONAL SDN. BHD.—See Can-One Berhad; *Int'l*, pg. 1276
KLUANG TIN AND CAN FACTORY SDN. BHD.—See Able Global Berhad; *Int'l*, pg. 63
KUNSHAN HUADE METAL PACKAGING CONTAINER CO., LTD.—See Crown Holdings, Inc.; *U.S. Public*, pg. 599
LITEC FRANCE S.A.S.—See Crown Holdings, Inc.; *U.S. Public*, pg. 599
METAL CONTAINER CORPORATION—See Anheuser-Busch InBev SA/NV; *Int'l*, pg. 465
METALGRAFICA IGUACU S.A.—See Companhia Siderurgica Nacional; *Int'l*, pg. 1748
MIVISA ENVASES S.A.U.—See Crown Holdings, Inc.; *U.S. Public*, pg. 598
MIVISA HUNGARY KFT.—See Crown Holdings, Inc.; *U.S. Public*, pg. 598
MIVISA MAROC, S.A.—See Crown Holdings, Inc.; *U.S. Public*, pg. 598
NATIONAL CANS & PACKING INDUSTRY LLC—See Al Batinah Development & Investment Holding Co. SAOG; *Int'l*, pg. 276
ORRVILLE COMPOSITE CONTAINER PLANT—See Greif Inc.; *U.S. Public*, pg. 966
PACIFIC MARKET INTERNATIONAL, LLC; *U.S. Private*, pg. 3068
PENNY PLATE, INC.; *U.S. Private*, pg. 3137
SEXTON CAN CO., INC.; *U.S. Private*, pg. 3620
SILGAN CAN COMPANY—See Silgan Holdings, Inc.; *U.S. Public*, pg. 1878
SILGAN CONTAINERS MANUFACTURING CORPORATION—See Silgan Holdings, Inc.; *U.S. Public*, pg. 1878
SILGAN CONTAINERS—See Silgan Holdings, Inc.; *U.S. Public*, pg. 1878
SILGAN HOLDINGS, INC.; *U.S. Public*, pg. 1878
SILGAN METAL PACKAGING STUPINO O.O.O.—See Silgan Holdings, Inc.; *U.S. Public*, pg. 1879
SILGAN METAL PACKAGING TCZEW S.A.—See Silgan Holdings, Inc.; *U.S. Public*, pg. 1879
SILGAN WHITE CAP LLC—See Silgan Holdings, Inc.; *U.S. Public*, pg. 1879
SONOCO METAL PACKAGING, LLC—See Sonoco Products Company; *U.S. Public*, pg. 1907
STAR CASES, LLC—See CE Star Holdings, LLC; *U.S. Private*, pg. 803
SUPERIOR METAL PRINTING (HUIYANG) CO., LTD.—See Crown Holdings, Inc.; *U.S. Public*, pg. 599
SUPERIOR MULTI-PACKAGING LIMITED—See Crown Holdings, Inc.; *U.S. Public*, pg. 599
SUPERIOR MULTI-PACKAGING (VIETNAM) CO., LTD—See Crown Holdings, Inc.; *U.S. Public*, pg. 599
UNSA AMBALAJ SANAYI VE TICARET ANONIM SIRKETI—See Greif Inc.; *U.S. Public*, pg. 968
WALLACE PACKAGING, LLC; *U.S. Private*, pg. 4431
WUXI HUAPENG CLOSURES COMPANY LIMITED—See CPMC Holdings Limited; *Int'l*, pg. 1826

332439 — OTHER METAL CONTAINER MANUFACTURING

ADVANCE DRUM SERVICE, INC.; *U.S. Private*, pg. 83
AIR-LOG—See General Electric Company; *U.S. Public*, pg. 918
ALUCON PUBLIC COMPANY LIMITED; *Int'l*, pg. 400
AMCOR TOBACCO PACKAGING POLSKA SPOLKA Z.O.O—See Amcor plc; *Int'l*, pg. 417
AMERICAN WELDING & TANK CO.—See Wind Point Advisors LLC; *U.S. Private*, pg. 4536
BALL PACKAGING EUROPE HANDELSGES MBH—See Ball Corporation; *U.S. Public*, pg. 267
BALL PACKAGING EUROPE LUBLIN SP. Z O.O.—See Ball Corporation; *U.S. Public*, pg. 267
BALL PACKAGING EUROPE RADOMSKO SP.Z O.O.—See Ball Corporation; *U.S. Public*, pg. 267
BALL PACKAGING EUROPE TRADING SP. Z O.O.—See Ball Corporation; *U.S. Public*, pg. 267
BEHRENS MANUFACTURING, LLC—See Mill City Capital, L.P.; *U.S. Private*, pg. 2730

BEKUPLAST GMBH; *Int'l*, pg. 962
BOX BOARD PRODUCTS, INC.—See Greif Inc.; *U.S. Public*, pg. 965
CAN-ONE (USA), INC.—See Can-One Berhad; *Int'l*, pg. 1276
CAN'T LIVE WITHOUT IT, LLC—See Lifetime Brands, Inc.; *U.S. Public*, pg. 1313
CASPIAN DRILLER PTE. LTD.—See China International Marine Containers (Group) Co., Ltd.; *Int'l*, pg. 1511
CHENGDU GOLDEN PHOENIX LIQUID NITROGEN CONTAINER COMPANY LIMITED—See Chart Industries, Inc.; *U.S. Public*, pg. 481
CHINA INTERNATIONAL MARINE CONTAINERS (GROUP) CO., LTD.; *Int'l*, pg. 1510
CIMC AUSTRALIA PTY LTD—See China International Marine Containers (Group) Co., Ltd.; *Int'l*, pg. 1511
CONTAINER COMPANY (ABERDEEN) LTD.—See First Reserve Management, L.P.; *U.S. Private*, pg. 1526
CONTAINER LIFE CYCLE MANAGEMENT LLC—See Greif Inc.; *U.S. Public*, pg. 967
CONTAINER RESEARCH CORPORATION; *U.S. Private*, pg. 1027
CPMC HOLDINGS LIMITED; *Int'l*, pg. 1825
CROWN BEVERAGE CANS SIHANOUKVILLE LIMITED—See Crown Holdings, Inc.; *U.S. Public*, pg. 597
CROWN CLOSURES SPAIN, S.L.—See Crown Holdings, Inc.; *U.S. Public*, pg. 598
CROWN HELLAS PACKAGING CAN SA—See Crown Holdings, Inc.; *U.S. Public*, pg. 597
CUBIC TRANSPORTATION SYSTEMS (ITMS) LIMITED—See Elliott Management Corporation; *U.S. Private*, pg. 1367
CUBIC TRANSPORTATION SYSTEMS (ITMS) LIMITED—See Veritas Capital Fund Management, LLC; *U.S. Private*, pg. 4361
DAERYUK CAN CO., LTD.; *Int'l*, pg. 1908
DAIRY FRESH, LLC—See Dean Foods Company; *U.S. Private*, pg. 1183
DALIAN CIMC LOGISTICS EQUIPMENT CO., LTD.—See China International Marine Containers (Group) Co., Ltd.; *Int'l*, pg. 1511
DART PORTABLE STORAGE, INC.—See Dart Transit Company; *U.S. Private*, pg. 1160
DERICHEBOURG ENTREPRISES-VALERCO - VALREN - ECOVAL—See Derichebourg S.A.; *Int'l*, pg. 2042
EMPTEEZY LTD; *Int'l*, pg. 2392
FCA, LLC—See Delos Capital, LLC; *U.S. Private*, pg. 1198
FISHER SCIENTIFIC COMPANY, LLC—See Thermo Fisher Scientific Inc.; *U.S. Public*, pg. 2148
FUMOA S.A.—See Aga Khan Development Network; *Int'l*, pg. 199
GENERAL STEEL DRUM LLC—See Myers Container, LLC; *U.S. Private*, pg. 2824
GRAHAM PACKAGING COMPANY BV—See Pactiv Evergreen Inc.; *U.S. Public*, pg. 1633
GRAHAM PACKAGING COMPANY OY—See Pactiv Evergreen Inc.; *U.S. Public*, pg. 1633
GRAHAM PACKAGING PLASTICS LTD.—See Pactiv Evergreen Inc.; *U.S. Public*, pg. 1633
GRAHAM PACKAGING POLAND SP. Z.O.O.—See Pactiv Evergreen Inc.; *U.S. Public*, pg. 1633
GRAHAM PLASTPAK PLASTIK AMBALAJ SANAYI A.S.—See Pactiv Evergreen Inc.; *U.S. Public*, pg. 1633
GREAT CHINA METAL IND. CO., LTD. - FUGANG PLANT—See Great China Metal Ind. Co., Ltd.; *Int'l*, pg. 3064
GREAT CHINA METAL IND. CO., LTD. - TOUFEN PLANT—See Great China Metal Ind. Co., Ltd.; *Int'l*, pg. 3064
GREIF BELGIUM B.V.B.A.—See Greif Inc.; *U.S. Public*, pg. 967
GREIF COLOMBIA S.A.—See Greif Inc.; *U.S. Public*, pg. 967
GREIF CONTAINERS, INC.—See Greif Inc.; *U.S. Public*, pg. 967
GREIF COSTA RICA S.A.—See Greif Inc.; *U.S. Public*, pg. 967
GREIF CZECH REPUBLIC A/S—See Greif Inc.; *U.S. Public*, pg. 967
GREIF EMBALAGENS INDUSTRIAIS DO BRASIL LTDA.—See Greif Inc.; *U.S. Public*, pg. 967
GREIF GERMANY GMBH—See Greif Inc.; *U.S. Public*, pg. 968
GREIF HELLAS—See Greif Inc.; *U.S. Public*, pg. 968
GREIF HUNGARY KFT—See Greif Inc.; *U.S. Public*, pg. 968
GREIF ITALIA SPA—See Greif Inc.; *U.S. Public*, pg. 968
GREIF JAMAICA LTD.—See Greif Inc.; *U.S. Public*, pg. 968
GREIF MALAYSIA SDN BHD—See Greif Inc.; *U.S. Public*, pg. 968
GREIF MEXICO, S.A. DE C.V.—See Greif Inc.; *U.S. Public*, pg. 968
GREIF NEDERLAND B.V.—See Greif Inc.; *U.S. Public*, pg. 968
GREIF NORWAY AS—See Greif Inc.; *U.S. Public*, pg. 968
GREIF PACKAGING LLC—See Greif Inc.; *U.S. Public*, pg. 968

332439 — OTHER METAL CONTAIN...

GREIF SINGAPORE PTE LTD—See Greif Inc.; *U.S. Public*, pg. 968
GREIF UK LTD.—See Greif Inc.; *U.S. Public*, pg. 968
G-SHANK ENTERPRISE CO., LTD. - BANG PA-IN FACTORY—See G-Shank Enterprise Co., Ltd.; *Int'l*, pg. 2862
G-SHANK ENTERPRISE CO., LTD. - QINGDAO FACTORY—See G-Shank Enterprise Co., Ltd.; *Int'l*, pg. 2863
G-SHANK ENTERPRISE CO., LTD. - SHANGHAI FACTORY—See G-Shank Enterprise Co., Ltd.; *Int'l*, pg. 2863
G-SHANK ENTERPRISE CO., LTD. - SHENZHEN FACTORY—See G-Shank Enterprise Co., Ltd.; *Int'l*, pg. 2863
G-SHANK ENTERPRISE CO., LTD. - SHENZHEN G-BAO FACTORY—See G-Shank Enterprise Co., Ltd.; *Int'l*, pg. 2863
G-SHANK ENTERPRISE CO., LTD. - SUZHOU FACTORY—See G-Shank Enterprise Co., Ltd.; *Int'l*, pg. 2863
G-SHANK ENTERPRISE CO., LTD. - TIANJIN FACTORY—See G-Shank Enterprise Co., Ltd.; *Int'l*, pg. 2863
G-SHANK ENTERPRISE CO., LTD. - XIAMEN FACTORY—See G-Shank Enterprise Co., Ltd.; *Int'l*, pg. 2863
GUANGDONG SHUN AN DA PACIFIC CONTAINER CO., LTD.; *Int'l*, pg. 3160
GUJARAT CONTAINERS LIMITED; *Int'l*, pg. 3176
GUJARAT CONTAINERS LIMITED - UNIT II—See GUJARAT CONTAINERS LIMITED; *Int'l*, pg. 3176
GUJARAT CONTAINERS LIMITED - UNIT I—See GUJARAT CONTAINERS LIMITED; *Int'l*, pg. 3176
HORIZON METALLIC INDUSTRIES L.L.C—See Gulf General Investment Company PSC; *Int'l*, pg. 3180
HOYER BELGIE N.V.—See Hoyer Group; *Int'l*, pg. 3498
HUNG DAO CONTAINER JOINT STOCK COMPANY; *Int'l*, pg. 3535
INTERNATIONAL PACKAGING CORP.; *U.S. Private*, pg. 2119
INTERNATIONAL PAPER MORTAGNE S.A.S.—See International Paper Company; *U.S. Public*, pg. 1157
JENSON & NICHOLSON (BANGLADESH) LIMITED—See Berger Paints Bangladesh Limited; *Int'l*, pg. 979
JINGMEN HONGTU SPECIAL AIRCRAFT MANUFACTURING CO., LTD—See China International Marine Containers (Group) Co., Ltd.; *Int'l*, pg. 1511
KOOKABURRA CONTAINERS PTY LIMITED—See United Rentals, Inc.; *U.S. Public*, pg. 2235
LIAONING CIMC VEHICLE LOGISTICS EQUIPMENTS CO., LTD.—See CIMC Vehicle (Group) Co., Ltd.; *Int'l*, pg. 1608
MAERSK CONTAINER INDUSTRI AS—See A.P. Moller-Maersk A/S; *Int'l*, pg. 26
MAERSK CONTAINER INDUSTRY DONGGUAN LTD.—See A.P. Moller-Maersk A/S; *Int'l*, pg. 26
MAUSER-WERKE GMBH—See Stone Canyon Industries, LLC; *U.S. Private*, pg. 3817
MAXON INDUSTRIES, S.A. DE C.V.—See Maxon Lift Corp.; *U.S. Private*, pg. 2619
MEYER STEEL DRUM INC.; *U.S. Private*, pg. 2692
MODEL DAIRY—See Dean Foods Company; *U.S. Private*, pg. 1183
MUELLER PACKAGING, LLC—See Mueller Industries, Inc.; *U.S. Public*, pg. 1484
MYERS CONTAINER, LLC; *U.S. Private*, pg. 2824
NEW CENTURY DECAL (SHENZHEN) LIMITED—See China COSCO Shipping Corporation Limited; *Int'l*, pg. 1495
NINGBO CIMC LOGISTICS EQUIPMENT CO., LTD.—See China International Marine Containers (Group) Co., Ltd.; *Int'l*, pg. 1512
NINGBO PACIFIC CONTAINER CO., LTD.—See China COSCO Shipping Corporation Limited; *Int'l*, pg. 1493
NORDISK AVIATION PRODUCTS AS—See TransDigm Group Incorporated; *U.S. Public*, pg. 2183
NORTH COAST CONTAINER CORP.—See Myers Container, LLC; *U.S. Private*, pg. 2824
PACK2PACK HALSTEREN B.V.—See Gilde Buy Out Partners B.V.; *Int'l*, pg. 2975
PHENIX-ROUSIES INDUSTRIES, S.A.—See Chief Industries, Inc.; *U.S. Private*, pg. 881
QIDONG PACIFIC PORT CO., LTD.—See China COSCO Shipping Corporation Limited; *Int'l*, pg. 1493
QIDONG SINGAMAS ENERGY EQUIPMENT CO., LTD.—See China COSCO Shipping Corporation Limited; *Int'l*, pg. 1493
QINGDAO CIMC CONTAINER MANUFACTURE CO., LTD—See China International Marine Containers (Group) Co., Ltd.; *Int'l*, pg. 1512
QINGDAO CIMC REEFER CONTAINER MANUFACTURE CO., LTD.—See China International Marine Containers (Group) Co., Ltd.; *Int'l*, pg. 1512
RECAN D.O.O.—See Ball Corporation; *U.S. Public*, pg. 267
ROYAL WOLF TRADING AUSTRALIA PTY LIMITED—See United Rentals, Inc.; *U.S. Public*, pg. 2235
RUBSTEEL AB—See Huhtamaki Oyj; *Int'l*, pg. 3526

SCT ACQUISITION, LLC—See Kratos Defense & Security Solutions, Inc.; *U.S. Public*, pg. 1277
SEA BOX, INC.; *U.S. Private*, pg. 3582
SECURITY MANUFACTURING CORPORATION—See American Locker Group Incorporated; *U.S. Private*, pg. 240
SHANGHAI PUDONG NEW AREA NEWCENTURY DECAL CO., LTD.—See China COSCO Shipping Corporation Limited; *Int'l*, pg. 1496
SHENZHEN SOUTHERN CIMC CONTAINERS SERVICE CO., LTD.—See China International Marine Containers (Group) Co., Ltd.; *Int'l*, pg. 1512
SHENZHEN SOUTHERN CIMC EASTERN LOGISTICS EQUIPMENT MANUFACTURING CO., LTD.—See China International Marine Containers (Group) Co., Ltd.; *Int'l*, pg. 1512
SIAPI S.R.L.—See ATS Corporation; *Int'l*, pg. 695
SILGAN WHITE CAP CORPORATION—See Silgan Holdings, Inc.; *U.S. Public*, pg. 1879
SILGAN WHITE CAP GMBH—See Silgan Holdings, Inc.; *U.S. Public*, pg. 1879
SKOLNIK INDUSTRIES INC.; *U.S. Private*, pg. 3683
SOCEMBAL SPRL—See Aga Khan Development Network; *Int'l*, pg. 199
SOUTHLINE METAL PRODUCTS COMPANY—See Greif Inc.; *U.S. Public*, pg. 968
SPECIAL PRODUCT COMPANY; *U.S. Private*, pg. 3748
STEEL TECHNOLOGY, LLC—See Helen of Troy Limited; *Int'l*, pg. 3329
SURETANK GROUP LTD.—See HitecVision AS; *Int'l*, pg. 3426
TAKEUCHI PRESS INDUSTRIES COMPANY LIMITED—See Alucon Public Company Limited; *Int'l*, pg. 400
TAYLOR-WHARTON AUSTRALIA PTY. LTD.—See Wind Point Advisors LLC; *U.S. Private*, pg. 4536
TAYLOR-WHARTON INTERNATIONAL LLC—See Wind Point Advisors LLC; *U.S. Private*, pg. 4536
TENNESSEE INDUSTRIAL ELECTRONICS, LLC—See Diploma PLC; *Int'l*, pg. 2129
THERMO OPTEK S.A.—See Thermo Fisher Scientific Inc.; *U.S. Public*, pg. 2154
THERMOS (CHINA) HOUSEWARES CO., LTD.—See Thermos L.L.C.; *U.S. Private*, pg. 4143
THERMOS L.L.C.; *U.S. Private*, pg. 4143
TIANJIN CIMC LOGISTICS EQUIPMENTS CO., LTD.—See China International Marine Containers (Group) Co., Ltd.; *Int'l*, pg. 1512
THE TIN BOX COMPANY; *U.S. Private*, pg. 4127
TRITON CONTAINER INTERNATIONAL LIMITED—See Brookfield Infrastructure Partners L.P.; *Int'l*, pg. 1190
VAN LEER CONTAINERS (NIGERIA) PLC—See Greif Inc.; *U.S. Public*, pg. 968
XINHUI CIMC CONTAINER CO., LTD.—See China International Marine Containers (Group) Co., Ltd.; *Int'l*, pg. 1512
YANGZHOU RUNYANG LOGISTICS EQUIPMENTS CO., LTD.—See China International Marine Containers (Group) Co., Ltd.; *Int'l*, pg. 1512
ZEMPER FRANCE S.A.R.L—See F.W. Thorpe plc; *Int'l*, pg. 2597
ZHANGZHOU CIMC CONTAINER CO., LTD.—See China International Marine Containers (Group) Co., Ltd.; *Int'l*, pg. 1513
ZIEMANN HOLVRIEKA N.V.—See China International Marine Containers (Group) Co., Ltd.; *Int'l*, pg. 1511

332510 — HARDWARE MANUFACTURING

ABLOY HIGH SECURITY LOCKS PRIVATE LTD—See ASSA ABLOY AB; *Int'l*, pg. 637
ABLOY OY—See ASSA ABLOY AB; *Int'l*, pg. 637
ABLOY UK LTD—See ASSA ABLOY AB; *Int'l*, pg. 636
ABLOY UK LTD—See ASSA ABLOY AB; *Int'l*, pg. 636
ACCELERATED CONCEPTS, INC.—See Digi International Inc.; *U.S. Public*, pg. 662
ACCELERATED CONCEPTS PTY. LTD.—See Digi International Inc.; *U.S. Public*, pg. 662
ACCURIDE INTERNATIONAL INC.; *U.S. Private*, pg. 55
ACME MANUFACTURING COMPANY INC.; *U.S. Private*, pg. 61
ACTRON MANUFACTURING, INC.; *U.S. Private*, pg. 70
ADAMS RITE EUROPE LIMITED—See ASSA ABLOY AB; *Int'l*, pg. 633
ADAMS RITE MANUFACTURING CO.—See ASSA ABLOY AB; *Int'l*, pg. 633
ADJUSTABLE CLAMP COMPANY; *U.S. Private*, pg. 79
ADVANTAGE MANUFACTURING CORP.—See ASSA ABLOY AB; *Int'l*, pg. 639
ADVANTUS CORPORATION; *U.S. Private*, pg. 95
AEROSPACE HOLDINGS, LLC—See Hallmark Financial Services, Inc.; *U.S. Public*, pg. 981
A & G MACHINE, INC.; *U.S. Private*, pg. 17
ALBA LOCKING PRODUCTS, LTD—See ASSA ABLOY AB; *Int'l*, pg. 640
A.L. HANSEN MANUFACTURING CO.; *U.S. Private*, pg. 27
ALLEGION A/S—See Allegion Public Limited Company; *Int'l*, pg. 335

ALLEGION B.V.—See Allegion Public Limited Company; *Int'l*, pg. 335
ALLEGION EMNIYET VE GUVENLIK SISTEMLERI SANAYI A.S.—See Allegion Public Limited Company; *Int'l*, pg. 335
ALLEGION NV—See Allegion Public Limited Company; *Int'l*, pg. 335
ALLEGION SECURITY TECHNOLOGIES (CHINA) CO., LTD.—See Allegion Public Limited Company; *Int'l*, pg. 335
ALLEGION (UK) LIMITED—See Allegion Public Limited Company; *Int'l*, pg. 335
ALLEGION US—See Allegion Public Limited Company; *Int'l*, pg. 335
ALLFAST FASTENING SYSTEMS, LLC—See TriMas Corporation; *U.S. Public*, pg. 2189
ALPHA CORPORATION; *Int'l*, pg. 367
ALPOS D.D.—See ALPOS, d.d.; *Int'l*, pg. 375
ALPOS HANDELS GMBH—See ALPOS, d.d.; *Int'l*, pg. 374
ALPOS MIZARSKA PROIZVODNJA, D.O.O.—See ALPOS, d.d.; *Int'l*, pg. 374
ALPOS POHISTVO, D.O.O.—See ALPOS, d.d.; *Int'l*, pg. 374
ALPOS POSEBNE STORITVE, D.O.O.—See ALPOS, d.d.; *Int'l*, pg. 374
ALPOS SP. Z.O.O.—See ALPOS, d.d.; *Int'l*, pg. 375
ALTIS AERO SYSTEMS LLC—See RTX Corporation; *U.S. Public*, pg. 1822
ALUMA-FORM INC.; *U.S. Private*, pg. 211
AMATOM ELECTRONIC HARDWARE, INC.; *U.S. Private*, pg. 216
ANAHOL S.A.—See Illinois Tool Works Inc.; *U.S. Public*, pg. 1101
ANCHOR LAS AB; *Int'l*, pg. 448
ANGEL METAL CO., LTD.—See ASSA ABLOY AB; *Int'l*, pg. 638
ARMOR SAFE TECHNOLOGIES—See Phelps Tointon Inc.; *U.S. Private*, pg. 3167
ARROW TRU-LINE, INC.—See MiddleGround Management, LP; *U.S. Public*, pg. 2711
ARX LIMITED—See Becton, Dickinson & Company; *U.S. Public*, pg. 288
ASCO SINTERING CO.; *U.S. Private*, pg. 348
ASETEK DANMARK A/S—See Asetek A/S; *Int'l*, pg. 606
ASIAN MICRO (THAILAND) CO., LTD.—See Asian Micro Holdings Ltd.; *Int'l*, pg. 618
A/S RUKO—See ASSA ABLOY AB; *Int'l*, pg. 632
ASSA ABLOY AUSTRALIA PACIFIC PTY LTD—See ASSA ABLOY AB; *Int'l*, pg. 633
ASSA ABLOY AUSTRIA GMBH—See ASSA ABLOY AB; *Int'l*, pg. 633
ASSA ABLOY BALTIC AS—See ASSA ABLOY AB; *Int'l*, pg. 633
ASSA ABLOY CHILE LTDA—See ASSA ABLOY AB; *Int'l*, pg. 633
ASSA ABLOY DANMARK A/S—See ASSA ABLOY AB; *Int'l*, pg. 633
ASSA ABLOY DEUTSCHLAND GMBH—See ASSA ABLOY AB; *Int'l*, pg. 633
ASSA ABLOY ENTRANCE SYSTEMS FRANCE SAS—See ASSA ABLOY AB; *Int'l*, pg. 633
ASSA ABLOY ENTRANCE SYSTEMS ITALY S.P.A.—See ASSA ABLOY AB; *Int'l*, pg. 633
ASSA ABLOY ENTRANCE SYSTEMS, SPOL. S R.O.—See ASSA ABLOY AB; *Int'l*, pg. 633
ASSA ABLOY ENTRANCE SYSTEMS (SUZHOU) CO., LTD.—See ASSA ABLOY AB; *Int'l*, pg. 633
ASSA ABLOY ES PRODUCTION S.R.O—See ASSA ABLOY AB; *Int'l*, pg. 633
ASSA ABLOY FORSAKRINGS AB—See ASSA ABLOY AB; *Int'l*, pg. 635
ASSA ABLOY GUOQIANG (SHANDONG) HARDWARE TECHNOLOGY CO., LTD—See ASSA ABLOY AB; *Int'l*, pg. 635
ASSA ABLOY HOSPITALITY (CANADA) LTD.—See ASSA ABLOY AB; *Int'l*, pg. 635
ASSA ABLOY HOSPITALITY GMBH—See ASSA ABLOY AB; *Int'l*, pg. 635
ASSA ABLOY HOSPITALITY IBERICA, S.L.—See ASSA ABLOY AB; *Int'l*, pg. 635
ASSA ABLOY HOSPITALITY LTD—See ASSA ABLOY AB; *Int'l*, pg. 635
ASSA ABLOY HOSPITALITY LTD—See ASSA ABLOY AB; *Int'l*, pg. 635
ASSA ABLOY HOSPITALITY LTD—See ASSA ABLOY AB; *Int'l*, pg. 635
ASSA ABLOY HOSPITALITY PTE LTD—See ASSA ABLOY AB; *Int'l*, pg. 635
ASSA ABLOY HOSPITALITY SAS—See ASSA ABLOY AB; *Int'l*, pg. 635
ASSA ABLOY HUNGARY KERESKEDELMI KFT.—See ASSA ABLOY AB; *Int'l*, pg. 635
ASSA ABLOY IDENTIFICATION TECHNOLOGY GROUP AB—See ASSA ABLOY AB; *Int'l*, pg. 635
ASSA ABLOY INDIA PRIVATE LTD.—See ASSA ABLOY AB; *Int'l*, pg. 635
ASSA ABLOY ITALIA S.P.A.—See ASSA ABLOY AB; *Int'l*, pg. 635

332510 — HARDWARE MANUFACTUR...

ASSA ABLOY JAPAN CO LTD—See ASSA ABLOY AB; *Int'l*, pg. 636
ASSA ABLOY KREDIT AB—See ASSA ABLOY AB; *Int'l*, pg. 636
ASSA ABLOY MALAYSIA SDN BHD—See ASSA ABLOY AB; *Int'l*, pg. 636
ASSA ABLOY NEDERLAND B.V.—See ASSA ABLOY AB; *Int'l*, pg. 636
ASSA ABLOY NEW ZEALAND LIMITED—See ASSA ABLOY AB; *Int'l*, pg. 636
ASSA ABLOY NV—See ASSA ABLOY AB; *Int'l*, pg. 636
ASSA ABLOY OCCIDENTE, SA DE CV—See ASSA ABLOY AB; *Int'l*, pg. 636
ASSA ABLOY PORTUGAL, LDA.—See ASSA ABLOY AB; *Int'l*, pg. 636
ASSA ABLOY PORTUGAL, UNIPESSOAL, LDA—See ASSA ABLOY AB; *Int'l*, pg. 636
ASSA ABLOY SICHERHEITSTECHNIK GMBH - BERLIN PLANT—See ASSA ABLOY AB; *Int'l*, pg. 636
ASSA ABLOY SOUTH ASIA PTE LTD—See ASSA ABLOY AB; *Int'l*, pg. 636
ASSA ABLOY SVENSK FASTIGHETS AB—See ASSA ABLOY AB; *Int'l*, pg. 636
ASSA ABLOY (SWITZERLAND) LTD.—See ASSA ABLOY AB; *Int'l*, pg. 632
ASSA, INC—See ASSA ABLOY AB; *Int'l*, pg. 637
ASSA INDUSTRIE AB—See ASSA ABLOY AB; *Int'l*, pg. 639
ASSA OEM AB—See ASSA ABLOY AB; *Int'l*, pg. 637
ASSOCIATED SPRING RAYMOND GMBH—See Barnes Group Inc.; *U.S. Public*, pg. 276
ASUS COMPUTER CZECH REPUBLIC S. R. O.—See ASUSTeK Computer Inc.; *Int'l*, pg. 663
ASUS CZECH SERVICE S. R. O.—See ASUSTeK Computer Inc.; *Int'l*, pg. 663
ASUS FRANCE SARL—See ASUSTeK Computer Inc.; *Int'l*, pg. 663
ASUS KOREA CO., LTD.—See ASUSTeK Computer Inc.; *Int'l*, pg. 663
ASUS MEXICO, S. A. DE C. V.—See ASUSTeK Computer Inc.; *Int'l*, pg. 663
ASUS NORDIC AB—See ASUSTeK Computer Inc.; *Int'l*, pg. 663
ASUS POLSKA SP. Z O. O.—See ASUSTeK Computer Inc.; *Int'l*, pg. 663
ASUS SERVICE AUSTRALIA PTY LIMITED—See ASUSTeK Computer Inc.; *Int'l*, pg. 663
ASUS TECHNOLOGY (HONG KONG) LIMITED—See ASUSTeK Computer Inc.; *Int'l*, pg. 663
ASUS TECHNOLOGY PTE. LIMITED—See ASUSTeK Computer Inc.; *Int'l*, pg. 663
ASUS TECHNOLOGY (VIETNAM) CO., LTD.—See ASUSTeK Computer Inc.; *Int'l*, pg. 663
ASUSTEK COMPUTER INC.; *Int'l*, pg. 663
ASUSTEK COMPUTER MALAYSIA SDN. BHD.—See ASUSTeK Computer Inc.; *Int'l*, pg. 663
ASUSTEK COMPUTER (S) PTE. LTD.—See ASUSTeK Computer Inc.; *Int'l*, pg. 663
ASUSTEK COMPUTERS (PTY) LIMITED—See ASUSTeK Computer Inc.; *Int'l*, pg. 664
ASUSTEK ITALY S. R. L.—See ASUSTeK Computer Inc.; *Int'l*, pg. 664
ASUSTEK (UK) LIMITED—See ASUSTeK Computer Inc.; *Int'l*, pg. 663
ATRACK TECHNOLOGY, INC.; *Int'l*, pg. 693
ATRACK TECHNOLOGY (TOKYO) INC.—See ATrack Technology, Inc.; *Int'l*, pg. 693
ATTWOOD CORPORATION—See Brunswick Corporation; *U.S. Public*, pg. 407
AUTOMOTIVE RACING PRODUCTS; *U.S. Private*, pg. 400
AVIS INDUSTRIAL CORPORATION; *U.S. Private*, pg. 407
AVOCET HARDWARE LTD.; *Int'l*, pg. 748
AXA STENMAN DEUTSCHLAND GMBH—See Allegion Public Limited Company; *Int'l*, pg. 335
AXA STENMAN FRANCE S.A.S.—See Allegion Public Limited Company; *Int'l*, pg. 335
AXA STENMAN INDUSTRIES B.V.—See Allegion Public Limited Company; *Int'l*, pg. 335
AXA STENMAN NEDERLAND B.V.—See Allegion Public Limited Company; *Int'l*, pg. 335
AXA STENMAN POLAND SP.Z.O.O.—See Allegion Public Limited Company; *Int'l*, pg. 335
BAB IKON GMBH SCHLIESSTECHNIK—See ASSA ABLOY AB; *Int'l*, pg. 639
BALDT, INC.; *U.S. Private*, pg. 458
BALDWIN HARDWARE CORPORATION—See Spectrum Brands Holdings, Inc.; *U.S. Public*, pg. 1917
BAND-IT COMPANY LTD.—See IDEX Corp; *U.S. Public*, pg. 1089
BAND-IT-IDEX, INC.—See IDEX Corp; *U.S. Public*, pg. 1089
BAND-IT R.S.A. (PTY) LTD.—See IDEX Corp; *U.S. Public*, pg. 1089
BAODEAN SECURITY PRODUCTS CO. LTD—See ASSA ABLOY AB; *Int'l*, pg. 639
BARTRONICS INDIA LTD.; *Int'l*, pg. 870
B.C LASEPARTNER A/S—See ASSA ABLOY AB; *Int'l*, pg. 639
B/E AEROSPACE CANADA COMPANY—See RTX Corporation; *U.S. Public*, pg. 1822
BELWITH PRODUCTS, LLC - HICKORY HARDWARE DIVISION—See Belwith Products, LLC; *U.S. Private*, pg. 522
BELWITH PRODUCTS, LLC - KEELER DIVISION—See Belwith Products, LLC; *U.S. Private*, pg. 522
BELWITH PRODUCTS, LLC; *U.S. Private*, pg. 522
BIOSTAR MICROTECH INTERNATIONAL CORP.; *Int'l*, pg. 1042
BIREPO A/S—See Addtech AB; *Int'l*, pg. 132
BLACKSMITHS DEPOT—See Kayne & Son Custom Hardware Inc.; *U.S. Private*, pg. 2266
BMW AUTOMOTIVE (IRELAND) LTD.—See Bayerische Motoren Werke Aktiengesellschaft; *Int'l*, pg. 911
BMW (GB) LTD.—See Bayerische Motoren Werke Aktiengesellschaft; *Int'l*, pg. 910
BMW MANUFACTURING INDUSTRIA DE MOTOS DA AMAZONIA LTDA.—See Bayerische Motoren Werke Aktiengesellschaft; *Int'l*, pg. 912
BMW M GMBH—See Bayerische Motoren Werke Aktiengesellschaft; *Int'l*, pg. 912
BOMMER INDUSTRIES, INC. - GAFFNEY PLANT—See Bommer Industries, Inc.; *U.S. Private*, pg. 612
BOMMER INDUSTRIES, INC.; *U.S. Private*, pg. 612
BOSSARD ITALIA S.R.L.—See Bossard Holding AG; *Int'l*, pg. 1117
BROOKS INSTRUMENT B.V.—See Illinois Tool Works Inc.; *U.S. Public*, pg. 1102
BROOKS INSTRUMENT KOREA, LTD.—See Illinois Tool Works Inc.; *U.S. Public*, pg. 1102
BURG-WACHTER KG; *Int'l*, pg. 1223
BW YEE SENG HARDWARE TRADING SDN. BHD.—See IJM Corporation Berhad; *Int'l*, pg. 3608
CANAAN INC.; *Int'l*, pg. 1277
CARDO DOOR PRODUCTION GMBH—See ASSA ABLOY AB; *Int'l*, pg. 634
CCL SECURITY PRODUCTS—See The Eastern Company; *U.S. Public*, pg. 2069
CELMA INDUKTA SA—See Cantoni Motor S.A.; *Int'l*, pg. 1299
CERRADURAS DE COLOMBIA - CERRACOL S.A.S.—See ASSA ABLOY AB; *Int'l*, pg. 639
CESSOT DECORATION SARL; *Int'l*, pg. 1424
C. HAGER & SONS HINGE MANUFACTURING COMPANY INC.; *U.S. Private*, pg. 705
CHARLES LEONARD NATIONAL, INC.—See Charles Leonard Inc.; *U.S. Private*, pg. 852
CHARLES LEONARD (WESTERN), INC.—See Charles Leonard Inc.; *U.S. Private*, pg. 852
CHEIL INDUSTRY CO. LTD—See ASSA ABLOY AB; *Int'l*, pg. 639
CHICAGO HARDWARE & FIXTURE COMPANY; *U.S. Private*, pg. 877
CHI CHENG ENTERPRISE CO., LTD.; *Int'l*, pg. 1474
CHIENG YENG ENT. CO., LTD.—See Leggett & Platt, Incorporated; *U.S. Public*, pg. 1301
CHIME BALL TECHNOLOGY CO., LTD.; *Int'l*, pg. 1479
CHITA KOGYO CO., LTD.; *Int'l*, pg. 1574
CH SWEESTECH DOOR SDN. BHD.—See Chuan Huat Resources Berhad; *Int'l*, pg. 1589
CHUBB UNION ZIMBABWE (PVT) LTD—See ASSA ABLOY AB; *Int'l*, pg. 639
CISA CERRADURAS S.A.—See Ingersoll Rand Inc.; *U.S. Public*, pg. 1120
CISA S.P.A.—See Ingersoll Rand Inc.; *U.S. Public*, pg. 1120
CITY LASEPARTNER A/S—See ASSA ABLOY AB; *Int'l*, pg. 639
CLARK PULLEY INDUSTRIES INC.—See AF Holding Company; *U.S. Public*, pg. 121
CLIMAX METAL PRODUCTS COMPANY—See RBC Bearings Incorporated; *U.S. Public*, pg. 1766
COLSON ASSOCIATES, INC.; *U.S. Private*, pg. 975
COLUMBIA NUT & BOLT LLC—See Park-Ohio Holdings Corp.; *U.S. Public*, pg. 1639
COMPONENTA MANUFACTURING OY—See Componenta Corporation; *Int'l*, pg. 1753
COMPONENT HARDWARE GROUP, INC.; *U.S. Private*, pg. 1002
COMPX FORT—See Contran Corporation; *U.S. Private*, pg. 1033
COMPX NATIONAL, INC.—See Contran Corporation; *U.S. Private*, pg. 1033
COMPX SECURITY PRODUCTS INC.—See Contran Corporation; *U.S. Private*, pg. 1033
CONNECTED SOLUTIONS GROUP, LLC; *U.S. Private*, pg. 1015
CONNECT TECH INC.—See HEICO Corporation; *U.S. Public*, pg. 1019
CONSOLIDATED AEROSPACE MANUFACTURING LLC—See Tinicum Enterprises, Inc.; *U.S. Private*, pg. 4174
COPERION K-TRON DEUTSCHLAND GMBH—See Hillenbrand, Inc.; *U.S. Public*, pg. 1036
COPERION K-TRON SALINA—See Hillenbrand, Inc.; *U.S. Public*, pg. 1037
COPERION (NANJING) MACHINERY CO., LTD.—See Hillenbrand, Inc.; *U.S. Public*, pg. 1036
CORBIN RUSSWIN, INC.—See ASSA ABLOY AB; *Int'l*, pg. 636
CORDSEN ENGINEERING GMBH—See Bechtle AG; *Int'l*, pg. 938
COREMAX CORP.; *Int'l*, pg. 1798
CRAWFORD COMBURSA S.L.U.—See ASSA ABLOY AB; *Int'l*, pg. 634
CRAWFORD HAFA GMBH—See ASSA ABLOY AB; *Int'l*, pg. 635
CRAWFORD-HAFA SRL—See ASSA ABLOY AB; *Int'l*, pg. 635
THE CROSBY GROUP LLC—See KKR & Co. Inc.; *U.S. Public*, pg. 1264
CWI INTERNATIONAL CHINA, LTD.—See Waxman Industries, Inc.; *U.S. Private*, pg. 4459
DAISUI CO., LTD.; *Int'l*, pg. 1942
DENY FONTAINE—See Groupe SFPI SA; *Int'l*, pg. 3111
DIEHL AEROSPACE, INC.—See Diehl Stiftung & Co. KG; *Int'l*, pg. 2114
DIEHL AEROSYSTEMS-HOLDING GMBH—See Diehl Stiftung & Co. KG; *Int'l*, pg. 2114
DIEHL AIRCABIN HUNGARY KFT.—See Diehl Stiftung & Co. KG; *Int'l*, pg. 2114
DIEHL SERVICE MODULES GMBH—See Diehl Stiftung & Co. KG; *Int'l*, pg. 2115
DITEC D.D. LAZIO S.R.L.—See ASSA ABLOY AB; *Int'l*, pg. 639
DITEC D.D. LOMBARDIA S.R.L.—See ASSA ABLOY AB; *Int'l*, pg. 639
DITEC ESPANA S.L.U.—See ASSA ABLOY AB; *Int'l*, pg. 639
DITEC TUR GMBH—See ASSA ABLOY AB; *Int'l*, pg. 639
DOCKYARD GENERAL ENGINEERING SERVICES (PVT) LTD. - MARINE & INDUSTRIAL HARDWARE DIVISION—See Colombo Dockyard PLC; *Int'l*, pg. 1702
DOMINANCE INDUSTRIES, INC.—See Owens Corning; *U.S. Public*, pg. 1626
DONGGUAN GEM ELECTRONICS & METAL CO., LTD.—See Gem Terminal Ind. Co., Ltd.; *Int'l*, pg. 2915
DORMA DOOR CONTROLS PTY LTD—See dormakaba Holding AG; *Int'l*, pg. 2178
DORMA-GLAS GMBH—See dormakaba Holding AG; *Int'l*, pg. 2178
DORMAKABA ACCESS INDONESIA, PT—See dormakaba Holding AG; *Int'l*, pg. 2178
DORMAKABA BULGARIA EOOD—See dormakaba Holding AG; *Int'l*, pg. 2178
DORMAKABA CESKO S.R.O—See dormakaba Holding AG; *Int'l*, pg. 2178
DORMAKABA EURASIA LLC—See dormakaba Holding AG; *Int'l*, pg. 2178
DORMAKABA HOLDING GMBH & CO. KGAA—See dormakaba Holding AG; *Int'l*, pg. 2178
DORMAKABA ITALIA SRL—See dormakaba Holding AG; *Int'l*, pg. 2179
DORMAKABA KENYA LIMITED—See dormakaba Holding AG; *Int'l*, pg. 2179
DORMAKABA MAGYARORSZAG ZRT.—See dormakaba Holding AG; *Int'l*, pg. 2178
DORMAKABA MAROC SARL—See dormakaba Holding AG; *Int'l*, pg. 2179
DORMAKABA NORGE AS—See dormakaba Holding AG; *Int'l*, pg. 2179
DORMAKABA PHILIPPINES INC.—See dormakaba Holding AG; *Int'l*, pg. 2179
DORMAKABA POLSKA SP. Z O.O.—See dormakaba Holding AG; *Int'l*, pg. 2179
DORMAKABA PRODUCTION MALAYSIA SDN. BHD.—See dormakaba Holding AG; *Int'l*, pg. 2179
DORMAKABA SCHWEIZ AG—See dormakaba Holding AG; *Int'l*, pg. 2179
DORMAKABA SUOMI OY—See dormakaba Holding AG; *Int'l*, pg. 2179
DORMAKABA (THAILAND) LTD.—See dormakaba Holding AG; *Int'l*, pg. 2178
DORMAKABA USA INC.—See dormakaba Holding AG; *Int'l*, pg. 2179
DORTONICS, INC.—See Sag Harbor Industries, Inc.; *U.S. Private*, pg. 3525
DOVER (SUZHOU) INDUSTRIAL EQUIPMENT MANUFACTURING CO., LTD.—See Dover Corporation; *U.S. Public*, pg. 679
DRIV-LOK, INC.; *U.S. Private*, pg. 1278
DRUCK- UND SPRITZGUSSWERK HETTICH GMBH & CO. KG—See Hettich Holding GmbH & Co. oHG; *Int'l*, pg. 3365
DSE INC.—See National Presto Industries, Inc; *U.S. Public*, pg. 1497
DUALIS GMBH IT SOLUTION—See Durr AG; *Int'l*, pg. 2230
EBERHARD HARDWARE MANUFACTURING LTD.—See The Eastern Company; *U.S. Public*, pg. 2069
EBERHARD MANUFACTURING DIVISION—See The Eastern Company; *U.S. Public*, pg. 2069
ECOPLASTIC CORPORATION; *Int'l*, pg. 2299
EFFEFF FRANCE S.A.S.—See ASSA ABLOY AB; *Int'l*, pg. 641
ELESA S.P.A.—See Brd. Klee A/S; *Int'l*, pg. 1143
ELMA ELECTRONIC GMBH—See Elma Electronic AG; *Int'l*, pg. 2367
ELMA ELECTRONIC ROMANIA SRL—See Elma Electronic AG; *Int'l*, pg. 2367

332510 — HARDWARE MANUFACTUR...

ELMA ELECTRONIC TECHNOLOGY (SHANGHAI) CO., LTD.—See Elma Electronic AG; *Int'l*, pg. 2367
ELMA ELECTRONIC UK LTD.—See Elma Electronic AG; *Int'l*, pg. 2367
EMKA BESCHLAGTEILE IBERICA S.L.—See EMKA-Beschlagteile GmbH & Co. KG; *Int'l*, pg. 2383
EMKA BOSNIA D.O.O.—See EMKA-Beschlagteile GmbH & Co. KG; *Int'l*, pg. 2383
EMKA FRANCE SA—See EMKA-Beschlagteile GmbH & Co. KG; *Int'l*, pg. 2383
EMKA INC.—See EMKA-Beschlagteile GmbH & Co. KG; *Int'l*, pg. 2383
EMKA INDUSTRIAL HARDWARE CO. LTD.—See EMKA-Beschlagteile GmbH & Co. KG; *Int'l*, pg. 2383
EMKA (UK) LTD.—See EMKA-Beschlagteile GmbH & Co. KG; *Int'l*, pg. 2383
EMTEK PRODUCTS, INC.—See ASSA ABLOY AB; *Int'l*, pg. 639
ENLIGHT CORPORATION; *Int'l*, pg. 2442
EPIC DIVERSITY SDN BHD—See Chin Hin Group Berhad; *Int'l*, pg. 1480
E.R. WAGNER CASTERS AND WHEELS DIV.—See E.R. Wagner Manufacturing Co.; *U.S. Private*, pg. 1307
E.R. WAGNER MANUFACTURING CO. - ENGINEERED PRODUCTS DIVISION—See E.R. Wagner Manufacturing Co.; *U.S. Private*, pg. 1307
E.R. WAGNER MANUFACTURING CO.; *U.S. Private*, pg. 1306
ESON PRECISION ENGINEERING (MALAYSIA) SDN. BHD.—See Eson Precision Ind. Co., Ltd.; *Int'l*, pg. 2504
EURO-ELZETT KFT.—See Groupe SFPI SA; *Int'l*, pg. 3111
EXCALIBUR VEHICLE ACCESSORIES (PTY) LTD—See ARGENT INDUSTRIAL LIMITED; *Int'l*, pg. 560
EXIDOR LIMITED—See ASSA ABLOY AB; *Int'l*, pg. 636
FANA NARZEDZIA SP.Z.O.O.—See Cantoni Motor S.A.; *Int'l*, pg. 1299
FEELER HARDWARE INDUSTRIAL CORPORATION—See Fair Friend Group; *Int'l*, pg. 2604
FERMETURES GROOM S.A.S.—See dormakaba Holding AG; *Int'l*, pg. 2177
FINISHLINE TECHNOLOGIES, INC.—See Spray Equipment & Service Center, Inc.; *U.S. Private*, pg. 3762
FLEXIBLE STEEL LACING COMPANY; *U.S. Private*, pg. 1544
FLEXI FORCE B.V.—See ASSA ABLOY AB; *Int'l*, pg. 639
FLEXIFORCE HUNGARY KFT.—See ASSA ABLOY AB; *Int'l*, pg. 639
FLEXI FORCE IBERICA, S.L.—See ASSA ABLOY AB; *Int'l*, pg. 639
FLEXI FORCE ITALIA S.R.L.—See ASSA ABLOY AB; *Int'l*, pg. 639
FLEXI FORCE POLAND SP. Z.O.O.—See ASSA ABLOY AB; *Int'l*, pg. 639
FLOBAL CORPORATION; *Int'l*, pg. 2707
FORTECH ELECTRONICS CO., LTD.—See Chaintech Technology Corp.; *Int'l*, pg. 1437
FORT SECURITE S.A.—See EMKA-Beschlagteile GmbH & Co. KG; *Int'l*, pg. 2383
FORTUNE BRANDS STORAGE & SECURITY LLC—See Fortune Brands Innovations, Inc.; *U.S. Public*, pg. 873
GAMBER-JOHNSON, LLC—See Main Street Capital Corporation; *U.S. Public*, pg. 1354
GEM INDUSTRIES CORPORATION; *U.S. Private*, pg. 1657
GEM INDUSTRIES—See Gem Industries Corporation; *U.S. Private*, pg. 1657
G.G. SCHMITT & SONS INC.—See Patrick Industries, Inc.; *U.S. Public*, pg. 1652
GIFLO ENGINEERING (PTY) LTD—See ARGENT INDUSTRIAL LIMITED; *Int'l*, pg. 560
GK MECHANICAL SYSTEMS LLC—See KKR & Co. Inc.; *U.S. Public*, pg. 1262
GREEN SHARE CO., LTD.—See Giga-Byte Technology Co., Ltd.; *Int'l*, pg. 2971
GRIMM INDUSTRIES PTE. LTD.—See GDS Global Limited; *Int'l*, pg. 2896
GUANGDONG KINEX HARDWARE PRODUCTS CO., LTD.—See Guangdong Kinlong Hardware Prdcts Co., Ltd.; *Int'l*, pg. 3157
GUANGDONG KINLONG HARDWARE PRDCTS CO., LTD.; *Int'l*, pg. 3157
GUANGDONG MINGZHU GROUP CO., LTD.; *Int'l*, pg. 3158
GUANGDONG SACA PRECISION MANUFACTURING CO., LTD.; *Int'l*, pg. 3159
GUANGDONG TOPSTRONG LIVING INNOVATION & INTEGRATION CO., LTD.; *Int'l*, pg. 3161
GUANGZHOU SHANGPIN HOME COLLECTION CO., LTD.; *Int'l*, pg. 3167
GUARDIAN GATE HARDWARE, LLC—See The Duchossois Group, Inc.; *U.S. Private*, pg. 4023
GUMSTIX INC.—See Altium Limited; *Int'l*, pg. 394
HAGA S/A INDUSTRIA E COMERCIO; *Int'l*, pg. 3206
HARDWYN INDIA LIMITED; *Int'l*, pg. 3273
HARKEN, INCORPORATED; *U.S. Private*, pg. 1864
HELTON INDUSTRIES LTD.—See ASSA ABLOY AB; *Int'l*, pg. 639
HENDERSON NEDERLANDS BV—See ASSA ABLOY AB; *Int'l*, pg. 639

HETTICH AMERICA, L.P.—See Hettich Holding GmbH & Co. oHG; *Int'l*, pg. 3365
HETTICH CR K.S.—See Hettich Holding GmbH & Co. oHG; *Int'l*, pg. 3365
HETTICH FRANKE GMBH & CO. KG—See Hettich Holding GmbH & Co. oHG; *Int'l*, pg. 3365
HETTICH FURNTECH GMBH & CO. KG—See Hettich Holding GmbH & Co. oHG; *Int'l*, pg. 3365
HETTICH LOGISTIK SERVICE GMBH & CO. KG—See Hettich Holding GmbH & Co. oHG; *Int'l*, pg. 3365
HETTICH MARKETING- UND VERTRIEBS GMBH & CO. KG—See Hettich Holding GmbH & Co. oHG; *Int'l*, pg. 3366
HETTICH-ONI GMBH & CO. KG—See Hettich Holding GmbH & Co. oHG; *Int'l*, pg. 3366
HETTICH STROTHMANN GMBH & CO. KG—See Hettich Holding GmbH & Co. oHG; *Int'l*, pg. 3366
HEYWOOD WILLIAMS COMPONENTS LIMITED—See ASSA ABLOY AB; *Int'l*, pg. 639
HIAWATHA, INC.—See Activar, Inc.; *U.S. Private*, pg. 68
HID CORPORATION LTD.—See ASSA ABLOY AB; *Int'l*, pg. 637
THE HILLMAN GROUP - TEMPE—See Hillman Solutions Corp.; *U.S. Public*, pg. 1038
HIPER GLOBAL UK LTD.—See HIPER Global Ltd.; *Int'l*, pg. 3402
HIPER GLOBAL US LTD.—See HIPER Global Ltd.; *Int'l*, pg. 3402
HLA COMPANY INC.; *U.S. Private*, pg. 1954
HOMAG TRADING AND SERVICES SDN. BHD.—See Durr AG; *Int'l*, pg. 2233
HONDA LOCK THAI CO., LTD.—See Honda Motor Co., Ltd.; *Int'l*, pg. 3460
HONGYUAN HARDWARE INDUSTRY & TRADING CO. LTD.; *Int'l*, pg. 3471
HOUCK INDUSTRIES, INC.; *U.S. Private*, pg. 1990
HUDSON LOCK, LLC—See Dominus Capital, L.P.; *U.S. Private*, pg. 1256
HUPSTEEL LIMITED; *Int'l*, pg. 3538
HYDRASEARCH COMPANY, INC.—See Dixon Valve & Coupling Company; *U.S. Private*, pg. 1246
IAMBA ARAD S.A.; *Int'l*, pg. 3568
IDD PARTS B.V.—See ASSA ABLOY AB; *Int'l*, pg. 639
THE ILLINOIS LOCK COMPANY—See The Eastern Company; *U.S. Public*, pg. 2069
ILS SPETH GMBH—See EMKA-Beschlagteile GmbH & Co. KG; *Int'l*, pg. 2383
IMPULSE NC, LLC—See Berkshire Hathaway Inc.; *U.S. Public*, pg. 310
INDUSTRIA E COMERCIO DE MAQUINAS PERFECTA CURITIBA LTDA.—See Illinois Tool Works Inc.; *U.S. Public*, pg. 1108
INDUSTRIAL REVOLUTION, INC.; *U.S. Private*, pg. 2068
INGERSOLL-RAND ARCHITECTURAL HARDWARE LIMITED—See Ingersoll Rand Inc.; *U.S. Public*, pg. 1121
INVERSORA LOCKEY DE VENEZUELA CA—See Ingersoll Rand Inc.; *U.S. Public*, pg. 1121
ISA INTELLIGENT SENSING ANYWHERE SA—See Anova Microsystems Inc.; *U.S. Private*, pg. 285
ITALTRACTOR LANDRONI LTDA.—See Titan International, Inc.; *U.S. Public*, pg. 2160
ITW AUTOMOTIVE KOREA, LLC—See Illinois Tool Works Inc.; *U.S. Public*, pg. 1104
ITW BRANDS—See Illinois Tool Works Inc.; *U.S. Public*, pg. 1104
ITW ELECTRONICS (SUZHOU) CO., LTD.—See Illinois Tool Works Inc.; *U.S. Public*, pg. 1105
ITW LYS FUSION S.R.L.—See Illinois Tool Works Inc.; *U.S. Public*, pg. 1106
ITW MARKING & CODING (SHANGHAI) CO., LTD.—See Illinois Tool Works Inc.; *U.S. Public*, pg. 1106
ITW PLASTIGLIDE—See Illinois Tool Works Inc.; *U.S. Public*, pg. 1107
ITW RAMSET/RED HEAD—See Illinois Tool Works Inc.; *U.S. Public*, pg. 1107
JOHN WAGNER ASSOCIATES, INC. - PACIFIC DIVISION—See John Wagner Associates, Inc.; *U.S. Private*, pg. 2225
JPM S.A.—See ASSA ABLOY AB; *Int'l*, pg. 639
KABA ACCESS CONTROL—See dormakaba Holding AG; *Int'l*, pg. 2177
KABA ILCO CORP.—See dormakaba Holding AG; *Int'l*, pg. 2177
KABA MAS LLC—See dormakaba Holding AG; *Int'l*, pg. 2177
KAE KRAFTWERKS- & ANLAGEN-ENGINEERING GMBH—See BKW AG; *Int'l*, pg. 1055
KASON INDUSTRIES INCORPORATED; *U.S. Private*, pg. 2264
KAYNE & SON CUSTOM HARDWARE INC.; *U.S. Private*, pg. 2264
KEYLINE CONSULTING SDN. BHD.—See Chuan Huat Resources Berhad; *Int'l*, pg. 1589
KIN LONG HARDWARE (INDIA) PRIVATE LIMITED—See Guangdong Kinlong Hardware Prdcts Co., Ltd.; *Int'l*, pg. 3157
KIRK KEY INTERLOCK COMPANY LLC—See Halma plc; *Int'l*, pg. 3231
KWIKSET CORPORATION—See Spectrum Brands Holdings, Inc.; *U.S. Public*, pg. 1917

LCN CLOSERS—See Allegion Public Limited Company; *Int'l*, pg. 335
LEGGETT & PLATT COMMERCIAL VEHICLE PRODUCTS, INC.—See Leggett & Platt, Incorporated; *U.S. Public*, pg. 1303
L.E. JOHNSON PRODUCTS INC.; *U.S. Private*, pg. 2365
LOCKMASTERS, INC.—See Dominus Capital, L.P.; *U.S. Private*, pg. 1256
LORD & SONS INC.; *U.S. Private*, pg. 2494
MAC VALVES, INC.-DUNDEE—See MAC Valves, Inc.; *U.S. Private*, pg. 2531
MARLBORO MANUFACTURING, INC.; *U.S. Private*, pg. 2583
MASONITE CZ SPOL S.R.O.—See Owens Corning; *U.S. Public*, pg. 1627
MASONITE DOORS PRIVATE LTD.—See Owens Corning; *U.S. Public*, pg. 1627
MASONITE IRELAND—See Owens Corning; *U.S. Public*, pg. 1627
MASTER LOCK COMPANY LLC—See Fortune Brands Innovations, Inc.; *U.S. Public*, pg. 873
MAYDAY MANUFACTURING CO.—See ESCO Technologies, Inc.; *U.S. Public*, pg. 794
MAYER & CO BESCHLAGE GMBH—See Guangdong Kinlong Hardware Prdcts Co., Ltd.; *Int'l*, pg. 3157
MCKINNEY PRODUCTS COMPANY—See ASSA ABLOY AB; *Int'l*, pg. 636
MCKISSICK PRODUCTS CO.—See KKR & Co. Inc.; *U.S. Public*, pg. 1264
MEDECO HIGH SECURITY LOCKS, INC.—See ASSA ABLOY AB; *Int'l*, pg. 636
MENUISERIE DU CENTRE—See Compagnie de Saint-Gobain SA; *Int'l*, pg. 1724
MIND SOLUTIONS, INC.; *U.S. Public*, pg. 1448
MIRANDA ASIA K.K.—See Belden, Inc.; *U.S. Public*, pg. 294
MIRANDA TECHNOLOGIES ASIA LTD.—See Belden, Inc.; *U.S. Public*, pg. 294
MIRANDA TECHNOLOGIES FRANCE SAS—See Belden, Inc.; *U.S. Public*, pg. 294
MOELLER MANUFACTURING & SUPPLY, INC.—See Tinicum Enterprises, Inc.; *U.S. Private*, pg. 4174
MUL-T-LOCK CZECH, S.R.O.—See ASSA ABLOY AB; *Int'l*, pg. 640
MUL-T-LOCK MACHINERY LTD.—See ASSA ABLOY AB; *Int'l*, pg. 640
MUL-T-LOCK TECHNOLOGIES ITALY SRL—See ASSA ABLOY AB; *Int'l*, pg. 640
MUL-T-LOCK USA, INC.—See ASSA ABLOY AB; *Int'l*, pg. 640
NARMOD SP. Z O.O.—See Cantoni Motor S.A.; *Int'l*, pg. 1299
NATIONAL INSTRUMENTS HUNGARY KFT.—See National Instruments Corporation; *U.S. Private*, pg. 2857
NATIONWIDE INDUSTRIES, INC.—See Harbour Group Industries, Inc.; *U.S. Private*, pg. 1860
NEPTUNE RESEARCH, LLC—See Wind Point Advisors LLC; *U.S. Private*, pg. 4534
NEW HAMPSHIRE INDUSTRIES INC.; *U.S. Private*, pg. 2896
NIELSEN HARDWARE CORPORATION—See Enerpac Tool Group Corp.; *U.S. Public*, pg. 766
NI HUNGARY KFT.—See National Instruments Corporation; *U.S. Private*, pg. 2857
NINGBO KIN LONG KEXING PRECISION MANUFACTURING CO., LTD.—See Guangdong Kinlong Hardware Prdcts Co., Ltd.; *Int'l*, pg. 3157
NORCRAFT COMPANIES, INC.—See MasterBrand, Inc.; *U.S. Public*, pg. 1394
NORMBAU BESCHLAGE UND AUSSTATTUNGS GMBH—See Allegion Public Limited Company; *Int'l*, pg. 335
NORMBAU FRANCE S.A.S.—See Ingersoll Rand Inc.; *U.S. Public*, pg. 1122
NORTON PACKAGING INC.; *U.S. Private*, pg. 2964
OCEANEERING SPACE SYSTEMS—See Oceaneering International, Inc.; *U.S. Public*, pg. 1563
ONITY CO., LIMITED—See Carrier Global Corporation; *U.S. Public*, pg. 443
ONITY LIMITED—See Carrier Global Corporation; *U.S. Public*, pg. 443
ONITY LTDA—See Carrier Global Corporation; *U.S. Public*, pg. 443
ONITY PTY LTD—See Carrier Global Corporation; *U.S. Public*, pg. 444
ONITY SAS—See Carrier Global Corporation; *U.S. Public*, pg. 444
ONITY, S.L.U.—See Carrier Global Corporation; *U.S. Public*, pg. 444
OPTIMA STANTRON CORP.—See Elma Electronic AG; *Int'l*, pg. 2367
OTTO MANNER PRAZISIONSFORMENBAU AG, SCHWEIZ—See Barnes Group Inc.; *U.S. Public*, pg. 277
OXO INTERNATIONAL INC.—See Helen of Troy Limited; *Int'l*, pg. 3329
PAUL HETTICH GMBH & CO. KG—See Hettich Holding GmbH & Co. oHG; *Int'l*, pg. 3366

N.A.I.C.S. INDEX

332613 — SPRING MANUFACTURIN...

P C HENDERSON (IRELAND) LIMITED—See ASSA ABLOY AB; *Int'l*, pg. 640
PEERLESS INDUSTRIES INC.; *U.S. Private*, pg. 3128
PENNENGINEERING FASTENING TECHNOLOGIES—See Tinicum Enterprises, Inc.; *U.S. Private*, pg. 4174
PETERSON SPRING-CIMA PLANT—See MiddleGround Management, LP; *U.S. Private*, pg. 2712
POLSKIE ZAKLADY LOTNICZE SP. ZO.O—See RTX Corporation; *U.S. Public*, pg. 1823
POMPANETTE COMPANY LLC; *U.S. Private*, pg. 3227
PORTAFEU SAS—See ASSA ABLOY AB; *Int'l*, pg. 640
PORTLAND WILLAMETTE—See Cardinal Aluminum Co.; *U.S. Private*, pg. 749
POSLAB TECHNOLOGY CORPORATION—See Ennoconn Corporation; *Int'l*, pg. 2443
PRATT & WHITNEY COMPONENT SOLUTIONS, INC.—See RTX Corporation; *U.S. Public*, pg. 1823
PRECISION INC.; *U.S. Private*, pg. 3245
PREMIERE LOCK COMPANY; *U.S. Private*, pg. 3251
PUNCH-LOK COMPANY—See Parrish Enterprises, Ltd.; *U.S. Private*, pg. 3100
RANDI A/S—See Allegion Public Limited Company; *Int'l*, pg. 335
RENIN CANADA CORPORATION—See Hilton Grand Vacations Inc.; *U.S. Public*, pg. 1040
THE RENOVATOR'S SUPPLY, INC.; *U.S. Private*, pg. 4104
REV-A-SHELF LLC—See Jones Plastic & Engineering Company, LLC; *U.S. Private*, pg. 2234
R.G. RAY CORPORATION; *U.S. Private*, pg. 3336
R.K.L. BUILDING SPECIALTIES CO., INC.—See Berkshire Hathaway Inc.; *U.S. Public*, pg. 312
ROCKY MOUNTAIN HARDWARE INC.; *U.S. Private*, pg. 3468
ROLLS-ROYCE MOTOR CARS LIMITED—See Bayerische Motoren Werke Aktiengesellschaft; *Int'l*, pg. 913
ROLLS-ROYCE MOTOR CARS NA LLC—See Bayerische Motoren Werke Aktiengesellschaft; *Int'l*, pg. 913
RONIS-DOM LTD.—See Groupe SFPI SA; *Int'l*, pg. 3111
RONIS S.A.S.—See Groupe SFPI SA; *Int'l*, pg. 3111
RUKO A/S—See ASSA ABLOY AB; *Int'l*, pg. 640
RUTLAND PRODUCTS CO.; *U.S. Private*, pg. 3508
RWM CASTERS COMPANY; *U.S. Private*, pg. 3509
SACOPAN, INC.—See Owens Corning; *U.S. Public*, pg. 1627
SARGENT & GREENLEAF, INC.—See OpenGate Capital Management, LLC; *U.S. Private*, pg. 3031
SARGENT MANUFACTURING COMPANY—See ASSA ABLOY AB; *Int'l*, pg. 636
SATURN FASTENERS INC.—See Fontana Luigi S.p.A.; *Int'l*, pg. 2726
SCHAEFER MARINE INC.; *U.S. Private*, pg. 3563
SCHLAGE DE MEXICO S.A. DE C.V.—See Ingersoll Rand Inc.; *U.S. Public*, pg. 1122
SCHLAGE LOCK COMPANY LLC—See Allegion Public Limited Company; *Int'l*, pg. 335
SECURE ENTERPRISES, LLC; *U.S. Private*, pg. 3593
SECURITECH GROUP, INC.—See ASSA ABLOY AB; *Int'l*, pg. 640
SHENZHEN KIN LONG HBS INTELLIGENT TECHNOLOGY CO., LTD.—See Guangdong Kinlong Hardware Prdcts Co., Ltd.; *Int'l*, pg. 3157
SILCA SOUTH AMERICA S.A.—See dormakaba Holding AG; *Int'l*, pg. 2178
SIMONSVOSS TECHNOLOGIES GMBH—See Allegion Public Limited Company; *Int'l*, pg. 335
SIMPSON MANUFACTURING COMPANY, INC.; *U.S. Public*, pg. 1882
SINGER VALVE, LLC—See Mueller Water Products, Inc.; *U.S. Public*, pg. 1486
SOLID AB—See ASSA ABLOY AB; *Int'l*, pg. 640
SOLIDSCAPE, INC.—See Groupe Gorge S.A.; *Int'l*, pg. 3103
SOUTHERN FOLGER DETENTION EQUIPMENT COMPANY—See Phelps Tointon Inc.; *U.S. Private*, pg. 3167
STANLEY SECURITY SOLUTIONS, INC.—See Stanley Black & Decker, Inc.; *U.S. Public*, pg. 1935
THE STEELWORKS CORPORATION—See Acme Manufacturing Company Inc.; *U.S. Private*, pg. 61
STRATTEC POWER ACCESS LLC—See Strattec Security Corporation; *U.S. Public*, pg. 1954
SUZHOU GEM OPTO-ELECTRONICS TERMINAL CO., LTD.—See Gem Terminal Ind. Co., Ltd.; *Int'l*, pg. 2915
TA AEROSPACE CO.—See TransDigm Group Incorporated; *U.S. Public*, pg. 2181
TECHNICAL AIRBORNE COMPONENTS INDUSTRIES SPRL—See TransDigm Group Incorporated; *U.S. Public*, pg. 2183
TELL MANUFACTURING, INC.—See Spectrum Brands Holdings, Inc.; *U.S. Public*, pg. 1917
TESA TALLERES DE ESCORIAZA S.A.U.—See ASSA ABLOY AB; *Int'l*, pg. 640
I-H MARINE SUPPLIES INC.; *U.S. Private*, pg. 3910
THE THOMAS MONAHAN COMPANY INC.; *U.S. Private*, pg. 4126
TIFFIN METAL PRODUCTS CO.—See Wellspring Capital Management LLC; *U.S. Private*, pg. 4477
TLHM CO. LTD.—See dormakaba Holding AG; *Int'l*, pg. 2178

TOP KNOBS USA, INC.—See The Jordan Company, L.P.; *U.S. Private*, pg. 4062
TRADEMARK HARDWARE INC.; *U.S. Private*, pg. 4202
TRAILBLAZER RESOURCES, INC.; *U.S. Private*, pg. 2179
TREND CONTROL SYSTEMS LIMITED—See Honeywell International Inc.; *U.S. Public*, pg. 1048
TRIANGLE BRASS MANUFACTURING COMPANY, INC.; *U.S. Private*, pg. 4226
TRIDON INC.—See TruArc Partners, L.P.; *U.S. Private*, pg. 4245
TRIOVING A.S.—See ASSA ABLOY AB; *Int'l*, pg. 641
TRUTH HARDWARE INC.—See Quanex Building Products Corp.; *U.S. Public*, pg. 1750
TYDENBROOKS SECURITY PRODUCTS GROUP—See Bertram Capital Management, LLC; *U.S. Private*, pg. 540
TYDENBROOKS SECURITY PRODUCTS GROUP—See Bertram Capital Management, LLC; *U.S. Private*, pg. 540
TYDENBROOKS SECURITY PRODUCTS GROUP—See Crimson Investment; *U.S. Private*, pg. 1100
TYDENBROOKS SECURITY PRODUCTS GROUP—See Crimson Investment; *U.S. Private*, pg. 1100
TYDEN (SUZHOU) SECURITY SEAL CO., LTD.—See Bertram Capital Management, LLC; *U.S. Private*, pg. 540
TYDEN (SUZHOU) SECURITY SEAL CO., LTD.—See Crimson Investment; *U.S. Private*, pg. 1100
VIBRACOUSTIC NANTES SAS—See Freudenberg SE; *Int'l*, pg. 2791
VICOR GMBH—See Vicor Corporation; *U.S. Public*, pg. 2296
VIETNAM GEM ELECTRONIC & METAL CO., LTD.—See Gem Terminal Ind. Co., Ltd.; *Int'l*, pg. 2915
VON DUPRIN LLC—See Allegion Public Limited Company; *Int'l*, pg. 335
VOSS INDUSTRIES, LLC—See Tinicum Enterprises, Inc.; *U.S. Private*, pg. 4174
WAH YUET HONG KONG LIMITED—See dormakaba Holding AG; *Int'l*, pg. 2178
WAH YUET INDUSTRIAL COMPANY LIMITED—See dormakaba Holding AG; *Int'l*, pg. 2178
WEBER-KNAPP COMPANY; *U.S. Private*, pg. 4465
WEISER LOCK CORPORATION—See Spectrum Brands Holdings, Inc.; *U.S. Public*, pg. 1917
WINNER INTERNATIONAL, LLC; *U.S. Private*, pg. 4542
WINZELER STAMPING CO.; *U.S. Private*, pg. 4546
WOLO MANUFACTURING CORP.—See 1847 Holdings LLC; *U.S. Public*, pg. 2
WOLVERINE COIL SPRING CO.; *U.S. Private*, pg. 4555
WORLD LOCK CO. LTD.—See The Eastern Company; *U.S. Public*, pg. 2069
YALE RESIDENTIAL SECURITY PRODUCTS, INC.—See ASSA ABLOY AB; *Int'l*, pg. 641
YALE SECURITY PRODUCTS S.P.A. (ITALY)—See ASSA ABLOY AB; *Int'l*, pg. 636
YALE SECURITY (SA) (PTY) LTD—See ASSA ABLOY AB; *Int'l*, pg. 641
YALE UK LTD.—See ASSA ABLOY AB; *Int'l*, pg. 636
YANTAI HUF TOOLS CO. LTD.—See Huf Hulsbeck & Furst GmbH & Co. KG; *Int'l*, pg. 3523
YARDLEY PRODUCTS CORPORATION—See Dixon Valve & Coupling Company; *U.S. Private*, pg. 1246
THE YOUNG ENGINEERS, INC.—See KKR & Co. Inc.; *U.S. Public*, pg. 1262
YSG DOOR SECURITY CONSULTANTS—See ASSA ABLOY AB; *Int'l*, pg. 637
ZAO ALPOS—See ALPOS, d.d.; *Int'l*, pg. 375
ZHEJIANG FACEA VEHICLE LOCKS CO LTD—See ASSA ABLOY AB; *Int'l*, pg. 641
ZPN BESEL-FORMIT LTD.—See Cantoni Motor S.A.; *Int'l*, pg. 1299

332613 — SPRING MANUFACTURING

ACME-MONACO CORPORATION; *U.S. Private*, pg. 61
ADVANEX EUROPE LTD.—See Advanex Inc.; *Int'l*, pg. 163
ADVANEX PRECISION COMPONENTS (DALIAN) CO., LTD.—See Advanex Inc.; *Int'l*, pg. 163
ADVANEX (THAILAND) LTD.—See Advanex Inc.; *Int'l*, pg. 163
AIR LIFT COMPANY; *U.S. Private*, pg. 139
ALMA UPPSALA AB—See Beijer Alma AB; *Int'l*, pg. 942
APM COIL SPRINGS SDN. BHD.—See APM Automotive Holdings Berhad; *Int'l*, pg. 516
APM SPRINGS (VIETNAM) CO. LTD.—See APM Automotive Holdings Berhad; *Int'l*, pg. 516
ARK TECHNOLOGIES INC.; *U.S. Private*, pg. 325
ASAHI-SEIKI MANUFACTURING CO., LTD MACHINERY DIVISION—See Asahi-Seiki Manufacturing Co., Ltd.; *Int'l*, pg. 599
ASAHI-SEIKI MANUFACTURING CO., LTD. PRECISION ENGINEERING DIVISION—See Asahi-Seiki Manufacturing Co., Ltd.; *Int'l*, pg. 599
ASSOCIATED SPRING CORPORATION—See OEP Capital Advisors, L.P.; *U.S. Private*, pg. 2998
ASSOCIATED SPRING—See OEP Capital Advisors, L.P.; *U.S. Private*, pg. 2998
ASSOCIATED SPRING—See OEP Capital Advisors, L.P.; *U.S. Private*, pg. 2998

ATLANTIC SPRING—See American Securities LLC; *U.S. Private*, pg. 249
AUTOMATIC SPRING COILING—See American Securities LLC; *U.S. Private*, pg. 249
AUTOMATIC SPRING PRODUCTS CORP.; *U.S. Private*, pg. 399
AXTONE HSW SP. Z.O.O.—See ITT Inc.; *U.S. Public*, pg. 1177
AXTONE S.A.—See ITT Inc.; *U.S. Public*, pg. 1177
AXTONE S.R.O.—See ITT Inc.; *U.S. Public*, pg. 1177
BAUMANN GMBH—See Baumann Federn AG; *Int'l*, pg. 895
BAUMANN MUELLES S.A.—See Baumann Federn AG; *Int'l*, pg. 895
BAUMANN SPRING CO. (S) PTE. LTD.—See Baumann Federn AG; *Int'l*, pg. 895
BAUMANN SPRINGS & COATING PVT. LTD.—See Baumann Federn AG; *Int'l*, pg. 895
BAUMANN SPRINGS (SHANGHAI) CO. LTD.—See Baumann Federn AG; *Int'l*, pg. 895
BAUMANN SPRINGS S.R.O.—See Baumann Federn AG; *Int'l*, pg. 895
BAUMANN SPRINGS TEXAS HOLDINGS LLC—See Baumann Federn AG; *Int'l*, pg. 895
BAUMANN SPRINGS TEXAS LTD.—See Baumann Federn AG; *Int'l*, pg. 895
BAUMANN SPRINGS USA, INC.—See Baumann Federn AG; *Int'l*, pg. 895
BEIJING DAEWON ASIA AUTOMOBILE SCIENCE & TECHNOLOGY CO., LTD.—See Daewon Kang Up Co., Ltd.; *Int'l*, pg. 1910
BETTS SPRING COMPANY, INC.; *U.S. Private*, pg. 547
CALDWELL MANUFACTURING COMPANY NORTH AMERICA, LLC—See ASSA ABLOY AB; *Int'l*, pg. 639
CAPITAL SPRING—See American Securities LLC; *U.S. Private*, pg. 249
CENTURY SPRING CORP.—See American Securities LLC; *U.S. Private*, pg. 249
CHUHATSU SEIKOU CO., LTD.—See Chuo Spring Co., Ltd.; *Int'l*, pg. 1599
CHUHATSU (THAILAND) CO., LTD. - HEMARAJ PLANT—See Chuo Spring Co., Ltd.; *Int'l*, pg. 1599
CHUHATSU (THAILAND) CO., LTD.—See Chuo Spring Co., Ltd.; *Int'l*, pg. 1599
CHUO SPRING CO., LTD. - FUJIOKA PLANT—See Chuo Spring Co., Ltd.; *Int'l*, pg. 1599
CHUO SPRING CO., LTD. - HEKINAN PLANT—See Chuo Spring Co., Ltd.; *Int'l*, pg. 1599
CHUO SPRING CO., LTD. - MIYOSHI PLANT—See Chuo Spring Co., Ltd.; *Int'l*, pg. 1599
CHUO SPRING CO., LTD.; *Int'l*, pg. 1599
COLONIAL SPRING COMPANY—See SEI MetalTek; *U.S. Private*, pg. 3599
COMMERCIAL SPRING AND TOOL COMPANY LIMITED; *Int'l*, pg. 1715
CONTITECH DAEWON AIRSPRING SYSTEMS CO. LTD.—See Daewon Kang Up Co., Ltd.; *Int'l*, pg. 1910
CORAZA SYSTEMS MALAYSIA SDN. BHD.—See Coraza Integrated Technology Berhad; *Int'l*, pg. 1795
COVENTRY COIL-O-MATIC (HARYANA) LIMITED; *Int'l*, pg. 1821
DAEWON EUROPE CO., LTD.—See Daewon Kang Up Co., Ltd.; *Int'l*, pg. 1910
DAEWON INDIA AUTOPARTS PRIVATE LIMITED—See Daewon Kang Up Co., Ltd.; *Int'l*, pg. 1910
DAEWON MEXICO S. DE R.L. DE C.V.—See Daewon Kang Up Co., Ltd.; *Int'l*, pg. 1910
DAEWON SPRING & SEAT LLC—See Daewon Kang Up Co., Ltd.; *Int'l*, pg. 1910
DAYTON PARTS, LLC—See Dorman Products, Inc.; *U.S. Public*, pg. 677
DIAMOND WIRE SPRING COMPANY; *U.S. Private*, pg. 1224
DUDEK & BOCK S. DE R.L. DE C.V.—See Dudek & Bock Spring Manufacturing Company; *U.S. Private*, pg. 1284
DUDEK & BOCK SPRING MANUFACTURING COMPANY; *U.S. Private*, pg. 1284
ENGINEERED SPRING PRODUCTS, INC.—See American Securities LLC; *U.S. Private*, pg. 249
ERNST W. VELLEUER GMBH & CO. KG—See Beijer Alma AB; *Int'l*, pg. 942
ESSC HOLDINGS, INC.—See American Securities LLC; *U.S. Private*, pg. 249
EUROPEAN SPRINGS & PRESSINGS LTD.—See Beijer Alma AB; *Int'l*, pg. 943
FABRIKA OPRUGA CACAK A.D.; *Int'l*, pg. 2599
FAWER LIAONING AUTOMOTIVE SPRING COMPANY LIMITED—See FAWER Automotive Parts Limited Company; *Int'l*, pg. 2624
FIRESTONE INDUSTRIAL PRODUCTS DIVISION—See Bridgestone Corporation; *Int'l*, pg. 1156
FRONTIER SPRINGS LTD.; *Int'l*, pg. 2796
GEM SOUTHEAST, INC.—See Gem Industries Corporation; *U.S. Private*, pg. 1657
HARDWARE PRODUCTS, LP—See SEI MetalTek; *U.S. Private*, pg. 3599
HELICAL PRODUCTS COMPANY—See American Securities LLC; *U.S. Private*, pg. 249
INDUSTRIAL DOOR CO. INC.; *U.S. Private*, pg. 2065

332613 — SPRING MANUFACTURIN...

INDUSTRIAL GAS SPRINGS INC.—See Barnes Group Inc.; *U.S. Public*, pg. 277
INDUSTRIAL GAS SPRINGS LIMITED—See Barnes Group Inc.; *U.S. Public*, pg. 277
JIANGSU DAEWON ASIA AUTOMOBILE SPRING CO., LTD.—See Daewon Kang Up Co., Ltd.; *Int'l*, pg. 1910
JOHN EVANS' SONS, INC.; *U.S. Private*, pg. 2221
KATO SPRING (SHANGHAI) CO., LTD.—See Advanex Inc.; *Int'l*, pg. 163
KHC DUDEK & BOCK LLC—See Dudek & Bock Spring Manufacturing Company; *U.S. Private*, pg. 1284
KITA USA, INC.—See Cohu, Inc.; *U.S. Public*, pg. 530
KUNSHAN CHUHO SPRING CO., LTD.—See Chuo Spring Co., Ltd.; *Int'l*, pg. 1599
LEE SPRING COMPANY LLC; *U.S. Private*, pg. 2413
LEGGETT & PLATT DO BRASIL LTDA.—See Leggett & Platt, Incorporated; *U.S. Public*, pg. 1303
LEGGETT & PLATT, INC. - OXFORD—See Leggett & Platt, Incorporated; *U.S. Public*, pg. 1303
LESJOFORS A/S—See Beijer Alma AB; *Int'l*, pg. 943
LESJOFORS AUTOMOTIVE AB—See Beijer Alma AB; *Int'l*, pg. 943
LESJOFORS GAS SPRINGS LV—See Beijer Alma AB; *Int'l*, pg. 943
LESJOFORS HEAVY SPRINGS UK LTD.—See Beijer Alma AB; *Int'l*, pg. 943
LESJOFORS INDUSTRIAL SPRINGS & PRESSINGS GMBH—See Beijer Alma AB; *Int'l*, pg. 943
LESJOFORS SPRINGS GMBH—See Beijer Alma AB; *Int'l*, pg. 943
LESJOFORS SPRINGS LV—See Beijer Alma AB; *Int'l*, pg. 943
LESJOFORS SPRINGS OY—See Beijer Alma AB; *Int'l*, pg. 943
LESJOFORS SPRINGS & PRESSINGS AB—See Beijer Alma AB; *Int'l*, pg. 943
LESJOFORS SPRINGS SLOVAKIA S.R.O.—See Beijer Alma AB; *Int'l*, pg. 943
LESJOFORS STOCK SPRING AB—See Beijer Alma AB; *Int'l*, pg. 943
LITEFLEX, LLC—See The Boler Company; *U.S. Private*, pg. 3996
L&P DENMARK APS—See Leggett & Platt, Incorporated; *U.S. Public*, pg. 1302
L&P SPRINGS ITALIA S.R.L.—See Leggett & Platt, Incorporated; *U.S. Public*, pg. 1302
LPT D.O.O.—See Leggett & Platt, Incorporated; *U.S. Public*, pg. 1302
MANGAL PRECISION PRODUCTS LIMITED - WORKS 1—See Amara Raja Energy & Mobility Limited; *Int'l*, pg. 412
MARYLAND PRECISION SPRING—See American Securities LLC; *U.S. Private*, pg. 250
MATTHEW WARREN SPRING—See American Securities LLC; *U.S. Private*, pg. 250
MAUDLIN & SON MANUFACTURING CO., INC.—See American Securities LLC; *U.S. Private*, pg. 250
METROL SPRINGS LTD.—See Beijer Alma AB; *Int'l*, pg. 943
MICHIGAN SPRING & STAMPING LLC—See Hines Corporation; *U.S. Private*, pg. 1949
MICROMATIC SPRING STAMPING CO.; *U.S. Private*, pg. 2703
MID-WEST SPRING & STAMPING, INC.; *U.S. Private*, pg. 2710
MOHAWK SPRING—See American Securities LLC; *U.S. Private*, pg. 250
MONTICELLO SPRING CORPORATION; *U.S. Private*, pg. 2777
MTC SUSPENSION INC.—See Genuine Parts Company; *U.S. Public*, pg. 932
MW INDUSTRIES, INC.—See American Securities LLC; *U.S. Private*, pg. 249
NAGASAKI-CHUHATSU CO., LTD.—See Chuo Spring Co., Ltd.; *Int'l*, pg. 1599
NEWCOMB SPRING CORP.; *U.S. Private*, pg. 2914
NHK-ASSOCIATED SPRING SUSPENSION COMPONENTS INC.—See OEP Capital Advisors, L.P.; *U.S. Private*, pg. 2998
NO-SAG PRODUCTS DIVISION—See Leggett & Platt, Incorporated; *U.S. Public*, pg. 1303
OY LESJOFORS AB—See Beijer Alma AB; *Int'l*, pg. 943
PA-TED SPRING CO. INC.; *U.S. Private*, pg. 3062
PETER BENESCH GMBH—See Hutter & Schrantz PMS Ges.m.b.H; *Int'l*, pg. 3540
PETERSON AMERICAN CORPORATION—See MiddleGround Management, LP; *U.S. Private*, pg. 2712
PETERSON SPRING EUROPE LTD.—See MiddleGround Management, LP; *U.S. Private*, pg. 2712
PETERSON SPRING-GEORGIA PLANT—See MiddleGround Management, LP; *U.S. Private*, pg. 2712
PETERSON SPRING-GREENVILLE PLANT—See MiddleGround Management, LP; *U.S. Private*, pg. 2712
PETERSON SPRING-MADISON HEIGHTS PLANT—See MiddleGround Management, LP; *U.S. Private*, pg. 2712
PETERSON SPRING-THREE RIVERS PLANT—See MiddleGround Management, LP; *U.S. Private*, pg. 2712
PLYMOUTH SPRING COMPANY, INC.—See Beijer Alma AB; *Int'l*, pg. 943
PONTOTOC SPRING—See American Securities LLC; *U.S. Private*, pg. 250
PRECISION PRODUCTS GROUP, INC.—See Auxo Investment Partners, LLC; *U.S. Private*, pg. 402
PRECISION PRODUCTS—See Auxo Investment Partners, LLC; *U.S. Private*, pg. 402
PRODOTTI BAUMANN SPA—See Baumann Federn AG; *Int'l*, pg. 895
P.T. APM ARMADA SUSPENSION—See APM Automotive Holdings Berhad; *Int'l*, pg. 516
P.T. CHUHATSU INDONESIA—See Chuo Spring Co., Ltd.; *Int'l*, pg. 1599
RESORTES ARGENTINA S.A.—See Barnes Group Inc.; *U.S. Public*, pg. 277
SAINT-GOBAIN PERFORMANCE PLASTICS RENCOL LIMITED—See Compagnie de Saint-Gobain SA; *Int'l*, pg. 1735
SAJET SYSTEM TECHNOLOGY (SUZHOU) CO., LTD.—See Chroma ATE Inc.; *Int'l*, pg. 1588
SAN DIEGO VISTA STEEL SERVICE CORPORATION—See Hanwa Co., Ltd.; *Int'l*, pg. 3263
SEI METALTEK; *U.S. Private*, pg. 3599
SK-PRUZINY, SPOL. S R.O.—See Hutter & Schrantz PMS Ges.m.b.H; *Int'l*, pg. 3540
SMALLEY STEEL RING COMPANY; *U.S. Private*, pg. 3690
SPRINGMASTERS—See American Securities LLC; *U.S. Private*, pg. 250
SPRINGS INC.—See Activar, Inc.; *U.S. Private*, pg. 68
SPRING TOLLMAN COMPANY, INC.; *U.S. Private*, pg. 3763
SPRING WORKS UTAH; *U.S. Private*, pg. 3763
SPUHL GMBH—See Leggett & Platt, Incorporated; *U.S. Public*, pg. 1303
STECE FJADRAR AB—See Beijer Alma AB; *Int'l*, pg. 943
STERLING SPRING LLC; *U.S. Private*, pg. 3807
STUMPP+SCHUELE GMBH—See Beijer Alma AB; *Int'l*, pg. 943
SUHM SPRING WORKS INC.; *U.S. Private*, pg. 3849
TAIWAN CHUHATSU FACTORY CO., LTD.—See Chuo Spring Co., Ltd.; *Int'l*, pg. 1599
TECHNOSPRING KFT.—See Hutter & Schrantz PMS Ges.m.b.H; *Int'l*, pg. 3540
TIANJIN LONGXING CO., LTD.—See Chuo Spring Co., Ltd.; *Int'l*, pg. 1599
TIANJIN ZHONGXING AUTOMOTIVE COMPONENTS CO., LTD.—See Chuo Spring Co., Ltd.; *Int'l*, pg. 1599
TOLLMAN SPRING COMPANY INC.; *U.S. Private*, pg. 4182
TWIST INC.; *U.S. Private*, pg. 4266
UNION SPRING & MANUFACTURING CORP.; *U.S. Private*, pg. 4285
VULCAN SPRING & MFG. CO.; *U.S. Private*, pg. 4416
WIRE PRODUCTS COMPANY INC.; *U.S. Private*, pg. 4546
XIAOGAN CHUHATSU LIOHO AUTOMOTIVE COMPONENTS CO., LTD.—See Chuo Spring Co., Ltd.; *Int'l*, pg. 1599
XIAOGAN ZHONGXING AUTOMOTIVE COMPONENTS CO., LTD.—See Chuo Spring Co., Ltd.; *Int'l*, pg. 1600

332618 — OTHER FABRICATED WIRE PRODUCT MANUFACTURING

ABBOTT INDUSTRIES INC.; *U.S. Private*, pg. 35
ACS INDUSTRIES, INC.; *U.S. Private*, pg. 66
ADC MANUFACTURING—See CRH plc; *Int'l*, pg. 1845
ADDLOGIX, INC.; *U.S. Private*, pg. 77
ADRIAN EQUIPMENT COMPANY INC.—See Adrian Steel Company Inc.; *U.S. Private*, pg. 82
AFC CABLE SYSTEMS, INC.—See Clayton, Dubilier & Rice, LLC; *U.S. Private*, pg. 919
ALBANY INTERNATIONAL FORMING FABRICS—See Albany International Corp.; *U.S. Public*, pg. 72
ALBORZ CABLE COMPANY; *Int'l*, pg. 299
ALLIED WIRE & CABLE INC. - MIDWESTERN DIVISION—See Allied Wire & Cable Inc.; *U.S. Private*, pg. 191
ALLIED WIRE & CABLE INC. - NEW ENGLAND DIVISION—See Allied Wire & Cable Inc.; *U.S. Private*, pg. 191
ALLIED WIRE & CABLE INC. - SOUTHEASTERN DIVISION—See Allied Wire & Cable Inc.; *U.S. Private*, pg. 191
ALLIED WIRE & CABLE INC. - WEST COAST DIVISION—See Allied Wire & Cable Inc.; *U.S. Private*, pg. 191
ALL-LIFTS, INC.—See Altamont Capital Partners; *U.S. Private*, pg. 204
ALTAK INC.; *U.S. Private*, pg. 204
ALUMI-GUARD, INC.—See CRH plc; *Int'l*, pg. 1845
AMACS PROCESS TOWER INTERNALS—See Rockwood Equity Partners, LLC; *U.S. Private*, pg. 3468
AMATEI INCORPORATED; *Int'l*, pg. 413
AMERICAN WIRE & CABLE COMPANY; *U.S. Private*, pg. 258
AMISTCO SEPARATION PRODUCTS, INC.—See Rockwood Equity Partners, LLC; *U.S. Private*, pg. 3468
AMPHENOL DC ELECTRONICS—See Amphenol Corporation; *U.S. Public*, pg. 127
AMPHENOL STEWARD ENTERPRISES, INC.—See Amphenol Corporation; *U.S. Public*, pg. 126
ANGOLA WIRE PRODUCTS INC.; *U.S. Private*, pg. 283
ANIXTER, INC.-CONNECTICUT—See WESCO International, Inc.; *U.S. Public*, pg. 2350
APACHE MILLS INC.; *U.S. Private*, pg. 290
AQ WIRING SYSTEMS CANADA INC.—See AQ Group AB; *Int'l*, pg. 527
AQ WIRING SYSTEMS NY, INC.—See AQ Group AB; *Int'l*, pg. 527
ARCELORMITTAL LAZARO CARDENAS S.A. DE C.V.—See ArcelorMittal S.A.; *Int'l*, pg. 544
ARGO PRODUCTS CO.; *U.S. Private*, pg. 320
ASHWORTH BELTS B.V.—See Ashworth Bros., Inc.; *U.S. Private*, pg. 350
ASHWORTH EUROPE, LTD—See Ashworth Bros., Inc.; *U.S. Private*, pg. 350
ASHWORTH JAPAN K.K.—See Ashworth Bros., Inc.; *U.S. Private*, pg. 350
ASTA INDIA PRIVATE LIMITED—See Global Equity Partners Beteiligungs-Management AG; *Int'l*, pg. 2996
ATLAS WIRE CORPORATION; *U.S. Private*, pg. 380
BAIRSTOW LIFTING PRODUCTS CO., INC.—See Altamont Capital Partners; *U.S. Private*, pg. 204
BAKER SALES—See Hindley Manufacturing Company, Inc.; *U.S. Private*, pg. 1948
BARBARAS DEVELOPMENT, INC.; *U.S. Private*, pg. 472
BAUMANN RESSORTS S.A.—See Baumann Federn AG; *Int'l*, pg. 895
BELDEN ELECTRONICS AMERICAS DIVISION—See Belden, Inc.; *U.S. Public*, pg. 293
BELT CONCEPTS OF AMERICA INC.—See The Goodyear Tire & Rubber Company; *U.S. Public*, pg. 2082
BERK-TEK ELECTRONICS DIVISION—See Leviton Manufacturing Company, Inc.; *U.S. Private*, pg. 2436
BETAFENCE DEUTSCHLAND GMBH—See CVC Capital Partners SICAV-FIS S.A.; *Int'l*, pg. 1885
BETAFENCE FRANCE SA—See CVC Capital Partners SICAV-FIS S.A.; *Int'l*, pg. 1885
BETAFENCE—See CVC Capital Partners SICAV-FIS S.A.; *Int'l*, pg. 1885
BETAFENCE SP ZOO—See CVC Capital Partners SICAV-FIS S.A.; *Int'l*, pg. 1885
BHARAT WIRE ROPES LIMITED; *Int'l*, pg. 1011
BIRMINGHAM RAIL LOCOMOTIVE CO.; *U.S. Private*, pg. 565
BIZLINK HOLDING INC.; *Int'l*, pg. 1053
BNZ MATERIALS, INC. - BILLERICA PLANT—See BNZ Materials, Inc.; *U.S. Private*, pg. 602
BRITZ & COMPANY; *U.S. Private*, pg. 657
BUFFALO WIRE WORKS CO., INC.; *U.S. Private*, pg. 681
THE BURLY CORPORATION OF NORTH AMERICA, INC.—See Mueller Inc.; *U.S. Private*, pg. 2810
CABLE MANUFACTURING, INC.; *U.S. Private*, pg. 711
CABLEX WIRE & CABLE (KUNSHAN) MFG. LIMITED—See Copartner Technology Corporation; *Int'l*, pg. 1793
CABLEX WIRE & CABLE (SHENZHEN) MFG CO., LTD.—See Copartner Technology Corporation; *Int'l*, pg. 1793
CAMBRIDGE ARCHITECTURAL—See Zurn Elkay Water Solutions Corporation; *U.S. Public*, pg. 2412
CAPARO WIRE LIMITED—See Caparo Group Ltd.; *Int'l*, pg. 1302
CARLISLE INTERCONNECT TECHNOLOGIES DE MEXICO—See Amphenol Corporation; *U.S. Public*, pg. 129
CARLISLE INTERCONNECT TECHNOLOGIES, INC.—See Amphenol Corporation; *U.S. Public*, pg. 129
THE CARPENTER GROUP; *U.S. Private*, pg. 4005
CARPENTER RIGGING—See The Carpenter Group; *U.S. Private*, pg. 4005
CAVERT WIRE COMPANY INCORPORATED; *U.S. Private*, pg. 795
CENTRAL WIRE INDUSTRIES LTD; *Int'l*, pg. 1410
C E PRECISION ASSEMBLIES, INC.—See Audax Group, Limited Partnership; *U.S. Private*, pg. 390
CHAMPLAIN CABLE CORP.—See American Industrial Acquisition Corporation; *U.S. Private*, pg. 237
CHANGZHOU TATSUTA CHINA ELECTRIC WIRE & CABLE CO., LTD.—See ENEOS Holdings, Inc.; *Int'l*, pg. 2416
CHARTER MANUFACTURING COMPANY, INC.; *U.S. Private*, pg. 858
CHENGDU SIWI SCIENCE AND TECHNOLOGY COMPANY LIMITED; *Int'l*, pg. 1469
CHONGQING PIGEON ELECTRIC WIRES & CABLES CO., LTD.—See Chongqing Machinery & Electronics Holding (Group) Co., Ltd.; *Int'l*, pg. 1580
CHUGOKU ELECTRIC WIRE & CABLE CO., LTD.—See ENEOS Holdings, Inc.; *Int'l*, pg. 2416
CLIPPER BELT LACER COMPANY—See Flexible Steel Lacing Company; *U.S. Private*, pg. 1544
CLOSETMAID LLC—See Griffon Corporation; *U.S. Public*, pg. 969
COAST WIRE & PLASTIC TECH, LLC—See Belden, Inc.; *U.S. Public*, pg. 293
COBB WIRE ROPE & SLING COMPANY INC.—See ALP Industries, Inc.; *U.S. Private*, pg. 196
COLEMAN CABLE, INC.—See Southwire Company, LLC; *U.S. Private*, pg. 3742

N.A.I.C.S. INDEX 332618 — OTHER FABRICATED WI...

COLLIS INC.—See Trive Capital Inc.; *U.S. Private*, pg. 4240
COMMERCIAL TRUCK & VAN EQUIPMENT INC.—See Adrian Steel Company Inc.; *U.S. Private*, pg. 82
CONSOLIDATED FABRICATORS CORP., BUILDING PRODUCTS DIVISION—See Consolidated Fabricators Corp; *U.S. Private*, pg. 1020
COPARTNER TECHNOLOGY (SHENZHEN) CO., LTD.—See Copartner Technology Corporation; *Int'l*, pg. 1793
COPPERWELD BIMETALLICS, LLC—See Fushi Copperweld, Inc.; *Int'l*, pg. 2849
COVE FOUR-SLIDE & STAMPING CORP.; *U.S. Private*, pg. 1071
CPI-LOUISIANA INC.—See CPI Wirecloth & Screens, Inc.; *U.S. Private*, pg. 1080
CVG ELECTRICAL SYSTEMS - MONONA—See Commercial Vehicle Group, Inc.; *U.S. Public*, pg. 547
CYBELE INDUSTRIES LIMITED; *Int'l*, pg. 1891
DEKORON UNITHERM, INC.—See Berkshire Hathaway Inc.; *U.S. Public*, pg. 309
DEKORON WIRE & CABLE ASIA PTE LTD—See Berkshire Hathaway Inc.; *U.S. Public*, pg. 310
DEKORON WIRE & CABLE, INC.—See Berkshire Hathaway Inc.; *U.S. Public*, pg. 309
DELTA WIRE & MFG.; *Int'l*, pg. 2020
DIAMOND MATERIALS TECH, INC.—See Groupe BPCE; *Int'l*, pg. 3097
DIVERSIFIED ULBRICH OF CANADA—See Ulbrich Stainless Steel & Special Metals, Inc.; *U.S. Private*, pg. 4275
DOMTECH, INC.; *Int'l*, pg. 2162
DSR CORP. - GWANGYANG STAINLESS STEEL FACTORY—See DSR Corp.; *Int'l*, pg. 2210
DSR QINGDAO LIMITED—See DSR Corp.; *Int'l*, pg. 2210
DSR WIRE CORPORATION; *Int'l*, pg. 2210
DSR WIRE CORPORATION - SUNCHEON FACTORY 1—See DSR Wire Corporation; *Int'l*, pg. 2210
DSR WIRE CORPORATION - SUNCHEON FACTORY 2—See DSR Wire Corporation; *Int'l*, pg. 2210
DSR WIRE CORPORATION - YULCHON FACTORY—See DSR Wire Corporation; *Int'l*, pg. 2210
DUR-O-WAL INC.—See Dayton Superior Corporation; *U.S. Private*, pg. 1178
EA CABLE ASSEMBLIES (HONGKONG) CO., LIMITED—See BizLink Holding Inc.; *Int'l*, pg. 1053
EASY HEAT LTD.—See Emerson Electric Co.; *U.S. Public*, pg. 740
ELMAT - SCHLAGHECK GMBH & CO. KG; *Int'l*, pg. 2367
ELMET TECHNOLOGIES INC.; *U.S. Private*, pg. 1376
EMGEE CABLES & COMMUNICATIONS LTD.; *Int'l*, pg. 2380
EMKA JSC; *Int'l*, pg. 2383
ENGINEERED WIRE PRODUCTS, INC.—See Contran Corporation; *U.S. Private*, pg. 1033
ESTAD STAMPING & MANUFACTURING COMPANY; *U.S. Private*, pg. 1428
EVERTOP WIRE CABLE CORPORATION; *Int'l*, pg. 2569
FELSTED PRODUCTS LLC—See Orscheln Group; *U.S. Private*, pg. 3045
FERTEK, INC.; *Int'l*, pg. 2646
FORT GLOSTER INDUSTRIES LIMITED—See Gloster Limited; *Int'l*, pg. 3011
FOX VALLEY STEEL & WIRE CO.; *U.S. Private*, pg. 1585
FOX WIRE LIMITED; *Int'l*, pg. 2756
FRANKLIN DISPLAY GROUP, INC.; *U.S. Private*, pg. 1597
FUJIKURA (CHINA) CO., LTD.—See Fujikura Ltd.; *Int'l*, pg. 2827
FUJIKURA COMPONENTS LTD.—See Fujikura Ltd.; *Int'l*, pg. 2828
FUJIKURA FEDERAL CABLES SDN BHD—See Fujikura Ltd.; *Int'l*, pg. 2828
FUJIKURA ZHUHAI CO., LTD.—See Fujikura Ltd.; *Int'l*, pg. 2829
FUTONG GROUP CO., LTD.; *Int'l*, pg. 2852
GALPRES A.D.; *Int'l*, pg. 2876
GAON CABLE CO., LTD. - GUNPO PLANT—See GAON Cable Co., Ltd.; *Int'l*, pg. 2882
GAON CABLE CO., LTD. - JEONJU PLANT—See GAON Cable Co., Ltd.; *Int'l*, pg. 2882
GENERAL CABLE EGYPT S.A.E.—See Emerging Investment Partners; *Int'l*, pg. 2379
GENUINE CABLE GROUP LLC—See Audax Group, Limited Partnership; *U.S. Private*, pg. 2942
GERMAIN ARMATURES; *Int'l*, pg. 2942
GKD-USA, INC.—See GKD - Gebr. Kufferath AG; *Int'l*, pg. 2983
GLASSMASTER CONTROLS COMPANY, INC.; *U.S. Private*, pg. 1707
GLOBAL ASCENT, INC.—See Team, Inc.; *U.S. Public*, pg. 1988
GLOBAL WIRE LTD.—See First Israel Turnaround Enterprise; *Int'l*, pg. 2685
GOC CO., LTD.; *Int'l*, pg. 3018
GR CABLES LIMITED; *Int'l*, pg. 3047
GRC ENTERPRISES, INC.; *U.S. Private*, pg. 1761
THE GREAT AMERICAN HANGER COMPANY INC.; *U.S. Private*, pg. 4037
GREENLEE TOOLS, INC.—See Emerson Electric Co.; *U.S. Public*, pg. 741

GREENLEE TOOLS, INC.—See Emerson Electric Co.; *U.S. Public*, pg. 741
GREENLEE TOOLS, INC.—See Emerson Electric Co.; *U.S. Public*, pg. 750
GREENLEE TOOLS, INC.—See Emerson Electric Co.; *U.S. Public*, pg. 750
GRIPLOCK SYSTEMS, LLC—See Salt Creek Capital Management, LLC; *U.S. Private*, pg. 3533
GRIPLOCK SYSTEMS, LLC—See Spell Capital Partners, LLC; *U.S. Private*, pg. 3754
GUANGDONG HOTATA TECHNOLOGY GROUP CO., LTD.; *Int'l*, pg. 3156
GUNNEBO A/S—See Gunnebo AB; *Int'l*, pg. 3184
GUNNEBO BALTIC SP Z O O—See Gunnebo AB; *Int'l*, pg. 3184
GUNNEBO INDUSTRIES—See Gunnebo AB; *Int'l*, pg. 3184
GUOSHENG FINANCIAL HOLDING INC.; *Int'l*, pg. 3187
HABASIT AMERICA - BUFFALO—See Habasit AG; *Int'l*, pg. 3202
HABASIT AMERICA, INC.—See Habasit AG; *Int'l*, pg. 3202
HABASIT AMERICA - MIDDLETOWN—See Habasit AG; *Int'l*, pg. 3202
HAI PHONG ELECTRICITY WATER MACHINE ASSEMBLY JOINT STOCK; *Int'l*, pg. 3209
HANGZHOU GAOXIN RUBBER & PLASTIC MATERIALS CO., LTD.; *Int'l*, pg. 3247
HARBOUR INDUSTRIES CANADA LTD.—See Berkshire Hathaway Inc.; *U.S. Public*, pg. 310
HARBOUR INDUSTRIES, INC.—See Berkshire Hathaway Inc.; *U.S. Public*, pg. 310
HELLERMANNTYTON AB DANMARK—See Aptiv PLC; *Int'l*, pg. 525
HELLERMANNTYTON GMBH - AUSTRIA—See Aptiv PLC; *Int'l*, pg. 525
HELLERMANNTYTON OY—See Aptiv PLC; *Int'l*, pg. 526
HELLERMANNTYTON S.L.—See Aptiv PLC; *Int'l*, pg. 526
HELLERMANNTYTON SRL-ARGENTINA—See Aptiv PLC; *Int'l*, pg. 526
HELLERMANNTYTON SRL—See Aptiv PLC; *Int'l*, pg. 526
HELLERMANNTYTON (WUXI) ELECTRICAL ACCESSORIES CO., LTD.—See Aptiv PLC; *Int'l*, pg. 525
HELUKABEL GMBH; *Int'l*, pg. 3338
HENDRICK SCREEN CO.—See Hendrick Manufacturing Company; *U.S. Private*, pg. 1914
HERAEUS MATERIALS SINGAPORE PTE. LTD. - CONTACT MATERIALS—See Heraeus Holding GmbH; *Int'l*, pg. 3358
HESCO BASTION LTD.—See CVC Capital Partners SICAV-FIS S.A.; *Int'l*, pg. 1886
HI-LEX CORPORATION - MIKKABI PLANT—See Hi-Lex Corporation; *Int'l*, pg. 3380
HI-LEX CORPORATION - SANDA-NISHI PLANT—See Hi-Lex Corporation; *Int'l*, pg. 3380
HI-LEX CORPORATION - SANDA PLANT—See Hi-Lex Corporation; *Int'l*, pg. 3380
HI-LEX KANTO, INC—See Hi-Lex Corporation; *Int'l*, pg. 3380
HOUSTON POST TENSION, INC.; *U.S. Private*, pg. 1994
HUA ENG WIRE & CABLE CO., LTD.; *Int'l*, pg. 3509
HYLAS B.V.—See CRH plc; *Int'l*, pg. 1844
HYOSUNG WIRE LUXEMBOURG S.A.—See Hyosung Corporation; *Int'l*, pg. 3552
INDEPENDENT NAIL COMPANY—See W.H. Maze Company; *U.S. Private*, pg. 4420
INSTEEL WIRE PRODUCTS COMPANY—See Insteel Industries, Inc.; *U.S. Public*, pg. 1134
INTERMETRO INDUSTRIES CORPORATION—See Emerson Electric Co.; *U.S. Public*, pg. 750
INTERMETRO INDUSTRIES CORPORATION—See Emerson Electric Co.; *U.S. Public*, pg. 750
INTERNATIONAL WIRE GROUP - INSULATED DIVISION—See Atlas Holdings, LLC; *U.S. Private*, pg. 376
IRISH DRIVER-HARRIS CO., LTD.—See Driver-Harris Company; *U.S. Private*, pg. 1278
JACKBURN MANUFACTURING INC.—See Knox Enterprises Inc.; *U.S. Private*, pg. 2324
JELLIFF CORPORATION - FLORIDA FACILITY—See Jelliff Corporation; *U.S. Private*, pg. 2198
JELLIFF CORPORATION; *U.S. Private*, pg. 2198
JIA XIN PLASTIC (SHENZHEN) CO., LTD.—See Copartner Technology Corporation; *Int'l*, pg. 1793
JIAZUO RAILWAY CABLE CO., LTD.—See China National Railway Signal & Communication Corp.; *Int'l*, pg. 1534
JOHN M. DEAN CO., LLC—See SEI MetalTek; *U.S. Private*, pg. 3599
JO YEH COMPANY LIMITED—See BizLink Holding Inc.; *Int'l*, pg. 1053
JUDSON A. SMITH COMPANY—See A.T. Wall Company; *U.S. Private*, pg. 28
KALAS MANUFACTURING, INC.; *U.S. Private*, pg. 2257
KASPAR WIRE WORKS, INC.—See The Kaspar Companies; *U.S. Private*, pg. 4064
KEATS MANUFACTURING COMPANY; *U.S. Private*, pg. 2271
THE KERITE COMPANY—See Berkshire Hathaway Inc.; *U.S. Public*, pg. 310
KEYSTONE CONSOLIDATED INDUSTRIES, INC.—See Contran Corporation; *U.S. Private*, pg. 1033
KOCH-OTTO YORK CO., INC.—See Koch Industries, Inc.; *U.S. Private*, pg. 2332
LACLEDE CHAIN MANUFACTURING CO., LLC - MARYVILLE—See C3 Capital Partners, LP; *U.S. Private*, pg. 710
LACLEDE CHAIN MANUFACTURING COMPANY, LLC—See C3 Capital Partners, LP; *U.S. Private*, pg. 710
L.A. DARLING COMPANY—See Berkshire Hathaway Inc.; *U.S. Public*, pg. 311
LAKE CABLE LLC; *U.S. Private*, pg. 2374
L&C CHANGSHA CABLE INDUSTRIES LTD.—See Leggett & Platt, Incorporated; *U.S. Public*, pg. 1302
LESJOFORS FJADRAR AB—See Beijer Alma AB; *Int'l*, pg. 943
LEVITON MANUFACTURING COMPANY, INC.; *U.S. Private*, pg. 2436
LHI TECHNOLOGY SHENZEN CO.—See Carlisle Companies Incorporated; *U.S. Public*, pg. 437
LIBLA INDUSTRIES INC.; *U.S. Private*, pg. 2447
LUMPI-BERNDORF DRAHT- UND SEILWERK GMBH—See Berndorf AG; *Int'l*, pg. 987
MARMON ENGINEERED WIRE & CABLE—See Berkshire Hathaway Inc.; *U.S. Public*, pg. 309
MASONRY REINFORCING CORPORATION AMERICA; *U.S. Private*, pg. 2603
MATRIX WIRE, INC.; *U.S. Private*, pg. 2612
MAZE LUMBER—See W.H. Maze Company; *U.S. Private*, pg. 4420
MAZZELLA LIFTING TECHNOLOGIES; *U.S. Private*, pg. 2623
M&B METAL PRODUCTS CO. INC.; *U.S. Private*, pg. 2524
MERCHANTS METALS, INC.—See The Sterling Group, L.P.; *U.S. Private*, pg. 4123
METALSPAND, INC.—See NMC Metals Inc.; *U.S. Private*, pg. 2931
METAL TEXTILES CORPORATION—See United Capital Corp.; *U.S. Private*, pg. 4288
METROPOLITAN WIRE CANADA, LTD.—See Emerson Electric Co.; *U.S. Public*, pg. 750
MHPS PLANT SERVICES PTY LTD—See Hitachi, Ltd.; *Int'l*, pg. 3423
MICHIGAN ROD PRODUCTS INC.; *U.S. Private*, pg. 2701
MID-SOUTH WIRE COMPANY, INC.; *U.S. Private*, pg. 2709
MIDWESTERN INDUSTRIES INC.; *U.S. Private*, pg. 2724
MID-WEST METAL PRODUCTS COMPANY INC.; *U.S. Private*, pg. 2710
MJM HOLDINGS INC.; *U.S. Private*, pg. 2753
MLP STEEL COMPANY; *U.S. Private*, pg. 2754
MOBO CO., LTD.—See GAON Cable Co., Ltd.; *Int'l*, pg. 2882
MODERN MACHINERY COMPANY—See Capital Machine Technologies, Inc.; *U.S. Private*, pg. 741
MOLECU WIRE CORPORATION; *U.S. Private*, pg. 2767
MOLEX HONG KONG/CHINA LTD.—See Koch Industries, Inc.; *U.S. Private*, pg. 2334
MOLEX INTERCONNECT (BEIJING) CO., LTD.—See Koch Industries, Inc.; *U.S. Private*, pg. 2334
MOLEX INTERCONNECT (SHANGHAI) CO., LTD.—See Koch Industries, Inc.; *U.S. Private*, pg. 2334
MTS SYSTEMS SRL—See Amphenol Corporation; *U.S. Public*, pg. 131
NASHVILLE WIRE PRODUCTS, INC. - MATERIAL HANDLING - BORDEAUX FACILITY—See Nashville Wire Products, Inc.; *U.S. Private*, pg. 2837
NASHVILLE WIRE PRODUCTS, INC. - MATERIAL HANDLING - FRANKFORT FACILITY—See Nashville Wire Products, Inc.; *U.S. Private*, pg. 2837
NASHVILLE WIRE PRODUCTS, INC. - NASHVILLE DISPLAY - DOVER FACILITY—See Nashville Wire Products, Inc.; *U.S. Private*, pg. 2837
NASHVILLE WIRE PRODUCTS, INC. - NASHVILLE DISPLAY - LEBANON FACILITY—See Nashville Wire Products, Inc.; *U.S. Private*, pg. 2837
NASHVILLE WIRE PRODUCTS, INC. - OEM PARTS - AUBURN FACILITY—See Nashville Wire Products, Inc.; *U.S. Private*, pg. 2837
NASHVILLE WIRE PRODUCTS, INC. - OEM PARTS - JUAREZ FACILITY—See Nashville Wire Products, Inc.; *U.S. Private*, pg. 2837
NASHVILLE WIRE PRODUCTS, INC. - OEM PARTS - WHITE BLUFF FACILITY—See Nashville Wire Products, Inc.; *U.S. Private*, pg. 2837
NASHVILLE WIRE PRODUCTS, INC.; *U.S. Private*, pg. 2836
NEPTCO INCORPORATED—See KKR & Co. Inc.; *U.S. Public*, pg. 1243
NEWARK WIRE CLOTH CO.; *U.S. Private*, pg. 2913
NEW YORK WIRE COMPANY—See Compagnie de Saint-Gobain SA; *Int'l*, pg. 1730
NILES FENCE & SECURITY PRODUCTS, LLC—See NMC Metals Inc.; *U.S. Private*, pg. 2931
NIPPON CABLE CO. LTD.—See Doppelmayr Group; *Int'l*, pg. 2175
NMC METALS INC.; *U.S. Private*, pg. 2931
NOVIA ASSOCIATES, INC.—See Hill & Smith PLC; *Int'l*, pg. 3392
NUMESH, INC.—See Fertek, Inc.; *Int'l*, pg. 2646

3519

332618 — OTHER FABRICATED WI...

OKLAHOMA STEEL & WIRE CO. INC.; *U.S. Private*, pg. 3007
THE OKONITE COMPANY; *U.S. Private*, pg. 4088
OMERIN USA, INC.—See Groupe OMERIN; *Int'l*, pg. 3109
ORSCHELN PRODUCTS LLC—See Orscheln Group; *U.S. Private*, pg. 3045
PARKER CHOMERICS—See Parker Hannifin Corporation; *U.S. Public*, pg. 1643
PEACE INDUSTRIES LTD.; *U.S. Private*, pg. 3122
PEERLESS CHAIN COMPANY—See The Carlyle Group Inc.; *U.S. Public*, pg. 2055
PELICAN WIRE COMPANY, INC.; *U.S. Private*, pg. 3131
PENGG DRAT S.R.O.—See Berndorf AG; *Int'l*, pg. 987
PENG USHA MARTIN PVT. LTD.—See Berndorf AG; *Int'l*, pg. 987
PENN POWER SYSTEMS—See Penn Power Group, LLC; *U.S. Private*, pg. 3134
PETERSON SPRING-MAUMEE PLANT—See Middle-Ground Management, LP; *U.S. Private*, pg. 2712
PHIFER WIRE PRODUCTS INC.; *U.S. Private*, pg. 3168
POLYMET CORPORATION; *U.S. Private*, pg. 3226
POSCO MVWPC S.A. DE C.V.—See DHSteel; *Int'l*, pg. 2100
PRAIRIE CABLE LLC.; *U.S. Private*, pg. 3242
PRECISION RESOURCE INC. - CANADA - CAMBRIDGE PLANT—See Precision Resource Inc.; *U.S. Private*, pg. 3246
PRECISION WIRE PRODUCTS INC.; *U.S. Private*, pg. 3247
PREMIER MANUFACTURING CORPORATION—See Trive Capital Inc.; *U.S. Private*, pg. 4240
P.T. JEMBO CABLE COMPANY—See Fujikura Ltd.; *Int'l*, pg. 2829
QUABBIN WIRE & CABLE CO. INC.; *U.S. Private*, pg. 3314
RADIX WIRE COMPANY; *U.S. Private*, pg. 3345
RFA-TECH LTD.—See Celsa Group; *Int'l*, pg. 1395
ROCHESTER WIRE & CABLE LLC—See Hexatronic Group AB; *Int'l*, pg. 3371
ROCKBESTOS-SUPRENANT CABLE CORP. OIL/PETROCHEMICAL DIVISION—See Berkshire Hathaway Inc.; *U.S. Public*, pg. 310
ROCKBESTOS-SUPRENANT CABLE CORP. TRANSPORTATION MARKET DIVISION—See Berkshire Hathaway Inc.; *U.S. Public*, pg. 310
ROCKBESTOS-SUPRENANT CABLE CORP. UTILITY/INDUSTRIAL MARKET DIVISION—See Berkshire Hathaway Inc.; *U.S. Public*, pg. 310
ROCKBESTOS-SURPRENANT CABLE CORP.—See Berkshire Hathaway Inc.; *U.S. Public*, pg. 310
ROM GROUP LIMITED—See Celsa Group; *Int'l*, pg. 1395
ROOFCLAD LTD.—See Alam Group of Companies; *Int'l*, pg. 289
RSCC AEROSPACE & DEFENSE—See Berkshire Hathaway Inc.; *U.S. Public*, pg. 310
RSCC WIRE & CABLE LLC—See Berkshire Hathaway Inc.; *U.S. Public*, pg. 310
SAFA, LLC—See AISIN Corporation; *Int'l*, pg. 251
SANLO, INC.—See Central Wire Industries Ltd; *Int'l*, pg. 1410
SCHLEGEL ENGINEERING KK—See Quanex Building Products Corp.; *U.S. Public*, pg. 1749
SCHNITZER SOUTHEAST, LLC—See Radius Recycling, Inc.; *U.S. Public*, pg. 1760
SCHULTE CORPORATION; *U.S. Private*, pg. 3570
SEVEN WIRE CO., LTD.—See General Engineering Public Company Limited; *Int'l*, pg. 2918
SHANGHAI NANYANG FUJIKURA CABLE CO., LTD.—See Fujikura Ltd.; *Int'l*, pg. 2829
SHERMAN WIRE COMPANY—See Contran Corporation; *U.S. Private*, pg. 1033
SHIN YA WIRE & CABLE (SHENZHEN) CO., LTD.—See Copartner Technology Corporation; *Int'l*, pg. 1793
SILVERADO CABLE COMPANY—See Phoenix Logistics, Inc.; *U.S. Private*, pg. 3173
SIVACO QUEBEC DIVISION—See The Heico Companies, L.L.C.; *U.S. Private*, pg. 4051
SMC SOUTH—See Sommer Metalcraft Corporation; *U.S. Private*, pg. 3712
SOCIETE INDUSTRIELLE DU TITANE, S.A.—See Contran Corporation; *U.S. Private*, pg. 1033
SOLON SPECIALTY WIRE CO.—See Leggett & Platt, Incorporated; *U.S. Public*, pg. 1303
SOMMER METALCRAFT CORPORATION; *U.S. Private*, pg. 3712
SOUTH BAY CABLE CORP.; *U.S. Private*, pg. 3719
SOUTHERN STEEL & WIRE CO. LLC—See Trive Capital Inc.; *U.S. Private*, pg. 4240
SOUTHWEST WIRE ROPE, L.P.—See Dot Family Holdings LLC; *U.S. Private*, pg. 1264
STAR GUIDE LIMITED—See Integer Holdings Corporation; *U.S. Public*, pg. 1135
STRAITS STEEL & WIRE COMPANY—See Trive Capital Inc.; *U.S. Private*, pg. 4240
STRAND-TECH MARTIN INCORPORATED—See Insteel Industries, Inc.; *U.S. Public*, pg. 1134
STREATER, INC.—See Berkshire Hathaway Inc.; *U.S. Public*, pg. 311
TALBOT INDUSTRIES, INC.—See Leggett & Platt, Incorporated; *U.S. Public*, pg. 1303
TATSUTA ELECTRIC WIRE & CABLE CO., LTD. - KYOTO WORKS—See ENEOS Holdings, Inc.; *Int'l*, pg. 2416
TATSUTA ELECTRIC WIRE & CABLE CO., LTD.—See ENEOS Holdings, Inc.; *Int'l*, pg. 2416
TELEDYNE STORM CABLE—See Teledyne Technologies Incorporated; *U.S. Public*, pg. 1995
TE WIRE & CABLE LLC—See Berkshire Hathaway Inc.; *U.S. Public*, pg. 310
THERM-O-LINK INC.; *U.S. Private*, pg. 4142
TOTOKU ELECTRIC CO., LTD.—See The Carlyle Group Inc.; *U.S. Public*, pg. 2055
TRANSWIRE (PTY.) LTD.—See ACTOM (Pty) Ltd.; *Int'l*, pg. 121
T&S PERFECTION CHAIN PRODUCTS, INC.; *U.S. Private*, pg. 3910
TWIN CITY WIRE, INC.; *U.S. Private*, pg. 4265
ULBRICH OF NEW ENGLAND—See Ulbrich Stainless Steel & Special Metals, Inc.; *U.S. Private*, pg. 4276
UNARCO INDUSTRIES LLC—See Berkshire Hathaway Inc.; *U.S. Public*, pg. 310
WANFU PLASTIC (SHENZHEN) CO., LTD.—See Copartner Technology Corporation; *Int'l*, pg. 1793
WAYNE WIRE CLOTH PRODUCTS, INC.; *U.S. Private*, pg. 4460
WEBSTER-PORTALLOY CHAINS, INC.—See MPE Partners, LLC; *U.S. Private*, pg. 2804
THE WESTERN GROUP; *U.S. Private*, pg. 4134
WEST PENN WIRE—See Belden, Inc.; *U.S. Public*, pg. 294
WHITEPATH FAB TECH INC.—See Cerberus Capital Management, L.P.; *U.S. Private*, pg. 838
WHITESELL WIRE FORM UNIT—See Whitesell Corporation; *U.S. Private*, pg. 4512
WHITMOR, INC.; *U.S. Private*, pg. 4513
WHITMOR/WIRENETICS; *U.S. Private*, pg. 4513
W.H. MAZE COMPANY; *U.S. Private*, pg. 4420
WILCAS CORP.; *U.S. Private*, pg. 4518
WIRE CLOTH MANUFACTURERS, INC.—See Graycliff Partners LP; *U.S. Private*, pg. 1761
WIREWAY/HUSKY CORPORATION; *U.S. Private*, pg. 4547
WOODSTOCK WIRE WORKS INC.; *U.S. Private*, pg. 4561
WUJIANG WANFENG PLASTIC CEMENT CO., LTD.—See Copartner Technology Corporation; *Int'l*, pg. 1793
WUXI HU AN WIRE AND CABLE CO., LTD.—See Hu An Cable Holdings Ltd.; *Int'l*, pg. 3509
WYTECH INDUSTRIES, INC.—See Vance Street Capital LLC; *U.S. Private*, pg. 4342

332710 — MACHINE SHOPS

2M TOOL COMPANY, INC.; *U.S. Private*, pg. 7
AAA SALES & ENGINEERING INC.—See Industrial Opportunity Partners, LLC; *U.S. Private*, pg. 2067
ABIST CO., LTD.; *Int'l*, pg. 62
ACCURATE METAL MACHINING, INC.—See HEICO Corporation; *U.S. Public*, pg. 1021
ACE PRECISION MACHINING CORP.; *U.S. Private*, pg. 57
ADVANCED MACHINE & ENGINEERING CO.; *U.S. Private*, pg. 90
ADVANCED PRECISION INC.—See The Jordan Company, L.P.; *U.S. Private*, pg. 4060
ADVANCED TECHNOLOGY MACHINING, INC.—See ESCO Technologies, Inc.; *U.S. Public*, pg. 793
ADVANCE TURNING & MANUFACTURING, INC.; *U.S. Private*, pg. 87
AERO DESIGN & MANUFACTURING, INC.; *U.S. Private*, pg. 118
A&K C.N.C. MACHINING, LLC—See Promus Holdings, LLC; *U.S. Private*, pg. 3284
AKRON GEAR & ENGINEERING INC.—See Forge Industries, Inc.; *U.S. Private*, pg. 1568
ALLEGHENY PLASTICS, INC. - PERFORMANCE PLASTICS DIVISION—See Allegheny Plastics Inc.; *U.S. Private*, pg. 176
ALLIED CHUCKER & ENGINEERING COMPANY; *U.S. Private*, pg. 185
ALLIED MECHANICAL—See Tower Industries Inc.; *U.S. Private*, pg. 4194
ALLIED PACIFIC—See Tower Industries Inc.; *U.S. Private*, pg. 4194
ALLOY CARBIDE COMPANY; *U.S. Private*, pg. 193
ALL WELD MACHINE & FABRICATION COMPANY; *U.S. Private*, pg. 173
ALPHA Q, INC.; *U.S. Private*, pg. 199
AMERICAN GRINDING AND MACHINE COMPANY; *U.S. Private*, pg. 235
AMERICAN INDUSTRIAL MACHINE—See BP Energy Partners, LLC; *U.S. Private*, pg. 629
ANCHOR METAL PROCESSING—See Anchor Manufacturing Group, Inc.; *U.S. Private*, pg. 273
ARMSTRONG TECHNOLOGY INC.; *U.S. Private*, pg. 332
ARWOOD MACHINE CORPORATION—See VulcanForms Inc.; *U.S. Private*, pg. 4416
ASCUTNEY METAL PRODUCTS—See Spirol International Corporation; *U.S. Private*, pg. 3758
ATEK ACCESS TECHNOLOGIES, LLC—See ATEK Companies, Inc.; *U.S. Private*, pg. 367
ATHENA MANUFACTURING, LP.; *U.S. Private*, pg. 367
ATLAS MACHINE AND SUPPLY INC.; *U.S. Private*, pg. 379

ATLAS MACHINING & WELDING, INC.; *U.S. Private*, pg. 379
AUGUSTA IRON & STEEL WORKS; *U.S. Private*, pg. 392
AUTOMATED METAL TECHNOLOGIES, INC.—See Naimor, Inc.; *U.S. Private*, pg. 2831
AZTALAN ENGINEERING, INC.; *U.S. Private*, pg. 415
BASIN PRECISION MACHINING LLC—See J Fitzgibbons LLC; *U.S. Private*, pg. 2153
BASSANI MANUFACTURING; *U.S. Private*, pg. 486
BAUGHMAN GROUP LTD; *U.S. Private*, pg. 490
BAYSIDE MACHINE CORP.; *U.S. Private*, pg. 497
BEATTY MACHINE & MFG. COMPANY; *U.S. Private*, pg. 507
BECKWOOD SERVICES, INC.—See Elbit Systems Limited; *Int'l*, pg. 2344
BEERE PRECISION PRODUCTS INC.; *U.S. Private*, pg. 514
BERANEK, INC.—See J & E Precision Tool, LLC; *U.S. Private*, pg. 2152
BOLTON AEROSPACE, INC.—See The Carlyle Group Inc.; *U.S. Public*, pg. 2054
BOSTON CENTERLESS INC.; *U.S. Private*, pg. 621
BOWMAN TOOL & MACHINING INC.—See Polaris, Inc.; *U.S. Public*, pg. 1701
BRACALENTE MANUFACTURING CO., INC.; *U.S. Private*, pg. 630
BUSCHE PERFORMANCE GROUP, INC.; *U.S. Private*, pg. 693
BYRNE TOOL & DIE INC.—See Byrne Electrical Specialists, Inc.; *U.S. Private*, pg. 701
CAPSTAN CALIFORNIA—See Capstan Inc.; *U.S. Private*, pg. 746
CARBOPRESS S.P.A.; *Int'l*, pg. 1321
CBS BORING & MACHINE COMPANY, INC.; *U.S. Private*, pg. 797
CENTERLINE MACHINING & GRINDING, INC.; *U.S. Private*, pg. 816
CENTRAL MACHINE & TOOL COMPANY—See Parrish Enterprises, Inc.; *U.S. Private*, pg. 3100
CENTURY TOOL & GAGE—See Century Tool & Gage; *U.S. Private*, pg. 834
CF GEAR HOLDINGS; *U.S. Private*, pg. 843
CHALMERS & KÜBECK, INC.; *U.S. Private*, pg. 845
CHANDLER INDUSTRIES - LAKE COUNTRY DIVISION—See Arch Equity Partners, LLC; *U.S. Private*, pg. 310
CLASSIC PRECISION, LLC—See Carlisle Companies Incorporated; *U.S. Public*, pg. 436
CLASSIC TURNING, INC.; *U.S. Private*, pg. 917
CM RECYCLING EQUIPMENT SOLUTIONS—See Bengal Machine; *U.S. Private*, pg. 526
CNC MACHINE GROUP INC.—See ZYCI LLC; *U.S. Private*, pg. 4611
COMPETITIVE ENGINEERING INC.; *U.S. Private*, pg. 1000
CONNECTICUT COINING, INC.—See MavenHill Capital; *U.S. Private*, pg. 2615
CONTINENTAL FIELD SYSTEMS INC.; *U.S. Private*, pg. 1028
CPK MANUFACTURING LLC—See Hill & Smith PLC; *Int'l*, pg. 3391
CREED-MONARCH, INC.; *U.S. Private*, pg. 1092
CROWN PARTS AND MACHINE INC.; *U.S. Private*, pg. 1111
CSC MACHINING—See Prescott Aerospace, Inc.; *U.S. Private*, pg. 3254
CUSTOM PRODUCTION GRINDING, INC.—See Blackwell Capital Group LLC; *U.S. Private*, pg. 577
D A E INDUSTRIES; *U.S. Private*, pg. 1136
DALTON CORPORATION - STRYKER PLANT—See Speyside Equity LLC; *U.S. Private*, pg. 3756
DAVIS TOOL INC.—See Bertram Capital Management, LLC; *U.S. Private*, pg. 539
D&B MACHINE, INC.; *U.S. Private*, pg. 1136
DELTA GEAR CO. INC.; *U.S. Private*, pg. 1200
D&G MACHINE PRODUCTS INC.; *U.S. Private*, pg. 1137
DMI WOLFGANG DRECHSLER GMBH—See DMI UK Ltd.; *Int'l*, pg. 2145
DOMAILLE ENGINEERING, LLC—See Onward Capital LLC; *U.S. Private*, pg. 3028
DOMAILLE ENGINEERING, LLC—See Thompson Street Capital Manager LLC; *U.S. Private*, pg. 4161
DOR-MAE INDUSTRIES; *U.S. Private*, pg. 1262
DOTY MACHINE WORKS, INC.—See Miller Mechanical Services, Inc.; *U.S. Private*, pg. 2735
DU PAGE PRECISION PRODUCTS CO.; *U.S. Private*, pg. 1282
DWA, INC.; *U.S. Private*, pg. 1295
DYNAMIC ENGINEERING INC.; *U.S. Private*, pg. 1298
EARTH TOOL COMPANY, LLC—See The Toro Company; *U.S. Public*, pg. 2135
ELASTEC/AMERICAN MARINE, INC.; *U.S. Private*, pg. 1350
ELCO INC.; *U.S. Private*, pg. 1350
ELLIOTT MACHINE WORKS, INC.—See Stellar Industries Inc.; *U.S. Private*, pg. 3799
ELLWOOD NATIONAL FORGE COMPANY, LLC—See Ellwood Group, Inc.; *U.S. Private*, pg. 1375

332710 — MACHINE SHOPS

ELLWOOD ROSE MACHINE, INC.—See Ellwood Group, Inc.; *U.S. Private*, pg. 1375
ENDURANCE FONDALMEC S.P.A.—See Affirma Capital Limited; *Int'l*, pg. 187
EUCLID INDUSTRIES INC.; *U.S. Private*, pg. 1432
FARMERS MARINE COPPER WORKS—See Four Winds Investment Corp.; *U.S. Private*, pg. 1583
FAVRE SARL—See BBG Baugerate GmbH; *Int'l*, pg. 920
FITZPATRICK MANUFACTURING CO.; *U.S. Private*, pg. 1537
FLOTURN INC.; *U.S. Private*, pg. 1551
F.R. DRAKE COMPANY—See The Middleby Corporation; *U.S. Public*, pg. 2113
FUJIKURA RICHARD MANUFACTURING INC.—See Fujikura Ltd.; *Int'l*, pg. 2828
FUTURE TECH METALS, INC.—See Avem Partners, LLC; *U.S. Private*, pg. 405
GALSTONBURY SOUTHERN GAGE—See Alpha Q, Inc.; *U.S. Private*, pg. 199
GAUM, INC.—See Universal Technical Resource Services, Inc.; *U.S. Private*, pg. 4306
GEARS & SPROCKETTS, INC.—See Headco Industries; *U.S. Private*, pg. 1891
GENERAL PLASTICS & COMPOSITES LP; *U.S. Private*, pg. 1666
GENERAL PROPELLER COMPANY, INC.; *U.S. Private*, pg. 1666
GENERAL TECHNOLOGY, INC.—See UCA Group Component Specialty Inc.; *U.S. Private*, pg. 4273
GENERAL TOOL COMPANY INC.; *U.S. Private*, pg. 1667
GKI INCORPORATED; *U.S. Private*, pg. 1704
GLENN MACHINE WORKS, INC.; *U.S. Private*, pg. 1710
GMT CORPORATION; *U.S. Private*, pg. 1723
GOODMAN BALL INC.—See C.E. Niehoff & Co.; *U.S. Private*, pg. 706
GREMADA INDUSTRIES INC.; *U.S. Private*, pg. 1783
GRENO INDUSTRIES INC.; *U.S. Private*, pg. 1783
GROEDITZER KURBELWELLE WILDAU GMBH—See Georgsmarienhutte Holding GmbH; *Int'l*, pg. 2940
GROVE INDUSTRIES, INC.—See Pine Grove Holdings, LLC; *U.S. Private*, pg. 3182
GROVER CORPORATION; *U.S. Private*, pg. 1795
G.S. PRECISION, INC. - KEENE DIVISION—See AE Industrial Partners, LP; *U.S. Private*, pg. 112
HAGER MACHINE & TOOL INC.—See Atec, Inc.; *U.S. Private*, pg. 365
HAHN & CLAY, LTD.; *U.S. Private*, pg. 1840
HANSEN ENGINEERING CO. INC.; *U.S. Private*, pg. 1856
HASCO INTERNORM LTD.—See Berndorf AG; *Int'l*, pg. 987
HASCO NORMALIEN MEXICO S.A. DE C.V.—See Berndorf AG; *Int'l*, pg. 987
HASCO POLSKA SP ZO.O.—See Berndorf AG; *Int'l*, pg. 987
HASCO PORTUGUESA LDA.—See Berndorf AG; *Int'l*, pg. 987
HASCO SINGAPORE (PTE) LTD.—See Berndorf AG; *Int'l*, pg. 987
HASCO SUISSE AG—See Berndorf AG; *Int'l*, pg. 987
HASCO TRADING (SHENZHEN) CO., LTD.—See Berndorf AG; *Int'l*, pg. 987
HEADCO MACHINE WORKS, INC.—See Headco Industries; *U.S. Private*, pg. 1891
H.M. DUNN COMPANY INC.; *U.S. Private*, pg. 1835
H. & S. SWANSONS' TOOL COMPANY—See The Jordan Company, L.P.; *U.S. Private*, pg. 4060
HUNTING ENERGY SERVICES - DOFFING DIV—See Hunting Plc; *Int'l*, pg. 3537
HYPRO INC.; *U.S. Private*, pg. 2020
IDL PRECISION MACHINING, INC.—See CORE Industrial Partners, LLC; *U.S. Private*, pg. 1048
ITW HEARTLAND GEARS—See Illinois Tool Works Inc.; *U.S. Public*, pg. 1106
JET MACHINE & MANUFACTURING—See Wulco Inc.; *U.S. Private*, pg. 4575
JIFFY AIR TOOL, INC.—See ShoreView Industries, LLC; *U.S. Private*, pg. 3642
J & S MACHINE; *U.S. Private*, pg. 2152
J.T. FENNELL CO. INC.; *U.S. Private*, pg. 2171
KELLER TECHNOLOGY CORPORATION; *U.S. Private*, pg. 2275
KEMP MANUFACTURING COMPANY; *U.S. Private*, pg. 2282
KENLEE PRECISION CORPORATION; *U.S. Private*, pg. 2284
KIMBER MFG. INC.; *U.S. Private*, pg. 2305
K&M MACHINE-FABRICATING INC.—See McLoughlin Enterprises Inc.; *U.S. Private*, pg. 2641
KOMAX CORPORATION; *U.S. Private*, pg. 2342
LASERAGE TECHNOLOGY CORP.—See AMETEK, Inc.; *U.S. Public*, pg. 120
LB STEEL, LLC—See L B Industries, Inc.; *U.S. Private*, pg. 2361
L&H INDUSTRIAL INC; *U.S. Private*, pg. 2362
THE L.H. THOMSON COMPANY, INC.; *U.S. Private*, pg. 4067
LINDQUIST MACHINE CORPORATION; *U.S. Private*, pg. 2460
LODOLCE MACHINE COMPANY, INC.; *U.S. Private*, pg. 2479
LOU-RICH, INC.—See Innovance, Inc.; *U.S. Private*, pg. 2081
MACHINISTS INCORPORATED; *U.S. Private*, pg. 2536
MAGIC CIRCLE MANUFACTURING DIVISION—See Acme Foundry, Inc.; *U.S. Private*, pg. 61
MAGNA MACHINE CO. INC.; *U.S. Private*, pg. 2546
MAGNUM MACHINING INCORPORATED; *U.S. Private*, pg. 2549
MAJOR TOOL & MACHINE, INC.; *U.S. Private*, pg. 2555
MARQUETTE COPPERSMITHING-MANUFACTURING DIVISION—See Marquette Coppersmithing Co., Inc.; *U.S. Private*, pg. 2587
MARTINEZ & TUREK, INC.; *U.S. Private*, pg. 2596
MATECH, INC.; *U.S. Private*, pg. 2609
MAXON FURNITURE, INC—See HNI Corporation; *U.S. Public*, pg. 1043
MB AEROSPACE STERLING HEIGHTS, INC.—See Barnes Group Inc.; *U.S. Public*, pg. 277
MCGILL MAINTENANCE LLP; *U.S. Private*, pg. 2634
MCLOUGHLIN ENTERPRISES INC.; *U.S. Private*, pg. 2641
MEGATECH A.Q. INC.—See MiddleGround Management, LP; *U.S. Private*, pg. 2712
MENDELL MACHINE AND MANUFACTURING, LLC—See Frazier & Company, Inc.; *U.S. Private*, pg. 1599
MIC GROUP—See J.B. Poindexter & Co., Inc.; *U.S. Private*, pg. 2158
MICRO-MECH INC.—See Ibiden Co., Ltd.; *Int'l*, pg. 3576
MID-AMERICAN MACHINE & EQUIPMENT, LLC.; *U.S. Private*, pg. 2707
MID-STATE MACHINE & FABRICATING INC—See CenterGate Capital, LP; *U.S. Private*, pg. 816
MID-STATE MACHINE PRODUCTS, INC.—See Insight Equity Holdings LLC; *U.S. Private*, pg. 2086
MID VALLEY INDUSTRIES, LLC—See Goldner Hawn Johnson & Morrison Inc.; *U.S. Private*, pg. 1735
MIETHER BEARING PRODUCTS, LLC—See Dunes Point Capital, LLC; *U.S. Public*, pg. 1288
MILLER MECHANICAL SERVICES, INC.; *U.S. Private*, pg. 2735
MINCE MASTER—See 2M Tool Company, Inc.; *U.S. Private*, pg. 7
M & M MANUFACTURING, INC.—See Rift Valley Equity Partners, LLC; *U.S. Private*, pg. 3435
MODERN INDUSTRIES, INC.; *U.S. Private*, pg. 2761
MONROE MACHINED PRODUCTS, INC.; *U.S. Private*, pg. 2773
MONTGOMERY MACHINE CO., INC.—See Oil States International, Inc.; *U.S. Public*, pg. 1565
MORBARK LLC—See Alamo Group Inc.; *U.S. Public*, pg. 71
MORRISON BERKSHIRE INC.; *U.S. Private*, pg. 2789
MUELLER FIELD OPERATIONS, INC.; *U.S. Private*, pg. 2810
NAIMOR, INC.; *U.S. Private*, pg. 2831
NATIONAL MACHINE COMPANY; *U.S. Private*, pg. 2859
NFM/WELDING ENGINEERS, INC.; *U.S. Private*, pg. 2923
NORMAN NOBLE INCORPORATED; *U.S. Private*, pg. 2938
NORTHERN IRON OF ST. PAUL, LLC; *U.S. Private*, pg. 2953
NORTHERN MACHINING & REPAIR, INC.; *U.S. Private*, pg. 2953
OEM PRESS SYSTEMS, INC.; *U.S. Private*, pg. 2997
OEM PRESS SYSTEMS (SHENZHEN) CO., LTD.—See OEM Press Systems, Inc.; *U.S. Private*, pg. 2997
OOO HASCO RU—See Berndorf AG; *Int'l*, pg. 987
OPEN LOOP ENERGY, INC.; *U.S. Private*, pg. 3029
PARADIGM METALS INC.; *U.S. Private*, pg. 3089
PARADIGM PRECISION - BERLIN—See AeroEquity Partners, LLC; *U.S. Private*, pg. 118
PARADIGM PRECISION - BERLIN—See The Carlyle Group Inc.; *U.S. Public*, pg. 2046
PARAMOUNT PRECISION PRODUCTS, INC.; *U.S. Private*, pg. 3093
PHB MACHINING DIVISION—See PHB Inc.; *U.S. Private*, pg. 3166
PIONEER PRODUCTS, INC.; *U.S. Private*, pg. 3188
PIPER PLASTICS INC.; *U.S. Private*, pg. 3189
PLASTIC DISTRIBUTORS & FABRICATORS, INC.—See Edgewater Capital Partners, L.P.; *U.S. Private*, pg. 1334
PRAGER INC.—See Zurn Elkay Water Solutions Corporation; *U.S. Public*, pg. 2413
PRECISE METAL PRODUCTS COMPANY; *U.S. Private*, pg. 3244
PRECISION AEROSPACE CORP.—See Shorehill Capital LLC; *U.S. Private*, pg. 3641
PRECISION COMPONENT INDUSTRIES, LLC—See Ohio Gratings, Inc.; *U.S. Private*, pg. 3004
PRECISION MACHINED PRODUCTS—See Mistequay Group Ltd.; *U.S. Private*, pg. 2750
PRECISION MACHINE MANUFACTURING CO.; *U.S. Private*, pg. 3245
PRECISION METAL PRODUCTS INC.; *U.S. Private*, pg. 3245
PRECISION SHAPES, INC.—See HC Private Investments LLC; *U.S. Private*, pg. 1888
PROCESS EQUIPMENT COMPANY OF TIPP CITY INC.; *U.S. Private*, pg. 3271
PRODUCTION TOOL CORPORATION; *U.S. Private*, pg. 3273
PRODUCTS SUPPORT INC.; *U.S. Private*, pg. 3274
PROFESSIONAL REBUILD & OPTIMAL SERVICE LLC; *U.S. Private*, pg. 3276
PROTOTYPE MACHINE CO. INC.; *U.S. Private*, pg. 3290
PT TRIMITRA TEHNIK—See Chien Wei Precise Technology Co., Ltd.; *Int'l*, pg. 1477
QCC, LLC—See Promus Holdings, LLC; *U.S. Private*, pg. 3284
Q-MACHINE—See Questar Corporation; *U.S. Private*, pg. 3326
QTM, INC.; *U.S. Private*, pg. 3314
QUASAR INDUSTRIES INC.; *U.S. Private*, pg. 3324
RAY INDUSTRIES, INC.—See Joshua Partners, LLC; *U.S. Private*, pg. 2237
R&B GRINDING CO. INC.; *U.S. Private*, pg. 3331
RCP SARL—See AmRest Holdings SE; *Int'l*, pg. 437
RDC MACHINE INC.; *U.S. Private*, pg. 3364
REINHART INDUSTRIES INC.; *U.S. Private*, pg. 3392
RESONETICS, LLC—See GTCR LLC; *U.S. Private*, pg. 1806
RICHLIND METAL FABRICATORS, INC.—See CORE Industrial Partners, LLC; *U.S. Private*, pg. 1048
R.L. HUDSON & COMPANY; *U.S. Private*, pg. 3338
R.M. KERNER CO.; *U.S. Private*, pg. 3339
ROCKTECH SYSTEMS, LLC—See Desktop Metal, Inc.; *U.S. Public*, pg. 656
ROYAL OAK INDUSTRIES INC.; *U.S. Private*, pg. 3493
RYERSON INC. - ATLANTA—See Ryerson Holding Corporation; *U.S. Public*, pg. 1829
RYERSON INC. - BURNS HARBOR—See Ryerson Holding Corporation; *U.S. Public*, pg. 1829
RYERSON INC. - COON RAPIDS—See Ryerson Holding Corporation; *U.S. Public*, pg. 1829
RYERSON INC. - LITTLE ROCK—See Ryerson Holding Corporation; *U.S. Public*, pg. 1829
RYERSON INC. - MEMPHIS—See Ryerson Holding Corporation; *U.S. Public*, pg. 1829
RYERSON INC. - MINNEAPOLIS—See Ryerson Holding Corporation; *U.S. Public*, pg. 1829
RYERSON INC. - SEATTLE—See Ryerson Holding Corporation; *U.S. Public*, pg. 1829
RYERSON INC.—See Ryerson Holding Corporation; *U.S. Public*, pg. 1829
SANDERS MANUFACTURING CO., INC.; *U.S. Private*, pg. 3543
S & D SPECIALTY, INC.; *U.S. Private*, pg. 3511
SEANAIR MACHINE CO., INC.—See AE Industrial Partners, LP; *U.S. Private*, pg. 112
SEANAIR MACHINE CO., INC.—See Broadtree Partners, LLC; *U.S. Private*, pg. 659
SHASTA INC.—See Shasta Holdings Company; *U.S. Private*, pg. 3627
SHOWA SEIKO CO., LTD.—See Hitachi Astemo, Ltd.; *Int'l*, pg. 3410
SMITHS MACHINE, LLC—See The Jordan Company, L.P.; *U.S. Private*, pg. 4060
SOUTHERN MANUFACTURING TECHNOLOGIES, INC.; *U.S. Private*, pg. 3733
SOUTHERN PRESTIGE INDUSTRIES, INC.; *U.S. Private*, pg. 3734
SOUTHERN TOOLING, INC.—See LFM Capital LLC; *U.S. Private*, pg. 2441
SPACE-CRAFT MANUFACTURING, INC.; *U.S. Private*, pg. 3744
SPECIALTY DESIGN & MANUFACTURING CO.—See Specialty Holdings Corp.; *U.S. Private*, pg. 3750
SPECIALTY HOLDINGS CORP.; *U.S. Private*, pg. 3750
SPECTRALYTICS, INC.—See The Cretex Companies, Inc.; *U.S. Private*, pg. 4016
SPENCER-HARRIS MACHINE & TOOL CO.—See FEMCO Holdings, LLC; *U.S. Private*, pg. 1494
SPINCRAFT—See Standex International; *U.S. Public*, pg. 1930
STAMPED PRODUCTS INC.—See Mid-South Industries, Inc.; *U.S. Private*, pg. 2708
STANLEY MACHINING & TOOL CORPORATION; *U.S. Private*, pg. 3783
STEWART TUBULAR PRODUCTS, INC.—See Pelican Energy Partners LP; *U.S. Private*, pg. 3130
STROM MANUFACTURING INC.—See Compass Precision LLC; *U.S. Private*, pg. 999
SUPERIOR COMPANIES INC.; *U.S. Private*, pg. 3876
SUPERIOR MACHINE COMPANY DIVISION—See Woodings Industrial Corporation; *U.S. Private*, pg. 4558
SUPREME MACHINED PRODUCTS COMPANY, INC.; *U.S. Private*, pg. 3882
S&W METAL PRODUCTS; *U.S. Private*, pg. 3514
SYLHAN LLC; *U.S. Private*, pg. 3898
TAURUS TOOL & ENGINEERING INC.—See L Squared Capital Management LP; *U.S. Private*, pg. 2362
TEAM INDUSTRIES ANDREWS, INC.—See TEAM Industries, Inc.; *U.S. Private*, pg. 3949
TEAM INDUSTRIES - PARK RAPIDS—See TEAM Industries, Inc.; *U.S. Private*, pg. 3949
TECHNIFORM METAL CURVING INC.; *U.S. Private*, pg. 3954
TENNECO AUTOMOTIVE WALKER—See Apollo Global Management, Inc.; *U.S. Public*, pg. 163

332710 — MACHINE SHOPS

TERRY'S MACHINE & MANUFACTURING, INC.—See Loar Group, Inc.; *U.S. Private*, pg. 2477
THALER MACHINE COMPANY INC.; *U.S. Private*, pg. 3979
THIERICA EQUIPMENT CORPORATION—See THI Inc.; *U.S. Private*, pg. 4144
THI INC.; *U.S. Private*, pg. 4144
TIBOR MACHINE PRODUCTS INC.; *U.S. Private*, pg. 4167
TOG MANUFACTURING CO., INC.; *U.S. Private*, pg. 4181
TOOLING SPECIALISTS INC.; *U.S. Private*, pg. 4186
TOTH INDUSTRIES, INC.; *U.S. Private*, pg. 4192
TOWER INDUSTRIES INC.; *U.S. Private*, pg. 4194
TRACE-A-MATIC CORPORATION; *U.S. Private*, pg. 4200
TRIANGLE MANUFACTURING CO. INC.; *U.S. Private*, pg. 4226
TRICONTINENT SCIENTIFIC, INC.—See Ingersoll Rand Inc.; *U.S. Public*, pg. 1120
TRI-STATE MACHINE, INC., *U.S. Private*, pg. 4224
TRIUMPH FABRICATIONS-FORT WORTH, INC.—See Arlington Capital Partners LLC; *U.S. Private*, pg. 328
TRIUMPH GEAR SYSTEMS-TORONTO, ULC—See Triumph Group, Inc.; *U.S. Public*, pg. 2197
TRIUMPH STRUCTURES-LOS ANGELES, INC.—See ATL Partners, LLC; *U.S. Private*, pg. 369
TRIUMPH STRUCTURES-LOS ANGELES, INC.—See British Columbia Investment Management Corp.; *Int'l*, pg. 1170
TRIUMPH STRUCTURES-WICHITA, INC.—See Triumph Group, Inc.; *U.S. Public*, pg. 2197
TSS TECHNOLOGIES INCORPORATED; *U.S. Private*, pg. 4254
TURNER MACHINE COMPANY, INC.; *U.S. Private*, pg. 4261
UCA GROUP COMPONENT SPECIALTY INC.; *U.S. Private*, pg. 4273
UNIVERSAL MACHINE CO. OF POTTSTOWN; *U.S. Private*, pg. 4305
U.S. AXLE, INC.; *U.S. Private*, pg. 4270
VANPRO, INC.; *U.S. Private*, pg. 4344
VERHOFF MACHINE & WELDING, INC.; *U.S. Private*, pg. 4360
VICKERS ENGINEERING, INC.; *U.S. Private*, pg. 4377
VULCAN MACHINE, INC.—See HC Private Investments LLC; *U.S. Private*, pg. 1888
VULCAN THREADED PRODUCTS, INC.—See Steel Dynamics, Inc.; *U.S. Public*, pg. 1942
WASHINGTON IRON WORKS, INC.—See Professional Rebuild & Optimal Service LLC; *U.S. Private*, pg. 3276
WATER WORKS FABRICATION, LLC—See Wind Point Advisors LLC; *U.S. Private*, pg. 4534
WESTBROOK MANUFACTURING INC.; *U.S. Private*, pg. 4488
WILCOX MACHINE & FAB, INC.; *U.S. Private*, pg. 4518
THE WILL-BURT CO., INC.; *U.S. Private*, pg. 4136
WSI INDUSTRIES, INC.—See Polaris, Inc.; *U.S. Public*, pg. 1701
ZIRCON PRECISION PRODUCTS, INC.; *U.S. Private*, pg. 4606
ZYCI LLC; *U.S. Private*, pg. 4611

332721 — PRECISION TURNED PRODUCT MANUFACTURING

A-1 MACHINING COMPANY—See Lionheart Ventures; *U.S. Private*, pg. 2464
ACU PHARMA UND CHEMIE GMBH—See BRENNTAG SE; *Int'l*, pg. 1146
ADVANEX INC.; *Int'l*, pg. 163
ADVANEX PRECISION COMPONENTS (DONGGUAN) CO., LTD.—See Advanex Inc.; *Int'l*, pg. 163
AKIMOTOSEIKIKOGYO CO., LTD.—See Fuji Seiki Co., Ltd.; *Int'l*, pg. 2817
ALCO MANUFACTURING CORPORATION LLC—See MiddleGround Management, LP; *U.S. Private*, pg. 2711
ALLAN TOOL & MACHINE CO., INC.; *U.S. Private*, pg. 174
ALLIED PRECISION TECHNOLOGIES (M) SDN. BHD.—See Allied Technologies Ltd.; *Int'l*, pg. 358
ALLIED TECH (S) PTE. LTD.—See Allied Technologies Ltd.; *Int'l*, pg. 358
ALPINE INDUSTRIES, INC.—See Adama Technologies Corp.; *U.S. Private*, pg. 73
ANDERSON EUROPE GMBH—See Anderson Industrial Corporation; *Int'l*, pg. 450
ARCH CUTTING TOOLS CORP.—See The Jordan Company, L.P.; *U.S. Private*, pg. 4060
ARCH PRECISION COMPONENTS CORP.—See Madison Dearborn Partners, LLC; *U.S. Private*, pg. 2540
ARLINGTON MACHINE & TOOL CO.—See Rift Valley Equity Partners, LLC; *U.S. Private*, pg. 3435
ASHLEY F. WARD, INC.; *U.S. Private*, pg. 350
AUTOCAM (CHINA) AUTOMOTIVE COMPONENTS CO., LTD.—See NN, Inc.; *U.S. Public*, pg. 1530
AUTOCAM CORPORATION—See NN, Inc.; *U.S. Public*, pg. 1530
AUTOCAM POLAND SP. Z.O.O.—See NN, Inc.; *U.S. Public*, pg. 1530
AUTOMATIC SCREW MACHINE PRODUCTS COMPANY, INC.—See Dubai Holding LLC; *Int'l*, pg. 2218

AVON MACHINING LLC—See Auxo Investment Partners, LLC; *U.S. Private*, pg. 402
BAUMGARTNER & LAMPERSTORFER INSTRUMENTS GMBH.; *Int'l*, pg. 895
BEAN'S BEST LLC; *U.S. Private*, pg. 506
BIEDERMANN MANUFACTURING INDUSTRIES; *U.S. Private*, pg. 551
BRAININ-ADVANCE INDUSTRIES, LLC—See NN, Inc.; *U.S. Public*, pg. 1531
BRAININ DE MEXICO S.A. DE C.V.—See NN, Inc.; *U.S. Public*, pg. 1531
BRAININ (FOSHAN) PRECISION ENGINEERED PRODUCTS, CO. LTD.—See NN, Inc.; *U.S. Public*, pg. 1531
BRITISH METAL TREATMENTS LIMITED—See Camellia Plc; *Int'l*, pg. 1271
BSL MANUFACTURING SDN. BHD.—See BSL Corporation Berhad; *Int'l*, pg. 1202
CAL-COMP PRECISION (THAILAND) LIMITED—See Cal-Comp Electronics (Thailand) pcl; *Int'l*, pg. 1261
CAMCRAFT INC.; *U.S. Private*, pg. 728
CANA-DATUM MOULDS LTD.; *Int'l*, pg. 1277
CASS SCREW MACHINE PRODUCTS LLC—See Heartland Equity Management LLC; *U.S. Private*, pg. 1900
CHARLESTON METAL PRODUCTS INC.; *U.S. Private*, pg. 856
CHEUNG WOH TECHNOLOGIES (JOHOR) SDN. BHD.—See Cheung Woh Technologies Ltd.; *Int'l*, pg. 1473
CHEUNG WOH TECHNOLOGIES (MALAYSIA) SDN. BHD.—See Cheung Woh Technologies Ltd.; *Int'l*, pg. 1473
CHIALIN PRECISION INDUSTRIAL CO., LTD.; *Int'l*, pg. 1475
CITIZEN MACHINERY CO., LTD.—See Citizen Watch Co., Ltd.; *Int'l*, pg. 1624
C. THORREZ INDUSTRIES INC.; *U.S. Private*, pg. 705
CT SYSTEMS—See K-F Management Company, Inc.; *U.S. Private*, pg. 2250
CURTIS SCREW COMPANY, LLC—See Curtis Screw Co., Inc.; *U.S. Private*, pg. 1127
DIRKSEN SCREW PRODUCTS CO.; *U.S. Private*, pg. 1236
DOLA INTERNATIONAL CORP.; *U.S. Private*, pg. 1254
DUPAGE MACHINE PRODUCTS, INC.; *U.S. Private*, pg. 1291
E C MOORE COMPANY; *U.S. Private*, pg. 1300
ELYRIA MANUFACTURING CORP.; *U.S. Private*, pg. 1377
ENG TEKNOLOGI SDN. BHD.—See Giovanni Agnelli B.V.; *Int'l*, pg. 2978
EXLAR CORP.—See Curtiss-Wright Corporation; *U.S. Public*, pg. 612
FB KJEDER AS—See Addtech AB; *Int'l*, pg. 133
FIJNMECHANISCHE INDUSTRIE VENRAY B.V.—See Aalberts N.V.; *Int'l*, pg. 34
FORESTACIONES OPERATIVAS DE MEXICO, S.A. DE C.V.—See Grupo Kuo, S.A.B. de C.V.; *Int'l*, pg. 3131
FRANZ FUNKE ZERSPANUNGSTECHNIK GMBH & CO.—See Gesco AG; *Int'l*, pg. 2945
F-TECH INC. - KAMEYAMA WADA PLANT—See F-Tech Inc.; *Int'l*, pg. 2595
FUJIFILM TECHNO PRODUCTS CO., LTD.—See FUJIFILM Holdings Corporation; *Int'l*, pg. 2825
FUJIMI EUROPE GMBH—See Fujimi Incorporated; *Int'l*, pg. 2829
FUJIMI SHENZHEN TECHNOLOGY CO., LTD.—See Fujimi Incorporated; *Int'l*, pg. 2829
GALGON INDUSTRIES INC.; *U.S. Private*, pg. 1637
GEMINI VALVE; *U.S. Private*, pg. 1658
GIKEN PRECISION ENGINEERING (S) PTE LTD—See GSS Energy Ltd.; *Int'l*, pg. 3150
GIKEN SAKATA (SINGAPORE) LIMITED; *Int'l*, pg. 2972
GKG PRECISION MACHINE CO., LTD.; *Int'l*, pg. 2983
GKN DRIVELINE LEGAZPI—See GKN plc; *Int'l*, pg. 2984
GL GMBH METALL- UND WERKSTATTTECHNIK; *Int'l*, pg. 2986
GLOBAL-TEK-MANUFACTURING LLC— See Crawford United Corporation; *U.S. Public*, pg. 592
GP COMPANIES INC.; *U.S. Private*, pg. 1747
GRIESHABER GMBH & CO. KG—See Grieshaber Holding GmbH; *Int'l*, pg. 3083
GRIMALDIS MEKANISKA VERKSTAD AB—See Grimaldi Industri AB; *Int'l*, pg. 3085
GROZ-BECKERT CARDING CHINA CO., LTD.—See Groz-Beckert KG; *Int'l*, pg. 3113
GROZ-BECKERT CARDING INDIA PRIVATE LIMITED—See Groz-Beckert KG; *Int'l*, pg. 3113
GROZ-BECKERT FRANCE S.A.—See Groz-Beckert KG; *Int'l*, pg. 3113
GROZ-BECKERT (YANTAI) TRADING CO., LTD.—See Groz-Beckert KG; *Int'l*, pg. 3113
HAMAMATSU ELECTRONIC PRESS CO., LTD.—See Hamamatsu Photonics K.K.; *Int'l*, pg. 3235
HARSHA ENGINEERS INTERNATIONAL LIMITED; *Int'l*, pg. 3279
HARTMAN FIJNMECHANISCHE INDUSTRIE B.V.—See *Int'l*, pg. 3280
HAYES SPECIALTY MACHINING, LTD.—See Enerpac Tool Group Corp.; *U.S. Public*, pg. 765
HEADER PRODUCTS INC.; *U.S. Private*, pg. 1891

HERKER INDUSTRIES INC.; *U.S. Private*, pg. 1925
HESTIKA FRANCE S.A.S—See Citizen Watch Co., Ltd.; *Int'l*, pg. 1625
HGEARS PADOVA S.P.A.—See hGears AG; *Int'l*, pg. 3378
HOSCO FITTINGS LLC—See Carlisle Companies Incorporated; *U.S. Public*, pg. 436
HUBL GMBH—See Gesco AG; *Int'l*, pg. 2945
INDUSTRIAL TECTONICS BEARINGS CORPORATION—See RBC Bearings Incorporated; *U.S. Public*, pg. 1766
KADDIS MANUFACTURING CORP.; *U.S. Private*, pg. 2253
KKSP PRECISION MACHINING, LLC—See Pine Grove Holdings, LLC; *U.S. Private*, pg. 3182
KNT MANUFACTURING INC.; *U.S. Private*, pg. 2325
KUO CONCENTRADORA, S.A. DE C.V.—See Grupo Kuo, S.A.B. de C.V.; *Int'l*, pg. 3131
LEYBOLD ITALIA S.R.L.—See Atlas Copco AB; *Int'l*, pg. 683
LEYBOLD UK LTD.—See Atlas Copco AB; *Int'l*, pg. 683
LUTCO, INC.; *U.S. Private*, pg. 2516
MACLEAN CURTIS, LLC - CORNELIUS PLANT—See MacLean-Fogg Company; *U.S. Private*, pg. 2537
MACLEAN CURTIS, LLC—See MacLean-Fogg Company; *U.S. Private*, pg. 2537
MANTH-BROWNELL INC.—See MiddleGround Management, LP; *U.S. Private*, pg. 2711
MASTER AUTOMATIC MACHINE COMPANY, INC.—See MacLean-Fogg Company; *U.S. Private*, pg. 2537
MEADEN SCREW PRODUCTS COMPANY; *U.S. Private*, pg. 2647
MELLING INDUSTRIES INC.—See Melling Tool Company Inc.; *U.S. Private*, pg. 2662
METAL SEAL & PRODUCTS, INC.; *U.S. Private*, pg. 2680
MEYER CANADA INC.—See Meyer Tool Inc.; *U.S. Private*, pg. 2693
MEYER TOOL POLAND SP. Z O. O.—See Meyer Tool Inc.; *U.S. Private*, pg. 2693
MICRO PRECISION GEAR TECHNOLOGY LIMITED—See Zurn Elkay Water Solutions Corporation; *U.S. Public*, pg. 2413
MICROPRECISION INC.; *U.S. Private*, pg. 2704
MIDWEST PRECISION LLC—See Shorehill Capital LLC; *U.S. Private*, pg. 3641
MILLENNIUM MANUFACTURING, INC.—See Bracalente Manufacturing Co., Inc.; *U.S. Private*, pg. 630
MILLTRONICS EUROPE B.V.—See Hurco Companies, Inc.; *U.S. Public*, pg. 1076
MITCHEL & SCOTT MACHINE COMPANY, INC.; *U.S. Private*, pg. 2750
MK CHAMBERS COMPANY; *U.S. Private*, pg. 2753
MT R&O LLC.—See Meyer Tool Inc.; *U.S. Private*, pg. 2693
NANOSCRIBE GMBH—See BICO Group AB; *Int'l*, pg. 1019
NIKKO METALS TAIWAN CO., LTD. - KUANYIN WORKS—See ENEOS Holdings, Inc.; *Int'l*, pg. 2416
NISSIN PRECISION METAL MANUFACTURING LIMITED—See Highway Holdings Limited; *Int'l*, pg. 3389
NOOK INDUSTRIES INC.; *U.S. Private*, pg. 2934
NORTH AMERICAN BOLT & SCREW CO. INC.; *U.S. Private*, pg. 2940
OBERG COSTA RCA, LTDA—See Oberg Industries Corp.; *U.S. Private*, pg. 2986
OBERG INDUSTRIES EUROPE, GMBH—See Oberg Industries Corp.; *U.S. Private*, pg. 2986
OERLIKON LEYBOLD VACUUM (TIANJIN) INTERNATIONAL TRADE CO. LTD.—See Atlas Copco AB; *Int'l*, pg. 683
OMNI COMPONENTS CORP.—See Aterian Investment Management, L.P.; *U.S. Private*, pg. 367
OWIN INDUSTRIAL SDN. BHD.—See Aimflex Berhad; *Int'l*, pg. 233
PHILIPPINE IINO CORPORATION—See Daido Metal Corporation; *Int'l*, pg. 1922
POHLMAN, INC.; *U.S. Private*, pg. 3221
POLI S.R.L.—See Westinghouse Air Brake Technologies Corporation; *U.S. Public*, pg. 2359
PRECINMAC, LP—See Bain Capital, LP; *U.S. Private*, pg. 442
PRECINMAC, LP—See Compass Advisers Group LLC; *U.S. Private*, pg. 998
PRECINMAC, LP—See Pine Island Capital Partners LLC; *U.S. Private*, pg. 3182
PRECISION PLUS, INC.; *U.S. Private*, pg. 3246
PRESCOTT PRODUCTS INC.—See Melling Tool Company Inc.; *U.S. Private*, pg. 2662
PRESSMETALL GUNZENHAUSEN GMBH & CO. KG—See CMP Capital Management-Partners GmbH; *Int'l*, pg. 1671
PRO-MANUFACTURED PRODUCTS, INC.—See Pine Grove Holdings, LLC; *U.S. Private*, pg. 3182
RAYCO TECHNOLOGIES PTE. LTD.—See Parker Hannifin Corporation; *U.S. Public*, pg. 1649
RIMA MANUFACTURING COMPANY; *U.S. Private*, pg. 3437
SARGENT AEROSPACE & DEFENSE, LLC—See RBC Bearings Incorporated; *U.S. Public*, pg. 1766
SBS INDUSTRIES, INC.—See Gladstone Management Corporation; *U.S. Private*, pg. 1705
SCHMEING GMBH & CO. KG—See Groz-Beckert KG; *Int'l*, pg. 3113

SHANGHAI HAKUDO PERCISION MATERIALS CO., LTD.—See Hakudo Co., Ltd.; *Int'l*, pg. 3220
SINOTECH ASIA LTD.—See Groz-Beckert KG; *Int'l*, pg. 3113
STANDARD HORSE NAIL COMPANY, LLC; *U.S. Private*, pg. 3778
STORK - TURBO BLADING - SNEEK—See Fluor Corporation; *U.S. Public*, pg. 860
SUPERIOR PRODUCTS, LLC.; *U.S. Private*, pg. 3880
SWAGELOK HY-LEVEL—See Swagelok Company; *U.S. Private*, pg. 3889
SWISS-TECH, LLC—See News-Press & Gazette Company; *U.S. Private*, pg. 2917
TECHNIQUES LLC—See Kirkwood Holding, Inc.; *U.S. Private*, pg. 2315
THREE M TOOL & MACHINE, INC.; *U.S. Private*, pg. 4164
TL MACHINE.; *U.S. Private*, pg. 4178
TRANS MACHINE TECHNOLOGIES; *U.S. Private*, pg. 4205
TRIANGLE MACHINE PRODUCT CO.—See Freeway Corporation; *U.S. Private*, pg. 1607
TSI FASTENER CO, INC.—See TSI Incorporated; *U.S. Private*, pg. 4253
TSI INSTRUMENT (BEIJING) CO.,LTD.—See TSI Incorporated; *U.S. Private*, pg. 4253
TSI INSTRUMENTS INDIA PRIVATE LIMITED—See TSI Incorporated; *U.S. Private*, pg. 4253
TSI INSTRUMENTS SINGAPORE PTE LTD.—See TSI Incorporated; *U.S. Private*, pg. 4253
VECO B.V.—See Gilde Buy Out Partners B.V.; *Int'l*, pg. 2975
W.A. THOMAS CO.; *U.S. Private*, pg. 4419
WEBER MANUFACTURING & SUPPLIES, INC.; *U.S. Private*, pg. 4465

332722 — BOLT, NUT, SCREW, RIVET, AND WASHER MANUFACTURING

3-V FASTENER CO, INC.—See Stanley Black & Decker, Inc.; *U.S. Public*, pg. 1931
A.AGRATI S.P.A.; *Int'l*, pg. 23
ABLOY MUL-T-LOCK MEXICO S.A. DE C.V.—See ASSA ABLOY AB; *Int'l*, pg. 637
ACCURATE AUTO PARTS, INC.—See Free Flow, Inc.; *U.S. Public*, pg. 884
ACUMENT GLOBAL TECHNOLOGIES INC.—See Fontana Luigi S.p.A.; *Int'l*, pg. 2726
AERO PRECISION PRODUCTS, INC.—See Mistequay Group Ltd.; *U.S. Private*, pg. 2749
AGRATI VIEUX CONDE S.A.S.—See A.Agrati S.p.A.; *Int'l*, pg. 23
AIR INDUSTRIES COMPANY—See Berkshire Hathaway Inc.; *U.S. Public*, pg. 314
ALBERT PASVAHL (GMBH & CO.); *Int'l*, pg. 297
ALLESCO INDUSTRIES INC.; *U.S. Private*, pg. 180
ALPHA STAMPING COMPANY—See The Alpha Group; *U.S. Private*, pg. 3984
AMERICAN JEBCO CORPORATION; *U.S. Private*, pg. 238
ANDERSON MANUFACTURING CO., INC.—See Big Shoulders Capital LLC; *U.S. Private*, pg. 554
ANILLO INDUSTRIES, INC.—See KKR & Co. Inc.; *U.S. Public*, pg. 1262
ARCONIC FASTENING SYSTEMS & RINGS - CARSON—See Howmet Aerospace Inc.; *U.S. Public*, pg. 1061
ARCONIC FASTENING SYSTEMS & RINGS - KINGSTON—See Howmet Aerospace Inc.; *U.S. Public*, pg. 1061
ARCONIC FASTENING SYSTEMS & RINGS - WACO—See Howmet Aerospace Inc.; *U.S. Public*, pg. 1061
ARCONIC GLOBAL FASTENERS LIMITED - LEICESTER—See Howmet Aerospace Inc.; *U.S. Public*, pg. 1062
ARCONIC GLOBAL FASTENERS LIMITED - REDDITCH—See Howmet Aerospace Inc.; *U.S. Public*, pg. 1062
ARCONIC GLOBAL FASTENERS & RINGS, INC.—See Howmet Aerospace Inc.; *U.S. Public*, pg. 1061
ARMATURE AD; *Int'l*, pg. 574
ARNOLD WRAGG LTD.—See ALA SpA; *Int'l*, pg. 289
ASSA ABLOY ENTRANCE SYSTEMS GMBH—See ASSA ABLOY AB; *Int'l*, pg. 633
ASSA ABLOY HONG KONG LIMITED—See ASSA ABLOY AB; *Int'l*, pg. 635
ASSA ABLOY KOREA CO., LTD.—See ASSA ABLOY AB; *Int'l*, pg. 636
ASSA ABLOY POLAND SP. Z O.O.—See ASSA ABLOY AB; *Int'l*, pg. 636
ASSA ABLOY SINGAPORE PTE LTD—See ASSA ABLOY AB; *Int'l*, pg. 636
ASSA ABLOY THAILAND LTD—See ASSA ABLOY AB; *Int'l*, pg. 636
ATF, INC.; *U.S. Private*, pg. 367
ATLAS BOLT & SCREW COMPANY—See Berkshire Hathaway Inc.; *U.S. Public*, pg. 310
AVDEL UK LTD.—See Stanley Black & Decker, Inc.; *U.S. Public*, pg. 1934
AVDEL USA LLC—See Stanley Black & Decker, Inc.; *U.S. Public*, pg. 1934

AVFAST (INDIA) PVT. LTD.—See Stanley Black & Decker, Inc.; *U.S. Public*, pg. 1932
AVIBANK MFG., INC.—See Berkshire Hathaway Inc.; *U.S. Public*, pg. 314
BAND-IT CLAMPS (ASIA) PTE., LTD.—See IDEX Corp; *U.S. Public*, pg. 1089
BAUMANN SPRINGS & PRESSINGS (UK) LTD.—See Baumann Federn AG; *Int'l*, pg. 895
BEAVER AEROSPACE & DEFENSE, INC.—See Heroux-Devtek Inc.; *Int'l*, pg. 3364
BE-BE A.D.; *Int'l*, pg. 932
BELA AUTOMOTIVES LIMITED; *Int'l*, pg. 963
B&G MANUFACTURING CO. INC.; *U.S. Private*, pg. 418
BIRMINGHAM FASTENER & SUPPLY INC. - B-FAST BOLT & SUPPLY DIVISION—See Birmingham Fastener & Supply Inc.; *U.S. Private*, pg. 564
BRAINARD RIVET COMPANY—See Fastener Industries Inc.; *U.S. Private*, pg. 1482
BRISTOL INDUSTRIES LLC—See Tinicum Enterprises, Inc.; *U.S. Private*, pg. 4174
BULTEN FASTENERS AB—See Bulten AB; *Int'l*, pg. 1214
BULTEN FASTENERS (TIANJIN) CO., LTD.—See Bulten AB; *Int'l*, pg. 1214
BULTEN GMBH—See Bulten AB; *Int'l*, pg. 1214
BULTEN HALLSTAHAMMAR AB—See Bulten AB; *Int'l*, pg. 1214
BULTEN LTD.—See Bulten AB; *Int'l*, pg. 1214
BULTEN NORTH AMERICA LLC—See Bulten AB; *Int'l*, pg. 1214
BULTEN POLSKA S.A.—See Bulten AB; *Int'l*, pg. 1214
BULTEN SWEDEN AB—See Bulten AB; *Int'l*, pg. 1214
CAPARO ATLAS FASTENINGS LIMITED—See Caparo Group Ltd.; *Int'l*, pg. 1301
CAPARO FASTENERS LIMITED—See Caparo Group Ltd.; *Int'l*, pg. 1301
CHANDLER PRODUCTS—See MW Industries, Inc.; *U.S. Private*, pg. 2822
CHERRY AEROSPACE LLC—See Berkshire Hathaway Inc.; *U.S. Public*, pg. 315
CHICAGO RIVET & MACHINE COMPANY-JEFFERSON DIVISION—See Chicago Rivet & Machine Company; *U.S. Public*, pg. 488
CHICAGO RIVET & MACHINE COMPANY; *U.S. Public*, pg. 488
CHUN YU BIO-TECH CO., LTD.—See Chun Yu Works & Co., Ltd.; *Int'l*, pg. 1596
CHUN YU WORKS & CO., LTD. - CHIASHING PLANT—See Chun Yu Works & Co., Ltd.; *Int'l*, pg. 1596
CHUN ZU MACHINERY INDUSTRY CO., LTD.—See Chun Yu Works & Co., Ltd.; *Int'l*, pg. 1596
CLENDENIN BROTHERS INC.; *U.S. Private*, pg. 940
CLEVELAND CITY FORGE; *U.S. Private*, pg. 940
COLD HEADING CO.; *U.S. Private*, pg. 965
COLEX INTERNATIONAL, LTD.—See NewAge Industries, Inc.; *U.S. Private*, pg. 2913
CONSOLIDATED METAL PRODUCTS, INC.; *U.S. Private*, pg. 1021
CONTINENTAL/MIDLAND, LLC—See A.Agrati S.p.A.; *Int'l*, pg. 23
DECKER MANUFACTURING CORP.; *U.S. Public*, pg. 645
DEEPAK FASTENERS LIMITED; *Int'l*, pg. 2002
DEEPAK FASTENERS (SHANNON) LTD.—See Deepak Fasteners Limited; *Int'l*, pg. 2002
DEEPAK FASTENERS (U.K.) LTD.—See Deepak Fasteners Limited; *Int'l*, pg. 2002
DESARROLLOS ESPECIALES DE SISTEMAS DE ANCLAJE, S.A.; *Int'l*, pg. 2044
EDSCO FASTENERS, LLC—See Commercial Metals Company; *U.S. Public*, pg. 546
EJR ERICH JAEGER ROZNOV S.R.O.—See AdCapital AG; *Int'l*, pg. 126
ELASTIC STOP NUT CORPORATION OF AMERICA—See KKR & Co. Inc.; *U.S. Public*, pg. 1262
ELGIN FASTENER GROUP—See MW Industries, Inc.; *U.S. Private*, pg. 2822
EMHART TEKNOLOGIES GMBH—See Stanley Black & Decker, Inc.; *U.S. Public*, pg. 1934
ENGTEX INDUSTRIES SDN. BHD.—See Engtex Group Berhad; *Int'l*, pg. 2436
EUROPEAN SPRINGS & PRESSINGS LTD—See Beijer Alma AB; *Int'l*, pg. 943
EYEEGO, LLC; *U.S. Public*, pg. 1453
FABORY MASTERS IN FASTENERS GROUP B.V.—See W.W. Grainger, Inc.; *U.S. Public*, pg. 2320
FABRISTEEL PRODUCTS—See Whitesell Corporation; *U.S. Private*, pg. 4512
FACIL EUROPE BVBA—See Facil Corporate BVBA; *Int'l*, pg. 2600
FACIL NORTH AMERICA, INC.—See Facil Corporate BVBA; *Int'l*, pg. 2600
FARFALLI; *Int'l*, pg. 2618
FAS-LINK CO., LTD.—See Hanwa Co., Ltd.; *Int'l*, pg. 3262
FASTENAL COMPANY; *U.S. Public*, pg. 823
FASTENER JAMHER TAIWAN INC.—See Stanley Black & Decker, Inc.; *U.S. Public*, pg. 1932
FASTRON CO.; *U.S. Private*, pg. 1483
FATIGUE TECHNOLOGY INC.—See Berkshire Hathaway Inc.; *U.S. Public*, pg. 315

FEDERAL SCREW WORKS-BIG RAPIDS DIV.—See Federal Screw Works; *U.S. Public*, pg. 826
FEDERAL SCREW WORKS; *U.S. Public*, pg. 826
FERDINAND GROSS CZECH, S.R.O.—See Ferdinand Gross GmbH & Co. KG; *Int'l*, pg. 2637
FERDINAND GROSS HUNGARY KFT.—See Ferdinand Gross GmbH & Co. KG; *Int'l*, pg. 2637
FERDINAND GROSS POLSKA SP Z O.O.—See Ferdinand Gross GmbH & Co. KG; *Int'l*, pg. 2637
FERDINAND GROSS ROMANIA S.R.L.—See Ferdinand Gross GmbH & Co. KG; *Int'l*, pg. 2637
THE FERRY CAP & SET SCREW COMPANY—See Dubai Holding LLC; *Int'l*, pg. 2218
FIRST LEXINGTON CORP.; *U.S. Private*, pg. 1520
FONTANA LUIGI S.P.A.; *Int'l*, pg. 2726
FORGO FASTENERS—See Valley Fastener Group LLC; *U.S. Private*, pg. 4333
FREEWAY CORPORATION; *U.S. Private*, pg. 1607
FREEWAY ROCKFORD—See Freeway Corporation; *U.S. Private*, pg. 1607
FREEWAY WASHER, LTD.—See Freeway Corporation; *U.S. Private*, pg. 1607
GEM-YEAR INDUSTRIAL CO., LTD.; *Int'l*, pg. 2915
G F D; *Int'l*, pg. 2861
GRADAC FAVRO A.D.; *Int'l*, pg. 3049
GROOV-PIN CORPORATION; *U.S. Private*, pg. 1792
GUANGZHOU EMHART FASTENING SYSTEMS CO., LTD.—See Stanley Black & Decker, Inc.; *U.S. Public*, pg. 1934
GUANGZHOU GEM-YEAR AUTO-PARTS CO., LTD.—See Gem-Year Industrial Co., Ltd.; *Int'l*, pg. 2915
HALIFAX RACK & SCREW CUTTING CO. LTD.; *Int'l*, pg. 3229
HGH HOLDINGS LTD.; *Int'l*, pg. 3378
HIGHLAND BOLT & NUT—See MNP Corporation; *U.S. Private*, pg. 2756
HINDLEY MANUFACTURING COMPANY, INC.; *U.S. Private*, pg. 1948
HI-PERFORMANCE FASTENING SYSTEMS—See American Securities LLC; *U.S. Private*, pg. 249
HIWIN JAPAN—See Hiwin Technologies Corp.; *Int'l*, pg. 3427
HIWIN SINGAPORE PTE. LTD.—See Hiwin Technologies Corp.; *Int'l*, pg. 3427
HIWIN S.R.L.—See Hiwin Technologies Corp.; *Int'l*, pg. 3427
HIWIN USA—See Hiwin Technologies Corp.; *Int'l*, pg. 3427
H&L TOOL COMPANY, INC.—See Chicago Rivet & Machine Company; *U.S. Public*, pg. 488
HOLBROOK MFG., INC.; *U.S. Private*, pg. 1961
HOLO-KROME COMPANY—See Fastenal Company; *U.S. Public*, pg. 824
H. PAULIN & CO., LIMITED—See Hillman Solutions Corp.; *U.S. Public*, pg. 1038
IFASTGROUPE AND COMPANY, LIMITED PARTNERSHIP—See The Heico Companies, L.L.C.; *U.S. Private*, pg. 4050
INFASCO DIVISION—See The Heico Companies, L.L.C.; *U.S. Private*, pg. 4050
INFASTECH CAMCAR MALAYSIA SBD. BHD—See Stanley Black & Decker, Inc.; *U.S. Public*, pg. 1932
INFASTECH (CHINA) LIMITED—See Stanley Black & Decker, Inc.; *U.S. Public*, pg. 1934
INFASTECH DECORAH, LLC—See Stanley Black & Decker, Inc.; *U.S. Public*, pg. 1932
INFASTECH (MALAYSIA) SDN BHD—See Stanley Black & Decker, Inc.; *U.S. Public*, pg. 1932
INFASTECH (SINGAPORE) PTE LTD—See Stanley Black & Decker, Inc.; *U.S. Public*, pg. 1934
INFASTEHC (SINGAPORE) PTE. LTD.—See Stanley Black & Decker, Inc.; *U.S. Public*, pg. 1933
ISELI PRECISION LLC—See Precision Plus, Inc.; *U.S. Private*, pg. 3246
ITW BUILDEX—See Illinois Tool Works Inc.; *U.S. Public*, pg. 1104
ITW POWERTRAIN FASTENING—See Illinois Tool Works Inc.; *U.S. Public*, pg. 1107
JENNMAR CORPORATION OF WEST VIRGINIA INC.—See Frank Calandra, Inc.; *U.S. Private*, pg. 1594
JENNMAR OF KENTUCKY INC.—See Frank Calandra, Inc.; *U.S. Private*, pg. 1594
JOHN HASSALL, LLC—See KKR & Co. Inc.; *U.S. Public*, pg. 1262
KERR LAKESIDE INC.; *U.S. Private*, pg. 2291
KESO GMBH—See ASSA ABLOY AB; *Int'l*, pg. 640
LASEPARTNER A/S—See ASSA ABLOY AB; *Int'l*, pg. 640
LAWSON PRODUCTS, INC.—See Distribution Solutions Group, Inc.; *U.S. Public*, pg. 669
LEDERER GMBH—See Freudenberg SE; *Int'l*, pg. 2789
LESJOFORS INDUSTRIFJADRAR AB—See Beijer Alma AB; *Int'l*, pg. 943
LESJOFORS STOCKHOLMS FJADER AB—See Beijer Alma AB; *Int'l*, pg. 943
LONG-LOK FASTENERS CORPORATION - LOCKING DIVISION WEST—See KKR & Co. Inc.; *U.S. Public*, pg. 1262
LONG-LOK FASTENERS CORPORATION—See KKR & Co. Inc.; *U.S. Public*, pg. 1262
MACLEAN-FOGG CO.; *U.S. Private*, pg. 2537

332722 — BOLT, NUT, SCREW, R...

MATENAER CORPORATION; *U.S. Private*, pg. 2609
METALAC SPS INDUSTRIA E COMERCIO LTDA.—See Berkshire Hathaway Inc.; *U.S. Public*, pg. 315
MNP CORPORATION; *U.S. Private*, pg. 2755
MNP STEEL & WIRE DIVISION—See MNP Corporation; *U.S. Private*, pg. 2756
NATIONAL RIVET & MANUFACTURING CO.; *U.S. Private*, pg. 2862
ND INDUSTRIES INC. - MIDWESTERN FASTENER PROCESSING DIVISION—See H.B. Fuller Company; *U.S. Public*, pg. 978
ND INDUSTRIES INC. - WESTERN FASTENER PROCESSING DIVISION—See H.B. Fuller Company; *U.S. Public*, pg. 978
NSS TECHNOLOGIES, INC.—See Berkshire Hathaway Inc.; *U.S. Public*, pg. 314
NUCOR FASTENERS—See Nucor Corporation; *U.S. Public*, pg. 1554
OHIO NUT & BOLT OF CANADA, LTD.—See Fastener Industries Inc.; *U.S. Private*, pg. 1482
ORBITFORM GROUP, LLC; *U.S. Private*, pg. 3038
PANALOK LIMITED—See Stanley Black & Decker, Inc.; *U.S. Public*, pg. 1933
PAUL R. BRILES INC.—See Berkshire Hathaway Inc.; *U.S. Public*, pg. 315
PENN ENGINEERING & MANUFACTURING CORP.—See Tinicum Enterprises, Inc.; *U.S. Private*, pg. 4174
PENNENGINEERING & MANUFACTURING CORP.—See Tinicum Enterprises, Inc.; *U.S. Private*, pg. 4174
PERMANENT TECHNOLOGIES, INC.; *U.S. Public*, pg. 1676
PIPE SHIELDS, INC.—See Piping Technology & Products Inc.; *U.S. Private*, pg. 3190
PORTLAND BOLT & MANUFACTURING CO., LLC; *U.S. Private*, pg. 3232
POWERS FASTENERS AUSTRALASIA PTY LIMITED—See Stanley Black & Decker, Inc.; *U.S. Public*, pg. 1933
POWERS FASTENERS (NZ) LIMITED & CO.—See Stanley Black & Decker, Inc.; *U.S. Public*, pg. 1933
PRECISION-HAYES INTERNATIONAL—See Enerpac Tool Group Corp.; *U.S. Public*, pg. 766
PRESTIGE STAMPING, INC.—See Auxo Investment Partners, LLC; *U.S. Private*, pg. 402
P&R FASTENERS INC.; *U.S. Private*, pg. 3059
PSM FASTENERS AB—See Bulten AB; *Int'l*, pg. 1214
PSM INTERNATIONAL HOLDINGS LTD.—See Bulten AB; *Int'l*, pg. 1214
PSM INTERNATIONAL LTD.—See Bulten AB; *Int'l*, pg. 1215
PT. MOONLION INDUSTRIES INDONESIA—See Chun Yu Works & Co., Ltd.; *Int'l*, pg. 1596
QRP, INC.—See Stanley Black & Decker, Inc.; *U.S. Public*, pg. 1934
RAIL PRODUCT SOLUTIONS LLC—See Caterpillar, Inc.; *U.S. Public*, pg. 453
RBC BEARINGS INC. - LINEAR PRECISION PRODUCTS DIVISION—See RBC Bearings Incorporated; *U.S. Public*, pg. 1766
RB&W CORPORATION OF CANADA—See Park-Ohio Holdings Corp.; *U.S. Public*, pg. 1640
RB&W-MANUFACTURING LLC—See Park-Ohio Holdings Corp.; *U.S. Public*, pg. 1640
ROBERTSON INC.—See Berkshire Hathaway Inc.; *U.S. Public*, pg. 311
ROCKFORD PRODUCTS, LLC—See BlackEagle Partners, LLC; *U.S. Private*, pg. 573
SEMBLEX CORPORATION; *U.S. Private*, pg. 3603
SHANGHAI CHUN ZU MACHINERY INDUSTRY CO., LTD.—See Chun Yu Works & Co., Ltd.; *Int'l*, pg. 1596
SHANNON PRECISION FASTENER, LLC; *U.S. Private*, pg. 3625
SHUR-LOK COMPANY—See Berkshire Hathaway Inc.; *U.S. Public*, pg. 315
SHUR-LOK INTERNATIONAL S.A.—See Berkshire Hathaway Inc.; *U.S. Public*, pg. 315
SKIFFY GMBH—See Essentra plc; *Int'l*, pg. 2511
SLIDEMATIC INDUSTRIES INC.; *U.S. Private*, pg. 3688
SOUTHERN IMPERIAL, INC.; *U.S. Private*, pg. 3732
SPIROL INTERNATIONAL CORPORATION; *U.S. Private*, pg. 3758
SPS TECHNOLOGIES - GREER STOP NUT—See Berkshire Hathaway Inc.; *U.S. Public*, pg. 315
SPS TECHNOLOGIES LIMITED—See Berkshire Hathaway Inc.; *U.S. Public*, pg. 315
SPS TECHNOLOGIES, LLC—See Berkshire Hathaway Inc.; *U.S. Public*, pg. 314
STANLEY ENGINEERED FASTENING—See Stanley Black & Decker, Inc.; *U.S. Public*, pg. 1934
STELFAST, INC.—See Nautic Partners, LLC; *U.S. Private*, pg. 2871
STILLWATER FASTENERS INC.—See Vertex Distribution; *U.S. Private*, pg. 4369
SUPERIOR WASHER & GASKET CORP.; *U.S. Private*, pg. 3881
TAPER-LOK CORP.—See First Reserve Management, L.P.; *U.S. Private*, pg. 1525
TFP CORPORATION; *U.S. Private*, pg. 3979
TRAMEC HILL FASTENER, LLC—See MacLean-Fogg Company; *U.S. Private*, pg. 2537
TRAYER PRODUCTS, INC.; *U.S. Private*, pg. 4215
TRI-STAR INDUSTRIES, INC.—See American Securities LLC; *U.S. Private*, pg. 250
UNIVERSAL THREAD GRINDING COMPANY; *U.S. Private*, pg. 4307
UTICA WASHERS—See MNP Corporation; *U.S. Private*, pg. 2756
VALLEY FASTENER GROUP LLC - NORTH COAST RIVET DIVISION—See Valley Fastener Group LLC; *U.S. Private*, pg. 4333
VALLEY FASTENER GROUP LLC; *U.S. Private*, pg. 4333
VERTEX DISTRIBUTION; *U.S. Private*, pg. 4369
WATER BLAST MANUFACTURING B.C. LTD.—See Exchange Income Corporation; *Int'l*, pg. 2579
WEJ-IT FASTENING SYSTEMS; *U.S. Private*, pg. 4473
WHITESELL CORPORATION; *U.S. Private*, pg. 4512
WILLIE WASHER MANUFACTURING CO.; *U.S. Private*, pg. 4527

332811 — METAL HEAT TREATING

ACCURATE BRAZING CORPORATION—See Aalberts N.V.; *Int'l*, pg. 33
AEROCRAFT HEAT TREATING CO., INC.—See Berkshire Hathaway Inc.; *U.S. Public*, pg. 313
AHC OBERFLACHENTECHNIK GMBH—See Aalberts N.V.; *Int'l*, pg. 33
AICHELIN GMBH—See Berndorf AG; *Int'l*, pg. 986
AIR WATER NV INC.—See Air Water Inc.; *Int'l*, pg. 239
AIR WATER NV (SHANGHAI) CO., LTD.—See Air Water Inc.; *Int'l*, pg. 239
AIR WATER (THAILAND) CO., LTD.—See Air Water Inc.; *Int'l*, pg. 239
AJAX METAL PROCESSING—See Cold Heading Co.; *U.S. Private*, pg. 965
AJAX TOCCO DE MEXICO, S.A. DE C.V.—See Park-Ohio Holdings Corp.; *U.S. Public*, pg. 1639
ALD THERMAL TREATMENT, INC.—See AMG Critical Materials N.V.; *Int'l*, pg. 425
ALFA-LAVAL (N.Z.) LTD.—See Alfa Laval AB; *Int'l*, pg. 311
ALFA LAVAL S.A.C.I.—See Alfa Laval AB; *Int'l*, pg. 311
ALFA LAVAL SINGAPORE PTE. LTD.—See Alfa Laval AB; *Int'l*, pg. 311
ALFE HEAT TREATING INC.—See Aalberts N.V.; *Int'l*, pg. 35
ANALYTIC STRESS RELIEVING, INC.—See The CapStreet Group LLC; *U.S. Private*, pg. 4004
APPLIED PROCESS, INC.—See High Street Capital Management, Inc.; *U.S. Private*, pg. 1937
AQUA BLASTING CORP.—See Battle Investment Group LLC; *U.S. Private*, pg. 489
ARMSTRONG HEAT TRANSFER GROUP—See Armstrong International, Inc.; *U.S. Private*, pg. 331
ATMOSPHERE HEAT TREATING INC.—See AFC-Holcroft LLC; *U.S. Public*, pg. 121
AUSTEMPER INC.—See AFC-Holcroft LLC; *U.S. Private*, pg. 121
BENTON HARBOR LLC—See Blackstone Inc.; *U.S. Public*, pg. 352
BLUEWATER THERMAL PROCESSION, LLC—See Blackstone Inc.; *U.S. Public*, pg. 352
BODYCOTE ARGENTINA SA—See Bodycote plc; *Int'l*, pg. 1097
BODYCOTE BRASIMET PROCESSAMENTO TERMICO S.A.—See Bodycote plc; *Int'l*, pg. 1097
BODYCOTE FRANCE—See Bodycote plc; *Int'l*, pg. 1097
BODYCOTE HARDIFF B.V.—See Bodycote plc; *Int'l*, pg. 1098
BODYCOTE HARDIFF GMBH—See Bodycote plc; *Int'l*, pg. 1098
BODYCOTE HARDINGSCENTRUM BV—See Bodycote plc; *Int'l*, pg. 1098
BODYCOTE HEAT TREATMENTS LTD.—See Bodycote plc; *Int'l*, pg. 1098
BODYCOTE HIP GMBH—See Bodycote plc; *Int'l*, pg. 1097
BODYCOTE H.I.P. LTD.—See Bodycote plc; *Int'l*, pg. 1097
BODYCOTE HIP N.V.—See Bodycote plc; *Int'l*, pg. 1097
BODYCOTE HOKEZELO KFT—See Bodycote plc; *Int'l*, pg. 1098
BODYCOTE HOT ISOSTATIC PRESSING AB—See Bodycote plc; *Int'l*, pg. 1098
BODYCOTE HOT ISOSTATIC PRESSING—See Bodycote plc; *Int'l*, pg. 1098
BODYCOTE HT S.R.O—See Bodycote plc; *Int'l*, pg. 1098
BODYCOTE IMT INC.—See Bodycote plc; *Int'l*, pg. 1098
BODYCOTE INTERNATIONAL INC.—See Bodycote plc; *Int'l*, pg. 1098
BODYCOTE ISTAS ISIL ISLEM SANAYI VE TICARET AS—See Bodycote plc; *Int'l*, pg. 1098
BODYCOTE ITALIA SRL—See Bodycote plc; *Int'l*, pg. 1098
BODYCOTE JAPAN K.K.—See Bodycote plc; *Int'l*, pg. 1098
BODYCOTE LAMPOKASITTELY OY—See Bodycote plc; *Int'l*, pg. 1098
BODYCOTE (NINGBO) HEAT TREATMENT CO. LIMITED—See Bodycote plc; *Int'l*, pg. 1097
BODYCOTE PLC; *Int'l*, pg. 1097

CORPORATE AFFILIATIONS

BODYCOTE POLSKA SP Z.O.O—See Bodycote plc; *Int'l*, pg. 1098
BODYCOTE RHEINTAL WARMEBEHANDLUNG AG—See Bodycote plc; *Int'l*, pg. 1098
BODYCOTE SAS—See Bodycote plc; *Int'l*, pg. 1098
BODYCOTE SCHWEIZ WARMEBEHANDLUNG AG—See Bodycote plc; *Int'l*, pg. 1098
BODYCOTE THERMAL PROCESSING—See Bodycote plc; *Int'l*, pg. 1098
BODYCOTE THERMAL PROCESSING—See Bodycote plc; *Int'l*, pg. 1098
BODYCOTE TRATAMENTE TERMICE SRL—See Bodycote plc; *Int'l*, pg. 1098
BODYCOTE TRATTAMENTI TERMICI SPA—See Bodycote plc; *Int'l*, pg. 1098
BODYCOTE VARMEBEHANDLING AB—See Bodycote plc; *Int'l*, pg. 1098
BODYCOTE VARMEBEHANDLING A/S—See Bodycote plc; *Int'l*, pg. 1098
BODYCOTE WARMEBEHANDLUNG GMBH—See Bodycote plc; *Int'l*, pg. 1098
BODYCOTE WARMEBEHANDLUNG GMBH—See Bodycote plc; *Int'l*, pg. 1098
BODYCOTE WARMEBEHANDLUNG MARCHTRENK GMBH—See Bodycote plc; *Int'l*, pg. 1098
BODYCOTE WARMEBEHANDLUNG WIEN GMBH—See Bodycote plc; *Int'l*, pg. 1098
BODYCOTE WUXI TECHNOLOGY CO. LIMITED—See Bodycote plc; *Int'l*, pg. 1098
BODYCOTE YTBEHANDLING AB—See Bodycote plc; *Int'l*, pg. 1098
BRADDOCK CARIBE METALLURGICAL, CORP.—See Braddock Metallurgical, Inc.; *U.S. Private*, pg. 631
BRADDOCK HEAT TREATING CO., INC.—See Braddock Metallurgical, Inc.; *U.S. Private*, pg. 631
BRADDOCK METALLURGICAL AEROSPACE - BOYNTON BEACH—See Braddock Metallurgical, Inc.; *U.S. Private*, pg. 631
BRADDOCK METALLURGICAL - ATLANTA—See Braddock Metallurgical, Inc.; *U.S. Private*, pg. 631
BRADDOCK METALLURGICAL - DAYTONA—See Braddock Metallurgical, Inc.; *U.S. Private*, pg. 631
BRADDOCK METALLURGICAL, INC.; *U.S. Private*, pg. 631
BRADDOCK METALLURGICAL - JACKSONVILLE—See Braddock Metallurgical, Inc.; *U.S. Private*, pg. 631
BRADDOCK METALLURGICAL - TAMPA—See Braddock Metallurgical, Inc.; *U.S. Private*, pg. 631
BRANNON STEEL; *Int'l*, pg. 1140
CALIFORNIA BRAZING COMPANY—See Trive Capital Inc.; *U.S. Private*, pg. 4240
CINCINNATI GEARING SYSTEMS INC.; *U.S. Private*, pg. 897
CIRCLE CITY HEAT TREATING, INC.—See Incertec Plating Corp.; *U.S. Private*, pg. 2053
CONTINENTAL HEAT TREATING, INC.; *U.S. Private*, pg. 1029
DANIELI CENTRO COMBUSTION SPA—See Danieli & C, Officine Meccaniche S.p.A.; *Int'l*, pg. 1962
DORRENBERG TRATAMIENTOS TERMICOS SL—See Gesco AG; *Int'l*, pg. 2945
DOWA THERMOTECH CO., LTD.—See Dowa Holdings Co., Ltd.; *Int'l*, pg. 2184
DOWA THERMOTECH MEXICO S.A. DE C.V.—See Dowa Holdings Co., Ltd.; *Int'l*, pg. 2184
DOWA THERMOTECH (THAILAND) CO., LTD.—See Dowa Holdings Co., Ltd.; *Int'l*, pg. 2184
EBTEC CORPORATION—See Aquasium Technology Limited; *Int'l*, pg. 528
ENHANCED POWDER COATING LTD.—See AZZ, Inc.; *U.S. Public*, pg. 259
ERIE STEEL, LTD.; *U.S. Private*, pg. 1420
GKN SINTER METALS LTD.—See GKN plc; *Int'l*, pg. 2985
GOGAS GOCH GMBH & CO. KG; *Int'l*, pg. 3022
HAERTEREI HAUCK GAIDORF GMBH—See Aalberts N.V.; *Int'l*, pg. 34
HAERTEREI HAUCK GMBH—See Aalberts N.V.; *Int'l*, pg. 34
HARTEREI HAUCK SUD GMBH—See Aalberts N.V.; *Int'l*, pg. 34
HAUCK HEAT TREATMENT LIMITED—See Aalberts N.V.; *Int'l*, pg. 34
HEAT & SURFACE TREATMENT B.V.—See Aalberts N.V.; *Int'l*, pg. 34
HEAT TREATING SERVICES CORPORATION OF AMERICA; *U.S. Private*, pg. 1901
HELIOS D.D; *Int'l*, pg. 3330
HI TECMETAL GROUP, INC.; *U.S. Private*, pg. 1931
IONBOND MEXICO - TECATE—See IHI Corporation; *Int'l*, pg. 3605
JARFALLA HARDVERKSTAD AB—See Georg Fischer AG; *Int'l*, pg. 2937
JASCO HEAT TREATING INC—See Jasco Tools Inc.; *U.S. Private*, pg. 2189
LABARGE COATING, LLC—See Womble Company Inc.; *U.S. Private*, pg. 4556
LAKE CITY HEAT TREATING CORP.—See Bodycote plc; *Int'l*, pg. 1098
LUCAS-MILHAUPT BRAZING MATERIALS (SUZHOU) CO.

N.A.I.C.S. INDEX

332812 — METAL COATING, ENGR...

LTD.—See Steel Partners Holdings L.P.; *U.S. Public*, pg. 1943
MAMESTA B V—See Aalberts N.V.; *Int'l*, pg. 35
MC IMPACTS METALS—See Commercial Metals Company; *U.S. Public*, pg. 547
METAL IMPROVEMENT COMPANY, LLC—See Curtiss-Wright Corporation; *U.S. Public*, pg. 612
METALLURGICAL SERVICE INC.—See Miller Consolidated Industries Inc.; *U.S. Private*, pg. 2733
METALS ENGINEERING, INC.; *U.S. Private*, pg. 2682
METATHERM S.A.S.—See Aalberts N.V.; *Int'l*, pg. 35
MILLER CONSOLIDATED INDUSTRIES INC.; *U.S. Private*, pg. 2733
MODERN INDUSTRIES INC., HEAT TREAT DIVISION—See Modern Industries Inc.; *U.S. Private*, pg. 2761
MODERN INDUSTRIES INC. - KERSEY PLANT—See Modern Industries Inc.; *U.S. Private*, pg. 2761
MODERN INDUSTRIES INC.; *U.S. Private*, pg. 2761
NIKKO FUJI PRECISION (WUXI) CO., LTD.—See ENEOS Holdings, Inc.; *Int'l*, pg. 2416
NITRUVID SAS—See Bodycote plc; *Int'l*, pg. 1098
PAULO PRODUCTS COMPANY INC.; *U.S. Private*, pg. 3114
PERFECTION STEEL TREATING—See MNP Corporation; *U.S. Private*, pg. 2756
SCRAP METAL SERVICES, LLC; *U.S. Private*, pg. 3579
SOLAR ATMOSPHERES, INC.; *U.S. Private*, pg. 3707
SPECIALTY STEEL TREATING INC.; *U.S. Private*, pg. 3750
STALSERVICE PRODUKTION I ANDERSTORP AB—See Aalberts N.V.; *Int'l*, pg. 35
SURFACE TREATMENT COMPANY N.V.—See Gimv NV; *Int'l*, pg. 2976
THERMAL TREATMENT CENTER INC.—See HI TecMetal Group, Inc.; *U.S. Private*, pg. 1931
THERMOCOMPACT SA—See Groupe BPCE; *Int'l*, pg. 3097
THORTEX—See Arlington Capital Partners LLC; *U.S. Private*, pg. 327
T. TERMICOS METASA, S.A.—See Aalberts N.V.; *Int'l*, pg. 35
T. TERMICOS SARASKETA, S.L.U—See Aalberts N.V.; *Int'l*, pg. 35
T. TERMICOS SOHETRASA, S.A.—See Aalberts N.V.; *Int'l*, pg. 36
T. TERMICOS TEY, S.L.—See Aalberts N.V.; *Int'l*, pg. 36
T. TERMICOS TRATERH, S.A.U—See Aalberts N.V.; *Int'l*, pg. 36
TTI GROUP LIMITED—See Aalberts N.V.; *Int'l*, pg. 36
VAC-MET, INC.—See Solar Atmospheres, Inc.; *U.S. Private*, pg. 3707
VACUHEAT GMBH—See AMG Critical Materials N.V.; *Int'l*, pg. 425
WALL COLMONOY CORPORATION; *U.S. Private*, pg. 4429
XYONICZ CORPORATION; *U.S. Private*, pg. 4584

332812 — METAL COATING, ENGRAVING (EXCEPT JEWELRY AND SILVERWARE), AND ALLIED SERVICES TO MANUFACTURERS

ADVANCED INDUSTRIAL COATINGS, INC.—See Crawford United Corporation; *U.S. Public*, pg. 592
AHC ITALIA S.R.L.—See Aalberts N.V.; *Int'l*, pg. 33
AHC OBERFLACHENTECHNIK GES.M.B.H.—See Aalberts N.V.; *Int'l*, pg. 33
AHC SURFACE TECHNOLOGY S.A.S.—See Aalberts N.V.; *Int'l*, pg. 33
ALMOND PRODUCTS INC—See Quoin Inc.; *U.S. Private*, pg. 3329
ALPHAFORM LTD—See Proto Labs, Inc.; *U.S. Public*, pg. 1729
THE ALPHA GROUP; *U.S. Private*, pg. 3984
ALUMINUM MAINTENANCE SYSTEMS OF TEXAS, INC.; *U.S. Private*, pg. 211
AMG COATING TECHNOLOGIES GMBH—See AMG Critical Materials N.V.; *Int'l*, pg. 425
AMZA LIMITED—See Element Solutions Inc.; *U.S. Public*, pg. 725
ANDOVER HEALTHCARE, INC.—See Milliken & Company; *U.S. Private*, pg. 2737
ANTI-FRICTION ENTERPRISES 1985—See Magni Group Inc.; *U.S. Private*, pg. 2547
A.O. SMITH - PROTECTIVE COATINGS DIVISION—See A. O. Smith Corporation; *U.S. Public*, pg. 11
APCO INDUSTRIES CO. LIMITED; *Int'l*, pg. 508
APS IRELAND, INC.—See Hancom, Inc.; *Int'l*, pg. 3242
APS MATERIALS, INC.—See Hancom, Inc.; *Int'l*, pg. 3242
ARCELORMITTAL DUDELANGE S.A.—See GFG Alliance Limited; *Int'l*, pg. 2956
ARIZONA GALVANIZING INC.—See AZZ, Inc.; *U.S. Public*, pg. 259
ARKANSAS GALVANIZING INC.—See AZZ, Inc.; *U.S. Public*, pg. 259
ATLAS PEN & PENCIL CORP.; *U.S. Private*, pg. 379
AZTEC CROWLEY—See AZZ, Inc.; *U.S. Public*, pg. 259
AZTEC, INC.—See Activar, Inc.; *U.S. Private*, pg. 68
AZTEC INDUSTRIES, INC.—See AZZ, Inc.; *U.S. Public*, pg. 259
AZTEC MANUFACTURING - WASKOM PARTNERSHIP, LTD.—See AZZ, Inc.; *U.S. Public*, pg. 259
AZZ GALVANIZING – CHATTANOOGA LLC—See AZZ, Inc.; *U.S. Public*, pg. 259
AZZ GALVANIZING - BIG SPRING, LLC—See AZZ, Inc.; *U.S. Public*, pg. 258
AZZ GALVANIZING - CHATTANOOGA LLC—See AZZ, Inc.; *U.S. Public*, pg. 258
AZZ GALVANIZING - KENNEDALE, LLC—See AZZ, Inc.; *U.S. Public*, pg. 258
AZZ GALVANIZING - KOSCIUSKO, LLC—See AZZ, Inc.; *U.S. Public*, pg. 258
AZZ GALVANIZING - MORGAN CITY, LLC—See AZZ, Inc.; *U.S. Public*, pg. 259
AZZ GALVANIZING - NASHVILLE—See AZZ, Inc.; *U.S. Public*, pg. 259
AZZ GALVANIZING - NEBRASKA, LLC—See AZZ, Inc.; *U.S. Public*, pg. 259
AZZ GALVANIZING - SAN ANTONIO, LLC—See AZZ, Inc.; *U.S. Public*, pg. 259
AZZ GALVANIZING SERVICES—See AZZ, Inc.; *U.S. Public*, pg. 259
AZZ SURFACE TECHNOLOGIES – ROWLETT LLC—See AZZ, Inc.; *U.S. Public*, pg. 259
AZZ SURFACE TECHNOLOGIES - GAINESVILLE LLC—See AZZ, Inc.; *U.S. Public*, pg. 259
AZZ SURFACE TECHNOLOGIES - GARLAND SOUTH LLC—See AZZ, Inc.; *U.S. Public*, pg. 259
AZZ SURFACE TECHNOLOGIES - TAMPA LLC—See AZZ, Inc.; *U.S. Public*, pg. 259
BARSON COMPOSITES CORP.; *U.S. Private*, pg. 482
BECK ARNLEY HOLDINGS LLC—See Apollo Global Management, Inc.; *U.S. Public*, pg. 160
BODYCOTE SINGAPORE PTE LTD—See Bodycote plc; *Int'l*, pg. 1098
BON CHEF INC.; *U.S. Private*, pg. 612
BRIGHTON-BEST INTERNATIONAL, INC.; *U.S. Private*, pg. 652
CACTUS COATINGS, INC.—See Marck & Associates, Inc.; *U.S. Private*, pg. 2571
CENTURY CORROSION TECHNOLOGIES, INC.—See First Reserve Management, L.P.; *U.S. Private*, pg. 1525
CHAMPION AMERICA; *U.S. Private*, pg. 846
CHEMART COMPANY; *U.S. Private*, pg. 871
CINCINNATI THERMAL SPRAY, INC.; *U.S. Private*, pg. 898
CN PRECISION CASING LIMITED—See CN Innovations Holdings Limited; *Int'l*, pg. 1673
COMMERCIAL COATING SERVICES INTERNATIONAL, LLC—See New Mountain Capital, LLC; *U.S. Private*, pg. 2899
COMMERCIAL STEEL TREATING CORP.; *U.S. Private*, pg. 984
CORTECROS D.O.O.—See Cortec Corporation; *U.S. Private*, pg. 1060
THE CROWN GROUP CO.—See PPG Industries, Inc.; *U.S. Public*, pg. 1710
CRYSTAL FINISHING SYSTEMS, INC.; *U.S. Private*, pg. 1115
CURTIS METAL FINISHING CO., INC.—See Commercial Steel Treating Corp.; *U.S. Private*, pg. 984
CYBERSHIELD, INC.; *U.S. Private*, pg. 1133
DEPOR INDUSTRIES INC.—See Magni Group Inc.; *U.S. Private*, pg. 2547
DETROIT ELECTRO-COATINGS CO. LLC; *U.S. Private*, pg. 1216
DEUTSCHE NICKEL GMBH; *Int'l*, pg. 2071
DEWAYNE'S QUALITY METAL COATINGS, LLC.; *U.S. Private*, pg. 1219
DIASFIN SA; *Int'l*, pg. 2106
DIESEL MARINE INTERNATIONAL DUBAI L.L.C.—See DMI UK Ltd.; *Int'l*, pg. 2146
DIVERSIFIED COATINGS INC.; *U.S. Private*, pg. 1241
DMI UK LTD.; *Int'l*, pg. 2145
DOUBLE G COATINGS COMPANY, L.P.—See Cleveland-Cliffs, Inc.; *U.S. Public*, pg. 514
DOUBLE G COATINGS COMPANY, L.P.—See United States Steel Corporation; *U.S. Public*, pg. 2236
DURALLOY AG—See Aalberts N.V.; *Int'l*, pg. 34
DURALLOY SUD GMBH—See Aalberts N.V.; *Int'l*, pg. 34
EASTERN ETCHING & MANUFACTURING CO.; *U.S. Private*, pg. 1319
ELECTRIC COATING TECHNOLOGIES, LLC—See Aurora Capital Group, LLC; *U.S. Private*, pg. 393
ELLISON SURFACE TECHNOLOGIES, INC.—See Bodycote plc; *Int'l*, pg. 1098
ESCO SPECIALTY COATINGS (GUANGZHOU) CO., LTD.—See Eternal Materials Co., Ltd.; *Int'l*, pg. 2520
EVAPORATED METAL FILMS CORPORATION—See Dynasil Corporation of America; *U.S. Private*, pg. 1299
FEINTOOL TENNESSEE, INC.—See Artemis Holding AG; *Int'l*, pg. 582
FERRO CORPORATION - EDISON SPECIALTY PLASTICS PLANT—See American Securities LLC; *U.S. Private*, pg. 251
FERRO KAPLAMA MALZEMELERI LIMITED SIRKETI—See American Securities LLC; *U.S. Private*, pg. 252
FRANK HILL ASSOCIATES; *U.S. Private*, pg. 1594
FRONTKEN (EAST MALAYSIA) SDN. BHD. - KUCHING PLANT—See Frontken Corporation Berhad; *Int'l*, pg. 2796
FRONTKEN (JOHOR) SDN. BHD.—See Frontken Corporation Berhad; *Int'l*, pg. 2796
FRONTKEN MALAYSIA SDN. BHD. - KULIM PLANT—See Frontken Corporation Berhad; *Int'l*, pg. 2796
FRONTKEN MALAYSIA SDN. BHD. - SHAH ALAM PLANT—See Frontken Corporation Berhad; *Int'l*, pg. 2796
FRONTKEN PHILIPPINES INC—See Frontken Corporation Berhad; *Int'l*, pg. 2796
FRONTKEN (SINGAPORE) PTE. LTD. - JURONG PLANT 1—See Frontken Corporation Berhad; *Int'l*, pg. 2796
FRONTKEN (THAILAND) CO. LTD.—See Frontken Corporation Berhad; *Int'l*, pg. 2796
GALVANO DIVISION—See The Heico Companies, L.L.C.; *U.S. Private*, pg. 4050
GAUTIER SPECIALTY METALS, LLC—See Reserve Group Management Company; *U.S. Private*, pg. 3404
GENERAL MAGNAPLATE CALIFORNIA—See General Magnaplate Corporation; *U.S. Private*, pg. 1665
GENERAL MAGNAPLATE CANADA LTD.—See General Magnaplate Corporation; *U.S. Private*, pg. 1666
GENERAL MAGNAPLATE CORPORATION; *U.S. Private*, pg. 1665
GENERAL MAGNAPLATE TEXAS—See General Magnaplate Corporation; *U.S. Private*, pg. 1666
GEORGE INDUSTRIES, INC.—See Valmont Industries, Inc.; *U.S. Public*, pg. 2273
GM NAMEPLATE INC.—See The Goldman Sachs Group, Inc.; *U.S. Public*, pg. 2080
GULF COAST GALVANIZING INC.—See AZZ, Inc.; *U.S. Public*, pg. 259
GUTMANN ALUMINIUM DRAHT GMBH—See ALCO Hellas S.A.; *Int'l*, pg. 301
HANDY & HARMAN LTD.—See Steel Partners Holdings L.P.; *U.S. Public*, pg. 1942
HAUZER TECHNO COATING B.V.—See IHI Corporation; *Int'l*, pg. 3604
H.C. STARCK, INC.—See Advent International Corporation; *U.S. Private*, pg. 102
H.C. STARCK, INC.—See The Carlyle Group Inc.; *U.S. Public*, pg. 2047
HG YANGON COMPANY LIMITED—See HG Metal Manufacturing Limited; *Int'l*, pg. 3375
HILL & SMITH INFRASTRUCTURE PRODUCTS INDIA PRIVATE LIMITED—See Hill & Smith PLC; *Int'l*, pg. 3391
HILONG PETROPIPE CO., LTD.—See Hilong Holding Limited; *Int'l*, pg. 3393
HOBSON GALVANIZING, INC.—See AZZ, Inc.; *U.S. Public*, pg. 259
IMPACT COATINGS AB—See Duroc AB; *Int'l*, pg. 2229
IMPREGLON, INC.—See Aalberts N.V.; *Int'l*, pg. 34
IMPREGLON, INC. - WOONSOCKET—See Aalberts N.V.; *Int'l*, pg. 34
INDUSTRIAL GALVANIZERS AMERICA, INC—See Valmont Industries, Inc.; *U.S. Public*, pg. 2273
INDUSTRIAL GALVANIZERS CORPORATION PTY. LTD.—See Valmont Industries, Inc.; *U.S. Public*, pg. 2273
I/N KOTE L.P.—See Cleveland-Cliffs, Inc.; *U.S. Public*, pg. 514
I/N TEK L.P.—See Cleveland-Cliffs, Inc.; *U.S. Public*, pg. 514
INTERCLAD—See The Egan Companies; *U.S. Private*, pg. 4025
INTERNATIONAL GALVANIZERS LP—See AZZ, Inc.; *U.S. Public*, pg. 259
IONBOND CONSETT—See IHI Corporation; *Int'l*, pg. 3605
JIANGSU TSC COATING CO., LTD.—See Hilong Holding Limited; *Int'l*, pg. 3393
JUPITER ALUMINUM CORPORATION - JUPITER COIL COATING DIVISION—See Jupiter Aluminum Corporation; *U.S. Private*, pg. 2245
K. COATINGS, LLC; *U.S. Private*, pg. 2251
KG COATING LIMITED—See Berkshire Hathaway Inc.; *U.S. Public*, pg. 314
KOREA PLASMA TECHNOLOGY U CO., LTD.—See Alutec Co., Ltd.; *Int'l*, pg. 401
KORNS GALVANIZING CO., INC.—See Hill & Smith PLC; *Int'l*, pg. 3392
L.B. FOSTER BALL WINCH, INC.—See L.B. Foster Company; *U.S. Public*, pg. 1278
LIBERTY COATING COMPANY LLC; *U.S. Private*, pg. 2443
MAGNA-TECH MANUFACTURING CORPORATION—See Henkel AG & Co. KGaA; *Int'l*, pg. 3353
MAGNI AMERICA DO SUL—See Magni Group Inc.; *U.S. Private*, pg. 2548
MAGNI EUROPE GMBH & CO. KG—See Magni Group Inc.; *U.S. Private*, pg. 2548
MAJESTIC ENGRAVING CORP.—See Schwaab Inc.; *U.S. Private*, pg. 3572
MANAR, INC. - PLASFINCO DIVISION—See Manar, Inc.; *U.S. Private*, pg. 2561
MANAR, INC. - TENNPLASCO - LAFAYETTE

3525

332812 — METAL COATING, ENGR...

DIVISION—See Manar, Inc.; *U.S. Private*, pg. 2561
MATERIAL SCIENCES CORPORATION - OHIO FACILITY—See Sky Island Capital LLC; *U.S. Private*, pg. 3684
MATERIAL SCIENCES CORPORATION—See Sky Island Capital LLC; *U.S. Private*, pg. 3684
MATERIAL SCIENCES CORPORATION - TORONTO FACILITY—See Sky Island Capital LLC; *U.S. Private*, pg. 3684
MATRIX SERVICE, INC.—See Matrix Service Company; *U.S. Public*, pg. 1397
MATTHEWS INTERNATIONAL (EFN) GMBH—See Matthews International Corporation; *U.S. Public*, pg. 1399
MATTHEWS INTERNATIONAL S.P.A.—See Matthews International Corporation; *U.S. Public*, pg. 1400
MAXFORD TECHNOLOGY LIMITED—See CN Innovations Holdings Limited; *Int'l*, pg. 1673
MEGGITT ADVANCED COMPOSITES LTD.—See Parker Hannifin Corporation; *U.S. Public*, pg. 1641
MESOCOAT INC.—See ABAKAN INC.; *U.S. Private*, pg. 34
METAL COATERS - HOUSTON PLANT—See Clayton, Dubilier & Rice, LLC; *U.S. Private*, pg. 921
METAL COATERS LP—See Clayton, Dubilier & Rice, LLC; *U.S. Private*, pg. 921
METAL COATERS OF GEORGIA—See Clayton, Dubilier & Rice, LLC; *U.S. Private*, pg. 921
METAL COATERS OF MISSISSIPPI—See Clayton, Dubilier & Rice, LLC; *U.S. Private*, pg. 921
METALLICS, INC.; *U.S. Private*, pg. 2681
METATHERM 74 S.A.S.—See Aalberts N.V.; *Int'l*, pg. 35
MICRO-AIR (TIANJIN) TECHNOLOGY CO., LTD.—See Frencken Group Limited; *Int'l*, pg. 2773
MIDWESTERN RUST PROOF CO.; *U.S. Private*, pg. 2724
MILAMAR COATINGS, LLC—See PPG Industries, Inc.; *U.S. Public*, pg. 1707
MILLER PRODUCTS INC.—See Quoin Inc.; *U.S. Private*, pg. 3329
MOLD-TECH S.A.R.L.—See Standex International; *U.S. Public*, pg. 1930
ND COMPOUND BLENDING DIVISION/MICHIGAN—See H.B. Fuller Company; *U.S. Public*, pg. 978
ND INDUSTRIES INC.—See H.B. Fuller Company; *U.S. Public*, pg. 978
ND INDUSTRIES—See H.B. Fuller Company; *U.S. Public*, pg. 978
NORTH AMERICAN GALVANIZING & COATINGS, INC.—See AZZ, Inc.; *U.S. Public*, pg. 259
NYLOK CORPORATION; *U.S. Private*, pg. 2976
OLD COUNTRY MILLWORK INC; *U.S. Private*, pg. 3008
OWEN INDUSTRIES, INC. - NORTHERN PLAINS FINISHING DIVISION—See Owen Industries, Inc.; *U.S. Private*, pg. 3054
PENTAGON COATING TECHNOLOGIES SDN. BHD.—See HPMT Holding Berhad; *Int'l*, pg. 3501
PLASMA TECHNOLOGY, INCORPORATED; *U.S. Private*, pg. 3198
POWDERCOAT SERVICES, INC.—See Meridian General, LLC; *U.S. Private*, pg. 2672
POWDER COTE II INC.; *U.S. Private*, pg. 3236
PRECISION COATING CO., INC.—See Katahdin Industries, Inc.; *U.S. Private*, pg. 2264
PREMIER GALVANIZING LIMITED—See Hill & Smith PLC; *Int'l*, pg. 3392
PRO-TEC COATING COMPANY, INC.—See United States Steel Corporation; *U.S. Public*, pg. 2236
PROTECTIVE COATINGS INC.—See Berkshire Hathaway Inc.; *U.S. Public*, pg. 314
PT FRONTKEN INDONESIA—See Frontken Corporation Berhad; *Int'l*, pg. 2796
PURE METAL GALVANIZING, ULC—See Valmont Industries, Inc.; *U.S. Public*, pg. 2274
QUICK TANKS INC.; *U.S. Private*, pg. 3326
RADIUS AEROSPACE, INC. - SHELBYVILLE—See Arlington Capital Partners LLC; *U.S. Private*, pg. 328
RIAG OBERFLACHENTECHNIK AG—See Aalberts N.V.; *Int'l*, pg. 35
ROESCH INC.; *U.S. Private*, pg. 3470
SHANGHAI TUBE-COTE PETROLEUM PIPE COATING CO., LTD.—See Hilong Holding Limited; *Int'l*, pg. 3393
SHERWIN-WILLIAMS CO. - INDUSTRIAL COATINGS DIVISION—See The Sherwin-Williams Company; *U.S. Public*, pg. 2128
SICHUAN HILONG PETROLEUM TECHNOLOGY CO., LTD.—See Hilong Holding Limited; *Int'l*, pg. 3393
SIGNCASTER CORPORATION; *U.S. Private*, pg. 3650
SILVERTIP ASSOCIATES, INC.—See Vance Street Capital LLC; *U.S. Private*, pg. 4342
SOUTH ATLANTIC LLC; *U.S. Private*, pg. 3719
SOUTHWEST UNITED CANADA, INC.—See Berkshire Hathaway Inc.; *U.S. Public*, pg. 315
SOUTHWEST UNITED DE MEXICO, S.A. DE C.V.—See Berkshire Hathaway Inc.; *U.S. Public*, pg. 315
SOUTHWEST UNITED INDUSTRIES, INC.—See Berkshire Hathaway Inc.; *U.S. Public*, pg. 315
SPECIALIST PROTECTIVE COATINGS LIMITED—See Billington Holdings Plc; *Int'l*, pg. 1031
SPECTRUM INDUSTRIES, INC.; *U.S. Private*, pg. 3752

SPRAYTEK, INC.—See Magni Group Inc.; *U.S. Private*, pg. 2548
STANDEX INTERNATIONAL GMBH, MOLD-TECH DIVISION SOUTH—See Standex International; *U.S. Public*, pg. 1931
STANDEX INTERNATIONAL GMBH, MOLD-TECH NORTH (GERMANY)—See Standex International; *U.S. Public*, pg. 1931
STANDEX INTERNATIONAL LIMITED—See Standex International; *U.S. Public*, pg. 1931
STANDEX INTERNATIONAL S.A./MOLD-TECH DIVISION—See Standex International; *U.S. Public*, pg. 1931
STANDEX INTERNATIONAL S.A.—See Standex International; *U.S. Public*, pg. 1931
STANDEX INTERNATIONAL S.R.L. - MOLD-TECH DIVISION—See Standex International; *U.S. Public*, pg. 1931
STAR SHINE MARKETING SDN. BHD.—See BlueScope Steel Limited; *Int'l*, pg. 1073
S+T GMBH & CO. KG—See Matthews International Corporation; *U.S. Public*, pg. 1399
STI HARTCHROM AG—See Arbonia AG; *Int'l*, pg. 538
STI HARTCHROM INC.—See Arbonia AG; *Int'l*, pg. 538
STI SURFACE TECHNOLOGIES INTERNATIONAL HOLDING AG—See Arbonia AG; *Int'l*, pg. 538
ST.LA. S.R.L.—See LCI Industries; *U.S. Public*, pg. 1296
ST. LOUIS METALLIZING CO.—See CIC Group, Inc.; *U.S. Private*, pg. 896
STUPP COATINGS, LLC—See Stupp Bros., Inc.; *U.S. Private*, pg. 3844
SUN BELT COATING, LLC—See Aalberts N.V.; *Int'l*, pg. 34
TEXAS INTERNAL PIPE COATING, LLC—See Hilong Holding Limited; *Int'l*, pg. 3393
THERMAL SPRAY SOLUTIONS, INC.—See Palladium Equity Partners, LLC; *U.S. Private*, pg. 3078
TIANJIN TUBE-COTE PETROLEUM PIPE COATING CO., LTD.—See Hilong Holding Limited; *Int'l*, pg. 3393
TRANSCO INC.; *U.S. Public*, pg. 4207
TRANSCO PRODUCTS INC.—See Transco Inc.; *U.S. Private*, pg. 4207
TREMCO CPG GERMANY GMBH—See RPM International Inc.; *U.S. Public*, pg. 1820
TREMCO CPG (INDIA) PRIVATE LIMITED—See RPM International Inc.; *U.S. Public*, pg. 1820
TRICOR DIRECT INC.—See Brady Corporation; *U.S. Public*, pg. 379
UNICOTE CORPORATION—See Howard Finishing LLC; *U.S. Private*, pg. 1994
UNITED GALVANIZING, INC.—See Valmont Industries, Inc.; *U.S. Public*, pg. 2274
UNITED WESTERN ENTERPRISES, INC.—See Ancor Holdings, L.P.; *U.S. Private*, pg. 275
VALLOUREC DRILLING PRODUCTS USA, INC.—See NOV, Inc.; *U.S. Public*, pg. 1547
VALMONT COATINGS WEST POINT GALVANIZING—See Valmont Industries, Inc.; *U.S. Public*, pg. 2274
VALSPAR POWDER COATINGS LTD.—See The Sherwin-Williams Company; *U.S. Public*, pg. 2129
VAPOR TECHNOLOGIES, INC.—See Masco Corporation; *U.S. Public*, pg. 1392
VIRTEK VISION INTERNATIONAL, INC.—See Vector Capital Management, L.P.; *U.S. Public*, pg. 4351
VITALINK KOREA CO., LTD.—See CN Innovations Holdings Limited; *Int'l*, pg. 1673
VITALINK THIN FILM TECHNOLOGY (SUZHOU) CO., LTD.—See CN Innovations Holdings Limited; *Int'l*, pg. 1673
VITALINK VIETNAM CO., LTD.—See CN Innovations Holdings Limited; *Int'l*, pg. 1673
VOIGT & SCHWEITZER LLC—See Hill & Smith PLC; *Int'l*, pg. 3392
VORTEQ ALLENTOWN, LLC—See Vorteq Coil Finishers, LLC; *U.S. Private*, pg. 4413
VORTEQ COIL FINISHERS, LLC; *U.S. Private*, pg. 4413
VORTEQ JACKSON, LLC—See Vorteq Coil Finishers, LLC; *U.S. Private*, pg. 4413
VORTEQ VALENCIA, LLC—See Vorteq Coil Finishers, LLC; *U.S. Private*, pg. 4413
VORTEQ WOODSTOCK, LLC—See Vorteq Coil Finishers, LLC; *U.S. Private*, pg. 4413
V&S AMBOY GALVANIZING LLC—See Hill & Smith PLC; *Int'l*, pg. 3392
V&S BRISTOL GALVANIZING LLC—See Hill & Smith PLC; *Int'l*, pg. 3392
V&S COLUMBUS GALANIZING LLC—See Hill & Smith PLC; *Int'l*, pg. 3392
V&S DETROIT GALVANIZING LLC—See Hill & Smith PLC; *Int'l*, pg. 3392
VULCAN PAINTERS INC.; *U.S. Private*, pg. 4416
WESTSIDE GALVANIZING SERVICES, INC.—See AZZ, Inc.; *U.S. Public*, pg. 259
WETZEL SP. Z.O.O.—See Matthews International Corporation; *U.S. Public*, pg. 1401
WINSKY INDUSTRY HONG KONG LIMITED—See CN Innovations Holdings Limited; *Int'l*, pg. 1673
WOMBLE COMPANY INC.; *U.S. Private*, pg. 4556
XCCENT INC.; *U.S. Private*, pg. 4580

332813 — ELECTROPLATING, PLATING, POLISHING, ANODIZING, AND COLORING

A-1 PLATING INC.; *U.S. Private*, pg. 21
ABBEY METAL FINISHING COMPANY LIMITED—See Camellia Plc; *Int'l*, pg. 1270
ABRAMS AIRBORNE MANUFACTURING, INC.; *U.S. Private*, pg. 39
ACME GALVANIZING, INC.—See AZZ, Inc.; *U.S. Public*, pg. 259
ADTEC ELECTROPLATING, INC.; *U.S. Private*, pg. 83
ADVANCED GRAPHICS TECHNOLOGIES, INC.—See Rotation Dynamics Corp.; *U.S. Private*, pg. 3486
AHC BENELUX B.V.—See Aalberts N.V.; *Int'l*, pg. 33
ALCO CAD-NICKEL CORP.; *U.S. Private*, pg. 153
ALLIED FINISHING INC.—See Decorative Castings Inc.; *U.S. Private*, pg. 1188
ALL METALS PROCESSING OF ORANGE COUNTY, LLC; *U.S. Private*, pg. 171
ALUMINUM COIL ANODIZING CORP.; *U.S. Private*, pg. 211
ANOPLATE CORPORATION; *U.S. Private*, pg. 285
AOTCO METAL FINISHING LLC; *U.S. Private*, pg. 289
APERAM STAINLESS SERVICES & SOLUTIONS USA, LLC—See Aperam SA; *Int'l*, pg. 508
ARCELORMITTAL GENT—See ArcelorMittal S.A.; *Int'l*, pg. 544
AREWAY LLC; *U.S. Private*, pg. 319
ARLINGTON PLATING COMPANY—See Enameled Steel; *U.S. Private*, pg. 1389
ARLINGTON PLATING COMPANY—See Midwestern Rust Proof Co.; *U.S. Private*, pg. 2724
BLUE STREAK FINISHERS, LTD.—See Coast Plating, Inc.; *U.S. Private*, pg. 954
BODYCOTE COATING CENTRUM BV—See Bodycote plc; *Int'l*, pg. 1097
BODYCOTE METALLURGICAL COATINGS LTD.—See Bodycote plc; *Int'l*, pg. 1098
BONNELL ALUMINUM (ELKHART), INC.—See Tredegar Corporation; *U.S. Public*, pg. 2187
B&T METALS CO.; *U.S. Private*, pg. 419
CADON PLATING COMPANY; *U.S. Private*, pg. 713
CEPLUS CO., LTD.—See Chuo Spring Co., Ltd.; *Int'l*, pg. 1599
CHEM-PLATE INDUSTRIES INC.; *U.S. Private*, pg. 871
CHEMTEC CHEMICALS B.V.—See RPM International Inc.; *U.S. Public*, pg. 1816
CHUGAI MINING CO. LTD. - MOCHIKOSHI PLANT—See Chugai Mining Co. Ltd.; *Int'l*, pg. 1594
COAST PLATING, INC.; *U.S. Private*, pg. 954
COIL SA/NV—See Coil S.A./N.V.; *Int'l*, pg. 1696
DAY-MET FINISHING CO. INC.—See Miller Consolidated Industries Inc.; *U.S. Private*, pg. 2733
DIEHL METAL APPLICATIONS GMBH—See Diehl Stiftung & Co. KG; *Int'l*, pg. 2115
DMI AUTOMOTIVE INC.—See DMI UK Ltd.; *Int'l*, pg. 2145
DMI GUANGZHOU LTD—See DMI UK Ltd.; *Int'l*, pg. 2145
DONHAD PTY. LTD.—See Valmont Industries, Inc.; *U.S. Public*, pg. 2273
EAST SIDE PLATING INC.; *U.S. Private*, pg. 1317
ELECTRO CHEMICAL FINISHING CO.; *U.S. Private*, pg. 1353
ELECTROCHEM SOLUTIONS, LLC—See Aterian Investment Management, L.P.; *U.S. Private*, pg. 366
ELECTRO-COATINGS OF CALIFORNIA INC.—See Acme Holdings, Inc.; *U.S. Private*, pg. 61
ELECTRO-COATINGS OF IOWA, INC.—See Acme Holdings, Inc.; *U.S. Private*, pg. 61
ELECTRO-COATINGS OF TEXAS, INC.—See Acme Holdings, Inc.; *U.S. Private*, pg. 61
ELECTRO PRIME INC.; *U.S. Private*, pg. 1353
ELM PLATING CO.; *U.S. Private*, pg. 1376
ENAMELED STEEL; *U.S. Private*, pg. 1389
ENDURO INDUSTRIES, INC.—See Black Diamond Capital Holdings, LLC; *U.S. Private*, pg. 570
ENTHONE SP. Z.O.O.—See Element Solutions Inc.; *U.S. Public*, pg. 726
ERIEVIEW METAL TREATING CO.; *U.S. Private*, pg. 1421
FOUNTAIN PLATING CO., INC.—See British Columbia Investment Management Corp.; *Int'l*, pg. 1170
GALVANOTECHNIK BAUM GMBH; *Int'l*, pg. 2876
GENERAL METAL FINISHING LLC—See NN, Inc.; *U.S. Public*, pg. 1531
GEORGE KOCH SONS EUROPE LTD.—See Koch Enterprises, Inc.; *U.S. Private*, pg. 2326
GOLDGROUP MINING INC.; *Int'l*, pg. 3033
GREENWOOD FABRICATING & PLATING; *U.S. Private*, pg. 1781
HAUSNER HARD - CHROME, INC.; *U.S. Private*, pg. 1880
HI-TECH METALS, INC.—See ESCO Technologies, Inc.; *U.S. Public*, pg. 794
HOHMAN PLATING & MANUFACTURING, LLC—See KKR & Co. Inc.; *U.S. Public*, pg. 1262
HYTEK FINISHES INC.—See TransDigm Group Incorporated; *U.S. Public*, pg. 2181
INCERTEC PLATING CORP.; *U.S. Private*, pg. 2053
INDIANA PICKLING & PROCESSING COMPANY—See Reliance Steel & Aluminum Co.; *U.S. Public*, pg. 1780

N.A.I.C.S. INDEX

332911 — INDUSTRIAL VALVE MA...

INDIANHEAD PLATING, INC.—See Aterian Investment Management, L.P.; *U.S. Private*, pg. 366
INDUPLATE, LLC—See Greystone Incorporated; *U.S. Private*, pg. 1786
INTERNATIONAL HARDCOAT, INC.; *U.S. Private*, pg. 2117
INTERPLEX INDUSTRIES INC.—See Blackstone Inc.; *U.S. Public*, pg. 355
IONBOND AG - NUREMBERG—See IHI Corporation; *Int'l*, pg. 3605
IONBOND AUSTRIA GMBH—See IHI Corporation; *Int'l*, pg. 3605
IONBOND NETHERLANDS B.V.—See IHI Corporation; *Int'l*, pg. 3605
IONBOND SWEDEN AB—See IHI Corporation; *Int'l*, pg. 3605
JONMANDY CORP.—See Ball Chain Mfg Co, Inc.; *U.S. Private*, pg. 459
KASPAR ELECTROPLATING CORPORATION—See The Kaspar Companies; *U.S. Private*, pg. 4064
KEELING & WALKER LTD—See Amalgamated Metal Corporation PLC; *Int'l*, pg. 408
KEYSTONE AUTOMOTIVE INDUSTRIES - STOCKTON—See LKQ Corporation; *U.S. Public*, pg. 1334
LAMINATORS INC.; *U.S. Private*, pg. 2380
LINCOLN INDUSTRIES; *U.S. Private*, pg. 2457
MACDERMID PANYU SPECIALTY CHEMICALS CO LTD—See Element Solutions Inc.; *U.S. Public*, pg. 727
MERIDIAN INTERNATIONAL GROUP, INC.; *U.S. Private*, pg. 2673
METAL FINISHING TECHNOLOGIES, INC.—See Battle Investment Group LLC; *U.S. Private*, pg. 489
METAL PREP TECHNOLOGY, INC.—See Aterian Investment Management, L.P.; *U.S. Private*, pg. 366
METAL SURFACES INC.; *U.S. Private*, pg. 2680
METKOTE LAMINATED PRODUCTS INC.—See FlashCo Manufacturing, Inc.; *U.S. Private*, pg. 1540
MUELLER CORPORATION; *U.S. Private*, pg. 2810
NEW BRUNSWICK PLATING INC.; *U.S. Private*, pg. 2892
ORBEL CORPORATION; *U.S. Private*, pg. 3038
OSBORN INTERNATIONAL GMBH—See Jason Industries, Inc.; *U.S. Private*, pg. 2190
OSBORN UNIPOL LDA.—See Jason Industries, Inc.; *U.S. Private*, pg. 2190
OSBORN UNIPOL (UK) LTD.—See Jason Industries, Inc.; *U.S. Private*, pg. 2190
OTR OBERFLACHENTECHNIK GMBH—See Fielmann Group AG; *Int'l*, pg. 2659
PAVCO, INC.; *U.S. Private*, pg. 3115
PILKINGTON METAL FINISHING LLC—See Aterian Investment Management, L.P.; *U.S. Private*, pg. 366
PIONEER METAL FINISHING LLC - ANODIZING & PLATING FACILITY—See Aterian Investment Management, L.P.; *U.S. Private*, pg. 366
PIONEER METAL FINISHING LLC - GAFFNEY DIVISION—See Aterian Investment Management, L.P.; *U.S. Private*, pg. 367
PIONEER METAL FINISHING LLC - MINNEAPOLIS DIVISION—See Aterian Investment Management, L.P.; *U.S. Private*, pg. 367
PIONEER METAL FINISHING LLC - MONROE DIVISION—See Aterian Investment Management, L.P.; *U.S. Private*, pg. 367
PIONEER METAL FINISHING LLC - OSHKOSH DIVISION—See Aterian Investment Management, L.P.; *U.S. Private*, pg. 367
PIONEER METAL FINISHING LLC—See Aterian Investment Management, L.P.; *U.S. Private*, pg. 366
PIONEER METAL FINISHING LLC - SOUTH BEND DIVISION—See Aterian Investment Management, L.P.; *U.S. Private*, pg. 367
PLATING FOR ELECTRONICS, LLC—See AOTCO Metal Finishing LLC; *U.S. Private*, pg. 289
PLATING TECHNOLOGY INC.; *U.S. Private*, pg. 3200
POLCO METAL FINISHING INC.—See Meridian International Group, Inc.; *U.S. Private*, pg. 2673
PPI AEROSPACE ACQUISITION LLC—See X-Ray Industries Inc.; *U.S. Private*, pg. 4579
PRECISION ENGINEERED PRODUCTS LLC - GENERAL METAL FINISHING—See NN, Inc.; *U.S. Public*, pg. 1531
PRECISION PLATING COMPANY, INC.—See Aalberts N.V.; *Int'l*, pg. 35
PRECISION PLATING INC.—See Precision Shooting Equipment Inc.; *U.S. Private*, pg. 3246
PRIDE METAL POLISHING, INC.—See Sky Island Capital LLC; *U.S. Private*, pg. 3684
PRIME PLATING INC—See Cyton Industries Inc.; *U.S. Private*, pg. 1136
PRL INC.; *U.S. Private*, pg. 3269
PSC INDUSTRIES, INC.—See PMC Capital Partners, LLC; *U.S. Private*, pg. 3218
PT. UYEMURA INDONESIA—See C.Uyemura & Co., Ltd.; *Int'l*, pg. 1244
RACK PROCESSING COMPANY, INC.; *U.S. Private*, pg. 3342
RICHMOND METAL FINISHING—See DWA, Inc.; *U.S. Private*, pg. 1295

RICHMOND PRESSED METAL WORKS, INC.—See DWA, Inc.; *U.S. Private*, pg. 1295
ROY METAL FINISHING CO, INC.—See Aalberts N.V.; *Int'l*, pg. 35
SAPORITO FINISHING COMPANY; *U.S. Private*, pg. 3548
SAV-ON PLATING, INC.; *U.S. Private*, pg. 3555
SAV-ON PLATING OF ARIZONA INC.—See Sav-On Plating, Inc.; *U.S. Private*, pg. 3555
SCHUMACHER COMPANY INCORPORATED; *U.S. Private*, pg. 3570
SGI SOCIETE DE GALVANOPLASTIE INDUSTRIELLE S.A.S.—See Aalberts N.V.; *Int'l*, pg. 35
SHALMET CORPORATION—See Carpenter Technology Corporation; *U.S. Public*, pg. 439
SHIELDS ACQUISITION COMPANY; *U.S. Private*, pg. 3635
SIFCO APPLIED SURFACE CONCEPTS—See SIFCO Industries, Inc.; *U.S. Public*, pg. 1877
SIFCO APPLIED SURFACE CONCEPTS SWEDEN AB—See SIFCO Industries, Inc.; *U.S. Public*, pg. 1877
SIFCO APPLIED SURFACE CONCEPTS (UK), LIMITED—See SIFCO Industries, Inc.; *U.S. Public*, pg. 1877
SIFCO ASC - FRANCE—See SIFCO Industries, Inc.; *U.S. Public*, pg. 1877
SOUTHEASTERN EQUIPMENT & SUPPLY, INC.; *U.S. Private*, pg. 3727
SOUTHWEST METAL FINISHING; *U.S. Private*, pg. 3740
SPECTRUM INDUSTRIES, INC. - DECORATIVE FINISHES DIVISION—See Spectrum Industries, Inc.; *U.S. Private*, pg. 3753
SUMCO, LLC; *U.S. Private*, pg. 3852
SUMIX CORPORATION—See C.Uyemura & Co., Ltd.; *Int'l*, pg. 1244
SUMMIT CORPORATION OF AMERICA; *U.S. Private*, pg. 3854
SUPERIOR METAL FINISHING, INC.—See Aterian Investment Management, L.P.; *U.S. Private*, pg. 367
SUPERIOR TECHNOLOGY CORP; *U.S. Private*, pg. 3880
SURFECT HOLDINGS, INC.; *U.S. Private*, pg. 3884
TECHMETALS, INC.; *U.S. Private*, pg. 3953
TEIKURO CORPORATION; *U.S. Private*, pg. 3958
TEMPEL STEEL COMPANY—See Worthington Industries, Inc.; *U.S. Public*, pg. 2382
TS INDUSTRIES INC.—See Graycliff Partners LP; *U.S. Private*, pg. 1761
US CHROME CORPORATION; *U.S. Private*, pg. 4318
VALEX CORP.—See Reliance Steel & Aluminum Co.; *U.S. Public*, pg. 1782
VALLEY PLATING WORKS; *U.S. Private*, pg. 4335
VANGUARD HOLDINGS; *U.S. Private*, pg. 4343
WESTFIELD ELECTROPLATING COMPANY; *U.S. Private*, pg. 4498
XYRON INC.—See ACCO Brands Corporation; *U.S. Public*, pg. 33

332911 — INDUSTRIAL VALVE MANUFACTURING

ADVANCED ENERGY INDUSTRIES SDN. BHD.—See Advanced Energy Industries, Inc.; *U.S. Public*, pg. 47
ADVANCED VALVE TECHNOLOGIES, LLC—See Wind Point Advisors LLC; *U.S. Private*, pg. 4534
AEGIS FLOW TECHNOLOGIES—See IDEX Corp; *U.S. Public*, pg. 1089
AKO ARMATUREN - SEPARATION GMBH—See Axel Johnson Gruppen AB; *Int'l*, pg. 762
ALCO VALVES GROUP LIMITED—See Graco, Inc.; *U.S. Public*, pg. 952
ALCO VALVES INC.—See Graco, Inc.; *U.S. Public*, pg. 952
ALCO VALVES (US), INC.—See Graco, Inc.; *U.S. Public*, pg. 952
AMERICAN AVK CO.—See AVK Holding A/S; *Int'l*, pg. 747
AMERICAN VALVE & HYDRANT CO.—See American Cast Iron Pipe Company; *U.S. Private*, pg. 226
AMF-BRUNS GMBH & CO. KG; *Int'l*, pg. 424
ANIMATICS GMBH—See Moog Inc.; *U.S. Public*, pg. 1469
ANNAPURNA BHASKARI GROUP; *Int'l*, pg. 473
APV BENELUX NV—See Lone Star Funds; *U.S. Private*, pg. 2485
AQUA-GAS MANUFACTURING LTD.—See AVK Holding A/S; *Int'l*, pg. 747
ARAD LTD.; *Int'l*, pg. 534
ARCA REGLER GMBH; *Int'l*, pg. 540
ARCA VALVULAS S.A. DE C.V.—See ARCA Regler GmbH; *Int'l*, pg. 540
ARGUS GMBH & CO. K.G.—See Flowserve Corporation; *U.S. Public*, pg. 855
ARMSTRONG INTERNATIONAL, INC.; *U.S. Private*, pg. 331
ARMSTRONG INTERNATIONAL, S.A.—See Armstrong International, Inc.; *U.S. Private*, pg. 331
ARTES VALVE & SERVICE GMBH—See ARCA Regler GmbH; *Int'l*, pg. 540
ASAHI AV VALVE (SHANGHAI) CO., LTD.—See Asahi Yukizai Corporation; *Int'l*, pg. 598
ASCO JOUCOMATIC PTY. LTD.—See Emerson Electric Co.; *U.S. Public*, pg. 741

ASCOMATICA S.A. DE C.V.—See Emerson Electric Co.; *U.S. Public*, pg. 741
ASCO NUMATICS SIRAI SRL—See Emerson Electric Co.; *U.S. Public*, pg. 740
ASCO VALVE, INC.—See Emerson Electric Co.; *U.S. Public*, pg. 750
ASTON PHOTONIC TECHNOLOGIES LIMITED—See Moog Inc.; *U.S. Public*, pg. 1469
AUMA RIESTER GMBH & CO. KG; *Int'l*, pg. 704
AUSTRALIAN VALVE GROUP PTY LTD—See Watts Water Technologies, Inc.; *U.S. Public*, pg. 2337
AVK HAUT MARNAISE S.A.S.—See AVK Holding A/S; *Int'l*, pg. 747
AVK HOLDING A/S; *Int'l*, pg. 746
AVK MITTELMANN ARMATUREN GMBH—See AVK Holding A/S; *Int'l*, pg. 747
AVK SYDDAL LTD.—See AVK Holding A/S; *Int'l*, pg. 747
AVK SYNTEC (ANHUI) CO. LTD.—See AVK Holding A/S; *Int'l*, pg. 747
AVK VALVES (ANHUI) CO., LTD.—See AVK Holding A/S; *Int'l*, pg. 747
AVK VALVES INDIA PVT. LTD.—See AVK Holding A/S; *Int'l*, pg. 747
AVK VALVES MANUFACTURING MALAYSIA SDN. BHD.—See AVK Holding A/S; *Int'l*, pg. 747
AWC FRAC VALVES INC.; *U.S. Private*, pg. 410
AZBIL CONTROL INSTRUMENTS (DALIAN) CO., LTD.—See Azbil Corporation; *Int'l*, pg. 777
AZZALIN SRL; *Int'l*, pg. 782
B&K, LLC—See Mueller Industries, Inc.; *U.S. Public*, pg. 1484
BMT CO., LTD. - YANGSAN FACTORY—See BMT Co., Ltd.; *Int'l*, pg. 1077
BONNEY FORGE CORPORATION - RP & C VALVE DIVISION—See Bonney Forge Corporation; *U.S. Private*, pg. 615
BOSHART INDUSTRIES INC.; *Int'l*, pg. 1116
BRAY CONTROLS ANDINA LTDA.—See Bray International, Inc.; *U.S. Private*, pg. 641
BRAY CONTROLS CANADA CORPORATION—See Bray International, Inc.; *U.S. Private*, pg. 641
BRAY CONTROLS FRANCE S.A.R.L—See Bray International, Inc.; *U.S. Private*, pg. 641
BRAY CONTROLS PACIFIC PTY. LTD.—See Bray International, Inc.; *U.S. Private*, pg. 641
BRAY CONTROLS PERU S.A.C—See Bray International, Inc.; *U.S. Private*, pg. 641
BRAY CONTROLS S.A.—See Bray International, Inc.; *U.S. Private*, pg. 641
BRAY CONTROLS SOUTHEAST ASIA PTE LTD—See Bray International, Inc.; *U.S. Private*, pg. 641
BRAY CONTROLS (UK) LTD.—See Bray International, Inc.; *U.S. Private*, pg. 641
BRAY CONTROLS VIETNAM COMPANY LTD.—See Bray International, Inc.; *U.S. Private*, pg. 641
BRAY INTERNATIONAL, INC. - BRAY CONTROLS BENELUX DIVISION—See Bray International, Inc.; *U.S. Private*, pg. 641
BRAY INTERNATIONAL, INC. - BRAY CONTROLS INDONESIA DIVISION—See Bray International, Inc.; *U.S. Private*, pg. 642
BRAY INTERNATIONAL, INC. - BRAY CONTROLS POLAND DIVISION—See Bray International, Inc.; *U.S. Private*, pg. 642
BRAY INTERNATIONAL, INC. - BRAY CONTROLS S. KOREA DIVISION—See Bray International, Inc.; *U.S. Private*, pg. 642
BRAY INTERNATIONAL, INC.; *U.S. Private*, pg. 641
BRAY TECHNICAL SERVICES INDIA PVT. LTD.—See Bray International, Inc.; *U.S. Private*, pg. 642
BRAY VALVULAS DE MEXICO S.A. DE C.V.—See Bray International, Inc.; *U.S. Private*, pg. 642
BROEN A/S—See Aalberts N.V.; *Int'l*, pg. 33
BROEN, INC.—See Aalberts N.V.; *Int'l*, pg. 33
BROEN MALAYSIA SDN. BHD.—See Aalberts N.V.; *Int'l*, pg. 33
BROEN S.A.—See Aalberts N.V.; *Int'l*, pg. 33
BROEN SINGAPORE PTE LTD—See Aalberts N.V.; *Int'l*, pg. 33
BROEN VALVES LTD.—See Aalberts N.V.; *Int'l*, pg. 33
BRYAN DONKIN VALVES LTD.—See AVK Holding A/S; *Int'l*, pg. 747
BS&B SAFETY SYSTEMS (INDIA) LTD.—See BS&B Safety Systems, LLC; *U.S. Private*, pg. 674
CAPITAL VALVES LIMITED—See NOV, Inc.; *U.S. Public*, pg. 1544
CASHCO, INC.—See May River Capital, LLC; *U.S. Private*, pg. 2620
CHEMTECH INDUSTRIAL VALVES LIMITED; *Int'l*, pg. 1463
CHEONGBO INDUSTRIAL CO., LTD.; *Int'l*, pg. 1470
CHONGQING CHUANYI AUTOMATION CO., LTD.; *Int'l*, pg. 1579
CIRCOR AEROSPACE, INC.—See KKR & Co. Inc.; *U.S. Public*, pg. 1242
CKD USA CORPORATION—See CKD Corporation; *Int'l*, pg. 1639
CLAYTON CORPORATION; *U.S. Private*, pg. 918

332911 — INDUSTRIAL VALVE MA...

CLAYTON PLASTICS CORP.—See Clayton Corporation; *U.S. Private*, pg. 918
CLOW CANADA INC.—See McWane, Inc.; *U.S. Private*, pg. 2645
CNNG SUFA TECHNOLOGY INDUSTRY CO LTD.—See China National Nuclear Corporation; *Int'l*, pg. 1532
COFELY DELTA CONTROLS BV—See ENGIE SA; *Int'l*, pg. 2430
CONTINENTAL DISC CORPORATION—See Tinicum Enterprises, Inc.; *U.S. Private*, pg. 4174
CONTROL DEVICES, LLC—See HBM Holdings Company; *U.S. Private*, pg. 1887
COPES-VULCAN—See SPX Technologies, Inc.; *U.S. Public*, pg. 1920
CRANE CHEMPHARMA FLOW SOLUTIONS—See Crane NXT, Co.; *U.S. Public*, pg. 590
CRANE ELECTRONICS, INC.—See Crane Group Limited; *Int'l*, pg. 1828
CRANE GLOBAL HOLDINGS S.L.—See Crane NXT, Co.; *U.S. Public*, pg. 590
CRANE LIMITED—See Crane NXT, Co.; *U.S. Public*, pg. 590
CRANE NINGJIN VALVE CO.—See Crane NXT, Co.; *U.S. Public*, pg. 590
CRANE OVERSEAS LLC—See Crane NXT, Co.; *U.S. Public*, pg. 591
CRANE PROCESS FLOW TECHNOLOGIES GMBH—See Crane NXT, Co.; *U.S. Public*, pg. 590
CRANE STOCKHAM VALVE LTD.—See Crane NXT, Co.; *U.S. Public*, pg. 590
CROSBY VALVE, INC.—See Emerson Electric Co.; *U.S. Public*, pg. 751
CURTISS-WRIGHT FLOW CONTROL CORPORATION—See Curtiss-Wright Corporation; *U.S. Public*, pg. 612
CYL KNIFE VALVES S.L.—See AVK Holding A/S; *Int'l*, pg. 747
DAMPER TECHNOLOGY CANADA—See AVK Holding A/S; *Int'l*, pg. 747
DAMPER TECHNOLOGY LTD. - LEICESTER PLANT—See AVK Holding A/S; *Int'l*, pg. 747
DAMPER TECHNOLOGY LTD.—See AVK Holding A/S; *Int'l*, pg. 747
DAVCO EQUIPMENT, INC.—See Flowserve Corporation; *U.S. Public*, pg. 855
DEFINOX (BEIJING) STAINLESS STEEL EQUIPMENT LTD—See Alfa Laval AB; *Int'l*, pg. 309
DEFINOX SAS—See Alfa Laval AB; *Int'l*, pg. 309
DELTAVALVE, LLC—See SCF Partners Ltd.; *U.S. Private*, pg. 3562
DEUTZ BENELUX B.V.—See DEUTZ AG; *Int'l*, pg. 2086
DEZURIK, INC.—See Granite Equity Partners LLC; *U.S. Private*, pg. 1755
DISTRIBUTION NOW FZE—See DNOW Inc.; *U.S. Public*, pg. 671
DMI YOUNG & CUNNINGHAM LTD.—See DMI UK Ltd.; *Int'l*, pg. 2145
DOUGLAS CHERO S.P.A.—See Schlumberger Limited; *U.S. Public*, pg. 1844
E. HAWLE ARMATURENWERKE GMBH; *Int'l*, pg. 2250
EL-O-MATIC BENELUX BV—See Emerson Electric Co.; *U.S. Public*, pg. 750
EMERSON AUTOMATION SOLUTIONS - GERMANY—See Emerson Electric Co.; *U.S. Public*, pg. 743
EMERSON INDUSTRIAL AUTOMATION POLAND SP. Z.O.O.—See Emerson Electric Co.; *U.S. Public*, pg. 745
EMERSON PROCESS MANAGEMENT LTDA.—See Emerson Electric Co.; *U.S. Public*, pg. 748
EMERSON PROCESS MANAGEMENT REGULATOR TECHNOLOGIES TULSA, LLC—See Emerson Electric Co.; *U.S. Public*, pg. 747
EMERSON PROCESS MANAGEMENT VALVE ACTUATION LLC—See Emerson Electric Co.; *U.S. Public*, pg. 748
EMERSON PROCESS MANAGEMENT-VALVE AUTOMATION—See Emerson Electric Co.; *U.S. Public*, pg. 748
ENGINEERED CONTROLS INTERNATIONAL LLC - REGO CRYO-FLOW PRODUCTS DIVISION—See Windjammer Capital Investors, LLC; *U.S. Private*, pg. 4537
ENGINEERED CONTROLS INTERNATIONAL LLC—See Windjammer Capital Investors, LLC; *U.S. Private*, pg. 4537
ERICHS ARMATUR AB—See AUMA Riester GmbH & Co. KG; *Int'l*, pg. 705
ESSEN TECH CO., LTD.; *Int'l*, pg. 2510
EVERGY METRO, INC.—See Evergy, Inc.; *U.S. Public*, pg. 801
EVERYTHING ICE, INC.; *U.S. Private*, pg. 1441
FABCO-AIR, INC.; *U.S. Private*, pg. 1546
FELUWA PUMPEN GMBH—See ARCA Regler GmbH; *Int'l*, pg. 540
FIKE CANADA, INC.—See Fike Corporation; *U.S. Private*, pg. 1505
FIKE JAPAN CORPORATION—See Fike Corporation; *U.S. Private*, pg. 1505
FINISHING BRANDS GERMANY GMBH—See Graco, Inc.; *U.S. Public*, pg. 953

FINISHING BRANDS (SHANGHAI) CO., LTD.—See Graco, Inc.; *U.S. Public*, pg. 953
FLO CONTROL, INC.; *U.S. Private*, pg. 1546
FLOMATIC CORPORATION—See Boshart Industries Inc.; *Int'l*, pg. 1116
FLOW CONTROLS S.A. DE C.V.—See Emerson Electric Co.; *U.S. Public*, pg. 744
FLOWSERVE AHAUS GMBH—See Flowserve Corporation; *U.S. Public*, pg. 855
FLOWSERVE CORPORATION; *U.S. Public*, pg. 855
FLOWSERVE CORP.—See Flowserve Corporation; *U.S. Public*, pg. 856
FLOWSERVE CORP.—See Flowserve Corporation; *U.S. Public*, pg. 856
FLOWSERVE EMA HOLDINGS, B.V.—See Flowserve Corporation; *U.S. Public*, pg. 855
FLOWSERVE S.R.L.—See Flowserve Corporation; *U.S. Public*, pg. 856
FLOWSERVE SWEDEN AB—See Flowserve Corporation; *U.S. Public*, pg. 856
FLOW-TEK INDUSTRIA E COMERCIO DE VALVULAS LTDA—See Bray International, Inc.; *U.S. Private*, pg. 642
FLUID CONTROL DIVISION—See Parker Hannifin Corporation; *U.S. Public*, pg. 1644
FORUM VALVE SOLUTIONS—See Forum Energy Technologies, Inc.; *U.S. Public*, pg. 873
FUKOKU CO., LTD. - AICHI PLANT—See Fukoku Co., Ltd.; *Int'l*, pg. 2838
GARMENDIA MACUS S.A.—See Air Products & Chemicals, Inc.; *U.S. Public*, pg. 66
GEA ASEPTOMAG AG—See GEA Group Aktiengesellschaft; *Int'l*, pg. 2897
GEA TUCHENHAGEN GMBH—See GEA Group Aktiengesellschaft; *Int'l*, pg. 2899
GEA TUCHENHAGEN POLSKA SP. Z O.O.—See GEA Group Aktiengesellschaft; *Int'l*, pg. 2900
GEBR. KEMPER GMBH & CO. KG; *Int'l*, pg. 2906
GEMA USA INC.—See Graco, Inc.; *U.S. Public*, pg. 953
GENERAL CONTROL EQUIPMENT COMPANY; *U.S. Private*, pg. 1664
GG MANUFACTURING S.R.L.—See Graco, Inc.; *U.S. Public*, pg. 953
GLENFIELD VALVES LIMITED—See AVK Holding A/S; *Int'l*, pg. 747
GLOBAL FLOW TECHNOLOGIES, INC.—See Forum Energy Technologies, Inc.; *U.S. Public*, pg. 874
GOODWIN KOREA LTD.—See Goodwin PLC; *Int'l*, pg. 3041
GOYEN CONTROLS CO. PTY LIMITED—See Emerson Electric Co.; *U.S. Public*, pg. 751
GRACO BVBA—See Graco, Inc.; *U.S. Public*, pg. 953
GRACO HIGH PRESSURE EQUIPMENT INC.—See Graco, Inc.; *U.S. Public*, pg. 953
GRACO MINNESOTA INC.—See Graco, Inc.; *U.S. Public*, pg. 953
GROTH CORPORATION—See Tinicum Enterprises, Inc.; *U.S. Private*, pg. 4174
GUANGZHOU ARCA VALVE LTD.—See ARCA Regler GmbH; *Int'l*, pg. 540
HAWA ENGINEERS LTD.; *Int'l*, pg. 3288
HENRY PRATT COMPANY, LLC—See Mueller Water Products, Inc.; *U.S. Public*, pg. 1485
HENRY TECHNOLOGIES - CHATHAM PLANT—See Hendricks Holding Company, Inc.; *U.S. Private*, pg. 1915
HENRY TECHNOLOGIES, INC.—See Hendricks Holding Company, Inc.; *U.S. Private*, pg. 1915
HEROSE GMBH; *Int'l*, pg. 3364
HFCONTROLS—See Doosan Corporation; *Int'l*, pg. 2173
HI-ALLOY VALVE LLC—See Movement Industries Corp.; *U.S. Public*, pg. 1480
HILTON VALVE, INC.—See Granite Equity Partners LLC; *U.S. Private*, pg. 1755
HOERBIGER AUSTRALIA PTY LTD.—See Hoerbiger Holding AG; *Int'l*, pg. 3440
HOLTER REGELARMATUREN GMBH & CO. KG; *Int'l*, pg. 3454
HOSIDEN SEIKO CORPORATION—See Hosiden Corporation; *Int'l*, pg. 3484
HS VALVE CO., LTD - FACTORY III—See HS VALVE CO., LTD; *Int'l*, pg. 3503
HS VALVE CO., LTD - FACTORY II—See HS VALVE CO., LTD; *Int'l*, pg. 3503
HS VALVE CO., LTD; *Int'l*, pg. 3503
HUMPHREY AUTOMATION—See Humphrey Products Corporation; *U.S. Private*, pg. 2007
HUSCO INTERNATIONAL, LTD.—See HUSCO International, Inc.; *U.S. Private*, pg. 2013
HUSCO-KAYABA HYDRAULICS (SHANGHAI) LTD.—See HUSCO International, Inc.; *U.S. Private*, pg. 2013
HY-LOK CORPORATION; *Int'l*, pg. 3543
INCOVA TECHNOLOGIES, INC.—See HUSCO International, Inc.; *U.S. Private*, pg. 2013
INSTRUMENT & VALVE SERVICES COMPANY—See Emerson Electric Co.; *U.S. Public*, pg. 748
INTERAPP AG—See AVK Holding A/S; *Int'l*, pg. 748
JATOS INC.—See Fuji Oozx Inc.; *Int'l*, pg. 2816
JIHOMORAVSKA ARMATURKA SPOL. S.R.O.—See Zurn Elkay Water Solutions Corporation; *U.S. Public*, pg. 2413
JINGMEN PRATT VALVE CO. LTD.—See Mueller Water Products, Inc.; *U.S. Public*, pg. 1485

KEIHIN VALVE CORP—See Hitachi Astemo, Ltd.; *Int'l*, pg. 3409
KENNEDY VALVE—See McWane, Inc.; *U.S. Private*, pg. 2645
KENTROL/SEVCO, INC.—See F.W. Webb Company; *U.S. Private*, pg. 1457
KOONTZ-WAGNER ELECTRIC COMPANY; *U.S. Private*, pg. 2343
K.P. MCNAMARA COMPANY, INC.—See HCI Equity Management, L.P.; *U.S. Private*, pg. 1889
K.P. MCNAMARA OF GEORGIA, INC—See HCI Equity Management, L.P.; *U.S. Private*, pg. 1889
KVC (UK) LTD—See Federal International (2000) Ltd; *Int'l*, pg. 2630
LE RESERVOIR MASSAL—See FAYAT SAS; *Int'l*, pg. 2625
LESLIE CONTROLS, INC.—See KKR & Co. Inc.; *U.S. Public*, pg. 1242
LIEBHERR-AEROSPACE BRASIL LTDA.—See Embraer S.A.; *Int'l*, pg. 2375
LYE MARKETING SDN. BHD.—See Engtex Group Berhad; *Int'l*, pg. 2436
MAASS FLANGE CORPORATION—See AFG Holdings, Inc.; *U.S. Private*, pg. 123
MAC VALVES ASIA, INC.—See MAC Valves, Inc.; *U.S. Private*, pg. 2531
MCWANE, INC. - AMERICAN R/D DIVISION—See McWane, Inc.; *U.S. Private*, pg. 2645
MCWANE SERVICES PRIVATE LTD—See McWane, Inc.; *U.S. Private*, pg. 2645
MDC VACUUM PRODUCTS, LLC; *U.S. Private*, pg. 2646
MEDICAL INFORMATION PROFESSIONAL SYSTEMS NV—See Roper Technologies, Inc.; *U.S. Public*, pg. 1812
MEGGITT (NORTH HOLLYWOOD), INC.—See Parker Hannifin Corporation; *U.S. Public*, pg. 1642
MEI SARL—See Crane NXT, Co.; *U.S. Public*, pg. 591
MERCURY MANUFACTURING COMPANY—See O2 Investment Partners, LLC; *U.S. Private*, pg. 2982
METALTECH SERVICE CENTER INC.—See Ironwood Capital Management LLC; *U.S. Private*, pg. 2140
METHVEN LIMITED—See GWA Group Limited; *Int'l*, pg. 3190
M&H VALVE CO.—See McWane, Inc.; *U.S. Private*, pg. 2645
MICROZERO CO., LTD.—See Hisaka Works, Ltd.; *Int'l*, pg. 3406
MILLIKIN VALVE, LLC—See Mueller Water Products, Inc.; *U.S. Public*, pg. 1485
MILTON INDUSTRIES, INC.—See Levine Leichtman Capital Partners, LLC; *U.S. Private*, pg. 2436
MIPS AUSTRIA GESMBH—See Roper Technologies, Inc.; *U.S. Public*, pg. 1812
MOGAS INDUSTRIES, INC.—See Flowserve Corporation; *U.S. Public*, pg. 856
MOOG CONTROLS (INDIA) PRIVATE LTD.—See Moog Inc.; *U.S. Public*, pg. 1470
MOOG NORDEN A.B.—See Moog Inc.; *U.S. Public*, pg. 1471
MOOG S.A.R.L.—See Moog Inc.; *U.S. Public*, pg. 1470
MUELLER CANADA HOLDINGS CORP.—See Mueller Water Products, Inc.; *U.S. Public*, pg. 1485
MUELLER CANADA LTD.—See Mueller Water Products, Inc.; *U.S. Public*, pg. 1485
MUELLER EUROPE INVESTMENT COMPANY LTD.—See Mueller Industries, Inc.; *U.S. Public*, pg. 1485
MUELLER INTERNATIONAL, LLC—See Mueller Water Products, Inc.; *U.S. Public*, pg. 1486
MUELLER SOUTHEAST, INC.—See Mueller Industries, Inc.; *U.S. Public*, pg. 1484
MUELLER SYSTEMS, LLC—See Mueller Water Products, Inc.; *U.S. Public*, pg. 1486
MUELLER WATER PRODUCTS, INC.; *U.S. Public*, pg. 1485
MULTIMAQ - PISTOLAS E EQUIPAMENTOS PARA PINTURA LTDA—See Graco, Inc.; *U.S. Public*, pg. 954
NETHERLOCKS SAFETY SYSTEMS—See Halma plc; *Int'l*, pg. 3233
NEWCO VALVES, LLC—See Schlumberger Limited; *U.S. Public*, pg. 1844
NEWMANS VALVE LLC—See Schlumberger Limited; *U.S. Public*, pg. 1844
NICHOLSON STEAM TRAP—See Emerson Electric Co.; *U.S. Public*, pg. 752
NIPPON FISHER CO., LTD.—See Emerson Electric Co.; *U.S. Public*, pg. 748
OKLAHOMA SAFETY EQUIPMENT CO. INC.—See Halma plc; *Int'l*, pg. 3231
OOO VAG ARMATUREN RUS—See Zurn Elkay Water Solutions Corporation; *U.S. Public*, pg. 2414
OPELLA LIMITED—See Fluidmaster, Inc.; *U.S. Private*, pg. 1552
ORBE CANADA INC.—See AVK Holding A/S; *Int'l*, pg. 748
PACE INDUSTRIES DE MEXICO, S.A. DE C.V.—See Kenner & Company, Inc.; *U.S. Private*, pg. 2286
PARKER HANNIFIN FLUID CONTROL DIVISION—See Parker Hannifin Corporation; *U.S. Public*, pg. 1644
PARKER HANNIFIN GENERAL VALVE OPERATION PNEUTRONICS DIVISION—See Parker Hannifin Corporation; *U.S. Public*, pg. 1647

N.A.I.C.S. INDEX

332912 — FLUID POWER VALVE A...

PARKER HANNIFIN MANUFACTURING FRANCE S.A.S.—See Parker Hannifin Corporation; *U.S. Public*, pg. 1646
PARKER HANNIFIN REFRIGERATING SPECIALTIES DIV.—See Parker Hannifin Corporation; *U.S. Public*, pg. 1644
PEGLER YORKSHIRE GROUP LTD.—See Aalberts N.V.; *Int'l*, pg. 35
PENTAIR VALVES & CONTROLS, INC. - CORONA—See Emerson Electric Co.; *U.S. Public*, pg. 751
PENTAIR VALVES & CONTROLS, INC. - PROPHETSTOWN—See Emerson Electric Co.; *U.S. Public*, pg. 751
PENTAIR VALVES & CONTROLS, INC.—See Emerson Electric Co.; *U.S. Public*, pg. 751
PENTAIR VALVES & CONTROLS, INC. - STAFFORD—See Emerson Electric Co.; *U.S. Public*, pg. 751
PENTAIR VALVES & CONTROLS INDIA PVT. LTD.—See Emerson Electric Co.; *U.S. Public*, pg. 751
PENTAIR VALVES & CONTROLS ITALIA S.R.L.—See Emerson Electric Co.; *U.S. Public*, pg. 751
PENTAIR VALVES & CONTROLS (M) SDN. BHD.—See Emerson Electric Co.; *U.S. Public*, pg. 751
PENTAIR VALVES & CONTROLS POLSKA SP. Z O.O.—See Emerson Electric Co.; *U.S. Public*, pg. 751
PENTAIR VALVES & CONTROLS (TAIWAN) LTD.—See Emerson Electric Co.; *U.S. Public*, pg. 751
PENTAIR VALVES & CONTROLS (THAILAND) LTD.—See Emerson Electric Co.; *U.S. Public*, pg. 751
PICUT ACQUISITION CORP—See Picut Manufacturing Company; *U.S. Private*, pg. 3176
PICUT MANUFACTURING COMPANY; *U.S. Private*, pg. 3176
PMV AUTOMATION AB—See Flowserve Corporation; *U.S. Public*, pg. 857
PREMIUM VALVE SERVICES, LLC—See Diefenthal Holdings, LLC; *U.S. Private*, pg. 1228
PRO-TECH VALVE SALES—See Forum Energy Technologies, Inc.; *U.S. Public*, pg. 874
PRUSS ARMATUREN AG—See Certina Holding AG; *Int'l*, pg. 1423
PTEC PRESSURE TECHNOLOGY GMBH—See Worthington Industries, Inc.; *U.S. Public*, pg. 2382
PT FLOWSERVE—See Flowserve Corporation; *U.S. Public*, pg. 857
RED VALVE CO., INC.—See Granite Equity Partners LLC; *U.S. Private*, pg. 1755
REGO EUROPE GMBH—See Windjammer Capital Investors, LLC; *U.S. Private*, pg. 4537
RICHARDS INDUSTRIES VALVE GROUP; *U.S. Private*, pg. 3429
RITEPRO CORPORATION—See Bray International, Inc.; *U.S. Private*, pg. 642
SAUDI VALVES MANUFACTURING CO. LTD.—See AVK Holding A/S; *Int'l*, pg. 748
SAUER-DANFOSS HIDRAULICA MOBIL LTDA.—See Danfoss A/S; *Int'l*, pg. 1961
SCHROEDAHL-ARAPP SPEZIALARMATUREN GMBH & CO. KG—See KKR & Co. Inc.; *U.S. Public*, pg. 1242
SEALWELD (USA), INC.—See Entegris, Inc.; *U.S. Public*, pg. 776
SEMPELL GMBH—See Emerson Electric Co.; *U.S. Public*, pg. 751
SEPPELFRICKE ARMATUREN GMBH & CO. OHG—See Aalberts N.V.; *Int'l*, pg. 35
SHERWOOD VALVE LLC—See Wind Point Advisors LLC; *U.S. Private*, pg. 4536
SHERWOOD VALVE LLC - VALLEY VIEW FACILITY—See Wind Point Advisors LLC; *U.S. Private*, pg. 4536
SHERWOOD VALVE—See Wind Point Advisors LLC; *U.S. Private*, pg. 4536
S.H. LEGGITT COMPANY INC.; *U.S. Private*, pg. 3517
SOFIS LIMITED—See Halma plc; *Int'l*, pg. 3233
SPENCE ENGINEERING CO., INC.—See Emerson Electric Co.; *U.S. Public*, pg. 752
S.P. KINNEY ENGINEERS, INC.; *U.S. Private*, pg. 3518
SPORLAN VALVE COMPANY—See Parker Hannifin Corporation; *U.S. Public*, pg. 1644
SPX FLOW CONTROL—See Lone Star Funds; *U.S. Private*, pg. 2486
SPX PROCESS EQUIPMENT—See SPX Technologies, Inc.; *U.S. Public*, pg. 1921
STANDARD MACHINE & MANUFACTURING CO.—See Dema Engineering Co.; *U.S. Private*, pg. 1203
THE STARFLO CORPORATION—See The Wm. Powell Company; *U.S. Private*, pg. 4138
STERLING FLUID SYSTEMS (HUNGARIA) KFT.—See Flowserve Corporation; *U.S. Public*, pg. 857
STERLING INDUSTRY CONSULT GMBH—See Flowserve Corporation; *U.S. Public*, pg. 857
STORM MANUFACTURING GROUP, INC.—See Storm Industries, Inc.; *U.S. Private*, pg. 3831
SURFACES & FINITIONS S.A.S.—See Graco, Inc.; *U.S. Public*, pg. 954
SYNESSO, INC.—See The Middleby Corporation; *U.S. Public*, pg. 2115
TAIWAN VALVE CO., LTD—See Emerson Electric Co.; *U.S. Public*, pg. 751

TAPCOENPRO UK LIMITED—See KKR & Co. Inc.; *U.S. Public*, pg. 1242
TAPCO INTERNATIONAL INC.—See Curtiss-Wright Corporation; *U.S. Public*, pg. 612
TEC ARTEC GMBH—See AVK Holding A/S; *Int'l*, pg. 748
TECNOMETAL—See Arcline Investment Management LP; *U.S. Private*, pg. 313
TERMINAL MANUFACTURING CO.—See Crane NXT, Co.; *U.S. Public*, pg. 592
TESCOM CORPORATION—See Emerson Electric Co.; *U.S. Public*, pg. 752
THERMAL EDGE, INC.; *U.S. Private*, pg. 4142
TYCO VALVES & CONTROLS (SICHUAN) CO., LTD.—See Emerson Electric Co.; *U.S. Public*, pg. 751
UNI-FORM COMPONENTS CO.—See Berkshire Hathaway Inc.; *U.S. Public*, pg. 311
UNITED BRASS WORKS INC.; *U.S. Private*, pg. 4288
U.S. PIPE VALVE & HYDRANT, LLC—See Mueller Water Products, Inc.; *U.S. Public*, pg. 2337
VAG ARMATUREN AT GMBH—See Zurn Elkay Water Solutions Corporation; *U.S. Public*, pg. 2414
VAG GMBH—See Aurelius Equity Opportunities SE & Co. KGaA; *Int'l*, pg. 710
VAG USA, LLC.—See Zurn Elkay Water Solutions Corporation; *U.S. Public*, pg. 2414
VAG VALVES CHILE S.A.—See Zurn Elkay Water Solutions Corporation; *U.S. Public*, pg. 2414
VAG VALVOLE ITALIA SRL—See Zurn Elkay Water Solutions Corporation; *U.S. Public*, pg. 2414
VALBART S.R.L.—See Flowserve Corporation; *U.S. Public*, pg. 857
VAL-MATIC VALVE AND MANUFACTURING CORP.; *U.S. Private*, pg. 4330
VALVE CONCEPTS, INC.—See May River Capital, LLC; *U.S. Private*, pg. 2620
VALVE & PRIMER CORPORATION—See Granite Equity Partners LLC; *U.S. Private*, pg. 1755
VALVTECHNOLOGIES INC.; *U.S. Private*, pg. 4338
VALVTRONIC S.A.—See Bray International, Inc.; *U.S. Private*, pg. 642
VINTROL, INC.—See Emerson Electric Co.; *U.S. Public*, pg. 752
VIRGO VALVES & CONTROLS PRIVATE LIMITED—See Emerson Electric Co.; *U.S. Public*, pg. 752
VON ROHR ARCA BV—See ARCA Regler GmbH; *Int'l*, pg. 540
VON ROHR ARMATUREN AG—See ARCA Regler GmbH; *Int'l*, pg. 540
VSH FABRIEKEN B.V.—See Aalberts N.V.; *Int'l*, pg. 36
V TEX CORPORATION—See Hitachi Zosen Corporation; *Int'l*, pg. 3412
V TEX KOREA CO., LTD.—See Hitachi Zosen Corporation; *Int'l*, pg. 3412
VTI VENTIL TECHNIK GMBH—See Aalberts N.V.; *Int'l*, pg. 36
WATERMAN INDUSTRIES, LLC—See CVF Capital Partners, Inc.; *U.S. Private*, pg. 1132
WATEROUS COMPANY—See American Cast Iron Pipe Company; *U.S. Private*, pg. 226
WATTS AUTOMATIC CONTROL VALVES, INC.—See Watts Water Technologies, Inc.; *U.S. Public*, pg. 2337
WATTS REGULATOR/WATTS ACV—See Watts Water Technologies, Inc.; *U.S. Public*, pg. 2338
WATTS VALVE (NINGBO) CO., LTD.—See Watts Water Technologies, Inc.; *U.S. Public*, pg. 2338
WATTS WATER TECHNOLOGIES (CANADA), INC.—See Watts Water Technologies, Inc.; *U.S. Public*, pg. 2338
WATTS WATER TECHNOLOGIES EMEA B.V.—See Watts Water Technologies, Inc.; *U.S. Public*, pg. 2338
WATTS WATER TECHNOLOGIES, INC.; *U.S. Public*, pg. 2338
WEKA AG—See ARCA Regler GmbH; *Int'l*, pg. 540
WELDMAC MANUFACTURING COMPANY—See TriMas Corporation; *U.S. Public*, pg. 2189
WILLIAM STEINEN MANUFACTURING CO.; *U.S. Private*, pg. 4525
THE WM. POWELL COMPANY; *U.S. Private*, pg. 4138
WORCESTER CONTROLS UK—See Flowserve Corporation; *U.S. Public*, pg. 857
WORLD VALVE B.V.—See AVK Holding A/S; *Int'l*, pg. 748
WOUTER WITZEL EUROVALVE B.V.—See AVK Holding A/S; *Int'l*, pg. 747
XOMOX CANADA LTD.—See Crane NXT, Co.; *U.S. Public*, pg. 590
XOMOX CORPORATION—See Crane NXT, Co.; *U.S. Public*, pg. 590
XOMOX FRANCE S.A.—See Crane NXT, Co.; *U.S. Public*, pg. 590
XOMOX HUNGARY KFT.—See Crane NXT, Co.; *U.S. Public*, pg. 590
XOMOX INTERNATIONAL GMBH & CO.—See Crane NXT, Co.; *U.S. Public*, pg. 590
XOMOX JAPAN LTD.—See Crane NXT, Co.; *U.S. Public*, pg. 590
XOMOX KOREA LTD.—See Crane NXT, Co.; *U.S. Public*, pg. 590
XOMOX SANMAR LTD.—See Crane NXT, Co.; *U.S. Public*, pg. 590

ZAHROOF VALVES, INC.—See Atlas Copco AB; *Int'l*, pg. 684

332912 — FLUID POWER VALVE AND HOSE FITTING MANUFACTURING

ABB SIFANG POWER SYSTEM CO., LTD.—See Beijing Sifang Automation Co., Ltd.; *Int'l*, pg. 957
AEROFIT, LLC—See Tinicum Enterprises, Inc.; *U.S. Private*, pg. 4174
AIR-WAY MANUFACTURING COMPANY; *U.S. Private*, pg. 140
ALFA LAVAL AUSTRALIA PTY LTD—See Alfa Laval AB; *Int'l*, pg. 309
ALFA LAVAL NEW ZEALAND LTD.—See Alfa Laval AB; *Int'l*, pg. 310
ALLEN AIRCRAFT PRODUCTS, INC. - AIRCRAFT DIVISION—See Allen Aircraft Products, Inc.; *U.S. Private*, pg. 178
AMPHENOL NELSON DUNN TECHNOLOGIES, INC.—See Amphenol Corporation; *U.S. Public*, pg. 128
ANDRITZ FLIESSBETT SYSTEME GMBH—See ANDRITZ AG; *Int'l*, pg. 453
ANNEX MANUFACTURING, INC.; *U.S. Private*, pg. 285
ARRAY PRODUCTS COMPANY, LLC; *U.S. Private*, pg. 334
ASCO SAS—See Emerson Electric Co.; *U.S. Public*, pg. 740
ASHISH POLYPLAST LTD.; *Int'l*, pg. 607
AVIC HEAVY MACHINERY CO., LTD.—See Aviation Industry Corporation of China; *Int'l*, pg. 741
BEMCO FULIDTECHNIK LLP—See BEMCO HYDRAULICS LTD; *Int'l*, pg. 969
BMT CO., LTD.; *Int'l*, pg. 1077
BOND FLUIDAIRE, INC. - WESTSIDE—See Exotic Automation & Supply, Inc.; *U.S. Private*, pg. 1449
BRIDGESTONE HOSEPOWER, LLC—See Bridgestone Corporation; *Int'l*, pg. 1156
CAMBRIDGE FLUID SYSTEMS LIMITED—See Ultra Clean Holdings, Inc.; *U.S. Public*, pg. 2223
CATERPILLAR FLUID SYSTEMS S.R.L.—See Caterpillar, Inc.; *U.S. Public*, pg. 450
CEPEX, S.A.U. (GRANOLLERS)—See Fluidra SA; *Int'l*, pg. 2714
CEPEX, S.A.U. (LA GARRIGA)—See Fluidra SA; *Int'l*, pg. 2714
CEPEX, S.A.U. (SANT JAUME DE LLIERCA)—See Fluidra SA; *Int'l*, pg. 2714
CEPEX S.A.U.—See Fluidra SA; *Int'l*, pg. 2714
CIRCOR, INC.—See KKR & Co. Inc.; *U.S. Public*, pg. 1242
CIRCOR INSTRUMENTATION TECHNOLOGIES, INC.—See KKR & Co. Inc.; *U.S. Public*, pg. 1242
CKD GLOBAL SERVICES CORPORATION—See CKD Corporation; *Int'l*, pg. 1639
CKD KOREA CORPORATION—See CKD Corporation; *Int'l*, pg. 1639
CLA-VAL AUTOMATIC CONTROL VALVES—See Griswold Industries, Inc.; *U.S. Private*, pg. 1790
CLA-VAL CANADA CORP.—See Griswold Industries, Inc.; *U.S. Private*, pg. 1790
CLA-VAL PACIFIC—See Griswold Industries, Inc.; *U.S. Private*, pg. 1791
CLINE HOSE & HYDRAULICS, LLC—See Bridgestone Corporation; *Int'l*, pg. 1156
CLIPPARD INSTRUMENT LABORATORY INC.; *U.S. Private*, pg. 945
COLDER PRODUCTS COMPANY LTD—See Dover Corporation; *U.S. Public*, pg. 679
COLDER PRODUCTS COMPANY—See Dover Corporation; *U.S. Public*, pg. 679
CONBRACO INDUSTRIES, INC. - PAGELAND—See Aalberts N.V.; *Int'l*, pg. 33
CONBRACO INDUSTRIES, INC.—See Aalberts N.V.; *Int'l*, pg. 33
CONTITECH FLUID AUTOMOTIVE ROMANIA SRL—See Continental Aktiengesellschaft; *Int'l*, pg. 1781
CRANE PAYMENT INNOVATIONS GMBH—See Crane NXT, Co.; *U.S. Public*, pg. 591
CRANE PAYMENT INNOVATIONS, INC.—See Crane NXT, Co.; *U.S. Public*, pg. 591
CRANE PROCESS FLOW TECHNOLOGIES LTD.—See Crane NXT, Co.; *U.S. Public*, pg. 590
CRANE VALVE SERVICES—See Crane NXT, Co.; *U.S. Public*, pg. 590
CRISSAIR, INC.—See ESCO Technologies, Inc.; *U.S. Public*, pg. 793
DAEMO ENGINEERING CO.; *Int'l*, pg. 1908
DAIKIN-SAUER-DANFOSS MANUFACTURING LTD.—See Daikin Industries, Ltd.; *Int'l*, pg. 1935
DAMAN PRODUCTS COMPANY, INC.—See Helios Technologies, Inc.; *U.S. Public*, pg. 1023
DANFOSS A/S WATER HYDRAULICS DIVISION—See Danfoss A/S; *Int'l*, pg. 1959
DELTA POWER CO.; *U.S. Private*, pg. 1201
DENSO MANUFACTURING ATHENS TENNESSEE, INC.—See Denso Corporation; *Int'l*, pg. 2029
DICHTELEMENTE HALLITE GMBH—See Compagnie Generale des Etablissements Michelin SCA; *Int'l*, pg. 1745
DIXON GROUP EUROPE LTD—See Dixon Valve & Cou-

332912 — FLUID POWER VALVE A...

pling Company; *U.S. Private*, pg. 1246
DIXONS DEUTSCHLAND GMBH—See Currys plc; *Int'l*, pg. 1879
DIXON VALVE & COUPLING COMPANY - DIXON BRASS DIVISION—See Dixon Valve & Coupling Company; *U.S. Private*, pg. 1246
DIXON VALVE & COUPLING COMPANY - DIXON POWHATAN DIVISION—See Dixon Valve & Coupling Company; *U.S. Private*, pg. 1246
DIXON VALVE & COUPLING COMPANY - DIXON SPECIALTY HOSE DIVISION—See Dixon Valve & Coupling Company; *U.S. Private*, pg. 1246
DIXON VALVE & COUPLING COMPANY; *U.S. Private*, pg. 1246
DK-LOK CORPORATION; *Int'l*, pg. 2139
DOEDIJNS HYDRAULICS B.V.—See IK Investment Partners Limited; *Int'l*, pg. 3609
DOEDIJNS PNEUMATICS B.V.—See IK Investment Partners Limited; *Int'l*, pg. 3609
DOVER SOUTHEAST ASIA (THAILAND) LTD.—See Dover Corporation; *U.S. Public*, pg. 681
EATON AEROSPACE LLC - CONVEYANCE SYSTEMS DIVISION, JACKSON—See Eaton Corporation plc; *Int'l*, pg. 2279
EATON GERMANY GMBH - AEROSPACE GROUP, CONVEYANCE SYSTEMS—See Eaton Corporation plc; *Int'l*, pg. 2279
EATON HYDRAULICS LLC - BEREA—See Eaton Corporation plc; *Int'l*, pg. 2280
EATON LTDA. - FLUID POWER DIVISION, GUARATINGUETA PLANT—See Eaton Corporation plc; *Int'l*, pg. 2280
EATON LTD. - HYDRAULIC SYSTEMS—See Eaton Corporation plc; *Int'l*, pg. 2280
ELBIT SYSTEMS LIMITED; *Int'l*, pg. 2344
EMERSON PROCESS MANAGEMENT—See Emerson Electric Co.; *U.S. Public*, pg. 746
EMERSON PROCESS MANAGEMENT—See Emerson Electric Co.; *U.S. Public*, pg. 746
EMERSON PROCESS MANAGEMENT VIRGO VALVES, INC.—See Emerson Electric Co.; *U.S. Public*, pg. 749
EP CLEVELAND, INC.—See Park-Ohio Holdings Corp.; *U.S. Public*, pg. 1639
E&S MANUFACTURING, INC.—See Array Products Company, LLC; *U.S. Private*, pg. 334
FACT, INC.; *Int'l*, pg. 2601
FASTER S.P.A.—See Helios Technologies, Inc.; *U.S. Public*, pg. 1023
FILTRONA SPECIAL FIBER PRODUCTS NINGBO CO., LTD.—See Essentra plc; *Int'l*, pg. 2511
FISHER CONTROLS INTERNATIONAL—See Emerson Electric Co.; *U.S. Public*, pg. 748
THE FITTING SOURCE, INC.—See Hydraulics International, Inc.; *U.S. Public*, pg. 2017
FLUIDOMAT UK PRIVATE LIMITED—See Fluidomat Ltd.; *Int'l*, pg. 2713
FLUID REGULATORS CORP.—See TransDigm Group Incorporated; *U.S. Public*, pg. 2181
FRONEK ANCHOR DARLING ENTERPRISES, INC—See Piping Technology & Products Inc.; *U.S. Public*, pg. 3190
GEORG FISCHER TPA SRL—See Georg Fischer AG; *Int'l*, pg. 2937
GIRMATIC AG; *Int'l*, pg. 2979
GOYEN CONTROLS CO UK LIMITED—See Emerson Electric Co.; *U.S. Public*, pg. 751
GRISWOLD INDUSTRIES, INC.; *U.S. Private*, pg. 1790
HOKE, INC.—See KKR & Co. Inc.; *U.S. Public*, pg. 1242
HUAIJI DENGYUN AUTO-PARTS (HOLDING) CO., LTD.; *Int'l*, pg. 3512
HUMPHREY PRODUCTS CORPORATION; *U.S. Private*, pg. 2007
HUNT VALVE COMPANY, INC.—See Arcline Investment Management LP; *U.S. Private*, pg. 313
HUSCO AUTOMOTIVE HOLDINGS, LLC.—See HUSCO International, Inc.; *U.S. Private*, pg. 2013
HUSCO HYDRAULICS PRIVATE LTD.—See HUSCO International, Inc.; *U.S. Private*, pg. 2013
HUSCO INTERNATIONAL, INC.; *U.S. Private*, pg. 2013
HYDAC FLUIDTECHNIK GMBH—See Hydac International GmbH; *Int'l*, pg. 3545
HYDRAFORCE INC.; *U.S. Private*, pg. 2017
HYDRAPOWER DYNAMICS LIMITED—See Park-Ohio Holdings Corp.; *U.S. Public*, pg. 1639
HYDRASPECMA DO BRAZIL LTDA.—See Aktieselskabet Schouw & Co.; *Int'l*, pg. 266
HYDRASPECMA HYDRAULIC SYSTEMS (TIANJIN) CO., LTD.—See Aktieselskabet Schouw & Co.; *Int'l*, pg. 266
HYDRASPECMA HYDRAULIKHUSET AB—See Aktieselskabet Schouw & Co.; *Int'l*, pg. 266
HYDRASPECMA INDIA PRIVATE LTD.—See Aktieselskabet Schouw & Co.; *Int'l*, pg. 266
HYDRASPECMA NORGE AS—See Aktieselskabet Schouw & Co.; *Int'l*, pg. 266
HYDRASPECMA SAMWON LTD.—See Aktieselskabet Schouw & Co.; *Int'l*, pg. 266
HYDRASPECMA USA INC.—See Aktieselskabet Schouw & Co.; *Int'l*, pg. 266

HYDRASPECMA WIRO AB—See Aktieselskabet Schouw & Co.; *Int'l*, pg. 266
HYDRO MATERIAL OY—See Addtech AB; *Int'l*, pg. 133
HY-LOK ASIA VALVES & FITTINGS PTE LTD.—See Hy-Lok Corporation; *Int'l*, pg. 3543
ICHOR SYSTEMS, INC.—See Francisco Partners Management, LP; *U.S. Private*, pg. 1590
INTERNATIONAL POLYMER SOLUTIONS INC.—See Graco, Inc.; *U.S. Public*, pg. 954
KADANT UNAFLEX LLC—See Kadant Inc.; *U.S. Public*, pg. 1212
LEGRIS DANMARK APS—See Parker Hannifin Corporation; *U.S. Public*, pg. 1645
LEGRIS DO BRASIL LTDA.—See Parker Hannifin Corporation; *U.S. Public*, pg. 1645
LEGRIS HUNGARIA KFT—See Parker Hannifin Corporation; *U.S. Public*, pg. 1645
LEGRIS INDIA PVT. LTD.—See Parker Hannifin Corporation; *U.S. Public*, pg. 1645
LEGRIS POLAND SP. Z.O.O.—See Parker Hannifin Corporation; *U.S. Public*, pg. 1645
LEGRIS S.A.S.—See Parker Hannifin Corporation; *U.S. Public*, pg. 1645
LEGRIS, S.R.O.—See Parker Hannifin Corporation; *U.S. Public*, pg. 1645
LOURDES INDUSTRIES INC.; *U.S. Private*, pg. 2500
MAC VALVES EUROPE, INC.—See MAC Valves, Inc.; *U.S. Private*, pg. 2531
MAC VALVES, INC.; *U.S. Private*, pg. 2531
MAC VALVES PACIFIC—See MAC Valves, Inc.; *U.S. Private*, pg. 2531
NEWAGE INDUSTRIES, INC. - ADVANTAPURE DIVISION—See NewAge Industries, Inc.; *U.S. Private*, pg. 2913
NEXUS VALVE, INC.—See Aalberts N.V.; *Int'l*, pg. 35
NYCOIL COMPANY—See Parker Hannifin Corporation; *U.S. Public*, pg. 1646
THE OILGEAR COMPANY—See Wynnchurch Capital, L.P.; *U.S. Private*, pg. 4578
OLAER AUSTRALIA PTY LTD—See Parker Hannifin Corporation; *U.S. Public*, pg. 1643
ORSCHELN TECHNOLOGIES PVT LTD.—See Orscheln Group; *U.S. Private*, pg. 3045
PARKER HANNIFIN A/S—See Parker Hannifin Corporation; *U.S. Public*, pg. 1645
PARKER HANNIFIN ESPANA SA—See Parker Hannifin Corporation; *U.S. Public*, pg. 1645
PARKER HANNIFIN GES.M.B.H.—See Parker Hannifin Corporation; *U.S. Public*, pg. 1645
PARKER HANNIFIN GMBH & CO. KG HOSE PRODUCTS DIVISION EUROPE—See Parker Hannifin Corporation; *U.S. Public*, pg. 1646
PARKER HANNIFIN GMBH—See Parker Hannifin Corporation; *U.S. Public*, pg. 1646
PARKER HANNIFIN GMBH—See Parker Hannifin Corporation; *U.S. Public*, pg. 1646
PARKER HANNIFIN HOSE PRODUCTS DIVISION—See Parker Hannifin Corporation; *U.S. Public*, pg. 1646
PARKER HANNIFIN HYDRAULIC VALVE DIV.—See Parker Hannifin Corporation; *U.S. Public*, pg. 1647
PARKER HANNIFIN INDUSTRIAL HOSE PRODUCTS DIVISION—See Parker Hannifin Corporation; *U.S. Public*, pg. 1646
PARKER HANNIFIN LIMITED—See Parker Hannifin Corporation; *U.S. Public*, pg. 1648
PARKER HANNIFIN MANUFACTURING SRL—See Parker Hannifin Corporation; *U.S. Public*, pg. 1648
PARKER HANNIFIN—See Crane NXT, Co.; *U.S. Public*, pg. 590
PARKER HANNIFIN STRATOFLEX PRODUCTS DIVISION-MANSFIELD HOSE PLANT—See Parker Hannifin Corporation; *U.S. Public*, pg. 1646
PARKER SPORLAN DIVISION—See Parker Hannifin Corporation; *U.S. Public*, pg. 1644
PENTAIR VALVES & CONTROLS, INC. - BATON ROUGE—See Emerson Electric Co.; *U.S. Public*, pg. 751
POLYFLON COMPANY—See Crane NXT, Co.; *U.S. Public*, pg. 590
POLYHOSE INDIA (RUBBER) PRIVATE LIMITED—See Caterpillar, Inc.; *U.S. Public*, pg. 453
PREECE, INC.; *U.S. Private*, pg. 3247
P.T. CRANE INDONESIA—See Crane NXT, Co.; *U.S. Public*, pg. 591
PUMP PRO'S, INC.—See Applied Industrial Technologies, Inc.; *U.S. Public*, pg. 171
REXNORD POWER TRANSMISSION PRODUCTS (TAICING) CO. LTD.—See Zurn Elkay Water Solutions Corporation; *U.S. Public*, pg. 2413
REXNORD TOLLOK SRL—See Zurn Elkay Water Solutions Corporation; *U.S. Public*, pg. 2413
RODNEY HUNT-FONTAINE, INC.—See Zurn Elkay Water Solutions Corporation; *U.S. Public*, pg. 2414
SCHRADER INTERNATIONAL BRASIL LTDA.—See Sensata Technologies Holding plc; *U.S. Public*, pg. 1866
SCHRADER INTERNATIONAL, INC.—See Sensata Technologies Holding plc; *U.S. Public*, pg. 1866

SCHRADER SAS—See Sensata Technologies Holding plc; *U.S. Public*, pg. 1866
SOCLA VALVES AND CONTROLS IBERICA SA—See Watts Water Technologies, Inc.; *U.S. Public*, pg. 2337
SPECMA DO BRASIL LTDA—See Aktieselskabet Schouw & Co.; *Int'l*, pg. 266
SPECMA HYDRAULIC U.S. INC.—See Aktieselskabet Schouw & Co.; *Int'l*, pg. 266
SPECMA HYDRAULIKHUSET AB—See Aktieselskabet Schouw & Co.; *Int'l*, pg. 266
SPECMA OY—See Aktieselskabet Schouw & Co.; *Int'l*, pg. 266
SUN HYDRAULICS CHINA CO., LTD.—See Helios Technologies, Inc.; *U.S. Public*, pg. 1023
SUN HYDRAULICS KOREA CORPORATION—See Helios Technologies, Inc.; *U.S. Public*, pg. 1024
SUN HYDRAULICS LIMITED—See Helios Technologies, Inc.; *U.S. Public*, pg. 1024
SUN HYDRAULIK GMBH—See Helios Technologies, Inc.; *U.S. Public*, pg. 1024
TACTAIR FLUID CONTROLS INC—See TransDigm Group Incorporated; *U.S. Public*, pg. 2183
TECNORD S.R.L.—See Delta Power Co.; *U.S. Private*, pg. 1201
TIANJIN TANGGU WATTS VALVE CO., LTD.—See Watts Water Technologies, Inc.; *U.S. Public*, pg. 2337
UNISOURCE MANUFACTURING, INC.—See AEA Investors LP; *U.S. Private*, pg. 115
VAG ARMATUREN CHILE LIMITADA—See Zurn Elkay Water Solutions Corporation; *U.S. Public*, pg. 2414
VAG VALVES FRANCE SARL—See Zurn Elkay Water Solutions Corporation; *U.S. Public*, pg. 2414
VAG VALVES UK LIMITED—See Zurn Elkay Water Solutions Corporation; *U.S. Public*, pg. 2414
VALLEY INDUSTRIES, LLP—See Emak S.p.A.; *Int'l*, pg. 2373
VANZANDT CONTROLS, LLC; *U.S. Private*, pg. 4345
VERNAY LABORATORIES, INC—See Vernay Laboratories, Inc.; *U.S. Private*, pg. 4368
VERNAY MANUFACTURING (SUZHOU) CO., LTD.—See Vernay Laboratories, Inc.; *U.S. Private*, pg. 4368
VERSA PRODUCTS COMPANY, INC.; *U.S. Private*, pg. 4369
VEXVE OY—See DevCo Partners Oy; *Int'l*, pg. 2086
WESTLOCK CONTROLS CORPORATION—See Crane NXT, Co.; *U.S. Public*, pg. 592
WUZHONG INSTRUMENT COMPANY LIMITED—See China Automation Group Limited; *Int'l*, pg. 1484
YOUNG & FRANKLIN, INC.—See TransDigm Group Incorporated; *U.S. Public*, pg. 2183

332913 — PLUMBING FIXTURE FITTING AND TRIM MANUFACTURING

ALPHA DIVISIONS PUBLIC COMPANY LIMITED; *Int'l*, pg. 368
AMERICAN BATH GROUP; *U.S. Private*, pg. 224
ANDERSON METALS, LLC—See Gemspring Capital Management, LLC; *U.S. Private*, pg. 1659
AQERO VERTRIEBS GMBH—See Development Bank of Japan, Inc.; *Int'l*, pg. 2087
ARROW FASTENER (U.K.) LIMITED—See Masco Corporation; *U.S. Public*, pg. 1391
A.Y. MCDONALD MANUFACTURING CO.; *U.S. Private*, pg. 29
BENJAMIN FRANKLIN PLUMBING; *U.S. Private*, pg. 526
BRASSTECH, INC.—See Masco Corporation; *U.S. Public*, pg. 1390
BURT PROCESS EQUIPMENT INC.; *U.S. Private*, pg. 692
CALIFORNIA FAUCETS INC.; *U.S. Private*, pg. 719
CELLO PRODUCTS INC.; *Int'l*, pg. 1394
THE CHICAGO FAUCET COMPANY—See Geberit AG; *Int'l*, pg. 2905
C.I. HOLDINGS BERHAD; *Int'l*, pg. 1243
CONTOUR SHOWERS LIMITED; *Int'l*, pg. 1785
CRANE BUILDING SERVICES & UTILITIES—See Crane NXT, Co.; *U.S. Public*, pg. 590
CRS S.P.A.—See Derichebourg S.A.; *Int'l*, pg. 2041
DAL-GEORG ROST & SOHNE SANITARARMATUREN GMBH—See Development Bank of Japan, Inc.; *Int'l*, pg. 2087
DEER BRIDGE PLUMBING & HEATING LTD.; *Int'l*, pg. 2003
DELTA FAUCET COMPANY—See Masco Corporation; *U.S. Public*, pg. 1391
DELTA FAUCET COMPANY—See Masco Corporation; *U.S. Public*, pg. 1391
DELTA FAUCET COMPANY—See Masco Corporation; *U.S. Public*, pg. 1391
DELTA FAUCET OF OKLAHOMA, INC.—See Masco Corporation; *U.S. Public*, pg. 1391
DOBY VERROLEC LTD—See Heitkamp & Thumann KG; *Int'l*, pg. 3326
DOE INDUSTRIES SDN. BHD.—See C.I. Holdings Berhad; *Int'l*, pg. 1243
D'VONTZ; *U.S. Private*, pg. 1139

N.A.I.C.S. INDEX

332919 — OTHER METAL VALVE A...

ELJER, INC.—See Sun Capital Partners, Inc.; *U.S. Private*, pg. 3858
ERICKSON CONSTRUCTION, LP—See Masco Corporation; *U.S. Public*, pg. 1390
FASMA A.D.; *Int'l*, pg. 2621
FERNCO INCORPORATED; *U.S. Private*, pg. 1497
FISHER MANUFACTURING COMPANY; *U.S. Private*, pg. 1534
FLUIDMASTER, INC.; *U.S. Private*, pg. 1552
FM MATTSSON MORA GROUP AB; *Int'l*, pg. 2717
FM MATTSSON MORA GROUP BELGIE NV—See FM Mattsson Mora Group AB; *Int'l*, pg. 2717
THE FORD METER BOX COMPANY, INC.; *U.S. Private*, pg. 4029
FRANKE AQUAROTTER GMBH—See Artemis Holding AG; *Int'l*, pg. 582
FRANKE CONSUMER PRODUCTS, INC.—See Artemis Holding AG; *Int'l*, pg. 582
FUDA FAUCET WORKS, INC.; *Int'l*, pg. 2804
FV S.A.; *Int'l*, pg. 2859
GENERAL ALUMINUM—See Park-Ohio Holdings Corp.; *U.S. Public*, pg. 1639
GENOVA EAST EUROPE—See Genova Products, Inc.; *U.S. Private*, pg. 1673
GENOVA WESTERN EUROPE—See Genova Products, Inc.; *U.S. Private*, pg. 1673
GEORG FISCHER LTD—See Georg Fischer AG; *Int'l*, pg. 2936
GEORG FISCHER PIPING SYSTEMS LTD—See Georg Fischer AG; *Int'l*, pg. 2936
GEORG FISCHER ROHRLEITUNGSSYSTEME AG—See Georg Fischer AG; *Int'l*, pg. 2937
GEORG FISCHER ROHRLEITUNGSSYSTEME (ELVETIA) S.A.—See Georg Fischer AG; *Int'l*, pg. 2936
GERBER PLUMBING FIXTURES CORPORATION; *U.S. Private*, pg. 1686
GLOBE UNION INDUSTRIAL CORP.; *Int'l*, pg. 3007
GROHE AG—See Development Bank of Japan, Inc.; *Int'l*, pg. 2087
GROHE AMERICA, INC.—See Development Bank of Japan, Inc.; *Int'l*, pg. 2088
GROHE A/S—See Development Bank of Japan, Inc.; *Int'l*, pg. 2087
GROHE AS—See Development Bank of Japan, Inc.; *Int'l*, pg. 2088
GROHEDAL SANITARSYSTEME GMBH & CO. KG—See Development Bank of Japan, Inc.; *Int'l*, pg. 2087
GROHE DEUTSCHLAND VERTRIEBS GMBH—See Development Bank of Japan, Inc.; *Int'l*, pg. 2088
GROHE ESPANA, S.A.—See Development Bank of Japan, Inc.; *Int'l*, pg. 2088
GROHE GMBH—See Development Bank of Japan, Inc.; *Int'l*, pg. 2088
GROHE JAPAN LTD.—See Development Bank of Japan, Inc.; *Int'l*, pg. 2088
GROHE LIMITED—See Development Bank of Japan, Inc.; *Int'l*, pg. 2088
GROHE NEDERLAND B.V.—See Development Bank of Japan, Inc.; *Int'l*, pg. 2088
GROHE N.V. S.A.—See Development Bank of Japan, Inc.; *Int'l*, pg. 2088
GROHE PACIFIC PTE. LTD.—See Development Bank of Japan, Inc.; *Int'l*, pg. 2088
GROHE POLSKA SP. Z O.O.—See Development Bank of Japan, Inc.; *Int'l*, pg. 2088
GROHE S.A.R.L.—See Development Bank of Japan, Inc.; *Int'l*, pg. 2088
GROHE S.P.A.—See Development Bank of Japan, Inc.; *Int'l*, pg. 2088
GROHE WATER TECHNOLOGY AG & CO. KG—See Development Bank of Japan, Inc.; *Int'l*, pg. 2088
HAFA BATHROOM GROUP AB; *Int'l*, pg. 3206
HAMAT GROUP LTD.; *Int'l*, pg. 3236
HANSGROHE A.B.—See Masco Corporation; *U.S. Public*, pg. 1390
HANSGROHE HANDELSGES.MBH—See Masco Corporation; *U.S. Public*, pg. 1390
HANSGROHE INTERNATIONAL GMBH—See Masco Corporation; *U.S. Public*, pg. 1390
HANSGROHE JAPAN KK—See Masco Corporation; *U.S. Public*, pg. 1390
HANSGROHE OOO—See Masco Corporation; *U.S. Public*, pg. 1391
HANSGROHE S.A.—See Masco Corporation; *U.S. Public*, pg. 1390
HANSGROHE SP. Z O.O.—See Masco Corporation; *U.S. Public*, pg. 1390
H.D. EICHELBERG & CO. GMBH—See Development Bank of Japan, Inc.; *Int'l*, pg. 2088
HOT SPRING SPAS NEW ZEALAND—See Masco Corporation; *U.S. Public*, pg. 1392
HUNTER INDUSTRIES INCORPORATED; *U.S. Private*, pg. 2010
HUPPE BELGIUM N.V./S.A.—See Masco Corporation; *U.S. Public*, pg. 1391
HUPPE B.V.—See Masco Corporation; *U.S. Public*, pg. 1391
HUPPE SPAIN, S.L.U.—See Masco Corporation; *U.S. Public*, pg. 1391

HUPPE SP. Z O.O.—See Masco Corporation; *U.S. Public*, pg. 1391
IDEAL STANDARD S.R.O.—See Anchorage Capital Group, L.L.C.; *U.S. Private*, pg. 274
IDEAL STANDARD S.R.O.—See CVC Capital Partners SICAV-FIS S.A.; *Int'l*, pg. 1888
JAY R. SMITH MFG. CO.; *U.S. Private*, pg. 2192
JB INDUSTRIES, INC.; *U.S. Private*, pg. 2193
J.R. SMITH MANUFACTURING COMPANY—See Jay R. Smith Mfg. Co.; *U.S. Private*, pg. 2192
JUST MANUFACTURING LLC—See Zurn Elkay Water Solutions Corporation; *U.S. Public*, pg. 2413
KALLISTA, INC.—See Kohler Company; *U.S. Private*, pg. 2339
KEENEY MANUFACTURING COMPANY—See United Plumbing Technologies; *U.S. Private*, pg. 4295
KERMI GMBH—See Arbonia AG; *Int'l*, pg. 538
KOHLER CANADA LTD.—See Kohler Company; *U.S. Private*, pg. 2339
KOHLER FRANCE S.A.S.—See Kohler Company; *U.S. Private*, pg. 2340
KOHLER JAPAN K.K.—See Kohler Company; *U.S. Private*, pg. 2340
LDR INDUSTRIES, INC.; *U.S. Private*, pg. 2404
LEE BRASS COMPANY; *U.S. Private*, pg. 2411
MAAX CANADA INC.—See American Bath Group; *U.S. Private*, pg. 224
MAAX INC.-VALDOSTA—See American Bath Group; *U.S. Private*, pg. 224
MAINFAUCET.COM—See Kenry Home Improvement Network, Inc.; *U.S. Private*, pg. 2287
MASCO CANADA LIMITED—See Masco Corporation; *U.S. Public*, pg. 1390
MASCOMEX S.A. DE C.V.—See Masco Corporation; *U.S. Public*, pg. 1392
MASCO RETAIL SALES SUPPORT, INC.—See Masco Corporation; *U.S. Public*, pg. 1391
MASCO SERVICES GROUP CORP.—See Masco Corporation; *U.S. Public*, pg. 1391
MCGUIRE MANUFACTURING—See Bead Industries Inc.; *U.S. Private*, pg. 505
MERIT BRASS COMPANY INC.; *U.S. Private*, pg. 2674
MIDLAND METAL MFG. CO., INC.—See Gemspring Capital Management, LLC; *U.S. Private*, pg. 1659
MOEN INCORPORATED—See Fortune Brands Innovations, Inc.; *U.S. Public*, pg. 873
PEERLESS FAUCET CORPORATION—See Masco Corporation; *U.S. Public*, pg. 1391
PLUMB SHOP—See Masco Corporation; *U.S. Public*, pg. 1392
POLYPIPE LIMITED - POLYPIPE TERRAIN DIVISION—See Genuit Group plc; *Int'l*, pg. 2930
PRICE PFISTER, INC.—See Spectrum Brands Holdings, Inc.; *U.S. Public*, pg. 1917
SIGNATURE HARDWARE; *U.S. Private*, pg. 3650
SPEAKMAN COMPANY; *U.S. Private*, pg. 3747
STANDARD HIDRAULICA, S.A.U.—See H.I.G. Capital, LLC; *U.S. Private*, pg. 1828
SYMMONS INDUSTRIES, INC.; *U.S. Private*, pg. 3899
TELSCO INDUSTRIES, INC.; *U.S. Private*, pg. 3962
TEMPERED PRODUCTS, INC.—See Masco Corporation; *U.S. Public*, pg. 1392
TRENTON PIPE NIPPLE COMPANY LLC—See Tailwind Capital Group, LLC; *U.S. Private*, pg. 3923
T&S BRASS & BRONZE WORKS, INC.; *U.S. Private*, pg. 3910
UNITED PLUMBING TECHNOLOGIES; *U.S. Private*, pg. 4295
VINYL CORP.—See Worthington Industries, Inc.; *U.S. Public*, pg. 2382
WATTS INDUSTRIES DEUTCHLAND GMBH—See Watts Water Technologies, Inc.; *U.S. Public*, pg. 2337
WATTS INDUSTRIES EUROPE B.V.—See Watts Water Technologies, Inc.; *U.S. Public*, pg. 2337
WAVIN ESTONIA OU—See Bharti Enterprises Limited; *Int'l*, pg. 1012
WAVIN-LABKO OY - PE FACTORY—See Bharti Enterprises Limited; *Int'l*, pg. 1013
WCM INDUSTRIES INC.; *U.S. Private*, pg. 4461
WOLSELEY CANADA INC.—See Ferguson plc; *Int'l*, pg. 2638
ZSI-FOSTER, INC.—See TruArc Partners, L.P.; *U.S. Private*, pg. 4245
ZURN INDUSTRIES LIMITED—See Zurn Elkay Water Solutions Corporation; *U.S. Public*, pg. 2414
ZURN PLUMBING PRODUCTS GROUP—See Zurn Elkay Water Solutions Corporation; *U.S. Public*, pg. 2413

332919 — OTHER METAL VALVE AND PIPE FITTING MANUFACTURING

AALBERTS INTEGRATED PIPING SYSTEMS APAC INC.—See Aalberts N.V.; *Int'l*, pg. 33
AALBERTS INTEGRATED PIPING SYSTEMS B.V.—See Aalberts N.V.; *Int'l*, pg. 33
AIRDROME PRECISION COMPONENTS—See Berkshire Hathaway Inc.; *U.S. Public*, pg. 313

ALBERT GREIFENBERG GMBH & CO. KG; *Int'l*, pg. 297
ALOYS F. DORNBRACHT GMBH & CO. KG; *Int'l*, pg. 365
AMERON INTERNATIONAL WATER TRANSMISSION GROUP—See NOV, Inc.; *U.S. Public*, pg. 1544
APEX VALVES LIMITED—See Watts Water Technologies, Inc.; *U.S. Public*, pg. 2337
A.P. SERVICES, LLC—See Curtiss-Wright Corporation; *U.S. Public*, pg. 612
AQUAMINE, LLC—See Victaulic Company; *U.S. Private*, pg. 4377
AQUATROL CORPORATION—See JM Process Systems Inc.; *U.S. Private*, pg. 2214
ASC ENGINEERED SOLUTIONS, LLC—See Tailwind Capital Group, LLC; *U.S. Private*, pg. 3923
ASSOCIATED VALVE—See Canerector Inc.; *Int'l*, pg. 1290
ATAM VALVES LIMITED; *Int'l*, pg. 666
AUTOMATIC MACHINE PRODUCTS COMPANY; *U.S. Private*, pg. 399
AXENICS, INC.; *U.S. Private*, pg. 412
BALON CORPORATION; *U.S. Private*, pg. 462
BETE FOG NOZZLE INC.; *U.S. Private*, pg. 545
BETTIS CANADA LTD.—See Emerson Electric Co.; *U.S. Public*, pg. 746
BETTS INDUSTRIES INC.; *U.S. Private*, pg. 547
BILFINGER SCHEVEN GMBH—See Bilfinger SE; *Int'l*, pg. 1026
BRASSCRAFT MANUFACTURING COMPANY—See Masco Corporation; *U.S. Public*, pg. 1390
BRASSCRAFT MANUFACTURING COMPANY—See Masco Corporation; *U.S. Public*, pg. 1390
BRASSCRAFT MANUFACTURING COMPANY—See Masco Corporation; *U.S. Public*, pg. 1390
BRITISH PIPE SUPPORTS (JINGJIANG) LIMITED—See Hill & Smith PLC; *Int'l*, pg. 3391
BS&B SAFETY SYSTEMS, LLC; *U.S. Private*, pg. 674
BUCHER UNIPEKTIN LTD—See Bucher Industries AG; *Int'l*, pg. 1208
CAMERON VALVES & MEASUREMENT - LITTLE ROCK—See Schlumberger Limited; *U.S. Public*, pg. 1844
CAMPBELL FITTINGS, INC.—See TruArc Partners, L.P.; *U.S. Private*, pg. 4245
CARPENTER & PATERSON INC.; *U.S. Private*, pg. 770
C&D VALVE LLC—See JB Industries, Inc.; *U.S. Private*, pg. 2193
C.E. MACPHERSON DIVISION OF CONREX STEEL LTD.—See Canerector Inc.; *Int'l*, pg. 1290
CENTURY INDUSTRIES COMPANY—See Emerson Electric Co.; *U.S. Public*, pg. 751
CHINA VALVES TECHNOLOGY, INC.; *Int'l*, pg. 1561
CHOMERICS - MEXICO—See Parker Hannifin Corporation; *U.S. Public*, pg. 1649
CIRCOR INTERNATIONAL, INC.—See KKR & Co. Inc.; *U.S. Public*, pg. 1242
CLARK-RELIANCE CORPORATION; *U.S. Private*, pg. 914
CLOW VALVE DIVISION—See McWane, Inc.; *U.S. Private*, pg. 2645
CMT ENGINEERING—See Caparo Group Ltd.; *Int'l*, pg. 1302
COOK-MFS, INC.—See Dover Corporation; *U.S. Public*, pg. 679
CROSBY-NATIONAL SWAGE CO.—See KKR & Co. Inc.; *U.S. Public*, pg. 1264
CURTISS-WRIGHT VALVE GROUP-FARRIS—See Curtiss-Wright Corporation; *U.S. Public*, pg. 611
CUSTOM ALLOYS CORPORATION—See J.F. Lehman & Company, Inc.; *U.S. Private*, pg. 2164
DANFOSS D.O.O.—See Danfoss A/S; *Int'l*, pg. 1961
DANFOSS S.A.—See Danfoss A/S; *Int'l*, pg. 1961
DEFINOX INC.—See Alfa Laval AB; *Int'l*, pg. 309
DELAVAN SPRAY, LLC—See R.W. Beckett Corporation; *U.S. Private*, pg. 3340
DESIGNED METAL CONNECTIONS, INC.—See Berkshire Hathaway Inc.; *U.S. Public*, pg. 314
DEUBLIN GMBH—See Hoerbiger Holding AG; *Int'l*, pg. 3439
DEUBLIN ITALIANA S.R.L.—See Hoerbiger Holding AG; *Int'l*, pg. 3439
DEUBLIN JAPAN LTD.—See Hoerbiger Holding AG; *Int'l*, pg. 3439
DEUBLIN KOREA CO. LTD.—See Hoerbiger Holding AG; *Int'l*, pg. 3439
DEUBLIN LTD.—See Hoerbiger Holding AG; *Int'l*, pg. 3439
DEUBLIN S.A.R.L.—See Hoerbiger Holding AG; *Int'l*, pg. 3440
DEXTER HYSOL AEROSPACE LLC—See Henkel AG & Co. KGaA; *Int'l*, pg. 3353
DIXON VALVE & COUPLING COMPANY - DIXON SANITARY DIVISION—See Dixon Valve & Coupling Company; *U.S. Private*, pg. 1246
DSO FLUID HANDLING CO., INC.—See Audax Group, Limited Partnership; *U.S. Private*, pg. 388
EAGLEBURGMANN JAPAN CO., LTD.—See Eagle Industry Co., Ltd.; *Int'l*, pg. 2265
EAGLEBURGMANN JAPAN CO., LTD.—See Freudenberg SE; *Int'l*, pg. 2784
EKK EAGLE (THAILAND) CO. LTD.—See Eagle Industry Co., Ltd.; *Int'l*, pg. 2265
ELKHART PRODUCTS CORP.-ELKHART PLANT—See

332919 — OTHER METAL VALVE A...

Mueller Industries, Inc.; *U.S. Public*, pg. 1484
ELKHART PRODUCTS CORPORATION-INDUSTRIAL DIVISION—See Mueller Industries, Inc.; *U.S. Public*, pg. 1484
ELKHART PRODUCTS CORPORATION—See Mueller Industries, Inc.; *U.S. Public*, pg. 1484
EMERSON AUTOMATION SOLUTIONS NETHERLANDS—See Emerson Electric Co.; *U.S. Public*, pg. 743
EMERSON PROCESS MANAGEMENT MAGYARORSZAG KFT.—See Emerson Electric Co.; *U.S. Public*, pg. 748
EMERSON SALES (UK) LIMITED—See Emerson Electric Co.; *U.S. Public*, pg. 749
ENGTEX DUCTILE IRON PIPES INDUSTRY SDN. BHD.—See Engtex Group Berhad; *Int'l*, pg. 2436
EQUALIZER FLANGE TOOL INNOVATION CO. LTD.—See Enerpac Tool Group Corp.; *U.S. Public*, pg. 765
EQUALIZER INTERNATIONAL INC.—See Enerpac Tool Group Corp.; *U.S. Public*, pg. 765
EVERLASTING VALVE CO.—See Armstrong International, Inc.; *U.S. Private*, pg. 332
EZEFLOW, INC.—See Allied Fitting LP; *U.S. Private*, pg. 186
FERRO S.A.; *Int'l*, pg. 2642
FIKE CORPORATION; *U.S. Private*, pg. 1505
FIKE EUROPE—See Fike Corporation; *U.S. Private*, pg. 1505
FITTERS DIVERSIFIED BERHAD; *Int'l*, pg. 2695
FULFLO SPECIALTIES—See Ruthman Pump & Engineering Inc.; *U.S. Private*, pg. 3508
GA INDUSTRIES, INC.—See Zurn Elkay Water Solutions Corporation; *U.S. Public*, pg. 2413
GEA MECHANICAL EQUIPMENT GMBH—See GEA Group Aktiengesellschaft; *Int'l*, pg. 2899
GENERAL PLUG & MANUFACTURING CO.; *U.S. Private*, pg. 1666
GENOYER S.A.—See Groupe BPCE; *Int'l*, pg. 3095
GEORG FISCHER SP. Z.O.O.—See Georg Fischer AG; *Int'l*, pg. 2937
GEORG FISCHER WAGA N.V.—See Georg Fischer AG; *Int'l*, pg. 2937
GLYNWED PIPE SYSTEMS LTD.—See Aliaxis S.A./N.V.; *Int'l*, pg. 324
GOLAN PIPE SYSTEMS APS—See Golan Plastic Products Ltd.; *Int'l*, pg. 3023
GREENVILLE METALS, INC.—See Berkshire Hathaway Inc.; *U.S. Public*, pg. 315
GRISWOLD CONTROLS; *U.S. Private*, pg. 1790
HALFEN GMBH—See CRH plc; *Int'l*, pg. 1844
HALLMARK CARDS, INC. - CENTER FIXTURE OPERATIONS—See Hallmark Cards, Inc.; *U.S. Private*, pg. 1844
HAM-LET (ISRAEL-CANADA) LTD.—See Ultra Clean Holdings, Inc.; *U.S. Public*, pg. 2223
HAMMOND VALVE CORP.—See Milwaukee Valve Company, Inc.; *U.S. Private*, pg. 2739
HARRIS/ARIZONA REBAR, INC.—See Nucor Corporation; *U.S. Public*, pg. 1553
HARRIS REBAR SEATTLE, INC.—See Nucor Corporation; *U.S. Public*, pg. 1553
HARRIS SALINAS REBAR , INC.—See Nucor Corporation; *U.S. Public*, pg. 1553
HEAT PIPE TECHNOLOGY, INC.—See Berkshire Hathaway Inc.; *U.S. Public*, pg. 312
HE HARBIN POWER PLANT VALVE CO., LTD.—See Harbin Electric Corporation; *Int'l*, pg. 3270
HENCO INDUSTRIES N.V.—See Aalberts N.V.; *Int'l*, pg. 34
HOLMGRENS METALL AKTIEBOLAGET—See Aalberts N.V.; *Int'l*, pg. 34
HYDRA-STOP, INC.—See IDEX Corp; *U.S. Public*, pg. 1089
HYDROLEVEL COMPANY—See C. Cowles & Co.; *U.S. Private*, pg. 705
IHARA SCIENCE CORPORATION; *Int'l*, pg. 3603
INCOE CORPORATION; *U.S. Private*, pg. 2054
IR SECURITY TECHNOLOGIES—See Ingersoll Rand Inc.; *U.S. Public*, pg. 1121
ITT ENGINEERED VALVES, LLC—See ITT Inc.; *U.S. Public*, pg. 1178
ITT INDUSTRIES INC.—See ITT Inc.; *U.S. Public*, pg. 1178
JAMES JONES COMPANY, LLC—See Mueller Water Products, Inc.; *U.S. Public*, pg. 1485
KADANT JOHNSON INC.—See Kadant Inc.; *U.S. Public*, pg. 1212
KEMPER VALVE & FITTINGS CORP.—See Caterpillar, Inc.; *U.S. Public*, pg. 452
KENNAMETAL ADVANCED MATERIALS SOLUTIONS GROUP—See Kennametal Inc.; *U.S. Public*, pg. 1221
KEYSTONE VALVE (KOREA) LLC—See Emerson Electric Co.; *U.S. Public*, pg. 751
KF INDUSTRIES, INC.—See KKR & Co. Inc.; *U.S. Public*, pg. 1242
KRAUSZ INDUSTRIES LTD.—See Mueller Water Products, Inc.; *U.S. Public*, pg. 1485
KRAUSZ USA INC.—See Mueller Water Products, Inc.; *U.S. Public*, pg. 1485
LASCO FITTINGS INC.—See Aalberts N.V.; *Int'l*, pg. 35
LEONARD VALVE COMPANY—See Bessemer Investment Partners LLC; *U.S. Private*, pg. 541
MARLEY POLSKA LTD.—See Etex SA/NV; *Int'l*, pg. 2522

MAROTTA CONTROLS, INC.; *U.S. Private*, pg. 2586
MATTSCO SUPPLY CO.; *U.S. Private*, pg. 2614
MICROFLEX INC.; *U.S. Private*, pg. 2703
MID-AMERICA FITTINGS, INC.—See Gemspring Capital Management, LLC; *U.S. Private*, pg. 1659
MILWAUKEE VALVE COMPANY, INC.; *U.S. Private*, pg. 2739
MOGAS INDUSTRIES, LTD—See Flowserve Corporation; *U.S. Public*, pg. 857
MORRISON BROTHERS COMPANY; *U.S. Private*, pg. 2789
MRC TRANSMARK—See MRC Global Inc.; *U.S. Public*, pg. 1481
MSI SUPPLY, INC.—See Winsupply, Inc.; *U.S. Private*, pg. 4545
MUELLER STEAM SPECIALTY—See Watts Water Technologies, Inc.; *U.S. Public*, pg. 2337
NELSON IRRIGATION CORPORATION; *U.S. Private*, pg. 2883
NIBCO INC.; *U.S. Private*, pg. 2924
NIBCO SP. Z O.O.—See NIBCO Inc.; *U.S. Private*, pg. 2924
NOR-CAL PRODUCTS, INC.—See Dr. Ing. K. Busch GmbH; *Int'l*, pg. 2193
OPW FUELING COMPONENTS—See Dover Corporation; *U.S. Public*, pg. 679
ORBIT IRRIGATION PRODUCTS INC.—See Platinum Equity, LLC; *U.S. Private*, pg. 3207
OZZIE'S PIPELINE PADDER, INC.; *U.S. Private*, pg. 3058
PACIFIC VALVES—See Crane NXT, Co.; *U.S. Public*, pg. 590
PARKER CANADA—See Parker Hannifin Corporation; *U.S. Public*, pg. 1645
PARKER HANNIFIN AFRICA PTY LTD.—See Parker Hannifin Corporation; *U.S. Public*, pg. 1644
PARKER HANNIFIN ALMELO—See Parker Hannifin Corporation; *U.S. Public*, pg. 1645
PARKER HANNIFIN A/S—See Parker Hannifin Corporation; *U.S. Public*, pg. 1645
PARKER HANNIFIN BV, NETHERLANDS SALES & SERVICE—See Parker Hannifin Corporation; *U.S. Public*, pg. 1645
PARKER HANNIFIN (CANADA) INC., CYLINDER DIVISION—See Parker Hannifin Corporation; *U.S. Public*, pg. 1647
PARKER HANNIFIN CORPORATION-EAST EUROPEAN SALES OFFICE—See Parker Hannifin Corporation; *U.S. Public*, pg. 1646
PARKER HANNIFIN CORP., SLOVENIA—See Parker Hannifin Corporation; *U.S. Public*, pg. 1646
PARKER HANNIFIN DE MEXICO—See Parker Hannifin Corporation; *U.S. Public*, pg. 1646
PARKER HANNIFIN FLUID POWER SYSTEMS & COMPONENTS CO., LTD.—See Parker Hannifin Corporation; *U.S. Public*, pg. 1645
PARKER HANNIFIN GMBH & CO. KG O-RING DIVISION EUROPE—See Parker Hannifin Corporation; *U.S. Public*, pg. 1649
PARKER HANNIFIN GMBH & CO. KG PACKING DIVISION EUROPE—See Parker Hannifin Corporation; *U.S. Public*, pg. 1649
PARKER HANNIFIN GMBH & CO. KG POLYFLEX DIVISION—See Parker Hannifin Corporation; *U.S. Public*, pg. 1646
PARKER HANNIFIN GMBH & CO.—See Parker Hannifin Corporation; *U.S. Public*, pg. 1644
PARKER HANNIFIN HOOGEZAND B.V.—See Parker Hannifin Corporation; *U.S. Public*, pg. 1646
PARKER HANNIFIN INDIA PVT. LTD.—See Parker Hannifin Corporation; *U.S. Public*, pg. 1647
PARKER HANNIFIN INDUSTRIAL S.R.O.—See Parker Hannifin Corporation; *U.S. Public*, pg. 1647
PARKER HANNIFIN JAPAN LTD.—See Parker Hannifin Corporation; *U.S. Public*, pg. 1648
PARKER HANNIFIN JAPAN LTD.—See Parker Hannifin Corporation; *U.S. Public*, pg. 1648
PARKER HANNIFIN KOREA—See Parker Hannifin Corporation; *U.S. Public*, pg. 1648
PARKER HANNIFIN MFG POLAND SP. Z.O.O.—See Parker Hannifin Corporation; *U.S. Public*, pg. 1646
PARKER HANNIFIN MOSCOW—See Parker Hannifin Corporation; *U.S. Public*, pg. 1646
PARKER HANNIFIN MOTION & CONTROL SALES DIVISION CANADA—See Parker Hannifin Corporation; *U.S. Public*, pg. 1647
PARKER HANNIFIN (NZ) LTD.—See Parker Hannifin Corporation; *U.S. Public*, pg. 1644
PARKER HANNIFIN (NZ) LTD.—See Parker Hannifin Corporation; *U.S. Public*, pg. 1644
PARKER HANNIFIN PLC—See Parker Hannifin Corporation; *U.S. Public*, pg. 1646
PARKER HANNIFIN PNEUMATIC DIVISION—See Parker Hannifin Corporation; *U.S. Public*, pg. 1644
PARKER HANNIFIN PORTUGAL, LDA—See Parker Hannifin Corporation; *U.S. Public*, pg. 1646
PARKER HANNIFIN, QUICK COUPLING DIV.—See Parker Hannifin Corporation; *U.S. Public*, pg. 1646
PARKER HANNIFIN SA CLIMATE & INDUSTRIAL CONTROLS—See Parker Hannifin Corporation; *U.S. Public*, pg. 1644

PARKER HANNIFIN S.A.—See Parker Hannifin Corporation; *U.S. Public*, pg. 1647
PARKER HANNIFIN, SA—See Parker Hannifin Corporation; *U.S. Public*, pg. 1647
PARKER HANNIFIN SPA FLUID CONTROL DIVISION—See Parker Hannifin Corporation; *U.S. Public*, pg. 1646
PARKER HANNIFIN SP. Z.O.O.—See Parker Hannifin Corporation; *U.S. Public*, pg. 1646
PARKER HANNIFIN S.R.O.—See Parker Hannifin Corporation; *U.S. Public*, pg. 1646
PARKER HANNIFIN TAIWAN CO. LTD.—See Parker Hannifin Corporation; *U.S. Public*, pg. 1649
PARKER HANNIFIN THAILAND CO. LTD.—See Parker Hannifin Corporation; *U.S. Public*, pg. 1649
PARKER HANNIFIN TUBE FITTINGS DIV.—See Parker Hannifin Corporation; *U.S. Public*, pg. 1646
PARKER SEAL DE MEXICO, S.A.—See Parker Hannifin Corporation; *U.S. Public*, pg. 1649
PEERLESS EUROPE LTD.—See CECO Environmental Corp.; *U.S. Public*, pg. 464
PENTAIR VALVES & CONTROLS BRASIL LTDA.—See Emerson Electric Co.; *U.S. Public*, pg. 751
PENTAIR VALVES & CONTROLS CANADA INC. - BURLINGTON OFFICE—See Emerson Electric Co.; *U.S. Public*, pg. 751
PENTAIR VALVES & CONTROLS SINGAPORE PTE. LTD.—See Emerson Electric Co.; *U.S. Public*, pg. 751
PERMA-PIPE CANADA, LTD.—See Perma-Pipe International Holdings, Inc.; *U.S. Public*, pg. 1676
PERMASWAGE S.A.—See Berkshire Hathaway Inc.; *U.S. Public*, pg. 314
PHD MANUFACTURING INC.; *U.S. Private*, pg. 3167
PIBIVIESSE S.R.L.—See Certina Holding AG; *Int'l*, pg. 1423
PIERCE FITTINGS—See Fresno Valves & Castings Inc.; *U.S. Private*, pg. 1610
PIMA VALVE, INC.—See Arcline Investment Management LP; *U.S. Private*, pg. 313
PIPING TECHNOLOGY & PRODUCTS INC.; *U.S. Private*, pg. 3190
PROGRAM WATER TECHNOLOGIES—See Sloan Valve Company; *U.S. Private*, pg. 3689
RAIN BIRD CORPORATION; *U.S. Private*, pg. 3347
RATHGIBSON JANESVILLE LLC—See Berkshire Hathaway Inc.; *U.S. Public*, pg. 314
RHINE RUHR PUMPS & VALVES (PTY.) LTD.—See Aliaxis S.A./N.V.; *Int'l*, pg. 324
RIVE TECHNOLOGY INC—See Standard Industries Holdings Inc.; *U.S. Private*, pg. 3780
ROMAC INDUSTRIES, INC.; *U.S. Private*, pg. 3475
SAINT-GOBAIN CANALIZACAO S.A.—See Compagnie de Saint-Gobain SA; *Int'l*, pg. 1729
SBS—See Groupe BPCE; *Int'l*, pg. 3095
SC VILMAR S.A.—See Groupe BPCE; *Int'l*, pg. 3095
SLOAN FLUSHMATE—See Sloan Valve Company; *U.S. Private*, pg. 3689
SLOAN VALVE COMPANY, FOUNDRY DIV.—See Sloan Valve Company; *U.S. Private*, pg. 3689
SLOAN VALVE COMPANY; *U.S. Private*, pg. 3689
SOCLA S.A.S.—See Watts Water Technologies, Inc.; *U.S. Public*, pg. 2337
SOFIS BV—See Halma plc; *Int'l*, pg. 3233
SOFIS GMBH—See Halma plc; *Int'l*, pg. 3233
SPECIAL FLANGE SERVICES, LTD.—See Groupe BPCE; *Int'l*, pg. 3095
SSP FITTINGS CORP.; *U.S. Private*, pg. 3769
STAHLWERK BOUS GMBH—See Georgsmarienhutte Holding GmbH; *Int'l*, pg. 2941
THE STARFLO CORPORATION—See The Wm. Powell Company; *U.S. Private*, pg. 4138
STEEL & O'BRIEN MANUFACTURING, INC.—See Edgewater Services, LLC; *U.S. Private*, pg. 1335
STERIDOSE SALES AB—See IDEX Corp; *U.S. Public*, pg. 1092
STERIDOSE SALES INC.—See IDEX Corp; *U.S. Public*, pg. 1092
STOCKHAM VALVES & FITTINGS, INC.—See Crane NXT, Co.; *U.S. Public*, pg. 590
STRAHMAN VALVES, INC.—See Audax Group, Limited Partnership; *U.S. Private*, pg. 388
SWAGELOK COMPANY; *U.S. Private*, pg. 3889
SWECO FAB, INC.—See Piping Technology & Products Inc.; *U.S. Private*, pg. 3190
TAISEI KOKI CO., LTD.—See Fair Friend Group; *Int'l*, pg. 2605
TASK FORCE TIPS LLC—See John S. Frey Enterprises; *U.S. Private*, pg. 2224
TYCO VALVES & CONTROLS DE MEXICO, S.A. DE C.V.—See Emerson Electric Co.; *U.S. Public*, pg. 751
UNIVOLT REMAT S.R.O.—See Dietzel GmbH; *Int'l*, pg. 2117
UPONOR OYJ—See Georg Fischer AG; *Int'l*, pg. 2937
VACCO INDUSTRIES INC.—See ESCO Technologies, Inc.; *U.S. Public*, pg. 794
VALTERRA PRODUCTS, INC.; *U.S. Private*, pg. 4337
VERNON TOOL COMPANY, LTD.—See Lincoln Electric Holdings, Inc.; *U.S. Public*, pg. 1318
VICTAULIC ASIA-PACIFIC—See Victaulic Company; *U.S. Private*, pg. 4377
VICTAULIC COMPANY OF CANADA LIMITED—See Victau-

332991 — BALL AND ROLLER BEA...

lic Company; *U.S. Private*, pg. 4377
VICTAULIC COMPANY; *U.S. Private*, pg. 4377
VICTAULIC EUROPE—See Victaulic Company; *U.S. Private*, pg. 4377
VICTAULIC FIRE SAFETY COMPANY, LLC—See Victaulic Company; *U.S. Private*, pg. 4377
VICTAULIC INTERNATIONAL—See Victaulic Company; *U.S. Private*, pg. 4377
VICTAULIC MIDDLE EAST—See Victaulic Company; *U.S. Private*, pg. 4377
VICTAULIC TOOL COMPANY—See Victaulic Company; *U.S. Private*, pg. 4377
WARD MANUFACTURING LLC - WISCONSIN NIPPLE FACILITY—See Tailwind Capital Group, LLC; *U.S. Private*, pg. 3923
WATTS CHESNEE—See Watts Water Technologies, Inc.; *U.S. Public*, pg. 2337
WEATHERTEC CORPORATION; *U.S. Private*, pg. 4463
WESTBROOK SALES & DISTRIBUTING CORP—See L.E. Simmons & Associates, Inc.; *U.S. Private*, pg. 2365
WFI INTERNATIONAL, INC.—See Bonney Forge Corporation; *U.S. Private*, pg. 615
WHITCO SUPPLY, LLC—See DNOW Inc.; *U.S. Public*, pg. 671
WORLD WIDE FITTINGS, INC.; *U.S. Private*, pg. 4567
WYSTRACH GMBH—See Hexagon Composites ASA; *Int'l*, pg. 3370
YORKSHIRE FITTINGS GYARTO KFT—See Aalberts N.V.; *Int'l*, pg. 36

332991 — BALL AND ROLLER BEARING MANUFACTURING

ABC BEARINGS LIMITED—See The Timken Company; *U.S. Public*, pg. 2133
ADCOLE CORPORATION—See Artemis Capital Partners Management Co., LLC; *U.S. Private*, pg. 340
AETNA BEARING COMPANY; *U.S. Private*, pg. 120
ALL POWER MANUFACTURING CO.—See RBC Bearings Incorporated; *U.S. Public*, pg. 1766
AMERICAN ROLLER BEARING CO., INC.; *U.S. Private*, pg. 246
AMERICAN ROLLER BEARING COMPANY; *U.S. Private*, pg. 246
ASIAN BEARING LTD.; *Int'l*, pg. 617
AUSTIN ENGINEERING CO. LTD.; *Int'l*, pg. 718
AUSTRALIAN TIMKEN PROPRIETARY LTD.—See The Timken Company; *U.S. Public*, pg. 2132
AUTOCAM INTERNATIONAL, LTD—See NN, Inc.; *U.S. Public*, pg. 1530
BAOTA INDUSTRY CO., LTD.; *Int'l*, pg. 856
BBL DAIDO PRIVATE LIMITED—See Daido Metal Corporation; *Int'l*, pg. 1921
BDI-BEARING DISTRIBUTORS, INC.; *U.S. Private*, pg. 500
BERLISS BEARING CO.—See FICODIS Inc.; *Int'l*, pg. 2653
BIMETAL BEARINGS LTD—See Daido Metal Corporation; *Int'l*, pg. 1921
BOUVERAT INDUSTRIES, S.A.S.—See NN, Inc.; *U.S. Public*, pg. 1530
CANADIAN TIMKEN LTD.—See The Timken Company; *U.S. Public*, pg. 2132
CHANGSHA BODE METALLURGIC MATERIAL CO., LTD.—See Fujian Longxi Bearing (Group) Corporation Limited; *Int'l*, pg. 2818
CHANGZHOU NRB CORPORATION; *Int'l*, pg. 1445
CHELSEA GRINDING CO.—See NN, Inc.; *U.S. Public*, pg. 1531
CHINA HUANCHI BEARING GROUP CO., LTD.; *Int'l*, pg. 1509
CS BEARING CO., LTD.; *Int'l*, pg. 1861
DAIDO INDUSTRIAL BEARINGS EUROPE LTD.—See Daido Metal Corporation; *Int'l*, pg. 1921
DAIDO INDUSTRIAL BEARINGS JAPAN CO., LTD.—See Daido Metal Corporation; *Int'l*, pg. 1921
DAIDO METAL CORPORATION - BIMETAL DIVISION—See Daido Metal Corporation; *Int'l*, pg. 1921
DAIDO METAL CORPORATION - GIFU FACTORY—See Daido Metal Corporation; *Int'l*, pg. 1921
DAIDO METAL CORPORATION - INUYAMA FACTORY—See Daido Metal Corporation; *Int'l*, pg. 1921
DAIDO METAL CORPORATION - MAEHARA FACTORY—See Daido Metal Corporation; *Int'l*, pg. 1921
DAIDO METAL CORPORATION; *Int'l*, pg. 1921
DAIDO METAL CZECH S.R.O.—See Daido Metal Corporation; *Int'l*, pg. 1921
DAIDO METAL MEXICO, S.A. DE C.V.—See Daido Metal Corporation; *Int'l*, pg. 1921
DAIDO METAL SAGA CO., LTD.—See Daido Metal Corporation; *Int'l*, pg. 1921
DAIDO METAL SALES CO., LTD—See Daido Metal Corporation; *Int'l*, pg. 1921
DAIDO METAL U.S.A. INC—See Daido Metal Corporation; *Int'l*, pg. 1921
DANAHER MOTION—See Danaher Corporation; *U.S. Public*, pg. 626
D&E BEARINGS AB; *Int'l*, pg. 1899
D&E BEARINGS OY; *Int'l*, pg. 1899

DECCAN BEARINGS LIMITED; *Int'l*, pg. 1999
DEL-TRON PRECISION, INC.; *U.S. Private*, pg. 1193
DESIGNATRONICS, INC. - QUALITY BEARINGS & COMPONENTS DIVISION—See Designatronics, Inc.; *U.S. Private*, pg. 1214
DODGE INDUSTRIAL AUSTRALIA PTY LTD.—See RBC Bearings Incorporated; *U.S. Public*, pg. 1766
DODGE INDUSTRIAL CANADA INC.—See RBC Bearings Incorporated; *U.S. Public*, pg. 1766
DODGE INDUSTRIAL INDIA PRIVATE LIMITED—See RBC Bearings Incorporated; *U.S. Public*, pg. 1766
DODGE MECHANICAL POWER TRANSMISSION MEXICO, S. DE R.L. DE C.V.—See RBC Bearings Incorporated; *U.S. Public*, pg. 1766
DURBAL METALLWARENFABRIK GMBH—See The Timken Company; *U.S. Public*, pg. 2133
DUROC LASER COATING AB—See Duc Long Gia Lai Group JSC; *Int'l*, pg. 2222
EDC, INC.—See Metallus Inc.; *U.S. Public*, pg. 1427
FASIL A.D.; *Int'l*, pg. 2621
FEDERAL-MOGUL DEVA GMBH—See Apollo Global Management, Inc.; *U.S. Public*, pg. 161
FEDERAL-MOGUL SA DE CV—See Apollo Global Management, Inc.; *U.S. Public*, pg. 161
FKL AD TEMERIN; *Int'l*, pg. 2697
FRANTZ MANUFACTURING COMPANY INC.; *U.S. Private*, pg. 1598
GALAXY BEARINGS LIMITED; *Int'l*, pg. 2871
GEBR. REINFURT GMBH & CO. KG—See Arcline Investment Management LP; *U.S. Private*, pg. 314
GGB, INC.—See The Timken Company; *U.S. Public*, pg. 2132
GLOBAL SUPPLY, A.S.—See HTC holding a.s.; *Int'l*, pg. 3508
HARMONIC PRECISION CORPORATION—See Harmonic Drive Systems Inc.; *Int'l*, pg. 3277
HCH BEARING AMERICAS—See China Huanchi Bearing Group Co., Ltd.; *Int'l*, pg. 1509
HEIM BEARINGS COMPANY—See RBC Bearings Incorporated; *U.S. Public*, pg. 1766
HEUNGKUK METALTECH CO., LTD.; *Int'l*, pg. 3366
HITACHI CABLE PHILIPPINES INC.—See Hitachi, Ltd.; *Int'l*, pg. 3415
HIWIN GMBH—See Hiwin Technologies Corp.; *Int'l*, pg. 3427
HIWIN TECHNOLOGIES CORP.; *Int'l*, pg. 3427
HOLMED, LLC—See NN, Inc.; *U.S. Public*, pg. 1531
IAG MAGNUM GMBH—See Georgsmarienhutte Holding GmbH; *Int'l*, pg. 2940
INDUSTRIAL TECTONICS BEARING CORP.—See RBC Bearings Incorporated; *U.S. Public*, pg. 1766
JIANGSU TWB BEARINGS CO., LTD.—See The Timken Company; *U.S. Public*, pg. 2132
JONATHAN ENGINEERED SOLUTIONS, CORP.—See JLL Partners, LLC; *U.S. Private*, pg. 2212
KD INDUSTRIES INC.—See Kendale Industries, Inc.; *U.S. Private*, pg. 2283
KEMEL ASIA PACIFIC PTE. LTD.—See Eagle Industry Co., Ltd.; *Int'l*, pg. 2265
KEMEL CO., LTD.—See Eagle Industry Co., Ltd.; *Int'l*, pg. 2265
KEMEL EUROPE LIMITED—See Eagle Industry Co., Ltd.; *Int'l*, pg. 2265
KENDALE INDUSTRIES, INC.; *U.S. Private*, pg. 2283
KILIAN MANUFACTURING CORPORATION—See Regal Rexnord Corporation; *U.S. Public*, pg. 1772
KINEX BEARINGS, A.S.—See CK Birla Group; *Int'l*, pg. 1636
KINEX-KLF, A.S.—See HTC holding a.s.; *Int'l*, pg. 3508
KOREA DRY BEARING CO., LTD.—See Daido Metal Corporation; *Int'l*, pg. 1922
LUBRITE TECHNOLOGIES—See U.S. Bronze Foundry & Machine, Inc.; *U.S. Private*, pg. 4270
MAGNUS—See Liam Ventures, Inc.; *U.S. Private*, pg. 2442
NADELLA S.P.A.—See The Timken Company; *U.S. Public*, pg. 2133
NAGEL CHASE INC.—See Payson Casters, Inc.; *U.S. Private*, pg. 3117
NATIONAL BEARINGS CO.—See Compagnie Generale des Etablissements Michelin SCA; *Int'l*, pg. 1745
NEXT POINT BEARING GROUP, LLC; *U.S. Private*, pg. 2920
NICE BALL BEARINGS INC.—See RBC Bearings Incorporated; *U.S. Public*, pg. 1766
NIHON TIMKEN K.K.—See The Timken Company; *U.S. Public*, pg. 2133
NN, INC.; *U.S. Public*, pg. 1530
NN LIFE SCIENCES DESIGN & DEVELOPMENT, LLC—See NN, Inc.; *U.S. Public*, pg. 1531
NN LIFE SCIENCES - VANDALIA, LLC—See NN, Inc.; *U.S. Public*, pg. 1531
NN NETHERLANDS B.V.—See NN, Inc.; *U.S. Public*, pg. 1531
OVERALL FORGE NOMINEES PTY LTD—See Berkshire Hathaway Inc.; *U.S. Public*, pg. 314
OVERALL FORGE PTY LTD—See Berkshire Hathaway Inc.; *U.S. Public*, pg. 314
PAYSON CASTERS, INC.; *U.S. Private*, pg. 3117

PAYSON NORCROSS—See Payson Casters, Inc.; *U.S. Private*, pg. 3117
PAYSON TEXAS, INC.—See Payson Casters, Inc.; *U.S. Private*, pg. 3117
PEER INC.—See Peer Chain Company; *U.S. Private*, pg. 3128
PERMAWICK COMPANY INC-INDIANA PLANT—See Permawick Company, Inc.; *U.S. Private*, pg. 3152
PHOENIX BEARINGS, LTD.—See RBC Bearings Incorporated; *U.S. Public*, pg. 1766
PMC ACQUISITION COMPANY, INC.—See NN, Inc.; *U.S. Public*, pg. 1531
PROGRESS RAIL - BEARING PLANT—See Caterpillar, Inc.; *U.S. Public*, pg. 453
PROGRESS RAIL - BEARING PLANT—See Caterpillar, Inc.; *U.S. Public*, pg. 453
RADIAL BEARING CORP.—See Torque Capital Group, LLC; *U.S. Private*, pg. 4189
RBC AIRCRAFT PRODUCTS, INC.—See RBC Bearings Incorporated; *U.S. Public*, pg. 1766
RBC BEARINGS INCORPORATED; *U.S. Public*, pg. 1766
RBC DE MEXICO S DE RL DE CV—See RBC Bearings Incorporated; *U.S. Public*, pg. 1766
RBC NICE BEARINGS, INC.—See RBC Bearings Incorporated; *U.S. Public*, pg. 1766
RBC PRECISION PRODUCTS-BREMEN, INC.—See RBC Bearings Incorporated; *U.S. Public*, pg. 1766
RBC PRECISION PRODUCTS-PLYMOUTH, INC.—See RBC Bearings Incorporated; *U.S. Public*, pg. 1766
RBC PRECISION PRODUCTS - PLYMOUTH—See RBC Bearings Incorporated; *U.S. Public*, pg. 1766
RBC SOUTHWEST PRODUCTS, INC.—See RBC Bearings Incorporated; *U.S. Public*, pg. 1766
REINFURT-CR, K.S.—See Arcline Investment Management LP; *U.S. Private*, pg. 314
RFK VALJCICI—See NN, Inc.; *U.S. Public*, pg. 1531
ROLLCO OY—See Addtech AB; *Int'l*, pg. 135
ROLLER BEARING COMPANY OF AMERICA INC.—See RBC Bearings Incorporated; *U.S. Public*, pg. 1766
ROLLON S.P.A.—See The Timken Company; *U.S. Public*, pg. 2133
RULMENTI S.A.—See Bera Holding A.S.; *Int'l*, pg. 978
SHUSTER CORPORATION—See Genuine Parts Company; *U.S. Public*, pg. 933
SOTEC GMBH—See Clariane SE; *Int'l*, pg. 1644
SPADONE ALFA SELF LUBRICATING PRODUCTS, LLC; *U.S. Private*, pg. 3744
SPECLINE, INC.—See RBC Bearings Incorporated; *U.S. Public*, pg. 1766
STANDARD LOCKNUT, LLC—See Tonka Bay Equity Partners LLC; *U.S. Private*, pg. 4185
STAUNTON CAPITAL, INC.; *U.S. Private*, pg. 3794
STURGE INDUSTRIES—See Bead Industries Inc.; *U.S. Private*, pg. 505
TIMKEN ARGENTINA S.R.L.—See The Timken Company; *U.S. Public*, pg. 2133
TIMKEN CANADA LP—See The Timken Company; *U.S. Public*, pg. 2133
THE TIMKEN COMPANY; *U.S. Public*, pg. 2132
TIMKEN DE MEXICO, S.A. DE C.V.—See The Timken Company; *U.S. Public*, pg. 2134
TIMKEN DEUTSCHLAND GMBH—See The Timken Company; *U.S. Public*, pg. 2133
TIMKEN DO BRASIL S.A. COMERCIO E INDUSTRIA LTDA.—See The Timken Company; *U.S. Public*, pg. 2134
TIMKEN EUROPE—See The Timken Company; *U.S. Public*, pg. 2133
TIMKEN GEARS & SERVICES INC.—See The Timken Company; *U.S. Public*, pg. 2133
TIMKEN GMBH—See The Timken Company; *U.S. Public*, pg. 2133
TIMKEN INDIA LTD.—See The Timken Company; *U.S. Public*, pg. 2133
TIMKEN INDIA MANUFACTURING PRIVATE LIMITED—See The Timken Company; *U.S. Public*, pg. 2133
TIMKEN ITALIA S.R.L.—See The Timken Company; *U.S. Public*, pg. 2133
TIMKEN ROMANIA SA—See The Timken Company; *U.S. Public*, pg. 2133
TIMKEN SINGAPORE PTE LTD.—See The Timken Company; *U.S. Public*, pg. 2133
TIMKEN SOUTH AFRICA PROPRIETARY LTD.—See The Timken Company; *U.S. Public*, pg. 2133
TIMKEN SUPER PRECISION—See The Timken Company; *U.S. Public*, pg. 2133
TIMKEN UK LTD.—See The Timken Company; *U.S. Public*, pg. 2134
TRIGON INTERNATIONAL LLC—See NN, Inc.; *U.S. Public*, pg. 1531
TSUBAKI NAKASHIMA CO., LTD—See The Carlyle Group Inc.; *U.S. Public*, pg. 2055
UNIVERSAL BEARINGS, INC.—See Hanwha Group; *Int'l*, pg. 3265
VALARD BEARINGS LTD—See Hudaco Industries Limited; *Int'l*, pg. 3521

332991 — BALL AND ROLLER BEA...

WAUCONDA TOOL & ENGINEERING LLC—See NN, Inc.; *U.S. Public*, pg. 1531

332992 — SMALL ARMS AMMUNITION MANUFACTURING

ADVANCED TECHNOLOGY INTERNATIONAL, LLC; *U.S. Private*, pg. 93
AMRON—See National Presto Industries, Inc; *U.S. Public*, pg. 1497
ARMORWORKS ENTERPRISES, LLC—See Littlejohn & Co., LLC; *U.S. Private*, pg. 2470
ASAHI SKB CO., LTD.—See Asahi Kasei Corporation; *Int'l*, pg. 596
BARNES BULLETS, LLC—See Sierra Bullets LLC; *U.S. Private*, pg. 3646
CHEMRING COUNTERMEASURES LTD—See Chemring Group PLC; *Int'l*, pg. 1463
COLEBROOK BOSSON & SAUNDERS (PRODUCTS) LIMITED—See MillerKnoll, Inc.; *U.S. Private*, pg. 1446
COLT DEFENSE LLC; *U.S. Private*, pg. 975
DANIEL DEFENSE; *U.S. Private*, pg. 1153
FEDERAL CARTRIDGE COMPANY—See Vista Outdoor Inc.; *U.S. Public*, pg. 2305
FIRSTEC CO., LTD.; *Int'l*, pg. 2688
HORNADY MANUFACTURING COMPANY; *U.S. Private*, pg. 1983
JAPAN SHOTSHELL LTD.—See Daicel Corporation; *Int'l*, pg. 1919
OLIN AUSTRALIA LIMITED—See Olin Corporation; *U.S. Public*, pg. 1570
OLIN CORPORATION - WINCHESTER DIVISION—See Olin Corporation; *U.S. Public*, pg. 1570
OTIS TECHNOLOGY, INC.; *U.S. Private*, pg. 3049
SAINT-GOBAIN WEBER LIMITED—See Compagnie de Saint-Gobain SA; *Int'l*, pg. 1727
SIERRA BULLETS LLC; *U.S. Private*, pg. 3646
SIMMEL DIFESA S.P.A.—See GIAT Industries S.A.; *Int'l*, pg. 2962
SINTERFIRE, INC.—See Argosy Capital Group, LLC; *U.S. Private*, pg. 321
WEST COAST SHOT INC.—See Metalico Inc.; *U.S. Private*, pg. 2681
WINCHESTER AUSTRALIA LIMITED—See Olin Corporation; *U.S. Public*, pg. 1570

332993 — AMMUNITION (EXCEPT SMALL ARMS) MANUFACTURING

ACBEL POLYTECH INC.; *Int'l*, pg. 78
ACTION MANUFACTURING CO.; *U.S. Private*, pg. 67
AIRSPLAT, CO.; *U.S. Private*, pg. 142
AMERICAN ORDNANCE LLC—See The Day & Zimmermann Group, Inc.; *U.S. Private*, pg. 4019
AMMO BROTHERS; *U.S. Private*, pg. 264
AMMO, INC.; *U.S. Public*, pg. 124
BYRNA TECHNOLOGIES INC.; *U.S. Public*, pg. 414
CHEMRING MILITARY PRODUCTS, INC.—See Global Ordnance LLC; *U.S. Private*, pg. 1716
DAY & ZIMMERMANN - MUNITIONS & GOVERNMENT—See The Day & Zimmermann Group, Inc.; *U.S. Private*, pg. 4019
FSP TECHNOLOGY INC.; *Int'l*, pg. 2800
GENERAL DYNAMICS ORDNANCE AND TACTICAL SYSTEMS-CANADA INC.—See General Dynamics Corporation; *U.S. Public*, pg. 914
GENERAL DYNAMICS ORDNANCE AND TACTICAL SYSTEMS - CANADA VALLEYFIELD INC.—See General Dynamics Corporation; *U.S. Public*, pg. 915
GENERAL DYNAMICS ORDNANCE AND TACTICAL SYSTEMS, INC.—See General Dynamics Corporation; *U.S. Public*, pg. 914
HEDCO DIV.—See The Dewey Electronics Corporation; *U.S. Public*, pg. 2067
IGMAN D.D. KONJIC; *Int'l*, pg. 3602
L3 FUZING & ORDNANCE SYSTEMS, INC.—See L3Harris Technologies, Inc.; *U.S. Public*, pg. 1284
NEXTER MUNITIONS S.A.—See GIAT Industries S.A.; *Int'l*, pg. 2962
NOBLES WORLDWIDE, INC.—See Ducommun Incorporated; *U.S. Public*, pg. 690
PITOMETER LOG DIV.—See The Dewey Electronics Corporation; *U.S. Public*, pg. 2067
REMINGTON ARMS COMPANY, INC. - AMMUNITION & COMPONENTS PLANT—See Cerberus Capital Management, L.P.; *U.S. Private*, pg. 839
RHEINMETALL DENEL MUNITION (PTY.) LTD.—See Denel SOC Ltd.; *Int'l*, pg. 2026
SCT ELECTRONICS LIMITED—See HNA International Investment Holdings Limited; *Int'l*, pg. 3433

332994 — SMALL ARMS, ORDNANCE, AND ORDNANCE ACCESSORIES MANUFACTURING

AECC AERO ENGINE CONTROL CO., LTD.; *Int'l*, pg. 171
AIRRATTLE INC.; *U.S. Private*, pg. 142
ALLOY SURFACES COMPANY, INC.—See Chemring Group PLC; *Int'l*, pg. 1463
AMTEC CORPORATION—See National Presto Industries, Inc; *U.S. Public*, pg. 1497
AO PRECISION MANUFACTURING LLC—See Juno Investments LLC; *U.S. Private*, pg. 2244
THE AUTOMOBLOX COMPANY—See Audax Group, Limited Partnership; *U.S. Private*, pg. 390
BENELLI ARMI S.P.A.—See Fabbrica d'Armi Pietro Beretta S.p.A.; *Int'l*, pg. 2598
BERETTA U.S.A. CORP.—See Fabbrica d'Armi Pietro Beretta S.p.A.; *Int'l*, pg. 2598
BHIC BOFORS ASIA SDN. BHD.—See Boustead Heavy Industries Corporation Berhad; *Int'l*, pg. 1120
BLOUNT INTERNATIONAL, INC.—See American Securities LLC; *U.S. Private*, pg. 247
BLOUNT INTERNATIONAL, INC.—See P2 Capital Partners, LLC; *U.S. Private*, pg. 3061
CENTURY ARMS, INC.—See Century International Arms Corporation; *U.S. Private*, pg. 833
COLT'S MANUFACTURING COMPANY, INC.—See Colt Defense LLC; *U.S. Private*, pg. 975
CRIMSON TRACE CORPORATION—See Smith & Wesson Brands, Inc.; *U.S. Public*, pg. 1896
DAISY MANUFACTURING COMPANY—See Bruckmann, Rosser, Sherrill & Co., LLC; *U.S. Private*, pg. 671
DEFENSE INDUSTRIES INTERNATIONAL, INC.; *Int'l*, pg. 2004
THE DEWEY ELECTRONICS CORPORATION; *U.S. Public*, pg. 2066
DIEHL DEFENCE GMBH & CO. KG—See Diehl Stiftung & Co. KG; *Int'l*, pg. 2115
THE ENTWISTLE CO.; *U.S. Private*, pg. 4026
FABBRICA D'ARMI PIETRO BERETTA S.P.A.; *Int'l*, pg. 2598
FN AMERICA, INC.—See Herstal, S.A.; *Int'l*, pg. 3364
FN AMERICA, LLC—See Herstal, S.A.; *Int'l*, pg. 3364
FN HERSTAL FAR EAST & AUSTRALASIA PTE. LTD.—See Herstal, S.A.; *Int'l*, pg. 3364
FN HERSTAL S.A.—See Herstal, S.A.; *Int'l*, pg. 3364
FNH UK LIMITED—See Herstal, S.A.; *Int'l*, pg. 3364
GAMO OUTDOOR USA, INC.—See Bruckmann, Rosser, Sherrill & Co., LLC; *U.S. Private*, pg. 671
GENERAL DYNAMICS ORDNANCE & TACTICAL SYSTEMS—See General Dynamics Corporation; *U.S. Public*, pg. 914
GLOBAL DIGITAL SOLUTIONS, INC.; *U.S. Public*, pg. 942
GREEN MOUNTAIN RIFLE BARREL CO. INC—See EBSCO Industries, Inc.; *U.S. Private*, pg. 1325
HECKLER & KOCH GMBH—See BAE Systems plc; *Int'l*, pg. 798
HERSTAL, S.A.; *Int'l*, pg. 3364
I.O. INCORPORATED; *U.S. Private*, pg. 2027
JAMES PURDEY & SONS LIMITED—See Compagnie Financiere Richemont S.A.; *Int'l*, pg. 1741
KNIGHT RIFLES, INC.—See EBSCO Industries, Inc.; *U.S. Private*, pg. 1325
KNIGHT'S ARMAMENT COMPANY; *U.S. Private*, pg. 2322
LUTH-AR, LLC; *U.S. Private*, pg. 2516
MANROY ENGINEERING LTD.—See Herstal, S.A.; *Int'l*, pg. 3365
THE MARLIN FIREARMS COMPANY, INC.—See Cerberus Capital Management, L.P.; *U.S. Private*, pg. 839
MAVERICK ARMS, INC.—See Mossberg Corporation; *U.S. Private*, pg. 2794
MECAR S.A.—See GIAT Industries S.A.; *Int'l*, pg. 2962
MILLETT INDUSTRIES—See Vista Outdoor Inc.; *U.S. Public*, pg. 2305
MOSSBERG CORPORATION; *U.S. Private*, pg. 2794
NEW WAY MOTOR & DIESEL ENGINEERING (PTY) LTD—See enX Group Limited; *Int'l*, pg. 2456
NEXTER SYSTEMS S.A.—See GIAT Industries S.A.; *Int'l*, pg. 2962
O.F. MOSSBERG & SONS, INC.—See Mossberg Corporation; *U.S. Private*, pg. 2794
PARA USA, LLC—See Cerberus Capital Management, L.P.; *U.S. Private*, pg. 839
REMINGTON ARMS COMPANY, INC. - MAYFIELD FIREARMS PLANT—See Cerberus Capital Management, L.P.; *U.S. Private*, pg. 839
REMINGTON ARMS COMPANY, INC.—See Cerberus Capital Management, L.P.; *U.S. Private*, pg. 839
REMINGTON OUTDOOR COMPANY INC.—See Cerberus Capital Management, L.P.; *U.S. Private*, pg. 839
ROBERT BOSCH TECNOLOGIA DE EMBALAGEM LTDA.—See CVC Capital Partners SICAV-FIS S.A.; *Int'l*, pg. 1884
SAKO LTD.—See Fabbrica d'Armi Pietro Beretta S.p.A.; *Int'l*, pg. 2598
SANDERSFIRE INTERNATIONAL LIMITED—See Goodwin PLC; *Int'l*, pg. 3042
SAVAGE ARMS, INC.—See Vista Outdoor Inc.; *U.S. Public*, pg. 2305
SAVAGE SPORTS CORPORATION—See Vista Outdoor Inc.; *U.S. Public*, pg. 2305
SELLMARK CORP.; *U.S. Private*, pg. 3603
SMITH & WESSON CORP.—See Smith & Wesson Brands, Inc.; *U.S. Public*, pg. 1896
STOEGER INDUSTRIES—See Fabbrica d'Armi Pietro Beretta S.p.A.; *Int'l*, pg. 2598
STURM, RUGER & COMPANY, INC.; *U.S. Public*, pg. 1958
STURM, RUGER-NEWPORT PLANT—See Sturm, Ruger & Company, Inc.; *U.S. Public*, pg. 1958
SURGICAL TABLES INC.—See ADDvise Group AB; *Int'l*, pg. 136
TRIUS TRAPS, LLC—See Lyman Products Corporation; *U.S. Private*, pg. 2520
TUG TECHNOLOGIES CORPORATION—See Textron Inc.; *U.S. Public*, pg. 2029
UNITED TACTICAL SYSTEMS, LLC; *U.S. Private*, pg. 4301
U.S. REPEATING ARMS COMPANY—See Herstal, S.A.; *Int'l*, pg. 3365
VEDDER HOLSTERS LLC; *U.S. Private*, pg. 4353
VERNEY-CARRON S.A.—See Cybergun SA; *Int'l*, pg. 1893
WEATHERBY, INC.; *U.S. Private*, pg. 4462

332996 — FABRICATED PIPE AND PIPE FITTING MANUFACTURING

ACCROTOOL, INC.; *U.S. Private*, pg. 54
ALCO INVESTMENT CO., INC.; *U.S. Private*, pg. 153
ALL METALS PROCESSING & LOGISTICS, INC.—See Reliance Steel & Aluminum Co.; *U.S. Public*, pg. 1779
AMERICAN BILTRITE INTELLECTUAL PROPERTIES INC.—See American Biltrite Inc.; *U.S. Public*, pg. 97
AMERICAN ROLL FORMED PRODUCTS CORP.; *U.S. Private*, pg. 246
ANVIL INTERNATIONAL, LLC—See Tailwind Capital Group, LLC; *U.S. Private*, pg. 3923
APPLIED FELTS, INC.—See Vortex Company, LLC; *U.S. Private*, pg. 4413
ARROW SYNDICATE PUBLIC COMPANY LIMITED; *Int'l*, pg. 579
ATCO ENERGY SOLUTIONS LTD—See ATCO Ltd.; *Int'l*, pg. 666
BENDING TECHNOLOGIES, INC.—See Activar, Inc.; *U.S. Private*, pg. 68
BENTECH INC.; *U.S. Private*, pg. 528
BHR HOCHDRUCK-ROHRLEITUNGSBAU GMBH—See Bilfinger SE; *Int'l*, pg. 1027
BORUSAN BIRLESIK BORU FABRIKALARI SANAYI VE TICARET AS; *Int'l*, pg. 1115
BRADLEY SERVICES, INC.—See Wind Point Advisors LLC; *U.S. Private*, pg. 4534
CAMBRIDGE METALS & PLASTICS, INC.—See Wind Point Advisors LLC; *U.S. Private*, pg. 4534
CAPITOL MANUFACTURING CO.—See Phoenix Forging Company, Inc.; *U.S. Private*, pg. 3173
CARAUSTAR INDUSTRIES, INC. - TAYLORS TUBE PLANT—See Greif Inc.; *U.S. Public*, pg. 966
CASTRONICS, INC.—See RNA, Inc.; *U.S. Private*, pg. 3452
CF ULTRA TECH—See Construction Forms, Inc.; *U.S. Private*, pg. 1023
CHATSWORTH PRODUCTS - GEORGETOWN—See Chatsworth Products Inc.; *U.S. Private*, pg. 868
CHINA PIPE GROUP LIMITED; *Int'l*, pg. 1540
CONSTRUCTION FORMS, INC.; *U.S. Private*, pg. 1023
CONTECH INC.—See Apax Partners LLP; *Int'l*, pg. 503
CONTROLS SOUTHEAST INC.—See AMETEK, Inc.; *U.S. Public*, pg. 118
CRC-EVANS CANADA LTD.—See CRC-Evans International, Inc.; *U.S. Private*, pg. 1087
CROSSPIPE SYSTEMS S.A.—See Golan Plastic Products Ltd.; *Int'l*, pg. 3023
CURTIS PRODUCTS INC.; *U.S. Private*, pg. 1126
CUSTOM MARINE INC.—See Contran Corporation; *U.S. Private*, pg. 1033
CUSTOM PIPE & COUPLING CO.—See Shapco, Inc.; *U.S. Private*, pg. 3625
DAEHO P&C CO., LTD. - BUSAN FACTORY—See DHSteel; *Int'l*, pg. 2100
DAKE COUPLINGS—See JSJ Corporation; *U.S. Private*, pg. 2241
DAVID HART AEROSPACE PIPES LIMITED—See Leggett & Platt, Incorporated; *U.S. Public*, pg. 1301
DEUBLIN COMPANY—See Hoerbiger Holding AG; *Int'l*, pg. 3439
DIPL. ING. K. DIETZEL GMBH; *Int'l*, pg. 2128
DSC LIMITED; *U.S. Private*, pg. 1281
DURAFLEX INC.; *U.S. Private*, pg. 1292
EAGLEBURGMANN CZECH S.R.O.—See Freudenberg SE; *Int'l*, pg. 2783
EAST COAST METALS SDN. BHD.—See Engtex Group Berhad; *Int'l*, pg. 2436
ENERPIPE, INC—See Enerfab, Inc.; *U.S. Private*, pg. 1393
EPIC PIPING, LLC—See Bernhard Capital Partners Management, LP; *U.S. Private*, pg. 537
ESSENTRA PIPE PROTECTION TECHNOLOGIES—See Essentra plc; *Int'l*, pg. 2511
ESSER-WERKE GMBH & CO. KG—See Construction Forms, Inc.; *U.S. Private*, pg. 1023
EUROFLEX TRANSMISSIONS (INDIA) PRIVATE LTD.—See Zurn Elkay Water Solutions Corporation; *U.S. Public*, pg. 2412
FABRICATED PIPE, INC.; *U.S. Private*, pg. 1458

FELKER BROTHERS CORPORATION - GLASGOW MANUFACTURING FACILITY—See Felker Brothers Corporation; *U.S. Private,* pg. 1493
FELKER BROTHERS CORPORATION - MARSHFIELD MANUFACTURING FACILITY—See Felker Brothers Corporation; *U.S. Private,* pg. 1493
FERGUSON FIRE & FABRICATION, INC.—See Ferguson plc; *Int'l,* pg. 2637
FIBER GLASS SYSTEMS L.P.—See NOV, Inc.; *U.S. Public,* pg. 1544
FINELINE SERVICES LIMITED—See Dialog Group Berhad; *Int'l,* pg. 2104
FITTINGS GMBH FORMSTUCKE + ANLAGEN—See HCS Beteiligungsgesellschaft mbH; *Int'l,* pg. 3299
FLOWORKS INTERNATIONAL LLC—See Wynnchurch Capital, L.P.; *U.S. Private,* pg. 4577
FRIATEC SARL—See Aliaxis S.A./N.V.; *Int'l,* pg. 324
FUTURE PIPE INDUSTRIES GROUP LTD.; *Int'l,* pg. 2857
GEBERIT PRODUZIONE S.P.A.—See Geberit AG; *Int'l,* pg. 2905
GEBERIT SALES LTD.—See Geberit AG; *Int'l,* pg. 2905
GEORG FISCHER FITTINGS GMBH—See Georg Fischer AG; *Int'l,* pg. 2935
GLOBE MECHANICAL, INC.; *U.S. Private,* pg. 1719
GLYNWED AB—See Aliaxis S.A./N.V.; *Int'l,* pg. 324
GLYNWED AG—See Aliaxis S.A./N.V.; *Int'l,* pg. 324
GLYNWED A/S—See Aliaxis S.A./N.V.; *Int'l,* pg. 324
GLYNWED B.V.—See Aliaxis S.A./N.V.; *Int'l,* pg. 324
GLYNWED N.V.—See Aliaxis S.A./N.V.; *Int'l,* pg. 324
GLYNWED PIPE SYSTEMS (ASIA) PTE. LTD.—See Aliaxis S.A./N.V.; *Int'l,* pg. 324
GLYNWED S.A.S.—See Aliaxis S.A./N.V.; *Int'l,* pg. 324
GLYNWED SRL—See Aliaxis S.A./N.V.; *Int'l,* pg. 324
GLYNWED S.R.O.—See Aliaxis S.A./N.V.; *Int'l,* pg. 324
GPS IBERICA S.L.—See Aliaxis S.A./N.V.; *Int'l,* pg. 324
HARRINGTON INDUSTRIAL PLASTICS LLC—See Bain Capital, LP; *U.S. Private,* pg. 432
HERCULES INDUSTRIES INC.; *U.S. Private,* pg. 1921
HG METAL PTE LTD—See HG Metal Manufacturing Limited; *Int'l,* pg. 3375
HIGH COUNTRY FUSION COMPANY, INC.; *U.S. Private,* pg. 1935
HIGH PRESSURE EQUIPMENT COMPANY—See Graco, Inc.; *U.S. Public,* pg. 953
HISTEEL CO., LTD.; *Int'l,* pg. 3408
HITACHI ZOSEN INOVA UK LTD.—See Hitachi Zosen Corporation; *Int'l,* pg. 3411
HITACHI ZOSEN KRB AG—See Hitachi Zosen Corporation; *Int'l,* pg. 3411
HOA PHAT STEEL PIPE CO., LTD.—See Hoa Phat Group Joint Stock Company; *Int'l,* pg. 3435
H-P PRODUCTS, INC.; *U.S. Private,* pg. 1824
HUIZHOU FUSHENG INSULATION MATERIALS LTD, INC.—See Auxo Investment Partners, LLC; *U.S. Private,* pg. 402
HYDRO TUBE ENTERPRISES, INC.; *U.S. Private,* pg. 2017
IDEAL WELDERS LTD.; *Int'l,* pg. 3589
INTERLAKEN TECHNOLOGY CORPORATION—See Wind Point Advisors LLC; *U.S. Private,* pg. 4534
IPLEX PIPELINES AUSTRALIA PTY LTD—See Fletcher Building Limited; *Int'l,* pg. 2699
IPLEX PIPELINES NZ LIMITED—See Fletcher Building Limited; *Int'l,* pg. 2699
J.B. SMITH MFG CO., LLC—See Mueller Water Products, Inc.; *U.S. Public,* pg. 1485
JTD ENTERPRISES INC.; *U.S. Private,* pg. 2241
JUNCO STEEL CORPORATION; *U.S. Private,* pg. 2244
KARL THEIS GMBH—See BayWa AG; *Int'l,* pg. 918
KE PERSSON AB—See H&M Hennes & Mauritz AB; *Int'l,* pg. 3192
KINGSTON BRIDGE ENGINEERING PTY LIMITED—See Fletcher Building Limited; *Int'l,* pg. 2700
KLAMFLEX PIPE COUPLINGS (PTY) LTD—See Zurn Elkay Water Solutions Corporation; *U.S. Public,* pg. 2413
LEGGETT & PLATT AEROSPACE MIDDLETOWN, LLC—See Leggett & Platt, Incorporated; *U.S. Public,* pg. 1303
LONG ISLAND PIPE SUPPLY, INC.—See Core & Main, Inc.; *U.S. Public,* pg. 576
MASKELL PIPE & SUPPLY, INC.—See Core & Main, Inc.; *U.S. Public,* pg. 576
MIDLAND INDUSTRIES. CO., INC.—See Gemspring Capital Management, LLC; *U.S. Private,* pg. 1659
MOLECOR (SEA) SDN. BHD.—See FITTERS Diversified Berhad; *Int'l,* pg. 2695
MOUNTAINEER FABRICATORS INC.; *U.S. Private,* pg. 2801
MPS ENTERPRISES, INC.—See Winsupply, Inc.; *U.S. Private,* pg. 4545
MUELLER COMERCIAL DE MEXICO S. DE R.L. DE C.V.—See Mueller Industries, Inc.; *U.S. Public,* pg. 1485
NELSON GLOBAL PRODUCTS, INC. - ARCADIA MANUFACTURING FACILITY—See Wind Point Advisors LLC; *U.S. Private,* pg. 4534
NELSON GLOBAL PRODUCTS, INC. - FORT WAYNE MANUFACTURING FACILITY—See Wind Point Advisors LLC; *U.S. Private,* pg. 4534
NELSON GLOBAL PRODUCTS, INC. - VIROQUA MANUFACTURING FACILITY—See Wind Point Advisors LLC; *U.S. Private,* pg. 4534
OIL STATES HYDROTECH—See Oil States International, Inc.; *U.S. Public,* pg. 1565
OIL STATES HYDROTECH SYSTEMS—See Oil States International, Inc.; *U.S. Public,* pg. 1565
PEORIA TUBE FORMING CORP.—See Wind Point Advisors LLC; *U.S. Private,* pg. 4534
PERMA-PIPE EGYPT FOR METAL FABRICATION & INSULATION INDUSTRIES (PERMA-PIPE EGYPT) S.A.E—See Perma-Pipe International Holdings, Inc.; *U.S. Public,* pg. 1676
PERMA-PIPE, INC.—See Perma-Pipe International Holdings, Inc.; *U.S. Public,* pg. 1676
PERMA-PIPE MIDDLE EAST FZC—See Perma-Pipe International Holdings, Inc.; *U.S. Public,* pg. 1676
PEXCOR MANUFACTURING CO., INC.—See Mueller Industries, Inc.; *U.S. Public,* pg. 1485
PIONEER PIPE, INC.; *U.S. Private,* pg. 3188
PIPE FABRICATING & SUPPLY COMPANY; *U.S. Private,* pg. 3189
PIPE FABRICATING & SUPPLY COMPANY - UTAH PLANT—See Pipe Fabricating & Supply Company; *U.S. Private,* pg. 3189
THE PIPE LINE DEVELOPMENT COMPANY; *U.S. Private,* pg. 4096
PIPELINE INDUCTION HEAT LIMITED—See CRC-Evans International, Inc.; *U.S. Private,* pg. 1087
PIPE SUPPORTS LTD—See Hill & Smith PLC; *Int'l,* pg. 3392
PRIMUS PROCESSAMENTO DE TUBOS S.A.—See IHI Corporation; *Int'l,* pg. 3606
R&B WAGNER CO. INC.; *U.S. Private,* pg. 3331
REPIPE-CALIFORNIA—See J.F. Lehman & Company, Inc.; *U.S. Private,* pg. 2163
RTI—See Groupe BPCE; *Int'l,* pg. 3095
SAINT-GOBAIN PAM UK—See Compagnie de Saint-Gobain SA; *Int'l,* pg. 1735
SAMWON TECH (EUROPE) LTD—See Aktieselskabet Schouw & Co.; *Int'l,* pg. 266
SHAW ALLOY PIPING PRODUCTS, LLC—See The Shaw Group Inc.; *U.S. Private,* pg. 4117
SHAW GROUP UK LIMITED—See The Shaw Group Inc.; *U.S. Private,* pg. 4117
SHAW NAPTECH, INC.—See The Shaw Group Inc.; *U.S. Private,* pg. 4117
SHAW NASS MIDDLE EAST WLL—See Abdulla Ahmed Nass Group WLL; *Int'l,* pg. 58
SHAW PROCESS FABRICATORS, INC.—See The Shaw Group Inc.; *U.S. Private,* pg. 4117
SMITH-BLAIR, INC.—See Xylem Inc.; *U.S. Public,* pg. 2395
SPECIALIZED FABRICATION EQUIPMENT GROUP, LLC—See Gladstone Management Corporation; *U.S. Private,* pg. 1705
SPECMA SP. Z.O.O.—See Aktieselskabet Schouw & Co.; *Int'l,* pg. 266
STANDEX AIR DISTRIBUTION PRODUCTS, INC. - GEORGIA—See Blue Wolf Capital Partners LLC; *U.S. Private,* pg. 596
STANDEX AIR DISTRIBUTION PRODUCTS, INC.—See Blue Wolf Capital Partners LLC; *U.S. Private,* pg. 596
STRAUB WERKE AG—See Aliaxis S.A./N.V.; *Int'l,* pg. 325
SUPERIOR DRILLPIPE MANUFACTURING—See Texas Steel Conversion, Inc.; *U.S. Private,* pg. 3977
TDW OFFSHORE SERVICES—See T.D. Williamson, Inc.; *U.S. Private,* pg. 3911
TEAM INDUSTRIES, INC.; *U.S. Private,* pg. 3949
TENNESSEE TUBEBENDING INC.—See Morris Coupling Company; *U.S. Private,* pg. 2787
THREADING & PRECISION MANUFACTURING LLC—See OFS International LLC; *U.S. Private,* pg. 3003
TROY TUBE & MANUFACTURING, CO.; *U.S. Private,* pg. 4243
TUBE FABRICATION INDUSTRIES, INC.; *U.S. Private,* pg. 4255
TUBE FORGINGS OF AMERICA INC.; *U.S. Private,* pg. 4255
TUBE PROCESSING CORP.; *U.S. Private,* pg. 4255
TUBE SPECIALTIES CO. INC.; *U.S. Private,* pg. 4255
TUBULAR SERVICES LP - JACINTOPORT PLANT—See Tubular Services LP; *U.S. Private,* pg. 4256
TUBULAR SERVICES LP - MCCARTY TUBING PLANT—See Tubular Services LP; *U.S. Private,* pg. 4256
UNITED PIPING, INC.—See APi Group Corporation; *Int'l,* pg. 514
UPONOR EPULETGEPESZETI KORLATOLT FELELOSSEGU TARSASAG—See Georg Fischer AG; *Int'l,* pg. 2937
U. S. STEEL TUBULAR PRODUCTS, INC.—See United States Steel Corporation; *U.S. Public,* pg. 2237
VARD PIPING AS—See Fincantieri S.p.A.; *Int'l,* pg. 2672
VARD PIPING TULCEA SRL—See Fincantieri S.p.A.; *Int'l,* pg. 2672
VSH FITTINGS B.V.—See Aalberts N.V.; *Int'l,* pg. 36
WEATHERFORD ARTIFICIAL LIFT SYSTEMS—See Weatherford International plc; *U.S. Public,* pg. 2339
WESTLAKE PIPE & FITTINGS CORPORATION—See Westlake Corporation; *U.S. Public,* pg. 2360
WOLFE ENGINEERING INC.; *U.S. Private,* pg. 4554

332999 — ALL OTHER MISCELLANEOUS FABRICATED METAL PRODUCT MANUFACTURING

5N PLUS INC.; *Int'l,* pg. 13
A&A MACHINE & FABRICATION, LLC.; *U.S. Private,* pg. 19
AB MONSTERAS METALL; *Int'l,* pg. 41
ACCRA MANUFACTURING, INC.—See Berkshire Hathaway Inc.; *U.S. Public,* pg. 314
ACCROFAB HOLDINGS LIMITED—See Endless LLP; *Int'l,* pg. 2403
ACEROLUX SL; *Int'l,* pg. 101
ACORN ENGINEERING COMPANY, INC.; *U.S. Private,* pg. 63
ADAMS MAGNETIC PRODUCTS CO.—See High Street Capital Management, Inc.; *U.S. Private,* pg. 1937
ADJ INDUSTRIES INC.—See CoorsTek, Inc.; *U.S. Private,* pg. 1043
ADRIAN STEEL COMPANY INC.; *U.S. Private,* pg. 82
ADVANCED BORING & TOOL COMPANY—See Utica Enterprises, Inc.; *U.S. Private,* pg. 4325
ADVANCED MATERIAL JAPAN CORPORATION—See Alconix Corporation; *Int'l,* pg. 302
ADVANCED STEEL & CRANE INC.—See EMC Limited; *Int'l,* pg. 2376
ADVANCED TECHNOLOGY & MATERIALS CO., LTD. - AMORPHOUS METAL PRODUCTS DIVISION—See Advanced Technology & Materials Co., Ltd.; *Int'l,* pg. 162
ADVANCED TECHNOLOGY & MATERIALS CO., LTD. - FUNCTIONAL MATERIALS DIVISION—See Advanced Technology & Materials Co., Ltd.; *Int'l,* pg. 162
ADVANCED TECHNOLOGY & MATERIALS CO., LTD. - INTERNATIONAL TRADING DIVISION—See Advanced Technology & Materials Co., Ltd.; *Int'l,* pg. 162
ADVANCED TECHNOLOGY & MATERIALS CO., LTD.; *Int'l,* pg. 162
ADVANCE METAL SUBSTRATE TECHNOLOGY SDN. BHD.—See Hexagon Holdings Berhad; *Int'l,* pg. 3370
ADVANCE TABCO, INC.—See Kinplex Corp.; *U.S. Private,* pg. 2313
ADVANCE TABCO, INC. - TEXAS—See Kinplex Corp.; *U.S. Private,* pg. 2313
ADX FIRE PROTECTION, INC.; *U.S. Private,* pg. 111
AESSEAL PLC; *Int'l,* pg. 182
AF GLOENCO INC. - GREENVILLE—See First Reserve Management, L.P.; *U.S. Private,* pg. 1525
AF GLOENCO INC.—See First Reserve Management, L.P.; *U.S. Private,* pg. 1525
AFRICA ISRAEL INDUSTRIES LTD.—See Africa Israel Investments Ltd.; *Int'l,* pg. 190
AFRIC INDUSTRIES SA; *Int'l,* pg. 189
AFT EUROPA KFT—See ARC Group Worldwide, Inc.; *U.S. Public,* pg. 179
AGI GREENPAC LIMITED; *Int'l,* pg. 209
AGUIA METAIS LTDA—See Aguia Resources Limited; *Int'l,* pg. 222
AGV GALVANIZING (M) SDN. BHD.—See AGV Group Limited; *Int'l,* pg. 222
AH INDUSTRIES A/S; *Int'l,* pg. 222
AIL INDUSTRIES CO., LTD.—See GIBCA Limited; *Int'l,* pg. 2962
AIRCOM MANUFACTURING, INC.—See Kimball Electronics, Inc.; *U.S. Public,* pg. 1228
AISIN SEIKI CO., LTD. - NISHIO DIE-CASTING PLANT—See AISIN Corporation; *Int'l,* pg. 253
AJU EGL CO., LTD.—See AJU Steel Co., Ltd.; *Int'l,* pg. 258
AKD ENGINEERING LIMITED—See Camellia Plc; *Int'l,* pg. 1270
ALBANY INTERNATIONAL CANADA CORP.—See Albany International Corp.; *U.S. Public,* pg. 72
ALBANY INTERNATIONAL DE MEXICO S.A. DE C.V.—See Albany International Corp.; *U.S. Public,* pg. 72
ALBANY INTERNATIONAL FRANCE S.A.S.—See Albany International Corp.; *U.S. Public,* pg. 72
ALBANY INTERNATIONAL LTD.—See Albany International Corp.; *U.S. Public,* pg. 72
ALBANY INTERNATIONAL OY—See Albany International Corp.; *U.S. Public,* pg. 72
ALBANY INTERNATIONAL TECIDOS TECNICOS LTDA.—See Albany International Corp.; *U.S. Public,* pg. 72
ALBERS MECHANICAL CONTRACTORS, INC.—See The Vollrath Company LLC; *U.S. Private,* pg. 4132
ALCONIX EUROPE GMBH—See Alconix Corporation; *Int'l,* pg. 302
ALCONIX HONG KONG CORP.,LTD.—See Alconix Corporation; *Int'l,* pg. 302
ALCONIX (MALAYSIA) SDN. BHD.—See Alconix Corporation; *Int'l,* pg. 302
ALCONIX SANSHIN CORPORATION—See Alconix Corporation; *Int'l,* pg. 302
ALCONIX (SHANGHAI) CORP.—See Alconix Corporation; *Int'l,* pg. 302
ALCONIX (TAIWAN) CORPORATION—See Alconix Corporation; *Int'l,* pg. 302

332999 — ALL OTHER MISCELLAN...

CORPORATE AFFILIATIONS

ALCONIX (THAILAND) LTD.—See Alconix Corporation; *Int'l*, pg. 302
AL JABER PRECISION ENGINEERING ESTABLISHMENT—See Al Jaber Group; *Int'l*, pg. 279
AL JABER SIGNS L.L.C.—See Al Jaber Group; *Int'l*, pg. 279
ALLEGHENY TECHNOLOGIES KOREA—See ATI Inc.; *U.S. Public*, pg. 222
ALLFLEX INTERNATIONAL DO BRASIL LTDA—See Merck & Co., Inc.; *U.S. Public*, pg. 1415
ALLFLEX SCR VOSTOK—See Merck & Co., Inc.; *U.S. Public*, pg. 1415
ALL MAGNETICS INC.; *U.S. Private*, pg. 171
ALL STAR BLEACHERS, INC.—See Summa Holdings, Inc.; *U.S. Private*, pg. 3852
ALPOS ALU, D.O.O.—See ALPOS, d.d.; *Int'l*, pg. 374
ALUMIL FRANCE S.A.S.—See Alumil Aluminium Industry S.A.; *Int'l*, pg. 400
AMAG COMPONENTS DEUTSCHLAND GMBH—See AMAG Austria Metall AG; *Int'l*, pg. 408
AMAG COMPONENTS KARLSRUHE GMBH—See AMAG Austria Metall AG; *Int'l*, pg. 408
AMEREX CORPORATION; *U.S. Private*, pg. 219
AMERICANA COMPANIES, INC.; *U.S. Private*, pg. 258
AMERICAN SPECIALTIES INC.; *U.S. Private*, pg. 255
AMERISTAR PERIMETER SECURITY USA, INC.—See ASSA ABLOY AB; *Int'l*, pg. 638
AMMCON CORP.—See Arcline Investment Management LP; *U.S. Private*, pg. 313
AMNODE AB; *Int'l*, pg. 429
AMOGREENTECH CO., LTD.; *Int'l*, pg. 429
AMS GMBH; *Int'l*, pg. 440
ANCHOR FABRICATION LTD.; *U.S. Private*, pg. 273
ANGLO ASIA ALLOYS VIETNAM CO., LTD.—See Daiki Aluminium Industry Co., Ltd.; *Int'l*, pg. 1931
ANH HUY CONSTRUCTION CO., LTD—See Hoa Binh Construction Group JSC; *Int'l*, pg. 3435
APEX TOOLS & ORTHOPEDICS CO.—See Berkshire Hathaway Inc.; *U.S. Public*, pg. 308
APPLIED ENGINEERING PTE. LTD.; *Int'l*, pg. 521
APPLIED FUSION INC.—See Francisco Partners Management, LP; *U.S. Private*, pg. 1590
AQ SPECIAL SHEET METAL AB—See AQ Group AB; *Int'l*, pg. 526
ARAYA INDUSTRIAL CO., LTD.; *Int'l*, pg. 536
ARCELORMITTAL ANCENIS—See ArcelorMittal S.A.; *Int'l*, pg. 543
ARDEN ENGINEERING, INC.—See Arlington Capital Partners LLC; *U.S. Private*, pg. 327
ARFMAN HEKWERK B.V.—See CRH plc; *Int'l*, pg. 1842
ARLAND TOOL & MANUFACTURING INC.; *U.S. Private*, pg. 326
THE ARMOR GROUP, INC.; *U.S. Private*, pg. 3988
ARMOUR PLASTICS LIMITED - RENAISSANCE BATHS DIVISION—See Armour Plastics Limited; *Int'l*, pg. 575
ARNOLD MAGNETIC TECHNOLOGIES LTD.—See Compass Diversified Holdings; *U.S. Public*, pg. 560
ARTISTIC FRAMING INC.; *U.S. Private*, pg. 343
ASAHI EITO CO., LTD.; *Int'l*, pg. 593
ASAHI-SEIKI MANUFACTURING CO., LTD.; *Int'l*, pg. 599
ASIAN STAR ANCHOR CHAIN CO., LTD. JIANGSU; *Int'l*, pg. 619
ASIA PRECISION PUBLIC COMPANY LIMITED; *Int'l*, pg. 615
ASW HOLDING CORPORATION; *U.S. Private*, pg. 363
ATI FLOWFORM PRODUCTS, LLC—See ATI Inc.; *U.S. Public*, pg. 221
ATLAS COPCO DRILLING SOLUTIONS LLC—See Atlas Copco AB; *Int'l*, pg. 681
ATLAS FIBRE COMPANY; *U.S. Private*, pg. 376
AT&M STAR ELECTRONIC COMPONENT CO., LTD.—See Advanced Technology & Materials Co., Ltd.; *Int'l*, pg. 162
AT PRECISION TOOLING SDN. BHD.—See AT Systematization Berhad; *Int'l*, pg. 664
ATTL ADVANCED MATERIALS CO., LTD.—See Advanced Technology & Materials Co., Ltd.; *Int'l*, pg. 162
A.T. WALL COMPANY; *U.S. Private*, pg. 28
AURUBIS ENGINEERING EAD—See Aurubis AG; *Int'l*, pg. 714
AURUBIS METAL PRODUCTS (SHANGHAI) CO., LTD—See Aurubis AG; *Int'l*, pg. 714
AURUBIS MORTARA S.P.A.—See Aurubis AG; *Int'l*, pg. 715
AURUBIS RUS LLC—See Aurubis AG; *Int'l*, pg. 715
AUTOMATIC EQUIPMENT CORPORATION; *U.S. Private*, pg. 399
AUTOMATIC PROCESSING INCORPORATED—See AZZ, Inc.; *U.S. Public*, pg. 259
AVINGTRANS PLC; *Int'l*, pg. 743
AVROT INDUSTRIES LTD.; *Int'l*, pg. 750
BAC KAN MINERAL JOINT STOCK CORPORATION; *Int'l*, pg. 793
BAHNTECHNIK BRAND-ERBISDORF GMBH—See Georgsmarienhutte Holding GmbH; *Int'l*, pg. 2940
BALLYMORE CO., INC.—See Graycliff Partners LP; *U.S. Private*, pg. 1760
BALTIC METALLTECHNIK GMBH—See Bader GmbH; *Int'l*, pg. 795
BAN SENG LEE INDUSTRIES SDN. BHD.—See BSL Corporation Berhad; *Int'l*, pg. 1202

BAOSTEEL DESHENG STAINLESS STEEL CO., LTD.—See China Baowu Steel Group Corp., Ltd.; *Int'l*, pg. 1485
BAOSTEEL GROUP XINJIANG BAYI IRON & STEEL CO., LTD.—See China Baowu Steel Group Corp., Ltd.; *Int'l*, pg. 1485
BAOSTEEL SPECIAL MATERIAL CO., LTD.—See China Baowu Steel Group Corp., Ltd.; *Int'l*, pg. 1485
BARLAGE GMBH; *Int'l*, pg. 866
BASIC AMERICAN METAL PRODUCTS—See GF Health Products, Inc.; *U.S. Private*, pg. 1689
BASLINI METALLI S.P.A.—See Baslini S.p.A.; *Int'l*, pg. 887
BAUER CORPORATION; *U.S. Private*, pg. 490
BAY INSULATION SYSTEMS, INC.—See Bay Industries Inc.; *U.S. Private*, pg. 493
BAYLESS ENGINEERING, INC.—See Tide Rock Holdings, LLC; *U.S. Private*, pg. 4167
BEAD INDUSTRIES INC.; *U.S. Private*, pg. 505
BEAR RIDGE MACHINE & FABRICATION, INC.—See Reading Anthracite Company; *U.S. Private*, pg. 3366
BE GROUP OU—See BE Group AB; *Int'l*, pg. 931
BEIJING ALLFLEX PLASTIC PRODUCTS CO., LTD.—See Merck & Co., Inc.; *U.S. Public*, pg. 1415
BEIJING ATAS METAL MATERIALS CO., LTD.—See Advanced Technology & Materials Co., Ltd.; *Int'l*, pg. 162
BEIJING ZHONG KE SAN HUAN HIGH-TECH CO., LTD.; *Int'l*, pg. 961
BERNDORF BAND LATINOAMERICA S.A.S.—See Berndorf AG; *Int'l*, pg. 987
BERNDORF STEEL BELT SYSTEMS CO. LTD.—See Berndorf AG; *Int'l*, pg. 987
BEST TECH & ENGINEERING LIMITED—See BT Wealth Industries Public Company Ltd.; *Int'l*, pg. 1204
BETAFENCE NV—See CVC Capital Partners SICAV-FIS S.A.; *Int'l*, pg. 1885
BM INNOTECH INDUSTRY COMPANY LIMITED—See Bangkok Sheet Metal Public Company Ltd.; *Int'l*, pg. 835
BMP METALS INC.; *Int'l*, pg. 1076
BMW INDUSTRIES LIMITED; *Int'l*, pg. 1078
BOBRICK WASHROOM EQUIPMENT, INC.—See ; *U.S. Private*, pg. 607
BOCHUMER VEREIN VERKEHRSTECHNIK GMBH; *Int'l*, pg. 1097
BOLAN CASTINGS LIMITED; *Int'l*, pg. 1102
BONAL TECHNOLOGIES, INC.—See Bonal International, Inc.; *U.S. Public*, pg. 368
BOOTZ MANUFACTURING COMPANY; *U.S. Private*, pg. 617
BRADFORD MACHINE CO—See HC Private Investments LLC; *U.S. Private*, pg. 1888
BRAIME GROUP PLC; *Int'l*, pg. 1136
BRALCO METALS—See Reliance Steel & Aluminum Co.; *U.S. Public*, pg. 1779
BREUER GMBH—See Horst Wellness GmbH & Co. KG; *Int'l*, pg. 3482
BROMFORD INDUSTRIES LIMITED; *Int'l*, pg. 1173
BUCKEYE FIRE EQUIPMENT COMPANY; *U.S. Private*, pg. 677
BUNTING MAGNETICS EUROPE LIMITED—See Bunting Magnetics Co.; *U.S. Private*, pg. 686
BURNES GROUP—See Cerberus Capital Management, L.P.; *U.S. Private*, pg. 837
BURSERYDS BRUK AB—See Illinois Tool Works Inc.; *U.S. Public*, pg. 1102
BUSCHE SOUTHFIELD, INC.—See Busche Performance Group, Inc.; *U.S. Private*, pg. 693
CAB INCORPORATED; *U.S. Private*, pg. 710
CAB INCORPORATED - TEXAS MFG. & DISTR. FACILITY—See CAB Incorporated; *U.S. Private*, pg. 710
CABINETRY DIVISION—See Zurn Elkay Water Solutions Corporation; *U.S. Public*, pg. 2412
CABLETEC INTERCONNECT COMPONENTS SYSTEMS LIMITED—See Diploma PLC; *Int'l*, pg. 2128
CAMACO LLC—See P&C Group, Inc.; *U.S. Private*, pg. 3058
CAMACO LORAIN MANUFACTURING—See P&C Group, Inc.; *U.S. Private*, pg. 3058
CAMBRIDGE ENGINEERED SOLUTIONS—See Zurn Elkay Water Solutions Corporation; *U.S. Public*, pg. 2412
CAMBRIDGE PRO FAB INC. - PLANT 2—See Cambridge Pro Fab Inc.; *Int'l*, pg. 1269
CAMBRIDGE PRO FAB INC. - PLANT 3—See Cambridge Pro Fab Inc.; *Int'l*, pg. 1269
CAMBRIDGE PRO FAB INC. - PLANT 4—See Cambridge Pro Fab Inc.; *Int'l*, pg. 1269
CAMBRIDGE PRO FAB INC.; *Int'l*, pg. 1269
CANYON PIPE & SUPPLY, INC.—See Nicholas Consolidated Inc.; *U.S. Private*, pg. 2925
CAPARO ENGINEERING LTD.—See Caparo Group Ltd.; *Int'l*, pg. 1301
CARISTRAP EUROPE D.O.O.—See Caristrap International Inc.; *U.S. Public*, pg. 1331
CAROLINA MACHINE & TOOL INC.; *U.S. Private*, pg. 768
CARRIS OF CONNECTICUT, INC.—See Carris Financial Corp.; *U.S. Private*, pg. 772
CARRS ENGINEERING LIMITED—See Carr's Group PLC; *Int'l*, pg. 1343

CAST METAL SERVICES PTY LIMITED—See Hitachi, Ltd.; *Int'l*, pg. 3415
CASTOR & LADDER PROPRIETARY LIMITED—See ARGENT INDUSTRIAL LIMITED; *Int'l*, pg. 560
CELL IMPACT AB—See Amasten Fastighets AB; *Int'l*, pg. 412
CENTERLINE MACHINE, INC.—See Dielectric Corporation; *U.S. Private*, pg. 1228
CENTRAL STATES, INC.; *U.S. Private*, pg. 825
CENTURY INDUSTRIES INC.; *U.S. Private*, pg. 833
CENTURY INDUSTRIES, LLC; *U.S. Private*, pg. 833
CERA SANITARYWARE LTD.; *Int'l*, pg. 1421
CGI AUTOMATED MANUFACTURING, INC.—See CORE Industrial Partners, LLC; *U.S. Private*, pg. 1048
CGT SHANGHAI TRADING CO. LTD.—See Canadian General Tower Limited; *Int'l*, pg. 1283
CHALLENGER PALLET & SUPPLY INC.; *U.S. Private*, pg. 845
CHANDLER INDUSTRIES -ARROW DIVISION—See Arch Equity Partners, LLC; *U.S. Public*, pg. 310
CHANDLER INDUSTRIES, INC.—See Arch Equity Partners, LLC; *U.S. Public*, pg. 310
CHANDLER INDUSTRIES - STREMEL DIVISION—See Arch Equity Partners, LLC; *U.S. Public*, pg. 310
CHATSWORTH PRODUCTS - CHATSWORTH—See Chatsworth Products Inc.; *U.S. Private*, pg. 868
CHEP AMERICAS—See Brambles Limited; *Int'l*, pg. 1138
CHIEF INDUSTRIES, INC. - CHIEF BUILDINGS DIVISION—See Chief Industries, Inc.; *U.S. Private*, pg. 881
CHINA DIVE COMPANY LIMITED; *Int'l*, pg. 1498
CHINA POWERPLUS LIMITED; *Int'l*, pg. 1542
CHINA SILVER GROUP LIMITED; *Int'l*, pg. 1551
CIFUNSA, S.A. DE C.V.—See Grupo Industrial Saltillo S.A. de C.V.; *Int'l*, pg. 3130
CINSA ENASA PRODUCTOS PARA EL HOGAR, S.A. DE C.V.—See Grupo Industrial Saltillo S.A. de C.V.; *Int'l*, pg. 3130
CIRCOR ENERGY PRODUCTS, INC—See KKR & Co. Inc.; *U.S. Public*, pg. 1242
CITY STEEL PUBLIC COMPANY LIMITED; *Int'l*, pg. 1628
CLIMAX ENGINEERED MATERIALS—See Freeport-McMoRan Inc.; *U.S. Public*, pg. 884
CLYDESDALE FORGE—See Caparo Group Ltd.; *Int'l*, pg. 1302
COLEUS CROWNS (UGANDA) LTD—See Anheuser-Busch InBev SA/NV; *Int'l*, pg. 464
COLEUS PACKAGING (PTY) LIMITED—See Anheuser-Busch InBev SA/NV; *Int'l*, pg. 464
COLIBRI SPINDLES LTD.—See Fukuda Corporation; *Int'l*, pg. 2839
COMAP ITALIA S.R.L.U.—See Aalberts N.V.; *Int'l*, pg. 33
COMAP N.V.—See Aalberts N.V.; *Int'l*, pg. 33
COMERCIAL DUOMO LIMITADA—See CRH plc; *Int'l*, pg. 1844
COMERCIALIZADORA LA MODERNA DE TOLUCA, S.A. DE C.V.—See Grupo La Moderna, S.A.B. de C.V.; *Int'l*, pg. 3131
COMESCO, S.A. DE C.V.—See Grupo Industrial Saltillo S.A. de C.V.; *Int'l*, pg. 3130
COMPART ASIA LIMITED—See Broadway Industrial Group Limited; *Int'l*, pg. 1172
CONCEPT MACHINE & TOOL INC.—See Industrial Machining Services, Inc.; *U.S. Private*, pg. 2067
CONSTELLIUM AUTOMOTIVE USA, LLC—See Constellium SE; *Int'l*, pg. 1776
CONSTELLIUM—See Constellium SE; *Int'l*, pg. 1776
CONSTELLIUM SWITZERLAND AG—See Constellium SE; *Int'l*, pg. 1776
CONSTELLIUM VALAIS SA—See Constellium SE; *Int'l*, pg. 1776
CONTECH LLC—See Marathon Asset Management LP; *U.S. Private*, pg. 2570
CONTINENTAL ALLOYS MIDDLE EAST FZE—See Reliance Steel & Aluminum Co.; *U.S. Public*, pg. 1779
CONTINENTAL ALLOYS & SERVICES INC.—See Reliance Steel & Aluminum Co.; *U.S. Public*, pg. 1779
CONTINENTAL ALLOYS & SERVICES INC.—See Reliance Steel & Aluminum Co.; *U.S. Public*, pg. 1779
CONTINENTAL ALLOYS & SERVICES LIMITED—See Reliance Steel & Aluminum Co.; *U.S. Public*, pg. 1779
CONTINENTAL ALLOYS & SERVICES (MALAYSIA) SDN. BHD.—See Reliance Steel & Aluminum Co.; *U.S. Public*, pg. 1779
CONTINENTAL ALLOYS & SERVICES PTE. LTD.—See Reliance Steel & Aluminum Co.; *U.S. Public*, pg. 1779
COOPER COATED COIL LTD.—See Cooper Coated Coil Management Limited; *Int'l*, pg. 1791
COOPER STANDARD AUTOMOTIVE POLSKA SP. Z.O.O.—See Cooper-Standard Holdings Inc.; *U.S. Public*, pg. 574
COOPER TOOLS, LLC - YORK PLANT—See Bain Capital, LP; *U.S. Private*, pg. 430
CORROSION PRODUCTS & EQUIPMENT, INC.; *U.S. Private*, pg. 1059
COTTERLAZ CONNECTORS SHENZHEN LTD.—See Aalberts N.V.; *Int'l*, pg. 33
COVER TECHNOLOGIES INC.; *Int'l*, pg. 1821

N.A.I.C.S. INDEX

332999 — ALL OTHER MISCELLAN...

C PRODUCTS DEFENSE, INC.; *U.S. Private*, pg. 702
CRAFT PATTERN & MOLD, INC.—See Delos Capital, LLC; *U.S. Private*, pg. 1199
CRAFT PATTERN & MOLD, INC.—See Silverfern Capital Management, LLC; *U.S. Private*, pg. 3663
CRENLO, LLC—See KPS Capital Partners, LP; *U.S. Private*, pg. 2347
CROWN ROLL LEAF INC.; *U.S. Private*, pg. 1112
CURTAINWALLS & WINDOWS, INC. - CW FABRICATION SYSTEMS DIVISION—See The Berlin Steel Construction Company; *U.S. Private*, pg. 3994
CYBERNAUT INTERNATIONAL HOLDINGS COMPANY LIMITED; *Int'l*, pg. 1893
DAIDO ELECTRONICS (THAILAND) CO., LTD.—See Daido Steel Co., Ltd.; *Int'l*, pg. 1922
DAIKI ALUMINIUM VIETNAM CO., LTD.—See Daiki Aluminium Industry Co., Ltd.; *Int'l*, pg. 1931
DAIKI OM ALUMINIUM INDUSTRY (PHILIPPINES) ,INC.—See Daiki Aluminium Industry Co., Ltd.; *Int'l*, pg. 1931
DALLMER LTD.—See DALLMER GmbH & Co. KG; *Int'l*, pg. 1954
DAMEN MARINE COMPONENTS GDANSK SP. Z O.O.—See Damen Shipyards Group; *Int'l*, pg. 1956
DAMEN MARINE COMPONENTS (SUZHOU) CO., LTD.—See Damen Shipyards Group; *Int'l*, pg. 1956
D AND O HOME COLLECTION CO., LTD.; *Int'l*, pg. 1898
DECOLAV, INC.; *U.S. Private*, pg. 1187
DELAFIELD CORPORATION; *U.S. Private*, pg. 1193
DELORO STELLITE, L.P.—See Kennametal Inc.; *U.S. Public*, pg. 1221
DELORO STELLITE UK LIMITED—See Kennametal Inc.; *U.S. Public*, pg. 1221
DELTA CONSOLIDATED INDUSTRIES, INC.—See Bain Capital, LP; *U.S. Private*, pg. 430
DELTA FABRICATION & MACHINE, INC.; *U.S. Private*, pg. 1200
DELTA FAUCET COMPANY INDIA PRIVATE LIMITED—See Masco Corporation; *U.S. Public*, pg. 1390
DELVA TOOL & MACHINE CORP.—See White Wolf Capital LLC; *U.S. Private*, pg. 4510
DESTRON FEARING CORPORATION—See Merck & Co., Inc.; *U.S. Public*, pg. 1415
DIMAR MANUFACTURING CORPORATION; *U.S. Private*, pg. 1232
DISA INDUSTRIE AG—See Altor Equity Partners AB; *Int'l*, pg. 395
DISTRIBUTION AND WAREHOUSING NETWORK LIMITED; *Int'l*, pg. 2136
DISTRIBUTION SANITAIRE CHAUFFAGE SAS—See Compagnie de Saint-Gobain SA; *Int'l*, pg. 1723
DITTO SALES INC.; *U.S. Private*, pg. 1240
DIVERSEY NEW ZEALAND LIMITED—See Sealed Air Corporation; *U.S. Public*, pg. 1853
DIVERSEY PERU S.A.C.—See Sealed Air Corporation; *U.S. Public*, pg. 1853
DMEGC GERMANY GMBH—See Hengdian Group DMEGC Magnetics Co., Ltd.; *Int'l*, pg. 3346
DOMINION BUILDING PRODUCTS—See ASSA ABLOY AB; *Int'l*, pg. 637
DONGGUAN CITY PRECIMET TRADING CO LTD—See Technic Incorporated; *U.S. Private*, pg. 3953
DONGGUAN TETSUWA METALS CO., LTD.—See Hanwa Co., Ltd.; *Int'l*, pg. 3262
DONGKUK INDUSTRIES CO., LTD. - POHANG FACTORY—See Dongkuk Industries Co., Ltd.; *Int'l*, pg. 2168
DONGKUK INDUSTRIES CO., LTD. - SIHEUNG FACTORY—See Dongkuk Industries Co., Ltd.; *Int'l*, pg. 2168
DORMONT MANUFACTURING CO.—See Watts Water Technologies, Inc.; *U.S. Public*, pg. 2338
DPH ASIA LTD—See Dichtungspartner Hamburg GmbH; *Int'l*, pg. 2111
DPH TURKEY—See Dichtungspartner Hamburg GmbH; *Int'l*, pg. 2111
D P WIRES LTD.; *Int'l*, pg. 1899
DROVERS ID PTY LTD—See Merck & Co., Inc.; *U.S. Public*, pg. 1416
DS4 S.R.L. —See EuroGroup Laminations S.p.A.; *Int'l*, pg. 2552
D'STYLE, INC.—See HNI Corporation; *U.S. Public*, pg. 1043
DUNLOP CONVEYOR BELTING GHANA LIMITED—See Compagnie Generale des Etablissements Michelin SCA; *Int'l*, pg. 1742
DUPREE, INC.; *U.S. Private*, pg. 1291
DURODYNE INC.—See Eaton Corporation plc; *Int'l*, pg. 2279
DYSON GROUP PLC; *Int'l*, pg. 2243
EASTCOAST STEEL LIMITED; *Int'l*, pg. 2271
E.B. TECNICA MEXICANA, S.A. DE C.V.—See Zurn Elkay Water Solutions Corporation; *U.S. Public*, pg. 2412
ECKA GRANULES METAL POWDERS LTD.—See Palladium Equity Partners, LLC; *U.S. Private*, pg. 3078
ELECTRIC MIRROR, INC.; *U.S. Private*, pg. 1352
ELITE CNC MACHINING, INC.; *U.S. Private*, pg. 1360
ELIZABETH-HATA INTERNATIONAL—See Operlo Group, LLC; *U.S. Private*, pg. 3032

ELIZA TINSLEY LTD.; *Int'l*, pg. 2363
ELKAY MANUFACTURING COMPANY—See Zurn Elkay Water Solutions Corporation; *U.S. Public*, pg. 2412
ELKHART BRASS MANUFACTURING COMPANY, INC.—See The Sterling Group, L.P.; *U.S. Private*, pg. 4122
ELK RIVER MACHINE CO.—See The Cretex Companies, Inc.; *U.S. Private*, pg. 4016
ELMA ASIA PACIFIC PTE. LTD.—See Elma Electronic AG; *Int'l*, pg. 2367
ELSA - SILGAN METAL PACKAGING S.A.—See Silgan Holdings, Inc.; *U.S. Public*, pg. 1878
ENDO MANUFACTURING CO., LTD.; *Int'l*, pg. 2405
ENDO METAL SLEEVE (THAILAND) CO., LTD.—See Endo Manufacturing Co., Ltd.; *Int'l*, pg. 2405
ENERGEROMONT RADNEVO EOOD—See Dietsmann N.V.; *Int'l*, pg. 2117
ENERGY ABSORPTION SYSTEMS, INC.—See Trinity Industries, Inc.; *U.S. Public*, pg. 2193
ENERGY ALLOYS UK LTD.—See Energy Alloys, LLC; *U.S. Private*, pg. 1393
ENSHU INDIA PRIVATE LIMITED—See Enshu Limited; *Int'l*, pg. 2446
ENSHU (USA) CORPORATION MEXICO R.O.W.I.—See Enshu Limited; *Int'l*, pg. 2446
ENTERTAINMENT METALS INC.; *U.S. Private*, pg. 1404
ENWARE PTY. LTD.—See Watts Water Technologies, Inc.; *U.S. Public*, pg. 2337
EP CONNECTORS GMBH—See AdCapital AG; *Int'l*, pg. 126
ESCALERAS, S. DE R.L. DE C.V.—See Cuprum S.A. de C.V.; *Int'l*, pg. 1878
ESTAB PLATT FRERES S.A.—See Carclo plc; *Int'l*, pg. 1321
EXERION PRECISION TECHNOLOGY OLOMOUC, S.R.O.—See Exerion Precision Technology Holding B.V.; *Int'l*, pg. 2584
THE EXPANDED METAL COMPANY LIMITED—See Gibraltar Industries, Inc.; *U.S. Public*, pg. 936
FAST & FLUID MANAGEMENT IBERICA—See IDEX Corp; *U.S. Public*, pg. 1090
FAZE THREE AUTOFAB LIMITED—See AUNDE Achter & Ebels GmbH; *Int'l*, pg. 705
FAZE THREE AUTOFAB LIMITED—See Faze Three Limited; *Int'l*, pg. 2627
F&B MFG. LLC—See Thunderbird LLC; *U.S. Private*, pg. 4166
FEATHERLITE INDUSTRIES LTD.—See Cuprum S.A. de C.V.; *Int'l*, pg. 1878
FEDERAL HOSE MANUFACTURING INC.—See The Crawford Group Inc.; *U.S. Private*, pg. 4016
FEDERAL-MOGUL OPERATIONS FRANCE SAS—See Apollo Global Management, Inc.; *U.S. Public*, pg. 161
FIRESTONE METAL PRODUCTS COMPANY, LLC - LAS VEGAS MANUFACTURING FACILITY—See Bridgestone Corporation; *Int'l*, pg. 1160
FIRESTONE METAL PRODUCTS COMPANY, LLC—See Bridgestone Corporation; *Int'l*, pg. 1159
THE FITZPATRICK COMPANY—See IDEX Corp; *U.S. Public*, pg. 1092
FIXINOX SA; *Int'l*, pg. 2696
FLEXIBLE METAL HOSE & RUBBER PRODUCTS; *U.S. Private*, pg. 1544
FLEXMAG INDUSTRIES INC.—See Compass Diversified Holdings; *U.S. Public*, pg. 560
FLOMET LLC—See ARC Group Worldwide, Inc.; *U.S. Public*, pg. 179
FLUID MANAGEMENT FRANCE SARL—See IDEX Corp; *U.S. Public*, pg. 1090
FMH AEROSPACE CORP.—See AMETEK, Inc.; *U.S. Public*, pg. 120
FMS ENTERPRISES MIGUN LTD.; *Int'l*, pg. 2717
FORE MACHINE COMPANY, INC.—See P4G Capital Management, LLC; *U.S. Private*, pg. 3062
FORSTER SWISS HOME AG; *Int'l*, pg. 2737
FOSHAN SHUNDE DISTRICT JINGYI WANXI COPPER INDUSTRY CO., LTD.—See Guangdong Jingyi Metal Co., Ltd.; *Int'l*, pg. 3157
FRANKE CONSUMER PRODUCTS, INC.—See Artemis Holding AG; *Int'l*, pg. 582
FRANKE KINDRED CANADA LIMITED—See Artemis Holding AG; *Int'l*, pg. 582
FRIED.V.NEUMAN GMBH—See CAG Holding GmbH; *Int'l*, pg. 1250
FTL LTD.—See IDEX Corp; *U.S. Public*, pg. 1090
FURUYA METAL AMERICAS INC—See Furuya Metal Co., Ltd.; *Int'l*, pg. 2848
FURUYA METAL CO., LTD. - CHITOSE PLANT—See Furuya Metal Co., Ltd.; *Int'l*, pg. 2848
FURUYA METAL CO., LTD. - TSUCHIURA PLANT—See Furuya Metal Co., Ltd.; *Int'l*, pg. 2848
FURUYA METAL CO., LTD. - TSUKUBA PLANT—See Furuya Metal Co., Ltd.; *Int'l*, pg. 2848
FURUYA METAL KOREA CO., LTD.—See Furuya Metal Co., Ltd.; *Int'l*, pg. 2848
GALA INDUSTRIES ASIA LIMITED—See Dover Corporation; *U.S. Public*, pg. 681
GALA KUNSTSTOFF- UND KAUTSCHUKMASCHINEN GMBH—See Dover Corporation; *U.S. Public*, pg. 681
GANTOIS SA; *Int'l*, pg. 2882

GARELICK MANUFACTURING CO.; *U.S. Private*, pg. 1644
G.D GERMANY—See Coesia S.p.A.; *Int'l*, pg. 1690
GEBERIT AG; *Int'l*, pg. 2904
GEBERIT APPARATE AG—See Geberit AG; *Int'l*, pg. 2904
GEBERIT HUTER GMBH—See Geberit AG; *Int'l*, pg. 2904
GEBERIT LICHTENSTEIN GMBH—See Geberit AG; *Int'l*, pg. 2904
GEBERIT PRODUKTIONS GMBH & CO. KG—See Geberit AG; *Int'l*, pg. 2905
GEBERIT VERTRIEBS GMBH & CO. KG—See Geberit AG; *Int'l*, pg. 2905
GEBERIT WEILHEIM GMBH—See Geberit AG; *Int'l*, pg. 2905
GEMINI ENGI-FAB LIMITED; *Int'l*, pg. 2916
GENERAL PRODUCTS PARTNERS INC.; *U.S. Private*, pg. 1666
GEORGE INDUSTRIES LLC—See Behrman Brothers Management Corp.; *U.S. Private*, pg. 515
GEORG FISCHER JRG AG—See Georg Fischer AG; *Int'l*, pg. 2936
GIBRALTAR CABLE BARRIER SYSTEMS, LP—See Framework Capital Partners; *U.S. Private*, pg. 1586
GIBRALTAR CABLE BARRIER SYSTEMS, LP—See Tecum Capital Partners, LLC; *U.S. Private*, pg. 3957
GIBRALTAR US, INC.; *U.S. Private*, pg. 1696
GKN SINTER METALS COMPONENTS GMBH—See GKN plc; *Int'l*, pg. 2985
GKN SINTER METALS FILTERS GMBH—See GKN plc; *Int'l*, pg. 2985
GKN SINTER METALS GMBH RADEVORMWALD GERMANY—See GKN plc; *Int'l*, pg. 2985
GKN SINTER METALS PRIVATE LTD—See GKN plc; *Int'l*, pg. 2985
GLOBAL EXPANDED METALS—See Omnimax Holdings, Inc.; *U.S. Private*, pg. 3017
GLOBAL MATERIAL TECHNOLOGIES, INC.—See ASW Holding Corporation; *U.S. Private*, pg. 363
GOFF'S ENTERPRISES INC.; *U.S. Private*, pg. 1726
GOOD FRIEND INTERNATIONAL HOLDINGS INC.; *Int'l*, pg. 3038
GRAPHIK DIMENSIONS, LLC—See H.I.G. Capital, LLC; *U.S. Private*, pg. 1827
GRAVITA GHANA LTD—See Gravita India Limited; *Int'l*, pg. 3062
GRAVITA INDIA LIMITED; *Int'l*, pg. 3062
GRAVITA MOZAMBIQUE LDA—See Gravita India Limited; *Int'l*, pg. 3062
GRAVITA USA INC.—See Gravita India Limited; *Int'l*, pg. 3062
GREAT AMERICAN PRODUCTS INC.—See Dyna Group International Inc.; *U.S. Public*, pg. 699
GREAT LAKES CASE & CABINET CO., INC.; *U.S. Private*, pg. 1764
GREENBRIER-MAXION EQUIPAMENTOS E SERVICOS FERROVIARIOS S.A.—See The Greenbrier Companies, Inc.; *U.S. Public*, pg. 2086
GREGORY INDUSTRIES, INC.; *U.S. Private*, pg. 1783
GROVE U.S. LLC—See The Manitowoc Company, Inc.; *U.S. Public*, pg. 2111
GSG GEORGSMARIENHUETTE SERVICE GESELLSCHAFT MBH—See Georgsmarienhutte Holding GmbH; *Int'l*, pg. 2940
GUARDIAN FALL PROTECTION, INC.; *U.S. Private*, pg. 1810
GUELPH TOOL INC.; *Int'l*, pg. 3172
G. VOLKL GMBH—See Dr. Aichhorn GmbH; *Int'l*, pg. 2190
HADADY CORPORATION; *U.S. Private*, pg. 1838
HAFA BATHROOM GROUP OY—See Hafa Bathroom Group AB; *Int'l*, pg. 3206
HALFEN S.R.L.—See CRH plc; *Int'l*, pg. 1844
HALSEY TAYLOR—See Zurn Elkay Water Solutions Corporation; *U.S. Public*, pg. 2412
HAMILTON CASTER & MFG. CO.; *U.S. Private*, pg. 1847
HAMILTON SAFE CO.—See Gunnebo AB; *Int'l*, pg. 3185
HANG YICK HOLDINGS COMPANY LIMITED; *Int'l*, pg. 3245
HANGZHOU DAHE THERMO-MAGNETICS CO., LTD. - VF DIVISION—See Ferrotec Holdings Corporation; *Int'l*, pg. 2643
HANGZHOU MEIBAH PRECISION MACHINERY CO., LTD.; *Int'l*, pg. 3249
HANNAY REELS INC.; *U.S. Private*, pg. 1855
HANSGROHE D.O.O.—See Masco Corporation; *U.S. Public*, pg. 1391
HANSGROHE LIMITED—See Masco Corporation; *U.S. Public*, pg. 1390
HANSOL LOGISTICS CO., LTD.—See Hansol Group; *Int'l*, pg. 3260
HANZA MECHANICS - ARJANG—See Hanza AB; *Int'l*, pg. 3267
HANZA MECHANICS TOREBODA—See Hanza AB; *Int'l*, pg. 3267
HARSCO INFRASTRUCTURE B.V.—See Enviri Corporation; *U.S. Public*, pg. 780
HARSCO METALS & MINERALS SAS—See Enviri Corporation; *U.S. Public*, pg. 780
HARTMANN TRESORE AG; *Int'l*, pg. 3280
HARTWELL CORPORATION—See TransDigm Group Incor-

332999 — ALL OTHER MISCELLAN...

porated; *U.S. Public,* pg. 2183
HASTINGS TECHNOLOGY METALS PTE LTD—See Hastings Technology Metals Limited; *Int'l,* pg. 3284
HAWS CORPORATION; *U.S. Private,* pg. 1883
HBD/THERMOID, INC.—See HBD Industries, Inc.; *U.S. Private,* pg. 1887
HBIS GROUP CHENGDE IRON & STEEL COMPANY—See HBIS Group Co., Ltd.; *Int'l,* pg. 3296
HEINRICH RENNER GMBH; *Int'l,* pg. 3324
HEXAGON VETEC SDN. BHD.—See Hexagon Holdings Berhad; *Int'l,* pg. 3370
HEYE SPECIAL STEEL CO., LTD.—See Advanced Technology & Materials Co., Ltd.; *Int'l,* pg. 162
HEYE & SUMMIT TOOLS CO., LTD—See Advanced Technology & Materials Co., Ltd.; *Int'l,* pg. 162
HIAP SENG ENGINEERING (THAILAND) CO., LTD.—See Hiap Seng Engineering Limited; *Int'l,* pg. 3382
HIGHLAND SUPPLY CORPORATION; *U.S. Private,* pg. 1939
HI-LINE INDUSTRIES II, INC.—See Sciens Capital Management LLC; *U.S. Private,* pg. 3574
HINDUSTAN SANITARYWARE & INDUSTRIES LTD (CD II)—See AGI Greenpac Limited; *Int'l,* pg. 209
HINDUSTAN SANITARYWARE & INDUSTRIES LTD (CD I)—See AGI Greenpac Limited; *Int'l,* pg. 209
HI-REL ALLOYS LTD.—See Windjammer Capital Investors, LLC; *U.S. Private,* pg. 4537
HI-REL LIDS LTD.—See Windjammer Capital Investors, LLC; *U.S. Private,* pg. 4538
HI-REL PRODUCTS, LLC—See Windjammer Capital Investors, LLC; *U.S. Private,* pg. 4538
HITACHI METALS ADVANCED MACHINING, LTD.—See Hitachi, Ltd.; *Int'l,* pg. 3420
HITACHI METALS KOREA CO., LTD.—See Hitachi, Ltd.; *Int'l,* pg. 3420
HITACHI METALS PRECISION INSTRUMENTS (SHENZHEN) LTD.—See Hitachi, Ltd.; *Int'l,* pg. 3420
HITACHI METALS SAN HUAN MAGNETIC MATERIALS (NANTONG) CO., LTD.—See Hitachi, Ltd.; *Int'l,* pg. 3420
HITACHI METALS TAIWAN, LTD.—See Hitachi, Ltd.; *Int'l,* pg. 3420
HITACHI METALS (THAILAND) LTD.—See Hitachi, Ltd.; *Int'l,* pg. 3420
HMS BERGBAU FZCO DUBAI LLC—See HMS Bergbau AG; *Int'l,* pg. 3432
HOA SEN GROUP; *Int'l,* pg. 3436
HOCHENG CO., LTD.—See Hocheng Corporation; *Int'l,* pg. 3437
HOCHENG PHILIPPINES CORPORATION—See Hocheng Corporation; *Int'l,* pg. 3437
HOEGANAES CORPORATION EUROPE GMBH—See GKN plc; *Int'l,* pg. 2986
HOFFMANN NEOPAC; *Int'l,* pg. 3440
HOGANAS AB; *Int'l,* pg. 3441
HOGAN MANUFACTURING INC.; *U.S. Private,* pg. 1961
H. O. SCHLUTER GMBH & CO. KG; *Int'l,* pg. 3194
H.S.F. SAMENWERKENDE FABRIEKEN B.V.—See Aalberts N.V.; *Int'l,* pg. 34
HUATRACO SCAFFOLD SDN BHD—See Hiap Teck Venture Berhad; *Int'l,* pg. 3382
HUATRACO SCAFFOLD SYSTEM SDN BHD—See Hiap Teck Venture Berhad; *Int'l,* pg. 3382
HUF ROMANIA S.R.L.—See Huf Hulsbeck & Furst GmbH & Co. KG; *Int'l,* pg. 3523
HUIDA SANITARY WARE CO., LTD.; *Int'l,* pg. 3526
HURTT FABRICATING CORP.; *U.S. Private,* pg. 2013
HUTCHINSON MANUFACTURING, INC.—See Daggett Ventures, LLC; *U.S. Private,* pg. 1144
HYDRATIGHT BV—See Enerpac Tool Group Corp.; *U.S. Public,* pg. 766
HYDRATIGHT EQUIPAMENTOS SERVICOS E INDUSTRIA LTDA.—See Enerpac Tool Group Corp.; *U.S. Public,* pg. 766
HYDRATIGHT FZE—See Enerpac Tool Group Corp.; *U.S. Public,* pg. 766
HYDRATIGHT INJECTASEAL DEUTSCHLAND GMBH—See Enerpac Tool Group Corp.; *U.S. Public,* pg. 766
HYDRATIGHT LTD.—See Enerpac Tool Group Corp.; *U.S. Public,* pg. 766
HYDRATIGHT NORGE AS—See Enerpac Tool Group Corp.; *U.S. Public,* pg. 766
HYDRATIGHT OPERATIONS, INC.—See Enerpac Tool Group Corp.; *U.S. Public,* pg. 766
HYDRATIGHT PTE. LTD.—See Enerpac Tool Group Corp.; *U.S. Public,* pg. 766
HYDRA-ZORB CO.—See TruArc Partners, L.P.; *U.S. Private,* pg. 4245
HYDRO LITHIUM INC; *Int'l,* pg. 3546
HYDUKE MACHINING SOLUTIONS INC.—See Hyduke Energy Services Inc.; *Int'l,* pg. 3548
HYPERION MATERIALS & TECHNOLOGIES (FRANCE) S.A.S.—See KKR & Co. Inc.; *U.S. Public,* pg. 1253
HYUNION HOLDING CO., LTD.; *Int'l,* pg. 3561
IBARAKI TECHNOS LTD.—See Hitachi, Ltd.; *Int'l,* pg. 3423
IDEAL CLAMP PRODUCTS, INC.—See TruArc Partners, L.P.; *U.S. Private,* pg. 4245
IDEAL JACOBS (XIAMEN) CORPORATION; *Int'l,* pg. 3589

IDEAL SHIELD, L.L.C.—See The Ideal Group, Inc.; *U.S. Private,* pg. 4055
IKM MEKANISKE AS—See IKM Gruppen AS; *Int'l,* pg. 3611
INDUSTRIAS ARGA, S.A. DE C.V.—See Hillenbrand, Inc.; *U.S. Public,* pg. 1035
INEX-SOLUTIONS GMBH—See Gesco AG; *Int'l,* pg. 2945
INOXPLATE, LTDA.—See Acerinox, S.A.; *Int'l,* pg. 101
INTEGRATED MAGNETICS; *U.S. Private,* pg. 2100
IOWA LASER TECHNOLOGY INC.—See O'Neal Industries, Inc.; *U.S. Private,* pg. 2979
ITW CODING PRODUCTS—See Illinois Tool Works Inc.; *U.S. Public,* pg. 1105
ITW FOILMARK—See Illinois Tool Works Inc.; *U.S. Public,* pg. 1105
ITW PRODUX—See Illinois Tool Works Inc.; *U.S. Public,* pg. 1107
JACOBS CHILE S.A.—See Jacobs Engineering Group, Inc.; *U.S. Public,* pg. 1185
JAPAN FABWELD CO., LTD.—See Hagihara Industries Inc.; *Int'l,* pg. 3207
JD NORMAN DE MEXICO, S. DE R.L. DE C.V.—See JD Norman Industries, Inc.; *U.S. Private,* pg. 2195
JD NORMAN INDUSTRIES, INC.; *U.S. Private,* pg. 2195
J & E PRECISION TOOL, LLC; *U.S. Private,* pg. 2152
JETMASTER (PTY) LTD—See ARGENT INDUSTRIAL LIMITED; *Int'l,* pg. 560
JFSL PROJECTS LTD.—See Jacobs Engineering Group, Inc.; *U.S. Public,* pg. 1185
JIREH METAL PRODUCTS, INC.; *U.S. Private,* pg. 2211
J.L. HALEY ENTERPRISES, INC.—See Aterian Investment Management, L.P.; *U.S. Private,* pg. 367
JOSAM COMPANY—See Watts Water Technologies, Inc.; *U.S. Public,* pg. 2337
KELPEN PLASTICS TECHNOLOGY SDN. BHD—See Ewein Berhad; *Int'l,* pg. 2576
KENNAMETAL LOGISTICS GMBH—See Kennametal Inc.; *U.S. Public,* pg. 1222
KENNAMETAL STELLITE S.R.L.—See Kennametal Inc.; *U.S. Public,* pg. 1222
KEYSTONE AUTOMATIC TECHNOLOGY, INC.—See MetalKraft Industries, Inc.; *U.S. Private,* pg. 2681
KILKEN PLATINUM PROPRIETARY LIMITED—See Andulela Investment Holdings Limited; *Int'l,* pg. 457
KMS FAB, LLC—See Reliance Steel & Aluminum Co.; *U.S. Public,* pg. 1780
KMS SOUTH, INC.—See Reliance Steel & Aluminum Co.; *U.S. Public,* pg. 1780
KNOX ASSOCIATES, INC.; *U.S. Private,* pg. 2324
KOHLER COMPANY; *U.S. Private,* pg. 2339
KOHLER (THAILAND) PUBLIC CO. LTD.—See Kohler Company; *U.S. Private,* pg. 2339
KOREA SHINKO MICROELECTRONICS CO., LTD.—See Fujitsu Limited; *Int'l,* pg. 2837
KOREA TECHNIC CO. LTD.—See Technic Incorporated; *U.S. Private,* pg. 3953
KURT MANUFACTURING CO. INC.; *U.S. Private,* pg. 2357
KVT-FASTENING AG—See Bossard Holding AG; *Int'l,* pg. 1117
LADDER INDUSTRIES, INC.—See Holden Industries, Inc.; *U.S. Private,* pg. 1962
L.A. GAUGE CO.; *U.S. Private,* pg. 2364
LAI INTERNATIONAL, INC.-MINNEAPOLIS—See Monroe Capital LLC; *U.S. Private,* pg. 2773
LAI INTERNATIONAL, INC.-MINNEAPOLIS—See The RLJ Companies, LLC; *U.S. Private,* pg. 4111
LAI INTERNATIONAL, INC.—See Monroe Capital LLC; *U.S. Private,* pg. 2773
LAI INTERNATIONAL, INC.—See The RLJ Companies, LLC; *U.S. Private,* pg. 4111
LAI INTERNATIONAL, INC.-WESTMINSTER—See Monroe Capital LLC; *U.S. Private,* pg. 2773
LAI INTERNATIONAL, INC.-WESTMINSTER—See The RLJ Companies, LLC; *U.S. Private,* pg. 4111
LANGFANG HUADE METAL PACKAGING CONTAINER CO., LTD.—See Crown Holdings, Inc.; *U.S. Public,* pg. 599
LAPOUYADE—See Blackstone Inc.; *U.S. Public,* pg. 348
LASERFLEX CORPORATION—See Ryerson Holding Corporation; *U.S. Public,* pg. 1829
LASER SPECIALTIES, INC.—See Lorraine Capital LLC; *U.S. Private,* pg. 2496
L.B. FOSTER RAIL TECHNOLOGIES CANADA LTD—See L.B. Foster Company; *U.S. Public,* pg. 1278
L. B. FOSTER RAIL TECHNOLOGIES, INC.—See L.B. Foster Company; *U.S. Public,* pg. 1278
LEADER TECH, INC.—See HEICO Corporation; *U.S. Public,* pg. 1020
LEED FABRICATION SERVICES, LLC—See First Reserve Management, L.P.; *U.S. Private,* pg. 1526
LEME, INC.—See Saugatuck Capital Company; *U.S. Private,* pg. 3554
LEWIS ENGINEERING COMPANY—See Jabil Inc.; *U.S. Public,* pg. 1181
LIBERTY SAFE & SECURITY PRODUCTS, INC.—See Compass Diversified Holdings; *U.S. Public,* pg. 560
LIPPERT COMPONENTS, INC.—See LCI Industries; *U.S. Public,* pg. 1295

LIQUIDMETAL TECHNOLOGIES, INC.; *U.S. Public,* pg. 1321
LISTA GMBH—See GreatStar Group Co., Ltd.; *Int'l,* pg. 3068
LITTLE ENTERPRISES, INC.—See OEP Capital Advisors, L.P.; *U.S. Private,* pg. 2999
LOUISVILLE LADDER INC.—See Cuprum S.A. de C.V.; *Int'l,* pg. 1878
MACK HILS, INC.; *U.S. Private,* pg. 2536
MAC LEAN PRECISION MACHINE CO.; *U.S. Private,* pg. 2531
MAGNAPLAN CORPORATION VISUAL PLANNING DIVISION—See Magnaplan Corporation; *U.S. Private,* pg. 2546
MAGNEQUENCH NEO POWDERS PTE. LTD.—See Brookfield Corporation; *Int'l,* pg. 1181
MAGNETIC COMPONENT ENGINEERING INC.; *U.S. Private,* pg. 2547
MAGNET LLC; *U.S. Private,* pg. 2547
MAGNUM MAGNETICS CORPORATION; *U.S. Private,* pg. 2549
MAITHAN ALLOYS LTD—See Bhagwati Syndicate Pvt. Ltd.; *Int'l,* pg. 1010
MANUFACTURING SUPPORT INDUSTRIES, INC.—See Craig Technologies, Inc.; *U.S. Private,* pg. 1083
MAPA SPONTEX ITALIA S.P.A.—See Newell Brands Inc.; *U.S. Public,* pg. 1514
MARINI MANUFACTURING, INC.; *U.S. Private,* pg. 2576
MARQUIS INDUSTRIES, INC.; *U.S. Private,* pg. 2587
MASKINERING OG SVEISESERVICE AS—See Schlumberger Limited; *U.S. Public,* pg. 1844
MATERIALS SCIENCE INTERNATIONAL, INC.; *U.S. Private,* pg. 2610
MATERION JAPAN LTD.—See Materion Corporation; *U.S. Public,* pg. 1395
MATERION TECHNICAL MATERIALS, INC.—See Materion Corporation; *U.S. Public,* pg. 1396
MECKLENBURGER METALLGUSS GMBH—See DIHAG Holding GmbH; *Int'l,* pg. 2124
MELCHER & FRENZEN ARMATUREN GMBH—See Aalberts N.V.; *Int'l,* pg. 35
MESA SAFE COMPANY, INC.; *U.S. Private,* pg. 2678
METALCRAFT OF MAYVILLE, INC.; *U.S. Private,* pg. 2680
METALEX LLC—See UPG Enterprises LLC; *U.S. Private,* pg. 4311
METAL FORMING & COINING CORP.—See Vickers Engineering, Inc.; *U.S. Private,* pg. 4377
METALIS HPS S.A.S.—See Aalberts N.V.; *Int'l,* pg. 35
METALIS POLSKA SP. Z.O.O.—See Aalberts N.V.; *Int'l,* pg. 35
METALLUS INC.; *U.S. Public,* pg. 1427
METALTECH CO., LTD.—See Hanwa Co., Ltd.; *Int'l,* pg. 3263
METEM CORPORATION—See General Electric Company; *U.S. Public,* pg. 918
METPAR CORP.; *U.S. Private,* pg. 2684
MICHAEL GLATT MASCHINENBAU GMBH—See Buechl Handels-und Beteiligungs-KG; *Int'l,* pg. 1211
MICRO MOLDING, INC.—See Frazier & Company, Inc.; *U.S. Private,* pg. 1599
MILESTONE METALS INC.; *U.S. Public,* pg. 2728
MILLER FABRICATION & CONSTRUCTION, INC.; *U.S. Private,* pg. 2734
MILLS PRODUCTS INC.; *U.S. Private,* pg. 2738
MINELAB ELECTRONICS PTY LTD—See Codan Limited; *Int'l,* pg. 1688
MITEK USA, INC.—See Berkshire Hathaway Inc.; *U.S. Public,* pg. 313
MOEN CHINA, LIMITED—See Fortune Brands Innovations, Inc.; *U.S. Public,* pg. 873
MORTON INDUSTRIES LLC; *U.S. Private,* pg. 2792
MULTRI PRECISION, LLC; *U.S. Private,* pg. 2813
MURDOCK-SUPER SECUR—See Acorn Engineering Company, Inc.; *U.S. Private,* pg. 63
MVG METALLVERKAUFSGESELLSCHAFT MBH & CO. KG—See GEA Group Aktiengesellschaft; *Int'l,* pg. 2903
NAMBE MILLS INC.; *U.S. Private,* pg. 2831
NAMITAKIKO CO., LTD.—See Carlit Co., Ltd.; *Int'l,* pg. 1338
NANTONG BAOSTEEL STEEL & IRON CO., LTD.—See China Baowu Steel Group Corp., Ltd.; *Int'l,* pg. 1486
NASEEJ FABRIC MANUFACTURING L.L.C.—See Dubai Islamic Bank PSJ; *Int'l,* pg. 2220
NEOMAX KINKI CO., LTD.—See Hitachi, Ltd.; *Int'l,* pg. 3423
NEOMAX KYUSHUU CO., LTD.—See Hitachi, Ltd.; *Int'l,* pg. 3423
NEO TECH PACKAGING (SHANGHAI) CO., LTD—See Crown Holdings, Inc.; *U.S. Public,* pg. 599
NEUMAN ALUMINIUM IMPACT EXTRUSION INC.—See CAG Holding GmbH; *Int'l,* pg. 1250
NEUMAN ALUMINIUM SERVICES S.R.O.—See CAG Holding GmbH; *Int'l,* pg. 1250
NEUMAN (XINHUI) ALLOY MATERIAL CO LTD—See CAG Holding GmbH; *Int'l,* pg. 1250
NEW STAR METALS, INC.—See Insight Equity Holdings LLC; *U.S. Private,* pg. 2086
NIKKO METALS TAIWAN CO., LTD.—See ENEOS Holdings, Inc.; *Int'l,* pg. 2416
NINGBO IRON & STEEL CO., LTD.—See China Baowu Steel Group Corp., Ltd.; *Int'l,* pg. 1486

N.A.I.C.S. INDEX

332999 — ALL OTHER MISCELLAN...

NIPPON MINING & METALS (SUZHOU) CO., LTD.—See ENEOS Holdings, Inc.; *Int'l*, pg. 2416
NIPPON PGM AMERICA INC.—See Dowa Holdings Co., Ltd.; *Int'l*, pg. 2184
NIPPON PUSNES CO., LTD.—See Hitachi Zosen Corporation; *Int'l*, pg. 3412
NITRAM, LLC; *U.S. Private*, pg. 2929
NORSK TITANIUM AS—See Rose Park Advisors LLC; *U.S. Private*, pg. 3481
NORTHWEST TERRITORIAL MINT, LLC.; *U.S. Private*, pg. 2962
NOSTALGIC IMAGES INC.; *U.S. Private*, pg. 2965
NUCOR COLD FINISH WISCONSIN, INC.—See Nucor Corporation; *U.S. Public*, pg. 1553
NUCOR-LMP INC.—See Nucor Corporation; *U.S. Public*, pg. 1554
NUCOR STEEL LONGVIEW LLC—See Nucor Corporation; *U.S. Public*, pg. 1554
NUCOR TUBULAR PRODUCTS MADISON LLC—See Nucor Corporation; *U.S. Public*, pg. 1554
NUMERICAL PRECISION, INC.—See Behrman Brothers Management Corp.; *U.S. Private*, pg. 515
NUMERICAL PRODUCTIONS, INC.—See Paramount Precision Products, Inc.; *U.S. Private*, pg. 3093
OATEY COMPANY; *U.S. Private*, pg. 2986
THE OCTOBER COMPANY, INC.; *U.S. Private*, pg. 4088
OGALLALA ELECTRONICS—See Compass Diversified Holdings; *U.S. Public*, pg. 560
OHKAWA CORP.—See Alconix Corporation; *Int'l*, pg. 302
OKINAWA BUNKA SHUTTER CO., LTD—See Bunka Shutter Co., Ltd.; *Int'l*, pg. 1216
OLYMPIC STEEL INC. - SILER CITY—See Olympic Steel Inc.; *U.S. Public*, pg. 1570
ONDAL MEDICAL SYSTEMS GMBH—See IK Investment Partners Limited; *Int'l*, pg. 3609
ONDAL MEDICAL SYSTEMS OF AMERICA, INC.—See IK Investment Partners Limited; *Int'l*, pg. 3610
O'NEAL MANUFACTURING SERVICES DIVISION—See O'Neal Industries, Inc.; *U.S. Private*, pg. 2979
ORMET CORP.; *U.S. Public*, pg. 1618
THE OSBORNE COINAGE COMPANY—See Groep Heylen Business & Building BV; *Int'l*, pg. 3087
PACIFIC RARE SPECIALTY METALS & CHEMICALS, INC.—See Coherent Corp.; *U.S. Public*, pg. 529
PACKLESS METAL HOSE INC.; *U.S. Private*, pg. 3073
PANDROL AUSTRALIA PTY LIMITED—See CVC Capital Partners SICAV-FIS S.A.; *Int'l*, pg. 1887
PASARGAD GROUP INTERNATIONAL TRADING COMPANY—See Bank Pasargad; *Int'l*, pg. 849
P&C GROUP, INC.; *U.S. Private*, pg. 3058
PEPCO MANUFACTURING COMPANY; *U.S. Private*, pg. 3143
PERFEKTA INC.—See Arlington Capital Partners LLC; *U.S. Private*, pg. 327
THE PERRYMAN COMPANY; *U.S. Private*, pg. 4093
PHOENIX ALUMINIUM 2011 LIMITED—See Fletcher Building Limited; *Int'l*, pg. 2700
PLAFOMETAL SAS—See Compagnie de Saint-Gobain SA; *Int'l*, pg. 1726
POLY-CHOKE—See Nitram, LLC; *U.S. Private*, pg. 2929
POLY PORTABLES INC.; *U.S. Private*, pg. 3225
PORCELAIN INDUSTRIES, INC.—See Incline MGMT Corp.; *U.S. Private*, pg. 2054
PORCELANIZADOS ENASA, S.A. DE C.V.—See Grupo Industrial Saltillo S.A. de C.V.; *Int'l*, pg. 3130
PORCHER LUXURY DESIGNS—See Sun Capital Partners, Inc.; *U.S. Private*, pg. 3858
PORTER'S GROUP, LLC—See Littlejohn & Co., LLC; *U.S. Private*, pg. 2471
PPG DECO SLOVAKIA, S.R.O.—See PPG Industries, Inc.; *U.S. Public*, pg. 1708
PPG SWITZERLAND GMBH—See PPG Industries, Inc.; *U.S. Public*, pg. 1709
PRECISION MANUFACTURING GROUP, LLC—See American Securities LLC; *U.S. Private*, pg. 250
PRECISION RESOURCE INC. - CONNECTICUT DIVISION—See Precision Resource Inc.; *U.S. Private*, pg. 3246
PRECISION RESOURCES INC.; *U.S. Private*, pg. 3246
PRECISION VALVE CORPORATION—See Peak Rock Capital LLC; *U.S. Private*, pg. 3124
PREFA ALUMINIUMPRODUKTE S.R.O.—See CAG Holding GmbH; *Int'l*, pg. 1250
PREFA FRANCE SARL—See CAG Holding GmbH; *Int'l*, pg. 1250
PREFA GMBH—See CAG Holding GmbH; *Int'l*, pg. 1250
PREFA HUNGARIA KFT.—See CAG Holding GmbH; *Int'l*, pg. 1250
PREFA ITALIA SRL—See CAG Holding GmbH; *Int'l*, pg. 1250
PREFA SCHWEIZ AG—See CAG Holding GmbH; *Int'l*, pg. 1250
PREMIER FAB, INC.—See Ameripipe Supply, Inc.; *U.S. Private*, pg. 260
PREMIER PRECISION GROUP LLC—See Spell Capital Partners, LLC; *U.S. Private*, pg. 3754
PREMIER PRECISION GROUP - RDS FACILITY—See Spell Capital Partners, LLC; *U.S. Private*, pg. 3754
PREMIER THERMAL SOLUTIONS LLC—See Aalberts N.V.; *Int'l*, pg. 35
PRIME METALS & ALLOYS, INC.—See Amerinac Holding Corp.; *U.S. Private*, pg. 260
PROSTEEL SECURITY PRODUCTS, INC.—See Promus Holdings, LLC; *U.S. Private*, pg. 3284
PROTO METALS ESCHENLOHE GMBH—See Proto Labs, Inc.; *U.S. Public*, pg. 1730
PROTOTYPE SOLUTIONS GROUP—See TruArc Partners, L.P.; *U.S. Private*, pg. 4245
PSM INTERNATIONAL FASTENERS LIMITED—See Bulten AB; *Int'l*, pg. 1215
PT.DAIKI TRADING INDONESIA—See Daiki Aluminium Industry Co., Ltd.; *Int'l*, pg. 1932
PT. HANWA ROYAL METALS—See Hanwa Co., Ltd.; *Int'l*, pg. 3263
PULSE SYSTEMS, LLC—See United American Healthcare Corp.; *U.S. Public*, pg. 2229
PUZ MEIBES SP. Z.O.O.—See Aalberts N.V.; *Int'l*, pg. 35
PWG PROFILROLLEN-WERKZEUGBAU GMBH—See CAG Holding GmbH; *Int'l*, pg. 1250
RADSATZFABRIK ILSENBURG GMBH—See Georgsmarienhutte Holding GmbH; *Int'l*, pg. 2941
RALOID CORPORATION—See Angeles Equity Partners, LLC; *U.S. Private*, pg. 282
RAPID SHEET METAL LLC—See Proto Labs, Inc.; *U.S. Public*, pg. 1730
RAUFOSS METALL GMBH—See Aalberts N.V.; *Int'l*, pg. 35
RED WOLF COMPANY, LLC—See Broadwind, Inc.; *U.S. Public*, pg. 392
REELCRAFT INDUSTRIES INC.—See Madison Industries, Inc.; *U.S. Private*, pg. 2543
RELIANCE STEEL & ALUMINUM CO.; *U.S. Public*, pg. 1779
RENA—See Mars, Incorporated; *U.S. Private*, pg. 2589
R.F. KNOX COMPANY, INC.; *U.S. Private*, pg. 3336
THE RITESCREEN COMPANY, LLC—See Seven Point Equity Partners, LLC; *U.S. Private*, pg. 3619
RITESCREEN—See Seven Point Equity Partners, LLC; *U.S. Private*, pg. 3619
RIVER STEEL, INC.; *U.S. Private*, pg. 3444
ROANWELL CORP. - ABSOLUTE MANUFACTURING DIVISION—See Roanwell Corporation; *U.S. Private*, pg. 3454
ROCHESTER METAL PRODUCTS CORP.; *U.S. Private*, pg. 3463
ROCKWOOD HOLDING COMPANY INC.; *U.S. Private*, pg. 3468
ROHL LLC—See Fortune Brands Innovations, Inc.; *U.S. Public*, pg. 873
RONSON CONSUMER PRODUCTS CORP.—See Zippo Manufacturing Company, Inc.; *U.S. Private*, pg. 4606
SAFARILAND, LLC - ONTARIO OFFICE—See Kanders & Company, Inc.; *U.S. Private*, pg. 2259
SAFEMARK SYSTEMS, LP—See ASSA ABLOY AB; *Int'l*, pg. 640
SAFE TIME, SPOL. S.R.O.—See Bergman & Beving AB; *Int'l*, pg. 980
SAFFIL LTD.—See Clearlake Capital Group, L.P.; *U.S. Private*, pg. 937
SANDVIK HYPERION TAIWAN LIMITED—See KKR & Co. Inc.; *U.S. Public*, pg. 1253
SANDVIK HYPERION (WUXI) CO., LTD.—See KKR & Co. Inc.; *U.S. Public*, pg. 1253
SAN EI METAL CO., LTD.—See Hanwa Co., Ltd.; *Int'l*, pg. 3263
SANITAS TROESCH AG—See Compagnie de Saint-Gobain SA; *Int'l*, pg. 1736
SANKEY AUSTRALIA—See CMG Pty. Ltd.; *Int'l*, pg. 1670
SCAFCO STEEL STUD MANUFACTURING CO.—See SCAFCO Corporation; *U.S. Private*, pg. 3560
SCE-SOCIETE DE CONCEPTION ET D'EDITION SAS—See A.S. Creation Tapeten AG; *Int'l*, pg. 28
SCHAFER DRIVELINE, LLC—See HBM Holdings Company; *U.S. Private*, pg. 1887
SCHAFFER PRECISION MACHINE SHOP, INC.—See Gremada Industries Inc.; *U.S. Private*, pg. 1783
SELEKTA INOVATIF (M) SDN. BHD.—See Giovanni Agnelli B.V.; *U.S. Private*, pg. 2978
SEMVAC A/S—See Westinghouse Air Brake Technologies Corporation; *U.S. Public*, pg. 2359
SENTRY GROUP, INC.; *U.S. Private*, pg. 3610
SENTRY SAFE, INC.—See Fortune Brands Innovations, Inc.; *U.S. Public*, pg. 873
SERRA LASER PRECISION, LLC—See LFM Capital LLC; *U.S. Private*, pg. 2441
SETTER GMBH & CO.—See Gesco AG; *Int'l*, pg. 2946
SHANGHAI ANTAI-ZHIGAO AMORPHOUS METAL CO., LTD.—See Advanced Technology & Materials Co., Ltd.; *Int'l*, pg. 162
SHANGHAI BAOHUA INTERNATIONAL TENDERING CO., LTD.—See China Baowu Steel Group Corp., Ltd.; *Int'l*, pg. 1486
SHANGHAI HITACHI METALS CABLE MATERIALS CO., LTD.—See Hitachi, Ltd.; *Int'l*, pg. 3424
SHAW AREVA MOX SERVICES, LLC; *U.S. Private*, pg. 3627
SHILOH INTERNACIONAL S.A. DE C.V.—See Shiloh Industries, Inc.; *U.S. Private*, pg. 3636
SHUNDE TUBE & ROD TECHNOLOGY CO., LTD.—See Guangdong Jingyi Metal Co., Ltd.; *Int'l*, pg. 3157
SIGNODE PACKAGING SYSTEMS LIMITED—See Illinois Tool Works Inc.; *U.S. Public*, pg. 1110
SIGNODE SYSTEMS (THAILAND) LTD.—See Illinois Tool Works Inc.; *U.S. Public*, pg. 1110
SILGAN METAL PACKAGING LEIPZIG GMBH—See Silgan Holdings, Inc.; *U.S. Public*, pg. 1879
SKODA JS A.S.—See Gazprombank JSC; *Int'l*, pg. 2892
SMARTCLIP NORDICS AB—See Bertelsmann SE & Co. KGaA; *Int'l*, pg. 996
SOCIETE DE COMMERCIALISATION DE FOURNITURES POUR L'INDUSTRIE ET LA CONSTRUCTION—See Compagnie de Saint-Gobain SA; *Int'l*, pg. 1737
SOCIETE DE CONSTRUCTION ET D'ASSEMBLAGES METALLIQUES SAS—See Amplifon S.p.A.; *Int'l*, pg. 436
SOCIETY AWARDS; *U.S. Private*, pg. 3703
SOHBI CRAFT POLAND SP.Z O.O.—See Hanwa Co., Ltd.; *Int'l*, pg. 3263
SOHBI KOHGEI (PHILS) INC.—See Hanwa Co., Ltd.; *Int'l*, pg. 3263
SOLAR ENERJI TEKNOLOJILERI VE METAL SANAYI TICARET A.S.—See Bozlu Holding; *Int'l*, pg. 1125
SOLARLENS CO., LTD.—See PPG Industries, Inc.; *U.S. Public*, pg. 1710
SONOCO ALCORE AB—See Sonoco Products Company; *U.S. Public*, pg. 1906
SPACE ENERGY CORPORATION—See ENEOS Holdings, Inc.; *Int'l*, pg. 2417
SPECMA WIRO AB—See Aktieselskabet Schouw & Co.; *Int'l*, pg. 266
SPS AEROSTRUCTURES LIMITED—See Berkshire Hathaway Inc.; *U.S. Public*, pg. 315
SPUN METALS, INC.—See Dubai Holding LLC; *Int'l*, pg. 2218
STAINTON METAL CO, LTD.—See Valmont Industries, Inc.; *U.S. Public*, pg. 2274
STANLEY STORAGE & WORKSPACE SYSTEMS—See Stanley Black & Decker, Inc.; *U.S. Public*, pg. 1935
STAR SHINE INDUSTRIES SDN. BHD.—See BlueScope Steel Limited; *Int'l*, pg. 1074
STEEL & ALLOY UTILITY PRODUCTS, INC.; *U.S. Private*, pg. 3795
STEEL INGENIERIA, S.A.—See Ferrovial S.A.; *Int'l*, pg. 2645
STEELTECH INDUSTRIAL FABRICATING CORPORATION—See J Fitzgibbons LLC; *U.S. Private*, pg. 2153
STERLING STEEL COMPANY, LLC—See Leggett & Platt, Incorporated; *U.S. Public*, pg. 1303
STOBA SONDERMASCHINEN GMBH—See Berndorf AG; *Int'l*, pg. 987
STREAMLINE COPPER & BRASS LTD.—See Mueller Industries, Inc.; *U.S. Public*, pg. 1485
SUPERIOR CANS & PAILS CONTAINERS (PUNE) PRIVATE LIMITED—See Crown Holdings, Inc.; *U.S. Public*, pg. 599
SUPERIOR FABRICATION COMPANY, LLC—See Reserve Group Management Company; *U.S. Private*, pg. 3405
SUSPA COMPART ASIA PTE. LTD.—See Andlinger & Company, Inc.; *U.S. Private*, pg. 279
SUSPA UK LTD.—See Andlinger & Company, Inc.; *U.S. Private*, pg. 279
SUSSEX WIRE, INC.—See Argosy Capital Group, LLC; *U.S. Private*, pg. 321
SWISSMETAL EAST ASIA LTD.—See Baoshida International Holding Group Co., Ltd.; *Int'l*, pg. 856
SYMBOLARTS, LLC; *U.S. Private*, pg. 3899
SYNTHANE-TAYLOR (CANADA) LIMITED—See Dunes Point Capital, LLC; *U.S. Private*, pg. 1289
TAPRITE-FASSCO MFG., INC.—See Aalberts N.V.; *Int'l*, pg. 36
TASMAN SINKWARE PTY LIMITED—See Fletcher Building Limited; *Int'l*, pg. 2701
TCR INDUSTRIES, INC.; *U.S. Private*, pg. 3943
TECHNETICS GROUP OXFORD, INC.—See Enpro Inc.; *U.S. Public*, pg. 775
TECHNIC INCORPORATED - CHALON PLANT—See Technic Incorporated; *U.S. Private*, pg. 3953
TEKUN ASAS SDN BHD (TASB)—See Ewein Berhad; *Int'l*, pg. 2576
TEMPEL CANADA CORPORATION—See Worthington Industries, Inc.; *U.S. Public*, pg. 2382
TEMPEL PRECISION METAL PRODUCTS INDIA PVT. LTD.—See Worthington Industries, Inc.; *U.S. Public*, pg. 2382
TEREXLIFT S.R.L.—See Terex Corporation; *U.S. Public*, pg. 2019
TERRASMART, LLC—See Gibraltar Industries, Inc.; *U.S. Public*, pg. 936
THERMACORE EUROPE LTD.—See The Goldman Sachs Group, Inc.; *U.S. Public*, pg. 2080
THERMACORE, INC.—See The Goldman Sachs Group, Inc.; *U.S. Public*, pg. 2080
THERMOPLASTICS ENGINEERING CORPORATION—See Broomfield Laboratories Inc.; *U.S. Private*, pg. 665

332999 — ALL OTHER MISCELLAN...

THETFORD CORP. MANUFACTURING FACILITY—See The Dyson-Kissner-Moran Corporation; *U.S. Private*, pg. 4024
THOMAS & SKINNER, INC.; *U.S. Private*, pg. 4154
THUNDERBIRD METALS PTY. LTD.—See ATHA Energy Corp.; *Int'l*, pg. 669
TINIUS OLSEN, LTD.—See Tinius Olsen, Inc.; *U.S. Private*, pg. 4175
TITANIUM, LTD.—See Titanium Fabrication Corporation; *U.S. Private*, pg. 4177
TITAN WHEEL CORPORATION OF ILLINOIS—See Titan International, Inc.; *U.S. Public*, pg. 2160
TIXIT—See Blackstone Inc.; *U.S. Public*, pg. 348
TJ COPE INC.—See Clayton, Dubilier & Rice, LLC; *U.S. Private*, pg. 919
TOGA MANUFACTURING, INC.—See Kinplex Corp.; *U.S. Private*, pg. 2313
TONG LUNG PHILIPPINES METAL INDUSTRY CO., INC.—See Spectrum Brands Holdings, Inc.; *U.S. Public*, pg. 1917
TOOLSPEC MANUFACTURING COMPANY LTD.—See Cooper Coated Coil Management Limited; *Int'l*, pg. 1791
TOPEKA METAL SPECIALTIES—See L B Industries, Inc.; *U.S. Private*, pg. 2361
TRIMASTER MANUFACTURING, INC.—See GenNx360 Capital Partners, L.P.; *U.S. Private*, pg. 1672
TRINITY HIGHWAY LEASING, INC.—See Trinity Industries, Inc.; *U.S. Public*, pg. 2194
TRUENORTH STEEL - BLAINE—See TrueNorth Steel Inc.; *U.S. Private*, pg. 4249
TRU-FLEX, LLC—See Wind Point Advisors LLC; *U.S. Private*, pg. 4534
TUBE BEND FORM INTERNATIONAL LIMITED—See Cooper Coated Coil Management Limited; *Int'l*, pg. 1791
TUBEX TUBENFABRIK WOLFSBERG GMBH—See CAG Holding GmbH; *Int'l*, pg. 1251
TW MANUFACTURING CO.—See Park-Ohio Holdings Corp.; *U.S. Public*, pg. 1640
ULBRICH SOLAR TECHNOLOGIES, INC.—See Ulbrich Stainless Steel & Special Metals, Inc.; *U.S. Private*, pg. 4276
ULTRA PLAY SYSTEMS, INC.—See Court Square Capital Partners, L.P.; *U.S. Private*, pg. 1070
UNICAST INC.—See Decisive Dividend Corporation; *Int'l*, pg. 2001
UNIRAC, INC.—See Tenex Capital Management, L.P.; *U.S. Private*, pg. 3966
URSCHEL ESPANA SL—See Urschel Laboratories Incorporated; *U.S. Private*, pg. 4316
VAAL SANITARYWARE (PROPRIETARY) LIMITED—See DISTRIBUTION AND WAREHOUSING NETWORK LIMITED; *Int'l*, pg. 2136
VACHERIE MACHINE DIVISION; *U.S. Private*, pg. 4329
VAC MAGNETIC JAPAN K.K.—See Ara Partners Group; *U.S. Private*, pg. 306
VAC MAGNETIC KOREA LTD.—See Ara Partners Group; *U.S. Private*, pg. 306
VAC NETHERLANDS B.V.—See Ara Partners Group; *U.S. Private*, pg. 306
VCI, INC.—See J Fitzgibbons LLC; *U.S. Private*, pg. 2153
VESTURE CORPORATION; *U.S. Private*, pg. 4373
VIDISPINE AB—See Bertelsmann SE & Co. KGaA; *Int'l*, pg. 996
VIKING LLC—See Dema Engineering Co.; *U.S. Private*, pg. 1203
VITRA BAD GMBH—See Eczacibasi Holding A.S.; *Int'l*, pg. 2301
VITRA USA INC.—See Eczacibasi Holding A.S.; *Int'l*, pg. 2302
VULCRAFT OF NEW YORK, INC.—See Nucor Corporation; *U.S. Public*, pg. 1555
WALL COLMONOY CORPORATION - WALL COLMONOY TECHNOLOGIES DIVISION—See Wall Colmonoy Corporation; *U.S. Private*, pg. 4429
WALL COLMONOY LIMITED—See Wall Colmonoy Corporation; *U.S. Private*, pg. 4429
WARREN FABRICATING CORPORATION - HUBBARD FACILITY—See Warren Fabricating Corporation; *U.S. Private*, pg. 4444
WATKINS DISTRIBUTION UK LIMITED—See Masco Corporation; *U.S. Public*, pg. 1391
WAYNE WIRE AIR BAG COMPONENTS, INC. - JUAREZ FACILITY—See Wayne Wire Cloth Products, Inc.; *U.S. Private*, pg. 4460
WECO MANUFACTURING GROUP—See Fairchild Capital Partners, LLC; *U.S. Private*, pg. 1462
WEDLAKE FABRICATING, INC.—See IES Holdings, Inc.; *U.S. Public*, pg. 1094
WEICOM S.R.L.—See Hillenbrand, Inc.; *U.S. Public*, pg. 1036
WEINGEROFF ENTERPRISES, INC.; *U.S. Private*, pg. 4472
WESKO INDUSTRIES, INC.—See Kinplex Corp.; *U.S. Private*, pg. 2313
WEST COAST ENGINEERING, INC—See Valmont Industries, Inc.; *U.S. Public*, pg. 2274
WESTEEL—See Ag Growth International Inc.; *Int'l*, pg. 198
WHIP INDUSTRIES INC.; *U.S. Private*, pg. 4506

WHITEHALL MANUFACTURING, INC.—See Acorn Engineering Company, Inc.; *U.S. Private*, pg. 63
WHITE METALS GROUP—See Plymouth Tube Company; *U.S. Private*, pg. 3216
WILLIAM T. SPAEDER CO., INC.; *U.S. Private*, pg. 4525
WINCO, INC.; *U.S. Private*, pg. 4533
WINCRAFT INCORPORATED—See Kynetic LLC; *U.S. Private*, pg. 2360
THE WINSFORD CORPORATION—See Winsford II Corporation; *U.S. Private*, pg. 4543
WINSFORD II CORPORATION; *U.S. Private*, pg. 4543
WISCO TAILORED BLANKS GMBH—See China Baowu Steel Group Corp., Ltd.; *Int'l*, pg. 1485
WITT INDUSTRIES, INC.—See The Armor Group, Inc.; *U.S. Private*, pg. 3988
W. L. GORE & ASSOCIATES (PACIFIC) PTE. LTD. - INDIA BRANCH—See W.L. Gore & Associates, Inc.; *U.S. Private*, pg. 4421
WOODWARD INDUSTRIES, INC.; *U.S. Private*, pg. 4561
WORLD GRAND HOLDINGS LIMITED—See AMVIG Holdings Limited; *Int'l*, pg. 442
WURTTEMBERGISCHE FILZTUCHFABRIK D. GESCHMAY GMBH—See Albany International Corp.; *U.S. Public*, pg. 72
XFS GLOBAL LLC; *U.S. Private*, pg. 4581
YANTAI TIEZHONGBAO STEEL PROCESSING CO., LTD.—See China International Marine Containers (Group) Co., Ltd.; *Int'l*, pg. 1513
YUMESHO LTD.—See Autobacs Seven Co., Ltd.; *Int'l*, pg. 726
ZHONGYUE POSCO (QINHUANGDAO) TINPLATE INDUSTRIAL CO., LIMITED—See GDH Limited; *Int'l*, pg. 2896
ZIPPER TECHNIK GMBH—See The Zippertubing Company; *U.S. Private*, pg. 4140
ZIPPO MANUFACTURING COMPANY, INC.; *U.S. Private*, pg. 4606
ZURN PEX, INC.—See Zurn Elkay Water Solutions Corporation; *U.S. Public*, pg. 2414

333111 — FARM MACHINERY AND EQUIPMENT MANUFACTURING

ADARSH PLANT PROTECT LTD.; *Int'l*, pg. 125
AEBI & CO. AG MASCHINENFABRIK—See Aebi Schmidt Holding AG; *Int'l*, pg. 170
AEBI SCHMIDT DEUTSCHLAND GMBH—See Aebi Schmidt Holding AG; *Int'l*, pg. 170
AEBI SCHMIDT NEDERLAND BV—See Aebi Schmidt Holding AG; *Int'l*, pg. 170
AEBI SCHMIDT POLSKA SP. Z O. O.—See Aebi Schmidt Holding AG; *Int'l*, pg. 170
AFAG GMBH—See Emerson Electric Co.; *U.S. Public*, pg. 740
AGCO AB—See AGCO Corporation; *U.S. Public*, pg. 58
AGCO ARGENTINA S.A.—See AGCO Corporation; *U.S. Public*, pg. 58
AGCO AUSTRIA GMBH—See AGCO Corporation; *U.S. Public*, pg. 58
AGCO CORPORATION; *U.S. Public*, pg. 58
AGCO DEUTSCHLAND GMBH—See AGCO Corporation; *U.S. Public*, pg. 58
AGCO MACHINERY LTD—See AGCO Corporation; *U.S. Public*, pg. 58
AGCO SUOMI OY—See AGCO Corporation; *U.S. Public*, pg. 58
AG GROWTH INDUSTRIES LIMITED PARTNERSHIP—See Ag Growth International Inc.; *Int'l*, pg. 198
AG GROWTH INTERNATIONAL - EDWARDS GRAIN GUARD DIVISION—See Ag Growth International Inc.; *Int'l*, pg. 198
AG GROWTH INTERNATIONAL INC.; *Int'l*, pg. 198
AGI EMEA S.R.L.—See Ag Growth International Inc.; *Int'l*, pg. 198
AGI SURETRACK LLC—See Ag Growth International Inc.; *Int'l*, pg. 198
AGRAVIS TECHNIK HESSEN-PFALZ GMBH—See AGRAVIS Raiffeisen AG; *Int'l*, pg. 215
AGRES SISTEMAS ELETRONICOS S.A.—See Emak S.p.A.; *Int'l*, pg. 2373
AGREVOLUTION, LLC—See AGCO Corporation; *U.S. Public*, pg. 58
AGRIFAC MACHINERY BV—See Exel Industries SA; *Int'l*, pg. 2582
AGRIFY CORPORATION; *U.S. Public*, pg. 63
AGRIPOWER LTD—See Exel Industries SA; *Int'l*, pg. 2582
AGRI-SERVICE, LLC—See AGCO Corporation; *U.S. Public*, pg. 58
AGTECH, LLC—See AGCO Corporation; *U.S. Public*, pg. 58
AIFARM LTD.; *Int'l*, pg. 231
ALAMO GROUP (EUROPE) LIMITED—See Alamo Group Inc.; *U.S. Public*, pg. 70
ALAMO GROUP (IL) INC.—See Alamo Group Inc.; *U.S. Public*, pg. 71
ALAMO MANUFACTURING SERVICES (UK) LIMITED—See Alamo Group Inc.; *U.S. Public*, pg. 70
ALFA-LAVAL MID EUROPE AG—See Alfa Laval AB; *Int'l*, pg. 309

ALFA LAVAL VENEZOLANA S.A.—See Alfa Laval AB; *Int'l*, pg. 311
AMADAS GROUP INC. - ALBANY PLANT—See Amadas Group Inc.; *U.S. Private*, pg. 215
AMADAS GROUP INC.; *U.S. Private*, pg. 215
AMARILLO WIND MACHINE COMPANY INC.—See Berkshire Hathaway Inc.; *U.S. Public*, pg. 311
AMAZONE H. DREYER GMBH & CO. KG; *Int'l*, pg. 413
AMCO MANUFACTURING, INC.—See Yetter Manufacturing Co., Inc.; *U.S. Private*, pg. 4588
AMEREQUIP CORPORATION; *U.S. Private*, pg. 219
AMITY TECHNOLOGY LLC; *U.S. Private*, pg. 263
ANDRITZ FEED & BIOFUEL MEXICO—See ANDRITZ AG; *Int'l*, pg. 453
ANGLIA HARVESTERS LTD.—See Claas KGaA mbH; *Int'l*, pg. 1641
API TECHNOLOGIES SAS—See Exel Industries SA; *Int'l*, pg. 2582
APPLEGATE LIVESTOCK EQUIPMENT, INC.—See Ag Growth International Inc.; *Int'l*, pg. 198
ARAG ARGENTINA S.A.U.—See Nordson Corporation; *U.S. Public*, pg. 1532
ARAG S.A. R.L.—See Nordson Corporation; *U.S. Public*, pg. 1532
ARIZONA MIST INC.—See Platinum Equity, LLC; *U.S. Private*, pg. 3207
ARTEC PULVERISATION SAS—See Bucher Industries AG; *Int'l*, pg. 1206
ART'S-WAY MANUFACTURING CO., INC.; *U.S. Public*, pg. 201
ARTS-WAY MANUFACTURING INTERNATIONAL LTD—See Art's-Way Manufacturing Co., Inc.; *U.S. Public*, pg. 201
ASIA AGRICULTURAL MACHINERY CO., LTD. - FIRST FACTORY—See Asia Agricultural Machinery Co., Ltd.; *Int'l*, pg. 609
ASIA AGRICULTURAL MACHINERY CO., LTD.; *Int'l*, pg. 609
A.T. FERRELL COMPANY, INC. - CLIPPER SEPARATION DIVISION—See A.T. Ferrell Company, Inc.; *U.S. Private*, pg. 28
A.T. FERRELL COMPANY, INC.; *U.S. Private*, pg. 28
AWETA -AUTOLINE, INC,—See FPS Food Processing Systems B.V.; *Int'l*, pg. 2757
AWETA SISTEMI S.P.A.—See FPS Food Processing Systems B.V.; *Int'l*, pg. 2757
BAJAJ STEEL INDUSTRIES LTD.; *Int'l*, pg. 804
BANCO JOHN DEERE S.A.—See Deere & Company; *U.S. Public*, pg. 646
BASAK TRAKTOR TARIM ZIRAAT VE IS MAKINALARI SANAYI TICARET A.S.—See ASKO Holding A.S.; *Int'l*, pg. 625
BAZOOKA FARMSTAR INC.—See Eldon C. Stutsman Inc.; *U.S. Private*, pg. 1351
BEALL MANUFACTURING, INC.; *U.S. Private*, pg. 505
BEHLEN MFG. CO. - BEHLEN COUNTRY DIVISION—See Behlen Mfg. Co.; *U.S. Private*, pg. 515
BELMONT HOLDINGS CORP.—See RGP Holding, Inc.; *U.S. Private*, pg. 3420
BERG EQUIPMENT CORPORATION; *U.S. Private*, pg. 530
BERTHOUD AGRICOLE SAS—See Exel Industries SA; *Int'l*, pg. 2582
BERTHOUD SPRAYERS LTD—See Exel Industries SA; *Int'l*, pg. 2582
BIGHAM BROTHERS, INC.—See Andrew W. Byrd & Co., LLC; *U.S. Private*, pg. 280
BILLY GOAT INDUSTRIES, INC.—See Briggs & Stratton Corporation; *U.S. Private*, pg. 650
BIOHELP - BIOLOGISCHER PFLANZENSCHUTZ- NUTZLINGSPRODUKTIONS-, HANDELS- UND BERATUNGS GMBH—See BayWa AG; *Int'l*, pg. 919
BLT BRANDENBURGER LANDTECHNIK GMBH—See Claas KGaA mbH; *Int'l*, pg. 1641
BOBCAT COMPANY—See HD Hyundai Infracore Co., Ltd.; *Int'l*, pg. 3300
BOMFORD TURNER LIMITED—See Alamo Group Inc.; *U.S. Public*, pg. 70
BOMFORD TURNER LIMITED—See Alamo Group Inc.; *U.S. Public*, pg. 70
BONDIOLI & PAVESI GS.M.B.H—See Bondioli & Pavesi S.p.A.; *Int'l*, pg. 1106
BOUMATIC LLC—See Madison One Holdings; *U.S. Private*, pg. 2544
BROWER EQUIPMENT—See Hawkeye Steel Products, Inc.; *U.S. Private*, pg. 1882
BUSH HOG, INC.—See Alamo Group Inc.; *U.S. Public*, pg. 71
CALIFORNIA TOMATO MACHINERY—See Westside Equipment Co.; *U.S. Private*, pg. 4500
CAPITOL EQUIPMENT—See Canerector Inc.; *Int'l*, pg. 1290
CARUELLE-NICOLAS SAS—See Exel Industries SA; *Int'l*, pg. 2582
CATERPILLAR EURASIA LLC—See Caterpillar, Inc.; *U.S. Public*, pg. 450
CEFETRA DIGITAL SERVICES S.L.—See BayWa AG; *Int'l*, pg. 917
CHASE PRODUCTS CO.—See The Starco Group, Inc.; *U.S. Private*, pg. 4121

N.A.I.C.S. INDEX
333111 — FARM MACHINERY AND ...

CHIEF INDUSTRIES, INC. - CHIEF AGRI/INDUSTRIAL DIVISION—See Chief Industries, Inc.; *U.S. Private*, pg. 881
CHORE-TIME/BROCK INTERNATIONAL—See Berkshire Hathaway Inc.; *U.S. Public*, pg. 303
CHORE-TIME CAGE SYSTEMS—See Berkshire Hathaway Inc.; *U.S. Public*, pg. 303
CHORE-TIME EQUIPMENT—See Berkshire Hathaway Inc.; *U.S. Public*, pg. 303
CLAAS AGRICOLTURA S.R.L.—See Claas KGaA mbH; *Int'l*, pg. 1640
CLAAS AGRICULTURAL MACHINERY PRIVATE LIMITED—See Claas KGaA mbH; *Int'l*, pg. 1640
CLAAS AMERICA LATINA REPRESENTACAO LTDA.—See Claas KGaA mbH; *Int'l*, pg. 1640
CLAAS ANLAGEMANAGEMENT GMBH—See Claas KGaA mbH; *Int'l*, pg. 1640
CLAAS ARGENTINA S.A.—See Claas KGaA mbH; *Int'l*, pg. 1640
CLAAS BORDESHOLM GMBH—See Claas KGaA mbH; *Int'l*, pg. 1640
CLAAS BRAUNSCHWEIG GMBH—See Claas KGaA mbH; *Int'l*, pg. 1641
CLAAS EASTERN LTD.—See Claas KGaA mbH; *Int'l*, pg. 1640
CLAAS E-SYSTEMS GMBH—See Claas KGaA mbH; *Int'l*, pg. 1640
CLAAS HUNGARIA KFT.—See Claas KGaA mbH; *Int'l*, pg. 1641
CLAAS IBERICA S.A.—See Claas KGaA mbH; *Int'l*, pg. 1641
CLAAS INDIA LTD.—See Claas KGaA mbH; *Int'l*, pg. 1641
CLAAS ITALIA S.P.A.—See Claas KGaA mbH; *Int'l*, pg. 1640
CLAAS MAIN-DONAU GMBH & CO. KG—See BayWa AG; *Int'l*, pg. 917
CLAAS MANNS LTD.—See Claas KGaA mbH; *Int'l*, pg. 1640
CLAAS MIDDLE EAST - FZE—See Claas KGaA mbH; *Int'l*, pg. 1640
CLAAS OMAHA INC.—See Claas KGaA mbH; *Int'l*, pg. 1641
CLAAS SAULGAU GMBH—See Claas KGaA mbH; *Int'l*, pg. 1641
CLAAS SELBSTFAHRENDE ERNTEMASCHINEN GMBH—See Claas KGaA mbH; *Int'l*, pg. 1641
CLAAS SUDOSTBAYERN GMBH—See BayWa AG; *Int'l*, pg. 917
CLAAS THURINGEN GMBH—See Claas KGaA mbH; *Int'l*, pg. 1641
CLAAS TRACTOR S.A.S.—See Claas KGaA mbH; *Int'l*, pg. 1640
CLAAS U.K. LTD.—See Claas KGaA mbH; *Int'l*, pg. 1641
CLAAS VERTRIEBSGESELLSCHAFT MBH—See Claas KGaA mbH; *Int'l*, pg. 1641
CLAAS WESER EMS GMBH—See Claas KGaA mbH; *Int'l*, pg. 1641
CLAAS WESTERN LTD.—See Claas KGaA mbH; *Int'l*, pg. 1640
CLAAS WURTTEMBERG GMBH—See BayWa AG; *Int'l*, pg. 917
CLIMATE LLC—See Bayer Aktiengesellschaft; *Int'l*, pg. 907
CMC SAS—See Exel Industries SA; *Int'l*, pg. 2582
CNH AMERICA - BENSON—See CNH Industrial N.V.; *Int'l*, pg. 1674
CNH AMERICA - FARGO—See CNH Industrial N.V.; *Int'l*, pg. 1674
CNH BELGIUM N.V.—See CNH Industrial N.V.; *Int'l*, pg. 1674
CNH CANADA, LTD.—See CNH Industrial N.V.; *Int'l*, pg. 1674
CNH DEUTSCHLAND GMBH—See CNH Industrial N.V.; *Int'l*, pg. 1674
CNH INDUSTRIAL ITALIA S.P.A.—See CNH Industrial N.V.; *Int'l*, pg. 1674
CNH SERVICES S.R.L.—See CNH Industrial N.V.; *Int'l*, pg. 1674
CNH U.K. LIMITED—See CNH Industrial N.V.; *Int'l*, pg. 1675
COGNEX SINGAPORE MANUFACTURING PTE. LTD.—See Cognex Corporation; *U.S. Public*, pg. 523
COMER INDUSTRIES (SHAOXING) COMPANY LTD.—See Comer Industries S.p.A.; *Int'l*, pg. 1710
CONTIFONTE SA—See Bucher Industries AG; *Int'l*, pg. 1208
CPM HOLDINGS, INC.—See Gilbert Global Equity Partners; *U.S. Private*, pg. 1698
CTB, INC.—See Berkshire Hathaway Inc.; *U.S. Public*, pg. 303
CTB INTERNATIONAL CORP.—See Berkshire Hathaway Inc.; *U.S. Public*, pg. 303
CUSTOM FABRICATING & REPAIR INC; *U.S. Private*, pg. 1128
DAEDONG CORPORATION; *Int'l*, pg. 1906
DANUSER MACHINE COMPANY, INC.; *U.S. Private*, pg. 1158
DEGELMAN INDUSTRIES LTD.; *Int'l*, pg. 2004
DETHMERS MANUFACTURING COMPANY; *U.S. Private*, pg. 1216
D&F EQUIPMENT SALES INC.; *U.S. Private*, pg. 1137
DIAMOND AUTOMATIONS INC.—See FPS Food Processing Systems B.V.; *Int'l*, pg. 2757
DIOSNA CS S.R.O.—See Hillenbrand, Inc.; *U.S. Public*, pg. 1036
DIOSNA DIERKS & SOHNE GMBH—See Hillenbrand, Inc.; *U.S. Public*, pg. 1036
DMI CANADA, INC.—See Otter Tail Corporation; *U.S. Public*, pg. 1624
DONGFENG ISEKI AGRICULTURAL MACHINERY (HUBEI) CO., LTD.—See Dongfeng Motor Corporation; *Int'l*, pg. 2166
DOUBLE L GROUP LTD.; *U.S. Private*, pg. 1265
DURAND WAYLAND INC.; *U.S. Private*, pg. 1292
DUTCH POWER COMPANY B.V.—See Alamo Group Inc.; *U.S. Public*, pg. 71
EAGLEBURGMANN NOVA MAGNETICS LTD.—See Freudenberg SE; *Int'l*, pg. 2784
EAGLE ENTERPRISES INC.—See W W Capital Corporation; *U.S. Private*, pg. 4417
EASTERN HARVESTERS LTD.—See Claas KGaA mbH; *Int'l*, pg. 1641
EKOTECHNIKA AG; *Int'l*, pg. 2339
ELANA AGROCREDIT; *Int'l*, pg. 2343
EMPYREAN CASHEWS LIMITED; *Int'l*, pg. 2392
ESCORTS KUBOTA LIMITED; *Int'l*, pg. 2502
EVANS MACTAVISH AGRICRAFT INC.; *U.S. Private*, pg. 1435
EXCEL AGRICULTURE—See Great Western Corporation Pty. Ltd.; *Int'l*, pg. 3066
EXCEL INDUSTRIES, INC.—See Stanley Black & Decker, Inc.; *U.S. Public*, pg. 1932
EXEL FINISHING PVT LTD—See Exel Industries SA; *Int'l*, pg. 2582
EXEL GSA SAS—See Exel Industries SA; *Int'l*, pg. 2582
EXEL INDUSTRIAL CANADA INC.—See Exel Industries SA; *Int'l*, pg. 2582
EXEL INDUSTRIAL E.P.E. LDTA—See Exel Industries SA; *Int'l*, pg. 2582
EXEL INDUSTRIAL E.P.E., S.A.—See Exel Industries SA; *Int'l*, pg. 2582
EXEL INDUSTRIES SA; *Int'l*, pg. 2582
EXEL LACKIER- UND BESCHICHTUNGSSYSTEME GMBH—See Exel Industries SA; *Int'l*, pg. 2582
EXEL NORTH AMERICA INC.—See Exel Industries SA; *Int'l*, pg. 2582
EXEL S.A. DE C.V.—See Exel Industries SA; *Int'l*, pg. 2582
FADAP A.D.; *Int'l*, pg. 2601
FANCOM B.V.—See Berkshire Hathaway Inc.; *U.S. Public*, pg. 303
FANCOM E.U.R.L.—See Berkshire Hathaway Inc.; *U.S. Public*, pg. 304
FARMTRAC TRACTORS EUROPE SPOLKA Z O.O.—See Escorts Kubota Limited; *Int'l*, pg. 2502
FATEX A.D.; *U.S. Private*, pg. 2623
FEDERAL MFG. CO.—See Leonard Green & Partners, L.P.; *U.S. Private*, pg. 2427
FEERUM S.A.; *Int'l*, pg. 2632
FIELDWISE, LLC—See Lindsay Corporation; *U.S. Public*, pg. 1319
FILATURES ET CORDERIES STE. GERMAINE—See Universal Cooperatives, Inc.; *U.S. Private*, pg. 4304
FINANZAUTO, S.A.—See Barloworld Ltd.; *Int'l*, pg. 866
FISCHER NEW SARL—See Exel Industries SA; *Int'l*, pg. 2582
FISKARS AUSTRALIA PTY. LIMITED—See Fiskars Oyj Abp; *Int'l*, pg. 2693
FISKARS BENELUX B.V.—See Fiskars Oyj Abp; *Int'l*, pg. 2694
FISKARS FINLAND OY AB—See Fiskars Oyj Abp; *Int'l*, pg. 2694
FISKARS HONG KONG LTD.—See Fiskars Oyj Abp; *Int'l*, pg. 2694
FISKARS UK LIMITED—See Fiskars Oyj Abp; *Int'l*, pg. 2694
FLORY INDUSTRIES, INC.; *U.S. Private*, pg. 1551
FORGES DE NIAUX; *Int'l*, pg. 2733
F.P. BOURGAULT INDUSTRIES LTD.; *Int'l*, pg. 2597
FPM AGROMEHANIKA A.D.; *Int'l*, pg. 2757
FRANK WALZ- UND SCHMIEDETECHNIK GMBH—See Gesco AG; *Int'l*, pg. 2945
GANDY COMPANY; *U.S. Private*, pg. 1641
GARANT GP—See Griffon Corporation; *U.S. Public*, pg. 969
GARBUIO S.P.A.; *Int'l*, pg. 2883
GEA FARM TECHNOLOGIES ACIER SAS—See GEA Group Aktiengesellschaft; *Int'l*, pg. 2898
GEA FARM TECHNOLOGIES ARGENTINA S.R.L.—See GEA Group Aktiengesellschaft; *Int'l*, pg. 2898
GEA FARM TECHNOLOGIES AUSTRIA GMBH—See GEA Group Aktiengesellschaft; *Int'l*, pg. 2898
GEA FARM TECHNOLOGIES BELGIUM N.V./S.A.—See GEA Group Aktiengesellschaft; *Int'l*, pg. 2898
GEA FARM TECHNOLOGIES BULGARIA EOOD—See GEA Group Aktiengesellschaft; *Int'l*, pg. 2898
GEA FARM TECHNOLOGIES CZ, SPOL. S.R.O.—See GEA Group Aktiengesellschaft; *Int'l*, pg. 2898
GEA FARM TECHNOLOGIES DO BRASIL, INDUSTRIA E COMERCIO DE EQUIPAMENTOS AGRICOLAS E PECUARIOS LTDA.—See GEA Group Aktiengesellschaft; *Int'l*, pg. 2899
GEA FARM TECHNOLOGIES DO BRASIL LTDA.—See GEA Group Aktiengesellschaft; *Int'l*, pg. 2899
GEA FARM TECHNOLOGIES GMBH—See GEA Group Aktiengesellschaft; *Int'l*, pg. 2898
GEA FARM TECHNOLOGIES IBERICA S.L.—See GEA Group Aktiengesellschaft; *Int'l*, pg. 2898
GEA FARM TECHNOLOGIES INC.—See GEA Group Aktiengesellschaft; *Int'l*, pg. 2899
GEA FARM TECHNOLOGIES (IRELAND) LTD.—See GEA Group Aktiengesellschaft; *Int'l*, pg. 2898
GEA FARM TECHNOLOGIES MULLERUP A/S—See GEA Group Aktiengesellschaft; *Int'l*, pg. 2898
GEA FARM TECHNOLOGIES NEDERLAND B.V.—See GEA Group Aktiengesellschaft; *Int'l*, pg. 2898
GEA FARM TECHNOLOGIES NEW ZEALAND LIMITED—See GEA Group Aktiengesellschaft; *Int'l*, pg. 2899
GEA FARM TECHNOLOGIES ROMANIA S.R.L.—See GEA Group Aktiengesellschaft; *Int'l*, pg. 2899
GEA FARM TECHNOLOGIES SLOVAKIA SPOL. S.R.O.—See GEA Group Aktiengesellschaft; *Int'l*, pg. 2899
GEA FARM TECHNOLOGIES SP. Z O.O.—See GEA Group Aktiengesellschaft; *Int'l*, pg. 2899
GEA FARM TECHNOLOGIES SUISSE AG—See GEA Group Aktiengesellschaft; *Int'l*, pg. 2899
GEA FARM TECHNOLOGIES TARIM EKIP. MAK. KIM. TEK. DAN. SAN. TIC. LTD. STI.—See GEA Group Aktiengesellschaft; *Int'l*, pg. 2899
GEA FARM TECHNOLOGIES (UK) LIMITED—See GEA Group Aktiengesellschaft; *Int'l*, pg. 2898
GEA WESTFALIASURGE CANADA COMPANY—See GEA Group Aktiengesellschaft; *Int'l*, pg. 2904
GEA WESTFALIASURGE CHILE S.A.—See GEA Group Aktiengesellschaft; *Int'l*, pg. 2904
GEA WESTFALIASURGE FRANCE SAS—See GEA Group Aktiengesellschaft; *Int'l*, pg. 2904
GEA WESTFALIASURGE NEDERLAND B.V.—See GEA Group Aktiengesellschaft; *Int'l*, pg. 2904
GEA WS SOUTHEAST, INC.—See GEA Group Aktiengesellschaft; *Int'l*, pg. 2903
G&G MANUFACTURING CO.; *U.S. Private*, pg. 1629
GINEGAR INDUSTRIA DE PLASTICOS LTDA.—See Ginegar Plastic Products Ltd.; *Int'l*, pg. 2976
GREENGRO TECHNOLOGIES INC.; *U.S. Public*, pg. 964
GREEN LINE EQUIPMENT - ALBION—See Green Line Equipment, Inc.; *U.S. Private*, pg. 1773
GREENYIELD BERHAD; *Int'l*, pg. 3078
GROWLIFE, INC.; *U.S. Public*, pg. 972
GSI BRASIL INDUSTRIA E COMERCIO DE EQUIPAMENTOS AGROPECUARIOS LTD—See AGCO Corporation; *U.S. Public*, pg. 58
GVM INC.; *U.S. Private*, pg. 1820
HAGIE MANUFACTURING COMPANY—See Deere & Company; *U.S. Public*, pg. 646
HARDEE BY EVH MANUFACTURING COMPANY, LLC; *U.S. Private*, pg. 1862
HARDI AUSTRALIA PTY. LTD.—See Exel Industries SA; *Int'l*, pg. 2582
HARDI EVRARD SA—See Exel Industries SA; *Int'l*, pg. 2582
HARDI GMBH—See Exel Industries SA; *Int'l*, pg. 2582
HARDI GMBH—See Exel Industries SA; *Int'l*, pg. 2582
HARDI KENYA LTD.—See Exel Industries SA; *Int'l*, pg. 2582
HARDI NORTH AMERICA INC—See Exel Industries SA; *Int'l*, pg. 2582
HARPER INDUSTRIES, INC.; *U.S. Private*, pg. 1867
HARSH INTERNATIONAL, INC.; *U.S. Private*, pg. 1872
HAWKEYE STEEL PRODUCTS, INC. - PRIDE OF THE FARM DIVISION—See Hawkeye Steel Products, Inc.; *U.S. Private*, pg. 1882
HAWKEYE STEEL PRODUCTS, INC.; *U.S. Private*, pg. 1882
HCC, INC.; *U.S. Private*, pg. 1888
H.D. HUDSON ASIA LIMITED—See H.D. Hudson Manufacturing Company; *U.S. Private*, pg. 1825
H.D. HUDSON MANUFACTURING COMPANY; *U.S. Private*, pg. 1825
HEIK HOLDING COMPANY INC.; *U.S. Private*, pg. 1904
HENKE MACHINE - BUFFALO EQUIPMENT—See Sinca Industries, Inc.; *U.S. Private*, pg. 3669
HERSCHEL PARTS, INC.—See F.P. Bourgault Industries Ltd.; *Int'l*, pg. 2597
HINIKER COMPANY; *U.S. Private*, pg. 1949
HOLMER MASCHINENBAU GMBH—See Exel Industries SA; *Int'l*, pg. 2582
H&S MANUFACTURING CO. INC.—See Heik Holding Company Inc.; *U.S. Private*, pg. 1904
HUSQVARNA COLOMBIA S.A.—See Husqvarna AB; *Int'l*, pg. 3539
HUSQVARNA DANMARK A/S—See Husqvarna AB; *Int'l*, pg. 3539
HUSQVARNA EESTI OSAUHING—See Husqvarna AB; *Int'l*, pg. 3539
HUSQVARNA FINANCE IRELAND LTD.—See Husqvarna AB; *Int'l*, pg. 3539
HUSQVARNA SLOVENSKO S.R.O.—See Husqvarna AB; *Int'l*, pg. 3539
HUSQVARNA SOUTH AFRICA (PROPRIETARY) LIMITED—See Husqvarna AB; *Int'l*, pg. 3539

333111 — FARM MACHINERY AND ...

ILEMO HARDI, S.A.U.—See Exel Industries SA; *Int'l*, pg. 2582
INGERSOLL PRODUCTS COMPANY—See Amerop Products; *U.S. Private*, pg. 261
INNOVATIVE GROWERS EQUIPMENT CANADA, INC.—See Hydrofarm Holdings Group, Inc.; *U.S. Public*, pg. 1079
INNOVATIVE GROWERS EQUIPMENT, INC.—See Hydrofarm Holdings Group, Inc.; *U.S. Public*, pg. 1079
JAMESWAY INCUBATOR COMPANY INC.—See FPS Food Processing Systems B.V.; *Int'l*, pg. 2757
JOHN DEERE BANK S.A.—See Deere & Company; *U.S. Public*, pg. 646
JOHN DEERE BRASIL LTDA.—See Deere & Company; *U.S. Public*, pg. 646
JOHN DEERE COMMERCIAL WORKSITE PRODUCTS, INC.—See Deere & Company; *U.S. Public*, pg. 646
JOHN DEERE CONSTRUCTION & FORESTRY COMPANY—See Deere & Company; *U.S. Public*, pg. 647
JOHN DEERE DUBUQUE WORKS—See Deere & Company; *U.S. Public*, pg. 647
JOHN DEERE ENGINE WORKS—See Deere & Company; *U.S. Public*, pg. 646
JOHN DEERE HARVESTER WORKS—See Deere & Company; *U.S. Public*, pg. 647
JOHN DEERE IBERICA S.A.—See Deere & Company; *U.S. Public*, pg. 646
JOHN DEERE LTD.—See Deere & Company; *U.S. Public*, pg. 646
JOHN DEERE OTTUMWA WORKS—See Deere & Company; *U.S. Public*, pg. 647
JOHN DEERE POWER PRODUCTS, INC.—See Deere & Company; *U.S. Public*, pg. 647
JOHN DEERE S.A. DE C.V.—See Deere & Company; *U.S. Public*, pg. 647
JOHN DEERE THIBODAUX, INC.—See Deere & Company; *U.S. Public*, pg. 647
JOHN DEERE WATERLOO WORKS—See Deere & Company; *U.S. Public*, pg. 647
JOHN DEERE WORLDWIDE AGRICULTURAL EQUIPMENT—See Deere & Company; *U.S. Public*, pg. 647
JOHN SHEARER LIMITED—See Arrowcrest Group Pty. Ltd.; *Int'l*, pg. 580
KELLY RYAN EQUIPMENT COMPANY; *U.S. Private*, pg. 2276
KERN MACHINERY; *U.S. Private*, pg. 2291
KIRBY MANUFACTURING INC.; *U.S. Private*, pg. 2314
KODIAK MFG. INC.—See KPS Capital Partners, LP; *U.S. Private*, pg. 2347
KOYKER MFG. CO.—See Sioux Steel Company; *U.S. Private*, pg. 3671
KREMLIN REXSON POLSKA SP. Z O.O.—See Exel Industries SA; *Int'l*, pg. 2583
KREMLIN REXSON S.P.A—See Exel Industries SA; *Int'l*, pg. 2583
KUHN-AUDUREAU SA—See Bucher Industries AG; *Int'l*, pg. 1209
KUHN-BLANCHARD SAS—See Bucher Industries AG; *Int'l*, pg. 1209
KUHN DO BRASIL S/A—See Bucher Industries AG; *Int'l*, pg. 1209
KUHN FARM MACHINERY PTY LTD—See Bucher Industries AG; *Int'l*, pg. 1209
KUHN FARM MACHINERY SARL—See Bucher Industries AG; *Int'l*, pg. 1209
KUHN-GELDROP B.V.—See Bucher Industries AG; *Int'l*, pg. 1209
KUHN-HUARD S.A.—See Bucher Industries AG; *Int'l*, pg. 1209
KUHN KRAUSE, INC.—See Bucher Industries AG; *Int'l*, pg. 1209
KUHN MGM SAS—See Bucher Industries AG; *Int'l*, pg. 1209
KUHN NORTH AMERICA, INC.—See Bucher Industries AG; *Int'l*, pg. 1209
KUHN S.A.—See Bucher Industries AG; *Int'l*, pg. 1209
KZ CO.—See IDEX Corp; *U.S. Public*, pg. 1091
LAGERHAUS TECHNIK-CENTER GMBH—See BayWa AG; *Int'l*, pg. 918
LANDOLL CORPORATION; *U.S. Private*, pg. 2386
LAVERDA S.P.A—See AGCO Corporation; *U.S. Public*, pg. 59
LEWIS M. CARTER MANUFACTURING CO.; *U.S. Private*, pg. 2439
LINDSAY MANUFACTURING COMPANY—See Lindsay Corporation; *U.S. Public*, pg. 1319
LINDSAY (TIANJIN) INDUSTRY CO., LTD.—See Lindsay Corporation; *U.S. Public*, pg. 1319
MACCARESE S.P.A.—See Edizione S.r.l.; *Int'l*, pg. 2312
MANN LAKE LTD.—See Grey Mountain Partners, LLC; *U.S. Private*, pg. 1784
MASSEY FERGUSON CORP.—See AGCO Corporation; *U.S. Public*, pg. 59
MASSEY FERGUSON TARIM MAKINELERI LTD—See AGCO Corporation; *U.S. Public*, pg. 59
MATROT EQUIPEMENTS SAS—See Exel Industries SA; *Int'l*, pg. 2582

MCCONNEL LTD.—See Alamo Group Inc.; *U.S. Public*, pg. 70
MECKLENBURGER LANDTECHNIK GMBH—See Claas KGaA mbH; *Int'l*, pg. 1641
MEC-TRACK S.R.L.—See Caterpillar, Inc.; *U.S. Public*, pg. 451
MEPU OY. - PYHARANTA FACTORY—See Ag Growth International Inc.; *Int'l*, pg. 198
MEPU OY—See Ag Growth International Inc.; *Int'l*, pg. 198
MILLER MANUFACTURING COMPANY—See Frandsen Corporation; *U.S. Private*, pg. 1593
MILLER-ST. NAZIANZ, INC.—See CNH Industrial N.V.; *Int'l*, pg. 1674
MITCHELL MILL SYSTEMS USA INC—See Ag Growth International Inc.; *Int'l*, pg. 198
MOBA B.V.—See FPS Food Processing Systems B.V.; *Int'l*, pg. 2757
MONOSEM, INC.—See Deere & Company; *U.S. Public*, pg. 647
MTD PRODUCTS DENMARK APS—See Stanley Black & Decker, Inc.; *U.S. Public*, pg. 1933
MTD PRODUCTS INDIA PRIVATE INDIA, LIMITED—See Stanley Black & Decker, Inc.; *U.S. Public*, pg. 1933
MUELLER LICHTENVOORDE B.V.—See Paul Mueller Company; *U.S. Public*, pg. 1655
MY-D HAN-D MFG. INC.; *U.S. Private*, pg. 2823
NAVTRONICS BVBA—See CNH Industrial N.V.; *Int'l*, pg. 1676
NETAFIM IRRIGATION INC.; *U.S. Private*, pg. 2887
NEW HOLLAND FIAT (INDIA) PRIVATE LIMITED—See CNH Industrial N.V.; *Int'l*, pg. 1676
NUVISION INDUSTRIES INC.—See Ag Growth International Inc.; *Int'l*, pg. 198
OLSON IRRIGATION SYSTEMS—See Xylem Inc.; *U.S. Public*, pg. 2394
OOO FRANK RUS—See Gesco AG; *Int'l*, pg. 2946
OOO GEA FARM TECHNOLOGIES RUS—See GEA Group Aktiengesellschaft; *Int'l*, pg. 2899
OUTDOOR POWER PRODUCTS HUSQVARNA KENYA LTD.—See Husqvarna AB; *Int'l*, pg. 3539
PAK AGRO PACKAGING (PRIVATE) LIMITED—See Hi-Tech Lubricants Ltd.; *Int'l*, pg. 3381
PAS REFORM HATCHERY TECHNOLOGIES BV—See Hydratec Industries NV; *Int'l*, pg. 3546
THE PERRY COMPANY; *U.S. Private*, pg. 4093
PETERSIME N.V.—See FPS Food Processing Systems B.V.; *Int'l*, pg. 2757
PICKUP OUTFITTERS—See The Perry Company; *U.S. Private*, pg. 4093
PLYMOUTH TUBE COMPANY - HOPKINSVILLE MILL—See Plymouth Tube Company; *U.S. Private*, pg. 3216
POWDER RIVER INC.; *U.S. Private*, pg. 3236
PRECISION PLANTING, LLC—See AGCO Corporation; *U.S. Public*, pg. 59
PRORA S.R.L.—See Garofalo Health Care SpA; *Int'l*, pg. 2886
PT DOULTON—See Fiskars Oyj Abp; *Int'l*, pg. 2694
RAVEN INDUSTRIES CANADA, INC.—See CNH Industrial N.V.; *Int'l*, pg. 1676
REINKE MANUFACTURING COMPANY, INC.; *U.S. Private*, pg. 3392
RHINOAG, INC.—See Alamo Group Inc.; *U.S. Public*, pg. 71
RITCHIE INDUSTRIES, INC.; *U.S. Private*, pg. 3441
ROUSSEAU SAS—See Alamo Group Inc.; *U.S. Public*, pg. 70
ROYAL DE BOER STALINRICHTINGEN B.V.—See Turntide Technologies Inc.; *U.S. Private*, pg. 4261
SANTA IZABEL AGRO INDUSTRIA LTDA.—See Alamo Group Inc.; *U.S. Public*, pg. 71
SBG INNOVATIE BV—See CNH Industrial N.V.; *Int'l*, pg. 1676
SCHWARZE INDUSTRIES AUSTRALIA PTY LTD.—See Alamo Group Inc.; *U.S. Public*, pg. 71
SHAVER MANUFACTURING COMPANY—See HCC, Inc.; *U.S. Private*, pg. 1888
SHORE MEASURING SYSTEMS—See Berkshire Hathaway Inc.; *U.S. Public*, pg. 303
SIA HUSQVARNA LATVIJA—See Husqvarna AB; *Int'l*, pg. 3540
SINCA INDUSTRIES, INC.; *U.S. Private*, pg. 3669
SINOI GMBH—See China National Building Material Group Co., Ltd.; *Int'l*, pg. 1526
SIOUX STEEL COMPANY; *U.S. Private*, pg. 3671
SLIMLINE MANUFACTURING LTD.—See Decisive Dividend Corporation; *Int'l*, pg. 2001
SMA FAUCHEUX SAS—See Alamo Group Inc.; *U.S. Public*, pg. 70
SOLECTRAC, INC.—See Ideanomics, Inc.; *U.S. Public*, pg. 1088
SOUTHERN HARVESTERS LTD.—See Claas KGaA mbH; *Int'l*, pg. 1641
SPAREX AGRIREPUESTOS SL—See AGCO Corporation; *U.S. Public*, pg. 59
SPAREX APS—See AGCO Corporation; *U.S. Public*, pg. 59
SPAREX HANDELS-UND VERTRIEBS GMBH—See AGCO Corporation; *U.S. Public*, pg. 59
SPAREX LIMITED VESTIGING HOLLAND BV—See AGCO

CORPORATE AFFILIATIONS

Corporation; *U.S. Public*, pg. 59
SPAREX POLSKA SP. Z.O.O.—See AGCO Corporation; *U.S. Public*, pg. 59
SPAREX PORTUGAL IMPORTACAO E COMERCIO DE PECAS LDA—See AGCO Corporation; *U.S. Public*, pg. 59
SPAREX S.A.R.L.—See AGCO Corporation; *U.S. Public*, pg. 59
SPEARHEAD MACHINERY LTD.—See Alamo Group Inc.; *U.S. Public*, pg. 70
SPEECO, INC.—See American Securities LLC; *U.S. Private*, pg. 247
SPEECO, INC.—See P2 Capital Partners, LLC; *U.S. Private*, pg. 3062
SPUDNIK EQUIPMENT COMPANY; *U.S. Private*, pg. 3765
STEINBERG MFG. CO. INC.—See Heik Holding Company Inc.; *U.S. Private*, pg. 1904
STEKLARNA ROGASKA D.O.O.—See Fiskars Oyj Abp; *Int'l*, pg. 2694
STEYR-CENTER NORD GMBH—See CNH Industrial N.V.; *Int'l*, pg. 1676
SUKUP MANUFACTURING CO; *U.S. Private*, pg. 3850
SUMMERS MANUFACTURING CO. INC.; *U.S. Private*, pg. 3853
SUNFLOWER MANUFACTURING INC.—See AGCO Corporation; *U.S. Public*, pg. 59
SVENSKA HARDI AB—See Exel Industries SA; *Int'l*, pg. 2582
TAYLOR FARMS FLORIDA INC.—See Taylor Fresh Foods Inc.; *U.S. Private*, pg. 3940
TECNOMA TECHNOLOGIES SAS—See Exel Industries SA; *Int'l*, pg. 2583
TITAN INTERTRACTOR GMBH—See Titan International, Inc.; *U.S. Public*, pg. 2160
TITAN TIRE CORPORATION OF FREEPORT—See Titan International, Inc.; *U.S. Public*, pg. 2160
TITAN TIRE CORPORATION OF UNION CITY—See Titan International, Inc.; *U.S. Public*, pg. 2160
T-L IRRIGATION CO.; *U.S. Private*, pg. 3910
THE TORO CO.—See The Toro Company; *U.S. Public*, pg. 2135
TRACTOR CENTRAL—See Tractor Central LLC; *U.S. Private*, pg. 4201
TRIPLE C, INC.—See HCC, Inc.; *U.S. Private*, pg. 1888
TROY-BILT LLC—See Stanley Black & Decker, Inc.; *U.S. Public*, pg. 1936
TURF FACTORY DIRECT LLC—See Sentinel Capital Partners, L.L.C.; *U.S. Private*, pg. 3609
TURF STAR INC.; *U.S. Private*, pg. 4259
TURKTRAKTOR VE ZIRAAT MAKINELERI AS—See CNH Industrial N.V.; *Int'l*, pg. 1676
TURUN KONEKESKUS OY—See AB Sagax; *Int'l*, pg. 41
TWOSE OF TIVERTON LTD.—See Aramark; *U.S. Public*, pg. 178
TYTAN HOLDINGS, INC.; *U.S. Public*, pg. 2211
UNIVERSAL HARVESTER CO., INC.—See Art's-Way Manufacturing Co., Inc.; *U.S. Public*, pg. 201
UNVERFERTH MANUFACTURING COMPANY INC.; *U.S. Private*, pg. 4311
USINES CLAAS FRANCE S.A.S.—See Claas KGaA mbH; *Int'l*, pg. 1641
VALMONT IRRIGATION DIVISION—See Valmont Industries, Inc.; *U.S. Public*, pg. 2274
VALMONT NORTHWEST—See Valmont Industries, Inc.; *U.S. Public*, pg. 2274
VALON KONE OOO—See Kadant Inc.; *U.S. Public*, pg. 1213
VALON KONE OOO—See Kadant Inc.; *U.S. Public*, pg. 1213
VALTRACTOR COMERCIO DE TRACTORES E MAQUINAS AGRICOLAS SA—See AGCO Corporation; *U.S. Public*, pg. 59
VALTRA INTERNATIONAL B.V.—See AGCO Corporation; *U.S. Public*, pg. 59
VENTURE PRODUCTS, INC.—See The Toro Company; *U.S. Public*, pg. 2135
VERMOREL SRL—See Exel Industries SA; *Int'l*, pg. 2583
WARATAH FORESTRY EQUIPMENT CANADA LIMITED—See Deere & Company; *U.S. Public*, pg. 647
WATERFORD WEDGWOOD DOULTON COMMERCIAL (SHANGHAI) LTD.—See Fiskars Oyj Abp; *Int'l*, pg. 2694
WESTERN HARVESTERS LTD.—See Claas KGaA mbH; *Int'l*, pg. 1641
WESTERN SALES (1986) LTD.—See Deere & Company; *U.S. Public*, pg. 647
WESTSIDE EQUIPMENT CO.; *U.S. Private*, pg. 4500
WIESE INDUSTRIES; *U.S. Private*, pg. 4516
WILKENS MANUFACTURING INC; *U.S. Private*, pg. 4520
WOODS EQUIPMENT COMPANY—See American Securities LLC; *U.S. Private*, pg. 247
WOODS EQUIPMENT COMPANY—See P2 Capital Partners, LLC; *U.S. Private*, pg. 3062
W W CAPITAL CORPORATION; *U.S. Private*, pg. 4417
WWRD IRELAND LIMITED—See Fiskars Oyj Abp; *Int'l*, pg. 2694
YETTER MANUFACTURING CO., INC.; *U.S. Private*, pg. 4588
ZETOR DEUTSCHLAND, GMBH—See HTC holding a.s.; *Int'l*, pg. 3508

N.A.I.C.S. INDEX

333120 — CONSTRUCTION MACHIN...

ZETOR FRANCE SARL—See HTC holding a.s.; *Int'l*, pg. 3508
ZETOR NORTH AMERICA, INC.—See HTC holding a.s.; *Int'l*, pg. 3508
ZETOR POLSKA, SP.Z O.O.—See HTC holding a.s.; *Int'l*, pg. 3508
ZETOR TRACTORS A.S.—See HTC holding a.s.; *Int'l*, pg. 3508
ZETOR UK, LTD.—See HTC holding a.s.; *Int'l*, pg. 3508

333112 — LAWN AND GARDEN TRACTOR AND HOME LAWN AND GARDEN EQUIPMENT MANUFACTURING

AGROFIX N.V.—See Husqvarna AB; *Int'l*, pg. 3538
AGUERREBERE S.A.—See Husqvarna AB; *Int'l*, pg. 3538
AMERICAN LAWN MOWER COMPANY; *U.S. Private*, pg. 239
AMGAZIT F.K. LTD.—See Stanley Black & Decker, Inc.; *U.S. Public*, pg. 1933
ARIENS COMPANY INC.; *U.S. Private*, pg. 322
ATLANTIC WATER GARDENS—See Argand Partners, LP; *U.S. Private*, pg. 319
BETTER HEADS LLC; *U.S. Private*, pg. 546
BIG E ENTERPRISES INC.; *U.S. Private*, pg. 553
BLOUNT, INC.—See American Securities LLC; *U.S. Private*, pg. 247
BLOUNT, INC.—See P2 Capital Partners, LLC; *U.S. Private*, pg. 3061
BRIGGS & STRATTON CANADA INC.—See Briggs & Stratton Corporation; *U.S. Private*, pg. 651
BRIGGS & STRATTON POWER PRODUCTS GROUP, LLC - MCDONOUGH—See Briggs & Stratton Corporation; *U.S. Private*, pg. 651
BRIGGS & STRATTON RSA (PROPRIETARY) LIMITED—See Briggs & Stratton Corporation; *U.S. Private*, pg. 651
BUHLER INDUSTRIES INC.—See ASKO Holding A.S.; *Int'l*, pg. 625
CLAAS FRANCE S.A.S.—See Claas KGaA mbH; *Int'l*, pg. 1641
CORAL CO. LTD.—See Husqvarna AB; *Int'l*, pg. 3539
COUNTRY HOME PRODUCTS INC.—See Generac Holdings Inc.; *U.S. Public*, pg. 912
CUST2MATE LTD.—See A2Z Smart Technologies Corp.; *Int'l*, pg. 30
DHG INC.—See Finn Corporation; *U.S. Private*, pg. 1510
EASTMAN INDUSTRIES; *U.S. Private*, pg. 1322
EASY GARDENER PRODUCTS, INC.—See Centre Lane Partners, LLC; *U.S. Private*, pg. 827
EMAK S.P.A.; *Int'l*, pg. 2373
EXMARK MANUFACTURING COMPANY INCORPORATED—See The Toro Company; *U.S. Public*, pg. 2135
FAULTLESS STARCH/BON AMI COMPANY - GARDEN WEASEL DIVISION—See Faultless Starch/Bon Ami Company; *U.S. Private*, pg. 1484
FINN CORPORATION; *U.S. Private*, pg. 1510
FIRST TRACTOR COMPANY LIMITED; *Int'l*, pg. 2688
FISHER-BARTON INCORPORATED; *U.S. Private*, pg. 1535
FISKARS DENMARK A/S—See Fiskars Oyj Abp; *Int'l*, pg. 2694
FISKARS GERMANY GMBH—See Elho BV; *Int'l*, pg. 2360
FISKARS ITALY S.R.L.—See Fiskars Oyj Abp; *Int'l*, pg. 2694
FISKARS POLAND SP. Z.O.O.—See Fiskars Oyj Abp; *Int'l*, pg. 2694
FORESTAL BOSQUES DEL PLATA S.A.—See Empresas CMPC S.A.; *Int'l*, pg. 2390
GARDENA FRANCE S.A.R.L.—See Husqvarna AB; *Int'l*, pg. 3539
GARDENA MANUFACTURING GMBH—See Husqvarna AB; *Int'l*, pg. 3539
GARDENA NORDEN AB—See Husqvarna AB; *Int'l*, pg. 3539
GARDENA NORDEN AB—See Husqvarna AB; *Int'l*, pg. 3539
GARDENA OSTERREICH GMBH—See Husqvarna AB; *Int'l*, pg. 3539
GARDENA SPOL.S.R.O.—See Husqvarna AB; *Int'l*, pg. 3539
GARDENS ALIVE!, INC.; *U.S. Private*, pg. 1643
GGP SWEDEN AB; *Int'l*, pg. 2958
GREAT STATES CORP.—See American Lawn Mower Company; *U.S. Private*, pg. 239
GREENWORKS (JIANGSU) CO., LTD.; *Int'l*, pg. 3077
HAYTER LIMITED—See The Toro Company; *U.S. Public*, pg. 2135
HELIOS TECHNOLOGIES, INC.; *U.S. Private*, pg. 1023
HONDA POWER EQUIPMENT MANUFACTURING, INC.—See Honda Motor Co., Ltd.; *Int'l*, pg. 3460
HORNBACH HOLDING AG & CO. KGAA; *Int'l*, pg. 3481
HOZELOCK LTD.—See Exel Industries SA; *Int'l*, pg. 2582
HUSQVARNA AB; *Int'l*, pg. 3538
HUSQVARNA AUSTRIA GMBH—See Husqvarna AB; *Int'l*, pg. 3539
HUSQVARNA CANADA CORP.—See Husqvarna AB; *Int'l*, pg. 3539
HUSQVARNA COMMERCIAL SOLUTIONS AUSTRIA GMBH—See Husqvarna AB; *Int'l*, pg. 3539
HUSQVARNA COMMERCIAL SOLUTIONS NORGE AS—See Husqvarna AB; *Int'l*, pg. 3539
HUSQVARNA CONSUMER OUTDOOR PRODUCTS N.A., INC.—See Husqvarna AB; *Int'l*, pg. 3539
HUSQVARNA DIRECT AB—See Husqvarna AB; *Int'l*, pg. 3539
HUSQVARNA FORESTRY PRODUCTS NA INC.—See Husqvarna AB; *Int'l*, pg. 3539
HUSQVARNA (INDIA) PRODUCTS PRIVATE LIMITED—See Husqvarna AB; *Int'l*, pg. 3539
HUSQVARNA LLC—See Husqvarna AB; *Int'l*, pg. 3539
HUSQVARNA MAGYARORSZAG KFT—See Husqvarna AB; *Int'l*, pg. 3539
HUSQVARNA OUTDOOR PRODUCTS - MCRAE—See Husqvarna AB; *Int'l*, pg. 3539
HUSQVARNA OUTDOOR PRODUCTS - ORANGEBURG—See Husqvarna AB; *Int'l*, pg. 3539
HUSQVARNA OUTDOOR PRODUCTS - SWAINSBORO—See Husqvarna AB; *Int'l*, pg. 3539
HUSQVARNA POLAND SP. Z O.O.—See Husqvarna AB; *Int'l*, pg. 3539
HUSQVARNA POLSKA SP.Z.O.O.—See Husqvarna AB; *Int'l*, pg. 3539
HUSQVARNA PROFESSIONAL PRODUCTS, INC.—See Husqvarna AB; *Int'l*, pg. 3539
HUSQVARNA TURF CARE—See Husqvarna AB; *Int'l*, pg. 3539
HUSQVARNA UK LTD.—See Husqvarna AB; *Int'l*, pg. 3539
INDOOR HARVEST, CORP.; *U.S. Public*, pg. 1116
IPOWER INC.; *U.S. Public*, pg. 1167
ISMAIL MOHAMMED ALDANAWI AL SADY GARDEN EQUIPMENT WLL—See Husqvarna AB; *Int'l*, pg. 3539
JACOBSEN TEXTRON—See Textron Inc.; *U.S. Public*, pg. 2028
JOHN DEERE CONSUMER & COMMERCIAL EQUIPMENT, INC.—See Deere & Company; *U.S. Public*, pg. 646
JOHN DEERE CREDIT SERVICES, INC.—See Deere & Company; *U.S. Public*, pg. 646
JOHN DEERE HORICON WORKS—See Deere & Company; *U.S. Public*, pg. 646
KAY HOME PRODUCTS—See Akerue Industries, LLC; *U.S. Private*, pg. 145
KOENIG EQUIPMENT INC.; *U.S. Private*, pg. 2336
M-B COMPANIES, INC. - AIRPORT SNOW REMOVAL DIVISION—See M-B Companies, Inc.; *U.S. Private*, pg. 2525
M. CASSAB COM. IND. LTDA—See Husqvarna AB; *Int'l*, pg. 3539
MOJACK DISTRIBUTORS; *U.S. Private*, pg. 2765
MTD AIRCAP—See Stanley Black & Decker, Inc.; *U.S. Public*, pg. 1933
MTD PRODUCTS LIMITED—See Stanley Black & Decker, Inc.; *U.S. Public*, pg. 1933
MTD SOUTHWEST INC.—See Stanley Black & Decker, Inc.; *U.S. Public*, pg. 1933
OHIO STEEL INDUSTRIES, INC.; *U.S. Private*, pg. 3005
OY HUSQVARNA COMMERCIAL SOLUTIONS FINLAND AB—See Husqvarna AB; *Int'l*, pg. 3539
PRECISION PRODUCTS, INC.—See Gleason Corporation; *U.S. Private*, pg. 1708
PREFERRED PRODUCTS, INC.—See United Natural Foods, Inc.; *U.S. Public*, pg. 2232
RAIN BIRD CORPORATION - RESIDENTIAL PRODUCTS DIVISION—See Rain Bird Corporation; *U.S. Private*, pg. 3347
RICHARD SANKEY & SON LTD.—See Fiskars Oyj Abp; *Int'l*, pg. 2694
SCHILLER GROUNDS CARE, INC.; *U.S. Private*, pg. 3565
SCOTTS CANADA LTD.—See The Scotts Miracle-Gro Company; *U.S. Public*, pg. 2127
THE SCOTTS COMPANY—See The Scotts Miracle-Gro Company; *U.S. Public*, pg. 2127
SFI SUPERIOR IMPLEMENTS—See First Reserve Management, L.P.; *U.S. Private*, pg. 1526
SIMPLICITY MANUFACTURING, INC.—See Briggs & Stratton Corporation; *U.S. Private*, pg. 651
S KLIER' NURSERY, INC.—See Magnuson Sod/Haag Services; *U.S. Private*, pg. 2549
THE TORO COMPANY; *U.S. Public*, pg. 2134
THE TORO CO.—See The Toro Company; *U.S. Public*, pg. 2135
THE TORO CO.—See The Toro Company; *U.S. Public*, pg. 2135
TORO MANUFACTURING LLC—See The Toro Company; *U.S. Public*, pg. 2135
TORO R&D COMPANY—See The Toro Company; *U.S. Public*, pg. 2135
TORO-WHEEL HORSE—See The Toro Company; *U.S. Public*, pg. 2135
THE TRAILERDANNOW CO.—See Elsan Ltd.; *Int'l*, pg. 2370

333120 — CONSTRUCTION MACHINERY MANUFACTURING

10G LLC—See Caterpillar, Inc.; *U.S. Public*, pg. 449
ACS INDUSTRIES INC.; *U.S. Private*, pg. 66
ACTION CONSTRUCTION EQUIPMENT LTD.; *Int'l*, pg. 119
AES FAMATEC—See FAYAT SAS; *Int'l*, pg. 2624
AGENT COMMERCIAL FRANCE DE GEITH INTERNATIONAL LTD.—See HD Hyundai Infracore Co., Ltd.; *Int'l*, pg. 3300
AG GROWTH INTERNATIONAL - WESTFIELD DIVISION—See Ag Growth International Inc.; *Int'l*, pg. 198
ALFRED RAITH GMBH; *Int'l*, pg. 317
ALINCO INCORPORATED; *Int'l*, pg. 328
AL JABER TRAILERS, STEEL AND METAL WORKS ESTABLISHMENT—See Al Jaber Group; *Int'l*, pg. 279
ALLEN ENGINEERING CORPORATION; *U.S. Private*, pg. 178
ALLINOV INC.—See Astec Industries, Inc.; *U.S. Public*, pg. 216
ALLTECH GROM GMBH—See Standard Industries Holdings Inc.; *U.S. Public*, pg. 3779
ALLTECH ITALIA S.R.L.—See Standard Industries Holdings Inc.; *U.S. Public*, pg. 3779
ALLU GROUP OY; *Int'l*, pg. 361
ALTEC INDUSTRIES INC.; *U.S. Private*, pg. 206
ALTRAD FORT BV—See Altrad Investment Authority SAS; *Int'l*, pg. 397
ALTRAD LESCHA GMBH—See Altrad Investment Authority SAS; *Int'l*, pg. 397
ALTRAD LIMEX D.O.O.—See Altrad Investment Authority SAS; *Int'l*, pg. 397
ALTRAD LIV D.O.O.—See Altrad Investment Authority SAS; *Int'l*, pg. 397
ALTRAD POLAND S.A.—See Altrad Investment Authority SAS; *Int'l*, pg. 397
ALTRAD RICHARD FRAISSE SAS—See Altrad Investment Authority SAS; *Int'l*, pg. 397
AMADAS INDUSTRIES INC—See Amadas Group Inc.; *U.S. Private*, pg. 215
AMERICAN AUGERS, INC.—See The Toro Company; *U.S. Public*, pg. 2134
AMMANN SWITZERLAND LTD; *Int'l*, pg. 429
ANCHOR COUPLING, INC.—See Caterpillar, Inc.; *U.S. Public*, pg. 449
ANCON BUILDING PRODUCTS PTY LTD—See CRH plc; *Int'l*, pg. 1842
ANCORA CHUMBADORES LTDA.; *Int'l*, pg. 449
ANHUI LIUGONG CRANE CO., LTD.—See Guangxi Liugong Machinery Co., Ltd.; *Int'l*, pg. 3163
ANHUI TUOSHAN HEAVY INDUSTRIES CO., LTD.; *Int'l*, pg. 470
ANVIL ATTACHMENTS, LLC; *U.S. Private*, pg. 289
ANVIL ATTACHMENTS, LLC—See Woodvine Group, LLC; *U.S. Private*, pg. 4561
APOLLO EARTHMOVERS LTD.—See Gujarat Apollo Industries Limited; *Int'l*, pg. 3176
AQ ANTON KFT—See AQ Group AB; *Int'l*, pg. 526
ARABIAN PROFILE COMPANY LIMITED—See GIBCA Limited; *Int'l*, pg. 2962
ARCELORMITTAL COATESVILLE—See Cleveland-Cliffs, Inc.; *U.S. Public*, pg. 514
ARGUS LIMITED; *U.S. Private*, pg. 322
ARROW CONSTRUCTION PRODUCTS LIMITED; *Int'l*, pg. 579
ASIATRAK (TIANJIN) LTD.—See Caterpillar, Inc.; *U.S. Public*, pg. 449
ASO FOAM CRETE CO., LTD.; *Int'l*, pg. 628
ASTEC, INC.—See Astec Industries, Inc.; *U.S. Public*, pg. 216
ASTEC MOBILE SCREENS, INC.—See Astec Industries, Inc.; *U.S. Public*, pg. 216
ATLANTA EQUIPMENT COMPANY INC—See Road Machinery & Supplies Company; *U.S. Private*, pg. 3453
ATLAS COPCO ANGOLA LDA—See Atlas Copco AB; *Int'l*, pg. 677
ATLAS COPCO APPLICATION CENTER EUROPE GMBH—See Atlas Copco AB; *Int'l*, pg. 679
ATLAS COPCO AUSTRALIA PTY LTD—See Atlas Copco AB; *Int'l*, pg. 677
ATLAS COPCO BOLIVIANA SA—See Atlas Copco AB; *Int'l*, pg. 678
ATLAS COPCO BULGARIA EOOD—See Atlas Copco AB; *Int'l*, pg. 678
ATLAS COPCO CHILENA S.A.C.—See Atlas Copco AB; *Int'l*, pg. 678
ATLAS COPCO LATVIJA SIA—See Atlas Copco AB; *Int'l*, pg. 679
ATLAS COPCO LIFTON EOOD—See Atlas Copco AB; *Int'l*, pg. 679
ATLAS COPCO MAKINALARI IMALAT AS—See Atlas Copco AB; *Int'l*, pg. 679
ATLAS COPCO NAMIBIA (PTY) LTD—See Atlas Copco AB; *Int'l*, pg. 679
ATLAS COPCO PERUANA SA—See Atlas Copco AB; *Int'l*, pg. 680
ATLAS COPCO POWERCRUSHER GMBH—See Atlas Copco AB; *Int'l*, pg. 679
ATLAS COPCO S.A.E.—See Atlas Copco AB; *Int'l*, pg. 680
ATLAS COPCO (SOUTH EAST ASIA) PTE LTD—See Atlas Copco AB; *Int'l*, pg. 677

333120 — CONSTRUCTION MACHIN...

ATLAS COPCO TAIWAN LTD—See Atlas Copco AB; *Int'l*, pg. 681
ATLAS HEAVY ENGINEERING PTY LTD—See Caterpillar, Inc.; *U.S. Public*, pg. 449
ATLAS MASCHINEN GMBH—See Terex Corporation; *U.S. Public*, pg. 2019
AXIA INCORPORATED—See Aurora Capital Group, LLC; *U.S. Private*, pg. 394
BADGER EQUIPMENT COMPANY—See Manitex International, Inc.; *U.S. Public*, pg. 1356
BALZER PACIFIC EQUIPMENT CO.; *U.S. Private*, pg. 463
BAOYE DAIWA INDUSTRIALIZED HOUSE MANUFACTURING CO., LTD.—See Daiwa House Industry Co., Ltd.; *Int'l*, pg. 1945
BARKO HYDRAULICS LLC—See The Heico Companies, L.L.C.; *U.S. Private*, pg. 4050
BARLOWORLD EQUIPMENT UK LIMITED—See Barloworld Ltd.; *Int'l*, pg. 866
BARRETT HOLDING COMPANY INC.; *U.S. Private*, pg. 479
BATICIM ENERJI ELEKTRIK URETIM A.S.—See BatiSoke Soke Cimento Sanayii TAS; *Int'l*, pg. 889
BAUER ANGOLA LDA.—See BAUER Aktiengesellschaft; *Int'l*, pg. 892
BAUER ENGINEERING GHANA LTD.—See BAUER Aktiengesellschaft; *Int'l*, pg. 892
BAUER EQUIPAMIENTOS DE PANAMA S.A.—See BAUER Aktiengesellschaft; *Int'l*, pg. 892
BAUER EQUIPMENT AMERICA INC.—See BAUER Aktiengesellschaft; *Int'l*, pg. 893
BAUER EQUIPMENT AUSTRALIA PTY. LTD.—See BAUER Aktiengesellschaft; *Int'l*, pg. 893
BAUER EQUIPMENT INDIA PRIVATE LIMITED—See BAUER Aktiengesellschaft; *Int'l*, pg. 893
BAUER EQUIPMENT UK LIMITED—See BAUER Aktiengesellschaft; *Int'l*, pg. 893
BAUER FONDATIONS SPECIALES EURL—See BAUER Aktiengesellschaft; *Int'l*, pg. 893
BAUER GEORGIA FOUNDATION SPECIALISTS LCC—See BAUER Aktiengesellschaft; *Int'l*, pg. 893
BAUER GEOTECHNICAL SPECIALIZED FOUNDATION LLC—See BAUER Aktiengesellschaft; *Int'l*, pg. 893
BAUER INTERNATIONAL FZE—See BAUER Aktiengesellschaft; *Int'l*, pg. 893
BAUER LEBANON FOUNDATION SPECIALISTS S.A.R.L.—See BAUER Aktiengesellschaft; *Int'l*, pg. 893
BAUER MACCHINE ITALIA SRL—See BAUER Aktiengesellschaft; *Int'l*, pg. 893
BAUER MAGYARORSZAG SPECIALIS MELYEPITO KFT.—See BAUER Aktiengesellschaft; *Int'l*, pg. 893
BAUER (MALAYASIA) SDN. BHD.—See BAUER Aktiengesellschaft; *Int'l*, pg. 891
BAUER MASCHINEN GMBH - ARESING PLANT—See BAUER Aktiengesellschaft; *Int'l*, pg. 892
BAUER MASCHINEN GMBH - EDELSHAUSEN PLANT—See BAUER Aktiengesellschaft; *Int'l*, pg. 892
BAUER MASCHINEN GMBH.—See BAUER Aktiengesellschaft; *Int'l*, pg. 892
BAUER MASZYNY POLSKA SP.Z.O.O.—See BAUER Aktiengesellschaft; *Int'l*, pg. 893
BAUER MIETPOOL GMBH.—See BAUER Aktiengesellschaft; *Int'l*, pg. 892
BAUER RENEWABLES LIMITED—See BAUER Aktiengesellschaft; *Int'l*, pg. 893
BAUER TECHNOLOGIES THAILAND CO., LTD.—See BAUER Aktiengesellschaft; *Int'l*, pg. 892
BAYWA RENT GMBH—See BayWa AG; *Int'l*, pg. 916
BELLE ENGINEERING LTD—See Altrad Investment Authority SAS; *Int'l*, pg. 398
BELLE GROUP INC.—See Altrad Investment Authority SAS; *Int'l*, pg. 398
BELL EQUIPMENT COMPANY SA (PTY) LIMITED—See Bell Equipment Limited; *Int'l*, pg. 966
BELL EQUIPMENT CO SWAZILAND (PROPRIETARY) LIMITED—See Bell Equipment Limited; *Int'l*, pg. 966
BELL EQUIPMENT MOZAMBIQUE LIMITADA—See Bell Equipment Limited; *Int'l*, pg. 966
BERENDSEN FLUID POWER PTY LIMITED; *Int'l*, pg. 978
BERGKAMP INC.; *U.S. Private*, pg. 531
BESSER QUINN MACHINE & FOUNDRY—See Besser Company; *U.S. Private*, pg. 542
BITUMA CORPORATION—See Gencor Industries, Inc.; *U.S. Public*, pg. 911
BLACK CAT BLADES LTD.; *Int'l*, pg. 1059
BLASTRAC NA, INC.—See Bard & Company, Inc.; *U.S. Private*, pg. 473
BOMA EQUIPMENT—See FAYAT SAS; *Int'l*, pg. 2624
BOMAG AMERICAS, INC.—See FAYAT SAS; *Int'l*, pg. 2624
BOMAG BRESIL—See FAYAT SAS; *Int'l*, pg. 2624
BOMAG CHEMNITZ—See FAYAT SAS; *Int'l*, pg. 2624
BOMAG GMBH—See FAYAT SAS; *Int'l*, pg. 2624
BOMAG MARINI LATIN AMERICA—See FAYAT SAS; *Int'l*, pg. 2624
BREINING MASCHINEN-UND FAHRZEUGBAU GMBH—See FAYAT SAS; *Int'l*, pg. 2624
BROKK AB—See Carl Bennet AB; *Int'l*, pg. 1332
BROKK, INC.—See Carl Bennet AB; *Int'l*, pg. 1332
BUCHER HIDRAULICA LTDA.—See Bucher Industries AG; *Int'l*, pg. 1207
BUCHER HYDRAULICS AG FRUTIGEN—See Bucher Industries AG; *Int'l*, pg. 1207
BUCHER HYDRAULICS ERDING GMBH—See Bucher Industries AG; *Int'l*, pg. 1207
BUCHER HYDRAULICS REMSCHEID GMBH—See Bucher Industries AG; *Int'l*, pg. 1207
BUCHER HYDRAULICS SUZHOU CO., LTD.—See Bucher Industries AG; *Int'l*, pg. 1207
BUCHER HYDRAULICS (WUXI) CO., LTD.—See Bucher Industries AG; *Int'l*, pg. 1207
BUCHER MUNICIPAL PTY LTD—See Bucher Industries AG; *Int'l*, pg. 1207
BUCHER UNIPEKTIN AG—See Bucher Industries AG; *Int'l*, pg. 1208
BUZZI SPA; *Int'l*, pg. 1230
CAMSO CIS LLC—See Compagnie Generale des Etablissements Michelin SCA; *Int'l*, pg. 1741
CAMSO DISTRIBUCION MEXICO, S.A. DE C.V.—See Compagnie Generale des Etablissements Michelin SCA; *Int'l*, pg. 1741
CAMSO DISTRIBUTION CANADA INC.—See Compagnie Generale des Etablissements Michelin SCA; *Int'l*, pg. 1742
CAMSO FRANCE SAS—See Compagnie Generale des Etablissements Michelin SCA; *Int'l*, pg. 1742
CAMSO HOLDING BRASIL LTDA—See Compagnie Generale des Etablissements Michelin SCA; *Int'l*, pg. 1742
CAMSO, INC.—See Compagnie Generale des Etablissements Michelin SCA; *Int'l*, pg. 1742
CAMSO INDUSTRIELLE HUNGARY KFT.—See Compagnie Generale des Etablissements Michelin SCA; *Int'l*, pg. 1742
CAMSO INTERNATIONAL S.A.R.L.—See Compagnie Generale des Etablissements Michelin SCA; *Int'l*, pg. 1742
CAMSO ITALY S.P.A.—See Compagnie Generale des Etablissements Michelin SCA; *Int'l*, pg. 1742
CAMSO JAPAN CO., LTD.—See Compagnie Generale des Etablissements Michelin SCA; *Int'l*, pg. 1742
CAMSO LASTIK TICARET LIMITED SIRKETI—See Compagnie Generale des Etablissements Michelin SCA; *Int'l*, pg. 1742
CAMSO NEW ZEALAND LIMITED—See Compagnie Generale des Etablissements Michelin SCA; *Int'l*, pg. 1742
CAMSO POLSKA S.A.—See Compagnie Generale des Etablissements Michelin SCA; *Int'l*, pg. 1742
CAMSO SCHWEIZ AG—See Compagnie Generale des Etablissements Michelin SCA; *Int'l*, pg. 1742
CAMSO SPAIN, S.L.—See Compagnie Generale des Etablissements Michelin SCA; *Int'l*, pg. 1742
CAMSO TAERYUK LTD.—See Compagnie Generale des Etablissements Michelin SCA; *Int'l*, pg. 1742
CAMSO UK LIMITED—See Compagnie Generale des Etablissements Michelin SCA; *Int'l*, pg. 1742
CAMSO, VIETNAM CO., LTD.—See Compagnie Generale des Etablissements Michelin SCA; *Int'l*, pg. 1742
CARGOTEC RUS LLC—See Cargotec Corporation; *Int'l*, pg. 1326
CARLISLE BRAKE PRODUCTS (UK) LIMITED—See Carlisle Companies Incorporated; *U.S. Public*, pg. 436
CASE BAUMASCHINEN AG.—See CNH Industrial N.V.; *Int'l*, pg. 1675
CASE CONSTRUCTION MACHINERY (SHANGHAI) CO., LTD.—See CNH Industrial N.V.; *Int'l*, pg. 1675
CATERPILLAR AMERICAS MEXICO, S. DE R.L. DE C.V.—See Caterpillar, Inc.; *U.S. Public*, pg. 449
CATERPILLAR ASIA PACIFIC HOLDING, INC.—See Caterpillar, Inc.; *U.S. Public*, pg. 449
CATERPILLAR BELGIUM S.A.—See Caterpillar, Inc.; *U.S. Public*, pg. 451
CATERPILLAR CANADA—See Caterpillar, Inc.; *U.S. Public*, pg. 449
CATERPILLAR CASTINGS KIEL GMBH—See Caterpillar, Inc.; *U.S. Public*, pg. 449
CATERPILLAR CENTRO DE FORMACION, S.L.—See Caterpillar, Inc.; *U.S. Public*, pg. 449
CATERPILLAR CHINA LIMITED—See Caterpillar, Inc.; *U.S. Public*, pg. 451
CATERPILLAR COMMERCIAL S.A.—See Caterpillar, Inc.; *U.S. Public*, pg. 449
CATERPILLAR DISTRIBUTION SERVICES EUROPE B.V.B.A.—See Caterpillar, Inc.; *U.S. Public*, pg. 449
CATERPILLAR EAST JAPAN LTD.—See Caterpillar, Inc.; *U.S. Public*, pg. 449
CATERPILLAR, EAST PEORIA PLANT—See Caterpillar, Inc.; *U.S. Public*, pg. 452
CATERPILLAR ELKADER LLC—See Caterpillar, Inc.; *U.S. Public*, pg. 449
CATERPILLAR ENERGY SOLUTIONS GMBH—See Caterpillar, Inc.; *U.S. Public*, pg. 450
CATERPILLAR FINANCE CORPORATION—See Caterpillar, Inc.; *U.S. Public*, pg. 450
CATERPILLAR FINANCE FRANCE S.A.—See Caterpillar, Inc.; *U.S. Public*, pg. 450
CATERPILLAR FINANCIAL LEASING, S.A.—See Caterpillar, Inc.; *U.S. Public*, pg. 450
CATERPILLAR FINANCIAL NEW ZEALAND LIMITED—See Caterpillar, Inc.; *U.S. Public*, pg. 450
CATERPILLAR FINANCIAL NORDIC SERVICES A.B.—See Caterpillar, Inc.; *U.S. Public*, pg. 450
CATERPILLAR FINANCIAL RECEIVABLES, INC.—See Caterpillar, Inc.; *U.S. Public*, pg. 450
CATERPILLAR FINANCIAL SERVICES ASIA PTE. LTD.—See Caterpillar, Inc.; *U.S. Public*, pg. 450
CATERPILLAR FINANCIAL SERVICES GMBH—See Caterpillar, Inc.; *U.S. Public*, pg. 450
CATERPILLAR FINANCIAL SERVICES KOREA, LTD.—See Caterpillar, Inc.; *U.S. Public*, pg. 450
CATERPILLAR FINANCIAL SERVICES NORWAY A/S—See Caterpillar, Inc.; *U.S. Public*, pg. 450
CATERPILLAR FINANCIAL SERVICES N.V.—See Caterpillar, Inc.; *U.S. Public*, pg. 450
CATERPILLAR FINANCIAL SERVICES POLAND SP. Z O.O.—See Caterpillar, Inc.; *U.S. Public*, pg. 450
CATERPILLAR FINANCIAL UKRAINE LLC—See Caterpillar, Inc.; *U.S. Public*, pg. 450
CATERPILLAR FRANCE S A S—See Caterpillar, Inc.; *U.S. Public*, pg. 451
CATERPILLAR GLOBAL MINING PTY. LTD.—See Caterpillar, Inc.; *U.S. Public*, pg. 450
CATERPILLAR HOLDING GERMANY GMBH—See Caterpillar, Inc.; *U.S. Public*, pg. 450
CATERPILLAR HYDRAULICS ITALIA S.R.L—See Caterpillar, Inc.; *U.S. Public*, pg. 450
CATERPILLAR, INC.; *U.S. Public*, pg. 449
CATERPILLAR INDIA PRIVATE LIMITED—See Caterpillar, Inc.; *U.S. Public*, pg. 451
CATERPILLAR INSURANCE SERVICES CORPORATION—See Caterpillar, Inc.; *U.S. Public*, pg. 451
CATERPILLAR INVESTMENT MANAGEMENT LTD.—See Caterpillar, Inc.; *U.S. Public*, pg. 451
CATERPILLAR JAPAN LTD.—See Caterpillar, Inc.; *U.S. Public*, pg. 451
CATERPILLAR MARINE ASIA PACIFIC PTE. LTD.—See Caterpillar, Inc.; *U.S. Public*, pg. 451
CATERPILLAR MARINE POWER UK LIMITED—See Caterpillar, Inc.; *U.S. Public*, pg. 451
CATERPILLAR MATERIELS ROUTIERS—See Caterpillar, Inc.; *U.S. Public*, pg. 451
CATERPILLAR MOTOREN VERWALTUNGS-GMBH—See Caterpillar, Inc.; *U.S. Public*, pg. 451
CATERPILLAR OEM SOLUTIONS GROUP—See Caterpillar, Inc.; *U.S. Public*, pg. 451
CATERPILLAR OF AUSTRALIA LTD.—See Caterpillar, Inc.; *U.S. Public*, pg. 452
CATERPILLAR OF AUSTRALIA PTY. LTD.—See Caterpillar, Inc.; *U.S. Public*, pg. 452
CATERPILLAR OF CANADA—See Caterpillar, Inc.; *U.S. Public*, pg. 452
CATERPILLAR OVERSEAS CREDIT CORPORATION S.A.—See Caterpillar, Inc.; *U.S. Public*, pg. 451
CATERPILLAR OVERSEAS SARL—See Caterpillar, Inc.; *U.S. Public*, pg. 451
CATERPILLAR PARTNERSHIP LTD.—See Caterpillar, Inc.; *U.S. Public*, pg. 451
CATERPILLAR PAVING PRODUCTS, INC.—See Caterpillar, Inc.; *U.S. Public*, pg. 451
CATERPILLAR PRECISION SEALS KOREA—See Caterpillar, Inc.; *U.S. Public*, pg. 451
CATERPILLAR PRODUCT DEVELOPMENT SARL—See Caterpillar, Inc.; *U.S. Public*, pg. 451
CATERPILLAR REMANUFACTURING LIMITED—See Caterpillar, Inc.; *U.S. Public*, pg. 452
CATERPILLAR RISK MANAGEMENT SERVICES LTD.—See Caterpillar, Inc.; *U.S. Public*, pg. 452
CATERPILLAR SERVIZI ITALIA SRL—See Caterpillar, Inc.; *U.S. Public*, pg. 452
CATERPILLAR SOLUTION ENGINEERING LTD.—See Caterpillar, Inc.; *U.S. Public*, pg. 452
CATERPILLAR TORREON S. DE R.L. DE C.V.—See Caterpillar, Inc.; *U.S. Public*, pg. 452
CATERPILLAR TRANSMISSIONS FRANCE S.A.R.L.—See Caterpillar, Inc.; *U.S. Public*, pg. 452
CATERPILLAR USED EQUIPMENT SERVICES INTERNATIONAL SARL—See Caterpillar, Inc.; *U.S. Public*, pg. 452
CATERPILLAR WEST JAPAN LTD.—See Caterpillar, Inc.; *U.S. Public*, pg. 452
CATERPILLAR WORK TOOLS B.V.—See Caterpillar, Inc.; *U.S. Public*, pg. 452
CATERPILLAR WORK TOOLS, INC.—See Caterpillar, Inc.; *U.S. Public*, pg. 452
CCCC SHANGHAI EQUIPMENT ENGINEERING CO., LTD.—See China Communications Construction Company Limited; *Int'l*, pg. 1490
CCCC XI'AN ROAD CONSTRUCTION MACHINERY CO., LTD.—See China Communications Construction Company Limited; *Int'l*, pg. 1490
CESAR SA—See Groupe Bruxelles Lambert SA; *Int'l*, pg. 3100
CHANGLIN COMPANY LIMITED; *Int'l*, pg. 1443
CHARLES MACHINE WORKS, INC.—See The Toro Company; *U.S. Public*, pg. 2134
CHENGDU XINZHU ROAD & BRIDGE MACHINERY CO., LTD.; *Int'l*, pg. 1469
CHICAGO MATERIALS CORPORATION—See K-Five Con-

N.A.I.C.S. INDEX

333120 — CONSTRUCTION MACHIN...

struction Corporation; *U.S. Private*, pg. 2251
CHICAGO PNEUMATIC BRASIL LTDA—See Atlas Copco AB; *Int'l*, pg. 681
CHINA NATIONAL MATERIALS COMPANY LIMITED; *Int'l*, pg. 1531
CIANBRO CORPORATION - EASTERN MANUFACTURING FACILITY—See Cianbro Corporation; *U.S. Private*, pg. 896
CIANBRO EQUIPMENT, LLC—See Cianbro Corporation; *U.S. Private*, pg. 896
CIMLINE INC.—See Hines Corporation; *U.S. Private*, pg. 1949
CINOXPLAN, S.L.—See The Middleby Corporation; *U.S. Public*, pg. 2113
CITIC HEAVY INDUSTRIES BRASIL—See CITIC Heavy Industries Co., Ltd.; *Int'l*, pg. 1621
CM ENERGY TECH CO., LTD.; *Int'l*, pg. 1665
CMI TEREX CORPORATION—See Terex Corporation; *U.S. Public*, pg. 2018
CNH AMERICA LLC—See CNH Industrial N.V.; *Int'l*, pg. 1674
CNH AMERICA - RACINE—See CNH Industrial N.V.; *Int'l*, pg. 1674
CNH AMERICA - WICHITA—See CNH Industrial N.V.; *Int'l*, pg. 1674
CNH BAUMASCHINEN GMBH—See CNH Industrial N.V.; *Int'l*, pg. 1674
CNH ITALIA S.P.A—See CNH Industrial N.V.; *Int'l*, pg. 1674
CNH LATIN AMERICA LTDA.—See CNH Industrial N.V.; *Int'l*, pg. 1674
COASTAL CONCRETE INC.; *U.S. Private*, pg. 955
COLUMBUS MCKINNON CORPORATION; *U.S. Public*, pg. 535
CONCRETE LEVELING SYSTEMS, INC.; *U.S. Public*, pg. 565
CONSTRUCTION TOOLS GMBH—See Epiroc AB; *Int'l*, pg. 2461
CONSTRUCTION TOOLS GMBH—See Epiroc AB; *Int'l*, pg. 2461
COUGAR INDUSTRIES, INC.—See Martin Engineering; *U.S. Private*, pg. 2595
COWIN EQUIPMENT COMPANY INC—See C&C Holding Inc.; *U.S. Private*, pg. 702
CRW CORPORATION; *U.S. Private*, pg. 1114
CUKUROVA INSAAT MAKINALARI SAN. VE TIC. A.S.—See Cukurova Holding A.S.; *Int'l*, pg. 1876
CUTTING EDGES PTY. LTD.—See Valmont Industries, Inc.; *U.S. Public*, pg. 2273
CWS INDUSTRIES (MFG) CORP.—See KPS Capital Partners, LP; *U.S. Private*, pg. 2347
DAGANG HOLDING GROUP CO. LTD.; *Int'l*, pg. 1912
DAISAN CO., LTD.; *Int'l*, pg. 1940
DANLEY CONSTRUCTION PRODUCTS PTY LTD—See Illinois Tool Works Inc.; *U.S. Public*, pg. 1102
DEERE-HITACHI CONSTRUCTION MACHINERY CORPORATION—See Deere & Company; *U.S. Public*, pg. 647
DEERE-HITACHI CONSTRUCTION MACHINERY CORPORATION—See Hitachi, Ltd.; *Int'l*, pg. 3415
DENSIT APS—See Illinois Tool Works Inc.; *U.S. Public*, pg. 1102
DENSIT ASIA PACIFIC SDN BHD—See Illinois Tool Works Inc.; *U.S. Public*, pg. 1102
DESIGNARC CO.—See Daiwa House Industry Co., Ltd.; *Int'l*, pg. 1946
DINGO RANGE PTY. LTD.—See Emerald Resources NL; *Int'l*, pg. 2378
DN TANKS, INC.; *U.S. Private*, pg. 1249
DONGIL METAL CO., LTD. - DASAN FACTORY—See Cheil Grinding Wheel Ind. Co., Ltd.; *Int'l*, pg. 1460
DOOSAN BOBCAT CHINA CO., LTD.—See Doosan Corporation; *Int'l*, pg. 2172
DOOSAN BOBCAT EMEA S.R.O.—See Doosan Corporation; *Int'l*, pg. 2172
DOOSAN BOBCAT GLOBAL COLLABORATION CENTER, INC.—See Doosan Corporation; *Int'l*, pg. 2172
DOOSAN BOBCAT INC—See Doosan Corporation; *Int'l*, pg. 2172
DOOSAN BOBCAT KOREA CO.—See Doosan Corporation; *Int'l*, pg. 2173
DOOSAN ELECTRO-MATERIALS (CHANGSHU) CO., LTD.—See Doosan Corporation; *Int'l*, pg. 2173
DOOSAN ELECTRO-MATERIALS (SHENZHEN) LIMITED—See Doosan Corporation; *Int'l*, pg. 2173
DOOSAN ELECTRO-MATERIALS VIETNAM CO., LTD.—See Doosan Corporation; *Int'l*, pg. 2173
DOOSAN H2 INNOVATION CO., LTD.—See Doosan Corporation; *Int'l*, pg. 2173
DOOSAN INFRACORE AMERICA CORPORATION—See HD Hyundai Infracore Co., Ltd.; *Int'l*, pg. 3299
DOOSAN INFRACORE INDIA PRIVATE CO., LTD.—See HD Hyundai Infracore Co., Ltd.; *Int'l*, pg. 3300
DOOSAN LOGISTICS EUROPE GMBH—See Doosan Corporation; *Int'l*, pg. 2173
DOOSAN MOBILITY INNOVATION (SHENZHEN) CO. LTD.—See Doosan Corporation; *Int'l*, pg. 2173
DOUGLAS DYNAMICS FINANCE COMPANY—See Douglas Dynamics, Inc.; *U.S. Public*, pg. 677

DREDGING SUPPLY COMPANY INC.; *U.S. Private*, pg. 1275
DSV ROAD AB—See DSV A/S; *Int'l*, pg. 2212
DUTTON-LAINSON COMPANY; *U.S. Private*, pg. 1295
DYNAPAC COMPACTION EQUIPMENT AB—See FAYAT SAS; *Int'l*, pg. 2624
DYNAPAC FRANCE SAS—See FAYAT SAS; *Int'l*, pg. 2624
DYNAPAC GMBH—See FAYAT SAS; *Int'l*, pg. 2624
DYO BOYA FABRIKALARI SANAYI VE TICARET AS; *Int'l*, pg. 2243
DY POWER CORPORATION—See DY Corporation; *Int'l*, pg. 2237
EAGLE INDUSTRY HOKKAIDO CO., LTD.—See Eagle Industry Co., Ltd.; *Int'l*, pg. 2265
EAGLE INDUSTRY (WUXI) CO., LTD.—See Eagle Industry Co., Ltd.; *Int'l*, pg. 2265
EAGLE SEALING RESEARCH & DEVELOPMENT (WUXI) CO., LTD.—See Eagle Industry Co., Ltd.; *Int'l*, pg. 2265
ED ETNYRE & CO. INC.—See Etnyre International Ltd. Inc.; *U.S. Private*, pg. 1432
EEI CORPORATION; *Int'l*, pg. 2317
EFFICIENCY PRODUCTION INCORPORATED; *U.S. Private*, pg. 1343
EGGING CO.; *U.S. Private*, pg. 1344
EKK EAGLE AMERICA INC.—See Eagle Industry Co., Ltd.; *Int'l*, pg. 2265
EKK EAGLE INDUSTRY MEXICO S.A. DE C.V.—See Eagle Industry Co., Ltd.; *Int'l*, pg. 2265
EKK EAGLE PRODUCTS INDIA PVT. LTD.—See Eagle Industry Co., Ltd.; *Int'l*, pg. 2265
EKK SALES EUROPE B.V.—See Eagle Industry Co., Ltd.; *Int'l*, pg. 2265
ELIVISION CO., LTD.; *Int'l*, pg. 2363
ELLICOTT DREDGE ENTERPRISES, LLC—See Markel Group Inc.; *U.S. Public*, pg. 1368
ELLICOTT DREDGES, LLC—See Markel Group Inc.; *U.S. Public*, pg. 1368
ELTRAK BULGARIA LTD.—See ELTRAK S.A.; *Int'l*, pg. 2371
E N BISSO & SON INC.; *U.S. Private*, pg. 1301
ENERGY TECHNOLOGIES INSTITUTE LLP—See Caterpillar, Inc.; *U.S. Public*, pg. 452
ENGCON AB; *Int'l*, pg. 2426
ENGCON IRELAND LTD.—See Engcon AB; *Int'l*, pg. 2426
ENGCON POLAND SP. Z O.O.—See Engcon AB; *Int'l*, pg. 2426
ENNIS - FLINT NEW ZEALAND—See PPG Industries, Inc.; *U.S. Public*, pg. 1707
ENNIS TRAFFIC SAFETY SOLUTIONS PTY LTD—See PPG Industries, Inc.; *U.S. Public*, pg. 1707
ENTEKRA, LLC—See Louisiana-Pacific Corporation; *U.S. Public*, pg. 1342
EPIROC AB; *Int'l*, pg. 2461
EPIROC DEUTSCHLAND GMBH—See Epiroc AB; *Int'l*, pg. 2462
EPIROC KOREA CO., LTD.—See Epiroc AB; *Int'l*, pg. 2462
EPIROC MAKINA AS—See Epiroc AB; *Int'l*, pg. 2462
EPIROC MALI SARL—See Epiroc AB; *Int'l*, pg. 2462
EPIROC MIDDLE EAST FZE—See Epiroc AB; *Int'l*, pg. 2462
EPIROC MINERIA E INGENIERIA CIVIL ESPANA, S.L.U—See Epiroc AB; *Int'l*, pg. 2462
EPIROC PHILIPPINES INC.—See Epiroc AB; *Int'l*, pg. 2462
EPIROC PORTUGAL UNIPESSOAL LDA—See Epiroc AB; *Int'l*, pg. 2462
EPIROC SRBIJA A.D.—See Epiroc AB; *Int'l*, pg. 2462
EPIROC TANZANIA LTD.—See Epiroc AB; *Int'l*, pg. 2462
EPIROC TASHKENT LLC—See Epiroc AB; *Int'l*, pg. 2462
EPIROC (THAILAND) LTD.—See Epiroc AB; *Int'l*, pg. 2461
EPIROC ZAMBIA LTD.—See Epiroc AB; *Int'l*, pg. 2462
EPIROC ZIMBABWE (PRIVATE) LTD.—See Epiroc AB; *Int'l*, pg. 2462
EQUIPMENT SERVICES GROUP, INC.—See Gencor Industries, Inc.; *U.S. Public*, pg. 911
ETERNA INDUSTRIES LIMITED—See Eterna Plc.; *Int'l*, pg. 2520
ETNYRE INTERNATIONAL LTD. INC.; *U.S. Private*, pg. 1432
ETS-LINDGREN OY—See ESCO Technologies, Inc.; *U.S. Public*, pg. 794
EUROLINERS—See Burelle S.A.; *Int'l*, pg. 1223
EVERCOMPOUNDS S.P.A.—See Caterpillar, Inc.; *U.S. Public*, pg. 452
EVERDIGM HEAVY EQUIPMENT & MACHINERY TRADING LLC—See Hyundai Everdigm Corp; *Int'l*, pg. 3556
EXENT CORP.; *Int'l*, pg. 2583
FEMA S.R.L.—See Chart Industries, Inc.; *U.S. Public*, pg. 481
FENNER DUNLOP MAROC SARL—See Compagnie Generale des Etablissements Michelin SCA; *Int'l*, pg. 1742
FERGUSON MANUFACTURING & EQUIPMENT COMPANY, INC.; *U.S. Private*, pg. 1497
FHI (NINGBO) CO., LTD.—See Formosa Plastics Corporation; *Int'l*, pg. 2735
FIBRA INGENIERIA Y CONSTRUCCION S.A.—See NOV, Inc.; *U.S. Public*, pg. 1544
FIELDERS MANUFACTURING PTY. LTD.—See BlueScope Steel Limited; *Int'l*, pg. 1073
FINISH LINE PRODUCTS, INC.—See Compagnie de Saint-Gobain SA; *Int'l*, pg. 1730

FISHER, LLC—See Douglas Dynamics, Inc.; *U.S. Public*, pg. 677
FIXIT AG; *Int'l*, pg. 2696
FLS JAPAN LTD.—See FLSmidth & Co. A/S; *Int'l*, pg. 2710
FLSMIDTH KREBS GMBH—See FLSmidth & Co. A/S; *Int'l*, pg. 2710
FLSMIDTH MAAG GEAR S.P.A.—See FLSmidth & Co. A/S; *Int'l*, pg. 2710
FLSMIDTH MAAG GEAR SP. Z O.O.—See FLSmidth & Co. A/S; *Int'l*, pg. 2710
FLSMIDTH MILANO S.R.L.—See FLSmidth & Co. A/S; *Int'l*, pg. 2710
FLSMIDTH MONGOLIA—See FLSmidth & Co. A/S; *Int'l*, pg. 2710
FLSMIDTH (PRIVATE) LTD.—See FLSmidth & Co. A/S; *Int'l*, pg. 2710
FLSMIDTH RUSLAND HOLDING A/S—See FLSmidth & Co. A/S; *Int'l*, pg. 2710
FLSMIDTH S.A.—See FLSmidth & Co. A/S; *Int'l*, pg. 2710
FLSMIDTH SP. Z.O.O.—See FLSmidth & Co. A/S; *Int'l*, pg. 2710
FLSMIDTH (UK) LIMITED—See FLSmidth & Co. A/S; *Int'l*, pg. 2710
FORMICA NORGE A/S—See HAL Trust N.V.; *Int'l*, pg. 3223
FORMOSA HEAVY INDUSTRIES CORP. - JEN-WU PLANT—See Formosa Plastics Corporation; *Int'l*, pg. 2735
FORMOSA HEAVY INDUSTRIES CORP. - MAI-LIAO PLANT—See Formosa Plastics Corporation; *Int'l*, pg. 2735
FROGCO AMPHIBIOUS EQUIPMENT, LLC—See Grey Mountain Partners, LLC; *U.S. Private*, pg. 1784
FUJI ASTEC, INC.—See Fuji Seal International, Inc.; *Int'l*, pg. 2816
FURUKAWA ROCK DRILL CO., LTD. - TAKASAKI FACTORY—See Furukawa Co., Ltd.; *Int'l*, pg. 2847
FURUKAWA ROCK DRILL CO., LTD. - YOSHII FACTORY—See Furukawa Co., Ltd.; *Int'l*, pg. 2847
FURUKAWA ROCK DRILL (SHANGHAI) CO., LTD.—See Furukawa Co., Ltd.; *Int'l*, pg. 2847
GAMMA-CIVIC CONSTRUCTION LTD—See Gamma-Civic Ltd; *Int'l*, pg. 2878
GEITH INC.—See HD Hyundai Infracore Co., Ltd.; *Int'l*, pg. 3300
GEITH INTERNATIONAL LTD—See HD Hyundai Infracore Co., Ltd.; *Int'l*, pg. 3300
GEITH INTERNATIONAL LTD.—See HD Hyundai Infracore Co., Ltd.; *Int'l*, pg. 3300
GENCOR INDUSTRIES, INC.; *U.S. Public*, pg. 911
GENERAL ASPHALT CO., INC.; *U.S. Private*, pg. 1660
GENIE GERMANY GMBH—See Terex Corporation; *U.S. Public*, pg. 2019
GERMAN-GULF ENTERPRISES LTD.—See Hydac International GmbH; *Int'l*, pg. 3544
GIKEN LTD.; *Int'l*, pg. 2972
GLOBAL PARTS, S.R.L—See HD Hyundai Infracore Co., Ltd.; *Int'l*, pg. 3300
GM DAEWOO AUSTRALIA PTY. LIMITED—See General Motors Company; *U.S. Public*, pg. 924
GRACE BAUPRODUKTE GMBH—See Standard Industries Holdings Inc.; *U.S. Private*, pg. 3779
GRACE CONSTRUCTION PRODUCTS N.V.—See Standard Industries Holdings Inc.; *U.S. Private*, pg. 3779
GRACE CONSTRUCTION PRODUCTS S.A.—See Standard Industries Holdings Inc.; *U.S. Private*, pg. 3779
GRACE TRADING (SHANGHAI) CO., LTD.—See Standard Industries Holdings Inc.; *U.S. Private*, pg. 3780
GREAVES PAKISTAN (PVT) LTD—See Cherat Cement Company Limited; *Int'l*, pg. 1471
GROUPE MECALAC S.A.; *Int'l*, pg. 3108
GRU COMEDIL S.R.L.—See Terex Corporation; *U.S. Public*, pg. 2019
GUANGXI LIUGONG MACHINERY CO., LTD.; *Int'l*, pg. 3163
GUNNEBO JOHNSON CORPORATION—See Gunnebo AB; *Int'l*, pg. 3184
HAE IN CORP.; *Int'l*, pg. 3205
HAEIN RESOURCES CO., LTD.—See Hae In Corp.; *Int'l*, pg. 3205
HAMM AG—See Deere & Company; *U.S. Public*, pg. 647
HAULOTTE GROUP SA; *Int'l*, pg. 3285
HAYNES CORPORATION—See Caterpillar, Inc.; *U.S. Public*, pg. 452
HBIS GROUP XUANHUA CONSTRUCTION MACHINERY CO., LTD.—See HBIS Group Co., Ltd.; *Int'l*, pg. 3296
HBIS RESOURCES CO., LTD.; *Int'l*, pg. 3296
HD HYUNDAI INFRACORE CO., LTD.; *Int'l*, pg. 3299
HEPCO HEAVY EQUIPMENT PRODUCTION COMPANY; *Int'l*, pg. 3356
H. GEIGER GMBH; *Int'l*, pg. 3194
HIAP TONG CORPORATION LTD.; *Int'l*, pg. 3382
HIGHWAY EQUIPMENT COMPANY; *U.S. Private*, pg. 1942
HIOLLE INDUSTRIES S.A.; *Int'l*, pg. 3401
HIROSHIMA EAGLE CO., LTD.—See Eagle Industry Co., Ltd.; *Int'l*, pg. 2265
HITACHI CONSTRUCTION MACHINERY ASIA AND PACIFIC PTE LTD.—See Hitachi, Ltd.; *Int'l*, pg. 3415
HITACHI CONSTRUCTION MACHINERY (CHINA) CO.,

LTD.—See Hitachi, Ltd.; *Int'l*, pg. 3415
HITACHI CONSTRUCTION MACHINERY CO., LTD.—See Hitachi, Ltd.; *Int'l*, pg. 3415
HITACHI CONSTRUCTION MACHINERY (EUROPE) N.V.—See Hitachi, Ltd.; *Int'l*, pg. 3415
HITACHI CONSTRUCTION MACHINERY LOADERS AMERICA INC.—See Hitachi, Ltd.; *Int'l*, pg. 3416
HITACHI CONSTRUCTION MACHINERY (M) SDN BHD—See Hitachi, Ltd.; *Int'l*, pg. 3415
HITACHI CONSTRUCTION MACHINERY (SHANGHAI) CO., LTD.—See Hitachi, Ltd.; *Int'l*, pg. 3415
HITACHI CONSTRUCTION MACHINERY (THAILAND) CO., LTD.—See Hitachi, Ltd.; *Int'l*, pg. 3415
HITACHI CONSTRUCTION MACHINERY ZAMBIA CO., LTD.—See Hitachi, Ltd.; *Int'l*, pg. 3416
HK TRACKS (WUXI) CO. LTD.—See Heungkuk Metaltech Co., Ltd.; *Int'l*, pg. 3366
H&L TOOTH COMPANY; *U.S. Private*, pg. 1823
HOA PHAT METAL PRODUCING CO., LTD.—See Hoa Phat Group Joint Stock Company; *Int'l*, pg. 3435
HUSQVARNA BELGIUM SA—See Husqvarna AB; *Int'l*, pg. 3539
HYDRA PLATFORMS MFG. INC.—See Terex Corporation; *U.S. Public*, pg. 2019
HYSTER-YALE MAXIMAL FORKLIFT (ZHEJIANG) CO., LTD.—See Hyster-Yale Materials Handling, Inc.; *U.S. Public*, pg. 1080
HYTEC ABU DHABI L.L.C.—See Al Jaber Group; *Int'l*, pg. 280
HYUNDAI CONSTRUCTION EQUIPMENT INDUSTRIAL CO., LTD.—See Hyundai Heavy Industries Co., Ltd.; *Int'l*, pg. 3557
HYUNDAI CONSTRUCTION EQUIPMENT U.S.A., INC.—See Hyundai Heavy Industries Co., Ltd.; *Int'l*, pg. 3557
HYUNDAI EVERDIGM AMERICA INC.—See Hyundai Everdigm Corp; *Int'l*, pg. 3556
HYUNDAI EVERDIGM CORP; *Int'l*, pg. 3556
IA BELL EQUIPMENT CO NAMIBIA (PROPRIETARY) LIMITED—See Bell Equipment Limited; *Int'l*, pg. 966
IHC HYDROHAMMER BV—See IHC Merwede Holding B.V.; *Int'l*, pg. 3603
IHLAS MOTOR A.S.—See Ihlas Holding A.S.; *Int'l*, pg. 3606
INGERSOLL-RAND SERVICIOS, S.A.—See Ingersoll Rand Inc.; *U.S. Public*, pg. 1121
INSTALLED BUILDING PRODUCTS OF FORT MYERS, LLC—See Installed Building Products, Inc.; *U.S. Public*, pg. 1133
INSTALLED BUILDING PRODUCTS OF JACKSONVILLE, LLC—See Installed Building Products, Inc.; *U.S. Public*, pg. 1133
INSTALLED BUILDING PRODUCTS OF MIAMI, LLC—See Installed Building Products, Inc.; *U.S. Public*, pg. 1133
INSTALLED BUILDING PRODUCTS OF TAMPA, LLC—See Installed Building Products, Inc.; *U.S. Public*, pg. 1133
INSTALLED BUILDING PRODUCTS OF WEST PALM, LLC—See Installed Building Products, Inc.; *U.S. Public*, pg. 1133
INSTALLED BUILDING PRODUCTS - PANHANDLE, LLC—See Installed Building Products, Inc.; *U.S. Public*, pg. 1132
INTERNATIONAL CONSTRUCTION EQUIPMENT; *U.S. Private*, pg. 2116
INTERTRACTOR AMERICA, CORP.—See Titan International, Inc.; *U.S. Public*, pg. 2160
IOWA MOLD TOOLING CO., INC.—See Oshkosh Corporation; *U.S. Public*, pg. 1620
IRBAL, S.A.—See Altrad Investment Authority SAS; *Int'l*, pg. 398
ISHIKAWAJIMA SCE (XIAMEN) CONSTRUCTION MACHINERY CO., LTD.—See IHI Corporation; *Int'l*, pg. 3605
ITW CONSTRUCTION PRODUCTS AS—See Illinois Tool Works Inc.; *U.S. Public*, pg. 1105
ITW CONSTRUCTION PRODUCTS ESPANA S.A.—See Illinois Tool Works Inc.; *U.S. Public*, pg. 1105
ITW CONSTRUCTION PRODUCTS ITALY SRL—See Illinois Tool Works Inc.; *U.S. Public*, pg. 1105
ITW CONSTRUCTION PRODUCTS OY—See Illinois Tool Works Inc.; *U.S. Public*, pg. 1105
JAPANLIFE CO., LTD.—See Hanwa Co., Ltd.; *Int'l*, pg. 3263
JEWELL ATTACHMENTS, LLC—See Stanley Black & Decker, Inc.; *U.S. Public*, pg. 1933
JIM TECHNOLOGY CORPORATION—See IHI Corporation; *Int'l*, pg. 3606
JLG EQUIPMENT SERVICES, INC.—See Oshkosh Corporation; *U.S. Public*, pg. 1620
JOHN DEERE DAVENPORT WORKS—See Deere & Company; *U.S. Public*, pg. 647
JOHN DEERE FORESTRY GROUP LLC—See Deere & Company; *U.S. Public*, pg. 647
JOHN DEERE WORLDWIDE CONSTRUCTION & FORESTRY—See Deere & Company; *U.S. Public*, pg. 647
JONES COMMUNICATIONS, INC.—See Comcast Corporation; *U.S. Public*, pg. 538
JOSEPH JINGOLI & SON, INC.; *U.S. Private*, pg. 2236

JOSEPH VOGELE AG—See Deere & Company; *U.S. Public*, pg. 647
JRB ATTACHMENTS, LLC—See Stanley Black & Decker, Inc.; *U.S. Public*, pg. 1933
KIMBLE MANUFACTURING COMPANY—See Hines Corporation; *U.S. Private*, pg. 1949
KINSHOFER APONOX OY—See Carl Bennet AB; *Int'l*, pg. 1332
KINSHOFER CZ S.R.O.—See Carl Bennet AB; *Int'l*, pg. 1332
KINSHOFER FRANCE S.A.R.L.—See Carl Bennet AB; *Int'l*, pg. 1332
KINSHOFER GMBH—See Carl Bennet AB; *Int'l*, pg. 1332
KINSHOFER UK LTD.—See Carl Bennet AB; *Int'l*, pg. 1332
KLEEMANN GMBH—See Deere & Company; *U.S. Public*, pg. 647
KOLBERG-PIONEER, INC.—See Astec Industries, Inc.; *U.S. Public*, pg. 216
KOMBET DZIALDOWO SP. Z O.O.—See Dekpol S.A.; *Int'l*, pg. 2006
KRESS CORPORATION; *U.S. Private*, pg. 2351
KT GRANT, INC.—See The Pritzker Organization, LLC; *U.S. Private*, pg. 4100
KUHN-MONTANA INDUSTRIA DE MAQUINAS, S/A—See Bucher Industries AG; *Int'l*, pg. 1209
LANCO INTERNATIONAL INC.; *U.S. Private*, pg. 2382
LATCHWAYS PLC—See MSA Safety Incorporated; *U.S. Public*, pg. 1481
THE LEONARD COMPANY; *U.S. Private*, pg. 4069
LEVEE LUMBER INC.; *U.S. Private*, pg. 2434
LIUGONG CONSTRUCTION MACHINERY N.A., LLC—See Guangxi Liugong Machinery Co., Ltd.; *Int'l*, pg. 3163
LIUGONG INDIA PVT. LTD.—See Guangxi Liugong Machinery Co., Ltd.; *Int'l*, pg. 3163
LIUGONG MACHINERY ASIA PACIFIC PTE. LTD.—See Guangxi Liugong Machinery Co., Ltd.; *Int'l*, pg. 3163
LIUGONG MACHINERY EUROPE B.V.—See Guangxi Liugong Machinery Co., Ltd.; *Int'l*, pg. 3163
LIUGONG MACHINERY HONG KONG CO., LTD.—See Guangxi Liugong Machinery Co., Ltd.; *Int'l*, pg. 3163
LIUGONG MACHINERY LATIN AMERICA, LTDA—See Guangxi Liugong Machinery Co., Ltd.; *Int'l*, pg. 3163
LIUGONG MACHINERY MIDDLE EAST FZE—See Guangxi Liugong Machinery Co., Ltd.; *Int'l*, pg. 3163
LIUGONG MACHINERY (POLAND) SP. Z O. O.—See Guangxi Liugong Machinery Co., Ltd.; *Int'l*, pg. 3163
LIUGONG MACHINERY RU, LLC—See Guangxi Liugong Machinery Co., Ltd.; *Int'l*, pg. 3163
LIUGONG MACHINERY SOUTH AFRICA (PTY) LTD—See Guangxi Liugong Machinery Co., Ltd.; *Int'l*, pg. 3163
LONDON (MTL) INC.—See Oshkosh Corporation; *U.S. Public*, pg. 1620
LOUGHBERRY MFG. CORP.—See The Fort Miller Group Inc.; *U.S. Private*, pg. 4030
MACGREGOR (CHN) LTD.—See Cargotec Corporation; *Int'l*, pg. 1328
MACGREGOR (ESP) S.A.—See Cargotec Corporation; *Int'l*, pg. 1328
MACGREGOR (GRC) E.P.E.—See Cargotec Corporation; *Int'l*, pg. 1328
MACGREGOR (HRV) D.O.O.—See Cargotec Corporation; *Int'l*, pg. 1328
MACGREGOR KAYABA LTD.—See Cargotec Corporation; *Int'l*, pg. 1329
MACGREGOR (KOR) LTD.—See Cargotec Corporation; *Int'l*, pg. 1328
MACGREGOR (POL) SP. Z O.O.—See Cargotec Corporation; *Int'l*, pg. 1328
MAEKAWA CONSTRUCTION CO., LTD.—See Freesia Macross Corporation; *Int'l*, pg. 2771
MAK BETEILIGUNGS GMBH—See Caterpillar, Inc.; *U.S. Public*, pg. 453
MANITOWOC CRANE GROUP COLOMBIA, S.A.S.—See The Manitowoc Company, Inc.; *U.S. Public*, pg. 2111
MANITOWOC GROUP (UK) LIMITED—See The Manitowoc Company, Inc.; *U.S. Public*, pg. 2111
MARINE TRAVELIFT, INC.; *U.S. Private*, pg. 2575
MARINI MAKINA A.S.—See FAYAT SAS; *Int'l*, pg. 2626
MARSH VENTURES INC.; *U.S. Private*, pg. 2591
MATEC CONSTRUCTION MACHINERY CO., LTD.—See Hoa Binh Construction Group JSC; *Int'l*, pg. 3435
MATHIEU—See FAYAT SAS; *Int'l*, pg. 2626
M-B COMPANIES, INC. - PAVEMENT MARKING EQUIPMENT DIVISION—See M-B Companies, Inc.; *U.S. Private*, pg. 2525
MCCLUNG-LOGAN EQUIPMENT COMPANY, INC.; *U.S. Private*, pg. 2628
MECALAC BAUMASCHINEN GMBH—See Groupe Mecalac S.A.; *Int'l*, pg. 3108
MIC INDUSTRIES INC.; *U.S. Private*, pg. 2697
MI-JACK PRODUCTS, INC.—See Lanco International Inc.; *U.S. Private*, pg. 2382
MINMETALS SANTOKU (GANZHOU) RARE EARTH MATERIAL CO., LTD.—See Hitachi, Ltd.; *Int'l*, pg. 3423
MIXER SYSTEMS INC.; *U.S. Private*, pg. 2752
MMG MITTELDEUTSCHE MONTAN GMBH.—See BAUER Aktiengesellschaft; *Int'l*, pg. 893

MOBILE TOWER CRANES (MTC) B.V.—See Arcomet & Co.; *Int'l*, pg. 550
MRT MANUFACTURING, INC.—See Utility One Source L.P.; *U.S. Private*, pg. 4326
MWM REAL ESTATE GMBH—See Caterpillar, Inc.; *U.S. Public*, pg. 453
NANCHANG KAMA CO., LTD.—See China Hi-Tech Group Corporation; *Int'l*, pg. 1508
NEW HOLLAND FIAT (INDIA) PVT. LTD. - PARTS DIVISION—See CNH Industrial N.V.; *Int'l*, pg. 1676
NEW HOLLAND FIAT (INDIA) PVT. LTD. - TRACTOR DIVISION—See CNH Industrial N.V.; *Int'l*, pg. 1676
NEW TECH MACHINERY CORP.—See Mazzella Lifting Technologies; *U.S. Private*, pg. 2623
NIHON KENKI LEASE CO., LTD.—See Caterpillar, Inc.; *U.S. Public*, pg. 453
NIPPON BAUER Y.K.—See BAUER Aktiengesellschaft; *Int'l*, pg. 893
NORTHERN STAR INDUSTRIES INC.; *U.S. Private*, pg. 2954
NOV DOWNHOLE—See NOV, Inc.; *U.S. Public*, pg. 1545
NOW NORWAY AS—See DNOW Inc.; *U.S. Public*, pg. 671
OAKS CONCRETE PRODUCTS LTD—See Brampton Brick Limited; *Int'l*, pg. 1139
OEM SOLUTIONS GROUP—See Caterpillar, Inc.; *U.S. Public*, pg. 453
O & K - HILFE GMBH—See CNH Industrial, N.V.; *Int'l*, pg. 1674
OOO BAUER MASCHINEN RUSSLAND—See BAUER Aktiengesellschaft; *Int'l*, pg. 893
OSIRIS CORP.; *U.S. Public*, pg. 1622
PACAL LLC; *U.S. Private*, pg. 3063
PACE ENGINEERING INC.; *U.S. Private*, pg. 3063
PACER BUILDING COMPONENTS INC.—See Atlas Engineered Products Ltd.; *Int'l*, pg. 685
PEARLMAN GROUP—See The Stephens Group, LLC; *U.S. Private*, pg. 4121
PEDERSHAAB A/S—See FLSmidth & Co. A/S; *Int'l*, pg. 2711
PEERLESS CONVEYOR & MANUFACTURING CO.—See The G.W. Van Keppel Company; *U.S. Private*, pg. 4031
PENGO ATTACHMENTS, INC. - COKATO—See Stanley Black & Decker, Inc.; *U.S. Public*, pg. 1933
PERKINS FRANCE (S.A.S.)—See Caterpillar, Inc.; *U.S. Public*, pg. 453
PERKINS MOTOREN GMBH—See Caterpillar, Inc.; *U.S. Public*, pg. 453
PETERSON PACIFIC INC.; *U.S. Private*, pg. 3160
PETTIBONE, LLC—See The Heico Companies, L.L.C.; *U.S. Private*, pg. 4050
PHILADELPHIA MIXING SOLUTIONS LTD.—See Lone Star Funds; *U.S. Private*, pg. 2485
PIERCE-PACIFIC MANUFACTURING INC.; *U.S. Private*, pg. 3179
POTAIN INDIA PVT. LTD.—See The Manitowoc Company, Inc.; *U.S. Public*, pg. 2111
POTAIN S.A.—See The Manitowoc Company, Inc.; *U.S. Public*, pg. 2111
POUJAUD SAS—See Altrad Investment Authority SAS; *Int'l*, pg. 398
POWER CURBERS INC.; *U.S. Private*, pg. 3237
POWER EQUIPMENT COMPANY; *U.S. Private*, pg. 3238
PROGRESS METAL RECLAMATION COMPANY—See Caterpillar, Inc.; *U.S. Public*, pg. 453
PROGRESS RAIL RACELAND CORPORATION—See Caterpillar, Inc.; *U.S. Public*, pg. 453
P.T. BAUER EQUIPMENT INDONESIA—See BAUER Aktiengesellschaft; *Int'l*, pg. 892
P.T. CATERPILLAR FINANCE INDONESIA—See Caterpillar, Inc.; *U.S. Public*, pg. 453
PT. CATERPILLAR INDONESIA—See Caterpillar, Inc.; *U.S. Public*, pg. 453
PTC OCEAN INDIEN—See FAYAT SAS; *Int'l*, pg. 2626
PTC—See FAYAT SAS; *Int'l*, pg. 2626
PT FYFE FIBRWRAP INDONESIA—See New Mountain Capital, LLC; *U.S. Private*, pg. 2900
PT. HITACHI CONSTRUCTION MACHINERY INDONESIA—See Hitachi, Ltd.; *Int'l*, pg. 3416
P.T. NATRA RAYA—See Caterpillar, Inc.; *U.S. Public*, pg. 451
RAPIDPARTS, INC.—See Caterpillar, Inc.; *U.S. Public*, pg. 453
REXCON, INC.—See Astec Industries, Inc.; *U.S. Public*, pg. 216
REXCON, LLC—See Astec Industries, Inc.; *U.S. Public*, pg. 216
RICHLAND, LLC; *U.S. Private*, pg. 3430
RIEDL G.M.B.H.—See GPI S.p.A.; *Int'l*, pg. 3046
RMS CRANES INC.—See First Reserve Management, L.P.; *U.S. Private*, pg. 1526
ROAD INFRASTRUCTURE INVESTMENT HOLDINGS, INC.—See PPG Industries, Inc.; *U.S. Public*, pg. 1710
ROADTEC, INC.—See Astec Industries, Inc.; *U.S. Public*, pg. 216
ROHR DREDGE NA, LLC—See Markel Group Inc.; *U.S. Public*, pg. 1368
ROYAL BOSKALIS WESTMINSTER N.V.—See HAL Trust N.V.; *Int'l*, pg. 3224
SAE—See FAYAT SAS; *Int'l*, pg. 2626

SAFEWORKS, LLC—See Brand Industrial Services, Inc.; *U.S. Private*, pg. 636
SAINT-GOBAIN STRADAL—See Compagnie de Saint-Gobain SA; *Int'l*, pg. 1736
SASE COMPANY, LLC—See Blue Point Capital Partners, LLC; *U.S. Private*, pg. 590
SAUBER MANUFACTURING CO; *U.S. Private*, pg. 3554
SCAI S.P.A—See Hitachi, Ltd.; *Int'l*, pg. 3416
SCARAB SWEEPERS LIMITED—See FAYAT SAS; *Int'l*, pg. 2626
SECMAIR—See FAYAT SAS; *Int'l*, pg. 2626
SECOROC GHANA LTD.—See Epiroc AB; *Int'l*, pg. 2463
SETOZAKI IRON WORKS CO., LTD.—See Hitachi Zosen Corporation; *Int'l*, pg. 3412
SF GMBH—See Freudenberg SE; *Int'l*, pg. 2790
SHANDONG LINGONG CONSTRUCTION MACHINERY—See AB Volvo; *Int'l*, pg. 42
SHANDONG ROCK DRILLING TOOLS CO., LTD.—See Epiroc AB; *Int'l*, pg. 2463
SHANGHAI JINTAI ENGINEERING MACHINERY CO., LTD.—See Guangxi Liugong Machinery Co., Ltd.; *Int'l*, pg. 3163
SIAC DO BRASIL LTDA.—See KPS Capital Partners, LP; *U.S. Private*, pg. 2347
SITECH SOUTH MS, LLC—See Puckett Machinery Company Inc.; *U.S. Private*, pg. 3301
SITTAB AB—See Addtech AB; *Int'l*, pg. 135
SKINCO COLOMBIT S.A.—See Etex SA/NV; *Int'l*, pg. 2522
SMIDTH & CO.—See FLSmidth & Co. A/S; *Int'l*, pg. 2712
SMITH SURFACE PREPARATION SYSTEMS INC.—See Graco, Inc.; *U.S. Public*, pg. 954
SOCIETE DE PROSPECTION ET D'INVENTIONS TECHNIQUES S.A.S.—See Illinois Tool Works Inc.; *U.S. Public*, pg. 1110
SOMERO ENTERPRISES INC.; *U.S. Public*, pg. 1902
SOUTH CENTRAL BUILDING SYSTEMS LTD.—See Atlas Engineered Products Ltd.; *Int'l*, pg. 685
SOUTHEAST INDUSTRIAL EQUIPMENT, INC.; *U.S. Private*, pg. 3725
SOUTHERN CALIFORNIA MATRIAL HANDLING INC.—See Caterpillar, Inc.; *U.S. Public*, pg. 454
SPA ATLAS COPCO ALGERIE—See Atlas Copco AB; *Int'l*, pg. 684
SPANCRETE MACHINERY CORP.—See Wells Concrete Products Company Inc.; *U.S. Private*, pg. 4476
SPM OIL & GAS INC.—See Caterpillar, Inc.; *U.S. Public*, pg. 453
SPURLINO MATERIALS, LLC; *U.S. Private*, pg. 3765
STERKOVNY A PISKOVNY BRNO A.S.—See Heidelberg Materials AG; *Int'l*, pg. 3310
STUDER PROFESSIONAL AUDIO GMBH—See Evertz Microsystems Limited; *Int'l*, pg. 2569
SUEYOSHI KOGYO CO., LTD.—See Fukoku Co., Ltd.; *Int'l*, pg. 2839
SUPERWINCH, LLC—See Kinderhook Industries, LLC; *U.S. Private*, pg. 2307
SUPERWINCH LTD.—See Kinderhook Industries, LLC; *U.S. Private*, pg. 2307
TABOR MACHINE COMPANY—See Brookfield Corporation; *Int'l*, pg. 1181
TBA ROMANIA S.R.L.—See Terex Corporation; *U.S. Public*, pg. 2019
TCM FRANCE S.A.S.—See Hitachi, Ltd.; *Int'l*, pg. 3416
TEREX ADVANCE MIXER, INC.—See Terex Corporation; *U.S. Public*, pg. 2018
TEREX COMPACT EQUIPMENT—See Terex Corporation; *U.S. Public*, pg. 2019
TEREX CRANES HUNGARY KFT.—See Terex Corporation; *U.S. Public*, pg. 2019
TEREX CRANES KOREA CO., LTD.—See Terex Corporation; *U.S. Public*, pg. 2019
TEREX CRANES PTY. LTD.—See Terex Corporation; *U.S. Public*, pg. 2019
TEREX CRANES WILMINGTON, INC.—See Terex Corporation; *U.S. Public*, pg. 2019
TEREX DEUTSCHLAND BAU-BETEILIGUNGEN GMBH—See Terex Corporation; *U.S. Public*, pg. 2019
TEREX DISTRIBUTION LIMITED—See Terex Corporation; *U.S. Public*, pg. 2020
TEREX INDIA PRIVATE LIMITED—See Terex Corporation; *U.S. Public*, pg. 2020
TEREX LATIN AMERICA EQUIPAMENTOS LTDA.—See Terex Corporation; *U.S. Public*, pg. 2020
TEREX LIFTING U.K. LIMITED—See Terex Corporation; *U.S. Public*, pg. 2019
TEREX MINERALS PROCESSING SYSTEMS—See Terex Corporation; *U.S. Public*, pg. 2020
TEREX NFLG (QUANZHOU) MOBILE PROCESSING EQUIPMENT CO LTD—See Terex Corporation; *U.S. Public*, pg. 2020
TEREX-TELELECT, INC.—See Terex Corporation; *U.S. Public*, pg. 2020
TEREX UTILITIES, INC.—See Terex Corporation; *U.S. Public*, pg. 2020
TEREX UTILITIES SOUTH—See Terex Corporation; *U.S. Public*, pg. 2020
TEREX UTILITIES WEST—See Terex Corporation; *U.S. Public*, pg. 2020

TEREX VERWALTUNGS GMBH—See Terex Corporation; *U.S. Public*, pg. 2020
TIMKEN MOTOR & CRANE SERVICES LLC—See The Timken Company; *U.S. Public*, pg. 2133
TRACMEC SRL—See BAUER Aktiengesellschaft; *Int'l*, pg. 894
TREMCO CPG SWEDEN AB—See RPM International Inc.; *U.S. Public*, pg. 1820
TRENCOR, INC.—See The Toro Company; *U.S. Public*, pg. 2134
TURBOMACH FRANCE S.A.R.L.—See Caterpillar, Inc.; *U.S. Public*, pg. 454
TURBOMACH GMBH—See Caterpillar, Inc.; *U.S. Public*, pg. 454
TURNER POWERTRAIN SYSTEMS LIMITED—See Caterpillar, Inc.; *U.S. Public*, pg. 454
UNDERGROUND INFRASTRUCTURE TECHNOLOGIES CORPORATION—See Hitachi Zosen Corporation; *Int'l*, pg. 3412
UNITED HEAVY MACHINERY PLANTS OJSC—See Gazprombank JSC; *Int'l*, pg. 2892
VALK MANUFACTURING COMPANY; *U.S. Private*, pg. 4332
VECTOR TECHNOLOGIES LTD.—See Holden Industries, Inc.; *U.S. Private*, pg. 1962
VERMEER CORPORATION; *U.S. Private*, pg. 4366
VIBCO INC.; *U.S. Private*, pg. 4376
VIKING-CIVES, LTD.—See Cives Corporation; *U.S. Private*, pg. 908
VINCE HAGAN COMPANY; *U.S. Private*, pg. 4384
VOLVO COMPACT EQUIPMENT S.A.S.—See AB Volvo; *Int'l*, pg. 44
VOLVO CONSTRUCTION EQUIPMENT CORPORATION—See AB Volvo; *Int'l*, pg. 43
VOLVO CONSTRUCTION EQUIPMENT EUROPE AB—See AB Volvo; *Int'l*, pg. 43
VOLVO CONSTRUCTION EQUIPMENT EUROPE GMBH—See AB Volvo; *Int'l*, pg. 43
VOLVO MASKIN AS—See AB Volvo; *Int'l*, pg. 45
VOSTA LMG DESIGN GMBH—See ASL Marine Holdings Ltd; *Int'l*, pg. 625
VOSTA LMG INDIA PVT. LTD.—See ASL Marine Holdings Ltd; *Int'l*, pg. 625
VOSTA LMG (ZHUHAI) LTD.—See ASL Marine Holdings Ltd; *Int'l*, pg. 625
WESTERN PRODUCTS; *U.S. Private*, pg. 4496
WHECO CORP.; *U.S. Private*, pg. 4505
WHOLESALE EQUIPMENT BROKERS; *U.S. Private*, pg. 4514
WIRTGEN GMBH—See Deere & Company; *U.S. Public*, pg. 647
THE WYCO TOOL COMPANY—See Badger Meter, Inc.; *U.S. Public*, pg. 263
XPART LIMITED—See Caterpillar, Inc.; *U.S. Public*, pg. 454
XTRATHERM UK LIMITED—See Mohawk Industries, Inc.; *U.S. Public*, pg. 1458
YAMATAKE ENGINEERING (M) SDN. BHD.—See Azbil Corporation; *Int'l*, pg. 777
YOWA ENGINEERING CO., LTD.—See Dowa Holdings Co., Ltd.; *Int'l*, pg. 2184

333131 — MINING MACHINERY AND EQUIPMENT MANUFACTURING

AFARAK SOUTH AFRICA (PTY) LTD.—See Afarak Group SE; *Int'l*, pg. 185
A.L. LEE CORP.—See Victory of West Virginia, Inc.; *U.S. Private*, pg. 4379
AMERICAN PULVERIZER COMPANY; *U.S. Private*, pg. 245
ARCELORMITTAL INFRASTRUCTURE G.P.—See ArcelorMittal S.A.; *Int'l*, pg. 544
ASTEC AUSTRALIA PTY LTD—See Astec Industries, Inc.; *U.S. Public*, pg. 216
ASTEC MOBILE MACHINERY GMBH—See Astec Industries, Inc.; *U.S. Public*, pg. 216
ATLAS COPCO BANGLADESH LTD.—See Atlas Copco AB; *Int'l*, pg. 677
ATLAS COPCO BLM S.R.L.—See Atlas Copco AB; *Int'l*, pg. 677
ATLAS COPCO BRASIL LTDA—See Atlas Copco AB; *Int'l*, pg. 678
ATLAS COPCO CANADA INC.—See Atlas Copco AB; *Int'l*, pg. 681
ATLAS COPCO CMT USA INC.—See Atlas Copco AB; *Int'l*, pg. 680
ATLAS COPCO CRAELIUS—See Atlas Copco AB; *Int'l*, pg. 678
ATLAS COPCO D.O.O.—See Atlas Copco AB; *Int'l*, pg. 681
ATLAS COPCO IAS GMBH—See Atlas Copco AB; *Int'l*, pg. 679
ATLAS COPCO INDUSTRIAL ZAMBIA LIMITED—See Atlas Copco AB; *Int'l*, pg. 679
ATLAS COPCO KOREA CO., LTD.—See Atlas Copco AB; *Int'l*, pg. 679
ATLAS COPCO LEVANT S.A.L—See Atlas Copco AB; *Int'l*, pg. 679
ATLAS COPCO LLC—See Atlas Copco AB; *Int'l*, pg. 679

ATLAS COPCO MAROC SA—See Atlas Copco AB; *Int'l*, pg. 679
ATLAS COPCO MEXICANA S.A. DE C.V.—See Atlas Copco AB; *Int'l*, pg. 679
ATLAS COPCO NIGERIA LTD.—See Atlas Copco AB; *Int'l*, pg. 680
ATLAS COPCO PERU S.A.C.—See Atlas Copco AB; *Int'l*, pg. 680
ATLAS COPCO POWER TECHNIQUE GMBH—See Atlas Copco AB; *Int'l*, pg. 680
ATLAS COPCO RENTAL LLC—See Atlas Copco AB; *Int'l*, pg. 680
ATLAS COPCO ROCK DRILLS AB—See Atlas Copco AB; *Int'l*, pg. 680
ATLAS COPCO SECOROC AB—See Atlas Copco AB; *Int'l*, pg. 680
ATLAS COPCO (SHANGHAI) TRADING CO., LTD.—See Atlas Copco AB; *Int'l*, pg. 677
ATLAS COPCO SRBIJA DOO—See Atlas Copco AB; *Int'l*, pg. 681
AUSTIN CANADA INC.—See Austin Engineering Ltd.; *Int'l*, pg. 718
AUSTIN ETT AFRICA LIMITED—See Austin Engineering Ltd.; *Int'l*, pg. 718
BILLITON BASE METALS—See BHP Group Limited; *Int'l*, pg. 1016
BOART LONGYEAR LTDA.—See Boart Longyear Ltd.; *Int'l*, pg. 1095
BOART LONGYEAR LTD.; *Int'l*, pg. 1094
BOART LONGYEAR S.A.—See Boart Longyear Ltd.; *Int'l*, pg. 1095
BREAKER TECHNOLOGY, INC.—See Astec Industries, Inc.; *U.S. Public*, pg. 216
BREAKER TECHNOLOGY LTD—See Astec Industries, Inc.; *U.S. Public*, pg. 216
BUCHER IBERICA SL—See Bucher Industries AG; *Int'l*, pg. 1207
BUCHER MUNICIPAL COUDES SARL—See Bucher Industries AG; *Int'l*, pg. 1207
BUCHER MUNICIPAL WERNBERG GMBH—See Bucher Industries AG; *Int'l*, pg. 1207
BUCYRUS AMERICA, INC.—See Caterpillar, Inc.; *U.S. Public*, pg. 450
BUCYRUS EUROPE GMBH—See Caterpillar, Inc.; *U.S. Public*, pg. 450
BUMECH SA; *Int'l*, pg. 1215
CANNA CORP; *U.S. Private*, pg. 734
CARBO CERAMICS (CHINA) COMPANY LTD.—See CARBO Ceramics Inc.; *U.S. Private*, pg. 748
CATERPILLAR GLOBAL MINING COLOMBIA S.A.S.—See Caterpillar, Inc.; *U.S. Public*, pg. 450
CATERPILLAR GLOBAL MINING EQUIPAMENTOS DE MINERACAO DO BRASIL LTDA.—See Caterpillar, Inc.; *U.S. Public*, pg. 450
CATERPILLAR GLOBAL MINING EUROPE GMBH—See Caterpillar, Inc.; *U.S. Public*, pg. 450
CATERPILLAR GLOBAL MINING HMS GMBH—See Caterpillar, Inc.; *U.S. Public*, pg. 450
CATERPILLAR GLOBAL MINING, LLC—See Caterpillar, Inc.; *U.S. Public*, pg. 450
CATERPILLAR UNDERGROUND MINING PTY. LTD.—See Caterpillar, Inc.; *U.S. Public*, pg. 452
CATERPILLAR XUZHOU LTD.—See Caterpillar, Inc.; *U.S. Public*, pg. 452
CATERPILLAR (ZHENGZHOU) LTD.—See Caterpillar, Inc.; *U.S. Public*, pg. 449
CENTER ROCK, INC.—See Sverica Capital Management LP; *U.S. Private*, pg. 3888
CENTRAL MINE EQUIPMENT COMPANY; *U.S. Private*, pg. 822
CENTRIFUGAL & MECHANICAL INDUSTRIES, INC.—See Elgin Equipment Group, LLC; *U.S. Private*, pg. 1359
CHENGDU DAHONGLI MACHINERY CO., LTD.; *Int'l*, pg. 1467
CHINA COAL PINGSHUO INDUSTRY COAL LIMITED LIABILITY CORPORATION—See China Coal Energy Company Limited; *Int'l*, pg. 1490
CHINA NATIONAL COAL MINING EQUIPMENT CO., LTD.—See China Coal Energy Company Limited; *Int'l*, pg. 1490
CITIC HIC GANDARA CENSA S.A.U.—See CITIC Heavy Industries Co., Ltd.; *Int'l*, pg. 1621
CMS QUARRIES SDN. BHD.—See Cahya Mata Sarawak Berhad; *Int'l*, pg. 1251
COMPANIA MSA DE ARGENTINA S.A.—See MSA Safety Incorporated; *U.S. Public*, pg. 1481
CONFLOW LIMITED; *Int'l*, pg. 1768
CONNEX SVT INC.—See Groupe Bruxelles Lambert SA; *Int'l*, pg. 3099
CONSEC CORPORATION - HIROSHIMA PLANT—See CONSEC CORPORATION; *Int'l*, pg. 1769
COPERION K-TRON GREAT BRITAIN LIMITED—See Hillenbrand, Inc.; *U.S. Public*, pg. 1036
CQMS RAZER PTY. LTD.—See Epiroc AB; *Int'l*, pg. 2461
DAMASCUS EQUIPMENT, LLC—See Spencer Mac Corporation; *U.S. Private*, pg. 3755
DCD-DORBYL HEAVY ENGINEERING

333131 — MINING MACHINERY AN...

VEREENIGING—See DCD-Dorbyl (Pty) Ltd.; *Int'l*, pg. 1991
DEILMANN-HANIEL MINING SYSTEMS, GMBH—See ATON GmbH; *Int'l*, pg. 688
DEISTER MACHINE CO. INC.; *U.S. Private*, pg. 1191
DERRICK CORPORATION; *U.S. Private*, pg. 1210
DK INDUSTRIAL SOLUTIONS, LLC—See Diethelm Keller Holding Limited; *Int'l*, pg. 2116
DOVER ARTIFICIAL LIFT PTY LTD—See Dover Corporation; *U.S. Public*, pg. 679
DOVER CORPORATION REGIONAL HEADQUARTERS—See Dover Corporation; *U.S. Public*, pg. 679
DRIL-QUIP TIW MEXICO S.A. DE C.V.—See Dril-Quip, Inc.; *U.S. Public*, pg. 687
DRUMMOND COMPANY, INC.; *U.S. Private*, pg. 1280
DRY SYSTEMS TECHNOLOGIES, INC.—See Alpha Natural Resources, Inc.; *U.S. Private*, pg. 199
EAGLE CRUSHER CO. INC.; *U.S. Private*, pg. 1309
EAGLE IRON WORKS, LLC—See McLanahan Corporation; *U.S. Private*, pg. 2640
EDI RAIL (MARYBOROUGH) PTY LTD.—See Downer EDI Limited; *Int'l*, pg. 2186
EIMCO ELECON INDIA LTD; *Int'l*, pg. 2332
ELGIN EQUIPMENT GROUP, LLC; *U.S. Private*, pg. 1359
ELGOOD-MAYO CORP.—See OceanSound Partners, LP; *U.S. Private*, pg. 2991
ELPHINSTONE PTY LTD; *Int'l*, pg. 2369
EPIROC CENTRAL AMERICA S.A.—See Epiroc AB; *Int'l*, pg. 2462
EPIROC CENTRAL ASIA LLP—See Epiroc AB; *Int'l*, pg. 2462
EPIROC FINLAND OY AB—See Epiroc AB; *Int'l*, pg. 2462
EPIROC FRANCE S.A.S.—See Epiroc AB; *Int'l*, pg. 2462
EPIROC JAPAN KK—See Epiroc AB; *Int'l*, pg. 2462
EPIROC MAROC SARL—See Epiroc AB; *Int'l*, pg. 2462
EPIROC MINING INDIA LTD.—See Epiroc AB; *Int'l*, pg. 2462
EPIROC MINING (NAMIBIA) (PTY) LTD.—See Epiroc AB; *Int'l*, pg. 2462
EPIROC NORGE AS—See Epiroc AB; *Int'l*, pg. 2462
EPIROC PERU S.A.—See Epiroc AB; *Int'l*, pg. 2462
EPIROC UKRAINE LLC—See Epiroc AB; *Int'l*, pg. 2462
EPOCH ENERGY TECHNOLOGY SDN BHD; *Int'l*, pg. 2463
ERIEZ MAGNETICS INDIA PRIVATE LIMITED—See Eriez Manufacturing Co. Inc.; *U.S. Private*, pg. 1421
ERIEZ MANUFACTURING CO. INC. - ERIEZ FLOTATION DIVISION - CANADA—See Eriez Manufacturing Co. Inc.; *U.S. Private*, pg. 1421
ERIEZ MANUFACTURING CO. INC. - ERIEZ FLOTATION DIVISION - CHILE—See Eriez Manufacturing Co. Inc.; *U.S. Private*, pg. 1421
ERIEZ MANUFACTURING CO. INC. - ERIEZ FLOTATION DIVISION - PERU—See Eriez Manufacturing Co. Inc.; *U.S. Private*, pg. 1421
ESAB (THAILAND) LTD.—See Enovis Corporation; *U.S. Public*, pg. 770
EURODRILL GMBH.—See BAUER Aktiengesellschaft; *Int'l*, pg. 893
FEECO INTERNATIONAL INC.; *U.S. Private*, pg. 1492
FLSMIDTH BUFFALO (PTY.) LTD.—See FLSmidth & Co. A/S; *Int'l*, pg. 2711
FLSMIDTH SPOKANE, INC.—See FLSmidth & Co. A/S; *Int'l*, pg. 2712
FORUM ENERGY TECHNOLOGIES, INC.; *U.S. Public*, pg. 873
FRANK CALANDRA, INC.; *U.S. Private*, pg. 1594
FURUKAWA ROCK DRILL KOREA CO., LTD.—See Furukawa Co., Ltd.; *Int'l*, pg. 2847
GE-FAIRCHILD LLC—See General Electric Company; *U.S. Public*, pg. 918
GENERAL STEEL & SUPPLY CO., INC.—See Fisher Industries; *U.S. Private*, pg. 1534
GEODRILL LIMITED; *Int'l*, pg. 2933
GEOMASINA A.D.; *Int'l*, pg. 2933
GETMAN CORPORATION; *U.S. Private*, pg. 1688
GI TECHNOLOGY GROUP CO., LTD.; *Int'l*, pg. 2960
GLOBALTECH CORPORATION PTY LTD—See Boart Longyear Ltd.; *Int'l*, pg. 1095
GL TECH CO., LTD.; *Int'l*, pg. 2986
GRAPHANO ENERGY LTD.; *Int'l*, pg. 3060
GUNDLACH EQUIPMENT CORPORATION—See Hillenbrand, Inc.; *U.S. Public*, pg. 1036
HALLIBURTON NETHERLANDS HOLDINGS B.V.—See Halliburton Company; *U.S. Public*, pg. 981
HALLIN MARINE SINGAPORE PTE LTD—See Superior Energy Services, Inc.; *U.S. Private*, pg. 3877
HBIS MINING—See HBIS Group Co., Ltd.; *Int'l*, pg. 3296
HINOWA S.P.A.—See Oshkosh Corporation; *U.S. Public*, pg. 1620
HOE LEONG CORPORATION LTD.; *Int'l*, pg. 3439
HONGHUA GOLDEN COAST EQUIPMENT FZE—See Honghua Group Ltd; *Int'l*, pg. 3470
HONGHUA GROUP LTD; *Int'l*, pg. 3470
HONGHUA INTERNATIONAL CO., LTD.—See Honghua Group Ltd; *Int'l*, pg. 3470
HUNTING ENERGY SERVICES (DRILLING TOOLS) INC.—See Hunting Plc; *Int'l*, pg. 3537
INGERSOLL-RAND (INDIA) PRIVATE LTD.—See Ingersoll Rand Inc.; *U.S. Public*, pg. 1121
JENNMAR CORPORATION—See Frank Calandra, Inc.; *U.S. Private*, pg. 1594
JOHNSON CRUSHERS INTERNATIONAL, INC.—See Astec Industries, Inc.; *U.S. Public*, pg. 216
J.W. JONES COMPANY, LLC; *U.S. Private*, pg. 2172
KENNAMETAL SP. Z O.O.—See Kennametal Inc.; *U.S. Public*, pg. 1222
K-TRON CHINA LTD.—See Hillenbrand, Inc.; *U.S. Public*, pg. 1036
LUDOWICI LIMITED—See FLSmidth & Co. A/S; *Int'l*, pg. 2711
MAETEHNIKA AS—See Eesti Energia AS; *Int'l*, pg. 2317
MARTIN ENGINEERING; *U.S. Private*, pg. 2595
MATRIX DESIGN GROUP, LLC—See Alliance Holdings GP, L.P.; *U.S. Private*, pg. 183
MCLANAHAN CORPORATION; *U.S. Private*, pg. 2640
MEGADIAMOND, INC.—See Schlumberger Limited; *U.S. Public*, pg. 1844
MERGER MINES CORP.; *U.S. Public*, pg. 1424
MODULAR TRAINING PTY LTD.—See Aquirian Limited; *Int'l*, pg. 528
MORGARDSHAMMAR AB—See Danieli & C. Officine Meccaniche S.p.A.; *Int'l*, pg. 1963
MSA AFRICA (PTY.) LTD.—See MSA Safety Incorporated; *U.S. Public*, pg. 1481
MSA-AUER VERTRIEBS GMBH—See MSA Safety Incorporated; *U.S. Public*, pg. 1482
MSA AUSTRALIA PTY. LIMITED—See MSA Safety Incorporated; *U.S. Public*, pg. 1481
MSA BELGIUM NV—See MSA Safety Incorporated; *U.S. Public*, pg. 1482
MSA (BRITAIN) LIMITED—See MSA Safety Incorporated; *U.S. Public*, pg. 1481
MSA DO BRASIL EQUIPAMENTOS E INSTRUMENTOS DE SEGURANCA LTDA.—See MSA Safety Incorporated; *U.S. Public*, pg. 1482
MSA INTERNATIONAL, INC.—See MSA Safety Incorporated; *U.S. Public*, pg. 1482
MSA ITALIANA S.P.A.—See MSA Safety Incorporated; *U.S. Public*, pg. 1482
MSA NEDERLAND, B.V.—See MSA Safety Incorporated; *U.S. Public*, pg. 1482
MSA NORDIC AB—See MSA Safety Incorporated; *U.S. Public*, pg. 1482
MSA OSTERREICH GMBH—See MSA Safety Incorporated; *U.S. Public*, pg. 1482
MSA PRODUKTION DEUTSCHLAND GMBH—See MSA Safety Incorporated; *U.S. Public*, pg. 1482
MSA SAFETY HUNGARY LTD.—See MSA Safety Incorporated; *U.S. Public*, pg. 1482
MSA SAFETY MALAYSIA SDN BHD—See MSA Safety Incorporated; *U.S. Public*, pg. 1482
MSA SAFETY POLAND SP.Z.O.O.—See MSA Safety Incorporated; *U.S. Public*, pg. 1482
MSA SCHWEIZ GMBH—See MSA Safety Incorporated; *U.S. Public*, pg. 1482
MSA SUZHOU SAFETY EQUIPMENT R&D CO., LTD.—See MSA Safety Incorporated; *U.S. Public*, pg. 1482
MSA TECHNOLOGIES AND ENTERPRISE SERVICES GMBH—See MSA Safety Incorporated; *U.S. Public*, pg. 1482
MSA TECHNOLOGIES AND ENTERPRISE SERVICES SAS—See MSA Safety Incorporated; *U.S. Public*, pg. 1482
MULTILIFT WELLTEC LLC—See Forum Energy Technologies, Inc.; *U.S. Public*, pg. 874
NEW CONCEPT MINING PERU S.A.C.—See Epiroc AB; *Int'l*, pg. 2463
NEW CONCEPT MINING (PTY) LTD—See Epiroc AB; *Int'l*, pg. 2463
NORSTONE A.S.—See Heidelberg Materials AG; *Int'l*, pg. 3315
NUMA TOOL CO.; *U.S. Private*, pg. 2973
OIL LIFT TECHNOLOGY PTY LTD—See Dover Corporation; *U.S. Public*, pg. 682
POWER TECHNIQUE NORTH AMERICA LLC—See Atlas Copco AB; *Int'l*, pg. 684
PT AUSTIN ENGINEERING INDONESIA—See Austin Engineering Ltd.; *Int'l*, pg. 718
QINGDAO TSC OFFSHORE EQUIPMENT CO., LTD—See CM Energy Tech Co., Ltd.; *Int'l*, pg. 1666
QUARRY & MINING MANUFACTURE PTY. LTD.—See E&A Limited; *Int'l*, pg. 2247
QUARRY & MINING MANUFACTURE (QLD) PTY. LTD.—See E&A Limited; *Int'l*, pg. 2247
RIMPULL CORPORATION; *U.S. Private*, pg. 3437
SALTUS INDUSTRIAL TECHNIQUE GMBH—See Atlas Copco AB; *Int'l*, pg. 684
SAND & GRUS AB JEHANDER—See Heidelberg Materials AG; *Int'l*, pg. 3315
SANSHELL PRODUCTS, INC.—See Frank Calandra, Inc.; *U.S. Private*, pg. 1594
SICHUAN HONGHUA ELECTRIC CO., LTD.—See Honghua Group Ltd; *Int'l*, pg. 3471
SIN CHEE HENG (BUTTERWORTH) SDN. BHD.—See Hextar Industries Berhad; *Int'l*, pg. 3373
SIN CHEE HENG (JOHORE) SDN. BHD.—See Hextar Industries Berhad; *Int'l*, pg. 3373
SIN CHEE HENG (KUANTAN) SDN. BHD.—See Hextar Industries Berhad; *Int'l*, pg. 3373
SIN CHEE HENG (SABAH) SDN. BHD.—See Hextar Industries Berhad; *Int'l*, pg. 3373
SIN CHEE HENG (SARAWAK) SDN. BHD.—See Hextar Industries Berhad; *Int'l*, pg. 3373
SIN CHEE HENG SDN. BHD.—See Hextar Industries Berhad; *Int'l*, pg. 3373
STEDMAN MACHINE COMPANY; *U.S. Private*, pg. 3795
STEWART & STEVENSON DE LAS AMERICAS COLOMBIA LTDA.—See Kirby Corporation; *U.S. Public*, pg. 1236
SVT GMBH—See Groupe Bruxelles Lambert SA; *Int'l*, pg. 3099
SYNATEC GMBH—See Atlas Copco AB; *Int'l*, pg. 684
TBS MINING SOLUTIONS PTY LTD.—See Aquirian Limited; *Int'l*, pg. 528
TECNIWELL S.R.L.—See Granite Construction Incorporated; *U.S. Public*, pg. 958
TEREX MATERIALS PROCESSING & MINING—See Terex Corporation; *U.S. Public*, pg. 2020
TEREX REDRILL—See Terex Corporation; *U.S. Public*, pg. 2020
TERRASOURCE GLOBAL CORPORATION DUNCAN—See Hillenbrand, Inc.; *U.S. Public*, pg. 1037
TOWNLEY MANUFACTURING COMPANY; *U.S. Private*, pg. 4198
TSC ENGINEERING LIMITED—See CM Energy Tech Co., Ltd.; *Int'l*, pg. 1666
TSC OFFSHORE CORPORATION—See CM Energy Tech Co., Ltd.; *Int'l*, pg. 1666
TSC OFFSHORE PTE. LIMITED—See CM Energy Tech Co., Ltd.; *Int'l*, pg. 1666
TSC OFFSHORE (UK) LIMITED—See CM Energy Tech Co., Ltd.; *Int'l*, pg. 1666
WILLIAMS PATENT CRUSHER & PULVERIZER CO., INC.; *U.S. Private*, pg. 4526
WORKSTRINGS INTERNATIONAL LIMITED—See Superior Energy Services, Inc.; *U.S. Private*, pg. 3877
WUXI-MSA SAFETY EQUIPMENT CO. LTD.—See MSA Safety Incorporated; *U.S. Public*, pg. 1482
XEROX AS—See Xerox Holdings Corporation; *U.S. Public*, pg. 2389

333132 — OIL AND GAS FIELD MACHINERY AND EQUIPMENT MANUFACTURING

ADVANCED GREEN ENERGY PTE LTD—See Advanced Holdings Ltd.; *Int'l*, pg. 159
AGENTIX CORP.; *U.S. Public*, pg. 60
AGGREGATE PLANT PRODUCTS CO.—See NOV, Inc.; *U.S. Public*, pg. 1543
AIR LIQUIDE GABOA—See Adenia Partners Ltd; *Int'l*, pg. 143
AIR LIQUID HOUPU HYDROGEN EQUIPMENT CO., LTD.—See Houpu Clean Energy Group Co., Ltd; *Int'l*, pg. 3490
AITKEN MANUFACTURING INC.—See INNOVATE Corp.; *U.S. Public*, pg. 1125
A.J. LUCAS GROUP LIMITED; *Int'l*, pg. 24
AKER SOLUTIONS INC.—See Aker Solutions ASA; *Int'l*, pg. 262
AKTOBE OIL EQUIPMENT PLANT JSC; *Int'l*, pg. 267
ALLIED TECHNOLOGY INC.—See Forum Energy Technologies, Inc.; *U.S. Public*, pg. 873
ALY ENERGY SERVICES, INC.; *U.S. Public*, pg. 89
AMERON BRASIL INDUSTRIA E COMERCIO DE TUBOS LTDA.—See NOV, Inc.; *U.S. Public*, pg. 1543
ANALYTICAL TECHNOLOGY & CONTROL LIMITED; *Int'l*, pg. 446
ANSA TECHNOLOGIES LIMITED—See ANSA McAL Limited; *Int'l*, pg. 477
APL DO BRASIL LTDA—See NOV, Inc.; *U.S. Public*, pg. 1543
APL MANAGEMENT PTE LTD—See NOV, Inc.; *U.S. Public*, pg. 1543
APL NORWAY AS—See NOV, Inc.; *U.S. Public*, pg. 1543
ARNETT & BURGESS OIL FIELD CONSTRUCTION LIMITED—See Quanta Services, Inc.; *U.S. Public*, pg. 1750
ARNETT & BURGESS PIPELINERS LTD.—See Quanta Services, Inc.; *U.S. Public*, pg. 1750
ARNETT & BURGESS PIPELINERS (ROCKIES) LLC—See Quanta Services, Inc.; *U.S. Public*, pg. 1750
AVECPALM MARKETING RESOURCES SDN. BHD.—See CB Industrial Product Holding Berhad; *Int'l*, pg. 1364
BAKER HUGHES ASIA PACIFIC LIMITED—See Baker Hughes Company; *U.S. Public*, pg. 264
BAKER HUGHES DO BRAZIL LTDA.—See Baker Hughes Company; *U.S. Public*, pg. 264
BAKER HUGHES - HUGHES CHRISTENSEN—See Baker Hughes Company; *U.S. Public*, pg. 264
BAKER HUGHES INTEQ GMBH—See Baker Hughes Company; *U.S. Public*, pg. 264
BAKER HUGHES INTEQ (M) SDN BHD—See Baker Hughes Company; *U.S. Public*, pg. 265

333132 — OIL AND GAS FIELD M...

BAKER HUGHES INTEQ—See Baker Hughes Company; *U.S. Public*, pg. 265
BAKER HUGHES INTERNATIONAL COOPERATIEF U.A.—See Baker Hughes Company; *U.S. Public*, pg. 265
BAKER HUGHES (NEDERLAND) B.V.—See Baker Hughes Company; *U.S. Public*, pg. 264
BASINTEK LLC—See Riverstone Holdings LLC; *U.S. Private*, pg. 3447
BAUER EQUIPMENT HONG KONG LTD.—See BAUER Aktiengesellschaft; *Int'l*, pg. 892
BAUER EQUIPMENT (MALAYASIA) SDN. BHD.—See BAUER Aktiengesellschaft; *Int'l*, pg. 892
BAUER EQUIPMENT (SHANGHAI) CO. LTD.—See BAUER Aktiengesellschaft; *Int'l*, pg. 892
BAUER TECHNOLOGIES FAR EAST PTE. LTD.—See BAUER Aktiengesellschaft; *Int'l*, pg. 892
BAUER TIANJIN TECHNOLOGIES CO. LTD.—See BAUER Aktiengesellschaft; *Int'l*, pg. 892
BEIJING SPC ENVIRONMENT PROTECTION TECH CO., LTD.; *Int'l*, pg. 957
BENCHMARK ENERGY PRODUCTS, LLC—See Select Water Solutions, Inc.; *U.S. Public*, pg. 1862
BENOIT PREMIUM THREADING, LLC; *U.S. Private*, pg. 528
BLUE1USA, LLC; *U.S. Private*, pg. 596
BLUEFIRE EQUIPMENT CORP.; *U.S. Private*, pg. 596
BLUE TEE CORPORATION; *U.S. Private*, pg. 594
BOART LONGYEAR CANADA—See Boart Longyear Ltd.; *Int'l*, pg. 1095
BORETS INTERNATIONAL LTD.—See Tangent Fund Management LLC; *U.S. Private*, pg. 3930
BRASBAUER EQUIPAMENTOS DE PERFURACAO LTDA.—See BAUER Aktiengesellschaft; *Int'l*, pg. 893
BRONCO MANUFACTURING LLC—See Akastor ASA; *Int'l*, pg. 260
BURCKHARDT COMPRESSION (DEUTSCHLAND) GMBH—See Burckhardt Compression Holding AG; *Int'l*, pg. 1220
BURCKHARDT COMPRESSION (ESPANA) S.A.—See Burckhardt Compression Holding AG; *Int'l*, pg. 1220
BURCKHARDT COMPRESSION (SHANGHAI) CO. LTD.—See Burckhardt Compression Holding AG; *Int'l*, pg. 1220
CACTUS, INC.; *U.S. Public*, pg. 418
CALFRAC WELL SERVICES (ARGENTINA) S.A.—See Calfrac Well Services Ltd.; *Int'l*, pg. 1263
CAMERON INTERNATIONAL CORPORATION—See Schlumberger Limited; *U.S. Public*, pg. 1843
CAMERON PETROLEUM (UK) LIMITED—See Schlumberger Limited; *U.S. Public*, pg. 1843
CAMERON RIG SOLUTIONS LLC—See Schlumberger Limited; *U.S. Public*, pg. 1843
CAMERON SENSE AS—See Schlumberger Limited; *U.S. Public*, pg. 1843
CAMERON SERVICES INTERNATIONAL PTY LTD—See Schlumberger Limited; *U.S. Public*, pg. 1843
CARBO CERAMICS INC.; *U.S. Private*, pg. 748
CASINJAC, INC.—See First Reserve Management, L.P.; *U.S. Private*, pg. 1526
CENTRIFUGAL SERVICES, INC.—See Brookfield Corporation; *Int'l*, pg. 1181
CGG SERVICES (UK) LTD.—See CGG; *Int'l*, pg. 1432
CHANCELLOR OIL TOOLS, INC.—See Team Oil Tools, LLC; *U.S. Private*, pg. 3950
CHEMTEC ENERGY SERVICES, LLC—See L.B. Foster Company; *U.S. Public*, pg. 1278
CHINA OIL HBP SCIENCE & TECHNOLOGY CO., LTD.; *Int'l*, pg. 1538
CITIZEN ENERGY OPERATING LLC; *U.S. Private*, pg. 902
COIL SERVICES (NORTH SEA) LIMITED—See NOV, Inc.; *U.S. Public*, pg. 1544
CONTROL FLOW INCORPORATED S. DE R. L. DE C.V.—See Control Flow Inc.; *U.S. Private*, pg. 1034
CONTROL FLOW INC.; *U.S. Private*, pg. 1034
CONTUBOS S.A.—See NOV, Inc.; *U.S. Public*, pg. 1544
COVENANT TESTING TECHNOLOGIES, LLC—See Kingswood Capital Management LLC; *U.S. Private*, pg. 2312
DANI INSTRUMENTS S.A.—See DANI Instruments SpA; *Int'l*, pg. 1962
DANI INSTRUMENTS SPA; *Int'l*, pg. 1962
DANLIN INDUSTRIES CORP.—See Arsenal Capital Management LP; *U.S. Private*, pg. 338
DELAWARE BASIN MIDSTREAM, LLC—See Occidental Petroleum Corporation; *U.S. Public*, pg. 1561
DELEUM PRIMERA SDN. BHD.—See Deleum Berhad; *Int'l*, pg. 2012
DELEUM ROTARY SERVICES SDN. BHD.—See Deleum Berhad; *Int'l*, pg. 2012
DIMITROVGRADKHIMMASH JSC—See HMS Hydraulic Machines & Systems Group plc; *Int'l*, pg. 3432
DOVER ARTIFICIAL LIFT INTERNATIONAL, LLC—See Dover Corporation; *U.S. Public*, pg. 679
DQ HOLDINGS (AUSTRALIA) PTY LTD—See Dril-Quip, Inc.; *U.S. Public*, pg. 687
DRECO ENERGY SERVICES ULC—See NOV, Inc.; *U.S. Public*, pg. 1544
DRIL-QUIP ASIA PACIFIC PTE LTD—See Dril-Quip, Inc.; *U.S. Public*, pg. 687
DRIL-QUIP DO BRASIL LTDA—See Dril-Quip, Inc.; *U.S. Public*, pg. 687
DRIL-QUIP (EUROPE) LIMITED—See Dril-Quip, Inc.; *U.S. Public*, pg. 687
DRIL-QUIP (EUROPE) LIMITED—See Dril-Quip, Inc.; *U.S. Public*, pg. 687
DRIL-QUIP (EUROPE) LIMITED—See Dril-Quip, Inc.; *U.S. Public*, pg. 687
DRIL-QUIP (EUROPE) LIMITED—See Dril-Quip, Inc.; *U.S. Public*, pg. 687
DRIL-QUIP (EUROPE) LIMITED—See Dril-Quip, Inc.; *U.S. Public*, pg. 687
DRIL-QUIP, INC.; *U.S. Public*, pg. 687
DRIL-QUIP LONDON—See Dril-Quip, Inc.; *U.S. Public*, pg. 687
DRIL-QUIP NEW ORLEANS—See Dril-Quip, Inc.; *U.S. Public*, pg. 687
DUAL DRIVE TECHNOLOGIES, LTD.—See Energy Transfer LP; *U.S. Public*, pg. 762
DUOLINE TECHNOLOGY—See Robroy Industries Inc.; *U.S. Private*, pg. 3463
EAB ENGINEERING AS—See Schlumberger Limited; *U.S. Public*, pg. 1844
EFX GLOBAL KL SDN BHD—See Enerflex Ltd.; *Int'l*, pg. 2418
ELMAR ENGINEERING LIMITED—See NOV, Inc.; *U.S. Public*, pg. 1544
ELMAR SERVICES LIMITED—See NOV, Inc.; *U.S. Public*, pg. 1544
ELMAR SERVICES PTY LTD—See NOV, Inc.; *U.S. Public*, pg. 1544
ENER-CORE, INC.; *U.S. Public*, pg. 760
ENERFLEX AUSTRALASIA HOLDINGS PTY. LTD.—See Enerflex Ltd.; *Int'l*, pg. 2418
ENERFLEX MENA LTD—See Enerflex Ltd.; *Int'l*, pg. 2418
ENERFLEX PROCESS PTY. LTD.—See Enerflex Ltd.; *Int'l*, pg. 2418
ENERFLEX PTE. LTD.—See Enerflex Ltd.; *Int'l*, pg. 2418
ENERFLEX SERVICE PTY. LTD.—See Enerflex Ltd.; *Int'l*, pg. 2418
ENERFLOW INDUSTRIES INC.—See NOV, Inc.; *U.S. Public*, pg. 1544
EN-FAB INC.; *U.S. Private*, pg. 1389
ENGINEERING SEISMOLOGY GROUP CANADA INC.—See Deep Imaging Technologies, Inc.; *U.S. Private*, pg. 1189
ENI TURKMENISTAN LTD—See Eni S.p.A.; *Int'l*, pg. 2437
ENTEQ UPSTREAM USA INC.—See Enteq Technologies plc; *Int'l*, pg. 2450
ENVIROTECHNOLOGIES INTERNATIONAL, INC.; *U.S. Public*, pg. 760
ESSENTRA PIPE PROTECTION TECHNOLOGIES—See Essentra plc; *Int'l*, pg. 2511
EUREKA PUMPS AS—See HitecVision AS; *Int'l*, pg. 3425
EXPO PARTES S.A. DE C.V.—See NOV, Inc.; *U.S. Public*, pg. 1544
EXTERRAN ENERGY SOLUTIONS, L.P.—See Enerflex Ltd.; *Int'l*, pg. 2418
EXTERRAN GENERAL HOLDINGS LLC—See Enerflex Ltd.; *Int'l*, pg. 2419
EXTREME TECHNOLOGIES, LLC—See Drilling Tools International Corp.; *U.S. Public*, pg. 688
FHE USA LLC - SAN ANTONIO—See J Fitzgibbons LLC; *U.S. Private*, pg. 2153
FHE USA LLC—See J Fitzgibbons LLC; *U.S. Private*, pg. 2153
FIBERSPAR CORPORATION—See NOV, Inc.; *U.S. Public*, pg. 1544
FIDMASH—See NOV, Inc.; *U.S. Public*, pg. 1544
FLARE INDUSTRIES, LLC—See Turnbridge Capital, LLC; *U.S. Private*, pg. 4260
FLOGISTIX, LP—See White Deer Management LLC; *U.S. Private*, pg. 4508
FLUX GROUP AS—See HitecVision AS; *Int'l*, pg. 3426
FOREMOST UNIVERSAL LP—See Foremost Income Fund; *Int'l*, pg. 2731
FORTH VALLEY ENGINEERING LIMITED—See NOV, Inc.; *U.S. Public*, pg. 1544
FORUM ARABIA LIMITED—See Forum Energy Technologies, Inc.; *U.S. Public*, pg. 873
FORUM ENERGY TECHNOLOGIES, INC. - FLOAT EQUIPMENT—See Forum Energy Technologies, Inc.; *U.S. Public*, pg. 873
FORUM ENERGY TECHNOLOGY (SHANGHAI) CO., LTD—See Forum Energy Technologies, Inc.; *U.S. Public*, pg. 873
FRAC TECHNOLOGY AS—See Nine Energy Service, Inc.; *U.S. Public*, pg. 1529
FRANK HENRY EQUIPMENT (1987) LTD.; *Int'l*, pg. 2761
FROG AGV SYSTEMS B.V.—See Oceaneering International, Inc.; *U.S. Public*, pg. 1562
GANSU HONGTENG OIL & GAS EQUIPMENT MANUFACTURING CO., LTD.—See Honghua Group Ltd; *Int'l*, pg. 3470
GARDNER DENVER, INC.—See Ingersoll Rand Inc.; *U.S. Public*, pg. 1118
GAS CONTROL EQUIPMENT IBERICA S.L.—See Enovis Corporation; *U.S. Public*, pg. 772
GAS CONTROL EQUIPMENT S.A. DE C.V.—See Enovis Corporation; *U.S. Public*, pg. 773
GASIN - GASES INDUSTRIAIS, S.A.R.L.—See Air Products & Chemicals, Inc.; *U.S. Public*, pg. 66
GASPROJECT S.A.—See Air Products & Chemicals, Inc.; *U.S. Public*, pg. 66
GAYLIN VIETNAM PTE LTD—See AMOS Group Limited; *Int'l*, pg. 430
GCE GAS CONTROL EQUIPMENT CO., LTD.—See Enovis Corporation; *U.S. Public*, pg. 772
GCE GAS CONTROL EQUIPMENT, INC.—See Enovis Corporation; *U.S. Public*, pg. 772
GCE GMBH—See Enovis Corporation; *U.S. Public*, pg. 772
GCE HUNGARIA KFT.—See Enovis Corporation; *U.S. Public*, pg. 772
GCE LATIN AMERICA LTD.—See Enovis Corporation; *U.S. Public*, pg. 772
GCE MUJELLI S.P.A.—See Enovis Corporation; *U.S. Public*, pg. 772
GCE PORTUGAL UNIPESSOAL LDA—See Enovis Corporation; *U.S. Public*, pg. 772
GCE ROMANIA S.R.L.—See Enovis Corporation; *U.S. Public*, pg. 772
GCE S.A.S.—See Enovis Corporation; *U.S. Public*, pg. 772
GCE SP. Z O.O.—See Enovis Corporation; *U.S. Public*, pg. 772
GE ENERGY & INDUSTRIAL SERVICES, INC.—See General Electric Company; *U.S. Public*, pg. 919
GE ENERGY OILFIELD TECHNOLOGY, INC.—See General Electric Company; *U.S. Public*, pg. 920
GE ENERGY OILFIELD TECHNOLOGY—See General Electric Company; *U.S. Public*, pg. 920
GEODYNAMICS, INC.—See Oil States International, Inc.; *U.S. Public*, pg. 1565
GE OIL & GAS U.K. LIMITED—See General Electric Company; *U.S. Public*, pg. 917
GEOPARK CHILE LIMITED-BERMUDA—See GeoPark Limited; *Int'l*, pg. 2934
G.E.S. GAS EQUIPMENT SERVICE GMBH—See Hoyer GmbH; *Int'l*, pg. 3498
G.E.S. OBERHAUSEN GMBH—See Hoyer GmbH; *Int'l*, pg. 3498
GRANT PRIDECO, L.P.—See NOV, Inc.; *U.S. Public*, pg. 1544
GRANT PRIDECO (SINGAPORE) PTE LTD—See NOV, Inc.; *U.S. Public*, pg. 1544
GREEN EQUIPMENT COMPANY—See Core & Main, Inc.; *U.S. Public*, pg. 576
GREYWOLF ENERGY SERVICES LTD.—See TETRA Technologies, Inc.; *U.S. Public*, pg. 2024
HAIMO AMERICA, INC.—See Haimo Technologies Group Corp.; *Int'l*, pg. 3211
HALLIBURTON MANUFACTURING & SERVICES LIMITED—See Halliburton Company; *U.S. Public*, pg. 980
HALLIBURTON SECURITY DBS—See Halliburton Company; *U.S. Public*, pg. 980
HILONG DRILL PIPE (WUXI) CO., LTD.—See Hilong Holding Limited; *Int'l*, pg. 3393
HILONG HOLDING LIMITED; *Int'l*, pg. 3393
HILONG PETROLEUM PIPE COMPANY LLC—See Hilong Holding Limited; *Int'l*, pg. 3393
HMS NEFTEMASH JSC—See HMS Hydraulic Machines & Systems Group plc; *Int'l*, pg. 3432
HONGHUA AMERICA, LLC—See Honghua Group Ltd; *Int'l*, pg. 3470
HONING INC.—See Dril-Quip, Inc.; *U.S. Public*, pg. 687
HUGHES CHRISTENSEN—See Baker Hughes Company; *U.S. Public*, pg. 264
HUNTING ALPHA (EPZ) LIMITED—See Hunting Plc; *Int'l*, pg. 3536
HUNTING ENERGY DE MEXICO S. DE R.L. DE C.V—See Hunting Plc; *Int'l*, pg. 3536
HUNTING ENERGY SAUDI ARABIA LLC—See Hunting Plc; *Int'l*, pg. 3536
HUNTING ENERGY SERVICES (AUSTRALIA) PTY. LTD.—See Hunting Plc; *Int'l*, pg. 3536
HUNTING ENERGY SERVICES (INTERNATIONAL) LIMITED—See Hunting Plc; *Int'l*, pg. 3536
HUNTING ENERGY SERVICES LLC—See Hunting Plc; *Int'l*, pg. 3537
HUNTING ENERGY SERVICES (NORWAY) AS—See Hunting Plc; *Int'l*, pg. 3536
HUNTING ENERGY SERVICES PTE. LTD.—See Hunting Plc; *Int'l*, pg. 3537
HUNTING ENERGY SERVICES (SOUTH AFRICA) PTY. LTD.—See Hunting Plc; *Int'l*, pg. 3536
HUNTING ENERGY SERVICES (WELL INTERVENTION) PTE. LTD.—See Hunting Plc; *Int'l*, pg. 3536
HUNTING ENERGY SERVICES (WUXI) CO., LTD.—See Hunting Plc; *Int'l*, pg. 3536
HUNTING PLC; *Int'l*, pg. 3536
HUNTING TITAN—See Hunting Plc; *Int'l*, pg. 3537
HYDRALIFT AS—See NOV, Inc.; *U.S. Public*, pg. 1545
HYDRALIFT FRANCE SAS—See NOV, Inc.; *U.S. Public*, pg. 1545
HYDRIL PRIVATE LTD—See General Electric Company; *U.S. Public*, pg. 919
HYDUKE DRILLING SOLUTIONS INC—See Hyduke Energy Services Inc.; *Int'l*, pg. 3548

333132 — OIL AND GAS FIELD M...

HYDUKE ENERGY SERVICES INC. - HYDUKE DESIGN & ENGINEERING DIVISION—See Hyduke Energy Services Inc.; *Int'l*, pg. 3548
HYDUKE ENERGY SERVICES INC.; *Int'l*, pg. 3548
IEOC PRODUCTION BV—See Eni S.p.A.; *Int'l*, pg. 2437
IKM PRODUCTION TECHNOLOGY UK LTD.—See IKM Gruppen AS; *Int'l*, pg. 3611
IKM PROMECH AS—See IKM Gruppen AS; *Int'l*, pg. 3611
INTELLISERV, INC.—See NOV, Inc.; *U.S. Public*, pg. 1545
INTERNATIONAL SNUBBING SERVICES—See Superior Energy Services, Inc.; *U.S. Private*, pg. 3877
INTERNATIONAL TUBULAR SERVICES DE MEXICO, S. DE R.I. DE C.V.—See Parker Wellbore Company; *U.S. Public*, pg. 1650
INTERNATIONAL TUBULARS FZE—See Parker Wellbore Company; *U.S. Public*, pg. 1650
IOS TUBULAR MANAGEMENT AS—See DNB Bank ASA; *Int'l*, pg. 2148
ITT BORNEMANN GMBH—See ITT Inc.; *U.S. Public*, pg. 1177
JIANGYIN TUBOSCOPE TUBULAR DEVELOPMENT CO., LTD.—See NOV, Inc.; *U.S. Public*, pg. 1545
J.L. BRYAN EQUIPMENT & LEASE SERVICE, INC.—See Empeiria Capital Partners LLC; *U.S. Private*, pg. 1384
J.W. WILLIAMS, INC.—See AECOM; *U.S. Public*, pg. 51
KIMRAY, INC.; *U.S. Private*, pg. 2306
KLEANGAS ENERGY TECHNOLOGIES, INC.; *U.S. Private*, pg. 2318
KLEMM BOHRTECHNIK GMBH.—See BAUER Aktiengesellschaft; *Int'l*, pg. 893
KOCH ENGINEERED SOLUTIONS, LLC—See Koch Industries, Inc.; *U.S. Private*, pg. 2332
LANZHOU HAIMO ENERGY TECHNOLOGY CO., LTD.—See Haimo Technologies Group Corp.; *Int'l*, pg. 3211
LEGACY MEASUREMENT SOLUTIONS, INC.—See White Deer Management LLC; *U.S. Private*, pg. 4508
LUFKIN INDUSTRIES LLC - OILFIELD DIVISION—See KPS Capital Partners, LP; *U.S. Private*, pg. 2347
LUFKIN INDUSTRIES LLC - POWER TRANSMISSION DIVISION—See KPS Capital Partners, LP; *U.S. Private*, pg. 2348
LUFKIN & PARTNERS LLC—See KPS Capital Partners, LP; *U.S. Private*, pg. 2348
LUSTER MEKANISKE INDUSTRI AS—See Schlumberger Limited; *U.S. Public*, pg. 1844
MATHEY DEARMAN, INC.—See Gladstone Management Corporation; *U.S. Private*, pg. 1705
MB AIR SYSTEMS LIMITED—See Ingersoll Rand Inc.; *U.S. Public*, pg. 1122
MENCK GMBH—See Buckthorn Partners LLP; *Int'l*, pg. 1210
MENCK GMBH—See OEP Capital Advisors, L.P.; *U.S. Private*, pg. 2997
MERPRO AMERICAS, INC.—See NOV, Inc.; *U.S. Public*, pg. 1545
MERPRO LIMITED—See NOV, Inc.; *U.S. Public*, pg. 1545
MEYER SERVICE, INC.; *U.S. Private*, pg. 2692
M. G. DYESS, INC.—See Quanta Services, Inc.; *U.S. Public*, pg. 1751
MHWIRTH AS—See Akastor ASA; *Int'l*, pg. 260
MHWIRTH AS—See Akastor ASA; *Int'l*, pg. 260
MHWIRTH AZERBAIJAN—See Akastor ASA; *Int'l*, pg. 260
MHWIRTH CANADA INC.—See Akastor ASA; *Int'l*, pg. 260
MHWIRTH DO BRASIL EQUIPAMENTOS LTDA—See Akastor ASA; *Int'l*, pg. 260
MHWIRTH GMBH—See Akastor ASA; *Int'l*, pg. 260
MHWIRTH INDIA PVT. LTD.—See Akastor ASA; *Int'l*, pg. 260
MHWIRTH LLC—See Akastor ASA; *Int'l*, pg. 260
MHWIRTH OFFSHORE PETROLEUM ENGINEERING (SHANGHAI) CO. LTD.—See Akastor ASA; *Int'l*, pg. 260
MHWIRTH PTY LTD—See Akastor ASA; *Int'l*, pg. 260
MHWIRTH (SINGAPORE) PTE. LTD.—See Akastor ASA; *Int'l*, pg. 260
MHWIRTH UK LTD.—See Akastor ASA; *Int'l*, pg. 260
MIDWESTERN MANUFACTURING CO. INC.—See Midwesco Industries Inc.; *U.S. Private*, pg. 2719
MONO PUMPS (AUSTRALIA) PROPRIETARY LIMITED—See NOV, Inc.; *U.S. Public*, pg. 1545
MUDLOGGING SYSTEMS, INC.—See ALS Limited; *Int'l*, pg. 379
NATIONAL OILWELL CANADA ULC—See NOV, Inc.; *U.S. Public*, pg. 1545
NATIONAL OILWELL DE MEXICO S.A. DE C.V.—See NOV, Inc.; *U.S. Public*, pg. 1546
NATIONAL OILWELL NORWAY MANUFACTURING AS—See NOV, Inc.; *U.S. Public*, pg. 1546
NATIONAL OILWELL POLAND S.P.Z.O.O.—See NOV, Inc.; *U.S. Public*, pg. 1546
NATIONAL OILWELL SERVICES DE MEXICO, S.A. DE C.V.—See NOV, Inc.; *U.S. Public*, pg. 1546
NATIONAL OILWELL VARCO DENMARK I/S—See NOV, Inc.; *U.S. Public*, pg. 1546
NATIONAL OILWELL VARCO-ESTEVAN SERVICE CENTER—See NOV, Inc.; *U.S. Public*, pg. 1546
NATIONAL OILWELL VARCO KOREA CO., LTD.—See NOV, Inc.; *U.S. Public*, pg. 1546

NATIONAL OILWELL VARCO, L.P.—See NOV, Inc.; *U.S. Public*, pg. 1546
NATIONAL OILWELL VARCO NORWAY AS—See NOV, Inc.; *U.S. Public*, pg. 1546
NATIONAL OILWELL VARCO PTE. LTD.—See NOV, Inc.; *U.S. Public*, pg. 1546
NATIONAL OILWELL VARCO-P&T SERVICIOS PETROLEROS—See NOV, Inc.; *U.S. Public*, pg. 1546
NATIONAL OILWELL VARCO RIG EQUIPMENT TRADING (SHANGHAI) CO., LTD.—See NOV, Inc.; *U.S. Public*, pg. 1546
NATIONAL OILWELL VARCO - SERVICE CENTER—See NOV, Inc.; *U.S. Public*, pg. 1546
NATIONAL OILWELL VARCO—See NOV, Inc.; *U.S. Public*, pg. 1546
NATIONAL OILWELL VARCO—See NOV, Inc.; *U.S. Public*, pg. 1546
NATIONAL OILWELL VARCO—See NOV, Inc.; *U.S. Public*, pg. 1546
NAVITAS PETROLEUM LIMITED PARTNERSHIP; *U.S. Public*, pg. 1500
NCS MULTISTAGE HOLDINGS, INC., *U.S. Public*, pg. 1503
NES FIRCROFT LIMITED—See AEA Investors LP; *U.S. Private*, pg. 114
NORWEGIAN PIPING AS—See HitecVision AS; *Int'l*, pg. 3426
NOV ASEP ELMAR (MIDDLE EAST) LIMITED—See NOV, Inc.; *U.S. Public*, pg. 1545
NOV-BLM SAS—See NOV, Inc.; *U.S. Public*, pg. 1545
NOV BRANDT EUROPE FRANCE—See NOV, Inc.; *U.S. Public*, pg. 1545
NOV BRANDT OILFIELD SERVICES MIDDLE EAST LLC—See NOV, Inc.; *U.S. Public*, pg. 1545
NOV DH DE MEXICO, S. DE R.L. DE C.V.—See NOV, Inc.; *U.S. Public*, pg. 1545
NOV DOWNHOLE AZERBAIJAN, LLC—See NOV, Inc.; *U.S. Public*, pg. 1545
NOV DOWNHOLE BOLIVIA S.R.L.—See NOV, Inc.; *U.S. Public*, pg. 1545
NOV DOWNHOLE DEL ECUADOR CIA. LTDA.—See NOV, Inc.; *U.S. Public*, pg. 1545
NOV DOWNHOLE EURASIA LIMITED—See NOV, Inc.; *U.S. Public*, pg. 1545
NOV DOWNHOLE GERMANY GMBH—See NOV, Inc.; *U.S. Public*, pg. 1545
NOV DOWNHOLE PTY LTD—See NOV, Inc.; *U.S. Public*, pg. 1545
NOV ENERFLOW ULC—See NOV, Inc.; *U.S. Public*, pg. 1545
NOV-FABTECH FZCO—See NOV, Inc.; *U.S. Public*, pg. 1545
NOV HOLDING GERMANY GMBH & CO KG—See NOV, Inc.; *U.S. Public*, pg. 1545
NOV, INC.; *U.S. Public*, pg. 1543
NOV KOSTROMA LLC—See NOV, Inc.; *U.S. Public*, pg. 1545
NOV RIG SOLUTIONS PTE. LTD.—See NOV, Inc.; *U.S. Public*, pg. 1545
NOV ROLLIGON—See NOV, Inc.; *U.S. Public*, pg. 1545
NOV SARA INDIA PRIVATE LIMITED—See NOV, Inc.; *U.S. Public*, pg. 1545
NOV WEST BV—See NOV, Inc.; *U.S. Public*, pg. 1545
NQL ENERGY SERVICES US, INC.—See NOV, Inc.; *U.S. Public*, pg. 1545
NRG MANUFACTURING, INC.—See First Reserve Management, L.P.; *U.S. Public*, pg. 1525
OCEANEERING ASSET INTEGRITY AS—See Oceaneering International, Inc.; *U.S. Public*, pg. 1562
OCEANEERING PIPETECH AS—See Oceaneering International, Inc.; *U.S. Public*, pg. 1563
OIL STATES INDUSTRIES (ASIA) PTE LTD.—See Oil States International, Inc.; *U.S. Public*, pg. 1565
OMEGA WELL MONITORING—See ALS Limited; *Int'l*, pg. 379
OMEGA WELL MONITORING—See ALS Limited; *Int'l*, pg. 379
ONESUBSEA GMBH—See Schlumberger Limited; *U.S. Public*, pg. 1844
ONESUBSEA LLC—See Schlumberger Limited; *U.S. Public*, pg. 1844
ONESUBSEA MALAYSIA SYSTEMS SDN BHD—See Schlumberger Limited; *U.S. Public*, pg. 1844
ONESUBSEA PROCESSING ASIA PACIFIC SDN. BHD.—See Schlumberger Limited; *U.S. Public*, pg. 1844
ONESUBSEA PROCESSING AS—See Schlumberger Limited; *U.S. Public*, pg. 1844
ONESUBSEA UK LIMITED—See Schlumberger Limited; *U.S. Public*, pg. 1844
OPTASENSE CANADA LTD.—See Luna Innovations Incorporated; *U.S. Public*, pg. 1349
OPTIMA SOLUTIONS U.K. LIMITED—See TETRA Technologies, Inc.; *U.S. Public*, pg. 2024
OPW FLUID TRANSFER SOLUTIONS (JIANG SU) CO., LTD.—See Dover Corporation; *U.S. Public*, pg. 682
ORIGIN INTERNATIONAL INC.—See Element Alpha SA; *Int'l*, pg. 2358
ORMED GMBH—See Enovis Corporation; *U.S. Public*, pg. 773

OTS INTERNATIONAL, INC.—See J Fitzgibbons LLC; *U.S. Private*, pg. 2153
OWEN OIL TOOLS LP—See Core Laboratories N.V.; *Int'l*, pg. 1798
PAKISTAN OILFIELDS LIMITED—See Attock Refinery Ltd; *Int'l*, pg. 697
PALMITECO ENGINEERING SDN. BHD.—See CB Industrial Product Holding Berhad; *Int'l*, pg. 1364
PDC LOGIC, LLC—See Intervale Capital, LLC; *U.S. Private*, pg. 2127
PESAKA INSPECTION SERVICES SDN.BHD.—See NOV, Inc.; *U.S. Public*, pg. 1546
PETROVALVE, INC.—See Flotek Industries, Inc.; *U.S. Public*, pg. 853
PETRO VEND SP. Z O.O.—See Dover Corporation; *U.S. Public*, pg. 682
PHOENIX OFFSHORE CO. LTD—See AMOS Group Limited; *Int'l*, pg. 430
PHOINIX GLOBAL LLC—See Forum Energy Technologies, Inc.; *U.S. Public*, pg. 874
PRAKLA BOHRTECHNIK GMBH.—See BAUER Aktiengesellschaft; *Int'l*, pg. 893
PROFIRE COMBUSTION, INC.—See Profire Energy, Inc.; *U.S. Public*, pg. 1724
PROFIRE ENERGY, INC.; *U.S. Public*, pg. 1724
PT. GAYLIN—See AMOS Group Limited; *Int'l*, pg. 430
PT H-TECH OILFIELD EQUIPMENT—See NOV, Inc.; *U.S. Public*, pg. 1546
PT HUNTING ENERGY ASIA—See Hunting Plc; *Int'l*, pg. 3537
QUAIL TOOLS, L.P.—See Parker Wellbore Company; *U.S. Public*, pg. 1650
QUALITY INDUSTRIAL CORP.—See Ilustrato Pictures International Inc.; *Int'l*, pg. 3617
QUARTZDYNE INC.—See Dover Corporation; *U.S. Public*, pg. 679
RANGER ENERGY SERVICES, INC.; *U.S. Public*, pg. 1762
RAUFOSS WATER & GAS AS—See Aalberts N.V.; *Int'l*, pg. 35
REAMCO, INC.—See Drilling Tools International Corp.; *U.S. Public*, pg. 688
REEDHYCALOG CIS, LLC—See NOV, Inc.; *U.S. Public*, pg. 1546
REED-HYCALOG DE MEXICO, S DE R.L. DE C.V.—See NOV, Inc.; *U.S. Public*, pg. 1546
RIFE RESOURCES LTD—See Freehold Royalties Ltd.; *Int'l*, pg. 2770
RUSSELL SUB-SURFACE SYSTEMS, LTD.—See NOV, Inc.; *U.S. Public*, pg. 1546
SAINT-GOBAIN NORPRO—See Compagnie de Saint-Gobain SA; *Int'l*, pg. 1730
SCHACHTBAU NORDHAUSEN GMBH - MECHANICAL ENGINEERING DIVISION—See BAUER Aktiengesellschaft; *Int'l*, pg. 893
SCHLEHUBER OIL TOOLS, LLC—See Intervale Capital, LLC; *U.S. Private*, pg. 2127
SCHLUMBERGER COMPLETION SYSTEMS—See Schlumberger Limited; *U.S. Public*, pg. 1844
SCHLUMBERGER LIMITED - DRILL BITS—See Schlumberger Limited; *U.S. Public*, pg. 1845
SEABOARD INTERNATIONAL, INC.; *U.S. Private*, pg. 3583
SHANGHAI BAUER TECHNOLOGIES CO. LTD.—See BAUER Aktiengesellschaft; *Int'l*, pg. 892
SHANGHAI SUNNEN MECHANICAL COMPANY, LTD.—See Sunnen Products Company; *U.S. Private*, pg. 3868
SIBNEFTEMASH JSC—See HMS Hydraulic Machines & Systems Group plc; *Int'l*, pg. 3432
SICHUAN JIAYUN OIL GAS EQUIPMENT CO., LTD.—See Fujian Snowman Co., Ltd.; *Int'l*, pg. 2819
SINOPEC OILFIELD EQUIPMENT CORPORATION—See China Petrochemical Corporation; *Int'l*, pg. 1540
SIVALLS, INC. - BROWNWOOD MANUFACTURING PLANT—See Sivalls, Inc.; *U.S. Private*, pg. 3677
SIVALLS, INC. - PAMPA MANUFACTURING PLANT—See Sivalls, Inc.; *U.S. Private*, pg. 3677
SOIL RECOVERY A/S—See NOV, Inc.; *U.S. Public*, pg. 1546
SOLARIS OILFIELD INFRASTRUCTURE, INC.; *U.S. Public*, pg. 1900
SOLARIS OILFIELD SITE SERVICES OPERATING, LLC—See Solaris Oilfield Infrastructure, Inc.; *U.S. Public*, pg. 1900
SONDEX LIMITED—See General Electric Company; *U.S. Public*, pg. 920
SOUTHTEX TREATERS, INC.—See Kinder Morgan, Inc.; *U.S. Public*, pg. 1233
SPECIALTY RENTAL TOOLS & SUPPLY, INC.; *U.S. Private*, pg. 3750
STAR FIBERGLASS HARBIN CO., LTD.—See NOV, Inc.; *U.S. Public*, pg. 1546
STEP OILTOOLS GMBH—See Akastor ASA; *Int'l*, pg. 260
STEWART & STEVENSON, LLC—See Kirby Corporation; *U.S. Public*, pg. 1236
STRATEGIC ASSET LEASING, INC.—See Redwoods Acquisition Corp.; *U.S. Public*, pg. 1771
SUBSEA TECHNOLOGIES LIMITED—See Helix Energy

N.A.I.C.S. INDEX

333241 — FOOD PRODUCT MACHIN...

Solutions Group, Inc.; *U.S. Public*, pg. 1024
SUNNEN AG—See Sunnen Products Company; *U.S. Private*, pg. 3868
SUNRISE OILFIELD SUPPLY, INC.—See Wingate Partners, LLP; *U.S. Private*, pg. 4541
SUPERIOR DRILLING PRODUCTS, INC.—See Drilling Tools International Corp.; *U.S. Public*, pg. 688
SUPERIOR ENERGY SERVICES (AUSTRALIA) PTY. LTD.—See Superior Energy Services, Inc.; *U.S. Private*, pg. 3877
SUPERIOR FABRICATION, INC.—See First Reserve Management, L.P.; *U.S. Private*, pg. 1526
SVT APAC PTE. LTD.—See Gesco AG; *Int'l*, pg. 2946
TAM INTERNATIONAL INC.; *U.S. Private*, pg. 3927
TAYLOR INDUSTRIES, LLC—See Basic Energy Services Inc.; *U.S. Public*, pg. 279
T.D. WILLIAMSON, INC.; *U.S. Private*, pg. 3911
TDW, INC.—See T.D. Williamson, Inc.; *U.S. Private*, pg. 3911
TDW PIGGING PRODUCTS—See T.D. Williamson, Inc.; *U.S. Private*, pg. 3911
TEAM OIL TOOLS, LLC; *U.S. Private*, pg. 3950
TEAM OIL TOOLS LP—See Intervale Capital, LLC; *U.S. Private*, pg. 2127
TESI S.P.A.—See GPI S.p.A.; *Int'l*, pg. 3046
THRU TUBING SOLUTIONS—See RPC, Inc.; *U.S. Public*, pg. 1816
TIW CORPORATION—See Dril-Quip, Inc.; *U.S. Public*, pg. 687
TIW HUNGARY LLC—See Dril-Quip, Inc.; *U.S. Public*, pg. 687
TIW INTERNATIONAL, LLC—See Dril-Quip, Inc.; *U.S. Public*, pg. 688
TREK, INC.—See Advanced Energy Industries, Inc.; *U.S. Public*, pg. 48
TRIANA ENERGY, LLC—See Morgan Stanley; *U.S. Public*, pg. 1474
TSC OFFSHORE CHINA LTD.—See CM Energy Tech Co., Ltd.; *Int'l*, pg. 1666
TSC OFFSHORE LIMITEDA—See CM Energy Tech Co., Ltd.; *Int'l*, pg. 1666
TS&M SUPPLY—See NOV, Inc.; *U.S. Public*, pg. 1546
TUBO-FGS, L.L.C.—See NOV, Inc.; *U.S. Public*, pg. 1547
TUBOSCOPE BRANDT DE VENEZUELA S.A.—See NOV, Inc.; *U.S. Public*, pg. 1547
TUBOSCOPE NORGE AS—See NOV, Inc.; *U.S. Public*, pg. 1547
TUBOSCOPE PIPELINE SERVICES INC.—See NOV, Inc.; *U.S. Public*, pg. 1546
TUBOSCOPE VETCO CANADA ULC—See NOV, Inc.; *U.S. Public*, pg. 1547
TUBOSCOPE VETCO MEXICO, S.A. DE C.V.—See NOV, Inc.; *U.S. Public*, pg. 1547
TUBOSCOPE VETCO MOSCOW CJSC—See NOV, Inc.; *U.S. Public*, pg. 1547
TUBOSCOPE VETCO (OSTERREICH) GMBH—See NOV, Inc.; *U.S. Public*, pg. 1547
TULSA MANUFACTURING PLANT—See T.D. Williamson, Inc.; *U.S. Private*, pg. 3911
ULTERRA DRILLING TECHNOLOGIES, L.P.—See Patterson-UTI Energy, Inc.; *U.S. Public*, pg. 1654
UNIVERSAL INDUSTRIAL GASES, LLC—See Nucor Corporation; *U.S. Public*, pg. 1555
US SYNTHETIC CORPORATION—See Dover Corporation; *U.S. Public*, pg. 679
VALLOUREC DRILLING OIL EQUIPMENT MANUFACTURING LLC—See NOV, Inc.; *U.S. Public*, pg. 1547
VALVISION AS—See HitecVision AS; *Int'l*, pg. 3426
VALVISION AS—See HitecVision AS; *Int'l*, pg. 3426
VARCO BJ BV—See NOV, Inc.; *U.S. Public*, pg. 1547
VARCO CANADA ULC—See NOV, Inc.; *U.S. Public*, pg. 1547
VARCO, L.P.—See NOV, Inc.; *U.S. Public*, pg. 1547
VARCO SARA (INDIA) PRIVATE LIMITED—See NOV, Inc.; *U.S. Public*, pg. 1547
VAREL INTERNATIONAL ENERGY SERVICES, INC.—See Blue Water Energy LLP; *Int'l*, pg. 1070
VINE RESOURCES INC.; *U.S. Private*, pg. 4385
WARRIOR RIG TECHNOLOGIES LIMITED—See Patterson-UTI Energy, Inc.; *U.S. Public*, pg. 1654
WEATHERFORD DIS MANUFACTURING (UK) LIMITED—See Weatherford International plc; *U.S. Public*, pg. 2340
WEATHERFORD OIL TOOL MIDDLE EAST LTD.—See Weatherford International plc; *U.S. Public*, pg. 2340
WEATHERFORD PRODUCTS, INC.—See Weatherford International plc; *U.S. Public*, pg. 2340
WEATHERFORD SAUDI ARABIA LTD.—See Weatherford International plc; *U.S. Public*, pg. 2341
WEATHERFORD U.K. LTD.—See Weatherford International plc; *U.S. Public*, pg. 2341
WELLKEEPER INC; *U.S. Private*, pg. 4475
WENZEL DOWNHOLE TOOLS EUROPE GMBH—See J Fitzgibbons LLC; *U.S. Private*, pg. 2153
WENZEL DOWNHOLE TOOLS LTD.—See J Fitzgibbons LLC; *U.S. Private*, pg. 2153
WENZEL DOWNHOLE TOOLS, U.S., INC.—See J Fitzgibbons LLC; *U.S. Private*, pg. 2153
WESTERN WELL TOOL INC.; *U.S. Private*, pg. 4498

WORLDWIDE OILFIELD MACHINE, INC.; *U.S. Private*, pg. 4570
XI'AN SITAN INSTRUMENT CO., LTD.—See Haimo Technologies Group Corp.; *Int'l*, pg. 3211
XL SYSTEMS EUROPE B.V.—See NOV, Inc.; *U.S. Public*, pg. 1547
ZEONS CORP.; *U.S. Public*, pg. 2402

333241 — FOOD PRODUCT MACHINERY MANUFACTURING

ABDULAZIZ & MANSOUR IBRAHIM ALBABTIN COMPANY; *Int'l*, pg. 58
ADS2 BRANDS LIMITED—See Ardian SAS; *Int'l*, pg. 555
ALFA LAVAL IBERIA S.A.—See Alfa Laval AB; *Int'l*, pg. 310
ALFA LAVAL INC.—See Alfa Laval AB; *Int'l*, pg. 309
ALFA LAVAL PARMA SRL—See Alfa Laval AB; *Int'l*, pg. 311
ALFA LAVAL S.A.—See Alfa Laval AB; *Int'l*, pg. 310
ALFA LAVAL S.P.A.—See Alfa Laval AB; *Int'l*, pg. 311
ALFA LAVAL US HOLDING INC.—See Alfa Laval AB; *Int'l*, pg. 309
ALI S.P.A.—See Ali Holding S.r.l.; *Int'l*, pg. 320
ALKAR-RAPIDPAK-MP EQUIPMENT, INC.—See The Middleby Corporation; *U.S. Public*, pg. 2113
ALLEGHENY BRADFORD CORPORATION; *U.S. Private*, pg. 175
ALLIANCE FOOD EQUIPMENT PROCESSING, LLC—See The Anderson Group, LLC; *U.S. Private*, pg. 3986
ALLIANCE PRODUCTS, LLC—See Sandstone Group, Inc.; *U.S. Private*, pg. 3545
ALLIED BIOTECH CORP.; *Int'l*, pg. 356
AMBACH ALI S.P.A.—See Ali Holding S.r.l.; *Int'l*, pg. 320
AMF AUTOMATION TECHNOLOGIES, LLC—See Markel Group Inc.; *U.S. Public*, pg. 1367
AMF BAKERY SYSTEMS—See Markel Group Inc.; *U.S. Public*, pg. 1368
ANDERSON INTERNATIONAL CORP.; *U.S. Private*, pg. 277
ANETSBERGER, LLC—See The Middleby Corporation; *U.S. Public*, pg. 2113
AOHATA CORPORATION, JAM FACTORY—See Aohata Corporation; *Int'l*, pg. 487
APV LTD.—See Lone Star Funds; *U.S. Private*, pg. 2485
APW WYOTT FOOD SERVICE EQUIPMENT, INC.—See Standex International; *U.S. Public*, pg. 1931
APW WYOTT FOOD SERVICE EQUIPMENT, INC.—See Standex International; *U.S. Public*, pg. 1931
ARBEITSGEMEINSCHAFT ZELLENKUHLERANLAGE KKW-ISAR GEA ENERGIETECHNIK GMBH-ALPINE BAU DEUTSCHLAND AG—See GEA Group Aktiengesellschaft; *Int'l*, pg. 2897
ARDE-BARINCO, INC.—See L3Harris Technologies, Inc.; *U.S. Public*, pg. 1279
ARMOR INOX S.A.—See The Middleby Corporation; *U.S. Public*, pg. 2113
ARMOR INOX UK LTD.—See The Middleby Corporation; *U.S. Public*, pg. 2114
ASAHI INDUSTRY CO., LTD.—See Hisaka Works, Ltd.; *Int'l*, pg. 3406
ASSOCIATED AMERICAN INDUSTRIES, INC.—See Standex International; *U.S. Public*, pg. 1930
ASTRA MANUFACTURING, INC.—See ShoreView Industries, LLC; *U.S. Private*, pg. 3642
A. SUTTER AG—See CRS Holding AG; *Int'l*, pg. 1859
ATLAS PACIFIC ENGINEERING COMPANY, INC.; *U.S. Private*, pg. 379
AUTO-BAKE PTY LTD—See The Middleby Corporation; *U.S. Public*, pg. 2113
BAKER PERKINS HOLDINGS LIMITED—See Blackstone Inc.; *U.S. Public*, pg. 360
BAKER PERKINS INC.—See Blackstone Inc.; *U.S. Public*, pg. 360
BARON ALI SPA—See Ali Holding S.r.l.; *Int'l*, pg. 320
B. BLEND MAQUINAS E BEBIDAS S.A.—See Whirlpool Corporation; *U.S. Public*, pg. 2367
BEECH OVENS PTY LTD—See The Middleby Corporation; *U.S. Public*, pg. 2113
BEEHIVE INC.—See Henry Crown & Company; *U.S. Private*, pg. 1917
BELSHAW BROTHERS, INC.—See Ali Holding S.r.l.; *Int'l*, pg. 322
BEPEX INTERNATIONAL, LLC; *U.S. Private*, pg. 529
BERTRAND-PUMA—See Ali Holding S.r.l.; *Int'l*, pg. 320
BEST EINDHOVEN BV—See Best N.V.; *Int'l*, pg. 999
BEST N.V.; *Int'l*, pg. 999
BETTCHER INDUSTRIES INC.—See KKR & Co. Inc.; *U.S. Public*, pg. 1241
BOMSOWA CO. LTD.; *Int'l*, pg. 1105
BONGARD S.A.—See Ali Holding S.r.l.; *Int'l*, pg. 322
BOTTOM LINE PROCESS TECHNOLOGIES, INC.; *U.S. Private*, pg. 623
BROASTER COMPANY LLC—See Broaster Company; *U.S. Private*, pg. 660
BRODERICK BROS. LIMITED; *Int'l*, pg. 1173
BROWN INTERNATIONAL CORP.—See Dover Corporation; *U.S. Public*, pg. 668
BUCHER-ALIMENTECH LTD—See Bucher Industries AG; *Int'l*, pg. 1208

BUCHER EXZEL, S.L.—See Bucher Industries AG; *Int'l*, pg. 1207
BUCHER MERK PROCESS GMBH—See Bucher Industries AG; *Int'l*, pg. 1207
BUCHER UNIPEKTIN SP. Z O.O.—See Bucher Industries AG; *Int'l*, pg. 1208
BUCHER VASLIN MS SA—See Bucher Industries AG; *Int'l*, pg. 1208
BUCHER VASLIN NORTH AMERICA, INC—See Bucher Industries AG; *Int'l*, pg. 1208
BUCHER VASLIN SA—See Bucher Industries AG; *Int'l*, pg. 1208
BUHLER AEROGLIDE—See Buhler AG; *Int'l*, pg. 1211
BUHLER INC.—See Buhler AG; *Int'l*, pg. 1212
BURFORD CORP.—See The Middleby Corporation; *U.S. Public*, pg. 2113
BURLODGE LTD.—See Ali Holding S.r.l.; *Int'l*, pg. 320
CADDY CORPORATION OF AMERICA; *U.S. Private*, pg. 712
CANDY TOY - INDUSTRIA E COMERCIO DE ALIMENTOS E PLASTICOS LTDA; *Int'l*, pg. 1289
CARPIGIANI CENTRO SUDAMERICA, SA—See Ali Holding S.r.l.; *Int'l*, pg. 320
CARPIGIANI GROUP—See Ali Holding S.r.l.; *Int'l*, pg. 320
CARRIER COMMERCIAL REFRIGERATION (THAILAND) LTD.—See Carrier Global Corporation; *U.S. Public*, pg. 440
CARTER DAY INTERNATIONAL, INC.; *U.S. Private*, pg. 775
CARTER-HOFFMANN, LLC—See The Middleby Corporation; *U.S. Public*, pg. 2113
CARVER INC.—See Lummus Corporation; *U.S. Private*, pg. 2514
CASA HERRERA INC.; *U.S. Private*, pg. 778
CB INDUSTRIAL PRODUCT HOLDING BERHAD; *Int'l*, pg. 1364
CFI—See Ali Holding S.r.l.; *Int'l*, pg. 320
CFS COMMERCIAL (BEIJING) LIMITED—See GEA Group Aktiengesellschaft; *Int'l*, pg. 2897
CFS ITALY S.P.A.—See GEA Group Aktiengesellschaft; *Int'l*, pg. 2897
CFS KOREA LTD.—See GEA Group Aktiengesellschaft; *Int'l*, pg. 2897
CFS NORDIC A/S—See GEA Group Aktiengesellschaft; *Int'l*, pg. 2897
CFS SWITZERLAND AG—See GEA Group Aktiengesellschaft; *Int'l*, pg. 2897
CFT DO BRASIL LTD—See ATS Corporation; *Int'l*, pg. 695
CFT PACKAGING USA INC.—See ATS Corporation; *Int'l*, pg. 695
CFT S.P.A.—See ATS Corporation; *Int'l*, pg. 695
CFT UKRAINE LTD—See ATS Corporation; *Int'l*, pg. 695
CHINA YOURAN DAIRY GROUP LIMITED; *Int'l*, pg. 1565
CLABO S.P.A.; *Int'l*, pg. 1641
CLEVELAND RANGE, LTD.—See Ali Holding S.r.l.; *Int'l*, pg. 322
CONAGRA BRANDS CANADA INC.—See Conagra Brands, Inc.; *U.S. Public*, pg. 564
CONVENIENCE FOOD SYSTEMS S.A. DE C.V.—See GEA Group Aktiengesellschaft; *Int'l*, pg. 2897
CONVOTHERM ELEKTROGERATE GMBH—See Ali Holding S.r.l.; *Int'l*, pg. 323
CORNELIUS BEVERAGE TECHNOLOGIES LIMITED—See Berkshire Hathaway Inc.; *U.S. Public*, pg. 309
CORNELIUS DEUTSCHLAND GMBH—See Berkshire Hathaway Inc.; *U.S. Public*, pg. 309
CORNELIUS ESPANA S.A.—See Berkshire Hathaway Inc.; *U.S. Public*, pg. 309
CORNELIUS ITALIA S.R.L.—See Berkshire Hathaway Inc.; *U.S. Public*, pg. 309
CORNELIUS OSTERREICH GES.M.B.H.—See Berkshire Hathaway Inc.; *U.S. Public*, pg. 309
CORNELIUS (SINGAPORE) PTE. LTD.—See Berkshire Hathaway Inc.; *U.S. Public*, pg. 309
CORNELIUS (TIANJIN) CO., LTD.—See Berkshire Hathaway Inc.; *U.S. Public*, pg. 309
CORNELIUS UKRAINE LLC—See Berkshire Hathaway Inc.; *U.S. Public*, pg. 309
CORNERSTONE FOODSERVICE GROUP, INC.—See ShoreView Industries, LLC; *U.S. Private*, pg. 3642
COZZINI, LLC—See The Middleby Corporation; *U.S. Public*, pg. 2113
COZZINI MIDDLEBY DE MEXICO, S. DE R.L.DE C.V.—See The Middleby Corporation; *U.S. Public*, pg. 2113
CP KELCO BELGIUM BVBA—See J.M. Huber Corporation; *U.S. Private*, pg. 2168
CPM EUROPE B.V.—See Gilbert Global Equity Partners; *U.S. Private*, pg. 1698
CPM EUROPE LTD.—See Gilbert Global Equity Partners; *U.S. Private*, pg. 1698
CRES-COR; *U.S. Private*, pg. 1093
CREST FOODS CO. INC.—See Harwood Capital LLP; *Int'l*, pg. 3282
CUSTOM METALCRAFT INC.; *U.S. Private*, pg. 1129
DAIRY SERVICE & MANUFACTURING INC.; *U.S. Private*, pg. 1146
DIESSEL AKTIENGESELLSCHAFT—See GEA Group Aktiengesellschaft; *Int'l*, pg. 2897

N.A.I.C.S. Index

333241 — FOOD PRODUCT MACHIN... CORPORATE AFFILIATIONS

DOVER REFRIGERATION & FOOD EQUIPMENT, INC.—See Dover Corporation; *U.S. Public*, pg. 680
DUKE MANUFACTURING COMPANY, INC. - ST. LOUIS FACTORY—See Duke Manufacturing Company, Inc.; *U.S. Private*, pg. 1285
DUKE MANUFACTURING C.R. S.R.O—See Duke Manufacturing Company, Inc.; *U.S. Private*, pg. 1285
DUNKLEY INTERNATIONAL—See Cherry Central Cooperative, Inc.; *U.S. Private*, pg. 874
THE DUPPS COMPANY; *U.S. Private*, pg. 4024
THE DUPPS COMPANY THERMAL TECHNOLOGY DIV.—See The Dupps Company; *U.S. Private*, pg. 4024
ECOLAB A/S—See Ecolab Inc.; *U.S. Public*, pg. 713
ECOLAB B.V.—See Ecolab Inc.; *U.S. Public*, pg. 713
ECOLAB COLOMBIA S.A.—See Ecolab Inc.; *U.S. Public*, pg. 713
ECOLAB ECUADOR CIA. LTDA.—See Ecolab Inc.; *U.S. Public*, pg. 713
ECOLAB EOOD—See Ecolab Inc.; *U.S. Public*, pg. 713
ECOLAB EUROPE GMBH—See Ecolab Inc.; *U.S. Public*, pg. 713
ECOLAB GMBH—See Ecolab Inc.; *U.S. Public*, pg. 713
ECOLAB HYGIENE D.O.O.—See Ecolab Inc.; *U.S. Public*, pg. 713
ECOLAB HYGIENE SYSTEMS GMBH—See Ecolab Inc.; *U.S. Public*, pg. 713
ECOLAB S. A.—See Ecolab Inc.; *U.S. Public*, pg. 714
ECOLAB S.A.—See Ecolab Inc.; *U.S. Public*, pg. 714
ECOLAB (SCHWEIZ) GMBH—See Ecolab Inc.; *U.S. Public*, pg. 713
ECOLAB SP. Z O.O.—See Ecolab Inc.; *U.S. Public*, pg. 714
ECOLAB SRL—See Ecolab Inc.; *U.S. Public*, pg. 714
ECOLAB USA INC.—See Ecolab Inc.; *U.S. Public*, pg. 714
EMERY THOMPSON MACHINE SUPPLY CO.—See The Middleby Corporation; *U.S. Public*, pg. 2113
ENODIS FRANCE SA—See Ali Holding S.r.l; *Int'l*, pg. 322
EVERSYS DIGITRONICS AG—See De'Longhi S.p.A.; *Int'l*, pg. 1997
EVERYWARE GLOBAL, INC.; *U.S. Private*, pg. 1441
FEDERAL INDUSTRIES—See Standex International; *U.S. Public*, pg. 1930
FELDMEIER EQUIPMENT, INC.; *U.S. Private*, pg. 1493
FILTRON ENGINEERS LIMITED; *Int'l*, pg. 2663
FIREX S.R.L.—See The Middleby Corporation; *U.S. Public*, pg. 2113
FOODNAMOO INC.; *Int'l*, pg. 2727
FOOD WARMING EQUIPMENT CO., INC.—See Hatco Corporation; *U.S. Private*, pg. 1879
FORMAX, INC.—See Henry Crown & Company; *U.S. Private*, pg. 1917
FOUNDRY ENGINEERING CORPORATION SDN. BHD.—See Golsta Sdn. Bhd.; *Int'l*, pg. 3037
FRONTMATEC HYGIENE GMBH—See KKR & Co. Inc.; *U.S. Public*, pg. 1241
FRONTMATEC SKIVE A/S—See KKR & Co. Inc.; *U.S. Public*, pg. 1241
FRONTMATEC TANDSLET A/S—See KKR & Co. Inc.; *U.S. Public*, pg. 1241
FRYMASTER, L.L.C.—See Ali Holding S.r.l; *Int'l*, pg. 322
FUKUTOME MEAT PACKERS LTD.; *Int'l*, pg. 2841
FYLDE FRESH & FABULOUS LTD.; *Int'l*, pg. 2860
GARDEL FOOD EQUIPMENT & CUTLERY; *U.S. Private*, pg. 1642
GEA AVAPAC LTD.—See GEA Group Aktiengesellschaft; *Int'l*, pg. 2897
GEA BREWERY SYSTEMS GMBH—See GEA Group Aktiengesellschaft; *Int'l*, pg. 2898
GEA CFS BAKEL B.V.—See GEA Group Aktiengesellschaft; *Int'l*, pg. 2898
GEA CFS BUHL GMBH—See GEA Group Aktiengesellschaft; *Int'l*, pg. 2898
GEA CFS GROUP B.V.—See GEA Group Aktiengesellschaft; *Int'l*, pg. 2898
GEA CFS INTERNATIONAL B.V.—See GEA Group Aktiengesellschaft; *Int'l*, pg. 2898
GEA CFS UDEN B.V.—See GEA Group Aktiengesellschaft; *Int'l*, pg. 2898
GEA CFS WEERT B.V.—See GEA Group Aktiengesellschaft; *Int'l*, pg. 2898
GEA CONVENIENCE FOOD TECHNOLOGIES B.V.—See GEA Group Aktiengesellschaft; *Int'l*, pg. 2898
GEA FARM TECHNOLOGIES AUSTRALIA PTY. LTD.—See GEA Group Aktiengesellschaft; *Int'l*, pg. 2898
GEA FOOD SOLUTIONS COMERCIALIZADORA LTDA—See GEA Group Aktiengesellschaft; *Int'l*, pg. 2899
GEA FOOD SOLUTIONS DENMARK A/S—See GEA Group Aktiengesellschaft; *Int'l*, pg. 2899
GEA FOOD SOLUTIONS FRANCE S.A.S.—See GEA Group Aktiengesellschaft; *Int'l*, pg. 2899
GEA FOOD SOLUTIONS GMBH—See GEA Group Aktiengesellschaft; *Int'l*, pg. 2898
GEA FOOD SOLUTIONS UKRAINE LLC—See GEA Group Aktiengesellschaft; *Int'l*, pg. 2899
GEA FOOD SOLUTIONS WEERT B.V.—See GEA Group Aktiengesellschaft; *Int'l*, pg. 2899
GEA MECHANICAL EQUIPMENT CANADA, INC.—See GEA Group Aktiengesellschaft; *Int'l*, pg. 2899
GEA NIRO SOAVI S.P.A.—See GEA Group Aktiengesellschaft; *Int'l*, pg. 2901
GEA PROCESS ENGINEERING INC. - FOOD & DAIRY DIVISION—See GEA Group Aktiengesellschaft; *Int'l*, pg. 2901
GEA PROCESS ENGINEERING INC.—See GEA Group Aktiengesellschaft; *Int'l*, pg. 2901
GEA PROCESS ENGINEERING (INDIA) LIMITED—See GEA Group Aktiengesellschaft; *Int'l*, pg. 2901
GEA PROCESS ENGINEERING NEDERLAND B.V.—See GEA Group Aktiengesellschaft; *Int'l*, pg. 2902
GEA PROCESS ENGINEERING N.V.—See GEA Group Aktiengesellschaft; *Int'l*, pg. 2901
GEA PROCESS ENGINEERING S.A.—See GEA Group Aktiengesellschaft; *Int'l*, pg. 2902
GEA PROCESS ENGINEERING (S.E.A.) PTE. LTD.—See GEA Group Aktiengesellschaft; *Int'l*, pg. 2901
GEA PROCESS ENGINEERING TAIWAN LTD.—See GEA Group Aktiengesellschaft; *Int'l*, pg. 2902
GEA PROCESS TECHNOLOGIES IRELAND LIMITED—See GEA Group Aktiengesellschaft; *Int'l*, pg. 2902
GEA PROCESS TECHNOLOGY NETHERLANDS B.V.—See GEA Group Aktiengesellschaft; *Int'l*, pg. 2902
GEA TDS GMBH—See GEA Group Aktiengesellschaft; *Int'l*, pg. 2903
GEA TUCHENHAGEN FRANCE SARL—See GEA Group Aktiengesellschaft; *Int'l*, pg. 2900
GEA WESTFALIA SEPARATING EQUIPMENT (TIANJIN) CO., LTD.—See GEA Group Aktiengesellschaft; *Int'l*, pg. 2900
GEA WESTFALIA SEPARATOR ARGENTINA S.A.—See GEA Group Aktiengesellschaft; *Int'l*, pg. 2900
GEA WESTFALIA SEPARATOR AUSTRALIA PTY. LTD.—See GEA Group Aktiengesellschaft; *Int'l*, pg. 2903
GEA WESTFALIA SEPARATOR AUSTRIA GMBH—See GEA Group Aktiengesellschaft; *Int'l*, pg. 2900
GEA WESTFALIA SEPARATOR BELGIUM N.V.—See GEA Group Aktiengesellschaft; *Int'l*, pg. 2900
GEA WESTFALIA SEPARATOR CANADA, INC.—See GEA Group Aktiengesellschaft; *Int'l*, pg. 2900
GEA WESTFALIA SEPARATOR CHILE S.A.—See GEA Group Aktiengesellschaft; *Int'l*, pg. 2900
GEA WESTFALIA SEPARATOR (CHINA) LTD.—See GEA Group Aktiengesellschaft; *Int'l*, pg. 2900
GEA WESTFALIA SEPARATOR CIS LTD.—See GEA Group Aktiengesellschaft; *Int'l*, pg. 2900
GEA WESTFALIA SEPARATOR CZ S.R.O.—See GEA Group Aktiengesellschaft; *Int'l*, pg. 2900
GEA WESTFALIA SEPARATOR DO BRASIL INDUSTRIA DE CENTRIFUGAS LTDA.—See GEA Group Aktiengesellschaft; *Int'l*, pg. 2901
GEA WESTFALIA SEPARATOR FRANCE SAS—See GEA Group Aktiengesellschaft; *Int'l*, pg. 2900
GEA WESTFALIA SEPARATOR HELLAS S.A.—See GEA Group Aktiengesellschaft; *Int'l*, pg. 2900
GEA WESTFALIA SEPARATOR HUNGARIA KFT.—See GEA Group Aktiengesellschaft; *Int'l*, pg. 2900
GEA WESTFALIA SEPARATOR ICELAND EHF—See GEA Group Aktiengesellschaft; *Int'l*, pg. 2900
GEA WESTFALIA SEPARATOR IRELAND LTD.—See GEA Group Aktiengesellschaft; *Int'l*, pg. 2900
GEA WESTFALIA SEPARATOR ITALIA S.R.L.—See GEA Group Aktiengesellschaft; *Int'l*, pg. 2900
GEA WESTFALIA SEPARATOR JAPAN K.K.—See GEA Group Aktiengesellschaft; *Int'l*, pg. 2900
GEA WESTFALIA SEPARATOR KOREA LTD.—See GEA Group Aktiengesellschaft; *Int'l*, pg. 2900
GEA WESTFALIA SEPARATOR (MALAYSIA) SDN BHD—See GEA Group Aktiengesellschaft; *Int'l*, pg. 2900
GEA WESTFALIA SEPARATOR MEXICANA S.A. DE C.V.—See GEA Group Aktiengesellschaft; *Int'l*, pg. 2900
GEA WESTFALIA SEPARATOR NORWAY AS—See GEA Group Aktiengesellschaft; *Int'l*, pg. 2900
GEA WESTFALIA SEPARATOR NZ LTD.—See GEA Group Aktiengesellschaft; *Int'l*, pg. 2900
GEA WESTFALIA SEPARATOR PHILIPPINES INC.—See GEA Group Aktiengesellschaft; *Int'l*, pg. 2900
GEA WESTFALIA SEPARATOR PRODUCTION FRANCE SAS—See Altifort France SAS; *Int'l*, pg. 393
GEA WESTFALIA SEPARATOR ROMANIA SRL—See GEA Group Aktiengesellschaft; *Int'l*, pg. 2900
GEA WESTFALIA SEPARATOR SANAYI VE TICARET LTD. STI.—See GEA Group Aktiengesellschaft; *Int'l*, pg. 2901
GEA WESTFALIA SEPARATOR SWEDEN AB—See GEA Group Aktiengesellschaft; *Int'l*, pg. 2901
GEA WESTFALIA SEPARATOR (THAILAND) LTD.—See GEA Group Aktiengesellschaft; *Int'l*, pg. 2900
GEA WESTFALIA SEPARATOR (TIANJIN) CO., LTD.—See GEA Group Aktiengesellschaft; *Int'l*, pg. 2900
GEA WESTFALIASURGE MEXICANA S.A. DE C.V. I.L.—See GEA Group Aktiengesellschaft; *Int'l*, pg. 2904
GEM EQUIPMENT OF OREGON INC.; *U.S. Private*, pg. 1657
GENERAL MILLS MARKETING, INC.—See General Mills, Inc.; *U.S. Public*, pg. 921
GERSTENBERG SCHRODER BRASIL LTDA.—See SPX Technologies, Inc.; *U.S. Public*, pg. 1921
G.G. DANDEKAR MACHINE WORKS LTD. - BHIWANDI PLANT—See G.G. Dandekar Properties Ltd.; *Int'l*, pg. 2865
GLOBAL SMOOTHIE SUPPLY, INC.; *U.S. Private*, pg. 1717
GOLDEN NOODLES NIGERIA LIMITED—See Flour Mills of Nigeria Plc.; *Int'l*, pg. 2709
GOLD MEDAL PRODUCTS CO.; *U.S. Private*, pg. 1728
GOLFETTO SANGATI S.R.L.—See GEA Group Aktiengesellschaft; *Int'l*, pg. 2903
GRAM EQUIPMENT A/S—See FSN Capital Partners AS; *Int'l*, pg. 2799
GRAM EQUIPMENT OF AMERICA INC.—See FSN Capital Partners AS; *Int'l*, pg. 2799
GRINDMASTER CORPORATION—See AB Electrolux; *Int'l*, pg. 40
G.S. BLODGETT CORPORATION—See The Middleby Corporation; *U.S. Public*, pg. 2114
GUANGZHOU JIAJIAMAI OILS AND FATS CO., LTD.—See Great-Sun Foods Co.,LTD.; *Int'l*, pg. 3066
HACKMAN OYJ ABP—See Ali Holding S.r.l; *Int'l*, pg. 321
HEAT & CONTROL, INC.; *U.S. Private*, pg. 1901
HEFEI TAIHE OPTOELECTRONIC TECHNOLOGY CO., LTD; *Int'l*, pg. 3308
HERSHEY ASIA PACIFIC PTE. LTD.—See The Hershey Co.; *U.S. Public*, pg. 2088
HERSHEY INDIA CONFECTIONERY PRIVATE LIMITED—See The Hershey Co.; *U.S. Public*, pg. 2089
HERSMEX S. DE R.L. DE C.V.—See The Hershey Co.; *U.S. Public*, pg. 2089
HINDS-BOCK CORPORATION—See The Middleby Corporation; *U.S. Public*, pg. 2114
HOLLYMATIC CORPORATION; *U.S. Private*, pg. 1966
HOLMAN COOKING EQUIPMENT INC.—See The Middleby Corporation; *U.S. Public*, pg. 2115
HOSHIZAKI MALAYSIA SDN. BHD.—See Hoshizaki Corporation; *Int'l*, pg. 3483
HOSHIZAKI PHILIPPINES CORPORATION—See Hoshizaki Corporation; *Int'l*, pg. 3484
H PIO CO., LTD.; *Int'l*, pg. 3191
HUBEI JUNEYAO GREAT HEALTH DAIRY CO., LTD.; *Int'l*, pg. 3518
ICL ORGANIC DAIRY PRODUCTS LIMITED; *Int'l*, pg. 3581
IDAHO STEEL PRODUCTS INC.; *U.S. Private*, pg. 2035
IDEX MPT INC.; *U.S. Private*, pg. 2038
IMC LTD—See The Middleby Corporation; *U.S. Public*, pg. 2114
IMI CORNELIUS HELLAS S.A.—See Berkshire Hathaway Inc.; *U.S. Public*, pg. 309
IMPERIAL MACHINE COMPANY LIMITED—See The Middleby Corporation; *U.S. Public*, pg. 2115
INGREDION VIETNAM COMPANY LIMITED—See Ingredion Incorporated; *U.S. Public*, pg. 1123
JBT ALCO-FOOD-MACHINES GMBH—See John Bean Technologies Corporation; *U.S. Public*, pg. 1191
JBT FOODTECH MADERA—See John Bean Technologies Corporation; *U.S. Public*, pg. 1191
JBT FOODTECH REDMOND—See John Bean Technologies Corporation; *U.S. Public*, pg. 1191
JBT FOODTECH SANDUSKY—See John Bean Technologies Corporation; *U.S. Public*, pg. 1191
JBT WOLF-TEC—See John Bean Technologies Corporation; *U.S. Public*, pg. 1191
JEONG POONG CO., LTD.—See Daesang Holdings Co., Ltd.; *Int'l*, pg. 1909
JOHN BEAN TECHNOLOGIES AUSTRALIA LTD.—See John Bean Technologies Corporation; *U.S. Public*, pg. 1191
JOHN BEAN TECHNOLOGIES CORPORATION; *U.S. Public*, pg. 1191
JOHN BEAN TECHNOLOGIES GMBH—See John Bean Technologies Corporation; *U.S. Public*, pg. 1191
JOHN BEAN TECHNOLOGIES IBERICA S.L.—See John Bean Technologies Corporation; *U.S. Public*, pg. 1191
JOHN BEAN TECHNOLOGIES INDIA PRIVATE LIMITED—See John Bean Technologies Corporation; *U.S. Public*, pg. 1191
JOHN BEAN TECHNOLOGIES K.K. CITRUS DIVISION—See John Bean Technologies Corporation; *U.S. Public*, pg. 1191
JOHN BEAN TECHNOLOGIES K.K.—See John Bean Technologies Corporation; *U.S. Public*, pg. 1191
JOHN BEAN TECHNOLOGIES N.V.—See John Bean Technologies Corporation; *U.S. Public*, pg. 1191
JOHN BEAN TECHNOLOGIES (SHANGHAI) CO., LTD.—See John Bean Technologies Corporation; *U.S. Public*, pg. 1191
JOHN BEAN TECHNOLOGIES SPAIN S.L.—See John Bean Technologies Corporation; *U.S. Public*, pg. 1192
JOHN BEAN TECHNOLOGIES S.P.A.—See John Bean Technologies Corporation; *U.S. Public*, pg. 1192
JOHS. LASSEN FJELLEBROEN A/S—See The Middleby Corporation; *U.S. Public*, pg. 2114
JOSPER, S.A.—See The Middleby Corporation; *U.S. Public*, pg. 2114
KEY TECHNOLOGY AUSTRALIA PTY. LTD.—See Warburg Pincus LLC; *U.S. Private*, pg. 4438
KEY TECHNOLOGY B.V.—See Warburg Pincus LLC; *U.S. Private*, pg. 4438

N.A.I.C.S. INDEX

333242 — SEMICONDUCTOR MACHI...

LAITRAM MACHINERY APS—See The Laitram LLC; *U.S. Private*, pg. 4067
LAITRAM MACHINERY INC.—See The Laitram LLC; *U.S. Private*, pg. 4067
LANCER CORPORATION—See Hoshizaki Corporation; *Int'l*, pg. 3484
LEVATI FOOD TECH S.R.L.—See ATS Corporation; *Int'l*, pg. 695
LINCAT LIMITED—See The Middleby Corporation; *U.S. Public*, pg. 2115
MACADAMS INTERNATIONAL (PTY) LTD.—See TRG Management LP; *U.S. Private*, pg. 4220
MADDOX METAL WORKS INC.; *U.S. Private*, pg. 2539
MAGNUSON CORPORATION—See Atlas Pacific Engineering Company, Inc.; *U.S. Private*, pg. 379
MARLEN INTERNATIONAL, INC.—See Warburg Pincus LLC; *U.S. Private*, pg. 4438
MARMON FOOD SERVICE EQUIPMENT—See Berkshire Hathaway Inc.; *U.S. Public*, pg. 303
MARSAL & SONS, INC.—See The Middleby Corporation; *U.S. Public*, pg. 2114
M-E-C COMPANY; *U.S. Private*, pg. 2526
MEYN AMERICA, LLC—See Berkshire Hathaway Inc.; *U.S. Public*, pg. 303
MEYN FOOD PROCESSING TECHNOLOGY B.V.—See Berkshire Hathaway Inc.; *U.S. Public*, pg. 303
MIDDLEBY AUSTRALIA PTY LTD—See The Middleby Corporation; *U.S. Public*, pg. 2114
MIDDLEBY CELFROST INNOVATIONS PVT LTD—See The Middleby Corporation; *U.S. Public*, pg. 2114
MIDDLEBY CHINA CORPORATION—See The Middleby Corporation; *U.S. Public*, pg. 2114
THE MIDDLEBY CORPORATION; *U.S. Public*, pg. 2113
MIDDLEBY COZZINI BRASIL EQUIPAMENTOS, LTDA—See The Middleby Corporation; *U.S. Public*, pg. 2114
MIDDLEBY ESPANA SLU—See The Middleby Corporation; *U.S. Public*, pg. 2114
MIDDLEBY KOREA CORPORATION—See The Middleby Corporation; *U.S. Public*, pg. 2114
MIDDLEBY MARSHALL, INC.—See The Middleby Corporation; *U.S. Public*, pg. 2114
MIDDLEBY MEXICO SA DE CV—See The Middleby Corporation; *U.S. Public*, pg. 2114
MIDDLEBY PHILIPPINES CORPORATION—See The Middleby Corporation; *U.S. Public*, pg. 2114
MIDDLEBY UK LTD—See The Middleby Corporation; *U.S. Public*, pg. 2114
THE MIDDLEBY WORLDWIDE EUROPE—See The Middleby Corporation; *U.S. Public*, pg. 2115
MP EQUIPMENT, LLC—See The Middleby Corporation; *U.S. Public*, pg. 2114
NATIONAL EQUIPMENT CORP.; *U.S. Private*, pg. 2853
NEWTON FOOD EQUIPMENT CO. LTD.—See Ali Holding S.r.l; *Int'l*, pg. 323
NIGHTFOOD, INC.—See NightFood Holdings, Inc.; *U.S. Public*, pg. 1528
NORSE DAIRY SYSTEMS LLC—See George Weston Limited; *Int'l*, pg. 2939
NORTHLAND ALUMINUM PRODUCTS INC. - NORDIC WARE DIVISION—See Northland Aluminum Products Inc.; *U.S. Private*, pg. 2955
NURISH.ME, INC.; *U.S. Public*, pg. 1555
NUTRINE CONFECTIONERY COMPANY PRIVATE LIMITED—See The Hershey Co.; *U.S. Public*, pg. 2089
NU-VU FOODSERVICE SYSTEMS—See The Middleby Corporation; *U.S. Public*, pg. 2115
OSA MACHINERY CO., LTD.—See General Packer Co., Ltd.; *Int'l*, pg. 2919
OY ECOLAB AB—See Ecolab Inc.; *U.S. Public*, pg. 716
OY SELECTA AB—See Allianz SE; *Int'l*, pg. 355
PACIFIC PACKAGING MACHINERY, INC.—See Leonard Green & Partners, L.P.; *U.S. Private*, pg. 2428
PAVAILLER S.A.S.—See Ali Holding S.r.l; *Int'l*, pg. 322
PAVAN S.P.A.—See GEA Group Aktiengesellschaft; *Int'l*, pg. 2903
PEERLESS FOOD EQUIPMENT LLC—See Hillenbrand, Inc.; *U.S. Public*, pg. 1037
THE PEERLESS GROUP—See Illinois Tool Works Inc.; *U.S. Public*, pg. 1111
PIPER PRODUCTS, INC.—See The Jordan Company, L.P.; *U.S. Private*, pg. 4060
PLANET PRODUCTS CORPORATION; *U.S. Private*, pg. 3196
PRIME EQUIPMENT GROUP, INC.—See John Bean Technologies Corporation; *U.S. Public*, pg. 1192
PROSEAL AMERICA, INC.—See John Bean Technologies Corporation; *U.S. Public*, pg. 1192
PROSEAL UK LIMITED—See John Bean Technologies Corporation; *U.S. Public*, pg. 1192
PROVISUR TECHNOLOGIES, INC.—See Henry Crown & Company; *U.S. Private*, pg. 1917
PT GEA WESTFALIA SEPARATOR INDONESIA—See GEA Group Aktiengesellschaft; *Int'l*, pg. 2901
PT WESTFALIA INDONESIA—See GEA Group Aktiengesellschaft; *Int'l*, pg. 2903
RAYTEC VISION S.P.A.—See ATS Corporation; *Int'l*, pg. 695
READING PRETZEL MACHINERY CORPORATION—See Markel Group Inc.; *U.S. Public*, pg. 1369
ROLEC PROZESS - UND BRAUTECHNIK GMBH—See ATS Corporation; *Int'l*, pg. 695
ROSENQVISTS FOOD TECHNOLOGIES—See Warburg Pincus LLC; *U.S. Private*, pg. 4438
ROSS INDUSTRIES INC.; *U.S. Private*, pg. 3485
SANI-MATIC, INC.; *U.S. Private*, pg. 3546
SANISERV—See The Affinis Group; *U.S. Private*, pg. 3983
SCANICO A/S—See The Middleby Corporation; *U.S. Public*, pg. 2115
SCHENCK PROCESS FCP EQUIPAMENTOS INDUSTRIAS LTDA.—See Hillenbrand, Inc.; *U.S. Public*, pg. 1037
SCHENCK PROCESS (THAILAND) LTD.—See Hillenbrand, Inc.; *U.S. Public*, pg. 1037
SELECTA AS—See Allianz SE; *Int'l*, pg. 355
SELECTA EESTI OSAUHING—See Allianz SE; *Int'l*, pg. 355
SENCOTEL S.L.—See Ali Holding S.r.l; *Int'l*, pg. 321
SHARPAK BRIDGWATER LIMITED—See Groupe Guillin SA; *Int'l*, pg. 3104
SHARPAK YATE LTD.—See Groupe Guillin SA; *Int'l*, pg. 3104
SHRENO LTD - FACTORY UNIT-1—See Alembic Limited; *Int'l*, pg. 306
SHRENO LTD - FACTORY UNIT-2—See Alembic Limited; *Int'l*, pg. 306
SOCAMEL DEUTSCHLAND GMBH—See Groupe Guillin SA; *Int'l*, pg. 3104
SOCAMEL ESPANA SL—See Groupe Guillin SA; *Int'l*, pg. 3104
SOCAMEL TECHNOLOGIES—See Groupe Guillin SA; *Int'l*, pg. 3104
SOLBERN LLC—See Markel Group Inc.; *U.S. Public*, pg. 1369
SOVOS BRANDS, INC.—See Campbell Soup Company; *U.S. Public*, pg. 427
SPX FLOW TECHNOLOGY COPENHAGEN A/S—See Lone Star Funds; *U.S. Private*, pg. 2486
STAINLESS SYSTEMS INC.; *U.S. Private*, pg. 3776
STANDEX COOKING SOLUTIONS GROUP—See Standex International; *U.S. Public*, pg. 1930
STANDEX FOOD SERVICE EQUIPMENT GROUP—See Standex International; *U.S. Public*, pg. 1930
STANDEX INTERNATIONAL CORPORATION; *U.S. Public*, pg. 1929
STAR MANUFACTURING INTERNATIONAL, INC.—See The Middleby Corporation; *U.S. Public*, pg. 2115
STEPHAN MACHINERY GMBH—See Capvis AG; *Int'l*, pg. 1318
STEWART SYSTEMS BAKING, LLC—See The Middleby Corporation; *U.S. Public*, pg. 2115
STOCK AMERICA, LLC—See Leonard Green & Partners, L.P.; *U.S. Private*, pg. 2428
STORK FOOD & DAIRY SYSTEMS B.V.—See John Bean Technologies Corporation; *U.S. Public*, pg. 1192
SVEBA-DAHLEN BALTIC OU—See The Middleby Corporation; *U.S. Public*, pg. 2115
SVEBA-DAHLEN ESPANA—See The Middleby Corporation; *U.S. Public*, pg. 2115
SVEBA-DAHLEN GROUP AB—See The Middleby Corporation; *U.S. Public*, pg. 2115
TAYLOR COMPANY—See The Middleby Corporation; *U.S. Public*, pg. 2115
T&C ITALIA S.R.L.—See Carlsberg A/S; *Int'l*, pg. 1341
TECHNO-AID CO., LTD.—See Aohata Corporation; *Int'l*, pg. 487
TECNO-STAR DUE S.R.L.—See Cremonini S.p.A.; *Int'l*, pg. 1838
THOMSEN GROUP LLC; *U.S. Private*, pg. 4162
TIPPER TIE, INC.—See John Bean Technologies Corporation; *U.S. Public*, pg. 1192
TONI TRADING SRL—See Bog'Art S.R.L.; *Int'l*, pg. 1100
TRAITOMIC A/S—See Carlsberg A/S; *Int'l*, pg. 1341
TROMP GROUP B.V.—See Markel Group Inc.; *U.S. Public*, pg. 1369
TURBOCHEF INTERNATIONAL—See The Middleby Corporation; *U.S. Public*, pg. 2115
TURBOCHEF TECHNOLOGIES EUROPE, LTD—See The Middleby Corporation; *U.S. Public*, pg. 2115
UAB SELECTA—See Allianz SE; *Int'l*, pg. 356
UNIFIED BRANDS INC.—See Electrolux Professional AB; *Int'l*, pg. 2353
UNIVEX CORPORATION; *U.S. Private*, pg. 4310
URSCHEL ASIA PACIFIC PTE. LTD.—See Urschel Laboratories Incorporated; *U.S. Private*, pg. 4316
URSCHEL CHINA LTD.—See Urschel Laboratories Incorporated; *U.S. Private*, pg. 4316
URSCHEL HELLAS—See Urschel Laboratories Incorporated; *U.S. Private*, pg. 4316
URSCHEL INDIA TRADING PRIVATE LIMITED—See Urschel Laboratories Incorporated; *U.S. Private*, pg. 4316
URSCHEL INTERNATIONAL LTD.—See Urschel Laboratories Incorporated; *U.S. Private*, pg. 4316
URSCHEL INTERNATIONAL LTD.—See Urschel Laboratories Incorporated; *U.S. Private*, pg. 4316
URSCHEL INTERNATIONAL LTD.—See Urschel Laboratories Incorporated; *U.S. Private*, pg. 4316
URSCHEL INTERNATIONAL LTD.—See Urschel Laboratories Incorporated; *U.S. Private*, pg. 4316
URSCHEL INTERNATIONAL LTD.—See Urschel Laboratories Incorporated; *U.S. Private*, pg. 4316
URSCHEL INTERNATIONAL LTD.—See Urschel Laboratories Incorporated; *U.S. Private*, pg. 4316
URSCHEL INTERNATIONAL POLSKA SP. Z O.O.—See Urschel Laboratories Incorporated; *U.S. Private*, pg. 4316
URSCHEL JAPAN—See Urschel Laboratories Incorporated; *U.S. Private*, pg. 4316
URSCHEL LABORATORIES INCORPORATED; *U.S. Private*, pg. 4316
URSCHEL (THAILAND) LTD.—See Urschel Laboratories Incorporated; *U.S. Private*, pg. 4316
VARIMIXER A/S—See The Middleby Corporation; *U.S. Public*, pg. 2115
VE.MA.C. SRL—See The Middleby Corporation; *U.S. Public*, pg. 2115
VENTILEX B.V.—See Electricite de France S.A.; *Int'l*, pg. 2352
VIKING COOKING SCHOOLS, LLC—See The Middleby Corporation; *U.S. Public*, pg. 2115
VOLLRATH SHANGHAI TRADING LIMITED—See The Vollrath Company LLC; *U.S. Private*, pg. 4132
W.D. LARAMORE MANUFACTURING INC.—See Hillenbrand, Inc.; *U.S. Public*, pg. 1037
WEILER & COMPANY, INC.—See Henry Crown & Company; *U.S. Private*, pg. 1917
WELBILT DEUTSCHLAND GMBH—See Ali Holding S.r.l; *Int'l*, pg. 323
WELBILT (HALESOWEN) LIMITED—See Ali Holding S.r.l; *Int'l*, pg. 323
WELBILT (SHANGHAI) FOODSERVICE CO., LTD.—See Ali Holding S.r.l; *Int'l*, pg. 323
WELBILT UK LIMITED—See Ali Holding S.r.l; *Int'l*, pg. 323
WESTFALIASURGE GMBH—See GEA Group Aktiengesellschaft; *Int'l*, pg. 2903
WESTON BRANDS, LLC—See Hamilton Beach Brands Holding Company; *U.S. Public*, pg. 981
WIKI PRATAMA SDN. BHD.—See Engtex Group Berhad; *Int'l*, pg. 2436
WIN-HOLT EQUIPMENT GROUP; *U.S. Private*, pg. 4532
WUNDER-BAR DISPENSING UK LTD.—See The Middleby Corporation; *U.S. Public*, pg. 2115
ZIAG PLANT ENGINEERING GMBH—See GEA Group Aktiengesellschaft; *Int'l*, pg. 2898

333242 — SEMICONDUCTOR MACHINERY MANUFACTURING

ACM RESEARCH, INC.; *U.S. Public*, pg. 35
ADVANTEST CANADA, INC.—See Advantest Corporation; *Int'l*, pg. 165
ADVANTEST FRANCE SAS—See Advantest Corporation; *Int'l*, pg. 166
ADVANTEST ISRAEL LTD.—See Advantest Corporation; *Int'l*, pg. 166
ADVANTEST ITALIA S.R.L.—See Advantest Corporation; *Int'l*, pg. 166
ADVANTEST (M) SDN. BHD.—See Advantest Corporation; *Int'l*, pg. 165
ADVANTEST SALES & SUPPORT (M) SDN. BHD.—See Advantest Corporation; *Int'l*, pg. 166
ADVANTEST TECHNOLOGY (SHANGHAI) CO., LTD.—See Advantest Corporation; *Int'l*, pg. 166
ADVANTEST TEST SOLUTIONS, INC.—See Advantest Corporation; *Int'l*, pg. 166
ADVANTEST VIETNAM CO., LTD.—See Advantest Corporation; *Int'l*, pg. 166
AEHR TEST SYSTEMS; *U.S. Public*, pg. 52
AEM (SUZHOU) CO., LTD.—See AEM Holdings Ltd.; *Int'l*, pg. 175
AIXTRON CHINA LTD.—See Aixtron SE; *Int'l*, pg. 255
AIXTRON KK—See Aixtron SE; *Int'l*, pg. 255
AIXTRON KOREA CO. LTD.—See Aixtron SE; *Int'l*, pg. 255
AIXTRON LTD.—See Aixtron SE; *Int'l*, pg. 255
AIXTRON TAIWAN CO. LTD.—See Aixtron SE; *Int'l*, pg. 255
AKROS SILICON, INC.—See Kinetic Technologies, Inc.; *U.S. Private*, pg. 2308
ALCOR MICRO CORPORATION LTD.; *Int'l*, pg. 303
ALGOLTEK TECHNOLOGY CO., LTD.; *Int'l*, pg. 318
ALLEGRO MICROSYSTEMS PHILIPPINES REALTY INC.—See Allegro MicroSystems, Inc.; *U.S. Public*, pg. 78
ALPHA 3 MANUFACTURING LIMITED—See Avnet, Inc.; *U.S. Public*, pg. 250
AMAZING MICROELECTRONIC CORP.; *Int'l*, pg. 413
AMKOR TECHNOLOGY, INC.; *U.S. Public*, pg. 124
AMTECH SYSTEMS, INC.; *U.S. Public*, pg. 133
APEVA SE—See Aixtron SE; *Int'l*, pg. 255
APPLIED MATERIALS CORP.—See Applied Materials, Inc.; *U.S. Public*, pg. 172
APPLIED MATERIALS GMBH & CO., KG—See Applied Materials, Inc.; *U.S. Public*, pg. 172
APPLIED MATERIALS, INC.; *U.S. Public*, pg. 172
APPLIED MATERIALS INDIA PRIVATE LIMITED—See Applied Materials, Inc.; *U.S. Public*, pg. 172
APPLIED MATERIALS KOREA, LTD.—See Applied Materi-

als, Inc.; *U.S. Public*, pg. 172
APPLIED MATERIALS SINGAPORE TECHNOLOGY PTE. LTD.—See Applied Materials, Inc.; *U.S. Public*, pg. 172
APPLIED MATERIALS SPV2, INC.—See Applied Materials, Inc.; *U.S. Public*, pg. 172
APS HOLDINGS CORPORATION; *Int'l*, pg. 523
APS KOREA, INC.—See Hancom, Inc.; *Int'l*, pg. 3242
ASIX ELECTRONICS CO. LTD.; *Int'l*, pg. 621
ASM ASSEMBLY AUTOMATION LTD.—See ASM INTERNATIONAL N.V.; *Int'l*, pg. 626
ASM GENITECH KOREA LTD.—See ASM INTERNATIONAL N.V.; *Int'l*, pg. 626
ASM INTERNATIONAL N.V.; *Int'l*, pg. 626
ASML BELGIUM BVBA—See ASML Holding N.V.; *Int'l*, pg. 627
ASML EQUIPMENT MALAYSIA SDN. BHD.—See ASML Holding N.V.; *Int'l*, pg. 627
ASML FRANCE S.A.R.L.—See ASML Holding N.V.; *Int'l*, pg. 627
ASML GERMANY GMBH—See ASML Holding N.V.; *Int'l*, pg. 627
ASML HONG KONG LTD.—See ASML Holding N.V.; *Int'l*, pg. 627
ASML JAPAN CO. LTD.—See ASML Holding N.V.; *Int'l*, pg. 627
ASML NETHERLANDS B.V.—See ASML Holding N.V.; *Int'l*, pg. 627
ASML PARTICIPATION US INC.—See ASML Holding N.V.; *Int'l*, pg. 627
ASML SINGAPORE PTE. LTD.—See ASML Holding N.V.; *Int'l*, pg. 627
ASML TAIWAN LTD.—See ASML Holding N.V.; *Int'l*, pg. 627
ASM PACIFIC ASSEMBLY PRODUCTS, INC.—See ASM INTERNATIONAL N.V.; *Int'l*, pg. 626
ASM TECHNOLOGY (HUIZHOU) CO. LIMITED—See ASM INTERNATIONAL N.V.; *Int'l*, pg. 626
AXCELIS TECHNOLOGIES GMBH—See Axcelis Technologies, Inc.; *U.S. Public*, pg. 255
AXCELIS TECHNOLOGIES, INC.; *U.S. Public*, pg. 255
AXCELIS TECHNOLOGIES LTD.—See Axcelis Technologies, Inc.; *U.S. Public*, pg. 255
AXCELIS TECHNOLOGIES LTD.—See Axcelis Technologies, Inc.; *U.S. Public*, pg. 255
AXCELIS TECHNOLOGIES PTE. LTD.—See Axcelis Technologies, Inc.; *U.S. Public*, pg. 255
AXCELIS TECHNOLOGIES, S.A.R.L.—See Axcelis Technologies, Inc.; *U.S. Public*, pg. 255
AXCELIS TECHNOLOGIES, S.R.L.—See Axcelis Technologies, Inc.; *U.S. Public*, pg. 255
BEAM GLOBAL; *U.S. Public*, pg. 287
BE SEMICONDUCTOR INDUSTRIES N.V.; *Int'l*, pg. 931
BESI APAC SDN. BHD.—See BE Semiconductor Industries N.V.; *Int'l*, pg. 931
BESI AUSTRIA GMBH—See BE Semiconductor Industries N.V.; *Int'l*, pg. 931
BESI AUSTRIA GMBH—See BE Semiconductor Industries N.V.; *Int'l*, pg. 931
BESI LESHAN CO., LTD.—See BE Semiconductor Industries N.V.; *Int'l*, pg. 931
BESI NORTH AMERICA, INC.—See BE Semiconductor Industries N.V.; *Int'l*, pg. 931
BESI PHILIPPINES, INC.—See BE Semiconductor Industries N.V.; *Int'l*, pg. 931
BESI (SHANGHAI) TRADING CO., LTD.—See BE Semiconductor Industries N.V.; *Int'l*, pg. 931
BESI SINGAPORE PTE. LTD.—See BE Semiconductor Industries N.V.; *Int'l*, pg. 931
BESI (THAI) S&S LTD.—See BE Semiconductor Industries N.V.; *Int'l*, pg. 931
BOSTON SEMI EQUIPMENT LLC; *U.S. Private*, pg. 622
BP MICROSYSTEMS, L.P.; *U.S. Private*, pg. 629
BRION TECHNOLOGIES—See ASML Holding N.V.; *Int'l*, pg. 627
BRION TECHNOLOGIES KK—See ASML Holding N.V.; *Int'l*, pg. 627
BRION TECHNOLOGIES (SHENZHEN) CO., LTD.—See ASML Holding N.V.; *Int'l*, pg. 627
BROOKS CCS JAPAN KK—See Azenta, Inc.; *U.S. Public*, pg. 257
BROOKS CCS RS AG—See Azenta, Inc.; *U.S. Public*, pg. 257
BRUCE TECHNOLOGIES, INC—See Amtech Systems, Inc.; *U.S. Public*, pg. 133
BSL UNIFY PTE. LTD.—See BSL Corporation Berhad; *Int'l*, pg. 1202
CAMMSYS CO., LTD; *Int'l*, pg. 1273
C C P CONTACT PROBES CO., LTD.; *Int'l*, pg. 1237
CENTROTHERM SITEC GMBH—See centrotherm photovoltaics AG; *Int'l*, pg. 1415
C&G HI TECH CO., LTD.; *Int'l*, pg. 1238
CHARMZONE GLOBAL CO., LTD.; *Int'l*, pg. 1451
CONCEPTRONIC—See CVD Equipment Corporation; *U.S. Public*, pg. 613
COVENTOR KOREA LIMITED—See Lam Research Corporation; *U.S. Public*, pg. 1289
COVENTOR SARL—See Lam Research Corporation; *U.S. Public*, pg. 1289

CRITERIA LABS, INC.—See Dover Corporation; *U.S. Public*, pg. 678
CSK INC.—See Atlas Copco AB; *Int'l*, pg. 681
CYMER B.V.—See ASML Holding N.V.; *Int'l*, pg. 627
CYMER, INC.—See ASML Holding N.V.; *Int'l*, pg. 627
CYMER JAPAN, INC.—See ASML Holding N.V.; *Int'l*, pg. 627
CYMER KOREA, INC.—See ASML Holding N.V.; *Int'l*, pg. 628
CYMER SEMICONDUCTOR EQUIPMENT (SHANGHAI) CO., LTD.—See ASML Holding N.V.; *Int'l*, pg. 628
CYMER SINGAPORE PTE. LTD.—See ASML Holding N.V.; *Int'l*, pg. 628
CYMER SOUTHEAST ASIA LTD.—See ASML Holding N.V.; *Int'l*, pg. 628
DAITRON TECHNOLOGY CO., LTD.—See Daitron Co., Ltd.; *Int'l*, pg. 1944
DECAWAVE (SHENZHEN) LIMITED—See Qorvo, Inc.; *U.S. Public*, pg. 1743
EAGLE TEST SYSTEMS, INC.—See Teradyne, Inc.; *U.S. Public*, pg. 2018
EEMS ITALIA S.P.A; *Int'l*, pg. 2317
ENTEGRIS JAPAN CO. LTD.—See Entegris, Inc.; *U.S. Public*, pg. 777
ENTEGRIS-JETALON SOLUTIONS, INC.—See Entegris, Inc.; *U.S. Public*, pg. 777
ENTREPIX ASIA PTD., LTD.—See Amtech Systems, Inc.; *U.S. Public*, pg. 133
ENVERV INC.—See Semtech Corporation; *U.S. Public*, pg. 1864
EPISIL PRECISION INC.; *Int'l*, pg. 2463
ESEC AG—See BE Semiconductor Industries N.V.; *Int'l*, pg. 931
EUGENE TECHNOLOGY CO., LTD.; *Int'l*, pg. 2526
EXPERT SEMICONDUCTOR TECH; *U.S. Private*, pg. 1450
FAITHTEK LIMITED—See GigaLane Co., Ltd.; *Int'l*, pg. 2971
FASFORD TECHNOLOGY CO., LTD.—See Fuji Corporation; *Int'l*, pg. 2809
FDK ENGINEERING CO., LTD.—See Fujitsu Limited; *Int'l*, pg. 2832
FERROTEC MATERIAL TECHNOLOGIES CORPORATION—See Ferrotec Holdings Corporation; *Int'l*, pg. 2643
FERROTEC POWER SEMICONDUCTOR (JAPAN) CORP.—See Ferrotec Holdings Corporation; *Int'l*, pg. 2643
FORMOSA DAIKIN ADVANCED CHEMICALS CO., LTD. - KAOHSIUNG REN-WU PLANT—See Formosa Plastics Corporation; *Int'l*, pg. 2735
FORMOSA DAIKIN ADVANCED CHEMICALS CO., LTD.—See Formosa Plastics Corporation; *Int'l*, pg. 2735
GALLANT MICRO MACHINING CO., LTD.; *Int'l*, pg. 2873
GALLANT PRECISION MACHINING CO., LTD.; *Int'l*, pg. 2873
GEMVAX & KAEL CO., LTD.; *Int'l*, pg. 2916
GIGAVIS CO., LTD.; *Int'l*, pg. 2972
GLOBAL STANDARD TECHNOLOGY CO., LTD.; *Int'l*, pg. 3001
GREMTEK SAS—See Diploma PLC; *Int'l*, pg. 2128
GST AMERICA INC.—See Global Standard Technology Co., Ltd.; *Int'l*, pg. 3001
GST TAIWAN LTD.—See Global Standard Technology Co., Ltd.; *Int'l*, pg. 3001
HANA WLS INC.—See Hana Micron Inc.; *Int'l*, pg. 3241
HERAEUS QUARZGLAS GMBH & CO. KG—See Heraeus Holding GmbH; *Int'l*, pg. 3358
HERMES MICROVISION, INC.—See ASML Holding N.V.; *Int'l*, pg. 628
HIGH TEMPERATURE SUPERCONDUCTORS, INC.; *U.S. Private*, pg. 2966
HITACHI HIGH-TECHNOLOGIES CORPORATION—See Hitachi, Ltd.; *Int'l*, pg. 3418
HONG LEONG INDUSTRIES BERHAD—See Hong Leong Investment Holdings Pte. Ltd.; *Int'l*, pg. 3468
HY-LOK EUROPE B.V.—See Hy-Lok Corporation; *Int'l*, pg. 3543
HY-LOK OCEANIA PTY. LTD.—See Hy-Lok Corporation; *Int'l*, pg. 3544
HY-LOK USA—See Hy-Lok Corporation; *Int'l*, pg. 3544
II-VI GMBH—See Coherent Corp.; *U.S. Public*, pg. 528
INSILICA, INC.; *U.S. Private*, pg. 2091
INTEGRATED DYNAMICS ENGINEERING INC.—See Aalberts N.V.; *Int'l*, pg. 34
INTERNATIONAL TEST SOLUTIONS, LLC—See Entegris, Inc.; *U.S. Public*, pg. 776
INTERPLEX ENGINEERED PRODUCTS, INC.—See Blackstone Inc.; *U.S. Public*, pg. 355
INTEST PTE. LTD.—See inTEST Corporation; *U.S. Public*, pg. 1159
INTEST THERMAL SOLUTIONS GMBH—See inTEST Corporation; *U.S. Public*, pg. 1159
INVENIOS, INC.; *U.S. Private*, pg. 2131
ISE LABS,CHINA, INC.—See ASE Technology Holding Co., Ltd.; *Int'l*, pg. 605
JORDAN VALLEY SEMICONDUCTOR CO LTD—See Bruker Corporation; *U.S. Public*, pg. 406
JORDAN VALLEY SEMICONDUCTORS, INC.—See Bruker Corporation; *U.S. Public*, pg. 406
JORDAN VALLEY SEMICONDUCTORS KOREA LTD.—See Bruker Corporation; *U.S. Public*, pg. 406
JORDAN VALLEY SEMICONDUCTORS, LTD.—See Bruker Corporation; *U.S. Public*, pg. 406
K-MAC TECHNOLOGY CORP.—See HB Solution Co., Ltd.; *Int'l*, pg. 3295
KOKUSAI ELECTRIC SEMICONDUCTOR SERVICE INC.—See KKR & Co. Inc.; *U.S. Public*, pg. 1258
LAM RESEARCH AG—See Lam Research Corporation; *U.S. Public*, pg. 1289
LAM RESEARCH CORPORATION; *U.S. Public*, pg. 1289
LAM RESEARCH CORPORATION—See Lam Research Corporation; *U.S. Public*, pg. 1289
LAM RESEARCH CORPORATION—See Lam Research Corporation; *U.S. Public*, pg. 1289
LAM RESEARCH (INDIA) PRIVATE LTD.—See Lam Research Corporation; *U.S. Public*, pg. 1289
LAM RESEARCH SERVICES LTD.—See Lam Research Corporation; *U.S. Public*, pg. 1290
LTX-CREDENCE ARMENIA L.L.C.—See Cohu, Inc.; *U.S. Public*, pg. 530
LTX-CREDENCE SINGAPORE PTE LTD.—See Cohu, Inc.; *U.S. Public*, pg. 530
MALAYSIAN PACIFIC INDUSTRIES BERHAD—See Hong Leong Investment Holdings Pte. Ltd.; *Int'l*, pg. 3468
MATERION ADVANCED MATERIALS TECHNOLOGIES AND SERVICES INC.—See Materion Corporation; *U.S. Public*, pg. 1395
MATTSON TECHNOLOGY, INC.—See Beijing E-Town International Investment & Development Co., Ltd.; *Int'l*, pg. 949
MATTSON TECHNOLOGY SINGAPORE PTE. LTD.—See Beijing E-Town International Investment & Development Co., Ltd.; *Int'l*, pg. 949
MATTSON TRADING (SHANGHAI) CO., LTD.—See Beijing E-Town International Investment & Development Co., Ltd.; *Int'l*, pg. 949
MICRON SEMICONDUCTOR PRODUCTS, INC.—See Micron Technology, Inc.; *U.S. Public*, pg. 1438
MICROSEMI SEMICONDUCTOR CORPORATION A/S—See Microchip Technology Incorporated; *U.S. Public*, pg. 1436
MICROSEMI SEMICONDUCTOR GMBH & CO. KG—See Microchip Technology Incorporated; *U.S. Public*, pg. 1436
MOLECULAR IMPRINTS, INC.—See Canon Inc.; *Int'l*, pg. 1297
NANOMETRICS CHINA COMPANY LTD.—See Onto Innovation Inc.; *U.S. Public*, pg. 1605
NIHON PALL MANUFACTURING LIMITED—See Danaher Corporation; *U.S. Public*, pg. 628
NOVA STAR INNOVATIONS, INC.; *U.S. Private*, pg. 2966
NOVELLUS SYSTEMS SEMICONDUCTOR EQUIPMENT SHANGHAI CO. LTD.—See Lam Research Corporation; *U.S. Public*, pg. 1290
NUCENT CO. LTD.—See EG Systems LLC; *U.S. Private*, pg. 1344
OEM GROUP EAST—See OEM Group, Inc.; *U.S. Private*, pg. 2997
OEM GROUP, INC.; *U.S. Private*, pg. 2997
OS NANO TECHNOLOGY CO., LTD.—See Bain Capital, LP; *U.S. Private*, pg. 434
PENSKE AUSTRALIA PTY. LTD.—See Penske Automotive Group, Inc.; *U.S. Public*, pg. 1665
PENSKE NEW ZEALAND—See Penske Automotive Group, Inc.; *U.S. Public*, pg. 1665
PHOTRONICS IDAHO, INC.—See Photronics, Inc.; *U.S. Public*, pg. 1689
PRINTEC CO., LTD.—See Air Water Inc.; *Int'l*, pg. 240
PRODUCTOS ESPECIALIZADOS DE MEXICO S. DE R.L. DE C.V—See DuPont de Nemours, Inc.; *U.S. Public*, pg. 694
PROTO LABS TOOLING GMBH—See Proto Labs, Inc.; *U.S. Public*, pg. 1730
QUANTUMTEK INNOVATIVES CORPORATION—See GigaLane Co., Ltd.; *Int'l*, pg. 2971
R2D AUTOMATION SAS—See Amtech Systems, Inc.; *U.S. Public*, pg. 134
RASCO GMBH—See Cohu, Inc.; *U.S. Public*, pg. 529
REALIZE CO., LTD.—See Future Innovation Group, Inc.; *Int'l*, pg. 2856
RITE TRACK EQUIPMENT SERVICES, LLC—See OEM Group, Inc.; *U.S. Private*, pg. 2997
RUBICON TECHNOLOGY, INC.; *U.S. Public*, pg. 1825
RUCKER & KOLLS INC—See Eico Inc.; *U.S. Private*, pg. 1346
SEMICONDUCTOR PROCESS EQUIPMENT CORPORATION; *U.S. Private*, pg. 3604
SHANGHAI CHANG WAH ELECTROMATERIALS INC.—See Chang Wah Technology Co., Ltd.; *Int'l*, pg. 1441
SH ASIA PACIFIC PTE. LTD.—See Chang Wah Technology Co., Ltd.; *Int'l*, pg. 1441
SH ELECTRONICS CHENGDU CO., LTD.—See Chang Wah Technology Co., Ltd.; *Int'l*, pg. 1441
SH ELECTRONICS SUZHOU CO., LTD.—See Chang Wah Technology Co., Ltd.; *Int'l*, pg. 1441
SHENZHEN EMBEST TECHNOLOGY CO., LTD.—See Avnet, Inc.; *U.S. Public*, pg. 254

SH PRECISION CHENGDU CO., LTD.—See Chang Wah Technology Co., Ltd.; *Int'l*, pg. 1441
SIGMAMELTEC LTD.—See Applied Materials, Inc.; *U.S. Public*, pg. 172
SNOWMAN MIDDLE EAST FZCO—See Fujian Snowman Co., Ltd.; *Int'l*, pg. 2819
SOGOTEC ENTERPRISE CO., LTD.—See Anderson Industrial Corporation; *Int'l*, pg. 450
SOLAR SICILY S.R.L.—See A2A S.p.A.; *Int'l*, pg. 29
SOLID STATE EQUIPMENT LLC; *U.S. Private*, pg. 3709
SPEEDLINE TECHNOLOGIES GMBH—See Illinois Tool Works Inc.; *U.S. Public*, pg. 1110
SPTS K.K.—See KLA Corporation; *U.S. Public*, pg. 1268
SPTS TECHNOLOGIES GMBH—See KLA Corporation; *U.S. Public*, pg. 1268
SPTS TECHNOLOGIES, INC.—See KLA Corporation; *U.S. Public*, pg. 1268
SPTS TECHNOLOGIES - KOREA—See KLA Corporation; *U.S. Public*, pg. 1268
SPTS TECHNOLOGIES LTD.—See KLA Corporation; *U.S. Public*, pg. 1268
SPTS TECHNOLOGIES - MALAYSIA—See KLA Corporation; *U.S. Public*, pg. 1268
SPTS TECHNOLOGIES PTE. LTD.—See KLA Corporation; *U.S. Public*, pg. 1268
SPTS TECHNOLOGIES (SHANGHAI) INC.—See KLA Corporation; *U.S. Public*, pg. 1268
SPTS TECHNOLOGIES - TAIWAN—See KLA Corporation; *U.S. Public*, pg. 1268
SURFACE MOUNT TECHNOLOGY CORPORATION; *U.S. Private*, pg. 3884
TACTRON ELEKTRONIK GMBH & CO. KG—See GigaLane Co., Ltd.; *Int'l*, pg. 2971
THERMONICS, INC.—See inTEST Corporation; *U.S. Public*, pg. 1159
ULTRA CLEAN HOLDINGS, INC.; *U.S. Public*, pg. 2223
ULTRA FINISH TECHNOLOGY CO., LTD.—See Hitachi Zosen Corporation; *Int'l*, pg. 3412
ULTRATECH KABUSHIKI KAISHA—See Veeco Instruments Inc.; *U.S. Public*, pg. 2276
USI AMERICA INC.—See ASE Technology Holding Co., Ltd.; *Int'l*, pg. 605
VARIAN SEMICONDUCTOR EQUIPMENT ASSOCIATES, INC.—See Applied Materials, Inc.; *U.S. Public*, pg. 173
VEECO JAPAN—See Veeco Instruments Inc.; *U.S. Public*, pg. 2277
VEECO KOREA LLC—See Veeco Instruments Inc.; *U.S. Public*, pg. 2277
VEECO SINGAPORE—See Veeco Instruments Inc.; *U.S. Public*, pg. 2277
VISHAY ELCTRONIC GMBH—See Vishay Intertechnology, Inc.; *U.S. Public*, pg. 2303
WOKEN TECHNOLOGY INC.—See GigaLane Co., Ltd.; *Int'l*, pg. 2971
XCERRA CORPORATION—See Cohu, Inc.; *U.S. Public*, pg. 530
ZETA INSTRUMENTS (SHANGHAI) CO., LTD.—See KLA Corporation; *U.S. Public*, pg. 1269

333243 — SAWMILL, WOODWORKING, AND PAPER MACHINERY MANUFACTURING

ALBANY INTERNATIONAL AB—See Albany International Corp.; *U.S. Public*, pg. 72
AMADA DO BRASIL LTDA.—See Amada Holdings Co., Ltd.; *Int'l*, pg. 404
AMADA LIANYUNGANG MACHINERY CO., LTD.—See Amada Holdings Co., Ltd.; *Int'l*, pg. 404
AMADA OCEANIA PTY. LTD.—See Amada Holdings Co., Ltd.; *Int'l*, pg. 403
AMERICAN PAPER CONVERTING LLC—See Ennis, Inc.; *U.S. Public*, pg. 768
ANDRITZ AB—See ANDRITZ AG; *Int'l*, pg. 452
ANDRITZ BRASIL LTDA.—See ANDRITZ AG; *Int'l*, pg. 452
ANDRITZ INGENIERIA S.A.—See ANDRITZ AG; *Int'l*, pg. 454
ANDRITZ K.K.—See ANDRITZ AG; *Int'l*, pg. 454
ANDRITZ PAPERCHINE—See ANDRITZ AG; *Int'l*, pg. 454
ANDRITZ PAPER MACHINERY LTD.—See ANDRITZ AG; *Int'l*, pg. 453
ANDRITZ PULP & PAPER—See ANDRITZ AG; *Int'l*, pg. 454
ANTHONY-ROSS COMPANY—See Clyde Blowers Capital IM LLP; *Int'l*, pg. 1665
ASC MACHINE TOOLS INC.; *U.S. Private*, pg. 345
ATLAS CONVERTING EQUIPMENT LIMITED; *Int'l*, pg. 676
BABCOCK POWER, INC.; *U.S. Private*, pg. 422
BAUER MASCHINEN GMBH - SCHROBENHAUSEN PLANT—See BAUER Aktiengesellschaft; *Int'l*, pg. 892
BAUMFOLDER CORPORATION—See Heidelberger Druckmaschinen AG; *Int'l*, pg. 3321
BEHRINGER ANLAGENBAU GMBH—See Behringer GmbH; *Int'l*, pg. 941
BEHRINGER EISELE GMBH—See Behringer GmbH; *Int'l*, pg. 941
BEHRINGER GMBH; *Int'l*, pg. 941
BENZ GMBH WERKZEUGSYSTEME—See Durr AG; *Int'l*, pg. 2232
BERNAL, LLC—See Auxo Investment Partners, LLC; *U.S. Private*, pg. 402
BMH TECHNOLOGY OY; *Int'l*, pg. 1076
BOBST ITALIA SPA—See Bobst Group S.A.; *Int'l*, pg. 1096
BOLTON EMERSON AMERICAS, LLC; *U.S. Private*, pg. 611
BONETTI CANADA INC.—See ANDRITZ AG; *Int'l*, pg. 455
BOWE SYSTEC AG; *Int'l*, pg. 1123
BRANDT KANTENTECHNIK GMBH—See Durr AG; *Int'l*, pg. 2232
CASCADES SONOCO, INC. - BIRMINGHAM—See Cascades Inc.; *Int'l*, pg. 1350
C. G. BRETTING MANUFACTURING CO., INC.; *U.S. Private*, pg. 705
THE CHALLENGE MACHINERY COMPANY; *U.S. Private*, pg. 4007
CHUNG HWA PULP CORP. - CHIUTANG MILL—See Chung Hwa Pulp Corp.; *Int'l*, pg. 1597
CHUNG HWA PULP CORP. - HUALIEN MILL—See Chung Hwa Pulp Corp.; *Int'l*, pg. 1597
CHUNG HWA PULP CORP. - TAITUNG MILL—See Chung Hwa Pulp Corp.; *Int'l*, pg. 1597
COMECART S.P.A—See Burgo Group S.p.A.; *Int'l*, pg. 1224
COMMIXT S.A.; *Int'l*, pg. 1719
CORLEY MANUFACTURING CO.; *U.S. Private*, pg. 1050
CREA S.R.L.—See Amada Holdings Co., Ltd.; *Int'l*, pg. 404
CURT G. JOA EUROPE GMBH—See Curt G. Joa, Inc.; *U.S. Private*, pg. 1126
CURT G. JOA, INC.; *U.S. Private*, pg. 1126
DELLE VEDOVE USA, INC.—See Cefla S.C.; *Int'l*, pg. 1389
DELTA PORTER-CABLE—See Stanley Black & Decker, Inc.; *U.S. Public*, pg. 1932
DIEHL WOODWORKING MACHINERY, INC.; *U.S. Private*, pg. 1219
DRVNA INDUSTRIJA SPACVA D.D; *Int'l*, pg. 2206
DUBUS INDUSTRIES; *Int'l*, pg. 2222
EDF EUROPE S.R.L.—See Guangdong Dongfang Science & Technology Co., Ltd.; *Int'l*, pg. 3153
ELSNER ENGINEERING WORKS INC.; *U.S. Private*, pg. 1377
ENBI GERMANY GMBH—See Platinum Equity, LLC; *U.S. Private*, pg. 3203
ENBI INDIANA, INC.—See Platinum Equity, LLC; *U.S. Private*, pg. 3203
ENBI ROCHESTER, INC.—See Platinum Equity, LLC; *U.S. Private*, pg. 3203
ENBI (ZHUHAI) INDUSTRIAL CO., LTD—See Platinum Equity, LLC; *U.S. Private*, pg. 3203
FRIZ KASCHIERTECHNIK GMBH—See Durr AG; *Int'l*, pg. 2232
GARDNER APOC—See Audax Group, Limited Partnership; *U.S. Private*, pg. 388
GL&V PULP & PAPER; *Int'l*, pg. 2986
GL&V USA INC. - HUDSON FALLS—See GL&V Pulp & Paper; *Int'l*, pg. 2987
GL&V USA INC. - LENOX—See GL&V Pulp & Paper; *Int'l*, pg. 2987
GL&V USA INC. - NASHUA—See GL&V Pulp & Paper; *Int'l*, pg. 2987
GRENZEBACH BSH GMBH—See Grenzebach Maschinenbau GmbH; *Int'l*, pg. 3081
GROUPE LEBEL INC.; *Int'l*, pg. 3106
GUANGZHOU KDT MACHINERY CO.,LTD; *Int'l*, pg. 3166
GUK-FALZMASCHINEN GRIESSER & KUNZMANN GMBH & CO. KG; *Int'l*, pg. 3177
HA MALAYSIA SDN. BHD.—See Durr AG; *Int'l*, pg. 2232
HMC CORPORATION—See HMC Corp.; *U.S. Private*, pg. 1955
HMC CORP.; *U.S. Private*, pg. 1954
H&M ROWELLS AB—See H&M Hennes & Mauritz AB; *Int'l*, pg. 3192
HOLLUND INDUSTRIAL MARINE, INC.; *U.S. Public*, pg. 1044
HOLM TRAVAROR AB; *Int'l*, pg. 3452
HOLZMA PLATTENAUFTEILTECHNIK GMBH—See Durr AG; *Int'l*, pg. 2232
HOLZMA PLATTENAUFTEILTECHNIK S.A.—See Durr AG; *Int'l*, pg. 2232
HOLZMA TECH GMBH—See Durr AG; *Int'l*, pg. 2232
HOMAG ASIA (PTE) LTD—See Durr AG; *Int'l*, pg. 2232
HOMAG ASIA (THAILAND) CO., LTD.—See Durr AG; *Int'l*, pg. 2233
HOMAG AUSTRALIA PTY LTD—See Durr AG; *Int'l*, pg. 2232
HOMAG CANADA INC—See Durr AG; *Int'l*, pg. 2232
HOMAG DANMARK A/S—See Durr AG; *Int'l*, pg. 2232
HOMAG ESOLUTION GMBH—See Durr AG; *Int'l*, pg. 2232
HOMAG FINANCE GMBH—See Durr AG; *Int'l*, pg. 2232
HOMAG GROUP AG—See Durr AG; *Int'l*, pg. 2232
HOMAG HOLZBEARBEITUNGSSYSTEME GMBH—See Durr AG; *Int'l*, pg. 2232
HOMAG INDIA PRIVATE LTD—See Durr AG; *Int'l*, pg. 2232
HOMAG ITALIA S.P.A—See Durr AG; *Int'l*, pg. 2232
HOMAG JAPAN CO. LTD—See Durr AG; *Int'l*, pg. 2232
HOMAG MACHINERY (SHANGHAI) CO., LTD.—See Durr AG; *Int'l*, pg. 2232
HOMAG MACHINERY SRODA SP. Z O.O—See Durr AG; *Int'l*, pg. 2232
HOMAG POLSKA SP.Z O.O—See Durr AG; *Int'l*, pg. 2232
HOMAG (SCHWEIZ) AG—See Durr AG; *Int'l*, pg. 2232
HOMAG SOUTH AMERICA LTDA—See Durr AG; *Int'l*, pg. 2232
HOMAG VERTRIEBS-BETEILIGUNGS GMBH—See Durr AG; *Int'l*, pg. 2232
HOMAG VERTRIEB & SERVICE GMBH—See Durr AG; *Int'l*, pg. 2232
HUNGARY ENBI KFT.—See Platinum Equity, LLC; *U.S. Private*, pg. 3203
HUYCK.WANGNER GERMANY GMBH—See ANDRITZ AG; *Int'l*, pg. 457
HUYCK.WANGNER ITALIA S.P.A—See ANDRITZ AG; *Int'l*, pg. 457
INDUSTRIAL ENGRAVING & MANUFACTURING CORP.; *U.S. Private*, pg. 2066
JAMES L. TAYLOR MANUFACTURING CO.; *U.S. Private*, pg. 2184
J.J. PLANK CORPORATION—See ANDRITZ AG; *Int'l*, pg. 457
JLT CLAMPS—See James L. Taylor Manufacturing Co.; *U.S. Private*, pg. 2184
JLY INVESTMENTS, INC.—See InCompass LLC; *U.S. Private*, pg. 2054
KADANT AUSTRALIA PTY. LTD.—See Kadant Inc.; *U.S. Public*, pg. 1212
KADANT BLACK CLAWSON LLC—See Kadant Inc.; *U.S. Public*, pg. 1212
KADANT CANADA CORP.—See Kadant Inc.; *U.S. Public*, pg. 1212
KADANT FIBERLINE (CHINA) CO.—See Kadant Inc.; *U.S. Public*, pg. 1212
KADANT INC.; *U.S. Public*, pg. 1212
KADANT JOHNSON CORPORATION (WUXI) LTD.—See Kadant Inc.; *U.S. Public*, pg. 1212
KADANT LAMORT AB—See Kadant Inc.; *U.S. Public*, pg. 1212
KADANT M-CLEAN AB—See Kadant Inc.; *U.S. Public*, pg. 1212
KADANT SOLUTIONS—See Kadant Inc.; *U.S. Public*, pg. 1212
KADANT UK LTD.—See Kadant Inc.; *U.S. Public*, pg. 1212
KAUKOMARKKINAT SHANGHAI LTD.—See Aspo Oyj; *Int'l*, pg. 631
KEMPSMITH MACHINE COMPANY; *U.S. Private*, pg. 2282
KLK HARDWOOD FLOORING SDN. BHD.—See Batu Kawan Berhad; *Int'l*, pg. 891
LORENTZEN & WETTRE AB—See ABB Ltd.; *Int'l*, pg. 49
MARQUIPWARDUNITED, INC.—See Barry-Wehmiller Companies, Inc.; *U.S. Private*, pg. 482
MARQUIPWARDUNITED, INC.—See Barry-Wehmiller Companies, Inc.; *U.S. Private*, pg. 482
MEREEN-JOHNSON MACHINE COMPANY—See North Central Equity LLC; *U.S. Private*, pg. 2943
MICOR AB—See Duroc AB; *Int'l*, pg. 2230
MTR MARTCO, LLC—See Triosim Corporation; *U.S. Private*, pg. 4236
NICHOLSON INDUSTRIES INC.; *U.S. Private*, pg. 2925
OLIVER MACHINERY CO.—See Chiu Ting Machinery Co., Ltd.; *Int'l*, pg. 1574
PAPER CONVERTING MACHINE COMPANY FAR EAST—See Barry-Wehmiller Companies, Inc.; *U.S. Private*, pg. 482
PAPER CONVERTING MACHINE COMPANY FAR EAST—See Barry-Wehmiller Companies, Inc.; *U.S. Private*, pg. 482
PAPER CONVERTING MACHINE COMPANY, LTD.—See Barry-Wehmiller Companies, Inc.; *U.S. Private*, pg. 482
PAPER CONVERTING MACHINE COMPANY—See Barry-Wehmiller Companies, Inc.; *U.S. Private*, pg. 482
PAPER CONVERTING MACHINE EUROPE GMBH—See Barry-Wehmiller Companies, Inc.; *U.S. Private*, pg. 482
PAPER MACHINERY CORPORATION; *U.S. Private*, pg. 3088
PENDU MANUFACTURING INC.; *U.S. Private*, pg. 3132
PESAKA TERENGGANU BERHAD—See Golden Pharos Berhad; *Int'l*, pg. 3031
PESAMA TIMBER CORPORATION SDN BHD—See Golden Pharos Berhad; *Int'l*, pg. 3031
REMACONTROL SWEDEN AB—See Image Systems AB; *Int'l*, pg. 3618
REMASAWCO AB—See Image Systems AB; *Int'l*, pg. 3618
RENHOLMEN AB—See Carl Bennet AB; *Int'l*, pg. 1332
RENHOLMEN AB—See Carl Bennet AB; *Int'l*, pg. 1332
RIVERSIDE TOOL CORP.—See Audax Group, Limited Partnership; *U.S. Private*, pg. 389
SANDUSKY INTERNATIONAL INC.—See MetalTek International; *U.S. Private*, pg. 2682
SANDUSKY LIMITED—See MetalTek International, *U.S. Private*, pg. 2682
SCHULER CONSULTING GMBH—See Durr AG; *Int'l*, pg. 2232
SHARIKAT MALAYSIA WOOD INDUSTRIES SDN BHD—See Mohawk Industries, Inc.; *U.S. Public*, pg. 1458
SHOPSMITH, INC.; *U.S. Private*, pg. 3640
SIERRAPINE LIMITED - MCKILLICAN AMERICAN - AMERICAN HARDWOODS DIVISION—See SierraPine Limited; *U.S. Private*, pg. 3648

SORB INDUSTRI AB—See Carl Bennet AB; *Int'l*, pg. 1332
SPANOLUX SPRL—See Mohawk Industries, Inc.; *U.S. Public*, pg. 1458
SULZER DAIICHI K.K.—See Daiichi Jitsugyo Co. Ltd.; *Int'l*, pg. 1927
TECCO GMBH—See Ilford Imaging Switzerland GmbH; *Int'l*, pg. 3614
TIDLAND CORPORATION—See Berwind Corporation; *U.S. Private*, pg. 541
TIPEX PTE LTD.—See Hanoi Beer Trading JSC; *Int'l*, pg. 3258
TRICO ENTERPRISES LLC.; *U.S. Private*, pg. 4229
USNR; *U.S. Private*, pg. 4323
VIKING ENGINEERING AND DEVELOPMENT INCORPORATED; *U.S. Private*, pg. 4382
WEINMANN HOLZBAUSYSTEMTECHNIK GMBH—See Durr AG; *Int'l*, pg. 2233
WOOD-MIZER PRODUCTS INC.; *U.S. Private*, pg. 4557
YATES-AMERICAN MACHINE COMPANY; *U.S. Private*, pg. 4587

333248 — ALL OTHER INDUSTRIAL MACHINERY MANUFACTURING

3D SYSTEMS - BURLINGTON—See 3D Systems Corporation; *U.S. Public*, pg. 4
4FRONT ENGINEERED SOLUTIONS, INC.—See ASSA ABLOY AB; *Int'l*, pg. 633
AALBORG INDUSTRIES LTDA—See Alfa Laval AB; *Int'l*, pg. 308
ABB AUTOMATION CO. LTD.—See ABB Ltd.; *Int'l*, pg. 54
ABB AUTOMATION GMBH—See ABB Ltd.; *Int'l*, pg. 50
ABB LTD.—See ABB Ltd.; *Int'l*, pg. 53
ABB MANUFACTURING SDN. BHD.—See ABB Ltd.; *Int'l*, pg. 53
ABB NG LTD—See ABB Ltd.; *Int'l*, pg. 53
ABB POWER AND AUTOMATION SYSTEMS LTD.—See ABB Ltd.; *Int'l*, pg. 55
ABB ROBOTICS AB—See ABB Ltd.; *Int'l*, pg. 49
ABB ROBOTICS—See ABB Ltd.; *Int'l*, pg. 49
ABB SAUDI ARABIA—See ABB Ltd.; *Int'l*, pg. 54
ABB SISTEMAS INDUSTRIALES AB—See ABB Ltd.; *Int'l*, pg. 55
ABB SOUTH AFRICA (PTY) LTD.—See ABB Ltd.; *Int'l*, pg. 55
ABB TECHNOLOGIES W.L.L.—See ABB Ltd.; *Int'l*, pg. 55
AB CARTER INC.; *U.S. Private*, pg. 33
AB DYNAMICS PLC; *Int'l*, pg. 39
ABERCROMBIE TEXTILES, LLC—See W.R. Berkley Corporation; *U.S. Public*, pg. 2316
AB GF SWEDENBORG—See Christian Berner Tech Trade AB; *Int'l*, pg. 1586
ACCESS LTD.—See AIDA Engineering, Ltd.; *Int'l*, pg. 231
ACCURA MACHINERY & MANUFACTURING (TAICANG) CO., LTD.; *Int'l*, pg. 94
ACCURI CYTOMETERS (EUROPE) LTD.—See Becton, Dickinson & Company; *U.S. Public*, pg. 288
ACCUWORX, LLC; *U.S. Private*, pg. 56
ACE APPARATEBAU CONSTRUCTION & ENGINEERING GMBH—See Christof Holding AG; *Int'l*, pg. 1587
ACEZ INSTRUMENTS PHILIPPINES CORPORATION—See Acez Instruments Pte. Ltd.; *Int'l*, pg. 102
ACEZ INSTRUMENTS (SHENZHEN) CO., LTD—See Acez Instruments Pte. Ltd.; *Int'l*, pg. 102
ACEZ SENSING PTE LTD.—See Acez Instruments Pte. Ltd.; *Int'l*, pg. 102
ACI CINCINNATI—See Amano Corporation; *Int'l*, pg. 410
ACME CRYOGENICS INC.—See Dover Corporation; *U.S. Public*, pg. 678
ACOEM GROUP; *Int'l*, pg. 107
ACROTEC UK LTD.—See Forsyth Capital Investors LLC; *U.S. Private*, pg. 1573
ADDMASTER CORPORATION; *U.S. Public*, pg. 40
ADEX BV—See Aalberts N.V.; *Int'l*, pg. 33
ADHESO-GRAPHICS, INC.; *U.S. Private*, pg. 79
ADM VENTURES INC.; *U.S. Private*, pg. 80
ADMV—See Coesia S.p.A.; *Int'l*, pg. 1690
ADVANCE PRODUCTS CORPORATION—See Industrial Innovations, Inc.; *U.S. Private*, pg. 2066
AEM HOLDINGS LTD.; *Int'l*, pg. 175
AGES SHARED SERVICES AB—See AGES Industri AB; *Int'l*, pg. 206
AGFA GRAPHICS SP. Z.O.O.—See Agfa-Gevaert N.V.; *Int'l*, pg. 207
AGFA GRAPHICS S.R.L.—See Agfa-Gevaert N.V.; *Int'l*, pg. 207
AGFA INDUSTRIES KOREA LTD.—See Agfa-Gevaert N.V.; *Int'l*, pg. 207
AGI BRASIL INDUSTRIA E COMERCIO S.A.—See Ag Growth International Inc.; *Int'l*, pg. 198
AGIE CHARMILLES CHINA (SHANGHAI) LTD—See Georg Fischer AG; *Int'l*, pg. 2934
AGIE CHARMILLES HOLDING LIMITED—See Georg Fischer AG; *Int'l*, pg. 2934
AGIE CHARMILLES KOREA CO LTD—See Georg Fischer AG; *Int'l*, pg. 2934

AGIE CHARMILLES LLC—See Georg Fischer AG; *Int'l*, pg. 2934
AGIE CHARMILLES LTDA—See Georg Fischer AG; *Int'l*, pg. 2934
AGIE CHARMILLES MANAGEMENT SA—See Georg Fischer AG; *Int'l*, pg. 2934
AGIE CHARMILLES NEW TECHNOLOGIES SA—See Georg Fischer AG; *Int'l*, pg. 2934
AGIE CHARMILLES S.R.O.—See Georg Fischer AG; *Int'l*, pg. 2934
AGSENSE, LLC—See Valmont Industries, Inc.; *U.S. Public*, pg. 2273
AIDA ENGINEERING CHINA CO., LTD.—See AIDA Engineering, Ltd.; *Int'l*, pg. 230
AIDA ENGINEERING, LTD.; *Int'l*, pg. 230
AIDA ENGINEERING (M) SDN. BHD.—See AIDA Engineering, Ltd.; *Int'l*, pg. 230
AIMT TRATERH, S.A.U.—See Aalberts N.V.; *Int'l*, pg. 33
AIR MONITOR CORP.—See Harbour Group Industries, Inc.; *U.S. Private*, pg. 1860
AKIYAMA INTERNATIONAL COMPANY LTD.; *Int'l*, pg. 263
AKIYAMA INTERNATIONAL CORP (USA)—See Akiyama International Company Ltd.; *Int'l*, pg. 263
ALD HOLCROFT VACUUM TECHNOLOGIES CO.—See AMG Critical Materials N.V.; *Int'l*, pg. 425
ALD OWN & OPERATE GMBH—See AMG Critical Materials N.V.; *Int'l*, pg. 425
ALD TRATAMIENTOS TERMICOS S.A. DE C.V.—See AMG Critical Materials N.V.; *Int'l*, pg. 425
ALFA LAVAL AB; *Int'l*, pg. 308
ALFA LAVAL (INDIA) LTD—See Alfa Laval AB; *Int'l*, pg. 308
ALFA LAVAL KOLDING A/S—See Alfa Laval AB; *Int'l*, pg. 310
ALFA LAVAL MID EUROPE GMBH—See Alfa Laval AB; *Int'l*, pg. 309
ALFA LAVAL NAKSKOV A/S—See Alfa Laval AB; *Int'l*, pg. 310
ALFA LAVAL POLSKA SP. ZOO—See Alfa Laval AB; *Int'l*, pg. 311
ALFA LAVAL VIETNAM LLC—See Alfa Laval AB; *Int'l*, pg. 311
AL-KHODARI INDUSTRIAL TRADING & SERVICES—See Abdullah Abdul Mohsin Al-Khodari Sons Company; *Int'l*, pg. 59
ALLEGHENY PLASTICS INC.; *U.S. Private*, pg. 176
ALLFLEX ARGENTIA S.A.—See Merck & Co., Inc.; *U.S. Public*, pg. 1415
ALLFLEX AUSTRALIA PTY LTD—See Merck & Co., Inc.; *U.S. Public*, pg. 1415
ALLFLEX DAN-MARK APS—See Merck & Co., Inc.; *U.S. Public*, pg. 1415
ALLFLEX GROUP GERMANY GMBH—See Merck & Co., Inc.; *U.S. Public*, pg. 1415
ALLFLEX NEW ZEALAND LIMITED—See Merck & Co., Inc.; *U.S. Public*, pg. 1415
ALLFLEX POLSKA SP Z O.O.—See Merck & Co., Inc.; *U.S. Public*, pg. 1415
ALLFLEX UK GROUP—See Merck & Co., Inc.; *U.S. Public*, pg. 1415
ALLIANCE MATERIAL HANDLING INC.; *U.S. Private*, pg. 183
ALLIED ENVIRONMENTAL SOLUTIONS, INC.—See Allied Resource Corporation; *U.S. Private*, pg. 187
ALL RING TECH CO., LTD.; *Int'l*, pg. 332
ALMCO, INC.—See Innovance, Inc.; *U.S. Private*, pg. 2081
ALPHA AUTOMOTIVE TECHNOLOGIES LLC—See IHI Corporation; *Int'l*, pg. 3604
ALPSGIKEN MYANMAR CO., LTD.—See Altech Corporation; *Int'l*, pg. 389
ALPSGIKEN TAIWAN CO., LTD.—See Altech Corporation; *Int'l*, pg. 389
AMADA ENGINEERING CO., LTD.—See Amada Holdings Co., Ltd.; *Int'l*, pg. 403
AMADA TOYO CO., LTD.—See Amada Holdings Co., Ltd.; *Int'l*, pg. 404
AMENDUNI NICOLA S.P.A.—See Acciaierie Valbruna S.p.A.; *Int'l*, pg. 89
AMERICAN HANDLING SYSTEMS, INC.; *U.S. Private*, pg. 235
AMERICAN KUHNE, INC.—See The Graham Group, Inc.; *U.S. Private*, pg. 4036
AMERICAN PERFORMANCE INDUSTRIES; *U.S. Private*, pg. 243
AMERICAN ROLLER COMPANY; *U.S. Private*, pg. 246
AMI INDUSTRIES, INC.; *U.S. Private*, pg. 263
AMS SPECTRAL UV—See Forsyth Capital Investors LLC; *U.S. Private*, pg. 1573
AMTECH ELECTRONICS INDIA LIMITED; *Int'l*, pg. 441
ANDERSON INDUSTRIAL CORPORATION - HOULUNG FACTORY—See Anderson Industrial Corporation; *Int'l*, pg. 450
ANDERSON & VREELAND, INC.; *U.S. Private*, pg. 276
ANDREW YULE & COMPANY LTD.; *Int'l*, pg. 452
ANDRITZ BIAX S.A.S.—See ANDRITZ AG; *Int'l*, pg. 454
ANDRITZ FEED & BIOFUEL A/S - VENEZUELA REPRESENTATIVE OFFICE—See ANDRITZ AG; *Int'l*, pg. 452
ANDRITZ FEED & BIOFUEL A/S - VIETNAM REPRESENTATIVE OFFICE—See ANDRITZ AG; *Int'l*, pg. 453

ANDRITZ FEED & BIOFUEL BRASIL LTDA.—See ANDRITZ AG; *Int'l*, pg. 452
ANDRITZ FIEDLER GMBH—See ANDRITZ AG; *Int'l*, pg. 453
ANDRITZ FRAUTECH S.R.L.—See ANDRITZ AG; *Int'l*, pg. 453
ANDRITZ HYDRO AB—See ANDRITZ AG; *Int'l*, pg. 453
ANDRITZ HYDRO AG ABMB BULACH—See ANDRITZ AG; *Int'l*, pg. 453
ANDRITZ HYDRO AS—See ANDRITZ AG; *Int'l*, pg. 453
ANDRITZ HYDRO S.A. DE C.V.—See ANDRITZ AG; *Int'l*, pg. 453
ANDRITZ HYDRO S.R.L. UNIPERSONALE—See ANDRITZ AG; *Int'l*, pg. 453
ANDRITZ JOCHMAN S.R.O.—See ANDRITZ AG; *Int'l*, pg. 454
ANDRITZ KMPT GMBH—See ANDRITZ AG; *Int'l*, pg. 454
ANDRITZ KMPT INC.—See ANDRITZ AG; *Int'l*, pg. 453
ANDRITZ LTD.—See ANDRITZ AG; *Int'l*, pg. 454
ANDRITZ PERFOJET S.A.S.—See ANDRITZ AG; *Int'l*, pg. 454
ANDRITZ SAS—See ANDRITZ AG; *Int'l*, pg. 454
ANDRITZ SEPARATION (INDIA) PRIVATE LTD.—See ANDRITZ AG; *Int'l*, pg. 454
ANDRITZ SINGAPORE PTE. LTD.—See ANDRITZ AG; *Int'l*, pg. 454
ANDRITZ SUNDWIG GMBH—See ANDRITZ AG; *Int'l*, pg. 455
ANDRITZ TECHNOLOGIES PVT. LTD.—See ANDRITZ AG; *Int'l*, pg. 454
ANHYDRO S.A.S—See Lone Star Funds; *U.S. Private*, pg. 2485
ANVA TITECH SYSTEM AB—See AnVa Tubes & Components AB; *Int'l*, pg. 486
A-ONE SEIMITSU INC.; *Int'l*, pg. 20
APB APPARATEBAU SCHWEISSTECHNIK GMBH—See Christof Holding AG; *Int'l*, pg. 1587
APEX ASIA PACIFIC PRIVATE LIMITED—See Apex International Co., Ltd.; *Int'l*, pg. 511
APEX EUROPE B.V.—See Apex International Co., Ltd.; *Int'l*, pg. 511
APEX ITALY S.R.L.—See Apex International Co., Ltd.; *Int'l*, pg. 511
APEX MACHINE CO.; *U.S. Private*, pg. 292
API FABRICACION, S.A.—See ACS, Actividades de Construccion y Servicios, S.A.; *Int'l*, pg. 110
APPLE FABRICATION COMPANY—See Triton Consolidated, Inc.; *U.S. Private*, pg. 4239
APPLIED CANADA, ULC—See Applied Industrial Technologies, Inc.; *U.S. Public*, pg. 170
APPLIED INDUSTRIAL TECHNOLOGIES, LP—See Applied Industrial Technologies, Inc.; *U.S. Public*, pg. 170
APPLIED MAINTENANCE SUPPLIES & SOLUTIONS, LLC—See Applied Industrial Technologies, Inc.; *U.S. Public*, pg. 170
APS TECHNOLOGY GROUP, INC.—See ABB Ltd.; *Int'l*, pg. 52
AQ GROUP AB; *Int'l*, pg. 526
ARBURG GMBH & CO.; *Int'l*, pg. 539
ARCURE; *Int'l*, pg. 552
ARMORFLEX INTERNATIONAL LIMITED—See Valmont Industries, Inc.; *U.S. Public*, pg. 2273
ARMOUR PLASTICS LIMITED - ENGINEERING DIVISION—See Armour Plastics Limited; *Int'l*, pg. 575
ARMSTRONG INDUSTRIAL CORPORATION LTD.; *Int'l*, pg. 575
AROOT CO., LTD.; *Int'l*, pg. 577
ART'S WAY VESSELS, INC.—See Art's-Way Manufacturing Co., Inc.; *U.S. Public*, pg. 201
ASAHI KASEI MICROZA (HANGZHOU) CO., LTD.—See Asahi Kasei Corporation; *Int'l*, pg. 596
ASAHI KASEI SPANDEX AMERICA, INC.—See Asahi Kasei Corporation; *Int'l*, pg. 596
ASAHI SEISAKUSHO CO., LTD.—See Ferrotec Holdings Corporation; *Int'l*, pg. 2643
ASIAN PLASTIC MACHINERY CO. LTD.—See Chen Hsong Holdings Ltd.; *Int'l*, pg. 1464
ASIA TECH IMAGE, INC.; *Int'l*, pg. 615
ASM ASSEMBLY EQUIPMENT (M) SDN. BHD.—See ASM INTERNATIONAL N.V.; *Int'l*, pg. 626
ASPEN AERIALS, INC.—See The Sterling Group, L.P.; *U.S. Private*, pg. 4123
ASSEMBLY & TEST - EUROPE GMBH—See ATS Corporation; *Int'l*, pg. 695
AT INFORMATION PRODUCTS; *U.S. Private*, pg. 363
ATLANTA ATTACHMENT COMPANY, INC.; *U.S. Private*, pg. 370
ATLAS COPCO APPLICATIONS INDUSTRIELLES S.A.S.—See Atlas Copco AB; *Int'l*, pg. 678
ATLAS COPCO (INDIA) LTD.—See Atlas Copco AB; *Int'l*, pg. 677
ATLAS COPCO (IRELAND) LTD—See Atlas Copco AB; *Int'l*, pg. 677
ATLAS COPCO PAKISTAN (PVT) LTD—See Atlas Copco AB; *Int'l*, pg. 680
ATLAS COPCO (SHANGHAI) PROCESS EQUIPMENT CO LTD—See Atlas Copco AB; *Int'l*, pg. 677
ATLAS COPCO (SHENYANG) CONSTRUCTION AND MIN-

N.A.I.C.S. INDEX

333248 — ALL OTHER INDUSTRIA...

ING EQUIPMENT LTD—See Atlas Copco AB; *Int'l*, pg. 677
ATLAS COPCO SOUTH AFRICA (PTY) LTD—See Atlas Copco AB; *Int'l*, pg. 679
ATLAS COPCO TOOLS GMBH—See Atlas Copco AB; *Int'l*, pg. 679
ATLAS COPCO (ZAMBIA) LTD—See Atlas Copco AB; *Int'l*, pg. 677
ATS ASSEMBLY & TEST, INC. - DAYTON—See ATS Corporation; *Int'l*, pg. 695
ATS CO., LTD.—See Daifuku Co., Ltd.; *Int'l*, pg. 1924
AULBACH ENTGRATUNGSTECHNIK GMBH; *Int'l*, pg. 704
AURORA LABS LIMITED; *Int'l*, pg. 714
AUSTAR LIFESCIENCES LIMITED; *Int'l*, pg. 716
AUTOCAM CORPORATION BOUVERAT INDUSTRIES—See NN, Inc.; *U.S. Public*, pg. 1530
AUTOMATIK PLASTICS MACHINERY GMBH—See Dover Corporation; *U.S. Public*, pg. 681
AUTOMATION TOOLING SYSTEMS ENTERPRISES, INC.—See ATS Corporation; *Int'l*, pg. 695
AUTOMED TECHNOLOGIES, INC.—See Cencora, Inc.; *U.S. Public*, pg. 467
AUTOQUIP CORPORATION—See Miner Enterprises, Inc.; *U.S. Private*, pg. 2741
AUXILIA GRAPHICA S.R.L.—See Sycamore Partners Management, LP; *U.S. Private*, pg. 3896
AVACO CO., LTD - DAEGU 1ST FACTORY—See AVACO CO., LTD; *Int'l*, pg. 733
AVERY DENNISON (HONG KONG) LTD.—See Avery Dennison Corporation; *U.S. Public*, pg. 243
AVERY DENNISON RETAIL BRANDING & INFORMATION SOLUTIONS - SAYRE—See Avery Dennison Corporation; *U.S. Public*, pg. 244
AVT INDUSTRITEKNIK AB—See Addtech AB; *Int'l*, pg. 131
AVURE TECHNOLOGIES INC.—See John Bean Technologies Corporation; *U.S. Public*, pg. 1191
A.W. MILLER TECHNICAL SALES, INC.—See A.W. Miller Technical Sales Inc.; *U.S. Private*, pg. 28
AWM MOLD SERVICE US INC.—See Adval Tech Holding AG; *Int'l*, pg. 155
AWM MOLD TECH INTERNATIONAL TRADING (SHANGHAI) CO. LTD.—See Adval Tech Holding AG; *Int'l*, pg. 155
AWM PLASTPACK LTD.—See Adval Tech Holding AG; *Int'l*, pg. 155
AWS ACHSLAGERWERK STASSFURT GMBH; *Int'l*, pg. 753
AXTEL INDUSTRIES LIMITED; *Int'l*, pg. 772
AZARAB INDUSTRIES; *Int'l*, pg. 776
AZBIL EUROPE NV—See Azbil Corporation; *Int'l*, pg. 777
AZBIL HONG KONG LIMITED—See Azbil Corporation; *Int'l*, pg. 777
AZBIL INDIA PRIVATE LIMITED—See Azbil Corporation; *Int'l*, pg. 777
AZBIL KIMMON TECHNOLOGY CORPORATION—See Azbil Corporation; *Int'l*, pg. 777
AZBIL MEXICO, S. DE R.L.DE C.V.—See Azbil Corporation; *Int'l*, pg. 777
AZBIL NORTH AMERICA RESEARCH & DEVELOPMENT, INC.—See Azbil Corporation; *Int'l*, pg. 777
AZBIL PRODUCTION (THAILAND) CO., LTD.—See Azbil Corporation; *Int'l*, pg. 777
AZBIL SAUDI LIMITED—See Azbil Corporation; *Int'l*, pg. 777
AZBIL TAIWAN CO., LTD.—See Azbil Corporation; *Int'l*, pg. 777
AZBIL VIETNAM CO., LTD.—See Azbil Corporation; *Int'l*, pg. 777
AZO CONTROLS GMBH—See AZO GmbH & Co. KG; *Int'l*, pg. 780
AZO EURL—See AZO GmbH & Co. KG; *Int'l*, pg. 780
AZO N.V.—See AZO GmbH & Co. KG; *Int'l*, pg. 780
BABCOCK WANSON SA—See Fonds de Consolidation et de Developpement des Entreprises; *Int'l*, pg. 2725
BACHEM AG—See Bachem Holding AG; *Int'l*, pg. 794
BAKER HUGHES (DEUTSCHLAND) HOLDING GMBH—See Baker Hughes Company; *U.S. Public*, pg. 264
BALCO, INC.—See CSW Industrials, Inc.; *U.S. Public*, pg. 601
BALDWIN AMERICAS CORPORATION—See Forsyth Capital Investors LLC; *U.S. Private*, pg. 1573
BALDWIN ASIA PACIFIC CORPORATION—See Forsyth Capital Investors LLC; *U.S. Private*, pg. 1573
BALDWIN EUROPE CONSOLIDATED INC.—See Forsyth Capital Investors LLC; *U.S. Private*, pg. 1573
BALDWIN GRAPHIC SYSTEMS, INC.—See Forsyth Capital Investors LLC; *U.S. Private*, pg. 1573
BALDWIN GRAPHIC SYSTEMS—See Forsyth Capital Investors LLC; *U.S. Private*, pg. 1573
BALDWIN IVT AB—See Forsyth Capital Investors LLC; *U.S. Private*, pg. 1573
BALDWIN-JAPAN LTD—See Forsyth Capital Investors LLC; *U.S. Private*, pg. 1573
BALDWIN JIMEK AB—See Forsyth Capital Investors LLC; *U.S. Private*, pg. 1573
BALDWIN OXY-DRY AMERICAS—See Forsyth Capital Investors LLC; *U.S. Private*, pg. 1573
BALDWIN PRINTING CONTROL EQUIPMENT (BEIJING) COMPANY, LTD.—See Forsyth Capital Investors LLC; *U.S. Private*, pg. 1573
BALDWIN PRINTING CONTROLS LTD.—See Forsyth Capital Investors LLC; *U.S. Private*, pg. 1573
BALDWIN TECHNOLOGY COMPANY, INC.—See Forsyth Capital Investors LLC; *U.S. Private*, pg. 1573
BALDWIN (UK) LTD.—See Forsyth Capital Investors LLC; *U.S. Private*, pg. 1573
BALEMASTER EUROPE BV—See Kadant Inc.; *U.S. Public*, pg. 1212
BALL & JEWELL DIVISION—See Harbour Group Industries, Inc.; *U.S. Private*, pg. 1860
BARLOWORLD EQUIPMENT (PTY) LIMITED—See Barloworld Ltd.; *Int'l*, pg. 866
BATLIBOI LTD.; *Int'l*, pg. 890
BAYNE MACHINE WORKS, INC.—See Terex Corporation; *U.S. Public*, pg. 2019
BAY PRODUCTS, INC., *U.S. Private*, pg. 494
BBS AUTOMATION BLAICHACH GMBH—See Durr AG; *Int'l*, pg. 2230
BBS AUTOMATION CHICAGO INC.—See Durr AG; *Int'l*, pg. 2230
BBS AUTOMATION GMBH—See Durr AG; *Int'l*, pg. 2230
BBS AUTOMATION GUADALAJARA S DE R.L. DE C.V.—See Durr AG; *Int'l*, pg. 2230
BBS AUTOMATION INDIA PRIVATE LTD.—See Durr AG; *Int'l*, pg. 2230
BBS AUTOMATION (KUNSHAN) CO., LTD.—See Durr AG; *Int'l*, pg. 2230
BBS AUTOMATION LIPANY S.R.O.—See Durr AG; *Int'l*, pg. 2230
BBS AUTOMATION PENANG SDN. BHD.—See Durr AG; *Int'l*, pg. 2230
BBS AUTOMATION (SUZHOU) CO., LTD.—See Durr AG; *Int'l*, pg. 2230
BBS AUTOMATION (TIANJIN) CO., LTD.—See Durr AG; *Int'l*, pg. 2230
BBS WINDING S.R.L.—See Durr AG; *Int'l*, pg. 2230
BCC FUBA INDIA LTD.; *Int'l*, pg. 926
BEE LINE COMPANY—See McLaughlin Body Co.; *U.S. Private*, pg. 2640
BEIJER ALMA AB; *Int'l*, pg. 942
BEIJING BEIREN FUJI PRINTING MACHINERY CO., LTD.—See Beijing Jingcheng Machinery Electric Holding Co., Ltd.; *Int'l*, pg. 953
BEIJING FIDIA MACHINERY & ELECTRONICS CO., LTD.—See FIDIA S.p.A.; *Int'l*, pg. 2654
BEIJING JINGCHENG MACHINERY ELECTRIC CO., LTD.; *Int'l*, pg. 952
BEIJING KER'KANG INSTRUMENT LIMITED COMPANY—See Halma plc; *Int'l*, pg. 3230
BEIJING NEW UNIVERSAL ENVIRONMENTAL ENGINEERING & TECHNOLOGY CO., LTD.—See Beijing New Universal Science and Technology Co., Ltd.; *Int'l*, pg. 954
BEIJING NEW UNIVERSAL SCIENCE AND TECHNOLOGY CO., LTD.; *Int'l*, pg. 954
BEIJING NO.2 MACHINE TOOL WORKS CO., LTD.—See Beijing Jingcheng Machinery Electric Holding Co., Ltd.; *Int'l*, pg. 953
BEIJING SIFANG TONGXING MECHANICAL TECHNOLOGY DEVELOPMENT CO., LTD.—See Beijing New Universal Science and Technology Co., Ltd.; *Int'l*, pg. 954
BEIJING TIANZHONGFANG ENVIRONMENTAL PROTECTION SCIENCE & TECHNOLOGY CO., LTD.—See Beijing New Universal Science and Technology Co., Ltd.; *Int'l*, pg. 954
BEIJING ZODNGOC AUTOMATIC TECHNOLOGY CO., LTD.—See Beijing Easpring Material Technology Co., Ltd.; *Int'l*, pg. 949
BELL & HOWELL - CANADA—See WestView Capital Partners, L.P.; *U.S. Private*, pg. 4501
BELL & HOWELL, LLC—See WestView Capital Partners, L.P.; *U.S. Private*, pg. 4501
BELL & HOWELL, LLC - WHEELING OFFICE—See WestView Capital Partners, L.P.; *U.S. Private*, pg. 4501
BELVAC PRODUCTION MACHINERY, INC.—See Dover Corporation; *U.S. Public*, pg. 679
BENKO PRODUCTS, INC., *U.S. Private*, pg. 526
BENTELER AUTOMOTIVE (CHINA) INVESTMENT CO. LTD.—See Benteler International AG; *Int'l*, pg. 976
BENTELER AUTOMOTIVE INDIA PRIVATE LIMITED—See Benteler International AG; *Int'l*, pg. 976
BENZ INCORPORATED—See Durr AG; *Int'l*, pg. 2232
BEREMA A/S—See Atlas Copco AB; *Int'l*, pg. 681
BESSER COMPANY; *U.S. Private*, pg. 542
BHDT GMBH—See Dr. Aichhorn GmbH; *Int'l*, pg. 2190
BICO GROUP AB; *Int'l*, pg. 1019
BIESSE ASIA PTE LTD.—See Biesse S.p.A.; *Int'l*, pg. 1020
BILFINGER CHEMSERV GMBH—See Bilfinger SE; *Int'l*, pg. 1026
BIO-CHEM FLUIDICS INC.—See Halma plc; *Int'l*, pg. 3231
BLACKSTONE NEY ULTRASONICS INC.—See Alpha Capital Partners, Ltd.; *U.S. Private*, pg. 197
BMB (SHANGHAI) INTERNATIONAL CORP.—See Brother Industries, Ltd.; *Int'l*, pg. 1196
BOBST BENELUX NV—See Bobst Group S.A.; *Int'l*, pg. 1095
BOBST BIELEFELD GMBH—See Bobst Group S.A.; *Int'l*, pg. 1095
BOBST (CHANGZHOU) LTD.—See Bobst Group S.A.; *Int'l*, pg. 1095
BOBST CIS LLC—See Bobst Group S.A.; *Int'l*, pg. 1095
BOBST FIRENZE S.R.L.—See Bobst Group S.A.; *Int'l*, pg. 1095
BOBST GRENCHEN AG—See Bobst Group S.A.; *Int'l*, pg. 1095
BOBST GROUP DEUTSCHLAND GMBH—See Bobst Group S.A.; *Int'l*, pg. 1095
BOBST IBERICA, S.L.—See Bobst Group S.A.; *Int'l*, pg. 1096
BOBST INDIA PRIVATE LTD.—See Bobst Group S.A.; *Int'l*, pg. 1096
BOBST ISTANBUL AMBALAJ A.S.—See Bobst Group S.A.; *Int'l*, pg. 1096
BOBST LAGOS LTD.—See Bobst Group S.A.; *Int'l*, pg. 1096
BOBST LYON SAS—See Bobst Group S.A.; *Int'l*, pg. 1096
BOBST MANCHESTER LTD.—See Bobst Group S.A.; *Int'l*, pg. 1096
BOBST MEERBUSCH GMBH—See Bobst Group S.A.; *Int'l*, pg. 1096
BOBST MEX SA—See Bobst Group S.A.; *Int'l*, pg. 1096
BOBST PARIS SAS—See Bobst Group S.A.; *Int'l*, pg. 1096
BOBST POLSKA SP. Z O.O.—See Bobst Group S.A.; *Int'l*, pg. 1096
BOBST S.A.—See Bobst Group S.A.; *Int'l*, pg. 1096
BOBST SCANDINAVIA APS—See Bobst Group S.A.; *Int'l*, pg. 1096
BOBST UK & IRELAND LTD.—See Bobst Group S.A.; *Int'l*, pg. 1096
BOBST VIETNAM CO. LTD.—See Bobst Group S.A.; *Int'l*, pg. 1096
BOLAITE (SHANGHAI) COMPRESSOR CO., LTD.—See Atlas Copco AB; *Int'l*, pg. 681
BOLZONI S.P.A.—See Hyster-Yale Materials Handling, Inc.; *U.S. Public*, pg. 1079
BOMBARDIER TRANSPORTATION EQUIPMENT (SUZHOU) CO., LTD.—See Alstom S.A.; *Int'l*, pg. 382
BONG GMBH—See Bong AB; *Int'l*, pg. 1107
BOSCH PACKAGING TECHNOLOGY—See CVC Capital Partners SICAV-FIS S.A.; *Int'l*, pg. 1884
BOWE CARDTEC GMBH—See BOWE SYSTEC AG; *Int'l*, pg. 1123
BRADKEN, INC.—See Hitachi, Ltd.; *Int'l*, pg. 3415
BRADY & MORRIS ENGINEERING CO. LTD.; *Int'l*, pg. 1135
BRAVE C&H SUPPLY CO., LTD.; *Int'l*, pg. 1141
BRECKNELL WILLIS COMPOSITES LTD.—See Westinghouse Air Brake Technologies Corporation; *U.S. Public*, pg. 2358
BRETECHE INDUSTRIE SAS—See Equistone Partners Europe Limited; *Int'l*, pg. 2486
BRIDGESTONE AMERICAS TIRE OPERATIONS, LLC - MUSCATINE MANUFACTURING FACILITY—See Cox Enterprises, Inc.; *U.S. Private*, pg. 1075
BRIGHTON TRU-EDGE HEADS—See Enerfab, Inc.; *U.S. Private*, pg. 1393
BRIGHT SHELAND INTERNATIONAL CO., LTD.; *Int'l*, pg. 1162
BROOKS AUTOMATION AG—See Azenta, Inc.; *U.S. Public*, pg. 258
BROTHER CENTRAL AND EASTERN EUROPE GMBH—See Brother Industries, Ltd.; *Int'l*, pg. 1196
BROTHER COMMERCIAL (THAILAND) LTD.—See Brother Industries, Ltd.; *Int'l*, pg. 1196
BROTHER IBERIA, S.L.U.—See Brother Industries, Ltd.; *Int'l*, pg. 1196
BROTHER INDUSTRIAL PRINTING (JAPAN), LTD.—See Brother Industries, Ltd.; *Int'l*, pg. 1197
BROTHER INDUSTRIES (PHILIPPINES), INC.—See Brother Industries, Ltd.; *Int'l*, pg. 1197
BROTHER INDUSTRIES TECHNOLOGY (MALAYSIA) SDN. BHD.—See Brother Industries, Ltd.; *Int'l*, pg. 1197
BROTHER INTERNATIONAL DEL PERU S.A.C.—See Brother Industries, Ltd.; *Int'l*, pg. 1196
BROTHER INTERNATIONAL KOREA CO., LTD.—See Brother Industries, Ltd.; *Int'l*, pg. 1196
BROTHER INTERNATIONAL TAIWAN LTD.—See Brother Industries, Ltd.; *Int'l*, pg. 1197
BROTHER MACHINERY (ASIA) LTD.—See Brother Industries, Ltd.; *Int'l*, pg. 1197
BROTHER MACHINERY SHANGHAI LTD.—See Brother Industries, Ltd.; *Int'l*, pg. 1197
BROTHER MACHINERY XIAN CO., LTD.—See Brother Industries, Ltd.; *Int'l*, pg. 1197
BROTHER NORDIC A/S—See Brother Industries, Ltd.; *Int'l*, pg. 1197
BROTHER POLSKA SP. Z O.O—See Brother Industries, Ltd.; *Int'l*, pg. 1196
BROTHER SALES, LTD.—See Brother Industries, Ltd.; *Int'l*, pg. 1197
BROTHER SEWING MACHINE (SHANGHAI) CO., LTD.—See Brother Industries, Ltd.; *Int'l*, pg. 1197
BROTHER SYSTEM TECHNOLOGY DEVELOPMENT (HANGZHOU) LTD.—See Brother Industries, Ltd.; *Int'l*, pg. 1197
BROTHER TECHNOLOGY (SHENZHEN) LTD.—See

Brother Industries, Ltd.; *Int'l*, pg. 1196
BROWN MACHINE GROUP—See Tenex Capital Management, L.P.; *U.S. Private*, pg. 3966
BROWN MACHINE, LLC—See Tenex Capital Management, L.P; *U.S. Private*, pg. 3966
BSAFE SYSTEMS AS—See Bergman & Beving AB; *Int'l*, pg. 980
BUCHER VASLIN SUDAMERICA—See Bucher Industries AG; *Int'l*, pg. 1208
BUHLER AEROGLIDE U.K.—See Buhler AG; *Int'l*, pg. 1211
BURCELIK BURSA CELIK DOKUM SANAYI AS; *Int'l*, pg. 1220
BURCKHARDT COMPRESSION (INDIA) PVT. LTD.—See Burckhardt Compression Holding AG; *Int'l*, pg. 1220
BURLINGTON AUTOMATION CORPORATION—See Lincoln Electric Holdings, Inc.; *U.S. Public*, pg. 1317
BUSICA LTD.—See Forval Corporation; *Int'l*, pg. 2745
BUSS-SMS-CANZLER GMBH; *Int'l*, pg. 1229
BUTLER AUTOMATIC, INC.; *U.S. Private*, pg. 696
BYNAS CO., LTD—See CDS Co., Ltd.; *Int'l*, pg. 1371
CADREX MANUFACTURING SOLUTIONS—See CORE Industrial Partners, LLC; *U.S. Private*, pg. 1048
CALIFORNIA PELLET MILL CO.—See Gilbert Global Equity Partners; *U.S. Private*, pg. 1699
CALTHERM CORPORATION—See Magnum Corporation; *U.S. Private*, pg. 2549
CALTROL, INC. - ESS DIVISION—See Caltrol, Inc.; *U.S. Private*, pg. 724
CAMOZZI DIGITAL S.R.L.—See Camozzi Group; *Int'l*, pg. 1273
CAMOZZI TECHNOPOLYMERS S.R.L.—See Camozzi Group; *Int'l*, pg. 1274
CAMPI SRL; *Int'l*, pg. 1274
CANMAX TECHNOLOGIES CO., LTD.; *Int'l*, pg. 1291
CANNON IV INC.—See Oval Partners; *U.S. Private*, pg. 3052
CANON BUSINESS MACHINES (PHILIPPINES), INC.—See Canon Inc.; *Int'l*, pg. 1293
CANON FINETECH NISCA INC.—See Canon Inc.; *Int'l*, pg. 1295
CANON PRODUCTION PRINTING NETHERLANDS B.V.—See Canon Inc.; *Int'l*, pg. 1296
CANON (SUZHOU) INC.—See Canon Inc.; *Int'l*, pg. 1292
CARD-MONROE CORP.; *U.S. Private*, pg. 749
CARLETON LIFE SUPPORT SYSTEMS INC.—See Eaton Corporation plc; *Int'l*, pg. 2277
CARLO GAVAZZI AUTOMATION (M) SDN BHD—See Carlo Gavazzi Holding AG; *Int'l*, pg. 1338
CARLO GAVAZZI SA—See Carlo Gavazzi Holding AG; *Int'l*, pg. 1339
CARL SCHENCK MACHINES EN INSTALLATIES B.V.—See Durr AG; *Int'l*, pg. 2230
CARL ZEISS QEC GMBH—See Carl-Zeiss-Stiftung; *Int'l*, pg. 1335
CAROLINA PREPRESS—See J.R. Cole Industries Inc.; *U.S. Private*, pg. 2170
CARRIER VIBRATING EQUIPMENT (SHANGHAI) CO., LTD.—See Carrier Vibrating Equipment, Inc.; *U.S. Private*, pg. 772
CASTFAST INDUSTRIAL COMPANY LIMITED—See Huscoke Holdings Limited; *Int'l*, pg. 3538
CEFLA FINISHING GROUP—See Cefla S.C.; *Int'l*, pg. 1389
CEFLA NORTH AMERICA INC.—See Cefla S.C.; *Int'l*, pg. 1389
CELLULAC LIMITED; *Int'l*, pg. 1395
CEMTREX, INC.; *U.S. Public*, pg. 466
CENTRAL MACHINE & MARINE INC.; *Int'l*, pg. 1408
CENTROTHERM PHOTOVOLTAICS AG; *Int'l*, pg. 1415
CERINNOV SAS—See Cerinnov Group SA; *Int'l*, pg. 1422
CERINNOV, UNIPESSOAL LDA.—See Cerinnov Group SA; *Int'l*, pg. 1422
CERULEAN LTD.—See Coesia S.p.A.; *Int'l*, pg. 1689
CFTC PRECISION SDN. BHD.—See China Fineblanking Technology Co., Ltd.; *Int'l*, pg. 1503
CHALLENGER LIFTS, INC.—See Snap-on Incorporated; *U.S. Public*, pg. 1897
CHANDNI MACHINES LIMITED—See Candour Techtex Ltd.; *Int'l*, pg. 1289
CHANGCHUN FAWER-IHI TURBO CO., LTD.—See IHI Corporation; *Int'l*, pg. 3604
CHARLES ROSS & SON COMPANY; *U.S. Private*, pg. 853
CHATHAM CORPORATION; *U.S. Private*, pg. 868
CHEMITHON CONSTRUCTORS LLC—See Chemithon Enterprises, Inc.; *U.S. Private*, pg. 872
THE CHEMITHON CORP.—See Chemithon Enterprises, Inc.; *U.S. Private*, pg. 872
CHENGDU LEEJUN INDUSTRIAL CO., LTD.; *Int'l*, pg. 1468
CHENGDU TECHCENT ENVIRONMENT INDUSTRY CO., LTD.; *Int'l*, pg. 1469
CHEN HSONG EUROPE B.V.—See Chen Hsong Holdings Ltd.; *Int'l*, pg. 1464
CHEN HSONG GERMANY GMBH—See Chen Hsong Holdings Ltd.; *Int'l*, pg. 1464
CHEN HSONG MACHINERY CO. LTD.—See Chen Hsong Holdings Ltd.; *Int'l*, pg. 1464
CHEN HSONG MACHINERY TAIWAN CO. LTD.—See Chen Hsong Holdings Ltd.; *Int'l*, pg. 1464
CHEN HSONG (MIDDLE EAST) FZE—See Chen Hsong Holdings Ltd.; *Int'l*, pg. 1464
CHEN HSONG MIDDLE EAST MAKINE TICARET ANONIM SIRKETI—See Chen Hsong Holdings Ltd.; *Int'l*, pg. 1464
CHEN HSONG SOUTH AMERICA IMPORTACAO, EXPORTACAO E COMERCIO DE EQUIPAMENTOS LTDA.—See Chen Hsong Holdings Ltd.; *Int'l*, pg. 1464
CHIA YI STEEL CO., LTD.; *Int'l*, pg. 1475
CHINA-EAST RESOURCES IMPORT & EXPORT CO., LTD.—See China Machinery Engineering Corporation; *Int'l*, pg. 1516
CHINA EQUIPMENT INTERNATIONAL TRADING CO., LTD.—See China Machinery Engineering Corporation; *Int'l*, pg. 1516
CHINA ERZHONG GROUP DEYANG HEAVY INDUSTRIES CO., LTD.; *Int'l*, pg. 1500
CHINA EVERBEST DEVELOPMENT INTERNATIONAL LIMITED—See China Machinery Engineering Corporation; *Int'l*, pg. 1516
CHINA FIRST HEAVY INDUSTRIES CO., LTD.; *Int'l*, pg. 1503
CHINA FUTEX HOLDINGS LIMITED; *Int'l*, pg. 1503
CHINA HP CO., LTD.—See HP Inc.; *U.S. Public*, pg. 1062
CHINA JIKAN RESEARCH INSTITUTE OF ENGINEERING INVESTIGATIONS & DESIGN, CO., LTD.—See China Machinery Engineering Corporation; *Int'l*, pg. 1516
CHINA MACHINERY ENGINEERING CORPORATION (PNG) LIMITED—See China Machinery Engineering Corporation; *Int'l*, pg. 1516
CHINA MACHINERY ENGINEERING HENAN CO., LTD.—See China Machinery Engineering Corporation; *Int'l*, pg. 1516
CHINA MACHINERY ENGINEERING WUXI CO., LTD.—See China Machinery Engineering Corporation; *Int'l*, pg. 1516
CHINA MACHINERY & EQUIPMENT INTERNATIONAL TENDERING CO., LTD.—See China Machinery Engineering Corporation; *Int'l*, pg. 1516
CHINA NATIONAL COMPLETE ENGINEERING CORPORATION—See China Machinery Engineering Corporation; *Int'l*, pg. 1516
CHINA NATIONAL GARMENTS GROUP CORPORATION—See China Hi-Tech Group Co., Ltd.; *Int'l*, pg. 1507
CHINA STEEL MACHINERY CORPORATION—See China Steel Corporation; *Int'l*, pg. 1555
CHINA TEXTILE SCIENCE & TECHNOLOGY CO., LTD.—See China Hi-Tech Group Co., Ltd.; *Int'l*, pg. 1507
CHRISTIAN MAYR GMBH & CO. KG; *Int'l*, pg. 1586
CHTC HEAVY INDUSTRY CO., LTD.—See China Hi-Tech Group Co., Ltd.; *Int'l*, pg. 1507
CHTC HOLDINGS CO., LTD.—See China Hi-Tech Group Co., Ltd.; *Int'l*, pg. 1507
CHTC INVESTMENT MANAGEMENT CO., LTD.—See China Hi-Tech Group Co., Ltd.; *Int'l*, pg. 1507
CHTC REAL ESTATE CO., LTD.—See China Hi-Tech Group Co., Ltd.; *Int'l*, pg. 1507
CHUGOKU MARINE PAINTS, LTD. - KYUSHU FACTORY—See Chugoku Marine Paints, Ltd.; *Int'l*, pg. 1595
CHUGOKU MARINE PAINTS, LTD. - SHIGA FACTORY—See Chugoku Marine Paints, Ltd.; *Int'l*, pg. 1595
CIC INTERNATIONAL LTD.; *U.S. Private*, pg. 896
CIE AUTOMOTIVE MAROC, S.A.R.L. D'AU—See Cie Automotive S.A.; *Int'l*, pg. 1604
CIMC USA INC.—See China International Marine Containers (Group) Co., Ltd.; *Int'l*, pg. 1511
CINCINNATI INDUSTRIAL MACHINERY—See The Armor Group, Inc.; *U.S. Private*, pg. 3988
CIPHERLAB ELECTRONICS TRADING (SHANGHAI) CO., LTD.—See Cipherlab Co., Ltd.; *Int'l*, pg. 1616
CIPHERLAB USA INC.—See Cipherlab Co., Ltd.; *Int'l*, pg. 1616
CIRCUIT CHEMISTRY EQUIPMENT—See Activar, Inc.; *U.S. Private*, pg. 68
CITIC HEAVY INDUSTRIES CO., LTD.; *Int'l*, pg. 1621
CITIC HEAVY MACHINERY CO., LTD.—See CITIC Group Corporation; *Int'l*, pg. 1620
CITIC HIC NORTH AMERICA CO., LTD.—See CITIC Heavy Industries Co., Ltd.; *Int'l*, pg. 1621
CITIC MACHINERY MANUFACTURING CO., LTD.—See CITIC Group Corporation; *Int'l*, pg. 1621
CITIZEN SYSTEMS EUROPE GMBH—See Citizen Watch Co., Ltd.; *Int'l*, pg. 1624
CKD CORPORATION - YOKKAICHI PLANT—See CKD Corporation; *Int'l*, pg. 1639
CKD MEXICO, S. DE R.L. DE C.V.—See CKD Corporation; *Int'l*, pg. 1639
CKD NIKKI DENSO CO., LTD.—See CKD Corporation; *Int'l*, pg. 1639
CKD VIETNAM ENGINEERING CO., LTD.—See CKD Corporation; *Int'l*, pg. 1639
CLARK EQUIPMENT CO.—See Doosan Corporation; *Int'l*, pg. 2172
CLEAN FACTOMATION, INC. - ASAN PLANT—See Daifuku Co., Ltd.; *Int'l*, pg. 1924
CLEAN FACTOMATION, INC.—See Daifuku Co., Ltd.; *Int'l*, pg. 1924
CLEMCO DANMARK APS—See Clemco Industries Corp.; *U.S. Private*, pg. 939
CLEMCO INTERNATIONAL GMBH—See Clemco Industries Corp.; *U.S. Private*, pg. 939
CLEMCO INTERNATIONAL, S.A.—See Clemco Industries Corp.; *U.S. Private*, pg. 939
CLEMCO KFT—See Clemco Industries Corp.; *U.S. Private*, pg. 939
CLINTON INDUSTRIES, INC.; *U.S. Private*, pg. 945
CLONDALKIN GROUP PLC—See Egeria Capital Management B.V.; *Int'l*, pg. 2323
CLYDE BERGEMANN MATERIALS HANDLING LTD—See Clyde Blowers Capital IM LLP; *Int'l*, pg. 1665
CLYDE BERGEMANN POWER GROUP AMERICAS INC. - AIR-GAS HANDLING PRODUCT DIVISION—See Clyde Blowers Capital IM LLP; *Int'l*, pg. 1665
CLYDE BERGEMANN POWER GROUP AMERICAS INC. - AIR POLLUTION CONTROL PRODUCT DIVISION—See Clyde Blowers Capital IM LLP; *Int'l*, pg. 1665
CLYDE BERGEMANN POWER GROUP AMERICAS INC. - MATERIAL HANDLING PRODUCT DIVISION—See Clyde Blowers Capital IM LLP; *Int'l*, pg. 1665
CMC INDUSTRIAL ELECTRONICS LTD.—See Ag Growth International Inc.; *Int'l*, pg. 198
CMC MAGNETICS CORPORATION; *Int'l*, pg. 1669
CMC TECHNOLOGIES ISRAEL LTD.; *Int'l*, pg. 1669
CMD CORPORATION; *U.S. Private*, pg. 950
CMEC BEIJING PROPERTY DEVELOPMENT CO., LTD.—See China Machinery Engineering Corporation; *Int'l*, pg. 1515
CMEC ENGINEERING MACHINERY IMPORT & EXPORT CO., LTD.—See China Machinery Engineering Corporation; *Int'l*, pg. 1515
CMEC GENERAL MACHINERY IMPORT & EXPORT CO., LTD.—See China Machinery Engineering Corporation; *Int'l*, pg. 1516
CMEC GROUP SHANGHAI INTERNATIONAL FORWARDING CO., LTD.—See China Machinery Engineering Corporation; *Int'l*, pg. 1516
CMEC GUINEA EQUATORIAL, S.L.—See China Machinery Engineering Corporation; *Int'l*, pg. 1516
CMEC INTERNATIONAL ENGINEERING CO., LTD.—See China Machinery Engineering Corporation; *Int'l*, pg. 1516
CMEC LANKA (PRIVATE) LIMITED—See China Machinery Engineering Corporation; *Int'l*, pg. 1516
CMEC MIDDLE EAST FZE—See China Machinery Engineering Corporation; *Int'l*, pg. 1516
CMEC PETROCHEMICAL-GENERAL MACHINERY CO., LTD.—See China Machinery Engineering Corporation; *Int'l*, pg. 1516
CMEC SAUDI FOR CONSTRUCTION LLC—See China Machinery Engineering Corporation; *Int'l*, pg. 1516
CMEC ZAMBIA DEVELOPMENT LIMITED—See China Machinery Engineering Corporation; *Int'l*, pg. 1516
CMIC ENMEI CO., LTD.—See China Machinery Engineering Corporation; *Int'l*, pg. 1516
CMJ CO., LTD.—See China Metal Products Co., Ltd.; *Int'l*, pg. 1523
CMK MECHANICS CORPORATION—See CMK Corporation; *Int'l*, pg. 1671
CMK MULTI CORPORATION—See CMK Corporation; *Int'l*, pg. 1671
COATS-WARNER CORPORATION—See Blower Dempsay Corporation; *U.S. Private*, pg. 584
COGENT TECHNOLOGIES, INC.—See Engage Technologies Corp.; *U.S. Private*, pg. 1397
COHESANT, INC.; *U.S. Private*, pg. 963
COJAFEX B.V.—See McDermott International, Inc.; *U.S. Public*, pg. 1405
COLD JET LLC; *U.S. Private*, pg. 965
COLEMAN MANUFACTURING LIMITED—See Westinghouse Air Brake Technologies Corporation; *U.S. Public*, pg. 2357
COLIN MEAR ENGINEERING LTD; *Int'l*, pg. 1698
COL-MET SPRAY BOOTHS, INC.; *U.S. Private*, pg. 965
COLOR IMAGING INC.; *U.S. Private*, pg. 972
COLUMBIA MACHINE INC.; *U.S. Private*, pg. 977
COMPANIA INDUSTRIAL EL VOLCAN SA; *Int'l*, pg. 1749
COMPASS CHEMICAL INTERNATIONAL LLC—See Bain Capital, LP; *U.S. Private*, pg. 441
COMPASS PRECISION LLC; *U.S. Private*, pg. 999
COMPONENT SPECIALTY, INC.—See UCA Group Component Specialty Inc.; *U.S. Private*, pg. 4273
COMPRESSION COMPONENTS & SERVICE, LLC—See Operio Group, LLC; *U.S. Private*, pg. 3032
THE CONAIR GROUP, INC.; *U.S. Private*, pg. 4013
CONEXA LLC; *U.S. Private*, pg. 1012
CONSEC CORPORATION; *Int'l*, pg. 1769
CONSOLIDATED BOTTLE CORPORATION—See Keystone Group, L.P.; *U.S. Private*, pg. 2297
CONTAINER GRAPHICS CORPORATION—See Container Graphics Corporation; *U.S. Private*, pg. 1026
CONTINENTAL TRADING CO. LLC—See GIBCA Limited; *Int'l*, pg. 2962
CONTITECH RUBBER INDUSTRIAL KFT.—See Continental Aktiengesellschaft; *Int'l*, pg. 1781

N.A.I.C.S. INDEX

333248 — ALL OTHER INDUSTRIA...

CONTRACT INDUSTRIAL TOOLING, INC.; *U.S. Private*, pg. 1032
CONTRATISTAS IHI E&C MEXICO, S.A.DE C.V.—See IHI Corporation; *Int'l*, pg. 3604
CONTROL PRINT LIMITED—See Control Print Ltd.; *Int'l*, pg. 1785
COORD3 S.R.L—See Atlas Copco AB; *Int'l*, pg. 680
COORSTEK ENGINEERED METALS ULC—See CoorsTek, Inc.; *U.S. Private*, pg. 1043
COORSTEK, INC. - COORSTEK TULSA FACILITY—See CoorsTek, Inc.; *U.S. Private*, pg. 1044
COORSTEK KK - HADANO FACILITY—See CoorsTek, Inc.; *U.S. Private*, pg. 1043
COORSTEK KK - KARIYA FACILITY—See CoorsTek, Inc.; *U.S. Private*, pg. 1043
COORSTEK KK - OGUNI FACILITY—See CoorsTek, Inc.; *U.S. Private*, pg. 1043
COORSTEK MACHINERY CORPORATION—See CoorsTek, Inc.; *U.S. Private*, pg. 1043
COPERION CORPORATION—See Hillenbrand, Inc.; *U.S. Public*, pg. 1036
COPERION PELLETIZING TECHNOLOGY GMBH—See Hillenbrand, Inc.; *U.S. Public*, pg. 1036
COSMOS MACHINERY LIMITED—See Cosmos Machinery Enterprises Limited; *Int'l*, pg. 1813
CPG INTERNATIONAL S.P.A.; *Int'l*, pg. 1824
CRABTREE OF GATESHEAD LTD.; *Int'l*, pg. 1827
CRAFTSMAN AUTOMATION LIMITED; *Int'l*, pg. 1827
CRAIG MANUFACTURING LTD.; *Int'l*, pg. 1827
CREO IL LTD.—See Eastman Kodak Company; *U.S. Public*, pg. 707
CROWN IRON WORKS COMPANY—See Gilbert Global Equity Partners; *U.S. Private*, pg. 1699
CROW TECHNOLOGIES 1977 LTD.; *Int'l*, pg. 1857
CSEPEL HOLDING PLC; *Int'l*, pg. 1864
CTCI MACHINERY CORPORATION—See CTCI Corporation; *Int'l*, pg. 1870
CUBIC KOREA INC. - BUSAN FACTORY—See Cubic Korea INC.; *Int'l*, pg. 1875
CUSTOM INDUSTRIES INC.; *U.S. Private*, pg. 1129
CUSTOM-PAK, INC. - DEWITT PLANT—See Custom-Pak, Inc.; *U.S. Private*, pg. 1130
CUSTOM PLASTICS INTERNATIONAL LTD.; *Int'l*, pg. 1880
CYG INSULATOR CO., LTD.—See ChangYuan Group Ltd.; *Int'l*, pg. 1444
DAEMYONG ENG CO., LTD - GUMI FACTORY—See AVACO CO., Ltd; *Int'l*, pg. 733
DAEMYONG ENG CO., LTD.—See AVACO CO., Ltd; *Int'l*, pg. 733
DAIDO ELECTRONICS (GUANGDONG) CO., LTD.—See Daido Steel Co., Ltd.; *Int'l*, pg. 1922
DAIDO GENERAL SERVICE CO., LTD.—See Daido Kogyo Co., Ltd.; *Int'l*, pg. 1920
DAIDO KENSETSU CO., LTD.—See Daido Kogyo Co., Ltd.; *Int'l*, pg. 1920
DAIDO KOGYO CO., LTD.; *Int'l*, pg. 1920
DAIDO PLANT INDUSTRIES CO., LTD.—See Daido Steel Co., Ltd.; *Int'l*, pg. 1923
DAIFUKU AMERICA CORPORATION—See Daifuku Co., Ltd.; *Int'l*, pg. 1925
DAIFUKU AUTOMATION (TIANJIN) CO., LTD.—See Daifuku Co., Ltd.; *Int'l*, pg. 1925
DAIFUKU CANADA INC.—See Daifuku Co., Ltd.; *Int'l*, pg. 1925
DAIFUKU (CHINA) CO., LTD.—See Daifuku Co., Ltd.; *Int'l*, pg. 1925
DAIFUKU (CHINA) MANUFACTURING CO., LTD.—See Daifuku Co., Ltd.; *Int'l*, pg. 1925
DAIFUKU CO., LTD. - SHIGA WORKS—See Daifuku Co., Ltd.; *Int'l*, pg. 1925
DAIFUKU CO., LTD.; *Int'l*, pg. 1924
DAIFUKU DESIGN & ENGINEERING CO., LTD.—See Daifuku Co., Ltd.; *Int'l*, pg. 1925
DAIFUKU EUROPE LTD.—See Daifuku Co., Ltd.; *Int'l*, pg. 1925
DAIFUKU INDIA PRIVATE LIMITED—See Daifuku Co., Ltd.; *Int'l*, pg. 1925
DAIFUKU KOREA CO., LTD. - CARWASH DIVISION—See Daifuku Co., Ltd.; *Int'l*, pg. 1925
DAIFUKU KOREA CO., LTD. - OVERSEAS DIVISION—See Daifuku Co., Ltd.; *Int'l*, pg. 1925
DAIFUKU KOREA CO., LTD.—See Daifuku Co., Ltd.; *Int'l*, pg. 1925
DAIFUKU LOGAN LTD—See Daifuku Co., Ltd.; *Int'l*, pg. 1925
DAIFUKU LOGISTIC TECHNOLOGY CO., LTD.—See Daifuku Co., Ltd.; *Int'l*, pg. 1925
DAIFUKU (MALAYSIA) SDN. BHD.—See Daifuku Co., Ltd.; *Int'l*, pg. 1925
DAIFUKU MANUFACTURING TECHNOLOGY CO., LTD.—See Daifuku Co., Ltd.; *Int'l*, pg. 1925
DAIFUKU MECHATRONICS (SINGAPORE) PTE. LTD.—See Daifuku Co., Ltd.; *Int'l*, pg. 1925
DAIFUKU PIONEER CO., LTD.—See Daifuku Co., Ltd.; *Int'l*, pg. 1925
DAIFUKU (THAILAND) LTD.—See Daifuku Co., Ltd.; *Int'l*, pg. 1925

DAIICHI ENGINEERING CO., LTD.—See Daiichi Jitsugyo Co. Ltd.; *Int'l*, pg. 1927
DAIKIN HYDRAULIC ENGINEERING CO., LTD.—See Daikin Industries, Ltd.; *Int'l*, pg. 1934
DAIKIN LUBRICATION PRODUCTS & ENGINEERING CO., LTD.—See Daikin Industries, Ltd.; *Int'l*, pg. 1934
DALAIN HUARUI HEAVY INDUSTRY INDIA COMPANY PRIVIATE LIMITED—See Dalian Huarui Heavy Industry Group Co., Ltd.; *Int'l*, pg. 1952
DALIAN ENERGAS GAS-SYSTEM CO., LTD.; *Int'l*, pg. 1951
DALIAN HAOSENREAD EQUIPMENT MANUFACTURE CO., LTD.—See Dalian Haosen Equipment Manufacturing Co., Ltd.; *Int'l*, pg. 1951
DALIAN HAOSEN SOFTWARE CO., LTD.—See Dalian Haosen Equipment Manufacturing Co., Ltd.; *Int'l*, pg. 1951
DALIAN HUARUI HEAVY INDUSTRY GROUP CO., LTD.; *Int'l*, pg. 1952
DALIAN MY GYM EDUCATION TECHNOLOGY CO., LTD.; *Int'l*, pg. 1952
DATATECHNIC S.A.S.—See Durr AG; *Int'l*, pg. 2233
DA TECHNOLOGY CO., LTD.; *Int'l*, pg. 1902
DATRON AG; *Int'l*, pg. 1982
DECKEL MAHO PFRONTEN GMBH—See DMG MORI Co., Ltd.; *Int'l*, pg. 2144
DECKEL MAHO SEEBACH GMBH—See DMG MORI Co., Ltd.; *Int'l*, pg. 2144
DEDERT CORPORATION; *U.S. Private*, pg. 1188
DE DIETRICH PROCESS SYSTEMS GMBH—See De Dietrich Process Systems S.A.; *Int'l*, pg. 1995
DE DIETRICH PROCESS SYSTEMS, INC.—See De Dietrich Process Systems S.A.; *Int'l*, pg. 1995
DE DIETRICH PROCESS SYSTEMS S.A. - GLASS-LINING PLANT—See De Dietrich Process Systems S.A.; *Int'l*, pg. 1995
DEDOES INDUSTRIES INC.; *U.S. Private*, pg. 1188
DEK PRINTING MACHINES GMBH—See Dover Corporation; *U.S. Public*, pg. 680
DEK PRINTING MACHINES LIMITED—See Dover Corporation; *U.S. Public*, pg. 680
DELACHAUX SA—See CVC Capital Partners SICAV-FIS S.A.; *Int'l*, pg. 1886
DE LA RUE CURRENCY (DIVISIONAL ENGINEERING UNIT)—See De La Rue plc; *Int'l*, pg. 1996
DELPHAX TECHNOLOGIES INC.; *U.S. Public*, pg. 651
DELPHAX TECHNOLOGIES LTD.—See Delphax Technologies Inc.; *U.S. Public*, pg. 651
DELTA EQUIPMENT S.A.—See Convum Ltd.; *Int'l*, pg. 1788
DELTA POWER SERVICES, LLC—See Babcock & Wilcox Enterprises, Inc.; *U.S. Public*, pg. 262
DENIS CIMAF INC.—See Alamo Group Inc.; *U.S. Public*, pg. 71
DESCO EQUIPMENT CORP.—See Apex Machine Co.; *U.S. Private*, pg. 293
DESOUTTER GMBH—See Atlas Copco AB; *Int'l*, pg. 682
DETROIT TOOL & ENGINEERING COMPANY—See Thompson Street Capital Manager LLC; *U.S. Private*, pg. 4161
DEUBLIN ASIA PACIFIC PTE LTD—See Hoerbiger Holding AG; *Int'l*, pg. 3439
DEUBLIN IBERICA, S.L.—See Hoerbiger Holding AG; *Int'l*, pg. 3439
DEUBLIN POLSKA SP. Z O.O—See Hoerbiger Holding AG; *Int'l*, pg. 3439
DEVILBISS AUTOMOTIVE REFINISHING—See Carlisle Companies Incorporated; *U.S. Public*, pg. 436
DHP INDIA LIMITED; *Int'l*, pg. 2100
DIAMOND POWER AUSTRALIA PTY., LTD.—See Babcock & Wilcox Enterprises, Inc.; *U.S. Public*, pg. 262
DIAMOND POWER CENTRAL & EASTERN EUROPE S.R.O.—See Babcock & Wilcox Enterprises, Inc.; *U.S. Public*, pg. 262
DIAMOND POWER FINLAND OY—See Babcock & Wilcox Enterprises, Inc.; *U.S. Public*, pg. 262
DIAMOND POWER GERMANY GMBH—See Babcock & Wilcox Enterprises, Inc.; *U.S. Public*, pg. 262
DIAMOND POWER INTERNATIONAL, INC.—See Babcock & Wilcox Enterprises, Inc.; *U.S. Public*, pg. 262
DIAMOND POWER MACHINE (HUBEI) CO., INC.—See Babcock & Wilcox Enterprises, Inc.; *U.S. Public*, pg. 262
DIAMOND POWER SERVICES S.E.A. LTD.—See Babcock & Wilcox Enterprises, Inc.; *U.S. Public*, pg. 262
DIAMOND POWER SPECIALTY COMPANY—See Babcock & Wilcox Enterprises, Inc.; *U.S. Public*, pg. 262
DIAMOND POWER SPECIALTY LTD.—See Babcock & Wilcox Enterprises, Inc.; *U.S. Public*, pg. 262
DIAMOND POWER SPECIALTY (PTY) LTD.—See Babcock & Wilcox Enterprises, Inc.; *U.S. Public*, pg. 262
DIAMOND POWER SWEDEN AB—See Babcock & Wilcox Enterprises, Inc.; *U.S. Public*, pg. 262
DIATEC S.R.L.—See ANDRITZ AG; *Int'l*, pg. 455
DIEFFENBACHER CZ HYDRAULICKE LISY, S.R.O—See Dieffenbacher Holding GmbH & Co. KG; *Int'l*, pg. 2114
DIEFFENBACHER MASCHINENFABRIK GMBH—See Dieffenbacher Holding GmbH & Co. KG; *Int'l*, pg. 2114
DIEFFENBACHER NORTH AMERICA, INC.—See Dieffenbacher Holding GmbH & Co. KG; *Int'l*, pg. 2114

DIGIDOC S.R.L.—See I.M.A. Industria Macchine Automatiche S.p.A.; *Int'l*, pg. 3565
DIGIPRINT AS—See Bergman & Beving AB; *Int'l*, pg. 980
DILLI INCORPORATED; *Int'l*, pg. 2125
DISA INDIA LTD—See Altor Equity Partners AB; *Int'l*, pg. 395
DISA INDUSTRIES A/S—See Altor Equity Partners AB; *Int'l*, pg. 395
DISCO HI-TEC MOROCCO SARL—See Disco Corporation; *Int'l*, pg. 2132
DISKUS WERKE AG; *Int'l*, pg. 2135
DITEMSA, S.A. DE C.V.; *Int'l*, pg. 2137
DIVERSE SUPPLY CHAIN (SG) PTE. LTD.—See 9R Limited; *Int'l*, pg. 17
DJK INNOVALUE CORPORATION—See Daiichi Jitsugyo Co. Ltd.; *Int'l*, pg. 1927
D&K CUSTOM MACHINE DESIGN INC.—See D&K Group, Inc.; *U.S. Private*, pg. 1138
DME COMPANY LLC—See Hillenbrand, Inc.; *U.S. Public*, pg. 1037
DME EUROPE C.V.B.A.—See Hillenbrand, Inc.; *U.S. Public*, pg. 1037
DMG ECOLINE GMBH—See DMG MORI Co., Ltd.; *Int'l*, pg. 2144
DMT DEMMINER MASCHINENBAU TECHNIK GMBH; *Int'l*, pg. 2146
DMW CORPORATION - MISHIMA PLANT—See DMW Corporation; *Int'l*, pg. 2147
DNP IMAGINGCOMM ASIA SDN. BHD.—See Dai Nippon Printing Co., Ltd.; *Int'l*, pg. 1914
DNP IMAGINGCOMM EUROPE B.V.—See Dai Nippon Printing Co., Ltd.; *Int'l*, pg. 1914
DNP MICRO TECHNICA CO., LTD.—See Dai Nippon Printing Co., Ltd.; *Int'l*, pg. 1915
DOCK PRODUCTS CANADA—See ASSA ABLOY AB; *Int'l*, pg. 633
DOHMEYER HOLDING BVBA—See Air Water Inc.; *Int'l*, pg. 240
DOLPHIN INTERNATIONAL BERHAD—See Asia Poly Holdings Berhad; *Int'l*, pg. 615
DOMINO ASIA PTE. LTD.—See Brother Industries, Ltd.; *Int'l*, pg. 1197
DOMINO CHINA LIMITED—See Brother Industries, Ltd.; *Int'l*, pg. 1197
DOMINO GRAPH TECH AG—See Brother Industries, Ltd.; *Int'l*, pg. 1197
DOMINO LASER GMBH—See Brother Industries, Ltd.; *Int'l*, pg. 1197
DOMINO PRINTING TECHNOLOGY LTD.—See Brother Industries, Ltd.; *Int'l*, pg. 1198
DONAGHYS AUSTRALIA PTY LTD—See Donaghys Limited; *Int'l*, pg. 2163
DONALDSON COLOMBIA S.A.S.—See Donaldson Company, Inc.; *U.S. Public*, pg. 675
DONCASTERS TRUCAST LTD.—See Dubai Holding LLC; *Int'l*, pg. 2218
DONGAH GEOLOGICAL ENGINEERING CO., LTD. - EUMSEONG PLANT—See DongAh Geological Engineering Co., Ltd.; *Int'l*, pg. 2165
DONGGUAN CHAOZHI NEW MATERIALS CO., LTD.—See Guangdong Dtech Technology Co., Ltd.; *Int'l*, pg. 3154
DONGGUAN DINGTAIXIN ELEC. CO., LTD.—See Guangdong Dtech Technology Co., Ltd.; *Int'l*, pg. 3154
DOOSAN BOBCAT SINGAPORE PTE. LTD.—See Doosan Corporation; *Int'l*, pg. 2173
DOOSAN DIGITAL INNOVATION AMERICA LLC—See Doosan Corporation; *Int'l*, pg. 2173
DOOSAN INFRACORE CHINA CO., LTD.—See Doosan Corporation; *Int'l*, pg. 2173
DOOSAN INFRACORE (CHINA) INVESTMENT CO., LTD.—See Doosan Corporation; *Int'l*, pg. 2173
DOOSAN INFRACORE GERMANY GMBH—See HD Hyundai Infracore Co., Ltd.; *Int'l*, pg. 3300
DOOSAN INTERNATIONAL SOUTH AFRICA PTY LTD—See Doosan Corporation; *Int'l*, pg. 2173
DOOSAN POWER SYSTEMS ARABIA COMPANY LIMITED—See Doosan Corporation; *Int'l*, pg. 2173
DOOSAN SKODA POWER S.R.O—See Doosan Corporation; *Int'l*, pg. 2173
DOOSAN TURBOMACHINERY SERVICES INC.—See Doosan Corporation; *Int'l*, pg. 2174
DORIGHT CO., LTD.; *Int'l*, pg. 2177
DORNIER GMBH—See Airbus SE; *Int'l*, pg. 242
DOVER ASIA TRADING PRIVATE LTD.—See Dover Corporation; *U.S. Public*, pg. 679
DOVER CORPORATION (CANADA) LIMITED—See Dover Corporation; *U.S. Public*, pg. 679
DOYLE SYSTEMS; *U.S. Private*, pg. 1270
DRAGON PRODUCTS LTD.—See Modern Group, Ltd.; *U.S. Private*, pg. 2761
DR. HONLE AG; *Int'l*, pg. 2192
DRS DATA & RESEARCH SERVICES PLC; *Int'l*, pg. 2206
DRS ENVIRONMENTAL SYSTEMS, INC.—See Charlesbank Capital Partners, LLC; *U.S. Private*, pg. 855
DSI EUROPE GMBH—See Vishay Precision Group, Inc.; *U.S. Public*, pg. 2303
DUBAI ISLAMIC BANK PRINTING PRESS LLC—See Dubai Islamic Bank PSJ; *Int'l*, pg. 2220

DUNDEE SUSTAINABLE TECHNOLOGIES INC.; *Int'l*, pg. 2226
DUOYUAN PRINTING, INC.—See Duoyuan Investments Limited; *Int'l*, pg. 2227
DURR AFRICA (PTY.) LTD.—See Durr AG; *Int'l*, pg. 2230
DURR ECOCLEAN S.A.S.—See Durr AG; *Int'l*, pg. 2231
DURR INDIA PRIVATE LTD.—See Durr AG; *Int'l*, pg. 2231
DURR KOREA INC.—See Durr AG; *Int'l*, pg. 2231
DURR MEGTEC LLC—See Durr AG; *Int'l*, pg. 2231
DURR SOMAC GMBH—See Durr AG; *Int'l*, pg. 2231
DURR SYSTEMS, INC.—See Durr AG; *Int'l*, pg. 2231
DURR SYSTEMS (MALAYSIA) SDN. BHD.—See Durr AG; *Int'l*, pg. 2231
DURR SYSTEMS MAROC SARL AU—See Durr AG; *Int'l*, pg. 2231
DURR (THAILAND) CO., LTD.—See Durr AG; *Int'l*, pg. 2230
DURR VIETNAM COMPANY LIMITED—See Durr AG; *Int'l*, pg. 2232
DYNAMIC DIES INC.; *U.S. Private*, pg. 1298
DYNAMIC ROBOTIC SOLUTIONS AB—See AIP, LLC; *U.S. Private*, pg. 137
DYNAMIC ROBOTIC SOLUTIONS GMBH—See AIP, LLC; *U.S. Private*, pg. 137
DYNAMIC ROBOTIC SOLUTIONS, INC.—See AIP, LLC; *U.S. Private*, pg. 137
EAGLEBURGMANN SINGAPORE PTE. LTD—See Freudenberg SE; *Int'l*, pg. 2784
EAGLEBURGMANN VIETNAM COMPANY LTD.—See Freudenberg SE; *Int'l*, pg. 2784
EAGLE HIGHCAST CO., LTD.—See Eagle Industry Co., Ltd.; *Int'l*, pg. 2265
EAGLE INDUSTRY CO., LTD. - SAITAMA FACTORY—See Eagle Industry Co., Ltd.; *Int'l*, pg. 2265
EAGLE INDUSTRY FRANCE S.A.S.—See Eagle Industry Co., Ltd.; *Int'l*, pg. 2265
THE EAST ASIATIC 2010 (THAILAND) COMPANY LTD.—See EAC Invest AS; *Int'l*, pg. 2262
EASTMAN KODAK COMPANY, SMALL SALES AND CUST SERV OFFICE—See Eastman Kodak Company; *U.S. Public*, pg. 707
EASTMAN MACHINE COMPANY; *U.S. Private*, pg. 1322
EBARA MACHINERY CHINA CO., LTD.—See Ebara Corporation; *Int'l*, pg. 2283
EBCO INDUSTRIES LTD.; *Int'l*, pg. 2284
EBNER GMBH & CO. KG; *Int'l*, pg. 2285
EBSCO INDUSTRIES, INC. - NSC INTERNATIONAL DIVISION—See EBSCO Industries, Inc.; *U.S. Private*, pg. 1325
ECA S.A.—See Groupe Gorge S.A.; *Int'l*, pg. 3103
ECOCA INDUSTRIAL CO., LTD.—See Fair Friend Group; *Int'l*, pg. 2604
ECO INDUSTRIAL SERVICES COMPANY LIMITED—See Frasers Property Limited; *Int'l*, pg. 2766
ECRM IMAGING SYSTEMS, INC.; *U.S. Private*, pg. 1330
EDL NGD (WA) PTY LTD—See CK Hutchison Holdings Limited; *Int'l*, pg. 1636
EDWARDS GMBH—See Atlas Copco AB; *Int'l*, pg. 682
EDWARD'S MANUFACTURING CO, INC.—See Tenex Capital Management, L.P.; *U.S. Private*, pg. 3966
EFI BRAZIL LTDA.—See Siris Capital Group, LLC; *U.S. Private*, pg. 3672
EFI CRETAPRINT S.L.—See Siris Capital Group, LLC; *U.S. Private*, pg. 3672
EFI K.K.—See Siris Capital Group, LLC; *U.S. Private*, pg. 3672
EICKHOFF AUSTRALIA PTY. LTD.—See Eickhoff Maschinenfabrik GmbH; *Int'l*, pg. 2328
EICKHOFF BERGBAUTECHNIK GMBH—See Eickhoff Maschinenfabrik GmbH; *Int'l*, pg. 2328
EICKHOFF (G.B.) LTD.—See Eickhoff Maschinenfabrik GmbH; *Int'l*, pg. 2328
EICKHOFF GIESSEREI GMBH—See Eickhoff Maschinenfabrik GmbH; *Int'l*, pg. 2328
EICKHOFF MINING TECHNOLOGY GMBH—See Eickhoff Maschinenfabrik GmbH; *Int'l*, pg. 2328
EICKHOFF POLONIA LTD.—See Eickhoff Maschinenfabrik GmbH; *Int'l*, pg. 2328
EICKHOFF PTY LTD—See Eickhoff Maschinenfabrik GmbH; *Int'l*, pg. 2328
EIKEN CHINA CO., LTD.—See EIKEN CHEMICAL CO. LTD.; *Int'l*, pg. 2332
EKATO RUHR- UND MISCHTECHNIK GMBH; *Int'l*, pg. 2338
ELECTRONICS FOR IMAGING AB—See Siris Capital Group, LLC; *U.S. Private*, pg. 3672
ELECTRONICS FOR IMAGING AUSTRALIA PTY. LTD.—See Siris Capital Group, LLC; *U.S. Private*, pg. 3672
ELECTRONICS FOR IMAGING B.V.—See Siris Capital Group, LLC; *U.S. Private*, pg. 3672
ELECTRONICS FOR IMAGING GMBH—See Siris Capital Group, LLC; *U.S. Private*, pg. 3673
ELECTRONICS FOR IMAGING, INC. - ARIZONA—See Siris Capital Group, LLC; *U.S. Private*, pg. 3672
ELECTRONICS FOR IMAGING, INC. - INKJET SOLUTIONS—See Siris Capital Group, LLC; *U.S. Private*, pg. 3672
ELECTRONICS FOR IMAGING ITALIA SRL—See Siris Capital Group, LLC; *U.S. Private*, pg. 3673
ELECTRONICS FOR IMAGING KOREA CO., LTD.—See Siris Capital Group, LLC; *U.S. Private*, pg. 3672
ELGIN NATIONAL INDUSTRIES, INC.—See Brookfield Corporation; *Int'l*, pg. 1181
ELGI RUBBER COMPANY LIMITED - CINCINNATI RETREAD SYSTEMS DIVISION—See Elgi Rubber Company Limited; *Int'l*, pg. 2360
ELKOME OY—See Addtech AB; *Int'l*, pg. 133
ELLIOTT EBARA TURBOMACHINERY CORPORATION—See Ebara Corporation; *Int'l*, pg. 2284
ELLIOTT TURBOMACHINERY CANADA, INC.—See Ebara Corporation; *Int'l*, pg. 2284
ELLWOOD CHROME CRANKSHAFT COMPANY—See Ellwood Group, Inc.; *U.S. Private*, pg. 1375
EMERSON ELECTRIC COMPANY (INDIA) PRIVATE LIMITED—See Emerson Electric Co.; *U.S. Public*, pg. 745
EMSE, INC.—See Daburn Electronics & Cable Corp.; *U.S. Private*, pg. 1144
ENERGY RECOVERY, INC.; *U.S. Public*, pg. 762
ENERPAC AS—See Enerpac Tool Group Corp.; *U.S. Public*, pg. 765
ENGELHARD SOUTH AFRICA (PTY.) LTD.—See BASF SE; *Int'l*, pg. 883
ENRIC (LANG FANG) ENERGY EQUIPMENT INTEGRATION CO., LTD.—See China International Marine Containers (Group) Co., Ltd.; *Int'l*, pg. 1511
ENVIPCO HOLDING N.V.; *Int'l*, pg. 2453
ENVIROKINETICS INC.; *U.S. Private*, pg. 1406
ENVIRONMENTAL TECTONICS CORPORATION; *U.S. Public*, pg. 781
ENVIROTHERM GMBH—See Allied Resource Corporation; *U.S. Private*, pg. 187
EPPENDORF VERTRIEB DEUTSCHLAND GMBH—See Eppendorf AG; *Int'l*, pg. 2464
EQUIPCERAMIC, S.A.; *Int'l*, pg. 2485
ERCON ASSOCIATES—See PMC Capital Partners, LLC; *U.S. Private*, pg. 3218
ERIEZ MAGNETICS EUROPE LTD—See Eriez Manufacturing Co. Inc.; *U.S. Private*, pg. 1421
ERIEZ MANUFACTURING CO. INC.; *U.S. Private*, pg. 1421
ESCADA INNOVATIONS LTD.—See Siris Capital Group, LLC; *U.S. Private*, pg. 3673
ESPEC CORP.; *Int'l*, pg. 2505
ESSEX INDUSTRIES, INC.; *U.S. Private*, pg. 1428
ESTIC AMERICA, INC.—See Estic Corporation; *Int'l*, pg. 2518
EST TOOLS CO., LTD.; *Int'l*, pg. 2517
ETC-PZL AEROSPACE INDUSTRIES SP Z O.O.—See Environmental Tectonics Corporation; *U.S. Public*, pg. 781
ETLA TECHNOLOGY (M) SDN.BHD.—See Frencken Group Limited; *Int'l*, pg. 2772
ETS GEORGES RENAULT S.A.S.—See Atlas Copco AB; *Int'l*, pg. 678
ETTLINGER KUNSTSTOFFMASCHINEN GMBH—See Dover Corporation; *U.S. Public*, pg. 681
ETTLINGER NORTH AMERICA LP—See Dover Corporation; *U.S. Public*, pg. 681
EUROMECCANICA S.P.A.—See Chien Wei Precise Technology Co., Ltd.; *Int'l*, pg. 1477
EURO M.E.C. GMBH—See China Machinery Engineering Corporation; *Int'l*, pg. 1516
EUROP CONCEPT—See Hiolle Industries S.A.; *Int'l*, pg. 3401
EUROSPAN FURNITURE SDN. BHD.—See Eurospan Holdings Berhad; *Int'l*, pg. 2558
EURO-TRAMCO B.V.—See Ag Growth International Inc.; *Int'l*, pg. 198
EVANS MACTAVISH AGRICRAFT—See Evans MacTavish Agricraft Inc.; *U.S. Private*, pg. 1435
EVATEC AG; *Int'l*, pg. 2560
EVATEC NA INC.—See Evatec AG; *Int'l*, pg. 2561
EVATHERM AG; *Int'l*, pg. 2561
EVATHERM GMBH—See EVATHERM AG; *Int'l*, pg. 2561
EVATHERM KFT.—See EVATHERM AG; *Int'l*, pg. 2561
EVERCEL, INC.; *U.S. Private*, pg. 1437
EVERYBOT, INC.; *Int'l*, pg. 2569
EVOQUA WATER TECHNOLOGIES—See Xylem Inc.; *U.S. Public*, pg. 2393
EVOQUA WATER TECHNOLOGIES—See Xylem Inc.; *U.S. Public*, pg. 2394
EXCEL FOUNDRY & MACHINE INC.—See FLSmidth & Co. A/S; *Int'l*, pg. 2712
EXCEL LASER TECHNOLOGY. PVT. LTD.—See Novanta Inc.; *U.S. Public*, pg. 1548
EXCEL TECHNOLOGY, INC.—See Novanta Inc.; *U.S. Public*, pg. 1548
EXONE AMERICAS LLC—See Desktop Metal, Inc.; *U.S. Public*, pg. 656
THE EXONE COMPANY—See Desktop Metal, Inc.; *U.S. Public*, pg. 656
EXONE GMBH—See Desktop Metal, Inc.; *U.S. Public*, pg. 656
EXONE ITALY S.R.L.—See Desktop Metal, Inc.; *U.S. Public*, pg. 656
EXONE KK—See Desktop Metal, Inc.; *U.S. Public*, pg. 656
EXONE PROPERTY GMBH—See Desktop Metal, Inc.; *U.S. Public*, pg. 656
EXONE SWEDEN AB—See Desktop Metal, Inc.; *U.S. Public*, pg. 656
FABMATICS GMBH; *Int'l*, pg. 2599
FABMATICS GMBH—See Fabmatics GmbH; *Int'l*, pg. 2599
FABRICO CENTRAL—See Audax Group, Limited Partnership; *U.S. Public*, pg. 387
FAIR FRIEND GROUP; *Int'l*, pg. 2604
FALMAC LIMITED; *Int'l*, pg. 2611
FALMAC MACHINERY (TIANJIN) LTD.—See Falmac Limited; *Int'l*, pg. 2611
FANDSTAN ELECTRIC GROUP LTD.—See Westinghouse Air Brake Technologies Corporation; *U.S. Public*, pg. 2358
FANDSTAN ELECTRIC LTD.—See Westinghouse Air Brake Technologies Corporation; *U.S. Public*, pg. 2358
FANUC LLC—See FANUC Corporation; *Int'l*, pg. 2614
FANUC ROBOMACHINE (SHENZHEN) LTD.—See FANUC Corporation; *Int'l*, pg. 2615
FARREL CORPORATION; *U.S. Private*, pg. 1480
FECO AJAX INC.—See Park-Ohio Holdings Corp.; *U.S. Public*, pg. 1639
FEI CPD B.V.—See Thermo Fisher Scientific Inc.; *U.S. Public*, pg. 2146
FELGUERA RAIL, S.A.U.—See Duro Felguera, S.A.; *Int'l*, pg. 2229
FENGXING CO., LTD.; *Int'l*, pg. 2634
FERROMATIK MILACRON GMBH—See Hillenbrand, Inc.; *U.S. Public*, pg. 1037
FERROMATIK MILACRON INDIA, LTD.—See Hillenbrand, Inc.; *U.S. Public*, pg. 1037
FFG WERKE GMBH—See Fair Friend Group; *Int'l*, pg. 2604
FFT PRODUKTIONSSYSTEME GMBH & CO. KG—See Fosun International Limited; *Int'l*, pg. 2750
FICO ASIA SDN. BHD.—See BE Semiconductor Industries N.V.; *Int'l*, pg. 931
FIDIA DO BRASIL COMERCIO DE EQUIPAMENTOS LTDA.—See FIDIA S.p.A.; *Int'l*, pg. 2655
FIEBIG & SCHILLINGS GMBH; *Int'l*, pg. 2655
FILTERMIST GMBH—See Absolent Air Care Group AB; *Int'l*, pg. 70
FILTISAC SA; *Int'l*, pg. 2663
FILTRAFINE PTE. LTD.—See Bright Sheland International Co., Ltd.; *Int'l*, pg. 1162
FINISHING BRANDS - INTERNATIONAL—See Carlisle Companies Incorporated; *U.S. Public*, pg. 436
FINN-LEY VAKUUM, S.R.O.—See Atlas Copco AB; *Int'l*, pg. 683
FIRESTONE INDUSTRIAL PRODUCTS, LLC - ARNHEM MANUFACTURING FACILITY—See Bridgestone Corporation; *Int'l*, pg. 1156
FIRESTONE PRODUTOS INDUSTRIAIS AV.—See Bridgestone Corporation; *Int'l*, pg. 1156
FIRST EIE SA; *Int'l*, pg. 2683
FIRST PLUS, INC.—See Iida Group Holdings Co., Ltd.; *Int'l*, pg. 3607
FLETCHER INDUSTRIES-INTERNATIONAL, INC.; *U.S. Private*, pg. 1542
FLI ENERGY LIMITED—See FLI International Limited; *Int'l*, pg. 2705
FLORIN GMBH—See DZ BANK AG Deutsche Zentral-Genossenschaftsbank; *Int'l*, pg. 2244
FLSMIDTH BOISE, INC.—See FLSmidth & Co. A/S; *Int'l*, pg. 2712
FLSMIDTH CONVEYOR ENGINEERING, INC.—See FLSmidth & Co. A/S; *Int'l*, pg. 2712
FLSMIDTH KREBS (BEIJING) LTD.—See FLSmidth & Co. A/S; *Int'l*, pg. 2712
FLSMIDTH KREBS INC.—See FLSmidth & Co. A/S; *Int'l*, pg. 2712
FLSMIDTH PFISTER GMBH—See FLSmidth & Co. A/S; *Int'l*, pg. 2712
FLSMIDTH PFISTER, INC.—See FLSmidth & Co. A/S; *Int'l*, pg. 2712
FLSMIDTH VENTOMATIC SPA—See FLSmidth & Co. A/S; *Int'l*, pg. 2710
FLS US HOLDINGS, INC.—See FLSmidth & Co. A/S; *Int'l*, pg. 2710
FLUID MANAGEMENT—See IDEX Corp; *U.S. Public*, pg. 1090
FLUIDOIL LIMITED—See FluidOil Limited; *Int'l*, pg. 2713
FLUIDOMAT LTD.; *Int'l*, pg. 2713
FMW INDUSTRIEANLAGENBAU GMBH—See HANNOVER Finanz GmbH; *Int'l*, pg. 3257
FOBOHA (GERMANY) GMBH—See Barnes Group Inc.; *U.S. Public*, pg. 277
FOBOHA (SWITZERLAND) AG—See Adval Tech Holding AG; *Int'l*, pg. 155
FOCUS LIGHTING & FIXTURES LIMITED; *Int'l*, pg. 2719
FOGG FILLER CO.—See Leonard Green & Partners, L.P.; *U.S. Private*, pg. 2427
FORMOSA HEAVY INDUSTRIES CORP.—See Formosa Plastics Corporation; *Int'l*, pg. 2735
FORMOSA PLASMA DISPLAY CORPORATION—See Formosa Plastics Corporation; *Int'l*, pg. 2735
FORTACO GROUP OY—See CapMan PLC; *Int'l*, pg. 1315
FRANCOTYP POSTALIA CANADA INC.—See Francotyp-

N.A.I.C.S. INDEX

333248 — ALL OTHER INDUSTRIA...

Postalia Holding AG; *Int'l*, pg. 2761
FRANCOTYP-POSTALIA, INC.—See Francotyp-Postalia Holding AG; *Int'l*, pg. 2761
FREUDENBERG ANLAGEN-UND WERKZEUGTECHNIK KG—See Freudenberg SE; *Int'l*, pg. 2785
FRIGOGLASS EAST AFRICA LTD.—See Frigoglass S.A.I.C.; *Int'l*, pg. 2792
FRIGOGLASS EURASIA LLC—See Frigoglass S.A.I.C.; *Int'l*, pg. 2792
FRIGOGLASS GMBH—See Frigoglass S.A.I.C.; *Int'l*, pg. 2792
FRIGOGLASS (GUANGZHOU) ICE COLD EQUIPMENT CO., LTD.—See Frigoglass S.A.I.C.; *Int'l*, pg. 2792
FRIGOGLASS INDIA PVT. LTD.—See Frigoglass S.A.I.C.; *Int'l*, pg. 2792
FRIGOGLASS NORDIC AS—See Frigoglass S.A.I.C.; *Int'l*, pg. 2792
FRIGOGLASS SOUTH AFRICA LTD.—See Frigoglass S.A.I.C.; *Int'l*, pg. 2792
FRIGOGLASS SP. Z O.O—See Frigoglass S.A.I.C.; *Int'l*, pg. 2792
FRIGOGLASS WEST AFRICA LIMITED—See Frigoglass S.A.I.C.; *Int'l*, pg. 2792
FRONTMATEC B.V.—See KKR & Co. Inc.; *U.S. Public*, pg. 1241
FRONTMATEC KOLDING A/S—See KKR & Co. Inc.; *U.S. Public*, pg. 1241
FSI ENERGY GROUP INC.; *Int'l*, pg. 2798
FSI INTERNATIONAL SERVICES LTD.—See FSI Energy Group Inc.; *Int'l*, pg. 2798
FUGRO-IMPROV, INC.—See Fugro N.V.; *Int'l*, pg. 2805
FUJIAN SANMING GEARBOX CO., LTD.—See Fujian Longxi Bearing (Group) Corporation Limited; *Int'l*, pg. 2818
FUJIFILM DIMATIX, INC.—See FUJIFILM Holdings Corporation; *Int'l*, pg. 2822
FUJI MACHINE AMERICA CORPORATION—See Fuji Corporation; *Int'l*, pg. 2809
FUJI MACHINE CHINA CO.,LTD.—See Fuji Corporation; *Int'l*, pg. 2809
FUJI ROTO GRAVURE SDN. BHD.—See Fuji Offset Plates Manufacturing Ltd; *Int'l*, pg. 2814
FUJITEC LANKA (PRIVATE) LTD.—See Fujitec Co., Ltd.; *Int'l*, pg. 2831
FUJITEC MYANMAR CO., LTD.—See Fujitec Co., Ltd.; *Int'l*, pg. 2831
FUJITEC PACIFIC, INC.—See Fujitec Co., Ltd.; *Int'l*, pg. 2831
FUJITEC (THAILAND) CO., LTD.—See Fujitec Co., Ltd.; *Int'l*, pg. 2831
FUJITEC URUGUAY S.A.—See Fujitec Co., Ltd.; *Int'l*, pg. 2831
FURUKAWA CASTEC CO., LTD.—See Furukawa Co., Ltd.; *Int'l*, pg. 2847
FURUKAWA ROCK DRILL INDIA PVT. LTD.—See Furukawa Co., Ltd.; *Int'l*, pg. 2847
FURUKAWA ROCK DRILL LATIN AMERICA S.A.—See Furukawa Co., Ltd.; *Int'l*, pg. 2847
FURUKAWA ROCK DRILL USA, INC.—See Furukawa Co., Ltd.; *Int'l*, pg. 2847
FUSION OEM; *U.S. Private*, pg. 1625
FUSIONTECH, INC.; *Int'l*, pg. 2849
GABLER ENGINEERING GMBH—See Hillenbrand, Inc.; *U.S. Public*, pg. 1036
GALA INDUSTRIES, INC.—See Dover Corporation; *U.S. Public*, pg. 681
GALE PACIFIC SPECIAL TEXTILES (NINGBO) LIMITED—See Gale Pacific Limited; *Int'l*, pg. 2872
GALFAB, INC.—See Cargotec Corporation; *Int'l*, pg. 1326
GALKIN AUTOMATED PRODUCTS CORP.—See Leggett & Platt, Incorporated; *U.S. Public*, pg. 1302
GALLUS DRUCKMASCHINEN GMBH—See Heidelberger Druckmaschinen AG; *Int'l*, pg. 3321
GALLUS FERD. RUESCH AG—See Heidelberger Druckmaschinen AG; *Int'l*, pg. 3321
GANGA FORGING LIMITED; *Int'l*, pg. 2880
GARIC LIMITED—See Bibby Line Group Limited; *Int'l*, pg. 1018
GATEWAY (TEXTILES) LIMITED—See Leggett & Platt, Incorporated; *U.S. Public*, pg. 1302
GEA BISCHOFF GMBH—See GEA Group Aktiengesellschaft; *Int'l*, pg. 2897
GEA BISCHOFF, INC.—See GEA Group Aktiengesellschaft; *Int'l*, pg. 2898
GEA FOOD SOLUTIONS NORTH AMERICA, INC.—See GEA Group Aktiengesellschaft; *Int'l*, pg. 2899
GEA MECHANICAL EQUIPMENT UK LIMITED—See GEA Group Aktiengesellschaft; *Int'l*, pg. 2901
GEA NU-CON LTD—See GEA Group Aktiengesellschaft; *Int'l*, pg. 2901
GEA NU-CON PTY. LTD.—See GEA Group Aktiengesellschaft; *Int'l*, pg. 2901
GEA PHARMA SYSTEMS (INDIA) PRIVATE LIMITED—See GEA Group Aktiengesellschaft; *Int'l*, pg. 2901
GEA PROCESS ENGINEERING CEE KFT.—See GEA Group Aktiengesellschaft; *Int'l*, pg. 2901
GEA PROCESS ENGINEERING CHILE S.A.—See GEA Group Aktiengesellschaft; *Int'l*, pg. 2901

GEA PROCESS ENGINEERING S.A. DE C.V.—See GEA Group Aktiengesellschaft; *Int'l*, pg. 2902
GEA PT FRANCE SAS—See GEA Group Aktiengesellschaft; *Int'l*, pg. 2901
GEARBOX EXPRESS, LLC; *U.S. Private*, pg. 1654
GEA UNIVALVE E.URL.—See GEA Group Aktiengesellschaft; *Int'l*, pg. 2903
GEA WESTFALIA SEPARATOR DEUTSCHLAND GMBH—See GEA Group Aktiengesellschaft; *Int'l*, pg. 2900
GEA WESTFALIA SEPARATOR POLSKA SP. Z O.O.—See GEA Group Aktiengesellschaft; *Int'l*, pg. 2900
GEA WESTFALIA SEPARATOR SOUTH AFRICA (PTY) LTD.—See GEA Group Aktiengesellschaft; *Int'l*, pg. 2901
GEA WESTFALIASURGE NORDIC A/S—See GEA Group Aktiengesellschaft; *Int'l*, pg. 2904
GEFIT LIVERNOIS ENGINEERING, LLC—See GEFIT S.p.A.; *Int'l*, pg. 2911
GEFIT S.P.A.; *Int'l*, pg. 2911
THE GEM CITY ENGINEERING CO., INC.—See CapitalWorks, LLC; *U.S. Private*, pg. 742
GENESYS INDUSTRIES INC.; *Int'l*, pg. 2922
GENETEC TECHNOLOGY BERHAD; *Int'l*, pg. 2922
GEORG FISCHER ENGINEERING AG—See Georg Fischer AG; *Int'l*, pg. 2935
GEORG FISCHER GESCHAFTSFUHRUNGS-GMBH—See Georg Fischer AG; *Int'l*, pg. 2935
GERBER SCIENTIFIC, INC. - GERBER TECHNOLOGY GROUP—See Vector Capital Management, L.P.; *U.S. Private*, pg. 4350
GERBER SCIENTIFIC INTERNATIONAL LDA.—See Vector Capital Management, L.P.; *U.S. Private*, pg. 4350
GERBER SCIENTIFIC LLC—See Vector Capital Management, L.P.; *U.S. Private*, pg. 4350
GERBER TECHNOLOGY GMBH—See Vector Capital Management, L.P.; *U.S. Private*, pg. 4351
GERBER TECHNOLOGY, LTD.—See Vector Capital Management, L.P.; *U.S. Private*, pg. 4351
GERBER TECHNOLOGY PTY. LTD.—See Vector Capital Management, L.P.; *U.S. Private*, pg. 4351
GERBER TECHNOLOGY SA DE CV—See Vector Capital Management, L.P.; *U.S. Private*, pg. 4351
GERBER TECHNOLOGY SARL—See Vector Capital Management, L.P.; *U.S. Private*, pg. 4351
GERRESHEIMER WERKZEUG- UND AUTOMATISIERUNGSTECHNIK GMBH—See Gerresheimer AG; *Int'l*, pg. 2944
GE-SHEN CORPORATION BERHAD; *Int'l*, pg. 2897
GESSNER/MILLER CORPORATION—See GHM Industries, Inc.; *U.S. Public*, pg. 1691
GF MACHINING SOLUTIONS SP. Z O.O.—See Georg Fischer AG; *Int'l*, pg. 2935
GHM INDUSTRIES, INC.; *U.S. Public*, pg. 1691
GIMATIC BULGARIA LTD.—See Barnes Group Inc.; *U.S. Public*, pg. 277
GIMATIC IBERIA S.L.—See Barnes Group Inc.; *U.S. Public*, pg. 277
GKD - GEBR. KUFFERATH AG; *Int'l*, pg. 2983
GLASTON EMERGING TECHNOLOGIES OY—See Glaston Oyj Abp; *Int'l*, pg. 2989
GLASTON MEXICO, S.A. DE C.V.—See Glaston Oyj Abp; *Int'l*, pg. 2989
GLASTON SPAIN S.L.—See Glaston Oyj Abp; *Int'l*, pg. 2989
GLASTON SWITZERLAND AG—See Glaston Oyj Abp; *Int'l*, pg. 2989
GLOBAL FINISHING SOLUTIONS LLC—See Curran Group, Inc.; *U.S. Private*, pg. 1125
GLOBAL WATER GROUP, INC.—See Eastern Water Resources Development & Management Public Company Limited; *Int'l*, pg. 2274
GLOBETRONICS TECHNOLOGY BHD.; *Int'l*, pg. 3007
GLORY F&C CO., LTD.—See GLORY Ltd.; *Int'l*, pg. 3009
GLORY INTERNATIONAL TRADING (SHANGHAI) CO., LTD.—See GLORY Ltd.; *Int'l*, pg. 3010
GLORY (PHILIPPINES) INC.—See GLORY Ltd.; *Int'l*, pg. 3009
GLUNZ & JENSEN HOLDING A/S; *Int'l*, pg. 3011
GLUNZ & JENSEN LTD.—See Glunz & Jensen Holding A/S; *Int'l*, pg. 3011
GLUNZ & JENSEN S.R.O.—See Glunz & Jensen Holding A/S; *Int'l*, pg. 3011
GODEX INTERNATIONAL CO., LTD.; *Int'l*, pg. 3019
GODREJ EFACEC AUTOMATION & ROBOTICS LTD.—See Efacec Capital, SGPS, S.A.; *Int'l*, pg. 2318
GODREJ EFACEC AUTOMATION & ROBOTICS LTD.—See Godrej & Boyce Mfg. Co. Ltd.; *Int'l*, pg. 3020
GOFF INC.; *U.S. Private*, pg. 1726
GOLSTA SDN. BHD.; *Int'l*, pg. 3037
GOM AMERICAS INC.—See Carl-Zeiss-Stiftung; *Int'l*, pg. 1336
GOM FRANCE SAS—See Carl-Zeiss-Stiftung; *Int'l*, pg. 1336
GOM GMBH—See Carl-Zeiss-Stiftung; *Int'l*, pg. 1336
GOM ITALIA S.R.L.—See Carl-Zeiss-Stiftung; *Int'l*, pg. 1336
GOM UK LIMITED—See Carl-Zeiss-Stiftung; *Int'l*, pg. 1336
GOODTECH SOLUTIONS MANUFACTURING AB—See BE Group AB; *Int'l*, pg. 931
GOSS GRAPHIC SYSTEMS JAPAN CORPORATION - SAYAMA—See AIP, LLC; *U.S. Private*, pg. 134

GOSS INTERNATIONAL AMERICAS, LLC—See AIP, LLC; *U.S. Private*, pg. 134
GOSS INTERNATIONAL EUROPE UK LTD.—See AIP, LLC; *U.S. Private*, pg. 134
GPN STROJIRNA S.R.O.—See Greiner Holding AG; *Int'l*, pg. 3079
GPS GLAS PRODUKTIONS SERVICE GMBH—See Compagnie de Saint-Gobain SA; *Int'l*, pg. 1735
GRADCO HOLDINGS, LLC; *U.S. Private*, pg. 1749
GRAFIX GMBH—See Dr. Honle AG; *Int'l*, pg. 2192
GRAHAM ENGINEERING CORPORATION—See The Graham Group, Inc.; *U.S. Private*, pg. 4036
GRAPHIC INNOVATORS INC.; *U.S. Private*, pg. 1757
GRAPHIC MEDIA PRODUCTS INC.; *U.S. Private*, pg. 1757
GRAPHIC PACKAGING INTERNATIONAL, INC. - CROSBY—See Graphic Packaging Holding Company; *U.S. Public*, pg. 959
GRAPHIC SYSTEMS SERVICES, INC.—See Eastman Kodak Company; *U.S. Public*, pg. 707
GRAPHIC VILLAGE, LLC—See Revitalize Capital; *U.S. Private*, pg. 3416
GRAVER TECHNOLOGIES LLC—See Berkshire Hathaway Inc.; *U.S. Public*, pg. 311
GREATOO (GUANGZHOU) ROBOT & INTELLIGENT MANUFACTURING CO., LTD.—See Greatoo Intelligent Equipment Inc.; *Int'l*, pg. 3067
GREENBELT RESOURCES CORP.; *U.S. Public*, pg. 964
GREENERPRINTER; *U.S. Private*, pg. 1777
GREENE, TWEED & CO., BENELUX B.V.—See Greene, Tweed & Co.; *U.S. Private*, pg. 1777
GREENE, TWEED & CO FRANCE SAS—See Greene, Tweed & Co.; *U.S. Private*, pg. 1777
GREENE, TWEED & CO. GMBH—See Greene, Tweed & Co.; *U.S. Private*, pg. 1777
GREENE, TWEED & CO. ITALIA S.R.L.—See Greene, Tweed & Co.; *U.S. Private*, pg. 1777
GREENE, TWEED & CO. JAPAN—See Greene, Tweed & Co.; *U.S. Private*, pg. 1777
GREENE, TWEED & CO., KOREA LTD.—See Greene, Tweed & Co.; *U.S. Private*, pg. 1777
GREENE, TWEED & CO., LIMITED—See Greene, Tweed & Co.; *U.S. Private*, pg. 1777
GREENE, TWEED & CO. PTE LTD.—See Greene, Tweed & Co.; *U.S. Private*, pg. 1777
GREENE, TWEED & CO. (SUISSE) SA—See Greene, Tweed & Co.; *U.S. Private*, pg. 1777
GREEN POINT (SINGAPORE) PTE. LTD.—See Far East Group Limited; *Int'l*, pg. 2616
GRENZEBACH MASCHINENBAU GMBH; *Int'l*, pg. 3081
GREYDON, INC.—See Leonard Green & Partners, L.P.; *U.S. Private*, pg. 2427
GROUP UP INDUSTRIAL CO., LTD.; *Int'l*, pg. 3090
GROZ-BECKERT KG; *Int'l*, pg. 3113
GROZ-BECKERT USA, INC.—See Groz-Beckert KG; *Int'l*, pg. 3113
G.S. COATING TECHNOLOGIES S.R.L.—See I.M.A. Industria Macchine Automatiche S.p.A.; *Int'l*, pg. 3565
GSN MASCHINEN-ANLAGEN-SERVICE GMBH; *Int'l*, pg. 3150
GT ADVANCED TECHNOLOGIES INC. - POLYSILICON DIVISION—See GT Advanced Technologies Inc.; *U.S. Private*, pg. 1801
GUANGDONG DTECH TECHNOLOGY CO., LTD.; *Int'l*, pg. 3154
GUANGDONG JINMING MACHINERY CO., LTD.; *Int'l*, pg. 3157
GUANGDONG JINMING MACHINERY CO., LTD.—See Guangdong Jinming Machinery Co., Ltd.; *Int'l*, pg. 3157
GUANGDONG JINMING MACHINERY CO., LTD.—See Guangdong Jinming Machinery Co., Ltd.; *Int'l*, pg. 3157
GUANGDONG JINMING MACHINERY CO., LTD.—See Guangdong Jinming Machinery Co., Ltd.; *Int'l*, pg. 3157
GUANGDONG ZHONGKE TIANYUAN NEW ENERGY TECHNOLOGY CO., LTD.—See China New Energy Limited; *Int'l*, pg. 1535
GUANGZHOU HAOZHI INDUSTRIAL CO., LTD.; *Int'l*, pg. 3165
GUANGZHOU MELCO INDUSTRIAL SUPPLIES CO., LTD.—See Cosmos Machinery Enterprises Limited; *Int'l*, pg. 1813
GUANGZHOU RISONG WELDSTONE INTELLIGENT EQUIPMENT CO., LTD.—See Guangzhou Risong Intelligent Technology Holding Co., Ltd.; *Int'l*, pg. 3167
GUDEL AUTOMATION GMBH—See Gudel Group AG; *Int'l*, pg. 3171
GUILD ASSOCIATES INC.; *U.S. Private*, pg. 1814
GULF BUSSINESS FORMS COMPANY W.L.L.—See First Investment Company K.S.C.C.; *Int'l*, pg. 2685
GUY BROWN PRODUCTS; *U.S. Private*, pg. 1820
GUYSON CORPORATION OF U.S.A.—See Guyson International Limited; *Int'l*, pg. 3189
GUYSON INTERNATIONAL LIMITED; *Int'l*, pg. 3189
GYROTRON TECHNOLOGY INC.; *U.S. Private*, pg. 1821
HAARSLEV INDUSTRIES A/S—See Altor Equity Partners AB; *Int'l*, pg. 394
HAARSLEV INDUSTRIES LTDA.—See Altor Equity Partners AB; *Int'l*, pg. 395

HAARSLEV INDUSTRIES SAC—See Altor Equity Partners AB; *Int'l*, pg. 395
HAARSLEV INDUSTRIES S.A.U.—See Altor Equity Partners AB; *Int'l*, pg. 395
HAARSLEV MACHINERY XUZHOU CO.—See Altor Equity Partners AB; *Int'l*, pg. 395
H A ECKHART & ASSOCIATES, INC.—See Arsenal Capital Management LP; *U.S. Private*, pg. 338
HAGIHANA MACHINERY (SHANGHAI) CO., LTD.—See Hagihara Industries Inc.; *Int'l*, pg. 3207
HAITIAN INTERNATIONAL GERMANY GMBH—See Haitian International Holdings Ltd.; *Int'l*, pg. 3217
HAITIAN INTERNATIONAL HOLDINGS LTD.; *Int'l*, pg. 3217
HAITIAN PLASTICS MACHINERY GROUP CO., LTD.—See Haitian International Holdings Ltd.; *Int'l*, pg. 3217
HALLITE SEALS AUSTRALIA PTY LIMITED—See Compagnie Generale des Etablissements Michelin SCA; *Int'l*, pg. 1742
HALLITE SHANGHAI COMPANY LIMITED—See Compagnie Generale des Etablissements Michelin SCA; *Int'l*, pg. 1742
HAMAI FUCHU FACTORY LTD.—See HAMAI INDUSTRIES LIMITED; *Int'l*, pg. 3235
HANDI QUILTER, INC.—See Branford Castle, Inc.; *U.S. Private*, pg. 639
HANGZHOU DAHE THERMO-MAGNETICS CO., LTD. (FTH)—See Ferrotec Holdings Corporation; *Int'l*, pg. 2643
HANGZHOU HIKROBOT TECHNOLOGY CO., LTD.—See Hangzhou Hikvision Digital Technology Co., Ltd.; *Int'l*, pg. 3247
HANKOOK PRECISION WORKS CO., LTD.—See Hankook Tire & Technology Co.,Ltd.; *Int'l*, pg. 3253
HAN KOOK STEEL & MILL CO., LTD.—See HNK Machine Tool Co., Ltd.; *Int'l*, pg. 3434
HANSEN INTERNATIONAL INC.; *U.S. Private*, pg. 1856
HANTRONG INVESTMENT CO., LTD.—See China Hi-Tech Group Co., Ltd.; *Int'l*, pg. 1507
HANYANG ENG CO., LTD.; *Int'l*, pg. 3267
HAOSEN AUTOMATION GMBH—See Dalian Haosen Equipment Manufacturing Co., Ltd.; *Int'l*, pg. 1952
HAOSEN AUTOMATION INDIA PRIVATE LIMITED—See Dalian Haosen Equipment Manufacturing Co., Ltd.; *Int'l*, pg. 1952
HAOSEN AUTOMATION NORTH AMERICA, INC.—See Dalian Haosen Equipment Manufacturing Co., Ltd.; *Int'l*, pg. 1952
HAOSEN HONG KONG LIMITED—See Dalian Haosen Equipment Manufacturing Co., Ltd.; *Int'l*, pg. 1952
HAOSEN INTELLIGENT EQUIPMENT (SHENZHEN) CO., LTD.—See Dalian Haosen Equipment Manufacturing Co., Ltd.; *Int'l*, pg. 1952
HAPPY JAPAN INC.—See Platinum Equity, LLC; *U.S. Private*, pg. 3208
HARPER CORPORATION OF AMERICA; *U.S. Private*, pg. 1867
HARVEY INDUSTRIES, LLC.; *U.S. Private*, pg. 1878
HAUHINCO MASCHINENFABRIK G. HAUSHERR JOCHUMS GMBH & CO. KG; *Int'l*, pg. 3285
HEBEI HUIJIN GROUP CO., LTD.; *Int'l*, pg. 3306
HEFEI MEYER OPTOELECTRONIC TECHNOLOGY INC.; *Int'l*, pg. 3307
HEFTER SYSTEMFORM GMBH—See Francotyp-Postalia Holding AG; *Int'l*, pg. 2761
HEIDELBERG BALTIC FINLAND OU—See Heidelberger Druckmaschinen AG; *Int'l*, pg. 3321
HEIDELBERG BENELUX BVBA—See Heidelberger Druckmaschinen AG; *Int'l*, pg. 3321
HEIDELBERG BENELUX B.V.—See Heidelberger Druckmaschinen AG; *Int'l*, pg. 3321
HEIDELBERGER DRUCKMASCHINEN AG; *Int'l*, pg. 3321
HEIDELBERGER DRUCKMASCHINEN UKRAINA LTD.—See Heidelberger Druckmaschinen AG; *Int'l*, pg. 3322
HEIDELBERG GRAFIK TICARET SERVIS LIMITED SIRKETI—See Heidelberger Druckmaschinen AG; *Int'l*, pg. 3321
HEIDELBERG GRAPHIC EQUIPMENT LIMITED—See Heidelberger Druckmaschinen AG; *Int'l*, pg. 3321
HEIDELBERG GRAPHIC EQUIPMENT LTD.—See Heidelberger Druckmaschinen AG; *Int'l*, pg. 3321
HEIDELBERG GRAPHICS TAIWAN LTD.—See Heidelberger Druckmaschinen AG; *Int'l*, pg. 3321
HEIDELBERG GRAPHICS (THAILAND) LTD.—See Heidelberger Druckmaschinen AG; *Int'l*, pg. 3321
HEIDELBERG INDIA PRIVATE LTD.—See Heidelberger Druckmaschinen AG; *Int'l*, pg. 3321
HEIDELBERG INTERNATIONAL LTD. A/S—See Heidelberger Druckmaschinen AG; *Int'l*, pg. 3321
HEIDELBERG ITALIA S.R.L.—See Heidelberger Druckmaschinen AG; *Int'l*, pg. 3321
HEIDELBERG MAGYARORSZAG KFT.—See Heidelberger Druckmaschinen AG; *Int'l*, pg. 3321
HEIDELBERG MANUFACTURING DEUTSCHLAND GMBH—See Heidelberger Druckmaschinen AG; *Int'l*, pg. 3321
HEIDELBERG WEB CARTON CONVERTING GMBH—See Heidelberger Druckmaschinen AG; *Int'l*, pg. 3322

HEINRICH KUPER GMBH & CO. KG; *Int'l*, pg. 3324
HELESI PLC; *Int'l*, pg. 3329
HELIOGRAPH HOLDING GMBH; *Int'l*, pg. 3330
HELVOET RUBBER & PLASTIC TECHNOLOGIES BV—See Hydratec Industries NV; *Int'l*, pg. 3546
HELVOET RUBBER & PLASTIC TECHNOLOGIES NV—See Hydratec Industries NV; *Int'l*, pg. 3546
HEMINA SPA—See IDEX Corp; *U.S. Public*, pg. 1090
HENGLI GROUP CO.,LTD.; *Int'l*, pg. 3346
HENGLI PETROCHEMICAL CO., LTD.; *Int'l*, pg. 3346
HERDER B.V.—See Alamo Group Inc.; *U.S. Public*, pg. 71
HERR INDUSTRIAL INC.; *U.S. Private*, pg. 1926
HIAB LOAD HANDLING EQUIPMENT (SHANGHAI) CO., LTD—See Cargotec Corporation; *Int'l*, pg. 1328
HIAB (PTY) LTD—See Cargotec Corporation; *Int'l*, pg. 1327
HILBER SOLAR GMBH; *Int'l*, pg. 3391
HI-LEX CORPORATION - KAIBARA PLANT—See Hi-Lex Corporation; *Int'l*, pg. 3380
HIL INDUSTRIS BERHAD; *Int'l*, pg. 3390
HIMILE (LIAONING) SCIENCE & TECHNOLOGY CO., LTD.—See Himile Mechanical Science & Technology Co., Ltd; *Int'l*, pg. 3397
HIMILE MECHANICAL SCIENCE & TECHNOLOGY CO., LTD; *Int'l*, pg. 3397
HIMILE MECHANICAL SCIENCE & TECHNOLOGY (KUNSHAN) CO., LTD.—See Himile Mechanical Science & Technology Co., Ltd; *Int'l*, pg. 3397
HIMILE MOLD (TIANJIN) CO., LTD.—See Himile Mechanical Science & Technology Co., Ltd; *Int'l*, pg. 3397
HINDUSTAN COMPOSITES LIMITED; *Int'l*, pg. 3399
HINIARATAKAN CORPORATION—See Daifuku Co., Ltd.; *Int'l*, pg. 1926
HI-P INTERNATIONAL LIMITED; *Int'l*, pg. 3381
HIRANO TECSEED CO., LTD.; *Int'l*, pg. 3403
HIRATA ENGINEERING S.A. DE C.V.—See Hirata Corporation; *Int'l*, pg. 3403
HIRATA FA ENGINEERING (S) PTE LTD—See Hirata Corporation; *Int'l*, pg. 3403
HISAKA WORKS (CHINA) CO., LTD.—See Hisaka Works, Ltd.; *Int'l*, pg. 3406
HISAKA WORKS, LTD. - KONOIKE PLANT—See Hisaka Works, Ltd.; *Int'l*, pg. 3406
HISAKA WORKS, LTD.; *Int'l*, pg. 3406
HITACHI HANBELL(SHANGHAI) PRECISE MACHINERY CO., LTD.—See Hitachi, Ltd.; *Int'l*, pg. 3417
HITACHI HIGH-TECHNOLOGIES IPC (M) SDN. BHD.—See Hitachi, Ltd.; *Int'l*, pg. 3418
HITACHI INDUSTRIAL EQUIPMENT MEXICO, S.A. DE C.V.—See Hitachi, Ltd.; *Int'l*, pg. 3419
HITACHI INDUSTRIAL EQUIPMENT NAKAJO ENGINEERING CO., LTD.—See Hitachi, Ltd.; *Int'l*, pg. 3419
HITACHI INDUSTRIAL EQUIPMENT (NANJING) CO., LTD.—See Hitachi, Ltd.; *Int'l*, pg. 3419
HITACHI INDUSTRIAL EQUIPMENT SYSTEMS (CHINA) CO., LTD.—See Hitachi, Ltd.; *Int'l*, pg. 3419
HITACHI INDUSTRIAL EQUIPMENT SYSTEMS CO., LTD.—See Hitachi, Ltd.; *Int'l*, pg. 3419
HITACHI INDUSTRIAL EQUIPMENT SYSTEMS (HONG KONG) CO., LTD.—See Hitachi, Ltd.; *Int'l*, pg. 3419
HITACHI INDUSTRIAL EQUIPMENT TECHNOLOGY SERVICE, CO., LTD.—See Hitachi, Ltd.; *Int'l*, pg. 3419
HITACHI ZOSEN FUKUI CORPORATION—See Hitachi Zosen Corporation; *Int'l*, pg. 3411
HITACHI-ZOSEN PLANT TECHNO-SERVICE CORPORATION—See Hitachi Zosen Corporation; *Int'l*, pg. 3411
HL ADVANCE TECHNOLOGIES (M) SDN. BHD.—See HLT Global Berhad; *Int'l*, pg. 3431
HNK MACHINE TOOL CO., LTD.; *Int'l*, pg. 3434
HOA PHAT EQUIPMENT & ACCESSORIES CO., LTD.—See Hoa Phat Group Joint Stock Company; *Int'l*, pg. 3435
HOERBIGER CANADA LTD.—See Hoerbiger Holding AG; *Int'l*, pg. 3440
HOERBIGER DE ARGENTINA S.A.—See Hoerbiger Holding AG; *Int'l*, pg. 3440
HOERBIGER DE CHILE S.A.—See Hoerbiger Holding AG; *Int'l*, pg. 3440
HOERBIGER FRANCE SAS—See Hoerbiger Holding AG; *Int'l*, pg. 3440
HOERBIGER MICRO FLUID GMBH—See Hoerbiger Holding AG; *Int'l*, pg. 3440
HOERBIGER SERVICE EGYPT, LLC—See Hoerbiger Holding AG; *Int'l*, pg. 3440
HOERBIGER SERVICE GMBH—See Hoerbiger Holding AG; *Int'l*, pg. 3440
HOERBIGER SERVICE HUNGARIA KFT.—See Hoerbiger Holding AG; *Int'l*, pg. 3440
HOERBIGER TURBOMACHINERY SERVICES B.V.B.A.—See Hoerbiger Holding AG; *Int'l*, pg. 3440
HOERBIGER VALVES (CHANGZHOU) CO., LTD.—See Hoerbiger Holding AG; *Int'l*, pg. 3440
HOERBIGER ZANDOV S.R.O.—See Hoerbiger Holding AG; *Int'l*, pg. 3440
HOKUDEN ASSOCIA CO., INC.—See Hokkaido Electric Power Co., Inc.; *Int'l*, pg. 3443
HOLY STONE ENTERPRISE CO., LTD.; *Int'l*, pg. 3454

HOMAG AUSTRIA GESELLSCHAFT M.B.H.—See Durr AG; *Int'l*, pg. 2233
HOMAG AUTOMATION GMBH—See Durr AG; *Int'l*, pg. 2233
HOMAG BOHRSYSTEME GMBH—See Durr AG; *Int'l*, pg. 2233
HOMAG ESPANA S.A.—See Durr AG; *Int'l*, pg. 2233
HOMAG GMBH—See Durr AG; *Int'l*, pg. 2233
HOMAG KANTENTECHNIK GMBH—See Durr AG; *Int'l*, pg. 2233
HOMAG PLATTENAUFTEILTECHNIK GMBH—See Durr AG; *Int'l*, pg. 2233
HOMAG SERVICES POLAND SP. Z O.O.—See Durr AG; *Int'l*, pg. 2233
HOMAG VIETNAM COMPANY LIMITED—See Durr AG; *Int'l*, pg. 2233
HONEYWELL LIFE SAFETY ROMANIA SRL—See Honeywell International Inc.; *U.S. Public*, pg. 1051
HORIZON TECHNOLOGY, INC.—See Biotage AB; *Int'l*, pg. 1042
HOSHIZAKI EUROPE LTD.—See Hoshizaki Corporation; *Int'l*, pg. 3483
HOSOKAWA MICRON FRANCE—See Hosokawa Micron Corporation; *Int'l*, pg. 3486
HOSOKAWA MICRON INTERNATIONAL INC.—See Hosokawa Micron Corporation; *Int'l*, pg. 3486
HOSOKAWA MICRON POWDER SYSTEMS—See Hosokawa Micron Corporation; *Int'l*, pg. 3486
HOWDEN AUSTRALIA PTY LIMITED—See Chart Industries, Inc.; *U.S. Public*, pg. 481
HP COLORSPAN—See HP Inc.; *U.S. Public*, pg. 1063
HPG INC.—See Balder Danmark A/S; *Int'l*, pg. 807
HPI, LLC.; *U.S. Private*, pg. 1997
HP INC CZECH REPUBLIC S.R.O.—See HP Inc.; *U.S. Public*, pg. 1063
HT KOREA CO., LTD—See Haitian International Holdings Ltd.; *Int'l*, pg. 3217
HTL AUSTRALASIA PTY. LTD.—See Enerpac Tool Group Corp.; *U.S. Public*, pg. 765
HUADIAN HEAVY INDUSTRIES CO.,LTD.; *Int'l*, pg. 3511
HU AN CABLE HOLDINGS LTD.; *Int'l*, pg. 3509
HUAXIAO PRECISION (SUZHOU) CO., LTD.—See CSG Smart Science & Technology Co., Ltd.; *Int'l*, pg. 1864
HUAYUAN (VIETNAM) MACHINERY CO., LTD.—See Haitian International Holdings Ltd.; *Int'l*, pg. 3217
HUNTING ENERGY SERVICES (UK) LIMITED—See Hunting Plc; *Int'l*, pg. 3536
HUSKY CIS LLC—See Platinum Equity, LLC; *U.S. Private*, pg. 3203
HUSKY DO BRASIL SISTEMAS DE INJECAO LTDA.—See Platinum Equity, LLC; *U.S. Private*, pg. 3204
HUSKY INJECTION MOLDING SYSTEMS ARGENTINA S.A.—See Platinum Equity, LLC; *U.S. Private*, pg. 3204
HUSKY INJECTION MOLDING SYSTEMS COLOMBIA LTD.—See Platinum Equity, LLC; *U.S. Private*, pg. 3204
HUSKY INJECTION MOLDING SYSTEMS IBERIA S.L.U.—See Platinum Equity, LLC; *U.S. Private*, pg. 3204
HUSKY INJECTION MOLDING SYSTEMS, INC.—See Platinum Equity, LLC; *U.S. Private*, pg. 3204
HUSKY INJECTION MOLDING SYSTEMS (INDIA) PRIVATE LIMITED—See Platinum Equity, LLC; *U.S. Private*, pg. 3203
HUSKY INJECTION MOLDING SYSTEMS (ISRAEL) LTD.—See Platinum Equity, LLC; *U.S. Private*, pg. 3203
HUSKY INJECTION MOLDING SYSTEMS KOREA INC—See Platinum Equity, LLC; *U.S. Private*, pg. 3204
HUSKY INJECTION MOLDING SYSTEMS LTD.—See Platinum Equity, LLC; *U.S. Private*, pg. 3203
HUSKY INJECTION MOLDING SYSTEMS (NORDIC) A/S—See Platinum Equity, LLC; *U.S. Private*, pg. 3203
HUSKY INJECTION MOLDING SYSTEMS S.A.—See Platinum Equity, LLC; *U.S. Private*, pg. 3204
HUSKY INJECTION MOLDING SYSTEMS (SHANGHAI) LTD.—See Platinum Equity, LLC; *U.S. Private*, pg. 3203
HUSKY INJECTION MOLDING SYSTEMS SINGAPORE PTE. LTD.—See Platinum Equity, LLC; *U.S. Private*, pg. 3204
HUSKY INJECTION MOLDING SYSTEMS (SOUTH AFRICA) PTY. LTD.—See Platinum Equity, LLC; *U.S. Private*, pg. 3203
HUSKY INJECTION MOLDING SYSTEMS (THAILAND) LTD.—See Platinum Equity, LLC; *U.S. Private*, pg. 3204
HUSQVARNA CONSTRUCTION PRODUCTS NORTH AMERICA, INC.—See Husqvarna AB; *Int'l*, pg. 3539
HYDRAQUIP CUSTOM SYSTEMS, INC.—See Employee Owned Holdings, Inc.; *U.S. Private*, pg. 1386
HYDRA TECH A/S—See BWB Partners P/S; *Int'l*, pg. 1232
HYDRODEC AUSTRALIA PTY. LTD.—See Hydrodec Group plc; *Int'l*, pg. 3547
HYDUKE ENERGY SERVICES INC. - HYDUKE MECHANICAL & MACHINING DIVISION—See Hyduke Energy Services Inc.; *Int'l*, pg. 3548
HYLAR METAL PRODUCTS—See Degelman Industries Ltd.; *Int'l*, pg. 2004
HYOSUNG CORPORATION - JOCHIWON PLANT—See Hyosung Corporation; *Int'l*, pg. 3550
HYULIM ROBOT CO., LTD.—See Dongbu Group; *Int'l*, pg. 2166

N.A.I.C.S. INDEX

HYUNDAI-WIA MACHINE AMERICA CORP.—See Hyundai Motor Company; *Int'l*, pg. 3560
IAI CORPORATION; *Int'l*, pg. 3568
IA KOREA CORP—See IAI Corporation; *Int'l*, pg. 3568
IAUTOMATION, INC.—See The Riverside Company; *U.S. Private*, pg. 4110
IDC USA, INC.—See Imaging Dynamics Company Ltd.; *Int'l*, pg. 3619
IDP AMERICAS, INC.—See IDP Corp., Ltd.; *Int'l*, pg. 3596
IFMA SA; *Int'l*, pg. 3599
IGEPA BELUX N.V.—See Printers' Service, Inc.; *U.S. Private*, pg. 3265
I&H ENGINEERING CO., LTD.—See IHI Corporation; *Int'l*, pg. 3604
IHI ASIA PACIFIC PTE. LTD.—See IHI Corporation; *Int'l*, pg. 3604
IHI ASIA PACIFIC (THAILAND) CO., LTD.—See IHI Corporation; *Int'l*, pg. 3604
IHI CANADA PROJECTS INC.—See IHI Corporation; *Int'l*, pg. 3604
IHI CHARGING SYSTEMS INTERNATIONAL GMBH—See IHI Corporation; *Int'l*, pg. 3604
IHI DALGAKIRAN MAKINA SANAYI VE TICARET A.S.—See IHI Corporation; *Int'l*, pg. 3604
IHI INSPECTION & INSTRUMENTATION CO., LTD.—See IHI Corporation; *Int'l*, pg. 3604
IHI METALTECH CO., LTD.—See IHI Corporation; *Int'l*, pg. 3604
IHI POWER GENERATION CORP.—See IHI Corporation; *Int'l*, pg. 3605
IHI POWER SYSTEM (THAILAND) CO., LTD.—See IHI Corporation; *Int'l*, pg. 3605
IHI (SHANGHAI) MANAGEMENT CO., LTD.—See IHI Corporation; *Int'l*, pg. 3604
IHI SOLID BIOMASS MALAYSIA SDN. BHD.—See IHI Corporation; *Int'l*, pg. 3605
IHI-SULLAIR COMPRESSION TECHNOLOGY (SUZHOU) CO., LTD.—See IHI Corporation; *Int'l*, pg. 3605
IHI SYSTEM TECHNOLOGY TAIWAN CO., LTD.—See IHI Corporation; *Int'l*, pg. 3605
IHI TAIWAN CORPORATION—See IHI Corporation; *Int'l*, pg. 3605
IHI TERRASUN SOLUTIONS INC.—See IHI Corporation; *Int'l*, pg. 3605
IHI TRANSPORT MACHINERY CO., LTD.—See IHI Corporation; *Int'l*, pg. 3604
IHI TURBO KOREA CO., LTD.—See IHI Corporation; *Int'l*, pg. 3605
IHI TURBO (THAILAND) CO., LTD.—See IHI Corporation; *Int'l*, pg. 3605
IHI VTN GMBH—See IHI Corporation; *Int'l*, pg. 3605
IHS GMBH—See Sabre Corporation; *U.S. Public*, pg. 1833
IKEGAI CORP—See Fair Friend Group; *Int'l*, pg. 2604
I MACHINE TECHNOLOGY LLC—See Chien Wei Precise Technology Co., Ltd.; *Int'l*, pg. 1477
IMAGE PROJECTIONS WEST, INC.; *U.S. Private*, pg. 2045
IMA PACIFIC CO. LTD.—See I.M.A. Industria Macchine Automatiche S.p.A.; *Int'l*, pg. 3565
IMA-PG INDIA PVT. LTD.—See I.M.A. Industria Macchine Automatiche S.p.A.; *Int'l*, pg. 3566
IMEX CO., LTD.—See Hitachi Zosen Corporation; *Int'l*, pg. 3411
IMPIKA SA—See Xerox Holdings Corporation; *U.S. Public*, pg. 2387
INC ENGINEERING CO., LTD.—See IHI Corporation; *Int'l*, pg. 3604
INCOMPASS LLC; *U.S. Private*, pg. 2054
INDCO, INC.—See Janel Corporation; *U.S. Public*, pg. 1187
INDICOR OF NC, LLC—See Clayton, Dubilier & Rice, LLC; *U.S. Private*, pg. 924
INDUCTOHEAT, INC.—See Indel, Inc.; *U.S. Private*, pg. 2055
INDUCTOTHERM HEATING & WELDING TECHNOLOGIES LTD—See Indel, Inc.; *U.S. Private*, pg. 2055
INDUSTRIAL DYNAMICS CO. LTD.; *U.S. Private*, pg. 2066
INDUSTRIAL FABRICATORS, INC.—See APi Group Corporation; *Int'l*, pg. 514
INDUSTRIAL MAGNETICS, INC.—See DNS Capital, LLC; *U.S. Private*, pg. 1249
INGECAL S.A.S.—See Durr AG; *Int'l*, pg. 2233
INGERSOLL-RAND (CHINA) INDUSTRIAL EQUIPMENT MANUFACTURING CO., LTD.—See Ingersoll Rand Inc.; *U.S. Public*, pg. 1120
INGERSOLL-RAND COMPANY—See Ingersoll Rand Inc.; *U.S. Public*, pg. 1120
INGERSOLL-RAND EUROPEAN SALES LIMITED—See Ingersoll Rand Inc.; *U.S. Public*, pg. 1121
INGERSOLL-RAND INTERNATIONAL LIMITED—See Ingersoll Rand Inc.; *U.S. Public*, pg. 1121
INGERSOLL-RAND ITALIA S.R.L.—See Ingersoll Rand Inc.; *U.S. Public*, pg. 1121
INGERSOLL-RAND SOUTH EAST ASIA (PTE.) LTD.—See Ingersoll Rand Inc.; *U.S. Public*, pg. 1121
INLAND NEWSPAPER MACHINERY LLC; *U.S. Private*, pg. 2078
INNOVATIVE IDM LLC; *U.S. Private*, pg. 2082
INNSE MILANO SPA—See Camozzi Group; *Int'l*, pg. 1274

INSTRON GMBH—See Illinois Tool Works Inc.; *U.S. Public*, pg. 1108
INSTRON (SHANGHAI) LTD.—See Illinois Tool Works Inc.; *U.S. Public*, pg. 1108
INTEGRATED DYNAMICS ENGINEERING LTD.—See Aalberts N.V.; *Int'l*, pg. 34
INTERCONTINENTAL CHEMICAL CORP; *U.S. Private*, pg. 2109
INTERHYDRAULIK ZEPRO GMBH—See Cargotec Corporation; *Int'l*, pg. 1328
INTERMAC DO BRASIL COMERCIO DE MAQUINAS E EQUIPAMENTOS LTDA.—See Biesse S.p.A.; *Int'l*, pg. 1020
INTERMECH LTD—See Atlas Copco AB; *Int'l*, pg. 677
INTHINC; *U.S. Private*, pg. 2128
INVERSIONES SONOCO DO CHILE DO LTDA.—See Sonoco Products Company; *U.S. Public*, pg. 1905
IP EMPAQUES DE MEXICO, S. DE R.L. DE C.V.—See International Paper Company; *U.S. Public*, pg. 1155
IROBOT (HK) LIMITED—See iRobot Corp.; *U.S. Public*, pg. 1171
IROBOT (INDIA) PRIVATE LIMITED—See iRobot Corp.; *U.S. Public*, pg. 1171
IROBOT - UK—See iRobot Corp.; *U.S. Public*, pg. 1171
ISHI POWER SDN BHD—See IHI Corporation; *Int'l*, pg. 3605
ISP OPTICS LATVIA, SIA—See LightPath Technologies, Inc.; *U.S. Public*, pg. 1315
ISRA VISION GMBH—See Atlas Copco AB; *Int'l*, pg. 682
ITALIANA AUDION S.R.L.—See Francotyp-Postalia Holding AG; *Int'l*, pg. 2761
ITT CANNON VEAM ITALIA S.R.L.—See ITT Inc.; *U.S. Public*, pg. 1177
ITT C'TREAT LLC—See ITT Inc.; *U.S. Public*, pg. 1177
ITW AUTOMOTIVE FINISHING—See Illinois Tool Works Inc.; *U.S. Public*, pg. 1104
ITW CONSTRUCTION PRODUCTS CZ S.R.O.—See Illinois Tool Works Inc.; *U.S. Public*, pg. 1105
ITW DYNATEC—See Illinois Tool Works Inc.; *U.S. Public*, pg. 1105
ITW GRAPHICS ASIA LIMITED—See Illinois Tool Works Inc.; *U.S. Public*, pg. 1106
ITW GRAPHICS KOREA CO. LTD.—See Illinois Tool Works Inc.; *U.S. Public*, pg. 1106
ITW HEARTLAND - STANDARD MACHINES—See Illinois Tool Works Inc.; *U.S. Public*, pg. 1106
ITW MORLOCK GMBH—See Illinois Tool Works Inc.; *U.S. Public*, pg. 1106
ITW SPRAYTEC S.A.S.—See Illinois Tool Works Inc.; *U.S. Public*, pg. 1107
ITW TEST & MEASUREMENT GMBH—See Illinois Tool Works Inc.; *U.S. Public*, pg. 1108
IWK PACKAGING SYSTEMS, INC.—See ATS Corporation; *Int'l*, pg. 695
IXMATION (ASIA) SDN. BHD.—See Durr AG; *Int'l*, pg. 2230
IXMATION (SUZHOU) CO., LTD.—See Durr AG; *Int'l*, pg. 2230
IXMATION (TIANJIN) CO., LTD.—See Durr AG; *Int'l*, pg. 2230
JAPAN POLYMARK CO. LTD.—See Illinois Tool Works Inc.; *U.S. Public*, pg. 1108
JARDIS INDUSTRIES INC.; *U.S. Private*, pg. 2188
JAZON SP. Z O.O.—See Chien Wei Precise Technology Co., Ltd.; *Int'l*, pg. 1477
JEFFREY RADER AB—See Hillenbrand, Inc.; *U.S. Public*, pg. 1037
JEFFREY RADER CANADA COMPANY—See Hillenbrand, Inc.; *U.S. Public*, pg. 1037
JENTSCHMANN AG—See Leggett & Platt, Incorporated; *U.S. Public*, pg. 1302
JERVIS B. WEBB COMPANY—See Daifuku Co., Ltd.; *Int'l*, pg. 1925
JEUMONT ELECTRIC—See Altawest Group; *Int'l*, pg. 388
JIANGSU IHI FENGDONG VACUUM TECHNOLOGY CO., LTD.—See IHI Corporation; *Int'l*, pg. 3606
JIANGYIN JINTIAN MACHINERY LIMITED—See Fountain Set (Holdings) Limited; *Int'l*, pg. 2754
JINGWEI TEXTILE MACHINERY COMPANY, LTD.—See China Hi-Tech Group Corporation; *Int'l*, pg. 1508
JLG EQUIPMENT SERVICES LIMITED—See Oshkosh Corporation; *U.S. Public*, pg. 1620
JLG FRANCE SARL—See Oshkosh Corporation; *U.S. Public*, pg. 1620
JLG INDUSTRIES GMBH—See Oshkosh Corporation; *U.S. Public*, pg. 1620
JLG INDUSTRIES, INC.—See Oshkosh Corporation; *U.S. Public*, pg. 1620
JOHN BEAN—See Snap-on Incorporated; *U.S. Public*, pg. 1897
JOHN BEAN TECHNOLOGIES (PROPRIETARY) LTD.—See John Bean Technologies Corporation; *U.S. Public*, pg. 1191
JOHN COCKERILL INDIA LIMITED—See Euremis Holding SA; *Int'l*, pg. 2530
JOT AUTOMATION LTD.—See Head Invest Oy; *Int'l*, pg. 3301
JOYCE/DAYTON CORP.—See Graham Holdings Company; *U.S. Public*, pg. 955

333248 — ALL OTHER INDUSTRIA...

J.R. AUTOMATION - STEVENSVILLE—See Hitachi, Ltd.; *Int'l*, pg. 3423
J.R. AUTOMATION TECHNOLOGIES, LLC—See Hitachi, Ltd.; *Int'l*, pg. 3423
KADANT GRANTEK INC.—See Kadant Inc.; *U.S. Public*, pg. 1212
KADANT JOHNSON ARGENTINA S.R.L.—See Kadant Inc.; *U.S. Public*, pg. 1212
KADANT JOHNSON EUROPE BV—See Kadant Inc.; *U.S. Public*, pg. 1212
KADANT JOHNSON FRANCE B.V.—See Kadant Inc.; *U.S. Public*, pg. 1212
KADANT LAMORT S.A.S.—See Kadant Inc.; *U.S. Public*, pg. 1212
KADANT MEXICO S.A. DE C.V.—See Kadant Inc.; *U.S. Public*, pg. 1212
KADANT SOUTH AMERICA LTDA.—See Kadant Inc.; *U.S. Public*, pg. 1212
KALIX—See Coesia S.p.A.; *Int'l*, pg. 1690
KALMAR FRANCE S.A.—See Cargotec Corporation; *Int'l*, pg. 1327
KALMAR SOUTH EAST ASIA PTE. LTD.—See Cargotec Corporation; *Int'l*, pg. 1327
KANSAI DESIGN CO., LTD.—See Hitachi Zosen Corporation; *Int'l*, pg. 3411
KASON CORP.—See May River Capital, LLC; *U.S. Private*, pg. 2620
KAYDON CUSTOM FILTRATION CORPORATION—See Madison Industries Holdings LLC; *U.S. Private*, pg. 2543
KEMEL CO., LTD. - KURE FACTORY—See Eagle Industry Co., Ltd.; *Int'l*, pg. 2265
KEMEL CO., LTD. - TAKASAGO FACTORY—See Eagle Industry Co., Ltd.; *Int'l*, pg. 2265
KENNAMETAL INDIA LTD.—See Kennametal Inc.; *U.S. Public*, pg. 1222
KEY MANUFACTURING INC—See Manar, Inc.; *U.S. Private*, pg. 2561
KITA MANUFACTURING CO., LTD.—See Cohu, Inc.; *U.S. Public*, pg. 529
KITO AMERICAS, INC.—See The Carlyle Group Inc.; *U.S. Public*, pg. 2055
KLEINMANN GMBH—See Illinois Tool Works Inc.; *U.S. Public*, pg. 1109
KLUIN WIJHE BV—See Aalberts N.V.; *Int'l*, pg. 34
KMT PRECISION GRINDING AB—See AIP, LLC; *U.S. Private*, pg. 137
KMT PRECISION GRINDING GMBH—See AIP, LLC; *U.S. Private*, pg. 138
KMT PRECISION GRINDING, INC.—See AIP, LLC; *U.S. Private*, pg. 138
KOCH CHEMICAL TECHNOLOGY GROUP LIMITED - KOCH-GLITSCH UK DIVISION—See Koch Industries, Inc.; *U.S. Public*, pg. 2332
KOCH CHEMICAL TECHNOLOGY GROUP LIMITED—See Koch Industries, Inc.; *U.S. Public*, pg. 2332
KOCH CHEMICAL TECHNOLOGY GROUP, LLC—See Koch Industries, Inc.; *U.S. Public*, pg. 2331
KOCH-GLITSCH B.V.B.A.—See Koch Industries, Inc.; *U.S. Private*, pg. 2332
KOCH-GLITSCH CANADA, LP—See Koch Industries, Inc.; *U.S. Public*, pg. 2332
KOCH HEAT TRANSFER COMPANY, LP—See Koch Industries, Inc.; *U.S. Public*, pg. 2331
KOCH HEAT TRANSFER COMPANY, S.R.L.—See Koch Industries, Inc.; *U.S. Public*, pg. 2332
KOCH HEAT TRANSFER TECHNOLOGY CO.—See Koch Industries, Inc.; *U.S. Public*, pg. 2332
KOCH INTERNATIONAL B.V—See Koch Industries, Inc.; *U.S. Private*, pg. 2332
KODAK GRAPHIC COMMUNICATIONS GROUP—See Eastman Kodak Company; *U.S. Public*, pg. 707
KODAK GRAPHIC COMMUNICATIONS—See Eastman Kodak Company; *U.S. Public*, pg. 707
KODAK GRAPHIC COMMUNICATIONS—See Eastman Kodak Company; *U.S. Public*, pg. 707
KODAK IL LTD—See Eastman Kodak Company; *U.S. Public*, pg. 707
KOLLMORGEN AUTOMATION AB—See Regal Rexnord Corporation; *U.S. Public*, pg. 1772
KOLLMORGEN SRL—See Regal Rexnord Corporation; *U.S. Public*, pg. 1772
THE KOREA HEAVY MACHINERY CO., LTD.—See HNK Machine Tool Co., Ltd.; *Int'l*, pg. 3434
KOREA SHINTO CO., LTD.—See Dong-A Socio Holdings Co., Ltd.; *Int'l*, pg. 2165
KRAUSSMAFFEI BERSTORFF GMBH—See China National Chemical Corporation; *Int'l*, pg. 1528
KRAUSSMAFFEI GROUP FRANCE SAS—See China National Chemical Corporation; *Int'l*, pg. 1528
KRAUSSMAFFEI GROUP GMBH—See China National Chemical Corporation; *Int'l*, pg. 1528
KRAUSSMAFFEI GROUP UK LTD.—See China National Chemical Corporation; *Int'l*, pg. 1528
KULA MAKINA IMALAT SAN. TIC. LTD. STI.—See Chien Wei Precise Technology Co., Ltd.; *Int'l*, pg. 1477
KURT MANUFACTURING CO. INC. - KURT INDUSTRIAL PRODUCTS DIVISION—See Kurt Manufacturing Co. Inc.; *U.S. Private*, pg. 2358

KURT MANUFACTURING CO. INC. - KURT MACHINING DIVISION—See Kurt Manufacturing Co. Inc.; *U.S. Private*, pg. 2358
KYOSAN DENSO MANUFACTURING KENTUCKY, LLC.—See Denso Corporation; *Int'l*, pg. 2032
LACHENMEIER APS—See Illinois Tool Works Inc.; *U.S. Public*, pg. 1109
LAKESHORE FITTINGS, INC.—See MiddleGround Management, LP; *U.S. Private*, pg. 2711
LAM RESEARCH ILLINOIS IAG, INC.—See Lam Research Corporation; *U.S. Public*, pg. 1290
LANCO ASSEMBLY SYSTEMS; *U.S. Private*, pg. 2382
LANDMARK EARTH SOLUTIONS, INC.—See Leggett & Platt, Incorporated; *U.S. Public*, pg. 1302
LAPMASTER GROUP HOLDINGS LLC—See Angeles Equity Partners, LLC; *U.S. Private*, pg. 282
LAPMASTER GROUP HOLDINGS LLC—See Bison Capital Asset Management, LLC; *U.S. Private*, pg. 566
LAPMASTER WOLTERS GMBH—See Angeles Equity Partners, LLC; *U.S. Private*, pg. 282
LAPMASTER WOLTERS GMBH—See Bison Capital Asset Management, LLC; *U.S. Private*, pg. 566
LAPMASTER WOLTERS LIMITED—See Angeles Equity Partners, LLC; *U.S. Private*, pg. 282
LAPMASTER WOLTERS LIMITED—See Bison Capital Asset Management, LLC; *U.S. Private*, pg. 566
LAPMASTER WOLTERS LLC—See Angeles Equity Partners, LLC; *U.S. Private*, pg. 282
LAPMASTER WOLTERS LLC—See Bison Capital Asset Management, LLC; *U.S. Private*, pg. 566
LASERCYCLE USA, INC.; *U.S. Private*, pg. 2395
LASIT LASER UK LTD.—See El.En. S.p.A.; *Int'l*, pg. 2342
LASIT SPA—See El.En. S.p.A.; *Int'l*, pg. 2342
LAVORWASH BRASIL IND. LTDA.—See Emak S.p.A.; *Int'l*, pg. 2373
L.B. FOSTER RAIL TECHNOLOGIES, INC.—See L.B. Foster Company; *U.S. Public*, pg. 1279
L.B. FOSTER UK LTD.—See L.B. Foster Company; *U.S. Public*, pg. 1279
LEGGETT & PLATT (SHANGHAI) MACHINERY TECHNOLOGY CO. LTD—See Leggett & Platt, Incorporated; *U.S. Public*, pg. 1302
LEVER MANUFACTURING CORP.—See Thermwell Products Co., Inc.; *U.S. Private*, pg. 4143
LH ACCESS TECHNOLOGY LIMITED—See Westinghouse Air Brake Technologies Corporation; *U.S. Public*, pg. 2358
LINX PRINTING TECHNOLOGIES LIMITED—See Danaher Corporation; *U.S. Public*, pg. 628
LLC ATLAS COPCO UKRAINE—See Atlas Copco AB; *Int'l*, pg. 683
LMP IMPIANTI SRL—See Owens Corning; *U.S. Public*, pg. 1626
LOCK INSPECTION SYSTEMS BV—See Illinois Tool Works Inc.; *U.S. Public*, pg. 1109
LOCK INSPECTION SYSTEMS LIMITED—See Illinois Tool Works Inc.; *U.S. Public*, pg. 1109
LOIBL ALLEN-SHERMAN-HOFF GMBH—See Babcock & Wilcox Enterprises, Inc.; *U.S. Public*, pg. 262
LOMA SYSTEMS-ILLINOIS—See Illinois Tool Works Inc.; *U.S. Public*, pg. 1109
LOMA SYSTEMS LTD—See Illinois Tool Works Inc.; *U.S. Public*, pg. 1109
LOMA SYSTEMS SRO—See Illinois Tool Works Inc.; *U.S. Public*, pg. 1109
LUDOWICI AUSTRALIA PTY LTD.—See FLSmidth & Co. A/S; *Int'l*, pg. 2711
LUKAS HYDRAULIK GMBH—See IDEX Corp; *U.S. Public*, pg. 1091
LUMMUS CORPORATION; *U.S. Private*, pg. 2514
LUSOSIDER PROJECTOS SIDERURGICOS S.A.—See Companhia Siderurgica Nacional; *Int'l*, pg. 1748
LUTETIA—See Henry Crown & Company; *U.S. Private*, pg. 1917
LYMAN PRODUCTS CORPORATION; *U.S. Private*, pg. 2520
MACAWBER BEEKAY PRIVATE LIMITED—See Clyde Blowers Capital IM LLP; *Int'l*, pg. 1665
MACDERMID PRINTING SOLUTIONS, LLC—See Element Solutions Inc.; *U.S. Public*, pg. 727
MACGREGOR HYDRAMARINE AS—See Cargotec Corporation; *Int'l*, pg. 1328
MACGREGOR PLIMSOLL (TIANJIN) CO., LTD—See Cargotec Corporation; *Int'l*, pg. 1329
MACKSON, INC.—See MetalTek International; *U.S. Private*, pg. 2682
MACTEK CORP.—See Pepperl+Fuchs Inc; *U.S. Private*, pg. 3145
MAERTIENS ROBOTEC GMBH—See Dieffenbacher Holding GmbH & Co. KG; *Int'l*, pg. 2114
MAGNADRIVE CORPORATION; *U.S. Private*, pg. 2546
MAGNAFLUX GMBH—See Illinois Tool Works Inc.; *U.S. Public*, pg. 1109
MAGNA INDUSTRIAL COMPANY LIMITED—See Illinois Tool Works Inc.; *U.S. Public*, pg. 1109
MAHR CORPORATION DE MEXICO S.A. DE C.V.—See Carl Mahr Holding GmbH; *Int'l*, pg. 1333

MAHR S.E.A. CO. LTD.—See Carl Mahr Holding GmbH; *Int'l*, pg. 1333
MA MICRO AUTOMATION GMBH—See Hitachi, Ltd.; *Int'l*, pg. 3423
MANAR, INC. - CEW ENTERPRISE DIVISION—See Manar, Inc.; *U.S. Private*, pg. 2561
MANAR, INC. - GTR DIVISION—See Manar, Inc.; *U.S. Private*, pg. 2561
MANGIAROTTI S.P.A.—See Brookfield Corporation; *Int'l*, pg. 1186
MANNER HONG KONG LIMITED—See Barnes Group Inc.; *U.S. Public*, pg. 277
MANNER JAPAN CO. LTD.—See Barnes Group Inc.; *U.S. Public*, pg. 278
MANNER USA, INC.—See Barnes Group Inc.; *U.S. Public*, pg. 277
MARANGONI TREAD N.A., INC.—See Borrachas Vipal SA; *Int'l*, pg. 1114
MAREN ENGINEERING CORPORATION—See Komar Industries, LLC; *U.S. Private*, pg. 2342
MARION GLASS EQUIPMENT & TECHNOLOGY COMPANY—See Ardagh Group S.A.; *Int'l*, pg. 553
MARK ANDY, INC.; *U.S. Private*, pg. 2577
MARKEM-IMAJE CORPORATION—See Dover Corporation; *U.S. Public*, pg. 680
MARKEM-IMAJE LTD.—See Dover Corporation; *U.S. Public*, pg. 682
MARKEM-IMAJE LTD.—See Dover Corporation; *U.S. Public*, pg. 682
MARKEM-IMAJE N.V.—See Dover Corporation; *U.S. Public*, pg. 680
MARKEM-IMAJE SPAIN S.A.U—See Dover Corporation; *U.S. Public*, pg. 682
MARK/TRECE INC.; *U.S. Private*, pg. 2578
MARLEY CANADIAN INC—See SPX Technologies, Inc.; *U.S. Public*, pg. 1921
MARTIN S.A.—See Bobst Group S.A.; *Int'l*, pg. 1096
MARZOLI MACHINES TEXTILE SRL—See Camozzi Group; *Int'l*, pg. 1274
MARZOLI TEXTILE MACHINERY MANUFACTURERS PRIVATE LIMITED—See Camozzi Group; *Int'l*, pg. 1274
MASA GMBH—See CGS Management AG; *Int'l*, pg. 1435
MASS FINISHING, INC.—See Innovance, Inc.; *U.S. Private*, pg. 2081
MATCO SEVICES, INC.—See Valmont Industries, Inc.; *U.S. Public*, pg. 2274
MATERIALS TRANSPORTATION CO.; *U.S. Private*, pg. 2610
MAT MISCHANLAGENTECHNIK GMBH.—See BAUER Aktiengesellschaft; *Int'l*, pg. 893
MATTHEWS SWEDOT AB—See Matthews International Corporation; *U.S. Public*, pg. 1400
MAXSYS FUEL SYSTEMS LTD.—See Lionheart Ventures; *U.S. Private*, pg. 2464
MAYR CORP.—See Christian Mayr GmbH & Co. KG; *Int'l*, pg. 1586
MAYR TRANSMISSIONS LTD.—See Christian Mayr GmbH & Co. KG; *Int'l*, pg. 1586
MCDONOUGH MANUFACTURING COMPANY; *U.S. Private*, pg. 2633
MCD S.A.S.—See Alfa Laval AB; *Int'l*, pg. 312
MCELROY MANUFACTURING, INC.; *U.S. Private*, pg. 2633
MCENEARNEY BUSINESS MACHINES LIMITED—See ANSA McAL Limited; *Int'l*, pg. 477
MCNEIL & NRM INC.; *U.S. Private*, pg. 2643
MECA & TECHNOLOGY MACHINE, INC.—See May River Capital, LLC; *U.S. Private*, pg. 2620
MECHANICAL EQUIPMENT COMPANY INC.; *U.S. Private*, pg. 2648
MECS EUROPE/AFRICA BVBA—See DuPont de Nemours, Inc.; *U.S. Public*, pg. 694
MEGA MANUFACTURING INC. - BERTSCH DIVISION—See Mega Manufacturing Inc.; *U.S. Private*, pg. 2660
MEGAPLAS ITALIA, S.P.A.—See Fomento de Construcciones y Contratas, S.A.; *Int'l*, pg. 2723
MEGATECH CORPORATION; *U.S. Public*, pg. 1414
MEGTEC SYSTEMS, INC.—See Durr AG; *Int'l*, pg. 2231
MEGTEC SYSTEMS SAS—See Durr AG; *Int'l*, pg. 2231
MEGTEC SYSTEMS SHANGHAI LTD—See Durr AG; *Int'l*, pg. 2231
MELCO INTERNATIONAL LLC; *U.S. Private*, pg. 2662
MENZEL, INC.; *U.S. Private*, pg. 2667
MERROW MACHINE COMPANY; *U.S. Private*, pg. 2676
METRIC INDUSTRIAL AS—See Addtech AB; *Int'l*, pg. 134
MEURER VERPACKUNGSSYSTEME GMBH—See Illinois Tool Works Inc.; *U.S. Public*, pg. 1109
MEXATRONIKA-TES LTD.—See Endress+Hauser (International) Holding AG; *Int'l*, pg. 2408
MEXPOL WERKZEUGMASCHINEN GMBH—See A-TEC Industries AG; *Int'l*, pg. 21
MEZGER HEFTSYSTEME GMBH—See Illinois Tool Works Inc.; *U.S. Public*, pg. 1109
MG TRADING AND DEVELOPMENT GMBH—See China Baowu Steel Group Corp., Ltd.; *Int'l*, pg. 1486
MICROFLUIDICS INTERNATIONAL CORPORATION—See IDEX Corp; *U.S. Public*, pg. 1091

MICRO IMAGING TECHNOLOGY, INC.; *U.S. Public*, pg. 1436
MICRONICS FILTRATION LTD.—See Vance Street Capital LLC; *U.S. Private*, pg. 4342
MICRONICS FILTRATION PTY. LTD.—See Vance Street Capital LLC; *U.S. Private*, pg. 4342
MICRONICS, INC.—See Vance Street Capital LLC; *U.S. Private*, pg. 4342
MICRO-POISE INDUSTRIAL EQUIPMENT (BEIJING) CO., LTD—See AMETEK, Inc.; *U.S. Public*, pg. 118
MICROPOISE MEASUREMENT SYSTEMS EUROPE GMBH—See AMETEK, Inc.; *U.S. Public*, pg. 118
MICRO-POISE MEASUREMENT SYSTEMS, LLC—See AMETEK, Inc.; *U.S. Public*, pg. 118
MILACRON CZECH REPUBLIC SPOL S.R.O.—See Hillenbrand, Inc.; *U.S. Public*, pg. 1037
MILACRON LLC—See Hillenbrand, Inc.; *U.S. Public*, pg. 1037
MILACRON MOLD-MASTERS SISTEMAS DE PROCESSAMENTO DE PLASTICOS LTDA.—See Hillenbrand, Inc.; *U.S. Public*, pg. 1037
MILACRON PLASTICS TECHNOLOGIES GROUP LLC—See Hillenbrand, Inc.; *U.S. Public*, pg. 1037
MILITARY PRODUCTS GROUP, INC.; *U.S. Private*, pg. 2729
MILLENNITEK LLC—See MS Technology, Inc.; *U.S. Private*, pg. 2806
MILLER PRODUCTS, INC.—See GHM Industries, Inc.; *U.S. Private*, pg. 1691
MING SUN ENTERPRISES (CHINA) LIMITED—See Cosmos Machinery Enterprises Limited; *Int'l*, pg. 1813
MIPAK POLYMERS LIMITED—See Hitech Corporation Ltd.; *Int'l*, pg. 3425
MISTEQUAY GROUP LTD. - BAY ROAD PLANT—See Mistequay Group Ltd.; *U.S. Private*, pg. 2749
MISTEQUAY GROUP LTD. - STANDISH PLANT—See Mistequay Group Ltd.; *U.S. Private*, pg. 2749
MISTEQUAY INTERNATIONAL (PVT) LIMITED—See Mistequay Group Ltd.; *U.S. Private*, pg. 2749
MITA-TEKNIK A/S—See Axcel Management A/S; *Int'l*, pg. 762
MODERN EQUIPMENT COMPANY, LLC—See Dunes Point Capital, LLC; *U.S. Private*, pg. 1288
MODULAR AUTOMATION IRELAND LTD.—See Ares Management Corporation; *U.S. Public*, pg. 190
MOLD-MASTERS (2007) LIMITED—See Hillenbrand, Inc.; *U.S. Public*, pg. 1037
MOLD-MASTERS EUROPA GMBH—See Hillenbrand, Inc.; *U.S. Public*, pg. 1037
MOLD-MASTERS HANDELSGESELLSCHAFT M.B.H.—See Hillenbrand, Inc.; *U.S. Public*, pg. 1037
MOLD-MASTERS KABUSHIKI KAISHA—See Hillenbrand, Inc.; *U.S. Public*, pg. 1037
MOLD-MASTERS (KUNSHAN) CO. LTD.—See Hillenbrand, Inc.; *U.S. Public*, pg. 1037
MOLD-MASTERS (U.K.) LTD.—See Hillenbrand, Inc.; *U.S. Public*, pg. 1037
MONARCH KNITTING MACHINERY (UK) LTD.—See Monarch Knitting Machinery Corp.; *U.S. Private*, pg. 2769
MONARCH MANUFACTURING CORP.—See Monarch Knitting Machinery Corp.; *U.S. Private*, pg. 2769
MOORFEED CORPORATION—See Executive Management Services Inc.; *U.S. Private*, pg. 1447
MOREHOUSE-COWLES—See IDEX Corp; *U.S. Public*, pg. 1091
MORGANA SYSTEMS LTD.—See Grimaldi Industri AB; *Int'l*, pg. 3085
MORRISON TEXTILE MACHINERY CO.; *U.S. Private*, pg. 2789
MOUVENT AG—See Bobst Group S.A.; *Int'l*, pg. 1096
MP BALANCE ENGINEERING—See AMETEK, Inc.; *U.S. Public*, pg. 118
M&R HOLDINGS INC.; *U.S. Private*, pg. 2525
M&R PRINTING EQUIPMENT INC.—See M&R Holdings Inc.; *U.S. Private*, pg. 2525
M&R SALES & SERVICE INC.—See M&R Holdings Inc.; *U.S. Private*, pg. 2525
M-SOLV LIMITED—See CN Innovations Holdings Limited; *Int'l*, pg. 1673
MS PRINTING SOLUTIONS S.R.L.—See Dover Corporation; *U.S. Public*, pg. 681
MULTILINE TECHNOLOGY, INC., PRINTED CIRCUIT BOARD DIVISION—See Multiline Technology Inc.; *U.S. Private*, pg. 2813
MULTILINE TECHNOLOGY, INC., PRINTING PRODUCTS DIVISION—See Multiline Technology Inc.; *U.S. Private*, pg. 2813
MULTILINE TECHNOLOGY INC.; *U.S. Private*, pg. 2813
MUNKEBO CLEMCO A/S—See Clemco Industries Corp.; *U.S. Private*, pg. 939
MUSTANG DYNAMOMETER; *U.S. Private*, pg. 2819
MW COMPONENTS—See MW Industries, Inc.; *U.S. Private*, pg. 2822
MW INDUSTRIES, INC.; *U.S. Private*, pg. 2822
NAI CRANES, LLC—See Dearborn Crane & Engineering Co.; *U.S. Private*, pg. 1185
NAKAN TECHNO CO., LTD.—See Helios Techno Holding Co., Ltd.; *Int'l*, pg. 3330

N.A.I.C.S. INDEX

333248 — ALL OTHER INDUSTRIA...

NANO PARTICLE TECHNOLOGY CENTER—See Hosokawa Micron Corporation; *Int'l*, pg. 3486

NANYANG DTECH CO., LTD.—See Guangdong Dtech Technology Co., Ltd.; *Int'l*, pg. 3154

NAPIER TURBOCHARGERS LIMITED—See Westinghouse Air Brake Technologies Corporation; *U.S. Public*, pg. 2358

NATIONAL TRUCK PARTS OF THE MIDWEST, INC.—See Illinois Tool Works Inc.; *U.S. Public*, pg. 1109

NATOLI ENGINEERING CO. INC.; *U.S. Private*, pg. 2866

NEK CO., LTD.—See Eagle Industry Co., Ltd.; *Int'l*, pg. 2265

NEKOOSA COATED PRODUCTS LLC—See Sentinel Capital Partners, L.L.C.; *U.S. Private*, pg. 3609

NEMAK ARGENTINA, S.R.L.—See ALFA, S.A.B. de C.V.; *Int'l*, pg. 313

NEMAK SLOVAKIA, S.R.O.—See ALFA, S.A.B. de C.V.; *Int'l*, pg. 313

NEW METAL ENGINEERING, LLC—See IHI Corporation; *Int'l*, pg. 3606

NEWTON OFFICINE MECCANICHE SRL—See Camozzi Group; *Int'l*, pg. 1274

NFM (DALIAN) MACHINERY CO., LTD.—See NFM/Welding Engineers, Inc.; *U.S. Private*, pg. 2923

NFM IDDON LTD.—See NFM/Welding Engineers, Inc.; *U.S. Private*, pg. 2923

NIIGATA POWER SYSTEMS (SINGAPORE) PTE. LTD.—See IHI Corporation; *Int'l*, pg. 3606

NIIGATA POWER SYTEMS (SHANGHAI) CO., LTD.—See IHI Corporation; *Int'l*, pg. 3606

NIKKO MECHANICS CO., LTD.—See Eternal Materials Co., Ltd.; *Int'l*, pg. 2521

NINGBO HAITIAN HUAYUAN MACHINERY CO., LTD.—See Haitian International Holdings Ltd.; *Int'l*, pg. 3217

NINGBO ZHAFIR PLASTICS MACHINERY CO., LTD.—See Haitian International Holdings Ltd.; *Int'l*, pg. 3217

NISHINIHON GENERATOR MFG. CO., LTD.—See Denyo Co., Ltd.; *Int'l*, pg. 2040

NISSEI GEAR MOTOR MFG. (CHANGZHOU) CO., LTD.—See Brother Industries, Ltd.; *Int'l*, pg. 1198

NISSEI TRADING (SHANGHAI) CO., LTD.—See Brother Industries, Ltd.; *Int'l*, pg. 1198

NISSIN KOKI CO., LTD.—See Fair Friend Group; *Int'l*, pg. 2604

NOGOON TOLGOI UUL LLC—See Endress+Hauser (International) Holding AG; *Int'l*, pg. 2408

NOL-TEC EUROPE, S.R.L.—See Nol-Tec Systems Inc.; *U.S. Private*, pg. 2933

NOL-TEC SYSTEMS (ASIA) PTE. LTD.—See Nol-Tec Systems Inc.; *U.S. Private*, pg. 2933

NOMIS D.O.O.—See Arburg GmbH & Co.; *Int'l*, pg. 539

NORDSON ANDINA LIMITADA—See Nordson Corporation; *U.S. Public*, pg. 1533

NORDSON AUSTRALIA PTY. LIMITED—See Nordson Corporation; *U.S. Public*, pg. 1533

NORDSON AUSTRALIA PTY., LTD.—See Nordson Corporation; *U.S. Public*, pg. 1533

NORDSON BENELUX B.V.—See Nordson Corporation; *U.S. Public*, pg. 1533

NORDSON CHINA CO., LTD.—See Nordson Corporation; *U.S. Public*, pg. 1533

NORDSON CORP. - ADHESIVE DISPENSING SYSTEMS DIVISION—See Nordson Corporation; *U.S. Public*, pg. 1533

NORDSON CORP. - INDUSTRIAL COATING SYSTEMS DIVISION—See Nordson Corporation; *U.S. Public*, pg. 1533

NORDSON CS, SPOL.S.R.O.—See Nordson Corporation; *U.S. Public*, pg. 1533

NORDSON DE MEXICO, S.A. DE C.V.—See Nordson Corporation; *U.S. Public*, pg. 1534

NORDSON DEUTSCHLAND GMBH—See Nordson Corporation; *U.S. Public*, pg. 1533

NORDSON DO BRASIL INDUSTRIA E COMERCIO LTDA.—See Nordson Corporation; *U.S. Public*, pg. 1534

NORDSON FINLAND OY—See Nordson Corporation; *U.S. Public*, pg. 1534

NORDSON FRANCE, S.A.—See Nordson Corporation; *U.S. Public*, pg. 1534

NORDSON GMBH (AUSTRIA)—See Nordson Corporation; *U.S. Public*, pg. 1534

NORDSON IBERICA S.A.—See Nordson Corporation; *U.S. Public*, pg. 1534

NORDSON ITALIA S.P.A—See Nordson Corporation; *U.S. Public*, pg. 1534

NORDSON K.K.—See Nordson Corporation; *U.S. Public*, pg. 1534

NORDSON (MALAYSIA) SDN. BHD.—See Nordson Corporation; *U.S. Public*, pg. 1533

NORDSON NORGE A/S—See Nordson Corporation; *U.S. Public*, pg. 1534

NORDSON POLSKA SP.Z.O.O.—See Nordson Corporation; *U.S. Public*, pg. 1534

NORDSON PORTUGAL EQUIPAMENTO INDUSTRIAL, LTDA.—See Nordson Corporation; *U.S. Public*, pg. 1534

NORDSON S.E. ASIA (PTE.), LTD.—See Nordson Corporation; *U.S. Public*, pg. 1534

NORDSON TECHNOLOGY B.V.—See Nordson Corporation; *U.S. Public*, pg. 1534

NORDSON XALOY ASIA (THAILAND) LTD.—See Nordson Corporation; *U.S. Public*, pg. 1534

NORDSON XALOY INCORPORATED—See Nordson Corporation; *U.S. Public*, pg. 1534

NOREVA GMBH—See Goodwin PLC; *Int'l*, pg. 3042

NORTH AMERICAN INDUSTRIAL SERVICES, INC.—See The Sterling Group, L.P.; *U.S. Private*, pg. 4123

NOVATECH, LLC; *U.S. Private*, pg. 2967

NUMERICAL CONCEPTS, INC.; *U.S. Private*, pg. 2973

NV STORAX BENELUX SA—See F. Ramada Investimentos, SGPS, S.A.; *Int'l*, pg. 2596

NYX INC.; *U.S. Private*, pg. 2977

OAKLAND AUTOMATION, LLC - NOVI PLANT—See Oakland Standard Co., LLC; *U.S. Private*, pg. 2985

OAKLAND AUTOMATION, LLC—See Oakland Standard Co., LLC; *U.S. Private*, pg. 2985

OERLIKON VACUUM RUSSIAN FEDERATION GERTNER SERVICE GMBH—See Atlas Copco AB; *Int'l*, pg. 684

OHIO MACHINERY CO. - MANTSINEN USA DIVISION—See Ohio Machinery Co.; *U.S. Private*, pg. 3004

OIL STATES QCS—See Oil States International, Inc.; *U.S. Public*, pg. 1565

OLIVOTTO GLASS TECHNOLOGIES S.P.A.—See China Glass Holdings Limited; *Int'l*, pg. 1504

OMMA S.R.L.—See Chargeurs SA; *Int'l*, pg. 1450

OMNI PRECISION SDN. BHD.—See Adval Tech Holding AG; *Int'l*, pg. 155

OMNI RAY AG—See Addtech AB; *Int'l*, pg. 134

O-M (U.S.A.), INC.—See Daiwabo Holdings Co., Ltd.; *Int'l*, pg. 1949

ONAMAC INDUSTRIES INC.—See Warburg Pincus LLC; *U.S. Private*, pg. 4437

ONNURI INDUSTRIAL MACHINERY CO. LTD—See Alfa Laval AB; *Int'l*, pg. 312

ORBITALUM TOOLS GMBH—See Illinois Tool Works Inc.; *U.S. Public*, pg. 1109

ORESUND UNLOADER DESIGN BUREAU AB—See FLSmidth & Co. A/S; *Int'l*, pg. 2712

OS MACHINERY CORP.—See Hokkan Holdings Limited; *Int'l*, pg. 3443

OSSIS CORPORATION—See Zimmer Biomet Holdings, Inc.; *U.S. Public*, pg. 2406

OTIS LIMITED—See Otis Worldwide Corporation; *U.S. Public*, pg. 1623

OTIS PACIFIC HOLDINGS B.V.—See Otis Worldwide Corporation; *U.S. Public*, pg. 1623

OT-LAS SRL—See El.En. S.p.A.; *Int'l*, pg. 2342

OTTO MANNER GMBH—See Barnes Group Inc.; *U.S. Public*, pg. 277

OVALSTRAPPING INC.—See Enterprises International Inc.; *U.S. Private*, pg. 1404

PACIFIC GREEN TECHNOLOGIES INC.; *U.S. Public*, pg. 1631

PACIFIC PLASTICS & ENGINEERING INC.—See The Cretex Companies, Inc.; *U.S. Private*, pg. 4016

PALL FILTERSYSTEMS GMBH—See Danaher Corporation; *U.S. Public*, pg. 629

PALL MEDISTAD BV—See Danaher Corporation; *U.S. Public*, pg. 630

PAL SALES LLC—See Asia Tele-Net & Technology Corporation Limited; *Int'l*, pg. 615

PAMARCO, INCORPORATED—See J.P. Kotts & Co.; *U.S. Private*, pg. 2170

PANHUIZEN GRAVEERINDUSTRIE B.V.—See Apex International Co., Ltd.; *Int'l*, pg. 511

PAR SYSTEMS, LLC—See Pohlad Companies; *U.S. Private*, pg. 3220

PEA GMBH—See AIRTECH JAPAN, LTD.; *Int'l*, pg. 249

PEAK TECHNOLOGIES, INC.—See Sole Source Capital LLC; *U.S. Private*, pg. 3708

PEERLESS ASIA PACIFIC PTE. LTD.—See CECO Environmental Corp.; *U.S. Public*, pg. 464

PEERLESS INDUSTRIAL GROUP, INC.—See The Carlyle Group Inc.; *U.S. Public*, pg. 2055

PEGASO S.R.L.—See Cellularline SpA; *Int'l*, pg. 1395

PENGO ATTACHMENTS, INC.—See Stanley Black & Decker, Inc.; *U.S. Public*, pg. 1933

PEREGRINE INDUSTRIES, INC.; *U.S. Public*, pg. 1673

PERFECBORE AG—See Fuji Corporation; *Int'l*, pg. 2810

PERPETUAL MACHINE COMPANY—See Textile Rubber & Chemical Co., Inc.; *U.S. Private*, pg. 3978

PFAFF-SILBERBLAU HEBEZEUGFABRIK GMBH—See Columbus McKinnon Corporation; *U.S. Public*, pg. 536

PFEIFFER VACUUM BRASIL LTDA—See Dr. Ing. K. Busch GmbH; *Int'l*, pg. 2194

PHARMASIENA SERVICE S.R.L.—See I.M.A. Industria Macchine Automatiche S.p.A.; *Int'l*, pg. 3566

PHENIX SYSTEMS SA—See 3D Systems Corporation; *U.S. Public*, pg. 4

PIERCE EQUIPMENT—See Ram Consolidated Industries, Inc.; *U.S. Private*, pg. 3350

PISTORA OY—See Illinois Tool Works Inc.; *U.S. Public*, pg. 1110

PITNEY BOWES (ASIA PACIFIC) PTE. LTD—See Pitney Bowes Inc.; *U.S. Public*, pg. 1694

THE PLASTEK GROUP - PLASTEK DO BRASIL DIVISION—See The Plastek Group; *U.S. Private*, pg. 4096

PLASTICAST HUNGARY KORLATOLT FELELOSSEGU TARSASAG—See Jabil Inc.; *U.S. Public*, pg. 1182

PM CONTROL SYSTEMS (AUST) PTY. LTD.—See Woodward, Inc.; *U.S. Public*, pg. 2377

PM CONTROL SYSTEMS PTE. LTD.—See Woodward, Inc.; *U.S. Public*, pg. 2377

PMFG, INC.—See CECO Environmental Corp.; *U.S. Public*, pg. 464

PNEU-MECH SYSTEMS MFG. LLC; *U.S. Private*, pg. 3219

POLYURETHANE MACHINERY CORPORATION—See PMC Capital Partners, LLC; *U.S. Private*, pg. 3218

POSH CONCEPT MANNEQUINS CO., LTD.—See Cosmos Machinery Enterprises Limited; *Int'l*, pg. 1813

POWER & ENERGY, INC.; *U.S. Private*, pg. 3237

PPT INDUSTRIAL MACHINES INC.—See Quality Products Inc.; *U.S. Private*, pg. 3320

PRACTICAL AUTOMATION INC.—See Alinabal Holdings Corporation; *U.S. Private*, pg. 168

PRECISION FLOW TECHNOLOGIES, INC.—See Francisco Partners Management, LP; *U.S. Private*, pg. 1590

PRECISION GEARS LTD.—See I.M.A. Industria Macchine Automatiche S.p.A.; *Int'l*, pg. 3566

PREMIER MILL CORP.—See SPX Technologies, Inc.; *U.S. Public*, pg. 1921

PRESSTEK EUROPE LTD.—See Mark Andy, Inc.; *U.S. Private*, pg. 2577

PRESSTEK LLC—See Mark Andy, Inc.; *U.S. Private*, pg. 2577

PRINTERS MERCHANDISING CORP.—See Printers' Service, Inc.; *U.S. Private*, pg. 3265

PRINTERS SERVICE OF FLORIDA, INC.—See Printers' Service, Inc.; *U.S. Private*, pg. 3265

PRISCO EUROPE BVBA—See Printers' Service, Inc.; *U.S. Private*, pg. 3265

PROCESS AUTOMATION (CHINA) LIMITED—See Asia Tele-Net & Technology Corporation Limited; *Int'l*, pg. 615

PROCESS AUTOMATION (SHENZHEN) LIMITED—See Asia Tele-Net & Technology Corporation Limited; *Int'l*, pg. 615

PROCOMAC ENGENHARIA LTDA.—See GEA Group Aktiengesellschaft; *Int'l*, pg. 2903

PRODUCTION CONTROL UNITS, INC.; *U.S. Private*, pg. 3273

THE PROVIDENT GROUP—See Anderson & Vreeland, Inc.; *U.S. Private*, pg. 276

PT ACEZ INSTRUMENTS INDONESIA—See Acez Instruments Pte. Ltd.; *Int'l*, pg. 102

PT. BOBST JAKARTA—See Bobst Group S.A.; *Int'l*, pg. 1096

PT CRESTEC INDONESIA—See Crestec Inc.; *Int'l*, pg. 1841

P.T. DAIFUKU INDONESIA—See Daifuku Co., Ltd.; *Int'l*, pg. 1926

PT DURR SYSTEMS INDONESIA—See Durr AG; *Int'l*, pg. 2233

PT FRIGOGLASS INDONESIA—See Frigoglass S.A.I.C.; *Int'l*, pg. 2792

PT. FUJITA KANKO INDONESIA—See Fujita Kanko Inc.; *Int'l*, pg. 2831

PTG HEAVY INDUSTRIES LIMITED—See Chongqing Machinery & Electronics Holding (Group) Co., Ltd.; *Int'l*, pg. 1580

PT. HITACHI HIGH-TECHNOLOGIES INDONESIA—See Hitachi, Ltd.; *Int'l*, pg. 3419

PT. IHI TRANSPORT MACHINERY INDONESIA—See IHI Corporation; *Int'l*, pg. 3606

PT. IHI TRANSPORT MACHINERY INDONESIA—See IHI Corporation; *Int'l*, pg. 3606

PT INGERSOLL-RAND INDONESIA—See Ingersoll Rand Inc.; *U.S. Public*, pg. 1122

PT.JAPAN ENGINEERING TECHNOLOGY—See Fair Friend Group; *Int'l*, pg. 2605

PT MANROLAND INDONESIA—See Allianz SE; *Int'l*, pg. 355

PT. PYROTEK INDONESIA—See Pyrotek Incorporated; *U.S. Private*, pg. 3311

PURALUBE GMBH—See Allied Resource Corporation; *U.S. Private*, pg. 187

PURALUBE INC.—See Allied Resource Corporation; *U.S. Private*, pg. 187

PURCELL SYSTEMS, INC.—See EnerSys; *U.S. Public*, pg. 767

PURSUIT MARINE DRIVE LIMITED—See Cellulac Limited; *Int'l*, pg. 1395

PYROBRAS COMERCIO E INDUSTRIA LTDA.—See Pyrotek Incorporated; *U.S. Private*, pg. 3311

PYROTEK BAHRAIN SPC—See Pyrotek Incorporated; *U.S. Private*, pg. 3311

PYROTEK CZ, S.R.O.—See Pyrotek Incorporated; *U.S. Private*, pg. 3311

PYROTEK DONGGUAN LIMITED—See Pyrotek Incorporated; *U.S. Private*, pg. 3311

PYROTEK (GUANGXI NANNING) HIGH TEMPERATURE MATERIALS CO., LTD.—See Pyrotek Incorporated; *U.S. Private*, pg. 3311

333248 — ALL OTHER INDUSTRIA...

PYROTEK INDIA PVT. LTD.—See Pyrotek Incorporated; *U.S. Private*, pg. 3311
PYROTEK JAPAN CO., LTD.—See Pyrotek Incorporated; *U.S. Private*, pg. 3311
PYROTEK PTY. LTD.—See Pyrotek Incorporated; *U.S. Private*, pg. 3311
PYROTEK (XI'AN) METAULLURGICAL MATERIALS CO., LTD.—See Pyrotek Incorporated; *U.S. Private*, pg. 3311
QINGDAO CHUN YUAN PRECISION MECHATRONIC CO., LTD.—See Chun Yuan Steel Industry Co., Ltd.; *Int'l*, pg. 1596
QUALITY CONTROLLED MANUFACTURING, INC; *U.S. Private*, pg. 3318
QUANTUMCORRUGATED S.R.L.—See Guangdong Dongfang Science & Technology Co., Ltd.; *Int'l*, pg. 3153
QUICKMILL INC.—See Batliboi Ltd.; *Int'l*, pg. 890
QUINTUS TECHNOLOGIES AB—See John Bean Technologies Corporation; *U.S. Public*, pg. 1191
QVF ENGINEERING GMBH—See De Dietrich Process Systems S.A.; *Int'l*, pg. 1995
QVF PROCESS SYSTEMS LTD.—See De Dietrich Process Systems S.A.; *Int'l*, pg. 1995
RADAR STAMPING TECHNOLOGIES S. DE R.L. DE C.V.—See Shiloh Industries, Inc.; *U.S. Private*, pg. 3636
RANSOHOFF—See Alpha Capital Partners, Ltd.; *U.S. Private*, pg. 197
RAVI INDUSTRIES LTD.—See Hayleys PLC; *Int'l*, pg. 3292
RAYTECH INDUSTRIES DIVISION—See Lyman Products Corporation; *U.S. Private*, pg. 2520
RCT HYDRAULIC-TOOLING AG—See Accu Holding AG; *Int'l*, pg. 94
RCT SACHSEN GMBH—See Accu Holding AG; *Int'l*, pg. 94
REDVIKING GROUP, LLC—See Lincoln Electric Holdings, Inc.; *U.S. Public*, pg. 1318
REDVIKING - RESEARCH TRIANGLE ENGINEERING CENTER—See Lincoln Electric Holdings, Inc.; *U.S. Public*, pg. 1318
REED MACHINERY, INC.; *U.S. Private*, pg. 3382
REFORM MASCHINENFABRIK ADOLF RABENSEIFNER GMBH & CO. KG—See ATON GmbH; *Int'l*, pg. 689
RELIANCE INDUSTRIAL PRODUCTS USA, LTD.—See Applied Industrial Technologies, Inc.; *U.S. Public*, pg. 171
REMTEC AUTOMATION LLC—See The C. M. Paula Company; *U.S. Private*, pg. 4003
RENTECH DEVELOPMENT CORPORATION—See Rentech, Inc.; *U.S. Private*, pg. 3400
RETHINK ROBOTICS, INC.; *U.S. Private*, pg. 3411
RIMROCK CORPORATION—See Lincoln Electric Holdings, Inc.; *U.S. Public*, pg. 1318
RIVERSIDE ENGINEERING, INC.—See FCF Partners, LP; *U.S. Private*, pg. 1485
RMH SYSTEMS, INC.; *U.S. Private*, pg. 3452
RMS EQUIPMENT LLC—See The Heico Companies, L.L.C.; *U.S. Private*, pg. 4050
RND AUTOMATION & ENGINEERING, LLC; *U.S. Private*, pg. 3452
ROBERINE B.V.—See Alamo Group Inc.; *U.S. Public*, pg. 71
ROCKWELL AUTOMATION CHILE S.A.—See Rockwell Automation, Inc.; *U.S. Public*, pg. 1806
ROCKWELL AUTOMATION TAIWAN CO., LTD.—See Rockwell Automation, Inc.; *U.S. Public*, pg. 1806
ROEHLEN ENGRAVING BF PERKINS—See Standex International; *U.S. Public*, pg. 1930
ROHR BAGGER GMBH—See Markel Group Inc.; *U.S. Public*, pg. 1369
ROKAS CONSTRUCTION, S.A.—See Iberdrola, S.A.; *Int'l*, pg. 3573
ROMAC INDUSTRIAL PARTS, INC.—See Kinderhook Industries, LLC; *U.S. Private*, pg. 2306
ROMAC INDUSTRIAL PARTS, INC.—See Kinderhook Industries, LLC; *U.S. Private*, pg. 2307
ROTADYNE—See Rotation Dynamics Corp.; *U.S. Private*, pg. 3486
ROTATION DYNAMICS CORP.; *U.S. Private*, pg. 3486
ROTEX EUROPE LTD.—See Hillenbrand, Inc.; *U.S. Public*, pg. 1036
ROTHTEC ENGRAVING CORP.; *U.S. Private*, pg. 3487
SABE S.A.S.—See Ag Growth International Inc.; *Int'l*, pg. 198
SABP ELTEKNIK AB—See Addtech AB; *Int'l*, pg. 135
SANGATECH CO., LTD.—See Bain Capital, LP; *U.S. Private*, pg. 435
SANKI CO LTD—See Daiken Corporation; *Int'l*, pg. 1931
SAPAL S.A.—See CVC Capital Partners SICAV-FIS S.A.; *Int'l*, pg. 1884
SARCLAD LTD.—See The Heico Companies, L.L.C.; *U.S. Private*, pg. 4051
SAS CRISTALLERIE DE SAINT PAUL—See Cerinnov Group SA; *Int'l*, pg. 1422
SATSUKI KIZAI CO., LTD.—See Futaba Corporation; *Int'l*, pg. 2851
SAUERESSIG DESIGN STUDIO GMBH—See Matthews International Corporation; *U.S. Public*, pg. 1401
SAUERESSIG FLEXO GMBH—See Matthews International Corporation; *U.S. Public*, pg. 1401
SAUERESSIG GMBH & CO. KG—See Matthews International Corporation; *U.S. Public*, pg. 1401

SAUERESSIG LTD.—See Matthews International Corporation; *U.S. Public*, pg. 1401
SAUERESSIG OOO—See Matthews International Corporation; *U.S. Public*, pg. 1401
SAUERESSIG POLSKA SP. Z.O.O.—See Matthews International Corporation; *U.S. Public*, pg. 1401
SAUER GMBH—See DMG MORI Co., Ltd.; *Int'l*, pg. 2144
S.C. ALLFLEX ROMANIA S.R.L.—See Merck & Co., Inc.; *U.S. Public*, pg. 1421
SCHENCK LTD—See Durr AG; *Int'l*, pg. 2233
SCHENCK PROCESS LLC—See Blackstone Inc.; *U.S. Public*, pg. 360
SCHENCK ROTEC INDIA LIMITED—See Durr AG; *Int'l*, pg. 2233
SCHENCK SHANGHAI MACHINERY CORPORATION LTD—See Durr AG; *Int'l*, pg. 2233
SCHENCK TREBEL CORPORATION—See Durr AG; *Int'l*, pg. 2233
SCHMITT EUROPE, LTD.—See Schmitt Industries, Inc.; *U.S. Public*, pg. 1846
SCHRAMM, INC.; *U.S. Private*, pg. 3569
SCOTT EQUIPMENT CO.; *U.S. Private*, pg. 3576
SCOTT TURBON MIXER, INC.—See Ebara Corporation; *Int'l*, pg. 2284
SCRIPTPRO LLC; *U.S. Private*, pg. 3580
SCULPTEO SAS—See BASF SE; *Int'l*, pg. 884
SEALED AIR AMERICAS MANUFACTURING S. DE R.L. DE C.V.—See Sealed Air Corporation; *U.S. Public*, pg. 1854
SELANDIA PARK A/S—See Glunz & Jensen Holding A/S; *Int'l*, pg. 3011
SELAS HEAT TECHNOLOGY COMPANY LLC—See Lionheart Ventures; *U.S. Private*, pg. 2464
SENCORPWHITE, INC.—See Connell Limited Partnership; *U.S. Private*, pg. 1017
SERCEL S.A—See CGG; *Int'l*, pg. 1432
SHAANXI BEIREN PRINTING MACHINERY CO., LTD.—See Beijing Jingcheng Machinery Electric Holding Co., Ltd.; *Int'l*, pg. 953
SHANGHAI CLYDE BERGEMANN MACHINERY COMPANY LTD.—See Clyde Blowers Capital IM LLP; *Int'l*, pg. 1665
SHANGHAI ESPEC ENVIRONMENTAL EQUIPMENT CO., LTD.—See ESPEC Corp.; *Int'l*, pg. 2505
SHANGHAI FLEETGUARD FILTER CO., LTD.—See Cummins Inc.; *U.S. Public*, pg. 606
SHANGHAI GOULDS PUMPS CO. LTD.—See ITT Inc.; *U.S. Public*, pg. 1178
SHANGHAI HUASHENG FUJITEC ESCALATOR CO., LTD.—See Fujitec Co., Ltd.; *Int'l*, pg. 2831
SHANGHAI INTERNATIONAL ENGINEERING CONSTRUCTION CONSULTING CO., LTD.—See ENN Natural Gas Co., Ltd.; *Int'l*, pg. 2443
SHANGHAI STAR MODERN AGRICULTURE EQUIPMENT CO., LTD.—See IHI Corporation; *Int'l*, pg. 3606
SHANGHAI YUNGTAY GIE CO., LTD.—See Hitachi, Ltd.; *Int'l*, pg. 3425
SHANGHAI ZHENHUA HEAVY INDUSTRY CO., LTD—See China Communications Construction Company Limited; *Int'l*, pg. 1491
SHANGHAI ZIMMER INTERNATIONAL TRADING CO. LTD. I.L.—See GEA Group Aktiengesellschaft; *Int'l*, pg. 2903
SHAOXING ADVANCE GEARBOX CO., LTD.—See Hangzhou Advance Gearbox Group Co., Ltd.; *Int'l*, pg. 3246
SHARP IMAGING AND INFORMATION COMPANY OF AMERICA—See Hon Hai Precision Industry Co., Ltd.; *Int'l*, pg. 3458
SHENYANG FIDIA NC & MACHINE CO., LTD.—See FIDIA S.p.A.; *Int'l*, pg. 2655
SHENZHEN BEIREN PRINTING CO., LTD.—See Beijing Jingcheng Machinery Electric Holding Co., Ltd.; *Int'l*, pg. 953
SHENZHEN CHEN HSONG MACHINERY CO. LTD.—See Chen Hsong Holdings Ltd.; *Int'l*, pg. 1464
SHICK TUBE-VEYOR CORPORATION—See Equistone Partners Europe Limited; *Int'l*, pg. 2486
SHILOH INDUSTRIES AB—See Shiloh Industries, Inc.; *U.S. Private*, pg. 3636
SHIMA CO., LTD.—See Daito Trust Construction Co., Ltd.; *Int'l*, pg. 1944
SHOWA INFORMATION SYSTEMS CO., LTD.—See Canon Inc.; *Int'l*, pg. 1296
S. HOWES, INC.; *U.S. Private*, pg. 3515
SICHUAN HONGHUA PETROLEUM EQUIPMENT CO., LTD.—See Honghua Group Ltd; *Int'l*, pg. 3471
SIMPSON TECHNOLOGIES CORPORATION—See Altor Equity Partners AB; *Int'l*, pg. 395
SIMPSON TECHNOLOGIES GMBH—See Altor Equity Partners AB; *Int'l*, pg. 395
SINGER AFRICA MIDDLE EAST LIMITED—See Platinum Equity, LLC; *U.S. Private*, pg. 3208
SINGER SEWING COMPANY—See Platinum Equity, LLC; *U.S. Private*, pg. 3208
SINLAND DEVELOPMENT PTE, LTD.—See China Machinery Engineering Corporation; *Int'l*, pg. 1516
SIRCUS S.R.L.—See Gruppo MutuiOnline S.p.A.; *Int'l*, pg. 3141
SIRIUS MACHINERY AB—See Coesia S.p.A.; *Int'l*, pg. 1690

SKARNES, INC.—See RMH Systems, Inc.; *U.S. Private*, pg. 3452
SLIPNAXOS AB—See 3M Company; *U.S. Public*, pg. 8
SLURRY-21 CO., LTD.—See Hitachi Zosen Corporation; *Int'l*, pg. 3412
SMB SCHWEDE MASCHINENBAU GMBH—See Crown Holdings, Inc.; *U.S. Public*, pg. 599
SMOOTH INVESTMENT CO., LTD.—See ANEST IWATA Corporation; *Int'l*, pg. 459
SMP SCHWEDE MASCHINENBAU WEISCHLITZ GMBH—See Crown Holdings, Inc.; *U.S. Public*, pg. 599
SNAP-ON EQUIPMENT HUNGARY KFT.—See Snap-on Incorporated; *U.S. Public*, pg. 1898
SNK EG TAIWAN CORPORATION—See Fair Friend Group; *Int'l*, pg. 2605
SNK ENGINEERING KOREA CO., LTD.—See Fair Friend Group; *Int'l*, pg. 2605
SNK INDIA PRIVATE LIMITED—See Fair Friend Group; *Int'l*, pg. 2605
SNK NANJING TECHNOLOGY CORPORATION—See Fair Friend Group; *Int'l*, pg. 2605
SNK THAI CO., LTD.—See Fair Friend Group; *Int'l*, pg. 2605
SOURCE TECHNOLOGIES, LLC—See StoneCalibre, LLC; *U.S. Private*, pg. 3828
SOUTHEASTERN INSTALLATION INC.; *U.S. Private*, pg. 3728
SPECMA HYDRAULIC SHANGHAI CO LTD—See Aktieselskabet Schouw & Co.; *Int'l*, pg. 266
SQUID INK MANUFACTURING, INC.—See Engage Technologies Corp.; *U.S. Private*, pg. 1397
SRS ENGINEERING, INC.; *U.S. Private*, pg. 3768
STAINLESS DESIGN CONCEPTS—See CVD Equipment Corporation; *U.S. Public*, pg. 613
STANDARD MOTOR PRODUCTS-INDEPENDENCE—See Standard Motor Products, Inc.; *U.S. Public*, pg. 1929
STANDARD TOOLS & EQUIPMENT CO. INC.—See Florida Capital Partners, Inc.; *U.S. Private*, pg. 1547
STANLEY BLACK & DECKER FINLAND OY—See Stanley Black & Decker, Inc.; *U.S. Public*, pg. 1934
STANLEY FASTENING SYSTEMS, L.P.—See Stanley Black & Decker, Inc.; *U.S. Public*, pg. 1935
THE STARCO GROUP, INC.; *U.S. Private*, pg. 4121
STARRETT KINEMETRIC ENGINEERING, INC.—See MiddleGround Management, LP; *U.S. Private*, pg. 2713
STC DIP SPIN—See Prab, Inc.; *U.S. Private*, pg. 3241
STEEGER USA, LLC—See Forsyth Capital Investors LLC; *U.S. Private*, pg. 1574
STELLAR INDUSTRIES INC.; *U.S. Private*, pg. 3799
STIGAB AB—See Addtech AB; *Int'l*, pg. 135
STIMAS ENGINEERING S.R.L.—See Durr AG; *Int'l*, pg. 2233
STOKVIS CELIX PORTUGAL UNIPESSOAL LDA—See Illinois Tool Works Inc.; *U.S. Public*, pg. 1110
STOLZ SEQUIPAG S.A.S.—See Alfa Laval AB; *Int'l*, pg. 312
STT ENVIRO CORP.—See Carmeuse Holding SA; *Int'l*, pg. 1342
STURTEVANT INC.; *U.S. Private*, pg. 3845
STYNER+BIENZ FORMTECH LTD.—See Adval Tech Holding AG; *Int'l*, pg. 155
SUAREZ MANUFACTURING INDUSTRIES—See Suarez Corporation Industries; *U.S. Private*, pg. 3847
SUMMIT VALVE & CONTROLS INC.—See Endress+Hauser (International) Holding AG; *Int'l*, pg. 2409
SUN DRILLING PRODUCTS CORP; *U.S. Private*, pg. 3863
SUNDS MDF TECHNOLOGIES AB—See Dieffenbacher Holding GmbH & Co. KG; *Int'l*, pg. 2114
SUPERIOR CONTROLS, INC.—See Lincoln Electric Holdings, Inc.; *U.S. Public*, pg. 1318
SUPFINA GRIESHABER GMBH & CO. KG—See Grieshaber Holding GmbH; *Int'l*, pg. 3083
SUPFINA MACHINE CO., INC.—See Grieshaber Holding GmbH; *Int'l*, pg. 3083
SUPPLIES DISTRIBUTORS S.A.—See GXO Logistics, Inc.; *U.S. Public*, pg. 976
SUPREME INTEGRATED TECHNOLOGY, INC.—See Employee Owned Holdings, Inc.; *U.S. Private*, pg. 1386
SURFACEPREP MOBILE LLC—See Nautic Partners, LLC; *U.S. Private*, pg. 2871
SUR-FORM CORPORATION—See Andrew W. Byrd & Co., LLC; *U.S. Private*, pg. 280
SWANSON-ANAHEIM CORP—See Swanson Systems, Inc.; *U.S. Private*, pg. 3891
SWECO—See Schlumberger Limited; *U.S. Public*, pg. 1846
SWENSON TECHNOLOGY, INC.—See GK Enterprises, Inc.; *U.S. Private*, pg. 1703
SYCOTEC GMBH & CO. KG—See Fukuda Corporation; *Int'l*, pg. 2839
SYNFORM CO., LTD.—See EQT AB; *Int'l*, pg. 2467
SYNVENTIVE MOLDING SOLUTIONS GMBH—See Barnes Group Inc.; *U.S. Public*, pg. 278
SYNVENTIVE MOLDING SOLUTIONS, INC.—See Barnes Group Inc.; *U.S. Public*, pg. 278
SYNVENTIVE MOLDING SOLUTIONS JBJ PRIVATE LIMITED—See Barnes Group Inc.; *U.S. Public*, pg. 277
SYNVENTIVE MOLDING SOLUTIONS K.K.—See Barnes Group Inc.; *U.S. Public*, pg. 277
SYNVENTIVE MOLDING SOLUTIONS PTE LTD.—See Barnes Group Inc.; *U.S. Public*, pg. 278

N.A.I.C.S. INDEX

333310 — COMMERCIAL AND SERV...

SYNVENTIVE MOLDING SOLUTIONS SL—See Barnes Group Inc.; *U.S. Public*, pg. 278
SYNVENTIVE MOLDING SOLUTIONS (SUZHOU) CO., LTD.—See Barnes Group Inc.; *U.S. Public*, pg. 277
SYSTEMONE TECHNOLOGIES INC.; *U.S. Private*, pg. 3907
SYSTEM TM A/S—See Durr AG; *Int'l*, pg. 2233
SYTECH—See Cummins Inc.; *U.S. Public*, pg. 609
TAIWAN DAIFUKU CO., LTD.—See Daifuku Co., Ltd.; *Int'l*, pg. 1926
TAIWAN DAIFUKU CO., LTD. - TAICHUNG PLANT—See Daifuku Co., Ltd.; *Int'l*, pg. 1926
TAKASHIMA GIKEN CO., LTD.—See IHI Corporation; *Int'l*, pg. 3606
TAMARIS INDUSTRIES SAS—See CVC Capital Partners SICAV-FIS S.A.; *Int'l*, pg. 1887
TAYLOR DEVICES, INC.; *U.S. Public*, pg. 1983
TECHNIC INCORPORATED-EQUIPMENT DIV.—See Technic Incorporated; *U.S. Private*, pg. 3953
TECHNIFAB PRODUCTS, INC.—See Crane Company; *U.S. Public*, pg. 589
TECHNO DAI-ICHI CO., LTD—See I-PEX Inc.; *Int'l*, pg. 3564
THE TECHNOLOGY STORE, INC.—See Scandium International Mining Corp; *U.S. Public*, pg. 1843
TELPAR, INC.—See Sole Source Capital LLC; *U.S. Private*, pg. 3708
TERLYN INDUSTRIES, INC.; *U.S. Private*, pg. 3969
TESSU SYSTEMS B.V.—See Absolent Air Care Group AB; *Int'l*, pg. 70
TEXAS OILPATCH SERVICES, LLC—See Applied Industrial Technologies, Inc.; *U.S. Public*, pg. 171
TEXMACO INFRASTRUCTURE & HOLDINGS LIMITED—See Adventz Group; *Int'l*, pg. 167
THAI CUBIC TECHNOLOGY CO., LTD. - SRIRACHA FACTORY—See Cubic Korea INC.; *Int'l*, pg. 1875
THERMISCHE RUCKSTANDSVERWERTUNG GMBH & CO. KG—See BASF SE; *Int'l*, pg. 885
THERMOTEC WEILBURG GMBH & CO. KG—See ESPEC Corp.; *Int'l*, pg. 2505
THIXOFORMING LLC—See ARC Group Worldwide, Inc.; *U.S. Public*, pg. 179
THOMAS ENGINEERING INC.; *U.S. Private*, pg. 4155
THOMSON NEFF GMBH—See Regal Rexnord Corporation; *U.S. Public*, pg. 1772
TIER ONE, LLC—See The Jordan Company, L.P.; *U.S. Private*, pg. 4060
TIMMERIJE B.V.—See Hydratec Industries NV; *Int'l*, pg. 3546
TLI ENTERPRISES INC.; *U.S. Private*, pg. 4178
TOLEDO ENGENERING COMPANY INC.; *U.S. Private*, pg. 4181
TOLLO LINEAR AB—See Regal Rexnord Corporation; *U.S. Public*, pg. 1772
TOMOIKE PRECISION MACHINERY (SHANGHAI) CO., LIMITED—See CDW Holding Ltd.; *Int'l*, pg. 1372
TOOLING & EQUIPMENT INTERNATIONAL CORP.—See General Motors Company; *U.S. Public*, pg. 929
TRAMCO EUROPE LIMITED—See Ag Growth International Inc.; *Int'l*, pg. 198
TRANSPACIFIC SUPERIOR PAK PTY LTD—See Cleanaway Waste Management Limited; *Int'l*, pg. 1655
TRIDENT GRAPHICS NA LLC—See Sonoco Products Company; *U.S. Public*, pg. 1909
TRU-STONE TECHNOLOGIES, INC.—See MiddleGround Management, LP; *U.S. Private*, pg. 2713
TTS MARINE KOREA CO., LTD.—See Cargotec Corporation; *Int'l*, pg. 1329
TTS MARINE OSTRAVA S.R.O—See Cargotec Corporation; *Int'l*, pg. 1329
TUBE FABRICATION MACHINERY LIMITED—See Addison Saws Limited; *Int'l*, pg. 129
TUFTCO CORPORATION; *U.S. Private*, pg. 4257
TVL AUSTRALIA PTY LTD—See Sabre Corporation; *U.S. Public*, pg. 1834
TWIN DISC POWER TRANSMISSION (SHANGHAI) CO. LTD.—See Twin Disc, Incorporated; *U.S. Public*, pg. 2207
UIC GMBH—See BDI - BioEnergy International AG; *Int'l*, pg. 929
ULTRA ELECTRONICS CARD SYSTEMS INC—See Advent International Corporation; *U.S. Private*, pg. 101
ULTRA ELECTRONICS CARD SYSTEMS LTD—See Advent International Corporation; *U.S. Private*, pg. 100
UNARCO MATERIAL HANDLING, INC.—See The Renco Group Inc.; *U.S. Private*, pg. 4104
UNION SPECIAL CORPORATION; *U.S. Private*, pg. 4285
UNITED SILICONE—See Illinois Tool Works Inc.; *U.S. Public*, pg. 1111
UNITEMP LIMITED—See ESPEC Corp.; *Int'l*, pg. 2505
UNIVERSAL INSTRUMENTS CORPORATION—See Francisco Partners Management, LP; *U.S. Private*, pg. 1592
US NUCLEAR CORP.; *U.S. Public*, pg. 2266
UYEMURA INTERNATIONAL (HONG KONG) CO., LTD.—See C.Uyemura & Co., Ltd.; *Int'l*, pg. 1244
VACUDYNE INC.—See Altair Corporation; *U.S. Public*, pg. 86
VALMONT POLSKA SP.Z O.O—See Valmont Industries, Inc.; *U.S. Public*, pg. 2274

VALMONT SM A/S—See Euro Steel Danmark A/S; *Int'l*, pg. 2531
VAUTID AUSTRIA GMBH—See DZ BANK AG Deutsche Zentral-Genossenschaftsbank; *Int'l*, pg. 2245
VAUTID-BELGIUM PGMBH—See DZ BANK AG Deutsche Zentral-Genossenschaftsbank; *Int'l*, pg. 2245
VELO3D, INC.; *U.S. Public*, pg. 2277
VERALTO CORPORATION; *U.S. Public*, pg. 2280
V.H.C LTD., INC.—See Cerberus Capital Management, L.P.; *U.S. Public*, pg. 839
VIDEOJET CHILE CODIFICADORA LIMITED—See Danaher Corporation; *U.S. Public*, pg. 631
VISION EXPERTS GMBH—See Atlas Copco AB; *Int'l*, pg. 683
V&N ADVANCED AUTOMATION SYSTEMS, LLC; *U.S. Private*, pg. 4327
VOLKER GMBH—See CoBe Capital LLC; *U.S. Public*, pg. 957
VOLVO GROUP VENTURE CAPITAL AB—See AB Volvo; *Int'l*, pg. 44
VPG SYSTEMS UK, LTD.—See Vishay Precision Group, Inc.; *U.S. Public*, pg. 2303
VSM SVERIGE AB—See Platinum Equity, LLC; *U.S. Private*, pg. 3208
VSM (UK) LTD—See Platinum Equity, LLC; *U.S. Private*, pg. 3208
VTU-ENGINEERING GMBH—See DPE Deutsche Private Equity GmbH; *Int'l*, pg. 2188
VULCANFORMS INC.; *U.S. Private*, pg. 4416
WABASH METAL PRODUCTS INC—See Harbour Group Industries, Inc.; *U.S. Private*, pg. 1860
WAGSTAFF INC.; *U.S. Private*, pg. 4426
WALCO MACHINES COMPANY INC.—See Chargeurs SA; *Int'l*, pg. 1450
WALISCHMILLER ENGINEERING GMBH—See Carr's Group PLC; *Int'l*, pg. 1343
WALKER MAGNETICS GROUP, INC.—See Alliance Holdings, Inc.; *U.S. Private*, pg. 183
WALL COLMONOY CORPORATION - AEROBRAZE ENGINEERED TECHNOLOGIES DIVISION—See Wall Colmonoy Corporation; *U.S. Private*, pg. 4429
WALTON/STOUT, INC.—See Harbour Group Industries, Inc.; *U.S. Private*, pg. 1860
WAREHOUSE AUTOMATION IBERIA, S.L.—See Illinois Tool Works Inc.; *U.S. Public*, pg. 1111
WASTEQUIP, LLC—See H.I.G. Capital, LLC; *U.S. Private*, pg. 1832
WAUSEON MACHINE AND MANUFACTURING, INC.; *U.S. Private*, pg. 4457
WAYNE TRAIL TECHNOLOGIES, INC.—See Lincoln Electric Holdings, Inc.; *U.S. Public*, pg. 1318
WAZANA BROTHERS INTERNATIONAL INC.; *U.S. Private*, pg. 4461
W BAR E INVESTMENTS CORP.; *U.S. Private*, pg. 4417
WEBB ROBOTICA S.R.L.—See EFORT Intelligent Equipment Co., Ltd.; *Int'l*, pg. 2321
WEBER PACKAGING SOLUTIONS, INC.; *U.S. Private*, pg. 4465
WEB PRINTING CONTROLS COMPANY INCORPORATED; *U.S. Private*, pg. 4464
WELLTEC MACHINERY LIMITED—See Cosmos Machinery Enterprises Limited; *Int'l*, pg. 1813
WESMAN SIMPSON TECHNOLOGIES PVT. LTD.—See Altor Equity Partners AB; *Int'l*, pg. 395
WESTERN PLASTICS—See Berkshire Hathaway Inc.; *U.S. Public*, pg. 300
WESTERN PRINTING MACHINERY CO.; *U.S. Private*, pg. 4496
WEYERHAEUSER COMPANY LIMITED—See Weyerhaeuser Company; *U.S. Public*, pg. 2365
WHEELABRATOR GROUP LTD.—See Altor Equity Partners AB; *Int'l*, pg. 395
WHITING CORPORATION—See GK Enterprises, Inc.; *U.S. Private*, pg. 1703
WHITING EQUIPMENT CANADA, INC.—See GK Enterprises, Inc.; *U.S. Private*, pg. 1703
THE WILLAMETTE VALLEY COMPANY - PRE-TEC DIVISION—See The Willamette Valley Company; *U.S. Private*, pg. 4136
WILLIAMS FORM ENGINEERING CORP.; *U.S. Private*, pg. 4525
WINTERTHUR TECHNOLOGIE AG—See 3M Company; *U.S. Public*, pg. 8
WINTERTHUR TECHNOLOGY UK LTD.—See 3M Company; *U.S. Public*, pg. 9
WIRTZ MANUFACTURING COMPANY INC.; *U.S. Private*, pg. 4547
WOLF ENERGY SERVICES INC.; *U.S. Public*, pg. 2376
THE WOLF MACHINE CO.; *U.S. Private*, pg. 4138
WSF INDUSTRIES, INC.; *U.S. Private*, pg. 4574
WUHAN RISONG HOKUTO AUTOMOTIVE EQUIPMENT CO., LTD.—See Guangzhou Risong Intelligent Technology Holding Co., Ltd.; *Int'l*, pg. 3167
WUHU NEW UNIVERSAL ENVIRONMENTAL SCIENCE & TECHNOLOGY CO., LTD.—See Beijing New Universal Science and Technology Co., Ltd.; *Int'l*, pg. 954
XEIKON AMERICA, INC.—See Koch Industries, Inc.; *U.S. Private*, pg. 2327

XEIKON AMERICA, INC.—See The Goldman Sachs Group, Inc.; *U.S. Public*, pg. 2077
XEIKON NV—See Koch Industries, Inc.; *U.S. Private*, pg. 2327
XEIKON NV—See The Goldman Sachs Group, Inc.; *U.S. Public*, pg. 2077
XEROX A/S—See Xerox Holdings Corporation; *U.S. Public*, pg. 2388
XEROX ISRAEL LTD—See Xerox Holdings Corporation; *U.S. Public*, pg. 2390
XIAN BROTHER INDUSTRIES CO., LTD.—See Brother Industries, Ltd.; *Int'l*, pg. 1198
XITRON, LLC—See Hybrid Software Group PLC; *Int'l*, pg. 3544
XYLEM WATER SOLUTIONS (HONG KONG) LIMITED—See Xylem Inc.; *U.S. Public*, pg. 2396
YIYANG RUBBER & PLASTICS MACHINERY GROUP CO, LTD—See China National Chemical Corporation; *Int'l*, pg. 1530
Y.M.P. (THAILAND) CO., LTD.—See Fair Friend Group; *Int'l*, pg. 2605
ZANA TOOLS SHPK—See Einhell Germany AG; *Int'l*, pg. 2334
ZELLER ENGINEERING GMBH—See Berry Global Group, Inc; *U.S. Public*, pg. 326
ZEPF TECHNOLOGIES UK LIMITED—See Diageo plc; *Int'l*, pg. 2103
ZHAFIR PLASTICS MACHINERY GMBH—See Haitian International Holdings Ltd.; *Int'l*, pg. 3217
ZHEJIANG TUOSHAN MACHINERY CO., LTD.—See Anhui Tuoshan Heavy Industries Co., Ltd.; *Int'l*, pg. 470
ZHONGSHE M&E IMPORT & EXPORT CO., LTD.—See China Machinery Engineering Corporation; *Int'l*, pg. 1516
ZIP-PAK—See Illinois Tool Works Inc.; *U.S. Public*, pg. 1109

333310 — COMMERCIAL AND SERVICE INDUSTRY MACHINERY MANUFACTURING

20 20 OPTICS PVT LTD—See EssilorLuxottica SA; *Int'l*, pg. 2512
3DM DIGITAL MANUFACTURING LTD.; *Int'l*, pg. 7
3M ITALIA S.P.A.—See 3M Company; *U.S. Public*, pg. 6
3NINE AB—See Grimaldi Industri AB; *Int'l*, pg. 3085
3S PHOTONICS S.A.S.—See Eurazeo SE; *Int'l*, pg. 2527
4D TECHNOLOGY CORPORATION—See Onto Innovation Inc.; *U.S. Public*, pg. 1605
AAREN SCIENTIFIC INC.—See Carl-Zeiss-Stiftung; *Int'l*, pg. 1334
ABILITY ENTERPRISE CO., LTD—See Abico Group; *Int'l*, pg. 61
ABSOLENT FILTERMIST INDIA PRIVATE LTD.—See Absolent Air Care Group AB; *Int'l*, pg. 70
ACCUTOME, INC.—See Halma plc; *Int'l*, pg. 3231
ACCU-TURN INC.—See Marini Manufacturing, Inc.; *U.S. Private*, pg. 2576
ACI HOLDINGS INC.—See Thermo Fisher Scientific Inc.; *U.S. Public*, pg. 2145
ACP INC.—See Ali Holding S.r.l; *Int'l*, pg. 322
ACRELEC GROUP SAS—See GLORY Ltd.; *Int'l*, pg. 3009
ACRISON, INC. - ACRISON INTERNATIONAL DIVISION—See Acrison, Inc.; *U.S. Private*, pg. 65
ACTION MANUFACTURING & SUPPLY, INC.—See Franklin Electric Co., Inc.; *U.S. Public*, pg. 878
ACTRO CO., LTD.; *Int'l*, pg. 121
ADEN FRANCE—See FAYAT SAS; *Int'l*, pg. 2624
ADP GAUSELMANN GMBH—See Gauselmann AG; *Int'l*, pg. 2890
ADVANCED THIN FILMS LLC—See IDEX Corp; *U.S. Public*, pg. 1089
ADVANCE OPTICAL—See EssilorLuxottica SA; *Int'l*, pg. 2513
AERO D.D.; *Int'l*, pg. 180
AEROMIX SYSTEMS, INC.—See Fluence Corporation Limited; *U.S. Public*, pg. 857
AETHER WATER SYSTEMS, LLC—See Nephros, Inc.; *U.S. Public*, pg. 1506
AFL INDUSTRIES, INC.—See RGF Environmental Group; *U.S. Private*, pg. 3420
AGFA CORPORATION—See Agfa-Gevaert N.V.; *Int'l*, pg. 208
AGFA-GEVAERT AB—See Agfa-Gevaert N.V.; *Int'l*, pg. 208
AGFA-GEVAERT AG/SA—See Agfa-Gevaert N.V.; *Int'l*, pg. 208
AGFA-GEVAERT ARGENTINA S.A.—See Agfa-Gevaert N.V.; *Int'l*, pg. 208
AGFA-GEVAERT B.V.—See Agfa-Gevaert N.V.; *Int'l*, pg. 208
AGFA-GEVAERT LTD.—See Agfa-Gevaert N.V.; *Int'l*, pg. 208
AGFA-GEVAERT N.V.; *Int'l*, pg. 207
AGFA-GEVAERT S.P.A.—See Agfa-Gevaert N.V.; *Int'l*, pg. 208
AGFA HEALTHCARE SPAIN, S.A.U.—See Agfa-Gevaert N.V.; *Int'l*, pg. 208
AGFA IMAGING PRODUCTS (SHENZHEN) CO., LTD.—See Agfa-Gevaert N.V.; *Int'l*, pg. 208
AGILENT TECHNOLOGIES, INC. - VACUUM

PRODUCTS—See Agilent Technologies, Inc.; *U.S. Public*, pg. 61
AGORA TC SP. Z O. O.—See Agora S.A.; *Int'l*, pg. 212
AIRTEC PNEUMATIC GMBH; *Int'l*, pg. 249
ALBIS OPTOELECTRONICS AG; *Int'l*, pg. 299
AL KAWTHAR COMPANY—See BERICAP GmbH & Co. KG; *Int'l*, pg. 980
ALKOSIGN LIMITED; *Int'l*, pg. 331
ALLIANCE LAUNDRY SYSTEMS LLC—See BDT Capital Partners, LLC; *U.S. Private*, pg. 502
ALL-PRO IMAGING CORP.—See Air Techniques, Inc.; *U.S. Private*, pg. 140
ALLTERRA DEUTSCHLAND GMBH—See Trimble, Inc.; *U.S. Public*, pg. 2190
ALLUXA, INC.—See Enpro Inc.; *U.S. Public*, pg. 774
ALPHA LENS COMPANY LTD.—See Carl-Zeiss-Stiftung; *Int'l*, pg. 1335
ALPHA LENS COMPANY LTD.—See EQT AB; *Int'l*, pg. 2472
ALPHATECH ALI S.P.A.—See Ali Holding S.r.l; *Int'l*, pg. 320
ALPINE RESEARCH OPTICS CORP.—See Altechna UAB; *Int'l*, pg. 389
ALTECHNA UAB; *Int'l*, pg. 389
ALTEK LAB INC.—See Altek Corporation; *Int'l*, pg. 389
ALTO-SHAAM INC.; *U.S. Private*, pg. 210
AMANO CORPORATION - HOSOE FACILITY—See Amano Corporation; *Int'l*, pg. 410
AMANO MCGANN CANADA INC.—See Amano Corporation; *Int'l*, pg. 411
AMBERTECH LIMITED; *Int'l*, pg. 414
AMERGRAPH CORPORATION; *U.S. Private*, pg. 219
AMERICAN DRYER CORPORATION—See Whirlpool Corporation; *U.S. Public*, pg. 2367
AMERICAN PHOTOCOPY EQUIPMENT COMPANY OF PITTSBURGH, LLC—See Xerox Holdings Corporation; *U.S. Public*, pg. 2387
AMERICAN PHOTONICS CO.; *U.S. Private*, pg. 243
AMSCOMATIC, INC.—See M&R Holdings Inc.; *U.S. Private*, pg. 2525
ANADOLU FLYGT POMPA PAZARLAMA VE TICARET AS—See Xylem Inc.; *U.S. Public*, pg. 2396
ANALYTICA BIO-ENERGY CORP.; *Int'l*, pg. 446
ANDRITZ FIBER DRYING LTD.—See ANDRITZ AG; *Int'l*, pg. 454
ANDRITZ SEPARATION GMBH—See ANDRITZ AG; *Int'l*, pg. 454
ANHUI BAILU ELECTRONIC TECHNOLOGY CO., LTD.—See Anhui Wanyi Science & Technology Co., Ltd.; *Int'l*, pg. 470
ANHUI RONGEN ENVIRONMENTAL PROTECTION TECHNOLOGY CO., LTD.—See Tennant Company; *U.S. Public*, pg. 2016
ANTON/BAUER INCORPORATED; *U.S. Private*, pg. 288
ANWELL TECHNOLOGIES LTD.; *Int'l*, pg. 486
A. O. SMITH ENTERPRISES LTD.—See A. O. Smith Corporation; *U.S. Public*, pg. 11
A.O. SMITH WATER PRODUCTS COMPANY B.V.—See A. O. Smith Corporation; *U.S. Public*, pg. 11
APLAB LIMITED-MUMBAI—See Aplab Limited; *Int'l*, pg. 515
APOGEE OPTOCOM CO., LTD.; *Int'l*, pg. 517
APPLIED IMAGE GROUP INC.; *U.S. Private*, pg. 298
APPLIED MATERIALS EUROPE BV—See Applied Materials, Inc.; *U.S. Public*, pg. 172
APPOTRONICS CORP., LTD.; *Int'l*, pg. 522
APP-TEK INTERNATIONAL PTY LTD—See Thermo Fisher Scientific Inc.; *U.S. Public*, pg. 2145
AQ PARKOPRINT AB—See AQ Group AB; *Int'l*, pg. 526
AQUAFINE CORPORATION—See Danaher Corporation; *U.S. Public*, pg. 624
AQUA PLUS WASSER- UND RECYCLINGSYSTEME GMBH—See Element Solutions Inc.; *U.S. Public*, pg. 725
AQUAPORIN US INC.—See Aquaporin A/S; *Int'l*, pg. 528
AQUATECH INTERNATIONAL CORP.; *U.S. Private*, pg. 303
AQUION PARTNERS L.P.; *U.S. Private*, pg. 305
AQUIRIAN TECHNOLOGY PTY LTD—See Aquirian Limited; *Int'l*, pg. 528
ARBORTECH—See Berkshire Hathaway Inc.; *U.S. Public*, pg. 299
ARGENCOS SA—See Godrej & Boyce Mfg. Co. Ltd.; *Int'l*, pg. 3020
ARGOSY RESEARCH, INC.; *Int'l*, pg. 563
ARIUS TECHNOLOGY INC.; *Int'l*, pg. 567
ARIUS TECHNOLOGY INC. - VAUGHAN—See Arius Technology Inc.; *Int'l*, pg. 567
ART ADVANCED RESEARCH TECHNOLOGIES INC.; *Int'l*, pg. 580
ARTEMIS OPTICAL LIMITED—See Gooch & Housego PLC; *Int'l*, pg. 3038
ARVEL INDUSTRIES SARL—See Bucher Industries AG; *Int'l*, pg. 1206
ARYLUX HUNGARY ELEKTROMECHANIKUS ALKATRESZGYARTO KFT—See Illinois Tool Works Inc.; *U.S. Public*, pg. 1101
ASAKAWA LENS WORKS CO., LTD.—See CHINO Corporation; *Int'l*, pg. 1570
ASCENTEK INTERNATIONAL COMPANY LIMITED—See Fuji Corporation; *Int'l*, pg. 2809

ASCENTEX INDUSTRY CORP.—See Fuji Corporation; *Int'l*, pg. 2809
ASE S.P.A.; *Int'l*, pg. 604
ASM FRONT-END MANUFACTURING SINGAPORE PTE LTD—See ASM INTERNATIONAL N.V.; *Int'l*, pg. 626
ASM JAPAN K.K.—See ASM INTERNATIONAL N.V.; *Int'l*, pg. 626
ASPEX CORPORATION—See Thermo Fisher Scientific Inc.; *U.S. Public*, pg. 2146
ASTRAL POOL AUSTRALIA PTY LIMITED—See Fluidra SA; *Int'l*, pg. 2713
ATLANTIC ZEISER, INC.—See Atlantic Zeiser GmbH & Co.; *Int'l*, pg. 676
ATLAS METAL INDUSTRIES INC.—See Mercury Aircraft Inc.; *U.S. Private*, pg. 2670
AURORA CORPORATION; *Int'l*, pg. 713
AURORA SINGAPORE CORP.—See Aurora Corporation; *Int'l*, pg. 713
AUTO BUTLER INC.; *U.S. Private*, pg. 397
AUTOLIV, INC.; *Int'l*, pg. 728
AUTOMATIC BAR CONTROLS, INC.—See The Middleby Corporation; *U.S. Public*, pg. 2113
AUTOMATIC PRODUCTS (UK) LIMITED—See Crane NXT, Co.; *U.S. Public*, pg. 591
AVERY WEIGH-TRONIX UK LIMITED—See Illinois Tool Works Inc.; *U.S. Public*, pg. 1101
AVID NORTH ASIA LIMITED—See Symphony Technology Group, LLC; *U.S. Private*, pg. 3901
AVID TECHNOLOGY EUROPE LTD.—See Symphony Technology Group, LLC; *U.S. Private*, pg. 3901
AVID TECHNOLOGY GMBH—See Symphony Technology Group, LLC; *U.S. Private*, pg. 3901
AVID TECHNOLOGY, INC. (S.E. ASIA) PTE. LTD.—See Symphony Technology Group, LLC; *U.S. Private*, pg. 3901
AVID TECHNOLOGY, INC.—See Symphony Technology Group, LLC; *U.S. Private*, pg. 3901
AVID TECHNOLOGY K.K.—See Symphony Technology Group, LLC; *U.S. Private*, pg. 3901
AVID TECHNOLOGY SALES LIMITED—See Symphony Technology Group, LLC; *U.S. Private*, pg. 3901
AVID TECHNOLOGY S.A.R.L—See Symphony Technology Group, LLC; *U.S. Private*, pg. 3901
AWETA G&P—See FPS Food Processing Systems B.V.; *Int'l*, pg. 2757
AZKOYEN COMERCIAL DEUTSCHLAND GMBH—See AZKOYEN S.A; *Int'l*, pg. 780
AZKOYEN INDUSTRIAL, S.A.—See AZKOYEN S.A.; *Int'l*, pg. 780
AZKOYEN S.A.; *Int'l*, pg. 780
AZO GMBH & CO. KG; *Int'l*, pg. 780
BAKERS PRIDE OVEN COMPANY—See Standex International; *U.S. Public*, pg. 1931
BALDWIN UV LTD.—See Forsyth Capital Investors LLC; *U.S. Private*, pg. 1573
BALLY WULFF AUTOMATEN GMBH; *Int'l*, pg. 809
BARBER-NICHOLS INC.—See Graham Corporation; *U.S. Public*, pg. 954
BARCLAY WATER MANAGEMENT, INC.—See Ecolab Inc.; *U.S. Public*, pg. 712
BASLER AG; *Int'l*, pg. 887
BASLER ASIA PTE. LTD.—See Basler AG; *Int'l*, pg. 887
BASLER VISION TECHNOLOGIES TAIWAN INC.—See Basler AG; *Int'l*, pg. 887
BASO PRECISION OPTICS LTD.—See Eastman Kodak Company; *U.S. Public*, pg. 706
BAUSCH & LOMB CANADA, INC.—See Bausch Health Companies Inc.; *Int'l*, pg. 896
BAUSCH & LOMB (M) SDN BHD—See Bausch Health Companies Inc.; *Int'l*, pg. 896
BAUSCH & LOMB SOUTH AFRICA PTY. LTD.—See Bausch Health Companies Inc.; *Int'l*, pg. 896
BAUSCH & LOMB VENEZUELA S.A.—See Bausch Health Companies Inc.; *Int'l*, pg. 896
BBGR S.A.—See EssilorLuxottica SA; *Int'l*, pg. 2512
BEAVER MACHINE CORPORATION; *Int'l*, pg. 935
BEDROCK AUTOMATION PLATFORMS, INC.—See Analog Devices, Inc.; *U.S. Public*, pg. 135
BEIJING ATLANTIC ZEISER TECH CO. LTD.—See Atlantic Zeiser GmbH & Co.; *Int'l*, pg. 676
BEIJING GRANT MEMBRANE SEPARATION EQUIPMENT CO., LTD.—See HNAC Technology Co., Ltd.; *Int'l*, pg. 3433
BEIJING HI-VAC ENVIRONMENTAL PROTECTION TECHNOLOGY CO., LTD.—See Hi-Vac Corporation; *U.S. Private*, pg. 1932
BEIJING NEWPORT SPECTRA-PHYSICS TECHNOLOGIES CO., LTD.—See MKS Instruments, Inc.; *U.S. Public*, pg. 1453
BEITLER MCKEE COMPANY—See EssilorLuxottica SA; *Int'l*, pg. 2513
BELANGER, INC.—See Dover Corporation; *U.S. Public*, pg. 678
BENZ RESEARCH & DEVELOPMENT CORPORATION—See TPG Capital, L.P.; *U.S. Public*, pg. 2169
BESSER PRONEQ, INC.—See Besser Company; *U.S. Private*, pg. 542

THE BETHLEHEM CORPORATION; *U.S. Private*, pg. 3994
BETHLEHEM INTL. SALES CORP.—See The Bethlehem Corporation; *U.S. Private*, pg. 3994
BETRIEBSGESELLSCHAFT PFORTNERHAUS MBH—See Fielmann Group AG; *Int'l*, pg. 2656
BINOPTICS CORP.—See MACOM Technology Solutions Holdings, Inc.; *U.S. Public*, pg. 1352
BIOCON 1, LLC—See Nephros, Inc.; *U.S. Public*, pg. 1506
BIOINGENIERIA DEHNER S.R.L.; *Int'l*, pg. 1038
BIO-UV GROUP; *Int'l*, pg. 1036
BLISS-BRET A.S.—See Haco N.V.; *Int'l*, pg. 3204
BLODGETT COMBI—See The Middleby Corporation; *U.S. Public*, pg. 2113
BLODGETT OVEN COMPANY INC—See The Middleby Corporation; *U.S. Public*, pg. 2113
BLOWER APPLICATION COMPANY, INC.—See Valesco Industries, Inc; *U.S. Private*, pg. 4331
BMW (US) HOLDING CORPORATION—See Bayerische Motoren Werke Aktiengesellschaft; *Int'l*, pg. 912
BOBRICK WASHROOM EQUIPMENT LIMITED—See Bobrick Washroom Equipment, Inc.; *U.S. Private*, pg. 607
BRADKEN-LONDON LTD.—See Hitachi, Ltd.; *Int'l*, pg. 3415
BRAIN POWER INTERNATIONAL LTD.—See Brain Power Inc.; *U.S. Private*, pg. 634
BRECONCHERRY LTD.—See GEA Group Aktiengesellschaft; *Int'l*, pg. 2897
BRET SA—See Haco N.V.; *Int'l*, pg. 3204
BRIGHTEN OPTIX CORPORATION; *Int'l*, pg. 1162
BRISTOL TOOL & GAUGE INTERNATIONAL GMBH—See Absolent Air Care Group AB; *Int'l*, pg. 70
BRITHOL MICHCOMA MOZAMBIQUE LIMITED; *Int'l*, pg. 1165
BROOKS TECHNOLOGY (SHANGHAI) LIMITED—See Azenta, Inc.; *U.S. Public*, pg. 258
BROTHER ENTERPRISE, LTD.—See Brother Industries, Ltd.; *Int'l*, pg. 1196
BROTHER INDUSTRIES, LTD.; *Int'l*, pg. 1196
BROTHER INDUSTRIES (SHENZHEN) LTD.—See Brother Industries, Ltd.; *Int'l*, pg. 1196
BROTHER INDUSTRIES (U.K.) LTD.—See Brother Industries, Ltd.; *Int'l*, pg. 1197
BROTHER INDUSTRIES (U.S.A.), INC.—See Brother Industries, Ltd.; *Int'l*, pg. 1197
BROTHER INDUSTRIES (VIETNAM) LTD.—See Brother Industries, Ltd.; *Int'l*, pg. 1197
BRUECKNER GROUP USA, INC. - FRASER—See Brueckner Group GmbH; *Int'l*, pg. 1199
BUNN-O-MATIC CORPORATION; *U.S. Private*, pg. 685
BURROUGHS, INC.—See Marlin Equity Partners, LLC; *U.S. Private*, pg. 2584
BUSHNELL OUTDOOR PRODUCTS, INC.—See Vista Outdoor, Inc.; *U.S. Public*, pg. 2304
BUSHNELL OUTDOOR PRODUCTS SAS—See Vista Outdoor, Inc.; *U.S. Public*, pg. 2304
BUSS AG—See Fabrel AG; *Int'l*, pg. 2599
BWT HUNGARIA KFT—See BWT Aktiengesellschaft; *Int'l*, pg. 1232
BWT WASSERTECHNIK GMBH—See BWT Aktiengesellschaft; *Int'l*, pg. 1232
CABLECAM, LLC—See Kroenke Sports & Entertainment, LLC; *U.S. Private*, pg. 2352
CABOT MICROELECTRONICS POLISHING CORPORATION—See Entegris, Inc.; *U.S. Public*, pg. 776
CADILLAC JACK, INC.—See Flutter Entertainment plc; *Int'l*, pg. 2715
CALIN TECHNOLOGY CO., LTD.; *Int'l*, pg. 1265
CALUMET PHOTOGRAPHIC BV—See Aurelius Equity Opportunities SE & Co. KGaA; *Int'l*, pg. 708
CALUMET PHOTOGRAPHIC GMBH—See Aurelius Equity Opportunities SE & Co. KGaA; *Int'l*, pg. 708
CAMMSYS GLOBAL CO., LTD.—See CAMMSYS CO., LTD; *Int'l*, pg. 1273
CAMMSYS VINA CO., LTD.—See CAMMSYS CO., LTD; *Int'l*, pg. 1273
CAMOS TECHNOLOGIES CO.,LTD.—See AAC Technologies Holdings Inc.; *Int'l*, pg. 31
CANON BULGARIA EOOD—See Canon Inc.; *Int'l*, pg. 1294
CANON DANMARK A/S—See Canon Inc.; *Int'l*, pg. 1294
CANON EMIRATES LLC—See Canon Inc.; *Int'l*, pg. 1293
CANON EURASIA A.S.—See Canon Inc.; *Int'l*, pg. 1293
CANON FINETECH INC. - FUKUI PLANT—See Canon Inc.; *Int'l*, pg. 1295
CANON FINETECH INC. - IBARAKI PLANT—See Canon Inc.; *Int'l*, pg. 1295
CANON FINETECH NISCA (SHENZHEN) INC.—See Canon Inc.; *Int'l*, pg. 1295
CANON INC., TAIWAN—See Canon Inc.; *Int'l*, pg. 1295
CANON KOREA CONSUMER IMAGING INC.—See Canon Inc.; *Int'l*, pg. 1295
CANON LATIN AMERICA, INC.—See Canon Inc.; *Int'l*, pg. 1297
CANON LUXEMBOURG S.A.—See Canon Inc.; *Int'l*, pg. 1294
CANON MACHINERY (DALIAN) CO., LTD.—See Canon Inc.; *Int'l*, pg. 1295
CANON OPTO (MALAYSIA) SDN. BHD.—See Canon Inc.; *Int'l*, pg. 1296

N.A.I.C.S. INDEX
333310 — COMMERCIAL AND SERV...

CANON OPTRON, INC.—See Canon Inc.; *Int'l*, pg. 1296
CANON PORTUGAL S.A.—See Canon Inc.; *Int'l*, pg. 1295
CANON RU LLC—See Canon Inc.; *Int'l*, pg. 1296
CANON (U.K.) LTD.—See Canon Inc.; *Int'l*, pg. 1293
CANON UK—See Canon Inc.; *Int'l*, pg. 1293
CANON VIRGINIA, INC.—See Canon Inc.; *Int'l*, pg. 1297
CANON WIND INC.—See Canon Inc.; *Int'l*, pg. 1297
CANON ZHONGSHAN BUSINESS MACHINES CO., LTD.—See Canon Inc.; *Int'l*, pg. 1292
CANON ZHUHAI, INC.—See Canon Inc.; *Int'l*, pg. 1292
CARBONAIR ENVIRONMENTAL SYSTEMS; *U.S. Private*, pg. 748
CARCLO PRECISION OPTICS—See Carclo plc; *Int'l*, pg. 1321
CARDINAL CARTRIDGE, INC.; *U.S. Private*, pg. 750
CARGOTEC SOLUTIONS LLC—See Cargotec Corporation; *Int'l*, pg. 1327
CARL ZEISS 3D AUTOMATION GMBH—See Carl-Zeiss-Stiftung; *Int'l*, pg. 1333
CARL ZEISS 3D METROLOGY SERVICES GMBH MUNCHEN—See Carl-Zeiss-Stiftung; *Int'l*, pg. 1333
CARL ZEISS 3D METROLOGY SERVICES GMBH PEINE—See Carl-Zeiss-Stiftung; *Int'l*, pg. 1333
CARL ZEISS 3D METROLOGY SERVICES GMBH—See Carl-Zeiss-Stiftung; *Int'l*, pg. 1333
CARL ZEISS AB—See Carl-Zeiss-Stiftung; *Int'l*, pg. 1333
CARL ZEISS AG—See Carl-Zeiss-Stiftung; *Int'l*, pg. 1333
CARL ZEISS AG—See Carl-Zeiss-Stiftung; *Int'l*, pg. 1334
CARL ZEISS ARGENTINA S.A.—See Carl-Zeiss-Stiftung; *Int'l*, pg. 1334
CARL ZEISS A/S—See Carl-Zeiss-Stiftung; *Int'l*, pg. 1333
CARL ZEISS B.V.—See Carl-Zeiss-Stiftung; *Int'l*, pg. 1334
CARL ZEISS CO. LTD.—See Carl-Zeiss-Stiftung; *Int'l*, pg. 1334
CARL ZEISS CO. LTD.—See Carl-Zeiss-Stiftung; *Int'l*, pg. 1334
CARL ZEISS DE MEXICO, S.A. DE C.V.—See Carl-Zeiss-Stiftung; *Int'l*, pg. 1336
CARL ZEISS D.O.O.—See Carl-Zeiss-Stiftung; *Int'l*, pg. 1336
CARL ZEISS D.O.O.—See Carl-Zeiss-Stiftung; *Int'l*, pg. 1336
CARL ZEISS FAR EAST COMPANY LIMITED—See Carl-Zeiss-Stiftung; *Int'l*, pg. 1334
CARL ZEISS GMBH—See Carl-Zeiss-Stiftung; *Int'l*, pg. 1334
CARL ZEISS IBERIA, S.L.—See Carl-Zeiss-Stiftung; *Int'l*, pg. 1334
CARL ZEISS INDIA PTE. LTD.—See Carl-Zeiss-Stiftung; *Int'l*, pg. 1334
CARL ZEISS INSTRUMENTS S.R.L.—See Carl-Zeiss-Stiftung; *Int'l*, pg. 1334
CARL ZEISS LTD.—See Carl-Zeiss-Stiftung; *Int'l*, pg. 1334
CARL ZEISS MEDITEC, INC.—See Carl-Zeiss-Stiftung; *Int'l*, pg. 1334
CARL ZEISS MENA FZE—See Carl-Zeiss-Stiftung; *Int'l*, pg. 1334
CARL ZEISS MICROSCOPY CO., LTD.—See Carl-Zeiss-Stiftung; *Int'l*, pg. 1335
CARL ZEISS MICROSCOPY GMBH—See Carl-Zeiss-Stiftung; *Int'l*, pg. 1335
CARL ZEISS MICROSCOPY LIMITED—See Carl-Zeiss-Stiftung; *Int'l*, pg. 1335
CARL ZEISS N.V-S.A.—See Carl-Zeiss-Stiftung; *Int'l*, pg. 1335
CARL ZEISS OPTON KFT.—See Carl-Zeiss-Stiftung; *Int'l*, pg. 1335
CARL ZEISS OY—See Carl-Zeiss-Stiftung; *Int'l*, pg. 1335
CARL ZEISS PTE. LTD.—See Carl-Zeiss-Stiftung; *Int'l*, pg. 1335
CARL ZEISS S.A.S—See Carl-Zeiss-Stiftung; *Int'l*, pg. 1335
CARL ZEISS SBE, LLC—See Carl-Zeiss-Stiftung; *Int'l*, pg. 1335
CARL ZEISS SHANGHAI CO., LTD.—See Carl-Zeiss-Stiftung; *Int'l*, pg. 1335
CARL ZEISS SPOL. S.R.O.—See Carl-Zeiss-Stiftung; *Int'l*, pg. 1336
CARL ZEISS SPORT OPTIKAI HUNGARIA KFT.—See Carl-Zeiss-Stiftung; *Int'l*, pg. 1335
CARL ZEISS SPORTS OPTICS GMBH—See Carl-Zeiss-Stiftung; *Int'l*, pg. 1334
CARL ZEISS SP. Z O. O.—See Carl-Zeiss-Stiftung; *Int'l*, pg. 1335
CARL-ZEISS-STIFTUNG; *Int'l*, pg. 1333
CARL ZEISS SUZHOU CO., LTD.—See Carl-Zeiss-Stiftung; *Int'l*, pg. 1335
CARL ZEISS TECHNIKA KFT.—See Carl-Zeiss-Stiftung; *Int'l*, pg. 1335
CARL ZEISS VISION AB—See Carl-Zeiss-Stiftung; *Int'l*, pg. 1335
CARL ZEISS VISION ARGENTINA S.A—See Carl-Zeiss-Stiftung; *Int'l*, pg. 1335
CARL ZEISS VISION AUSTRALIA GROUP PTY. LTD.—See Carl-Zeiss-Stiftung; *Int'l*, pg. 1335
CARL ZEISS VISION AUSTRALIA LTD.—See Carl-Zeiss-Stiftung; *Int'l*, pg. 1335
CARL ZEISS VISION AUSTRALIA LTD.—See EQT AB; *Int'l*, pg. 2473

CARL ZEISS VISION BELGIUM NV—See Carl-Zeiss-Stiftung; *Int'l*, pg. 1335
CARL ZEISS VISION BRASIL INDUSTRIA OPTICA LTDA.—See Carl-Zeiss-Stiftung; *Int'l*, pg. 1335
CARL ZEISS VISION BRASIL INDUSTRIA OPTICA LTDA.—See EQT AB; *Int'l*, pg. 2473
CARL ZEISS VISION COLUMBIA LTDA.—See Carl-Zeiss-Stiftung; *Int'l*, pg. 1335
CARL ZEISS VISION DANMARK A/S—See Carl-Zeiss-Stiftung; *Int'l*, pg. 1335
CARL ZEISS VISION ESPANA—See Carl-Zeiss-Stiftung; *Int'l*, pg. 1335
CARL ZEISS VISION FRANCE HOLDING S.A.S.—See Carl-Zeiss-Stiftung; *Int'l*, pg. 1335
CARL ZEISS VISION GMBH—See Carl-Zeiss-Stiftung; *Int'l*, pg. 1335
CARL ZEISS VISION GMBH—See EQT AB; *Int'l*, pg. 2473
CARL ZEISS VISION (GUANGZHOU) LTD.—See Carl-Zeiss-Stiftung; *Int'l*, pg. 1335
CARL ZEISS VISION (GUANGZHOU) LTD.—See EQT AB; *Int'l*, pg. 2473
CARL ZEISS VISION HUNGARY OPTIKAI KFT.—See Carl-Zeiss-Stiftung; *Int'l*, pg. 1335
CARL ZEISS VISION INTERNATIONAL GMBH—See Carl-Zeiss-Stiftung; *Int'l*, pg. 1335
CARL ZEISS VISION INTERNATIONAL GMBH—See EQT AB; *Int'l*, pg. 2472
CARL ZEISS VISION ITALIA SPA—See Carl-Zeiss-Stiftung; *Int'l*, pg. 1336
CARL ZEISS VISION ITALIA SPA—See EQT AB; *Int'l*, pg. 2473
CARL ZEISS VISION (MALAYSIA) SDN. BHD.—See Carl-Zeiss-Stiftung; *Int'l*, pg. 1335
CARL ZEISS VISION MANUFACTURA DE MEXICO S. DE R.L. DE C.V.—See Carl-Zeiss-Stiftung; *Int'l*, pg. 1336
CARL ZEISS VISION MEXICO S. DE R.L. DE C.V.—See Carl-Zeiss-Stiftung; *Int'l*, pg. 1336
CARL ZEISS VISION PORTUGAL S.A.—See Carl-Zeiss-Stiftung; *Int'l*, pg. 1336
CARL ZEISS VISION SINGAPORE PTE. LTD.—See Carl-Zeiss-Stiftung; *Int'l*, pg. 1336
CARL ZEISS VISION—See Carl-Zeiss-Stiftung; *Int'l*, pg. 1335
CARL ZEISS VISION—See Carl-Zeiss-Stiftung; *Int'l*, pg. 1335
CARL ZEISS VISION—See EQT AB; *Int'l*, pg. 2472
CARL ZEISS VISION—See EQT AB; *Int'l*, pg. 2473
CARL ZEISS VISION SOUTH AFRICA LTD.—See Carl-Zeiss-Stiftung; *Int'l*, pg. 1336
CARL ZEISS VISION SWISS AG—See Carl-Zeiss-Stiftung; *Int'l*, pg. 1336
CARL ZEISS VISION SWISS AG—See EQT AB; *Int'l*, pg. 2473
CARL ZEISS VISION UK LTD.—See Carl-Zeiss-Stiftung; *Int'l*, pg. 1336
CARL ZEISS VISION UK LTD.—See EQT AB; *Int'l*, pg. 2473
CARL ZEISS VISION VENEZUELA INDUSTRIA OPTICA C.A.—See Carl-Zeiss-Stiftung; *Int'l*, pg. 1336
CARL ZEISS VISION VENEZUELA INDUSTRIA OPTICA C.A.—See EQT AB; *Int'l*, pg. 2473
CARL ZEISS X-RAY MICROSCOPY, INC.—See Carl-Zeiss-Stiftung; *Int'l*, pg. 1336
CAR-O-LINER COMMERCIAL AB—See Snap-on Incorporated; *U.S. Public*, pg. 1897
CAR-O-LINER HOLDING AB—See Snap-on Incorporated; *U.S. Public*, pg. 1897
CASIX INC.—See H&Q Asia Pacific, Ltd.; *U.S. Private*, pg. 1823
CASSAVANT MACHINING, INC.—See Gallant Capital Partners, LLC; *U.S. Private*, pg. 1639
CATCH THE MOMENT; *U.S. Private*, pg. 788
CATERPILLAR GLOBAL MINING CZECH REPUBLIC, A.S.—See Caterpillar, Inc.; *U.S. Public*, pg. 450
CATERPILLAR PROPULSION AB—See Caterpillar, Inc.; *U.S. Public*, pg. 451
CATERPILLAR PROPULSION PRODUCTION AB—See Caterpillar, Inc.; *U.S. Public*, pg. 451
CATERPILLAR PROPULSION PRODUCTION PTE. LTD.—See Caterpillar, Inc.; *U.S. Public*, pg. 451
CATERPILLAR PROPULSION SWEDEN AB—See Caterpillar, Inc.; *U.S. Public*, pg. 452
CATERPILLAR RAMOS ARIZPE, S. DE R.L. DE C.V.—See Caterpillar, Inc.; *U.S. Public*, pg. 452
CATERPILLAR REMANUFACTURING SERVICES RADOM POLAND—See Caterpillar, Inc.; *U.S. Public*, pg. 452
CATERPILLAR SERVICES GERMANY GMBH—See Caterpillar, Inc.; *U.S. Public*, pg. 452
CBC CO (MILAN) LTD.—See CBC Co., Ltd.; *Int'l*, pg. 1365
CBC CO. (PARIS) LTD.—See CBC Co., Ltd.; *Int'l*, pg. 1365
CBC (DEUTSCHLAND) GMBH—See CBC Co., Ltd.; *Int'l*, pg. 1365
CBC (EUROPE) LTD.—See CBC Co., Ltd.; *Int'l*, pg. 1365
CBC OPTICAL INDUSTRIES BD CO., LTD. See CBC Co., Ltd.; *Int'l*, pg. 1365
CBC OPTRONICS (BEIJING) CO., LTD.—See CBC Co., Ltd.; *Int'l*, pg. 1365
CBC (POLAND) SP.Z.O.O.—See CBC Co., Ltd.; *Int'l*, pg. 1365

CBC.S PTE LTD - TRADE DIVISION—See CBC Co., Ltd.; *Int'l*, pg. 1365
CBDMD, INC.; *U.S. Public*, pg. 456
CELESTRON, LLC; *U.S. Private*, pg. 806
CELLI S.P.A.—See Ardian SAS; *Int'l*, pg. 555
CENTENNIAL OPTICAL LTD.; *Int'l*, pg. 1402
CERINNOV INC.—See Cerinnov Group SA; *Int'l*, pg. 1422
CERTIKIN INTERNATIONAL LTD.—See Fluidra SA; *Int'l*, pg. 2714
CHAMBON SRL—See Haco N.V.; *Int'l*, pg. 3204
CHANGCHUN UP OPTOTECH CO., LTD.; *Int'l*, pg. 1442
CHARLES BESELER CO.; *U.S. Private*, pg. 851
CHEMFREE CORPORATION—See Berwind Corporation; *U.S. Private*, pg. 541
CHEMITHON ENGINEERS PVT. LTD.—See Chemithon Enterprises, Inc.; *U.S. Private*, pg. 872
CHEMSPEC EUROPE LIMITED—See RPM International Inc.; *U.S. Public*, pg. 1816
CHINA MACHINERY ENGINEERING SUZHOU CO., LTD.—See China Machinery Engineering Corporation; *Int'l*, pg. 1516
CHIYODA INTEGRE CO., LTD.; *Int'l*, pg. 1575
CHLORIDE GROUP LIMITED—See Emerson Electric Co.; *U.S. Public*, pg. 742
CHRIST PHARMA & LIFE SCIENCE SHANGHAI LTD.—See BWT Aktiengesellschaft; *Int'l*, pg. 1233
CHROMACOL LIMITED—See Thermo Fisher Scientific Inc.; *U.S. Public*, pg. 2145
CIPAG SA—See Ariston Thermo S.p.A.; *Int'l*, pg. 567
CITY OPTICAL PTY LTD.—See EssilorLuxottica SA; *Int'l*, pg. 2512
CLACK CORPORATION; *U.S. Private*, pg. 909
CLASSROOM TECHNOLOGY SOLUTIONS, INC.—See Galaxy Next Generation, Inc.; *U.S. Public*, pg. 895
CLEANAWAY SUPERIOR PAK PTY LTD—See Cleanaway Waste Management Limited; *Int'l*, pg. 1655
CLEARFIELD, INC.; *U.S. Public*, pg. 512
CLEMCO INDUSTRIES CORP.; *U.S. Private*, pg. 939
CLEMENTINA-CLEMCO HOLDING INC.; *U.S. Private*, pg. 940
CLERIO VISION INC.; *U.S. Private*, pg. 940
CLEVELAND RANGE LLC—See Ali Holding S.r.l.; *Int'l*, pg. 322
CLEXTRAL INC.—See Groupe Legris Industries; *Int'l*, pg. 3106
CLEXTRAL SAS—See Groupe Legris Industries; *Int'l*, pg. 3106
CLOVER TECHNOLOGIES GROUP LLC; *U.S. Private*, pg. 947
CLYDE BERGEMANN LIMITED—See Clyde Blowers Capital IM LLP; *Int'l*, pg. 1665
COAST TO COAST ENTERTAINMENT LLC—See Elaut International N.V.; *Int'l*, pg. 2343
COBURN TECHNOLOGIES (U.K.), LTD.—See Coburn Technologies, Inc.; *U.S. Private*, pg. 958
COCA-COLA WEST JAPAN CUSTOMER SERVICE CO LTD—See Coca-Cola Bottlers Japan Holdings Inc.; *Int'l*, pg. 1684
CODA, INC.; *U.S. Private*, pg. 960
COFCO CAPITAL HOLDINGS CO., LTD.; *Int'l*, pg. 1691
COFFEE DAY GLOBAL LTD. - VENDING DIVISION—See Affirma Capital Limited; *Int'l*, pg. 187
COGES ESPANA MEDIOS DE PAGO, S.L.—See AZKOYEN S.A; *Int'l*, pg. 780
COGES S.P.A.—See AZKOYEN S.A; *Int'l*, pg. 780
COGNEX HUNGARY KFT.—See Cognex Corporation; *U.S. Public*, pg. 523
COGNEX INTERNATIONAL, INC.—See Cognex Corporation; *U.S. Public*, pg. 523
COGNEX UK LTD.—See Cognex Corporation; *U.S. Public*, pg. 523
COHERENT BV—See Coherent Corp.; *U.S. Public*, pg. 527
COHERENT CORP.; *U.S. Public*, pg. 526
COHERENT JAPAN, INC.—See Coherent Corp.; *U.S. Public*, pg. 527
COIN ACCEPTORS, INC.; *U.S. Private*, pg. 964
COLDWATER MACHINE COMPANY, LLC—See Lincoln Electric Holdings, Inc.; *U.S. Public*, pg. 1317
COLE-PARMER INDIA PVT. LTD—See GTCR LLC; *U.S. Private*, pg. 1804
COLORLINK JAPAN CO., LTD.—See Arisawa Manufacturing Co., Ltd.; *Int'l*, pg. 566
COMBI WEAR PARTS—See The Riverside Company; *U.S. Private*, pg. 4109
COMPACTION & RECYCLING EQUIPMENT, INC.—See Deep Green Waste & Recycling, Inc.; *U.S. Public*, pg. 645
COMPONENTA ALBIN AB—See Componenta Corporation; *Int'l*, pg. 1753
CONAIR BRAZIL—See The Conair Group, Inc.; *U.S. Private*, pg. 4013
CONAIR EAST ASIA—See The Conair Group, Inc.; *U.S. Private*, pg. 4013
CONAIR EUROPE LTD.—See The Conair Group, Inc.; *U.S. Private*, pg. 4013
CONAIR MEXICANA S.A. DE C.V.—See The Conair Group, Inc.; *U.S. Private*, pg. 4013
CONAIR PACIFIC EQUIPMENT PTE. LTD.

333310 — COMMERCIAL AND SERV...

PHILIPPINES—See The Conair Group, Inc.; *U.S. Private*, pg. 4013
CONAIR PACIFIC EQUIPMENT PTE. LTD.—See The Conair Group, Inc.; *U.S. Private*, pg. 4013
CONAIRPRO INC.—See American Securities LLC; *U.S. Private*, pg. 248
CONSOLIDATED TECHNOLOGIES, INC.—See Thermo Fisher Scientific Inc.; *U.S. Public*, pg. 2149
COOPERVISION CANADA CORP.—See The Cooper Companies, Inc.; *U.S. Public*, pg. 2066
COOPERVISION GMBH—See The Cooper Companies, Inc.; *U.S. Public*, pg. 2066
COOPERVISION LIMITED—See The Cooper Companies, Inc.; *U.S. Public*, pg. 2066
COOPERVISION NEDERLAND BV—See The Cooper Companies, Inc.; *U.S. Public*, pg. 2066
COOPERVISION RUS LLC—See The Cooper Companies, Inc.; *U.S. Public*, pg. 2066
COOPERVISION S.A.S.—See The Cooper Companies, Inc.; *U.S. Public*, pg. 2066
CORE-FLEX OPTICAL (SUZHOU) CO., LTD.—See Coretronic Corporation; *Int'l*, pg. 1800
CORINNE MCCORMARK, INC—See EssilorLuxottica SA; *Int'l*, pg. 2514
CORNELIUS DE MEXICO SA DE CV—See Berkshire Hathaway Inc.; *U.S. Public*, pg. 309
CORNING NETOPTIX, INC.—See Corning Incorporated; *U.S. Public*, pg. 578
CORNING TROPEL CORP.—See Corning Incorporated; *U.S. Public*, pg. 578
COROB INDIA PVT. LTD.—See Graco, Inc.; *U.S. Public*, pg. 953
COROB OY—See Graco, Inc.; *U.S. Public*, pg. 953
COROB S.P.A.—See Graco, Inc.; *U.S. Public*, pg. 952
COSTAR GROUP CO., LTD.; *Int'l*, pg. 1815
CPAC EQUIPMENT, INC.—See Buckingham Capital, LLC; *U.S. Private*, pg. 678
CPAC EUROPE N.V.—See Buckingham Capital, LLC; *U.S. Private*, pg. 678
CPAC ITALIA S.R.L—See Buckingham Capital, LLC; *U.S. Private*, pg. 678
CRANE MERCHANDISING SYSTEMS LTD.—See Crane NXT, Co.; *U.S. Public*, pg. 590
CRANE PAYMENT & MERCHANDISING TECHNOLOGIES—See Crane NXT, Co.; *U.S. Public*, pg. 591
CRANE PAYMENTS INNOVATIONS, INC.—See Crane NXT, Co.; *U.S. Public*, pg. 591
CRITICAL IMAGING, LLC; *U.S. Private*, pg. 1101
CROSSBOWS OPTICAL LTD—See EssilorLuxottica SA; *Int'l*, pg. 2514
CRT CUSTOM PRODUCTS, INC.; *U.S. Private*, pg. 1113
CSCEC SCIMEE SCI & TECH CO., LTD.; *Int'l*, pg. 1863
CUBIC DATA SYSTEMS, INC.—See Elliott Management Corporation; *U.S. Private*, pg. 1367
CUBIC DATA SYSTEMS, INC.—See Veritas Capital Fund Management, LLC; *U.S. Private*, pg. 4361
CUBIC FOREIGN SALES, INC.—See Elliott Management Corporation; *U.S. Private*, pg. 1368
CUBIC FOREIGN SALES, INC.—See Veritas Capital Fund Management, LLC; *U.S. Private*, pg. 4361
CUBIC MICROCHIP DEVELOPMENT CORPORATION—See Elliott Management Corporation; *U.S. Private*, pg. 1368
CUBIC MICROCHIP DEVELOPMENT CORPORATION—See Veritas Capital Fund Management, LLC; *U.S. Private*, pg. 4361
CULLIGAN AUSTRALIA PTY LTD.—See BDT Capital Partners, LLC; *U.S. Private*, pg. 502
CULLIGAN ESPANA S.A.—See BDT Capital Partners, LLC; *U.S. Private*, pg. 502
CULLIGAN FRANCE—See BDT Capital Partners, LLC; *U.S. Private*, pg. 502
CULLIGAN INTERNATIONAL COMPANY—See BDT Capital Partners, LLC; *U.S. Private*, pg. 502
CULLIGAN ITALIANA S.P.A.—See BDT Capital Partners, LLC; *U.S. Private*, pg. 502
CULLIGAN (UK) LTD.—See BWT Aktiengesellschaft; *Int'l*, pg. 1233
CUMMINS-ALLISON GMBH—See Crane NXT, Co.; *U.S. Public*, pg. 591
CUMMINS-ALLISON INC.—See Crane NXT, Co.; *U.S. Public*, pg. 591
CUMMINS-ALLISON LTD.—See Crane NXT, Co.; *U.S. Public*, pg. 591
CUMMINS ALLISON SAS—See Crane NXT, Co.; *U.S. Public*, pg. 591
CURTISS-WRIGHT CORPORATION; *U.S. Public*, pg. 611
CVI LASER INTERNATIONAL LLC—See IDEX Corp; *U.S. Public*, pg. 1089
CVI LASER LIMITED—See IDEX Corp; *U.S. Public*, pg. 1089
CVI LASER OPTICS—See IDEX Corp; *U.S. Public*, pg. 1090
CVI TECHNICAL OPTICS COMPANY LTD.—See IDEX Corp; *U.S. Public*, pg. 1090
DAEHO TECHNOLOGY KOREA CO., LTD.; *Int'l*, pg. 1907
DAEMYUNG OPTICAL CO. LTD.—See Hoya Corporation; *Int'l*, pg. 3495

DAGE TEST SYSTEMS (SUZHOU) CO. LTD.—See Nordson Corporation; *U.S. Public*, pg. 1532
DAHILL OFFICE TECHNOLOGY CORPORATION—See Xerox Holdings Corporation; *U.S. Public*, pg. 2387
DAHLE NORTH AMERICA, INC.—See Erwin Muller Gruppe GmbH; *Int'l*, pg. 2500
DAICEL MICRO OPTICS CO. LTD.—See Daicel Corporation; *Int'l*, pg. 1919
DALIAN FUJI BINGSHAN VENDING MACHINE CO., LTD.—See Fuji Electric Co., Ltd.; *Int'l*, pg. 2810
DALLMEIER ELECTRONIC ESPANA, S.L.—See Dallmeier electronic GmbH & Co. KG; *Int'l*, pg. 1954
DANA CANADA CORPORATION—See Dana Incorporated; *U.S. Public*, pg. 622
DANFOSS DISTRICT HEATING S.R.L.—See Danfoss A/S; *Int'l*, pg. 1959
DAQI ENVIRONMENTAL PROTECTION ENGINEERING (DALIAN) CO., LTD.—See Daiki Axis Co., Ltd.; *Int'l*, pg. 1932
DARCOR LIMITED; *Int'l*, pg. 1972
DATACARD CANADA, INC.—See DataCard Corporation; *U.S. Private*, pg. 1164
DATACARD CORPORATION; *U.S. Private*, pg. 1164
DATACARD DEUTSCHLAND GMBH—See DataCard Corporation; *U.S. Private*, pg. 1164
DATACARD EQUIPMENT—See DataCard Corporation; *U.S. Private*, pg. 1164
DATACARD FRANCE S.A—See DataCard Corporation; *U.S. Private*, pg. 1164
DATACARD JAPAN LTD.—See DataCard Corporation; *U.S. Private*, pg. 1164
DATACARD LTD.—See DataCard Corporation; *U.S. Private*, pg. 1164
DATACARD SERVICE—See DataCard Corporation; *U.S. Private*, pg. 1164
DATACOLOR INC.—See Datacolor AG; *Int'l*, pg. 1977
DATECS LTD.; *Int'l*, pg. 1981
D-DESIGN NORDIC AB—See Symphony Technology Group, LLC; *U.S. Private*, pg. 3901
DEGIDESIGN ITALY S.R.L—See Symphony Technology Group, LLC; *U.S. Private*, pg. 3901
DEKRA VISATEC GMBH—See DEKRA e.V.; *Int'l*, pg. 2010
DE LA RUE CIS—See De La Rue plc; *Int'l*, pg. 1996
DE LA RUE LTD.—See De La Rue plc; *Int'l*, pg. 1996
DE LA RUE (MALAYSIA) SDN. BHD.—See De La Rue plc; *Int'l*, pg. 1996
DE LA RUE SYSTEMS LIMITED—See De La Rue plc; *Int'l*, pg. 1996
DE LA RUE (THAILAND) LIMITED—See De La Rue plc; *Int'l*, pg. 1996
DELFIELD COMPANY—See Ali Holding S.r.l; *Int'l*, pg. 322
DENITECH CORPORATION—See Xerox Holdings Corporation; *U.S. Public*, pg. 2387
DESERT AIRE CORP.—See Multistack, LLC; *U.S. Private*, pg. 2813
DEXTER APACHE HOLDINGS, INC.; *U.S. Private*, pg. 1220
DIEDRICH MANUFACTURING, INC.—See City Capital Advisors, LLC; *U.S. Private*, pg. 905
DI. ENVIRO CORPORATION—See DI Corp.; *Int'l*, pg. 2101
DIGITALOPTICS CORPORATION JAPAN GK—See Adeia Inc.; *U.S. Public*, pg. 40
DIGITAL VISION SYSTEMS INC—See Image Systems AB; *Int'l*, pg. 3618
DIGITAL VISION SYSTEMS LTD.—See Image Systems AB; *Int'l*, pg. 3618
DIOPTICS MEDICAL PRODUCTS INC.—See EssilorLuxottica SA; *Int'l*, pg. 2513
DIVERSE OPTICS, INC.; *U.S. Private*, pg. 1241
D&K EUROPE LTD.—See D&K Group, Inc.; *U.S. Private*, pg. 1138
DMP CORPORATION—See Element Solutions Inc.; *U.S. Public*, pg. 725
DMT SOLUTIONS GLOBAL CORPORATION—See Platinum Equity, LLC; *U.S. Private*, pg. 3202
DOCTER OPTICS ASIA LTD.—See Hella GmbH & Co. KGaA; *Int'l*, pg. 3331
DONALDSON AUSTRALASIA PTY. LTD.—See Donaldson Company, Inc.; *U.S. Public*, pg. 675
DONALDSON FILTRATION SYSTEMS (PTY.) LTD.—See Donaldson Company, Inc.; *U.S. Public*, pg. 675
DONALDSON S.A. DE C.V.—See Donaldson Company, Inc.; *U.S. Public*, pg. 676
DONGGUAN KWAN HONG ELECTRONICS CO. LTD.—See Deswell Industries, Inc.; *Int'l*, pg. 2047
DONGGUAN YUTONG OPTICAL TECHNOLOGY CO., LTD.; *Int'l*, pg. 2167
DORON PRECISION SYSTEMS, INC.; *U.S. Private*, pg. 1263
DOUGLAS MACHINES CORPORATION—See CNL Strategic Capital Management LLC; *U.S. Private*, pg. 952
DOWA TECHNO ENGINEERING CO., LTD.—See Dowa Holdings Co., Ltd.; *Int'l*, pg. 2184
D&R MACHINE COMPANY, INC.—See CORE Industrial Partners, LLC; *U.S. Private*, pg. 1048
DR. SCHMIDT INTRAOCULARLINSEN GMBH—See HumanOptics AG; *Int'l*, pg. 3530
D&S CAR WASH EQUIPMENT CO.; *U.S. Private*, pg. 1138

CORPORATE AFFILIATIONS

DUKE MANUFACTURING COMPANY, INC.; *U.S. Private*, pg. 1285
DURAY/J.F. DUNCAN INDUSTRIES, INC.; *U.S. Private*, pg. 1293
DUROC ENGINEERING I GOTEBORG AB—See Duroc AB; *Int'l*, pg. 2229
DUROC ENGINEERING I UMEA AB—See Duroc AB; *Int'l*, pg. 2229
DURR SYSTEMS SPAIN—See Durr AG; *Int'l*, pg. 2231
DYNACOLOR CO., LTD.; *Int'l*, pg. 2239
DYNAMIC VENDING, INC.—See Compass Group PLC; *Int'l*, pg. 1751
EADS SODERN NORTH AMERICA, INC.—See Airbus SE; *Int'l*, pg. 243
THE EAGLE GROUP; *U.S. Private*, pg. 4024
EAGLE INTERNATIONAL, LLC—See Tennant Company; *U.S. Public*, pg. 2016
EAGLE PRODUCT INSPECTION LLC—See Mettler-Toledo International, Inc.; *U.S. Public*, pg. 1432
EARTHWISE ENVIRONMENTAL, INC.—See Nolan Capital, Inc.; *U.S. Private*, pg. 2934
EASTERN MANAGED PRINT NETWORK, LLC—See Xerox Holdings Corporation; *U.S. Public*, pg. 2387
EASTERN OPTICAL LABORATORIES LTD.—See EssilorLuxottica SA; *Int'l*, pg. 2512
EASTMAN KODAK COMPANY; *U.S. Public*, pg. 706
EASTMAN PARK MICROGRAPHICS, INC. - DALLAS—See Eastman Park Micrographics, Inc.; *U.S. Private*, pg. 1322
EBARA CORPORATION; *Int'l*, pg. 2282
EBARA-ELLIOTT SERVICE (TAIWAN) CO., LTD.—See Ebara Corporation; *Int'l*, pg. 2284
EBARA ENGINEERING SINGAPORE PTE. LTD.—See Ebara Corporation; *Int'l*, pg. 2283
EBARA PRECISION MACHINERY KOREA INC.—See Ebara Corporation; *Int'l*, pg. 2283
EBARA QINGDAO CO. LTD.—See Ebara Corporation; *Int'l*, pg. 2283
EBARA (THAILAND) LIMITED—See Ebara Corporation; *Int'l*, pg. 2282
ECOLAB DEUTSCHLAND GMBH—See Ecolab Inc.; *U.S. Public*, pg. 713
ECOLAB EXPORT GMBH—See Ecolab Inc.; *U.S. Public*, pg. 713
ECOLAB LIMITED—See Ecolab Inc.; *U.S. Public*, pg. 713
ECOSYSTEM CONSULTING SERVICE, INC.—See GZA GeoEnvironmental Inc.; *U.S. Private*, pg. 1822
EDC EUROPEAN EXCAVATOR DESIGN CENTER BETEILIGUNGS-GMBH—See Caterpillar, Inc.; *U.S. Public*, pg. 452
EDESIX LIMITED—See Motorola Solutions, Inc.; *U.S. Public*, pg. 1477
EDMUND INDUSTRIAL OPTICS INC.; *U.S. Private*, pg. 1337
EDMUND OPTICS CHINA CO. LTD.—See Edmund Industrial Optics Inc.; *U.S. Private*, pg. 1337
EDMUND OPTICS GMBH—See Edmund Industrial Optics Inc.; *U.S. Private*, pg. 1337
EDMUND OPTICS JAPAN LTD.—See Edmund Industrial Optics Inc.; *U.S. Private*, pg. 1337
EDMUND OPTICS KOREA LTD.—See Edmund Industrial Optics Inc.; *U.S. Private*, pg. 1337
EDMUND OPTICS LTD.—See Edmund Industrial Optics Inc.; *U.S. Private*, pg. 1337
EDMUND OPTICS SINGAPORE PTE. LTD.—See Edmund Industrial Optics Inc.; *U.S. Private*, pg. 1337
EDMUND OPTICS—See Edmund Industrial Optics Inc.; *U.S. Private*, pg. 1337
EDUCATION CARTOGRAPHY & ILLUSTRATION JSC; *Int'l*, pg. 2315
EDWARDS INDIA PRIVATE LTD.—See Atlas Copco AB; *Int'l*, pg. 682
EDWARDS ISRAEL VACUUM LTD.—See Atlas Copco AB; *Int'l*, pg. 682
EDWARDS LTD.—See Atlas Copco AB; *Int'l*, pg. 682
EDWARDS S.R.O.—See Atlas Copco AB; *Int'l*, pg. 682
EGRO SUISSE AG—See Ali Holding S.r.l; *Int'l*, pg. 321
ELAS NV—See Haco N.V.; *Int'l*, pg. 3204
ELECTRIC H2O, INC.—See Global Water Technologies, Inc.; *U.S. Public*, pg. 945
ELECTROLUX LAUNDRY SYSTEMS DENMARK A/S—See AB Electrolux; *Int'l*, pg. 40
ELECTROLUX LAUNDRY SYSTEMS SWEDEN AB—See AB Electrolux; *Int'l*, pg. 40
ELECTROLUX PROFESSIONAL, INC.—See AB Electrolux; *Int'l*, pg. 40
ELECTRO-MOTIVE TECHNICAL CONSULTING CO. (BEIJING) LTD.—See Caterpillar, Inc.; *U.S. Public*, pg. 452
ELECTRO-OPTIX, INC.; *U.S. Private*, pg. 1354
ELEGANCE OPTICAL INTERNATIONAL HOLDINGS LTD.; *Int'l*, pg. 2355
ELOMA GMBH—See Ali Holding S.r.l; *Int'l*, pg. 322
EL-TRADE SP. Z O.O.—See Warner Bros. Discovery, Inc.; *U.S. Public*, pg. 2326
ELWOOD NATIONAL CRANKSHAFT SERVICES—See Ellwood Group, Inc.; *U.S. Private*, pg. 1375
E.MAGINE OPTICAL, INC.—See EssilorLuxottica SA; *Int'l*, pg. 2514
EMERSON ELECTRIC (CHINA) HOLDING CO., LTD.—See

N.A.I.C.S. INDEX

333310 — COMMERCIAL AND SERV...

Emerson Electric Co.; *U.S. Public*, pg. 744
EMERSON ELECTRIC NEDERLAND BV—See Emerson Electric Co.; *U.S. Public*, pg. 745
EMERSON FZE—See Emerson Electric Co.; *U.S. Public*, pg. 745
EMERSON MACHINERY & EQUIPMENT (SHENZHEN) CO., LTD.—See Emerson Electric Co.; *U.S. Public*, pg. 745
EMERSON NETWORK POWER CO., LTD.—See Emerson Electric Co.; *U.S. Public*, pg. 745
EMP TECHNOLOGIES, LTD.—See Pyrotek Incorporated; *U.S. Private*, pg. 3310
EMSCO INC.; *U.S. Private*, pg. 1388
ENABLENCE TECHNOLOGIES INC.; *Int'l*, pg. 2395
ENODIS CORPORATION—See Ali Holding S.r.l; *Int'l*, pg. 322
ENPLAS HI-TECH (SINGAPORE) PTE. LTD.—See ENPLAS CORPORATION; *Int'l*, pg. 2445
ENPLAS LABORATORIES, INC.—See ENPLAS CORPORATION; *Int'l*, pg. 2445
ENPLAS (VIETNAM) CO., LTD.—See ENPLAS CORPORATION; *Int'l*, pg. 2445
ENV SERVICES, INC.—See Donaldson Company, Inc.; *U.S. Public*, pg. 676
EOS GMBH ELECTRO OPTICAL SYSTEMS; *Int'l*, pg. 2458
EPICOR INC.—See Xylem Inc.; *U.S. Public*, pg. 2393
EPILOG CORPORATION; *U.S. Private*, pg. 1413
ESCHENBACH OPTIK GMBH—See Equistone Partners Europe Limited; *Int'l*, pg. 2486
ESCHENBACH OPTIK OF AMERICA, INC.—See Equistone Partners Europe Limited; *Int'l*, pg. 2486
ESL DEFENCE LTD—See Textron Inc.; *U.S. Public*, pg. 2029
ESMACH S.P.A.—See Ali Holding S.r.l; *Int'l*, pg. 322
ESSILOR ASIA PACIFIC PTE LTD.—See EssilorLuxottica SA; *Int'l*, pg. 2512
ESSILOR D.O.O—See EssilorLuxottica SA; *Int'l*, pg. 2512
ESSILOR INDIA PVT LTD—See EssilorLuxottica SA; *Int'l*, pg. 2512
ESSILOR IRELAND LTD.—See EssilorLuxottica SA; *Int'l*, pg. 2513
ESSILOR LTD.—See EssilorLuxottica SA; *Int'l*, pg. 2513
ESSILORLUXOTTICA SA; *Int'l*, pg. 2512
ESSILOR OF AMERICA, INC.—See EssilorLuxottica SA; *Int'l*, pg. 2513
ESSILOR OPTICAL LABORATORY POLSKA SP. Z.O.O.—See EssilorLuxottica SA; *Int'l*, pg. 2513
ESSILOR ROMANIA SRL—See EssilorLuxottica SA; *Int'l*, pg. 2513
ESSILOR SOUTH AFRICA (PTY) LTD.—See EssilorLuxottica SA; *Int'l*, pg. 2513
ETERNAL OPTICAL MATERIAL (SUZHOU) CO., LTD.—See Eternal Materials Co., Ltd.; *Int'l*, pg. 2521
EUGEN LAGLER GMBH; *Int'l*, pg. 2526
EUROPTEC GMBH—See Glas Trosch Holding AG; *Int'l*, pg. 2988
EURO TECH HOLDINGS COMPANY LIMITED; *Int'l*, pg. 2531
EVER HARVEST INTERNATIONAL GROUP INC.; *Int'l*, pg. 2562
EVERSYS S.A.—See De'Longhi S.p.A.; *Int'l*, pg. 1997
EVOQUA WATER TECHNOLOGIES—See Xylem Inc.; *U.S. Public*, pg. 2394
EVOQUA WATER TECHNOLOGIES—See Xylem Inc.; *U.S. Public*, pg. 2394
EXCELITAS TECHNOLOGIES CORP.—See AEA Investors LP; *U.S. Private*, pg. 113
EXCELITAS TECHNOLOGIES SINGAPORE PTE. LTD.—See AEA Investors LP; *U.S. Private*, pg. 113
EXPERIAN AUSTRALIA PTY. LTD.—See Experian plc; *Int'l*, pg. 2587
EXPERIAN AUSTRALIA PTY. LTD. - SYDNEY OFFICE—See Experian plc; *Int'l*, pg. 2587
EXPERIAN DATA SERVICES S.R.L.—See Experian plc; *Int'l*, pg. 2587
EXPERIAN DEUTSCHLAND HOLDING GMBH—See Experian plc; *Int'l*, pg. 2586
EXPERIAN HONG KONG LTD.—See Experian plc; *Int'l*, pg. 2587
EXPERIAN NEDERLAND B.V.—See Experian plc; *Int'l*, pg. 2587
EYAL OPTICAL IND. LTD.—See EssilorLuxottica SA; *Int'l*, pg. 2516
EYECITY.COM, INC.; *U.S. Public*, pg. 817
EYE DESIGNS, LLC—See Vision Service Plan; *U.S. Private*, pg. 4391
FABRINET—See H&Q Asia Pacific, Ltd.; *U.S. Private*, pg. 1823
FALCON FOODSERVICE EQUIPMENT—See Ali Holding S.r.l; *Int'l*, pg. 322
FARO TECHNOLOGIES, INC - LASER DIVISION—See FARO Technologies, Inc.; *U.S. Public*, pg. 823
FARREL LTD.—See Farrel Corporation; *U.S. Private*, pg. 1480
FAT S.A.—See Haco N.V.; *Int'l*, pg. 3204
FAWN ENGINEERING CORP.—See The Wittern Group; *U.S. Private*, pg. 4138

FAWN VENDING SYSTEMS, INC.—See The Wittern Group; *U.S. Private*, pg. 4138
FEHA LASERTEC HALLE GMBH; *Int'l*, pg. 2632
FEI ASIA PACIFIC CO., LTD.—See Thermo Fisher Scientific Inc.; *U.S. Public*, pg. 2146
FEI COMPANY JAPAN LTD.—See Thermo Fisher Scientific Inc.; *U.S. Public*, pg. 2146
FEI COMPANY OF USA (S.E.A.) PTE. LTD.—See Thermo Fisher Scientific Inc.; *U.S. Public*, pg. 2146
FEI DEUTSCHLAND GMBH—See Thermo Fisher Scientific Inc.; *U.S. Public*, pg. 2146
FEI ELECTRON OPTICS INTERNATIONAL B.V.—See Thermo Fisher Scientific Inc.; *U.S. Public*, pg. 2147
FEI FRANCE SAS—See Thermo Fisher Scientific Inc.; *U.S. Public*, pg. 2147
FEI GLOBAL HOLDINGS C.V.—See Thermo Fisher Scientific Inc.; *U.S. Public*, pg. 2147
FEI NORWAY HOLDING AS—See Thermo Fisher Scientific Inc.; *U.S. Public*, pg. 2147
FEI TRONDHEIM AS—See Thermo Fisher Scientific Inc.; *U.S. Public*, pg. 2147
FEI UK LTD.—See Thermo Fisher Scientific Inc.; *U.S. Public*, pg. 2147
FELLOWES (AUSTRALIA) PTY LTD—See Fellowes, Inc.; *U.S. Private*, pg. 1494
FELLOWES GERMANY GMBH—See Fellowes, Inc.; *U.S. Private*, pg. 1494
FELLOWES, INC.; *U.S. Private*, pg. 1494
FERSON TECHNOLOGIES, INC.—See OSI Systems, Inc.; *U.S. Public*, pg. 1621
FESTO DIDACTIC INC.—See Festo AG & Co. KG; *Int'l*, pg. 2647
FESTO DIDACTIC LTD.—See Festo AG & Co. KG; *Int'l*, pg. 2647
FEY LAMELOVE KROUZKY PRODEJE S.R.O.—See Fey Lamellenringe GmbH & Co. KG; *Int'l*, pg. 2649
FFGS TECHNO SERVICE CO., LTD.—See FUJIFILM Holdings Corporation; *Int'l*, pg. 2821
FG GROUP HOLDINGS INC.—See Kingsway Financial Services Inc.; *U.S. Public*, pg. 1234
FGX CANADA-FOSTERGRANT—See EssilorLuxottica SA; *Int'l*, pg. 2514
FGX EUROPE, LTD.—See EssilorLuxottica SA; *Int'l*, pg. 2514
FGX INTERNATIONAL LIMITED CHINA—See EssilorLuxottica SA; *Int'l*, pg. 2514
FHP EXPORT GMBH—See Freudenberg SE; *Int'l*, pg. 2785
FIELMANN AG & CO. IM CENTRUM OHG—See Fielmann Group AG; *Int'l*, pg. 2658
FIELMANN AG & CO. OHG LUDWIGSPLATZ—See Fielmann Group AG; *Int'l*, pg. 2658
FIELMANN AG & CO. OHG SCHNELSEN—See Fielmann Group AG; *Int'l*, pg. 2658
FIELMANN AG & CO. RHEYDT OHG—See Fielmann Group AG; *Int'l*, pg. 2657
FIELMANN AG & CO. VENLOER STRASSE OHG—See Fielmann Group AG; *Int'l*, pg. 2658
FIELMANN AG - VAREL—See Fielmann Group AG; *Int'l*, pg. 2658
FIELMANN AUGENOPTIK IM CENTRUM AG & CO. OHG—See Fielmann Group AG; *Int'l*, pg. 2658
FIELMANN GROUP AG; *Int'l*, pg. 2655
FILMTOOLS; *U.S. Private*, pg. 1506
FILTERMIST ASIA PTE. LTD.—See Absolent Air Care Group AB; *Int'l*, pg. 70
FILTERMIST SHANGHAI LTD.—See Absolent Air Care Group AB; *Int'l*, pg. 70
FILTROX AG—See CRS Holding AG; *Int'l*, pg. 1859
FINAXO ENVIRONNEMENT SA; *Int'l*, pg. 2670
FINGER LAKES INSTRUMENTATION, LLC—See IDEX Corp; *U.S. Public*, pg. 1090
FIREARMS SIMULATION SYSTEMS INC.—See Advanced Interactive Systems; *U.S. Private*, pg. 90
FIRE KING SECURITY PRODUCTS, LLC—See Pfingsten Partners, LLC; *U.S. Private*, pg. 3164
FIRST HYDROGEN CORP.; *Int'l*, pg. 2684
FISHER CLINICAL SERVICES PTE LTD.—See Thermo Fisher Scientific Inc.; *U.S. Public*, pg. 2147
FISHER & PAYKEL APPLIANCES ITALY S.P.A.—See Haier Smart Home Co., Ltd.; *Int'l*, pg. 3210
FISHER SCIENTIFIC A/S—See Thermo Fisher Scientific Inc.; *U.S. Public*, pg. 2147
FISHER SCIENTIFIC D.O.O.—See Thermo Fisher Scientific Inc.; *U.S. Public*, pg. 2148
FISHER SCIENTIFIC GMBH—See Thermo Fisher Scientific Inc.; *U.S. Public*, pg. 2148
FISHER SCIENTIFIC IRELAND LIMITED—See Thermo Fisher Scientific Inc.; *U.S. Public*, pg. 2148
FISHER SCIENTIFIC (M) SDN BHD—See Thermo Fisher Scientific Inc.; *U.S. Public*, pg. 2147
FISHER SCIENTIFIC, UNIPESSOAL, LDA.—See Thermo Fisher Scientific Inc.; *U.S. Public*, pg. 2148
FLAME SEAL PRODUCTS, INC.; *U.S. Public*, pg. 852
FLEXPRINT, LLC—See Oval Partners; *U.S. Private*, pg. 3052
FLIR INTEGRATED IMAGING SOLUTIONS—See Teledyne Technologies Incorporated; *U.S. Public*, pg. 1993
FLIR OUTDOOR & TACTICAL SYSTEMS—See Teledyne

Technologies Incorporated; *U.S. Public*, pg. 1993
FLOWBIRD SVERIGE AB—See Astorg Partners S.A.S.; *Int'l*, pg. 656
FLOWSERVE GMBH—See Flowserve Corporation; *U.S. Public*, pg. 856
FL SELENIA LUXCO S.C.A.—See Vestar Capital Partners, LLC; *U.S. Public*, pg. 4371
FLSMIDTH SALT LAKE CITY, INC.—See FLSmidth & Co. A/S; *Int'l*, pg. 2712
FLUXDATA INC.—See Halma plc; *Int'l*, pg. 3231
FLUXTEK INTERNATIONAL CORP.; *Int'l*, pg. 2715
FORENTA L.P.; *U.S. Private*, pg. 1566
FO SHAN MANITOWOC FOODSERVICE CO.—See Ali Holding S.r.l; *Int'l*, pg. 322
FOTO FANTASY, INC.—See Dai Nippon Printing Co., Ltd.; *Int'l*, pg. 1914
FOUNTAIN S.A.; *Int'l*, pg. 2754
FRANCOTYP-POSTALIA FRANCE SAS—See Francotyp-Postalia Holding AG; *Int'l*, pg. 2761
FRANCOTYP-POSTALIA GMBH—See Francotyp-Postalia Holding AG; *Int'l*, pg. 2761
FRANCOTYP-POSTALIA LTD.—See Francotyp-Postalia Holding AG; *Int'l*, pg. 2761
FRANCOTYP-POSTALIA NV—See Francotyp-Postalia Holding AG; *Int'l*, pg. 2761
FRANCOTYP-POSTALIA SVERIGE AB—See Francotyp-Postalia Holding AG; *Int'l*, pg. 2761
FRANKE FOODSERVICE SYSTEMS AG—See Artemis Holding AG; *Int'l*, pg. 582
FRANKE FOODSERVICE SYSTEMS, INC.—See Artemis Holding AG; *Int'l*, pg. 582
FRANKE KAFFEEMASCHINEN AG—See Artemis Holding AG; *Int'l*, pg. 582
FRANKE KUCHENTECHNIK AG—See Artemis Holding AG; *Int'l*, pg. 582
FRANKLIN ELECTRONIC PUBLISHERS, INC.; *U.S. Private*, pg. 1597
FRESHBREW VENDING—See FreshBrew Group USA, L.P.; *U.S. Private*, pg. 1610
FRIMONT, S.P.A.—See Ali Holding S.r.l; *Int'l*, pg. 321
FRONTIER INDUSTRIAL TECHNOLOGY—See Delta Industrial Services, Inc.; *U.S. Private*, pg. 1200
FSS INC.—See Advanced Interactive Systems; *U.S. Private*, pg. 90
FTNON ALMELO B.V.—See John Bean Technologies Corporation; *U.S. Public*, pg. 1191
FUJIAN FORECAM OPTICS CO., LTD.; *Int'l*, pg. 2817
FUJIAN ZHONGSHE MACHINERY & EQUIPMENT IMP. & EXP. CO., LTD.—See China Machinery Engineering Corporation; *Int'l*, pg. 1516
FUJICOLOR SVERIGE AB—See FUJIFILM Holdings Corporation; *Int'l*, pg. 2822
FUJI ELECTRIC DEVICE TECHNOLOGY AMERICA, INC.—See Fuji Electric Co., Ltd.; *Int'l*, pg. 2811
FUJIFILM ASIA PACIFIC PTE. LTD.—See FUJIFILM Holdings Corporation; *Int'l*, pg. 2821
FUJIFILM (CHINA) INVESTMENT CO., LTD.—See FUJIFILM Holdings Corporation; *Int'l*, pg. 2821
FUJIFILM CORPORATION—See FUJIFILM Holdings Corporation; *Int'l*, pg. 2821
FUJIFILM DENMARK A/S—See FUJIFILM Holdings Corporation; *Int'l*, pg. 2821
FUJIFILM FRANCE S.A.S.—See FUJIFILM Holdings Corporation; *Int'l*, pg. 2822
FUJIFILM IMAGING SYSTEMS CO., LTD.—See FUJIFILM Holdings Corporation; *Int'l*, pg. 2824
FUJIFILM IMAGING SYSTEMS (SUZHOU) CO., LTD.—See FUJIFILM Holdings Corporation; *Int'l*, pg. 2822
FUJIFILM OPTICS CO., LTD.—See FUJIFILM Holdings Corporation; *Int'l*, pg. 2824
FUJIFILM OPTO MATERIALS CO., LTD.—See FUJIFILM Holdings Corporation; *Int'l*, pg. 2824
FUJIFILM SERICOL BRASIL PRODUTOS PARA IMPRESSAO LTDA—See FUJIFILM Holdings Corporation; *Int'l*, pg. 2823
FUJIFILM SVERIGE AB—See Axel Johnson Gruppen AB; *Int'l*, pg. 764
FUJIMAK CORPORATION; *Int'l*, pg. 2829
FUJINON (EUROPE) GMBH—See FUJIFILM Holdings Corporation; *Int'l*, pg. 2822
FUJIPREAM CORPORATION; *Int'l*, pg. 2830
FUJITSU FRONTECH LIMITED - NIIGATA PLANT—See Fujitsu Limited; *Int'l*, pg. 2834
FUJITSU FRONTECH NORTH AMERICA INC.—See Fujitsu Limited; *Int'l*, pg. 2834
FUJITSU FRONTECH (SHANGHAI) LIMITED—See Fujitsu Limited; *Int'l*, pg. 2834
FULONGMA GROUP CO., LTD.; *Int'l*, pg. 2843
FURUKAWA DENSHI CO., LTD. - OPTICAL COMPONENTS PLANT—See Furukawa Co., Ltd.; *Int'l*, pg. 2847
FUTURECORE CO LTD; *Int'l*, pg. 2858
FUTURE OPTICS FL INC—See EssilorLuxottica SA; *Int'l*, pg. 2514
F.W. WEBB COMPANY - WEBB WATER SYSTEMS DIVISION—See F.W. Webb Company; *U.S. Private*, pg. 1457
G9PHARMA CO. LTD; *Int'l*, pg. 2867
GA BRAUN INC.; *U.S. Private*, pg. 1632

GALESBURG MANUFACTURING CO.; *U.S. Private*, pg. 1637
GAMAJET CLEANING SYSTEMS, INC.—See Alfa Laval AB; *Int'l*, pg. 309
GAMECARD-JOYCO HOLDINGS, INC.; *Int'l*, pg. 2877
GARLAND COMMERCIAL RANGES, LTD.—See Ali Holding S.r.l; *Int'l*, pg. 322
GASPER ENGINEERING, INC—See Arsenal Capital Management LP; *U.S. Private*, pg. 338
GEA NIRO SOAVI U.K.—See GEA Group Aktiengesellschaft; *Int'l*, pg. 2901
GEERPRES INC.; *U.S. Private*, pg. 1655
GEL S.P.A.; *Int'l*, pg. 2913
GEMTRON DE MEXICO S.A. DE C.V.—See Carl-Zeiss-Stiftung; *Int'l*, pg. 1336
GENERAL DYNAMICS GLOBAL IMAGING TECHNOLOGIES, INC. - ROCHESTER HILLS—See General Dynamics Corporation; *U.S. Public*, pg. 915
GENERATIONS IN AVIATION, INC.—See Atlantic Street Capital Management LLC; *U.S. Private*, pg. 374
GENIE UK LIMITED—See Terex Corporation; *U.S. Public*, pg. 2019
GEOMATEC CO., LTD. - AKO FACTORY—See GEOMATEC Co., Ltd.; *Int'l*, pg. 2933
GEOMATEC CO., LTD. - KANNARI FACTORY—See GEOMATEC Co., Ltd.; *Int'l*, pg. 2933
GEOMATEC (WUXI) CO., LTD.; *Int'l*, pg. 2933
GEOVISION VIETNAM SYSTEMS CO., LTD.—See GeoVision Inc.; *Int'l*, pg. 2942
GESCO AG; *Int'l*, pg. 2945
GEV GMBH—See Advent International Corporation; *U.S. Private*, pg. 96
GEV GMBH—See Centerbridge Partners, L.P.; *U.S. Private*, pg. 812
GEWETE GELDWECHSEL- UND SICHERHEITSTECHNIK GMBH—See Gauselmann AG; *Int'l*, pg. 2890
GKB OPHTHALMICS LTD.; *Int'l*, pg. 2983
GLASS FAB INC.; *U.S. Private*, pg. 1706
GLASTON ESTONIA OU—See Glaston Oyj Abp; *Int'l*, pg. 2989
GLASTON FINLAND OY—See Glaston Oyj Abp; *Int'l*, pg. 2989
GLASTON FRANCE S.A.S.U.—See Glaston Oyj Abp; *Int'l*, pg. 2989
GLASTON GERMANY GMBH—See Glaston Oyj Abp; *Int'l*, pg. 2989
GLASTON MIDDLE EAST—See Glaston Oyj Abp; *Int'l*, pg. 2989
GLASTON NORTH AMERICA (USA), INC—See Glaston Oyj Abp; *Int'l*, pg. 2989
GLASTON OYJ ABP; *Int'l*, pg. 2989
GLASTON SERVICES LTD. OY—See Glaston Oyj Abp; *Int'l*, pg. 2989
GLASTON SINGAPORE PTE. LTD.—See Glaston Oyj Abp; *Int'l*, pg. 2989
GLASTON SOUTH AMERICA LTDA.—See Glaston Oyj Abp; *Int'l*, pg. 2989
GLASTON UK LTD.—See Glaston Oyj Abp; *Int'l*, pg. 2989
GLOBAL PAYMENT TECHNOLOGIES (EUROPE) LIMITED—See Global Payment Technologies, Inc.; *U.S. Public*, pg. 943
GLOBAL PAYMENT TECHNOLOGIES, INC.; *U.S. Public*, pg. 942
GLOBALSIM, INC.; *U.S. Private*, pg. 1719
GLORY AUSTRIA GMBH—See GLORY Ltd.; *Int'l*, pg. 3009
GLORY CURRENCY AUTOMATION INDIA PVT. LTD.—See GLORY Ltd.; *Int'l*, pg. 3009
GLORY FRANCE—See GLORY Ltd.; *Int'l*, pg. 3009
GLORY FRIENDLY CO., LTD.—See GLORY Ltd.; *Int'l*, pg. 3009
GLORY GLOBAL SOLUTIONS (BRASIL) MAQUINAS E EQUIPAMENTOS LTDA.—See GLORY Ltd.; *Int'l*, pg. 3010
GLORY GLOBAL SOLUTIONS (CANADA) INC.—See GLORY Ltd.; *Int'l*, pg. 3010
GLORY GLOBAL SOLUTIONS (FRANCE) S.A.S.—See GLORY Ltd.; *Int'l*, pg. 3010
GLORY GLOBAL SOLUTIONS (GERMANY) GMBH—See GLORY Ltd.; *Int'l*, pg. 3010
GLORY GLOBAL SOLUTIONS INC.—See GLORY Ltd.; *Int'l*, pg. 3010
GLORY GLOBAL SOLUTIONS (INTERNATIONAL) LTD.—See GLORY Ltd.; *Int'l*, pg. 3009
GLORY GLOBAL SOLUTIONS LTD—See GLORY Ltd.; *Int'l*, pg. 3010
GLORY GLOBAL SOLUTIONS (NETHERLANDS) BV—See GLORY Ltd.; *Int'l*, pg. 3010
GLORY GLOBAL SOLUTIONS—See GLORY Ltd.; *Int'l*, pg. 3010
GLORY GLOBAL SOLUTIONS (SPAIN) S.A.—See GLORY Ltd.; *Int'l*, pg. 3010
GLORY IPO CHINA LTD.—See GLORY Ltd.; *Int'l*, pg. 3009
GLORY KIKI CO., LTD.—See GLORY Ltd.; *Int'l*, pg. 3010
GLORY LTD. - SAITAMA FACTORY—See GLORY Ltd.; *Int'l*, pg. 3009
GLORY SCIENCE CO., LTD.—See Cheng Eui Precision Industry Co., Ltd.; *Int'l*, pg. 1465

GLORY SYSTEM CREATE LTD.—See GLORY Ltd.; *Int'l*, pg. 3009
GLUNZ & JENSEN, INC.—See Glunz & Jensen Holding A/S; *Int'l*, pg. 3011
GMEINER GMBH—See Bucher Industries AG; *Int'l*, pg. 1208
GNBS ECO CO.,LTD; *Int'l*, pg. 3016
GOLD RAIN ENTERPRISES CORP.; *Int'l*, pg. 3026
GOLFZON CO., LTD.; *Int'l*, pg. 3035
GOOCH & HOUSEGO (CALIFORNIA) LLC—See Gooch & Housego PLC; *Int'l*, pg. 3038
GOOCH & HOUSEGO JAPAN KK—See Gooch & Housego PLC; *Int'l*, pg. 3038
GOOCH & HOUSEGO (PALO ALTO) LLC—See Gooch & Housego PLC; *Int'l*, pg. 3038
GOOCH & HOUSEGO PLC; *Int'l*, pg. 3037
GOOCH & HOUSEGO (UK) LIMITED—See Gooch & Housego PLC; *Int'l*, pg. 3038
GOODTECH RECOVERY TECHNOLOGY AS—See Goodtech ASA; *Int'l*, pg. 3041
GOODTECH SOLUTIONS AB—See Goodtech ASA; *Int'l*, pg. 3041
GOODWAY TECHNOLOGIES CORPORATION; *U.S. Private*, pg. 1740
GOPRO, INC.; *U.S. Public*, pg. 952
GOTAVERKEN MILJO AB—See Babcock & Wilcox Enterprises, Inc.; *U.S. Public*, pg. 263
GRACO KK—See Graco, Inc.; *U.S. Public*, pg. 953
GRACO MANUFACTURING CO. INC.—See Alfred Karcher GmbH & Co. KG; *Int'l*, pg. 316
GRACO N.V.—See Graco, Inc.; *U.S. Public*, pg. 953
GRADCO (JAPAN), LTD.—See Gradco Holdings, LLC; *U.S. Private*, pg. 1749
GRADCO (USA), INC.—See Gradco Holdings, LLC; *U.S. Private*, pg. 1749
GRANDIMPIANTI I.L.E. ALI SPA.—See Ali Holding S.r.l; *Int'l*, pg. 321
GRANITE WATER WORKS, INC.—See Core & Main, Inc.; *U.S. Public*, pg. 576
GRAVER WATER SYSTEMS LLC—See Berkshire Hathaway Inc.; *U.S. Public*, pg. 311
GREAT LAKES COATING LABORATORY—See Carl-Zeiss-Stiftung; *Int'l*, pg. 1335
GREAT LAKES COATING LABORATORY—See EQT AB; *Int'l*, pg. 2473
GREAT WALL (OPTICAL) PLASTIC WORKS LTD.—See Cosmos Machinery Enterprises Limited; *Int'l*, pg. 1813
GREEN DIAMOND EQUIPMENT LTD.; *Int'l*, pg. 3070
GREEN TURTLE AMERICAS, LTD—See Zurn Elkay Water Solutions Corporation; *U.S. Public*, pg. 2413
GREENWALD INDUSTRIES DIVISION—See The Eastern Company; *U.S. Public*, pg. 2069
GRENOBLOISE D'ELECTRONIQUE ET D'AUTOMATISMES; *Int'l*, pg. 3081
GRINM ELECTRO-OPTIC MATERIALS CO., LTD.—See Grinm Advanced Materials Co., Ltd.; *Int'l*, pg. 3087
GROENEVELD BRILLEN EN CONTACTLENZEN B.V.—See Fielmann Group AG; *Int'l*, pg. 2658
GRUPO LAMOSA S.A. DE C.V.; *Int'l*, pg. 3131
GUANGDONG JINMA ENTERTAINMENT CORPORATION LIMITED; *Int'l*, pg. 3157
GUANGDONG LIANXUN PRECISION MANUFACTURING CO.,LTD.; *Int'l*, pg. 3158
GUANGDONG NEW GRAND PACKING CO.,LTD; *Int'l*, pg. 3158
GUANGHE LANDSCAPE CULTURE COMMUNICATION CO., LTD; *Int'l*, pg. 3162
GUANGZHOU BOTNY CHEMICAL CO., LTD.—See China Aluminum Cans Holdings Limited; *Int'l*, pg. 1482
GUANGZHOU LUXVISIONS INNOVATION TECHNOLOGY LIMITED; *Int'l*, pg. 3166
H2O INNOVATION INC.—See Ember Infrastructure Management, LP; *U.S. Private*, pg. 1378
HACO AUSTRALIA PERTH—See Haco N.V.; *Int'l*, pg. 3204
HACO B.V.—See Haco N.V.; *Int'l*, pg. 3204
HACO CANADA INC.—See Haco N.V.; *Int'l*, pg. 3204
HACO FAR EAST PTE LTD—See Haco N.V.; *Int'l*, pg. 3204
HACO MACHINERY PRIVATE LIMITED—See Haco N.V.; *Int'l*, pg. 3204
HACO - MUBEA SYSTEME GMBH—See Haco N.V.; *Int'l*, pg. 3204
HACO SAS—See Haco N.V.; *Int'l*, pg. 3204
HACO SL—See Haco N.V.; *Int'l*, pg. 3205
HACO TRADING COMPANY NV—See Haco N.V.; *Int'l*, pg. 3204
HAESUNG OPTICS CO., LTD.; *Int'l*, pg. 3206
HALCYON METAL COMPANY LIMITED—See Halcyon Technology Public Company Limited; *Int'l*, pg. 3227
HALOSOURCE CORP.; *U.S. Private*, pg. 1846
HALOSOURCE, INC.—See Halosource Corp.; *U.S. Private*, pg. 1846
HALOX TECHNOLOGIES, INC.—See IDEX Corp; *U.S. Public*, pg. 1090
HANGZHOU JIZHI MECHATRONIC CO., LTD.; *Int'l*, pg. 3249
HANIL VACUUM CO., LTD.; *Int'l*, pg. 3252
HARDEN TECHNOLOGIES INC.; *Int'l*, pg. 3272
HARN R/O SYSTEMS, INC.—See Komline-Sanderson Corporation; *U.S. Private*, pg. 2342

HAROLD JOHNSON OPTICAL LABORATORIES, INC.—See Truist Financial Corporation; *U.S. Public*, pg. 2200
HARRICK SCIENTIFIC PRODUCTS, INC.—See Ampersand Management LLC; *U.S. Private*, pg. 265
HATCO CORPORATION; *U.S. Private*, pg. 1879
HAYLEYS PHOTOPRINT LTD—See Hayleys PLC; *Int'l*, pg. 3292
HAYWARD INDUSTRIAL PRODUCTS, INC.—See CCMP Capital Advisors, LP; *U.S. Private*, pg. 800
HAYWARD INDUSTRIAL PRODUCTS, INC.—See MSD Capital, L.P.; *U.S. Private*, pg. 2807
H. CEGIELSKI - POZNAN S.A.; *Int'l*, pg. 3194
HEADWORKS INTERNATIONAL INC.; *U.S. Private*, pg. 1891
HEATH CONSULTANTS INC. DAMAGE PREVENTION SERVICES—See Heath Consultants Incorporated; *U.S. Private*, pg. 1902
HEATH CONSULTANTS INCORPORATED, INTERNATIONAL SALES—See Heath Consultants Incorporated; *U.S. Private*, pg. 1902
HEBERT KANNEGIESSER GMBH; *Int'l*, pg. 3306
HELIO VISION GERMANY GMBH—See Aldeyra Therapeutics, Inc.; *U.S. Public*, pg. 74
HELLA GUTMANN MOBILITY GMBH—See Hella GmbH & Co. KGaA; *Int'l*, pg. 3332
HELLMA AXIOM, INC.—See Hellma GmbH & Co. KG; *Int'l*, pg. 3334
HERAEUS AMBA AUSTRALIA PTY. LTD.—See Heraeus Holding GmbH; *Int'l*, pg. 3357
HERAEUS QUARTZ AMERICA, LLC—See Heraeus Holding GmbH; *Int'l*, pg. 3358
HERBERT KANNEGIESSER GES. MBH—See Hebert Kannegiesser GmbH; *Int'l*, pg. 3306
HIBER ALI SPA—See Ali Holding S.r.l; *Int'l*, pg. 321
HI-LITE CAMERA COMPANY LIMITED—See Highway Holdings Limited; *Int'l*, pg. 3389
HINIKER COMPANY - COSTER ENGINEERING DIVISION—See Hiniker Company; *U.S. Private*, pg. 1949
HI-P LENS TECHNOLOGY (SHANGHAI) CO., LTD.—See Hi-P International Limited; *Int'l*, pg. 3381
HI-VAC CORPORATION; *U.S. Private*, pg. 1932
HK AMERICA INC.—See HK Co., Ltd.; *Int'l*, pg. 3428
HK CO., LTD.; *Int'l*, pg. 3428
HNT ELECTRONICS CO.,LTD; *Int'l*, pg. 3434
HOBART CORPORATION—See Illinois Tool Works Inc.; *U.S. Public*, pg. 1103
HOEV CO., LTD—See Hoya Corporation; *Int'l*, pg. 3495
HOFFMAN/NEW YORKER INC.; *U.S. Private*, pg. 1960
HOFLAND OPTIEK B.V.—See Fielmann Group AG; *Int'l*, pg. 2659
HOH SEPARTEC OY—See BWT Aktiengesellschaft; *Int'l*, pg. 1233
HOH VATTENTEKNIK AB—See BWT Aktiengesellschaft; *Int'l*, pg. 1233
HOLT JAPAN INC.—See Hoya Corporation; *Int'l*, pg. 3494
HON HAI PRECISION INDUSTRY CO., LTD. - TAIPEI OFFICE—See Hon Hai Precision Industry Co., Ltd.; *Int'l*, pg. 3457
HORIBA TRADING (SHANGHAI) CO., LTD.—See HORIBA Ltd; *Int'l*, pg. 3477
HORIZON LAMPS, INC.—See Forsyth Capital Investors LLC; *U.S. Private*, pg. 1573
HORUS VISION, LLC; *U.S. Private*, pg. 1984
HOSHIZAKI AMERICA, INC.—See Hoshizaki Corporation; *Int'l*, pg. 3484
HOSHIZAKI CORPORATION; *Int'l*, pg. 3483
HOSHIZAKI LANCER PTY LTD.—See Hoshizaki Corporation; *Int'l*, pg. 3483
HOSOKAWA ALPINE AKTIENGESELLSCHAFT & CO. OHG—See Hosokawa Micron Corporation; *Int'l*, pg. 3486
THE HOTSY CORPORATION—See Alfred Karcher GmbH & Co. KG; *Int'l*, pg. 316
HOUPU CLEAN ENERGY GROUP CO., LTD; *Int'l*, pg. 3490
HOYA CANDEO OPTRONICS CORPORATION—See Hoya Corporation; *Int'l*, pg. 3494
HOYA CORPORATION - AKISHIMA FACILITY—See Hoya Corporation; *Int'l*, pg. 3494
HOYA CORPORATION - ATLANTA FACILITY—See Hoya Corporation; *Int'l*, pg. 3497
HOYA CORPORATION - CLEVELAND FACILITY—See Hoya Corporation; *Int'l*, pg. 3497
HOYA CORPORATION - DALLAS FACILITY—See Hoya Corporation; *Int'l*, pg. 3497
HOYA CORPORATION - DAYTON FACILITY—See Hoya Corporation; *Int'l*, pg. 3497
HOYA CORPORATION - EUGENE FACILITY—See Hoya Corporation; *Int'l*, pg. 3497
HOYA CORPORATION - HARTFORD FACILITY—See Hoya Corporation; *Int'l*, pg. 3497
HOYA CORPORATION - KNOXVILLE FACILITY—See Hoya Corporation; *Int'l*, pg. 3497
HOYA CORPORATION - LARGO FACILITY—See Hoya Corporation; *Int'l*, pg. 3497
HOYA CORPORATION - LEWISTON FACILITY—See Hoya Corporation; *Int'l*, pg. 3497

N.A.I.C.S. INDEX

333310 — COMMERCIAL AND SERV...

HOYA CORPORATION - MIYAGI FACTORY—See Hoya Corporation; *Int'l*, pg. 3494
HOYA CORPORATION - MODESTO FACILITY—See Hoya Corporation; *Int'l*, pg. 3497
HOYA CORPORATION - NEW ORLEANS FACILITY—See Hoya Corporation; *Int'l*, pg. 3497
HOYA CORPORATION - OGAWA FACTORY—See Hoya Corporation; *Int'l*, pg. 3494
HOYA CORPORATION - PORTLAND FACILITY—See Hoya Corporation; *Int'l*, pg. 3497
HOYA CORPORATION - SAN ANTONIO FACILITY—See Hoya Corporation; *Int'l*, pg. 3497
HOYA CORPORATION - YAMAGATA FACTORY—See Hoya Corporation; *Int'l*, pg. 3495
HOYA GLASS DISK PHILIPPINES, INC.—See Hoya Corporation; *Int'l*, pg. 3495
HOYA HOLDINGS, INC.—See Hoya Corporation; *Int'l*, pg. 3496
HOYA LENS BELGIUM N.V.—See Hoya Corporation; *Int'l*, pg. 3496
HOYA LENS BELGUIM B.V.—See Hoya Corporation; *Int'l*, pg. 3496
HOYA LENS CANADA, INC. - MONTREAL FACILITY—See Hoya Corporation; *Int'l*, pg. 3496
HOYA LENS CANADA, INC.—See Hoya Corporation; *Int'l*, pg. 3496
HOYA LENS CANADA, INC. - TORONTO FACILITY—See Hoya Corporation; *Int'l*, pg. 3496
HOYA LENS CANADA, INC. - VANCOUVER FACILITY—See Hoya Corporation; *Int'l*, pg. 3496
HOYA LENS CZ A.S—See Hoya Corporation; *Int'l*, pg. 3496
HOYA LENS DENMARK A/S—See Hoya Corporation; *Int'l*, pg. 3496
HOYA LENS DEUTSCHLAND GMBH—See Hoya Corporation; *Int'l*, pg. 3496
HOYA LENS FINLAND OY—See Hoya Corporation; *Int'l*, pg. 3496
HOYA LENS FRANCE S.A.—See Hoya Corporation; *Int'l*, pg. 3496
HOYA LENS GUANGZHOU LTD.—See Hoya Corporation; *Int'l*, pg. 3495
HOYA LENS HONG KONG LTD.—See Hoya Corporation; *Int'l*, pg. 3495
HOYA LENS HUNGARY RT—See Hoya Corporation; *Int'l*, pg. 3496
HOYA LENS IBERIA S.A.—See Hoya Corporation; *Int'l*, pg. 3496
HOYA LENS IBERIA S.A.—See Hoya Corporation; *Int'l*, pg. 3496
HOYA LENS INDIA PVT.LTD—See Hoya Corporation; *Int'l*, pg. 3495
HOYA LENS ITALIA S.P.A.—See Hoya Corporation; *Int'l*, pg. 3496
HOYA LENS KOREA CO., LTD.—See Hoya Corporation; *Int'l*, pg. 3495
HOYA LENS MANUFACTURING HUNGARY RT—See Hoya Corporation; *Int'l*, pg. 3495
HOYA LENS MANUFACTURING MALAYSIA SDN. BHD.—See Hoya Corporation; *Int'l*, pg. 3495
HOYA LENS NEDERLAND B.V.—See Hoya Corporation; *Int'l*, pg. 3496
HOYA LENS PHILIPPINES, INC.—See Hoya Corporation; *Int'l*, pg. 3495
HOYA LENS POLAND SP. Z.O.O.—See Hoya Corporation; *Int'l*, pg. 3496
HOYA LENS SHANGHAI LTD.—See Hoya Corporation; *Int'l*, pg. 3495
HOYA LENS (S) PTE. LTD.—See Hoya Corporation; *Int'l*, pg. 3495
HOYA LENS SWEDEN AB—See Hoya Corporation; *Int'l*, pg. 3496
HOYA LENS TAIWAN LTD.—See Hoya Corporation; *Int'l*, pg. 3496
HOYA LENS THAILAND LTD.—See Hoya Corporation; *Int'l*, pg. 3496
HOYA LENS VIETNAM LTD.—See Hoya Corporation; *Int'l*, pg. 3496
HOYA MEDICAL SINGAPORE PTE. LTD.—See Hoya Corporation; *Int'l*, pg. 3496
HOYA OPTICAL (ASIA) CO., LTD—See Hoya Corporation; *Int'l*, pg. 3496
HOYA OPTICAL TECHNOLOGY (SUZHOU) LTD.—See Hoya Corporation; *Int'l*, pg. 3496
HOYA OPTICAL TECHNOLOGY (WEIHAI) CO., LTD.—See Hoya Corporation; *Int'l*, pg. 3496
HOYA OPTICS (THAILAND) LTD.—See Hoya Corporation; *Int'l*, pg. 3496
HOYA OPTO-ELECTRONICS QINGDAO LTD.—See Hoya Corporation; *Int'l*, pg. 3496
HOYA SURGICAL OPTICS, INC. ATLANTA FACILITY—See Hoya Corporation; *Int'l*, pg. 3497
HOYA SURGICAL OPTICS, INC. - CHICAGO FACILITY—See Hoya Corporation; *Int'l*, pg. 3497
HOYA SURGICAL OPTICS, INC. - CLEVELAND FACILITY—See Hoya Corporation; *Int'l*, pg. 3497
HOYA SURGICAL OPTICS, INC. - DALLAS FACILITY—See Hoya Corporation; *Int'l*, pg. 3497
HOYA SURGICAL OPTICS, INC. - DAYTON FACILITY—See Hoya Corporation; *Int'l*, pg. 3497
HOYA SURGICAL OPTICS, INC. - EUGENE FACILITY—See Hoya Corporation; *Int'l*, pg. 3497
HOYA SURGICAL OPTICS, INC. - HARTFORD FACILITY—See Hoya Corporation; *Int'l*, pg. 3497
HOYA SURGICAL OPTICS, INC. - KNOXVILLE FACILITY—See Hoya Corporation; *Int'l*, pg. 3497
HOYA SURGICAL OPTICS, INC. - LARGO FACILITY—See Hoya Corporation; *Int'l*, pg. 3497
HOYA SURGICAL OPTICS, INC. - LEWISTON FACILITY—See Hoya Corporation; *Int'l*, pg. 3497
HOYA SURGICAL OPTICS, INC. - MODESTO FACILITY—See Hoya Corporation; *Int'l*, pg. 3497
HOYA SURGICAL OPTICS, INC. - PORTLAND FACILITY—See Hoya Corporation; *Int'l*, pg. 3497
HOYA SURGICAL OPTICS, INC. - SAN ANTONIO FACILITY—See Hoya Corporation; *Int'l*, pg. 3497
HOYA SURGICAL OPTICS, INC. - SAN DIEGO FACILITY—See Hoya Corporation; *Int'l*, pg. 3497
HOYA SURGICAL OPTICS, INC. - ST. LOUIS FACILITY—See Hoya Corporation; *Int'l*, pg. 3497
HOYA TECHNOSURGICAL CORPORATION—See Hoya Corporation; *Int'l*, pg. 3498
HP IMAGING & PRINTING GROUP—See HP Inc.; *U.S. Public*, pg. 1063
HUBEI DOTI-MICRO TECHNOLOGY CO., LTD.; *Int'l*, pg. 3517
HUMANOPTICS DEUTSCHLAND VERWALTUNGS GMBH—See HumanOptics AG; *Int'l*, pg. 3530
HUNGERFORD & TERRY INC.; *U.S. Private*, pg. 2007
HUNTER ASSOCIATES LABORATORY; *U.S. Private*, pg. 2009
HYDROCHEM (S) PTE LTD—See Hyflux Ltd; *Int'l*, pg. 3548
HYFLUX CONSUMER PRODUCTS PTE. LTD.—See Hyflux Ltd; *Int'l*, pg. 3548
HYFLUX ENGINEERING (INDIA) PVT LTD—See Hyflux Ltd; *Int'l*, pg. 3548
HYFLUX LIFESTYLE PRODUCTS (INDIA) PVT LTD—See Hyflux Ltd; *Int'l*, pg. 3548
HYFLUX (MALAYSIA) SDN BHD—See Hyflux Ltd; *Int'l*, pg. 3548
HYFLUX MEMBRANE MANUFACTURING (S) PTE.LTD—See Hyflux Ltd; *Int'l*, pg. 3548
IBSEN PHOTONICS A/S—See Foss A/S; *Int'l*, pg. 2749
I.D. ELECTROQUIMICA, S.L.—See Fluidra SA; *Int'l*, pg. 2714
IDIS AMERICA CO., LTD.—See IDIS Co., Ltd.; *Int'l*, pg. 3595
IDIS BENELUX BV—See IDIS Co., Ltd.; *Int'l*, pg. 3595
IDIS EUROPE LIMITED—See IDIS Co., Ltd.; *Int'l*, pg. 3595
IER—See Financiere de L'Odet; *Int'l*, pg. 2667
IHI CORPORATION; *Int'l*, pg. 3603
II-VI DEUTSCHLAND GMBH—See Coherent Corp.; *U.S. Public*, pg. 528
II-VI INFRARED LASER (SUZHOU) CO., LTD.—See Coherent Corp.; *U.S. Public*, pg. 528
II-VI INFRARED—See Coherent Corp.; *U.S. Public*, pg. 528
II-VI OPTICS (SUZHOU) CO., LTD.—See Coherent Corp.; *U.S. Public*, pg. 528
II-VI SINGAPORE PTE., LTD.—See Coherent Corp.; *U.S. Public*, pg. 528
ILAPAK ASIA—See ILAPAK S.A.; *Int'l*, pg. 3613
ILAPAK DO BRASIL LTDA—See ILAPAK S.A.; *Int'l*, pg. 3613
ILAPAK FRANCE S.A.—See ILAPAK S.A.; *Int'l*, pg. 3613
ILAPAK HUNGARY—See ILAPAK S.A.; *Int'l*, pg. 3613
ILAPAK INC.—See ILAPAK S.A.; *Int'l*, pg. 3613
ILAPAK ITALIA S.P.A.—See ILAPAK S.A.; *Int'l*, pg. 3613
ILAPAK (LANGFANG) PACKAGING MACHINERY CO.,LTD—See ILAPAK S.A.; *Int'l*, pg. 3613
ILAPAK LTD—See ILAPAK S.A.; *Int'l*, pg. 3613
ILAPAK S.A.; *Int'l*, pg. 3613
ILAPAK SNG—See ILAPAK S.A.; *Int'l*, pg. 3613
ILAPAK SP. Z O.O.—See ILAPAK S.A.; *Int'l*, pg. 3613
ILAPAK VERPACKUNGSMASCHINEN GMBH—See ILAPAK S.A.; *Int'l*, pg. 3613
ILENS SDN BHD—See Hoya Corporation; *Int'l*, pg. 3496
ILFORD IMAGING SWITZERLAND GMBH; *Int'l*, pg. 3614
IMAGE ONE CORP.; *U.S. Public*, pg. 2044
IMAGE SYSTEMS AB; *Int'l*, pg. 3618
IMAGING BUSINESS MACHINES LLC; *U.S. Private*, pg. 2046
IMAX CORPORATION; *Int'l*, pg. 3620
IMAX VR, LLC—See Imax Corporation; *Int'l*, pg. 3620
IM CO., LTD.; *Int'l*, pg. 3617
IMMEDIA SEMICONDUCTOR, INC.—See Amazon.com, Inc.; *U.S. Public*, pg. 90
IMPULSA SOLUCIONES TECNOLOGICAS, S.L.—See AZKOYEN S.A; *Int'l*, pg. 780
INDUSTRIAL LAUNDRY SERVICES, LLC—See EVI Industries, Inc.; *U.S. Public*, pg. 803
INGENICO ARGENTINA—See Apollo Global Management, Inc.; *U.S. Public*, pg. 151
INGENICO GMBH—See Apollo Global Management, Inc.; *U.S. Public*, pg. 151
INGENICO IBERIA, SL—See Apollo Global Management, Inc.; *U.S. Public*, pg. 151
INGENICO ITALIA SPA—See Apollo Global Management, Inc.; *U.S. Public*, pg. 151
INGENICO (UK) LTD.—See Apollo Global Management, Inc.; *U.S. Public*, pg. 151
INLAND FINANCE COMPANY—See The Wittern Group; *U.S. Public*, pg. 4138
INNOVATIVE EYEWEAR, INC.; *U.S. Public*, pg. 1126
INRAD OPTICS, INC.—See Edgewater Capital Partners, L.P.; *U.S. Private*, pg. 1335
INRAD OPTICS, INC.—See Edgewater Capital Partners, L.P.; *U.S. Private*, pg. 1335
INRAD OPTICS, INC.—See SK Capital Partners, LP; *U.S. Private*, pg. 3679
INRAD OPTICS, INC.—See SK Capital Partners, LP; *U.S. Private*, pg. 3679
INSCERCO MANUFACTURING INC.; *U.S. Private*, pg. 2085
INSIGHT TECHNOLOGY INCORPORATED—See L3Harris Technologies, Inc.; *U.S. Public*, pg. 1281
INTERCAST EUROPE S.R.L.—See EssilorLuxottica SA; *Int'l*, pg. 2515
INTERCLEAN EQUIPMENT, LLC—See Oakland Standard Co., LLC; *U.S. Private*, pg. 2985
INTERFLEX DATENSYSTEME GESMBH—See Ingersoll Rand Inc.; *U.S. Public*, pg. 1121
INTERNATIONAL LOTTERY & TOTALIZATOR SYSTEMS, INC.—See Berjaya Corporation Berhad; *Int'l*, pg. 983
INTERNET ACCESS GMBH LILIBIT BERLIN GESELLSCHAFT FUR KOMMUNIKATION UND DIGITALTECHNIK—See Francotyp-Postalia Holding AG; *Int'l*, pg. 2761
INTEVAC ASIA PRIVATE LIMITED—See Intevac, Inc.; *U.S. Public*, pg. 1159
INVERNESS CORPORATION—See Berkshire Hathaway Inc.; *U.S. Public*, pg. 316
INVERNESS UK—See Berkshire Hathaway Inc.; *U.S. Public*, pg. 316
IPEK SPEZIAL-TV GMBH—See IDEX Corp; *U.S. Public*, pg. 1092
IQINVISION, INC.—See Vicon Industries, Inc.; *U.S. Private*, pg. 4377
IROBOT CORP.; *U.S. Public*, pg. 1171
ISP OPTICS CORP.—See LightPath Technologies, Inc.; *U.S. Public*, pg. 1315
ISRA SURFACE VISION INC.—See Atlas Copco AB; *Int'l*, pg. 682
ISRA VISION AG—See Atlas Copco AB; *Int'l*, pg. 682
ISRA VISION LTD.—See Atlas Copco AB; *Int'l*, pg. 682
ISRA VISION SYSTEMS INC.—See Atlas Copco AB; *Int'l*, pg. 682
ISRA VISION VISTEK A.S.—See Atlas Copco AB; *Int'l*, pg. 683
ITT WATER & WASTEWATER U.S.A., INC.—See ITT Inc.; *U.S. Public*, pg. 1178
ITW HIGHLAND—See Illinois Tool Works Inc.; *U.S. Public*, pg. 1106
IXMATION INC.—See Durr AG; *Int'l*, pg. 2230
JABIL CIRCUIT AUSTRIA GMBH—See Jabil Inc.; *U.S. Public*, pg. 1181
JABIL CIRCUIT DE CHIHUAHUA S. DE R.L. DE C.V.—See Jabil Inc.; *U.S. Public*, pg. 1181
JABIL CIRCUIT GYARTO K.F.T.—See Jabil Inc.; *U.S. Public*, pg. 1181
JABIL CIRCUIT INDIA PVT. LTD.—See Jabil Inc.; *U.S. Public*, pg. 1181
JABIL CIRCUIT ITALIA, S.R.L—See Jabil Inc.; *U.S. Public*, pg. 1181
JABIL CIRCUIT ITALIA, S.R.L.—See Jabil Inc.; *U.S. Public*, pg. 1181
JABIL CIRCUIT POLAND SP. Z O.O.—See Jabil Inc.; *U.S. Public*, pg. 1181
JABIL GLOBAL SERVICES NETHERLANDS B.V.—See Jabil Inc.; *U.S. Public*, pg. 1181
JACKSON WWS, INC.—See Hoshizaki Corporation; *Int'l*, pg. 3484
JENNY PRODUCTS, INC.; *U.S. Private*, pg. 2200
JETSTREAM OF HOUSTON, LLP—See Federal Signal Corporation; *U.S. Public*, pg. 826
J. HVIDTVED LARSEN IRELAND LTD.—See Bucher Industries AG; *Int'l*, pg. 1209
J. HVIDTVED LARSEN UK LTD.—See Bucher Industries AG; *Int'l*, pg. 1209
JIM COLEMAN COMPANY; *U.S. Private*, pg. 2208
JITA OY—See Georg Fischer AG; *Int'l*, pg. 2937
J&L METROLOGY, INC.; *U.S. Private*, pg. 2154
JML OPTICAL INDUSTRIES, LLC—See Truist Financial Corporation; *U.S. Public*, pg. 2200
JOHNSTON SWEEPERS LTD—See Bucher Industries AG; *Int'l*, pg. 1208
JUFFALI-POLYONE MASTER BATCHES COMPANY—See Avient Corporation; *U.S. Public*, pg. 247
KADIAC CO., LTD—See Coca-Cola Bottlers Japan Holdings Inc.; *Int'l*, pg. 1684
KAISER OPTICAL SYSTEMS, INC.—See Endress+Hauser (International) Holding AG; *Int'l*, pg. 2407
KAISER OPTICAL SYSTEMS SARL—See RTX Corporation; *U.S. Public*, pg. 1823
KANNEGIESSER AUE GMBH—See Hebert Kannegiesser GmbH; *Int'l*, pg. 3306
KANNEGIESSER AUGSBURG GMBH—See Hebert Kann-

333310 — COMMERCIAL AND SERV...   CORPORATE AFFILIATIONS

egiesser GmbH; *Int'l*, pg. 3306
KANNEGIESSER AUSTRALIA PTY LTD.—See Hebert Kannegiesser GmbH; *Int'l*, pg. 3306
KANNEGIESSER GMBH—See Hebert Kannegiesser GmbH; *Int'l*, pg. 3306
KANNEGIESSER ITALIA S.R.L.—See Hebert Kannegiesser GmbH; *Int'l*, pg. 3306
KARCHER AB—See Alfred Karcher GmbH & Co. KG; *Int'l*, pg. 316
KARCHER AG—See Alfred Karcher GmbH & Co. KG; *Int'l*, pg. 316
KARCHER AS—See Alfred Karcher GmbH & Co. KG; *Int'l*, pg. 316
KARCHER CLEANING SYSTEMS SDN. BHD.—See Alfred Karcher GmbH & Co. KG; *Int'l*, pg. 316
KARCHER FLOOR CARE, INC.—See Alfred Karcher GmbH & Co. KG; *Int'l*, pg. 316
KARCHER FZE—See Alfred Karcher GmbH & Co. KG; *Int'l*, pg. 316
KARCHER LIMITED—See Alfred Karcher GmbH & Co. KG; *Int'l*, pg. 316
KARCHER MEXICO, S.A. DE C.V.—See Alfred Karcher GmbH & Co. KG; *Int'l*, pg. 316
KARCHER (UK) LTD.—See Alfred Karcher GmbH & Co. KG; *Int'l*, pg. 316
KARCHER UKRAINE—See Alfred Karcher GmbH & Co. KG; *Int'l*, pg. 317
KAYPENTAX—See Hoya Corporation; *Int'l*, pg. 3495
KBCO, THE POLARIZED LENS COMPANY—See EssilorLuxottica SA; *Int'l*, pg. 2513
KEGEL COMPANY INC.; *U.S. Private*, pg. 2273
KERSTAR LTD.—See Absolent Air Care Group AB; *Int'l*, pg. 70
KEYCAST LJUNGBY AB—See The Riverside Company; *U.S. Private*, pg. 4109
KEY TECHNOLOGY, INC.—See Warburg Pincus LLC; *U.S. Private*, pg. 4437
KIN + CARTA PLC—See BC Partners LLP; *Int'l*, pg. 925
KINETICO DENMARK APS—See Axel Johnson Gruppen AB; *Int'l*, pg. 765
KINETICO FRANCE SARL—See Axel Johnson Gruppen AB; *Int'l*, pg. 765
KINETICO GERMANY GMBH—See Axel Johnson Gruppen AB; *Int'l*, pg. 765
KINETICO INCORPORATED—See Axel Johnson Gruppen AB; *Int'l*, pg. 765
KINETICO INCORPORATED—See Axel Johnson Gruppen AB; *Int'l*, pg. 765
KINETICO UK LIMITED—See Axel Johnson Gruppen AB; *Int'l*, pg. 765
THE KINGSLAND ENGINEERING CO. LTD—See Haco N.V.; *Int'l*, pg. 3205
KODAK ALARIS GERMANY GMBH—See Eastman Kodak Company; *U.S. Public*, pg. 707
KODAK AMERICAS LTDA.—See Eastman Kodak Company; *U.S. Public*, pg. 707
KODAK ARGENTINA S.A.I.C.—See Eastman Kodak Company; *U.S. Public*, pg. 707
KODAK CANADA INC.—See Eastman Kodak Company; *U.S. Public*, pg. 707
KODAK DE COLOMBIA, SAS—See Eastman Kodak Company; *U.S. Public*, pg. 707
KODAK DE MEXICO S.A. DE C.V.—See Eastman Kodak Company; *U.S. Public*, pg. 708
KODAK DIGITAL PRODUCTS CENTER—See Eastman Kodak Company; *U.S. Public*, pg. 707
KODAK ELECTRONIC PRODUCTS (SHANGHAI) COMPANY LIMITED—See Eastman Kodak Company; *U.S. Public*, pg. 707
KODAK GRAPHIC COMMUNICATIONS CANADA COMPANY—See Eastman Kodak Company; *U.S. Public*, pg. 707
KODAK IMAGING NETWORK, INC.—See Eastman Kodak Company; *U.S. Public*, pg. 707
KODAK INDIA LIMITED—See Eastman Kodak Company; *U.S. Public*, pg. 707
KODAK JAPAN INDUSTRIES LTD.—See Eastman Kodak Company; *U.S. Public*, pg. 707
KODAK (KENYA) LIMITED—See Eastman Kodak Company; *U.S. Public*, pg. 707
KODAK LIMITED—See Eastman Kodak Company; *U.S. Public*, pg. 707
KODAK NEDERLAND BV—See Eastman Kodak Company; *U.S. Public*, pg. 707
KODAK-PATHE SAS—See Eastman Kodak Company; *U.S. Public*, pg. 708
KODAK, S.A.—See Eastman Kodak Company; *U.S. Public*, pg. 708
KOLUSZKY FOUNDRY SP. Z.O.O.—See Haco N.V.; *Int'l*, pg. 3205
KOMAR INDUSTRIES, LLC; *U.S. Private*, pg. 2342
KORVIS AUTOMATION INC.; *U.S. Private*, pg. 2344
KREFFT GROBKUCHENTECHNIK GMBH—See Ali Holding S.r.l; *Int'l*, pg. 321
KROMO ALI SPA—See Ali Holding S.r.l; *Int'l*, pg. 321
KROY LLC—See Pubco Corporation; *U.S. Private*, pg. 3298
KUNSHAN ECO WATER SYSTEMS CO., LTD—See Hyflux Ltd; *Int'l*, pg. 3548

L2F INC.—See The Middleby Corporation; *U.S. Public*, pg. 2114
L-3 COMMUNICATIONS BRASHEAR—See L3Harris Technologies, Inc.; *U.S. Public*, pg. 1282
L-3 COMMUNICATIONS SSG-TINSLEY—See L3Harris Technologies, Inc.; *U.S. Public*, pg. 1283
L-3 COMMUNICATIONS WESTWOOD CORPORATION-TANO DIVISION—See L3Harris Technologies, Inc.; *U.S. Public*, pg. 1283
L-3 EOTECH, INC.—See L3Harris Technologies, Inc.; *U.S. Public*, pg. 1283
L-3 SONOMA EO—See L3Harris Technologies, Inc.; *U.S. Public*, pg. 1283
L-3 WESCAM INC.—See L3Harris Technologies, Inc.; *U.S. Public*, pg. 1283
LABORATOIRES FUJIFILM SA—See FUJIFILM Holdings Corporation; *Int'l*, pg. 2822
LAB VISION CORPORATION—See Thermo Fisher Scientific Inc.; *U.S. Public*, pg. 2152
LA MARZOCCO INTERNATIONAL, LLC—See De'Longhi S.p.A.; *Int'l*, pg. 1997
LANDA WATER CLEANING SYSTEMS—See Alfred Karcher GmbH & Co. KG; *Int'l*, pg. 316
LAPAK ISRAEL LTD—See ILAPAK S.A.; *Int'l*, pg. 3613
LAVORWASH BRASIL IND. E COM. LTDA—See Emak S.p.A.; *Int'l*, pg. 2373
LAVORWASH FRANCE S.A.S.—See Emak S.p.A.; *Int'l*, pg. 2373
LAVORWASH IBERICA S.L.—See Emak S.p.A.; *Int'l*, pg. 2373
LAVORWASH POLSKA S.P. Z O.O.—See Emak S.p.A.; *Int'l*, pg. 2373
LD DIDACTIC GMBH—See Aurelius Equity Opportunities SE & Co. KGaA; *Int'l*, pg. 708
LEC INDUSTRIES CO., LTD.—See Daiki Axis Co., Ltd.; *Int'l*, pg. 1932
LEICA CAMERA AG—See Blackstone Inc.; *U.S. Public*, pg. 360
LEICA CAMERA, INC.—See Blackstone Inc.; *U.S. Public*, pg. 360
LEICA GEOSYSTEMS LTD.—See Hexagon AB; *Int'l*, pg. 3367
LEUPOLD & STEVENS, INC.; *U.S. Private*, pg. 2433
LFA MACHINES DFW, LLC—See Operio Group, LLC; *U.S. Private*, pg. 3032
LFA MACHINES OXFORD LTD.—See Operio Group, LLC; *U.S. Private*, pg. 3032
LIBERTO OF HARLINGEN INC.—See Liberto Specialty Company Inc.; *U.S. Private*, pg. 2442
LIGHTWORKS OPTICAL SYSTEMS, INC.—See Coherent Corp.; *U.S. Public*, pg. 529
LIGHTWORKS OPTICAL SYSTEMS, INC.—See Coherent Corp.; *U.S. Public*, pg. 529
LIMITED LIABILITY COMPANY BAUSCH & LOMB—See Bausch Health Companies Inc.; *Int'l*, pg. 897
LINAIR BIO-SCIENCE PTE. LTD.—See Acesian Partners Limited; *Int'l*, pg. 102
LOHMANN TAIWAN CO. LTD., TAIWAN—See Eli Lilly & Company; *U.S. Public*, pg. 733
LOPREST WATER TREATMENT COMPANY—See Water Remediation Technology LLC; *U.S. Private*, pg. 4451
LUMENERA CORPORATION—See Teledyne Technologies Incorporated; *U.S. Public*, pg. 1992
LUMENTUM HOLDINGS INC.; *U.S. Public*, pg. 1348
LUMETRICS, INC.; *U.S. Private*, pg. 2514
LUMITHERA, INC.; *U.S. Private*, pg. 2514
LUXEMBOURG MOUNTING CENTER S.A.—See The Goodyear Tire & Rubber Company; *U.S. Public*, pg. 2084
LUXOTTICA GROUP S.P.A.—See EssilorLuxottica SA; *Int'l*, pg. 2515
LYNX PRODUCT GROUP, LLC.—See Chalmers Group of Companies; *Int'l*, pg. 1438
MACGREGOR PLIMSOLL PTE LTD—See Cargotec Corporation; *Int'l*, pg. 1328
MACGREGOR SHANGHAI TRADING CO., LTD.—See Cargotec Corporation; *Int'l*, pg. 1328
M.A.IND. S.R.L.—See Brookfield Corporation; *Int'l*, pg. 1182
MALAYSIAN HOYA LENS SDN. BHD.—See Hoya Corporation; *Int'l*, pg. 3496
MANITOWOC CRANE GROUP ASIA PTE, LTD.—See The Manitowoc Company, Inc.; *U.S. Public*, pg. 2111
MANITOWOC FSG MANUFACTURA MEXICO, S. DE R.L. DE C.V.—See Ali Holding S.r.l; *Int'l*, pg. 322
MARATHON EQUIPMENT COMPANY—See Terex Corporation; *U.S. Public*, pg. 2019
MARCHON ITALIA S.R.L.—See Vision Service Plan; *U.S. Private*, pg. 4391
MARCHON PORTUGAL UNIPESSOAL LDA—See Vision Service Plan; *U.S. Private*, pg. 4391
MARENO ALI S.P.A.—See Ali Holding S.r.l; *Int'l*, pg. 321
MARQUE TDI - TECHNOLOGIAS DE CODIFICACAO S.A.—See Brother Industries, Ltd.; *Int'l*, pg. 1198
MARUESU GT CO., LTD.—See GLORY LTD.; *Int'l*, pg. 3010
MATERION PRECISION OPTICS AND THIN FILM COATINGS INC.—See Materion Corporation; *U.S. Public*, pg. 1396
MATTHEWS STUDIO EQUIPMENT, INC.; *U.S. Private*, pg. 2613

MAX LEVY AUTOGRAPH, INC.—See Coherent Corp.; *U.S. Public*, pg. 529
MECHTRONIX TEXTRON CANADA INC.—See Textron Inc.; *U.S. Public*, pg. 2029
MECO U.K.—See Mechanical Equipment Company Inc.; *U.S. Private*, pg. 2648
MEI AUTO PAYMENT SYSTEM (SHANGHAI) LTD.—See Crane NXT, Co.; *U.S. Public*, pg. 591
MEIP INTERNATIONAL, S.L.—See Fluidra SA; *Int'l*, pg. 2714
MEISTERHAUS LABORATORIO OPTICO LTDA.—See Carl-Zeiss-Stiftung; *Int'l*, pg. 1336
MEIZHOU CHAOHUA CNC TECHNOLOGY CO., LTD.—See Guangdong Chaohua Technology Co., Ltd.; *Int'l*, pg. 3153
MELLES GRIOT AB—See IDEX Corp; *U.S. Public*, pg. 1091
MELLES GRIOT B.V.—See IDEX Corp; *U.S. Public*, pg. 1091
MERATECH RUS GROUP LLC—See Ecolab Inc.; *U.S. Public*, pg. 714
MERKUR FREIZEIT LEASING GMBH—See Gauselmann AG; *Int'l*, pg. 2890
METALAST S.A.—See Fluidra SA; *Int'l*, pg. 2714
METAVAC LLC—See Thermo Fisher Scientific Inc.; *U.S. Public*, pg. 2149
METCHEM, INC.—See Ascent Industries Co.; *U.S. Public*, pg. 210
METCRAFT INC.; *U.S. Private*, pg. 2683
METTLER TOLEDO ANALYSE INDUSTRIELLE S.A.R.L.—See Mettler-Toledo International, Inc.; *U.S. Public*, pg. 1432
METTLER-TOLEDO A/S—See Mettler-Toledo International, Inc.; *U.S. Public*, pg. 1432
METTLER-TOLEDO A/S—See Mettler-Toledo International, Inc.; *U.S. Public*, pg. 1432
METTLER-TOLEDO IND. E COM. LTDA.—See Mettler-Toledo International, Inc.; *U.S. Public*, pg. 1432
METTLER TOLEDO INSTRUMENTS (SHANGHAI) LTD.—See Mettler-Toledo International, Inc.; *U.S. Public*, pg. 1432
METTLER-TOLEDO S.A. DE C.V.—See Mettler-Toledo International, Inc.; *U.S. Public*, pg. 1433
METTLER-TOLEDO SP. Z.O.O.—See Mettler-Toledo International, Inc.; *U.S. Public*, pg. 1433
MICHINOKU SERVICE CO., LTD.—See Hitachi Zosen Corporation; *Int'l*, pg. 3411
MICROANALYTICS—See Volatile Analysis Corporation; *U.S. Private*, pg. 4410
MICROS SYSTEMS UK LIMITED - BOLTON—See Oracle Corporation; *U.S. Public*, pg. 1612
MIDWEST REMEDIATION INC.; *U.S. Private*, pg. 2723
MIE FUJI CO., LTD.—See Fuji Electric Co., Ltd.; *Int'l*, pg. 2812
MINCO MANUFACTURING, LLC; *U.S. Private*, pg. 2740
MINDS-EYE-VIEW, INC.; *U.S. Private*, pg. 2741
MINUTE KEY, INC.; *U.S. Private*, pg. 2745
MIYAZAKI CANON INC.—See Canon Inc.; *Int'l*, pg. 1298
MIYAZAKI DAISHIN CANON CO., LTD.—See Canon Inc.; *Int'l*, pg. 1298
MOLDED FIBER GLASS WATER TREATMENT PRODUCTS—See Molded Fiber Glass Companies; *U.S. Private*, pg. 2766
MOLINS SRO—See Coesia S.p.A.; *Int'l*, pg. 1690
MONITORING SOLUTIONS, INC.; *U.S. Private*, pg. 2771
MONO EQUIPMENT LTD.—See Ali Holding S.r.l; *Int'l*, pg. 322
MONROE SYSTEMS FOR BUSINESS—See Carolina Wholesale Office Machine Company, Inc.; *U.S. Private*, pg. 769
MONSTER DIGITAL, INC.; *U.S. Public*, pg. 1465
MORITEX CORPORATION—See Cognex Corporation; *U.S. Public*, pg. 523
MORITEX NORTH AMERICA, INC.—See Cognex Corporation; *U.S. Public*, pg. 523
MOVING IMAGE TECHNOLOGIES, INC.; *U.S. Public*, pg. 1480
MRC SMART TECHNOLOGY SOLUTIONS, INC.—See Xerox Holdings Corporation; *U.S. Public*, pg. 2388
MSA ITALIA S.R.L.—See MSA Safety Incorporated; *U.S. Public*, pg. 1482
MST & ASSOCIATES INC.—See Southern Pan Services Company; *U.S. Private*, pg. 3734
MUSTANG DYNAMOMETER, LOS ANGELES—See Mustang Dynamometer; *U.S. Private*, pg. 2819
MUSTANG VACUUM SYSTEMS INC.—See Mustang Dynamometer; *U.S. Private*, pg. 2819
M Y H COMERCIAL E INDUSTRIAL LIMITADA—See Air Products & Chemicals, Inc.; *U.S. Public*, pg. 66
NAGASAKI CANON INC.—See Canon Inc.; *Int'l*, pg. 1298
NALCO DANMARK APS—See Ecolab Inc.; *U.S. Public*, pg. 715
NASU NIKON CO., LTD.—See EssilorLuxottica SA; *Int'l*, pg. 2512
NATIONAL CARWASH SOLUTIONS, INC.—See Berkshire Partners LLC; *U.S. Public*, pg. 535
NATIONALLINK, INC.; *U.S. Private*, pg. 2865
NATIONAL VISION - ST. CLOUD OPTICAL

LABOARTORY—See KKR & Co. Inc.; *U.S. Public*, pg. 1261

NAVITAR COATING LABS, INC.—See AMETEK, Inc.; *U.S. Public*, pg. 121

NAVITAR INDUSTRIES, LLC—See AMETEK, Inc.; *U.S. Public*, pg. 121

NECCHI S.P.A.—See CF Italia srl; *Int'l*, pg. 1429

NEGAFILE SYSTEMS—See The Graham Group, Inc.; *U.S. Private*, pg. 4037

NEPTUNE TECHNOLOGY GROUP INC.—See Roper Technologies, Inc.; *U.S. Public*, pg. 1812

NEWBOLD LLC—See Fort Point Capital, LLC; *U.S. Private*, pg. 1574

NEWBURY FRANKLIN INDUSTRIALS LLC—See Ironwood Capital Management LLC; *U.S. Private*, pg. 2140

NEWELL EUROPE SARL—See Newell Brands Inc.; *U.S. Public*, pg. 1514

NEWELL RUBBERMAID ARGENTINA S.A.—See Newell Brands Inc.; *U.S. Public*, pg. 1514

NEWELL RUBBERMAID UK SERVICES LIMITED—See Newell Brands Inc.; *U.S. Public*, pg. 1514

NEW ENGLAND LOW VISION & BLINDNESS; *U.S. Private*, pg. 2894

NEWFIELD INFORMATION TECHNOLOGY LLC—See Xerox Holdings Corporation; *U.S. Public*, pg. 2388

NEW FOCUS—See MKS Instruments, Inc.; *U.S. Public*, pg. 1453

NEWPORT OPTO-ELECTRONICS TECHNOLOGIES (SINGAPORE) PTE. LTD.—See MKS Instruments, Inc.; *U.S. Public*, pg. 1453

NEWPORT SPECTRA-PHYSICS GMBH—See MKS Instruments, Inc.; *U.S. Public*, pg. 1453

NEXTSCAN INC.—See Digital Check Corp.; *U.S. Private*, pg. 1230

NICHIZO HOKKAIDO SERVICE CORP.—See Hitachi Zosen Corporation; *Int'l*, pg. 3411

NIECO EQUIPMENT CORPORATION; *U.S. Private*, pg. 2926

NIGHT OPTICS USA, INC.—See Vista Outdoor Inc.; *U.S. Public*, pg. 2305

NIHON PALL LTD.—See Danaher Corporation; *U.S. Public*, pg. 629

NIIGATA MACHINE TECHNO CO., LTD.—See Fair Friend Group; *Int'l*, pg. 2604

NIKON-ESSILOR CO., LTD.—See EssilorLuxottica SA; *Int'l*, pg. 2512

NIKON-TRIMBLE CO., LTD.—See Trimble, Inc.; *U.S. Public*, pg. 2190

NIMBUS WATER SYSTEMS—See Axel Johnson Gruppen AB; *Int'l*, pg. 765

NIPPON CONLUX CO. LTD.—See Crane NXT, Co.; *U.S. Public*, pg. 591

NIPPON DONALDSON LTD.—See Donaldson Company, Inc.; *U.S. Public*, pg. 676

NIPPON POLAROID KABUSHIKI KAISHA—See Gordon Brothers Group, LLC; *U.S. Private*, pg. 1742

NIPPON POLAROID KABUSHIKI KAISHA—See Hilco Trading, LLC; *U.S. Private*, pg. 1943

NISCA CORPORATION—See Canon Inc.; *Int'l*, pg. 1295

NKT PHOTONICS A/S—See Hamamatsu Photonics K.K.; *Int'l*, pg. 3235

NORCO INC. - EPHRATA FILL GAS PLANT—See Norco, Inc.; *U.S. Private*, pg. 2936

NORCO INC. - LEWISTON FILL GAS PLANT—See Norco, Inc.; *U.S. Private*, pg. 2936

NORCO INC. - MOSES LAKE A.S.U. PLANT—See Norco, Inc.; *U.S. Private*, pg. 2936

NORCO INC. - NAMPA A.S.U. PLANT—See Norco, Inc.; *U.S. Private*, pg. 2936

NORDSON ASIA PACIFIC, LTD.—See Nordson Corporation; *U.S. Public*, pg. 1533

NORDSON ASYMTEK K.K.—See Nordson Corporation; *U.S. Public*, pg. 1533

NORDSON CORPORATION; *U.S. Public*, pg. 1532

NORDSON KOREA—See Nordson Corporation; *U.S. Public*, pg. 1534

NORDSON SVERIGE AB—See Nordson Corporation; *U.S. Public*, pg. 1534

NORTHROP GRUMMAN SYNOPTICS—See Northrop Grumman Corporation; *U.S. Public*, pg. 1540

NOUVEAU EYEWEAR, INC.—See SunTx Capital Partners, L.P.; *U.S. Private*, pg. 3874

NSS ENTERPRISES, INC. - NSS EUROPEAN DIVISION—See NSS Enterprises, Inc.; *U.S. Private*, pg. 2970

NSS ENTERPRISES, INC.; *U.S. Private*, pg. 2970

NUARC COMPANY, INC.—See M&R Holdings Inc.; *U.S. Private*, pg. 2525

NUARC WESTERN DIV.—See M&R Holdings Inc.; *U.S. Private*, pg. 2525

NUVONIC—See Halma plc; *Int'l*, pg. 3231

OCEAN OPTICS BV—See Halma plc; *Int'l*, pg. 3232

OCLARO PHOTONICS, INC.—See Lumentum Holdings Inc.; *U.S. Public*, pg. 1348

OCLARO TECHNOLOGY, INC.—See Lumentum Holdings Inc.; *U.S. Public*, pg. 1348

OCLARO TECHNOLOGY LIMITED—See Lumentum Holdings Inc.; *U.S. Public*, pg. 1348

OCP ASIA, INC.—See Koch Industries, Inc.; *U.S. Private*, pg. 2335

ODATE ECOMANAGE CORPORATION—See Hitachi Zosen Corporation; *Int'l*, pg. 3412

OEM - ALI S.P.A—See Ali Holding S.r.l.; *Int'l*, pg. 321

OIP N.V.—See Elbit Systems Limited; *Int'l*, pg. 2345

OITA CANON INC.—See Canon Inc.; *Int'l*, pg. 1298

OLDEMT LIMITED—See Pitney Bowes Inc.; *U.S. Public*, pg. 1695

OLD TUCSON COMPANY; *U.S. Private*, pg. 3009

OLMSTED-KIRK EQUIPMENT & SUPPLY CO.—See Olmsted-Kirk Paper Company; *U.S. Private*, pg. 3011

OMEGA OPTIX S.R.O.—See EssilorLuxottica SA; *Int'l*, pg. 2516

OMI—See EssilorLuxottica SA; *Int'l*, pg. 2515

OMNISENSE SYSTEMS PRIVATE LIMITED—See BH Global Corporation Limited; *Int'l*, pg. 1009

ONDA ENTERTAINMENT CO., LTD.—See CHA Biotech Co., Ltd.; *Int'l*, pg. 1435

ONITY, INC.—See Carrier Global Corporation; *U.S. Public*, pg. 441

OPC CORPORATION—See TPG Capital, L.P.; *U.S. Public*, pg. 2175

OPEX CORPORATION; *U.S. Private*, pg. 3032

OPGAL - OPTRONICS INDUSTRIES LTD.—See Elbit Systems Limited; *Int'l*, pg. 2345

OPHIR OPTICS, LLC—See MKS Instruments, Inc.; *U.S. Public*, pg. 1453

OPHIR OPTRONICS GMBH—See MKS Instruments, Inc.; *U.S. Public*, pg. 1453

OPHIR OPTRONICS SOLUTIONS LTD.—See MKS Instruments, Inc.; *U.S. Public*, pg. 1453

OPINICUS TEXTRON INC.—See Textron Inc.; *U.S. Public*, pg. 1453

OPTEX SYSTEMS HOLDINGS, INC.; *U.S. Public*, pg. 1609

OPTICAL COATINGS JAPAN—See AGC Inc.; *Int'l*, pg. 204

OPTICAL GAGING PRODUCTS INC.—See Quality Vision International Inc.; *U.S. Private*, pg. 3321

OPTICS BALZERS AG—See Materion Corporation; *U.S. Public*, pg. 1396

OPTICS BALZERS GMBH—See Materion Corporation; *U.S. Public*, pg. 1396

OPTICS BALZERS JENA GMBH—See Materion Corporation; *U.S. Public*, pg. 1396

OPTICS BALZERS MALAYSIA SDN. BHD.—See Materion Corporation; *U.S. Public*, pg. 1396

OPTICS BALZERS USA INC.—See Materion Corporation; *U.S. Public*, pg. 1396

OPTIGRATE CORPORATION—See IPG Photonics Corporation; *U.S. Public*, pg. 1167

OPTIKER CARL GMBH—See Fielmann Group AG; *Int'l*, pg. 2659

OPTIK HESS GMBH & CO. KG—See Fielmann Group AG; *Int'l*, pg. 2659

OPTIMAX SYSTEMS, INC.; *U.S. Private*, pg. 3034

OPTIQUE CRISTAL INC—See EssilorLuxottica SA; *Int'l*, pg. 2516

OPTISWISS AG—See Carl-Zeiss-Stiftung; *Int'l*, pg. 1336

OPTISWISS FRANCE SARL—See Carl-Zeiss-Stiftung; *Int'l*, pg. 1336

OPTOMETRICS CORPORATION—See Dynasil Corporation of America; *U.S. Private*, pg. 1299

OPTOSIGMA CORP.; *U.S. Private*, pg. 3036

OPT-SCIENCES CORPORATION; *U.S. Public*, pg. 1608

ORDERMAN GMBH—See NCR Voyix Corporation.; *U.S. Public*, pg. 1503

ORLACO GMBH—See Stoneridge, Inc.; *U.S. Public*, pg. 1951

ORLACO INC.—See Stoneridge, Inc.; *U.S. Public*, pg. 1951

OTSUKA WELLNESS VENDING CO., LTD.—See Earth Corporation; *Int'l*, pg. 2268

OXOID LIMITED—See Thermo Fisher Scientific Inc.; *U.S. Public*, pg. 2150

PACIFIC, INC.—See Hines Corporation; *U.S. Private*, pg. 1949

PALL ASIA INTERNATIONAL LTD.—See Danaher Corporation; *U.S. Public*, pg. 629

PALL CORPORATION FILTRATION & SEPARATIONS LTD.—See Danaher Corporation; *U.S. Public*, pg. 629

PALL CORTLAND—See Danaher Corporation; *U.S. Public*, pg. 629

PALL EUROPE LTD.—See Danaher Corporation; *U.S. Public*, pg. 629

PALL FRANCE—See Danaher Corporation; *U.S. Public*, pg. 629

PALL INDIA PVT. LTD.—See Danaher Corporation; *U.S. Public*, pg. 629

PALL ITALIA S.R.L—See Danaher Corporation; *U.S. Public*, pg. 630

PALL NEW ZEALAND LTD.—See Danaher Corporation; *U.S. Public*, pg. 630

PALL NORGE A/S—See Danaher Corporation; *U.S. Public*, pg. 630

PALL SINGAPORE TAIWAN BRANCH HOLDING COMPANY PTE LTD.—See Danaher Corporation; *U.S. Public*, pg. 630

PALL SOUTH AFRICA (PTY) LIMITED—See Danaher Corporation; *U.S. Public*, pg. 630

PALL TECHNOLOGIES SA—See Danaher Corporation; *U.S. Public*, pg. 630

PANAVISION INC.—See Cerberus Capital Management, L.P.; *U.S. Private*, pg. 839

PANAVISION INTERNATIONAL, LP—See Cerberus Capital Management, L.P.; *U.S. Private*, pg. 839

PARAGON WATER SYSTEMS, INC.—See BDT Capital Partners, LLC; *U.S. Public*, pg. 502

PARKER CHOMERICS OPTICAL PRODUCTS—See Parker Hannifin Corporation; *U.S. Public*, pg. 1643

PARKER COMPANY, INC—See Ariens Company Inc.; *U.S. Private*, pg. 322

PARKER HANNIFIN DAEDAL DIVISION—See Parker Hannifin Corporation; *U.S. Public*, pg. 1644

PARKER HANNIFIN INDUSTRIA E COMERCIO LTDA.—See Parker Hannifin Corporation; *U.S. Public*, pg. 1644

PARKER HANNIFIN PLC - INSTRUMENTATION DIVISION—See Parker Hannifin Corporation; *U.S. Public*, pg. 1648

PARKER HANNIFIN—See Parker Hannifin Corporation; *U.S. Public*, pg. 1645

PARKINSON TECHNOLOGIES, INC.; *U.S. Private*, pg. 3098

PARKTRON TECHNOLOGY CO., LTD—See Chung-Hsin Electric & Machinery Manufacturing Corp.; *Int'l*, pg. 1597

PARTECH, INC.—See PAR Technology Corporation; *U.S. Public*, pg. 1636

PDQ MANUFACTURING, INC.—See Dover Corporation; *U.S. Public*, pg. 679

PELLERIN MILNOR CORPORATION; *U.S. Private*, pg. 3131

PENTAX CANADA INC.—See Hoya Corporation; *Int'l*, pg. 3495

PENTAX EUROPE GMBH—See Hoya Corporation; *Int'l*, pg. 3495

PENTAX FRANCE LIFE CARE S.A.S.—See Hoya Corporation; *Int'l*, pg. 3495

PENTAX NEDERLAND B.V.—See Hoya Corporation; *Int'l*, pg. 3495

PENTAX SINTAI OPTICAL INSTRUMENT (SHENZHEN) CO., LTD.—See Hoya Corporation; *Int'l*, pg. 3495

PENTAX U.K. LIMITED—See Hoya Corporation; *Int'l*, pg. 3495

PERBIO SCIENCE PROJEKT AB—See Thermo Fisher Scientific Inc.; *U.S. Public*, pg. 2151

PERFERX OPTICAL CO. INC.—See EssilorLuxottica SA; *Int'l*, pg. 2513

PERSPECTICS—See EssilorLuxottica SA; *Int'l*, pg. 2516

PHARMAGG SYSTEMTECHNIK GMBH—See Hebert Kannegiesser GmbH; *Int'l*, pg. 3306

PHOSEON TECHNOLOGY, INC.—See AEA Investors LP; *U.S. Private*, pg. 113

PHOTOGENIC PROFESSIONAL LIGHTING—See Promark International Inc.; *U.S. Private*, pg. 3282

PHOTOMETRICS—See Teledyne Technologies Incorporated; *U.S. Public*, pg. 1992

PHOTOMETRICS UK LIMITED—See Roper Technologies, Inc.; *U.S. Public*, pg. 1812

PHOTONIS FRANCE S.A.S.—See Ardian SAS; *Int'l*, pg. 556

PHOTONIS TECHNOLOGIES S.A.S.—See Ardian SAS; *Int'l*, pg. 556

PHOTO-SONICS INC.; *U.S. Private*, pg. 3174

PHOTRON USA, INC.—See Imagica Group Inc.; *Int'l*, pg. 3619

PIONEER ENVIRONMENTAL TECHNOLOGY PTE LTD—See AnnAik Limited; *Int'l*, pg. 473

PITCO FRIALATOR INC.—See The Middleby Corporation; *U.S. Public*, pg. 2113

PITNEY BOWES AUSTRALIA FAS PTY. LIMITED—See Pitney Bowes Inc.; *U.S. Public*, pg. 1694

PITNEY BOWES BRASIL EQUIPAMENTOS E SERVICOS LTDA—See Pitney Bowes Inc.; *U.S. Public*, pg. 1694

PITNEY BOWES CANADA LP—See Pitney Bowes Inc.; *U.S. Public*, pg. 1695

PITNEY BOWES (IRELAND) LIMITED—See Pitney Bowes Inc.; *U.S. Public*, pg. 1694

PITNEY BOWES SVENSKA AB—See Pitney Bowes Inc.; *U.S. Public*, pg. 1695

PITNEY BOWES (THAILAND) LIMITED—See Pitney Bowes Inc.; *U.S. Public*, pg. 1694

PLEATCO, LLC—See Align Capital Partners, LLC; *U.S. Private*, pg. 167

PLX, INC.—See Edgewater Capital Partners, L.P.; *U.S. Private*, pg. 1335

PLX, INC.—See SK Capital Partners, LP; *U.S. Private*, pg. 3679

PMA INDUSTRIES—See Ancor Holdings, L.P.; *U.S. Private*, pg. 275

POLAROID CORPORATION—See Gordon Brothers Group, LLC; *U.S. Private*, pg. 1742

POLAROID CORPORATION—See Hilco Trading, LLC; *U.S. Private*, pg. 1943

POLAROID DE MEXICO S.A. DE C.V.—See Gordon Brothers Group, LLC; *U.S. Private*, pg. 1742

POLAROID DE MEXICO S.A. DE C.V.—See Hilco Trading, LLC; *U.S. Private*, pg. 1943

333310 — COMMERCIAL AND SERV...

POLAROID (ESPANA) S.A.—See Gordon Brothers Group, LLC; *U.S. Private*, pg. 1742
POLAROID (ESPANA) S.A.—See Hilco Trading, LLC; *U.S. Private*, pg. 1943
POLAROID GMBH—See Gordon Brothers Group, LLC; *U.S. Private*, pg. 1742
POLAROID GMBH—See Hilco Trading, LLC; *U.S. Private*, pg. 1943
POLAROID (U.K.) LIMITED—See Gordon Brothers Group, LLC; *U.S. Private*, pg. 1742
POLAROID (U.K.) LIMITED—See Hilco Trading, LLC; *U.S. Private*, pg. 1943
POLYCOM UK LTD.—See HP Inc.; *U.S. Public*, pg. 1065
POWERSCREEN INTERNATIONAL LIMITED—See Terex Corporation; *U.S. Public*, pg. 2020
PRAMA HIKVISION INDIAN PRIVATE LIMITED—See Hangzhou Hikvision Digital Technology Co., Ltd.; *Int'l*, pg. 3248
PRECISION OPTICS CORPORATION, INC.; *U.S. Public*, pg. 1713
PREOPTIX CO., LTD.—See Delta Electronics, Inc.; *Int'l*, pg. 2018
PREOPTIX (JIANG SU) CO., LTD.—See Delta Electronics, Inc.; *Int'l*, pg. 2018
PRINCE CASTLE, INC.—See Berkshire Hathaway Inc.; *U.S. Public*, pg. 310
PRINCETON INSTRUMENTS INC.—See Teledyne Technologies Incorporated; *U.S. Public*, pg. 1992
PRINTER COMPONENTS INC.—See Floturn Inc.; *U.S. Private*, pg. 1551
PROCOIN GMBH—See Giesecke & Devrient GmbH; *Int'l*, pg. 2970
PRODPI INC.; *U.S. Private*, pg. 3272
PROMAC ITALIA SRL—See Ali Holding S.r.l.; *Int'l*, pg. 321
PRO OPTIC CANADA INC.—See EssilorLuxottica SA; *Int'l*, pg. 2516
PROPHOTONIX LIMITED—See Union Park Capital; *U.S. Private*, pg. 4284
PT. DAIKI AXIS INDONESIA—See Daiki Axis Co., Ltd.; *Int'l*, pg. 1932
PT PALL FILTRATION INDONESIA—See Danaher Corporation; *U.S. Public*, pg. 629
PT. SCHOTT IGAR GLASS—See Carl-Zeiss-Stiftung; *Int'l*, pg. 1336
PULLMAFLEX U.K. LIMITED—See Leggett & Platt, Incorporated; *U.S. Public*, pg. 1303
PURATION, INC.—See American Cannabis Innovations Conglomerated; *U.S. Private*, pg. 226
PURE H2O BIO-TECHNOLOGIES, INC.; *U.S. Private*, pg. 3305
PURE WATER SOLUTIONS, INC.—See Xylem Inc.; *U.S. Public*, pg. 2394
PVT SYSTEMS—See Cataract Steel Industries, Inc.; *U.S. Private*, pg. 788
QED TECHNOLOGIES INTERNATIONAL, INC.—See Quad-C Management, Inc.; *U.S. Private*, pg. 3315
QINGDAO JIAONAN EBARA ELECTRIC POWER CO., LTD.—See Ebara Corporation; *Int'l*, pg. 2284
QIOPTIQ LTD.—See AEA Investors LP; *U.S. Private*, pg. 114
QIOPTIQ PHOTONICS GMBH & CO. KG—See AEA Investors LP; *U.S. Private*, pg. 114
QIOPTIQ PHOTONICS LIMITED—See AEA Investors LP; *U.S. Private*, pg. 114
QUADRO ENGINEERING CORP—See IDEX Corp; *U.S. Public*, pg. 1091
QUALITY VISION INTERNATIONAL INC. - CERTIFIED COMPARATOR PRODUCTS DIVISION—See Quality Vision International Inc.; *U.S. Private*, pg. 3321
QUANTRONIX, INC.; *U.S. Private*, pg. 3322
QUANTURN LIMITED—See Galaxy Entertainment Group Limited; *Int'l*, pg. 2871
QUESTAR CORPORATION; *U.S. Private*, pg. 3326
QUIKSERV CORP.—See River Associates Investments, LLC; *U.S. Private*, pg. 3443
RACINE INDUSTRIES INC.; *U.S. Private*, pg. 3342
RAINSOFT WATER TREATMENT SYSTEMS—See Aquion Partners L.P.; *U.S. Private*, pg. 305
RANCILIO GROUP S.P.A.—See Ali Holding S.r.l.; *Int'l*, pg. 321
RATHENOWER OPTIK GMBH—See Fielmann Group AG; *Int'l*, pg. 2659
RAYTHEON ELCAN OPTICAL TECHNOLOGIES—See RTX Corporation; *U.S. Public*, pg. 1824
RAYTHEON SPAIN—See RTX Corporation; *U.S. Public*, pg. 1825
REALD INC.—See Rizvi Traverse Management LLC; *U.S. Private*, pg. 3449
REBELLION PHOTONICS, INC.—See Honeywell International Inc.; *U.S. Public*, pg. 1051
REFRESH WATERS PTY LTD. - OZ WATER FILTERS—See Eneco Refresh Limited; *Int'l*, pg. 2411
REICHERT, INC.—See AMETEK, Inc.; *U.S. Public*, pg. 116
RESEARCH ELECTRO-OPTICS INC—See AEA Investors LP; *U.S. Private*, pg. 114
RES-KEM LLC—See Ecolab Inc.; *U.S. Public*, pg. 716
RESTORATION CLEANERS, LLC; *U.S. Private*, pg. 3410
REXAIR, LLC—See Rhone Group, LLC; *U.S. Private*, pg. 3424
RHINO TOOL HOUSE—See Blue Sea Capital Management LLC; *U.S. Private*, pg. 592
RICCAR AMERICA, INC.—See Tacony Corporation; *U.S. Private*, pg. 3921
RICHARDS CORPORATION; *U.S. Private*, pg. 3428
RIMOLDI DA AMAZONIA IND. E COM. LTDA.—See CF Italia srl; *Int'l*, pg. 1429
ROBOSOFT NV—See Haco N.V.; *Int'l*, pg. 3205
ROCKWELL AUTOMATION A/S—See Rockwell Automation, Inc.; *U.S. Public*, pg. 1805
ROCKWELL AUTOMATION (N.Z.) LTD.—See Rockwell Automation, Inc.; *U.S. Public*, pg. 1805
ROCKWELL COLLINS OPTRONICS, INC.—See RTX Corporation; *U.S. Public*, pg. 1823
ROCKWELL COLLINS SIMULATION & TRAINING SOLUTIONS LLC—See RTX Corporation; *U.S. Public*, pg. 1823
ROCKY MOUNTAIN INSTRUMENT, INC.; *U.S. Private*, pg. 3469
RODENSTOCK CANADA INC.—See Compass Advisers Group LLC; *U.S. Private*, pg. 999
ROLIC TECHNOLOGIES LTD.—See BASF SE; *Int'l*, pg. 884
ROLIC TECHNOLOGIES (SHANGHAI) CO., LTD.—See BASF SE; *Int'l*, pg. 884
ROPER SCIENTIFIC GMBH—See Roper Technologies, Inc.; *U.S. Public*, pg. 1813
ROPER SCIENTIFIC, INC.—See Teledyne Technologies Incorporated; *U.S. Public*, pg. 1992
ROPER SCIENTIFIC SAS—See Roper Technologies, Inc.; *U.S. Public*, pg. 1813
ROSCO LABORATORIES, INC.; *U.S. Private*, pg. 3481
ROSS OPTICAL INDUSTRIES, INC.—See Precision Optics Corporation, Inc.; *U.S. Public*, pg. 1713
ROTARY LIFT—See Dover Corporation; *U.S. Public*, pg. 679
ROTHENBERGER WERKZEUGE PRODUKTION GMBH—See Dr. Helmut Rothenberger Holding GmbH; *Int'l*, pg. 2192
ROYAL VENDORS, INC.; *U.S. Private*, pg. 3494
RPC PHOTONICS, INC.—See Viavi Solutions Inc.; *U.S. Public*, pg. 2295
RSA ENTGRAT- U. TRENN-SYSTEME VERWALTUNGS-GMBH—See BayernLB Holding AG; *Int'l*, pg. 914
RSA SYSTEMES EBAVURAGE ET TRONCONNAGE S.A.R.L.—See BayernLB Holding AG; *Int'l*, pg. 914
RUG DOCTOR, LLC—See Ares Management Corporation; *U.S. Public*, pg. 191
RUYS HANDELSVERENIGING B.V—See Francotyp-Postalia Holding AG; *Int'l*, pg. 2761
RVISION INC.—See COMSovereign Holding Corp.; *U.S. Public*, pg. 562
SAINT-GOBAIN SEVA—See Compagnie de Saint-Gobain SA; *Int'l*, pg. 1735
SALSNES NORTH AMERICA INC—See Aqua-Pure Ventures Inc.; *Int'l*, pg. 527
THE SALVAJOR COMPANY; *U.S. Private*, pg. 4113
SANITAIRE DIVISION—See Xylem Inc.; *U.S. Public*, pg. 2396
SANITHERM INC.—See Clean Harbors, Inc.; *U.S. Public*, pg. 510
SA PHOTONICS, INC.; *U.S. Private*, pg. 3519
SAPPHIRE SCIENTIFIC INC.—See RPM International Inc.; *U.S. Public*, pg. 1820
SAPPLICATOR LTD—See Acrison, Inc.; *U.S. Private*, pg. 65
SAROPH SWEDEN AB—See Thermo Fisher Scientific Inc.; *U.S. Public*, pg. 2152
SATISLOH AG—See EssilorLuxottica SA; *Int'l*, pg. 2516
SATISLOH ASIA LTD.—See EssilorLuxottica SA; *Int'l*, pg. 2516
SATISLOH IBERICA SL—See EssilorLuxottica SA; *Int'l*, pg. 2516
SATISLOH ITALY SPA—See EssilorLuxottica SA; *Int'l*, pg. 2516
SATISLOH ZHONGSHAN LTD—See EssilorLuxottica SA; *Int'l*, pg. 2516
SB MANUFACTURING, INC.—See Berry Companies, Inc.; *U.S. Private*, pg. 538
SCANJET MARINE & SYSTEMS AB—See Alfa Laval AB; *Int'l*, pg. 312
SCANTRON CORPORATION - DATA MANAGEMENT SOLUTIONS—See Transom Capital Group, LLC; *U.S. Private*, pg. 4210
SCANTRON CORPORATION—See Transom Capital Group, LLC; *U.S. Private*, pg. 4209
SCHOTT SPEZIALGLAS AG—See Carl-Zeiss-Stiftung; *Int'l*, pg. 1337
SCHOTT TAIWAN LTD.—See Carl-Zeiss-Stiftung; *Int'l*, pg. 1337
SCHRODER MASCHINENBAU GMBH & CO KG—See John Bean Technologies Corporation; *U.S. Public*, pg. 1192
SCIENTIFIC MICROSCOPES INC.; *U.S. Private*, pg. 3574
S.C.M. BLISS SAS—See Haco N.V.; *Int'l*, pg. 3205
SCOTSMAN GROUP LLC—See Ali Holding S.r.l.; *Int'l*, pg. 321
SCOTSMAN ICE SYSTEMS (SHANGHAI) CO., LTD.—See Ali Holding S.r.l.; *Int'l*, pg. 321
SEILER INSTRUMENT AND MANUFACTURING CO. INC.; *U.S. Private*, pg. 3599

SEIWA SANGYO CO., LTD.—See Alfresa Holdings Corporation; *Int'l*, pg. 317
SELECTA DEUTSCHLAND GMBH—See Allianz SE; *Int'l*, pg. 355
SELECTA OLLAND B.V.—See Allianz SE; *Int'l*, pg. 355
SELECTIVEND INC.—See The Wittern Group; *U.S. Private*, pg. 4138
SEMROCK, INC.—See IDEX Corp; *U.S. Public*, pg. 1092
SENSUS & CESKA REPUBLIKA SPOL. S R.O.—See Xylem Inc.; *U.S. Public*, pg. 2394
SENSUS FRANCE HOLDINGS SAS—See Xylem Inc.; *U.S. Public*, pg. 2394
SENSUS GMBH HANNOVER—See Xylem Inc.; *U.S. Public*, pg. 2394
SENSUS MANUFACTURING (SHANGHAI) CO., LTD.—See Xylem Inc.; *U.S. Public*, pg. 2395
SEPARATION DYNAMICS, INC.; *U.S. Private*, pg. 3611
SERVER PRODUCTS INC.; *U.S. Private*, pg. 3614
SEWER EQUIPMENT CO. OF AMERICA; *U.S. Private*, pg. 3620
SFAM SOCIETE FRANCAISE D'AMPOULES MECANIQUES SARL—See Carl-Zeiss-Stiftung; *Int'l*, pg. 1337
SHAMIR INSIGHT, INC.—See EssilorLuxottica SA; *Int'l*, pg. 2516
SHAMIR OPTICAL INDUSTRY LTD.—See EssilorLuxottica SA; *Int'l*, pg. 2516
SHAMIR USA, INC.—See EssilorLuxottica SA; *Int'l*, pg. 2516
SHANGRAO YUTONG OPTICAL TECHNOLOGY CO., LTD.—See Dongguan Yutong Optical Technology Co., Ltd.; *Int'l*, pg. 2167
SHARP KOREA CORPORATION LTD.—See Hon Hai Precision Industry Co., Ltd.; *Int'l*, pg. 3458
SHARP MANUFACTURING FRANCE S.A.—See Hon Hai Precision Industry Co., Ltd.; *Int'l*, pg. 3458
SHINSHU FUJI ELECTRIC CO., LTD.—See Fuji Electric Co., Ltd.; *Int'l*, pg. 2813
SHOP-VAC CORPORATION—See GreatStar Group Co., Ltd.; *U.S. Private*, pg. 3067
SHRED-TECH INC.—See The Heico Companies, L.L.C.; *U.S. Private*, pg. 4051
SIA HANSAMATRIX INNOVATION—See HansaMatrix AS; *Int'l*, pg. 3259
SIA HANSAMATRIX VENTSPILS—See HansaMatrix AS; *Int'l*, pg. 3259
SICHUAN HONGDA PETROLEUM & NATURAL GAS CO., LTD.—See Houpu Clean Energy Group Co., Ltd; *Int'l*, pg. 3490
SIGNET ARMORLITE (ASIA) PTE LTD—See EssilorLuxottica SA; *Int'l*, pg. 2516
SIGNET ARMORLITE IBERICA SA—See EssilorLuxottica SA; *Int'l*, pg. 2516
SIGNET ARMORLITE OPTIC GMBH—See EssilorLuxottica SA; *Int'l*, pg. 2516
SIHI GROUP B.V.—See Flowserve Corporation; *U.S. Public*, pg. 857
SKYPERSONIC, INC.—See Red Cat Holdings, Inc.; *U.S. Public*, pg. 1769
SMIF EQUIPMENT (TIANJIN) CO., LTD—See Azenta, Inc.; *U.S. Public*, pg. 258
SMITH-VICTOR CORPORATION—See Promark International Inc.; *U.S. Private*, pg. 3282
SNUGZ USA INC; *U.S. Private*, pg. 3701
SOGEFI INDUSTRIA DE AUTOPECAS LTDA.—See Compagnia Finanziaria de Benedetti S.p.A.; *Int'l*, pg. 1722
SOLARX EYEWEAR LLC; *U.S. Private*, pg. 3708
SOLX, INC.; *U.S. Private*, pg. 3711
SOMAT COMPANY—See Illinois Tool Works Inc.; *U.S. Public*, pg. 1110
SOUTHBEND—See The Middleby Corporation; *U.S. Public*, pg. 2115
SOUTHWEST LENS CORP.—See EssilorLuxottica SA; *Int'l*, pg. 2514
SPACETECH, INC.—See Astrotech Corporation; *U.S. Public*, pg. 218
SPARTAN TOOL—See The Heico Companies, L.L.C.; *U.S. Private*, pg. 4050
SPATIAL ENERGY, LLC—See Advent International Corporation; *U.S. Private*, pg. 103
SPECTRAL SYSTEMS LLC—See Artemis Capital Partners Management Co., LLC; *U.S. Private*, pg. 341
SPECTRA-PHYSICS, K.K.—See MKS Instruments, Inc.; *U.S. Public*, pg. 1453
SPEEDOTRON CORPORATION—See Promark International Inc.; *U.S. Private*, pg. 3282
SPENUZZA BROTHERS INC.; *U.S. Private*, pg. 3755
SPHERICAL OPTICS (PTY) LTD.—See EssilorLuxottica SA; *Int'l*, pg. 2516
SPITZ INC.—See Elevate Entertainment, Inc.; *U.S. Private*, pg. 1358
SPUHL AG—See Leggett & Platt, Incorporated; *U.S. Public*, pg. 1303
SPX GENFARE—See SPX Technologies, Inc.; *U.S. Public*, pg. 1921
SPY OPTIC SRL—See Alvarez & Marsal, Inc.; *U.S. Private*, pg. 212
SRECO-FLEXIBLE INCORPORATED; *U.S. Private*, pg. 3767
STAAR SURGICAL AG NIEDERLASSUNG

N.A.I.C.S. INDEX

333413 — INDUSTRIAL AND COMM...

GERMANY—See STAAR Surgical Co.; *U.S. Public*, pg. 1924

STAAR SURGICAL COMPANY AG—See STAAR Surgical Co.; *U.S. Public*, pg. 1924

STANDARD CHANGE-MAKERS INC.; *U.S. Private*, pg. 3778

STANDLEY'S SYSTEMS, INC; *U.S. Private*, pg. 3782

THE STAPLEX COMPANY, INC.; *U.S. Private*, pg. 4120

STARRETT PRECISION OPTICAL LIMITED—See Middle-Ground Management, LP; *U.S. Private*, pg. 2713

STEFAN SYDOR OPTICS, INC.; *U.S. Private*, pg. 3797

STENOGRAPH LLC—See The Heico Companies, L.L.C.; *U.S. Private*, pg. 4051

STERISIL, INC.—See Avista Capital Partners, L.P.; *U.S. Private*, pg. 409

STERNO PRODUCTS, LLC—See Compass Diversified Holdings; *U.S. Public*, pg. 560

STEWART BUSINESS SYSTEMS, LLC—See Xerox Holdings Corporation; *U.S. Public*, pg. 2388

STINGRAY OPTICS, LLC—See Gooch & Housego PLC; *Int'l*, pg. 3038

STONEAGE, INC.; *U.S. Private*, pg. 3827

STORK PLASTICS MACHINERY B.V.—See Fluor Corporation; *U.S. Public*, pg. 860

STORM VULCAN MATTONI; *U.S. Private*, pg. 3831

SUMOTO S.R.L.—See Ebara Corporation; *Int'l*, pg. 2284

SUNTECH OPTICS INC.—See EssilorLuxottica SA; *Int'l*, pg. 2514

SUSPA PNEUMATICS INDIA PVT. LTD.—See Andlinger & Company, Inc.; *U.S. Private*, pg. 279

SUTHERLIN OPTICAL COMPANY—See EssilorLuxottica SA; *Int'l*, pg. 2514

SWEDA CANADA INC.—See Sweda Corporation; *U.S. Private*, pg. 3891

SWEDA CORPORATION; *U.S. Private*, pg. 3891

SWEEPSTER ATTACHMENTS LLC; *U.S. Private*, pg. 3891

SWIFT INSTRUMENTS, INC.-TECHNICAL INSTRUMENTS DIV.—See Swift Optical Instruments, Inc.; *U.S. Private*, pg. 3893

SWIFT OPTICAL INSTRUMENTS, INC.; *U.S. Private*, pg. 3893

SYSTEM PLAST, LLC—See Emerson Electric Co.; *U.S. Public*, pg. 752

TAFT ENGINEERING, INC.—See Watts Water Technologies, Inc.; *U.S. Public*, pg. 2337

TAIWAN OPLINK COMMUNICATIONS, INC.—See Koch Industries, Inc.; *U.S. Private*, pg. 2335

TALLEY MACHINERY CORPORATION—See Tingue, Brown & Co.; *U.S. Private*, pg. 4173

TCR BUSINESS SYSTEMS, INC.—See NCR Voyix Corporation.; *U.S. Public*, pg. 1503

TECHNETICS GROUP U.K. LTD.—See Enpro Inc.; *U.S. Public*, pg. 775

TECNICAS DE ENTIBACION, S.A.U.—See Duro Felguera, S.A.; *Int'l*, pg. 2229

TELEDYNE SCIENTIFIC & IMAGING, LLC—See Teledyne Technologies Incorporated; *U.S. Public*, pg. 1995

TENNANT COMPANY COMMERCIAL, USA—See Tennant Company; *U.S. Public*, pg. 2016

TENNANT HOLDING B.V.—See Tennant Company; *U.S. Public*, pg. 2016

TEXAS DIGITAL SYSTEMS, INC.—See NCR Voyix Corporation.; *U.S. Public*, pg. 1503

THERMEDICS DETECTION DE ARGENTINA S.A.—See Thermo Fisher Scientific Inc.; *U.S. Public*, pg. 2152

THERMO ASSET MANAGEMENT SERVICES INC.—See Thermo Fisher Scientific Inc.; *U.S. Public*, pg. 2152

THERMO EBERLINE LLC—See Thermo Fisher Scientific Inc.; *U.S. Public*, pg. 2152

THERMO EGS GAUGING, INC.—See Thermo Fisher Scientific Inc.; *U.S. Public*, pg. 2152

THERMO ENVIRONMENTAL INSTRUMENTS INC.—See Thermo Fisher Scientific Inc.; *U.S. Public*, pg. 2152

THERMO FISHER FINANCIAL SERVICES INC.—See Thermo Fisher Scientific Inc.; *U.S. Public*, pg. 2152

THERMO FISHER SCIENTIFIC - METAVAC—See Thermo Fisher Scientific Inc.; *U.S. Public*, pg. 2153

THERMO FISHER SCIENTIFIC (SCHWEIZ) AG—See Thermo Fisher Scientific Inc.; *U.S. Public*, pg. 2153

THERMO FISHER SCIENTIFIC (ZURICH) AG—See Thermo Fisher Scientific Inc.; *U.S. Public*, pg. 2153

THERMO GAMMA-METRICS PTY LTD—See Thermo Fisher Scientific Inc.; *U.S. Public*, pg. 2154

THERMO KEYTEK LLC—See Thermo Fisher Scientific Inc.; *U.S. Public*, pg. 2154

THERMO LIFE SCIENCES AB—See Thermo Fisher Scientific Inc.; *U.S. Public*, pg. 2152

THERMO NITON ANALYZERS LLC—See Thermo Fisher Scientific Inc.; *U.S. Public*, pg. 2154

THERMO RAMSEY S.A.—See Thermo Fisher Scientific Inc.; *U.S. Public*, pg. 2154

THOMAS L. GREEN & COMPANY, INC.—See Markel Group Inc.; *U.S. Public*, pg. 1369

THOMEKO EESTI OU—See Danish Crown AmbA; *Int'l*, pg. 1964

THOMEKO OY—See Danish Crown AmbA; *Int'l*, pg. 1964

TIANJIN CANON CO., LTD.—See Canon Inc.; *Int'l*, pg. 1292

TIDEL ENGINEERING, L.P.—See Littlejohn & Co., LLC; *U.S. Private*, pg. 2472

TIFFEN MANUFACTURING CORP.—See Topspin Partners, L.P.; *U.S. Private*, pg. 4188

TOBU CO., LTD.—See Daiki Axis Co., Ltd.; *Int'l*, pg. 1932

TOKHEIM HENGSHAN TECHNOLOGIES (GUANGZHOU) CO. LTD.—See Dover Corporation; *U.S. Public*, pg. 683

TORNADO INDUSTRIES, INC.—See Tacony Corporation; *U.S. Private*, pg. 3921

TRANSITIONS OPTICAL LIMITED—See EssilorLuxottica SA; *Int'l*, pg. 2514

TRANSITIONS OPTICAL PHILIPPINES, INC.—See EssilorLuxottica SA; *Int'l*, pg. 2514

TRANSITIONS OPTICAL (S) PTE. LTD—See EssilorLuxottica SA; *Int'l*, pg. 2514

TRANSITIONS OPTICAL (THAILAND) LTD.—See EssilorLuxottica SA; *Int'l*, pg. 2514

TRANSPACIFIC MANUFACTURING SYSTEMS PTY LTD—See Cleanaway Waste Management Limited; *Int'l*, pg. 1655

TRITECH INTERNATIONAL LIMITED—See Moog Inc.; *U.S. Public*, pg. 1471

TRU SIMULATION + TRAINING INC.—See Textron Inc.; *U.S. Public*, pg. 2028

TRUVOX INTERNATIONAL LIMITED—See Tacony Corporation; *U.S. Private*, pg. 3921

TURNTIDE TECHNOLOGIES INC.; *U.S. Private*, pg. 4261

TUTHILL TRANSFER SYSTEMS—See Tuthill Corporation; *U.S. Private*, pg. 4263

UAB HELLA LITHUANIA—See Hella GmbH & Co. KGaA; *Int'l*, pg. 3333

UCM AG—See Durr AG; *Int'l*, pg. 2233

ULTRAFRYER SYSTEMS, INC.—See Standex International; *U.S. Public*, pg. 1931

UNION TECH AUTOMATION SDN. BHD.—See Aimflex Berhad; *Int'l*, pg. 233

UNISYN VOTING SOLUTIONS, INC.—See Berjaya Corporation Berhad; *Int'l*, pg. 983

UNITEC LLC—See New Mountain Capital, LLC; *U.S. Private*, pg. 2900

UNITED SERVICE EQUIPMENT COMPANY—See Standex International; *U.S. Public*, pg. 1931

USI, INC.; *U.S. Private*, pg. 4323

UTILITY PROTECTION SERVICES-EAST—See Heath Consultants Incorporated; *U.S. Private*, pg. 1902

VECTA VENDING SOLUTIONS S.P.A.—See AB Electrolux; *Int'l*, pg. 41

VEHICLE SERVICE GROUP, LLC—See Dover Corporation; *U.S. Public*, pg. 679

VEROMATIC INTERNATIONAL BV—See Godrej & Boyce Mfg. Co. Ltd.; *Int'l*, pg. 3021

V-GEN LTD.—See MKS Instruments, Inc.; *U.S. Public*, pg. 1453

VIAVI SOLUTIONS DE MEXICO S.A. DE C.V.—See Viavi Solutions Inc.; *U.S. Public*, pg. 2295

VIDEK, INC.; *U.S. Private*, pg. 4380

VIDEOJET TECHNOLOGIES INC.—See Danaher Corporation; *U.S. Public*, pg. 631

VISION CARE COMPANY—See Hoya Corporation; *Int'l*, pg. 3498

VISION EASE, LP—See Wind Point Advisors LLC; *U.S. Private*, pg. 4536

VISION ENGINEERING INC.; *U.S. Private*, pg. 4390

VISION RESEARCH, INC.—See AMETEK, Inc.; *U.S. Public*, pg. 118

VOLANKA LTD—See Hayleys PLC; *Int'l*, pg. 3292

WASHTEC—See Ali Holding S.r.l; *Int'l*, pg. 322

WATERCARE CORPORATION—See A. O. Smith Corporation; *U.S. Public*, pg. 12

WATERMILL EXPRESS—See Watermill Express LLC; *U.S. Private*, pg. 4454

WATER RESOURCES INTERNATIONAL, INC.; *U.S. Private*, pg. 4451

WATER SERVICES OF AMERICA, INC.; *U.S. Private*, pg. 4451

WAVEX TECHNOLOGIES PTE. LTD.—See HKC International Holdings Limited; *Int'l*, pg. 3428

WAVIN-LABKO OY—See Bharti Enterprises Limited; *Int'l*, pg. 1013

WAVIN LATVIA SIA—See Bharti Enterprises Limited; *Int'l*, pg. 1012

WEATHERFORD (U.K.) LIMITED—See Weatherford International plc; *U.S. Public*, pg. 2339

WEAVEXX, LLC—See ANDRITZ AG; *Int'l*, pg. 457

WELLS BLOOMFIELD LLC—See The Middleby Corporation; *U.S. Public*, pg. 2115

WESTFALISCHE WASSER UND UMWELTANALYTIK GMBH—See Gelsenwasser AG; *Int'l*, pg. 2913

WEST PHARMACEUTICAL SERVICES SINGAPORE PTE. LTD—See West Pharmaceutical Services, Inc.; *U.S. Public*, pg. 2353

WIDNI OY—See Axel Johnson Gruppen AB; *Int'l*, pg. 762

WILD GOOSE CANNING TECHNOLOGIES INC.; *U.S. Private*, pg. 4518

WILLIAM F. WHITE INTERNATIONAL INC.—See Ashtead Group Plc; *Int'l*, pg. 609

WILLIAMS GUN SIGHT COMPANY, INC.; *U.S. Private*, pg. 4526

WINDSOR INDUSTRIES, INC.—See Alfred Karcher GmbH & Co. KG; *Int'l*, pg. 316

WINGSCAPES, INC..—See EBSCO Industries, Inc.; *U.S. Private*, pg. 1325

WINSTON INDUSTRIES, LLC; *U.S. Private*, pg. 4544

WINTERTHUR TECHNOLOGY TAICANG CO. LTD.—See 3M Company; *U.S. Public*, pg. 9

WMS GAMING INC.—See Light & Wonder, Inc.; *U.S. Public*, pg. 1315

XACTI CORPORATION—See Advantage Partners LLP; *Int'l*, pg. 164

XEROX CARE & QUALITY SOLUTIONS, INC.—See Xerox Holdings Corporation; *U.S. Public*, pg. 2390

XEROX COMERCIO E INDUSTRIA LTDA—See Xerox Holdings Corporation; *U.S. Public*, pg. 2391

XEROX CZECH REPUBLIC S R.O.—See Xerox Holdings Corporation; *U.S. Public*, pg. 2388

XEROX DO BRASIL S.A.—See Xerox Holdings Corporation; *U.S. Public*, pg. 2391

THE XEROX FOUNDATION INC.—See Xerox Holdings Corporation; *U.S. Public*, pg. 2388

XEROX INTERNATIONAL PARTNERS—See FUJIFILM Holdings Corporation; *Int'l*, pg. 2825

XEROX MANUFACTURING NEDERLAND B.V.—See Xerox Holdings Corporation; *U.S. Public*, pg. 2389

XEROX (NETHERLAND) B.V.—See Xerox Holdings Corporation; *U.S. Public*, pg. 2389

XGIGA COMMUNICATION TECHNOLOGY CO., LTD.—See Amphenol Corporation; *U.S. Public*, pg. 132

X-RITE, INCORPORATED—See Danaher Corporation; *U.S. Public*, pg. 632

YONG KANG LAVORWASH EQUIPMENT CO., LTD.—See Emak S.p.A.; *Int'l*, pg. 2373

YOUNGER OPTICS EUROPE S.R.O.—See Younger Mfg. Co.; *U.S. Public*, pg. 4594

YOUNGOPTICS INC.—See Coretronic Corporation; *Int'l*, pg. 1800

ZEISS-BELOMO OOO—See Carl-Zeiss-Stiftung; *Int'l*, pg. 1337

ZEP INC. - NIAGARA NATIONAL DIVISION—See New Mountain Capital, LLC; *U.S. Private*, pg. 2904

ZETA INSTRUMENTS, INC.—See KLA Corporation; *U.S. Public*, pg. 1269

ZODIAC POOL SYSTEMS, INC. - POLARIS PRODUCTS—See The Carlyle Group Inc.; *U.S. Public*, pg. 2057

ZODIAC POOL SYSTEMS, INC.—See The Carlyle Group Inc.; *U.S. Public*, pg. 2057

ZYGO CORPORATION—See AMETEK, Inc.; *U.S. Public*, pg. 119

ZYGO ELECTRO-OPTICS GROUP MANUFACTURING CENTER—See AMETEK, Inc.; *U.S. Public*, pg. 119

ZYGO RICHMOND, INC.—See AMETEK, Inc.; *U.S. Public*, pg. 119

333413 — INDUSTRIAL AND COMMERCIAL FAN AND BLOWER AND AIR PURIFICATION EQUIPMENT MANUFACTURING

AAF INTERNATIONAL B.V.—See Daikin Industries, Ltd.; *Int'l*, pg. 1936

ABC INDUSTRIES INC.—See Branford Castle, Inc.; *U.S. Private*, pg. 639

ABSOLENT AIR CARE GROUP AB; *Int'l*, pg. 69

ABSOLENT (BEIJING) CO., LTD.—See Absolent Air Care Group AB; *Int'l*, pg. 70

ABSOLENT GMBH—See Absolent Air Care Group AB; *Int'l*, pg. 70

ABSOLENT INC.—See Absolent Air Care Group AB; *Int'l*, pg. 70

ABSOLENT JAPAN LTD.—See Absolent Air Care Group AB; *Int'l*, pg. 70

ABSOLENT SAS—See Absolent Air Care Group AB; *Int'l*, pg. 70

ABSOLENT S.R.L.—See Absolent Air Care Group AB; *Int'l*, pg. 70

ACME ENGINEERING AND MANUFACTURING CORP.; *U.S. Private*, pg. 60

ADVANCE ROSS ELECTRONICS CORPORATION—See Chartwell Investments; *U.S. Private*, pg. 859

AEROVENT—See Twin City Fan Companies, Ltd.; *U.S. Private*, pg. 4265

AIRCO—See Ingersoll Rand Inc.; *U.S. Public*, pg. 1120

AIR-DRY COMPANY OF AMERICA LLC—See TransDigm Group Incorporated; *U.S. Public*, pg. 2181

AIREFRESH INDUSTRIES (M) SDN. BHD.—See Ancom Nylex Berhad; *Int'l*, pg. 449

AIRLANCO INC.—See Ag Growth International Inc.; *Int'l*, pg. 198

AIRMASTER FAN COMPANY; *U.S. Private*, pg. 141

AIR SAMPLER DIV.—See The Staplex Company, Inc.; *U.S. Private*, pg. 4121

AIRSAN CORPORATION—See Clover Creek Partners, LLC; *U.S. Private*, pg. 947

AIRTECH JAPAN, LTD. - CLEAN SUPPLY FACTORY—See AIRTECH JAPAN, LTD.; *Int'l*, pg. 249

AIRTECH JAPAN, LTD. - GUNMA FACTORY—See

333413 — INDUSTRIAL AND COMM...

AIRTECH JAPAN, LTD.; *Int'l*, pg. 249
AIRTECH JAPAN, LTD. - KAZO FACTORY—See AIRTECH JAPAN, LTD.; *Int'l*, pg. 249
AIRTECH JAPAN, LTD. - SOKA FACTORY—See AIRTECH JAPAN, LTD.; *Int'l*, pg. 249
AIRTECH JAPAN, LTD.; *Int'l*, pg. 249
ALLEN-SHERMAN-HOFF—See Babcock & Wilcox Enterprises, Inc.; *U.S. Private*, pg. 262
ALTEC INDUSTRIES INC.—See Altec Industries Inc.; *U.S. Private*, pg. 206
AMANO CORPORATION—See Amano Corporation; *Int'l*, pg. 410
AMANO VIETNAM CO., LTD.—See Amano Corporation; *Int'l*, pg. 411
AMETEK PRECISION MOTION CONTROL - ROTRON/NAUTILAIR BLOWERS—See AMETEK, Inc.; *U.S. Public*, pg. 117
AMETEK ROTRON - EL CAJON—See AMETEK, Inc.; *U.S. Public*, pg. 117
AMETEK ROTRON—See AMETEK, Inc.; *U.S. Public*, pg. 117
ANDRITZ S.R.L.—See ANDRITZ AG; *Int'l*, pg. 454
APEL INTERNATIONAL, LLC—See Align Capital Partners, LLC; *U.S. Private*, pg. 167
ATLANTIC VENTILATION—See Atlantic Societe Francaise Develop Thermique S.A.; *Int'l*, pg. 675
ATMUS FILTRATION TECHNOLOGIES INC.; *U.S. Public*, pg. 224
AZEN MANUFACTURING PTE. LTD.—See Twin City Fan Companies, Ltd.; *U.S. Private*, pg. 4265
BAHNSON, INC.—See Bahnson Holdings, Inc.; *U.S. Private*, pg. 425
BASF CATALYSTS LLC - ENVIRONMENTAL TECHNOLOGIES—See BASF SE; *Int'l*, pg. 875
BECKETT AIR INC.; *U.S. Private*, pg. 511
BECO ENGINEERING COMPANY; *U.S. Private*, pg. 512
BHA ALTAIR, LLC—See Parker Hannifin Corporation; *U.S. Public*, pg. 1640
BIOWIND GROUP S.A. - MANUFACTURING PLANT—See Biowind Group S.A.; *Int'l*, pg. 1045
BIOWIND GROUP S.A.; *Int'l*, pg. 1045
BLACK & DECKER IBERICA S.COM POR A.—See Stanley Black & Decker, Inc.; *U.S. Public*, pg. 1936
BOFA AMERICAS INC.—See Donaldson Company, Inc.; *U.S. Public*, pg. 675
BOFA INTERNATIONAL LTD.—See Donaldson Company, Inc.; *U.S. Public*, pg. 675
BUFFALO AIR HANDLING—See Ampco-Pittsburgh Corporation; *U.S. Public*, pg. 126
BUFFALO FILTER LLC—See CONMED Corporation; *U.S. Public*, pg. 567
CAMFIL AB; *Int'l*, pg. 1272
CAMFIL AG—See Camfil AB; *Int'l*, pg. 1272
CAMFIL AIRFILTER SDN. BHD.—See Camfil AB; *Int'l*, pg. 1272
CAMFIL A/S—See Camfil AB; *Int'l*, pg. 1272
CAMFIL AUSTRALIA PTY LTD—See Camfil AB; *Int'l*, pg. 1272
CAMFIL AUSTRIA GMBH—See Camfil AB; *Int'l*, pg. 1272
CAMFIL BV—See Camfil AB; *Int'l*, pg. 1272
CAMFIL CANADA INC.—See Camfil AB; *Int'l*, pg. 1272
CAMFIL ESPANA SA—See Camfil AB; *Int'l*, pg. 1272
CAMFIL INDIA PVT. LTD.—See Camfil AB; *Int'l*, pg. 1272
CAMFIL (IRL) LTD—See Camfil AB; *Int'l*, pg. 1272
CAMFIL LTD.—See Camfil AB; *Int'l*, pg. 1272
CAMFIL NEW ZEALAND LIMITED—See Camfil AB; *Int'l*, pg. 1272
CAMFIL NORGE AS—See Camfil AB; *Int'l*, pg. 1272
CAMFIL OY—See Camfil AB; *Int'l*, pg. 1272
CAMFIL POLSKA SP. Z O.O.—See Camfil AB; *Int'l*, pg. 1272
CAMFIL SA—See Camfil AB; *Int'l*, pg. 1272
CAMFIL SPA—See Camfil AB; *Int'l*, pg. 1272
CAMFIL S.R.O.—See Camfil AB; *Int'l*, pg. 1272
CAMFIL UAE—See Camfil AB; *Int'l*, pg. 1272
CAMFIL USA, INC.—See Camfil AB; *Int'l*, pg. 1272
CANADIAN PUREGAS EQUIPMENT LIMITED; *Int'l*, pg. 1285
CECO ENVIRONMENTAL CORP.; *U.S. Public*, pg. 463
CECO ENVIRONMENTAL MIDDLE EAST DMCC—See CECO Environmental Corp.; *U.S. Public*, pg. 463
CECO FILTERS INC.—See CECO Environmental Corp.; *U.S. Public*, pg. 463
CECO GROUP, INC.—See CECO Environmental Corp.; *U.S. Public*, pg. 463
CERTAINTEED MACHINE WORKS—See Compagnie de Saint-Gobain SA; *Int'l*, pg. 1729
C.G. WOOD COMPANY, INC.—See Madison Dearborn Partners, LLC; *U.S. Private*, pg. 2541
CHAMBON SAS—See Haco N.V.; *Int'l*, pg. 3204
CHICAGO BLOWER CORPORATION; *U.S. Private*, pg. 877
CIRCUL-AIRE INC—See Madison Industries Holdings LLC; *U.S. Private*, pg. 2543
CLARAGE—See Twin City Fan Companies, Ltd.; *U.S. Private*, pg. 4265
CLARCOR AIR FILTRATION PRODUCTS INC.—See Parker Hannifin Corporation; *U.S. Public*, pg. 1641
CLID SYSTEMES SAS—See Haco N.V.; *Int'l*, pg. 3204

CLIMET INSTRUMENTS CO.—See Venturedyne, Ltd.; *U.S. Private*, pg. 4358
CNTUS CO.,LTD; *Int'l*, pg. 1679
COFIMCO FAN (CHANGSHU) CO., LTD.—See Chart Industries, Inc.; *U.S. Public*, pg. 481
COFIMCO INTERNATIONAL (SHANGHAI) TRADING CO, INC.—See Chart Industries, Inc.; *U.S. Public*, pg. 481
COFIMCO S.R.L.—See Chart Industries, Inc.; *U.S. Public*, pg. 481
COLUMBUS INDUSTRIES, INC.; *U.S. Private*, pg. 979
CUSTOM FILTER, LLC—See Audax Group, Limited Partnership; *U.S. Private*, pg. 389
DAITRON (NETHERLANDS) B.V.—See Daitron Co., Ltd.; *Int'l*, pg. 1944
DELBAG GMBH—See Hengst SE & Co. KG; *Int'l*, pg. 3347
DELBAG S.A.S.—See Hengst SE & Co. KG; *Int'l*, pg. 3347
DELBAG S.R.O.—See Hengst SE & Co. KG; *Int'l*, pg. 3347
DIALOG TECHNIVAC LTD.—See Dialog Group Berhad; *Int'l*, pg. 2104
DINAIR CLEAN AIR OY—See Daikin Industries, Ltd.; *Int'l*, pg. 1936
DINGS DYNAMICS CO.—See Venturedyne, Ltd.; *U.S. Private*, pg. 4358
DINGS MAGNETIC CO.—See Venturedyne, Ltd.; *U.S. Private*, pg. 4358
DIVERSITECH EQUIPMENT & SALES (1984) LTD.—See Absolent Air Care Group AB; *Int'l*, pg. 70
DONALDSON COMPANY, INC.; *U.S. Public*, pg. 675
DONALDSON FAR EAST LTD.—See Donaldson Company, Inc.; *U.S. Public*, pg. 676
DONALDSON FILTER COMPONENTS LTD.—See Donaldson Company, Inc.; *U.S. Public*, pg. 675
DONALDSON FILTRATION (ASIA PACIFIC) PTE. LTD.—See Donaldson Company, Inc.; *U.S. Public*, pg. 676
DONALDSON FILTRATION (GB) LTD.—See Donaldson Company, Inc.; *U.S. Public*, pg. 675
DONALDSON FILTRATION MAGYARORSZAG KFT.—See Donaldson Company, Inc.; *U.S. Public*, pg. 675
DONALDSON FILTRATION MALAYSIA SDN BHD—See Donaldson Company, Inc.; *U.S. Public*, pg. 676
DONALDSON FILTRATION NORWAY A.S.—See Donaldson Company, Inc.; *U.S. Public*, pg. 675
DONALDSON FILTROS IBERICA S.L.—See Donaldson Company, Inc.; *U.S. Public*, pg. 675
DONALDSON FRANCE, S.A.S.—See Donaldson Company, Inc.; *U.S. Public*, pg. 675
DONALDSON GMBH—See Donaldson Company, Inc.; *U.S. Public*, pg. 675
DONALDSON IBERICA SOLUCIONES EN FILTRACION, S.L.—See Donaldson Company, Inc.; *U.S. Public*, pg. 675
DONALDSON KOREA CO., LTD.—See Donaldson Company, Inc.; *U.S. Public*, pg. 676
DONALDSON SCANDINAVIA A.P.S.—See Donaldson Company, Inc.; *U.S. Public*, pg. 675
DONALDSON SCHWEIZ GMBH—See Donaldson Company, Inc.; *U.S. Public*, pg. 675
DONALDSON (WUXI) FILTERS CO., LTD.—See Donaldson Company, Inc.; *U.S. Public*, pg. 675
DRINKSTATION, INC.—See PepsiCo, Inc.; *U.S. Public*, pg. 1668
DUCON TECHNOLOGIES INC.; *U.S. Private*, pg. 1284
DURR UNIVERSAL, INC.—See Durr AG; *Int'l*, pg. 2231
DUSTEX LLC—See Insight Equity Holdings LLC; *U.S. Private*, pg. 2086
DUST FREE, LP—See CSW Industrials, Inc.; *U.S. Public*, pg. 601
EBARA FAN & BLOWER CO., LTD.—See Ebara Corporation; *Int'l*, pg. 2283
EBARA HAMADA BLOWER CO., LTD.—See Ebara Corporation; *Int'l*, pg. 2282
EBARA JITSUGYO CO., LTD.; *Int'l*, pg. 2284
ECE CO., LTD.—See Ebara Corporation; *Int'l*, pg. 2282
ENTOLETER LLC; *U.S. Private*, pg. 1405
EVOQUA WATER TECHNOLOGIES—See Xylem Inc.; *U.S. Public*, pg. 2394
EXHAUSTO A/S—See Aldes Aeraulique SAS; *Int'l*, pg. 304
EXHAUSTO GMBH—See Aldes Aeraulique SAS; *Int'l*, pg. 304
FILTERMIST SYSTEMS LTD.—See Absolent Air Care Group AB; *Int'l*, pg. 70
FILTRAFINE CORPORATION—See Bright Sheland International Co., Ltd.; *Int'l*, pg. 1162
FILTRAFINE JAPAN INC.—See Bright Sheland International Co., Ltd.; *Int'l*, pg. 1162
FILTRATION GROUP CORPORATION—See Madison Industries Holdings LLC; *U.S. Private*, pg. 2543
FISHER-KLOSTERMAN, INC.—See CECO Environmental Corp.; *U.S. Public*, pg. 463
FLEX-KLEEN—See CECO Environmental Corp.; *U.S. Public*, pg. 464
FOCUSED PHOTONICS (HANGZHOU), INC.; *Int'l*, pg. 2720
FREUDENBERG FILTRATION TECHNOLOGIES SE & CO. KG—See Freudenberg SE; *Int'l*, pg. 2786
FREUDENBERG & VILENE FILTER (THAILAND) CO., LTD.—See Freudenberg SE; *Int'l*, pg. 2785

FS PRECISION TECH CO. LLC—See Brookfield Corporation; *Int'l*, pg. 1181
FUJIAN LONGKING CO., LTD.; *Int'l*, pg. 2818
FURNACE CONSTRUCTION CREMATORS LIMITED—See Matthews International Corporation; *U.S. Public*, pg. 1399
FU SHENG INDUSTRIAL CO., LTD.—See Brookfield Corporation; *Int'l*, pg. 1181
FU SHENG USA INC—See Brookfield Corporation; *Int'l*, pg. 1181
GEA HOVEX B.V.—See GEA Group Aktiengesellschaft; *Int'l*, pg. 2899
GKG ASIA PTE. LTD.—See GKG Precision Machine Co., Ltd.; *Int'l*, pg. 2983
GKL VENTILATIE TECHNIEK B.V.—See Grafton Group plc; *Int'l*, pg. 3050
GLASFLOSS INDUSTRIES; *U.S. Private*, pg. 1706
GLENDALE MEMORIAL HOSPITAL & HEALTH CENTER—See Catholic Health Initiatives; *U.S. Private*, pg. 789
GREENHECK FAN CORPORATION; *U.S. Private*, pg. 1778
HACO A.S.—See Haco N.V.; *Int'l*, pg. 3204
HACO (AUSTRALIA) PTY LTD—See Haco N.V.; *Int'l*, pg. 3205
HACO G. KOUZARIS LTD.—See Haco N.V.; *Int'l*, pg. 3204
HACO MACHINERY (MALAYSIA) SDN BHD—See Haco N.V.; *Int'l*, pg. 3205
HACO (NINGBO) INTERNATIONAL TRADING CO., LTD.—See Haco N.V.; *Int'l*, pg. 3204
HAI PHONG ELECTRICAL MECHANICAL JSC; *Int'l*, pg. 3209
HA KOVOCHEM SPOL S.R.O.—See Huettenes-Albertus Chemische Werke GmbH; *Int'l*, pg. 3523
HANDOK CLEAN TECH CO., LTD.; *Int'l*, pg. 3243
HARTZELL FAN, INC.—See Hartzell Industries, Inc.; *U.S. Private*, pg. 1874
HEALTHWAY HOME PRODUCTS, INC.—See AE Industrial Partners, LP; *U.S. Private*, pg. 112
HEE ENVIRONMENTAL ENGINEERING, LLC—See CECO Environmental Corp.; *U.S. Public*, pg. 463
HENGST MIDDLE EAST FZE—See Hengst SE & Co. KG; *Int'l*, pg. 3347
HENGST OF NORTH AMERICA, INC.—See Hengst SE & Co. KG; *Int'l*, pg. 3347
HENGST SE & CO. KG; *Int'l*, pg. 3347
HF GROUP INC.; *U.S. Private*, pg. 1928
HI AIR KOREA CO., LTD.; *Int'l*, pg. 3379
HICKOK AE LLC—See Crawford United Corporation; *U.S. Public*, pg. 592
HI-KALIBRE EQUIPMENT LTD.; *Int'l*, pg. 3380
HORTON INC—See Horton Inc.; *U.S. Private*, pg. 1984
HOWDEN AFRICA HOLDINGS LIMITED—See Chart Industries, Inc.; *U.S. Public*, pg. 482
HOWDEN AIR & GAS INDIA PRIVATE LIMITED—See Chart Industries, Inc.; *U.S. Public*, pg. 481
HOWDEN ALPHAIR VENTILATING SYSTEMS INC.—See Chart Industries, Inc.; *U.S. Public*, pg. 481
HOWDEN AXIAL FANS AB—See Chart Industries, Inc.; *U.S. Public*, pg. 481
HOWDEN AXIAL FANS APS—See Chart Industries, Inc.; *U.S. Public*, pg. 481
HOWDEN COVENT FANS INC.—See Chart Industries, Inc.; *U.S. Public*, pg. 481
HOWDEN DONKIN (PROPRIETARY) LIMITED—See Chart Industries, Inc.; *U.S. Public*, pg. 481
HOWDEN FFP (PROPRIETARY) LIMITED—See Chart Industries, Inc.; *U.S. Public*, pg. 481
HOWDEN MELBOURNE PTY LIMITED—See Chart Industries, Inc.; *U.S. Public*, pg. 482
HOWDEN MIDDLE EAST FZE—See Chart Industries, Inc.; *U.S. Public*, pg. 482
HOWDEN NORTH AMERICA, INC.—See Chart Industries, Inc.; *U.S. Public*, pg. 482
HOWDEN SOLYVENT (INDIA) PVT LTD—See Chart Industries, Inc.; *U.S. Public*, pg. 482
HOWDEN THOMASSEN FAR EAST PTE LTD—See Chart Industries, Inc.; *U.S. Public*, pg. 482
HOWDEN TURBO FANS OY—See Chart Industries, Inc.; *U.S. Public*, pg. 482
HOWDEN USA COMPANY—See Chart Industries, Inc.; *U.S. Public*, pg. 482
HUDSON PRODUCTS CORPORATION—See Chart Industries, Inc.; *U.S. Public*, pg. 482
HYGROMATIK GMBH—See Carel Industries S.p.A.; *Int'l*, pg. 1324
IONEX RESEARCH CORP.; *U.S. Private*, pg. 2134
ITW AIR MANAGEMENT—See Illinois Tool Works Inc.; *U.S. Public*, pg. 1104
K&B DUCT—See CECO Environmental Corp.; *U.S. Public*, pg. 463
KOCH FILTER CORPORATION—See Canada Pension Plan Investment Board; *Int'l*, pg. 1281
KRONOS ADVANCED TECHNOLOGIES, INC.; *U.S. Private*, pg. 2353
LAU INDUSTRIES—See Canada Pension Plan Investment Board; *Int'l*, pg. 1281
LE BOZEC FILTRATION ET SYSTEMES, S.A.S.—See Donaldson Company, Inc.; *U.S. Public*, pg. 676

N.A.I.C.S. INDEX

LFG SPECIALTIES, L.L.C.—See The Shaw Group Inc.; *U.S. Private*, pg. 4117
LOREN COOK COMPANY; *U.S. Private*, pg. 2495
L & T HOWDEN PRIVATE LTD.—See Chart Industries, Inc.; *U.S. Public*, pg. 482
LUBRITECH ARGENTINA, S.R.L—See Enovis Corporation; *U.S. Public*, pg. 773
LUBRITECH CARIBBEAN LIMITED—See Enovis Corporation; *U.S. Public*, pg. 773
LUBRITECH DO BRASIL SERVICOS DE LUBRIFICACAO LTDA.—See Enovis Corporation; *U.S. Public*, pg. 773
LUFT- UND THERMOTECHNIK BAYREUTH GMBH—See Durr AG; *Int'l*, pg. 2233
LYDALL GUTSCHE GMBH & CO. KG—See Lydall, Inc.; *U.S. Public*, pg. 1349
MARADYNE MOBILE PRODUCTS—See Dreison International, Inc.; *U.S. Private*, pg. 1276
MAS AIR SYSTEMS, LLC—See The New York Blower Company, Inc.; *U.S. Private*, pg. 4083
MCGILL AIRCLEAN CORP.—See The McGill Corporation; *U.S. Private*, pg. 4076
MECHANOVENT CORPORATION—See The New York Blower Company, Inc.; *U.S. Private*, pg. 4083
MEGGITT AIRDYNAMICS, INC.—See Parker Hannifin Corporation; *U.S. Public*, pg. 1642
MET-PRO TECHNOLOGIES LLC—See CECO Environmental Corp.; *U.S. Public*, pg. 463
MICRON (M) SDN. BHD.—See Channel Micron Holdings Company Limited; *Int'l*, pg. 1446
MIDWESCO FILTER RESOURCES, INC.—See Perma-Pipe International Holdings, Inc.; *U.S. Public*, pg. 1676
MIDWESCO MECHANICAL AND ENERGY, INC.—See Perma-Pipe International Holdings, Inc.; *U.S. Public*, pg. 1676
MIDWEST INTERNATIONAL STANDARD PRODUCTS, INC.; *U.S. Private*, pg. 2722
MOLEKULE GROUP, INC.; *U.S. Public*, pg. 1458
MOORE FANS LLC; *U.S. Private*, pg. 2780
MORRISON PRODUCTS INC.; *U.S. Private*, pg. 2789
NADI AIRTECHNICS PRIVATE LIMITED—See Twin City Fan Companies, Ltd.; *U.S. Private*, pg. 4265
NADI AIRTECHNICS PRIVATE LIMITED - UNIT 4—See Twin City Fan Companies, Ltd.; *U.S. Private*, pg. 4265
NATIONAL FILTER MEDIA—See Perma-Pipe International Holdings, Inc.; *U.S. Public*, pg. 1676
NEW BUSCH CO., INC.—See CECO Environmental Corp.; *U.S. Public*, pg. 463
THE NEW YORK BLOWER COMPANY, INC.; *U.S. Private*, pg. 4083
NICOTRA GEBHARDT AB—See Regal Rexnord Corporation; *U.S. Public*, pg. 1773
NICOTRA GEBHARDT LTD.—See Regal Rexnord Corporation; *U.S. Public*, pg. 1773
NICOTRA GEBHARDT PTE LTD—See Regal Rexnord Corporation; *U.S. Public*, pg. 1773
NICOTRA GEBHARDT PVT. LTD.—See Regal Rexnord Corporation; *U.S. Public*, pg. 1773
NICOTRA GEBHARDT S.A.—See Regal Rexnord Corporation; *U.S. Public*, pg. 1773
NICOTRA GEBHARDT S.P.A—See Regal Rexnord Corporation; *U.S. Public*, pg. 1773
NOVELAIRE TECHNOLOGIES; *U.S. Private*, pg. 2968
NUOVE ENERGIE SRL—See Enel S.p.A.; *Int'l*, pg. 2414
OBERLIN FILTER GMBH—See Production Service Company; *U.S. Private*, pg. 3273
OBERLIN FILTER LTD.—See Production Service Company; *U.S. Private*, pg. 3273
OFFSHORE CLEANING SYSTEMS, LLC.; *U.S. Private*, pg. 3002
PALL AUSTRALIA PTY LTD—See Danaher Corporation; *U.S. Public*, pg. 629
PALL AUSTRIA FILTER GMBH—See Danaher Corporation; *U.S. Public*, pg. 629
PALL ESPANA S.A.U.—See Danaher Corporation; *U.S. Public*, pg. 629
PALL FILTER (BEIJING) CO., LTD.—See Danaher Corporation; *U.S. Public*, pg. 629
PALL FILTRATION PTE LTD.—See Danaher Corporation; *U.S. Public*, pg. 629
PALL NORDEN AB—See Danaher Corporation; *U.S. Public*, pg. 630
PALL POLAND LTD.—See Danaher Corporation; *U.S. Public*, pg. 630
PALL (SCHWEIZ) AG—See Danaher Corporation; *U.S. Public*, pg. 630
PCI INDUSTRIES INC.; *U.S. Private*, pg. 3120
PEERLESS BLOWERS—See HBD Industries, Inc.; *U.S. Private*, pg. 1887
PERMA-PIPE INTERNATIONAL HOLDINGS, INC.; *U.S. Public*, pg. 1676
PNEUMATIC PRODUCTS CORP.—See SPX Technologies, Inc.; *U.S. Public*, pg. 1921
PRIDE INTERNATIONAL (SHANGHAI)CO., LTD.—See Bright Sheland International Co., Ltd.; *Int'l*, pg. 1162
PROCESS EQUIPMENT INC.—See Carousel Capital Partners; *U.S. Private*, pg. 769
PROVENTIA EMISSION CONTROL OY—See Head Invest Oy; *Int'l*, pg. 3301

PSP INDUSTRIES INC.—See The Herrick Corporation; *U.S. Private*, pg. 4052
PT. DONALDSON FILTRATION INDONESIA—See Donaldson Company, Inc.; *U.S. Public*, pg. 676
P.T. PANATA JAYA MANDIRI—See Donaldson Company, Inc.; *U.S. Public*, pg. 676
PURAFIL, INC.—See Madison Industries Holdings LLC; *U.S. Private*, pg. 2543
PURIFICATION CELLUTIONS, LLC—See Ingevity Corporation; *U.S. Public*, pg. 1122
QUATRO AIR TECHNOLOGIES INC.—See Absolent Air Care Group AB; *Int'l*, pg. 70
RASHED AL-RASHED & SONS-DONALDSON COMPANY LTD.—See Donaldson Company, Inc.; *U.S. Public*, pg. 676
RASTERPUNKT-DRUCKVORSTUFEFURVERPAKUNGEN GMBH—See Matthews International Corporation; *U.S. Public*, pg. 1400
RENSA FILTRATION, INC.—See Audax Group, Limited Partnership; *U.S. Private*, pg. 389
REVCOR, INC.; *U.S. Private*, pg. 3413
ROBINSON FANS, INC.; *U.S. Private*, pg. 3461
SCS FILTRATION PTY LTD—See Atlas Copco AB; *Int'l*, pg. 684
SIA KENTEK LATVIJA—See Diploma PLC; *Int'l*, pg. 2129
SICELUB COLOMBIA LTDA.—See KKR & Co. Inc.; *U.S. Public*, pg. 1242
SICELUB IBERICO S.L.—See KKR & Co. Inc.; *U.S. Public*, pg. 1242
SIMA-SACA—See Haco N.V.; *Int'l*, pg. 3205
SLY, INC.; *U.S. Private*, pg. 3690
SOLBERG MANUFACTURING INC.; *U.S. Private*, pg. 3708
THE SPENCER TURBINE CO.—See Alliance Holdings, Inc.; *U.S. Private*, pg. 183
SPX FLOW TECHNOLOGY AUSTRALIA—See Lone Star Funds; *U.S. Private*, pg. 2486
SPX FLOW TECHNOLOGY USA, INC.—See Lone Star Funds; *U.S. Private*, pg. 2486
STERNVENT CO., INC.—See Durex Inc.; *U.S. Private*, pg. 1293
STF SVENSKA TEXTILFILTER AB—See Daikin Industries, Ltd.; *Int'l*, pg. 1936
STRIONAIR, INC.—See Carrier Global Corporation; *U.S. Public*, pg. 442
STROBIC AIR CORPORATION—See Dominus Capital, L.P.; *U.S. Private*, pg. 1257
SUDDEUTSCHE WOHNUNGSBAU GMBH—See ACS, Actividades de Construccion y Servicios, S.A.; *Int'l*, pg. 114
SURCO PRODUCTS, INC.; *U.S. Private*, pg. 3883
TCF VZDUCHOTECHNIKA LTD.—See Twin City Fan Companies, Ltd.; *U.S. Private*, pg. 4265
TECHNO SCIENCE, INC.—See DIC Corporation; *Int'l*, pg. 2111
TERMOVENT KOMERC D.O.O.—See Arbonia AG; *Int'l*, pg. 538
TERRA UNIVERSAL INC.; *U.S. Private*, pg. 3970
THERMADYNE DE MEXICO S.A. DE C.V.—See Enovis Corporation; *U.S. Public*, pg. 773
TLT BABCOCK EUROPE KFT.—See Enovis Corporation; *U.S. Public*, pg. 773
TLT-BABCOCK, INC.—See The New York Blower Company, Inc.; *U.S. Private*, pg. 4083
TLT BABCOCK INDIA PRIVATE LIMITED—See Enovis Corporation; *U.S. Public*, pg. 773
TOMI ENVIRONMENTAL SOLUTIONS, INC.; *U.S. Public*, pg. 2162
TORIT DCE GMBH—See Donaldson Company, Inc.; *U.S. Public*, pg. 675
TRI-DIM FILTER CORPORATION—See Team Solutions Project Group, Inc.; *U.S. Private*, pg. 3950
TULLP B.V.—See GEA Group Aktiengesellschaft; *Int'l*, pg. 2903
TURBO PRECLEANER INC—See Dreison International, Inc.; *U.S. Private*, pg. 1276
TVS FILTERS—See Align Capital Partners, LLC; *U.S. Private*, pg. 167
TWIN CITY FAN & BLOWER—See Twin City Fan Companies, Ltd.; *U.S. Private*, pg. 4265
TWIN CITY FAN COMPANIES, LTD.; *U.S. Private*, pg. 4265
TWIN CITY VENTCO—See Twin City Fan Companies, Ltd.; *U.S. Private*, pg. 4265
UAB KENTEK LIETUVA—See Diploma PLC; *Int'l*, pg. 2129
ULTRAFILTER AG—See Donaldson Company, Inc.; *U.S. Public*, pg. 676
ULTRAFILTER S.A.S.—See Donaldson Company, Inc.; *U.S. Public*, pg. 675
UV FLU TECHNOLOGIES, INC.; *U.S. Public*, pg. 2268
V2R, LLC—See Revcor, Inc.; *U.S. Private*, pg. 3413
VENTAMATIC LTD.; *U.S. Private*, pg. 4357
VOLKES AIR LIMITED—See SPX Technologies, Inc.; *U.S. Public*, pg. 1921
VORNADO AIR, LLC—See AEA Investors LP; *U.S. Private*, pg. 116
WACO ASSOCIATES INC. - SAN DIEGO OFFICE—See Waco Associates Inc.; *U.S. Private*, pg. 4424
WALKER FILTRATION INC.—See Atlas Copco AB; *Int'l*, pg. 681

WALKER FILTRATION LIMITED—See Atlas Copco AB; *Int'l*, pg. 681
WEB PRODUCTS INC.—See The Lackey Group; *U.S. Private*, pg. 4067
WEMS INC.; *U.S. Private*, pg. 4480
WESTERN FILTER CORPORATION—See Donaldson Company, Inc.; *U.S. Public*, pg. 676
WOOLEE AIRTECH KOREA CO., LTD.—See AIRTECH JAPAN, LTD.; *Int'l*, pg. 249
WUHAN LONGKING EP TECHNOLOGIES CO., LTD—See Fujian Longking Co., Ltd.; *Int'l*, pg. 2818
ZHF (USA), INC.; *U.S. Private*, pg. 4603

333414 — HEATING EQUIPMENT (EXCEPT WARM AIR FURNACES) MANUFACTURING

2G ENERGY INC.—See 2G Energy AG; *Int'l*, pg. 5
AAGES S.A.; *Int'l*, pg. 31
AAVID NIAGARA LLC—See The Goldman Sachs Group, Inc.; *U.S. Public*, pg. 2080
ADVANCED ENERGY SYSTEMS, LLC—See Arthur J. Gallagher & Co.; *U.S. Public*, pg. 202
AFG RUS—See Arbonia AG; *Int'l*, pg. 537
AHASOLAR TECHNOLOGIES LIMITED; *Int'l*, pg. 222
AICHELIN HEAT TREATMENT SYSTEMS (BEIJING) CO., LTD.—See Berndorf AG; *Int'l*, pg. 986
AICHELIN HEAT TREATMENT SYSTEMS INC.—See Berndorf AG; *Int'l*, pg. 986
AICHELIN SERVICE GMBH—See Berndorf AG; *Int'l*, pg. 986
AIR-CON TECHNOLOGIES, INC.—See Regal Rexnord Corporation; *U.S. Public*, pg. 1772
AIRTEX MANUFACTURING PARTNERSHIP; *Int'l*, pg. 249
ALARKO CARRIER SANAYI VE TICARET A.S.—See Alarko Holding A.S.; *Int'l*, pg. 291
ALFA LAVAL AALBORG BV—See Alfa Laval AB; *Int'l*, pg. 308
ALFA LAVAL FRANCE SAS—See Alfa Laval AB; *Int'l*, pg. 309
ALFA-LAVAL IRAN CO.—See Alfa Laval AB; *Int'l*, pg. 311
ALFA-PLAM A.D.; *Int'l*, pg. 314
ALLEARTH RENEWABLES, INC.; *U.S. Private*, pg. 175
AMBRELL B.V.—See inTEST Corporation; *U.S. Public*, pg. 1159
AMBRELL LIMITED—See inTEST Corporation; *U.S. Public*, pg. 1159
AMERICAN WATER HEATER COMPANY—See A. O. Smith Corporation; *U.S. Public*, pg. 11
ANJI TECHNOLOGY CO., LTD.; *Int'l*, pg. 472
A. O. SMITH (CHINA) ENVIRONMENTAL PRODUCTS CO., LTD.—See A. O. Smith Corporation; *U.S. Public*, pg. 11
APM CLIMATE CONTROL SDN. BHD.—See APM Automotive Holdings Berhad; *Int'l*, pg. 516
ARABI INDUSTRIAL SERVICES & SUPPLIES CO.—See Arabi Holding Group Company K.S.C.C.; *Int'l*, pg. 532
ARBONIA MANAGEMENT AG—See Arbonia AG; *Int'l*, pg. 537
ARBONIA RIESA GMBH—See Arbonia AG; *Int'l*, pg. 538
ARBONIA SERVICES AG—See Arbonia AG; *Int'l*, pg. 538
ARBONIA SOLUTIONS AG—See Arbonia AG; *Int'l*, pg. 538
ARCTIC FOX, LLC—See Harbour Group Industries, Inc.; *U.S. Private*, pg. 1860
ATLANTA ENERGY PRIVATE LIMITED—See Atlanta Limited; *Int'l*, pg. 674
ATMOR INDUSTRIES LTD.—See Ariston Holding N.V.; *Int'l*, pg. 567
AUGUST BROTJE GMBH—See BDR Thermea Group B.V.; *Int'l*, pg. 930
AVENIR ENERGIE SA; *Int'l*, pg. 738
BABCOCK-HITACHI DONGFANG BOILER CO., LTD.—See Hitachi, Ltd.; *Int'l*, pg. 3423
BABCOCK WANSON ITALIANA—See CNIM Constructions Industrielles de la Mediterranee SA; *Int'l*, pg. 1677
BABCOCK WANSON UK LTD.—See CNIM Constructions Industrielles de la Mediterranee SA; *Int'l*, pg. 1677
BABCOCK & WILCOX MEGTEC, LLC—See Durr AG; *Int'l*, pg. 2231
BABCOCK & WILCOX ME HOLDINGS LIMITED—See Babcock & Wilcox Enterprises, Inc.; *U.S. Public*, pg. 262
BABCOCK & WILCOX SPIG, INC.—See Babcock & Wilcox Enterprises, Inc.; *U.S. Public*, pg. 262
BADGER FIRE PROTECTION INC.—See Carrier Global Corporation; *U.S. Public*, pg. 440
BAUERHIN-ELEKTRO-WARME GMBH—See Lear Corporation; *U.S. Public*, pg. 1296
BAXI A/S—See BDR Thermea Group B.V.; *Int'l*, pg. 930
BAXI GROUP LTD.—See BDR Thermea Group B.V.; *Int'l*, pg. 930
BAXI POTTERTON LTD.—See BDR Thermea Group B.V.; *Int'l*, pg. 930
BAXI S.P.A.—See BDR Thermea Group B.V.; *Int'l*, pg. 930
BCS MANAGMENT COMPANY—See Vari Corporation; *U.S. Private*, pg. 4346
BEARWARD ENGINEERING LIMITED—See Westinghouse Air Brake Technologies Corporation; *U.S. Public*, pg. 2357
BEARWARD LIMITED—See Westinghouse Air Brake Tech-

333414 — HEATING EQUIPMENT (...

nologies Corporation; *U.S. Public*, pg. 2357
BEIJING AILIYANG SOLAR ENERGY TECHNOLOGY CO. LTD.—See China Solar & Clean Energy Solutions, Inc.; *Int'l*, pg. 1552
BEIJING DELI SOLAR TECHNOLOGY DEVELOPMENT CO., LTD.—See China Solar & Clean Energy Solutions, Inc.; *Int'l*, pg. 1552
BEN ARNOLD CO., INC.; *U.S. Private*, pg. 522
BERNDORF BADERBAU DEUTSCHLAND GMBH—See Berndorf AG; *Int'l*, pg. 986
BLACK & DECKER (THAILAND) LIMITED—See Stanley Black & Decker, Inc.; *U.S. Public*, pg. 1936
BLOOM COMBUSTION (INDIA) PRIVATE LTD.—See Caledonia Investments plc; *Int'l*, pg. 1262
BLOOM ENGINEERING CO. INC.—See Caledonia Investments plc; *Int'l*, pg. 1262
BLUE SKY ENERGY; *U.S. Private*, pg. 593
BOUSTEAD INTERNATIONAL HEATERS LIMITED—See Boustead Singapore Limited; *Int'l*, pg. 1120
BOYERTOWN FOUNDRY COMPANY—See Mestek, Inc.; *U.S. Public*, pg. 1426
BRADFORD-WHITE CORPORATION; *U.S. Private*, pg. 632
BROEN FINLAND OY—See Aalberts N.V.; *Int'l*, pg. 33
BROEN LTD.—See Aalberts N.V.; *Int'l*, pg. 33
BROEN RAUFOSS AB—See Aalberts N.V.; *Int'l*, pg. 33
BROEN VALVES (BEIJING) CO., LTD.—See Aalberts N.V.; *Int'l*, pg. 33
BROEN-ZAWGAZ SP. Z.O.O.—See Aalberts N.V.; *Int'l*, pg. 33
CANEFCO LIMITED; *Int'l*, pg. 1289
CATARACT STEEL INDUSTRIES, INC.; *U.S. Private*, pg. 787
CENTREX TECHNICAL SALES, LLC; *U.S. Private*, pg. 829
CHEMIDRO S.P.A.—See Bharti Enterprises Limited; *Int'l*, pg. 1012
CHINA CREATIVE GLOBAL HOLDINGS LIMITED; *Int'l*, pg. 1496
CHINVEST SAS; *Int'l*, pg. 1571
CLARY SOLAR; *U.S. Private*, pg. 915
CLEARVUE (ASIA) PTE.LTD.—See ClearVue Technologies Limited; *Int'l*, pg. 1657
COEN COMPANY, INC.—See Koch Industries, Inc.; *U.S. Private*, pg. 2331
CONERGY INDIA—See Kawa Capital Management, Inc.; *U.S. Private*, pg. 2266
CORONA CORPORATION; *Int'l*, pg. 1802
CREOTECH INSTRUMENTS S.A.; *Int'l*, pg. 1839
DAI-ICHI HIGH FREQUENCY CO., LTD.; *Int'l*, pg. 1917
DANFOSS GESELLSCHAFT M.B.H.—See Danfoss A/S; *Int'l*, pg. 1960
DANFOSS GMBH—See Danfoss A/S; *Int'l*, pg. 1960
DANFOSS HAGO INC.—See Danfoss A/S; *Int'l*, pg. 1960
DANFOSS HEATING DIVISION—See Danfoss A/S; *Int'l*, pg. 1960
DANFOSS HEAT PUMPS UK LTD.—See Danfoss A/S; *Int'l*, pg. 1960
DANFOSS INC.—See Danfoss A/S; *Int'l*, pg. 1960
DANFOSS MICRO CHANNEL HEAT EXCHANGER (JIAXING) CO., LTD.—See Danfoss A/S; *Int'l*, pg. 1960
DANFOSS OTOMASYON VE URUNLERI TIC LTD.—See Danfoss A/S; *Int'l*, pg. 1960
DE DIETRICH PROCESS SYSTEMS S.A.; *Int'l*, pg. 1995
DENKI KOGYO (CHANGZHOU) HEAT TREATMENT EQUIPMENT CO., LTD.—See DKK Co., Ltd.; *Int'l*, pg. 2139
DENKO TECHNO HEAT CO., LTD.—See DKK Co., Ltd.; *Int'l*, pg. 2139
DENSO FUKUSHIMA CORPORATION—See Denso Corporation; *Int'l*, pg. 2031
DENSO SISTEMAS TERMICOS ESPANA S.A.—See Denso Corporation; *Int'l*, pg. 2030
DESA LLC—See H.I.G. Capital, LLC; *U.S. Private*, pg. 1829
DE-STA-CO SHANGHAI CO., LTD.—See Stabilus; *U.S. Private*, pg. 3774
DETROIT STOKER CO.; *U.S. Private*, pg. 1216
DKK MANUFACTURING (THAILAND) CO., LTD.—See DKK Co., Ltd.; *Int'l*, pg. 2139
DOMNICK HUNTER GROUP LTD.—See Parker Hannifin Corporation; *U.S. Public*, pg. 1645
DOMOTEC SA—See Ariston Thermo S.p.A.; *Int'l*, pg. 567
DRU BELGIUM—See DRU Verwarming B.V.; *Int'l*, pg. 2206
DRU VERWARMING B.V.; *Int'l*, pg. 2206
DUCOMMUN AEROSTRUCTURES—See Ducommun Incorporated; *U.S. Public*, pg. 690
EBARA REFRIGERATION EQUIPMENT & SYSTEMS CO., LTD.—See Ebara Corporation; *Int'l*, pg. 2283
ECLIPSE INC.—See Honeywell International Inc.; *U.S. Public*, pg. 1047
ECOLIBRIUM SOLAR, INC.—See Tenex Capital Management, L.P.; *U.S. Private*, pg. 3966
ECOMB AB; *Int'l*, pg. 2296
EFD INDUCTION AB—See Arendals Fossekompani ASA; *Int'l*, pg. 558
EFD INDUCTION AS—See Arendals Fossekompani ASA; *Int'l*, pg. 558
EFD INDUCTION CO. LTD.—See Arendals Fossekompani ASA; *Int'l*, pg. 558
EFD INDUCTION GES.M.B.H—See Arendals Fossekompani ASA; *Int'l*, pg. 558
EFD INDUCTION GMBH—See Arendals Fossekompani ASA; *Int'l*, pg. 558
EFD INDUCTION INC.—See Arendals Fossekompani ASA; *Int'l*, pg. 558
EFD INDUCTION K.K.—See Arendals Fossekompani ASA; *Int'l*, pg. 558
EFD INDUCTION LTDA.—See Arendals Fossekompani ASA; *Int'l*, pg. 559
EFD INDUCTION LTD.—See Arendals Fossekompani ASA; *Int'l*, pg. 559
EFD INDUCTION PVT. LTD.—See Arendals Fossekompani ASA; *Int'l*, pg. 559
EFD INDUCTION S.A—See Arendals Fossekompani ASA; *Int'l*, pg. 559
EFD INDUCTION (SHANGHAI) CO. LTD.—See Arendals Fossekompani ASA; *Int'l*, pg. 558
EFD INDUCTION SL—See Arendals Fossekompani ASA; *Int'l*, pg. 559
EFD INDUCTION SP. Z O O—See Arendals Fossekompani ASA; *Int'l*, pg. 559
EFD INDUCTION SRL—See Arendals Fossekompani ASA; *Int'l*, pg. 559
EFM SALES COMPANY—See Vari Corporation; *U.S. Private*, pg. 4346
ELCO DO BRAZIL LTDA.—See Regal Rexnord Corporation; *U.S. Public*, pg. 1773
EMA INDIA LTD.; *Int'l*, pg. 2372
EMBASSY INDUSTRIES, INC.—See Mestek, Inc.; *U.S. Public*, pg. 1426
ENDLESS SOLAR CORPORATION PTY LIMITED; *Int'l*, pg. 2403
ENFINITY FRANCE SARL—See Enfinity N.V.; *Int'l*, pg. 2425
ENFINITY ITALIA SRL—See Enfinity N.V.; *Int'l*, pg. 2425
ENFINITY PHILIPPINES RENEWABLE RESOURCES INC.—See Enfinity N.V.; *Int'l*, pg. 2425
ENFINITY THAILAND LIMITED—See Enfinity N.V.; *Int'l*, pg. 2425
ENOGIA SA; *Int'l*, pg. 2444
ENSIGN RIBBON BURNERS, LLC—See Lionheart Ventures; *U.S. Private*, pg. 2464
ENTECH SA; *Int'l*, pg. 2450
EPIC ENERGY LTD. - NAVI MUMBAI WORKS—See Epic Energy Ltd.; *Int'l*, pg. 2460
EV PARKING SERVICE CO., LTD.; *Int'l*, pg. 2560
FIVES NORTH AMERICAN COMBUSTION, INC.—See FIVES, Societe Anonyme; *Int'l*, pg. 2696
FLAMCO B.V.—See Aalberts N.V.; *Int'l*, pg. 34
FLAMCO FLEXCON B.V.—See Aalberts N.V.; *Int'l*, pg. 34
FLAMCO GMBH—See Aalberts N.V.; *Int'l*, pg. 34
FLAMCO S.A.R.L.—See Aalberts N.V.; *Int'l*, pg. 34
FLATWORK TECHNOLOGIES LLC; *U.S. Private*, pg. 1541
FORNEY CORPORATION—See Graham Holdings Company; *U.S. Public*, pg. 954
FUJI ELECTRIC (ZHUHAI) CO., LTD.—See Fuji Electric Co., Ltd.; *Int'l*, pg. 2811
GAS-FIRED PRODUCTS, INC.; *U.S. Private*, pg. 1648
GAS-FIRED PRODUCTS (U.K.) LTD.—See Gas-Fired Products, Inc.; *U.S. Private*, pg. 1648
GEMINA TERMIX PRODUCTION A/S—See Danfoss A/S; *Int'l*, pg. 1961
GIANT FACTORIES INC.—See A. O. Smith Corporation; *U.S. Public*, pg. 12
GLOBAL WARMING SOLUTIONS, INC.; *U.S. Public*, pg. 945
GREENTECH ENERGIESYSTEME GMBH—See Christof Holding AG; *Int'l*, pg. 1587
GROUPE OUELLET CANADA INC.; *Int'l*, pg. 3109
GRUPO TERMOINDUSTRIAL ECA, S.A. DE C.V.; *Int'l*, pg. 3137
GUANGZHOU DEVOTION DOMESTIC BOILERS MANUFACTURING CO. LTD.—See Devotion Energy Group Limited; *Int'l*, pg. 2090
GUANGZHOU DEVOTION THERMAL FACILITY CO., LTD.—See Devotion Energy Group Limited; *Int'l*, pg. 2090
GUANGZHOU SEAGULL KITCHEN & BATH PRODUCTS CO., LTD.; *Int'l*, pg. 3167
HANWHA Q CELLS AUSTRALIA PTY. LTD.—See Hanwha Group; *Int'l*, pg. 3265
HANWHA Q CELLS JAPAN CO., LTD.—See Hanwha Group; *Int'l*, pg. 3265
HANWHA Q CELLS MALAYSIA—See Hanwha Group; *Int'l*, pg. 3265
HANWHA Q CELLS USA CORP.—See Hanwha Group; *Int'l*, pg. 3265
HANWHA SOLAR AMERICA LLC—See Hanwha Group; *Int'l*, pg. 3265
HANWHA SOLARONE GMBH—See Hanwha Group; *Int'l*, pg. 3265
HANWHA SOLARONE (SHANGHAI) CO., LTD.—See Hanwha Group; *Int'l*, pg. 3265
HANWHA SOLARONE TECHNOLOGY CO., LTD.—See Hanwha Group; *Int'l*, pg. 3265
HAUCK MANUFACTURING COMPANY—See Honeywell International Inc.; *U.S. Public*, pg. 1048
HAYWARD POOL PRODUCTS CANADA, INC.—See CCMP Capital Advisors, LP; *U.S. Private*, pg. 800
HAYWARD POOL PRODUCTS CANADA, INC.—See MSD Capital, L.P.; *U.S. Private*, pg. 2807
H.B. SMITH CO., INC.; *U.S. Private*, pg. 1825
HDT GLOBAL, INC.—See Nexus Capital Management LP; *U.S. Private*, pg. 2922
HEARTH & HOME TECHNOLOGIES, INC.—See HNI Corporation; *U.S. Public*, pg. 1043
HEAT AUTHORITY, LLC—See Thermon Group Holdings, Inc.; *U.S. Public*, pg. 2155
HEATRAE SAIDIA HEATING LTD.—See BDR Thermea Group B.V.; *Int'l*, pg. 930
HEIZKORPER PROLUX AG—See Arbonia AG; *Int'l*, pg. 538
HEURTEY PETROCHEM GMBH—See Heurtey Petrochem SA; *Int'l*, pg. 3366
HEURTEY PETROCHEM INDIA PVT LTD—See Heurtey Petrochem SA; *Int'l*, pg. 3366
HORN GLASS INDUSTRIES AG—See Certina Holding AG; *Int'l*, pg. 1423
IBC SOLAR A.E.—See IBC Solar AG; *Int'l*, pg. 3569
IBC SOLAR AUSTRIA GMBH—See IBC Solar AG; *Int'l*, pg. 3569
IBC SOLAR B.V.—See IBC Solar AG; *Int'l*, pg. 3569
IBC SOLAR PROJECTS PRIVATE LIMITED—See IBC Solar AG; *Int'l*, pg. 3570
IBC SOLAR SRL—See IBC Solar AG; *Int'l*, pg. 3570
IBC SOLAR TEKNIK SDN BHD—See IBC Solar AG; *Int'l*, pg. 3570
ICMA RETIREMENT CORPORATION; *Int'l*, pg. 3582
ICMA S.A.; *Int'l*, pg. 3582
INNOVATIVE HEARTH PRODUCTS—See TRM Equity LLC; *U.S. Private*, pg. 4241
INTERNATIONAL COMFORT PRODUCTS CORPORATION—See Carrier Global Corporation; *U.S. Public*, pg. 442
JENSEN METAL PRODUCTS INC.; *U.S. Private*, pg. 2201
JOHNSON GAS APPLIANCE CO.; *U.S. Private*, pg. 2228
JOHN ZINK INTERNATIONAL LUXEMBOURG S.A.R.L.—See Koch Industries, Inc.; *U.S. Private*, pg. 2331
JOHN ZINK KEU GMBH—See Koch Industries, Inc.; *U.S. Private*, pg. 2331
JOTUL AS—See OpenGate Capital Management, LLC; *U.S. Private*, pg. 3030
JOTUL HISPANIA, S.L.—See OpenGate Capital Management, LLC; *U.S. Private*, pg. 3030
JOTUL ITALIA SRL—See OpenGate Capital Management, LLC; *U.S. Private*, pg. 3030
JOTUL NORTH AMERICA INC.—See OpenGate Capital Management, LLC; *U.S. Private*, pg. 3030
JOTUL POLSKA SP. Z O.O.—See OpenGate Capital Management, LLC; *U.S. Private*, pg. 3030
KANMOR CONTROL SYSTEMS LTD.—See Watts Water Technologies, Inc.; *U.S. Public*, pg. 4352
KEMCO SYSTEMS, CO. LLC—See CECO Environmental Corp.; *U.S. Public*, pg. 463
KERMI SP.Z.O.O.—See Arbonia AG; *Int'l*, pg. 538
KFXO-TV—See News-Press & Gazette Company; *U.S. Private*, pg. 2917
KOCH-ASIA PACIFIC, INC. - JOHN ZINK ASIA-PACIFIC DIVISION—See Koch Industries, Inc.; *U.S. Private*, pg. 2332
KOCH HEAT TRANSFER CANADA, LP—See Koch Industries, Inc.; *U.S. Private*, pg. 2332
KUNSHAN DOWA THERMO FURNACE CO., LTD.—See Dowa Holdings Co., Ltd.; *Int'l*, pg. 2184
LAM RESEARCH HOLDING GMBH—See Lam Research Corporation; *U.S. Public*, pg. 1289
L.B. WHITE COMPANY INC.; *U.S. Private*, pg. 2364
LPI, INC.; *U.S. Private*, pg. 2507
MARSHALL EXCELSIOR COMPANY—See Dover Corporation; *U.S. Public*, pg. 679
MAXON B.V.—See Honeywell International Inc.; *U.S. Public*, pg. 1048
MAXON COMBUSTION SYSTEMS AB—See Honeywell International Inc.; *U.S. Public*, pg. 1048
MAXON COMBUSTION SYSTEMS A/S—See Honeywell International Inc.; *U.S. Public*, pg. 1048
MAXON COMBUSTION SYSTEMS LTD.—See Honeywell International Inc.; *U.S. Public*, pg. 1048
MAXON CORPORATION—See Honeywell International Inc.; *U.S. Public*, pg. 1048
MAXON GMBH—See Honeywell International Inc.; *U.S. Public*, pg. 1048
MAXON GMBH—See Honeywell International Inc.; *U.S. Public*, pg. 1048
MAXON S.A.R.L.—See Honeywell International Inc.; *U.S. Public*, pg. 1048
MEIBES METALL-TECHNIK SP. Z.O.O.—See Aalberts N.V.; *Int'l*, pg. 35
MEIBES SK S.R.O.—See Aalberts N.V.; *Int'l*, pg. 35
MEIBES S.R.O.—See Aalberts N.V.; *Int'l*, pg. 35
MEIBES SYSTEM-TECHNIK GMBH—See Aalberts N.V.; *Int'l*, pg. 35
MESSERSCHMID ENERGIESYSTEME GMBH—See EnBW Energie Baden-Wurttemberg AG; *Int'l*, pg. 2399
MESTEK CANADA INC.—See Mestek, Inc.; *U.S. Public*, pg. 1426

N.A.I.C.S. INDEX

MIDCO INTERNATIONAL, INC.; *U.S. Private*, pg. 2710
MODINE PLIEZHAUSEN GMBH—See Modine Manufacturing Company; *U.S. Public*, pg. 1455
MONESSEN HOLDING COMPANY—See HNI Corporation; *U.S. Public*, pg. 1043
MUNSTER SIMMS ENGINEERING LIMITED—See Brunswick Corporation; *U.S. Public*, pg. 408
NATIONAL PRESTO INDUSTRIES, INC; *U.S. Public*, pg. 1497
NEDERLANDSE RADIATEUREN FABRIEK BV—See Banco Products (I) Ltd.; *Int'l*, pg. 824
NEW YORKER BOILER CO. INC.—See Burnham Holdings, Inc.; *U.S. Public*, pg. 412
NEXTRACKER INC.; *U.S. Public*, pg. 1527
NIHON DENNETSU CO., LTD.—See Air Water Inc.; *Int'l*, pg. 240
NRF POLAND SPOLKA. Z.O.O—See Banco Products (I) Ltd.; *Int'l*, pg. 824
OASIS MATERIALS CORPORATION—See Arsenal Capital Management LP; *U.S. Private*, pg. 338
OUELLET CANADA INC.—See Groupe Ouellet Canada Inc.; *Int'l*, pg. 3109
OWL OIL INC.; *U.S. Private*, pg. 3055
PARKER HANNIFIN CORP. FILTRATION & SEPARATION DIVISION—See Parker Hannifin Corporation; *U.S. Public*, pg. 1645
PARKER HANNIFIN STRATOFLEX—See Parker Hannifin Corporation; *U.S. Public*, pg. 1646
POWER FLAME INC.—See Astec Industries, Inc.; *U.S. Public*, pg. 216
PRODUCTIVE HEAT TREATMENT CO. LTD.—See Chen Hsong Holdings Ltd.; *Int'l*, pg. 1464
PT ALFA LAVAL INDONESIA—See Alfa Laval AB; *Int'l*, pg. 312
PUMC HOLDING CORPORATION; *U.S. Private*, pg. 3303
PVI INDUSTRIES LLC—See Watts Water Technologies, Inc.; *U.S. Public*, pg. 2337
PV REPOWER INC.—See Abalance Corporation Ltd.; *Int'l*, pg. 48
RAAB KARCHER SANITAR HEIZUNG FLIESEN GMBH—See Compagnie de Saint-Gobain SA; *Int'l*, pg. 1733
RENESOLA SINGAPORE PTE. LTD.—See EMEREN GROUP LTD; *U.S. Public*, pg. 739
RESEAU ENERGIES SAS—See Brookfield Corporation; *Int'l*, pg. 1188
RESERVOIRS X. PAUCHARD—See FAYAT SAS; *Int'l*, pg. 2626
RIELLO CANADA INC.—See Carrier Global Corporation; *U.S. Public*, pg. 444
RIELLO HUNGARY KERESKEDELMI ZARTKORUEN MUKODO RESZVENYTARSASAG—See Carrier Global Corporation; *U.S. Public*, pg. 444
RIELLO LTD.—See Carrier Global Corporation; *U.S. Public*, pg. 444
RIELLO RO S.R.L.—See Carrier Global Corporation; *U.S. Public*, pg. 444
RILEY POWER, INC.—See Babcock Power, Inc.; *U.S. Private*, pg. 422
ROTEX HEATING SYSTEMS GMBH—See Daikin Industries, Ltd.; *Int'l*, pg. 1934
ROTEX POLSKA SP. Z O.O.—See Daikin Industries, Ltd.; *Int'l*, pg. 1936
RUG RIELLO URZADZENIA GRZEWCZE SA—See Carrier Global Corporation; *U.S. Public*, pg. 444
RUTLAND PRODUCTS, INC.—See Rutland Products Co.; *U.S. Public*, pg. 3508
R.W. BECKETT CORPORATION; *U.S. Private*, pg. 3340
SABIANA S.P.A.—See Arbonia AG; *Int'l*, pg. 538
SAFED SUISSE S.A.—See Berndorf AG; *Int'l*, pg. 987
SALUS NORTH AMERICA, INC.—See Computime Group Limited; *Int'l*, pg. 1761
SAS CLIPS HIOLLE—See Hiolle Industries S.A.; *Int'l*, pg. 3401
SCHWANK INC.; *U.S. Private*, pg. 3572
SCHWANK INC.—See Schwank Inc.; *U.S. Private*, pg. 3572
SECURITE CHEMINEES INTERNATIONAL LTEE—See Lennox International Inc.; *U.S. Public*, pg. 1308
SHANGHAI DATUN ENERGY RESOURCES TECHNOLOGY DEVELOPMENT COMPANY LIMITED—See China Coal Energy Company Limited; *Int'l*, pg. 1490
SIMPLEX ARMATUREN & SYSTEME GMBH—See Aalberts N.V.; *Int'l*, pg. 35
SLANT/FIN CORPORATION; *U.S. Private*, pg. 3687
SLANT/FIN, LTD/LTEE.—See Slant/Fin Corporation; *U.S. Private*, pg. 3687
SOFINTER S.P.A.—See Gammon India Limited; *Int'l*, pg. 2879
SOLARAY CORPORATION; *U.S. Private*, pg. 3707
SOLAHMAX TECHNOLOGY, INC.; *U.S. Public*, pg. 1900
SOLARTECH UNIVERSAL CORP.; *U.S. Public*, pg. 3708
SPECIFIED AIR SOLUTIONS LLC—See Madison Industries Holdings LLC; *U.S. Private*, pg. 2543
SPX PROCESS EQUIPMENT—See SPX Technologies, Inc.; *U.S. Public*, pg. 1921
STABILIS SOLUTIONS, INC.; *U.S. Public*, pg. 1924
STAMM INTERNATIONAL CORPORATION; *U.S. Private*, pg. 3777

STANDARD FORGED PRODUCTS, LLC—See Arcosa, Inc.; *U.S. Public*, pg. 186
S.T. JOHNSON CO.; *U.S. Private*, pg. 3519
SUNEARTH, INC.—See Solaray Corporation; *U.S. Private*, pg. 3707
SWEQUIPOS, S.A. DE C.V.—See Schlumberger Limited; *U.S. Public*, pg. 1846
TACO INCORPORATED; *U.S. Private*, pg. 3920
TALLERES DEL AGUA SL—See Fluidra SA; *Int'l*, pg. 2714
TENNANT CEE GMBH—See Tennant Company; *U.S. Public*, pg. 2016
TENNANT CLEANING SYSTEM & EQUIPMENT CO. LTD.—See Tennant Company; *U.S. Public*, pg. 2016
TENNANT SALES & SERVICE SPAIN S.A.—See Tennant Company; *U.S. Public*, pg. 2016
THERMASYS, CORP.—See Wellspring Capital Management LLC; *U.S. Private*, pg. 4478
THERMAX BABCOCK & WILCOX ENERGY SOLUTIONS PRIVATE LIMITED—See Babcock & Wilcox Enterprises, Inc.; *U.S. Public*, pg. 263
THERMON AUSTRALIA PTY. LTD.—See Thermon Group Holdings, Inc.; *U.S. Public*, pg. 2155
THERMON FAR EAST, LTD.—See Thermon Group Holdings, Inc.; *U.S. Public*, pg. 2155
THERMON FRANCE SAS—See Thermon Group Holdings, Inc.; *U.S. Public*, pg. 2155
THERMO PRODUCTS, LLC—See Burnham Holdings, Inc.; *U.S. Public*, pg. 412
THERMOR—See Atlantic Societe Francaise Develop Thermique S.A.; *Int'l*, pg. 675
THERMOWATT PROFESSIONAL S.R.L.—See Ariston Holding N.V.; *Int'l*, pg. 567
TRANTECH RADIATOR PRODUCTS, INC.—See Industrial Opportunity Partners, LLC; *U.S. Private*, pg. 2067
TRAVIS INDUSTRIES INC.; *U.S. Private*, pg. 4214
TUTELAR OIL SERVICES CO. (PVT) LTD.—See Desh Garments Limited; *Int'l*, pg. 2045
UNITED STATES STOVE COMPANY; *U.S. Private*, pg. 4300
UPONOR NORTH AMERICA—See Georg Fischer AG; *Int'l*, pg. 2938
UPONOR USA—See Georg Fischer AG; *Int'l*, pg. 2938
VARI CORPORATION; *U.S. Private*, pg. 4346
WATLOW AUSTRALIA PTY. LTD.—See Tinicum Enterprises, Inc.; *U.S. Private*, pg. 4174
WATLOW DE MEXICO S.A. DE C.V.—See Tinicum Enterprises, Inc.; *U.S. Private*, pg. 4175
WATLOW ENGINEERING—See Tinicum Enterprises, Inc.; *U.S. Private*, pg. 4174
WATLOW POLYMER TECHNOLOGIES, INC.—See Tinicum Enterprises, Inc.; *U.S. Private*, pg. 4174
WATLOW ST. LOUIS, INC.—See Tinicum Enterprises, Inc.; *U.S. Private*, pg. 4175
WEIL-MCLAIN—See SPX Technologies, Inc.; *U.S. Public*, pg. 1922
WILLIAMS FURNACE CO.—See Bee Street Holdings LLC; *U.S. Private*, pg. 513
WOLF GMBH—See CENTROTEC SE; *Int'l*, pg. 1415
WUXI JIACHENG SOLAR ENERGY TECHNOLOGY CO., LTD.—See EMEREN GROUP LTD; *U.S. Public*, pg. 739

333415 — AIR-CONDITIONING AND WARM AIR HEATING EQUIPMENT AND COMMERCIAL AND INDUSTRIAL REFRIGERATION EQUIPMENT MANUFACTURING

9R LIMITED; *Int'l*, pg. 17
AAON, INC.; *U.S. Public*, pg. 12
ABB AUTOMATION TECHNOLOGIES AB—See ABB Ltd.; *Int'l*, pg. 49
ABEL BUILDING SOLUTIONS—See ANSA McAl Limited; *Int'l*, pg. 477
ABSAL COMPANY; *Int'l*, pg. 69
ACMA ENGINEERS PRIVATE LIMITED—See Acma Ltd.; *Int'l*, pg. 107
ACS GROUP, INC.—See Harbour Group Industries, Inc.; *U.S. Private*, pg. 1860
ADAMS MFG. CO.; *U.S. Private*, pg. 74
ADAMS THERMAL SYSTEMS, INC.; *U.S. Private*, pg. 75
ADELT MECHANICAL WORKS LTD.—See ENGIE SA; *Int'l*, pg. 2430
ADVANCED DISTRIBUTOR PRODUCTS LLC—See Lennox International Inc.; *U.S. Public*, pg. 1307
ADVANTIX SYSTEMS; *U.S. Private*, pg. 95
AEC, INC.—See Harbour Group Industries, Inc.; *U.S. Private*, pg. 1860
AERIS ENVIRONMENTAL LLC—See Aeris Environmental Ltd; *Int'l*, pg. 180
AEROFIN CORP—See Ampco-Pittsburgh Corporation; *U.S. Public*, pg. 126
AHI CARRIER FZC—See Carrier Global Corporation; *U.S. Public*, pg. 440
AHMET YAR REFRIGERATING INDUSTRY CO.—See Carrier Global Corporation; *U.S. Public*, pg. 441
AHT COOLING SYSTEMS GMBH—See Daikin Industries, Ltd.; *Int'l*, pg. 1932
AIR CHANGE INTERNATIONAL LIMITED; *Int'l*, pg. 236

AIR CHANGE PTY LTD—See Air Change International Limited; *Int'l*, pg. 236
AIRCONDITIONING DIRECT PTY. LTD.—See Beijer Ref AB; *Int'l*, pg. 943
AIREDALE AIR CONDITIONING S.A. PTY LTD—See Modine Manufacturing Company; *U.S. Public*, pg. 1454
AIREDALE GROUP LIMITED—See Modine Manufacturing Company; *U.S. Public*, pg. 1454
AIREDALE NORTH AMERICA, INC.—See Modine Manufacturing Company; *U.S. Public*, pg. 1454
AIREX INC.; *Int'l*, pg. 247
AIR INSTAL B.V.—See CENTROTEC SE; *Int'l*, pg. 1414
AIRLINE PETROLEUM, CO.—See Santarelli & Sons Oil Co., Inc.; *U.S. Private*, pg. 3548
AIR ROVER, INC.—See Guardian Capital Partners, LLC; *U.S. Private*, pg. 1810
AIR SYSTEM COMPONENTS, INC.—See Canada Pension Plan Investment Board; *Int'l*, pg. 1278
AIRTEX MANUFACTURING PARTNERSHIP - CALGARY HEAT TRANSFER PLANT—See Airtex Manufacturing Partnership; *Int'l*, pg. 249
AIRTEX MANUFACTURING PARTNERSHIP - EDMONTON FACTORY—See Airtex Manufacturing Partnership; *Int'l*, pg. 249
AIRTEX MANUFACTURING PARTNERSHIP - NEWMARKET FACTORY—See Airtex Manufacturing Partnership; *Int'l*, pg. 249
AIRVANCE GROUP; *Int'l*, pg. 250
AIR WATER SAFETY SERVICE INC.—See Air Water Inc.; *Int'l*, pg. 239
ALCO CONTROLS SPOL. S.R.O.—See Emerson Electric Co.; *U.S. Public*, pg. 745
ALDES AERAULIQUE SAS; *Int'l*, pg. 304
ALFA LAVAL HES SA—See Alfa Laval AB; *Int'l*, pg. 309
ALFA LAVAL ITALY S.R.L.—See Alfa Laval AB; *Int'l*, pg. 312
ALFA LAVAL LTDA—See Alfa Laval AB; *Int'l*, pg. 310
ALFA LAVAL NEW ZEELAND PTY. LTD.—See Alfa Laval AB; *Int'l*, pg. 312
ALFA LAVAL NORDICK AB—See Alfa Laval AB; *Int'l*, pg. 310
ALFA LAVAL (PORTUGAL) LDA—See Alfa Laval AB; *Int'l*, pg. 308
ALFA LAVAL S.A.S—See Alfa Laval AB; *Int'l*, pg. 311
ALFA LAVAL (SHANGHAI) TECHNOLOGIES CO LTD—See Alfa Laval AB; *Int'l*, pg. 308
ALFA LAVAL (TAICANG) TECHNOLOGIES CO. LTD.—See Alfa Laval AB; *Int'l*, pg. 308
ALFA LAVAL TECHNOLOGIES EQUIPMENT AND SERVICE SOLUTIONS LLC—See Alfa Laval AB; *Int'l*, pg. 312
ALFA LAVAL VANTAA OY—See Alfa Laval AB; *Int'l*, pg. 310
ALLIED AIR ENTERPRISES INC.—See Lennox International Inc.; *U.S. Public*, pg. 1307
AMBER ENTERPRISES INDIA LIMITED; *Int'l*, pg. 414
AMERICAN AIR FILTER INTERNATIONAL, INC.—See Daikin Industries, Ltd.; *Int'l*, pg. 1936
AMERICAN AIR FILTER MANUFACTURING SDN. BHD.—See Daikin Industries, Ltd.; *Int'l*, pg. 1932
AMETEK HUGHES-TREITLER—See AMETEK, Inc.; *U.S. Public*, pg. 116
AMETEK THERMAL SYSTEMS, INC—See AMETEK, Inc.; *U.S. Public*, pg. 119
ANDREWS SYKES GROUP PLC; *Int'l*, pg. 452
APPLIED COOLING TECHNOLOGY LLC—See DMI UK Ltd.; *Int'l*, pg. 2145
ARAGONESA DE POSTVENTA S.L.U.—See Brookfield Corporation; *Int'l*, pg. 1188
THE ARCTICOM GROUP, LLC; *U.S. Private*, pg. 3987
ARISTON THERMO S.P.A.; *Int'l*, pg. 567
ARKTON SP. Z O.O.—See Berling S.A.; *Int'l*, pg. 986
ARMATURENWERK ALTENBURG GMBH—See BITZER SE; *Int'l*, pg. 1051
ARMCOR AIR SOLUTIONS PTY. LTD.—See Beijer Ref AB; *Int'l*, pg. 943
ARROW FLUID POWER—See Arrow Pneumatics Inc.; *U.S. Private*, pg. 335
ARROW PNEUMATICS INC.; *U.S. Private*, pg. 335
ARTIC TEMP, INC.—See Imperial Brown Inc.; *U.S. Private*, pg. 2049
ASAHI KOGYOSHA CO., LTD. - EQUIPMENT DIVISION—See Asahi Kogyosha Co., Ltd.; *Int'l*, pg. 598
AS SISUSTAJA—See Carrier Global Corporation; *U.S. Public*, pg. 441
ATLANTIC CLIMATISATION ET VENTILATION S.A.S.—See Atlantic Societe Francaise Develop Thermique S.A.; *Int'l*, pg. 675
ATLANTIC DUCT CLEANING, INC.—See The Operand Group II LLC; *U.S. Private*, pg. 4088
ATLANTIC SFDT—See Atlantic Societe Francaise Develop Thermique S.A.; *Int'l*, pg. 675
AUSTCOLD REFRIGERATION PTY LTD—See Enovis Corporation; *U.S. Public*, pg. 770
AUSTIN LAZ & COMPANY PLC.; *Int'l*, pg. 718
AUSTRALIAN AIRCONDITIONING DISTRIBUTORS PTY. LTD.—See Beijer Ref AB; *Int'l*, pg. 943
AUTOMOTIVE CLIMATE CONTROL, INC.; *U.S. Private*, pg. 400
AUTORAD, INC.—See Alfa Laval AB; *Int'l*, pg. 309
AZ KLIMA A.S.—See CEZ, a.s.; *Int'l*, pg. 1426
BABCOCK WANSON ESPANA SA—See CNIM Construc-

tions Industrielles de la Mediterranee SA; *Int'l*, pg. 1677
BAC COOLING SYSTEMS (SUZHOU) CO., LTD.—See AMSTED Industries Incorporated; *U.S. Private*, pg. 267
BAC DALIAN CO., LTD.—See AMSTED Industries Incorporated; *U.S. Private*, pg. 267
BAC JAPAN CO., LTD.—See AMSTED Industries Incorporated; *U.S. Private*, pg. 267
BAC MALAYSIA, SDN. BHD.—See AMSTED Industries Incorporated; *U.S. Private*, pg. 267
BALCKE-DUERR ITALIANA, S.R.L.—See SPX Technologies, Inc.; *U.S. Public*, pg. 1921
BALLY REFRIGERATED BOXES, INC.—See United Refrigeration, Inc.; *U.S. Private*, pg. 4296
BALTIC MASTER—See Carrier Global Corporation; *U.S. Public*, pg. 441
BALTIMORE AIRCOIL AUST. PTY.LTD.—See AMSTED Industries Incorporated; *U.S. Private*, pg. 267
BALTIMORE AIRCOIL COMPANY S.A. (PTY) LTD.—See AMSTED Industries Incorporated; *U.S. Private*, pg. 268
BALTIMORE AIRCOIL COMPANY—See AMSTED Industries Incorporated; *U.S. Private*, pg. 267
BALTIMORE AIRCOIL INTERNATIONAL NV—See AMSTED Industries Incorporated; *U.S. Private*, pg. 267
BALTIMORE AIRCOIL ITALIA S.R.L.—See AMSTED Industries Incorporated; *U.S. Private*, pg. 267
BARD MANUFACTURING COMPANY; *U.S. Private*, pg. 473
BAR INDUSTRIESERVICE GMBH—See Bilfinger SE; *Int'l*, pg. 1024
BARKELL LIMITED—See Modine Manufacturing Company; *U.S. Public*, pg. 1455
BASX, LLC—See AAON, Inc.; *U.S. Public*, pg. 12
B/E AEROSPACE THERMAL & POWER MANAGEMENT—See RTX Corporation; *U.S. Public*, pg. 1822
BEIJER REF AB; *Int'l*, pg. 943
BEIJER REF BELGIUM B.V.—See Beijer Ref AB; *Int'l*, pg. 944
BEIJER REF LITHUANIA UAB—See Beijer Ref AB; *Int'l*, pg. 944
BEIJER REF SUPPORT NORWAY AS—See Beijer Ref AB; *Int'l*, pg. 944
BELIMO AB—See BELIMO Holding AG; *Int'l*, pg. 964
BELIMO AIRCONTROLS (USA), INC.—See BELIMO Holding AG; *Int'l*, pg. 964
BELIMO AUTOMATION DEUTSCHLAND GMBH—See BELIMO Holding AG; *Int'l*, pg. 964
BELIMO AUTOMATION INDIA PRIVATE LIMITED—See BELIMO Holding AG; *Int'l*, pg. 965
BELIMO AUTOMATION MALAYSIA SDN. BHD.—See BELIMO Holding AG; *Int'l*, pg. 964
BELIMO AUTOMATION (SHANGHAI) CO., LTD.—See BELIMO Holding AG; *Int'l*, pg. 965
BELIMO BELGIUM B.V.—See BELIMO Holding AG; *Int'l*, pg. 965
BELIMO FINLAND OY—See BELIMO Holding AG; *Int'l*, pg. 965
BELIMO HOLDING AG; *Int'l*, pg. 964
BELIMO ITALIA S.R.L.—See BELIMO Holding AG; *Int'l*, pg. 965
BELIMO TECHNOLOGY (USA), INC.—See BELIMO Holding AG; *Int'l*, pg. 965
BELIMO TURKEY OTOMASYON A.S.—See BELIMO Holding AG; *Int'l*, pg. 965
BEPCO, INC.; *U.S. Private*, pg. 529
BEREVA S.R.L.—See BELIMO Holding AG; *Int'l*, pg. 965
BEVERAGE-AIR CO.—See Haier Smart Home Co., Ltd.; *Int'l*, pg. 3210
BGR ENERGY SYSTEMS LIMITED - AIR FIN COOLER DIVISION—See BGR Energy Systems Limited; *Int'l*, pg. 1008
B. GRIMM GROUP; *Int'l*, pg. 788
BHARAT REFRIGERATIONS PRIVATE LIMITED—See Ice Make Refrigeration Ltd.; *Int'l*, pg. 3579
BIMI INTERNATIONAL MEDICAL INC.; *Int'l*, pg. 1032
BINGSHAN REFRIGERATION & HEAT TECHNOLOGIES CO., LTD.; *Int'l*, pg. 1033
BITZER ANDINA SPA—See BITZER SE; *Int'l*, pg. 1051
BITZER AUSTRALIA PTY LIMITED—See BITZER SE; *Int'l*, pg. 1051
BITZER ELECTRONICS A/S—See BITZER SE; *Int'l*, pg. 1051
BITZER INDUSTRIAL EQUIPMENT (BEIJING) CO., LTD.—See BITZER SE; *Int'l*, pg. 1051
BITZER INVERTERTECHNOLOGIE GMBH—See BITZER SE; *Int'l*, pg. 1051
BITZER KENYA LTD.—See BITZER SE; *Int'l*, pg. 1051
BITZER KUHLMASCHINENBAU GMBH—See BITZER SE; *Int'l*, pg. 1051
BITZER KUHLMASCHINENBAU SCHKEUDITZ GMBH—See BITZER SE; *Int'l*, pg. 1051
BITZER NEW ZEALAND PTY. LTD.—See BITZER SE; *Int'l*, pg. 1051
BITZER SA—See BITZER SE; *Int'l*, pg. 1051
BITZER SE—See BITZER SE; *Int'l*, pg. 1052
BITZER SL—See BITZER SE; *Int'l*, pg. 1052
BITZER US, INC.—See BITZER SE; *Int'l*, pg. 1052

BLACK DIAMOND PLUMBING & MECHANICAL, INC.; *U.S. Private*, pg. 571
BLISS REFRIGERATION LTD.—See GEA Group Aktiengesellschaft; *Int'l*, pg. 2897
BLUEFORS OY—See DevCo Partners Oy; *Int'l*, pg. 2086
BLUE STAR LIMITED; *Int'l*, pg. 1070
BLUE STAR LIMITED - THANE FACILITY—See Blue Star Limited; *Int'l*, pg. 1070
BLUE STAR LTD.—See Blue Star Limited; *Int'l*, pg. 1070
BLUE STAR LTD.—See Blue Star Limited; *Int'l*, pg. 1070
BLUE STAR LTD.—See Blue Star Limited; *Int'l*, pg. 1070
BLUE STAR LTD.—See Blue Star Limited; *Int'l*, pg. 1070
BLUE STAR NORTH AMERICA INC.—See Blue Star Limited; *Int'l*, pg. 1070
BMB ENTERPRISES; *U.S. Private*, pg. 600
BOREAL INTERNATIONAL CORPORATION—See Watsco, Inc.; *U.S. Public*, pg. 2336
BRINK CLIMATE SYSTEMS B.V.—See CENTROTEC SE; *Int'l*, pg. 1414
BRINK CLIMATE SYSTEMS DEUTSCHLAND GMBH—See CENTROTEC SE; *Int'l*, pg. 1414
BRITANNIA KITCHEN VENTILATION LIMITED—See The Middleby Corporation; *U.S. Public*, pg. 2115
BROKERBAY INC.—See Carrier Global Corporation; *U.S. Public*, pg. 440
BUNDY KFT—See Sun Capital Partners, Inc.; *U.S. Private*, pg. 3861
BUNDY REFRIGERACAO BRASIL IND E COMERCIO—See Sun Capital Partners, Inc.; *U.S. Private*, pg. 3861
BUNDY REFRIGERATION INTERNATIONAL HOLDING B.V.—See Sun Capital Partners, Inc.; *U.S. Private*, pg. 3861
BUNDY REFRIGERATION SP. ZO.O.—See Sun Capital Partners, Inc.; *U.S. Private*, pg. 3861
BUNDY REFRIGERATION S.R.L.—See Sun Capital Partners, Inc.; *U.S. Private*, pg. 3861
CALDERYS FRANCE SAS—See Groupe Bruxelles Lambert SA; *Int'l*, pg. 3099
CALIQUA AG—See ENGIE SA; *Int'l*, pg. 2429
CALIQUA POWERTEC GMBH—See ENGIE SA; *Int'l*, pg. 2429
CAREL ELECTRONIC SUZHOU LTD.—See Carel Industries S.p.A.; *Int'l*, pg. 1324
CAREL RUSSIA LLC—See Carel Industries S.p.A.; *Int'l*, pg. 1324
CARLISLE HARDCAST EUROPE B.V.—See Carlisle Companies Incorporated; *U.S. Public*, pg. 436
CARLISLE HARDCAST INC.—See Carlisle Companies Incorporated; *U.S. Public*, pg. 436
CARRIER AIRCONDITIONING & REFRIGERATION LIMITED—See Carrier Global Corporation; *U.S. Public*, pg. 440
CARRIER AIR CONDITIONING SALES & SERVICE (SHANGHAI) CO LTD—See Carrier Global Corporation; *U.S. Public*, pg. 440
CARRIER AIRCON LANKA PRIVATE LIMITED—See Carrier Global Corporation; *U.S. Public*, pg. 440
CARRIER AKTIEBOLAG—See Carrier Global Corporation; *U.S. Public*, pg. 440
CARRIER AUSTRALIA PTY LTD—See Carrier Global Corporation; *U.S. Public*, pg. 440
CARRIER CHLADIACA TECHNIKA SLOVAKIA S.R.O.—See Carrier Global Corporation; *U.S. Public*, pg. 440
CARRIER CHLADICI TECHNIKA SPOL. S.R.O.—See Carrier Global Corporation; *U.S. Public*, pg. 441
CARRIER CHLODNICTWO POLSKA SP. Z O.O.—See Carrier Global Corporation; *U.S. Public*, pg. 441
CARRIER ENTERPRISE CANADA, L.P.—See Watsco, Inc.; *U.S. Public*, pg. 2336
CARRIER ENTERPRISE MEXICO S. DE R.L. DE C.V.—See Watsco, Inc.; *U.S. Public*, pg. 2336
CARRIER GUAM, INC.—See Carrier Global Corporation; *U.S. Public*, pg. 442
CARRIER HUTESTECHNIKA FORGALMAZO MAGYARORSZAG KFT—See Carrier Global Corporation; *U.S. Public*, pg. 441
CARRIER KALTETECHNIK AUSTRIA GES.M.B.—See Carrier Global Corporation; *U.S. Public*, pg. 441
CARRIER KALTETECHNIK DEUTSCHLAND GMBH—See Carrier Global Corporation; *U.S. Public*, pg. 441
CARRIER KALTETECHNIK SCHWEIZ AG—See Carrier Global Corporation; *U.S. Public*, pg. 441
CARRIER MEXICO S.A. DE C.V.—See Carrier Global Corporation; *U.S. Public*, pg. 442
CARRIER MIDEA INDIA PRIVATE LIMITED—See Carrier Global Corporation; *U.S. Public*, pg. 442
CARRIER REFRIGERATION DENMARK A/S—See Carrier Global Corporation; *U.S. Public*, pg. 443
CARRIER REFRIGERATION IRELAND—See Carrier Global Corporation; *U.S. Public*, pg. 441
CARRIER REFRIGERATION NORWAY AS—See Carrier Global Corporation; *U.S. Public*, pg. 443
CARRIER REFRIGERATION OPERATION ITALY SPA—See Carrier Global Corporation; *U.S. Public*, pg. 441
CARRIER REFRIGERATION UK LTD.—See Carrier Global Corporation; *U.S. Public*, pg. 443
CARRIER RENTAL SYSTEMS ASIA PTE LTD—See Carrier Global Corporation; *U.S. Public*, pg. 443
CARRIER RENTAL SYSTEMS (UK) LIMITED—See Carrier Global Corporation; *U.S. Public*, pg. 443
CARRIER TRANSICOLD HONG KONG LIMITED—See Carrier Global Corporation; *U.S. Public*, pg. 443
CARRIER TRANSICOLD SCANDINAVIA A/S—See Carrier Global Corporation; *U.S. Public*, pg. 443
CARRIER TRANSICOLD—See Penn Power Group, LLC; *U.S. Private*, pg. 3134
CARRIER TRANSICOLD (UK) LIMITED—See Carrier Global Corporation; *U.S. Public*, pg. 443
CASTELMAC, S.P.A.—See Ali Holding S.r.l; *Int'l*, pg. 321
CEI ENTERPRISES, INC.—See Astec Industries, Inc.; *U.S. Public*, pg. 216
CHANGSHU TIANYIN ELECTROMECHANICAL CO., LTD.; *Int'l*, pg. 1444
CHARLES HASLER AG—See Beijer Ref AB; *Int'l*, pg. 944
CHIGO HOLDING LIMITED; *Int'l*, pg. 1478
CHINA ENERGY TECHNOLOGY CORP., LTD.; *Int'l*, pg. 1500
CHO THAVEE THERMOTECH COMPANY LIMITED—See Cho Thavee Public Company Limited; *Int'l*, pg. 1576
CHUBB DEUTSCHLAND GMBH—See Carrier Global Corporation; *U.S. Public*, pg. 443
CHUGAI AIR SYSTEM CO., LTD.—See Chugai Ro Co., Ltd.; *Int'l*, pg. 1594
C.I. GROUP PUBLIC COMPANY LIMITED; *Int'l*, pg. 1243
CK COMPANY CO., LTD.; *Int'l*, pg. 1636
CLASSIC AIR'S ONE HOUR HEATING & AIR CONDITIONING; *U.S. Private*, pg. 916
CLIMAESPACO—See ENGIE SA; *Int'l*, pg. 2431
CLIMATE & CONTROLS BENELUX B.V.—See Carrier Global Corporation; *U.S. Public*, pg. 443
CLIMATE PROS, LLC—See Saw Mill Capital LLC; *U.S. Private*, pg. 3557
CLIMATE TECHNOLOGIES PTY LTD; *Int'l*, pg. 1659
CLIMESPACE—See ENGIE SA; *Int'l*, pg. 2431
COFELY AXIMA—See ENGIE SA; *Int'l*, pg. 2429
COFELY KALTETECHNIK GMBH—See ENGIE SA; *Int'l*, pg. 2430
COLBY EQUIPMENT COMPANY INC.; *U.S. Private*, pg. 965
COLCAB (PTY) LTD.—See TRG Management LP; *U.S. Private*, pg. 4220
COMBAT HVAC LIMITED—See Madison Industries Holdings LLC; *U.S. Private*, pg. 2543
COMFORT EXPERT B.V.—See CENTROTEC SE; *Int'l*, pg. 1414
COMFORT INSTITUTE, INC.—See Aeroseal, LLC; *U.S. Private*, pg. 119
COMFORT-SERVICE PJSC; *Int'l*, pg. 1711
COMPONENTES DELFA, C.A.—See General Motors Company; *U.S. Public*, pg. 923
CONCEPCION CARRIER AIR CONDITIONING CORPORATION—See Concepcion Industrial Corporation; *Int'l*, pg. 1764
CONDARIA 87 S.R.L.—See Dometic Group AB; *Int'l*, pg. 2160
CONTROLLED TEMP SUPPLY, LLC—See Gryphon Investors, LLC; *U.S. Private*, pg. 1798
COOLERADO CORP; *U.S. Private*, pg. 1039
COOLING TECHNOLOGY BY NATURAL GAS CO. (GAS CHILL) S.A.E.—See Egyptian Kuwaiti Holding; *Int'l*, pg. 2327
COPELAND CANADA, LTD.—See Emerson Electric Co.; *U.S. Public*, pg. 742
COPELAND CORPORATION LLC—See Emerson Electric Co.; *U.S. Public*, pg. 743
COPELAND GMBH—See Emerson Electric Co.; *U.S. Public*, pg. 743
COPELAND ITALIA S.A.R.L.—See Emerson Electric Co.; *U.S. Public*, pg. 744
CORNELIUS INC. - GLENDALE HEIGHTS—See Berkshire Hathaway Inc.; *U.S. Public*, pg. 309
CROWNTONKA CALIFORNIA, INC.—See Rainey Road Holdings, Inc.; *U.S. Private*, pg. 3348
CROWNTONKA, INC.—See Rainey Road Holdings, Inc.; *U.S. Private*, pg. 3347
CRYOMECH, INC.—See DevCo Partners Oy; *Int'l*, pg. 2086
CUSTOM COILS INC.—See US Holdings Corporation; *U.S. Private*, pg. 4319
DAEWOO ELECTRONICS CORPORATION—See Dongbu Group; *Int'l*, pg. 2165
DAI-DAN CO LTD - TECHNICAL DEVELOPMENT DIVISION—See DAI-DAN Co Ltd; *Int'l*, pg. 1917
DAI-DAN SERVICE KANTO CO., LTD.—See DAI-DAN Co Ltd; *Int'l*, pg. 1917
DAIKIN AC (AMERICAS), INC.—See Daikin Industries, Ltd.; *Int'l*, pg. 1932
DAIKIN AC SPAIN, S.A.—See Daikin Industries, Ltd.; *Int'l*, pg. 1932
DAIKIN AIRCONDITIONING BELGIUM NV—See Daikin Industries, Ltd.; *Int'l*, pg. 1933
DAIKIN AIRCONDITIONING CENTRAL EUROPE GMBH—See Daikin Industries, Ltd.; *Int'l*, pg. 1933
DAIKIN AIRCONDITIONING FRANCE SAS—See Daikin Industries, Ltd.; *Int'l*, pg. 1933
DAIKIN AIRCONDITIONING GERMANY GMBH—See Dai-

N.A.I.C.S. INDEX

333415 — AIR-CONDITIONING AN...

kin Industries, Ltd.; *Int'l*, pg. 1933
DAIKIN AIRCONDITIONING (HONG KONG) LTD.—See Daikin Industries, Ltd.; *Int'l*, pg. 1933
DAIKIN AIRCONDITIONING INDIA PVT. LTD. - RAJASTHAN FACTORY—See Daikin Industries, Ltd.; *Int'l*, pg. 1933
DAIKIN AIRCONDITIONING ITALY S.P.A.—See Daikin Industries, Ltd.; *Int'l*, pg. 1933
DAIKIN AIR CONDITIONING (M) SDN. BHD.—See Daikin Industries, Ltd.; *Int'l*, pg. 1932
DAIKIN AIRCONDITIONING NETHERLANDS B.V.—See Daikin Industries, Ltd.; *Int'l*, pg. 1933
DAIKIN AIRCONDITIONING PHILIPPINES, INC.—See Daikin Industries, Ltd.; *Int'l*, pg. 1933
DAIKIN AIR-CONDITIONING (SHANGHAI) CO., LTD. - HUIZHOU BRANCH—See Daikin Industries, Ltd.; *Int'l*, pg. 1933
DAIKIN AIR-CONDITIONING (SHANGHAI) CO., LTD.—See Daikin Industries, Ltd.; *Int'l*, pg. 1933
DAIKIN AIR CONDITIONING SINGAPORE PTE. LTD.—See Daikin Industries, Ltd.; *Int'l*, pg. 1933
DAIKIN AIRCONDITIONING SOUTH AFRICA PTY. LTD.—See Daikin Industries, Ltd.; *Int'l*, pg. 1933
DAIKIN AIR-CONDITIONING TECHNOLOGY (SHANGHAI), LTD.—See Daikin Industries, Ltd.; *Int'l*, pg. 1933
DAIKIN AIRCONDITIONING (THAILAND) LTD.—See Daikin Industries, Ltd.; *Int'l*, pg. 1933
DAIKIN AIRCONDITIONING U.K., LTD.—See Daikin Industries, Ltd.; *Int'l*, pg. 1933
DAIKIN AMERICA, INC.—See Daikin Industries, Ltd.; *Int'l*, pg. 1933
DAIKIN APPLIED AMERICAS INC.—See Daikin Industries, Ltd.; *Int'l*, pg. 1936
DAIKIN APPLIED EUROPE S.P.A.—See Daikin Industries, Ltd.; *Int'l*, pg. 1933
DAIKIN APPLIED SYSTEMS CO., LTD.—See Daikin Industries, Ltd.; *Int'l*, pg. 1933
DAIKIN APPLIED (UK) LTD.—See Daikin Industries, Ltd.; *Int'l*, pg. 1933
DAIKIN ASIA SERVICING PTE., LTD.—See Daikin Industries, Ltd.; *Int'l*, pg. 1934
DAIKIN AUSTRALIA PTY. LTD.—See Daikin Industries, Ltd.; *Int'l*, pg. 1934
DAIKIN CHEMICAL EUROPE GMBH—See Daikin Industries, Ltd.; *Int'l*, pg. 1934
DAIKIN (CHINA) INVESTMENT CO., LTD.—See Daikin Industries, Ltd.; *Int'l*, pg. 1932
DAIKIN COMPRESSOR INDUSTRIES, LTD.—See Daikin Industries, Ltd.; *Int'l*, pg. 1934
DAIKIN DEVICE CZECH REPUBLIC S.R.O.—See Daikin Industries, Ltd.; *Int'l*, pg. 1934
DAIKIN ELECTRONIC DEVICES MALAYSIA SDN. BHD.—See Daikin Industries, Ltd.; *Int'l*, pg. 1934
DAIKIN EUROPE COORDINATION CENTER NV—See Daikin Industries, Ltd.; *Int'l*, pg. 1934
DAIKIN EUROPE N.V.—See Daikin Industries, Ltd.; *Int'l*, pg. 1934
DAIKIN FLUOROCHEMICALS (CHINA) CO., LTD.—See Daikin Industries, Ltd.; *Int'l*, pg. 1934
DAIKIN FLUORO COATINGS (SHANGHAI) CO., LTD.—See Daikin Industries, Ltd.; *Int'l*, pg. 1934
DAIKIN FUORO COATINGS (SHANGHAI) CO., LTD.—See Daikin Industries, Ltd.; *Int'l*, pg. 1934
DAIKIN HVAC SOLUTION HOKKAIDO CO., LTD.—See Daikin Industries, Ltd.; *Int'l*, pg. 1934
DAIKIN HVAC SOLUTION NIIGATA CO., LTD.—See Daikin Industries, Ltd.; *Int'l*, pg. 1934
DAIKIN INDUSTRIES, LTD. - KANAOKA FACTORY—See Daikin Industries, Ltd.; *Int'l*, pg. 1934
DAIKIN INDUSTRIES, LTD. - RINKAI FACTORY—See Daikin Industries, Ltd.; *Int'l*, pg. 1934
DAIKIN INDUSTRIES, LTD. - SHIGA PLANT—See Daikin Industries, Ltd.; *Int'l*, pg. 1934
DAIKIN INDUSTRIES, LTD.; *Int'l*, pg. 1932
DAIKIN INDUSTRIES (THAILAND) LTD.—See Daikin Industries, Ltd.; *Int'l*, pg. 1934
DAIKIN ISITMA VE SOGUTMA SISTEMLERI SANAYI TICARET A.S.—See Daikin Industries, Ltd.; *Int'l*, pg. 1934
DAIKIN KOREA CO., LTD.—See Daikin Industries, Ltd.; *Int'l*, pg. 1934
DAIKIN MALAYSIA SDN. BHD.—See Daikin Industries, Ltd.; *Int'l*, pg. 1935
DAIKIN MANUFACTURING GERMANY GMBH—See Daikin Industries, Ltd.; *Int'l*, pg. 1935
DAIKIN MARINE (SHANGHAI) CO., LTD.—See Daikin Industries, Ltd.; *Int'l*, pg. 1935
DAIKIN MCQUAY AR CONDICIONADO BRASIL LTDA.—See Daikin Industries, Ltd.; *Int'l*, pg. 1932
DAIKIN MIDDLE EAST & AFRICA FZE—See Daikin Industries, Ltd.; *Int'l*, pg. 1935
DAIKIN MR ENGINEERING CO., LTD.—See Daikin Industries, Ltd.; *Int'l*, pg. 1934
DAIKIN REFRIGERATION MALAYSIA SDN. BHD.—See Daikin Industries, Ltd.; *Int'l*, pg. 1935
DAIKIN RESEARCH & DEVELOPMENT MALAYSIA SDN. BHD.—See Daikin Industries, Ltd.; *Int'l*, pg. 1935
DAIKIN STEEL MALAYSIA SDN. BHD.—See Daikin Industries, Ltd.; *Int'l*, pg. 1935

DAIKIN TRADING (THAILAND) LTD.—See Daikin Industries, Ltd.; *Int'l*, pg. 1935
DAIWA INDUSTRIES LTD.; *Int'l*, pg. 1947
DANFOSS COMMERCIAL COMPRESSORS LTD.—See Danfoss A/S; *Int'l*, pg. 1959
DANTHERM COOLING INC.—See Dansk Industri Invest A/S; *Int'l*, pg. 1968
DATA AIRE, INC.—See Construction Specialties, Inc.; *U.S. Private*, pg. 1024
DEFLECTO CANADA LIMITED—See Jordan Industries, Inc.; *U.S. Private*, pg. 2235
DELTA-T CORP.—See Madison Industries Holdings LLC; *U.S. Private*, pg. 2543
DEM PRODUCTION AB—See Beijer Ref AB; *Int'l*, pg. 944
DENSO AIRCOOL CORPORATION—See Denso Corporation; *Int'l*, pg. 2031
DENSO AIR SYSTEMS CZECH S.R.O—See Denso Corporation; *Int'l*, pg. 2029
DENSO AIR SYSTEMS MICHIGAN, INC.—See Denso Corporation; *Int'l*, pg. 2029
DENSO AIR SYSTEMS TOYOSHINA CORPORATION—See Denso Corporation; *Int'l*, pg. 2029
DENSO MANUFACTURING CZECH S.R.O.—See Denso Corporation; *Int'l*, pg. 2031
DENSO THERMAL SYSTEMS POLSKA SP.Z.O.O.—See Denso Corporation; *Int'l*, pg. 2031
DESMON S.P.A.—See The Middleby Corporation; *U.S. Public*, pg. 2113
DLVA, INC.; *U.S. Private*, pg. 1248
DOMETIC ASIA CO. LTD.—See Dometic Group AB; *Int'l*, pg. 2160
DOMETIC AUSTRIA GMBH—See Dometic Group AB; *Int'l*, pg. 2160
DOMETIC BENELUX B.V.—See Dometic Group AB; *Int'l*, pg. 2160
DOMETIC DENMARK A/S—See Dometic Group AB; *Int'l*, pg. 2160
DOMETIC DEUTSCHLAND GMBH—See Dometic Group AB; *Int'l*, pg. 2160
DOMETIC FINLAND OY—See Dometic Group AB; *Int'l*, pg. 2160
DOMETIC ITALY S.R.L.—See Dometic Group AB; *Int'l*, pg. 2160
DOMETIC KK—See Dometic Group AB; *Int'l*, pg. 2160
DOMETIC KOREA CO., LTD.—See Dometic Group AB; *Int'l*, pg. 2160
DOMETIC MIDDLE EAST FZCO—See Dometic Group AB; *Int'l*, pg. 2160
DOMETIC MX, S DE RL DE CV—See Dometic Group AB; *Int'l*, pg. 2160
DOMETIC NEW ZEALAND LTD.—See Dometic Group AB; *Int'l*, pg. 2160
DOMETIC NORWAY AS—See Dometic Group AB; *Int'l*, pg. 2160
DOMETIC POLAND SPOLKA Z OGRANICZONA ODPOWIEDZIALNOSCIA—See Dometic Group AB; *Int'l*, pg. 2160
DOMETIC PTE. LTD.—See Dometic Group AB; *Int'l*, pg. 2160
DOMETIC (PTY) LTD.—See Dometic Group AB; *Int'l*, pg. 2160
DOMETIC RUS LIMITED LIABILITY COMPANY—See Dometic Group AB; *Int'l*, pg. 2160
DOMETIC S.A.S—See Dometic Group AB; *Int'l*, pg. 2160
DOMETIC SEITZ AB—See Dometic Group AB; *Int'l*, pg. 2160
DOMETIC (SHENZHEN) TRADING CO. LTD.—See Dometic Group AB; *Int'l*, pg. 2160
DOMETIC SLOVAKIA S.R.O.—See Dometic Group AB; *Int'l*, pg. 2160
DOMETIC SPAIN SL—See Dometic Group AB; *Int'l*, pg. 2160
DOMETIC SWITZERLAND AG—See Dometic Group AB; *Int'l*, pg. 2160
DOVER ENGINEERED SYSTEMS, INC.—See Dover Corporation; *U.S. Public*, pg. 679
DRESDNER KUHLANLAGENBAU GMBH—See Dussmann Stiftung & Co. KGaA; *Int'l*, pg. 2233
DRI-EAZ PRODUCTS, INC.—See RPM International Inc.; *U.S. Public*, pg. 1816
DUCTSOX CORPORATION—See Rite-Hite Holding Corporation; *U.S. Private*, pg. 3442
DUNHAM-BUSH, INC.—See Berjaya Corporation Berhad; *Int'l*, pg. 984
DUNHAM-BUSH (MALAYSIA) BERHAD—See Berjaya Corporation Berhad; *Int'l*, pg. 984
DURO DYNE CORPORATION; *U.S. Private*, pg. 1293
DYNAC SDN. BHD.; *Int'l*, pg. 2238
DYNAIR INC.—See Carlisle Companies Incorporated; *U.S. Public*, pg. 436
ECM TECHNOLOGIES SAS; *Int'l*, pg. 2292
ECODYNE HEAT EXCHANGERS, INC.—See Berkshire Hathaway Inc.; *U.S. Public*, pg. 311
EID S.A.S.—See Beijer Ref AB; *Int'l*, pg. 944
ELECTRA CONSUMER PRODUCTS (1970) LTD.—See Elco Limited; *Int'l*, pg. 2345
ELECTRONIC MODULAR SERVICES LIMITED—See Car-

rier Global Corporation; *U.S. Public*, pg. 443
EMERSON CLIMATE TECHNOLOGIES, INC.—See Emerson Electric Co.; *U.S. Public*, pg. 743
EMERSON CLIMATE TECHNOLOGIES MEXICO SA DE CV—See Emerson Electric Co.; *U.S. Public*, pg. 744
EMERSON COMERCIO EM TECNOLOGIA DE CLIMATIZACAO LTDA—See Emerson Electric Co.; *U.S. Public*, pg. 744
EMERSON NETWORK POWER ITALIA—See Vertiv Holdings Co; *U.S. Public*, pg. 2288
ENERGY LABS INC.—See Vertiv Holdings Co; *U.S. Public*, pg. 2289
ENGINIA S.R.L.—See Carel Industries S.p.A.; *Int'l*, pg. 1324
ENO S.A.S.; *Int'l*, pg. 2444
ENRAD AB; *Int'l*, pg. 2445
ENTEREX INTERNATIONAL LIMITED; *Int'l*, pg. 2450
EPTA S.P.A.; *Int'l*, pg. 2466
ESI CONTROLS LTD.—See Addtech AB; *Int'l*, pg. 133
ETABLISSEMENTS BRANCHER S.A.S.—See Lennox International Inc.; *U.S. Public*, pg. 1307
FAIVELEY RAILWAY TRADING CO., LTD.—See Westinghouse Air Brake Technologies Corporation; *U.S. Public*, pg. 2357
FAIVELEY TRANSPORT LEIPZIG GMBH & CO KG—See Westinghouse Air Brake Technologies Corporation; *U.S. Public*, pg. 2357
FAR EAST REFRIGERATION (M) SDN. BHD.—See Far East Group Limited; *Int'l*, pg. 2616
FEDDERS ELECTRIC AND ENGINEERING LIMITED; *Int'l*, pg. 2629
FILTER QUEEN INC.—See HMI Industries Inc.; *U.S. Private*, pg. 1955
FISEN CORP.; *U.S. Private*, pg. 1533
FLAMCO KFT.—See Aalberts N.V.; *Int'l*, pg. 34
FOGCO SYSTEMS INC.—See Pinewell Capital LLC; *U.S. Private*, pg. 3184
FOSTORIA INDUSTRIES, INC.—See TPI Corp.; *U.S. Private*, pg. 4200
FRIGINOX—See Ali Holding S.r.l.; *Int'l*, pg. 321
FRIGOBLOCK GROSSKOPF GMBH—See Ingersoll Rand Inc.; *U.S. Public*, pg. 1120
FRIGOGLASS S.A.I.C.; *Int'l*, pg. 2792
FRIGOTEHNICA S.A.—See Axxess Capital; *Int'l*, pg. 772
FRIGRITE REFRIGERATION PTY LTD—See Crayon Group AS; *Int'l*, pg. 1829
FRIULINOX ALI SPA—See Ali Holding S.r.l.; *Int'l*, pg. 321
FUJINE SANGYO CO., LTD.—See Alconix Corporation; *Int'l*, pg. 302
FUJITSU GENERAL AMERICA, INC.—See Fujitsu Limited; *Int'l*, pg. 2833
GAC CORPORATION - ANJO PLANT—See Denso Corporation; *Int'l*, pg. 2032
GAC CORPORATION—See Denso Corporation; *Int'l*, pg. 2032
GACTEL TURNKEY PROJECTS LIMITED—See Gammon India Limited; *Int'l*, pg. 2879
GAMKO B.V.—See Illinois Tool Works Inc.; *U.S. Public*, pg. 1103
GAROVAGLIO & ZORRAQUIN SA; *Int'l*, pg. 2886
GASCO AFFILIATES, LLC—See CI Capital Partners LLC; *U.S. Private*, pg. 895
GEA AEROFREEZE SYSTEMS, INC.—See GEA Group Aktiengesellschaft; *Int'l*, pg. 2897
GEA AWP GMBH—See GEA Group Aktiengesellschaft; *Int'l*, pg. 2897
GEA EGI ENERGIAGAZDALKODASI ZRT.—See GEA Group Aktiengesellschaft; *Int'l*, pg. 2898
GEA GENEGLACE S.A.S.—See GEA Group Aktiengesellschaft; *Int'l*, pg. 2899
GEA GRASSO PHILIPPINES, INC.—See GEA Group Aktiengesellschaft; *Int'l*, pg. 2902
GEA GRASSO (THAILAND) CO. LTD.—See GEA Group Aktiengesellschaft; *Int'l*, pg. 2902
GEA GRASSO TOV—See GEA Group Aktiengesellschaft; *Int'l*, pg. 2902
GEA GRASSO UAB—See GEA Group Aktiengesellschaft; *Int'l*, pg. 2902
GEA GRENCO LTD.—See GEA Group Aktiengesellschaft; *Int'l*, pg. 2899
GEA ISISAN TESISAT INSAAT TAAHHUT TICARET VE SANAYI A.S.—See GEA Group Aktiengesellschaft; *Int'l*, pg. 2899
GEA KLIMATYZACJA SPOLKA Z O.O.—See GEA Group Aktiengesellschaft; *Int'l*, pg. 2899
GEA LYOPHIL GMBH—See GEA Group Aktiengesellschaft; *Int'l*, pg. 2899
GEA PHARMA SYSTEMS AG—See GEA Group Aktiengesellschaft; *Int'l*, pg. 2901
GEA PROCESS ENGINEERING LTD.—See GEA Group Aktiengesellschaft; *Int'l*, pg. 2901
GEA PROCESS ENGINEERING S.A.S.—See GEA Group Aktiengesellschaft; *Int'l*, pg. 2902
GEA PROCESS ENGINEERING Z O.O.—See GEA Group Aktiengesellschaft; *Int'l*, pg. 2902
GEA REFRIGERATION AFRICA (PTY) LTD.—See GEA Group Aktiengesellschaft; *Int'l*, pg. 2902
GEA REFRIGERATION FRANCE SAS—See Ardian SAS; *Int'l*, pg. 556

333415 — AIR-CONDITIONING AN...

GEA REFRIGERATION GERMANY GMBH—See GEA Group Aktiengesellschaft; *Int'l*, pg. 2902
GEA REFRIGERATION IBERICA S.A.—See GEA Group Aktiengesellschaft; *Int'l*, pg. 2902
GEA REFRIGERATION PHILIPPINES, INC.—See GEA Group Aktiengesellschaft; *Int'l*, pg. 2902
GEA REFRIGERATION ROMANIA S.R.L.—See GEA Group Aktiengesellschaft; *Int'l*, pg. 2902
GEA REFRIGERATION TECHNOLOGIES GMBH—See GEA Group Aktiengesellschaft; *Int'l*, pg. 2902
GEA REFRIGERATION TECHNOLOGIES INDIA PVT LTD.—See GEA Group Aktiengesellschaft; *Int'l*, pg. 2903
GEA REFRIGERATION TECHNOLOGIES IRELAND—See GEA Group Aktiengesellschaft; *Int'l*, pg. 2903
GEA REFRIGERATION TECHNOLOGIES—See GEA Group Aktiengesellschaft; *Int'l*, pg. 2902
GEA REFRIGERATION TECHNOLOGY CO., LTD.—See GEA Group Aktiengesellschaft; *Int'l*, pg. 2903
GEA REFRIGERATION TECHNOLOGY (SUZHOU) CO., LTD.—See GEA Group Aktiengesellschaft; *Int'l*, pg. 2903
GEA REFRIGERATION (THAILAND) CO. LTD.—See GEA Group Aktiengesellschaft; *Int'l*, pg. 2902
GEA REFRIGERATION UK LTD.—See GEA Group Aktiengesellschaft; *Int'l*, pg. 2903
GEA REFRIGERATION VIETNAM CO. LTD.—See GEA Group Aktiengesellschaft; *Int'l*, pg. 2903
GEA SISTEMAS DE RESFRIAMENTO LTDA.—See GEA Group Aktiengesellschaft; *Int'l*, pg. 2903
GEI INDUSTRIAL SYSTEMS LTD.; *Int'l*, pg. 2912
GEM REFRIGERATOR COMPANY, INC.; *U.S. Private*, pg. 1657
GENERAL FILTERS, INC.; *U.S. Private*, pg. 1665
GENTHERM ASIA PACIFIC INCORPORATED—See Gentherm Incorporated; *U.S. Public*, pg. 931
GK DRIVE SYSTEMS (SUZHOU) CO., LTD.—See Dana Incorporated; *U.S. Public*, pg. 623
GLACIER BAY TECHNOLOGY; *U.S. Private*, pg. 1704
GOLDSTEIN ESWOOD COMMERCIAL COOKING PTY LTD—See The Middleby Corporation; *U.S. Public*, pg. 2114
GOODMAN GLOBAL, INC.—See Daikin Industries, Ltd.; *Int'l*, pg. 1935
GOODMAN MANUFACTURING COMPANY, L.P.—See Daikin Industries, Ltd.; *Int'l*, pg. 1935
GORDON BROTHERS INDUSTRIES PTY. LIMITED - BENDIGO FACTORY—See Gordon Brothers Industries Pty. Limited; *Int'l*, pg. 3042
GRASSO COMPONENTES IBERICA LDA.—See GEA Group Aktiengesellschaft; *Int'l*, pg. 2903
GRASSO REFRIGERATION SYSTEMS SHANGHAI CO., LTD.—See GEA Group Aktiengesellschaft; *Int'l*, pg. 2903
GREE AIR CONDITIONER (VIETNAM) CO., LTD.—See Gree Electric Appliances, Inc. of Zhuhai; *Int'l*, pg. 3068
GREE AIRCONS LLP—See Gree Electric Appliances, Inc. of Zhuhai; *Int'l*, pg. 3068
GREE ELECTRIC APPLIANCES DO BRASIL LTDA—See Gree Electric Appliances, Inc. of Zhuhai; *Int'l*, pg. 3068
GREE GMBH—See Gree Electric Appliances, Inc. of Zhuhai; *Int'l*, pg. 3068
GREE INC.—See Gree Electric Appliances, Inc. of Zhuhai; *Int'l*, pg. 3068
GREEINDIA AIR CONDITONERS & APPLIANCES LTD.—See Gree Electric Appliances, Inc. of Zhuhai; *Int'l*, pg. 3068
GREEMAK GROUP DOO—See Gree Electric Appliances, Inc. of Zhuhai; *Int'l*, pg. 3068
GREE MALAYSIA SDN. BHD.—See Gree Electric Appliances, Inc. of Zhuhai; *Int'l*, pg. 3068
GREEN POINT PTY. LTD.—See BITZER SE; *Int'l*, pg. 1052
GREE PRODUCTS FRANCE SAS—See Gree Electric Appliances, Inc. of Zhuhai; *Int'l*, pg. 3068
GREE PRODUCTS, S.L.—See Gree Electric Appliances, Inc. of Zhuhai; *Int'l*, pg. 3068
GRUPO TH MANTENIMIENTO, S.L.—See Helvetia Holding AG; *Int'l*, pg. 3339
GSW WATER HEATERS—See A. O. Smith Corporation; *U.S. Public*, pg. 11
GUANGDONG SHENLING ENVIRONMENTAL SYSTEMS CO., LTD.; *Int'l*, pg. 3160
GUANGZHOU GOALAND ENERGY CONSERVATION TECH CO., LTD.; *Int'l*, pg. 3165
GULF AIR CONDITIONING MANUFACTURING INDUSTRIES L.L.C—See GIBCA Limited; *Int'l*, pg. 2962
HAAKON INDUSTRIES (CANADA) LTD.; *Int'l*, pg. 3201
HALLA VISTEON CLIMATE CONTROL (NANCHANG) CO., LTD.—See Hahn & Company; *Int'l*, pg. 3208
HANGZHOU ZHONGTAI CRYOGENIC TECHNOLOGY CORPORATION; *Int'l*, pg. 3251
HARBIN AIR CONDITIONING CO., LTD.; *Int'l*, pg. 3270
HARSCO INDUSTRIAL AIR-X-CHANGERS—See Chart Industries, Inc.; *U.S. Public*, pg. 481
HARTFORD COMPRESSORS INC.—See Berjaya Corporation Berhad; *Int'l*, pg. 984
HAWS AG—See Haws Corporation; *U.S. Private*, pg. 1884
HCR, INC.—See Jamison Door Company; *U.S. Private*, pg. 2186
HEAT CONTROLLER, INC.—See Motors & Armatures, Inc.; *U.S. Private*, pg. 2797

HEATCRAFT REFRIGERATION (WUXI) CO. LTD.—See Lennox International Inc.; *U.S. Public*, pg. 1307
HEATCRAFT TASMANIA PTY LTD—See Lennox International Inc.; *U.S. Public*, pg. 1307
HEATEC JIETONG HOLDINGS LTD; *Int'l*, pg. 3304
HEMAIR SYSTEMS INDIA LTD.—See AIRTECH JAPAN, LTD.; *Int'l*, pg. 249
HENCO FLOOR N.V.—See Aalberts N.V.; *Int'l*, pg. 34
HENGLI INDUSTRIAL DEVELOPMENT GROUP CO., LTD.; *Int'l*, pg. 3346
HENRY TECHNOLOGIES CANADA—See Hendricks Holding Company, Inc.; *U.S. Private*, pg. 1915
HENRY TECHNOLOGIES LIMITED—See Hendricks Holding Company, Inc.; *U.S. Private*, pg. 1915
HEROFLON S.P.A.—See Daikin Industries, Ltd.; *Int'l*, pg. 1935
HILL PHOENIX COSTA RICA, SOCIEDAD DE RESPONSABILIDAD LIMITADA—See Dover Corporation; *U.S. Public*, pg. 681
HILL PHOENIX INC.—See Dover Corporation; *U.S. Public*, pg. 679
HITACHI EUROPE LTD. - AIR CONDITIONING AND REFRIGERATION GROUP DIVISION—See Hitachi, Ltd.; *Int'l*, pg. 3417
HITACHI EUROPE S.R.L.—See Hitachi, Ltd.; *Int'l*, pg. 3417
HITACHI TECHNOLOGIES AND SERVICES LTD.—See Hitachi, Ltd.; *Int'l*, pg. 3422
HONEYWELL BUILDING SOLUTIONS—See Honeywell International Inc.; *U.S. Public*, pg. 1048
HONGSHENG HEAT EXCHANGER MANUFACTURING CO.,LTD; *Int'l*, pg. 3471
HORIZON SCIENTIFIC, INC.—See Standex International; *U.S. Public*, pg. 1930
HOSHIZAKI EUROPE B.V.—See Hoshizaki Corporation; *Int'l*, pg. 3483
HOSHIZAKI SUZHOU CO., LTD.—See Hoshizaki Corporation; *Int'l*, pg. 3484
HUBEI DONPER ELECTROMECHANICAL GROUP CO., LTD.; *Int'l*, pg. 3517
HUMICLIMA EST, S.A.—See ACS, Actividades de Construccion y Servicios, S.A.; *Int'l*, pg. 114
HUNTAIR INC.; *U.S. Private*, pg. 2009
HVAC STORES; *U.S. Private*, pg. 2015
HYDAC COOLING GMBH—See Hydac International GmbH; *Int'l*, pg. 3545
HYDROGEN ENERGY CO., LTD.—See Fujian Snowman Co., Ltd.; *Int'l*, pg. 2819
HYDRO INNOVATIONS, LLC—See CEA Industries Inc.; *U.S. Public*, pg. 463
ILSHINBIOBASE CO., LTD.; *Int'l*, pg. 3616
IMPERIAL BROWN INC.; *U.S. Private*, pg. 2049
INAIRE (PVT) LTD.—See Daikin Industries, Ltd.; *Int'l*, pg. 1935
INGERSOLL-RAND (CHINA) INVESTMENT COMPANY LIMITED—See Ingersoll Rand Inc.; *U.S. Public*, pg. 1120
INGERSOLL-RAND DO BRASIL LTDA.—See Ingersoll Rand Inc.; *U.S. Public*, pg. 1122
INSULATED STRUCTURES (1989) (PTY) LIMITED—See TRG Management LP; *U.S. Private*, pg. 4220
INTERNATIONAL COMFORT PRODUCTS CORPORATION (CANADA)—See Carrier Global Corporation; *U.S. Public*, pg. 442
INVENTOR A.G.S.A.—See Beijer Ref AB; *Int'l*, pg. 944
INVENTOR CONCEPT S.R.L.—See Beijer Ref AB; *Int'l*, pg. 944
JOAO DE DEUS & FILHOS S.A.—See Denso Corporation; *Int'l*, pg. 2031
JOE'S REFRIGERATION, INC.; *U.S. Private*, pg. 2219
JUFFALI AIR CONDITIONING, MECHANICAL & ELECTRICAL COMPANY - DUCTWORK FACILITY—See E.A. Juffali & Brothers Company; *Int'l*, pg. 2250
JUFFALI AIR CONDITIONING, MECHANICAL & ELECTRICAL COMPANY - LOW VOLTAGE PANEL BOARD FACILITY—See E.A. Juffali & Brothers Company; *Int'l*, pg. 2250
KAIRAK INC.—See Illinois Tool Works Inc.; *U.S. Public*, pg. 1108
KE2 THERM SOLUTIONS, INC.—See Acuity Brands, Inc.; *U.S. Public*, pg. 37
KEIHIN AIRCON NORTH AMERICA, INC.—See Hitachi Astemo, Ltd.; *Int'l*, pg. 3409
KERMI S.R.O.—See Arbonia AG; *Int'l*, pg. 538
KETEMA LP—See Alfa Laval AB; *Int'l*, pg. 309
KIDDE BRASIL LTDA—See Carrier Global Corporation; *U.S. Public*, pg. 443
KIMO RHVAC CONTROLS GMBH—See BITZER SE; *Int'l*, pg. 1052
KOLPAK—See Ali Holding S.r.l; *Int'l*, pg. 322
KONI NORTH AMERICA, INC.—See ITT Inc.; *U.S. Public*, pg. 1178
KYSOR WARREN CORP.—See EPTA S.p.a.; *Int'l*, pg. 2466
KYSOR/WARREN DE MEXICO, S. DE R.L. DE C.V.—See Lennox International Inc.; *U.S. Public*, pg. 1307
KYSOR WARREN EPTA US CORP.—See EPTA S.p.a.; *Int'l*, pg. 2466
LEER INC.—See Dexter Apache Holdings, Inc.; *U.S. Private*, pg. 1220

LENNOX FRANCE S.A.S.—See Lennox International Inc.; *U.S. Public*, pg. 1307
LENNOX INDUSTRIES INC.—See Lennox International Inc.; *U.S. Public*, pg. 1307
LENNOX INTERNATIONAL INC.; *U.S. Public*, pg. 1307
LENNOX POLSKA SP. Z.O.O.—See Lennox International Inc.; *U.S. Public*, pg. 1308
LGL GERMANY GMBH—See Lennox International Inc.; *U.S. Public*, pg. 1307
LIEBERT CANADA—See Emerson Electric Co.; *U.S. Public*, pg. 744
LINDE REFRIGERATION SYSTEMS LTD.—See Carrier Global Corporation; *U.S. Public*, pg. 441
LUVATA CZECH S.R.O.—See Fedders Electric and Engineering Limited; *Int'l*, pg. 2629
LYTRON INCORPORATED—See The Goldman Sachs Group, Inc.; *U.S. Public*, pg. 2080
MAERSK CONTAINER INDUSTRY QINGDAO LTD.—See A.P. Moller-Maersk A/S; *Int'l*, pg. 26
MANITOWOC FSG OPERATIONS, LLC—See The Manitowoc Company, Inc.; *U.S. Public*, pg. 2111
MANITOWOC ICE, INC.—See Ali Holding S.r.l; *Int'l*, pg. 322
MANITOWOC WESTERN COMPANY, INC.—See The Manitowoc Company, Inc.; *U.S. Public*, pg. 2111
MARLEY MEXICANA S.A. DE C.V.—See SPX Technologies, Inc.; *U.S. Public*, pg. 1921
MARSHAL OFFSHORE & MARINE ENGINEERING CO. LTD.—See 9R Limited; *Int'l*, pg. 17
MARVAIR—See Thor Industries, Inc.; *U.S. Public*, pg. 2156
MASTER-BILT PRODUCTS—See Ten Oaks Group; *U.S. Private*, pg. 3964
MAULTECH CORPORATION—See Denso Corporation; *Int'l*, pg. 2032
MCQUAY INTERNATIONAL-CHILLER PRODUCTS—See Daikin Industries, Ltd.; *Int'l*, pg. 1936
MENTOR BUSINESS SYSTEMS LIMITED—See Carrier Global Corporation; *U.S. Public*, pg. 443
MERINO-ODD SDN. BHD.—See DAI-DAN Co Ltd; *Int'l*, pg. 1917
METALAIRE, INC.—See J.T. Walker Industries, Inc.; *U.S. Private*, pg. 2171
MGR EQUIPMENT CORP.; *U.S. Private*, pg. 2695
MICRO MATIC USA, INC.; *U.S. Private*, pg. 2702
MILE HIGH EQUIPMENT LLC—See Ali Holding S.r.l; *Int'l*, pg. 321
MISR REFRIGERATION & AIR CONDITIONING MANUFACTURING COMPANY S.A.E.—See Carrier Global Corporation; *U.S. Public*, pg. 443
MISTAMERICA CORPORATION; *U.S. Private*, pg. 2749
MODINE, INC.—See Modine Manufacturing Company; *U.S. Public*, pg. 1455
MODINE JACKSONVILLE INC.—See Modine Manufacturing Company; *U.S. Public*, pg. 1455
MODINE UDEN B.V.—See Modine Manufacturing Company; *U.S. Public*, pg. 1455
MORITANI DAIKIN CO, LTD.—See Daikin Industries, Ltd.; *Int'l*, pg. 1936
MUELINK & GROL B.V.—See Egeria Capital Management B.V.; *Int'l*, pg. 2323
MUELLER REFRIGERATION LLC—See Mueller Industries, Inc.; *U.S. Public*, pg. 1484
MULTIPLEX COMPANY INC.; *U.S. Private*, pg. 2813
MULTISTACK, LLC; *U.S. Private*, pg. 2813
NAILOR INDUSTRIES; *U.S. Private*, pg. 2831
NATIONAL TRADE SUPPLY, LLC; *U.S. Private*, pg. 2864
NED AIR B.V.—See CENTROTEC SE; *Int'l*, pg. 1414
NEWELL RUBBERMAID GERMAN HOLDING GMBH—See Newell Brands Inc.; *U.S. Public*, pg. 1514
NIAGARA BLOWER COMPANY—See Alfa Laval AB; *Int'l*, pg. 309
NICOTRA GEBHARDT GMBH—See Regal Rexnord Corporation; *U.S. Public*, pg. 1773
NIPPON OTIS ELEVATOR COMPANY—See Otis Worldwide Corporation; *U.S. Public*, pg. 1623
NISSENS A/S—See Standard Motor Products, Inc.; *U.S. Public*, pg. 1929
NORFOXX REFRIGERATION, LLC—See Saw Mill Capital LLC; *U.S. Private*, pg. 3557
NOR-LAKE INC.—See Ten Oaks Group; *U.S. Private*, pg. 3964
NORTH SEA VENTILATION LIMITED—See Dynac Sdn. Bhd.; *Int'l*, pg. 2239
NORTH STAR ICE EQUIPMENT CORPORATION; *U.S. Private*, pg. 2947
NOVENCO A/S—See Hi Air Korea Co., Ltd.; *Int'l*, pg. 3379
NOVENCO B.V.—See Hi Air Korea Co., Ltd.; *Int'l*, pg. 3379
NYLE CORPORATION; *U.S. Private*, pg. 2976
OLIVE TREE ENERGY, LLC; *U.S. Private*, pg. 3010
ONEROOF ENERGY GROUP, INC.; *U.S. Public*, pg. 1603
OOO GEA REFRIGERATION RUS—See GEA Group Aktiengesellschaft; *Int'l*, pg. 2903
OSAKA TECHNOCRAT. CO., LTD.—See Chofu Seisakusho Co., Ltd.; *Int'l*, pg. 1577
O.Y.L. MANUFACTURING COMPANY, SDN. BHD. (OYLM)—See Daikin Industries, Ltd.; *Int'l*, pg. 1936
PALL INTERNATIONAL SARL—See Danaher Corporation; *U.S. Public*, pg. 630

N.A.I.C.S. INDEX

333511 — INDUSTRIAL MOLD MAN...

PARKER AIRTEK—See Parker Hannifin Corporation; *U.S. Public*, pg. 1645
PARKER HANNIFIN A/S—See Parker Hannifin Corporation; *U.S. Public*, pg. 1645
PARKER HANNIFIN CLIMATE & INDUSTRIAL CONTROLS GROUP—See Parker Hannifin Corporation; *U.S. Public*, pg. 1644
PARKER HANNIFIN MOBILE BUSINESS UNIT—See Parker Hannifin Corporation; *U.S. Public*, pg. 1644
PARKER HANNIFIN REFRIGERATION & AIR CONDITIONING DIVISION—See Parker Hannifin Corporation; *U.S. Public*, pg. 1644
PCH METALS S.A.S.—See Callista Private Equity GmbH & Co. KG; *Int'l*, pg. 1265
PENNBARRY—See Canada Pension Plan Investment Board; *Int'l*, pg. 1278
PERFECT AIR & HOME IMPROVEMENT INC.; *U.S. Private*, pg. 3148
PERLICK CORPORATION; *U.S. Private*, pg. 3152
PERMASENSE LIMITED—See Emerson Electric Co.; *U.S. Public*, pg. 751
PHOENIX MANUFACTURING, INC.—See Bee Street Holdings LLC; *U.S. Private*, pg. 513
PHOENIX PEACH, LLC—See Baum Capital Partners Management LLC; *U.S. Private*, pg. 490
POLARIS ALI SPA.—See Ali Holding S.r.l; *Int'l*, pg. 321
PROGNOST SYSTEMS GMBH—See Burckhardt Compression Holding AG; *Int'l*, pg. 1221
PRO-KLIMA D.O.O.—See CENTROTEC SE; *Int'l*, pg. 1414
PSL ENGINEERING PVT. LTD.—See Fedders Electric and Engineering Limited; *Int'l*, pg. 2630
PT APM AUTO COMPONENTS INDONESIA—See APM Automotive Holdings Berhad; *Int'l*, pg. 516
PT BERCA CARRIER INDONESIA—See Carrier Global Corporation; *U.S. Public*, pg. 444
PT. DAIKIN MANUFACTURING INDONESIA—See Daikin Industries, Ltd.; *Int'l*, pg. 1936
PT. FAR EAST REFRIGERATION INDONESIA—See Far East Group Limited; *Int'l*, pg. 2616
PT. SNOWMAN MANDIRI INDONESIA—See Fujian Snowman Co., Ltd.; *Int'l*, pg. 2819
PYRAMID AIRTECH PVT. LTD.—See AIRTECH JAPAN, LTD.; *Int'l*, pg. 249
PZP HEATING A.S.—See Arbonia AG; *Int'l*, pg. 538
Q-CARRIER (B) SENDIRIAN BERHAD—See Carrier Global Corporation; *U.S. Public*, pg. 444
QINGDAO HAIER-CARRIER REFRIGERATION EQUIPMENT COMPANY LIMITED—See Carrier Global Corporation; *U.S. Public*, pg. 444
RAINEY ROAD LLC—See Rainey Road Holdings, Inc.; *U.S. Private*, pg. 3347
RAPID ENGINEERING INC.; *U.S. Private*, pg. 3355
REALCOLD NEW ZEALAND LTD.—See Beijer Ref AB; *Int'l*, pg. 945
REFCOMP ITALY S.R.L.—See Fujian Snowman Co., Ltd.; *Int'l*, pg. 2819
REFPLUS INC.—See Madison Industries Holdings LLC; *U.S. Private*, pg. 2543
RESEARCH PRODUCTS CORPORATION - APRILAIRE DIVISION—See Research Products Corporation; *U.S. Private*, pg. 3404
RESEARCH PRODUCTS CORPORATION; *U.S. Private*, pg. 3404
RESTORATION INDUSTRIES, INC.; *U.S. Private*, pg. 3410
RIELLO S.A.—See Carrier Global Corporation; *U.S. Public*, pg. 444
RIELLO S.P.A.—See RTX Corporation; *U.S. Public*, pg. 1825
ROYAL GEA GRASSO HOLDING NV-REFRIGERATION DIVISION—See GEA Group Aktiengesellschaft; *Int'l*, pg. 2902
R & Y AC COMPRESSOR, INC.; *U.S. Private*, pg. 3331
SANTARELLI & SONS OIL CO., INC.; *U.S. Private*, pg. 3548
SAS DECTRON COMPANY—See Madison Industries Holdings LLC; *U.S. Private*, pg. 2543
SAUDI REFRIGERATORS MANUFACTURING CO.LTD.—See E.A. Juffali & Brothers Company; *Int'l*, pg. 2251
SAUNA360 GROUP OY—See Masco Corporation; *U.S. Public*, pg. 1392
SAVELYS GDF SUEZ—See ENGIE SA; *Int'l*, pg. 2434
SCHOMBURG REFRIGERATION CO, INC—See Benedict Refrigeration Service, Inc.; *U.S. Private*, pg. 525
SCM REF AB—See Beijer Ref AB; *Int'l*, pg. 945
SCROLL COMPRESSORS LLC—See Emerson Electric Co.; *U.S. Public*, pg. 744
SHANDONG GRAD GROUP—See Chung-Hsin Electric & Machinery Manufacturing Corp.; *Int'l*, pg. 1597
SHANGHAI GENERAL FUJI REFRIGERATION EQUIPMENT CO., LTD.—See Fuji Electric Co., Ltd.; *Int'l*, pg. 2813
SILVER KING REFRIGERATION, INC—See Berkshire Hathaway Inc.; *U.S. Public*, pg. 310
SINCLAIR GLOBAL GROUP S.R.O.—See Beijer Ref AB; *Int'l*, pg. 945
SINGHAGIRI (PVT) LTD.—See Daikin Industries, Ltd.; *Int'l*, pg. 1936
SITE SUPPORT SERVICES, INC.—See Tate Engineering Systems Inc.; *U.S. Private*, pg. 3936
SME DEUTSCHLAND GMBH—See Dana Incorporated; *U.S. Public*, pg. 623
SME SHANGHAI CO., LTD.—See Dana Incorporated; *U.S. Public*, pg. 623
SMEVA B.V.—See Carrier Global Corporation; *U.S. Public*, pg. 442
SMEV S.R.L.—See Dometic Group AB; *Int'l*, pg. 2160
SMITHCO ENGINEERING INC.; *U.S. Private*, pg. 3697
SMITH SERVICES, INC.; *U.S. Private*, pg. 3695
SODASTREAM DIRECT LLC—See PepsiCo, Inc.; *U.S. Public*, pg. 1672
SODASTREAM INDUSTRIES LTD.—See PepsiCo, Inc.; *U.S. Public*, pg. 1672
SODASTREAM (SA) (PTY) LTD.—See PepsiCo, Inc.; *U.S. Public*, pg. 1672
SPX COOLING TECHNOLOGIES FRANCE SA—See SPX Technologies, Inc.; *U.S. Public*, pg. 1921
SPX COOLING TECHNOLOGIES INC.—See SPX Technologies, Inc.; *U.S. Public*, pg. 1921
SPX COOLING TECHNOLOGIES—See SPX Technologies, Inc.; *U.S. Public*, pg. 1921
SPX COOLING TECHNOLOGIES TRADING DMCC—See SPX Technologies, Inc.; *U.S. Public*, pg. 1921
SPX COOLING TECHNOLOGIES UK LTD.—See SPX Technologies, Inc.; *U.S. Public*, pg. 1921
SPX COOLING TECHNOLOGIES (ZHANGJIAKOU) CO. LTD.—See SPX Technologies, Inc.; *U.S. Public*, pg. 1921
SPX DE MEXICO, S.A. DE C.V.—See Lone Star Funds; *U.S. Private*, pg. 2487
SPX DRY COOLING USA, LLC—See SPX Technologies, Inc.; *U.S. Public*, pg. 1921
SPX FLOW TECHNOLOGY CRAWLEY LIMITED—See Lone Star Funds; *U.S. Private*, pg. 2486
SPX FLOW TECHNOLOGY DANMARK A/S—See Lone Star Funds; *U.S. Private*, pg. 2486
SPX FLOW TECHNOLOGY HANSE GMBH—See Lone Star Funds; *U.S. Private*, pg. 2486
SPX FLOW TECHNOLOGY (INDIA) PRIVATE LIMITED—See Lone Star Funds; *U.S. Private*, pg. 2486
SPX FLOW TECHNOLOGY KOREA CO., LTD.—See Lone Star Funds; *U.S. Private*, pg. 2486
SPX FLOW TECHNOLOGY MOERS GMBH—See Lone Star Funds; *U.S. Private*, pg. 2486
SPX FLOW TECHNOLOGY NEW ZEALAND LIMITED—See Lone Star Funds; *U.S. Private*, pg. 2486
SPX FLOW TECHNOLOGY NORDERSTEDT GMBH—See Lone Star Funds; *U.S. Private*, pg. 2486
SPX FLOW TECHNOLOGY SINGAPORE PTE. LTD.—See Lone Star Funds; *U.S. Private*, pg. 2486
SPX FLOW TECHNOLOGY STOCKHOLM AB—See Lone Star Funds; *U.S. Private*, pg. 2486
SPX INDIA PRIVATE LIMITED—See Lone Star Funds; *U.S. Private*, pg. 2487
SPX ITALIA S.R.L—See Lone Star Funds; *U.S. Private*, pg. 2487
SPX MIDDLE EAST FZE—See Lone Star Funds; *U.S. Private*, pg. 2487
SPX (SCHWEIZ) AG—See Lone Star Funds; *U.S. Private*, pg. 2486
SPX TECHNOLOGIES, INC.; *U.S. Public*, pg. 1920
STAJAC INDUSTRIES, INC.; *U.S. Private*, pg. 3776
SUBURBAN MANUFACTURING, CO.—See Thor Industries, Inc.; *U.S. Public*, pg. 2156
SUPER RADIATOR COILS LTD.; *U.S. Private*, pg. 3875
SVENSKA ROTOR MASKINER AB—See Fujian Snowman Co., Ltd.; *Int'l*, pg. 2819
TAIWAN HITACHI CO., LTD.—See Hitachi, Ltd.; *Int'l*, pg. 3424
TECUMSEH DO BRASIL, LTDA.—See Atlas Holdings, LLC; *U.S. Private*, pg. 378
TECUMSEH DO BRASIL, LTDA.—See Mueller Industries, Inc.; *U.S. Public*, pg. 1485
TECUMSEH EURO-MALAYSIA SDN. BHD—See Atlas Holdings, LLC; *U.S. Private*, pg. 378
TECUMSEH EURO-MALAYSIA SDN. BHD—See Mueller Industries, Inc.; *U.S. Public*, pg. 1485
TECUMSEH EUROPE SA—See Atlas Holdings, LLC; *U.S. Private*, pg. 378
TECUMSEH EUROPE SA—See Mueller Industries, Inc.; *U.S. Public*, pg. 1485
TEI STRUTHERS WELLS—See Babcock Power, Inc.; *U.S. Private*, pg. 422
TEKGARD, INC.—See Advanced Cooling Technologies, Inc.; *U.S. Private*, pg. 88
TEXAS FIRE & SAFETY—See Highview Capital, LLC; *U.S. Private*, pg. 1942
THERMAL CARE INC.—See Perma-Pipe International Holdings, Inc.; *U.S. Public*, pg. 1676
THERMAL CORPORATION—See Nailor Industries, Inc.; *U.S. Private*, pg. 2831
THOMPSON HVAC—See Thompson Industrial Services, LLC; *U.S. Private*, pg. 4159
TOSHIBA CARRIER AIR CONDITIONING (CHINA) CO., LTD.—See Carrier Global Corporation; *U.S. Public*, pg. 444
TOSHIBA CARRIER AIRCONDITIONING SALES (SHANGHAI) CO., LTD.—See Carrier Global Corporation; *U.S. Public*, pg. 444
TOSHIBA CARRIER CORPORATION—See Carrier Global Corporation; *U.S. Public*, pg. 444
TOSHIBA CARRIER EUROPE S.A.S.—See Carrier Global Corporation; *U.S. Public*, pg. 444
TOSHIBA CARRIER NORTH AMERICA, INC.—See Carrier Global Corporation; *U.S. Public*, pg. 444
TOSHIBA CARRIER (THAILAND) CO., LTD.—See Carrier Global Corporation; *U.S. Public*, pg. 444
TOWN & COUNTRY SERVICES; *U.S. Private*, pg. 4196
TRANE DEUTSCHLAND GMBH—See Ingersoll Rand Inc.; *U.S. Public*, pg. 1122
TRANS C.A.S. S.R.L.—See Compa S.A.; *Int'l*, pg. 1721
TRANTER SOLARICE GMBH—See Alfa Laval AB; *Int'l*, pg. 310
TRAULSEN—See Illinois Tool Works Inc.; *U.S. Public*, pg. 1104
TROLEX CORP.; *U.S. Private*, pg. 4241
TRYBA ENERGIES SAS—See Atrya SAS; *Int'l*, pg. 694
TT-COIL A/S—See Beijer Ref AB; *Int'l*, pg. 945
TT-COIL NORGE AS—See Beijer Ref AB; *Int'l*, pg. 945
TYLER REFRIGERATION CORP.—See Haier Smart Home Co., Ltd.; *Int'l*, pg. 3210
UD-RD HOLDING COMPANY LIMITED—See Lone Star Funds; *U.S. Private*, pg. 2487
UGI HVAC ENTERPRISES, INC.—See UGI Corporation; *U.S. Public*, pg. 2223
UNITED ELECTRIC COMPANY, L.P.—See Carrier Global Corporation; *U.S. Public*, pg. 442
UNITED REFRIGERATOR SDN BHD—See Carrier Global Corporation; *U.S. Public*, pg. 442
UTC CANADA CORPORATION—See RTX Corporation; *U.S. Public*, pg. 1825
VARD ACCOMMODATION AS—See Fincantieri S.p.A.; *Int'l*, pg. 2671
VARD ACCOMMODTION TULCEA SRL—See Fincantieri S.p.A.; *Int'l*, pg. 2671
VENSTAR, INC.—See Daikin Industries, Ltd.; *Int'l*, pg. 1936
VICTORY CLIMATE SYSTEMS—See Hickman Investments Inc.; *U.S. Private*, pg. 1933
VICTORY REFRIGERATION COMPANY LLC—See Ali Holding S.r.l; *Int'l*, pg. 322
VIDEOJET ARGENTINA S.R.L.—See Danaher Corporation; *U.S. Public*, pg. 631
VIKING AIRTECH PTE. LTD.—See 9R Limited; *Int'l*, pg. 17
VIKING AIRTECH SDN. BHD.—See 9R Limited; *Int'l*, pg. 17
VIKING AIRTECH (SHANGHAI) CO., LTD.—See 9R Limited; *Int'l*, pg. 17
VIKING AIRTECH (YANTAI) CO., LTD.—See 9R Limited; *Int'l*, pg. 17
VILTER MANUFACTURING LLC—See Emerson Electric Co.; *U.S. Public*, pg. 744
VULGANUS OY—See Aspo Oyj; *Int'l*, pg. 632
WARMAFLOOR (GB) LTD.—See Bharti Enterprises Limited; *Int'l*, pg. 1012
WESTERN REFRIGERATION PVT. LTD.—See Hoshizaki Corporation; *Int'l*, pg. 3484
WHIRLPOOL CORP. - LA VERGNE—See Whirlpool Corporation; *U.S. Public*, pg. 2367
WILLIAMS REFRIGERATION AUSTRALIA PTY. LTD.—See Ali Holding S.r.l; *Int'l*, pg. 322
WILLIAMS REFRIGERATION LTD.—See Ali Holding S.r.l; *Int'l*, pg. 322
WOLF POWER SYSTEMS GMBH—See CENTROTEC SE; *Int'l*, pg. 1415
WOLSELEY HVAC R GROUP—See Ferguson plc; *Int'l*, pg. 2638
WORLD DRYER CORPORATION—See Zurn Elkay Water Solutions Corporation; *U.S. Public*, pg. 2413
XCEL ERECTORS, INC.—See SPX Technologies, Inc.; *U.S. Public*, pg. 1921
XETEX INC.; *U.S. Private*, pg. 4581
XI'AN DAIKIN QING'AN COMPRESSOR CO., LTD.—See Daikin Industries, Ltd.; *Int'l*, pg. 1937
XYLEM INC.—See Xylem Inc.; *U.S. Public*, pg. 2396
ZANOTTI S.P.A.—See Daikin Industries, Ltd.; *Int'l*, pg. 1937
ZEKS COMPRESSED AIR SOLUTIONS LLC—See Ingersoll Rand Inc.; *U.S. Public*, pg. 1122
ZERO ZONE, INC. - REFRIGERATION SYSTEMS DIVISION—See Zero Zone, Inc.; *U.S. Private*, pg. 4602
ZERO ZONE, INC.; *U.S. Private*, pg. 4602

333511 — INDUSTRIAL MOLD MANUFACTURING

A-1 FIBER GLASS, INC.; *U.S. Private*, pg. 21
A-1 TOOL CORPORATION—See Triangle Tool Corporation; *U.S. Private*, pg. 4226
AALBERS TOOL & MOLD INC.; *Int'l*, pg. 32
ABB POWER TECHNOLOGIES AB—See ABB Ltd.; *Int'l*, pg. 49
ACE CORPORATION HOLDINGS LIMITED—See Berry Global Group, Inc; *U.S. Public*, pg. 320
ACE MOLD (HEFEI) COMPANY LIMITED—See Berry Global Group, Inc; *U.S. Public*, pg. 320
ACE MOLD INDUSTRIAL (SHENZHEN) COMPANY

333511 — INDUSTRIAL MOLD MAN...

LIMITED—See Berry Global Group, Inc; *U.S. Public*, pg. 320
ACE MOLD (SHANGHAI) COMPANY LIMITED—See Berry Global Group, Inc; *U.S. Public*, pg. 320
ACE PLASTICS (SHENZHEN) COMPANY LIMITED—See Berry Global Group, Inc; *U.S. Public*, pg. 320
ACE PLASTICS (ZHUHAI) COMPANY LIMITED—See Berry Global Group, Inc; *U.S. Public*, pg. 320
ADVAL TECH (GRENCHEN) AG—See Adval Tech Holding AG; *Int'l*, pg. 155
ADVAL TECH (HUNGARY) KFT.—See Adval Tech Holding AG; *Int'l*, pg. 155
ADVAL TECH (MEXICO) S.A. DE C.V.—See Adval Tech Holding AG; *Int'l*, pg. 155
ADVAL TECH (SUZHOU) CO. LTD.—See Adval Tech Holding AG; *Int'l*, pg. 155
AFT-HUNGARY KFT.—See ARC Group Worldwide, Inc.; *U.S. Public*, pg. 179
ASSOCIATED TOOLMAKERS LTD.—See The Eastern Company; *U.S. Public*, pg. 2069
A-TECH SOLUTION CO., LTD. - CHEONAN FACTORY—See A-TECH Solution Co., Ltd.; *Int'l*, pg. 21
A-TECH SOLUTION CO., LTD. - GWANG-JU FACTORY—See A-TECH Solution Co., Ltd.; *Int'l*, pg. 21
A-TECH SOLUTION CO., LTD.; *Int'l*, pg. 21
ATLAS DIE, LLC - CHEM-MILLING DIVISION—See Auxo Investment Partners, LLC; *U.S. Private*, pg. 402
AVK PLAST A/S—See AVK Holding A/S; *Int'l*, pg. 747
AVK PLASTICS B.V.—See AVK Holding A/S; *Int'l*, pg. 747
BACVIET INDUSTRY JOINT STOCK COMPANY—See Bacviet Steel JSC; *Int'l*, pg. 795
BACVIET STRUCTURE STEEL BUILDING COMPANY LIMITED—See Bacviet Steel JSC; *Int'l*, pg. 795
BERRY ACE PACKAGING (JIAXING) COMPANY LIMITED—See Berry Global Group, Inc; *U.S. Public*, pg. 320
BESSER CO.—See Besser Company; *U.S. Private*, pg. 542
BIG 3 PRECISION MOLD SERVICES, LLC—See The Eastern Company; *U.S. Public*, pg. 2069
CARLSON TOOL & MANUFACTURING CORP.; *U.S. Private*, pg. 765
CASETEK HOLDINGS LIMITED; *Int'l*, pg. 1351
CAVAFORM, INC.—See Crestview Partners, L.P.; *U.S. Private*, pg. 1099
CDM TOOL & MANUFACTURING CO., INC.—See Jacsten Holdings, LLC; *U.S. Private*, pg. 2180
CENTURY TOOL & GAGE; *U.S. Private*, pg. 834
CEPS, INC.; *U.S. Private*, pg. 835
CHANGZHOU FUJI SEIKI CO., LTD.—See Fuji Seiki Co., Ltd.; *Int'l*, pg. 2817
CHEEFAT METAL PRODUCTS & PLASTIC PLATING CO., LTD.—See China Aerospace International Holdings Limited; *Int'l*, pg. 1481
CHEEYUEN SURFACE TREAMENT (HUIZHOU) CO., LTD.—See China Aerospace International Holdings Limited; *Int'l*, pg. 1481
CHEMFAB JAPAN, LTD.—See Compagnie de Saint-Gobain SA; *Int'l*, pg. 1732
CLUSTER TECHNOLOGY CO., LTD.; *Int'l*, pg. 1664
CONSTRUCTION PRODUCTS INC.—See Wilian Holding Co., Inc.; *U.S. Private*, pg. 4520
DAIDO DMS (THAILAND) CO., LTD.—See Daido Steel Co., Ltd.; *Int'l*, pg. 1922
DAIDONG ELECTRONICS (THAILAND) CO., LTD.—See Daidong Electronics Co., Ltd.; *Int'l*, pg. 1924
DAIDONG MOLD & PLASTICS (SHANGHAI) CO., LTD.—See Daidong Electronics Co., Ltd.; *Int'l*, pg. 1924
DELTA TOOLING CO. INC.; *U.S. Private*, pg. 1202
DEMPSEY INDUSTRIES, INC.—See TruArc Partners, L.P.; *U.S. Private*, pg. 4245
D-M-E (CHINA) LIMITED—See Hillenbrand, Inc.; *U.S. Public*, pg. 1036
D-M-E MOLD TECHNOLOGY (SHENZHEN) COMPANY LTD.—See Hillenbrand, Inc.; *U.S. Public*, pg. 1036
D-M-E NORMALIEN GMBH—See Hillenbrand, Inc.; *U.S. Public*, pg. 1036
DONGHUA MACHINERY LTD.—See Cosmos Machinery Enterprises Limited; *Int'l*, pg. 1813
DYNAMIC DESIGN CO., LTD.; *Int'l*, pg. 2240
E'MOLD MANUFACTURING (KUNSHAN) CO., LTD.—See Accrelist Ltd.; *Int'l*, pg. 93
ENGINEERED MOLDING TECHNOLOGY LLC—See Repligen Corporation; *U.S. Public*, pg. 1784
ENPLAS (U.S.A.), INC.—See ENPLAS CORPORATION; *Int'l*, pg. 2445
ESON PRECISION ENGINEERING S.A. DE C.V.—See Eson Precision Ind. Co., Ltd.; *Int'l*, pg. 2504
ESON SLOVAKIA A.S.—See Eson Precision Ind. Co., Ltd.; *Int'l*, pg. 2504
ESTERLE MOLD & MACHINE CO. INC.; *U.S. Private*, pg. 1429
EVA PRECISION INDUSTRIAL (SUZHOU) LIMITED—See EVA Precision Industrial Holdings Limited; *Int'l*, pg. 2560
FAIRWAY INJECTION MOLDS, INC.—See BlackBern Partners LLC; *U.S. Private*, pg. 573
FAIRWAY INJECTION MOLDS, INC.—See Lee Equity Partners LLC; *U.S. Private*, pg. 2413

FAWN DE MEXICO—See National Molding Corporation; *U.S. Private*, pg. 2859
FICO B.V.—See BE Semiconductor Industries N.V.; *Int'l*, pg. 931
FOBOHA (US) INC.—See Adval Tech Holding AG; *Int'l*, pg. 155
FOXCONN OY—See Hon Hai Precision Industry Co., Ltd.; *Int'l*, pg. 3457
FRANCHINO MOLD & ENGINEERING CO.; *U.S. Private*, pg. 1587
F & S TOOL, INC.—See Berry Global Group, Inc; *U.S. Public*, pg. 322
FUJI SEIKI CO., LTD. - MATSUYAMA FACTORY—See Fuji Seiki Co., Ltd.; *Int'l*, pg. 2817
FUJI SEIKI CO., LTD.; *Int'l*, pg. 2817
FUTABA CORPORATION - CHONAN MACHINERY & TOOLING FACTORY II—See Futaba Corporation; *Int'l*, pg. 2850
FUTABA JTW (THAILAND) LTD.—See Futaba Corporation; *Int'l*, pg. 2850
FU YU MOULDING & TOOLING (CHONGQING) CO., LTD.—See Fu Yu Corporation Limited; *Int'l*, pg. 2801
FU YU MOULDING & TOOLING (ZHUHAI) CO., LTD.—See Fu Yu Corporation Limited; *Int'l*, pg. 2801
FWB KUNSTSTOFFTECHNIK GMBH—See Hella GmbH & Co. KGaA; *Int'l*, pg. 3331
GALLANT MICRO. MACHINING (SUZHOU) CO., LTD.—See Gallant Precision Machining Co., Ltd.; *Int'l*, pg. 2873
GERRESHEIMER WERKZEUGBAU WACKERSDORF GMBH—See Gerresheimer AG; *Int'l*, pg. 2944
GF-TEC GMBH.—See BAUER Aktiengesellschaft; *Int'l*, pg. 893
GI TECH CO LTD.; *Int'l*, pg. 2960
GONGIN PRECISION INDUSTRIAL CO., LTD.; *Int'l*, pg. 3037
GOODWIN REFRACTORY SERVICES HOLDINGS LIMITED—See Goodwin PLC; *Int'l*, pg. 3041
GRAHAM PACKAGING COMPANY ITALIA S.R.L.—See Pactiv Evergreen Inc.; *U.S. Public*, pg. 1633
GRUBER SYSTEMS INC.; *U.S. Private*, pg. 1797
GTM PLASTICS INC.; *U.S. Private*, pg. 1807
GUANGZHOU KINTE ELECTRIC INDUSTRIAL CO., LTD.—See China National Electric Apparatus Research Institute Co., Ltd.; *Int'l*, pg. 1531
GUJARAT TOOLROOM LIMITED; *Int'l*, pg. 3177
GURIT TOOLING (TAICANG) CO., LTD.—See Gurit Holding AG; *Int'l*, pg. 3188
G+W GMBH—See AVK Holding A/S; *Int'l*, pg. 748
HANGZHOU AMPHENOL JET INTERCONNECT TECHNOLOGY CO. LTD.—See Amphenol Corporation; *U.S. Public*, pg. 130
HASCO FORM-SERVICE AB—See Berndorf AG; *Int'l*, pg. 987
HASCO FRANCE S.A.R.L.—See Berndorf AG; *Int'l*, pg. 987
HAYCO MANUFACTURING LTD.; *Int'l*, pg. 3290
HI-P (CHENGDU) MOLD BASE MANUFACTURING CO., LTD.—See Hi-P International Limited; *Int'l*, pg. 3381
HI-P (CHENGDU) PRECISION PLASTIC MANUFACTURING CO., LTD.—See Hi-P International Limited; *Int'l*, pg. 3381
HI-P POLAND SP. Z O.O.—See Hi-P International Limited; *Int'l*, pg. 3381
HI-P (THAILAND) CO., LTD.—See Hi-P International Limited; *Int'l*, pg. 3381
HI-TECH MOLD & ENGINEERING; *U.S. Private*, pg. 1932
HOA SEN BUILDING MATERIAL ONE MEMBER LIMITED LIABILITIES COMPANY—See Hoa Sen Group; *Int'l*, pg. 3436
HOEI PLASTICS CO., LTD.—See Fuji Electric Co., Ltd.; *Int'l*, pg. 2812
HOSIDEN PLASTICS CORPORATION—See Hosiden Corporation; *Int'l*, pg. 3484
HUF TOOLS GMBH—See Huf Hulsbeck & Furst GmbH & Co. KG; *Int'l*, pg. 3523
IDI COMPOSITE MATERIAL (SHANGHAI) CO., LTD—See Industrial Dielectrics Holdings, Inc.; *U.S. Private*, pg. 2065
IKEGAI METAL CORP—See Fair Friend Group; *Int'l*, pg. 2604
IKKA TECHNOLOGY DONGGUAN CO., LTD.—See Abico Group; *Int'l*, pg. 61
INTEGRITY MOLD, INC.—See BlackBern Partners LLC; *U.S. Private*, pg. 573
INTEGRITY MOLD, INC.—See Lee Equity Partners LLC; *U.S. Private*, pg. 2413
INTERPLEX NAS ELECTRONICS GMBH—See Blackstone Inc.; *U.S. Public*, pg. 355
JSP MOLD LLC—See JSP International; *U.S. Private*, pg. 2241
JUBILEE INDUSTRIES HOLDINGS LTD.—See Accrelist Ltd.; *Int'l*, pg. 93
JUBILEE INDUSTRIES (S) PTE LTD.—See Accrelist Ltd.; *Int'l*, pg. 93
JUBILEE MANUFACTURING SDN BHD—See Accrelist Ltd.; *Int'l*, pg. 93
KANSAS PLASTICS COMPANY INC.—See MacLean-Fogg Company; *U.S. Private*, pg. 2537

CORPORATE AFFILIATIONS

KISHIN CORPORATION—See Futaba Corporation; *Int'l*, pg. 2851
KUMSUNG INDUSTRIAL CO., LTD.—See Daewon Cable Co., Ltd.; *Int'l*, pg. 1909
KUNSHAN ESON PRECISION ENGINEERING CO., LTD.—See Eson Precision Ind. Co., Ltd.; *Int'l*, pg. 2504
MAGNETICS—See Spang & Company; *U.S. Private*, pg. 3744
MASTER MOLD—See The Plastek Group; *U.S. Private*, pg. 4096
MATRIX COMPOSITES, INC.—See ITT Inc.; *U.S. Public*, pg. 1178
METRO MOLD & DESIGN, INC.; *U.S. Private*, pg. 2686
MODELL TECHNIK GMBH & CO. FORMENBAU KG—See Gesco AG; *Int'l*, pg. 2946
MODELS & TOOLS INC.; *U.S. Private*, pg. 2759
MOLD BASE INDUSTRIES INC.; *U.S. Private*, pg. 2766
MOLD CRAFT, INC.—See BlackBern Partners LLC; *U.S. Private*, pg. 573
MOLD CRAFT, INC.—See Lee Equity Partners LLC; *U.S. Private*, pg. 2413
MOLDMAKERS INCORPORATED—See MGS Manufacturing Group, Inc.; *U.S. Private*, pg. 2695
MOLD MASTERS INTL. LLC; *U.S. Private*, pg. 2766
MOLD-TECH SINGAPORE PTE. LTD.—See Standex International; *U.S. Public*, pg. 1930
MONROE MOLD, LLC—See Talon LLC; *U.S. Private*, pg. 3927
MULTIWIN DE MEXICO S.A. DE C.V.—See Eson Precision Ind. Co., Ltd.; *Int'l*, pg. 2504
NATIONAL TOOL & MANUFACTURING COMPANY; *U.S. Private*, pg. 2864
NEMAK CZECH REPUBLIC, S.R.O.—See ALFA, S.A.B. de C.V.; *Int'l*, pg. 313
NEMAK DILLINGEN GMBH—See ALFA, S.A.B. de C.V.; *Int'l*, pg. 313
NEMAK LINZ GMBH—See ALFA, S.A.B. de C.V.; *Int'l*, pg. 313
NMC SHANGHAI, LTD.—See National Molding Corporation; *U.S. Private*, pg. 2859
NYPROMOLD INC.; *U.S. Private*, pg. 2977
OMNI ENGINEERING SHANGHAI CO. LTD—See Adval Tech Holding AG; *Int'l*, pg. 155
PENN ERIE DIVISION—See The Plastek Group; *U.S. Private*, pg. 4096
PIERSON INDUSTRIES INC.; *U.S. Private*, pg. 3179
PLANFURO GLOBAL, S.A.—See F. Ramada Investimentos, SGPS, S.A.; *Int'l*, pg. 2596
PLASTECH CORPORATION—See Frandsen Corporation; *U.S. Private*, pg. 1593
PLASTIC MOLD TECHNOLOGY, INC.; *U.S. Private*, pg. 3198
PMI INDUSTRIES, INC.—See BAM Enterprises, Inc.; *U.S. Private*, pg. 463
PRECISION MOULDS, LTD.—See Mattel, Inc.; *U.S. Public*, pg. 1399
PREMIUM PLASTIC SOLUTIONS LLC—See Wembly Enterprises LLC; *U.S. Private*, pg. 4480
PRINCIPAL MANUFACTURING CORP.; *U.S. Private*, pg. 3264
PRISM PLASTICS, INC. - MEADVILLE PLANT—See Berkshire Hathaway Inc.; *U.S. Public*, pg. 311
PROPER GROUP INTERNATIONAL; *U.S. Private*, pg. 3285
PROPER POLYMERS OF ANDERSON—See Proper Group International; *U.S. Private*, pg. 3285
PROPER TOOLING—See Proper Group International; *U.S. Private*, pg. 3285
PROTO LABS, INC.; *U.S. Public*, pg. 1729
PRO-WESTERN PLASTICS LTD.—See Berry Global Group, Inc; *U.S. Public*, pg. 322
PT. DAIDO DMS INDONESIA—See Daido Steel Co., Ltd.; *Int'l*, pg. 1923
PT. FUJI SEIKI INDONESIA—See Fuji Seiki Co., Ltd.; *Int'l*, pg. 2817
PYRAMID MOLD & TOOL—See Crestview Partners, L.P.; *U.S. Private*, pg. 1099
QT INDUSTRIES LLC; *U.S. Private*, pg. 3314
QUALITY MOLD INC.; *U.S. Private*, pg. 3320
RAO DESIGN INTERNATIONAL, INC.; *U.S. Private*, pg. 3355
R & B PLASTICS MACHINERY, LLC—See Talon LLC; *U.S. Private*, pg. 3927
REI PROMAX TECHNOLOGIES PTE LTD—See Chasen Holdings Limited; *Int'l*, pg. 1457
ROMAC INDUSTRIES, INC. - ROMAC FOUNDRY DIVISION—See Romac Industries, Inc.; *U.S. Private*, pg. 3475
RONNINGEN RESEARCH & DEVELOPMENT CO; *U.S. Private*, pg. 3478
SEAWAY PLASTICS ENGINEERING, INC.; *U.S. Private*, pg. 3592
SEISHIN (THAILAND) CO., LTD.—See Daiki Aluminium Industry Co., Ltd.; *Int'l*, pg. 1932
SEITZ LLC—See Andlinger & Company, Inc.; *U.S. Private*, pg. 279
SHANGHAI FUJI SEIKI CO., LTD.—See Fuji Seiki Co., Ltd.; *Int'l*, pg. 2817
SHANGHAI ITW PLASTICS & METAL CO., LTD.—See

N.A.I.C.S. INDEX

333514 — SPECIAL DIE AND TOO...

Illinois Tool Works Inc.; *U.S. Public*, pg. 1110
SIMPLY-X GMBH—See CTS Eventim AG & Co. KGAA; *Int'l*, pg. 1874
SINXON PLASTIC (DONG GUAN) CO., LTD.—See COXON Precise Industrial Co., Ltd.; *Int'l*, pg. 1823
SINYON PLASTIC INDUSTRIAL CO., LTD.—See COXON Precise Industrial Co., Ltd.; *Int'l*, pg. 1823
SOUTHWEST MOLD, INC.—See TruArc Partners, L.P.; *U.S. Private*, pg. 4245
SPECIAL MOLD ENGINEERING INC.; *U.S. Private*, pg. 3748
SPECIALTY MANUFACTURING CO.; *U.S. Private*, pg. 3750
SRS (QINGDAO) CASTING MATERIALS COMPANY LIMITED—See Goodwin PLC; *Int'l*, pg. 3042
STRADAL ENVIRONNEMENT—See Compagnie de Saint-Gobain SA; *Int'l*, pg. 1737
SUNTOOL CO., LTD.—See Eson Precision Ind. Co., Ltd.; *Int'l*, pg. 2504
SYBRIDGE TECHNOLOGIES, INC.—See Crestview Partners, L.P.; *U.S. Private*, pg. 1099
TECH MOLD, INC.; *U.S. Private*, pg. 3952
TECNO MATIC EUROPE S.R.O.—See Ingersoll Rand Inc.; *U.S. Public*, pg. 1122
TEUSCHER KUNSTSTOFF-TECHNIK LTD—See Adval Tech Holding AG; *Int'l*, pg. 155
THAAI TECH SOLUTIONS PVT. LTD.—See A-TECH Solution Co., Ltd.; *Int'l*, pg. 21
THAI FUJI SEIKI CO., LTD.—See Fuji Seiki Co., Ltd.; *Int'l*, pg. 2817
THERMOPLAY BRASIL SISTEMAS DE INJECAO LTDA—See Barnes Group Inc.; *U.S. Public*, pg. 278
THERMOPLAY DEUTSCHLAND GMBH—See Barnes Group Inc.; *U.S. Public*, pg. 278
THERMOPLAY HOT RUNNER SYSTEMS (BEIJING) CO. LTD—See Barnes Group Inc.; *U.S. Public*, pg. 278
THERMOPLAY INDIA PRIVATE LIMITED—See Barnes Group Inc.; *U.S. Public*, pg. 278
THERMOPLAY PORTUGAL UNIPESSOAL LDA—See Barnes Group Inc.; *U.S. Public*, pg. 278
THERMOPLAY S.P.A.—See Barnes Group Inc.; *U.S. Public*, pg. 278
THERMOPLAY U.K. LTD.—See Barnes Group Inc.; *U.S. Public*, pg. 278
TIRAD S.R.O.—See Hillenbrand, Inc.; *U.S. Public*, pg. 1037
TITRON INDUSTRIES LIMITED—See AMCO United Holding Limited; *Int'l*, pg. 416
TOHOKU RUBBER CO., LTD.—See Hitachi, Ltd.; *Int'l*, pg. 3424
TRIANGLE TOOL CO.—See The Plastek Group; *U.S. Private*, pg. 4096
TRITECH INTERNATIONAL, LLC—See C&G SYSTEMS INC.; *Int'l*, pg. 1238
TSU-KONG CO., LTD.—See ChangChun Group; *Int'l*, pg. 1442
UNIBLOC-PUMP, INC.—See May River Capital, LLC; *U.S. Private*, pg. 2620
VWH VORRICHTUNGS- UND WERKZEUGBAU HERSCHBACH GMBH—See Gesco AG; *Int'l*, pg. 2945
WG STROHWIG TOOL & DIE INC.; *U.S. Private*, pg. 4503
WHITEFIELD PLASTICS CORPORATION—See Mearthane Products Corporation; *U.S. Private*, pg. 2648
WUXI DAIDONG ELECTRONICS CO., LTD.—See Daidong Electronics Co., Ltd.; *Int'l*, pg. 1924
WUXI SINGUAN METAL SCIENCE & TECHNOLOGY CO., LTD.—See Eson Precision Ind. Co., Ltd.; *Int'l*, pg. 2504
YANTAI JIRAY ELECTRONIC TECHNOLOGY CO., LTD.—See Eson Precision Ind. Co., Ltd.; *Int'l*, pg. 2504
YANTAI ZHENGYI PRECISION ELECTRONIC CO., LTD.—See Eson Precision Ind. Co., Ltd.; *Int'l*, pg. 2504
YUKA PRECISION (WUJIANG) CO., LTD.—See Audix Corporation; *Int'l*, pg. 702
ZOLTRIX MATERIAL (GUANGZHOU) LIMITED—See CN Innovations Holdings Limited; *Int'l*, pg. 1673

333514 — SPECIAL DIE AND TOOL, DIE SET, JIG, AND FIXTURE MANUFACTURING

AAPICO HITECH TOOLING CO., LTD.—See AAPICO Hitech plc; *Int'l*, pg. 37
ABA-PGT INC.; *U.S. Private*, pg. 33
ACRO INDUSTRIES INC.; *U.S. Private*, pg. 65
ADAPTIVE TECHNOLOGIES CORP.—See Kennametal Inc.; *U.S. Public*, pg. 1222
ADVANCED MACHINING & TOOLING, INC.—See Shorehill Capital LLC; *U.S. Private*, pg. 3641
A.F.C. TOOL COMPANY INC.—See F.C. Industries Inc.; *U.S. Private*, pg. 1456
ALEXANDER MACHINE & TOOL COMPANY, INC.—See Behrman Brothers Management Corp.; *U.S. Private*, pg. 515
AMERICAN TOOLING CENTER, INC.; *U.S. Private*, pg. 257
THE ANCHOR DANLY COMPANY—See Connell Limited Partnership; *U.S. Private*, pg. 1017
ANKARSRUM DIE CASTING AB—See AB Monsteras Metall; *Int'l*, pg. 41
APPLIED COMPOSITES ENGINEERING, INC.—See AE Industrial Partners, LP; *U.S. Private*, pg. 111
ARMADA TOOLWORKS LIMITED; *Int'l*, pg. 574
ARMINTOOL MANUFACTURING & ARMIN MOLD CORPORATION; *U.S. Private*, pg. 330
ASAHI DIAMOND AMERICA, INC.—See Asahi Diamond Industrial Co. Ltd.; *Int'l*, pg. 592
ASAHI DIAMOND INDUSTRIAL CO. LTD. - CHIBA NO.2 FACTORY—See Asahi Diamond Industrial Co. Ltd.; *Int'l*, pg. 592
ASDEX CORPORATION—See Aichi Steel Corporation; *Int'l*, pg. 230
ATLANTIC GASKET CORP.; *U.S. Private*, pg. 373
ATLAS DIE, LLC - ATLANTA PLANT—See Auxo Investment Partners, LLC; *U.S. Private*, pg. 402
ATLAS DIE, LLC - GREENSBORO PLANT—See Auxo Investment Partners, LLC; *U.S. Private*, pg. 402
ATLAS DIE, LLC—See Auxo Investment Partners, LLC; *U.S. Private*, pg. 402
ATLAS TOOL INC.; *U.S. Private*, pg. 380
AUTO CRAFT TOOL & DIE CO.—See Arsenal Capital Management LP; *U.S. Private*, pg. 338
BAKER INDUSTRIES, INC.—See Lincoln Electric Holdings, Inc.; *U.S. Public*, pg. 1317
BAYLOFF STAMPED PRODUCTS, INC.; *U.S. Private*, pg. 496
BE&H EXTRUSION DIES, INC.—See Exco Technologies Limited; *Int'l*, pg. 2580
BEST CUTTING DIE CO.; *U.S. Private*, pg. 542
BIG 3 PRECISION PRODUCTS, INC.—See The Eastern Company; *U.S. Public*, pg. 2069
BRONSON & BRATTON INC.; *U.S. Private*, pg. 662
BTD MANUFACTURING, INC.—See Otter Tail Corporation; *U.S. Public*, pg. 1624
CAMERON TOOL CORP.—See Tool Tech, Inc.; *U.S. Private*, pg. 4185
CARR LANE MANUFACTURING CO.; *U.S. Private*, pg. 771
C&A TOOL ENGINEERING, INC.—See Development Bank of Japan, Inc.; *Int'l*, pg. 2087
CENTRAL EXTRUSION DIE CO—See Cockburn Enterprises Inc.; *U.S. Private*, pg. 959
CENTURY, INC.; *U.S. Private*, pg. 834
CENTURY SPECIALTIES—See Century, Inc.; *U.S. Private*, pg. 834
CHEN HSONG PRECISION MOULD CO., LTD.—See Chen Hsong Holdings Ltd.; *Int'l*, pg. 1464
CHICAGO ROLL CO., INC.—See Roll-Kraft, Inc.; *U.S. Private*, pg. 3474
COAST COMPOSITES, INC.—See AIP, LLC; *U.S. Private*, pg. 133
COCKBURN ENTERPRISES INC.; *U.S. Private*, pg. 959
COMPOSIDIE INC.; *U.S. Private*, pg. 1002
CONTAINER GRAPHICS CORPORATION; *U.S. Private*, pg. 1026
CONVEX MOLD, INC.—See Sonoco Products Company; *U.S. Public*, pg. 1906
CORRADAS.P.A.—See EuroGroup Laminations S.p.A.; *Int'l*, pg. 2552
CUPPLES' J & J COMPANY INCORPORATED; *U.S. Private*, pg. 1123
CUSTOM TOOL AND MANUFACTURING COMPANY; *U.S. Private*, pg. 1125
DANLY IEM SET DIVISION—See Connell Limited Partnership; *U.S. Private*, pg. 1017
DATUM INDUSTRIES, LLC—See Huizenga Manufacturing Group, Inc.; *U.S. Private*, pg. 2004
DAYTON PRECISION PUNCH INC.—See F.C. Industries Inc.; *U.S. Private*, pg. 1456
DEMMER ENGINEERING & MACHINE CO.; *U.S. Private*, pg. 1203
DIECRAFT AUSTRALIA PTY. LTD.—See Tupperware Brands Corporation; *U.S. Public*, pg. 2204
DIELINE CORP.—See Synergis Technologies Group; *U.S. Private*, pg. 3903
DIELINK—See Synergis Technologies Group; *U.S. Private*, pg. 3903
DIE SERVICES INTERNATIONAL, LLC; *U.S. Private*, pg. 1228
DIE-TECH INDUSTRIES, INC.; *U.S. Private*, pg. 1228
DISCO-SEA EUROPE S.R.L.—See Disco Corporation; *Int'l*, pg. 2132
D&M TOOL CORPORATION—See Specialty Manufacturers, Inc.; *U.S. Private*, pg. 3750
DONGGUAN JINNJIXING PRECISION OPTICAL CO., LTD.—See CHIALIN Precision Industrial Co., Ltd.; *Int'l*, pg. 1475
DOVER—See Danaher Corporation; *U.S. Public*, pg. 626
DRT MFG. COMPANY; *U.S. Private*, pg. 1279
DURA-METAL PRODUCTS CORP.—See KKR & Co. Inc.; *U.S. Public*, pg. 1252
FASOM AUTOMATION SYSTEMS, INC.—See Lincoln Electric Holdings, Inc.; *U.S. Public*, pg. 1317
EDCO, INC.—See Exco Technologies Limited; *Int'l*, pg. 2580
EHRHARDT TOOL & MACHINE, LLC—See Dunes Point Capital, LLC; *U.S. Private*, pg. 1288
ELGA AKTIEBOLAG—See Illinois Tool Works Inc.; *U.S. Public*, pg. 1103
ELIZABETH CARBIDE DIE CO. INC.—See Operio Group, LLC; *U.S. Private*, pg. 3032
ENEFCO USA, INC. - GLOBALDIE DIVISION—See Argosy Capital Group, LLC; *U.S. Private*, pg. 321
ENTERPRISE TOOL & DIE, INC.; *U.S. Private*, pg. 1404
EXCO ENGINEERING—See Exco Technologies Limited; *Int'l*, pg. 2580
EXCO EXTRUSION DIES, INC.—See Exco Technologies Limited; *Int'l*, pg. 2580
EXCO TECHNOLOGIES LIMITED; *Int'l*, pg. 2580
EXCO TOOLING SOLUTIONS—See Exco Technologies Limited; *Int'l*, pg. 2580
EXTRUSION DIES INDUSTRIES, LLC—See Nordson Corporation; *U.S. Public*, pg. 1532
FANCORT INDUSTRIES, INC.; *U.S. Private*, pg. 1472
F.C. INDUSTRIES INC.; *U.S. Private*, pg. 1455
FEHRMAN TOOL & DIE INC.—See The Velocity Group, Inc.; *U.S. Private*, pg. 4130
FEINTOOL CINCINNATI, INC.—See Artemis Holding AG; *Int'l*, pg. 582
FORT WAYNE WIRE DIE INC.; *U.S. Private*, pg. 1575
FOX VALLEY TOOL & DIE, INC.; *U.S. Private*, pg. 1585
FRONTIER TOOLING & DESIGN, INC.—See Andersen Corporation; *U.S. Private*, pg. 275
FROST CONVERTING SYSTEMS, INC.—See Matthews International Corporation; *U.S. Public*, pg. 1399
F.TECH MFG. (THAILAND) LTD.—See F-Tech Inc.; *Int'l*, pg. 2595
FUJI DIE CO., LTD. - HADANO 1 & 2 FACTORY—See Fuji Die Co., Ltd.; *Int'l*, pg. 2810
FUJI DIE CO., LTD. - KORIYAMA 2 FACTORY—See Fuji Die Co., Ltd.; *Int'l*, pg. 2810
FUJI DIE CO., LTD. - MOJI FACTORY—See Fuji Die Co., Ltd.; *Int'l*, pg. 2810
FUJI DIE CO., LTD. - NAGOYA FACTORY—See Fuji Die Co., Ltd.; *Int'l*, pg. 2810
FUJI DIE CO., LTD. - OSAKA FACTORY—See Fuji Die Co., Ltd.; *Int'l*, pg. 2810
FUJI DIE CO., LTD.; *Int'l*, pg. 2810
FUJILLOY THAILAND CO., LTD.—See Fuji Die Co., Ltd.; *Int'l*, pg. 2810
FUKUDA ENGINEERING CO., LTD.—See F-Tech Inc.; *Int'l*, pg. 2595
FUTABA CORPORATION - AKASHI MACHINERY & TOOLING FACTORY—See Futaba Corporation; *Int'l*, pg. 2850
FUTABA CORPORATION - CHONAN MACHINERY & TOOLING FACTORY—See Futaba Corporation; *Int'l*, pg. 2850
FUTABA CORPORATION - CHOSEI MACHINERY & TOOLING FACTORY—See Futaba Corporation; *Int'l*, pg. 2850
FUTABA CORPORATION - MUTSUZAWA MACHINERY & TOOLING FACTORY—See Futaba Corporation; *Int'l*, pg. 2850
FUTURAMIC TOOL & ENGINEERING COMPANY INC.; *U.S. Private*, pg. 1626
GASBARRE PRODUCTS INC., MCKEE CARBIDE TOOL DIVISION—See Gasbarre Products Inc.; *U.S. Private*, pg. 1648
GENESEE A & B, INC.—See Genesee Group, Inc.; *U.S. Private*, pg. 1669
G&H DIVERSIFIED MANUFACTURING LP; *U.S. Private*, pg. 1629
GREINER EXTRUSION GROUP GMBH—See Greiner Holding AG; *Int'l*, pg. 3079
HAMMILL MANUFACTURING COMPANY INC.; *U.S. Private*, pg. 1849
HANSON INTERNATIONAL INC.; *U.S. Private*, pg. 1856
HENAN LILIANG DIAMOND CO., LTD.; *Int'l*, pg. 3342
HILL ENGINEERING, INC.—See Mestek, Inc.; *U.S. Public*, pg. 1426
HIROSE SEIKO CO., LTD.—See Honda Motor Co., Ltd.; *Int'l*, pg. 3460
HODEN SEIMITSU KAKO KENKYUSHO CO., LTD.; *Int'l*, pg. 3438
HONDA ENGINEERING NORTH AMERICA—See Honda Motor Co., Ltd.; *Int'l*, pg. 3461
HS DIE & ENGINEERING, INC.; *U.S. Private*, pg. 1998
ILJIN DIAMOND CO LTD - ANSAN PLANT—See Iljin Diamond Co Ltd; *Int'l*, pg. 3614
ILJIN DIAMOND CO LTD - EUMSEONG PLANT—See Iljin Diamond Co Ltd; *Int'l*, pg. 3614
INDUSTRIAL MACHINING SERVICES, INC.; *U.S. Private*, pg. 2066
THE INVENTORS SHOP LLC—See Sea Box, Inc.; *U.S. Private*, pg. 3582
ITW BELGIUM S.P.R.L.—See Illinois Tool Works Inc.; *U.S. Public*, pg. 1104
JERGENS INC.; *U.S. Private*, pg. 2201
JRL VENTURES, INC.; *U.S. Private*, pg. 2240
K & S TOOL, DIE & MANUFACTURING, INC.; *U.S. Private*, pg. 2249
KUNSHAN JINNJI PRECISION MOLD CO., LTD.—See CHIALIN Precision Industrial Co., Ltd.; *Int'l*, pg. 1475
KYODO DIE-WORKS (THAILAND) CO., LTD.—See Hoden Seimitsu Kako Kenkyusho, Co., Ltd.; *Int'l*, pg. 3438
KYUSHU F-TECH INC.—See F-Tech Inc.; *Int'l*, pg. 2595
LC MANUFACTURING LLC—See MW Universal Inc.; *U.S. Private*, pg. 2822
L.H. CARBIDE CORPORATION—See L.H. Industries Corp.; *U.S. Private*, pg. 2366

333514 — SPECIAL DIE AND TOO...

LINK TOOL & DIE—See MNP Corporation; *U.S. Private*, pg. 2756
MAJESTIC INDUSTRIES INC.—See GenNx360 Capital Partners, L.P.; *U.S. Private*, pg. 1672
MANTZ AUTOMATION, INC.; *U.S. Private*, pg. 2567
MID-STATES FORGING DIE & TOOL CO.—See Modern Drop Forge Co.; *U.S. Private*, pg. 2760
MIDWAY DIE, LLC—See Auxo Investment Partners, LLC; *U.S. Private*, pg. 402
MISTEQUAY GROUP LTD.; *U.S. Private*, pg. 2749
MOLDMAKERS DIE CAST TOOLING DIVISION INC.—See MGS Manufacturing Group, Inc.; *U.S. Private*, pg. 2695
MOLEX SINGAPORE PTE. LTD.—See Koch Industries, Inc.; *U.S. Private*, pg. 2334
MTD MICRO MOLDING; *U.S. Private*, pg. 2809
MXL INDUSTRIES, INC.—See The Pritzker Group - Chicago, LLC; *U.S. Private*, pg. 4099
NANOTECHNOLOGY MANUFACTURING PTE. LTD.—See Fu Yu Corporation Limited; *Int'l*, pg. 2801
NEW CRAFT TOOL & DIE—See MNP Corporation; *U.S. Private*, pg. 2756
NORDSON EXTRUSION DIES INDUSTRIES. LLC—See Nordson Corporation; *U.S. Public*, pg. 1534
NORDSON PPS (SHANGHAI) CO., LTD.—See Nordson Corporation; *U.S. Public*, pg. 1534
OBERG ARIZONA—See Oberg Industries Corp.; *U.S. Private*, pg. 2986
OBERG INDUSTRIES, INC.—See Oberg Industries Corp.; *U.S. Private*, pg. 2986
OBERG INDUSTRIES—See Oberg Industries Corp.; *U.S. Private*, pg. 2986
OMG, INC.—See Steel Partners Holdings L.P.; *U.S. Public*, pg. 1943
OXBOW MACHINE PRODUCTS INC.; *U.S. Private*, pg. 3056
PANAVISE TOOL (CHANGZHOU), LLC—See Panavise Products, Inc.; *U.S. Private*, pg. 3085
PARAGON DIE & ENGINEERING COMPANY; *U.S. Private*, pg. 3091
PENN STATE TOOL & DIE CORPORATION; *U.S. Private*, pg. 3135
PENN UNITED TECHNOLOGIES, INC.; *U.S. Private*, pg. 3135
PHB TOOL & DIE—See PHB Inc.; *U.S. Private*, pg. 3167
POLYGON SOLUTIONS, INC.; *U.S. Private*, pg. 3225
PORTER PRECISION PRODUCTS COMPANY; *U.S. Private*, pg. 3232
PRECISION GRINDING & MANUFACTURING; *U.S. Private*, pg. 3245
PRECISION PUNCH CORPORATION; *U.S. Private*, pg. 3246
PRODELCON SDN. BHD.—See Globaltec Formation Berhad; *Int'l*, pg. 3004
P.T. ASAHI DIAMOND INDUSTRIAL INDONESIA—See Asahi Diamond Industrial Co. Ltd.; *Int'l*, pg. 592
PT. FUJILLOY INDONESIA—See Fuji Die Co., Ltd.; *Int'l*, pg. 2810
PT. ITT FLUID TECHNOLOGY INDONESIA—See ITT Inc.; *U.S. Public*, pg. 1178
QUALA-DIE, INC.—See Penn United Technologies, Inc.; *U.S. Private*, pg. 3135
QUALITY TOOL INC.; *U.S. Private*, pg. 3321
RAILTECH BOUTET INC.—See CVC Capital Partners SICAV-FIS S.A.; *Int'l*, pg. 1887
RING PRECISON COMPONENTS—See PMT Group Inc; *U.S. Private*, pg. 3219
SEILKOP INDUSTRIES INC.; *U.S. Private*, pg. 3599
SERVICE TOOL & DIE, INC.; *U.S. Private*, pg. 3616
SE SETCO SERVICE COMPANY—See Holden Industries, Inc.; *U.S. Private*, pg. 1962
SE SETCO SERVICE COMPANY—See The Timken Company; *U.S. Public*, pg. 2133
SFC KOENIG AG—See IDEX Corp; *U.S. Public*, pg. 1092
SHANGHAI XU HUI DIAMOND INDUSTRIAL CO., LTD.—See Asahi Diamond Industrial Co. Ltd.; *Int'l*, pg. 592
SHILOH INDUSTRIES—See Shiloh Industries, Inc.; *U.S. Private*, pg. 3636
SHINHAN DIAMOND INDUSTRIAL CO., LTD.—See Asahi Diamond Industrial Co. Ltd.; *Int'l*, pg. 592
SHINWA DIE CO., LTD.—See Fuji Die Co., Ltd.; *Int'l*, pg. 2810
SHIPPO ASAHI MOULDS (THAILAND) CO., LTD.—See Daido Metal Corporation; *Int'l*, pg. 1922
SOUTHERN STEEL & WIRE INC.—See Highland Supply Corporation; *U.S. Private*, pg. 1939
STANEK TOOL CORP.—See Jacsten Holdings, LLC; *U.S. Private*, pg. 2181
STILLWATER TECHNOLOGIES, LLC—See Brixey & Meyer, Inc.; *U.S. Private*, pg. 658
SUPERIOR DIE SET CORP.; *U.S. Private*, pg. 3876
SUPERIOR PRODUCTION LLC; *U.S. Private*, pg. 3880
TELLA TOOL & MANUFACTURING COMPANY; *U.S. Private*, pg. 3962
TESSY AUTOMATION, LLC—See Tessy Plastics Corp; *U.S. Private*, pg. 3973
TIANJIN HEXING MECHATRONICS TECHNOLOGY CO., LTD.—See Hoden Seimitsu Kako Kenkyusho Co., Ltd.; *Int'l*, pg. 3438
TITAN, INC.—See The Burke Porter Group; *U.S. Private*, pg. 4003
TMK MANUFACTURING, INC.—See Aterian Investment Management, L.P.; *U.S. Private*, pg. 367
TOOL TECH, INC.; *U.S. Private*, pg. 4185
TRIANGLE TOOL CORPORATION; *U.S. Private*, pg. 4226
VI MANUFACTURING INC.; *U.S. Private*, pg. 4375
VOTAW PRECISION TECHNOLOGIES, INC.—See Doerfer Corporation; *U.S. Private*, pg. 1253
VOTAW PRECISION TECHNOLOGIES, INC.—See Stone River Capital Partners, LLC; *U.S. Private*, pg. 3826
VOTAW PRECISION TECHNOLOGIES, INC.—See Wynnchurch Capital, L.P.; *U.S. Private*, pg. 4577
WEST PHARMACEUTICAL SERVICES CORNWALL LTD.—See West Pharmaceutical Services, Inc.; *U.S. Public*, pg. 2353
WILSON TOOL INTERNATIONAL INC.; *U.S. Private*, pg. 4531
WIND MILL WOODWORKING, INC.—See Amerhart Limited; *U.S. Private*, pg. 219
WORLDIA NICE NOVA DIAMOND TECHNOLOGY (JIAXING) CO., LTD.—See Beijing Worldia Diamond Tools Co., Ltd.; *Int'l*, pg. 961
WORTHINGTON CYLINDER CORPORATION—See Worthington Industries, Inc.; *U.S. Public*, pg. 2383
YUMEI TECHNOLOGIES SDN. BHD.—See Advanced Systems Automation Limited; *Int'l*, pg. 162

333515 — CUTTING TOOL AND MACHINE TOOL ACCESSORY MANUFACTURING

ACME INDUSTRIAL COMPANY—See Jergens Inc.; *U.S. Private*, pg. 2201
ADVAL TECH HOLDING AG; *Int'l*, pg. 155
A.G. DAVIS/AA GAGE; *U.S. Private*, pg. 25
AGI-VR/WESSON INC—See The Jordan Company, L.P.; *U.S. Private*, pg. 4060
AKELA LTD.—See Thermwood Corporation; *U.S. Private*, pg. 4143
ALVORD-POLK INC.; *U.S. Private*, pg. 214
AMADA TOOL PRECISION CO., LTD.—See Amada Holdings Co., Ltd.; *Int'l*, pg. 404
AMERICAN DRILL BUSHING CO.; *U.S. Private*, pg. 231
AMERICAN HOFMANN CORPORATION; *U.S. Private*, pg. 236
ANCA GMBH—See ANCA Pty Ltd; *Int'l*, pg. 447
ANCA PTY LTD; *Int'l*, pg. 447
ANCA (UK) LTD—See ANCA Pty Ltd; *Int'l*, pg. 447
ANCA (USA) INC—See ANCA Pty Ltd; *Int'l*, pg. 447
ANDRITZ IGGESUND TOOLS AB—See ANDRITZ AG; *Int'l*, pg. 452
APOLLO MACHINE & WELDING LTD.; *Int'l*, pg. 518
ARCH GLOBAL PRECISION LLC—See The Jordan Company, L.P.; *U.S. Private*, pg. 4060
ASAHI DIAMOND DE MEXICO, S.A. DE C.V.—See Asahi Diamond Industrial Co. Ltd.; *Int'l*, pg. 592
ASAHI DIAMOND INDUSTRIAL EUROPE SAS—See Asahi Diamond Industrial Co. Ltd.; *Int'l*, pg. 592
ASAHI DIAMOND INDUSTRIAL GERMANY GMBH—See Asahi Diamond Industrial Co. Ltd.; *Int'l*, pg. 592
ASAHI DIAMOND INDUSTRIAL MALAYSIA SDN. BHD.—See Asahi Diamond Industrial Co. Ltd.; *Int'l*, pg. 592
ASAHI DIAMOND INDUSTRIAL SCANDINAVIA AB—See Asahi Diamond Industrial Co. Ltd.; *Int'l*, pg. 592
ASAHI DIAMOND (THAILAND) CO., LTD.—See Asahi Diamond Industrial Co. Ltd.; *Int'l*, pg. 592
ASG JERGENS INC.—See Jergens Inc.; *U.S. Private*, pg. 2201
ASHLAND TECHNOLOGIES, INC.; *U.S. Private*, pg. 349
ASKO, INC.—See ANDRITZ AG; *Int'l*, pg. 455
ATS AUTOMATION TOOLING SYSTEMS GMBH - WINNENDEN—See ATS Corporation; *Int'l*, pg. 695
AVANTEC AUSTRIA GMBH—See AVANTEC Zerspantechnik GmbH; *Int'l*, pg. 735
AVANTEC ZERSPANTECHNIK GMBH; *Int'l*, pg. 735
BASF CHEMCAT THAILAND LIMITED—See BASF SE; *Int'l*, pg. 872
BEIJING WORLDIA DIAMOND TOOLS CO., LTD.; *Int'l*, pg. 960
BERNDORF AG; *Int'l*, pg. 986
BERTRAM & GRAF GMBH—See Steel Partners Holdings L.P.; *U.S. Public*, pg. 1943
BFT GMBH—See Dr. Aichhorn GmbH; *Int'l*, pg. 2190
BITNER TOOLING TECHNOLOGIES—See L Squared Capital Management LP; *U.S. Private*, pg. 2362
BLOUNT EUROPE, S.A.—See American Securities LLC; *U.S. Private*, pg. 247
BLOUNT EUROPE, S.A.—See P2 Capital Partners, LLC; *U.S. Private*, pg. 3061
BLOUNT GMBH—See American Securities LLC; *U.S. Private*, pg. 247
BLOUNT GMBH—See P2 Capital Partners, LLC; *U.S. Private*, pg. 3061
BLOUNT JAPAN, INC.—See American Securities LLC; *U.S. Private*, pg. 247
BLOUNT JAPAN, INC.—See P2 Capital Partners, LLC; *U.S. Private*, pg. 3062
BLOUNT UK LTD.—See American Securities LLC; *U.S. Private*, pg. 247
BLOUNT UK LTD.—See P2 Capital Partners, LLC; *U.S. Private*, pg. 3062
BRINKMAN INTERNATIONAL GROUP, INC.; *U.S. Private*, pg. 655
BRODERNA INGEMAR OCH BO MEKANISKA AB—See CTT Systems AB; *Int'l*, pg. 1874
BYSTRONIC UK LTD.—See Bystronic AG; *Int'l*, pg. 1236
CAL SDI, INC.; *U.S. Private*, pg. 715
CALTROL, INC.; *U.S. Private*, pg. 723
CAMERON—See The Stratford-Cambridge Group Co.; *U.S. Private*, pg. 4123
CEDIMA GMBH; *Int'l*, pg. 1388
CHANGSHA DIALINE NEW MATERIAL SCIENCE & TECHNOLOGY CO., LTD.; *Int'l*, pg. 1444
CHICAGO RIVET & MACHINE COMPANY-ALBIA DIVISION—See Chicago Rivet & Machine Company; *U.S. Public*, pg. 488
C & H PRECISION LIMITED—See Avingtrans plc; *Int'l*, pg. 743
COGSDILL TOOL PRODUCTS, INC.; *U.S. Private*, pg. 962
COMINIX INDIA PRIVATE LIMITED—See Cominix Co., Ltd.; *Int'l*, pg. 1714
COMINIX TRADING PHILIPPINES, INC.—See Cominix Co., Ltd.; *Int'l*, pg. 1714
COMPOSITE PRODUCTS LIMITED—See Avingtrans plc; *Int'l*, pg. 743
CONCUT, INC.—See Dixie Diamond Manufacturing, Inc.; *U.S. Private*, pg. 1245
CORDED STRAP (NZ) LIMITED—See Bunzl plc; *Int'l*, pg. 1218
CRAFTSTECH, INC.—See KKR & Co. Inc.; *U.S. Public*, pg. 1252
CUTLITE PENTA SRL—See El.En. S.p.A.; *Int'l*, pg. 2341
CUTTING SPECIALISTS, INC.—See Beall Manufacturing, Inc.; *U.S. Private*, pg. 505
DANIELS GROUP INC.; *U.S. Private*, pg. 1156
DE NEERS TOOLS LIMITED; *Int'l*, pg. 1996
DE-STA-CO (ASIA) COMPANY, LIMITED—See Stabilus; *U.S. Private*, pg. 3774
DE-STA-CO BENELUX B.V.—See Stabilus; *U.S. Private*, pg. 3774
DE-STA-CO EUROPE GMBH—See Stabilus; *U.S. Private*, pg. 3774
DETROIT EDGE TOOL COMPANY; *U.S. Private*, pg. 1216
DIAMOND INNOVATIONS INTERNATIONAL SALES—See KKR & Co. Inc.; *U.S. Public*, pg. 1253
DIJET GMBH—See DIJET Industrial Co., Ltd; *Int'l*, pg. 2125
DIJET INDUSTRIAL CO., LTD - MIE PLANT—See DIJET Industrial Co., Ltd; *Int'l*, pg. 2125
DIJET INDUSTRIAL CO., LTD - TONDABAYASHI PLANT—See DIJET Industrial Co., Ltd; *Int'l*, pg. 2125
DISCO CORPORATION - CHINO PLANT—See Disco Corporation; *Int'l*, pg. 2131
DISCO CORPORATION - KURE PLANT—See Disco Corporation; *Int'l*, pg. 2132
DISCO CORPORATION - KUWABATA PLANT—See Disco Corporation; *Int'l*, pg. 2132
DMG MORI SEIKI INDIA PVT. LTD.—See DMG MORI Co., Ltd.; *Int'l*, pg. 2145
DMG MORI SPARE PARTS GMBH—See DMG MORI Co., Ltd.; *Int'l*, pg. 2144
DORRENBERG SPECIAL STEELS PTE. LTD.—See Gesco AG; *Int'l*, pg. 2945
DUVAL PRECISION GRINDING INC.—See Peter Pan Bus Lines, Inc.; *U.S. Private*, pg. 3159
DYNAMIC INSTRUMENTS INC.—See Technology for Energy Corporation; *U.S. Private*, pg. 3955
DYNATECT MANUFACTURING, INC.—See 3i Group plc; *Int'l*, pg. 8
DYNATEX INTERNATIONAL; *U.S. Private*, pg. 1300
EDGECRAFT CORPORATION—See The Legacy Companies; *U.S. Private*, pg. 4069
EINHELL FINLAND OY—See Einhell Germany AG; *Int'l*, pg. 2333
ELEMENT SIX GMBH—See Anglo American PLC; *Int'l*, pg. 462
ELEMENT SIX (PRODUCTION) PROPRIETARY LIMITED—See Anglo American PLC; *Int'l*, pg. 462
ELUMATEC AG—See Cifin S.r.l.; *Int'l*, pg. 1606
EMKAY TAPS & CUTTING TOOLS LTD.; *Int'l*, pg. 2383
ENERPAC TOOL GROUP CORP.; *U.S. Public*, pg. 765
THE ENTWISTLE CO - DANVILLE FACILITY—See Brodart Co.; *U.S. Private*, pg. 661
ES INDUSTRY CO LTD; *Int'l*, pg. 2500
EUROTEKNA S.R.L.—See I.M.A. Industria Macchine Automatiche S.p.A.; *Int'l*, pg. 3565
FABRICA DE SCULE RASNOV SA; *Int'l*, pg. 2599
FALL MACHINE COMPANY, LLC—See White Wolf Capital LLC; *U.S. Private*, pg. 4510
FESCO SYSTEMS LLC; *U.S. Private*, pg. 1499
FIRSTAR PRECISION CORP.—See Empowered Ventures, Inc.; *U.S. Private*, pg. 1387

333517 — MACHINE TOOL MANUFA...

FLEXBAR MACHINE CORP.; *U.S. Private*, pg. 1543
FLORIDA KNIFE CO.; *U.S. Private*, pg. 1549
FLOW ASIA CORPORATION—See AIP, LLC; *U.S. Private*, pg. 137
FLOW ULTRA HIGH PRESSURE WATERJET TECHNOLOGY (SHANGHAI) CO., LTD.—See AIP, LLC; *U.S. Private*, pg. 137
FORKARDT DEUTSCHLAND GMBH—See Privet Fund Management, LLC; *U.S. Private*, pg. 3269
FORKARDT FRANCE SAS—See Privet Fund Management, LLC; *U.S. Private*, pg. 3269
FORKARDT INC.—See Privet Fund Management, LLC; *U.S. Private*, pg. 3269
FRANK LEMEKS TOW—See Gesco AG; *Int'l*, pg. 2945
FRENCKEN MECHATRONICS B.V.—See Frencken Group Limited; *Int'l*, pg. 2772
FRENCKEN TECHNICAL PROJECTS ASSEMBLY B.V.—See Frencken Group Limited; *Int'l*, pg. 2772
FUJI AIR TOOLS CO., LTD—See Atlas Copco AB; *Int'l*, pg. 679
FUJI ROZAI CO., LTD.—See ARE Holdings, Inc.; *Int'l*, pg. 557
GENHAM DIAMOND TOOLING, INC.—See L Squared Capital Management LP; *U.S. Private*, pg. 2361
GEORG KESEL GMBH & CO. KG—See Gesco AG; *Int'l*, pg. 2945
GLEASON CUTTING TOOLS CORPORATION—See Gleason Corporation; *U.S. Private*, pg. 1708
GLEASON-PFAUTER MASCHINENFABRIK GMBH—See Gleason Corporation; *U.S. Private*, pg. 1708
GREENLEAF CORPORATION; *U.S. Private*, pg. 1778
HALCYON TECHNOLOGY (M) SDN. BHD.—See Halcyon Technology Public Company Limited; *Int'l*, pg. 3227
HALCYON TECHNOLOGY (PHILIPPINES) INC.—See Halcyon Technology Public Company Limited; *Int'l*, pg. 3227
HALCYON TECHNOLOGY PUBLIC COMPANY LIMITED; *Int'l*, pg. 3227
HANWA AEROSPACE USA—See Hanwha Group; *Int'l*, pg. 3264
HARDINGE MACHINE TOOLS B.V.—See Privet Fund Management, LLC; *U.S. Private*, pg. 3269
H.B. CARBIDE COMPANY—See Star Cutter Company; *U.S. Private*, pg. 3784
HC GROUP SEARCH INC.—See HC Group, Inc.; *Int'l*, pg. 3297
HEBI HAICHANG SPECIAL EQUIPMENT CO LTD—See China Auto Electronics Group Limited; *Int'l*, pg. 1483
HEINRICH CO.—See Ace Stamping & Machine Co, Inc.; *U.S. Private*, pg. 57
HENAN HUANGHE WHIRLWIND CO., LTD.; *Int'l*, pg. 3342
HERRAMIENTAS CLEVELAND, S.A. DE C.V.—See Dalian Top-Eastern Group Co., Ltd.; *Int'l*, pg. 1953
HEUS MANUFACTURING COMPANY, INC.; *U.S. Private*, pg. 1928
HI-LIFE TOOLS—See Berkshire Hathaway Inc.; *U.S. Public*, pg. 315
HITTCO TOOLS LIMITED; *Int'l*, pg. 3427
HONDA ENGINEERING ASIAN CO., LTD.—See Honda Motor Co., Ltd.; *Int'l*, pg. 3461
HONDA ENGINEERING EUROPE LTD.—See Honda Motor Co., Ltd.; *Int'l*, pg. 3461
HOUGEN MANUFACTURING INC.; *U.S. Private*, pg. 1990
HOVIS PRECISION PRODUCTS INC.—See DRT Mfg. Company; *U.S. Private*, pg. 1279
HPMT DEUTSCHLAND GMBH—See HPMT Holding Berhad; *Int'l*, pg. 3501
HPMT (SHENZHEN) LIMITED—See HPMT Holding Berhad; *Int'l*, pg. 3501
HPTEC GMBH—See Hunan Nonferrous Metals Corporation Ltd.; *Int'l*, pg. 3533
HUSQVARNA CONSTRUCTION PRODUCTS NORTH AMERICA, INC. - CORONA—See Husqvarna AB; *Int'l*, pg. 3539
HWACHEON ASIA PACIFIC PTE LTD—See Hwacheon Machine Tool Co., Ltd.; *Int'l*, pg. 3541
HWACHEON MACHINERY AMERICA, INC.—See Hwacheon Machine Tool Co., Ltd.; *Int'l*, pg. 3542
HWACHEON MACHINERY EUROPE GMBH—See Hwacheon Machine Tool Co., Ltd.; *Int'l*, pg. 3542
HWACHEON MACHINE TOOL VIETNAM CO., LTD.—See Hwacheon Machine Tool Co., Ltd.; *Int'l*, pg. 3541
HYPERION MATERIALS & TECHNOLOGIES DE MEXICO S.A. DE C.V.—See KKR & Co. Inc.; *U.S. Public*, pg. 1253
HYPEX INC.; *U.S. Private*, pg. 2019
IG-MEX, S. DE R.L. DE C.V.—See Regal Rexnord Corporation; *U.S. Public*, pg. 1773
IMCO CARBIDE TOOL INC.; *U.S. Private*, pg. 2046
INGERSOLL CUTTING TOOL COMPANY—See Berkshire Hathaway Inc.; *U.S. Public*, pg. 307
INGERSOLL WERKZEUGE GMBH—See Berkshire Hathaway Inc.; *U.S. Public*, pg. 307
INTERTECH WORLDWIDE CORPORATION; *U.S. Private*, pg. 2127
INTRA, CORP.; *U.S. Private*, pg. 2129
IPD NEDERLAND B.V.—See MSCI Inc.; *U.S. Public*, pg. 1483
JADE EQUIPMENT CORP.—See The Jordan Company, L.P.; *U.S. Private*, pg. 4060

JW GLASS RECYCLING CO., LTD.—See ARE Holdings, Inc.; *Int'l*, pg. 557
KBC TOOLS INCORPORATED - MACHINERY DIVISION—See KBC Tools Incorporated; *U.S. Private*, pg. 2268
KENNAMETAL METALWORKING SOLUTIONS & SERVICES GROUP—See Kennametal Inc.; *U.S. Public*, pg. 1222
KMT GMBH—See AIP, LLC; *U.S. Private*, pg. 138
KMT WATERJET SYSTEMS, INC.—See AIP, LLC; *U.S. Private*, pg. 138
KOREMURA ASAHI DIAMOND INDUSTRIAL CO., LTD.—See Asahi Diamond Industrial Co. Ltd.; *Int'l*, pg. 592
LAPMASTER INDIA PRIVATE LIMITED—See Angeles Equity Partners, LLC; *U.S. Private*, pg. 282
LAPMASTER INDIA PRIVATE LIMITED—See Bison Capital Asset Management, LLC; *U.S. Private*, pg. 566
LAWN STAR PTY. LTD.—See Einhell Germany AG; *Int'l*, pg. 2333
LUCAS-MILHAUPT WARWICK LLC.—See Steel Partners Holdings L.P.; *U.S. Public*, pg. 1943
LUMENTUM OPERATIONS LLC—See Lumentum Holdings Inc.; *U.S. Public*, pg. 1348
MACHINEFABRIEK GEBRS.FRENCKEN B.V.—See Frencken Group Limited; *Int'l*, pg. 2773
M.A. FORD MANUFACTURING CO.; *U.S. Private*, pg. 2527
MAHR, SPOL S.R.O.—See Carl Mahr Holding GmbH; *Int'l*, pg. 1333
MASTERCUT TOOL CORP.; *U.S. Private*, pg. 2608
MASTER WORK-HOLDING, INC.—See Rohm Products of America; *U.S. Private*, pg. 3473
MATVEST INC.; *U.S. Private*, pg. 2614
MICHIGAN DRILL CORPORATION; *U.S. Private*, pg. 2700
MILLSTAR LLC—See Galaxy Technologies Corp.; *U.S. Private*, pg. 1636
MISTEQUAY—See Mistequay Group Ltd.; *U.S. Private*, pg. 2749
MULTI-METALS; *U.S. Private*, pg. 2812
MUL-T-LOCK MACHINERY LTD.—See ASSA ABLOY AB; *Int'l*, pg. 640
NAP GLADU - MARIEVILLE—See Audax Group, Limited Partnership; *U.S. Private*, pg. 389
NAP GLADU—See Audax Group, Limited Partnership; *U.S. Private*, pg. 389
NED CORP.; *U.S. Private*, pg. 2879
THE NEW JERSEY WIRE STITCHING MACHINE CO.—See Precision Automation Co., Inc.; *U.S. Private*, pg. 3244
NIAGARA CUTTER, INC.; *U.S. Private*, pg. 2924
NORBAR TORQUE TOOLS (NZ) LIMITED—See Snap-on Incorporated; *U.S. Public*, pg. 1898
NORDSON RUSSIA LIMITED LIABILITY COMPANY—See Nordson Corporation; *U.S. Public*, pg. 1534
NORTH AMERICAN TOOL CORPORATION—See L Squared Capital Management LP; *U.S. Private*, pg. 2361
OHIO METAL WORKING PRODUCTS CO., INC.—See Art's-Way Manufacturing Co., Inc.; *U.S. Public*, pg. 201
OOO SUNNEN RUS—See Sunnen Products Company; *U.S. Private*, pg. 3868
O.S. WALKER CO. INC.—See Alliance Holdings, Inc.; *U.S. Private*, pg. 183
OTT-JAKOB SPANNTECHNIK GMBH—See Fukuda Corporation; *Int'l*, pg. 2839
OY ATLAS COPCO ROTEX AB—See Atlas Copco AB; *Int'l*, pg. 684
PALMGREN STEEL PRODUCTS, INC.—See Colovos Company; *U.S. Private*, pg. 975
PARTSMASTER, INC.—See Distribution Solutions Group, Inc.; *U.S. Public*, pg. 669
P&B HOLDINGS, INC.; *U.S. Private*, pg. 3058
PETER WOLTERS JAPAN CO., LTD.—See Angeles Equity Partners, LLC; *U.S. Private*, pg. 282
PETER WOLTERS JAPAN CO., LTD.—See Bison Capital Asset Management, LLC; *U.S. Private*, pg. 566
PFERD-RUEGGEBERG BVBA—See August Rueggeberg GmbH & Co. KG PFERD-Werkzeuge; *Int'l*, pg. 703
PFERD-VSM SP.Z.O.O.—See August Rueggeberg GmbH & Co. KG PFERD-Werkzeuge; *Int'l*, pg. 703
PMC-COLINET, INC.—See Park-Ohio Holdings Corp.; *U.S. Public*, pg. 1639
POWERS FASTENERS INC.—See Stanley Black & Decker, Inc.; *U.S. Public*, pg. 1933
PRODUCTIVE SOLUTIONS, INC.—See River Associates Investments, LLC; *U.S. Private*, pg. 3443
PRODUCTOS ELECTRICOS APLICADOS, S. DE R.L. DE C.V.—See Regal Rexnord Corporation; *U.S. Public*, pg. 1773
PTM CORPORATION; *U.S. Private*, pg. 3298
REGAL BELOIT (WUXI) CO., LTD.—See Regal Rexnord Corporation; *U.S. Public*, pg. 1773
RIKEN SEIKO CO., LTD.—See Daido Steel Co., Ltd.; *Int'l*, pg. 1923
THE RIPLEY COMPANY—See CapitalWorks, LLC; *U.S. Private*, pg. 742
ROTHENBERGER USA LLC—See Dr. Helmut Rothenberger Holding GmbH; *Int'l*, pg. 2191
ROTOMETRICS INTERNATIONAL A/S—See MPE Partners, LLC; *U.S. Private*, pg. 2803
SANISTAL A/S—See Ahlsell AB; *Int'l*, pg. 223
SCHAUBLIN GMBH—See RBC Bearings Incorporated; *U.S. Public*, pg. 1766
SL INDUSTRIES, INC.—See Steel Partners Holdings L.P.; *U.S. Public*, pg. 1943
SOUTHERN GAGE INC.—See Alpha Q, Inc.; *U.S. Private*, pg. 199
SPECTRUM TRACER SERVICES, LLC—See NCS Multistage Holdings, Inc.; *U.S. Public*, pg. 1503
SPEEDGRIP CHUCK, INC.—See The Stratford-Cambridge Group Co.; *U.S. Private*, pg. 4123
SPIRALOCK CORPORATION—See Stanley Black & Decker, Inc.; *U.S. Public*, pg. 1934
STAR CUTTER COMPANY - ELK RAPIDS ENGINEERING DIVISION—See Star Cutter Company; *U.S. Private*, pg. 3784
STAR CUTTER COMPANY; *U.S. Private*, pg. 3784
STAR SU FEDERAL DE MEXICO S.A. DE C.V—See Star Cutter Company; *U.S. Private*, pg. 3784
SUZHOU ALLIED TECH CO., LTD.—See Allied Technologies Ltd.; *Int'l*, pg. 358
SYNEO, LLC—See Arcline Investment Management LP; *U.S. Private*, pg. 315
TAEGUTEC LTD—See Berkshire Hathaway Inc.; *U.S. Public*, pg. 308
TAT EE METROLOGY SDN BHD—See Chien Wei Precise Technology Co., Ltd.; *Int'l*, pg. 1477
TELEDYNE LTD.—See Teledyne Technologies Incorporated; *U.S. Public*, pg. 1994
TOOLTEC (QINGDAO) TOOL CO LTD—See Atlas Copco AB; *Int'l*, pg. 684
TORCHMATE, INC.—See Lincoln Electric Holdings, Inc.; *U.S. Public*, pg. 1318
TOYO KNIFE COMPANY, LTD—See Ferrotec Holdings Corporation; *Int'l*, pg. 2643
UNIVERSAL / DEVLIEG LLC—See Mistequay Group Ltd.; *U.S. Private*, pg. 2750
VERMEER MV SOLUTIONS, INC—See Vermeer Corporation; *U.S. Private*, pg. 4366
VIKING DRILL & TOOL INC.; *U.S. Private*, pg. 4382
VISTA METALS INC.; *U.S. Private*, pg. 4403
WEB INDUSTRIES, INC.—See Web Industries Inc.; *U.S. Private*, pg. 4464
WERKZEUGBAU LAICHINGEN GMBH—See Gesco AG; *Int'l*, pg. 2946
WORLDIA EUROPE GMBH—See Beijing Worldia Diamond Tools Co., Ltd.; *Int'l*, pg. 960
ZENITH CUTTER CO.; *U.S. Private*, pg. 4601
ZHONGBAN TRADE SHANGHAI CO., LTD.—See Cominix Co., Ltd.; *Int'l*, pg. 1714
ZHUZHOU CEMENTED CARBIDE CUTTING TOOLS CO., LTD.—See Hunan Nonferrous Metals Corporation Ltd.; *Int'l*, pg. 3533

333517 — MACHINE TOOL MANUFACTURING

3M COMPANY - MONTROSE—See 3M Company; *U.S. Public*, pg. 5
ABPRO BIO CO., LTD.; *Int'l*, pg. 67
ACOT TOOLING XIAMEN LTD.—See Acma Ltd.; *Int'l*, pg. 107
ADDISONMCKEE INC.—See Albion Investors, LLC; *U.S. Private*, pg. 153
ADDISON SAWS LIMITED; *Int'l*, pg. 129
ADTEX FUJI CO., LTD.—See Fuji Corporation; *Int'l*, pg. 2809
AGFM HOLDING CORPORATION; *U.S. Private*, pg. 127
AGIE CHARMILLES MACHINE TOOL CO., LTD.—See Georg Fischer AG; *Int'l*, pg. 2934
AGIE CHARMILLES SALES LTD.—See Georg Fischer AG; *Int'l*, pg. 2934
AGIE CHARMILLES SOUTH EAST ASIA PTE LTD—See Georg Fischer AG; *Int'l*, pg. 2934
AGIE S.P.A.—See Georg Fischer AG; *Int'l*, pg. 2934
AHRESTY KUMAMOTO CORPORATION—See Ahresty Corporation; *Int'l*, pg. 226
AHRESTY TECHNO SERVICE CORPORATION—See Ahresty Corporation; *Int'l*, pg. 226
AHRESTY TOCHIGI CORPORATION—See Ahresty Corporation; *Int'l*, pg. 226
AIDA HONG KONG, LTD.—See AIDA Engineering, Ltd.; *Int'l*, pg. 230
AIDA PRESSEN GMBH—See AIDA Engineering, Ltd.; *Int'l*, pg. 230
AIDA STAMPING TECHNOLOGY (INDIA) PVT LTD.—See AIDA Engineering, Ltd.; *Int'l*, pg. 230
AIDA STAMPING TECHNOLOGY (THAILAND) CO., LTD.—See AIDA Engineering, Ltd.; *Int'l*, pg. 230
ALATNICA A.D.; *Int'l*, pg. 292
ALGER MANUFACTURING, LLC; *U.S. Private*, pg. 166
ALINABAL ENGINEERED PRODUCTS—See Alinabal Holdings Corporation; *U.S. Private*, pg. 168
ALLEN FRANCE SAS—See Illinois Tool Works Inc.; *U.S. Public*, pg. 1101
ALTRAD PLETTAC ASSCO GMBH—See Altrad Investment Authority SAS; *Int'l*, pg. 397

333517 — MACHINE TOOL MANUFA...   CORPORATE AFFILIATIONS

ALTRUST PRECISION TOOLING (DONGGUAN) CO., LTD.—See Combine Will International Holdings Limited; *Int'l*, pg. 1709
AMADA ASIA PTE. LTD.—See Amada Holdings Co., Ltd.; *Int'l*, pg. 403
AMADA HOLDINGS CO., LTD.; *Int'l*, pg. 403
AMADA LIANYUNGANG MACHINE TOOL CO., LTD—See Amada Holdings Co., Ltd.; *Int'l*, pg. 404
AMADA MACHINE TOOLS (THAILAND) CO., LTD—See Amada Holdings Co., Ltd.; *Int'l*, pg. 403
AMADA OUTILLAGE S.A.—See Amada Holdings Co., Ltd.; *Int'l*, pg. 404
AMADA SHANGHAI MACHINE TECH CO., LTD—See Amada Holdings Co., Ltd.; *Int'l*, pg. 404
AMERICAN METAL TECHNOLOGIES, LLC; *U.S. Private*, pg. 241
AMERICAN PRECISION INDUSTRIES INC.—See Fortive Corporation; *U.S. Public*, pg. 870
AMRU AND HANWHA INTERNATIONAL CO., LTD.—See Hanwha Group; *Int'l*, pg. 3265
ANCA DO BRASIL—See ANCA Pty Ltd; *Int'l*, pg. 448
ANDERSON-COOK INC. - CLINTON TWP. PLANT—See Anderson-Cook Inc.; *U.S. Private*, pg. 278
ANDERSON-COOK INC. - FRASER PLANT—See Anderson-Cook Inc.; *U.S. Private*, pg. 278
ANDERSON-COOK INC. - SHANGHAI PLANT—See Anderson-Cook Inc.; *U.S. Private*, pg. 278
ANDERSON-COOK INC.; *U.S. Private*, pg. 278
ANDERSON-COOK INC. - STRATFORD PLANT—See Anderson-Cook Inc.; *U.S. Private*, pg. 278
ANDRITZ IGGESUND TOOLS CANADA INC.—See ANDRITZ AG; *Int'l*, pg. 454
ANDRITZ KAISER GMBH—See ANDRITZ AG; *Int'l*, pg. 454
ANVA ARION SWEDEN AB—See AnVa Tubes & Components AB; *Int'l*, pg. 486
APPLICATION SPECIALTIES, INC.—See DXP Enterprises, Inc.; *U.S. Public*, pg. 697
ARCH CUTTING TOOLS - FLUSHING, LLC—See The Jordan Company, L.P.; *U.S. Private*, pg. 4060
A.S.A.P INDUSTRIES MANUFACTURING, LLC—See Boyne Capital Management, LLC; *U.S. Private*, pg. 628
ATLAS COPCO DRILLING SOLUTIONS—See Atlas Copco AB; *Int'l*, pg. 681
ATLAS COPCO KFT—See Atlas Copco AB; *Int'l*, pg. 679
ATS MACHINE TOOL DIVISION—See ATS Corporation; *Int'l*, pg. 695
AUROTEK CORPORATION - TAOYUAN FACTORY—See Aurotek Corporation; *Int'l*, pg. 714
AVDEL ITALIA S.R.L.—See Stanley Black & Decker, Inc.; *U.S. Public*, pg. 1931
AVDEL SPAIN SA—See Stanley Black & Decker, Inc.; *U.S. Public*, pg. 1931
AVERY INDIA LIMITED—See Illinois Tool Works Inc.; *U.S. Public*, pg. 1101
AVERY MALAYSIA SDN BHD—See Illinois Tool Works Inc.; *U.S. Public*, pg. 1101
AVERY WEIGH-TRONIX (SUZHOU) WEIGHING TECHNOLOGY CO. LTD.—See Illinois Tool Works Inc.; *U.S. Public*, pg. 1101
AVIC AVIATION HIGH-TECHNOLOGY CO., LTD.—See Aviation Industry Corporation of China; *Int'l*, pg. 741
AWEA MECHANTRONIC CO., LTD.; *Int'l*, pg. 753
AWEA MECHANTRONIC CO., LTD. - TAIWAN TAICHUNG FACTORY—See Awea Mechantronic Co., Ltd.; *Int'l*, pg. 753
AWEA MECHANTRONIC (SUZHOU) LTD.—See Awea Mechantronic Co., Ltd.; *Int'l*, pg. 753
AWEBA WERKZEUGBAU GMBH—See ANDRITZ AG; *Int'l*, pg. 455
AXLY PRODUCTION MACHINING INC.—See Gemini Group, Inc.; *U.S. Private*, pg. 1657
AXYZ AUTOMATION INC.—See AXYZ Automation Group Inc.; *Int'l*, pg. 773
THE BAIRD MACHINERY CORPORATION; *U.S. Private*, pg. 3991
BAKUER S.P.A.; *Int'l*, pg. 806
BALTEC MASCHINENBAU AG; *Int'l*, pg. 812
BANGALORE INTEGRATED SYSTEM SOLUTIONS PRIVATE LTD—See Illinois Tool Works Inc.; *U.S. Public*, pg. 1101
BANSON TOOL HIRE LIMITED—See Frank Key Group Limited; *Int'l*, pg. 2761
BARDONS & OLIVER, INC.; *U.S. Private*, pg. 474
BARNES INTERNATIONAL, INC.—See Komline-Sanderson Corporation; *U.S. Private*, pg. 2342
BARRANCA DIAMOND PRODUCTS, INC.—See MK Diamond Products, Inc.; *U.S. Private*, pg. 2753
BARTH INDUSTRIES, CO. LP—See NESCO, Inc.; *U.S. Private*, pg. 2886
BASE SPOLKA Z OGRANICZONA ODPOWIEDZIALNOSCIA—See Hellman & Friedman LLC; *U.S. Private*, pg. 1911
BAUCH ENGINEERING GMBH & CO. KG; *Int'l*, pg. 891
BAUER MANUFACTURING INC.—See BAUER Aktiengesellschaft; *Int'l*, pg. 892
BAYLOFF STAMPED PRODUCTS DETROIT, INC.—See Bayloff Stamped Products, Inc.; *U.S. Private*, pg. 496
BEIJING DAHENG LASER EQUIPMENT CO., LTD.—See Daheng New Epoch Technology, Inc.; *Int'l*, pg. 1913
BEIJING NO. 1 MACHINE TOOL PLANT—See Beijing Jingcheng Machinery Electric Holding Co., Ltd.; *Int'l*, pg. 953
BELCO INDUSTRIES, INC. - FAMCO MACHINE DIVISION—See Belco Industries, Inc.; *U.S. Private*, pg. 517
BELCO INDUSTRIES, INC.; *U.S. Private*, pg. 517
BENDTEC, INC.—See Bernhard Capital Partners Management, LP; *U.S. Private*, pg. 537
BENTELER GLASS PROCESSING GMBH—See Benteler International AG; *Int'l*, pg. 977
BEST WAY MECHANTRONIC CO.—See Awea Mechantronic Co., Ltd.; *Int'l*, pg. 753
BIRK MANUFACTURING, INC.; *U.S. Private*, pg. 564
BLACK & DECKER SSC CO., LTD.—See Stanley Black & Decker, Inc.; *U.S. Public*, pg. 1932
BLACKHAWK ENGINEERING, INC.—See Cie Automotive S.A.; *Int'l*, pg. 1604
BLOWTHERM S.P.A.; *Int'l*, pg. 1065
BOART LONGYEAR INC.—See Boart Longyear Ltd.; *Int'l*, pg. 1095
BOBST CENTRAL EUROPE LIMITED—See Bobst Group S.A.; *Int'l*, pg. 1095
BOBST (LATINOAMERICA NORTE Y CARIBE) S.A. DE C.V.—See Bobst Group S.A.; *Int'l*, pg. 1095
BOLDUC LEROUX INC.; *Int'l*, pg. 1102
BOLTEX INC.; *U.S. Private*, pg. 611
BOSUN CO LTD; *Int'l*, pg. 1118
BOURN & KOCH FELLOWS SERVICES GROUP—See Berkshire Hathaway Inc.; *U.S. Public*, pg. 298
BOURN & KOCH, INC.—See Berkshire Hathaway Inc.; *U.S. Public*, pg. 298
BRAMMER FRANCE—See Advent International Corporation; *U.S. Private*, pg. 98
BRINEY TOOLING SYSTEMS, INC.—See Gemini Group, Inc.; *U.S. Private*, pg. 1657
BRINKMAN PRODUCTS INC—See Brinkman International Group, Inc.; *U.S. Private*, pg. 655
BROOKS INSTRUMENT INDIA PRIVATE LIMITED—See Illinois Tool Works Inc.; *U.S. Public*, pg. 1102
BROOKS INSTRUMENT SINGAPORE PTE, LTD.—See Illinois Tool Works Inc.; *U.S. Public*, pg. 1102
BROWN & SHARPE INC—See Hexagon AB; *Int'l*, pg. 3367
BRUBAKER TOOL CORPORATION—See Talbot Holdings Inc.; *U.S. Private*, pg. 3925
BSL CORPORATION BERHAD; *Int'l*, pg. 1202
BTM COMPANY, LLC—See CapitalSouth Corp.; *U.S. Private*, pg. 742
BUTECH BLISS; *U.S. Private*, pg. 696
BYSTRONIC AUSTRIA GMBH—See Bystronic AG; *Int'l*, pg. 1236
BYSTRONIC LASER AG—See Bystronic AG; *Int'l*, pg. 1236
BYSTRONIC MASCHINEN AG—See Glaston Oyj Abp; *Int'l*, pg. 2989
BYSTRONIC SALES AG—See Bystronic AG; *Int'l*, pg. 1236
BYSTRONIC UK LTD.—See Bystronic AG; *Int'l*, pg. 1236
CALIFORNIA SERVICE TOOL INC.; *U.S. Private*, pg. 720
CAMOZZI GROUP - LUMEZZANE PLANT—See Camozzi Group; *Int'l*, pg. 1273
CAMOZZI GROUP - POLPENAZZE PLANT—See Camozzi Group; *Int'l*, pg. 1273
CAMOZZI GROUP; *Int'l*, pg. 1273
CAMOZZI MANUFACTURING SRL—See Camozzi Group; *Int'l*, pg. 1274
CAMOZZI PNEUMATIK AB—See Camozzi Group; *Int'l*, pg. 1274
CAPITAL TECHNOLOGIES, INC.—See Hess Industries, Inc.; *U.S. Private*, pg. 1927
CARRARO INDIA LTD.—See FLY Srl; *Int'l*, pg. 2715
CARVER, INC.—See Harbour Group Industries, Inc.; *U.S. Private*, pg. 1860
C DUGARD LTD; *Int'l*, pg. 1237
CERINNOV GROUP SA; *Int'l*, pg. 1422
CHANG TYPE INDUSTRIAL CO., LTD.; *Int'l*, pg. 1441
CHARLES G. ALLEN CO.; *U.S. Private*, pg. 852
CHARMILLES TECHNOLOGIES SA—See Georg Fischer AG; *Int'l*, pg. 2934
CHEVALIER MACHINERY CO., LTD.—See Falcon Machine Tools Co. Ltd.; *Int'l*, pg. 2611
CHEVALIER MACHINERY, INC.—See Falcon Machine Tools Co. Ltd.; *Int'l*, pg. 2611
CHICAGO RIVET & MACHINE COMPANY-TYRONE DIVISION—See Chicago Rivet & Machine Company; *U.S. Public*, pg. 488
CHIEN WEI PRECISE TECHNOLOGY CO., LTD.; *Int'l*, pg. 1477
CHINA RAILWAY CONSTRUCTION HEAVY INDUSTRY CORPORATION LIMITED—See China Railway Construction Corporation Limited; *Int'l*, pg. 1543
CHISHOLM, BOYD & WHITE CO.—See Venturedyne, Ltd.; *U.S. Private*, pg. 4358
CHIU TING INDUSTRIAL (HUIZHOU) CO., LTD.—See Chiu Ting Machinery Co., Ltd.; *Int'l*, pg. 1574
CHONGQING MACHINE TOOLS (GROUP) CO., LTD.—See Chongqing Machinery & Electronics Holding (Group) Co., Ltd.; *Int'l*, pg. 1580
CHUN ZU MACHINERY IND. CO., LTD.—See Chun Yu Works & Co., Ltd.; *Int'l*, pg. 1596
CIFUNSA DEL BAJIO, S.A. DE C.V.—See Grupo Industrial Saltillo S.A. de C.V.; *Int'l*, pg. 3130
THE CINCINNATI GILBERT MACHINE TOOL COMPANY, LLC; *U.S. Private*, pg. 4010
CINCINNATI INCORPORATED; *U.S. Private*, pg. 898
CINETIC GIUSTINA S.R.L.—See FIVES, Societe Anonyme; *Int'l*, pg. 2696
CIRCOR AEROSPACE—See KKR & Co. Inc.; *U.S. Public*, pg. 1242
CITIZEN MACCHINE ITALIA S.R.L.—See Citizen Watch Co., Ltd.; *Int'l*, pg. 1623
CITIZEN MACHINERY MIYANO CO., LTD.—See Citizen Watch Co., Ltd.; *Int'l*, pg. 1624
CITIZEN MACHINERY PHILIPPINES INC.—See Citizen Watch Co., Ltd.; *Int'l*, pg. 1624
CKS PRECISION MACHINING, INC.—See Gemini Group, Inc.; *U.S. Private*, pg. 1658
CLIFFORD-JACOBS FORGING COMPANY—See Mission Essential Personnel, LLC; *U.S. Private*, pg. 2747
CLIMAX GMBH—See Gladstone Management Corporation; *U.S. Private*, pg. 1705
CLIMAX PORTABLE MACHINE TOOLS, INC.—See Gladstone Management Corporation; *U.S. Private*, pg. 1705
CN PRECISION CASING (SHENZHEN) COMPANY LIMITED—See CN Innovations Holdings Limited; *Int'l*, pg. 1673
COHERENT EUROPE B.V.—See Coherent Corp.; *U.S. Public*, pg. 527
COHERENT ITALIA S.R.L.—See Coherent Corp.; *U.S. Public*, pg. 527
COHERENT SINGAPORE PTE., LTD.—See Coherent Corp.; *U.S. Public*, pg. 527
COIL TUBING TECHNOLOGY, INC.; *U.S. Private*, pg. 964
COLORADO FABRICATION LLC—See Kirkwood Holding, Inc.; *U.S. Private*, pg. 2315
COLOVOS COMPANY; *U.S. Private*, pg. 975
COMER INDUSTRIES S.P.A. - CAVRIAGO UNIT—See Comer Industries S.p.A.; *Int'l*, pg. 1710
COMER INDUSTRIES S.P.A. - MANTOVA UNIT—See Comer Industries S.p.A.; *Int'l*, pg. 1710
COMER INDUSTRIES S.P.A. - MATERA UNIT—See Comer Industries S.p.A.; *Int'l*, pg. 1710
COMMODORE MANUFACTURING CORPORATION; *U.S. Private*, pg. 985
COMPASS SYSTEMS & SALES, INC.—See Alston Capital Partners LLC; *U.S. Private*, pg. 203
COMPONENTA A.S.—See Componenta Corporation; *Int'l*, pg. 1753
COMPRESSOR PRODUCTS INTERNATIONAL—See Enpro Inc.; *U.S. Public*, pg. 774
CONSOLIDATED TOOL, INC.—See Gemini Group, Inc.; *U.S. Private*, pg. 1658
CONTINENTAL MACHINES, INC.—See DoAll Company; *U.S. Private*, pg. 1250
CP TOOLS KOREA CO. LTD.—See Atlas Copco AB; *Int'l*, pg. 681
CRANKSHAFT MACHINE COMPANY—See Avis Industrial Corporation; *U.S. Private*, pg. 407
CUTLITE DO BRASIL LTDA—See El.En. S.p.A.; *Int'l*, pg. 2341
DAIDO DIE & MOLD STEEL SOLUTIONS CO., LTD.—See Daido Steel Co., Ltd.; *Int'l*, pg. 1922
DAIDO MACHINERY CO., LTD.—See Daido Steel Co., Ltd.; *Int'l*, pg. 1922
DAIHEN CORPORATION - ROKKO PLANT—See Daihen Corporation; *Int'l*, pg. 1926
DAIHEN INC.—See Daihen Corporation; *Int'l*, pg. 1926
DAIHEN INDUSTRIAL MACHINERY CORPORATION—See Daihen Corporation; *Int'l*, pg. 1926
DAIHEN TECHNOS CO., LTD.—See Daihen Corporation; *Int'l*, pg. 1926
DAIHEN VARSTROJ WELDING CUTTING AND ROBOTICS D.D.—See Daihen Corporation; *Int'l*, pg. 1926
DALIAN TONGHAI MACHINERY & ELECTRONIC EQUIPMENT CO., LTD.; *Int'l*, pg. 1952
DALLAS INDUSTRIES, INC.; *U.S. Private*, pg. 1149
DANIELI FATA HUNTER, INC.—See Danieli & C. Officine Meccaniche S.p.A.; *Int'l*, pg. 1963
DATRON FRANCE SAS—See Datron AG; *Int'l*, pg. 1982
DATRON TECHNOLOGY CZ S.R.O.—See Datron AG; *Int'l*, pg. 1982
DATRON TECHNOLOGY S.R.O.—See Datron AG; *Int'l*, pg. 1982
DATRON TOOL TECHNOLOGY GMBH—See Datron AG; *Int'l*, pg. 1982
DBG CANADA LIMITED; *Int'l*, pg. 1988
DECKEL MAHO GILDEMEISTER (SHANGHAI) MACHINE TOOLS CO., LTD.—See DMG MORI Co., Ltd.; *Int'l*, pg. 2144
DELL MARKING SYSTEMS INC.—See Gage Corporation; *U.S. Private*, pg. 1634
DESOUTTER S.A.—See Atlas Copco AB; *Int'l*, pg. 682
DESPATCH INDUSTRIES LIMITED PARTNERSHIP—See Illinois Tool Works Inc.; *U.S. Public*, pg. 1102
DEWALT INDUSTRIAL TOOLS S.P.A.—See Stanley Black & Decker, Inc.; *U.S. Public*, pg. 1932

DEXKO GLOBAL, INC.—See Brookfield Corporation; *Int'l*, pg. 1175
DIEFFENBACHER HOLDING GMBH & CO. KG; *Int'l*, pg. 2114
DIEFFENBACHER SCHENCK PANEL GMBH—See Dieffenbacher Holding GmbH & Co. KG; *Int'l*, pg. 2114
DIEFFENBACHER SYSTEM-AUTOMATION GMBH—See Dieffenbacher Holding GmbH & Co. KG; *Int'l*, pg. 2114
DIEHL WERKZEUGBAU SEEBACH GMBH—See Diehl Stiftung & Co. KG; *Int'l*, pg. 2115
DIJET INDUSTRIAL CO., LTD; *Int'l*, pg. 2125
DISCO CORPORATION; *Int'l*, pg. 2131
DISCO HI-TEC CZECH S.R.O.—See Disco Corporation; *Int'l*, pg. 2132
DISSTON COMPANY—See CAL SDI, INC.; *U.S. Private*, pg. 715
DMG MORI AKTIENGESELLSCHAFT—See DMG MORI Co., Ltd.; *Int'l*, pg. 2143
DMG MORI AUSTRALIA PTY. LTD.—See DMG MORI Co., Ltd.; *Int'l*, pg. 2144
DMG MORI BELUX BVBA - SPRL—See DMG MORI Co., Ltd.; *Int'l*, pg. 2144
DMG MORI BERLIN GMBH—See DMG MORI Co., Ltd.; *Int'l*, pg. 2143
DMG MORI CO., LTD. - PLANT 1—See DMG MORI Co., Ltd.; *Int'l*, pg. 2144
DMG MORI CO., LTD.; *Int'l*, pg. 2143
DMG MORI CZECH S.R.O.—See DMG MORI Co., Ltd.; *Int'l*, pg. 2144
DMG MORI DEUTSCHLAND GMBH—See DMG MORI Co., Ltd.; *Int'l*, pg. 2143
DMG MORI EUROPE AG—See DMG MORI Co., Ltd.; *Int'l*, pg. 2143
DMG MORI FINLAND OY AB—See DMG MORI Co., Ltd.; *Int'l*, pg. 2144
DMG MORI FRANCE - LYON—See DMG MORI Co., Ltd.; *Int'l*, pg. 2144
DMG MORI GREECE LTD.—See DMG MORI Co., Ltd.; *Int'l*, pg. 2144
DMG MORI HAMBURG GMBH—See DMG MORI Co., Ltd.; *Int'l*, pg. 2143
DMG MORI MACHINE TOOLS TRADING CO., LTD.—See DMG MORI Co., Ltd.; *Int'l*, pg. 2144
DMG MORI (MALAYSIA) SDN. BHD.—See DMG MORI Co., Ltd.; *Int'l*, pg. 2145
DMG MORI NORWAY AS—See DMG MORI Co., Ltd.; *Int'l*, pg. 2144
DMG MORI PHILIPPINES INC.—See DMG MORI Co., Ltd.; *Int'l*, pg. 2144
DMG MORI ROMANIA S.R.L.—See DMG MORI Co., Ltd.; *Int'l*, pg. 2144
DMG MORI SALES & SERVICE CO., LTD.—See DMG MORI Co., Ltd.; *Int'l*, pg. 2145
DMG MORI SCHWEIZ AG—See DMG MORI Co., Ltd.; *Int'l*, pg. 2144
DMG MORI SEIKI CO., LTD. - NARA CAMPUS NO. 1 PLANT—See DMG MORI Co., Ltd.; *Int'l*, pg. 2145
DMG MORI SEIKI (THAILAND) CO., LTD.—See DMG MORI Co., Ltd.; *Int'l*, pg. 2145
DMG MORI STUTTGART GMBH—See DMG MORI Co., Ltd.; *Int'l*, pg. 2145
DMG MORI SWEDEN AB—See DMG MORI Co., Ltd.; *Int'l*, pg. 2145
DMG MORI (THAILAND) CO., LTD.—See DMG MORI Co., Ltd.; *Int'l*, pg. 2143
DMG MORI USA, INC.—See DMG MORI Co., Ltd.; *Int'l*, pg. 2145
DMG MORI USED MACHINES CO., LTD.—See DMG MORI Co., Ltd.; *Int'l*, pg. 2145
DMG MORI VIET NAM CO., LTD.—See DMG MORI Co., Ltd.; *Int'l*, pg. 2145
DRAKE MANUFACTURING SERVICE CO., LLC—See UniWorld Capital, L.P.; *U.S. Private*, pg. 4281
DUBUIS ET CIE S.A.S.—See Stanley Black & Decker, Inc.; *U.S. Public*, pg. 1932
DUER CAROLINA COIL, INC.—See American Securities LLC; *U.S. Private*, pg. 249
DUFIEUX INDUSTRIE S.A.S.—See Evolem S.A.; *Int'l*, pg. 2572
DUFU INDUSTRIES SERVICES PTE LTD—See Dufu Technology Corp. Berhad; *Int'l*, pg. 2223
DUGARD MIDDLE EAST—See C Dugard Ltd; *Int'l*, pg. 1238
DUGARD RUS LLC—See C Dugard Ltd; *Int'l*, pg. 1238
DURA-BOND BEARING CO.—See Melling Tool Company Inc.; *U.S. Private*, pg. 2662
DUROC ENGINEERING I HELSINGBORG AB—See Duroc AB; *Int'l*, pg. 2229
DUROC MACHINE TOOL AB—See Duroc AB; *Int'l*, pg. 2229
DUROC MACHINE TOOL SIA—See Duroc AB; *Int'l*, pg. 2229
DUROC TOOLING I OLOFSTROM AB—See Duroc AB; *Int'l*, pg. 2229
EFCO INC.—See Park-Ohio Holdings Corp.; *U.S. Public*, pg. 1638
EINHELL TURKEY DIS TICARET A.S.—See Einhell Germany AG; *Int'l*, pg. 2333
EISENWERK ARNSTADT GMBH—See DIHAG Holding GmbH; *Int'l*, pg. 2124

ELECTROIMPACT INC.; *U.S. Private*, pg. 1354
EL.EN. S.P.A.; *Int'l*, pg. 2341
ELLWOOD NATIONAL CRANKSHAFT SERVICES—See Ellwood Group, Inc.; *U.S. Private*, pg. 1375
EMHART TEKNOLOGIES B.V.—See Stanley Black & Decker, Inc.; *U.S. Public*, pg. 1932
EMHART TEKNOLOGIES LLC—See Stanley Black & Decker, Inc.; *U.S. Public*, pg. 1932
EMIC EQUIPAMENTOS E SISTEMAS DE ENSAIO LTDA.—See Illinois Tool Works Inc.; *U.S. Public*, pg. 1103
EM KOREA CO., LTD.; *Int'l*, pg. 2372
EMP FRAS- UND MESSTECHNIK GMBH—See Fair Friend Group; *Int'l*, pg. 2604
EMUGE-FRANKEN B.V.—See EMUGE-Werk Richard Glimpel GmbH & Co. KG; *Int'l*, pg. 2394
EMUGE-FRANKEN HASSAS KESICI TAKIM SANAYI LTD. STI.—See EMUGE-Werk Richard Glimpel GmbH & Co. KG; *Int'l*, pg. 2394
EMUGE-WERK RICHARD GLIMPEL GMBH & CO. KG; *Int'l*, pg. 2394
ENERPAC FRANCE S.A.S.—See Enerpac Tool Group Corp.; *U.S. Public*, pg. 765
ENGIS CORPORATION; *U.S. Private*, pg. 1399
ENSHU LIMITED - HAMAKITA FACTORY—See Enshu Limited; *Int'l*, pg. 2446
ENSHU LIMITED; *Int'l*, pg. 2446
EONMETALL TECHNOLOGY SDN. BHD.—See Eonmetall Group Berhad; *Int'l*, pg. 2458
EO TECHNICS CO., LTD.; *Int'l*, pg. 2457
EPIROC BULGARIA EOOD—See Epiroc AB; *Int'l*, pg. 2461
EPIROC DRILLING SOLUTIONS LLC—See Epiroc AB; *Int'l*, pg. 2462
EPIROC DRILLING TOOLS AB—See Epiroc AB; *Int'l*, pg. 2462
EPIROC DRILLING TOOLS LLC—See Epiroc AB; *Int'l*, pg. 2462
EPIROC RUS LLC—See Epiroc AB; *Int'l*, pg. 2462
EPIROC TAJIKISTAN LLC—See Epiroc AB; *Int'l*, pg. 2462
ERIKS SEALS & PLASTICS, INC.—See LKCM Headwater Investments; *U.S. Private*, pg. 2475
ESAB AUTOMATION LTD.—See Enovis Corporation; *U.S. Public*, pg. 770
ESAB CUTTING SYSTEMS—See Enovis Corporation; *U.S. Public*, pg. 770
ESAB KFT—See Enovis Corporation; *U.S. Public*, pg. 770
ETERNAL MATERIALS CO., LTD.; *Int'l*, pg. 2520
ETLA TECHNOLOGY (WUXI) CO.,LTD.—See Frencken Group Limited; *Int'l*, pg. 2772
EURO METALL KFT.—See DIHAG Holding GmbH; *Int'l*, pg. 2124
EVA PRECISION INDUSTRIAL HOLDINGS LIMITED; *Int'l*, pg. 2560
EVERITE MACHINE PRODUCTS CO.—See Arcline Investment Management LP; *U.S. Private*, pg. 313
EVOLUT S.P.A.—See EFORT Intelligent Equipment Co., Ltd.; *Int'l*, pg. 2321
EVOLUT (WUHU) ROBOTICS CO., LTD.—See EFORT Intelligent Equipment Co., Ltd.; *Int'l*, pg. 2321
EXTRUDE HONE KK—See Kennametal Inc.; *U.S. Public*, pg. 1221
EXTRUDE HONE LLC—See Kennametal Inc.; *U.S. Public*, pg. 1221
FACOM BELGIE BVBA—See Stanley Black & Decker, Inc.; *U.S. Public*, pg. 1932
FAIR FRIEND ENTERPRISE CO., LTD.—See Fair Friend Group; *Int'l*, pg. 2604
FAIRSKQ (TAIWAN) CO., LTD.—See Fair Friend Group; *Int'l*, pg. 2604
FALCON MACHINE TOOLS CO. LTD.; *Int'l*, pg. 2611
FANUC OCEANIA PTY. LIMITED—See FANUC Corporation; *Int'l*, pg. 2615
FANUC SOUTH AFRICA PTY. LIMITED—See FANUC Corporation; *Int'l*, pg. 2615
FARINA PRESSE S.R.L.—See ANDRITZ AG; *Int'l*, pg. 455
FEINMECHANIK MICHAEL DECKEL GMBH & CO. KG; *Int'l*, pg. 2632
FEINTOOL BEIJING SWISSTEC—See Artemis Holding AG; *Int'l*, pg. 582
FEINTOOL FRANCE S.A.R.L.—See Artemis Holding AG; *Int'l*, pg. 582
FEINTOOL INTERNATIONAL MANAGEMENT LTD.—See Artemis Holding AG; *Int'l*, pg. 582
FEINTOOL ITALIA S.R.L.—See Artemis Holding AG; *Int'l*, pg. 582
FEINTOOL JAPAN CO., LTD.—See Artemis Holding AG; *Int'l*, pg. 582
FEINTOOL PARTS & COMPONENTS LTD.—See Artemis Holding AG; *Int'l*, pg. 582
FEINTOOL RESEARCH & DEVELOPMENT AG—See Artemis Holding AG; *Int'l*, pg. 582
FEINTOOL SYSTEM PARTS AG—See Artemis Holding AG; *Int'l*, pg. 582
FEINTOOL SYSTEM PARTS ETTLINGEN GMBH—See Artemis Holding AG; *Int'l*, pg. 582
FEINTOOL SYSTEM PARTS JENA GMBH—See Artemis Holding AG; *Int'l*, pg. 582

FEINTOOL TEILE & KOMPONENTEN AG—See Artemis Holding AG; *Int'l*, pg. 582
FERMAT CZ. S.R.O.—See FERMAT Group, a.s.; *Int'l*, pg. 2638
FERMAT GROUP, A.S.; *Int'l*, pg. 2638
FERMAT MACHINERY PVT. LTD.—See FERMAT Group, a.s.; *Int'l*, pg. 2638
FINEPART SWEDEN AB; *Int'l*, pg. 2674
FIRST TECHNOLOGY (BEIJING) LTD.—See Fuji Corporation; *Int'l*, pg. 2809
FISCHER AG PRAZISIONSSPINDELN; *Int'l*, pg. 2692
FIVES MACHINING SYSTEMS, INC. - FOND DU LAC—See FIVES, Societe Anonyme; *Int'l*, pg. 2696
FIVES MACHINING SYSTEMS, INC. - HEBRON—See FIVES, Societe Anonyme; *Int'l*, pg. 2696
FIVES MACHINING SYSTEMS, INC.—See FIVES, Societe Anonyme; *Int'l*, pg. 2696
FLOW EUROPE GMBH—See AIP, LLC; *U.S. Private*, pg. 137
FOLEY-UNITED/NEARY DIVISION—See Foley-Belsaw Company; *U.S. Private*, pg. 1558
FORI AUTOMATION LLC—See Lincoln Electric Holdings, Inc.; *U.S. Public*, pg. 1317
FORKARDT INDIA LLP—See Privet Fund Management, LLC; *U.S. Private*, pg. 3269
FORMTEK, INC.—See Mestek, Inc.; *U.S. Public*, pg. 1426
FOSTER REFRIGERATOR FRANCE S.A.S.—See Illinois Tool Works Inc.; *U.S. Public*, pg. 1103
FP STENCIL SDN. BHD.—See FoundPac Group Berhad; *Int'l*, pg. 2754
FRAEN MACHINING CORPORATION; *U.S. Private*, pg. 1586
FREESIA MACROSS CORPORATION; *Int'l*, pg. 2771
FREUND-TURBO CORPORATION—See Freund Corporation; *Int'l*, pg. 2791
FUGRO-IMPROV LTD.—See Fugro N.V.; *Int'l*, pg. 2808
FUJI HONING INDUSTRIAL CO., LTD.—See Fair Friend Group; *Int'l*, pg. 2604
FUJI INDIA CORPORATION PRIVATE LIMITED—See Fuji Corporation; *Int'l*, pg. 2809
FUJI LINEAR CORPORATION—See Fuji Corporation; *Int'l*, pg. 2809
FUJI MACHINE MFG. CO., LTD. - FUJIOKA PLANT—See Fuji Corporation; *Int'l*, pg. 2810
GAMKO REFRIGERATION EURL—See Illinois Tool Works Inc.; *U.S. Public*, pg. 1103
GASBARRE PRODUCTS INC.; *U.S. Private*, pg. 1648
GAY LEE CORPORATION—See L Squared Capital Management LP; *U.S. Private*, pg. 2362
GEMINI PLASTICS DE MEXICO S. DE R.L. DE C.V.—See Gemini Group, Inc.; *U.S. Private*, pg. 1658
GEMINI PLASTICS, INC.—See Gemini Group, Inc.; *U.S. Private*, pg. 1658
GENERAL BROACH COMPANY—See Utica Enterprises, Inc.; *U.S. Private*, pg. 4325
GEORGE T. SCHMIDT, INC.; *U.S. Private*, pg. 1683
GERMANY DINAS SEMICONDUCTOR LASER CO., LTD.—See Coherent Corp.; *U.S. Public*, pg. 527
GERTNER SERVICE GMBH—See Atlas Copco AB; *Int'l*, pg. 683
GF MACHINING SOLUTIONS LTD.—See Georg Fischer AG; *Int'l*, pg. 2934
GIBBS-HUNGARY DIE CASTING KFT.—See Koch Enterprises, Inc.; *U.S. Private*, pg. 2326
GIEBELER GMBH; *Int'l*, pg. 2968
GILDEMEISTER DREHMASCHINEN GMBH—See DMG MORI Co., Ltd.; *Int'l*, pg. 2144
GILDEMEISTER ITALIANA S.P.A.—See DMG MORI Co., Ltd.; *Int'l*, pg. 2144
GKN AEROSPACE MUNCIE INC—See GKN plc; *Int'l*, pg. 2984
GKN SINTER METALS ST THOMAS LTD—See GKN plc; *Int'l*, pg. 2985
GLEASON GEAR TECHNOLOGY (SUZHOU) CO., LTD.—See Gleason Corporation; *U.S. Private*, pg. 1708
GLEASON-PFAUTER MASCHINENFABRIK GMBH—See Gleason Corporation; *U.S. Private*, pg. 1708
THE GLEASON WORKS—See Gleason Corporation; *U.S. Private*, pg. 1708
GLEBAR COMPANY, INC.—See Arcline Investment Management LP; *U.S. Private*, pg. 313
GLOBAL GEAR & MACHINING—See Innovative Manufacturing Solutions Corp.; *U.S. Private*, pg. 2082
GNB CORPORATION—See Ellison Technologies Inc.; *U.S. Private*, pg. 1374
GOODWAY MACHINE CORP.; *Int'l*, pg. 3041
GOODWAY (SUZHOU) MACHINE CORP.—See GOODWAY MACHINE CORP.; *Int'l*, pg. 3041
GRAEBENER PRESS SYSTEMS INC.—See ANDRITZ AG; *Int'l*, pg. 456
GREENFIELD INDUSTRIES CANADA INC.—See Dalian Top-Eastern Group Co., Ltd.; *Int'l*, pg. 1953
GREENFIELD INDUSTRIES, INC.—See Dalian Top-Eastern Group Co., Ltd.; *Int'l*, pg. 1953
GRK CANADA LIMITED—See Illinois Tool Works Inc.; *U.S. Public*, pg. 1103
GROUPE GORGE S.A.; *Int'l*, pg. 3103
GSN RETOOLING-MAINTENANCE, INC.—See GSN

333517 — MACHINE TOOL MANUFA...

Maschinen-Anlagen-Service GmbH; *Int'l*, pg. 3150
GWS TOOL GROUP, LLC—See L Squared Capital Management LP; *U.S. Private*, pg. 2361
HACO N.V.; *Int'l*, pg. 3204
HAMAI CO., LTD.; *Int'l*, pg. 3235
HAMMOND MACHINERY, INC.; *U.S. Private*, pg. 1850
HANGZHOU ADVANCE FORGING CO., LTD.—See Hangzhou Advance Gearbox Group Co., Ltd.; *Int'l*, pg. 3246
HANGZHOU WAGEN PRECISION TOOLING CO., LTD.—See Ferrotec Holdings Corporation; *Int'l*, pg. 2643
HANITA METAL WORKS, LTD.—See Kennametal Inc.; *U.S. Public*, pg. 1221
HANWHA AMERICA DEVELOPMENT INC.—See Hanwha Group; *Int'l*, pg. 3265
HANWHA CANADA DEVELOPMENT INC.—See Hanwha Group; *Int'l*, pg. 3265
HANWHA CHINA—See Hanwha Group; *Int'l*, pg. 3265
HANWHA (H.K.) CO., LTD.—See Hanwha Group; *Int'l*, pg. 3265
HANWHA INTERNATIONAL INDIA PVT. LTD.—See Hanwha Group; *Int'l*, pg. 3265
HANWHA INTERNATIONAL (S) PTE LTD.—See Hanwha Group; *Int'l*, pg. 3265
HANWHA MACHINERY AMERICA INC.—See Hanwha Group; *Int'l*, pg. 3266
HANWHA SAUDI CONTRACTING CO., LTD.—See Hanwha Group; *Int'l*, pg. 3265
HANWHA TECHM CO., LTD. - CHANGWON PLANT—See Hanwha Group; *Int'l*, pg. 3266
HANWHA TECHM CO., LTD.—See Hanwha Group; *Int'l*, pg. 3266
HANWHA TECHM (SUZHOU) CO., LTD.—See Hanwha Group; *Int'l*, pg. 3266
HANWHA TECHM USA LLC—See Hanwha Group; *Int'l*, pg. 3266
HARDINGE BROTHERS, INC.—See Privet Fund Management, LLC; *U.S. Private*, pg. 3269
HARDINGE GMBH—See Privet Fund Management, LLC; *U.S. Private*, pg. 3269
HARDINGE INC.—See Privet Fund Management, LLC; *U.S. Private*, pg. 3269
HARDINGE MACHINE (SHANGHAI) CO., LTD.—See Privet Fund Management, LLC; *U.S. Private*, pg. 3269
HARDINGE MACHINE TOOLS B.V. - TAIWAN REPRESENTATIVE OFFICE—See Privet Fund Management, LLC; *U.S. Private*, pg. 3269
HARTNESS INTERNATIONAL EUROPE, GMBH—See Illinois Tool Works Inc.; *U.S. Public*, pg. 1103
HASCO AUSTRIA GESELLSCHAFT M.B.H—See Berndorf AG; *Int'l*, pg. 987
HASCO CANADA INC.—See Berndorf AG; *Int'l*, pg. 987
HASCO ENCOUNTER LTD.—See Berndorf AG; *Int'l*, pg. 987
HASCO HASENCLEVER GMBH & CO. KG—See Berndorf AG; *Int'l*, pg. 987
HASCO IBERICA S.L.U.—See Berndorf AG; *Int'l*, pg. 987
HASCO INDIA PVT. LTD.—See Berndorf AG; *Int'l*, pg. 987
HECKLER AG; *Int'l*, pg. 3307
HEFEI METALFORMING INTELLIGENT MANUFACTURING CO., LTD.; *Int'l*, pg. 3307
HEINRICH SCHMID MASCHINEN-UND WERKZEUGBAU AG—See Artemis Holding AG; *Int'l*, pg. 582
HEM INC.; *U.S. Private*, pg. 1913
HERBER ENGINEERING AB—See Duc Long Gia Lai Group JSC; *Int'l*, pg. 2222
HESS INDUSTRIES, INC.; *U.S. Private*, pg. 1927
HESS INDUSTRIES, INC.—See Hess Industries, Inc.; *U.S. Private*, pg. 1927
HIGHYAG LASERTECHNOLOGIE GMBH—See Coherent Corp.; *U.S. Public*, pg. 528
HIKOKI POWER TOOLS DEUTSCHLAND GMBH—See KKR & Co. Inc.; *U.S. Public*, pg. 1257
HILIFT JACK CO.—See The Bloomfield Manufacturing Co., Inc.; *U.S. Private*, pg. 3995
HILTI AG; *Int'l*, pg. 3394
HMB, SPOL. S R.O.—See FERMAT Group, a.s.; *Int'l*, pg. 2639
HMT INTERNATIONAL LIMITED—See HMT Limited; *Int'l*, pg. 3433
HMT LIMITED; *Int'l*, pg. 3433
HMT MACHINE TOOLS LIMITED—See HMT Limited; *Int'l*, pg. 3433
HOBART ANDINA S.A.S.—See Illinois Tool Works Inc.; *U.S. Public*, pg. 1103
HOBART GESELLSCHAFT MIT BESCHRANKTER HAFTUNG—See Illinois Tool Works Inc.; *U.S. Public*, pg. 1103
HOBART NEDERLAND B.V.—See Illinois Tool Works Inc.; *U.S. Public*, pg. 1104
HOBART SCANDINAVIA APS—See Illinois Tool Works Inc.; *U.S. Public*, pg. 1104
HOLROYD PRECISION LTD.—See Chongqing Machinery & Electronics Holding (Group) Co., Ltd.; *Int'l*, pg. 1580
HOP CHEONG TECHNOLOGY LIMITED—See HNA International Investment Holdings Limited; *Int'l*, pg. 3433
HORST SPRENGER GMBH RECYCLING-TOOLS—See Stanley Black & Decker, Inc.; *U.S. Public*, pg. 1932

HOWA MACHINERY, LTD.; *Int'l*, pg. 3492
H. PAULIN & CO., LTD. - CAPITAL METAL INDUSTRIES—See Hillman Solutions Corp.; *U.S. Public*, pg. 1038
H. PAULIN & CO., LTD. - LONG-LOK CANADA—See Hillman Solutions Corp.; *U.S. Public*, pg. 1038
H. PAULIN & CO., LTD. - PRECISION FASTENERS—See Hillman Solutions Corp.; *U.S. Public*, pg. 1038
H. PAULIN & CO., LTD. - PRO-TIP—See Hillman Solutions Corp.; *U.S. Public*, pg. 1038
HPM AMERICA DIVISION—See Taylor's Industrial Services, L.L.C.; *U.S. Private*, pg. 3941
HUNAN YUJING MACHINERY CO., LTD.; *Int'l*, pg. 3534
HUNTER DOUGLAS ASSEMBLY AUTOMATION AB—See 3G Capital Partners L.P.; *U.S. Private*, pg. 11
HURCO GMBH—See Hurco Companies, Inc.; *U.S. Public*, pg. 1076
HWACHEON MACHINERY CO., LTD.; *Int'l*, pg. 3542
HWACHEON MACHINE TOOL CO., LTD.; *Int'l*, pg. 3541
HYPERTHERM INC.; *U.S. Private*, pg. 2019
I.A.M.U. S.A.; *Int'l*, pg. 3565
ICM—See Dalian Tonghai Machinery & Electronic Equipment Co., Ltd.; *Int'l*, pg. 1952
IDEAL MACHINING & SUPPLY INC.; *U.S. Private*, pg. 2036
IDRA LIMITED—See Idra s.r.l.; *Int'l*, pg. 3596
IDRA NORTH AMERICA—See Idra s.r.l.; *Int'l*, pg. 3596
IDRAPRINCE, INC.—See Buhler AG; *Int'l*, pg. 1212
IDRA S.R.L.; *Int'l*, pg. 3596
IKM WELLDRONE TECHNOLOGY AS—See IKM Gruppen AS; *Int'l*, pg. 3612
ILLIG MASCHINENBAU GMBH & CO. KG; *Int'l*, pg. 3615
IMT FORGE GROUP—See Mission Essential Personnel, LLC; *U.S. Private*, pg. 2747
INDUSTRIAL INNOVATIONS, INC.; *U.S. Private*, pg. 2066
INDUSTRIAL METAL PRODUCTS CORP.; *U.S. Private*, pg. 2067
INFASTECH KABUSHIKI KAISHA—See Stanley Black & Decker, Inc.; *U.S. Public*, pg. 1932
INFASTECH (KOREA) LIMITED—See Stanley Black & Decker, Inc.; *U.S. Public*, pg. 1932
INGERSOLL MACHINES TOOLS, INC. (IMTA)—See Camozzi Group; *Int'l*, pg. 1274
INGERSOLL PRODUCTION SYSTEMS—See Dalian Tonghai Machinery & Electronic Equipment Co., Ltd.; *Int'l*, pg. 1952
INNSE-BERARDI SPA—See Camozzi Group; *Int'l*, pg. 1274
INN SP Z.O.O.—See Illinois Tool Works Inc.; *U.S. Public*, pg. 1104
INSTRON STRUCTURAL TESTING SYSTEMS GMBH—See Illinois Tool Works Inc.; *U.S. Public*, pg. 1108
INTA TECHNOLOGIES CORPORATION—See Francisco Partners Management, LP; *U.S. Private*, pg. 1590
INTERPLEX ELECTRONIC (DALIAN) CO., LTD.—See Blackstone Inc.; *U.S. Public*, pg. 354
INVESTMENT TOOLING INTERNATIONAL LIMITED—See Valmont Industries, Inc.; *U.S. Public*, pg. 2273
ISCAR ALATI D.O.O—See Berkshire Hathaway Inc.; *U.S. Public*, pg. 307
ISCAR AUSTRIA GMBH—See Berkshire Hathaway Inc.; *U.S. Public*, pg. 307
ISCAR BENELUX S.A.—See Berkshire Hathaway Inc.; *U.S. Public*, pg. 307
ISCAR BULGARIA LTD—See Berkshire Hathaway Inc.; *U.S. Public*, pg. 307
ISCAR CR S.R.O.—See Berkshire Hathaway Inc.; *U.S. Public*, pg. 307
ISCAR FRANCE SAS—See Berkshire Hathaway Inc.; *U.S. Public*, pg. 307
ISCAR GERMANY GMBH—See Berkshire Hathaway Inc.; *U.S. Public*, pg. 307
ISCAR HARTMETALL AG—See Berkshire Hathaway Inc.; *U.S. Public*, pg. 307
ISCAR HUNGARY KFT.—See Berkshire Hathaway Inc.; *U.S. Public*, pg. 307
ISCAR IBERICA AS—See Berkshire Hathaway Inc.; *U.S. Public*, pg. 307
ISCAR ITALIA SRL—See Berkshire Hathaway Inc.; *U.S. Public*, pg. 307
ISCAR LTD.—See Berkshire Hathaway Inc.; *U.S. Public*, pg. 307
ISCAR NETHERLANDS BV—See Berkshire Hathaway Inc.; *U.S. Public*, pg. 307
ISCAR POLAND SP. Z O.O—See Berkshire Hathaway Inc.; *U.S. Public*, pg. 307
ISCAR PORTUGAL SA—See Berkshire Hathaway Inc.; *U.S. Public*, pg. 307
ISCAR RUSSIA LLC—See Berkshire Hathaway Inc.; *U.S. Public*, pg. 307
ISCAR SLOVENIJA D.O.O.—See Berkshire Hathaway Inc.; *U.S. Public*, pg. 307
ISCAR SR, S.R.O.—See Berkshire Hathaway Inc.; *U.S. Public*, pg. 307
ISCAR SVERIGE AB—See Berkshire Hathaway Inc.; *U.S. Public*, pg. 307
ISCAR TOOLS LTD.—See Berkshire Hathaway Inc.; *U.S. Public*, pg. 307

ISCAR TOOLS SRL—See Berkshire Hathaway Inc.; *U.S. Public*, pg. 307
ITW ANGLEBOARD AB—See Illinois Tool Works Inc.; *U.S. Public*, pg. 1104
ITW CANADA INVESTMENTS LIMITED PARTNERSHIP—See Illinois Tool Works Inc.; *U.S. Public*, pg. 1105
ITW CONSTRUCTION PRODUCTS APS—See Illinois Tool Works Inc.; *U.S. Public*, pg. 1105
ITW CONTAMINATION CONTROL B.V.—See Illinois Tool Works Inc.; *U.S. Public*, pg. 1105
ITW CPM S.A.S.—See Illinois Tool Works Inc.; *U.S. Public*, pg. 1105
ITW DENMARK APS—See Illinois Tool Works Inc.; *U.S. Public*, pg. 1105
ITW (DEUTSCHLAND) GMBH—See Illinois Tool Works Inc.; *U.S. Public*, pg. 1104
ITW GUNTHER S.A.S.—See Illinois Tool Works Inc.; *U.S. Public*, pg. 1106
ITW JAPAN LTD.—See Illinois Tool Works Inc.; *U.S. Public*, pg. 1106
JACKSONLEA POLISHING MATERIALS CO. LTD.—See Jason Industries, Inc.; *U.S. Private*, pg. 2190
JARVIS CUTTING TOOLS; *U.S. Private*, pg. 2188
JASCSONLEA DE MEXICO S.A. DE C.V.—See Jason Industries, Inc.; *U.S. Private*, pg. 2190
JASCO TOOLS INC.; *U.S. Private*, pg. 2189
JIANGSU GUOQIANG TOOLS CO., LTD.—See Stanley Black & Decker, Inc.; *U.S. Public*, pg. 1933
JOBS AUTOMAZIONE S.P.A. - SACHMAN DIVISION—See Fair Friend Group; *Int'l*, pg. 2604
JOBS AUTOMAZIONE S.P.A.—See Fair Friend Group; *Int'l*, pg. 2604
JOH. FRIEDRICH BEHRENS AG—See GreatStar Group Co., Ltd.; *Int'l*, pg. 3067
JONES PLASTIC & ENGINEERING COMPANY, LLC - CAMDEN DIVISION—See Jones Plastic & Engineering Company, LLC; *U.S. Private*, pg. 2233
JONES PLASTIC & ENGINEERING COMPANY, LLC - JEFFERSONTOWN DIVISION—See Jones Plastic & Engineering Company, LLC; *U.S. Private*, pg. 2233
JONES PLASTIC & ENGINEERING COMPANY, LLC - WILLIAMSBURG DIVISION—See Jones Plastic & Engineering Company, LLC; *U.S. Private*, pg. 2233
JONES PLASTIC & ENGINEERING DE MONTERREY, S.A. DE C.V.—See Jones Plastic & Engineering Company, LLC; *U.S. Private*, pg. 2234
JONES & SHIPMAN HARDINGE LIMITED—See Privet Fund Management, LLC; *U.S. Private*, pg. 3269
JONES & SHIPMAN S.A.R.L.—See Privet Fund Management, LLC; *U.S. Private*, pg. 3269
JPW INDUSTRIES INC.—See Tenex Capital Management, L.P.; *U.S. Private*, pg. 3966
KABUKU INC.—See Futaba Corporation; *Int'l*, pg. 2850
KANT-SLAM DOOR CHECK CO.—See The Bloomfield Manufacturing Co., Inc.; *U.S. Private*, pg. 3995
KAO FONG MACHINERY CO., LTD.—See Hota Industrial Mfg. Co., Ltd.; *Int'l*, pg. 3487
KARLE UND JUNG GMBH—See Dieffenbacher Holding GmbH & Co. KG; *Int'l*, pg. 2114
KASPER MACHINE CO.; *U.S. Private*, pg. 2264
KAUFMAN MFG. COMPANY; *U.S. Private*, pg. 2265
KEBE ERSATZTEILE GMBH—See Enovis Corporation; *U.S. Public*, pg. 771
KENCI S.L.—See Kennametal Inc.; *U.S. Public*, pg. 1222
KENNAMETAL BELGIUM S.P.R.L.—See Kennametal Inc.; *U.S. Public*, pg. 1222
KENNAMETAL DE MEXICO, S.A. DE C.V.—See Kennametal Inc.; *U.S. Public*, pg. 1223
KENNAMETAL EUROPE HOLDING GMBH—See Kennametal Inc.; *U.S. Public*, pg. 1221
KENNAMETAL EXTRUDE HONE LIMITED—See Kennametal Inc.; *U.S. Public*, pg. 1221
KENNAMETAL EXTRUDE HONE LTD.—See Kennametal Inc.; *U.S. Public*, pg. 1221
KENNAMETAL HARDPOINT (TAIWAN) INC.—See Kennametal Inc.; *U.S. Public*, pg. 1222
KENNAMETAL INC.; *U.S. Public*, pg. 1221
KENNAMETAL KESICI TAKIMLAR SANAYI VE TICARET ANONIM SIRKETI—See Kennametal Inc.; *U.S. Public*, pg. 1222
KENNAMETAL KOREA LTD.—See Kennametal Inc.; *U.S. Public*, pg. 1222
KENNAMETAL LOGISTICS UK LTD.—See Kennametal Inc.; *U.S. Public*, pg. 1222
KENNAMETAL POLSKA SP. Z.O.O.—See Kennametal Inc.; *U.S. Public*, pg. 1222
KENNAMETAL SHARED SERVICES PRIVATE LIMITED—See Kennametal Inc.; *U.S. Public*, pg. 1222
KEYANG ELECTRIC MACHINERY CO., LTD. - ANSAN PLANT—See Haesung Industrial Co., Ltd.; *Int'l*, pg. 3206
KEYANG ELECTRIC MACHINERY CO., LTD. - CHEONAN PLANT—See Haesung Industrial Co., Ltd.; *Int'l*, pg. 3206
KEYANG ELECTRIC MACHINERY CO., LTD.—See Haesung Industrial Co., Ltd.; *Int'l*, pg. 3205
KEYANG ELECTRIC MACHINERY (JIANGSU) CO., LTD.—See Haesung Industrial Co., Ltd.; *Int'l*, pg. 3205
KEYANG ELECTRIC MACHINERY (SUZHOU) CO.,

333517 — MACHINE TOOL MANUFA...

LTD.—See Haesung Industrial Co., Ltd.; *Int'l,* pg. 3206
KMT GROUP AB—See AIP, LLC; *U.S. Private,* pg. 137
KNUDSON MANUFACTURING, INC.; *U.S. Private,* pg. 2325
KOBOT SYSTEMS PTY LTD.—See Fuji Corporation; *Int'l,* pg. 2810
KOMO MACHINE INC.; *U.S. Private,* pg. 2342
KRB MACHINERY CO. INC.; *U.S. Private,* pg. 2350
KROFAM INC.; *U.S. Private,* pg. 2352
K-TEK CORPORATION, INC.—See Griffiths Corporation; *U.S. Private,* pg. 1789
KUNSHAN FUJI MACHINE MFG. CO., LTD.—See Fuji Corporation; *Int'l,* pg. 2810
KURT MANUFACTURING CO. INC. - KURT MANUFACTURING CORPORATE, GEAR, AND MACHINING DIVISION—See Kurt Manufacturing Co. Inc.; *U.S. Private,* pg. 2358
KYOUEI CO., LTD.—See Ichinen Holdings Co., Ltd.; *Int'l,* pg. 3580
LANDIS MACHINE—See NESCO, Inc.; *U.S. Private,* pg. 2886
LCM PRECISION TECHNOLOGY S.R.L.—See Hurco Companies, Inc.; *U.S. Public,* pg. 1076
LINTORFER EISENGIESSEREI GMBH—See DIHAG Holding GmbH; *Int'l,* pg. 2124
LITTLE ROCK TOOLS INC.—See Jasco Tools Inc.; *U.S. Private,* pg. 2189
L. KELLENBERGER & CO. AG—See Privet Fund Management, LLC; *U.S. Private,* pg. 3269
LLC CAMOZZI—See Camozzi Group; *Int'l,* pg. 1274
LOADPOINT BEARINGS LIMITED—See GL Tech Co., Ltd.; *Int'l,* pg. 2986
LOCKFORMER COMPANY—See Mestek, Inc.; *U.S. Public,* pg. 1426
LOGITECH LIMITED—See Roper Technologies, Inc.; *U.S. Public,* pg. 1812
LSP TECHNOLOGIES, INC.; *U.S. Private,* pg. 2509
LUCAS SARL—See A.J. Lucas Group Limited; *Int'l,* pg. 24
LUNA AB—See Bergman & Beving AB; *Int'l,* pg. 980
LUREN PRECISION CO., LTD.—See Hiwin Technologies Corp.; *Int'l,* pg. 3427
L'USINAGE ELECTRIQUE SARL—See Georg Fischer AG; *Int'l,* pg. 2935
MACHINE SOLUTIONS, INC.—See Forsyth Capital Investors LLC; *U.S. Private,* pg. 1573
MACHINE TOOLS INTERNATIONAL SP. Z O.O.—See C Dugard Ltd; *Int'l,* pg. 1238
MAE MACHINES (BEIJING) CO., LTD.—See Gesco AG; *Int'l,* pg. 2945
MAG IAS GMBH—See Fair Friend Group; *Int'l,* pg. 2604
MAG MAINTENANCE UK LIMITED—See MAG IAS Holdings, Inc.; *U.S. Private,* pg. 2545
MAGNETO SPECIAL ANODES B.V.—See Xylem Inc.; *U.S. Public,* pg. 2394
MARKUSSON PROFESSIONAL GRINDERS AB—See Emak S.p.A.; *Int'l,* pg. 2373
MARTIN SPROCKET & GEAR, INC. - MISSISSAUGA—See Martin Sprocket & Gear, Inc.; *U.S. Private,* pg. 2596
MATE PRECISION TOOLING INC.; *U.S. Private,* pg. 2609
MATRIX MACHINE TOOL (COVENTRY) LIMITED—See Hiwin Technologies Corp.; *Int'l,* pg. 3427
MCLEAN INCORPORATED; *U.S. Private,* pg. 2641
MECANIZACIONES DEL SUR-MECASUR, S.A.—See Cie Automotive S.A.; *Int'l,* pg. 1604
MEGA MANUFACTURING INC.; *U.S. Private,* pg. 2660
MELLING TOOL COMPANY INC. - MELLING CYLINDER SLEEVES DIVISION—See Melling Tool Company Inc.; *U.S. Private,* pg. 2662
MELLING TOOL COMPANY INC. - MELLING SINTERED METALS DIVISION—See Melling Tool Company Inc.; *U.S. Private,* pg. 2662
METRIC MACHINING; *U.S. Private,* pg. 2684
MEUSELWITZ GUSS EISENGIESSEREI GMBH—See DIHAG Holding GmbH; *Int'l,* pg. 2124
M.HART DO BRASIL LTDA.—See Stanley Black & Decker, Inc.; *U.S. Public,* pg. 1933
MICROMATIC, LLC; *U.S. Private,* pg. 2703
MILWAUKEE SLIDE AND SPINDLE—See Belco Industries, Inc.; *U.S. Private,* pg. 517
MODEL 2 MACHINING, INC.—See Generation Growth Capital, Inc.; *U.S. Private,* pg. 1668
MONARCH INDUSTRIES LIMITED—See Bank of Montreal; *Int'l,* pg. 847
MONARCH INDUSTRIES LIMITED—See Business Development Bank of Canada; *Int'l,* pg. 1229
MONARCH INDUSTRIES LIMITED—See Export Development Canada; *Int'l,* pg. 2590
MONTRESOR & CO. S.R.L.—See Biesse S.p.A.; *Int'l,* pg. 1020
MOORE TOOL COMPANY, INC.—See PMT Group Inc; *U.S. Private,* pg. 3219
MORI SEIKI BRASIL LTDA.—See DMG MORI Co., Ltd.; *Int'l,* pg. 2145
MORI SEIKI ESPANA S.A.—See DMG MORI Co., Ltd.; *Int'l,* pg. 2145
MORI SEIKI HONG KONG LTD.—See DMG MORI Co., Ltd.; *Int'l,* pg. 2145
MORI SEIKI ISRAEL LTD.—See DMG MORI Co., Ltd.; *Int'l,* pg. 2145
MORI SEIKI (SHANGHAI) CO., LTD.—See DMG MORI Co., Ltd.; *Int'l,* pg. 2145
MORI SEIKI TECHNO GMBH—See DMG MORI Co., Ltd.; *Int'l,* pg. 2145
MORI SEIKI TECHNO LTD.—See DMG MORI Co., Ltd.; *Int'l,* pg. 2145
MOSEY MANUFACTURING COMPANY INCORPORATED; *U.S. Private,* pg. 2793
MUDANJIANG OTC WELDING MACHINES CO., LTD.—See Daihen Corporation; *Int'l,* pg. 1926
MUSASHI SEIMITSU CO., LTD.—See Honda Motor Co., Ltd.; *Int'l,* pg. 3463
NACHI MACHINING TECHNOLOGY CO.; *U.S. Private,* pg. 2830
NANJING EASTERN LASER CO., LTD.—See Coherent Corp.; *U.S. Public,* pg. 527
NANJING EASTERN TECHNOLOGIES COMPANY, LTD.—See Coherent Corp.; *U.S. Public,* pg. 527
NATIONAL MACHINERY LLC—See Alpha Capital Partners, Ltd.; *U.S. Private,* pg. 197
NORDSON B.V.—See Nordson Corporation; *U.S. Public,* pg. 1533
NORMAC INCORPORATED; *U.S. Private,* pg. 2938
OCEAN MACHINERY—See Citizen Watch Co., Ltd.; *Int'l,* pg. 1624
OLIVER INSTRUMENT COMPANY; *U.S. Private,* pg. 3011
OMAX CORP.; *U.S. Private,* pg. 3015
OOO KENNAMETAL—See Kennametal Inc.; *U.S. Public,* pg. 1223
OSBORN INTERNATIONAL AB—See Jason Industries, Inc.; *U.S. Private,* pg. 2190
OSBORN SINGAPORE PTE LTD.—See Jason Industries, Inc.; *U.S. Private,* pg. 2190
OSBORN UNIPOL SAS—See Jason Industries, Inc.; *U.S. Private,* pg. 2190
OSBORN-UNIPOL SL—See Jason Industries, Inc.; *U.S. Private,* pg. 2190
OTC DAIHEN ASIA CO., LTD.—See Daihen Corporation; *Int'l,* pg. 1926
OTC DAIHEN EUROPE GMBH—See Daihen Corporation; *Int'l,* pg. 1926
OTC INDUSTRIAL (QINGDAO) CO., LTD.—See Daihen Corporation; *Int'l,* pg. 1926
PANAVISE PRODUCTS, INC.; *U.S. Private,* pg. 3085
PARKER HANNIFIN HYDRAULIC FILTER DIVISION—See Parker Hannifin Corporation; *U.S. Public,* pg. 1645
PAUL BEIER GMBH WERKZEUG- UND MASCHINENBAU & CO. KG—See Gesco AG; *Int'l,* pg. 2946
PCC ROLLMET, INC.—See Berkshire Hathaway Inc.; *U.S. Public,* pg. 314
PEDDINGHAUS CORPORATION; *U.S. Private,* pg. 3127
PENTA LASER ZHEJIANG CO., LTD.—See El.En. S.p.A.; *Int'l,* pg. 2342
PFAFF MASCHINENBAU GMBH—See FLSmidth & Co. A/S; *Int'l,* pg. 2711
PFERD AUSTRALIA (PTY.) LTD.—See August Rueggeberg GmbH & Co. KG PFERD-Werkzeuge; *Int'l,* pg. 703
PFERD-RUEGGEBERG B.V.—See August Rueggeberg GmbH & Co. KG PFERD-Werkzeuge; *Int'l,* pg. 703
PFERD RUEGGEBERG FRANCE—See August Rueggeberg GmbH & Co. KG PFERD-Werkzeuge; *Int'l,* pg. 703
PFERD-RUEGGEBERG GES.M.B.H—See August Rueggeberg GmbH & Co. KG PFERD-Werkzeuge; *Int'l,* pg. 703
PFERD-TOOLS PVT. LTD.—See August Rueggeberg GmbH & Co. KG PFERD-Werkzeuge; *Int'l,* pg. 703
PLASMA AUTOMATION, INC.; *U.S. Private,* pg. 3198
PLS PACIFIC LASER SYSTEMS LLC—See Danaher Corporation; *U.S. Public,* pg. 629
PMC INDUSTRIES INC.—See Park-Ohio Holdings Corp.; *U.S. Public,* pg. 1639
PMT GROUP INC; *U.S. Private,* pg. 3219
POWER PACKER EUROPA B.V.—See Enerpac Tool Group Corp.; *U.S. Public,* pg. 766
POWER-PACKER NORTH AMERICA, INC.—See Enerpac Tool Group Corp.; *U.S. Public,* pg. 766
PRC LASER CORP.—See Coherent Corp.; *U.S. Public,* pg. 527
PRESSL, SPOL. S R.O.—See FERMAT Group, a.s.; *Int'l,* pg. 2639
P.R. HOFFMAN MACHINE PRODUCTS, INC.—See Amtech Systems, Inc.; *U.S. Public,* pg. 134
P&R INDUSTRIES INC.; *U.S. Private,* pg. 3059
THE PRODUCTO MACHINE CO.—See PMT Group Inc; *U.S. Private,* pg. 3219
PROFILE METAL FORMING INC.; *U.S. Private,* pg. 3277
PT AIDA STAMPING TECHNOLOGY INDONESIA—See AIDA Engineering, Ltd.; *Int'l,* pg. 231
PT. DMG MORI INDONESIA—See DMG MORI Co., Ltd.; *Int'l,* pg. 2145
PT. DMG MORI SEIKI INDONESIA—See DMG MORI Co., Ltd.; *Int'l,* pg. 2145
PTG DEUTSCHLAND GMBH—See Chongqing Machinery & Electronics Holding (Group) Co., Ltd.; *Int'l,* pg. 1580
PTX-PENTRONIX, INC.—See Gasbarre Products Inc.; *U.S. Private,* pg. 1648
QPI MULTIPRESS, INC.—See Quality Products Inc.; *U.S. Private,* pg. 3321
QPM AEROSPACE INC.; *U.S. Private,* pg. 3313
RAPPOLD WINTERTHUR TECHNOLOGIE GMBH—See 3M Company; *U.S. Public,* pg. 8
RAWL AUSTRALASIA PTY. LTD.—See Stanley Black & Decker, Inc.; *U.S. Public,* pg. 1934
REGAL BELOIT SPAIN, S.A.—See Regal Rexnord Corporation; *U.S. Public,* pg. 1773
REGION SUPPLIERS PTE LTD—See GRP Limited; *Int'l,* pg. 3114
RIDGE TOOL COMPANY—See Emerson Electric Co.; *U.S. Public,* pg. 749
ROFIN-BAASEL CANADA LTD.—See Coherent Corp.; *U.S. Public,* pg. 527
ROFIN-BAASEL, INC.—See Coherent Corp.; *U.S. Public,* pg. 527
ROFIN-SINAR, INC.—See Coherent Corp.; *U.S. Public,* pg. 527
ROFIN-SINAR TECHNOLOGIES EUROPE S.L.—See Coherent Corp.; *U.S. Public,* pg. 528
ROHM PRODUCTS OF AMERICA; *U.S. Private,* pg. 3473
ROPER WHITNEY OF ROCKFORD INC.; *U.S. Private,* pg. 3480
ROTEA D.O.O.—See August Rueggeberg GmbH & Co. KG PFERD-Werkzeuge; *Int'l,* pg. 703
ROTHENBERGER USA - WEST COAST OPERATIONS—See Dr. Helmut Rothenberger Holding GmbH; *Int'l,* pg. 2191
ROTOMETRICS, INC.—See MPE Partners, LLC; *U.S. Private,* pg. 2803
SANDERS SAWS, INC.—See K2 Diamond Company; *U.S. Private,* pg. 2253
SATISLOH PHOTONICS AG—See EssilorLuxottica SA; *Int'l,* pg. 2516
SAUTEC AS—See Epiroc AB; *Int'l,* pg. 2463
SAW MART LTD—See Addison Saws Limited; *Int'l,* pg. 129
SCHIRNHOFER WERKZEUGMASCHINEN & WERKZEUGE GMBH—See Grieshaber Holding GmbH; *Int'l,* pg. 3083
SCHMIEDEBERGER GIESSEREI GMBH—See DIHAG Holding GmbH; *Int'l,* pg. 2125
SCHULER AUTOMATION GMBH & CO. KG—See ANDRITZ AG; *Int'l,* pg. 456
SCHULER (DALIAN) FORMING TECHNOLOGIES CO., LTD.—See ANDRITZ AG; *Int'l,* pg. 456
SCHULER PRESSES UK LIMITED—See ANDRITZ AG; *Int'l,* pg. 456
SEALANT SYSTEMS INTERNATIONAL, INC.—See Illinois Tool Works Inc.; *U.S. Public,* pg. 1110
S.E.E. SISTEMAS INDUSTRIA E COMERCIO LTDA.—See Illinois Tool Works Inc.; *U.S. Public,* pg. 1110
S.E. HUFFMAN CORP.—See The Springs Company; *U.S. Private,* pg. 4120
SELWAY CORPORATION; *U.S. Private,* pg. 3603
SENECA FALLS MACHINES; *U.S. Private,* pg. 3606
SERBIA ISCAR TOOLS D.O.O.—See Berkshire Hathaway Inc.; *U.S. Public,* pg. 307
SES AUTOMATION INC.—See SES, LLC; *U.S. Private,* pg. 3617
SETCO MIDWEST SERVICE CENTER—See Holden Industries, Inc.; *U.S. Private,* pg. 1962
SETCO SALES COMPANY—See Holden Industries, Inc.; *U.S. Private,* pg. 1962
SHANGHAI CAMOZZI AUTOMATION CONTROL CO, LTD.—See Camozzi Group; *Int'l,* pg. 1274
SHANGHAI HANHONG PRECISION MACHINERY CO., LTD.—See Ferrotec Holdings Corporation; *Int'l,* pg. 2643
SHANGHAI HUATENG METAL PROCESSING CO., LTD.—See Chun Yuan Steel Industry Co., Ltd.; *Int'l,* pg. 1596
SHANGHAI JACKSONLEA POLISHING MATERIALS CO., LTD.—See Jason Industries, Inc.; *U.S. Private,* pg. 2190
SHB STAHL- UND HARTGUSSWERK BOESDORF GMBH—See DIHAG Holding GmbH; *Int'l,* pg. 2125
SHENZHEN KBF LASER TECH CO., LTD.—See El.En. S.p.A.; *Int'l,* pg. 2342
SHIN NIPPON KOKI CO. LTD. - MISAKI—See Fair Friend Group; *Int'l,* pg. 2605
SHIN NIPPON KOKI CO. LTD.—See Fair Friend Group; *Int'l,* pg. 2604
SHIROKI SEIKEI CO., LTD.—See AISIN Corporation; *Int'l,* pg. 254
SIEBURG INTERNATIONAL, INC.; *U.S. Private,* pg. 3646
SIGMA TECHNOLOGY S.R.L.—See Fair Friend Group; *Int'l,* pg. 2604
SIGNODE (ESPANA) S.A.—See Crown Holdings, Inc.; *U.S. Public,* pg. 599
SKY THRIVE RAMBAUDI S.R.L.—See Fair Friend Group; *Int'l,* pg. 2604
SNK GMBH—See Fair Friend Group; *Int'l,* pg. 2605
SOMBUR TOOL & DIE—See MNP Corporation; *U.S. Private,* pg. 2756
SORTIMAT TECHNOLOGY PVT. LTD.—See ATS Corporation; *Int'l,* pg. 695
SOTRAS SRL—See El.En. S.p.A.; *Int'l,* pg. 2342
SOUTHWESTERN INDUSTRIES, INC.; *U.S. Private,* pg. 3741

333517 — MACHINE TOOL MANUFA...

SPEZIALGUSS WETZLAR GMBH—See DIHAG Holding GmbH; *Int'l*, pg. 2125
SPG NETHERLANDS B.V.—See Illinois Tool Works Inc.; *U.S. Public*, pg. 1110
SPG PACKAGING UK LTD—See Illinois Tool Works Inc.; *U.S. Public*, pg. 1110
SPRINGFIELD MANUFACTURING LLC—See The Springs Company; *U.S. Private*, pg. 4120
STABIL DRILL SPECIALITIES, L.L.C.—See Superior Energy Services, Inc.; *U.S. Public*, pg. 3877
STABIL DRILL SPECIALTIES, L.L.C.—See Superior Energy Services, Inc.; *U.S. Public*, pg. 3877
STANKOWENDT RUSSIA—See 3M Company; *U.S. Public*, pg. 9
STANLEY BLACK & DECKER AUSTRIA GMBH—See Stanley Black & Decker, Inc.; *U.S. Public*, pg. 1934
STANLEY BLACK & DECKER BELGIUM BVBA—See Stanley Black & Decker, Inc.; *U.S. Public*, pg. 1934
STANLEY BLACK & DECKER CZECH REPUBLIC S.R.O.—See Stanley Black & Decker, Inc.; *U.S. Public*, pg. 1934
STANLEY BLACK & DECKER DEUTSCHLAND GMBH—See Stanley Black & Decker, Inc.; *U.S. Public*, pg. 1934
STANLEY BLACK & DECKER FRANCE S.A.S.—See Stanley Black & Decker, Inc.; *U.S. Public*, pg. 1934
STANLEY BLACK & DECKER IBERICA, S.L.—See Stanley Black & Decker, Inc.; *U.S. Public*, pg. 1934
STANLEY BLACK & DECKER IRELAND—See Stanley Black & Decker, Inc.; *U.S. Public*, pg. 1934
STANLEY BLACK & DECKER NETHERLANDS B.V.—See Stanley Black & Decker, Inc.; *U.S. Public*, pg. 1934
STANLEY BLACK & DECKER NORWAY AS—See Stanley Black & Decker, Inc.; *U.S. Public*, pg. 1934
STANLEY BLACK & DECKER POLSKA SP. Z O.O.—See Stanley Black & Decker, Inc.; *U.S. Public*, pg. 1934
STAR-SU LLC.—See Star Cutter Company; *U.S. Private*, pg. 3784
SUMMIT MACHINE TOOL MANUFACTURING LLC—See LSB Industries, Inc.; *U.S. Public*, pg. 1344
SUMMIT TOOLING INC.—See CORE Industrial Partners, LLC; *U.S. Private*, pg. 1049
SUND BIRSTA AB—See Danieli & C. Officine Meccaniche S.p.A.; *Int'l*, pg. 1963
SUPERB INDUSTRIES, INC.; *U.S. Private*, pg. 3875
SUPERIOR DRILLING SOLUTIONS, LLC—See Drilling Tools International Corp.; *U.S. Public*, pg. 688
SWATY D.D.—See Avtotehna, d.d.; *Int'l*, pg. 751
SWELDX AB—See Illinois Tool Works Inc.; *U.S. Public*, pg. 1111
SWISSTEC SOURCING VIETNAM JOINT STOCK COMPANY—See Einhell Germany AG; *Int'l*, pg. 2334
SYNRAD, INC.—See Novanta Inc.; *U.S. Public*, pg. 1548
TAIYO KOKI CO., LTD.—See DMG MORI Co., Ltd.; *Int'l*, pg. 2145
TAPIO GMBH—See Durr AG; *Int'l*, pg. 2233
TARUS PRODUCTS INC.; *U.S. Private*, pg. 3934
TESA TECHNOLOGY UK LTD—See Hexagon AB; *Int'l*, pg. 3369
THERMWOOD CORPORATION; *U.S. Private*, pg. 4143
THIRODE GRANDES CUISINES POLIGNY SAS—See Illinois Tool Works Inc.; *U.S. Public*, pg. 1111
THUMB TOOL & ENGINEERING CO.—See Gemini Group, Inc.; *U.S. Private*, pg. 1658
TIMESAVERS INC.—See Holden Industries, Inc.; *U.S. Private*, pg. 1962
TIMESAVERS INTERNATIONAL BV—See Holden Industries, Inc.; *U.S. Private*, pg. 1962
TITMAN TIP TOOLS LIMITED—See Checkit plc; *Int'l*, pg. 1459
TOOLING TECHNOLOGY, LLC—See GenNx360 Capital Partners, L.P.; *U.S. Private*, pg. 1672
TOUGHBUILT INDUSTRIES, INC.; *U.S. Public*, pg. 2165
T PROJECT CO., LTD.—See DMG MORI Co., Ltd.; *Int'l*, pg. 2145
TRIBUS ENTERPRISES, INC.; *U.S. Private*, pg. 4228
TRI TOOL INC.; *U.S. Private*, pg. 4221
TRI TOOL INTERNATIONAL—See Tri Tool Inc.; *U.S. Private*, pg. 4221
TRI TOOL POWER SERVICES, INC.—See Tri Tool Inc.; *U.S. Private*, pg. 4221
TUNGALOY CORP.—See Berkshire Hathaway Inc.; *U.S. Public*, pg. 308
TWINAPLATE LIMITED—See Illinois Tool Works Inc.; *U.S. Public*, pg. 1111
TYROLIA TECHNOLOGY GMBH—See Head B.V.; *Int'l*, pg. 3300
UNICHEMICALS INDUSTRIA E COMERCIO LTDA.—See Illinois Tool Works Inc.; *U.S. Public*, pg. 1111
U.S. BROACH & MACHINE COMPANY—See Avis Industrial Corporation; *U.S. Private*, pg. 407
VALFIVRE ITALIA SRL—See El.En. S.p.A.; *Int'l*, pg. 2342
VALON KONE AB—See Kadant Inc.; *U.S. Public*, pg. 1213
VALON KONE AB—See Kadant Inc.; *U.S. Public*, pg. 1213
VEECO PROCESS EQUIPMENT INC.—See Veeco Instruments Inc.; *U.S. Public*, pg. 2277
VICTOR TECHNOLOGIES GROUP, INC.—See Enovis Corporation; *U.S. Public*, pg. 771

VIET ITALIA S.R.L.—See Biesse S.p.A.; *Int'l*, pg. 1020
VITRONICS SOLTEC B.V.—See Illinois Tool Works Inc.; *U.S. Public*, pg. 1111
WALDRICH COBURG WERKZEUGMASCHINENFABRIK GMBH—See Beijing Jingcheng Machinery Electric Holding Co., Ltd.; *Int'l*, pg. 953
WALLNER TOOLING/EXPAC INC.; *U.S. Private*, pg. 4431
WALSH PARTS & SERVICE; *U.S. Private*, pg. 4433
WALZENGIESSEREI COSWIG GMBH—See DIHAG Holding GmbH; *Int'l*, pg. 2125
WARDJET, INC.—See AXYZ Automation Group Inc.; *Int'l*, pg. 773
W.A. WHITNEY CO.—See Mega Manufacturing Inc.; *U.S. Private*, pg. 2660
WELDON SOLUTIONS; *U.S. Private*, pg. 4474
WELLS MANUFACTURING LLC; *U.S. Private*, pg. 4476
WERKZEUGBAU LEIPZIG GMBH—See Gesco AG; *Int'l*, pg. 2946
WHELAN MACHINE & TOOL, LLC—See Gremada Industries Inc.; *U.S. Private*, pg. 1783
WHEMCO, INC.—See Park Corp.; *U.S. Private*, pg. 3096
WILLIAMS WHITE & COMPANY—See Doerfer Corporation; *U.S. Private*, pg. 1253
WILSON TOOL CANADA INC.—See Wilson Tool International Inc.; *U.S. Private*, pg. 4531
WINTERTHUR SCHLEIFTECHNIK AG—See 3M Company; *U.S. Public*, pg. 9
WOODINGS INDUSTRIAL CORPORATION; *U.S. Private*, pg. 4558
WOODLAWN MANUFACTURING, LTD.—See National Presto Industries, Inc; *U.S. Public*, pg. 1497
WRIGHT-K TECHNOLOGY, INC.; *U.S. Private*, pg. 4573
XLO INDIA LIMITED—See Hindustan Hardy Limited; *Int'l*, pg. 3400
ZDAS, A.S.—See CEFC China Energy Company Limited; *Int'l*, pg. 1389

333519 — ROLLING MILL AND OTHER METALWORKING MACHINERY MANUFACTURING

ACM-SERVICE COMPANY LLC—See Chien Wei Precise Technology Co., Ltd.; *Int'l*, pg. 1477
ADELWIGGINS GROUP—See TransDigm Group Incorporated; *U.S. Public*, pg. 2181
AICHI TECHNO METAL FUKAUMI CO., LTD.—See Aichi Steel Corporation; *Int'l*, pg. 230
AMADA (INDIA) PVT. LTD.—See Amada Holdings Co., Ltd.; *Int'l*, pg. 403
AMAERO INTERNATIONAL LIMITED; *Int'l*, pg. 407
AMERICAN PELLET MILL SERVICES, INC.—See Buhler AG; *Int'l*, pg. 1212
AML3D LIMITED; *Int'l*, pg. 429
AUTOMATION SPECIALISTS, INC.; *U.S. Private*, pg. 399
BEMCOR INC.—See Beatty Machine & Mfg. Company; *U.S. Private*, pg. 507
BONAL INTERNATIONAL, INC.; *U.S. Public*, pg. 368
BORGWARNER PDS TECHNOLOGIES, L.L.C.—See BorgWarner Inc.; *U.S. Public*, pg. 370
BOXPLAN GMBH & CO. KG—See Bobst Group S.A.; *Int'l*, pg. 1096
BRADBURY COMPANY, INC.; *U.S. Private*, pg. 631
BRANER USA, INC.—See Holleway Capital Partners LLC; *U.S. Private*, pg. 1964
CAMOZZI ADVANCED MANUFACTURING S.P.A.—See Camozzi Group; *Int'l*, pg. 1273
CAMOZZI AUTOMATION S.P.A.—See Camozzi Group; *Int'l*, pg. 1273
CBP ENGINEERING CORP.; *U.S. Private*, pg. 797
CENTURY ROLLFORMING INC.—See Century, Inc.; *U.S. Private*, pg. 834
CINETIC AUTOMATION—See FIVES, Societe Anonyme; *Int'l*, pg. 2696
COE PRESS EQUIPMENT CORP.; *U.S. Private*, pg. 960
COMPONENTA CASTINGS OY—See Componenta Corporation; *Int'l*, pg. 1753
DANIELI & C. OFFICINE MECCANICHE S.P.A.; *Int'l*, pg. 1962
DANIELI CORPORATION—See Danieli & C. Officine Meccaniche S.p.A.; *Int'l*, pg. 1962
DANIELI GERMANY GMBH—See Danieli & C. Officine Meccaniche S.p.A.; *Int'l*, pg. 1963
DANIELI MORGARDSHAMMAR SA—See Danieli & C. Officine Meccaniche S.p.A.; *Int'l*, pg. 1963
ESKO BRNO S.R.O—See Danaher Corporation; *U.S. Public*, pg. 626
FENES S.A.—See Cantoni Motor S.A.; *Int'l*, pg. 1299
FIVES DMS—See FIVES, Societe Anonyme; *Int'l*, pg. 2696
FORMTEK ASIA-PACIFIC—See Mestek, Inc.; *U.S. Public*, pg. 1426
FUJI CORPORATION; *Int'l*, pg. 2809
GEFIT DALIAN INDUSTRIAL TECHNOLOGY CO., LTD.—See GEFIT S.p.A.; *Int'l*, pg. 2912
GEFIT S.P.A. - GEFIT MOULDS & ASSEMBLY DIVISION—See GEFIT S.p.A.; *Int'l*, pg. 2911
GEFTECH KFT.—See GEFIT S.p.A.; *Int'l*, pg. 2912
GEORGE KOCH SONS LLC—See Koch Enterprises, Inc.; *U.S. Private*, pg. 2326

GOLDEN STATE ENGINEERING INC.; *U.S. Private*, pg. 1733
HENGERDA NEW MATERIALS (FUJIAN) CO., LTD.; *Int'l*, pg. 3346
HOVER-DAVIS, INC.—See Francisco Partners Management, LP; *U.S. Private*, pg. 1590
KARL EUGEN FISCHER GMBH—See Deutsche Beteiligungs AG; *Int'l*, pg. 2063
KENNAMETAL (SHANGHAI) CO., LTD.—See Kennametal Inc.; *U.S. Public*, pg. 1221
KENNAMETAL SOUTH AFRICA (PTY.) LTD.—See Kennametal Inc.; *U.S. Public*, pg. 1222
KENNAMETAL (THAILAND) CO., LTD.—See Kennametal Inc.; *U.S. Public*, pg. 1221
LOMAR MACHINE & TOOL CO.; *U.S. Private*, pg. 2483
METRO MACHINE & ENGINEERING CORP.—See Doering Company, LLC; *U.S. Private*, pg. 1253
MHCG, INC.—See Hitachi, Ltd.; *Int'l*, pg. 3423
MITSUBISHI-HITACHI METALS MACHINERY, INC.—See Hitachi, Ltd.; *Int'l*, pg. 3423
MITSUBISHI-HITACHI METALS MACHINERY (SHANGHAI), INC.—See Hitachi, Ltd.; *Int'l*, pg. 3423
MITSUBISHI-HITACHI METALS MACHINERY USA, INC.—See Hitachi, Ltd.; *Int'l*, pg. 3423
MITSUBISHI-HITACHI POWER SYSTEMS EUROPE GMBH—See Hitachi, Ltd.; *Int'l*, pg. 3423
ND MANUFACTURING ENGINEERING GROUP—See H.B. Fuller Company; *U.S. Public*, pg. 978
OHIO PICKLING & PROCESSING—See MNP Corporation; *U.S. Private*, pg. 2756
P/A INDUSTRIES, INC.; *U.S. Private*, pg. 3061
P/A INDUSTRIES-METAL STAMPING EQUIPMENT—See P/A Industries, Inc.; *U.S. Private*, pg. 3061
P/A INDUSTRIES—See P/A Industries, Inc.; *U.S. Private*, pg. 3061
PARK CORP.; *U.S. Private*, pg. 3096
PERFECTO INDUSTRIES INC.; *U.S. Private*, pg. 3148
PIC DESIGN INC.—See RBC Bearings Incorporated; *U.S. Public*, pg. 1766
PIPELINE ENGINEERING LTD—See KKR & Co. Inc.; *U.S. Public*, pg. 1242
RAPPOLD, HERMANN & CO. GMBH—See E.ON SE; *Int'l*, pg. 2259
ROSKAMP CHAMPION—See Gilbert Global Equity Partners; *U.S. Private*, pg. 1699
ROYLE SYSTEMS GROUP; *U.S. Private*, pg. 3494
RWC INC.; *U.S. Private*, pg. 3508
SCHULER (CHINA) CO., LTD.—See ANDRITZ AG; *Int'l*, pg. 456
SCOTCHMAN INDUSTRIES, INC.—See Krofam Inc.; *U.S. Private*, pg. 2353
SIN YEN TECHNOLOGIES SDN. BHD.—See FoundPac Group Berhad; *Int'l*, pg. 2754
SPECIALTY STRIP & OSCILLATING, INC.; *U.S. Private*, pg. 3751
SUNNEN PRODUCTS COMPANY; *U.S. Private*, pg. 3868
SWECO EUROPE S.A.—See Schlumberger Limited; *U.S. Public*, pg. 1846
THE TAYLOR-WINFIELD CORPORATION—See Olympus Partners; *U.S. Private*, pg. 3014
TELEDYNE SEABOTIX INC.—See Teledyne Technologies Incorporated; *U.S. Public*, pg. 1995
UNION ELECTRIC STEEL BVBA—See Ampco-Pittsburgh Corporation; *U.S. Public*, pg. 126
UNITED ROLLS INC.—See Park Corp.; *U.S. Private*, pg. 3096
UTICA PRODUCTS, INC.—See Utica Enterprises, Inc.; *U.S. Private*, pg. 4325
VALMONT COATINGS INC—See Valmont Industries, Inc.; *U.S. Public*, pg. 2274
VERTEX FASTENERS, INC.—See Leggett & Platt, Incorporated; *U.S. Public*, pg. 1304
WES-TECH AUTOMATION SOLUTIONS; *U.S. Private*, pg. 4482
XTEK EUROPE S.R.O.—See Xtek, Inc.; *U.S. Private*, pg. 4583
YODER - FORMTEK METAL FORMING, INC.—See Mestek, Inc.; *U.S. Public*, pg. 1426

333611 — TURBINE AND TURBINE GENERATOR SET UNITS MANUFACTURING

AHT SYNGAS TECHNOLOGY NV; *Int'l*, pg. 226
ALSTOM ALGERIE S.P.A.—See Alstom S.A.; *Int'l*, pg. 380
ALSTOM AUSTRALIA LTD—See Alstom S.A.; *Int'l*, pg. 380
ALSTOM DEUTSCHLAND AG—See Alstom S.A.; *Int'l*, pg. 380
ALSTOM GULF AREA—See Alstom S.A.; *Int'l*, pg. 380
ALSTOM K.K.—See Alstom S.A.; *Int'l*, pg. 380
ALSTOM POWER TURBOMACHINES SA—See General Electric Company; *U.S. Public*, pg. 917
ALSTOM PROJECTS INDIA LTD—See General Electric Company; *U.S. Public*, pg. 917
ALSTOM RENEWABLE POWER CANADA INC.—See Alstom S.A.; *Int'l*, pg. 381
ALSTOM SWITZERLAND LTD—See Alstom S.A.; *Int'l*, pg. 381

N.A.I.C.S. INDEX

333612 — SPEED CHANGER, INDU...

AMERICAN GOVERNOR CO.—See Emerson Electric Co.; *U.S. Public*, pg. 740
AMSC WINDTEC GMBH—See American Superconductor Corporation; *U.S. Public*, pg. 110
ANDRITZ ENERGY & ENVIRONMENT GMBH—See ANDRITZ AG; *Int'l*, pg. 452
ANDRITZ HYDRO AG—See ANDRITZ AG; *Int'l*, pg. 453
ANDRITZ HYDRO GMBH—See ANDRITZ AG; *Int'l*, pg. 453
ANDRITZ KFT.—See ANDRITZ AG; *Int'l*, pg. 454
ANEMOI LLC; *U.S. Private*, pg. 281
ARISTA POWER, INC.; *U.S. Public*, pg. 192
ASSOCIATED SPRING RAYMOND (SHANGHAI) CO., LTD.—See OEP Capital Advisors, L.P.; *U.S. Private*, pg. 2998
BAJUENERGY WIND GMBH—See BKW AG; *Int'l*, pg. 1054
BARBOUR STOCKWELL INCORPORATED; *U.S. Private*, pg. 472
BARNES GROUP SPAIN SRL—See Barnes Group Inc.; *U.S. Public*, pg. 277
BATTERY ELECTRIC VEHICLE & ELECTRONIC PRODUCTS TESTING CENTER CO., LTD.—See Energy Absolute Public Company Limited; *Int'l*, pg. 2422
BEIJING BEIZHONG STEAM TURBINE GENERATOR CO., LTD.—See Beijing Jingcheng Machinery Electric Holding Co., Ltd.; *Int'l*, pg. 953
BEIJING JINGCHENG NEW ENERGY CO., LTD.—See Beijing Jingcheng Machinery Electric Holding Co., Ltd.; *Int'l*, pg. 953
BEMCO FLUIDTECHNIK LLP—See BEMCO HYDRAULICS LTD; *Int'l*, pg. 969
BGR BOILERS PRIVATE LIMITED—See BGR Energy Systems Limited; *Int'l*, pg. 1008
BGR TURBINES COMPANY PRIVATE LIMITED—See BGR Energy Systems Limited; *Int'l*, pg. 1008
BILFINGER MASCHINENBAU GMBH & CO KG—See Bilfinger SE; *Int'l*, pg. 1027
BRIGGS & STRATTON CORPORATION; *U.S. Private*, pg. 650
BRITWIND LTD.—See Ecotricity Group Ltd.; *Int'l*, pg. 2300
BROADWIND HEAVY FABRICATIONS, INC.—See Broadwind, Inc.; *U.S. Public*, pg. 392
BUCHER HYDRAULICS AG—See Bucher Industries AG; *Int'l*, pg. 1207
BUCHER HYDRAULICS FRUHGEN AG—See Bucher Industries AG; *Int'l*, pg. 1207
BUCHER HYDRAULICS S.P.A.—See Bucher Industries AG; *Int'l*, pg. 1207
CAPSTONE GREEN ENERGY CORPORATION; *U.S. Private*, pg. 746
CAPSTONE TURBINE INTERNATIONAL, INC.—See Capstone Green Energy Corporation; *U.S. Private*, pg. 746
CATERPILLAR CHINA INVESTMENT CO., LTD.—See Caterpillar, Inc.; *U.S. Public*, pg. 451
CHENG POWER SYSTEMS, INC.—See NRG Energy, Inc.; *U.S. Public*, pg. 1549
CHINA MING YANG WIND POWER GROUP LIMITED; *Int'l*, pg. 1524
CHROMALLOY GAS TURBINE EUROPA B.V.—See Veritas Capital Fund Management, LLC; *U.S. Private*, pg. 4364
CLAYTON SALES & SERVICE LTD.—See Clayton Industries Co.; *U.S. Private*, pg. 918
CLIPPER WINDPOWER, LLC—See Platinum Equity, LLC; *U.S. Private*, pg. 3202
COMBUSTION PARTS INC.—See Allied Power Group, LLC; *U.S. Private*, pg. 187
CUMMINS INC.—See Cummins Inc.; *U.S. Public*, pg. 606
CUMMINS KOMATSU ENGINE COMPANY—See Cummins Inc.; *U.S. Public*, pg. 606
DESARROLLOS EOLICOS, S.A.—See EDP - Energias de Portugal, S.A.; *Int'l*, pg. 2314
DIVISAO TURBINAS SOLAR S.A. DE C.V.—See Caterpillar, Inc.; *U.S. Public*, pg. 453
DONGFANG ELECTRIC CORPORATION LIMITED; *Int'l*, pg. 2166
DONGFANG ELECTRIC (WUHAN) NUCLEAR EQUIPEMENT CO., LTD.—See Dongfang Electric Corporation Limited; *Int'l*, pg. 2166
DOOSAN HEAVY INDUSTRIES VIETNAM CO., LTD.—See Doosan Corporation; *Int'l*, pg. 2173
ELLIOTT COMPANY—See Ebara Corporation; *Int'l*, pg. 2284
ENGINEERED MACHINED PRODUCTS INC.—See Concentric AB; *Int'l*, pg. 1764
ENIKON A.D.; *Int'l*, pg. 2439
FICONT INDUSTRY BEIJING CO., LTD.; *Int'l*, pg. 2653
FIRST MODE IPP LIMITED—See Anglo American PLC; *Int'l*, pg. 462
FLORIDA TURBINE TECHNOLOGIES INC.—See Kratos Defense & Security Solutions, Inc.; *U.S. Public*, pg. 1276
FREEMAN ENCLOSURE SYSTEMS, LLC—See IES Holdings, Inc.; *U.S. Public*, pg. 1094
GAIA-WIND LTD.; *Int'l*, pg. 2869
GAS TURBINE EFFICIENCY AB—See Gas Turbine Efficiency, LLC; *U.S. Private*, pg. 1647
GE ENERGY—See General Electric Company; *U.S. Public*, pg. 917
GE ENERGY—See General Electric Company; *U.S. Public*, pg. 917

GE HYDRO FRANCE—See General Electric Company; *U.S. Public*, pg. 917
GENERAC BRASIL LTDA—See Generac Holdings Inc.; *U.S. Public*, pg. 912
GE PACKAGED POWER, INC.—See General Electric Company; *U.S. Public*, pg. 917
GE PACKAGED POWER, L.P.—See General Electric Company; *U.S. Public*, pg. 917
GE POWER NORWAY AS—See General Electric Company; *U.S. Public*, pg. 917
GE POWER SWEDEN AB—See General Electric Company; *U.S. Public*, pg. 917
GE POWER SWEDEN AB—See General Electric Company; *U.S. Public*, pg. 917
GESTAMP WIND—See Corporacion Gestamp SL; *Int'l*, pg. 1804
GRENERGY RENOVABLES SA; *Int'l*, pg. 3080
GURIT BALSA, S.L.—See Gurit Holding AG; *Int'l*, pg. 3188
GURIT COMPOSITE COMPONENTS LTD.—See Gurit Holding AG; *Int'l*, pg. 3188
GURIT (HUNGARY) KFT.—See CARBOPRESS S.p.A.; *Int'l*, pg. 1321
GURIT ITALY S.R.L.—See Gurit Holding AG; *Int'l*, pg. 3188
HALUS POWER SYSTEMS; *U.S. Private*, pg. 1846
HANGZHOU ADVANCE WIND-POWER GEARBOX CO., LTD.—See Hangzhou Advance Gearbox Group Co., Ltd.; *Int'l*, pg. 3246
HANGZHOU STEAM TURBINE CO., LTD.; *Int'l*, pg. 3250
HARBIN ELECTRICAL MACHINERY COMPANY LIMITED—See Harmonicare Medical Holdings Ltd.; *Int'l*, pg. 3278
HARBIN ELECTRIC COMPANY LIMITED—See Harbin Electric Corporation; *Int'l*, pg. 3270
HAWTHORNE POWER SYSTEMS—See Hawthorne Machinery Company; *U.S. Private*, pg. 1884
HELIX WIND, CORP.—See Better For You Wellness, Inc.; *U.S. Public*, pg. 326
HITACHI HIGH TECHNOLOGIES EUROPE GMBH—See Hitachi, Ltd.; *Int'l*, pg. 3418
HITACHI POWER SOLUTIONS CO., LTD.—See Hitachi, Ltd.; *Int'l*, pg. 3420
HOWMET CASTINGS & SERVICES, INC. - WHITEHALL CASTING—See Howmet Aerospace Inc.; *U.S. Public*, pg. 1061
HUAYI ELECTRIC COMPANY LIMITED; *Int'l*, pg. 3516
ICARUS WIND ENERGY, INC.; *U.S. Private*, pg. 2029
IHI JET SERVICE CO., LTD.—See IHI Corporation; *Int'l*, pg. 3605
JEUMONT ELECTRIC INDIA PRIVATE LIMITED—See Altawest Group; *Int'l*, pg. 388
JSB GROUP A/S—See Gurit Holding AG; *Int'l*, pg. 3188
KEYSTONE TOWER SYSTEMS, INC.—See NOV, Inc.; *U.S. Public*, pg. 1545
KINECO EXEL COMPOSITES INDIA PRIVATE LIMITED—See Exel Composites Oyj; *Int'l*, pg. 2582
KOHLER - GENERATOR DIVISION—See Kohler Company; *U.S. Private*, pg. 2339
L.A. TURBINE—See Chart Industries, Inc.; *U.S. Public*, pg. 482
LM WIND POWER A/S—See General Electric Company; *U.S. Public*, pg. 917
MONT SAINTE-MARGUERITE WIND FARM L.P.—See Canada Pension Plan Investment Board; *Int'l*, pg. 1281
NATURENER RIM ROCK WIND ENERGY, LLC—See Morgan Stanley; *U.S. Public*, pg. 1475
NEW WAY POWER (PTY) LIMITED—See enX Group Limited; *Int'l*, pg. 2456
NORTHERN POWER SYSTEMS CORP.; *U.S. Private*, pg. 2954
NUOVO PIGNONE S.P.A.—See General Electric Company; *U.S. Public*, pg. 919
NUVUS GRO CORP.; *U.S. Private*, pg. 2975
OGIN, INC.—See Exelon Corporation; *U.S. Public*, pg. 807
PARCO EOLICO DEL SAN GOTTARDO SA—See Azienda Elettrica Ticinese; *Int'l*, pg. 779
PIKA ENERGY, INC.—See Generac Holdings Inc.; *U.S. Public*, pg. 912
POWERDYNE INTERNATIONAL, INC.; *U.S. Public*, pg. 1705
PRECISION ENGINE CONTROLS CORPORATION—See Parker Hannifin Corporation; *U.S. Public*, pg. 1643
PROTON ENERGY SYSTEMS, INC.; *U.S. Private*, pg. 3290
P.T. SOLAR SERVICES INDONESIA—See Caterpillar, Inc.; *U.S. Public*, pg. 453
PURENERGY RENEWABLES, LTD—See Abengoa S.A.; *Int'l*, pg. 59
PURENERGY RENEWABLES, LTD—See Algonquin Power & Utilities Corp.; *Int'l*, pg. 319
RULMECA CORPORATION; *U.S. Private*, pg. 3503
SAFREMA ENERGY EUROPE—See Safrema Energy LLC; *U.S. Private*, pg. 3525
SAFREMA ENERGY LLC; *U.S. Private*, pg. 3525
SEEGER-ORBIS GMBH & CO. OHG—See Barnes Group Inc.; *U.S. Public*, pg. 277
SIFCO TURBINE COMPONENT SERVICES—See SIFCO Industries, Inc.; *U.S. Public*, pg. 1877
SOLAR TURBINES CANADA LTD.—See Caterpillar, Inc.; *U.S. Public*, pg. 454

SOLAR TURBINES EUROPE S.A.—See Caterpillar, Inc.; *U.S. Public*, pg. 454
SOLAR TURBINES INCORPORATED—See Caterpillar, Inc.; *U.S. Public*, pg. 453
SOLAR TURBINES INDIA PRIVATE LIMITED—See Caterpillar, Inc.; *U.S. Public*, pg. 454
SOLAR TURBINES INTERNATIONAL COMPANY—See Caterpillar, Inc.; *U.S. Public*, pg. 454
SOLAR TURBINES SERVICES NIGERIA LTD.—See Caterpillar, Inc.; *U.S. Public*, pg. 454
SOLAR TURBINES SERVICES OF ARGENTINA S.R.L.—See Caterpillar, Inc.; *U.S. Public*, pg. 454
STEELWIND NORDENHAM GMBH—See AG der Dillinger Huttenwerke; *Int'l*, pg. 197
STORK USA, INC.—See Fluor Corporation; *U.S. Public*, pg. 860
STROMSHOLMEN AB—See Barnes Group Inc.; *U.S. Public*, pg. 277
STS TURBO, INC.; *U.S. Private*, pg. 3843
TAS ENERGY, INC.—See Comfort Systems USA, Inc.; *U.S. Public*, pg. 544
TECH DEVELOPMENT INC.—See General Electric Company; *U.S. Public*, pg. 919
TECUMSEH POWER COMPANY—See Platinum Equity, LLC; *U.S. Private*, pg. 3208
THOMASSEN ENERGY B.V.—See Cassa Depositi e Prestiti S.p.A.; *Int'l*, pg. 1354
TPI COMPOSITES INC.—See Landmark Growth Capital Partners, LP; *U.S. Private*, pg. 2385
TURBINAS SOLAR DE VENEVUELA C.A.—See Caterpillar, Inc.; *U.S. Public*, pg. 454
TURBINAS SOLAR, S.A. DE C.V.—See Caterpillar, Inc.; *U.S. Public*, pg. 454
TURBINE ENGINE COMPONENTS TECHNOLOGIES CORP.—See Stony Point Group, Inc.; *U.S. Private*, pg. 3830
TURBOCAM INTERNATIONAL; *U.S. Private*, pg. 4259
TURBOMACH PAKISTAN (PRIVATE) LIMITED—See Caterpillar, Inc.; *U.S. Public*, pg. 454
TURBOMACH S.A.—See Caterpillar, Inc.; *U.S. Public*, pg. 454
TURBOSERVICES SDN. BHD.—See Deleum Berhad; *Int'l*, pg. 2012
TUTHILL CORPORATION; *U.S. Private*, pg. 4262
VERICOR POWER SYSTEMS LLC—See CSL Capital Management, LLC; *U.S. Private*, pg. 1117
WESTLAKE EPOXY GMBH—See Westlake Corporation; *U.S. Public*, pg. 2360
WOODWARD AKEN GMBH—See Woodward, Inc.; *U.S. Public*, pg. 2378
WOODWARD, INC. - LOVELAND—See Woodward, Inc.; *U.S. Public*, pg. 2378
WOODWARD INDIA PRIVATE LIMITED—See Woodward, Inc.; *U.S. Public*, pg. 2378
WOODWARD KEMPEN GMBH—See Woodward, Inc.; *U.S. Public*, pg. 2378
XZERES CORP.; *U.S. Private*, pg. 4584

333612 — SPEED CHANGER, INDUSTRIAL HIGH-SPEED DRIVE, AND GEAR MANUFACTURING

ABB SWITZERLAND LTD - DRIVES—See ABB Ltd.; *Int'l*, pg. 54
ACE PILLAR CO., LTD; *Int'l*, pg. 94
ALTRA INDUSTRIAL MOTION RUSSIA OOO—See Regal Rexnord Corporation; *U.S. Public*, pg. 1772
AMARILLO GEAR COMPANY INC.—See Berkshire Hathaway Inc.; *U.S. Public*, pg. 311
AMOTECH KOREA INC.—See Amotech Co Ltd; *Int'l*, pg. 430
BAODING TIANWEI BAOBIAN ELECTRIC CO., LTD.; *Int'l*, pg. 856
BAUER GEAR MOTOR FINLAND OY AB—See Regal Rexnord Corporation; *U.S. Public*, pg. 1772
BAUER GEAR MOTOR LIMITED—See Regal Rexnord Corporation; *U.S. Public*, pg. 1772
BENGAL MACHINE; *U.S. Private*, pg. 526
BISON GEAR & ENGINEERING CORPORATION—See AMETEK, Inc.; *U.S. Public*, pg. 120
BONDY LMT A/S—See Addtech AB; *Int'l*, pg. 132
BONFIGLIOLI ITALIA S.P.A.—See Bonfiglioli Riduttori S.p.A.; *Int'l*, pg. 1106
BONFIGLIOLI RIDUTTORI S.P.A.; *Int'l*, pg. 1106
BONFIGLIOLI USA, INC.—See Bonfiglioli Riduttori S.p.A.; *Int'l*, pg. 1106
BONFIGLIOLI VECTRON GMBH—See Brd. Klee A/S; *Int'l*, pg. 1143
BOSTON GEAR—See Regal Rexnord Corporation; *U.S. Public*, pg. 1772
BRAD FOOTE GEAR WORKS, INC.—See Broadwind, Inc.; *U.S. Public*, pg. 392
BREVINI AUSTRALIA PTY LTD—See Dana Incorporated; *U.S. Public*, pg. 621
BREVINI CANADA LIMITED—See Dana Incorporated; *U.S. Public*, pg. 621

3595

333612 — SPEED CHANGER, INDU...

BREVINI ESPANA S.A.—See Dana Incorporated; *U.S. Public*, pg. 621
BREVINI JAPAN LTD—See Dana Incorporated; *U.S. Public*, pg. 621
BREVINI KOREA CO., LTD.—See Dana Incorporated; *U.S. Public*, pg. 621
BREVINI LATINO-AMERICANA IND. & CO. LTD.—See Dana Incorporated; *U.S. Public*, pg. 622
BREVINI NORGE AS—See Dana Incorporated; *U.S. Public*, pg. 622
BREVINI POWER TRANSMISSION FRANCE—See Dana Incorporated; *U.S. Public*, pg. 622
BREVINI THAILAND CO. LTD.—See Dana Incorporated; *U.S. Public*, pg. 622
BREVINI USA INC.—See Dana Incorporated; *U.S. Public*, pg. 622
BREVINI YANCHENG PLANETARY DRIVES CO. LTD.—See Dana Incorporated; *U.S. Public*, pg. 622
BRUINHOF BV—See The Carlyle Group Inc.; *U.S. Public*, pg. 2046
THE C.A. LAWTON COMPANY; *U.S. Private*, pg. 4003
CARRARO ARGENTINA S.A.—See FLY Srl; *Int'l*, pg. 2715
CARRARO CHINA DRIVE SYSTEM CO., LTD.—See FLY Srl; *Int'l*, pg. 2715
CARRARO DRIVE TECH DO BRASIL INC.—See FLY Srl; *Int'l*, pg. 2715
CARRARO S.P.A.—See FLY Srl; *Int'l*, pg. 2715
CARRARO TECHNOLOGIES INDIA PVT. LTD.—See FLY Srl; *Int'l*, pg. 2715
CASTEX TECHNOLOGIES LIMITED—See Amtek Auto Limited; *Int'l*, pg. 441
CENTA ANTRIEBE KIRSCHEY GMBH—See Zurn Elkay Water Solutions Corporation; *U.S. Public*, pg. 2413
CIMA S.P.A.—See Coesia S.p.A.; *Int'l*, pg. 1689
CONDUCTIX-WAMPFLER B.V.—See CVC Capital Partners SICAV-FIS S.A.; *Int'l*, pg. 1886
CONE DRIVE OPERATIONS INC.—See The Timken Company; *U.S. Public*, pg. 2132
DANA BREVINI POWER - TRANSMISSION S.P.A.—See Dana Incorporated; *U.S. Public*, pg. 622
DANFOSS BAUER GMBH—See Danfoss A/S; *Int'l*, pg. 1959
DAVALL GEARS LTD.—See Illinois Tool Works Inc.; *U.S. Public*, pg. 1105
DAVID BROWN GEAR INDUSTRIES AUSTRALIA PTY. LTD.—See Clyde Blowers Capital IM LLP; *Int'l*, pg. 1665
DESIGNATRONICS, INC. - QUALITY TRANSMISSION COMPONENTS DIVISION—See Designatronics, Inc.; *U.S. Private*, pg. 1214
DHHI GERMANY GMBH—See Dalian Huarui Heavy Industry Group Co., Ltd.; *Int'l*, pg. 1952
DONGWON OLEV CORP.—See Dongwon Enterprise Co., Ltd.; *Int'l*, pg. 2171
DRIVESERVICE SRL—See FLY Srl; *Int'l*, pg. 2715
DURST—See Regal Rexnord Corporation; *U.S. Public*, pg. 1773
EUCLID UNIVERSAL CORP.—See Jordan Industries, Inc.; *U.S. Public*, pg. 2235
FABO KERESKEDELMI ES SZOLGALTATO KFT.—See AUMA Riester GmbH & Co. KG; *Int'l*, pg. 705
FEINTOOL TECHNOLOGY AG—See Certina Holding AG; *Int'l*, pg. 1423
FLENDER CORPORATION—See The Carlyle Group Inc.; *U.S. Public*, pg. 2046
FLENDER DE MEXICO, S.A. DE C.V.—See The Carlyle Group Inc.; *U.S. Public*, pg. 2047
FLENDER GES.M.B.H.—See The Carlyle Group Inc.; *U.S. Public*, pg. 2046
FLENDER GMBH—See The Carlyle Group Inc.; *U.S. Public*, pg. 2046
FLENDER GRAFFENSTADEN S.A.—See The Carlyle Group Inc.; *U.S. Public*, pg. 2047
FLENDER IBERICA S.A.—See The Carlyle Group Inc.; *U.S. Public*, pg. 2047
FLENDER LIMITED—See The Carlyle Group Inc.; *U.S. Public*, pg. 2047
FLSMIDTH MAAG GEAR AG—See FLSmidth & Co. A/S; *Int'l*, pg. 2710
FUJIAN SPICER DRIVETRAIN SYSTEM CO., LTD.—See Dana Incorporated; *U.S. Public*, pg. 623
GEARTEC, INC.—See United Stars Inc.; *U.S. Private*, pg. 4298
GEFRAN S.P.A.; *Int'l*, pg. 2912
GFC ANTRIEBSSYSTEME GMBH—See AUMA Riester GmbH & Co. KG; *Int'l*, pg. 705
GLOBAL TECHNOS LTD.—See Hota Industrial Mfg. Co., Ltd.; *Int'l*, pg. 3487
GUILIN FUDA CO., LTD.; *Int'l*, pg. 3173
HARMONIC AD, INC.—See Harmonic Drive Systems Inc.; *Int'l*, pg. 3277
HARMONIC DRIVE L.L.C.—See Harmonic Drive Systems Inc.; *Int'l*, pg. 3277
HARMONIC DRIVE SE—See Harmonic Drive Systems Inc.; *Int'l*, pg. 3277
HARMONIC DRIVE SYSTEMS INC.; *Int'l*, pg. 3277
HAVLIK GEAR—See Mill City Capital, L.P.; *U.S. Private*, pg. 2730
HENGSHAN GEAR CO., LTD—See Hunan Oil Pump Co., Ltd.; *Int'l*, pg. 3533

THE HORSBURGH & SCOTT CO.—See GenNx360 Capital Partners, L.P.; *U.S. Private*, pg. 1672
HOTATECH, INC.—See Hota Industrial Mfg. Co., Ltd.; *Int'l*, pg. 3487
JKF AMERICAS INC.—See Bengal & Assam Company Ltd.; *Int'l*, pg. 973
J.K. FENNER (INDIA) LTD.—See Bengal & Assam Company Ltd.; *Int'l*, pg. 973
JUKEN SWISS TECHNOLOGY AG—See Frencken Group Limited; *Int'l*, pg. 2773
LEESON ELECTRIC - GROVE GEAR—See Regal Rexnord Corporation; *U.S. Public*, pg. 1773
MARTIN SPROCKET & GEAR, INC.; *U.S. Private*, pg. 2596
MICROMOTION GMBH—See Harmonic Drive Systems Inc.; *Int'l*, pg. 3277
MILWAUKEE GEAR COMPANY—See Regal Rexnord Corporation; *U.S. Public*, pg. 1773
NICHOLS PORTLAND, LLC.—See Altus Capital Partners, Inc.; *U.S. Private*, pg. 211
NORD GEAR CORPORATION—See Getriebebau NORD GmbH & Co. KG; *Int'l*, pg. 2953
NORD GEAR LIMITED—See Getriebebau NORD GmbH & Co. KG; *Int'l*, pg. 2953
NORD GEAR LTD.—See Getriebebau NORD GmbH & Co. KG; *Int'l*, pg. 2953
NUTTALL GEAR LLC—See Regal Rexnord Corporation; *U.S. Public*, pg. 1772
THE OILGEAR COMPANY - FREMONT—See Wynnchurch Capital, L.P.; *U.S. Private*, pg. 4578
O&K ANTRIEBSTECHNIK GMBH—See Bonfiglioli Riduttori S.p.A.; *Int'l*, pg. 1106
OVERTON CHICAGO GEAR INC.—See Hicks Holdings, LLC; *U.S. Private*, pg. 1934
OVERTON CHICAGO GEAR INC.—See The Riverside Company; *U.S. Private*, pg. 4108
OVERTON CHICAGO GEAR INC.—See Weinberg Capital Group, Inc.; *U.S. Private*, pg. 4471
OY JENS S. AB—See Axel Johnson Gruppen AB; *Int'l*, pg. 763
PEERLESS-WINSMITH, INC.—See HBD Industries, Inc.; *U.S. Private*, pg. 1887
PENN LOCOMOTIVE GEAR—See Berkshire Hathaway Inc.; *U.S. Public*, pg. 311
PENN MACHINE COMPANY—See Berkshire Hathaway Inc.; *U.S. Public*, pg. 311
PERFECTION GEAR, INC.—See HBD Industries, Inc.; *U.S. Private*, pg. 1887
PHILADELPHIA GEAR CORPORATION—See The Timken Company; *U.S. Public*, pg. 2133
PRECISION GEARS, INC.—See United Stars Inc.; *U.S. Private*, pg. 4298
REDUCTORES DE MEXICO S.A.—See Berkshire Hathaway Inc.; *U.S. Public*, pg. 311
RELIANCE GEAR LTD.—See First Israel Mezzanine Investors Ltd.; *Int'l*, pg. 2685
ROC SPICER, LTD.—See Dana Incorporated; *U.S. Public*, pg. 623
SAMICK ADM CO., LTD.—See Harmonic Drive Systems Inc.; *Int'l*, pg. 3277
SCHAFER GEAR WORKS ROSCOE, LLC—See HBM Holdings Company; *U.S. Private*, pg. 1887
SCHAFER INDUSTRIES, INC.—See HBM Holdings Company; *U.S. Private*, pg. 1887
SEW-EURODRIVE INC.; *U.S. Private*, pg. 3619
SIAP S.P.A.—See FLY Srl; *Int'l*, pg. 2716
SIEMENS AB—See The Carlyle Group Inc.; *U.S. Public*, pg. 2047
SIEMENS GEARED MOTORS GMBH—See The Carlyle Group Inc.; *U.S. Public*, pg. 2047
SIEMENS LTD.—See The Carlyle Group Inc.; *U.S. Public*, pg. 2047
SPRUIT TRANSMISSIES BV—See Axel Johnson Gruppen AB; *Int'l*, pg. 763
SUNLIGHT ELECTRICAL (VIETNAM) CO., LTD.—See Chint Group Corporation; *Int'l*, pg. 1571
TEAM INDUSTRIES - AUDUBON—See TEAM Industries, Inc.; *U.S. Private*, pg. 3949
TORQTEK DESIGN & MANUFACTURING, LLC; *U.S. Private*, pg. 4189
UNITED STATES GEAR CORPORATION; *U.S. Private*, pg. 4299
VACON LTD—See Danfoss A/S; *Int'l*, pg. 1961
VELVET DRIVE—See Regal Rexnord Corporation; *U.S. Public*, pg. 1774
WARRENS MOTORS INC.—See Barbados Shipping & Trading Co. Ltd.; *Int'l*, pg. 858

333613 — MECHANICAL POWER TRANSMISSION EQUIPMENT MANUFACTURING

ABB STRIEBEL & JOHN GMBH—See ABB Ltd.; *Int'l*, pg. 50
ACCURATE INC.—See Advanex Inc.; *Int'l*, pg. 163
AGO AG ENERGIE + ANLAGEN—See HCS Beteiligungsgesellschaft mbH; *Int'l*, pg. 3299
AIR BEARING TECHNOLOGY, INC.—See KLA Corporation; *U.S. Public*, pg. 1267

ALCATEL-LUCENT TELETAS TELEKOMUNIKASYON AS; *Int'l*, pg. 300
ALINABAL MOTION TRANSFER DEVICES—See Alinabal Holdings Corporation; *U.S. Private*, pg. 168
ALLIED TRANSMISSIONS (S.E.A.) PTE LTD—See Dana Incorporated; *U.S. Public*, pg. 621
ALPHA PROCESS CONTROLS (INTERNATIONAL) LTD.—See ACCEDO Group Ltd.; *Int'l*, pg. 79
ALTRA INDUSTRIAL MOTION, INC.—See Regal Rexnord Corporation; *U.S. Public*, pg. 1772
ALUMINIUM DIE CASTING S.R.L.—See Regal Rexnord Corporation; *U.S. Public*, pg. 1772
AMERIDRIVES INTERNATIONAL, LLC—See Regal Rexnord Corporation; *U.S. Public*, pg. 1772
ANDRITZ HYDRO GMBH—See ANDRITZ AG; *Int'l*, pg. 453
APAR INDUSTRIES LTD.; *Int'l*, pg. 501
AS DITTON PIEVADKEZU RUPNICA; *Int'l*, pg. 589
ASTROSYSTEMS AUTOMATION—See North Atlantic Industries Inc.; *U.S. Private*, pg. 2942
BARNIER ET FILS; *Int'l*, pg. 866
BEARING ENGINEERS, INC.—See Frontenac Company LLC; *U.S. Private*, pg. 1613
BEIJING MOBIS TRANSMISSION CO., LTD.—See Hyundai Motor Company; *Int'l*, pg. 3558
BEIJING SUPLET POWER CO., LTD; *Int'l*, pg. 958
B.W. ELLIOTT MANUFACTURING COMPANY, LLC—See Enerpac Tool Group Corp.; *U.S. Public*, pg. 765
THE CARLYLE JOHNSON MACHINE COMPANY, LLC; *U.S. Private*, pg. 4005
CAVOTEC ALFO GMBH—See Cavotec SA; *Int'l*, pg. 1362
CAVOTEC AUSTRALIA—See Cavotec SA; *Int'l*, pg. 1362
CAVOTEC CANADA INC.—See Cavotec SA; *Int'l*, pg. 1362
CAVOTEC CONNECTORS AB—See Cavotec SA; *Int'l*, pg. 1362
CAVOTEC DANMARK AS—See Cavotec SA; *Int'l*, pg. 1362
CAVOTEC DEUTSCHLAND GMBH—See Cavotec SA; *Int'l*, pg. 1362
CAVOTEC DEUTSCHLAND HOLDINGS GMBH—See Cavotec SA; *Int'l*, pg. 1362
CAVOTEC FINLAND OY—See Cavotec SA; *Int'l*, pg. 1362
CAVOTEC FLADUNG GMBH—See Cavotec SA; *Int'l*, pg. 1362
CAVOTEC HONG KONG LTD.—See Cavotec SA; *Int'l*, pg. 1362
CAVOTEC INDIA LTD.—See Cavotec SA; *Int'l*, pg. 1362
CAVOTEC LATIN AMERICA S.A.—See Cavotec SA; *Int'l*, pg. 1362
CAVOTEC MICRO-CONTROL AS—See Cavotec SA; *Int'l*, pg. 1362
CAVOTEC MICRO-CONTROL GMBH—See Cavotec SA; *Int'l*, pg. 1362
CAVOTEC MIDDLE EAST FZE—See Cavotec SA; *Int'l*, pg. 1362
CAVOTEC MOORMASTER LTD—See Cavotec SA; *Int'l*, pg. 1362
CAVOTEC NEDERLAND B.V.—See Cavotec SA; *Int'l*, pg. 1362
CAVOTEC NORGE AS—See Cavotec SA; *Int'l*, pg. 1363
CAVOTEC RMS SA—See Cavotec SA; *Int'l*, pg. 1363
CAVOTEC SA; *Int'l*, pg. 1362
CAVOTEC SHANGHAI LTD.—See Cavotec SA; *Int'l*, pg. 1363
CAVOTEC SINGAPORE PTE LTD.—See Cavotec SA; *Int'l*, pg. 1363
CAVOTEC SOUTH AFRICA (PTY.) LTD.—See Cavotec SA; *Int'l*, pg. 1363
CAVOTEC SPECIMAS S.P.A.—See Cavotec SA; *Int'l*, pg. 1363
CAVOTEC SVERIGE AB—See Cavotec SA; *Int'l*, pg. 1363
CAVOTEC (SWISS) S.A.—See Cavotec SA; *Int'l*, pg. 1362
CAVOTEC USA INC.—See Cavotec SA; *Int'l*, pg. 1363
CENTA TRANSM. FAR EAST PTE LTD.—See Zurn Elkay Water Solutions Corporation; *U.S. Public*, pg. 2412
CENTRAL AREA ELECTRICAL MECHANICAL JOINT STOCK COMPANY; *Int'l*, pg. 1404
C-FLEX BEARING CO., INC.; *U.S. Private*, pg. 704
CGIT SYSTEMS, INC.—See AZZ, Inc.; *U.S. Public*, pg. 259
CHINA HIGH SPEED TRANSMISSION EQUIPMENT GROUP CO., LTD.—See Fullshare Holdings Limited; *Int'l*, pg. 2843
CIMCO MARINE AB; *Int'l*, pg. 1609
COCKERILL MAINTENANCE & INGENIERIE SA—See Euremis Holding SA; *Int'l*, pg. 2530
CONDUCTIX-WAMPFLER AG—See CVC Capital Partners SICAV-FIS S.A.; *Int'l*, pg. 1886
CONDUCTIX-WAMPFLER LTD.—See CVC Capital Partners SICAV-FIS S.A.; *Int'l*, pg. 1887
CVTECH-IBC INC.; *Int'l*, pg. 1890
DAIDO CORPORATION OF AMERICA—See Daido Kogyo Co., Ltd.; *Int'l*, pg. 1920
DAIDO INDUSTRIA DE CORRENTES DA AMAZONIA LTDA.—See Daido Kogyo Co., Ltd.; *Int'l*, pg. 1920
DAIDO INDUSTRIAL E COMERCIAL LTDA.—See Daido Kogyo Co., Ltd.; *Int'l*, pg. 1920
DANFOSS A/S—See Danfoss A/S; *Int'l*, pg. 1959
DIAMOND CHAIN COMPANY—See The Timken Company; *U.S. Public*, pg. 2132

N.A.I.C.S. INDEX

333618 — OTHER ENGINE EQUIPM...

DIAMOND CHAIN UK LTD—See The Timken Company; *U.S. Public*, pg. 2132
DIAMOND POWER INFRASTRUCTURE LTD.; *Int'l*, pg. 2105
D.I.D ASIA CO., LTD.—See Daido Kogyo Co., Ltd.; *Int'l*, pg. 1920
D.I.D CO., LTD.—See Daido Kogyo Co., Ltd.; *Int'l*, pg. 1920
D.I.D VIETNAM CO., LTD.—See Daido Kogyo Co., Ltd.; *Int'l*, pg. 1920
DODGE MANUFACTURING COMPANY—See ABB Ltd.; *Int'l*, pg. 51
DOERING COMPANY, LLC; *U.S. Private*, pg. 1253
DOVER ENERGY, INC.—See Dover Corporation; *U.S. Public*, pg. 679
DRIVE SOURCE INTERNATIONAL, INC.—See TGP Investments, LLC; *U.S. Private*, pg. 3979
DYNAMIC SEALING TECHNOLOGIES, INC.—See Kadant Inc.; *U.S. Public*, pg. 1212
DYNATECT POLYCLUTCH—See 3i Group plc; *Int'l*, pg. 8
ECE INDUSTRIES LIMITED; *Int'l*, pg. 2288
E.C. STYBERG ENGINEERING CO., INC.; *U.S. Private*, pg. 1305
EKSPAN LIMITED—See RPM International Inc.; *U.S. Public*, pg. 1816
EMCO LTD.; *Int'l*, pg. 2376
ENERGOMONTAJ S.A. - HIDRO DIVISION—See Energomontaj S.A.; *Int'l*, pg. 2421
EPIC ENERGY LTD.; *Int'l*, pg. 2460
ESCO COUPLINGS N.V.—See Esco Financial & Engineering Company S.A/N.V.; *Int'l*, pg. 2501
ESCO COUPLINGS & TRANSMISSIONS PRIVATE LIMITED—See Esco Financial & Engineering Company S.A/N.V.; *Int'l*, pg. 2501
ESCO POWER N.V.—See Esco Financial & Engineering Company S.A/N.V.; *Int'l*, pg. 2501
ESCO TRANSMISSIONS N.V.—See Esco Financial & Engineering Company S.A/N.V.; *Int'l*, pg. 2502
ESCO TRANSMISSIONS S.A.—See Esco Financial & Engineering Company S.A/N.V.; *Int'l*, pg. 2502
FALLBROOK TECHNOLOGIES INC.; *U.S. Private*, pg. 1467
FB CHAIN LIMITED—See Addtech AB; *Int'l*, pg. 133
FB KEDJOR AB—See Addtech AB; *Int'l*, pg. 133
FLENDER POWER TRANSMISSION (PTY.) LTD.—See The Carlyle Group Inc.; *U.S. Public*, pg. 2047
FORCE CONTROL INDUSTRIES, INC.; *U.S. Private*, pg. 1563
FUJIAN LONGXI BEARING (GROUP) CORPORATION LIMITED; *Int'l*, pg. 2818
FUJITSU NETWORK COMMUNICATIONS - RICHARDSON PLANT—See Fujitsu Limited; *Int'l*, pg. 2833
GALLI GIOVANNI & C. S.R.L.—See El.En. S.p.A.; *Int'l*, pg. 2342
GE POWER CONVERSION FRANCE SAS—See General Electric Company; *U.S. Public*, pg. 917
GE POWER CONVERSION—See General Electric Company; *U.S. Public*, pg. 917
GE POWER CONVERSION UK LTD.—See General Electric Company; *U.S. Public*, pg. 917
GETRAG FORD TRANSMISSIONS GMBH—See Ford Motor Company; *U.S. Public*, pg. 866
GKN DRIVELINE KIEL—See GKN plc; *Int'l*, pg. 2984
GKN DRIVELINE WALSALL LTD—See GKN plc; *Int'l*, pg. 2985
GKN RIBEMONT SARL—See GKN plc; *Int'l*, pg. 2985
GUANGDONG ELECTRIC POWER DEVELOPMENT CO., LTD.—See Guangdong Yudean Group Co., Ltd.; *Int'l*, pg. 3162
GUANGDONG YANGSHAN UNITED PRECISION MANUFACTURING CO., LTD.; *Int'l*, pg. 3162
GUARDIAN COUPLINGS LLC—See Regal Rexnord Corporation; *U.S. Public*, pg. 1772
GUARDIAN IND., INC.—See Regal Rexnord Corporation; *U.S. Public*, pg. 1772
HANKUK CHAIN INDUSTRIAL CO., LTD.—See Daedong Corporation; *Int'l*, pg. 1906
HELIX UNIFORMED LTD.—See Preformed Line Products Company; *U.S. Public*, pg. 1714
HEPHAIST SEIKO CO., LTD. - AKITA FACTORY—See Heheist Co., Ltd.; *Int'l*, pg. 3308
HOKURIKU BANDO, INC.—See Bando Chemical Industries, Ltd.; *Int'l*, pg. 830
HUB CITY, INC.—See Regal Rexnord Corporation; *U.S. Public*, pg. 1773
HUDACO INDUSTRIES LIMITED - BEARINGS INTERNATIONAL DIVISION—See Hudaco Industries Limited; *Int'l*, pg. 3521
HUNTING SUBSEA TECHNOLOGIES—See Hunting Plc; *Int'l*, pg. 3537
HYSPAN PRECISION PRODUCTS, INC.; *U.S. Private*, pg 2020
INDUSTRIAL MOTION CONTROL, LLC—See Stabilus; *U.S. Private*, pg. 3774
INERTIA DYNAMICS, INC.—See Matrix International Ltd.; *U.S. Private*, pg. 2612
INPRO/SEAL LLC—See Dover Corporation; *U.S. Public*, pg. 681
ITALTRASFO SRL—See ABB Ltd.; *Int'l*, pg. 54
JAKOB ANTRIEBSTECHNIK GMBH—See Fukuda Corporation; *Int'l*, pg. 2839
KAMATICS CORPORATION—See Arcline Investment Management LP; *U.S. Private*, pg. 314
KINGSBURY GMBH—See Kingsbury Inc.; *U.S. Private*, pg. 2311
KINGSBURY INC.; *U.S. Private*, pg. 2311
KMC YTBEHANDLING AB—See Addtech AB; *Int'l*, pg. 134
KOREA CRAWLER TRACK LTD.—See Hoe Leong Corporation Ltd.; *Int'l*, pg. 3439
L-3 COMMUNICATIONS WESTWOOD CORPORATION—See L3Harris Technologies, Inc.; *U.S. Public*, pg. 1283
LESAGE SAS—See Brookfield Corporation; *Int'l*, pg. 1188
LM WIND POWER BLADES (POLAND) SP. Z.O.O.—See General Electric Company; *U.S. Public*, pg. 920
LOVEJOY CURTIS, LLC—See The Timken Company; *U.S. Public*, pg. 2133
LOVEJOY INC.—See The Timken Company; *U.S. Public*, pg. 2133
MAGNETIC POWER SYSTEMS INC.—See Berwind Corporation; *U.S. Private*, pg. 541
MARBAISE HANLO LS GMBH—See Emerson Electric Co.; *U.S. Public*, pg. 750
MARTIN SPROCKET & GEAR DE MEXICO, S.A. DE C.V.—See Martin Sprocket & Gear, Inc.; *U.S. Private*, pg. 2596
MARTIN SPROCKET & GEAR (SHANGHAI) CO., LTD.—See Martin Sprocket & Gear, Inc.; *U.S. Private*, pg. 2596
MASKA POWER TRANSMISSION (CHANGZHOU) CO. LTD.—See ABB Ltd.; *Int'l*, pg. 49
MAUREY MANUFACTURING CORPORATION; *U.S. Private*, pg. 2615
MCWANE, INC. - ANACO DIVISION—See McWane, Inc.; *U.S. Private*, pg. 2645
MDCGROUP, INC.—See Argo Graphics Inc.; *Int'l*, pg. 562
METRONICS, INC.—See The Carlyle Johnson Machine Company, LLC; *U.S. Private*, pg. 4005
MILLER BEARINGS DIVISION - MIAMI—See Genuine Parts Company; *U.S. Public*, pg. 933
NERA INFOCOM (M) SDN BHD—See Ennoconn Corporation; *Int'l*, pg. 2443
NERA TELECOMMUNICATIONS (TAIWAN) CO. LTD—See Ennoconn Corporation; *Int'l*, pg. 2443
NEXEN GROUP INC.; *U.S. Private*, pg. 2919
NEXTER MECHANICS S.A.—See GIAT Industries S.A.; *Int'l*, pg. 2962
PEERLESS GEAR LLC—See Certified Parts Corporation; *U.S. Private*, pg. 841
POWER SOLUTIONS INTERNATIONAL, INC.; *U.S. Public*, pg. 1705
PREFORMED LINE PRODUCTS (GREAT BRITAIN) LTD.—See Preformed Line Products Company; *U.S. Public*, pg. 1714
P.T. DAIDO INDONESIA MANUFACTURING—See Daido Kogyo Co., Ltd.; *Int'l*, pg. 1921
PT. JAPAN AE POWER SYSTEMS INDONESIA—See Hitachi, Ltd.; *Int'l*, pg. 3424
PT. NERA INDONESIA—See Ennoconn Corporation; *Int'l*, pg. 2443
RBC TRANSPORT DYNAMICS CORPORATION—See RBC Bearings Incorporated; *U.S. Public*, pg. 1766
REELL PRECISION MANUFACTURING CORP.; *U.S. Private*, pg. 3383
REXNORD CANADA LIMITED—See Zurn Elkay Water Solutions Corporation; *U.S. Public*, pg. 2413
REXNORD INDUSTRIES, LLC—See Zurn Elkay Water Solutions Corporation; *U.S. Public*, pg. 2413
R.J. CORMAN RAILPOWER—See R.J. Corman Railroad Group LLC; *U.S. Private*, pg. 3337
R+L HYDRAULICS GMBH—See The Timken Company; *U.S. Public*, pg. 2133
ROLLA SP PROPELLERS SA—See Twin Disc, Incorporated; *U.S. Public*, pg. 2206
ROLLCO AB—See Addtech AB; *Int'l*, pg. 135
ROLLCO A/S—See Addtech AB; *Int'l*, pg. 135
ROLLCO NORGE AS—See Addtech AB; *Int'l*, pg. 135
ROLLCO TAIWAN CO., LTD. —See Addtech AB; *Int'l*, pg. 135
ROLLON CORPORATION—See The Timken Company; *U.S. Public*, pg. 2133
SAN FILIPPO S.R.L.—See Gruppo MutuiOnline S.p.A; *Int'l*, pg. 3141
SKIFFY LTD.—See Essentra plc; *Int'l*, pg. 2512
S.S. WHITE TECHNOLOGIES INC.; *U.S. Private*, pg. 3518
S S WHITE TECHNOLOGIES UK LIMITED—See S.S. White Technologies Inc.; *U.S. Private*, pg. 3518
STOCK DRIVE PRODUCTS—See Designatronics, Inc.; *U.S. Private*, pg. 1214
STROMAG FRANCE SAS—See Regal Rexnord Corporation, *U.S. Public*, pg. 1772
SVENDBORG BRAKES APS—See Regal Rexnord Corporation; *U.S. Public*, pg. 1772
SVENDBORG BRAKES PERU S.A.C.—See Regal Rexnord Corporation; *U.S. Public*, pg. 1772
TB WOOD'S CORPORATION—See Regal Rexnord Corporation; *U.S. Public*, pg. 1772
TB WOOD'S INCORPORATED—See Regal Rexnord Corporation; *U.S. Public*, pg. 1772
TECUMSEH POWER COMPANY—See Platinum Equity, LLC; *U.S. Private*, pg. 3208
TIMKEN ILS DAYTON, INC.—See The Timken Company; *U.S. Public*, pg. 2133
TRINITY MEYER UTILITY STRUCTURES, LLC—See Trinity Industries, Inc.; *U.S. Public*, pg. 2194
TWIN DISC INTERNATIONAL, S.A.—See Twin Disc, Incorporated; *U.S. Public*, pg. 2207
TWIN DISC ITALIA SRL—See Twin Disc, Incorporated; *U.S. Public*, pg. 2207
WARNER ELECTRIC (SINGAPORE) PTY, LTD.—See Regal Rexnord Corporation; *U.S. Public*, pg. 1772
WARNER ELECTRIC (TAIWAN) LTD.—See Regal Rexnord Corporation; *U.S. Public*, pg. 1772
WARNER ELECTRIC (THAILAND) LTD.—See Regal Rexnord Corporation; *U.S. Public*, pg. 1772
WARTSILA JOVYATLAS EUROATLAS GMBH—See L3Harris Technologies, Inc.; *U.S. Public*, pg. 1284
WAUKESHA BEARINGS CORP.—See Dover Corporation; *U.S. Public*, pg. 679
WEASLER ENGINEERING INC.—See Enerpac Tool Group Corp.; *U.S. Public*, pg. 766
WHEELER INDUSTRIES, INC.—See Jenkins Electric Co.; *U.S. Private*, pg. 2199
W.M. BERG INC.—See Zurn Elkay Water Solutions Corporation; *U.S. Public*, pg. 2413
XTEK, INC.; *U.S. Private*, pg. 4583
ZURN ELKAY WATER SOLUTIONS CORPORATION; *U.S. Public*, pg. 2412

333618 — OTHER ENGINE EQUIPMENT MANUFACTURING

511220 N.B. INC.—See Immersion Corporation; *U.S. Public*, pg. 1112
AFSI EUROPE S.R.O.—See Caterpillar, Inc.; *U.S. Public*, pg. 449
AFSI EUROPE S.R.O.—See Donaldson Company, Inc.; *U.S. Public*, pg. 675
AKASAKA DIESELS LIMITED - NAKAMINATO FACTORY—See Akasaka Diesels Limited; *Int'l*, pg. 260
AKASAKA DIESELS LIMITED; *Int'l*, pg. 259
AKASAKA DIESELS LIMITED - TOYODA FACTORY—See Akasaka Diesels Limited; *Int'l*, pg. 260
ALERT ENGINE PARTS (PTY) LIMITED—See Dubai World Corporation; *Int'l*, pg. 2221
ALLIED MOTION CANADA INC.—See Allient Inc.; *U.S. Public*, pg. 80
AMERICAN POWER GROUP CORPORATION; *U.S. Public*, pg. 108
ANADOLU MOTOR URETIM VE PAZARLAMA A.S.—See AG Anadolu Grubu Holding A.S.; *Int'l*, pg. 197
ANCA MOTION PTY. LTD.—See ANCA Pty Ltd; *Int'l*, pg. 448
ANHUI QUANCHAI ENGINE CO., LTD.; *Int'l*, pg. 469
ARLEIGH INTERNATIONAL LIMITED—See LKQ Corporation; *U.S. Public*, pg. 1333
AVL AST D.O.O.—See AVL List GmbH; *Int'l*, pg. 748
AVL AUTOKUT ENGINEERING LTD.—See AVL List GmbH; *Int'l*, pg. 748
AVL CECHY SPOL. S R.O.—See AVL List GmbH; *Int'l*, pg. 748
AVL DEUTSCHLAND GMBH—See AVL List GmbH; *Int'l*, pg. 748
AVL IBERICA S.A.—See AVL List GmbH; *Int'l*, pg. 748
AVL ITALY S.R.L.—See AVL List GmbH; *Int'l*, pg. 748
AVL LIST NORDISKA AB—See AVL List GmbH; *Int'l*, pg. 748
AVL UNITED KINGDOM LIMITED—See AVL List GmbH; *Int'l*, pg. 748
BAKER HUGHES HOLDINGS LLC—See Baker Hughes Company; *U.S. Public*, pg. 264
BEMAC CORPORATION; *Int'l*, pg. 968
BLUTIP POWER TECHNOLOGIES LTD.; *Int'l*, pg. 1075
BMW MOTOREN GMBH—See Bayerische Motoren Werke Aktiengesellschaft; *Int'l*, pg. 910
BOLEY TOOL & MACHINE WORKS; *U.S. Private*, pg. 610
BOMBARDIER AEROSPACE BELFAST—See Bombardier Inc.; *Int'l*, pg. 1103
BOMBARDIER CAPITAL INTERNATIONAL B.V.—See Bombardier Inc.; *Int'l*, pg. 1104
BOMBARDIER CREDIT RECEIVABLES CORPORATION—See Bombardier Inc.; *Int'l*, pg. 1104
BOMBARDIER MASS TRANSIT CORPORATION—See Alstom S.A.; *Int'l*, pg. 382
BOMBARDIER MEXICO, S.A. DE C.V.—See Alstom S.A.; *Int'l*, pg. 382
BOMBARDIER RECREATIONAL PRODUCTS - JOHNSON & EVINRUDE—See Bain Capital, LP; *U.S. Private*, pg. 431
BOMBARDIER TRANSPORTATION AG—See Alstom S.A.; *Int'l*, pg. 382
BOMBARDIER TRANSPORTATION AUSTRIA GMBH—See Alstom S.A.; *Int'l*, pg. 382
BOMBARDIER TRANSPORTATION (BAHNTECHNOLOGIE) GERMANY GMBH—See Alstom S.A.; *Int'l*, pg. 382

333618 — OTHER ENGINE EQUIPM...

BOMBARDIER TRANSPORTATION CANADA - TRANSIT SYSTEMS—See Alstom S.A.; *Int'l*, pg. 382
BOMBARDIER TRANSPORTATION CZECH REPUBLIC A/S—See Alstom S.A.; *Int'l*, pg. 382
BOMBARDIER TRANSPORTATION SA—See Alstom S.A.; *Int'l*, pg. 383
BRANCO MOTORES LTDA.—See Briggs & Stratton Corporation; *U.S. Private*, pg. 650
BRIGGS & STRATTON INDIA PRIVATE LIMITED—See Briggs & Stratton Corporation; *U.S. Private*, pg. 651
BRIGGS & STRATTON INTERNATIONAL SALES—See Briggs & Stratton Corporation; *U.S. Private*, pg. 651
BRIGGS & STRATTON JAPAN KK—See Briggs & Stratton Corporation; *U.S. Private*, pg. 651
BRIGGS & STRATTON (MALAYSIA) SDN. BHD.—See Briggs & Stratton Corporation; *U.S. Private*, pg. 650
BRIGGS & STRATTON NETHERLANDS B.V.—See Briggs & Stratton Corporation; *U.S. Private*, pg. 651
BRIGGS & STRATTON REPRESENTACAO DE MOTORES E PRODUCTOS DE FORCA DO BRASIL LTDA.—See Briggs & Stratton Corporation; *U.S. Private*, pg. 651
BRIGGS & STRATTON (SHANGHAI) INTERNATIONAL TRADING CO., LTD.—See Briggs & Stratton Corporation; *U.S. Private*, pg. 650
BRIGGS & STRATTON SWEDEN AB—See Briggs & Stratton Corporation; *U.S. Private*, pg. 651
CAB CAKARAN CORPORATION BERHAD; *Int'l*, pg. 1245
CAPE INDUSTRIES LTD.; *Int'l*, pg. 1303
CARBON RX INC.—See Delta CleanTech Inc.; *Int'l*, pg. 2016
CASCADIA MOTION, LLC—See BorgWarner Inc.; *U.S. Public*, pg. 371
CATERPILLAR CLEANAIR SYSTEMS, INC.—See Caterpillar, Inc.; *U.S. Public*, pg. 449
CATERPILLAR MOTOREN GMBH & CO. KG—See Caterpillar, Inc.; *U.S. Public*, pg. 451
CENTA TRANSMISJONER A.S.—See Zurn Elkay Water Solutions Corporation; *U.S. Public*, pg. 2413
CENTA TRANSMISSIONER A/S—See Zurn Elkay Water Solutions Corporation; *U.S. Public*, pg. 2413
CENTA TRANSMISSIONI S.R.L.—See Zurn Elkay Water Solutions Corporation; *U.S. Public*, pg. 2413
CENTA TRANSMISSIONS FAR EAST PTE LTD—See Zurn Elkay Water Solutions Corporation; *U.S. Public*, pg. 2413
CENTA TRANSMISSIONS LTD.—See Zurn Elkay Water Solutions Corporation; *U.S. Public*, pg. 2413
CENTA TRANSMISSIONS PTY LTD.—See Zurn Elkay Water Solutions Corporation; *U.S. Public*, pg. 2413
CHALWYN LIMITED—See Roper Technologies, Inc.; *U.S. Public*, pg. 1810
CHANGCHAI CO., LTD.; *Int'l*, pg. 1442
CHARLES EQUIPMENT ENERGY SYSTEMS LLC; *U.S. Private*, pg. 852
CHINOOK INDUSTRIAL LTD.; *Int'l*, pg. 1571
COATES INTERNATIONAL, LTD.; *U.S. Public*, pg. 520
CUMMINS BELGIUM N.V.—See Cummins Inc.; *U.S. Public*, pg. 605
CUMMINS BRASIL LTDA.—See Cummins Inc.; *U.S. Public*, pg. 605
CUMMINS CORPORATION—See Cummins Inc.; *U.S. Public*, pg. 605
CUMMINS DEUTSCHLAND GMBH—See Cummins Inc.; *U.S. Public*, pg. 605
CUMMINS DISTRIBUTOR BELGIUM SA—See Cummins Inc.; *U.S. Public*, pg. 605
CUMMINS ENGINE COMPANY PTY LIMITED—See Cummins Inc.; *U.S. Public*, pg. 605
CUMMINS FILTRATION CO. LTD.—See Cummins Inc.; *U.S. Public*, pg. 605
CUMMINS FILTRATION, INC.—See Cummins Inc.; *U.S. Public*, pg. 605
CUMMINS FILTRATION SARL—See Cummins Inc.; *U.S. Public*, pg. 605
CUMMINS GENERATOR TECHNOLOGIES—See Cummins Inc.; *U.S. Public*, pg. 606
CUMMINS HOLLAND B.V.—See Cummins Inc.; *U.S. Public*, pg. 606
CUMMINS HONG KONG LTD.—See Cummins Inc.; *U.S. Public*, pg. 606
CUMMINS INC.; *U.S. Public*, pg. 605
CUMMINS ITALIA S.P.A.—See Cummins Inc.; *U.S. Public*, pg. 606
CUMMINS JUAREZ, S.A. DE C.V.—See Cummins Inc.; *U.S. Public*, pg. 606
CUMMINS, LTD.—See Cummins Inc.; *U.S. Public*, pg. 607
CUMMINS MAKINA SANAYI VE TICARET LIMITED SIRKETI—See Cummins Inc.; *U.S. Public*, pg. 606
CUMMINS MIDDLE EAST FZE—See Cummins Inc.; *U.S. Public*, pg. 606
CUMMINS NATURAL GAS ENGINES, INC.—See Cummins Inc.; *U.S. Public*, pg. 606
CUMMINS NORTHEAST INC.—See Cummins Inc.; *U.S. Public*, pg. 606
CUMMINS N.V.—See Cummins Inc.; *U.S. Public*, pg. 606
CUMMINS ROMANIA SRL—See Cummins Inc.; *U.S. Public*, pg. 607
CUMMINS SALES AND SERVICE—See Cummins Inc.; *U.S. Public*, pg. 607
CUMMINS SALES & SERVICE SINGAPORE PTE LTD—See Cummins Inc.; *U.S. Public*, pg. 606
CUMMINS SOUTHERN PLAINS, LLC—See Cummins Inc.; *U.S. Public*, pg. 607
CUMMINS TURBO TECHNOLOGIES LTD.—See Cummins Inc.; *U.S. Public*, pg. 607
CUMMINS WESTERN CANADA LIMITED PARTNERSHIP—See Cummins Inc.; *U.S. Public*, pg. 607
DAECHANG SOLUTION CO., LTD.; *Int'l*, pg. 1906
DAECHANG SOLUTION CO., LTD. - ULJU FACTORY—See Daechang Solution Co., Ltd.; *Int'l*, pg. 1906
DAMEN SCHELDE MARINE SERVICES PTE LTD.—See Damen Shipyards Group; *Int'l*, pg. 1956
DD POWER (PTY) LIMITED—See Hudaco Industries Limited; *Int'l*, pg. 3521
DENSO AUSTRALIAN AUTOMOTIVE AIR PTY. LTD.—See Denso Corporation; *Int'l*, pg. 2032
DENSO BARCELONA S.A.—See Denso Corporation; *Int'l*, pg. 2031
DENYO EUROPE B.V.—See Denyo Co., Ltd.; *Int'l*, pg. 2040
DETROIT CHILE S.A.; *Int'l*, pg. 2048
DEUTZ BETEILLIGUNG GMBH—See DEUTZ AG; *Int'l*, pg. 2086
DEUTZ DO BRASIL LTDA.—See DEUTZ AG; *Int'l*, pg. 2086
DEUTZ UK LTD.—See DEUTZ AG; *Int'l*, pg. 2086
DIESEL RECON UK—See Cummins Inc.; *U.S. Public*, pg. 605
DIMO (PVT) LTD.—See Diesel & Motor Engineering PLC; *Int'l*, pg. 2116
DMI DIESEL OFFSHORE (S) PTE LTD.—See DMI UK Ltd.; *Int'l*, pg. 2145
DMI NANTONG LTD—See DMI UK Ltd.; *Int'l*, pg. 2145
DONGFENG CUMMINS ENGINE CO., LTD.—See Cummins Inc.; *U.S. Public*, pg. 607
DONGFENG CUMMINS ENGINE CO., LTD.—See Dongfeng Motor Corporation; *Int'l*, pg. 2166
DRE DRAEXLMAIER ELEKTROTEK S.R.O.—See Draexlmaier Gruppe; *Int'l*, pg. 2198
DUING D.O.O.—See 2G Energy AG; *Int'l*, pg. 5
ELAC SONAR GMBH—See Cohort plc; *Int'l*, pg. 1696
ELECTRO-MOTIVE CANADA CO.—See Caterpillar, Inc.; *U.S. Public*, pg. 453
ELECTRO-MOTIVE DIESEL, INC.—See Caterpillar, Inc.; *U.S. Public*, pg. 453
ENCONNEX LLC; *U.S. Private*, pg. 1390
ENGINE SYSTEMS, INC.—See Kirby Corporation; *U.S. Public*, pg. 1235
ENOVATION CONTROLS, LTD.—See Helios Technologies, Inc.; *U.S. Public*, pg. 1023
ENPRO HOLDINGS, INC.—See Enpro Inc.; *U.S. Public*, pg. 774
ENVIRONMENTAL SOLUTIONS WORLDWIDE, INC.; *U.S. Public*, pg. 781
FAIRBANKS MORSE, LLC—See Arcline Investment Management LP; *U.S. Private*, pg. 313
FLEETGUARD FILTERS PVT. LTD.—See Cummins Inc.; *U.S. Public*, pg. 606
FURUNO FRANCE S.A.S.—See Furuno Electric Co., Ltd.; *Int'l*, pg. 2848
GE ENERGY (USA), LLC—See General Electric Company; *U.S. Public*, pg. 919
GENERAL ENGINE PRODUCTS LLC—See MacAndrews & Forbes Incorporated; *U.S. Private*, pg. 2532
GENERAL ENGINE PRODUCTS LLC—See The Renco Group Inc.; *U.S. Private*, pg. 4104
GLOBE MOTORS DE MEXICO, S.A. DE C.V.—See Allient Inc.; *U.S. Public*, pg. 80
GLOBE MOTORS, INC.—See Allient Inc.; *U.S. Public*, pg. 80
GNUTTI CARLO S.P.A.; *Int'l*, pg. 3017
GNUTTI CARLO SWEDEN AB—See Gnutti Carlo S.p.A.; *Int'l*, pg. 3017
GNUTTI CARLO USA, INC.—See Gnutti Carlo S.p.A.; *Int'l*, pg. 3017
GNUTTI LTD.—See Gnutti Carlo S.p.A.; *Int'l*, pg. 3017
GUANGXI YUCHAI MACHINERY CO. LTD.—See Hong Leong Investment Holdings Pte. Ltd.; *Int'l*, pg. 3469
HANGZHOU ADVANCE MASSON MARINE TRANSMISSION CO., LTD.—See Hangzhou Advance Gearbox Group Co., Ltd.; *Int'l*, pg. 3246
HANS BELL EQUIPMENT LTD.—See Daeyang Electric Co., Ltd.; *Int'l*, pg. 1911
HANWHA ENGINE CO., LTD.; *Int'l*, pg. 3264
HEDEMORA DIESEL AB—See Engenco Limited; *Int'l*, pg. 2427
HEFEI RONG AN POWER MACHINERY CO., LTD.—See China Huarong Energy Co. Ltd.; *Int'l*, pg. 1509
HITACHI ZOSEN MARINE ENGINE CO., LTD.—See Hitachi Zosen Corporation; *Int'l*, pg. 3412
HITACHI ZOSEN TRADING (SHANGHAI) CO., LTD.—See Hitachi Zosen Corporation; *Int'l*, pg. 3412
HSD MARINE INDUSTRY(DALIAN) CO., LTD.—See Hanwha Engine Co., Ltd.; *Int'l*, pg. 3264
HTC-AED, A.S.—See HTC holding a.s.; *Int'l*, pg. 3508
HUBEI SUPER-ELEC AUTO ELECTRIC MOTOR LTD., LIABILITY CO.—See Bain Capital, LP; *U.S. Private*, pg. 428
THE HUNSLET ENGINE COMPANY LIMITED—See Westinghouse Air Brake Technologies Corporation; *U.S. Public*, pg. 2359
IAERO GROUP; *U.S. Private*, pg. 2027
IHI DO BRASIL REPRESENTACOES LTDA.—See IHI Corporation; *Int'l*, pg. 3604
IHI POWER SYSTEMS CO., LTD.—See IHI Corporation; *Int'l*, pg. 3605
IMPCO TECHNOLOGIES, INC.—See Genisys Controls, LLC; *U.S. Private*, pg. 1671
IMPCO TECHNOLOGIES (JAPAN) CO, LTD.—See Genisys Controls, LLC; *U.S. Private*, pg. 1671
INDUSTRIAL PARTS DEPOT INC.; *U.S. Private*, pg. 2067
INDUSTRIAL POWER ALLIANCE, LTD.—See Cummins Inc.; *U.S. Public*, pg. 607
ISOTTA FRASCHINI MOTORI S.P.A.—See Fincantieri S.p.A.; *Int'l*, pg. 2671
IVECO LTD.—See CNH Industrial N.V.; *Int'l*, pg. 1675
JACOBS VEHICLE SYSTEMS, INC.—See Cummins Inc.; *U.S. Public*, pg. 608
JD NORMAN LYDNEY LIMITED—See JD Norman Industries, Inc.; *U.S. Private*, pg. 2195
KIRBY ENGINE SYSTEMS, INC.—See Kirby Corporation; *U.S. Public*, pg. 1235
KOHLER DE MEXICO, S.A. DE C.V.—See Kohler Company; *U.S. Private*, pg. 2340
KOMATSU CUMMINS ENGINE CO., LTD.—See Cummins Inc.; *U.S. Public*, pg. 608
KONTAK MANUFACTURING CO. LTD.—See General Electric Company; *U.S. Public*, pg. 918
L-3 MAS CANADA—See L3Harris Technologies, Inc.; *U.S. Public*, pg. 1283
LEWMAR LTD.—See LCI Industries; *U.S. Public*, pg. 1295
LEWMAR NORTH EUROPE LTD.—See LCI Industries; *U.S. Public*, pg. 1295
LOMBARDINI S.R.L..—See Kohler Company; *U.S. Private*, pg. 2340
LS MARINE CO., LTD.—See Daeyang Electric Co., Ltd.; *Int'l*, pg. 1911
MARINE POWER INTERNATIONAL PTY. LTD.—See Brunswick Corporation; *U.S. Public*, pg. 408
MARSHALL ENGINES, INC.; *U.S. Private*, pg. 2592
MERCURY MARINE GROUP—See Brunswick Corporation; *U.S. Public*, pg. 408
MERCURY MARINE LTD.—See Brunswick Corporation; *U.S. Public*, pg. 408
MERCURY MARINE SINGAPORE PTE LTD—See Brunswick Corporation; *U.S. Public*, pg. 408
MOTORTECH AMERICAS LLC—See Generac Holdings Inc.; *U.S. Public*, pg. 912
MOTORTECH GMBH—See Generac Holdings Inc.; *U.S. Public*, pg. 912
MOTORTECH POLSKA SP. Z.O.O.—See Generac Holdings Inc.; *U.S. Public*, pg. 912
MOTORTECH SHANGHAI CO., LTD.—See Generac Holdings Inc.; *U.S. Public*, pg. 912
MWM GMBH—See Caterpillar, Inc.; *U.S. Public*, pg. 452
NAVICO AUSTRALIA PTY LIMITED—See Brunswick Corporation; *U.S. Public*, pg. 408
NIIGATA POWER SYSTEMS (EUROPE) B.V.—See IHI Corporation; *Int'l*, pg. 3606
NIPPON DIESEL SERVICE GMBH—See Daeyang Electric Co., Ltd.; *Int'l*, pg. 1911
NISSAN MARINE & POWER PRODUCTS—See Tohatsu America Corporation; *U.S. Private*, pg. 4181
OIL PURIFICATION SYSTEMS, INC.; *U.S. Private*, pg. 3006
OPTIMAX ENGINE INC.—See Genuine Parts Company; *U.S. Public*, pg. 932
O.S. ENGINES MFG. CO., LTD.—See Futaba Corporation; *Int'l*, pg. 2851
PC DIESEL PTY. LTD.—See Engenco Limited; *Int'l*, pg. 2427
PERKINS ENGINES COMPANY LTD.—See Caterpillar, Inc.; *U.S. Public*, pg. 453
PERKINS ENGINES INC—See Caterpillar, Inc.; *U.S. Public*, pg. 453
PERKINS INDIA PRIVATE LIMITED—See Caterpillar, Inc.; *U.S. Public*, pg. 453
PERKINS INTERNATIONAL INC.—See Caterpillar, Inc.; *U.S. Public*, pg. 453
PLEASURECRAFT ENGINE GROUP—See Correct Craft, Inc.; *U.S. Private*, pg. 1058
POWER SYSTEMS MFG., LLC—See Hanwha Group; *Int'l*, pg. 3266
POWERTRAIN PRODUCTS CORP.—See Sun Capital Partners, Inc.; *U.S. Private*, pg. 3860
PRODUCTOS MARINE DE MEXICO, S.A. DE C.V.—See Brunswick Corporation; *U.S. Public*, pg. 408
PT. HITZ INDONESIA—See Hitachi Zosen Corporation; *Int'l*, pg. 3412
QUINCY COMPRESSOR INC.—See Atlas Copco AB; *Int'l*, pg. 680
RESET PTE LIMITED—See CME Group, Inc.; *U.S. Public*, pg. 517
RIVAL TECHNOLOGIES, INC.; *U.S. Public*, pg. 1800
SAIC FIAT POWERTRAIN HONGYAN CO. LTD.—See CNH Industrial N.V.; *Int'l*, pg. 1676
SERVICE CENTER MILAN S.R.L.—See DEUTZ AG; *Int'l*, pg. 2086
SHANDONG HUAYUAN LAIDONG INTERNAL COMBUS-

N.A.I.C.S. INDEX

333912 — AIR AND GAS COMPRES...

TION ENGINE CO., LTD.—See China Hi-Tech Group Corporation; *Int'l*, pg. 1508
SHANGHAI KAINING IMPORT & EXPORT CO., LTD.—See China Hi-Tech Group Corporation; *Int'l*, pg. 1508
SHORT BLOCK TECHNOLOGIES, INC.; *U.S. Private*, pg. 3642
SPECTECH FRANCE SAS—See ALA SpA; *Int'l*, pg. 289
SPRINGFIELD REMANUFACTURING CORP. HEAVY DUTY DIV—See SRC Holdings Corporation; *U.S. Private*, pg. 3767
SRC HOLDINGS CORPORATION; *U.S. Private*, pg. 3767
STATURE ELECTRIC, INC.—See Allient Inc.; *U.S. Public*, pg. 80
STEWART & STEVENSON SERVICES, INC.—See BAE Systems plc; *Int'l*, pg. 796
STX HEAVY INDUSTRY CO. LTD.—See Dalian Huarui Heavy Industry Group Co., Ltd.; *Int'l*, pg. 1952
SUN MURPHY INTERNATIONAL TRADING (SHANGHAI) CO., LTD—See Helios Technologies, Inc.; *U.S. Public*, pg. 1024
SUNPOWER, INC.—See AMETEK, Inc.; *U.S. Public*, pg. 118
TECOGEN INC.; *U.S. Public*, pg. 1989
THRUSTMASTER OF TEXAS, INC.; *U.S. Private*, pg. 4165
TOHATSU AMERICA CORPORATION; *U.S. Private*, pg. 4181
UZUSHIO ENTERPRISE CO., LTD.—See Daeyang Electric Co., Ltd.; *Int'l*, pg. 1911
VALUEPART INC.—See Deere & Company; *U.S. Public*, pg. 647
VOLVO PENTA TURKEY—See AB Volvo; *Int'l*, pg. 42
VOSSLOH LOCOMOTIVES GMBH—See CRRC Corporation Limited; *Int'l*, pg. 1859
WABTEC EUROPE GMBH—See Westinghouse Air Brake Technologies Corporation; *U.S. Public*, pg. 2359
WOODWARD FST, INC.—See Woodward, Inc.; *U.S. Public*, pg. 2378
WOODWARD L'ORANGE GMBH—See Woodward, Inc.; *U.S. Public*, pg. 2378
WUXI CUMMINS TURBO TECHNOLOGIES CO., LTD.—See Cummins Inc.; *U.S. Public*, pg. 607
WUXI WORLDBEST KAMA POWER CO., LTD.—See China Hi-Tech Group Corporation; *Int'l*, pg. 1508

333912 — AIR AND GAS COMPRESSOR MANUFACTURING

ABAC AMERICAN IMC INC—See Atlas Copco AB; *Int'l*, pg. 677
ABAC ARIA COMPRESSA S.P.A—See Atlas Copco AB; *Int'l*, pg. 677
ABAC DMS AIR COMPRESSORS PTE LTD—See Atlas Copco AB; *Int'l*, pg. 677
ABAC FRANCE S.A.S.—See Atlas Copco AB; *Int'l*, pg. 677
ABAC UK LTD—See Atlas Copco AB; *Int'l*, pg. 677
AGRE KOMPRESSOREN GMBH—See Atlas Copco AB; *Int'l*, pg. 679
AICHI TOKEI DENKI CO., LTD.; *Int'l*, pg. 230
AIR GUNSA S.R.L—See ANEST IWATA Corporation; *Int'l*, pg. 458
AIR PRODUCTS SP. Z.O.O.—See Air Products & Chemicals, Inc.; *U.S. Public*, pg. 66
AIRTAC (FUJIAN) INTELLIGENT EQUIPMENT CO., LTD.—See Airtac International Group; *Int'l*, pg. 248
AIRTAC INDUSTRIAL (MALAYSIA) SDN. BHD.—See Airtac International Group; *Int'l*, pg. 249
AIRTAC (JIANGSU) AUTOMATION CO., LTD.—See Airtac International Group; *Int'l*, pg. 248
AIRTAC (TIANJIN) INTELLIGENT TECHNOLOGY CO., LTD.—See Airtac International Group; *Int'l*, pg. 248
ALLMAND BROS., INC.—See Briggs & Stratton Corporation; *U.S. Private*, pg. 650
ALUP CZ SPOL. S.R.O—See Atlas Copco AB; *Int'l*, pg. 677
ALUP GRASSAIR KOMPRESSOREN BV—See Atlas Copco AB; *Int'l*, pg. 677
ALUP KOMPRESSOREN B.V.—See Atlas Copco AB; *Int'l*, pg. 677
ALUP KOMPRESSOREN GMBH—See Atlas Copco AB; *Int'l*, pg. 677
ANEST IWATA AIR ENGINEERING INC.—See ANEST IWATA Corporation; *Int'l*, pg. 458
ANEST IWATA CORPORATION; *Int'l*, pg. 458
ANEST IWATA DEUTSCHLAND GMBH—See ANEST IWATA Corporation; *Int'l*, pg. 458
ANEST IWATA EUROPE GMBH—See ANEST IWATA Corporation; *Int'l*, pg. 458
ANEST IWATA ITALIA S.R.L—See ANEST IWATA Corporation; *Int'l*, pg. 458
ANEST IWATA KOREA CORPORATION—See ANEST IWATA Corporation; *Int'l*, pg. 458
ANEST IWATA MOTHERSON LIMITED—See ANEST IWATA Corporation; *Int'l*, pg. 458
ANEST IWATA SEGI CORPORATION—See ANEST IWATA Corporation; *Int'l*, pg. 458
ANEST IWATA SOUTHEAST ASIA CO., LTD.—See ANEST IWATA Corporation; *Int'l*, pg. 458
ANEST IWATA SPARMAX CO., LTD.—See ANEST IWATA Corporation; *Int'l*, pg. 458

ANEST IWATA TAIWAN CORPORATION—See ANEST IWATA Corporation; *Int'l*, pg. 458
ANEST IWATA USA INC.—See ANEST IWATA Corporation; *Int'l*, pg. 458
ANGI ENERGY SYSTEMS, INC.—See Vontier Corporation; *U.S. Public*, pg. 2308
APATOR MINING SP. Z.O.O.—See Apator S.A.; *Int'l*, pg. 501
APO PUMPS & COMPRESSORS, LLC—See DXP Enterprises, Inc.; *U.S. Public*, pg. 697
ARIEL CORPORATION; *U.S. Private*, pg. 322
ARKOS GROUP LLC—See Burckhardt Compression Holding AG; *Int'l*, pg. 1220
ATELIERS BUSCH S.A.—See Dr. Ing. K. Busch GmbH; *Int'l*, pg. 2192
ATLAS COPCO AIRPOWER N.V.—See Atlas Copco AB; *Int'l*, pg. 678
ATLAS COPCO AIRTEC—See Atlas Copco AB; *Int'l*, pg. 678
ATLAS COPCO ASSEMBLY SYSTEMS LLC—See Atlas Copco AB; *Int'l*, pg. 681
ATLAS COPCO BEHEER B.V.—See Atlas Copco AB; *Int'l*, pg. 679
ATLAS COPCO BH D.O.O.—See Atlas Copco AB; *Int'l*, pg. 677
ATLAS COPCO (BOTSWANA) (PTY) LTD—See Atlas Copco AB; *Int'l*, pg. 677
ATLAS COPCO CENTRAL ASIA LLP—See Atlas Copco AB; *Int'l*, pg. 678
ATLAS COPCO CHINA/HONG KONG—See Atlas Copco AB; *Int'l*, pg. 678
ATLAS COPCO COLOMBIA LTDA—See Atlas Copco AB; *Int'l*, pg. 678
ATLAS COPCO COMPRESSEURS S.A.S—See Atlas Copco AB; *Int'l*, pg. 678
ATLAS COPCO COMPRESSORS LLC—See Atlas Copco AB; *Int'l*, pg. 680
ATLAS COPCO COMPTEC LLC—See Atlas Copco AB; *Int'l*, pg. 680
ATLAS COPCO CREPELLE S.A.S.—See Atlas Copco AB; *Int'l*, pg. 678
ATLAS COPCO ENERGAS GMBH—See Atlas Copco AB; *Int'l*, pg. 679
ATLAS COPCO GES.M.B.H.—See Atlas Copco AB; *Int'l*, pg. 679
ATLAS COPCO HURRICANE LLC—See Atlas Copco AB; *Int'l*, pg. 680
ATLAS COPCO INDUSTRIAL AIR—See Atlas Copco AB; *Int'l*, pg. 678
ATLAS COPCO INDUSTRIAL TECHNIQUE S.R.L.—See Atlas Copco AB; *Int'l*, pg. 680
ATLAS COPCO ITALIA S.P.A.—See Atlas Copco AB; *Int'l*, pg. 679
ATLAS COPCO KOMPRESSORTEKNIK A/S—See Atlas Copco AB; *Int'l*, pg. 679
ATLAS COPCO LTD—See Atlas Copco AB; *Int'l*, pg. 681
ATLAS COPCO MAFI-TRENCH COMPANY LLC—See Atlas Copco AB; *Int'l*, pg. 680
ATLAS COPCO MCT GMBH—See Atlas Copco AB; *Int'l*, pg. 679
ATLAS COPCO (NI) LTD—See Atlas Copco AB; *Int'l*, pg. 681
ATLAS COPCO OIL-FREE AIR—See Atlas Copco AB; *Int'l*, pg. 678
ATLAS COPCO (PHILIPPINES) INC.—See Atlas Copco AB; *Int'l*, pg. 677
ATLAS COPCO PORTABLE AIR—See Atlas Copco AB; *Int'l*, pg. 678
ATLAS COPCO (SCHWEIZ) AG—See Atlas Copco AB; *Int'l*, pg. 677
ATLAS COPCO S.R.O.—See Atlas Copco AB; *Int'l*, pg. 680
ATLAS COPCO S.R.O.—See Atlas Copco AB; *Int'l*, pg. 681
ATLAS COPCO (THAILAND) LTD—See Atlas Copco AB; *Int'l*, pg. 677
ATLAS COPCO TOOLS CENTRAL EUROPE GMBH—See Atlas Copco AB; *Int'l*, pg. 679
ATOMI CORP.—See Dugan Production Corp.; *U.S. Private*, pg. 1285
ATS ELGI LIMITED—See ELGI Equipments Limited; *Int'l*, pg. 2359
AZBIL TELSTAR, S.L.U.—See Azbil Corporation; *Int'l*, pg. 777
BAUER COMPRESSEURS S.A.R.L.—See BAUER COMP Holding AG; *Int'l*, pg. 894
BAUER COMPRESSORI S.R.L. UNIPERSONALE—See BAUER COMP Holding AG; *Int'l*, pg. 894
BAUER COMPRESSORS ASIA PTE LTD—See BAUER COMP Holding AG; *Int'l*, pg. 894
BAUER COMPRESSORS CO. LTD.—See BAUER COMP Holding AG; *Int'l*, pg. 894
BAUER COMPRESSORS INC.—See BAUER COMP Holding AG; *Int'l*, pg. 894
BAUER KOMPRESSOREN AUSTRALIA PTY LTD—See BAUER COMP Holding AG; *Int'l*, pg. 894
BAUER KOMPRESSOREN CHINA LTD. See BAUER COMP Holding AG; *Int'l*, pg. 894
BAUER KOMPRESSOREN EGYPT LTD.—See BAUER COMP Holding AG; *Int'l*, pg. 894
BAUER KOMPRESSOREN GCC FZE—See BAUER COMP Holding AG; *Int'l*, pg. 894

BAUER KOMPRESSOREN GMBH—See BAUER COMP Holding AG; *Int'l*, pg. 894
BAUER KOMPRESSOREN INDIA PVT. LTD.—See BAUER COMP Holding AG; *Int'l*, pg. 894
BAUER KOMPRESSOREN SHANGHAI LTD.—See BAUER COMP Holding AG; *Int'l*, pg. 894
BAUER-POSEIDON KOMPRESSOREN GES.M.B.H.—See BAUER COMP Holding AG; *Int'l*, pg. 894
BEIJING JINGCHENG ENVIRONMENTAL PROTECTION DEVELOPMENT CO., LTD.—See Beijing Jingcheng Machinery Electric Holding Co., Ltd.; *Int'l*, pg. 953
BEIJING JINGGHENG COMPRESSOR CO., LTD—See Beijing Jingcheng Machinery Electric Co., Ltd.; *Int'l*, pg. 952
BGR ENERGY SYSTEMS LIMITED - OIL & GAS EQUIPMENT DIVISION—See BGR Energy Systems Limited; *Int'l*, pg. 1009
BNM STENSTRUP A/S—See Dr. Ing. K. Busch GmbH; *Int'l*, pg. 2192
BOCK AUSTRALIA PTY. LTD.—See GEA Group Aktiengesellschaft; *Int'l*, pg. 2897
BRISTOL COMPRESSORS INTERNATIONAL, INC.—See Garrison Investment Group LP; *U.S. Private*, pg. 1645
BROOKS AUTOMATION, INC. CTI-CRYOGENICS PRODUCTS CENTER—See Atlas Copco AB; *Int'l*, pg. 682
BUMHAN INDUSTRIES CO., LTD.; *Int'l*, pg. 1215
BURCKHARDT COMPRESSION AG—See Burckhardt Compression Holding AG; *Int'l*, pg. 1220
BURCKHARDT COMPRESSION HOLDING AG; *Int'l*, pg. 1220
BURCKHARDT COMPRESSION (JAPAN) LTD.—See Burckhardt Compression Holding AG; *Int'l*, pg. 1220
BURCKHARDT COMPRESSION KOREA BUSAN LTD.—See Burckhardt Compression Holding AG; *Int'l*, pg. 1220
BURCKHARDT COMPRESSION KOREA LTD.—See Burckhardt Compression Holding AG; *Int'l*, pg. 1221
BURCKHARDT COMPRESSION (MIDDLE EAST) FZE—See Burckhardt Compression Holding AG; *Int'l*, pg. 1220
BURCKHARDT COMPRESSION (NETHERLANDS) BV—See Burckhardt Compression Holding AG; *Int'l*, pg. 1220
BURCKHARDT COMPRESSION (SAUDI ARABIA) LLC—See Burckhardt Compression Holding AG; *Int'l*, pg. 1220
BURCKHARDT COMPRESSION SINGAPORE PTE LTD.—See Burckhardt Compression Holding AG; *Int'l*, pg. 1221
BURCKHARDT COMPRESSION SOUTH AFRICA (PTY) LTD.—See Burckhardt Compression Holding AG; *Int'l*, pg. 1221
BURCKHARDT COMPRESSION (UK) LTD.—See Burckhardt Compression Holding AG; *Int'l*, pg. 1220
BURCKHARDT KOMPRESOR SAN. VE TIC. LTD.—See Burckhardt Compression Holding AG; *Int'l*, pg. 1221
BUSCH AG—See Dr. Ing. K. Busch GmbH; *Int'l*, pg. 2192
BUSCH ARGENTINA S.R.L.—See Dr. Ing. K. Busch GmbH; *Int'l*, pg. 2192
BUSCH AUSTRALIA PTY. LTD.—See Dr. Ing. K. Busch GmbH; *Int'l*, pg. 2192
BUSCH AUSTRIA GMBH—See Dr. Ing. K. Busch GmbH; *Int'l*, pg. 2192
BUSCH B.V.—See Dr. Ing. K. Busch GmbH; *Int'l*, pg. 2192
BUSCH CHILE S. A.—See Dr. Ing. K. Busch GmbH; *Int'l*, pg. 2192
BUSCH CLEAN AIR S.A.—See Dr. Ing. K. Busch GmbH; *Int'l*, pg. 2192
BUSCH DO BRASIL LTDA.—See Dr. Ing. K. Busch GmbH; *Int'l*, pg. 2193
BUSCH FRANCE S.A.S.—See Dr. Ing. K. Busch GmbH; *Int'l*, pg. 2192
BUSCH IRELAND LTD.—See Dr. Ing. K. Busch GmbH; *Int'l*, pg. 2193
BUSCH ISRAEL LTD.—See Dr. Ing. K. Busch GmbH; *Int'l*, pg. 2193
BUSCH ITALIA S.R.L.—See Dr. Ing. K. Busch GmbH; *Int'l*, pg. 2193
BUSCH KOREA LTD.—See Dr. Ing. K. Busch GmbH; *Int'l*, pg. 2193
BUSCH LBERICA S.A—See Dr. Ing. K. Busch GmbH; *Int'l*, pg. 2193
BUSCH MALAYSIA SDN BHD—See Dr. Ing. K. Busch GmbH; *Int'l*, pg. 2193
BUSCH MANUFACTURING KOREA LTD.—See Dr. Ing. K. Busch GmbH; *Int'l*, pg. 2193
BUSCH MANUFACTURING LLC—See Dr. Ing. K. Busch GmbH; *Int'l*, pg. 2193
BUSCH NEW ZEALAND LTD.—See Dr. Ing. K. Busch GmbH; *Int'l*, pg. 2193
BUSCH N.V.—See Dr. Ing. K. Busch GmbH; *Int'l*, pg. 2193
BUSCH POLSKA SP. Z O.O.—See Dr. Ing. K. Busch GmbH; *Int'l*, pg. 2193
BUSCH TAIWAN CORPORATION—See Dr. Ing. K. Busch GmbH; *Int'l*, pg. 2193
BUSCH (UK) LTD.—See Dr. Ing. K. Busch GmbH; *Int'l*, pg. 2192
BUSCH VACUUM INDIA PVT LTD.—See Dr. Ing. K. Busch GmbH; *Int'l*, pg. 2193

333912 — AIR AND GAS COMPRES...

BUSCH VACUUM KFT.—See Dr. Ing. K. Busch GmbH; *Int'l*, pg. 2193
BUSCH VACUUM MEXICO S DE R.L. DE C.V—See Dr. Ing. K. Busch GmbH; *Int'l*, pg. 2193
BUSCH VACUUM RUSSIA OOO—See Dr. Ing. K. Busch GmbH; *Int'l*, pg. 2193
BUSCH VACUUM (SHANGHAI) CO. LTD.—See Dr. Ing. K. Busch GmbH; *Int'l*, pg. 2193
BUSCH VACUUM SINGAPORE PTE. LTD.—See Dr. Ing. K. Busch GmbH; *Int'l*, pg. 2193
BUSCH VACUUM SOUTH AFRICA (PTY) LTD.—See Dr. Ing. K. Busch GmbH; *Int'l*, pg. 2193
BUSCH VACUUM TECHNICS INC.—See Dr. Ing. K. Busch GmbH; *Int'l*, pg. 2193
BUSCH VACUUM (THAILAND) CO. LTD.—See Dr. Ing. K. Busch GmbH; *Int'l*, pg. 2193
BUSCH VAKUUM S.R.O.—See Dr. Ing. K. Busch GmbH; *Int'l*, pg. 2193
BUSCH VAKUUMTEKNIK AB—See Dr. Ing. K. Busch GmbH; *Int'l*, pg. 2193
BUSCH VAKUUMTEKNIK AS—See Dr. Ing. K. Busch GmbH; *Int'l*, pg. 2193
BUSCH VAKUUMTEKNIK OY—See Dr. Ing. K. Busch GmbH; *Int'l*, pg. 2193
CAMPBELL HAUSFELD—See Berkshire Hathaway Inc.; *U.S. Public*, pg. 299
CECCATO ARIA COMPRESSA S.P.A.—See Atlas Copco AB; *Int'l*, pg. 679
CENTURY TRADING CO., LTD—See ANEST IWATA Corporation; *Int'l*, pg. 458
CHANGHONG HUAYI COMPRESSOR CO., LTD.; *Int'l*, pg. 1443
CHART DISTRIBUTION & STORAGE SYSTEMS INC.—See Chart Industries, Inc.; *U.S. Public*, pg. 481
CHONGQING GAS COMPRESSOR FACTORY CO., LTD.—See Chongqing Machinery & Electronics Holding (Group) Co., Ltd.; *Int'l*, pg. 1580
CHONGQING GENERAL INDUSTRY (GROUP) CO., LTD—See Chongqing Machinery & Electronics Holding (Group) Co., Ltd.; *Int'l*, pg. 1580
CLEANTECH ENERGY PTY. LTD.—See Delorean Corporation Limited; *Int'l*, pg. 2015
COMPAIR (AUSTRALASIA) LTD.—See Ingersoll Rand Inc.; *U.S. Public*, pg. 1119
COMPAIR DRUCKLUFTTECHNIK—See Ingersoll Rand Inc.; *U.S. Public*, pg. 1119
COMPAIR KOREA CO., LTD.—See Ingersoll Rand Inc.; *U.S. Public*, pg. 1119
COMPAIR SOUTH AFRICA (PTY) LTD.—See Ingersoll Rand Inc.; *U.S. Public*, pg. 1119
COMPOSITES BUSCH S.A.—See Dr. Ing. K. Busch GmbH; *Int'l*, pg. 2193
COMPRESSEURS MAUGUIERE S.A.S.—See Atlas Copco AB; *Int'l*, pg. 678
COMPRESSEURS WORTHINGTON CREYSSENSAC S.A.S.—See Atlas Copco AB; *Int'l*, pg. 678
COMPRESSOR ENGINEERING CORPORATION; *U.S. Private*, pg. 1003
COMPRESSOR PRODUCTS INTERNATIONAL GMBH—See Enpro Inc.; *U.S. Public*, pg. 774
COMPRESSOR PRODUCTS INTERNATIONAL LTD.—See Enpro Inc.; *U.S. Public*, pg. 774
COMPRESSOR SAZI TABRIZ CO.; *Int'l*, pg. 1754
COMPRESSOR SYSTEMS INC.—See EQT AB; *Int'l*, pg. 2478
COMPRESSOR WORLD, LLC; *U.S. Private*, pg. 1003
CONVUM LTD.; *Int'l*, pg. 1787
COOK COMPRESSION LIMITED—See Dover Corporation; *U.S. Public*, pg. 678
COOK COMPRESSION, LLC—See Dover Corporation; *U.S. Public*, pg. 678
COOPER MACHINERY SERVICES—See Arcline Investment Management LP; *U.S. Private*, pg. 313
CORKEN, INC.—See IDEX Corp; *U.S. Public*, pg. 1091
CPI PACIFIC PTY LIMITED—See Enpro Inc.; *U.S. Public*, pg. 774
CTA HOLDING; *Int'l*, pg. 1869
CURTIS-TOLEDO, INC.—See Brookfield Corporation; *Int'l*, pg. 1181
CUSTOM DESIGNED COMPRESSOR SYSTEMS, INC.; *U.S. Public*, pg. 612
DANFOSS COMMERCIAL COMPRESSORS S.A.—See Danfoss A/S; *Int'l*, pg. 1959
DANFOSS TURBOCOR COMPRESSORS INC.—See Danfoss A/S; *Int'l*, pg. 1961
DCC LPG LTD.—See DCC plc; *Int'l*, pg. 1990
DEWALT INDUSTRIAL TOOL COMPANY—See Stanley Black & Decker, Inc.; *U.S. Public*, pg. 1932
DR. ING. K. BUSCH GMBH; *Int'l*, pg. 2192
DRYERTECH INDUSTRIES LTD.; *Int'l*, pg. 2207
DURR SYSTEMS CZECH REPUBLIC A.S.—See Durr AG; *Int'l*, pg. 2231
EAGLE COMPRESSORS INC.—See Paratech, Inc.; *U.S. Private*, pg. 3093
EBARA TECHNOLOGIES INC.—See Ebara Corporation; *Int'l*, pg. 2283
EDMAC EUROPE N.V.—See Atlas Copco AB; *Int'l*, pg. 682
EDWARDS SAS—See Atlas Copco AB; *Int'l*, pg. 682
EKOMAK ENDUSTRIYEL KOMPRESOR MAKINE SANAYIVETICARET A.S.—See Atlas Copco AB; *Int'l*, pg. 682
ELAINE, INC.; *U.S. Private*, pg. 1349
ELGI COMPRESSORS (M) SDN. BHD.—See ELGI Equipments Limited; *Int'l*, pg. 2359
ELGI COMPRESSORS USA INC.—See ELGI Equipments Limited; *Int'l*, pg. 2360
ELGI EQUIPMENTS AUSTRALIA PTY LTD.—See ELGI Equipments Limited; *Int'l*, pg. 2360
ELGI EQUIPMENTS LIMITED - PRESSURE VESSEL DIVISION—See ELGI Equipments Limited; *Int'l*, pg. 2360
ELGI EQUIPMENTS LIMITED; *Int'l*, pg. 2359
ELGI EQUIPMENTS LTD.—See ELGI Equipments Limited; *Int'l*, pg. 2360
ELGI EQUIPMENTS PTY LTD.—See ELGI Equipments Limited; *Int'l*, pg. 2360
ELGI EQUIPMENTS (ZHEJIANG) LIMITED—See ELGI Equipments Limited; *Int'l*, pg. 2360
ELLIOTT TURBOMACHINERY LTD.—See Ebara Corporation; *Int'l*, pg. 2284
EMBRACO S.A.—See Whirlpool Corporation; *U.S. Public*, pg. 2368
EMCO WHEATON GMBH—See Ingersoll Rand Inc.; *U.S. Public*, pg. 1119
ENERFLEX ENERGY SYSTEMS INC.—See Enerflex Ltd.; *Int'l*, pg. 2418
ENERFLEX ENERGY SYSTEMS (WYOMING) INC.—See Enerflex Ltd.; *Int'l*, pg. 2418
ENRIC (BENGBU) COMPRESSOR CO., LTD.—See China International Marine Containers (Group) Co., Ltd.; *Int'l*, pg. 1511
EXLAIR (NZ) LIMITED—See Atlas Copco AB; *Int'l*, pg. 682
EXTERRAN PERU SELVA S.R.L.—See Enerflex Ltd.; *Int'l*, pg. 2419
FIAC S.P.A.—See Atlas Copco AB; *Int'l*, pg. 682
FNA GROUP, INC.; *U.S. Private*, pg. 1555
THE FOUNTAINHEAD GROUP, INC.; *U.S. Private*, pg. 4030
FUJITSU COMPONENT (MALAYSIA) SDN, BHD.—See FUJITSU COMPONENT LIMITED; *Int'l*, pg. 2832
FW MURPHY PRODUCTION CONTROLS LLC—See Dover Corporation; *U.S. Public*, pg. 679
GARDNER DENVER AUSTRIA GMBH—See Ingersoll Rand Inc.; *U.S. Public*, pg. 1118
GARDNER DENVER BELGIUM NV—See Ingersoll Rand Inc.; *U.S. Public*, pg. 1118
GARDNER DENVER CANADA CORP.—See Ingersoll Rand Inc.; *U.S. Public*, pg. 1118
GARDNER DENVER CZ + SK, S.R.O.—See Ingersoll Rand Inc.; *U.S. Public*, pg. 1118
GARDNER DENVER DENMARK A/S—See Ingersoll Rand Inc.; *U.S. Public*, pg. 1119
GARDNER DENVER DEUTSCHLAND GMBH—See Ingersoll Rand Inc.; *U.S. Public*, pg. 1119
GARDNER DENVER DRUM LTD.—See Ingersoll Rand Inc.; *U.S. Public*, pg. 1119
GARDNER DENVER ENGINEERED PRODUCTS INDIA PTE LTD.—See Ingersoll Rand Inc.; *U.S. Public*, pg. 1119
GARDNER DENVER FRANCE SAS—See Ingersoll Rand Inc.; *U.S. Public*, pg. 1119
GARDNER DENVER HONG KONG LTD.—See Ingersoll Rand Inc.; *U.S. Public*, pg. 1119
GARDNER DENVER INDUSTRIES AUSTRALIA PTY LTD.—See Ingersoll Rand Inc.; *U.S. Public*, pg. 1119
GARDNER DENVER JAPAN LTD.—See Ingersoll Rand Inc.; *U.S. Public*, pg. 1119
GARDNER DENVER LTD.—See Ingersoll Rand Inc.; *U.S. Public*, pg. 1119
GARDNER DENVER MACHINERY (SHANGHAI) CO. LTD.—See Ingersoll Rand Inc.; *U.S. Public*, pg. 1119
GARDNER DENVER NASH AUSTRALIA—See Ingersoll Rand Inc.; *U.S. Public*, pg. 1119
GARDNER DENVER NASH BRASIL INDUSTRIA E COMERCIO DE BOMBAS LTDA.—See Ingersoll Rand Inc.; *U.S. Public*, pg. 1119
GARDNER DENVER NASH LLC—See Ingersoll Rand Inc.; *U.S. Public*, pg. 1119
GARDNER DENVER NASH SINGAPORE PTE LTD.—See Ingersoll Rand Inc.; *U.S. Public*, pg. 1119
GARDNER DENVER NEDERLAND BV—See Ingersoll Rand Inc.; *U.S. Public*, pg. 1119
GARDNER DENVER NEW ZEALAND LTD.—See Ingersoll Rand Inc.; *U.S. Public*, pg. 1119
GARDNER DENVER PETROLEUM PUMPS, LLC—See Ingersoll Rand Inc.; *U.S. Public*, pg. 1118
GARDNER DENVER PTE. LTD.—See Ingersoll Rand Inc.; *U.S. Public*, pg. 1118
GARDNER DENVER - ROBUSCHI DIVISION—See Ingersoll Rand Inc.; *U.S. Public*, pg. 1119
GARDNER DENVER SLOVAKIA S.R.O.—See Ingersoll Rand Inc.; *U.S. Public*, pg. 1119
GARDNER DENVER SRL—See Ingersoll Rand Inc.; *U.S. Public*, pg. 1119
GARDNER DENVER TAIWAN LTD.—See Ingersoll Rand Inc.; *U.S. Public*, pg. 1119
GARDNER DENVER (THAILAND) CO., LTD.—See Ingersoll Rand Inc.; *U.S. Public*, pg. 1118
GARDNER DENVER THOMAS GMBH—See Ingersoll Rand Inc.; *U.S. Public*, pg. 1119
GARDNER DENVER THOMAS, INC.—See Ingersoll Rand Inc.; *U.S. Public*, pg. 1119
GARDNER DENVER THOMAS - MONROE—See Ingersoll Rand Inc.; *U.S. Public*, pg. 1119
GARDNER DENVER THOMAS PNEUMATIC SYSTEMS (WUXI) CO., LTD.—See Ingersoll Rand Inc.; *U.S. Public*, pg. 1119
GARDNER DENVER TRADING (SHANGHAI) CO. LTD.—See Ingersoll Rand Inc.; *U.S. Public*, pg. 1119
GARLOCK INDIA PRIVATE LIMITED—See Enpro Inc.; *U.S. Public*, pg. 775
GAST ASIA, INC.—See IDEX Corp; *U.S. Public*, pg. 1090
GAST MANUFACTURING, INC.—See IDEX Corp; *U.S. Public*, pg. 1090
GD INDUSTRIAL PRODUCTS MALAYSIA SDN—See Ingersoll Rand Inc.; *U.S. Public*, pg. 1118
GUANGDONG AIRTAC INTELLIGENT EQUIPMENT CO., LTD.—See Airtac International Group; *Int'l*, pg. 249
GUANGZHOU WANBAO GROUP CO., LTD.; *Int'l*, pg. 3168
HALDEX CONCENTRIC PLC.—See Haldex AB; *Int'l*, pg. 3228
HANGZHOU OXYGEN PLANT GROUP CO., LTD.; *Int'l*, pg. 3249
HANKISON INTERNATIONAL; *U.S. Private*, pg. 1853
HANSHIN MACHINERY CO., LTD.; *Int'l*, pg. 3260
HITACHI GLOBAL AIR POWER US, LLC—See Hitachi, Ltd.; *Int'l*, pg. 3417
HITACHI INDUSTRIAL EQUIPMENT (SUZHOU) COMPRESSOR CO., LTD.—See Hitachi, Ltd.; *Int'l*, pg. 3419
HITACHI INDUSTRIAL EQUIPMENT SYSTEMS CO., LTD. - AIR COMPRESSOR SYSTEM DIVISION—See Hitachi, Ltd.; *Int'l*, pg. 3419
HITACHI INDUSTRIAL EQUIPMENT SYSTEMS CO., LTD. - EBINA DIVISION—See Hitachi, Ltd.; *Int'l*, pg. 3419
HITACHI INDUSTRIAL EQUIPMENT SYSTEMS CO., LTD. - SAGAMI DIVISION—See Hitachi, Ltd.; *Int'l*, pg. 3419
HOERBIGER CORPORATION OF AMERICA, INC.—See Hoerbiger Holding AG; *Int'l*, pg. 3440
HOKUETSU INDUSTRIES CO., LTD.; *Int'l*, pg. 3444
HOWDEN BC COMPRESSORS—See Chart Industries, Inc.; *U.S. Public*, pg. 481
HOWDEN CKD COMPRESSORS S.R.O—See Chart Industries, Inc.; *U.S. Public*, pg. 481
HOWDEN COMPRESSORS INC—See Chart Industries, Inc.; *U.S. Public*, pg. 482
HOWDEN COMPRESSORS LIMITED—See Chart Industries, Inc.; *U.S. Public*, pg. 481
HOWDEN GROUP LTD.—See Chart Industries, Inc.; *U.S. Public*, pg. 481
HOWDEN THOMASSEN COMPRESSORS INDIA PRIVATE LIMITED—See Chart Industries, Inc.; *U.S. Public*, pg. 482
HOWDEN THOMASSEN COMPRESSORS—See Chart Industries, Inc.; *U.S. Public*, pg. 482
HUANGSHI DONGBEI ELECTRICAL APPLIANCE CO., LTD.; *Int'l*, pg. 3513
HUAYI COMPRESSOR BARCELONA, S.L.—See Changhong Huayi Compressor Co., Ltd.; *Int'l*, pg. 1443
HYCOMP, INC.; *U.S. Private*, pg. 2016
ILMVAC TRADING (SHANGHAI) CO. LTD.—See Ingersoll Rand Inc.; *U.S. Public*, pg. 1119
ILS INOVATIVE LABORSYSTEME GMBH—See Ingersoll Rand Inc.; *U.S. Public*, pg. 1120
I.M.W. CNG BANGLADESH LTD.—See Clean Energy Fuels Corp.; *U.S. Public*, pg. 508
IMW INDUSTRIES LTD.—See Clean Energy Fuels Corp.; *U.S. Public*, pg. 508
INDUSTRIE MECCANICHE DI BAGNOLO S.R.L.—See Chart Industries, Inc.; *U.S. Public*, pg. 482
INGERSOLL-RAND AIR SOLUTIONS HIBON SARL—See Ingersoll Rand Inc.; *U.S. Public*, pg. 1120
INGERSOLL-RAND COLOMBIA S.A.S—See Ingersoll Rand Inc.; *U.S. Public*, pg. 1120
INGERSOLL-RAND COMPANY LIMITED (UK)—See Ingersoll Rand Inc.; *U.S. Public*, pg. 1121
INGERSOLL-RAND COMPANY SA (PTY) LTD.—See Ingersoll Rand Inc.; *U.S. Public*, pg. 1121
INGERSOLL-RAND INDUSTRIAL TECHNOLOGIES - COMPRESSED AIR SOLUTIONS—See Ingersoll Rand Inc.; *U.S. Public*, pg. 1121
INGERSOLL-RAND ITALIANA S.P.A.—See Ingersoll Rand Inc.; *U.S. Public*, pg. 1121
INGERSOLL-RAND POLSKA SP.Z.O.O.—See Ingersoll Rand Inc.; *U.S. Public*, pg. 1121
INGERSOLL RAND S.E. ASIA (PRIVATE) LIMITED—See Ingersoll Rand Inc.; *U.S. Public*, pg. 1121
INGERSOLL-RAND WORLDWIDE CAPITAL S.A.R.L.—See Ingersoll Rand Inc.; *U.S. Public*, pg. 1121
INNOVATIVE VACUUM SOLUTIONS, INC.—See Atlas Copco AB; *Int'l*, pg. 683
IRMER + ELZE KOMPRESSOREN GMBH—See Atlas Copco AB; *Int'l*, pg. 679
IWATA SERVICE & SALES(M) SDN. BHD.—See ANEST IWATA Corporation; *Int'l*, pg. 458
JAMES HOWDEN GROUP LIMITED—See Chart Industries, Inc.; *U.S. Public*, pg. 482

N.A.I.C.S. INDEX

JAVAC PTY. LTD.—See Atlas Copco AB; *Int'l*, pg. 683
JIAXIPERA COMPRESSOR LIMITED COMPANY—See Changhong Huayi Compressor Co., Ltd.; *Int'l*, pg. 1443
KAZANKOMPESSORMASH OJSC—See HMS Hydraulic Machines & Systems Group plc; *Int'l*, pg. 3432
LEYBOLD DO BRASIL LTDA.—See Atlas Copco AB; *Int'l*, pg. 683
LEYBOLD FRANCE SAS—See Atlas Copco AB; *Int'l*, pg. 683
LEYBOLD FRANCE S.A.S.—See Atlas Copco AB; *Int'l*, pg. 683
LEYBOLD HISPANICA S.A.—See Atlas Copco AB; *Int'l*, pg. 683
LEYBOLD INDIA PVT LTD.—See Atlas Copco AB; *Int'l*, pg. 683
LEYBOLD IRELAND—See Atlas Copco AB; *Int'l*, pg. 683
LEYBOLD ITALIA SRL—See Atlas Copco AB; *Int'l*, pg. 683
LEYBOLD JAPAN CO., LTD.—See Atlas Copco AB; *Int'l*, pg. 683
LEYBOLD JAPAN CO., LTD.—See Atlas Copco AB; *Int'l*, pg. 683
LEYBOLD KOREA LTD.—See Atlas Copco AB; *Int'l*, pg. 683
LEYBOLD NEDERLAND B.V.—See Atlas Copco AB; *Int'l*, pg. 683
LEYBOLD SCHWEIZ AG—See Atlas Copco AB; *Int'l*, pg. 683
LEYBOLD SINGAPORE PTE LTD—See Atlas Copco AB; *Int'l*, pg. 683
LEYBOLD TAIWAN LTD—See Atlas Copco AB; *Int'l*, pg. 683
LEYBOLD (TIANJIN) INTERNATIONAL TRADE CO., LTD.—See Atlas Copco AB; *Int'l*, pg. 683
LEYBOLD USA INC.—See Atlas Copco AB; *Int'l*, pg. 683
LIUZHOU TECH MACHINERY CO., LTD.—See Atlas Copco AB; *Int'l*, pg. 683
LIVNICA PRECIZNIH ODLIVAKA D.O.O.—See Bet Shemesh Engines Holdings (1997) Ltd.; *Int'l*, pg. 1001
MAGNUM VENUS PRODUCTS; *U.S. Private*, pg. 2549
MATTEI COMPRESSORS INC.; *U.S. Private*, pg. 2613
MULTIAIR ITALIA S.R.L.—See Atlas Copco AB; *Int'l*, pg. 679
MVP MANUFACTURING—See Magnum Venus Products; *U.S. Private*, pg. 2549
NIPPON BUSCH K.K.—See Dr. Ing. K. Busch GmbH; *Int'l*, pg. 2193
NORTHFIELD PRECISION INSTRUMENT CORP.; *U.S. Public*, pg. 1539
NORWALK COMPRESSOR COMPANY, INC.; *U.S. Private*, pg. 2964
OERLIKON LEYBOLD VACUUM DRESDEN GMBH—See Atlas Copco AB; *Int'l*, pg. 683
OERLIKON LEYBOLD VACUUM INDIA PVT. LTD.—See Atlas Copco AB; *Int'l*, pg. 683
OINA VV AKTIEBOLAG—See Ingersoll Rand Inc.; *U.S. Public*, pg. 1122
OY ATLAS COPCO AB—See Atlas Copco AB; *Int'l*, pg. 684
OY ATLAS COPCO KOMPRESSORIT AB—See Atlas Copco AB; *Int'l*, pg. 684
PMH DRUCKLUFT GMBH—See Atlas Copco AB; *Int'l*, pg. 684
POWEREX IWATA AIR TECHNOLOGY, INC.—See ANEST IWATA Corporation; *Int'l*, pg. 458
PRESSURE COMPRESSORES LTDA.—See Atlas Copco AB; *Int'l*, pg. 684
PROGNOST MACHINERY DIAGNOSTICS EQUIPMENT & SERVICES LLC—See Burckhardt Compression Holding AG; *Int'l*, pg. 1221
PT ELGI EQUIPMENTS INDONESIA—See ELGI Equipments Limited; *Int'l*, pg. 2360
RENO A/S—See Atlas Copco AB; *Int'l*, pg. 684
RIX INDUSTRIES; *U.S. Private*, pg. 3448
ROBUSCHI DO BRASIL LTD.—See Ingersoll Rand Inc.; *U.S. Public*, pg. 1119
ROBUSCHI FLUID TECHNOLOGY (SHANGHAI) CO. LTD.—See Ingersoll Rand Inc.; *U.S. Public*, pg. 1119
ROBUSCHI FRANCE SARL—See Ingersoll Rand Inc.; *U.S. Public*, pg. 1119
ROTAIR S.P.A.—See ELGI Equipments Limited; *Int'l*, pg. 2360
ROTORCOMP VERDICHTER GMBH—See BAUER COMP Holding AG; *Int'l*, pg. 894
R.P. ADAMS COMPANY, INC.—See SERFILCO, Ltd.; *U.S. Private*, pg. 3613
RUNTECH SYSTEMS, INC.—See Ingersoll Rand Inc.; *U.S. Public*, pg. 1122
RUNTECH SYSTEMS OY—See Ingersoll Rand Inc.; *U.S. Public*, pg. 1122
SAS BELAIR—See ELGI Equipments Limited; *Int'l*, pg. 2360
SCALES INDUSTRIAL TECHNOLOGIES, INC.—See Atlas Copco AB; *Int'l*, pg. 684
SCHNEIDER BOHEMIA SPOL S.R.O.—See Atlas Copco AB; *Int'l*, pg. 684
SCHNEIDER DRUCKLUFT GMBH—See Atlas Copco AB; *Int'l*, pg. 684
SCHNEIDER-SLOVENSKO TLAKOVA VZDUCHOTECHNIKA SPOL. S R.O.—See Atlas Copco AB; *Int'l*, pg. 684
SCHULER PRESSEN GMBH - WAGHAUSEL—See ANDRITZ AG; *Int'l*, pg. 456
SCOTT FETZER COMPANY—See Berkshire Hathaway Inc.; *U.S. Public*, pg. 299
SCROLL TECHNOLOGIES—See Danfoss A/S; *Int'l*, pg. 1961
SENSEAIR AB—See Asahi Kasei Corporation; *Int'l*, pg. 597
SERVI-COMPRESORES, C.A.—See Enerflex Ltd.; *Int'l*, pg. 2419
SHANGHAI BOLAITE COMPRESSOR CO LTD—See Atlas Copco AB; *Int'l*, pg. 684
SHENYANG YUANDA COMPRESSOR CO. LTD.—See Burckhardt Compression Holding AG; *Int'l*, pg. 1221
SHINANO FUJITSU LIMITED—See FUJITSU COMPONENT LIMITED; *Int'l*, pg. 2832
STERLING FLUID SYSTEMS (ITALY) S.P.A.—See Flowserve Corporation; *U.S. Public*, pg. 857
SULLAIR ARGENTINA S.A.—See Hitachi, Ltd.; *Int'l*, pg. 3417
SULLAIR ASIA PTE. LTD.—See Hitachi, Ltd.; *Int'l*, pg. 3424
SULLAIR OF HOUSTON, INC.—See HOLT Texas, LTD.; *U.S. Private*, pg. 1969
SULLAIR TAIWAN LLC—See Hitachi, Ltd.; *Int'l*, pg. 3417
SUPER PRODUCTS LLC—See Alamo Group Inc.; *U.S. Public*, pg. 71
TAMROTOR KOMPRESSORIT OY—See Ingersoll Rand Inc.; *U.S. Public*, pg. 1120
TAMROTOR MARINE COMPRESSORS AS—See Ingersoll Rand Inc.; *U.S. Public*, pg. 1120
TECHFLUID NORD S.A.S.—See Atlas Copco AB; *Int'l*, pg. 684
TECUMSEH PRODUCTS COMPANY LLC—See Atlas Holdings, LLC; *U.S. Private*, pg. 378
TECUMSEH PRODUCTS COMPANY LLC—See Mueller Industries, Inc.; *U.S. Public*, pg. 1485
TECUMSEH PRODUCTS INDIA PVT. LTD.—See Atlas Holdings, LLC; *U.S. Private*, pg. 378
TECUMSEH PRODUCTS INDIA PVT. LTD.—See Mueller Industries, Inc.; *U.S. Public*, pg. 1485
TELSTAR INDUSTRIAL, S.L.—See Azbil Corporation; *Int'l*, pg. 777
TEVAK S.R.O.—See Atlas Copco AB; *Int'l*, pg. 684
THOMAS INDUSTRIES INC.—See Ingersoll Rand Inc.; *U.S. Public*, pg. 1120
UE COMPRESSION, LLC—See Lion Equity Partners, LLC; *U.S. Private*, pg. 2463
ULTRA ELECTRONICS PRECISION AIR SYSTEMS LTD—See Advent International Corporation; *U.S. Private*, pg. 101
UNICCOMP GMBH—See BAUER COMP Holding AG; *Int'l*, pg. 894
VAKUTEK—See Dr. Ing. K. Busch GmbH; *Int'l*, pg. 2194
VAN AIR, INC.; *U.S. Private*, pg. 4338
VAN AIR SYSTEMS INC—See Van Air, Inc.; *U.S. Private*, pg. 4338
WABCO COMPRESSOR MANUFACTURING CO.—See Cummins Inc.; *U.S. Public*, pg. 609
WUXI PNEUMATECH AIR/GAS PURITY EQUIPMENT CO LTD—See Atlas Copco AB; *Int'l*, pg. 684
YTM-INDUSTRIAL OY—See Atlas Copco AB; *Int'l*, pg. 684

333914 — MEASURING, DISPENSING, AND OTHER PUMPING EQUIPMENT MANUFACTURING

ABEL EQUIPOS, S.A.—See Hillenbrand, Inc.; *U.S. Public*, pg. 1036
ABEL GMBH—See Hillenbrand, Inc.; *U.S. Public*, pg. 1035
ABEL PUMPS, L.P.—See IDEX Corp; *U.S. Public*, pg. 1089
AB GERMA—See ADDvise Group AB; *Int'l*, pg. 136
AC CUSTOM PUMPS DIVISION—See Xylem Inc.; *U.S. Public*, pg. 2395
A.C. DISPENSING EQUIPMENT INC.; *Int'l*, pg. 23
ADIXEN VACUUM PRODUCTS SAS—See Dr. Ing. K. Busch GmbH; *Int'l*, pg. 2194
AEROCONTROLEX GROUP—See TransDigm Group Incorporated; *U.S. Public*, pg. 2181
AIR DIMENSIONS, INC.—See Ingersoll Rand Inc.; *U.S. Public*, pg. 1118
AISAN INDUSTRY FRANCE SA—See Aisan Industry Co., Ltd.; *Int'l*, pg. 250
AISIN CORPORATION - NISHIO ENGINE COMPONENT PLANT—See AISIN Corporation; *Int'l*, pg. 251
AKRON BRASS COMPANY—See IDEX Corp; *U.S. Public*, pg. 1089
ALEDCO, INC.—See DXP Enterprises, Inc.; *U.S. Public*, pg. 697
ALFA LAVAL FLOW EQUIPMENT (KUNSHAN) CO LTD—See Alfa Laval AB; *Int'l*, pg. 308
ALFA LAVAL LIMITED—See Alfa Laval AB; *Int'l*, pg. 310
ALFA LAVAL LIMITED—See Alfa Laval AB; *Int'l*, pg. 310
ALLWEILER A/S—See KKR & Co. Inc.; *U.S. Public*, pg. 1242
ALLWEILER GMBH—See KKR & Co. Inc.; *U.S. Public*, pg. 1242
ALYAN PUMP CO.—See Bain Capital, LP; *U.S. Private*, pg. 432
AMT PUMP COMPANY—See The Gorman-Rupp Company; *U.S. Public*, pg. 2085
ANDRITZ PUMPS GERMANY GMBH—See ANDRITZ AG; *Int'l*, pg. 454
ANDRITZ RITZ GMBH—See ANDRITZ AG; *Int'l*, pg. 454
ANNEX-TECHNIK GMBH—See LKQ Corporation; *U.S. Public*, pg. 1333
APEX PRECISION TECHNOLOGY INC.; *U.S. Private*, pg. 293
APOLLO GOESSNITZ GMBH—See HMS Hydraulic Machines & Systems Group plc; *Int'l*, pg. 3432
APTARGROUP, INC.- CONGERS—See AptarGroup, Inc.; *U.S. Public*, pg. 175
AR WILFLEY & SONS INC.; *U.S. Private*, pg. 306
ASPACOIL LTD; *Int'l*, pg. 628
ASSOCIATED FUEL PUMP SYSTEMS CORP.—See Denso Corporation; *Int'l*, pg. 2031
AXFLOW A/S—See Axel Johnson Gruppen AB; *Int'l*, pg. 762
AXFLOW AS—See Axel Johnson Gruppen AB; *Int'l*, pg. 763
AXFLOW GMBH—See Axel Johnson Gruppen AB; *Int'l*, pg. 763
AXFLOW LDA.—See Axel Johnson Gruppen AB; *Int'l*, pg. 763
AXFLOW SA—See Axel Johnson Gruppen AB; *Int'l*, pg. 763
B27, LLC—See DXP Enterprises, Inc.; *U.S. Public*, pg. 697
BAKERCORP B.V.—See United Rentals, Inc.; *U.S. Public*, pg. 2235
BAKERCORP INTERNATIONAL HOLDINGS, INC.—See United Rentals, Inc.; *U.S. Public*, pg. 2235
BANDAK GROUP—See Herkules Capital AS; *Int'l*, pg. 3362
BANJO CORPORATION—See IDEX Corp; *U.S. Public*, pg. 1089
BENNETT PUMP COMPANY—See Hines Corporation; *U.S. Private*, pg. 1949
BERG COMPANY, LLC.; *U.S. Private*, pg. 530
BEST EQUIPMENT SERVICE & SALES COMPANY, LLC—See DXP Enterprises, Inc.; *U.S. Public*, pg. 697
BEST INSTRUMENTS CO., LTD.—See A&D Co., Ltd.; *Int'l*, pg. 19
BIJUR LUBRICATING CORPORATION—See Summa Holdings, Inc.; *U.S. Private*, pg. 3852
BLACK HORSE LLC—See Caterpillar, Inc.; *U.S. Public*, pg. 449
BOBRUISK MACHINE BUILDING PLANT OJSC—See HMS Hydraulic Machines & Systems Group plc; *Int'l*, pg. 3432
BOMBAS BORNEMANN S.R.L.—See ITT Inc.; *U.S. Public*, pg. 1177
BOMBAS GOULDS DE MEXICO S. DE R.L. DE C.V.—See ITT Inc.; *U.S. Public*, pg. 1177
BORNEMANN EXZENTERSCHNECKENPUMPEN GMBH—See ITT Inc.; *U.S. Public*, pg. 1177
BORNEMANN INC.—See ITT Inc.; *U.S. Public*, pg. 1177
BORNEMANN MIDDLE EAST FZE—See ITT Inc.; *U.S. Public*, pg. 1177
BORNEMANN PUMPS ASIA PTE. LTD.—See ITT Inc.; *U.S. Public*, pg. 1177
BORNEMANN PUMPS & SYSTEMS CO. LTD—See ITT Inc.; *U.S. Public*, pg. 1177
BORNEMANN S.A. DE C.V.—See ITT Inc.; *U.S. Public*, pg. 1177
BRAN & LUEBBE GMBH—See SPX Technologies, Inc.; *U.S. Public*, pg. 1920
BRITVIC AQUA LIBRA CO LIMITED—See Britvic plc; *Int'l*, pg. 1171
BUFFALO PUMPS, INC.—See Ampco-Pittsburgh Corporation; *U.S. Public*, pg. 126
BURCKHARDT COMPRESSION (BRASIL) LTDA.—See Burckhardt Compression Holding AG; *Int'l*, pg. 1220
BURCKHARDT COMPRESSION (FRANCE) S.A.S—See Burckhardt Compression Holding AG; *Int'l*, pg. 1220
BUSCH GVT LTD.—See Dr. Ing. K. Busch GmbH; *Int'l*, pg. 2192
CAT PUMPS DEUTSCHLAND GMBH—See Diversified Dynamics Corporation; *U.S. Private*, pg. 1242
CAT PUMPS-INTERNATIONAL DIVISION—See Diversified Dynamics Corporation; *U.S. Private*, pg. 1242
CAT PUMPS (UK) LTD.—See Diversified Dynamics Corporation; *U.S. Private*, pg. 1242
CENLUB INDUSTRIES LTD. - FARIDABAD PLANT - I—See Cenlub Industries Ltd.; *Int'l*, pg. 1401
CHAMPIONX OILFIELD SOLUTIONS NIGERIA LIMITED—See ChampionX Corporation; *U.S. Public*, pg. 478
CHONGQING PUMP INDUSTRY CO., LTD.—See Chongqing Machinery & Electronics Holding (Group) Co., Ltd.; *Int'l*, pg. 1580
CIRCOR NAVAL SOLUTIONS, LLC—See KKR & Co. Inc.; *U.S. Public*, pg. 1242
CLAUDE LAVAL CORPORATION—See Lindsay Corporation; *U.S. Public*, pg. 1319
CLYDE PUMPS INDIA PVT LIMITED—See Lone Star Funds; *U.S. Private*, pg. 2485
CLYDE PUMPS UNION CANADA LIMITED—See Lone Star Funds; *U.S. Private*, pg. 2485
CLYDE UNION INC.—See Lone Star Funds; *U.S. Private*, pg. 2485
CLYDE UNION LTD—See Lone Star Funds; *U.S. Private*, pg. 2485
CLYDE UNION S.A.S.—See Lone Star Funds; *U.S. Private*, pg. 2485
COFFIN TURBO PUMP INC.; *U.S. Private*, pg. 961
COMERCIALIZADORA DE ELECTRODOS VENEZUELA

COMELVEN C.A.—See Enovis Corporation; *U.S. Public,* pg. 772
COMET S.P.A.—See Emak S.p.A.; *Int'l,* pg. 2373
COMET USA, INC.—See Emak S.p.A.; *Int'l,* pg. 2373
CON FORMS—See Construction Forms, Inc.; *U.S. Private,* pg. 1023
COOPER ALLOY CORPORATION; *U.S. Private,* pg. 1040
COORSTEK, INC. - COORSTEK NEW MILLS FACILITY—See CoorsTek, Inc.; *U.S. Private,* pg. 1043
CORNELIUS, INC.—See Berkshire Hathaway Inc.; *U.S. Public,* pg. 308
CORNELL PUMP COMPANY—See Roper Technologies, Inc.; *U.S. Public,* pg. 1811
CORPORACION EG S.A.; *Int'l,* pg. 1803
CRANE FLUID HANDLING—See Crane NXT, Co.; *U.S. Public,* pg. 590
CRANE PUMPS AND SYSTEMS CANADA, INC.—See Crane NXT, Co.; *U.S. Public,* pg. 590
CRANE PUMPS & SYSTEMS INC.—See Crane NXT, Co.; *U.S. Public,* pg. 590
CRYSTAL MOUNTAIN PRODUCTS LTD.—See Epsilon Healthcare Ltd.; *Int'l,* pg. 2466
DAIKIN SWEDEN A.B.—See Daikin Industries, Ltd.; *Int'l,* pg. 1935
DANFOSS POWER SOLUTIONS S.R.L.—See Danfoss A/S; *Int'l,* pg. 1960
DAVEY PRODUCTS NZ LIMITED—See Amotiv Limited; *Int'l,* pg. 431
DAVEY PRODUCTS PTY. LTD.—See Amotiv Limited; *Int'l,* pg. 431
DAVID BROWN GEAR SYSTEMS LIMITED—See Clyde Blowers Capital IM LLP; *Int'l,* pg. 1665
DEAN PUMP—See CECO Environmental Corp.; *U.S. Public,* pg. 464
DICALITE HOLDINGS INC.—See RGP Holding, Inc.; *U.S. Private,* pg. 3420
DISPENDIX GMBH—See BICO Group AB; *Int'l,* pg. 1019
DISPENSE SYSTEMS INTERNATIONAL—See Aalberts N.V.; *Int'l,* pg. 34
DIXON PUMPS, INC.—See Madison Dearborn Partners, LLC; *U.S. Private,* pg. 2542
DKM—See Groupe Legris Industries; *Int'l,* pg. 3106
DOSAGE 2000 S.A.R.L.—See Nordson Corporation; *U.S. Public,* pg. 1532
DOVER ENERGY AUTOMATION, LLC—See Dover Corporation; *U.S. Public,* pg. 679
DOVER FUELING SOLUTIONS UK LIMITED—See Dover Corporation; *U.S. Public,* pg. 680
DRESCHER ASOCIADOS SRL—See Atlas Copco AB; *Int'l,* pg. 683
DSI GETRANKEARMATUREN GMBH & CO. KG—See Aalberts N.V.; *Int'l,* pg. 34
DYNAMATIC LIMITED UK—See Dynamatic Technologies Limited; *Int'l,* pg. 2239
DYNAMATIC TECHNOLOGIES LIMITED; *Int'l,* pg. 2239
EBARA-DENSAN TAIWAN MANUFACTURING CO., LTD.—See Ebara Corporation; *Int'l,* pg. 2283
EBARA ESPANA BOMBAS S.A.—See Ebara Corporation; *Int'l,* pg. 2283
EBARA FLUID MACHINERY KOREA CO., LTD.—See Ebara Corporation; *Int'l,* pg. 2283
EBARA HAI DUONG COMPANY LTD.—See Ebara Corporation; *Int'l,* pg. 2283
EBARA INDUSTRIAS MECANICAS E COMERCIO LTDA.—See Ebara Corporation; *Int'l,* pg. 2283
EBARA INTERNATIONAL CORP.—See Ebara Corporation; *Int'l,* pg. 2283
EBARA MACHINERY INDIA PRIVATE LIMITED—See Ebara Corporation; *Int'l,* pg. 2283
EBARA MACHINERY ZIBO CO., LTD.—See Ebara Corporation; *Int'l,* pg. 2283
EBARA PUMPS AUSTRALIA PTY. LTD.—See Ebara Corporation; *Int'l,* pg. 2283
EBARA PUMPS EUROPE S.P.A.—See Ebara Corporation; *Int'l,* pg. 2283
EBARA PUMPS MALAYSIA SDN. BHD.—See Ebara Corporation; *Int'l,* pg. 2283
EBARA PUMPS MIDDLE EAST FZE—See Ebara Corporation; *Int'l,* pg. 2283
EBARA VIETNAM PUMP COMPANY LIMITED—See Ebara Corporation; *Int'l,* pg. 2283
EBARA YOSHIKURA HYDRO-TECH CO., LTD.—See Ebara Corporation; *Int'l,* pg. 2283
EBS-RAY PUMPS PTY. LTD.—See Dover Corporation; *U.S. Public,* pg. 681
E-CARBON FAR EAST LTD.—See Westinghouse Air Brake Technologies Corporation; *U.S. Public,* pg. 2357
ECOTECH MARINE; *U.S. Private,* pg. 1330
ENERGY STEEL AND SUPPLY COMPANY—See Avingtrans plc; *Int'l,* pg. 743
ENGINEERED FLUID INC.; *U.S. Private,* pg. 1398
ENGINEERED MACHINERY, INC.—See Clayton, Dubilier & Rice, LLC; *U.S. Private,* pg. 926
ENOVIS CORPORATION; *U.S. Public,* pg. 770
ESAB AKTIENGESELLSCHAFT—See Enovis Corporation; *U.S. Public,* pg. 770
ESAB PERSTORP AB—See Enovis Corporation; *U.S. Public,* pg. 771

ESAB RUSSIA BV—See Enovis Corporation; *U.S. Public,* pg. 771
ESTABROOK CORPORATION; *U.S. Private,* pg. 1428
EVERDIGM AMERICA INC.—See Hyundai Everdigm Corp; *Int'l,* pg. 3556
EXTREME PUMP SOLUTIONS—See Divergent Energy Services Corp.; *Int'l,* pg. 2137
FAIRMOUNT AUTOMATION, INC.—See Enovis Corporation; *U.S. Public,* pg. 772
FAIVELEY TRANSPORT RAIL TECHNOLOGIES INDIA LIMITED—See Westinghouse Air Brake Technologies Corporation; *U.S. Public,* pg. 2357
FEDERAL PUMP CORP.—See Bain Capital, LP; *U.S. Private,* pg. 432
FEILONG AUTO COMPONENTS CO., LTD.; *Int'l,* pg. 2632
FINDER POMPE S.P.A.—See Dover Corporation; *U.S. Public,* pg. 681
FINDER POMPES—See Dover Corporation; *U.S. Public,* pg. 681
FINISH THOMPSON, INC.; *U.S. Private,* pg. 1510
FLINT HYDROSTATICS, INC.—See Clearlake Capital Group, L.P.; *U.S. Private,* pg. 933
FLINT & WALLING INC.—See Zoeller Co.; *U.S. Private,* pg. 4607
FLOWSERVE (BELGIUM) BVBA—See Flowserve Corporation; *U.S. Public,* pg. 855
FLOWSERVE CORP.—See Flowserve Corporation; *U.S. Public,* pg. 855
FLOWSERVE CORP.—See Flowserve Corporation; *U.S. Public,* pg. 855
FLOWSERVE CORP.—See Flowserve Corporation; *U.S. Public,* pg. 856
FLOWSERVE CORP.—See Flowserve Corporation; *U.S. Public,* pg. 856
FLOWSERVE CORP.—See Flowserve Corporation; *U.S. Public,* pg. 856
FLOWSERVE DORTMUND VERWALTUNGS GMBH—See Flowserve Corporation; *U.S. Public,* pg. 856
FLOWSERVE HAMBURG GMBH—See Flowserve Corporation; *U.S. Public,* pg. 856
FLOWSERVE LTDA.—See Flowserve Corporation; *U.S. Public,* pg. 856
FLOWSERVE LTD.—See Flowserve Corporation; *U.S. Public,* pg. 856
FLOWSERVE NIIGATA WORTHINGTON COMPANY LTD.—See Flowserve Corporation; *U.S. Public,* pg. 856
FLOWSERVE PUMPS LIMITED—See Flowserve Corporation; *U.S. Public,* pg. 856
FLOWSERVE S.A. DE C.V.—See Flowserve Corporation; *U.S. Public,* pg. 856
FLOWSERVE S.A.—See Flowserve Corporation; *U.S. Public,* pg. 856
FLOWSERVE S. DE R.L. DE C.V.—See Flowserve Corporation; *U.S. Public,* pg. 855
FLOWSERVE SIHI AUSTRIA GMBH—See Flowserve Corporation; *U.S. Public,* pg. 856
FLOWSERVE SIHI CZ S.R.O.—See Flowserve Corporation; *U.S. Public,* pg. 855
FLOWSERVE SIHI (FRANCE) SAS—See Flowserve Corporation; *U.S. Public,* pg. 856
FLOWSERVE SIHI GERMANY GMBH—See Flowserve Corporation; *U.S. Public,* pg. 855
FLOWSERVE SIHI (ITALY) S.R.L.—See Flowserve Corporation; *U.S. Public,* pg. 855
FLOWSERVE SIHI (SPAIN) S.L.—See Flowserve Corporation; *U.S. Public,* pg. 855
FLOWSERVE S.P.A.—See Flowserve Corporation; *U.S. Public,* pg. 856
FLOWSERVE (THAILAND) LTD.—See Flowserve Corporation; *U.S. Public,* pg. 855
FLOWSERVE WORTHINGTON S.R.L.—See Flowserve Corporation; *U.S. Public,* pg. 856
FLOWTRONEX PSI, LLC—See Motor Controls, Inc.; *U.S. Private,* pg. 2797
FLSMIDTH KREBS AFRICA (PTY.) LTD.—See FLSmidth & Co. A/S; *Int'l,* pg. 2711
FLSMIDTH KREBS CHILE LIMITADA—See FLSmidth & Co. A/S; *Int'l,* pg. 2710
FLUID EQUIPMENT DEVELOPMENT COMPANY LLC; *U.S. Private,* pg. 1552
FLUID MANAGEMENT, INC.—See IDEX Corp; *U.S. Public,* pg. 1090
FLUITRON, INC.—See Ara Partners Group; *U.S. Private,* pg. 306
FRAMO AS—See Alfa Laval AB; *Int'l,* pg. 311
FRAMO DO BRASIL LTDA.—See Alfa Laval AB; *Int'l,* pg. 312
FRAMO FLATEY AS—See Alfa Laval AB; *Int'l,* pg. 311
FRAMO FLATOY AS—See Alfa Laval AB; *Int'l,* pg. 312
FRAMO FUSA AS—See Alfa Laval AB; *Int'l,* pg. 311
FRAMO HOLSNEY AS—See Alfa Laval AB; *Int'l,* pg. 311
FRAMO HOUSTON INC.—See Alfa Laval AB; *Int'l,* pg. 311
FRAMO KOREA LTD.—See Alfa Laval AB; *Int'l,* pg. 311
FRAMO NEDERLAND BV—See Alfa Laval AB; *Int'l,* pg. 311
FRAMO NIPPON KK—See Alfa Laval AB; *Int'l,* pg. 311
FRAMO SERVICES AS—See Alfa Laval AB; *Int'l,* pg. 311
FRAMO SHANGHAI AS—See Alfa Laval AB; *Int'l,* pg. 312
FRAMO SINGAPORE PTE. LTD.—See Alfa Laval AB; *Int'l,* pg. 312

FRANKLIN ELECTRIC GERMANY HOLDING GMBH—See Franklin Electric Co., Inc.; *U.S. Public,* pg. 878
FRANKLIN ELECTRIC (SEA) PTY. LTD.—See Franklin Electric Co., Inc.; *U.S. Public,* pg. 878
FRANKLIN ELECTRIC (SUZHOU) CO., LTD.—See Franklin Electric Co., Inc.; *U.S. Public,* pg. 878
FRANKLIN FUELING SYSTEMS—See Franklin Electric Co., Inc.; *U.S. Public,* pg. 878
FRANZ SUTER GMBH-PUMPEN UND SYSTEME; *Int'l,* pg. 2763
FREE FLOW, INC.; *U.S. Public,* pg. 884
FRISTAM PUMPEN F. STAMP GMBH & CO. KG; *Int'l,* pg. 2793
FRISTAM PUMPS USA, LIMITED PARTNERSHIP—See FRISTAM Pumpen F. Stamp GmbH & Co. KG; *Int'l,* pg. 2793
FURMANITE INTERNATIONAL LTD. - IPSCO—See Team, Inc.; *U.S. Public,* pg. 1987
FURUKAWA INDUSTRIAL MACHINERY SYSTEMS CO., LTD. - OYAMA UNIT—See Furukawa Co., Ltd.; *Int'l,* pg. 2847
FURUKAWA INDUSTRIAL MACHINERY SYSTEMS CO., LTD.—See Furukawa Co., Ltd.; *Int'l,* pg. 2847
FURUKAWA INDUSTRIAL MACHINERY SYSTEMS CO., LTD. - TOCHIGI UNIT—See Furukawa Co., Ltd.; *Int'l,* pg. 2847
FYBROC—See CECO Environmental Corp.; *U.S. Public,* pg. 464
G.A. KIESEL GMBH; *Int'l,* pg. 2865
GARDNER DENVER OBERDORFER PUMPS, INC.—See Ingersoll Rand Inc.; *U.S. Public,* pg. 1119
GARDNER DENVER WATER JETTING SYSTEMS, INC.—See Ingersoll Rand Inc.; *U.S. Public,* pg. 1119
GASBOY INTERNATIONAL, INC.—See Danaher Corporation; *U.S. Public,* pg. 627
GEA NIRO SOAVI BRAZIL—See GEA Group Aktiengesellschaft; *Int'l,* pg. 2901
GEA WIEGAND GMBH—See GEA Group Aktiengesellschaft; *Int'l,* pg. 2903
GEA WIEGAND (SCHWEIZ) GMBH—See GEA Group Aktiengesellschaft; *Int'l,* pg. 2903
GEIGER PUMP & EQUIPMENT COMPANY—See AEA Investors LP; *U.S. Private,* pg. 113
GEMA SWITZERLAND AG—See Graco, Inc.; *U.S. Public,* pg. 953
GEOTECHNICAL INSTRUMENTS (U.K.) LIMITED—See Graco, Inc.; *U.S. Public,* pg. 953
GIANT INDUSTRIES, INC.; *U.S. Private,* pg. 1695
GILBARCO GMBH & CO. KG—See Vontier Corporation; *U.S. Public,* pg. 2308
GILBARCO INC.—See Vontier Corporation; *U.S. Public,* pg. 2308
GILBARCO LATIN AMERICA ANDINA LTDA.—See Vontier Corporation; *U.S. Public,* pg. 2309
GILBARCO LATIN AMERICA SRL—See Vontier Corporation; *U.S. Public,* pg. 2309
GILBARCO VEEDER-ROOT AB—See Vontier Corporation; *U.S. Public,* pg. 2309
GILBARCO VEEDER-ROOT ASIA PTE. LTD.—See Vontier Corporation; *U.S. Public,* pg. 2309
GILBARCO VEEDER-ROOT AS—See Vontier Corporation; *U.S. Public,* pg. 2309
GILBARCO VEEDER-ROOT ITALY—See Vontier Corporation; *U.S. Public,* pg. 2309
GILBARCO VEEDER-ROOT OU—See Vontier Corporation; *U.S. Public,* pg. 2309
GILBARCO VEEDER ROOT SPOLKA Z.O.O.—See Vontier Corporation; *U.S. Public,* pg. 2309
GILBARCO VEEDER ROOT S.R.L.—See Vontier Corporation; *U.S. Public,* pg. 2309
GILBARCO VEEDER-ROOT UK—See Vontier Corporation; *U.S. Public,* pg. 2309
GKN SINTER METALS DE ARGENTINA S.A.—See Concentric AB; *Int'l,* pg. 1764
GOODWIN INDUSTRIA E COMERCIO DE VALVULAS DE RETENCAO E BOMBAS SUBMERSAS LTDA.—See Goodwin PLC; *Int'l,* pg. 3041
GOODWIN INTERNATIONAL LTD.—See Goodwin PLC; *Int'l,* pg. 3041
GOODWIN (SHANXI) PUMP CO., LTD.—See Goodwin PLC; *Int'l,* pg. 3041
THE GORMAN-RUPP COMPANY; *U.S. Public,* pg. 2085
GORMAN-RUPP EUROPE B.V.—See The Gorman-Rupp Company; *U.S. Public,* pg. 2085
GORMAN-RUPP INDUSTRIES—See The Gorman-Rupp Company; *U.S. Public,* pg. 2085
GORMAN-RUPP OF CANADA LIMITED—See The Gorman-Rupp Company; *U.S. Public,* pg. 2085
GOULDS PUMPS CO. LTD.—See ITT Inc.; *U.S. Public,* pg. 1177
GOULDS PUMPS, INC. - LOS ANGELES—See ITT Inc.; *U.S. Public,* pg. 1177
GOULDS PUMPS, INC. - MEMPHIS—See ITT Inc.; *U.S. Public,* pg. 1177
GOULDS PUMPS, INC.—See ITT Inc.; *U.S. Public,* pg. 1177
GOULDS PUMPS (NY), INC.—See ITT Inc.; *U.S. Public,* pg. 1177

N.A.I.C.S. INDEX

333914 — MEASURING, DISPENSI...

GOULDS PUMPS U.K. LTD.—See ITT Inc.; *U.S. Public*, pg. 1177
GOULDS WATER TECHNOLOGY - AUBURN—See Xylem Inc.; *U.S. Public*, pg. 2396
GOULDS WATER TECHNOLOGY - LUBBOCK—See Xylem Inc.; *U.S. Public*, pg. 2396
GOULDS WATER TECHNOLOGY PHILIPPINES, INC.—See Xylem Inc.; *U.S. Public*, pg. 2396
GOULDS WATER TECHNOLOGY - SENECA FALLS—See Xylem Inc.; *U.S. Public*, pg. 2395
GOULDS WATER TECHNOLOGY - SLATON—See Xylem Inc.; *U.S. Public*, pg. 2396
GRACO, INC.; *U.S. Public*, pg. 952
GRAYMILLS CORPORATION; *U.S. Private*, pg. 1761
GREAT PLAINS INDUSTRIES, INC.—See Great Plains Ventures, Inc.; *U.S. Private*, pg. 1767
GRINDEX AB—See Xylem Inc.; *U.S. Public*, pg. 2396
GRINDEX PUMPS LLC—See Xylem Inc.; *U.S. Public*, pg. 2396
GROENEVELD UK LIMITED—See The Timken Company; *U.S. Public*, pg. 2132
GUANGDONG LINGXIAO PUMP INDUSTRY CO., LTD.; *Int'l*, pg. 3158
GUSHER PUMPS, INC.—See Ruthman Pump & Engineering Inc.; *U.S. Private*, pg. 3508
GUSMER SUDAMERICA S.A.—See Graco, Inc.; *U.S. Public*, pg. 953
GWE BUDAFILTER KFT.—See BAUER Aktiengesellschaft; *Int'l*, pg. 893
HADER INDUSTRIES INC.; *U.S. Private*, pg. 1839
HAI DUONG PUMP MANUFACTURING JOINT STOCK COMPANY; *Int'l*, pg. 3208
HALE PRODUCTS INC.—See IDEX Corp; *U.S. Public*, pg. 1090
HANYU GROUP JOINT-STOCK CO., LTD.; *Int'l*, pg. 3267
HASKEL EUROPE LTD. - ABERDEEN—See BC Partners LLP; *Int'l*, pg. 922
HASKEL EUROPE LTD. - ABERDEEN—See The Carlyle Group Inc.; *U.S. Public*, pg. 2044
HASKEL EUROPE LTD.—See BC Partners LLP; *Int'l*, pg. 922
HASKEL EUROPE LTD.—See The Carlyle Group Inc.; *U.S. Public*, pg. 2044
HASKEL INTERNATIONAL, LLC—See BC Partners LLP; *Int'l*, pg. 922
HASKEL INTERNATIONAL, LLC—See The Carlyle Group Inc.; *U.S. Public*, pg. 2044
HASKEL SISTEMAS DE FLUIDOS ESPANA, S.R.L.—See BC Partners LLP; *Int'l*, pg. 922
HASKEL SISTEMAS DE FLUIDOS ESPANA, S.R.L.—See The Carlyle Group Inc.; *U.S. Public*, pg. 2044
HAYWARD GORDON LTD—See Ebara Corporation; *Int'l*, pg. 2284
HIBAR CHINA CO. LTD.—See Tesla, Inc.; *U.S. Public*, pg. 2021
HIBAR SYSTEMS EUROPE GMBH—See Tesla, Inc.; *U.S. Public*, pg. 2021
HIBAR SYSTEMS LIMITED—See Tesla, Inc.; *U.S. Public*, pg. 2021
HITACHI PUMP MANUFACTURE (WUXI) CO., LTD.—See Hitachi, Ltd.; *Int'l*, pg. 3420
HMS HYDRAULIC MACHINES & SYSTEMS GROUP PLC; *Int'l*, pg. 3432
HMS LIVHYDROMASH JSC—See HMS Hydraulic Machines & Systems Group plc; *Int'l*, pg. 3432
HOERBIGER AUTOMATISIERUNGSTECHNIK GMBH—See Hoerbiger Holding AG; *Int'l*, pg. 3440
HOLLAND PUMP MFG., INC.—See Arcus Infrastructure Partners LLP; *Int'l*, pg. 553
HOMA PUMPENFABRIK GMBH; *Int'l*, pg. 3454
HOUTTUIN B.V.—See KKR & Co. Inc.; *U.S. Public*, pg. 1242
HOWDEN GROUP BV—See Chart Industries, Inc.; *U.S. Public*, pg. 482
HUNAN JIALI MACHINERY CO., LTD—See Hunan Oil Pump Co., Ltd.; *Int'l*, pg. 3533
HYDROMASHSERVICE JSC—See HMS Hydraulic Machines & Systems Group plc; *Int'l*, pg. 3432
HYDRONOVA AUSTRALIA-NZ PTY LTD—See Dover Corporation; *U.S. Public*, pg. 681
HYDRO NOVA EUROPE, LTD.—See Dover Corporation; *U.S. Public*, pg. 681
HYDRO SERVICE A/S—See Addtech AB; *Int'l*, pg. 133
HYDRO SYSTEMS EUROPE, LTD.—See Dover Corporation; *U.S. Public*, pg. 681
HYOSUNG EBARA CO., LTD.—See Ebara Corporation; *Int'l*, pg. 2284
HYOSUNG EBARA CO., LTD.—See Flowserve Corporation; *U.S. Public*, pg. 856
HYOSUNG EBARA CO., LTD.—See Hyosung Corporation; *Int'l*, pg. 3551
HYOSUNG GOODSPRINGS, INC.—See Hyosung Advanced Materials Co., Ltd.; *Int'l*, pg. 3550
HYTEC AUTOMOTIVE—See DeBartolo Holdings, LLC; *U.S. Private*, pg. 1186
IDEX ASIA PACIFIC PTE. LTD.—See IDEX Corp; *U.S. Public*, pg. 1090
IDEX FLUID & METERING PVT. LTD.—See IDEX Corp; *U.S. Public*, pg. 1090

IDEX HEALTH & SCIENCE GMBH—See IDEX Corp; *U.S. Public*, pg. 1092
IDEX INDIA PRIVATE LTD.—See IDEX Corp; *U.S. Public*, pg. 1091
IMO INDUSTRIES INC.—See KKR & Co. Inc.; *U.S. Public*, pg. 1242
IMPO MOTOR POMPA SANAYI VE TICARET A.S.—See Franklin Electric Co., Inc.; *U.S. Public*, pg. 878
INDUSTRIAS ROTOR PUMP S.A.—See Franklin Electric Co., Inc.; *U.S. Public*, pg. 878
INGERSOLL-RAND (AUSTRALIA) LTD.—See Ingersoll Rand Inc.; *U.S. Public*, pg. 1121
INTEGRATED DESIGNS L.P.—See Roper Technologies, Inc.; *U.S. Public*, pg. 1812
INTEGRATED DISPENSE SOLUTIONS, LLC—See Carlisle Companies Incorporated; *U.S. Public*, pg. 436
ITT BOMBAS GOULDS DO BRASIL LTDA.—See ITT Inc.; *U.S. Public*, pg. 1177
ITT CORP. - SANTA ANA—See ITT Inc.; *U.S. Public*, pg. 1178
ITT GOULDS PUMPS COLUMBIA S.A.S.—See ITT Inc.; *U.S. Public*, pg. 1178
ITT INDUSTRIES SPAIN SL—See ITT Inc.; *U.S. Public*, pg. 1178
ITT RHEINHUTTE BENELUX B.V.—See ITT Inc.; *U.S. Public*, pg. 1178
ITT RHEINHUTTE PUMPEN CO., LTD.—See ITT Inc.; *U.S. Public*, pg. 1178
ITT RHEINHUTTE PUMPEN GMBH—See ITT Inc.; *U.S. Public*, pg. 1178
ITUBOMBAS LOCACAO COMERCIO IMPORTACAO E EXPORTACAO LTDA.—See Atlas Copco AB; *Int'l*, pg. 683
ITW DYNATEC G.M.B.H.—See Illinois Tool Works Inc.; *U.S. Public*, pg. 1105
ITW INDUSTRIAL FINISHING—See Illinois Tool Works Inc.; *U.S. Public*, pg. 1106
JABSCO MARINE ITALIA S.R.L.—See Xylem Inc.; *U.S. Public*, pg. 2396
JAMES E. WATSON & CO.—See Atlas Copco AB; *Int'l*, pg. 683
KNIGHT CANADA LIMITED—See IDEX Corp; *U.S. Public*, pg. 1091
KYOSAN DENKI CO., LTD.—See Denso Corporation; *Int'l*, pg. 2032
LAING THERMOTECH, INC.—See Xylem Inc.; *U.S. Public*, pg. 2396
LAWRENCE PUMPS, INC.—See Flowserve Corporation; *U.S. Public*, pg. 856
LAWRENCE PUMPS (SHANGHAI) COMPANY LIMITED—See Flowserve Corporation; *U.S. Public*, pg. 856
LIBERTY PUMPS; *U.S. Private*, pg. 2447
LINDBERG/MPH—See Resilience Capital Partners, LLC; *U.S. Private*, pg. 3405
LIVNYNASOS JSC—See HMS Hydraulic Machines & Systems Group plc; *Int'l*, pg. 3432
LIYANG SIFANG STAINLESS STEEL PRODUCTS CO., LTD—See Alfa Laval AB; *Int'l*, pg. 308
LOWARA GMBH—See Xylem Inc.; *U.S. Public*, pg. 2396
LOWARA S.R.L.—See Xylem Inc.; *U.S. Public*, pg. 2396
LUFKIN ARGENTINA, S.A.—See KPS Capital Partners, LP; *U.S. Private*, pg. 2348
LUFKIN INDUSTRIES - CALGARY—See KPS Capital Partners, LP; *U.S. Private*, pg. 2348
LUFKIN INDUSTRIES SRL—See KPS Capital Partners, LP; *U.S. Private*, pg. 2348
MAAG AUTOMATIK GMBH—See Dover Corporation; *U.S. Public*, pg. 681
MAAG PUMP SYSTEMS AG—See Dover Corporation; *U.S. Public*, pg. 681
MAAG PUMP SYSTEMS GMBH—See Dover Corporation; *U.S. Public*, pg. 682
MARCH MANUFACTURING INC.; *U.S. Private*, pg. 2571
MCNALLY INDUSTRIES, LLC; *U.S. Private*, pg. 2643
MEFIAG USA—See CECO Environmental Corp.; *U.S. Public*, pg. 464
METROPOLITAN INDUSTRIES, INC.; *U.S. Private*, pg. 2688
MICROPUMP, INC.—See IDEX Corp; *U.S. Public*, pg. 1091
MILTON ROY EUROPE—See BC Partners LLP; *Int'l*, pg. 922
MILTON ROY EUROPE—See The Carlyle Group Inc.; *U.S. Public*, pg. 2044
MILTON ROY - HARTELL DIVISION—See BC Partners LLP; *Int'l*, pg. 922
MILTON ROY - HARTELL DIVISION—See The Carlyle Group Inc.; *U.S. Public*, pg. 2044
MILTON ROY LIQUID METRONICS INCORPORATED—See BC Partners LLP; *Int'l*, pg. 922
MILTON ROY LIQUID METRONICS INCORPORATED—See The Carlyle Group Inc.; *U.S. Public*, pg. 2044
MILTON ROY, LLC—See BC Partners LLP; *Int'l*, pg. 922
MILTON ROY, LLC—See The Carlyle Group Inc.; *U.S. Public*, pg. 2044
MONO PUMPS LIMITED—See NOV, Inc.; *U.S. Public*, pg. 1545

MONO PUMPS (MANUFACTURING) LIMITED—See NOV, Inc.; *U.S. Public*, pg. 1545
MOUVEX SASU—See Dover Corporation; *U.S. Public*, pg. 682
MOYNO, INC.—See NOV, Inc.; *U.S. Public*, pg. 1545
MP PUMPS, INC.—See KKR & Co. Inc.; *U.S. Public*, pg. 1239
MWI CORPORATION; *U.S. Private*, pg. 2822
M.W. SMITH EQUIPMENT, INC.—See DXP Enterprises, Inc.; *U.S. Public*, pg. 697
NAF AB—See ANDRITZ AG; *Int'l*, pg. 452
NANCHONG THREE-CIRCLE ELECTRONICS CO., LTD.—See Chaozhou Three-Circle Group Co., Ltd.; *Int'l*, pg. 1447
NASOSENERGOMASH SUMY JSC—See HMS Hydraulic Machines & Systems Group plc; *Int'l*, pg. 3432
NATIONAL OILWELL VARCO MSW S.A.—See NOV, Inc.; *U.S. Public*, pg. 1546
NATIONAL PROCESS EQUIPMENT, INC.—See DXP Enterprises, Inc.; *U.S. Public*, pg. 697
NATIONAL PUMP COMPANY - LUBBOCK—See The Gorman-Rupp Company; *U.S. Public*, pg. 2085
NATIONAL PUMP COMPANY—See The Gorman-Rupp Company; *U.S. Public*, pg. 2085
NETZSCH ARGENTINA S. A.—See Erich Netzsch GmbH & Co. Holding KG; *Int'l*, pg. 2491
NETZSCH ASIA PACIFIC PTE LTD.—See Erich Netzsch GmbH & Co. Holding KG; *Int'l*, pg. 2491
NETZSCH CESKA REPUBLIKA S.R.O.—See Erich Netzsch GmbH & Co. Holding KG; *Int'l*, pg. 2493
NETZSCH DO BRASIL LTDA.—See Erich Netzsch GmbH & Co. Holding KG; *Int'l*, pg. 2492
NETZSCH ESPANA S.A.—See Erich Netzsch GmbH & Co. Holding KG; *Int'l*, pg. 2491
NETZSCH-FEINMAHLTECHNIK GMBH—See Erich Netzsch GmbH & Co. Holding KG; *Int'l*, pg. 2492
NETZSCH FRERES S.A.R.L.—See Erich Netzsch GmbH & Co. Holding KG; *Int'l*, pg. 2492
NETZSCH GERATEBAU GMBH—See Erich Netzsch GmbH & Co. Holding KG; *Int'l*, pg. 2492
NETZSCH INSTRUMENTS SP.Z.O.O.—See Erich Netzsch GmbH & Co. Holding KG; *Int'l*, pg. 2492
NETZSCH KOREA CO. LTD—See Erich Netzsch GmbH & Co. Holding KG; *Int'l*, pg. 2492
NETZSCH LANZHOU PUMPS CO. LTD.—See Erich Netzsch GmbH & Co. Holding KG; *Int'l*, pg. 2492
NETZSCH MALAYSIA SDN.BHD—See Erich Netzsch GmbH & Co. Holding KG; *Int'l*, pg. 2492
NETZSCH MASTERMIX LTD.—See Erich Netzsch GmbH & Co. Holding KG; *Int'l*, pg. 2492
NETZSCH MILANTECNICA S.R.L.—See Erich Netzsch GmbH & Co. Holding KG; *Int'l*, pg. 2492
NETZSCH-OILFIELD PRODUCTS GMBH—See Erich Netzsch GmbH & Co. Holding KG; *Int'l*, pg. 2492
NETZSCH PUMPS NORTH AMERICA, LLC—See Erich Netzsch GmbH & Co. Holding KG; *Int'l*, pg. 2492
NETZSCH (SHANGHAI) MACHINERY AND INSTRUMENTS CO. LTD.—See Erich Netzsch GmbH & Co. Holding KG; *Int'l*, pg. 2491
NETZSCH THAILAND LTD.—See Erich Netzsch GmbH & Co. Holding KG; *Int'l*, pg. 2492
NETZSCH TROCKENMAHLTECHNIK GMBH—See Erich Netzsch GmbH & Co. Holding KG; *Int'l*, pg. 2493
NETZSCH WERBE- UND SERVICE- GMBH—See Erich Netzsch GmbH & Co. Holding KG; *Int'l*, pg. 2492
NIZHNEVARTOVSKREMSERVIS CJSC—See HMS Hydraulic Machines & Systems Group plc; *Int'l*, pg. 3432
NORDSON SEALANT EQUIPMENT, INC.—See Nordson Corporation; *U.S. Public*, pg. 1533
NOVA-TECH INTERNATIONAL, INC.; *U.S. Private*, pg. 2966
NOV AUSTRALIA PTY LTD—See NOV, Inc.; *U.S. Public*, pg. 1545
OBL SRL—See IDEX Corp; *U.S. Public*, pg. 1091
OOO NETZSCH PUMPS RUS—See Erich Netzsch GmbH & Co. Holding KG; *Int'l*, pg. 2493
ORENCO SYSTEMS INC.; *U.S. Private*, pg. 3040
ORION INSTRUMENTS, LLC.—See AMETEK, Inc.; *U.S. Public*, pg. 121
PALMSTIERNA INTERNATIONAL AB—See Flowserve Corporation; *U.S. Public*, pg. 857
PARKER HANNIFIN PAN AMERICAN DIVISION—See Parker Hannifin Corporation; *U.S. Public*, pg. 1643
PATTERSON PUMP COMPANY—See The Gorman-Rupp Company; *U.S. Public*, pg. 2085
PATTERSON PUMP IRELAND LIMITED—See The Gorman-Rupp Company; *U.S. Public*, pg. 2085
PCM GROUP UK LTD—See Gevelot S.A.; *Int'l*, pg. 2954
PCM POMPES—See Gevelot S.A.; *Int'l*, pg. 2954
PCM PUMPS LTD.—See Gevelot S.A.; *Int'l*, pg. 2954
PCM TRADING (SHANGHAI) CO. LTD—See Gevelot S.A.; *Int'l*, pg. 2954
PENGUIN PUMPS, INC—See Finish Thompson, Inc.; *U.S. Private*, pg. 1510
PFEIFFER VACUUM BENELUX B.V.—See Dr. Ing. K. Busch GmbH; *Int'l*, pg. 2193
PFEIFFER VACUUM COMPONENTS & SOLUTIONS GMBH—See Dr. Ing. K. Busch GmbH; *Int'l*, pg. 2194

333914 — MEASURING, DISPENSI...

PFEIFFER VACUUM GMBH—See Dr. Ing. K. Busch GmbH; Int'l, pg. 2194
PFEIFFER VACUUM ROMANIA S.R.L.—See Dr. Ing. K. Busch GmbH; Int'l, pg. 2194
PFEIFFER VACUUM SAS—See Dr. Ing. K. Busch GmbH; Int'l, pg. 2194
PFEIFFER VACUUM TAIWAN CORPORATION LTD.—See Dr. Ing. K. Busch GmbH; Int'l, pg. 2193
PFEIFFER VACUUM TECHNOLOGY AG—See Dr. Ing. K. Busch GmbH; Int'l, pg. 2193
PIONEER PUMP LTD.—See Franklin Electric Co., Inc.; U.S. Public, pg. 879
PIONEER PUMP PTY. LTD.—See Franklin Electric Co., Inc.; U.S. Public, pg. 879
PMI OPERATING COMPANY, LTD.—See DXP Enterprises, Inc.; U.S. Public, pg. 697
POWER ASSOCIATES INTERNATIONAL, INC—See Crossplane Capital Management LP; U.S. Private, pg. 1107
PRODUCTION PUMP SYSTEMS, INC.—See DXP Enterprises, Inc.; U.S. Public, pg. 697
PSG GERMANY GMBH—See Dover Corporation; U.S. Public, pg. 682
P.T. EBARA INDONESIA—See Ebara Corporation; Int'l, pg. 2284
PT. EBARA TURBOMACHINERY SERVICES INDONESIA—See Ebara Corporation; Int'l, pg. 2284
PULSAFEEDER EUROPE B.V.—See IDEX Corp; U.S. Public, pg. 1091
PULSAFEEDER INC.—See IDEX Corp; U.S. Public, pg. 1091
PUMPER PARTS LLC—See IDEX Corp; U.S. Public, pg. 1092
PUMPMAN, LLC—See Bain Capital, LP; U.S. Private, pg. 432
PUMPNSEAL AUSTRALIA PTY LIMITED—See Diploma PLC; Int'l, pg. 2129
PUMP & POWER EQUIPMENT, LLC—See DXP Enterprises, Inc.; U.S. Public, pg. 698
PUMPS & MOTORS OF BELIZE LTD.—See Endress+Hauser (International) Holding AG; Int'l, pg. 2409
QED ENVIRONMENTAL SYSTEMS, INC.—See Graco, Inc.; U.S. Public, pg. 954
QUADNA INC.—See DXP Enterprises, Inc.; U.S. Public, pg. 698
QUINN PUMPS (CALIFORNIA) INC.—See KPS Capital Partners, LP; U.S. Private, pg. 2348
QUINN PUMPS CANADA LTD.—See KPS Capital Partners, LP; U.S. Private, pg. 2348
QUINN PUMPS INC.—See KPS Capital Partners, LP; U.S. Private, pg. 2348
REVERSO PUMPS, INC.—See Crawford United Corporation; U.S. Public, pg. 592
REWITEC GMBH—See Croda International plc; Int'l, pg. 1853
RICHTER-CHEMIE-TECHNIK GMBH—See IDEX Corp; U.S. Public, pg. 1091
RICHTER PUMPS AND VALVES INC.—See IDEX Corp; U.S. Public, pg. 1091
RMSPUMPTOOLS LIMITED—See ChampionX Corporation; U.S. Public, pg. 478
ROPER PUMP COMPANY—See Roper Technologies, Inc.; U.S. Public, pg. 1813
RUHRPUMPEN DO BRASIL IND. E COM DE BOMBAS HIDRAULICAS LTDA.—See Corporacion EG S.A.; Int'l, pg. 1803
RUHRPUMPEN GMBH—See Corporacion EG S.A.; Int'l, pg. 1803
RUHRPUMPEN, INC. - ORLAND PLANT—See Corporacion EG S.A.; Int'l, pg. 1803
RUHRPUMPEN INC.—See Corporacion EG S.A.; Int'l, pg. 1803
RUHRPUMPEN LIMITED—See Corporacion EG S.A.; Int'l, pg. 1803
RULE DIVISION—See Xylem Inc.; U.S. Public, pg. 2396
RUTHMAN PUMP & ENGINEERING INC.; U.S. Private, pg. 3508
SAUDI MECHANICAL INDUSTRIES CO.—See Arab Petroleum Investments Corporation; Int'l, pg. 531
SEAQUIST GENERAL PLASTICS—See AptarGroup, Inc.; U.S. Public, pg. 175
SENSUS SERVICES DEUTSCHLAND GMBH—See Xylem Inc.; U.S. Public, pg. 2395
SERFILCO INTERNATIONAL, LTD.—See SERFILCO, Ltd.; U.S. Private, pg. 3613
SHARPE MIXERS, INC.—See Ebara Corporation; Int'l, pg. 2284
SILGAN DISPENSING SYSTEMS BARCELONA, S.L.—See Silgan Holdings, Inc.; U.S. Public, pg. 1879
SILGAN DISPENSING SYSTEMS CANADA LTD.—See Silgan Holdings, Inc.; U.S. Public, pg. 1879
SILGAN DISPENSING SYSTEMS FRANCE S.A.S.—See Silgan Holdings, Inc.; U.S. Public, pg. 1879
SILGAN DISPENSING SYSTEMS HEMER GMBH—See Silgan Holdings, Inc.; U.S. Public, pg. 1879
SILGAN DISPENSING SYSTEMS INDIA PRIVATE LIMITED—See Silgan Holdings, Inc.; U.S. Public, pg. 1879
SILGAN DISPENSING SYSTEMS MEXICO OPERADORA, S.A. DE C.V.—See Silgan Holdings, Inc.; U.S. Public, pg. 1879
SILGAN DISPENSING SYSTEMS MEXICO, S.A. DE C.V.—See Silgan Holdings, Inc.; U.S. Public, pg. 1879
SILGAN DISPENSING SYSTEMS MILANO S.R.L.—See Silgan Holdings, Inc.; U.S. Public, pg. 1879
SILGAN DISPENSING SYSTEMS STATERSVILLE LLC—See Silgan Holdings, Inc.; U.S. Public, pg. 1879
SILGAN DISPENSING SYSTEMS VICENZA S.R.L.—See Silgan Holdings, Inc.; U.S. Public, pg. 1879
SILGAN DISPENSING SYSTEMS (WUXI) CO., LTD.—See Silgan Holdings, Inc.; U.S. Public, pg. 1878
SIMMONS SIRVEY CORPORATION—See Dover Corporation; U.S. Public, pg. 682
SIPCON INSTRUMENT INDUSTRIES PVT. LTD.—See Chien Wei Precise Technology Co., Ltd.; Int'l, pg. 1477
S&N PUMP (AFRICA) LTDA—See Lone Star Funds; U.S. Private, pg. 2485
SOLARES CONTROLS—See Applied Industrial Technologies, Inc.; U.S. Public, pg. 171
SOLDACENTRO SA—See Enovis Corporation; U.S. Public, pg. 773
SOUTHWEST OILFIELD PRODUCTS, INC.—See CLEANTEK Industries Inc.; Int'l, pg. 1655
SOUTHWEST WATERWORKS CONTRACTORS, INC.—See Bain Capital, LP; U.S. Private, pg. 433
SPX FLOW TECHNOLOGY BELGIUM NV—See Lone Star Funds; U.S. Private, pg. 2486
SPX FLOW TECHNOLOGY JAPAN, INC.—See Lone Star Funds; U.S. Private, pg. 2486
SPX FLOW TECHNOLOGY MEXICO S.A. DE C.V.—See Lone Star Funds; U.S. Private, pg. 2486
SPX FLOW TECHNOLOGY (PTY) LIMITED—See Lone Star Funds; U.S. Private, pg. 2486
SPX FLOW TECHNOLOGY SANTORSO S.R.L.—See Lone Star Funds; U.S. Private, pg. 2486
SPX FLOW TECHNOLOGY SAS—See Lone Star Funds; U.S. Private, pg. 2486
SPX FLOW TECHNOLOGY SVERIGE AB—See Lone Star Funds; U.S. Private, pg. 2486
SPX NETHERLANDS B.V.—See Lone Star Funds; U.S. Private, pg. 2487
SPX SERVICOS INDUSTRIAIS LTDA.—See Lone Star Funds; U.S. Private, pg. 2487
STANDARD PUMP, INC.—See May River Capital, LLC; U.S. Private, pg. 2620
STANDEX INTERNATIONAL S.R.L. - PROCON DIVISION—See Standex International; U.S. Public, pg. 1931
STANDEX IRELAND LTD.—See Standex International; U.S. Public, pg. 1931
STERLING FLUID SYSTEMS (AUSTRIA) GMBH—See Flowserve Corporation; U.S. Public, pg. 857
STERLING FLUID SYSTEMS (POLSKA) SP.Z.O.O.—See Flowserve Corporation; U.S. Public, pg. 857
STERLING SIHI BULGARIA EOOD—See Flowserve Corporation; U.S. Public, pg. 857
STERLING SIHI (NETHERLANDS) B.V.—See Flowserve Corporation; U.S. Public, pg. 857
STIG WAHLSTROM HYDRAULIK AB—See Addtech AB; Int'l, pg. 135
SUNBELT POWER CONTROLS INC.—See Innovative IDM LLC; U.S. Private, pg. 2082
SUNDYNE, LLC—See BC Partners LLP; Int'l, pg. 922
SUNDYNE, LLC—See The Carlyle Group Inc.; U.S. Public, pg. 2044
SUNTEC INDUSTRIES INC.; U.S. Private, pg. 3873
SUPERIOR OIL FIELD SERVICES L.L.C.—See Gulf Petroleum Investment Co. S.A.K.C.; Int'l, pg. 3182
SVANEHOJ DANMARK A/S—See ITT Inc.; U.S. Public, pg. 1178
SVENSKA TEKNISK BYRA AB—See Axel Johnson Gruppen AB; Int'l, pg. 765
SYSTECON LLC—See ENGIE SA; Int'l, pg. 2429
TACO (CANADA) LTD.—See Taco Incorporated; U.S. Private, pg. 3920
TACO ELECTRONIC SOLUTIONS, INC.—See Taco Incorporated; U.S. Private, pg. 3920
THOMPSON PUMP AND MANUFACTURING CO., INC.; U.S. Private, pg. 4160
THOMPSONS, KELLY & LEWIS PTY LTD—See Flowserve Corporation; U.S. Public, pg. 857
TIMKEN ILS CHELTENHAM LIMITED—See The Timken Company; U.S. Public, pg. 2133
TOKHEIM GUARDIAN VENTURE SDN. BHD—See Dover Corporation; U.S. Public, pg. 683
TOKHEIM INDIA PRIVATE LIMITED—See Dover Corporation; U.S. Public, pg. 683
TOKHEIM NETHERLANDS B.V.—See Dover Corporation; U.S. Public, pg. 683
TOKHEIM SOFITAM APPLICATIONS—See Dover Corporation; U.S. Public, pg. 683
TOKUPI CO., LTD.—See Fukuda Corporation; Int'l, pg. 2839
TUSHACO PUMPS PRIVATE LIMITED—See Enovis Corporation; U.S. Public, pg. 773
TUTHILL CORPORATION PUMP GROUP—See Tuthill Corporation; U.S. Private, pg. 4263
TUTHILL FILL-RITE DIVISION—See Tuthill Corporation; U.S. Private, pg. 4263
TUTHILL MEXICO, S RL CV—See Tuthill Corporation; U.S. Private, pg. 4262
TUTHILL UK LTD—See Tuthill Corporation; U.S. Private, pg. 4263
TUTHILL VACUUM & BLOWER SYSTEMS, INC.—See Ingersoll Rand Inc.; U.S. Public, pg. 1122
UAB GILBARCO VEEDER-ROOT—See Vontier Corporation; U.S. Public, pg. 2309
UE MANUFACTURING LLC—See Kirby Corporation; U.S. Public, pg. 1235
ULVAC CRYOGENICS KOREA INC.—See Azenta, Inc.; U.S. Public, pg. 258
ULVAC CRYOGENICS NINGBO INC.—See Azenta, Inc.; U.S. Public, pg. 258
VALCO CINCINNATI INC.; U.S. Private, pg. 4330
VAL-TEX, LLC—See Entegris, Inc.; U.S. Public, pg. 777
VARISCO S.R.L.—See Atlas Copco AB; Int'l, pg. 684
VARMA & VELAVERK EHF.—See Endress+Hauser (International) Holding AG; Int'l, pg. 2409
VERMES MICRODISPENSING GMBH—See Chaozhou Three-Circle Group Co., Ltd.; Int'l, pg. 1447
VERSA-MATIC TOOL, INC.—See IDEX Corp; U.S. Public, pg. 1092
VERTICAL S.P.A.—See Franklin Electric Co., Inc.; U.S. Public, pg. 879
VIKING PUMP (EUROPE) LTD.—See IDEX Corp; U.S. Public, pg. 1092
VIKING PUMP, INC.—See IDEX Corp; U.S. Public, pg. 1092
VIKING PUMP OF CANADA, INC.—See IDEX Corp; U.S. Public, pg. 1092
WANNER ENGINEERING INC.; U.S. Private, pg. 4436
WARREN RUPP, INC.—See IDEX Corp; U.S. Public, pg. 1092
WATERTRONICS, LLC—See Lindsay Corporation; U.S. Public, pg. 1320
WAYNE FUELING SYSTEMS LLC—See Dover Corporation; U.S. Public, pg. 683
WAYNE FUELING SYSTEMS SWEDEN AB—See Dover Corporation; U.S. Public, pg. 683
WAYNE WATER SYSTEMS—See Berkshire Hathaway Inc.; U.S. Public, pg. 300
WDM PUMPS, INC.—See Corporacion EG S.A.; Int'l, pg. 1803
WEBB PUMP—See F.W. Webb Company; U.S. Private, pg. 1457
WEIL PUMP CO. INC.—See Wilo USA LLC; U.S. Private, pg. 4529
WILLIAMS INSTRUMENT COMPANY—See BC Partners LLP; Int'l, pg. 922
WILLIAMS INSTRUMENT COMPANY—See The Carlyle Group Inc.; U.S. Public, pg. 2044
WILO USA LLC; U.S. Private, pg. 4529
WORKDRY INTERNATIONAL LIMITED—See Arcus Infrastructure Partners LLP; Int'l, pg. 553
WORTHINGTON S.P.A.—See Flowserve Corporation; U.S. Public, pg. 857
WORTHINGTON S.R.L.—See Flowserve Corporation; U.S. Public, pg. 857
WRIGHT FLOW TECHHNOLOGIES, INC.—See IDEX Corp; U.S. Public, pg. 1092
WRIGHT FLOW TECHNOLOGIES LIMITED—See IDEX Corp; U.S. Public, pg. 1092
WRIGHT FLOW TECHNOLOGIES LTD.—See IDEX Corp; U.S. Public, pg. 1092
WRIGHT FLOW TECHNOLOGIES—See IDEX Corp; U.S. Public, pg. 1092
W.S. DARLEY & CO., INC.; U.S. Private, pg. 4422
XYLEM ANALYTICS GERMANY GMBH—See Xylem Inc.; U.S. Public, pg. 2396
XYLEM APPLIED WATER SYSTEMS - GUELPH—See Xylem Inc.; U.S. Public, pg. 2396
XYLEM APPLIED WATER SYSTEMS - OTTAWA—See Xylem Inc.; U.S. Public, pg. 2396
XYLEM APPLIED WATER SYSTEMS - SAINT-LAURENT—See Xylem Inc.; U.S. Public, pg. 2396
XYLEM INC. - APPLIED WATER SYSTEMS—See Xylem Inc.; U.S. Public, pg. 2395
XYLEM INC. - BELL & GOSSETT DIVISION—See Xylem Inc.; U.S. Public, pg. 2396
XYLEM INC. - WATER SOLUTIONS—See Xylem Inc.; U.S. Public, pg. 2396
XYLEM SHARED SERVICES SP. Z.O.Q.—See Xylem Inc.; U.S. Public, pg. 2397
XYLEM WATER SOLUTIONS AB—See Xylem Inc.; U.S. Public, pg. 2396
XYLEM WATER SOLUTIONS ARGENTINA S.A.—See Xylem Inc.; U.S. Public, pg. 2396
XYLEM WATER SOLUTIONS AUSTRIA GMBH—See Xylem Inc.; U.S. Public, pg. 2396
XYLEM WATER SOLUTIONS AUSTRIA GMBH—See Xylem Inc.; U.S. Public, pg. 2396
XYLEM WATER SOLUTIONS COLOMBIA LTDA.—See Xylem Inc.; U.S. Public, pg. 2397
XYLEM WATER SOLUTIONS DENMARK APS—See Xylem Inc.; U.S. Public, pg. 2397

N.A.I.C.S. INDEX

333921 — ELEVATOR AND MOVING...

XYLEM WATER SOLUTIONS ESPANA S.A.—See Xylem Inc.; *U.S. Public*, pg. 2397
XYLEM WATER SOLUTIONS FLORIDA LLC—See Xylem Inc.; *U.S. Public*, pg. 2397
XYLEM WATER SOLUTIONS INDIA PRIVATE LIMITED—See Xylem Inc.; *U.S. Public*, pg. 2397
XYLEM WATER SOLUTIONS INDIA PVT. LTD.—See Xylem Inc.; *U.S. Public*, pg. 2397
XYLEM WATER SOLUTIONS IRELAND LTD.—See Xylem Inc.; *U.S. Public*, pg. 2397
XYLEM WATER SOLUTIONS NEW ZEALAND LIMITED—See Xylem Inc.; *U.S. Public*, pg. 2397
XYLEM WATER SOLUTIONS PERU S.A.—See Xylem Inc.; *U.S. Public*, pg. 2397
XYLEM WATER SOLUTIONS PORTUGAL, UNIPESSOA LDA—See Xylem Inc.; *U.S. Public*, pg. 2397
XYLEM WATER SOLUTIONS SINGAPORE PTE. LTD.—See Xylem Inc.; *U.S. Public*, pg. 2397
XYLEM WATER SOLUTIONS SOUTH AFRICA (PTY) LTD.—See Xylem Inc.; *U.S. Public*, pg. 2397
XYLEM WATER SOLUTIONS SUOMI OY—See Xylem Inc.; *U.S. Public*, pg. 2397
XYLEM WATER SOLUTIONS UK LTD.—See Xylem Inc.; *U.S. Public*, pg. 2397
XYLEM WATER SOLUTIONS U.S.A., INC. - INDIANAPOLIS—See Xylem Inc.; *U.S. Public*, pg. 2397
XYLEM WATER SOLUTIONS U.S.A., INC.—See Xylem Inc.; *U.S. Public*, pg. 2397
XYLEM WATER SYSTEMS HUNGARY KFT—See Xylem Inc.; *U.S. Public*, pg. 2397
YEMEN LUBRICANTS MANUFACTURING COMPANY LTD.—See Hayel Saeed Anam Group of Companies; *Int'l*, pg. 3291
ZOELLER CO.; *U.S. Private*, pg. 4607

333921 — ELEVATOR AND MOVING STAIRWAY MANUFACTURING

4B ELEVATOR COMPONENTS LIMITED—See Braime Group Plc; *Int'l*, pg. 1136
AARON INDUSTRIES LTD.; *Int'l*, pg. 37
ACCREDITED HOME ELEVATOR, INC.—See Aldine Capital Partners, Inc.; *U.S. Private*, pg. 159
ACCREDITED HOME ELEVATOR, INC.—See Stoic Holdings LLC; *U.S. Private*, pg. 3816
ACROW INDIA LTD.; *Int'l*, pg. 109
ADDERACARE AB; *Int'l*, pg. 128
AFFINITY ELEVATOR COMPANY, LLC—See L Squared Capital Management LP; *U.S. Private*, pg. 2362
AITKEN SPENCE ELEVATORS (PVT) LTD—See Aitken Spence PLC; *Int'l*, pg. 254
AMERICAN ELEVATOR GROUP; *U.S. Private*, pg. 231
AUTOMATED SYSTEMS INC.; *U.S. Private*, pg. 399
BAGBY ELEVATOR COMPANY, INC.; *U.S. Private*, pg. 425
BOSTOCK COMPANY, INC.; *U.S. Private*, pg. 621
CANNY ELEVATOR CO., LTD.; *Int'l*, pg. 1292
CARGILL AG HORIZONS—See Cargill, Inc.; *U.S. Private*, pg. 755
CHAMPION ELEVATOR CORP.; *U.S. Private*, pg. 846
CHANGJIANG RUNFA MEDICINE CO., LTD.; *Int'l*, pg. 1443
CHINA ENERGINE INTERNATIONAL (HOLDINGS) LIMITED; *Int'l*, pg. 1500
CITY LIFT PARKING, LLC; *U.S. Private*, pg. 906
COMPRESSOR PRODUCTS INTERNATIONAL SOUTH KOREA—See Enpro Inc.; *U.S. Public*, pg. 774
COMPUTERIZED ELEVATOR CONTROL CORP.—See Advent International Corporation; *U.S. Private*, pg. 106
COMPUTERIZED ELEVATOR CONTROL CORP.—See Cinven Limited; *Int'l*, pg. 1615
ECE INDUSTRIES LIMITED - ELEVATOR DIVISION—See ECE Industries Limited; *Int'l*, pg. 2288
EITA ELEVATOR (MALAYSIA) SDN. BHD.—See Eita Resources Berhad; *Int'l*, pg. 2336
EITA RESEARCH & DEVELOPMENT SDN. BHD.—See Eita Resources Berhad; *Int'l*, pg. 2336
EITA RESOURCES BERHAD; *Int'l*, pg. 2336
EITA-SCHNEIDER (MFG) SDN. BHD.—See Eita Resources Berhad; *Int'l*, pg. 2336
ELEVADORES OTIS, S.A. DE C.V.—See Otis Worldwide Corporation; *U.S. Public*, pg. 1623
ELEVATOR EQUIPMENT CORPORATION; *U.S. Private*, pg. 1358
ELEVATOR RESEARCH MANUFACTURING CORP.—See Dewhurst Group plc; *Int'l*, pg. 2091
ELEVATOR SERVICE LLC—See Carroll Capital LLC; *U.S. Private*, pg. 773
EMLAK KONUT ASANSOR SISTEMLERI SANAYI VE TICARET A.S.—See Emlak Konut Gayrimenkul Yatirim Ortakligi AS; *Int'l*, pg. 2384
FLYING TECHNOLOGY CO., LTD.; *Int'l*, pg. 2716
FUJITEC AMERICA INC—See Fujitec Co., Ltd.; *Int'l*, pg. 2831
FUJITEC CANADA, INC.—See Fujitec Co., Ltd.; *Int'l*, pg. 2831
FUJITEC CO., LTD.; *Int'l*, pg. 2831
FUJITEC EGYPT CO., LTD.—See Fujitec Co., Ltd.; *Int'l*, pg. 2831

FUJITEC ELEVATOR CO. INC.—See Fujitec Co., Ltd.; *Int'l*, pg. 2831
FUJITEC INDIA PRIVATE LTD.—See Fujitec Co., Ltd.; *Int'l*, pg. 2831
FUJITEC KOREA CO., LTD.—See Fujitec Co., Ltd.; *Int'l*, pg. 2831
FUJITEC SINGAPORE CORPORATION LIMITED—See Fujitec Co., Ltd.; *Int'l*, pg. 2831
FUJITEC TAIWAN CO., LTD.—See Fujitec Co., Ltd.; *Int'l*, pg. 2831
FURUTEC ELECTRICAL SDN. BHD.—See Eita Resources Berhad; *Int'l*, pg. 2337
GAL CANADA ELEVATOR PRODUCTS CORP.—See Golden Gate Capital Management II, LLC; *U.S. Private*, pg. 1732
GAL MANUFACTURING CORPORATION—See Golden Gate Capital Management II, LLC; *U.S. Private*, pg. 1732
GENERAL ELEVATOR CO., LTD.; *Int'l*, pg. 2918
GUANGZHOU GUANGRI STOCK CO., LTD.; *Int'l*, pg. 3165
HALLEY ELEVATOR COMPANY, INC.—See 3Phase Elevator Corp; *U.S. Private*, pg. 14
HANGZHOU HUNING ELEVATOR PARTS CO., LTD.; *Int'l*, pg. 3248
HANKOOK OTIS ELEVATOR COMPANY—See Otis Worldwide Corporation; *U.S. Public*, pg. 1623
HANS LUTZ MASCHINENFABRIK GMBH & CO. KG; *Int'l*, pg. 3259
HAUENSTEIN & BURMEISTER, INC.; *U.S. Private*, pg. 1880
HIRATA CORPORATION OF EUROPE LTD—See Hirata Corporation; *Int'l*, pg. 3403
HITACHI ELEVATOR ASIA PTE. LTD.—See Hitachi, Ltd.; *Int'l*, pg. 3416
HITACHI ELEVATOR (CAMBODIA) CO., LTD.—See Hitachi, Ltd.; *Int'l*, pg. 3416
HITACHI ELEVATOR (CHENGDU) CO., LTD.—See Hitachi, Ltd.; *Int'l*, pg. 3416
HITACHI ELEVATOR ENGINEERING (MALAYSIA) SDN. BHD.—See Hitachi, Ltd.; *Int'l*, pg. 3417
HITACHI ELEVATOR (GUANGZHOU) ESCALATOR CO., LTD.—See Hitachi, Ltd.; *Int'l*, pg. 3417
HITACHI ELEVATOR MOTOR (GUANGZHOU) CO., LTD.—See Hitachi, Ltd.; *Int'l*, pg. 3416
HITACHI ELEVATOR SAUDI ARABIA LIMITED—See Hitachi, Ltd.; *Int'l*, pg. 3417
HITACHI LIFT INDIA PVT. LTD.—See Hitachi, Ltd.; *Int'l*, pg. 3420
HUASHENG FUJITEC ELEVATOR CO. LTD.—See Fujitec Co., Ltd.; *Int'l*, pg. 2831
HYUNDAI ELEVATOR CO., LTD.—See Hyundai Group; *Int'l*, pg. 3557
HYUNDAI ELEVATOR CO., LTD.—See Hyundai Group; *Int'l*, pg. 3557
IFE ELEVATORS CO., LTD; *Int'l*, pg. 3599
INCLINATOR COMPANY OF AMERICA, INC.; *U.S. Private*, pg. 2053
JARDINE SCHINDLER LIFTS LTD.—See Otis Worldwide Corporation; *U.S. Public*, pg. 1623
LAPEYRE STAIR, INC.—See The Laitram LLC; *U.S. Private*, pg. 4067
LM LIFTMATERIAL GMBH—See Bain Capital, LP; *U.S. Private*, pg. 452
MATOT INC.; *U.S. Private*, pg. 2611
MEMCO LIMITED—See Halma plc; *Int'l*, pg. 3232
MINNESOTA ELEVATOR INC.; *U.S. Private*, pg. 2743
MONITOR CONTROLS INC—See Halma plc; *Int'l*, pg. 3231
NATIONAL WHEEL-O-VATOR CO. INC.—See Advent International Corporation; *U.S. Private*, pg. 106
NATIONAL WHEEL-O-VATOR CO. INC.—See Cinven Limited; *Int'l*, pg. 1615
O'LEARY'S MATERIAL HANDLING SERVICES PTY LTD—See Cargotec Corporation; *Int'l*, pg. 1329
ORACLE ELEVATOR COMPANY—See L Squared Capital Management LP; *U.S. Private*, pg. 2362
OTIS A.S.—See Otis Worldwide Corporation; *U.S. Public*, pg. 1623
OTIS CANADA, INC.—See Otis Worldwide Corporation; *U.S. Public*, pg. 1623
OTIS ELEVATOR (CHINA) COMPANY LIMITED—See Otis Worldwide Corporation; *U.S. Public*, pg. 1623
OTIS ELEVATOR (CHINA) INVESTMENT COMPANY LIMITED—See Otis Worldwide Corporation; *U.S. Public*, pg. 1623
OTIS ELEVATOR COMPANY (INDIA) LIMITED—See Otis Worldwide Corporation; *U.S. Public*, pg. 1623
OTIS ELEVATOR COMPANY—See Otis Worldwide Corporation; *U.S. Public*, pg. 1622
OTIS ELEVATOR COMPANY (TAIWAN) LIMITED—See Otis Worldwide Corporation; *U.S. Public*, pg. 1623
OTIS ELEVATOR CO. PTY. LTD.—See Otis Worldwide Corporation; *U.S. Public*, pg. 1623
OTIS ELEVATOR LIMITED—See Otis Worldwide Corporation; *U.S. Public*, pg. 1623
OTIS GESELLSCHAFT M.B.H.—See Otis Worldwide Corporation; *U.S. Public*, pg. 1623
OTIS GMBH & CO. OHG—See Otis Worldwide Corporation; *U.S. Public*, pg. 1623
OTIS HOLDINGS GMBH & CO. OHG—See Otis Worldwide Corporation; *U.S. Public*, pg. 1623

OTIS S.A.—See Otis Worldwide Corporation; *U.S. Public*, pg. 1623
OTIS S.C.S.—See Otis Worldwide Corporation; *U.S. Public*, pg. 1623
OTIS SERVIZ, S.R.L.—See Otis Worldwide Corporation; *U.S. Public*, pg. 1623
PEELLE ASIA PACIFIC, PTE. LTD.—See The Peelle Company; *U.S. Private*, pg. 4092
THE PEELLE COMPANY LTD.—See The Peelle Company; *U.S. Private*, pg. 4092
THE PEELLE COMPANY; *U.S. Private*, pg. 4092
PT. FUJITEC INDONESIA—See Fujitec Co., Ltd.; *Int'l*, pg. 2831
RETRO ELEVATOR CORP.; *U.S. Private*, pg. 3412
SEMATIC ELEVADORES MEXICO S. DE R.L. DE C.V.—See Bain Capital, LP; *U.S. Private*, pg. 452
SEMATIC ELEVATOR PRODUCTS (CHANGSHU) CO., LTD.—See Bain Capital, LP; *U.S. Private*, pg. 452
SEMATIC HUNGARIA KFT—See Bain Capital, LP; *U.S. Private*, pg. 452
SEMATIC S.P.A.—See Bain Capital, LP; *U.S. Private*, pg. 452
SEMATIC S.P.A. - SUISIO PLANT—See Bain Capital, LP; *U.S. Private*, pg. 452
SEMATIC USA, INC.—See Bain Capital, LP; *U.S. Private*, pg. 452
SETEM S.A.R.L.—See Braime Group Plc; *Int'l*, pg. 1136
SHANGHAI CHEVALIER TRADING CO., LTD.—See Chevalier International Holdings Limited; *Int'l*, pg. 1474
SHANGHAI YUNGTAY ELEVATOR EQUIPMENT CO., LTD.—See Hitachi, Ltd.; *Int'l*, pg. 3425
SHENZHEN KESONG TECHNOLOGY CO., LTD.—See China Security Co., Ltd.; *Int'l*, pg. 1550
SIAM-HITACHI ELEVATOR CO., LTD. - CHONBURI FACTORY—See Hitachi, Ltd.; *Int'l*, pg. 3424
SIAM-HITACHI ELEVATOR CO., LTD.—See Hitachi, Ltd.; *Int'l*, pg. 3424
SIGMA ELEVATOR (HK) LIMITED—See Otis Worldwide Corporation; *U.S. Public*, pg. 1623
SPECTRA COLOR, INC.—See Arsenal Capital Management LP; *U.S. Private*, pg. 337
THYSSEN DOVER ELEVATOR (CANADA) LTD.—See Advent International Corporation; *U.S. Private*, pg. 107
THYSSEN DOVER ELEVATOR (CANADA) LTD.—See Cinven Limited; *Int'l*, pg. 1615
THYSSENKRUPP ACCESSIBILITY B.V.—See Advent International Corporation; *U.S. Private*, pg. 106
THYSSENKRUPP ACCESSIBILITY B.V.—See Cinven Limited; *Int'l*, pg. 1614
THYSSENKRUPP ELEVADORES S.A.C.—See Advent International Corporation; *U.S. Private*, pg. 106
THYSSENKRUPP ELEVADORES S.A.C.—See Cinven Limited; *Int'l*, pg. 1614
THYSSENKRUPP ELEVADORES, S.A. DE C.V.—See Advent International Corporation; *U.S. Private*, pg. 106
THYSSENKRUPP ELEVADORES, S.A. DE C.V.—See Cinven Limited; *Int'l*, pg. 1614
THYSSENKRUPP ELEVADORES S.A.—See Advent International Corporation; *U.S. Private*, pg. 106
THYSSENKRUPP ELEVADORES S.A.—See Advent International Corporation; *U.S. Private*, pg. 106
THYSSENKRUPP ELEVADORES S.A.—See Advent International Corporation; *U.S. Private*, pg. 106
THYSSENKRUPP ELEVADORES S.A.—See Advent International Corporation; *U.S. Private*, pg. 106
THYSSENKRUPP ELEVADORES S.A.—See Advent International Corporation; *U.S. Private*, pg. 106
THYSSENKRUPP ELEVADORES S.A.—See Advent International Corporation; *U.S. Private*, pg. 106
THYSSENKRUPP ELEVADORES S.A.—See Cinven Limited; *Int'l*, pg. 1614
THYSSENKRUPP ELEVADORES S.A.—See Cinven Limited; *Int'l*, pg. 1614
THYSSENKRUPP ELEVADORES S.A.—See Cinven Limited; *Int'l*, pg. 1614
THYSSENKRUPP ELEVADORES S.A.—See Cinven Limited; *Int'l*, pg. 1614
THYSSENKRUPP ELEVADORES S.A.—See Cinven Limited; *Int'l*, pg. 1614
THYSSENKRUPP ELEVADORES S.A.—See Cinven Limited; *Int'l*, pg. 1614
THYSSENKRUPP ELEVADORES, S.L.—See Advent International Corporation; *U.S. Private*, pg. 106
THYSSENKRUPP ELEVADORES, S.L.—See Cinven Limited; *Int'l*, pg. 1614
THYSSENKRUPP ELEVADORES, S.R.L.—See Advent International Corporation; *U.S. Private*, pg. 106
THYSSENKRUPP ELEVADORES, S.R.L.—See Cinven Limited; *Int'l*, pg. 1614
THYSSENKRUPP ELEVATOR AMERICAS CORP.—See Advent International Corporation; *U.S. Private*, pg. 106
THYSSENKRUPP ELEVATOR AMERICAS CORP.—See Cinven Limited; *Int'l*, pg. 1615
THYSSENKRUPP ELEVATOR A/S—See Advent International Corporation; *U.S. Private*, pg. 106
THYSSENKRUPP ELEVATOR A/S—See Advent International Corporation; *U.S. Private*, pg. 106

333921 — ELEVATOR AND MOVING...

THYSSENKRUPP ELEVATOR A/S—See Cinven Limited; *Int'l*, pg. 1614
THYSSENKRUPP ELEVATOR A/S—See Cinven Limited; *Int'l*, pg. 1614
THYSSENKRUPP ELEVATOR (BD) PVT. LTD.—See Advent International Corporation; *U.S. Private*, pg. 106
THYSSENKRUPP ELEVATOR (BD) PVT. LTD.—See Cinven Limited; *Int'l*, pg. 1614
THYSSENKRUPP ELEVATOR CANADA LTD.—See Advent International Corporation; *U.S. Private*, pg. 107
THYSSENKRUPP ELEVATOR CANADA LTD.—See Cinven Limited; *Int'l*, pg. 1615
THYSSENKRUPP ELEVATOR CAPITAL CORP.—See Advent International Corporation; *U.S. Private*, pg. 106
THYSSENKRUPP ELEVATOR CAPITAL CORP.—See Cinven Limited; *Int'l*, pg. 1615
THYSSENKRUPP ELEVATOR CORP.—See Advent International Corporation; *U.S. Private*, pg. 106
THYSSENKRUPP ELEVATOR CORP.—See Cinven Limited; *Int'l*, pg. 1615
THYSSENKRUPP ELEVATOR & ESCALATOR (SHANGHAI) CO.LTD.—See Advent International Corporation; *U.S. Private*, pg. 106
THYSSENKRUPP ELEVATOR & ESCALATOR (SHANGHAI) CO.LTD.—See Cinven Limited; *Int'l*, pg. 1614
THYSSENKRUPP ELEVATOR (HK) LTD.—See Advent International Corporation; *U.S. Private*, pg. 106
THYSSENKRUPP ELEVATOR (HK) LTD.—See Cinven Limited; *Int'l*, pg. 1614
THYSSENKRUPP ELEVATOR INC.—See Advent International Corporation; *U.S. Private*, pg. 106
THYSSENKRUPP ELEVATOR INC.—See Cinven Limited; *Int'l*, pg. 1615
THYSSENKRUPP ELEVATOR (INDIA) PRIVATE LIMITED—See Advent International Corporation; *U.S. Private*, pg. 106
THYSSENKRUPP ELEVATOR (INDIA) PRIVATE LIMITED—See Cinven Limited; *Int'l*, pg. 1614
THYSSENKRUPP ELEVATOR INNOVATION CENTER, S.A.—See Advent International Corporation; *U.S. Private*, pg. 107
THYSSENKRUPP ELEVATOR INNOVATION CENTER, S.A.—See Cinven Limited; *Int'l*, pg. 1615
THYSSENKRUPP ELEVATOR (KOREA) LTD. - CHEONAN PLANT—See Advent International Corporation; *U.S. Private*, pg. 106
THYSSENKRUPP ELEVATOR (KOREA) LTD. - CHEONAN PLANT—See Cinven Limited; *Int'l*, pg. 1614
THYSSENKRUPP ELEVATOR (KOREA) LTD.—See Advent International Corporation; *U.S. Private*, pg. 106
THYSSENKRUPP ELEVATOR (KOREA) LTD.—See Cinven Limited; *Int'l*, pg. 1614
THYSSENKRUPP ELEVATOR MANUFACTURING FRANCE S.A.S.—See Advent International Corporation; *U.S. Private*, pg. 107
THYSSENKRUPP ELEVATOR MANUFACTURING FRANCE S.A.S.—See Cinven Limited; *Int'l*, pg. 1615
THYSSENKRUPP ELEVATOR MANUFACTURING INC.—See Advent International Corporation; *U.S. Private*, pg. 107
THYSSENKRUPP ELEVATOR MANUFACTURING INC.—See Cinven Limited; *Int'l*, pg. 1615
THYSSENKRUPP ELEVATOR MANUFACTURING SPAIN S.L.—See Advent International Corporation; *U.S. Private*, pg. 107
THYSSENKRUPP ELEVATOR MANUFACTURING SPAIN S.L.—See Cinven Limited; *Int'l*, pg. 1615
THYSSENKRUPP ELEVATOR—See Advent International Corporation; *U.S. Private*, pg. 106
THYSSENKRUPP ELEVATOR—See Cinven Limited; *Int'l*, pg. 1615
THYSSENKRUPP ELEVATOR SOUTHERN EUROPE, AFRICA & MIDDLE EAST, S.L.U.—See Advent International Corporation; *U.S. Private*, pg. 107
THYSSENKRUPP ELEVATOR SOUTHERN EUROPE, AFRICA & MIDDLE EAST, S.L.U.—See Cinven Limited; *Int'l*, pg. 1615
THYSSENKRUPP ELEVATORS (SHANGHAI) CO., LTD.—See Advent International Corporation; *U.S. Private*, pg. 107
THYSSENKRUPP ELEVATORS (SHANGHAI) CO., LTD.—See Cinven Limited; *Int'l*, pg. 1615
THYSSENKRUPP NORTHERN ELEVATOR LTD.—See Advent International Corporation; *U.S. Private*, pg. 107
THYSSENKRUPP NORTHERN ELEVATOR LTD.—See Cinven Limited; *Int'l*, pg. 1615
TK ELEVATOR—See Advent International Corporation; *U.S. Private*, pg. 106
TK ELEVATOR—See Cinven Limited; *Int'l*, pg. 1614
UNION IRON INC.—See Ag Growth International Inc.; *Int'l*, pg. 198
VANTAGE ELEVATOR SOLUTIONS—See Golden Gate Capital Management II, LLC; *U.S. Private*, pg. 1732
VERTICAL DIMENSIONS, LLC—See Golden Gate Capital Management II, LLC; *U.S. Private*, pg. 1732
WAUPACA ELEVATOR CO, INC.—See Gardner Standard LLC; *U.S. Private*, pg. 1644
WISCONSIN ELEVATOR COMPANY, LLC—See Gardner Standard LLC; *U.S. Private*, pg. 1644
YUNGTAY ENGINEERING CO., LTD.—See Hitachi, Ltd.; *Int'l*, pg. 3424
YUNGTAY ENGINEERING CO., LTD. - TAOYUAN FACTORY—See Hitachi, Ltd.; *Int'l*, pg. 3425
ZARDOYA OTIS, S.A.—See Otis Worldwide Corporation; *U.S. Public*, pg. 1623

333922 — CONVEYOR AND CONVEYING EQUIPMENT MANUFACTURING

4B AFRICA ELEVATOR COMPONENTS (PTY) LIMITED—See Braime Group Plc; *Int'l*, pg. 1136
4B BRAIME (CHANGZHOU) INDUSTRIAL CONTROL EQUIPMENT COMPANY LIMITED—See Braime Group Plc; *Int'l*, pg. 1136
4B BRAIME COMPONENTS LIMITED—See Braime Group Plc; *Int'l*, pg. 1136
AEROCOM FRANCE S.A.R.L.—See aerocom GmbH & Co.; *Int'l*, pg. 180
AEROCOM GCT S.R.L.—See aerocom GmbH & Co.; *Int'l*, pg. 180
AEROCOM GMBH & CO.; *Int'l*, pg. 180
ALBA MANUFACTURING INC.; *U.S. Private*, pg. 151
ALLIED UNIKING CORPORATION; *U.S. Private*, pg. 188
AMERICAN OVERHEAD CONVEYOR—See Payson Casters, Inc.; *U.S. Private*, pg. 3117
ANCRA SYSTEMS BV—See The Heico Companies, L.L.C.; *U.S. Private*, pg. 4050
ANHUI SHENGYUN ENVIRONMENT PROTECTION GROUP CO., LTD.; *Int'l*, pg. 469
APOLLO MASCHINENBAU GMBH—See Gujarat Apollo Industries Limited; *Int'l*, pg. 3176
ARBON EQUIPMENT CORPORATION—See Rite-Hite Holding Corporation; *U.S. Private*, pg. 3441
ARROWHEAD CONVEYOR CORPORATION, INC.; *U.S. Private*, pg. 336
ASGCO MANUFACTURING, INC.; *U.S. Private*, pg. 349
ASHWORTH BROS., INC.; *U.S. Private*, pg. 350
ASHWORTH FACTORY SERVICE CORPORATION—See Ashworth Bros., Inc.; *U.S. Private*, pg. 350
ATS AUTOMATION MALAYSIA SDN. BHD.—See ATS Corporation; *Int'l*, pg. 695
AUTOMATION & MODULAR COMPONENTS, INC.; *U.S. Private*, pg. 399
BATCO CORPORATION LTD.—See Ag Growth International Inc.; *Int'l*, pg. 198
BAY EQUIPMENT CORP.—See HEICO Corporation; *U.S. Public*, pg. 1019
BELL EQUIPMENT RUSSLAND LLC—See Bell Equipment Limited; *Int'l*, pg. 966
BELT POWER LLC—See Platte River Ventures, LLC; *U.S. Private*, pg. 3211
BISHOP LIFTING PRODUCTS, INC.—See Altamont Capital Partners, Inc.; *U.S. Private*, pg. 204
BONEAL INCORPORATED; *U.S. Private*, pg. 614
BRIDGESTONE DIVERSIFIED PRODUCTS (CHINA) CO., LTD.—See Bridgestone Corporation; *Int'l*, pg. 1158
BRIDGESTONE DIVERSIFIED PRODUCTS EAST CO., LTD.—See Bridgestone Corporation; *Int'l*, pg. 1158
BRIDGESTONE ENGINEERED PRODUCTS OF ASIA, SDN BHD.—See Bridgestone Corporation; *Int'l*, pg. 1158
BULLDOG AUTOMATION, LLC—See Huizenga Manufacturing Group, Inc.; *U.S. Private*, pg. 2004
BUSSE/SJI—See Arrowhead Conveyor Corporation, Inc.; *U.S. Private*, pg. 336
CAMBRIDGE INTERNATIONAL, INC.—See Zurn Elkay Water Solutions Corporation; *U.S. Public*, pg. 2412
CAMOTION, INC.—See Pohlad Companies; *U.S. Private*, pg. 3220
CARRIER VIBRATING EQUIPMENT, INC.; *U.S. Private*, pg. 772
CENTRAL CONVEYOR CO., LTD.—See IHI Corporation; *Int'l*, pg. 3604
THE CHANTLAND COMPANY—See Precision Inc.; *U.S. Private*, pg. 3245
CHANTLAND MHS CO.—See PVS Chemicals, Inc.; *U.S. Private*, pg. 3308
CIGNYS-SAGINAW; *U.S. Private*, pg. 897
CINETIC SORTING CORP.—See FIVES, Societe Anonyme; *Int'l*, pg. 2696
CLYDE PROCESS LTD.—See Blackstone Inc.; *U.S. Public*, pg. 360
CONTITECH CONVEYOR BELT GROUP—See Continental Aktiengesellschaft; *Int'l*, pg. 1781
CONTITECH TRANSPORTBANDSYSTEME GMBH—See Continental Aktiengesellschaft; *Int'l*, pg. 1781
CONTITECH TRANSPORTBANDSYSTEME GMBH—See Continental Aktiengesellschaft; *Int'l*, pg. 1781
CONVEYOR AGGREGATE PRODUCTS CORP.—See Purvis Bearing Service Ltd.; *U.S. Private*, pg. 3307
CONVEYOR TECHNOLOGIES INC.; *U.S. Private*, pg. 1036
COPERION K-TRON ASIA PTE. LTD.—See Hillenbrand, Inc.; *U.S. Public*, pg. 1036
COPERION K-TRON (SCHWEIZ) GMBH—See Hillenbrand, Inc.; *U.S. Public*, pg. 1036
CUSTOM CONVEYOR CORP.—See Schwing Bioset, Inc.; *U.S. Private*, pg. 3573
CUSTOM-METAL FABRICATORS, INC.; *U.S. Private*, pg. 1130
CVTEC CO., LTD.—See AISIN Corporation; *Int'l*, pg. 253
DAIDO CHAIN (CHANGSHU) CO., LTD.—See Daido Kogyo Co., Ltd.; *Int'l*, pg. 1920
DAIRY CONVEYOR CORPORATION; *U.S. Private*, pg. 1145
DAMIA AGRICULTURAL PRODUCTS COMPANY LTD.—See Future Arab Investment Co.; *Int'l*, pg. 2852
DAMON TECHNOLOGY GROUP CORP., LTD.; *Int'l*, pg. 1957
DAVIDSON-KENNEDY CO.; *U.S. Private*, pg. 1172
DEMATIC CORP.—See KKR & Co. Inc.; *U.S. Public*, pg. 1254
DEMATIC CORP.—See The Goldman Sachs Group, Inc.; *U.S. Public*, pg. 2078
DEMATIC GMBH—See KKR & Co. Inc.; *U.S. Public*, pg. 1254
DEMATIC GMBH—See KKR & Co. Inc.; *U.S. Public*, pg. 1254
DEMATIC GMBH—See The Goldman Sachs Group, Inc.; *U.S. Public*, pg. 2078
DEMATIC GMBH—See The Goldman Sachs Group, Inc.; *U.S. Public*, pg. 2078
DEMATIC PTY. LTD.—See KKR & Co. Inc.; *U.S. Public*, pg. 1254
DEMATIC PTY. LTD.—See The Goldman Sachs Group, Inc.; *U.S. Public*, pg. 2079
DOPPELMAYR SEILBAHNEN GMBH—See Doppelmayr Group; *Int'l*, pg. 2174
DORNER MANUFACTURING CORP.; *U.S. Private*, pg. 1263
DOUGLAS MANUFACTURING CO, INC.—See Rulmeca Corporation; *U.S. Private*, pg. 3503
DR. ING. GOSSLING MASCHINENFABRIK GMBH; *Int'l*, pg. 2192
DUNLOP SERVICE B.V.—See Compagnie Generale des Etablissements Michelin SCA; *Int'l*, pg. 1742
DURR POLAND SP. Z O.O.—See Durr AG; *Int'l*, pg. 2231
DURR SYSTEMS GMBH—See Durr AG; *Int'l*, pg. 2231
DURR SYSTEM SPAIN SA—See Durr AG; *Int'l*, pg. 2231
DURR SYSTEMS—See Durr AG; *Int'l*, pg. 2231
DYNAMIC AIR INC.; *U.S. Private*, pg. 1297
EGEMIN AUTOMATION INC.; *U.S. Private*, pg. 1344
EICKHOFF MASCHINENFABRIK GMBH; *Int'l*, pg. 2328
EMI CORP.; *U.S. Private*, pg. 1382
ESBELT, S.A.—See Asgco Manufacturing, Inc.; *U.S. Private*, pg. 349
ESSMUELLER COMPANY; *U.S. Private*, pg. 1428
EVERLANCE CO., LTD.; *Int'l*, pg. 2567
EXMAC AUTOMATION LIMITED—See L3Harris Technologies, Inc.; *U.S. Public*, pg. 1281
FATA AUTOMATION LIMITED—See CIEM S.p.A.; *Int'l*, pg. 1605
FB KETJUTEKNIIKKA OY—See Addtech AB; *Int'l*, pg. 133
FB KETTEN GMBH—See Addtech AB; *Int'l*, pg. 133
FENNER CONVEYOR BELTING PRIVATE LIMITED—See Compagnie Generale des Etablissements Michelin SCA; *Int'l*, pg. 1744
FENNER CONVEYOR BELTING (SOUTH AFRICA) (PTY) LIMITED—See Compagnie Generale des Etablissements Michelin SCA; *Int'l*, pg. 1744
FENNER DUNLOP (ATLANTA), INC.—See Compagnie Generale des Etablissements Michelin SCA; *Int'l*, pg. 1744
FENNER DUNLOP AUSTRALIA PTY. LTD.—See Compagnie Generale des Etablissements Michelin SCA; *Int'l*, pg. 1744
FENNER DUNLOP (BRACEBRIDGE) INC.—See Compagnie Generale des Etablissements Michelin SCA; *Int'l*, pg. 1744
FENNER DUNLOP BV—See Compagnie Generale des Etablissements Michelin SCA; *Int'l*, pg. 1745
FENNER DUNLOP CONVEYOR SYSTEMS & SERVICES, LLC.—See Compagnie Generale des Etablissements Michelin SCA; *Int'l*, pg. 1744
FENNER DUNLOP ITALIA S.R.L.—See Compagnie Generale des Etablissements Michelin SCA; *Int'l*, pg. 1742
FENNER DUNLOP LIMITED—See Compagnie Generale des Etablissements Michelin SCA; *Int'l*, pg. 1744
FENNER DUNLOP (PORT CLINTON), INC.—See Compagnie Generale des Etablissements Michelin SCA; *Int'l*, pg. 1744
FENNER DUNLOP SARL—See Compagnie Generale des Etablissements Michelin SCA; *Int'l*, pg. 1742
FENNER DUNLOP S.L.—See Compagnie Generale des Etablissements Michelin SCA; *Int'l*, pg. 1742
FENNER DUNLOP (TOLEDO), LLC—See Compagnie Generale des Etablissements Michelin SCA; *Int'l*, pg. 1744
FESTO AG & CO. KG; *Int'l*, pg. 2646
FIELDQUIP PTY LTD.—See Alamo Group Inc.; *U.S. Public*, pg. 71
FLEETWOODGOLDCOWYARD AMBEC, INC.—See Barry-Wehmiller Companies, Inc.; *U.S. Private*, pg. 481
FLEETWOODGOLDCOWYARD—See Barry-Wehmiller Companies, Inc.; *U.S. Private*, pg. 481

N.A.I.C.S. INDEX

333923 — OVERHEAD TRAVELING ...

FLEETWOODGOLDCOWYARD—See Barry-Wehmiller Companies, Inc.; *U.S. Private*, pg. 481
FLEXCO (AUST) PTY. LTD—See Flexible Steel Lacing Company; *U.S. Private*, pg. 1544
FLEXCO CONVEYING EQUIPMENT TRADING (SHANGHAI) CO., LTD.—See Flexible Steel Lacing Company; *U.S. Private*, pg. 1544
FLEXLINK AB—See Coesia S.p.A.; *Int'l*, pg. 1689
FMH CONVEYORS, LLC - JONESBORO OPERATIONS—See Warburg Pincus LLC; *U.S. Private*, pg. 4437
FMH CONVEYORS LLC—See Warburg Pincus LLC; *U.S. Private*, pg. 4437
F.N. SHEPPARD & CO.; *U.S. Private*, pg. 1456
FORBO SIEGLING (THAILAND) CO. LTD.—See Forbo Holding Ltd.; *Int'l*, pg. 2730
FOSHAN GOLDEN MILKY WAY INTELLIGENT EQUIPMENT CO., LTD.; *Int'l*, pg. 2748
FROST EUROPE, S.L.—See Frost Inc.; *U.S. Private*, pg. 1616
FROST INC.; *U.S. Private*, pg. 1616
FROST LINKS, INC.—See Frost Inc.; *U.S. Private*, pg. 1616
FUJITEC VENEZUELA C.A.—See Fujitec Co., Ltd.; *Int'l*, pg. 2831
GARVEY CORPORATION—See Columbus McKinnon Corporation; *U.S. Public*, pg. 536
GEA NU-CON MANUFACTURING LIMITED—See GEA Group Aktiengesellschaft; *Int'l*, pg. 2901
GOESSLING USA, INC.—See Dr. Ing. Gossling Maschinenfabrik GmbH; *Int'l*, pg. 2192
GOWER CORPORATION; *U.S. Private*, pg. 1747
THE GSI GROUP (SHANGHAI) CO. LTD—See AGCO Corporation; *U.S. Public*, pg. 59
HANS BINDER MASCHINENBAU GMBH—See EnWave Corporation; *Int'l*, pg. 2456
HANSEN MANUFACTURING CORP.—See Ag Growth International Inc.; *Int'l*, pg. 198
HARRY MAJOR MACHINE & TOOL CO.; *U.S. Private*, pg. 1872
HARVEST INTERNATIONAL INC.; *U.S. Private*, pg. 1875
HENRY FILTERS (EUROPE) LTD.—See Durr AG; *Int'l*, pg. 2233
HIMEC CONVEYORS INC—See Harris Companies; *U.S. Private*, pg. 1869
HMS PRODUCTS CO.; *U.S. Private*, pg. 1955
HOMECARE PRODUCTS, INC.; *U.S. Private*, pg. 1973
HORIZON SYSTEMS, INC.; *U.S. Private*, pg. 1982
HUACHANGDA INTELLIGENT EQUIPMENT GROUP CO., LTD.; *Int'l*, pg. 3511
HYTROL CONVEYOR CO., INC.; *U.S. Private*, pg. 2020
IAMECH TECHNOLOGY INC.—See Contrel Technology Co., Ltd.; *Int'l*, pg. 1785
INTELLIGRATED, INC.—See Honeywell International Inc.; *U.S. Public*, pg. 1051
INTERNATIONAL LIFT SYSTEMS, LLC—See KPS Capital Partners, LP; *U.S. Private*, pg. 2347
INTERSYSTEMS INTERNATIONAL, LLC—See AGCO Corporation; *U.S. Public*, pg. 58
INTRALOX (INDIA) PRIVATE LTD.—See The Laitram LLC; *U.S. Private*, pg. 4067
INTRALOX LLC—See The Laitram LLC; *U.S. Private*, pg. 4067
INTRALOX SHANGHAI LTD.—See The Laitram LLC; *U.S. Private*, pg. 4067
IZUTECH CORPORATION - SHINSHIRO PLANT—See Fair Friend Group; *Int'l*, pg. 2604
IZUTECH CORPORATION—See Fair Friend Group; *Int'l*, pg. 2604
JERVIS B. WEBB COMPANY LTD.—See Daifuku Co., Ltd.; *Int'l*, pg. 1925
JERVIS B. WEBB COMPANY OF CANADA LTD.—See Daifuku Co., Ltd.; *Int'l*, pg. 1925
JOHN BEAN TECHNOLOGIES AUTOMATED GUIDED VEHICLES, INC.—See Oshkosh Corporation; *U.S. Public*, pg. 1620
JORGENSEN CONVEYORS, INC.—See Innovance, Inc.; *U.S. Private*, pg. 2081
JOY GLOBAL CONVEYORS INC.—See Stellex Capital Management LP; *U.S. Private*, pg. 3800
KEY HANDLING SYSTEMS, INC.; *U.S. Private*, pg. 2293
KLATT FORDERTECHNIK GMBH—See Hormann Holding GmbH & Co. KG; *Int'l*, pg. 3480
KLEENLINE, LLC—See Leonard Green & Partners, L.P.; *U.S. Private*, pg. 2428
KNIGHT INDUSTRIES & ASSOCIATES INC.; *U.S. Private*, pg. 2322
K-TRON PROCESS GROUP—See Hillenbrand, Inc.; *U.S. Public*, pg. 1037
THE LAITRAM LLC; *U.S. Private*, pg. 4067
LANE CONVEYORS & DRIVES, INC.; *U.S. Private*, pg. 2387
MACGREGOR (PRT) LDA.—See Cargotec Corporation; *Int'l*, pg. 1328
MADA S.P.A.—See CIEM S.p.A.; *Int'l*, pg. 1605
MALLARD MANUFACTURING CORP.—See MacLean-Fogg Co.; *U.S. Private*, pg. 2537
MATERIAL HANDLING SYSTEMS, INC.—See Thomas H. Lee Partners, L.P.; *U.S. Private*, pg. 4156
MAYFRAN INTERNATIONAL, B.V.—See Mayfran International, Inc.; *U.S. Private*, pg. 2622
MAYFRAN INTERNATIONAL, INC.; *U.S. Private*, pg. 2622
METZGAR CONVEYOR COMPANY; *U.S. Private*, pg. 2691
MEYER INDUSTRIES INC.; *U.S. Private*, pg. 2692
MOHLER MATERIAL HANDLING, INC.; *U.S. Private*, pg. 2765
MOTAN, INC.; *U.S. Private*, pg. 2795
MOUAT COMPANY INC.; *U.S. Private*, pg. 2797
MYOTOKU LTD. - IWATE PLANT—See Convum Ltd.; *Int'l*, pg. 1788
NCC AUTOMATED SYSTEMS, INC.—See ATS Corporation; *Int'l*, pg. 695
NEXEL INDUSTRIES, INC.—See Global Industrial Company; *U.S. Public*, pg. 942
NOL-TEC SYSTEMS INC.; *U.S. Private*, pg. 2933
NUMINA GROUP, INCORPORATED; *U.S. Private*, pg. 2973
OHIO BLOW PIPE COMPANY; *U.S. Private*, pg. 3003
OLPIDURR S.T.A—See Durr AG; *Int'l*, pg. 2233
OVERHEAD CONVEYOR CO.; *U.S. Private*, pg. 3053
PACIFIC CONVEYOR SYSTEMS, INC.—See Blower Dempsay Corporation; *U.S. Private*, pg. 584
PARKER HANNIFIN B.V.—See Parker Hannifin Corporation; *U.S. Public*, pg. 1646
PARKER HANNIFIN DANMARK A/S—See Parker Hannifin Corporation; *U.S. Public*, pg. 1646
PARKER HANNIFIN PLC—See Parker Hannifin Corporation; *U.S. Public*, pg. 1644
POWERSCREEN USA LLC—See Terex Corporation; *U.S. Public*, pg. 2020
PPM TECHNOLOGIES EMEA LTD.—See Warburg Pincus LLC; *U.S. Private*, pg. 4438
PPM TECHNOLOGIES INDIA LTD.—See Warburg Pincus LLC; *U.S. Private*, pg. 4438
PRAB, INC.; *U.S. Private*, pg. 3241
PRODUCTION INDUSTRIES INC.—See Frost Inc.; *U.S. Private*, pg. 1616
PRO SYSTEMS, LLC—See Lincoln Electric Holdings, Inc.; *U.S. Public*, pg. 1318
RAPID INDUSTRIES, INC.; *U.S. Private*, pg. 3356
REA INDIA PTE. LTD.—See News Corporation; *U.S. Public*, pg. 1521
REGIONAL SUPPLY, LLC—See Platte River Ventures, LLC; *U.S. Private*, pg. 3211
REXNORD ASIA PACIFIC PTE. LTD.—See Zurn Elkay Water Solutions Corporation; *U.S. Public*, pg. 2413
REXNORD FINANCE BV—See Zurn Elkay Water Solutions Corporation; *U.S. Public*, pg. 2413
REXNORD FLATTOP EUROPE BV—See Zurn Elkay Water Solutions Corporation; *U.S. Public*, pg. 2413
REXNORD FLATTOP EUROPE SRL—See Zurn Elkay Water Solutions Corporation; *U.S. Public*, pg. 2413
REXNORD I.H. B.V.—See Zurn Elkay Water Solutions Corporation; *U.S. Public*, pg. 2413
REXNORD KETTE GMBH—See Zurn Elkay Water Solutions Corporation; *U.S. Public*, pg. 2413
REXNORD MARBETT SRL—See Zurn Elkay Water Solutions Corporation; *U.S. Public*, pg. 2413
REXNORD MIDDLE EAST FZE—See Zurn Elkay Water Solutions Corporation; *U.S. Public*, pg. 2413
REXNORD S.A. DE C.V.—See Zurn Elkay Water Solutions Corporation; *U.S. Public*, pg. 2413
RITE-HITE MATERIAL HANDLING EQUIPMENT (KUNSHAN) CO., LTD.—See Rite-Hite Holding Corporation; *U.S. Private*, pg. 3442
ROTEC INDUSTRIES INC.; *U.S. Private*, pg. 3486
SCREW CONVEYOR INDUSTRIES; *U.S. Private*, pg. 3579
SCREW CONVEYOR INDUSTRIES - VISALIA PLANT—See Screw Conveyor Industries; *U.S. Private*, pg. 3579
SCREW CONVEYOR INDUSTRIES - WINONA PLANT—See Screw Conveyor Industries; *U.S. Private*, pg. 3579
SENTRY EQUIPMENT ERECTORS INC.—See Leonard Green & Partners, L.P.; *U.S. Private*, pg. 2428
SHUTTLEWORTH EUROPE N.V.—See Leonard Green & Partners, L.P.; *U.S. Private*, pg. 2428
SHUTTLEWORTH, LLC—See Leonard Green & Partners, L.P.; *U.S. Private*, pg. 2428
SIMPLICITY ENGINEERING, INC.—See Terex Corporation; *U.S. Public*, pg. 2020
SI SYSTEMS, INC.—See Paragon Technologies, Inc.; *U.S. Public*, pg. 1637
SOUTHERN SYSTEMS, INC.; *U.S. Private*, pg. 3735
SPAREX MASCHINENSUBEHOR HANDELSGESELLSCHAFT M.B.H—See AGCO Corporation; *U.S. Public*, pg. 59
SPARKS BELTING COMPANY—See JSJ Corporation; *U.S. Private*, pg. 2241
SPECTRUM AUTOMATION COMPANY—See Huizenga Manufacturing Group, Inc.; *U.S. Private*, pg. 2004
STACY EQUIPMENT CO.—See MPE Partners, LLC; *U.S. Private*, pg. 2804
STEEL STORAGE SYSTEMS, INC.; *U.S. Private*, pg. 3796
STOCK EQUIPMENT COMPANY INC.—See Blackstone Inc.; *U.S. Public*, pg. 360
STOCK REDLER LIMITED—See Blackstone Inc.; *U.S. Public*, pg. 360
SUN BELT INC.—See Platte River Ventures, LLC; *U.S. Private*, pg. 3211
SUPERIOR INDUSTRIES, INC.; *U.S. Private*, pg. 3878
SYNTRON MATERIAL HANDLING GROUP, LLC—See Kadrant Inc.; *U.S. Public*, pg. 1212
TANGSHAN DBT MACHINERY CO., LTD.—See Caterpillar, Inc.; *U.S. Public*, pg. 454
TEREX GB LIMITED—See Terex Corporation; *U.S. Public*, pg. 2019
THOMAS CONVEYOR COMPANY; *U.S. Private*, pg. 4155
TRAMCO INC.—See Ag Growth International Inc.; *Int'l*, pg. 198
TRANSTEX BELTING—See Forbo Holding Ltd.; *Int'l*, pg. 2729
TRIBELT B.V.—See Beijer Alma AB; *Int'l*, pg. 943
TRIPLE/S DYNAMICS, INC.; *U.S. Private*, pg. 4237
TUTTLE, INC.—See LFM Capital LLC; *U.S. Private*, pg. 2441
UNEX MANUFACTURING, INC.; *U.S. Private*, pg. 4281
VAN GORP CORPORATION—See Precision Inc.; *U.S. Private*, pg. 3245
VAN OWEN GROUP ACQUISITION COMPANY; *U.S. Private*, pg. 4340
VIS GMBH—See ManpowerGroup Inc.; *U.S. Public*, pg. 1362
WARD INDUSTRIAL EQUIPMENT LTD—See Dynamic Technologies Group Inc.; *Int'l*, pg. 2241
WEBB-STILES COMPANY; *U.S. Private*, pg. 4464
WEBSTER INDUSTRIES INC.—See MPE Partners, LLC; *U.S. Private*, pg. 2803
WEBSTER MANUFACTURING CO.—See MPE Partners, LLC; *U.S. Private*, pg. 2804
WESTERN PNEUMATICS, INC.—See Insight Equity Holdings LLC; *U.S. Private*, pg. 2086
WESTFALIA TECHNOLOGIES, INC.; *U.S. Private*, pg. 4498
WILLIAM W. MEYER & SONS INC.; *U.S. Private*, pg. 4525
WIN WIN, INC.; *U.S. Private*, pg. 4532
WPS INDUSTRIES INC.; *U.S. Private*, pg. 4571

333923 — OVERHEAD TRAVELING CRANE, HOIST, AND MONORAIL SYSTEM MANUFACTURING

ACCO MATERIAL HANDLING SOLUTIONS, INC.—See KKR & Co. Inc.; *U.S. Public*, pg. 1239
ACE WINCHES NORGE AS—See Ashtead Technology Holdings Plc; *Int'l*, pg. 609
ADC BRETAGNE—See FAYAT SAS; *Int'l*, pg. 2624
ADC MEDITERRANEE—See FAYAT SAS; *Int'l*, pg. 2624
ADC NORD—See FAYAT SAS; *Int'l*, pg. 2624
ADC NORMANDIE—See FAYAT SAS; *Int'l*, pg. 2624
ADC RHONE-ALPES—See FAYAT SAS; *Int'l*, pg. 2624
ADC SUD-OUEST—See FAYAT SAS; *Int'l*, pg. 2624
AHERN AUSTRALIA PTY. LTD.—See Xtreme Manufacturing, LLC; *U.S. Private*, pg. 4583
AICHI AUS PTY LTD—See Aichi Corporation; *Int'l*, pg. 229
ALFRED CHEYNE ENGINEERING LIMITED—See Ashtead Technology Holdings Plc; *Int'l*, pg. 609
ALLIED SYSTEMS COMPANY; *U.S. Private*, pg. 188
ALLIED SYSTEMS—See Allied Systems Company; *U.S. Private*, pg. 188
ALLSAFE JUNGFALK GMBH & CO. KG; *Int'l*, pg. 360
AMERICAN CRANE & EQUIPMENT CORPORATION - SERVICE, PARTS & STANDARD CRANE DIVISION—See American Crane & Equipment Corporation; *U.S. Private*, pg. 229
AMERICAN CRANE & EQUIPMENT CORPORATION; *U.S. Private*, pg. 229
AMERICAN EQUIPMENT, INC.—See Rotunda Capital Partners LLC; *U.S. Private*, pg. 3487
AMESBURY TRUTH—See Quanex Building Products Corp.; *U.S. Public*, pg. 1749
ANCRA ABT AB—See The Heico Companies, L.L.C.; *U.S. Private*, pg. 4050
ANCRA AUSTRALIA PTY. LTD.—See The Heico Companies, L.L.C.; *U.S. Private*, pg. 4050
ANCRA ESPANA—See The Heico Companies, L.L.C.; *U.S. Private*, pg. 4050
ANCRA INTERNATIONAL LLC—See The Heico Companies, L.L.C.; *U.S. Private*, pg. 4050
ANCRA INTERNATIONAL SARL—See The Heico Companies, L.L.C.; *U.S. Private*, pg. 4050
ANCRA JAPAN LTD.—See allsafe JUNGFALK GmbH & Co. KG; *Int'l*, pg. 360
ARCOMET & CO.; *Int'l*, pg. 550
BCES—See FAYAT SAS; *Int'l*, pg. 2624
BEIJING JINGCHENG HEAVY INDUSTRY CO., LTD.—See Beijing Jingcheng Machinery Electric Holding Co., Ltd.; *Int'l*, pg. 953
BULBULOGLU VINC SANAYII VE TICARET A.S.—See FAYAT SAS; *Int'l*, pg. 2624
CARGOTEC FRANCE S.A.S.—See Cargotec Corporation; *Int'l*, pg. 1326
CARGOTEC SWEDEN AB—See Cargotec Corporation; *Int'l*, pg. 1327
CAVOTEC GROUP HOLDINGS NV—See Cavotec SA; *Int'l*, pg. 1362

333923 — OVERHEAD TRAVELING ...

CAVOTEC KOREA LTD—See Cavotec SA; *Int'l*, pg. 1363
CHESTER HOIST—See Columbus McKinnon Corporation; *U.S. Public*, pg. 535
CM HOIST DIVISION—See Columbus McKinnon Corporation; *U.S. Public*, pg. 535
COMETE—See FAYAT SAS; *Int'l*, pg. 2625
CRANETECH, INC.—See Balance Point Capital Advisors, LLC; *U.S. Private*, pg. 457
CRANE TECH SOLUTIONS, LLC; *U.S. Private*, pg. 1085
CRANEX LIMITED; *Int'l*, pg. 1828
DEARBORN CRANE & ENGINEERING CO.; *U.S. Private*, pg. 1185
DOPPELMAYR FRANCE S.A.—See Doppelmayr Group; *Int'l*, pg. 2174
DOWNS CRANE & HOIST CO, INC.; *U.S. Private*, pg. 1269
DP WINCH—See Dover Corporation; *U.S. Public*, pg. 679
DUBAI CRANES & TECHNICAL SERVICES LTD.—See Dubai Investments PJSC; *Int'l*, pg. 2219
DURAFERRO INDUSTRIA E COMERCIO LTDA.—See Bardella S.A. Industrias Mecanicas; *Int'l*, pg. 864
DY CORPORATION; *Int'l*, pg. 2237
DY IKSAN—See DY Corporation; *Int'l*, pg. 2237
DYNACON, INC.—See Forum Energy Technologies, Inc.; *U.S. Public*, pg. 873
EAGLE CREEK, INC.—See V. F. Corporation; *U.S. Public*, pg. 2268
ELITE TOOLS LTD.—See Atlantic China Welding Consumables, Inc.; *Int'l*, pg. 674
ENCORE METALS—See Reliance Steel & Aluminum Co.; *U.S. Public*, pg. 1781
FERING D.D.; *Int'l*, pg. 2638
FIROUZA ENGINEERING COMPANY; *Int'l*, pg. 2681
FISKARS BRANDS GERMANY GMBH—See Fiskars Oyj Abp; *Int'l*, pg. 2693
FISKARS DANMARK A/S—See Fiskars Oyj Abp; *Int'l*, pg. 2694
FISKARS FRANCE S.A.R.L.—See Fiskars Oyj Abp; *Int'l*, pg. 2694
FISKARS NORGE A/S—See Fiskars Oyj Abp; *Int'l*, pg. 2694
FURUKAWA UNIC CORPORATION - SAKURA UNIT—See Furukawa Co., Ltd.; *Int'l*, pg. 2847
FURUKAWA UNIC CORPORATION—See Furukawa Co., Ltd.; *Int'l*, pg. 2847
FURUKAWA UNIC (THAILAND) CO., LTD.—See Furukawa Co., Ltd.; *Int'l*, pg. 2847
GENIE AUSTRALIA PTY. LTD.—See Terex Corporation; *U.S. Public*, pg. 2019
GENIE BRASIL LTDA—See Terex Corporation; *U.S. Public*, pg. 2019
GENIE FRANCE S.A.R.L.—See Terex Corporation; *U.S. Public*, pg. 2019
GENIE INDUSTRIES IBERICA, S.L.—See Terex Corporation; *U.S. Public*, pg. 2019
GENIE INDUSTRIES, INC.—See Terex Corporation; *U.S. Public*, pg. 2019
GENIE MANUFACTURING, INC.—See Terex Corporation; *U.S. Public*, pg. 2019
HARRINGTON HOISTS, INC.—See The Carlyle Group Inc.; *U.S. Public*, pg. 2055
HIAB CRANES, S.L.—See Cargotec Corporation; *Int'l*, pg. 1326
HIAB LTD.—See Cargotec Corporation; *Int'l*, pg. 1327
HIAB S.A. DE C.V.—See Cargotec Corporation; *Int'l*, pg. 1327
HIAB S.A./N.V.—See Cargotec Corporation; *Int'l*, pg. 1327
INDEPENDENT ROUGH TERRAIN CENTER LLC—See Congruent Investment Partners, LLC; *U.S. Private*, pg. 1014
INDEPENDENT ROUGH TERRAIN CENTER LLC—See IBC Management, Inc.; *U.S. Private*, pg. 2028
INTEGRATED MACHINERY SOLUTIONS, LLC—See DeSHAZO Service Company, LLC; *U.S. Private*, pg. 1213
INTERSEAS SHIPPING (PRIVATE) LIMITED—See Baker Technology Limited; *Int'l*, pg. 805
JERED, LLC—See Pohlad Companies; *U.S. Private*, pg. 3220
JLG DEUTSCHLAND GMBH—See Oshkosh Corporation; *U.S. Public*, pg. 1620
JLG INDUSTRIES, INC.—See Oshkosh Corporation; *U.S. Public*, pg. 1620
JLG INDUSTRIES (ITALIA) S.R.L.—See Oshkosh Corporation; *U.S. Public*, pg. 1620
JLG LATINO AMERICANA LTDA.—See Oshkosh Corporation; *U.S. Public*, pg. 1620
JLG SVERIGE AB—See Oshkosh Corporation; *U.S. Public*, pg. 1620
KALMAR B.V.—See Cargotec Corporation; *Int'l*, pg. 1327
KALMAR INDUSTRIES AB—See Cargotec Corporation; *Int'l*, pg. 1327
KALMAR INDUSTRIES OY AB—See Cargotec Corporation; *Int'l*, pg. 1327
KRANBAU KOETHEN GMBH—See Georgsmarienhutte Holding GmbH; *Int'l*, pg. 2940
LIFTUP AS—See Alfa Laval AB; *Int'l*, pg. 312
LOGLIFT JONSERED AB—See Cargotec Corporation; *Int'l*, pg. 1327
MACGREGOR (CYPRUS) LTD.—See Cargotec Corporation; *Int'l*, pg. 1328
MANITEX INTERNATIONAL, INC.; *U.S. Public*, pg. 1356
MANITOWOC CRANES, INC.—See The Manitowoc Company, Inc.; *U.S. Public*, pg. 2111
MANITOWOC RE-MANUFACTURING, INC.—See The Manitowoc Company, Inc.; *U.S. Public*, pg. 2111
MARMON CRANE SERVICES, INC.—See Berkshire Hathaway Inc.; *U.S. Public*, pg. 309
MGX EQUIPMENT SERVICES, LLC—See The Manitowoc Company, Inc.; *U.S. Public*, pg. 2111
MOFFETT ENGINEERING LTD—See Cargotec Corporation; *Int'l*, pg. 1329
MOTA GROUP, INC.; *U.S. Private*, pg. 2795
OMH, INC.; *U.S. Private*, pg. 3016
OSHKOSH-JLG (SHANGHAI) ENTERPRISE DEVELOPMENT CO., LTD.—See Oshkosh Corporation; *U.S. Public*, pg. 1621
PACCAR WINCH DIVISION—See PACCAR Inc.; *U.S. Public*, pg. 1631
PLATFORMA ELEVADORAS JLG IBERICA S.L.—See Oshkosh Corporation; *U.S. Public*, pg. 1620
PLATNICK STEEL & ENGINEERING, INC.—See Spencer Mac Corporation; *U.S. Private*, pg. 3755
QIQIHAR RAILWAY ROLLING STOCK CO., LTD.—See CRRC Corporation Limited; *Int'l*, pg. 1859
RAMSEY INDUSTRIES INC.—See Gridiron Capital, LLC; *U.S. Private*, pg. 1786
RAMSEY WINCH COMPANY INC.—See Gridiron Capital, LLC; *U.S. Private*, pg. 1786
RE.MAC.UT, S.R.L.—See NOV, Inc.; *U.S. Public*, pg. 1546
SEA DEEP SHIPYARD PTE. LTD—See Baker Technology Limited; *Int'l*, pg. 805
SHORELINE INDUSTRIES, INC.—See Otter Tail Corporation; *U.S. Public*, pg. 1624
SHUTTLELIFT, INC.—See Marine Travelift, Inc.; *U.S. Private*, pg. 2575
SICHUAN CHANGJIANG ENGINEERING CRANE CO., LTD.—See Terex Corporation; *U.S. Public*, pg. 2019
SIEMPELKAMP KRANTECHNIK GMBH—See G. Siempelkamp GmbH & Co. KG; *Int'l*, pg. 2865
SNORKEL EUROPE LIMITED—See Xtreme Manufacturing, LLC; *U.S. Private*, pg. 4583
SNORKEL INTERNATIONAL, LLC—See Xtreme Manufacturing, LLC; *U.S. Private*, pg. 4583
STAHL CRANESYSTEMS GMBH—See Columbus McKinnon Corporation; *U.S. Public*, pg. 536
STAHL CRANESYSTEMS (INDIA) PVT. LTD.—See Columbus McKinnon Corporation; *U.S. Public*, pg. 536
STAHL CRANESYSTEMS TRADING (SHANGHAI) CO. LTD.—See Columbus McKinnon Corporation; *U.S. Public*, pg. 536
STIEFEL GMBH & CO. KG—See GSK plc; *Int'l*, pg. 3149
SUMNER MANUFACTURING CO., INC.—See Southwire Company, LLC; *U.S. Private*, pg. 3742
TC/AMERICAN CRANE COMPANY—See Orion Financial Corp.; *U.S. Private*, pg. 3043
TC/AMERICAN CRANE COMPANY—See Stewart Capital Partners LLC; *U.S. Private*, pg. 3811
TEREX CRANES, INC.—See Terex Corporation; *U.S. Public*, pg. 2019
TEREX ITALIA S.R.L.—See Terex Corporation; *U.S. Public*, pg. 2019
TEREX LIFTING AUSTRALIA PTY. LTD.—See Terex Corporation; *U.S. Public*, pg. 2019
TEREX MALAYSIA SDN BHD—See Terex Corporation; *U.S. Public*, pg. 2020
TEREX MATERIAL HANDLING AG—See Terex Corporation; *U.S. Public*, pg. 2020
TEREX MATERIAL HANDLING A/S—See Terex Corporation; *U.S. Public*, pg. 2020
TEREX MATERIAL HANDLING GMBH—See Terex Corporation; *U.S. Public*, pg. 2020
TEREX MATERIAL HANDLING SPOL. S.R.O.—See Terex Corporation; *U.S. Public*, pg. 2020
TEREX MATERIAL HANDLING SP. Z O.O.—See Terex Corporation; *U.S. Public*, pg. 2020
TEREX SOUTH DAKOTA, INC.—See Terex Corporation; *U.S. Public*, pg. 2020
TIANJIN GOLDSUN WIRE ROPE LTD.—See Golik Holdings Limited; *Int'l*, pg. 3036
TK RENTALS SDN. BHD.—See Hextar Industries Berhad; *Int'l*, pg. 3373
TORSIT BV—See Henkel + Gerlach GmbH & Co. KG; *Int'l*, pg. 3348
TTS BOHAI MACHINERY CO., LTD.—See Cargotec Corporation; *Int'l*, pg. 1329
TTS MARINE SHANGHAI CO., LTD.—See Cargotec Corporation; *Int'l*, pg. 1329
TTS OFFSHORE HANDLING EQUIPMENT AS—See Cargotec Corporation; *Int'l*, pg. 1329
TULSA WINCH, INC.—See Dover Corporation; *U.S. Public*, pg. 679
TUTT BRYANT GROUP LIMITED - CRANE HIRE DIVISION—See Affirma Capital Limited; *Int'l*, pg. 188
UNIFIED INDUSTRIES, INC.—See Columbus McKinnon Corporation; *U.S. Public*, pg. 536
WALTCO LIFT CORP.—See Cargotec Corporation; *Int'l*, pg. 1329
WERGA-TOOLS GMBH—See Fiskars Oyj Abp; *Int'l*, pg. 2694
WHEELTRONIC LTD.—See Snap-on Incorporated; *U.S. Public*, pg. 1899
WILHITE CRANE SERVICE, INC.; *U.S. Private*, pg. 4520
WINDHOFF BAHN- UND ANLAGENTECHNIK GMBH—See Georgsmarienhutte Holding GmbH; *Int'l*, pg. 2941
ZENAR CORPORATION; *U.S. Private*, pg. 4601

333924 — INDUSTRIAL TRUCK, TRACTOR, TRAILER, AND STACKER MACHINERY MANUFACTURING

ACCO MATERIAL HANDLING SOLUTIONS, INC. - NUTTING DIVISION—See KKR & Co. Inc.; *U.S. Public*, pg. 1239
AEBI SCHMIDT NORGE AS—See Aebi Schmidt Holding AG; *Int'l*, pg. 170
AGCO MEXICO S DE RL DE CV—See AGCO Corporation; *U.S. Public*, pg. 58
A.G. PRUDEN & CIA. S.A.—See KKR & Co. Inc.; *U.S. Public*, pg. 1254
A.G. PRUDEN & CIA. S.A.—See The Goldman Sachs Group, Inc.; *U.S. Public*, pg. 2079
AICHI CORPORATION; *Int'l*, pg. 229
AL-BABTAIN BODY MANUFACTURING CO.—See Al-Babtain Group; *Int'l*, pg. 284
AL-GHAZI TRACTORS LIMITED; *Int'l*, pg. 285
ALLOY CUSTOM PRODUCTS, LLC—See Cryogenic Industrial Solutions, Inc.; *U.S. Private*, pg. 1115
AMERICAN TRAILER WORKS, INC.—See Bain Capital, LP; *U.S. Private*, pg. 436
ANHUI HELI CO., LTD.; *Int'l*, pg. 467
ARROW ENGINE COMPANY—See TriMas Corporation; *U.S. Public*, pg. 2189
ASKO HOLDING A.S.; *Int'l*, pg. 624
AURAMO OY—See Hyster-Yale Materials Handling, Inc.; *U.S. Public*, pg. 1079
AUTO CRANE COMPANY—See Gridiron Capital, LLC; *U.S. Private*, pg. 1786
BETA FUELING SYSTEMS, LLC—See Alfons Haar Maschinenbau GmbH & Co. KG; *Int'l*, pg. 315
BLADES TECHNOLOGY LTD.—See RTX Corporation; *U.S. Public*, pg. 1821
BOLIN AUTO & TRUCK PARTS CO., INC.—See American Securities LLC; *U.S. Private*, pg. 248
BOLZONI AURAMO BV—See Hyster-Yale Materials Handling, Inc.; *U.S. Public*, pg. 1080
BOLZONI AURAMO GMBH—See Hyster-Yale Materials Handling, Inc.; *U.S. Public*, pg. 1080
BOLZONI AURAMO INC.—See Hyster-Yale Materials Handling, Inc.; *U.S. Public*, pg. 1079
BOLZONI AURAMO (PTY) LTD—See Hyster-Yale Materials Handling, Inc.; *U.S. Public*, pg. 1079
BOLZONI AURAMO (WUXI) FORKLIFT TRUCK ATTACHMENT CO. LTD.—See Hyster-Yale Materials Handling, Inc.; *U.S. Public*, pg. 1079
BOLZONI CAPITAL HOLDING B.V.—See Hyster-Yale Materials Handling, Inc.; *U.S. Public*, pg. 1079
BOLZONI (HEBEI) FORKS—See Hyster-Yale Materials Handling, Inc.; *U.S. Public*, pg. 1079
BOLZONI ITALIA SRL—See Hyster-Yale Materials Handling, Inc.; *U.S. Public*, pg. 1079
BOLZONI SARL—See Hyster-Yale Materials Handling, Inc.; *U.S. Public*, pg. 1080
BOLZONI SOUTH AMERICA LTDA.—See Hyster-Yale Materials Handling, Inc.; *U.S. Public*, pg. 1080
BPR-RICO EQUIPMENT INC.; *U.S. Private*, pg. 630
BRODERSON MANUFACTURING CORP.—See Lanco International Inc.; *U.S. Private*, pg. 2382
BROMMA (MALAYSIA) SDN. BHD.—See Cargotec Corporation; *Int'l*, pg. 1326
BUCHER LANDTECHNIK AG—See Bucher Industries AG; *Int'l*, pg. 1208
CAPACITY OF TEXAS, INC. - LAYMOR DIVISION—See AIP, LLC; *U.S. Private*, pg. 135
CAPACITY OF TEXAS, INC.—See AIP, LLC; *U.S. Private*, pg. 135
CARGOTEC NETHERLANDS B.V.—See Cargotec Corporation; *Int'l*, pg. 1326
CAVOTEC INTERNATIONAL LTD—See Cavotec SA; *Int'l*, pg. 1362
CONCORD CONCRETE PUMPS INC.; *Int'l*, pg. 1764
CROWN EQUIPMENT CORPORATION; *U.S. Private*, pg. 1111
CURTIS INDUSTRIES, LLC—See Nautic Partners, LLC; *U.S. Private*, pg. 2868
CUSTOM TRUCK & EQUIPMENT, LLC—See Custom Truck One Source, Inc.; *U.S. Public*, pg. 612
DAIMLER TRUCK AUSTRALIA PACIFIC PTY. LTD.—See Daimler Truck Holding AG; *Int'l*, pg. 1938
DAIMLER TRUCK SOUTHERN AFRICA LTD.—See Daimler Truck Holding AG; *Int'l*, pg. 1938
DEL EQUIPMENT (UK) LTD.—See Cargotec Corporation; *Int'l*, pg. 1327
DELLNER BRAKES AB; *Int'l*, pg. 2013
DEUTRUCK GMBH; *Int'l*, pg. 2049

333924 — INDUSTRIAL TRUCK, T...

DOEPKER INDUSTRIES LTD.; *Int'l*, pg. 2153
DOOSAN INDUSTRIAL VEHICLE AMERICA CORP.—See Doosan Corporation; *Int'l*, pg. 2173
DOOSAN INDUSTRIAL VEHICLE EUROPE N.V.—See Doosan Corporation; *Int'l*, pg. 2173
DOOSAN INDUSTRIAL VEHICLE U.K. LTD.—See Doosan Corporation; *Int'l*, pg. 2173
DOOSAN INFRACORE XINJIANG MACHINERY CO., LTD.—See HD Hyundai Infracore Co., Ltd.; *Int'l*, pg. 3300
DOVER FRANCE HOLDINGS, S.A.S.—See Dover Corporation; *U.S. Public*, pg. 680
EDNIL D.O.O. SARAJEVO—See KKR & Co. Inc.; *U.S. Public*, pg. 1254
EDNIL D.O.O. SARAJEVO—See The Goldman Sachs Group, Inc.; *U.S. Public*, pg. 2079
ELECTRIC TRACTOR CORP; *Int'l*, pg. 2349
EMPIRE SOUTHERN TIER EQUIPMENT CORP.—See Leuner Inc.; *U.S. Private*, pg. 2433
EUROCRANE (CHINA) CO., LTD.; *Int'l*, pg. 2534
EXPRESS CUSTOM TRAILERS MFG. INC.; *Int'l*, pg. 2590
EXTREME ENGINEERING, INC.—See LCI Industries; *U.S. Public*, pg. 1295
FENWICK-LINDE S.A.R.L.—See KKR & Co. Inc.; *U.S. Public*, pg. 1254
FENWICK-LINDE S.A.R.L.—See The Goldman Sachs Group, Inc.; *U.S. Public*, pg. 2079
FLUID UTVA A.D.; *Int'l*, pg. 2713
FONTAINE FIFTH WHEEL COMPANY—See Berkshire Hathaway Inc.; *U.S. Public*, pg. 310
FONTAINE MODIFICATION COMPANY—See Berkshire Hathaway Inc.; *U.S. Public*, pg. 310
FORANKRA AB—See Axel Johnson Gruppen AB; *Int'l*, pg. 764
FORK-CO USA SALES LLC; *U.S. Private*, pg. 1569
FROMMELT SAFETY—See Rite-Hite Holding Corporation; *U.S. Private*, pg. 3442
FULTRA SAPI DE CV; *Int'l*, pg. 2843
FURUKAWA MACHINERY ASIA SDN. BHD.—See Furukawa Co., Ltd.; *Int'l*, pg. 2847
FURUKAWA UNYU CO., LTD.—See Furukawa Co., Ltd.; *Int'l*, pg. 2847
GAUSSIN SA; *Int'l*, pg. 2891
GEESINKNORBA AB—See Geesink Group B.V.; *Int'l*, pg. 2911
GENERAL TRANSERVICE INC.—See Global Capital Corp.; *U.S. Private*, pg. 1712
GKN SANKEY LTD.—See GKN plc; *Int'l*, pg. 2985
GLOBAL CAPITAL CORP.; *U.S. Private*, pg. 1712
GLOBE TRAILER MANUFACTURING, INC.; *U.S. Private*, pg. 1720
THE GODWIN GROUP; *U.S. Private*, pg. 4033
GRASDORF GMBH; *Int'l*, pg. 3061
GREENKRAFT, INC.; *U.S. Public*, pg. 964
GROFF TRACTOR & EQUIPMENT, INC; *U.S. Private*, pg. 1791
GUANGDONG UCAN ROBOT TECHNOLOGY CO., LTD.—See Guangdong Dtech Technology Co., Ltd.; *Int'l*, pg. 3154
HANGCHA GROUP CO., LTD.—See GreatStar Group Co., Ltd.; *Int'l*, pg. 3067
HANS H. MEYER GMBH—See Hyster-Yale Materials Handling, Inc.; *U.S. Public*, pg. 1080
HANSLER MANUTENTION, INC—See Hansler Industries; *Int'l*, pg. 3260
HARLO CORPORATION; *U.S. Private*, pg. 1865
HARMAR; *U.S. Private*, pg. 1866
HARPER TRUCKS, INC.; *U.S. Private*, pg. 1868
THE HEIL CO.—See Terex Corporation; *U.S. Public*, pg. 2019
HEIL TRAILER INTERNATIONAL, CO. - HEIL ATHENS MANUFACTURING FACILITY—See AIP, LLC; *U.S. Private*, pg. 134
HEIL TRAILER INTERNATIONAL, CO. - HEIL TANK SERVICE - MANUFACTURING FACILITY—See AIP, LLC; *U.S. Private*, pg. 134
HEINRICH DE FRIES GMBH; *Int'l*, pg. 3324
HELI AMERICA INC.—See Anhui Heli Co., Ltd.; *Int'l*, pg. 467
HELI SOUTHEAST ASIA CO., LTD.—See Anhui Heli Co., Ltd.; *Int'l*, pg. 467
HIAB AB—See Cargotec Corporation; *Int'l*, pg. 1326
HIAB DENMARK A/S—See Cargotec Corporation; *Int'l*, pg. 1326
HIAB HANA CO. LTD.—See Cargotec Corporation; *Int'l*, pg. 1326
HIAB S.A.—See Cargotec Corporation; *Int'l*, pg. 1327
HILMAN, INC.; *U.S. Private*, pg. 1947
HOVE AMERICAS INC.—See Hove A/S; *Int'l*, pg. 3492
HOVE BRASIL EQUIPAMENTOS E SERVICOS DE LUBRIFICACAO LTDA.—See Hove A/S; *Int'l*, pg. 3492
HOVE LUBRICANTS INDIA PRIVATE LIMITED—See Hove A/S; *Int'l*, pg. 3492
HUMPHREY COMPANIES LLC; *U.S. Private*, pg. 2007
HYSTER FRANCE S.A.R.L.—See Hyster-Yale Materials Handling, Inc.; *U.S. Public*, pg. 1080
HYSTER-YALE GROUP, INC.—See Hyster-Yale Materials Handling, Inc.; *U.S. Public*, pg. 1080
HYSTER-YALE MATERIALS HANDLING GMBH—See Hyster-Yale Materials Handling, Inc.; *U.S. Public*, pg. 1080
IBERCARRETILLAS OM ESPANA S.A.—See KKR & Co. Inc.; *U.S. Public*, pg. 1255
IBERCARRETILLAS OM ESPANA S.A.—See The Goldman Sachs Group, Inc.; *U.S. Public*, pg. 2079
IMG COMPANIES, LLC—See Francisco Partners Management, LP; *U.S. Private*, pg. 1590
IM RAKOVICA U RESTRUKTURIRANJU A.D.; *Int'l*, pg. 3617
INTERMETRO INDUSTRIES CORPORATION—See Emerson Electric Co.; *U.S. Public*, pg. 750
JERVIS B. WEBB COMPANY—See Daifuku Co., Ltd.; *Int'l*, pg. 1925
JLG INDUSTRIES (UNITED KINGDOM) LIMITED—See Oshkosh Corporation; *U.S. Public*, pg. 1620
JLG NEW ZEALAND ACCESS EQUIPMENT & SERVICE—See Oshkosh Corporation; *U.S. Public*, pg. 1620
KALMAR INDUSTRIES MAGNUM DIVISION—See Cargotec Corporation; *Int'l*, pg. 1327
KALMAR USA INC.—See Cargotec Corporation; *Int'l*, pg. 1327
KAMA CO., LTD.—See China Hi-Tech Group Corporation; *Int'l*, pg. 1508
KION NORTH AMERICA CORPORATION—See KKR & Co. Inc.; *U.S. Public*, pg. 1255
KION NORTH AMERICA CORPORATION—See The Goldman Sachs Group, Inc.; *U.S. Public*, pg. 2079
KNL HOLDINGS, LLC; *U.S. Private*, pg. 2322
LANDOLL CORPORATION - DREXEL—See Landoll Corporation; *U.S. Private*, pg. 2386
LEKTRO INC.—See John Bean Technologies Corporation; *U.S. Public*, pg. 1192
LIFT-A-LOFT CORPORATION; *U.S. Private*, pg. 2452
LIFTER CHINA LTD COMPANY—See Generac Holdings Inc.; *U.S. Public*, pg. 912
LIFTKING MANUFACTURING CORP.—See Lanco International Inc.; *U.S. Private*, pg. 2382
LIFTOMATIC MATERIAL HANDLING INC.; *U.S. Private*, pg. 2452
LINDE (CHINA) FORKLIFT TRUCK CORP., LTD.—See KKR & Co. Inc.; *U.S. Public*, pg. 1255
LINDE (CHINA) FORKLIFT TRUCK CORP., LTD.—See The Goldman Sachs Group, Inc.; *U.S. Public*, pg. 2079
LINDE FORDERTECHNIK GMBH—See KKR & Co. Inc.; *U.S. Public*, pg. 1255
LINDE FORDERTECHNIK GMBH—See The Goldman Sachs Group, Inc.; *U.S. Public*, pg. 2079
LINDE HEAVY TRUCK DIVISION LTD.—See KKR & Co. Inc.; *U.S. Public*, pg. 1255
LINDE HEAVY TRUCK DIVISION LTD.—See The Goldman Sachs Group, Inc.; *U.S. Public*, pg. 2079
LINDE HIGH LIFT CHILE S.A.—See KKR & Co. Inc.; *U.S. Public*, pg. 1255
LINDE HIGH LIFT CHILE S.A.—See The Goldman Sachs Group, Inc.; *U.S. Public*, pg. 2079
LINDE LANSING FORDERTECHNIK AG—See KKR & Co. Inc.; *U.S. Public*, pg. 1255
LINDE LANSING FORDERTECHNIK AG—See The Goldman Sachs Group, Inc.; *U.S. Public*, pg. 2079
LINDE MATERIAL HANDLING (AUSTRALIA) PTY. LTD.—See KKR & Co. Inc.; *U.S. Public*, pg. 1255
LINDE MATERIAL HANDLING (AUSTRALIA) PTY. LTD.—See The Goldman Sachs Group, Inc.; *U.S. Public*, pg. 2079
LINDE MATERIAL HANDLING CESKA REPUBLICA S.R.O.—See KKR & Co. Inc.; *U.S. Public*, pg. 1255
LINDE MATERIAL HANDLING CESKA REPUBLICA S.R.O.—See The Goldman Sachs Group, Inc.; *U.S. Public*, pg. 2079
LINDE MATERIAL HANDLING DO BRASIL LTDA.—See KKR & Co. Inc.; *U.S. Public*, pg. 1255
LINDE MATERIAL HANDLING DO BRASIL LTDA.—See The Goldman Sachs Group, Inc.; *U.S. Public*, pg. 2079
LINDE MATERIAL HANDLING GMBH—See KKR & Co. Inc.; *U.S. Public*, pg. 1254
LINDE MATERIAL HANDLING GMBH—See The Goldman Sachs Group, Inc.; *U.S. Public*, pg. 2079
LINDE MATERIAL HANDLING IBERICA S.A.—See KKR & Co. Inc.; *U.S. Public*, pg. 1255
LINDE MATERIAL HANDLING IBERICA S.A.—See The Goldman Sachs Group, Inc.; *U.S. Public*, pg. 2079
LINDE MATERIAL HANDLING ITALIA S.P.A.—See KKR & Co. Inc.; *U.S. Public*, pg. 1255
LINDE MATERIAL HANDLING ITALIA S.P.A.—See The Goldman Sachs Group, Inc.; *U.S. Public*, pg. 2079
LINDE MATERIAL HANDLING (PTY) LTD.—See KKR & Co. Inc.; *U.S. Public*, pg. 1255
LINDE MATERIAL HANDLING (PTY) LTD.—See The Goldman Sachs Group, Inc.; *U.S. Public*, pg. 2079
LINDE MATERIAL HANDLING (UK) LTD.—See KKR & Co. Inc.; *U.S. Public*, pg. 1255
LINDE MATERIAL HANDLING (UK) LTD.—See The Goldman Sachs Group, Inc.; *U.S. Public*, pg. 2079
LINDE VILICARI HRVATSKA D.O.O.—See KKR & Co. Inc.; *U.S. Public*, pg. 1255
LINDE VILICARI HRVATSKA D.O.O.—See The Goldman Sachs Group, Inc.; *U.S. Public*, pg. 2079
LIUZHOU LIUGONG FORKLIFT CO., LTD.—See Guangxi Liugong Machinery Co., Ltd.; *Int'l*, pg. 3163
LLC FURUKAWA UNIC RUS—See Furukawa Co., Ltd.; *Int'l*, pg. 2847
LLC HANS H. MEYER OOO—See Hyster-Yale Materials Handling, Inc.; *U.S. Public*, pg. 1080
LONG REACH INC.—See Allied Systems Company; *U.S. Private*, pg. 188
MAGLINE, INC.; *U.S. Private*, pg. 2546
MAGLINER DO BRASIL—See Magline, Inc.; *U.S. Private*, pg. 2546
MAGLINER INTERNATIONAL LLC—See Magline, Inc.; *U.S. Private*, pg. 2546
MAGLINE SANO GMBH—See Magline, Inc.; *U.S. Private*, pg. 2546
MANITEX, INC.—See Manitex International, Inc.; *U.S. Public*, pg. 1356
MANSKE MATERIAL HANDLING, INC.—See Richards Supply Company; *U.S. Private*, pg. 3429
MCCULLOUGH INDUSTRIES, INC.—See Olympic Steel Inc.; *U.S. Public*, pg. 1570
MERITOR HVS AB—See Cummins Inc.; *U.S. Public*, pg. 608
MEYER GMBH—See Hyster-Yale Materials Handling, Inc.; *U.S. Public*, pg. 1080
MJ PROMOTIONS, INC.—See Lanco International Inc.; *U.S. Private*, pg. 2382
MOTOCAR SERVICE COMPANY (MSC)—See KKR & Co. Inc.; *U.S. Public*, pg. 1255
MOTOCAR SERVICE COMPANY (MSC)—See The Goldman Sachs Group, Inc.; *U.S. Public*, pg. 2079
NACCO MATERIALS HANDLING GROUP BRASIL LTDA.—See Hyster-Yale Materials Handling, Inc.; *U.S. Public*, pg. 1080
NACCO MATERIALS HANDLING GROUP, LTD.—See Hyster-Yale Materials Handling, Inc.; *U.S. Public*, pg. 1080
NACCO MATERIALS HANDLING GROUP PTY. LTD.—See Hyster-Yale Materials Handling, Inc.; *U.S. Public*, pg. 1080
NACCO MATERIALS HANDLING LTD. - CRAIGAVON PLANT—See Hyster-Yale Materials Handling, Inc.; *U.S. Public*, pg. 1080
NIIGATA TRSNSYS CO., LTD.—See IHI Corporation; *Int'l*, pg. 3606
NMC/WOLLARD COMPANY; *U.S. Private*, pg. 2931
NORBA A/S—See Geesink Group B.V.; *Int'l*, pg. 2911
OLDENBURG GROUP, INC. - DEFENSE DIVISION—See Oldenburg Group, Inc.; *U.S. Private*, pg. 3010
OM CARRELLI ELEVATORI S.P.A.—See KKR & Co. Inc.; *U.S. Public*, pg. 1255
OM CARRELLI ELEVATORI S.P.A.—See The Goldman Sachs Group, Inc.; *U.S. Public*, pg. 2079
OVERLAND TANK, INC.—See Tenex Capital Management, L.P.; *U.S. Private*, pg. 3966
PACIFIC TRUCK & TRAILER—See Great Western Leasing & Sales, LLC; *U.S. Private*, pg. 1768
PARTINGTON ENGINEERING LIMITED—See ARGENT INDUSTRIAL LIMITED; *Int'l*, pg. 561
PETERBILT MOTORS CO.—See PACCAR Inc.; *U.S. Public*, pg. 1631
PETTIBONE TRAVERSE LIST LLC—See The Heico Companies, L.L.C.; *U.S. Private*, pg. 4050
PJ TRAILERS, INC.—See Bain Capital, LP; *U.S. Private*, pg. 436
PLANK ENTERPRISES INC.; *U.S. Private*, pg. 3196
PM ARGENTINA SISTEMAS DE ELEVACION S.A.—See Manitex International, Inc.; *U.S. Public*, pg. 1356
PM CHILE S.P.A.—See Manitex International, Inc.; *U.S. Public*, pg. 1356
PM EQUIPMENT TRADING FZE—See Manitex International, Inc.; *U.S. Public*, pg. 1356
PM OIL & STEEL IBERICA S.L.—See Manitex International, Inc.; *U.S. Public*, pg. 1356
PM OIL & STEEL S.P.A.—See Manitex International, Inc.; *U.S. Public*, pg. 1356
PRESTO LIFTS INC.—See Allied Systems Company; *U.S. Private*, pg. 188
ROURA IRON WORKS INC.—See Roura Iron Works, Inc.; *U.S. Private*, pg. 3489
ROYAL TRACTOR CO., INC.—See Greenbriar Equity Group, L.P.; *U.S. Private*, pg. 1776
ROYAL TRUCK & EQUIPMENT, LLC—See Alamo Group Inc.; *U.S. Public*, pg. 71
RUSH SALES COMPANY—See Tenex Capital Management, L.P.; *U.S. Private*, pg. 3966
RUSH TRUCK CENTERS OF ARIZONA, INC.—See Rush Enterprises, Inc.; *U.S. Public*, pg. 1826
SELLICK EQUIPMENT LIMITED—See Avis Industrial Corporation; *U.S. Private*, pg. 408
SHANDONG KAMA AUTOMOBILE MANUFACTURING CO., LTD.—See China Hi-Tech Group Corporation; *Int'l*, pg. 1508
SINOTRANS & CSC SHIPBUILDING INDUSTRY CORPORATION - HONGGUANG PORT MACHINERY PLANT—See China Merchants Group Limited; *Int'l*, pg. 1521

333924 — INDUSTRIAL TRUCK, T...

S & N PUMP COMPANY—See Lone Star Funds; *U.S. Private,* pg. 2485
SOUTHWORTH INTERNATIONAL GROUP INC.; *U.S. Private,* pg. 3742
SOUTHWORTH PRODUCTS CORP.—See Southworth International Group Inc.; *U.S. Private,* pg. 3743
SPX FLOW TECHNOLOGY FINLAND OY—See Lone Star Funds; *U.S. Private,* pg. 2486
SPX FLOW TECHNOLOGY WARENDORF GMBH—See Lone Star Funds; *U.S. Private,* pg. 2486
STECO, LLC—See KNL Holdings, LLC; *U.S. Private,* pg. 2322
STILL AG—See KKR & Co. Inc.; *U.S. Public,* pg. 1255
STILL AG—See The Goldman Sachs Group, Inc.; *U.S. Public,* pg. 2079
STILL CR, SPOL. S R.O.—See KKR & Co. Inc.; *U.S. Public,* pg. 1255
STILL CR, SPOL. S R.O.—See The Goldman Sachs Group, Inc.; *U.S. Public,* pg. 2079
STILL DANMARK A/S—See KKR & Co. Inc.; *U.S. Public,* pg. 1255
STILL DANMARK A/S—See The Goldman Sachs Group, Inc.; *U.S. Public,* pg. 2079
STILL GESELLSCHAFT M.B.H.—See KKR & Co. Inc.; *U.S. Public,* pg. 1255
STILL GESELLSCHAFT M.B.H.—See The Goldman Sachs Group, Inc.; *U.S. Public,* pg. 2079
STILL GMBH—See KKR & Co. Inc.; *U.S. Public,* pg. 1255
STILL GMBH—See The Goldman Sachs Group, Inc.; *U.S. Public,* pg. 2079
STILL INTERN TRANSPORT B.V.—See KKR & Co. Inc.; *U.S. Public,* pg. 1255
STILL INTERN TRANSPORT B.V.—See The Goldman Sachs Group, Inc.; *U.S. Public,* pg. 2079
STILL ITALIA S.P.A.—See KKR & Co. Inc.; *U.S. Public,* pg. 1255
STILL ITALIA S.P.A.—See The Goldman Sachs Group, Inc.; *U.S. Public,* pg. 2079
STILL MATERIALS HANDLING LTD.—See KKR & Co. Inc.; *U.S. Public,* pg. 1255
STILL MATERIALS HANDLING LTD.—See The Goldman Sachs Group, Inc.; *U.S. Public,* pg. 2079
STILL N.V.—See KKR & Co. Inc.; *U.S. Public,* pg. 1255
STILL N.V.—See The Goldman Sachs Group, Inc.; *U.S. Public,* pg. 2080
STILL S.A.—See KKR & Co. Inc.; *U.S. Public,* pg. 1255
STILL S.A.—See The Goldman Sachs Group, Inc.; *U.S. Public,* pg. 2080
STILL S.A.S.—See KKR & Co. Inc.; *U.S. Public,* pg. 1255
STILL S.A.S.—See The Goldman Sachs Group, Inc.; *U.S. Public,* pg. 2080
STILL WAGNER GMBH & CO. KG—See KKR & Co. Inc.; *U.S. Public,* pg. 1255
STILL WAGNER GMBH & CO. KG—See The Goldman Sachs Group, Inc.; *U.S. Public,* pg. 2080
SUMITOMO NAACO MATERIALS HANDLING CO., LTD.—See Hyster-Yale Materials Handling, Inc.; *U.S. Public,* pg. 1080
TAYLOR-DUNN MANUFACTURING COMPANY—See Polaris, Inc.; *U.S. Public,* pg. 1701
TERAFLEX, INC.—See Clearlake Capital Group, L.P.; *U.S. Private,* pg. 938
TEREX EQUIPMENT LIMITED—See AB Volvo; *Int'l,* pg. 43
TRANSCO RAILWAY PRODUCTS INC.—See Berkshire Hathaway Inc.; *U.S. Public,* pg. 312
VAC-CON, INC.—See Holden Industries, Inc.; *U.S. Private,* pg. 1962
VACTOR MANUFACTURING, INC.—See Federal Signal Corporation; *U.S. Public,* pg. 826
VALTRACTOR SA—See AGCO Corporation; *U.S. Public,* pg. 59
VALTRA DO BRASIL S.A.—See AGCO Corporation; *U.S. Public,* pg. 59
VALTRA GMBH—See AGCO Corporation; *U.S. Public,* pg. 59
VALTRA, INC.—See AGCO Corporation; *U.S. Public,* pg. 59
VALTRA TRACTORES S.A.—See AGCO Corporation; *U.S. Public,* pg. 59
VALTRA TRACTORES S.A.—See AGCO Corporation; *U.S. Public,* pg. 59
VALTRA TRACTORS (UK) LTD.—See AGCO Corporation; *U.S. Public,* pg. 59
VALTRA TRAKTOR AB—See AGCO Corporation; *U.S. Public,* pg. 59
VALTRA VERTRIEBS GMBH—See AGCO Corporation; *U.S. Public,* pg. 59
VISA LIGHTING CORPORATION—See Oldenburg Group, Inc.; *U.S. Private,* pg. 3010
VISHAY BLH CANADA—See Vishay Intertechnology, Inc.; *U.S. Public,* pg. 2303
WASP INC.; *U.S. Private,* pg. 4450
WELDSHIP CORPORATION—See Markel Group Inc.; *U.S. Public,* pg. 1369
WILLAMSEN-GODWIN TRUCK BODY COMPANY—See The Godwin Group; *U.S. Private,* pg. 4033
XTREME MANUFACTURING, LLC; *U.S. Private,* pg. 4583

333991 — POWER-DRIVEN HANDTOOL MANUFACTURING

AIR TOOL SERVICE COMPANY—See ShoreView Industries, LLC; *U.S. Private,* pg. 3642
AMADA CANADA LTD.—See Amada Holdings Co., Ltd.; *Int'l,* pg. 404
AMERICAN PNEUMATIC TOOLS—See Atlas Copco AB; *Int'l,* pg. 681
ANDREAS STIHL AG & CO.; *Int'l,* pg. 451
ANEST IWATA IBERICA S.L.—See ANEST IWATA Corporation; *Int'l,* pg. 458
APEX TOOL GROUP GMBH & CO. OHG—See Bain Capital, LP; *U.S. Private,* pg. 430
APEX TOOL GROUP, LLC - DAYTON POWER TOOLS PLANT—See Bain Capital, LP; *U.S. Private,* pg. 430
APEX TOOL GROUP, LLC - POWER TOOL DIVISION—See Bain Capital, LP; *U.S. Private,* pg. 430
ARROW FASTENER CO., LLC—See Masco Corporation; *U.S. Public,* pg. 1389
ATLAS COPCO CONSTRUCTION TOOLS AB—See Atlas Copco AB; *Int'l,* pg. 678
ATLAS COPCO KK—See Atlas Copco AB; *Int'l,* pg. 679
BLACK & DECKER HOLDINGS GMBH; *Int'l,* pg. 1056
BLACK & DECKER POLSKA SP.Z.O.O.—See Stanley Black & Decker, Inc.; *U.S. Public,* pg. 1932
BLACK & DECKER PUERTO RICO—See Stanley Black & Decker, Inc.; *U.S. Public,* pg. 1936
BLACK & DECKER (U.S.) INC.—See Stanley Black & Decker, Inc.; *U.S. Public,* pg. 1932
CAMCORP MANUFACTURING, INC.—See Camrost-Felcorp Inc.; *Int'l,* pg. 1275
CHICAGO PNEUMATIC TOOL COMPANY LLC—See Atlas Copco AB; *Int'l,* pg. 681
CONTINENTAL TOOL GROUP INCORPORATED—See ShoreView Industries, LLC; *U.S. Private,* pg. 3642
COUNTRYWIDE HARDWARE, INC.—See ShoreView Industries, LLC; *U.S. Private,* pg. 3642
CPS PRODUCTS, INC.—See Harbour Group Industries, Inc.; *U.S. Private,* pg. 1860
DAC TECHNOLOGIES GROUP INTERNATIONAL, INC.; *U.S. Public,* pg. 620
DE POAN PNEUMATIC CORP.; *Int'l,* pg. 1996
DESOUTTER ITALIANA S.R.L.—See Atlas Copco AB; *Int'l,* pg. 682
DIAL A.D.; *Int'l,* pg. 2103
DYNABRADE DO BRASIL LTDA.—See Dynabrade, Inc.; *U.S. Private,* pg. 1297
DYNABRADE EUROPE S.A.R.L.—See Dynabrade, Inc.; *U.S. Private,* pg. 1297
DYNABRADE, INC.; *U.S. Private,* pg. 1297
DYNABRADE INDIA ABRASIVE POWER TOOLS PVT. LTD.—See Dynabrade, Inc.; *U.S. Private,* pg. 1297
EAGLEBURGMANN AUSTRALASIA PTY. LTD. - MELBOURNE—See Eagle Industry Co., Ltd.; *Int'l,* pg. 2265
EAGLEBURGMANN AUSTRALASIA PTY. LTD. - MELBOURNE—See Freudenberg SE; *Int'l,* pg. 2783
EINHELL AUSTRALIA PTY. LTD.—See Einhell Germany AG; *Int'l,* pg. 2332
EINHELL BENELUX B.V.—See Einhell Germany AG; *Int'l,* pg. 2332
EINHELL BIH D.O.O.—See Einhell Germany AG; *Int'l,* pg. 2333
EINHELL BRASIL COM. DISTR. FERR. E EQUIP. LTDA—See Ancora Chumbadores Ltda.; *Int'l,* pg. 449
EINHELL BULGARIA LTD.—See Einhell Germany AG; *Int'l,* pg. 2333
EINHELL CHILE S.A.—See Einhell Germany AG; *Int'l,* pg. 2333
EINHELL CROATIA D.O.O—See Einhell Germany AG; *Int'l,* pg. 2333
EINHELL D. O. O.—See Einhell Germany AG; *Int'l,* pg. 2332
EINHELL ESPANA—See Einhell Germany AG; *Int'l,* pg. 2333
EINHELL FRANCE S.A.S.—See Einhell Germany AG; *Int'l,* pg. 2333
EINHELL GERMANY AG; *Int'l,* pg. 2332
EINHELL HELLAS S.A.—See Einhell Germany AG; *Int'l,* pg. 2333
EINHELL HUNGARIA LTD.—See Einhell Germany AG; *Int'l,* pg. 2333
EINHELL ITALIA S.R.L.—See Einhell Germany AG; *Int'l,* pg. 2333
EINHELL POLSKA SP. Z.O.O.—See Einhell Germany AG; *Int'l,* pg. 2333
EINHELL PORTUGAL LDA.—See Einhell Germany AG; *Int'l,* pg. 2333
EINHELL ROMANIA S.R.L.—See Einhell Germany AG; *Int'l,* pg. 2333
EINHELL SCHWEIZ AG—See Einhell Germany AG; *Int'l,* pg. 2333
EINHELL SKANDINAVIA APS—See Einhell Germany AG; *Int'l,* pg. 2333
EINHELL SLOVAKIA S.R.O.—See Einhell Germany AG; *Int'l,* pg. 2333
EINHELL UK LTD.—See Einhell Germany AG; *Int'l,* pg. 2333
EINHELL UKRAINE TOV—See Einhell Germany AG; *Int'l,* pg. 2333
EINHELL UNICORE S.R.O.—See Einhell Germany AG; *Int'l,* pg. 2333
EMERSON BRAZIL—See Emerson Electric Co.; *U.S. Public,* pg. 743
EMERSON JAPAN LTD.—See Emerson Electric Co.; *U.S. Public,* pg. 745
ESTIC CORPORATION; *Int'l,* pg. 2518
FLORIDA PNEUMATIC MANUFACTURING CORPORATION—See ShoreView Industries, LLC; *U.S. Private,* pg. 3642
FURUKAWA ROCK DRILL USA CO., LTD. - BREAKER DIVISION—See Furukawa Co., Ltd.; *Int'l,* pg. 2847
GEORGES RENAULT S.A.—See Atlas Copco AB; *Int'l,* pg. 678
GREEN MANUFACTURING, INC.—See ShoreView Industries, LLC; *U.S. Private,* pg. 3642
HAMATON AUTOMOTIVE TECHNOLOGY CO., LTD.; *Int'l,* pg. 3236
HANS EINHELL (CHINA) CHONGQING CO., LTD.—See Einhell Germany AG; *Int'l,* pg. 2333
HANS EINHELL OSTERREICH GMBH—See Einhell Germany AG; *Int'l,* pg. 2333
HANSI ANHAI FAR EAST LTD.—See Einhell Germany AG; *Int'l,* pg. 2333
HIKOKI POWER TOOLS BELGIUM N.V./S.A.—See KKR & Co. Inc.; *U.S. Public,* pg. 1257
HIKOKI POWER TOOLS HUNGARY KFT.—See KKR & Co. Inc.; *U.S. Public,* pg. 1257
HIKOKI POWER TOOLS (MALAYSIA) SDN. BHD.—See KKR & Co. Inc.; *U.S. Public,* pg. 1257
HIKOKI POWER TOOLS NETHERLANDS B.V.—See KKR & Co. Inc.; *U.S. Public,* pg. 1257
HIKOKI POWER TOOLS OSTERREICH GMBH—See KKR & Co. Inc.; *U.S. Public,* pg. 1257
HIKOKI POWER TOOLS ROMANIA S.R.L.—See KKR & Co. Inc.; *U.S. Public,* pg. 1257
HIKOKI POWER TOOLS (SINGAPORE) PTE.LTD.—See KKR & Co. Inc.; *U.S. Public,* pg. 1257
HIKOKI POWER TOOLS (THAILAND) CO.,LTD.—See KKR & Co. Inc.; *U.S. Public,* pg. 1257
HILTI AG, WERK THURINGEN—See Hilti AG; *Int'l,* pg. 3394
HILTI ARGENTINA, S.A.—See Hilti AG; *Int'l,* pg. 3394
HILTI (AUST.) PTY. LTD.—See Hilti AG; *Int'l,* pg. 3394
HILTI AUSTRIA GMBH—See Hilti AG; *Int'l,* pg. 3394
HILTI BELGIUM N.V.—See Hilti AG; *Int'l,* pg. 3394
HILTI (BULGARIA) EOOD—See Hilti AG; *Int'l,* pg. 3394
HILTI (CANADA) CORPORATION—See Hilti AG; *Int'l,* pg. 3394
HILTI CARIBE INC.—See Hilti AG; *Int'l,* pg. 3394
HILTI CHILE LIMITADA—See Hilti AG; *Int'l,* pg. 3394
HILTI (CHINA) LTD.—See Hilti AG; *Int'l,* pg. 3394
HILTI COLOMBIA S.A.—See Hilti AG; *Int'l,* pg. 3394
HILTI COMPLETE SYSTEMS UAB—See Hilti AG; *Int'l,* pg. 3394
HILTI CROATIA D.O.O.—See Hilti AG; *Int'l,* pg. 3394
HILTI CR SPOL. S.R.O.—See Hilti AG; *Int'l,* pg. 3394
HILTI DENMARK A/S—See Hilti AG; *Int'l,* pg. 3394
HILTI DEUTSCHLAND GMBH—See Hilti AG; *Int'l,* pg. 3394
HILTI DISTRIBUTION LTD.—See Hilti AG; *Int'l,* pg. 3394
HILTI DO BRASIL COMERCIAL LTDA.—See Hilti AG; *Int'l,* pg. 3395
HILTI EESTI OU—See Hilti AG; *Int'l,* pg. 3394
HILTI ENTWICKLUNG BEFESTIGUNGSTECHNIK GMBH—See Hilti AG; *Int'l,* pg. 3394
HILTI ENTWICKLUNG ELEKTROWERZEUGE GMBH—See Hilti AG; *Int'l,* pg. 3394
HILTI ESPANOLA S.A.—See Hilti AG; *Int'l,* pg. 3394
HILTI FAR EAST PRIVATE LTD.—See Hilti AG; *Int'l,* pg. 3394
HILTI (FASTENING SYSTEMS) LTD.—See Hilti AG; *Int'l,* pg. 3394
HILTI FRANCE S.A.—See Hilti AG; *Int'l,* pg. 3394
HILTI (GT. BRITAIN) LIMITED—See Hilti AG; *Int'l,* pg. 3394
HILTI HELLAS S.A.—See Hilti AG; *Int'l,* pg. 3394
HILTI HOLDING GMBH—See Hilti AG; *Int'l,* pg. 3395
HILTI (HONG KONG) LTD.—See Hilti AG; *Int'l,* pg. 3394
HILTI HUNGARIA SZOLGALTATO KFT.—See Hilti AG; *Int'l,* pg. 3395
HILTI, INC.—See Hilti AG; *Int'l,* pg. 3395
HILTI INDIA PRIVATE LIMITED—See Hilti AG; *Int'l,* pg. 3395
HILTI INSAAT MALZEMELERI TICARET A.S.—See Hilti AG; *Int'l,* pg. 3395
HILTI ITALIA S.P.A.—See Hilti AG; *Int'l,* pg. 3395
HILTI (JAPAN) LTD.—See Hilti AG; *Int'l,* pg. 3394
HILTI (KOREA) COMPANY LTD.—See Hilti AG; *Int'l,* pg. 3394
HILTI KUNSTSTOFFTECHNIK GMBH—See Hilti AG; *Int'l,* pg. 3395
HILTI (MALAYSIA), SDN. BHD.—See Hilti AG; *Int'l,* pg. 3394
HILTI MEXICANA, S.A. DE C.V.—See Hilti AG; *Int'l,* pg. 3395
HILTI NEDERLAND B.V.—See Hilti AG; *Int'l,* pg. 3395
HILTI (PHILIPPINES), INC.—See Hilti AG; *Int'l,* pg. 3394
HILTI (POLAND) SP. ZO.O.—See Hilti AG; *Int'l,* pg. 3394
HILTI (PORTUGAL), PRODUCTOS E SERVICOS LDA.—See Hilti AG; *Int'l,* pg. 3394
HILTI (SCHWEIZ) AG—See Hilti AG; *Int'l,* pg. 3394
HILTI SERVICES LIMITED—See Hilti AG; *Int'l,* pg. 3395

N.A.I.C.S. INDEX

333992 — WELDING AND SOLDERI...

HILTI SLOVAKIA SPOL. S.R.O.—See Hilti AG; *Int'l*, pg. 3395
HILTI SLOVENIJA D.O.O.—See Hilti AG; *Int'l*, pg. 3395
HILTI (SOUTH AFRICA) PTY. LTD.—See Hilti AG; *Int'l*, pg. 3394
HILTI (SUOMI) OY—See Hilti AG; *Int'l*, pg. 3394
HILTI SVENSKA AB—See Hilti AG; *Int'l*, pg. 3395
HILTI TAIWAN CO., LTD.—See Hilti AG; *Int'l*, pg. 3395
HILTI (UKRAINE) LTD.—See Hilti AG; *Int'l*, pg. 3394
HOLMATRO N.V.—See Madison Industries Holdings LLC; *U.S. Private*, pg. 2543
HONDA POWER EQUIPMENT SWEDEN A.B.—See Honda Motor Co., Ltd.; *Int'l*, pg. 3462
HUSQVARNA ZENOAH CO., LTD—See Husqvarna AB; *Int'l*, pg. 3539
HY-TECH MACHINE, INC.—See ShoreView Industries, LLC; *U.S. Private*, pg. 3642
INGERSOLL-RAND (GUILIN) TOOLS COMPANY LIMITED—See Ingersoll Rand Inc.; *U.S. Public*, pg. 1120
INGERSOLL-RAND INDUSTRIAL TECHNOLOGIES - TOOLS & LIFTING/MATERIAL HANDLING SOLUTIONS—See Ingersoll Rand Inc.; *U.S. Public*, pg. 1122
INVERSIONES HILTI DE VENEZUELA S.A.—See Hilti AG; *Int'l*, pg. 3395
IRWIN INDUSTRIAL TOOL COMPANY—See Newell Brands Inc.; *U.S. Public*, pg. 1514
ISABERG RAPID AB—See ACCO Brands Corporation; *U.S. Public*, pg. 33
KOKI HOLDINGS CO., LTD.—See KKR & Co. Inc.; *U.S. Public*, pg. 1257
KOKI SALES CO., LTD.—See KKR & Co. Inc.; *U.S. Public*, pg. 1257
LABOR SAVING DEVICES, INC.—See George Risk Industries, Inc.; *U.S. Public*, pg. 934
LEVIAT AG—See CRH plc; *Int'l*, pg. 1845
MAHR MALAYSIA SDN. BHD.—See Carl Mahr Holding GmbH; *Int'l*, pg. 1333
MASTERFIX POLAND LTD. SP.Z.O.O—See Stanley Black & Decker, Inc.; *U.S. Public*, pg. 1934
MASTERFIX PRODUCTS U.K. LTD.—See Stanley Black & Decker, Inc.; *U.S. Public*, pg. 1933
NOVALIA S.A.S.—See Durr AG; *Int'l*, pg. 2233
NWL DENMARK SERVICES APS—See Newell Brands Inc.; *U.S. Public*, pg. 1514
OSBORN INTERNATIONAL GMBH—See Jason Industries, Inc.; *U.S. Private*, pg. 2190
OSBORN INTERNATIONAL SRL—See Jason Industries, Inc.; *U.S. Private*, pg. 2190
PARATECH, INC.; *U.S. Private*, pg. 3093
PEACE INDUSTRIES INC. - SPOTNAILS DIVISION—See Peace Industries Ltd.; *U.S. Private*, pg. 3122
P&F INDUSTRIES, INC.—See ShoreView Industries, LLC; *U.S. Private*, pg. 3642
PRIMEX LTDA.—See Aiphone Co., Ltd.; *Int'l*, pg. 235
REEDHYCALOG UK LTD—See NOV, Inc.; *U.S. Public*, pg. 1546
RIDGE TOOL AUSTRALIA PTY., LTD.—See Emerson Electric Co.; *U.S. Public*, pg. 751
RIDGE TOOL GMBH & CO. OHG—See Emerson Electric Co.; *U.S. Public*, pg. 749
RIDGE TOOL N.V.—See Emerson Electric Co.; *U.S. Public*, pg. 752
SKIL EUROPE B.V.—See Emerson Electric Co.; *U.S. Public*, pg. 752
SNA EUROPE (FRANCE) SARL—See Snap-on Incorporated; *U.S. Public*, pg. 1898
SNA EUROPE (SPAIN)—See Snap-on Incorporated; *U.S. Public*, pg. 1898
SNA GERMANY GMBH—See Snap-on Incorporated; *U.S. Public*, pg. 1898
SNAP-ON EQUIPMENT S.R.L.—See Snap-on Incorporated; *U.S. Public*, pg. 1898
SNAP-ON TOOLS HONG KONG LIMITED—See Snap-on Incorporated; *U.S. Public*, pg. 1898
SNAP-ON TOOLS ITALIA S.R.L.—See Snap-on Incorporated; *U.S. Public*, pg. 1898
STANLEY HYDRAULIC TOOLS—See Stanley Black & Decker, Inc.; *U.S. Public*, pg. 1935
STANLEY WORKS (EUROPE) AG—See Stanley Black & Decker, Inc.; *U.S. Public*, pg. 1936
THE STANLEY WORKS PTY. LTD.—See Stanley Black & Decker, Inc.; *U.S. Public*, pg. 1936
STIHL, INC.—See Andreas Stihl AG & Co.; *Int'l*, pg. 451
STIHL LTD—See Andreas Stihl AG & Co.; *Int'l*, pg. 451
STIHL PARTS, INC.—See Andreas Stihl AG & Co.; *Int'l*, pg. 451
SVENSKA EINHELL AB—See Einhell Germany AG; *Int'l*, pg. 2334
TAUREX DRILL BITS LLC—See Intervale Capital, LLC; *U.S. Private*, pg. 2127
VIRAX S.A.—See Dr. Helmut Rothenberger Holding GmbH; *Int'l*, pg. 2192
VON ARX AG—See Emerson Electric Co.; *U.S. Public*, pg. 749
WEBER SCREWDRIVING SYSTEMS INC.; *U.S. Private*, pg. 4465
WELLER TOOLS GMBH—See Bain Capital, LP; *U.S. Private*, pg. 430

ZEPHYR MANUFACTURING CO., INC.—See SHG Holdings Corp.; *U.S. Private*, pg. 3635
ZIRCON CORPORATION; *U.S. Private*, pg. 4606

333992 — WELDING AND SOLDERING EQUIPMENT MANUFACTURING

AB RINCO ULTRASONICS SVERIGE—See Crest Group Inc.; *U.S. Private*, pg. 1096
ACE PRODUCTION TECHNOLOGIES, INC.—See Nordson Corporation; *U.S. Public*, pg. 1532
ACRO AUTOMATION SYSTEMS INC.; *U.S. Private*, pg. 65
ADOR WELDING LTD; *Int'l*, pg. 152
AEGIS BUSINESS LTD.—See Century Plyboards (I) Ltd.; *Int'l*, pg. 1419
AKTIESELSKABET ESAB—See Enovis Corporation; *U.S. Public*, pg. 770
A-L COMPRESSED GASES, INC.; *U.S. Private*, pg. 22
ALCOTEC WIRE CORPORATION—See Enovis Corporation; *U.S. Public*, pg. 770
ALENT ASSEMBLY SOLUTIONS BRASIL SOLDAS LTDA.—See Element Solutions Inc.; *U.S. Public*, pg. 726
ALPHA METALS, INC.—See Element Solutions Inc.; *U.S. Public*, pg. 726
AMA INDUSTRIAL COMPANY; *Int'l*, pg. 403
AMERICAN TORCH TIP CO. INC.; *U.S. Private*, pg. 257
ARCAM AB—See General Electric Company; *U.S. Public*, pg. 919
ARC MACHINES GMBH—See Enovis Corporation; *U.S. Public*, pg. 770
ARC MACHINES INC.—See Enovis Corporation; *U.S. Public*, pg. 770
ARMATRON INTERNATIONAL, INC.; *U.S. Private*, pg. 330
ASCOTECH S.A. DE C.V.—See Emerson Electric Co.; *U.S. Public*, pg. 741
AS ESAB—See Enovis Corporation; *U.S. Public*, pg. 770
ASIA GIKEN CO., LTD.—See Carlit Co., Ltd.; *Int'l*, pg. 1338
ATLANTIC CHINA WELDING CONSUMABLES, INC.; *Int'l*, pg. 674
AUTOROBOT-STREFA SP Z O.O.—See EFORT Intelligent Equipment Co., Ltd.; *Int'l*, pg. 2321
BANGLADESH WELDING ELECTRODES LIMITED; *Int'l*, pg. 836
BERNARD WELDING—See Illinois Tool Works Inc.; *U.S. Public*, pg. 1101
BOBSHELL ELECTRODES LIMITED; *Int'l*, pg. 1095
BROCO, INC.; *U.S. Private*, pg. 661
CHAMBERLAIN MANUFACTURING CORP.—See The Duchossois Group, Inc.; *U.S. Private*, pg. 4023
CHARTER INTERNATIONAL PLC—See Enovis Corporation; *U.S. Public*, pg. 770
CHOSUN WELDING POHANG CO., LTD.—See CS HOLDINGS CO., LTD.; *Int'l*, pg. 1861
CIGWELD (M) SDN BHD—See Enovis Corporation; *U.S. Public*, pg. 771
CIGWELD PTY LTD.—See Enovis Corporation; *U.S. Public*, pg. 771
CONARCO ALAMBRES Y SOLDADURAS S.A—See Enovis Corporation; *U.S. Public*, pg. 772
CRC-EVANS AUTOMATIC WELDING, INC.—See CRC-Evans International, Inc.; *U.S. Private*, pg. 1087
DAWSON METAL COMPANY INC.; *U.S. Private*, pg. 1176
D & H INDIA LIMITED; *Int'l*, pg. 1898
DNF CO LTD - ELECTRONIC MATERIAL DIVISION—See DNF Co., Ltd.; *Int'l*, pg. 2148
EATON INDUSTRIES (NETHERLANDS) B.V.—See Eaton Corporation plc; *Int'l*, pg. 2281
ECZACIBASI-LINCOLN ELECTRIC ASKAYNAK CO.—See Eczacibasi Holding A.S.; *Int'l*, pg. 2301
ELECTRO-ARCO S.A.—See Lincoln Electric Holdings, Inc.; *U.S. Public*, pg. 1317
ELECTRON BEAM TECHNOLOGIES, INC.; *U.S. Private*, pg. 1355
EMERSON ELECTRIC (CHINA) HOLDINGS CO., LTD.—See Emerson Electric Co.; *U.S. Public*, pg. 744
EMERSON ELECTRIC KOREA LTD.—See Emerson Electric Co.; *U.S. Public*, pg. 745
EMERSON ELECTRIC (MALAYSIA) SDN. BHD.—See Emerson Electric Co.; *U.S. Public*, pg. 744
EMERSON ELECTRIC (THAILAND) LIMITED—See Emerson Electric Co.; *U.S. Public*, pg. 744
EMERSON ENERGY SYSTEMS ARGENTINA S.A.—See Emerson Electric Co.; *U.S. Public*, pg. 745
EMERSON JAPAN, LTD., FUSITE DIVISION—See Emerson Electric Co.; *U.S. Public*, pg. 745
EMERSON PROCESS MANAGEMENT S.R.O.—See Emerson Electric Co.; *U.S. Public*, pg. 748
EMERSON RETAIL SERVICES EUROPE GMBH—See Emerson Electric Co.; *U.S. Public*, pg. 744
ENGINEERING AIDS SDN BHD; *Int'l*, pg. 2435
ESAB AB—See Enovis Corporation; *U.S. Public*, pg. 770
ESAB AFRICA WELDING AND CUTTING (PROPRIETARY) LIMITED—See Enovis Corporation; *U.S. Public*, pg. 770
ESAB AG—See Enovis Corporation; *U.S. Public*, pg. 770
ESAB APS—See Enovis Corporation; *U.S. Public*, pg. 770
ESAB A/S—See Enovis Corporation; *U.S. Public*, pg. 770

ESAB CUTTING SYSTEMS—See Enovis Corporation; *U.S. Public*, pg. 771
ESAB EGYPT—See Enovis Corporation; *U.S. Public*, pg. 770
ESAB FRANCE SAS—See Enovis Corporation; *U.S. Public*, pg. 770
THE ESAB GROUP, INC.—See Enovis Corporation; *U.S. Public*, pg. 771
ESAB GROUP (UK) LTD.—See Enovis Corporation; *U.S. Public*, pg. 770
ESAB IBERICA S.A.—See Enovis Corporation; *U.S. Public*, pg. 770
ESAB INDIA LTD.—See Enovis Corporation; *U.S. Public*, pg. 770
ESAB INTERNATIONAL AB—See Enovis Corporation; *U.S. Public*, pg. 770
ESAB (MALAYSIA) SDN BHD—See Enovis Corporation; *U.S. Public*, pg. 770
ESAB MEXICO S.A. DE C.V.—See Enovis Corporation; *U.S. Public*, pg. 770
ESAB MIDDLE EAST—See Enovis Corporation; *U.S. Public*, pg. 771
ESAB NEDERLAND B.V.—See Enovis Corporation; *U.S. Public*, pg. 771
ESAB OY—See Enovis Corporation; *U.S. Public*, pg. 771
ESAB S.A. INDUSTRIA E COMERCIO—See Enovis Corporation; *U.S. Public*, pg. 771
ESAB SALDATURA S.P.A.—See Enovis Corporation; *U.S. Public*, pg. 771
ESAB SEAH CORPORATION—See Enovis Corporation; *U.S. Public*, pg. 771
ESAB SLOVAKIA SRO—See Enovis Corporation; *U.S. Public*, pg. 771
ESAB SVERIGE AB—See Enovis Corporation; *U.S. Public*, pg. 771
ESAB TYUMEN LIMITED LIABILITY COMPANY—See Enovis Corporation; *U.S. Public*, pg. 771
ESAB WELDING & CUTTING PRODUCTS (SHANGHAI) CO LIMITED—See Enovis Corporation; *U.S. Public*, pg. 771
ESAB WELDING & CUTTING PRODUCTS—See Enovis Corporation; *U.S. Public*, pg. 771
ESAB WELDING & CUTTING PRODUCTS—See Enovis Corporation; *U.S. Public*, pg. 771
ESAB WELDING EQUIPMENT AB—See Enovis Corporation; *U.S. Public*, pg. 771
ESAB WELDING PRODUCTS (JIANGSU) CO LIMITED—See Enovis Corporation; *U.S. Public*, pg. 771
ETI ELEKTROELEMENT, D.D.—See Andlinger & Company, Inc.; *U.S. Private*, pg. 278
FENGDA COMPANY LIMITED—See Atlantic China Welding Consumables, Inc.; *Int'l*, pg. 674
FORWARD TECHNOLOGY, INC.—See Crest Group Inc.; *U.S. Private*, pg. 1096
FUSITE, B.V.—See Emerson Electric Co.; *U.S. Public*, pg. 744
FUSITE JAPAN—See Emerson Electric Co.; *U.S. Public*, pg. 744
GAS-ARC GROUP LIMITED—See Enovis Corporation; *U.S. Public*, pg. 773
GEE LTD.—See BMT Group Limited; *Int'l*, pg. 1078
HARJU ELEKTER AS; *Int'l*, pg. 3277
HARRIS CALORIFIC GMBH—See Lincoln Electric Holdings, Inc.; *U.S. Public*, pg. 1317
HARRIS CALORIFIC INTERNATIONAL SP. Z O.O.—See Lincoln Electric Holdings, Inc.; *U.S. Public*, pg. 1317
HARRIS CALORIFIC S.R.L.—See Lincoln Electric Holdings, Inc.; *U.S. Public*, pg. 1317
HARRIS EURO S.L.—See Lincoln Electric Holdings, Inc.; *U.S. Public*, pg. 1317
HEINZ SOYER BOLZENSCHWEISSTECHNIK GMBH; *Int'l*, pg. 3325
HIT WELDING INDUSTRY CO., LTD.; *Int'l*, pg. 3408
HKS-PROZESSTECHNIK GMBH—See Enovis Corporation; *U.S. Public*, pg. 773
HOBART BROTHERS COMPANY—See Illinois Tool Works Inc.; *U.S. Public*, pg. 1103
HORMANN AUTOMOTIVE BIELEFELD GMBH—See Hormann Holding GmbH & Co. KG; *Int'l*, pg. 3480
IAW DE MEXICO, S.A. DE C.V.—See Atlantic China Welding Consumables, Inc.; *Int'l*, pg. 674
ITW DYNATEC KABUSHIKI KAISHA—See Illinois Tool Works Inc.; *U.S. Public*, pg. 1105
ITW WELDING PRODUCTS GROUP FZE—See Illinois Tool Works Inc.; *U.S. Public*, pg. 1108
ITW WELDING PRODUCTS ITALY SRL—See Illinois Tool Works Inc.; *U.S. Public*, pg. 1108
JETLINE ENGINEERING—See Illinois Tool Works Inc.; *U.S. Public*, pg. 1108
LASERLINE GMBH—See CEWE Stiftung & Co. KGaA; *Int'l*, pg. 1425
LES INDUSTRIES RAILWEL INC.—See CVC Capital Partners SICAV-FIS S.A.; *Int'l*, pg. 1887
LINCOLN CANADA HOLDINGS ULC—See Lincoln Electric Holdings, Inc.; *U.S. Public*, pg. 1317
LINCOLN ELECTRIC BELGIUM—See Lincoln Electric Holdings, Inc.; *U.S. Public*, pg. 1317
LINCOLN ELECTRIC BESTER SP. Z O.O.—See Lincoln

3611

333992 — WELDING AND SOLDERI...

Electric Holdings, Inc.; *U.S. Public*, pg. 1317
THE LINCOLN ELECTRIC COMPANY (ASIA PACIFIC) PTE. LTD.—See Lincoln Electric Holdings, Inc.; *U.S. Public*, pg. 1318
THE LINCOLN ELECTRIC COMPANY AUSTRALIA PTY. LTD.—See Lincoln Electric Holdings, Inc.; *U.S. Public*, pg. 1318
LINCOLN ELECTRIC COMPANY (INDIA) PRIVATE LIMITED—See Lincoln Electric Holdings, Inc.; *U.S. Public*, pg. 1317
LINCOLN ELECTRIC CZ S.R.O.—See Lincoln Electric Holdings, Inc.; *U.S. Public*, pg. 1317
LINCOLN ELECTRIC DEUTSCHLAND—See Lincoln Electric Holdings, Inc.; *U.S. Public*, pg. 1317
LINCOLN ELECTRIC DO BRASIL INDUSTRIA E COMERCIO LTDA.—See Lincoln Electric Holdings, Inc.; *U.S. Public*, pg. 1318
LINCOLN ELECTRIC EUROPE B.V.—See Lincoln Electric Holdings, Inc.; *U.S. Public*, pg. 1317
LINCOLN ELECTRIC EUROPE S.L.—See Lincoln Electric Holdings, Inc.; *U.S. Public*, pg. 1317
LINCOLN ELECTRIC FRANCE S.A.S.—See Lincoln Electric Holdings, Inc.; *U.S. Public*, pg. 1317
LINCOLN ELECTRIC HELI (ZHENGZHOU) WELDING MATERIALS COMPANY LTD.—See Lincoln Electric Holdings, Inc.; *U.S. Public*, pg. 1317
LINCOLN ELECTRIC HOLDINGS, INC.; *U.S. Public*, pg. 1316
LINCOLN ELECTRIC IBERIA, S.L.—See Lincoln Electric Holdings, Inc.; *U.S. Public*, pg. 1317
LINCOLN ELECTRIC JAPAN K.K.—See Lincoln Electric Holdings, Inc.; *U.S. Public*, pg. 1317
LINCOLN ELECTRIC LUXEMBOURG S.A.R.L.—See Lincoln Electric Holdings, Inc.; *U.S. Public*, pg. 1317
LINCOLN ELECTRIC MALAYSIA SDN. BHD.—See Lincoln Electric Holdings, Inc.; *U.S. Public*, pg. 1317
LINCOLN ELECTRIC MAQUINAS, S. DE R.L. DE C.V.—See Lincoln Electric Holdings, Inc.; *U.S. Public*, pg. 1317
LINCOLN ELECTRIC MEXICANA S.A. DE C.V.—See Lincoln Electric Holdings, Inc.; *U.S. Public*, pg. 1317
LINCOLN ELECTRIC MIDDLE EAST FZE—See Lincoln Electric Holdings, Inc.; *U.S. Public*, pg. 1317
LINCOLN ELECTRIC PORTUGAL, S.A.—See Lincoln Electric Holdings, Inc.; *U.S. Public*, pg. 1317
LINCOLN ELECTRIC S.A.—See Lincoln Electric Holdings, Inc.; *U.S. Public*, pg. 1317
LINCOLN ELECTRIC SPAIN, S.L.—See Lincoln Electric Holdings, Inc.; *U.S. Public*, pg. 1317
LINCOLN ELECTRIC (THAILAND) LTD.—See Lincoln Electric Holdings, Inc.; *U.S. Public*, pg. 1317
LINCOLN ELECTRIC (U.K.) LTD.—See Lincoln Electric Holdings, Inc.; *U.S. Public*, pg. 1317
LINCOLN SMITWELD BELGIUM S.A.—See Lincoln Electric Holdings, Inc.; *U.S. Public*, pg. 1318
LUCAS MILHAUPT RIBERAC SA—See Steel Partners Holdings L.P.; *U.S. Public*, pg. 1943
M2K-LASER GMBH—See Coherent Corp.; *U.S. Public*, pg. 528
MACDERMID ALPHA ELECTRONICS SOLUTIONS, INC.—See Element Solutions Inc.; *U.S. Public*, pg. 726
MECASONIC ESPANA SA—See Crest Group Inc.; *U.S. Private*, pg. 1096
MECASONIC SA—See Crest Group Inc.; *U.S. Private*, pg. 1096
MECASONIC UK LTD—See Crest Group Inc.; *U.S. Private*, pg. 1096
META VISION SYSTEMS LIMITED—See Stanley Black & Decker, Inc.; *U.S. Public*, pg. 1933
MILLER ELECTRIC MANUFACTURING CO.—See Illinois Tool Works Inc.; *U.S. Public*, pg. 1109
MOELLER ELECTRIC NV/SA—See Eaton Corporation plc; *Int'l*, pg. 2281
MOGEMA 3.0—See Aalberts N.V.; *Int'l*, pg. 35
MOGEMA VESSEM BV—See Aalberts N.V.; *Int'l*, pg. 35
THE NANJING LINCOLN ELECTRIC CO., LTD.—See Lincoln Electric Holdings, Inc.; *U.S. Public*, pg. 1318
NI WELDING SUPPLY, L.L.C.; *U.S. Private*, pg. 2924
O.C.I.M. S.R.L.—See Enovis Corporation; *U.S. Public*, pg. 771
OERLIKON SCANDINAVIA AB—See Lincoln Electric Holdings, Inc.; *U.S. Public*, pg. 1317
OERLIKON SCHWEISSTECHNIK AG—See Lincoln Electric Holdings, Inc.; *U.S. Public*, pg. 1317
OERLIKON SCHWEISSTECHNIK GMBH—See Lincoln Electric Holdings, Inc.; *U.S. Public*, pg. 1317
OK INTERNATIONAL (UK) LTD.—See Dover Corporation; *U.S. Public*, pg. 681
O.R. LASERTECHNOLOGIE GMBH—See Coherent Corp.; *U.S. Public*, pg. 527
O-Z GEDNEY COMPANY LLC—See Emerson Electric Co.; *U.S. Public*, pg. 740
PHILIPPINE WELDING EQUIPMENT, INC.—See Enovis Corporation; *U.S. Public*, pg. 771
PLANT PERFORMANCE SERVICES INC.; *U.S. Private*, pg. 3197
POWERLASE TECHNOLOGIES LIMITED—See ANDRITZ AG; *Int'l*, pg. 456
PR. A. I. SRL—See Illinois Tool Works Inc.; *U.S. Public*, pg. 1110
PRC LASER EUROPE N.V.—See Coherent Corp.; *U.S. Public*, pg. 528
PRO CRANE SERVICES PROPRIETARY LIMITED—See ARGENT INDUSTRIAL LIMITED; *Int'l*, pg. 561
PT CIGWELD INDONESIA—See Enovis Corporation; *U.S. Public*, pg. 771
PT LINCOLN ELECTRIC INDONESIA—See Lincoln Electric Holdings, Inc.; *U.S. Public*, pg. 1318
PT LINCOLN INDOWELD—See Lincoln Electric Holdings, Inc.; *U.S. Public*, pg. 1318
PT VICTOR TEKNOLOGI INDONESIA—See Enovis Corporation; *U.S. Public*, pg. 771
QUALITEK DELTA PHILIPPINES—See Qualitek International Inc.; *U.S. Private*, pg. 3317
QUALITEK ELECTRONIC SHENZHEN CHINA—See Qualitek International Inc.; *U.S. Private*, pg. 3317
QUALITEK SINGAPORE PTE. LTD.—See Qualitek International Inc.; *U.S. Private*, pg. 3317
RAILTECH SCHLATTER SYSTEMS, S.A.S.—See CVC Capital Partners SICAV-FIS S.A.; *Int'l*, pg. 1887
RANKIN INDUSTRIES, INC.—See Broco, Inc.; *U.S. Private*, pg. 661
READY WELDER CORPORATION—See Broco, Inc.; *U.S. Private*, pg. 661
RINCO ULTRASONICS AG—See Crest Group Inc.; *U.S. Private*, pg. 1096
RINCO ULTRASONICS DANMARK A/S—See Crest Group Inc.; *U.S. Private*, pg. 1096
RINCO ULTRASONICS GMBH—See Crest Group Inc.; *U.S. Private*, pg. 1096
RINCO ULTRASONICS (INDIA) PRIVATE LIMITED—See Crest Group Inc.; *U.S. Private*, pg. 1096
RINCO ULTRASONICS ITALIA S.R.L.—See Crest Group Inc.; *U.S. Private*, pg. 1096
RINCO ULTRASONICS (SHANGHAI) CO., LTD.—See Crest Group Inc.; *U.S. Private*, pg. 1096
RINCO ULTRASONICS USA INC.—See Crest Group Inc.; *U.S. Private*, pg. 1096
ROBOLUTION GMBH—See Lincoln Electric Holdings, Inc.; *U.S. Public*, pg. 1318
ROFIN BAASEL BENELUX BV—See Coherent Corp.; *U.S. Public*, pg. 528
ROFIN-BAASEL ESPANA SL—See Coherent Corp.; *U.S. Public*, pg. 528
ROFIN-BAASEL FRANCE SA—See Coherent Corp.; *U.S. Public*, pg. 528
ROMAN MANUFACTURING INC.; *U.S. Private*, pg. 3476
S.A. ESAB N.V.—See Enovis Corporation; *U.S. Public*, pg. 771
SAF-OERLIKON MALAYSIA SWDN BHD—See Lincoln Electric Holdings, Inc.; *U.S. Public*, pg. 1318
SCHERWO STEUERUNGSTECHNIK GMBH—See ATON GmbH; *Int'l*, pg. 689
SCIAKY WELDING MACHINES LTD.—See Phillips Service Industries, Inc. (PSI); *U.S. Private*, pg. 3171
THE SHANGHAI LINCOLN ELECTRIC CO., LTD.—See Lincoln Electric Holdings, Inc.; *U.S. Public*, pg. 1318
SIVACO ONTARIO PROCESSING DIVISION—See The Heico Companies, L.L.C.; *U.S. Private*, pg. 4051
SMART AUTOMATION SYSTEMS; *U.S. Private*, pg. 3691
SMITH EQUIPMENT—See Illinois Tool Works Inc.; *U.S. Public*, pg. 1110
SOLDADURAS WEST ARCO S.A.S.—See Enovis Corporation; *U.S. Public*, pg. 773
SOLDEX S.A.—See Enovis Corporation; *U.S. Public*, pg. 773
SSCO MANUFACTURING, INC.—See Lincoln Electric Holdings, Inc.; *U.S. Public*, pg. 1318
STOODY COMPANY—See Enovis Corporation; *U.S. Public*, pg. 774
TBI INDUSTRIES GMBH—See Enovis Corporation; *U.S. Public*, pg. 773
TECHMETA SA—See Bodycote plc; *Int'l*, pg. 1098
TECHNICAL DEVICES CO.; *U.S. Private*, pg. 3954
TECTOWELD INC.—See Hicks Lightning Protection, Inc.; *U.S. Private*, pg. 1934
TEUREMA SL—See EUROLLS S.p.A.; *Int'l*, pg. 2553
THERMADYNE JAPAN LTD.—See Enovis Corporation; *U.S. Public*, pg. 771
THERMADYNE (SHANGHAI) CO. LTD.—See Enovis Corporation; *U.S. Public*, pg. 771
THERMADYNE VICTOR LTDA.—See Enovis Corporation; *U.S. Public*, pg. 773
TOKAI YOGYO CO., LTD.—See Alconix Corporation; *Int'l*, pg. 303
TOP ELECTRODES SDN. BHD.—See Atlantic China Welding Consumables, Inc.; *Int'l*, pg. 674
UHRHAN & SCHWILL SCHWEISSTECHNIK GMBH—See Lincoln Electric Holdings, Inc.; *U.S. Public*, pg. 1318
UHRHAN & SCHWILL SCHWEISSTECHNIK GMBH—See Lincoln Electric Holdings, Inc.; *U.S. Public*, pg. 1318
UNIWELD PRODUCTS INC.; *U.S. Private*, pg. 4310
VAUTID INDIA PRIVATE LIMITED—See DZ BANK AG Deutsche Zentral-Genossenschaftsbank; *Int'l*, pg. 2245
VAUTID LATAM S.A.—See DZ BANK AG Deutsche Zentral-Genossenschaftsbank; *Int'l*, pg. 2245
VAUTID MIDDLE EAST F.Z.E—See DZ BANK AG Deutsche Zentral-Genossenschaftsbank; *Int'l*, pg. 2245
VAUTID NORTH AMERICA, INC.—See DZ BANK AG Deutsche Zentral-Genossenschaftsbank; *Int'l*, pg. 2245
VERTIV DEL PERU S.A.C.—See Vertiv Holdings Co; *U.S. Public*, pg. 2289
VICTOR EQUIPMENT COMPANY—See Enovis Corporation; *U.S. Public*, pg. 771
VICTOR EQUIPMENT DE MEXICO, S.A. DE C.V.—See Enovis Corporation; *U.S. Public*, pg. 771
VICTOR TECHNOLOGIES ASIA SDN BHD—See Enovis Corporation; *U.S. Public*, pg. 771
VICTOR TECHNOLOGIES AUSTRALIA PTY LTD.—See Enovis Corporation; *U.S. Public*, pg. 774
VICTOR TECHNOLOGIES CANADA LTD.—See Enovis Corporation; *U.S. Public*, pg. 774
VICTOR TECHNOLOGIES INTERNATIONAL, INC.—See Enovis Corporation; *U.S. Public*, pg. 774
VICTOR TECHNOLOGIES S.R.L.—See Enovis Corporation; *U.S. Public*, pg. 772
VIZIENT MANUFACTURING SOLUTIONS, INC.—See Lincoln Electric Holdings, Inc.; *U.S. Public*, pg. 1318
WALL LENK CORPORATION; *U.S. Private*, pg. 4430
WEARTECH INTERNATIONAL LIMITED—See Lincoln Electric Holdings, Inc.; *U.S. Public*, pg. 1318
WEATHERFORD CANADA PARTNERSHIP—See Weatherford International plc; *U.S. Public*, pg. 2340
WELDING TECHNOLOGY CORPORATION—See Welding Technology Corporation; *U.S. Private*, pg. 4474
WESTERN ENTERPRISES DIVISION—See Berkshire Hathaway Inc.; *U.S. Public*, pg. 300
WESTERN PNEUMATIC TUBE COMPANY, LLC—See Leggett & Platt, Incorporated; *U.S. Public*, pg. 1304
WOLF ROBOTICS, LLC—See Lincoln Electric Holdings, Inc.; *U.S. Public*, pg. 1318
WTC—See Welding Technology Corporation; *U.S. Private*, pg. 4474
WUHAN TOPWIN OPTOELECTRONICS TECHNOLOGY CO. LTD.—See MKS Instruments, Inc.; *U.S. Public*, pg. 1452

333993 — PACKAGING MACHINERY MANUFACTURING

THE AAGARD GROUP, LLC; *U.S. Private*, pg. 3980
ABC PACKAGING MACHINE CORPORATION; *U.S. Private*, pg. 36
ACCRAPLY, INC.—See Barry-Wehmiller Companies, Inc.; *U.S. Private*, pg. 481
ACMA GD—See Coesia S.p.A.; *Int'l*, pg. 1690
ACMA S.P.A.—See Coesia S.p.A.; *Int'l*, pg. 1689
AEM (HONGKONG) PTE LTD—See AEM Holdings Ltd.; *Int'l*, pg. 175
ALFONS HAAR MASCHINENBAU GMBH & CO. KG; *Int'l*, pg. 315
ALHAMRANI INDUSTRIAL GROUP LTD—See Alhamrani Group; *Int'l*, pg. 319
ALLPAX PRODUCTS LLC—See Leonard Green & Partners, L.P.; *U.S. Private*, pg. 2427
ALTECH NEW MATERIALS (SUZHOU) CO., LTD.—See Altech Co., Ltd.; *Int'l*, pg. 388
AMERICAN FUJI TECHNICAL SERVICES, INC—See Fuji Seal International, Inc.; *Int'l*, pg. 2816
AMERICAN PLASTIC TECHNOLOGIES, INC.—See Rao Design International, Inc.; *U.S. Private*, pg. 3355
ARMINAK & ASSOCIATES, INC.—See TriMas Corporation; *U.S. Public*, pg. 2189
ARPAC LLC—See Warburg Pincus LLC; *U.S. Private*, pg. 4437
ASANO LABORATORIES CO., LTD.—See Daiichi Jitsugyo Co. Ltd.; *Int'l*, pg. 1927
A/S CHRISTIAN BERNER—See Christian Berner Tech Trade AB; *Int'l*, pg. 1586
ASH PLASTIC PRODUCTS LIMITED—See Hill & Smith PLC; *Int'l*, pg. 3391
ATCOM TECHNOLOGIES LTD.; *Int'l*, pg. 667
AVERY WEIGH-TRONIX, LLC—See Illinois Tool Works Inc.; *U.S. Public*, pg. 1101
BARRY-WEHMILLER COMPANIES, INC.; *U.S. Private*, pg. 481
BELVAC CR, SPOL S.R.O.—See Dover Corporation; *U.S. Public*, pg. 678
BELVAC MIDDLE EAST FZE—See Dover Corporation; *U.S. Public*, pg. 678
B+ EQUIPMENT SAS—See Sealed Air Corporation; *U.S. Public*, pg. 1852
BETTER PACKAGES, INC.—See Clearlake Capital Group, L.P.; *U.S. Private*, pg. 935
BEVCORP, LLC—See John Bean Technologies Corporation; *U.S. Public*, pg. 1191
BG CONTAINER GLASS PUBLIC COMPANY LIMITED; *Int'l*, pg. 1006
B.H. BUNN COMPANY; *U.S. Private*, pg. 420
B&H MANUFACTURING COMPANY; *U.S. Private*, pg. 418
BOBST ITALIA SPA—See Bobst Group S.A.; *Int'l*, pg. 1096
BOSCH PACKAGING SERVICES—See CVC Capital Partners SICAV-FIS S.A.; *Int'l*, pg. 1884

N.A.I.C.S. INDEX

333993 — PACKAGING MACHINERY...

BOSCH PACKAGING TECHNOLOGY (CHENGDU) CO., LTD.—See CVC Capital Partners SICAV-FIS S.A.; *Int'l*, pg. 1884
BOSCH PACKAGING TECHNOLOGY (HANGZHOU) CO., LTD.—See CVC Capital Partners SICAV-FIS S.A.; *Int'l*, pg. 1884
BOSCH PACKAGING TECHNOLOGY, INC.—See CVC Capital Partners SICAV-FIS S.A.; *Int'l*, pg. 1884
BOSCH PACKAGING TECHNOLOGY K.K.—See CVC Capital Partners SICAV-FIS S.A.; *Int'l*, pg. 1884
BOSCH PACKAGING TECHNOLOGY LTD.—See CVC Capital Partners SICAV-FIS S.A.; *Int'l*, pg. 1884
BOSCH PACKAGING TECHNOLOGY (SINGAPORE) PTE. LTD.—See CVC Capital Partners SICAV-FIS S.A.; *Int'l*, pg. 1884
BRAUSSE EUROPE BV—See Bobst Group S.A.; *Int'l*, pg. 1096
BRENTON, LLC.—See Leonard Green & Partners, L.P.; *U.S. Private*, pg. 2427
BRUECKNER GROUP USA, INC.—See Bruckner Group GmbH; *Int'l*, pg. 1199
CAMPBELL WRAPPER CORPORATION; *U.S. Private*, pg. 731
CAN LINES INC.; *U.S. Private*, pg. 732
CARGOSCAN AS—See Mettler-Toledo International, Inc.; *U.S. Public*, pg. 1432
CHARLES BESELER CO. - SHRINK PACKAGING DIVISION—See Charles Beseler Co.; *U.S. Private*, pg. 851
CHRISTIAN BERNER AS—See Christian Berner Tech Trade AB; *Int'l*, pg. 1586
CHRISTIAN BERNER OY—See Christian Berner Tech Trade AB; *Int'l*, pg. 1586
CKD SHIKOKU SEIKO CORPORATION—See CKD Corporation; *Int'l*, pg. 1639
CORNIANI ACMA GD—See Coesia S.p.A.; *Int'l*, pg. 1690
COZZOLI MACHINE COMPANY; *U.S. Private*, pg. 1079
CP PACKAGING, LLC.—See The Middleby Corporation; *U.S. Public*, pg. 2113
CRAWFORD PACKAGING INC.; *Int'l*, pg. 1829
CROWN PACKAGING LUX I S.A.R.L.—See Crown Holdings, Inc.; *Int'l*, pg. 598
CVC TECHNOLOGIES, INC.; *Int'l*, pg. 1889
C V C TECHNOLOGIES, INC.—See CVC Technologies, Inc.; *Int'l*, pg. 1889
DAIO PACKAGE CORPORATION—See Daio Paper Corporation; *Int'l*, pg. 1939
DAIO POSTAL CHEMICAL CORPORATION—See Daio Paper Corporation; *Int'l*, pg. 1939
DAVIS BUSINESS UNIT—See Douglas Machine, Inc.; *U.S. Private*, pg. 1267
DEKAPRINT S.A.; *Int'l*, pg. 2005
DELKOR SYSTEMS INC.; *U.S. Private*, pg. 1197
DOMINO PRINT AND APPLY AB—See Brother Industries, Ltd.; *Int'l*, pg. 1197
DOUGLAS MACHINE, INC.; *U.S. Private*, pg. 1267
EASTEY ENTERPRISES INC.—See Engage Technologies Corp.; *U.S. Private*, pg. 1397
EDL MASSMAN, LLC—See Granite Equity Partners LLC; *U.S. Private*, pg. 1755
ELECSTER OYJ; *Int'l*, pg. 2348
ELLIOTT MANUFACTURING COMPANY, INC.—See Granite Equity Partners LLC; *U.S. Private*, pg. 1755
EMHART GLASS MANUFACTURING INC.—See Bucher Industries AG; *Int'l*, pg. 1208
EMINIS AMBALAJ SANAYI VE TICARET A.S.; *Int'l*, pg. 2381
ENGAGE TECHNOLOGIES, INC.—See Castlight Health, Inc.; *U.S. Public*, pg. 448
EPI LABELERS LLC—See Leonard Green & Partners, L.P.; *U.S. Private*, pg. 2427
ESPERA-WERKE GMBH; *Int'l*, pg. 2505
FAMECCANICA NORTH AMERICA, INC.—See The Procter & Gamble Company; *U.S. Public*, pg. 2120
FINLOGIC S.P.A.; *Int'l*, pg. 2675
FISCHBEIN DEUTSCHLAND GMBH—See Warburg Pincus LLC; *U.S. Private*, pg. 4437
FISCHBEIN PACKAGING (S) PTE LTD.—See Warburg Pincus LLC; *U.S. Private*, pg. 4437
FISCHBEIN S.A.—See Warburg Pincus LLC; *U.S. Private*, pg. 4437
FISCHBEIN-SAXON, LTD.—See Warburg Pincus LLC; *U.S. Private*, pg. 4437
FLEETWOOD-SIGNODE—See Crown Holdings, Inc.; *U.S. Public*, pg. 599
FOCKE & CO. (GMBH & CO.) VERPACKUNGSMASCHINEN; *Int'l*, pg. 2718
FOCKE & CO., INC.—See Focke & Co. (GmbH & Co.) Verpackungsmaschinen; *Int'l*, pg. 2718
FOPAC MASCHINENBAU GMBH—See Focke & Co. (GmbH & Co.) Verpackungsmaschinen; *Int'l*, pg. 2718
FORMECA OY—See Amitec Oy; *Int'l*, pg. 428
FOWLER PRODUCTS COMPANY, LLC—See Leonard Green & Partners, L.P.; *U.S. Private*, pg. 2427
FUJI FLEX, INC.—See Fuji Seal International, Inc.; *Int'l*, pg. 2816
FUJI LABEL CO., LTD.—See DIC Corporation; *Int'l*, pg. 2109

FUJI SEAL EUROPE B.V.—See Fuji Seal International, Inc.; *Int'l*, pg. 2816
FUJI SEAL FRANCE S.A.S.—See Fuji Seal International, Inc.; *Int'l*, pg. 2816
FUJI SEAL INTERNATIONAL, INC - NARA FACTORY—See Fuji Seal International, Inc.; *Int'l*, pg. 2816
FUJI SEAL PACKAGING DE MEXICO, S.A. DE C.V—See Fuji Seal International, Inc.; *Int'l*, pg. 2816
FUJI SEAL POLAND SP.ZO.O.—See Fuji Seal International, Inc.; *Int'l*, pg. 2816
FUJI SEAL SOUTHEAST ASIA, INC.—See Fuji Seal International, Inc.; *Int'l*, pg. 2816
FUJI TACK EAST, INC.—See Fuji Seal International, Inc.; *Int'l*, pg. 2816
FUNENG ORIENTAL EQUIPMENT TECHNOLOGY CO., LTD.; *Int'l*, pg. 2846
G.D CHINA LIMITED—See Coesia S.p.A.; *Int'l*, pg. 1690
G.D DO BRASIL—See Coesia S.p.A.; *Int'l*, pg. 1690
GD INDONESIA—See Coesia S.p.A.; *Int'l*, pg. 1690
G.D JAPAN—See Coesia S.p.A.; *Int'l*, pg. 1690
GDM SPA—See Coesia S.p.A.; *Int'l*, pg. 1690
G.D RUSSIAN FEDERATION—See Coesia S.p.A.; *Int'l*, pg. 1690
G.D SOUTH EAST ASIA—See Coesia S.p.A.; *Int'l*, pg. 1690
GD S.P.A.—See Coesia S.p.A.; *Int'l*, pg. 1689
GEA PROCOMAC S.P.A. - PACKAGING UNIT—See GEA Group Aktiengesellschaft; *Int'l*, pg. 2902
GEA PROCOMAC S.P.A.—See GEA Group Aktiengesellschaft; *Int'l*, pg. 2902
GENERAL PACKER AMERICA CORPORATION—See General Packer Co., Ltd.; *Int'l*, pg. 2919
GENERAL PACKER CHINA CO., LTD.—See General Packer Co., Ltd.; *Int'l*, pg. 2919
GERBER SCIENTIFIC, INC. - GERBER INNOVATIONS DIVISION—See Vector Capital Management, L.P.; *U.S. Private*, pg. 4351
GIMA S.P.A.—See I.M.A. Industria Macchine Automatiche S.p.A.; *Int'l*, pg. 3565
GOODTECH PACKAGING SYSTEMS AS—See Goodtech ASA; *Int'l*, pg. 3041
GOULD SOUTHERN—See Stephen Gould Corporation; *U.S. Private*, pg. 3802
GRAPHIC WEST PACKAGING MACHINERY, LLC; *U.S. Private*, pg. 1758
GREAT EASTERN INDUSTRIES LIMITED—See Feng Tay Enterprises Co., Ltd.; *Int'l*, pg. 2634
GUANGDONG DONGFANG SCIENCE & TECHNOLOGY CO., LTD.; *Int'l*, pg. 3153
GUANGDONG TENGEN INDUSTRIAL GROUP CO., LTD.; *Int'l*, pg. 3161
GUANGZHOU TECH-LONG PACKAGING MACHINERY CO., LTD.; *Int'l*, pg. 3168
HAAR CZ S.R.O.—See Alfons Haar Maschinenbau GmbH & Co. KG; *Int'l*, pg. 315
HAAR FRANCE SAS—See Alfons Haar Maschinenbau GmbH & Co. KG; *Int'l*, pg. 315
HAMER-FISCHBEIN LLC - FISCHBEIN DIVISION—See Warburg Pincus LLC; *U.S. Private*, pg. 4437
HAMER-FISCHBEIN LLC—See Warburg Pincus LLC; *U.S. Private*, pg. 4437
HANGZHOU ZHONGYA MACHINERY CO., LTD.; *Int'l*, pg. 3252
HANMERE POLYTHENE LTD—See Chiltern Capital LLP; *Int'l*, pg. 1479
HAPA AG—See Coesia S.p.A.; *Int'l*, pg. 1690
HARBIN BOSHI AUTOMATION CO., LTD.; *Int'l*, pg. 3270
HARPAK-ULMA PACKAGING, LLC; *U.S. Private*, pg. 1867
HARTNESS INTERNATIONAL INC.—See Illinois Tool Works Inc.; *U.S. Public*, pg. 1103
HASSIA PACKAGING PVT. LTD.—See I.M.A. Industria Macchine Automatiche S.p.A.; *Int'l*, pg. 3565
HAYSSEN PACKING TECHNOLOGIES, INC.—See Barry-Wehmiller Companies, Inc.; *U.S. Private*, pg. 482
HEAT SEAL LLC; *U.S. Private*, pg. 1901
H. ERBEN LIMITED—See Keystone Group, L.P.; *U.S. Private*, pg. 2297
H.-H. FOCKE GMBH & CO. KG—See Focke & Co. (GmbH & Co.) Verpackungsmaschinen; *Int'l*, pg. 2718
HOCHLAND ROMANIA SRL—See Hochland SE; *Int'l*, pg. 3437
HORIX MANUFACTURING COMPANY; *U.S. Private*, pg. 1980
THE HUDSON-SHARP MACHINE COMPANY—See Barry-Wehmiller Companies, Inc.; *U.S. Private*, pg. 482
HUHTAMAKI DO BRASIL LTDA.—See Huhtamaki Oyj; *Int'l*, pg. 3526
HUHTAMAKI FLEXIBLE PACKAGING GERMANY GMBH & CO. KG—See Huhtamaki Oyj; *Int'l*, pg. 3524
HUHTAMAKI INDIA LIMITED; *Int'l*, pg. 3524
HUHTAMAKI RUSSIA—See Huhtamaki Oyj; *Int'l*, pg. 3525
HUNAN CHINA SUN PHARMACEUTICAL MACHINERY CO., LTD.; *Int'l*, pg. 3531
ID TECHNOLOGY LLC—See Leonard Green & Partners, L.P.; *U.S. Private*, pg. 2427
ILAPAK (BEIJING) PACKAGING MACHINERY CO. LTD.—See I.M.A. Industria Macchine Automatiche S.p.A.; *Int'l*, pg. 3566
ILAPAK INTERNATIONAL SA—See I.M.A. Industria Macchine Automatiche S.p.A.; *Int'l*, pg. 3566
ILAPAK ITALIA S.P.A. - FILLDOSE DIVISION—See ILAPAK S.A.; *Int'l*, pg. 3613
ILPRA BENELUX BV—See Ilpra SpA; *Int'l*, pg. 3616
ILPRA DEUTSCHLAND GMBH—See Ilpra SpA; *Int'l*, pg. 3616
ILPRA HONG KONG LTD.—See Ilpra SpA; *Int'l*, pg. 3616
ILPRA SPA; *Int'l*, pg. 3616
ILPRA SYSTEMS ESPANA SL—See Ilpra SpA; *Int'l*, pg. 3616
ILPRA SYSTEMS UK LTD.—See Ilpra SpA; *Int'l*, pg. 3616
I.M.A. INDUSTRIA MACCHINE AUTOMATICHE S.P.A.; *Int'l*, pg. 3565
IMA PACKAGING & PROCESSING EQUIPMENT CO., LTD.—See I.M.A. Industria Macchine Automatiche S.p.A.; *Int'l*, pg. 3566
INLINE FILLING SYSTEMS, LLC—See The Middleby Corporation; *U.S. Public*, pg. 2114
IPI S.R.L.—See Coesia S.p.A.; *Int'l*, pg. 1690
ITW HI-CONE—See Illinois Tool Works Inc.; *U.S. Public*, pg. 1106
ITW MERITEX SDN. BHD.—See Illinois Tool Works Inc.; *U.S. Public*, pg. 1106
ITW MIMA SYSTEMS S.A.S.—See Illinois Tool Works Inc.; *U.S. Public*, pg. 1106
ITW MULLER—See Illinois Tool Works Inc.; *U.S. Public*, pg. 1106
IWK VERPACKUNGSTECHNIK GMBH—See ATS Corporation; *Int'l*, pg. 695
JBT FOODTECH CITRUS SYSTEMS—See John Bean Technologies Corporation; *U.S. Public*, pg. 1191
KJO SYSTEMS SDN. BHD.—See Can-One Berhad; *Int'l*, pg. 1276
KLIKLOK CORPORATION; *U.S. Private*, pg. 2320
KLIKLOK INTERNATIONAL—See Kliklok Corporation; *U.S. Private*, pg. 2320
LABEL-AIRE, INC.—See Impaxx, Inc.; *U.S. Private*, pg. 2049
LABELING SYSTEMS LLC—See Leonard Green & Partners, L.P.; *U.S. Private*, pg. 2428
LAETUS GMBH—See Coesia S.p.A.; *Int'l*, pg. 1690
LANTECH INC.; *U.S. Private*, pg. 2391
LOVESHAW—See Illinois Tool Works Inc.; *U.S. Public*, pg. 1109
MASSMAN AUTOMATION DESIGNS, LLC—See Granite Equity Partners LLC; *U.S. Private*, pg. 1755
MATRIX PACKAGING MACHINERY, LLC—See Leonard Green & Partners, L.P.; *U.S. Private*, pg. 2428
MEHEEN MANUFACTURING, INC.—See Wild Goose Canning Technologies Inc.; *U.S. Private*, pg. 4518
MERKEL FREUDENBERG FLUIDTECHNIC GMBH—See Freudenberg SE; *Int'l*, pg. 2789
MGS MACHINE CORPORATION; *U.S. Private*, pg. 2695
MIDDLEBY PACKAGING SOLUTIONS, LLC—See The Middleby Corporation; *U.S. Public*, pg. 2114
NERCON ENGINEERING & MANUFACTURING INC.; *U.S. Private*, pg. 2885
NEW ENGLAND MACHINERY, INC.—See Granite Equity Partners LLC; *U.S. Private*, pg. 1755
NJM-CLI PACKAGING SYSTEMS INTERNATIONAL; *U.S. Private*, pg. 2931
NJM PACKAGING—See Leonard Green & Partners, L.P.; *U.S. Private*, pg. 2428
NJM PACKAGING—See Leonard Green & Partners, L.P.; *U.S. Private*, pg. 2428
NOVAFLEX SAS—See Bobst Group S.A.; *Int'l*, pg. 1096
OHLSON PACKAGING, INC.—See Warburg Pincus LLC; *U.S. Private*, pg. 4438
OMK LTD.—See Daiwabo Holdings Co., Ltd.; *Int'l*, pg. 1949
O-M MACHINERY LTD.—See Daiwabo Holdings Co., Ltd.; *Int'l*, pg. 1949
OMTEC LTD.—See Daiwabo Holdings Co., Ltd.; *Int'l*, pg. 1949
OOO FINNPACK—See Elecster Oyj; *Int'l*, pg. 2348
ORGAPACK GMBH—See Illinois Tool Works Inc.; *U.S. Public*, pg. 1109
OSGOOD INDUSTRIES, INC.—See CVC Capital Partners SICAV-FIS S.A.; *Int'l*, pg. 1884
OSSID LLC—See Leonard Green & Partners, L.P.; *U.S. Private*, pg. 2428
PACKAGE MACHINERY COMPANY, INC.; *U.S. Private*, pg. 3072
PACKSIZE INTERNATIONAL, LLC; *U.S. Private*, pg. 3073
PAGO ETIKETTIERSYSTEME GMBH—See Fuji Seal International, Inc.; *Int'l*, pg. 2817
PAGO S.R.L.—See Fuji Seal International, Inc.; *Int'l*, pg. 2817
THE PAPER PRODUCTS LTD.—See Huhtamaki Oyj; *Int'l*, pg. 3526
PARSONS-EAGLE PACKAGING SYSTEMS—See Campbell Wrapper Corporation; *U.S. Private*, pg. 731
PARSONS-EAGLE PACKAGING SYSTEMS—See Campbell Wrapper Corporation; *U.S. Private*, pg. 731
PHARMAWORKS INC.; *U.S. Private*, pg. 3165
PNEUMATICSCALEANGELUS—See Barry-Wehmiller Companies, Inc.; *U.S. Private*, pg. 482
PNEUMATICSCALEANGELUS—See Barry-Wehmiller Companies, Inc.; *U.S. Private*, pg. 482

333993 — PACKAGING MACHINERY...

PNEUMATIC SCALE CORPORATION—See Barry-Wehmiller Companies, Inc.; *U.S. Private*, pg. 482
PPI TECHNOLOGIES GLOBAL, LLC; *U.S. Private*, pg. 3240
PRODUCT MOVERS, LLC; *U.S. Private*, pg. 3273
PROMACH, INC.—See Leonard Green & Partners, L.P.; *U.S. Private*, pg. 2427
PROSEAL AUSTRALIA PTY. LTD.—See John Bean Technologies Corporation; *U.S. Public*, pg. 1192
PT. FUJI SEAL INDONESIA—See Fuji Seal International, Inc.; *Int'l*, pg. 2816
QUANDEL VERPACKUNGS- UND FOERDERTECHNIK GMBH—See Illinois Tool Works Inc.; *U.S. Public*, pg. 1110
R.A. JONES & CO. INC.—See Coesia S.p.A.; *Int'l*, pg. 1690
R.A. JONES & CO.—See Coesia S.p.A.; *Int'l*, pg. 1690
R.A JONES GROUP LTD—See Coesia S.p.A.; *Int'l*, pg. 1690
RENNCO LLC—See Leonard Green & Partners, L.P.; *U.S. Private*, pg. 2428
RESCASET CONCEPT—See Groupe Guillin SA; *Int'l*, pg. 3104
RICE LAKE DE MEXICO—See Rice Lake Weighing Systems, Inc.; *U.S. Private*, pg. 3425
RIEKE CORPORATION—See TriMas Corporation; *U.S. Public*, pg. 2189
ROVEMA GMBH—See Franz Haniel & Cie. GmbH; *Int'l*, pg. 2763
SACMO—See Coesia S.p.A.; *Int'l*, pg. 1690
SANNER GMBH—See GHO Capital Partners LLP; *Int'l*, pg. 2959
SCHOELLER ARCA SYSTEMS GROUP B.V.—See OEP Capital Advisors, L.P.; *U.S. Private*, pg. 3000
SEALCOAT TECHNOLOGIES LLC—See BERICAP GmbH & Co. KG; *Int'l*, pg. 981
SEALED AIR SHRINK EQUIPMENT—See Sealed Air Corporation; *U.S. Public*, pg. 1855
SERPA PACKAGING SOLUTIONS, LLC—See Leonard Green & Partners, L.P.; *U.S. Private*, pg. 2428
SHANKLIN CORPORATION—See Sealed Air Corporation; *U.S. Public*, pg. 1855
SHIPPERS SUPPLY INC—See Central National Gottesman Inc.; *U.S. Private*, pg. 823
SIGNODE CANADA—See Crown Holdings, Inc.; *U.S. Public*, pg. 599
SIGNODE DENMARK APS—See Crown Holdings, Inc.; *U.S. Public*, pg. 599
SIGNODE FINLAND OY—See Crown Holdings, Inc.; *U.S. Public*, pg. 599
SIGNODE HONG KONG LIMITED—See Crown Holdings, Inc.; *U.S. Public*, pg. 599
SIGNODE INDUSTRIAL GROUP MEXICO, R.L. DE C.V.—See Crown Holdings, Inc.; *U.S. Public*, pg. 600
SIGNODE INDUSTRIAL GROUP US INC.—See Crown Holdings, Inc.; *U.S. Public*, pg. 600
SIGNODE KABUSHIKI KAISHA—See Crown Holdings, Inc.; *U.S. Public*, pg. 599
SIGNODE NORWAY AS—See Crown Holdings, Inc.; *U.S. Public*, pg. 600
SIGNODE PACKAGING GROUP (MALAYSIA) SDN BHD—See Crown Holdings, Inc.; *U.S. Public*, pg. 599
SIGNODE PACKAGING SYSTEMS EUROPE - UK & IRELAND—See Crown Holdings, Inc.; *U.S. Public*, pg. 600
SIGNODE PACKAGING SYSTEMS—See Crown Holdings, Inc.; *U.S. Public*, pg. 599
SIGNODE POLSKA SP. Z O.O.—See Crown Holdings, Inc.; *U.S. Public*, pg. 600
SIGNODE SYSTEM GMBH—See Crown Holdings, Inc.; *U.S. Public*, pg. 600
SIGNODE UK LTD.—See Crown Holdings, Inc.; *U.S. Public*, pg. 600
SIMS MANUFACTURING CO. INC.—See Michelsen Packaging Co. Inc.; *U.S. Private*, pg. 2700
SK STOK—See FLSmidth & Co. A/S; *Int'l*, pg. 2712
SNAP-ON TOOLS KOREA LTD.—See Snap-on Incorporated; *U.S. Public*, pg. 1899
SNAP-ON TOOLS PRIVATE LIMITED—See Snap-on Incorporated; *U.S. Public*, pg. 1899
SNAP-ON TOOLS SINGAPORE PTE LTD—See Snap-on Incorporated; *U.S. Public*, pg. 1899
SONOCO CANADA CORPORATION—See Sonoco Products Company; *U.S. Public*, pg. 1905
SONOCO CANADA CORPORATION—See Sonoco Products Company; *U.S. Public*, pg. 1905
SONOCO FLEXIBLE PACKAGING—See Sonoco Products Company; *U.S. Public*, pg. 1906
SONOCO LURGAN—See Sonoco Products Company; *U.S. Public*, pg. 1906
SONOCO NEW ZEALAND LTD.—See Sonoco Products Company; *U.S. Public*, pg. 1905
SONOCO PRODUCTS MALAYSIA SDN BHD—See Sonoco Products Company; *U.S. Public*, pg. 1905
SPG PACKAGING SYSTEMS GMBH—See Crown Holdings, Inc.; *U.S. Public*, pg. 599
SPREAFICO AUTOMATION S.R.L.—See I.M.A. Industria Macchine Automatiche S.p.A.; *Int'l*, pg. 3566
STANDARD-KNAPP, INC.; *U.S. Private*, pg. 3782

STRAPEX AUSTRIA GES. MBH—See Illinois Tool Works Inc.; *U.S. Public*, pg. 1111
STRAPEX EMBALAGEM L.D.A.—See Illinois Tool Works Inc.; *U.S. Public*, pg. 1111
STRAPEX GMBH—See Illinois Tool Works Inc.; *U.S. Public*, pg. 1111
STRAPEX GMBH—See Illinois Tool Works Inc.; *U.S. Public*, pg. 1111
STRAPEX S.A.S.—See Illinois Tool Works Inc.; *U.S. Public*, pg. 1111
STRAPEX S.P.R.L.—See Illinois Tool Works Inc.; *U.S. Public*, pg. 1111
STRAPEX SRL—See Illinois Tool Works Inc.; *U.S. Public*, pg. 1111
SYNTEGON TECHNOLOGY GMBH—See CVC Capital Partners SICAV-FIS S.A.; *Int'l*, pg. 1884
SYSTEMS TECHNOLOGY, INC.; *U.S. Private*, pg. 3908
TAYLOR PRODUCTS; *U.S. Private*, pg. 3940
TEKNOWEB CONVERTING S.R.L.—See I.M.A. Industria Macchine Automatiche S.p.A.; *Int'l*, pg. 3566
TEKNOWEB N.A. LLC—See I.M.A. Industria Macchine Automatiche S.p.A.; *Int'l*, pg. 3566
TEMPRESS TECHNOLOGIES INC.—See Oil States International, Inc.; *U.S. Public*, pg. 1565
THIELE TECHNOLOGIES, INC.—See Barry-Wehmiller Companies, Inc.; *U.S. Private*, pg. 482
THIELE TECHNOLOGIES - REEDLEY—See Barry-Wehmiller Companies, Inc.; *U.S. Private*, pg. 482
TISSUE MACHINERY COMPANY S.P.A.—See I.M.A. Industria Macchine Automatiche S.p.A.; *Int'l*, pg. 3566
TMC NORTH AMERICA INC.—See I.M.A. Industria Macchine Automatiche S.p.A.; *Int'l*, pg. 3566
TRIANGLE PACKAGE MACHINERY CO.; *U.S. Private*, pg. 4226
TRIO PACKAGING CORP; *U.S. Private*, pg. 4236
TRIOPLAST NYBORG A/S—See Altor Equity Partners AB; *Int'l*, pg. 396
ULTRASOURCE LLC; *U.S. Private*, pg. 4278
UNIVERSAL PACKAGING SYSTEMS, INC.—See Universal Packaging Systems, Inc.; *U.S. Private*, pg. 4306
U.S. BOTTLERS MACHINERY COMPANY; *U.S. Private*, pg. 4270
VERITIV EXPRESS—See Clayton, Dubilier & Rice, LLC; *U.S. Private*, pg. 929
VISTECH MANUFACTURING SOLUTIONS, LLC—See Angeles Equity Partners, LLC; *U.S. Private*, pg. 282
VLINK OPTICS CORPORATION—See Advanced Fiber Resources (Zhuhai) Ltd; *Int'l*, pg. 159
VOLPAK PACKAGING MACHINES—See Coesia S.p.A.; *Int'l*, pg. 1690
VOLPAK S.A—See Coesia S.p.A.; *Int'l*, pg. 1690
VUSIONGROUP—See BOE Technology Group Co., Ltd.; *Int'l*, pg. 1099
WEILER LABELING SYSTEMS, LLC—See Leonard Green & Partners, L.P.; *U.S. Private*, pg. 2428
WEXXAR PACKAGING INC.—See Leonard Green & Partners, L.P.; *U.S. Private*, pg. 2428
ZANDER & INGESTROM AB—See Christian Berner Tech Trade AB; *Int'l*, pg. 1586

333994 — INDUSTRIAL PROCESS FURNACE AND OVEN MANUFACTURING

9183-7252 QUEBEC INC.—See Parker Hannifin Corporation; *U.S. Public*, pg. 1640
AFC-HOLCROFT LLC; *U.S. Private*, pg. 121
AICHI CERATEC CORPORATION—See Aichi Steel Corporation; *Int'l*, pg. 230
AIROIL FLAREGAS PVT. LTD.; *Int'l*, pg. 248
AJAX ELECTRIC CO.; *U.S. Private*, pg. 143
AJAX TOCCO INTERNATIONAL LTD.—See Park-Ohio Holdings Corp.; *U.S. Public*, pg. 1639
AJAX TOCCO MAGNETHERMIC CANADA LIMITED—See Park-Ohio Holdings Corp.; *U.S. Public*, pg. 1639
AJAX TOCCO MAGNETHERMIC CORPORATION—See Park-Ohio Holdings Corp.; *U.S. Public*, pg. 1639
AJAX TOCCO MAGNETHERMIC CORPORATION—See Park-Ohio Holdings Corp.; *U.S. Public*, pg. 1639
AJAX TOCCO MAGNETHERMIC CORPORATION—See Park-Ohio Holdings Corp.; *U.S. Public*, pg. 1639
AJAX TOCCO MAGNETHERMIC GMBH—See Park-Ohio Holdings Corp.; *U.S. Public*, pg. 1639
AKITA ZINC CO., LTD.—See Dowa Holdings Co., Ltd.; *Int'l*, pg. 2182
ALD INDUSTRIE- UND MONTAGEPARK STAAKEN GMBH—See AMG Critical Materials N.V.; *Int'l*, pg. 425
ALD THERMO TECHNOLOGIES FAR EAST CO., LTD.—See AMG Critical Materials N.V.; *Int'l*, pg. 425
ALD VACUUM TECHNOLOGIES GMBH—See AMG Critical Materials N.V.; *Int'l*, pg. 425
ALD VACUUM TECHNOLOGIES, INC.—See AMG Critical Materials N.V.; *Int'l*, pg. 425
ALD VACUUMJE TECHNOLOGII QOO—See AMG Critical Materials N.V.; *Int'l*, pg. 425
ALPHA 1 INDUCTION SERVICE CENTER—See Indel, Inc.; *U.S. Private*, pg. 2055

AMBRELL CORPORATION—See inTEST Corporation; *U.S. Public*, pg. 1159
AMERICAN FIREGLASS; *U.S. Private*, pg. 234
ANDRITZ MAERZ GMBH—See ANDRITZ AG; *Int'l*, pg. 454
ANEMOSTAT PRODUCTS—See Mestek, Inc.; *U.S. Public*, pg. 1426
APROGEN KIC INC.; *Int'l*, pg. 522
ASML IRELAND LTD.—See ASML Holding N.V.; *Int'l*, pg. 627
AXON LLC—See Leonard Green & Partners, L.P.; *U.S. Private*, pg. 2427
BANANZA AIR MANAGEMENT SYSTEMS, INC.—See Rapid Engineering Inc.; *U.S. Private*, pg. 3355
BELCO INDUSTRIES INC.; *U.S. Private*, pg. 517
BONE FRONTIER COMPANY—See Grey Mountain Partners, LLC; *U.S. Private*, pg. 1784
BORN HEATERS CANADA, ULC—See Primoris Services Corporation; *U.S. Public*, pg. 1718
BOSIO D.O.O.—See Berndorf AG; *Int'l*, pg. 987
BTU (FRANCE)—See Amtech Systems, Inc.; *U.S. Public*, pg. 133
BTU LTD.—See Amtech Systems, Inc.; *U.S. Public*, pg. 133
C.A. LITZLER CO., INC.; *U.S. Private*, pg. 705
CAMBRIDGE VACUUM ENGINEERING INC.—See Aquasium Technology Limited; *Int'l*, pg. 528
CAMBRIDGE VACUUM ENGINEERING LIMITED—See Aquasium Technology Limited; *Int'l*, pg. 528
CANERECTOR INC.; *Int'l*, pg. 1289
CENTORR VACUUM INDUSTRIES, INC.; *U.S. Private*, pg. 818
CENTROTHERM SUD EUROPE SAS—See centrotherm photovoltaics AG; *Int'l*, pg. 1415
CHENTRONICS CORPORATION—See Koch Industries, Inc.; *U.S. Private*, pg. 2331
CHUGAI ENGINEERING CO.,LTD.—See Chugai Ro Co., Ltd.; *Int'l*, pg. 1594
CHUGAI PLANT CO., LTD.—See Chugai Ro Co., Ltd.; *Int'l*, pg. 1594
CHUGAI RO ALUMINUM (SHANDONG) CO., LTD.—See Chugai Ro Co., Ltd.; *Int'l*, pg. 1594
CHUGAI RO CO., LTD. - KOKURA FACTORY—See Chugai Ro Co., Ltd.; *Int'l*, pg. 1594
CHUGAI RO CO., LTD. - SAKAI WORKS—See Chugai Ro Co., Ltd.; *Int'l*, pg. 1594
CHUGAI RO CO., LTD.; *Int'l*, pg. 1594
CHUGAI RO SHANGHAI CO., LTD.—See Chugai Ro Co., Ltd.; *Int'l*, pg. 1594
CHUGAI RO (THAILAND) CO., LTD.—See Chugai Ro Co., Ltd.; *Int'l*, pg. 1594
CHUGAI RO THERMAL ENGINEERING (SHANGHAI) CO., LTD.—See Chugai Ro Co., Ltd.; *Int'l*, pg. 1594
C.I. HAYES—See Gasbarre Products Inc.; *U.S. Private*, pg. 1648
CIMPROGETTI S.P.A.—See HANNOVER Finanz GmbH; *Int'l*, pg. 3257
COMMUNICATION SCIENCE CORPORATION—See Fair Friend Group; *Int'l*, pg. 2604
CONSARC ENGINEERING LIMITED—See Indel, Inc.; *U.S. Private*, pg. 2055
CONSOLIDATED ENGINEERING CO; *U.S. Private*, pg. 1020
CPM WOLVERINE PROCTOR LLC - LEXINGTON—See Gilbert Global Equity Partners; *U.S. Private*, pg. 1698
CPM WOLVERINE PROCTOR LLC—See Gilbert Global Equity Partners; *U.S. Private*, pg. 1698
CPM WOLVERINE PROCTOR LTD.—See Gilbert Global Equity Partners; *U.S. Private*, pg. 1698
DAIKI ENGINEERING CO., LTD.—See Daiki Aluminium Industry Co., Ltd.; *Int'l*, pg. 1931
DAIKI ENGINEERING (SEA) SDN BHD—See Daiki Aluminium Industry Co., Ltd.; *Int'l*, pg. 1931
DAIKI ENGINEERING THAI CO., LTD.—See Daiki Aluminium Industry Co., Ltd.; *Int'l*, pg. 1931
DAIKI-SIGMA ENGINEERING (CHINA) INC.—See Daiki Aluminium Industry Co., Ltd.; *Int'l*, pg. 1931
DEDERT (SHANGHAI) DRYING AND EVAPORATING TECHNOLOGY CO., LTD—See Dedert Corporation; *U.S. Private*, pg. 1188
DENKI KOGYO CO., LTD. - ATSUGI PLANT—See DKK Co., Ltd.; *Int'l*, pg. 2139
DENKI KOGYO CO., LTD. - SUZUKA PLANT—See DKK Co., Ltd.; *Int'l*, pg. 2139
DENKIRO SERVICE CO., LTD.; *Int'l*, pg. 2027
DENKO TECHNO HEAT CO., LTD. - HAMAMATSU PLANT—See DKK Co., Ltd.; *Int'l*, pg. 2139
DESPATCH INDUSTRIES INC.—See Illinois Tool Works Inc.; *U.S. Public*, pg. 1102
DESPATCH INDUSTRIES, INC.—See Illinois Tool Works Inc.; *U.S. Public*, pg. 1102
DKK OF AMERICA, INC.—See DKK Co., Ltd.; *Int'l*, pg. 2139
DKK (THAILAND) CO., LTD.—See DKK Co., Ltd.; *Int'l*, pg. 2139
DOBLE LEMKE GMBH—See ESCO Technologies, Inc.; *U.S. Public*, pg. 793
DURR SYSTEMS INC. - PLYMOUTH—See Durr AG; *Int'l*, pg. 2231
DYNATECH FURNACES PVT. LTD.—See AMG Critical Materials N.V.; *Int'l*, pg. 425

N.A.I.C.S. INDEX

333995 — FLUID POWER CYLINDE...

EATGOOD SWEDEN AB; *Int'l*, pg. 2277
ECU INTERNATIONAL—See Allcargo Logistics Limited; *Int'l*, pg. 334
EFD INDUCAO BRASIL LTD.—See Arendals Fossekompani ASA; *Int'l*, pg. 558
EFD INDUCTION MARCOUSSIS S.A.—See Arendals Fossekompani ASA; *Int'l*, pg. 559
ELECTROTHERM INDIA LTD - ENGINEERING & PROJECT DIVISION—See Electrotherm India Ltd; *Int'l*, pg. 2355
ENERCON INDUSTRIES CORPORATION; *U.S. Private*, pg. 1392
FAST HEAT INC.; *U.S. Private*, pg. 1482
FURNACE ENGINEERING PTY LTD—See ESPEC Corp.; *Int'l*, pg. 2505
FURNACES NUCLEAR APPLICATIONS GRENOBLE S.A.—See AMG Critical Materials N.V.; *Int'l*, pg. 425
GASBARRE PRODUCTS INC., SINTERITE FURNACE DIVISION—See Gasbarre Products Inc.; *U.S. Private*, pg. 1648
GIG KARASEK GMBH—See Dr. Aichhorn GmbH; *Int'l*, pg. 2190
GILLESPIE & POWERS INC.—See Gillespie Powers Refrigeration & Engineering; *U.S. Private*, pg. 1700
GLENRO INC.; *U.S. Private*, pg. 1711
GMH BLANKSTAHL GMBH—See Georgsmarienhutte Holding GmbH; *Int'l*, pg. 2940
THE GRIEVE CORPORATION; *U.S. Private*, pg. 4039
HAMWORTHY COMBUSTION ENGINEERING (KOREA) CO. LTD.—See Koch Industries, Inc.; *U.S. Private*, pg. 2331
HAMWORTHY COMBUSTION ENGINEERING LIMITED—See Koch Industries, Inc.; *U.S. Private*, pg. 2331
HAMWORTHY COMBUSTION ENGINEERING S.R.L.—See Koch Industries, Inc.; *U.S. Private*, pg. 2331
HAMWORTHY PEABODY COMBUSTION INC.—See Koch Industries, Inc.; *U.S. Private*, pg. 2331
HANWHA MACHINERY CO., LTD.—See Hanwha Group; *Int'l*, pg. 3266
HEATEC, INC.—See Astec Industries, Inc.; *U.S. Public*, pg. 216
HEBELER PROCESS SOLUTIONS, LLC—See Hebeler Corporation; *U.S. Private*, pg. 1902
HEINRICH GEISSLER GMBH—See Georgsmarienhutte Holding GmbH; *Int'l*, pg. 2940
HEURTEY PETROCHEM BRASIL LTDA.—See Heurtey Petrochem SA; *Int'l*, pg. 3366
HEURTEY PETROCHEM MANUFACTURING S.A.—See Heurtey Petrochem SA; *Int'l*, pg. 3366
HEURTEY PETROCHEM ROMANIA SRL—See Heurtey Petrochem SA; *Int'l*, pg. 3366
HEURTEY PETROCHEM SA; *Int'l*, pg. 3366
HEURTEY PETROCHEM SOUTH AFRICA (PTY) LTD—See Heurtey Petrochem SA; *Int'l*, pg. 3366
HEURTEY PETROCHEM TECHNOLOGY (BEIJING) LTD.—See Heurtey Petrochem SA; *Int'l*, pg. 3366
HIGHTEMP FURNACES LTD.—See Dowa Holdings Co., Ltd.; *Int'l*, pg. 2184
HKF INC.; *U.S. Private*, pg. 1953
HOTMIX ASPHALT EQUIPMENT CO.; *U.S. Private*, pg. 1989
HOTMIX PARTS; *U.S. Private*, pg. 1989
INDUCTION EQUIPMENT (INDIA) PRIVATE LIMITED—See Park-Ohio Holdings Corp.; *U.S. Public*, pg. 1639
INDUCTOTHERM CORP.—See Indel, Inc.; *U.S. Private*, pg. 2055
INDUCTOTHERM EUROPE LIMITED—See Indel, Inc.; *U.S. Private*, pg. 2055
INDUCTOTHERM GROUP BRASIL LTDA—See Indel, Inc.; *U.S. Private*, pg. 2055
INDUCTOTHERM GROUP FRANCE—See Indel, Inc.; *U.S. Private*, pg. 2055
INDUCTOTHERM PTY., LTD.—See Indel, Inc.; *U.S. Private*, pg. 2055
INDUSTRIAL ENGINEERING & EQUIPMENT CO. INC.; *U.S. Private*, pg. 2066
INOVA LAB S.R.L.—See Park-Ohio Holdings Corp.; *U.S. Public*, pg. 1639
INTERNATIONAL THERMAL SYSTEMS, LLC; *U.S. Private*, pg. 2121
J.L. BECKER COMPANY—See Gasbarre Products Inc.; *U.S. Private*, pg. 1648
KOSHUHA CO., LTD.—See DKK Co., Ltd.; *Int'l*, pg. 2139
LEPEL CORPORATION—See Indel, Inc.; *U.S. Private*, pg. 2055
LIAM VENTURES, INC.; *U.S. Private*, pg. 2442
L.L.C. HEURTEY PETROCHEM RUS—See Heurtey Petrochem SA; *Int'l*, pg. 3366
L & L SPECIAL FURNACE CO., INC.; *U.S. Private*, pg. 2361
NEON BLOOM, INC.; *U.S. Private*, pg. 1506
NIPPON SELAS CO., LTD.—See Lionheart Ventures; *U.S. Private*, pg. 2464
NOVATEC INC.; *U.S. Private*, pg. 2967
ONQUEST, INC.—See Primoris Services Corporation; *U.S. Public*, pg. 1718
PETRO-CHEM DEVELOPMENT COMPANY, INC.—See Heurtey Petrochem SA; *Int'l*, pg. 3366

PETRO-CHEM DEVELOPMENT COMPANY, INC.—See Heurtey Petrochem SA; *Int'l*, pg. 3366
PETRO-CHEM KOREA CO. LTD.—See Heurtey Petrochem SA; *Int'l*, pg. 3366
PHOENIX INTERNATIONAL, INC.—See JMC Capital Partners LLC; *U.S. Private*, pg. 2215
PLEISSNER GUSS GMBH—See Georgsmarienhutte Holding GmbH; *Int'l*, pg. 2941
PT. DOWA THERMOTECH INDONESIA—See Dowa Holdings Co., Ltd.; *Int'l*, pg. 2184
RESOURCE RECYCLING, LLC—See European Metal Recycling Limited; *Int'l*, pg. 2557
ROBAM APPLIANCES PVT. LTD.—See Hangzhou Robam Appliances Co., Ltd.; *Int'l*, pg. 3250
SAET INDUCTION EQUIPMENT (SHANGHAI) CO. LTD.—See Park-Ohio Holdings Corp.; *U.S. Public*, pg. 1640
SAET S.P.A.—See Park-Ohio Holdings Corp.; *U.S. Public*, pg. 1640
SAFED INDUSTRIEOFEN GMBH—See Berndorf AG; *Int'l*, pg. 987
SELAS WAERMETECHNIK GMBH—See Lionheart Ventures; *U.S. Private*, pg. 2464
SHERWOOD-TEMPLETON COAL COMPANY, INC.—See Templeton Coal Company, Inc.; *U.S. Private*, pg. 3963
SPX FLOW TECHNOLOGY CANADA INC—See Lone Star Funds; *U.S. Private*, pg. 2486
STIMAS S.R.L.—See Durr AG; *Int'l*, pg. 2233
SURFACE COMBUSTION, INC.; *U.S. Private*, pg. 3883
SUZHOU EBRAIN ELECTRONICS CO., LTD.—See Ebrains, Inc.; *Int'l*, pg. 2286
TAIWAN CHUGAI RO CO., LTD.—See Chugai Ro Co., Ltd.; *Int'l*, pg. 1594
TEMPCO ELECTRIC HEATER CORP; *U.S. Private*, pg. 3963
THERMAL TECHNOLOGY INC.—See GT Advanced Technologies Inc.; *U.S. Private*, pg. 1801
THERMA-TRON-X INC—See TTX Holdings Inc.; *U.S. Private*, pg. 4255
THERMIQUE INDUSTRIE VIDE—See AMG Critical Materials N.V.; *Int'l*, pg. 425
TPI CORP.; *U.S. Private*, pg. 4200
TPS, LLC—See Resilience Capital Partners, LLC; *U.S. Private*, pg. 3405
TRENT, INC.; *U.S. Private*, pg. 4218
TTX HOLDINGS INC.; *U.S. Private*, pg. 4255
UOP CALLIDUS—See Honeywell International Inc.; *U.S. Private*, pg. 1052
VULCAN ELECTRIC COMPANY; *U.S. Private*, pg. 4415
VULCAN ENGINEERING CO.—See Wafra Investment Advisory Group, Inc.; *U.S. Private*, pg. 4425
WATLOW COLUMBIA, INC.—See Tinicum Enterprises, Inc.; *U.S. Private*, pg. 4175
WATLOW ELECTRIC MANUFACTURING COMPANY—See Tinicum Enterprises, Inc.; *U.S. Private*, pg. 4174
WATLOW GMBH—See Tinicum Enterprises, Inc.; *U.S. Private*, pg. 4174
WATLOW HANNIBAL—See Tinicum Enterprises, Inc.; *U.S. Private*, pg. 4175
WELBILT INTERNATIONAL LTD.—See Ali Holding S.r.l; *Int'l*, pg. 323
WISTA STAHLHANDEL WITTEN GMBH—See Georgsmarienhutte Holding GmbH; *Int'l*, pg. 2941
YAMAZAKI DENKI CO., LTD.—See Denkiro Service Co., Ltd.; *Int'l*, pg. 2027
ZPF FOUNDRY4 GMBH—See DZ BANK AG Deutsche Zentral-Genossenschaftsbank; *Int'l*, pg. 2245

333995 — FLUID POWER CYLINDER AND ACTUATOR MANUFACTURING

AEROFLEX NANJING—See Advent International Corporation; *U.S. Private*, pg. 99
AEROFLUID CO., LTD.—See Hydac International GmbH; *Int'l*, pg. 3544
AGILITY FUEL SOLUTIONS LLC—See Hexagon Composites ASA; *Int'l*, pg. 3370
AGRAMKOW ASIA PACIFIC PTE. LTD.—See Durr AG; *Int'l*, pg. 2230
AGRAMKOW DO BRASIL LTDA.—See Durr AG; *Int'l*, pg. 2230
AGRAMKOW FLUID SYSTEMS A/S—See Durr AG; *Int'l*, pg. 2230
ALPOS PROIZVODNJA ORODIJ, D.O.O.—See ALPOS, d.d.; *Int'l*, pg. 374
A-T CONTROLS, INC—See MiddleGround Management, LP; *U.S. Private*, pg. 2712
AUMA ACTUATORS (S) PTE. LTD.—See AUMA Riester GmbH & Co. KG; *Int'l*, pg. 704
AUMA-LUSA REPRESENTATIVE OFFICE, LDA.—See AUMA Riester GmbH & Co. KG; *Int'l*, pg. 705
AUMA MEXICO S. DE R.L. DE C.V.—See AUMA Riester GmbH & Co. KG; *Int'l*, pg. 704
BAR GMBH—See Watts Water Technologies, Inc.; *U.S. Public*, pg. 2337
BAR PNEUMATISCHE STEUERUNGSSYSTEME

GMBH—See Watts Water Technologies, Inc.; *U.S. Public*, pg. 2337
BELIMO CUSTOMIZATION (USA), INC.—See BELIMO Holding AG; *Int'l*, pg. 965
BELLOWSTECH, LLC—See American Securities LLC; *U.S. Private*, pg. 250
BIFFI ITALIA S.R.L.—See Emerson Electric Co.; *U.S. Public*, pg. 742
BNT HIDRAULIKA D.D. NOVI TRAVNIK; *Int'l*, pg. 1093
BUCHER HYDRAULICS CO., LTD—See Bucher Industries AG; *Int'l*, pg. 1207
BUCHER HYDRAULICS CORP—See Bucher Industries AG; *Int'l*, pg. 1207
BUCHER HYDRAULICS KK—See Bucher Industries AG; *Int'l*, pg. 1207
CDA INTERCORP LLC—See TransDigm Group Incorporated; *U.S. Public*, pg. 2182
CERTIFIED POWER SOLUTIONS; *U.S. Private*, pg. 841
CKD (CHINA) CORPORATION—See CKD Corporation; *Int'l*, pg. 1639
CKD CORPORATION; *Int'l*, pg. 1639
CKD SINGAPORE PTE LTD—See CKD Corporation; *Int'l*, pg. 1639
CKD THAI CORPORATION LTD.—See CKD Corporation; *Int'l*, pg. 1639
CMC MARINE, INC.—See T-H Marine Supplies Inc.; *U.S. Private*, pg. 3910
CORTLAND COMPANY, INC.—See Enerpac Tool Group Corp.; *U.S. Public*, pg. 765
CROSS MANUFACTURING INC.; *U.S. Private*, pg. 1105
CROWNE GROUP LLC; *U.S. Private*, pg. 1112
CTS OF CANADA, LTD.—See CTS Corporation; *U.S. Public*, pg. 603
CUSTOM FLUIDPOWER PTY. LTD.—See Helios Technologies, Inc.; *U.S. Public*, pg. 1023
CUSTOM HOISTS, INC.—See Standex International; *U.S. Public*, pg. 1930
CVI LASER SAS—See IDEX Corp; *U.S. Public*, pg. 1090
DATASENSING S.R.L.—See Datalogic S.p.A.; *Int'l*, pg. 1978
DELTA-P TECHNOLOGIES LTD.—See Hydac International GmbH; *Int'l*, pg. 3544
DESTACO—See Stabilus; *U.S. Private*, pg. 3774
DIPLOMA PLC; *Int'l*, pg. 2128
DOWTY PROPELLERS—See General Electric Company; *U.S. Public*, pg. 918
EATON CYLINDER—See Eaton Corporation plc; *Int'l*, pg. 2280
EATON INDUSTRIES (NETHERLANDS) B.V. - HYDRAULICS DIVISION—See Eaton Corporation plc; *Int'l*, pg. 2281
EDRIVE ACTUATORS, INC.—See Graham Holdings Company; *U.S. Public*, pg. 955
EEM TECNOLOGIAS DE ACCIONAMIENTO Y CONTROL, S.A.—See Hydac International GmbH; *Int'l*, pg. 3544
ELEB-EMBRAER—See Embraer S.A.; *Int'l*, pg. 2375
ELEKTRO-METALL EXPORT GMBH—See TransDigm Group Incorporated; *U.S. Public*, pg. 2182
EL-MASRY INDUSTRIAL SERVICES LLC—See Hydac International GmbH; *Int'l*, pg. 3544
EL-O-MATIC USA, INC.—See Emerson Electric Co.; *U.S. Public*, pg. 746
ENERGY MANUFACTURING COMPANY, INC.—See Ligon Industries LLC; *U.S. Private*, pg. 2455
ENERPAC CORP.—See Enerpac Tool Group Corp.; *U.S. Public*, pg. 765
ENERTORK LTD.; *Int'l*, pg. 2424
FISHER HYDRAULICS, INC.—See Ligon Industries LLC; *U.S. Private*, pg. 2455
FLUID AIR CONTROLS LLC—See The Stratford-Cambridge Group Co.; *U.S. Private*, pg. 4123
FLUIDPOWER GROUP SERVICES UK LIMITED—See Flowtech Fluidpower plc; *Int'l*, pg. 2709
FLUITRONICS GMBH; *Int'l*, pg. 2714
FRIEDERICH-HYDROTECH S.A.R.L.—See Hydac International GmbH; *Int'l*, pg. 3544
GENERAL DYNAMICS OTS (VERSATRON), INC.—See General Dynamics Corporation; *U.S. Public*, pg. 914
GONZALEZ PICO SYSTEMS INC.—See Gonzalez Design Engineering Company Inc.; *U.S. Private*, pg. 1737
GREAT BEND INDUSTRIES—See Ligon Industries LLC; *U.S. Private*, pg. 2455
HADER-SEITZ INC.—See Hader Industries Inc.; *U.S. Private*, pg. 1839
HALLITE SEALS AMERICAS, LLC—See Compagnie Generale des Etablissements Michelin SCA; *Int'l*, pg. 1742
HELICAL AUTO-TECHNOLOGY PVT LTD—See Helical Technology Limited; *Int'l*, pg. 3330
HELICAL TECHNOLOGY LIMITED; *Int'l*, pg. 3330
HEXAGON LINCOLN, INC.—See Hexagon Composites ASA; *Int'l*, pg. 3370
HEXAGON RAUFOSS AS—See Hexagon Composites ASA; *Int'l*, pg. 3370
HIWIN MIKROSYSTEM CORP.; *Int'l*, pg. 3427
HOL-MAC CORPORATION; *U.S. Private*, pg. 1961
HYDAC CO., LTD.—See Hydac International GmbH; *Int'l*, pg. 3545
HYDAC CORPORATION, ACCUMULATOR DIVISION—See Hydac Technology Corporation; *U.S. Private*, pg. 2016

333995 — FLUID POWER CYLINDE...

HYDAC D.O.O.—See Hydac International GmbH; *Int'l*, pg. 3545
HYDAC DRIVE CENTER GMBH—See Hydac International GmbH; *Int'l*, pg. 3545
HYDAC SPOL. S R.O.—See Hydac International GmbH; *Int'l*, pg. 3545
HYDAC SYSTEMS & SERVICES GMBH—See Hydac International GmbH; *Int'l*, pg. 3545
HYDAC TECHNOLOGY GMBH—See Hydac International GmbH; *Int'l*, pg. 3545
HYDAC TECHNOLOGY PTE. LTD.—See Hydac International GmbH; *Int'l*, pg. 3545
HYDAC TECNOLOGIA, UNIPESSOAL, LDA.—See Hydac International GmbH; *Int'l*, pg. 3545
HYDRATECH, LLC—See Ligon Industries LLC; *U.S. Private*, pg. 2455
HYDROPHI TECHNOLOGIES GROUP, INC.; *U.S. Private*, pg. 2018
HYDROSAAR GMBH—See Hydac International GmbH; *Int'l*, pg. 3545
HYSER C.A.—See Hydac International GmbH; *Int'l*, pg. 3545
HYSONIC PHILIPPINES INC.—See HYSONIC Co., Ltd.; *Int'l*, pg. 3554
IDEX CORP; *U.S. Public*, pg. 1089
IDEX DO BRASIL SERVICOS E VENDAS LTDA.—See IDEX Corp; *U.S. Public*, pg. 1091
IDEX TECHNOLOGY (SUZHOU) CO., LTD.—See IDEX Corp; *U.S. Public*, pg. 1091
JIANGYIN KAIYAN METAL MANUFACTURING CO., LTD.—See Changzhou Kaidi Electrical, Inc.; *Int'l*, pg. 1445
KAIDI ELECTRICAL EUROPE GMBH—See Changzhou Kaidi Electrical, Inc.; *Int'l*, pg. 1445
KAIDI LLC—See Changzhou Kaidi Electrical, Inc.; *Int'l*, pg. 1445
KALMAR DANMARK A/S—See Cargotec Corporation; *Int'l*, pg. 1327
KONGAZ A.S.—See Bera Holding A.S.; *Int'l*, pg. 978
KURODA PNEUMATICS LTD.—See Parker Hannifin Corporation; *U.S. Public*, pg. 1641
M-CKD PRECISION SDN. BHD.—See CKD Corporation; *Int'l*, pg. 1639
MILWAUKEE CYLINDER—See Enerpac Tool Group Corp.; *U.S. Public*, pg. 766
MORIN ACTUATOR—See Emerson Electric Co.; *U.S. Public*, pg. 751
NOVASENTIS, INC.—See General Motors Company; *U.S. Public*, pg. 926
PARKER HANNIFIN CYLINDER DIVISION—See Parker Hannifin Corporation; *U.S. Public*, pg. 1647
PARKER HANNIFIN CYLINDER DIVISION, SWEDEN—See Parker Hannifin Corporation; *U.S. Public*, pg. 1647
PARKER HANNIFIN GEAR PUMP DIVISION—See Parker Hannifin Corporation; *U.S. Public*, pg. 1647
PARKER HANNIFIN GMBH & CO. KG HYDRAULIC CONTROLS DIVISION EUROPE—See Parker Hannifin Corporation; *U.S. Public*, pg. 1647
PARKER HANNIFIN MANUFACTURING LTD.-CYLINDER DIVISION—See Parker Hannifin Corporation; *U.S. Public*, pg. 1647
PARKER HANNIFIN MOBILE CYLINDER DIVISION—See Parker Hannifin Corporation; *U.S. Public*, pg. 1647
PARKER HANNIFIN PNEUMATIC DIVISION-NORTH AMERICA—See Parker Hannifin Corporation; *U.S. Public*, pg. 1644
PARKER HANNIFIN SPA CYLINDER DIVISION—See Parker Hannifin Corporation; *U.S. Public*, pg. 1647
PARKER-HELAC DIVISION—See Parker Hannifin Corporation; *U.S. Public*, pg. 1647
PENINSULAR CYLINDER CO.—See Avis Industrial Corporation; *U.S. Private*, pg. 408
PENTAIR VALVES & CONTROLS CANADA INC.—See Emerson Electric Co.; *U.S. Public*, pg. 751
PHD INC.; *U.S. Private*, pg. 3167
PRECISION HYDRAULIC CYLINDERS INC.—See Leggett & Platt, Incorporated; *U.S. Public*, pg. 1303
PRINCE MANUFACTURING CORPORATION; *U.S. Private*, pg. 3264
PSC INDUSTRIES, INC. - GRAHAM HYDRAULICS DIVISION—See PMC Capital Partners, LLC; *U.S. Private*, pg. 3218
PT. HYDAC TECHNOLOGY INDONESIA—See Hydac International GmbH; *Int'l*, pg. 3545
RAMROD INDUSTRIES LLC—See Ligon Industries LLC; *U.S. Private*, pg. 2455
RMS HYDRAULIC SERVICES CO.—See Road Machinery & Supplies Company; *U.S. Private*, pg. 3453
ROLLON JAPAN KK—See The Timken Company; *U.S. Public*, pg. 2133
SAUDI GULF HYDRAULICS CO., LTD.—See Hydac International GmbH; *Int'l*, pg. 3545
SEABEE CORPORATION CYLINDERS—See Ligon Industries LLC; *U.S. Private*, pg. 2455
SEATORQUE CONTROL SYSTEMS, LLC; *U.S. Private*, pg. 3591
SERVI GROUP AS—See Ferd AS; *Int'l*, pg. 2636
SERVOTRONICS, INC.; *U.S. Public*, pg. 1872
SHAW DEVELOPMENT, LLC—See Madison Dearborn Partners, LLC; *U.S. Private*, pg. 2542
THE SHEFFER CORPORATION—See The Ralph J. Stolle Company; *U.S. Private*, pg. 4102
SONO-TEK CORPORATION; *U.S. Public*, pg. 1904
SPX HYDRAULIC TECHNOLOGIES—See SPX Technologies, Inc.; *U.S. Public*, pg. 1921
STANDARD BIOTOOLS INC.; *U.S. Public*, pg. 1928
SUSPA, INC.—See Andlinger & Company, Inc.; *U.S. Private*, pg. 279
SUZHOU BUCHER HYDRAULICS CO. LTD—See Bucher Industries AG; *Int'l*, pg. 1207
TAIWAN CKD CORPORATION—See CKD Corporation; *Int'l*, pg. 1639
TAIYO PARKER FLUIDPOWER (SHANGHAI) CO., LTD.—See Parker Hannifin Corporation; *U.S. Public*, pg. 1650
TEXAS HYDRAULICS, INC.—See Wynnchurch Capital, L.P.; *U.S. Private*, pg. 4578

333996 — FLUID POWER PUMP AND MOTOR MANUFACTURING

AISAN BITRON LOUNY S.R.O.—See Aisan Industry Co., Ltd.; *Int'l*, pg. 250
ALBIN PUMP SAS—See Ingersoll Rand Inc.; *U.S. Public*, pg. 1118
ALFA LAVAL S.R.L.—See Alfa Laval AB; *Int'l*, pg. 311
ALL-FLO PUMP COMPANY, LIMITED—See Dover Corporation; *U.S. Public*, pg. 680
ANNAPURNA KENMORE TUBE PRODUCTS PVT. LTD.—See Annapurna Bhaskari Group; *Int'l*, pg. 473
ANNAPURNA KENMORE TUBE PRODUCTS PVT. LTD.—See Parker Hannifin Corporation; *U.S. Public*, pg. 1640
A. O. SMITH WATER PRODUCTS—See A. O. Smith Corporation; *U.S. Public*, pg. 11
ARATRON HYDRAULIKK AS—See Addtech AB; *Int'l*, pg. 132
ARMSTRONG FLUID HANDLING—See Armstrong International, Inc.; *U.S. Private*, pg. 331
AXFLOW SAS—See Axel Johnson Gruppen AB; *Int'l*, pg. 763
BARNES DE COLOMBIA S.A.—See Corporacion EG S.A.; *Int'l*, pg. 1803
BECKETT CORPORATION—See General Foam Plastics Corp.; *U.S. Private*, pg. 1665
BEGA ELECTROMOTOR SA; *Int'l*, pg. 940
BEIJING HUADE HYDRAULIC INDUSTRIAL GROUP CO., LTD.—See Beijing Jingcheng Machinery Electric Holding Co., Ltd.; *Int'l*, pg. 953
BOWHEAD MANUFACTURING COMPANY, LLC—See Ukpeagvik Inupiat Corporation; *U.S. Private*, pg. 4275
BREVINI FLUID POWER FRANCE SAS—See Dana Incorporated; *U.S. Public*, pg. 621
BREVINI FLUID POWER GMBH—See Dana Incorporated; *U.S. Public*, pg. 621
BREVINI IRELAND LIMITED—See Dana Incorporated; *U.S. Public*, pg. 621
BREVINI NEW ZEALAND LIMITED—See Dana Incorporated; *U.S. Public*, pg. 622
BREVINI SVENSKA AB—See Dana Incorporated; *U.S. Public*, pg. 622
BUCHER HYDRAULICS DACHAU GMBH—See Bucher Industries AG; *Int'l*, pg. 1207
BUCHER HYDRAULICS GMBH—See Bucher Industries AG; *Int'l*, pg. 1207
BUCHER HYDRAULICS—See Bucher Industries AG; *Int'l*, pg. 1207
BUCHER HYDRAULICS—See Bucher Industries AG; *Int'l*, pg. 1207
CHAMPIONX CORPORATION; *U.S. Public*, pg. 478
CIRCOR NAVAL SOLUTIONS, LLC—See KKR & Co. Inc.; *U.S. Public*, pg. 1242
CONCENTRIC AB; *Int'l*, pg. 1763
CONCENTRIC BIRMINGHAM LTD.—See Concentric AB; *Int'l*, pg. 1763
CONCENTRIC HOF GMBH—See Concentric AB; *Int'l*, pg. 1763
CONCENTRIC INNOVATIONS AB—See Concentric AB; *Int'l*, pg. 1763
CONCENTRIC ITASCA INC.—See Concentric AB; *Int'l*, pg. 1763
CONCENTRIC KOREA LLC—See Concentric AB; *Int'l*, pg. 1763
CONCENTRIC PUMPS PUNE PVT. LTD.—See Concentric AB; *Int'l*, pg. 1764
CONCENTRIC PUMPS (SUZHOU) CO. LTD.—See Concentric AB; *Int'l*, pg. 1764
CONCENTRIC ROCKFORD INC.—See Concentric AB; *Int'l*, pg. 1764
CONCENTRIC SRL—See Concentric AB; *Int'l*, pg. 1764
CRANE MERGER CO. LLC—See Crane NXT, Co.; *U.S. Public*, pg. 591
CUSTOM FLUIDPOWER VIETNAM COMPANY LTD.—See Helios Technologies, Inc.; *U.S. Public*, pg. 1023
DAICEL SAFETY SYSTEMS (JIANGSU) CO., LTD.—See Daicel Corporation; *Int'l*, pg. 1919

DAICEL SAFETY SYSTEMS KOREA, INC.—See Daicel Corporation; *Int'l*, pg. 1919
DANAHER MOTION CHINA—See Danaher Corporation; *U.S. Public*, pg. 626
DANFOSS POWER SOLUTIONS, INC.—See Danfoss A/S; *Int'l*, pg. 1960
DENSO MANUFACTURING HUNGARY LTD.—See Denso Corporation; *Int'l*, pg. 2031
DOSATRON INTERNATIONAL SAS—See Ingersoll Rand Inc.; *U.S. Public*, pg. 1118
DOVER PUMP SOLUTIONS GROUP—See Dover Corporation; *U.S. Public*, pg. 680
EAGLE INDUSTRY SALES (SHANGHAI) CO., LTD.—See Eagle Industry Co., Ltd.; *Int'l*, pg. 2265
EAST WEST MANUFACTURING, LLC; *U.S. Private*, pg. 1318
ECO ENERGY PUMPS, INC.; *U.S. Private*, pg. 1328
ELEKTOR INDUSTRIES INC.; *U.S. Private*, pg. 1357
ELIS DANMARK A/S—See Eurazeo SE; *Int'l*, pg. 2528
FASCO AUSTRALIA PTY. LTD.—See Regal Rexnord Corporation; *U.S. Public*, pg. 1773
FENWICK-LINDE HYDRAULICS—See KKR & Co. Inc.; *U.S. Public*, pg. 1255
FENWICK-LINDE HYDRAULICS—See The Goldman Sachs Group, Inc.; *U.S. Public*, pg. 2079
FINE SINTER CO., LTD. - KAWAGOE PLANT—See Fine Sinter Co., Ltd.; *Int'l*, pg. 2673
FLOWTECH FLUIDPOWER PLC; *Int'l*, pg. 2709
FLOWTECHNOLOGY BENELUX B.V.—See Flowtech Fluidpower plc; *Int'l*, pg. 2709
FLYGT NIPPON K.K.—See Xylem Inc.; *U.S. Public*, pg. 2396
FRANKLIN ELECTRIC INDUSTRIA DE MOTOBOMBAS SA—See Franklin Electric Co., Inc.; *U.S. Public*, pg. 878
GOYEN VALVE LLC—See Emerson Electric Co.; *U.S. Public*, pg. 751
GRACO AUSTRALIA PTY LTD—See Graco, Inc.; *U.S. Public*, pg. 953
GRACO AUTOMOTIVE TECHNOLOGY CENTER—See Graco, Inc.; *U.S. Public*, pg. 953
GRACO KOREA, INC.—See Graco, Inc.; *U.S. Public*, pg. 953
GRACO SHANGHAI OFFICE—See Graco, Inc.; *U.S. Public*, pg. 953
GRACO SOUTH DAKOTA INC.—See Graco, Inc.; *U.S. Public*, pg. 953
GURTNER—See Gevelot S.A.; *Int'l*, pg. 2954
HAWE HYDRAULIK SE; *Int'l*, pg. 3288
HAWE NORTH AMERICA, INC.—See HAWE Hydraulik SE; *Int'l*, pg. 3288
HAYWARD TYLER FLUID HANDLING LTD—See Avingtrans plc; *Int'l*, pg. 744
HAYWARD TYLER GROUP LIMITED—See Avingtrans plc; *Int'l*, pg. 743
HAYWARD TYLER GROUP PLC—See Avingtrans plc; *Int'l*, pg. 743
HAYWARD TYLER HOLDINGS LIMITED—See Avingtrans plc; *Int'l*, pg. 744
HAYWARD TYLER INC.—See Avingtrans plc; *Int'l*, pg. 744
HAYWARD TYLER INDIA PRIVATE LIMITED—See Avingtrans plc; *Int'l*, pg. 744
HAYWARD TYLER PUMPS (KUNSHAN) CO., LTD—See Avingtrans plc; *Int'l*, pg. 744
HIDROSTAL S.A.; *Int'l*, pg. 3384
HITACHI INDUSTRIAL EQUIPMENT SYSTEMS CO., LTD. - NARASHINO DIVISION—See Hitachi, Ltd.; *Int'l*, pg. 3419
HOVE A/S; *Int'l*, pg. 3492
HYDAC INTERNATIONAL GMBH; *Int'l*, pg. 3544
HYDAC LTD.—See Hydac International GmbH; *Int'l*, pg. 3545
HYDAC PROCESS TECHNOLOGY GMBH—See Hydac International GmbH; *Int'l*, pg. 3545
HYDAC PTY. LTD.—See Hydac International GmbH; *Int'l*, pg. 3545
HYDRAULICS INTERNATIONAL, INC. - PUMPS DIVISION—See Hydraulics International, Inc.; *U.S. Private*, pg. 2017
HYDRAULIC SPECIALISTS AUSTRALIA PTY. LTD.; *Int'l*, pg. 3546
HYDRO MOBILE INC.; *Int'l*, pg. 3546
HYDROTECH COMPANY LTD.; *Int'l*, pg. 3548
HYUNDAI INDUSTRIAL CO., LTD.—See Aisan Industry Co., Ltd.; *Int'l*, pg. 250
IFH GROUP INC.; *U.S. Private*, pg. 2039
IHD INDUSTRIES PVT. LTD.—See Aisan Industry Co., Ltd.; *Int'l*, pg. 251
IKM HYDRAULIC SERVICES AS—See IKM Gruppen AS; *Int'l*, pg. 3611
INDUSTRIAL EQUIPMENT & PARTS INC.—See Winsupply, Inc.; *U.S. Private*, pg. 4545
INDUSTRIAS MECANICAS LAGO, S.A.U—See Fluidra SA; *Int'l*, pg. 2714
INNOTEK CORPORATION; *U.S. Private*, pg. 2081
KEMEL SALES & SERVICE (SHANGHAI) CO., LTD.—See Eagle Industry Co., Ltd.; *Int'l*, pg. 2265
KRACHT GMBH—See Atlas Copco AB; *Int'l*, pg. 683
LARZEP, S.A.—See Enerpac Tool Group Corp.; *U.S. Public*, pg. 766

N.A.I.C.S. INDEX

333998 — ALL OTHER MISCELLAN...

LBM S.R.L.—See Compass Diversified Holdings; *U.S. Public*, pg. 560
MECHANICAL TOOL & ENGINEERING CO.; *U.S. Private*, pg. 2649
MILTON ROY INDUSTRIAL (SHANGHAI) CO., LTD.—See Ingersoll Rand Inc.; *U.S. Public*, pg. 1122
MOMENTUM ENGINEERED SYSTEMS, INC.—See Flexaseal Engineered Seals and Systems, LLC; *U.S. Private*, pg. 1543
MUNRO COMPANIES, INC.; *U.S. Private*, pg. 2814
NELSON HYDRAULICS LIMITED—See Flowtech Fluidpower plc; *Int'l*, pg. 2709
NETZSCH VIETNAM LIMITED—See Erich Netzsch GmbH & Co. Holding KG; *Int'l*, pg. 2493
NORD (CHINA) POWER TRANSMISSION CO., LTD.—See Getriebebau NORD GmbH & Co. KG; *Int'l*, pg. 2953
OERLIKON LEYBOLD VACUUM GMBH—See Atlas Copco AB; *Int'l*, pg. 683
OILGEAR TOWLER GMBH—See Wynnchurch Capital, L.P.; *U.S. Private*, pg. 4578
OILGEAR TOWLER LTD.—See Wynnchurch Capital, L.P.; *U.S. Private*, pg. 4578
OILGEAR TOWLER S.A.—See Wynnchurch Capital, L.P.; *U.S. Private*, pg. 4578
OILGEAR TOWLER SAS—See Wynnchurch Capital, L.P.; *U.S. Private*, pg. 4578
O.T. OIL TECHNOLOGY S.R.L.—See Dana Incorporated; *U.S. Public*, pg. 623
PARKER FILTRATION B.V.—See Parker Hannifin Corporation; *U.S. Public*, pg. 1644
PARKER FILTRATION & SEPARATION BV—See Parker Hannifin Corporation; *U.S. Public*, pg. 1644
PARKER HANNIFIN AUTOMATION GROUP—See Parker Hannifin Corporation; *U.S. Public*, pg. 1644
PARKER HANNIFIN CHILE LIMITADA—See Parker Hannifin Corporation; *U.S. Public*, pg. 1644
PARKER HANNIFIN CORP. - FLUID SYSTEMS DIVISION—See Parker Hannifin Corporation; *U.S. Public*, pg. 1648
PARKER HANNIFIN CUSTOM CYLINDER OPERATIONS—See Parker Hannifin Corporation; *U.S. Public*, pg. 1647
PARKER HANNIFIN CZECH REPUBLIC SRO—See Parker Hannifin Corporation; *U.S. Public*, pg. 1645
PARKER HANNIFIN DE MEXICO S.A. DE C.V.—See Parker Hannifin Corporation; *U.S. Public*, pg. 1645
PARKER HANNIFIN FILTRATION GROUP—See Parker Hannifin Corporation; *U.S. Public*, pg. 1645
PARKER HANNIFIN FLUID SYSTEM CONNECTORS GROUP—See Parker Hannifin Corporation; *U.S. Public*, pg. 1645
PARKER HANNIFIN FRANCE SAS—See Parker Hannifin Corporation; *U.S. Public*, pg. 1646
PARKER HANNIFIN GB LTD.—See Parker Hannifin Corporation; *U.S. Public*, pg. 1646
PARKER HANNIFIN HYDRAULICS GROUP—See Parker Hannifin Corporation; *U.S. Public*, pg. 1647
PARKER HANNIFIN INSTRUMENTATION GROUP—See Parker Hannifin Corporation; *U.S. Public*, pg. 1647
PARKER HANNIFIN INTEGRATED HYDRAULLICS DIVISION—See Parker Hannifin Corporation; *U.S. Public*, pg. 1647
PARKER-HANNIFIN INTERNATIONAL CORP.—See Parker Hannifin Corporation; *U.S. Public*, pg. 1649
PARKER HANNIFIN LLC—See Parker Hannifin Corporation; *U.S. Public*, pg. 1648
PARKER HANNIFIN MANUFACTURING BELGIUM BVBA—See Parker Hannifin Corporation; *U.S. Public*, pg. 1648
PARKER HANNIFIN MANUFACTURING FINLAND OY—See Parker Hannifin Corporation; *U.S. Public*, pg. 1648
PARKER HANNIFIN MANUFACTURING SPAIN SL—See Parker Hannifin Corporation; *U.S. Public*, pg. 1648
PARKER HANNIFIN MOBILE SYSTEMS DIVISION—See Parker Hannifin Corporation; *U.S. Public*, pg. 1647
PARKER HANNIFIN NETHERLANDS HOLDINGS 2 B.V.—See Parker Hannifin Corporation; *U.S. Public*, pg. 1648
PARKER HANNIFIN NICHOLS AIRBORNE DIV—See Parker Hannifin Corporation; *U.S. Public*, pg. 1649
PARKER HANNIFIN OILDYNE DIVISION—See Parker Hannifin Corporation; *U.S. Public*, pg. 1647
PARKER HANNIFIN SRL—See Parker Hannifin Corporation; *U.S. Public*, pg. 1649
PARKER HANNIFIN SWEDEN SALES AB—See Parker Hannifin Corporation; *U.S. Public*, pg. 1649
PARKER HANNIFIN TUBE FITTINGS DIVISION-CUSTOM MANUFACTURING BUSINESS UNIT—See Parker Hannifin Corporation; *U.S. Public*, pg. 1646
PARKER HAREKET VE KONTROL SISTEMLERI TIC. A.S.—See Parker Hannifin Corporation; *U.S. Public*, pg. 1649
PARKER HOSE BV—See Parker Hannifin Corporation; *U.S. Public*, pg. 1649
PARKER ITALY HOLDING S.R.L.—See Parker Hannifin Corporation; *U.S. Public*, pg. 1649

PARKER KOREA LTD.—See Parker Hannifin Corporation; *U.S. Public*, pg. 1649
PARKER LKLIM KONTROL SISTEMLERI SANAYI VE TIC AS—See Parker Hannifin Corporation; *U.S. Public*, pg. 1649
PARKER POLYFLEX BV—See Parker Hannifin Corporation; *U.S. Public*, pg. 1649
PARKER SERVICIO'S DE MEXICO, S.A. DE C.V.—See Parker Hannifin Corporation; *U.S. Public*, pg. 1649
PCM DEUTSCHLAND GMBH—See Gevelot S.A.; *Int'l*, pg. 2954
PCM EUROPE S.A.S.—See Gevelot S.A.; *Int'l*, pg. 2954
PCM GROUP ITALIA SRL—See Gevelot S.A.; *Int'l*, pg. 2954
PCM MANUFACTURING FRANCE S.A.S.—See Gevelot S.A.; *Int'l*, pg. 2954
PCM S.A.—See Gevelot S.A.; *Int'l*, pg. 2954
PCM TECHNOLOGIES S.A.S.—See Gevelot S.A.; *Int'l*, pg. 2954
PNEUMAX CO. LTD—See Atlas Copco AB; *Int'l*, pg. 684
PORTESCAP SINGAPORE PTE. LTD.—See Danaher Corporation; *U.S. Public*, pg. 626
PORTESCAP—See Danaher Corporation; *U.S. Public*, pg. 626
PORTESCAP—See Danaher Corporation; *U.S. Public*, pg. 626
PORTESCAP—See Danaher Corporation; *U.S. Public*, pg. 626
PROREMAN PTY LTD.—See Epiroc AB; *Int'l*, pg. 2463
PSG CALIFORNIA LLC—See Dover Corporation; *U.S. Public*, pg. 682
P.T. EBARA INDONESIA—See Ebara Corporation; *Int'l*, pg. 2284
PUMPMAN HOLDINGS LLC—See Bain Capital, LP; *U.S. Private*, pg. 432
PUMPTECH, LLC—See Pike Street Capital, LP; *U.S. Private*, pg. 3180
RAM-PAC INTERNATIONAL INC.—See Hader Industries Inc.; *U.S. Private*, pg. 1839
ROCKY MOUNTAIN HYDROSTATICS, LLC—See HEICO Corporation; *U.S. Public*, pg. 1021
ROTARY POWER LIMITED—See British Engines Ltd.; *Int'l*, pg. 1961
SAUER-DANFOSS GMBH & CO. OHG—See Danfoss A/S; *Int'l*, pg. 1961
SAUER-DANFOSS GMBH—See Danfoss A/S; *Int'l*, pg. 1961
SIAM DENSO MANUFACTURING CO., LTD.—See Denso Corporation; *Int'l*, pg. 2033
SPX FLOW TECHNOLOGY ETTEN-LEUR B.V—See Lone Star Funds; *U.S. Private*, pg. 2486
SPX FLOW TECHNOLOGY NORWAY AS—See Lone Star Funds; *U.S. Private*, pg. 2486
STAFFORDSHIRE HYDRAULIC SERVICES LIMITED—See Graco, Inc.; *U.S. Public*, pg. 954
SYDEX FLOW LTDA.—See Gevelot S.A.; *Int'l*, pg. 2954
SYDEX SINGAPORE LTD.—See Gevelot S.A.; *Int'l*, pg. 2955
SYDEX SRL—See Gevelot S.A.; *Int'l*, pg. 2954
SYDEX USA LLC—See Gevelot S.A.; *Int'l*, pg. 2955
TACO CO., LTD.—See Azbil Corporation; *Int'l*, pg. 777
TADAKIKO CO., LTD.—See Hitachi, Ltd.; *Int'l*, pg. 3424
TAIYO, LTD.—See Parker Hannifin Corporation; *U.S. Public*, pg. 1649
TAIYO TECH CO., LTD.—See Parker Hannifin Corporation; *U.S. Public*, pg. 1650
TERRA DRIVE SYSTEMS, INC.—See HCI Equity Management, L.P.; *U.S. Private*, pg. 1889
THERMEDX LLC—See Stryker Corporation; *U.S. Public*, pg. 1957
TOKHEIM BELGIUM—See Dover Corporation; *U.S. Public*, pg. 683
TSC MANUFACTURING & SUPPLY, LLC—See CM Energy Tech Co., Ltd.; *Int'l*, pg. 1666
UNICO DEUTSCHLAND GMBH—See Regal Rexnord Corporation; *U.S. Public*, pg. 1774
UNICO (UK) LTD.—See Regal Rexnord Corporation; *U.S. Public*, pg. 1774
VEKTOR AG—See Girmatic AG; *Int'l*, pg. 2979
WADE COUPLINGS LTD.—See Crane NXT, Co.; *U.S. Public*, pg. 591
WELCH-ILMVAC—See Ingersoll Rand Inc.; *U.S. Public*, pg. 1119
WHITE KNIGHT FLUID HANDLING, INC.—See Graco, Inc.; *U.S. Public*, pg. 954
YOW BELL CASTING (TAI CANG) CO., LTD.—See Chia Yi Steel Co., Ltd.; *Int'l*, pg. 1475
YSI (UK) LTD.—See Xylem Inc.; *U.S. Public*, pg. 2395

333998 — ALL OTHER MISCELLANEOUS GENERAL PURPOSE MACHINERY MANUFACTURING

3M PURIFICATION PTY. LIMITED—See 3M Company; *U.S. Public*, pg. 7
AB BEST MATIC—See Ingersoll Rand Inc.; *U.S. Public*, pg. 1120
ABCO AUTOMATION, INC.; *U.S. Private*, pg. 36
ABG ALLGEMEINE BAUMASCHINEN-GESELLSCHAFT MBH—See AB Volvo; *Int'l*, pg. 43
ABG-FRANCE E.U.R.L—See Ingersoll Rand Inc.; *U.S. Public*, pg. 1120
ABG-IBERICA—See Ingersoll Rand Inc.; *U.S. Public*, pg. 1120
ACCELERATED PRODUCTION SYSTEMS LIMITED—See Dover Corporation; *U.S. Public*, pg. 678
ACCRAPLY, INC.—See Barry-Wehmiller Companies, Inc.; *U.S. Private*, pg. 481
A.C.E. (SHANGHAI) TRADING CO. LTD.—See Atlas Converting Equipment Limited; *Int'l*, pg. 676
ACTUANT INDIA PVT. LTD.—See Enerpac Tool Group Corp.; *U.S. Public*, pg. 765
ACTUANT KOREA LTD.—See Enerpac Tool Group Corp.; *U.S. Public*, pg. 765
ADAPTIVE VISION SPOLKA Z OGRANICZONA ODPOWIEDZIALNOSCIA—See Zebra Technologies Corporation; *U.S. Public*, pg. 2401
A&D KOREA LIMITED—See A&D Co., Ltd.; *Int'l*, pg. 18
A&D SCALES CO., LTD.—See A&D Co., Ltd.; *Int'l*, pg. 19
ADVANCED MACHINE & TOOL CORP.; *U.S. Private*, pg. 90
ADVANCED TEST CONCEPTS, LLC—See Dr. Ing. K. Busch GmbH; *Int'l*, pg. 2193
A&D WEIGHING PTY. LTD.—See A&D Co., Ltd.; *Int'l*, pg. 18
AERO - BOND CORP.—See Rift Valley Equity Partners, LLC; *U.S. Private*, pg. 3435
AEROWASH AB; *Int'l*, pg. 182
AFCON HOLDINGS LTD.; *Int'l*, pg. 185
AF SRL—See Generac Holdings Inc.; *U.S. Public*, pg. 912
THE A.H. EMERY COMPANY; *U.S. Private*, pg. 3980
AIRLINE HYDRAULICS CORPORATION; *U.S. Private*, pg. 141
AIR & LIQUID SYSTEMS CORPORATION—See Ampco-Pittsburgh Corporation; *U.S. Public*, pg. 126
AIROBOTICS LTD.—See Ondas Holdings, Inc.; *U.S. Public*, pg. 1602
AIR PRODUCTS & CHEMICALS, INC.—See Air Products & Chemicals, Inc.; *U.S. Public*, pg. 64
AIRTAC (CHINA) CO., LTD.—See Airtac International Group; *Int'l*, pg. 248
AIRTAC CO., LTD.—See Airtac International Group; *Int'l*, pg. 249
AIRTAC INDUSTRIAL CO., LTD.—See Airtac International Group; *Int'l*, pg. 249
AIRTAC USA CORPORATION—See Airtac International Group; *Int'l*, pg. 249
ALFA LAVAL MOATTI SAS—See Alfa Laval AB; *Int'l*, pg. 309
ALFONS HAAR LIMITED—See Alfons Haar Maschinenbau GmbH & Co. KG; *Int'l*, pg. 315
ALGAS-SDI INTERNATIONAL LLC—See Honeywell International Inc.; *U.S. Public*, pg. 1047
ALLIS TOOL & MACHINE CORP.; *U.S. Private*, pg. 192
ALLOY BELLOWS & PRECISION WELDING—See Shelburne Corp.; *U.S. Private*, pg. 3630
ALLOY SPECIALTIES INC.—See J & E Precision Tool, LLC; *U.S. Private*, pg. 2152
AMERICAN BALER COMPANY—See Avis Industrial Corporation; *U.S. Private*, pg. 407
AMERICAN FELT & FILTER COMPANY; *U.S. Private*, pg. 233
AMERICAN LEAK DETECTION, INC.—See Water Intelligence Inc; *U.S. Public*, pg. 2334
AMETEK CHATILLON FORCE MEASUREMENT PRODUCTS—See AMETEK, Inc.; *U.S. Public*, pg. 117
AMG RESOURCES CORP. - LLANELLI FACILITY—See AMG Resources Corp.; *U.S. Private*, pg. 262
AMIAD WATER SYSTEMS LTD.; *Int'l*, pg. 427
ANDRITZ SEPARATION INC.—See ANDRITZ AG; *Int'l*, pg. 453
ANHUI YINGLIU ELECTROMECHANICAL CO., LTD.; *Int'l*, pg. 470
ANVA GMBH—See AnVa Tubes & Components AB; *Int'l*, pg. 486
ARISTOCRAT ARGENTINA S.A.—See Aristocrat Leisure Limited; *Int'l*, pg. 566
ARMSTRONG INTERNATIONAL MEXICO S DE RL DE CV—See Armstrong International, Inc.; *U.S. Private*, pg. 331
ARMSTRONG MOLD CORP.; *U.S. Private*, pg. 332
ARROW SINTERED PRODUCTS—See Arrow Pneumatics Inc.; *U.S. Private*, pg. 335
ASEM, S.R.L.—See Rockwell Automation, Inc.; *U.S. Public*, pg. 1805
ASM ASSEMBLY SYSTEMS LLC—See ASM INTERNATIONAL N.V.; *Int'l*, pg. 626
ASSEMBLY & MANUFACTURING SYSTEMS, INC.; *U.S. Private*, pg. 353
ASTRO MANUFACTURING & DESIGN, INC.; *U.S. Private*, pg. 362
ATC (ITALIA) S.R.L.—See Airtac International Group; *Int'l*, pg. 248
AT ENGINEERING SOLUTION SDN. BHD.—See AT Systematization Berhad; *Int'l*, pg. 664
ATLAS CONVERTING EQUIPMENT (INDIA) PVT. LTD.—See Atlas Converting Equipment Limited; *Int'l*, pg. 676
ATLAS CONVERTING NORTH AMERICA, INC.—See Atlas

Converting Equipment Limited; *Int'l*, pg. 676
ATLAS INDUSTRIES INC.; *U.S. Private*, pg. 379
ATS CAROLINA INC.—See ATS Corporation; *Int'l*, pg. 695
ATS OHIO INC.—See ATS Corporation; *Int'l*, pg. 695
ATS SORTIMAT USA LLC—See ATS Corporation; *Int'l*, pg. 695
ATS SYSTEMS OREGON INC.—See ATS Corporation; *Int'l*, pg. 695
AUDUBON MACHINERY CORP.; *U.S. Private*, pg. 391
AUTOMATED INDUSTRIAL MACHINERY, INC.; *U.S. Private*, pg. 399
AUTOMATION ENGINEERING CORPORATION; *U.S. Private*, pg. 399
AUTOMATION TOOL COMPANY; *U.S. Private*, pg. 400
AUTOTAC, INC.—See Oakland Standard Co., LLC; *U.S. Private*, pg. 2985
AVERY WEIGH-TRONIX, INC.—See Illinois Tool Works Inc.; *U.S. Public*, pg. 1101
AVERY WEIGH-TRONIX INTERNATIONAL LIMITED—See Illinois Tool Works Inc.; *U.S. Public*, pg. 1101
AVIFIL SAS—See Parker Hannifin Corporation; *U.S. Public*, pg. 1640
AVON CORPORATION LTD.; *Int'l*, pg. 749
AWG FITTINGS GMBH—See IDEX Corp; *U.S. Public*, pg. 1089
AZMAYESH INDUSTRIAL FACTORIES COMPANY; *Int'l*, pg. 780
BADER GMBH; *Int'l*, pg. 795
BALYO APAC PTE LTD—See Balyo SA; *Int'l*, pg. 813
BALYO SA—See Balyo SA; *Int'l*, pg. 813
BARDELLA S.A. INDUSTRIAS MECANICAS; *Int'l*, pg. 864
BAY ADVANCED TECHNOLOGIES LLC - AUSTIN—See Bay Advanced Technologies LLC; *U.S. Private*, pg. 491
BAYSHORE TRUCK EQUIPMENT COMPANY—See Illinois Tool Works Inc.; *U.S. Public*, pg. 1101
BEAM A/S—See Bucher Industries AG; *Int'l*, pg. 1207
BEL ENGINEERING (UK) LTD—See British Engines Ltd.; *Int'l*, pg. 1171
BEMCO HYDRAULICS LTD; *Int'l*, pg. 968
BIESSE AMERICA, INC.—See Biesse S.p.A.; *Int'l*, pg. 1020
BIESSE S.P.A.; *Int'l*, pg. 1020
BINKS—See Illinois Tool Works Inc.; *U.S. Public*, pg. 1102
BIOMICROLAB, INC.—See SPT Labtech Limited; *U.S. Private*, pg. 3765
BL AUTOTEC, LTD.—See Bando Chemical Industries, Ltd.; *Int'l*, pg. 830
BL - PEGSON LIMITED—See Terex Corporation; *U.S. Public*, pg. 2020
BLUE RIVER TECHNOLOGY, INC.—See Deere & Company; *U.S. Public*, pg. 646
BMS BVBA—See Alpha Associes Conseil SAS; *Int'l*, pg. 366
BMS VISION LTD.—See Alpha Associes Conseil SAS; *Int'l*, pg. 366
BOBST GRENCHEN AG—See Bobst Group S.A.; *Int'l*, pg. 1095
BONSO ELECTRONICS INTERNATIONAL INC.; *Int'l*, pg. 1109
BONSO ELECTRONICS (SHENZHEN) CO. LIMITED—See Bonso Electronics International Inc; *Int'l*, pg. 1109
BORE-MAX CORP.—See Golden Gate Capital Management II, LLC; *U.S. Private*, pg. 1732
BOSTON DYNAMICS INC.—See Hyundai Motor Company; *Int'l*, pg. 3558
BRADLEY LIFTING CORPORATION—See Xtek, Inc.; *U.S. Private*, pg. 4583
BROCK ELECTRONICS LTD.—See Fuji Corporation; *Int'l*, pg. 2809
BULLEX, INC.—See Lakeland Industries, Inc.; *U.S. Public*, pg. 1288
BURCELIK VANA SANAYI VE TICARET A.S.; *Int'l*, pg. 1220
BWT AQUA AG—See BWT Aktiengesellschaft; *Int'l*, pg. 1232
CALORIC ANLAGENBAU GMBH; *Int'l*, pg. 1265
CALSPAN AERO SYSTEMS ENGINEERING, INC.—See Calspan Technology Holding Corporation; *U.S. Private*, pg. 723
CANADIAN GENERAL FILTERS LIMITED—See General Filters, Inc.; *U.S. Private*, pg. 1665
CARDINAL SCALE MANUFACTURING CO.; *U.S. Private*, pg. 750
CARPENTERIE METALLICHE DI COLZATE S.R.L.—See G. Siempelkamp GmbH & Co. KG; *Int'l*, pg. 2864
CAS CORPORATION - CAS CHEMICAL FACTORY—See CAS Corporation; *Int'l*, pg. 1349
CAS CORPORATION - RUTHERFORD BRANCH—See CAS Corporation; *Int'l*, pg. 1349
CAS CORPORATION; *Int'l*, pg. 1349
CAS POLSKA SP. Z O.O.—See CAS Corporation; *Int'l*, pg. 1349
CAS WEIGHING INDIA PVT. LTD.—See CAS Corporation; *Int'l*, pg. 1349
CAS (ZHEJIANG) ELECTRONICS CO., LTD.—See CAS Corporation; *Int'l*, pg. 1349
CAT SCALE COMPANY—See Iowa 80 Group, Inc.; *U.S. Private*, pg. 2134
CCC HEAVY DUTY TRUCK PARTS COMPANY—See Platinum Equity, LLC; *U.S. Private*, pg. 3209

CELCOR LTD.—See Illinois Tool Works Inc.; *U.S. Public*, pg. 1102
CENTRISYS CORPORATION—See Chengdu Techcent Environment Industry Co., Ltd.; *Int'l*, pg. 1469
CENTURY FIRE PROTECTION, LLC—See FirstService Corporation; *Int'l*, pg. 2691
CERTEX LIFTING LTD - OIL & GAS DIVISION—See Axel Johnson Gruppen AB; *Int'l*, pg. 764
CERTEX LIFTING LTD - RENEWABLES DIVISION—See Axel Johnson Gruppen AB; *Int'l*, pg. 764
CERTEX RUS ZAO—See Axel Johnson Gruppen AB; *Int'l*, pg. 764
CFT GMBH; *Int'l*, pg. 1430
CHASSIX, INC.—See Platinum Equity, LLC; *U.S. Private*, pg. 3201
CHEMCO MANUFACTURING COMPANY INC.; *U.S. Private*, pg. 871
CINETIC LANDIS LTD.—See FIVES, Societe Anonyme; *Int'l*, pg. 2696
CKD EUROPE B.V.—See CKD Corporation; *Int'l*, pg. 1639
CLAYTON INDUSTRIES LTD.; *U.S. Private*, pg. 918
CLINE TOOL & SERVICE COMPANY—See Bertram Capital Management, LLC; *U.S. Private*, pg. 539
CLORDISYS SOLUTIONS INC.—See Aterian Investment Management, L.P.; *U.S. Private*, pg. 366
CLYDE BERGEMANN INC.—See Clyde Blowers Capital IM LLP; *Int'l*, pg. 1645
CMA (WUHU) ROBOTICS CO., LTD.—See EFORT Intelligent Equipment Co., Ltd.; *Int'l*, pg. 2321
CMCO MATERIAL HANDLING (PTY), LTD.—See Columbus McKinnon Corporation; *U.S. Public*, pg. 535
CMC RECYCLING—See Commercial Metals Company; *U.S. Public*, pg. 545
COESIA S.P.A.; *Int'l*, pg. 1689
COGES FRANCE, S.A.S.—See AZKOYEN S.A.; *Int'l*, pg. 780
COILHOSE PNEUMATICS INC.; *U.S. Private*, pg. 964
COLONY HARDWARE CORP.—See Audax Group, Limited Partnership; *U.S. Private*, pg. 387
COLUMBUS JACK CORPORATION—See Quality Products Inc.; *U.S. Private*, pg. 3320
COLUMBUS MCKINNON ENGINEERED PRODUCTS GMBH—See Columbus McKinnon Corporation; *U.S. Public*, pg. 536
COLUMBUS MCKINNON (SHANGHAI) INTERNATIONAL TRADING CO. LTD.—See Columbus McKinnon Corporation; *U.S. Public*, pg. 535
COMET TECHNOLOGIES USA, INC. - EBEAM TECHNOLOGIES—See Tri-City Electric Co.; *U.S. Private*, pg. 4221
CORTLAND FIBRON BX LIMITED—See Enerpac Tool Group Corp.; *U.S. Public*, pg. 765
COS.MEC S.R.L.—See Freund Corporation; *Int'l*, pg. 2791
CPI LUBRICATION - CC TECHNOLOGY—See Enpro Inc.; *U.S. Public*, pg. 774
CPI LUBRICATION - PREMIER LUBRICATION SYSTEMS—See Enpro Inc.; *U.S. Public*, pg. 774
C-P MANUFACTURING, INC.—See IMS Recycling Service Inc.; *U.S. Private*, pg. 2051
CRAFT MACHINE WORKS INC.; *U.S. Private*, pg. 1081
CRC-EVANS B.V.—See CRC-Evans International, Inc.; *U.S. Private*, pg. 1087
CRONIFER U.K. LTD.—See CRONIMET Holding GmbH; *Int'l*, pg. 1854
CUBIC DEFENCE AUSTRALIA PTY. LIMITED—See Elliott Management Corporation; *U.S. Private*, pg. 1367
CUBIC DEFENCE AUSTRALIA PTY. LIMITED—See Veritas Capital Fund Management, LLC; *U.S. Private*, pg. 4361
CUBIC TRANSPORTATION SYSTEMS CANADA, LTD.—See Elliott Management Corporation; *U.S. Private*, pg. 1368
CUBIC TRANSPORTATION SYSTEMS CANADA, LTD.—See Veritas Capital Fund Management, LLC; *U.S. Private*, pg. 4362
CUMBERLAND ENGINEERING CORPORATION—See Harbour Group Industries, Inc.; *U.S. Private*, pg. 1860
CUMMINS SCOTT & ENGLISH MALAYSIA SDN. BHD.—See Cummins Inc.; *U.S. Public*, pg. 607
CUNO LATINA LTDA.—See 3M Company; *U.S. Public*, pg. 7
CYGNUS MANUFACTURING CO.; *U.S. Private*, pg. 1134
DAGE-MTI OF MICHIGAN CITY, INC.; *U.S. Private*, pg. 1144
DAIFUKU CLEANROOM AUTOMATION AMERICA CORPORATION—See Daifuku Co., Ltd.; *Int'l*, pg. 1925
DAIFUKU NORTH AMERICA HOLDING COMPANY—See Daifuku Co., Ltd.; *Int'l*, pg. 1925
DAIFUKU (SUZHOU) CLEANROOM AUTOMATION CO., LTD.—See Daifuku Co., Ltd.; *Int'l*, pg. 1925
DAIWA HEAVY INDUSTRY CO,. LTD.; *Int'l*, pg. 1944
DAKOTA TUBE INC.; *U.S. Private*, pg. 1147
DANCUTTER A/S—See Halma plc; *Int'l*, pg. 3231
DAVID PAJIC DAKA A.D.; *Int'l*, pg. 1983
DE DIETRICH PROCESS SYSTEMS-ROSENMUND DIVISION—See De Dietrich Process Systems S.A.; *Int'l*, pg. 1995
DELTA INDUSTRIAL SERVICES, INC.; *U.S. Private*, pg. 1200
DES-CASE CORPORATION—See The Timken Company; *U.S. Public*, pg. 2132

DETECTO SCALE COMPANY—See Cardinal Scale Manufacturing Co.; *U.S. Private*, pg. 751
DFI AMERICA, LLC—See DFI Inc.; *Int'l*, pg. 2095
D.I.D PHILIPPINES INC.—See Daido Kogyo Co., Ltd.; *Int'l*, pg. 1920
DISTECH SYSTEMS, INC.—See Gleason Corporation; *U.S. Private*, pg. 1708
DL MARTIN CO.; *U.S. Private*, pg. 1247
DONG YANG P&F CO., LTD - GIMPO FACTORY—See DYPNF CO.,LTD; *Int'l*, pg. 2243
DOSMATIC U.S.A., INC.—See Dover Corporation; *U.S. Public*, pg. 679
DOVER ARTIFICIAL LIFT, LLC—See Dover Corporation; *U.S. Public*, pg. 679
DOVER ENGINEERED SYSTEMS UK LTD—See Dover Corporation; *U.S. Public*, pg. 679
DOVER FLUIDS UK LTD—See Dover Corporation; *U.S. Public*, pg. 680
DOVER LUXEMBOURG FINANCE S.A.R.L.—See Dover Corporation; *U.S. Public*, pg. 680
DOVER PUMP SOLUTIONS GROUP (EUROPE) GMBH—See Dover Corporation; *U.S. Public*, pg. 680
DROGOBYCH TRUCK CRANE PLANT PJSC; *Int'l*, pg. 2205
DUCOMMUN—See Ducommun Incorporated; *U.S. Public*, pg. 690
DUFF-NORTON—See Columbus McKinnon Corporation; *U.S. Public*, pg. 536
DYNAMIC DESIGN SOLUTIONS, INC.; *U.S. Private*, pg. 1298
DYPNF CO.,LTD; *Int'l*, pg. 2243
EAGLE TECHNOLOGIES GROUP; *U.S. Private*, pg. 1311
EAST CHICAGO MACHINE TOOL CORPORATION—See Kadant Inc.; *U.S. Public*, pg. 1212
EATON AEROSPACE LLC - HYDRAULIC SYSTEMS DIVISION, JACKSON—See Eaton Corporation plc; *Int'l*, pg. 2279
EATON FILTRATION LLC - RONNINGEN-PETTER—See Eaton Corporation plc; *Int'l*, pg. 2280
EATON FILTRATION LLC—See Eaton Corporation plc; *Int'l*, pg. 2280
ECO-TEK HOLDINGS LIMITED; *Int'l*, pg. 2293
EDI GMBH—See Nordson Corporation; *U.S. Public*, pg. 1532
E.I. SPECTRA, LLC—See BelHealth Investment Partners LLC; *U.S. Private*, pg. 517
ELGA AB—See Illinois Tool Works Inc.; *U.S. Public*, pg. 1103
ELRO (U.K.) LIMITED—See Illinois Tool Works Inc.; *U.S. Public*, pg. 1103
ELUMATEC FRANCE S.A.S.—See Cifin S.r.l.; *Int'l*, pg. 1606
EMERSON NETWORK POWER (SOUTH AFRICA) (PTY) LTD—See Emerson Electric Co.; *U.S. Public*, pg. 745
EMERY WINSLOW SCALE COMPANY—See The A.H. Emery Company; *U.S. Private*, pg. 3980
ENERGIZER GROUP FRANCE SAS—See Edgewell Personal Care Company; *U.S. Public*, pg. 718
ENERPAC HYDRAULICS (INDIA) PVT. LTD.—See Enerpac Tool Group Corp.; *U.S. Public*, pg. 765
ENERPAC INTEGRATED SOLUTIONS B.V—See Enerpac Tool Group Corp.; *U.S. Public*, pg. 765
ENTEGRIS GP, INC.—See Entegris, Inc.; *U.S. Public*, pg. 776
ENTERPRISES INTERNATIONAL INC.; *U.S. Private*, pg. 1404
ETS RAOUL LENOIR SAS—See CVC Capital Partners SICAV-FIS S.A.; *Int'l*, pg. 1887
EVAC E.U.R.L.—See Bridgepoint Group Plc; *Int'l*, pg. 1153
EVAC GERMANY GMBH—See Bridgepoint Group Plc; *Int'l*, pg. 1153
EVAC VACUUM SYSTEMS (SHANGHAI) CO., LTD.—See Bridgepoint Group Plc; *Int'l*, pg. 1153
EVANTIC—See Edgewater Capital Partners, L.P.; *U.S. Private*, pg. 1334
EXILE TECHNOLOGIES CORPORATION—See GEOSPACE TECHNOLOGIES CORPORATION; *U.S. Public*, pg. 934
EXILE TECHNOLOGIES LIMITED—See GEOSPACE TECHNOLOGIES CORPORATION; *U.S. Public*, pg. 934
EXXONMOBIL CORPORATION—See Exxon Mobil Corporation; *U.S. Public*, pg. 815
FAIRBANKS SCALES INC.; *U.S. Private*, pg. 1462
FALCON ASPHALT REPAIR EQUIPMENT; *U.S. Private*, pg. 1466
FAMECCANICA MACHINERY (SHANGHAI) CO., LTD.—See The Procter & Gamble Company; *U.S. Public*, pg. 2120
FANUC ADRIA D.O.O.—See FANUC Corporation; *Int'l*, pg. 2614
FANUC AUTOMATION ISRAEL LTD.—See FANUC Corporation; *Int'l*, pg. 2614
FANUC AUTOMATION ROMANIA S.R.L.—See FANUC Corporation; *Int'l*, pg. 2614
FANUC BENELUX BV—See FANUC Corporation; *Int'l*, pg. 2614
FANUC CZECH S.R.O.—See FANUC Corporation; *Int'l*, pg. 2614
FANUC MEXICO S.A. DE C.V.—See FANUC Corporation; *Int'l*, pg. 2614

N.A.I.C.S. INDEX

333998 — ALL OTHER MISCELLAN...

FANUC NORDIC AB—See FANUC Corporation; *Int'l*, pg. 2614
FANUC OSTERREICH GMBH—See FANUC Corporation; *Int'l*, pg. 2614
FANUC SERBIA D.O.O.—See FANUC Corporation; *Int'l*, pg. 2614
FANUC SLOVAKIA S.R.O.—See FANUC Corporation; *Int'l*, pg. 2614
FANUC SOUTH AMERICA EQUIPAMENTOS DE AUTOMACAO E SERVICOS LTDA.—See FANUC Corporation; *Int'l*, pg. 2614
FANUC TURKEY ENDUSTRIYEL OTOMASYON TIC. LTD. STI.—See FANUC Corporation; *Int'l*, pg. 2614
FANUC UKRAINE LLC—See FANUC Corporation; *Int'l*, pg. 2614
FERRY INDUSTRIES INC.; *U.S. Private*, pg. 1498
FILTERTEK B.V.—See Illinois Tool Works Inc.; *U.S. Public*, pg. 1103
FILTERTEK DE MEXICO, S.A. DE C.V.—See Illinois Tool Works Inc.; *U.S. Public*, pg. 1103
FILTERTEK DO BRAZIL INDUSTRIA E COMMERCIO LTDA.—See Illinois Tool Works Inc.; *U.S. Public*, pg. 1103
FILTERTEK INC.—See Illinois Tool Works Inc.; *U.S. Public*, pg. 1103
FILTERTEK, S.A.—See Illinois Tool Works Inc.; *U.S. Public*, pg. 1103
FILTRA-SYSTEMS COMPANY—See The Chickasaw Nation; *U.S. Private*, pg. 4008
FITNESS PLUS EQUIPMENT SERVICES INC.; *U.S. Private*, pg. 1536
FITRASYON ARITIM SISTEMLERI SANAYIVE TICARET FTS—See Amiad Water Systems Ltd.; *Int'l*, pg. 427
FLEXFAB HORIZONS INTERNATIONAL, LLC; *U.S. Private*, pg. 1544
FLEXFAB LLC—See Flexfab Horizons International, LLC; *U.S. Private*, pg. 1544
FLOW BANGALORE WATERJET PVT. LTD.—See AIP, LLC; *U.S. Private*, pg. 137
FLUID CONSERVATION SYSTEMS INC—See Halma plc; *Int'l*, pg. 3231
FLUIDPOINT, A.S.—See Convum Ltd.; *Int'l*, pg. 1788
FORGEPRO INDIA PRIVATE LIMITED—See Daifuku Co., Ltd.; *Int'l*, pg. 1926
FORTE LUBRICANTS LIMITED—See Illinois Tool Works Inc.; *U.S. Public*, pg. 1103
FOSTER REFRIGERATOR (U.K.)—See Illinois Tool Works Inc.; *U.S. Public*, pg. 1103
FREEMS CORPORATION; *Int'l*, pg. 2770
FRYMAKORUMA AG—See Capvis AG; *Int'l*, pg. 1318
FUJI AMERICA CORPORATION—See Fuji Corporation; *Int'l*, pg. 2809
FUJI MACHINE MANUFACTURING (EUROPE) GMBH—See Fuji Corporation; *Int'l*, pg. 2810
FUJISHOJI CO., LTD.; *Int'l*, pg. 2830
FUSION GROUP LTD.—See AVK Holding A/S; *Int'l*, pg. 747
FUSION ITALIA S.R.L—See AVK Holding A/S; *Int'l*, pg. 747
GAMKO REFRIGERATION U.K. LIMITED—See Illinois Tool Works Inc.; *U.S. Public*, pg. 1103
GASBARRE PRODUCTS—See Gasbarre Products Inc.; *U.S. Private*, pg. 1648
GAST GROUP LTD.—See IDEX Corp; *U.S. Public*, pg. 1090
GATLIN CORPORATION—See Applied Industrial Technologies, Inc.; *U.S. Public*, pg. 171
GEFRAN BRASIL ELETTROEL. LTDA.—See Gefran S.p.A.; *Int'l*, pg. 2912
GEFRAN DRIVES & MOTION S.R.L.—See Gefran S.p.A.; *Int'l*, pg. 2912
GEFRAN SIEI DRIVES TECH. CO., LTD.—See Gefran S.p.A.; *Int'l*, pg. 2912
GENERAL PACKER CO., LTD.; *Int'l*, pg. 2919
GENESIS ATC; *U.S. Private*, pg. 1669
GENESIS SYSTEMS GROUP, LLC—See IPG Photonics Corporation; *U.S. Public*, pg. 1167
GEOSPACE ENGINEERING RESOURCES INTERNATIONAL, INC.—See GEOSPACE TECHNOLOGIES CORPORATION; *U.S. Public*, pg. 934
GEOSPACE TECHNOLOGIES CANADA, INC.—See GEOSPACE TECHNOLOGIES CORPORATION; *U.S. Public*, pg. 934
GHM INDUSTRIES, INC. - MILLER LIFTING PRODUCTS DIVSION—See GHM Industries, Inc.; *U.S. Private*, pg. 1691
GIKEN LTD. - TOKYO FACTORY—See GIKEN Ltd.; *Int'l*, pg. 2972
GIKEN SEKO CO., LTD. - KANSAI FACTORY—See GIKEN Ltd.; *Int'l*, pg. 2972
GILETTA S.P.A.—See Bucher Industries AG; *Int'l*, pg. 1208
GISAB GALLIVARE INDUSTRISERVICE AB—See Axel Johnson Gruppen AB; *Int'l*, pg. 763
GOERTEK SHINNEI TECHNOLOGY CO., LTD.—See GoerTek Inc.; *Int'l*, pg. 3021
GOODTECH GMBH—See Grant Thornton International Limited; *Int'l*, pg. 3059
GOSA FOM A.D.; *Int'l*, pg. 3043
GRAINGER & WORRALL MACHINING LTD—See Grainger & Worrall Limited; *Int'l*, pg. 3052
GRG BANKING EQUIPMENT CO., LTD.—See Guangzhou Radio Group Co., Ltd.; *Int'l*, pg. 3167
GROUPE R.Y. BEAUDOIN, INC.; *Int'l*, pg. 3110
GSF EUROPE B.V.—See Parker Hannifin Corporation; *U.S. Public*, pg. 1641
G. SIEMPELKAMP GMBH & CO. KG; *Int'l*, pg. 2864
GUANGDONG SENSSUN WEIGHING APPARATUS GROUP LTD.; *Int'l*, pg. 3160
GUNNEBO DO BRASIL LTDA—See Gunnebo AB; *Int'l*, pg. 3184
GUSMER ENTERPRISES, INC.; *U.S. Private*, pg. 1819
GUSMER ENTERPRISES, INC.—See Gusmer Enterprises, Inc.; *U.S. Private*, pg. 1819
G.W. SPRINKLER A/S—See Carrier Global Corporation; *U.S. Public*, pg. 441
HAAR NEDERLAND CV—See Alfons Haar Maschinenbau GmbH & Co. KG; *Int'l*, pg. 315
HAAR POLSKA SP. Z O.O.—See Alfons Haar Maschinenbau GmbH & Co. KG; *Int'l*, pg. 316
HANWHA TECHM CO., LTD. - ASAN 1 PLANT—See Hanwha Group; *Int'l*, pg. 3266
HAULOTTE AUSTRALIA PTY LTD.—See Haulotte Group SA; *Int'l*, pg. 3285
HAULOTTE DO BRAZIL LTDA.A—See Haulotte Group SA; *Int'l*, pg. 3285
HAULOTTE HUBARBEITSBUHNEN GMBH—See Haulotte Group SA; *Int'l*, pg. 3285
HAULOTTE IBERICA S.L—See Haulotte Group SA; *Int'l*, pg. 3285
HAULOTTE INDIA PRIVATE LIMITED—See Haulotte Group SA; *Int'l*, pg. 3285
HAULOTTE ITALIA S.R.L.—See Haulotte Group SA; *Int'l*, pg. 3285
HAULOTTE MEXICO S.A. DE C.V.—See Haulotte Group SA; *Int'l*, pg. 3285
HAULOTTE MIDDLE EAST FZE—See Haulotte Group SA; *Int'l*, pg. 3285
HAULOTTE NETHERLANDS B.V—See Haulotte Group SA; *Int'l*, pg. 3285
HAULOTTE POLSKA SP. Z O.O.—See Haulotte Group SA; *Int'l*, pg. 3285
HAULOTTE SCANDINAVIA AB—See Haulotte Group SA; *Int'l*, pg. 3285
HAULOTTE SHANGHAI CO., LTD.—See Haulotte Group SA; *Int'l*, pg. 3285
HAULOTTE SINGAPORE PTE LTD.—See Haulotte Group SA; *Int'l*, pg. 3285
HAULOTTE TRADING (SHANGHAI) CO., LTD.—See Haulotte Group SA; *Int'l*, pg. 3285
HAULOTTE UK LTD.—See Haulotte Group SA; *Int'l*, pg. 3285
HAULOTTE VOSTOK OOO—See Haulotte Group SA; *Int'l*, pg. 3285
HEBELER CORPORATION; *U.S. Private*, pg. 1902
HEBETECHNIK GESELLSCHAFT GMBH—See Columbus McKinnon Corporation; *U.S. Public*, pg. 535
HEINKEL FILTERING SYSTEMS INC.—See HEINKEL Process Technology GmbH; *Int'l*, pg. 3323
HEINKEL PROCESS TECHNOLOGY GMBH; *Int'l*, pg. 3323
HELLER INDUSTRIES INC.; *U.S. Private*, pg. 1907
HENRY FILTERS, INC.—See Komline-Sanderson Corporation; *U.S. Private*, pg. 2342
HERO EUROPE S.R.L—See I.C.T.C. Holdings Corporation; *Int'l*, pg. 3565
HERO LATIN AMERICA SISTEMAS TINTOMETRICOS LTDA—See I.C.T.C. Holdings Corporation; *Int'l*, pg. 3565
HERO PRODUCTS INDIA PVT. LTD.—See I.C.T.C. Holdings Corporation; *Int'l*, pg. 3565
HEXCEL POTTSVILLE CORPORATION—See Hexcel Corporation; *U.S. Public*, pg. 1033
HILLIARD CORPORATION; *U.S. Public*, pg. 1038
HIRATA AUTOMATED MACHINERY (SHANGHAI) CO., LTD.—See Hirata Corporation; *Int'l*, pg. 3403
HIRSCH MASCHINENBAU GMBH—See Hirsch Servo AG; *Int'l*, pg. 3405
HOBART CANADA CORP.—See Illinois Tool Works Inc.; *U.S. Public*, pg. 1103
HOBART SALES & SERVICE, INC.—See Illinois Tool Works Inc.; *U.S. Public*, pg. 1104
HOLMATRO, INC.—See Madison Industries Holdings LLC; *U.S. Private*, pg. 2543
HOMAG FRANCE S.A—See Durr AG; *Int'l*, pg. 2232
HONG KONG ACE PILLAR ENTERPRISE CO., LTD.—See ACE PILLAR Co., Ltd; *Int'l*, pg. 94
HORMANN AUTOMOTIVE EISLINGEN GMBH—See Hormann Holding GmbH & Co. KG; *Int'l*, pg. 3480
HORMANN AUTOMOTIVE GUSTAVSBURG GMBH—See Hormann Holding GmbH & Co. KG; *Int'l*, pg. 3480
HORMANN AUTOMOTIVE PENZBERG GMBH—See Hormann Holding GmbH & Co. KG; *Int'l*, pg. 3480
HORMANN AUTOMOTIVE SAARBRUCKEN GMBH—See Hormann Holding GmbH & Co. KG; *Int'l*, pg. 3480
HORMANN AUTOMOTIVE ST. WENDEL GMBH—See Hormann Holding GmbH & Co. KG; *Int'l*, pg. 3480
HORMANN AUTOMOTIVE WACKERSDORF GMBH—See Hormann Holding GmbH & Co. KG; *Int'l*, pg. 3480
H. PAULIN & CO., LTD. - JEYCO MACHINE PRODUCTS—See Hillman Solutions Corp.; *U.S. Public*, pg. 1038
H.R. BLACK CO. INC.—See Komline-Sanderson Corporation; *U.S. Private*, pg. 2342
HUAMING POWER EQUIPMENT CO., LTD.; *Int'l*, pg. 3513
HYDAC AS—See Hydac International GmbH; *Int'l*, pg. 3544
HYDAC CORPORATION—See Hydac International GmbH; *Int'l*, pg. 3544
HYDAC D.O.O.—See Hydac International GmbH; *Int'l*, pg. 3545
HYDAC ELECTRONIC GMBH—See Hydac International GmbH; *Int'l*, pg. 3545
HYDAC ELECTRONIC, S.R.O.—See Hydac International GmbH; *Int'l*, pg. 3545
HYDAC ENGINEERING AG—See Hydac International GmbH; *Int'l*, pg. 3545
HYDAC EOOD—See Hydac International GmbH; *Int'l*, pg. 3544
HYDAC FILTERTECHNIK GMBH—See Hydac International GmbH; *Int'l*, pg. 3545
HYDAC HYDRAULIK GES.M.B.H.—See Hydac International GmbH; *Int'l*, pg. 3545
HYDAC (INDIA) PVT. LTD.—See Hydac International GmbH; *Int'l*, pg. 3544
HYDAC INTERNATIONAL SA DE CV—See Hydac International GmbH; *Int'l*, pg. 3545
HYDAC KOREA CO. LTD.—See Hydac International GmbH; *Int'l*, pg. 3545
HYDAC N.V.—See Hydac International GmbH; *Int'l*, pg. 3545
HYDAC S.R.O.—See Hydac International GmbH; *Int'l*, pg. 3545
HYDAC TECHNOLOGY ARGENTINA S.R.L.—See Hydac International GmbH; *Int'l*, pg. 3545
HYDAC TECHNOLOGY CORPORATION, ELECTRONIC DIVISION—See Hydac Technology Corporation; *U.S. Private*, pg. 2016
HYDAC TECHNOLOGY CORPORATION, HYCON DIVISION—See Hydac Technology Corporation; *U.S. Private*, pg. 2016
HYDAC TECHNOLOGY CORPORATION; *U.S. Private*, pg. 2016
HYDAC TECHNOLOGY (HONGKONG) LTD.—See Hydac International GmbH; *Int'l*, pg. 3545
HYDAC TECHNOLOGY LTD.—See Hydac International GmbH; *Int'l*, pg. 3545
HYDAC TECHNOLOGY PTY LTD—See Hydac International GmbH; *Int'l*, pg. 3545
HYDAC TECNOLOGIA CHILE LTDA—See Hydac International GmbH; *Int'l*, pg. 3545
HYDAC TECNOLOGIA LTDA—See Hydac International GmbH; *Int'l*, pg. 3545
HYER INDUSTRIES INC.; *U.S. Private*, pg. 2018
HY-PRO CORPORATION—See Donaldson Company, Inc.; *U.S. Public*, pg. 676
HYUNDAI MOVEX CO., LTD.; *Int'l*, pg. 3560
IAI ROBOT (THAILAND) CO., LTD.—See IAI Corporation; *Int'l*, pg. 3568
IAI (SHANGHAI) CO., LTD.—See IAI Corporation; *Int'l*, pg. 3568
I.C.T.C. HOLDINGS CORPORATION; *Int'l*, pg. 3565
ILJINENERGY CO., LTD. - PLANT 2—See Iljin Power Co., Ltd.; *Int'l*, pg. 3615
ILJIN POWER CO., LTD.; *Int'l*, pg. 3615
ILLINOIS TOOL WORKS INC.; *U.S. Public*, pg. 1101
INDUSTRIAL FILTER PUMP MANUFACTURING CO; *U.S. Private*, pg. 2066
INDUSTRIAL MAINTENANCE, WELDING & MACHINING CO, INC.; *U.S. Private*, pg. 2067
INFAIMON DO BRASIL VISAO ARTIFICIAL LTDA—See MiddleGround Management, LP; *U.S. Private*, pg. 2712
INFAIMON MEXICO S.A.DE C.V.—See MiddleGround Management, LP; *U.S. Private*, pg. 2712
INFAIMON S.L.U.—See MiddleGround Management, LP; *U.S. Private*, pg. 2712
INFAIMON UNIPESSOAL, LDA.—See MiddleGround Management, LP; *U.S. Private*, pg. 2712
INGENIERIA Y SERVICIOS METALCROM LTDA.—See Parker Hannifin Corporation; *U.S. Public*, pg. 1641
INGERSOLL-RAND COMPANY (CHILE) Y CIA LTDA.—See Ingersoll Rand Inc.; *U.S. Public*, pg. 1121
INGERSOLL-RAND EQUIPEMENTS DE PRODUCTION S.A.S.—See Ingersoll Rand Inc.; *U.S. Public*, pg. 1121
INGERSOLL-RAND HOLDINGS LTD.—See Ingersoll Rand Inc.; *U.S. Public*, pg. 1121
INSTRON SINGAPORE PTE LIMITED—See Illinois Tool Works Inc.; *U.S. Public*, pg. 1108
INTERNATIONAL PIPE MACHINERY CORP.—See Besser Company; *U.S. Private*, pg. 542
INTOUCH TECHNOLOGIES, INC.; *U.S. Private*, pg. 2129
IRCON INC.—See Fortive Corporation; *U.S. Public*, pg. 870
ISHIKAWAJIMA-HARIMA SUL-AMERICA LTDA.—See IHI Corporation; *Int'l*, pg. 3605
ITALTINTO EQUIPMENTS PVT. LIMITED—See I.C.T.C. Holdings Corporation; *Int'l*, pg. 3565
ITECMA S.A.S.—See Illinois Tool Works Inc.; *U.S. Public*, pg. 1104
ITW CONSTRUCTION PRODUCTS AB—See Illinois Tool Works Inc.; *U.S. Public*, pg. 1105
ITW COVID SECURITY GROUP INC.—See Illinois Tool Works Inc.; *U.S. Public*, pg. 1105

333998 — ALL OTHER MISCELLAN...

ITW FOOD EQUIPMENT GROUP LLC—See Illinois Tool Works Inc.; *U.S. Public*, pg. 1106
ITW GLOBAL INVESTMENTS INC.—See Illinois Tool Works Inc.; *U.S. Public*, pg. 1106
I.T.W. INC.—See Illinois Tool Works Inc.; *U.S. Public*, pg. 1104
ITW PERFORMANCE PLASTIC (SHANGHAI) CO. LTD.—See Illinois Tool Works Inc.; *U.S. Public*, pg. 1106
ITW SHIPPERS S.P.R.L.—See Illinois Tool Works Inc.; *U.S. Public*, pg. 1107
ITW STRETCH PACKAGING PARTS & TECHNICAL ASSISTANCE—See Illinois Tool Works Inc.; *U.S. Public*, pg. 1107
ITW TEST & MEASUREMENT (CHINA) CO., LTD.—See Illinois Tool Works Inc.; *U.S. Public*, pg. 1108
JABIL CHAD AUTOMATION—See Jabil Inc.; *U.S. Public*, pg. 1180
JABIL CIRCUIT DE MEXICO, S DE RL DE C.V.—See Jabil Inc.; *U.S. Public*, pg. 1181
JAQUES INTERNATIONAL HOLDINGS PTY. LTD.—See Terex Corporation; *U.S. Public*, pg. 2020
JAQUES (THAILAND) LIMITED—See Terex Corporation; *U.S. Public*, pg. 2020
JENS S. TRANSMISSIONER A/S—See Axel Johnson Gruppen AB; *Int'l*, pg. 763
JL FILTRATION INC.—See Clean Harbors, Inc.; *U.S. Public*, pg. 510
JLG INDUSTRIES, INC.—See Oshkosh Corporation; *U.S. Public*, pg. 1620
JORDAN TECHNOLOGIES, LLC—See Turnbridge Capital, LLC; *U.S. Private*, pg. 4260
JRH INDUSTRIES LLC; *U.S. Private*, pg. 2240
KADANT JOHNSON DEUTSCHLAND GMBH—See Kadant Inc.; *U.S. Public*, pg. 1212
KAHLE ENGINEERING CO.; *U.S. Private*, pg. 2254
KAPTAS OY—See Addtech AB; *Int'l*, pg. 134
KARCHER NORTH AMERICA—See Alfred Karcher GmbH & Co. KG; *Int'l*, pg. 316
KAUTEX MACHINES, INC.; *U.S. Private*, pg. 2265
KDF FLUID TREATMENT INC.—See Palladium Equity Partners, LLC; *U.S. Private*, pg. 3078
KELCO INDUSTRIES INC; *U.S. Private*, pg. 2274
KENSEI INDUSTRY CO., LTD.—See A&D Co., Ltd.; *Int'l*, pg. 19
KIDDE-DEUGRA BRANDSCHUTZSYSTEME GMBH—See RTX Corporation; *U.S. Public*, pg. 1822
KIDDE GRAVINER LTD.—See RTX Corporation; *U.S. Public*, pg. 1822
KMI SYSTEMS INC.; *U.S. Private*, pg. 2321
KNIGHT, LLC—See IDEX Corp; *U.S. Public*, pg. 1091
KNIGHTSCOPE, INC.; *U.S. Public*, pg. 1269
KOCH MEMBRANE SYSTEMS, INC.—See Koch Industries, Inc.; *U.S. Private*, pg. 2332
KOMLINE-SANDERSON CORPORATION; *U.S. Private*, pg. 2342
L3 OCEANSERVER, INC.—See L3Harris Technologies, Inc.; *U.S. Public*, pg. 1284
LAVERDA AGCO SPA—See AGCO Corporation; *U.S. Public*, pg. 59
LDI INDUSTRIES, INC.; *U.S. Private*, pg. 2404
LECTRODRYER LLC; *U.S. Private*, pg. 2410
LIANYNGANG JUMP PETROLEUM AND CHEMICAL MACHINERY CO., LTD.—See Dover Corporation; *U.S. Public*, pg. 681
LINDGREN R.F. ENCLOSURES, INC.—See ESCO Technologies, Inc.; *U.S. Public*, pg. 794
LINDSAY INTERNATIONAL (ANZ) PTY LTD.—See Lindsay Corporation; *U.S. Public*, pg. 1319
LINDSAY TRANSPORTATION SOLUTIONS, INC.—See Lindsay Corporation; *U.S. Public*, pg. 1319
LINER PRODUCTS, LLC—See Granite Construction Incorporated; *U.S. Public*, pg. 957
LITRA CO., LTD.—See A&D Co., Ltd.; *Int'l*, pg. 19
L-K INDUSTRIES, INC.—See Dorilton Capital Advisors LLC; *U.S. Private*, pg. 1263
LLOYD MATERIALS TESTING—See AMETEK, Inc.; *U.S. Public*, pg. 117
LOCK INSPECTION SYSTEMES FRANCE SARL—See Illinois Tool Works Inc.; *U.S. Public*, pg. 1109
LOEPFE BROTHERS LTD.—See Alpha Associes Conseil SAS; *Int'l*, pg. 367
LTS SCALE COMPANY, LLC—See Main Street Capital Holdings, LLC; *U.S. Private*, pg. 2551
LUDOWICI INDIA PRIVATE LIMITED—See FLSmidth & Co. A/S; *Int'l*, pg. 2711
LUDOWICI LLC—See FLSmidth & Co. A/S; *Int'l*, pg. 2711
LUDOWICI MINING PROCESS INDIA PVT LIMITED—See FLSmidth & Co. A/S; *Int'l*, pg. 2711
LUDOWICI SCREENS LLC—See FLSmidth & Co. A/S; *Int'l*, pg. 2711
MAE-EITEL INC.—See Gesco AG; *Int'l*, pg. 2945
MAGNEMOTION INC.—See Rockwell Automation, Inc.; *U.S. Public*, pg. 1805
MANITOWOC CRANE GROUP AUSTRALIA PTY LTD.—See The Manitowoc Company, Inc.; *U.S. Public*, pg. 2111
MANITOWOC CRANE GROUP FRANCE SAS—See The Manitowoc Company, Inc.; *U.S. Public*, pg. 2111

MANITOWOC CRANE GROUP NETHERLANDS B.V.—See The Manitowoc Company, Inc.; *U.S. Public*, pg. 2111
MANITOWOC CRANE GROUP POLAND SP—See The Manitowoc Company, Inc.; *U.S. Public*, pg. 2111
MARIOFF CORPORATION OY—See Carrier Global Corporation; *U.S. Public*, pg. 441
MARKEM-IMAJE CSAT GMBH—See Dover Corporation; *U.S. Public*, pg. 682
MARKEM-IMAJE INDUSTRIES—See Dover Corporation; *U.S. Public*, pg. 682
MARKEM-IMAJE LIMITED—See Dover Corporation; *U.S. Public*, pg. 682
MARKEM-IMAJE S.A.—See Dover Corporation; *U.S. Public*, pg. 682
MARKEM PTE. LTD.—See Dover Corporation; *U.S. Public*, pg. 681
MARK RITE LINES EQUIPMENT CO, INC.—See Federal Signal Corporation; *U.S. Public*, pg. 826
MARVEL ENGINEERING COMPANY; *U.S. Private*, pg. 2597
MAS AUTOMATION CORP.—See Chroma ATE Inc.; *Int'l*, pg. 1588
MEASUREMENT SYSTEMS INTERNATIONAL, INC.—See Rice Lake Weighing Systems, Inc.; *U.S. Private*, pg. 3425
MEC DELACHAUX S.R.L.—See CVC Capital Partners SICAV-FIS S.A.; *Int'l*, pg. 1887
MERRICK INDUSTRIES INC—See Tannehill International Industries; *U.S. Private*, pg. 3931
MERRICK INDUSTRIES PVT. LTD.—See Tannehill International Industries; *U.S. Private*, pg. 3931
METALEX MANUFACTURING INC.; *U.S. Private*, pg. 2680
METTLER-TOLEDO INC.—See Mettler-Toledo International, Inc.; *U.S. Public*, pg. 1432
METTLER-TOLEDO INGOLD, INC.—See Mettler-Toledo International, Inc.; *U.S. Public*, pg. 1432
METTLER-TOLEDO SALES INTERNATIONAL GMBH—See Mettler-Toledo International, Inc.; *U.S. Public*, pg. 1433
MICHIGAN CUSTOM MACHINES, INC.; *U.S. Private*, pg. 2700
MI-T-M CORPORATION; *U.S. Private*, pg. 2696
MMLJ, INC.; *U.S. Private*, pg. 2755
MODERN PACKAGING, INC.—See Leonard Green & Partners, L.P.; *U.S. Private*, pg. 2428
MOGEMA B.V.—See Aalberts N.V.; *Int'l*, pg. 35
MONOTARO CO., LTD.—See W.W. Grainger, Inc.; *U.S. Public*, pg. 2320
MONOTECH OF MISSISSIPPI INC.—See The Herrick Corporation; *U.S. Private*, pg. 4052
MOTT CORP.—See IDEX Corp; *U.S. Public*, pg. 1091
NATIONAL BULK EQUIPMENT, INC.; *U.S. Private*, pg. 2849
NCH ESPANOLA S.A.—See NCH Corporation; *U.S. Private*, pg. 2875
NCH - HUNGARY KFT.—See NCH Corporation; *U.S. Private*, pg. 2875
NCH NORGE AS—See NCH Corporation; *U.S. Private*, pg. 2876
NETZSCH CANADA, INC.—See Erich Netzsch GmbH & Co. Holding KG; *Int'l*, pg. 2491
NETZSCH-CONDUX MAHLTECHNIK GMBH—See Erich Netzsch GmbH & Co. Holding KG; *Int'l*, pg. 2492
NETZSCH PREMIER TECHNOLOGIES, LLC.—See Erich Netzsch GmbH & Co. Holding KG; *Int'l*, pg. 2492
NETZSCH TECHNOLOGIES, INDIA PVT. LTD.—See Erich Netzsch GmbH & Co. Holding KG; *Int'l*, pg. 2492
NEW CASTLE ROLLS, INC.—See Nordson Corporation; *U.S. Public*, pg. 1533
NEW LACHAUSSEE S.A.—See George Forrest International S.A.; *Int'l*, pg. 2938
NINGBO AIRTAC AUTOMATIC INDUSTRIAL CO., LTD.—See Airtac International Group; *Int'l*, pg. 249
NITROCISION, LLC—See IHI Corporation; *Int'l*, pg. 3604
NORCO INDUSTRIES, INC.; *U.S. Private*, pg. 2936
NORDSON PACIFIC, INC.—See Nordson Corporation; *U.S. Public*, pg. 1534
NORDSON PPS GMBH—See Nordson Corporation; *U.S. Public*, pg. 1534
NORDSON XALOY K.K.—See Nordson Corporation; *U.S. Public*, pg. 1534
NORTH AMERICAN FILTER CORPORATION; *U.S. Private*, pg. 2940
NOXON AB—See Beijer Alma AB; *Int'l*, pg. 943
OBERLIN FILTER COMPANY—See Production Service Company; *U.S. Private*, pg. 3273
OE SOLUTIONS AS—See Axel Johnson Gruppen AB; *Int'l*, pg. 763
OHAUS CORPORATION—See Mettler-Toledo International, Inc.; *U.S. Public*, pg. 1433
OLAER HYDRAULICS (INDIA) PVT. LTD.—See Parker Hannifin Corporation; *U.S. Public*, pg. 1643
OLAER TIANJIN HYDRAULIC MANUFACTURING CO.,LTD.—See Parker Hannifin Corporation; *U.S. Public*, pg. 1643
ONVALLA COMPANY LIMITED—See Alla Public Company Limited; *Int'l*, pg. 332
OREGON DISTRIBUTION LTD—See American Securities LLC; *U.S. Private*, pg. 247

OREGON DISTRIBUTION LTD—See P2 Capital Partners, LLC; *U.S. Private*, pg. 3062
ORWAK AB—See Accent Equity Partners AB; *Int'l*, pg. 81
ORWAK POLSKA SP. Z O.O.—See Accent Equity Partners AB; *Int'l*, pg. 81
PACIFIC OZONE TECHNOLOGY INC.—See Xylem Inc.; *U.S. Public*, pg. 2394
PALL AEROPOWER CORPORATION—See Danaher Corporation; *U.S. Public*, pg. 629
PALL (CANADA) LIMITED—See Danaher Corporation; *U.S. Public*, pg. 629
PALL FILTRATION AND SEPARATIONS GROUP—See Danaher Corporation; *U.S. Public*, pg. 629
PALL KOREA LIMITED—See Danaher Corporation; *U.S. Public*, pg. 630
PALL LIFE SCIENCES PUERTO RICO, LLC—See Danaher Corporation; *U.S. Public*, pg. 630
PALL MANUFACTURING UK LIMITED—See Danaher Corporation; *U.S. Public*, pg. 630
PARKER HANNIFIN ESSC SP Z.O.O.—See Parker Hannifin Corporation; *U.S. Public*, pg. 1645
PARKER HANNIFIN FILTRATION PRODUCTS AND SYSTEMS (SHANGHAI) CO., LTD.—See Parker Hannifin Corporation; *U.S. Public*, pg. 1645
PARKER HANNIFIN FILTRATION & SEPARATION DIVISION-BALSTON PRODUCTS—See Parker Hannifin Corporation; *U.S. Public*, pg. 1645
PARKER HANNIFIN MANUFACTURING GERMANY GMBH & CO. KG—See Parker Hannifin Corporation; *U.S. Public*, pg. 1648
PARKER HANNIFIN MANUFACTURING NETHERLANDS (FILTRATION AND SEPARATION) B.V.—See Parker Hannifin Corporation; *U.S. Public*, pg. 1648
PARKER HANNIFIN MANUFACTURING NETHERLANDS (FILTRATION) B.V.—See Parker Hannifin Corporation; *U.S. Public*, pg. 1648
PARKER HANNIFIN MANUFACTURING NETHERLANDS (HOSE) B.V.—See Parker Hannifin Corporation; *U.S. Public*, pg. 1648
PARKER HANNIFIN MANUFACTURING NETHERLANDS (PNEUMATIC) B.V.—See Parker Hannifin Corporation; *U.S. Public*, pg. 1648
PARKER HANNIFIN MANUFACTURING POLAND SP Z.O.O.—See Parker Hannifin Corporation; *U.S. Public*, pg. 1648
PARKER HANNIFIN MOTION & CONTROL (SHANGHAI) CO. LTD.—See Parker Hannifin Corporation; *U.S. Public*, pg. 1648
PARKER HANNIFIN PROCESS ADVANCED FILTRATION DIVISION—See Parker Hannifin Corporation; *U.S. Public*, pg. 1645
PARKER HANNIFIN RACOR - FILTERS—See Parker Hannifin Corporation; *U.S. Public*, pg. 1645
PARKER HANNIFIN RACOR—See Parker Hannifin Corporation; *U.S. Public*, pg. 1645
PARKER HANNIFIN REFRIGERATION & AIR CONDITIONING (WUXI) CO., LTD.—See Parker Hannifin Corporation; *U.S. Public*, pg. 1648
PARKER HANNIFIN STRATOFLEX PRODUCTS DIV—See Parker Hannifin Corporation; *U.S. Public*, pg. 1646
PARLE FREUND MACHINERY PRIVATE LIMITED—See Freund Corporation; *Int'l*, pg. 2791
PATHEON FRANCE S.A.S.—See Thermo Fisher Scientific Inc.; *U.S. Public*, pg. 2151
PENNSYLVANIA SCALE COMPANY—See The A.H. Emery Company; *U.S. Private*, pg. 3980
PENN UNITED COSTA RICA SA—See Penn United Technologies, Inc.; *U.S. Private*, pg. 3135
PEP FILTERS, INC.—See Amiad Water Systems Ltd.; *Int'l*, pg. 427
PEPPERL+FUCHS INC; *U.S. Private*, pg. 3145
PERBIX MACHINE COMPANY, INC.—See Tesla, Inc.; *U.S. Public*, pg. 2021
PEREGRINE ENERGY CORP.; *U.S. Private*, pg. 3147
PERENNIAL ENERGY, LLC—See Commerce Bancshares, Inc.; *U.S. Public*, pg. 544
PETERSON PACIFIC CORP.—See Astec Industries, Inc.; *U.S. Public*, pg. 216
PHENIX TECHNOLOGY, INC.—See ESCO Technologies, Inc.; *U.S. Public*, pg. 794
PITTSFIELD PRODUCTS INC.; *U.S. Private*, pg. 3192
POLI S.P.A—See Westinghouse Air Brake Technologies Corporation; *U.S. Public*, pg. 2359
POLTANK, S.A.U.—See Fluidra SA; *Int'l*, pg. 2714
PRECISION AUTOMATION CO., INC.; *U.S. Private*, pg. 3244
PREMIER HYDRAULICS, LLC—See JRH Industries LLC; *U.S. Private*, pg. 2240
PRODUCTION SERVICE COMPANY; *U.S. Private*, pg. 3273
PRO PRODUCTS, INC.—See AFM Capital Partners, Inc.; *U.S. Private*, pg. 123
PROTECT PLUS AIR, LLC—See Freudenberg SE; *Int'l*, pg. 2786
PT METTLER-TOLEDO INDONESIA—See Mettler-Toledo International, Inc.; *U.S. Public*, pg. 1433
PTR BALER & COMPACTOR COMPANY—See Komar Industries, LLC; *U.S. Private*, pg. 2342

N.A.I.C.S. INDEX

334111 — ELECTRONIC COMPUTER...

PUREX INTERNATIONAL LIMITED—See Brother Industries, Ltd.; *Int'l*, pg. 1198
QUANTUM INTERNATIONAL CORP.; *U.S. Public*, pg. 1754
THE RDI GROUP—See Ardian SAS; *Int'l*, pg. 556
REEL-O-MATIC, INC.; *U.S. Private*, pg. 3383
RELIABLE AUTOMATIC SPRINKLER CO., INC.; *U.S. Private*, pg. 3393
RELIABLE FIRE SPRINKLER AUSTRALIA PTY. LTD.—See Reliable Automatic Sprinkler Co., Inc.; *U.S. Private*, pg. 3393
RELIABLE FIRE SPRINKLER LTD.—See Reliable Automatic Sprinkler Co., Inc.; *U.S. Private*, pg. 3393
RICE LAKE WEIGHING SYSTEMS EUROPE B.V.—See Rice Lake Weighing Systems, Inc.; *U.S. Private*, pg. 3425
RICE LAKE WEIGHING SYSTEMS, INC.; *U.S. Private*, pg. 3425
THE ROCKY MOUNTAIN TRUCK CENTER—See Interstate Companies, Inc.; *U.S. Private*, pg. 2124
ROSEDALE PRODUCTS INC.; *U.S. Private*, pg. 3482
ROTEX INC.; *U.S. Private*, pg. 3486
SAVIO MACCHINE TESSILI S.P.A.—See Alpha Associes Conseil SAS; *Int'l*, pg. 366
SCHALTBAU MACHINE ELECTRICS LTD.—See The Carlyle Group Inc.; *U.S. Public*, pg. 2053
SCHRADER DUNCAN LIMITED - PNEUMATICS BUSINESS UNIT—See Duncan Engineering Limited; *Int'l*, pg. 2225
SCHREIBER LLC—See Axel Johnson Gruppen AB; *Int'l*, pg. 765
SCHULTES PRECISION MANUFACTURING, INC.—See Helios Technologies, Inc.; *U.S. Public*, pg. 1023
SCHWING BIOSET, INC.; *U.S. Private*, pg. 3573
SCHWING BIOSET—See Schwing Bioset, Inc.; *U.S. Private*, pg. 3573
SEDO TREEPOINT GMBH—See Alpha Associes Conseil SAS; *Int'l*, pg. 367
SENSIA LLC—See Rockwell Automation, Inc.; *U.S. Public*, pg. 1807
SENSORMATE AG—See Gefran S.p.A.; *Int'l*, pg. 2912
SERFILCO, LTD.; *U.S. Private*, pg. 3613
SES, LLC; *U.S. Private*, pg. 3617
SHANGHAI-FANUC ROBOTICS CO., LTD.—See FANUC Corporation; *Int'l*, pg. 2615
SHASTA HOLDINGS COMPANY; *U.S. Private*, pg. 3627
SHOWA CORPORATION - ASABA PLANT—See Hitachi Astemo, Ltd.; *Int'l*, pg. 3410
SICHUAN BLUESTAR MACHINERY CO, LTD—See China National Chemical Corporation; *Int'l*, pg. 1529
SIEMPELKAMP BEHALTERTECHNIK GMBH—See G. Siempelkamp GmbH & Co. KG; *Int'l*, pg. 2864
SIEMPELKAMP MASCHINEN- UND ANLAGENBAU GMBH—See G. Siempelkamp GmbH & Co. KG; *Int'l*, pg. 2865
SIEMPELKAMP NIS INGENIEURGESELLSCHAFT MBH—See G. Siempelkamp GmbH & Co. KG; *Int'l*, pg. 2865
SIEMPELKAMP (WUXI) MACHINERY MANUFACTURING CO. LTD.—See G. Siempelkamp GmbH & Co. KG; *Int'l*, pg. 2864
SILENTBLOC UK LTD—See Dellner Brakes AB; *Int'l*, pg. 2014
SOGEFI FILTRATION D.O.O.—See Compagnia Finanziaria de Benedetti S.p.A.; *Int'l*, pg. 1722
SOLAYTEC B.V.—See Amtech Systems, Inc.; *U.S. Public*, pg. 134
SOUTHERN FILTER MEDIA LLC; *U.S. Private*, pg. 3731
SOUTH PARK CORPORATION; *U.S. Private*, pg. 3723
SPECMA COMPONENT AB—See Aktieselskabet Schouw & Co.; *Int'l*, pg. 266
SPECTRUM SEI MICROWAVE, INC.—See AEA Investors LP; *U.S. Private*, pg. 113
SPENCO ENGINEERING COMPANY LTD—See AGCO Corporation; *U.S. Public*, pg. 59
SPIRIT GLOBAL ENERGY SOLUTIONS CANADA LTD.—See Dover Corporation; *U.S. Public*, pg. 682
STAUFF CORPORATION; *U.S. Private*, pg. 3794
STEMMER IMAGING AB—See MiddleGround Management, LP; *U.S. Private*, pg. 2712
STEMMER IMAGING AG—See MiddleGround Management, LP; *U.S. Private*, pg. 2713
STEMMER IMAGING A/S—See MiddleGround Management, LP; *U.S. Private*, pg. 2712
STEMMER IMAGING B.V.—See MiddleGround Management, LP; *U.S. Private*, pg. 2713
STEMMER IMAGING GES.M.B.H.—See MiddleGround Management, LP; *U.S. Private*, pg. 2713
STEMMER IMAGING LTD.—See MiddleGround Management, LP; *U.S. Private*, pg. 2713
STEMMER IMAGING OY—See MiddleGround Management, LP; *U.S. Private*, pg. 2713
STEMMER IMAGING S.A.S.—See MiddleGround Management, LP; *U.S. Private*, pg. 2713
STEMMER IMAGING SP.Z O.O.—See MiddleGround Management, LP; *U.S. Private*, pg. 2713
STEMMER IMAGING S.R.L.—See MiddleGround Management, LP; *U.S. Private*, pg. 2713
STERLING-VELCON FILTERS CORP.—See Parker Hannifin Corporation; *U.S. Public*, pg. 1649
STRAINRITE INC.; *U.S. Private*, pg. 3833
STROTHMANN MACHINES & HANDLING GMBH—See G. Siempelkamp GmbH & Co. KG; *Int'l*, pg. 2865
SUPERIOR AUTOMATIC SPRINKLER CO.; *U.S. Private*, pg. 3876
SUZHOU SUPER PILLAR AUTOMATION EQUIPMENT CO., LTD.—See ACE PILLAR Co., Ltd; *Int'l*, pg. 94
SWANSON-ERIE CORPORATION—See Swanson Systems, Inc.; *U.S. Private*, pg. 3891
SWANSON SYSTEMS, INC.; *U.S. Private*, pg. 3891
TA INDUSTRIES INC.—See CSW Industrials, Inc.; *U.S. Public*, pg. 602
TAIWAN FANUC CORPORATION—See FANUC Corporation; *Int'l*, pg. 2615
TAIWAN FANUC ROBOTICS CORPORATION—See FANUC Corporation; *Int'l*, pg. 2615
TAKUMI MACHINERY CO., LTD.—See Liberty Diversified International Inc.; *U.S. Private*, pg. 2444
TANNEHILL INTERNATIONAL INDUSTRIES; *U.S. Private*, pg. 3931
TC NU-STAR, INC.; *U.S. Private*, pg. 3942
TECH-FLO CONSULTING, LLC—See RedBird Capital Partners L.P.; *U.S. Private*, pg. 3377
TELEROBOT LABS SRL—See Danieli & C. Officine Meccaniche S.p.A.; *Int'l*, pg. 1963
TELESTACK, LIMITED—See Astec Industries, Inc.; *U.S. Public*, pg. 216
TEMPOSONICS GMBH & CO. KG—See Amphenol Corporation; *U.S. Public*, pg. 132
TENCO INC.—See Alamo Group Inc.; *U.S. Public*, pg. 71
TENCO INDUSTRIES, INC.—See Alamo Group Inc.; *U.S. Public*, pg. 71
TENCO (USA), INC.—See Alamo Group Inc.; *U.S. Public*, pg. 71
TENNANT AUSTRALIA—See Tennant Company; *U.S. Public*, pg. 2016
TENNANT COMPANY; *U.S. Public*, pg. 2015
TENNANT EUROPE N.V.—See Tennant Company; *U.S. Public*, pg. 2016
TENNANT GMBH & CO. KG—See Tennant Company; *U.S. Public*, pg. 2016
TENNANT N.V.—See Tennant Company; *U.S. Public*, pg. 2016
TENNANT S.A.—See Tennant Company; *U.S. Public*, pg. 2016
TEREX GERMANY GMBH & CO. K.G.—See Terex Corporation; *U.S. Public*, pg. 2020
THERMOTRON INDUSTRIES—See Venturedyne, Ltd.; *U.S. Private*, pg. 4358
THURNE TEKNIK AB—See Addtech AB; *Int'l*, pg. 135
THURNE TEKNIK AB—See Addtech AB; *Int'l*, pg. 135
TIANJIN ACE PILLAR CO., LTD.—See ACE PILLAR Co., Ltd; *Int'l*, pg. 94
TIME MANUFACTURING COMPANY—See The Sterling Group, L.P.; *U.S. Private*, pg. 4123
TRANSACT TECHNOLOGIES INCORPORATED; *U.S. Public*, pg. 2179
TRIDYNE PROCESS SYSTEMS, INC.; *U.S. Private*, pg. 4230
TSA GRIDDLE SYSTEMS INC.—See Gilbert Global Equity Partners; *U.S. Private*, pg. 1699
TWINCO INC.; *U.S. Private*, pg. 4266
TWIN FILTER N.A., INC.—See Parker Hannifin Corporation; *U.S. Public*, pg. 1650
UNICLIP VERPACKUNGSTECHNIK GMBH—See Dover Corporation; *U.S. Public*, pg. 683
US MOTION, INC.—See Frencken Group Limited; *Int'l*, pg. 2773
VEGA CONVEYORS & AUTOMATION PRIVATE LIMITED—See Daifuku Co., Ltd.; *Int'l*, pg. 1926
VENTAPP GMBH—See G. Siempelkamp GmbH & Co. KG; *Int'l*, pg. 2865
VERSACHEM CHILE S.A.—See Illinois Tool Works Inc.; *U.S. Public*, pg. 1111
VERSEIDAG AG—See Gilde Buy Out Partners B.V.; *Int'l*, pg. 2974
VISHAY BLH—See Vishay Intertechnology, Inc.; *U.S. Public*, pg. 2303
VISHAY TRANSDUCERS LTD.—See Vishay Intertechnology, Inc.; *U.S. Public*, pg. 2303
VITRONICS SOLTEC CORPORATION—See Illinois Tool Works Inc.; *U.S. Public*, pg. 1111
VITRONICS SOLTEC TECHNOLOGIES (SUZHOU) CO., LTD.—See Illinois Tool Works Inc.; *U.S. Public*, pg. 1111
WACHS CANADA LTD.—See Illinois Tool Works Inc.; *U.S. Public*, pg. 1111
WASSER FILTRATION INC.; *U.S. Private*, pg. 4450
WAUSAU EQUIPMENT COMPANY, INC.—See Alamo Group Inc.; *U.S. Public*, pg. 71
WAYNE WIRE CLOTH PRODUCTS HILLMAN DIVISION—See Wayne Wire Cloth Products, Inc.; *U.S. Private*, pg. 4460
WEASLER ENGINEERING B.V—See Enerpac Tool Group Corp.; *U.S. Public*, pg. 766
WEASLER ENGINEERING, KFT—See Enerpac Tool Group Corp.; *U.S. Public*, pg. 766
WEATHERFORD KOPP GMBH—See Weatherford International plc; *U.S. Public*, pg. 2340
WEIGH-TRONIX CANADA, ULC—See Illinois Tool Works Inc.; *U.S. Public*, pg. 1111
WEI KUANG AUTOMATIC EQUIPMENT (XIAMEN) CO., LTD.—See Chroma ATE Inc.; *Int'l*, pg. 1588
WEIR SPM; *U.S. Private*, pg. 4472
WELDING INDUSTRIES PTY LIMITED—See Illinois Tool Works Inc.; *U.S. Public*, pg. 1111
WEST BOND INC.; *U.S. Private*, pg. 4483
WESTCON INSTRUMENTACAO INDUSTRIAL LTDA—See CHINO Corporation; *Int'l*, pg. 1571
WESTERMO NETWORK TECHNOLOGIES AB—See Ependion AB; *Int'l*, pg. 2459
WILSEY TOOL CO., INC.—See The Jordan Company, L.P.; *U.S. Private*, pg. 4060
W.S. BADGER COMPANY, INC; *U.S. Private*, pg. 4422
YIXING TAIXING ENVIRONTAEC CO. LTD.—See Amiad Water Systems Ltd.; *Int'l*, pg. 427
Z-LYFTEN PRODUKTION AB—See Cargotec Corporation; *Int'l*, pg. 1329

334111 — ELECTRONIC COMPUTER MANUFACTURING

2CRSI CORPORATION—See 2Crsi SA; *Int'l*, pg. 4
2CRSI ME FZE—See 2Crsi SA; *Int'l*, pg. 4
2CRSI UK LTD.—See 2Crsi SA; *Int'l*, pg. 4
AAEON TECHNOLOGY INC.—See ASUSTeK Computer Inc.; *Int'l*, pg. 663
ABACO SYSTEMS LIMITED—See AMETEK, Inc.; *U.S. Public*, pg. 119
ABCO ELECTRONICS VINA CO., LTD.—See ABCO Electronics Co., Ltd.; *Int'l*, pg. 57
ABCO TECH CO., LTD.—See ABCO Electronics Co., Ltd.; *Int'l*, pg. 57
ABICO NETCOM CO., LTD.; *Int'l*, pg. 61
ABOCOM SYSTEMS, INC. - MIAO-LIH HSUAN FACTORY—See AboCom Systems, Inc.; *Int'l*, pg. 66
ACBEL ELECTRONIC (WUHAN) CO., LTD.—See AcBel Polytech Inc.; *Int'l*, pg. 78
ACBEL POLYTECH (PHILIPPINES) INC.—See AcBel Polytech Inc.; *Int'l*, pg. 78
ACER AFRICA PTY. LTD.—See Acer Incorporated; *Int'l*, pg. 98
ACER AMERICA CORPORATION—See Acer Incorporated; *Int'l*, pg. 98
ACER AMERICA CORPORATION—See Acer Incorporated; *Int'l*, pg. 98
ACER CIS, INC.—See Acer Incorporated; *Int'l*, pg. 98
ACER COMPUTEC MEXICO, S.A. DE C.V.—See Acer Incorporated; *Int'l*, pg. 98
ACER COMPUTER AUSTRALIA PTY. LTD.—See Acer Incorporated; *Int'l*, pg. 98
ACER COMPUTER B.V. BENELUX—See Acer Incorporated; *Int'l*, pg. 98
ACER COMPUTER CO., LTD.—See Acer Incorporated; *Int'l*, pg. 98
ACER COMPUTER CZECH AND SLOVAK REPUBLICS—See Acer Incorporated; *Int'l*, pg. 98
ACER COMPUTER (FAR EAST) LIMITED—See Acer Incorporated; *Int'l*, pg. 98
ACER COMPUTER FINLAND OY—See Acer Incorporated; *Int'l*, pg. 98
ACER COMPUTER FRANCE S.A.R.L.—See Acer Incorporated; *Int'l*, pg. 98
ACER COMPUTER GMBH—See Acer Incorporated; *Int'l*, pg. 99
ACER COMPUTER (M.E.) LTD.—See Acer Incorporated; *Int'l*, pg. 98
ACER COMPUTER NEW ZEALAND LTD.—See Acer Incorporated; *Int'l*, pg. 99
ACER COMPUTER NORWAY A/S—See Acer Incorporated; *Int'l*, pg. 99
ACER COMPUTER (SINGAPORE) PTE. LTD.—See Acer Incorporated; *Int'l*, pg. 99
ACER COMPUTER SWEDEN AB—See Acer Incorporated; *Int'l*, pg. 99
ACER DENMARK A/S—See Acer Incorporated; *Int'l*, pg. 99
ACER DO BRASIL LIMITADA—See Acer Incorporated; *Int'l*, pg. 99
ACER GADGET INC.; *Int'l*, pg. 98
ACER INCORPORATED; *Int'l*, pg. 98
ACER INDIA (PVT) LTD.—See Acer Incorporated; *Int'l*, pg. 99
ACER INFORMATION SERVICES INTERNATIONAL—See Acer Incorporated; *Int'l*, pg. 99
ACER ITALY S.R.L.—See Acer Incorporated; *Int'l*, pg. 99
ACER JAPAN CORPORATION—See Acer Incorporated; *Int'l*, pg. 99
ACER LATIN AMERICA, INC.—See Acer Incorporated; *Int'l*, pg. 99
ACER PHILIPPINES, INC.—See Acer Incorporated; *Int'l*, pg. 99
ACER SALES & SERVICES SDN. BHD.—See Acer Incorporated; *Int'l*, pg. 99
ACER SERVICE CORPORATION—See Acer Incorporated; *Int'l*, pg. 99

334111 — ELECTRONIC COMPUTER...

ACER VIETNAM CO., LTD.—See Acer Incorporated; *Int'l*, pg. 99
AFFORDABLE ROBOTIC & AUTOMATION LTD.; *Int'l*, pg. 188
AITECH SPACE SYSTEMS INC—See AITECH Rugged Computer Systems; *U.S. Private*, pg. 143
AMLEX HOLDINGS BHD; *Int'l*, pg. 429
AMPIRE CO., LTD.; *Int'l*, pg. 433
APLEX TECHNOLOGY, INC.; *Int'l*, pg. 515
APPLE ASIA LIMITED—See Apple Inc.; *U.S. Public*, pg. 169
APPLE BENELUX B.V. - BELGIUM OFFICE—See Apple Inc.; *U.S. Public*, pg. 169
APPLE BENELUX B.V.—See Apple Inc.; *U.S. Public*, pg. 169
APPLE COMPUTER MEXICO S.A. DE C.V.—See Apple Inc.; *U.S. Public*, pg. 169
APPLE FRANCE SARL—See Apple Inc.; *U.S. Public*, pg. 169
APPLE GES.MBH—See Apple Inc.; *U.S. Public*, pg. 169
APPLE GMBH—See Apple Inc.; *U.S. Public*, pg. 169
APPLE INDIA PRIVATE LIMITED—See Apple Inc.; *U.S. Public*, pg. 169
APPLE JAPAN, INC.—See Apple Inc.; *U.S. Public*, pg. 169
APPLE PTY. LIMITED—See Apple Inc.; *U.S. Public*, pg. 169
APPLE SALES INTERNATIONAL—See Apple Inc.; *U.S. Public*, pg. 169
APPLIDE CORPORATION; *Int'l*, pg. 521
APPLIED DYNAMICS INTERNATIONAL, LTD.—See Applied Dynamics International; *U.S. Private*, pg. 298
APPLIED DYNAMICS INTERNATIONAL; *U.S. Private*, pg. 298
ASBIS BULGARIA LIMITED—See ASBISc Enterprises Plc; *Int'l*, pg. 600
ASBIS D.O.O.—See ASBISc Enterprises Plc; *Int'l*, pg. 600
ASBIS POLAND SP. Z O.O.—See ASBISc Enterprises Plc; *Int'l*, pg. 600
ASBIS ROMANIA S.R.L.—See ASBISc Enterprises Plc; *Int'l*, pg. 600
ASBIS SK SP.L SR.O—See ASBISc Enterprises Plc; *Int'l*, pg. 600
ASBIS SLOVENIA D.O.O.—See ASBISc Enterprises Plc; *Int'l*, pg. 600
ASETEK A/S; *Int'l*, pg. 606
ASUS HOLLAND B.V.—See ASUSTeK Computer Inc.; *Int'l*, pg. 663
ATEN INFOTECH N.V.—See Aten International Co., Ltd.; *Int'l*, pg. 668
ATON SYSTEMES S.A.—See Actia Group SA; *Int'l*, pg. 118
AURES TECHNOLOGIES GMBH—See Aures Technologies; *Int'l*, pg. 710
AURES TECHNOLOGIES INC.—See Aures Technologies; *Int'l*, pg. 710
AURES TECHNOLOGIES PTY. LTD.—See Aures Technologies; *Int'l*, pg. 710
AVALDATA CORPORATION; *Int'l*, pg. 734
AVANT TECHNOLOGIES OF PR, INC.; *U.S. Private*, pg. 404
AVER INFORMATION INC.—See AVer Information Inc.; *Int'l*, pg. 739
AVIATION COMMUNICATION & SURVEILLANCE SYSTEMS, LLC—See L3Harris Technologies, Inc.; *U.S. Public*, pg. 1281
AVNET ELECTRONICS TECHNOLOGY (SHENZHEN) LIMITED—See Avnet, Inc.; *U.S. Public*, pg. 251
AVNET EMG ELEKTRONISCHE BAUELEMENTE GMBH—See Avnet, Inc.; *U.S. Public*, pg. 250
AVNET EMG FRANCE—See Avnet, Inc.; *U.S. Public*, pg. 250
AVNET EUROPE BV—See Avnet, Inc.; *U.S. Public*, pg. 251
AXIOMTEK ITALIA S.R.L—See Axiomtek Co., Ltd; *Int'l*, pg. 769
AXIOMTEK TEKDEUTSCHLAND GMBH—See Axiomtek Co., Ltd; *Int'l*, pg. 769
AYON CYBERSECURITY, INC.—See Video Display Corporation; *U.S. Public*, pg. 2296
BEIJER ELECTRONICS AS—See Ependion AB; *Int'l*, pg. 2459
BEIJER ELECTRONICS A/S—See Ependion AB; *Int'l*, pg. 2459
BEIJER ELECTRONICS CORP.—See Ependion AB; *Int'l*, pg. 2459
BEIJER ELECTRONICS GMBH & CO. KG—See Ependion AB; *Int'l*, pg. 2459
BEIJER ELECTRONICS KOREA CO., LTD.—See Ependion AB; *Int'l*, pg. 2459
BEIJER ELECTRONICS TRADING (SHANGHAI) CO., LTD.—See Ependion AB; *Int'l*, pg. 2459
BEIJER ELECTRONICS UK LTD.—See Ependion AB; *Int'l*, pg. 2459
BEIJER ELEKTRONIK VE TIC. A.S.—See Ependion AB; *Int'l*, pg. 2459
BIPROGY INC.; *Int'l*, pg. 1045
BLACKBOARD INC.—See Class Technologies Inc.; *U.S. Private*, pg. 915
BOLDATA TECHNOLOGY, INC.; *U.S. Private*, pg. 610
BOSTON IT SOLUTIONS PVT. LTD.—See 2Crsi SA; *Int'l*, pg. 4
BOSTON SERVER & STORAGE SOLUTIONS GMBH—See 2Crsi SA; *Int'l*, pg. 4

BRITE COMPUTERS; *U.S. Private*, pg. 657
CAL-COMP OPTICAL ELECTRONICS (SUZHOU) COMPANY LIMITED—See Cal-Comp Electronics (Thailand) pcl; *Int'l*, pg. 1261
CASIO (CHINA) CO., LTD.—See Casio Computer Co., Ltd.; *Int'l*, pg. 1353
CASIO COMPUTER CO., LTD.; *Int'l*, pg. 1353
CCS INFOTECH LIMITED; *Int'l*, pg. 1369
CCS INFOTECH SINGAPORE PTE LTE—See CCS Infotech Limited; *Int'l*, pg. 1369
CCUR HOLDINGS INC.; *U.S. Public*, pg. 461
CERMETEK MICROELECTRONICS, INC.; *U.S. Public*, pg. 476
CHENBRO GMBH—See Chenbro Micom Co., Ltd.; *Int'l*, pg. 1465
CHENMING ELECTRONIC TECHNOLOGY USA, INC.—See Chenming Electronic Tech. Corp.; *Int'l*, pg. 1470
CHENPOWER INFORMATION TECHNOLOGY (SHANGHAI) CO., LTD.—See Chenbro Micom Co., Ltd.; *Int'l*, pg. 1465
CHINA AHOKU TECHLAND ELECTRONICS LTD.—See Ahoku Electronic Company; *Int'l*, pg. 225
CHINA GREATWALL TECHNOLOGY GROUP CO., LTD.—See China Electronics Corporation; *Int'l*, pg. 1499
CLARIENCE TECHNOLOGIES, LLC—See Genstar Capital, LLC; *U.S. Private*, pg. 1676
CLEVO COMPANY; *Int'l*, pg. 1658
COMPAL ELECTRONICS, INC.; *Int'l*, pg. 1746
COMPUTING AND PRINTING GLOBAL SERVICES MEXICO, S. DE R.L. DE C.V.—See HP Inc.; *U.S. Public*, pg. 1062
COMPUTING AND PRINTING MEXICO, S. DE R.L. DE C.V.—See HP Inc.; *U.S. Public*, pg. 1062
CONCURRENT NIPPON CORPORATION—See CCUR Holdings Inc.; *U.S. Public*, pg. 461
COTS TECHNOLOGY CO., LTD.; *Int'l*, pg. 1817
CRAY INC.—See Hewlett Packard Enterprise Company; *U.S. Public*, pg. 1030
CRAY INC.—See Hewlett Packard Enterprise Company; *U.S. Public*, pg. 1030
CRAY KOREA, INC.—See Hewlett Packard Enterprise Company; *U.S. Public*, pg. 1030
CREATIVE NEWTECH LIMITED; *Int'l*, pg. 1833
CRESTRON ELECTRONICS, INC.; *U.S. Private*, pg. 1097
CROWN MICRO INC—See BOLData Technology, Inc.; *U.S. Private*, pg. 610
CUBIX CORPORATION; *U.S. Private*, pg. 1120
CURTISS-WRIGHT FLOW CONTROL SERVICE, LLC—See Curtiss-Wright Corporation; *U.S. Public*, pg. 612
CYBER ENERGY CO., LTD.—See CyberPower Systems, Inc.; *Int'l*, pg. 1893
CYBOZU MEDIA AND TECHNOLOGY CO.,LTD.—See Cybozu Inc.; *Int'l*, pg. 1894
DAIKOKU DENKI CO., LTD.; *Int'l*, pg. 1937
DANAHER MOTION SARO AB—See Danaher Corporation; *U.S. Public*, pg. 626
DATALOGIC AUSTRALIA PTY LTD—See Datalogic S.p.A.; *Int'l*, pg. 1978
DATALOGIC DO BRAZIL COMERCIO DE EQUIPAMENTOS E AUTOMACAO LTDA.—See Datalogic S.p.A.; *Int'l*, pg. 1978
DATALOGIC HUNGARY KFT—See Datalogic S.p.A.; *Int'l*, pg. 1978
DATALOGIC SINGAPORE ASIA PACIFIC PTE LTD.—See Datalogic S.p.A.; *Int'l*, pg. 1978
DATALOGIC SLOVAKIA S.R.O.—See Datalogic S.p.A.; *Int'l*, pg. 1978
DATALOGIC TECHNOLOGIA DE MEXICO S.R.L.—See Datalogic S.p.A.; *Int'l*, pg. 1978
DATALOGIC USA, INC.—See Datalogic S.p.A.; *Int'l*, pg. 1978
DATALOGIC VIETNAM LLC—See Datalogic S.p.A.; *Int'l*, pg. 1978
DATAVAN INTERNATIONAL CORP.; *Int'l*, pg. 1981
DAWNING INFORMATION INDUSTRY CO., LTD.; *Int'l*, pg. 1984
DBG TECHNOLOGY CO., LTD.; *Int'l*, pg. 1988
DBUB GROUP, INC.; *Int'l*, pg. 1989
DEDICATED COMPUTING, LLC—See McNally Capital, LLC; *U.S. Private*, pg. 2643
DELL INC. - NASHVILLE—See Dell Technologies Inc.; *U.S. Public*, pg. 649
DELL INC.—See Dell Technologies Inc.; *U.S. Public*, pg. 649
DERKWOO ELECTRONICS CO., LTD.; *Int'l*, pg. 2042
DIGI INTERNATIONAL INC.; *U.S. Public*, pg. 661
DIGITAL CHINA (SHENZHEN) LIMITED—See Digital China Holdings Limited; *Int'l*, pg. 2121
DIVERSIFIED TECHNOLOGY INC.—See Ergon, Inc.; *U.S. Private*, pg. 1417
DK UIL (TIANJIN) ELECTRONICS CO., LTD—See Dongkuk Steel Mill Co., Ltd.; *Int'l*, pg. 2169
DMG MORI DIGITAL CO., LTD.—See DMG MORI Co., Ltd.; *Int'l*, pg. 2144
DONGGUAN FOUND CHAIN IOT CO., LTD.—See Everspring Industry Co., Ltd.; *Int'l*, pg. 2569
DYNABOOK AMERICAS, INC.—See Hon Hai Precision Industry Co., Ltd.; *Int'l*, pg. 3457

CORPORATE AFFILIATIONS

DYNAMIC DECISIONS INC.; *U.S. Private*, pg. 1298
DYNATEM, INC.—See Eurotech S.p.A.; *Int'l*, pg. 2558
EARTH-PANDA MAGNETIC APPLICATION TECH CO., LTD.—See Earth-Panda Advance Magnetic Material Co., Ltd.; *Int'l*, pg. 2268
EARTH-PANDA (SUZHOU) MAGNET CO., LTD.—See Earth-Panda Advance Magnetic Material Co., Ltd.; *Int'l*, pg. 2268
EARTH-PANDA (TIANJIN) ELECTRICAL CO., LTD.—See Earth-Panda Advance Magnetic Material Co., Ltd.; *Int'l*, pg. 2268
EASTERN LOGICA INFOWAY LTD.; *Int'l*, pg. 2273
EBV ELEKTRONIK ISRAEL (2008) LTD.—See Avnet, Inc.; *U.S. Public*, pg. 252
ELECTRONICS MANUFACTURING SOLUTIONS—See Benchmark Electronics, Inc.; *U.S. Public*, pg. 296
ELITEGROUP COMPUTER SYSTEMS (JAPAN) CO., LTD.—See Elitegroup Computer Systems Co., Ltd.; *Int'l*, pg. 2363
ELMA ELECTRONIC AG; *Int'l*, pg. 2367
ELMA ELECTRONIC INC.—See Elma Electronic AG; *Int'l*, pg. 2367
ELUOMENG LIMITED—See Avnet, Inc.; *U.S. Public*, pg. 253
EMC AUSTRALIA PTY LIMITED—See Dell Technologies Inc.; *U.S. Public*, pg. 650
EMC COMPUTER SYSTEMS AS, NORWAY—See Dell Technologies Inc.; *U.S. Public*, pg. 650
EMC COMPUTER SYSTEMS VENEZUELA, S.A.—See Dell Technologies Inc.; *U.S. Public*, pg. 651
EMDOOR INFORMATION CO., LTD.; *Int'l*, pg. 2376
EMERSON ARGENTINA S.A.—See Emerson Electric Co.; *U.S. Public*, pg. 743
EM-TEC GMBH—See Dover Corporation; *U.S. Public*, pg. 683
ENGLANDER ENTERPRISES, INC.; *U.S. Private*, pg. 1399
ENVIPCO PORTUGAL UNIPESSOAL LDA.—See Envipco Holding N.V.; *Int'l*, pg. 2453
EUROCOM CORPORATION; *Int'l*, pg. 2534
EVANS & SUTHERLAND COMPUTER CORPORATION - DIGITAL THEATER DIVISION—See Elevate Entertainment, Inc.; *U.S. Private*, pg. 1358
EVERSPRING TECH USA, INC.—See Everspring Industry Co., Ltd.; *Int'l*, pg. 2569
EXPERT COMPUTER INTERNATIONAL; *U.S. Private*, pg. 1450
FIRST INTERNATIONAL COMPUTER, INC.; *Int'l*, pg. 2684
FLEXTRONICS DESIGN, S.R.O.—See Flex Ltd.; *Int'l*, pg. 2702
FLEXTRONICS DIGITAL DESIGN JAPAN, LTD.—See Flex Ltd.; *Int'l*, pg. 2703
FLEXTRONICS TECHNOLOGY (SHENZHEN) CO., LTD.—See Flex Ltd.; *Int'l*, pg. 2704
FLYTECH TECHNOLOGY CO., LTD.; *Int'l*, pg. 2716
FLYTECH TECHNOLOGY HONG KONG LTD.—See Flytech Technology Co., Ltd.; *Int'l*, pg. 2716
FLYTECH TECHNOLOGY (U.S.A.) INC.—See Flytech Technology Co., Ltd.; *Int'l*, pg. 2716
FORTUNE INFORMATION SYSTEMS CORP.; *Int'l*, pg. 2743
FOXCONN CORPORATION—See Hon Hai Precision Industry Co., Ltd.; *Int'l*, pg. 3457
FRACTAL GAMING GROUP AB; *Int'l*, pg. 2758
FUJITSU AMERICA, INC.—See Fujitsu Limited; *Int'l*, pg. 2833
FUJITSU AUSTRALIA PTY. LTD.—See Fujitsu Limited; *Int'l*, pg. 2833
FUJITSU BUSINESS COMMUNICATION SYSTEMS, INC.- SALES & MARKETING—See Fujitsu Limited; *Int'l*, pg. 2833
FUJITSU CANADA, INC.—See Fujitsu Limited; *Int'l*, pg. 2834
FUJITSU CONSULTING S.A.—See Fujitsu Limited; *Int'l*, pg. 2834
FUJITSU FRONTECH LTD.—See Fujitsu Limited; *Int'l*, pg. 2834
FUJITSU GENERAL LTD.—See Fujitsu Limited; *Int'l*, pg. 2834
FUJITSU LIMITED; *Int'l*, pg. 2832
FUJITSU MICRODEVICES LTD.—See Fujitsu Limited; *Int'l*, pg. 2835
FUJITSU NEW ZEALAND LTD.—See Fujitsu Limited; *Int'l*, pg. 2836
FUJITSU PC ASIA PACIFIC LTD—See Fujitsu Limited; *Int'l*, pg. 2835
FUJITSU SERVICE A/S—See Fujitsu Limited; *Int'l*, pg. 2836
FUJITSU SERVICES AB—See Fujitsu Limited; *Int'l*, pg. 2836
FUJITSU SERVICES GMBH—See Fujitsu Limited; *Int'l*, pg. 2836
FUJITSU SERVICES—See Fujitsu Limited; *Int'l*, pg. 2836
FUJITSU TECHNOLOGY SOLUTIONS GESMBH—See Fujitsu Limited; *Int'l*, pg. 2836
FUSHAN TECHNOLOGY (VIETNAM) LIMITED LIABILITY COMPANY—See Hon Hai Precision Industry Co., Ltd.; *Int'l*, pg. 3457
GATEWAY HONG KONG LTD—See Acer Incorporated; *Int'l*, pg. 99
GATEWAY, INC.—See Acer Incorporated; *Int'l*, pg. 99

N.A.I.C.S. INDEX

334111 — ELECTRONIC COMPUTER...

GATEWAY US RETAIL, INC.—See Acer Incorporated; *Int'l*, pg. 99
G.B.T. TECHNOLOGY TRADING GMBH—See Giga-Byte Technology Co., Ltd.; *Int'l*, pg. 2971
GE INTELLIGENT PLATFORMS, INC. - HUNTSVILLE—See Emerson Electric Co.; *U.S. Public*, pg. 749
GENERAL DYNAMICS MISSION SYSTEMS, INC.—See General Dynamics Corporation; *U.S. Public*, pg. 914
GIGA-BYTE TECHNOLOGY CO., LTD.; *Int'l*, pg. 2971
GIGABYTE TECHNOLOGY PTY. LTD.—See Giga-Byte Technology Co., Ltd.; *Int'l*, pg. 2971
GLORY AZ SYSTEM CO., LTD.—See GLORY Ltd.; *Int'l*, pg. 3009
GRANITE MICROSYSTEMS INC.; *U.S. Private*, pg. 1756
GREAT WALL TECHNOLOGY CO., LTD.—See China Electronics Corporation; *Int'l*, pg. 1499
GUANGZHOU DIGITAL CHINA LIMITED—See Digital China Group Co., Ltd.; *Int'l*, pg. 2121
HABIB IT SOLUTIONS PVT LTD.—See Habib Group of Companies; *Int'l*, pg. 3203
HAKKO ELECTRONICS CO., LTD.—See Fuji Electric Co., Ltd.; *Int'l*, pg. 2812
HASEE COMPUTER CO., LTD.; *Int'l*, pg. 3282
HECTRONIC AB—See discoverIE Group plc; *Int'l*, pg. 2133
HELLA SLOVAKIA LIGHTING S.R.O.—See Hella GmbH & Co. KGaA; *Int'l*, pg. 3332
HELO CORP.; *U.S. Public*, pg. 1024
HEWLETT-PACKARD ARABIA LLC—See HP Inc.; *U.S. Public*, pg. 1063
HEWLETT-PACKARD DEVELOPMENT COMPANY, L.P.—See HP Inc.; *U.S. Public*, pg. 1063
HEWLETT-PACKARD ENTERPRISES, LLC—See HP Inc.; *U.S. Public*, pg. 1063
HEWLETT-PACKARD ESPANOLA S.L.—See HP Inc.; *U.S. Public*, pg. 1063
HEWLETT-PACKARD INDIGO LTD.—See HP Inc.; *U.S. Public*, pg. 1064
HEWLETT-PACKARD INDUSTRIAL PRINTING LTD.—See HP Inc.; *U.S. Public*, pg. 1064
HEWLETT-PACKARD LUXEMBOURG S.C.A.—See HP Inc.; *U.S. Public*, pg. 1064
HEWLETT-PACKARD MANUFACTURING LTD.—See Hewlett Packard Enterprise Company; *U.S. Public*, pg. 1032
HEWLETT-PACKARD MEXICO - MONTERREY/NUEVO LEON—See Hewlett Packard Enterprise Company; *U.S. Public*, pg. 1032
HEWLETT-PACKARD MEXICO S. DE R.L. DE C.V.—See Hewlett Packard Enterprise Company; *U.S. Public*, pg. 1032
HEWLETT-PACKARD (NIGERIA) LIMITED—See Hewlett Packard Enterprise Company; *U.S. Public*, pg. 1031
HEWLETT-PACKARD OPERATIONS MEXICO, S. DE R.L. DE C.V.—See Hewlett Packard Enterprise Company; *U.S. Public*, pg. 1032
HEWLETT-PACKARD POLSKA SP. Z.O.O.—See HP Inc.; *U.S. Public*, pg. 1064
HEWLETT-PACKARD SERVICES SAUDI ARABIA COMPANY—See HP Inc.; *U.S. Public*, pg. 1064
HEWLETT-PACKARD TECHNOLOGY (SHANGHAI) CO. LTD.—See HP Inc.; *U.S. Public*, pg. 1064
HEWLETT-PACKARD TRADING (SHANGHAI) CO. LTD.—See HP Inc.; *U.S. Public*, pg. 1064
HIGHAIM TECHNOLOGY INC.—See Ennoconn Corporation; *Int'l*, pg. 2443
HOLMAK HEATX B.V.—See CENTROTEC SE; *Int'l*, pg. 1414
HONEYWELL SCANNING & MOBILITY—See Honeywell International Inc.; *U.S. Public*, pg. 1050
HP AUSTRIA GMBH—See HP Inc.; *U.S. Public*, pg. 1062
HP BELGIUM BVBA—See HP Inc.; *U.S. Public*, pg. 1062
HP BRASIL INDUSTRIA E COMERCIO DE EQUIPAMENTOS ELETRONICOS LTDA—See HP Inc.; *U.S. Public*, pg. 1062
HP COMPUTING AND PRINTING D.O.O.—See HP Inc.; *U.S. Public*, pg. 1062
HP COMPUTING AND PRINTING SYSTEMS INDIA PRIVATE LIMITED—See HP Inc.; *U.S. Public*, pg. 1062
HPCP-COMPUTING AND PRINTING PORTUGAL, UNIPESSOAL, LDA.—See HP Inc.; *U.S. Public*, pg. 1063
HP DEUTSCHLAND GMBH—See HP Inc.; *U.S. Public*, pg. 1062
HP FINLAND OY—See HP Inc.; *U.S. Public*, pg. 1063
HP INC ARGENTINA S.R.L.—See HP Inc.; *U.S. Public*, pg. 1063
HP INC CHILE COMERCIAL LIMITADA—See HP Inc.; *U.S. Public*, pg. 1063
HP INC COSTA RICA LIMITADA—See HP Inc.; *U.S. Public*, pg. 1063
HP INC DANMARK APS—See HP Inc.; *U.S. Public*, pg. 1063
HP INC MAGYARORSZAG KFT—See HP Inc.; *U.S. Public*, pg. 1063
HP INC POLSKA SP. Z O.O.—See HP Inc.; *U.S. Public*, pg. 1063
HP INC ROMANIA SRL—See HP Inc.; *U.S. Public*, pg. 1063
HP INC SLOVAKIA, S.R.O.—See HP Inc.; *U.S. Public*, pg. 1063
HP INC TUNISIE SARL—See HP Inc.; *U.S. Public*, pg. 1063
HP ITALY S.R.L.—See HP Inc.; *U.S. Public*, pg. 1063
HP NEDERLAND B.V.—See HP Inc.; *U.S. Public*, pg. 1063
HP NORGE AS—See HP Inc.; *U.S. Public*, pg. 1063
HP PPS AUSTRALIA PTY LTD—See HP Inc.; *U.S. Public*, pg. 1063
HP-PPS ECUADOR CIA. LTDA—See HP Inc.; *U.S. Public*, pg. 1063
HP PPS MALAYSIA SDN. BHD.—See HP Inc.; *U.S. Public*, pg. 1063
HP PPS MAROC SARL—See HP Inc.; *U.S. Public*, pg. 1063
HP PPS MULTIMEDIA SDN. BHD.—See HP Inc.; *U.S. Public*, pg. 1063
HP PPS SINGAPORE (SALES) PTE. LTD.—See HP Inc.; *U.S. Public*, pg. 1063
HP PPS SVERIGE AB—See HP Inc.; *U.S. Public*, pg. 1063
HP PRINTING AND PERSONAL SYSTEMS HELLAS EPE—See HP Inc.; *U.S. Public*, pg. 1063
HP PRINTING & COMPUTING SOLUTIONS, S.L.U.—See HP Inc.; *U.S. Public*, pg. 1063
HP SCHWEIZ GMBH—See HP Inc.; *U.S. Public*, pg. 1063
HP SOLUTIONS CREATION AND DEVELOPMENT SERVICES S.L.U.—See HP Inc.; *U.S. Public*, pg. 1063
HP SOUTH AFRICA PROPRIETARY LIMITED—See HP Inc.; *U.S. Public*, pg. 1063
HP TAIWAN INFORMATION TECHNOLOGY LTD.—See HP Inc.; *U.S. Public*, pg. 1063
HUMANSOFT SZERVIZ KFT.—See 4iG Nyrt.; *Int'l*, pg. 12
HYRICAN INFORMATIONSSYSTEME AG; *Int'l*, pg. 3554
IBASE TECHNOLOGY (USA), INC.; *U.S. Private*, pg. 2028
IBM (CHINA) INVESTMENT COMPANY LIMITED—See International Business Machines Corporation; *U.S. Public*, pg. 1145
IBM CONGO SARL—See International Business Machines Corporation; *U.S. Public*, pg. 1146
IBM DEUTSCHLAND GMBH—See International Business Machines Corporation; *U.S. Public*, pg. 1146
IBM EESTI OSAUHING—See International Business Machines Corporation; *U.S. Public*, pg. 1146
IBM GLOBAL FINANCING CANADA CORPORATION—See International Business Machines Corporation; *U.S. Public*, pg. 1147
IBM GLOBAL FINANCING DEUTSCHLAND GMBH—See International Business Machines Corporation; *U.S. Public*, pg. 1147
IBM GLOBAL FINANCING ESPANA, S.L.U.—See International Business Machines Corporation; *U.S. Public*, pg. 1147
IBM GLOBAL FINANCING FINLAND OY—See International Business Machines Corporation; *U.S. Public*, pg. 1147
IBM GLOBAL FINANCING SCHWEIZ GMBH—See International Business Machines Corporation; *U.S. Public*, pg. 1147
IBM IRELAND PRODUCT DISTRIBUTION LIMITED—See International Business Machines Corporation; *U.S. Public*, pg. 1147
IBM MAURITIUS—See International Business Machines Corporation; *U.S. Public*, pg. 1147
IBM NEDERLAND FINANCIERINGEN B.V.—See International Business Machines Corporation; *U.S. Public*, pg. 1147
IBM QATAR SSC—See International Business Machines Corporation; *U.S. Public*, pg. 1148
IBM SYSTEMS & TECHNOLOGY—See International Business Machines Corporation; *U.S. Public*, pg. 1148
IBM TAIWAN CORPORATION—See International Business Machines Corporation; *U.S. Public*, pg. 1148
IBM UNITED KINGDOM LIMITED—See International Business Machines Corporation; *U.S. Public*, pg. 1148
IDT INTERNATIONAL LIMITED; *Int'l*, pg. 3596
IHSE GMBH ASIA PACIFIC PTE. LTD.—See Brockhaus Private Equity GmbH; *Int'l*, pg. 1172
IHSE GMBH—See Brockhaus Private Equity GmbH; *Int'l*, pg. 1172
IHSE USA LLC—See Brockhaus Private Equity GmbH; *Int'l*, pg. 1172
IMAGE MICROSYSTEMS, INC.; *U.S. Private*, pg. 2044
INSEEGO INTERNATIONAL HOLDINGS LTD.—See Inseego Corp.; *U.S. Public*, pg. 1129
INSPIRED GAMING GROUP LIMITED—See Inspired Entertainment Inc; *U.S. Public*, pg. 1131
INTEL CORPORATION U.K. LTD.—See Intel Corporation; *U.S. Public*, pg. 1138
INTERNATIONAL BUSINESS MACHINES SENEGAL—See International Business Machines Corporation; *U.S. Public*, pg. 1149
IROBOT (SHANGHAI) LTD.—See iRobot Corp.; *U.S. Public*, pg. 1171
ITRONIX CORPORATION—See General Dynamics Corporation; *U.S. Public*, pg. 916
IVIEW DIGITAL VIDEO SOLUTIONS INC.—See Creative Vistas Inc.; *Int'l*, pg. 1834
JANUS DISPLAYS; *U.S. Private*, pg. 2188
JAVA CONNECTIONS LLC; *U.S. Private*, pg. 2191
JUNIPER SYSTEMS—See Campbell Scientific, Inc.; *U.S. Private*, pg. 730
KIMBALL ELECTRONICS, INC.; *U.S. Public*, pg. 1228
LITEYE SYSTEMS, INC.—See Highlander Partners, L.P.; *U.S. Private*, pg. 1939
LOGITECH FAR EAST LTD.—See Logitech International S.A.; *U.S. Public*, pg. 1341
LOGITECH UK LTD—See Logitech International S.A.; *U.S. Public*, pg. 1341
LUCILLE MAUD CORPORATION; *U.S. Private*, pg. 2511
MERCURY SYSTEMS, INC.; *U.S. Public*, pg. 1422
MERCURY SYSTEMS - TRUSTED MISSION SOLUTIONS, INC.—See Mercury Systems, Inc.; *U.S. Public*, pg. 1422
MICRON SYSTEMS INTEGRATION, INC.—See Micron Technology, Inc.; *U.S. Public*, pg. 1438
MICROWAY, INC.; *U.S. Private*, pg. 2705
MIDI INGENIERIE S.A.S.—See HENSOLDT AG; *Int'l*, pg. 3356
MIRAC NETWORKS (DONGGUAN) CO., LTD.—See Alpha Networks Inc.; *Int'l*, pg. 369
MOBILEDEMAND, LC; *U.S. Private*, pg. 2758
NATEL ENGINEERING CO., INC. - AGAVE PLANT—See Natel Engineering Company, Inc.; *U.S. Private*, pg. 2838
NC NETWORK FACTORY, CO., LTD.—See Di-Nikko Engineering Co., Ltd.; *Int'l*, pg. 2101
NSI BVBA—See discoverIE Group plc; *Int'l*, pg. 2133
NVIS INC.; *U.S. Private*, pg. 2975
NYXIO TECHNOLOGIES CORPORATION; *U.S. Private*, pg. 2977
OBVIUS; *U.S. Private*, pg. 2988
ONE STOP SYSTEMS, INC.; *U.S. Public*, pg. 1602
OOO HEWLETT-PACKARD RUS—See HP Inc.; *U.S. Public*, pg. 1064
ORBITAL INFRASTRUCTURE GROUP, INC.; *U.S. Public*, pg. 1615
ORBOTECH ASIA LTD.—See KLA Corporation; *U.S. Public*, pg. 1268
ORBOTECH ELECTRONICS (SHENZHEN) CO., LTD.—See KLA Corporation; *U.S. Public*, pg. 1268
ORBOTECH ELECTRONICS (SUZHOU) CO., LTD.—See KLA Corporation; *U.S. Public*, pg. 1268
ORIGIN PC, LLC—See EagleTree Capital, LP; *U.S. Private*, pg. 1311
OY IBM FINLAND AB—See International Business Machines Corporation; *U.S. Public*, pg. 1149
PALM COMERCIO DE APARELHOS ELETRONICOS LTDA.—See HP Inc.; *U.S. Public*, pg. 1064
PALM EUROPE LIMITED—See HP Inc.; *U.S. Public*, pg. 1064
PINNACLE SYSTEMS LTD.—See Symphony Technology Group, LLC; *U.S. Private*, pg. 3902
POLYWELL COMPUTERS, INC.; *U.S. Private*, pg. 3226
PRIMA ELECTRONIC SERVICES LIMITED—See OSI Systems, Inc.; *U.S. Public*, pg. 1622
PROMARK TECHNOLOGY, INC.—See Hainan Traffic Administration Holding Co., Ltd.; *Int'l*, pg. 3215
PT ACER INDONESIA—See Acer Incorporated; *Int'l*, pg. 99
PT HEWLETT-PACKARD INDONESIA—See HP Inc.; *U.S. Public*, pg. 1064
QUALTRAX INC.—See HgCapital Trust plc; *Int'l*, pg. 3378
RARE EARTH MAGNESIUM TECHNOLOGY GROUP HOLDINGS LIMITED—See Century Sunshine Group Holdings Limited; *Int'l*, pg. 1419
RECAB AB—See Addtech AB; *Int'l*, pg. 135
SAVANT SYSTEMS, INC.; *U.S. Private*, pg. 3556
SECTOR 5, INC.; *U.S. Public*, pg. 1855
SHANGHAI DIGITAL CHINA LIMITED—See Digital China Group Co., Ltd.; *Int'l*, pg. 2121
SHANGHAI GLOBAL SOURCING CONSULTING CO., LTD.—See Carrefour SA; *Int'l*, pg. 1346
SHANGHAI HEWLETT-PACKARD CO. LTD.—See Hewlett Packard Enterprise Company; *U.S. Public*, pg. 1031
SHENZHEN KAIFA TECHNOLOGY CO., LTD.—See China Electronics Corporation; *Int'l*, pg. 1499
SHIMANE FUJITSU LIMITED—See Fujitsu Limited; *Int'l*, pg. 2837
SHUGART CORPORATION; *U.S. Private*, pg. 3644
SILICON MECHANICS, INC.—See Cerberus Capital Management, L.P.; *U.S. Private*, pg. 839
SMC (COMERCIAL OFFSHORE DE MACAU) LIMITADA—See The Singing Machine Company, Inc.; *U.S. Public*, pg. 2130
SOCKET MOBILE, INC.; *U.S. Public*, pg. 1899
SOFTWARE AG CHILE S.A.—See Silver Lake Group, LLC; *U.S. Private*, pg. 3659
SOFTWARE AG, S.A. DE C.V.—See Silver Lake Group, LLC; *U.S. Private*, pg. 3660
SPECTRALINK CORPORATION—See HP Inc.; *U.S. Public*, pg. 1065
SPTS TECHNOLOGIES LTD.—See KLA Corporation; *U.S. Public*, pg. 1269
SPTS TECHNOLOGIES SAS—See KLA Corporation; *U.S. Public*, pg. 1269
STRATUS TECHNOLOGIES, INC.—See Penguin Solutions, Inc.; *U.S. Public*, pg. 1661
SYNAPTICS JAPAN (K.K.) LIMITED—See Synaptics Incorporated; *U.S. Public*, pg. 1969
SYNTELLECT, INC.—See Enghouse Systems Limited; *Int'l*, pg. 2428
TAIWAN AHOKU ELECTRONIC COMPANY—See Ahoku Electronic Company; *Int'l*, pg. 225
TANGENT COMPUTER INC.; *U.S. Private*, pg. 3930

334111 — ELECTRONIC COMPUTER...

TECHNOLOGY RECOVERY GROUP LTD.; *U.S. Private*, pg. 3955
TELEDYNE LECROY XENA APS.—See Teledyne Technologies Incorporated; *U.S. Public*, pg. 1994
TERADATA OPERATIONS, INC.—See Teradata Corporation; *U.S. Public*, pg. 2017
TERADATA SAUDI ARABIA LLC—See Teradata Corporation; *U.S. Public*, pg. 2017
TEXAS INSTRUMENTS ITALIA S.R.L.—See Texas Instruments Incorporated; *U.S. Public*, pg. 2026
THECUS TECHNOLOGY CORP.—See Ennoconn Corporation; *Int'l*, pg. 2443
THECUS U.S.A., INC.—See Ennoconn Corporation; *Int'l*, pg. 2443
TODD ENTERPRISES INC.; *U.S. Private*, pg. 4181
TOLL MICROELECTRONICS CO., LTD.—See Fortune Oriental Company Limited; *Int'l*, pg. 2744
TRANQUIL PC LTD.—See 2Crsi SA; *Int'l*, pg. 4
UAB HEWLETT-PACKARD—See HP Inc.; *U.S. Public*, pg. 1065
UNIVERSAL SYSTEMS, INC.; *U.S. Public*, pg. 2262
URBAN FT GROUP, INC.; *U.S. Public*, pg. 4314
VADATECH, INC.; *U.S. Private*, pg. 4329
VECOW CO., LTD.—See Ennoconn Corporation; *Int'l*, pg. 2443
WITEKIO GMBH—See Avnet, Inc.; *U.S. Public*, pg. 254
WYSE TECHNOLOGY AUSTRALIA PTY LIMITED—See Dell Technologies Inc.; *U.S. Public*, pg. 650
WYSE TECHNOLOGY (UK) LIMITED—See Dell Technologies Inc.; *U.S. Public*, pg. 650
XEROX SOUTH AFRICA (PROPRIETARY) LIMITED—See Xerox Holdings Corporation; *U.S. Public*, pg. 2390
ZHUHAI HERALD DATANETICS LIMITED—See Herald Holdings Limited; *Int'l*, pg. 3358

334112 — COMPUTER STORAGE DEVICE MANUFACTURING

3PAR INC.—See Hewlett Packard Enterprise Company; *U.S. Public*, pg. 1030
ACBEL (USA) POLYTECH INC.—See AcBel Polytech Inc.; *Int'l*, pg. 78
ACCESS INFORMATION INFORMATION MANAGEMENT SHARED SERVICES LLC—See Berkshire Partners LLC; *U.S. Private*, pg. 534
ADATA ELECTRONICS (SHANGHAI) CO., LTD.—See ADATA Technology Co., Ltd.; *Int'l*, pg. 126
ADATA TECHNOLOGY (HK) CO. LTD.—See ADATA Technology Co., Ltd.; *Int'l*, pg. 126
ADATA TECHNOLOGY (SUZHOU) CO., LTD.—See ADATA Technology Co., Ltd.; *Int'l*, pg. 126
ALANCO TECHNOLOGIES, INC.; *U.S. Public*, pg. 71
ALLIANCE STORAGE TECHNOLOGIES, INC.; *U.S. Private*, pg. 184
ALLSOP, INC.; *U.S. Private*, pg. 193
AMETHYSTUM STORAGE TECHNOLOGY CO., LTD.; *Int'l*, pg. 424
AMINO COMMUNICATIONS AB—See Aferian plc; *Int'l*, pg. 185
AMPEX CORPORATION; *U.S. Private*, pg. 266
AMPEX DATA SYSTEMS CORPORATION—See Ampex Corporation; *U.S. Private*, pg. 266
ANWELL PRECISION TECHNOLOGY (HK) LIMITED—See Anwell Technologies Ltd.; *Int'l*, pg. 486
ANWELL SOLAR TECHNOLOGIES LIMITED—See Anwell Technologies Ltd.; *Int'l*, pg. 486
AOF IMAGING TECHNOLOGY, JAPAN LTD.—See Asia Optical Co., Inc.; *Int'l*, pg. 613
APACER ELECTRONIC (SHANGHAI) CO., LTD.—See Apacer Technology Inc.; *Int'l*, pg. 500
APACER MEMORY AMERICA, INC.—See Apacer Technology Inc.; *Int'l*, pg. 500
APACER TECHNOLOGIES PVT LTD.—See Apacer Technology Inc.; *Int'l*, pg. 500
APACER TECHNOLOGY CORP.—See Apacer Technology Inc.; *Int'l*, pg. 500
APACER TECHNOLOGY INC.; *Int'l*, pg. 500
APPRO INTERNATIONAL, INC.—See Hewlett Packard Enterprise Company; *U.S. Public*, pg. 1030
ARTS OPTICAL INTERNATIONAL HOLDINGS LTD; *Int'l*, pg. 585
ASUS EUROPE B.V.—See ASUSTeK Computer Inc.; *Int'l*, pg. 663
ATP ELECTRONICS, INC.—See Actiontec Electronics, Inc.; *U.S. Private*, pg. 68
AVENTIS SYSTEMS, INC.; *U.S. Private*, pg. 405
AVERE SYSTEMS, INC.—See Microsoft Corporation; *U.S. Public*, pg. 1439
BEIJING EGOVA CO., LTD.; *Int'l*, pg. 949
BEIJING JINGKAI INFORMATION STORAGE TECHNOLOGY CO., LTD.—See Amethystum Storage Technology Co., Ltd.; *Int'l*, pg. 424
BEIJING POLYSTAR DIGIDISC CO., LTD.—See China Poly Group Corporation; *Int'l*, pg. 1541
BENQ MATERIALS CORP.; *Int'l*, pg. 975
BIGL TECHNOLOGIES (CHONGQING) CO., LTD.—See Broadway Industrial Group Limited; *Int'l*, pg. 1172
BIGL TECHNOLOGIES (SHENZHEN) CO., LTD.—See Broadway Industrial Group Limited; *Int'l*, pg. 1172
BIGL TECHNOLOGIES (THAILAND) CO., LTD.—See Broadway Industrial Group Limited; *Int'l*, pg. 1172
BIGL TECHNOLOGIES (WUXI) CO., LTD.—See Broadway Industrial Group Limited; *Int'l*, pg. 1172
BROOKS AUTOMATION (GERMANY) GMBH MISTELGAU—See Azenta, Inc.; *U.S. Public*, pg. 257
BROOKS AUTOMATION ISRAEL, LTD.—See Azenta, Inc.; *U.S. Public*, pg. 257
BROOKS AUTOMATION TAIWAN COMPANY LTD.—See Azenta, Inc.; *U.S. Public*, pg. 257
CAMBEX CORPORATION; *U.S. Public*, pg. 425
CANDELIS, INC.—See Candle Acquisition Corporation; *U.S. Private*, pg. 733
CARD CENTER LTD.—See Chams Holding Company; *Int'l*, pg. 1440
CENTRAL FILES, INC.—See Berkshire Partners LLC; *U.S. Private*, pg. 534
CHECKOUTSTORE INC.; *U.S. Private*, pg. 869
CHERRY EUROPE GMBH—See Cherry SE; *Int'l*, pg. 1472
CIPHERMAX, INC.; *U.S. Private*, pg. 899
CLEARPOINT ENTERPRISES, INC.; *U.S. Private*, pg. 938
COHERENT - PORTLAND—See Coherent Corp.; *U.S. Public*, pg. 527
COMFOR STORES A.S.—See AB S.A.; *Int'l*, pg. 41
CRESTEC (MALAYSIA) SDN BHD—See Crestec Inc.; *Int'l*, pg. 1841
DATADIRECT NETWORKS INC.; *U.S. Private*, pg. 1165
DATA DISTRIBUTING, LLC; *U.S. Private*, pg. 1162
DATAPULSE TECHNOLOGY LTD.; *Int'l*, pg. 1979
DATA STORAGE CORPORATION; *U.S. Public*, pg. 635
DELTA ELECTRONICS (HONG KONG) LTD.—See Delta Electronics, Inc.; *Int'l*, pg. 2016
DELTA ELECTRONICS INTERNATIONAL LTD.—See Delta Electronics, Inc.; *Int'l*, pg. 2018
DNP IMAGING COMMUNICATION (SHANGHAI) CO., LTD.—See Dai Nippon Printing Co., Ltd.; *Int'l*, pg. 1914
DROBO, INC.—See StorCentric, Inc.; *U.S. Private*, pg. 3831
DYNAMIC SYSTEMS, INC.; *U.S. Private*, pg. 1299
EDGE SOLUTIONS INC.; *U.S. Private*, pg. 1334
EDGE TECH CORP.; *U.S. Private*, pg. 1334
EDP EUROPE—See Engineered Data Products, LLC; *U.S. Private*, pg. 1398
EMC CORPORATION - SOUTHBOROUGH—See Dell Technologies Inc.; *U.S. Public*, pg. 651
ENPLAS (HONG KONG) LIMITED—See ENPLAS CORPORATION; *Int'l*, pg. 2444
EN POINTE TECHNOLOGIES, INC.—See Din Global Corp.; *U.S. Private*, pg. 1233
F5 NETWORKS, INC. - LOWELL—See F5, Inc.; *U.S. Public*, pg. 819
FARO SPAIN S.L.U.—See FARO Technologies, Inc.; *U.S. Public*, pg. 823
FIDELITY VOICE AND DATA; *U.S. Private*, pg. 1503
FORTUNE ORIENTAL COMPANY LIMITED; *Int'l*, pg. 2744
FREEIT DATA SOLUTIONS, INC.,; *U.S. Private*, pg. 1604
GIGAFAST INC.; *U.S. Private*, pg. 1697
GREAT WALL BROADBAND NETWORK SERVICE CO., LTD.—See CITIC Group Corporation; *Int'l*, pg. 1621
GREAT WALL BROADBAND NETWORK SERVICE CO., LTD.—See Dr. Peng Telecom & Media Group Co., Ltd.; *Int'l*, pg. 2194
GSE CO., LTD.; *Int'l*, pg. 3144
HGST EUROPE, LTD.—See Western Digital Corporation; *U.S. Public*, pg. 2355
HGST, INC.—See Western Digital Corporation; *U.S. Public*, pg. 2355
HGST JAPAN CO., LTD.—See Western Digital Corporation; *U.S. Public*, pg. 2355
HGST PHILIPPINES CORP.—See Western Digital Corporation; *U.S. Public*, pg. 2355
HGST SINGAPORE PTE. LTD.—See Western Digital Corporation; *U.S. Public*, pg. 2355
HGST (THAILAND) LTD.—See Western Digital Corporation; *U.S. Public*, pg. 2355
HITACHI COMPUTER PRODUCTS (EUROPE) S.A.S.—See Hitachi, Ltd.; *Int'l*, pg. 3415
HITACHI DATA SYSTEMS AG—See Hitachi, Ltd.; *Int'l*, pg. 3413
HITACHI ELECTRONIC PRODUCTS (M) SDN BHD—See Hitachi, Ltd.; *Int'l*, pg. 3416
HITACHI GLOBAL STORAGE PRODUCTS (SHENZHEN) CO., LTD.—See Western Digital Corporation; *U.S. Public*, pg. 2355
HITACHI GLOBAL STORAGE TECHNOLOGIES CONSULTING (SHANGHAI) CO., LTD.—See Western Digital Corporation; *U.S. Public*, pg. 2355
HITACHI GLOBAL STORAGE TECHNOLOGIES MALAYSIA SDN. BHD.—See Western Digital Corporation; *U.S. Public*, pg. 2355
HITACHI GLOBAL STORAGE TECHNOLOGIES PHILIPPINES CORP.—See Western Digital Corporation; *U.S. Public*, pg. 2355
HITACHI GLOBAL STORAGE TECHNOLOGIES (SHENZHEN) CO., LTD.—See Western Digital Corporation; *U.S. Public*, pg. 2355
HITACHI-LG DATA STORAGE (HUIZHOU) LTD.—See Hitachi, Ltd.; *Int'l*, pg. 3422
HITACHI-LG DATA STORAGE, INC.—See Hitachi, Ltd.; *Int'l*, pg. 3422
HITACHI-LG DATA STORAGE KOREA, INC.—See Hitachi, Ltd.; *Int'l*, pg. 3422
INONET COMPUTER GMBH—See Eurotech S.p.A.; *Int'l*, pg. 2558
INPHASE TECHNOLOGIES, INC.—See Signal Lake Management LLC; *U.S. Private*, pg. 3649
INTERNATIONAL ASSEMBLY SPECIALISTS S.A. DE C.V.—See Shugart Corporation; *U.S. Private*, pg. 3644
INTEVAC (SHENZHEN) CO. LTD.—See Intevac, Inc.; *U.S. Public*, pg. 1159
I/OMAGIC CORPORATION; *U.S. Private*, pg. 2027
IOSAFE, INC.—See CRU Data Security Group, LLC; *U.S. Private*, pg. 1113
ISCM TECHNOLOGY (THAILAND) CO., LTD.—See D'nonce Technology Bhd.; *Int'l*, pg. 1900
ISILON SYSTEMS, LLC—See Dell Technologies Inc.; *U.S. Public*, pg. 651
JAPAN LANTRONIX K.K.—See Lantronix, Inc.; *U.S. Public*, pg. 1293
JENSEN INFORMATION TECHNOLOGIES INC; *U.S. Private*, pg. 2200
KOFAX AUSTRIA GMBH—See Clearlake Capital Group, L.P.; *U.S. Private*, pg. 936
KOFAX AUSTRIA GMBH—See TA Associates, Inc.; *U.S. Private*, pg. 3916
KPS (BEIJING) PETROLEUM EQUIPMENT TRADING CO, LTD.—See Dover Corporation; *U.S. Public*, pg. 681
KRATOS-INTEGRAL SYSTEMS, INC.—See Kratos Defense & Security Solutions, Inc.; *U.S. Public*, pg. 1276
LINCOLN ARCHIVES INC.—See Lincoln Securities Corp.; *U.S. Private*, pg. 2459
MICROBOARDS TECHNOLOGY, LLC; *U.S. Private*, pg. 2703
MMRGLOBAL, INC.; *U.S. Private*, pg. 2755
MOBILE STORAGE (UK) LTD.—See WillScot Mobile Mini Holdings Corp.; *U.S. Public*, pg. 2372
MODUSLINK DE MEXICO, S.R.L. DE C.V.—See Steel Connect, Inc.; *U.S. Public*, pg. 1941
MOUNTAIN SECURE SYSTEMS (MSS)—See Phillips Service Industries, Inc. (PSI); *U.S. Private*, pg. 3171
NCR ITALIA S.R.L.—See NCR Voyix Corporation.; *U.S. Public*, pg. 1503
NCR VOYIX CORPORATION.; *U.S. Public*, pg. 1501
NETAPP BELGIUM BVBA—See NetApp, Inc.; *U.S. Public*, pg. 1507
NETAPP (CHINA) LTD.—See NetApp, Inc.; *U.S. Public*, pg. 1507
NETAPP, INC.; *U.S. Public*, pg. 1507
NETAPP INDIA PRIVATE LTD.—See NetApp, Inc.; *U.S. Public*, pg. 1507
NETAPP ISRAEL SALES LTD.—See NetApp, Inc.; *U.S. Public*, pg. 1507
NETAPP JAPAN K.K.—See NetApp, Inc.; *U.S. Public*, pg. 1507
NETAPP MEXICO—See NetApp, Inc.; *U.S. Public*, pg. 1507
NETAPP (SHANGHAI) COMMERCIAL CO., LTD.—See NetApp, Inc.; *U.S. Public*, pg. 1507
NETAPP UK LTD.—See NetApp, Inc.; *U.S. Public*, pg. 1507
NETEZZA CORPORATION—See International Business Machines Corporation; *U.S. Public*, pg. 1149
NETWORK APPLIANCE BV THE NETHERLANDS—See NetApp, Inc.; *U.S. Public*, pg. 1507
NETWORK APPLIANCE INDIA—See NetApp, Inc.; *U.S. Public*, pg. 1507
NIMBLE STORAGE, INC.—See Hewlett Packard Enterprise Company; *U.S. Public*, pg. 1032
NTI CORPORATION; *U.S. Private*, pg. 2971
OVERLAND STORAGE, INC.; *U.S. Private*, pg. 3053
OVERLAND STORAGE SARL—See Overland Storage, Inc.; *U.S. Private*, pg. 3053
POSTPATH LLC—See Cisco Systems, Inc.; *U.S. Public*, pg. 500
POWERTHRU—See Phillips Service Industries, Inc. (PSI); *U.S. Private*, pg. 3171
PRESILIENT, LLC; *U.S. Private*, pg. 3255
PRISM INTERGRATED SDN BHD—See Iron Mountain Incorporated; *U.S. Public*, pg. 1174
P.T. TEAC ELECTRONICS INDONESIA—See Evolution Capital Management LLC; *U.S. Private*, pg. 1443
PURE STORAGE, INC.; *U.S. Public*, pg. 1738
QUALSTAR CORPORATION; *U.S. Public*, pg. 1748
QUANTUM CORP. - IRVINE—See Quantum Corporation; *U.S. Public*, pg. 1754
QUANTUM CORPORATION; *U.S. Public*, pg. 1753
QUANTUM CORP. - PIKES PEAK OPERATIONS—See Quantum Corporation; *U.S. Public*, pg. 1754
QUANTUM SARL—See Quantum Corporation; *U.S. Public*, pg. 1754
QUANTUM STORAGE AUSTRALIA PTY, LTD.—See Quantum Corporation; *U.S. Public*, pg. 1754
QUANTUM STORAGE SINGAPORE PTE. LTD.—See Quantum Corporation; *U.S. Public*, pg. 1754
QUANTUM STORAGE UK, LTD.—See Quantum Corporation; *U.S. Public*, pg. 1754

N.A.I.C.S. INDEX

RACKMOUNT SOLUTIONS, INC.; *U.S. Private*, pg. 3342
RARE SYSTEMS INC.; *U.S. Private*, pg. 3356
SANDISK IL LTD.—See Western Digital Corporation; *U.S. Public*, pg. 2355
SANDISK INDIA - BANGALORE—See Western Digital Corporation; *U.S. Public*, pg. 2355
SANDISK ISRAEL (TEFEN) LTD.—See Western Digital Corporation; *U.S. Public*, pg. 2355
SANDISK LLC—See Western Digital Corporation; *U.S. Public*, pg. 2355
SANDISK MANUFACTURING LIMITED—See Western Digital Corporation; *U.S. Public*, pg. 2356
SANDISK STORAGE MALAYSIA SDN. BHD.—See Western Digital Corporation; *U.S. Public*, pg. 2356
SANDISK TRADING (SHANGHAI) CO. LTD.—See Western Digital Corporation; *U.S. Public*, pg. 2356
SATIVUS TECH CORP.; *U.S. Public*, pg. 1841
SERVERS DIRECT, LLC—See Equus Holdings, Inc.; *U.S. Private*, pg. 1417
SOFTWARE AG BRASIL INFORMATICA E SERVICOS LTDA—See Silver Lake Group, LLC; *U.S. Private*, pg. 3659
SOFTWARE AG VENEZUELA C.A.—See Silver Lake Group, LLC; *U.S. Private*, pg. 3660
SOLIDFIRE, INC.—See NetApp, Inc.; *U.S. Public*, pg. 1507
SOUTHERN DATA STORAGE, INC.; *U.S. Private*, pg. 3731
SWAPDRIVE, INC.—See Gen Digital Inc.; *U.S. Public*, pg. 910
SYSTERRA COMPUTER GMBH—See Addtech AB; *Int'l*, pg. 135
TAIYONIC LTD-(TAIYO)—See Northern Technologies International Corporation; *U.S. Public*, pg. 1538
TEAC ELECTRONICS (M) SDN. BHD.—See Evolution Capital Management LLC; *U.S. Private*, pg. 1443
TEGILE SYSTEMS PRIVATE LIMITED—See Western Digital Corporation; *U.S. Public*, pg. 2355
TRADETHEMARKETS.COM; *U.S. Private*, pg. 4202
UD INFO CORP.—See Apacer Technology Inc.; *Int'l*, pg. 500
UMEDISC LIMITED—See Anwell Technologies Ltd.; *Int'l*, pg. 486
UNION SQUARE MUSIC LTD.—See Bertelsmann SE & Co. KGaA; *Int'l*, pg. 990
VERBATIM AMERICAS, LLC—See CMC Magnetics Corporation; *Int'l*, pg. 1669
VERBATIM AUSTRALIA PTY LTD—See CMC Magnetics Corporation; *Int'l*, pg. 1669
VERBATIM ESPANA S.A—See CMC Magnetics Corporation; *Int'l*, pg. 1669
VERBATIM GMBH—See CMC Magnetics Corporation; *Int'l*, pg. 1669
VERBATIM (HONG KONG) LIMITED—See CMC Magnetics Corporation; *Int'l*, pg. 1669
VERBATIM ITALIA SPA A SOCIO UNICO—See CMC Magnetics Corporation; *Int'l*, pg. 1669
VERBATIM LIMITED—See CMC Magnetics Corporation; *Int'l*, pg. 1669
VERBATIM MARKETING INDIA PVT. LTD.—See CMC Magnetics Corporation; *Int'l*, pg. 1669
VERBATIM (SHENZHEN) INT'L TRADING CORP. LTD.—See CMC Magnetics Corporation; *Int'l*, pg. 1669
VERBATIM TAIWAN INTERNATIONAL TRADING CORPORATE LTD.—See CMC Magnetics Corporation; *Int'l*, pg. 1669
VERISTOR SYSTEMS, INC.; *U.S. Private*, pg. 4360
VIOLIN MEMORY DATA STORAGE SYSTEM COMPANY, LTD.—See Quantum Corporation; *U.S. Public*, pg. 1754
VIOLIN MEMORY EMEA LTD.—See Quantum Corporation; *U.S. Public*, pg. 1754
VIOLIN MEMORY, INC.—See Quantum Corporation; *U.S. Public*, pg. 1754
VIOLIN MEMORY K.K.—See Quantum Corporation; *U.S. Public*, pg. 1754
VIOLIN MEMORY SINGAPORE PTE. LTD.—See Quantum Corporation; *U.S. Public*, pg. 1754
VYCON, INC.—See Calnetix Technologies, LLC.; *U.S. Private*, pg. 723
WALA, INC.—See Data443 Risk Mitigation, Inc.; *U.S. Public*, pg. 635
WESTERN DIGITAL CORPORATION; *U.S. Public*, pg. 2355
WESTERN DIGITAL TECHNOLOGIES, INC.—See Western Digital Corporation; *U.S. Public*, pg. 2355
WINTEC INDUSTRIES INC.; *U.S. Private*, pg. 4545
XEROX S.P.A.—See Xerox Holdings Corporation; *U.S. Public*, pg. 2389
XIOTECH CORPORATION—See Oak Investment Partners; *U.S. Private*, pg. 2983
YASKAWA BROOKS AUTOMATION, INC.—See Azenta, Inc.; *U.S. Public*, pg. 258
ZHUHAI CRESTEC HUAGUANG ELECTRONICS TECHNOLOGY CO., LTD.—See Crestec Inc.; *Int'l*, pg. 1841

334118 — COMPUTER TERMINAL AND OTHER COMPUTER PERIPHERAL EQUIPMENT MANUFACTURING

3DCONNEXION GMBH—See Logitech International S.A.; *U.S. Public*, pg. 1341
3DCONNEXION INC.—See Logitech International S.A.; *U.S. Public*, pg. 1341
3M TOUCH SYSTEMS, INC.—See 3M Company; *U.S. Public*, pg. 7
4FRONT SERVICES LIMITED—See NCR Voyix Corporation.; *U.S. Public*, pg. 1501
AAC MICROTECH (CHANGZHOU) CO., LTD.—See AAC Technologies Holdings Inc.; *Int'l*, pg. 31
ABETECH, INC.; *U.S. Private*, pg. 38
ABKO CO., LTD.; *Int'l*, pg. 62
ACCTON TECHNOLOGY CORPORATION; *Int'l*, pg. 93
ACCU-SORT SYSTEMS, INC.—See Danaher Corporation; *U.S. Public*, pg. 624
ACCU-TECH SYSTEMS, LTD.—See Amano Corporation; *Int'l*, pg. 410
ACCU-TIME SYSTEMS, INC.—See Amano Corporation; *Int'l*, pg. 410
ACER TECHNOLOGIES CORP.—See Acer Incorporated; *Int'l*, pg. 99
ACER TECHNOLOGY, INC.—See Acer Incorporated; *Int'l*, pg. 99
ACS (INDIA) LIMITED—See Dell Technologies Inc.; *U.S. Public*, pg. 649
ACTIVE KEY GMBH—See Cherry SE; *Int'l*, pg. 1472
ADVANCED INPUT DEVICES, INC.—See TransDigm Group Incorporated; *U.S. Public*, pg. 2180
ADVANCED MICRO DEVICES (CHINA) CO. LTD.—See Advanced Micro Devices, Inc.; *U.S. Public*, pg. 48
ADVANCED MICRO DEVICES GLOBAL SERVICES (M) SDN. BHD.—See Advanced Micro Devices, Inc.; *U.S. Public*, pg. 48
ADVANCED MICRO DEVICES INC.—See Advanced Micro Devices, Inc.; *U.S. Public*, pg. 48
ADVANCED MICRO DEVICES (SHANGHAI) CO. LTD.—See Advanced Micro Devices, Inc.; *U.S. Public*, pg. 48
ADVAN INT'L CORP.—See Barco N.V.; *Int'l*, pg. 863
ADVANTECH AUTOMATION CORP.—See Advantech Co., Ltd.; *Int'l*, pg. 164
ADVA OPTICAL NETWORKING ISRAEL LTD—See ADTRAN Holdings, Inc.; *U.S. Public*, pg. 44
AFIX TECHNOLOGIES, INC.—See Aware, Inc.; *U.S. Public*, pg. 254
AFOR SDN. BHD.—See Epicentre Holdings Limited; *Int'l*, pg. 2460
AGFA-GEVAERT DO BRASIL LTDA.—See Agfa-Gevaert N.V.; *Int'l*, pg. 208
AGFA MATERIALS CORPORATION—See Agfa-Gevaert N.V.; *Int'l*, pg. 208
AGFA MATERIALS JAPAN LTD.—See Agfa-Gevaert N.V.; *Int'l*, pg. 208
AGFA MATERIALS TAIWAN CO., LTD.—See Agfa-Gevaert N.V.; *Int'l*, pg. 208
AHEARN & SOPER INC.; *Int'l*, pg. 222
AHEARN & SOPER INC.—See Ahearn & Soper Inc.; *Int'l*, pg. 223
AISIN ENGINEERING CO., LTD.—See AISIN Corporation; *Int'l*, pg. 252
ALCADON AB—See DistIT AB; *Int'l*, pg. 2136
ALCADON A/S—See DistIT AB; *Int'l*, pg. 2136
ALIENWARE LIMITED—See Dell Technologies Inc.; *U.S. Public*, pg. 649
ALLIED TELESYN INTERNATIONAL, INC.; *U.S. Private*, pg. 188
ALLIED TELESYN INTERNATIONAL LTD.—See ALLIED TELESIS HOLDINGS K.K.; *Int'l*, pg. 358
ALLSOP EUROPE LIMITED—See Allsop, Inc.; *U.S. Private*, pg. 193
ALTEK CORPORATION; *Int'l*, pg. 389
AMANO CINCINNATI CANADA, INC.—See Amano Corporation; *Int'l*, pg. 410
AMBIR TECHNOLOGY, INC.; *U.S. Private*, pg. 218
AMD ADVANCED MICRO DEVICES (ROU) S.R.L.—See Advanced Micro Devices, Inc.; *U.S. Public*, pg. 48
AMERICAN MEGATRENDS INDIA PVT. LTD.—See HGGC, LLC; *U.S. Private*, pg. 1928
AMERICAN MEGATRENDS INTERNATIONAL GMBH—See HGGC, LLC; *U.S. Private*, pg. 1929
AMERICAN RELIANCE INC.; *U.S. Private*, pg. 245
AMT DATASOUTH CORPORATION—See AMT Datasouth Corporation; *U.S. Private*, pg. 268
ANALOG TECH KK—See Analog Devices, Inc.; *U.S. Public*, pg. 135
ANDES TECHNOLOGY CORPORATION; *Int'l*, pg. 450
ANIXA BIOSCIENCES, INC.; *U.S. Public*, pg. 137
ANNAPOLIS MICRO SYSTEMS, INC.; *U.S. Private*, pg. 284
ANTEC INCORPORATED; *U.S. Private*, pg. 287
AOPEN INC.—See Acer Incorporated; *Int'l*, pg. 98
APPLE INC.; *U.S. Public*, pg. 169
APPLE OPERATIONS EUROPE—See Apple Inc.; *U.S. Public*, pg. 169
APPLIED CO., LTD.; *Int'l*, pg. 521
ARBOR TECHNOLOGY CORP.; *Int'l*, pg. 538
ARISTOCRAT TECHNOLOGIES NZ LIMITED—See Aristocrat Leisure Limited; *Int'l*, pg. 566
ARROW VALUE RECOVERY BELGIUM BVBA—See Arrow Electronics, Inc.; *U.S. Public*, pg. 198
ARROW VALUE RECOVERY CZECH REPUBLIC SRO—See Arrow Electronics, Inc.; *U.S. Public*, pg. 198
ARROW VALUE RECOVERY EMEA BV—See Arrow Electronics, Inc.; *U.S. Public*, pg. 198
ARROW VALUE RECOVERY FRANCE SAS—See Arrow Electronics, Inc.; *U.S. Public*, pg. 198
ARROW VALUE RECOVERY GERMANY GMBH—See Arrow Electronics, Inc.; *U.S. Public*, pg. 198
ARROW VALUE RECOVERY NETHERLANDS BV—See Arrow Electronics, Inc.; *U.S. Public*, pg. 198
ARROW VALUE RECOVERY UK LTD—See Arrow Electronics, Inc.; *U.S. Public*, pg. 198
ASANTE TECHNOLOGIES, INC.; *U.S. Private*, pg. 345
ASI BUSINESS SOLUTIONS, LLC—See Xerox Holdings Corporation; *U.S. Public*, pg. 2387
ASPEN TECHNOLOGY WLL—See Emerson Electric Co.; *U.S. Public*, pg. 741
ASROCK INC.; *U.S. Public*, pg. 632
ASTRONOVA GMBH—See AstroNova, Inc.; *U.S. Public*, pg. 218
ASTRONOVA, INC.; *U.S. Public*, pg. 217
ASTRONOVA (SHANGHAI) TRADING CO., LTD—See AstroNova, Inc.; *U.S. Public*, pg. 218
ASTRONOVA (SINGAPORE) PTE LTD.—See AstroNova, Inc.; *U.S. Public*, pg. 218
AT COMPUS S.R.O.—See AB S.A.; *Int'l*, pg. 41
AT COMPUTERS HOLDING A.S.—See AB S.A.; *Int'l*, pg. 41
ATEN INTERNATIONAL CO., LTD.; *Int'l*, pg. 668
ATI TECHNOLOGIES ULC—See Advanced Micro Devices, Inc.; *U.S. Public*, pg. 48
ATMI INTERNATIONAL TRADING CO. LTD.—See Entegris, Inc.; *U.S. Public*, pg. 776
ATMI TAIWAN CO. LTD.—See Entegris, Inc.; *U.S. Public*, pg. 776
ATRONIX INC.; *U.S. Private*, pg. 382
AUDIOCODES USA—See AudioCodes Ltd.; *Int'l*, pg. 702
AURAS TECHNOLOLGY CO., LTD.; *Int'l*, pg. 707
AURORA GROUP DANMARK A/S—See DistIT AB; *Int'l*, pg. 2136
AURORA GROUP FINLAND OY—See DistIT AB; *Int'l*, pg. 2136
AURORA GROUP NORGE AS—See DistIT AB; *Int'l*, pg. 2136
AURORA GROUP SVERIGE AB—See DistIT AB; *Int'l*, pg. 2136
AUTOCONT A.S.—See AutoCont Control Systems, s.r.o.; *Int'l*, pg. 726
AUTOCONT CONTROL SYSTEMS, S.R.O.; *Int'l*, pg. 726
AVERMEDIA TECHNOLOGIES INC.; *Int'l*, pg. 739
AVISION INC.; *Int'l*, pg. 744
AVOCENT CORPORATION—See Vertiv Holdings Co; *U.S. Public*, pg. 2288
AYDIN DISPLAYS, INC.—See Elbit Systems Limited; *Int'l*, pg. 2344
AZTECH LABS INC.—See Aztech Group Ltd.; *Int'l*, pg. 781
BALLY TECHNOLOGIES, INC.—See Light & Wonder, Inc.; *U.S. Public*, pg. 1314
BANDRICH INC.—See HTC Corporation; *Int'l*, pg. 3508
BANTA GLOBAL TURNKEY LLC—See Chatham Asset Management, LLC; *U.S. Private*, pg. 862
BARCO SVERIGE AB—See Barco N.V.; *Int'l*, pg. 863
BARCOVIEW TEXEN SAS—See Barco N.V.; *Int'l*, pg. 864
BARCO VISUAL (BEIJING) ELECTRONICS CO., LTD.—See Barco N.V.; *Int'l*, pg. 863
BARCREST GROUP LTD.—See Light & Wonder, Inc.; *U.S. Public*, pg. 1314
BASLER FRANCE S.A.—See Basler AG; *Int'l*, pg. 887
B.A.T.M. GERMANY GMBH—See BATM Advanced Communications Ltd.; *Int'l*, pg. 890
BCDVIDEO; *U.S. Private*, pg. 499
BEHAVIOR TECH COMPUTER CORPORATION - CHUNG LI FACTORY—See Behavior Tech Computer Corporation; *Int'l*, pg. 941
BEHAVIOR TECH COMPUTER CORPORATION; *Int'l*, pg. 941
BEHAVIOR TECH COMPUTER CORPORATION—See Behavior Tech Computer Corporation; *Int'l*, pg. 941
BEHAVIOR TECH COMPUTER EUROPE B.V.—See Behavior Tech Computer Corporation; *Int'l*, pg. 941
BEIJING BOE MARKETING CO., LTD.—See BOE Technology Group Co., Ltd.; *Int'l*, pg. 1099
BEIJING BOE REAL ESTATE CO., LTD.—See BOE Technology Group Co., Ltd.; *Int'l*, pg. 1099
BEIJING BOE SENSING TECHNOLOGY CO., LTD.—See BOE Technology Group Co., Ltd.; *Int'l*, pg. 1099
BEIJING BOE VACUUM ELECTRONICS CO., LTD.—See BOE Technology Group Co., Ltd.; *Int'l*, pg. 1099
BEIJING BOE VIDEO TECHNOLOGY CO., LTD.—See BOE Technology Group Co., Ltd.; *Int'l*, pg. 1099
BEIJING BRAIN CELL SOFTWARE CORPORATION LIMITED—See Fujitsu Limited; *Int'l*, pg. 2833
BEIJING YINGHE CENTURY CO., LTD.—See BOE Technology Group Co., Ltd.; *Int'l*, pg. 1099
BENQ CORPORATION; *Int'l*, pg. 975
BEST IPRODUCTS.COM LLC; *U.S. Private*, pg. 543
BIN CHUAN ENTERPRISE CORP.; *Int'l*, pg. 1032
BIOME GROW INC.; *Int'l*, pg. 1039
BIOSTAR MICROTECH (U.S.A) CORP.—See Biostar Microtech International Corp.; *Int'l*, pg. 1042

334118 — COMPUTER TERMINAL A...

BIOTEK INSTRUMENTS SOUTH KOREA LTD.—See Agilent Technologies, Inc.; *U.S. Public*, pg. 62
BIOTEK INSTRUMENTS (SWITZERLAND) GMBH—See Agilent Technologies, Inc.; *U.S. Public*, pg. 61
BIXOLON AMERICA INC.—See Bixolon Co Ltd; *Int'l*, pg. 1052
BLACK BOX CORPORATION—See Black Box Limited; *Int'l*, pg. 1056
BOCA SYSTEMS, INC.; *U.S. Private*, pg. 607
BOE HEALTHCARE INVESTMENT & MANAGEMENT CO., LTD.—See BOE Technology Group Co., Ltd.; *Int'l*, pg. 1099
BOE SMART TECHNOLOGY CO., LTD.—See BOE Technology Group Co., Ltd.; *Int'l*, pg. 1099
B.O.S. BETTER ONLINE SOLUTIONS LTD.; *Int'l*, pg. 790
BOUNDLESS TECHNOLOGIES, INC.—See Video Display Corporation; *U.S. Public*, pg. 2297
BOXX TECHNOLOGIES, LLC—See Craftsman Capital Partners, LLC; *U.S. Private*, pg. 1082
BRADY POLSKA SP. Z.O.O.—See Brady Corporation; *U.S. Public*, pg. 379
BRADY VIETNAM COMPANY LIMITED—See Brady Corporation; *U.S. Public*, pg. 379
BROOKS AUTOMATION FRANCE SAS—See Azenta, Inc.; *U.S. Public*, pg. 257
BROTHER HOLDING (EUROPE) LTD.—See Brother Industries, Ltd.; *Int'l*, pg. 1196
BROWAVE CORPORATION; *Int'l*, pg. 1198
CABLE ACCESSORIES (AUSTRALIA) PTY LTD—See Adamantem Capital Management Pty Limited; *Int'l*, pg. 123
CALIFORNIA DIGITAL INC.; *U.S. Private*, pg. 719
CANON COMPONENTS, INC.—See Canon Inc.; *Int'l*, pg. 1293
CANON ELECTRONICS, INC.—See Canon Inc.; *Int'l*, pg. 1293
CANON FINETECH INC.—See Canon Inc.; *Int'l*, pg. 1295
CANON VIETNAM CO., LTD.—See Canon Inc.; *Int'l*, pg. 1297
CASHWAY FINTECH CO., LTD.; *Int'l*, pg. 1352
CASING MACRON TECHNOLOGY CO., LTD.; *Int'l*, pg. 1352
CEIBA TECHNOLOGIES; *U.S. Private*, pg. 805
CEI LIMITED—See AEM Holdings Ltd.; *Int'l*, pg. 175
CELESTIX NETWORKS, INC.; *U.S. Private*, pg. 806
CELESTIX NETWORKS PTE. LTD.—See Celestix Networks, Inc.; *U.S. Private*, pg. 806
CELLFIE GLOBAL CO.,LTD.; *Int'l*, pg. 1393
CENTON ELECTRONICS, INC.; *U.S. Private*, pg. 818
CENTURY SAGE SCIENTIFIC HOLDINGS LIMITED; *Int'l*, pg. 1419
CFTC PRECISION (HUIAN) LIMITED—See China Fineblanking Technology Co., Ltd.; *Int'l*, pg. 1503
CHATSWORTH DATA CORPORATION—See CDC Data, LLC; *U.S. Private*, pg. 802
CHECKIT PLC; *Int'l*, pg. 1459
CHENBRO MICOM CO., LTD.; *Int'l*, pg. 1465
CHENBRO MICOM (USA) INC.—See Chenbro Micom Co., Ltd.; *Int'l*, pg. 1465
CHEONGHO ICT CO., LTD.; *Int'l*, pg. 1470
CHERRY SE; *Int'l*, pg. 1472
CHEUNG WOH TECHNOLOGIES LTD.; *Int'l*, pg. 1473
CHIARO TECHNOLOGIES LLC—See Cognex Corporation; *U.S. Public*, pg. 522
CHICONY AMERICA INC.—See Chicony Electronics Co., Ltd.; *Int'l*, pg. 1476
CHICONY ELECTRONICS CEZ S.R.O—See Chicony Electronics Co., Ltd.; *Int'l*, pg. 1476
CHICONY ELECTRONICS CO., LTD.; *Int'l*, pg. 1476
CHICONY ELECTRONICS (DONGGUAN) CO., LTD.—See Chicony Electronics Co., Ltd.; *Int'l*, pg. 1476
CHICONY ELECTRONICS GMBH—See Chicony Electronics Co., Ltd.; *Int'l*, pg. 1476
CHICONY ELECTRONICS (MAINLAND CHINA II) CO., LTD.—See Chicony Electronics Co., Ltd.; *Int'l*, pg. 1476
CHICONY POWER TECHNOLOGY HONG KONG LIMITED—See Chicony Power Technology Co., Ltd.; *Int'l*, pg. 1476
CHUNGHO COMNET CO., LTD. - GIMPO FACTORY—See Cheongho ICT Co., Ltd.; *Int'l*, pg. 1471
CHUNTEX ELECTRONIC CO., LTD.; *Int'l*, pg. 1598
CINEMASSIVE DISPLAYS, LLC—See HaiVision Systems, Inc.; *Int'l*, pg. 3218
CISCO THV LLC—See Cisco Systems, Inc.; *U.S. Public*, pg. 499
CITIZEN SYSTEMS EUROPE CORPORATION—See Citizen Watch Co., Ltd.; *Int'l*, pg. 1624
CLEARCUBE TECHNOLOGY, INC.; *U.S. Private*, pg. 932
CMICRO CORPORATION—See Imasen Electric Industrial Co., Ltd.; *Int'l*, pg. 3620
COBIUS HEALTHCARE SOLUTIONS, LLC—See PCP Enterprise, L.P.; *U.S. Private*, pg. 3121
COMPAL BROADBAND NETWORKS, INC.; *Int'l*, pg. 1746
COMPSEE, INC.—See Control Solutions, Inc.; *U.S. Private*, pg. 1034
COMPU B LTD.; *Int'l*, pg. 1754
COMPUCASE ENTERPRISE CO., LTD.; *Int'l*, pg. 1754
COMPUCASE EUROPE GMBH—See Compucase Enterprise Co., Ltd.; *Int'l*, pg. 1754

COMPUCASE JAPAN CO., LTD.—See Compucase Enterprise Co., Ltd.; *Int'l*, pg. 1754
COMPUCASE UK. LTD.—See Compucase Enterprise Co., Ltd.; *Int'l*, pg. 1754
COMPU-LINK CORPORATION; *U.S. Private*, pg. 1003
COMPUTERS & CONTROLS LTD.; *Int'l*, pg. 1760
COMPUTER TECHNOLOGY LINK CORP; *U.S. Private*, pg. 1005
COMPUTRONICS HOLDINGS LIMITED; *Int'l*, pg. 1761
CONCURRENT TECHNOLOGIES INC.—See Concurrent Technologies Plc; *Int'l*, pg. 1766
CONRAC ASIA DISPLAY PRODUCTS PTE LTD.—See Data Modul AG; *Int'l*, pg. 1976
CONRAC GMBH.—See Data Modul AG; *Int'l*, pg. 1976
CONRAC LTDA.—See Data Modul AG; *Int'l*, pg. 1976
CONRAC MENA FZE—See Data Modul AG; *Int'l*, pg. 1976
CONRAC SOUTH AFRICA (PTY) LTD.—See Data Modul AG; *Int'l*, pg. 1976
CONTEC CO., LTD.—See Daifuku Co., Ltd.; *Int'l*, pg. 1924
CONTROL CABLE INC.; *U.S. Private*, pg. 1034
CONTROL MODULE, INC.; *U.S. Private*, pg. 1034
CORETRONIC CORPORATION; *Int'l*, pg. 1800
CORETRONIC SYSTEM ENGINEERING CORPORATION—See Coretronic Corporation; *Int'l*, pg. 1800
CORO GLOBAL INC.; *U.S. Public*, pg. 579
CORSAIR COMPONENTS, INC.—See EagleTree Capital, LP; *U.S. Private*, pg. 1311
CPC PLC—See Avnet, Inc.; *U.S. Public*, pg. 254
CREATIVE TECHNOLOGY CENTRE PTE LTD—See Creative Technology Ltd.; *Int'l*, pg. 1833
CREATIVE TECHNOLOGY (CHINA) CO., LTD.—See Creative Technology Ltd.; *Int'l*, pg. 1833
CREATIVE TECHNOLOGY LTD.; *Int'l*, pg. 1833
CROSSCONTROL OY—See Enerpac Tool Group. Corp.; *U.S. Public*, pg. 765
CROSSROADS SYSTEMS, INC.; *U.S. Public*, pg. 596
CROSSROADS SYSTEMS (TEXAS), INC.—See Crossroads Systems, Inc.; *U.S. Public*, pg. 596
CROWDSPARK LTD; *Int'l*, pg. 1857
CRYPTERA A/S—See Diebold Nixdorf, Inc.; *U.S. Public*, pg. 659
CSI ACQUISITION CORP.; *U.S. Private*, pg. 1117
CURSOR CONTROLS LIMITED—See discoverIE Group plc; *Int'l*, pg. 2133
CUSTOM INTEGRATED TECHNOLOGY INC.—See Canon Inc.; *Int'l*, pg. 1297
CYPRESS TECHNOLOGIES CORP.; *U.S. Private*, pg. 1135
DAIKOKU DENKI CO., LTD. - KASUGAI DIVISION—See Daikoku Denki Co., Ltd.; *Int'l*, pg. 1937
DAIKOKU DENKI CO., LTD. - KOZOJI DIVISION—See Daikoku Denki Co., Ltd.; *Int'l*, pg. 1937
DAIKOKU DENKI CO., LTD. - SAKASHITA DIVISION—See Daikoku Denki Co., Ltd.; *Int'l*, pg. 1937
DALY COMPUTERS INC.; *U.S. Private*, pg. 1150
DANDELTACO A/S—See DistIT AB; *Int'l*, pg. 2136
DARFON ELECTRONICS CORPORATION—See BenQ Corporation; *Int'l*, pg. 975
DATADIRECT TECHNOLOGIES CORP.—See Progress Software Corporation; *U.S. Public*, pg. 1725
DATALOGIC ADC S.R.L.—See Datalogic S.p.A.; *Int'l*, pg. 1978
DATALOGIC AUTOMATION S.R.L.—See Datalogic S.p.A.; *Int'l*, pg. 1978
DATALUX CORPORATION; *U.S. Private*, pg. 1165
DATA MODUL AG; *Int'l*, pg. 1976
DATA MODUL FRANCE, S.A.R.L.—See Data Modul AG; *Int'l*, pg. 1976
DATA MODUL INC.—See Data Modul AG; *Int'l*, pg. 1976
DATA TRANSLATION, INC.—See National Instruments Corporation; *U.S. Public*, pg. 2856
DATENTECHNIK AG; *Int'l*, pg. 1982
DDS, INC.; *Int'l*, pg. 1994
DEBITEK, INC.—See Global Payments Inc.; *U.S. Public*, pg. 944
DELL (CHINA) COMPANY LIMITED—See Dell Technologies Inc.; *U.S. Public*, pg. 649
DELL GESM.B.H.—See Dell Technologies Inc.; *U.S. Public*, pg. 649
DELL GMBH—See Dell Technologies Inc.; *U.S. Public*, pg. 649
DELL INDIA PRIVATE LTD.—See Dell Technologies Inc.; *U.S. Public*, pg. 649
DELTA NETWORKS, INC.—See Delta Electronics, Inc.; *Int'l*, pg. 2018
DEVLIN ELECTRONICS LIMITED; *Int'l*, pg. 2089
DEWHURST LTD.—See Dewhurst Group plc; *Int'l*, pg. 2091
DFI INC.; *Int'l*, pg. 2095
DFS B.V.—See Dell Technologies Inc.; *U.S. Public*, pg. 649
DIEBOLD ATM CIHAZLARI SANAYI VE TICARET A.S.—See Diebold Nixdorf, Inc.; *U.S. Public*, pg. 659
DIEBOLD AUSTRALIA PTY. LTD.—See Diebold Nixdorf, Inc.; *U.S. Public*, pg. 659
DIEBOLD BELGIUM—See Diebold Nixdorf, Inc.; *U.S. Public*, pg. 660
DIEBOLD FRANCE—See Diebold Nixdorf, Inc.; *U.S. Public*, pg. 660

DIEBOLD HUNGARY LTD.—See Diebold Nixdorf, Inc.; *U.S. Public*, pg. 660
DIEBOLD LATIN AMERICA OPERATIONAL HEADQUARTERS—See Diebold Nixdorf, Inc.; *U.S. Public*, pg. 660
DIEBOLD LUXEMBOURG—See Diebold Nixdorf, Inc.; *U.S. Public*, pg. 660
DIEBOLD NIXDORF AG—See Diebold Nixdorf, Inc.; *U.S. Public*, pg. 660
DIEBOLD NIXDORF AG—See Diebold Nixdorf, Inc.; *U.S. Public*, pg. 660
DIEBOLD NIXDORF B.V.—See Diebold Nixdorf, Inc.; *U.S. Public*, pg. 660
DIEBOLD NIXDORF SL—See Diebold Nixdorf, Inc.; *U.S. Public*, pg. 660
DIEBOLD NIXDORF S.R.L.—See Diebold Nixdorf, Inc.; *U.S. Public*, pg. 660
DIEBOLD NIXDORF SRL—See Diebold Nixdorf, Inc.; *U.S. Public*, pg. 660
DIEBOLD OF NEVADA, INC.—See Diebold Nixdorf, Inc.; *U.S. Public*, pg. 661
DIEBOLD OLTP—See Diebold Nixdorf, Inc.; *U.S. Public*, pg. 660
DIEBOLD PARAGUAY—See Diebold Nixdorf, Inc.; *U.S. Public*, pg. 660
DIEBOLD (THAILAND) CO., LTD.—See Diebold Nixdorf, Inc.; *U.S. Public*, pg. 659
DIEBOLD VIETNAM COMPANY LIMITED—See Diebold Nixdorf, Inc.; *U.S. Public*, pg. 661
DIGITAL CHINA TECHNOLOGY LIMITED—See Digital China Holdings Limited; *Int'l*, pg. 2121
DIGITAL GRAPHICS INCORPORATION; *Int'l*, pg. 2122
DIGITAL MEDIA PROFESSIONALS INC.; *Int'l*, pg. 2122
DIGITAL PHOTONICS CORP.—See Anderson Industrial Corporation; *Int'l*, pg. 450
DIGITECH SYSTEMS CO., LTD.; *Int'l*, pg. 2123
DILON TECHNOLOGIES LLC; *U.S. Private*, pg. 1232
DISCRETIX, INC.—See Discretix Technologies Ltd.; *Int'l*, pg. 2135
DISPLAYLINK (UK) LIMITED—See Synaptics Incorporated; *U.S. Public*, pg. 1969
DLOG GESELLSCHAFT FUR ELEKTRONISCHE DATENTECHNIK MBH—See Advantech Co., Ltd.; *Int'l*, pg. 164
DOCUMENT CAPTURE TECHNOLOGIES INC.; *U.S. Private*, pg. 1252
DOMINO PRINTING SCIENCES PLC—See Brother Industries, Ltd.; *Int'l*, pg. 1197
DOMINO UK LTD.—See Brother Industries, Ltd.; *Int'l*, pg. 1198
DOVE DATA PRODUCTS INC.; *U.S. Private*, pg. 1268
DRUCKERFACHMANN.DE GMBH—See Droege Group AG; *Int'l*, pg. 2205
DSK CO., LTD.; *Int'l*, pg. 2210
DUAGON AG—See Deutsche Beteiligungs AG; *Int'l*, pg. 2063
DYNABOOK EUROPE GMBH—See Hon Hai Precision Industry Co., Ltd.; *Int'l*, pg. 3457
DYNABOOK INC.—See Hon Hai Precision Industry Co., Ltd.; *Int'l*, pg. 3457
EASTMAN PARK MICROGRAPHICS, INC.; *U.S. Private*, pg. 1322
EATON CORP. - ELECTRICAL SECTOR, COLUMBUS—See Eaton Corporation plc; *Int'l*, pg. 2279
ECLIPSE CASH SYSTEMS, LLC—See Further Global Capital Management, L.P.; *U.S. Private*, pg. 1625
EFAX.COM INC.—See Ziff Davis, Inc.; *U.S. Public*, pg. 2404
EFI CRETAPRINT, S.L.—See Siris Capital Group, LLC; *U.S. Private*, pg. 3672
EIZO CORPORATION; *Int'l*, pg. 2337
EIZO DISPLAY TECHNOLOGIES (SUZHOU) CO., LTD.—See EIZO Corporation; *Int'l*, pg. 2337
EIZO NORDIC AB—See EIZO Corporation; *Int'l*, pg. 2337
EIZO TECHNOLOGIES GMBH—See EIZO Corporation; *Int'l*, pg. 2337
EKWB D.O.O.; *Int'l*, pg. 2340
ELECOM CO., LTD.; *Int'l*, pg. 2348
ELECTION SYSTEMS & SOFTWARE INC.—See Lee Enterprises, Incorporated; *U.S. Public*, pg. 1298
ELECTION SYSTEMS & SOFTWARE INC.—See McCarthy Group, LLC; *U.S. Private*, pg. 2626
ELECTRONICS FOR IMAGING, INC.—See Siris Capital Group, LLC; *U.S. Private*, pg. 3672
ELO TOUCH SOLUTIONS (BELGIUM) NV—See Crestview Partners, L.P.; *U.S. Private*, pg. 1098
ELO TOUCH SOLUTIONS, INC. - ROCHESTER—See Crestview Partners, L.P.; *U.S. Private*, pg. 1098
ELO TOUCH SOLUTIONS, INC.—See Crestview Partners, L.P.; *U.S. Private*, pg. 1098
ELO TOUCH SOLUTIONS SINGAPORE PTE LTD—See Crestview Partners, L.P.; *U.S. Private*, pg. 1098
ELSOFT RESEARCH BERHAD; *Int'l*, pg. 2370
EMC COMPUTER SYSTEMS A/S—See Dell Technologies Inc.; *U.S. Public*, pg. 650
EMERSON NETWORK POWER, ENERGY SYSTEMS—See Vertiv Holdings Co; *U.S. Public*, pg. 2289
EMIRATES TECHNOLOGY COMPANY (EMITAC); *Int'l*, pg. 2382

N.A.I.C.S. INDEX

334118 — COMPUTER TERMINAL A...

ENCORE NETWORKS INC.; *U.S. Private*, pg. 1391
ENFORA, INC.—See Inseego Corp.; *U.S. Public*, pg. 1129
ENNOCONN CORPORATION; *Int'l*, pg. 2443
EPENDION AB; *Int'l*, pg. 2459
EPICENTRE PTE. LTD.—See Epicentre Holdings Limited; *Int'l*, pg. 2460
EPICENTRE SOLUTIONS PTE. LTD.—See Epicentre Holdings Limited; *Int'l*, pg. 2460
ERGOTRON, INC.—See The Sterling Group, L.P.; *U.S. Private*, pg. 4122
EROOMSYSTEM SPE, INC.—See eRoomSystem Technologies, Inc.; *U.S. Private*, pg. 1423
EROOMSYSTEM TECHNOLOGIES, INC.; *U.S. Private*, pg. 1423
E-SEEK, INC.—See Bundesdruckerei GmbH; *Int'l*, pg. 1216
E-SEEK, INC.—See Giesecke & Devrient GmbH; *Int'l*, pg. 2970
EUROTECH FRANCE S.A.S.—See Eurotech S.p.A.; *Int'l*, pg. 2558
EUROTECH INC.—See Eurotech S.p.A.; *Int'l*, pg. 2558
EUROTECH INC.—See Eurotech S.p.A.; *Int'l*, pg. 2558
EZENIA! INC.; *U.S. Public*, pg. 818
FAB UNIVERSAL CORP.; *U.S. Private*, pg. 1458
FATPIPE NETWORKS INC.; *U.S. Private*, pg. 1483
FEIGE INTELLIGENT TECHNOLOGY CO., LTD.—See Great Wall Motor Company Limited; *Int'l*, pg. 3066
FINDELTACO OY—See DistIT AB; *Int'l*, pg. 2136
FIRICH ENTERPRISES CO., LTD; *Int'l*, pg. 2679
FLEXTRONICS GLOBAL SERVICES (MANCHESTER) LIMITED—See Flex Ltd.; *Int'l*, pg. 2702
FLYTECH ELECTRONIC (SHANGHAI) CO., LTD.—See Flytech Technology Co., Ltd.; *Int'l*, pg. 2716
FLYTECH TECHNOLOGY CO., LTD. - TAIPEI FACTORY—See Flytech Technology Co., Ltd.; *Int'l*, pg. 2716
FOCUS MEDIA TECHNOLOGY (SHANGAHI) CO., LTD.—See Focus Media Holding Limited; *Int'l*, pg. 2753
FORTRESS TECHNOLOGIES, INC.—See General Dynamics Corporation; *U.S. Public*, pg. 913
FOUNDER TECHNOLOGY GROUP CORP.; *Int'l*, pg. 2753
FUJI ELECTRIC CORP OF AMERICA—See Fuji Electric Co., Ltd.; *Int'l*, pg. 2811
FUJIFILM MICRODISKS USA, INC.—See FUJIFILM Holdings Corporation; *Int'l*, pg. 2823
FUJIPREAM CORPORATION - HIMEJI FACTORY—See Fujipream Corporation; *Int'l*, pg. 2830
FUJIPREAM CORPORATION - PV FACTORY—See Fujipream Corporation; *Int'l*, pg. 2830
FUJITSU COMPONENTS (MALAYSIA) SDN. BHD.—See Fujitsu Limited; *Int'l*, pg. 2834
FUJITSU DIE-TECH CORPORATION OF THE PHILIPPINE—See Fujitsu Limited; *Int'l*, pg. 2834
FUJITSU ISOTEC LIMITED—See Fujitsu Limited; *Int'l*, pg. 2834
FUJITSU IT PRODUCTS LTD.—See Fujitsu Limited; *Int'l*, pg. 2834
FUJITSU PERIPHERALS LIMITED—See Fujitsu Limited; *Int'l*, pg. 2835
FUJITSU TECHNOLOGY SOLUTIONS OOO—See Fujitsu Limited; *Int'l*, pg. 2837
FUJITSU TECHNOLOGY SOLUTIONS SP. Z O.O.—See Fujitsu Limited; *Int'l*, pg. 2837
FUZHOU BOE OPTOELECTRONICS TECHNOLOGY CO., LTD.—See BOE Technology Group Co., Ltd.; *Int'l*, pg. 1099
GATEWAY MANUFACTURING LLC—See Acer Incorporated; *Int'l*, pg. 99
G.B.T. INC.,—See Giga-Byte Technology Co., Ltd.; *Int'l*, pg. 2971
GECMA COMPONENTS ELECTRONIC GMBH—See Eaton Corporation plc; *Int'l*, pg. 2278
GENERAL DYNAMICS ITRONIX EUROPE LTD.—See General Dynamics Corporation; *U.S. Public*, pg. 915
GENNUM CORP. - OTTAWA DESIGN CENTER—See Semtech Corporation; *U.S. Public*, pg. 1864
GENNUM UK LIMITED—See Semtech Corporation; *U.S. Public*, pg. 1864
GENUINE ZEBRA TECHNOLOGIES TRADING (SHANGHAI) CO., LTD.—See Zebra Technologies Corporation; *U.S. Public*, pg. 2401
GGI TECHNOLOGY LTD.—See Gunze Limited; *Int'l*, pg. 3185
GLOBAL INDUSTRIAL COMPANY; *U.S. Public*, pg. 942
GOLDPAC GROUP LIMITED; *Int'l*, pg. 3034
GOOD WAY TECHNOLOGY CO., LTD.; *Int'l*, pg. 3039
GRANDSTREAM NETWORKS, INC.; *U.S. Private*, pg. 1754
GRASS VALLEY CANADA—See Black Dragon Capital LLC; *U.S. Private*, pg. 571
GTCO CALCOMP, INC.—See Centre Lane Partners, LLC; *U.S. Private*, pg. 828
GUANGZHOU TECSUN SCIENCE & TECHNOLOGY CO., LTD.; *Int'l*, pg. 3161
GUANGZHOU SHIZHEN INFORMATION TECHNOLOGY CO., LTD.—See Guangzhou Shiyuan Electronics Co., Ltd; *Int'l*, pg. 3168
GUILLEMOT CORPORATION S.A.; *Int'l*, pg. 3174
GUNZE TECHNOLOGIES USA CORP.—See Gunze Limited; *Int'l*, pg. 3185

HAMA GMBH & CO KG; *Int'l*, pg. 3234
HANNSPREE, INC.—See HannStar Display Corporation; *Int'l*, pg. 3257
HANNSTOUCH SOLUTION INC.; *Int'l*, pg. 3258
HANSOL LCD INC.—See Hansol Group; *Int'l*, pg. 3260
HANVON MANUFACTURER CO., LTD—See Hanwang Technology Co., Ltd.; *Int'l*, pg. 3264
HANWANG TECHNOLOGY CO., LTD.; *Int'l*, pg. 3263
HAUPPAUGE COMPUTER WORKS GMBH—See HAUPPAUGE DIGITAL, INC.; *U.S. Public*, pg. 988
HAUPPAUGE COMPUTER WORKS INC.—See HAUPPAUGE DIGITAL, INC.; *U.S. Public*, pg. 988
HAUPPAUGE COMPUTER WORKS SARL—See HAUPPAUGE DIGITAL, INC.; *U.S. Public*, pg. 988
HAUPPAUGE COMPUTER WORKS SARL—See HAUPPAUGE DIGITAL, INC.; *U.S. Public*, pg. 988
HAUPPAUGE COMPUTER WORKS UK LTD.—See HAUPPAUGE DIGITAL, INC.; *U.S. Public*, pg. 988
HAUPPAUGE DIGITAL ASIA PTE LTD.—See HAUPPAUGE DIGITAL, INC.; *U.S. Public*, pg. 988
HAUPPAUGE DIGITAL, INC.; *U.S. Public*, pg. 988
HAUPPAUGE DIGITAL, INC.—See HAUPPAUGE DIGITAL, INC.; *U.S. Public*, pg. 988
HEC KOREA CO.,LTD.—See Compucase Enterprise Co., Ltd.; *Int'l*, pg. 1754
HERGO ERGONOMIC SUPPORT SYSTEMS, INC.; *U.S. Private*, pg. 1921
HEWLETT PACKARD ENTERPRISE BV—See Hewlett Packard Enterprise Company; *U.S. Public*, pg. 1031
HEWLETT-PACKARD (M) SDN. BHD.—See Hewlett Packard Enterprise Company; *U.S. Public*, pg. 1031
HIGH TOUCH, INC.; *U.S. Private*, pg. 1937
HIMAX IMAGING, INC.—See Himax Technologies, Inc.; *Int'l*, pg. 3396
HIMAX TECHNOLOGIES (SHENZHEN) CO., LTD.—See Himax Technologies, Inc.; *Int'l*, pg. 3397
HIMAX TECHNOLOGIES (SUZHOU) CO., LTD.—See Himax Technologies, Inc.; *Int'l*, pg. 3397
HITACHI COMPUTER PRODUCTS (AMERICA), INC.—See Hitachi, Ltd.; *Int'l*, pg. 3413
HITACHI FINANCIAL EQUIPMENT SYSTEM(SHENZHEN) CO., LTD.—See Hitachi, Ltd.; *Int'l*, pg. 3417
HITACHI-OMRON TERMINAL SOLUTIONS, CORP.—See Hitachi, Ltd.; *Int'l*, pg. 3422
HITACHI TERMINALS MECHATRONICS PHILIPPINES CORPORATION—See Hitachi, Ltd.; *Int'l*, pg. 3422
HITACHI TERMINAL SOLUTIONS INDIA PRIVATE LIMITED—See Hitachi, Ltd.; *Int'l*, pg. 3422
HITACHI TERMINAL SOLUTIONS KOREA CO., LTD.—See Hitachi, Ltd.; *Int'l*, pg. 3422
HMS INDUSTRIAL NETWORKS APS—See HMS Networks AB; *Int'l*, pg. 3433
HMS INDUSTRIAL NETWORKS GMBH—See HMS Networks AB; *Int'l*, pg. 3433
HMS INDUSTRIAL NETWORKS INC.—See HMS Networks AB; *Int'l*, pg. 3433
HMS INDUSTRIAL NETWORKS INDIA PRIVATE LTD.—See HMS Networks AB; *Int'l*, pg. 3433
HMS INDUSTRIAL NETWORKS K.K.—See HMS Networks AB; *Int'l*, pg. 3433
HMS INDUSTRIAL NETWORKS S.R.L.—See HMS Networks AB; *Int'l*, pg. 3433
HOOLEON CORPORATION; *U.S. Private*, pg. 1978
HOTWAY TECHNOLOGY CORPORATION—See Ban Leong Technologies Limited; *Int'l*, pg. 814
HOYA DIGITAL SOLUTIONS CORPORATION—See Hoya Corporation; *Int'l*, pg. 3495
HPC SYSTEMS, INC.; *Int'l*, pg. 3500
HP INC.; *U.S. Public*, pg. 1062
HYBRICON CORPORATION—See ACS Integrated Systems, Inc.; *U.S. Private*, pg. 66
HYGON INFORMATION TECHNOLOGY CO. LTD.; *Int'l*, pg. 3549
ICAD, INC.; *U.S. Public*, pg. 1083
ICHIA TECHNOLOGIES INC.; *Int'l*, pg. 3579
IDEMIA AUSTRALASIA PTY. LTD.—See Advent International Corporation; *U.S. Private*, pg. 102
IDEMIA IDENTITY & SECURITY CANADA, INC.—See Advent International Corporation; *U.S. Private*, pg. 102
IDEMIA IDENTITY & SECURITY SUCURSAL COLOMBIA—See Advent International Corporation; *U.S. Private*, pg. 102
IDEMIA IDENTITY & SECURITY UK LIMITED—See Advent International Corporation; *U.S. Private*, pg. 102
IDEMIA THE NETHERLANDS B.V.—See Advent International Corporation; *U.S. Private*, pg. 102
IDP CORP., LTD.; *Int'l*, pg. 3596
IDVATION GMBH—See H2APEX Group SCA; *Int'l*, pg. 3200
IEI INTEGRATION CORP.; *Int'l*, pg. 3597
IFI TECHNOLOGY USA CORP.—See IEI Integration Corp.; *Int'l*, pg. 3597
IGO, INC.—See Steel Partners Holdings L.P.; *U.S. Public*, pg. 1943
IMMERSION CANADA, INC.—See Immersion Corporation; *U.S. Public*, pg. 1112
IMPRINT ENTERPRISES INC.; *U.S. Private*, pg. 2051
INDUSTRIAL ELECTRONIC ENGINEERS, INC.; *U.S. Private*, pg. 2066

INFINIDAT INC.; *U.S. Private*, pg. 2070
INFOCUS CORPORATION—See Image Holdings Corporation; *U.S. Private*, pg. 2044
INGENICO CORP.—See Apollo Global Management, Inc.; *U.S. Public*, pg. 151
INTEGRATED BIOMETRICS, INC.—See Reserve Group Management Company; *U.S. Public*, pg. 3404
INTEL CORP. IBERIA, S.A.—See Intel Corporation; *U.S. Public*, pg. 1138
INTEL MALAYSIA SDN. BERHAD—See Intel Corporation; *U.S. Public*, pg. 1138
INTEL SEMICONDUCTOR (DALIAN) LTD.—See Intel Corporation; *U.S. Public*, pg. 1138
INTERFACE TECHNOLOGY (CHENGDU) CO., LTD.—See General Interface Solution (GIS) Holding Ltd.; *Int'l*, pg. 2918
INTERMEC BY HONEYWELL—See Honeywell International Inc.; *U.S. Public*, pg. 1050
INTERMEC, INC.—See Honeywell International Inc.; *U.S. Public*, pg. 1050
INTERMEC (SOUTH AMERICA) LTDA.—See Honeywell International Inc.; *U.S. Public*, pg. 1050
INTERMEC TECHNOLOGIES AB—See Honeywell International Inc.; *U.S. Public*, pg. 1050
INTERMEC TECHNOLOGIES AUSTRALIA PTY. LIMITED—See Honeywell International Inc.; *U.S. Public*, pg. 1050
INTERMEC TECHNOLOGIES CORPORATION—See Honeywell International Inc.; *U.S. Public*, pg. 1050
INTERMEC TECHNOLOGIES, S.L.U.—See Honeywell International Inc.; *U.S. Public*, pg. 1050
ION NETWORKS, INC.—See AEA Investors LP; *U.S. Private*, pg. 113
ISRA VISION POLYMETRIC GMBH—See Atlas Copco AB; *Int'l*, pg. 683
IWASAKI SEISAKUSHO CO., LTD.—See Daifuku Co., Ltd.; *Int'l*, pg. 1926
JADAK, LLC—See Novanta Inc.; *U.S. Public*, pg. 1548
JUNIPER NETWORKS (US), INC.—See Juniper Networks, Inc.; *U.S. Public*, pg. 1211
KENSINGTON TECHNOLOGY GROUP—See ACCO Brands Corporation; *U.S. Public*, pg. 33
KEY TRONIC COMPUTER PERIPHERALS (SHANGHAI) CO. LTD—See Key Tronic Corporation; *U.S. Public*, pg. 1225
KINGSTON TECHNOLOGY COMPANY, INC.; *U.S. Private*, pg. 2312
K.K. ARISTOCRAT TECHNOLOGIES—See Aristocrat Leisure Limited; *Int'l*, pg. 566
KNURR GMBH—See Vertiv Holdings Co; *U.S. Public*, pg. 2289
KNURR-MECOR GMBH—See Vertiv Holdings Co; *U.S. Public*, pg. 2289
KODAK OY—See Eastman Kodak Company; *U.S. Public*, pg. 708
KODAK SA/NV—See Eastman Kodak Company; *U.S. Public*, pg. 708
LAMBDA SYSTEM INC.—See Core Corporation; *Int'l*, pg. 1797
LEGEND CORPORATE SERVICES PTY LTD—See Adamantem Capital Management Pty Limited; *Int'l*, pg. 123
LIFESIZE COMMUNICATIONS, GMBH—See Logitech International S.A.; *U.S. Public*, pg. 1341
LIFESIZE COMMUNICATIONS LIMITED—See Logitech International S.A.; *U.S. Public*, pg. 1341
LIVESCRIBE, INC.—See Anoto Group AB; *Int'l*, pg. 474
LOCKHEED MARTIN SYSTEMS INTEGRATION - OWEGO—See Lockheed Martin Corporation; *U.S. Public*, pg. 1338
LOGICOOL CO., LTD.—See Logitech International S.A.; *U.S. Public*, pg. 1341
LOGITECH AUSTRALIA COMPUTER PERIPHERALS PTY, LIMITED—See Logitech International S.A.; *U.S. Public*, pg. 1341
LOGITECH ENGINEERING & DESIGNS INDIA PRIVATE LIMITED—See Logitech International S.A.; *U.S. Public*, pg. 1341
LOGITECH GMBH—See Logitech International S.A.; *U.S. Public*, pg. 1341
LOGITECH HONG KONG, LIMITED—See Logitech International S.A.; *U.S. Public*, pg. 1341
LOGITECH INC.—See Logitech International S.A.; *U.S. Public*, pg. 1341
LOGITECH INTERNATIONAL S.A.; *U.S. Public*, pg. 1341
LOGITECH IRELAND SERVICES LIMITED—See Logitech International S.A.; *U.S. Public*, pg. 1341
LOGITECH KOREA LTD.—See Logitech International S.A.; *U.S. Public*, pg. 1341
LOGITECH TECHNOLOGY (SUZHOU) CO., LTD.—See Logitech International S.A.; *U.S. Public*, pg. 1341
LUMINEX BV—See DiaSorin S.p.A.; *Int'l*, pg. 2106
MAD CATZ EUROPE LIMITED—See Mad Catz Interactive Inc.; *U.S. Private*, pg. 2538
MAD CATZ GMBH—See Mad Catz Interactive Inc.; *U.S. Private*, pg. 2539
MAD CATZ INTERACTIVE ASIA LIMITED—See Mad Catz Interactive Inc.; *U.S. Private*, pg. 2539
MAD CATZ INTERACTIVE INC.; *U.S. Private*, pg. 2538

334118 — COMPUTER TERMINAL A...

MAD CATZ SAS—See Mad Catz Interactive Inc.; *U.S. Private*, pg. 2539
MAGMA—See One Stop Systems, Inc.; *U.S. Public*, pg. 1602
MAG-TEK INC.; *U.S. Private*, pg. 2545
MARBURG TECHNOLOGY INC.; *U.S. Private*, pg. 2570
MART BV—See Siris Capital Group, LLC; *U.S. Private*, pg. 3673
MARWAY POWER SYSTEMS INC—See HEICO Corporation; *U.S. Public*, pg. 1021
MATROX ELECTRONIC SYSTEMS LTD.—See Zebra Technologies Corporation; *U.S. Public*, pg. 2401
MAXIMATECC AB—See Enerpac Tool Group Corp.; *U.S. Public*, pg. 766
MEASUREMENT COMPUTING CORPORATION—See National Instruments Corporation; *U.S. Public*, pg. 2856
MEN MIKRO ELEKTRONIK GMBH—See Deutsche Beteiligungs AG; *Int'l*, pg. 2063
MERCURY COMPUTER SYSTEMS LTD.—See Mercury Systems, Inc.; *U.S. Public*, pg. 1422
METROLOGIC ASIA (PTE) LTD.—See Honeywell International Inc.; *U.S. Public*, pg. 1050
METROLOGIC DO BRASIL LTDA.—See Honeywell International Inc.; *U.S. Public*, pg. 1050
METROLOGIC INSTRUMENTS, INC.—See Honeywell International Inc.; *U.S. Public*, pg. 1050
MICROMICR CORPORATION; *U.S. Private*, pg. 2704
MICRON TECHNOLOGY OF VIRGINIA—See Micron Technology, Inc.; *U.S. Public*, pg. 1438
MICROSOFT ENTERTAINMENT & DEVICES DIVISION—See Microsoft Corporation; *U.S. Public*, pg. 1440
MIE BROTHER PRECISION INDUSTRIES, LTD.—See Brother Industries, Ltd.; *Int'l*, pg. 1198
MIKROELEKTRONIK AR-GE TASARIM VE TICARET LTD. CO.—See Aselsan Elektronik Sanayi Ve Ticaret AS; *Int'l*, pg. 605
MILWAUKEE PC INC.; *U.S. Private*, pg. 2739
MINDSPEED TECHNOLOGIES (K.K.)—See MACOM Technology Solutions Holdings, Inc.; *U.S. Public*, pg. 1352
MITEK SYSTEMS, INC., *U.S. Public*, pg. 1451
MOBIUS PARTNERS ENTERPRISE SOLUTIONS; *U.S. Private*, pg. 2758
MODERN ELECTRONICS ESTABLISHMENT (MEE)—See Al Faisaliah Group; *Int'l*, pg. 277
MYRICOM, INC.—See CSP Inc.; *U.S. Public*, pg. 601
NANJING AIMECHATEC LTD.—See Aimechatec Ltd.; *Int'l*, pg. 233
NANJING HITACHI TECHNO. CO., LTD.—See Hitachi, Ltd.; *Int'l*, pg. 3423
NANO PRECISION CORPORATION—See Coretronic Corporation; *Int'l*, pg. 1800
NCR CHILE INDUSTRIAL Y COMERCIAL LIMITADA—See NCR Voyix Corporation; *U.S. Public*, pg. 1503
NCR DEL PERU S.A.—See NCR Voyix Corporation.; *U.S. Public*, pg. 1503
NCR GOVERNMENT SYSTEMS LLC—See NCR Voyix Corporation.; *U.S. Public*, pg. 1503
NCR SOLUTIONS DE MEXICO S. DE R.L. DE C.V.—See NCR Voyix Corporation.; *U.S. Public*, pg. 1503
THE NEAT COMPANY; *U.S. Private*, pg. 4082
NEBULA, INC., *U.S. Private*, pg. 2879
NER DATA PRODUCTS, INC.—See NER Holdings Inc.; *U.S. Private*, pg. 2885
NETGEAR, INC.; *U.S. Public*, pg. 1508
NETWORK IMAGING SOLUTIONS INC.; *U.S. Private*, pg. 2889
NETWORK INSTRUMENTS, LLC—See Viavi Solutions Inc.; *U.S. Public*, pg. 2295
NEW ENGLAND TECHNOLOGY GROUP, INC.; *U.S. Private*, pg. 2894
NIHON MERCURY COMPUTER SYSTEMS K.K.—See Mercury Systems, Inc.; *U.S. Public*, pg. 1422
NINGBO GIGA-BYTE TECHNOLOGY CO., LTD.—See Giga-Byte Technology Co., Ltd.; *Int'l*, pg. 2971
NORDELTACO A/S—See DistIT AB; *Int'l*, pg. 2136
NOVATECH, LLC - ORION UTILITY AUTOMATION DIVISION—See NovaTech, LLC; *U.S. Private*, pg. 2967
NUTFIELD TECHNOLOGY, INC.—See FARO Technologies, Inc.; *U.S. Public*, pg. 823
NUVON, INC.—See Francisco Partners Management, LP; *U.S. Private*, pg. 1589
OA LABORATORY CO., LTD. - FUJISAWA PLANT—See FUJISOFT INCORPORATED; *Int'l*, pg. 2830
OBERON, INC.—See Chatsworth Products Inc.; *U.S. Private*, pg. 868
OCP GROUP, INC.—See Blackstone Inc.; *U.S. Public*, pg. 355
ONE STOP DISPLAYS, LLC—See New Vision Display, Inc.; *U.S. Private*, pg. 2907
ONYX HEALTHCARE USA, INC.—See ASUSTeK Computer Inc.; *Int'l*, pg. 664
OPENCONNECT SYSTEMS, INC.—See Bain Capital, LP; *U.S. Private*, pg. 442
OPTOMA TECHNOLOGY, INC.—See Coretronic Corporation; *Int'l*, pg. 1800
PARKEON GMBH—See Astorg Partners S.A.S.; *Int'l*, pg. 657
PARKEON PTY LTD.—See Astorg Partners S.A.S.; *Int'l*, pg. 657
PARKEON S.A.S.—See Astorg Partners S.A.S.; *Int'l*, pg. 656
PARKEON S.A.S.—See Astorg Partners S.A.S.; *Int'l*, pg. 657
PARKEON S.L.U.—See Astorg Partners S.A.S.; *Int'l*, pg. 657
PARKEON S.P.A.—See Astorg Partners S.A.S.; *Int'l*, pg. 657
PARVUS CORP.—See Curtiss-Wright Corporation; *U.S. Public*, pg. 611
PATRIOT MEMORY—See Peripheral Devices & Products Systems Inc.; *U.S. Public*, pg. 3151
PEERLESS SYSTEMS CORPORATION—See LCV Capital Management, LLC; *U.S. Private*, pg. 2404
POINDUS SYSTEMS CORP.—See Flytech Technology Co., Ltd.; *Int'l*, pg. 2716
THE PORTLAND GROUP, INC.—See NVIDIA Corporation; *U.S. Public*, pg. 1558
POS-X, LLC—See Custom SpA; *Int'l*, pg. 1881
PRECISION ELECTRONIQUE—See Agilent Technologies, Inc.; *U.S. Public*, pg. 62
PRINTEK INC.; *U.S. Private*, pg. 3265
PRINTRONIX, INC.—See Acacia Research Corporation; *U.S. Public*, pg. 27
QATAR DATAMATION SYSTEMS—See Emirates Technology Company (EMITAC); *Int'l*, pg. 2382
QOSMOS SA—See Enea AB; *Int'l*, pg. 2410
QUANTUM STORAGE JAPAN CORPORATION—See Quantum Corporation; *U.S. Public*, pg. 1754
QUMU CORPORATION—See Enghouse Systems Limited; *Int'l*, pg. 2427
RAZER INC.; *U.S. Private*, pg. 3359
REDOCTANE, INC.—See Microsoft Corporation; *U.S. Public*, pg. 1438
RGB SYSTEMS INC.; *U.S. Private*, pg. 3420
RIMAGE JAPAN CO., LTD.—See Equus Holdings, Inc.; *U.S. Private*, pg. 1417
RKON, INC.; *U.S. Private*, pg. 3450
ROBOSERVER SYSTEMS CORP.; *U.S. Public*, pg. 1804
RUGGED INFORMATION TECHNOLOGY EQUIPMENT CORP.—See AstroNova, Inc.; *U.S. Public*, pg. 218
SANDVINE CORPORATION—See Francisco Partners Management, LP; *U.S. Private*, pg. 1591
SCAN COIN AB—See ACON Investments, LLC; *U.S. Private*, pg. 63
SCAN COIN, INC.—See ACON Investments, LLC; *U.S. Private*, pg. 63
SCAN-OPTICS, LLC—See Patriarch Partners, LLC; *U.S. Private*, pg. 3109
SCEPTRE INDUSTRIES, INC.—See Compal Electronics, Inc.; *Int'l*, pg. 1746
SCEPTRE TECHNOLOGIES INC.; *U.S. Private*, pg. 3562
SCM MICROSYSTEMS JAPAN, INC.—See Identiv, Inc.; *U.S. Public*, pg. 1089
SECURE DIGITAL, INC.; *U.S. Private*, pg. 3593
SECUREWORKS EUROPE S.R.L.—See Dell Technologies Inc.; *U.S. Public*, pg. 651
SHARP NEC DISPLAY SOLUTIONS, LTD.—See Hon Hai Precision Industry Co., Ltd.; *Int'l*, pg. 3459
SHENZHEN KAFIA MAGNETIC RECORDING CO., LTD—See China Electronics Corporation; *Int'l*, pg. 1499
SHINKO ELECTRONICS (SINGAPORE) PTE. LTD.—See Fujitsu Limited; *Int'l*, pg. 2838
SILICON MOUNTAIN MEMORY, INC.—See Silicon Mountain Holdings, Inc.; *U.S. Private*, pg. 3652
SITIME CORP.; *U.S. Public*, pg. 1889
SMART PACKAGING SOLUTIONS SAS—See Agfa-Gevaert N.V.; *Int'l*, pg. 209
SMART TECHNOLOGIES ULC—See Hon Hai Precision Industry Co., Ltd.; *Int'l*, pg. 3457
SOFTWARE AG SAUDI ARABIA LLC—See Silver Lake Group, LLC; *U.S. Private*, pg. 3660
SPECTRA LOGIC CORPORATION; *U.S. Private*, pg. 3751
SPRAYCOOL, INC.—See Parker Hannifin Corporation; *U.S. Public*, pg. 1643
SPYR, INC.; *U.S. Public*, pg. 1922
STEELCLOUD LLC; *U.S. Public*, pg. 3796
SUPER MICRO COMPUTER, INC.; *U.S. Public*, pg. 1966
SUPER MICRO COMPUTER TAIWAN INC.—See Super Micro Computer, Inc.; *U.S. Public*, pg. 1966
SUPERMICRO TECHNOLOGY (BEIJING) CO., LTD.—See Super Micro Computer, Inc.; *U.S. Public*, pg. 1966
SUZHOU MOBYDATA SMART SYSTEM CO. LTD.—See Datalogic S.p.A.; *Int'l*, pg. 1978
SYNAPTICS EUROPE SARL—See Synaptics Incorporated; *U.S. Public*, pg. 1969
SYNAPTICS INCORPORATED; *U.S. Public*, pg. 1969
SYNNEX CO., LTD.—See TD Synnex Corp; *U.S. Public*, pg. 1984
SYSTECH SOLUTIONS, INC.—See Dover Corporation; *U.S. Public*, pg. 682
TAIWAN CONTEC CO., LTD.—See Daifuku Co., Ltd.; *Int'l*, pg. 1925
TB GERMANY GMBH—See Turtle Beach Corporation; *U.S. Public*, pg. 2205
TEAC CORPORATION—See Evolution Capital Management LLC; *U.S. Private*, pg. 1442
TOM ONLINE INC.—See CK Hutchison Holdings Limited; *Int'l*, pg. 1638
TOP GLORY ELECTRONICS CO., LTD.—See Behavior Tech Computer Corporation; *Int'l*, pg. 941
TORNIK INC.—See WESCO International, Inc.; *U.S. Public*, pg. 2350
TOUCHTEK CORPORATION—See Hong Tai Electric Industrial Co., Ltd.; *Int'l*, pg. 3469
TRANAX TECHNOLOGIES INC.; *U.S. Private*, pg. 4205
TRANSITION NETWORKS—See Pineapple Energy Inc.; *U.S. Public*, pg. 1691
TRENTON SYSTEMS INC; *U.S. Private*, pg. 4218
TRENTON TECHNOLOGY INC.—See Trenton Systems Inc; *U.S. Private*, pg. 4218
TRIMBLE CORVALLIS—See Trimble, Inc.; *U.S. Public*, pg. 2192
TROJANLABEL APS—See AstroNova, Inc.; *U.S. Public*, pg. 218
TWO TECHNOLOGIES, INC., *U.S. Private*, pg. 4267
TYRRELLTECH, INC., *U.S. Private*, pg. 4269
UBEE INTERACTIVE, INC.; *U.S. Private*, pg. 4273
UBIQCONN TECHNOLOGY INC.—See FIC Global, INC; *Int'l*, pg. 2653
UCAMCO N.V.—See ESO Partners L.P.; *Int'l*, pg. 2504
ULTIMATE TECHNOLOGY CORPORATION; *U.S. Private*, pg. 4277
UNICOMP, INC., *U.S. Private*, pg. 4282
UNIVERSAL DISPLAY CORPORATION HONG KONG, LIMITED—See Universal Display Corporation; *U.S. Public*, pg. 2255
VERIFONE AUSTRALIA (HAPL) PTY LTD—See British Columbia Investment Management Corp.; *Int'l*, pg. 1170
VERIFONE AUSTRALIA (HAPL) PTY LTD—See Francisco Partners Management, LP; *U.S. Private*, pg. 1592
VERIFONE, INC.—See British Columbia Investment Management Corp.; *Int'l*, pg. 1170
VERIFONE, INC.—See Francisco Partners Management, LP; *U.S. Private*, pg. 1592
VERIFONE LATIN AMERICA & THE CARIBBEAN—See British Columbia Investment Management Corp.; *Int'l*, pg. 1170
VERIFONE LATIN AMERICA & THE CARIBBEAN—See Francisco Partners Management, LP; *U.S. Private*, pg. 1592
VERIFONE NEW ZEALAND—See British Columbia Investment Management Corp.; *Int'l*, pg. 1170
VERIFONE NEW ZEALAND—See Francisco Partners Management, LP; *U.S. Private*, pg. 1592
VERIFONE SYSTEMS (CHINA), INC.—See British Columbia Investment Management Corp.; *Int'l*, pg. 1170
VERIFONE SYSTEMS (CHINA), INC.—See Francisco Partners Management, LP; *U.S. Private*, pg. 1592
VIDEX, INC.; *U.S. Private*, pg. 4381
VIEWSONIC CORPORATION; *U.S. Private*, pg. 4381
VIKING TECHNOLOGY—See Sanmina Corporation; *U.S. Public*, pg. 1841
VIRTRA, INC.; *U.S. Public*, pg. 2299
VMWARE MALAYSIA SDN. BHD.—See Dell Technologies Inc.; *U.S. Public*, pg. 651
VMWARE MEXICO S. DE R.L. DE C.V.—See Dell Technologies Inc.; *U.S. Public*, pg. 651
VMWARE POLAND SP. Z O.O.—See Dell Technologies Inc.; *U.S. Public*, pg. 651
VMWARE SOUTH AFRICA (PTY.) LTD.—See Dell Technologies Inc.; *U.S. Public*, pg. 651
WAVELAB, INC.—See Comba Telecom Systems Holdings Limited; *Int'l*, pg. 1708
WEBDYN—See BNP Paribas SA; *Int'l*, pg. 1089
WEBSCAN, INC.—See Cognex Corporation; *U.S. Public*, pg. 523
WIEDENBACH APPARATEBAU GMBH—See Brother Industries, Ltd.; *Int'l*, pg. 1198
WINCOR NIXDORF N.V.—See Diebold Nixdorf, Inc.; *U.S. Public*, pg. 660
WMS INDUSTRIES INC.—See Light & Wonder, Inc.; *U.S. Public*, pg. 1315
WUXI EASYWAY MODEL DESIGN & MANUFACTURE CO., LTD.—See 3D Systems Corporation; *U.S. Public*, pg. 4
XEROX CANADA LTD.—See Xerox Holdings Corporation; *U.S. Public*, pg. 2390
XEROX LIMITED AG—See Xerox Holdings Corporation; *U.S. Public*, pg. 2389
XEROX REAL ESTATE & GENERAL SERVICES—See Xerox Holdings Corporation; *U.S. Public*, pg. 2390
YOUNG-IN SCIENTIFIC CO., LTD.—See Agilent Technologies, Inc.; *U.S. Public*, pg. 62
YOUNG LIGHTING TECHNOLOGY ING.—See Coretronic Corporation; *Int'l*, pg. 1800
ZEBRA TECHNOLOGIES AB—See Zebra Technologies Corporation; *U.S. Public*, pg. 2402
ZEBRA TECHNOLOGIES B.V.—See Zebra Technologies Corporation; *U.S. Public*, pg. 2402
ZEBRA TECHNOLOGIES CORPORATION; *U.S. Public*, pg. 2401
ZEBRA TECHNOLOGIES CORP.—See Zebra Technologies Corporation; *U.S. Public*, pg. 2402
ZEBRA TECHNOLOGIES INTERNATIONAL, LLC—See Zebra Technologies Corporation; *U.S. Public*, pg. 2402
ZHEJIANG BOE DISPLAY TECHNOLOGY CO., LTD.—See BOE Technology Group Co., Ltd.; *Int'l*, pg. 1099
Z MICROSYSTEMS INC.; *U.S. Private*, pg. 4596

N.A.I.C.S. INDEX

334210 — TELEPHONE APPARATUS...

ZNYX NETWORKS, INC.; *U.S. Private*, pg. 4607

334210 — TELEPHONE APPARATUS MANUFACTURING

ACROPOLIS TELECOM S.A.; *Int'l*, pg. 109
ACTELIS NETWORKS, INC.; *U.S. Public*, pg. 36
ADTRAN EUROPE LIMITED—See ADTRAN Holdings, Inc.; *U.S. Public*, pg. 43
ADTRAN, INC.—See ADTRAN Holdings, Inc.; *U.S. Public*, pg. 43
ADVANCETEC INDUSTRIES INC.; *U.S. Private*, pg. 93
ADVA OPTICAL NETWORKING AS—See ADTRAN Holdings, Inc.; *U.S. Public*, pg. 44
ADVA OPTICAL NETWORKING CORP.—See ADTRAN Holdings, Inc.; *U.S. Public*, pg. 44
ADVA OPTICAL NETWORKING HONG KONG, LTD.—See ADTRAN Holdings, Inc.; *U.S. Public*, pg. 44
ADVA OPTICAL NETWORKING (SHENZHEN) LTD—See ADTRAN Holdings, Inc.; *U.S. Public*, pg. 44
ADVA OPTICAL NETWORKING SP. Z.O.O.—See ADTRAN Holdings, Inc.; *U.S. Public*, pg. 44
AESP, INC.; *U.S. Private*, pg. 120
AEWIN TECHNOLOGIES CO., LTD.; *Int'l*, pg. 183
AIMVALLEY B.V.; *Int'l*, pg. 234
AIRVANA, INC.; *U.S. Private*, pg. 142
AIRVANA NETWORKS INDIA PRIVATE LIMITED—See Airvana, Inc.; *U.S. Private*, pg. 142
ALCADON GROUP AB; *Int'l*, pg. 299
ALLIED TELESYN INTERNATIONAL S.R.L.—See ALLIED TELESIS HOLDINGS K.K.; *Int'l*, pg. 359
ALPHA NETWORKS INC.; *Int'l*, pg. 368
ALPHA SOLUTIONS CO., LTD.—See Alpha Networks Inc.; *Int'l*, pg. 369
ALTIGEN COMMUNICATIONS, INC., *U.S. Public*, pg. 88
ALVARION LTD.; *Int'l*, pg. 401
AMERICAN TEL-A-SYSTEMS INC.; *U.S. Private*, pg. 256
AMERITEC CORPORATION; *U.S. Private*, pg. 261
AMPED WIRELESS LIMITED; *U.S. Private*, pg. 265
AMPHENOL NETWORK SOLUTIONS, INC.—See Amphenol Corporation; *U.S. Public*, pg. 128
AMPHITECH; *Int'l*, pg. 433
ASCOM HPF SA—See Ascom Holding AG; *Int'l*, pg. 603
ATLINKS GROUP LIMITED; *Int'l*, pg. 687
AUDIOCODES CALIFORNIA—See AudioCodes Ltd.; *Int'l*, pg. 701
AUDIOCODES LTD.; *Int'l*, pg. 701
AUDIOSEARS CORPORATION; *U.S. Private*, pg. 391
AVAYA INC.—See Silver Lake Group, LLC; *U.S. Private*, pg. 3655
AVAYA INC.—See TPG Capital, L.P.; *U.S. Public*, pg. 2168
AZ-TECHNOLOGY SDN BHD—See Aztech Group Ltd.; *Int'l*, pg. 781
BEIJING EDIMAX SCIENCE & TECHNOLOGY CO., LTD.—See Edimax Technology Co., Ltd.; *Int'l*, pg. 2310
BILLION ELECTRIC CO., LTD.; *Int'l*, pg. 1031
BLACKBERRY LIMITED; *Int'l*, pg. 1060
BLACKBERRY UK LIMITED—See BlackBerry Limited; *Int'l*, pg. 1060
BOGEN COMMUNICATIONS, INC.—See Bogen Communications International Inc.; *U.S. Public*, pg. 367
BOGEN COMMUNICATIONS INTERNATIONAL INC.; *U.S. Public*, pg. 367
BOTAI TECHNOLOGY LIMITED; *Int'l*, pg. 1118
BRIGHTSTAR DOMINICANA S.A.—See Brightstar Capital Partners, L.P.; *U.S. Private*, pg. 653
BUSINESS MARKETERS GROUP, INC.—See Halma plc; *Int'l*, pg. 3230
BYD ELECTRONIC INTERNATIONAL CO LTD—See BYD Company Limited; *Int'l*, pg. 1234
CALIX INC. - DEVELOPMENT CENTER—See Calix Inc.; *U.S. Public*, pg. 424
CALIX—See Calix Inc.; *U.S. Public*, pg. 424
CALL-EM-ALL LLC; *U.S. Private*, pg. 721
CALL MANAGEMENT PRODUCTS INC.; *U.S. Private*, pg. 721
CAMEO COMMUNICATION, INC.; *Int'l*, pg. 1271
CASTLENET TECHNOLOGY, INC.; *Int'l*, pg. 1357
CAVENDISH KINETICS B.V.—See Qorvo, Inc.; *U.S. Public*, pg. 1743
C-COR INCORPORATED—See CommScope Holding Company, Inc.; *U.S. Public*, pg. 548
CEECO, INC.; *U.S. Private*, pg. 805
CELLY S.P.A.—See Esprinet S.p.A.; *Int'l*, pg. 2506
CERAGON NETWORKS PHILIPPINES, INC.—See Ceragon Networks Ltd.; *Int'l*, pg. 1421
CHINA ELECTRONICS TECHNOLOGY GROUP CORPORATION; *Int'l*, pg. 1499
CHONGQING XINWEI TELECOM TECHNOLOGY CO., LTD.—See Beijing Xinwei Technology Group Co., Ltd.; *Int'l*, pg. 961
CIENA COMMUNICATIONS, INC.—See Ciena Corporation; *U.S. Public*, pg. 494
CIG SHANGHAI CO., LTD.; *Int'l*, pg. 1606
CISCO NORWAY AS—See Cisco Systems, Inc.; *U.S. Public*, pg. 497
CISCO SYSTEMS (CHINA) NETWORKING TECHNOLOGY CO., LTD.—See Cisco Systems, Inc.; *U.S. Public*, pg. 497
CISCO SYSTEMS LLC—See Cisco Systems, Inc.; *U.S. Public*, pg. 498
CISCO SYSTEMS MACEDONIA DOOEL SKOPJE—See Cisco Systems, Inc.; *U.S. Public*, pg. 498
CISCO VIDEO TECHNOLOGIES INDIA PRIVATE LIMITED—See Cisco Systems, Inc.; *U.S. Public*, pg. 499
CIVITELLA & CIA LTDA—See Klein Tools Inc.; *U.S. Private*, pg. 2319
CLARITY—See HP Inc.; *U.S. Public*, pg. 1064
CLEARONE, INC.; *U.S. Public*, pg. 512
CMR PHILIPPINES, INC.—See Amphenol Corporation; *U.S. Public*, pg. 129
COMARCO WIRELESS TECHNOLOGIES, INC.—See Comarco, Inc.; *U.S. Public*, pg. 980
COMBA TELECOM LTDA—See Comba Telecom Systems Holdings Limited; *Int'l*, pg. 1708
COMMUNICATION WEAVER CO., LTD.; *Int'l*, pg. 1720
CONDUCTIX-WAMPFLER O.O.O.—See CVC Capital Partners SICAV-FIS S.A.; *Int'l*, pg. 1887
CORIANT AMERICA, INC.—See Marlin Equity Partners, LLC; *U.S. Private*, pg. 2584
CORTELCO, INC.—See Cortelco Systems Holding Corp.; *U.S. Private*, pg. 1060
COVEROO, INC.—See Zazzle, Inc.; *U.S. Private*, pg. 4598
CRITICAL TELECOM INC.—See BATM Advanced Communications Ltd.; *Int'l*, pg. 890
CXTEC; *U.S. Private*, pg. 1133
CYBERTAN TECHNOLOGY, INC.; *Int'l*, pg. 1894
DBTEL; *Int'l*, pg. 1989
D-LINK CORPORATION, INC.; *Int'l*, pg. 1900
D-LINK MALAYSIA SDN. BHD.—See D-Link Corporation, Inc.; *Int'l*, pg. 1900
DONGGUAN YOUXUN ELECTRONICS CO., LTD.—See Alpha Networks Inc.; *Int'l*, pg. 369
DRAYTEK CORPORATION; *Int'l*, pg. 2200
DURATEL S.P.A.—See EcoTec s.r.l.; *Int'l*, pg. 2300
ECI TELECOM LTD.—See Ribbon Communications Inc.; *U.S. Public*, pg. 1796
ECS TELECOM CO., LTD.; *Int'l*, pg. 2301
EDIMAX TECHNOLOGY CO., LTD.; *Int'l*, pg. 2310
EKINOPS S.A.; *Int'l*, pg. 2338
ELECTRONIC TELE-COMMUNICATIONS, INC.; *U.S. Public*, pg. 725
ELECTRO STANDARDS LABORATORIES INC.; *U.S. Private*, pg. 1353
EXTREME NETWORKS NETHERLANDS BV—See Extreme Networks, Inc.; *U.S. Public*, pg. 813
EXTREME NETWORKS TECHNOLOGY CO. (BEIJING) LTD.—See Extreme Networks, Inc.; *U.S. Public*, pg. 813
FIBERWAVE CORP.; *U.S. Private*, pg. 1502
FIFO WIRELESS; *U.S. Private*, pg. 1505
FIH MOBILE LIMITED—See Hon Hai Precision Industry Co., Ltd.; *Int'l*, pg. 3457
FINISAR CORP. - FREMONT—See Coherent Corp.; *U.S. Public*, pg. 528
FLEXTRONICS MANUFACTURING MEXICO, S.A. DE C.V.—See Flex Ltd.; *Int'l*, pg. 2703
FLORIDA MICROELECTRONICS, LLC—See Francisco Partners Management, LP; *U.S. Private*, pg. 1589
FRANKLIN WIRELESS CORPORATION; *U.S. Public*, pg. 883
FRTEK CO., LTD.; *Int'l*, pg. 2797
FUJITSU NETWORK COMMUNICATIONS INC.—See Fujitsu Limited; *Int'l*, pg. 2833
GENERAL DATACOMM INDUSTRIES, INC.; *U.S. Public*, pg. 913
GIGASET COMMUNICATIONS GMBH—See Gigaset AG; *Int'l*, pg. 2972
GLOBAL TEL LINK CORPORATION—See American Securities LLC; *U.S. Private*, pg. 249
GN NETCOM INC.—See GN Store Nord A/S; *Int'l*, pg. 3016
GROUP SENSE MOBILE-TECH LIMITED—See Century Sunshine Group Holdings Limited; *Int'l*, pg. 1419
HITACHI TELECOM (USA), INC.—See Hitachi, Ltd.; *Int'l*, pg. 3414
HITRON TECHNOLOGIES AMERICAS INC.—See Hitron Technologies Inc.; *Int'l*, pg. 3427
HITRON TECHNOLOGIES EUROPE HOLDING B.V.—See Hitron Technologies Inc.; *Int'l*, pg. 3427
HITRON TECHNOLOGIES (SIP) INC.—See Hitron Technologies Inc.; *Int'l*, pg. 3427
HKC TECHNOLOGY LIMITED—See HKC International Holdings Limited; *Int'l*, pg. 3428
HKC TECHNOLOGY (SHANGHAI) CO. LTD.—See HKC International Holdings Limited; *Int'l*, pg. 3428
HSQ TECHNOLOGY INC—See Wind Point Advisors LLC; *U.S. Private*, pg. 4535
HUBBELL PREMISE WIRING—See Hubbell Incorporated; *U.S. Public*, pg. 1067
HUBER+SUHNER CUBE OPTICS AG—See Huber + Suhner AG; *Int'l*, pg. 3519
ILYA CO., LTD. - PYEONGTAEK FACTORY—See Enterpartners Co., LTD; *Int'l*, pg. 2451
ILYA CO., LTD. - WEIHAI FACTORY—See Enterpartners Co., LTD; *Int'l*, pg. 2451
INTEL CORPORATION - PARSIPPANY OFFICE—See Intel Corporation; *U.S. Public*, pg. 1138
INTERACTIVE DIGITAL TECHNOLOGIES INC.—See Hitron Technologies Inc.; *Int'l*, pg. 3427
INTERDIGITAL - MELVILLE—See InterDigital, Inc.; *U.S. Public*, pg. 1144
IWATSU HONG KONG, LTD.—See AI Holdings Corp.; *Int'l*, pg. 227
IWATSU (MALAYSIA) SDN. BHD.—See AI Holdings Corp.; *Int'l*, pg. 227
JIETECH TRADING (SUZHOU) INC.—See Hitron Technologies Inc.; *Int'l*, pg. 3427
KAJ LARSEN COMMUNICATION A/S—See Aiphone Co., Ltd.; *Int'l*, pg. 235
LAKE COMMUNICATIONS LIMITED—See Searchlight Capital Partners, L.P.; *U.S. Private*, pg. 3589
LEVITON NETWORK SOLUTIONS—See Leviton Manufacturing Company, Inc.; *U.S. Private*, pg. 2437
LIGHTWIRE LLC—See Cisco Systems, Inc.; *U.S. Public*, pg. 499
LUXMOBILE GROUP; *U.S. Private*, pg. 2518
MEDTELL LTD—See MedTel Services, LLC; *U.S. Private*, pg. 2659
MESSAGE PROCESSING INTERNATIONAL, INC.; *U.S. Public*, pg. 1426
MICROSEMI FREQUENCY & TIME CORPORATION—See Microchip Technology Incorporated; *U.S. Public*, pg. 1436
MICROSEMI FREQUENCY & TIME GMBH—See Microchip Technology Incorporated; *U.S. Public*, pg. 1436
MICROSOFT MOBILE DEUTSCHLAND GMBH—See Microsoft Corporation; *U.S. Public*, pg. 1441
MICRO VOICE APPLICATIONS, INC.; *U.S. Private*, pg. 2702
MOTOROLA SOLUTIONS FRANCE SAS—See Motorola Solutions, Inc.; *U.S. Public*, pg. 1478
MULTI-TECH SYSTEMS INC.—See Northlane Capital Partners, LLC; *U.S. Private*, pg. 2956
MYEDGE LLC; *U.S. Private*, pg. 2824
NETCOMM WIRELESS LIMITED—See Casa Systems, Inc.; *U.S. Private*, pg. 778
NETCOMM WIRELESS—See Casa Systems, Inc.; *U.S. Private*, pg. 778
NETGEAR DENMARK APS—See NETGEAR, Inc.; *U.S. Public*, pg. 1508
NETGEAR HONG KONG LIMITED—See NETGEAR, Inc.; *U.S. Public*, pg. 1508
NETGEAR RESEARCH INDIA PVT. LTD.—See NETGEAR, Inc.; *U.S. Public*, pg. 1508
NETGEAR RUSSIA LLC—See NETGEAR, Inc.; *U.S. Public*, pg. 1508
NETWORK EQUIPMENT TECHNOLOGIES, INC.—See Ribbon Communications Inc.; *U.S. Public*, pg. 1797
NEWTON INSTRUMENT COMPANY; *U.S. Private*, pg. 2918
NSGDATACOM, INC.; *U.S. Private*, pg. 2970
ONEACCESS SA—See Ekinops S.A.; *Int'l*, pg. 2338
OPLINK COMMUNICATIONS, LLC—See Koch Industries, Inc.; *U.S. Private*, pg. 2335
OPTOPLEX CORP.; *U.S. Public*, pg. 3036
PATTON ELECTRONICS CO.; *U.S. Private*, pg. 3111
PIONEER COMMUNICATIONS CORP—See EQT AB; *Int'l*, pg. 2470
PLAMEX, S.A. DE C.V.—See HP Inc.; *U.S. Public*, pg. 1064
PLANTRONICS, INC.—See HP Inc.; *U.S. Public*, pg. 1064
POLYCOM ASIA PACIFIC PTE LTD.—See HP Inc.; *U.S. Public*, pg. 1064
POLYCOM (FRANCE), S.A.R.L.—See HP Inc.; *U.S. Public*, pg. 1064
POLYCOM GLOBAL LIMITED—See HP Inc.; *U.S. Public*, pg. 1064
POLYCOM, INC. - AUSTIN—See HP Inc.; *U.S. Public*, pg. 1065
POLYCOM, INC.—See HP Inc.; *U.S. Public*, pg. 1064
POLYCOM, INC. - WESTMINSTER—See HP Inc.; *U.S. Public*, pg. 1065
POLYCOM ISRAEL LTD.—See HP Inc.; *U.S. Public*, pg. 1064
POLYCOM (JAPAN) K.K.—See HP Inc.; *U.S. Public*, pg. 1064
POLYCOM NORWAY AS—See HP Inc.; *U.S. Public*, pg. 1065
POLYCOM RUSSIA—See HP Inc.; *U.S. Public*, pg. 1065
POLYCOM TELECOMUNICACOES DO BRASIL LTDA.—See HP Inc.; *U.S. Public*, pg. 1065
PROTEL INC.—See Warburg Pincus LLC; *U.S. Private*, pg. 4438
QUINTRON SYSTEMS, INC.—See Godspeed Capital Management LP; *U.S. Private*, pg. 1725
RADIO DATA TECHNOLOGY LTD.—See CML Microsystems Plc; *Int'l*, pg. 1671
RAULAND-BORG CORPORATION—See AMETEK, Inc.; *U.S. Public*, pg. 118
RIBBON COMMUNICATIONS MALAYSIA SDN. BHD.—See Ribbon Communications Inc.; *U.S. Public*, pg. 1797
SA JAPAN KK—See Cisco Systems, Inc.; *U.S. Public*, pg. 500
SCIENTIFIC-ATLANTA, LLC—See Cisco Systems, Inc.; *U.S. Public*, pg. 500
SHENZHEN XINWEI TELECOM TECHNOLOGY CO.,

334210 — TELEPHONE APPARATUS...

LTD.—See Beijing Xinwei Technology Group Co., Ltd.; *Int'l*, pg. 961
SHORETEL, INC.—See Searchlight Capital Partners, L.P.; *U.S. Private*, pg. 3589
SILIGENCE SAS—See ASUSTeK Computer Inc.; *Int'l*, pg. 663
SMARTPHONE EXPERTS LLC; *U.S. Private*, pg. 3692
SMT TECHNOLOGIES SDN. BHD.—See EG Industries Berhad; *Int'l*, pg. 2322
SONUS NETWORKS AUSTRALIA PTY LTD.—See Ribbon Communications Inc.; *U.S. Public*, pg. 1797
STAR2STAR COMMUNICATIONS, LLC—See Comcast Corporation; *U.S. Public*, pg. 537
SUTTLE APPARATUS CORPORATION—See Pineapple Energy Inc.; *U.S. Public*, pg. 1691
TELAMON TECHNOLOGIES CORP—See Telamon Corporation; *U.S. Private*, pg. 3959
TELEDEX CORPORATION; *U.S. Private*, pg. 3960
TELIT COMMUNICATIONS PLC—See DBAY Advisors Limited; *Int'l*, pg. 1987
TELIT COMMUNICATIONS S.P.A.—See DBAY Advisors Limited; *Int'l*, pg. 1988
TELLABS OPERATIONS, INC.—See Marlin Equity Partners, LLC; *U.S. Private*, pg. 2585
TELULAR CORPORATION—See AMETEK, Inc.; *U.S. Public*, pg. 122
TEO TECHNOLOGIES; *U.S. Private*, pg. 3968
TOLLGRADE COMMUNICATIONS, INC.—See Enghouse Systems Limited; *Int'l*, pg. 2428
TOLLGRADE GERMANY GMBH—See Enghouse Systems Limited; *Int'l*, pg. 2428
TOLLGRADE UK LIMITED—See Enghouse Systems Limited; *Int'l*, pg. 2428
ULTRA ELECTRONICS DNE TECHNOLOGIES, INC.—See Advent International Corporation; *U.S. Private*, pg. 101
ULTRATEC, INC.; *U.S. Private*, pg. 4278
VARI TRONICS COMPANY, INC.; *U.S. Private*, pg. 4346
VERIZON COMMUNICATIONS INC. - JOHNSTOWN, PA—See Verizon Communications Inc.; *U.S. Public*, pg. 2285
VIDEO GUIDANCE, INC.; *U.S. Private*, pg. 4380
VOICE-TECH, INC.; *U.S. Private*, pg. 4409
WAVESPLITTER TECHNOLOGIES, INC.; *U.S. Private*, pg. 4458
WESTELL TECHNOLOGIES, INC.; *U.S. Public*, pg. 2354
WINDSTREAM D&E, INC.—See Windstream Holdings, Inc.; *U.S. Public*, pg. 2373
WISTRON NEXUS INC.—See Acer Incorporated; *Int'l*, pg. 100
WORLDGATE COMMUNICATIONS, INC.; *U.S. Private*, pg. 4568
WORLD KINECT CORPORATION; *U.S. Public*, pg. 2380
XYBERNAUT CORPORATION; *U.S. Private*, pg. 4583
YUNKE CHINA INFORMATION TECHNOLOGY LIMITED—See Digital China Holdings Limited; *Int'l*, pg. 2121

334220 — RADIO AND TELEVISION BROADCASTING AND WIRELESS COMMUNICATIONS EQUIPMENT MANUFACTURING

2M-TEK, INC.—See Parker Wellbore Company; *U.S. Public*, pg. 1650
4CABLE TV INTERNATIONAL, INC.; *U.S. Public*, pg. 9
5BARZ INTERNATIONAL INC.; *U.S. Public*, pg. 16
AAC WIRELESS TECHNOLOGIES AB—See AAC Technologies Holdings Inc.; *Int'l*, pg. 31
ABER ELECTRONICS LIMITED—See Creo Medical Group PLC; *Int'l*, pg. 1838
ABOCOM SYSTEMS, INC.; *Int'l*, pg. 66
AB VILNIAUS VINGIS; *Int'l*, pg. 42
ACBZ IMPORTACAO E COMERCIO LTDA.—See ASUSTeK Computer Inc.; *Int'l*, pg. 663
AC&C INTERNATIONAL CO., LTD.; *Int'l*, pg. 74
ACCURIS NETWORKS LIMITED—See ESW Capital, LLC; *U.S. Private*, pg. 1430
ACE ANTENNA CO., LTD.—See Ace Technologies Corp.; *Int'l*, pg. 95
ACE ANTENNA COMPANY INC.—See Ace Technologies Corp.; *Int'l*, pg. 95
ACE ANTENNA INDIA PRIVATE LIMITED—See Ace Technologies Corp.; *Int'l*, pg. 95
ACE TECHNOLOGIES CORP.; *Int'l*, pg. 95
ACTIVE CONTROL TECHNOLOGY INC.; *Int'l*, pg. 120
ACTIVE NETWORK IPICO (US) INC.—See Global Payments Inc.; *U.S. Public*, pg. 943
ADEUNIS RF; *Int'l*, pg. 145
ADRONICS/ELROB MANUFACTURING; *U.S. Private*, pg. 82
ADVANCED ENERGY INDUSTRIES, INC.—See Advanced Energy Industries, Inc.; *U.S. Public*, pg. 47
ADVANCED MICROWAVE, INC.—See NeoMagic Corporation; *U.S. Public*, pg. 1506
ADVANCETC LIMITED; *Int'l*, pg. 163
THE AEGIS MOBILE, LLC; *U.S. Private*, pg. 3982
AEROSCOUT, INC.; *U.S. Private*, pg. 119
AETHERCOMM INC.—See Veritas Capital Fund Management, LLC; *U.S. Private*, pg. 4362
AGC MULTI MATERIAL EUROPE SA—See AGC Inc.; *Int'l*, pg. 202
AIPTEK INTERNATIONAL INC.; *Int'l*, pg. 235
AIRSPAN COMMUNICATIONS LTD.—See Airspan Networks Holdings Inc.; *U.S. Public*, pg. 68
AIRSPAN COMMUNICATIONS (SHANGHAI) CO. LTD.—See Airspan Networks Holdings Inc.; *U.S. Public*, pg. 68
AIRSPAN JAPAN KK (KABUSHIKI KAISHA)—See Airspan Networks Holdings Inc.; *U.S. Public*, pg. 68
AIRSPAN NETWORKS (ISRAEL) LTD—See Airspan Networks Holdings Inc.; *U.S. Public*, pg. 68
AIRSPAN NETWORKS PTY LTD—See Airspan Networks Holdings Inc.; *U.S. Public*, pg. 68
AIRTIME MANAGEMENT AND PROGRAMMING SDN. BHD.—See Astro All Asia Networks plc; *Int'l*, pg. 662
AIR-TRAK—See EROAD Limited; *Int'l*, pg. 2496
AIRWAVE SOLUTIONS LIMITED—See Motorola Solutions, Inc.; *U.S. Public*, pg. 1478
ALARIS ANTENNAS PROPRIETARY LIMITED—See Alaris Holdings Limited; *Int'l*, pg. 291
ALARIS HOLDINGS LIMITED; *Int'l*, pg. 291
ALBATRON TECHNOLOGY CO., LTD.; *Int'l*, pg. 293
ALIEN TECHNOLOGY CORPORATION; *U.S. Private*, pg. 167
ALLGON AB—See Bure Equity AB; *Int'l*, pg. 1221
ALLIED TELESIS HOLDINGS K.K.; *Int'l*, pg. 358
ALLIED TELESIS (HONG KONG) LTD.—See ALLIED TELESIS HOLDINGS K.K.; *Int'l*, pg. 358
ALLIS COMMUNICATIONS CO., LTD.—See Allis Electric Co., Ltd.; *Int'l*, pg. 359
ALLOY COMPUTER PRODUCTS (AUSTRALIA) PTY. LTD.; *Int'l*, pg. 360
ALLOY COMPUTER PRODUCTS LLC—See Alloy Computer Products (Australia) Pty. Ltd.; *Int'l*, pg. 360
ALOYS INC.; *Int'l*, pg. 365
AMERICAN MICROWAVE CORPORATION—See Ironwave Technologies LLC; *U.S. Private*, pg. 2140
AMETEK PROGRAMMABLE POWER, INC.—See AMETEK, Inc.; *U.S. Public*, pg. 118
AMIMON, LTD.; *Int'l*, pg. 427
AM NETWORKS; *U.S. Private*, pg. 214
AMOTECH CO., LTD. - ANTENNA DIVISION—See Amotech Co Ltd; *Int'l*, pg. 431
AMPHENOL ANTENNA SOLUTIONS, INC.—See Amphenol Corporation; *U.S. Public*, pg. 127
AMPHENOL PROCOM, INC.—See Amphenol Corporation; *U.S. Public*, pg. 128
AMPHENOL T&M ANTENNAS, INC.—See Amphenol Corporation; *U.S. Public*, pg. 128
AMPLIDAN A/S—See L3Harris Technologies, Inc.; *U.S. Public*, pg. 1280
AMPLIFIER RESEARCH CORP.—See AMETEK, Inc.; *U.S. Public*, pg. 120
AMPLITECH GROUP, INC.; *U.S. Public*, pg. 133
AMTRAN VIETNAM TECHNOLOGY COMPANY LIMITED—See AmTRAN Technology; *Int'l*, pg. 442
ANAREN COMMUNICATIONS SUZHOU CO., LTD.—See TTM Technologies, Inc.; *U.S. Public*, pg. 2203
ANAREN MICROWAVE, INC.—See TTM Technologies, Inc.; *U.S. Public*, pg. 2203
ANDREA ELECTRONICS CORPORATION; *U.S. Public*, pg. 136
ANDREW TELECOMMUNICATIONS DE REYNOSA S DE RL DE CV—See CommScope Holding Company, Inc.; *U.S. Public*, pg. 548
ANHUI TATFOOK TECHNOLOGY CO., LTD; *Int'l*, pg. 469
ANTENEX, INC.—See DuPont de Nemours, Inc.; *U.S. Public*, pg. 693
ANTENNACRAFT CO.—See RS Legacy Corporation; *U.S. Private*, pg. 3496
ANTENNA DEVELOPMENT CORPORATION—See Blue Canyon Technologies LLC; *U.S. Private*, pg. 586
ANTENNA PRODUCTS CORPORATION—See Phazar Corp.; *U.S. Private*, pg. 3166
ANTENNA & TECHNOLOGY CORP.—See Ace Technologies Corp.; *Int'l*, pg. 95
ANTRONIX INC.; *U.S. Private*, pg. 288
API DELEVAN, INC.—See Danaher Corporation; *U.S. Public*, pg. 623
ARCADYAN TECHNOLOGY CORPORATION—See Compal Electronics, Inc.; *Int'l*, pg. 1746
ARC WIRELESS, INC.—See ARC Group Worldwide, Inc.; *U.S. Public*, pg. 179
ARC WIRELESS, LLC—See ARC Group Worldwide, Inc.; *U.S. Public*, pg. 179
ARELIS SAS; *Int'l*, pg. 558
ARIES INDUSTRIES INC.; *U.S. Private*, pg. 322
ARION TECHNOLOGY INC.; *Int'l*, pg. 565
ARRIS SOLUTIONS, INC. - CHICAGO—See CommScope Holding Company, Inc.; *U.S. Public*, pg. 548
ARRIS SOLUTIONS, INC. - HORSHAM—See CommScope Holding Company, Inc.; *U.S. Public*, pg. 548
ARRIS SOLUTIONS, INC.—See CommScope Holding Company, Inc.; *U.S. Public*, pg. 548
ARROW-COMMUNICATION LABS INC—See Northern CATV Sales Inc.; *U.S. Private*, pg. 2952

CORPORATE AFFILIATIONS

ARROW ELECTRONICS KOREA LTD.—See Arrow Electronics, Inc.; *U.S. Public*, pg. 195
ARTEL—See Atrel VideoSystems; *U.S. Private*, pg. 382
ARYA ELECTRONICS IRAN CO.; *Int'l*, pg. 588
ASCOM SECURITY SOLUTIONS AG—See Ascom Holding AG; *Int'l*, pg. 603
ASC SIGNAL DIVISION - MANUFACTURING—See Kratos Defense & Security Solutions, Inc.; *U.S. Public*, pg. 1275
ASIA ICOM INC.—See ICOM INCORPORATED; *Int'l*, pg. 3582
AS-IP TECH, INC.; *U.S. Public*, pg. 209
ASKEY DO BRASIL TECNOLOGIA LTDA.—See ASUSTeK Computer Inc.; *Int'l*, pg. 663
ASKEY INTERNATIONAL CORP.—See ASUSTeK Computer Inc.; *Int'l*, pg. 663
ASKEY TECHNOLOGY (JIANGSU) LTD.—See ASUSTeK Computer Inc.; *Int'l*, pg. 663
ASTEELFLASH DESIGN SOLUTIONS HAMBURG GMBH—See ASE Technology Holding Co., Ltd.; *Int'l*, pg. 604
ASTEELFLASH DEVELOPPEMENT—See ASE Technology Holding Co., Ltd.; *Int'l*, pg. 604
ASTEELFLASH EST—See ASE Technology Holding Co., Ltd.; *Int'l*, pg. 604
ASTEELFLASH HERSFELD GMBH—See ASE Technology Holding Co., Ltd.; *Int'l*, pg. 605
ASTEELFLASH NORMANDIE—See ASE Technology Holding Co., Ltd.; *Int'l*, pg. 605
ASTRA MICROWAVE PRODUCTS LIMITED; *Int'l*, pg. 658
ASTRO STROBEL KOMMUNIKATIONSSYSTEME GMBH; *Int'l*, pg. 662
ATC FIBRA DE COLOMBIA, S.A.S.—See American Tower Corporation; *U.S. Public*, pg. 110
AUTELAN TECHNOLOGY INTERNATIONAL LIMITED—See Beijing AUTELAN Technology Co. Ltd.; *Int'l*, pg. 945
AVCON INFORMATION TECHNOLOGY CO., LTD.; *Int'l*, pg. 737
AVENIR TELECOM FRANCE—See Avenir Telecom S.A.; *Int'l*, pg. 738
AVENIR TELECOM ROMANIA—See Avenir Telecom S.A.; *Int'l*, pg. 738
AVENIR TELECOM SPAIN—See Avenir Telecom S.A.; *Int'l*, pg. 738
AVIAT COMMUNICATIONS TECHNOLOGY (SHENZHEN) COMPANY LTD.—See Aviat Networks, Inc.; *U.S. Public*, pg. 245
AVIAT NETWORKS BRASIL SERVICOS EM COMMUNICACOES LTDA.—See Aviat Networks, Inc.; *U.S. Public*, pg. 245
AVIAT NETWORKS CANADA ULC—See Aviat Networks, Inc.; *U.S. Public*, pg. 245
AVIAT NETWORKS COMMUNICATION SOLUTIONS LIMITED—See Aviat Networks, Inc.; *U.S. Public*, pg. 245
AVIAT NETWORKS COTE D'IVOIRE—See Aviat Networks, Inc.; *U.S. Public*, pg. 245
AVIAT NETWORKS DE MEXICO, S.A. DE C.V.—See Aviat Networks, Inc.; *U.S. Public*, pg. 245
AVIAT NETWORKS SAUDI ARABIA—See Aviat Networks, Inc.; *U.S. Public*, pg. 245
AVIAT NETWORKS (UK) LIMITED—See Aviat Networks, Inc.; *U.S. Public*, pg. 245
AVIAT U.S., INC. - SAN ANTONIO—See Aviat Networks, Inc.; *U.S. Public*, pg. 246
AVIAT U.S., INC.—See Aviat Networks, Inc.; *U.S. Public*, pg. 245
AV TECH CORPORATION; *Int'l*, pg. 733
AXCERA, LLC—See GigaHertz LLC; *U.S. Private*, pg. 1697
AXESSTEL KOREA, INC.—See Axesstel, Inc.; *U.S. Private*, pg. 412
AXIA NETMEDIA CORPORATION—See BCE Inc.; *Int'l*, pg. 926
AXXCELERA BROADBAND WIRELESS INC.—See Moseley Associates, Inc.; *U.S. Private*, pg. 2793
AZUREWAVE TECHNOLOGIES, INC.; *Int'l*, pg. 782
BAE SYSTEMS-INTEGRATED ELECTRONIC SOLUTIONS—See BAE Systems plc; *Int'l*, pg. 797
BAN LOONG HOLDINGS LTD.; *Int'l*, pg. 814
BARCO SIMULATIONS—See Barco N.V.; *Int'l*, pg. 864
BARTEC PIXAVI AS—See Charterhouse Capital Partners LLP; *Int'l*, pg. 1455
BAYLIN TECHNOLOGIES INC.; *Int'l*, pg. 914
BEAM COMMUNICATIONS PTY. LTD.; *Int'l*, pg. 932
BEAM COMMUNICATIONS PTY LTD.—See Beam Communications Pty. Ltd.; *Int'l*, pg. 932
BEETEL TELETECH LIMITED—See Brightstar Capital Partners, L.P.; *U.S. Private*, pg. 653
BEIJING AUTELAN TECHNOLOGY CO. LTD.; *Int'l*, pg. 945
BEKEN CORPORATION; *Int'l*, pg. 962
BELDEN GRASS VALLEY ASIA LIMITED—See Belden, Inc.; *U.S. Public*, pg. 293
BELDEN GRASS VALLEY INDUSTRIA E COMERCIO E SERVICOS LTDA.—See Belden, Inc.; *U.S. Public*, pg. 293
BELL-PARK CO., LTD.; *Int'l*, pg. 966
BHARAT ELECTRONICS LIMITED; *Int'l*, pg. 1010
BINATONE ELECTRONICS INTERNATIONAL LTD.; *Int'l*, pg. 1033

N.A.I.C.S. INDEX

BIOQUEST CORP.; *U.S. Public*, pg. 338
BITEK PTY LTD.; *Int'l*, pg. 1050
BJG ELECTRONICS, INC.—See Audax Group, Limited Partnership; *U.S. Public*, pg. 387
BK TECHNOLOGIES CORPORATION; *U.S. Public*, pg. 340
BLACKBERRY LTD. - WATERLOO MANUFACTURING FACILITY—See BlackBerry Limited; *Int'l*, pg. 1060
BLACK & DECKER MACAO—See Stanley Black & Decker, Inc.; *U.S. Public*, pg. 1936
BLACKLINE SAFETY CORP.; *Int'l*, pg. 1061
BLAUPUNKT INTERNATIONAL GMBH & CO. KG—See Aurelius Equity Opportunities SE & Co. KGaA; *Int'l*, pg. 707
BLONDER TONGUE LABORATORIES, INC.; *U.S. Public*, pg. 362
BLUECOM CO., LTD.; *Int'l*, pg. 1071
BOKWANG HI-TECH CO., LTD—See Bokwang TS Co.; *Int'l*, pg. 1102
BOKWANG TS CO.; *Int'l*, pg. 1102
BOOMSENSE TECHNOLOGY CO., LTD.; *Int'l*, pg. 1111
BROADCAST ELECTRONICS, INC.; *U.S. Private*, pg. 658
BROADCAST ELECTRONICS, INC.—See Audax Group, Limited Partnership; *U.S. Private*, pg. 386
BROADCAST MARKETING GROUP, INC.; *U.S. Public*, pg. 388
BROADCAST MICROWAVE SERVICES EUROPE GMBH—See Vislink Technologies Inc.; *U.S. Public*, pg. 2304
BROADCAST MICROWAVE SERVICES, INC.—See Vislink Technologies Inc.; *U.S. Public*, pg. 2304
BROWNING PRODUCTIONS & ENTERTAINMENT, INC.; *U.S. Private*, pg. 669
BYD ELECTRONIC HUNGARY KFT—See BYD Company Limited; *Int'l*, pg. 1234
CABASSE GROUP; *Int'l*, pg. 1245
CALAMP CORP.; *U.S. Public*, pg. 422
CALIFORNIA AMPLIFIER S.A.R.L—See CalAmp Corp.; *U.S. Public*, pg. 422
CALIX INC.; *U.S. Public*, pg. 424
CAMBRIDGE BROADBAND NETWORKS LIMITED; *Int'l*, pg. 1269
CAREVIEW COMMUNICATIONS, INC.; *U.S. Public*, pg. 435
CARRIERCOMM INC.—See Moseley Associates, Inc.; *U.S. Private*, pg. 2793
CASIO INDIA COMPANY PRIVATE LTD—See Casio Computer Co., Ltd.; *Int'l*, pg. 1353
CASIO PHILIPPINES CORPORATION—See Casio Computer Co., Ltd.; *Int'l*, pg. 1353
CBC AMERICA CO., LTD.—See CBC Co., Ltd.; *Int'l*, pg. 1365
CELLO ELECTRONICS (UK) LTD.; *Int'l*, pg. 1394
CELLSTAR (ASIA) CORPORATION LIMITED; *Int'l*, pg. 1394
CELLSTAR CHILE, S.A.; *Int'l*, pg. 1394
CELPAD, INC.; *U.S. Public*, pg. 808
CENTRON COMMUNICATION SYSTEM (XIAMEN) CO., LTD—See Centron Telecom International Holding Ltd; *Int'l*, pg. 1414
CENTURION ELECTRONICS (SHANGHAI) LIMITED—See DuPont de Nemours, Inc.; *U.S. Public*, pg. 693
CEOTRONICS, INC.—See CeoTronics AG; *Int'l*, pg. 1420
CEOTRONICS (SCHWEIZ) AG—See CeoTronics AG; *Int'l*, pg. 1420
CERAGON ITALY—See Ceragon Networks Ltd.; *Int'l*, pg. 1421
CERAGON MOSCOW—See Ceragon Networks Ltd.; *Int'l*, pg. 1421
CERAGON NETWORKS, INC.—See Ceragon Networks Ltd.; *Int'l*, pg. 1421
CERAGON NETWORKS (INDIA) PRIVATE LIMITED—See Ceragon Networks Ltd.; *Int'l*, pg. 1421
CERAGON NETWORKS LTD.; *Int'l*, pg. 1421
CERAGON NETWORKS S.A. DE C.V.—See Ceragon Networks Ltd.; *Int'l*, pg. 1421
CERAGON NETWORKS (UK) LIMITED—See Ceragon Networks Ltd.; *Int'l*, pg. 1421
CERAGON POLAND—See Ceragon Networks Ltd.; *Int'l*, pg. 1421
CHELTON AVIONICS, INC—See TransDigm Group Incorporated; *U.S. Public*, pg. 2180
CHENGDU EOPTOLINK TECHNOLOGY INC.; *Int'l*, pg. 1467
CHENZHOU XIPOINT TECHNOLOGY CO., LTD.—See Gospell Digital Technology Co., Ltd.; *Int'l*, pg. 3043
CHINA AEROSPACE TIMES ELECTRONICS CO., LTD.; *Int'l*, pg. 1481
CHINA DIGITAL TV HOLDING CO., LTD.; *Int'l*, pg. 1497
CHINA DIGITAL VIDEO HOLDINGS LIMITED; *Int'l*, pg. 1498
CHINA ELECTRONICS TECHNOLOGY CO., LTD.; *Int'l*, pg. 1499
CHINA E-WALLET PAYMENT GROUP LIMITED; *Int'l*, pg. 1498
CHINA TIANYING INC.; *Int'l*, pg. 1559
CIRCUIT AUTOMATION INC—See Parker Hannifin Corporation; *U.S. Public*, pg. 1650
CISTERA NETWORKS, INC.; *U.S. Public*, pg. 501
CJ E&M JAPAN INC.—See CJ Corporation; *Int'l*, pg. 1632

CLARY CORPORATION; *U.S. Private*, pg. 915
CLASSIFIED SOLUTIONS GROUP, INC.; *U.S. Private*, pg. 917
CLAVIS TECHNOLOGIES INTERNATIONAL CO., LTD.; *Int'l*, pg. 1653
CLEARDAY, INC.; *U.S. Public*, pg. 512
CLEARTRONIC, INC.; *U.S. Public*, pg. 513
CL INTERNATIONAL CO., LTD.; *Int'l*, pg. 1640
CMK CORPORATION - KIBAN CENTER PLANT—See CMK Corporation; *Int'l*, pg. 1670
COBRA ELECTRONICS CORPORATION—See Monomoy Capital Partners LLC; *U.S. Private*, pg. 2772
COJOT OY—See Alaris Holdings Limited; *Int'l*, pg. 291
COMANT INDUSTRIES, INC—See Advent International Corporation; *U.S. Private*, pg. 99
COMARK COMMUNICATIONS, LLC; *U.S. Public*, pg. 980
COMBA TELECOM INDIA PRIVATE LIMITED—See Comba Telecom Systems Holdings Limited; *Int'l*, pg. 1708
COMMSCOPE, INC.—See CommScope Holding Company, Inc.; *U.S. Public*, pg. 548
COMMSCOPE SOLUTIONS GERMANY GMBH—See CommScope Holding Company, Inc.; *U.S. Public*, pg. 549
COMMSCOPE TECHNOLOGIES LLC—See CommScope Holding Company, Inc.; *U.S. Public*, pg. 548
COMMUNICATION POWER CORP. (CPC); *U.S. Private*, pg. 988
COMMUNICATIONS & POWER INDUSTRIES CANADA INC.—See Odyssey Investment Partners, LLC; *U.S. Private*, pg. 2994
COMMUNICATIONS & POWER INDUSTRIES LLC - BEVERLY MICROWAVE DIVISION—See Odyssey Investment Partners, LLC; *U.S. Private*, pg. 2994
COMMUNICATIONS & POWER INDUSTRIES LLC - COMMUNICATIONS & MEDICAL PRODUCTS DIVISION—See Odyssey Investment Partners, LLC; *U.S. Private*, pg. 2994
COMMUNICATIONS & POWER INDUSTRIES LLC - ECONCO DIVISION—See Odyssey Investment Partners, LLC; *U.S. Private*, pg. 2994
COMMUNICATIONS & POWER INDUSTRIES LLC - MICROWAVE POWER PRODUCTS DIVISION—See Odyssey Investment Partners, LLC; *U.S. Private*, pg. 2995
COMMUNICATIONS & POWER INDUSTRIES LLC - SATCOM EAST DIVISION—See Odyssey Investment Partners, LLC; *U.S. Private*, pg. 2995
COMMUNICATIONS & POWER INDUSTRIES LLC - SATCOM WEST DIVISION—See Odyssey Investment Partners, LLC; *U.S. Private*, pg. 2995
COMMUNICATIONS & POWER INDUSTRIES LLC—See Odyssey Investment Partners, LLC; *U.S. Private*, pg. 2994
COMPLETE INNOVATIONS INC.—See PowerFleet, Inc.; *U.S. Public*, pg. 1706
COMROD INC.; *U.S. Private*, pg. 1006
COMSONICS, INC.; *U.S. Private*, pg. 1006
COMTECH PST CORP.—See Comtech Telecommunications Corp.; *U.S. Public*, pg. 563
COMTECH SATELLITE NETWORK TECHNOLOGIES, INC.—See Comtech Telecommunications Corp.; *U.S. Public*, pg. 563
COMTECH SYSTEMS, INC.—See Comtech Telecommunications Corp.; *U.S. Public*, pg. 563
COMTECH TELECOMMUNICATIONS CORP.; *U.S. Public*, pg. 562
COMTECH XICOM TECHNOLOGY, INC.—See Comtech Telecommunications Corp.; *U.S. Public*, pg. 563
CONNEX TELECOMMUNICATIONS INC.; *Int'l*, pg. 1769
CONTINENTAL ELECTRONICS CORPORATION—See Lone Star Investment Advisors, LLC; *U.S. Private*, pg. 2489
CONTINENTAL LENSA S.A.—See Lone Star Investment Advisors, LLC; *U.S. Private*, pg. 2489
CONTROL4 CORPORATION—See Resideo Technologies, Inc.; *U.S. Public*, pg. 1790
CORETEX LIMITED—See EROAD Limited; *Int'l*, pg. 2496
CORNING MOBILEACCESS, INC.—See Corning Incorporated; *U.S. Public*, pg. 578
COSHIP ELECTRONICS CO., LTD.; *Int'l*, pg. 1810
COWON SYSTEMS INC.; *Int'l*, pg. 1822
COX MEDIA GROUP, LLC—See Apollo Global Management, Inc.; *U.S. Public*, pg. 163
COXON PRECISE INDUSTRIAL CO., LTD.; *Int'l*, pg. 1823
CPI INTERNATIONAL, INC.—See Odyssey Investment Partners, LLC; *U.S. Private*, pg. 2994
CPI LOCUS MICROWAVE, INC.—See Odyssey Investment Partners, LLC; *U.S. Private*, pg. 2994
CPI RADANT TECHNOLOGIES DIVISION INC.—See Odyssey Investment Partners, LLC; *U.S. Private*, pg. 2994
CPI SATCOM & ANTENNA TECHNOLOGIES INC.—See Odyssey Investment Partners, LLC; *U.S. Private*, pg. 2994
CRANE AEROSPACE STC MICROWAVE SYSTEM OLEKTRON—See Crano NXT, Co.; *U.S. Public*, pg. 589
CRESCEND TECHNOLOGIES, L.L.C.; *U.S. Private*, pg. 1093
CRESCENT N.V.; *Int'l*, pg. 1839
CRIMSON TIDE PLC; *Int'l*, pg. 1850
CRUCIALTEC CO., LTD.; *Int'l*, pg. 1859

C&S ANTENNAS, INC.—See Amphenol Corporation; *U.S. Public*, pg. 127
CS CORPORATION; *Int'l*, pg. 1861
CTT INC.; *U.S. Public*, pg. 1119
CTX VIRTUAL TECHNOLOGIES, INC.; *U.S. Public*, pg. 603
CUSTOM MICROWAVE, INC.—See Trive Capital Inc.; *U.S. Private*, pg. 4240
DAHENG NEW EPOCH TECHNOLOGY, INC.; *Int'l*, pg. 1913
DAI TELECOM LTD.—See DBAY Advisors Limited; *Int'l*, pg. 1987
DALIAN HARADA INDUSTRY CO., LTD.—See HARADA INDUSTRY CO., LTD.; *Int'l*, pg. 3269
DANSK BEREDSSKABSKOMMUNIKATION A/S—See Motorola Solutions, Inc.; *U.S. Public*, pg. 1477
DATRON WORLD COMMUNICATIONS, INC.—See Cyberlux Corporation; *U.S. Public*, pg. 617
DAVID CLARK COMPANY INCORPORATED; *U.S. Private*, pg. 1169
DAYANG TECHNOLOGY DEVELOPMENT INC.—See Daheng New Epoch Technology, Inc.; *Int'l*, pg. 1913
DECA SYSTEM INC.; *Int'l*, pg. 1999
DEEPMIND PLATFORM CO., LTD.; *Int'l*, pg. 2003
DELTA GREEN TIANJIN INDUSTRIES CO., LTD.—See Delta Electronics, Inc.; *Int'l*, pg. 2018
DENKI KOGYO CO., LTD. - KANUMA PLANT—See DKK Co., Ltd.; *Int'l*, pg. 2139
DENKO SEISAKUSHO CO., LTD.—See DKK Co., Ltd.; *Int'l*, pg. 2139
DE&T CO., LTD.; *Int'l*, pg. 1997
DEVICEANYWHERE; *U.S. Private*, pg. 1218
DIELECTRIC, LLC—See Sinclair, Inc.; *U.S. Public*, pg. 1885
DIGITAL LIGHTWAVE, INC.; *U.S. Private*, pg. 1230
DIGITAL MULTIMEDIA TECHNOLOGY CO., LTD.; *Int'l*, pg. 2122
D-LINK (INDIA) LTD—See D-Link Corporation, Inc.; *Int'l*, pg. 1900
DONGGUAN ACE TECHNOLOGY CO., LTD.—See Ace Technologies Corp.; *Int'l*, pg. 95
DORO A/S, NORWAY—See Doro AB; *Int'l*, pg. 2179
DORO HONG KONG LTD—See Doro AB; *Int'l*, pg. 2179
DORO SAS—See Doro AB; *Int'l*, pg. 2179
DRAGONWAVE HFCL INDIA PRIVATE LIMITED—See HFCL Limited; *Int'l*, pg. 3375
DRAGONWAVE MEXICO S.A. DE C.V.—See Transform-X, Inc.; *U.S. Private*, pg. 4208
DRAGONWAVE-X—See Transform-X, Inc.; *U.S. Private*, pg. 4208
DSNL CO LTD; *Int'l*, pg. 2210
DTC COMMUNICATIONS, INC.—See Advent International Corporation; *U.S. Private*, pg. 99
DUKANE CORPORATION-AUDIO VISUAL DIVISION—See Dukane Corporation; *U.S. Private*, pg. 1285
DUKANE CORPORATION; *U.S. Private*, pg. 1285
DUKANE CORPORATION-ULTRASONICS DIVISION—See Dukane Corporation; *U.S. Private*, pg. 1285
DURA-LINE CORPORATION—See Grupo Empresarial Kaluz S.A. de C.V.; *Int'l*, pg. 3127
DURA-LINE CORP. - SPARKS PLANT—See Grupo Empresarial Kaluz S.A. de C.V.; *Int'l*, pg. 3127
DYNASTREAM INNOVATIONS INC.—See Garmin Ltd.; *Int'l*, pg. 2885
DZS INC.; *U.S. Public*, pg. 700
E3 GROUP SA—See Grupo Arbulu S.L.; *Int'l*, pg. 3120
E3 SYSTEMS ITALY—See Grupo Arbulu S.L.; *Int'l*, pg. 3120
E3 SYSTEMS MALTA—See Grupo Arbulu S.L.; *Int'l*, pg. 3120
E3 SYSTEMS USA—See Grupo Arbulu S.L.; *Int'l*, pg. 3120
EAGLE COMTRONICS INC.; *U.S. Private*, pg. 1308
EARTHSEARCH COMMUNICATIONS, INC.—See EAST COAST DIVERSIFIED CORPORATION; *U.S. Private*, pg. 1316
EASTONE CENTURY TECHNOLOGY CO., LTD.; *Int'l*, pg. 2274
E-BAND COMMUNICATIONS, LLC—See Moseley Associates, Inc.; *U.S. Private*, pg. 2793
ECESSA CORPORATION—See TheIPGuys.Net LLC; *U.S. Private*, pg. 4141
ECHOSTAR CORPORATION; *U.S. Public*, pg. 711
ECHOSTAR DATA NETWORKS CORPORATION—See EchoStar Corporation; *U.S. Public*, pg. 711
EEG ENTERPRISES, INC.—See Ai-Media Technologies Limited; *Int'l*, pg. 227
ELECTRO PARTES DE MATAMOROS, S.A. DE C.V.—See The Hines Group, Inc.; *U.S. Private*, pg. 4053
ELEKTROVEZE PROIZVODNJA A.D.; *Int'l*, pg. 2357
ELEXA CONSUMER PRODUCTS INC.; *U.S. Private*, pg. 1358
ENENSYS TECHNOLOGIES SA; *Int'l*, pg. 2415
ENERGOUS CORPORATION; *U.S. Public*, pg. 762
ENGINEERED ENDEAVORS INC.—See Emerson Electric Co.; *U.S. Public*, pg. 749
E-PATH COMMUNICATIONS, INC.; *U.S. Private*, pg. 1302
ERF WIRELESS, INC.; *U.S. Public*, pg. 1417
ETIHAD ETISALAT COMPANY; *Int'l*, pg. 2523
ETM-ELECTROMATIC INC.; *U.S. Private*, pg. 1432
EUROATLAS GESELLSCHAFT FUR LEISTUNG-

334220 — RADIO AND TELEVISIO...

SELEKTRONIK GMBH—See L3Harris Technologies, Inc.; *U.S. Public*, pg. 1281
EVER CREATE PROFITS LIMITED—See HNA International Investment Holdings Limited; *Int'l*, pg. 3433
EVERTZ UK LIMITED—See Evertz Microsystems Limited; *Int'l*, pg. 2569
EVS BROADCAST EQUIPMENT IBERICA S.L.—See EVS Broadcast Equipment S.A.; *Int'l*, pg. 2574
EVS BROADCAST EQUIPMENT LTD.—See EVS Broadcast Equipment S.A.; *Int'l*, pg. 2574
EVS BROADCAST EQUIPMENT S.A.; *Int'l*, pg. 2574
EVS CANADA INC.—See EVS Broadcast Equipment S.A.; *Int'l*, pg. 2574
EVS DEUTSCHLAND GMBH—See EVS Broadcast Equipment S.A.; *Int'l*, pg. 2574
EVS FRANCE DEVELOPPEMENT S.A.R.L.—See EVS Broadcast Equipment S.A.; *Int'l*, pg. 2574
EVS FRANCE S.A.—See EVS Broadcast Equipment S.A.; *Int'l*, pg. 2574
EVS INC.—See EVS Broadcast Equipment S.A.; *Int'l*, pg. 2574
EVS ITALY S.R.L.—See EVS Broadcast Equipment S.A.; *Int'l*, pg. 2574
EXFO FINLAND OY—See EXFO Inc.; *Int'l*, pg. 2584
EXFO SERVICE ASSURANCE INC.—See EXFO Inc.; *Int'l*, pg. 2584
EXTREME NETWORKS CANADA, INC.—See Extreme Networks, Inc.; *U.S. Public*, pg. 813
EXTREME NETWORKS, INC.; *U.S. Public*, pg. 813
EYESVISION CORP.; *Int'l*, pg. 2593
EZCONN CORPORATION; *Int'l*, pg. 2593
FARNCOMBE FRANCE SARL—See Blackstreet Capital Holdings LLC; *U.S. Private*, pg. 577
FAVITE INC.- RFID DIVISION—See FAVITE Inc.; *Int'l*, pg. 2623
FEI-ELCOM TECH, INC.—See Frequency Electronics, Inc.; *U.S. Public*, pg. 885
FEI-ZYFER, INC.—See Frequency Electronics, Inc.; *U.S. Public*, pg. 885
FIBERPLEX TECHNOLOGIES, LLC—See Patton Electronics Co.; *U.S. Private*, pg. 3111
FIBOCOM WIRELESS, INC.; *Int'l*, pg. 2652
FILTRONIC BROADBAND LTD.—See Filtronic plc; *Int'l*, pg. 2663
FILTRONIC PLC; *Int'l*, pg. 2663
FILTRONIC (SUZHOU) TELECOMMUNICATION PRODUCTS CO. LTD.—See Filtronic plc; *Int'l*, pg. 2663
FINEDIGITAL INC.; *Int'l*, pg. 2674
FORTUNE WIRELESS, INC.—See Paychex, Inc.; *U.S. Public*, pg. 1655
FREIGHTWATCH INTERNATIONAL (USA), INC.—See Carrier Global Corporation; *U.S. Public*, pg. 442
FSK ELECTRONICS SA (PTY) LTD—See The Carlyle Group Inc.; *U.S. Public*, pg. 2045
FUJITSU LIMITED - NASU PLANT—See Fujitsu Limited; *Int'l*, pg. 2835
FUJITSU LIMITED - SUZAKA PLANT—See Fujitsu Limited; *Int'l*, pg. 2835
FUJITSU SEMICONDUCTOR WIRELESS PRODUCTS, INC.—See Intel Corporation; *U.S. Public*, pg. 1139
FUNA INTERNATIONAL OY—See L3Harris Technologies, Inc.; *U.S. Public*, pg. 1281
FUNA INTERNATIONAL SRL—See L3Harris Technologies, Inc.; *U.S. Public*, pg. 1281
FUNKWERK AG—See Hormann Holding GmbH & Co. KG; *Int'l*, pg. 3479
FUNKWERK PLETTAC ELECTRONIC GMBH—See Hormann Holding GmbH & Co. KG; *Int'l*, pg. 3479
FUSITE USA—See Emerson Electric Co.; *U.S. Public*, pg. 744
FUTABA CORPORATION - CHOSEI ELECTRONIC SYSTEMS FACTORY—See Futaba Corporation; *Int'l*, pg. 2850
FUTABA CORPORATION; *Int'l*, pg. 2850
GAMMA NU THETA INC.—See Hyulim Networks Co., Ltd.; *Int'l*, pg. 3555
GAOYAO ACEDIE CASTING TECHNOLOGY CO., LTD.—See Ace Technologies Corp.; *Int'l*, pg. 95
GAOYAO ACE MECHATRONIX CO., LTD.—See Ace Technologies Corp.; *Int'l*, pg. 95
GAOYAO G-ACE INDUSTRY CO., LTD.—See Ace Technologies Corp.; *Int'l*, pg. 95
GAPWAVES AB; *Int'l*, pg. 2883
GARMIN (ASIA) CORPORATION—See Garmin Ltd.; *Int'l*, pg. 2885
GARMIN POLSKA SP. Z O.O.—See Garmin Ltd.; *Int'l*, pg. 2885
GARMIN SINGAPORE PTE. LTD—See Garmin Ltd.; *Int'l*, pg. 2885
GARMIN USA, INC.—See Garmin Ltd.; *Int'l*, pg. 2885
GATESAIR, INC. - QUINCY—See The Gores Group, LLC; *U.S. Private*, pg. 4034
GATESAIR, INC.—See The Gores Group, LLC; *U.S. Private*, pg. 4034
GDC TECHNOLOGY LIMITED—See Huayi Brothers Media Corp.; *Int'l*, pg. 3515
GEEYA TECHNOLOGY CO., LTD.; *Int'l*, pg. 2911

GEMINI TRAZE RFID PVT. LTD.—See Gemini Communication Ltd.; *Int'l*, pg. 2916
GENERAL DYNAMICS VERTEX RSI—See General Dynamics Corporation; *U.S. Public*, pg. 916
GEOTAB, INC.; *Int'l*, pg. 2941
GEOTRAQ INC.—See ALT5 Sigma Corporation; *U.S. Public*, pg. 85
GIGAHERTZ LLC; *U.S. Private*, pg. 1697
GIGALANE CO., LTD.; *Int'l*, pg. 2971
GILAT SATELLITE NETWORKS LTD.; *Int'l*, pg. 2973
GI PROVISION LIMITED—See Global Invacom Group Limited; *Int'l*, pg. 2998
GLARUN TECHNOLOGY CO., LTD.; *Int'l*, pg. 2988
GLOBAL INVACOM LIMITED—See Global Invacom Group Limited; *Int'l*, pg. 2998
GLOBAL INVACOM MANUFACTURING PTE LTD—See Global Invacom Group Limited; *Int'l*, pg. 2998
GLOBAL INVACOM MANUFACTURING (SHANGHAI) CO., LTD.—See Global Invacom Group Limited; *Int'l*, pg. 2998
GLOBAL INVACOM MANUFACTURING (UK) LIMITED—See Global Invacom Group Limited; *Int'l*, pg. 2998
GLOBAL INVACOM WAVEGUIDE—See Global Invacom Group Limited; *Int'l*, pg. 2998
GPS SOURCE, INC.—See General Dynamics Corporation; *U.S. Public*, pg. 913
GRASS VALLEY FRANCE SAS—See Black Dragon Capital LLC; *U.S. Private*, pg. 571
GRASS VALLEY USA, LLC—See Black Dragon Capital LLC; *U.S. Private*, pg. 571
THE GREATER WASHINGTON EDUCATIONAL TELECOMMUNICATIONS ASSOCIATION, INC.; *U.S. Private*, pg. 4038
GREEN PACKET (SHANGHAI) LTD.—See Green Packet Berhad; *Int'l*, pg. 3072
GROUND CONTROL SYSTEMS, INC.—See Horizon Capital LLP; *Int'l*, pg. 3479
GUANGDONG SHENGLU TELECOMMUNICATION TECH CO., LTD.; *Int'l*, pg. 3160
GUANGZHOU ECHOM SCIENCE & TECHNOLOGY CO., LTD.; *Int'l*, pg. 3165
GUANGZHOU HAIGE COMMUNICATIONS GROUP INCORPORATED COMPANY; *Int'l*, pg. 3165
GUANGZHOU HI-TARGET NAVIGATION TECH CO., LTD.; *Int'l*, pg. 3166
HAGENUK MARINEKOMMUNIKATION GMBH—See Airbus SE; *Int'l*, pg. 242
HA-HO KFT.—See Aiphone Co., Ltd.; *Int'l*, pg. 235
HANGZHOU CNCR-IT CO., LTD.; *Int'l*, pg. 3247
HANYANG NAVICOM CO., LTD—See Hanyang Eng Co., Ltd.; *Int'l*, pg. 3267
HARADA COMMUNICATION SYSTEMS CO., LTD.—See HARADA INDUSTRY CO., LTD.; *Int'l*, pg. 3269
HARADA INDUSTRIES (MEXICO), S.A.DE C.V.—See HARADA INDUSTRY CO., LTD.; *Int'l*, pg. 3269
HARADA INDUSTRIES VIETNAM LIMITED—See HARADA INDUSTRY CO., LTD.; *Int'l*, pg. 3269
HARMONIC, INC.; *U.S. Public*, pg. 985
HARMONIC INTERNATIONAL AUSTRALIA PTY. LTD.—See Harmonic, Inc.; *U.S. Public*, pg. 985
HARMONIC INTERNATIONAL LIMITED—See Harmonic, Inc.; *U.S. Public*, pg. 985
HARMONIC TECHNOLOGIES (BEIJING) CO. LTD.—See Harmonic, Inc.; *U.S. Public*, pg. 986
HARMONIC (UK) LIMITED—See Harmonic, Inc.; *U.S. Public*, pg. 985
HARRIS COMMUNICATION ARGENTINA SA—See Aviat Networks, Inc.; *U.S. Public*, pg. 246
HARRIS COMMUNICATIONS (AUSTRALIA) PTY. LTD.—See L3Harris Technologies, Inc.; *U.S. Public*, pg. 1279
HARRIS COMMUNICATIONS EGYPT, LLC—See L3Harris Technologies, Inc.; *U.S. Public*, pg. 1279
HARRIS COMMUNICATIONS FZCO—See L3Harris Technologies, Inc.; *U.S. Public*, pg. 1279
HARRIS COMUNICACOES PARTICIPACOES DO BRASIL LTDA.—See L3Harris Technologies, Inc.; *U.S. Public*, pg. 1279
HARRIS CORP. - COMMUNICATIONS DIVISION—See L3Harris Technologies, Inc.; *U.S. Public*, pg. 1279
HARRIS SOFTWARE SYSTEMS PTY. LTD.—See L3Harris Technologies, Inc.; *U.S. Public*, pg. 1280
HELLENIC TELEVISION LTD.; *Int'l*, pg. 3334
HENGXIN TECHNOLOGY CO., LTD.; *Int'l*, pg. 3347
H.H. BENFIELD ELECTRIC SUPPLY COMPANY INC. - BENFIELD DATA COMM DIVISION—See H.H. Benfield Electric Supply Company Inc.; *U.S. Private*, pg. 1826
HITACHI EUROPE GMBH - DIGITAL MEDIA GROUP—See Hitachi, Ltd.; *Int'l*, pg. 3417
HITACHI KOKUSAI ELECTRIC CANADA, LTD.—See KKR & Co. Inc.; *U.S. Public*, pg. 1257
HITACHI KOKUSAI ELECTRIC SERVICES INC.—See KKR & Co. Inc.; *U.S. Public*, pg. 1257
HOLJERON CORPORATION—See Matthews International Corporation; *U.S. Public*, pg. 1400
HOMECAST CO., LTD.; *Int'l*, pg. 3455
HONDA ELECTRON CO., LTD.—See G Three Holdings Corp.; *Int'l*, pg. 2862

HONEYWELL AEROSPACE - NORCROSS—See Honeywell International Inc.; *U.S. Public*, pg. 1047
HONEYWELL TCAS INC.—See L3Harris Technologies, Inc.; *U.S. Public*, pg. 1281
HOSIDEN CORPORATION-TOKYO FACTORY—See Hosiden Corporation; *Int'l*, pg. 3484
H&S HIGHTECH CORP.; *Int'l*, pg. 3193
HTC AMERICA, INC.—See HTC Corporation; *Int'l*, pg. 3508
HTC CORPORATION; *Int'l*, pg. 3508
HTC NETHERLANDS B.V.—See HTC Corporation; *Int'l*, pg. 3508
HUBER + SUHNER (HONG KONG) LTD.—See Huber + Suhner AG; *Int'l*, pg. 3519
HUBER + SUHNER (SINGAPORE) PTE. LTD.—See Huber + Suhner AG; *Int'l*, pg. 3519
HUBER + SUHNER (UK) LTD.—See Huber + Suhner AG; *Int'l*, pg. 3519
HUIZHOU SPEED WIRELESS TECHNOLOGY CO., LTD.; *Int'l*, pg. 3527
HUMAX CO., LTD.—See Humax Holdings Co., Ltd.; *Int'l*, pg. 3530
HUNEED TECHNOLOGIES; *Int'l*, pg. 3534
HYTEC GERATEBAU GMBH—See DZS Inc.; *U.S. Public*, pg. 701
HYTERA COMMUNICATIONS (CANADA) INC.—See Hytera Communications Corporation Limited; *Int'l*, pg. 3555
HYTERA COMMUNICATIONS CORPORATION LIMITED; *Int'l*, pg. 3554
HYTERA COMMUNICATIONS FZCO—See Hytera Communications Corporation Limited; *Int'l*, pg. 3555
HYTERA COMMUNICATIONS (HONG KONG) COMPANY LIMITED—See Hytera Communications Corporation Limited; *Int'l*, pg. 3555
HYTERA COMMUNICATIONS (UK) CO., LTD.—See Hytera Communications Corporation Limited; *Int'l*, pg. 3555
HYTERA US INC.—See Hytera Communications Corporation Limited; *Int'l*, pg. 3555
ICOA, INC.; *U.S. Public*, pg. 1086
ICOE (SHANGHAI) TECHNOLOGIES CO., LTD.—See Beijing BDstar Navigation Co., Ltd.; *Int'l*, pg. 946
ICOM AMERICA LICENSE HOLDING LLC—See ICOM INCORPORATED; *Int'l*, pg. 3582
ICOM (AUSTRALIA) PTY. LTD.—See ICOM INCORPORATED; *Int'l*, pg. 3582
ICOM (EUROPE) GMBH—See ICOM INCORPORATED; *Int'l*, pg. 3582
ICOM FRANCE S.A.S.—See ICOM INCORPORATED; *Int'l*, pg. 3583
ICOM INCORPORATED; *Int'l*, pg. 3582
ICOM INFORMATION PRODUCTS INC.—See ICOM INCORPORATED; *Int'l*, pg. 3583
ICOMM INTERNATIONAL LANKA (PVT) LTD—See ICOMM Tele Limited; *Int'l*, pg. 3583
ICOMM TELE LIMITED; *Int'l*, pg. 3583
ICOMM TELE LIMITED - TOWERS UNIT—See ICOMM Tele Limited; *Int'l*, pg. 3583
ICOMM TELE LIMITED - TURNKEY SERVICES DIVISION—See ICOMM Tele Limited; *Int'l*, pg. 3583
ICOM SPAIN, S.L.—See ICOM INCORPORATED; *Int'l*, pg. 3583
ICOM (UK) LTD.—See ICOM INCORPORATED; *Int'l*, pg. 3582
IDENTIV, INC.; *U.S. Public*, pg. 1088
IFOTEC SA—See BNP Paribas SA; *Int'l*, pg. 1089
IKEGAMI ELECTRONICS (EUROPE) GMBH—See Ikegami Tsushinki Co., Ltd.; *Int'l*, pg. 3610
IKEGAMI TSUSHINKI CO., LTD.-OVERSEAS SALES DIVISION—See Ikegami Tsushinki Co., Ltd.; *Int'l*, pg. 3610
IKEGAMI TSUSHINKI CO., LTD.; *Int'l*, pg. 3610
ILSI AMERICA LLC; *U.S. Private*, pg. 2043
IMAGINE COMMUNICATIONS - ARGENTINA—See The Gores Group, LLC; *U.S. Private*, pg. 4035
IMAGINE COMMUNICATIONS - AUSTRIA—See The Gores Group, LLC; *U.S. Private*, pg. 4035
IMAGINE COMMUNICATIONS - BRAZIL—See The Gores Group, LLC; *U.S. Private*, pg. 4035
IMAGINE COMMUNICATIONS CANADA LTD.—See The Gores Group, LLC; *U.S. Private*, pg. 4035
IMAGINE COMMUNICATIONS - CHINA—See The Gores Group, LLC; *U.S. Private*, pg. 4035
IMAGINE COMMUNICATIONS CORP. - CHESAPEAKE—See The Gores Group, LLC; *U.S. Private*, pg. 4035
IMAGINE COMMUNICATIONS CORP. - NORTHRIDGE—See The Gores Group, LLC; *U.S. Private*, pg. 4035
IMAGINE COMMUNICATIONS - FRANCE—See The Gores Group, LLC; *U.S. Private*, pg. 4035
IMAGINE COMMUNICATIONS - GERMANY—See The Gores Group, LLC; *U.S. Private*, pg. 4035
IMAGINE COMMUNICATIONS - HONG KONG—See The Gores Group, LLC; *U.S. Private*, pg. 4035
IMAGINE COMMUNICATIONS - HUNGARY—See The Gores Group, LLC; *U.S. Private*, pg. 4035
IMAGINE COMMUNICATIONS - INDIA—See The Gores Group, LLC; *U.S. Private*, pg. 4035

N.A.I.C.S. INDEX

334220 — RADIO AND TELEVISIO...

IMAGINE COMMUNICATIONS - JAPAN—See The Gores Group, LLC; *U.S. Private*, pg. 4035
IMPACT POWER, INC.—See Allis Electric Co., Ltd.; *Int'l*, pg. 359
IMPINJ, INC.; *U.S. Public*, pg. 1113
IM TECH INC; *Int'l*, pg. 3617
INFINERA CORPORATION; *U.S. Public*, pg. 1117
INFINITE QL SDN. BHD.—See AWC Berhad; *Int'l*, pg. 752
INFOSONICS EL SALVADOR S.A. DE C.V.—See Simply, Inc.; *U.S. Public*, pg. 1882
INFOSONICS LATIN AMERICA, INC.—See Simply, Inc.; *U.S. Public*, pg. 1882
INFOSONICS S.A.—See Simply, Inc.; *U.S. Public*, pg. 1882
INNOVA TELECOMMUNICATION COMPANY LIMITED—See ALT Telecom PCL; *Int'l*, pg. 383
INNOVATIVE CONCEPTS, INC.—See Elbit Systems Limited; *Int'l*, pg. 2344
INNOVATIVE POWER PRODUCTS, INC.; *U.S. Private*, pg. 2083
INSTRUMENTS FOR INDUSTRIES, INC.—See AMETEK, Inc.; *U.S. Public*, pg. 119
INTAC INTERNATIONAL, INC.—See Remark Holdings, Inc.; *U.S. Public*, pg. 1782
INTEGRATED MICROWAVE TECHNOLOGIES, LLC—See Vislink Technologies, Inc.; *U.S. Public*, pg. 2304
INTENO BROADBAND TECHNOLOGY AS—See Amplex AB; *Int'l*, pg. 434
INTENO BVBA—See Amplex AB; *Int'l*, pg. 433
INTENO DENMARK A/S—See Amplex AB; *Int'l*, pg. 434
INTENO NETMEDIA OY AB—See Amplex AB; *Int'l*, pg. 434
INTERCEL TELECOMS GROUP, INC.; *U.S. Private*, pg. 2109
INTERDIGITAL INTERNATIONAL, INC.—See InterDigital, Inc.; *U.S. Public*, pg. 1144
INTERNATIONAAL HANDELSKANTOOR B.V.—See Aiphone Co., Ltd.; *Int'l*, pg. 235
INTERSTATE ELECTRONICS CORPORATION—See L3Harris Technologies, Inc.; *U.S. Public*, pg. 1281
INTERTRONIC SOLUTIONS INC.—See Calian Group Ltd.; *U.S. Public*, pg. 1264
ION MEDIA SONGS, INC.—See The E.W. Scripps Company; *U.S. Public*, pg. 2067
IPICO, INC.—See Brookfield Corporation; *Int'l*, pg. 1189
IPICO SOUTH AFRICA (PTY) LTD.—See Brookfield Corporation; *Int'l*, pg. 1189
IRADIO INC.—See ANSA McAl Limited; *Int'l*, pg. 477
IRONWOOD ELECTRONICS INC.—See HEICO Corporation; *U.S. Public*, pg. 1020
ITRON, INC.; *U.S. Public*, pg. 1175
IWATSU ELECTRIC CO LTD—See AI Holdings Corp.; *Int'l*, pg. 227
JABIL CIRCUIT, INC. - SAN JOSE PLANT—See Jabil Inc.; *U.S. Public*, pg. 1181
JABIL CIRCUIT, LTD.—See Jabil Inc.; *U.S. Public*, pg. 1181
JABIL CIRCUIT OF MICHIGAN, INC.—See Jabil Inc.; *U.S. Public*, pg. 1181
JANTEQ AUSTRALIA PTY. LIMITED—See General Dynamics Corporation; *U.S. Public*, pg. 916
JANTEQ CORP.—See General Dynamics Corporation; *U.S. Public*, pg. 916
JAST, S.A.—See ViaSat, Inc.; *U.S. Public*, pg. 2292
JAYBEAM LIMITED—See Amphenol Corporation; *U.S. Public*, pg. 130
JIANGMEN ACE SURFACE TREATMENT CO., LTD.—See Ace Technologies Corp.; *Int'l*, pg. 95
JIANGSU A-KERR BIO-IDENTIFICATION TECHNOLOGY CO., LTD.—See Huizhou Speed Wireless Technology Co., Ltd.; *Int'l*, pg. 3527
JIANGSU HENGXIN TECHNOLOGY CO., LTD.—See Hengxin Technology Ltd.; *Int'l*, pg. 3347
JMGT STUDIOS SATELLITE TELEVISION NETWORK, LLC; *U.S. Private*, pg. 2215
KABELSIGNAL AG—See EVN AG; *Int'l*, pg. 2571
KAJEET, INC.; *U.S. Private*, pg. 2256
KEYMILE GMBH—See DZS Inc.; *U.S. Public*, pg. 701
KEYMILE NETWORKS GMBH—See DZS Inc.; *U.S. Public*, pg. 701
KIMBALL ELECTRONICS (THAILAND), LTD.—See Kimball Electronics, Inc.; *U.S. Public*, pg. 1228
KNURR ELECTRONICS GMBH—See Vertiv Holdings Co; *U.S. Public*, pg. 2289
KRATOS-GENERAL MICROWAVE ISRAEL—See Kratos Defense & Security Solutions, Inc.; *U.S. Public*, pg. 1276
KVH INDUSTRIES INC; *U.S. Public*, pg. 1277
L-3 APPLIED TECHNOLOGIES, INC.—See L3Harris Technologies, Inc.; *U.S. Public*, pg. 1281
L-3 AVIATION RECORDERS—See L3Harris Technologies, Inc.; *U.S. Public*, pg. 1281
L-3 COMMUNICATIONS ASA LIMITED—See L3Harris Technologies, Inc.; *U.S. Public*, pg. 1281
L-3 COMMUNICATIONS AUSTRALIA GROUP PTY LTD—See L3Harris Technologies, Inc.; *U.S. Public*, pg. 1281
L-3 COMMUNICATIONS CORP. - PULSE SCIENCES—See L3Harris Technologies, Inc.; *U.S. Public*, pg. 1284
L-3 COMMUNICATIONS ELAC NAUTIK GMBH—See L3Harris Technologies, Inc.; *U.S. Public*, pg. 1282
L-3 COMMUNICATIONS ELECTRON DEVICES—See L3Harris Technologies, Inc.; *U.S. Public*, pg. 1282
L-3 COMMUNICATIONS KOREA CO., LTD.—See L3Harris Technologies, Inc.; *U.S. Public*, pg. 1280
L-3 COMMUNICATIONS NARDA MICROWAVE-EAST—See L3Harris Technologies, Inc.; *U.S. Public*, pg. 1282
L-3 COMMUNICATIONS NARDA SATELLITE NETWORKS—See L3Harris Technologies, Inc.; *U.S. Public*, pg. 1282
L-3 COMMUNICATIONS OCEANIA PTY LIMITED—See L3Harris Technologies, Inc.; *U.S. Public*, pg. 1283
L-3 COMMUNICATIONS RANDTRON ANTENNA SYSTEMS—See L3Harris Technologies, Inc.; *U.S. Public*, pg. 1283
L-3 COMMUNICATIONS TELEMETRY-WEST—See L3Harris Technologies, Inc.; *U.S. Public*, pg. 1283
L-3 NARDA-MITEQ—See L3Harris Technologies, Inc.; *U.S. Public*, pg. 1283
L3 TECHNOLOGIES, INC.—See L3Harris Technologies, Inc.; *U.S. Public*, pg. 1280
L3 UNIDYNE, INC.—See L3Harris Technologies, Inc.; *U.S. Public*, pg. 1284
L3 WESTWOOD CORPORATION—See L3Harris Technologies, Inc.; *U.S. Public*, pg. 1284
LAIRD TECHNOLOGIES JAPAN, INC.—See DuPont de Nemours, Inc.; *U.S. Public*, pg. 693
LAIRD TECHNOLOGIES (M) SDN BHD—See DuPont de Nemours, Inc.; *U.S. Public*, pg. 693
LAIRD TECHNOLOGIES (SEA) PTE LIMITED—See DuPont de Nemours, Inc.; *U.S. Public*, pg. 693
LAIRD TECHNOLOGIES TAIWAN, INC.—See DuPont de Nemours, Inc.; *U.S. Public*, pg. 693
LBA GROUP, INC.; *U.S. Private*, pg. 2403
L-COM GLOBAL CONNECTIVITY CORP. - FLORIDA—See Genstar Capital, LLC; *U.S. Private*, pg. 1677
L-COM, INC.—See Genstar Capital, LLC; *U.S. Private*, pg. 1677
LECSTAR TELECOM, INC.—See Integracore, Inc.; *U.S. Private*, pg. 2098
LESJOFORS CHINA LTD—See Beijer Alma AB; *Int'l*, pg. 943
LEWMAR MARINE LTD.—See LCI Industries; *U.S. Public*, pg. 1295
LIGHTSMYTH TECHNOLOGIES, INC.—See Coherent Corp.; *U.S. Public*, pg. 528
LINDSAY INTERNATIONAL (ANZ) PTY LTD.—See Lindsay Corporation; *U.S. Public*, pg. 1319
LOCATION BASED TECHNOLOGIES INC.; *U.S. Public*, pg. 1337
LOGMEIN AUS PTY LTD—See Elliott Management Corporation; *U.S. Private*, pg. 1368
LOGMEIN AUS PTY LTD—See Francisco Partners Management, LP; *U.S. Private*, pg. 1590
LOUD TECHNOLOGIES INC.; *U.S. Public*, pg. 1342
LS RESEARCH, LLC—See DuPont de Nemours, Inc.; *U.S. Public*, pg. 693
LYMAN BROS.; *U.S. Private*, pg. 2520
MARANTZ JAPAN INC.—See Bain Capital, LP; *U.S. Private*, pg. 438
THE MARQUIE GROUP, INC.; *U.S. Public*, pg. 2112
MARTHA STEWART LIVING OMNIMEDIA, INC.—See Marquee Brands LLC; *U.S. Private*, pg. 2586
THE MARYGOLD COMPANIES, INC.; *U.S. Public*, pg. 2112
MASTER PYROSERVE SDN BHD—See FITTERS Diversified Berhad; *Int'l*, pg. 2695
MASTODON DESIGN LLC—See CACI International Inc.; *U.S. Public*, pg. 418
MEASAT RADIO COMMUNICATIONS SDN. BHD.—See Astro All Asia Networks plc; *Int'l*, pg. 662
METEOR COMMUNICATIONS CORPORATION, INC.—See Berkshire Hathaway Inc.; *U.S. Public*, pg. 303
MFJ ENTERPRISES INC.; *U.S. Private*, pg. 2693
MICROCONNEX CORPORATION—See Amphenol Corporation; *U.S. Public*, pg. 129
MICROELECTRONICS TECHNOLOGY INC. (MTI)—See Microelectronics Technology Company; *U.S. Private*, pg. 2703
MICROFAB, INC.—See Edgewater Capital Partners, L.P.; *U.S. Private*, pg. 1335
MICRO-MODE PRODUCTS, INC.—See ITT Inc.; *U.S. Public*, pg. 1178
MICROPHASE CORPORATION—See Ault Alliance, Inc.; *U.S. Public*, pg. 227
MICROWAVE SPECIALTY COMPANY—See Rantec Microwave Systems, Inc.; *U.S. Private*, pg. 3355
MIDWEST COMPUTER REGISTER CORP.—See FEI, Inc; *U.S. Private*, pg. 1493
MINI-SYSTEMS, INC. - ELECTRONIC PACKAGE DIVISION—See Mini-Systems, Inc.; *U.S. Private*, pg. 2742
MITEL NETWORKS CORPORATION—See Searchlight Capital Partners, L.P.; *U.S. Private*, pg. 3588
MITEL NETWORKS, INC.—See Searchlight Capital Partners, L.P.; *U.S. Private*, pg. 3589
MITEL TECHNOLOGIES, INC.—See Searchlight Capital Partners, L.P.; *U.S. Private*, pg. 3589
MOBILE CREATE CO., LTD.—See Future Innovation Group, Inc.; *Int'l*, pg. 2856
MONARCH ANTENNA, INC.—See Aptiv PLC; *Int'l*, pg. 524
MOPHIE INC.—See Evercel, Inc.; *U.S. Private*, pg. 1437
MOSELEY ASSOCIATES, INC.; *U.S. Private*, pg. 2793
MOTOROLA ARABIA, INC.—See Motorola Solutions, Inc.; *U.S. Public*, pg. 1478
MOTOROLA (CHINA) ELECTRONICS LTD.—See Motorola Solutions, Inc.; *U.S. Public*, pg. 1478
MOTOROLA ELECTRONIC GMBH—See Motorola Solutions, Inc.; *U.S. Public*, pg. 1478
MOTOROLA ELECTRONICS SDN. BHD.—See Motorola Solutions, Inc.; *U.S. Public*, pg. 1478
MOTOROLA GMBH—See Motorola Solutions, Inc.; *U.S. Public*, pg. 1478
MOTOROLA LIMITED—See Motorola Solutions, Inc.; *U.S. Public*, pg. 1478
MOTOROLA S.A.S.—See Motorola Solutions, Inc.; *U.S. Public*, pg. 1478
MOTOROLA SOLUTIONS ARGENTINA, S.A.—See Motorola Solutions, Inc.; *U.S. Public*, pg. 1478
MOTOROLA SOLUTIONS (CHINA) CO. LTD.—See Motorola Solutions, Inc.; *U.S. Public*, pg. 1478
MOTOROLA SOLUTIONS GERMANY GMBH—See Motorola Solutions, Inc.; *U.S. Public*, pg. 1478
MOTOROLA SOLUTIONS, INC.; *U.S. Public*, pg. 1477
MOTOROLA SOLUTIONS ISRAEL LIMITED—See Motorola Solutions, Inc.; *U.S. Public*, pg. 1478
MOTOROLA SOLUTIONS MALAYSIA SDN. BHD.—See Motorola Solutions, Inc.; *U.S. Public*, pg. 1478
MOTOROLA SOLUTIONS SINGAPORE PTE LTD—See Motorola Solutions, Inc.; *U.S. Public*, pg. 1478
MOTOROLA TECHNOLOGY SDN. BHD.—See Motorola Solutions, Inc.; *U.S. Public*, pg. 1478
MOVIUS INTERACTIVE CORPORATION—See Movius Interactive Corporation; *U.S. Private*, pg. 2802
MPHASE TECHNOLOGIES, INC.; *U.S. Public*, pg. 1480
MU-DEL ELECTRONICS, INC.—See Ironwave Technologies LLC; *U.S. Private*, pg. 2140
MULTITONE ELECTRONICS PLC—See Champion Technology Holdings Ltd; *Int'l*, pg. 1440
MWAVE INDUSTRIES, LLC—See Alaris Holdings Limited; *Int'l*, pg. 291
NAUTICAL, LUIS ARBULU, S.L.U.—See Grupo Arbulu S.L.; *Int'l*, pg. 3120
NAVAL ELECTRONICS AB—See Advent International Corporation; *U.S. Private*, pg. 100
NERA TELECOMMUNICATIONS LTD. (INDONESIA)—See Ennoconn Corporation; *Int'l*, pg. 2443
NEW BEDFORD PANORAMEX CORPORATION; *U.S. Private*, pg. 2892
NEWTEL CORPORATION COMPANY LIMITED—See Digilife Technologies Limited; *Int'l*, pg. 2119
NORTECH SYSTEMS -AUGUSTA—See Nortech Systems Incorporated; *U.S. Public*, pg. 1536
NORTECH SYSTEMS -BEMIDJI—See Nortech Systems Incorporated; *U.S. Public*, pg. 1536
NORTECH SYSTEMS INCORPORATED; *U.S. Public*, pg. 1536
NORTECH SYSTEMS -INTERCON 1—See Nortech Systems Incorporated; *U.S. Public*, pg. 1536
NORTECH SYSTEMS -MERRIFIELD—See Nortech Systems Incorporated; *U.S. Public*, pg. 1536
NORTHROP GRUMMAN ELECTRONIC SYSTEMS—See Northrop Grumman Corporation; *U.S. Public*, pg. 1540
NORTHROP GRUMMAN - NAVIGATION SYSTEMS—See Northrop Grumman Corporation; *U.S. Public*, pg. 1540
NORTHSTAR ELECTRONICS, INC.; *U.S. Public*, pg. 1541
NUCOURSE DISTRIBUTION INC.; *U.S. Private*, pg. 2972
OHB COSMOS INTERNATIONAL LAUNCH SERVICES GMBH—See Hiscox Ltd.; *Int'l*, pg. 3407
OLSON TECHNOLOGY INC.; *U.S. Private*, pg. 3012
OPTION WIRELESS HONG KONG LIMITED—See Crescent N.V.; *Int'l*, pg. 1839
ORBAN—See Nabro Able LLC; *U.S. Private*, pg. 2829
ORBITAL SATCOM CORP.—See NextPlat Corp.; *U.S. Public*, pg. 1526
ORBITAL SCIENCES CORPORATION—See Northrop Grumman Corporation; *U.S. Public*, pg. 1541
OROLIA SWITZERLAND SA—See Eurazeo SE; *Int'l*, pg. 2528
OXBLUE CORPORATION—See Hexagon AB; *Int'l*, pg. 3369
PACTROL CONTROLS LTD.—See Emerson Electric Co.; *U.S. Public*, pg. 751
PARADISE DATACOM LLC—See Teledyne Technologies Incorporated; *U.S. Public*, pg. 1994
PARADISE DATACOM LTD—See Teledyne Technologies Incorporated; *U.S. Public*, pg. 1994
PARKERVISION, INC.; *U.S. Public*, pg. 1650
PDI COMMUNICATION SYSTEMS INC.; *U.S. Private*, pg. 3121
PHAZAR ANTENNA CORP.—See Phazar Corp.; *U.S. Private*, pg. 3166
PINNACLE SYSTEMS, INC.—See Symphony Technology Group, LLC; *U.S. Private*, pg. 3901
POINTER ARGENTINA S.A.—See PowerFleet, Inc.; *U.S. Public*, pg. 1706
POINTER DO BRASIL COMERCIAL LTDA.—See PowerFleet, Inc.; *U.S. Public*, pg. 1706
POINTER LOGISTICA Y MONITOREO, S.A. DE C.V.—See PowerFleet, Inc.; *U.S. Public*, pg. 1706

334220 — RADIO AND TELEVISIO... CORPORATE AFFILIATIONS

POINTER SA (PTY) LTD.—See PowerFleet, Inc.; *U.S. Public*, pg. 1706
POLSKIE BADANIA INTERNETU SP. Z O. O.—See Agora S.A.; *Int'l*, pg. 213
POWERFLEET GMBH—See PowerFleet, Inc.; *U.S. Public*, pg. 1706
POWERFLEET, INC.; *U.S. Public*, pg. 1706
POWERSPHYR INC.; *U.S. Private*, pg. 3240
POWERSTORM HOLDINGS, INC.; *U.S. Private*, pg. 3240
P.P.C.; *U.S. Public*, pg. 3060
PRECISION COMMUNICATION SERVICES CORP.—See Jabil Inc.; *U.S. Public*, pg. 1182
PRECISION OPTICAL TECHNOLOGIES, INC.—See Belden, Inc.; *U.S. Public*, pg. 294
PRIME TECHNOLOGICAL SERVICES, LLC; *U.S. Private*, pg. 3262
PRO-ACTIVE PROJECTS LIMITED—See Content Ventures Limited; *Int'l*, pg. 1779
PROCOM DEUTSCHLAND GMBH—See Amphenol Corporation; *U.S. Public*, pg. 132
PROXIM WIRELESS CORPORATION; *U.S. Public*, pg. 1731
P.T. AIRSPAN NETWORKS INDONESIA—See Airspan Networks Holdings Inc.; *U.S. Public*, pg. 68
QUALCOMM CDMA TECHNOLOGIES ASIA-PACIFIC PTE. LTD.—See QUALCOMM Incorporated; *U.S. Public*, pg. 1747
QUALCOMM ISRAEL LTD—See QUALCOMM Incorporated; *U.S. Public*, pg. 1747
QUINTECH ELECTRONICS & COMMUNICATIONS, INC.—See Evertz Microsystems Limited; *Int'l*, pg. 2569
RADIO FREE ASIA; *U.S. Private*, pg. 3344
RADIO FREQUENCY SYSTEMS GMBH—See Radio Frequency Systems, Inc.; *U.S. Private*, pg. 3344
RADIO FREQUENCY SYSTEMS, INC.; *U.S. Private*, pg. 3344
RADVISION COMMUNICATION DEVELOPMENT (BEIJING) CO. LTD.—See Silver Lake Group, LLC; *U.S. Private*, pg. 3656
RADVISION COMMUNICATION DEVELOPMENT (BEIJING) CO. LTD.—See TPG Capital, L.P.; *U.S. Public*, pg. 2169
RADVISION FRANCE S.A.R.L.—See Silver Lake Group, LLC; *U.S. Private*, pg. 3656
RADVISION FRANCE S.A.R.L.—See TPG Capital, L.P.; *U.S. Public*, pg. 2169
RADVISION (HK) LTD.—See Silver Lake Group, LLC; *U.S. Private*, pg. 3656
RADVISION (HK) LTD.—See TPG Capital, L.P.; *U.S. Public*, pg. 2169
RADVISION JAPAN KK—See Silver Lake Group, LLC; *U.S. Private*, pg. 3656
RADVISION JAPAN KK—See TPG Capital, L.P.; *U.S. Public*, pg. 2169
RADVISION LTD.—See Silver Lake Group, LLC; *U.S. Private*, pg. 3656
RADVISION LTD.—See TPG Capital, L.P.; *U.S. Public*, pg. 2169
RADVISION (UK) LTD.—See Silver Lake Group, LLC; *U.S. Private*, pg. 3656
RADVISION (UK) LTD.—See TPG Capital, L.P.; *U.S. Public*, pg. 2169
RAMONA RESEARCH, INC.—See HEICO Corporation; *U.S. Public*, pg. 1020
RAVEN ANTENNA SYSTEMS, INC.—See Global Invacom Group Limited; *Int'l*, pg. 2998
RAYSAT ANTENNA SYSTEMS LLC—See Gilat Satellite Networks Ltd.; *Int'l*, pg. 2973
RECTEC TECHNOLOGY & COMMUNICATION—See Northeast Oklahoma Electric Cooperative Inc.; *U.S. Private*, pg. 2951
REDSTONE AEROSPACE CORPORATION—See Coherent Corp.; *U.S. Public*, pg. 529
REGAL BELOIT SPAIN SA—See Regal Rexnord Corporation; *U.S. Public*, pg. 1773
REL-TECH ELECTRONICS, INC.—See RF Industries, Ltd.; *U.S. Public*, pg. 1796
RFM INTEGRATED DEVICE INC.—See Akoustis Technologies, Inc.; *U.S. Public*, pg. 69
RF NEULINK—See Raveon Technologies Corporation; *U.S. Private*, pg. 3357
R. L. DRAKE HOLDINGS, LLC—See Blonder Tongue Laboratories, Inc.; *U.S. Public*, pg. 362
R. L. DRAKE, LLC—See Blonder Tongue Laboratories, Inc.; *U.S. Public*, pg. 362
ROCKWELL AUTOMATION LDA—See Rockwell Automation, Inc.; *U.S. Public*, pg. 1806
ROSCOR CORPORATION; *U.S. Private*, pg. 3481
RUCKUS WIRELESS, INC.—See CommScope Holding Company, Inc.; *U.S. Public*, pg. 548
SABRE COMMUNICATIONS CORP.—See The Jordan Company, L.P.; *U.S. Private*, pg. 4061
SCHROFF TECHNOLOGIES INTERNATIONAL, INC.—See RF Industries, Ltd.; *U.S. Public*, pg. 1796
SCHWAIGER GMBH—See VOXX International Corporation; *U.S. Public*, pg. 2311
SCREEN FUTURE S.R.L.—See DB Elettronica Telecomunicazioni SpA; *Int'l*, pg. 1986

SEACHANGE INTERNATIONAL, INC.; *U.S. Public*, pg. 1851
SEASPACE CORP.; *U.S. Private*, pg. 3591
SEATEL, INC.—See Advent International Corporation; *U.S. Private*, pg. 100
SECTRACK N.V.—See Geotab, Inc.; *Int'l*, pg. 2941
SECURE COMMUNICATION SYSTEMS, INC.—See Vance Street Capital LLC; *U.S. Private*, pg. 4342
SEKIDENKO, INC.—See Advanced Energy Industries, Inc.; *U.S. Public*, pg. 47
SENSOR SYSTEMS INC.—See HEICO Corporation; *U.S. Public*, pg. 1021
SEPURA DEUTSCHLAND GMBH—See Hytera Communications Corporation Limited; *Int'l*, pg. 3555
SHANGHAI HARADA NEW AUTOMOTIVE ANTENNA CO., LTD.—See HARADA INDUSTRY CO., LTD.; *Int'l*, pg. 3269
SHENZHEN HYAN MICROELECTRONICS CO., LTD.—See Anhui Tatfook Technology Co., Ltd; *Int'l*, pg. 469
SHIN AH LIMITED—See Ace Technologies Corp.; *Int'l*, pg. 95
SIDUS SPACE, INC.; *U.S. Public*, pg. 1876
SILICON LABORATORIES CANADA ULC—See Silicon Laboratories Inc.; *U.S. Public*, pg. 1880
SIMPSON ELECTRIC COMPANY; *U.S. Private*, pg. 3668
SITO MOBILE LTD.; *U.S. Public*, pg. 1890
SIXNET WIRELESS PRODUCT GROUP USA—See HMS Networks AB; *Int'l*, pg. 3433
SKYWORKS SOLUTIONS OY—See Skyworks Solutions, Inc.; *U.S. Public*, pg. 1893
SMOOTH OPERATIONS (PRODUCTIONS) LIMITED—See Songtradr, Inc.; *U.S. Private*, pg. 3713
SOMERA COMMUNICATIONS PTE. LTD.—See Jabil Inc.; *U.S. Public*, pg. 1182
SONIC FOUNDRY, INC.; *U.S. Public*, pg. 1903
SONIM TECHNOLOGIES, INC.; *U.S. Public*, pg. 1903
SONIM TECHNOLOGIES (INDIA) PRIVATE LIMITED—See Sonim Technologies, Inc.; *U.S. Public*, pg. 1903
SONIM TECHNOLOGIES (SHENZHEN) LIMITED—See Sonim Technologies, Inc.; *U.S. Public*, pg. 1903
SOUNDCRAFT CANADA—See Evertz Microsystems Limited; *Int'l*, pg. 2569
SOUTHWEST MICROWAVE INC.; *U.S. Private*, pg. 3740
SPECIALTY MICROWAVE CORP.—See Amplitech Group, Inc.; *U.S. Public*, pg. 133
SPECTRANETIX, INC.; *U.S. Private*, pg. 3751
SPECTRUM CONTROL GMBH—See Allient Inc.; *U.S. Public*, pg. 80
SPEED (KOREA) WIRELESS TECHNOLOGY CO., LTD.—See Huizhou Speed Wireless Technology Co., Ltd.; *Int'l*, pg. 3527
SPEED (TAIWAN) WIRELESS TECHNOLOGY CO., LTD.—See Huizhou Speed Wireless Technology Co., Ltd.; *Int'l*, pg. 3527
SPEED TECHNOLOGY (USA) CO., LTD.—See Huizhou Speed Wireless Technology Co., Ltd.; *Int'l*, pg. 3527
SPICE CSL INTERNATIONAL SDN. BHD.—See Digilife Technologies Limited; *Int'l*, pg. 2120
SRAMPORT - TRANSMISSOES MECHANICAS, LDA.—See SRAM International Corporation; *U.S. Private*, pg. 3767
SR TELECOM & CO. S.E.C.—See Groupe Lagasse Inc.; *Int'l*, pg. 3106
STADIUM ASIA—See Cicor Technologies Ltd.; *Int'l*, pg. 1603
STADIUM POWER LIMITED—See Cicor Technologies Ltd.; *Int'l*, pg. 1603
STAHLGRUBER COMMUNICATION CENTER GMBH—See Brodos AG; *Int'l*, pg. 1173
STARENT NETWORKS BEIJING CO., LTD.—See Cisco Systems, Inc.; *U.S. Public*, pg. 500
STARENT NETWORKS, CORP.—See Cisco Systems, Inc.; *U.S. Public*, pg. 500
STITCHER INC.—See Liberty Media Corporation; *U.S. Public*, pg. 1311
STUDER DEUTSCHLAND GMBH—See Evertz Microsystems Limited; *Int'l*, pg. 2569
SUNBRITETV LLC; *U.S. Private*, pg. 3865
SUPERCLICK, INC.—See AT&T Inc.; *U.S. Public*, pg. 220
SUTRO TOWER, INC.—See Nexstar Media Group, Inc.; *U.S. Public*, pg. 1524
SUZHOU KEYANG PHOTOELECTRICITY TECHNOLOGY CO., LTD.—See Huizhou Speed Wireless Technology Co., Ltd.; *Int'l*, pg. 3527
SUZHOU RAKEN TECHNOLOGY LTD.—See AmTRAN Technology; *Int'l*, pg. 442
SYMEO GMBH—See Analog Devices, Inc.; *U.S. Public*, pg. 136
SYMEO SP. Z O.O.—See Analog Devices, Inc.; *U.S. Public*, pg. 136
SYNTONICS LLC—See Ironwave Technologies LLC; *U.S. Private*, pg. 2140
SYSTEMS ENGINEERING & MANAGEMENT, CO.—See The O'Neil Group Company, LLC; *U.S. Private*, pg. 4087
TACTICAL COMMAND INDUSTRIES, INC.—See Kanders & Company, Inc.; *U.S. Private*, pg. 2259
TCI INTERNATIONAL, INC.—See SPX Technologies, Inc.; *U.S. Public*, pg. 1922

TDS TELECOM—See Telephone & Data Systems, Inc.; *U.S. Public*, pg. 1997
TEAM SA—See Advent International Corporation; *U.S. Private*, pg. 99
TECHNICAL COMMUNICATIONS CORPORATION; *U.S. Public*, pg. 1988
TECHNO IKEGAMI CO., LTD—See Ikegami Tsushinki Co., Ltd.; *Int'l*, pg. 3610
TEK INDUSTRIES INC.; *U.S. Private*, pg. 3958
TELEDYNE GERMANY GMBH—See Teledyne Technologies Incorporated; *U.S. Public*, pg. 1993
TELEDYNE PARADISE DATACOM LIMITED—See Teledyne Technologies Incorporated; *U.S. Public*, pg. 1994
TELEDYNE PARADISE DATACOM, LLC—See Teledyne Technologies Incorporated; *U.S. Public*, pg. 1994
TELEFUNKEN RADIO COMMUNICATIONS SYSTEMS GMBH—See Elbit Systems Limited; *Int'l*, pg. 2345
TELEMUNDO 314 REDWOOD LLC—See Comcast Corporation; *U.S. Public*, pg. 541
TELEMUNDO LAS VEGAS LLC—See Comcast Corporation; *U.S. Public*, pg. 541
TELEMUNDO OF ARIZONA LLC—See Comcast Corporation; *U.S. Public*, pg. 542
TELEMUNDO OF CHICAGO LLC—See Comcast Corporation; *U.S. Public*, pg. 542
TELEMUNDO OF DENVER LLC—See Comcast Corporation; *U.S. Public*, pg. 542
TELEMUNDO OF FRESNO LLC—See Comcast Corporation; *U.S. Public*, pg. 542
TELEMUNDO OF NEW ENGLAND LLC—See Comcast Corporation; *U.S. Public*, pg. 542
TELEMUNDO OF NEW MEXICO LLC—See Comcast Corporation; *U.S. Public*, pg. 542
TELEMUNDO OF NORTHERN CALIFORNIA LLC—See Comcast Corporation; *U.S. Public*, pg. 542
TELEMUNDO OF PUERTO RICO LLC—See Comcast Corporation; *U.S. Public*, pg. 542
TELEMUNDO OF SAN DIEGO LLC—See Comcast Corporation; *U.S. Public*, pg. 542
TELEMUNDO RIO GRANDE VALLEY, LLC—See Comcast Corporation; *U.S. Public*, pg. 541
TELIT WIRELESS SOLUTIONS CO., LTD.—See DBAY Advisors Limited; *Int'l*, pg. 1988
TELIT WIRELESS SOLUTIONS INC.—See DBAY Advisors Limited; *Int'l*, pg. 1988
TELLABS AB—See Marlin Equity Partners, LLC; *U.S. Private*, pg. 2585
TELLABS COMMUNICATIONS INTERNATIONAL LIMITED—See Marlin Equity Partners, LLC; *U.S. Private*, pg. 2585
TELLABS COMMUNICATIONS (MALAYSIA) SDN. BHD.—See Marlin Equity Partners, LLC; *U.S. Private*, pg. 2585
TELLABS DEUTSCHLAND GMBH—See Marlin Equity Partners, LLC; *U.S. Private*, pg. 2585
TELLABS DO BRASIL, LTDA.—See Marlin Equity Partners, LLC; *U.S. Private*, pg. 2585
TELLABS INDIA PRIVATE LIMITED—See Marlin Equity Partners, LLC; *U.S. Private*, pg. 2585
TELLABS PTY LIMITED—See Marlin Equity Partners, LLC; *U.S. Private*, pg. 2585
TELLABS SOUTH AFRICA (PROPRIETARY) LIMITED—See Marlin Equity Partners, LLC; *U.S. Private*, pg. 2585
TELTECH COMMUNICATIONS, LLC; *U.S. Private*, pg. 3962
TELVUE CORPORATION; *U.S. Private*, pg. 3963
TERADYNE, INC.-MEMORY TEST DIVISION—See Teradyne, Inc.; *U.S. Public*, pg. 2018
TERRAN ORBITAL CORPORATION—See Lockheed Martin Corporation; *U.S. Public*, pg. 1339
TETRA IRELAND COMMUNICATIONS LIMITED—See eircom Holdings (Ireland) Limited; *Int'l*, pg. 2334
TEXTLOCAL LTD.—See Cisco Systems, Inc.; *U.S. Public*, pg. 500
THINKLOGICAL, LLC—See Belden, Inc.; *U.S. Public*, pg. 294
THOMSON BROADCAST SAS—See Arelis SAS; *Int'l*, pg. 558
THOUSANDEYES GERMANY GMBH—See Cisco Systems, Inc.; *U.S. Public*, pg. 500
TIME DOMAIN CORP.—See Bonaventure Capital LLC; *U.S. Private*, pg. 613
TIME DOMAIN CORP.—See Fidelis Capital LLC; *U.S. Private*, pg. 1502
TKH SECURITY SOLUTIONS USA—See Vector Capital Management, L.P.; *U.S. Private*, pg. 4352
TOUCHPOINT GROUP HOLDINGS, INC.; *U.S. Public*, pg. 2165
TOWERTEL S.P.A.—See EI Towers S.p.A.; *Int'l*, pg. 2328
TRANSCORE, LP—See Roper Technologies, Inc.; *U.S. Public*, pg. 1813
TRANS-TECH, INC.—See Skyworks Solutions, Inc.; *U.S. Public*, pg. 1893
TRIAD RF SYSTEMS INC.—See Comrod Inc.; *U.S. Private*, pg. 1006
TRIVEC-AVANT CORPORATION—See Advent International Corporation; *U.S. Private*, pg. 100
UBIQUITI INC.; *U.S. Public*, pg. 2217

N.A.I.C.S. INDEX

334290 — OTHER COMMUNICATION...

ULTIMATTE CORPORATION—See Blackmagic Design Pty. Ltd.; *Int'l*, pg. 1061
UNISTRONG TECHNOLOGY (S) PTE. LTD.—See Beijing UniStrong Science & Technology Co., Ltd.; *Int'l*, pg. 959
UNITED STATES ALUMOWELD CO. INC.—See Fujikura Ltd.; *Int'l*, pg. 2829
UTAH SCIENTIFIC, INC.; *U.S. Private*, pg. 4324
VDO-PH INTERNATIONAL, INC.; *U.S. Private*, pg. 4349
VECAST, INC.; *U.S. Private*, pg. 4349
VERYKOOL USA, INC.—See Simply, Inc.; *U.S. Public*, pg. 1882
VIASAT AUSTRALIA PTY LIMITED—See ViaSat, Inc.; *U.S. Public*, pg. 2292
VIASAT, INC.; *U.S. Public*, pg. 2291
VIASAT UK LIMITED—See ViaSat, Inc.; *U.S. Public*, pg. 2292
VICON DEUTSCHLAND GMBH—See Vicon Industries, Inc.; *U.S. Private*, pg. 4377
VICON INDUSTRIES LIMITED—See Vicon Industries, Inc.; *U.S. Private*, pg. 4377
VICOR CORPORATION; *U.S. Public*, pg. 2296
VICOR ITALY SRL—See Vicor Corporation; *U.S. Public*, pg. 2296
VICOR U.K. LTD.—See Vicor Corporation; *U.S. Public*, pg. 2296
VIEWCAST.COM, INC.; *U.S. Public*, pg. 2297
VISIONGLOBAL CORP.; *U.S. Public*, pg. 2304
VISLINK TECHNOLOGIES INC.; *U.S. Public*, pg. 2304
VISTA POINT TECHNOLOGIES, INC.—See Flex Ltd.; *Int'l*, pg. 2703
VISTA POINT TECHNOLOGIES, INC.—See Flex Ltd.; *Int'l*, pg. 2703
VOCERA COMMUNICATIONS, INC.—See Stryker Corporation; *U.S. Public*, pg. 1958
VOICE ASSIST, INC.; *U.S. Public*, pg. 2308
VXI CORPORATION—See GN Store Nord A/S; *Int'l*, pg. 3016
WAKAYAMA ICOM INC.—See ICOM INCORPORATED; *Int'l*, pg. 3583
WAVESTREAM CORP.—See Gilat Satellite Networks Ltd.; *Int'l*, pg. 2973
WENZEL INTERNATIONAL INC.—See Arcline Investment Management LP; *U.S. Private*, pg. 313
WESTERMO NERATEC AG—See Ependion AB; *Int'l*, pg. 2459
WI2WI CORPORATION; *U.S. Public*, pg. 2369
WINEGARD COMPANY; *U.S. Private*, pg. 4540
WIRELESS COMMUNICATIONS INC.; *U.S. Private*, pg. 4546
WI-SKY INFLIGHT, INC.; *U.S. Private*, pg. 4515
WOODHEAD INDUSTRIES, INC.—See Koch Industries, Inc.; *U.S. Private*, pg. 2335
WORLD MOBILE HOLDINGS INC.; *U.S. Public*, pg. 2381
WXXI PUBLIC BROADCASTING COUNCIL; *U.S. Private*, pg. 4575
WYNNCOM, INC.—See Fortran Corporation; *U.S. Private*, pg. 872
XCEIVE CORPORATION—See Sofinnova Ventures, Inc.; *U.S. Private*, pg. 3704
XSTREAM NORTH AMERICA, INC.—See SeaChange International, Inc.; *U.S. Public*, pg. 1851
XSTREAM SP. Z O.O.—See SeaChange International, Inc.; *U.S. Public*, pg. 1851
YSI NANOTECH—See Xylem Inc.; *U.S. Public*, pg. 2395
ZEBRA ENTERPRISE SOLUTIONS B.V.B.A.—See Zebra Technologies Corporation; *U.S. Public*, pg. 2402
ZETRON, INC.—See Codan Limited; *Int'l*, pg. 1688

334290 — OTHER COMMUNICATIONS EQUIPMENT MANUFACTURING

3ONEDATA CO., LTD.; *Int'l*, pg. 9
8X8, INC.; *U.S. Public*, pg. 10
ABB INDUSTRIES LLC—See ABB Ltd.; *Int'l*, pg. 51
ABCELEC—See FAYAT SAS; *Int'l*, pg. 2624
ACLARA POWER-LINE SYSTEMS INC.—See Hubbell Incorporated; *U.S. Public*, pg. 1067
ACLARA TECHNOLOGIES LLC—See Hubbell Incorporated; *U.S. Public*, pg. 1067
ADDSINO CO., LTD.; *Int'l*, pg. 131
ADVANCED DETECTION SYSTEMS—See Venturedyne, Ltd.; *U.S. Private*, pg. 4358
ADVANCED POWER ELECTRONICS CORP.; *Int'l*, pg. 161
ADVANCED POWERLINE TECHNOLOGIES, INC.; *U.S. Public*, pg. 49
ADVANTECH ADVANCED MICROWAVE TECHNOLOGIES INC.; *Int'l*, pg. 164
ADVANTECH WIRELESS TECHNOLOGIES (USA) INC.—See Baylin Technologies Inc.; *Int'l*, pg. 914
AIPHONE COMMUNICATIONS (VIETNAM) CO., LTD.—See Aiphone Co., Ltd.; *Int'l*, pg. 235
AIRWALK COMMUNICATIONS, INC.—See Ubee Interactive, Inc.; *U.S. Private*, pg. 4273
AKUVOX (XIAMEN) NETWORKS CO., LTD.—See Fujian Star-net Communication Co.,Ltd; *Int'l*, pg. 2819
ALBA TRAFFIC MANAGEMENT LIMITED—See Breedon Group plc; *Int'l*, pg. 1144

ALLEGION (AUSTRALIA) PTY LIMITED—See Allegion Public Limited Company; *Int'l*, pg. 335
ALLEGION CANADA INC.—See Allegion Public Limited Company; *Int'l*, pg. 335
ALLEGION FU HSING LIMITED—See Allegion Public Limited Company; *Int'l*, pg. 335
ALPHA NETWORKS (CHANGSHU) CO., LTD.—See Alpha Networks Inc.; *Int'l*, pg. 369
ALPHA NETWORKS (CHENGDU) CO., LTD.—See Alpha Networks Inc.; *Int'l*, pg. 369
ALPHA NETWORKS (DONGGUAN) CO., LTD.—See Alpha Networks Inc.; *Int'l*, pg. 369
ALPHA NETWORKS VIETNAM COMPANY LIMITED—See Alpha Networks Inc.; *Int'l*, pg. 369
ALPHA SYSTEMS INC.; *Int'l*, pg. 369
ALPHA TECHNICAL SERVICES INC.—See Alpha Networks Inc.; *Int'l*, pg. 369
ALPS COMMUNICATION DEVICES TECHNOLOGY(SHANGHAI) CO., LTD.—See Alps Alpine Co., Ltd.; *Int'l*, pg. 375
ALSTOM SIGNALING INC.—See Alstom S.A.; *Int'l*, pg. 381
ALSTOM SIGNALING OPERATION, LLC—See Alstom S.A.; *Int'l*, pg. 381
ALSTOM TRANSPORTATION INC.—See Alstom S.A.; *Int'l*, pg. 381
ALT TELECOM PCL; *Int'l*, pg. 383
AMERICAN HEARING SYSTEMS INC—See GN Store Nord A/S; *Int'l*, pg. 3016
AMPAC EUROPE LIMITED—See Halma plc; *Int'l*, pg. 3230
AMPAC NZ LIMITED—See Halma plc; *Int'l*, pg. 3230
AMPHENOL CANADA CORP.—See Amphenol Corporation; *U.S. Public*, pg. 127
AMPHENOL TECHNICAL PRODUCTS INTERNATIONAL—See Amphenol Corporation; *U.S. Public*, pg. 127
ANDREW SATCOM AFTICA (PTY.) LTD.—See CommScope Holding Company, Inc.; *U.S. Public*, pg. 548
ANDREW TELECOMMUNICATIONS INDIA PVT. LTD. (ATGV)—See CommScope Holding Company, Inc.; *U.S. Public*, pg. 548
ANGELCARE MONITORS INC.—See Angelcare Holding Inc.; *Int'l*, pg. 459
A NOVO COMLINK ESPANA SL—See Hainan Traffic Administration Holding Co., Ltd.; *Int'l*, pg. 3213
ANRITSU S.R.L—See Anritsu Corporation; *Int'l*, pg. 476
APEX SIGNAL CORPORATION—See North Atlantic Industries Inc.; *U.S. Private*, pg. 2942
APOLLO (BEIJING) FIRE PRODUCTS CO. LTD.—See Halma plc; *Int'l*, pg. 3230
APOLLO FIRE DETECTORS LIMITED—See Halma plc; *Int'l*, pg. 3230
APOLLO GMBH—See Halma plc; *Int'l*, pg. 3230
APPLIED SIGNAL TECHNOLOGY—See RTX Corporation; *U.S. Public*, pg. 1825
APPLIED SIGNAL TECHNOLOGY—See RTX Corporation; *U.S. Public*, pg. 1825
APX GROUP HOLDINGS, INC.—See NRG Energy, Inc.; *U.S. Public*, pg. 1551
ARGUS SECURITY S.R.L.—See Halma plc; *Int'l*, pg. 3230
ARIMA COMMUNICATIONS CORPORATION—See Arima Photovoltaic & Optical Corp.; *Int'l*, pg. 565
ARLO TECHNOLOGIES, INC.; *U.S. Public*, pg. 193
ARTAFLEX INC.; *Int'l*, pg. 581
ARTIZA NETWORKS, INC.; *Int'l*, pg. 585
ASCOM (BELGIUM) NV—See Ascom Holding AG; *Int'l*, pg. 603
ASCOM B.V.—See Ascom Holding AG; *Int'l*, pg. 603
ASCOM COLOMBIA S.A.—See Ascom Holding AG; *Int'l*, pg. 603
ASCOM DENMARK A/S—See Ascom Holding AG; *Int'l*, pg. 603
ASCOM DEUTSCHLAND GMBH—See Ascom Holding AG; *Int'l*, pg. 603
ASCOM (FINLAND) OY—See Ascom Holding AG; *Int'l*, pg. 602
ASCOM IMMOBILIEN AG—See Ascom Holding AG; *Int'l*, pg. 602
ASCOM INDIA PVT LTD—See Ascom Holding AG; *Int'l*, pg. 603
ASCOM INTEGRATED WIRELESS PTY LTD—See Ascom Holding AG; *Int'l*, pg. 603
ASCOM NORWAY—See Ascom Holding AG; *Int'l*, pg. 603
ASCOM POLAND SP. Z.O.O.—See Ascom Holding AG; *Int'l*, pg. 603
ASCOM (SCHWEIZ) AG—See Ascom Holding AG; *Int'l*, pg. 602
ASCOM SYSTEC AG—See Ascom Holding AG; *Int'l*, pg. 603
ASCOM (UK) LTD.—See Ascom Holding AG; *Int'l*, pg. 603
ASELSAN ELEKTRONIK SANAYI VE TICARET AS; *Int'l*, pg. 605
ASSA ABLOY AUSTRALIA PTY LTD—See ASSA ABLOY AB; *Int'l*, pg. 633
ASSA ABLOY GLOBAL SOLUTIONS AB—See ASSA ABLOY AB; *Int'l*, pg. 635
ASSA ABLOY HOSPITALITY SHANGHAI LTD—See ASSA ABLOY AB; *Int'l*, pg. 635
A/S SAF TEHNIKA; *Int'l*, pg. 28

ASTI CORPORATION - FUKUROI FACTORY—See ASTI Corporation; *Int'l*, pg. 654
ASTI CORPORATION - HAMAMATSU FACTORY—See ASTI Corporation; *Int'l*, pg. 654
ASTI CORPORATION - IWATA FACTORY—See ASTI Corporation; *Int'l*, pg. 654
ASTI CORPORATION - KAKEGAWA FACTORY—See ASTI Corporation; *Int'l*, pg. 654
ASTI CORPORATION - MIYAKODA FACTORY—See ASTI Corporation; *Int'l*, pg. 654
ASTI CORPORATION; *Int'l*, pg. 654
ASTI TRANSPORTATION SYSTEMS INC.—See New Enterprise Stone & Lime Co., Inc.; *U.S. Private*, pg. 2895
ASTRA MICROWAVE PRODUCTS LIMITED - UNIT-II—See Astra Microwave Products Limited; *Int'l*, pg. 658
ATLAS AUTOS (PRIVATE) LIMITED - KARACHI PLANT—See Atlas Group of Companies; *Int'l*, pg. 685
ATLAS AUTOS (PRIVATE) LIMITED - SHEIKHUPURA PLANT—See Atlas Group of Companies; *Int'l*, pg. 685
ATLAS GENTECH (NZ) LIMITED—See WESCO International, Inc.; *U.S. Public*, pg. 2350
AUDEN TECHNO CORP.; *Int'l*, pg. 701
AUDIOCODES, BEIJING—See AudioCodes Ltd.; *Int'l*, pg. 702
AUSTCO COMMUNICATIONS SYSTEMS PTY. LTD.—See Azure Healthcare Limited; *Int'l*, pg. 782
AUSTCO MARKETING & SERVICE (ASIA) PTE. LTD.—See Azure Healthcare Limited; *Int'l*, pg. 782
AUSTCO MARKETING & SERVICE (CANADA) LTD.—See Azure Healthcare Limited; *Int'l*, pg. 782
AUSTCO MARKETING & SERVICE (UK) LTD.—See Azure Healthcare Limited; *Int'l*, pg. 782
AUSTCO MARKETING & SERVICE (USA) LTD.—See Azure Healthcare Limited; *Int'l*, pg. 782
AUSTDAC PTY. LIMITED—See Hubbell Incorporated; *U.S. Public*, pg. 1066
AVANTEL LTD.; *Int'l*, pg. 735
AVAYA AUSTRALIA PTY LTD—See Silver Lake Group, LLC; *U.S. Private*, pg. 3655
AVAYA AUSTRALIA PTY LTD—See TPG Capital, L.P.; *U.S. Public*, pg. 2168
AVAYA BELGIUM SPRL—See Silver Lake Group, LLC; *U.S. Private*, pg. 3655
AVAYA BELGIUM SPRL—See TPG Capital, L.P.; *U.S. Public*, pg. 2169
AVAYA CHINA - BEIJING OFFICE—See Silver Lake Group, LLC; *U.S. Private*, pg. 3655
AVAYA CHINA - BEIJING OFFICE—See TPG Capital, L.P.; *U.S. Public*, pg. 2168
AVAYA CHINA - GUANGZHOU OFFICE—See Silver Lake Group, LLC; *U.S. Private*, pg. 3655
AVAYA CHINA - GUANGZHOU OFFICE—See TPG Capital, L.P.; *U.S. Public*, pg. 2168
AVAYA CHINA - SHANGHAI OFFICE—See Silver Lake Group, LLC; *U.S. Private*, pg. 3655
AVAYA CHINA - SHANGHAI OFFICE—See TPG Capital, L.P.; *U.S. Public*, pg. 2168
AVAYA CZECH REPUBLIC—See Silver Lake Group, LLC; *U.S. Private*, pg. 3655
AVAYA CZECH REPUBLIC—See TPG Capital, L.P.; *U.S. Public*, pg. 2169
AVAYA HONG KONG CO. LTD.—See Silver Lake Group, LLC; *U.S. Private*, pg. 3655
AVAYA HONG KONG CO. LTD.—See TPG Capital, L.P.; *U.S. Public*, pg. 2168
AVAYA JAPAN—See Silver Lake Group, LLC; *U.S. Private*, pg. 3655
AVAYA JAPAN—See TPG Capital, L.P.; *U.S. Public*, pg. 2168
AVAYA KOREA—See Silver Lake Group, LLC; *U.S. Private*, pg. 3655
AVAYA KOREA—See TPG Capital, L.P.; *U.S. Public*, pg. 2168
AVAYA MALAYSIA—See Silver Lake Group, LLC; *U.S. Private*, pg. 3655
AVAYA MALAYSIA—See TPG Capital, L.P.; *U.S. Public*, pg. 2168
AVAYA NEDERLAND B.V.—See Silver Lake Group, LLC; *U.S. Private*, pg. 3656
AVAYA NEDERLAND B.V.—See TPG Capital, L.P.; *U.S. Public*, pg. 2169
AVAYA PHILIPPINES—See Silver Lake Group, LLC; *U.S. Private*, pg. 3655
AVAYA PHILIPPINES—See TPG Capital, L.P.; *U.S. Public*, pg. 2168
AVAYA SINGAPORE—See Silver Lake Group, LLC; *U.S. Private*, pg. 3655
AVAYA SINGAPORE—See TPG Capital, L.P.; *U.S. Public*, pg. 2168
AVAYA THAILAND—See Silver Lake Group, LLC; *U.S. Private*, pg. 3655
AVAYA THAILAND—See TPG Capital, L.P.; *U.S. Public*, pg. 2168
AVAYA UK—See Silver Lake Group, LLC; *U.S. Private*, pg. 3656
AVAYA UK—See TPG Capital, L.P.; *U.S. Public*, pg. 2169
AVIAT NETWORKS MALAYSIA SDN. BHD.—See Aviat Networks, Inc.; *U.S. Public*, pg. 245

334290 — OTHER COMMUNICATION...

AVIAT NETWORKS (NZ) LIMITED—See Aviat Networks, Inc.; *U.S. Public*, pg. 245
AVIAT NETWORKS PHILIPPINES, INC.—See Aviat Networks, Inc.; *U.S. Public*, pg. 245
AVIAT NETWORKS POLSKA SP. Z.O.O.—See Aviat Networks, Inc.; *U.S. Public*, pg. 245
AVIAT NETWORKS SAUDI TELECOM & INFORMATION TECHNOLOGY CO.—See Aviat Networks, Inc.; *U.S. Public*, pg. 245
AVIAT NETWORKS (THAILAND) LTD.—See Aviat Networks, Inc.; *U.S. Public*, pg. 245
AVIAT STORITVENO PODJETJE, D.O.O.—See Aviat Networks, Inc.; *U.S. Public*, pg. 246
AVIRE ELEVATOR TECHNOLOGY INDIA PTE. LTD.—See Halma plc; *Int'l*, pg. 3230
AVIRE ELEVATOR TECHNOLOGY SHANGHAI LTD.—See Halma plc; *Int'l*, pg. 3230
AVIRE GLOBAL PTE. LTD.—See Halma plc; *Int'l*, pg. 3230
AVIRE LIMITED—See Halma plc; *Int'l*, pg. 3230
AVIRE S.R.O.—See Halma plc; *Int'l*, pg. 3230
AV TECH CORPORATION - SANCHONG FACTORY—See Av Tech Corporation; *U.S. Private*, pg. 733
AVTEC INC.; *U.S. Private*, pg. 410
AXESSTEL, INC.; *U.S. Public*, pg. 412
BAE SYSTEMS ENTERPRISES LIMITED—See BAE Systems plc; *Int'l*, pg. 796
BAK EUROPE GMBH—See BAK International Ltd.; *Int'l*, pg. 804
BARCO, INC.—See Barco N.V.; *Int'l*, pg. 864
BARTEC VODEC LTD.—See Charterhouse Capital Partners LLP; *Int'l*, pg. 1455
BATM ADVANCED COMMUNICATIONS LTD.; *Int'l*, pg. 890
BEIJING INHAND NETWORKS TECHNOLOGY CO., LTD.; *Int'l*, pg. 952
BEIJING RAILWAY SIGNAL CO., LTD.—See China National Railway Signal & Communication Corp.; *Int'l*, pg. 1534
BEIJING TRICOLOR TECHNOLOGY CO., LTD.; *Int'l*, pg. 959
BEL TONE INDIA LIMITED—See GN Store Nord A/S; *Int'l*, pg. 3016
BELWITH PRODUCTS, LLC - FIRST WATCH SECURITY DIVISION—See Belwith Products, LLC; *U.S. Private*, pg. 522
BONSO ELECTRONICS LIMITED—See Bonso Electronics International Inc.; *Int'l*, pg. 1109
BRADY GMBH—See Brady Corporation; *U.S. Public*, pg. 378
BRITON EMS LIMITED—See OSI Systems, Inc.; *U.S. Public*, pg. 1621
BRK BRANDS, INC.—See Resideo Technologies, Inc.; *U.S. Public*, pg. 1789
BURKE E. PORTER MACHINERY COMPANY—See China Everbright Group Limited; *Int'l*, pg. 1501
C10 COMMUNICATIONS PTY LTD.—See Casa Systems, Inc.; *U.S. Private*, pg. 778
CAF SIGNALLING, S.L.U.—See Construcciones y Auxiliar de Ferrocarriles S.A.; *Int'l*, pg. 1776
CANTRONIC SECURITY SYSTEMS (CHINA) CO., LTD.—See Cantronic Systems Inc.; *Int'l*, pg. 1300
CASEY FIRE SYSTEMS, INC.—See Wind Point Advisors LLC; *U.S. Private*, pg. 4535
CASSIDIAN S.A.S.—See Airbus SE; *Int'l*, pg. 242
CCOP INTERNATIONAL (THAILAND) CO. LTD.—See Lumentum Holdings Inc.; *U.S. Public*, pg. 1348
C ENTERPRISES, L.P.—See RF Industries, Ltd.; *U.S. Public*, pg. 1796
CENTRAL SECURITY DISTRIBUTION PTY. LTD.—See WESCO International, Inc.; *U.S. Public*, pg. 2350
CEOTRONICS AG; *Int'l*, pg. 1420
CEOTRONICS S.L.—See CeoTronics AG; *Int'l*, pg. 1420
CERILLION INC.—See Cerillion plc; *Int'l*, pg. 1422
CERILLION TECHNOLOGIES INDIA PRIVATE LIMITED—See Cerillion plc; *Int'l*, pg. 1422
CERILLION TECHNOLOGIES LIMITED—See Cerillion plc; *Int'l*, pg. 1422
C.G. DEVELOPMENT LIMITED—See Universal Electronics, Inc.; *U.S. Public*, pg. 2255
CHECKPOINT SYSTEMS DANMARK A/S—See CCL Industries Inc.; *Int'l*, pg. 1368
CHECKPOINT SYSTEMS, INC.—See CCL Industries Inc.; *Int'l*, pg. 1367
CHECKPOINT SYSTEMS INDIA PRIVATE LIMITED—See CCL Industries Inc.; *Int'l*, pg. 1368
CHECKPOINT SYSTEMS JAPAN CO. LTD.—See CCL Industries Inc.; *Int'l*, pg. 1368
CHINA ALL ACCESS (HOLDINGS) LIMITED; *Int'l*, pg. 1482
CHINA NATIONAL RAILWAY SIGNAL & COMMUNICATION CORP.; *Int'l*, pg. 1534
CHINA SECURITY & FIRE IOT SENSING (SHENZHEN) CO., LTD.—See China Security Co., Ltd.; *Int'l*, pg. 1550
CHINA SECURITY &FIRE XULONG ELECTRONIC & TECHNOLOGY CO., LTD.—See China Security Co., Ltd.; *Int'l*, pg. 1550
CHONGQING MAS GEYI SCIENCE & TECHNOLOGY CO., LTD.—See Chongqing MAS Sci. & Tech. Co., Ltd.; *Int'l*, pg. 1580
CIANBRO CORPORATION - RICKERS WHARF MARINE FACILITY—See Cianbro Corporation; *U.S. Private*, pg. 896
CISCO DO BRASIL LTDA.—See Cisco Systems, Inc.; *U.S. Public*, pg. 499
CISCO SYSTEMS CAPITAL (INDIA) PRIVATE LIMITED—See Cisco Systems, Inc.; *U.S. Public*, pg. 498
CLAL INFORMATION TECHNOLOGY—See Access Industries, Inc.; *U.S. Private*, pg. 51
CLEAR-COM, LLC—See HM Electronics Incorporated; *U.S. Private*, pg. 1954
CNS LINK CO., LTD.; *Int'l*, pg. 1678
COBHAM DEFENCE COMMUNICATIONS LTD.—See Advent International Corporation; *U.S. Private*, pg. 99
COBHAM ELECTRONIC SYSTEMS INC.—See Advent International Corporation; *U.S. Private*, pg. 99
CODAN LIMITED; *Int'l*, pg. 1687
CODE 3, INC.—See Ecco Safety Group; *U.S. Private*, pg. 1326
COLUMBIA WEATHER SYSTEMS, INC.—See Hinds Instruments, Inc.; *U.S. Private*, pg. 1948
COMBA TELECOM TECHNOLOGY (GUANGZHOU) LIMITED—See Comba Telecom Systems Holdings Limited; *Int'l*, pg. 1708
COMET ELECTRONICS, LLC—See Comet Industries Inc.; *U.S. Private*, pg. 981
COMMSCOPE CABOS DO BRASIL LTDA—See CommScope Holding Company, Inc.; *U.S. Public*, pg. 549
COMMSCOPE, INC. - WESTCHESTER—See CommScope Holding Company, Inc.; *U.S. Public*, pg. 549
COMMSCOPE SOLUTIONS INTERNATIONAL, INC. BACHENBULACH—See CommScope Holding Company, Inc.; *U.S. Public*, pg. 549
COMMSCOPE SOLUTIONS IRELAND LTD.—See CommScope Holding Company, Inc.; *U.S. Public*, pg. 549
COMNET TELECOM SUPPLY, INC.; *U.S. Private*, pg. 998
COMPUTER SERVICE COMPANY—See Steiny & Company, Inc.; *U.S. Private*, pg. 3799
COMSYS NET CORPORATION—See COMSYS Holdings Corporation; *Int'l*, pg. 1762
CONTINENTAL INSTRUMENTS, LLC—See Napco Security Technologies, Inc.; *U.S. Public*, pg. 1491
CONVERGENT NETWORKS INC.; *U.S. Private*, pg. 1035
COOPER FULLEON LIMITED—See Eaton Corporation plc; *Int'l*, pg. 2278
CORINEX COMMUNICATIONS CORP.; *Int'l*, pg. 1801
CORNET TECHNOLOGY GMBH—See Cornet Technology Inc.; *U.S. Private*, pg. 1053
CORNET TECHNOLOGY INC.; *U.S. Private*, pg. 1053
CORNET TECHNOLOGY (INDIA) PRIVATE LIMITED—See Cornet Technology Inc.; *U.S. Private*, pg. 1053
CPI MALIBU DIVISION—See Odyssey Investment Partners, LLC; *U.S. Private*, pg. 2994
CRESCO WIRELESS, INC.—See Cresco, Ltd.; *Int'l*, pg. 1840
CRSC WANQUAN SIGNAL EQUIPMENT CO., LTD.—See China Railway Signal & Communication Corporation Ltd.; *Int'l*, pg. 1544
CTM LYNG AS—See Addtech AB; *Int'l*, pg. 132
CUBIC CYBER SOLUTIONS, INC.—See Elliott Management Corporation; *U.S. Private*, pg. 1367
CUBIC CYBER SOLUTIONS, INC.—See Veritas Capital Fund Management, LLC; *U.S. Private*, pg. 4361
CXR ANDERSON JACOBSON SAS; *Int'l*, pg. 1891
DAEATI CO., LTD.; *Int'l*, pg. 1905
DAEMYUNG SONOSEASON CO., LTD.; *Int'l*, pg. 1908
DAEYANG ELECTRIC CO., LTD. - ELECTRICAL / ELECTRONIC DIVISON—See Daeyang Electric Co., Ltd.; *Int'l*, pg. 1911
DAIKO TSUSAN CO., LTD.; *Int'l*, pg. 1937
DAMAC PRODUCTS, INC.—See Littlejohn & Co., LLC; *U.S. Private*, pg. 2471
DEI HOLDINGS, INC. - DIRECTED DIVISION—See Charlesbank Capital Partners, LLC; *U.S. Private*, pg. 855
DELTA ENERGY SYSTEMS (CZECH REPUBLIC) SPOL. S.R.O.—See Delta Electronics, Inc.; *Int'l*, pg. 2016
DELTA INFORMATION SYSTEMS INC.; *U.S. Private*, pg. 1201
DELTA SCIENTIFIC CORP.; *U.S. Private*, pg. 1201
DENSO YAMAGATA CO., LTD.—See Denso Corporation; *Int'l*, pg. 2032
DESON INNOVATIVE LIMITED—See Deson Development International Holdings Ltd; *Int'l*, pg. 2045
DEVOTEAM GMBH—See Devoteam SA; *Int'l*, pg. 2089
DIGITAL RECEIVER TECHNOLOGY INC.—See The Boeing Company; *U.S. Public*, pg. 2039
DINGLI CORPORATION LTD.; *Int'l*, pg. 2127
DKK CO., LTD.; *Int'l*, pg. 2139
DOM-METALUX S.A.S.—See Groupe SFPI SA; *Int'l*, pg. 3111
DONG-GUAN LI YUAN ELECTRONICS CO., LTD.—See Everspring Industry Co., Ltd.; *Int'l*, pg. 2569
DRI CORPORATION; *U.S. Private*, pg. 1277
DUOLUN TECHNOLOGY CO., LTD.; *Int'l*, pg. 2227
DW DIGITAL WIRELESS INC—See DDS Wireless International Inc.; *Int'l*, pg. 1994
EBRAHIM K. KANOO COMPANY B.S.C - SECURITY 1 DIVISION—See Ebrahim K. Kanoo Company B.S.C.; *Int'l*, pg. 2286
ECOLINK INTELLIGENT TECHNOLOGY, INC.—See Universal Electronics, Inc.; *U.S. Public*, pg. 2255
ECONOLITE CONTROL PRODUCTS, INC.—See Econolite Group, Inc.; *U.S. Private*, pg. 1330
ECONOLITE GROUP, INC.; *U.S. Private*, pg. 1330
EDGEWATER WIRELESS SYSTEMS INC.; *Int'l*, pg. 2309
EGAN VISUAL INC.; *Int'l*, pg. 2322
ELBIT SECURITY SYSTEMS LTD.—See Elbit Systems Limited; *Int'l*, pg. 2344
ELECTRONIC SYSTEMS TECHNOLOGY, INC.; *U.S. Public*, pg. 724
ELFAB LIMITED—See Halma plc; *Int'l*, pg. 3231
ELGIGANTEN A/S—See Currys plc; *Int'l*, pg. 1879
ELLEAIR PRODUCT CO., LTD.—See Daio Paper Corporation; *Int'l*, pg. 1940
ELPAS, INC.—See Halma plc; *Int'l*, pg. 3231
EPI (HOLDINGS) LIMITED; *Int'l*, pg. 2459
ESCO TECHNOLOGIES, INC.; *U.S. Public*, pg. 793
ETEN INFORMATION SYSTEM CO., LTD.—See Acer Incorporated; *Int'l*, pg. 99
EXELIS C4I PTY LTD.—See L3Harris Technologies, Inc.; *U.S. Public*, pg. 1279
EXFO TELECOM EQUIPMENT (SHENZHEN) CO. LTD.—See EXFO Inc.; *Int'l*, pg. 2584
FEDERAL SIGNAL CORPORATION; *U.S. Public*, pg. 826
FEDERAL SIGNAL CREDIT CORPORATION—See Federal Signal Corporation; *U.S. Public*, pg. 826
FEDERAL SIGNAL VAMA, S.A.—See Federal Signal Corporation; *U.S. Public*, pg. 826
FFE LIMITED—See Halma plc; *Int'l*, pg. 3231
FFLO - INSIDE AUTO PARTS, INC.—See Free Flow, Inc.; *U.S. Public*, pg. 884
FHF BERGBAUTECHNIK GMBH & CO. KG—See Eaton Corporation plc; *Int'l*, pg. 2281
FHF FUNKE+HUSTER FERNSIG GMBH—See Eaton Corporation plc; *Int'l*, pg. 2281
FIBROLAN LTD.; *Int'l*, pg. 2653
FINISAR AUSTRALIA PTY. LTD.—See Coherent Corp.; *U.S. Public*, pg. 528
FINISAR CORP. - HORSHAM—See Coherent Corp.; *U.S. Public*, pg. 528
FINISAR CORPORATION—See Coherent Corp.; *U.S. Public*, pg. 528
FINISAR ISRAEL LTD.—See Coherent Corp.; *U.S. Public*, pg. 528
FIRE AND SECURITY HARDWARE PTY LIMITED—See Allegion Public Limited Company; *Int'l*, pg. 335
FIREANGEL SAFETY TECHNOLOGY GROUP PLC; *Int'l*, pg. 2678
FIRECOM, INC.—See Wind Point Advisors LLC; *U.S. Private*, pg. 4535
FIRETRACE AEROSPACE, LLC—See Halma plc; *Int'l*, pg. 3231
FIRST ALERT (CANADA) INC.—See Newell Brands Inc.; *U.S. Public*, pg. 1514
FIRST ALERT, INC.—See Resideo Technologies, Inc.; *U.S. Public*, pg. 1789
FLEXTRONICS LAVAL S.N.C.—See Flex Ltd.; *Int'l*, pg. 2703
FLEXTRONICS MANUFACTURING (ZHUHAI) CO., LTD.—See Flex Ltd.; *Int'l*, pg. 2703
FORSIDE CO., LTD.; *Int'l*, pg. 2737
FORTH CORPORATION PUBLIC COMPANY LIMITED; *Int'l*, pg. 2738
FORWARD INNOVATIONS GMBH—See Forward Industries, Inc.; *U.S. Public*, pg. 874
FREUND-VECTOR CORPORATION—See Freund Corporation; *Int'l*, pg. 2791
FUJIAN STAR-NET COMMUNICATION CO.,LTD; *Int'l*, pg. 2819
FUJITSU ESPANA, S.A.—See Fujitsu Limited; *Int'l*, pg. 2836
FUJITSU TELECOMMUNICATIONS EUROPE LIMITED—See Fujitsu Limited; *Int'l*, pg. 2837
FUJITSU TELECOMMUNICATIONS FRANCE SAS—See Fujitsu Limited; *Int'l*, pg. 2837
FUJITSU TELECOM NETWORKS LIMITED—See Fujitsu Limited; *Int'l*, pg. 2837
FUNKWERK IOT GMBH—See Hormann Holding GmbH & Co. KG; *Int'l*, pg. 3479
FUNKWERK TECHNOLOGIES GMBH—See Hormann Holding GmbH & Co. KG; *Int'l*, pg. 3480
FUNK WERK VIDEO SYSTEME GMBH—See Hormann Holding GmbH & Co. KG; *Int'l*, pg. 3479
FURUNO HELLAS S.A.—See Furuno Electric Co., Ltd.; *Int'l*, pg. 2848
FUTURE INNOVATION GROUP, INC.; *Int'l*, pg. 2856
GAI-TRONICS LIMITED—See Hubbell Incorporated; *U.S. Public*, pg. 1066
GAS MEASUREMENT INSTRUMENTS LIMITED—See Teledyne Technologies Incorporated; *U.S. Public*, pg. 1992
GENERAL DYNAMICS GOVERNMENT SYSTEMS CORPORATION—See General Dynamics Corporation; *U.S. Public*, pg. 914
GENERAL DYNAMICS MISSION SYSTEMS, INC.—See General Dynamics Corporation; *U.S. Public*, pg. 915
GENEW TECHNOLOGIES CO., LTD.; *Int'l*, pg. 2922
GENOHCO, INC.; *Int'l*, pg. 2925
GEOFON A.D.; *Int'l*, pg. 2933

N.A.I.C.S. INDEX

334290 — OTHER COMMUNICATION...

GEORGE RISK INDUSTRIES, INC.; *U.S. Public*, pg. 934
GIGA-BYTE COMMUNICATION INC.—See Giga-Byte Technology Co., Ltd.; *Int'l*, pg. 2971
GIGA-BYTE TECHNOLOGY CO., LTD. - GIGABYTE NAN-PING FACTORY—See Giga-Byte Technology Co., Ltd.; *Int'l*, pg. 2971
GIV-TECH, INC.—See Global Information, Inc.; *Int'l*, pg. 2997
GLOBAL INVACOM GROUP LIMITED; *Int'l*, pg. 2998
GLOBAL INVACOM SDN. BHD.—See Global Invacom Group Limited; *Int'l*, pg. 2998
GLOBALSAT WORLDCOM CORP.; *Int'l*, pg. 3004
GLOBALSTAR JAPAN, INC.—See Globalstar, Inc.; *U.S. Public*, pg. 946
GN NETCOM A/S—See GN Store Nord A/S; *Int'l*, pg. 3016
GN RESOUND LTD.—See GN Store Nord A/S; *Int'l*, pg. 3016
GN RESOUND PTY. LTD.—See GN Store Nord A/S; *Int'l*, pg. 3016
GN STORE NORD A/S; *Int'l*, pg. 3015
GOHIGH NETWORKS CO., LTD.; *Int'l*, pg. 3022
GREENPAGES—See GreenPages, Inc.; *U.S. Private*, pg. 1779
GREEN VALLEY - UNITED KINGDOM—See Black Dragon Capital LLC; *U.S. Private*, pg. 571
GREENWOODS COMMUNICATIONS LTD.; *Int'l*, pg. 3077
GUANGDONG CREATE CENTURY INTELLIGENT EQUIPMENT GROUP CORPORATION LIMITED; *Int'l*, pg. 3153
GUARDIAR USA LLC; *U.S. Private*, pg. 1810
GULF SECURITY TECHNOLOGY CO., LTD.—See Carrier Global Corporation; *U.S. Public*, pg. 441
GUNNEBO ENTRANCE CONTROL LTD.—See Gunnebo AB; *Int'l*, pg. 3184
GUNNEBO ENTRANCE CONTROL SARL—See Gunnebo AB; *Int'l*, pg. 3184
GUNNEBO INTRANCE CONTROL S.P.A.—See Gunnebo AB; *Int'l*, pg. 3184
HABTECH COMMUNICATIONS—See APi Group Corporation; *Int'l*, pg. 514
HALMA AUSTRALASIA PTY LTD—See Halma plc; *Int'l*, pg. 3231
HANCHANG CORPORATION; *Int'l*, pg. 3242
HANS FOLGSAARD A/S—See Addtech AB; *Int'l*, pg. 133
HARBOR COMMUNICATIONS, LLC—See Telapex Inc.; *U.S. Private*, pg. 3959
HARRIS CANADA SYSTEMS, INC.—See L3Harris Technologies, Inc.; *U.S. Public*, pg. 1279
HARRIS SYSTEMS LIMITED—See L3Harris Technologies, Inc.; *U.S. Public*, pg. 1280
HAVIS, INC.; *U.S. Private*, pg. 1881
HAYAT COMMUNICATIONS CO. K.S.C.C.; *Int'l*, pg. 3290
HELLERMANNTYTON LTD. - MANCHESTER—See Aptiv PLC; *Int'l*, pg. 525
HELLERMANNTYTON (PTY.) LTD.—See Aptiv PLC; *Int'l*, pg. 525
HELLO DIRECT, INC.—See Synergy Communications Management; *U.S. Private*, pg. 3904
HETRONIC INTERNATIONAL, INC.—See Methode Electronics, Inc.; *U.S. Public*, pg. 1428
HETRONIC SWISS AG—See Methode Electronics, Inc.; *U.S. Public*, pg. 1428
HETRONIC USA, INC.—See Methode Electronics, Inc.; *U.S. Public*, pg. 1428
HITACHI COMMUNICATION TECHNOLOGIES AMERICA, INC. - HCTA PACKET CORE DIVISION—See Hitachi, Ltd.; *Int'l*, pg. 3413
HITACHI COMMUNICATION TECHNOLOGIES AMERICA, INC.—See Hitachi, Ltd.; *Int'l*, pg. 3413
HITACHI RAIL STS MALAYSIA SDN. BHD.—See Hitachi, Ltd.; *Int'l*, pg. 3421
HITRON SYSTEMS INC. - CHINA FACTORY—See Hitron Systems Inc.; *Int'l*, pg. 3427
HITRON SYSTEMS INC.; *Int'l*, pg. 3427
HM ELECTRONICS INCORPORATED; *U.S. Private*, pg. 1954
HMS INDUSTRIAL NETWORKS PTY. LTD.—See HMS Networks AB; *Int'l*, pg. 3433
HOCHIKI ASIA PACIFIC PTE. LTD.—See Hochiki Corporation; *Int'l*, pg. 3437
HOCHIKI AUSTRALIA PTY LTD—See Hochiki Corporation; *Int'l*, pg. 3437
HOCHIKI CORPORATION; *Int'l*, pg. 3437
HOCHIKI MIDDLE EAST FZE—See Hochiki Corporation; *Int'l*, pg. 3437
HOCHIKI SERVICIOS, S. DE R.L. DE C.V.—See Hochiki Corporation; *Int'l*, pg. 3437
HOME CONTROL INTERNATIONAL LIMITED; *Int'l*, pg. 3454
HOSIDEN BESSON LTD—See Hosiden Corporation; *Int'l*, pg. 3484
HTL LIMITED—See HFCL Limited; *Int'l*, pg. 3375
HUAWEI TECHNOLOGIES CO., LTD.—See Huawei Investment & Holding Co., Ltd.; *Int'l*, pg. 3515
HYFIRE WIRELESS FIRE SOLUTIONS LTD.—See Halma plc; *Int'l*, pg. 3232
HYT AMERICA, INC.—See Hytera Communications Corporation Limited; *Int'l*, pg. 3554
HYTERA MOBILFUNK GMBH—See Hytera Communications Corporation Limited; *Int'l*, pg. 3555
HYULIM NETWORKS CO., LTD.; *Int'l*, pg. 3555
IC REALTIME, LLC.; *U.S. Private*, pg. 2029
IHS NIGERIA PLC; *Int'l*, pg. 3607
I'LL INC.; *Int'l*, pg. 3562
INFORMATION DISPLAY COMPANY—See Carmanah Technologies Corporation; *Int'l*, pg. 1341
INSTALARME INDUSTRIA E COMERCIO LTDA—See Allied Universal Manager LLC; *U.S. Private*, pg. 190
INTRUSION INC.; *U.S. Public*, pg. 1159
JARIET TECHNOLOGIES, INC.—See L3Harris Technologies, Inc.; *U.S. Public*, pg. 1280
JAVELIN INNOVATIONS INC.—See Gilo Ventures, LLC; *U.S. Private*, pg. 1701
JETSTREAM OF HOUSTON, INC.—See Federal Signal Corporation; *U.S. Public*, pg. 826
JNPR SWEDEN AB—See Juniper Networks, Inc.; *U.S. Public*, pg. 1211
JUNIPER NETWORKS AUSTRALIA LTD.—See Juniper Networks, Inc.; *U.S. Public*, pg. 1211
JUNIPER NETWORKS BRAZIL LTD.—See Juniper Networks, Inc.; *U.S. Public*, pg. 1211
JUNIPER NETWORKS B.V.—See Juniper Networks, Inc.; *U.S. Public*, pg. 1211
JUNIPER NETWORKS CHINA LTD.—See Juniper Networks, Inc.; *U.S. Public*, pg. 1211
JUNIPER NETWORKS FINLAND OY—See Juniper Networks, Inc.; *U.S. Public*, pg. 1211
JUNIPER NETWORKS FRANCE SARL—See Juniper Networks, Inc.; *U.S. Public*, pg. 1211
JUNIPER NETWORKS (HONG KONG) LTD.—See Juniper Networks, Inc.; *U.S. Public*, pg. 1211
JUNIPER NETWORKS INDIA PRIVATE LTD.—See Juniper Networks, Inc.; *U.S. Public*, pg. 1211
JUNIPER NETWORKS IRELAND LTD.—See Juniper Networks, Inc.; *U.S. Public*, pg. 1211
JUNIPER NETWORKS ITALY S.R.L.—See Juniper Networks, Inc.; *U.S. Public*, pg. 1211
JUNIPER NETWORKS KOREA, INC.—See Juniper Networks, Inc.; *U.S. Public*, pg. 1211
JUNIPER NETWORKS MALAYSIA SDN. BHD.—See Juniper Networks, Inc.; *U.S. Public*, pg. 1211
JUNIPER NETWORKS MEXICO S.A. DE C.V.—See Juniper Networks, Inc.; *U.S. Public*, pg. 1211
JUNIPER NETWORKS (SINGAPORE) PTE. LTD.—See Juniper Networks, Inc.; *U.S. Public*, pg. 1211
JUNIPER NETWORKS SPAIN SRL—See Juniper Networks, Inc.; *U.S. Public*, pg. 1211
JUNIPER NETWORKS SWITZERLAND GMBH—See Juniper Networks, Inc.; *U.S. Public*, pg. 1211
JUNIPER NETWORKS TAIWAN LIMITED CO.—See Juniper Networks, Inc.; *U.S. Public*, pg. 1211
JUNIPER NETWORKS U.K. LTD.—See Juniper Networks, Inc.; *U.S. Public*, pg. 1211
JUPITER TECHNOLOGY (WUXI) CO., LTD.—See Microelectronics Technology Company; *U.S. Public*, pg. 2703
KAC ALARM COMPANY LIMITED—See Honeywell International; *U.S. Public*, pg. 1051
KIDDE PRODUCTS LIMITED—See Carrier Global Corporation; *U.S. Public*, pg. 441
KNIGHT SECURITY SYSTEMS, LLC—See Sentinel Capital Partners, L.L.C.; *U.S. Private*, pg. 3609
KO HARTOG VERKEERSTECHNIEK B.V.—See Addtech AB; *Int'l*, pg. 134
KUSTOM SIGNALS, INC.—See Ecco Safety Group; *U.S. Private*, pg. 1326
KYMETA CORPORATION; *U.S. Private*, pg. 2360
L-3 COMMUNICATIONS EO/IR INC—See L3Harris Technologies, Inc.; *U.S. Public*, pg. 1282
L-3 COMMUNICATIONS ESSCO COLLINS LTD.—See Odyssey Investment Partners, LLC; *U.S. Private*, pg. 2994
L-3 COMMUNICATIONS MOBILE-VISION, INC.—See L3Harris Technologies, Inc.; *U.S. Public*, pg. 1282
L-3 COMMUNICATIONS SECURITY AND DETECTION SYSTEMS, INC.—See L3Harris Technologies, Inc.; *U.S. Public*, pg. 1283
L-3 COMMUNICATIONS SINGAPORE PTE LTD—See L3Harris Technologies, Inc.; *U.S. Public*, pg. 1283
L-3 COMMUNICATIONS UK LTD—See L3Harris Technologies, Inc.; *U.S. Public*, pg. 1283
L3 LATITUDE, LLC—See L3Harris Technologies, Inc.; *U.S. Public*, pg. 1284
LAIRD TECHNOLOGIES S.R.O.—See DuPont de Nemours, Inc.; *U.S. Public*, pg. 693
LAMDA HELLIX S.A—See Digital Realty Trust, Inc.; *U.S. Public*, pg. 663
LANTRONIX, INC.; *U.S. Public*, pg. 1293
LIMOTEC BVBA—See Halma plc; *Int'l*, pg. 3232
LIUPANSHUI MAS TECHNOLOGY CO., LTD.—See Chongqing MAS Sci. & Tech. Co., Ltd.; *Int'l*, pg. 1580
LJ NETWORK HOLDING BV—See CalAmp Corp.; *U.S. Public*, pg. 422
LOGOS COMMUNICATIONS, INC.—See Black Box Limited; *Int'l*, pg. 1058
LOJACK CORPORATION—See CalAmp Corp.; *U.S. Public*, pg. 422
LOJACK EQUIPMENT IRELAND LIMITED—See CalAmp Corp.; *U.S. Public*, pg. 422
MACE SECURITY INTERNATIONAL, INC.; *U.S. Public*, pg. 1351
MARIOFF GMBH—See Carrier Global Corporation; *U.S. Public*, pg. 443
MARIOFF HI-FOG S.L.U.—See Carrier Global Corporation; *U.S. Public*, pg. 443
MARIOFF LTD.—See Carrier Global Corporation; *U.S. Public*, pg. 443
MARIOFF SAS—See Carrier Global Corporation; *U.S. Public*, pg. 443
MARIOFF SKANDINAVIEN AB—See Carrier Global Corporation; *U.S. Public*, pg. 443
MARIOFF SRL—See Carrier Global Corporation; *U.S. Public*, pg. 443
MARLBOROUGH COMMUNICATIONS LIMITED—See Cohort plc; *Int'l*, pg. 1696
MAS METAMAP (BEIJING) SOFTWARE TECHNOLOGY CO., LTD.—See Chongqing MAS Sci. & Tech. Co., Ltd.; *Int'l*, pg. 1580
MAS ZHONGTAI (BEIJING) TECHNOLOGY CO., LTD.—See Chongqing MAS Sci. & Tech. Co., Ltd.; *Int'l*, pg. 1580
MATICMIND SPA—See Ascom Holding AG; *Int'l*, pg. 603
MAX-VIZ, INC.—See Astronics Corporation; *U.S. Public*, pg. 217
MCMURDO, INC.—See Eurazeo SE; *Int'l*, pg. 2528
MEISEI ELECTRIC CO., LTD.—See IHI Corporation; *Int'l*, pg. 3606
MERCURY SYSTEMS, INC. - RF INTEGRATED SOLUTIONS—See Mercury Systems, Inc.; *U.S. Public*, pg. 1422
METRAX GMBH—See OSI Systems, Inc.; *U.S. Public*, pg. 1621
MINETEC PTY LTD.—See Codan Limited; *Int'l*, pg. 1688
MINIM, INC.; *U.S. Public*, pg. 1449
MOBILE COMMUNICATIONS AMERICA, INC.—See Sentinel Capital Partners, L.L.C.; *U.S. Private*, pg. 3609
MOLD-TECH (DONGGUAN) CO. LTD.—See Standex International; *U.S. Public*, pg. 1930
MOLEX PREMISE NETWORKS, INC.—See Koch Industries, Inc.; *U.S. Private*, pg. 2335
MORTON PHOTONICS, INC.—See Coldquanta, Inc.; *U.S. Private*, pg. 966
MSA SORDIN AB—See MSA Safety Incorporated; *U.S. Public*, pg. 1482
NADY SYSTEMS, INC.; *U.S. Private*, pg. 2830
NAHUELSAT S.A.—See Airbus SE; *Int'l*, pg. 247
NAPCO DR, S.A.—See Napco Security Technologies, Inc.; *U.S. Public*, pg. 1491
NATIONAL SIGNAL, INC.—See Hill & Smith PLC; *Int'l*, pg. 3392
NEST LABS, INC.—See Alphabet Inc.; *U.S. Public*, pg. 84
NEXTGENID, INC.—See Zeva Inc.; *U.S. Private*, pg. 4603
NIHON CORNET TECHNOLOGY K.K.—See Cornet Technology Inc.; *U.S. Private*, pg. 1053
NORAN TEL, INC.—See Westell Technologies, Inc.; *U.S. Public*, pg. 2354
NOTIFIER CO.—See Honeywell International Inc.; *U.S. Public*, pg. 1050
NUTMEG UTILITY PRODUCTS INC.; *U.S. Private*, pg. 2974
OA LABORATORY CO., LTD.—See FUJISOFT INCORPORATED; *Int'l*, pg. 2830
ON4 COMMUNICATIONS INC.; *U.S. Public*, pg. 1601
ONE FOR ALL IBERIA S.L.—See Universal Electronics, Inc.; *U.S. Public*, pg. 2255
ON-RAMP WIRELESS, INC.; *U.S. Private*, pg. 3019
OPTIMUS S.A.—See Aiphone Co., Ltd.; *Int'l*, pg. 235
OPTION GERMANY GMBH—See Crescent N.V.; *Int'l*, pg. 1839
OPTION WIRELESS LTD—See Crescent N.V.; *Int'l*, pg. 1839
ORBITAL SYSTEMS, LTD.—See Odyssey Investment Partners, LLC; *U.S. Private*, pg. 2995
ORION ENTRANCE CONTROL, INC.; *U.S. Private*, pg. 3042
PADGETT COMMUNICATIONS, INC.; *U.S. Private*, pg. 3073
PALOMAR PRODUCTS INC.—See TransDigm Group Incorporated; *U.S. Public*, pg. 2181
PANDUIT INT—See Panduit Corp.; *U.S. Private*, pg. 3085
PEAK NANO OPTICS, LLC—See L3Harris Technologies, Inc.; *U.S. Public*, pg. 1284
PHASE ELECTRONICS LTD.—See Everspring Industry Co., Ltd.; *Int'l*, pg. 2569
PICOMETRIX, LLC—See Luna Innovations Incorporated; *U.S. Public*, pg. 1349
PLANTRONICS LIMITED—See HP Inc.; *U.S. Public*, pg. 1064
PLANTRONICS PTY. LIMITED—See HP Inc.; *U.S. Public*, pg. 1064
PLANTRONICS RUS LLC—See HP Inc.; *U.S. Public*, pg. 1064
POSITIVEID CORPORATION; *U.S. Private*, pg. 3233
POTTER ELECTRIC SIGNAL COMPANY, LLC—See KKR & Co. Inc.; *U.S. Public*, pg. 1263
POTTERS INDUSTRIAL LIMITADA—See Ecovyst Inc.; *U.S. Public*, pg. 717
PRECO ELECTRONICS, LLC—See Sensata Technologies

N.A.I.C.S. Index

334290 — OTHER COMMUNICATION... CORPORATE AFFILIATIONS

Holding plc; *U.S. Public*, pg. 1865
PREFERRED TECHNOLOGY SYSTEMS, LLC.—See Source Capital, LLC; *U.S. Private*, pg. 3718
PROJECTIONS, INC.; *U.S. Private*, pg. 3281
PROPRIETARY CONTROL SYSTEMS CORP.—See TTIK Inc.; *U.S. Private*, pg. 4255
PS TECHNOLOGIES, LLC—See Black Box Limited; *Int'l*, pg. 1058
PTMW INC.; *U.S. Private*, pg. 3298
QENEX COMMUNICATIONS, INC.; *U.S. Public*, pg. 1742
QMAX COMMUNICATIONS PTE LTD.—See Creative Technology Ltd.; *Int'l*, pg. 1833
RAPISCAN SYSTEMS HONG KONG LIMITED—See OSI Systems, Inc.; *U.S. Public*, pg. 1622
RAVEON TECHNOLOGIES CORPORATION; *U.S. Private*, pg. 3357
RAYTHEON APPLIED SIGNAL TECHNOLOGY, INC.—See RTX Corporation; *U.S. Public*, pg. 1825
RMD INSTRUMENTS CORPORATION—See Dynasil Corporation of America; *U.S. Private*, pg. 1300
ROANWELL CORPORATION; *U.S. Private*, pg. 3453
ROBICHAUX AUTOMATION & CONTROL, INC.—See J.F. Lehman & Company, Inc.; *U.S. Private*, pg. 2164
ROCKWELL COLLINS, INC.—See RTX Corporation; *U.S. Public*, pg. 1822
ROSS TECHNOLOGY CORPORATION; *U.S. Private*, pg. 3485
RUIJIE NETWORKS CO., LTD.—See Fujian Star-net Communication Co.,Ltd; *Int'l*, pg. 2819
SAM TAIHANG ELECTRONICS CO LTD—See L3Harris Technologies, Inc.; *U.S. Public*, pg. 1284
SANMINA-SCI ENCLOSURE SYSTEMS (SHENZHEN) LTD.—See Sanmina Corporation; *U.S. Public*, pg. 1840
SCOTTEL VOICE & DATA, INC.—See Black Box Limited; *Int'l*, pg. 1058
SDP TELECOM INC.—See Koch Industries, Inc.; *U.S. Private*, pg. 2335
SECURITY PLUS ALARMS, LLC—See Arvig Enterprises, Inc.; *U.S. Private*, pg. 345
SENTORARU DENSHI SEIGYO CO., LTD.—See Futaba Corporation; *Int'l*, pg. 2851
SENTRY TECHNOLOGY CORPORATION; *U.S. Public*, pg. 1868
SHORETEL AUSTRALIA PTY. LTD.—See Searchlight Capital Partners, L.P.; *U.S. Private*, pg. 3589
SIERRA MICROWAVE TECHNOLOGY, LLC—See HEICO Corporation; *U.S. Public*, pg. 1020
SILICON LABORATORIES INC.; *U.S. Public*, pg. 1879
SIMONSVOSS SECURITY TECHNOLOGIES (ASIA) PTE. LTD.—See Allegion Public Limited Company; *Int'l*, pg. 335
SIMONSVOSS TECHNOLOGIES BV—See Allegion Public Limited Company; *Int'l*, pg. 335
SIMONSVOSS TECHNOLOGIES SAS—See Allegion Public Limited Company; *Int'l*, pg. 335
SKYLINE PARTNERS TECHNOLOGY, LLC—See COMSovereign Holding Corp.; *U.S. Public*, pg. 562
SMA RAILWAY TECHNOLOGY GMBH—See Beijing Dinghan Technology Group Co., Ltd.; *Int'l*, pg. 948
SMOKE GUARD, INC.—See CSW Industrials, Inc.; *U.S. Public*, pg. 602
SOLACOM TECHNOLOGIES (US), INC.—See Comtech Telecommunications Corp.; *U.S. Public*, pg. 563
SPACE ENGINEERING S.P.A.—See Airbus SE; *Int'l*, pg. 247
SPERRY MARINE CANADA LIMITED—See Northrop Grumman Corporation; *U.S. Public*, pg. 1540
STANLEY CONVERGENT SECURITY SOLUTIONS, INC.—See Stanley Black & Decker, Inc.; *U.S. Public*, pg. 1934
STAR HEADLIGHT AND LANTERN CO., INC.; *U.S. Private*, pg. 3784
STIG WAHLSTROM OY—See Addtech AB; *Int'l*, pg. 135
STN SCHIFFSELEKTRIK VERWALTUNGS GMBH—See L3Harris Technologies, Inc.; *U.S. Public*, pg. 1284
SYSTECH CORPORATION; *U.S. Private*, pg. 3906
SYSTEM SENSOR—See Honeywell International Inc.; *U.S. Public*, pg. 1049
TALK-A-PHONE CO.; *U.S. Private*, pg. 3926
TALLYSMAN WIRELESS INC.—See Calian Group Ltd.; *Int'l*, pg. 1264
TECH ELECTRONICS OF COLORADO, LLC—See Tronicom Corp.; *U.S. Private*, pg. 4241
TECHNICAL INNOVATION, LLC—See Diversified Specialties, Inc.; *U.S. Private*, pg. 1243
TELCO SYSTEMS—See BATM Advanced Communications Ltd.; *Int'l*, pg. 890
TELEBYTE, INC.; *U.S. Private*, pg. 3960
TELEDYNE E2V LIMITED—See Teledyne Technologies Incorporated; *U.S. Public*, pg. 1995
TELEGENIX INC.—See Indel, Inc.; *U.S. Private*, pg. 2055
TELENAV, INC.; *U.S. Private*, pg. 3960
TELEPHONICS CORPORATION—See TTM Technologies, Inc.; *U.S. Public*, pg. 2203
TELE-TECTOR OF MARYLAND, INC.—See GTCR LLC; *U.S. Private*, pg. 1802
TELKONET COMMUNICATIONS, INC.—See TELKONET, INC.; *U.S. Public*, pg. 1999
TELOGY NETWORKS, INC.—See Texas Instruments Incorporated; *U.S. Public*, pg. 2026
TESAT-SPACECOM GESCHAFTSFUHRUNG GMBH—See Airbus SE; *Int'l*, pg. 243
TOMEI TSUSHIN KOGYO CO., LTD.—See COMSYS Holdings Corporation; *Int'l*, pg. 1762
TPA TRAFFIC & PARKING AUTOMATION SYSTEMS—See Ascom Holding AG; *Int'l*, pg. 603
TRACSTAR SYSTEMS, INC.—See Advent International Corporation; *U.S. Private*, pg. 100
TRILLIANT INCORPORATED; *U.S. Private*, pg. 4231
TRINITY INDUSTRIES—See Trinity Industries, Inc.; *U.S. Public*, pg. 2194
TRL TECHNOLOGY LIMITED—See L3Harris Technologies, Inc.; *U.S. Public*, pg. 1284
UEI DO BRASIL CONTROLES REMOTOS LTDA.—See Universal Electronics, Inc.; *U.S. Public*, pg. 2255
ULTRA ELECTRONICS MARITIME SYSTEMS—See Advent International Corporation; *U.S. Private*, pg. 100
VALCOM, INC.; *U.S. Private*, pg. 4330
VESTCOM INTERNATIONAL, INC.—See Charlesbank Capital Partners, LLC; *U.S. Private*, pg. 856
VIAVI SOLUTIONS HABERLESME TEST VE OLCUM TEKNOLOJILERI TICARET LIMITED SIRKETI—See Viavi Solutions Inc.; *U.S. Public*, pg. 2295
VIBES TECHNOLOGIES, INC.—See Black Box Limited; *Int'l*, pg. 1058
VICON INDUSTRIES, INC.; *U.S. Private*, pg. 4377
VICTOR PRODUCTS USA INCORPORATED—See Federal Signal Corporation; *U.S. Public*, pg. 826
VIDEOLOCITY INTERNATIONAL, INC.; *U.S. Private*, pg. 4380
VIKING ELECTRONICS, INC.—See Eaton Corporation plc; *Int'l*, pg. 2282
VIPER COMMUNICATION SYSTEMS—See Microwave Transmission Systems, Inc.; *U.S. Private*, pg. 2705
VISIX, INC.; *U.S. Private*, pg. 4393
VMS ALARMS; *U.S. Private*, pg. 4408
VTEL PRODUCTS CORPORATION; *U.S. Private*, pg. 4415
WABTEC CONTROL SYSTEMS PTY LTD—See Westinghouse Air Brake Technologies Corporation; *U.S. Public*, pg. 2359
WABTEC EQUIPAMENTOS FERROVIARIOS LTDA.—See Westinghouse Air Brake Technologies Corporation; *U.S. Public*, pg. 2359
WALTER KIDDE PORTABLE EQUIPMENT INC.—See Carrier Global Corporation; *U.S. Public*, pg. 441
WARTSILA MARINE SYSTEMS KOREA CO. LTD.—See L3Harris Technologies, Inc.; *U.S. Public*, pg. 1284
WESTEK ELECTRONICS INC.; *U.S. Private*, pg. 4490
WESTERN-CULLEN-HAYES INC.; *U.S. Private*, pg. 4498
WESTERN PACIFIC SIGNAL, LLC—See Econolite Group, Inc.; *U.S. Private*, pg. 1330
WILLO PRODUCTS COMPANY INC.; *U.S. Private*, pg. 4528
WITS CO., LTD.—See Chemtronics Co., Ltd.; *Int'l*, pg. 1464
XTERA COMMUNICATIONS, INC.—See H.I.G. Capital, LLC; *U.S. Private*, pg. 1833
ZETRON AUSTRALASIA PTY LTD.,—See Codan Limited; *Int'l*, pg. 1688
ZETRON, INC.—See Codan Limited; *Int'l*, pg. 1688
ZHONE TECHNOLOGIES S. DE R.L. DE C.V.—See DZS Inc.; *U.S. Public*, pg. 701

334310 — AUDIO AND VIDEO EQUIPMENT MANUFACTURING

AAMP OF FLORIDA, INC.; *U.S. Private*, pg. 32
ACME HOLDINGS BERHAD; *Int'l*, pg. 107
ACOUSTIC ENERGY LIMITED—See Formosa Prosonic Industries Berhad; *Int'l*, pg. 2736
ACTIA DO BRASIL IND. E COM. LTDA.—See Actia Group SA; *Int'l*, pg. 118
ACTIA VIDEO BUS, S.A.—See Actia Group SA; *Int'l*, pg. 118
ACTION INDUSTRIES (M) SDN. BHD.—See Action Electronics Co., Ltd.; *Int'l*, pg. 119
ADAM AUDIO GMBH—See Focusrite plc; *Int'l*, pg. 2720
ADAM AUDIO USA, INC.—See Focusrite plc; *Int'l*, pg. 2720
ADVANCE DISPLAY TECHNOLOGIES, INC.; *U.S. Private*, pg. 83
ALCO ELECTRONICS LIMITED—See Alco Holdings Limited; *Int'l*, pg. 301
ALCORN MCBRIDE, INC.; *U.S. Private*, pg. 154
ALESIS, L.P.—See inMusic, LLC; *U.S. Private*, pg. 2080
ALIPHCOM; *U.S. Private*, pg. 168
ALLEN AUDIO, INC.—See Allen Organ Company; *U.S. Private*, pg. 179
ALPHA VIDEO & AUDIO, INC.; *U.S. Private*, pg. 200
ALPINE ELECTRONICS MANUFACTURING OF EUROPE LTD.—See Alps Alpine Co., Ltd.; *Int'l*, pg. 375
ALTEC LANSING LLC—See Prophet Equity L.P.; *U.S. Private*, pg. 3286
A- MAX TECHNOLOGY (CHINA) LTD.—See A-Max Technology Limited; *Int'l*, pg. 20
A-MAX TECHNOLOGY GMBH—See A-Max Technology Limited; *Int'l*, pg. 20
A-MAX TECHNOLOGY LIMITED; *Int'l*, pg. 20
A-MAX TECHNOLOGY MCO CO., LTD.—See A-Max Technology Limited; *Int'l*, pg. 20
AMERICON, LLC—See Babcock & Wilcox Enterprises, Inc.; *U.S. Public*, pg. 262
AMEXCOM ELECTRONICS, INC.—See Compal Electronics, Inc.; *Int'l*, pg. 1746
AMPLIFIER TECHNOLOGIES, INC.; *U.S. Private*, pg. 266
ANAM ELECTRONICS CO., LTD - CONSUMER A/V DIVISION—See Anam Electronics Co., Ltd.; *Int'l*, pg. 446
ANAM ELECTRONICS CO., LTD.; *Int'l*, pg. 446
ANTENNA INTERNATIONAL—See The Wicks Group of Companies, LLC; *U.S. Private*, pg. 4135
APOGEE SOUND INTERNATIONAL, LLC—See Bogen Communications International Inc.; *U.S. Public*, pg. 367
ARCHOS S.A.; *Int'l*, pg. 549
ARLO TECHNOLOGIES INTERNATIONAL LTD.—See Arlo Technologies, Inc.; *U.S. Public*, pg. 193
ARMOUR AUTOMOTIVE LIMITED—See AAMP of Florida, Inc.; *U.S. Private*, pg. 32
ARRIS GLOBAL LTD.—See CommScope Holding Company, Inc.; *U.S. Public*, pg. 548
ARTIVISION TECHNOLOGIES PTE. LTD.; *Int'l*, pg. 585
ASM SERVICES AND SUPPORT IRELAND LTD.—See ASM INTERNATIONAL N.V.; *Int'l*, pg. 626
ASM TECHNOLOGY SINGAPORE PTE LTD—See ASM INTERNATIONAL N.V.; *Int'l*, pg. 626
ATEME S.A.; *Int'l*, pg. 668
ATLAS SOUND—See MiTek Corporation; *U.S. Private*, pg. 2751
ATOMOS; *Int'l*, pg. 688
ATREND USA; *U.S. Private*, pg. 382
ATS ACOUSTICS; *U.S. Private*, pg. 382
AUDIO RESEARCH CORPORATION—See Fine Sounds S.p.A.; *Int'l*, pg. 2673
AUDIO-TECHNICA CORPORATION; *Int'l*, pg. 701
AUDIO-TECHNICA (GREATER CHINA) LIMITED—See Audio-Technica Corporation; *Int'l*, pg. 701
AUDIO-TECHNICA LIMITED (UK)—See Audio-Technica Corporation; *Int'l*, pg. 701
AUDIO-TECHNICA (S.E.A.) PTE. LTD.—See Audio-Technica Corporation; *Int'l*, pg. 701
AUDIO-TECHNICA U.S., INC.—See Audio-Technica Corporation; *Int'l*, pg. 701
AUDIO VIDEO SYSTEMS, INC. (AVS); *U.S. Private*, pg. 391
AUVITRONICS LIMITED - MANUFACTURING UNIT-1—See House of Habib; *Int'l*, pg. 3491
AUVITRONICS LIMITED—See House of Habib; *Int'l*, pg. 3491
AVANTE SYSTEMS, INC.; *Int'l*, pg. 735
AV CONCEPT SINGAPORE PTE LTD.—See AV Concept Holdings Ltd; *Int'l*, pg. 733
AVIGILON CORPORATION—See Motorola Solutions, Inc.; *U.S. Public*, pg. 1477
AXIS COMMUNICATIONS BV—See Canon Inc.; *Int'l*, pg. 1293
AXIS COMMUNICATIONS GMBH—See Canon Inc.; *Int'l*, pg. 1293
AXIS COMMUNICATIONS KK—See Canon Inc.; *Int'l*, pg. 1293
AXIS COMMUNICATIONS KOREA CO. LTD.—See Canon Inc.; *Int'l*, pg. 1293
AXIS COMMUNICATIONS OOO—See Canon Inc.; *Int'l*, pg. 1293
AXIS COMMUNICATIONS PTY LTD—See Canon Inc.; *Int'l*, pg. 1293
AXIS COMMUNICATIONS (SA) (PTY) LTD—See Canon Inc.; *Int'l*, pg. 1293
AXIS COMMUNICATIONS—See Canon Inc.; *Int'l*, pg. 1293
AXIS COMMUNICATIONS (S) PTE LTD—See Canon Inc.; *Int'l*, pg. 1293
AXIS COMMUNICATIONS TAIWAN CO., LTD.—See Canon Inc.; *Int'l*, pg. 1293
AXIS COMMUNICATIONS (UK) LTD—See Canon Inc.; *Int'l*, pg. 1293
BANG & OLUFSEN ASIA PTE. LTD.—See Bang & Olufsen a/s; *Int'l*, pg. 831
BANG & OLUFSEN A/S; *Int'l*, pg. 831
BANG & OLUFSEN DANMARK A/S—See Bang & Olufsen a/s; *Int'l*, pg. 831
BANG & OLUFSEN DEUTSCHLAND GMBH—See Bang & Olufsen a/s; *Int'l*, pg. 831
BANG & OLUFSEN ESPANA S.A.—See Bang & Olufsen a/s; *Int'l*, pg. 831
BANG & OLUFSEN EXPANSION A/S—See Bang & Olufsen a/s; *Int'l*, pg. 831
BANG & OLUFSEN FRANCE S.A.—See Bang & Olufsen a/s; *Int'l*, pg. 831
BANG & OLUFSEN ICEPOWER A/S—See Bang & Olufsen a/s; *Int'l*, pg. 831
BANG & OLUFSEN JAPAN K.K.—See Bang & Olufsen a/s; *Int'l*, pg. 831
BANG & OLUFSEN SVENSKA AB—See Bang & Olufsen a/s; *Int'l*, pg. 831
B&C SPEAKERS BRASIL COMERCIO DE EQUIPAMENTOS DE AUDIO LTDA.—See B&C Speakers SpA; *Int'l*, pg. 783
B&C SPEAKERS NA (USA), LLC—See B&C Speakers SpA; *Int'l*, pg. 783
B&C SPEAKERS SPA; *Int'l*, pg. 783
BEAMZ INTERACTIVE, INC.; *U.S. Public*, pg. 287

N.A.I.C.S. INDEX

334310 — AUDIO AND VIDEO EQU...

BEATS ELECTRONICS, LLC—See Apple Inc.; *U.S. Public*, pg. 169
BEC TERO ENTERTAINMENT CO., LTD.—See BEC World Public Company Limited; *Int'l*, pg. 936
BEIJING HANBANG TECHNOLOGY CORP.; *Int'l*, pg. 951
BEIJING JETSEN TECHNOLOGY CO., LTD.; *Int'l*, pg. 952
BESTECHNIC SHANGHAI CO., LTD.; *Int'l*, pg. 1000
BEYERDYNAMIC GMBH & CO KG; *Int'l*, pg. 1005
BIAMP SYSTEMS, LLC—See AMETEK, Inc.; *U.S. Public*, pg. 118
B&K COMPONENTS LTD.; *U.S. Private*, pg. 418
BLACKMAGIC DESIGN PTY. LTD.; *Int'l*, pg. 1061
BLAUPUNKT AUDIOVISION GMBH & CO. KG—See Aurelius Equity Opportunities SE & Co. KGaA; *Int'l*, pg. 707
BLAUPUNKT CAR AUDIO SYSTEMS GMBH & CO. KG—See Aurelius Equity Opportunities SE & Co. KGaA; *Int'l*, pg. 708
BLUELINEA SA; *Int'l*, pg. 1072
BLUE MICROPHONES, LLC—See Transom Capital Group, LLC; *U.S. Private*, pg. 4209
BOGEN CORPORATION—See Bogen Communications International Inc.; *U.S. Public*, pg. 367
BOSE A/S—See Bose Corporation; *U.S. Private*, pg. 619
BOSE CORPORATION INDIA PRIVATE LIMITED—See Bose Corporation; *U.S. Private*, pg. 619
BOSE CORPORATION; *U.S. Private*, pg. 619
BOSE ELECTRONICS (SHANGHAI) CO. LIMITED—See Bose Corporation; *U.S. Private*, pg. 619
BOSE GMBH—See Bose Corporation; *U.S. Private*, pg. 620
BOSE K.K.—See Bose Corporation; *U.S. Private*, pg. 620
BOSE N.V.—See Bose Corporation; *U.S. Private*, pg. 620
BOSE PTY. LTD.—See Bose Corporation; *U.S. Private*, pg. 620
BOSE S.A. DE C.V.—See Bose Corporation; *U.S. Private*, pg. 620
BOSE S.A.R.L.—See Bose Corporation; *U.S. Private*, pg. 620
BOSE S.P.A.—See Bose Corporation; *U.S. Private*, pg. 620
BOSE SYSTEMS CORPORATION—See Bose Corporation; *U.S. Private*, pg. 620
BOSTON ACOUSTICS, INC.—See Bain Capital, LP; *U.S. Private*, pg. 438
BPM BROADCAST & PROFESSIONAL MEDIA GMBH—See Avemio AG; *Int'l*, pg. 738
BRETFORD MANUFACTURING INC.; *U.S. Private*, pg. 646
BROADSIGHT SYSTEMS INC.—See CBC Co., Ltd.; *Int'l*, pg. 1365
CABASSE S.A.—See Cabasse Group; *Int'l*, pg. 1245
CALCOM VISION LTD.; *Int'l*, pg. 1262
CALIFONE INTERNATIONAL, INC.—See School Specialty, Inc.; *U.S. Public*, pg. 1848
CAVERIN SOLUTIONS S.A.—See Econocom Group SA; *Int'l*, pg. 2297
CERWIN-VEGA, INC.—See Gibson Brands, Inc.; *U.S. Private*, pg. 1696
CHINA SKYRISE DIGITAL SERVICE INC.; *Int'l*, pg. 1552
CHONGQING ELECTRONICS LIMITED—See Central Wealth Group Holdings Limited; *Int'l*, pg. 1410
CHUGOKU FUNAI ELECTRIC CO., LTD.—See Funai Electric Co., Ltd.; *Int'l*, pg. 2844
CHUNGHSIN TECHNOLOGY GROUP CO., LTD; *Int'l*, pg. 1597
CISCO SYSTEMS—See Cisco Systems, Inc.; *U.S. Public*, pg. 500
CITY ANIMATION CO; *U.S. Private*, pg. 905
CLARION ASIA PTE. LTD.—See FORVIA SE; *Int'l*, pg. 2745
CLARION AUSTRALIA PTY. LTD.—See FORVIA SE; *Int'l*, pg. 2745
CLARION CO.; LTD.—See FORVIA SE; *Int'l*, pg. 2745
CLARION EUROPE S.A.S.—See FORVIA SE; *Int'l*, pg. 2745
CLARION (G.B.) LTD.—See FORVIA SE; *Int'l*, pg. 2745
CLARION (HK) INDUSTRIES CO., LTD.—See FORVIA SE; *Int'l*, pg. 2745
CLARION HUNGARY ELECTRONICS KFT—See FORVIA SE; *Int'l*, pg. 2745
CLARION (MALAYSIA) SDN. BHD.—See FORVIA SE; *Int'l*, pg. 2745
CLARION MANUFACTURING CORPORATION OF AMERICA—See FORVIA SE; *Int'l*, pg. 2745
CLARION (TAIWAN) MANUFACTURING CO., LTD.—See FORVIA SE; *Int'l*, pg. 2745
COMCAM INTERNATIONAL, INC.; *U.S. Public*, pg. 981
COMHEAR, INC.; *U.S. Private*, pg. 981
COMMUSONIC INDUSTRIES LIMITED—See Alco Holdings Limited; *Int'l*, pg. 301
CONFERENCE TECHNOLOGIES, INC.; *U.S. Private*, pg. 1013
CONRAC, INC.; *U.S. Private*, pg. 1018
CORPORATE COFFEE SYSTEMS, LLC—See Aramark; *U.S. Public*, pg. 176
COURTSMART DIGITAL SYSTEMS, INC.; *U.S. Private*, pg. 1070
COWON INDONESIA—See Cowon Systems Inc.; *Int'l*, pg. 1822
CRANFORD CONTROLS LIMITED—See Halma plc; *Int'l*, pg. 3231
CREST AUDIO—See Peavey Electronics Corporation; *U.S. Private*, pg. 3126

CTS ELECTRONIC COMPONENTS, INC.—See CTS Corporation; *U.S. Public*, pg. 603
CTS ELECTRONIC COMPONENTS, INC.—See CTS Corporation; *U.S. Public*, pg. 603
CUSTOM PLUS DISTRIBUTING, LLC—See Resideo Technologies, Inc.; *U.S. Public*, pg. 1790
CX TECHNOLOGY CORPORATION; *Int'l*, pg. 1891
DAEWOO ELECTRONICS AMERICA, INC.—See Dongbu Group; *Int'l*, pg. 2165
DAEWOO ELECTRONICS EUROPE GMBH—See Dongbu Group; *Int'l*, pg. 2165
DAEWOO ELECTRONICS (M) SDN. BHD.—See Dongbu Group; *Int'l*, pg. 2165
DAEWOO ELECTRONICS (PANAMA) S.A.—See Dongbu Group; *Int'l*, pg. 2165
DAEWOO ELECTRONICS SALES U.K. LIMITED—See Dongbu Group; *Int'l*, pg. 2165
DALLMEIER KOREA CO., LTD—See Dallmeier electronic GmbH & Co. KG; *Int'l*, pg. 1954
DANTAX A/S; *Int'l*, pg. 1969
DANTAX RADIO A/S—See Dantax A/S; *Int'l*, pg. 1969
D&B AUDIOTECHNIK GMBH—See Ardian SAS; *Int'l*, pg. 556
DEFINITIVE TECHNOLOGY, INC.—See Charlesbank Capital Partners, LLC; *U.S. Private*, pg. 855
DEI HOLDINGS, INC.—See Charlesbank Capital Partners, LLC; *U.S. Private*, pg. 855
DELPHI DELCO ELECTRONICS DE MEXICO S.A. DE C.V.—See Aptiv PLC; *Int'l*, pg. 524
DENON CORPORATION—See Bain Capital, LP; *U.S. Private*, pg. 438
DENSO TEN DE MEXICO, S.A. DE C.V.—See Denso Corporation; *Int'l*, pg. 2030
DESIGN & INSTALLATION DIVISION—See KVL Audio Visual Services; *U.S. Private*, pg. 2359
DEXXON GMBH—See Dexxon Groupe SA; *Int'l*, pg. 2093
DIGITAL ALLY, INC.; *U.S. Public*, pg. 662
DIGITAL VIDEO SYSTEMS, INC.; *U.S. Private*, pg. 1231
DK MUSIC PUBLISHING CO., LTD.—See DAIICHIKOUSHO CO., LTD.; *Int'l*, pg. 1930
D&M PREMIUM SOUND SOLUTIONS, LLC—See Masimo Corporation; *U.S. Public*, pg. 1392
DOLBY AUSTRALIA PTY. LTD.—See Dolby Laboratories, Inc.; *U.S. Public*, pg. 672
DOLBY INTERNATIONAL AB—See Dolby Laboratories, Inc.; *U.S. Public*, pg. 672
DONGGUAN CLARION ORIENT ELECTRONICS CO., LTD.—See FORVIA SE; *Int'l*, pg. 2745
DONGGUAN DONGFA TEAC AUDIO CO., LTD.—See Evolution Capital Management LLC; *U.S. Private*, pg. 1443
DORANCO, INC.; *U.S. Private*, pg. 1262
DOREMI LABS, INC.—See Dolby Laboratories, Inc.; *U.S. Public*, pg. 672
DPI, INC.; *U.S. Private*, pg. 1270
DRAPER INC.; *U.S. Private*, pg. 1272
DREAMUS COMPANY; *Int'l*, pg. 2203
DRONE VOLT SA; *Int'l*, pg. 2206
DTS (ASIA) LIMITED—See Xperi Inc.; *U.S. Public*, pg. 2392
DTS GUANGZHOU—See Xperi Inc.; *U.S. Public*, pg. 2392
DTS, INC.—See Xperi Inc.; *U.S. Public*, pg. 2391
DTS JAPAN KK—See Xperi Inc.; *U.S. Public*, pg. 2392
DTS LICENSING LIMITED—See Xperi Inc.; *U.S. Public*, pg. 2392
DTS LICENSING PTE. LTD.—See Xperi Inc.; *U.S. Public*, pg. 2392
DTS, LLC—See Xperi Inc.; *U.S. Public*, pg. 2392
DTS WASHINGTON LLC—See Xperi Inc.; *U.S. Public*, pg. 2392
DYNABOOK SINGAPORE PTE. LTD—See Hon Hai Precision Industry Co., Ltd.; *Int'l*, pg. 3457
EASTECH ELECTRONICS (SG) PTE. LTD.—See Eastern Holding Limited; *Int'l*, pg. 2272
EASTECH (HUIZHOU) CO., LTD.—See Eastern Holding Limited; *Int'l*, pg. 2272
EASTECH SYSTEMS (HUIYANG) CO., LTD—See Eastern Holding Limited; *Int'l*, pg. 2272
EASTERN ASIA INDUSTRIES SDN. BHD—See Eastern Asia Technology Ltd.; *Int'l*, pg. 2271
EASTERN HOLDING LIMITED; *Int'l*, pg. 2272
EAVS SA; *Int'l*, pg. 2282
ECO VOLT CO.,LTD.; *Int'l*, pg. 2292
EDIFIER TECHNOLOGY INC.; *Int'l*, pg. 2309
EIGHTEEN SOUND S.R.L.—See B&C Speakers SpA; *Int'l*, pg. 784
EIZO AUSTRIA GMBH—See EIZO Corporation; *Int'l*, pg. 2337
EIZO EUROPE GMBH—See EIZO Corporation; *Int'l*, pg. 2337
EIZO LIMITED—See EIZO Corporation; *Int'l*, pg. 2337
E-LEAD ELECTRONIC TECHNOLOGY (JIANGSU) CO., LTD.—See E-Lead Electronic Co., Ltd.; *Int'l*, pg. 2248
ELECTRONICA CLARION, S.A. DE C.V.—See FORVIA SE; *Int'l*, pg. 2745
ELECTRONICA CLARION, S.A. DE C.V.—See FORVIA SE; *Int'l*, pg. 2745
ELECTROSONIC, INC.—See Helvar Merca Oy AB; *Int'l*, pg. 3339
EMERSON CLIMATE TECHNOLOGIES ARABIA LIMITED

CO.—See Emerson Electric Co.; *U.S. Public*, pg. 743
EMERSON RADIO CORP.; *U.S. Public*, pg. 752
EMINENCE SPEAKER LLC.—See B&C Speakers SpA; *Int'l*, pg. 784
EMOTIVA AUDIO CORPORATION—See Jade Design, Inc.; *U.S. Private*, pg. 2181
EPOS GROUP A/S—See Demant A/S; *Int'l*, pg. 2023
ESOTERIC COMPANY—See Evolution Capital Management LLC; *U.S. Private*, pg. 1443
ESTEC CORPORATION—See Foster Electric Co., Ltd.; *Int'l*, pg. 2749
EUPHON COMMUNICATIONS S.P.A.; *Int'l*, pg. 2526
EVERTZ MICROSYSTEMS LIMITED; *Int'l*, pg. 2569
EVERTZ MICROSYSTEMS LTD.—See Evertz Microsystems Limited; *Int'l*, pg. 2569
EXEO ENTERTAINMENT, INC.; *U.S. Public*, pg. 807
F.G.S. CO., LTD.—See Funai Electric Co., Ltd.; *Int'l*, pg. 2844
FIRST ENGINEERING CO., LTD.—See Hibino Corporation; *Int'l*, pg. 3383
FLAT AUDIO TECHNOLOGIES, LLC; *U.S. Private*, pg. 1540
FOCUSRITE PLC; *Int'l*, pg. 2720
FORMOSA PROSONIC INDUSTRIES BERHAD; *Int'l*, pg. 2736
FORMOSA PROSONIC TECHNICS SDN. BHD.—See Formosa Prosonic Industries Berhad; *Int'l*, pg. 2736
FOSTER ELECTRIC CO., (HEYUAN) LTD.—See Foster Electric Co., Ltd.; *Int'l*, pg. 2749
FOSTER ELECTRIC CO., LTD.; *Int'l*, pg. 2749
FOSTER ELECTRIC CO., (TAIWAN) LTD.—See Foster Electric Co., Ltd.; *Int'l*, pg. 2749
FOSTER ELECTRIC (DA NANG) CO., LTD.—See Foster Electric Co., Ltd.; *Int'l*, pg. 2749
FOSTER ELECTRIC IPO (THAILAND) LTD.—See Foster Electric Co., Ltd.; *Int'l*, pg. 2749
FOSTER ELECTRIC (NANNING) CO., LTD.—See Foster Electric Co., Ltd.; *Int'l*, pg. 2749
FOSTER ELECTRIC (QUANG NGAI) CO., LTD.—See Foster Electric Co., Ltd.; *Int'l*, pg. 2749
FOSTER ELECTRIC (SINGAPORE) PTE. LTD.—See Foster Electric Co., Ltd.; *Int'l*, pg. 2749
FOSTER ELECTRIC (THILAWA) CO., LTD.—See Foster Electric Co., Ltd.; *Int'l*, pg. 2749
FOSTER ELECTRIC (U.S.A.), INC.—See Foster Electric Co., Ltd.; *Int'l*, pg. 2749
FOSTER ELECTRIC (VIETNAM) CO., LTD.—See Foster Electric Co., Ltd.; *Int'l*, pg. 2749
FOSTER ELECTRIC (VIETNAM) CO., LTD. - VIETNAM FACTORY 2—See Foster Electric Co., Ltd.; *Int'l*, pg. 2749
FOUGEROLLE S.A.—See Eiffage S.A.; *Int'l*, pg. 2330
FUJIKON INDUSTRIAL HOLDINGS LTD; *Int'l*, pg. 2826
FU LOGITEC CO., LTD.; *Int'l*, pg. 2801
FUNAI DEUTSCHLAND—See Funai Electric Co., Ltd.; *Int'l*, pg. 2844
FUNAI ELECTRIC ADVANCED APPLIED TECHNOLOGY RESEARCH INSTITUTE INC.—See Funai Electric Co., Ltd.; *Int'l*, pg. 2844
FUNAI ELECTRIC CO., LTD.; *Int'l*, pg. 2844
FUNAI ELECTRIC EUROPE SP. Z.O.O.—See Funai Electric Co., Ltd.; *Int'l*, pg. 2844
FUNAI ELECTRIC (H.K.) LTD.—See Funai Electric Co., Ltd.; *Int'l*, pg. 2844
FUNAI ELECTRIC (MALASIYA) SDN. BHD.—See Funai Electric Co., Ltd.; *Int'l*, pg. 2844
FUNAI TECHO-SYSTEMS CO., LTD.—See Funai Electric Co., Ltd.; *Int'l*, pg. 2845
FUNAI (THAILAND) CO., LTD.—See Funai Electric Co., Ltd.; *Int'l*, pg. 2844
GATEKEEPER SYSTEMS INC.; *Int'l*, pg. 2889
GEMINI SOUND PRODUCTS CORP.; *U.S. Private*, pg. 1658
GENASYS, INC.; *U.S. Public*, pg. 911
GENCOM TECHNOLOGIES LTD.—See Hills Limited; *Int'l*, pg. 3393
GENER8 MEDIA CORP.; *Int'l*, pg. 2917
GENERAL COMMUNICATIONS—See Hills Limited; *Int'l*, pg. 3393
GETTOP ACOUSTIC CO., LTD.; *Int'l*, pg. 2953
GGEC AMERICA, INC.—See GuoGuang Electric Company Limited; *Int'l*, pg. 3186
GGEC HONG KONG LTD.—See GuoGuang Electric Company Limited; *Int'l*, pg. 3186
GN AUDIO USA, INC.—See GN Store Nord A/S; *Int'l*, pg. 3015
GOVISION, LP—See Atairos Group, Inc.; *U.S. Private*, pg. 363
GP ELECTRONICS LIMITED—See Gold Peak Technology Group Limited; *Int'l*, pg. 3025
GRAFFITI ENTERTAINMENT, INC.—See Azure Holding Group Corp.; *U.S. Private*, pg. 416
GUANGDONG ANJUBAO DIGITAL TECHNOLOGY CO., LTD.; *Int'l*, pg. 3152
GUANGZHOU DTS DIGITAL THEATER SYSTEM, CO. LTD—See Xperi Inc.; *U.S. Public*, pg. 2392
GUANGZHOU PANYU JIU SHUI KENG FOSTER ELECTRIC FACTORY—See Foster Electric Co., Ltd.; *Int'l*, pg. 2750

334310 — AUDIO AND VIDEO EQU...

GUOGUANG ELECTRIC COMPANY LIMITED; *Int'l*, pg. 3186
HAIVISION NETWORK VIDEO INC.—See HaiVision Systems, Inc.; *Int'l*, pg. 3218
HAIVISION SYSTEMS, INC.; *Int'l*, pg. 3218
HANCHIH ELECTRONICS (SHENZHEN) CO., LTD.—See Hanpin Electron Co., Ltd.; *Int'l*, pg. 3258
HANGZHOU CENTURY CO., LTD.; *Int'l*, pg. 3246
HANGZHOU HIKVISION DIGITAL TECHNOLOGY CO., LTD.; *Int'l*, pg. 3247
HANPIN BVI INTERNATIONAL CO., LTD.—See Hanpin Electron Co., Ltd.; *Int'l*, pg. 3258
HANPIN BVI INTL CO., LTD.—See Hanpin Electron Co., Ltd.; *Int'l*, pg. 3258
HARMONIC EUROPE S.A.S.—See Harmonic, Inc.; *U.S. Public*, pg. 985
HARMONIC TECHNOLOGIES (HK) LIMITED—See Harmonic, Inc.; *U.S. Public*, pg. 986
HARMONIC VIDEO SYSTEMS LTD.—See Harmonic, Inc.; *U.S. Public*, pg. 986
HEADSETS.COM, INC.; *U.S. Private*, pg. 1891
HECO AUDIO-PRODUKTE GMBH—See VOXX International Corporation; *U.S. Public*, pg. 2311
H.F.T. INDUSTRIAL LTD.—See Funai Electric Co., Ltd.; *Int'l*, pg. 2844
HIBINO ASIA PACIFIC (SHANGHAI) LIMITED—See Hibino Corporation; *Int'l*, pg. 3383
HIBINO CORPORATION; *Int'l*, pg. 3383
HIBINO MEDIA TECHNICAL CORPORATION—See Hibino Corporation; *Int'l*, pg. 3383
HIKVISION AUSTRALIA PTY CO., LTD.—See Hangzhou Hikvision Digital Technology Co., Ltd.; *Int'l*, pg. 3247
HIKVISION AZERBAIJAN LIMITED LIABILITY—See Hangzhou Hikvision Digital Technology Co., Ltd.; *Int'l*, pg. 3247
HIKVISION CANADA INC.—See Hangzhou Hikvision Digital Technology Co., Ltd.; *Int'l*, pg. 3247
HIKVISION CZECH S.R.O.—See Hangzhou Hikvision Digital Technology Co., Ltd.; *Int'l*, pg. 3247
HIKVISION DEUTSCHLAND GMBH—See Hangzhou Hikvision Digital Technology Co., Ltd.; *Int'l*, pg. 3247
HIKVISION DO BRASIL COMERCIO DE EQUIPAMENTOS DE SEGURANCA LTDA.—See Hangzhou Hikvision Digital Technology Co., Ltd.; *Int'l*, pg. 3248
HIKVISION FRANCE SAS—See Hangzhou Hikvision Digital Technology Co., Ltd.; *Int'l*, pg. 3247
HIKVISION FZE—See Hangzhou Hikvision Digital Technology Co., Ltd.; *Int'l*, pg. 3247
HIKVISION ITALY S.R.L—See Hangzhou Hikvision Digital Technology Co., Ltd.; *Int'l*, pg. 3247
HIKVISION KAZAKHSTAN LIMITED LIABILITY PARTNERSHIP—See Hangzhou Hikvision Digital Technology Co., Ltd.; *Int'l*, pg. 3247
HIKVISION KOREA LIMITED—See Hangzhou Hikvision Digital Technology Co., Ltd.; *Int'l*, pg. 3247
HIKVISION LLC—See Hangzhou Hikvision Digital Technology Co., Ltd.; *Int'l*, pg. 3248
HIKVISION (MALAYSIA) SDN. BHD.—See Hangzhou Hikvision Digital Technology Co., Ltd.; *Int'l*, pg. 3247
HIKVISION MEXICO S.A.DE C.V.—See Hangzhou Hikvision Digital Technology Co., Ltd.; *Int'l*, pg. 3248
HIKVISION NEW ZEALAND LIMITED—See Hangzhou Hikvision Digital Technology Co., Ltd.; *Int'l*, pg. 3248
HIKVISION PAKISTAN (SMC-PRIVATE) LIMITED—See Hangzhou Hikvision Digital Technology Co., Ltd.; *Int'l*, pg. 3248
HIKVISION POLAND SPOLKA Z OGRANICZONA ODPOWIEDZIALNOSCIA—See Hangzhou Hikvision Digital Technology Co., Ltd.; *Int'l*, pg. 3248
HIKVISION SINGAPORE PTE. LTD.—See Hangzhou Hikvision Digital Technology Co., Ltd.; *Int'l*, pg. 3248
HIKVISION SOUTH AFRICA (PTY) CO., LTD.—See Hangzhou Hikvision Digital Technology Co., Ltd.; *Int'l*, pg. 3248
HIKVISION SPAIN, S.L.—See Hangzhou Hikvision Digital Technology Co., Ltd.; *Int'l*, pg. 3248
HIKVISION TECHNOLOGY EGYPT JSC—See Hangzhou Hikvision Digital Technology Co., Ltd.; *Int'l*, pg. 3248
HIKVISION TECHNOLOGY ISRAEL CO., LTD.—See Hangzhou Hikvision Digital Technology Co., Ltd.; *Int'l*, pg. 3248
HIKVISION TURKEY TECHNOLOGY & SECURITY SYSTEMS COMMERCE CORPORATION—See Hangzhou Hikvision Digital Technology Co., Ltd.; *Int'l*, pg. 3248
HIKVISION UK LIMITED—See Hangzhou Hikvision Digital Technology Co., Ltd.; *Int'l*, pg. 3248
HIKVISION USA, INC.—See Hangzhou Hikvision Digital Technology Co., Ltd.; *Int'l*, pg. 3248
HILLS INDUSTRIES ANTENNA & TV SYSTEMS—See Hills Limited; *Int'l*, pg. 3393
HILLS INDUSTRIES DIRECT ALARM SUPPLIES—See Hills Limited; *Int'l*, pg. 3393
HITACHI HOME ELECTRONICS ASIA (S) PTE. LTD.—See Hitachi, Ltd.; *Int'l*, pg. 3414
HITEVISION CO., LTD.; *Int'l*, pg. 3426
HIVI ACOUSTICS TECHNOLOGY CO., LTD.; *Int'l*, pg. 3427
HIWAVE (HONG KONG) LIMITED—See FLAT Audio Technologies, LLC; *U.S. Private*, pg. 1541

HOLMBERG FRANCE SAS—See Holmberg GmbH & Co. KG; *Int'l*, pg. 3452
HONEYWELL VIDEO SYSTEMS—See Honeywell International Inc.; *U.S. Public*, pg. 1051
HOSIDEN KYUSHU CORPORATION—See Hosiden Corporation; *Int'l*, pg. 3484
HYMNARIO-EAW (HUIYANG) CO., LTD.—See Eastern Holding Limited; *Int'l*, pg. 2272
I3 INTERNATIONAL INC.; *Int'l*, pg. 3566
IDIS CO., LTD.; *Int'l*, pg. 3595
IMMEDIA, LLC; *U.S. Private*, pg. 2047
INFINITY WIRELESS, INC.—See OwnersEdge Inc.; *U.S. Private*, pg. 3055
INNOVACOM, INC.; *U.S. Public*, pg. 1125
INTER TECHNOLOGIES CORPORATION (ITC); *U.S. Private*, pg. 2106
INVISION AUTOMOTIVE SYSTEMS, INC.—See VOXX International Corporation; *U.S. Public*, pg. 2311
ION AUDIO, LLC—See inMusic, LLC; *U.S. Private*, pg. 2080
ITALIAN TOMATO LTD.—See BANDAI NAMCO Holdings Inc.; *Int'l*, pg. 829
JOYO ELECTRIC CO., LTD.—See Beijing Sojo Electric Company Limited; *Int'l*, pg. 957
JWIN ELECTRONICS CORP.; *U.S. Private*, pg. 2247
KALEIDESCAPE, INC.; *U.S. Private*, pg. 2257
KH ELECTRON CO., LTD.—See Corstone Corporation; *U.S. Private*, pg. 1060
KLIPSCH GROUP, INC.—See VOXX International Corporation; *U.S. Public*, pg. 2311
KOSS CORPORATION; *U.S. Public*, pg. 1275
KOSS EUROPE S.A.—See Koss Corporation; *U.S. Public*, pg. 1275
KRELL INDUSTRIES, INC.; *U.S. Private*, pg. 2351
L3 MOBILE-VISION, INC.—See Keystone Group, L.P.; *U.S. Private*, pg. 2296
LEGACY AUDIO, INC.; *U.S. Private*, pg. 2416
LIFESIZE COMMUNICATIONS, INC.—See Logitech International S.A.; *U.S. Public*, pg. 1341
LLC HIKVISION TASHKENT—See Hangzhou Hikvision Digital Technology Co., Ltd.; *Int'l*, pg. 3248
LOGIC INTEGRATION INC.; *U.S. Private*, pg. 2481
LOUDSPEAKER COMPONENTS, L.L.C.; *U.S. Private*, pg. 2498
LSI SACO TECHNOLOGIES, INC.—See LSI Industries Inc.; *U.S. Public*, pg. 1344
M3 ELECTRONIC GMBH—See DISA LIMITED; *Int'l*, pg. 2131
MAC AUDIO ELECTRONIC GMBH—See VOXX International Corporation; *U.S. Public*, pg. 2311
MACKIE DESIGNS S.P.A.—See LOUD Technologies Inc.; *U.S. Public*, pg. 1342
MAGNAT AUDIO-PRODUKTE GMBH—See VOXX International Corporation; *U.S. Public*, pg. 2311
MARANTZ EUROPE B.V.—See Bain Capital, LP; *U.S. Private*, pg. 438
MARANTZ FRANCE SAS—See Bain Capital, LP; *U.S. Private*, pg. 438
MARANTZ GMBH—See Bain Capital, LP; *U.S. Private*, pg. 438
MARANTZ ITALY SRL—See Bain Capital, LP; *U.S. Private*, pg. 439
MARANTZ UK LTD.—See Bain Capital, LP; *U.S. Private*, pg. 439
MARTIN AUDIO LTD.—See Focusrite plc; *Int'l*, pg. 2720
MARTIN AUDIO US, LLC—See Focusrite plc; *Int'l*, pg. 2720
MAX SOUND CORPORATION; *U.S. Public*, pg. 1402
MCINTOSH LABORATORY, INC.—See Fine Sounds S.p.A.; *Int'l*, pg. 2673
MECHDYNE CANADA—See Mechdyne Corp.; *U.S. Private*, pg. 2649
MECHDYNE CORP.; *U.S. Private*, pg. 2649
MESA/BOOGIE LIMITED; *U.S. Private*, pg. 2678
MEYER SOUND LABORATORIES INC.; *U.S. Private*, pg. 2692
MICROSOFT MOBILE INC.—See Microsoft Corporation; *U.S. Public*, pg. 1441
MITEK CORPORATION - MONROE FACILITY—See MiTek Corporation; *U.S. Public*, pg. 2751
MITEK CORPORATION; *U.S. Private*, pg. 2751
MOGAMI DENKI CORPORATION—See EQT AB; *Int'l*, pg. 2470
MOGAMI DONGGUAN ELECTRONICS CO., LTD.—See EQT AB; *Int'l*, pg. 2470
MONSTER, LLC—See Monster Products, Inc.; *U.S. Private*, pg. 2774
MOONBLINK COMMUNICATIONS; *U.S. Private*, pg. 2779
MOTOROLA DE MEXICO, S.A.—See Motorola Solutions, Inc.; *U.S. Public*, pg. 1479
NAMCO ENTERTAINMENT INC.—See BANDAI NAMCO Holdings Inc.; *Int'l*, pg. 829
NEURILINK LLC—See AVI Systems, Inc.; *U.S. Private*, pg. 406
NEW WAVE INNOVATIONS, LLC—See MarineMax, Inc.; *U.S. Public*, pg. 1367
NOKIA MOBILE PHONES WIRELESS DATA—See Microsoft Corporation; *U.S. Public*, pg. 1441
NUMARK INDUSTRIES, L.P.—See inMusic, LLC; *U.S. Private*, pg. 2080

OPTIMAL MEDIA PRODUCTION GMBH—See Edel SE & Co. KGaA; *Int'l*, pg. 2305
OPTIM INCORPORATED—See Juno Investments LLC; *U.S. Private*, pg. 2244
OU BO-SOFT—See Bang & Olufsen a/s; *Int'l*, pg. 831
PACIFIC COMMUNICATIONS PTY. LTD.—See Hills Limited; *Int'l*, pg. 3393
PARAMOUNT PICTURES ENTERTAINMENT CANADA INC.—See National Amusements, Inc.; *U.S. Private*, pg. 2843
PCTV SYSTEMS—See HAUPPAUGE DIGITAL, INC.; *U.S. Public*, pg. 988
PEAVEY COMMERCIAL AUDIO—See Peavey Electronics Corporation; *U.S. Private*, pg. 3126
PEAVEY ELECTRONICS CORPORATION; *U.S. Private*, pg. 3126
PEAVEY ELECTRONICS LTD.—See Peavey Electronics Corporation; *U.S. Private*, pg. 3126
PHASE LINEAR—See VOXX International Corporation; *U.S. Public*, pg. 2311
PHOENIX GOLD—See PHX AP Acquisitions LLC; *U.S. Private*, pg. 3174
PHORUS, INC.—See Xperi Inc.; *U.S. Public*, pg. 2392
PHOTRON EUROPE LIMITED—See Imagica Group Inc.; *Int'l*, pg. 3618
PHOTRON LIMITED—See Imagica Group Inc.; *Int'l*, pg. 3618
PIONEER AUTOMOTIVE TECHNOLOGY—See EQT AB; *Int'l*, pg. 2470
PIONEER CORPORATION—See EQT AB; *Int'l*, pg. 2470
PIONEER DO BRASIL LTDA—See EQT AB; *Int'l*, pg. 2471
PIONEER ELECTRONICS AUSTRALIA PTY LTD—See EQT AB; *Int'l*, pg. 2470
PIONEER EUROPE N.V—See EQT AB; *Int'l*, pg. 2471
PIONEER GULF, FZE—See EQT AB; *Int'l*, pg. 2471
PIONEER (HK) LTD.—See EQT AB; *Int'l*, pg. 2470
PIONEER INDIA ELECTRONICS PRIVATE LTD—See EQT AB; *Int'l*, pg. 2471
PIONEER TECHNOLOGY (MALAYSIA) SDN. BHD.—See EQT AB; *Int'l*, pg. 2471
PIXELINK, INC.—See AMETEK, Inc.; *U.S. Public*, pg. 121
PLAYNETWORK, INC.—See Vector Capital Management, L.P.; *U.S. Private*, pg. 4351
POLK AUDIO, INC.—See Charlesbank Capital Partners, LLC; *U.S. Private*, pg. 855
PRO-VISION INC.—See JMC Capital Partners LLC; *U.S. Private*, pg. 2215
PT. HIKVISION TECHNOLOGY INDONESIA—See Hangzhou Hikvision Digital Technology Co., Ltd.; *Int'l*, pg. 3248
P.T. SHARP ELECTRONICS INDONESIA—See Hon Hai Precision Industry Co., Ltd.; *Int'l*, pg. 3457
QSC, LLC; *U.S. Private*, pg. 3314
QUAD VIDEO HALO, INC.—See Quad Video Holdings Corporation; *U.S. Private*, pg. 3315
QUAD VIDEO HOLDINGS CORPORATION; *U.S. Private*, pg. 3315
QUAM-NICHOLS COMPANY; *U.S. Private*, pg. 3322
RADIO ENGINEERING INDUSTRIES; *U.S. Private*, pg. 3343
RADIO FREQUENCY SYSTEMS PTY. LTD.—See Radio Frequency Systems, Inc.; *U.S. Private*, pg. 3344
RADIO FREQUENCY SYSTEMS SINGAPORE PTE LTD—See Radio Frequency Systems, Inc.; *U.S. Private*, pg. 3344
RAPID DIE & MOLDING CO.; *U.S. Private*, pg. 3355
RDDS AVIONICS LIMITED—See Croma Security Solutions Group Plc; *Int'l*, pg. 1853
REDFLEX HOLDINGS LIMITED—See Verra Mobility Corporation; *U.S. Public*, pg. 2286
REDFLEX TRAFFIC SYSTEMS INC.—See Verra Mobility Corporation; *U.S. Public*, pg. 2286
REELEX CO., LTD.—See Chuo Spring Co., Ltd.; *Int'l*, pg. 1599
REKOR RECOGNITION SYSTEMS—See Rekor Systems, Inc.; *U.S. Public*, pg. 1778
REQUEST, INC.; *U.S. Private*, pg. 3403
REVOLUTIONARY CONCEPTS, INC.; *U.S. Private*, pg. 3417
ROCKFORD CORPORATION—See Patrick Industries, Inc.; *U.S. Public*, pg. 1653
ROGERS STEREO INC.; *U.S. Private*, pg. 3472
ROKU, INC.; *U.S. Public*, pg. 1808
SAKAR INTERNATIONAL, INC.; *U.S. Public*, pg. 3530
SAMBON (H.K.) ELECTRONICS LIMITED—See Corstone Corporation; *U.S. Private*, pg. 1060
SANSHIN ELECTRIC CO., LTD.—See Bain Capital, LP; *U.S. Private*, pg. 435
SANSHIN (MALAYSIA) SDN. BHD.—See Bain Capital, LP; *U.S. Private*, pg. 435
SCAN-SPEAK A/S—See Eastern Holding Limited; *Int'l*, pg. 2272
SDI TECHNOLOGIES, INC.; *U.S. Private*, pg. 3581
SEACHANGE INDIA PRIVATE, LTD.—See SeaChange International, Inc.; *U.S. Public*, pg. 1851
SEILOX; *U.S. Private*, pg. 3599
SELECT SOUND SERVICE, INC.—See Communications Engineering Co.; *U.S. Private*, pg. 988

N.A.I.C.S. INDEX

334412 — BARE PRINTED CIRCUI...

SENNHEISER COMMUNICATIONS A/S—See Demant A/S; *Int'l*, pg. 2024
SERVICE TECH AV; *U.S. Private*, pg. 3616
SHANGHAI AXIS COMMUNICATION EQUIPMENT TRADING CO. LTD—See Canon Inc.; *Int'l*, pg. 1293
SHANGHAI PIONEER SPEAKERS CO., LTD.—See EQT AB; *Int'l*, pg. 2471
SHARP APPLIANCES (THAILAND) LTD.—See Hon Hai Precision Industry Co., Ltd.; *Int'l*, pg. 3457
SHARP CORPORATION—See Hon Hai Precision Industry Co., Ltd.; *Int'l*, pg. 3457
SHARP ELECTRONICA ESPANA S.A.—See Hon Hai Precision Industry Co., Ltd.; *Int'l*, pg. 3458
SHARP INDIA LIMITED—See Hon Hai Precision Industry Co., Ltd.; *Int'l*, pg. 3458
SHORTHAND CENTER TSUKUBA CO., LTD.—See Advanced Media, Inc.; *Int'l*, pg. 161
SHURE INCORPORATED; *U.S. Private*, pg. 3644
SKAR AUDIO, INC.; *U.S. Private*, pg. 3681
SKULLCANDY AUDIO (SHENZHEN) CO., LTD.—See Mill Road Capital Management LLC; *U.S. Private*, pg. 2730
SKULLCANDY INTERNATIONAL GMBH—See Mill Road Capital Management LLC; *U.S. Private*, pg. 2730
SKULLCANDY NORDIC AB—See Mill Road Capital Management LLC; *U.S. Private*, pg. 2730
SMBT PUBLISHING (THAILAND) CO., LTD.—See BEC World Public Company Limited; *Int'l*, pg. 936
SNAP ONE, LLC—See Resideo Technologies, Inc.; *U.S. Public*, pg. 1790
S'NEXT JAPAN CO. LTD.—See Koch Industries, Inc.; *U.S. Private*, pg. 2334
S'NEXT PHILIPPINES—See Koch Industries, Inc.; *U.S. Private*, pg. 2334
S & O ELECTRONICS (MALAYSIA) SDN. BHD.—See Hon Hai Precision Industry Co., Ltd.; *Int'l*, pg. 3457
SONOS, INC.; *U.S. Public*, pg. 1909
SONUS FABER S.P.A.—See Fine Sounds S.p.A.; *Int'l*, pg. 2673
SOUNDCAST LLC—See Hancock Park Associates, LP; *U.S. Private*, pg. 1852
SOUNDCHECK, LLC—See Live Nation Entertainment, Inc.; *U.S. Public*, pg. 1330
SOUNDCHIP SA—See Synaptics Incorporated; *U.S. Public*, pg. 1969
SOUND VIDEO SOLUTIONS, INC.; *U.S. Private*, pg. 3717
SPEAKERBUS, INC.; *U.S. Private*, pg. 3747
STAGE FRONT PRESENTATION SYSTEMS; *U.S. Private*, pg. 3775
STEREO VISION ENTERTAINMENT, INC.; *U.S. Public*, pg. 1945
STEWART FILMSCREEN CORPORATION - OHIO—See Stewart Filmscreen Corporation; *U.S. Public*, pg. 3811
STEWART FILMSCREEN CORPORATION; *U.S. Public*, pg. 3811
STILLWATER DESIGNS & AUDIO; *U.S. Private*, pg. 3812
SZ HANBANG TECHNOLOGY CO., LTD.—See Beijing Hanbang Technology Corp.; *Int'l*, pg. 951
TAIWAN TEAC CORPORATION—See Evolution Capital Management LLC; *U.S. Private*, pg. 1443
TANDBERG ASA—See Cisco Systems, Inc.; *U.S. Public*, pg. 500
TEAC AUDIO (CHINA) CO., LTD.—See Evolution Capital Management LLC; *U.S. Private*, pg. 1443
TEAC EUROPE GMBH.—See Evolution Capital Management LLC; *U.S. Private*, pg. 1443
TEAC MANUFACTURING SOLUTIONS CORPORATION—See Evolution Capital Management LLC; *U.S. Private*, pg. 1443
TEAC MANUFACTURING SOLUTIONS CORPORATION—See Evolution Capital Management LLC; *U.S. Private*, pg. 1443
TEAC NEDERLAND B.V.—See Evolution Capital Management LLC; *U.S. Private*, pg. 1443
TECTONIC ELEMENTS LTD.—See FLAT Audio Technologies, LLC; *U.S. Private*, pg. 1541
TOHOKU PIONEER CORPORATION - YONEZAWA PLANT—See EQT AB; *Int'l*, pg. 2471
TOHOKU PIONEER (THAILAND) CO., LTD.—See EQT AB; *Int'l*, pg. 2471
TOHOKU PIONEER (VIETNAM) CO., LTD.—See EQT AB; *Int'l*, pg. 2471
TOTAL RECALL CORPORATION—See Ares Management Corporation; *U.S. Public*, pg. 189
TOTAL VIDEO PRODUCTS, INC.—See Fernandez Holdings, Inc.; *U.S. Private*, pg. 1497
TRIAD SPEAKERS, INC.—See Resideo Technologies, Inc.; *U.S. Public*, pg. 1790
TYMPHANY-CHINA—See Tymphany Corp.; *U.S. Private*, pg. 4268
TYMPHANY CORP.; *U.S. Private*, pg. 4268
TYMPHANY-HONG KONG—See Tymphany Corp.; *U.S. Private*, pg. 4268
UCA SYSTEMS INC.; *U.S. Private*, pg. 4273
ULTRA ELECTRONICS SONAR & COMMUNICATIONS SYSTEMS—See Advent International Corporation; *U.S. Private*, pg. 101
UNGO SECURITY CORPORATION—See FORVIA SE; *Int'l*, pg. 2745

UNIVERSAL ELECTRONICS BV—See Universal Electronics, Inc.; *U.S. Public*, pg. 2255
UNIVERSAL ELECTRONICS, INC.; *U.S. Public*, pg. 2255
UNIVERSAL ELECTRONICS—See Universal Electronics, Inc.; *U.S. Public*, pg. 2255
VELODYNE ACOUSTICS, INC.; *U.S. Private*, pg. 4355
VIALTA, INC.; *U.S. Private*, pg. 4375
VIDEO COMMUNICATION FRANCE S.A.—See Bertelsmann SE & Co. KGaA; *Int'l*, pg. 996
VIDEON CENTRAL, INC.; *U.S. Private*, pg. 4380
VIEVU LLC—See Axon Enterprise, Inc.; *U.S. Public*, pg. 256
VISTACOM, INC.—See Conference Technologies, Inc.; *U.S. Private*, pg. 1013
VISTEON AMAZONAS LTDA.—See Visteon Corporation; *U.S. Public*, pg. 2305
VIZIO, INC.—See VIZIO Holding Corp.; *U.S. Public*, pg. 2307
VUZIX CORPORATION; *U.S. Public*, pg. 2314
WADIA DIGITAL—See Fine Sounds S.p.A.; *Int'l*, pg. 2673
WATCHGUARD, INC.—See Motorola Solutions, Inc.; *U.S. Public*, pg. 1479
WESTONE LABORATORIES, INC.—See HealthEdge Investment Partners, LLC; *U.S. Private*, pg. 1896
WIDEBAND SYSTEMS, INC.—See Delta Information Systems Inc.; *U.S. Private*, pg. 1201
WIPLIANCE, LLC; *U.S. Private*, pg. 4546
XIAMEN CLARION ELECTRICAL ENTERPRISE CO., LTD.—See FORVIA SE; *Int'l*, pg. 2745
XIUM CORPORATION; *U.S. Private*, pg. 4581
XOS DIGITAL INC.—See Catapult Group International Ltd.; *Int'l*, pg. 1358
YOKOHAMA CREATIVE CENTER—See BANDAI NAMCO Holdings Inc.; *Int'l*, pg. 829
YOKOHAMA MIRAI-KENKYUSHO—See BANDAI NAMCO Holdings Inc.; *Int'l*, pg. 829
YORKTEL, INC.—See Yorktel, Inc.; *U.S. Private*, pg. 4591
ZAGG INCORPORATED—See Evercel, Inc.; *U.S. Private*, pg. 1437
ZONE DEFENSE, LLC—See JMC Capital Partners LLC; *U.S. Private*, pg. 2215

334412 — BARE PRINTED CIRCUIT BOARD MANUFACTURING

4DSP LLC—See AMETEK, Inc.; *U.S. Public*, pg. 119
ABONMAX CO., LTD; *Int'l*, pg. 67
ACTIONTEC ELECTRONICS, INC.; *U.S. Private*, pg. 68
ADVANCED CIRCUITS, INC.—See IGP Industries, LLC; *U.S. Private*, pg. 2039
AE CORPORATION (M) SDN. BHD.—See AE Multi Holdings Berhad; *Int'l*, pg. 170
AE MULTI HOLDINGS BERHAD; *Int'l*, pg. 170
AGILITY MFG, INC.; *U.S. Private*, pg. 128
AKM ELECTRONICS TECHNOLOGY (SUZHOU) COMPANY LIMITED—See AKM Industrial Company Limited; *Int'l*, pg. 264
AKM INDUSTRIAL COMPANY LIMITED; *Int'l*, pg. 264
ALL QUALITY & SERVICES INC.; *U.S. Private*, pg. 171
AMALLION ENTERPRISE (THAILAND) CORPORATION LTD.—See AE Multi Holdings Berhad; *Int'l*, pg. 170
AMERICAN BOARD COMPANIES, INC.—See The MATCO Group, Inc.; *U.S. Private*, pg. 4075
AMPHENOL INVOTEC LIMITED—See Amphenol Corporation; *U.S. Public*, pg. 128
AMPHENOL TRACKWISE DESIGNS LIMITED—See Amphenol Corporation; *U.S. Public*, pg. 129
ANAREN CERAMICS, INC.—See TTM Technologies, Inc.; *U.S. Public*, pg. 2203
ANSEN CORPORATION; *U.S. Private*, pg. 285
AOI ELECTRONICS CO., LTD.; *Int'l*, pg. 487
AOSHIKANG TECHNOLOGY CO., LTD.; *Int'l*, pg. 498
APCB INC.; *Int'l*, pg. 508
APCT, INC.—See IGP Industries, LLC; *U.S. Private*, pg. 2039
APEX CIRCUIT (THAILAND) CO., LTD.—See Apex International Co., Ltd.; *Int'l*, pg. 511
APEX INTERNATIONAL CO., LTD.; *Int'l*, pg. 511
ASIA VETS HOLDINGS LTD.; *Int'l*, pg. 616
AT&S AMERICAS LLC—See AT&S Austria Technologie & Systemtechnik Aktiengesellschaft; *Int'l*, pg. 665
AT&S ASIA PACIFIC LIMITED—See AT&S Austria Technologie & Systemtechnik Aktiengesellschaft; *Int'l*, pg. 665
AT&S AUSTRIA TECHNOLOGIE & SYSTEMTECHNIK AKTIENGESELLSCHAFT; *Int'l*, pg. 664
AT&S CHINA CO. LTD.—See AT&S Austria Technologie & Systemtechnik Aktiengesellschaft; *Int'l*, pg. 665
AT&S DEUTSCHLAND GMBH—See AT&S Austria Technologie & Systemtechnik Aktiengesellschaft; *Int'l*, pg. 665
AT&S INDIA PRIVATE LIMITED—See AT&S Austria Technologie & Systemtechnik Aktiengesellschaft; *Int'l*, pg. 665
AT&S (TAIWAN) CO., LTD.—See AT&S Austria Technologie & Systemtechnik Aktiengesellschaft; *Int'l*, pg. 665
AUTOMOBILE & PCB INC.; *Int'l*, pg. 730
AVG ADVANCED TECHNOLOGIES LP; *U.S. Private*, pg. 406
AVISONIC TECHNOLOGY CORP.—See ELAN Microelectronic Corp.; *Int'l*, pg. 2342

BAKER TECHNOLOGY ASSOCIATES, INC.; *U.S. Private*, pg. 456
BENCHMARK ELECTRONICS, INC.; *U.S. Public*, pg. 295
BENCHMARK ELECTRONICS INC.—See Benchmark Electronics, Inc.; *U.S. Public*, pg. 295
BESTBRIGHT ELECTRONICS CO., LTD.—See Brightking Holdings Limited; *Int'l*, pg. 1162
BH CO., LTD.; *Int'l*, pg. 1009
THE BOEING CO. - EL PASO—See The Boeing Company; *U.S. Public*, pg. 2040
BOMIN ELECTRONICS CO., LTD.; *Int'l*, pg. 1104
BRIGHTKING (BEIJING) CO., LTD.—See Brightking Holdings Limited; *Int'l*, pg. 1163
BRIGHTKING ELECTRONICS CO., LTD.—See Brightking Holdings Limited; *Int'l*, pg. 1162
BRIGHTKING ELECTRONICS INC.—See Brightking Holdings Limited; *Int'l*, pg. 1162
BRIGHTKING ENTERPRISE (H.K) CO., LTD—See Brightking Holdings Limited; *Int'l*, pg. 1163
BRIGHTKING (SHANGAI) CO., LTD.—See Brightking Holdings Limited; *Int'l*, pg. 1163
BRIGHTKING (SHENZHEN) CO., LTD.—See Brightking Holdings Limited; *Int'l*, pg. 1163
BRUNSWICK GMBH—See Brunswick Corporation; *U.S. Public*, pg. 407
BRUNSWICK NETHERLANDS B.V.—See Brunswick Corporation; *U.S. Public*, pg. 407
BURTON INDUSTRIES INC.; *U.S. Private*, pg. 693
CAMSING INTERNATIONAL HOLDING LIMITED; *Int'l*, pg. 1275
CAREER ELECTRONIC (KUNSHAN) CO., LTD.—See Career Technology (MFG.) Co., Ltd.; *Int'l*, pg. 1323
CARLIN SYSTEMS INC.; *U.S. Private*, pg. 764
CARTEL ELECTRONICS, INC.—See IGP Industries, LLC; *U.S. Private*, pg. 2039
CERAMATE TECHNICAL (SUZHOU) CO., LTD.—See Brightking Holdings Limited; *Int'l*, pg. 1162
CHEER TIME ENTERPRISES CO., LTD - KUEI-SHAN PLANT—See Cheer Time Enterprises Co., Ltd.; *Int'l*, pg. 1459
CHEER TIME ENTERPRISES CO., LTD.; *Int'l*, pg. 1459
CHEMITALIC DENMARK A/S; *Int'l*, pg. 1462
CHEMITALIC SUZHOU LTD.—See Chemitalic Denmark A/S; *Int'l*, pg. 1462
CHINA CIRCUIT TECHNOLOGY (SHANTOU) CORPORATION—See Guangdong Goworld Co., Ltd.; *Int'l*, pg. 3154
CHIN POON INDUSTRIAL CO., LTD.; *Int'l*, pg. 1480
CICOR AMERICAS INC.—See Cicor Technologies Ltd.; *Int'l*, pg. 1603
CICOR ASIA PTE. LTD.—See Cicor Technologies Ltd.; *Int'l*, pg. 1603
CICOR ELECTRONIC SOLUTIONS DIVISION—See Cicor Technologies Ltd.; *Int'l*, pg. 1603
CICOREL SA—See Cicor Technologies Ltd.; *Int'l*, pg. 1603
CICOR TECHNOLOGIES LTD.; *Int'l*, pg. 1603
CIRCUIT CONNECT, INC.—See Infinitum Electric, Inc.; *U.S. Private*, pg. 2071
CIRCUITS WEST, INC.—See Daniel P. O'Reilly & Company; *U.S. Private*, pg. 1156
CIRCUIT SYSTEMS (INDIA) LIMITED; *Int'l*, pg. 1618
CIRCUIT WORKS CORPORATION—See IDEX Corp; *U.S. Public*, pg. 1091
CLOUD AIR CO., LTD.; *Int'l*, pg. 1661
CMKC (DONG GUAN) LTD.—See CMK Corporation; *Int'l*, pg. 1671
CMKC (HONG KONG) LTD.—See CMK Corporation; *Int'l*, pg. 1671
CMK CORPORATION - G STATION PLANT—See CMK Corporation; *Int'l*, pg. 1670
CMK CORPORATION - NIIGATA SATELLITE PLANT—See CMK Corporation; *Int'l*, pg. 1670
CMK CORPORATION; *Int'l*, pg. 1670
CMK CORPORATION (THAILAND) CO., LTD.—See CMK Corporation; *Int'l*, pg. 1670
CMK ELECTRONICS (WUXI) CO., LTD.—See CMK Corporation; *Int'l*, pg. 1671
CMK EUROPE N.V.—See CMK Corporation; *Int'l*, pg. 1671
CMK KANBARA ELECTRONIC CORPORATION—See CMK Corporation; *Int'l*, pg. 1671
CMK NIIGATA CORPORATION—See CMK Corporation; *Int'l*, pg. 1671
CMK PRODUCTS CORPORATION—See CMK Corporation; *Int'l*, pg. 1671
COFIDUR SA; *Int'l*, pg. 1692
COGISCAN INC.—See Durr AG; *Int'l*, pg. 2230
COMPEQ MANUFACTURING CO., LTD. - LUCHU PLANT—See Compeq Manufacturing Co., Ltd.; *Int'l*, pg. 1753
COMPEQ MANUFACTURING CO., LTD.; *Int'l*, pg. 1753
COMPEQ MANUFACTURING(HUIZHOU) CO., LTD.—See Compeq Manufacturing Co., Ltd.; *Int'l*, pg. 1753
COMPEQ MANUFACTURING(SUZHOU) CO., LTD.—See Compeq Manufacturing Co., Ltd.; *Int'l*, pg. 1753
COMPUTROL, INC.—See Armstrong International, Inc.; *U.S. Private*, pg. 332
COPPER CLAD MULTILAYER PRODUCTS INC.; *U.S. Private*, pg. 1045

334412 — BARE PRINTED CIRCUIT... — CORPORATE AFFILIATIONS

CREONIX, LLC—See Elbit Systems Limited; *Int'l*, pg. 2344
CSUN MFG. LTD.; *Int'l*, pg. 1868
CTS ELECTRONICS MANUFACTURING SOLUTIONS—See Benchmark Electronics, Inc.; *U.S. Public*, pg. 295
CURAMIK ELECTRONICS, INC.—See Rogers Corporation; *U.S. Public*, pg. 1808
DAEDUCK ELECTRONICS CO., LTD.—See DAEDUCK Co., Ltd.; *Int'l*, pg. 1906
DAIWA CIRCUIT MODULE CO., LTD.—See Hokuriku Electric Industry Co., Ltd.; *Int'l*, pg. 3444
DAP CO., LTD.; *Int'l*, pg. 1970
DEK ASIA PACIFIC PRIVATE LIMITED—See Dover Corporation; *U.S. Public*, pg. 680
DELTA GROUP ELECTRONIC INC.; *U.S. Private*, pg. 1200
DIGITTRON TECHNOLOGIES, INC.—See Pivot International, Inc.; *U.S. Private*, pg. 3192
DONG GUAN HONG YUEN ELECTRONICS LTD.—See China Aerospace International Holdings Limited; *Int'l*, pg. 1481
DOWA POWER DEVICE CO., LTD.—See Dowa Holdings Co., Ltd.; *Int'l*, pg. 2183
DYNAMIC ELECTRONICS CO., LTD.; *Int'l*, pg. 2240
DYNAMIC ELECTRONICS (HUANGSHI) CO., LTD.—See Dynamic Electronics Co., Ltd.; *Int'l*, pg. 2240
DYNAMIC ELECTRONICS (KUNSHAN) CO., LTD.—See Dynamic Electronics Co., Ltd.; *Int'l*, pg. 2240
DYNAMIC PCB ELECTRONICS CO., LTD.—See Dynamic Electronics Co., Ltd.; *Int'l*, pg. 2240
DYNAMIC & PROTO CIRCUITS INC.; *Int'l*, pg. 2239
EECO SWITCH (UK)—See Transico Incorporated; *U.S. Private*, pg. 4208
EG INDUSTRIES BERHAD; *Int'l*, pg. 2322
ELECTRONIC SERVICES CORPORATION OF AMERICA; *U.S. Private*, pg. 1356
ELECTROPAC CO., INC.—See Mass Design, Inc.; *U.S. Private*, pg. 2603
ELITE ELECTRONIC MATERIAL CO., LTD. - KUNSHAN PLANT—See Elite Material Co., Ltd.; *Int'l*, pg. 2362
ELITE ELECTRONIC MATERIAL (KUNSHAN) CO., LTD.—See Elite Material Co., Ltd.; *Int'l*, pg. 2362
ELITE ELECTRONIC MATERIAL (ZHONGSHAN) CO., LTD.—See Elite Material Co., Ltd.; *Int'l*, pg. 2362
ELITE MATERIAL CO., LTD. - HSINCHU PLANT—See Elite Material Co., Ltd.; *Int'l*, pg. 2362
ELITE SEMICONDUCTOR MICROELECTRONICS TECHNOLOGY INC.; *Int'l*, pg. 2362
ELMA BUSTRONIC CORP.—See Elma Electronic AG; *Int'l*, pg. 2367
ELNA PRINTED CIRCUITS CO., LTD.—See Global Brands Manufacture Ltd.; *Int'l*, pg. 2993
ENE TECHNOLOGY INC.; *Int'l*, pg. 2410
ENSILICA INDIA PRIVATE LIMITED—See Ensilica Plc; *Int'l*, pg. 2447
EPEC ENGINEERED TECHNOLOGIES; *U.S. Private*, pg. 1411
EV ADVANCED MATERIAL CO., LTD.; *Int'l*, pg. 2560
FABRICATED COMPONENTS CORPORATION; *U.S. Private*, pg. 1458
FINE-LINE CIRCUITS LIMITED; *Int'l*, pg. 2673
FIRAN TECHNOLOGY GROUP CORPORATION; *Int'l*, pg. 2678
FIRST HI-TEC ENTERPRISE CO., LTD.; *Int'l*, pg. 2684
FLEXIUM INTERCONNECT, INC - KUNSHAN PLANT—See Flexium Interconnect, Inc.; *Int'l*, pg. 2705
FLEXIUM INTERCONNECT, INC.; *Int'l*, pg. 2705
FLEXTRONICS INTERNATIONAL PA, INC.—See Flex Ltd.; *Int'l*, pg. 2703
FLEXTRONICS INTERNATIONAL USA, INC.—See Flex Ltd.; *Int'l*, pg. 2703
FLEXTRONICS INTERNATIONAL USA INC.—See Flex Ltd.; *Int'l*, pg. 2703
FTG CIRCUITS - CHATSWORTH—See Firan Technology Group Corporation; *Int'l*, pg. 2678
FTG CIRCUITS FREDERICKSBURG INC.—See Firan Technology Group Corporation; *Int'l*, pg. 2678
FTG CIRCUITS - TORONTO—See Firan Technology Group Corporation; *Int'l*, pg. 2678
FUJIKURA ELECTRONICS (THAILAND) LTD. - NAVANAKORN FACTORY 3—See Fujikura Ltd.; *Int'l*, pg. 2828
FUJITSU INTERCONNECT TECHNOLOGIES LIMITED—See Fujitsu Limited; *Int'l*, pg. 2833
GENERAL MICROCIRCUITS, INC.—See East West Manufacturing, LLC; *U.S. Private*, pg. 1319
GENERALPLUS TECHNOLOGY INC.; *Int'l*, pg. 2920
GENIE ELECTRONICS COMPANY; *U.S. Private*, pg. 1671
GLOBAL BRANDS MANUFACTURE (DONGGUAN) LTD.—See Global Brands Manufacture Ltd.; *Int'l*, pg. 2993
GLOBAL BRANDS MANUFACTURE LTD - CHINA GUANGDONG HUANGJIAN PCBA PLANT—See Global Brands Manufacture Ltd.; *Int'l*, pg. 2993
GLOBAL BRANDS MANUFACTURE LTD.; *Int'l*, pg. 2993
GOLD CIRCUIT ELECTRONICS - CHANGSHU PLANT—See Gold Circuit Electronics; *Int'l*, pg. 3024
GOLD CIRCUIT ELECTRONICS - CHUNG LI PLANT—See Gold Circuit Electronics; *Int'l*, pg. 3024
GOLD CIRCUIT ELECTRONICS; *Int'l*, pg. 3023

GRAPHIC RESEARCH INC; *U.S. Private*, pg. 1757
GS SWISS PCB AG—See H2APEX Group SCA; *Int'l*, pg. 3199
GUANGDONG CHAMPION ASIA ELECTRONICS CO., LTD.; *Int'l*, pg. 3153
GUANGDONG CHAOHUA TECHNOLOGY CO., LTD.; *Int'l*, pg. 3153
GUANGDONG ELLINGTON ELECTRONICS TECH CO., LTD.; *Int'l*, pg. 3154
GUANGZHOU MEADVILLE ELECTRONICS CO., LTD.; *Int'l*, pg. 3167
GUANGZHOU TAIHUA MULTILAYER CIRCUIT BOARD CO., LTD.—See Guangdong Chaohua Technology Co., Ltd.; *Int'l*, pg. 3153
GUH CIRCUIT INDUSTRY (PG) SDN. BHD.—See GUH Holdings Berhad; *Int'l*, pg. 3173
GUH CIRCUIT INDUSTRY (SUZHOU) CO., LTD.—See GUH Holdings Berhad; *Int'l*, pg. 3173
GUH HOLDINGS BERHAD; *Int'l*, pg. 3173
GUL TECHNOLOGIES SINGAPORE LTD.; *Int'l*, pg. 3178
GULTECH (SUZHOU) ELECTRONICS CO., LTD.—See Gul Technologies Singapore Ltd.; *Int'l*, pg. 3178
GULTECH (WUXI) ELECTRONICS CO., LTD.—See Gul Technologies Singapore Ltd.; *Int'l*, pg. 3178
HANNSTAR BOARD CORPORATION; *Int'l*, pg. 3257
HI-P (SUZHOU) ELECTRONICS TECHNOLOGY CO., LTD.—See Hi-P International Limited; *Int'l*, pg. 3381
HI-TECH ELECTRONIC MANUFACTURING, INC.; *U.S. Private*, pg. 1932
HOKURIKU (SINGAPORE) PTE., LTD.—See Hokuriku Electric Industry Co., Ltd.; *Int'l*, pg. 3445
HOLADAY CIRCUITS, INC.—See Firan Technology Group Corporation; *Int'l*, pg. 2678
HONG YUEN ELECTRONICS LIMITED—See China Aerospace International Holdings Limited; *Int'l*, pg. 1481
HUIZHOU LIEN SHUN ELECTRONICS CO., LTD.—See Brightking Holdings Limited; *Int'l*, pg. 1162
HUIZHOU UNIPLUS ELECTRONICS CO., LTD.—See Guangdong Chaohua Technology Co., Ltd.; *Int'l*, pg. 3153
HYUN WOO INDUSTRIAL CO., LTD; *Int'l*, pg. 3555
IBIDEN CIRCUITS OF AMERICA CORP.—See Ibiden Co., Ltd.; *Int'l*, pg. 3575
IBIDEN CO., LTD. - OGAKI PLANT—See Ibiden Co., Ltd.; *Int'l*, pg. 3575
IBIDEN ELECTRONICS (BEIJING) CO., LTD.—See Ibiden Co., Ltd.; *Int'l*, pg. 3575
IBIDEN ELECTRONICS TECHNOLOGY (SHANGHAI) CO.—See Ibiden Co., Ltd.; *Int'l*, pg. 3575
IBIDEN SINGAPORE PTE. LTD.—See Ibiden Co., Ltd.; *Int'l*, pg. 3576
ICAPE HOLDING S.A.; *Int'l*, pg. 3578
IEC ELECTRONICS CORP.—See Goldberg Lindsay & Co., LLC; *U.S. Private*, pg. 1729
IMI INC.—See Firan Technology Group Corporation; *Int'l*, pg. 2678
INEDA SYSTEMS INC.—See Intel Corporation; *U.S. Public*, pg. 1138
INEDA SYSTEMS PVT. LTD.—See Intel Corporation; *U.S. Public*, pg. 1138
INITIAL TECHNOLOGY PTE LTD—See Compeq Manufacturing Co., Ltd.; *Int'l*, pg. 1753
INTEGRATED CIRCUIT PACKAGING CORPORATION; *U.S. Private*, pg. 2099
INTHINC, INC.—See ORBCOMM, Inc.; *U.S. Public*, pg. 1614
I. TECHNICAL SERVICES LLC—See Prime Technological Services, LLC; *U.S. Private*, pg. 3262
JABIL CIRCUIT, INC. - TEMPE PLANT—See Jabil Inc.; *U.S. Public*, pg. 1181
JABIL CIRCUIT JAPAN, INC.—See Jabil Inc.; *U.S. Public*, pg. 1181
JATON CORP.; *U.S. Private*, pg. 2191
JIANGSU BOMIN ELECTRONICS CO., LTD.—See Bomin Electronics Co., Ltd.; *Int'l*, pg. 1105
JR CONTROLS INC.; *U.S. Private*, pg. 2239
KALEX CIRCUIT BOARD (CHINA) LIMITED—See TTM Technologies, Inc.; *U.S. Public*, pg. 2203
KFE HONG KONG CO., LIMITED—See Cosmos Machinery Enterprises Limited; *Int'l*, pg. 1813
KYODEN CO., LTD.—See The Carlyle Group Inc.; *U.S. Public*, pg. 2048
LENTHOR ENGINEERING, LLC—See Arsenal Capital Management LP; *U.S. Private*, pg. 338
LIBRA INDUSTRIES, INCORPORATED; *U.S. Private*, pg. 2447
LOGIC PD, INC.—See Compass Group, LLC; *U.S. Private*, pg. 999
LONE STAR CIRCUITS INC.; *U.S. Private*, pg. 2484
MASS DESIGN, INC.; *U.S. Private*, pg. 2603
MASTERWORK ELECTRONICS INC.; *U.S. Private*, pg. 2608
MCDONALD TECHNOLOGIES INTERNATIONAL INC.; *U.S. Private*, pg. 2632
MEIZHOU TAIHUA PRINTED CIRCUIT BOARD CO., LTD.—See Guangdong Chaohua Technology Co., Ltd.; *Int'l*, pg. 3153
MICRON CORPORATION; *U.S. Private*, pg. 2704

MICRON MEMORY JAPAN - HIROSHIMA PLANT—See Micron Technology, Inc.; *U.S. Public*, pg. 1437
MID-SOUTH ELECTRONICS, INC.—See Mid-South Industries, Inc.; *U.S. Private*, pg. 2708
MINCO EC AG—See Minco Products, Inc.; *U.S. Private*, pg. 2740
MINCO GMBH—See Minco Products, Inc.; *U.S. Private*, pg. 2740
MINCO LTD—See Minco Products, Inc.; *U.S. Private*, pg. 2740
MINCO PRODUCTS, INC.; *U.S. Private*, pg. 2740
THE MOREY CORPORATION; *U.S. Private*, pg. 4080
MTI ELECTRONICS INC.—See Insight Equity Holdings LLC; *U.S. Private*, pg. 2086
MULTITEST ELECTRONIC SYSTEMS, INC.—See Cohu, Inc.; *U.S. Public*, pg. 530
NAM HING CIRCUIT BOARD COMPANY LIMITED—See China Environmental Energy Investment Limited; *Int'l*, pg. 1500
NEXLOGIC TECHNOLOGIES INC.; *U.S. Private*, pg. 2919
ORIENTAL PRINTED CIRCUITS, INC.—See TTM Technologies, Inc.; *U.S. Public*, pg. 2203
ORIENTAL PRINTED CIRCUITS (USA), INC.—See TTM Technologies, Inc.; *U.S. Public*, pg. 2203
OSDA, INC.—See Foxtronics EMS; *U.S. Private*, pg. 1585
PARAGON ELECTRONIC SYSTEMS INC.; *U.S. Private*, pg. 3091
PARK AEROSPACE CORPORATION; *U.S. Public*, pg. 1637
P.C.B. CENTER (THAILAND) CO., LTD.—See Aspocomp Group Oyj; *Int'l*, pg. 632
PHILWAY PRODUCTS, INC.; *U.S. Private*, pg. 3171
PHOTOCHEMIE AG—See Cicor Technologies Ltd.; *Int'l*, pg. 1603
PHOTO ETCH TECHNOLOGY—See Align Capital Partners, LLC; *U.S. Private*, pg. 167
PHYSPEED, LLC—See MaxLinear, Inc.; *U.S. Public*, pg. 1403
PLEXUS CORP. SERVICES (UK) LIMITED—See Plexus Corp.; *U.S. Public*, pg. 1698
PLEXUS CORP.; *U.S. Public*, pg. 1698
PLEXUS INTERNATIONAL SERVICES, INC.—See Plexus Corp.; *U.S. Public*, pg. 1698
PLEXUS SERVICES CORP.—See Plexus Corp.; *U.S. Public*, pg. 1698
PLEXUS—See Plexus Corp.; *U.S. Public*, pg. 1698
PPI/TIME ZERO INC.—See Insight Equity Holdings LLC; *U.S. Private*, pg. 2086
PRINCETON TECHNOLOGY CORP.—See Intervala, LLC; *U.S. Private*, pg. 2127
PROJECTS UNLIMITED, INC.; *U.S. Private*, pg. 3281
PT CICOR PANATEC—See Cicor Technologies Ltd.; *Int'l*, pg. 1603
PTL INFORMATION TECHNOLOGY SERVICES CORP.—See Plexus Corp.; *U.S. Public*, pg. 1698
QUALITEK—See Westak, Inc.; *U.S. Private*, pg. 4488
QUALITY CIRCUITS INC.; *U.S. Private*, pg. 3318
QUAL-PRO CORPORATION; *U.S. Private*, pg. 3317
RAVEN INDUSTRIES, INC. - ELECTRONIC SYSTEMS DIVISION—See CNH Industrial N.V.; *Int'l*, pg. 1676
RAVEN INDUSTRIES, INC. - FLOW CONTROL DIVISION—See CNH Industrial N.V.; *Int'l*, pg. 1676
R & D CIRCUITS, INC.—See Guardian Capital Partners, LLC; *U.S. Private*, pg. 1810
RIVERSIDE ELECTRONICS LTD.; *U.S. Private*, pg. 3445
ROGERS CORPORATION; *U.S. Public*, pg. 1807
ROGERS N.V.—See Rogers Corporation; *U.S. Public*, pg. 1808
ROYAL CIRCUIT SOLUTIONS, INC.—See Summit Interconnect, Inc.; *U.S. Private*, pg. 3855
RTP CORP.; *U.S. Private*, pg. 3498
RYOHOKU DENSHI CO., LTD.—See Hokuriku Electric Industry Co., Ltd.; *Int'l*, pg. 3445
SAE CIRCUITS COLORADO INC.; *U.S. Private*, pg. 3523
SAKI CORPORATION—See DMG MORI Co., Ltd.; *Int'l*, pg. 2145
SALINE LECTRONICS, INC.—See Crestview Partners, L.P.; *U.S. Private*, pg. 1098
SANMINADE MEXICO S.A. DE C.V.—See Sanmina Corporation; *U.S. Public*, pg. 1841
SANMINA-SCI AB—See Sanmina Corporation; *U.S. Public*, pg. 1840
SANMINA-SCI GERMANY GMBH—See Sanmina Corporation; *U.S. Public*, pg. 1840
SANMINA-SCI GMBH—See Sanmina Corporation; *U.S. Public*, pg. 1840
SANMINA-SCI HUNGARY ELECTRONICS MANUFACTURING LIMITED LIABILITY COMPANY—See Sanmina Corporation; *U.S. Public*, pg. 1840
SANMINA-SCI IRELAND—See Sanmina Corporation; *U.S. Public*, pg. 1841
SANMINA-SCI ISRAEL MEDICAL SYSTEMS, LTD.—See Sanmina Corporation; *U.S. Public*, pg. 1841
SANMINA-SCI MANCHESTER PLANT—See Sanmina Corporation; *U.S. Public*, pg. 1841
SANMINA-SCI OPTICAL TECHNOLOGY (SHENZHEN) LTD.—See Sanmina Corporation; *U.S. Public*, pg. 1841
SANMINA-SCI RSP DE MEXICO S.A. DE C.V.—See Sanmina Corporation; *U.S. Public*, pg. 1841

N.A.I.C.S. INDEX

334413 — SEMICONDUCTOR AND R...

SANMINA-SCI SYSTEMS DE MEXICO S.A. DE C.V.—See Sanmina Corporation; *U.S. Public*, pg. 1841
SANMINA-SCI SYSTEMS JAPAN, LTD.—See Sanmina Corporation; *U.S. Public*, pg. 1841
SANMINA-SCI SYSTEMS (MALAYSIA) SND BHD—See Sanmina Corporation; *U.S. Public*, pg. 1841
SANMINA-SCI SYSTEMS SINGAPORE PTE. LTD.—See Sanmina Corporation; *U.S. Public*, pg. 1841
SANMINA-SCI SYSTEMS (THAILAND) LIMITED—See Sanmina Corporation; *U.S. Public*, pg. 1841
SANMINA-SCI TECHNOLOGY INDIA PRIVATE LIMITED—See Sanmina Corporation; *U.S. Public*, pg. 1841
SATOSEN CO., LTD.—See Arisawa Manufacturing Co., Ltd.; *Int'l*, pg. 566
SCHOTT NORTH AMERICA, INC. - BARON SYSTEMS & SOLUTIONS DIVISION—See Carl-Zeiss-Stiftung; *Int'l*, pg. 1337
SEMI-KINETICS INC.—See Gonzalez Design Engineering Company Inc.; *U.S. Private*, pg. 1737
SHENNAN CIRCUIT COMPANY LIMITED - LONGGANG FACTORY—See AVIC International Holdings Limited; *Int'l*, pg. 742
SHENNAN CIRCUIT COMPANY LIMITED—See AVIC International Holdings Limited; *Int'l*, pg. 742
SHENZHEN BOMIN ELECTRONIC CO., LTD.—See Bomin Electronics Co., Ltd.; *Int'l*, pg. 1105
SILICON FOREST ELECTRONICS, INC.; *U.S. Private*, pg. 3652
SILICON LABORATORIES ASIA PACIFIC, LIMITED—See Silicon Laboratories Inc.; *U.S. Public*, pg. 1879
SILICON LABORATORIES FRANCE SAS—See Silicon Laboratories Inc.; *U.S. Public*, pg. 1880
SILICON LABORATORIES GMBH—See Silicon Laboratories Inc.; *U.S. Public*, pg. 1880
SILICON LABORATORIES INTERNATIONAL PTE. LTD.—See Silicon Laboratories Inc.; *U.S. Public*, pg. 1880
SILICON LABORATORIES UK LIMITED—See Silicon Laboratories Inc.; *U.S. Public*, pg. 1880
SILICON LABORATORIES Y.K.—See Silicon Laboratories Inc.; *U.S. Public*, pg. 1880
SKY COMPUTERS, INC.; *U.S. Private*, pg. 3684
SMTC CORPORATION—See H.I.G. Capital, LLC; *U.S. Private*, pg. 1833
SMTC MANUFACTURING CORPORATION OF CALIFORNIA—See H.I.G. Capital, LLC; *U.S. Private*, pg. 1833
SMTC MANUFACTURING CORPORATION OF CANADA—See H.I.G. Capital, LLC; *U.S. Private*, pg. 1834
SMTC NOVA SCOTIA COMPANY—See H.I.G. Capital, LLC; *U.S. Private*, pg. 1834
SOLIDMICRON TECHNOLOGIES PTE LTD—See Fu Yu Corporation Limited; *Int'l*, pg. 2801
SOPARK CORP.; *U.S. Private*, pg. 3715
SOUTH BAY CIRCUITS INC.; *U.S. Private*, pg. 3719
SOUTH COAST CIRCUITS, INC.—See Summit Interconnect, Inc.; *U.S. Private*, pg. 3855
SPANG & COMPANY; *U.S. Private*, pg. 3744
SPECIALIZED COATING SERVICES—See Tide Rock Holdings, LLC; *U.S. Private*, pg. 4168
STADIUM ELECTRONICS LIMITED—See Cicor Technologies Ltd.; *Int'l*, pg. 1603
STENTECH, INC.—See Align Capital Partners, LLC; *U.S. Private*, pg. 167
SUMMIT INTERCONNECT, INC.; *U.S. Private*, pg. 3855
SUNTRON NORTHEAST EXPRESS—See Blum Capital Partners, L.P.; *U.S. Private*, pg. 599
SUNTRON NORTHEAST EXPRESS—See HCI Equity Management, L.P.; *U.S. Private*, pg. 1889
SUNTRON NORTHEAST OPERATIONS—See Blum Capital Partners, L.P.; *U.S. Private*, pg. 599
SUNTRON NORTHEAST OPERATIONS—See HCI Equity Management, L.P.; *U.S. Private*, pg. 1889
SUZHOU CICOR TECHNOLOGY CO., LTD.—See Cicor Technologies Ltd.; *Int'l*, pg. 1603
SWISSTRONICS CONTRACT MANUFACTURING AG—See Cicor Technologies Ltd.; *Int'l*, pg. 1603
SYPRIS ELECTRONICS, LLC—See Sypris Solutions, Inc.; *U.S. Public*, pg. 1972
SYSTEL SA—See Cicor Technologies Ltd.; *Int'l*, pg. 1603
SYSTRONICS S.R.L.—See Cicor Technologies Ltd.; *Int'l*, pg. 1603
TAI HONG CIRCUIT IND. CO., LTD.—See ChangChun Group; *Int'l*, pg. 1442
TAIWAN UYEMURA CO., LTD.—See C.Uyemura & Co., Ltd.; *Int'l*, pg. 1244
TAT CHUN PRINTED CIRCUIT BOARD COMPANY LIMITED—See China Silver Technology; *Int'l*, pg. 1552
TECH CIRCUITS INC.—See IGP Industries, LLC; *U.S. Private*, pg. 2039
TEKNETIX INC.; *U.S. Private*, pg. 3958
TETRAD ELECTRONICS INC.; *U.S. Private*, pg. 3973
TEXAS INSTRUMENTS NORWAY AS—See Texas Instruments Incorporated; *U.S. Public*, pg. 2026
TEXATRONICS INC.; *U.S. Private*, pg. 3978

THINFLEX CORP.—See Arisawa Manufacturing Co., Ltd.; *Int'l*, pg. 566
TOKYO KAKOKI CO., LTD.—See Astena Holdings Co., Ltd.; *Int'l*, pg. 653
TOKYO KAKOKI (SHANGHAI) CO., LTD.—See Astena Holdings Co., Ltd.; *Int'l*, pg. 653
TRINAMIC, INC.—See Analog Devices, Inc.; *U.S. Public*, pg. 136
TRINAMIC MOTION CONTROL GMBH & CO. KG—See Analog Devices, Inc.; *U.S. Public*, pg. 136
TT ELECTRONICS IOT SOLUTIONS LIMITED—See Cicor Technologies Ltd.; *Int'l*, pg. 1603
TTM TECHNOLOGIES ADVANCED CIRCUITS DIV.—See TTM Technologies, Inc.; *U.S. Public*, pg. 2203
TTM TECHNOLOGIES, INC.; *U.S. Public*, pg. 2203
VANGUARD EMS, INC.; *U.S. Private*, pg. 4343
VIASYSTEMS TECHNOLOGIES CORP., L.L.C. - CANADA—See TTM Technologies, Inc.; *U.S. Public*, pg. 2203
VIASYSTEMS TECHNOLOGIES CORP., L.L.C. - FOREST GROVE—See TTM Technologies, Inc.; *U.S. Public*, pg. 2203
VIASYSTEMS TECHNOLOGIES CORP., L.L.C. - SAN JOSE—See TTM Technologies, Inc.; *U.S. Public*, pg. 2203
VIRTEX ENTERPRISES LP—See Insight Equity Holdings LLC; *U.S. Private*, pg. 2086
VULCAN FLEX CIRCUIT CORPOATION—See Vulcan Electric Company; *U.S. Private*, pg. 4416
WELLEX CORPORATION; *U.S. Private*, pg. 4475
WESCO SERVICES, LLC—See WESCO International, Inc.; *U.S. Public*, pg. 2352
WESTAK OF OREGON INC.—See Westak, Inc.; *U.S. Private*, pg. 4488
WESTERN ELECTRONICS LLC—See DBSI, Inc.; *U.S. Private*, pg. 1179
WINTRONICS INC.; *U.S. Private*, pg. 4545
WORLD ELECTRONICS SALES & SERVICE; *U.S. Private*, pg. 4565
YAMANASHI SANKO CO., LTD.—See CMK Corporation; *Int'l*, pg. 1671
ZENTECH DALLAS, LLC—See BlackBern Partners LLC; *U.S. Private*, pg. 573
ZENTECH FREDERICKSBURG LLC—See BlackBern Partners LLC; *U.S. Private*, pg. 573
ZENTECH MANUFACTURING, INC.—See BlackBern Partners LLC; *U.S. Private*, pg. 573
ZHONGSHAN TAT CHUN PRINTED CIRCUIT BOARD COMPANY LIMITED—See China Silver Technology; *Int'l*, pg. 1552
ZHUHAI GREE DAIKIN DEVICE CO., LTD.—See Daikin Industries, Ltd.; *Int'l*, pg. 1937

334413 — SEMICONDUCTOR AND RELATED DEVICE MANUFACTURING

3D-SHAPE GMBH—See Atlas Copco AB; *Int'l*, pg. 682
3PEAK, INC.; *Int'l*, pg. 9
ABB SWITZERLAND LTD - SEMICONDUCTORS—See ABB Ltd.; *Int'l*, pg. 54
ABILIS SYSTEMS SARL—See ALi Corporation; *Int'l*, pg. 320
ABOV SEMICONDUCTOR CO., LTD.; *Int'l*, pg. 67
ABSOLICON SOLAR COLLECTOR AB; *Int'l*, pg. 70
ACE HIGHTECH CO., LTD.; *Int'l*, pg. 94
ACTIONS SEMICONDUCTOR CO., LTD.; *Int'l*, pg. 119
ACTSOLAR, INC.—See Texas Instruments Incorporated; *U.S. Public*, pg. 2025
ADANI GREEN ENERGY LTD.—See Adani Enterprises Limited; *Int'l*, pg. 125
ADAPTIVE PLASMA TECHNOLOGY CORPORATION; *Int'l*, pg. 125
ADAPT LASER SYSTEMS, LLC—See Boyne Capital Management, LLC; *U.S. Private*, pg. 628
ADATA TECHNOLOGY CO., LTD.; *Int'l*, pg. 126
ADCOLE CORPORATION - AEROSPACE DIVISION—See Artemis Capital Partners Management, LLC; *U.S. Private*, pg. 340
ADLINK TECHNOLOGY, INC.; *Int'l*, pg. 150
ADTECHNOLOGY CO., LTD.; *Int'l*, pg. 154
ADVANCED ANALOG TECHNOLOGY, INC.; *Int'l*, pg. 157
ADVANCED DIGITAL CHIPS INC.; *Int'l*, pg. 158
ADVANCED ENERGY RENEWABLES, INC.—See Advanced Energy Industries, Inc.; *U.S. Public*, pg. 47
ADVANCED MICRO DEVICES, INC.; *U.S. Public*, pg. 48
ADVANCED MICRO DEVICES (U.K.) LIMITED—See Advanced Micro Devices, Inc.; *U.S. Public*, pg. 48
ADVANCED MICRO-FABRICATION EQUIPMENT, INC.; *Int'l*, pg. 161
ADVANCED NANO PRODUCTS CO., LTD. - DAEJEON FACILITY—See Advanced Nano Products Co., Ltd.; *Int'l*, pg. 161
ADVANCED OPTICAL COMPONENTS—See Coherent Corp.; *U.S. Public*, pg. 528
ADVANCED OPTOELECTRONIC TECHNOLOGY INC.; *Int'l*, pg. 161
ADVANCED PHOTONIX, INC.—See Luna Innovations Incorporated; *U.S. Public*, pg. 1348

ADVANCED SEMICONDUCTOR ENGINEERING, INC.—See ASE Technology Holding Co., Ltd.; *Int'l*, pg. 604
ADVANCED SEMICONDUCTOR MANUFACTURING CORPORATION LIMITED; *Int'l*, pg. 162
ADVANCED SYSTEMS AUTOMATION LIMITED; *Int'l*, pg. 162
ADVANTEST ACADEMY, KK.—See Advantest Corporation; *Int'l*, pg. 165
ADVANTEST AMERICA INC.—See Advantest Corporation; *Int'l*, pg. 165
ADVANTEST - BOBLINGEN—See Advantest Corporation; *Int'l*, pg. 165
ADVANTEST (CHINA) CO., LTD.—See Advantest Corporation; *Int'l*, pg. 165
ADVANTEST COMPONENT, INC. - SENDAI FACTORY—See Advantest Corporation; *Int'l*, pg. 165
ADVANTEST COMPONENT, INC.—See Advantest Corporation; *Int'l*, pg. 165
ADVANTEST (EUROPE) GMBH—See Advantest Corporation; *Int'l*, pg. 165
ADVANTEST EUROPE SYSTEMS GMBH—See Advantest Corporation; *Int'l*, pg. 165
ADVANTEST SHANGHAI CO., LTD.—See Advantest Corporation; *Int'l*, pg. 166
ADVANTEST SYSTEMS CORPORATION—See Advantest Corporation; *Int'l*, pg. 166
ADVANTEST (THAILAND) LTD.—See Advantest Corporation; *Int'l*, pg. 165
ADVA OPTICAL NETWORKING NORTH AMERICA, INC. - CHATSWORTH—See ADTRAN Holdings, Inc.; *U.S. Public*, pg. 44
ADVENT TECHNOLOGIES HOLDINGS, INC.; *U.S. Public*, pg. 49
AEGIS LIGHTWAVE, INC.; *U.S. Private*, pg. 116
AEHR TEST SYSTEMS GMBH—See Aehr Test Systems; *U.S. Public*, pg. 52
AEHR TEST SYSTEMS JAPAN K.K.—See Aehr Test Systems; *U.S. Public*, pg. 52
AEI POWER GMBH—See Advanced Energy Industries, Inc.; *U.S. Public*, pg. 47
AEI POWER INDIA PVT. LTD.—See Advanced Energy Industries, Inc.; *U.S. Public*, pg. 47
AEM MICROTRONICS (SUZHOU) CO., LTD.—See AEM Holdings Ltd.; *Int'l*, pg. 175
AEM SINGAPORE PTE. LTD.—See AEM Holdings Ltd.; *Int'l*, pg. 175
AEM TESTECH (SHANGHAI) CO., LTD.—See AEM Holdings Ltd.; *Int'l*, pg. 175
AEROFLEX INCORPORATED—See Advent International Corporation; *U.S. Private*, pg. 99
AGAPE PACKAGE MANUFACTURING (SHANGHAI) LTD.—See Alpha and Omega Semiconductor Limited; *Int'l*, pg. 366
AGC ELECTRONICS CO., LTD.—See AGC Inc.; *Int'l*, pg. 201
AIBIT CO., LTD.; *Int'l*, pg. 228
AIC CORPORATION BERHAD—See Globaltec Formation Berhad; *Int'l*, pg. 3004
AIR WATER MATERIALS INC.—See Air Water Inc.; *Int'l*, pg. 239
AIXTRON SE; *Int'l*, pg. 254
AJINEXTEK CO., LTD.; *Int'l*, pg. 256
ALCHIP TECHNOLOGIES, KK—See Alchip Technologies, Limited; *Int'l*, pg. 301
ALCHIP TECHNOLOGIES, LIMITED; *Int'l*, pg. 301
ALCOR MICRO (SHENZHEN) CORPORATION LTD.—See Alcor Micro Corporation Ltd.; *Int'l*, pg. 303
ALI (CHINA) CORPORATION—See ALi Corporation; *Int'l*, pg. 320
ALI CORPORATION; *Int'l*, pg. 320
ALI (HSINCHU) CORPORATION—See ALi Corporation; *Int'l*, pg. 320
ALIMCO FINANCIAL CORPORATION; *U.S. Private*, pg. 168
ALIONTEK CORPORATION—See Ferrotec Holdings Corporation; *Int'l*, pg. 2642
ALI (SHANGHAI) CORPORATION—See ALi Corporation; *Int'l*, pg. 320
ALI (ZHUHAI) CORPORATION—See ALi Corporation; *Int'l*, pg. 320
ALLEGRO MICROSYSTEMS ARGENTINA, S.A.—See Allegro MicroSystems, Inc.; *U.S. Public*, pg. 78
ALLEGRO MICROSYSTEMS FRANCE SAS—See Allegro MicroSystems, Inc.; *U.S. Public*, pg. 78
ALLEGRO MICROSYSTEMS GERMANY GMBH—See Allegro MicroSystems, Inc.; *U.S. Public*, pg. 78
ALLEGRO MICROSYSTEMS MARKETING INDIA PRIVATE LIMITED—See Allegro MicroSystems, Inc.; *U.S. Public*, pg. 78
ALLEGRO (SHANGHAI) MICRO ELECTRONICS COMMERCIAL & TRADING CO., LTD.—See Allegro MicroSystems, Inc.; *U.S. Public*, pg. 78
ALLIANCE SEMICONDUCTOR (INDIA) PRIVATE LIMITED—See Alimco Financial Corporation; *U.S. Private*, pg. 168
ALL SENSORS, CORP.; *U.S. Private*, pg. 172
ALLWINNER TECHNOLOGY CO., LTD.; *Int'l*, pg. 361

3643

334413 — SEMICONDUCTOR AND R...

ALPHA AND OMEGA SEMICONDUCTOR (SHANGHAI) CO., LTD.—See Alpha and Omega Semiconductor Limited; *Int'l*, pg. 366
ALPHA AND OMEGA SEMICONDUCTOR (SHENZHEN) CO., LTD.—See Alpha and Omega Semiconductor Limited; *Int'l*, pg. 366
ALPHA AND OMEGA SEMICONDUCTOR (TAIWAN) LTD.—See Alpha and Omega Semiconductor Limited; *Int'l*, pg. 366
ALPHA ASSEMBLY SOLUTIONS BELGIUM NV—See Element Solutions Inc.; *U.S. Public*, pg. 725
ALPHA ASSEMBLY SOLUTIONS BRASIL SOLDAS LTDA—See Element Solutions Inc.; *U.S. Public*, pg. 726
ALPHA ASSEMBLY SOLUTIONS KOREA LTD—See Element Solutions Inc.; *U.S. Public*, pg. 726
ALPHA ASSEMBLY SOLUTIONS NETHERLANDS B.V.—See Element Solutions Inc.; *U.S. Public*, pg. 726
ALPHA ASSEMBLY SOLUTIONS (SHENZEN) CO. LTD—See Element Solutions Inc.; *U.S. Public*, pg. 726
ALPHA ASSEMBLY SOLUTIONS (TAIWAN) LIMITED—See Element Solutions Inc.; *U.S. Public*, pg. 726
ALPHA HOLDINGS, INC.; *Int'l*, pg. 368
ALPHA MICROELECTRONICS CORP.; *Int'l*, pg. 368
ALPHA & OMEGA SEMICONDUCTOR (HONG KONG) LIMITED—See Alpha and Omega Semiconductor Limited; *Int'l*, pg. 366
ALPHA & OMEGA SEMICONDUCTOR (SHENZHEN) LIMITED—See Alpha and Omega Semiconductor Limited; *Int'l*, pg. 366
ALPHAWAVE IP GROUP PLC; *Int'l*, pg. 370
ALPINE ELECTRONICS AUSTRALIA PTY. LIMITED—See Alps Alpine Co., Ltd.; *Int'l*, pg. 375
ALPINE ELECTRONICS (CHINA) COMPANY LIMITED—See Alps Alpine Co., Ltd.; *Int'l*, pg. 375
ALPINE ELECTRONICS DE ESPANA, S.A.—See Alps Alpine Co., Ltd.; *Int'l*, pg. 375
ALPINE ELECTRONICS (EUROPE) GMBH—See Alps Alpine Co., Ltd.; *Int'l*, pg. 375
ALPINE ELECTRONICS FRANCE S.A.R.L.—See Alps Alpine Co., Ltd.; *Int'l*, pg. 375
ALPINE ELECTRONICS GMBH—See Alps Alpine Co., Ltd.; *Int'l*, pg. 375
ALPINE ELECTRONICS MARKETING INC.—See Alps Alpine Co., Ltd.; *Int'l*, pg. 375
ALPINE ELECTRONICS OF CANADA, INC.—See Alps Alpine Co., Ltd.; *Int'l*, pg. 375
ALPINE ELECTRONICS OF U.K. LIMITED—See Alps Alpine Co., Ltd.; *Int'l*, pg. 375
ALPINE ITALIA S.P.A.—See Alps Alpine Co., Ltd.; *Int'l*, pg. 375
ALPINE PRECISION, INC.—See Alps Alpine Co., Ltd.; *Int'l*, pg. 375
ALPINE TECHNOLOGY MANUFACTURING, INC.—See Alps Alpine Co., Ltd.; *Int'l*, pg. 376
ALPS ACCOUNTING CENTRE—See Alps Alpine Co., Ltd.; *Int'l*, pg. 376
ALPS(CHINA)CO., LTD.—See Alps Alpine Co., Ltd.; *Int'l*, pg. 376
ALPS ELECTRIC EUROPA GMBH—See Alps Alpine Co., Ltd.; *Int'l*, pg. 376
ALPS ELECTRIC EUROPE GMBH—See Alps Alpine Co., Ltd.; *Int'l*, pg. 376
ALPS ELECTRIC (IRELAND) LIMITED—See Alps Alpine Co., Ltd.; *Int'l*, pg. 376
ALPS ELECTRIC KOREA CO.—See Alps Alpine Co., Ltd.; *Int'l*, pg. 376
ALPS ELECTRIC (MALAYSIA) SDN, BHD.—See Alps Alpine Co., Ltd.; *Int'l*, pg. 376
ALPS ELECTRIC (SINGAPORE), PTE. LTD.—See Alps Alpine Co., Ltd.; *Int'l*, pg. 376
ALPS ELECTRIC (S) PTE. LTD.—See Alps Alpine Co., Ltd.; *Int'l*, pg. 376
ALPS ELECTRIC (USA), INC.—See Alps Alpine Co., Ltd.; *Int'l*, pg. 376
ALPS PRECISION (MALAYSIA) SDN. BHD.—See Alps Alpine Co., Ltd.; *Int'l*, pg. 376
ALSENTIS LLC—See Methode Electronics, Inc.; *U.S. Public*, pg. 1428
ALTAFLEX—See OSI Systems, Inc.; *U.S. Public*, pg. 1621
AMBARELLA, INC.; *U.S. Public*, pg. 92
AMBARELLA SHANGHAI CO., LTD.—See Ambarella, Inc.; *U.S. Public*, pg. 92
AMBARELLA TAIWAN LTD.—See Ambarella, Inc.; *U.S. Public*, pg. 92
AMD ADVANCED MICRO DEVICES ISRAEL LTD.—See Advanced Micro Devices, Inc.; *U.S. Public*, pg. 48
AMD ADVANCED RESEARCH LLC—See Advanced Micro Devices, Inc.; *U.S. Public*, pg. 48
AMD FAR EAST, LTD.—See Advanced Micro Devices, Inc.; *U.S. Public*, pg. 48
AMD INDIA PRIVATE LIMITED—See Advanced Micro Devices, Inc.; *U.S. Public*, pg. 48
AMD TECHNOLOGIES (CHINA) CO. LTD.—See Advanced Micro Devices, Inc.; *U.S. Public*, pg. 48
AMD TECHNOLOGY DEVELOPMENT (BEIJING) CO.—See Advanced Micro Devices, Inc.; *U.S. Public*, pg. 48
AMEC INTERNATIONAL PTE LTD.—See Advanced Micro-Fabrication Equipment, Inc.; *Int'l*, pg. 161
AMEC JAPAN CO., INC.—See Advanced Micro-Fabrication Equipment, Inc.; *Int'l*, pg. 161
AMEC KML INC.—See Advanced Micro-Fabrication Equipment, Inc.; *Int'l*, pg. 161
AMEC KOREA LIMITED—See Advanced Micro-Fabrication Equipment, Inc.; *Int'l*, pg. 161
AMEC NANCHANG LTD.—See Advanced Micro-Fabrication Equipment, Inc.; *Int'l*, pg. 161
AMEC NORTH AMERICA, INC.—See Advanced Micro-Fabrication Equipment, Inc.; *Int'l*, pg. 161
AMEC TAIWAN LTD.—See Advanced Micro-Fabrication Equipment, Inc.; *Int'l*, pg. 161
AMEC XIAMEN LTD.—See Advanced Micro-Fabrication Equipment, Inc.; *Int'l*, pg. 161
AMERICAN ELECTRONIC COMPONENTS, INC.; *U.S. Private*, pg. 231
AMICCOM ELECTRONICS CORP.; *Int'l*, pg. 427
AMI SEMICONDUCTOR CANADA COMPANY—See ON Semiconductor Corporation; *U.S. Public*, pg. 1600
AMKOR ADVANCED TECHNOLOGY TAIWAN, INC.—See Amkor Technology, Inc.; *U.S. Public*, pg. 124
AMKOR ASSEMBLY & TEST (SHANGHAI) CO., LTD.—See Amkor Technology, Inc.; *U.S. Public*, pg. 124
AMKOR TECHNOLOGY GERMANY GMBH—See Amkor Technology, Inc.; *U.S. Public*, pg. 124
AMKOR TECHNOLOGY KOREA, INC.—See Amkor Technology, Inc.; *U.S. Public*, pg. 124
AMKOR TECHNOLOGY MALAYSIA SDN. BHD.—See Amkor Technology, Inc.; *U.S. Public*, pg. 124
AMKOR TECHNOLOGY PHILIPPINES, INC.—See Amkor Technology, Inc.; *U.S. Public*, pg. 124
AMKOR TECHNOLOGY TAIWAN LTD.—See Amkor Technology, Inc.; *U.S. Public*, pg. 124
AMLOGIC SHANGHAI CO., LTD.; *Int'l*, pg. 429
AMPERE COMPUTING LLC; *U.S. Private*, pg. 265
AMPHENOL ADVANCED SENSORS PUERTO RICO, LLC—See Amphenol Corporation; *U.S. Public*, pg. 126
AMPHENOL ADVANCED SENSORS—See Amphenol Corporation; *U.S. Public*, pg. 126
AMPLITUDE LASER INC.—See Amplitude Technologies SA; *Int'l*, pg. 436
AMPLITUDE SYSTEMES, S.A.—See Amplitude Technologies SA; *Int'l*, pg. 436
AMS AG; *Int'l*, pg. 438
ANALOG DEVICES (CHINA) CO. LTD.—See Analog Devices, Inc.; *U.S. Public*, pg. 134
ANALOG DEVICES, INC. - GREENSBORO—See Analog Devices, Inc.; *U.S. Public*, pg. 135
ANALOG DEVICES, INC. - SAN JOSE—See Analog Devices, Inc.; *U.S. Public*, pg. 135
ANALOG DEVICES, INC.; *U.S. Public*, pg. 134
ANALOG DEVICES, INC. - WILMINGTON—See Analog Devices, Inc.; *U.S. Public*, pg. 135
ANALOG DEVICES (SHANGHAI) CO. LTD.—See Analog Devices, Inc.; *U.S. Public*, pg. 134
ANALOG DEVICES S.L.—See Analog Devices, Inc.; *U.S. Public*, pg. 135
ANALOG INTEGRATIONS CORP.; *Int'l*, pg. 446
ANAPASS, INC.; *Int'l*, pg. 447
ANCHOR SEMICONDUCTOR, INC.—See KLA Corporation; *U.S. Public*, pg. 1267
ANP USA INC.—See Advanced Nano Products Co., Ltd.; *Int'l*, pg. 161
ANSWER TECHNOLOGY CO., LTD.; *Int'l*, pg. 479
APACT CO., LTD.; *Int'l*, pg. 500
APEX MICROTECHNOLOGY, CORP.—See HEICO Corporation; *U.S. Public*, pg. 1020
APEX PRECISION POWER—See Cirrus Logic, Inc.; *U.S. Public*, pg. 496
AP MEMORY TECHNOLOGY CORPORATION; *Int'l*, pg. 499
APPLIED MATERIALS (CHINA) HOLDINGS, LTD.—See Applied Materials, Inc.; *U.S. Public*, pg. 172
APPLIED MATERIALS (CHINA), INC.—See Applied Materials, Inc.; *U.S. Public*, pg. 172
APPLIED MATERIALS WEB COATING GMBH—See Applied Materials, Inc.; *U.S. Public*, pg. 172
APPLIED MICRO CIRCUITS CORPORATION CANADA—See MACOM Technology Solutions Holdings, Inc.; *U.S. Public*, pg. 1352
APPLIED MICRO CIRCUITS CORPORATION—See MACOM Technology Solutions Holdings, Inc.; *U.S. Public*, pg. 1352
APPLIED OPTOELECTRONICS, INC.; *U.S. Public*, pg. 173
APPLIED VENTURES, LLC—See Applied Materials, Inc.; *U.S. Public*, pg. 172
APS CHINA CORPORATION—See APS Holdings Corporation; *Int'l*, pg. 523
APS VIETANM CO. LTD.—See APS Holdings Corporation; *Int'l*, pg. 523
APTINA INDIA PRIVATE LIMITED—See ON Semiconductor Corporation; *U.S. Public*, pg. 1600
APTINA (UK) LIMITED—See ON Semiconductor Corporation; *U.S. Public*, pg. 1600
AQ COMPONENTS MJALLOM AB—See AQ Group AB; *Int'l*, pg. 526
ARCADIA OPTRONIX INC.—See Advanced Fiber Resources (Zhuhai) Ltd; *Int'l*, pg. 159
ARCTECH SOLAR (CHANGZHOU) CO., LTD.—See Arctech Solar Holding Co., Ltd.; *Int'l*, pg. 551
ARCTECH SOLAR, INC.—See Arctech Solar Holding Co., Ltd.; *Int'l*, pg. 551
ARCTECH SOLAR INDIA PVT. LTD.—See Arctech Solar Holding Co., Ltd.; *Int'l*, pg. 551
ARCTECH SOLAR (JAPAN) CO., LTD.—See Arctech Solar Holding Co., Ltd.; *Int'l*, pg. 551
ARCTECH SOLAR (SHANGHAI) COMPANY—See Arctech Solar Holding Co., Ltd.; *Int'l*, pg. 551
ARDENT CONCEPTS, INC.—See Amphenol Corporation; *U.S. Public*, pg. 129
ARES GREEN TECHNOLOGY CORPORATION—See Frontken Corporation Berhad; *Int'l*, pg. 2796
ARGIL, INC.—See Gentex Corporation; *U.S. Public*, pg. 931
ARTEMIS ELECTRICALS & PROJECTS LTD.; *Int'l*, pg. 581
ARTERIS, INC.; *U.S. Public*, pg. 201
ARTERIS S.A.—See Arteris, Inc.; *U.S. Public*, pg. 201
ARTERY TECHNOLOGY COMPANY—See Faraday Technology Corporation; *Int'l*, pg. 2617
ARTERY TECHNOLOGY CORPORATION, LTD.—See Faraday Technology Corporation; *Int'l*, pg. 2618
ASAHI KASEI MICRODEVICES EUROPE GMBH—See Asahi Kasei Corporation; *Int'l*, pg. 595
ASAHI KASEI MICRODEVICES (SHANGHAI) CO., LTD.—See Asahi Kasei Corporation; *Int'l*, pg. 595
ASAHI KASEI MICRODEVICES TAIWAN CORP.—See Asahi Kasei Corporation; *Int'l*, pg. 595
ASA MULTIPLATE SDN BHD—See Advanced Systems Automation Limited; *Int'l*, pg. 162
ASCENT SOLAR TECHNOLOGIES, INC.; *U.S. Public*, pg. 210
ASE (CHUNG LI), INC.—See ASE Technology Holding Co., Ltd.; *Int'l*, pg. 604
ASE ELECTRONICS (M) SDN. BHD.—See ASE Technology Holding Co., Ltd.; *Int'l*, pg. 604
ASE KAOHSIUNG—See ASE Technology Holding Co., Ltd.; *Int'l*, pg. 604
ASE KOREA INC.—See ASE Technology Holding Co., Ltd.; *Int'l*, pg. 604
ASE (KUNSHAN) INC.—See ASE Technology Holding Co., Ltd.; *Int'l*, pg. 604
ASE SINGAPORE PTE. LTD.—See ASE Technology Holding Co., Ltd.; *Int'l*, pg. 604
ASE TEST LIMITED—See ASE Technology Holding Co., Ltd.; *Int'l*, pg. 604
ASFLOW CO LTD.; *Int'l*, pg. 606
ASMEDIA TECHNOLOGY INC.; *Int'l*, pg. 627
ASM JAPAN K.K. - NAGAOKA FACTORY—See ASM INTERNATIONAL N.V.; *Int'l*, pg. 626
ASM LASER SEPARATION INTERNATIONAL (ALSI) B.V.—See ASM INTERNATIONAL N.V.; *Int'l*, pg. 626
ASM NUTOOL, INC.—See ASM INTERNATIONAL N.V.; *Int'l*, pg. 626
ASM PACIFIC TECHNOLOGY LTD.—See ASM INTERNATIONAL N.V.; *Int'l*, pg. 626
ASM SEMICONDUCTOR MATERIALS (SHENZHEN) CO. LTD.—See ASM INTERNATIONAL N.V.; *Int'l*, pg. 626
ASM TECHNOLOGY (M) SDN. BHD.—See ASM INTERNATIONAL N.V.; *Int'l*, pg. 626
ASPEED TECHNOLOGY INC.; *Int'l*, pg. 628
ASTANA SOLAR LLP—See Canadian Solar Inc.; *Int'l*, pg. 1286
ASTANA SOLAR LLP—See ECM Technologies SAS; *Int'l*, pg. 2292
ASTI HOLDINGS LIMITED; *Int'l*, pg. 654
ASTI (USA), INC.—See ASTI Holdings Limited; *Int'l*, pg. 655
ASTRIA SEMICONDUCTOR HOLDINGS, INC—See FormFactor, Inc.; *U.S. Public*, pg. 868
ASTRONERGY—See Chint Group Corporation; *Int'l*, pg. 1571
ASTYX GMBH—See General Motors Company; *U.S. Public*, pg. 923
ATOMERA INCORPORATED; *U.S. Public*, pg. 225
AT SEMICON CO., LTD.; *Int'l*, pg. 664
AUDIX CORPORATION; *Int'l*, pg. 702
AUDIX TECHNOLOGY (WUJIANG) CO., LTD.—See Audix Corporation; *Int'l*, pg. 702
AUO CORPORATION; *Int'l*, pg. 706
AUSTIN MANUFACTURING SERVICES LP; *U.S. Private*, pg. 396
AUSTRIAMICROSYSTEMS GERMANY GMBH—See ams AG; *Int'l*, pg. 440
AUSTRIAMICROSYSTEMS (PHILIPPINES) INC.—See ams AG; *Int'l*, pg. 440
AUSTRIAMICROSYSTEMS USA INC—See ams AG; *Int'l*, pg. 440
AVAGO TECHNOLOGIES U.S. INC.—See Broadcom Inc.; *U.S. Public*, pg. 388
AVAGO TECHNOLOGIES WIRELESS (U.S.A.) MANUFACTURING INC.—See Broadcom Inc.; *U.S. Public*, pg. 388
AVI-TECH HOLDINGS LIMITED; *Int'l*, pg. 741
AVNET EMBEDDED GMBH—See Avnet, Inc.; *U.S. Public*, pg. 251
AVNET EMG GMBH—See Avnet, Inc.; *U.S. Public*, pg. 250
AVNET SILICA—See Avnet, Inc.; *U.S. Public*, pg. 250
AVO PHOTONICS, INC.—See Halma plc; *Int'l*, pg. 3230

N.A.I.C.S. INDEX

334413 — SEMICONDUCTOR AND R...

AXELL CORPORATION; *Int'l*, pg. 767
AXSUN TECHNOLOGIES, INC.—See AEA Investors LP; *U.S. Private*, pg. 113
AXT, INC.; *U.S. Public*, pg. 256
AZELIS FRANCE SAS—See EQT AB; *Int'l*, pg. 2469
AZENTA LIFE SCIENCES CANADA, INC.—See Azenta, Inc.; *Int'l*, pg. 257
AZFIN SEMICONDUCTORS PTE LTD—See Aztech Group Ltd.; *Int'l*, pg. 781
AZUR SPACE SOLAR POWER GMBH—See 5N Plus Inc.; *Int'l*, pg. 13
BAE SYSTEMS IMAGING SOLUTIONS—See BAE Systems plc; *Int'l*, pg. 797
BAI INC.; *U.S. Private*, pg. 425
BALDER D.O.O.—See Kimberly-Clark Corporation; *U.S. Public*, pg. 1229
BALLARD UNMANNED SYSTEMS, INC.—See Honeywell International Inc.; *U.S. Public*, pg. 1047
BARUN ELECTRONICS CO., LTD.; *Int'l*, pg. 870
BASF FUEL CELL INC.—See BASF SE; *Int'l*, pg. 876
BAY MICROSYSTEMS, INC.; *U.S. Private*, pg. 494
BCD SEMICONDUCTOR CORP—See Diodes Incorporated; *U.S. Public*, pg. 667
BCD SEMICONDUCTOR LIMITED—See Diodes Incorporated; *U.S. Public*, pg. 667
BCD SEMICONDUCTOR (TAIWAN) COMPANY LIMITED—See Diodes Incorporated; *U.S. Public*, pg. 667
BCD (SHANGHAI) MICRO-ELECTRONICS LIMITED—See Diodes Incorporated; *U.S. Public*, pg. 667
BCNC CO., LTD.; *Int'l*, pg. 928
BCNC USA, INC.—See BCnC Co., Ltd.; *Int'l*, pg. 928
BEAMMWAVE AB; *Int'l*, pg. 932
BEIJING BOYU SEMICONDUCTOR VESSEL CRAFTWORK TECHNOLOGY CO., LTD.—See AXT, Inc.; *U.S. Public*, pg. 256
BEIJING DVT TECHNOLOGY CO., LTD.—See Daheng New Epoch Technology, Inc.; *Int'l*, pg. 1913
BEIJING ENERGY INTERNATIONAL HOLDING CO., LTD.; *Int'l*, pg. 949
BEIJING GAONENG DAHENG ACCELERATOR TECHNOLOGY CO. LTD.—See Daheng New Epoch Technology, Inc.; *Int'l*, pg. 1913
BEIJING HAMAMATSU PHOTON TECHNIQUES, INC.—See Hamamatsu Photonics K.K.; *Int'l*, pg. 3235
BEIJING HUAFENG TEST & CONTROL TECHNOLOGY CO., LTD.; *Int'l*, pg. 951
BEIJING JINGYUNTONG TECHNOLOGY CO., LTD.; *Int'l*, pg. 953
BEIJING SWT OPTICAL COMMUNICATIONS TECHNOLOGIES, CO., LTD.—See Beijing SWT Communications Co., Ltd.; *Int'l*, pg. 958
BEIJING TONGMEI XTAL TECHNOLOGY CO, LTD.—See AXT, Inc.; *U.S. Public*, pg. 256
BENCHMARQ MICROELECTRONICS CORPORATION OF SOUTH KOREA—See Texas Instruments Incorporated; *U.S. Public*, pg. 2025
BIFFA LEICESTER LIMITED—See Biffa Group Limited; *Int'l*, pg. 1020
BIONOVATE TECHNOLOGIES CORP; *U.S. Private*, pg. 562
BLOOM ENERGY CORPORATION; *U.S. Public*, pg. 362
BLOOM ENERGY (INDIA) PVT. LTD.—See Bloom Energy Corporation; *U.S. Public*, pg. 362
BLUECHIIP LIMITED; *Int'l*, pg. 1070
BLUGLASS LIMITED; *Int'l*, pg. 1075
BOE SEMI-CONDUCTOR CO., LTD.—See BOE Technology Group Co., Ltd.; *Int'l*, pg. 1099
BORON PRODUCTS, LLC—See 3M Company; *U.S. Public*, pg. 8
BORTEX GLOBAL LIMITED; *Int'l*, pg. 1115
BOURNS (XIAMEN) LTD.—See Bourns, Inc.; *U.S. Private*, pg. 624
BRAINHOLE TECHNOLOGY LIMITED; *Int'l*, pg. 1137
BRIGHT CRYSTAL COMPANY LIMITED—See Bright Led Electronics Corp.; *Int'l*, pg. 1161
BRIGHT LED ELECTRONICS CORP.; *Int'l*, pg. 1161
BRITE-STRIKE TACTICAL ILLUMINATION PRODUCTS, INC.; *U.S. Public*, pg. 388
BROADCOM CORPORATION—See Broadcom Inc.; *U.S. Public*, pg. 388
BROADCOM SINGAPORE PTE. LTD.—See Broadcom Inc.; *U.S. Public*, pg. 388
BROADCOM UK LTD.—See Broadcom Inc.; *U.S. Public*, pg. 388
BROADEX TECHNOLOGIES CO., LTD.; *Int'l*, pg. 1172
BROOKS AUTOMATION, INC.—See Azenta, Inc.; *U.S. Public*, pg. 257
BROOKS AUTOMATION KOREA, LTD.—See Azenta, Inc.; *U.S. Public*, pg. 257
BROOKS AUTOMATION LUXEMBOURG SARL—See Azenta, Inc.; *U.S. Public*, pg. 257
BROOKS CCS GMBH—See Azenta, Inc.; *U.S. Public*, pg. 257
BROOKS JAPAN K.K.—See Azenta, Inc.; *U.S. Public*, pg. 257
BV TEKNIK A/S—See Addtech AB; *Int'l*, pg. 132
CABOT MICROELECTRONICS SINGAPORE PTE. LTD.—See Entegris, Inc.; *U.S. Public*, pg. 776
CA JAPAN, LTD.—See Broadcom Inc.; *U.S. Public*, pg. 389
CAL-COMP AUTOMATION AND INDUSTRIAL 4.0 SERVICE (THAILAND) CO., LTD.—See Cal-Comp Electronics (Thailand) pcl; *Int'l*, pg. 1260
CAL-COMP OPTICAL ELECTRONICS (YUEYANG) CO., LTD.—See Cal-Comp Electronics (Thailand) pcl; *Int'l*, pg. 1261
CAL-COMP PRECISION HOLDING CO., LTD.—See Cal-Comp Electronics (Thailand) pcl; *Int'l*, pg. 1261
CAL-COMP PRECISION (YUEYANG) CO., LTD.—See Cal-Comp Electronics (Thailand) pcl; *Int'l*, pg. 1261
CALVATEC LIMITED—See Analog Devices, Inc.; *U.S. Public*, pg. 135
CAMECA TAIWAN CORP. LTD.—See AMETEK, Inc.; *U.S. Public*, pg. 117
CANADIAN SOLAR (AUSTRALIA) PTY., LTD.—See Canadian Solar Inc.; *Int'l*, pg. 1286
CANADIAN SOLAR EMEA GMBH—See Canadian Solar Inc.; *Int'l*, pg. 1286
CANADIAN SOLAR JAPAN K.K.—See Canadian Solar Inc.; *Int'l*, pg. 1286
CANADIAN SOLAR MANUFACTURING (SUZHOU) INC.—See Canadian Solar Inc.; *Int'l*, pg. 1286
CANADIAN SOLAR (USA) INC.—See Canadian Solar Inc.; *Int'l*, pg. 1286
CANON ANELVA CORPORATION—See Canon Inc.; *Int'l*, pg. 1292
CANON MACHINERY (MALAYSIA) SDN BHD.—See Canon Inc.; *Int'l*, pg. 1295
CANON OPTICAL INDUSTRIAL EQUIPMENT (SHANGHAI) INC.—See Canon Inc.; *Int'l*, pg. 1292
CANYON SEMICONDUCTOR INC.—See Diodes Incorporated; *U.S. Public*, pg. 667
CAPRES A/S—See KLA Corporation; *U.S. Public*, pg. 1267
CARDXX, INC.; *U.S. Public*, pg. 434
CAREER TECHNOLOGY (SUZHOU) CO., LTD.—See Career Technology (MFG.) Co., Ltd.; *Int'l*, pg. 1323
CARLO GAVAZZI INDUSTRI A/S—See Carlo Gavazzi Holding AG; *Int'l*, pg. 1339
CARL ZEISS CMP GMBH—See Carl-Zeiss-Stiftung; *Int'l*, pg. 1334
CARL ZEISS JENA GMBH—See Carl-Zeiss-Stiftung; *Int'l*, pg. 1334
CARL ZEISS MEDITEC VERTRIEBSGESELLSCHAFT MBH—See Carl-Zeiss-Stiftung; *Int'l*, pg. 1334
CARL ZEISS SMT GMBH—See Carl-Zeiss-Stiftung; *Int'l*, pg. 1335
CARL ZEISS SPECTROSCOPY GMBH—See Carl-Zeiss-Stiftung; *Int'l*, pg. 1335
CARMANAH TECHNOLOGIES CORPORATION; *Int'l*, pg. 1341
CASCADE MICROTECH, INC.—See FormFactor, Inc.; *U.S. Public*, pg. 868
CASCADETEQ INC.—See AP Memory Technology Corporation; *Int'l*, pg. 499
CASTRICO CO., LTD.; *Int'l*, pg. 1358
CBD EVISION PTE LTD—See Challenger Technologies Ltd.; *Int'l*, pg. 1438
CBOL CORP.; *U.S. Private*, pg. 797
C&CI PARTNERS CO., LTD.—See CoAsia Holdings Co., Ltd.; *Int'l*, pg. 1680
C&D SEMICONDUCTOR SERVICES, INC.; *U.S. Private*, pg. 702
CEEG (SHANGHAI) SOLAR SCIENCE TECHNOLOGY CO., LTD.—See China Sunergy Co., Ltd.; *Int'l*, pg. 1556
CENTRAL SEMICONDUCTOR CORP; *U.S. Private*, pg. 824
CENTROSOLAR GLAS GMBH & CO. KG—See Ducatt NV; *Int'l*, pg. 2223
CENTROTHERM PHOTOVOLTAICS TECHNOLOGY GMBH—See centrotherm photovoltaics AG; *Int'l*, pg. 1415
CENTROTHERM PHOTOVOLTAICS TECHNOLOGY SHANGHAI CO. LTD.—See centrotherm photovoltaics AG; *Int'l*, pg. 1415
CENTUM ELECTRONICS LTD.; *Int'l*, pg. 1416
CEVA FRANCE—See CEVA, Inc.; *U.S. Public*, pg. 476
CEVA, INC.; *U.S. Public*, pg. 476
CHAMPION MICROELECTRONIC CORP.; *Int'l*, pg. 1440
CHAMPION MICROELECTRONIC—See Champion Microelectronic Corp.; *Int'l*, pg. 1440
CHANGZHOU EGING PV TECHNOLOGY CO., LTD.—See EGing Photovoltaic Technology Co., Ltd.; *Int'l*, pg. 2324
CHANGZHOU GALAXY ELECTRICAL CO., LTD—See Galaxy Semiconductor Co., Ltd.; *Int'l*, pg. 2871
CHARM ENGINEERING CO., LTD.; *Int'l*, pg. 1451
CHEMRING DEFENCE GERMANY GMBH—See Chemring Group PLC; *Int'l*, pg. 1463
CHEMRING EOD LIMITED—See Chemring Group PLC; *Int'l*, pg. 1463
CHEMTRONICS CO., LTD. - PYEONGTAEK PLANT—See Chemtronics Co., Ltd.; *Int'l*, pg. 1464
CHEMTRONICS CO., LTD. - SEJONG PLANT—See Chemtronics Co., Ltd.; *Int'l*, pg. 1464
CHEMTRONICS CO., LTD.; *Int'l*, pg. 1464
CHEMTRONICS CO., LTD. - YONGIN PLANT—See Chemtronics Co., Ltd.; *Int'l*, pg. 1464
CHENDU PERFECT TECHNOLOGY CO., LTD.—See Hangzhou Silan Microelectronics Co., Ltd.; *Int'l*, pg. 3250
CHENGDU MONOLITHIC POWER SYSTEMS CO., LTD.—See Monolithic Power Systems, Inc.; *U.S. Public*, pg. 1464
CHINA SOLAR ENERGY HOLDINGS LIMITED; *Int'l*, pg. 1552
CHIPBOND TECHNOLOGY CORPORATION; *Int'l*, pg. 1572
CHIP HOPE CO., LTD.; *Int'l*, pg. 1572
CHIPMOS ASSEMBLY FAB—See ChipMOS Technologies Inc.; *Int'l*, pg. 1573
CHIPMOS GOLD BUMPING FAB—See ChipMOS Technologies Inc.; *Int'l*, pg. 1573
CHIPMOS JAPAN INC.—See ChipMOS Technologies Inc.; *Int'l*, pg. 1573
CHIPMOS TECHNOLOGIES INC.; *Int'l*, pg. 1573
CHIPMOS TESTING FAB—See ChipMOS Technologies Inc.; *Int'l*, pg. 1573
CHIPMOS U.S.A., INC.—See ChipMOS Technologies Inc.; *Int'l*, pg. 1573
CHIPONE TECHNOLOGY (BEIJING) CO., LTD.; *Int'l*, pg. 1573
CHIPSEA TECHNOLOGIES (SHENZHEN) CORP.; *Int'l*, pg. 1573
CHIPS&MEDIA, INC.; *Int'l*, pg. 1573
CHIP SUPPLY INC.—See Behrman Brothers Management Corp.; *U.S. Private*, pg. 515
CHONGQING DAQO NEW ENERGY CO., LTD.—See Daqo New Energy Corp.; *Int'l*, pg. 1971
CHUNBO ADVANCED MATERIALS CO. LTD.—See Chunbo Co., Ltd.; *Int'l*, pg. 1596
CHUNBO CO., LTD.; *Int'l*, pg. 1596
CHUNBO FINE CHEM CO., LTD.—See Chunbo Co., Ltd.; *Int'l*, pg. 1596
CHUNGHWA LEADING PHOTONICS TECH CO., LTD.—See Chunghwa Telecom Co., Ltd.; *Int'l*, pg. 1598
CHUNGHWA PRECISION TEST TECH. USA CORPORATION—See Chunghwa Telecom Co., Ltd.; *Int'l*, pg. 1598
CICOR REINHARDT MICROTECH AG—See Cicor Technologies Ltd.; *Int'l*, pg. 1603
CIRRUS LOGIC, INC.; *U.S. Public*, pg. 496
CIRRUS LOGIC INTERNATIONAL LTD.—See Cirrus Logic, Inc.; *U.S. Public*, pg. 496
CIRRUS LOGIC INTERNATIONAL (UK) LTD.—See Cirrus Logic, Inc.; *U.S. Public*, pg. 496
CIRRUS LOGIC K.K.—See Cirrus Logic, Inc.; *U.S. Public*, pg. 496
CIRTEK ELECTRONICS CORPORATION—See Cirtek Holdings Philippines Corp.; *Int'l*, pg. 1618
CI SYSTEMS (ISRAEL) LTD.; *Int'l*, pg. 1601
CKD CORPORATION - KASUGAI PLANT—See CKD Corporation; *Int'l*, pg. 1639
CLEARSPEED TECHNOLOGY PLC; *Int'l*, pg. 1657
CLIPSOL S.A.—See ENGIE SA; *Int'l*, pg. 2428
CMC MATERIALS, INC.—See Entegris, Inc.; *U.S. Public*, pg. 776
CML MICROCIRCUITS (SINGAPORE) PTE. LTD.—See CML Microsystems Plc; *Int'l*, pg. 1671
CML MICROCIRCUITS (UK) LTD.—See CML Microsystems Plc; *Int'l*, pg. 1671
CML MICROCIRCUITS (USA) INC.—See CML Microsystems Plc; *Int'l*, pg. 1671
CMR GROUP LTD.—See Amphenol Corporation; *U.S. Public*, pg. 129
C.M.R. U.S.A., INC.—See Amphenol Corporation; *U.S. Public*, pg. 129
COADNA HOLDINGS, INC.—See Coherent Corp.; *U.S. Public*, pg. 526
COASIA CORPORATION—See CoAsia Holdings Co., Ltd.; *Int'l*, pg. 1680
COASIA ELECTRONICS CORP.—See CoAsia Holdings Co., Ltd.; *Int'l*, pg. 1680
COASIA NEXELL CO., LTD.—See CoAsia Holdings Co., Ltd.; *Int'l*, pg. 1680
COASIA SEMI KOREA CO., LTD.—See CoAsia Holdings Co., Ltd.; *Int'l*, pg. 1680
COBHAM MAL LIMITED—See Advent International Corporation; *U.S. Private*, pg. 99
CODA OCTOPUS GROUP, INC.; *U.S. Public*, pg. 521
CODI-M CO., LTD.; *Int'l*, pg. 1688
COHERENT ITALIA—See Coherent Corp.; *U.S. Public*, pg. 527
COHERENT KOREA, LTD.—See Coherent Corp.; *U.S. Public*, pg. 527
COHERENT LASER INDIA PVT. LTD.—See Coherent Corp.; *U.S. Public*, pg. 527
COHU SEMICONDUCTOR TEST GMBH—See Cohu, Inc.; *U.S. Public*, pg. 529
COLORLIGHT CLOUD TECH LTD.; *Int'l*, pg. 1704
COMET AG—See Comet Holding AG; *Int'l*, pg. 1710
COME TRUE BIOMEDICAL, INC.; *Int'l*, pg. 1710
COMMONWEALTH LAMINATING & COATING, INC.—See Eastman Chemical Company; *U.S. Public*, pg. 704
COMMTONE SOLUTION CO. LTD—See Discretix Technologies Ltd.; *Int'l*, pg. 2134
COMPONENTES INTEL DE COSTA RICA—See Intel Corporation; *U.S. Public*, pg. 1138
COMPONENT RE-ENGINEERING COMPANY, INC.—See

334413 — SEMICONDUCTOR AND R...

Tinicum Enterprises, Inc.; *U.S. Private*, pg. 4174
COMPUGRAPHICS INTERNATIONAL LTD.—See Element Solutions Inc.; *U.S. Public*, pg. 725
COMPUGRAPHICS JENA GMBH—See Element Solutions Inc.; *U.S. Public*, pg. 725
COMPUGRAPHICS U.S.A. INC. - AUSTIN—See Element Solutions Inc.; *U.S. Public*, pg. 725
COMPUGRAPHICS U.S.A. INC.—See Element Solutions Inc.; *U.S. Public*, pg. 725
COMTEC SOLAR INTERNATIONAL (M) SDN. BHD.—See Comtec Solar Systems Group Limited; *Int'l*, pg. 1762
COMTEC SOLAR (JIANGSU) CO., LIMITED—See Comtec Solar Systems Group Limited; *Int'l*, pg. 1762
CONERGY PTE LTD—See Kawa Capital Management, Inc.; *U.S. Private*, pg. 2266
CONTINENTAL DEVICE INDIA PRIVATE LIMITED; *Int'l*, pg. 1783
CONTROL MESURE REGULATION (UK) LIMITED—See Amphenol Corporation; *U.S. Public*, pg. 130
CONVERSANT INTELLECTUAL PROPERTY MANAGEMENT INCORPORATED—See Sterling Partners; *U.S. Private*, pg. 3806
CONVERSANT IP JAPAN K.K.—See Sterling Partners; *U.S. Private*, pg. 3806
COORSTEK, INC. - COORSTEK OREGON OPERATIONS FACILITY—See CoorsTek, Inc.; *U.S. Private*, pg. 1044
COORSTEK, INC. - COORSTEK TENNESSEE FACILITY—See CoorsTek, Inc.; *U.S. Private*, pg. 1044
COORSTEK, INC. - COORSTEK VISTA FACILITY—See CoorsTek, Inc.; *U.S. Private*, pg. 1044
COORSTEK, INC. - COORSTEK WORCESTER FACILITY—See CoorsTek, Inc.; *U.S. Private*, pg. 1044
CORUS MANUFACTURING LTD.—See Lam Research Corporation; *U.S. Public*, pg. 1289
COSMO ELECTRONICS CORPORATION; *Int'l*, pg. 1811
COSTRONIC S.A.—See Amphenol Corporation; *U.S. Public*, pg. 130
CRANE ELECTRONICS CORPORATION—See Crane NXT, Co.; *U.S. Public*, pg. 589
CREATIVE SENSOR INC.; *Int'l*, pg. 1833
CREDENCE SYSTEMS (M) SDN BHD—See Cohu, Inc.; *U.S. Public*, pg. 530
CREDENCE SYSTEMS PTE. LTD.—See Cohu, Inc.; *U.S. Public*, pg. 530
CREE HONG KONG LIMITED—See Wolfspeed, Inc.; *U.S. Public*, pg. 2377
CROCUS TECHNOLOGY INTERNATIONAL INC.—See Allegro MicroSystems, Inc.; *U.S. Public*, pg. 78
CRYSTAL IS, INC.—See Asahi Kasei Corporation; *Int'l*, pg. 596
CSI SOLAR TECHNOLOGIES INC.—See Canadian Solar Inc.; *Int'l*, pg. 1286
CSI SOLARTRONICS (CHANGSHU) CO., LTD.—See Canadian Solar Inc.; *Int'l*, pg. 1286
CSMC TECHNOLOGIES CORPORATION—See China Resources (Holdings) Co., Ltd.; *Int'l*, pg. 1548
CSR INDIA PRIVATE LIMITED—See QUALCOMM Incorporated; *U.S. Public*, pg. 1748
CSR TECHNOLOGY (INDIA) PRIVATE LIMITED—See QUALCOMM Incorporated; *U.S. Public*, pg. 1748
CSUN AUSTRALIA PTY. LTD.—See China Sunergy Co., Ltd.; *Int'l*, pg. 1556
CSUN - CHINA SUNERGY CLEAN TECH INC.—See China Sunergy Co., Ltd.; *Int'l*, pg. 1556
CSUN - CHINA SUNERGY EUROPE GMBH—See China Sunergy Co., Ltd.; *Int'l*, pg. 1556
CSUN - CHINA SUNERGY (SOUTH AFRICA) CO., LTD.—See China Sunergy Co., Ltd.; *Int'l*, pg. 1556
CSUN EURASIA ENERGY SYSTEMS INDUSTRY & TRADE INC.—See China Sunergy Co., Ltd.; *Int'l*, pg. 1556
CSUN JAPAN SOLAR ENERGY CO., LTD.—See China Sunergy Co., Ltd.; *Int'l*, pg. 1556
CSUN RENEWABLE ENERGY (FRANCE) S.A.R.L.—See China Sunergy Co., Ltd.; *Int'l*, pg. 1556
CTF SOLAR GMBH—See China National Building Material Group Co., Ltd.; *Int'l*, pg. 1525
CYANCONNODE HOLDINGS PLC; *Int'l*, pg. 1891
CYBEROPTICS CHINA COMPANY LTD.—See Nordson Corporation; *U.S. Public*, pg. 1532
CYBEROPTICS SEMICONDUCTOR, INC.—See Nordson Corporation; *U.S. Public*, pg. 1532
CYCLEO SAS—See Semtech Corporation; *U.S. Public*, pg. 1864
CYG ET CO., LTD.—See ChangYuan Group Ltd.; *Int'l*, pg. 1444
CYMECHS INC.; *Int'l*, pg. 1896
CYNTEC CO., LTD.—See Delta Electronics, Inc.; *Int'l*, pg. 2016
CYOPTICS, INC.—See Broadcom Inc.; *U.S. Public*, pg. 388
DAEWON SEMICONDUCTOR PACKAGING INDUSTRIAL CORPORATION - IMS DAEWON FACTORY—See Daewon Semiconductor Packaging Industrial Corporation; *Int'l*, pg. 1910
DAIHEN ADVANCED MACHINERY (CHANGSHU) CO., LTD.—See Daihen Corporation; *Int'l*, pg. 1926
DAITRON CO., LTD.; *Int'l*, pg. 1944
DAITRON (H.K.) CO., LTD.—See Daitron Co., Ltd.; *Int'l*, pg. 1944

DAITRON (MALAYSIA) SDN. BHD.—See Daitron Co., Ltd.; *Int'l*, pg. 1944
DALIAN ALPINE ELECTRONICS CO., LTD.—See Alps Alpine Co., Ltd.; *Int'l*, pg. 376
DAN DONG ALPINE ELECTRONICS, INC.—See Alps Alpine Co., Ltd.; *Int'l*, pg. 376
DARWIN PRECISIONS CORPORATION; *Int'l*, pg. 1973
DASAN NETWORKS, INC.; *Int'l*, pg. 1973
DATA I/O CANADA CORPORATION—See Data I/O Corporation; *U.S. Public*, pg. 635
DATA I/O INTERNATIONAL, INC.—See Data I/O Corporation; *U.S. Public*, pg. 635
DATANG NXP SEMICONDUCTORS CO., LTD.—See Datang Telecom Technology Co., Ltd.; *Int'l*, pg. 1979
DAVICOM SEMICONDUCTOR, INC.; *Int'l*, pg. 1983
DAW TECHNOLOGIES, INC.; *U.S. Private*, pg. 1175
DECAWAVE LIMITED—See Qorvo, Inc.; *U.S. Public*, pg. 1743
DELSOLAR (WUJIANG) LTD.—See Delta Electronics, Inc.; *Int'l*, pg. 2016
DELTA DESIGN SINGAPORE PTE. LTD.—See Cohu, Inc.; *U.S. Public*, pg. 529
DELTA ELECTRONICS, INC.; *Int'l*, pg. 2016
DENSO ELECTRONICS CORPORATION—See Denso Corporation; *Int'l*, pg. 2029
DIAGNOSYS SYSTEMS, INC.—See Astronics Corporation; *U.S. Public*, pg. 217
DIAKOPTO INC.—See ANSYS, Inc.; *U.S. Public*, pg. 139
DI CORP.; *Int'l*, pg. 2101
DI CORP. - THE DONGTAN PLANT—See DI Corp.; *Int'l*, pg. 2101
DIGI INTERNATIONAL—See Digi International Inc.; *U.S. Public*, pg. 662
DIGITAL LUMENS, INC.—See Skyview Capital, LLC; *U.S. Private*, pg. 3686
DIGITAL VOICE SYSTEMS, INC.; *U.S. Private*, pg. 1231
DILAS DIODE LASER, INC.—See Coherent Corp.; *U.S. Public*, pg. 527
DILAS DIODENLASER GMBH—See Coherent Corp.; *U.S. Public*, pg. 527
DIODES CO. LTD.—See Diodes Incorporated; *U.S. Public*, pg. 667
DIODES INCORPORATED; *U.S. Public*, pg. 667
DIODES ZETEX GMBH—See Diodes Incorporated; *U.S. Public*, pg. 667
DIODES ZETEX NEUHAUS GMBH—See Diodes Incorporated; *U.S. Public*, pg. 667
DIODES ZETEX SEMICONDUCTORS LTD—See Diodes Incorporated; *U.S. Public*, pg. 667
DIRECT POWER AND WATER CORPORATION—See Preformed Line Products Company; *U.S. Public*, pg. 1714
DISCO HI-TEC (MALAYSIA) SDN. BHD.—See Disco Corporation; *Int'l*, pg. 2132
DISCO HI-TEC (THAILAND) CO., LTD.—See Disco Corporation; *Int'l*, pg. 2132
DISCO TECHNOLOGY (SHANGHAI) CO., LTD.—See Disco Corporation; *Int'l*, pg. 2132
DISCRETIX TECHNOLOGIES K.K.—See Discretix Technologies Ltd.; *Int'l*, pg. 2135
DISCRETIX TECHNOLOGIES LTD.; *Int'l*, pg. 2134
DISCRETIX TECHNOLOGIES LTD.—See Discretix Technologies Ltd.; *Int'l*, pg. 2135
DLG HANBIT CO., LTD.—See Duc Long Gia Lai Group JSC; *Int'l*, pg. 2222
DNEX SEMICONDUCTOR SDN. BHD.—See Dagang NeXchange Berhad; *Int'l*, pg. 1912
DNP FINE ELECTRONICS CO., LTD.—See Dai Nippon Printing Co., Ltd.; *Int'l*, pg. 1914
DNP LSI DESIGN CO., LTD.—See Dai Nippon Printing Co., Ltd.; *Int'l*, pg. 1914
D & O GREEN TECHNOLOGIES BERHAD; *Int'l*, pg. 1898
DOMINANT OPTO TECHNOLOGIES KOREA INC.—See D & O Green Technologies Berhad; *Int'l*, pg. 1898
DOMINANT OPTO TECHNOLOGIES NORTH AMERICA, INC.—See D & O Green Technologies Berhad; *Int'l*, pg. 1898
DOMINANT OPTO TECHNOLOGIES SDN. BHD.—See D & O Green Technologies Berhad; *Int'l*, pg. 1898
DOMINANT OPTO TECHNOLOGIES (SHANGHAI) CO., LTD.—See D & O Green Technologies Berhad; *Int'l*, pg. 1898
DOMINANT SEMICONDUCTORS (EUROPE GMBH)—See D & O Green Technologies Berhad; *Int'l*, pg. 1898
DONGBU HITEK CO., LTD.—See Dongbu Group; *Int'l*, pg. 2166
DONGJIN SEMICHEM CO., LTD.; *Int'l*, pg. 2168
DONGWOON ANATECH CO., LTD.; *Int'l*, pg. 2171
DONG YANG ENERGY CO., LTD.—See Dongyang Engineering & Construction Corp.; *Int'l*, pg. 2171
DOOSAN CORPORATION - JEUNGPYEONG FACTORY—See Doosan Corporation; *Int'l*, pg. 2173
DOWA ELECTRONIC MATERIALS CO., LTD.—See Dowa Holdings Co., Ltd.; *Int'l*, pg. 2183
DOWA SEMICONDUCTOR AKITA CO., LTD.—See Dowa Holdings Co., Ltd.; *Int'l*, pg. 2183
DSPG EDINBURGH LTD.—See Synaptics Incorporated; *U.S. Public*, pg. 1969

DSP GROUP HK LIMITED—See Synaptics Incorporated; *U.S. Public*, pg. 1969
DSP GROUP, INC.—See Synaptics Incorporated; *U.S. Public*, pg. 1969
DSP GROUP LTD.—See Synaptics Incorporated; *U.S. Public*, pg. 1969
DSP TECHNOLOGY INDIAN PRIVATE LIMITED—See Synaptics Incorporated; *U.S. Public*, pg. 1969
DT FINE ELECTRONICS CO., LTD.—See Dai Nippon Printing Co., Ltd.; *Int'l*, pg. 1915
DUKSAN HI-METAL CO., LTD.; *Int'l*, pg. 2224
DUK SAN NEOLUX CO., LTD.; *Int'l*, pg. 2224
DYESOL AUSTRALIA PTY. LTD.—See Greatcell Solar Ltd.; *Int'l*, pg. 3067
DYESOL INDUSTRIES PTY. LTD.—See Greatcell Solar Ltd.; *Int'l*, pg. 3067
DYESOL UK LTD.—See Greatcell Solar Ltd.; *Int'l*, pg. 3067
EAST TEXAS INTEGRATED CIRCUITS, INC.—See Broadcom Inc.; *U.S. Public*, pg. 388
ECI TECHNOLOGY INTERNATIONAL, INC.—See KLA Corporation; *U.S. Public*, pg. 1267
ECM GREENTECH SASU—See ECM Technologies SAS; *Int'l*, pg. 2292
ECOARK, INC.—See RiskOn International, Inc.; *U.S. Public*, pg. 1799
ECOMAL AUSTRIA GES.MBH—See Vishay Intertechnology, Inc.; *U.S. Public*, pg. 2302
ECOMAL FINLAND OY—See Vishay Intertechnology, Inc.; *U.S. Public*, pg. 2302
ECOMAL FRANCE S.A.—See Vishay Intertechnology, Inc.; *U.S. Public*, pg. 2302
ECOMAL ITALY SRL—See Vishay Intertechnology, Inc.; *U.S. Public*, pg. 2302
ECOMAL NEDERLAND BV—See Vishay Intertechnology, Inc.; *U.S. Public*, pg. 2302
ECOMAL SCHWEIZ A.G.—See Vishay Intertechnology, Inc.; *U.S. Public*, pg. 2302
ECOMAL UK LTD.—See Vishay Intertechnology, Inc.; *U.S. Public*, pg. 2302
EDWARDS S.P.A.—See Atlas Copco AB; *Int'l*, pg. 682
EDWARDS VACUO LTDA—See Atlas Copco AB; *Int'l*, pg. 682
EGALAX-EMPIA TECHNOLOGY, INC.; *Int'l*, pg. 2322
EG SYSTEMS LLC; *U.S. Private*, pg. 1344
E+HPS ENGINEERING (SUZHOU) CO., LTD—See Ellipsiz Ltd.; *Int'l*, pg. 2366
EINFOCHIPS, INC.—See eInfochips Limited; *Int'l*, pg. 2332
EINFOCHIPS LIMITED; *Int'l*, pg. 2332
EJECTT INC; *Int'l*, pg. 2337
EKPO FUEL CELL TECHNOLOGIES GMBH—See ElringKlinger AG; *Int'l*, pg. 2369
ELAN (H.K.) MICROELECTRONIC CORP.—See ELAN Microelectronic Corp.; *Int'l*, pg. 2342
ELAN (H.K.) MICROELECTRONICS CORP.—See ELAN Microelectronic Corp.; *Int'l*, pg. 2342
ELAN MICROELECTRONIC CORP SHANGHAI LTD.—See ELAN Microelectronic Corp.; *Int'l*, pg. 2342
ELECTRIQ POWER HOLDINGS, INC.; *U.S. Public*, pg. 723
ELECTRO-MATIC VENTURES, INC.; *U.S. Private*, pg. 1354
ELECTRONICS INDUSTRY PUBLIC COMPANY LIMITED; *Int'l*, pg. 2354
ELK CORPORATION; *Int'l*, pg. 2363
ELLIPSIZ SEMILAB (SHANGHAI) CO.—See Ellipsiz Ltd.; *Int'l*, pg. 2366
ELLIPSIZ SINGAPORE PTE LTD—See Ellipsiz Ltd.; *Int'l*, pg. 2366
ELMOS JAPAN K.K.—See ELMOS Semiconductor AG; *Int'l*, pg. 2368
ELMOS N.A. INC—See ELMOS Semiconductor AG; *Int'l*, pg. 2368
ELMOS SEMICONDUCTOR AG; *Int'l*, pg. 2368
ELMOS SEMICONDUCTOR SINGAPORE PTE. LTD.—See ELMOS Semiconductor AG; *Int'l*, pg. 2368
ELMOS SEMICONDUCTOR TECHNOLOGY (SHANGHAI) CO., LTD.—See ELMOS Semiconductor AG; *Int'l*, pg. 2368
ELPIDA MEMORY (EUROPE) SARL—See Micron Technology, Inc.; *U.S. Public*, pg. 1437
ELPIDA MEMORY (KOREA) CO., LTD.—See Micron Technology, Inc.; *U.S. Public*, pg. 1437
ELSOFT SYSTEMS SDN. BHD.—See Elsoft Research Berhad; *Int'l*, pg. 2370
ELTOSCH GRAFIX AMERICA INC.—See Dr. Honle AG; *Int'l*, pg. 2192
EMBEDWAY TECHNOLOGIES (SHANGHAI) CORPORATION; *Int'l*, pg. 2374
EMCORE CORPORATION; *U.S. Public*, pg. 739
EMEMORY TECHNOLOGY, INC.; *Int'l*, pg. 2377
EMERALD PRECISION ENGINEERING SDN. BHD.—See Advanced Systems Automation Limited; *Int'l*, pg. 162
EMEREN GROUP LTD; *U.S. Public*, pg. 739
EMINENT ELECTRONIC TECHNOLOGY, CO., LTD.—See ELAN Microelectronic Corp.; *Int'l*, pg. 2342
EMISENSE TECHNOLOGIES, LLC—See CoorsTek, Inc.; *U.S. Private*, pg. 1044
ENABLENCE USA COMPONENTS, INC.—See Enablence Technologies Inc.; *Int'l*, pg. 2395
ENECSYS PLC; *Int'l*, pg. 2411

N.A.I.C.S. INDEX

334413 — SEMICONDUCTOR AND R...

ENERGETIQ TECHNOLOGY, INC.—See Hamamatsu Photonics K.K.; *Int'l*, pg. 3235
ENERGIA INNOVACION Y DESARROLLO FOTOVOLTAICO S.A.; *Int'l*, pg. 2420
ENERGY MATTERS PTY LTD—See SunEdison, Inc.; *U.S. Private*, pg. 3866
ENFIS LIGHTING—See Bould Opportunities PLC; *Int'l*, pg. 1119
ENFIS LIMITED—See Bould Opportunities PLC; *Int'l*, pg. 1119
ENFIS LTD.—See Bould Opportunities PLC; *Int'l*, pg. 1119
ENNOSTAR INC.; *Int'l*, pg. 2443
ENOMOTO PHILIPPINE MANUFACTURING INC.—See Enomoto Co., Ltd.; *Int'l*, pg. 2444
ENPHASE ENERGY AUSTRALIA PTY. LTD.—See Enphase Energy, Inc.; *U.S. Public*, pg. 774
ENPHASE ENERGY, INC.; *U.S. Public*, pg. 774
ENPHASE ENERGY NEW ZEALAND LIMITED—See Enphase Energy, Inc.; *U.S. Public*, pg. 774
ENPHASE ENERGY S.A.S.—See Enphase Energy, Inc.; *U.S. Public*, pg. 774
ENPHASE ENERGY S.R.L.—See Enphase Energy, Inc.; *U.S. Public*, pg. 774
ENPHASE ENERGY UK LIMITED—See Enphase Energy, Inc.; *U.S. Public*, pg. 774
ENPHASE SERVICE COMPANY, LLC—See Enphase Energy, Inc.; *U.S. Public*, pg. 774
ENPHASE SOLAR ENERGY PRIVATE LIMITED—See Enphase Energy, Inc.; *U.S. Public*, pg. 774
ENPLAS SEIKI CORPORATION—See ENPLAS CORPORATION; *Int'l*, pg. 2445
ENPLAS SEMICONDUCTOR PERIPHERAL CORPORATION—See ENPLAS CORPORATION; *Int'l*, pg. 2445
ENTEGRIS CANADA LIMITED—See Entegris, Inc.; *U.S. Public*, pg. 776
ENTEGRIS GMBH—See Entegris, Inc.; *U.S. Public*, pg. 776
ENTEGRIS, INC.; *U.S. Public*, pg. 776
ENTEGRIS MALAYSIA SDN. BHD.—See Entegris, Inc.; *U.S. Public*, pg. 776
EOPLEX LIMITED—See ASTI Holdings Limited; *Int'l*, pg. 655
EPILEDS TECHNOLOGIES, INC.; *Int'l*, pg. 2460
EPIWORKS, INC.—See Coherent Corp.; *U.S. Public*, pg. 528
EPURON EPE—See Kawa Capital Management, Inc.; *U.S. Private*, pg. 2266
EQUIPMENTS CELL CO., LTD.; *Int'l*, pg. 2485
EQUIPTEST ENGINEERING PTE. LTD.—See Cohu, Inc.; *U.S. Public*, pg. 529
ERIS TECHNOLOGY CO—See Diodes Incorporated; *U.S. Public*, pg. 667
ESEC (SINGAPORE) PTE. LTD.—See BE Semiconductor Industries N.V.; *Int'l*, pg. 931
ESPRESSIF SYSTEMS SHANGHAI CO., LTD.; *Int'l*, pg. 2506
ESS TECH, INC.; *U.S. Public*, pg. 794
ESS TECHNOLOGY, INC.—See Imperium Partners Group, LLC; *U.S. Private*, pg. 2050
ES TECHNOLOGY LTD.—See Coherent Corp.; *U.S. Public*, pg. 528
ETROVISION TECHNOLOGY CO., LTD.—See Chung-Hsin Electric & Machinery Manufacturing Corp.; *Int'l*, pg. 1597
EVANS & SUTHERLAND COMPUTER CORPORATION - SIMULATION DIVISION—See Elevate Entertainment, Inc.; *U.S. Private*, pg. 1358
EVERLIGHT ELECTRONICS CO., LTD.; *Int'l*, pg. 2567
EVERSPIN TECHNOLOGIES, INC; *U.S. Public*, pg. 802
EVOLUCIA INC.; *U.S. Private*, pg. 1442
EVOLVE MANUFACTURING TECHNOLOGIES; *U.S. Private*, pg. 1443
EXCITON TECHNOLOGY; *Int'l*, pg. 2580
EXERION PRECISION TECHNOLOGY HOLDING B.V.; *Int'l*, pg. 2584
EXICON CO., LTD.; *Int'l*, pg. 2584
EXPONENT LIMITED—See Exponent, Inc.; *U.S. Public*, pg. 812
FABTECH INC.—See Diodes Incorporated; *U.S. Public*, pg. 667
FARADAY TECHNOLOGY CHINA CORPORATION—See Faraday Technology Corporation; *Int'l*, pg. 2618
FARADAY TECHNOLOGY CORPORATION—See Faraday Technology Corporation; *Int'l*, pg. 2618
FARADAY TECHNOLOGY CORPORATION—See Faraday Technology Corporation; *Int'l*, pg. 2618
FARADAY TECHNOLOGY JAPAN CORPORATION—See Faraday Technology Corporation; *Int'l*, pg. 2618
FARADAY TECHNOLOGY VIETNAM COMPANY LIMITED—See Faraday Technology Corporation; *Int'l*, pg. 2618
FARO BENELUX B.V.—See FARO Technologies, Inc.; *U.S. Public*, pg. 823
FARO EUROPE GMBH & CO. KG—See FARO Technologies, Inc.; *U.S. Public*, pg. 823
FARO SINGAPORE PTE. LTD.—See FARO Technologies, Inc.; *U.S. Public*, pg. 823
FDK CORPORATION - KOSAI PLANT—See Fujitsu Limited; *Int'l*, pg. 2832

FEATURE INTEGRATION TECHNOLOGY, INC.; *Int'l*, pg. 2629
FEI COMPANY—See Thermo Fisher Scientific Inc.; *U.S. Public*, pg. 2146
FEI FREMONT—See Thermo Fisher Scientific Inc.; *U.S. Public*, pg. 2147
FERROTEC CERAMICS CORPORATION—See Ferrotec Holdings Corporation; *Int'l*, pg. 2643
FERROTEC CORPORATION SINGAPORE PTE LTD—See Ferrotec Holdings Corporation; *Int'l*, pg. 2643
FERROTEC SILICON CORPORATION—See Ferrotec Holdings Corporation; *Int'l*, pg. 2643
FERROTEC TAIWAN CO., LTD.—See Ferrotec Holdings Corporation; *Int'l*, pg. 2643
FHR ANLAGENBAU GMBH—See centrotherm photovoltaics AG; *Int'l*, pg. 1415
FICO INTERNATIONAL B.V.—See BE Semiconductor Industries N.V.; *Int'l*, pg. 931
FICO TOOLING LESHAN COMPANY LTD.—See BE Semiconductor Industries N.V.; *Int'l*, pg. 931
FIDELIX CO., LTD.; *Int'l*, pg. 2654
FINE SEMITECH CORP.; *Int'l*, pg. 2673
FINETECHNIX CO., LTD.; *Int'l*, pg. 2674
FINISAR MALAYSIA SDN. BHD.—See Coherent Corp.; *U.S. Public*, pg. 528
FINISAR SHANGHAI INC.—See Coherent Corp.; *U.S. Public*, pg. 528
FIRST SOLAR, INC.; *U.S. Public*, pg. 847
FIRST SOLAR MALAYSIA SDN. BHD.—See First Solar, Inc.; *U.S. Public*, pg. 847
FLEXTRONICS SEMICONDUCTOR, INC.—See Flex Ltd.; *Int'l*, pg. 2703
FNS TECH CO.,LTD; *Int'l*, pg. 2718
FOCUS LIGHTINGS TECH CO., LTD.; *Int'l*, pg. 2719
FONROCHE ENERGIE SAS—See Eurazeo SE; *Int'l*, pg. 2528
FORHOUSE CORPORATION - DA-YA FACTORY—See Darwin Precisions Corporation; *Int'l*, pg. 1973
FORHOUSE CORPORATION - XIAMEN FACTORY—See Darwin Precisions Corporation; *Int'l*, pg. 1973
FORMFACTOR EUROPE GMBH—See FormFactor, Inc.; *U.S. Public*, pg. 868
FORMFACTOR GMBH—See FormFactor, Inc.; *U.S. Public*, pg. 868
FORMFACTOR, INC.; *U.S. Public*, pg. 868
FORMFACTOR K.K.—See FormFactor, Inc.; *U.S. Public*, pg. 868
FORMFACTOR KOREA, INC.—See FormFactor, Inc.; *U.S. Public*, pg. 868
FORMOSA EPITAXY INCORPORATION—See Ennostar Inc.; *Int'l*, pg. 2443
FORZA SILICON CORPORATION—See AMETEK, Inc.; *U.S. Public*, pg. 120
FOSHAN NATIONSTAR OPTOELECTRONICS CO., LTD. - LED LIGHTING DIVISION—See Foshan Nationstar Optoelectronics Co., Ltd.; *Int'l*, pg. 2748
FOSHAN NATIONSTAR OPTOELECTRONICS CO., LTD.; *Int'l*, pg. 2748
FOXSEMICON INTEGRATED TECHNOLOGY INC.—See Hon Hai Precision Industry Co., Ltd.; *Int'l*, pg. 3457
FREIBERGER COMPOUND MATERIALS GMBH—See Federmann Enterprises, Ltd.; *Int'l*, pg. 2631
FREIBERGER COMPOUND MATERIALS TAIWAN LTD.—See Federmann Enterprises, Ltd.; *Int'l*, pg. 2631
FREIBERGER COMPOUND MATERIALS USA, INC.—See Federmann Enterprises, Ltd.; *Int'l*, pg. 2631
FRONTGRADE COLORADO SPRINGS LLC—See Veritas Capital Fund Management, LLC; *U.S. Private*, pg. 4362
F.S.E CORPORATION—See Contrel Technology Co., Ltd.; *Int'l*, pg. 1785
FUJIAN ACETRON NEW MATERIALS CO., LTD.; *Int'l*, pg. 2817
FUJIAN RAYNEN TECHNOLOGY CO., LTD.; *Int'l*, pg. 2819
FUJI ELECTRIC BRAZIL-EUIPAMENTOS DE ENERGIA LTDA. (FEB)—See Fuji Electric Co., Ltd.; *Int'l*, pg. 2811
FUJI ELECTRIC PHILIPPINES, INC.—See Fuji Electric Co., Ltd.; *Int'l*, pg. 2811
FUJI ELECTRIC POWER SEMICONDUCTOR CO., LTD.—See Fuji Electric Co., Ltd.; *Int'l*, pg. 2811
FUJI ELECTRIC TAIWAN CO., LTD.—See Fuji Electric Co., Ltd.; *Int'l*, pg. 2812
FUJI ELECTRIC TSUGARU SEMICONDUCTOR CO., LTD.—See Fuji Electric Co., Ltd.; *Int'l*, pg. 2812
FUJIFILM ELECTRONIC MATERIALS (EUROPE) S.R.L.—See FUJIFILM Holdings Corporation; *Int'l*, pg. 2822
FUJIFILM ELECTRONIC MATERIALS MANUFACTURING KOREA CO., LTD.—See FUJIFILM Holdings Corporation; *Int'l*, pg. 2824
FUJIFILM ELECTRONIC MATERIALS U.S.A., INC.—See FUJIFILM Holdings Corporation; *Int'l*, pg. 2822
FUJIFILM ELECTRONIC MATERIALS U.S.A. INC.—See FUJIFILM Holdings Corporation; *Int'l*, pg. 2822
FUJITSU SEMICONDUCTOR AMERICA, INC—See Fujitsu Limited; *Int'l*, pg. 2835
FUJITSU SEMICONDUCTOR ASIA PTE. LTD.—See Fujitsu Limited; *Int'l*, pg. 2835
FUJITSU SEMICONDUCTOR EMBEDDED SOLUTIONS AUSTRIA GMBH—See Fujitsu Limited; *Int'l*, pg. 2835
FUJITSU SEMICONDUCTOR EUROPE GMBH—See Fujitsu Limited; *Int'l*, pg. 2835
FUJITSU SEMICONDUCTOR LIMITED—See Fujitsu Limited; *Int'l*, pg. 2835
FUJITSU SEMICONDUCTOR PACIFIC ASIA LIMITED—See Fujitsu Limited; *Int'l*, pg. 2835
FUJITSU SEMICONDUCTOR (SHANGHAI) CO., LTD.—See Fujitsu Limited; *Int'l*, pg. 2835
FULCRUM MICROSYSTEMS, INC.—See Intel Corporation; *U.S. Public*, pg. 1138
FURUKAWA DENSHI CO., LTD. - SEMICONDUCTOR MATERIALS PLANT—See Furukawa Co., Ltd.; *Int'l*, pg. 2847
FUTURE ELECTRONICS CORP., BRAZIL—See Future Electronics Inc.; *Int'l*, pg. 2854
FUTURE ELECTRONICS CORP., FRANCE—See Future Electronics Inc.; *Int'l*, pg. 2855
FUTURE ELECTRONICS LTD.—See Future Electronics Inc.; *Int'l*, pg. 2855
FUZHOU ROCKCHIP ELECTRONICS CO., LTD.; *Int'l*, pg. 2859
GALAXIA ELECTRONICS CO., LTD.—See Hyosung Corporation; *Int'l*, pg. 3550
GALAXY SEMICONDUCTOR CO., LTD.; *Int'l*, pg. 2871
GALLANT PRECISION INDUSTRIES (SUZHOU) CO., LTD.—See Gallant Precision Machining Co., Ltd.; *Int'l*, pg. 2873
GANSU GOLDEN SOLAR CO., LTD; *Int'l*, pg. 2881
GCL SYSTEM INTEGRATION TECHNOLOGY CO., LTD.—See Golden Concord Holdings Limited; *Int'l*, pg. 3028
GCS HOLDINGS, INC.; *Int'l*, pg. 2895
GCT SEMICONDUCTOR, INC.—See GCT Semiconductor Holding, Inc.; *U.S. Public*, pg. 908
GENCELL LTD.; *Int'l*, pg. 2917
GENESEM INC.; *Int'l*, pg. 2921
GENESIS PHOTONICS INC.; *Int'l*, pg. 2921
GENIUS ELECTRONIC OPTICAL (XIAMEN) CO., LTD.—See Genius Electronic Optical Co., Ltd.; *Int'l*, pg. 2924
GEO SEMICONDUCTOR INC.—See indie Semiconductor, Inc.; *U.S. Public*, pg. 1116
GI CO., LTD.—See BCnC Co., Ltd.; *Int'l*, pg. 928
GIGADEVICE SEMICONDUCTOR (BEIJING) INC; *Int'l*, pg. 2971
GIGADEVICE SEMICONDUCTOR (HEFEI) INC.—See GigaDevice Semiconductor (Beijing) Inc; *Int'l*, pg. 2971
GIGA SOLAR MATERIALS CORP.; *Int'l*, pg. 2971
GIGASTONE CORPORATION; *Int'l*, pg. 2972
GIGASTORAGE CORP.; *Int'l*, pg. 2972
GINTECH ENERGY CORPORATION; *Int'l*, pg. 2977
GLOBAL COMMUNICATION SEMICONDUCTORS, INC.—See GCS Holdings, Inc.; *Int'l*, pg. 2895
GLOBAL MIXED-MODE TECHNOLOGY INC.; *Int'l*, pg. 2999
GLOBAL UNICHIP CORP.; *Int'l*, pg. 3002
GLOBETRONICS MANUFACTURING SDN. BHD.—See Globetronics Technology Bhd.; *Int'l*, pg. 3007
GLYN GMBH & CO. KG; *Int'l*, pg. 3011
GLYN SWITZERLAND—See GLYN GmbH & Co. KG; *Int'l*, pg. 3011
GOERTEK INC.; *Int'l*, pg. 3021
GOKE MICROELECTRONICS CO., LTD.; *Int'l*, pg. 3022
GOLDEN CENTURY INTERNATIONAL HOLDINGS GROUP LIMITED; *Int'l*, pg. 3028
GP SOLAR GMBH—See centrotherm photovoltaics AG; *Int'l*, pg. 1415
GRAND VENTURE TECHNOLOGY LIMITED; *Int'l*, pg. 3057
GRAND VENTURE TECHNOLOGY SDN. BHD.—See Grand Venture Technology Limited; *Int'l*, pg. 3057
GRAND VENTURE TECHNOLOGY (SUZHOU) CO., LTD.—See Grand Venture Technology Limited; *Int'l*, pg. 3057
GREATCELL SOLAR LTD.; *Int'l*, pg. 3066
GRINDING & DICING SERVICES, INC.—See Akoustis Technologies, Inc.; *U.S. Public*, pg. 69
GRINM ADVANCED MATERIALS CO., LTD.; *Int'l*, pg. 3087
GSI TECHNOLOGY, INC.; *U.S. Public*, pg. 973
G-SMATT GLOBAL CO., LTD.; *Int'l*, pg. 2863
GT ADVANCED CZ LLC—See GT Advanced Technologies Inc.; *U.S. Private*, pg. 1801
GT ADVANCED TECHNOLOGIES INC.; *U.S. Private*, pg. 1801
GT ADVANCED TECHNOLOGIES LIMITED—See GT Advanced Technologies Inc.; *U.S. Private*, pg. 1801
GT SOLAR (SHANGHAI) CO., LTD.—See GT Advanced Technologies Inc.; *U.S. Private*, pg. 1801
GUANGDONG ELECTRONIC INFORMATION INDUSTRIAL GROUP CO., LTD.—See Guangdong Rising Assets Management Co., Ltd.; *Int'l*, pg. 3159
GUANGDONG FUXIN TECHNOLOGY CO., LTD.; *Int'l*, pg. 3154
GUANGDONG LEADYO IC TESTING CO., LTD.; *Int'l*, pg. 3158
GV (GEUMVIT CORP.) JAPAN CO., LTD.—See GeumVit Corp.; *Int'l*, pg. 2954

GV (GEUMVIT CORP.) (YANTAI) CO., LTD.—See GeumVit Corp.; *Int'l*, pg. 2954
HAESUNG DS CO., LTD. - CHANGWON FACTORY—See HAESUNG DS Co., Ltd.; *Int'l*, pg. 3205
HAESUNG DS CO., LTD.; *Int'l*, pg. 3205
HAGIWARA ELECTRIC HOLDINGS CO., LTD.; *Int'l*, pg. 3207
HAGIWARA ENGINEERING CO., LTD.—See Hagiwara Electric Holdings Co., Ltd.; *Int'l*, pg. 3207
HAKKODA DENSHI CO., LTD.—See Ferrotec Holdings Corporation; *Int'l*, pg. 2643
HAMAMATSU CORPORATION - FACTORY—See Hamamatsu Photonics K.K.; *Int'l*, pg. 3235
HAMAMATSU PHOTONICS K.K. - ELECTRON TUBE DIVISION—See Hamamatsu Photonics K.K.; *Int'l*, pg. 3235
HAMAMATSU PHOTONICS K.K. - SOLID STATE DIVISION—See Hamamatsu Photonics K.K.; *Int'l*, pg. 3235
HAMAMATSU PHOTONICS K.K.; *Int'l*, pg. 3235
HAMAMATSU PHOTONICS K.K. - SYSTEMS DIVISION—See Hamamatsu Photonics K.K.; *Int'l*, pg. 3235
HANA MATERIALS INC.; *Int'l*, pg. 3241
HANA MICRON INC.; *Int'l*, pg. 3241
HANA SEMICONDUCTOR (AYUTTHAYA) CO., LTD.—See Hana Microelectronics Public Company Limited; *Int'l*, pg. 3241
HANA SEMICONDUCTOR (BKK) CO., LTD.—See Hana Microelectronics Public Company Limited; *Int'l*, pg. 3241
HANCOM GMD INC.—See Hancom With Inc.; *Int'l*, pg. 3242
HANGZHOU MPS SEMICONDUCTOR TECHNOLOGY LTD.—See Monolithic Power Systems, Inc.; *U.S. Public*, pg. 1464
HANGZHOU SEMICONDUCTOR WAFER CO., LTD.—See Ferrotec Holdings Corporation; *Int'l*, pg. 2643
HANGZHOU SILAN AZUER CO., LTD.—See Hangzhou Silan Microelectronics Co., Ltd.; *Int'l*, pg. 3250
HANGZHOU SILAN INTEGRATED CIRCUIT CO., LTD.—See Hangzhou Silan Microelectronics Co., Ltd.; *Int'l*, pg. 3250
HANGZHOU SILAN MICROELECTRONICS CO., LTD.; *Int'l*, pg. 3250
HANGZHOU SILAN OPTRONICS TECHNOLOGY CO., LTD—See Hangzhou Silan Microelectronics Co., Ltd.; *Int'l*, pg. 3250
HANGZHOU YOUWANG ELECTRONICS CO., LTD.—See Hangzhou Silan Microelectronics Co., Ltd.; *Int'l*, pg. 3250
HANMI SEMICONDUCTOR CO., LTD.; *Int'l*, pg. 3256
HANSOL IONES CO., LTD; *Int'l*, pg. 3261
HANVON C-PEN TECHNOLOGY CO., LTD.—See Hanwang Technology Co., Ltd.; *Int'l*, pg. 3264
HANWHA Q CELLS CO., LTD—See Hanwha Group; *Int'l*, pg. 3265
HANYANG DIGITECH CO., LTD.; *Int'l*, pg. 3267
HAVERTON WTV LIMITED—See EQTEC plc; *Int'l*, pg. 2483
HB TECHNOLOGY INC. - CHEONAN-SI PLANT—See HB Technology Inc.; *Int'l*, pg. 3295
HC SEMITEK CORPORATION; *Int'l*, pg. 3297
HD HYUNDAI ENERGY SOLUTIONS CO.,LTD.; *Int'l*, pg. 3299
HEXIS GMBH—See Hexis AG; *Int'l*, pg. 3371
HGH INFRARED SYSTEMS INC.; *U.S. Private*, pg. 1930
HG SEMICONDUCTOR LIMITED; *Int'l*, pg. 3375
HIGH COMPONENTS AOMORI CO., LTD.—See AOI Electronics, Co., Ltd.; *Int'l*, pg. 488
HIGH POWER LIGHTING CORP.; *Int'l*, pg. 3386
HIGH Q LASER GMBH—See MKS Instruments, Inc.; *U.S. Public*, pg. 1453
HIMAX IGI PRECISION LTD.—See Himax Technologies, Inc.; *Int'l*, pg. 3396
HIMAX IMAGING, LTD.—See Himax Technologies, Inc.; *Int'l*, pg. 3396
HIMAX TECHNOLOGIES, INC.; *Int'l*, pg. 3396
HIMAX TECHNOLOGIES JAPAN LTD—See Himax Technologies, Inc.; *Int'l*, pg. 3397
HIMAX TECHNOLOGIES KOREA LTD.—See Himax Technologies, Inc.; *Int'l*, pg. 3397
HIRATA CORPORATION; *Int'l*, pg. 3403
HITACHI EUROPE LTD. - POWER DEVICE DIVISION—See Hitachi, Ltd.; *Int'l*, pg. 3417
HITACHI HIGH-TECH CORPORATION—See Hitachi, Ltd.; *Int'l*, pg. 3418
HITACHI HIGH-TECH DIAGNOSTICS (SHANGHAI) CO., LTD.—See Hitachi, Ltd.; *Int'l*, pg. 3418
HITACHI HIGH-TECHNOLOGIES KOREA CO., LTD.—See Hitachi, Ltd.; *Int'l*, pg. 3419
HITACHI HIGH-TECH (SHANGHAI) CO., LTD.—See Hitachi, Ltd.; *Int'l*, pg. 3418
HITACHI PLANT TECHNOLOGIES (VIETNAM) CO., LTD.—See Hitachi, Ltd.; *Int'l*, pg. 3420
HLB INNOVATION CO.,LTD.; *Int'l*, pg. 3430
HODOGAYA CHEMICAL CO., LTD. - KORIYAMA PLANT—See Hodogaya Chemical Co., Ltd.; *Int'l*, pg. 3438
HOFFMAN INSTRUMENTATION SUPPLY, INC.—See Ultra Clean Holdings, Inc.; *U.S. Public*, pg. 2223
HOLON CO., LTD.—See A&D Co., Ltd.; *Int'l*, pg. 19

HOLTEK SEMICONDUCTOR (CHINA) INC.—See Holtek Semiconductor Inc.; *Int'l*, pg. 3453
HOLTEK SEMICONDUCTOR INC.; *Int'l*, pg. 3453
HOLTEK SEMICONDUCTOR INC.—See Holtek Semiconductor Inc.; *Int'l*, pg. 3454
HOLTEK SEMICONDUCTOR (INDIA) PVT. LTD.—See Holtek Semiconductor Inc.; *Int'l*, pg. 3453
HOLTEK SEMICONDUCTOR (USA), INC.—See Holtek Semiconductor Inc.; *Int'l*, pg. 3453
HONG KONG FUJIDENKI CO., LTD.—See Fuji Electric Co., Ltd.; *Int'l*, pg. 2812
HORIBA ADVANCED TECHNO CO., LTD. - KYOTO FACTORY—See HORIBA Ltd; *Int'l*, pg. 3476
HORIBA KOREA CO., LTD. - BUCHEON FACTORY—See HORIBA Ltd; *Int'l*, pg. 3476
HORIBA STEC, CO., LTD. - ASO FACTORY—See HORIBA Ltd; *Int'l*, pg. 3476
HORIBA STEC KOREA LTD.—See HORIBA Ltd; *Int'l*, pg. 3476
HOSHINE SILICON (LUZHOU) INDUSTRY CO., LTD.—See Hoshine Silicon Industry Co., Ltd.; *Int'l*, pg. 3482
HOSHINE SILICON (SHANSHAN) INDUSTRY CO., LTD.—See Hoshine Silicon Industry Co., Ltd.; *Int'l*, pg. 3482
HOUSING TECHNOLOGY CORP.—See Europtronic Group Ltd.; *Int'l*, pg. 2557
H&S HIGHTECH CORP. - CHINA FACTORY—See H&S HighTech Corp.; *Int'l*, pg. 3193
HT MICRON—See Hana Micron Inc.; *Int'l*, pg. 3241
HUA HONG SEMICONDUCTOR LIMITED; *Int'l*, pg. 3509
HUBEI JIUZHIYANG INFRARED SYSTEM CO., LTD; *Int'l*, pg. 3518
HUGA OPTOTECH INC.—See Ennostar Inc.; *Int'l*, pg. 2443
HUNDREDYEARS CO., LTD.—See Fantasista Co., Ltd.; *Int'l*, pg. 2613
HY-LINE AG—See Blue Cap AG; *Int'l*, pg. 1067
HY-LINE COMMUNICATION PRODUCTS VERTRIEBS GMBH—See Blue Cap AG; *Int'l*, pg. 1067
HY-LINE COMPUTER COMPONENTS VERTRIEBS GMBH—See Blue Cap AG; *Int'l*, pg. 1067
HY-LINE HOLDING GMBH—See Blue Cap AG; *Int'l*, pg. 1067
HY-LINE POWER COMPONENTS VERTRIEBS GMBH—See Blue Cap AG; *Int'l*, pg. 1067
HY-LOK CANADA INC.—See Hy-Lok Corporation; *Int'l*, pg. 3543
HY-LOK CHINA—See Hy-Lok Corporation; *Int'l*, pg. 3543
HYSITRON, INC.—See Bruker Corporation; *U.S. Public*, pg. 406
HYTEK MICROSYSTEMS, INC.—See Natel Engineering Company, Inc.; *U.S. Private*, pg. 2838
IA INC.; *Int'l*, pg. 3568
IA POWERTRON CO., LTD.—See iA Inc.; *Int'l*, pg. 3568
IBIDEN PHILIPPINES, INC.—See Ibiden Co., Ltd.; *Int'l*, pg. 3575
ICERA INC.—See NVIDIA Corporation; *U.S. Public*, pg. 1558
ICERA INC.—See NVIDIA Corporation; *U.S. Public*, pg. 1558
I-CHIPS TECHNOLOGY INC.—See Imagica Group Inc.; *Int'l*, pg. 3619
I-CHIUN PRECISION ELECTRIC INDUSTRY (CHINA) CO., LTD.—See I-CHIUN PRECISION INDUSTRY CO., LTD.; *Int'l*, pg. 3562
I-CHIUN PRECISION ELECTRIC (NANJING) CO., LTD.—See I-CHIUN PRECISION INDUSTRY CO., LTD.; *Int'l*, pg. 3562
I-CHIUN PRECISION INDUSTRY CO., LTD. - NANJING PLANT—See I-CHIUN PRECISION INDUSTRY CO., LTD.; *Int'l*, pg. 3563
I-CHIUN PRECISION INDUSTRY CO., LTD.—See I-CHIUN PRECISION INDUSTRY CO., LTD.; *Int'l*, pg. 3562
ICHOR HOLDINGS, LP—See Francisco Partners Management, LP; *U.S. Private*, pg. 1590
I&C TECHNOLOGY CO., LTD.; *Int'l*, pg. 3562
IDENTICARE LIMITED—See Animalcare Group plc; *Int'l*, pg. 471
I-FACTORY CO., LTD.; *Int'l*, pg. 3563
II-VI LASER ENTERPRISE GMBH—See Coherent Corp.; *U.S. Public*, pg. 528
IK SEMICON CO., LTD.; *Int'l*, pg. 3610
ILJIN DISPLAY CO., LTD.; *Int'l*, pg. 3614
ILJIN SEMICONDUCTOR CO., LTD.—See Iljin Display Co., Ltd.; *Int'l*, pg. 3614
IMAGINATION TECHNOLOGIES GROUP LIMITED—See Canyon Bridge Capital Partners, Inc.; *Int'l*, pg. 1300
IMAGINATION TECHNOLOGIES INDIA PVT. LTD.—See Canyon Bridge Capital Partners, Inc.; *Int'l*, pg. 1300
IMAGINATION TECHNOLOGIES LTD.—See Canyon Bridge Capital Partners, Inc.; *Int'l*, pg. 1300
IMAGIS CO., LTD.; *Int'l*, pg. 3619
INDUSTRIEALPINE BAUTRAGER GMBH—See ELMOS Semiconductor AG; *Int'l*, pg. 2368
INMUSIC GMBH—See inMusic, LLC; *U.S. Private*, pg. 2080
INNERSENSE—See KLA Corporation; *U.S. Public*, pg. 1268
INNOPOWER TECHNOLOGY CORPORATION—See Faraday Technology Corporation; *Int'l*, pg. 2618
INNOVATIVE NANOTECH INCORPORATED—See Chroma ATE Inc.; *Int'l*, pg. 1588

INTEGRATED MATERIALS, INC.—See Ferrotec Holdings Corporation; *Int'l*, pg. 2643
INTEL CHINA LTD.—See Intel Corporation; *U.S. Public*, pg. 1138
INTEL CHINA LTD.—See Intel Corporation; *U.S. Public*, pg. 1138
INTEL CORPORATION - CHANDLER OFFICE—See Intel Corporation; *U.S. Public*, pg. 1138
INTEL CORPORATION; *U.S. Public*, pg. 1136
INTEL CZECH TRADINGS, INC.—See Intel Corporation; *U.S. Public*, pg. 1138
INTEL ELECTRONICS (MALAYSIA) SDN. BHD.—See Intel Corporation; *U.S. Public*, pg. 1138
INTEL INDONESIA CORPORATION—See Intel Corporation; *U.S. Public*, pg. 1138
INTEL IRELAND LTD.—See Intel Corporation; *U.S. Public*, pg. 1138
INTEL ISRAEL (74) LIMITED—See Intel Corporation; *U.S. Public*, pg. 1138
INTEL KABUSHIKI KAISHA—See Intel Corporation; *U.S. Public*, pg. 1138
INTEL MASSACHUSETTS, INC.—See Intel Corporation; *U.S. Public*, pg. 1138
INTEL MEDITERRANEAN TRADING COMPANY—See Intel Corporation; *U.S. Public*, pg. 1138
INTEL MOBILE COMMUNICATIONS GMBH—See Intel Corporation; *U.S. Public*, pg. 1138
INTEL SA CORP—See Intel Corporation; *U.S. Public*, pg. 1138
INTEL SEMICONDUCTOR LTD.—See Intel Corporation; *U.S. Public*, pg. 1139
INTEL SEMICONDUCTOR LTD.—See Intel Corporation; *U.S. Public*, pg. 1139
INTEL SEMICONDUCTOR LTD.—See Intel Corporation; *U.S. Public*, pg. 1139
INTEL SEMICONDUCTOR LTD.—See Intel Corporation; *U.S. Public*, pg. 1139
INTEL SEMICONDUTORES DO BRASIL LTDA.—See Intel Corporation; *U.S. Public*, pg. 1139
INTEL TECHNOLOGIES, INC.—See Intel Corporation; *U.S. Public*, pg. 1139
INTEL TECHNOLOGY INDIA PVT. LTD.—See Intel Corporation; *U.S. Public*, pg. 1139
INTEL TECHNOLOGY PHILIPPINES, INC.—See Intel Corporation; *U.S. Public*, pg. 1139
INTEL TECHNOLOGY POLAND—See Intel Corporation; *U.S. Public*, pg. 1139
INTELTECH S.A. DE C.V.—See Intel Corporation; *U.S. Public*, pg. 1139
INTEL TECNOLOGIA DE ARGENTINA S.A.—See Intel Corporation; *U.S. Public*, pg. 1139
INTEL TECNOLOGIA DE COLOMBIA S.A.—See Intel Corporation; *U.S. Public*, pg. 1139
INTEL TECNOLOGIA DE MEXICO, S.A. DE C.V.—See Intel Corporation; *U.S. Public*, pg. 1139
INTERDIGITAL, INC.; *U.S. Public*, pg. 1143
INTERNATIONAL TEST SOLUTIONS KOREA LIMITED—See Entegris, Inc.; *U.S. Public*, pg. 776
INTERPLEX TECHNOLOGY PTE. LTD.—See Blackstone Inc.; *U.S. Public*, pg. 355
INTERPOINT U.K. LTD.—See Crane NXT, Co.; *U.S. Public*, pg. 589
INTEST SILICON VALLEY CORPORATION—See inTEST Corporation; *U.S. Public*, pg. 1159
INVENSAS CORPORATION—See Adeia Inc.; *U.S. Public*, pg. 41
IOTA COMMUNICATIONS, INC.; *U.S. Public*, pg. 1167
IPG PHOTONICS CORPORATION; *U.S. Public*, pg. 1167
IPG PHOTONICS (JAPAN) LTD.—See IPG Photonics Corporation; *U.S. Public*, pg. 1167
IPG PHOTONICS (KOREA) LTD.—See IPG Photonics Corporation; *U.S. Public*, pg. 1167
ISE LABS, INC.—See ASE Technology Holding Co., Ltd.; *Int'l*, pg. 604
ISOLINK, INC.—See Skyworks Solutions, Inc.; *U.S. Public*, pg. 1893
ISRA VISION GRAPHIKON GMBH—See Atlas Copco AB; *Int'l*, pg. 682
IXYS CORPORATION—See Littelfuse, Inc.; *U.S. Public*, pg. 1327
IXYS GLOBAL SERVICES GMBH—See Littelfuse, Inc.; *U.S. Public*, pg. 1327
IXYS LONG BEACH INC.—See Littelfuse, Inc.; *U.S. Public*, pg. 1327
IXYS SEMICONDUCTOR GMBH—See Littelfuse, Inc.; *U.S. Public*, pg. 1327
IXYS SEMICONDUCTORS GMBH—See Littelfuse, Inc.; *U.S. Public*, pg. 1327
IXYS UK WESTCODE LIMITED—See Littelfuse, Inc.; *U.S. Public*, pg. 1327
I-ZOU HI-TECH (SZN) CO., LTD.—See I-CHIUN PRECISION INDUSTRY CO., LTD.; *Int'l*, pg. 3563
JABIL CIRCUIT (BEIJING) LIMITED—See Jabil Inc.; *U.S. Public*, pg. 1180
JABIL CIRCUIT (SUZHOU) LTD.—See Jabil Inc.; *U.S. Public*, pg. 1181
JABIL DO BRASIL INDUSTRIA ELETROELETRONICA LTDA.—See Jabil Inc.; *U.S. Public*, pg. 1181

N.A.I.C.S. INDEX

334413 — SEMICONDUCTOR AND R...

JAPAN ENGINEERING CO., LTD.—See Advantest Corporation; *Int'l*, pg. 166
J-DEVICES CORPORATION—See Amkor Technology, Inc.; *U.S. Public*, pg. 124
JDSU DO BRASIL LTDA. & CIA—See Viavi Solutions Inc.; *U.S. Public*, pg. 2295
JIANGSU LINYANG SOLARFUN CO., LTD.—See Hanwha Group; *Int'l*, pg. 3265
JIREH SEMICONDUCTOR INCORPORATED—See Alpha and Omega Semiconductor Limited; *Int'l*, pg. 366
JOHNSON SMITH COMPANY; *U.S. Private*, pg. 2229
JSI MICROELECTRONICS—See JMAR, LLC; *U.S. Private*, pg. 2215
JST PERFORMANCE, INC.—See Genstar Capital, LLC; *U.S. Private*, pg. 1676
K1 SOLUTION, INC.—See Federmann Enterprises, Ltd.; *Int'l*, pg. 2631
KAILO ENERGY—See Global Unicorn Holdings, Inc.; *U.S. Private*, pg. 1718
KANTO SANYO SEMICONDUCTOR CO., LTD.—See ON Semiconductor Corporation; *U.S. Public*, pg. 1601
KAZAKHSTAN SOLAR SILICON LLP—See Canadian Solar Inc.; *Int'l*, pg. 1286
KAZAKHSTAN SOLAR SILICON LLP—See ECM Technologies SAS; *Int'l*, pg. 2292
KINETIC TECHNOLOGIES, INC.; *U.S. Private*, pg. 2308
KLA-TENCOR ASIA-PAC DISTRIBUTION CORPORATION—See KLA Corporation; *U.S. Public*, pg. 1268
KNOWLES ELECTRONICS AUSTRIA GMBH—See Knowles Corporation; *U.S. Public*, pg. 1270
KOBRITE TAIWAN CORPORATION—See Bright Led Electronics Corp.; *Int'l*, pg. 1161
KOKUSAI ELECTRIC ASIA PACIFIC CO., LTD.—See KKR & Co. Inc.; *U.S. Public*, pg. 1258
KOKUSAI ELECTRIC EUROPE GMBH—See KKR & Co. Inc.; *U.S. Public*, pg. 1258
KOPIN CORPORATION; *U.S. Public*, pg. 1271
KOREA SUNERGY CO., LTD—See China Sunergy Co., Ltd.; *Int'l*, pg. 1556
L3 ELECTRON DEVICES, INC.—See L3Harris Technologies, Inc.; *U.S. Public*, pg. 1284
L3 MICREO PTY LIMITED—See L3Harris Technologies, Inc.; *U.S. Public*, pg. 1284
LAM RESEARCH B.V.—See Lam Research Corporation; *U.S. Public*, pg. 1289
LAM RESEARCH CO., LTD. - HIROSHIMA SERVICE CENTER—See Lam Research Corporation; *U.S. Public*, pg. 1289
LAM RESEARCH CO., LTD.—See Lam Research Corporation; *U.S. Public*, pg. 1289
LAM RESEARCH CO., LTD.—See Lam Research Corporation; *U.S. Public*, pg. 1289
LAM RESEARCH CORPORATION—See Lam Research Corporation; *U.S. Public*, pg. 1289
LAM RESEARCH GMBH—See Lam Research Corporation; *U.S. Public*, pg. 1289
LAM RESEARCH INTERNATIONAL SARL—See Lam Research Corporation; *U.S. Public*, pg. 1290
LAM RESEARCH (IRELAND) LIMITED—See Lam Research Corporation; *U.S. Public*, pg. 1289
LAM RESEARCH (ISRAEL) LTD.—See Lam Research Corporation; *U.S. Public*, pg. 1289
LAM RESEARCH KOREA LTD.—See Lam Research Corporation; *U.S. Public*, pg. 1290
LAM RESEARCH SAS—See Lam Research Corporation; *U.S. Public*, pg. 1290
LAM RESEARCH SAS—See Lam Research Corporation; *U.S. Public*, pg. 1290
LAM RESEARCH SERVICE CO., LTD.—See Lam Research Corporation; *U.S. Public*, pg. 1290
LAM RESEARCH SRL—See Lam Research Corporation; *U.S. Public*, pg. 1290
LASER 2000 GMBH—See Gimv NV; *Int'l*, pg. 2976
LASIT LASER DEUTSCHLAND GMBH—See El.En. S.p.A.; *Int'l*, pg. 2342
LASIT LASER IBERICA, S.L.—See El.En. S.p.A.; *Int'l*, pg. 2342
LASIT LASER POLSKA SP. Z O.O.—See El.En. S.p.A.; *Int'l*, pg. 2342
LATTICE SEMICONDUCTEURS SARL—See Lattice Semiconductor Corporation; *U.S. Public*, pg. 1294
LATTICE SEMICONDUCTOR CORPORATION; *U.S. Public*, pg. 1294
LATTICE SEMICONDUCTOR GMBH—See Lattice Semiconductor Corporation; *U.S. Public*, pg. 1294
LATTICE SEMICONDUCTOR JAPAN KK—See Lattice Semiconductor Corporation; *U.S. Public*, pg. 1294
LATTICE SEMICONDUCTOR K.K.—See Lattice Semiconductor Corporation; *U.S. Public*, pg. 1294
LATTICE SEMICONDUCTOR (PH) CORPORATION—See Lattice Semiconductor Corporation; *U.S. Public*, pg. 1294
LATTICE SEMICONDUCTOR (SHANGHAI) CO. LTD.—See Lattice Semiconductor Corporation; *U.S. Public*, pg. 1294
LATTICE SEMICONDUCTOR S.R.L.—See Lattice Semiconductor Corporation; *U.S. Public*, pg. 1294
LATTICE SEMICONDUCTOR UK LIMITED—See Lattice Semiconductor Corporation; *U.S. Public*, pg. 1294

LATTICE SG PTE. LTD.—See Lattice Semiconductor Corporation; *U.S. Public*, pg. 1294
LEADTECH CO., LTD.—See Helios Techno Holding Co., Ltd.; *Int'l*, pg. 3330
LESHAN-PHOENIX SEMICONDUCTOR CO., LTD.—See ON Semiconductor Corporation; *U.S. Public*, pg. 1600
LID TECHNOLOGIES INC.—See Amphenol Corporation; *U.S. Public*, pg. 130
LIGHTPATH TECHNOLOGIES, INC.; *U.S. Public*, pg. 1315
LINEAR TECHNOLOGY AB—See Analog Devices, Inc.; *U.S. Public*, pg. 135
LINEAR TECHNOLOGY GK—See Analog Devices, Inc.; *U.S. Public*, pg. 135
LINEAR TECHNOLOGY (ITALY) S.R.L.—See Analog Devices, Inc.; *U.S. Public*, pg. 135
LINEAR TECHNOLOGY K.K.—See Analog Devices, Inc.; *U.S. Public*, pg. 135
LINEAR TECHNOLOGY S.A.R.L.—See Analog Devices, Inc.; *U.S. Public*, pg. 135
LINEAR TECHNOLOGY SEMICONDUCTOR MEXICO S. DE R.L. DE C.V.—See Analog Devices, Inc.; *U.S. Public*, pg. 135
LINEAR TECHNOLOGY (U.K.) LTD.—See Analog Devices, Inc.; *U.S. Public*, pg. 135
LITI RESEARCH & DEVELOPMENT INC.—See KKR & Co. Inc.; *U.S. Public*, pg. 1259
LOGIC DEVICES INCORPORATED; *U.S. Private*, pg. 2481
LTRIM TECHNOLOGIES—See Constellation Software Inc.; *Int'l*, pg. 1774
LTX-CREDENCE ITALIA S.R.L.—See Cohu, Inc.; *U.S. Public*, pg. 530
LTX-CREDENCE SYSTEMS KK—See Cohu, Inc.; *U.S. Public*, pg. 530
LUMASENSE TECHNOLOGIES BENELUX B.V.—See Advanced Energy Industries, Inc.; *U.S. Public*, pg. 47
LUMEDYNE TECHNOLOGIES INCORPORATED—See Alphabet Inc.; *U.S. Public*, pg. 83
LUMILEDS LLC—See Apollo Global Management, Inc.; *U.S. Public*, pg. 153
LUMINA POWER, INC.—See HEICO Corporation; *U.S. Public*, pg. 1020
LUNAR INVESTMENT, LLC—See Enpro Inc.; *U.S. Public*, pg. 775
MACOM JAPAN LIMITED—See MACOM Technology Solutions Holdings, Inc.; *U.S. Public*, pg. 1352
MACOM TECHNOLOGY SOLUTIONS (BANGALORE) PRIVATE LIMITED—See MACOM Technology Solutions Holdings, Inc.; *U.S. Public*, pg. 1352
MACOM TECHNOLOGY SOLUTIONS CANADA INC—See MACOM Technology Solutions Holdings, Inc.; *U.S. Public*, pg. 1352
M/ACOM TECHNOLOGY SOLUTIONS (CORK) LIMITED—See MACOM Technology Solutions Holdings, Inc.; *U.S. Public*, pg. 1352
M/A-COM TECHNOLOGY SOLUTIONS INC.—See MA-COM Technology Solutions Holdings, Inc.; *U.S. Public*, pg. 1352
M/A-COM TECHNOLOGY SOLUTIONS (UK) LIMITED—See MACOM Technology Solutions Holdings, Inc.; *U.S. Public*, pg. 1352
MAGNOLIA SOLAR, INC.—See RiskOn International, Inc.; *U.S. Public*, pg. 1799
MAINBRIGHT ENTERPRISES LTD.—See Bright Led Electronics Corp.; *Int'l*, pg. 1161
MALAYSIAN SH ELECTRONICS SDN. BHD.—See Chang Wah Technology Co., Ltd.; *Int'l*, pg. 1441
MARLOW INDUSTRIES, INC.—See Coherent Corp.; *U.S. Public*, pg. 529
MARPORT AMERICAS, INC.—See Amphenol Corporation; *U.S. Public*, pg. 131
MARPORT EHF—See Amphenol Corporation; *U.S. Public*, pg. 131
MARPORT FRANCE SAS—See Amphenol Corporation; *U.S. Public*, pg. 131
MARPORT NORGE AS—See Amphenol Corporation; *U.S. Public*, pg. 131
MARPORT SOUTH AFRICA (PTY) LTD.—See Amphenol Corporation; *U.S. Public*, pg. 131
MARPORT SPAIN SL—See Amphenol Corporation; *U.S. Public*, pg. 131
MARPORT UK LTD.—See Amphenol Corporation; *U.S. Public*, pg. 131
MASIMO SEMICONDUCTOR, INC.—See Masimo Corporation; *U.S. Public*, pg. 1392
MATERION PRECISION OPTICS AND THIN FILM COATINGS CORPORATION—See Materion Corporation; *U.S. Public*, pg. 1395
MATTSON THERMAL PRODUCTS GMBH—See Beijing E-Town International Investment & Development Co., Ltd.; *Int'l*, pg. 949
MAXIM DIRECT—See Analog Devices, Inc.; *U.S. Public*, pg. 135
MAXIM INDIA INTEGRATED CIRCUIT DESIGN PVT LTD—See Analog Devices, Inc.; *U.S. Public*, pg. 135
MAXIM INTEGRATED PRODUCTS GMBH—See Analog Devices, Inc.; *U.S. Public*, pg. 135
MAXIM INTEGRATED PRODUCTS, INC.—See Analog Devices, Inc.; *U.S. Public*, pg. 135

MAXIM INTEGRATED PRODUCTS NETHERLANDS B.V.—See Analog Devices, Inc.; *U.S. Public*, pg. 135
MAXIM INTEGRATED PRODUCTS (THAILAND) CO., LTD.—See Analog Devices, Inc.; *U.S. Public*, pg. 135
MAXIM INTEGRATED PRODUCTS UK LIMITED—See Analog Devices, Inc.; *U.S. Public*, pg. 135
MAXIM INTEGRATED S.A.—See Analog Devices, Inc.; *U.S. Public*, pg. 136
MAXIM PHILIPPINES OPERATING CORPORATION—See Analog Devices, Inc.; *U.S. Public*, pg. 136
MAXIUM TECHNOLOGIES (SHANGHAI) INC.—See Hiyes International Co., Ltd.; *Int'l*, pg. 3427
MAXLINEAR HISPANIA, S.L.—See MaxLinear, Inc.; *U.S. Public*, pg. 1403
MAXLINEAR, INC.; *U.S. Public*, pg. 1402
MAXLINEAR JAPAN GK—See MaxLinear, Inc.; *U.S. Public*, pg. 1403
MAXLINEAR SHANGHAI LIMITED—See MaxLinear, Inc.; *U.S. Public*, pg. 1403
MAXLINEAR TECHNOLOGIES PRIVATE LIMITED—See MaxLinear, Inc.; *U.S. Public*, pg. 1403
MCG KINGSPORT, INC.—See Moog Inc.; *U.S. Public*, pg. 1469
MCT ASIA (PENANG) SDN BHD—See Cohu, Inc.; *U.S. Public*, pg. 530
MCT WORLDWIDE LLC - MALAYSIA FACILITY—See Cohu, Inc.; *U.S. Public*, pg. 530
MEGAHUNT TECHNOLOGIES INC.—See Hi Sun Technology (China) Limited; *Int'l*, pg. 3380
MEI LLC—See S&P Global Inc.; *U.S. Public*, pg. 1830
MEIVAC, INC.—See Ferrotec Holdings Corporation; *Int'l*, pg. 2643
MELLANOX TECHNOLOGIES, INC.—See NVIDIA Corporation; *U.S. Public*, pg. 1558
MELLANOX TECHNOLOGIES, LTD.—See NVIDIA Corporation; *U.S. Public*, pg. 1558
MEMC KUCHING SDN. BHD.—See SunEdison, Inc.; *U.S. Private*, pg. 3866
MEMC PASADENA, INC.—See SunEdison, Inc.; *U.S. Private*, pg. 3866
MEMSIC, INC.—See China Oceanwide Holdings Group Co., Ltd.; *Int'l*, pg. 1538
MEMSIC, INC.—See IDG Capital; *Int'l*, pg. 3594
MERIT SENSOR SYSTEMS, INC.—See Merit Medical Systems, Inc.; *U.S. Public*, pg. 1425
MESTA ELECTRONICS INC—See Hammond Power Solutions Inc.; *Int'l*, pg. 3239
METANOIA COMMUNICATIONS INC.—See ELAN Microelectronic Corp.; *Int'l*, pg. 2343
METRYX, LTD.—See Lam Research Corporation; *U.S. Public*, pg. 1290
MICROCHIP TECHNOLOGY INCORPORATED; *U.S. Public*, pg. 1436
MICROCHIP TECHNOLOGY (THAILAND) CO., LTD.—See Microchip Technology Incorporated; *U.S. Public*, pg. 1436
MICRO-CONTROLE SPECTRA-PHYSICS S.A.S.—See MKS Instruments, Inc.; *U.S. Public*, pg. 1453
MICRO ENGINEERING, INC.—See Solitron Devices, Inc.; *U.S. Public*, pg. 1901
MICRO INDUSTRIES CORPORATION; *U.S. Private*, pg. 2702
MICRON AKITA, INC.—See Micron Technology, Inc.; *U.S. Public*, pg. 1437
MICRON JAPAN, LTD.—See Micron Technology, Inc.; *U.S. Public*, pg. 1437
MICRON MEMORY JAPAN, INC.—See Micron Technology, Inc.; *U.S. Public*, pg. 1437
MICRON MEMORY TAIWAN CO., LTD.—See Micron Technology, Inc.; *U.S. Public*, pg. 1437
MICRON SEMICONDUCTOR KOREA CO., LTD.—See Micron Technology, Inc.; *U.S. Public*, pg. 1438
MICRON SEMICONDUCTOR (XIAMEN) CO., LTD.—See Micron Technology, Inc.; *U.S. Public*, pg. 1438
MICRON SEMICONDUCTOR (XI'AN) CO., LTD.—See Micron Technology, Inc.; *U.S. Public*, pg. 1438
MICRON TECHNOLOGY, INC.; *U.S. Public*, pg. 1437
MICRON TECHNOLOGY SERVICES, INC.—See Micron Technology, Inc.; *U.S. Public*, pg. 1438
MICRON TECHNOLOGY TEXAS, LLC—See Micron Technology, Inc.; *U.S. Public*, pg. 1438
MICROPAC INDUSTRIES INC.; *U.S. Public*, pg. 1438
MICROSEMI COMMUNICATIONS, INC.—See Microchip Technology Incorporated; *U.S. Public*, pg. 1436
MICROSEMI CORP. - ANALOG MIXED SIGNAL GROUP—See Microchip Technology Incorporated; *U.S. Public*, pg. 1436
MICROSEMI CORP. - MASSACHUSETTS—See Microchip Technology Incorporated; *U.S. Public*, pg. 1400
MICROSEMI CORP. - POWER PRODUCTS GROUP—See Microchip Technology Incorporated; *U.S. Public*, pg. 1436
MICROSEMI CORP. - RF POWER PRODUCTS—See Microchip Technology Incorporated; *U.S. Public*, pg. 1436
MICROSEMI CORP. - SCOTTSDALE—See Microchip Technology Incorporated; *U.S. Public*, pg. 1436
MICROSEMI SEMICONDUCTOR ULC—See Microchip Technology Incorporated; *U.S. Public*, pg. 1437

334413 — SEMICONDUCTOR AND R...

MICROSEMI SEMICONDUCTOR (U.S.) INC.—See Microchip Technology Incorporated; *U.S. Public*, pg. 1437
MICROSEMI STORAGE SOLUTIONS, INC.—See Microchip Technology Incorporated; *U.S. Public*, pg. 1437
MICROSENSE, LLC—See KLA Corporation; *U.S. Public*, pg. 1268
MICROSS MANCHESTER—See Behrman Brothers Management Corp.; *U.S. Private*, pg. 515
MICROWAVE TECHNOLOGY, INC.—See CML Microsystems Plc; *Int'l*, pg. 1671
MIMIX BROADBAND, INC.—See MACOM Technology Solutions Holdings, Inc.; *U.S. Public*, pg. 1352
MINDSPEED TECHNOLOGIES, INC.—See MACOM Technology Solutions Holdings, Inc.; *U.S. Public*, pg. 1352
MIRION TECHNOLOGIES (CANBERRA), INC.—See Mirion Technologies, Inc.; *U.S. Public*, pg. 1450
MISSON SOLAR LIMITED—See Foresight Solar Fund Limited; *Int'l*, pg. 2732
MIYOTA DEVELOPMENT CENTER OF AMERICA, INC.—See Citizen Watch Co., Ltd.; *Int'l*, pg. 1623
MJO INDUSTRIES, INC.; *U.S. Private*, pg. 2753
MOBIX LABS, INC.—See Mobix Labs, Inc.; *U.S. Public*, pg. 1454
MONOLITHIC POWER SPAIN, S.L.—See Monolithic Power Systems, Inc.; *U.S. Public*, pg. 1465
MONOLITHIC POWER SYSTEMS, INC.; *U.S. Public*, pg. 1464
MORGAN SOLAR INC.—See Enbridge Inc.; *Int'l*, pg. 2397
MPS EUROPE SARL—See Monolithic Power Systems, Inc.; *U.S. Public*, pg. 1464
MPS INTERNATIONAL KOREA CO., LTD.—See Monolithic Power Systems, Inc.; *U.S. Public*, pg. 1464
MPS INTERNATIONAL (SHANGHAI) LTD.—See Monolithic Power Systems, Inc.; *U.S. Public*, pg. 1464
MPS INTERNATIONAL (TAIWAN) LTD.—See Monolithic Power Systems, Inc.; *U.S. Public*, pg. 1464
MPS JAPAN K.K.—See Monolithic Power Systems, Inc.; *U.S. Public*, pg. 1464
MPS TECH SWITZERLAND SARL—See Monolithic Power Systems, Inc.; *U.S. Public*, pg. 1465
M.SETEK CO., LTD.—See AUO Corporation; *Int'l*, pg. 706
MULTITEST ELECTRONIC SYSTEMS (PENANG) SDN. BHD.—See Cohu, Inc.; *U.S. Public*, pg. 530
MULTITEST ELEKTRONISCHE SYSTEME GMBH—See Cohu, Inc.; *U.S. Public*, pg. 530
MUNDRA SOLAR TECHNOPARK PRIVATE LIMITED—See Adani Enterprises Limited; *Int'l*, pg. 125
MUSIC SEMICONDUCTORS PHILIPPINES, INC—See Greenergy Holdings Inc.; *Int'l*, pg. 3074
MU-TEST S.A.S.—See AEM Holdings Ltd.; *Int'l*, pg. 175
NANCHANG CREATIVE SENSOR TECHNOLOGY CO., LTD.—See Creative Sensor Inc.; *Int'l*, pg. 1833
NANJING DRAGON TREASURE BOAT DEVELOPMENT CO., LTD.—See ASTI Holdings Limited; *Int'l*, pg. 655
NANJING RENEWABLE ENERGY CO., LTD.—See China Sunergy Co., Ltd.; *Int'l*, pg. 1556
NANOMETRICS U.K. LTD.—See Onto Innovation Inc.; *U.S. Public*, pg. 1605
NANOTEC INTERNATIONAL GMBH—See Hanmi Semiconductor Co., Ltd.; *Int'l*, pg. 3256
NANTERO, INC.; *U.S. Private*, pg. 2833
NATEL ENGINEERING COMPANY, INC.; *U.S. Private*, pg. 2838
NATIONAL INSTRUMENTS DRESDEN GMBH—See National Instruments Corporation; *U.S. Private*, pg. 2857
NATIONAL SEMICONDUCTOR CORPORATION—See Texas Instruments Incorporated; *U.S. Public*, pg. 2025
NATIONAL SEMICONDUCTOR (MAINE), INC.—See Texas Instruments Incorporated; *U.S. Public*, pg. 2025
NATIONAL SEMICONDUTORES DA AMERICA DO SUL LTDA.—See Texas Instruments Incorporated; *U.S. Public*, pg. 2026
NATIONAL SEMICONDUTORES DO BRASIL LTDA.—See Texas Instruments Incorporated; *U.S. Public*, pg. 2026
NAVITAS SEMICONDUCTOR CORPORATION; *U.S. Public*, pg. 1500
NAVITAS SYSTEMS, LLC—See East Penn Manufacturing Co., Inc.; *U.S. Private*, pg. 1317
NCR FINANCIAL SOLUTIONS GROUP LTD.—See NCR Voyix Corporation; *U.S. Public*, pg. 1503
NEMICON CORPORATION—See Broadcom Inc.; *U.S. Public*, pg. 390
NEOMAGIC CORPORATION; *U.S. Public*, pg. 1506
NESTEK KOREA CO., LTD.—See AEM Holdings Ltd.; *Int'l*, pg. 175
NETLIST, INC.; *U.S. Public*, pg. 1508
NETRONOME, INC.; *U.S. Private*, pg. 2888
NEW ENGLAND LEAD BURNING CO.; *U.S. Private*, pg. 2894
NEXPLANAR CORPORATION—See Entegris, Inc.; *U.S. Public*, pg. 776
NG MICROSYSTEMS INDIA PVT. LTD.—See Trident Microsystems, Inc.; *U.S. Private*, pg. 4230
NIHON ENTEGRIS K.K.—See Entegris, Inc.; *U.S. Public*, pg. 777
NINGBO ANJI MICROELECTRONICS TECHNOLOGY CO., LTD.—See Anji Microelectronics Technology Shanghai Co., Ltd.; *Int'l*, pg. 472

NISHI TOKYO CHEMIX CORPORATION—See AICA Kogyo Company, Limited; *Int'l*, pg. 229
NITRIDE SOLUTIONS INC.; *U.S. Private*, pg. 2929
NOPTEL OY—See Herstal, S.A.; *Int'l*, pg. 3365
NORTH CAROLINA RENEWABLE PROPERTIES, LLC—See Duke Energy Corporation; *U.S. Public*, pg. 691
NORTH PENN TECHNOLOGY, INC.—See PMC Capital Partners, LLC; *U.S. Private*, pg. 3217
NOVAR CONTROLS CORPORATION—See Honeywell International Inc.; *U.S. Public*, pg. 1051
NVE CORPORATION; *U.S. Public*, pg. 1558
NVIDIA ARC GMBH—See NVIDIA Corporation; *U.S. Public*, pg. 1558
NVIDIA CORPORATION; *U.S. Public*, pg. 1558
NVIDIA DEVELOPMENT UK LIMITED—See NVIDIA Corporation; *U.S. Public*, pg. 1558
NVIDIA GK—See NVIDIA Corporation; *U.S. Public*, pg. 1558
NVIDIA SEMICONDUCTOR (SHENZHEN) CO., LTD.—See NVIDIA Corporation; *U.S. Public*, pg. 1558
NVIDIA TECHNOLOGY UK LIMITED—See NVIDIA Corporation; *U.S. Public*, pg. 1558
O2MICRO (CHINA) CO., LTD—See Forebright Capital Management Ltd.; *Int'l*, pg. 2731
O2MICRO INTERNATIONAL LTD.—See Forebright Capital Management Ltd.; *Int'l*, pg. 2731
ODYSSEY SEMICONDUCTOR TECHNOLOGIES, INC.—See Power Integrations, Inc.; *U.S. Public*, pg. 1705
OEM GROUP AUSTRIA—See OEM Group, Inc.; *U.S. Private*, pg. 2997
OEM GROUP JAPAN CO., LTD.—See OEM Group, Inc.; *U.S. Private*, pg. 2997
THE OHIO MOULDING CORPORATION - OMCO SOLAR DIVISION—See The Ohio Moulding Corporation; *U.S. Private*, pg. 4088
OHIZUMI MFG CO., LTD. - TOWADA PLANT—See Ferrotec Holdings Corporation; *Int'l*, pg. 2643
OHIZUMI MFG (THAILAND) CO., LTD.—See Ferrotec Holdings Corporation; *Int'l*, pg. 2643
OMEGA SEMICONDUCTOR SDN. BHD.—See D & Q Green Technologies Berhad; *Int'l*, pg. 1898
OMNICHIP SP. Z O.O.—See Atende S.A.; *Int'l*, pg. 668
OMNI-ID USA, INC.—See ASSA ABLOY AB; *Int'l*, pg. 637
OMNIVISION TECHNOLOGIES, INC.—See CITIC Group Corporation; *Int'l*, pg. 1619
OMNIVISION TECHNOLOGIES, INC.—See CITIC Securities Co., Ltd.; *Int'l*, pg. 1622
OMNIVISION TECHNOLOGIES, INC.—See Hua Capital Management Co., Ltd.; *Int'l*, pg. 3509
OMNIVISION TECHNOLOGIES SINGAPORE PTE. LTD—See CITIC Group Corporation; *Int'l*, pg. 1619
OMNIVISION TECHNOLOGIES SINGAPORE PTE. LTD—See CITIC Securities Co., Ltd.; *Int'l*, pg. 1622
OMNIVISION TECHNOLOGIES SINGAPORE PTE. LTD—See Hua Capital Management Co., Ltd.; *Int'l*, pg. 3509
ONETREE MICRODEVICES, INC.—See Analog Devices, Inc.; *U.S. Public*, pg. 136
ON SEMICONDUCTOR CONNECTIVITY SOLUTIONS, INC.—See ON Semiconductor Corporation; *U.S. Public*, pg. 1600
ON SEMICONDUCTOR CORPORATION; *U.S. Public*, pg. 1600
ON SEMICONDUCTOR CZECH REPUBLIC A.S.—See ON Semiconductor Corporation; *U.S. Public*, pg. 1600
ON SEMICONDUCTOR GERMANY GMBH—See ON Semiconductor Corporation; *U.S. Public*, pg. 1600
ON SEMICONDUCTOR HONG KONG DESIGN LTD.—See ON Semiconductor Corporation; *U.S. Public*, pg. 1600
ON SEMICONDUCTOR IMAGE SENSOR BVBA—See ON Semiconductor Corporation; *U.S. Public*, pg. 1600
ON SEMICONDUCTOR ITALY S.R.L—See ON Semiconductor Corporation; *U.S. Public*, pg. 1600
ON SEMICONDUCTOR LEASING BVBA—See ON Semiconductor Corporation; *U.S. Public*, pg. 1600
ON SEMICONDUCTOR SLOVAKIA A.S.—See ON Semiconductor Corporation; *U.S. Public*, pg. 1600
ON SEMICONDUCTOR—See ON Semiconductor Corporation; *U.S. Public*, pg. 1600
ON SEMICONDUCTOR—See ON Semiconductor Corporation; *U.S. Public*, pg. 1600
ON SEMICONDUCTOR SWITZERLAND S.A.—See ON Semiconductor Corporation; *U.S. Public*, pg. 1600
ON SEMICONDUCTOR TECHNOLOGY INDIA PRIVATE LIMITED—See ON Semiconductor Corporation; *U.S. Public*, pg. 1600
ON SEMICONDUCTOR TECHNOLOGY JAPAN LTD.—See ON Semiconductor Corporation; *U.S. Public*, pg. 1600
ONTO INNOVATION EUROPE, B.V.—See Onto Innovation Inc.; *U.S. Public*, pg. 1605
ONTO INNOVATION SOUTHEAST ASIA PTE. LIMITED—See Onto Innovation Inc.; *U.S. Public*, pg. 1605
OPTIZ INC.—See China Wafer Level CSP Co., Ltd.; *Int'l*, pg. 1562
ORBOTECH LT SOLAR, LLC—See KLA Corporation; *U.S. Public*, pg. 1268

OSI LASER DIODE, INC.—See OSI Systems, Inc.; *U.S. Public*, pg. 1621
OSI OPTOELECTRONICS INC.—See OSI Systems, Inc.; *U.S. Public*, pg. 1621
OSI OPTOELECTRONICS LIMITED.—See OSI Systems, Inc.; *U.S. Public*, pg. 1621
OSRAM CONTINENTAL ROMANIA S.R.L.—See ams AG; *Int'l*, pg. 438
OSRAM OPTO SEMICONDUCTORS, INC.—See ams AG; *Int'l*, pg. 439
OSRAM SL GMBH—See ams AG; *Int'l*, pg. 438
OTOSENSE INC.—See Analog Devices, Inc.; *U.S. Public*, pg. 136
PENGUIN SOLUTIONS, INC.; *U.S. Public*, pg. 1661
PERASO INC.; *U.S. Public*, pg. 1672
PFC FLEXIBLE CIRCUITS LIMITED—See OSI Systems, Inc.; *U.S. Public*, pg. 1622
PHOTOCHEMICAL CO., LTD.—See Hamamatsu Photonics K.K.; *Int'l*, pg. 3235
PHOTONIC SENSE GMBH—See Hellma GmbH & Co. KG; *Int'l*, pg. 3334
PHOTRONICS CALIFORNIA, INC.—See Photronics, Inc.; *U.S. Public*, pg. 1689
PHOTRONICS, INC.; *U.S. Public*, pg. 1689
PHOTRONICS KOREA, LTD.—See Photronics, Inc.; *U.S. Public*, pg. 1689
PHOTRONICS MZD, GMBH.—See Photronics, Inc.; *U.S. Public*, pg. 1689
PHOTRONICS SINGAPORE PTE, LTD.—See Photronics, Inc.; *U.S. Public*, pg. 1689
PHOTRONICS UK, LTD.—See Photronics, Inc.; *U.S. Public*, pg. 1689
PI-CRYSTAL INC.—See Daicel Corporation; *Int'l*, pg. 1919
PIXELWORKS CORPORATION—See Pixelworks, Inc.; *U.S. Public*, pg. 1695
PIXELWORKS, INC.; *U.S. Public*, pg. 1695
PIXELWORKS SEMICONDUCTOR TECHNOLOGY (SHANGHAI) CO. LTD.—See Pixelworks, Inc.; *U.S. Public*, pg. 1695
PIXELWORKS SEMICONDUCTOR TECHNOLOGY (TAIWAN) INC.—See Pixelworks, Inc.; *U.S. Public*, pg. 1696
PK, INC—See Photronics, Inc.; *U.S. Public*, pg. 1689
PKLT—See Photronics, Inc.; *U.S. Public*, pg. 1689
PLASMART, INC.—See MKS Instruments, Inc.; *U.S. Public*, pg. 1453
PLASMA-THERM, LLC; *U.S. Private*, pg. 3198
PNY TECHNOLOGIES, INC.; *U.S. Private*, pg. 3219
THE POWER HOUSE, INC.; *U.S. Private*, pg. 4097
POWER INTEGRATIONS (EUROPE) LIMITED—See Power Integrations, Inc.; *U.S. Public*, pg. 1705
POWER INTEGRATIONS GMBH—See Power Integrations, Inc.; *U.S. Public*, pg. 1705
POWER INTEGRATIONS, INC.; *U.S. Public*, pg. 1705
POWER INTEGRATIONS, K.K.—See Power Integrations, Inc.; *U.S. Public*, pg. 1705
POWER INTEGRATIONS SINGAPORE PTE. LIMITED—See Power Integrations, Inc.; *U.S. Public*, pg. 1705
PRAXAIR CHEMAX SEMICONDUCTOR MATERIALS CO., LTD.—See China Petrochemical Development Corp.; *Int'l*, pg. 1540
PRECISION SILICON JAPAN CO., LTD.—See Episil Precision Inc.; *Int'l*, pg. 2463
PRIMESTAR SOLAR, INC.—See General Electric Company; *U.S. Public*, pg. 919
PRISM SOLAR TECHNOLOGIES INCORPORATED—See Genie Energy Ltd.; *U.S. Public*, pg. 931
PROBE SPECIALISTS INC.—See Boston Semi Equipment LLC; *U.S. Private*, pg. 622
PSI TECHNOLOGIES HOLDINGS, INC.—See Ayala Corporation; *Int'l*, pg. 774
PTS PROGRESSIVE ENGINEERING CO., LTD.—See Hanmi Semiconductor Co., Ltd.; *Int'l*, pg. 3256
PULSETECH PRODUCTS CORPORATION; *U.S. Private*, pg. 3303
PURE WAFER INC.—See ZelnickMedia Corp.; *U.S. Private*, pg. 4600
PYRAMID SEMICONDUCTOR CORP.—See HEICO Corporation; *U.S. Public*, pg. 1020
Q-CELLS ASIA LTD.—See Hanwha Group; *Int'l*, pg. 3265
QORVO (BEIJING) CO., LTD.—See Qorvo, Inc.; *U.S. Public*, pg. 1743
QORVO CALIFORNIA, INC.—See Qorvo, Inc.; *U.S. Public*, pg. 1743
QORVO COSTA RICA S.R.L.—See Qorvo, Inc.; *U.S. Public*, pg. 1743
QORVO GERMANY HOLDING GMBH—See Qorvo, Inc.; *U.S. Public*, pg. 1743
QORVO JAPAN YK—See Qorvo, Inc.; *U.S. Public*, pg. 1743
QORVO KOREA LTD.—See Qorvo, Inc.; *U.S. Public*, pg. 1743
QORVO MUNICH GMBH—See Qorvo, Inc.; *U.S. Public*, pg. 1743
QORVO SHANGHAI LTD.—See Qorvo, Inc.; *U.S. Public*, pg. 1743
QORVO TEXAS, LLC—See Qorvo, Inc.; *U.S. Public*, pg. 1743

334413 — SEMICONDUCTOR AND R...

QORVO UK LIMITED—See Qorvo, Inc.; *U.S. Public*, pg. 1743

QUALCOMM ATHEROS HONG KONG—See QUALCOMM Incorporated; *U.S. Public*, pg. 1747

QUALCOMM ATHEROS, INC.—See QUALCOMM Incorporated; *U.S. Public*, pg. 1747

QUALCOMM ATHEROS TAIWAN—See QUALCOMM Incorporated; *U.S. Public*, pg. 1747

QUALCOMM ATHEROS TECHNOLOGY (MACAO COMMERCIAL OFFSHORE) LIMITED—See QUALCOMM Incorporated; *U.S. Public*, pg. 1747

QUALCOMM CDMA TECHNOLOGIES—See QUALCOMM Incorporated; *U.S. Public*, pg. 1747

QUALCOMM TECHNOLOGIES INTERNATIONAL, LTD.—See QUALCOMM Incorporated; *U.S. Public*, pg. 1748

QUALCOMM WIRELESS SEMI CONDUCTOR TECHNOLOGIES LIMITED—See QUALCOMM Incorporated; *U.S. Public*, pg. 1748

QUANTUM3D INC.—See Havelsan Hava Elektronik Sanayi ve Ticaret AS; *Int'l*, pg. 3287

QUANZHOU RAYNEN AUTOMATION TECHNOLOGY CO., LTD.—See Fujian Raynen Technology Co., Ltd.; *Int'l*, pg. 2819

QUICKLOGIC CORPORATION; *U.S. Public*, pg. 1756

QUICKLOGIC INTERNATIONAL INC.—See QuickLogic Corporation; *U.S. Public*, pg. 1756

QUICKLOGIC SOFTWARE (INDIA) PRIVATE LTD.—See QuickLogic Corporation; *U.S. Public*, pg. 1756

RAMBUS INC.; *U.S. Public*, pg. 1762

RAMBUS KOREA, INC.—See Rambus Inc.; *U.S. Public*, pg. 1762

RAPID BRIDGE LLC—See QUALCOMM Incorporated; *U.S. Public*, pg. 1747

RAYOTEK SCIENTIFIC, INC.—See Artemis Capital Partners Management Co., LLC; *U.S. Private*, pg. 341

RBI SOLAR KK—See Gibraltar Industries, Inc.; *U.S. Public*, pg. 936

R&D ALTANOVA, INC.—See Advantest Corporation; *Int'l*, pg. 166

REACTION TECHNOLOGY EPI, LLC—See Littelfuse, Inc.; *U.S. Public*, pg. 1327

REALIZE CO., LTD. - KITSUKI PLANT—See Future Innovation Group, Inc.; *Int'l*, pg. 2856

REC SITE SERVICES PTE LTD—See China National Chemical Corporation; *Int'l*, pg. 1527

REC SOLAR, INC.—See Duke Energy Corporation; *U.S. Public*, pg. 691

REC SOLAR PTE. LTD.—See China National Chemical Corporation; *Int'l*, pg. 1527

REGO S. DE R.L. DE C.V.—See Windjammer Capital Investors, LLC; *U.S. Private*, pg. 4537

REINHARDT MICROTECH GMBH—See Cicor Technologies Ltd.; *Int'l*, pg. 1603

REISEN ENERGY CO., LTD.—See AJ Advance Technology Public Company Limited; *Int'l*, pg. 255

RENARD MANUFACTURING CO. INC.—See Wetherill Associates Inc.; *U.S. Private*, pg. 4502

RENESOLA DEUTSCHLAND GMBH—See EMEREN GROUP LTD; *U.S. Public*, pg. 739

REVASUM, INC.; *U.S. Public*, pg. 1792

RF360 EUROPE GMBH—See QUALCOMM Incorporated; *U.S. Public*, pg. 1748

RHE MICROSYSTEMS GMBH—See Cicor Technologies Ltd.; *Int'l*, pg. 1603

ROCKETICK, INC.—See Cadence Design Systems, Inc.; *U.S. Public*, pg. 419

ROCKETICK TECHNOLOGIES LTD.—See Cadence Design Systems, Inc.; *U.S. Public*, pg. 419

ROFIN-BAASEL CHINA CO., LTD.—See Coherent Corp.; *U.S. Public*, pg. 527

ROFIN-BAASEL JAPAN CORP.—See Coherent Corp.; *U.S. Public*, pg. 527

ROFIN-BAASEL TAIWAN LTD.—See Coherent Corp.; *U.S. Public*, pg. 527

RP CONSTRUCTION SERVICES, LLC—See Quanta Services, Inc.; *U.S. Public*, pg. 1752

RSM ELECTRON POWER INC.; *U.S. Private*, pg. 3497

SAANKHYA LABS PVT. LTD.—See General Motors Company; *U.S. Public*, pg. 928

SABRE TECHNOLOGY HOLDINGS PTE. LTD.—See Sabre Corporation; *U.S. Public*, pg. 1833

SAINT-GOBAIN SOLAR S.R.L.—See Compagnie de Saint-Gobain SA; *Int'l*, pg. 1735

SAINT-GOBAIN SOLAR SYSTEMS S.A.—See Compagnie de Saint-Gobain SA; *Int'l*, pg. 1728

SAINT-GOBAIN SOLAR SYSTEMS SA—See Compagnie de Saint-Gobain SA; *Int'l*, pg. 1735

SANKALP SEMICONDUCTOR PRIVATE LIMITED—See HCL Technologies Ltd.; *Int'l*, pg. 3299

SANKALP USA INC.—See HCL Technologies Ltd.; *Int'l*, pg. 3299

SANKGUJ SEMICONDUCTOR PRIVATE LIMITED—See HCL Technologies Ltd.; *Int'l*, pg. 3299

SANYO SEMICONDUCTOR CO., LTD.—See ON Semiconductor Corporation; *U.S. Public*, pg. 1601

SANYO SEMICONDUCTOR MANUFACTURING PHILIPPINES CORPORATION—See ON Semiconductor Corporation; *U.S. Public*, pg. 1601

SANYO SEMICONDUCTOR (THAILAND) CO., LTD.—See ON Semiconductor Corporation; *U.S. Public*, pg. 1601

SCG CZECH DESIGN CENTER S.R.O.—See ON Semiconductor Corporation; *U.S. Public*, pg. 1601

SCG HONG KONG SAR LTD.—See ON Semiconductor Corporation; *U.S. Public*, pg. 1601

SCHOTT NORTH AMERICA., INC. - ELECTRONIC PACKAGING DIVISION—See Carl-Zeiss-Stiftung; *Int'l*, pg. 1337

SCHRADER-BRIDGEPORT INTERNATIONAL, INC.—See Sensata Technologies Holding plc; *U.S. Public*, pg. 1865

SCI ENGINEERED MATERIALS, INC.; *U.S. Public*, pg. 1848

SEA CHANGE ASIA PACIFIC OPERATIONS PTE. LTD.—See SeaChange International, Inc.; *U.S. Public*, pg. 1851

SEMCO INSTRUMENTS, INC.—See TransDigm Group Incorporated; *U.S. Public*, pg. 2183

SEMEQUIP, INC.—See 3M Company; *U.S. Public*, pg. 8

SEMICOA CORPORATION—See Vance Street Capital LLC; *U.S. Private*, pg. 4342

SEMICONDUCTOR COMPONENTS INDUSTRIES OF RHODE ISLAND, INC.—See ON Semiconductor Corporation; *U.S. Public*, pg. 1601

SEMICONDUCTOR COMPONENTS INDUSTRIES SINGAPORE PTE. LTD.—See ON Semiconductor Corporation; *U.S. Public*, pg. 1601

SEMTECH ADVANCED SYSTEMS INDIA PRIVATE LIMITED—See Semtech Corporation; *U.S. Public*, pg. 1864

SEMTECH CORPORATION; *U.S. Public*, pg. 1864

SEMTECH CORPUS CHRISTI S.A. DE C.V.—See Semtech Corporation; *U.S. Public*, pg. 1864

SEMTECH EMEA LIMITED—See Semtech Corporation; *U.S. Public*, pg. 1864

SEMTECH EUROPE LIMITED—See Semtech Corporation; *U.S. Public*, pg. 1864

SEMTECH GERMANY GMBH—See Semtech Corporation; *U.S. Public*, pg. 1864

SEMTECH (INTERNATIONAL) AG—See Semtech Corporation; *U.S. Public*, pg. 1864

SEMTECH LTD.—See Semtech Corporation; *U.S. Public*, pg. 1864

SEMTECH NETHERLANDS BV—See Semtech Corporation; *U.S. Public*, pg. 1864

SEMTECH SAN DIEGO—See Semtech Corporation; *U.S. Public*, pg. 1864

SEMTECH SEMICONDUCTOR (SHANGHAI) CO. LTD.—See Semtech Corporation; *U.S. Public*, pg. 1864

SEMTECH SEMICONDUCTOR (SHENZHEN) COMPANY LIMITED—See Semtech Corporation; *U.S. Public*, pg. 1864

SENDYNE CORP.—See Sensata Technologies Holding plc; *U.S. Public*, pg. 1865

SENSATA GERMANY GMBH—See Sensata Technologies Holding plc; *U.S. Public*, pg. 1866

SENSATA TECHNOLOGIES DE MEXICO S DE RL DE CV—See Sensata Technologies Holding plc; *U.S. Public*, pg. 1866

SENSCIENT, LTD.—See MSA Safety Incorporated; *U.S. Public*, pg. 1482

SENSL TECHNOLOGIES LIMITED—See ON Semiconductor Corporation; *U.S. Public*, pg. 1601

SENSOR KOGYO CO.,LTD. - GONOHE PLANT—See Ferrotec Holdings Corporation; *Int'l*, pg. 2643

SENSOR KOGYO CO., LTD. - HACHINOHE PLANT—See Ferrotec Holdings Corporation; *Int'l*, pg. 2643

SENSOR KOGYO CO., LTD.—See Ferrotec Holdings Corporation; *Int'l*, pg. 2643

SHANGHAI COMTEC SOLAR TECHNOLOGY CO., LTD.—See Comtec Solar Systems Group Limited; *Int'l*, pg. 1762

SHANGHAI KAIHONG ELECTRONIC CO., LTD.—See Diodes Incorporated; *U.S. Public*, pg. 667

SHANGHAI SHENHE THERMO-MAGNETICS CO., LTD. - PV MATERIAL DIVISION—See Ferrotec Holdings Corporation; *Int'l*, pg. 2643

SHANGHAI SHENHE THERMO-MAGNETICS CO., LTD. - SILICON MATERIAL DIVISION—See Ferrotec Holdings Corporation; *Int'l*, pg. 2643

SHARP SEMICONDUCTOR INDONESIA—See Hon Hai Precision Industry Co., Ltd.; *Int'l*, pg. 3459

SHELLBACK SEMICONDUCTOR TECHNOLOGY—See OEM Group, Inc.; *U.S. Private*, pg. 2997

SHENZHEN HAILIANG STORAGE PRODUCTS CO., LTD.—See Western Digital Corporation; *U.S. Public*, pg. 2355

SHOUGANG CONCORD TECHNOLOGY HOLDINGS LIMITED—See HNA International Investment Holdings Limited; *Int'l*, pg. 3433

SIEB & MEYER AG—See Fukuda Corporation; *Int'l*, pg. 2839

SIFIVE, INC.; *U.S. Private*, pg. 3648

SIGE SEMICONDUCTOR (EUROPE) LIMITED—See Skyworks Solutions, Inc.; *U.S. Public*, pg. 1893

SIGE SEMICONDUCTOR (U.S.), CORP.—See Skyworks Solutions, Inc.; *U.S. Public*, pg. 1893

SILFEX, INCORPORATED—See Lam Research Corporation; *U.S. Public*, pg. 1290

SILICONIX INCORPORATED—See Vishay Intertechnology, Inc.; *U.S. Public*, pg. 2302

SILICON LABORATORIES NORWAY AS—See Silicon Laboratories Inc.; *U.S. Public*, pg. 1880

SILICON POWER CORPORATION; *U.S. Private*, pg. 3652

SILICON STORAGE TECHNOLOGY INC.—See Microchip Technology Incorporated; *U.S. Public*, pg. 1437

SILICON TECHNOLOGY CORPORATION—See Carlit Co., Ltd.; *Int'l*, pg. 1338

SILICONWARE PRECISION INDUSTRIES CO., LTD. - CHANGHUA FACILITY—See ASE Technology Holding Co., Ltd.; *Int'l*, pg. 605

SILICONWARE PRECISION INDUSTRIES CO., LTD. - HSINCHU IG FACILITY—See ASE Technology Holding Co., Ltd.; *Int'l*, pg. 605

SILICONWARE PRECISION INDUSTRIES CO., LTD. - HSINCHU IIIG FACILITY—See ASE Technology Holding Co., Ltd.; *Int'l*, pg. 605

SILICONWARE PRECISION INDUSTRIES CO., LTD.—See ASE Technology Holding Co., Ltd.; *Int'l*, pg. 605

SILICONWARE TECHNOLOGY (SUZHOU) LIMITED—See ASE Technology Holding Co., Ltd.; *Int'l*, pg. 605

SILTERRA MALAYSIA SDN BHD—See Dagang NeXchange Berhad; *Int'l*, pg. 1912

SKYWATER TECHNOLOGY, INC.; *U.S. Public*, pg. 1893

SKYWORKS SOLUTIONS DE MEXICO, S. DE R.L. DE C.V.—See Skyworks Solutions, Inc.; *U.S. Public*, pg. 1893

SKYWORKS SOLUTIONS, INC.; *U.S. Public*, pg. 1893

SL LINK CO.,LTD.—See Fortune Oriental Company Limited; *Int'l*, pg. 2744

SMART MODULAR TECHNOLOGIES, INC.—See Penguin Solutions, Inc.; *U.S. Public*, pg. 1661

SMC JAPAN—See Microchip Technology Incorporated; *U.S. Public*, pg. 1437

SNJ ENTERPRISES, INC.—See Dometic Group AB; *Int'l*, pg. 2160

SNOWBUSH MEXICO S.A.P.I. DE C.V.—See Semtech Corporation; *U.S. Public*, pg. 1864

SOLAERO TECHNOLOGIES CORP.—See Rocket Lab USA, Inc.; *U.S. Public*, pg. 1804

SOLARDEC CVBA—See Deceuninck NV; *Int'l*, pg. 2000

SOLARFLARE COMMUNICATIONS, INC.—See Advanced Micro Devices, Inc.; *U.S. Public*, pg. 49

SOLAR QUARTZ TECHNOLOGIES, INC.; *U.S. Public*, pg. 1900

SOLID STATE DEVICES, INC.; *U.S. Private*, pg. 3709

SOLITRON DEVICES, INC.; *U.S. Public*, pg. 1901

SONICS, INC.; *U.S. Private*, pg. 3714

SOUND DESIGN TECHNOLOGIES LTD.—See ON Semiconductor Corporation; *U.S. Public*, pg. 1601

SPACE MICRO INC.—See Voyager Space Holdings, Inc.; *U.S. Private*, pg. 4414

SPARTON BECKWOOD, LLC—See Elbit Systems Limited; *Int'l*, pg. 2344

SPARTON BROOKSVILLE, LLC—See Elbit Systems Limited; *Int'l*, pg. 2344

SPECTRA7 MICROSYSTEMS INC.; *U.S. Public*, pg. 1915

SPECTROLAB INC.—See The Boeing Company; *U.S. Public*, pg. 2041

SPIRE CORPORATION; *U.S. Private*, pg. 3757

SPIRE TECHNOLOGIES PTE LTD—See ASTI Holdings Limited; *Int'l*, pg. 655

SPIRE TECHNOLOGIES (TAIWAN) LTD.—See ASTI Holdings Limited; *Int'l*, pg. 655

STARCHIPS TECHNOLOGY INC.—See ASE Technology Holding Co., Ltd.; *Int'l*, pg. 604

STELLA CHEMIFA SINGAPORE PTE. LTD.—See Hitachi, Ltd.; *Int'l*, pg. 3424

STRATOS INTERNATIONAL, INC.—See Emerson Electric Co.; *U.S. Public*, pg. 752

SUNEDISON SEMICONDUCTOR BV—See SunEdison, Inc.; *U.S. Private*, pg. 3867

SUNGEN INTERNATIONAL LIMITED—See Anwell Technologies Ltd.; *Int'l*, pg. 486

SUN MATERIALS TECHNOLOGY CO., LTD.—See China Ruyi Holdings Limited; *Int'l*, pg. 1549

SUNPOWER CORPORATION—See Enphase Energy, Inc.; *U.S. Public*, pg. 774

SUZHOU ENABLENCE PHOTONIC TECHNOLOGIES CO., LTD.—See Enablence Technologies Inc.; *Int'l*, pg. 2395

SUZHOU EPILEDS CO., LTD.—See Epileds Technologies, Inc.; *Int'l*, pg. 2460

SWEDISH MICROWAVE AB—See Beijer Alma AB; *Int'l*, pg. 943

SYNAPTICS JAPAN GK—See Synaptics Incorporated; *U.S. Public*, pg. 1969

SYNCOMM CORPORATION LTD.—See Alcor Micro Corporation Ltd.; *Int'l*, pg. 303

SYNCROMATICS CORP.—See Grupo Tecnologico e Industrial GMV, S.A.; *Int'l*, pg. 3135

SYSTEM GENERAL CORPORATION—See ON Semiconductor Corporation; *U.S. Public*, pg. 1601

SYSTEM SOLUTIONS CO., LTD.—See ON Semiconductor Corporation; *U.S. Public*, pg. 1601

TAICHUNG PHOTRONICS PHOTOMASK CO., LTD.—See

334413 — SEMICONDUCTOR AND R...

Photronics, Inc.; *U.S. Public,* pg. 1689
TAITRON COMPONENTS INCORPORATED E REPRESENTACOES DO BRASIL LTDA—See Taitron Components Incorporated; *U.S. Public,* pg. 1979
TAITRON COMPONENTS INCORPORATED TAIWAN—See Taitron Components Incorporated; *U.S. Public,* pg. 1979
TAITRON COMPONENTS MEXICO, S.A. DE C.V.—See Taitron Components Incorporated; *U.S. Public,* pg. 1979
TAIWAN DONGJIN SEMICHEM CO., LTD.—See Dongjin Semichem Co., Ltd.; *Int'l,* pg. 2168
TAIZHOU MINGXIN MICROELECTRONICS CO., LTD.—See Daheng New Epoch Technology, Inc.; *Int'l,* pg. 1913
TALUS MANUFACTURING, LTD.—See Lam Research Corporation; *U.S. Public,* pg. 1290
TDI-ENTERPRISE POWER SYSTEMS—See TDI Power Systems; *U.S. Private,* pg. 3944
TDI POWER SYSTEMS; *U.S. Private,* pg. 3944
TECHNETICS GROUP JAPAN LTD.—See Enpro Inc.; *U.S. Public,* pg. 775
TECHNIC (SUZHOU) SEMICONDUCTOR ENGINEERING CO., LTD—See Technic Incorporated; *U.S. Private,* pg. 3953
TECHPOINT, INC.; *U.S. Public,* pg. 1988
TECH SEMICONDUCTOR SINGAPORE PTE. LTD.—See Canon Inc.; *Int'l,* pg. 1296
TEK INDIA—See Hanmi Semiconductor Co., Ltd.; *Int'l,* pg. 3256
TELEDYNE DALSA, INC.—See Teledyne Technologies Incorporated; *U.S. Public,* pg. 1993
TELEDYNE MICROELECTRONIC TECHNOLOGIES—See Teledyne Technologies Incorporated; *U.S. Public,* pg. 1994
TELFORD INDUSTRIES PTE LTD—See ASTI Holdings Limited; *Int'l,* pg. 655
TELFORD SERVICE (MELAKA) SDN. BHD.—See ASTI Holdings Limited; *Int'l,* pg. 655
TELFORD SERVICE SDN. BHD.—See ASTI Holdings Limited; *Int'l,* pg. 655
TELFORD SVC. PHILS., INC.—See ASTI Holdings Limited; *Int'l,* pg. 655
TELFORD TECHNOLOGIES (SHANGHAI) PTE LTD—See ASTI Holdings Limited; *Int'l,* pg. 655
TEL NEXX, INC.—See ASM INTERNATIONAL N.V.; *Int'l,* pg. 626
TEMPRESS SYSTEMS, INC.—See Amtech Systems, Inc.; *U.S. Public,* pg. 134
TERADYNE, INC.-INTEGRA TEST DIVISION—See Teradyne, Inc.; *U.S. Public,* pg. 2018
TERRA SOLAR NORTH AMERICA, INC.—See China Solar Energy Holdings Limited; *Int'l,* pg. 1552
TESNA INC. - ANSEONG FACTORY—See Doosan Tesna Inc; *Int'l,* pg. 2174
TESSERA, INC. - YOKOHAMA FACILITY—See Adeia Inc.; *U.S. Public,* pg. 41
TEXAS ADVANCED OPTOELECTRONIC SOLUTIONS, INC.—See ams AG; *Int'l,* pg. 440
TEXAS INSTRUMENTS AUSTIN INCORPORATED—See Texas Instruments Incorporated; *U.S. Public,* pg. 2026
TEXAS INSTRUMENTS AUSTRALIA PTY LIMITED—See Texas Instruments Incorporated; *U.S. Public,* pg. 2026
TEXAS INSTRUMENTS BUSINESS EXPANSION GMBH—See Texas Instruments Incorporated; *U.S. Public,* pg. 2026
TEXAS INSTRUMENTS CANADA LIMITED—See Texas Instruments Incorporated; *U.S. Public,* pg. 2026
TEXAS INSTRUMENTS FINLAND OY—See Texas Instruments Incorporated; *U.S. Public,* pg. 2026
TEXAS INSTRUMENTS INCORPORATED; *U.S. Public,* pg. 2025
TEXAS INSTRUMENTS (INDIA) PRIVATE LIMITED—See Texas Instruments Incorporated; *U.S. Public,* pg. 2026
TEXAS INSTRUMENTS JAPAN SEMICONDUCTOR LIMITED—See Texas Instruments Incorporated; *U.S. Public,* pg. 2026
TEXAS INSTRUMENTS MALAYSIA SDN. BHD.—See Texas Instruments Incorporated; *U.S. Public,* pg. 2026
TEXAS INSTRUMENTS MARKETING & FINANCE GMBH & CO. KG—See Texas Instruments Incorporated; *U.S. Public,* pg. 2026
TEXAS INSTRUMENTS MELBOURNE INCORPORATED—See Texas Instruments Incorporated; *U.S. Public,* pg. 2026
TEXAS INSTRUMENTS RUSSIA SALES OOO—See Texas Instruments Incorporated; *U.S. Public,* pg. 2026
TEXAS INSTRUMENTS SEMICONDUCTOR GROUP—See Texas Instruments Incorporated; *U.S. Public,* pg. 2026
TEXAS INSTRUMENTS SEMICONDUCTOR MANUFACTURING (CHENGDU) CO., LTD.—See Texas Instruments Incorporated; *U.S. Public,* pg. 2026
TEXAS INSTRUMENTS SEMICONDUCTOR TECHNOLOGIES (SHANGHAI) CO., LTD.—See Texas Instruments Incorporated; *U.S. Public,* pg. 2026
TEXAS INSTRUMENTS SINGAPORE (PTE.) LTD.—See Texas Instruments Incorporated; *U.S. Public,* pg. 2026
TEXAS INSTRUMENTS SUNNYVALE INCORPORATED—See Texas Instruments Incorporated; *U.S. Public,* pg. 2026

TEXAS INSTRUMENTS TUCSON CORPORATION—See Texas Instruments Incorporated; *U.S. Public,* pg. 2026
TEXAS INSTRUMENTS (UK) LIMITED—See Diodes Incorporated; *U.S. Public,* pg. 667
THINK SILICON RESEARCH & TECHNOLOGY SINGLE MEMBER S.A.—See Applied Materials, Inc.; *U.S. Public,* pg. 172
TIGO ENERGY MERGECO, INC—See Tigo Energy, Inc; *U.S. Public,* pg. 2158
TI (PHILIPPINES), INC.—See Texas Instruments Incorporated; *U.S. Public,* pg. 2026
TOHO KASEI CO., LTD.—See Daikin Industries, Ltd.; *Int'l,* pg. 1936
TOHOKU ALPS, CO., LTD.—See Alps Alpine Co., Ltd.; *Int'l,* pg. 376
TOPCO SCIENTIFIC (SHANGHAI) CO., LTD.—See Federmann Enterprises, Ltd.; *Int'l,* pg. 2631
TOP DYNAMIC ENTERPRISES LIMITED - DONGGUAN FACTORY—See Brainhole Technology Limited; *Int'l,* pg. 1137
TREBOR INTERNATIONAL, INC.—See IDEX Corp; *U.S. Public,* pg. 1092
TRIAD SEMICONDUCTOR; *U.S. Private,* pg. 4225
TRIDENT MICROELECTRONICS, LTD.—See Trident Microsystems, Inc.; *U.S. Private,* pg. 4230
TRIDENT MICROSYSTEMS (EUROPE) B.V.—See Trident Microsystems, Inc.; *U.S. Private,* pg. 4230
TRIDENT MICROSYSTEMS (EUROPE) GMBH—See Trident Microsystems, Inc.; *U.S. Private,* pg. 4230
TRINAMIX GMBH—See BASF SE; *Int'l,* pg. 885
TRINITY TECHNOLOGIES, INC.; *U.S. Public,* pg. 4235
TRINNO TECHNOLOGY CO., LTD.—See iA Inc.; *Int'l,* pg. 3568
TRIP TECHNOLOGIES, INC.; *U.S. Public,* pg. 2194
TRIUNE IP, LLC—See Semtech Corporation; *U.S. Public,* pg. 1864
TRIUNE SYSTEMS, LLC—See Semtech Corporation; *U.S. Public,* pg. 1864
TUYAR MIKROELEKTRONIK SANAYI VE TICARET ANONIM SIRKETI—See Aselsan Elektronik Sanayi Ve Ticaret AS; *Int'l,* pg. 606
TWILIGHT NOW, LLC—See Now Electronics; Inc.; *U.S. Private,* pg. 2968
TWILIGHT NOW, LLC—See Twilight Technology, Inc.; *U.S. Private,* pg. 4264
TWILIGHT TECHNOLOGY, INC.; *U.S. Private,* pg. 4264
ULTRA CLEAN ASIA PACIFIC, PTE LTD—See Ultra Clean Holdings, Inc.; *U.S. Public,* pg. 2223
ULTRA CLEAN TECHNOLOGY SYSTEMS AND SERVICE, INC.—See Ultra Clean Holdings, Inc.; *U.S. Public,* pg. 2223
UNIGEN CORPORATION; *U.S. Private,* pg. 4283
UNIKORN SEMICONDUCTOR CORPORATION—See Ennostar Inc.; *Int'l,* pg. 2444
UNITIVE ELECTRONICS INC.; *U.S. Private,* pg. 4302
UNITY SEMICONDUCTOR CORPORATION—See Rambus Inc.; *U.S. Public,* pg. 1762
UNIVERSAL DISPLAY CORPORATION; *U.S. Public,* pg. 2254
UNIVERSAL TECHNIC SAS—See Danaher Corporation; *U.S. Public,* pg. 631
US SENSOR SYSTEMS INC.—See Acorn Energy, Inc.; *U.S. Public,* pg. 36
UTAH STATE UNIVERSITY, SPACE DYNAMICS LABORATORY; *U.S. Private,* pg. 4324
UWIZ TECHNOLOGY CO., LTD.—See American Securities LLC; *U.S. Private,* pg. 252
VARIAN KOREA LTD.—See Applied Materials, Inc.; *U.S. Public,* pg. 173
VARIAN SEMICONDUCTOR EQUIPMENT ASSOCIATES PACRIM PTE. LTD.—See Applied Materials, Inc.; *U.S. Public,* pg. 172
VASCO DATA SECURITY NV/SA—See OneSpan Inc.; *U.S. Public,* pg. 1604
VEECO COMPOUND SEMICONDUCTOR INC.—See Veeco Instruments Inc.; *U.S. Public,* pg. 2276
VEECO INSTRUMENTS INC.; *U.S. Public,* pg. 2276
VEECO PRECISION SURFACE PROCESSING LLC—See Veeco Instruments Inc.; *U.S. Public,* pg. 2277
VEGA MESSTECHNIK AG—See Grieshaber Holding GmbH; *Int'l,* pg. 3083
VIAVI SOLUTIONS AB—See Viavi Solutions Inc.; *U.S. Public,* pg. 2295
VIAVI SOLUTIONS DEUTSCHLAND GMBH—See Viavi Solutions Inc.; *U.S. Public,* pg. 2295
VIAVI SOLUTIONS FRANCE SAS—See Viavi Solutions Inc.; *U.S. Public,* pg. 2295
VIAVI SOLUTIONS INC.; *U.S. Public,* pg. 2295
VIAVI SOLUTIONS ITALIA S.R.L.—See Viavi Solutions Inc.; *U.S. Public,* pg. 2295
VIAVI SOLUTIONS JAPAN K.K.—See Viavi Solutions Inc.; *U.S. Public,* pg. 2295
VIAVI SOLUTIONS SPAIN, S.A.—See Viavi Solutions Inc.; *U.S. Public,* pg. 2295
VICOR HONG KONG LTD.—See Vicor Corporation; *U.S. Public,* pg. 2296
VIOLIN MEMORY FEDERAL SYSTEMS, INC.—See Quantum Corporation; *U.S. Public,* pg. 1754

CORPORATE AFFILIATIONS

VIRTIUM TECHNOLOGY, INC.—See Court Square Capital Partners, L.P.; *U.S. Private,* pg. 1070
VISHAY BCCOMPONENTS BEYSCHLAG GMBH—See Vishay Intertechnology, Inc.; *U.S. Public,* pg. 2302
VISHAY GENERAL SEMICONDUCTOR OF TAIWAN, LTD.—See Vishay Intertechnology, Inc.; *U.S. Public,* pg. 2302
VISHAY HONG KONG LTD.—See Vishay Intertechnology, Inc.; *U.S. Public,* pg. 2303
VISHAY KOREA CO. LTD.—See Vishay Intertechnology, Inc.; *U.S. Public,* pg. 2303
VISHAY RESISTORS BELGIUM BVBA—See Vishay Intertechnology, Inc.; *U.S. Public,* pg. 2303
VISHAY SEMICONDUCTOR GES.MBH—See Vishay Intertechnology, Inc.; *U.S. Public,* pg. 2303
VISHAY SEMICONDUCTOR INDIA LTD.—See Vishay Intertechnology, Inc.; *U.S. Public,* pg. 2303
VIXAR INC.—See ams AG; *U.S. Public,* pg. 439
VIXS SYSTEMS INC.—See Pixelworks, Inc.; *U.S. Public,* pg. 1696
VSUN JAPAN CO., LTD.—See Abalance Corporation Ltd.; *Int'l,* pg. 48
WAFERING TECHNOLOGY CORPORATION—See GIGASTORAGE Corp.; *Int'l,* pg. 2972
WAFER SPACE SEMICONDUCTORS TECHNOLOGIES PVT. LTD.—See Alten S.A.; *Int'l,* pg. 391
WATT FUEL CELL CORP.; *U.S. Public,* pg. 4456
WEIHAI CHINA GLASS SOLAR COMPANY LIMITED—See China Glass Holdings Limited; *Int'l,* pg. 1504
WHI GLOBAL, LLC—See Rift Valley Equity Partners, LLC; *U.S. Private,* pg. 3435
WISA TECHNOLOGIES, INC.; *U.S. Public,* pg. 2376
WOLFSPEED, INC.; *U.S. Public,* pg. 2376
WOLFSPEED—See Wolfspeed, Inc.; *U.S. Public,* pg. 2377
WOOJIN ELECTRO-NITE INC.—See Heraeus Holding GmbH; *Int'l,* pg. 3358
WUXI CHINA RESOURCES HUAJING MICROELECTRONICS CO., LTD.—See China Resources (Holdings) Co., Ltd.; *Int'l,* pg. 1548
WUXI CREATIVE SENSOR TECHNOLOGY CO., LTD—See Creative Sensor Inc.; *Int'l,* pg. 1833
XCERRA CORPORATION - MILPITAS—See Cohu, Inc.; *U.S. Public,* pg. 530
XIAMEN SILAN ADVANCED COMPOUND SEMICONDUCTOR CO., LTD.—See Hangzhou Silan Microelectronics Co., Ltd.; *Int'l,* pg. 3250
XIAMEN SILAN MICROCHIP MANUFACTURING CO., LTD.—See Hangzhou Silan Microelectronics Co., Ltd.; *Int'l,* pg. 3250
XILINX BENELUX B.V.B.A.—See Advanced Micro Devices, Inc.; *U.S. Public,* pg. 49
XILINX DEVELOPMENT CORPORATION—See Advanced Micro Devices, Inc.; *U.S. Public,* pg. 49
XILINX GMBH—See Advanced Micro Devices, Inc.; *U.S. Public,* pg. 49
XILINX HONG KONG LIMITED—See Advanced Micro Devices, Inc.; *U.S. Public,* pg. 49
XILINX, INC.- ALBUQUERQUE—See Advanced Micro Devices, Inc.; *U.S. Public,* pg. 49
XILINX, INC.- LONGMONT—See Advanced Micro Devices, Inc.; *U.S. Public,* pg. 49
XILINX, INC.—See Advanced Micro Devices, Inc.; *U.S. Public,* pg. 48
XILINX INDIA TECHNOLOGY SERVICES PVT. LTD.—See Advanced Micro Devices, Inc.; *U.S. Public,* pg. 49
XILINX IRELAND—See Advanced Micro Devices, Inc.; *U.S. Public,* pg. 49
XILINX K.K.—See Advanced Micro Devices, Inc.; *U.S. Public,* pg. 49
XILINX LTD.—See Advanced Micro Devices, Inc.; *U.S. Public,* pg. 49
XINJIANG DAQO NEW ENERGY CO. LTD.—See Daqo New Energy Corp.; *Int'l,* pg. 1971
XINJIANG EASTERN HOSHINE SILICON INDUSTRY CO., LTD.—See Hoshine Silicon Industry Co., Ltd.; *Int'l,* pg. 3483
XINJIANG JINSONG SILICON INDUSTRY CO., LTD.—See Hoshine Silicon Industry Co., Ltd.; *Int'l,* pg. 3483
XINJIANG WESTERN HOSHINE SILICON INDUSTRY CO., LTD.—See Hoshine Silicon Industry Co., Ltd.; *Int'l,* pg. 3483
YANG TING TECH CO., LTD.—See ASE Technology Holding Co., Ltd.; *Int'l,* pg. 605
YEA SHIN TECHNOLOGY CO., LTD.—See Diodes Incorporated; *U.S. Public,* pg. 667
ZENTRI, INC.—See Silicon Laboratories Inc.; *U.S. Public,* pg. 1880
ZETEX INC.—See Diodes Incorporated; *U.S. Public,* pg. 667
ZHEJIANG YUHUI SOLAR ENERGY SOURCE CO., LTD.—See EMEREN GROUP LTD; *U.S. Public,* pg. 739
ZHONG SHAN ENOMOTO CO. LTD.—See Enomoto Co., Ltd.; *Int'l,* pg. 2444
ZHONGSHAN RUIKE NEW ENERGY CO., LTD.—See China Ming Yang Wind Power Group Limited; *Int'l,* pg. 1524
ZILOG INC.—See Littelfuse, Inc.; *U.S. Public,* pg. 1327
ZIPTRONIX, INC.—See Adeia Inc.; *U.S. Public,* pg. 41

N.A.I.C.S. INDEX

ZOLL MEDICAL ITALIA SRL—See Asahi Kasei Corporation; *Int'l*, pg. 598

334416 — CAPACITOR, RESISTOR, COIL, TRANSFORMER, AND OTHER INDUCTOR MANUFACTURING

ABB XI'AN POWER CAPACITOR COMPANY LIMITED—See ABB Ltd.; *Int'l*, pg. 49
ABCO ELECTRONICS CO., LTD.; *Int'l*, pg. 57
ABCO HUNGARY KFT—See ABCO Electronics Co., Ltd.; *Int'l*, pg. 57
ABCO SLOVAKIA SRO—See ABCO Electronics Co., Ltd.; *Int'l*, pg. 57
ADVANCE MOLD & MANUFACTURING INC.—See Flex Ltd.; *Int'l*, pg. 2703
AEM, INC; *U.S. Private*, pg. 117
AEROSPACE CH UAV CO., LTD.; *Int'l*, pg. 181
ALCON ELECTRONICS PVT. LTD.—See HEICO Corporation; *U.S. Public*, pg. 1019
ALFRED TRONSER GMBH; *Int'l*, pg. 317
ALPHA ELECTRONICS CORP.—See Vishay Precision Group, Inc.; *U.S. Public*, pg. 2303
ALSTOM BRASIL LTDA.—See Alstom S.A.; *Int'l*, pg. 380
ALTIUM B.V.—See Altium Limited; *Int'l*, pg. 393
AMERICA PRECISION INDUSTRY - SURFACE MOUNT DIVISION—See Danaher Corporation; *U.S. Public*, pg. 626
AMOTECH CO LTD; *Int'l*, pg. 430
AMOTECH CO., LTD. - VARISTOR DIVISION—See Amotech Co Ltd; *Int'l*, pg. 431
AMPHENOL THERMOMETRICS (UK) LIMITED—See Amphenol Corporation; *U.S. Public*, pg. 129
ANGSTROHM PRECISION, INC.—See Vishay Intertechnology, Inc.; *U.S. Public*, pg. 2302
ANHUI JUAN KUANG ELECTRIC CO., LTD.; *Int'l*, pg. 469
APAQ TECHNOLOGY CO., LTD.; *Int'l*, pg. 500
APAQ TECHNOLOGY CO., LTD. - WUXI FACTORY—See Apaq Technology Co., Ltd.; *Int'l*, pg. 501
ARCELORMITTAL SAGUNTO SL—See ArcelorMittal S.A.; *Int'l*, pg. 1
ARIZONA CAPACITORS, INC.—See Electro Technik Industries; *U.S. Private*, pg. 1354
THE ARNOLD ENGINEERING CO.—See Compass Diversified Holdings; *U.S. Public*, pg. 560
ARNOLD MAGNETIC TECHNOLOGIES CORPORATION—See Compass Diversified Holdings; *U.S. Public*, pg. 560
AUDIX HI-TECH INVESTMENT CO., LTD.—See Audix Corporation; *Int'l*, pg. 702
AUTOMATIC ELECTRIC EUROPE B.V.; *Int'l*, pg. 730
AVAAK, INC—See NETGEAR, Inc.; *U.S. Public*, pg. 1508
AVID SYSTEMS, INC.—See Symphony Technology Group, LLC; *U.S. Private*, pg. 3901
BADGER MAGNETICS, INC.; *U.S. Private*, pg. 424
BEEHIVE COILS LTD; *Int'l*, pg. 939
BEL FUSE EUROPE LTD.—See Bel Fuse Inc.; *U.S. Public*, pg. 292
BEL FUSE INC.; *U.S. Public*, pg. 292
BEL POWER (HANGZHOU) CO. LTD.—See Bel Fuse Inc.; *U.S. Public*, pg. 292
BEL STEWART S.R.O.—See Bel Fuse Inc.; *U.S. Public*, pg. 293
BEL TRANSFORMER INC.—See Bel Fuse Inc.; *U.S. Public*, pg. 293
BILPOWER LIMITED - BARODA UNIT—See Bilpower Limited; *Int'l*, pg. 1031
BILPOWER LTD - KANCHAD PLANT—See Bilpower Limited; *Int'l*, pg. 1031
BILPOWER LTD - UTTRANCHAL PLANT—See Bilpower Limited; *Int'l*, pg. 1031
BLUESCOPE COATED PRODUCTS LLC—See BlueScope Steel Limited; *Int'l*, pg. 1072
BOURNS DE MEXICO S DE RL DE CV—See Bourns, Inc.; *U.S. Private*, pg. 624
BREVE TUFVASSONS SP. Z O.O.—See Addtech AB; *Int'l*, pg. 132
BROMANCO BJORKGREN AB—See Amplex AB; *Int'l*, pg. 434
CADDOCK ELECTRONICS, INC.; *U.S. Private*, pg. 712
CADDOCK NETWORK DIVISION—See Caddock Electronics, Inc.; *U.S. Private*, pg. 712
CAL-COMP INDUSTRIA E COMERCIO DE ELETRONICOS E INFORMATICA LTD.—See Cal-Comp Electronics (Thailand) pcl; *Int'l*, pg. 1261
CAPXON ELECTRONIC INDUSTRIAL COMPANY LIMITED—See Capxon International Electronic Co Ltd; *Int'l*, pg. 1318
CAPXON ELECTRONIC (SHENZHEN) CO. LTD.—See Capxon International Electronic Co Ltd; *Int'l*, pg. 1318
CAP-XX LTD.; *Int'l*, pg. 1301
CARTE INTERNATIONAL INC.; *Int'l*, pg. 1348
C.D. ELECTRONICA DE MEXICO, S.A. DE C.V.—See Knowles Corporation; *U.S. Public*, pg. 1270
CEC-COILS SINGAPORE PTE LTD.—See CEC International Holdings Limited; *Int'l*, pg. 1372

CG POWER SYSTEMS BELGIUM NV—See Avantha Group; *Int'l*, pg. 736
CG POWER SYSTEMS IRELAND LTD.—See Avantha Group; *Int'l*, pg. 736
CHANT SINCERE CO., LTD.; *Int'l*, pg. 1446
CHINA POWER EQUIPMENT, INC.; *Int'l*, pg. 1542
CHINA TITANS ENERGY TECHNOLOGY GROUP CO., LTD.; *Int'l*, pg. 1559
CLOVER HITECHNOLOGY CO., LTD.; *Int'l*, pg. 1663
COILCRAFT, INC.; *U.S. Private*, pg. 964
COILS ELECTRONIC CO., LIMITED—See CEC International Holdings Limited; *Int'l*, pg. 1372
COILS ELECTRONIC (ZHONGSHAN) CO., LTD.—See CEC International Holdings Limited; *Int'l*, pg. 1372
COILS INC.; *U.S. Private*, pg. 964
COMET MECHANICAL EQUIPMENT (SHANGHAI) CO. LTD—See Comet Holding AG; *Int'l*, pg. 1710
COMET TECHNOLOGIES USA, INC. - PLASMA CONTROL TECHNOLOGIES—See Comet Holding AG; *Int'l*, pg. 1710
COMPONENTS CORPORATION OF AMERICA, INC.; *U.S. Private*, pg. 1002
COOPER POWER SYSTEMS, LLC - NACOGDOCHES PLANT—See Eaton Corporation plc; *Int'l*, pg. 2278
CORNELL DUBILIER ELECTRONICS, INC.—See Knowles Corporation; *U.S. Public*, pg. 1270
CORNELL DUBILIER MARKETING, INC.—See Knowles Corporation; *U.S. Public*, pg. 1270
CORRY MICRONICS, INC.—See Arcline Investment Management LP; *U.S. Private*, pg. 313
COTO TECHNOLOGY, INC.—See The Dyson-Kissner-Moran Corporation; *U.S. Private*, pg. 4024
COWELL FASHION CO., LTD.; *Int'l*, pg. 1822
CROWN JOY INTERNATIONAL LTD.—See FSP Technology Inc.; *Int'l*, pg. 2800
CTS AUTOMOTIVE—See CTS Corporation; *U.S. Public*, pg. 603
CURTISS-WRIGHT CONTROLS INTEGRATED SENSING—See Curtiss-Wright Corporation; *U.S. Public*, pg. 611
CUSTOM MAGNETICS, INC.; *U.S. Private*, pg. 1129
DAEJOO ELECTRONIC MATERIALS CO., LTD.; *Int'l*, pg. 1907
DAEWOO ELECTRONIC EQUIPMENT CO., LTD—See DAEWOO ELECTRONIC COMPONENTS Co, Ltd.; *Int'l*, pg. 1910
DAIHEN CORPORATION - CHITOSE PLANT—See Daihen Corporation; *Int'l*, pg. 1926
DAIHEN CORPORATION - KANEHIRA PLANT—See Daihen Corporation; *Int'l*, pg. 1926
DAIHEN CORPORATION - MIE PLANT—See Daihen Corporation; *Int'l*, pg. 1926
DAIHEN ELECTRIC CO., LTD.—See Daihen Corporation; *Int'l*, pg. 1926
DAIHEN ENGINEERING CO., LTD.—See Daihen Corporation; *Int'l*, pg. 1926
DAIHEN OTC (BEIJING) CO., LTD.—See Daihen Corporation; *Int'l*, pg. 1926
DAIHOKU INDUSTRY CO., LTD.—See Daihen Corporation; *Int'l*, pg. 1926
DATACON HUNGARY TERMELO KFT.—See BE Semiconductor Industries N.V.; *Int'l*, pg. 931
DAWONSYS CO., LTD.; *Int'l*, pg. 1984
DELTA ELECTRONICS (SWEDEN) AB—See Delta Electronics, Inc.; *Int'l*, pg. 2018
DELTA ENERGY SYSTEMS (INDIA) PRIVATE LTD.—See Delta Electronics, Inc.; *Int'l*, pg. 2018
DEXTER MAGNETIC TECHNOLOGIES, INC.—See Tinicum Enterprises, Inc.; *U.S. Private*, pg. 4174
DONGGUAN COILS ELECTRONIC CO. LTD.—See CEC International Holdings Limited; *Int'l*, pg. 1372
EAGLERIES JAPAN CO., LTD.—See Eaglerise Electric & Electronic (China) Co., Ltd.; *Int'l*, pg. 2266
EAGLERISE ELECTRIC & ELECTRONIC (CHINA) CO., LTD.; *Int'l*, pg. 2266
EAGLERISE ELECTRIC & ELECTRONIC (JIAN) CO., LTD.—See Eaglerise Electric & Electronic (China) Co., Ltd.; *Int'l*, pg. 2266
EAGLERISE-MAGROOTS TECHNOLOGY SHENZHEN CORPORATION LIMITED—See Eaglerise Electric & Electronic (China) Co., Ltd.; *Int'l*, pg. 2266
EAO FRANCE SAS—See EAO AG; *Int'l*, pg. 2267
EDOM TECHNOLOGY CO., LTD.; *Int'l*, pg. 2313
EFACEC USA, INC.—See Efacec Capital, SGPS, S.A.; *Int'l*, pg. 2318
EG POWER ELECTRONICS (INDIA) PVT. LTD.—See Amplex AB; *Int'l*, pg. 434
EKARAT ENGINEERING PUBLIC COMPANY LIMITED; *Int'l*, pg. 2338
ELCO LIMITED; *Int'l*, pg. 2345
ELECTRO TECHNIK INDUSTRIES; *U.S. Private*, pg. 1354
ELECTROTHERM INDIA LTD; *Int'l*, pg. 2354
ELECTRUM AUTOMATION AB—See Addtech AB; *Int'l*, pg. 133
ELEROM S.A. ROMAN; *Int'l*, pg. 2359
ELMA CO., LTD.—See Gunze Limited; *Int'l*, pg. 3185
EMEK ELEKTRIK ENDÜSTRISI A.S.; *Int'l*, pg. 2376
EMERSON NETWORK POWER SURGE PROTECTION,

INC.—See Vertiv Holdings Co; *U.S. Public*, pg. 2289
ENGTEK (THAILAND) CO., LTD.—See Giovanni Agnelli B.V.; *Int'l*, pg. 2978
ETAL GROUP AB—See Amplex AB; *Int'l*, pg. 434
EUROPTRONIC ELECTRONIC (SHENZHEN) CO., LTD.—See Europtronic Group Ltd.; *Int'l*, pg. 2557
EUROPTRONIC GROUP LTD.; *Int'l*, pg. 2557
EUROPTRONIC (SINGAPORE) PTE. LTD.—See Europtronic Group Ltd.; *Int'l*, pg. 2557
EUROPTRONIC (TAIWAN) IND. CORP.—See Europtronic Group Ltd.; *Int'l*, pg. 2557
EXA THERMOMETRICS INDIA PRIVATE LIMITED—See Amphenol Corporation; *U.S. Public*, pg. 130
EXXELIA SAS—See HEICO Corporation; *U.S. Public*, pg. 1019
FLUX A/S—See discoverIE Group plc; *Int'l*, pg. 2133
FLUX INTERNATIONAL LTD.—See discoverIE Group plc; *Int'l*, pg. 2133
FORTRESS SYSTEMS PTY LIMITED—See Halma plc; *Int'l*, pg. 3231
FOSHAN NORATEL ELECTRIC CO., LTD.—See discoverIE Group plc; *Int'l*, pg. 2133
FOSS FIBEROPTISK SYSTEMSALG AS—See discoverIE Group plc; *Int'l*, pg. 2133
FOSS FIBRE OPTICS S.R.O—See discoverIE Group plc; *Int'l*, pg. 2133
FSK (THAILAND) CO., LTD.—See Foster Electric Co., Ltd.; *Int'l*, pg. 2133
FUJIAN TORCH ELECTRON TECHNOLOGY CO., LTD.; *Int'l*, pg. 2820
FUNKWERK SECURITY COMMUNICATIONS GMBH—See Hormann Holding GmbH & Co. KG; *Int'l*, pg. 3479
GAOZHOU COILS ELECTRONIC CO. LTD.—See CEC International Holdings Limited; *Int'l*, pg. 1372
HAMMOND POWER SOLUTIONS, INC.; *U.S. Private*, pg. 1850
HA NOI TRANSFORMER MANUFACTURING & ELECTRIC MATERIAL JOINT STOCK COMPANY; *Int'l*, pg. 3201
HAN RYUK ELECTRONICS CO., LTD.—See Hokuriku Electric Industry Co., Ltd.; *Int'l*, pg. 3444
HDK (THAILAND) CO., LTD.—See Hokuriku Electric Industry Co., Ltd.; *Int'l*, pg. 3444
HNSPOWERTECH CORP.—See H&S HighTech Corp.; *Int'l*, pg. 3193
HOKUDEN (MALAYSIA) SDN. BHD.—See Hokuriku Electric Industry Co., Ltd.; *Int'l*, pg. 3444
HOKURIKU (DONGGUAN) CO., LTD - 2ND FACTORY—See Hokuriku Electric Industry Co., Ltd.; *Int'l*, pg. 3444
HOKURIKU ELECTRIC (GUANG DONG) CO., LTD. - 1ST FACTORY—See Hokuriku Electric Industry Co., Ltd.; *Int'l*, pg. 3445
HOKURIKU ELECTRIC INDUSTRY CO., LTD.; *Int'l*, pg. 3444
HOKURIKU (MALAYSIA), SDN. BHD.—See Hokuriku Electric Industry Co., Ltd.; *Int'l*, pg. 3445
HOLY STONE ENTERPRISE CO., LTD. - DONGGUAN PLANT—See Holy Stone Enterprise Co., Ltd.; *Int'l*, pg. 3454
HONEY HOPE HONESTY ENTERPRISE CO., LTD.; *Int'l*, pg. 3465
HORIBA UK LIMITED—See HORIBA Ltd; *Int'l*, pg. 3477
HOSIDEN SINGAPORE PTE. LTD.—See Hosiden Corporation; *Int'l*, pg. 3484
HUA JUNG ELECTRONICS (GUANG DONG) CO., LTD.—See Hua Jung Components Co., Ltd.; *Int'l*, pg. 3509
HUA JUNG ELECTRONICS (SHANGHAI) CO., LTD.—See Hua Jung Components Co., Ltd.; *Int'l*, pg. 3509
HUBBELL POWER SYSTEMS, INC. - WADSWORTH—See Hubbell Incorporated; *U.S. Public*, pg. 1067
HUNAN AIHUA GROUP CO., LTD.; *Int'l*, pg. 3531
HYOSUNG INDUSTRIAL PG—See Hyosung Corporation; *Int'l*, pg. 3551
HYTRONICS CORP.—See Electro Technik Industries; *U.S. Private*, pg. 1354
ILJIN ELECTRIC CO., LTD.—See Iljin Display Co., Ltd.; *Int'l*, pg. 3614
IMPULSERADAR SWEDEN AB—See Addtech AB; *Int'l*, pg. 134
INDUCTIVE TECHNOLOGIES, INC.—See Electro Technik Industries; *U.S. Private*, pg. 1354
INDUSTRIA ELETROMECANICA BALESTRO LTDA.—See Hubbell Incorporated; *U.S. Public*, pg. 1067
INTERNATIONAL COMPONENTS CORPORATION; *U.S. Private*, pg. 2116
IOXUS, INC.—See Systematic Power Solutions, LLC; *U.S. Private*, pg. 3907
JAMES ELECTRONICS INC.—See Custom Magnetics, Inc.; *U.S. Private*, pg. 1129
JENNINGS TECHNOLOGY—See ABB Ltd.; *Int'l*, pg. 52
JOHANSON DIELECTRICS, INC.; *U.S. Private*, pg. 2219
JOHANSON MANUFACTURING CORPORATION; *U.S. Private*, pg. 2219
JX NIPPON COIL CENTER CO., LTD.—See ENEOS Holdings, Inc.; *Int'l*, pg. 2416
KNOWLES CAZENOVIA INC.—See Knowles Corporation; *U.S. Public*, pg. 1270

334416 — CAPACITOR, RESISTOR...

KNOWLES CAZENOVIA—See Knowles Corporation; *U.S. Public*, pg. 1270
KNOWLES (UK) LTD—See Knowles Corporation; *U.S. Public*, pg. 1270
KOREA TRANSFORMER CO. LTD.—See Diamond Electric Mfg. Co., Ltd.; *Int'l*, pg. 2105
KUNSHAN YUAN MAO ELECTRONICS TECHNOLOGY CO., LTD.—See Global Brands Manufacture Ltd.; *Int'l*, pg. 2993
KURZ-KASCH WABASH—See Monomoy Capital Partners LLC; *U.S. Private*, pg. 2772
KYUHEN CO., INC.—See Daihen Corporation; *Int'l*, pg. 1926
LOGITECH (STREAMING MEDIA) SA—See Logitech International S.A.; *U.S. Public*, pg. 1341
MAGNETIKA, INC.; *U.S. Private*, pg. 2547
MARSHALL ELECTRIC CORPORATION; *U.S. Private*, pg. 2592
MD TECH PHILS., INC.—See Hokuriku Electric Industry Co., Ltd.; *Int'l*, pg. 3445
MICRO-OHM CORPORATION; *U.S. Private*, pg. 2702
MINI-SYSTEMS, INC.; *U.S. Private*, pg. 2742
MYRRA POWER SP ZOO—See discoverIE Group plc; *Int'l*, pg. 2133
MYRRA SAS—See discoverIE Group plc; *Int'l*, pg. 2133
NATIONAL ELECTRIC COIL; *U.S. Private*, pg. 2853
NESSCAP KOREA CO., LTD—See Tesla, Inc.; *U.S. Public*, pg. 2021
NIC COMPONENTS CORP.—See Arrow Electronics, Inc.; *U.S. Public*, pg. 199
NOARK ELECTRIC (EUROPE) S.R.O.—See Chint Group Corporation; *Int'l*, pg. 1571
NORATEL AS—See discoverIE Group plc; *Int'l*, pg. 2133
NORATEL DENMARK A/S—See discoverIE Group plc; *Int'l*, pg. 2133
NORATEL FINLAND OY—See discoverIE Group plc; *Int'l*, pg. 2133
NORATEL GERMANY AG—See discoverIE Group plc; *Int'l*, pg. 2133
NORATEL INDIA POWER COMPONENTS PVT LTD—See discoverIE Group plc; *Int'l*, pg. 2133
NORATEL INTERNATIONAL PVT LTD—See discoverIE Group plc; *Int'l*, pg. 2133
NORATEL NORTH AMERICA INC.—See discoverIE Group plc; *Int'l*, pg. 2133
NORATEL POWER ENGINEERING INC.—See discoverIE Group plc; *Int'l*, pg. 2133
NORATEL SP Z.O.O—See discoverIE Group plc; *Int'l*, pg. 2133
NORATEL SWEDEN AB—See discoverIE Group plc; *Int'l*, pg. 2133
NORATEL UK LTD—See discoverIE Group plc; *Int'l*, pg. 2133
NOVACAP LLC—See Dover Corporation; *U.S. Public*, pg. 682
ONYX POWER INC.—See Eaton Corporation plc; *Int'l*, pg. 2282
PARALLAX POWER SUPPLIES LLC; *U.S. Private*, pg. 3092
PIONEER POWER SOLUTIONS, INC.; *U.S. Public*, pg. 1693
PIONEER TRANSFORMERS LTD.—See Guggenheim Partners, LLC; *U.S. Private*, pg. 1812
PLITRON MANUFACTURING INCORPORATED—See discoverIE Group plc; *Int'l*, pg. 2133
PRECISION ELECTRONIC COIL MFG. CO.; *U.S. Private*, pg. 3244
PRINTED CIRCUITS INTERNATIONAL INCORPORATED—See Platinum Equity, LLC; *U.S. Private*, pg. 3206
PROCALY SAS—See Amphenol Corporation; *U.S. Public*, pg. 132
QORVO FLORIDA, INC.—See Qorvo, Inc.; *U.S. Public*, pg. 1743
QUALITY COILS INCORPORATED; *U.S. Private*, pg. 3318
RADYNE CORPORATION—See Indel, Inc.; *U.S. Private*, pg. 2055
RAYCOM ELECTRONICS, INC.—See Electro Technik Industries; *U.S. Private*, pg. 1354
RCD COMPONENTS INC.—See The Jordan Company, L.P.; *U.S. Private*, pg. 4063
RENCO ELECTRONICS INC.—See Standex International; *U.S. Public*, pg. 1930
RFI CORPORATION—See Advent International Corporation; *U.S. Private*, pg. 100
RICHEY CAPACITOR INC.; *U.S. Private*, pg. 3429
RIEDON, INC.; *U.S. Private*, pg. 3434
RIWISA AG, KUNSTSTOFFWERKE HAGGLINGEN—See Flex Ltd.; *Int'l*, pg. 2704
SAG HARBOR INDUSTRIES, INC.; *U.S. Private*, pg. 3525
S&C ELECTRIC (CHINA) COMPANY LTD.—See S&C Electric Company; *U.S. Private*, pg. 3512
S&C ELECTRIC EUROPE LTD.—See S&C Electric Company; *U.S. Private*, pg. 3513
S&C ELECTRIC MEXICANA, S. DE R.L. DE C.V.—See S&C Electric Company; *U.S. Private*, pg. 3513
SEI ELECTRONICS INC.; *U.S. Private*, pg. 3598
SHANGHAI EAGLERIES ELECTRIC & ELECTRONIC CO., LTD.—See Eaglerise Electric & Electronic (China) Co., Ltd.; *Int'l*, pg. 2266
SIGNAL TRANSFORMER CO., INC.—See Bel Fuse Inc.; *U.S. Public*, pg. 293
SONDERBORG VRKTOJSFABRIK A/S—See Flex Ltd.; *Int'l*, pg. 2704
SOUTH HAVEN COIL INC.—See Humphrey Products Corporation; *U.S. Private*, pg. 2007
SPECTRUM CONTROL DE MEXICO, S.A. DE C.V.—See Allient Inc.; *U.S. Public*, pg. 80
SPECTRUM CONTROL TECHNOLOGY INC.—See Allient Inc.; *U.S. Public*, pg. 80
STACOENERGY PRODUCTS CO.—See Components Corporation of America, Inc.; *U.S. Private*, pg. 1002
STANDEX ELECTRONICS, INC.—See Standex International; *U.S. Public*, pg. 1930
STONITE COIL CORPORATION; *U.S. Private*, pg. 3830
SUREFLEX, INC.—See The Eastern Company; *U.S. Public*, pg. 2069
SWIFT LEVIC MAGNETS—See Compass Diversified Holdings; *U.S. Public*, pg. 560
SYSTEMATIC POWER MANUFACTURING, LLC—See Systematic Power Solutions, LLC; *U.S. Private*, pg. 3907
TABUCHI ELECTRIC CO., LTD.—See Diamond Electric Mfg. Co., Ltd.; *Int'l*, pg. 2105
TABUCHI ELECTRIC COMPANY OF AMERICA—See Diamond Electric Mfg. Co., Ltd.; *Int'l*, pg. 2105
TABUCHI ELECTRIC U.K. LTD.—See Diamond Electric Mfg. Co., Ltd.; *Int'l*, pg. 2105
TAIPEI HOKURIKU ELECTRIC INDUSTRY CO., LTD.—See Hokuriku Electric Industry Co., Ltd.; *Int'l*, pg. 3445
TCI, LLC—See Allient Inc.; *U.S. Public*, pg. 80
TDI-CIRCUITEK—See TDI Power Systems; *U.S. Private*, pg. 3944
TELEDYNE E2V (UK) LIMITED—See Teledyne Technologies Incorporated; *U.S. Public*, pg. 1995
TIANJIN HANA INTERNATIONAL TRADING CO., LTD.—See ABCO Electronics Co., Ltd.; *Int'l*, pg. 57
TIANJIN HOKURIKU ELECTRIC INDUSTRY CO., LTD.—See Hokuriku Electric Industry Co., Ltd.; *Int'l*, pg. 3445
TONICHI FERRITE CO., LTD.—See CEC International Holdings Limited; *Int'l*, pg. 1372
TRAFO CZ, A.S.—See CEZ, a.s.; *Int'l*, pg. 1429
TRONSER, INC.—See Alfred Tronser GmbH; *Int'l*, pg. 317
TUFVASSONS TRANSFORMATOR AB—See Addtech AB; *Int'l*, pg. 135
U.S. SENSOR CORP.—See Littelfuse, Inc.; *U.S. Public*, pg. 1327
VICTOR MINING INDUSTRY GROUP, INC.; *U.S. Public*, pg. 2296
VISHAY AMERICAS, INC.—See Vishay Intertechnology, Inc.; *U.S. Public*, pg. 2302
VISHAY ELECTRONICA PORTUGAL LDA.—See Vishay Intertechnology, Inc.; *U.S. Public*, pg. 2303
VISHAY ELECTRONIC GMBH—See Vishay Intertechnology, Inc.; *U.S. Public*, pg. 2303
VISHAY ISRAEL LIMITED—See Vishay Intertechnology, Inc.; *U.S. Public*, pg. 2303
VISHAY LTD.—See Vishay Intertechnology, Inc.; *U.S. Public*, pg. 2303
VISHAY PRECISION FOIL, INC.—See Vishay Precision Group, Inc.; *U.S. Public*, pg. 2304
VISHAY S.A.—See Vishay Intertechnology, Inc.; *U.S. Public*, pg. 2303
WABASH TECHNOLOGIES, INC.—See Sensata Technologies Holding plc; *U.S. Public*, pg. 1866
WAHA ELECTRIC SUPPLY COMPANY OF SAUDI ARABIA—See Ali Zaid Al-Quraishi & Brothers Co.; *Int'l*, pg. 323
WATERLOO DE NOGALES, S.A. DE C.V.—See Fortune Brands Innovations, Inc.; *U.S. Public*, pg. 873
THE WINATIC CORP.—See Electro Technik Industries; *U.S. Private*, pg. 1354
ZHONGSHAN COILS METALWORK CO., LTD.—See CEC International Holdings Limited; *Int'l*, pg. 1372
ZHONGSHAN MYRRA ELECTRONIC CO., LTD.—See discoverIE Group plc; *Int'l*, pg. 2134

334417 — ELECTRONIC CONNECTOR MANUFACTURING

ABELCONN LLC; *U.S. Private*, pg. 37
ACES ELECTRONIC CO., LTD.; *Int'l*, pg. 102
ADO OPTRONIC CORP.; *Int'l*, pg. 152
AIRBORN INC.—See Koch Industries, Inc.; *U.S. Private*, pg. 2333
ALTIUM EUROPE GMBH—See Altium Limited; *Int'l*, pg. 393
ALTIUM INFORMATION TECHNOLOGY (SHANGHAI) CO., LTD.—See Altium Limited; *Int'l*, pg. 393
AMPHENOL AEROSPACE & INDUSTRIAL OPERATIONS—See Amphenol Corporation; *U.S. Public*, pg. 126
AMPHENOL AIR LB GMBH—See Amphenol Corporation; *U.S. Public*, pg. 128
AMPHENOL ASSEMBLETECH (XIAMEN) CO., LTD.—See Amphenol Corporation; *U.S. Public*, pg. 128
AMPHENOL AUSTRALIA PTY. LTD.—See Amphenol Corporation; *U.S. Public*, pg. 128
AMPHENOL (CHANGZHOU) ADVANCED CONNECTOR CO. LTD.—See Amphenol Corporation; *U.S. Public*, pg. 126
AMPHENOL CNT (XIAN) TECHNOLOGY CO., LTD.—See Amphenol Corporation; *U.S. Public*, pg. 127
AMPHENOL COMMERCIAL PRODUCTS (CHENGDU) CO. LTD.—See Amphenol Corporation; *U.S. Public*, pg. 127
AMPHENOL CONNEXUS AB—See Amphenol Corporation; *U.S. Public*, pg. 128
AMPHENOL CONNEXUS AEOU—See Amphenol Corporation; *U.S. Public*, pg. 128
AMPHENOL CONNEXUS OU—See Amphenol Corporation; *U.S. Public*, pg. 127
AMPHENOL CORPORATION; *U.S. Public*, pg. 126
AMPHENOL CUSTOM CABLE, INC.—See Amphenol Corporation; *U.S. Public*, pg. 128
AMPHENOL DAESHIN ELECTRONIC & PRECISION CO., LTD.—See Amphenol Corporation; *U.S. Public*, pg. 127
AMPHENOL DO BRASIL LTDA.—See Amphenol Corporation; *U.S. Public*, pg. 128
AMPHENOL EAST ASIA ELECTRONIC TECHNOLOGY (SHENZHEN) CO. LTD.—See Amphenol Corporation; *U.S. Public*, pg. 127
AMPHENOL EAST ASIA ELECT. TECH. SHENZHEN CO., LTD.—See Amphenol Corporation; *U.S. Public*, pg. 127
AMPHENOL FCI ASIA PTE. LTD.—See Amphenol Corporation; *U.S. Public*, pg. 127
AMPHENOL FCI BESANCON SA—See Amphenol Corporation; *U.S. Public*, pg. 127
AMPHENOL FCI CONNECTORS SINGAPORE PTE LTD - THAILAND REPRESENTATIVE OFFICE—See Amphenol Corporation; *U.S. Public*, pg. 127
AMPHENOL FIBER TECHNOLOGY (SHENZHEN) CO., LTD.—See Amphenol Corporation; *U.S. Public*, pg. 127
AMPHENOL FILEC, S.A.S.—See Amphenol Corporation; *U.S. Public*, pg. 127
AMPHENOL INTERCONNECT INDIA PRIVATE LIMITED—See Amphenol Corporation; *U.S. Public*, pg. 128
AMPHENOL INTERNATIONAL MILITARY AEROSPACE & INDUSTRIAL OPERATIONS—See Amphenol Corporation; *U.S. Public*, pg. 128
AMPHENOL JAPAN, LTD.—See Amphenol Corporation; *U.S. Public*, pg. 128
AMPHENOL KAI JACK (SHENAHEN) CO. LTD.—See Amphenol Corporation; *U.S. Public*, pg. 128
AMPHENOL LIMITED—See Amphenol Corporation; *U.S. Public*, pg. 128
AMPHENOL MALAYSIA SDN BHD—See Amphenol Corporation; *U.S. Public*, pg. 128
AMPHENOL MCP KOREA LIMITED—See Amphenol Corporation; *U.S. Public*, pg. 128
AMPHENOL MOBILE CONNECTOR SOLUTIONS (CHANGZHOU) CO., LTD.—See Amphenol Corporation; *U.S. Public*, pg. 128
AMPHENOL MOBILE CONSUMER PRODUCTS GROUP—See Amphenol Corporation; *U.S. Public*, pg. 128
AMPHENOL OMNICONNECT INDAI PRIVATE LIMITED—See Amphenol Corporation; *U.S. Public*, pg. 128
AMPHENOL PCD INC.—See Amphenol Corporation; *U.S. Public*, pg. 128
AMPHENOL PCD (SHENZHEN) CO., LTD.—See Amphenol Corporation; *U.S. Public*, pg. 128
AMPHENOL TAIWAN CORP.—See Amphenol Corporation; *U.S. Public*, pg. 128
AMPHENOL TCS DE MEXICO S.A. DE C.V.—See Amphenol Corporation; *U.S. Public*, pg. 129
AMPHENOL TCS IRELAND LTD.—See Amphenol Corporation; *U.S. Public*, pg. 129
AMPHENOL TCS (MALAYSIA) SDN BHD—See Amphenol Corporation; *U.S. Public*, pg. 129
AMPHENOL TCS SDN BHD—See Amphenol Corporation; *U.S. Public*, pg. 129
AMPHENOL TCS—See Amphenol Corporation; *U.S. Public*, pg. 129
AMPHENOL TECHNOLOGY (SHENZHEN) CO. LTD.—See Amphenol Corporation; *U.S. Public*, pg. 127
AMPHENOL TECVOX LLC—See Amphenol Corporation; *U.S. Public*, pg. 129
AMPHENOL-TFC (CHANGZHOU) COMMUNICATIONS EQUIPMENT CO., LTD.—See Amphenol Corporation; *U.S. Public*, pg. 132
AMPHENOL TFC DO BRASIL LTDA.—See Amphenol Corporation; *U.S. Public*, pg. 132
AMPHENOL TIANJIN CO. LTD.—See Amphenol Corporation; *U.S. Public*, pg. 129
AMPHENOL-TUCHEL ELECTRONICS GMBH—See Amphenol Corporation; *U.S. Public*, pg. 129
ANT PRECISION INDUSTRY CO., LTD.; *Int'l*, pg. 479
ANYTEK TECHNOLOGY CORPORATION LTD—See Amphenol Corporation; *U.S. Public*, pg. 129
ASMPT GMBH & CO. KG; *Int'l*, pg. 628
AUTOMOTIVE ELECTRONIC CONTROLS—See Methode Electronics, Inc.; *U.S. Public*, pg. 1428

N.A.I.C.S. INDEX

334417 — ELECTRONIC CONNECTO...

AVIC FORSTAR SCIENCE & TECHNOLOGY CO., LTD.—See Aviation Industry Corporation of China; *Int'l*, pg. 741
AVIEL ELECTRONICS—See RF Industries, Ltd.; *U.S. Public*, pg. 1796
B&B ELECTRONICS MANUFACTURING COMPANY; *U.S. Private*, pg. 417
BEIJING ZOHETEC CO., LTD; *Int'l*, pg. 961
BEL CONNECTOR INC.—See Bel Fuse Inc.; *U.S. Public*, pg. 292
BEL STEWART CONNECTOR SYSTEMS, INC.—See Bel Fuse Inc.; *U.S. Public*, pg. 293
BERND RICHTER GMBH—See Amphenol Corporation; *U.S. Public*, pg. 129
BERND RICHTER U.S.A., INC.—See Amphenol Corporation; *U.S. Public*, pg. 129
BEST CHIPS CO., LTD.; *Int'l*, pg. 998
BTSR INTERNATIONAL S.P.A.; *Int'l*, pg. 1206
BURNDY LLC—See Hubbell Incorporated; *U.S. Public*, pg. 1066
CABLE CORPORATION OF INDIA LTD.; *Int'l*, pg. 1246
CABLESCAN B.V.—See Amphenol Corporation; *U.S. Public*, pg. 129
CABLESCAN LIMITED—See Amphenol Corporation; *U.S. Public*, pg. 129
CANARE CORPORATION OF KOREA—See Canare Electric Co., Ltd.; *Int'l*, pg. 1288
CANARE CORPORATION—See Canare Electric Co., Ltd.; *Int'l*, pg. 1288
CANARE ELECTRIC CORPORATION OF TIANJIN CO., LTD.—See Canare Electric Co., Ltd.; *Int'l*, pg. 1288
CANARE ELECTRIC INDIA PRIVATE LIMITED—See Canare Electric Co., Ltd.; *Int'l*, pg. 1288
CANARE ELECTRIC (SHANGHAI) CO., LTD.—See Canare Electric Co., Ltd.; *Int'l*, pg. 1288
CANARE EUROPE GMBH—See Canare Electric Co., Ltd.; *Int'l*, pg. 1288
CANARE MIDDLE EAST FZCO—See Canare Electric Co., Ltd.; *Int'l*, pg. 1288
CANARE SINGAPORE PRIVATE LIMITED—See Canare Electric Co., Ltd.; *Int'l*, pg. 1288
CASCO AUTOMOTIVE SINGAPORE PTE., LTD.—See Amphenol Corporation; *U.S. Public*, pg. 129
CASCO DO BRASIL LTDA—See Amphenol Corporation; *U.S. Public*, pg. 129
CELLULARLINE SPA; *Int'l*, pg. 1395
CHENG EUI PRECISION INDUSTRY CO., LTD.; *Int'l*, pg. 1465
CHINA HOSIDEN CO., LTD.—See Hosiden Corporation; *Int'l*, pg. 3484
CHINA RESOURCES MICROELECTRONICS LTD.—See China Resources (Holdings) Co., Ltd.; *Int'l*, pg. 1548
CINCH CONNECTIVITY SOLUTIONS - WASECA—See Bel Fuse Inc.; *U.S. Public*, pg. 293
CINCH CONNECTORS DE MEXICO, S.A. DE C.V.—See Bel Fuse Inc.; *U.S. Public*, pg. 293
CINCH CONNECTORS INC.—See Bel Fuse Inc.; *U.S. Public*, pg. 293
CINCH CONNECTORS LTD.—See Bel Fuse Inc.; *U.S. Public*, pg. 293
CLEMENTS NATIONAL COMPANY—See Aptiv PLC; *Int'l*, pg. 526
CMP PRODUCTS LIMITED—See British Engines Ltd.; *Int'l*, pg. 1171
CNERGENZ BERHAD; *Int'l*, pg. 1673
CNPLUS CO., LTD.; *Int'l*, pg. 1678
COMPONENTA USA, LLC—See Componenta Corporation; *Int'l*, pg. 1753
CONCRAFT HOLDING CO., LTD.; *Int'l*, pg. 1765
CONCRAFT PRECISION ELECTRONIC (BAOYING) CO., LTD.—See Concraft Holding Co., Ltd.; *Int'l*, pg. 1765
CONCRAFT PRECISION INDUSTRIAL CO., LTD.—See Concraft Holding Co., Ltd.; *Int'l*, pg. 1765
CONNECTRONICS CORP.—See HEICO Corporation; *U.S. Public*, pg. 1020
CONTEC EMS CO., LTD.—See Daifuku Co., Ltd.; *Int'l*, pg. 1925
COOPER INTERCONNECT, INC. - CAMARILLO—See Eaton Corporation plc; *Int'l*, pg. 2278
COOPER INTERCONNECT, INC. - LA GRANGE—See Eaton Corporation plc; *Int'l*, pg. 2278
COOPER INTERCONNECT, INC. - MOORPARK—See Eaton Corporation plc; *Int'l*, pg. 2278
COOPER INTERCONNECT, INC.—See Eaton Corporation plc; *Int'l*, pg. 2278
COTTERLAZ JEAN S.A.S.—See Aalberts N.V.; *Int'l*, pg. 34
CRISTEK INTERCONNECTS, INC.—See Windjammer Capital Investors, LLC; *U.S. Private*, pg. 4537
CVD EQUIPMENT CORPORATION; *U.S. Public*, pg. 613
CVILUX CORPORATION; *Int'l*, pg. 1889
CVILUX ELECTRONICS (DONGGUAN) CO., LTD.—See CviLux Corporation; *Int'l*, pg. 1889
CVILUX KOREA CORPORATION—See CviLux Corporation; *Int'l*, pg. 1889
CVILUX LAO CO., LTD.—See CviLux Corporation; *Int'l*, pg. 1889
CVILUX SDN BHD—See CviLux Corporation; *Int'l*, pg. 1889
CVILUX TECHNOLOGY (SHENZHEN) CORPORATION—See CviLux Corporation; *Int'l*, pg. 1889
CVILUX USA CORPORATION—See CviLux Corporation; *Int'l*, pg. 1889
DAI-ICHI SEIKO CO., LTD. - OGORI PLANT—See I-PEX Inc.; *Int'l*, pg. 3564
DAI-ICHI SEIKO CO., LTD. - ONOJO PLANT—See I-PEX Inc.; *Int'l*, pg. 3564
DAI-ICHI SEIKO CO., LTD. - TACHIARAI PLANT—See I-PEX Inc.; *Int'l*, pg. 3564
DAI-ICHI SEIKO CO., LTD. - YAMANASHI PLANT—See I-PEX Inc.; *Int'l*, pg. 3564
DATAMATE DIVISION—See Methode Electronics, Inc.; *U.S. Public*, pg. 1428
DATAMATE PRODUCTS GROUP—See Methode Electronics, Inc.; *U.S. Public*, pg. 1428
DCX-CHOL ENTERPRISES, INC. - NEWVAC / DCX DIVISION—See DCX-CHOL Enterprises, Inc.; *U.S. Private*, pg. 1180
DCX-CHOL ENTERPRISES, INC. - SMI DIVISION—See DCX-CHOL Enterprises, Inc.; *U.S. Private*, pg. 1180
DDK LTD. - MOKA PLANT—See Fujikura Ltd.; *Int'l*, pg. 2827
DDK (SHANGHAI) LTD.—See Fujikura Ltd.; *Int'l*, pg. 2827
DDK (THAILAND) LTD.—See Fujikura Ltd.; *Int'l*, pg. 2827
DIELECTRIC SCIENCES, INC.—See HEICO Corporation; *U.S. Public*, pg. 1020
D'NONCE TECHNOLOGY BHD.; *Int'l*, pg. 1899
DONGGUAN JIAHONG ELECTRONICS CO., LTD.—See CHIALIN Precision Industrial Co., Ltd.; *Int'l*, pg. 1475
DONGGUAN MOLEX SOUTH-CHINA CONNECTOR CO. LTD.—See Koch Industries, Inc.; *U.S. Private*, pg. 2334
DONGGUAN QUNHAN ELECTRONICS CO.,LTD.—See CviLux Corporation; *Int'l*, pg. 1889
ED PRODUCTS LTD.—See Amphenol Corporation; *U.S. Public*, pg. 130
EDWIN DEUTGEN, KUNSTOFFTECHNIK GMBH—See Amphenol Corporation; *U.S. Public*, pg. 130
ELECTRONIC MANUFACTURING TECHNOLOGY, LLC—See Elbit Systems Limited; *Int'l*, pg. 2345
ELSA ERNI SYSTEM—See ERNI Electronics GmbH; *Int'l*, pg. 2494
ERNI ELECTRONICS GMBH; *Int'l*, pg. 2494
ERNI ELECTRONICS, INC.—See ERNI Electronics GmbH; *Int'l*, pg. 2494
ERNI ELECTRONIC SOLUTIONS GMBH—See FIDELITAS Industrieholding GmbH; *Int'l*, pg. 2654
ERNI ELECTRONICS (THAILAND) CO. LTD.—See ERNI Electronics GmbH; *Int'l*, pg. 2494
ESCHA BAUELEMENTE GMBH; *Int'l*, pg. 2501
EXCEL CELL ELECTRONIC CO., LTD.; *Int'l*, pg. 2577
FCI CONNECTOR MALAYSIA SDN. BHD.—See Amphenol Corporation; *U.S. Public*, pg. 127
FCI CONNECTORS HONG KONG LTD.—See Amphenol Corporation; *U.S. Public*, pg. 127
FCI CONNECTORS MALAYSIA SDN. BHD.—See Amphenol Corporation; *U.S. Public*, pg. 130
FCI CONNECTORS SWEDEN AB—See Amphenol Corporation; *U.S. Public*, pg. 127
FCI DEUTSCHLAND GMBH—See Amphenol Corporation; *U.S. Public*, pg. 127
FCI OEN CONNECTORS LTD—See Amphenol Corporation; *U.S. Public*, pg. 127
FCI USA LLC - AUTOMOTIVE—See Amphenol Corporation; *U.S. Public*, pg. 127
FCI USA LLC—See Amphenol Corporation; *U.S. Public*, pg. 127
FILCON ELECTRONIC GMBH—See Diploma PLC; *Int'l*, pg. 2128
FILCONN, INC.—See PEI-Genesis Inc.; *U.S. Private*, pg. 3130
FILEC-LECTRIC SARL—See Amphenol Corporation; *U.S. Public*, pg. 130
FLEXUS ELECTRONIC INC.—See Amphenol Corporation; *U.S. Public*, pg. 130
FLUKE NEDERLAND B.V.—See Fortive Corporation; *U.S. Public*, pg. 870
FOOSUNGTECH CO., LTD.—See Foosung Co., Ltd.; *Int'l*, pg. 2728
FOXCONN INTERCONNECT TECHNOLOGY JAPAN CO., LTD.—See Hon Hai Precision Industry Co., Ltd.; *Int'l*, pg. 3456
FUJIKURA PRECISION LTD.—See Fujikura Ltd.; *Int'l*, pg. 2828
GAMESMAN LTD.—See TransDigm Group Incorporated; *U.S. Public*, pg. 2180
GE AVIATION SYSTEMS LTD. - EASTLEIGH—See General Electric Company; *U.S. Public*, pg. 918
GEM TERMINAL IND. CO., LTD.; *Int'l*, pg. 2915
GOOCH & HOUSEGO (TORQUAY) LIMITED—See Gooch & Housego PLC; *Int'l*, pg. 3038
GUANGZHOU AMPHENOL SINCERE FLEX CIRCUITS CO. LTD.—See Amphenol Corporation; *U.S. Public*, pg. 127
HANGZHOU AMPHENOL PHOENIX TELECOM PARTS CO., LTD.—See Amphenol Corporation; *U.S. Public*, pg. 128
HFCL LIMITED; *Int'l*, pg. 3375
HIROSE ELECTRIC EUROPE B.V—See Hirose Electric Co., Ltd.; *Int'l*, pg. 3405
HIROSE ELECTRIC HONG KONG CO., LTD.—See Hirose Electric Co., Ltd.; *Int'l*, pg. 3405
HIROSE ELECTRIC HONG KONG TRADING CO., LTD.—See Hirose Electric Co., Ltd.; *Int'l*, pg. 3405
HIROSE ELECTRIC MALAYSIA SDN BHD—See Hirose Electric Co., Ltd.; *Int'l*, pg. 3405
HIROSE ELECTRIC SINGAPORE PTE.LTD—See Hirose Electric Co., Ltd.; *Int'l*, pg. 3405
HIROSE ELECTRIC TAIWAN CO., LTD.—See Hirose Electric Co., Ltd.; *Int'l*, pg. 3405
HIROSE ELECTRIC TRADING (SHANGHAI) CO., LTD.—See Hirose Electric Co., Ltd.; *Int'l*, pg. 3405
HIROSE ELECTRIC (U.S.A.), INC.—See Hirose Electric Co., Ltd.; *Int'l*, pg. 3405
HOLLAND ELECTRONICS, INC.—See Amphenol Corporation; *U.S. Public*, pg. 130
HONG RI DA TECHNOLOGY COMPANY LIMITED; *Int'l*, pg. 3469
HOSIDEN CORPORATION (M) SDN. BHD.—See Hosiden Corporation; *Int'l*, pg. 3484
HOYUAN GREEN ENERGY CO.,LTD; *Int'l*, pg. 3499
HST (HONGKONG) LTD—See Hirose Electric Co., Ltd.; *Int'l*, pg. 3405
IBIDEN FINLAND—See Ibiden Co., Ltd.; *Int'l*, pg. 3575
ICHINOSEKI HIROSE ELECTRIC CO., LTD.—See Hirose Electric Co., Ltd.; *Int'l*, pg. 3405
IDEAL ANDERSON TECHNOLOGIES (SHENZHEN) LTD.—See IDEAL Industries Inc.; *U.S. Private*, pg. 2036
IDEAL INDUSTRIES SAS—See IDEAL Industries Inc; *U.S. Private*, pg. 2036
IEH CORPORATION; *U.S. Public*, pg. 1094
INTRO CORP.—See Audax Group, Limited Partnership; *U.S. Private*, pg. 388
IONIX AEROSPACE LIMITED—See Amphenol Corporation; *U.S. Public*, pg. 130
IONIX SYSTEMS OU—See Amphenol Corporation; *U.S. Public*, pg. 130
I-SHENG ELECTRIC WIRE & CABLE CO., LTD. - I-SHENG MANUFACTURING (SONG GANG) FACTORY—See I-Sheng Electric Wire & Cable Co., Ltd.; *Int'l*, pg. 3565
ITT BIW CONNECTOR SYSTEMS, LLC—See ITT Inc.; *U.S. Public*, pg. 1177
ITT CANNON DE MEXICO S.A. DE C.V.—See ITT Inc.; *U.S. Public*, pg. 1177
ITT CANNON INTERNATIONAL, INC.—See ITT Inc.; *U.S. Public*, pg. 1177
ITT VEAM LLC—See ITT Inc.; *U.S. Public*, pg. 1178
JOHNSTECH INTERNATIONAL CORP.; *U.S. Private*, pg. 2229
JOSLYN SUNBANK COMPANY LLC—See TransDigm Group Incorporated; *U.S. Public*, pg. 2181
KE ELEKTRONIK GMBH—See Amphenol Corporation; *U.S. Public*, pg. 130
KE OSTROV-ELEKTRIK S.R.O.—See Amphenol Corporation; *U.S. Public*, pg. 130
KE OSTROV ELEKTRIK S.R.O.—See Amphenol Corporation; *U.S. Public*, pg. 130
KE OSTROV ELEKTRIK S.R.O.—See Amphenol Corporation; *U.S. Public*, pg. 130
KE PRESOV ELEKTRIK, S.R.O.—See Amphenol Corporation; *U.S. Public*, pg. 130
KNURR-SPEOTRA (S.E.A.) PTE. LTD.—See Vertiv Holdings Co; *U.S. Public*, pg. 2289
KOLLMORGEN CORPORATION—See Regal Rexnord Corporation; *U.S. Public*, pg. 1772
KONFEKTION E ELECTRONIK GMBH—See Amphenol Corporation; *U.S. Public*, pg. 130
KORIYAMA HIROSE ELECTRIC CO., LTD—See Hirose Electric Co., Ltd.; *Int'l*, pg. 3405
KUNSHAN DRAGONSTATE ELECTRONIC TECHNOLOGY CO., LTD.—See Concraft Holding Co., Ltd.; *Int'l*, pg. 1765
LAGUNA DAI-ICHI, INC.—See I-PEX Inc.; *Int'l*, pg. 3564
LAND WIN ELECTRONIC CORP.—See Koch Industries, Inc.; *U.S. Private*, pg. 2335
LESCO DISTRIBUTING; *U.S. Private*, pg. 2432
LINXENS—See Astorg Partners S.A.S.; *Int'l*, pg. 656
MELLANOX TECHNOLOGIES DENMARK A/S—See NVIDIA Corporation; *U.S. Public*, pg. 1558
MERITEC—See Ohio Associated Enterprises; *U.S. Private*, pg. 3003
MERRIMACK RIVER PRECISION INDUSTRIAL CORPORATION—See CX Technology Corporation; *Int'l*, pg. 1891
METHODE DEVELOPMENT COMPANY—See Methode Electronics, Inc.; *U.S. Public*, pg. 1428
METHODE ELECTRONICS ASIA PTE, LTD.—See Methode Electronics, Inc.; *U.S. Public*, pg. 1428
METHODE ELECTRONICS, INC.; *U.S. Public*, pg. 1428
METHODE ELECTRONICS INDIA, PRIVATE LTD.—See Methode Electronics, Inc.; *U.S. Public*, pg. 1428
METHODE ELECTRONICS IRELAND, LTD.—See Methode Electronics, Inc.; *U.S. Public*, pg. 1428
METHODE ELECTRONICS (SHANGHAI) CO. LTD.—See Methode Electronics, Inc.; *U.S. Public*, pg. 1428
METHODE ELECTRONICS—See Methode Electronics, Inc.; *U.S. Public*, pg. 1428
METHODE POWER SOLUTIONS GROUP—See Methode

334417 — ELECTRONIC CONNECTO...

Electronics, Inc.; *U.S. Public*, pg. 1428
MINCO SA—See Minco Products, Inc.; *U.S. Private*, pg. 2740
MOLEX BRAZIL LTDA.—See Koch Industries, Inc.; *U.S. Private*, pg. 2334
MOLEX ELECTRONICS LTD.—See Koch Industries, Inc.; *U.S. Private*, pg. 2334
MOLEX INTERCONNECT GMBH—See Koch Industries, Inc.; *U.S. Private*, pg. 2334
MOLEX INTERNATIONAL, INC.—See Koch Industries, Inc.; *U.S. Private*, pg. 2334
MOLEX IRELAND LTD.—See Koch Industries, Inc.; *U.S. Private*, pg. 2334
MOLEX KOREA CO., LTD.—See Koch Industries, Inc.; *U.S. Private*, pg. 2334
MOLEX LLC—See Koch Industries, Inc.; *U.S. Private*, pg. 2333
MOLEX S.A. DE C.V.—See Koch Industries, Inc.; *U.S. Private*, pg. 2335
MOLEX TAIWAN LTD.—See Koch Industries, Inc.; *U.S. Private*, pg. 2334
MOLEX ZETRONIC S.R.L. UNICO SOCIO—See Koch Industries, Inc.; *U.S. Private*, pg. 2334
NETWORK BUSINESS PRODUCTS—See Methode Electronics, Inc.; *U.S. Public*, pg. 1429
NEWTECH SCIENTIFIC TECHNOLOGY CORP.—See CHIALIN Precision Industrial Co., Ltd.; *Int'l*, pg. 1475
NSI INDUSTRIES, LLC—See Odyssey Investment Partners, LLC; *U.S. Private*, pg. 2995
OHIO ASSOCIATED ENTERPRISES; *U.S. Private*, pg. 3003
OPTERNUS COMPONENTS GMBH—See Hexatronic Group AB; *Int'l*, pg. 3371
OPTOKON D.O.O.—See Methode Electronics, Inc.; *U.S. Public*, pg. 1429
OPTOKON POLSKA SP. Z O.O.—See Methode Electronics, Inc.; *U.S. Public*, pg. 1429
PARAMETRIC TECHNOLOGY MEXICO, S.A. DE C.V.—See PTC Inc.; *U.S. Public*, pg. 1735
PARKER HANNIFIN AUTOMOTIVE CONNECTORS DO BRAZIL—See Parker Hannifin Corporation; *U.S. Public*, pg. 1645
PARKER HANNIFIN CONNECTORS, LTD.—See Parker Hannifin Corporation; *U.S. Public*, pg. 1645
PIHER SENSORS & CONTROLS S.A.—See Amphenol Corporation; *U.S. Public*, pg. 132
POLYMICRO TECHNOLOGIES, LLC—See Koch Industries, Inc.; *U.S. Private*, pg. 2335
POSITRONIC ASIA PTE LTD.—See Positronic Industries, Inc.; *U.S. Private*, pg. 3234
POSITRONIC INDUSTRIES CARIBE, INC.—See Positronic Industries, Inc.; *U.S. Private*, pg. 3234
POSITRONIC INDUSTRIES, INC.; *U.S. Private*, pg. 3234
POSITRONIC INDUSTRIES S.A.S.—See Positronic Industries, Inc.; *U.S. Private*, pg. 3234
POSITRONIC INTERCONNECTS PVT. LTD.—See Positronic Industries, Inc.; *U.S. Private*, pg. 3234
POSITRONIC JAPAN CO LTD—See Positronic Industries, Inc.; *U.S. Private*, pg. 3234
POST GLOVER LIFELINK INC.; *U.S. Private*, pg. 3234
PRECISION FIBER OPTICS LTD.—See Fujikura Ltd.; *Int'l*, pg. 2829
PROCOM A/S—See Amphenol Corporation; *U.S. Public*, pg. 132
P.T HIROSE ELECTRIC INDONESIA—See Hirose Electric Co., Ltd.; *Int'l*, pg. 3405
QUATECH, LLC—See B&B Electronics Manufacturing Company; *U.S. Private*, pg. 417
QUELL CORP.—See HEICO Corporation; *U.S. Public*, pg. 1020
RF CABLE ASSEMBLIES DIVISION—See RF Industries, Ltd.; *U.S. Public*, pg. 1796
RF CONNECTORS DIVISION—See RF Industries, Ltd.; *U.S. Public*, pg. 1796
RF INDUSTRIES, LTD.; *U.S. Public*, pg. 1795
ROCHESTER INDUSTRIAL CONTROL, INC.—See Cerberus Capital Management, L.P.; *U.S. Private*, pg. 838
SEALTRON INC.—See AMETEK, Inc.; *U.S. Public*, pg. 116
SEALTRON INC.—See AMETEK, Inc.; *U.S. Public*, pg. 116
SHANGHAI AMPHENOL AIRWAVE COMMUNICATION ELECTRONIC CO., LTD.—See Amphenol Corporation; *U.S. Public*, pg. 128
SHOGYO INTERNATIONAL CORPORATION; *U.S. Private*, pg. 3639
SIA OPTOKON BALTIC—See Methode Electronics, Inc.; *U.S. Public*, pg. 1429
SOLID SEALING TECHNOLOGY, INC.—See HEICO Corporation; *U.S. Public*, pg. 1021
SOURIAU S.A.S.—See TransDigm Group Incorporated; *U.S. Public*, pg. 2181
SOURIAU USA INC.—See TransDigm Group Incorporated; *U.S. Public*, pg. 2181
SPECTRA STRIP CABLE PRODUCTS—See Amphenol Corporation; *U.S. Public*, pg. 132
SPECTRA STRIP LTD.—See Amphenol Corporation; *U.S. Public*, pg. 132
SSI TECHNOLOGIES GMBH—See Amphenol Corporation; *U.S. Public*, pg. 132
SUZHOU CHIALIN PRECISION INDUSTRIAL CO., LTD.—See CHIALIN Precision Industrial Co., Ltd.; *Int'l*, pg. 1475
TEKA INTERCONNECTION SYSTEMS, INC.—See Blackstone Inc.; *U.S. Public*, pg. 355
TELECT DE MEXICO S. DE R.L. DE C.V.—See Amphenol Corporation; *U.S. Public*, pg. 132
TELEDYNE IMPULSE- PDM LTD.—See Teledyne Technologies Incorporated; *U.S. Public*, pg. 1993
TELEDYNE OIL & GAS—See Teledyne Technologies Incorporated; *U.S. Public*, pg. 1994
TELEDYNE REYNOLDS INC.—See Teledyne Technologies Incorporated; *U.S. Public*, pg. 1995
TFC SOUTH AMERICA S.A.—See Amphenol Corporation; *U.S. Public*, pg. 132
THAI DAI-ICHI SEIKO CO., LTD - THAI PLANT—See I-PEX Inc.; *Int'l*, pg. 3564
THOMAS & BETTS CORPORATION—See ABB Ltd.; *Int'l*, pg. 52
TIANJIN AMPHENOL KAE CO., LTD.—See Amphenol Corporation; *U.S. Public*, pg. 132
TRANSIGO LTD.—See Evolution AB; *Int'l*, pg. 2572
TR MANUFACTURING, LLC—See Corning Incorporated; *U.S. Public*, pg. 579
U-JIN CABLE INDUSTRIAL CO., LTD.—See Amphenol Corporation; *U.S. Public*, pg. 132
ULTRA ELECTRONICS ICE, INC.—See Advent International Corporation; *U.S. Private*, pg. 101
VIDEOJET TECHNOLOGIES LTD—See Danaher Corporation; *U.S. Public*, pg. 632
VIETNAM DAI-ICHI SEIKO CO., LTD. - VIETNAM PLANT—See I-PEX Inc.; *Int'l*, pg. 3564
WEH GMBH—See Fukuda Corporation; *Int'l*, pg. 2839
WORSWICK INDUSTRIES, INC.—See RF Industries, Ltd.; *U.S. Public*, pg. 1796

334418 — PRINTED CIRCUIT ASSEMBLY (ELECTRONIC ASSEMBLY) MANUFACTURING

3S PHOTONICS S.A.S - MARCOUSSIS—See Eurazeo SE; *Int'l*, pg. 2527
AAEON TECHNOLOGY GMBH—See ASUSTeK Computer Inc.; *Int'l*, pg. 663
ADCOTRON EMS INC.—See East West Manufacturing, LLC; *U.S. Private*, pg. 1318
ADVANCED ASSEMBLY LLC—See Summit Interconnect, Inc.; *U.S. Private*, pg. 3855
ADVANCED ENERGY INDUSTRIES, INC.; *U.S. Public*, pg. 46
ADVANCED ENERGY SINGAPORE, PTE. LTD.—See Advanced Energy Industries, Inc.; *U.S. Public*, pg. 47
ADVANCED INTEGRATED MANUFACTURING CORP. LTD.; *Int'l*, pg. 160
ADVANCED MANUFACTURING CORP SDN. BHD.—See Advanced Integrated Manufacturing Corp. Ltd.; *Int'l*, pg. 160
ADVANTECH EMBEDDED EPLATFORM GROUP—See Advantech Co., Ltd.; *Int'l*, pg. 164
AKM ELECTRONICS INDUSTRIAL (PANYU) LTD—See AKM Industrial Company Limited; *Int'l*, pg. 264
AKM ELECTRONIC TECHNOLOGY (SUZHOU) COMPANY LIMITED—See AKM Industrial Company Limited; *Int'l*, pg. 264
ALLCOM PRODUCTS LLC—See Oblong, Inc.; *U.S. Public*, pg. 1560
ALL FLEX FLEXIBLE CIRUITS, LLC—See Granite Equity Partners LLC; *U.S. Private*, pg. 1755
ALTIUM JAPAN KK—See Altium Limited; *Int'l*, pg. 393
AMDOCS CANADA, INC.—See Amdocs Limited; *Int'l*, pg. 419
AMDOCS FRANCE—See Amdocs Limited; *Int'l*, pg. 419
AMERICAN COMPUTER DEVELOPMENT, INC.; *U.S. Private*, pg. 227
AMPTECH, INC.—See New Water Capital, L.P.; *U.S. Private*, pg. 2908
APPLIED TECHNICAL SERVICES CORPORATION—See Goldberg Lindsay & Co., LLC; *U.S. Private*, pg. 1729
ASHOKA TECHNOLOGIES PRIVATE LIMITED—See Ashoka Buildcon Ltd.; *Int'l*, pg. 608
ASIA PACIFIC SATELLITE LNC.; *Int'l*, pg. 614
ASPECT SOFTWARE—See Vector Capital Management, L.P.; *U.S. Private*, pg. 4350
AVI-TECH ELECTRONICS PTE. LTD.—See Avi-Tech Holdings Limited; *Int'l*, pg. 741
BENCHMARK ELECTRONICS INC. - NEW HAMPSHIRE DIVISION—See Benchmark Electronics, Inc.; *U.S. Public*, pg. 295
CAL-COMP ELECTRONICS (USA) CO., LTD.—See Cal-Comp Electronics (Thailand) pcl; *Int'l*, pg. 1260
CANYON MANUFACTURING SERVICES, INC.; *U.S. Private*, pg. 736
CASSIDIAN SOLUTIONS S.A.U.—See Airbus SE; *Int'l*, pg. 242
CEI INTERNATIONAL INVESTMENTS (VIETNAM) LIMITED—See AEM Holdings Ltd.; *Int'l*, pg. 175
CEI PTE. LTD.—See AEM Holdings Ltd.; *Int'l*, pg. 175
CICOR ANAM LTD.—See Cicor Technologies Ltd.; *Int'l*, pg. 1603

CONCURRENT MANUFACTURING SOLUTIONS LLC—See Balmoral Funds LLC; *U.S. Private*, pg. 461
CONCURRENT TECHNOLOGIES PLC; *Int'l*, pg. 1766
CSUN TECHNOLOGY (GUANGZHOU) CO., LTD.—See CSUN MFG. LTD.; *Int'l*, pg. 1868
DIGITALOPTICS CORPORATION ISRAEL LIMITED—See Adeia Inc.; *U.S. Public*, pg. 40
DIGITALOPTICS CORPORATION KOREA LIMITED—See Adeia Inc.; *U.S. Public*, pg. 40
DIGITALOPTICS CORPORATION TAIWAN LIMITED—See Adeia Inc.; *U.S. Public*, pg. 40
DRACO PCB PUBLIC COMPANY LIMITED—See Chin Poon Industrial Co., Ltd.; *Int'l*, pg. 1480
DSD, LTD.—See Disco Corporation; *Int'l*, pg. 2131
ECI TELECOM IBERICA S.A.—See Ribbon Communications Inc.; *U.S. Public*, pg. 1797
ECI TELECOM LTD. - CHINA—See Ribbon Communications Inc.; *U.S. Public*, pg. 1797
ECI TELECOM (PHILIPPINES), INC.—See Ribbon Communications Inc.; *U.S. Public*, pg. 1797
ECI TELECOM (SINGAPORE)—See Ribbon Communications Inc.; *U.S. Public*, pg. 1797
EISO ENTERPRISE CO., LTD.; *Int'l*, pg. 2336
ELITE MATERIAL CO., LTD. - TAOYUAN PLANT—See Elite Material Co., Ltd.; *Int'l*, pg. 2362
EMERSON ENERGY SYSTEMS—See Emerson Electric Co.; *U.S. Public*, pg. 745
ENDICOTT INTERCONNECT TECHNOLOGIES, INC.; *U.S. Private*, pg. 1391
EPIC TECHNOLOGIES, LLC—See Natel Engineering Company, Inc.; *U.S. Private*, pg. 2838
FLEXTRONICS ELECTRONICS TECHNOLOGY (SUZHOU) CO., LTD.—See Flex Ltd.; *Int'l*, pg. 2702
FLEXTRONICS MANUFACTURING (H.K.) LTD.—See Flex Ltd.; *Int'l*, pg. 2703
FOCUSLIGHT SWITZERLAND SA—See Focuslight Technologies Inc.; *Int'l*, pg. 2720
FORMOSA ADVANCED TECHNOLOGIES CO., LTD.; *Int'l*, pg. 2734
FUJIKURA ELECTRONICS (THAILAND) LTD. - PRACHINBURI FACTORY 1—See Fujikura Ltd.; *Int'l*, pg. 2828
GENTHERM TECHNOLOGIES (SHANGHAI) CO. LTD.—See Gentherm Incorporated; *U.S. Public*, pg. 932
GIA TZOONG ENTERPRISE CO., LTD.; *Int'l*, pg. 2960
GPV AMERICAS MEXICO S.A.P.I DE CV—See Aktieselskabet Schouw & Co.; *Int'l*, pg. 266
GPV ASIA (THAILAND) CO., LTD.—See Aktieselskabet Schouw & Co.; *Int'l*, pg. 266
GPV AUSTRIA CABLE GMBH—See Aktieselskabet Schouw & Co.; *Int'l*, pg. 266
GPV AUSTRIA GMBH—See Aktieselskabet Schouw & Co.; *Int'l*, pg. 266
GREEN POINT TECHNOLOGY (SHENZHEN) CO., LTD.—See Jabil Inc.; *U.S. Public*, pg. 1180
GREENRAY INDUSTRIES—See TechniCorp International II; *U.S. Private*, pg. 3954
HANA MICROELECTRONICS (JIAXING) CO., LTD.—See Hana Microelectronics Public Company Limited; *Int'l*, pg. 3241
HANA MICROELECTRONICS PUBLIC CO., LTD.—See Hana Microelectronics Public Company Limited; *Int'l*, pg. 3241
HANKUK CARBON CO., LTD. - HAMYANG PLANT—See HANKUK CARBON Co., Ltd.; *Int'l*, pg. 3254
HANKUK CARBON CO., LTD.; *Int'l*, pg. 3254
HDK MICRO DEVICES CO., LTD.—See Hokuriku Electric Industry Co., Ltd.; *Int'l*, pg. 3444
HENKEL ELECTRONIC MATERIALS LLC—See Henkel AG & Co. KGaA; *Int'l*, pg. 3353
HERAEUS CONTACT MATERIALS DIVISION—See Heraeus Holding GmbH; *Int'l*, pg. 3358
HERAEUS MATERIALS SINGAPORE PTE. LTD.—See Heraeus Holding GmbH; *Int'l*, pg. 3357
HOKURIKU SEIKI CO., LTD.—See Hokuriku Electric Industry Co., Ltd.; *Int'l*, pg. 3445
IBIDEN CO., LTD. - GAMA PLANT—See Ibiden Co., Ltd.; *Int'l*, pg. 3575
IBIDEN CO., LTD. - GODO PLANT—See Ibiden Co., Ltd.; *Int'l*, pg. 3575
IBIDEN CO., LTD. - OGAKI CENTRAL PLANT—See Ibiden Co., Ltd.; *Int'l*, pg. 3575
IBIDEN CO., LTD.; *Int'l*, pg. 3575
INFINITUM ELECTRIC, INC.; *U.S. Private*, pg. 2071
INTEGRATED MICROELECTRONICS, INC.—See Ayala Corporation; *Int'l*, pg. 774
INTERVALA, LLC; *U.S. Private*, pg. 2127
ITW EAE MEXICO, S DE RL DE CV—See Illinois Tool Works Inc.; *U.S. Public*, pg. 1105
JABIL ADVANCED MECHANICAL SOLUTIONS, INC.—See Jabil Inc.; *U.S. Public*, pg. 1180
JABIL CIRCUIT FINANCIAL, INC.—See Jabil Inc.; *U.S. Public*, pg. 1181
JABIL INC.; *U.S. Public*, pg. 1180
JABIL JAPAN, INC.—See Jabil Inc.; *U.S. Public*, pg. 1181
JABIL (MAURITIUS) HOLDINGS LTD.—See Jabil Inc.; *U.S. Public*, pg. 1180
KASALIS INC.—See Jabil Inc.; *U.S. Public*, pg. 1181
KEY TRONIC CORPORATION; *U.S. Public*, pg. 1225

N.A.I.C.S. INDEX

KIMBALL ELECTRONICS INDIANAPOLIS, INC.—See Kimball Electronics, Inc.; *U.S. Public*, pg. 1228
LARITECH INC.; *U.S. Private*, pg. 2392
MC TEST SERVICE, INC. - BOSTON—See H.I.G. Capital, LLC; *U.S. Private*, pg. 1833
MC TEST SERVICE, INC. - MEXICO—See H.I.G. Capital, LLC; *U.S. Private*, pg. 1833
MC TEST SERVICE, INC.—See H.I.G. Capital, LLC; *U.S. Private*, pg. 1833
MEDTEL SERVICES, LLC; *U.S. Private*, pg. 2659
MERCURY SYSTEMS SARL—See Mercury Systems, Inc.; *U.S. Public*, pg. 1422
MICROSEMI ISRAEL, LTD.—See Microchip Technology Incorporated; *U.S. Public*, pg. 1437
MOEN (SHANGHAI) KITCHEN & BATH PRODUCTS CO., LTD.—See Fortune Brands Innovations, Inc.; *U.S. Public*, pg. 873
MULTEK BRAZIL LTDA—See Flex Ltd.; *Int'l*, pg. 2704
MULTEK HONG KONG LIMITED—See Flex Ltd.; *Int'l*, pg. 2704
NAPROTEK, INC.—See Edgewater Capital Partners, L.P.; *U.S. Private*, pg. 1335
NEOPHOTONICS CORPORATION—See Lumentum Holdings Inc.; *U.S. Public*, pg. 1348
NEXTER ELECTRONICS S.A.—See GIAT Industries S.A.; *Int'l*, pg. 2962
NOKIA MOBILE PHONES—See Microsoft Corporation; *U.S. Public*, pg. 1441
NOKIA MOBILE PHONES—See Microsoft Corporation; *U.S. Public*, pg. 1441
OAI ELECTRONICS INC.—See Rooney Holdings, Inc.; *U.S. Private*, pg. 3479
OPTIMUM DESIGN ASSOCIATES, INC.—See Crestview Partners, L.P.; *U.S. Private*, pg. 1098
OSI ELECTRONICS, INC.—See OSI Systems, Inc.; *U.S. Public*, pg. 1621
OSI ELECTRONICS (UK) LTD.—See OSI Systems, Inc.; *U.S. Public*, pg. 1621
PENTEK SYSTEMS, INC.—See Mercury Systems, Inc.; *U.S. Public*, pg. 1422
POWER-ONE INC.—See ABB Ltd.; *Int'l*, pg. 52
PRECICO GROUP SDN BHD—See Frencken Group Limited; *Int'l*, pg. 2773
PRIMUS TECHNOLOGIES CORP.—See OEP Capital Advisors, L.P.; *U.S. Private*, pg. 3000
PRODUCTION TECHNOLOGY—See Fuji Corporation; *Int'l*, pg. 2810
PT SURYA TEKNOLOGI BATAM—See AEM Holdings Ltd.; *Int'l*, pg. 175
RESTRONICS CO., INC—See Fuji Corporation; *Int'l*, pg. 2810
SEGUE ELECTRONICS, INC.; *U.S. Private*, pg. 3598
SHYE FENG ENTERPRISE (THAILAND) CO., LTD.—See Apex International Co., Ltd.; *Int'l*, pg. 511
SMARTECH ELECTRONICS CO., LTD.—See Fuji Corporation; *Int'l*, pg. 2810
SPARTON CORPORATION—See Elbit Systems Limited; *Int'l*, pg. 2344
SYNTELLECT LTD—See Enghouse Systems Limited; *Int'l*, pg. 2428
TELEDYNE LABTECH LIMITED—See Teledyne Technologies Incorporated; *U.S. Public*, pg. 1994
TELEDYNE LABTECH LTD. - MILTON KEYNES PLANT—See Teledyne Technologies Incorporated; *U.S. Public*, pg. 1994
TELIGENTEMS, LLC—See Prime Technological Services, LLC; *U.S. Private*, pg. 3262
TELLABS OY—See Marlin Equity Partners, LLC; *U.S. Private*, pg. 2585
USI JAPAN CO., LTD.—See ASE Technology Holding Co., Ltd.; *Int'l*, pg. 604
USI SCIENTIFIC INDUSTRIAL (SHANGHAI) CO., LTD.—See ASE Technology Holding Co., Ltd.; *Int'l*, pg. 604
USI@WORK, INC.—See ASE Technology Holding Co., Ltd.; *Int'l*, pg. 605
WESTING GREEN (TIANJIN) PLASTIC CO., LTD—See Jabil Inc.; *U.S. Public*, pg. 1182
XEROX CANADA I LIMITED PARTNERSHIP—See Xerox Holdings Corporation; *U.S. Public*, pg. 2387

334419 — OTHER ELECTRONIC COMPONENT MANUFACTURING

3CEMS GROUP - FREMONT BRANCH—See FIC Global, INC; *Int'l*, pg. 2653
3DLABS—See Creative Technology Ltd.; *Int'l*, pg. 1833
3D PLUS SAS—See HEICO Corporation; *U.S. Public*, pg. 1020
3D PLUS U.S.A., INC.—See HEICO Corporation; *U.S. Public*, pg. 1020
3M INNOVATION SINGAPORE PTE LTD—See 3M Company; *U.S. Public*, pg. 6
3S KOREA CO., LTD.; *Int'l*, pg. 9
4B ASIA PACIFIC COMPANY LIMITED—See Braime Group Plc; *Int'l*, pg. 1136
7C SOLARPARKEN AG; *Int'l*, pg. 15

AAR AIRCRAFT COMPONENT SERVICES-NEW YORK—See AAR Corp.; *U.S. Public*, pg. 13
AAVID CHINA—See The Goldman Sachs Group, Inc.; *U.S. Public*, pg. 2080
AAVID INDIA—See The Goldman Sachs Group, Inc.; *U.S. Public*, pg. 2080
AAVID—See The Goldman Sachs Group, Inc.; *U.S. Public*, pg. 2080
AAVID THERMALLOY S.R.L.—See The Goldman Sachs Group, Inc.; *U.S. Public*, pg. 2080
ABB D.O.O.—See ABB Ltd.; *Int'l*, pg. 55
ABB (HONG KONG) LTD.—See ABB Ltd.; *Int'l*, pg. 49
ABCHIMIE—See KKR & Co. Inc.; *U.S. Public*, pg. 1242
ABCO ELECTRONICS CO., LTD. - ABCO SHENYANG PLANT—See ABCO Electronics Co., Ltd.; *Int'l*, pg. 57
ABCO ELECTRONICS CO., LTD. - ABCO WEIHAI PLANT—See ABCO Electronics Co., Ltd.; *Int'l*, pg. 57
ABCO ELECTRONICS CO., LTD. - ABCO YANTAI PLANT—See ABCO Electronics Co., Ltd.; *Int'l*, pg. 57
ABLEMEX, S.A. DE C.V.—See SigmaTron International, Inc.; *U.S. Public*, pg. 1877
ACACIA RESEARCH CORPORATION; *U.S. Public*, pg. 27
ACCEL ELEKTRONIKA UAB—See Littelfuse, Inc.; *U.S. Public*, pg. 1326
ACCEL INNOVATIONS LIMITED—See Accel Group Holdings Limited; *Int'l*, pg. 79
ACCESSO TECHNOLOGY GROUP PLC; *Int'l*, pg. 89
ACCRELIST A.I. TECH PTE. LTD.—See Accrelist Ltd.; *Int'l*, pg. 93
ACCUSPEC ELECTRONICS, LLC—See Armstrong Holdings, Inc.; *U.S. Private*, pg. 331
ACES DONG GUAN—See Aces Electronic Co., Ltd.; *Int'l*, pg. 102
ACME PACKET, INC.—See Oracle Corporation; *U.S. Public*, pg. 1610
ACOPIAN TECHNICAL COMPANY; *U.S. Private*, pg. 63
ACPA TECHNOLOGY CO., LTD.—See Ahoku Electronic Company; *Int'l*, pg. 225
ACTIA 3E S.A.—See Actia Group SA; *Int'l*, pg. 118
ACTIA ELECTRONICS, INC.—See Actia Group SA; *Int'l*, pg. 118
ACTIA GROUP SA; *Int'l*, pg. 117
ACTIA TELEMATICS SERVICES SA—See Actia Group SA; *Int'l*, pg. 118
ACTION ELECTRONICS CO., LTD.; *Int'l*, pg. 119
ACULA TECHNOLOGY CORP.; *Int'l*, pg. 121
ADALET—See Berkshire Hathaway Inc.; *U.S. Public*, pg. 299
ADI CORPORATION; *Int'l*, pg. 145
ADLINK TECHNOLOGY B.V.—See ADLINK Technology, Inc.; *Int'l*, pg. 150
ADLINK TECHNOLOGY KOREA LTD.—See ADLINK Technology, Inc.; *Int'l*, pg. 150
ADLINK TECHNOLOGY LTD.—See ADLINK Technology, Inc.; *Int'l*, pg. 151
ADLINK TECHNOLOGY SARL—See ADLINK Technology, Inc.; *Int'l*, pg. 151
ADTEC PLASMA TECHNOLOGY CHINA LTD.—See Adtec Plasma Technology Co., Ltd.; *Int'l*, pg. 154
ADVANCED CERAMIC X CORPORATION; *Int'l*, pg. 157
ADVANCED CONNECTION TECHNOLOGY INC.; *Int'l*, pg. 158
ADVANCE DIGITAL, INC.—See Advance Local LLC; *U.S. Private*, pg. 83
ADVANCED INTERCONNECT MANUFACTURING, INC.—See Floturn Inc.; *U.S. Public*, pg. 1551
ADVANCED MANUFACTURING CORPORATION PTE. LTD.—See Advanced Integrated Manufacturing Corp.; *Int'l*, pg. 160
ADVANCED MEDIA, INC.; *Int'l*, pg. 160
ADVANCED MICRO DEVICES (SINGAPORE) PTE. LTD.—See Advanced Micro Devices, Inc.; *U.S. Public*, pg. 48
ADVANCED MP TECHNOLOGY INC.—See Wynnchurch Capital, L.P.; *U.S. Private*, pg. 4576
ADVANCED QUARTZ MATERIAL (HANGZHOU) CO., LTD.—See Ferrotec Holdings Corporation; *Int'l*, pg. 2643
ADVANTOR SYSTEMS CORPORATION—See V2X, Inc.; *U.S. Public*, pg. 2270
AE KOREA, LTD.—See Advanced Energy Industries, Inc.; *U.S. Public*, pg. 47
AEMTEC GMBH—See capiton AG; *Int'l*, pg. 1314
AE PRECISION POWER PRODUCTS PVT. LTD.—See Advanced Energy Industries, Inc.; *U.S. Public*, pg. 47
AERO-MODEL INC.—See The Zippertubing Company; *U.S. Private*, pg. 4140
AFROTECH INC.; *U.S. Private*, pg. 119
AFERIAN PLC; *Int'l*, pg. 185
AFPD PTE., LTD.—See AUO Corporation; *Int'l*, pg. 706
AGC ELECTRONICS AMERICA, INC.—See AGC Inc.; *Int'l*, pg. 200
AGC ELECTRONICS TAIWAN INC.—See AGC Inc.; *Int'l*, pg. 203
AGC SEIMI CHEMICAL CO., LTD. - KASHIMA PLANT—See AGC Inc.; *Int'l*, pg. 202
AGC SEIMI CHEMICAL CO., LTD.—See AGC Inc.; *Int'l*, pg. 202

334419 — OTHER ELECTRONIC CO...

AGILE MAGNETICS, INC.—See Standex International; *U.S. Public*, pg. 1930
AHA CO., LTD.; *Int'l*, pg. 222
AHEAD MAGNETICS, INC.; *U.S. Private*, pg. 130
AHOKU TECHLAND ELECTRONICS LTD.—See Ahoku Electronic Company; *Int'l*, pg. 225
AIMECHATEC LTD.; *Int'l*, pg. 232
AIMHIGH GLOBAL CORP.; *Int'l*, pg. 233
AIPHONE CO., LTD.; *Int'l*, pg. 234
AIPHONE S.A.S.—See Aiphone Co., Ltd.; *Int'l*, pg. 235
AIRMAR EMEA EURL—See Amphenol Corporation; *U.S. Public*, pg. 126
AIRSPEED, LLC—See Mercury Aircraft Inc.; *U.S. Private*, pg. 2670
AISHIDA CO., LTD.; *Int'l*, pg. 251
AISIN CORPORATION - HANDA ELECTRONICS PLANT—See AISIN Corporation; *Int'l*, pg. 251
AISIN ELECTRONICS ILLINOIS, LLC—See AISIN Corporation; *Int'l*, pg. 252
AJINOMOTO FINE-TECHNO CO., INC.—See Ajinomoto Company, Inc.; *Int'l*, pg. 256
AKAPP STEMMANN BV—See Westinghouse Air Brake Technologies Corporation; *U.S. Public*, pg. 2358
AKIBA HOLDINGS CO., LTD.; *Int'l*, pg. 263
AKITA RARE METALS CO., LTD—See Dowa Holdings Co., Ltd.; *Int'l*, pg. 2183
AKT AMERICA, INC.—See Applied Materials, Inc.; *U.S. Public*, pg. 172
ALBER GMBH—See Invacare Corporation; *U.S. Private*, pg. 2130
ALCO HOLDINGS LIMITED; *Int'l*, pg. 301
ALCOM ELECTRONICOS DE MEXICO, S.A. DE C.V.—See Alps Alpine Co., Ltd.; *Int'l*, pg. 375
ALDER OPTOMECHANICAL CORP.—See Alltek Technology Corporation; *Int'l*, pg. 360
ALDETEC, INC.—See Greenbriar Equity Group, L.P.; *U.S. Private*, pg. 1775
ALEIS PTY LTD—See Merck & Co., Inc.; *U.S. Public*, pg. 1415
ALFALIGHT, INC.—See Gooch & Housego PLC; *U.S. Private*, pg. 3038
AL HASSAN GHAZI IBRAHIM SHAKER; *Int'l*, pg. 279
ALLCOMM (H.K.) LIMITED—See Alltronics Holdings Limited; *Int'l*, pg. 361
ALLIED TECHNOLOGIES LTD.; *Int'l*, pg. 358
ALLTEK MARINE ELECTRONICS CORP.—See Alltek Technology Corporation; *Int'l*, pg. 360
ALLTRONICS HOLDINGS LIMITED; *Int'l*, pg. 361
ALLTRONICS TECH. MFTG. LIMITED—See Alltronics Holdings Limited; *Int'l*, pg. 361
ALPHA ASSEMBLY SOLUTIONS SINGAPORE PTE LTD—See Element Solutions Inc.; *U.S. Public*, pg. 726
ALPINE CUSTOMER SERVICE (USA), INC.—See Alps Alpine Co., Ltd.; *Int'l*, pg. 375
ALPINE DO BRASIL LTDA—See Alps Alpine Co., Ltd.; *Int'l*, pg. 375
ALPINE ELECTRONICS, INC.—See Alps Alpine Co., Ltd.; *Int'l*, pg. 375
ALPINE ELECTRONICS OF MIDDLE EAST, FZCO—See Alps Alpine Co., Ltd.; *Int'l*, pg. 375
ALPINE ELECTRONICS OF SILICON VALLEY, INC.—See Alps Alpine Co., Ltd.; *Int'l*, pg. 375
ALPINE OF ASIA PACIFIC INDIA PVT., LTD.—See Alps Alpine Co., Ltd.; *Int'l*, pg. 375
ALPINE TECHNOLOGY MANUFACTURING (THAILAND) CO., LTD.—See Alps Alpine Co., Ltd.; *Int'l*, pg. 375
ALPS ALPIN ASIA CO., LTD.—See Alps Alpine Co., Ltd.; *Int'l*, pg. 376
ALPS ALPINE CO., LTD.; *Int'l*, pg. 375
ALPS ALPINE NORTH AMERICA, INC.—See Alps Alpine Co., Ltd.; *Int'l*, pg. 376
ALPS ALPINE VIETNAM CO., LTD.—See Alps Alpine Co., Ltd.; *Int'l*, pg. 376
ALPS DE MEXICO S. DE R.L. DE C.V.—See Alps Alpine Co., Ltd.; *Int'l*, pg. 376
ALPS ELECTRIC CO., LTD. - FURUKAWA PLANT—See Alps Alpine Co., Ltd.; *Int'l*, pg. 376
ALPS ELECTRIC CO., LTD. - KAKUDA PLANT—See Alps Alpine Co., Ltd.; *Int'l*, pg. 376
ALPS ELECTRIC CO., LTD. - NAGAOKA PLANT—See Alps Alpine Co., Ltd.; *Int'l*, pg. 376
ALPS ELECTRIC CO., LTD. - ONAHAMA PLANT—See Alps Alpine Co., Ltd.; *Int'l*, pg. 376
ALPS ELECTRIC CO., LTD. - TAIRA PLANT—See Alps Alpine Co., Ltd.; *Int'l*, pg. 376
ALPS ELECTRIC CO., LTD. - WAKUYA PLANT—See Alps Alpine Co., Ltd.; *Int'l*, pg. 376
ALPS ELECTRIC CZECH, S.R.O.—See Alps Alpine Co., Ltd.; *Int'l*, pg. 375
ALPS ELECTRIC EUROPE GMBH - DORTMUND PLANT—See Alps Alpine Co., Ltd.; *Int'l*, pg. 376
ALPS ELECTRIC (INDIA) PRIVATE LIMITED—See Alps Alpine Co., Ltd.; *Int'l*, pg. 376
ALPS ELECTRIC (MALAYSIA) SDN.BHD. - JENGKA PLANT—See Alps Alpine Co., Ltd.; *Int'l*, pg. 376
ALPS ELECTRONICS HONG KONG LIMITED—See Alps Alpine Co., Ltd.; *Int'l*, pg. 376
AMATECH AG; *Int'l*, pg. 413

AMERICA II GROUP, LLC—See Wynnchurch Capital, L.P.; *U.S. Private*, pg. 4576
AMERICAN AUDIO COMPONENT INC.—See AAC Technologies Holdings Inc.; *Int'l*, pg. 31
AMERICAN INDUSTRIAL SYSTEMS, INC.—See Hon Hai Precision Industry Co., Ltd.; *Int'l*, pg. 3456
AMERICAN INTERNATIONAL COMMUNICATIONS, INC.; *U.S. Private*, pg. 238
AMERICAN INTERNATIONAL COMMUNICATIONS JACKSONVILLE—See American International Communications, Inc.; *U.S. Private*, pg. 238
AMERICAN TACK & HARDWARE CO. INC.—See Amertac Holdings Inc.; *U.S. Private*, pg. 261
AMERICAN TEC ELECTRONIC INDIA PVT LTD.—See Fuji Corporation; *Int'l*, pg. 2809
AMERTAC HOLDINGS INC.; *U.S. Private*, pg. 261
AMERTEK COMPUTER (SHENZHEN) CO. LTD.—See FIC Global, INC; *Int'l*, pg. 2653
AMETEK MOTORS (SHANGHAI) CO., LTD.—See AMETEK, Inc.; *U.S. Public*, pg. 119
AMETEK NORDIC AB—See AMETEK, Inc.; *U.S. Public*, pg. 119
AMITRONIC OY—See Addtech AB; *Int'l*, pg. 131
AMOSENSE CO., LTD.; *Int'l*, pg. 430
AMOTECH CO., LTD. - SHANDONG FACTORY—See Amotech Co Ltd; *Int'l*, pg. 431
AMPEX CORPORATION - COLORADO SPRINGS SERVICE FACILITY—See Ampex Corporation; *U.S. Private*, pg. 266
AMPEX DATA INTERNATIONAL CORPORATION—See Ampex Corporation; *U.S. Private*, pg. 266
AMPHENOL ALDEN PRODUCTS COMPANY—See Amphenol Corporation; *U.S. Public*, pg. 128
AMPHENOL ALDEN PRODUCTS MEXICO, S.A. DE C.V.—See Amphenol Corporation; *U.S. Public*, pg. 128
AMPHENOL COMMERCIAL AND INDUSTRIAL UK, LIMITED—See Amphenol Corporation; *U.S. Public*, pg. 127
AMPHENOL COMMERCIAL INTERCONNECT KOREA CO. LTD.—See Amphenol Corporation; *U.S. Public*, pg. 127
AMPHENOL FCI CONNECTORS SINGAPORE PTE. LTD.—See Amphenol Corporation; *U.S. Public*, pg. 127
AMPHENOL FIBER OPTIC TECHNOLOGY (SHENZHEN) CO., LTD.—See Amphenol Corporation; *U.S. Public*, pg. 127
AMPHENOL GESELLSCHAFT M.B.H.—See Amphenol Corporation; *U.S. Public*, pg. 127
AMPHENOL GRIFFITH ENTERPRISES, LLC—See Amphenol Corporation; *U.S. Public*, pg. 128
AMPHENOL OPTIMIZE MEXICO S.A. DE C.V.—See Amphenol Corporation; *U.S. Public*, pg. 128
AMPHENOL PHITEK, LIMITED—See Amphenol Corporation; *U.S. Public*, pg. 128
AMPHENOL PRINTED CIRCUITS, INC.—See Amphenol Corporation; *U.S. Public*, pg. 126
AMPHENOL PROVENS SAS—See Amphenol Corporation; *U.S. Public*, pg. 128
AMPHENOL SENSING KOREA COMPANY LIMITED—See Amphenol Corporation; *U.S. Public*, pg. 128
AMPHENOL TECHNOLOGY MACEDONIA—See Amphenol Corporation; *U.S. Public*, pg. 129
AMPHENOL TEL-AD LIMITED—See Amphenol Corporation; *U.S. Public*, pg. 129
AMPHENOL THERMOMETRICS, INC.—See Amphenol Corporation; *U.S. Public*, pg. 129
AMPHENOL THERMOMETRICS (UK) LIMITED—See Amphenol Corporation; *U.S. Public*, pg. 129
AMPHENOL TUCHEL INDUSTRIAL GMBH—See Amphenol Corporation; *U.S. Public*, pg. 129
AMPLE ELECTRONIC TECHNOLOGY CO., LTD.; *Int'l*, pg. 433
AMPTEK, INC.—See AMETEK, Inc.; *U.S. Public*, pg. 120
AMTRAN TECHNOLOGY; *Int'l*, pg. 442
ANALOG DEVICES IRELAND LTD.—See Analog Devices, Inc.; *U.S. Public*, pg. 134
ANALOGIC CANADA CORPORATION—See Altaris Capital Partners, LLC; *U.S. Private*, pg. 205
ANALOG MODULES, INC.—See HEICO Corporation; *U.S. Public*, pg. 1020
ANCOM COMPONENTS SDN. BHD.—See Ancom Nylex Berhad; *Int'l*, pg. 449
ANDEN CO., LTD.—See Denso Corporation; *Int'l*, pg. 2028
ANHUI SHINY ELECTRONIC TECHNOLOGY COMPANY LIMITED; *Int'l*, pg. 469
ANIXTER (CIS) LLC—See WESCO International, Inc.; *U.S. Public*, pg. 2350
ANIXTER PUERTO RICO, INC.—See WESCO International, Inc.; *U.S. Public*, pg. 2350
ANJI MICROELECTRONICS TECHNOLOGY SHANGHAI CO., LTD.; *Int'l*, pg. 472
ANKER INNOVATIONS TECHNOLOGY CO., LTD.; *Int'l*, pg. 472
ANRITSU DEVICES CO., LTD.—See Anritsu Corporation; *Int'l*, pg. 475
ANTYCIP IBERICA SL—See HENSOLDT AG; *Int'l*, pg. 3355
ANTYCIP TECHNOLOGIES S.A.S.—See HENSOLDT AG; *Int'l*, pg. 3355

AOF IMAGING TECHNOLOGY LIMITED—See Asia Optical Co., Inc.; *Int'l*, pg. 613
AOMORI DDK LTD.—See Fujikura Ltd.; *Int'l*, pg. 2827
AOMORI FUJIKURA KANAYA LTD.—See Fujikura Ltd.; *Int'l*, pg. 2827
APACHE DESIGN, INC.—See ANSYS, Inc.; *U.S. Public*, pg. 139
APAC OPTO ELECTRONICS, INC.; *Int'l*, pg. 500
APC TECHNOLOGY GROUP PLC; *Int'l*, pg. 507
APEM, INC.—See IDEC Corporation; *Int'l*, pg. 3589
APEM S.A.—See IDEC Corporation; *Int'l*, pg. 3589
APEX ACE HOLDING LIMITED; *Int'l*, pg. 509
APEX SCIENCE & ENGINEERING CORP.; *Int'l*, pg. 512
API CONTROL SYSTEMS SOLUTIONS INC; *U.S. Private*, pg. 294
API / INMET, INC.—See AEA Investors LP; *U.S. Private*, pg. 113
API MICROELECTRONICS LIMITED—See AEA Investors LP; *U.S. Private*, pg. 113
API TECHNOLOGIES CORP.—See AEA Investors LP; *U.S. Private*, pg. 113
API / WEINSCHEL, INC.—See AEA Investors LP; *U.S. Private*, pg. 113
APLUS PRODUCTS LLC—See Diversified Electronics Inc.; *U.S. Private*, pg. 1242
APM AUTO ELECTRICS SDN. BHD.—See APM Automotive Holdings Berhad; *Int'l*, pg. 516
APPLETON GROUP - MEMPHIS—See Emerson Electric Co.; *U.S. Public*, pg. 740
APPLETON GRP LLC—See Emerson Electric Co.; *U.S. Public*, pg. 740
APPLIED MATERIALS FRANCE SARL—See Applied Materials, Inc.; *U.S. Public*, pg. 172
APPLIED MATERIALS GMBH—See Applied Materials, Inc.; *U.S. Public*, pg. 172
APPLIED MATERIALS IRELAND LTD.—See Applied Materials, Inc.; *U.S. Public*, pg. 172
APPLIED MATERIALS ISRAEL, LTD.—See Applied Materials, Inc.; *U.S. Public*, pg. 172
APPLIED MATERIALS ITALIA S.R.L.—See Applied Materials, Inc.; *U.S. Public*, pg. 172
APPLIED MATERIALS JAPAN, INC.—See Applied Materials, Inc.; *U.S. Public*, pg. 172
APPLIED MATERIALS SOUTH EAST ASIA PTE. LTD.—See Applied Materials, Inc.; *U.S. Public*, pg. 172
APPLIED SCIENTIFIC INSTRUMENTATION, INC.; *U.S. Private*, pg. 299
AQ INDUCTIVES HUNGARY KFT—See AQ Group AB; *Int'l*, pg. 526
AQ PLASTRONIC AD—See AQ Group AB; *Int'l*, pg. 526
ARCHOS GMBH—See Archos S.A.; *Int'l*, pg. 549
ARCHOS INC.—See Archos S.A.; *Int'l*, pg. 549
ARCHOS UK LTD.—See Archos S.A.; *Int'l*, pg. 549
ARCHSAT INVESTMENTS (GAUTENG)(PTY) LTD—See Ellies Holdings Limited; *Int'l*, pg. 2366
ARCHSAT INVESTMENTS (NATAL) (PTY) LTD—See Ellies Holdings Limited; *Int'l*, pg. 2366
ARCVISION TECHNOLOGY CORP.—See Ac&C International Co., Ltd.; *Int'l*, pg. 74
ARDATEM—See Gerard Perrier Industrie S.A.; *Int'l*, pg. 2942
ARGO TRANSDATA CORPORATION—See The Eastern Company; *U.S. Public*, pg. 2069
ARIES ELECTRONICS INC.; *U.S. Private*, pg. 322
ARIMA OPTOELECTRONICS CORPORATION—See Arima Photovoltaic & Optical Corp.; *Int'l*, pg. 565
ARIMA PHOTOVOLTAIC & OPTICAL CORP.; *Int'l*, pg. 565
ARIMON TECHNOLOGIES INC.; *U.S. Private*, pg. 323
ARISAWA KENPAN CO., LTD.—See Arisawa Manufacturing Co., Ltd.; *Int'l*, pg. 565
ARISTOCRAT INTERNATIONAL PTY LTD—See Aristocrat Leisure Limited; *Int'l*, pg. 566
ARISTOCRAT LEISURE CYPRUS LIMITED—See Aristocrat Leisure Limited; *Int'l*, pg. 566
ARISTOCRAT (MACAU) PTY LIMITED—See Aristocrat Leisure Limited; *Int'l*, pg. 566
ARISTOCRAT SERVICE MEXICO, S.A. DE C.V.—See Aristocrat Leisure Limited; *Int'l*, pg. 566
ARISTOCRAT TECHNICAL SERVICES PTY LTD—See Aristocrat Leisure Limited; *Int'l*, pg. 566
ARISTOCRAT TECHNOLOGIES EUROPE (HOLDINGS) LIMITED—See Aristocrat Leisure Limited; *Int'l*, pg. 566
ARISTOCRAT TECHNOLOGIES INDIA PRIVATE LTD—See Aristocrat Leisure Limited; *Int'l*, pg. 566
ARISTOCRAT TECHNOLOGIES SPAIN S.L—See Aristocrat Leisure Limited; *Int'l*, pg. 566
ARISTOCRAT TECHNOLOGY GAMING SYSTEMS PTY LIMITED—See Aristocrat Leisure Limited; *Int'l*, pg. 566
ARLON EMD LLC—See CriticalPoint Capital, LLC; *U.S. Private*, pg. 1102
ARMORLINK SH CORP.—See IEI Integration Corp.; *Int'l*, pg. 3597
ARROW ARGENTINA S.A.—See Arrow Electronics, Inc.; *U.S. Public*, pg. 195
ARROW ELECTRONICS ASIA (S) PTE LTD—See Arrow Electronics, Inc.; *U.S. Public*, pg. 195
ARROW ELECTRONICS HELLAS S.A.—See Arrow Electronics, Inc.; *U.S. Public*, pg. 197

ARROW ELECTRONICS INDIA PRIVATE LTD.—See Arrow Electronics, Inc.; *U.S. Public*, pg. 195
ARROW ELECTRONICS JAPAN K.K.—See Arrow Electronics, Inc.; *U.S. Public*, pg. 197
ARROW ELECTRONICS (S) PTE LTD.—See Arrow Electronics, Inc.; *U.S. Public*, pg. 195
ARROW ELECTRONICS TAIWAN LTD.—See Arrow Electronics, Inc.; *U.S. Public*, pg. 195
ARROW S-TECH NORWAY AS—See Arrow Electronics, Inc.; *U.S. Public*, pg. 198
ARRYX, INC.—See Haemonetics Corporation; *U.S. Public*, pg. 979
ARTESYN EMBEDDED COMPUTING, INC.—See Penguin Solutions, Inc.; *U.S. Public*, pg. 1661
ARTESYN EMBEDDED POWER—See Advanced Energy Industries, Inc.; *U.S. Public*, pg. 47
ARTESYN EMBEDDED TECHNOLOGIES, INC.—See Platinum Equity, LLC; *U.S. Private*, pg. 3201
ASAHI KAKO CO., LTD.—See Daiwabo Holdings Co., Ltd.; *Int'l*, pg. 1949
ASAHI KASEI E-MATERIALS CORP.—See Asahi Kasei Corporation; *Int'l*, pg. 595
ASAHI KASEI EMD CORPORATION—See Asahi Kasei Corporation; *Int'l*, pg. 595
ASAHI KASEI MICRODEVICES CORP.—See Asahi Kasei Corporation; *Int'l*, pg. 595
ASAHI KASEI TECHNOSYSTEM CORP.—See Asahi Kasei Corporation; *Int'l*, pg. 596
ASBIS BALTICS SIA—See ASBISc Enterprises Plc; *Int'l*, pg. 600
ASBIS MIDDLE EAST FZE—See ASBISc Enterprises Plc; *Int'l*, pg. 600
ASCO POWER TECHNOLOGIES LIMITED—See Emerson Electric Co.; *U.S. Public*, pg. 740
ASE JAPAN CO., LTD.—See ASE Technology Holding Co., Ltd.; *Int'l*, pg. 604
ASETRONICS AG; *Int'l*, pg. 606
ASIA INDUSTRY DEVELOPMENT CO., LTD.—See Asia Holdings Co., Ltd.; *Int'l*, pg. 613
ASI AUTOMATIKK AS—See Addtech AB; *Int'l*, pg. 131
ASM ASSEMBLY EQUIPMENT BANGKOK LIMITED—See ASM INTERNATIONAL N.V.; *Int'l*, pg. 626
ASM BELGIUM N.V.—See ASM INTERNATIONAL N.V.; *Int'l*, pg. 626
ASM FRONT-END SALES AND SERVICES TAIWAN CO. LTD.—See ASM INTERNATIONAL N.V.; *Int'l*, pg. 626
ASOLID TECHNOLOGY CO., LTD.; *Int'l*, pg. 628
ASPLEX SP. Z.O.O.—See Acer Incorporated; *Int'l*, pg. 99
ASPOCOMP AB—See Aspocomp Group Oyj; *Int'l*, pg. 632
ASPOCOMP OY—See Aspocomp Group Oyj; *Int'l*, pg. 632
ASPOCOMP (THAILAND) CO., LTD.—See Aspocomp Group Oyj; *Int'l*, pg. 632
ASSA ABLOY ASIA PACIFIC LTD—See ASSA ABLOY AB; *Int'l*, pg. 633
ASSA ABLOY (SA) (PTY) LTD—See ASSA ABLOY AB; *Int'l*, pg. 632
ASSOCIATED INDUSTRIES CHINA, INC.; *Int'l*, pg. 649
ASTEELFLASH GERMANY GMBH—See ASE Technology Holding Co., Ltd.; *Int'l*, pg. 605
ASTEELFLASH GROUP—See ASE Technology Holding Co., Ltd.; *Int'l*, pg. 604
ASTEELFLASH MEXICO S.A. DE C.V.—See ASE Technology Holding Co., Ltd.; *Int'l*, pg. 605
ASTEELFLASH SCHWANDORF GMBH—See ASE Technology Holding Co., Ltd.; *Int'l*, pg. 605
ASTEELFLASH TUNISIE S.A.—See ASE Technology Holding Co., Ltd.; *Int'l*, pg. 605
ASTEELFLASH USA CORP.—See ASE Technology Holding Co., Ltd.; *Int'l*, pg. 605
ASTI ELECTRONICS INDIA PRIVATE LIMITED—See ASTI Corporation; *Int'l*, pg. 654
ASTRA MICROWAVE PRODUCTS LIMITED - UNIT-I—See Astra Microwave Products Limited; *Int'l*, pg. 658
ASUNA CO., LTD.—See Arisawa Manufacturing Co., Ltd.; *Int'l*, pg. 566
ATECT KOREA CORPORATION—See Atect Corporation; *Int'l*, pg. 668
AT&S KLAGENFURT LEITERPLATTEN GMBH—See AT&S Austria Technologie & Systemtechnik Aktiengesellschaft; *Int'l*, pg. 665
ATTENTI LTD.—See Apax Partners LLP; *Int'l*, pg. 502
ATTENTI US, INC.—See Apax Partners LLP; *Int'l*, pg. 502
ATX NETWORKS CORP.—See H.I.G. Capital, LLC; *U.S. Private*, pg. 1828
ATX S.A.—See Emerson Electric Co.; *U.S. Public*, pg. 740
AUDEARA LIMITED; *Int'l*, pg. 700
AUDIX TECHNOLOGY (XIAMEN) CO., LTD.—See Audix Corporation; *Int'l*, pg. 702
AUO GREEN ENERGY AMERICA CORP.—See AUO Corporation; *Int'l*, pg. 706
AUO GREEN ENERGY EUROPE B.V.—See AUO Corporation; *Int'l*, pg. 706
AU OPTRONICS KOREA LTD.—See AUO Corporation; *Int'l*, pg. 706
AU OPTRONICS MANUFACTURING (SHANGHAI) CORP.—See AUO Corporation; *Int'l*, pg. 706
AU OPTRONICS (SHANGHAI) CO., LTD.—See AUO Corporation; *Int'l*, pg. 706

N.A.I.C.S. INDEX

334419 — OTHER ELECTRONIC CO...

AU OPTRONICS (SLOVAKIA) S.R.O.—See AUO Corporation; *Int'l*, pg. 706
AUTOTECH TECH LIMITED PARTNERSHIP—See AVG Advanced Technologies LP; *U.S. Private*, pg. 406
AUTRONIC STEUER- UND REGELTECHNIK GMBH—See FORTEC Elektronik AG; *Int'l*, pg. 2738
AVACO CO., LTD; *Int'l*, pg. 733
AVALON TECHNOLOGIES LIMITED; *Int'l*, pg. 734
AVANSTRATE KOREA INC.—See Hoya Corporation; *Int'l*, pg. 3495
AVATEC CO., LTD.; *Int'l*, pg. 737
AV CONCEPT HOLDINGS LTD; *Int'l*, pg. 733
AVER INFORMATION, INC.—See AVer Information Inc.; *Int'l*, pg. 739
AVG-LTI LP—See AVG Advanced Technologies LP; *U.S. Private*, pg. 406
AVIC ELECTROMECHANICAL SYSTEMS CO., LTD.—See Aviation Industry Corporation of China; *Int'l*, pg. 741
AVIDSEN—See HF Company; *Int'l*, pg. 3374
AVNET HONG KONG LIMITED—See Avnet, Inc.; *U.S. Public*, pg. 251
AVOCENT REDMOND CORP.—See Vertiv Holdings Co; *U.S. Public*, pg. 2288
AVTECHTYEE, INC.—See TransDigm Group Incorporated; *U.S. Public*, pg. 2182
AWP, INC.—See Kohlberg & Company, LLC; *U.S. Private*, pg. 2337
AXCEN PHOTONICS CORPORATION; *Int'l*, pg. 762
AXCESS INTERNATIONAL, INC.; *U.S. Private*, pg. 412
AXIOM MANUFACTURING SERVICES LIMITED—See Elate Holdings Limited; *Int'l*, pg. 2343
AXIS TECHNOLOGIES GROUP, INC.; *U.S. Public*, pg. 255
AYON VISUAL SOLUTIONS—See Video Display Corporation; *U.S. Public*, pg. 2296
AZBIL TAISHIN CO., LTD.—See Azbil Corporation; *Int'l*, pg. 777
AZ DISPLAYS, INC.—See Zettler Components, Inc.; *U.S. Private*, pg. 4603
AZKOYEN MEDIOS DE PAGO, S.A.—See AZKOYEN S.A; *Int'l*, pg. 780
AZTECH GROUP LTD.; *Int'l*, pg. 781
BACCARAT SA—See Fortune Fountain (Beijing) Holding Group Co., Ltd.; *Int'l*, pg. 2743
BAE SYSTEMS ELECTRONICS LIMITED—See BAE Systems plc; *Int'l*, pg. 796
BAE SYSTEMS INFORMATION AND ELECTRONIC SYSTEMS INTEGRATION INC.—See BAE Systems plc; *Int'l*, pg. 797
BAE SYSTEMS SAUDI ARABIA—See BAE Systems plc; *Int'l*, pg. 796
BALVER ZINN JOSEF JOST GMBH & CO. KG; *Int'l*, pg. 812
BARCO MANUFACTURING S.R.O.—See Barco N.V.; *Int'l*, pg. 863
BARCO SAS—See Barco N.V.; *Int'l*, pg. 863
BARCO VISUAL (BEIJING) TRADING CO., LTD.—See Barco N.V.; *Int'l*, pg. 863
BASF ELECTRONIC MATERIALS GMBH—See BASF SE; *Int'l*, pg. 878
BASF ELECTRONIC MATERIALS (SHANGHAI) CO. LTD.—See BASF SE; *Int'l*, pg. 878
BASF SUISSE S.A.—See BASF SE; *Int'l*, pg. 881
BASF TODA BATTERY MATERIALS LLC—See BASF SE; *Int'l*, pg. 882
BASLER ELECTRIC COMPANY - BASLER ELECTRIC FACILITY—See Basler Electric Company; *U.S. Private*, pg. 485
BASLER ELECTRIC COMPANY - BASLER ELECTRIC FACILITY—See Basler Electric Company; *U.S. Private*, pg. 485
BASLER ELECTRIC FRANCE SAS—See Basler Electric Company; *U.S. Private*, pg. 485
BB ELECTRONICS A/S; *Int'l*, pg. 920
BB ELECTRONICS SUZHOU CO. LTD.—See BB Electronics A/S; *Int'l*, pg. 920
BDT BAVARIA DIGITAL TECHNIK GMBH—See AdCapital AG; *Int'l*, pg. 126
BEAD INDUSTRIES INC - BEAD ELECTRONICS DIVISION—See Bead Industries Inc.; *U.S. Private*, pg. 505
BECAR SRL—See Beghelli S.p.A.; *Int'l*, pg. 941
BEE ELECTRONIC MACHINES LTD.; *Int'l*, pg. 938
BEIJING AEROSPACE CHANGFENG CO., LTD.; *Int'l*, pg. 945
BEIJING BAYI SPACE LCD TECHNOLOGY CO., LTD.; *Int'l*, pg. 946
BEIJING BOE CHATANI ELECTRONICS CO., LTD.—See BOE Technology Group Co., Ltd.; *Int'l*, pg. 1099
BEIJING BOE DISPLAY TECHNOLOGY CO., LTD.—See BOE Technology Group Co., Ltd.; *Int'l*, pg. 1099
BEIJING BOE OPTOELECTRONICS TECHNOLOGY CO., LTD.—See BOE Technology Group Co., Ltd.; *Int'l*, pg. 1099
BEIJING BOE VACUUM TECHNOLOGY CO., LTD.—See BOE Technology Group Co., Ltd.; *Int'l*, pg. 1099
BEIJING CHANGFENG KEWEI PHOTOELECTRIC CO., LTD.—See Beijing Aerospace Changfeng Co., Ltd.; *Int'l*, pg. 945

BEIJING DAHAO TECHNOLOGY CORPORATION LIMITED; *Int'l*, pg. 948
BEIJING PHILISENSE TECHNOLOGY CO., LTD.; *Int'l*, pg. 955
BEIJING XIAOCHENG TECHNOLOGY STOCK CO., LTD; *Int'l*, pg. 961
BEIJING XINWEI TECHNOLOGY GROUP CO., LTD.; *Int'l*, pg. 961
BEIJING YUANLIU HONGYUAN ELECTRONIC TECHNOLOGY CO., LTD.; *Int'l*, pg. 961
BEIJING ZUOJIANG TECHNOLOGY CO., LTD.; *Int'l*, pg. 961
BEI SENSORS NORTH AMERICA—See Sensata Technologies Holding plc; *U.S. Public*, pg. 1866
BEI SENSORS SAS—See Sensata Technologies Holding plc; *U.S. Public*, pg. 1865
BEJING DAHENG CREATIVE TECHNOLOGY CO., LTD.—See Daheng New Epoch Technology, Inc.; *Int'l*, pg. 1913
BEL FUSE AMERICA, INC.—See Bel Fuse Inc.; *U.S. Public*, pg. 292
BEL FUSE LTD.—See Bel Fuse Inc.; *U.S. Public*, pg. 292
BEL FUSE (MACAO COMMERICAL OFFSHORE) LIMITED—See Bel Fuse Inc.; *U.S. Public*, pg. 292
BELL AND MCCOY INC.; *U.S. Private*, pg. 518
BEL POWER EUROPE S.R.L.—See Bel Fuse Inc.; *U.S. Public*, pg. 292
BEL POWER SOLUTIONS CO. LTD.—See Bel Fuse Inc.; *U.S. Public*, pg. 293
BEL POWER SOLUTIONS INC.—See Bel Fuse Inc.; *U.S. Public*, pg. 293
BEL POWER SOLUTIONS LTD.—See Bel Fuse Inc.; *U.S. Public*, pg. 293
BENCHMARK ELECTRONICS INC.—See Benchmark Electronics, Inc.; *U.S. Public*, pg. 295
BENCHMARK ELECTRONICS INC.—See Benchmark Electronics, Inc.; *U.S. Public*, pg. 295
THE BERGQUIST COMPANY - BIGFORK FACILITY—See GGI Solutions; *Int'l*, pg. 2957
THE BERGQUIST COMPANY - CANNON FALLS FACILITY—See Henkel AG & Co. KGaA; *Int'l*, pg. 3353
THE BERGQUIST COMPANY GMBH—See Henkel AG & Co. KGaA; *Int'l*, pg. 3353
THE BERGQUIST COMPANY KOREA, LTD.—See Henkel AG & Co. KGaA; *Int'l*, pg. 3353
THE BERGQUIST COMPANY—See Henkel AG & Co. KGaA; *Int'l*, pg. 3353
BERNECKER + RAINER INDUSTRIE ELEKTRONIK GMBH—See ABB Ltd.; *Int'l*, pg. 56
BERNER EAZYMATIC AG—See Hormann KG Verkaufsgesellschaf; *Int'l*, pg. 3480
BERNIER CONNECT SAS—See HEICO Corporation; *U.S. Public*, pg. 1020
BESTEC ELECTRONICS USA—See Bestec Power Electronics Co., Ltd.; *Int'l*, pg. 1000
BEST MODULES CORP.—See Holtek Semiconductor Inc.; *Int'l*, pg. 3453
BEST SOLUTION TECHNOLOGY INC.—See Holtek Semiconductor Inc.; *Int'l*, pg. 3453
BETAMEK BERHAD; *Int'l*, pg. 1002
BIOLOG DEVICE CO., LTD.; *Int'l*, pg. 1039
BIOLUMIX, INC.—See Neogen Corporation; *U.S. Public*, pg. 1505
BIOMARK, INC.; *U.S. Private*, pg. 562
BIO MEDIC DATA SYSTEMS INC—See Bio Medic Corporation; *U.S. Private*, pg. 561
BK-ELECTRONIC GMBH—See Resideo Technologies, Inc.; *U.S. Public*, pg. 1790
BK HOLDINGS CO., LTD; *Int'l*, pg. 1054
BLACKHAWK INC.—See Sagewind Capital LLC; *U.S. Private*, pg. 3528
BLINK CHARGING CO.; *U.S. Public*, pg. 361
BLINK MOBILITY, LLC—See Blink Charging Co.; *U.S. Public*, pg. 361
BLUCOM VINA CO., LTD.—See Bluecom Co., Ltd.; *Int'l*, pg. 1071
BLUE STAR ENGINEERING & ELECTRONICS LTD.—See Blue Star Limited; *Int'l*, pg. 1070
BOE (HEBEI) MOBILE TECHNOLOGY CO., LTD.—See BOE Technology Group Co., Ltd.; *Int'l*, pg. 1099
BOE HYUNDAI LCD (BEIJING) DISPLAY TECHNOLOGY CO., LTD.—See BOE Technology Group Co., Ltd.; *Int'l*, pg. 1099
BOE (KOREA) CO., LTD.—See BOE Technology Group Co., Ltd.; *Int'l*, pg. 1099
BOMAR CRYSTAL COMPANY—See BOMAR EXO LLC; *U.S. Private*, pg. 612
BONTRONIC GMBH—See Gerard Perrier Industrie S.A.; *Int'l*, pg. 2942
BOURNS ASIA PACIFIC INC.—See Bourns, Inc.; *U.S. Private*, pg. 624
BOURNS ELECTRONICS (TAIWAN) LTD.—See Bourns, Inc.; *U.S. Private*, pg. 624
BOURNS LTD.—See Bourns, Inc.; *U.S. Private*, pg. 624
BOYD THERMAL SYSTEMS TAIWAN INC.—See The Goldman Sachs Group, Inc.; *U.S. Public*, pg. 2080
BOZHON PRECISION INDUSTRY TECHNOLOGY CO., LTD.; *Int'l*, pg. 1125

BPE SRL—See Dana Incorporated; *U.S. Public*, pg. 621
BPS COOPERATIEF U.A.—See Bel Fuse Inc.; *U.S. Public*, pg. 292
BRANSON DE MEXICO, S.A. DE C.V.—See Emerson Electric Co.; *U.S. Public*, pg. 742
BRICARD S.A.—See Ingersoll Rand Inc.; *U.S. Public*, pg. 1120
BRIGHTKING HOLDINGS LIMITED; *Int'l*, pg. 1162
BRIGHT LED ELECTRONICS CORP. - CHINA FACTORY—See Bright Led Electronics Corp.; *Int'l*, pg. 1161
BROADBAND TELCOM POWER, INC.—See E.ON SE; *Int'l*, pg. 2258
BROADEX TECHNOLOGIES UK LTD.—See Broadex Technologies Co., Ltd.; *Int'l*, pg. 1172
BROADTEAM ELECTRONICS (GUANGZHOU) INC.—See FIC Global, INC; *Int'l*, pg. 2653
BROAD TECHNOLOGY (GUANGZHOU) INC.—See FIC Global, INC; *Int'l*, pg. 2653
BROAD TECHNOLOGY INCORPORATED—See FIC Global, INC; *Int'l*, pg. 2653
BUCHER AUTOMATION HUNGARY KFT.—See Bucher Industries AG; *Int'l*, pg. 1206
BULL GROUP CO., LTD.; *Int'l*, pg. 1214
BUTLER AVIONICS, INC.—See Butler National Corporation; *U.S. Public*, pg. 413
BYRNE ELECTRICAL SPECIALISTS, INC.; *U.S. Private*, pg. 701
C3-ILEX LLC—See L3Harris Technologies, Inc.; *U.S. Public*, pg. 1281
CABOT SUPERMETALS K.K.—See Cabot Corporation; *U.S. Public*, pg. 417
CAL-COMP ELECTRONICS - MAHACHAI—See Cal-Comp Electronics (Thailand) pcl; *Int'l*, pg. 1260
CAL-COMP ELECTRONICS - PETCHABURI—See Cal-Comp Electronics (Thailand) pcl; *Int'l*, pg. 1260
CAL-COMP ELECTRONICS (SUZHOU) COMPANY LIMITED—See Cal-Comp Electronics (Thailand) pcl; *Int'l*, pg. 1260
CAL-COMP ELECTRONICS (THAILAND) PCL; *Int'l*, pg. 1260
CALLIDUS CORPORATION; *U.S. Private*, pg. 722
CALSONIC KANSEI (GUANGZHOU) CORP.—See KKR & Co. Inc.; *U.S. Public*, pg. 1260
CALSONIC KANSEI (HAIMEN) CAR AIR-CONDITIONING COMPRESSOR CORPORATION—See KKR & Co. Inc.; *U.S. Public*, pg. 1260
CALSONIC KANSEI KOREA CORPORATION—See KKR & Co. Inc.; *U.S. Public*, pg. 1260
CALSONIC KANSEI (MALAYSIA) SDN.BHD.—See KKR & Co. Inc.; *U.S. Public*, pg. 1260
CALSONIC KANSEI MEXICANA, S.A. DE R.L. DE C.V.—See KKR & Co. Inc.; *U.S. Public*, pg. 1260
CALSONIC KANSEI MOTHERSON AUTO PRODUCTS PRIVATE LIMITED—See KKR & Co. Inc.; *U.S. Public*, pg. 1260
CALSONIC KANSEI (SHANGHAI) CORP.—See KKR & Co. Inc.; *U.S. Public*, pg. 1260
CALSONIC KANSEI (WUXI) CORPORATION—See KKR & Co. Inc.; *U.S. Public*, pg. 1260
CAMELOT ELECTRONIC TECHNOLOGY CO., LTD; *Int'l*, pg. 1271
CANADIAN SOLAR INC.; *Int'l*, pg. 1285
CANON ELECTRONICS VIETNAM CO., LTD.—See Canon Inc.; *Int'l*, pg. 1297
CANON ELECTRON TUBES & DEVICES CO., LTD.—See Canon Inc.; *Int'l*, pg. 1293
CANON ENGINEERING HONG KONG CO., LTD.—See Canon Inc.; *Int'l*, pg. 1295
CANON MACHINERY INC.—See Canon Inc.; *Int'l*, pg. 1295
CANON OPTICAL INDUSTRIAL EQUIPMENT SERVICE (SHANGHAI) INC.—See Canon Inc.; *Int'l*, pg. 1292
CANON TOKKI CORPORATION—See Canon Inc.; *Int'l*, pg. 1296
CARDINAL COGEN, INC.—See General Electric Company; *U.S. Public*, pg. 916
CARDINALUHP LLC—See AMETEK, Inc.; *U.S. Public*, pg. 120
CARLO GAVAZZI AUTOMACAO LTDA—See Carlo Gavazzi Holding AG; *Int'l*, pg. 1338
CARLO GAVAZZI AUTOMATION HONG KONG LTD—See Carlo Gavazzi Holding AG; *Int'l*, pg. 1338
CARLO GAVAZZI AUTOMATION (KUNSHAN) CO LTD—See Carlo Gavazzi Holding AG; *Int'l*, pg. 1339
CARLO GAVAZZI CONTROLS SPA—See Carlo Gavazzi Holding AG; *Int'l*, pg. 1339
CARLO GAVAZZI GMBH—See Carlo Gavazzi Holding AG; *Int'l*, pg. 1338
CARLO GAVAZZI GMBH—See Carlo Gavazzi Holding AG; *Int'l*, pg. 1339
CARLO GAVAZZI LTD—See Carlo Gavazzi Holding AG; *Int'l*, pg. 1339
CARLO GAVAZZI MEXICO S.A. DE C.V.—See Carlo Gavazzi Holding AG; *Int'l*, pg. 1339
CARLO GAVAZZI OY AB—See Carlo Gavazzi Holding AG; *Int'l*, pg. 1339
CARLO GAVAZZI SA—See Carlo Gavazzi Holding AG; *Int'l*, pg. 1339

CARRIER FIRE & SECURITY—See Carrier Global Corporation; *U.S. Public*, pg. 440
CARTER DUNCAN CORPORATION; *U.S. Private*, pg. 775
CASCADIA BLOCKCHAIN GROUP CORP.; *Int'l*, pg. 1351
CASIL OPTOELECTRONIC PRODUCT DEVELOPMENT LIMITED—See China Aerospace International Holdings Limited; *Int'l*, pg. 1481
CASIO ELECTRONIC MANUFACTURING CO., LTD.—See Casio Computer Co., Ltd.; *Int'l*, pg. 1353
CASIO ELECTRONICS (SHAOGUAN) CO., LTD.—See Casio Computer Co., Ltd.; *Int'l*, pg. 1353
CASIO ELECTRONICS (SHENZHEN) CO., LTD.—See Casio Computer Co., Ltd.; *Int'l*, pg. 1353
CASIO LATIN AMERICA S.A.—See Casio Computer Co., Ltd.; *Int'l*, pg. 1353
CASIO MARKETING (THAILAND) CO., LTD.—See Casio Computer Co., Ltd.; *Int'l*, pg. 1353
CASIO MICRONICS CO., LTD.—See Casio Computer Co., Ltd.; *Int'l*, pg. 1353
CASIO MIDDLE EAST & AFRICA FZE—See Casio Computer Co., Ltd.; *Int'l*, pg. 1353
CASIO TIMEPIECE (DONGGUAN) CO., LTD.—See Casio Computer Co., Ltd.; *Int'l*, pg. 1353
CASTECH INC.; *Int'l*, pg. 1355
CAVENDISH KINETICS, INC.—See Qorvo, Inc.; *U.S. Public*, pg. 1743
CCT TECH (HK) LIMITED—See CCT Fortis Holdings Limited; *Int'l*, pg. 1369
CDZ.T S.R.L.—See Emerson Electric Co.; *U.S. Public*, pg. 742
CE GLOBAL SOURCING TAIWAN CO LTD.—See HPI AG; *Int'l*, pg. 3500
C-E (HONG KONG) LTD.—See Citizen Watch Co., Ltd.; *Int'l*, pg. 1623
CEI INTERNATIONAL INVESTMENTS (VN) LTD.—See AEM Holdings Ltd.; *Int'l*, pg. 175
CELETRONIX USA, INC.—See Jabil Inc.; *U.S. Public*, pg. 1180
CELLSTOP SYSTEMS, INC.; *Int'l*, pg. 1394
CELLULAR SPECIALTIES INC.—See Westell Technologies, Inc.; *U.S. Public*, pg. 2354
CENTERA PHOTONICS INC.—See Elite Advanced Laser Corporation; *Int'l*, pg. 2362
CENTRICA HIVE CANADA INC.—See Centrica plc; *Int'l*, pg. 1413
CENTRICA HIVE LIMITED—See Centrica plc; *Int'l*, pg. 1413
CENTRICA HIVE US INC.—See Centrica plc; *Int'l*, pg. 1413
CENTROID, INC.—See Hicks Holdings, LLC; *U.S. Private*, pg. 1934
CENTROID, INC.—See The Riverside Company; *U.S. Private*, pg. 4108
CENTROID, INC.—See Weinberg Capital Group, Inc.; *U.S. Private*, pg. 4471
CERAMIC & MICROWAVE PRODUCTS—See Dover Corporation; *U.S. Public*, pg. 679
CERCO LLC; *U.S. Private*, pg. 840
CERTIFIED MANUFACTURING, INC.; *U.S. Private*, pg. 841
CETRON ELECTRONICS MANUFACTURING DIVISION—See Richardson Electronics, Ltd.; *U.S. Public*, pg. 1797
CEVA IRELAND LIMITED—See CEVA, Inc.; *U.S. Public*, pg. 476
CHANGSHA JINGJIA MICROELECTRONICS CO., LTD.; *Int'l*, pg. 1444
CHANG WAH ELECTRONMATERIALS, INC.; *Int'l*, pg. 1441
CHANG WAH TECHNOLOGY CO., LTD.; *Int'l*, pg. 1441
CHANGYUAN GROUP LTD.; *Int'l*, pg. 1444
CHANGZHOU AOHONG ELECTRONICS CO., LTD.; *Int'l*, pg. 1445
CHANGZHOU GIKEN PRECISION CO., LTD.—See GSS Energy Ltd.; *Int'l*, pg. 3150
CHANGZHOU HAIHONG ELECTRONICS CO., LTD.—See Changzhou Aohong Electronics Co., Ltd.; *Int'l*, pg. 1445
CHANGZHOU MINKING ELECTRONICS CO., LTD.—See China Security & Surveillance Technology, Inc.; *Int'l*, pg. 1550
CHANGZHOU ZHONGYING SCIENCE & TECHNOLOGY CO., LTD.; *Int'l*, pg. 1446
CHANNEL TECHNOLOGIES GROUP, INC.—See Blue Wolf Capital Partners LLC; *U.S. Private*, pg. 594
CHAOZHOU THREE-CIRCLE GROUP CO., LTD.; *Int'l*, pg. 1447
CHARLES E. GILLMAN COMPANY—See ITT Inc.; *U.S. Public*, pg. 1179
CHATSWORTH PRODUCTS INTERNATIONAL, LTD.—See Chatsworth Products Inc.; *U.S. Private*, pg. 868
CHECKPOINT MANUFACTURING JAPAN CO., LTD.—See CCL Industries Inc.; *Int'l*, pg. 1368
CHEIL TECHNOLOGY CORP.; *Int'l*, pg. 1460
CHEMRING ENERGETIC DEVICES, INC.—See Chemring Group PLC; *Int'l*, pg. 1463
CHENGDU BOE OPTOELECTRONICS TECHNOLOGY CO., LTD.—See BOE Technology Group Co., Ltd.; *Int'l*, pg. 1099
CHENGDU CORPRO TECHNOLOGY CO., LTD.; *Int'l*, pg. 1467
CHENGDU M&S ELECTRONICS TECHNOLOGY CO., LTD.; *Int'l*, pg. 1468

CHENGDU RML TECHNOLOGY CO., LTD.; *Int'l*, pg. 1468
CHENGDU XUGUANG ELECTRONICS CO., LTD.; *Int'l*, pg. 1469
CHENGDU ZHIMINGDA ELECTRONICS CO., LTD.; *Int'l*, pg. 1470
CHENG MEI MATERIALS TECHNOLOGY CORPORATION; *Int'l*, pg. 1466
CHENMING ELECTRONIC (DONGGUAN) CO., LTD.—See Chenming Electronic Tech. Corp.; *Int'l*, pg. 1470
CHEVAL ELECTRONIC ENCLOSURE CO. LTD.—See Blackstone Inc.; *U.S. Public*, pg. 354
CHEVILLOT S.A.S.—See Merck & Co., Inc.; *U.S. Public*, pg. 1415
CHICONY POWER TECHNOLOGY CO., LTD.; *Int'l*, pg. 1476
CHIEFTEK PRECISION CO., LTD.; *Int'l*, pg. 1476
CHINA NATIONAL ELECTRONIC DEVICES CORP.—See Beijing Shiji Information Technology Co., Ltd.; *Int'l*, pg. 956
CHINA SECURITY & SURVEILLANCE MANUFACTURING (PRC), INC.—See China Security & Surveillance Technology, Inc.; *Int'l*, pg. 1550
CHINA SINGYES NEW MATERIALS HOLDINGS LIMITED; *Int'l*, pg. 1552
CHINA SPACESAT CO., LTD.; *Int'l*, pg. 1553
CHINA ZHENHUA (GROUP) SCIENCE & TECHNOLOGY CO., LTD.; *Int'l*, pg. 1567
CHLORIDE POWER PROTECTION PTY. LTD.—See Emerson Electric Co.; *U.S. Public*, pg. 742
CHLORIDE POWER PROTECTION—See Vertiv Holdings Co; *U.S. Public*, pg. 2288
CHLORIDE SRL—See Emerson Electric Co.; *U.S. Public*, pg. 742
CHONGQING CEC-TECHNOLOGY LIMITED—See CEC International Holdings Limited; *Int'l*, pg. 1372
CHONGQING YUXIN PINGRUI ELECTRONIC CO., LTD.; *Int'l*, pg. 1581
CICOR DEUTSCHLAND GMBH—See Cicor Technologies Ltd.; *Int'l*, pg. 1603
CICOR ECOTOOL PTE LTD.—See Cicor Technologies Ltd.; *Int'l*, pg. 1603
CICOR VIETNAM COMPANY LTD.—See Cicor Technologies Ltd.; *Int'l*, pg. 1603
CIDRA PRECISION SERVICES, LLC—See IDEX Corp; *U.S. Public*, pg. 1090
CINCH CONNECTIVITY SOLUTIONS (SHANGHAI) CO., LTD.—See Bel Fuse Inc.; *U.S. Public*, pg. 293
CIONA TECHNOLOGIES LLC—See SRC Holdings Corporation; *U.S. Private*, pg. 3767
CIRCLE RING NETWORK SDN BHD; *Int'l*, pg. 1617
CIRCUIT FABOLOGY MICROELECTRONICS EQUIPMENT CO., LTD.; *Int'l*, pg. 1618
CIRCUITRONICS, INC; *U.S. Private*, pg. 900
CIRCUIT TREE MEDICAL, INC.—See STAAR Surgical Co.; *U.S. Public*, pg. 1924
CIRMAKER TECHNOLOGY CORPORATION; *Int'l*, pg. 1618
CITIZEN ELECTRONICS (CHINA) CO., LTD.—See Citizen Watch Co., Ltd.; *Int'l*, pg. 1623
CITIZEN ELECTRONICS TIMEL CO., LTD.—See Citizen Watch Co., Ltd.; *Int'l*, pg. 1623
CITIZEN FINETECH MIYOTA CO., LTD. - KITAMIMAKI WORKS—See Citizen Watch Co., Ltd.; *Int'l*, pg. 1623
CITIZEN FINETECH MIYOTA CO., LTD.—See Citizen Watch Co., Ltd.; *Int'l*, pg. 1623
CITIZEN MICRO CO., LTD.—See Citizen Watch Co., Ltd.; *Int'l*, pg. 1624
CITIZEN MICRO DEVICES (SUZHOU) CO., LTD.—See Citizen Watch Co., Ltd.; *Int'l*, pg. 1624
CITIZEN PRECISION GUANGZHOU CO., LTD.—See Citizen Watch Co., Ltd.; *Int'l*, pg. 1623
CITIZEN PRECISION HACHINOHE CO., LTD.—See Citizen Watch Co., Ltd.; *Int'l*, pg. 1623
CITIZEN SYSTEMS JAPAN CO., LTD.—See Citizen Watch Co., Ltd.; *Int'l*, pg. 1624
CKD (SHANGHAI) CORPORATION—See CKD Corporation; *Int'l*, pg. 1639
CLEAN ENERGY TECHNOLOGIES, INC.; *U.S. Public*, pg. 508
CLEVER DEVICES LTD.; *U.S. Private*, pg. 942
CLINTON ELECTRONICS CORPORATION; *U.S. Private*, pg. 944
CMC ELECTRONICS ME INC.—See TransDigm Group Incorporated; *U.S. Public*, pg. 2180
CMK ENTERPRISES, INC.—See Electronic Technologies International, Inc.; *U.S. Private*, pg. 1356
CM VISUAL TECHNOLOGY CORP.—See Himax Technologies, Inc.; *Int'l*, pg. 3396
COADNA PHOTONICS, INC.—See Coherent Corp.; *U.S. Public*, pg. 524
COASIA ELECTRONICS CORP. (SHANGHAI) LIMITED—See CoAsia Microelectronics Corp.; *Int'l*, pg. 1681
COASIA ELECTRONICS CORP. (SHENZHEN) LIMITED—See CoAsia Microelectronics Corp.; *Int'l*, pg. 1681
COASIA ELECTRONICS CORP. (SINGAPORE) PTE. LTD.—See CoAsia Microelectronics Corp.; *Int'l*, pg. 1681

COASIA KOREA CO., LTD.—See CoAsia Microelectronics Corp.; *Int'l*, pg. 1681
COASIA MICROELECTRONICS CORP.; *Int'l*, pg. 1681
COBHAM ANTENNA SYSTEMS—See Advent International Corporation; *U.S. Private*, pg. 99
COBHAM TRACKING AND LOCATING LIMITED—See Advent International Corporation; *U.S. Private*, pg. 99
CODE SYSTEMS INC.—See VOXX International Corporation; *U.S. Public*, pg. 2311
COHERENT JAPAN, INC.—See Coherent Corp.; *U.S. Public*, pg. 527
COHERENT KAISERSLAUTERN GMBH—See Coherent Corp.; *U.S. Public*, pg. 527
COHUHD—See Cohu, Inc.; *U.S. Public*, pg. 529
COHU, INC.; *U.S. Public*, pg. 529
COHU MALAYSIA SDN. BHD.—See Cohu, Inc.; *U.S. Public*, pg. 529
COKYVINA JOINT STOCK COMPANY; *Int'l*, pg. 1696
COLUMBIA ELEKTRONIK AB—See Addtech AB; *Int'l*, pg. 132
COMACRAFT SDN BHD—See Dynavest Pte. Ltd.; *Int'l*, pg. 2242
COMET TECHNOLOGIES KOREA CO. LTD.—See Comet Holding AG; *Int'l*, pg. 1710
COMMUNICATION ASSOCIATES—See Belden, Inc.; *U.S. Public*, pg. 294
COMMUNICATION NETWORKS, LLC—See ACRE, LLC; *U.S. Private*, pg. 65
COMPAL MEXICO—See Compal Electronics, Inc.; *Int'l*, pg. 1746
COMPONENTES AVANZADOS DE MEXICO, S.A. DE C.V.—See Emerson Electric Co.; *U.S. Public*, pg. 742
COMPONENT INTERTECHNOLOGIES, INC.; *U.S. Private*, pg. 1002
COMPOTECH AB—See Addtech AB; *Int'l*, pg. 132
COMPTOIR COMMERCIAL INTERNATIONAL N.V.—See Aiphone Co., Ltd.; *Int'l*, pg. 235
COMPUTATIONAL SYSTEMS, INCORPORATED—See Emerson Electric Co.; *U.S. Public*, pg. 742
COMTEL HOLDINGS INC.; *U.S. Private*, pg. 1006
CONCORD CONTROL SYSTEMS LIMITED; *Int'l*, pg. 1765
CONDUCTIVE INKJET TECHNOLOGY LIMITED—See Carclo plc; *Int'l*, pg. 1321
CONELEC OF FLORIDA, LLC—See Main Street Capital Holdings, LLC; *U.S. Private*, pg. 2551
CONHUI (HUIZHOU) SEMICONDUCTOR COMPANY LIMITED—See China Aerospace International Holdings Limited; *Int'l*, pg. 1481
CONNECTICUT ELECTRIC, INC.—See Thompson Street Capital Manager LLC; *U.S. Private*, pg. 4161
CONOLOG CORPORATION; *U.S. Public*, pg. 1018
CONTEL CORPORATION LIMITED; *Int'l*, pg. 1779
CONTINENTAL MICROWAVE & TOOL CO, INC—See Advent International Corporation; *U.S. Private*, pg. 99
CONTROL4 APAC PTY. LTD.—See Resideo Technologies, Inc.; *U.S. Public*, pg. 1790
CONTROL4 EUROPE DOO BELGRADE—See Resideo Technologies, Inc.; *U.S. Public*, pg. 1790
CONTROL4 GERMANY GMBH—See Resideo Technologies, Inc.; *U.S. Public*, pg. 1790
CONXALL CORPORATION—See HEICO Corporation; *U.S. Public*, pg. 1021
COOLER MASTER TECHNOLOGY INC.—See Ban Leong Technologies Limited; *Int'l*, pg. 814
CO-OPERATIVE INDUSTRIES DEFENSE, LLC—See ITT Inc.; *U.S. Public*, pg. 1179
COORSTEK TOKUYAMA CORPORATION—See CoorsTek, Inc.; *U.S. Private*, pg. 1043
COPELAND DE MEXICO, S.A. DE C.V.—See Emerson Electric Co.; *U.S. Public*, pg. 743
CORELASE OY—See Coherent Corp.; *U.S. Public*, pg. 527
CORELIS INC.—See Sagewind Capital LLC; *U.S. Private*, pg. 3527
CORETRONIC PROJECTION (KUNSHAN) CO., LTD.—See Coretronic Corporation; *Int'l*, pg. 1800
CORNELL DUBILIER PROPERTY CORP.—See Knowles Corporation; *U.S. Public*, pg. 1270
CORNERSTONE NETWORKS CO., LTD.; *Int'l*, pg. 1801
CORNING INC. - HARRODSBURG PLANT—See Corning Incorporated; *U.S. Public*, pg. 578
COSMO COMMUNICATIONS CORPORATON; *Int'l*, pg. 1811
COSNINE CO., LTD.; *Int'l*, pg. 1814
COSONIC ACOUSTIC (HK) TECHNOLOGY CO., LIMITED—See Cosonic Intelligent Technologies Co., Ltd.; *Int'l*, pg. 1814
COSONIC ELECTROACOUSTIC TECHNOLOGY CO., LTD.—See Cosonic Intelligent Technologies Co., Ltd.; *Int'l*, pg. 1814
COSONIC INTELLIGENT TECHNOLOGIES CO., LTD.; *Int'l*, pg. 1814
COTHERM S.A.S.—See Atlantic Societe Francaise Develop Thermique S.A.; *Int'l*, pg. 675
COTTONS POINT DESIGN; *U.S. Private*, pg. 1064
COUNTERBALANCE CORPORATION—See South Chester Tube Company; *U.S. Private*, pg. 3721
CPT DRIVES & POWER PCL; *Int'l*, pg. 1826
CPT TECHNOLOGY (GROUP) CO., LTD.; *Int'l*, pg. 1826

334419 — OTHER ELECTRONIC CO...

N.A.I.C.S. INDEX

CRANE AEROSPACE & ELECTRONICS, KELTEC OPERATION—See Crane NXT, Co.; *U.S. Public*, pg. 589
CRANE AEROSPACE, INC.—See Crane NXT, Co.; *U.S. Public*, pg. 589
CRANE ELECTRONICS, INC.—See Crane NXT, Co.; *U.S. Public*, pg. 589
CRANE ELECTRONICS LTD.—See Crane Group Limited; *Int'l*, pg. 1828
CRAWFORD PRODUCTION ROMANIA SRL—See ASSA ABLOY AB; *Int'l*, pg. 635
CREATION TECHNOLOGIES LP—See Goldberg Lindsay & Co., LLC; *U.S. Private*, pg. 1729
CREATIVE LABS SRL—See Creative Technology Ltd.; *Int'l*, pg. 1833
CREATIVE TECHNOLOGY (CHINA) CO., LTD.—See Creative Technology Ltd.; *Int'l*, pg. 1833
CREATIVE TECHNOLOGY (CHINA) CO., LTD.—See Creative Technology Ltd.; *Int'l*, pg. 1833
CREE FAYETTEVILLE, INC.—See Wolfspeed, Inc.; *U.S. Public*, pg. 2377
CROSBY EUROPE N.V.—See KKR & Co. Inc.; *U.S. Public*, pg. 1264
CRRC YONGJI ELECTRIC CO., LTD.—See CRRC Corporation Limited; *Int'l*, pg. 1858
CRUCIALTEC USA, INC.—See CrucialTec Co., Ltd.; *Int'l*, pg. 1859
CRYSTALWISE TECHNOLOGY, INC.; *Int'l*, pg. 1860
CSE SEMAPHORE AUSTRALIA PTY LTD—See CSE Global Ltd.; *Int'l*, pg. 1863
CSE SEMAPHORE BELGIUM SA—See CSE Global Ltd.; *Int'l*, pg. 1863
CSE SEMAPHORE INC—See CSE Global Ltd.; *Int'l*, pg. 1863
CTS AUTOMOTIVE, L.L.C.—See CTS Corporation; *U.S. Public*, pg. 603
CTS CORPORATION; *U.S. Public*, pg. 602
CTS VALPEY CORPORATION—See CTS Corporation; *U.S. Public*, pg. 603
CUBICON INC.—See HyVISION SYSTEM INC.; *Int'l*, pg. 3561
CUSTOM CABLE INDUSTRIES INC.—See HWI Partners, LLC; *U.S. Private*, pg. 2015
CUSTOM SECURITY INDUSTRIES INC.—See Sentry Technology Corporation; *U.S. Public*, pg. 1868
CVILUX TECHNOLOGY (CHONGQING) CORPORATION—See CviLux Corporation; *Int'l*, pg. 1889
CVILUX TECHNOLOGY (SUZHOU) CO., LTD.—See CviLux Corporation; *Int'l*, pg. 1889
CWB AUTOMOTIVE ELECTRONICS CO., LTD.; *Int'l*, pg. 1890
CYBRID TECHNOLOGIES, INC.; *Int'l*, pg. 1894
CYGIA CO., LTD.—See ChangYuan Group Ltd.; *Int'l*, pg. 1444
CYG TIANGONG CO., LTD.—See ChangYuan Group Ltd.; *Int'l*, pg. 1444
CYTTA CORP.; *U.S. Public*, pg. 618
DABURN ELECTRONICS & CABLE CORP.; *U.S. Private*, pg. 1143
DAEDUCK ELECTRONICS CO., LTD. - ANSAN PLANT #1—See DAEDUCK Co., Ltd.; *Int'l*, pg. 1906
D&A ELECTRICAL SYSTEMS SDN. BHD.—See Draexlmaier Gruppe; *Int'l*, pg. 2198
DAEWOO ELECTRONIC COMPONENTS CO., LTD.; *Int'l*, pg. 1910
DAEWOO ELECTRONIC COMPONENTS SUZHOU A&T TECHNOLOGY CO., LTD.—See DAEWOO ELECTRONIC COMPONENTS Co, Ltd.; *Int'l*, pg. 1910
DAEWOO ELECTRONIC COMPONENTS VIETNAM CORPORATION—See DAEWOO ELECTRONIC COMPONENTS Co, Ltd.; *Int'l*, pg. 1910
DAGE PRECISION INDUSTRIES LIMITED—See Nordson Corporation; *U.S. Public*, pg. 1532
DAIDO ELECTRONICS (SUZHOU) CO., LTD.—See Daido Steel Co., Ltd.; *Int'l*, pg. 1922
DAIDONG ELECTRONICS CO., LTD.; *Int'l*, pg. 1924
DAI-ICHI SEIKO AMERICA, INC.—See I-PEX Inc.; *Int'l*, pg. 3563
DAI-ICHI SEIKO CO., LTD. - JOHOR BAHRU FACTORY—See I-PEX Inc.; *Int'l*, pg. 3563
DAI-ICHI SEIKO I-PEX CO., LTD.—See I-PEX Inc.; *Int'l*, pg. 3563
DAIICHI SEIKO (M) SDN. BHD.—See I-PEX Inc.; *Int'l*, pg. 3564
DAIKEN-DAUER-DANFOSS LTD.—See Danfoss A/S; *Int'l*, pg. 1960
DAI NIPPON PRINTING CO. (TAIWAN), LTD.—See Dai Nippon Printing Co., Ltd.; *Int'l*, pg. 1915
DAISHINKU (AMERICA) CORP—See Daishinku Corp.; *Int'l*, pg. 1942
DAISHINKU CORP. - KANZAKI PLANT—See Daishinku Corp.; *Int'l*, pg. 1942
DAISHINKU CORP. - NISHIWAKI PLANT—See Daishinku Corp.; *Int'l*, pg. 1942
DAISHINKU CORP.; *Int'l*, pg. 1942
DAISHINKU CORP. - TOKUSHIMA PRODUCTION DIVISION—See Daishinku Corp.; *Int'l*, pg. 1942
DAISHINKU CORP. - TOTTORI PRODUCTION DIVISION—See Daishinku Corp.; *Int'l*, pg. 1942
DAISHINKU (DEUTSCHLAND) GMBH—See Daishinku Corp.; *Int'l*, pg. 1942
DAISHINKU (SINGAPORE) PTE. LTD—See Daishinku Corp.; *Int'l*, pg. 1942
DAISHINKU (THAILAND) CO., LTD.—See Daishinku Corp.; *Int'l*, pg. 1942
DAITO CHEMIX CORPORATION - FUKUI PLANT—See Daito Chemix Corporation; *Int'l*, pg. 1943
DAITO CHEMIX CORPORATION - SHIZUOKA PLANT—See Daito Chemix Corporation; *Int'l*, pg. 1943
DAITO DENSO CO., LTD.—See Daitron Co., Ltd.; *Int'l*, pg. 1944
DAITO ELECTRON CO., LTD. - EM MACHIDA FACTORY—See Daitron Co., Ltd.; *Int'l*, pg. 1944
DAITRON INC.—See Daitron Co., Ltd.; *Int'l*, pg. 1944
DAITRON (SHANGHAI) CO., LTD.—See Daitron Co., Ltd.; *Int'l*, pg. 1944
DAKTRONICS FRANCE SARL—See Daktronics, Inc.; *U.S. Public*, pg. 621
DAKTRONICS FZE—See Daktronics, Inc.; *U.S. Public*, pg. 620
DAKTRONICS, GMBH—See Daktronics, Inc.; *U.S. Public*, pg. 621
DAKTRONICS IRELAND CO. LTD.—See Daktronics, Inc.; *U.S. Public*, pg. 621
DAKTRONICS JAPAN, INC.—See Daktronics, Inc.; *U.S. Public*, pg. 621
DAKTRONICS SHANGHAI LTD.—See Daktronics, Inc.; *U.S. Public*, pg. 621
DAKTRONICS UK, LTD.—See Daktronics, Inc.; *U.S. Public*, pg. 621
DALIAN ALPS ELECTRONICS CO., LTD.—See Alps Alpine Co., Ltd.; *Int'l*, pg. 376
DANDONG ALPS ELECTRONICS CO., LTD.—See Alps Alpine Co., Ltd.; *Int'l*, pg. 376
DANFOSS AG—See Danfoss A/S; *Int'l*, pg. 1959
DANFOSS (ANSHAN) CONTROLS CO. LTD.—See Danfoss A/S; *Int'l*, pg. 1959
DANFOSS AS—See Danfoss A/S; *Int'l*, pg. 1959
DANFOSS AS—See Danfoss A/S; *Int'l*, pg. 1959
DANFOSS (AUSTRALIA) PTY. LTD.—See Danfoss A/S; *Int'l*, pg. 1959
DANFOSS CO. LTD.—See Danfoss A/S; *Int'l*, pg. 1959
DANFOSS DISTRIBUTION SERVICES A/S—See Danfoss A/S; *Int'l*, pg. 1959
DANFOSS DO BRASIL INDUSTRIA E COMERCIO LTDA.—See Danfoss A/S; *Int'l*, pg. 1961
DANFOSS EOOD—See Danfoss A/S; *Int'l*, pg. 1960
DANFOSS ESSLINGEN GMBH—See Danfoss A/S; *Int'l*, pg. 1960
DANFOSS FZCO—See Danfoss A/S; *Int'l*, pg. 1960
DANFOSS HF.—See Danfoss A/S; *Int'l*, pg. 1961
DANFOSS INDUSTRIES LIMITED—See Danfoss A/S; *Int'l*, pg. 1960
DANFOSS INDUSTRIES PTE. LTD.—See Danfoss A/S; *Int'l*, pg. 1960
DANFOSS INDUSTRIES PVT. LIMITED—See Danfoss A/S; *Int'l*, pg. 1960
DANFOSS INDUSTRIES SDN BHD—See Danfoss A/S; *Int'l*, pg. 1960
DANFOSS IXA A/S—See Danfoss A/S; *Int'l*, pg. 1960
DANFOSS KFT.—See Danfoss A/S; *Int'l*, pg. 1960
DANFOSS LDA.—See Danfoss A/S; *Int'l*, pg. 1960
DANFOSS LIMITED—See Danfoss A/S; *Int'l*, pg. 1960
DANFOSS LLC—See Danfoss A/S; *Int'l*, pg. 1960
DANFOSS LLP—See Danfoss A/S; *Int'l*, pg. 1960
DANFOSS LTD—See Danfoss A/S; *Int'l*, pg. 1960
DANFOSS POLAND SP.Z.O.O.—See Danfoss A/S; *Int'l*, pg. 1960
DANFOSS POWER ELECTRONICS A/S—See Danfoss A/S; *Int'l*, pg. 1960
DANFOSS POWER SOLUTIONS GMBH & CO. OHG—See Danfoss A/S; *Int'l*, pg. 1960
DANFOSS POWER SOLUTIONS LTDA.—See Danfoss A/S; *Int'l*, pg. 1960
DANFOSS POWER SOLUTIONS OY AB—See Danfoss A/S; *Int'l*, pg. 1960
DANFOSS POWER SOLUTIONS PTY. LTD.—See Danfoss A/S; *Int'l*, pg. 1960
DANFOSS POWER SOLUTIONS—See Danfoss A/S; *Int'l*, pg. 1960
DANFOSS REDAN A/S—See Danfoss A/S; *Int'l*, pg. 1961
DANFOSS S.A. DE C.V.—See Danfoss A/S; *Int'l*, pg. 1961
DANFOSS SPOL. S.R.O.—See Danfoss A/S; *Int'l*, pg. 1961
DANFOSS S.R.O.—See Danfoss A/S; *Int'l*, pg. 1961
DANFOSS (THAILAND) CO. LTD.—See Danfoss A/S; *Int'l*, pg. 1959
DANFOSS T.O.V.—See Danfoss A/S; *Int'l*, pg. 1961
DANFOSS TRATA D.O.O.—See Danfoss A/S; *Int'l*, pg. 1961
DANFOSS UAB—See Danfoss A/S; *Int'l*, pg. 1961
DANRIVER TECHNOLOGY (GUANGZHOU) INC.—See FIC Global, INC; *Int'l*, pg. 2653
DAR IBTIKAR AL IRAQ FOR GENERAL SERVICES AND GENERAL TRADE LLC—See Emerson Electric Co.; *U.S. Public*, pg. 742
DARWIN PRECISIONS (SUZHOU) CORP.—See AUO Corporation; *Int'l*, pg. 706
DARWIN PRECISIONS (XIAMEN) CORP.—See AUO Corporation; *Int'l*, pg. 706
DASAN SOLUETA CO.,LTD.; *Int'l*, pg. 1973
DATA MODUL ELECTRONIC TECHNOLOGY (SHANGHAI) CO., LTD.—See Data Modul AG; *Int'l*, pg. 1976
DATA MODUL IBERIA S.L.—See Data Modul AG; *Int'l*, pg. 1976
DATA MODUL POLSKA SP. Z O.O—See Data Modul AG; *Int'l*, pg. 1976
DATASONIC MANUFACTURING SDN. BHD.—See Datasonic Group Berhad; *Int'l*, pg. 1979
DATATRONIC DISTRIBUTION, INC.—See Datronix Holdings Limited; *Int'l*, pg. 1982
DBG TECHNOLOGY (INDIA) PRIVATE LIMITED—See DBG Technology Co., Ltd.; *Int'l*, pg. 1988
D-BOX TECHNOLOGIES INC.; *Int'l*, pg. 1900
DCM DRAEXLMAIER COMPONENTS AUTOMOTIVE DE MEXICO S.A. DE C.V.—See Draexlmaier Gruppe; *Int'l*, pg. 2198
DDK (VIETNAM) LTD.—See Fujikura Ltd.; *Int'l*, pg. 2827
DE AMERTEK CORPORATION INC.; *U.S. Private*, pg. 1181
DEL MAR AVIONICS; *U.S. Private*, pg. 1192
DELPHI ELECTRICAL CENTERS (SHANGHAI) CO., LTD.—See Aptiv PLC; *Int'l*, pg. 524
DELTA ELECTRONICS (AUTOMOTIVE) AMERICAS INC.—See Delta Electronics, Inc.; *Int'l*, pg. 2016
DELTA ELECTRONICS EUROPE LTD.—See Delta Electronics, Inc.; *Int'l*, pg. 2018
DELTA ELECTRONICS (FRANCE) S.A.S.—See Delta Electronics, Inc.; *Int'l*, pg. 2016
DELTA ELECTRONICS (SLOVAKIA) S.R.O.—See Delta Electronics, Inc.; *Int'l*, pg. 2018
DELTA ENERGY SYSTEMS (UK) LIMITED—See Delta Electronics, Inc.; *Int'l*, pg. 2018
DELTA NETWORKS (DONGGUAN) CO., LTD.—See Delta Electronics, Inc.; *Int'l*, pg. 2018
DELTA PLUS CESKA REPUBLIKA S.R.O.—See Delta Plus Group; *Int'l*, pg. 2019
DELTA PLUS CROATIA D.O.O.—See Delta Plus Group; *Int'l*, pg. 2020
DELTA PLUS-E SA—See Delta Plus Group; *Int'l*, pg. 2020
DELTA PLUS HELLAS SRL—See Delta Plus Group; *Int'l*, pg. 2020
DELTA PLUS POLSKA SP ZO.O—See Delta Plus Group; *Int'l*, pg. 2020
DELTA PLUS SICUREX SRL—See Delta Plus Group; *Int'l*, pg. 2020
DELTA PLUS SLOVENSKO SRO—See Delta Plus Group; *Int'l*, pg. 2020
DELTATECH CONTROLS GMBH—See Sensata Technologies Holding plc; *U.S. Public*, pg. 1865
DELTEC SHUNTS, LLC—See Riedon, Inc.; *U.S. Private*, pg. 3434
DELTON TECHNOLOGY (GUANGZHOU) INC.—See FIC Global, INC; *Int'l*, pg. 2653
DELTRON LTD.; *Int'l*, pg. 2022
DEM MANUFACTURING—See Avnet, Inc.; *U.S. Public*, pg. 250
DENSO IWATE CORPORATION—See Denso Corporation; *Int'l*, pg. 2032
DEPO AUTO PARTS IND. CO., LTD.; *Int'l*, pg. 2041
DESIGNATRONICS, INC. - ALL METRIC SMALL PARTS DIVISION—See Designatronics, Inc.; *U.S. Private*, pg. 1214
DEXATEK TECHNOLOGY LTD.—See Ennoconn Corporation; *Int'l*, pg. 2443
DFE DRAXLMAIER FAHRZEUGELEKTRIK GMBH—See Draexlmaier Gruppe; *Int'l*, pg. 2198
DHAUTOWARE CO LTD; *Int'l*, pg. 2099
DIALIGHT CORPORATION—See Dialight plc; *Int'l*, pg. 2104
DIALIGHT PLC; *Int'l*, pg. 2104
DICON FIBEROPTICS, INC.; *U.S. Private*, pg. 1227
D.ID CORPORATION; *Int'l*, pg. 1901
DIGITAL APPLIANCE CONTROLS DE MEXICO, S.A. DE C.V.—See SigmaTron International, Inc.; *U.S. Public*, pg. 1877
DIGITRONIC GMBH; *Int'l*, pg. 2124
DIGNITANA AB; *Int'l*, pg. 2124
DIGUANG INTERNATIONAL DEVELOPMENT COMPANY LTD.; *Int'l*, pg. 2124
DIRECTED ENERGY, INC.—See Berkeley Nucleonics Corp.; *U.S. Private*, pg. 532
DISPLAY TECH CO., LTD.; *Int'l*, pg. 2135
DIVERSIFIED TECHNICAL SYSTEMS, INC.—See Vishay Precision Group, Inc.; *U.S. Public*, pg. 2303
DJ PRECISION CO., LTD.—See I-PEX Inc.; *Int'l*, pg. 3563
DK ELECTRONIC MATERIALS, INC.; *Int'l*, pg. 2138
DK TECH; *Int'l*, pg. 2100
DMEGC JAPAN CORPORATION LIMITED—See Hengdian Group DMEGC Magnetics Co., Ltd.; *Int'l*, pg. 3346
DMEGC SOLAR USA, LLC—See Hengdian Group DMEGC Magnetics Co., Ltd.; *Int'l*, pg. 3346
DMEGC UK SOLAR PV—See Hengdian Group DMEGC Magnetics Co., Ltd.; *Int'l*, pg. 3346
DMS CO., LTD.; *Int'l*, pg. 2146
DNF CO., LTD - DNF ULSAN PLANT—See DNF Co., Ltd.; *Int'l*, pg. 2148

D'NONCE (JOHORE) SDN. BHD.—See D'nonce Technology Bhd.; *Int'l*, pg. 1899
DNP COLOR TECHNO KAMEYAMA CO., LTD.—See Dai Nippon Printing Co., Ltd.; *Int'l*, pg. 1914
DNP ELECTRONICS AMERICA, LLC—See Dai Nippon Printing Co., Ltd.; *Int'l*, pg. 1914
DNP PRECISION DEVICES CO., LTD.—See Dai Nippon Printing Co., Ltd.; *Int'l*, pg. 1915
DONGBU HITEK FABRICATION 2—See Dongbu Group; *Int'l*, pg. 376
DONGGUAN ALPS ELECTRONICS CO., LTD.—See Alps Alpine Co., Ltd.; *Int'l*, pg. 376
DONGGUAN AOHAI TECHNOLOGY CO., LTD.; *Int'l*, pg. 2167
DONGGUAN DAEJOO ELECTRONIC MATERIALS CO., LTD.—See Daejoo Electronic Materials Co., Ltd.; *Int'l*, pg. 1907
DONGGUAN DINGTONG PRECISION METAL CO., LTD.; *Int'l*, pg. 2167
DONGGUAN FUKOKU RUBBER & PLASTICS INDUSTRY CO., LTD.—See Fukoku Co., Ltd.; *Int'l*, pg. 2838
DONGGUAN JETCROWN TECHNOLOGY LIMITED—See Deswell Industries, Inc.; *Int'l*, pg. 2047
DONGGUAN MENTECH OPTICAL & MAGNETIC CO., LTD. - MORGAN HILL BRANCH—See Dongguan Mentech Optical & Magnetic Co., Ltd.; *Int'l*, pg. 2167
DONGGUAN MENTECH OPTICAL & MAGNETIC CO., LTD.; *Int'l*, pg. 2167
DONGGUAN TARRY ELECTRONICS CO., LTD.; *Int'l*, pg. 2167
DONGGUAN TEAC ELECTRONICS CO., LTD.—See Evolution Capital Management LLC; *U.S. Private*, pg. 1443
DONGNAN ELECTRONICS CO., LTD.; *Int'l*, pg. 2169
DONGXU OPTOELECTRONIC TECHNOLOGY CO., LTD.; *Int'l*, pg. 2171
DOOSAN CORPORATION - IKSAN FACTORY—See Doosan Corporation; *Int'l*, pg. 2173
DP SERVICE S.R.L.—See Codere S.A.; *Int'l*, pg. 1688
DRAEXLMAIER GRUPPE; *Int'l*, pg. 2198
DREAMTECH CO., LTD.; *Int'l*, pg. 2203
DR. FRITZ FAULHABER GMBH & CO. KG; *Int'l*, pg. 2191
DRM SISTEME ELECTRICE SRL—See Draexlmaier Gruppe; *Int'l*, pg. 2198
DSA ONCORE; *U.S. Private*, pg. 1281
DSE DRAXLMAIER SYSTEMY ELEKTRYCZNE SP. Z O.O.—See Draexlmaier Gruppe; *Int'l*, pg. 2198
DSM COMPUTER GMBH—See Avnet, Inc.; *U.S. Public*, pg. 252
DSV DRAXLMAIER SYSTEMVERKABELUNGEN GMBH—See Draexlmaier Gruppe; *Int'l*, pg. 2198
DTR DRAXLMAIER SISTEME TEHNICE ROMANIA S.R.L.—See Draexlmaier Gruppe; *Int'l*, pg. 2198
DUOTECH SERVICES, INC—See Bernhard Capital Partners Management, LP; *U.S. Private*, pg. 537
DUPAR CONTROLS INC.—See Dewhurst Group plc; *Int'l*, pg. 2091
DUPONT PERFORMANCE SOLUTIONS (SINGAPORE) PTE. LTD.—See Celanese Corporation; *U.S. Public*, pg. 465
DUPONT PERFORMANS COZUMLERI ENDUSTRIYEL URUNLER TICARET LIMITED SIRKETI—See Celanese Corporation; *U.S. Public*, pg. 465
DUPONT ROMANIA S.R.L.—See Corteva, Inc.; *U.S. Public*, pg. 582
DVDO, INC.—See Lattice Semiconductor Corporation; *U.S. Public*, pg. 1294
DVS DRAXLMAIER VERDRAHTUNGSSYSTEME GMBH—See Draexlmaier Gruppe; *Int'l*, pg. 2198
DYNAMIC EUROPE LTD.—See Invacare Corporation; *U.S. Private*, pg. 2130
DYNAMIC PROGRESS INTERNATIONAL LIMITED—See Alltronics Holdings Limited; *Int'l*, pg. 361
DYNAMIC SOURCE MANUFACTURING INC.; *Int'l*, pg. 2240
DYNAVEST PTE. LTD.; *Int'l*, pg. 2242
DYNAVEST TECHNOLOGIES (SUZHOU) CO, LTD—See Dynavest Pte. Ltd.; *Int'l*, pg. 2242
DYNAVEST (THAILAND) CO, LTD—See Dynavest Pte. Ltd.; *Int'l*, pg. 2242
DYNAVISION LTD.; *Int'l*, pg. 2242
DYNNIQ UK LTD—See Egeria Capital Management B.V.; *Int'l*, pg. 2323
E3 ENERGIE EFFIZIENZ EXPERTEN GMBH—See BayWa AG; *Int'l*, pg. 917
EASTECH ELECTRONICS (TAIWAN) INC.—See Eastern Asia Technology Ltd.; *Int'l*, pg. 2271
EASTERN ASIA TECHNOLOGY LTD.; *Int'l*, pg. 2271
EASTPRINT, INC.—See East West Manufacturing, LLC; *U.S. Private*, pg. 1319
EBARA DENSAN LTD.—See Ebara Corporation; *Int'l*, pg. 2282
EBERLE DESIGN, INC.—See Vance Street Capital LLC; *U.S. Private*, pg. 4342
EBV ELEKTRONIK SP. Z O.O.—See Avnet, Inc.; *U.S. Public*, pg. 252
EBV ELEKTRONIK TOV—See Avnet, Inc.; *U.S. Public*, pg. 252
EBW ELECTRONICS, INC.; *U.S. Private*, pg. 1326

ECLAT FOREVER MACHINERY CO., LTD.; *Int'l*, pg. 2291
ECLIPTEK, LLC—See ILSI America LLC; *U.S. Private*, pg. 2043
ECOMAL DEUTSCHLAND GMBH—See Vishay Intertechnology, Inc.; *U.S. Public*, pg. 2302
ECOPRO CO., LTD.; *Int'l*, pg. 2299
E& CORPORATION CO., LTD.; *Int'l*, pg. 2246
ECR AG—See H2APEX Group SCA; *Int'l*, pg. 3199
EDECLINSEYSYSTEM CO.,LTD.—See Fuji Corporation; *Int'l*, pg. 2809
EDISON OPTO CORP.; *Int'l*, pg. 2311
EDOM ELECTRONIC TECHNOLOGY (SHANGHAI) CO., LTD.—See EDOM Technology Co., Ltd.; *Int'l*, pg. 2313
EDOM TECHNOLOGY JAPAN CO., LTD.—See EDOM Technology Co., Ltd.; *Int'l*, pg. 2313
EDO WESTERN CORP.—See L3Harris Technologies, Inc.; *U.S. Public*, pg. 1279
EDS MANUFACTURING INC.; *U.S. Private*, pg. 1338
EDT-EUROPE APS—See Emerging Display Tech; *Int'l*, pg. 2379
EDT-JAPAN CORP.—See Emerging Display Tech; *Int'l*, pg. 2379
EECO, INC.—See Emerson Electric Co; *U.S. Public*, pg. 742
EFUN TECHNOLOGY CO., LTD.; *Int'l*, pg. 2322
EFW INC.—See Elbit Systems Limited; *Int'l*, pg. 2344
EGIDE SA; *Int'l*, pg. 2324
EGIDE USA, INC.—See Egide SA; *Int'l*, pg. 2324
EINHELL MIDDLE EAST TRADING FZC—See Einhell Germany AG; *Int'l*, pg. 2333
E INK CORPORATION—See E Ink Holdings, Inc.; *Int'l*, pg. 2246
E INK HOLDINGS, INC; *Int'l*, pg. 2246
E INVESTMENT & DEVELOPMENT CO., LTD.; *Int'l*, pg. 2246
EIZO ENGINEERING CORPORATION—See EIZO Corporation; *Int'l*, pg. 2337
EIZO NANAO MS CORPORATION—See EIZO Corporation; *Int'l*, pg. 2337
ELAN MICROELECTRONIC CORP.; *Int'l*, pg. 2342
ELBIT SYSTEMS ELECTRO-OPTICS ELOP LTD.—See Elbit Systems Limited; *Int'l*, pg. 2344
ELBIT SYSTEMS EW AND SIGINT - ELISRA LTD—See Elbit Systems Limited; *Int'l* pg. 2344
ELBIT SYSTEMS LAND AND C4I LTD.—See Elbit Systems Limited; *Int'l*, pg. 2344
ELCOMTEC CO., LTD; *Int'l*, pg. 2345
ELECTRICAL COMPONENTS INTERNATIONAL, INC.—See Cerberus Capital Management, L.P.; *U.S. Private*, pg. 838
ELECTRICAL COMPONENTS INTERNATIONAL—See Cerberus Capital Management, L.P.; *U.S. Private*, pg. 838
ELECTROCUBE INCORPORATED; *U.S. Private*, pg. 1354
ELECTROLUX DE CHILE S.A.—See AB Electrolux; *Int'l*, pg. 41
ELECTRONICA NSC DE MEXICO, S.A. DE C.V.—See Texas Instruments Incorporated; *U.S. Public*, pg. 2025
ELECTRONIC INDUSTRIES CO.; *Int'l*, pg. 2354
ELECTRONIC INSTRUMENTATION & TECHNOLOGY; *U.S. Private*, pg. 1355
ELECTRONIC SECURITY DEVICES, INC.—See ASSA ABLOY AB; *Int'l*, pg. 639
ELECTRONIC TECHNOLOGIES INTERNATIONAL, INC.; *U.S. Private*, pg. 1356
ELECTRO OPTIC SYSTEMS HOLDINGS LIMITED; *Int'l*, pg. 2353
ELEKTROBIT NIPPON K.K.—See Continental Aktiengesellschaft; *Int'l*, pg. 1783
ELEKTRON COMPONENTS TUNISIE SARL—See Checkit plc; *Int'l*, pg. 1459
ELITE ADVANCED LASER CORPORATION; *Int'l*, pg. 2362
E-LITECOM CO., LTD.; *Int'l*, pg. 2249
ELITE MATERIAL CO., LTD.; *Int'l*, pg. 2362
ELKON ELEKTRIK SANAYI VE TICARET AS—See Electricite de France S.A.; *Int'l*, pg. 2351
ELLIES ELECTRONICS (BLOEMFONTEIN)(PTY) LTD—See Ellies Holdings Limited; *Int'l*, pg. 2366
ELLIES ELECTRONICS (CAPE)(PTY) LTD—See Ellies Holdings Limited; *Int'l*, pg. 2366
ELLIES ELECTRONICS (NATAL)(PTY) LTD—See Ellies Holdings Limited; *Int'l*, pg. 2366
ELLIES ELECTRONICS (NELSPRUIT)(PTY) LTD—See Ellies Holdings Limited; *Int'l*, pg. 2366
ELLIES ELECTRONICS (PIETERSBURG)(PTY) LTD—See Ellies Holdings Limited; *Int'l*, pg. 2366
ELLIES HOLDINGS LIMITED; *Int'l*, pg. 2365
ELLIES (PTY) LTD—See Ellies Holdings Limited; *Int'l*, pg. 2366
ELLIPSIZ COMMUNICATIONS (NZ) LIMITED—See Ellipsiz Ltd.; *Int'l*, pg. 2366
ELLIPSIZ LTD.; *Int'l*, pg. 2366
ELMA ELECTRONIC GMBH—See Elma Electronic AG; *Int'l*, pg. 2367
ELMOS SEMICONDUCTOR SUD GMBH—See ELMOS Semiconductor AG; *Int'l*, pg. 2368
EL-O-MATIC GMBH—See Emerson Electric Co.; *U.S. Public*, pg. 743

ELP CORPORATION; *Int'l*, pg. 2369
ELTEC ELEKTRONIK AG—See CornerstoneCapital Verwaltungs AG; *Int'l*, pg. 1801
ELTECH A/S—See Addtech AB; *Int'l*, pg. 133
EMB CO., LTD.; *Int'l*, pg. 2374
EMCON EMANATION CONTROL LTD.—See AEA Investors LP; *U.S. Private*, pg. 113
EMDT AMERICA INC.—See Kopin Corporation; *U.S. Public*, pg. 1271
EMERGENCY POWER SYSTEMS LIMITED—See Emerson Electric Co.; *U.S. Public*, pg. 743
EMERGING DISPLAY TECHNOLOGIES CORP.; *Int'l*, pg. 2378
EMERGING DISPLAY TECHNOLOGIES CORP.—See Emerging Display Tech; *Int'l*, pg. 2379
EMERGING DISPLAY TECHNOLOGIES CO.,—See Emerging Display Tech; *Int'l*, pg. 2379
EMERSON CLIMATE TECHNOLOGIES FZE—See Emerson Electric Co.; *U.S. Public*, pg. 745
EMERSON CLIMATE TECHNOLOGIES (INDIA) LIMITED—See Emerson Electric Co.; *U.S. Public*, pg. 743
EMERSON CLIMATE TECHNOLOGIES S.R.L.—See Emerson Electric Co.; *U.S. Public*, pg. 743
EMERSON ELECTRIC CO. (INDIA) PRIVATE LTD.—See Emerson Electric Co.; *U.S. Public*, pg. 744
EMERSON LLC—See Emerson Electric Co.; *U.S. Public*, pg. 746
EMERSON NETWORK POWER DO BRASIL LTDA—See Emerson Electric Co.; *U.S. Public*, pg. 745
EMERSON NETWORK POWER ENTERPRISE SRL—See Emerson Electric Co.; *U.S. Public*, pg. 745
EMERSON NETWORK POWER INDUSTRIAL SYSTEMS SAS—See Emerson Electric Co.; *U.S. Public*, pg. 742
EMERSON NETWORK POWER SAS—See Emerson Electric Co.; *U.S. Public*, pg. 742
EMERSON NETWORK POWER (SINGAPORE) PTE. LTD.—See Vertiv Holdings Co; *U.S. Public*, pg. 2288
EMERSON NETWORK POWER (THAILAND) CO. LTD.—See Vertiv Holdings Co; *U.S. Public*, pg. 2288
EMERSON (PHILIPPINES) CORPORATION—See Emerson Electric Co.; *U.S. Public*, pg. 744
EMERSON PROCESS MANAGEMENT EUROPE GMBH—See Emerson Electric Co.; *U.S. Public*, pg. 748
EMERSON PROCESS MANAGEMENT KFT.—See Emerson Electric Co.; *U.S. Public*, pg. 747
EMERSON PROCESS MANAGEMENT NV—See Emerson Electric Co.; *U.S. Public*, pg. 748
EMERSON PROCESS MANAGEMENT REGULATOR TECHNOLOGIES, INC.—See Emerson Electric Co.; *U.S. Public*, pg. 747
EMERSON PROCESS MANAGEMENT S.R.L.—See Emerson Electric Co.; *U.S. Public*, pg. 748
EMF CORPORATION; *U.S. Private*, pg. 1382
EMG, INC.; *U.S. Private*, pg. 1382
EMNI CO., LTD; *Int'l*, pg. 2385
EMPEROR CULTURE GROUP LIMITED; *Int'l*, pg. 2386
EMPOWER RF SYSTEMS, INC.; *U.S. Private*, pg. 1387
EMS DEVELOPMENT CORPORATION—See Advent International Corporation; *U.S. Private*, pg. 100
EMSONIC CO., LTD—See EXA E&C Inc.; *Int'l*, pg. 2576
EM TECH CO., LTD.—See EO Technics Co., Ltd.; *Int'l*, pg. 2457
EM TEST (SWITZERLAND) GMBH—See AMETEK, Inc.; *U.S. Public*, pg. 120
EM TEST (USA), INC.—See AMETEK, Inc.; *U.S. Public*, pg. 120
EMTRON ELECTRONIC GMBH—See FORTEC Elektronik AG; *Int'l*, pg. 2738
EMW; *Int'l*, pg. 2395
ENCITECH CONNECTORS AB—See Beijer Alma AB; *Int'l*, pg. 942
ENDRICH BAUELEMENTE VERTRIEBS GMBH; *Int'l*, pg. 2409
ENERTEC SYSTEMS 2001 LTD.—See Ault Alliance, Inc.; *U.S. Public*, pg. 227
ENERZENT CO., LTD.; *Int'l*, pg. 2425
ENGINEERING DESIGN TEAM, INC.—See HEICO Corporation; *U.S. Public*, pg. 1020
ENICS AG—See Ahlstrom Capital Oy; *Int'l*, pg. 225
ENNOTECH (KUNSHAN) TECHNOLOGY CO., LTD.—See Ennoconn Corporation; *Int'l*, pg. 2443
ENOMOTO CO., LTD.; *Int'l*, pg. 2444
ENOMOTO HONG KONG CO.LTD.—See Enomoto Co., Ltd.; *Int'l*, pg. 2444
ENOVA SYSTEMS INC.; *U.S. Public*, pg. 770
ENPLAS MICROTECH, INC.—See ENPLAS CORPORATION; *Int'l*, pg. 2445
ENPLAS SEMICONDUCTOR PERIPHERALS PTE. LTD.—See ENPLAS CORPORATION; *Int'l*, pg. 2445
ENSILICA PLC; *Int'l*, pg. 2447
ENSURGE MICROPOWER ASA; *Int'l*, pg. 2449
ENTEGRIS SAS—See Entegris, Inc.; *U.S. Public*, pg. 776
ENTEK INTERNATIONAL UK LTD.—See Entek Holding LLC; *U.S. Private*, pg. 1403
ENTIRE TECHNOLOGY CO., LTD.; *Int'l*, pg. 2452
EOLITE SYSTEMS, SAS—See MKS Instruments, Inc.; *U.S. Public*, pg. 1452

N.A.I.C.S. INDEX

334419 — OTHER ELECTRONIC CO...

EO TECHNICS CO., LTD.—See EO Technics Co., Ltd.; *Int'l*, pg. 2457
EO TECHNICS INDIA PVT. LTD—See EO Technics Co., Ltd.; *Int'l*, pg. 2457
EO TECHNICS SINGAPORE PTE., LTD.—See EO Technics Co., Ltd.; *Int'l*, pg. 2457
EO TECHNICS TAIWAN CO., LTD.—See EO Technics Co., Ltd.; *Int'l*, pg. 2457
EPC POWER CORP.—See Cleanhill Partners; *U.S. Private*, pg. 931
EPC POWER CORP.—See The Goldman Sachs Group, Inc.; *U.S. Public*, pg. 2076
E P E CORP.—See Intervala, LLC; *U.S. Private*, pg. 2127
EPICRYSTAL CORPORATION (CHANGZHOU) LTD.—See Ennostar Inc.; *Int'l*, pg. 2443
EPISIL TECHNOLOGIES, INC.; *Int'l*, pg. 2463
EPISKY CORPORATION (XIAMEN) LTD.—See Ennostar Inc.; *Int'l*, pg. 2443
E.S.C. ELECTRONICS CORP.; *U.S. Private*, pg. 1307
ESCORT TEKNOLOJI YATIRIM A.S.; *Int'l*, pg. 2502
ESI-PYROPHOTONICS LASERS, INC.—See MKS Instruments, Inc.; *U.S. Public*, pg. 1452
ESON PRECISION IND. CO., LTD.; *Int'l*, pg. 2504
ESPEY MFG. & ELECTRONICS CORP.; *U.S. Public*, pg. 794
ETAL, INC.—See Amplex AB; *Int'l*, pg. 434
ETREND HIGHTECH CORP.; *Int'l*, pg. 2524
ETS-LINDGREN LIMITED—See ESCO Technologies, Inc.; *U.S. Public*, pg. 794
EUROFINS MASER B.V.—See Eurofins Scientific S.E.; *Int'l*, pg. 2545
EUROIMPIANTI ELECTRONIC S.P.A.—See Argo Finanziaria S.p.A.; *Int'l*, pg. 562
EVERBRITE ELECTRONICS, INC—See Everbrite, LLC; *U.S. Private*, pg. 1437
EVERBRITE TECHNOLOGY CO., LTD.; *Int'l*, pg. 2563
EVERDISPLAY OPTRONICS SHANGHAI CO., LTD.; *Int'l*, pg. 2563
EVERFOCUS ELECTRONICS (BEIJING) CO., LTD.—See EverFocus Electronics Co., Ltd.; *Int'l*, pg. 2565
EVERFOCUS ELECTRONICS CORP.—See EverFocus Electronics Co., Ltd.; *Int'l*, pg. 2565
EVERLIGHT ELECTRONICS (SUZHOU) LTD.—See Everlight Electronics Co., Ltd.; *Int'l*, pg. 2567
EVERTECHNO CO., LTD.; *Int'l*, pg. 2569
EVOQUA WATER TECHNOLOGIES CANADA—See Xylem Inc.; *U.S. Public*, pg. 2394
EXCEET GROUP AG—See H2APEX Group SCA; *Int'l*, pg. 3199
EXCEL CELL ELECTRONIC ANHUI CO., LTD.—See Excel Cell Electronic Co., Ltd.; *Int'l*, pg. 2577
EXCEL CELL ELECTRONIC (SUZHOU) CO., LTD.—See Excel Cell Electronic Co., Ltd.; *Int'l*, pg. 2577
EXCELITAS CANADA, INC.—See AEA Investors LP; *U.S. Private*, pg. 113
EXCELITAS TECHNOLOGIES GMBH & CO. KG—See AEA Investors LP; *U.S. Private*, pg. 113
EXCELITAS TECHNOLOGIES PHILIPPINES, INC.—See AEA Investors LP; *U.S. Private*, pg. 113
EXCELSIOR CAPITAL LTD.; *Int'l*, pg. 2578
EXERION PRECISION TECHNOLOGY ULFT NL B.V.—See Exerion Precision Technology Holding B.V.; *Int'l*, pg. 2584
FAE TECHNOLOGY S.P.A.; *Int'l*, pg. 2601
FAIR-RITE PRODUCTS CORP.; *U.S. Private*, pg. 1462
FAITAL S.P.A.—See Alps Alpine Co., Ltd.; *Int'l*, pg. 376
FARGO ASSEMBLY OF EUROPE LTD—See Cerberus Capital Management, L.P.; *U.S. Private*, pg. 838
FARRAND CONTROLS DIVISION—See Ruhle Companies, Inc.; *U.S. Private*, pg. 3503
FCI CONNECTORS KOREA LTD.—See Amphenol Corporation; *U.S. Public*, pg. 127
FCI CONNECTORS SHANGHAI CO. LTD.—See Amphenol Corporation; *U.S. Public*, pg. 127
FCI ELECTRONICS HUNGARY KFT—See Amphenol Corporation; *U.S. Public*, pg. 127
FCI JAPAN K. K.—See Amphenol Corporation; *U.S. Public*, pg. 127
FCI TAIWAN LTD—See Amphenol Corporation; *U.S. Public*, pg. 127
FDK CORPORATION - SANYO PLANT—See Fujitsu Limited; *Int'l*, pg. 2832
FDK CORPORATION—See Fujitsu Limited; *Int'l*, pg. 2832
FDK LANKA (PVT) LTD.—See Fujitsu Limited; *Int'l*, pg. 2832
FEI COMMUNICATIONS, INC.—See Frequency Electronics, Inc.; *U.S. Public*, pg. 885
FEI GOVERNMENT SYSTEMS, INC.—See Frequency Electronics, Inc.; *U.S. Public*, pg. 885
FENIX MANUFACTURING SOLUTIONS, LLC; *U.S. Private*, pg. 1495
FEP FAHRZEUGELEKTRIK PIRNA GMBH—See Amphenol Corporation; *U.S. Public*, pg. 130
FERRANTI TECHNOLOGIES LIMITED—See Elbit Systems Limited; *Int'l*, pg. 2345
FERROAMP ELEKTRONIK AB; *Int'l*, pg. 2642
FERROTEC (AN HUI) TECHNOLOGY DEVELOPMENT CO., LTD.; *Int'l*, pg. 2642
FERROTEC KOREA CORPORATION—See Ferrotec Holdings Corporation; *Int'l*, pg. 2643

FERROTEC POWER SEMICONDUCTOR GMBH—See Ferrotec Holdings Corporation; *Int'l*, pg. 2643
FERROTEC SEMICONDUCTOR MATERIAL CORPORATION—See Ferrotec Holdings Corporation; *Int'l*, pg. 2643
FF SYSTEMS INC.; *U.S. Private*, pg. 1500
FIBEROPTICS TECHNOLOGY INC.; *U.S. Private*, pg. 1502
FIDIA CO.—See FIDIA S.p.A.; *Int'l*, pg. 2654
FIDIA DO BRASIL LTDA.—See FIDIA S.p.A.; *Int'l*, pg. 2654
FIDIA GMBH—See FIDIA S.p.A.; *Int'l*, pg. 2654
FIDIA IBERICA S.A.—See FIDIA S.p.A.; *Int'l*, pg. 2655
FIDIA MACHINERY & ELECTRONICS CO. LTD.—See FIDIA S.p.A.; *Int'l*, pg. 2655
FIDIA S.A.R.L.—See FIDIA S.p.A.; *Int'l*, pg. 2655
FIDIA S.P.A.; *Int'l*, pg. 2654
FILTRONIC AB—See Danaher Corporation; *U.S. Public*, pg. 626
FILTRONIC WIRELESS LTD.—See Filtronic plc; *Int'l*, pg. 2663
FILTRONIC WIRELESS LTD.—See Filtronic plc; *Int'l*, pg. 2663
FINEDNC. CO., LTD.; *Int'l*, pg. 2674
FINE DNC CO., LTD.—See Finetechnix Co., Ltd.; *Int'l*, pg. 2674
FINEMAT APPLIED MATERIALS CO., LTD.; *Int'l*, pg. 2674
FINETEK CO., LTD; *Int'l*, pg. 2674
FIRSTCOME ELECTRONICS LTD.—See Citizen Watch Co., Ltd.; *Int'l*, pg. 1625
FIRSTMARK AEROSPACE CORPORATION—See Hicks Holdings, LLC; *U.S. Private*, pg. 1934
FIRSTMARK AEROSPACE CORPORATION—See The Riverside Company; *U.S. Private*, pg. 4108
FIRSTMARK AEROSPACE CORPORATION—See Weinberg Capital Group, Inc.; *U.S. Private*, pg. 4471
FITIPOWER INTEGRATED TECHNOLOGY, INC.; *Int'l*, pg. 2695
FLEXPOINT SENSOR SYSTEMS, INC.; *U.S. Public*, pg. 853
FLEXPOWER INDIA PRIVATE LIMITED—See Flex Ltd.; *Int'l*, pg. 2702
FLEX-TEC INC.—See Cerberus Capital Management, L.P.; *U.S. Private*, pg. 838
FLEXTRONICS AMERICA, LLC—See Flex Ltd.; *Int'l*, pg. 2703
FLEXTRONICS AUTOMOTIVE INC—See Flex Ltd.; *Int'l*, pg. 2702
FLEXTRONICS BRASIL LTDA.—See Flex Ltd.; *Int'l*, pg. 2703
FLEXTRONICS COMPUTING (SUZHOU) CO. LTD.—See Flex Ltd.; *Int'l*, pg. 2702
FLEXTRONICS ENCLOSURES (HONG KONG) LTD.—See Flex Ltd.; *Int'l*, pg. 2702
FLEXTRONICS GLOBAL ENCLOSURES (SINGAPORE) PTE. LTD.—See Flex Ltd.; *Int'l*, pg. 2702
FLEXTRONICS GLOBAL SERVICES CANADA INC.—See Flex Ltd.; *Int'l*, pg. 2702
FLEXTRONICS GROUP SWEDEN AB—See Flex Ltd.; *Int'l*, pg. 2702
FLEXTRONICS INTERNATIONAL AB—See Flex Ltd.; *Int'l*, pg. 2702
FLEXTRONICS INTERNATIONAL CORK B.V.—See Flex Ltd.; *Int'l*, pg. 2702
FLEXTRONICS INTERNATIONAL DENMARK A/S—See Flex Ltd.; *Int'l*, pg. 2702
FLEXTRONICS INTERNATIONAL KFT.—See Flex Ltd.; *Int'l*, pg. 2702
FLEXTRONICS INTERNATIONAL—See Flex Ltd.; *Int'l*, pg. 2702
FLEXTRONICS INTERNATIONAL—See Flex Ltd.; *Int'l*, pg. 2702
FLEXTRONICS INTERNATIONAL TAIWAN LTD.—See Flex Ltd.; *Int'l*, pg. 2703
FLEXTRONICS INTERNATIONAL USA INC. AUSTIN—See Flex Ltd.; *Int'l*, pg. 2703
FLEXTRONICS INTERNATIONAL USA INC.—See Flex Ltd.; *Int'l*, pg. 2703
FLEXTRONICS INTERNATIONAL USA INC.—See Flex Ltd.; *Int'l*, pg. 2703
FLEXTRONICS (ISRAEL) LTD—See Flex Ltd.; *Int'l*, pg. 2702
FLEXTRONICS JAPAN K.K.—See Flex Ltd.; *Int'l*, pg. 2703
FLEXTRONICS MANUFACTURING JUAREZ, S.A. DE C.V.—See Flex Ltd.; *Int'l*, pg. 2703
FLEXTRONICS MANUFACTURING MEXICO, S.A. DE C.V.—See Flex Ltd.; *Int'l*, pg. 2703
FLEXTRONICS MANUFACTURING (PENANG) SDN. BHD.—See Flex Ltd.; *Int'l*, pg. 2703
FLEXTRONICS MANUFACTURING (SINGAPORE) PTE. LTD.—See Flex Ltd.; *Int'l*, pg. 2703
FLEXTRONICS (NANJING) TECHNOLOGY CO., LTD—See Flex Ltd.; *Int'l*, pg. 2702
FLEXTRONICS NETWORK SERVICES SWEDEN AB—See Flex Ltd.; *Int'l*, pg. 2703
FLEXTRONICS ROMANIA SRL—See Flex Ltd.; *Int'l*, pg. 2704
FLEXTRONICS SERVICIOS GUADALAJARA, S.A. DE C.V.—See Flex Ltd.; *Int'l*, pg. 2704
FLEXTRONICS (SHANGHAI) CO., LTD.—See Flex Ltd.; *Int'l*, pg. 2702

FLEXTRONICS SPECIAL BUSINESS SOLUTIONS—See Flex Ltd.; *Int'l*, pg. 2704
FLEXTRONICS SYSTEMS TEXAS LTD.—See Flex Ltd.; *Int'l*, pg. 2703
FLEXTRONICS TECHNOLOGIES (INDIA) PVT LTD.—See Flex Ltd.; *Int'l*, pg. 2704
FLEXTRONICS TECHNOLOGY (PENANG) SDN. BHD.—See Flex Ltd.; *Int'l*, pg. 2704
FLEXTRONICS TECHNOLOGY (SHANGHAI) CO., LTD.—See Flex Ltd.; *Int'l*, pg. 2704
FLEXTRONICS TECHNOLOGY (SHENZHEN) CO., LTD.—See Flex Ltd.; *Int'l*, pg. 2704
FLOATOGRAPH TECHNOLOGIES, LLC; *U.S. Private*, pg. 1546
FLOTURN PHOTORECEPTOR (KUNSHAN) CO., LTD.—See Floturn Inc.; *U.S. Private*, pg. 1551
FLUKE ITALIA S.R.L.—See Fortive Corporation; *U.S. Public*, pg. 870
FLUKE OPERATIONS B.V.—See Danaher Corporation; *U.S. Public*, pg. 627
FOCUS H&S CO., LTD.; *Int'l*, pg. 2719
FOCUSLIGHT TECHNOLOGIES INC.; *Int'l*, pg. 2720
FORHOUSE CORPORATION - MALAYSIAN FACTORY—See Darwin Precisions Corporation; *Int'l*, pg. 1973
FORMOSA ELECTRONIC INDUSTRIES INC.; *Int'l*, pg. 2734
FORTEC ELEKTRONIK AG; *Int'l*, pg. 2737
FORTEC SWITZERLAND AG—See FORTEC Elektronik AG; *Int'l*, pg. 2738
FORTEC TECHNOLOGY UK LIMITED—See FORTEC Elektronik AG; *Int'l*, pg. 2738
FORTH CORPORATION PUBLIC COMPANY LIMITED - FORTH FACTORY—See Forth Corporation Public Company Limited; *Int'l*, pg. 2738
FORTH DIMENSION DISPLAYS—See Kopin Corporation; *U.S. Public*, pg. 1271
FORTRON/SOURCE CORP.; *U.S. Private*, pg. 1577
FORYOU CORPORATION; *Int'l*, pg. 2747
FORYOU GENERAL ELECTRONICS CO., LTD.—See Foryou Corporation; *Int'l*, pg. 2747
FOSTER ELECTRIC CO., (GUANGZHOU) LTD.—See Foster Electric Co., Ltd.; *Int'l*, pg. 2749
FOTONATION LIMITED; *Int'l*, pg. 2753
FOXCONN TECHNOLOGY CO., LTD.—See Hon Hai Precision Industry Co., Ltd.; *Int'l*, pg. 3456
FOX ELECTRONICS AS—See Addtech AB; *Int'l*, pg. 133
FP INOVOLABS GMBH—See Francotyp-Postalia Holding AG; *Int'l*, pg. 2761
FPT SEMICONDUCTOR JOINT STOCK COMPANY—See FPT Corporation; *Int'l*, pg. 2757
FRAKO CAPACITORS & PLANT CONSTRUCTION GMBH—See AdCapital AG; *Int'l*, pg. 126
FREEBIRD SEMICONDUCTOR CORPORATION—See HEICO Corporation; *U.S. Public*, pg. 1021
FREEDOM ELECTRONICS LLC—See SPP Management Services, LLC; *U.S. Private*, pg. 3762
FREQUENCY ELECTRONICS, INC.; *U.S. Public*, pg. 885
FSP GROUP USA CORP.—See FSP Technology Inc.; *Int'l*, pg. 2800
FSP TECHNOLOGY INC.—See FSP Technology Inc.; *Int'l*, pg. 2800
FSP TECHNOLOGY USA INC.—See FSP Technology Inc.; *Int'l*, pg. 2800
FUJIAN FORY CO., LTD.—See Fujian Furi Electronics Co., Ltd.; *Int'l*, pg. 2818
FUJIAN FURI ELECTRONICS CO., LTD.; *Int'l*, pg. 2818
FUJIAN SUPERTECH ADVANCED MATERIAL CO., LTD.; *Int'l*, pg. 2820
FUJI ELECTRIC INDUSTRY CO., LTD. - KUSATSU FACTORY—See FUJI ELECTRIC INDUSTRY CO., LTD.; *Int'l*, pg. 2813
FUJI ELECTRIC INDUSTRY CO., LTD. - SHIN-ASAHI FACTORY—See FUJI ELECTRIC INDUSTRY CO., LTD.; *Int'l*, pg. 2813
FUJI ELECTRIC INDUSTRY CO., LTD.; *Int'l*, pg. 2813
FUJIFILM ELECTRONIC MATERIALS (EUROPE) N.V.—See FUJIFILM Holdings Corporation; *Int'l*, pg. 2821
FUJIFILM OPT-ELECTRONICS (TIANJIN) CO., LTD.—See FUJIFILM Holdings Corporation; *Int'l*, pg. 2824
FUJIKURA AUTOMOTIVE VIETNAM LTD.—See Fujikura Ltd.; *Int'l*, pg. 2828
FUJIKURA ELECTRONICS SHANGHAI LTD.—See Fujikura Ltd.; *Int'l*, pg. 2828
FUJIKURA ELECTRONICS (THAILAND) LTD. - AYUTTHAYA FACTORY 1—See Fujikura Ltd.; *Int'l*, pg. 2828
FUJIKURA ELECTRONICS (THAILAND) LTD. - LAMPHUN FACTORY 1—See Fujikura Ltd.; *Int'l*, pg. 2828
FUJIKURA ELECTRONICS (THAILAND) LTD. - NAVANAKORN FACTORY 2—See Fujikura Ltd.; *Int'l*, pg. 2828
FUJIKURA ELECTRONICS (THAILAND) LTD.—See Fujikura Ltd.; *Int'l*, pg. 2828
FUJIKURA ELECTRONICS VIETNAM LTD.—See Fujikura Ltd.; *Int'l*, pg. 2828
FUJIKURA LTD.; *Int'l*, pg. 2827
FUJI MACHINE MFG. CO., LTD. - OKAZAKI PLANT—See Fuji Corporation; *Int'l*, pg. 2810

FUJITA DEVICE CO., LTD.—See FUJITA ENGINEERING Co., Ltd.; *Int'l*, pg. 2831
FUJITSU COMPONENTS (CHANGZHOU) CO., LTD.—See FUJITSU COMPONENT LIMITED; *Int'l*, pg. 2832
FUJITSU COMPONENTS HONG KONG CO., LIMITED—See Fujitsu Limited; *Int'l*, pg. 2834
FUJITSU DENSO INTERNATIONAL LIMITED—See Fujitsu Limited; *Int'l*, pg. 2834
FUJITSU LIMITED - AIZU WAKAMATSU PLANT—See Fujitsu Limited; *Int'l*, pg. 2835
FUJITSU LIMITED - MIE PLANT—See Fujitsu Limited; *Int'l*, pg. 2835
FUJITSU LIMITED - NUMAZU PLANT—See Fujitsu Limited; *Int'l*, pg. 2835
FUJITSU LIMITED - OYAMA PLANT—See Fujitsu Limited; *Int'l*, pg. 2835
FUJITSU SEMICONDUCTOR EUROPE GMBH—See Fujitsu Limited; *Int'l*, pg. 2835
FUNAI ELECTRIC EUROPE SP. Z.O.O. - FRENCH BUSINESS UNIT—See Funai Electric Co., Ltd.; *Int'l*, pg. 2844
FUNAI ELECTRIC EUROPE SP. Z.O.O. - GERMAN BUSINESS UNIT—See Funai Electric Co., Ltd.; *Int'l*, pg. 2844
FUNAI ELECTRIC EUROPE SP. Z.O.O. - POLISH BUSINESS UNIT—See Funai Electric Co., Ltd.; *Int'l*, pg. 2844
FUNCTION INTERNATIONAL PUBLIC COMPANY LIMITED; *Int'l*, pg. 2845
FURUNO CHINA CO., LIMITED—See Furuno Electric Co., Ltd.; *Int'l*, pg. 2847
FURUNO DONGGUAN CO., LTD.—See Furuno Electric Co., Ltd.; *Int'l*, pg. 2847
FURUNO ELECTRIC CO., LTD.; *Int'l*, pg. 2847
FURUNO HONG KONG CO., LTD.—See Furuno Electric Co., Ltd.; *Int'l*, pg. 2848
FURUNO KANSAI HANBAI CO., LTD.—See Furuno Electric Co., Ltd.; *Int'l*, pg. 2848
FURUNO KOREA CO., LTD.—See Furuno Electric Co., Ltd.; *Int'l*, pg. 2848
FUTABA CORPORATION OF AMERICA—See Futaba Corporation; *Int'l*, pg. 2850
FUTABA CORPORATION OF HUIZHOU—See Futaba Corporation; *Int'l*, pg. 2850
FUTABA CORPORATION OF THE PHILIPPINES—See Futaba Corporation; *Int'l*, pg. 2850
FUTABA ELECTRONICS (BEIJING) CO., LTD.—See Futaba Corporation; *Int'l*, pg. 2850
FUTABA (EUROPE) GMBH—See Futaba Corporation; *Int'l*, pg. 2850
FUTABA MOBILE DISPLAY CORPORATION—See Futaba Corporation; *Int'l*, pg. 2850
FUTABA PRECISION CO., LTD.—See Futaba Corporation; *Int'l*, pg. 2850
FUTABA PRECISION DIE & MOLD MACHINERY (CHINA) CO., LTD.—See Futaba Corporation; *Int'l*, pg. 2850
FUTABA PRECISION MOULD (SHENZHEN) CORPORATION, LTD.—See Futaba Corporation; *Int'l*, pg. 2850
FUTABA (VIETNAM) CO., LTD.—See Futaba Corporation; *Int'l*, pg. 2850
FUTURE ELECTRONICS CORP., ITALY—See Future Electronics Inc.; *Int'l*, pg. 2855
GALAXIA DEVICE CO., LTD.—See Hyosung Corporation; *Int'l*, pg. 3550
GALTRONICS CORPORATION LTD.—See Baylin Technologies Inc.; *Int'l*, pg. 914
GANZHOU YIHAO NEW MATERIALS CO., LTD.; *Int'l*, pg. 2882
GARO AB; *Int'l*, pg. 2885
GE AVIATION SYSTEMS LLC - POMPANO BEACH—See General Electric Company; *U.S. Public*, pg. 918
GEFRAN DEUTSCHLAND GMBH—See Gefran S.p.A.; *Int'l*, pg. 2912
GEFRAN INDIA LTD.—See Gefran S.p.A.; *Int'l*, pg. 2912
GEFRAN SIEI DRIVES TECHNOLOGY (SHANGHAI) CO.,LTD—See Gefran S.p.A.; *Int'l*, pg. 2912
GEMMA—See HITIM Group; *Int'l*, pg. 3426
GEMSTAR TECHNOLOGY (CHINA) CO. LIMITED—See Universal Electronics, Inc.; *U.S. Public*, pg. 2255
GENERAL INTERFACE SOLUTION (GIS) HOLDING LTD.; *Int'l*, pg. 2918
GENERAL MICROWAVE CORPORATION—See Kratos Defense & Security Solutions, Inc.; *U.S. Public*, pg. 1276
GENERALPLUS TECHNOLOGY (H.K.) CO., LIMITED—See Generalplus Technology Inc.; *Int'l*, pg. 2920
GENIMOUS TECHNOLOGY CO., LTD.; *Int'l*, pg. 2923
GENNBIO INC.; *Int'l*, pg. 2925
GEOMATEC CO., LTD.; *Int'l*, pg. 2933
GERAER BATTERIE-DIENST GMBH; *Int'l*, pg. 2942
GERAL AUTOMATION SA—See Gerard Perrier Industrie S.A.; *Int'l*, pg. 2942
GERAL CONSTRUCTIONS ELECTRIQUES ET TRAVAUX INDUSTRIELS SAS—See Gerard Perrier Industrie S.A.; *Int'l*, pg. 2942
GERLING APPLIED ENGINEERING, INC.—See Harald Quandt Holding GmbH; *Int'l*, pg. 3270
GEROME TECHNOLOGIES, INC.—See Audax Group, Limited Partnership; *U.S. Private*, pg. 387
GET ELECTRONIQUE S.A.S.—See Airbus SE; *Int'l*, pg. 246
GGI SOLUTIONS; *Int'l*, pg. 2957

GILLAM-FEI, S.A.—See Frequency Electronics, Inc.; *U.S. Public*, pg. 885
GILLET TUBES TECHNOLOGIES S.A.S.—See Apollo Global Management, Inc.; *U.S. Public*, pg. 162
GLASS ONE TECHNOLOGY CORPORATION; *Int'l*, pg. 2989
GLASS ONE TECHNOLOGY TAIWAN CORPORATION—See Glass One Technology Corporation; *Int'l*, pg. 2989
GLOBAL EQUIPMENT SERVICES & MANUFACTURING VIETNAM COMPANY LIMITED—See Kimball Electronics, Inc.; *U.S. Public*, pg. 1228
GLOBAL LIGHTING TECHNOLOGIES INC.; *Int'l*, pg. 2998
GLOBALTECH CORPORATION; *U.S. Public*, pg. 946
GLOBAL TECH LED LLC; *U.S. Private*, pg. 1718
GLOBAL VIEW COMPANY LIMITED; *Int'l*, pg. 3002
GLOTECH INDUSTRIAL CORP.; *Int'l*, pg. 3011
G. LUFFT MESS- UND REGELTECHNIK GMBH—See Danaher Corporation; *U.S. Public*, pg. 627
G.M.I. TECHNOLOGY INC.; *Int'l*, pg. 2866
GM SINGAPORE PTE. LIMITED—See General Motors Company; *U.S. Public*, pg. 924
GODEX EUROPE GMBH—See Godex International Co., Ltd.; *Int'l*, pg. 3019
GODEX INTERNATIONAL AMERICA, LLC—See Godex International Co., Ltd.; *Int'l*, pg. 3019
GO ELEMENT CO., LTD.; *Int'l*, pg. 3017
GOERTEK KOREA TECHNOLOGY INC.—See GoerTek Inc.; *Int'l*, pg. 3021
GOERTEK TECHNOLOGY JAPAN CO., LTD.—See GoerTek Inc.; *Int'l*, pg. 3021
GOLDEN STATE ENVIRONMENTAL TEDAGUA CORPORATION, S.A.—See ACS, Actividades de Construccion y Servicios, S.A.; *Int'l*, pg. 112
GOOCH & HOUSEGO (DEUTSCHLAND) GMBH—See Gooch & Housego PLC; *Int'l*, pg. 3038
GOOD SKY RELAY (SHENZHEN) CO., LTD.—See Excel Cell Electronic Co., Ltd.; *Int'l*, pg. 2577
GOOD WILL INSTRUMENT CO., LTD.; *Int'l*, pg. 3039
GOWANDA - GEC LLC—See The Jordan Company, L.P.; *U.S. Private*, pg. 4063
GP ACOUSTICS (UK) LIMITED—See Gold Peak Technology Group Limited; *Int'l*, pg. 3025
GP ELECTRONICS (SZ) LIMITED—See Gold Peak Technology Group Limited; *Int'l*, pg. 3025
GPS INDUSTRIES, LLC—See Ingersoll Rand Inc.; *U.S. Public*, pg. 1120
GPV ESTONIA AS—See Aktieselskabet Schouw & Co.; *Int'l*, pg. 266
GPV GERMANY GMBH—See Aktieselskabet Schouw & Co.; *Int'l*, pg. 266
GPV GROUP A/S—See Aktieselskabet Schouw & Co.; *Int'l*, pg. 266
GPV INTERNATIONAL A/S—See Aktieselskabet Schouw & Co.; *Int'l*, pg. 266
GPV LANKA (PRIVATE), LTD.—See Aktieselskabet Schouw & Co.; *Int'l*, pg. 266
GPV SLOVAKIA (NOVA) S.R.O.—See Aktieselskabet Schouw & Co.; *Int'l*, pg. 266
GPV SLOVAKIA S.R.O.—See Aktieselskabet Schouw & Co.; *Int'l*, pg. 266
GPV SWEDEN AB—See Aktieselskabet Schouw & Co.; *Int'l*, pg. 266
GPV SWITZERLAND SA—See Aktieselskabet Schouw & Co.; *Int'l*, pg. 266
GPV ZHONGSHAN CO., LTD.—See Aktieselskabet Schouw & Co.; *Int'l*, pg. 266
GRAINIT S.R.L.—See Corteva, Inc.; *U.S. Public*, pg. 584
GRASPHERE JAPAN CO., LTD.—See Central Security Patrols Co., Ltd.; *Int'l*, pg. 1410
GRAVITA GEORGIA LIMITED—See Gravita India Limited; *Int'l*, pg. 3062
GRAVITY MEDIA GROUP LIMITED; *Int'l*, pg. 3062
GREATEK ELECTRONICS INC.; *Int'l*, pg. 3067
GREEN BALLAST, INC.; *U.S. Private*, pg. 1771
GREEVE LIMITED—See Elate Holdings Limited; *Int'l*, pg. 2343
GRESHAM POWER ELECTRONICS LIMITED—See Ault Alliance, Inc.; *U.S. Public*, pg. 227
GROLLEAU SAS—See Flex Ltd.; *Int'l*, pg. 2704
GROUP DEKKO - MERRIAM—See Graham Holdings Company; *U.S. Public*, pg. 955
GRUPO RAF, S.A. DE C.V.; *Int'l*, pg. 3134
G-SHANK ENTERPRISE CO., LTD.; *Int'l*, pg. 2862
GS YUASA POWER ELECTRONICS LTD.—See GS Yuasa Corporation; *Int'l*, pg. 3143
GUANGDONG ANJUBAO DISPLAY TECHNOLOGY CO., LTD.—See Guangdong Anjubao Digital Technology Co., Ltd.; *Int'l*, pg. 3152
GUANGDONG FENGHUA ADVANCED TECHNOLOGY (HOLDING) CO., LTD.; *Int'l*, pg. 3154
GUANGDONG GOWORLD CO., LTD.; *Int'l*, pg. 3154
GUANGDONG GREEN PRECISION COMPONENTS CO., LTD.; *Int'l*, pg. 3154
GUANGDONG HEC TECHNOLOGY HOLDING CO., LTD.; *Int'l*, pg. 3155
GUANGDONG KINGSHINE ELECTRONIC TECHNOLOGY COMPANY LIMITED; *Int'l*, pg. 3157

GUANGDONG LITE ARRAY COMPANY LIMITED—See Global-Tech Advanced Innovations Inc.; *Int'l*, pg. 3003
GUANGDONG STONESONIC DIGITAL TECHNIQUE CO., LTD.—See China Security & Surveillance Technology, Inc.; *Int'l*, pg. 1550
GUANGDONG ZHENYE TECHNOLOGY CO., LTD.; *Int'l*, pg. 3162
GUANGZHOU AMPHENOL ELECTRONICS CO., LTD.—See Amphenol Corporation; *U.S. Public*, pg. 130
GUANGZHOU FANGBANG ELECTRONICS CO., LTD.; *Int'l*, pg. 3165
GUANGZHOU HAOYANG ELECTRONIC CO., LTD.; *Int'l*, pg. 3165
GUANGZHOU SHIYUAN ELECTRONICS CO., LTD; *Int'l*, pg. 3168
GUANGZHOU SHIYUAN ELECTRONIC TECHNOLOGY CO., LTD.; *Int'l*, pg. 3168
GUANGZHOU TERMBRAY ELECTRONICS TECHNOLOGIES COMPANY LIMITED—See TTM Technologies, Inc.; *U.S. Public*, pg. 2203
GUARDIAN ELECTRIC MANUFACTURING COMPANY—See Kelco Industries Inc.; *U.S. Private*, pg. 2274
GUDEL GROUP AG; *Int'l*, pg. 3171
GUESTLOGIX INC.; *Int'l*, pg. 3173
GUIZHOU SPACE APPLIANCE CO., LTD.; *Int'l*, pg. 3175
GUJARAT PERSTORP ELECTRONICS LTD.; *Int'l*, pg. 3177
GVS ARGENTINA SA—See GVS S.p.A.; *Int'l*, pg. 3190
GVS FILTRATION CO., LTD.—See GVS S.p.A.; *Int'l*, pg. 3190
GVS FILTRATION SDN. BHD.—See GVS S.p.A.; *Int'l*, pg. 3190
GVS JAPAN KK—See GVS S.p.A.; *Int'l*, pg. 3190
GVS KOREA LTD.—See GVS S.p.A.; *Int'l*, pg. 3190
GVS MICROFILTRAZIONE S.R.L.—See GVS S.p.A.; *Int'l*, pg. 3190
GVS RUSSIA LLC—See GVS S.p.A.; *Int'l*, pg. 3190
GVS TECHNOLOGY (SUZHOU) CO., LTD.—See GVS S.p.A.; *Int'l*, pg. 3190
G.W. LISK COMPANY, INC.; *U.S. Private*, pg. 1631
H2APEX GROUP SCA; *Int'l*, pg. 3199
HAGIWARA ELECTRONICS CO., LTD.—See Hagiwara Electric Holdings Co., Ltd.; *Int'l*, pg. 3207
HAGIWARA ELECTRONICS INDIA PRIVATE LIMITED—See Hagiwara Electric Holdings Co., Ltd.; *Int'l*, pg. 3207
HAGIWARA HOKUTO TECHNO CO., LTD.—See Hagiwara Electric Holdings Co., Ltd.; *Int'l*, pg. 3207
HAGIWARA (SHANGHAI) CO., LTD.—See Hagiwara Electric Holdings Co., Ltd.; *Int'l*, pg. 3207
HAGIWARA TECHNO SOLUTIONS CO. LTD.—See Hagiwara Electric Holdings Co., Ltd.; *Int'l*, pg. 3207
HAGIWARA TECHNO SOLUTIONS (SHANGHAI) CO., LTD.—See Hagiwara Electric Holdings Co., Ltd.; *Int'l*, pg. 3207
HAIER SMART HOME CO., LTD.; *Int'l*, pg. 3209
HALMA TRADING AND SERVICES INDIA PVT LTD—See Halma plc; *Int'l*, pg. 3232
HAMLIN ELECTRONICS (SUZHOU) LIMITED—See Littelfuse, Inc.; *U.S. Public*, pg. 1327
HAMMOND EXPANDERS DIVISION - MALAYSIA PLANT—See Hammond Group, Inc.; *U.S. Private*, pg. 1849
HANA MICRODISPLAY TECHNOLOGIES, INC.—See Hana Microelectronics Public Company Limited; *Int'l*, pg. 3241
HANA MICROELECTRONICS PUBLIC COMPANY LIMITED; *Int'l*, pg. 3241
HANGZHOU DAHE THERMO-MAGNETICS CO., LTD. - QUARTZ DIVISION—See Ferrotec Holdings Corporation; *Int'l*, pg. 2643
HANGZHOU EVERFINE PHOTO-E-INFO CO., LTD.; *Int'l*, pg. 3247
HANGZHOU GREENDA ELECTRONIC MATERIALS CO., LTD.; *Int'l*, pg. 3247
HANGZHOU LION ELECTRONICS CO., LTD.; *Int'l*, pg. 3249
HANGZHOU MDK OPTO ELECTRONIC CORP., LTD.; *Int'l*, pg. 3249
HANNSPREE DISPLAY TECHNOLOGY (NANJING) INC.—See HannStar Display Corporation; *Int'l*, pg. 3257
HANNSTAR DISPLAY CORPORATION - NEIHU PLANT—See HannStar Display Corporation; *Int'l*, pg. 3257
HANNSTAR DISPLAY CORPORATION; *Int'l*, pg. 3257
HANNSTAR DISPLAY CORPORATION - TAINAN PLANT—See HannStar Display Corporation; *Int'l*, pg. 3257
HANNSTAR DISPLAY (NANJING) CORPORATION—See HannStar Display Corporation; *Int'l*, pg. 3257
HANP INC.; *Int'l*, pg. 3258
HANSOL TECHNICS CO., LTD.; *Int'l*, pg. 3261
HANZA ELECTRIC (SUZHOU) CO. LTD.—See Hanza AB; *Int'l*, pg. 3267
HAOSEN ULTRA-PRECISION CO., LTD.—See Dalian Haosen Equipment Manufacturing Co., Ltd.; *Int'l*, pg. 1952
HARBIN XINGUANG OPTIC-ELECTRONICS TECHNOLOGY CO., LTD.; *Int'l*, pg. 3271

N.A.I.C.S. INDEX

334419 — OTHER ELECTRONIC CO...

HARMONY ELECTRONICS CORP—See Daishinku Corp.; *Int'l*, pg. 1942
HARMONY ELECTRONICS (DONGGUAN) CO., LTD.—See Daishinku Corp.; *Int'l*, pg. 1942
HARMONY ELECTRONICS (THAILAND) CO LTD—See Daishinku Corp.; *Int'l*, pg. 1942
HARRIS CORP. - ELECTRONIC SYSTEMS DIVISION—See L3Harris Technologies, Inc.; *U.S. Public*, pg. 1279
HARRIS CORP. - SPACE & INTELLIGENCE SYSTEMS DIVISION—See L3Harris Technologies, Inc.; *U.S. Public*, pg. 1280
HARVATEK CORPORATION; *Int'l*, pg. 3280
HAYAMA INDUSTRIES CO., LTD.—See AOI Electronics Co., Ltd.; *Int'l*, pg. 488
HAYDON LINEAR MOTORS (CHANGZHOU) CO., LTD.—See AMETEK, Inc.; *U.S. Public*, pg. 120
H&B DESIGN CO., LTD.; *Int'l*, pg. 3191
HB SOLUTION CO., LTD.; *Int'l*, pg. 3295
HB TECHNOLOGY INC.; *Int'l*, pg. 3295
HCC AEGIS INC.—See AMETEK, Inc.; *U.S. Public*, pg. 116
HCC INDUSTRIES INTERNATIONAL—See AMETEK, Inc.; *U.S. Public*, pg. 116
HCC INDUSTRIES INTERNATIONAL—See AMETEK, Inc.; *U.S. Public*, pg. 116
HDC LABS CO., LTD.; *Int'l*, pg. 3300
HD VIEW 360, INC.; *U.S. Private*, pg. 1890
HEADWALL PHOTONICS, INC.; *U.S. Private*, pg. 1891
HEBEI SINOPACK ELECTRONIC TECHNOLOGY CO., LTD.; *Int'l*, pg. 3306
HEFEI XINSHENG OPTOELECTRONICS TECHNOLOGY CO., LTD.—See BOE Technology Group Co., Ltd.; *Int'l*, pg. 1099
HELIATEK GMBH; *Int'l*, pg. 3329
HENAN CARVE ELECTRONICS TECHNOLOGY CO., LTD.; *Int'l*, pg. 3342
HENAN THINKER AUTOMATIC EQUIPMENT CO., LTD.; *Int'l*, pg. 3343
HENGDIAN GROUP DMEGC MAGNETICS CO., LTD.; *Int'l*, pg. 3346
HENGSTLER GMBH—See Fortive Corporation; *U.S. Public*, pg. 870
HENKEL US OPERATIONS CORPORATION - TCLAD DIVISION—See Henkel AG & Co. KGaA; *Int'l*, pg. 3353
HEP TECH CO., LTD.; *Int'l*, pg. 3356
HERAEUS NOBLELIGHT AMERICA LLC—See AEA Investors LP; *U.S. Private*, pg. 113
HERLEY CTI—See Advent International Corporation; *U.S. Private*, pg. 101
HERLEY GMI EYAL LTD.—See Kratos Defense & Security Solutions, Inc.; *U.S. Public*, pg. 1276
HERLEY NEW ENGLAND—See Advent International Corporation; *U.S. Private*, pg. 101
HERMETIC SEAL—See AMETEK, Inc.; *U.S. Public*, pg. 116
HETRONIC ASIA—See Methode Electronics, Inc.; *U.S. Public*, pg. 1428
HEWTECH (LIANYUNGANG) ELECTRONICS CO., LTD.—See Hirakawa Hewtech Corp.; *Int'l*, pg. 3403
HEWTECH PHILIPPINES ELECTRONICS CORP.—See Hirakawa Hewtech Corp.; *Int'l*, pg. 3403
HEXA ANALISA SDN. BHD.—See Fibon Berhad; *Int'l*, pg. 2652
HFC CONTROLS. CORP.—See Doosan Corporation; *Int'l*, pg. 2174
HF COMPANY; *Int'l*, pg. 3374
HF SCIENTIFIC, INC.—See Watts Water Technologies, Inc.; *U.S. Public*, pg. 2337
HID CHINA LTD.—See ASSA ABLOY AB; *Int'l*, pg. 637
HID GLOBAL GMBH—See ASSA ABLOY AB; *Int'l*, pg. 637
HID GLOBAL SDN. BHD.—See ASSA ABLOY AB; *Int'l*, pg. 637
HID GLOBAL SWITZERLAND S.A.—See ASSA ABLOY AB; *Int'l*, pg. 637
HID INDIA PRIVATE LTD—See ASSA ABLOY AB; *Int'l*, pg. 637
HIGGSTEC, INC.; *Int'l*, pg. 3385
HIGHBROAD ADVANCED MATERIAL (HEFEI) CO., LTD.; *Int'l*, pg. 3386
HIGHER WAY ELECTRONIC CO., LTD.; *Int'l*, pg. 3387
HIGHMAG TECHNOLOGY (SHENZHEN), LTD.—See Advanced Technology & Materials Co., Ltd.; *Int'l*, pg. 162
HIGH VOLTAGE TECHNOLOGY LIMITED—See HEICO Corporation; *U.S. Public*, pg. 1020
HILLCREST LABORATORIES, INC.—See CEVA, Inc.; *U.S. Public*, pg. 476
HIMS CO., LTD.; *Int'l*, pg. 3397
HINDUSTHAN URBAN INFRASTRUCTURE LTD.; *Int'l*, pg. 3400
HIPER GLOBAL LTD ; *Int'l*, pg. 3402
HIRSCHMANN AUTOMATION & CONTROL GMBH—See Belden, Inc.; *U.S. Public*, pg. 294
HITACHI BRASIL LTDA.—See Hitachi, Ltd.; *Int'l*, pg. 3415
HITACHI CONSUMER ELECTRONICS CO., LTD.—See Hitachi, Ltd.; *Int'l*, pg. 3416
HITACHI DRIVES & AUTOMATION GMBH—See Hitachi, Ltd.; *Int'l*, pg. 3416
HITACHI ELECTRONIC DEVICES (WUJIANG) CO., LTD.—See Hitachi, Ltd.; *Int'l*, pg. 3416
HITACHI EUROPE LTD. - DIGITAL MEDIA GROUP DIVISION—See Hitachi, Ltd.; *Int'l*, pg. 3417
HITACHI HIGH-TECH HONG KONG LIMITED—See Hitachi, Ltd.; *Int'l*, pg. 3418
HITACHI HIGH-TECHNOLOGIES (S) PTE. LTD.—See Hitachi, Ltd.; *Int'l*, pg. 3418
HITACHI HIGH-TECHNOLOGIES TAIWAN CORPORATION—See Hitachi, Ltd.; *Int'l*, pg. 3419
HITACHI HI-SYSTEM21 CO., LTD.—See Hitachi, Ltd.; *Int'l*, pg. 3417
HITACHI INDUSTRIAL EQUIPMENT SYSTEMS CO., LTD. - TAGA DIVISION—See Hitachi, Ltd.; *Int'l*, pg. 3419
HITACHI KOKUSAI LINEAR EQUIPAMENTOS ELETRONICOS S/A—See Hitachi, Ltd.; *Int'l*, pg. 3415
HITACHI MEDIA ELECTRONICS CO., LTD.—See Hitachi, Ltd.; *Int'l*, pg. 3420
HITACHI SOUTH AMERICA, ARGENTINA S.A.—See Hitachi, Ltd.; *Int'l*, pg. 3421
HITACHI TERMINAL MECHATRONICS, CORP.—See Hitachi, Ltd.; *Int'l*, pg. 3422
HITEC SENSOR SOLUTIONS, INC.—See Bridgepoint Group Plc; *Int'l*, pg. 1155
HOKURIKU INTERNATIONAL (THAILAND) CO., LTD.—See Hokuriku Electric Industry Co., Ltd.; *Int'l*, pg. 3445
HOLDERS COMPONENTS LIMITED—See Holders Technology plc; *Int'l*, pg. 3449
HOLLYLAND (CHINA) ELECTRONICS TECHNOLOGY CORPORATION LIMITED—See Hollyland Group Holdings Limited; *Int'l*, pg. 3452
HONG KONG AIC LIMITED—See Hitachi, Ltd.; *Int'l*, pg. 3423
HONGLI ZHIHUI GROUP CO., LTD.; *Int'l*, pg. 3471
HONYI INTERNATIONA CO., LTD.; *Int'l*, pg. 3472
HORIBA STEC, CO., LTD.—See HORIBA Ltd; *Int'l*, pg. 3476
HORNG TONG ENTERPRISE CO., LTD.; *Int'l*, pg. 3482
HOSIDEN AMERICA CORP—See Hosiden Corporation; *Int'l*, pg. 3484
HOSIDEN CORPORATION - CHINA HOSIDEN LCD FACTORY—See Hosiden Corporation; *Int'l*, pg. 3484
HOSIDEN ELECTRONICS (MALAYSIA) SDN. BHD—See Hosiden Corporation; *Int'l*, pg. 3484
HOSIDEN ELECTRONICS (SHANGHAI) CO., LTD—See Hosiden Corporation; *Int'l*, pg. 3484
HOSIDEN F.D. CORPORATION—See Hosiden Corporation; *Int'l*, pg. 3484
HOSIDEN (THAILAND) CO., LTD—See Hosiden Corporation; *Int'l*, pg. 3484
HOSIDEN VIETNAM (BAC GIANG) CO., LTD—See Hosiden Corporation; *Int'l*, pg. 3484
HOTRON PRECISION ELECTRONIC INDUSTRIAL CO. LTD.; *Int'l*, pg. 3489
HOYA ELECTRONICS KOREA CO., LTD.—See Hoya Corporation; *Int'l*, pg. 3495
HOYA ELECTRONICS MALAYSIA SDN. BHD.—See Hoya Corporation; *Int'l*, pg. 3495
HOYA ELECTRONICS SINGAPORE PTE. LTD.—See Hoya Corporation; *Int'l*, pg. 3495
HOYA MICROELECTRONICS TAIWAN CO., LTD.—See Hoya Corporation; *Int'l*, pg. 3496
H. PAULIN & CO., LTD. - DOMINION FITTINGS—See Hillman Solutions Corp.; *U.S. Public*, pg. 1038
HTC EUROPE CO., LTD.—See HTC Corporation; *Int'l*, pg. 3508
HUA JUNG COMPONENTS CO., LTD.; *Int'l*, pg. 3509
HUBEI FEILIHUA QUARTZ GLASS CO., LTD.; *Int'l*, pg. 3517
HUBEI GEOWAY INVESTMENT CO., LTD.; *Int'l*, pg. 3517
HUBEI ZHONGYI TECHNOLOGY INC.; *Int'l*, pg. 3519
HUF ELECTRONICS BRETTEN GMBH—See Huf Hulsbeck & Furst GmbH & Co. KG; *Int'l*, pg. 3523
HUIYANG CCT TELECOMMUNICATIONS PRODUCTS CO., LTD—See CCT Fortis Holdings Limited; *Int'l*, pg. 1370
HUIZHOU CHINA EAGLE ELECTRONIC TECHNOLOGY CO., LTD.; *Int'l*, pg. 3527
HU LANE ASSOCIATE, INC.; *Int'l*, pg. 3509
HYOSUNG EUROPE S.R.L.—See Hyosung Corporation; *Int'l*, pg. 3551
HYOSUNG INTERNATIONAL (HK) LTD.—See Hyosung Corporation; *Int'l*, pg. 3551
HYSONIC CO., LTD.; *Int'l*, pg. 3554
HYUNDAI BIOSCIENCE CO., LTD.; *Int'l*, pg. 3555
HZO, INC.—See Evercel, Inc.; *U.S. Private*, pg. 1437
I2S SA; *Int'l*, pg. 3566
IBIDEN ELECTRONICS INDUSTRIES CO., LTD.—See Ibiden Co., Ltd.; *Int'l*, pg. 3575
IBIDEN ELECTRONICS MALAYSIA SDN. BHD.—See Ibiden Co., Ltd.; *Int'l*, pg. 3575
IBIDEN PHILIPPINES LANDHOLDING, INC.—See Ibiden Co., Ltd.; *Int'l*, pg. 3575
IBO TECHNOLOGY COMPANY LIMITED; *Int'l*, pg. 3576
I-BUS CORPORATION; *U.S. Private*, pg. 2026
ICD CO., LTD.; *Int'l*, pg. 3579
I-CHIUN PRECISION INDUSTRY CO., LTD.; *Int'l*, pg. 3562
IDEAS, INC.; *U.S. Private*, pg. 2037
IDEMIA GERMANY GMBH—See Advent International Corporation; *U.S. Private*, pg. 102
IDENTISYS, INC.; *U.S. Private*, pg. 2037
IDEVICES, LLC—See Hubbell Incorporated; *U.S. Public*, pg. 1067
IEC ELECTRONICS - ALBUQUERQUE—See Goldberg Lindsay & Co., LLC; *U.S. Private*, pg. 1729
II-VI WIDE BAND GAP, INC.—See Coherent Corp.; *U.S. Public*, pg. 529
ILWOUL GML CO.,LTD; *Int'l*, pg. 3617
I.M.A. S.R.L.—See Koch Industries, Inc.; *U.S. Private*, pg. 2335
IM FLASH TECHNOLOGIES, LLC—See Micron Technology, Inc.; *U.S. Public*, pg. 1437
IMMERSION JAPAN K.K.—See Immersion Corporation; *U.S. Public*, pg. 1112
IMMERSION LIMITED—See Immersion Corporation; *U.S. Public*, pg. 1112
IMMERSION (SHANGHAI) SCIENCE & TECHNOLOGY CO., LTD.—See Immersion Corporation; *U.S. Public*, pg. 1112
IMPACT SCIENCE & TECHNOLOGY, INC.—See L3Harris Technologies, Inc.; *U.S. Public*, pg. 1280
INFINITE RF HOLDINGS, INC.—See Genstar Capital, LLC; *U.S. Private*, pg. 1677
INIVEN—See Conolog Corporation; *U.S. Private*, pg. 1018
INNCOM INTERNATIONAL INC.—See Honeywell International Inc.; *U.S. Public*, pg. 1048
INNOAUTO TECHNOLOGIES INC.—See Hitron Technologies Inc.; *Int'l*, pg. 3427
INNOVATIVE DESIGN SOLUTIONS, INC.—See LCI Industries; *U.S. Public*, pg. 1295
INNOVATIVE ELECTRONIC DESIGNS, INC.—See MiTek Corporation; *U.S. Private*, pg. 2751
INNOVISTA SENSORS—See The Carlyle Group Inc.; *U.S. Public*, pg. 2047
INPRINT CORPORATION—See ARC DOCUMENT SOLUTIONS, INC.; *U.S. Public*, pg. 179
INSERVCO, INC.—See Centre Lane Partners, LLC; *U.S. Private*, pg. 827
INSPECTORES Y CONSULTORES IBERCAL S.L.U.—See Enel S.p.A.; *Int'l*, pg. 2414
INSTANTEL INC.—See Stanley Black & Decker, Inc.; *U.S. Public*, pg. 1935
INTEGRATED COMBAT SYSTEMS, INC.—See Orbit International Corp.; *U.S. Public*, pg. 1614
INTEGRATED MICROWAVE CORPORATION—See Knowles Corporation; *U.S. Public*, pg. 1270
INTEK HONDURAS, S.A. DE C.V.—See Endress+Hauser (International) Holding AG; *Int'l*, pg. 2408
INTEK NICARAGUA, S.A.—See Endress+Hauser (International) Holding AG; *Int'l*, pg. 2408
INTELLICOM INNOVATION AB—See HMS Networks AB; *Int'l*, pg. 3433
INTERCONNECT CABLE TECHNOLOGIES CORP. - ASIA—See Interconnect Cable Technologies Corp.; *U.S. Private*, pg. 2109
INTERCONNECT CABLE TECHNOLOGIES CORP.; *U.S. Private*, pg. 2109
INTERFACE OPTOELECTRONCIS (SHENZHEN) CO., LTD.—See General Interface Solution (GIS) Holding Ltd.; *Int'l*, pg. 2918
INTERFACE OPTOELECTRONCIS (WUXI) CO., LTD.—See General Interface Solution (GIS) Holding Ltd.; *Int'l*, pg. 2918
INTERFACE OPTOELECTRONICS (SHENZHEN) CO., LTD.—See General Interface Solution (GIS) Holding Ltd.; *Int'l*, pg. 2918
INTERFACE OPTOELECTRONICS (WUXI) CO., LTD.—See General Interface Solution (GIS) Holding Ltd.; *Int'l*, pg. 2918
INTERLINK ELECTRONICS, K.K.—See Interlink Electronics, Inc.; *U.S. Public*, pg. 1144
INTERNATIONAL CRYSTAL MANUFACTURING, INC.; *U.S. Private*, pg. 2116
INTERNATIONAL ELECTRONIC RESEARCH CORP.—See CTS Corporation; *U.S. Public*, pg. 603
INTERNATIONAL ENTERPRISES, INC.—See Elbit Systems Limited; *Int'l*, pg. 2344
INTRICON CORPORATION; *U.S. Public*, pg. 1159
INTRINSIC SAFETY EQUIPMENT OF TEXAS, INC.—See Emerson Electric Co.; *U.S. Public*, pg. 750
INVERIS TRAINING SOLUTIONS, INC.—See Parker Hannifin Corporation; *U.S. Public*, pg. 1642
INVUE SECURITY PRODUCTS; *U.S. Private*, pg. 2133
I-O DATA DEVICE, INC.; *Int'l*, pg. 3563
ION BEAM MILLING, INC.—See Semi-General, Inc.; *U.S. Private*, pg. 3603
I-PEX CO., LTD—See I-PEX Inc.; *Int'l*, pg. 3564
I-PEX ELECTRONICS (H.K.) LTD.—See I-PEX Inc.; *Int'l*, pg. 3564
I-PEX EUROPE SARL—See I-PEX Inc.; *Int'l*, pg. 3564
I-PEX GLOBAL OPERATIONS, INC.—See I-PEX Inc.; *Int'l*, pg. 3564
I-PEX INC.; *Int'l*, pg. 3563
I-PEX KOREA CO., LTD.—See I-PEX Inc.; *Int'l*, pg. 3564
I-PEX (SHANGHAI) CO., LTD.—See I-PEX Inc.; *Int'l*, pg. 3564
IRCAMERAS LLC—See HEICO Corporation; *U.S. Public*, pg. 1020
IRIVER INC—See Dreamus Company; *Int'l*, pg. 2203

334419 — OTHER ELECTRONIC CO...   CORPORATE AFFILIATIONS

ISECURETRAC CORP.—See Corrisoft LLC; *U.S. Private*, pg. 1059
I-SHENG ELECTRONICS (KUNSHAN) CO., LTD.—See I-Sheng Electric Wire & Cable Co., Ltd.; *Int'l*, pg. 3565
ISMECA MALAYSIA SDN. BHD.—See Cohu, Inc.; *U.S. Public*, pg. 529
ISMECA USA, INC.—See Cohu, Inc.; *U.S. Public*, pg. 529
ISOLA GMBH—See TPG Capital, L.P.; *U.S. Public*, pg. 2174
ITT AEROSPACE CONTROLS LLC—See ITT Inc.; *U.S. Public*, pg. 1177
ITT BRASIL EQUIPAMENTOSPARA BOMBEAMENTO E TRATAMENTO DE AGUA E EFLUENTES LTDA—See ITT Inc.; *U.S. Public*, pg. 1177
ITW ELECTRONIC BUSINESS ASIA CO., LIMITED—See Illinois Tool Works Inc.; *U.S. Public*, pg. 1105
ITW INDUSTRY B.V.—See Illinois Tool Works Inc.; *U.S. Public*, pg. 1106
ITW REYFLEX FRANCE S.A.S.—See Illinois Tool Works Inc.; *U.S. Public*, pg. 1107
ITW SPEEDLINE EQUIPMENT (SUZHOU) CO. LTD.—See Illinois Tool Works Inc.; *U.S. Public*, pg. 1107
ITW SWITCHES—See Illinois Tool Works Inc.; *U.S. Public*, pg. 1107
IZOBLOK GMBH—See BEWi ASA; *Int'l*, pg. 1004
JACO ELECTRONICS, INC.; *U.S. Public*, pg. 1183
J A ELECTRONIC MANUFACTURING CO, INC.—See Brand Industrial Services, Inc.; *U.S. Private*, pg. 636
JA ELECTRONICS COMPANY—See Brance Krachy Company, Inc.; *U.S. Private*, pg. 635
JANCO ELECTRONICS INC.; *U.S. Public*, pg. 2186
JAYBEAM WIRELESS SAS—See Amphenol Corporation; *U.S. Public*, pg. 130
JCHYUN SYSTEMS, INC.—See Creative Technology Ltd.; *Int'l*, pg. 1833
JENKINS ELECTRIC CO.; *U.S. Private*, pg. 2199
JEROME INDUSTRIES CORP.—See Tinicum Enterprises, Inc.; *U.S. Private*, pg. 4174
JETTER AUTOMATION HUNGARY KFT.—See Bucher Industries AG; *Int'l*, pg. 1209
JETTER AUTOMATION TECHNOLOGY (SHANGHAI) CO., LTD.—See Bucher Industries AG; *Int'l*, pg. 1209
JIANGSU CANYANG OPTOELECTRONICS LTD.—See Ennostar Inc.; *Int'l*, pg. 2444
JIAXING GLEAD ELECTRONICS CO., LTD.—See Beijing BDstar Navigation Co., Ltd.; *Int'l*, pg. 946
J-TEQ EMS SOLUTIONS LTD.—See Avnet, Inc.; *U.S. Public*, pg. 253
JUKEN KOGYO CO. LTD.—See EMNI Co., Ltd; *Int'l*, pg. 2385
JUKEN OPTICS (YANTAI) CO. LTD.—See EMNI Co., Ltd; *Int'l*, pg. 2385
JUKEN TECHNOLOGY (DONG-GUAN) CO. LTD.—See EMNI Co., Ltd; *Int'l*, pg. 2385
JUKEN TECHNOLOGY ENGINEERING SDN. BHD.—See EMNI Co., Ltd; *Int'l*, pg. 2385
JUKEN TECHNOLOGY (HUIZHOU) CO. LTD.—See EMNI Co., Ltd; *Int'l*, pg. 2385
JX METALS PRECISION TECHNOLOGY CO., LTD.—See ENEOS Holdings, Inc.; *Int'l*, pg. 2416
KAI JIA COMPUTER ACCESSORY CO., LTD.—See Casetek Holdings Limited; *Int'l*, pg. 1351
KAJAANI PROCESS MEASUREMENTS LTD.—See ABB Ltd.; *Int'l*, pg. 49
KAYSER LIMITED—See Highway Holdings Limited; *Int'l*, pg. 3389
KE ELEKTRONIK GMBH—See Amphenol Corporation; *U.S. Public*, pg. 130
KEIHIN AUTO PARTS (THAILAND) CO., LTD. - 2ND PLANT—See Hitachi Astemo, Ltd.; *Int'l*, pg. 3409
KELTA, INC.; *U.S. Private*, pg. 2281
KELTRON ELECTRONICS CORP.; *U.S. Private*, pg. 2281
KEMIAO GARMENT HOLDING GROUP; *U.S. Public*, pg. 1220
KENTEC ELECTRONICS LTD.—See Hochiki Corporation; *Int'l*, pg. 3437
KEVLIN CORPORATION—See Advent International Corporation; *U.S. Private*, pg. 100
KIMBALL ELECTRONICS MEXICO, INC.—See Kimball Electronics, Inc.; *U.S. Public*, pg. 1228
KIMBALL ELECTRONICS (NANJING) CO., LTD.—See Kimball Electronics, Inc.; *U.S. Public*, pg. 1228
KIMBALL ELECTRONICS TAMPA, INC.—See Kimball Electronics, Inc.; *U.S. Public*, pg. 1228
KINECTIQ INC.; *U.S. Private*, pg. 2307
KISHIN MEGATEC CO., LTD.—See Futaba Corporation; *Int'l*, pg. 2851
KISHIN VIETNAM CO., LTD.—See Futaba Corporation; *Int'l*, pg. 2851
KJ PRETECH ASIA HOLDING CO. LTD.—See EMNI Co., Ltd; *Int'l*, pg. 2385
KLINGENBURG UK LTD.—See Carel Industries S.p.A.; *Int'l*, pg. 1324
K&L MICROWAVE, INC.—See Dover Corporation; *U.S. Public*, pg. 679
KNOWLES CORPORATION; *U.S. Public*, pg. 1270
KNOWLES ELECTRONICS DENMARK APS—See Knowles Corporation; *U.S. Public*, pg. 1270

KNOWLES ELECTRONICS, LLC—See Knowles Corporation; *U.S. Public*, pg. 1270
KNOWLES ELECTRONICS (MALAYSIA) SDN. BHD.—See Knowles Corporation; *U.S. Public*, pg. 1270
KNOWLES ELECTRONICS TAIWAN, LTD.—See Knowles Corporation; *U.S. Public*, pg. 1270
KOBRITE DONGGUAN CORPORATION—See Bright Led Electronics Corp.; *Int'l*, pg. 1161
KODAK MEXICANA, S.A. DE C.V.—See Eastman Kodak Company; *U.S. Public*, pg. 707
KODAK OOO—See Eastman Kodak Company; *U.S. Public*, pg. 708
KOFU CASIO CO., LTD.—See Casio Computer Co., Ltd.; *Int'l*, pg. 1353
KOOKJE ELECTRIC KOREA CO., LTD.—See KKR & Co. Inc.; *U.S. Public*, pg. 1257
KOREA HOSIDEN ELECTRONICS CO., LTD.—See Hosiden Corporation; *Int'l*, pg. 3484
KOSO CORPORATION—See Hamamatsu Photonics K.K.; *Int'l*, pg. 3235
KTC MANAGEMENT CORPORATION—See The Goldman Sachs Group, Inc.; *U.S. Public*, pg. 2080
K-TRONICS (SUZHOU) TECHNOLOGY CO., LTD.—See BOE Technology Group Co., Ltd.; *Int'l*, pg. 1099
KUHNE ELECTRONIC GMBH—See Alaris Holdings Limited; *Int'l*, pg. 291
KYUSYU DAISHINKU CORP—See Daishinku Corp.; *Int'l*, pg. 1942
L3 ADAPTIVE METHODS—See L3Harris Technologies, Inc.; *U.S. Public*, pg. 1284
L3 AVIATION PRODUCTS, INC.—See L3Harris Technologies, Inc.; *U.S. Public*, pg. 1284
L-3 COMMUNICATIONS AEROMET, INC.—See L3Harris Technologies, Inc.; *U.S. Public*, pg. 1281
L-3 COMMUNICATIONS CINCINNATI ELECTRONICS CORPORATION—See L3Harris Technologies, Inc.; *U.S. Public*, pg. 1282
L-3 COMMUNICATIONS CYTERRA CORPORATION—See L3Harris Technologies, Inc.; *U.S. Public*, pg. 1282
L-3 COMMUNICATIONS ELECTRON DEVICES—See L3Harris Technologies, Inc.; *U.S. Public*, pg. 1282
L-3 COMMUNICATIONS ELECTRON TECHNOLOGIES INC—See L3Harris Technologies, Inc.; *U.S. Public*, pg. 1282
L-3 COMMUNICATIONS NARDA MICROWAVE-WEST—See L3Harris Technologies, Inc.; *U.S. Public*, pg. 1282
L-3 COMMUNICATIONS SONOMA EO INC—See L3Harris Technologies, Inc.; *U.S. Public*, pg. 1283
LABSPHERE, INC.—See Halma plc; *Int'l*, pg. 3231
LAIRD TECHNOLOGIES, INC.—See DuPont de Nemours, Inc.; *U.S. Public*, pg. 693
LAIRD TECHNOLOGIES KOREA Y.H—See DuPont de Nemours, Inc.; *U.S. Public*, pg. 693
LAIRD TECHNOLOGIES S. DE R. L. DE C V.—See DuPont de Nemours, Inc.; *U.S. Public*, pg. 693
LAIRD TECHNOLOGIES (SHANGHAI) LIMITED—See DuPont de Nemours, Inc.; *U.S. Public*, pg. 693
LAIRD TECHNOLOGIES (SHENZHEN) LIMITED—See DuPont de Nemours, Inc.; *U.S. Public*, pg. 693
LAKE REGION MEDICAL GMBH—See Integer Holdings Corporation; *U.S. Public*, pg. 1135
LAKE REGION MEDICAL - SALEM—See Integer Holdings Corporation; *U.S. Public*, pg. 1135
LAM RESEARCH (SHANGHAI) CO., LTD.—See Lam Research Corporation; *U.S. Public*, pg. 1289
LASERCUT INC.—See El.En. S.p.A.; *Int'l*, pg. 2342
LASER IMAGING SYSTEMS GMBH & CO. KG—See KLA Corporation; *U.S. Public*, pg. 1268
LCR ELECTRONICS, INC.—See Tinicum Enterprises, Inc.; *U.S. Private*, pg. 4174
LEANTEQ CO., LTD.—See Enpro Inc.; *U.S. Public*, pg. 775
LEEMAH CORPORATION; *U.S. Private*, pg. 2415
LEEMAH ELECTRONICS INC.—See Leemah Corporation; *U.S. Private*, pg. 2415
LEGACY TECHNOLOGIES INC.; *U.S. Private*, pg. 2417
LEMSYS SA—See Teradyne, Inc.; *U.S. Public*, pg. 2018
LEXEL IMAGING SYSTEMS INC.; *U.S. Private*, pg. 2440
LEXTAR ELECTRONICS (CHUZHOU) CORP.—See Ennostar Inc.; *Int'l*, pg. 2444
LEXTAR ELECTRONICS CORP.—See Ennostar Inc.; *Int'l*, pg. 2444
LEXTAR ELECTRONICS (XIAMEN) CORP.—See Ennostar Inc.; *Int'l*, pg. 2444
LIMITED LIABILITY COMPANY CASIO—See Casio Computer Co., Ltd.; *Int'l*, pg. 1353
LIMTECH BIOMETRIC SOLUTIONS (PROPRIETARY) LIMITED—See Hosken Consolidated Investments Limited; *Int'l*, pg. 3485
LINEARIZER TECHNOLOGY, INC.—See MACOM Technology Solutions Holdings, Inc.; *U.S. Public*, pg. 1352
LIQUIDYN GMBH—See Nordson Corporation; *U.S. Public*, pg. 1533
LISA DRAXLMAIER GMBH—See Draexlmaier Gruppe; *Int'l*, pg. 2198
LISK CONTROL TECHNOLOGY (SUZHOU) CO., LTD.—See G.W. Lisk Company, Inc.; *U.S. Private*, pg. 1631

LISK IRELAND LTD.—See G.W. Lisk Company, Inc.; *U.S. Private*, pg. 1631
LITTELFUSE LT, UAB—See Littelfuse, Inc.; *U.S. Public*, pg. 1327
LMI CONNECTORS—See ABB Ltd.; *Int'l*, pg. 52
LOGITEK INC.—See North Atlantic Industries Inc.; *U.S. Private*, pg. 2942
LSI ADL TECHNOLOGY INC.—See LSI Industries Inc.; *U.S. Public*, pg. 1344
LUCIX CORP.—See HEICO Corporation; *U.S. Public*, pg. 1020
LUMEX, INC.—See Illinois Tool Works Inc.; *U.S. Public*, pg. 1109
LUTHI ELEKTRONIK-FEINMECHANIK AG—See AMETEK, Inc.; *U.S. Public*, pg. 120
LUXLITE (SHENZHEN) CORPORATION LIMITED—See Ennostar Inc.; *Int'l*, pg. 2444
LYNN ELECTRONICS CORPORATION—See Odyssey Investment Partners, LLC; *U.S. Private*, pg. 2995
MACLEAN POWER CANADA—See Centerbridge Partners, L.P.; *U.S. Private*, pg. 815
MACLEAN POWER, LLC—See Centerbridge Partners, L.P.; *U.S. Private*, pg. 815
MACLEAN SENIOR INDUSTRIES LLC—See Centerbridge Partners, L.P.; *U.S. Private*, pg. 815
MACROLINK, INC.—See RTX Corporation; *U.S. Public*, pg. 1822
MAGNETIKA, INC.-GARDENA—See Magnetika, Inc.; *U.S. Private*, pg. 2547
MANAGE INC.; *U.S. Private*, pg. 2559
MARCOLE ENTERPRISES LLC—See Wilcas Corp.; *U.S. Private*, pg. 4518
MARCON DENSO CO., LTD.—See Denso Corporation; *Int'l*, pg. 2032
MARELLI AUTOMOTIVE COMPONENTS (GUANGZHOU) CORPORATION—See KKR & Co. Inc.; *U.S. Public*, pg. 1260
MARELLI AUTOMOTIVE COMPONENTS (WUXI) CORPORATION—See KKR & Co. Inc.; *U.S. Public*, pg. 1260
MARELLI AUTOMOTIVE SYSTEMS EUROPE PLC - FRANCE BRANCH OFFICE—See KKR & Co. Inc.; *U.S. Public*, pg. 1260
MARELLI AUTOMOTIVE SYSTEMS EUROPE PLC—See KKR & Co. Inc.; *U.S. Public*, pg. 1260
MARELLI AUTOMOTIVE SYSTEMS UK LIMITED—See KKR & Co. Inc.; *U.S. Public*, pg. 1260
MARELLI BARCELONA ESPANA S.A.U.—See KKR & Co. Inc.; *U.S. Public*, pg. 1260
MARELLI CHINA HOLDING COMPANY—See KKR & Co. Inc.; *U.S. Public*, pg. 1260
MARELLI DO BRASIL INDUSTRIA E COMERCIO LTDA—See KKR & Co. Inc.; *U.S. Public*, pg. 1260
MARELLI PLOIESTI ROMANIA S.R.L.—See KKR & Co. Inc.; *U.S. Public*, pg. 1260
MARELLI R&D CO., LIMITED—See KKR & Co. Inc.; *U.S. Public*, pg. 1260
MARELLI (THAILAND) CO., LTD—See KKR & Co. Inc.; *U.S. Public*, pg. 1260
MARELLI TOOLING (GUANGZHOU) CORPORATION—See KKR & Co. Inc.; *U.S. Public*, pg. 1260
MARELLI (XIANG YANG) CORPORATION—See KKR & Co. Inc.; *U.S. Public*, pg. 1260
MASA DA AMAZONIA LTDA.—See Flex Ltd.; *Int'l*, pg. 2704
MASTERNAUT AB—See Compagnie Generale des Etablissements Michelin SCA; *Int'l*, pg. 1743
MASTERNAUT DEUTSCHLAND GMBH—See Compagnie Generale des Etablissements Michelin SCA; *Int'l*, pg. 1743
MAST MICROWAVE—See Advent International Corporation; *U.S. Private*, pg. 100
MATRIX-FOCALSPOT, INC.—See Nordson Corporation; *U.S. Public*, pg. 1533
MATRIX INSPECTION SYSTEMS, PTE. LTD.—See Nordson Corporation; *U.S. Public*, pg. 1533
MATRIX (SUZHOU) TRADING CO., LTD.—See Nordson Corporation; *U.S. Public*, pg. 1533
MATRIX TECHNOLOGIES GMBH—See Nordson Corporation; *U.S. Public*, pg. 1533
MATSUE DAI-ICHI SEIKO CO., LTD—See I-PEX Inc.; *Int'l*, pg. 3564
MAURER ELECTRONICS GMBH—See Bundesdruckerei GmbH; *Int'l*, pg. 1215
MAURY MICROWAVE INC.—See Artemis Capital Partners Management Co., LLC; *U.S. Private*, pg. 340
MAXITROL COMPANY - MAXITROL ELECTRONICS DIVISION—See Maxitrol Company; *U.S. Private*, pg. 2619
MAXWELL TECHNOLOGIES KOREA CO., LTD—See Tesla, Inc.; *U.S. Public*, pg. 2021
MCGREGOR & ASSOCIATES, INC.; *U.S. Private*, pg. 2635
MEC A/S—See IDEC Corporation; *Int'l*, pg. 3589
MECOMB (THAILAND) LTD.—See Fuji Corporation; *Int'l*, pg. 2810
MEDIAMATICS, INC.—See Texas Instruments Incorporated; *U.S. Public*, pg. 2025

N.A.I.C.S. INDEX

334419 — OTHER ELECTRONIC CO...

MEFIAG B.V.—See CECO Environmental Corp.; *U.S. Public*, pg. 464

MEGLAB ELECTRONIQUE INC.—See Epiroc AB; *Int'l*, pg. 2463

MEL MICRON EUROPE LTD.—See Micron Technology, Inc.; *U.S. Public*, pg. 1437

MEMTRON TECHNOLOGIES CO.—See TransDigm Group Incorporated; *U.S. Public*, pg. 2180

MERCURY COMMERCIAL ELECTRONICS, INC.—See Mercury Systems, Inc.; *U.S. Public*, pg. 1422

MERCURY ELECTRONICS & PLASTICS MANUFACTURING—See Brunswick Corporation; *U.S. Public*, pg. 408

MERRIMAC INDUSTRIES INC.—See Crane NXT, Co.; *U.S. Public*, pg. 591

METHODE DATAMATE PRODUCTS—See Methode Electronics, Inc.; *U.S. Public*, pg. 1429

METHODE ELECTRONICS EUROPE LTD.—See Methode Electronics, Inc.; *U.S. Public*, pg. 1429

METRO INDUSTRIES, INC.—See Emerson Electric Co.; *U.S. Public*, pg. 750

METRONIC SAS—See HF Company; *Int'l*, pg. 3374

MICRO-COAX, INC.—See Amphenol Corporation; *U.S. Public*, pg. 129

MICROCRAFT K.K.—See Infinite Graphics Incorporated; *U.S. Public*, pg. 1117

MICROLAB/FXR LLC—See RF Industries, Ltd.; *U.S. Public*, pg. 1796

MICROMETALS INC.; *U.S. Private*, pg. 2704

MICRONET LTD.—See Tingo Group, Inc.; *U.S. Public*, pg. 2159

MICROPLACE INC.—See eBay Inc.; *U.S. Public*, pg. 709

MICROPROSS SAS—See National Instruments Corporation; *U.S. Private*, pg. 2856

MICROSS COMPONENTS, INC. - ELECTRO-MECHANICAL SERVICES, HATFIELD—See Behrman Brothers Management Corp.; *U.S. Private*, pg. 515

MICROSS COMPONENTS, INC.—See Behrman Brothers Management Corp.; *U.S. Private*, pg. 515

MICROVISION, INC.; *U.S. Public*, pg. 1444

MICROWAVE FILTER COMPANY, INC.; *U.S. Public*, pg. 1444

MIDCON CABLES LLC; *U.S. Private*, pg. 2710

MIDWEST MICROWAVE SOLUTIONS, INC.—See HEICO Corporation; *U.S. Public*, pg. 1020

MIKROS SYSTEMS CORPORATION—See McKean Defense Group LLC; *U.S. Private*, pg. 2637

THE MILLENNIA DESIGN—See Millennia Group Inc.; *U.S. Private*, pg. 2731

MILLENNIA GROUP INC.; *U.S. Private*, pg. 2731

MINING CONTROLS, LLC—See Brookfield Corporation; *Int'l*, pg. 1181

MIYACHI CORPORATION—See Amada Holdings Co., Ltd.; *Int'l*, pg. 404

MKS ENI PRODUCTS—See MKS Instruments, Inc.; *U.S. Public*, pg. 1452

MOLEX CONNECTIVITY GMBH - LEINFELDEN-ECHTERDINGEN—See Koch Industries, Inc.; *U.S. Private*, pg. 2334

MOLEX ELEKTRONIK GMBH—See Koch Industries, Inc.; *U.S. Private*, pg. 2334

MOLEX KNUTSEN DANMARK A/S—See Koch Industries, Inc.; *U.S. Private*, pg. 2334

MONZITE CORPORATION—See Omni-Lite Industries Canada Inc.; *U.S. Public*, pg. 1572

MOOG COMPONENTS GROUP—See Moog Inc.; *U.S. Public*, pg. 1470

MOOG DO BRASIL CONTROLES LTDA—See Moog Inc.; *U.S. Public*, pg. 1470

MOOG ITALIANA SRL—See Moog Inc.; *U.S. Public*, pg. 1470

MOOG READING LIMITED—See Moog Inc.; *U.S. Public*, pg. 1470

MOSYS INC.—See Peraso Inc.; *U.S. Public*, pg. 1673

MOSYS INTERNATIONAL, INC.—See Peraso Inc.; *U.S. Public*, pg. 1673

MOTOREDUCTORES U.S., S.A. DE C.V.—See Emerson Electric Co.; *U.S. Public*, pg. 750

MSC TECHNOLOGIES GMBH—See Avnet, Inc.; *U.S. Public*, pg. 253

MS INTERNATIONAL CORP.—See Fuji Corporation; *Int'l*, pg. 2810

MSI TRANSDUCERS CORP.—See Amphenol Corporation; *U.S. Public*, pg. 130

M-TRON INDUSTRIES, LTD.—See M-tron Industries, Inc.; *U.S. Public*, pg. 1351

MUEGGE GMBH—See Harald Quandt Holding GmbH; *Int'l*, pg. 3270

MULTEK DISPLAY (HONG KONG) LIMITED—See Flex Ltd.; *Int'l*, pg. 2704

MULTEK FLEXIBLE CIRCUITS, INC.—See Flex Ltd.; *Int'l*, pg. 2703

NAKOR INC.—See DAEDUCK Co., Ltd.; *Int'l*, pg. 1906

NAMCO CONTROLS CORPORATION—See Danaher Corporation; *U.S. Public*, pg. 628

NANOFLEX POWER CORPORATION; *U.S. Public*, pg. 1490

NAN YA PRINTED CIRCUIT BOARD CORPORATION—See Formosa Plastics Corporation; *Int'l*, pg. 2736

NARRAGANSETT IMAGING—See Global Imaging Holdings Realty, LLC; *U.S. Private*, pg. 1714

NASCENTECHNOLOGY MANUFACTURING, INC.—See Newawa Technology, Inc.; *U.S. Private*, pg. 2913

NCR (NZ) CORPORATION—See NCR Voyix Corporation; *U.S. Public*, pg. 1502

NEL FREQUENCY CONTROLS, INC.—See Genstar Capital, LLC; *U.S. Private*, pg. 1673

NETCOM, INC.—See Cedar Creek Partners LLC; *U.S. Private*, pg. 804

NETLIST ELECTRONICS (SUZHOU) CO., LTD.—See Netlist, Inc.; *U.S. Public*, pg. 1509

NEW PRODUCT INTEGRATION SOLUTIONS, INC.—See Amphenol Corporation; *U.S. Public*, pg. 131

NEW VISION DISPLAY, INC.; *U.S. Private*, pg. 2907

NIC COMPONENTS ASIA PTE LTD.—See Arrow Electronics, Inc.; *U.S. Public*, pg. 199

NIELSEN KELLERMAN INC.; *U.S. Private*, pg. 2927

NIKKO FUJI ELECTRONICS DONGGUAN CO., LTD.—See ENEOS Holdings, Inc.; *Int'l*, pg. 2416

NINGBO ALPS ELECTRONICS CO., LTD.—See Alps Alpine Co., Ltd.; *Int'l*, pg. 376

NISHIKI ELECTRONICS CO., LTD.—See Alps Alpine Co., Ltd.; *Int'l*, pg. 376

N.J. FROMENT & CO. LIMITED—See Emerson Electric Co.; *U.S. Public*, pg. 750

NLIGHT, INC.; *U.S. Public*, pg. 1530

NOCA AS—See Guardian Capital Group Limited; *Int'l*, pg. 3170

NOLIAC AS—See CTS Corporation; *U.S. Public*, pg. 603

NORCOR TECHNOLOGIES CORPORATION; *U.S. Private*, pg. 2936

NORDAUTOMATION AB—See Addtech AB; *Int'l*, pg. 134

NORDSON ADVANCED TECHNOLOGY (JAPAN) K.K.—See Nordson Corporation; *U.S. Public*, pg. 1533

NORDSON ADVANCED TECHNOLOGY (SINGAPORE) PTE. LTD.—See Nordson Corporation; *U.S. Public*, pg. 1533

NORDSON ASYMTEK, INC.—See Nordson Corporation; *U.S. Public*, pg. 1533

NORDSON BKG LLC—See Nordson Corporation; *U.S. Public*, pg. 1533

NORDSON DAGE, INC.—See Nordson Corporation; *U.S. Public*, pg. 1533

NORDSON EFD LLC—See Nordson Corporation; *U.S. Public*, pg. 1533

NORDSON MARCH, INC.—See Nordson Corporation; *U.S. Public*, pg. 1534

NORDSON S.E. ASIA (PTE.) LIMITED,—See Nordson Corporation; *U.S. Public*, pg. 1534

NORDSON YESTECH, INC.—See Nordson Corporation; *U.S. Public*, pg. 1534

NORSAT INTERNATIONAL INC.—See Hytera Communications Corporation Limited; *Int'l*, pg. 3555

NOVA ELECTRIC—See Technology Dynamics, Inc.; *U.S. Private*, pg. 3955

NOVA MICROWAVE, INC.—See Electro Technik Industries; *U.S. Private*, pg. 1354

NUERA COMMUNICATIONS SINGAPORE PTE LTD.—See AudioCodes Ltd.; *Int'l*, pg. 702

NUTSTEEL INDUSTRIA METALURGICA LTDA—See Emerson Electric Co.; *U.S. Public*, pg. 750

NUVOTRONICS, INC.—See Elliott Management Corporation; *U.S. Private*, pg. 1368

NUVOTRONICS, INC.—See Veritas Capital Fund Management, LLC; *U.S. Private*, pg. 4362

NU-WAY SPEAKER PRODUCTS INC.; *U.S. Private*, pg. 2972

NVIDIA FZ-LLC—See NVIDIA Corporation; *U.S. Public*, pg. 1558

OCEAN OPTICS GERMANY—See Halma plc; *Int'l*, pg. 3232

OCLARO TECHNOLOGY (SHENZHEN) CO., LTD.—See Lumentum Holdings Inc.; *U.S. Public*, pg. 1348

OCTOPART INC.—See Altium Limited; *Int'l*, pg. 394

OCULUS VR, LLC—See Meta Platforms, Inc.; *U.S. Public*, pg. 1427

ODC NIMBUS INC—See Dubilier & Company, Inc.; *U.S. Private*, pg. 1283

OECO LLC—See Parker Hannifin Corporation; *U.S. Public*, pg. 1643

OHMEGA TECHNOLOGIES, INC.—See Arcline Investment Management LP; *U.S. Private*, pg. 315

OMEGA ELECTRONICS MANUFACTURING SERVICES; *U.S. Private*, pg. 3015

OMNIPLESS MANUFACTURING (PROPRIETARY) LIMITED—See Advent International Corporation; *U.S. Private*, pg. 100

OOO DANFOSS—See Danfoss A/S; *Int'l*, pg. 1961

OOO FIDIA—See FIDIA S.p.A.; *Int'l*, pg. 2655

OPTO 22; *U.S. Private*, pg. 3035

OPTOMA (CHINA & H.K.) LIMITED—See Coretronic Corporation; *Int'l*, pg. 1800

OPTOMA DEUTSCHLAND GMBH—See Coretronic Corporation; *Int'l*, pg. 1800

OPTOMA EUROPE LIMITED—See Coretronic Corporation; *Int'l*, pg. 1800

OPTOMA SCANDINAVIA. A.S.—See Coretronic Corporation; *Int'l*, pg. 1800

OPTOMA USA—See Coretronic Corporation; *Int'l*, pg. 1800

OPTRON SCIENTIFIC COMPANY INC.—See US Nuclear Corp.; *U.S. Public*, pg. 2267

OPUS RS EUROPE S.L.—See Searchlight Capital Partners, L.P.; *U.S. Private*, pg. 3590

ORBISAT INDUSTRIA E AEROLEVANTAMENTO S.A.—See Embraer S.A.; *Int'l*, pg. 2376

ORBIT INTERNATIONAL CORP.; *U.S. Public*, pg. 1614

ORBOTECH SINGAPORE CORPORATION PTE. LTD.—See KLA Corporation; *U.S. Public*, pg. 1268

ORDOS YUANSHENG OPTOELECTRONICS CO., LTD.—See BOE Technology Group Co., Ltd.; *Int'l*, pg. 1099

OSI OPTOELECTRONICS AS—See OSI Systems, Inc.; *U.S. Public*, pg. 1621

OUSTER, INC.; *U.S. Public*, pg. 1624

PACE INC.; *U.S. Private*, pg. 3063

PACIFIC AEROSPACE & ELECTRONICS, INC.—See TransDigm Group Incorporated; *U.S. Public*, pg. 2181

PACIFIC INSIGHT ELECTRONICS CORP.—See Methode Electronics, Inc.; *U.S. Public*, pg. 1429

PACIFIC POWER SOURCE, INC.; *U.S. Private*, pg. 3070

PAKTRON CAPACITORS—See Milestone Partners Ltd.; *U.S. Private*, pg. 2729

PALOMAR DISPLAY PRODUCTS, INC.; *U.S. Private*, pg. 3082

PALOMAR TECHNOLOGIES GMBH—See Palomar Technologies Companies, LLC; *U.S. Private*, pg. 3082

PALOMAR TECHNOLOGIES INC.—See Palomar Technologies Companies, LLC; *U.S. Private*, pg. 3082

PALOMAR TECHNOLOGIES PTE LTD.—See Palomar Technologies Companies, LLC; *U.S. Private*, pg. 3082

PANTEK TECHNOLOGY CORP.—See Alltek Technology Corporation; *Int'l*, pg. 360

PARA SYSTEMS INC.—See Components Corporation of America, Inc.; *U.S. Private*, pg. 1002

PASCALL ELECTRONICS LTD.—See TransDigm Group Incorporated; *U.S. Public*, pg. 2182

PCB GROUP, INC.—See Amphenol Corporation; *U.S. Public*, pg. 131

PCB PIEZOTRONICS BVBA—See Amphenol Corporation; *U.S. Public*, pg. 131

PCB PIEZOTRONICS EUROPE GMBH—See Amphenol Corporation; *U.S. Public*, pg. 131

PCB PIEZOTRONICS INC.—See Amphenol Corporation; *U.S. Public*, pg. 131

PCI LIMITED—See Platinum Equity, LLC; *U.S. Private*, pg. 3206

PCI-SHANGHAI ELECTRONIC COMPANY LTD.—See Platinum Equity, LLC; *U.S. Private*, pg. 3206

PC&S TECHNOLOGIES GMBH—See Berndorf AG; *Int'l*, pg. 987

PCTEL (TIANJIN) ELECTRONICS COMPANY LTD.—See Amphenol Corporation; *U.S. Public*, pg. 132

PEERLESS INSTRUMENT CO., INC.—See Curtiss-Wright Corporation; *U.S. Public*, pg. 612

PENCHEM TECHNOLOGIES SDN. BHD.—See Frencken Group Limited; *Int'l*, pg. 2773

PERCEPTION DIGITAL TECHNOLOGY (SHENZHEN) LIMITED—See HongDa Financial Holding Limited; *Int'l*, pg. 3470

PERCEPTRON, INC.—See Atlas Copco AB; *Int'l*, pg. 680

PGC WIRE AND CABLE, LLC—See Proto Labs, Inc.; *U.S. Public*, pg. 1729

PHOENIX LOGISTICS, INC.; *U.S. Private*, pg. 3173

PHOTON DYNAMICS, INC.—See KLA Corporation; *U.S. Public*, pg. 1268

PHOTONIS USA PENNSYLVANIA, INC.—See Ardian SAS; *Int'l*, pg. 556

PI INNOVO LLC—See Dana Incorporated; *U.S. Public*, pg. 623

PIONEER CHINA HOLDING CO LTD—See EQT AB; *Int'l*, pg. 2470

PIONEER ELECTRONICS(THAILAND) CO LTD—See EQT AB; *Int'l*, pg. 2470

PIONEERFA CORP—See EQT AB; *Int'l*, pg. 2471

PIONEER HIGH FIDELITY TAIWAN CO.,LTD—See EQT AB; *Int'l*, pg. 2471

PLANAR MONOLITHICS INDUSTRIES, INC.—See Arcline Investment Management LP; *U.S. Private*, pg. 315

PLATINUM TOOLS INC.—See Odyssey Investment Partners, LLC; *U.S. Private*, pg. 2995

PMP AUTO COMPONENTS PVT. LTD.—See Ashok Piramal Group; *Int'l*, pg. 608

POINDUS SYSTEMS UK LIMITED—See Compal Electronics, Inc.; *Int'l*, pg. 1746

POWER DIGITAL COMMUNICATION CO., LTD.—See Cal-Comp Electronics (Thailand) pcl; *Int'l*, pg. 1261

POWERMAT TECHNOLOGIES LTD.—See General Motors Company; *U.S. Public*, pg. 928

POWER-ONE ITALY S.P.A.—See ABB Ltd.; *Int'l*, pg. 52

POWER TECHNOLOGY, INC.; *U.S. Public*, pg. 3239

POWERTRON GMBH—See Vishay Precision Group, Inc.; *U.S. Public*, pg. 2303

PRAIRIE TECHNOLOGIES, INC.—See Bruker Corporation; *U.S. Public*, pg. 407

N.A.I.C.S. Index

334419 — OTHER ELECTRONIC CO... CORPORATE AFFILIATIONS

PRECISION DEVICES INCORPORATED; *U.S. Private*, pg. 3244
PRECISION TECHNOLOGY INC.—See Insight Equity Holdings LLC; *U.S. Private*, pg. 2086
PRECISION WIRELESS LLC—See Amphenol Corporation; *U.S. Public*, pg. 132
PRECITOOL-FENWICK NV—See Fuji Corporation; *Int'l*, pg. 2810
PREMIER COIL SOLUTIONS, INC.; *U.S. Private*, pg. 3249
PRIME FOUNDATION INC.—See FIC Global, INC; *Int'l*, pg. 2653
PRIME TECHNOLOGY (GUANGZHOU) INC.—See FIC Global, INC; *Int'l*, pg. 2653
PRISMATIBRO AB—See Addtech AB; *Int'l*, pg. 134
PRITCHARD BROWN, LLC.; *U.S. Private*, pg. 3268
PROGRESSIVE DYNAMICS, INC.; *U.S. Private*, pg. 3279
PSI REPAIR SERVICES, INC.—See Phillips Service Industries, Inc. (PSI); *U.S. Private*, pg. 3171
PT. ENPLAS INDONESIA—See ENPLAS CORPORATION; *Int'l*, pg. 2445
PT ESG PANATEC—See Cicor Technologies Ltd.; *Int'l*, pg. 1603
PT FLEXTRONICS TECHNOLOGY INDONESIA—See Flex Ltd.; *Int'l*, pg. 2704
PUREDEPTH, INC.—See Aptiv PLC; *Int'l*, pg. 524
PYRONIX LIMITED—See Hangzhou Hikvision Digital Technology Co., Ltd.; *Int'l*, pg. 3248
PYROPRESS ENGINEERING COMPANY LIMITED (THE)—See Caterpillar, Inc.; *U.S. Public*, pg. 453
QINGDAO DAEJOO ELECTRONIC MATERIALS CO., LTD.—See Daejoo Electronic Materials Co., Ltd.; *Int'l*, pg. 1907
QINGDAO HOSIDEN ELECTRONICS CO., LTD.—See Hosiden Corporation; *Int'l*, pg. 3484
QINGDAO KOWA SEIKO CO., LTD.—See FUJITSU COMPONENT LIMITED; *Int'l*, pg. 2832
QORVO INTERNATIONAL PTE. LTD.—See Qorvo, Inc.; *U.S. Public*, pg. 1743
QORVO OREGON, INC.—See Qorvo, Inc.; *U.S. Public*, pg. 1743
Q-TECH CORPORATION; *U.S. Private*, pg. 3312
QTERICS, INC.—See Lattice Semiconductor Corporation; *U.S. Public*, pg. 1294
QUALCOMM MEMS TECHNOLOGIES, INC.—See QUALCOMM Incorporated; *U.S. Public*, pg. 1748
QUALITY COMPONENTS, INC.—See Emerson Electric Co.; *U.S. Public*, pg. 751
QUANTUM CORP. - SANTA MARIA—See Quantum Corporation; *U.S. Public*, pg. 1754
QUANTUM MATERIALS CORP.; *U.S. Private*, pg. 3323
QUEST RAIL LLC—See Orscheln Group; *U.S. Private*, pg. 3045
RADIANT ELITE INVESTMENTS LIMITED—See General Interface Solution (GIS) Holding Ltd.; *Int'l*, pg. 2918
RADIODETECTION B.V.—See SPX Technologies, Inc.; *U.S. Public*, pg. 1921
RADIUS POWER INC.—See Tinicum Enterprises, Inc.; *U.S. Private*, pg. 4174
RALTRON ELECTRONICS CORP.—See Rami Technology Group; *U.S. Private*, pg. 3351
RALTRON ISRAEL LTD.—See Rami Technology Group; *U.S. Private*, pg. 3351
RALTRON KOREA CO., LTD.—See Rami Technology Group; *U.S. Private*, pg. 3351
RAMBUS DELAWARE LLC—See Rambus Inc.; *U.S. Public*, pg. 1762
RAMI TECHNOLOGY GROUP; *U.S. Private*, pg. 3351
RAMI TECHNOLOGY (S) PTE LTD—See Rami Technology Group; *U.S. Private*, pg. 3351
RASANT-ALCOTEC BESCHICHTUNGSTECHNIK GMBH—See Coherent Corp.; *U.S. Public*, pg. 528
RBI SOLAR, INC.—See Gibraltar Industries, Inc.; *U.S. Public*, pg. 936
RDI, INC.; *U.S. Private*, pg. 3364
REACH TECHNOLOGY, INC.—See Novanta Inc.; *U.S. Public*, pg. 1548
REC AMERICAS, LLC—See China National Chemical Corporation; *Int'l*, pg. 1527
RECO BIOTEK CO., LTD.—See General Interface Solution (GIS) Holding Ltd.; *Int'l*, pg. 2918
RECO TECHNOLOGY (CHENGDU) CO., LTD.—See General Interface Solution (GIS) Holding Ltd.; *Int'l*, pg. 2919
REC SOLAR EMEA GMBH—See China National Chemical Corporation; *Int'l*, pg. 1527
RED HAWK NETWORK ESSENTIALS, INC.—See Belden, Inc.; *U.S. Public*, pg. 294
REGAL ELECTRONICS, INC.; *U.S. Private*, pg. 3385
RHEA ELECTRONIQUE—See Hiolle Industries S.A.; *Int'l*, pg. 3401
R H LABORATORIES, INC.—See HEICO Corporation; *U.S. Public*, pg. 1021
RICH FULL INTERNATIONAL INDUSTRIES LIMITED—See CCT Fortis Holdings Limited; *Int'l*, pg. 1370
RICH SALES, INC.—See Fuji Corporation; *Int'l*, pg. 2810
RI MING (SHANGHAI) CO., LTD.—See Casetek Holdings Limited; *Int'l*, pg. 1351
RI-TENG COMPUTER ACCESSORY (SHANGHAI) CO., LTD.—See Casetek Holdings Limited; *Int'l*, pg. 1351
RJR POLYMERS INC.; *U.S. Private*, pg. 3449
ROFIN-BAASEL UK LTD.—See Coherent Corp.; *U.S. Public*, pg. 528
ROFIN-SINAR UK LTD.—See CMR GmbH; *Int'l*, pg. 1672
ROGERS CORP. - ADVANCED CIRCUIT MATERIALS DIVISION - FLEXIBLE PRODUCTS—See Rogers Corporation; *U.S. Public*, pg. 1808
ROGERS CORP. - ADVANCED CIRCUIT MATERIALS DIVISION - HIGH FREQUENCY PRODUCTS—See Rogers Corporation; *U.S. Public*, pg. 1808
ROHM & HAAS ELECTRONIC MATERIALS CMP KOREA LTD.—See DuPont de Nemours, Inc.; *U.S. Public*, pg. 694
ROLIC TECHNOLOGIES AG—See BASF SE; *Int'l*, pg. 884
RONAN ENGINEERING LTD.—See Ronan Engineering Company; *U.S. Private*, pg. 3477
ROTEC TECHNOLOGY GMBH—See FORTEC Elektronik AG; *Int'l*, pg. 2738
ROTOTECH ELECTRICAL COMPONENTS INC.; *U.S. Private*, pg. 3487
RUBICON WORLDWIDE LLC—See Rubicon Technology, Inc.; *U.S. Public*, pg. 1825
RUHLE COMPANIES, INC.; *U.S. Private*, pg. 3503
SAE POWER COMPANY, INC.—See SAE Power; *U.S. Private*, pg. 3523
SAE POWER INC—See SAE Power; *U.S. Private*, pg. 3523
SAE POWER; *U.S. Private*, pg. 3523
SAFARI CIRCUITS, INC.; *U.S. Private*, pg. 3523
SAFEPLACE LTD.—See ASSA ABLOY AB; *Int'l*, pg. 640
SAIA-BURGESS BENELUX B.V.—See Honeywell International Inc.; *U.S. Public*, pg. 1052
SAIA BURGESS CONTROLS AG—See Honeywell International Inc.; *U.S. Public*, pg. 1052
SAINT-GOBAIN QUARTZ S.A.S.—See Compagnie de Saint-Gobain SA; *Int'l*, pg. 1735
SAM ELECTRONICS NEDERLAND B.V.—See L3Harris Technologies, Inc.; *U.S. Public*, pg. 1284
SAMTEC, INC.; *U.S. Private*, pg. 3538
S AND Y INDUSTRIES, INC.; *U.S. Private*, pg. 3512
SANMINA CORPORATION - KUNSHAN—See Sanmina Corporation; *U.S. Public*, pg. 1840
SANMINA FRANCE SAS—See Sanmina Corporation; *U.S. Public*, pg. 1840
SANMINA SAS—See Sanmina Corporation; *U.S. Public*, pg. 1840
SANMINA-SCI DE MEXICO S.A. DE C.V.—See Sanmina Corporation; *U.S. Public*, pg. 1841
SAN TECHNOLOGY, INC.—See Hitachi, Ltd.; *Int'l*, pg. 3424
SANTIER INC.—See Egide SA; *Int'l*, pg. 2324
SANTON HOLLAND B.V.—See discoverIE Group plc; *Int'l*, pg. 2133
SARATOGA INDUSTRIES DIVISION—See Espey Mfg. & Electronics Corp.; *U.S. Public*, pg. 794
SAUER-DANFOSS AB—See Danfoss A/S; *Int'l*, pg. 1960
SAUER-DANFOSS APS—See Danfoss A/S; *Int'l*, pg. 1960
SAUER-DANFOSS A.S.—See Danfoss A/S; *Int'l*, pg. 1961
SBC DEUTSCHLAND GMBH—See Honeywell International Inc.; *U.S. Public*, pg. 1052
SC ELECTROLUX ROMANIA SA—See AB Electrolux; *Int'l*, pg. 41
SCHOTT NORTH AMERICA, INC. - LIGHTING & IMAGING DIVISION—See Carl-Zeiss-Stiftung; *Int'l*, pg. 1337
SCIENTIFIC COMPONENTS CORP.; *U.S. Private*, pg. 3574
SEACOMP DISPLAYS, INC.; *U.S. Private*, pg. 3584
SECURE SYSTEMS & TECHNOLOGIES LTD—See AEA Investors LP; *U.S. Private*, pg. 113
SELECTRON INDUSTRIAL COMPANY; *U.S. Private*, pg. 3601
SEMFLEX, INC.—See Emerson Electric Co.; *U.S. Public*, pg. 752
SENSATA TECHNOLOGIES BAOYING CO., LTD.—See Sensata Technologies Holding plc; *U.S. Public*, pg. 1865
SENSATA TECHNOLOGIES CHANGZHOU CO., LTD.—See Sensata Technologies Holding plc; *U.S. Public*, pg. 1865
SENSATA TECHNOLOGIES INDIANA, INC.—See Sensata Technologies Holding plc; *U.S. Public*, pg. 1866
SENSATA TECHNOLOGIES MEX DISTRIBUTION, S.A. DE C.V.—See Sensata Technologies Holding plc; *U.S. Public*, pg. 1865
SENVA INC.—See Carel Industries S.p.A.; *Int'l*, pg. 1324
SHANGHAI DAEJOO ELECTRONIC MATERIALS CO., LTD.—See Daejoo Electronic Materials Co., Ltd.; *Int'l*, pg. 1907
SHANGHAI DAI-ICHI SEIKO MOULD & PLASTICS CO., LTD. - MINHANG PLANT—See I-PEX Inc.; *Int'l*, pg. 3564
SHANGHAI DAI-ICHI SEIKO MOULD & PLASTICS CO., LTD.—See I-PEX Inc.; *Int'l*, pg. 3564
SHANGHAI HDK MICRO DEVICES CO., LTD.—See Hokuriku Electric Industry Co., Ltd.; *Int'l*, pg. 3445
SHANGHAI SIMCONIX ELECTRONIC COMPANY LTD.—See Vishay Intertechnology, Inc.; *U.S. Public*, pg. 2302
SHANGHAI VIASYSTEMS EMS COMPANY LIMITED—See TTM Technologies, Inc.; *U.S. Public*, pg. 2203
SHANTOU GOWORLD DISPLAY CO., LTD.—See Guangdong Goworld Co., Ltd.; *Int'l*, pg. 3154
SHARECAT SOLUTIONS AS—See Borea AS; *Int'l*, pg. 1113
SHARP ELECTRONICS (EUROPE) LIMITED—See Hon Hai Precision Industry Co., Ltd.; *Int'l*, pg. 3458
SHARP ELECTRONICS RUSSIA LLC—See Hon Hai Precision Industry Co., Ltd.; *Int'l*, pg. 3458
SHARP ELECTRONICS (VIETNAM) COMPANY LIMITED—See Hon Hai Precision Industry Co., Ltd.; *Int'l*, pg. 3458
SHARP MANUFACTURING POLAND SP. Z O. O.—See Hon Hai Precision Industry Co., Ltd.; *Int'l*, pg. 3458
SHARP MIE CORPORATION—See Hon Hai Precision Industry Co., Ltd.; *Int'l*, pg. 3459
SHARP NIIGATA ELECTRONICS CORPORATION—See Hon Hai Precision Industry Co., Ltd.; *Int'l*, pg. 3459
SHARP YONAGO CORPORATION—See Hon Hai Precision Industry Co., Ltd.; *Int'l*, pg. 3459
SHENG RUI ELECTRONIC TECHNOLOGY (SHANGHAI) CO., LTD.—See Casetek Holdings Limited; *Int'l*, pg. 1351
SHENZHEN COSON ELECTRONIC CO. LTD.—See China Security & Surveillance Technology, Inc.; *Int'l*, pg. 1550
SHENZHEN JUNTIAN HENGXUN TECHNOLOGY CO., LTD.—See Bomin Electronics Co., Ltd.; *Int'l*, pg. 1105
SHENZHEN LONGHORN SECURITY TECHNOLOGY CO., LTD.—See China Security & Surveillance Technology, Inc.; *Int'l*, pg. 1550
SHENZHEN MARY PHOTOELECTRICITY CO., LTD.—See Fujian Furi Electronics Co., Ltd.; *Int'l*, pg. 2818
SHENZHEN RUIJING INDUSTRIAL CO. LTD.—See CETC Acoustic-Optic-Electronic Technology Inc.; *Int'l*, pg. 1424
SHENZHEN RUNLITE TECHNOLOGY CO., LTD.—See Fujian Furi Electronics Co., Ltd.; *Int'l*, pg. 2818
SHENZHEN SUCCESS ELECTRONICS CO., LTD. - YU SHUN ELECTRONICS FACTORY—See Aishida Co., Ltd.; *Int'l*, pg. 251
SHENZHEN TOTECH TECHNOLOGIES CO., LTD.—See Aiphone Co., Ltd.; *Int'l*, pg. 235
SHENZHEN ZHONG HAN SCIENCE & TECH. CO., LTD.—See FSP Technology Inc.; *Int'l*, pg. 2800
SHINKO ELECTRIC AMERICA, INC.—See Fujitsu Limited; *Int'l*, pg. 2838
SHINKO ELECTRIC INDUSTRIES CO., LTD. - ARAI PLANT—See Fujitsu Limited; *Int'l*, pg. 2838
SHINKO ELECTRIC INDUSTRIES CO., LTD. - KYOGASE PLANT—See Fujitsu Limited; *Int'l*, pg. 2838
SHINKO ELECTRIC INDUSTRIES CO., LTD. - TAKAOKA PLANT—See Fujitsu Limited; *Int'l*, pg. 2838
SHINKO ELECTRIC INDUSTRIES CO., LTD. - WAKAHO PLANT—See Fujitsu Limited; *Int'l*, pg. 2838
SHINKO ELECTRIC INDUSTRIES (WUXI) CO., LTD.—See Fujitsu Limited; *Int'l*, pg. 2838
SHINKO ELECTRONICS (MALAYSIA) SDN. BHD.—See Fujitsu Limited; *Int'l*, pg. 2838
SIA DANFOSS—See Danfoss A/S; *Int'l*, pg. 1961
SIAM CALSONIC CO., LIMITED.—See KKR & Co. Inc.; *U.S. Public*, pg. 1260
S.I. DE MEXICO S.A. DE C.V.—See Standex International; *U.S. Public*, pg. 1930
SIE COMPUTING SOLUTIONS, INC.—See AbelConn LLC; *U.S. Private*, pg. 37
SIENNA CORPORATION INC.; *U.S. Private*, pg. 3646
SIGMATRON ELECTRONIC TECHNOLOGY CO., LTD.—See SigmaTron International, Inc.; *U.S. Public*, pg. 1877
SIMONSVOSS TECHNOLOGIES AG—See Allegion Public Limited Company; *Int'l*, pg. 335
SINGAPORE DAI-ICHI PTE. LTD.—See I-PEX Inc.; *Int'l*, pg. 3564
SINOMA ADVANCED MATERIALS CO. LTD.—See China National Materials; *Int'l*, pg. 1532
SITRA AUTOMAZIONE SRL—See FIDIA S.p.A.; *Int'l*, pg. 2655
SKYWORKS GLOBAL PTE LTD—See Skyworks Solutions, Inc.; *U.S. Public*, pg. 1893
SKYWORKS SEMICONDUCTOR—See Skyworks Solutions, Inc.; *U.S. Public*, pg. 1893
SKYWORKS SOLUTIONS COMPANY, LIMITED—See Skyworks Solutions, Inc.; *U.S. Public*, pg. 1893
SKYWORKS SOLUTIONS KOREA LIMITED—See Skyworks Solutions, Inc.; *U.S. Public*, pg. 1893
SKYWORKS SOLUTIONS LIMITED—See Skyworks Solutions, Inc.; *U.S. Public*, pg. 1893
SKYWORKS SOLUTIONS WORLDWIDE, INC.—See Skyworks Solutions, Inc.; *U.S. Public*, pg. 1893
SLING MEDIA, INC.—See EchoStar Corporation; *U.S. Public*, pg. 711
SMART ELECTRONICS & ASSEMBLY, INC.—See Vance Street Capital LLC; *U.S. Private*, pg. 4342
SMARTRAC TECHNOLOGY GMBH—See Avery Dennison Corporation; *U.S. Public*, pg. 245
SMARTRAC TECHNOLOGY LTD.—See Avery Dennison Corporation; *U.S. Public*, pg. 245
SMARTRAC TECHNOLOGY US INC.—See Avery Dennison Corporation; *U.S. Public*, pg. 245
SMARTWAVE TECHNOLOGIES CORP.—See Northlane Capital Partners, LLC; *U.S. Private*, pg. 2956
SMARTWITNESS USA LLC—See Sensata Technologies Holding plc; *U.S. Public*, pg. 1866
SMS TECHNOLOGIES, INC.—See Cal-Comp Electronics (Thailand) pcl; *Int'l*, pg. 1261

SMTC ASIA LTD.—See H.I.G. Capital, LLC; *U.S. Private*, pg. 1833
SMTC DE CHIHUAHUA S.A. DE C.V.—See H.I.G. Capital, LLC; *U.S. Private*, pg. 1834
SMTC ELECTRONICS DONGGUAN COMPANY LIMITED—See H.I.G. Capital, LLC; *U.S. Private*, pg. 1833
SMTC ELECTRONICS (SUZHOU) COMPANY LIMITED—See H.I.G. Capital, LLC; *U.S. Private*, pg. 1833
SOLIDSTATE CONTROLS, LLC—See AMETEK, Inc.; *U.S. Public*, pg. 121
SOLIDSTATE CONTROLS MEXICO, S.A. DE C.V.—See AMETEK, Inc.; *U.S. Public*, pg. 121
SOLTERRA RENEWABLE TECHNOLOGIES, INC.—See Quantum Materials Corp.; *U.S. Public*, pg. 3323
SOUND TECHNOLOGY, INC.—See Altaris Capital Partners, LLC; *U.S. Private*, pg. 205
SOUTHCHINA ENGINEERING & MANUFACTURING LIMITED—See Alltronics Holdings Limited; *Int'l*, pg. 361
SOUTHWEST VACUUM DEVICES, INC.—See Video Display Corporation; *U.S. Public*, pg. 2296
SPANG & COMPANY-BOONEVILLE PLANT—See Spang & Company; *U.S. Private*, pg. 3744
SPARTON ELECTRONICS FLORIDA, INC.—See Elbit Systems Limited; *Int'l*, pg. 2344
SPARTON MEDICAL SYSTEMS COLORADO, LLC—See Elbit Systems Limited; *Int'l*, pg. 2345
SPARTON MEDICAL SYSTEMS, INC.—See Elbit Systems Limited; *Int'l*, pg. 2344
SPARTRONICS LLC—See OEP Capital Advisors, L.P.; *U.S. Private*, pg. 3000
SPECTRALCAST, INC.; *U.S. Public*, pg. 1915
SPECTRO ANALYTICAL INSTRUMENTS INC.—See AMETEK, Inc.; *U.S. Public*, pg. 118
SPECTRUM CONTROL, INC.—See Allient Inc.; *U.S. Public*, pg. 80
SPECULATIVE PRODUCT DESIGN, LLC; *U.S. Private*, pg. 3753
SPEECH DESIGN GMBH—See Bogen Communications International Inc.; *U.S. Public*, pg. 367
SPIKE TECHNOLOGIES LLC—See QUALCOMM Incorporated; *U.S. Public*, pg. 1748
SPITFIRE CONTROLS (VIETNAM) CO. LTD.—See Sigma-Tron International, Inc.; *U.S. Public*, pg. 1878
SRCTEC, LLC—See SRC, Inc.; *U.S. Private*, pg. 3767
SSAC LLC—See Littelfuse, Inc.; *U.S. Public*, pg. 1327
SSD DRIVES, INC.—See Parker Hannifin Corporation; *U.S. Public*, pg. 1644
STABIL PRODUKT ELEKTROTECHNIKAI KFT.—See Standard Motor Products, Inc.; *U.S. Public*, pg. 1929
STACK ELECTRONICS LTD—See Stack Electronics; *U.S. Private*, pg. 3774
STALCOP L.P.—See 13i Capital Corporation; *U.S. Private*, pg. 3
STANDARD COMPONENTS DE MEXICO S.A.—See SigmaTron International, Inc.; *U.S. Public*, pg. 1878
STANDEX ELECTRONICS JAPAN CORPORATION—See Standex International; *U.S. Public*, pg. 1930
STANDEX HOLDINGS LIMITED—See Standex International; *U.S. Public*, pg. 1931
STAR MICROWAVE, INC.—See Electro Technik Industries; *U.S. Private*, pg. 1354
S-TEAM ELEKTRONIK GMBH—See Koch Industries, Inc.; *U.S. Private*, pg. 2334
STOCKNET—See The Hearst Corporation; *U.S. Private*, pg. 4045
STONERIDGE ASIA PACIFIC ELECTRONICS (SUZHOU) CO. LTD.—See Stoneridge, Inc.; *U.S. Public*, pg. 1951
STONERIDGE ELECTRONICS, INC.—See Stoneridge, Inc.; *U.S. Public*, pg. 1951
STONERIDGE ELECTRONICS LTD.—See Stoneridge, Inc.; *U.S. Public*, pg. 1951
STRUTHERS ELECTRONICS CORPORATION; *U.S. Private*, pg. 3842
SUN PACIFIC POWER CORP.—See Sun Pacific Holding Corp; *U.S. Public*, pg. 1963
SUNTRON GULF COAST OPERATIONS—See Blum Capital Partners, L.P.; *U.S. Private*, pg. 599
SUNTRON GULF COAST OPERATIONS—See HCI Equity Management, L.P.; *U.S. Private*, pg. 1889
SURFACE TECHNOLOGY ABERDEEN LTD.—See Quaker Chemical Corporation; *U.S. Public*, pg. 1747
SURFACE TECHNOLOGY AUSTRALIA—See Quaker Chemical Corporation; *U.S. Public*, pg. 1747
SURFACE TECHNOLOGY (COVENTRY) LTD.—See Quaker Chemical Corporation; *U.S. Public*, pg. 1747
SURFACE TECHNOLOGY (EAST KILBRIDE) LTD.—See Quaker Chemical Corporation; *U.S. Public*, pg. 1747
SURFACE TECHNOLOGY (LEEDS) LTD.—See Quaker Chemical Corporation; *U.S. Public*, pg. 1747
SUZHOU BOE CHATANI ELECTRONICS CO., LTD.—See BOE Technology Group Co., Ltd.; *Int'l*, pg. 1099
SUZHOU CMR ELECTRONIC DEVICES CO., LTD.—See Amphenol Corporation; *U.S. Public*, pg. 132
SUZHOU CUIZHUO DIANZI LTD.—See Adtec Plasma Technology Co., Ltd.; *U.S. Public*, pg. 154
SUZHOU DELTA PLUS PERSONAL PROTECTION—See Delta Plus Group; *Int'l*, pg. 2020
SUZO-HAPP GROUP—See ACON Investments, LLC; *U.S. Private*, pg. 62
SWINDON SILICON SYSTEMS LIMITED—See Sensata Technologies Holding plc; *U.S. Public*, pg. 1866
SWITCHCRAFT FAR EAST COMPANY, LTD.—See HEICO Corporation; *U.S. Public*, pg. 1021
SWITCHCRAFT INC.—See HEICO Corporation; *U.S. Public*, pg. 1020
SYNQOR INC.; *U.S. Private*, pg. 3904
SYPRIS SOLUTIONS, INC.; *U.S. Public*, pg. 1972
SYSTRONICS (INDIA) LTD.—See Ambalal Sarabhai Enterprises Ltd.; *Int'l*, pg. 413
TACTICAL SUPPORT EQUIPMENT INC.; *U.S. Private*, pg. 3921
TACTUS TECHNOLOGY, INC.—See General Motors Company; *U.S. Public*, pg. 929
TAEYANG ELECTRONICS CO., LTD. - WAEGWAN FACTORY—See GenNBio Inc.; *Int'l*, pg. 2925
TAICANG ALPINE ELECTRONICS CO., LTD.—See Alps Alpine Co., Ltd.; *Int'l*, pg. 376
TAIPEI HOKURIKU CO., LTD.—See Hokuriku Electric Industry Co., Ltd.; *Int'l*, pg. 3445
TAIWAN DAEJOO ELECTRONIC MATERIALS CO., LTD.—See Daejoo Electronic Materials Co., Ltd.; *Int'l*, pg. 1907
TAIWAN FUTABA ELECTRONICS CORPORATION—See Futaba Corporation; *Int'l*, pg. 2851
TAIWAN JUKEN CO. LTD.—See EMNI Co., Ltd; *Int'l*, pg. 2385
TAIWAN MARINE ELECTRIC CO., LTD.—See Allis Electric Co., Ltd.; *Int'l*, pg. 359
TAIWAN SHINKO ELECTRONICS CO., LTD.—See Fujitsu Limited; *Int'l*, pg. 2838
TAIYO AMERICA, INC.—See Parker Hannifin Corporation; *U.S. Public*, pg. 1649
TARUTIN KESTER CO., LTD.—See Illinois Tool Works Inc.; *U.S. Public*, pg. 1111
TATSUTA ELECTRONIC MATERIALS MALAYSIA SDN. BHD.—See ENEOS Holdings, Inc.; *Int'l*, pg. 2416
TCI CERAMICS—See National Magnetics Group, Inc.; *U.S. Private*, pg. 2859
TECHMA CORPORATION—See Denso Corporation; *Int'l*, pg. 2033
TECHNIC ASIA-PACIFIC SDN. BHD.—See Technic Incorporated; *U.S. Private*, pg. 3953
TECHNIC (CHINA-HK) LTD.—See Technic Incorporated; *U.S. Private*, pg. 3953
TECHNICORP INTERNATIONAL II; *U.S. Private*, pg. 3954
TECHNOLOGIEPARK TENINGEN GMBH—See Ascom Holding AG; *Int'l*, pg. 603
TECHNOLOGY DYNAMICS, INC.; *U.S. Private*, pg. 3955
TECHNO QUARTZ INC.—See GL Sciences Inc.; *Int'l*, pg. 2986
TECHSPAN SYSTEMS—See Hill & Smith PLC; *Int'l*, pg. 3392
TECHWIN OPTO-ELECTRONICS CO., LTD.—See CHIA-LIN Precision Industrial Co., Ltd.; *Int'l*, pg. 1476
TECMAG, INC.—See Avingtrans plc; *Int'l*, pg. 744
TELCA 2000—See ENGIE SA; *Int'l*, pg. 2434
TELEDYNE COUGAR—See Teledyne Technologies Incorporated; *U.S. Public*, pg. 1993
TELEDYNE E2V, INC.—See Teledyne Technologies Incorporated; *U.S. Public*, pg. 1995
TELEDYNE LECROY GMBH—See Teledyne Technologies Incorporated; *U.S. Public*, pg. 1994
TELEDYNE LECROY INDIA TRADING PRIVATE LTD.—See Teledyne Technologies Incorporated; *U.S. Public*, pg. 1994
TELEDYNE LECROY JAPAN CORPORATION—See Teledyne Technologies Incorporated; *U.S. Public*, pg. 1994
TELEDYNE LECROY KOREA, LTD.—See Teledyne Technologies Incorporated; *U.S. Public*, pg. 1994
TELEDYNE LECROY, S.A.—See Teledyne Technologies Incorporated; *U.S. Public*, pg. 1994
TELEDYNE LECROY SINGAPORE PTE. LTD.—See Teledyne Technologies Incorporated; *U.S. Public*, pg. 1994
TELEDYNE LECROY, S.R.L.—See Teledyne Technologies Incorporated; *U.S. Public*, pg. 1994
TELEDYNE REAL TIME SYSTEMS INC.—See Teledyne Technologies Incorporated; *U.S. Public*, pg. 1995
TELEDYNE RESON B.V.—See Teledyne Technologies Incorporated; *U.S. Public*, pg. 1995
TELEDYNE RESON GMBH—See Teledyne Technologies Incorporated; *U.S. Public*, pg. 1995
TELEDYNE RESON, INC.—See Teledyne Technologies Incorporated; *U.S. Public*, pg. 1995
TELEPHONICS SWEDEN AB—See TTM Technologies, Inc.; *U.S. Public*, pg. 2203
TELESIS TECHNOLOGIES INC.—See Bertram Capital Management, LLC; *U.S. Private*, pg. 540
TELESIS TECHNOLOGIES INC.—See Crimson Investment; *U.S. Public*, pg. 1100
TEMPO AUTOMATION HOLDINGS, INC.; *U.S. Public*, pg. 1999
TEMPO EUROPE LIMITED—See Emerson Electric Co.; *U.S. Public*, pg. 742
TEMPO EUROPE LIMITED—See Emerson Electric Co.; *U.S. Public*, pg. 750
TESEQ AG—See AMETEK, Inc.; *U.S. Public*, pg. 119
TEXAS INSTRUMENTS DENMARK A/S—See Texas Instruments Incorporated; *U.S. Public*, pg. 2026
TEXAS INSTRUMENTS DEUTSCHLAND GMBH—See Texas Instruments Incorporated; *U.S. Public*, pg. 2026
TEXAS INSTRUMENTS ISRAEL LTD.—See Texas Instruments Incorporated; *U.S. Public*, pg. 2026
TEXAS INSTRUMENTS PALO ALTO INCORPORATED—See Texas Instruments Incorporated; *U.S. Public*, pg. 2026
TFI TELEMARK—See APT, Inc.; *U.S. Private*, pg. 302
THAI WIRE & CABLE SERVICES CO., LTD.—See Hayakawa Densen Kogyo Co., Ltd.; *Int'l*, pg. 3289
THIIM A/S—See Addtech AB; *Int'l*, pg. 135
THOMAS ELECTRONICS INC.; *U.S. Private*, pg. 4155
THUNDERLINE Z, INC.—See Emerson Electric Co.; *U.S. Public*, pg. 744
TIANJIN ALPS ELECTRONICS CO., LTD.—See Alps Alpine Co., Ltd.; *Int'l*, pg. 376
TIANJIN CENTRAL ELECTRONIC CORPORATION—See Commax Co., Ltd.; *Int'l*, pg. 1714
TIANJIN EO TECHNICS CO., LTD—See EO Technics Co., Ltd.; *Int'l*, pg. 2457
TIANJIN KDS CORP.—See Daishinku Corp.; *Int'l*, pg. 1942
TIANJIN LAIRD TECHNOLOGIES LIMITED—See DuPont de Nemours, Inc.; *U.S. Public*, pg. 694
TIANMA EUROPE GMBH—See AVIC International Holdings Limited; *Int'l*, pg. 742
TIANMA MICRO-ELECTRONICS CO., LTD.—See AVIC International Holdings Limited; *Int'l*, pg. 742
TIME TIMER LLC; *U.S. Public*, pg. 4172
TINGO GROUP, INC.; *U.S. Public*, pg. 2159
TLC ELECTRONICS, INC.; *U.S. Private*, pg. 4178
TOFIC CO. LTD.—See AT&S Austria Technologie & Systemtechnik Aktiengesellschaft; *Int'l*, pg. 665
TOHOKU HIROSE ELECTRIC CO., LTD.—See Hirose Electric Co., Ltd.; *Int'l*, pg. 3405
TOHOKU PIONEER CORPORATION—See EQT AB; *Int'l*, pg. 2471
TOTAL ELECTRONICS, LLC—See Cal-Comp Electronics (Thailand) pcl; *Int'l*, pg. 1261
TOUCHSENSOR TECHNOLOGIES, L.L.C.—See Methode Electronics, Inc.; *U.S. Public*, pg. 1429
TOUCHSTONE PRECISION, INC.—See I-PEX Inc.; *Int'l*, pg. 3564
TPE DE MEXICO, S. DE R.L. DE C.V.—See RBC Bearings Incorporated; *U.S. Public*, pg. 1766
TRAKA PLC—See ASSA ABLOY AB; *Int'l*, pg. 640
TRANSDUCERS DIRECT, LLC; *U.S. Private*, pg. 4207
TRANS-LUX CORPORATION; *U.S. Public*, pg. 2179
TRANS WORLD CONNECTION—See Unlimited Services of Wisconsin, Inc.; *U.S. Public*, pg. 4310
TRENDYLITE CORPORATION—See Ennostar Inc.; *Int'l*, pg. 2444
TRIPPE MANUFACTURING COMPANY; *U.S. Private*, pg. 4238
TRI-STAR ELECTRONICS INTERNATIONAL, INC.—See Carlisle Companies Incorporated; *U.S. Public*, pg. 437
TRITON SERVICES INC.; *U.S. Private*, pg. 4239
TROIS TAKAYA ELECTRONICS (THAILAND) CO., LTD.—See Di-Nikko Engineering Co., Ltd.; *Int'l*, pg. 2101
TROMBETTA MOTION TECHNOLOGIES, INC.—See Fulham & Co., Inc.; *U.S. Private*, pg. 1620
TSE; *U.S. Private*, pg. 4252
TTE FILTERS, LLC—See The Jordan Company, L.P.; *U.S. Private*, pg. 4063
TURTLE BEACH CORPORATION; *U.S. Public*, pg. 2205
TURTLE BEACH EUROPE LIMITED—See Turtle Beach Corporation; *U.S. Public*, pg. 2205
TUSONIX INC.—See CTS Corporation; *U.S. Public*, pg. 603
TWIN FILTER SOUTH AMERICA LTDA—See Parker Hannifin Corporation; *U.S. Public*, pg. 1650
UEC ELECTRONICS, LLC—See Greenbriar Equity Group, L.P.; *U.S. Private*, pg. 1775
UNICIRCUIT, INC.—See TTM Technologies, Inc.; *U.S. Public*, pg. 2203
UNIROYAL GLOBAL ENGINEERED PRODUCTS, INC.; *U.S. Public*, pg. 2227
UNITED LED CORPORATION (SHANDONG) LIMITED—See Ennostar Inc.; *Int'l*, pg. 2444
UNIVERSAL SCIENTIFIC INDUSTRIAL CO., LTD.—See ASE Technology Holding Co., Ltd.; *Int'l*, pg. 604
UNIVERSAL SCIENTIFIC INDUSTRIAL (SHANGHAI) CO., LTD.—See ASE Technology Holding Co., Ltd.; *Int'l*, pg. 604
UPSTREAMNET COMMUNICATIONS GMBH—See DigitalBridge Group, Inc.; *U.S. Public*, pg. 665
UPSTREAMNET COMMUNICATIONS GMBH—See EQT AB; *Int'l*, pg. 2482
UQM TECHNOLOGIES, INC.—See Danfoss A/S; *Int'l*, pg. 1961
UST-ALDETEC GROUP—See Greenbriar Equity Group, L.P.; *U.S. Private*, pg. 1775
U.S. TECHNOLOGIES INC.—See Greenbriar Equity Group, L.P.; *U.S. Private*, pg. 1776

334419 — OTHER ELECTRONIC CO...

UTHE TECHNOLOGY, INC.—See Crest Group Inc.; *U.S. Private*, pg. 1096
UTIS CO., LTD—See Rogers Corporation; *U.S. Public*, pg. 1808
VACON FRANCE S.A.S.—See Danfoss A/S; *Int'l*, pg. 1962
VALORE (SHENZHEN) PRIVATE LIMITED—See Challenger Technologies Ltd.; *Int'l*, pg. 1438
VARTECH SYSTEMS, INC.; *U.S. Public*, pg. 2276
VDC DISPLAY SYSTEMS—See Video Display Corporation; *U.S. Public*, pg. 2296
VEECO MALAYSIA SDN. BHD.—See Veeco Instruments Inc.; *U.S. Public*, pg. 2277
VEECO SOLAR EQUIPMENT INC.—See Veeco Instruments Inc.; *U.S. Public*, pg. 2277
VEONEER, INC.—See SSW Partners LP; *U.S. Private*, pg. 3770
VERSA ELECTRONICS—See Versa Companies; *U.S. Private*, pg. 4368
VIASYSTEMS ASIA LIMITED—See TTM Technologies, Inc.; *U.S. Public*, pg. 2203
VIDEO DISPLAY CORPORATION; *U.S. Public*, pg. 2296
VIDEO DISPLAY NOVATRON TUBE DIVISION—See Video Display Corporation; *U.S. Public*, pg. 2297
VIETNAM DAI-ICHI SEIKO CO., LTD.—See I-PEX Inc.; *Int'l*, pg. 3564
VIGILANT TECHNOLOGY INC.—See BATM Advanced Communications Ltd.; *Int'l*, pg. 890
VIMAX (KUNSHAN) CO., LTD.—See Coretronic Corporation; *Int'l*, pg. 1800
VINGCARD ELSAFE AS—See ASSA ABLOY AB; *Int'l*, pg. 641
VINX SYSTEM SERVICE (THAILAND) CO., LTD.—See FUJISOFT INCORPORATED; *Int'l*, pg. 2830
VISHAY BCCOMPONENTS HONG KONG LTD.—See Vishay Intertechnology, Inc.; *U.S. Public*, pg. 2302
VISHAY CELTRON TECHNOLOGIES, INC.—See Vishay Precision Group, Inc.; *U.S. Public*, pg. 2303
VISHAY COMPONENTS (HUIZHOU) CO. LTD.—See Vishay Intertechnology, Inc.; *U.S. Public*, pg. 2302
VISHAY PME FRANCE SARL—See Vishay Precision Group, Inc.; *U.S. Public*, pg. 2304
VISHAY PRECISION FOIL K.K.—See Vishay Precision Group, Inc.; *U.S. Public*, pg. 2304
VISHAY PRECISION TRANSDUCERS INDIA PRIVATE LIMITED—See Vishay Precision Group, Inc.; *U.S. Public*, pg. 2304
VISTA POINT TECHNOLOGIES, INC.—See Flex Ltd.; *Int'l*, pg. 2703
VISTA POINT TECHNOLOGIES (MALAYSIA) SDN. BHD.—See Flex Ltd.; *Int'l*, pg. 2704
VISUAL COMMUNICATIONS COMPANY, INC.; *U.S. Private*, pg. 4404
VITESSE SYSTEMS—See Trive Capital Inc.; *U.S. Private*, pg. 4240
V-TEK INCORPORATED; *U.S. Private*, pg. 4328
WABASH TECHNOLOGIES DE MEXICO, S DE R L DE C V—See Sensata Technologies Holding plc; *U.S. Public*, pg. 1866
WAFO SCHNECKEN UND ZYLINDER GMBH—See Nordson Corporation; *U.S. Public*, pg. 1535
WATTS INSULATION NV—See Watts Water Technologies, Inc.; *U.S. Public*, pg. 2338
WAVELENGTH ELECTRONICS LIMITED—See APC Technology Group plc; *Int'l*, pg. 508
WAYGATE TECHNOLOGIES USA, LP—See Baker Hughes Company; *U.S. Public*, pg. 265
WB-PRC LASER SERVICE GMBH—See Coherent Corp.; *U.S. Public*, pg. 528
WESCO AIRCRAFT HARDWARE CORP. - ELECTRICAL PRODUCTS GROUP—See Platinum Equity, LLC; *U.S. Private*, pg. 3210
WESTEK LIGHTING—See Amertac Holdings Inc.; *U.S. Private*, pg. 261
WILBRECHT LEDCO, INC.; *U.S. Private*, pg. 4517
WILLIAMS ADVANCED MATERIALS INC.—See Materion Corporation; *U.S. Public*, pg. 1396
WINCHESTER INTERCONNECT RF CORPORATION—See Aptiv PLC; *Int'l*, pg. 526
WINTECH CO., LTD.—See EO Technics Co., Ltd.; *Int'l*, pg. 2457
W. L. GORE & ASSOCIATES, CO., LTD.—See W.L. Gore & Associates, Inc.; *U.S. Public*, pg. 4421
WONJIN PRECISION CO., LTD.—See Futaba Corporation; *Int'l*, pg. 2851
WOODHEAD SOFTWARE & ELECTRONICS S.A.S.U.—See Koch Industries, Inc.; *U.S. Private*, pg. 2335
WOODWARD IDS BULGARIA EOOD—See Woodward, Inc.; *U.S. Public*, pg. 2378
WOVEN ELECTRONICS LLC—See RTX Corporation; *U.S. Public*, pg. 1822
WUJIANG SIGMATRON ELECTRONICS CO., LTD.—See SigmaTron International, Inc.; *U.S. Public*, pg. 1878
WUXI ALPS ELECTRONICS CO., LTD.—See Alps Alpine Co., Ltd.; *Int'l*, pg. 377
XANTREX TECHNOLOGY, INC.—See Windjammer Capital Investors, LLC; *U.S. Private*, pg. 4538
XCEL POWER SYSTEMS LTD.—See TransDigm Group Incorporated; *U.S. Public*, pg. 2182
XIAMEN BOE ELECTRONICS CO., LTD.—See BOE Technology Group Co., Ltd.; *Int'l*, pg. 1099
XI'AN XINHAI MICROELECTRONICS TECHNOLOGY CO., LTD.—See Chipsea Technologies (Shenzhen) Corp.; *Int'l*, pg. 1573
XTREME RFID—See Cascade Engineering, Inc.; *U.S. Private*, pg. 779
XUZHOU HIRSCHMANN ELECTRONICS CO., LTD.—See Belden, Inc.; *U.S. Public*, pg. 294
XYMOX TECHNOLOGIES INC.—See Brookfield Corporation; *Int'l*, pg. 1182
YALE LA FONTE SISTEMAS DE SEGURANCA LTDA—See ASSA ABLOY AB; *Int'l*, pg. 641
YAMAGATA CASIO CO., LTD.—See Casio Computer Co., Ltd.; *Int'l*, pg. 1353
YDC CORPORATION—See Future Corporation; *Int'l*, pg. 2853
YMC CO., LTD.—See Dream T Entertainment Co., Ltd.; *Int'l*, pg. 2203
YOKOGAWA DIGITAL COMPUTER CORPORATION—See DTS Corporation; *Int'l*, pg. 2217
YSI (HONG KONG) LTD.—See Xylem Inc.; *U.S. Public*, pg. 2395
YUTAKA ELECTRIC MANUFACTURING COMPANY LTD.—See Glass One Technology Corporation; *Int'l*, pg. 2989
ZAO HIKVISION—See Hangzhou Hikvision Digital Technology Co., Ltd.; *Int'l*, pg. 3248
ZAO RIDAN—See Danfoss A/S; *Int'l*, pg. 1962
Z-AXIS, INC.—See Video Display Corporation; *U.S. Public*, pg. 2297
ZEBRA TECHNOLOGIES ARGENTINA S.A.—See Zebra Technologies Corporation; *U.S. Public*, pg. 2402
ZETTLER CONTROLS, INC.—See Zettler Components, Inc.; *U.S. Private*, pg. 4603
ZETTLER ELECTRONICS NEDERLAND B.V.—See Zettler Components, Inc.; *U.S. Private*, pg. 4603
ZHEIJANG HOLIP ELECTRONIC TECHNOLOGY CO. LTD.—See Danfoss A/S; *Int'l*, pg. 1962
ZHUHAI DAVID ELECTRONICS CO., LTD.—See Chant Sincere Co., Ltd.; *Int'l*, pg. 1446
ZHUHAI SINGYES NEW MATERIALS TECHNOLOGY CO. LTD.—See China Singyes New Materials Holdings Limited; *Int'l*, pg. 1552
ZONAR SYSTEMS, LLC—See Continental Aktiengesellschaft; *Int'l*, pg. 1783
Z-WAVE ALLIANCE, LLC—See Silicon Laboratories Inc.; *U.S. Public*, pg. 1880
ZYGO PTE. LTD.—See AMETEK, Inc.; *U.S. Public*, pg. 119

334510 — ELECTROMEDICAL AND ELECTRO-THERAPEUTIC APPARATUS MANUFACTURING

3B MEDICAL, INC.; *U.S. Private*, pg. 8
3-D MATRIX ASIA PTE. LTD.—See 3-D Matrix, Ltd.; *Int'l*, pg. 6
ABBOTT MEDICAL DEVICES TRADING (SHANGHAI) CO., LTD.—See Abbott Laboratories; *U.S. Public*, pg. 17
ABBOTT POINT OF CARE INTERNATIONAL—See Abbott Laboratories; *U.S. Public*, pg. 14
ABBOTT VASCULAR INC.—See Abbott Laboratories; *U.S. Public*, pg. 18
ABBOTT VASCULAR INSTRUMENTS DEUTSCHLAND GMBH—See Abbott Laboratories; *U.S. Public*, pg. 18
ABBOTT VASCULAR JAPAN CO., LTD.—See Abbott Laboratories; *U.S. Public*, pg. 18
ACCELERATED CARE PLUS CORP.—See Patient Square Capital, L.P.; *U.S. Private*, pg. 3106
ACCENTUS MEDICAL PLC—See Coller Capital Ltd.; *Int'l*, pg. 1699
ACTIGRAPH, LLC—See ArchiMed SAS; *Int'l*, pg. 548
ACUTUS MEDICAL, INC.; *U.S. Public*, pg. 37
ADALTIS SRL—See BATM Advanced Communications Ltd.; *Int'l*, pg. 890
ADAPTIVE SWITCH LABORATORIES, INC.—See Invacare Corporation; *U.S. Private*, pg. 2130
A&D ELECTRONICS (SHENZHEN) CO., LTD.—See A&D Co., Ltd.; *Int'l*, pg. 18
ADMEDUS SARL—See Anteris Technologies Ltd.; *Int'l*, pg. 482
AD STYLA SP. Z O.O.—See Demant A/S; *Int'l*, pg. 2022
ADTEC PLASMA TECHNOLOGY VIETNAM CO., LTD.—See Adtec Plasma Technology Co., Ltd.; *Int'l*, pg. 154
ADVANCED CERAMICS TECHNOLOGY (M) SDN. BHD.—See Crest Group Inc.; *U.S. Private*, pg. 1095
ADVANCED HANDLING LTD—See Amplex AB; *Int'l*, pg. 434
AGFA-GEVAERT HEALTHCARE GMBH—See Agfa-Gevaert N.V.; *Int'l*, pg. 208
AGFA HEALTHCARE AG—See Agfa-Gevaert N.V.; *Int'l*, pg. 207
AGFA HEALTHCARE SWEDEN AB—See Agfa-Gevaert N.V.; *Int'l*, pg. 207
AKOUSTICA MEDICA M EPE—See Demant A/S; *Int'l*, pg. 2023

ALEVA NEUROTHERAPEUTICS SA—See BNP Paribas SA; *Int'l*, pg. 1089
ALLIANCE SPORTS GROUP, L.P.; *U.S. Private*, pg. 184
ALLTEC ANGEWANDTE LASERLICHT TECHNOLOGIE GMBH—See Danaher Corporation; *U.S. Public*, pg. 624
ALPHASENSE LIMITED—See AMETEK, Inc.; *U.S. Public*, pg. 119
ALPINION MEDICAL SYSTEMS CO., LTD.—See Iljin Display Co., Ltd.; *Int'l*, pg. 3614
ALTIMATE MEDICAL, INC.—See Rockwood Equity Partners, LLC; *U.S. Private*, pg. 3468
AMBU A/S; *Int'l*, pg. 416
AMERICAN MEDICAL SYSTEMS, INC.-SAN JOSE—See Endo International plc; *Int'l*, pg. 2404
AMIGO MOBILITY INTERNATIONAL, INC.; *U.S. Private*, pg. 263
AMPLIFON DEUTSCHLAND GMBH—See Amplifon S.p.A.; *Int'l*, pg. 435
AMPLITUDE TECHNOLOGIES SA; *Int'l*, pg. 436
AMPLIVOX LTD.—See Demant A/S; *Int'l*, pg. 2023
ANALOGIC MEDICAL EQUIPMENT (SHANGHAI) CO. LTD.—See Altaris Capital Partners, LLC; *U.S. Private*, pg. 205
ANALYTICA LIMITED; *Int'l*, pg. 446
ANDON HEALTH CO., LTD.; *Int'l*, pg. 451
ANGIODYNAMICS CANADA INC.—See AngioDynamics, Inc.; *U.S. Public*, pg. 137
ANSHAN HYMSON SCIENCE & TECHNOLOGY CO., LTD.—See Hymson Laser Technology Group Co Ltd; *Int'l*, pg. 3549
APDM, INC.—See Astorg Partners S.A.S.; *Int'l*, pg. 657
APE ANGEWANDTE PHYSIK & ELEKTRONIK GMBH; *Int'l*, pg. 508
APEC (ASIA) LIMITED—See Freudenberg SE; *Int'l*, pg. 2782
APEX BIOTECHNOLOGY CORP.; *Int'l*, pg. 509
AQUARIUS SURGICAL TECHNOLOGIES INC.; *Int'l*, pg. 528
AQUATEC OPERATIONS GMBH—See Invacare Corporation; *U.S. Private*, pg. 2130
ARADIGM CORPORATION; *U.S. Public*, pg. 175
ARCOMA AB; *Int'l*, pg. 550
ARGES GMBH—See Novanta Inc.; *U.S. Public*, pg. 1548
ARKRAY FACTORY LTD.—See ARKRAY, Inc.; *Int'l*, pg. 571
ARKRAY FACTORY PINGHU, INC.—See ARKRAY, Inc.; *Int'l*, pg. 571
ARKRAY FACTORY SHANGHAI, INC.—See ARKRAY, Inc.; *Int'l*, pg. 571
ARKRAY INDUSTRY, INC.—See ARKRAY, Inc.; *Int'l*, pg. 571
ARKRAY LTD.—See ARKRAY, Inc.; *Int'l*, pg. 571
ARKRAY TECH XI'AN, INC.—See ARKRAY, Inc.; *Int'l*, pg. 572
AROCELL AB; *Int'l*, pg. 577
ARTECH ULTRASONIC SYSTEMS AG—See Crest Group Inc.; *U.S. Private*, pg. 1095
ARX BVBA—See Becton, Dickinson & Company; *U.S. Public*, pg. 288
ASAHI INTECC LATIN PROMOCAO DE VENDAS E COMERCIO DE PRODUTOS CIRURGICOS LTDA.—See Asahi Intecc Co., Ltd.; *Int'l*, pg. 594
ASPEN LABORATORIES, INC.—See CONMED Corporation; *U.S. Public*, pg. 567
ATCOR MEDICAL PTY LIMITED—See CardieX Limited; *Int'l*, pg. 1321
ATOS MEDICAL BRASIL LTDA.—See Coloplast A/S; *Int'l*, pg. 1703
ATOS MEDICAL JAPAN INC.—See Coloplast A/S; *Int'l*, pg. 1703
ATOS MEDICAL LTD.—See Coloplast A/S; *Int'l*, pg. 1703
ATOS MEDICAL POLAND SP. Z O.O.—See Coloplast A/S; *Int'l*, pg. 1703
ATOS MEDICAL S.L.—See Coloplast A/S; *Int'l*, pg. 1703
ATOS MEDICAL UK LTD.—See Coloplast A/S; *Int'l*, pg. 1703
ATRION CORPORATION—See Nordson Corporation; *U.S. Public*, pg. 1532
AUTOBIO DIAGNOSTICS CO., LTD; *Int'l*, pg. 726
AUTOLOGIC DIAGNOSTICS, INC.—See Searchlight Capital Partners, L.P.; *U.S. Private*, pg. 3590
AUTOLOGIC DIAGNOSTICS LTD.—See Searchlight Capital Partners, L.P.; *U.S. Private*, pg. 3590
AUTOLOGIC DIAGNOSTICS PTY. LTD.—See Searchlight Capital Partners, L.P.; *U.S. Private*, pg. 3590
AVISION BRASIL LTDA.—See Avision Inc.; *Int'l*, pg. 744
AVITA MEDICAL AMERICAS LLC—See Avita Medical, Inc.; *U.S. Public*, pg. 249
AVITA MEDICAL EUROPE LTD.—See Avita Medical, Inc.; *U.S. Public*, pg. 249
AXELGAARD MANUFACTURING CO., LTD.; *U.S. Private*, pg. 412
AXESS ULTRASOUND, LLC—See Ascension Health Alliance; *U.S. Private*, pg. 346
BAXTER ONCOLOGY GMBH—See Baxter International Inc.; *U.S. Public*, pg. 281
BECKMAN COULTER HONG KONG LTD.—See Danaher Corporation; *U.S. Public*, pg. 624
BEIJING DAHENG MEDICAL EQUIPMENT CO., LTD.—See Daheng New Epoch Technology, Inc.; *Int'l*, pg. 1913

N.A.I.C.S. INDEX 334510 — ELECTROMEDICAL AND ...

BELTONE ELECTRONICS LLC—See GN Store Nord A/S; *Int'l*, pg. 3016
BELTONE EUROPE HOLDINGS APS—See GN Store Nord A/S; *Int'l*, pg. 3016
BERGMAN DIAGNOSTIKA AS—See Addtech AB; *Int'l*, pg. 132
BERKELEY NUCLEONICS CORP.; *U.S. Private*, pg. 532
BERNAFON AG—See Demant A/S; *Int'l*, pg. 2023
BERNAFON CANADA LTD.—See Demant A/S; *Int'l*, pg. 2023
BERNAFON HORGERATE GMBH—See Demant A/S; *Int'l*, pg. 2023
BERNAFON, LLC—See Demant A/S; *Int'l*, pg. 2023
BERNAFON NEDERLAND B.V.—See Demant A/S; *Int'l*, pg. 2023
BERNAFON (UK) LTD.—See Demant A/S; *Int'l*, pg. 2023
BEST MEDICAL CANADA, LTD.—See Best Medical International, Inc.; *U.S. Private*, pg. 543
BEST MEDICAL INTERNATIONAL, INC.; *U.S. Private*, pg. 543
BIOELECTRONICS CORP.; *U.S. Public*, pg. 335
BIOLITEC AG; *Int'l*, pg. 1039
BIOLITEC ITALIA SRL—See biolitec AG; *Int'l*, pg. 1039
BIOLITEC (M) SDN. BHD.—See biolitec AG; *Int'l*, pg. 1039
BIOLITEC PHARMA (IRELAND) LTD.—See biolitec AG; *Int'l*, pg. 1039
BIOMAGNETICS DIAGNOSTICS CORP.; *U.S. Public*, pg. 337
BIOMERICA, INC.; *U.S. Public*, pg. 337
BIONESS, INC.—See Bioventus Inc.; *U.S. Public*, pg. 339
BIOPROD BIOMEDICINSKI PRODUKTI D.O.O.—See Baxter International Inc.; *U.S. Public*, pg. 281
BIOPTIK TECHNOLOGY, INC.; *Int'l*, pg. 1041
BIOSENSE WEBSTER INC.—See Johnson & Johnson; *U.S. Public*, pg. 1194
BIOSIG TECHNOLOGIES, INC.; *U.S. Public*, pg. 338
BIOTRONIK GMBH & CO.; *Int'l*, pg. 1044
BODYMEDIA, INC.—See AliphCom; *U.S. Private*, pg. 168
BOSTON SCIENTIFIC - ARDEN HILLS/SAINT PAUL—See Boston Scientific Corporation; *U.S. Public*, pg. 374
BOSTON SCIENTIFIC - ELECTROPHYSIOLOGY - LOWELL—See Boston Scientific Corporation; *U.S. Public*, pg. 374
BOSTON SCIENTIFIC INTERNATIONAL B.V.—See Boston Scientific Corporation; *U.S. Public*, pg. 374
BOSTON SCIENTIFIC INTERNATIONAL S.A.—See Boston Scientific Corporation; *U.S. Public*, pg. 374
BOSTON SCIENTIFIC JAPAN K.K.—See Boston Scientific Corporation; *U.S. Public*, pg. 374
BOSTON SCIENTIFIC LIMITED—See Boston Scientific Corporation; *U.S. Public*, pg. 374
BOULE MEDICAL AB—See Boule Diagnostics AB; *Int'l*, pg. 1119
BOULE MEDICAL (BEIJING) CO. LTD—See Boule Diagnostics AB; *Int'l*, pg. 1119
BREATHRESEARCH INC.—See AireHealth, LLC; *U.S. Private*, pg. 141
BRIDGER PHOTONICS, INC.; *U.S. Private*, pg. 649
BRONCUS MEDICAL, INC; *U.S. Private*, pg. 662
BSP - BIOLOGICAL SIGNAL PROCESSING LTD.; *Int'l*, pg. 1202
CAMBRIDGE NUTRITIONAL SCIENCES PLC; *Int'l*, pg. 1269
CANDELA CORPORATION—See Apax Partners LLP; *Int'l*, pg. 506
CARCLO DIAGNOSTIC SOLUTIONS LTD—See Carclo plc; *Int'l*, pg. 1321
CARDIAC SCIENCE CORPORATION—See Asahi Kasei Corporation; *Int'l*, pg. 597
CARDIAQ VALVE TECHNOLOGIES, INC.—See Edwards Lifesciences Corporation; *U.S. Public*, pg. 720
CARDIEX LIMITED; *Int'l*, pg. 1321
CARDIODYNAMICS INTERNATIONAL CORPORATION—See FUJIFILM Holdings Corporation; *Int'l*, pg. 2823
CARDIODYNE, INC.—See Integra LifeSciences Holdings Corporation; *U.S. Public*, pg. 1135
CARDIOS SISTEMAS COMERCIAL E INDUSTRIAL LTDA.—See Halma plc; *Int'l*, pg. 3231
CAREFUSION ASIA (HK) LIMITED—See Becton, Dickinson & Company; *U.S. Public*, pg. 291
CARLISLE MEDICAL TECHNOLOGIES (DONGGUAN) CO., LTD—See Carlisle Companies Incorporated; *U.S. Public*, pg. 436
CARL ZEISS CO., LTD.—See Carl-Zeiss-Stiftung; *Int'l*, pg. 1334
CARL ZEISS MEDITEC AG—See Carl-Zeiss-Stiftung; *Int'l*, pg. 1333
CARSEN MEDICAL INC.—See Diploma PLC; *Int'l*, pg. 2128
CATHRX LTD; *Int'l*, pg. 1361
CAT TECHNOLOGIES LTD—See BATM Advanced Communications Ltd.; *Int'l*, pg. 890
CELERIS D.O.O.—See Cipla Ltd.; *Int'l*, pg. 1616
CELLERATION, INC.—See Adynxx, Inc.; *U.S. Public*, pg. 50
CENEFOM CORPORATION LIMITED—See BenQ Materials Corp.; *Int'l*, pg. 975
CERAMOPTEC GMBH—See biolitec AG; *Int'l*, pg. 1039

CHALGREN ENTERPRISES—See The Graham Group, Inc.; *U.S. Private*, pg. 4037
CHECK-CAP LTD.; *Int'l*, pg. 1459
CHINA WAH YAN HEALTHCARE LTD.; *Int'l*, pg. 1562
CHOKSI ASIA PRIVATE LIMITED; *Int'l*, pg. 1577
CHO-PAT—See Medi-Dyne Healthcare Products Ltd.; *U.S. Private*, pg. 2651
CLARION MEDICAL TECHNOLOGIES INC.—See ALPHAEON Corporation; *U.S. Private*, pg. 200
CLEVELAND MEDICAL DEVICES, INC.; *U.S. Private*, pg. 941
COCHLEAR AG—See Cochlear Limited; *Int'l*, pg. 1686
COCHLEAR AMERICAS INC—See Cochlear Limited; *Int'l*, pg. 1686
COCHLEAR BENELUX NV—See Cochlear Limited; *Int'l*, pg. 1686
COCHLEAR BONE ANCHORED SOLUTIONS AB—See Cochlear Limited; *Int'l*, pg. 1687
COCHLEAR CANADA INC—See Cochlear Limited; *Int'l*, pg. 1687
COCHLEAR DEUTSCHLAND GMBH & CO. KG—See Cochlear Limited; *Int'l*, pg. 1687
COCHLEAR EUROPE LIMITED—See Cochlear Limited; *Int'l*, pg. 1687
COCHLEAR FRANCE SAS—See Cochlear Limited; *Int'l*, pg. 1687
COCHLEAR (HK) LIMITED—See Cochlear Limited; *Int'l*, pg. 1686
COCHLEAR KOREA LIMITED—See Cochlear Limited; *Int'l*, pg. 1687
COCHLEAR MEDICAL DEVICE COMPANY INDIA PRIVATE LIMITED—See Cochlear Limited; *Int'l*, pg. 1687
COCHLEAR NORDIC AB—See Cochlear Limited; *Int'l*, pg. 1687
COCHLEAR SWEDEN HOLDINGS AB—See Cochlear Limited; *Int'l*, pg. 1687
COCHLEAR TIBBI CIHAZLAR VE SAGLIK HIZMETLERI LIMITED SIRKETI—See Cochlear Limited; *Int'l*, pg. 1687
COCHLEAR VERWALTUNGS GMBH—See Cochlear Limited; *Int'l*, pg. 1687
CO-DIAGNOSTICS, INC.; *U.S. Public*, pg. 520
CODMAN & SHURTLEFF, INC.—See Johnson & Johnson; *U.S. Public*, pg. 1195
COHERENT DEOS—See Coherent Corp.; *U.S. Public*, pg. 527
COHERENT KOREA LTD.—See Coherent Corp.; *U.S. Public*, pg. 527
COHERENT SCOTLAND LTD.—See Coherent Corp.; *U.S. Public*, pg. 527
COLOPLAST UKRAINE A/S—See Coloplast A/S; *Int'l*, pg. 1704
COMET ELECTRONICS CO. LTD.—See Comet Holding AG; *Int'l*, pg. 1710
COMPUMEDICS EUROPE GMBH—See Compumedics Limited; *Int'l*, pg. 1757
COMPUMEDICS FRANCE SAS—See Compumedics Limited; *Int'l*, pg. 1757
COMPUMEDICS GERMANY GMBH—See Compumedics Limited; *Int'l*, pg. 1757
COMPUMEDICS LIMITED - COMPUMEDICS SLEEP DIVISION—See Compumedics Limited; *Int'l*, pg. 1757
COMPUMEDICS LIMITED - NEUROSCAN DIVISION—See Compumedics Limited; *Int'l*, pg. 1757
COMPUMEDICS LIMITED; *Int'l*, pg. 1757
CONCENTRIC MEDICAL, INC.—See Stryker Corporation; *U.S. Public*, pg. 1955
CONMED DEUTSCHLAND GMBH—See CONMED Corporation; *U.S. Public*, pg. 567
CONMED FRANCE SAS—See CONMED Corporation; *U.S. Public*, pg. 567
CONMED LINVATEC AUSTRALIA PTY. LTD—See CONMED Corporation; *U.S. Public*, pg. 567
CONMED LINVATEC BIOMATERIALS OY—See CONMED Corporation; *U.S. Public*, pg. 567
CONMED U.K. LTD.—See CONMED Corporation; *U.S. Public*, pg. 567
CONTINUUM SERVICES LLC—See Abbott Laboratories; *U.S. Public*, pg. 19
COOK VASCULAR INCORPORATED—See Cook Group Incorporated; *U.S. Private*, pg. 1037
COOLTOUCH, INC.—See Apax Partners LLP; *Int'l*, pg. 506
COSMAN MEDICAL, LLC—See Boston Scientific Corporation; *U.S. Public*, pg. 374
C-RAD AB; *Int'l*, pg. 1239
CREATE MEDIC CO. LTD.; *Int'l*, pg. 1832
CROSSROADS EXTREMITY SYSTEMS, LLC—See Johnson & Johnson; *U.S. Public*, pg. 1194
CRYONIC MEDICAL; *Int'l*, pg. 1860
CUE HEALTH INC.; *U.S. Public*, pg. 604
CURATIVE MEDICAL DEVICES GMBH—See ResMed Inc.; *U.S. Public*, pg. 1790
CURATIVE MEDICAL INC.—See ResMed Inc.; *U.S. Public*, pg. 1790
CURATIVE MEDICAL TECHNOLOGY (SUZHOU) LTD—See ResMed Inc.; *U.S. Public*, pg. 1790
CURBELL MEDICAL PRODUCTS, INC.—See Curbell, Inc.; *U.S. Private*, pg. 1124
CURETIS NV; *Int'l*, pg. 1878

CURIUM SAS; *Int'l*, pg. 1878
CURLIN MEDICAL INC.—See Moog Inc.; *U.S. Public*, pg. 1470
CUTERA AUSTRALIA PTY LTD—See Cutera, Inc.; *U.S. Public*, pg. 613
CUTERA, INC.; *U.S. Public*, pg. 612
CYNOSURE FRANCE S.A.R.L.—See Clayton, Dubilier & Rice, LLC; *U.S. Private*, pg. 922
CYNOSURE PTY LTD—See Clayton, Dubilier & Rice, LLC; *U.S. Private*, pg. 922
CYNOSURE SARL—See El.En. S.p.A.; *Int'l*, pg. 2341
CYNOSURE UK LTD—See El.En. S.p.A.; *Int'l*, pg. 2341
DAICEL CHIRAL TECHNOLOGIES (CHINA) CO., LTD.—See Daicel Corporation; *Int'l*, pg. 1918
DAWON NEXVIEW CO.,LTD.; *Int'l*, pg. 1984
DELPHI MEDICAL SYSTEMS CORPORATION—See Aptiv PLC; *Int'l*, pg. 524
DEMANT SCHWEIZ AG—See Demant A/S; *Int'l*, pg. 2023
DFI CO.,LTD.—See DFI Inc.; *Int'l*, pg. 2095
DIASORIN MOLECULAR LLC—See DiaSorin S.p.A.; *Int'l*, pg. 2106
DIGIRAD IMAGING SOLUTIONS, INC.—See Star Equity Holdings, Inc.; *U.S. Public*, pg. 1937
DIGITAL HEARING (UK) LTD.—See Demant A/S; *Int'l*, pg. 2023
DIRECT CONVERSION AB—See Varex Imaging Corporation; *U.S. Public*, pg. 2275
DIRUI INDUSTRIAL CO., LTD.; *Int'l*, pg. 2130
DMS HEALTH TECHNOLOGIES, INC.; *U.S. Private*, pg. 1249
DOCUSOFT SP. Z O.O.—See Arcus S.A.; *Int'l*, pg. 553
DOLOMITE AB—See Invacare Corporation; *U.S. Private*, pg. 2130
DRTECH CORPORATION; *Int'l*, pg. 2206
DWL USA INC.—See Compumedics Limited; *Int'l*, pg. 1757
EAGLE ACTUATOR COMPONENTS GMBH & CO. KG—See Eagle Industry Co., Ltd.; *Int'l*, pg. 2265
EARGO, INC.—See Patient Square Capital, L.P.; *U.S. Private*, pg. 3106
ECKERT & ZIEGLER BEBIG GMBH—See Eckert & Ziegler Strahlen- und Medizintechnik AG; *Int'l*, pg. 2290
EDAN DIAGNOSTICS, INC.—See Edan Instruments, Inc.; *Int'l*, pg. 2303
EDAN INSTRUMENTS, INC.; *Int'l*, pg. 2303
EDAP RUSSIA—See EDAP TMS S.A.; *Int'l*, pg. 2304
EDAP TMS FRANCE S.A.—See EDAP TMS S.A.; *Int'l*, pg. 2304
EDAP TMS KOREA—See EDAP TMS S.A.; *Int'l*, pg. 2304
EDAP TMS S.A.; *Int'l*, pg. 2304
EDWARDS LIFESCIENCES COSTA RICA, S.R.L.—See Edwards Lifesciences Corporation; *U.S. Public*, pg. 720
EIKEN CHEMICAL CO. LTD.; *Int'l*, pg. 2332
E.I. MEDICAL IMAGING; *U.S. Private*, pg. 1305
EKF DIAGNOSTICS INC.—See EKF Diagnostics Holdings PLC; *Int'l*, pg. 2338
ELECTROMEDICAL PRODUCTS INTERNATIONAL, INC.—See Tillery Capital LLC; *U.S. Private*, pg. 4171
ELEKTA HELLAS EPE—See Elekta AB; *Int'l*, pg. 2355
ELEKTA LLC—See Elekta AB; *Int'l*, pg. 2355
ELEKTA LTD.—See Elekta AB; *Int'l*, pg. 2355
ELEKTA MEDICAL SA DE CV—See Elekta AB; *Int'l*, pg. 2355
ELEKTA MEDIKAL SISTEMLER TICARET A.S.—See Elekta AB; *Int'l*, pg. 2356
ELEKTA PTE LTD.—See Elekta AB; *Int'l*, pg. 2356
ELEKTA SERVICES S.R.O.—See Elekta AB; *Int'l*, pg. 2356
ELEKTA SOLUTIONS AB—See Elekta AB; *Int'l*, pg. 2356
ELEKTA SP.Z.O.O—See Elekta AB; *Int'l*, pg. 2356
ELEXXION AG; *Int'l*, pg. 2359
ELLEX MEDICAL LASERS LIMITED; *Int'l*, pg. 2365
ELLEX MEDICAL PTY LTD.—See Ellex Medical Lasers Limited; *Int'l*, pg. 2365
ELLEX SERVICES EUROPE S.A.R.L—See Ellex Medical Lasers Limited; *Int'l*, pg. 2365
ENDOCHOICE, INC.—See Boston Scientific Corporation; *U.S. Public*, pg. 375
ENDOSTIM, INC.; *U.S. Private*, pg. 1392
ENDPOINT CLINICAL—See Laboratory Corporation of America Holdings; *U.S. Public*, pg. 1286
E-QURE CORP.; *U.S. Private*, pg. 1302
ERIKA B-CURE LASER LTD.; *Int'l*, pg. 2493
ESAOTE ASIA PACIFIC DIAGNOSTIC PRIVATE LIMITED—See Esaote S.p.A.; *Int'l*, pg. 2501
ESAOTE BENELUX N.V.—See Esaote S.p.A.; *Int'l*, pg. 2501
ESAOTE BIOMEDICA DEUTSCHLAND GMBH—See Esaote S.p.A.; *Int'l*, pg. 2501
ESAOTE CHINA LTD.—See Esaote S.p.A.; *Int'l*, pg. 2501
ESAOTE ESPANA S.A.—See Esaote S.p.A.; *Int'l*, pg. 2501
ESAOTE EUROPE B.V.—See Esaote S.p.A.; *Int'l*, pg. 2501
ESAOTE FRANCE S.A.R.L.—See Esaote S.p.A.; *Int'l*, pg. 2501
ESAOTE HEALTHCARE DO BRASIL—See Esaote S.p.A.; *Int'l*, pg. 2501
ESAOTE LATINOAMERICA S.A.—See Esaote S.p.A.; *Int'l*, pg. 2501
ESAOTE MEDICAL SAS—See Esaote S.p.A.; *Int'l*, pg. 2501
ESAOTE NORTH AMERICA INC.—See Esaote S.p.A.; *Int'l*, pg. 2501

334510 — ELECTROMEDICAL AND ...

ESAOTE S.P.A.; *Int'l*, pg. 2501
ESAOTE UK—See Esaote S.p.A.; *Int'l*, pg. 2501
ESCALON MEDICAL CORP.; *U.S. Public*, pg. 793
ESCALON PENNSYLVANIA, INC.—See Escalon Medical Corp.; *U.S. Public*, pg. 793
ETS LINDGREN JAPAN, INC.—See ESCO Technologies, Inc.; *U.S. Public*, pg. 794
EUROFINS HUMAN FACTORS MD, LLC—See Eurofins Scientific S.E.; *Int'l*, pg. 2544
EUROFINS LIMED LTD.—See Eurofins Scientific S.E.; *Int'l*, pg. 2545
EVALVE, INC.—See Abbott Laboratories; *U.S. Public*, pg. 19
EXALENZ BIOSCIENCE INC.—See Meridian Bioscience Inc.; *U.S. Public*, pg. 1424
EXALENZ BIOSCIENCE LTD.—See Meridian Bioscience Inc.; *U.S. Public*, pg. 1424
FAMILY MEDICAL SUPPLY LLC—See Invacare Corporation; *U.S. Private*, pg. 2130
FANNIN (UK) LIMITED—See ICU Medical, Inc.; *U.S. Public*, pg. 1087
FILMECC USA, INC.—See Asahi Intecc Co., Ltd.; *Int'l*, pg. 594
FIMI S.R.L.—See Barco N.V.; *Int'l*, pg. 864
FIRST CHECK DIAGNOSTICS, LLC—See Abbott Laboratories; *U.S. Public*, pg. 19
FISHER & PAYKEL HEALTHCARE LIMITED—See Fisher & Paykel Healthcare Corporation Limited; *Int'l*, pg. 2693
FISIOBIOS S.R.L.—See Bios S.p.A.; *Int'l*, pg. 1041
FLUOPTICS IMAGING INC.—See Getinge AB; *Int'l*, pg. 2949
FLUOPTICS S.A.S.—See Getinge AB; *Int'l*, pg. 2949
FMC SMAD S.A.S.—See Fresenius Medical Care AG; *Int'l*, pg. 2775
FONAR CORPORATION; *U.S. Public*, pg. 863
FRESENIUS MEDICAL CARE AUSTRALIA PTY LTD.—See Fresenius Medical Care AG; *Int'l*, pg. 2774
FRESENIUS MEDICAL CARE NEDERLAND B.V.—See Fresenius Medical Care AG; *Int'l*, pg. 2775
FRESENIUS MEDICAL CARE (SCHWEIZ) AG—See Fresenius Medical Care AG; *Int'l*, pg. 2774
FRESENIUS MEDICAL CARE SOUTH AFRICA (PTY) LTD.—See Fresenius Medical Care AG; *Int'l*, pg. 2775
FRESENIUS MEDICAL CARE (U.K.) LTD.—See Fresenius Medical Care AG; *Int'l*, pg. 2774
FRITZ STEPHAN GMBH; *Int'l*, pg. 2794
FUJIFILM SONOSITE, INC.—See FUJIFILM Holdings Corporation; *Int'l*, pg. 2825
G2POWER CO., LTD.; *Int'l*, pg. 2866
GAMBRO AB—See Baxter International Inc.; *U.S. Public*, pg. 281
GAMBRO BICART—See Baxter International Inc.; *U.S. Public*, pg. 282
GAMBRO CHINA LTD.—See Baxter International Inc.; *U.S. Public*, pg. 281
GAMBRO DASCO S.P.A.—See Baxter International Inc.; *U.S. Public*, pg. 281
GAMBRO/HOSPAL GMBH—See Baxter International Inc.; *U.S. Public*, pg. 282
GAMBRO/HOSPAL INDUSTRIE S.A.—See Baxter International Inc.; *U.S. Public*, pg. 282
GAMBRO/HOSPAL LTD.—See Baxter International Inc.; *U.S. Public*, pg. 282
GAMBRO INC.—See Baxter International Inc.; *U.S. Public*, pg. 281
GAMBRO KOREA LTD.—See Baxter International Inc.; *U.S. Public*, pg. 282
GAMBRO MEDICAL PRODUCTS (SHANGHAI) CO. LTD.—See Baxter International Inc.; *U.S. Public*, pg. 281
GAMBRO MEOPTA S.R.O.—See Baxter International Inc.; *U.S. Public*, pg. 282
GAMBRO PTY. LTD. (SYDNEY)—See Baxter International Inc.; *U.S. Public*, pg. 282
GAMBRO RESEARCH—See Baxter International Inc.; *U.S. Public*, pg. 282
GAMBRO S.P.A.—See Baxter International Inc.; *U.S. Public*, pg. 281
GAMBRO S.P.A.—See Baxter International Inc.; *U.S. Public*, pg. 281
GAMBRO UF SOLUTIONS, INC.—See Baxter International Inc.; *U.S. Public*, pg. 282
GAMMEX RMI GMBH—See Gammex RMI Inc.; *U.S. Private*, pg. 1641
GAMMEX RMI LIMITED—See Gammex RMI Inc.; *U.S. Private*, pg. 1641
GE HEALTHCARE LIMITED—See General Electric Company; *U.S. Public*, pg. 917
GE MEDICAL SYSTEMS INFORMATION TECHNOLOGIES, INC.—See GE HealthCare Technologies Inc.; *U.S. Public*, pg. 909
GENEMATRIX INC.; *Int'l*, pg. 2917
GENETIC SIGNATURES LIMITED; *Int'l*, pg. 2922
GERRESHEIMER ESSEN GMBH—See Gerresheimer AG; *Int'l*, pg. 2943
GERRESHEIMER HOLDINGS GMBH—See Gerresheimer AG; *Int'l*, pg. 2943
GERRESHEIMER SHUANGFENG PHARMACEUTICAL PACKAGING (ZHENJIANG) CO. LTD.—See Gerresheimer AG; *Int'l*, pg. 2944

GETINGE LINAC TECHNOLOGIES SA—See Getinge AB; *Int'l*, pg. 2950
GLYCOREX TRANSPLANTATION AB; *Int'l*, pg. 3011
GN EJENDOMME A/S—See GN Store Nord A/S; *Int'l*, pg. 3015
GN HEARING A/S—See GN Store Nord A/S; *Int'l*, pg. 3015
GN HEARING BENELUX B.V.—See GN Store Nord A/S; *Int'l*, pg. 3015
GN HEARING CARE CANADA LTD—See GN Store Nord A/S; *Int'l*, pg. 3015
GN HEARING CARE CORPORATION—See GN Store Nord A/S; *Int'l*, pg. 3015
GN HEARING CARE S.A.—See GN Store Nord A/S; *Int'l*, pg. 3015
GN HEARING GMBH—See GN Store Nord A/S; *Int'l*, pg. 3016
GN HEARING INDIA PRIVATE LIMITED—See GN Store Nord A/S; *Int'l*, pg. 3015
GN HEARING JAPAN K.K.—See GN Store Nord A/S; *Int'l*, pg. 3015
GN HEARING KOREA CO., LTD.—See GN Store Nord A/S; *Int'l*, pg. 3015
GN HEARING (MALAYSIA) SDN. BHD.—See GN Store Nord A/S; *Int'l*, pg. 3015
GN HEARING NEW ZEALAND LIMITED—See GN Store Nord A/S; *Int'l*, pg. 3015
GN HEARING NORWAY AS—See GN Store Nord A/S; *Int'l*, pg. 3015
GN HEARING PTE. LTD.—See GN Store Nord A/S; *Int'l*, pg. 3015
GN HEARING SAS—See GN Store Nord A/S; *Int'l*, pg. 3015
GN HEARING SVERIGE AB—See GN Store Nord A/S; *Int'l*, pg. 3015
GN HEARING SWITZERLAND AG—See GN Store Nord A/S; *Int'l*, pg. 3015
GN NETCOM (IBERICA) S.A.—See GN Store Nord A/S; *Int'l*, pg. 3016
GN RESOUND AB—See GN Store Nord A/S; *Int'l*, pg. 3016
GN RESOUND AG—See GN Store Nord A/S; *Int'l*, pg. 3016
GN RESOUND CHINA LTD.—See GN Store Nord A/S; *Int'l*, pg. 3016
GN RESOUND CORPORATION—See GN Store Nord A/S; *Int'l*, pg. 3016
GN RESOUND DO BRAZIL LTDA.—See GN Store Nord A/S; *Int'l*, pg. 3016
GN RESOUND HEARING CARE EQU. (SHANGHAI)—See GN Store Nord A/S; *Int'l*, pg. 3016
GN RESOUND INDIA PRIVATE LIMITED—See GN Store Nord A/S; *Int'l*, pg. 3016
GN RESOUND NORGE AS—See GN Store Nord A/S; *Int'l*, pg. 3016
GN RESOUND S.A.S—See GN Store Nord A/S; *Int'l*, pg. 3016
GN RESOUND SINGAPORE PTE. LTD.—See GN Store Nord A/S; *Int'l*, pg. 3016
GN US HOLDINGS INC.; *U.S. Private*, pg. 1723
GOLD STANDARD DIAGNOSTICS HORSHAM, INC.—See Eurofins Scientific S.E.; *Int'l*, pg. 2550
GOLD STANDARD DIAGNOSTICS KASSEL GMBH—See Eurofins Scientific S.E.; *Int'l*, pg. 2550
GRASON-STADLER, INC.—See Demant A/S; *Int'l*, pg. 2023
GREINER BIO-ONE GMBH—See Greiner Holding AG; *Int'l*, pg. 3079
GREINER BIO-ONE INTERNATIONAL GMBH—See Greiner Holding AG; *Int'l*, pg. 3079
GRUENDLER GMBH—See ResMed Inc.; *U.S. Public*, pg. 1790
GUANGDONG TRANSTEK MEDICAL ELECTRONICS CO., LTD; *Int'l*, pg. 3161
GUANGZHOU HYMSON LASER CO., LTD.—See Hymson Laser Technology Group Co Ltd; *Int'l*, pg. 3549
GUANGZHOU RUOYUCHEN TECHNOLOGY CO., LTD.; *Int'l*, pg. 3167
GUERBET GROSSHANDEL MIT PHARMAZEUTISCHEN PRODUKTEN GES.M.B.H.—See Guerbet SA; *Int'l*, pg. 3172
GUERBET IMAGING PANAMA S. A.—See Guerbet SA; *Int'l*, pg. 3172
GUERBET MEXICANA S. A. DE C. V.—See Guerbet SA; *Int'l*, pg. 3172
GUERBET PRODUTOS RADIOLOGICOS LTDA.—See Guerbet SA; *Int'l*, pg. 3172
GUYMARK UK LIMITED—See Demant A/S; *Int'l*, pg. 2023
HANGZHOU SHENHAO TECHNOLOGY CO., LTD.; *Int'l*, pg. 3250
HARPOON MEDICAL, INC.—See Edwards Lifesciences Corporation; *U.S. Public*, pg. 721
HARTFIEL AUTOMATION; *U.S. Private*, pg. 1873
HC ITALIA SRL—See Heidelberg Materials AG; *Int'l*, pg. 3310
HEALTH SCIENCES CORPORATION—See SMK Imaging, LLC; *U.S. Private*, pg. 3698
HEALTHTRONICS, INC.—See Altaris Capital Partners, LLC; *U.S. Private*, pg. 206
HEARING HEALTHCARE MANAGEMENT, INC.—See Demant A/S; *Int'l*, pg. 2023
HEARING SUPPLIES SA—See Amplifon S.p.A.; *Int'l*, pg. 435

HEARTBEAM, INC.; *U.S. Public*, pg. 1017
HELENA LABORATORIES (AUSTRALIA) PTY. LTD.—See Helena Laboratories Corporation; *U.S. Private*, pg. 1906
HELENA LABORATORIES (UK) LIMITED—See Helena Laboratories Corporation; *U.S. Private*, pg. 1906
HEMOCUE AB—See Danaher Corporation; *U.S. Public*, pg. 630
HERAEUS CZ S.R.O.—See Heraeus Holding GmbH; *Int'l*, pg. 3357
HILL-ROM S.A.S.—See Baxter International Inc.; *U.S. Public*, pg. 283
HILL-ROM SOCIEDADE UNIPESSOAL, LDA—See Baxter International Inc.; *U.S. Public*, pg. 282
HINDUSTAN PHOTO FILMS MANUFACTURING COMPANY LIMITED; *Int'l*, pg. 3400
HITACHI ALOKA MEDICAL, LTD.—See Hitachi, Ltd.; *Int'l*, pg. 3413
HITACHI MEDICAL (GUANGZHOU) CO., LTD.—See Hitachi, Ltd.; *Int'l*, pg. 3420
HITACHI MEDICAL SYSTEMS UK LTD.—See Hitachi, Ltd.; *Int'l*, pg. 3420
HMCM, INC.—See FONAR Corporation; *U.S. Public*, pg. 863
HOGY MEDICAL CO. LTD. - MIHO PLANT NO. 1—See Hogy Medical Co., Ltd.; *Int'l*, pg. 3442
HOGY MEDICAL CO., LTD. - MIHO PLANT NO. 2—See Hogy Medical Co., Ltd.; *Int'l*, pg. 3442
HOGY MEDICAL CO., LTD.; *Int'l*, pg. 3442
HOREN DEVENTER BV—See Amplifon S.p.A.; *Int'l*, pg. 435
HORIBA ABX LTDA.—See HORIBA Ltd; *Int'l*, pg. 3475
HOTSPUR TECHNOLOGIES, INC.—See Teleflex Incorporated; *U.S. Public*, pg. 1995
HOYA CORPORATION - PENTAX LIFECARE DIVISION, MEDICAL INSTRUMENT SBU—See Hoya Corporation; *Int'l*, pg. 3495
HOYA CORPORATION - PENTAX LIFECARE DIVISION—See Hoya Corporation; *Int'l*, pg. 3494
HUAGONG TECH COMPANY LIMITED; *Int'l*, pg. 3512
HUAKANG BIOMEDICAL HOLDINGS CO., LTD.; *Int'l*, pg. 3512
HUESTIS MACHINE CORP.—See Best Medical International, Inc.; *U.S. Private*, pg. 543
HYMSON (JIANGMEN) LASER INTELLIGENT EQUIPMENTS CO., LTD.—See Hymson Laser Technology Group Co Ltd; *Int'l*, pg. 3549
HYMSON LASER INTELLIGENT EQUIPMENTS (JIANGSU) CO., LTD.—See Hymson Laser Technology Group Co Ltd; *Int'l*, pg. 3550
IBP MEDICAL GMBH—See Mesa Laboratories, Inc.; *U.S. Public*, pg. 1426
ICECURE MEDICAL LTD.; *Int'l*, pg. 3579
II-VI SUWTECH, INC.—See Coherent Corp.; *U.S. Public*, pg. 529
IMA AUTOMATION MALAYSIA SDN. BHD.—See I.M.A. Industria Macchine Automatiche S.p.A.; *Int'l*, pg. 3565
IMRICOR MEDICAL SYSTEMS, INC.; *U.S. Private*, pg. 2051
IMT B.V.—See Xylem Inc.; *U.S. Public*, pg. 2394
IMUNON, INC.; *U.S. Public*, pg. 1114
INARI MEDICAL, INC.; *U.S. Public*, pg. 1114
INHEALTH TECHNOLOGIES—See Freudenberg SE; *Int'l*, pg. 2789
INOVA LABS, INC.—See ResMed Inc.; *U.S. Public*, pg. 1790
INSIGHTEC LTD.—See Elbit Imaging Ltd.; *Int'l*, pg. 2344
INTERACOUSTICS A/S—See Demant A/S; *Int'l*, pg. 2024
INTERACOUSTICS DO BRASIL. COM. DE EQUIP. MEDICOS LTDA.—See Demant A/S; *Int'l*, pg. 2024
INTERACOUSTICS PTY. LTD.—See Demant A/S; *Int'l*, pg. 2024
INTERACTIVE MOTION TECHNOLOGIES, INC.—See Bionik Laboratories Corp.; *Int'l*, pg. 1040
INTERMED EQUIPAMENTO MEDICO HOSPITALAR LTDA.—See Becton, Dickinson & Company; *U.S. Public*, pg. 292
INTRAOP MEDICAL CORP.—See Firsthand Capital Management, Inc.; *U.S. Private*, pg. 1532
INTRICON DATRIX CORPORATION—See IntriCon Corporation; *U.S. Public*, pg. 1159
INVACARE AG—See Invacare Corporation; *U.S. Private*, pg. 2130
INVACARE A/S—See Invacare Corporation; *U.S. Private*, pg. 2130
INVACARE AUSTRIA GMBH—See Invacare Corporation; *U.S. Private*, pg. 2130
INVACARE DOLOMITE AB—See Invacare Corporation; *U.S. Private*, pg. 2130
INVACARE EC-HONG A/S—See Invacare Corporation; *U.S. Private*, pg. 2130
INVACARE GMBH—See Invacare Corporation; *U.S. Private*, pg. 2130
INVACARE INTERNATIONAL SARL—See Invacare Corporation; *U.S. Private*, pg. 2131
INVACARE IRELAND LTD.—See Invacare Corporation; *U.S. Private*, pg. 2131
INVACARE OUTCOMES MANAGEMENT LLC—See Invacare Corporation; *U.S. Private*, pg. 2131
INVACARE REA AB—See Invacare Corporation; *U.S. Private*, pg. 2131

N.A.I.C.S. INDEX

334510 — ELECTROMEDICAL AND ...

INVACARE, S.A.—See Invacare Corporation; *U.S. Private*, pg. 2131
IONIQ SCIENCES, INC.; *U.S. Private*, pg. 2134
IRADIMED CORPORATION; *U.S. Public*, pg. 1171
IRIDEX CORPORATION; *U.S. Public*, pg. 1171
ISOMET (UK) LTD.—See Isomet Corporation; *U.S. Private*, pg. 2146
ITAMAR MEDICAL LTD.—See Asahi Kasei Corporation; *Int'l*, pg. 597
ITL HEALTHCARE PTY LIMITED—See Merit Medical Systems, Inc.; *U.S. Public*, pg. 1425
KABUSHIKI KAISHA HELENA KENKYUJYO—See Helena Laboratories Corporation; *U.S. Private*, pg. 1906
KIGRE, INC.—See L3Harris Technologies, Inc.; *U.S. Public*, pg. 1281
KNIT-RITE INC.; *U.S. Private*, pg. 2322
KUSCHALL AG—See Invacare Corporation; *U.S. Private*, pg. 2131
KYUSHU CREATE MEDIC CO., LTD.—See CREATE MEDIC CO. LTD.; *Int'l*, pg. 1832
LABORATORIO ANALISI CLINICHE MEDICHE IANNACCONE S.R.L.—See Bios S.p.A.; *Int'l*, pg. 1041
LAIDE AUDITIVE SA—See Amplifon S.p.A.; *Int'l*, pg. 435
LANDAUER, INC.—See Fortive Corporation; *U.S. Public*, pg. 871
LASER CONTROL SYSTEMS LIMITED.—See FARO Technologies, Inc.; *U.S. Public*, pg. 823
LASEROP LTD.—See AEM Holdings Ltd.; *Int'l*, pg. 175
LASER QUANTUM GMBH—See Novanta Inc.; *U.S. Public*, pg. 1548
LASER QUANTUM LIMITED—See Novanta Inc.; *U.S. Public*, pg. 1548
LASER VENTURES, INC.—See Altaris Capital Partners, LLC; *U.S. Private*, pg. 206
LAYERWISE NV—See 3D Systems Corporation; *U.S. Public*, pg. 4
LENSAR, INC.; *U.S. Public*, pg. 1308
LIDCO LIMITED—See Masimo Corporation; *U.S. Public*, pg. 1392
LIFESYNC CORPORATION—See HealthEdge Investment Partners, LLC; *U.S. Private*, pg. 1896
LUMENIS (GERMANY) GMBH—See Boston Scientific Corporation; *U.S. Public*, pg. 375
LUMENIS INDIA PRIVATE LTD—See Boston Scientific Corporation; *U.S. Public*, pg. 375
LUMENIS (ITALY) SRL—See Boston Scientific Corporation; *U.S. Public*, pg. 375
MAGELLAN DIAGNOSTICS, INC.—See Meridian Bioscience Inc.; *U.S. Public*, pg. 1424
MAHR METROLOGY INDIA PRIVATE LTD.—See Carl Mahr Holding GmbH; *Int'l*, pg. 1333
MAICO DIAGNOSTIC GMBH—See Demant A/S; *Int'l*, pg. 2024
MAQUET, INC.—See Getinge AB; *Int'l*, pg. 2951
MAQUET MEDICAL SYSTEMS USA LLC—See Getinge AB; *Int'l*, pg. 2951
MARIBO MEDICO A/S—See ResMed Inc.; *U.S. Public*, pg. 1790
MASIMO ASIA PACIFIC PTE. LTD.—See Masimo Corporation; *U.S. Public*, pg. 1392
MASIMO KOREA, LLC—See Masimo Corporation; *U.S. Public*, pg. 1392
MEDISCAN GMBH & CO. KG—See Greiner Holding AG; *Int'l*, pg. 3079
MEDWORK GMBH—See FUJIFILM Holdings Corporation; *Int'l*, pg. 2826
MEVION MEDICAL SYSTEMS, INC.; *U.S. Private*, pg. 2691
MICROMASS HOLDINGS LTD.—See Waters Corporation; *U.S. Public*, pg. 2334
MICRON PRODUCTS, INC.—See Micron Solutions, Inc.; *U.S. Public*, pg. 1437
MICRON SOLUTIONS, INC.; *U.S. Public*, pg. 1437
MIDMARK DIAGNOSTICS GROUP—See Midmark Corporation; *U.S. Private*, pg. 2716
MIRACLE-EAR, INC.—See Amplifon S.p.A.; *Int'l*, pg. 435
MIRADRY, INC.—See 1315 Capital LLC; *U.S. Private*, pg. 3
MISSISSIPPI VALLEY REGIONAL BLOOD CENTER; *U.S. Private*, pg. 2748
MOCOM S.R.L.—See Cefla S.C.; *Int'l*, pg. 1390
MORTARA INSTRUMENT, INC.—See Baxter International Inc.; *U.S. Public*, pg. 283
MOTION CONTROL, INC.—See Patient Square Capital, L.P.; *U.S. Private*, pg. 3107
MOTUS GI HOLDINGS, INC.; *U.S. Public*, pg. 1479
NANOVIBRONIX, INC.; *U.S. Public*, pg. 1490
NATIONAL ELECTRICAL MANUFACTURERS ASSOCIATION - MEDICAL IMAGING AND TECHNOLOGY ALLIANCE DIVISION—See National Electrical Manufacturers Association; *U.S. Private*, pg. 2853
NATIONAL ULTRASOUND, INC.—See Avista Capital Partners, L.P.; *U.S. Private*, pg. 408
NATUS MEDICAL INC.—See ArchiMed SAS; *Int'l*, pg. 549
NATUS NEUROLOGY INCORPORATED—See ArchiMed SAS; *Int'l*, pg. 549
NEURELEC S.A.S.—See Demant A/S; *Int'l*, pg. 2024
NEUROSIGMA, INC.; *U.S. Private*, pg. 2890
NEUWAVE MEDICAL, INC.—See Johnson & Johnson; *U.S. Public*, pg. 1196

NEW WORLD TECHNOLOGIES, INC.; *U.S. Private*, pg. 2908
NIPPON ENVIRONMENT AMENITY CO., LTD.—See Hibino Corporation; *Int'l*, pg. 3383
NON-INVASIVE MONITORING SYSTEMS, INC.; *U.S. Public*, pg. 1532
NOVA BIOMEDICAL K.K.—See Nova Biomedical Corporation; *U.S. Private*, pg. 2965
NOVANTA EUROPE GMBH—See Novanta Inc.; *U.S. Public*, pg. 1548
NOVANTA ITALY SRL—See Novanta Inc.; *U.S. Public*, pg. 1548
NU-MED PLUS, INC.; *U.S. Public*, pg. 1552
OMEGA DIAGNOSTICS LIMITED—See Cambridge Nutritional Sciences Plc; *Int'l*, pg. 1269
OPHIR JAPAN LTD.—See MKS Instruments, Inc.; *U.S. Public*, pg. 1453
OPHIR OPTRONICS SOLUTIONS LTD.—See MKS Instruments, Inc.; *U.S. Public*, pg. 1453
OPHIR SPIRICON EUROPE GMBH—See MKS Instruments, Inc.; *U.S. Public*, pg. 1453
OPHIR-SPIRICON, LLC—See MKS Instruments, Inc.; *U.S. Public*, pg. 1453
OPTOPOL TECHNOLOGY S.A.—See Canon Inc.; *Int'l*, pg. 1294
OPTO SENSORS HONG KONG LIMITED—See OSI Systems, Inc.; *U.S. Public*, pg. 1621
ORTHOMERICA PRODUCTS INC.; *U.S. Private*, pg. 3045
ORTHOSENSOR, INC.—See Stryker Corporation; *U.S. Public*, pg. 1956
OTICON AS—See Demant A/S; *Int'l*, pg. 2024
OTICON A/S—See Demant A/S; *Int'l*, pg. 2024
OTICON CANADA LTD.—See Demant A/S; *Int'l*, pg. 2024
OTICON DENMARK A/S—See Demant A/S; *Int'l*, pg. 2024
OTICON ESPANA S.A.—See Demant A/S; *Int'l*, pg. 2024
OTICON GMBH—See Demant A/S; *Int'l*, pg. 2024
OTICON, INC.—See Demant A/S; *Int'l*, pg. 2024
OTICON LIMITED—See Demant A/S; *Int'l*, pg. 2024
OTICON MALAYSIA SDN—See Demant A/S; *Int'l*, pg. 2024
OTICON MEDICAL AB—See Demant A/S; *Int'l*, pg. 2024
OTICON MEDICAL MAROC—See Demant A/S; *Int'l*, pg. 2024
OTICON NEDERLAND B.V.—See Demant A/S; *Int'l*, pg. 2024
OTICON POLSKA PRODUCTION SP. Z O.O.—See Demant A/S; *Int'l*, pg. 2024
OTICON SHANGHAI HEARING TECHNOLOGY CO. LTD.—See Demant A/S; *Int'l*, pg. 2024
OTIX GLOBAL, INC.—See Demant A/S; *Int'l*, pg. 2024
OTOMETRICS FRANCE—See ArchiMed SAS; *Int'l*, pg. 549
OTOMETRICS GMBH—See ArchiMed SAS; *Int'l*, pg. 549
OUTSET MEDICAL, INC.; *U.S. Public*, pg. 1625
OY OTICON AB—See Demant A/S; *Int'l*, pg. 2024
PALOMAR MEDICAL TECHNOLOGIES, LLC—See Clayton, Dubilier & Rice, LLC; *U.S. Private*, pg. 922
PENTAX ITALIA S.R.L.—See Hoya Corporation; *Int'l*, pg. 3498
PERISTEL S.A.—See Getinge AB; *Int'l*, pg. 2952
PHONIC EAR INC.—See Demant A/S; *Int'l*, pg. 2024
PHYSIO-CONTROL, INC.—See Stryker Corporation; *U.S. Public*, pg. 1956
PHYSIO-CONTROL MANUFACTURING, INC.—See Stryker Corporation; *U.S. Public*, pg. 1956
PHYSIO-CONTROL OPERATIONS NETHERLANDS B.V.—See Stryker Corporation; *U.S. Public*, pg. 1956
PILOT BLANKENFELDE MEDIZINISCH-ELEKTRONISCHE GERATE GMBH—See Amplifon S.p.A.; *Int'l*, pg. 435
POLAREAN IMAGING PLC—See Amphion Innovations plc; *Int'l*, pg. 433
POLAREAN, INC.—See Amphion Innovations plc; *Int'l*, pg. 433
POSITRON CORP.; *U.S. Private*, pg. 3234
PRECHECK HEALTH SERVICES, INC.; *U.S. Private*, pg. 3243
PRECHECK HEALTH SERVICES, INC.; *U.S. Private*, pg. 3243
PREDICTIVE THERAPEUTICS, LLC—See Predictive Technology Group, Inc.; *U.S. Public*, pg. 1714
PREMIER MEDICAL CORPORATION—See New Mountain Capital, LLC; *U.S. Private*, pg. 2903
PRO THERAPY SUPPLIES; *U.S. Private*, pg. 3270
PROXY BIOMEDICAL LTD.—See Sealed Air Corporation; *U.S. Public*, pg. 1854
PULSE VETERINARY TECHNOLOGIES, LLC—See Zomedica Corp.; *U.S. Public*, pg. 2410
PULSION MEDICAL SYSTEMS IBERICA S.L.—See Getinge AB; *Int'l*, pg. 2952
PULSION MEDICAL UK LTD.—See Getinge AB; *Int'l*, pg. 2952
PYNG MEDICAL CORP.—See Teleflex Incorporated; *U.S. Public*, pg. 1996
RAPID BIOSENSOR SYSTEMS LIMIT—See Xylem Inc.; *U.S. Public*, pg. 2394
REDHAWK MEDICAL PRODUCTS UK LTD.—See Redhawk Holdings Corp.; *U.S. Public*, pg. 1770
REFLECTANCE MEDICAL, INC.—See Sotera Wireless, Inc.; *U.S. Private*, pg. 3716

RENALYSIS MEDICAL CARE CO. LTD.—See Hi-Clearance, Inc.; *Int'l*, pg. 3380
RESMED (BEIJING) MEDICAL DEVICE CO., LTD—See ResMed Inc.; *U.S. Public*, pg. 1791
RESMED INDIA PRIVATE LTD—See ResMed Inc.; *U.S. Public*, pg. 1791
RESMED NORWAY AS—See ResMed Inc.; *U.S. Public*, pg. 1791
RESMED PARIS SAS—See ResMed Inc.; *U.S. Public*, pg. 1791
RESMED SENSOR TECHNOLOGIES LTD.—See ResMed Inc.; *U.S. Public*, pg. 1791
RESTORATIVE CARE OF AMERICA, INC.—See Restorative Care of America; *U.S. Private*, pg. 3410
RESTORATIVE CARE OF AMERICA; *U.S. Private*, pg. 3410
ROCKWELL MEDICAL, INC.; *U.S. Public*, pg. 1807
ROLAND CONSULT STASCHE & FINGER GMBH—See Gaush Meditech Ltd.; *Int'l*, pg. 2891
RRTS UNIPESSOAL LDA—See Elekta AB; *Int'l*, pg. 2356
RUDOLF RIESTER GMBH—See Halma plc; *Int'l*, pg. 3232
SANBOR CORPORATION; *U.S. Private*, pg. 3542
SCHENCK ROTEC GMBH—See Durr AG; *Int'l*, pg. 2233
THE SCOTTCARE CORPORATION—See Berkshire Hathaway Inc.; *U.S. Public*, pg. 300
SCOTT SPECIALTIES INC.; *U.S. Private*, pg. 3577
SENSIR INC.—See Epiroc AB; *Int'l*, pg. 2463
SHANGHAI GENOMICS, INC.,—See GNI Group Ltd.; *Int'l*, pg. 3017
SI-BONE, INC.; *U.S. Public*, pg. 1876
SIGHT SCIENCES, INC.; *U.S. Public*, pg. 1877
SIVANTOS GMBH—See EQT AB; *Int'l*, pg. 2480
SIVANTOS INDIA PVT. LTD.—See EQT AB; *Int'l*, pg. 2480
SLUCHADLOVA AKUSTIKA SPOL S.R.O.—See GN Store Nord A/S; *Int'l*, pg. 3016
SMITHS MEDICAL AUSTRALASIA PTY. LTD.—See ICU Medical, Inc.; *U.S. Public*, pg. 1087
SMITHS MEDICAL DEUTSCHLAND GMBH—See ICU Medical, Inc.; *U.S. Public*, pg. 1087
SMITHS MEDICAL INTERNATIONAL LTD.—See ICU Medical, Inc.; *U.S. Public*, pg. 1087
SMITHS MEDICAL JAPAN LTD.—See ICU Medical, Inc.; *U.S. Public*, pg. 1087
SMITHS MEDICAL (SOUTH AFRICA) PTY. LTD.—See ICU Medical, Inc.; *U.S. Public*, pg. 1087
SMK IMAGING, LLC; *U.S. Private*, pg. 3698
SOLENO THERAPEUTICS, INC.; *U.S. Public*, pg. 1900
SOLTA MEDICAL, INC.—See Bausch Health Companies Inc.; *U.S. Public*, pg. 898
SOLUETA VINA CO., LTD.—See Dasan Solueta Co.,Ltd.; *Int'l*, pg. 1973
SOLUSCOPE SAS—See Ecolab Inc.; *U.S. Public*, pg. 716
SONACARE MEDICAL, LLC; *U.S. Private*, pg. 3712
SONOSITE, INC.—See FUJIFILM Holdings Corporation; *Int'l*, pg. 2823
SOUTHERN CALIFORNIA BRAIDING, INC.—See Goldberg Lindsay & Co., LLC; *U.S. Private*, pg. 1729
SPACELABS MEDICAL, INC.—See OSI Systems, Inc.; *U.S. Public*, pg. 1622
SPACELABS MEDICAL UK S.P.A.—See OSI Systems, Inc.; *U.S. Public*, pg. 1622
SPARTON ONYX, LLC—See Elbit Systems Limited; *Int'l*, pg. 2345
SPECIALIZED MEDICAL SERVICES, INC.—See New Mountain Capital, LLC; *U.S. Private*, pg. 2903
SPEEDUS CORP.; *U.S. Public*, pg. 1917
SS INNOVATIONS INTERNATIONAL, INC.; *U.S. Public*, pg. 1922
STANDEX MEDER ELECTRONICS GMBH—See Standex International; *U.S. Public*, pg. 1931
STANDEX-MEDER ELECTRONICS (SHANGHAI) CO., LTD.—See Standex International; *U.S. Public*, pg. 1931
STAR EQUITY HOLDINGS, INC.; *U.S. Public*, pg. 1937
STARKEY LABORATORIES, INC.; *U.S. Private*, pg. 3787
STEREOTAXIS, INC.; *U.S. Public*, pg. 1945
STERIPAC GMBH—See Eurofins Scientific S.E.; *Int'l*, pg. 2552
STRYKER GMBH—See Stryker Corporation; *U.S. Public*, pg. 1956
STRYKER-OSTEONICS SA—See Stryker Corporation; *U.S. Public*, pg. 1957
STRYKER SALES CORPORATION—See Stryker Corporation; *U.S. Public*, pg. 1957
STRYKER SOUTH AFRICA (PROPRIETARY) LIMITED—See Stryker Corporation; *U.S. Public*, pg. 1957
STRYKER SPINE SA—See Stryker Corporation; *U.S. Public*, pg. 1957
STRYKER SPINE SAS—See Stryker Corporation; *U.S. Public*, pg. 1957
STRYKER (SUZHOU) MEDICAL TECHNOLOGY CO LTD.—See Stryker Corporation; *U.S. Public*, pg. 1956
SYNERGETICS, INC.—See Bausch Health Companies Inc.; *Int'l*, pg. 897
SYNERON CANDELA CANADA—See Apax Partners LLP; *Int'l*, pg. 506
SYNERON MEDICAL LTD.—See Apax Partners LLP; *Int'l*, pg. 506

334510 — ELECTROMEDICAL AND ...

TAICHA MEDICAL CORP.—See Hi-Clearance, Inc.; *Int'l*, pg. 3380
TECHNICAL GAS PRODUCTS, INC.; *U.S. Private*, pg. 3954
TECHSHOT, INC.—See Redwire Corporation; *U.S. Public*, pg. 1771
TELSTAR LIFE SCIENCE SOLUTIONS—See Azbil Corporation; *Int'l*, pg. 777
TERARECON, INC.—See Symphony Innovation, LLC; *U.S. Private*, pg. 3900
THERMO FISHER DIAGNOSTICS OY—See Thermo Fisher Scientific Inc.; *U.S. Public*, pg. 2152
TIVIC HEALTH SYSTEMS, INC.; *U.S. Public*, pg. 2161
TODD RESEARCH LIMITED—See Image Scan Holdings plc; *Int'l*, pg. 3618
TOMOTHERAPY BELGIUM BVBA—See Accuray Incorporated; *U.S. Public*, pg. 33
TOPERA, INC.—See Abbott Laboratories; *U.S. Public*, pg. 21
TRAC TELECOMS & RADIO LTD—See Ecolab Inc.; *U.S. Public*, pg. 712
TREACE MEDICAL CONCEPTS, INC.; *U.S. Public*, pg. 2186
TRIANGLE BIOSYSTEMS INC.—See Harvard Bioscience, Inc.; *U.S. Public*, pg. 987
TRICE MEDICAL, INC; *U.S. Private*, pg. 4228
TRIFOIL IMAGING—See Psilos Group Managers, LLC; *U.S. Private*, pg. 3297
TRIMEDYNE, INC.; *U.S. Private*, pg. 4232
TRIOLAB A/S—See Addtech AB; *Int'l*, pg. 135
TRUMPF MED (AUST) PTY. LIMITED—See Baxter International Inc.; *U.S. Public*, pg. 283
TRUMPF MEDICAL SYSTEMS, INC.—See Baxter International Inc.; *U.S. Public*, pg. 283
TRUMPF MEDICAL SYSTEMS (TAICANG) CO., LTD.—See Baxter International Inc.; *U.S. Public*, pg. 283
TRUMPF MEDIZIN SYSTEME BETEILIGUNGS GMBH—See Baxter International Inc.; *U.S. Public*, pg. 283
TRUMPF MEDIZIN SYSTEME GMBH & CO. KG—See Baxter International Inc.; *U.S. Public*, pg. 283
U.K. MEDICAL, LTD.—See Becton, Dickinson & Company; *U.S. Public*, pg. 292
ULTRASONIX MEDICAL CORPORATION—See Altaris Capital Partners, LLC; *U.S. Private*, pg. 205
UMWELT- UND INGENIEURTECHNIK GMBH DRESDEN—See General Atomics; *U.S. Private*, pg. 1664
VACUTEC MESSTECHNIK GMBH—See Hormann Holding GmbH & Co. KG; *Int'l*, pg. 3480
VAPOTHERM, INC.—See Perceptive Advisors, LLC; *U.S. Private*, pg. 3146
VASO CORPORATION; *U.S. Public*, pg. 2276
VERATHON INC.—See Roper Technologies, Inc.; *U.S. Public*, pg. 1814
VERATHON MEDICAL (CANADA) ULC—See Roper Technologies, Inc.; *U.S. Public*, pg. 1814
VERATHON MEDICAL (EUROPE) B.V.—See Roper Technologies, Inc.; *U.S. Public*, pg. 1814
VERATHON MEDICAL (FRANCE) S.A.R.L.—See Roper Technologies, Inc.; *U.S. Public*, pg. 1814
VIDACARE CORP.—See Teleflex Incorporated; *U.S. Public*, pg. 1996
VIDAR SYSTEMS CORPORATION—See 3D Systems Corporation; *U.S. Public*, pg. 4
VIDEOJET TECHNOLOGIES B.V.—See Danaher Corporation; *U.S. Public*, pg. 632
VIDEOJET TECHNOLOGIES CANADA L.P.—See Danaher Corporation; *U.S. Public*, pg. 632
VIDEOJET TECHNOLOGIES EUROPE B.V.—See Danaher Corporation; *U.S. Public*, pg. 632
VIDEOJET TECHNOLOGIES JSC—See Danaher Corporation; *U.S. Public*, pg. 632
VIDEOJET TECHNOLOGIES MEXICO S. DE R.L. DE C.V.—See Danaher Corporation; *U.S. Public*, pg. 632
VIDEOJET X-RITE K.K.—See Danaher Corporation; *U.S. Public*, pg. 632
VISIOMED GROUP LTD—See Avita Medical, Inc.; *U.S. Public*, pg. 249
VITALWEAR, INC.; *U.S. Private*, pg. 4405
WARNER INSTRUMENTS LLC—See Harvard Bioscience, Inc.; *U.S. Public*, pg. 987
WELCH ALLYN DO BRASIL COMERCIA DE EQUIPMENTOS MEDICOS, LTDA—See Baxter International Inc.; *U.S. Public*, pg. 284
WIDEX HEARING AID CO., INC.—See EQT AB; *Int'l*, pg. 2480
WIDEX HORGERATE AG—See EQT AB; *Int'l*, pg. 2481
W.O.M. WORLD OF MEDICINE GMBH—See Novanta Inc.; *U.S. Public*, pg. 1548
W.O.M. WORLD OF MEDICINE PRODUKTIONS-GMBH—See Novanta Inc.; *U.S. Public*, pg. 1548
XOFT, INC.—See iCad, Inc.; *U.S. Public*, pg. 1083
ZOLL MEDICAL CORPORATION—See Asahi Kasei Corporation; *Int'l*, pg. 597
ZYNEX, INC.; *U.S. Public*, pg. 2414

334511 — SEARCH, DETECTION, NAVIGATION, GUIDANCE, AERONAUTICAL, AND NAUTICAL SYSTEM AND INSTRUMENT MANUFACTURING

3D LASER SYSTEME GMBH—See Trimble, Inc.; *U.S. Public*, pg. 2190
AAR AIRCRAFT COMPONENT SERVICES-AMSTERDAM—See AAR Corp.; *U.S. Public*, pg. 13
ACCONEER AB; *Int'l*, pg. 90
ACME LIFT COMPANY, LLC; *U.S. Private*, pg. 61
ACTIONTOP ELECTRONICS (SHENZHEN) CO. LTD—See Cantronic Systems Inc.; *Int'l*, pg. 1299
ADACEL SYSTEMS, INC.—See Adacel Technologies Limited; *Int'l*, pg. 123
ADCOLE CORPORATION—See Artemis Capital Partners Management Co., LLC; *U.S. Private*, pg. 340
ADVANCED RADAR CORPORATION—See NDP, LLC; *U.S. Private*, pg. 2876
ADVANCED TECHNICAL SOLUTIONS IN SCANDINAVIA AB—See FARO Technologies, Inc.; *U.S. Public*, pg. 823
AEROANTENNA TECHNOLOGY, INC.—See HEICO Corporation; *U.S. Public*, pg. 1020
AEROELITE LIMITED—See L3Harris Technologies, Inc.; *U.S. Public*, pg. 1280
AERO-INSTRUMENTS CO., LLC—See TransDigm Group Incorporated; *U.S. Public*, pg. 2181
AERO INVENTORY (JAPAN) KK—See Aero Inventory plc; *Int'l*, pg. 180
AERO INVENTORY (USA) INC—See Aero Inventory plc; *Int'l*, pg. 180
AERONAUTICAL & GENERAL INSTRUMENTS LIMITED—See HWH Investments Limited; *Int'l*, pg. 3543
AEROSTRUCTURES ACQUISITION, LLC—See AE Industrial Partners, LP; *U.S. Private*, pg. 111
AEVEX AEROSPACE; *U.S. Private*, pg. 120
AIRBORNE SYSTEMS FRANCE—See TransDigm Group Incorporated; *U.S. Public*, pg. 2181
AIRBORNE SYSTEMS GROUP LIMITED—See TransDigm Group Incorporated; *U.S. Public*, pg. 2181
AIRBORNE SYSTEMS NORTH AMERICA OF NJ INC.—See TransDigm Group Incorporated; *U.S. Public*, pg. 2181
AIRBOSS DEFENSE GROUP LTD.—See AirBoss of America Corp.; *Int'l*, pg. 241
AIRCRAFT PERFORMANCE GROUP, INC.—See Liberty Hall Capital Partners, L.P.; *U.S. Private*, pg. 2444
AIREON LLC—See Iridium Communications Inc.; *U.S. Public*, pg. 1171
AMETEK AEROSPACE & DEFENSE DIVISION—See AMETEK, Inc.; *U.S. Public*, pg. 116
AMETEK AMERON, LLC—See AMETEK, Inc.; *U.S. Public*, pg. 117
ANHUI SUN-CREATE ELECTRONICS CO., LTD.; *Int'l*, pg. 469
ANSCHUETZ SINGAPORE PTE. LTD.—See DMB Dr. Dieter Murrmann Beteiligungsgesellschaft mbH; *Int'l*, pg. 2142
ANSCHUTZ GMBH—See DMB Dr. Dieter Murrmann Beteiligungsgesellschaft mbH; *Int'l*, pg. 2142
APLISENS S.A.; *Int'l*, pg. 515
APOLLO MICRO SYSTEMS LIMITED; *Int'l*, pg. 518
APPLANIX LLC—See Trimble, Inc.; *U.S. Public*, pg. 2190
APPLIED ENERGETICS, INC.; *U.S. Public*, pg. 170
APSS S.R.L.—See L3Harris Technologies, Inc.; *U.S. Public*, pg. 1280
APSYS—See Airbus SE; *Int'l*, pg. 246
ARGON ST, INC.—See The Boeing Company; *U.S. Public*, pg. 2039
ARMTEC COUNTERMEASURES CO. - DEFENSE TECHNOLOGIES-ARO—See TransDigm Group Incorporated; *U.S. Public*, pg. 2180
ARMTEC COUNTERMEASURES CO.—See TransDigm Group Incorporated; *U.S. Public*, pg. 2180
ARMTEC COUTERMEASURES CO.—See TransDigm Group Incorporated; *U.S. Public*, pg. 2180
A/S KELVIN HUGHES—See HENSOLDT AG; *Int'l*, pg. 3355
ASSURED TELEMATICS INC.—See Pegasus TransTech, LLC; *U.S. Private*, pg. 3130
ASTRONAUTICS C.A. LTD.—See Astronautics Corporation of America; *U.S. Private*, pg. 362
ASTRONAUTICS CORPORATION OF AMERICA - PLANT 4—See Astronautics Corporation of America; *U.S. Private*, pg. 362
ASTRONAUTICS CORPORATION OF AMERICA; *U.S. Private*, pg. 362
ASTRONAUTICS U.K.—See Astronautics Corporation of America; *U.S. Private*, pg. 362
ASTRONICS AEROSAT CORPORATION—See Astronics Corporation; *U.S. Public*, pg. 217
ATK AEROSPACE SYSTEMS—See Northrop Grumman Corporation; *U.S. Public*, pg. 1540
ATLANTIS SYSTEMS CORP.—See BPLI Holdings Inc.; *Int'l*, pg. 1132
ATLANTIS SYSTEMS INTERNATIONAL INC.—See BPLI Holdings Inc.; *Int'l*, pg. 1133
ATLAS ELEKTRONIK GMBH—See Airbus SE; *Int'l*, pg. 241
ATLAS ELEKTRONIK UK LTD.—See Airbus SE; *Int'l*, pg. 242
ATLAS MARIDAN APS—See Airbus SE; *Int'l*, pg. 242
ATLAS NAVAL SYSTEMS MALAYSIA SDN BHD—See Airbus SE; *Int'l*, pg. 242
ATLAS NORTH AMERICA, LLC—See Airbus SE; *Int'l*, pg. 242
AUTONOMOUS SURFACE VEHICLES LIMITED—See L3Harris Technologies, Inc.; *U.S. Public*, pg. 1280
AUTRONICS CORPORATION—See Curtiss-Wright Corporation; *U.S. Public*, pg. 611
AVALEX TECHNOLOGIES CORPORATION; *U.S. Private*, pg. 403
AVER INFORMATION INC.; *Int'l*, pg. 739
AVIAOK INTERNATIONAL LLC; *Int'l*, pg. 741
AVIC AIRBORNE SYSTEMS CO., LTD.; *Int'l*, pg. 742
AVION SOLUTIONS, INC.; *U.S. Private*, pg. 407
AV TECH CORPORATION - CCTV PRODUCT DIVISION—See Av Tech Corporation; *Int'l*, pg. 733
BAE SYSTEMS AUSTRALIA LIMITED—See BAE Systems plc; *Int'l*, pg. 796
BAE SYSTEMS-COMMUNICATION, NAVIGATION, IDENTIFICATION & RECONNAISSANCE—See BAE Systems plc; *Int'l*, pg. 798
BAE SYSTEMS-COMMUNICATIONS, NAVIGATION, IDENTIFICATION & RECONNAISSANCE—See BAE Systems plc; *Int'l*, pg. 798
BAE SYSTEMS CUSTOMER SOLUTIONS—See BAE Systems plc; *Int'l*, pg. 796
BAE SYSTEMS-ELECTRONICS & INTEGRATED SOLUTIONS—See BAE Systems plc; *Int'l*, pg. 797
BAE SYSTEMS INDIA (SERVICES) PVT. LTD—See BAE Systems plc; *Int'l*, pg. 796
BAE SYSTEMS-INFORMATION WARFARE—See BAE Systems plc; *Int'l*, pg. 798
BAE SYSTEMS INTEGRATED SYSTEM TECHNOLOGIES—See BAE Systems plc; *Int'l*, pg. 796
BAE SYSTEMS—See BAE Systems plc; *Int'l*, pg. 797
BAE SYSTEMS—See BAE Systems plc; *Int'l*, pg. 797
BAE SYSTEMS—See BAE Systems plc; *Int'l*, pg. 798
BANTEC, INC.; *U.S. Public*, pg. 275
BARCO FEDERAL SYSTEMS LLC—See Barco N.V.; *Int'l*, pg. 864
BDSTAR INFORMATION SERVICE CO., LTD.—See Beijing BDstar Navigation Co., Ltd.; *Int'l*, pg. 946
BEIJING ADVANCED VIDEOINFO TECHNOLOGY CO., LTD—See Cantronic Systems Inc.; *Int'l*, pg. 1299
BEIJING BDSTAR NAVIGATION CO., LTD.; *Int'l*, pg. 946
BEIJING HIGHLANDER DIGITAL TECHNOLOGY CO., LTD.; *Int'l*, pg. 951
BEIJING UNISTRONG SCIENCE & TECHNOLOGY CO., LTD.; *Int'l*, pg. 959
BENMAR MARINE ELECTRONICS, INC.; *U.S. Private*, pg. 526
BENTELER DEFENSE GMBH—See Benteler International AG; *Int'l*, pg. 976
BERKSHIRE MANUFACTURED PRODUCTS, INC.—See Waverly Partners Inc.; *U.S. Private*, pg. 4458
BG T&A CO.; *Int'l*, pg. 1007
THE BOEING CO. - HUNTSVILLE—See The Boeing Company; *U.S. Public*, pg. 2040
BOSSARD AEROSPACE GERMANY GMBH—See Bossard Holding AG; *Int'l*, pg. 1117
BOSSARD NEDERLAND B.V.—See Bossard Holding AG; *Int'l*, pg. 1117
BRIMROSE-ACOUSTO OPTIC COMPONENTS DIVISION—See Brimrose Corporation of America; *U.S. Private*, pg. 654
BRIMROSE CORPORATION OF AMERICA; *U.S. Private*, pg. 654
BRIMROSE-NIR PROCESS ANALYSIS DIVISION—See Brimrose Corporation of America; *U.S. Private*, pg. 654
BROOKES & GATEHOUSE, LTD.—See Brunswick Corporation; *U.S. Public*, pg. 408
BSE—See BSE Industrial Contractors; *U.S. Private*, pg. 675
BT REDCARE GROUP—See BT Group plc; *Int'l*, pg. 1203
BVR TECHNOLOGIES CO.—See Kaney Aerospace, Inc.; *U.S. Private*, pg. 2260
B.V. VEGA MEET - EN REGELTECHNIEK—See Grieshaber Holding GmbH; *Int'l*, pg. 3083
CASSIDIAN COMMUNICATIONS GMBH—See Airbus SE; *Int'l*, pg. 242
CASTLES TECHNOLOGY EUROPE S.R.L.—See Castles Technology Co., Ltd; *Int'l*, pg. 1357
CASTLES TECHNOLOGY INTERNATIONAL CORP.—See Castles Technology Co., Ltd; *Int'l*, pg. 1357
CASTLES TECHNOLOGY SINGAPORE PTE. LTD.—See Castles Technology Co., Ltd; *Int'l*, pg. 1357
CASTLES TECHNOLOGY SPAIN SL—See Castles Technology Co., Ltd; *Int'l*, pg. 1357
CAUSEWAY AERO GROUP LTD.; *Int'l*, pg. 1361
CENTURY RETAIL EUROPE B.V.—See Hangzhou Century Co., Ltd.; *Int'l*, pg. 3246
CHARTCO LTD.—See Equistone Partners Europe Limited; *Int'l*, pg. 2486
CHELTON LIMITED—See TransDigm Group Incorporated; *U.S. Public*, pg. 2180
CHEMRING SENSORS & ELECTRONIC SYSTEMS, INC.—See Chemring Group PLC; *Int'l*, pg. 1463
CHENGDU SPACEON ELECTRONICS CO., LTD.; *Int'l*, pg. 1469

N.A.I.C.S. INDEX

334511 — SEARCH, DETECTION, ...

CHINA AEROSPACE INTERNATIONAL HOLDINGS LIMITED; *Int'l*, pg. 1481
CHINA HARZONE INDUSTRY CO., LTD.; *Int'l*, pg. 1507
CHRONOTRACK SYSTEMS CORP.—See Leonard Green & Partners, L.P.; *U.S. Private*, pg. 2426
CHRONOTRACK SYSTEMS CORP.—See TPG Capital, L.P.; *U.S. Public*, pg. 2174
CHRONOTRACK SYSTEMS EUROPE B.V.—See Leonard Green & Partners, L.P.; *U.S. Private*, pg. 2426
CHRONOTRACK SYSTEMS EUROPE B.V.—See TPG Capital, L.P.; *U.S. Public*, pg. 2174
CHUN YU WORKS & CO., LTD.; *Int'l*, pg. 1596
CIRCUTECH INTERNATIONAL HOLDINGS LIMITED; *Int'l*, pg. 1618
CLOUD CAP TECHNOLOGY, INC.—See RTX Corporation; *U.S. Public*, pg. 1821
CMC ELECTRONICS AURORA LLC—See TransDigm Group Incorporated; *U.S. Public*, pg. 2180
CMC ELECTRONICS INC. - OTTAWA—See TransDigm Group Incorporated; *U.S. Public*, pg. 2180
CMC ELECTRONICS INC.—See TransDigm Group Incorporated; *U.S. Public*, pg. 2180
CML GROUP LTD—See Teledyne Technologies Incorporated; *U.S. Public*, pg. 1994
COBHAM MOTION CONTROL—See Advent International Corporation; *U.S. Public*, pg. 99
CODA OCTOPUS PRODUCTS LTD.—See Coda Octopus Group, Inc.; *U.S. Public*, pg. 521
COLLINS AEROSPACE - CHESHIRE—See RTX Corporation; *U.S. Public*, pg. 1821
COMMUTER AIR TECHNOLOGY; *U.S. Private*, pg. 997
COMPUDYNE CORPORATION—See Frontenac Company LLC; *U.S. Private*, pg. 1613
COMTEK ADVANCED STRUCTURES LTD—See Searchlight Capital Partners, L.P.; *U.S. Private*, pg. 3588
CONMED CORPORATION; *U.S. Public*, pg. 567
CRAME, S.A.—See Grupo Arbulu S.L.; *Int'l*, pg. 3120
CRITICAL SOLUTIONS INTERNATIONAL, INC.—See AirBoss of America Corp.; *Int'l*, pg. 241
CROWCON DETECTION INSTRUMENTS LIMITED—See Halma plc; *Int'l*, pg. 3231
CT-VIDEO GMBH—See CeoTronics AG; *Int'l*, pg. 1420
DELTA DRONE SA; *Int'l*, pg. 2016
DETECT CANADA—See DeTect, Inc.; *U.S. Private*, pg. 1216
DETECT EU LTD.—See DeTect, Inc.; *U.S. Private*, pg. 1216
DETECT, INC. - AVIATION & SECURITY SYSTEMS GROUP—See DeTect, Inc.; *U.S. Private*, pg. 1216
DETECT, INC. - METEOROLOGICAL RADAR GROUP—See DeTect, Inc.; *U.S. Private*, pg. 1216
DETECT, INC.; *U.S. Private*, pg. 1216
DEVICE 4U SDN. BHD.—See AWC Berhad; *Int'l*, pg. 752
DI-NIKKO ENGINEERING CO., LTD. - TODOROKU FACTORY—See Di-Nikko Engineering Co., Ltd.; *Int'l*, pg. 2101
DME CORPORATION—See Astronics Corporation; *U.S. Public*, pg. 217
DRS TECHNOLOGIES CANADA LTD.—See DEV Information Technology Pvt. Ltd.; *Int'l*, pg. 2086
DSME E&R LTD.—See Hanwha Ocean Co., Ltd.; *Int'l*, pg. 3266
DUKANE SEACOM, INC.—See HEICO Corporation; *U.S. Public*, pg. 1020
DY4 SYSTEMS, INC.—See Curtiss-Wright Corporation; *U.S. Public*, pg. 612
DYNA-EMPIRE, INC.; *U.S. Private*, pg. 1297
EASAT RADAR SYSTEMS LIMITED—See Goodwin PLC; *Int'l*, pg. 3041
EATON AEROSPACE LLC - ELECTRICAL SENSING & CONTROLS DIVISION, COSTA MESA—See Eaton Corporation plc; *Int'l*, pg. 2279
EATON AEROSPACE LLC - ELECTRICAL SENSING & CONTROLS DIVISION, GLENOLDEN—See Eaton Corporation plc; *Int'l*, pg. 2279
EATON AEROSPACE LLC - ELECTRICAL SENSING & CONTROLS DIVISION, GRAND RAPIDS—See Eaton Corporation plc; *Int'l*, pg. 2279
EATON AEROSPACE LLC - ELECTRICAL SENSING & CONTROLS DIVISION, SARASOTA—See Eaton Corporation plc; *Int'l*, pg. 2279
ECONOLITE CANADA, INC.—See Econolite Group, Inc.; *U.S. Private*, pg. 1330
EDGE AUTONOMY SLO, LLC—See AE Industrial Partners, LP; *U.S. Private*, pg. 112
EESTERLINE SENSORS SERVICES AMERICAS, INC.—See TransDigm Group Incorporated; *U.S. Public*, pg. 2180
ELBIT SYSTEMS OF AMERICA, LLC—See Elbit Systems Limited; *Int'l*, pg. 2344
ELDEC CORPORATION—See Crane NXT, Co.; *U.S. Public*, pg. 589
ELECSYS CORPORATION—See Lindsay Corporation; *U.S. Public*, pg. 1319
ELECTRO OPTIC SYSTEMS PTY LIMITED—See Electro Optic Systems Holdings Limited; *Int'l*, pg. 2353
ELITE AEROSPACE GROUP, INC.; *U.S. Private*, pg. 1360
ENSCO AVIONICS CANADA INC.—See Ensco Inc.; *U.S. Private*, pg. 1402

ENSCO AVIONICS, INC.—See Ensco Inc.; *U.S. Private*, pg. 1402
ENSCO RAIL AUSTRALIA PTY LTD—See Ensco Inc.; *U.S. Private*, pg. 1402
ENSCO RAIL, INC.—See Ensco Inc.; *U.S. Private*, pg. 1402
ENTERPRISE ELECTRONICS CORPORATION—See International Business Machines Corporation; *U.S. Public*, pg. 1151
EOS SPACE SYSTEMS PTY LIMITED—See Electro Optic Systems Holdings Limited; *Int'l*, pg. 2353
ESCORT, INC.—See Monomoy Capital Partners LLC; *U.S. Private*, pg. 2772
ESTERLINE DEFENSE GROUP—See TransDigm Group Incorporated; *U.S. Public*, pg. 2180
ESTERLINE ENGINEERED MATERIALS-NMC AEROSPACE—See TransDigm Group Incorporated; *U.S. Public*, pg. 2181
ESTERLINE SENSORS SERVICES AMERICAS, INC.—See TransDigm Group Incorporated; *U.S. Public*, pg. 2180
EUROAVIONICS SCHW EIZ AG—See HENSOLDT AG; *Int'l*, pg. 3355
EUROAVIONICS US HOLDCO. INC.—See HENSOLDT AG; *Int'l*, pg. 3355
EURONAV LTD.—See Euronav NV; *Int'l*, pg. 2554
EVERFOCUS ELECTRONICS AG—See EverFocus Electronics Co., Ltd.; *Int'l*, pg. 2565
EVERFOCUS ELECTRONICS CO., LTD.; *Int'l*, pg. 2565
EVERFOCUS ELECTRONICS (INDIA) PRIVATE LTD.—See EverFocus Electronics Co., Ltd.; *Int'l*, pg. 2565
EVERFOCUS JAPAN CORP.—See EverFocus Electronics Co., Ltd.; *Int'l*, pg. 2565
EVPU DEFENCE A.S.—See EVPU a.s.; *Int'l*, pg. 2573
EWR WEATHER RADAR SYSTEMS; *U.S. Private*, pg. 1444
EXTANT COMPONENTS GROUP HOLDINGS, INC.—See TransDigm Group Incorporated; *U.S. Public*, pg. 2182
FERNAU LIMITED—See Moog Inc.; *U.S. Public*, pg. 1470
FIDELITY TECHNOLOGIES CORP.; *U.S. Public*, pg. 1503
FIELDTECH AVIONICS & INSTRUMENTS, INC.; *U.S. Private*, pg. 1504
FIGEAC-AERO SA; *Int'l*, pg. 2660
FIRSTMARK CORP.—See Hicks Holdings, LLC; *U.S. Private*, pg. 1934
FIRSTMARK CORP.—See The Riverside Company; *U.S. Private*, pg. 4108
FIRSTMARK CORP.—See Weinberg Capital Group, Inc.; *U.S. Private*, pg. 4471
FLIR COMMERCIAL SYSTEMS, INC.—See Teledyne Technologies Incorporated; *U.S. Public*, pg. 1993
FLIR SYSTEMS CV—See Teledyne Technologies Incorporated; *U.S. Public*, pg. 1993
FLIR SYSTEMS LTD.—See Teledyne Technologies Incorporated; *U.S. Public*, pg. 1993
FLYHT AEROSPACE SOLUTIONS LTD.—See Firan Technology Group Corporation; *Int'l*, pg. 2678
FREEFLIGHT SYSTEMS, LTD.—See The Jordan Company, L.P.; *U.S. Private*, pg. 4059
FUTURECOM SYSTEMS GROUP INC.—See Motorola Solutions, Inc.; *U.S. Public*, pg. 1477
G2METRIC—See Searchlight Capital Partners, L.P.; *U.S. Private*, pg. 3588
GARMIN ARGENTINA SRL—See Garmin Ltd.; *Int'l*, pg. 2884
GARMIN AT, INC.—See Garmin Ltd.; *Int'l*, pg. 2885
GARMIN AUSTRIA GMBH—See Garmin Ltd.; *Int'l*, pg. 2885
GARMIN CHILE LDA—See Garmin Ltd.; *Int'l*, pg. 2884
GARMIN CHINA CO. LTD.—See Garmin Ltd.; *Int'l*, pg. 2884
GARMIN CORPORATION—See Garmin Ltd.; *Int'l*, pg. 2885
GARMIN CZECH S.R.O—See Garmin Ltd.; *Int'l*, pg. 2884
GARMIN (EUROPE) LTD.—See Garmin Ltd.; *Int'l*, pg. 2885
GARMIN HRVATSKA D.O.O.—See Garmin Ltd.; *Int'l*, pg. 2884
GARMIN IBERIA S.A.—See Garmin Ltd.; *Int'l*, pg. 2884
GARMIN INTERNATIONAL, INC.—See Garmin Ltd.; *Int'l*, pg. 2884
GARMIN ITALIA S.P.A.—See Garmin Ltd.; *Int'l*, pg. 2885
GARMIN LTD.; *Int'l*, pg. 2884
GARMIN NEW ZEALAND LTD.—See Garmin Ltd.; *Int'l*, pg. 2885
GARMIN NORDIC DENMARK A/S—See Garmin Ltd.; *Int'l*, pg. 2885
GARMIN NORDIC FINLAND OY—See Garmin Ltd.; *Int'l*, pg. 2885
GARMIN NORDIC NORWAY AS—See Garmin Ltd.; *Int'l*, pg. 2885
GARMIN NORDIC SWEDEN AB—See Garmin Ltd.; *Int'l*, pg. 2885
GARMIN NORGE AS—See Garmin Ltd.; *Int'l*, pg. 2885
GARMIN SWITZERLAND GMBH—See Garmin Ltd.; *Int'l*, pg. 2885
GARMIN (THAILAND) LTD.—See Garmin Ltd.; *Int'l*, pg. 2884
GARMIN, TRGOVINA IN SERVIS, D.O.O.—See Garmin Ltd.; *Int'l*, pg. 2885
GARMIN VIETNAM LTD.—See Garmin Ltd.; *Int'l*, pg. 2885
GAVIAL ITC—See Gavial Engineering & Manufacturing; *U.S. Private*, pg. 1652
GAZOMAT SARL; *Int'l*, pg. 2891
GE AVIATION SYSTEMS LLC - BOHEMIA—See General Electric Company; *U.S. Public*, pg. 918

GE AVIATION SYSTEMS LLC - GRAND RAPIDS—See General Electric Company; *U.S. Public*, pg. 918
GENERAL ATOMICS—See General Atomics; *U.S. Private*, pg. 1663
GENERAL ATOMICS SYSTEMS INTEGRATION, LLC—See General Atomics; *U.S. Private*, pg. 1663
GENERAL OCEANS AS; *Int'l*, pg. 2919
GENIUS TRAFFIC SYSTEM COMPANY LIMITED—See Forth Corporation Public Company Limited; *Int'l*, pg. 2738
GEODETICS INCORPORATED—See AEVEX Aerospace; *U.S. Private*, pg. 120
GEODIGITAL INTERNATIONAL INC.; *Int'l*, pg. 2933
GEOTAG INC.; *U.S. Private*, pg. 1685
GEOTRAC SYSTEMS INC.—See Trimble, Inc.; *U.S. Public*, pg. 2190
GIL GMBH—See Trimble, Inc.; *U.S. Public*, pg. 2190
GLOBAL TOOLING SYSTEMS INC.—See AIP, LLC; *U.S. Private*, pg. 133
GPS INSIGHT LLC—See Accel Partners L.P.; *U.S. Private*, pg. 48
GPS INSIGHT LLC—See KKR & Co. Inc.; *U.S. Private*, pg. 1238
GRANITE STATE MANUFACTURING—See Allard Nazarian Group Inc.; *U.S. Private*, pg. 175
GREINA TECHNOLOGIES, INC.—See Alps Alpine Co., Ltd.; *Int'l*, pg. 376
GROUND PENETRATING RADAR SYSTEMS, LLC—See Kohlberg & Company, LLC; *U.S. Private*, pg. 2338
GRUPO ARBULU S.L.; *Int'l*, pg. 3120
GSN MAQUINARIA-SERVICIOS-CNC, S.A. DE C.V.—See GSN Maschinen-Anlagen-Service GmbH; *Int'l*, pg. 3150
GT ADVANCED TECHNOLOGIES TAIWAN CO., LTD.—See GT Advanced Technologies Inc.; *U.S. Private*, pg. 1801
GUANGZHOU HANGXIN AVIATION TECHNOLOGY CO., LTD.; *Int'l*, pg. 3165
HARDSTAFF BARRIERS LIMITED—See Hill & Smith PLC; *Int'l*, pg. 3391
HARRIS CORP. - ELECTRONIC SYSTEMS DIVISION - AMITYVILLE—See L3Harris Technologies, Inc.; *U.S. Public*, pg. 1279
HARRIS CORP. - ELECTRONIC SYSTEMS DIVISION - RADAR & RECONNAISSANCE SYSTEMS - VAN NUYS—See L3Harris Technologies, Inc.; *U.S. Public*, pg. 1279
HARRIS CORP. - ELECTRONIC SYSTEMS DIVISION - RECONNAISSANCE & SURVEILLANCE SYSTEMS - MORGAN HILL—See L3Harris Technologies, Inc.; *U.S. Public*, pg. 1280
HARRIS CORP. - ELECTRONIC SYSTEMS DIVISION - SONAR & COMMAND SYSTEMS - CHESAPEAKE—See L3Harris Technologies, Inc.; *U.S. Public*, pg. 1280
HARRIS CORP. - GEOSPATIAL SYSTEMS DIVISION—See L3Harris Technologies, Inc.; *U.S. Public*, pg. 1280
HARRIS CORP. - NIGHT VISION & COMMUNICATIONS SOLUTIONS DIVISION—See L3Harris Technologies, Inc.; *U.S. Public*, pg. 1279
HARRIS CORP. - NIGHT VISION—See Elbit Systems Limited; *Int'l*, pg. 2344
HAVELSAN HAVA ELEKTRONIK SANAYI VE TICARET AS; *Int'l*, pg. 3287
HEMISPHERE GNSS (USA) INC.—See CNH Industrial N.V.; *Int'l*, pg. 1675
HERLEY LANCASTER—See Advent International Corporation; *U.S. Private*, pg. 101
HF GROUP INC. - HOUSTON FEARLESS 76 DIVISION—See HF Group Inc.; *U.S. Private*, pg. 1928
HONEYWELL AIR TRANSPORT SYSTEMS—See Honeywell International Inc.; *U.S. Public*, pg. 1047
HONEYWELL CANADA, INC.—See Honeywell International Inc.; *U.S. Public*, pg. 1051
HONEYWELL ENGINE SYSTEMS & SERVICES—See Honeywell International Inc.; *U.S. Public*, pg. 1047
HONEYWELL FEDERAL MANUFACTURING TECHNOLOGY—See Honeywell International Inc.; *U.S. Public*, pg. 1047
HONEYWELL JAPAN INC.—See Honeywell International Inc.; *U.S. Public*, pg. 1051
HONEYWELL PTE. LTD.—See Honeywell International Inc.; *U.S. Public*, pg. 1051
HONEYWELL SAFETY PRODUCTS EUROPE SAS—See Honeywell International Inc.; *U.S. Public*, pg. 1051
HONEYWELL UK LIMITED—See Honeywell International Inc.; *U.S. Public*, pg. 1051
HOYA CORPORATION USA—See Hoya Corporation; *Int'l*, pg. 3496
HUMMINBIRD—See Johnson Outdoors Inc.; *U.S. Public*, pg. 1200
HYDROID, INC.—See Huntington Ingalls Industries, Inc.; *U.S. Public*, pg. 1072
HYDROSCIENCE TECHNOLOGIES, INC.; *U.S. Private*, pg. 2018
IMAGE SENSING SYSTEMS EUROPE LIMITED—See Autoscope Technologies Corporation; *U.S. Public*, pg. 238
IMAGE SENSING SYSTEMS HK LIMITED—See Autoscope Technologies Corporation; *U.S. Public*, pg. 239
INFINITY TECHNOLOGY, INC.; *U.S. Private*, pg. 2072

334511 — SEARCH, DETECTION, ...

INSTRON LIMITED—See Illinois Tool Works Inc.; *U.S. Public*, pg. 1108
INTUITIVE MACHINES, INC.; *U.S. Public*, pg. 1160
IQGEO GROUP PLC—See KKR & Co. Inc.; *U.S. Public*, pg. 1253
ITT CANNON GMBH—See ITT Inc.; *U.S. Public*, pg. 1177
ITT CANNON KOREA LTD.—See ITT Inc.; *U.S. Public*, pg. 1177
ITT CORPORATION INDIA PVT. LTD.—See ITT Inc.; *U.S. Public*, pg. 1178
ITT ITALIA S.R.L.—See ITT Inc.; *U.S. Public*, pg. 1178
IVIGIL CORPORATION—See Ac&C International Co., Ltd.; *Int'l*, pg. 74
JACOTTET INDUSTRIE SAS—See Carclo plc; *Int'l*, pg. 1321
JENA-OPTRONIK GMBH—See Airbus SE; *Int'l*, pg. 245
JOBY AVIATION, INC.; *U.S. Public*, pg. 1190
JOHNSON OUTDOORS MARINE ELECTRONICS, INC.—See Johnson Outdoors Inc.; *U.S. Public*, pg. 1201
KEARFOTT CORPORATION—See Astronautics Corporation of America; *U.S. Private*, pg. 362
KEARFOTT GUIDANCE & NAVIGATION CORPORATION - KEARFOTT MOTION SYSTEM DIVISION—See Astronautics Corporation of America; *U.S. Private*, pg. 362
KEARFOTT GUIDANCE & NAVIGATION CORPORATION—See Astronautics Corporation of America; *U.S. Private*, pg. 362
KELVIN HUGHES LIMITED—See HENSOLDT AG; *Int'l*, pg. 3355
KELVIN HUGHES (NEDERLAND) B.V.—See HENSOLDT AG; *Int'l*, pg. 3355
KELVIN HUGHES (SINGAPORE) PTE. LTD.—See HENSOLDT AG; *Int'l*, pg. 3355
KLEIN MARINE SYSTEMS, INC.—See General Oceans AS; *Int'l*, pg. 2919
KMC SYSTEMS INC.—See Elbit Systems Limited; *Int'l*, pg. 2344
KOLLSMAN, INC.—See Elbit Systems Limited; *Int'l*, pg. 2344
KONI BV—See ITT Inc.; *U.S. Public*, pg. 1178
KSARIA CORPORATION—See ITT Inc.; *U.S. Public*, pg. 1179
L-3 AVIONICS SYSTEMS, INC.—See L3Harris Technologies, Inc.; *U.S. Public*, pg. 1281
L-3 CHESAPEAKE SCIENCES CORPORATION—See L3Harris Technologies, Inc.; *U.S. Public*, pg. 1281
L-3 COMMUNICATIONS ELECTRONIC SYSTEMS—See L3Harris Technologies, Inc.; *U.S. Public*, pg. 1282
L-3 COMMUNICATIONS KLEIN ASSOCIATES, INC.—See L3Harris Technologies, Inc.; *U.S. Public*, pg. 1282
L-3 COMMUNICATIONS MARINE HOLDINGS AS—See L3Harris Technologies, Inc.; *U.S. Public*, pg. 1282
L-3 COMMUNICATIONS MARINE SYSTEMS UK LTD—See L3Harris Technologies, Inc.; *U.S. Public*, pg. 1282
L-3 INTERSTATE ELECTRONICS CORPORATION—See L3Harris Technologies, Inc.; *U.S. Public*, pg. 1283
L3 MARIPRO, INC.—See L3Harris Technologies, Inc.; *U.S. Public*, pg. 1284
L-3 MUSTANG TECHNOLOGY—See L3Harris Technologies, Inc.; *U.S. Public*, pg. 1283
L3 OCEANIA PTY LIMITED—See L3Harris Technologies, Inc.; *U.S. Public*, pg. 1284
L-3 SYSTEMS & IMAGERY—See L3Harris Technologies, Inc.; *U.S. Public*, pg. 1283
LEACH INTERNATIONAL EUROPE S.A.—See TransDigm Group Incorporated; *U.S. Public*, pg. 2181
LIAONING DAOHENG TECHNOLOGY CO., LTD—See Cantronic Systems Inc.; *Int'l*, pg. 1300
LIGHTRIDGE SOLUTIONS—See ATL Partners, LLC; *U.S. Private*, pg. 369
LITTELFUSE SEMICONDUCTOR (WUXI) COMPANY—See Littelfuse, Inc.; *U.S. Public*, pg. 1327
LOADRITE LIMITED—See Trimble, Inc.; *U.S. Public*, pg. 2190
LOCI CONTROLS, INC.; *U.S. Private*, pg. 2478
LOCKHEED MARTIN CORPORATION; *U.S. Public*, pg. 1337
LOCKHEED MARTIN ENGINE INVESTMENTS, LLC—See Lockheed Martin Corporation; *U.S. Public*, pg. 1338
LOCKHEED MARTIN INTEGRATED SYSTEMS, INC.—See Lockheed Martin Corporation; *U.S. Public*, pg. 1338
LOCKHEED MARTIN INTEGRATED TECHNOLOGY, LLC—See Lockheed Martin Corporation; *U.S. Public*, pg. 1338
LOCKHEED MARTIN OPERATIONS SUPPORT, INC.—See Lockheed Martin Corporation; *U.S. Public*, pg. 1338
LOCKHEED MARTIN SIPPICAN COUNTERMEASURE SYSTEMS—See Lockheed Martin Corporation; *U.S. Public*, pg. 1338
LOCKHEED MARTIN SIPPICAN, INC.—See Lockheed Martin Corporation; *U.S. Public*, pg. 1338
LOUIS BERGER SERVICES INC.—See Kingswood Capital Management LLC; *U.S. Private*, pg. 2312
LUXIUM SOLUTIONS, LLC—See Edgewater Capital Partners, L.P.; *U.S. Private*, pg. 1335
LUXIUM SOLUTIONS, LLC—See SK Capital Partners, LP; *U.S. Private*, pg. 3679

LYNGSO MARINE A/S—See L3Harris Technologies, Inc.; *U.S. Public*, pg. 1284
MACDONALD, DETTWILER AND ASSOCIATES CORP.—See Advent International Corporation; *U.S. Private*, pg. 103
MAGELLAN NAVIGATION, INC.—See Shah Capital Partners, LP; *U.S. Public*, pg. 3623
M/D TOTCO—See NOV, Inc.; *U.S. Public*, pg. 1545
MEGGITT AEROSPACE LIMITED—See Parker Hannifin Corporation; *U.S. Public*, pg. 1642
MEGGITT DEFENCE SYSTEMS LTD.—See Parker Hannifin Corporation; *U.S. Public*, pg. 1642
MEGGITT PLC - ANGOULEME FACILITY—See Parker Hannifin Corporation; *U.S. Public*, pg. 1642
MEGGITT PLC - ARCHAMPS FACILITY—See Parker Hannifin Corporation; *U.S. Public*, pg. 1642
MEGGITT PLC - BASINGSTOKE FACILITY—See Parker Hannifin Corporation; *U.S. Public*, pg. 1642
MEGGITT PLC - FRIBOURG FACILITY—See Parker Hannifin Corporation; *U.S. Public*, pg. 1642
MEGGITT PLC - HCL - MEGGITT ODC FACTORY—See Parker Hannifin Corporation; *U.S. Public*, pg. 1642
MEGGITT PLC - MEGGITT SHANGHAI FACILITY—See Parker Hannifin Corporation; *U.S. Public*, pg. 1642
MEGGITT-USA, INC. - GERMANTOWN FACILITY—See Parker Hannifin Corporation; *U.S. Public*, pg. 1642
MEPS DEVICES SDN. BHD.—See AWC Berhad; *Int'l*, pg. 752
MICRO SYSTEMS, INC.—See Kratos Defense & Security Solutions, Inc.; *U.S. Public*, pg. 1276
MINE SAFETY APPLIANCES COMPANY-INSTRUMENT DIVISION—See MSA Safety Incorporated; *U.S. Public*, pg. 1482
MOOG AIRCRAFT GROUP—See Moog Inc.; *U.S. Public*, pg. 1469
MOOG AIRCRAFT GROUP - TORRANCE—See Moog Inc.; *U.S. Public*, pg. 1469
MOOG FERNAU LIMITED—See Moog Inc.; *U.S. Public*, pg. 1470
MOOG INC.; *U.S. Public*, pg. 1469
MTI POLYFAB INC.—See 3M Company; *U.S. Public*, pg. 5
N2 IMAGING SYSTEMS, LLC—See RTX Corporation; *U.S. Public*, pg. 1821
NAL RESEARCH CORP.—See Blue Sky Network, LLC; *U.S. Private*, pg. 593
NANOTRON TECHNOLOGIES GMBH—See XTI Aerospace, Inc.; *U.S. Public*, pg. 2393
NAVCOM DEFENSE ELECTRONICS, INC.—See TransDigm Group Incorporated; *U.S. Public*, pg. 2182
NAVERUS, INC.—See General Electric Company; *U.S. Public*, pg. 919
NAVICO, INC.—See Brunswick Corporation; *U.S. Public*, pg. 408
NAVIONICS INC.—See Garmin Ltd.; *Int'l*, pg. 2885
NAVIONICS SRL—See Garmin Ltd.; *Int'l*, pg. 2885
NAVMAN WIRELESS AUSTRALIA PTY.LTD.—See Vontier Corporation; *U.S. Public*, pg. 2309
NAVTECH RADAR LIMITED—See Halma plc; *Int'l*, pg. 3232
NEANY INC.; *U.S. Private*, pg. 2877
NEXALA LTD—See Trimble, Inc.; *U.S. Public*, pg. 2190
NEXEYA FRANCE SAS—See HENSOLDT AG; *Int'l*, pg. 3355
NON-INTRUSIVE INSPECTION TECHNOLOGY, INC. - CHARLOTTESVILLE FACILITY—See Chemring Group PLC; *Int'l*, pg. 1463
NON-INTRUSIVE INSPECTION TECHNOLOGY, INC.—See Chemring Group PLC; *Int'l*, pg. 1463
NORTH NIGHT VISION TECHNOLOGY CO., LTD.—See China North Industries Group Corporation; *Int'l*, pg. 1536
NORTHROP GRUMMAN AEROSPACE SYSTEMS-BETHPAGE—See Northrop Grumman Corporation; *U.S. Public*, pg. 1540
NORTHROP GRUMMAN ELECTRONIC SYSTEMS—See Northrop Grumman Corporation; *U.S. Public*, pg. 1540
NORTHROP GRUMMAN INTELLIGENCE, SURVEILLANCE & RECONNAISSANCE SYSTEMS—See Northrop Grumman Corporation; *U.S. Public*, pg. 1540
NORTHROP GRUMMAN INTERNATIONAL, INC.—See Northrop Grumman Corporation; *U.S. Public*, pg. 1541
NORTHROP GRUMMAN ITALIA S.P.A.—See Northrop Grumman Corporation; *U.S. Public*, pg. 1540
NORTHROP GRUMMAN LITEF GMBH—See Northrop Grumman Corporation; *U.S. Public*, pg. 1540
NORTHROP GRUMMAN MISSION SYSTEMS EUROPE LIMITED—See Northrop Grumman Corporation; *U.S. Public*, pg. 1541
NORTHROP GRUMMAN-NORDEN SYSTEMS—See Northrop Grumman Corporation; *U.S. Public*, pg. 1540
NORTHROP GRUMMAN SPERRY MARINE GMBH & CO. KG—See Northrop Grumman Corporation; *U.S. Public*, pg. 1540
NORTHROP GRUMMAN SPERRY MARINE LIMITED—See Northrop Grumman Corporation; *U.S. Public*, pg. 1540
NORTHROP GRUMMAN-XETRON—See Northrop Grumman Corporation; *U.S. Public*, pg. 1540
NORTHSTAR MARINE ELECTRONICS—See Altor Equity Partners AB; *Int'l*, pg. 395
NOVATEL INC.—See Hexagon AB; *Int'l*, pg. 3368

NRPL AERO OY—See Goodwin PLC; *Int'l*, pg. 3042
OCEANSCIENCE GROUP, LTD.—See Teledyne Technologies Incorporated; *U.S. Public*, pg. 1992
ODYSSEY INDUSTRIES, LLC—See AIP, LLC; *U.S. Private*, pg. 133
OPTECH INC.—See Teledyne Technologies Incorporated; *U.S. Public*, pg. 1993
PACIFIC DESIGN TECHNOLOGIES, INC.—See AMETEK, Inc.; *U.S. Public*, pg. 116
PACIFIC SCIENTIFIC HTL—See Parker Hannifin Corporation; *U.S. Public*, pg. 1643
PALL GMBH—See Danaher Corporation; *U.S. Public*, pg. 629
PALMER ENVIRONMENTAL LIMITED—See Halma plc; *Int'l*, pg. 3232
PARKER HANNIFIN, CONTROL SYSTEMS DIVISION—See Parker Hannifin Corporation; *U.S. Public*, pg. 1649
PARKER HANNIFIN CORPORATION; *U.S. Public*, pg. 1640
PENNY & GILES AEROSPACE LTD.—See Curtiss-Wright Corporation; *U.S. Public*, pg. 611
PGA ELECTRONIC S.A.—See Astronics Corporation; *U.S. Public*, pg. 217
PHOTONIS USA, INC.—See Ardian SAS; *Int'l*, pg. 556
POINTER, INC.—See PowerFleet, Inc.; *U.S. Public*, pg. 1706
POINT MOBILE CO., LTD.—See BG T&A Co.; *Int'l*, pg. 1007
PRECISE TIME & FREQUENCY, LLC—See The LGL Group, Inc.; *U.S. Public*, pg. 2109
PRIORIA ROBOTICS, INC.; *U.S. Private*, pg. 3266
PROLEC LTD—See Carl Bennet AB; *Int'l*, pg. 1332
PYROBAN BENELUX B.V.—See Caterpillar, Inc.; *U.S. Public*, pg. 453
PYROBAN GROUP LIMITED—See Caterpillar, Inc.; *U.S. Public*, pg. 453
Q-FREE AMERICA LATINA LTDA.—See Guardian Capital Group Limited; *Int'l*, pg. 3170
Q/G HOLLAND B.V.—See Quad/Graphics, Inc.; *U.S. Public*, pg. 1744
QUAD/GRAPHICS EUROPE SP. Z O.O—See Quad/Graphics, Inc.; *U.S. Public*, pg. 1744
QUANERGY PERCEPTION TECHNOLOGIES, INC.—See Quanergy Systems, Inc.; *U.S. Public*, pg. 1749
QUANERGY SYSTEMS, INC.; *U.S. Public*, pg. 1749
QUANTEM FBO GROUP LLC; *U.S. Private*, pg. 3322
QWIP TECHNOLOGIES, INC.—See Cantronic Systems Inc.; *Int'l*, pg. 1300
RADIO FREQUENCY SIMULATION SYSTEMS, INC.—See Vadatech, Inc.; *U.S. Private*, pg. 4329
RADIO RESEARCH INSTRUMENT CO.; *U.S. Private*, pg. 3344
RANTEC MICROWAVE SYSTEMS, INC.; *U.S. Private*, pg. 3355
RAPTOR SCIENTIFIC LLC—See L Squared Capital Management LP; *U.S. Private*, pg. 2362
RAYMARINE INC.—See Teledyne Technologies Incorporated; *U.S. Public*, pg. 1993
RAYMARINE UK LTD.—See Teledyne Technologies Incorporated; *U.S. Public*, pg. 1993
RAYTHEON ANSCHUETZ GMBH SHANGHAI—See DMB Dr. Dieter Murmann Beteiligungsgesellschaft mbH; *Int'l*, pg. 2142
RAYTHEON AUSTRALIA PTY LTD—See RTX Corporation; *U.S. Public*, pg. 1824
RAYTHEON CANADA LIMITED—See RTX Corporation; *U.S. Public*, pg. 1824
RAYTHEON CANADA LIMITED - WATERLOO—See RTX Corporation; *U.S. Public*, pg. 1824
RAYTHEON COMPANY—See RTX Corporation; *U.S. Public*, pg. 1824
RAYTHEON DEUTSCHLAND GMBH—See RTX Corporation; *U.S. Public*, pg. 1824
RAYTHEON INTEGRATED DEFENSE SYSTEMS—See RTX Corporation; *U.S. Public*, pg. 1824
RAYTHEON INTERNATIONAL, INC.—See RTX Corporation; *U.S. Public*, pg. 1824
RAYTHEON SPACE & AIRBORNE SYSTEMS—See RTX Corporation; *U.S. Public*, pg. 1825
RAYTHEON SYSTEMS LIMITED—See RTX Corporation; *U.S. Public*, pg. 1825
RAYTHEON VISION SYSTEMS—See RTX Corporation; *U.S. Public*, pg. 1825
REAL-TIME LABORATORIES, LLC—See Elbit Systems Limited; *Int'l*, pg. 2344
REDWIRE CORPORATION; *U.S. Public*, pg. 1770
REDWIRE,LLC—See Redwire Corporation; *U.S. Public*, pg. 1771
RESEARCH ELECTRONICS INTERNATIONAL, LLC—See HEICO Corporation; *U.S. Public*, pg. 1020
RF IDEAS, INC.—See Roper Technologies, Inc.; *U.S. Public*, pg. 1812
ROCKWELL COLLINS AUSTRALIA PTY LIMITED—See RTX Corporation; *U.S. Public*, pg. 1823
ROCKWELL COLLINS CONTROL TECHNOLOGIES, LLC—See RTX Corporation; *U.S. Public*, pg. 1823
ROCKWELL COLLINS DEUTSCHLAND GMBH—See RTX Corporation; *U.S. Public*, pg. 1823
ROCKWELL COLLINS DO BRASIL LTDA.—See RTX Cor-

N.A.I.C.S. INDEX

334512 — AUTOMATIC ENVIRONME...

poration; *U.S. Public*, pg. 1823
ROGERSON KRATOS—See Rogerson Aircraft Corporation; *U.S. Private*, pg. 3472
ROSEMOUNT AEROSPACE INC.—See RTX Corporation; *U.S. Public*, pg. 1821
ROSEMOUNT AEROSPACE INC. - UNION—See RTX Corporation; *U.S. Public*, pg. 1822
ROSEMOUNT AEROSPACE LIMITED—See RTX Corporation; *U.S. Public*, pg. 1822
ROSEMOUNT TANK RADAR AB—See Emerson Electric Co.; *U.S. Public*, pg. 748
SAGEMCOM MAGYARORSZAG ELEKTRONIKAI KFT.—See Charterhouse Capital Partners LLP; *Int'l*, pg. 1456
SAM ELECTRONICS GMBH—See L3Harris Technologies, Inc.; *U.S. Public*, pg. 1284
SCANMATIC AS—See Arendals Fossekompani ASA; *Int'l*, pg. 559
SCHONSTEDT INSTRUMENT, CO.—See SPX Technologies, Inc.; *U.S. Public*, pg. 1922
SECO MANUFACTURING COMPANY INC—See Trimble, Inc.; *U.S. Public*, pg. 2191
SENSORS & SOFTWARE INC.—See SPX Technologies, Inc.; *U.S. Public*, pg. 1922
SENSORS UNLIMITED, INC.—See RTX Corporation; *U.S. Public*, pg. 1821
SEVENCS GMBH—See Teledyne Technologies Incorporated; *U.S. Public*, pg. 1992
SGX EUROPE SP. Z.O.O.—See Amphenol Corporation; *U.S. Public*, pg. 132
SGX SENSORTECH LTD.—See Baird Financial Group, Inc.; *U.S. Private*, pg. 453
SHENZHEN HUANGHE DIGITAL TECHNOLOGY CO. LTD.—See Cantronic Systems Inc.; *Int'l*, pg. 1300
SHOTOVER CAMERA SYSTEMS LP—See Helinet Aviation Services LLC; *U.S. Private*, pg. 1906
SHOTOVER SYSTEMS LTD.—See Helinet Aviation Services LLC; *U.S. Private*, pg. 1906
S+H SYSTEMTECHNIK GMBH—See Trimble, Inc.; *U.S. Public*, pg. 2191
SIGNIA AEROSPACE—See Arcline Investment Management LP; *U.S. Private*, pg. 315
SIMMONDS PRECISION PRODUCTS INC.—See RTX Corporation; *U.S. Public*, pg. 1822
SIRCHIE FINGERPRINT LABS; *U.S. Private*, pg. 3671
SL MONTEVIDEO TECHNOLOGY, INC.—See Steel Partners Holdings L.P.; *U.S. Public*, pg. 1943
SMART DESIGN TECHNOLOGY CO., LTD.—See Hotai Motor Co., Ltd.; *Int'l*, pg. 3487
SMT INDUSTRIES CO. LTD.—See EG Industries Berhad; *Int'l*, pg. 2322
SOCIETE D'ETUDES ET DE FABRICATIONS ELECTRONIQUES ET ELECTRIQUES—See Amphenol Corporation; *U.S. Public*, pg. 132
SODERN S.A.—See Airbus SE; *Int'l*, pg. 246
SONARTECH ATLAS PTY. LTD.—See Airbus SE; *Int'l*, pg. 242
SONATECH INC.—See Blue Wolf Capital Partners LLC; *U.S. Private*, pg. 594
SOUND OCEAN SYSTEMS, INC.—See Okeanus Science & Technology, LLC; *U.S. Private*, pg. 3007
SPARC RESEARCH LLC—See SPARC Holding Company; *U.S. Private*, pg. 3745
SPECTRONIC DENMARK A/S—See Advent International Corporation; *U.S. Private*, pg. 100
SPEKTRA AGRI SRL—See Trimble, Inc.; *U.S. Public*, pg. 2191
SPEKTRA S.P.A.—See Trimble, Inc.; *U.S. Public*, pg. 2191
SPERRY MARINE INC.—See Northrop Grumman Corporation; *U.S. Public*, pg. 1540
SUMMIT MACHINE, LLC—See Berkshire Hathaway Inc.; *U.S. Public*, pg. 315
SURVEILLANCE AUSTRALIA PTY LIMITED—See Advent International Corporation; *U.S. Private*, pg. 100
SYSCOR CONTROLS & AUTOMATION INC.—See Enbridge Inc.; *U.S. Public*, pg. 2397
SYSTRON-DONNER CORPORATION—See EMCORE Corporation; *U.S. Public*, pg. 739
TDG GERMANY GMBH—See TransDigm Group Incorporated; *U.S. Public*, pg. 2183
TECH SOURCE, INC.—See EIZO Corporation; *Int'l*, pg. 2337
TEKLA KOREA—See Trimble, Inc.; *U.S. Public*, pg. 2191
TEKLA (SEA) PTE. LTD.—See Trimble, Inc.; *U.S. Public*, pg. 2191
TELEDYNE BENTHOS, INC.—See Teledyne Technologies Incorporated; *U.S. Public*, pg. 1992
TELEDYNE BLUEVIEW, INC.—See Teledyne Technologies Incorporated; *U.S. Public*, pg. 1993
TELEDYNE CDL, INC.—See Teledyne Technologies Incorporated; *U.S. Public*, pg. 1993
TELEDYNE FLIR, LLC—See Teledyne Technologies Incorporated; *U.S. Public*, pg. 1993
TELEDYNE FRANCE SAS—See Teledyne Technologies Incorporated; *U.S. Public*, pg. 1993
TELEDYNE GAVIA EHF.—See Teledyne Technologies Incorporated; *U.S. Public*, pg. 1993
TELEDYNE JUDSON TECHNOLOGIES—See Teledyne Technologies Incorporated; *U.S. Public*, pg. 1995
TELEDYNE RD INSTRUMENTS, INC.—See Teledyne Technologies Incorporated; *U.S. Public*, pg. 1994
TELEDYNE RESON A/S—See Teledyne Technologies Incorporated; *U.S. Public*, pg. 1994
TELEDYNE TAPTONE—See Teledyne Technologies Incorporated; *U.S. Public*, pg. 1993
TELEDYNE TSS LIMITED—See Teledyne Technologies Incorporated; *U.S. Public*, pg. 1995
TELENAV DO BRASIL SERVICOS DE LOCALIZACAO LTDA.—See Telenav, Inc.; *U.S. Private*, pg. 3960
TELETRAC NAVMAN (UK) LTD.—See Vontier Corporation; *U.S. Public*, pg. 2309
TELETRAC NAVMAN US LTD.—See Vontier Corporation; *U.S. Public*, pg. 2309
TEXTRON SYSTEMS CORPORATION—See Textron Inc.; *U.S. Public*, pg. 2029
THALES-RAYTHEON SYSTEMS COMPANY LLC—See RTX Corporation; *U.S. Public*, pg. 1825
TIDELAND SIGNAL CORPORATION—See Xylem Inc.; *U.S. Public*, pg. 2395
TIE TIE IOT TECHNOLOGY CO., LTD.—See HBIS Group Co., Ltd.; *Int'l*, pg. 3296
TRAFFICMASTER LTD—See Vector Capital Management, L.P.; *U.S. Private*, pg. 4353
TRIMBLE AB—See Trimble, Inc.; *U.S. Public*, pg. 2191
TRIMBLE BRASIL SOLUCOES LTDA—See Trimble, Inc.; *U.S. Public*, pg. 2192
TRIMBLE DAYTON—See Trimble, Inc.; *U.S. Public*, pg. 2192
TRIMBLE EUROPE B.V.—See Trimble, Inc.; *U.S. Public*, pg. 2192
TRIMBLE FRANCE S.A.S.—See Trimble, Inc.; *U.S. Public*, pg. 2192
TRIMBLE GMBH—See Trimble, Inc.; *U.S. Public*, pg. 2192
TRIMBLE HUNGARY KFT—See Trimble, Inc.; *U.S. Public*, pg. 2192
TRIMBLE ITALIA SRL—See Trimble, Inc.; *U.S. Public*, pg. 2192
TRIMBLE JEAN GMBH—See Trimble, Inc.; *U.S. Public*, pg. 2192
TRIMBLE KAISERSLAUTERN GMBH—See Trimble, Inc.; *U.S. Public*, pg. 2192
TRIMBLE LOADRITE CHILE SPA—See Trimble, Inc.; *U.S. Public*, pg. 2192
TRIMBLE MEXICO S DE RL—See Trimble, Inc.; *U.S. Public*, pg. 2192
TRIMBLE MOBILITY SOLUTIONS INDIA LIMITED—See Trimble, Inc.; *U.S. Public*, pg. 2192
TRIMBLE NAVIGATION CHILE LIMITADA—See Trimble, Inc.; *U.S. Public*, pg. 2192
TRIMBLE NAVIGATION INDIA PVT LIMITED—See Trimble, Inc.; *U.S. Public*, pg. 2192
TRIMBLE NAVIGATION NEW ZEALAND LIMITED—See Trimble, Inc.; *U.S. Public*, pg. 2192
TRIMBLE RAILWAYS GMBH—See Trimble, Inc.; *U.S. Public*, pg. 2192
TRIMBLE RUS LLC—See Trimble, Inc.; *U.S. Public*, pg. 2192
TRIMBLE SOLUTIONS MALAYSIA SDN BHD—See Trimble, Inc.; *U.S. Public*, pg. 2193
TRIMBLE SOUTH AFRICA DISTRIBUTION HOLDINGS PTY LTD.—See Trimble, Inc.; *U.S. Public*, pg. 2193
TRIMBLE SWEDEN A.B.—See Trimble, Inc.; *U.S. Public*, pg. 2193
TRIMBLE TERRASAT GMBH—See Trimble, Inc.; *U.S. Public*, pg. 2193
TRIMBLE UK LIMITED—See Trimble, Inc.; *U.S. Public*, pg. 2193
TRUEPOINT TECHNOLOGY CO., LTD.—See Beijing BDStar Navigation Co., Ltd.; *Int'l*, pg. 946
TRUEPOSITION, INC.—See Liberty Broadband Corporation; *U.S. Public*, pg. 1311
TTF AEROSPACE, INC.—See Commercial Aircraft Interiors, LLC; *U.S. Public*, pg. 983
ULITEP, SPOL. S R.O.—See CEZ, a.s.; *Int'l*, pg. 1429
ULTRA ELECTRONICS CANADA INC.—See Advent International Corporation; *U.S. Private*, pg. 100
ULTRA ELECTRONICS FLIGHTLINE SYSTEMS—See Advent International Corporation; *U.S. Private*, pg. 101
ULTRA ELECTRONICS HERLEY—See Advent International Corporation; *U.S. Private*, pg. 101
ULTRA ELECTRONICS HOLDINGS LIMITED—See Advent International Corporation; *U.S. Private*, pg. 100
ULTRA ELECTRONICS OCEAN SYSTEMS INC.—See Advent International Corporation; *U.S. Private*, pg. 101
ULTRA ELECTRONICS SML TECHNOLOGIES LTD.—See Advent International Corporation; *U.S. Private*, pg. 101
UNDERSEA SENSOR SYSTEMS INC.—See Advent International Corporation; *U.S. Private*, pg. 101
UNIDUX ELECTRONICS LIMITED—See Avnet, Inc.; *U.S. Public*, pg. 251
UNIGRAPHIC, INC.—See Quad/Graphics, Inc.; *U.S. Public*, pg. 1745
UNITED GEAR & ASSEMBLY—See United Stars Inc.; *U.S. Private*, pg. 4298
UNITED TECHNOLOGIES CANADA, LTD.—See RTX Corporation; *U.S. Public*, pg. 1825
UNUSUAL MACHINES, INC.; *U.S. Public*, pg. 2263
VALENCE SURFACE TECHNOLOGIES LLC—See ATL Partners, LLC; *U.S. Private*, pg. 369
VALENCE SURFACE TECHNOLOGIES LLC—See British Columbia Investment Management Corp.; *U.S. Public*, pg. 1170
VEHICLE TRACKING SOLUTIONS, LLC; *U.S. Private*, pg. 4354
VELODYNE LIDAR, INC.—See Ouster, Inc.; *U.S. Public*, pg. 1624
VERIPOS INC.—See Hexagon AB; *Int'l*, pg. 3368
VIGILANT TECHNOLOGIES LTD—See BATM Advanced Communications Ltd.; *Int'l*, pg. 890
VIRGIN ORBIT HOLDINGS, INC.; *U.S. Private*, pg. 4387
WAVETRONIX CORP.—See Electro Technik Industries; *U.S. Private*, pg. 1354
WHEELS UP PARTNERS LLC—See Wheels Up Experience Inc.; *U.S. Public*, pg. 2366
WHITE'S ELECTRONICS; *U.S. Private*, pg. 4510
WOODWARD MPC.—See Woodward, Inc.; *U.S. Public*, pg. 2378
XI'AN SYSTEM SENSOR ELECTRONICS LTD.—See Honeywell International Inc.; *U.S. Public*, pg. 1049
XYLEM (NANJING) CO. LTD—See Xylem Inc.; *U.S. Public*, pg. 2396
XYLEM (SHANGHAI) TRADING CO., LTD.—See Xylem Inc.; *U.S. Public*, pg. 2396
YULISTA HOLDING, LLC—See Chiulista Services, Inc.; *U.S. Private*, pg. 887
ZETTLEX (UK) LIMITED—See Novanta Inc.; *U.S. Public*, pg. 1548

334512 — AUTOMATIC ENVIRONMENTAL CONTROL MANUFACTURING FOR RESIDENTIAL, COMMERCIAL, AND APPLIANCE USE

ACSL LTD; *Int'l*, pg. 117
ADVANCED THERMAL SCIENCES CORPORATION—See RTX Corporation; *U.S. Public*, pg. 1822
ADVANTAGE ENGINEERING INCORPORATED; *U.S. Private*, pg. 94
AGM CONTAINER CONTROLS, INC.; *U.S. Private*, pg. 128
AIRCOM PNEUMATIC GMBH—See Fukuda Corporation; *Int'l*, pg. 2839
ALL SENSORS GMBH—See Amphenol Corporation; *U.S. Public*, pg. 126
AMANO CORPORATION; *Int'l*, pg. 410
AM CONSERVATION GROUP, INC.—See Kohlberg & Company, LLC; *U.S. Private*, pg. 2337
AMERICAN AUTO-MATRIX INC.—See ABB Ltd.; *Int'l*, pg. 56
ANNAPURNA ELECTRONICS & SERVICES PVT. LTD.—See Annapurna Bhaskari Group; *Int'l*, pg. 473
APCOM INC.—See A. O. Smith Corporation; *U.S. Public*, pg. 11
ARCOPLAST INC.—See Germfree Laboratories Inc.; *U.S. Private*, pg. 1687
ARMSTRONG INTERNATIONAL PRIVATE LIMITED—See Armstrong International, Inc.; *U.S. Private*, pg. 331
ARMSTRONG SERVICE FRANCE S.A.—See Armstrong International, Inc.; *U.S. Private*, pg. 332
ARMSTRONG SERVICE, INC.—See Armstrong International, Inc.; *U.S. Private*, pg. 332
ARTUS SAS—See Parker Hannifin Corporation; *U.S. Public*, pg. 1643
ASIA NEO TECH INDUSTRIAL CO., LTD.; *Int'l*, pg. 613
ATS AUTOMATION INC.; *U.S. Private*, pg. 382
AUTOMATED LOGIC CORPORATION—See Carrier Global Corporation; *U.S. Public*, pg. 440
AUTOMATION COMPONENTS, INC.—See Arcline Investment Management LP; *U.S. Private*, pg. 313
AUTOMATION TECHNIQUE SA; *Int'l*, pg. 730
AUTRONICA FIRE AND SECURITY AS—See Carrier Global Corporation; *U.S. Public*, pg. 440
BAY ADVANCED TECHNOLOGIES LLC; *U.S. Private*, pg. 491
CAREL ACR SYSTEMS INDIA PVT. LTD.—See Carel Industries S.p.A.; *Int'l*, pg. 1324
CAREL ASIA LTD.—See Carel Industries S.p.A.; *Int'l*, pg. 1324
CAREL AUSTRALIA PTY LTD—See Carel Industries S.p.A.; *Int'l*, pg. 1324
CAREL CONTROLS IBERICA SL—See Carel Industries S.p.A.; *Int'l*, pg. 1324
CAREL CONTROLS SOUTH AFRICA PTY LTD—See Carel Industries S.p.A.; *Int'l*, pg. 1324
CAREL DEUTSCHLAND GMBH—See Carel Industries S.p.A.; *Int'l*, pg. 1324
CAREL FRANCE SAS—See Carel Industries S.p.A.; *Int'l*, pg. 1324
CAREL JAPAN CO., LTD.—See Carel Industries S.p.A.; *Int'l*, pg. 1324
CAREL MEXICANA S. DE RL. DE CV.—See Carel Industries S.p.A.; *Int'l*, pg. 1324
CAREL MIDDLE EAST DWC-CLC—See Carel Industries S.p.A.; *Int'l*, pg. 1324
CAREL NORDIC AB—See Carel Industries S.p.A.; *Int'l*, pg. 1324
CAREL SUD AMERICA INSTRUMENTACAO ELETRONICA

334512 — AUTOMATIC ENVIRONME...

LTDA—See Carel Industries S.p.A.; *Int'l*, pg. 1324
CAREL (THAILAND) CO. LTD.—See Carel Industries S.p.A.; *Int'l*, pg. 1324
CAREL UK LTD.—See Carel Industries S.p.A.; *Int'l*, pg. 1324
CAREL UKRAINE LLC—See Carel Industries S.p.A.; *Int'l*, pg. 1324
CARNES COMPANY INCORPORATED; *U.S. Private*, pg. 766
CHANNEL PRODUCTS, INC.—See Weinberg Capital Group, Inc.; *U.S. Private*, pg. 4471
CLIMALEVEL ENERGIESYSTEME GMBH; *Int'l*, pg. 1659
COMMAX CO., LTD.; *Int'l*, pg. 1714
COMRADE APPLIANCES LIMITED; *Int'l*, pg. 1761
COMVERGE, INC.—See Itron, Inc.; *U.S. Public*, pg. 1175
COPLUS INC.; *Int'l*, pg. 1793
CORMETECH, INC.; *U.S. Private*, pg. 1050
C.R.C. S.R.L.—See Carel Industries S.p.A.; *Int'l*, pg. 1324
CYLON CONTROLS LTD.—See ABB Ltd.; *Int'l*, pg. 56
CYLON CONTROLS (UK) LIMITED—See ABB Ltd.; *Int'l*, pg. 56
CYLON ENERGY INC.—See ABB Ltd.; *Int'l*, pg. 56
CYLON GMBH—See ABB Ltd.; *Int'l*, pg. 56
DAIO ENGINEERING CO., LTD.—See Daio Paper Corporation; *Int'l*, pg. 1939
DAIWA ENERGY CO., LTD.—See Daiwa House Industry Co., Ltd.; *Int'l*, pg. 1945
DALIAN HAOSEN EQUIPMENT MANUFACTURING CO., LTD.; *Int'l*, pg. 1951
DANFOSS AB—See Danfoss A/S; *Int'l*, pg. 1959
DANFOSS A/S APPLIANCE CONTROLS DIV.—See Danfoss A/S; *Int'l*, pg. 1959
DANFOSS A/S BUILDING CONTROLS DIV.—See Danfoss A/S; *Int'l*, pg. 1959
DANFOSS A/S - COMFORT CONTROLS DIVISION—See Danfoss A/S; *Int'l*, pg. 1959
DANFOSS A/S REFRIGERATION & A/C CONTROLS DIVISION—See Danfoss A/S; *Int'l*, pg. 1959
DANFOSS BURNER COMPONENTS DIVISION—See Danfoss A/S; *Int'l*, pg. 1960
DANFOSS RANDALL LIMITED—See Danfoss A/S; *Int'l*, pg. 1961
DANFOSS S.R.L.—See Danfoss A/S; *Int'l*, pg. 1961
DENSO AIR SYSTEMS CORPORATION—See Denso Corporation; *Int'l*, pg. 2029
DENSO WAVE INC.—See Denso Corporation; *Int'l*, pg. 2032
DERLITE CO LTD.—See Active Energy Group plc; *Int'l*, pg. 120
DESIGN ENVIROMENTS, INC.—See Blackford Capital LLC; *U.S. Private*, pg. 574
DINEX, INC.—See Fuji Media Holdings, Inc.; *Int'l*, pg. 2813
DONGFANG ELECTRONICS CO., LTD.; *Int'l*, pg. 2166
DURR AIS S.A. DE C.V.—See Durr AG; *Int'l*, pg. 2230
DURR ANLAGENBAU GMBH—See Durr AG; *Int'l*, pg. 2231
DURR BRASIL LTDA.—See Durr AG; *Int'l*, pg. 2231
DURR DE MEXICO S.A. DE C.V.—See Durr AG; *Int'l*, pg. 2232
DURR LTD.—See Durr AG; *Int'l*, pg. 2231
DURRPOL SP.Z.O.O.—See Durr AG; *Int'l*, pg. 2232
DY AMERICA INC.—See DY Corporation; *Int'l*, pg. 2237
EARTH ENVIRONMENTAL SERVICE CO., LTD.—See Earth Corporation; *Int'l*, pg. 2268
EATON GMBH—See Eaton Corporation plc; *Int'l*, pg. 2281
EBARA DENSAN (QINGDAO) TECHNOLOGY CO., LTD.—See Ebara Corporation; *Int'l*, pg. 2283
EFORT INTELLIGENT EQUIPMENT CO., LTD.; *Int'l*, pg. 2321
EINDEC CORPORATION LIMITED; *Int'l*, pg. 2332
ELCAT INC.; *U.S. Private*, pg. 1350
ELECTROFILM MANUFACTURING COMPANY LLC—See ITT Inc.; *U.S. Public*, pg. 1177
ELODRIVE GMBH; *Int'l*, pg. 2368
ELSTER S.R.O.—See Honeywell International Inc.; *U.S. Public*, pg. 1047
EMERSON APPLIANCE CONTROLS—See Emerson Electric Co.; *U.S. Public*, pg. 743
EMERSON CLIMATE TECHNOLOGIES GMBH—See Emerson Electric Co.; *U.S. Public*, pg. 743
EMERSON CLIMATE TECHNOLOGIES RETAIL SOLUTIONS, INC.—See Emerson Electric Co.; *U.S. Public*, pg. 744
EMERSON PROCESS MANAGEMENT AS—See Emerson Electric Co.; *U.S. Public*, pg. 746
EMERSON PROCESS MANAGEMENT GMBH & CO. OHG—See Emerson Electric Co.; *U.S. Public*, pg. 746
ENALASYS CORP.; *U.S. Private*, pg. 1389
ENGINEERED SPECIALTY PRODUCTS, INC.; *U.S. Private*, pg. 1398
ESPEC ENVIRONMENTAL EQUIPMENT (SHANGHAI) CO., LTD.—See ESPEC Corp.; *Int'l*, pg. 2505
ESPEC KOREA CORP.—See ESPEC Corp.; *Int'l*, pg. 2505
ESPEC NORTH AMERICA INC.—See ESPEC Corp.; *Int'l*, pg. 2505
EUCLID LABS S.R.L.; *Int'l*, pg. 2525
EUROPE ENVIRONMENT S.A.—See Europlasma SA; *Int'l*, pg. 2557
EVA-DRY; *U.S. Private*, pg. 1434
EVER SOURCE SCIENCE & TECHNOLOGY DEVELOPMENT GROUP CO., LIMITED—See CHYY Development Group Limited; *Int'l*, pg. 1600
EVOQUA WATER TECHNOLOGIES—See Xylem Inc.; *U.S. Public*, pg. 2393
FASTEMS OY AB—See Helvar Merca Oy AB; *Int'l*, pg. 3339
FESTO AB—See Festo AG & Co. KG; *Int'l*, pg. 2646
FESTO AS—See Festo AG & Co. KG; *Int'l*, pg. 2647
FESTO B.V.—See Festo AG & Co. KG; *Int'l*, pg. 2647
FESTO CO., LTD.—See Festo AG & Co. KG; *Int'l*, pg. 2647
FESTO D.O.O. LJUBLJANA—See Festo AG & Co. KG; *Int'l*, pg. 2648
FESTO INC.—See Festo AG & Co. KG; *Int'l*, pg. 2647
FESTO K.K.—See Festo AG & Co. KG; *Int'l*, pg. 2647
FESTO KOREA CO. LTD.—See Festo AG & Co. KG; *Int'l*, pg. 2647
FESTO LIMITED—See Festo AG & Co. KG; *Int'l*, pg. 2647
FESTO PNEUMATIC S.A.—See Festo AG & Co. KG; *Int'l*, pg. 2647
FESTO PNEUMATIC S.A.—See Festo AG & Co. KG; *Int'l*, pg. 2647
FESTO PTE. LTD.—See Festo AG & Co. KG; *Int'l*, pg. 2647
FESTO (PTY.) LTD.—See Festo AG & Co. KG; *Int'l*, pg. 2646
FESTO SDN. BHD.—See Festo AG & Co. KG; *Int'l*, pg. 2648
FESTO S.I.A.—See Festo AG & Co. KG; *Int'l*, pg. 2648
FESTO SPOL. S.R.O.—See Festo AG & Co. KG; *Int'l*, pg. 2648
FESTO SP.Z.O.O.—See Festo AG & Co. KG; *Int'l*, pg. 2648
FESTO S.R.L.—See Festo AG & Co. KG; *Int'l*, pg. 2648
FESTO U.A.B.—See Festo AG & Co. KG; *Int'l*, pg. 2648
FIELDWARE, LLC; *U.S. Private*, pg. 1504
GENBYTE TECHNOLOGY, INC.; *Int'l*, pg. 2916
GENERAL MONITORS IRELAND LIMITED—See MSA Safety Incorporated; *U.S. Public*, pg. 1481
GENTHERM MEDICAL, LLC—See Gentherm Incorporated; *U.S. Public*, pg. 932
GREATECH INTEGRATION (M) SDN. BHD.—See Greatech Technology Berhad; *Int'l*, pg. 3067
GROENEVELD-BEKA CANADA INC.—See The Timken Company; *U.S. Public*, pg. 2132
GROENEVELD-BEKA GMBH—See The Timken Company; *U.S. Public*, pg. 2132
GROENEVELD UK LIMITED—See The Timken Company; *U.S. Public*, pg. 2132
HACH SALES & SERVICE CANADA LTD.—See Danaher Corporation; *U.S. Public*, pg. 627
HART & COOLEY, INC.—See Egeria Capital Management B.V.; *Int'l*, pg. 2323
HEBEI SAILHERO ENVIRONMENTAL PROTECTION HIGH-TECH CO., LTD.; *Int'l*, pg. 3306
HELEN OF TROY CANADA, INC.—See Helen of Troy Limited; *Int'l*, pg. 3328
HELEN OF TROY L.P.—See Helen of Troy Limited; *Int'l*, pg. 3328
HERAEUS ELECTRO-NITE CO., LLC—See Heraeus Holding GmbH; *Int'l*, pg. 3357
HERAEUS ELECTRO-NITE—See Heraeus Holding GmbH; *Int'l*, pg. 3357
HOERBIGER-ORIGA CORP.—See Hoerbiger Holding AG; *Int'l*, pg. 3440
HONEYWELL AUTOMATION & CONTROL SOLUTIONS—See Honeywell International Inc.; *U.S. Public*, pg. 1047
HONEYWELL ELECTRONIC MATERIALS—See Honeywell International Inc.; *U.S. Public*, pg. 1047
HONEYWELL ENVIRONMENTAL & COMBUSTION CONTROLS—See Honeywell International Inc.; *U.S. Public*, pg. 1048
HONEYWELL INTERNATIONAL INC.; *U.S. Public*, pg. 1046
HONEYWELL PROCESS SOLUTIONS—See Honeywell International Inc.; *U.S. Public*, pg. 1049
HONEYWELL SENSORS, INC.—See Honeywell International Inc.; *U.S. Public*, pg. 1051
HOSOKAWA MICRON B.V.—See Hosokawa Micron Corporation; *Int'l*, pg. 3486
HOSOKAWA MICRON GMBH—See Hosokawa Micron Corporation; *Int'l*, pg. 3486
HOSOKAWA MICRON LTD.—See Hosokawa Micron Corporation; *Int'l*, pg. 3486
HOSOKAWA MICRON LTD.—See Hosokawa Micron Corporation; *Int'l*, pg. 3486
HS TECHNOLOGY CO., LTD.—See DY Corporation; *Int'l*, pg. 2237
HYMSON LASER TECHNOLOGY GROUP CO LTD; *Int'l*, pg. 3549
ICEMENERG SERVICE SA—See CNTEE TRANSELECTRICA SA; *Int'l*, pg. 1678
INNOVATIVE CLIMATIC TECHNOLOGIES CORP.; *U.S. Public*, pg. 1126
INTEGRATED CONTROL SYSTEMS INC.; *U.S. Private*, pg. 2099
INTEGRATED CONTROL SYSTEMS INC.—See Integrated Control Systems Inc.; *U.S. Private*, pg. 2099
INTEGRATED CONTROL SYSTEMS INC.—See Integrated Control Systems Inc.; *U.S. Private*, pg. 2099
JACKSON SYSTEMS, LLC; *U.S. Private*, pg. 2178
JETTER AG—See Bucher Industries AG; *Int'l*, pg. 1207
JTOP CO., LTD.—See EDION Corporation; *Int'l*, pg. 2310
KAZ CANADA, INC.—See Helen of Troy Limited; *Int'l*, pg. 3329

CORPORATE AFFILIATIONS

KAZ CONSUMER PRODUCTS, S.L.U.—See Helen of Troy Limited; *Int'l*, pg. 3329
KAZ EUROPE SARL—See Helen of Troy Limited; *Int'l*, pg. 3329
KAZ FRANCE SAS—See Helen of Troy Limited; *Int'l*, pg. 3329
KAZ HAUSGERATE GMBH—See Helen of Troy Limited; *Int'l*, pg. 3329
KAZ HOME APPLIANCE (SHENZHEN) COMPANY LIMITED—See Helen of Troy Limited; *Int'l*, pg. 3329
KAZ USA, INC.—See Helen of Troy Limited; *Int'l*, pg. 3329
LAVO GALLERY SDN. BHD.—See Focus Dynamics Group Berhad; *Int'l*, pg. 2719
LINK ELECTRIC & SAFETY CONTROL CO.; *U.S. Private*, pg. 2461
LORD & COMPANY TECHNOLOGIES, INC.—See Sentinel Capital Partners, L.L.C.; *U.S. Private*, pg. 3609
LOVE CONTROLS CORPORATION—See Arcline Investment Management LP; *U.S. Private*, pg. 313
MARATHON PRODUCTS, INC.—See Harbour Group Industries, Inc.; *U.S. Private*, pg. 1861
MARCHI THERMAL SYSTEMS, INC.—See Ultra Clean Holdings, Inc.; *U.S. Public*, pg. 2223
MAXITROL COMPANY; *U.S. Private*, pg. 2619
MERRICK ENVIRONMENTAL TECHNOLOGIES—See Tannehill International Industries; *U.S. Private*, pg. 3931
MERTIK MAXITROL GMBH & CO., KG—See Maxitrol Company; *U.S. Private*, pg. 2619
MUELLER SV, LTD.—See Mueller Water Products, Inc.; *U.S. Public*, pg. 1485
NOVA COMET S.R.L.—See Aalberts N.V.; *Int'l*, pg. 35
NOVAR GMBH—See Honeywell International Inc.; *U.S. Public*, pg. 1051
NUVVE HOLDING CORP.; *U.S. Public*, pg. 1556
OHGA ELECTRONICS CO., LTD.—See Holy Stone Enterprise Co., Ltd.; *Int'l*, pg. 3454
OOO FESTO-RF—See Festo AG & Co. KG; *Int'l*, pg. 2648
PCB PIEZOTRONICS GMBH—See Amphenol Corporation; *U.S. Public*, pg. 132
PELIA GEBAEUDESYSTEME GMBH—See 3U Holding AG; *Int'l*, pg. 10
PHOENIX CONTROLS CORPORATION—See Honeywell International Inc.; *U.S. Public*, pg. 1047
PHONETICS, INC.; *U.S. Private*, pg. 3174
PILOMAT S.R.L.—See Hormann KG Verkaufsgesellschaft; *Int'l*, pg. 3481
PRENTKE ROMICH COMPANY; *U.S. Private*, pg. 3252
REED NATIONAL COMPANY—See Mestek, Inc.; *U.S. Public*, pg. 1426
RESIDENTIAL CONTROL SYSTEMS, INC.—See Universal Electronics, Inc.; *U.S. Public*, pg. 2255
R. L. STONE COMPANY, INC.—See Applied Industrial Technologies, Inc.; *U.S. Public*, pg. 171
ROBERTSHAW CONTROLS COMPANY—See One Rock Capital Partners, LLC; *U.S. Private*, pg. 3023
ROCKWELL AUTOMATION (CHINA) COMPANY LIMITED—See Rockwell Automation, Inc.; *U.S. Public*, pg. 1805
ROCKWELL AUTOMATION G.M.B.H.—See Rockwell Automation, Inc.; *U.S. Public*, pg. 1806
ROCKWELL AUTOMATION S.R.O.—See Rockwell Automation, Inc.; *U.S. Public*, pg. 1806
RUSKIN COMPANY—See Canada Pension Plan Investment Board; *Int'l*, pg. 1281
SENSATA TECHNOLOGIES AUTOMOTIVE SENSORS (SHANGHAI) CO., LTD.—See Sensata Technologies Holding plc; *U.S. Public*, pg. 1865
SENSATA TECHNOLOGIES GERMANY GMBH—See Sensata Technologies Holding plc; *U.S. Public*, pg. 1865
SENSATA TECHNOLOGIES HOLLAND B.V.—See Sensata Technologies Holding plc; *U.S. Public*, pg. 1865
SENSATA TECHNOLOGIES KOREA LIMITED—See Sensata Technologies Holding plc; *U.S. Public*, pg. 1865
SENSATA TECHNOLOGIES MALAYSIA SDN. BHD.—See Sensata Technologies Holding plc; *U.S. Public*, pg. 1865
SENSATA TECHNOLOGIES SENSORES E CONTROLES DO BRASIL LTDA.—See Sensata Technologies Holding plc; *U.S. Public*, pg. 1865
SENSATA TECHNOLOGIES SINGAPORE PTE. LTD.—See Sensata Technologies Holding plc; *U.S. Public*, pg. 1865
SENSATA TECHNOLOGIES TAIWAN CO., LTD.—See Sensata Technologies Holding plc; *U.S. Public*, pg. 1866
SENSATRONICS, LLC; *U.S. Private*, pg. 3607
SENSCIENT INC.; *U.S. Private*, pg. 3607
SERES ENVIRONNEMENT S.A.S—See Electricite de France S.A.; *Int'l*, pg. 2350
SHENZHEN HW AUTOMATION EQUIPMENT CO., LTD.—See CSG Smart Science & Technology Co., Ltd.; *Int'l*, pg. 1865
SIGMATRON US - WEST COAST—See SigmaTron International, Inc.; *U.S. Public*, pg. 1877
SINGLE TEMPERIERTECHNIK GMBH—See Arbonia AG; *Int'l*, pg. 537
SITELOGIQ GOVERNMENT SOLUTIONS LLC—See Brookfield Corporation; *Int'l*, pg. 1182
STEMMER IMAGING AG—See MiddleGround Management, LP; *U.S. Private*, pg. 2712
TECHNICAL MARKETING MANUFACTURING INC.—See

N.A.I.C.S. INDEX

334513 — INSTRUMENTS AND REL...

Hamilton Robinson LLC; *U.S. Private*, pg. 1848
TECHNOLOG LIMITED—See Roper Technologies, Inc.; *U.S. Public*, pg. 1813
TGA INDUSTRIES LIMITED—See Danaher Corporation; *U.S. Public*, pg. 631
THERM-O-DISC, INCORPORATED—See One Rock Capital Partners, LLC; *U.S. Private*, pg. 3023
VERANTIS CORPORATION—See Tanglewood Investments Inc.; *U.S. Private*, pg. 3931
VIET AN ENVIRONMENT TECHNOLOGY JOINT STOCK COMPANY—See Endress+Hauser (International) Holding AG; *Int'l*, pg. 2409
VISHAY PRECISION GROUP CANADA ULC—See Vishay Precision Group, Inc.; *U.S. Public*, pg. 2303
VOCOLLECT, INC.—See Honeywell International Inc.; *U.S. Public*, pg. 1050
WATLOW WINONA, INC.—See Tinicum Enterprises, Inc.; *U.S. Private*, pg. 4175
WATTMASTER CONTROLS, INC.—See AAON, Inc.; *U.S. Public*, pg. 12
WELLINGTON DRIVE TECHNOLOGIES PTE LTD—See AoFrio Limited; *Int'l*, pg. 487
WELLINGTON MOTOR TECNOLOJILERI SAN TIC LTD STI—See AoFrio Limited; *Int'l*, pg. 487
WGL ENERGY SERVICES, INC.—See AltaGas Ltd.; *Int'l*, pg. 384
WHITE-RODGERS—See Emerson Electric Co.; *U.S. Public*, pg. 744
WOODWARD CONTROLS (SUZHOU) CO., LTD.—See Woodward, Inc.; *U.S. Public*, pg. 2378
WOODWARD (TIANJIN) CONTROLS COMPANY LIMITED—See Woodward, Inc.; *U.S. Public*, pg. 2377
YANTAI EBARA AIR CONDITIONING EQUIPMENT CO., LTD.—See Ebara Corporation; *Int'l*, pg. 2284

334513 — INSTRUMENTS AND RELATED PRODUCTS MANUFACTURING FOR MEASURING, DISPLAYING, AND CONTROLLING INDUSTRIAL PROCESS VARIABLES

A1-CBISS LIMITED—See Diploma PLC; *Int'l*, pg. 2128
AAGE HEMPEL GROUP—See Grupo Arbulu S.L.; *Int'l*, pg. 3120
ABB ENGINEERING (SHANGHAI) LTD.—See ABB Ltd.; *Int'l*, pg. 49
ABB INC. - AUTOMATION TECHNOLOGIES INSTRUMENTATION PRODUCTS—See ABB Ltd.; *Int'l*, pg. 51
ABB INC. - AUTOMATION TECHNOLOGIES—See ABB Ltd.; *Int'l*, pg. 51
ABB LTD.—See ABB Ltd.; *Int'l*, pg. 53
ABB LTD. - STONEHOUSE—See ABB Ltd.; *Int'l*, pg. 53
ABB SACE S.P.A.—See ABB Ltd.; *Int'l*, pg. 54
ACCUMETRICS, INC.—See Amphenol Corporation; *U.S. Public*, pg. 130
ACCUSONIC TECHNOLOGIES—See IDEX Corp; *U.S. Public*, pg. 1089
ACEZ INSTRUMENTS PTE. LTD.; *Int'l*, pg. 102
ACRISON, INC.; *U.S. Private*, pg. 65
ACROS ORGANICS B.V.B.A.—See Thermo Fisher Scientific Inc.; *U.S. Public*, pg. 2145
ACT TEST PANELS, INC.—See Talon LLC; *U.S. Private*, pg. 3927
ADCOLE FAR EAST LTD.—See Artemis Capital Partners Management Co., LLC; *U.S. Private*, pg. 340
ADCOLE GMBH—See Artemis Capital Partners Management Co., LLC; *U.S. Private*, pg. 340
ADS LLC—See IDEX Corp; *U.S. Public*, pg. 1089
ADVANCED CAE, INC.—See Advanced Holdings Ltd.; *Int'l*, pg. 159
ADVANCED CAE LTD.—See Advanced Holdings Ltd.; *Int'l*, pg. 159
ADVANCED CAE PTE. LTD.—See Advanced Holdings Ltd.; *Int'l*, pg. 159
ADVANCED CAE SAUDI ARABIA COMPANY LTD.—See Advanced Holdings Ltd.; *Int'l*, pg. 159
ADVANCED CONTROLS CO., LTD.—See Advanced Holdings Ltd.; *Int'l*, pg. 159
ADVANCED CONTROLS PTE. LTD. - BEIJING REPRESENTATIVE OFFICE—See Advanced Holdings Ltd.; *Int'l*, pg. 159
ADVANCED CONTROLS PTE. LTD.—See Advanced Holdings Ltd.; *Int'l*, pg. 159
ADVANCED TEMPERATURE TEST SYSTEMS GMBH—See FormFactor, Inc.; *U.S. Public*, pg. 868
ADVANSOR A/S—See Dover Corporation; *U.S. Public*, pg. 678
ADVANTECH CZECH S.R.O.—See Advantech Co., Ltd.; *Int'l*, pg. 164
ADVANTEST CORPORATION - GUNMA FACTORY 2—See Advantest Corporation; *Int'l*, pg. 166
ADVANTEST CORPORATION - GUNMA FACTORY—See Advantest Corporation; *Int'l*, pg. 165
ADVANTEST EUROPE R&D S.A.R.L.—See Advantest Corporation; *Int'l*, pg. 165
ADVANTEST (MALAYSIA) SDN. BHD.—See Advantest Corporation; *Int'l*, pg. 165

ADVANTEST (SINGAPORE) PTE. LTD.—See Advantest Corporation; *Int'l*, pg. 165
AEROTECH LTD—See Aerotech Inc.; *U.S. Private*, pg. 119
AFRICAN RESONANCE BUSINESS SOLUTIONS PROPRIETARY LIMITED—See Capital Appreciation Ltd.; *Int'l*, pg. 1309
AFS FORECOURT SOLUTIONS PROPRIETARY LIMITED—See Vontier Corporation; *U.S. Public*, pg. 2308
AGGREKO UK LTD.—See I Squared Capital Advisors (US) LLC; *U.S. Private*, pg. 2021
AIR COMM CORPORATION—See Arcline Investment Management LP; *U.S. Private*, pg. 312
AIRKIT S.A.; *Int'l*, pg. 248
AIROIL FLAREGAS PVT. LTD. - INDRAD WORKS—See Airoil Flaregas Pvt. Ltd.; *Int'l*, pg. 248
ALBERT LABS INTERNATIONAL CORP.; *Int'l*, pg. 297
ALICAT SCIENTIFIC, INC.—See Halma plc; *Int'l*, pg. 3231
ALICAT SCIENTIFIC INDIA PRIVATE LIMITED—See Halma plc; *Int'l*, pg. 3230
ALICONA CORPORATION—See Bruker Corporation; *U.S. Public*, pg. 404
ALICONA GMBH—See Bruker Corporation; *U.S. Public*, pg. 404
ALICONA IMAGING GMBH—See Bruker Corporation; *U.S. Public*, pg. 404
ALICONA KOREA PCIFIC LTD.—See Bruker Corporation; *U.S. Public*, pg. 404
ALICONA SARL—See Bruker Corporation; *U.S. Public*, pg. 404
ALICONA S.R.L.—See Bruker Corporation; *U.S. Public*, pg. 404
ALICONA UK LIMITED—See Bruker Corporation; *U.S. Public*, pg. 404
ALLMESS GMBH—See Itron, Inc.; *U.S. Public*, pg. 1175
ALPHA SPECIALTY PRODUCTS INC.; *U.S. Private*, pg. 199
ALPHA TECHNOLOGIES SERVICES LLC—See Roper Technologies, Inc.; *U.S. Public*, pg. 1811
AMANO CORPORATION - TSUKUI FACILITY—See Amano Corporation; *Int'l*, pg. 410
AMANO MALAYSIA SDN.BHD.—See Amano Corporation; *Int'l*, pg. 410
AMANO TIME & PARKING SPAIN, S.A.—See Amano Corporation; *Int'l*, pg. 411
AMERICAN AIRES, INC.; *Int'l*, pg. 422
AMERICAN AUTOGARD LLC—See Zurn Elkay Water Solutions Corporation; *U.S. Public*, pg. 2412
AMERICAN TERATEC, INC.—See Makke LLC; *U.S. Private*, pg. 2556
AMERIDRIVES COUPLINGS—See Regal Rexnord Corporation; *U.S. Public*, pg. 1772
AMETEK DREXELBROOK—See AMETEK, Inc.; *U.S. Public*, pg. 117
AMETEK ELECTRONIC INSTRUMENTS GROUP—See AMETEK, Inc.; *U.S. Public*, pg. 116
AMETEK INSTRUMENTOS, S.L.—See AMETEK, Inc.; *U.S. Public*, pg. 120
AMETEK LAND, INC.—See AMETEK, Inc.; *U.S. Public*, pg. 118
AMETEK POWER INSTRUMENTS—See AMETEK, Inc.; *U.S. Public*, pg. 117
AMETEK SOLARTRON ISA—See AMETEK, Inc.; *U.S. Public*, pg. 117
AMOT CONTROLS CORPORATION—See Roper Technologies, Inc.; *U.S. Public*, pg. 1810
AMOT CONTROLS GMBH—See Roper Technologies, Inc.; *U.S. Public*, pg. 1810
AMTECH WORLD CORPORATION—See Roper Technologies, Inc.; *U.S. Public*, pg. 1810
ANALOG DEVICES INDIA PVT. LTD.—See Analog Devices, Inc.; *U.S. Public*, pg. 134
ANALYTICAL INDUSTRIES INC.—See Battery Ventures, L.P.; *U.S. Public*, pg. 489
ANASIA - EGYPT (S.A.E.)—See Endress+Hauser (International) Holding AG; *Int'l*, pg. 2405
ANDERSON INSTRUMENT CO., INC.—See Fortive Corporation; *U.S. Public*, pg. 870
ANDRITZ SAVONLINNA WORKS OY—See ANDRITZ AG; *Int'l*, pg. 454
ANDRITZ SEPARATION ITALY S.R.L.—See ANDRITZ AG; *Int'l*, pg. 454
ANDRITZ SEPARATION & PUMP TECHNOLOGIES INDIA PRIVATE LIMITED—See ANDRITZ AG; *Int'l*, pg. 455
ANHUI LANDUN PHOTOELECTRON CO., LTD.; *Int'l*, pg. 469
APATOR POWOGAZ S.A.—See Apator S.A.; *Int'l*, pg. 501
APEX INSTRUMENTS, INC.; *U.S. Private*, pg. 292
APPLITEK NV/SA; *Int'l*, pg. 521
ARABIAN METERING COMPANY—See Itron, Inc.; *U.S. Public*, pg. 1175
ARABI GULF SERVICES & INDUSTRIAL SUPPLIES CO.—See Arabi Holding Group Company K.S.C.C.; *Int'l*, pg. 532
ARCELORMITTAL RODANGE & SCHIFFLANGE S.A.—See ArcelorMittal S.A.; *Int'l*, pg. 545
ARGA CONTROLS, INC.—See Electro Switch Corporation; *U.S. Private*, pg. 1353

ARIMA DISPLAY CORPORATION—See Arima Photovoltaic & Optical Corp.; *Int'l*, pg. 565
ARISAWA MANUFACTURING CO., LTD. - 3D MATERIAL DIVISION—See Arisawa Manufacturing Co., Ltd.; *Int'l*, pg. 565
ARISAWA MANUFACTURING CO., LTD. - CIRCUIT MATERIAL DIVISION—See Arisawa Manufacturing Co., Ltd.; *Int'l*, pg. 565
ARISAWA MANUFACTURING CO., LTD. - ELECTRICAL INSULATING & COMPOSITE MATERIAL DIVISION—See Arisawa Manufacturing Co., Ltd.; *Int'l*, pg. 565
ARISAWA MANUFACTURING CO., LTD. - ELECTRONIC MATERIAL DIVISION—See Arisawa Manufacturing Co., Ltd.; *Int'l*, pg. 565
ARISAWA MANUFACTURING CO., LTD. - NAKADAHARA FACTORY—See Arisawa Manufacturing Co., Ltd.; *Int'l*, pg. 565
ARISAWA MANUFACTURING CO., LTD. - NAKADAHARA-NISHI FACTORY—See Arisawa Manufacturing Co., Ltd.; *Int'l*, pg. 566
ARIS MAURITIUS LIMITED—See Endress+Hauser (International) Holding AG; *Int'l*, pg. 2405
ARIS TRADING LTD.—See Endress+Hauser (International) Holding AG; *Int'l*, pg. 2405
ARIZONA INSTRUMENT LLC; *U.S. Private*, pg. 324
ARPLAMA N.V.; *Int'l*, pg. 578
ARYA INSTRUMENT CO.—See Endress+Hauser (International) Holding AG; *Int'l*, pg. 2405
ASEA BROWN BOVERI LTD.—See ABB Ltd.; *Int'l*, pg. 55
ASTEX GMBH—See MKS Instruments, Inc.; *U.S. Public*, pg. 1452
A-TECH CORP.; *U.S. Private*, pg. 22
ATI INDUSTRIAL AUTOMATION, INC.—See Novanta Inc.; *U.S. Public*, pg. 1548
AURORA SOLAR TECHNOLOGIES INC.; *Int'l*, pg. 714
AUTOGARD ASIA PACIFIC PTY LTD—See Zurn Elkay Water Solutions Corporation; *U.S. Public*, pg. 2412
AUTOMATED MEASUREMENT & CONTROL CORPORATION—See Makke LLC; *U.S. Private*, pg. 2556
AUTOMATIKOS IRANGA UAB—See Harju Elekter AS; *Int'l*, pg. 3277
AUTOMATION & CONTROLS ENGINEERING LTD.; *Int'l*, pg. 730
AUTOMATION SOLUTIONS LTD.—See Endress+Hauser (International) Holding AG; *Int'l*, pg. 2405
AVANTEC SARL—See Thermo Fisher Scientific Inc.; *U.S. Public*, pg. 2148
AVENTICS GMBH—See Emerson Electric Co.; *U.S. Public*, pg. 742
AVESCO MARKETING CORPORATION; *Int'l*, pg. 739
AZONIX CORPORATION—See Crane NXT, Co.; *U.S. Public*, pg. 589
BADGER METER CZECH REPUBLIC—See Badger Meter, Inc.; *U.S. Public*, pg. 263
BADGER METER DE LAS AMERICAS, S.A. DE C.V.—See Badger Meter, Inc.; *U.S. Public*, pg. 263
BADGER METER EUROPE, GMBH—See Badger Meter, Inc.; *U.S. Public*, pg. 263
BADGER METER, INC. - RACINE—See Badger Meter, Inc.; *U.S. Public*, pg. 263
BALYO SA; *Int'l*, pg. 813
BARBEN ANALYZER TECHNOLOGY, LLC—See AMETEK, Inc.; *U.S. Public*, pg. 118
BARCO ELEKTRONIK SISTEMLERI SAN.TIC. A.S—See Barco N.V.; *Int'l*, pg. 863
BARCO SINGAPORE PRIVATE LIMITED—See Barco N.V.; *Int'l*, pg. 863
BARTEC TECHNOR AS—See Charterhouse Capital Partners LLP; *Int'l*, pg. 1455
BASSO INDUSTRY CORPORATION; *Int'l*, pg. 888
BAVARIA ELECTRODES GMBH—See Graphite India Ltd; *Int'l*, pg. 3061
BBG BAUGERATE GMBH; *Int'l*, pg. 920
BDI CANADA, INC.—See Forge Industries, Inc.; *U.S. Private*, pg. 1568
BDI. CO., LTD; *Int'l*, pg. 929
BEIJING ARITIME INTELLIGENT CONTROL CO., LTD.; *Int'l*, pg. 945
BEIJING CHIEFTAIN CONTROL ENGINEERING TECHNOLOGY CO., LTD.; *Int'l*, pg. 947
BEIJING DAHENG ELECTRIC CO., LTD.—See Daheng New Epoch Technology, Inc.; *Int'l*, pg. 1913
BEIJING FORTUNE DRAEGER SAFETY EQUIPMENT CO., LTD.—See Draegerwerk AG & Co. KGaA; *Int'l*, pg. 2196
BEIJING SDL TECHNOLOGY CO., LTD.; *Int'l*, pg. 955
BEIJING STARNETO TECHNOLOGY CO.,LTD; *Int'l*, pg. 957
BEMIND A.D.; *Int'l*, pg. 969
BERTHOLD TECHNOLOGIES GMBH & CO. KG; *Int'l*, pg. 997
BGK FINISHING SYSTEMS—See Carlisle Companies Incorporated; *U.S. Public*, pg. 436
BILFINGER INDUSTRIAL AUTOMATION SERVICES LTD.—See Bilfinger SE; *Int'l*, pg. 1027
BIODOT, INC.—See ATS Corporation; *Int'l*, pg. 695
BIO-PROTECH INC; *Int'l*, pg. 1035

3679

BIOSYNERGY, INC.—See Harbour Group Industries, Inc.; *U.S. Private*, pg. 1861
BOSE SYSTEMS CORPORATION - ELECTROFORCE SYSTEMS GROUP—See Bose Corporation; *U.S. Private*, pg. 620
B.R.A.H.M.S. AUSTRIA GMBH—See Thermo Fisher Scientific Inc.; *U.S. Public*, pg. 2154
B.R.A.H.M.S. BIOTECH GMBH—See Thermo Fisher Scientific Inc.; *U.S. Public*, pg. 2154
BRISTOL BABCOCK AB—See Emerson Electric Co.; *U.S. Public*, pg. 748
BRITISH ROTOTHERM COMPANY LTD.; *Int'l*, pg. 1171
BTU EUROPE LTD.—See Amtech Systems, Inc.; *U.S. Public*, pg. 133
BUDZAR INDUSTRIES INC.—See Shelburne Corp.; *U.S. Private*, pg. 3630
CALIFORNIA ANALYTICAL INSTRUMENTS, INC.—See The Carlyle Group Inc.; *U.S. Public*, pg. 2046
CAMPBELL SCIENTIFIC AFRICA (PTY) LTD.—See Campbell Scientific, Inc.; *U.S. Private*, pg. 730
CAMPBELL SCIENTIFIC AUSTRALIA PTY LTD—See Campbell Scientific, Inc.; *U.S. Private*, pg. 730
CAMPBELL SCIENTIFIC CANADA CORP.—See Campbell Scientific, Inc.; *U.S. Private*, pg. 730
CAMPBELL SCIENTIFIC DO BRASIL, LTDA.—See Campbell Scientific, Inc.; *U.S. Private*, pg. 730
CAMPBELL SCIENTIFIC, INC.; *U.S. Private*, pg. 730
CAMPBELL SCIENTIFIC SPAIN, S.L.—See Campbell Scientific, Inc.; *U.S. Private*, pg. 730
CAPITAL SAFETY ROW LTD—See 3M Company; *U.S. Public*, pg. 8
CARL MAHR HOLDING GMBH; *Int'l*, pg. 1332
CARL ZEISS 3D METROLOGY SERVICES GMBH KOLN—See Carl-Zeiss-Stiftung; *Int'l*, pg. 1333
CARL ZEISS AUTOMATED INSPECTION GMBH & CO. KG—See Carl-Zeiss-Stiftung; *Int'l*, pg. 1334
CARL ZEISS DO BRASIL LTDA.—See Carl-Zeiss-Stiftung; *Int'l*, pg. 1336
CARL ZEISS FIXTURE SYSTEMS GMBH—See Carl-Zeiss-Stiftung; *Int'l*, pg. 1334
CARL ZEISS IMT CO., LTD.—See Carl-Zeiss-Stiftung; *Int'l*, pg. 1334
CARL ZEISS IMT IBERIA S.L.U.—See Carl-Zeiss-Stiftung; *Int'l*, pg. 1334
CARL ZEISS INDUSTRIAL METROLOGY, LLC—See Carl-Zeiss-Stiftung; *Int'l*, pg. 1334
CARL ZEISS INDUSTRIELLE MESSTECHNIK AUSTRIA GMBH—See Carl-Zeiss-Stiftung; *Int'l*, pg. 1334
CARL ZEISS OIM GMBH—See Carl-Zeiss-Stiftung; *Int'l*, pg. 1335
CARL ZEISS SLOVAKIA, S.R.O.—See Carl-Zeiss-Stiftung; *Int'l*, pg. 1335
CAROMETEC A/S—See KKR & Co. Inc.; *U.S. Public*, pg. 1241
CASCADE AUTOMATION SYSTEMS B.V.—See CHINO Corporation; *Int'l*, pg. 1570
CASCADE TECHNOLOGIES LIMITED—See Emerson Electric Co.; *U.S. Public*, pg. 742
CASELLA ESPANA SA—See IDEAL Industries Inc; *U.S. Private*, pg. 2036
CEPHEID ITALY SRL—See Danaher Corporation; *U.S. Public*, pg. 625
CEPHEID PROPRIETARY LIMITED—See Danaher Corporation; *U.S. Public*, pg. 625
CERES TECHNOLOGIES, INC.—See Atlas Copco AB; *Int'l*, pg. 682
CG AUTOMATION SOLUTIONS USA INC.—See Avantha Group; *Int'l*, pg. 735
CHANDLER ENGINEERING COMPANY LLC—See AMETEK, Inc.; *U.S. Public*, pg. 117
CHANGSHA HIGH-TECH DEVELOPMENT ZONE KAIQUAN MECHANICAL & ELECTRICAL TECHNOLOGY CO., LTD.—See Endress+Hauser (International) Holding AG; *Int'l*, pg. 2405
CHEMKO TECHNICAL SERVICES, INC.—See Astro Pak Corporation; *U.S. Private*, pg. 362
CHEMTRAK, INC.; *U.S. Private*, pg. 872
CHENGDU HUAMAOKEXIN AUTOMATION CONTROL ENGINEERING CO., LTD.—See Endress+Hauser (International) Holding AG; *Int'l*, pg. 2405
CHENGDU QINCHUAN IOT TECHNOLOGY CO., LTD.; *Int'l*, pg. 1468
CHIEF ENVIRONMENTAL PRODUCTS—See Chief Industries, Inc.; *U.S. Private*, pg. 881
CHINA HIGH PRECISION AUTOMATION GROUP LIMITED; *Int'l*, pg. 1508
CHINO CORPORATION INDIA PVT. LTD.—See CHINO Corporation; *Int'l*, pg. 1570
CHINO CORPORATION; *Int'l*, pg. 1570
CHROMA ATE INC. - LIN-KOU FACTORY—See Chroma ATE Inc.; *Int'l*, pg. 1588
CHROMATIC PRODUCTIONS, INC.—See H.I.G. Capital, LLC; *U.S. Private*, pg. 1834
C.I.M.C.I SARL—See Endress+Hauser (International) Holding AG; *Int'l*, pg. 2405
C.K. ENVIRONMENT A/S—See Addtech AB; *Int'l*, pg. 132
CLEMEX TECHNOLOGIES INC.; *Int'l*, pg. 1657
CLYDE BERGEMANN CANADA LTD.—See Clyde Blowers Capital IM LLP; *Int'l*, pg. 1665
CLYDE BERGEMANN EESTI AS—See Clyde Blowers Capital IM LLP; *Int'l*, pg. 1665
CLYDE BERGEMANN GMBH—See Clyde Blowers Capital IM LLP; *Int'l*, pg. 1665
CLYDE BERGEMANN POLSKA SP. Z O.O.—See Clyde Blowers Capital IM LLP; *Int'l*, pg. 1665
CMC HI TEC CONTROLLING SOLUTIONS LTD.—See CMC Technologies Israel Ltd.; *Int'l*, pg. 1669
COGNEX CORPORATION; *U.S. Public*, pg. 522
COHESIVE TECHNOLOGIES INC.—See Thermo Fisher Scientific Inc.; *U.S. Public*, pg. 2145
COILCRAFT CPS—See Coilcraft, Inc.; *U.S. Private*, pg. 964
COILCRAFT CPS TAIWAN—See Coilcraft, Inc.; *U.S. Private*, pg. 964
COILCRAFT EUROPE LTD—See Coilcraft, Inc.; *U.S. Private*, pg. 964
COILCRAFT HONG KONG LTD.—See Coilcraft, Inc.; *U.S. Private*, pg. 964
COILCRAFT JAPAN, INC.—See Coilcraft, Inc.; *U.S. Private*, pg. 964
COILCRAFT SINGAPORE PTE. LTD.—See Coilcraft, Inc.; *U.S. Private*, pg. 964
COLE-PARMER CANADA COMPANY—See Thermo Fisher Scientific Inc.; *U.S. Public*, pg. 2148
COLE-PARMER INSTRUMENT COMPANY, LLC—See GTCR LLC; *U.S. Private*, pg. 1804
COMAP S.A.—See Aalberts N.V.; *Int'l*, pg. 33
COMIN KHMERE CO., LTD.—See Endress+Hauser (International) Holding AG; *Int'l*, pg. 2406
COMPUTIME GROUP LIMITED; *Int'l*, pg. 1760
CONAX TECHNOLOGIES LLC; *U.S. Private*, pg. 1008
COOPER-ATKINS CORPORATION - GAINESVILLE FLORIDA FACILITY—See Emerson Electric Co.; *U.S. Public*, pg. 742
COOPER CROUSE-HINDS ICI—See Eaton Corporation plc; *Int'l*, pg. 2277
COPERION K-TRON PITMAN, INC.—See Hillenbrand, Inc.; *U.S. Public*, pg. 1037
COSCO SHIPPING TECHNOLOGY CO., LTD.—See China COSCO Shipping Corporation Limited; *Int'l*, pg. 1493
COSPOWER ENGINEERING LTD.; *Int'l*, pg. 1814
COX FLOW MEASUREMENT, INC.—See Badger Meter, Inc.; *U.S. Public*, pg. 263
CRANE CONTROLS, INC.—See Crane NXT, Co.; *U.S. Public*, pg. 589
CRANE NXT, CO.; *U.S. Public*, pg. 589
CRAWFORD UNITED CORPORATION; *U.S. Public*, pg. 592
CREAFORM FRANCE S.A.S.—See AMETEK, Inc.; *U.S. Public*, pg. 120
CREAFORM SHANGHAI LTD.—See AMETEK, Inc.; *U.S. Public*, pg. 120
CREATE TECHNOLOGY & SCIENCE CO., LTD.; *Int'l*, pg. 1832
CRYOPACK VERIFICATION TECHNOLOGIES, INC.—See Integreon Global; *U.S. Private*, pg. 2102
CSG INTELLIGENCE TECHNOLOGY (HEFEI) CO., LTD.—See CSG Smart Science & Technology Co., Ltd.; *Int'l*, pg. 1864
CSG INTELLIGENT ELECTRICAL TECHNOLOGY CO., LTD.—See CSG Smart Science & Technology Co., Ltd.; *Int'l*, pg. 1864
CUBIC DEFENCE NEW ZEALAND LTD.—See Elliott Management Corporation; *U.S. Private*, pg. 1367
CUBIC DEFENCE NEW ZEALAND LTD.—See Veritas Capital Fund Management, LLC; *U.S. Private*, pg. 4361
CUBIC SENSOR & INSTRUMENT CO., LTD.; *Int'l*, pg. 1875
CUBIC TECHNOLOGIES PTE. LTD.—See Elliott Management Corporation; *U.S. Private*, pg. 1367
CUBIC TECHNOLOGIES PTE. LTD.—See Veritas Capital Fund Management, LLC; *U.S. Private*, pg. 4361
CUSTOM CONTROL SOLUTIONS, INC.; *U.S. Private*, pg. 1128
CYBEROPTICS LTD.—See Nordson Corporation; *U.S. Public*, pg. 1532
CYBEROPTICS (SINGAPORE) PTE. LTD.—See Nordson Corporation; *U.S. Public*, pg. 1532
DAEYANG INSTRUMENT CO., LTD—See Daeyang Electric Co., Ltd.; *Int'l*, pg. 1911
DAKIN ENGINEERING PTE LTD—See CHINO Corporation; *Int'l*, pg. 1570
DALIAN NEW ORIENTAL INTERNATIONAL INSTRUMENT INDUSTRY & TRADE CO., LTD.—See Endress+Hauser (International) Holding AG; *Int'l*, pg. 2406
DALIAN ZHIYUN AUTOMATION CO., LTD.; *Int'l*, pg. 1953
DANAHER CORPORATION; *U.S. Public*, pg. 623
DANFOSS A/S FLOW DIV.—See Danfoss A/S; *Int'l*, pg. 1959
DANFOSS A/S INDUSTRIAL CONTROLS DIV.—See Danfoss A/S; *Int'l*, pg. 1959
DANFOSS S.A.R.L.—See Danfoss A/S; *Int'l*, pg. 1961
DANFOSS SILICON POWER GMBH—See Danfoss A/S; *Int'l*, pg. 1961
DANFOSS SP. Z.O.O.—See Danfoss A/S; *Int'l*, pg. 1961
DANIEL CANADA—See Emerson Electric Co.; *U.S. Public*, pg. 746
DANIEL MEASUREMENT & CONTROL INC.—See Emerson Electric Co.; *U.S. Public*, pg. 746

DAQ ELECTRONICS, INC.; *U.S. Private*, pg. 1158
DATALOGIC AUTOMATION, INC.—See Datalogic S.p.A.; *Int'l*, pg. 1978
DATA PHYSICS CORP.—See Battery Ventures, L.P.; *U.S. Private*, pg. 488
DELTA SYSTEMS & AUTOMATION INC.—See ILAPAK S.A.; *Int'l*, pg. 3613
DEVICOR MEDICAL EUROPE GMBH—See Danaher Corporation; *U.S. Public*, pg. 626
DH EUROPE FINANCE SA—See Danaher Corporation; *U.S. Public*, pg. 625
DIBA JAPAN KK—See Halma plc; *Int'l*, pg. 3231
DICKSON/UNIGAGE, INC.—See May River Capital, LLC; *U.S. Private*, pg. 2620
DIEHL AKO STIFTUNG & CO. KG—See Diehl Stiftung & Co. KG; *Int'l*, pg. 2114
DIEHL CONTROLS MEXICO S.A. DE C.V.—See Diehl Stiftung & Co. KG; *Int'l*, pg. 2115
DIEHL CONTROLS (NANJING) CO. LTD.—See Diehl Stiftung & Co. KG; *Int'l*, pg. 2115
DIEHL CONTROLS NORTH AMERICA INC.—See Diehl Stiftung & Co. KG; *Int'l*, pg. 2115
DIEHL CONTROLS POLSKA SP. Z O.O.—See Diehl Stiftung & Co. KG; *Int'l*, pg. 2115
DIETERICH STANDARD INC.—See Emerson Electric Co.; *U.S. Public*, pg. 747
DIFFUSION SARL—See Endress+Hauser (International) Holding AG; *Int'l*, pg. 2406
DIGITRON INSTRUMENTATION LIMITED—See British Rototherm Company Ltd.; *Int'l*, pg. 1171
DIONEX CORPORATION—See Thermo Fisher Scientific Inc.; *U.S. Public*, pg. 2146
DKK-TOA CORPORATION; *Int'l*, pg. 2139
DOLAN-JENNER INDUSTRIES INC.—See Danaher Corporation; *U.S. Public*, pg. 626
DONG-IL SHIMADZU CORP.—See DI Corp.; *Int'l*, pg. 2101
DONGIL TECHNOLOGY LTD.; *Int'l*, pg. 2168
DP FESTO—See Festo AG & Co. KG; *Int'l*, pg. 2646
DRAEGER CANADA LTD.—See Draegerwerk AG & Co. KGaA; *Int'l*, pg. 2196
DRAEGER CROATIA D.O.O.—See Draegerwerk AG & Co. KGaA; *Int'l*, pg. 2196
DRAEGER MEDICAL HISPANIA S.A.—See Draegerwerk AG & Co. KGaA; *Int'l*, pg. 2196
DRAEGER MEDICAL ITALIANA S.P.A.—See Draegerwerk AG & Co. KGaA; *Int'l*, pg. 2196
DRAEGER MEDICAL SOUTH AFRICA (PTY) LTD—See Draegerwerk AG & Co. KGaA; *Int'l*, pg. 2196
DRAEGER SAFETY AUSTRIA GMBH—See Draegerwerk AG & Co. KGaA; *Int'l*, pg. 2197
DRAEGER SAFETY LTD.—See Draegerwerk AG & Co. KGaA; *Int'l*, pg. 2197
DRAEGER SAFETY NEDERLAND B V—See Draegerwerk AG & Co. KGaA; *Int'l*, pg. 2197
DRAEGER SAFETY NORGE A/S—See Draegerwerk AG & Co. KGaA; *Int'l*, pg. 2197
DRAEGER SAFETY PACIFIC LTD.—See Draegerwerk AG & Co. KGaA; *Int'l*, pg. 2197
DRAEGER SAFETY S.A.—See Draegerwerk AG & Co. KGaA; *Int'l*, pg. 2197
DRAEGER SAFETY (SCHWEIZ) AG—See Draegerwerk AG & Co. KGaA; *Int'l*, pg. 2197
DRAEGER SAFETY SWEDEN AB—See Draegerwerk AG & Co. KGaA; *Int'l*, pg. 2197
DRAGER SAFETY DANMARK A/S—See Draegerwerk AG & Co. KGaA; *Int'l*, pg. 2197
DUNKERMOTOREN FRANCE SAS—See AMETEK, Inc.; *U.S. Public*, pg. 120
DUNKERMOTOREN ITALIA S.R.L.—See AMETEK, Inc.; *U.S. Public*, pg. 120
DUNKERMOTOREN SUBOTICA D.O.O.—See AMETEK, Inc.; *U.S. Public*, pg. 120
DUNKERMOTOREN TAICANG CO., LTD.—See AMETEK, Inc.; *U.S. Public*, pg. 120
DUNKERMOTOREN USA INC.—See AMETEK, Inc.; *U.S. Public*, pg. 120
DWYER INSTRUMENTS, LLC—See Arcline Investment Management LP; *U.S. Private*, pg. 313
DWYER INSTRUMENTS LTD—See Arcline Investment Management LP; *U.S. Private*, pg. 313
DWYER INSTRUMENTS PTY LTD—See Arcline Investment Management LP; *U.S. Private*, pg. 313
DYNA IMAGE CORPORATION—See Diodes Incorporated; *U.S. Public*, pg. 667
DYNISCO EUROPE GMBH—See Roper Technologies, Inc.; *U.S. Public*, pg. 1811
EATON CORP. ELECTRICAL SECTOR, WATERTOWN—See Eaton Corporation plc; *Int'l*, pg. 2279
EATON ELEKTROTECHNIKA S.R.O.—See Eaton Corporation plc; *Int'l*, pg. 2280
ECKELMANN AG; *Int'l*, pg. 2289
ECN AUTOMATION EL SALVADOR S.A. DE C.V.—See Endress+Hauser (International) Holding AG; *Int'l*, pg. 2406
EIWA CORPORATION; *Int'l*, pg. 2337
ELDEC FRANCE S.A.R.L.—See Crane NXT, Co.; *U.S. Public*, pg. 589

N.A.I.C.S. INDEX
334513 — INSTRUMENTS AND REL...

ELECTRONIC CONTROLS DESIGN; *U.S. Private*, pg. 1355
ELECTRONIC DESIGN FOR INDUSTRY, INC.—See Turnbridge Capital, LLC; *U.S. Private*, pg. 4260
ELECTRO-OPTICAL INDUSTRIES, LLC—See HGH Infrared Systems Inc.; *U.S. Private*, pg. 1930
ELECTRO-SENSORS, INC.; *U.S. Public*, pg. 723
ELSTER AMERICAN METER COMPANY, LLC—See Honeywell International Inc.; *U.S. Public*, pg. 1047
ELSTER N.V./S.A.—See Honeywell International Inc.; *U.S. Public*, pg. 1048
EMERSON ELECTRIC CANADA LIMITED—See Emerson Electric Co.; *U.S. Public*, pg. 744
EMERSON ELECTRIC (M) SDN BHD—See Emerson Electric Co.; *U.S. Public*, pg. 744
EMERSON INDUSTRIAL AUTOMATION BELGIUM NV—See Emerson Electric Co.; *U.S. Public*, pg. 745
EMERSON INDUSTRIAL AUTOMATION ITALY SPA—See Emerson Electric Co.; *U.S. Public*, pg. 745
EMERSON JAPAN, LTD.—See Emerson Electric Co.; *U.S. Public*, pg. 745
EMERSON NETWORK POWER HOLDING S.R.L.—See Vertiv Holdings Co; *U.S. Public*, pg. 2288
EMERSON PROCESS MANAGEMENT AG—See Emerson Electric Co.; *U.S. Public*, pg. 746
EMERSON PROCESS MANAGEMENT ASIA PACIFIC PTE LTD—See Emerson Electric Co.; *U.S. Public*, pg. 747
EMERSON PROCESS MANAGEMENT AUSTRALIA PTY LIMITED—See Emerson Electric Co.; *U.S. Public*, pg. 747
EMERSON PROCESS MANAGEMENT BV—See Emerson Electric Co.; *U.S. Public*, pg. 747
EMERSON PROCESS MANAGEMENT GMBH & CO. OHG—See Emerson Electric Co.; *U.S. Public*, pg. 747
EMERSON PROCESS MANAGEMENT, LDA—See Emerson Electric Co.; *U.S. Public*, pg. 748
EMERSON PROCESS MANAGEMENT LIMITED—See Emerson Electric Co.; *U.S. Public*, pg. 747
EMERSON PROCESS MANAGEMENT LIMITED—See Emerson Electric Co.; *U.S. Public*, pg. 747
EMERSON PROCESS MANAGEMENT ROSEMOUNT INC.—See Emerson Electric Co.; *U.S. Public*, pg. 747
EMERSON PROCESS MANAGEMENT S.A.—See Emerson Electric Co.; *U.S. Public*, pg. 748
EMERSON PROCESS MANAGEMENT—See Emerson Electric Co.; *U.S. Public*, pg. 746
EMERSON REMOTE AUTOMATION SOLUTIONS—See Emerson Electric Co.; *U.S. Public*, pg. 748
E-MOTIVE DISPLAY PTE. LIMITED—See Halma plc; *Int'l*, pg. 3231
ENDRESS+HAUSER ANALYTICAL INSTRUMENTS (SUZHOU) CO., LTD.—See Endress+Hauser (International) Holding AG; *Int'l*, pg. 2406
ENDRESS+HAUSER COLOMBIA S.A.S.—See Endress+Hauser (International) Holding AG; *Int'l*, pg. 2407
ENDRESS+HAUSER (DEUTSCHLAND) GMBH+CO. KG.—See Endress+Hauser (International) Holding AG; *Int'l*, pg. 2406
ENDRESS+HAUSER FLOWTEC AG—See Endress+Hauser (International) Holding AG; *Int'l*, pg. 2407
ENDRESS+HAUSER FLOWTEC (BRASIL) FLUXOMETROS LTDA.—See Endress+Hauser (International) Holding AG; *Int'l*, pg. 2407
ENDRESS+HAUSER GROUP SERVICES AG—See Endress+Hauser (International) Holding AG; *Int'l*, pg. 2407
ENDRESS+HAUSER INC.—See Endress+Hauser (International) Holding AG; *Int'l*, pg. 2407
ENDRESS+HAUSER INFOSERVE GMBH+CO. KG—See Endress+Hauser (International) Holding AG; *Int'l*, pg. 2407
ENDRESS+HAUSER INTERNATIONAL AG—See Endress+Hauser (International) Holding AG; *Int'l*, pg. 2407
ENDRESS+HAUSER (INTERNATIONAL) HOLDING AG; *Int'l*, pg. 2405
ENDRESS+HAUSER LTD.—See Endress+Hauser (International) Holding AG; *Int'l*, pg. 2407
ENDRESS+HAUSER (MAGYARORSZAG) KFT.—See Endress+Hauser (International) Holding AG; *Int'l*, pg. 2406
ENDRESS+HAUSER OY—See Endress+Hauser (International) Holding AG; *Int'l*, pg. 2407
ENDRESS+HAUSER PANAMA INC.—See Endress+Hauser (International) Holding AG; *Int'l*, pg. 2407
ENDRESS+HAUSER PHILIPPINES INC.—See Endress+Hauser (International) Holding AG; *Int'l*, pg. 2407
ENDRESS & HAUSER PROCESS AUTOMATION (UAE) TRADING LLC—See Endress+Hauser (International) Holding AG; *Int'l*, pg. 2406
ENDRESS+HAUSER PROCESS SOLUTIONS AG—See Endress+Hauser (International) Holding AG; *Int'l*, pg. 2407
ENDRESS+HAUSER SE+CO. KG.—See Endress+Hauser (International) Holding AG; *Int'l*, pg. 2408
ENDRESS+HAUSER SICESTHERM S.R.L.—See Endress+Hauser (International) Holding AG; *Int'l*, pg. 2408
ENDRESS+HAUSER (SUZHOU) AUTOMATION INSTRUMENTATION CO., LTD.—See Endress+Hauser (International) Holding AG; *Int'l*, pg. 2406
ENDRESS+HAUSER SYSTEMPLAN GMBH—See Endress+Hauser (International) Holding AG; *Int'l*, pg. 2408
ENDRESS+HAUSER (VIETNAM) CO. LTD.—See Endress+Hauser (International) Holding AG; *Int'l*, pg. 2406
ENDRESS+HAUSER WETZER (SUZHOU) CO. LTD.—See Endress+Hauser (International) Holding AG; *Int'l*, pg. 2408
ENDRESS+HAUSER WETZER USA INC.—See Endress+Hauser (International) Holding AG; *Int'l*, pg. 2408
ENERTIME SAS; *Int'l*, pg. 2424
EN OM FRA, S.A.—See Nova Ventures Group Corp.; *U.S. Private*, pg. 2966
ENVEA CHINA LTD.—See The Carlyle Group Inc.; *U.S. Public*, pg. 2046
ENVEA GLOBAL SAS—See The Carlyle Group Inc.; *U.S. Public*, pg. 2046
ENVEA GMBH—See The Carlyle Group Inc.; *U.S. Public*, pg. 2046
ENVEA INC.—See The Carlyle Group Inc.; *U.S. Public*, pg. 2046
ENVEA INDIA PVT LTD—See The Carlyle Group Inc.; *U.S. Public*, pg. 2046
ENVEA PROCESS GMBH—See The Carlyle Group Inc.; *U.S. Public*, pg. 2046
ENVEA UK LTD.—See The Carlyle Group Inc.; *U.S. Public*, pg. 2046
ERICH NETZSCH GMBH & CO. HOLDING KG; *Int'l*, pg. 2491
ERIE SCIENTIFIC COMPANY OF PUERTO RICO—See Thermo Fisher Scientific Inc.; *U.S. Public*, pg. 2146
ESAUTOMOTION S.P.A.— *Int'l*, pg. 2501
ESC SERVICES, INC.—See Rockwell Automation, Inc.; *U.S. Public*, pg. 1805
ESPEC CORP. - FUKUCHIYAMA PLANT—See ESPEC Corp.; *U.S. Public*, pg. 2505
ESTERLINE TECHNOLOGIES CORPORATION—See TransDigm Group Incorporated; *U.S. Public*, pg. 2180
ETION CONNECT (PTY) LTD.—See Etion Limited; *Int'l*, pg. 2523
ETS LINDGREN ENGINEERING INDIA PRIVATE LIMITED—See ESCO Technologies, Inc.; *U.S. Public*, pg. 793
EUROTECH LTD.—See Eurotech S.p.A.; *Int'l*, pg. 2558
EVEREST INGENIERIA SRL—See Endress+Hauser (International) Holding AG; *Int'l*, pg. 2408
EVEST CORPORATION—See Hitachi, Ltd.; *Int'l*, pg. 3424
FAGKAUP EHF.—See Endress+Hauser (International) Holding AG; *Int'l*, pg. 2408
THE FALK SERVICE CORPORATION—See Zurn Elkay Water Solutions Corporation; *U.S. Public*, pg. 2414
FAST EQUIPAMENTOS E SERVICOS LDA.—See Endress+Hauser (International) Holding AG; *Int'l*, pg. 2408
FERROCONTROL STEUERUNGSSYSTEME GMBH & CO. KG—See Eckelmann AG; *Int'l*, pg. 2290
FERVI SPA; *Int'l*, pg. 2646
FESTO A/S—See Festo AG & Co. KG; *Int'l*, pg. 2646
FESTO BELGIUM N.V./S.A.—See Festo AG & Co. KG; *Int'l*, pg. 2647
FESTO BRASIL LTDA.—See Festo AG & Co. KG; *Int'l*, pg. 2647
FESTO BULGARIA EOOD—See Festo AG & Co. KG; *Int'l*, pg. 2647
FESTO C.A.—See Festo AG & Co. KG; *Int'l*, pg. 2647
FESTO CHILE SA—See Festo AG & Co. KG; *Int'l*, pg. 2647
FESTO (CHINA) LTD.—See Festo AG & Co. KG; *Int'l*, pg. 2646
FESTO CONTROLS PVT. LTD.—See Festo AG & Co. KG; *Int'l*, pg. 2647
FESTO D.O.O.—See Festo AG & Co. KG; *Int'l*, pg. 2648
FESTO GMBH—See Festo AG & Co. KG; *Int'l*, pg. 2647
FESTO KFT.—See Festo AG & Co. KG; *Int'l*, pg. 2647
FESTO LIMITED—See Festo AG & Co. KG; *Int'l*, pg. 2647
FESTO LIMITED—See Festo AG & Co. KG; *Int'l*, pg. 2647
FESTO LIMITED—See Festo AG & Co. KG; *Int'l*, pg. 2647
FESTO LTDA.—See Festo AG & Co. KG; *Int'l*, pg. 2647
FESTO LTD.—See Festo AG & Co. KG; *Int'l*, pg. 2647
FESTO LTD.—See Festo AG & Co. KG; *Int'l*, pg. 2647
FESTO OY AB EESTI FILIAAL—See Festo AG & Co. KG; *Int'l*, pg. 2647
FESTO OY—See Festo AG & Co. KG; *Int'l*, pg. 2647
FESTO PNEUMATIC S.K.—See Festo AG & Co. KG; *Int'l*, pg. 2647
FESTO PTY. LTD.—See Festo AG & Co. KG; *Int'l*, pg. 2647
FESTO SAN. VE TIC A.S.—See Festo AG & Co. KG; *Int'l*, pg. 2648
FESTO S.A.—See Festo AG & Co. KG; *Int'l*, pg. 2648
FESTO S.P.A.—See Festo AG & Co. KG; *Int'l*, pg. 2648
FESTO SPOL. S.R.O.—See Festo AG & Co. KG; *Int'l*, pg. 2648
FILTRATION LAB INC.; *Int'l*, pg. 2663
FISHER MEXICO, S. DE R.L. DE C.V.—See Thermo Fisher Scientific Inc.; *U.S. Public*, pg. 2147
FISHER SCIENTIFIC AG—See Thermo Fisher Scientific Inc.; *U.S. Public*, pg. 2145
FISHER SCIENTIFIC GTF AB—See Thermo Fisher Scientific Inc.; *U.S. Public*, pg. 2148
FISHER SCIENTIFIC (HONG KONG) LIMITED—See Thermo Fisher Scientific Inc.; *U.S. Public*, pg. 2147
FISHER SCIENTIFIC JAPAN, LTD.—See Thermo Fisher Scientific Inc.; *U.S. Public*, pg. 2148
FISHER SCIENTIFIC OF THE NETHERLANDS B.V.—See Thermo Fisher Scientific Inc.; *U.S. Public*, pg. 2148
FISHER SCIENTIFIC S.A.S.—See Thermo Fisher Scientific Inc.; *U.S. Public*, pg. 2148
FISHER SCIENTIFIC, SPOL. S.R.O—See Thermo Fisher Scientific Inc.; *U.S. Public*, pg. 2148
FIT HOLDING CO., LTD.—See Cheng Eui Precision Industry Co., Ltd.; *Int'l*, pg. 1465
FLIR SYSTEMS AB—See Teledyne Technologies Incorporated; *U.S. Public*, pg. 1993
FLIR SYSTEMS COMPANY LTD.—See Teledyne Technologies Incorporated; *U.S. Public*, pg. 1992
FLIR UNMANNED AERIAL SYSTEMS AS—See Teledyne Technologies Incorporated; *U.S. Public*, pg. 1992
FLOWMETRICS, INC—See Hydraulics International, Inc.; *U.S. Private*, pg. 2017
FLSMIDTH INDUSTRIAL SOLUTIONS MAKINE SANAYI VE TICARET A.S.—See FLSmidth & Co. A/S; *Int'l*, pg. 2710
FLUIDIGM (SHANGHAI) INSTRUMENT TECHNOLOGY COMPANY LIMITED—See Standard BioTools Inc.; *U.S. Public*, pg. 1928
FONTAINE USA INC.—See Zurn Elkay Water Solutions Corporation; *U.S. Public*, pg. 2412
FOOD AUTOMATION - SERVICE TECHNIQUES, INC.; *U.S. Private*, pg. 1560
FORCECON TECH. CO., LTD.; *Int'l*, pg. 2730
FORTRESS INTERLOCKS PTY LIMITED—See Halma plc; *Int'l*, pg. 3231
FRAMATOME INC.—See Electricite de France S.A.; *Int'l*, pg. 2351
FRANKLIN CONTROL SYSTEMS, INC.—See Franklin Electric Co., Inc.; *U.S. Public*, pg. 878
FREPART AB—See Amplex AB; *Int'l*, pg. 433
FUGRO OCEANOR AS—See Fugro N.V.; *Int'l*, pg. 2807
FUJIAN SANMING DOUBLE-WHEEL CHEMICAL MACHINERY CO. LTD—See China National Chemical Corporation; *Int'l*, pg. 1527
FUJICOPIAN CO., LTD. - OKAYAMA PLANT—See Fujicopian Co., Ltd.; *Int'l*, pg. 2820
FUJITSU OPTICAL COMPONENTS AMERICA, INC.—See Fujitsu Limited; *Int'l*, pg. 2835
FUJITSU SERVICES LIMITED—See Fujitsu Limited; *Int'l*, pg. 2835
FUTABA CORPORATION - CHOSEI ELECTRON TUBE FACTORY—See Futaba Corporation; *Int'l*, pg. 2850
FUTABA CORPORATION - CHOSEI VFD MODULE FACTORY—See Futaba Corporation; *Int'l*, pg. 2850
FUTABA CORPORATION - MOBARA ELECTRON TUBE FACTORY—See Futaba Corporation; *Int'l*, pg. 2850
GASALARM A.D.; *Int'l*, pg. 2887
GATEWORKS, CORP.; *U.S. Private*, pg. 1651
GE DRUCK HOLDINGS LIMITED—See General Electric Company; *U.S. Public*, pg. 916
GEFRAN, INC.—See Gefran S.p.A.; *Int'l*, pg. 2912
GE INTELLIGENT PLATFORMS, INC.—See Emerson Electric Co.; *U.S. Public*, pg. 749
GENERAL MONITORS INC.—See MSA Safety Incorporated; *U.S. Public*, pg. 1481
GEORGE WILSON INDUSTRIES LIMITED; *Int'l*, pg. 2939
GEORG FISCHER SIGNET LLC—See Georg Fischer AG; *Int'l*, pg. 2936
GEOTECH ENVIRONMENTAL EQUIPMENT, INC.; *U.S. Private*, pg. 1685
GEOTECH INSTRUMENTS—See Geotech Environmental Equipment, Inc.; *U.S. Private*, pg. 1685
GERMANY AEROTECH GMBH—See Aerotech Inc.; *U.S. Private*, pg. 119
GES AUTOMATION TECHNOLOGY INC.—See Edwin L. Heim Company Inc.; *U.S. Private*, pg. 1342
GHM MESSTECHNIK GMBH - STANDORT GREISINGER—See GHM Messtechnik GmbH; *Int'l*, pg. 2959
GHM MESSTECHNIK GMBH - STANDORT HONSBERG—See GHM Messtechnik GmbH; *Int'l*, pg. 2959
GHM MESSTECHNIK GMBH - STANDORT MARTENS—See GHM Messtechnik GmbH; *Int'l*, pg. 2959
GIO AUTOMATION TECHNOLOGY CO., LTD.—See Hitachi, Ltd.; *Int'l*, pg. 3425
GOK REGLER- UND ARMATUREN- GESELLSCHAFT MBH & CO. KG; *Int'l*, pg. 3022
GRANT INDUSTRIAL CONTROLS INC.; *U.S. Private*, pg. 1756
GREYLINE INSTRUMENTS INC.—See Harbour Group Industries, Inc.; *U.S. Private*, pg. 1860
GREYLINE INSTRUMENTS, INC.—See Harbour Group In-

334513 — INSTRUMENTS AND REL...

dustries, Inc.; *U.S. Private,* pg. 1860
GSI ELECTRONIQUE INC—See AGCO Corporation; *U.S. Public,* pg. 58
GSI GROUP EUROPE GMBH—See Novanta Inc.; *U.S. Public,* pg. 1548
GUIDED WAVE INC.—See IGP Industries, LLC; *U.S. Private,* pg. 2040
HACH LANGE FINANCE GMBH—See Danaher Corporation; *U.S. Public,* pg. 627
HAMLIN, INC,—See Littelfuse, Inc.; *U.S. Public,* pg. 1327
HAMMOND MANUFACTURING CO. LTD.; *Int'l,* pg. 3238
HANGZHOU WINMATION AUTOMATION COMPANY LIMITED—See ABB Ltd.; *Int'l,* pg. 3
HANSON RESEARCH CORP.—See Teledyne Technologies Incorporated; *U.S. Public,* pg. 1993
HARDY PROCESS SOLUTIONS, INC.—See Technology for Energy Corporation; *U.S. Private,* pg. 3955
HAWCO LTD.—See Bay Tree Private Equity LLP; *Int'l,* pg. 901
HAWKE INTERNATIONAL—See Hubbell Incorporated; *U.S. Public,* pg. 1066
HAYDON KERK MOTION SOLUTIONS, INC.-KERK PRODUCTS DIVISION—See AMETEK, Inc.; *U.S. Public,* pg. 116
HEFEI HENGCHANG AUTOMATION CONTROL CO., LTD.—See Endress+Hauser (International) Holding AG; *Int'l,* pg. 2408
HEFEI QUNYING SCIENCE & TECHNOLOGY CO., LTD.—See Endress+Hauser (International) Holding AG; *Int'l,* pg. 2408
HEIDRIVE GMBH—See Allient Inc.; *U.S. Public,* pg. 80
HERALD DATANETICS LIMITED—See Herald Holdings Limited; *Int'l,* pg. 3358
HEXAGON AB; *Int'l,* pg. 3367
HICHROM LIMITED—See Avantor, Inc.; *U.S. Public,* pg. 242
HIGH PRECISION DEVICES, INC.—See FormFactor, Inc.; *U.S. Public,* pg. 868
HINDS INSTRUMENTS, INC.; *U.S. Private,* pg. 1948
HIOKI E.E. CORPORATION; *Int'l,* pg. 3401
HITACHI INSTRUMENT (DALIAN) CO., LTD.—See Hitachi, Ltd.; *Int'l,* pg. 3419
HOLOMETRIC TECHNOLOGIES FORSCHUNGS- UND ENTWICKLUNGS-GMBH—See Carl-Zeiss-Stiftung; *Int'l,* pg. 1336
HONEYWELL ENRAF AMERICAS, INC.—See Honeywell International Inc.; *U.S. Public,* pg. 1049
HONEYWELL SENSING & CONTROL—See Honeywell International Inc.; *U.S. Public,* pg. 1050
HONEYWELL TECHNOLOGY SOLUTIONS QATAR LTD.—See Honeywell International Inc.; *U.S. Public,* pg. 1051
HONEYWELL TEKNOLOJI ANONIM SIRKETI—See Honeywell International Inc.; *U.S. Public,* pg. 1051
HORIBA LTD; *Int'l,* pg. 3474
H.O. TRERICE COMPANY; *U.S. Private,* pg. 1835
HOWELL INSTRUMENTS INC; *U.S. Private,* pg. 1996
HSH-SYSTEME FUR PROZESS-IT GMBH—See AZO GmbH & Co. KG; *Int'l,* pg. 780
HUAXIAO PRECISION INDUSTRY (SUZHOU) CO., LTD.—See CSG Smart Science & Technology Co., Ltd.; *Int'l,* pg. 1864
HURCO MACHINE TOOL PRODUCTION COMPANY—See Hurco Companies, Inc.; *U.S. Public,* pg. 1076
IAC ACOUSTICS AUSTRALIA—See AEA Investors LP; *U.S. Private,* pg. 114
IAC NORDIC A/S—See AEA Investors LP; *U.S. Private,* pg. 114
I B E JUNUZOVIC D.O.O.—See Endress+Hauser (International) Holding AG; *Int'l,* pg. 2408
ICONTRONIC SDN. BHD.; *Int'l,* pg. 3586
IDEAL INDUSTRIES AUSTRALIA—See IDEAL Industries Inc; *U.S. Private,* pg. 2036
IDEAL INDUSTRIES BRASIL LTDA.—See IDEAL Industries Inc; *U.S. Private,* pg. 2036
IDEAL INDUSTRIES (CANADA) CORP.—See IDEAL Industries Inc; *U.S. Private,* pg. 2036
IDEAL INDUSTRIES CHINA L.L.C.—See IDEAL Industries Inc; *U.S. Private,* pg. 2036
IDEAL INDUSTRIES GMBH—See IDEAL Industries Inc; *U.S. Private,* pg. 2036
IDEAL INDUSTRIES, INC. - CASELLA MEASUREMENT DIVISION—See IDEAL Industries Inc; *U.S. Private,* pg. 2036
IDEAL INDUSTRIES MEXICO—See IDEAL Industries Inc; *U.S. Private,* pg. 2036
IDEAL INDUSTRIES (U.K.) LIMITED—See IDEAL Industries Inc; *U.S. Private,* pg. 2036
IDEX HEALTH & SCIENCE GMBH—See IDEX Corp; *U.S. Public,* pg. 1090
IDEX HEALTH & SCIENCE LLC—See IDEX Corp; *U.S. Public,* pg. 1090
I+G ELECTRICAL SERVICES CO. LTD.—See Endress+Hauser (International) Holding AG; *Int'l,* pg. 2408
IKM INSTRUTEK AS—See IKM Gruppen AS; *Int'l,* pg. 3611
IKM SUBSEA UK LTD—See IKM Gruppen AS; *Int'l,* pg. 3611
IME INTERMOUNTAIN ELECTRIC, INC.—See Quanta Services, Inc.; *U.S. Public,* pg. 1751

IMPRESS SENSORS & SYSTEMS LIMITED—See Sensata Technologies Holding plc; *U.S. Public,* pg. 1865
INDEV GAUGING SYSTEMS, INC.—See Numina Group, Incorporated; *U.S. Private,* pg. 2973
INDUSTRIAL INTERFACE LIMITED—See Sensata Technologies Holding plc; *U.S. Public,* pg. 1865
INNOVATIVE PRODUCT ACHIEVEMENTS LLC—See Roper Technologies, Inc.; *U.S. Public,* pg. 1811
INNOVATIVE SENSOR TECHNOLOGY IST AG—See Endress+Hauser (International) Holding AG; *Int'l,* pg. 2408
INSENSYS LIMITED—See Moog Inc.; *U.S. Public,* pg. 1469
IN-SITU, INC.; *U.S. Public,* pg. 2052
INSTRUMENTS FOR INDUSTRY, INC.—See AMETEK, Inc.; *U.S. Public,* pg. 120
INSTRUMETRICS INDUSTRIAL CONTROL LTD.—See Endress+Hauser (International) Holding AG; *Int'l,* pg. 2408
INTALYSIS PTY LTD—See Thermo Fisher Scientific Inc.; *U.S. Public,* pg. 2154
INTEGRATED FLOW SOLUTIONS, LLC—See DXP Enterprises, Inc.; *U.S. Public,* pg. 697
INTELLIGENTE SENSORSYSTEME DRESDEN GMBH—See Amphenol Corporation; *U.S. Public,* pg. 130
INTELLIGENT INSTRUMENTATION, INC.; *U.S. Private,* pg. 2105
INTERNATIONAL METALS & CHEMICALS GROUP; *U.S. Private,* pg. 2119
IRCON CHINA—See Fortive Corporation; *U.S. Public,* pg. 870
IRIS POWER LP—See Koch Industries, Inc.; *U.S. Private,* pg. 2331
ISOTRON SYSTEMS B.V.—See Addtech AB; *Int'l,* pg. 134
ISRA VISION PARSYTEC AG—See Atlas Copco AB; *Int'l,* pg. 682
ITALGALVANO (TECHNIC GROUP) SLOVAKIA—See Technic Incorporated; *U.S. Private,* pg. 3953
ITRON INDIA PRIVATE LIMITED—See Itron, Inc.; *U.S. Public,* pg. 1176
ITRON METERING SOLUTIONS UK LTD—See Itron, Inc.; *U.S. Public,* pg. 1176
ITW MAGNAFLUX—See Illinois Tool Works Inc.; *U.S. Public,* pg. 1106
JETTER DISTRIBUTION LTD.—See Bucher Industries AG; *Int'l,* pg. 1207
JETTER OY—See Bucher Industries AG; *Int'l,* pg. 1207
J. PARPALA OY—See ANDRITZ AG; *Int'l,* pg. 456
JUNGE CONTROL, INC.—See Ag Growth International Inc.; *Int'l,* pg. 198
KADANT PAAL S.A.U.—See Kadant Inc.; *U.S. Public,* pg. 1207
KEYSIGHT TECHNOLOGIES, INC.; *U.S. Public,* pg. 1226
KEYSIGHT TECHNOLOGIES JAPAN G.K.—See Keysight Technologies, Inc.; *U.S. Public,* pg. 1227
KEYSIGHT TECHNOLOGIES UK LIMITED—See Keysight Technologies, Inc.; *U.S. Public,* pg. 1227
KEYTROLLER, LLC—See PowerFleet, Inc.; *U.S. Public,* pg. 1706
KING NUTRONICS CORPORATION—See L Squared Capital Management LP; *U.S. Private,* pg. 2362
KOREA CHINO CORPORATION—See CHINO Corporation; *Int'l,* pg. 1571
KREATECH BIOTECHNOLOGY BV—See Danaher Corporation; *U.S. Public,* pg. 628
K-TEK INSTRUMENTS (PTY) LTD.—See ABB Ltd.; *Int'l,* pg. 55
K-TRON ELECTRONICS—See Hillenbrand, Inc.; *U.S. Public,* pg. 1037
K-TRON INTERNATIONAL, INC.—See Hillenbrand, Inc.; *U.S. Public,* pg. 1036
KUNMING CONDELL ELECTRONICS CO., LTD.—See Endress+Hauser (International) Holding AG; *Int'l,* pg. 2408
L-3 COMMUNICATIONS-DISPLAY SYSTEMS—See L3Harris Technologies, Inc.; *U.S. Public,* pg. 1283
LAND INSTRUMENTS INTERNATIONAL—See AMETEK, Inc.; *U.S. Public,* pg. 118
LCR HALLCREST LLC—See Harbour Group Industries, Inc.; *U.S. Private,* pg. 1861
LCR HALLCREST LTD—See Harbour Group Industries, Inc.; *U.S. Private,* pg. 1861
THE LEE COMPANY; *U.S. Private,* pg. 4068
LEICA BIOSYSTEMS IMAGING INC.—See Danaher Corporation; *U.S. Public,* pg. 628
LEICA GEOSYSTEMS AG METROLOGY DIVISION—See Hexagon AB; *Int'l,* pg. 3367
LEICA MICROSYSTEMS TRADING (SHANGHAI) LTD.—See Danaher Corporation; *U.S. Public,* pg. 628
LION LABORATORIES LIMITED—See MPD, Inc.; *U.S. Private,* pg. 2803
LIPPERT ADLINK TECHNOLOGY GMBH—See ADLINK Technology, Inc.; *Int'l,* pg. 151
LITTELFUSE STARTCO—See Littelfuse, Inc.; *U.S. Public,* pg. 1327
LORENTZEN & WAETTRE SKANDINAVIEN AB—See ABB Ltd.; *Int'l,* pg. 49
LUMASENSE TECHNOLOGIES, INC.—See Advanced Energy Industries, Inc.; *U.S. Public,* pg. 47

LUMASENSE TECHNOLOGIES SARL—See Advanced Energy Industries, Inc.; *U.S. Public,* pg. 47
MAGNETROL INSTRUMENTATION INDUSTRIAL LTDA.—See AMETEK, Inc.; *U.S. Public,* pg. 121
MAGNETROL INTERNATIONAL INC.—See AMETEK, Inc.; *U.S. Public,* pg. 121
MAGNETROL INTERNATIONAL, INC.—See AMETEK, Inc.; *U.S. Public,* pg. 121
MAGNETROL INTERNATIONAL N.V.—See AMETEK, Inc.; *U.S. Public,* pg. 121
MAGNETROL INTERNATIONAL—See AMETEK, Inc.; *U.S. Public,* pg. 121
MAGNETROL INTERNATIONAL, INC.—See AMETEK, Inc.; *U.S. Public,* pg. 121
MAGNETROL INTERNATIONAL, INC.—See AMETEK, Inc.; *U.S. Public,* pg. 121
MAGNETROL INTERNATIONAL, INC.—See AMETEK, Inc.; *U.S. Public,* pg. 121
MAGNETROL INTERNATIONAL, INC.—See AMETEK, Inc.; *U.S. Public,* pg. 121
MAGYAR & ASSOCIATES; *U.S. Private,* pg. 2550
MAHR FEDERAL, INC.—See Carl Mahr Holding GmbH; *Int'l,* pg. 1333
MALEMA ENGINEERING CORP.—See Dover Corporation; *U.S. Public,* pg. 682
MAMAC SYSTEMS (ASIA) PTE LIMITED—See Mamac Systems Inc.; *U.S. Private,* pg. 2558
MAMAC SYSTEMS (CANADA) LIMITED—See Mamac Systems Inc.; *U.S. Private,* pg. 2558
MAMAC SYSTEMS INC.; *U.S. Private,* pg. 2558
MAMAC SYSTEMS PTY LIMITED—See Mamac Systems Inc.; *U.S. Private,* pg. 2559
MAMAC SYSTEMS (UK) LIMITED—See Mamac Systems Inc.; *U.S. Private,* pg. 2559
MARATHON SENSORS INC.—See Halma plc; *Int'l,* pg. 3231
MARINE ELECTRIC SYSTEMS, INC.; *U.S. Private,* pg. 2575
MARINE INSTRUMENTS S.A.—See Grupo Arbulu S.L.; *Int'l,* pg. 3120
MAWI-THERM TEMPERATUR-PROZESSTECHNIK GMBH—See CHINO Corporation; *Int'l,* pg. 1571
MAXCESS INTERNATIONAL CORPORATION—See Berwind Corporation; *U.S. Private,* pg. 541
MAXON COMBUSTION EQUIPMENT SHANGHAI CO. LTD.—See Honeywell International Inc.; *U.S. Public,* pg. 1048
MAXON INTERNATIONAL B.V.B.A.—See Honeywell International Inc.; *U.S. Public,* pg. 1048
MEGGITT SA—See Parker Hannifin Corporation; *U.S. Public,* pg. 1642
MEGGITT (XIAMEN) SENSORS & CONTROLS CO LIMITED—See Parker Hannifin Corporation; *U.S. Public,* pg. 1641
MERCOID DIV.—See Arcline Investment Management LP; *U.S. Private,* pg. 313
MERIAM INSTRUMENT—See Berkshire Hathaway Inc.; *U.S. Public,* pg. 300
MESA LABORATORIES, INC.; *U.S. Public,* pg. 1425
METHODE MEXICO, S.A. DE C.V.—See Methode Electronics, Inc.; *U.S. Public,* pg. 1428
METTLER-TOLEDO AG—See Mettler-Toledo International, Inc.; *U.S. Public,* pg. 1432
METTLER-TOLEDO INGOLD INC.—See Mettler-Toledo International, Inc.; *U.S. Public,* pg. 1432
M.H. RHODES CRAMER, LLC—See CapitalWorks, LLC; *U.S. Private,* pg. 742
MICHELL INSTRUMENTS, INC.—See Battery Ventures, L.P.; *U.S. Private,* pg. 489
MICHELL INSTRUMENTS LIMITED—See Battery Ventures, L.P.; *U.S. Private,* pg. 489
MICRO CONTROL SYSTEMS INC.; *U.S. Private,* pg. 2702
MILJOCO CORP.—See Arcline Investment Management LP; *U.S. Private,* pg. 313
MILMEGA LIMITED—See AMETEK, Inc.; *U.S. Public,* pg. 121
MIRION TECHNOLOGIES (CANBERRA UK) LIMITED—See Mirion Technologies, Inc.; *U.S. Public,* pg. 1450
MIROITERIES DE L'OUEST SEMIVER CLIMAVER—See Compagnie de Saint-Gobain SA; *Int'l,* pg. 1724
MKS ASTEX PRODUCTS—See MKS Instruments, Inc.; *U.S. Public,* pg. 1452
MKS DENMARK APS—See MKS Instruments, Inc.; *U.S. Public,* pg. 1452
MKS INSTRUMENTS DEUTSCHLAND GMBH—See MKS Instruments, Inc.; *U.S. Public,* pg. 1453
MKS INSTRUMENTS, INC.; *U.S. Public,* pg. 1452
MKS INSTRUMENTS UK LTD.—See MKS Instruments, Inc.; *U.S. Public,* pg. 1453
MKS JAPAN, INC.—See MKS Instruments, Inc.; *U.S. Public,* pg. 1453
MKS MATERIALS DELIVERY PRODUCTS—See MKS Instruments, Inc.; *U.S. Public,* pg. 1453
MKS MSC, INC.—See MKS Instruments, Inc.; *U.S. Public,* pg. 1453
MMI BUSINESS SERVICES FZE—See Endress+Hauser

N.A.I.C.S. INDEX

334513 — INSTRUMENTS AND REL...

(International) Holding AG; *Int'l*, pg. 2408
MOKON—See Windjammer Capital Investors, LLC; *U.S. Private*, pg. 4538
MOORE INDUSTRIES-EUROPE INC.—See Moore Industries International Inc.; *U.S. Private*, pg. 2780
MOORE INDUSTRIES INTERNATIONAL INC.; *U.S. Private*, pg. 2780
MOUNTZ, INC.—See Snap-on Incorporated; *U.S. Public*, pg. 1897
MSA DE MEXICO, S.A. DE C.V.—See MSA Safety Incorporated; *U.S. Public*, pg. 1482
MT INDUSTRIAL SUPPLIES & SERVICES CO. LTD.—See Endress+Hauser (International) Holding AG; *Int'l*, pg. 2408
MUELLER CO. LTD.—See Mueller Water Products, Inc.; *U.S. Public*, pg. 1486
NANODROP TECHNOLOGIES LLC—See Thermo Fisher Scientific Inc.; *U.S. Public*, pg. 2149
NAO, INC.; *U.S. Private*, pg. 2834
NATIONAL INSTRUMENTS CORPORATION; *U.S. Private*, pg. 2856
NATIONAL METER AND AUTOMATION, INC.—See Badger Meter, Inc.; *U.S. Public*, pg. 263
NAVTEAM A/S—See Grupo Arbulu S.L.; *Int'l*, pg. 3120
NDC TECHNOLOGIES, INC.—See Nordson Corporation; *U.S. Public*, pg. 1533
NDC TECHNOLOGIES LIMITED—See Nordson Corporation; *U.S. Public*, pg. 1533
NDC TECHNOLOGIES SRL—See Nordson Corporation; *U.S. Public*, pg. 1533
NDI EUROPE GMBH—See Roper Technologies, Inc.; *U.S. Public*, pg. 1812
NDS SURGICAL IMAGING BV—See Novanta Inc.; *U.S. Public*, pg. 1548
NDS SURGICAL IMAGING, LLC—See Novanta Inc.; *U.S. Public*, pg. 1548
NETZSCH TAURUS INSTRUMENTS GMBH—See Erich Netzsch GmbH & Co. Holding KG; *Int'l*, pg. 2493
NEU AUTOMATION SAS—See Groupe SFPI SA; *Int'l*, pg. 3111
NEWALL ELECTRONICS INC.—See Sensata Technologies Holding plc; *U.S. Public*, pg. 1866
NEWALL MEASUREMENT SYSTEMS LTD.—See Sensata Technologies Holding plc; *U.S. Public*, pg. 1866
NEWPORT ELECTRONICS, INC.—See Arcline Investment Management LP; *U.S. Private*, pg. 314
NEXTRON CORPORATION—See Powell Industries, Inc.; *U.S. Public*, pg. 1705
NK ENGINEERING CO., LTD.—See Endress+Hauser (International) Holding AG; *Int'l*, pg. 2408
NORCROSS CORPORATION—See Saint Clair Systems, Inc.; *U.S. Private*, pg. 3529
NORDSON ASYMTEK, INC.—See Nordson Corporation; *U.S. Public*, pg. 1533
NORTHERN DIGITAL INC.—See Roper Technologies, Inc.; *U.S. Public*, pg. 1812
NOSHOK INC.; *U.S. Private*, pg. 2965
NOVODIRECT GMBH—See Thermo Fisher Scientific Inc.; *U.S. Public*, pg. 2148
NUNC A/S—See Thermo Fisher Scientific Inc.; *U.S. Public*, pg. 2149
N.V. DRAEGER SAFETY BELGIUM S.A.—See Draegerwerk AG & Co. KGaA; *Int'l*, pg. 2198
OBCORP LLC—See AMETEK, Inc.; *U.S. Public*, pg. 121
O'BRIEN BVBA—See AMETEK, Inc.; *U.S. Public*, pg. 121
OEP, INC.—See Zurn Elkay Water Solutions Corporation; *U.S. Public*, pg. 2413
OGP MESSTECHNIK GMBH—See Quality Vision International Inc.; *U.S. Private*, pg. 3321
OGP SHANGHAI CO. LTD.—See Quality Vision International Inc.; *U.S. Private*, pg. 3321
OHIZUMI MFG. CO., LTD.—See Ferrotec Holdings Corporation; *Int'l*, pg. 2643
OMEGA ENGINEERING, INC.—See Arcline Investment Management LP; *U.S. Private*, pg. 314
OMS MOTION, INC.; *U.S. Private*, pg. 3018
ONE PLUS CORP.—See ParkerGale, LLC; *U.S. Private*, pg. 3098
ONERAIN, INC.; *U.S. Private*, pg. 3025
ONIX SYSTEMS INC.—See Thermo Fisher Scientific Inc.; *U.S. Public*, pg. 2149
OPSENS INC.—See Haemonetics Corporation; *U.S. Public*, pg. 979
OPTICAL GAGING (S) PTE, LTD—See Quality Vision International Inc.; *U.S. Private*, pg. 3321
OPTOSKAND AB—See Coherent Corp.; *U.S. Public*, pg. 528
ORBOTECH LTD.—See KLA Corporation; *U.S. Public*, pg. 1288
ORMCO LLC—See Danaher Corporation; *U.S. Public*, pg. 629
OXOID AB—See Thermo Fisher Scientific Inc.; *U.S. Public*, pg. 2150
OXOID AG—See Thermo Fisher Scientific Inc.; *U.S. Public*, pg. 2150
OXOID AS—See Thermo Fisher Scientific Inc.; *U.S. Public*, pg. 2150
OXOID BV—See Thermo Fisher Scientific Inc.; *U.S. Public*, pg. 2150
OXOID DEUTSCHLAND GMBH—See Thermo Fisher Scientific Inc.; *U.S. Public*, pg. 2150
OXOID N.V.—See Thermo Fisher Scientific Inc.; *U.S. Public*, pg. 2150
OXOID S.P.A—See Thermo Fisher Scientific Inc.; *U.S. Public*, pg. 2150
PALL TECHNOLOGY UK LIMITED—See Danaher Corporation; *U.S. Public*, pg. 630
PAR GOVERNMENT SYSTEMS CORPORATION—See Booz Allen Hamilton Holding Corporation; *U.S. Public*, pg. 369
PARKER HANNIFIN DE MEXICO-SEAL DE MATAMOROS FACILITY—See Parker Hannifin Corporation; *U.S. Public*, pg. 1649
PARKER HANNIFIN (ESPANA) S.A.—See Parker Hannifin Corporation; *U.S. Public*, pg. 1644
PARKER HANNIFIN - INSTRUMENTATION PRODUCTS DIV—See Parker Hannifin Corporation; *U.S. Public*, pg. 1647
PARKER HANNIFIN MANUFACTURING GERMANY GMBH & CO. KG AEROSPACE HYDRAULIC DIVISION—See Parker Hannifin Corporation; *U.S. Public*, pg. 1643
PARKER HANNIFIN MOTION AND CONTROL—See Parker Hannifin Corporation; *U.S. Public*, pg. 1647
PARKER HANNIFIN PRECISION FLUIDICS DIVISION—See Parker Hannifin Corporation; *U.S. Public*, pg. 1647
PARKER HANNIFIN SINGAPORE PTE. LTD.—See Parker Hannifin Corporation; *U.S. Public*, pg. 1649
PARKER HANNIFIN VERIFLO DIVISION—See Parker Hannifin Corporation; *U.S. Public*, pg. 1647
PCME LTD.—See The Carlyle Group Inc.; *U.S. Public*, pg. 2046
PCTEL EUROPE AB—See Amphenol Corporation; *U.S. Public*, pg. 132
PEAK DRINK DISPENSE LIMITED—See The Middleby Corporation; *U.S. Public*, pg. 2115
PENNY & GILES CONTROLS INC.—See Curtiss-Wright Corporation; *U.S. Public*, pg. 611
PENNY & GILES CONTROLS LTD.—See Curtiss-Wright Corporation; *U.S. Public*, pg. 611
PENNY & GILES CONTROLS LTD.—See Curtiss-Wright Corporation; *U.S. Public*, pg. 611
PENNY & GILES GMBH—See Curtiss-Wright Corporation; *U.S. Public*, pg. 612
PERBIO SCIENCE BVBA—See Thermo Fisher Scientific Inc.; *U.S. Public*, pg. 2151
PHASE ANALYZER COMPANY LTD.—See Roper Technologies, Inc.; *U.S. Public*, pg. 1812
PHENOMENEX, INC.—See Danaher Corporation; *U.S. Public*, pg. 630
PHOTONIKA LLC—See Endress+Hauser (International) Holding AG; *Int'l*, pg. 2409
PHOTONIS NETHERLANDS B.V.—See Ardian SAS; *Int'l*, pg. 556
PH TRADING W.L.L.—See Endress+Hauser (International) Holding AG; *Int'l*, pg. 2409
PIHER INTERNATIONAL GMBH—See Parker Hannifin Corporation; *U.S. Public*, pg. 1643
PLEXUS CORP. LIMITED—See Plexus Corp.; *U.S. Public*, pg. 1698
PLEXUS CORP. (UK) LIMITED—See Plexus Corp.; *U.S. Public*, pg. 1698
PLEXUS MANUFACTURING SDN. BHD.—See Plexus Corp.; *U.S. Public*, pg. 1698
PLEXUS SERVICIOS S. DE R.L. DE C.V.—See Plexus Corp.; *U.S. Public*, pg. 1698
PLEXUS (XIAMEN) CO., LTD.—See Plexus Corp.; *U.S. Public*, pg. 1698
POWERVAR CANADA INC.—See AMETEK, Inc.; *U.S. Public*, pg. 118
POWERVAR DEUTSCHLAND GMBH—See AMETEK, Inc.; *U.S. Public*, pg. 118
POWERVAR, LTD.—See AMETEK, Inc.; *U.S. Public*, pg. 118
PRECISION FABRICATING & CLEANING CO—See Precision Resources Inc.; *U.S. Private*, pg. 3246
PRECISION HYDRAULIC CYLINDERS (UK) LIMITED—See Leggett & Platt, Incorporated; *U.S. Public*, pg. 1303
PRECISION HYDRAULICS PRIVATE LIMITED—See Leggett & Platt, Incorporated; *U.S. Public*, pg. 1303
PRECISION TECHNOLOGIES PTE LTD—See Danaher Corporation; *U.S. Public*, pg. 626
PRIME ATLANTIC GLOBAL INSTRUMENTS LIMITED—See Endress+Hauser (International) Holding AG; *Int'l*, pg. 2409
PROCESS AUTOMATION LTD.—See Endress+Hauser (International) Holding AG; *Int'l*, pg. 2409
PROCESS CONTROL SERVICES, INC.—See Applied Industrial Technologies, Inc.; *U.S. Public*, pg. 171
PROCESS & ENERGY SOLUTIONS, S.A.—See Endress+Hauser (International) Holding AG; *Int'l*, pg. 2409
PROCESS SOLUTIONS, INC.—See New Mountain Capital, LLC; *U.S. Private*, pg. 2900
PROCON ENGINEERING LTD.—See NOV, Inc.; *U.S. Public*, pg. 1546
PROXEON BIOSYSTEMS A/S—See Thermo Fisher Scientific Inc.; *U.S. Public*, pg. 2149
PT. ENDRESS+HAUSER INDONESIA—See Endress+Hauser (International) Holding AG; *Int'l*, pg. 2409
PT. FESTO—See Festo AG & Co. KG; *Int'l*, pg. 2648
PT MECOINDO—See Itron, Inc.; *U.S. Public*, pg. 1176
PT ROCKWELL AUTOMATION INDONESIA—See Rockwell Automation, Inc.; *U.S. Public*, pg. 1805
PUNCH PLASTX EVERGEM NV—See Iep Invest SA; *Int'l*, pg. 3597
PUNCH PLASTX SRO—See Iep Invest SA; *Int'l*, pg. 3597
PUNCH SRO—See Iep Invest SA; *Int'l*, pg. 3597
PYROMETER INSTRUMENT CO., INC.—See Makke LLC; *U.S. Private*, pg. 2556
QINGDAO AIKETE AUTOMATION INSTRUMENT CO., LTD.—See Endress+Hauser (International) Holding AG; *Int'l*, pg. 2409
Q-LAB CORP.; *U.S. Private*, pg. 3312
QUALITY THERMISTOR, INC.—See CTS Corporation; *U.S. Public*, pg. 603
QUANZHOU FENGZE NICE MECHANICAL & ELECTRICAL EQUIPMENT CO., LTD.—See Endress+Hauser (International) Holding AG; *Int'l*, pg. 2409
QUATUOR S.A.—See Thermo Fisher Scientific Inc.; *U.S. Public*, pg. 2154
RADIOMETER MEDICAL APS—See Danaher Corporation; *U.S. Public*, pg. 631
RADIOMETER TURKU OY—See Danaher Corporation; *U.S. Public*, pg. 631
RAM OPTICAL INSTRUMENTATION INC.—See Quality Vision International Inc.; *U.S. Private*, pg. 3321
RAYTEK CORPORATION—See Fortive Corporation; *U.S. Public*, pg. 870
RED LION CONTROLS INC.—See HMS Networks AB; *Int'l*, pg. 3433
REMASAWCO AS—See Image Systems AB; *Int'l*, pg. 3618
RESPONDER SYSTEMS CORPORATION—See AMETEK, Inc.; *U.S. Public*, pg. 121
RESTEK CORPORATION; *U.S. Private*, pg. 3408
REX AUTOMATISIERUNGSTECHNIK GMBH—See Eckelmann AG; *Int'l*, pg. 2290
REXNORD AUSTRALIA PTY LTD.—See Zurn Elkay Water Solutions Corporation; *U.S. Public*, pg. 2413
REXNORD DO BRASIL INDUSTRIAL LTDA—See Zurn Elkay Water Solutions Corporation; *U.S. Public*, pg. 2413
REXNORD FLAT TOP ITALY SRL—See Zurn Elkay Water Solutions Corporation; *U.S. Public*, pg. 2413
REXNORD FRANCE HOLDINGS SAS—See Zurn Elkay Water Solutions Corporation; *U.S. Public*, pg. 2413
RGF ENVIRONMENTAL GROUP; *U.S. Private*, pg. 3420
ROCHESTER SENSORS, LLC—See Renovo Capital, LLC; *U.S. Private*, pg. 3399
ROCKWELL AUTOMATION CANADA LTD.—See Rockwell Automation, Inc.; *U.S. Public*, pg. 1805
ROCKWELL AUTOMATION DRIVES SYSTEMS—See Rockwell Automation, Inc.; *U.S. Public*, pg. 1806
ROCKWELL AUTOMATION, INC.; *U.S. Public*, pg. 1805
ROCKWELL AUTOMATION KOREA LTD.—See Rockwell Automation, Inc.; *U.S. Public*, pg. 1806
ROCKWELL AUTOMATION MIDDLE EAST—See Rockwell Automation, Inc.; *U.S. Public*, pg. 1806
RODA DEACO VALVE, INC.—See Roper Technologies, Inc.; *U.S. Public*, pg. 1813
ROFIN-BAASEL LASERTECH GMBH & CO. KG—See Coherent Corp.; *U.S. Public*, pg. 528
ROFIN-SINAR LASER GMBH—See Coherent Corp.; *U.S. Public*, pg. 527
ROHRBACK COSASCO SYSTEMS, INC.—See Halma plc; *Int'l*, pg. 3232
ROHRBACK COSASCO SYSTEMS UK LTD.—See Halma plc; *Int'l*, pg. 3232
ROPER TECHNOLOGIES, INC.; *U.S. Public*, pg. 1810
ROSEMOUNT MEASUREMENT LIMITED—See Emerson Electric Co.; *U.S. Public*, pg. 752
ROSEMOUNT NUCLEAR INSTRUMENTS—See Emerson Electric Co.; *U.S. Public*, pg. 747
ROSEMOUNT SPECIALTY PRODUCTS LLC—See Emerson Electric Co.; *U.S. Public*, pg. 747
RUDOLPH TECHNOLOGIES, INC.—See Onto Innovation Inc.; *U.S. Public*, pg. 1605
SABO-ARMATUREN SERVICE GMBH—See Emerson Electric Co.; *U.S. Public*, pg. 752
SAINT CLAIR SYSTEMS, INC.; *U.S. Private*, pg. 3529
SATA SARL—See Endress+Hauser (International) Holding AG; *Int'l*, pg. 2409
SAYAMA CORPORATION—See Air Water Inc.; *Int'l*, pg. 240
SCHENCK PROCESS HOLDING GMBH—See Blackstone Inc.; *U.S. Public*, pg. 360
SCHMITT INDUSTRIES, INC.; *U.S. Public*, pg. 1846
SCHUFF STEEL-GULF COAST, INC.—See INNOVATE Corp.; *U.S. Public*, pg. 1126
SEDEMA S.A.—See CHINO Corporation; *Int'l*, pg. 1571
SENSATA TECHNOLOGIES GMBH—See Sensata Technologies Holding plc; *U.S. Public*, pg. 1866
SENSITECH INC. - REDMOND PLANT—See Carrier Global Corporation; *U.S. Public*, pg. 442

334513 — INSTRUMENTS AND REL...

SENSITECH INC.—See Carrier Global Corporation; *U.S. Public*, pg. 442
SENSOR SCIENTIFIC, INC.—See CTS Corporation; *U.S. Public*, pg. 603
SENSORS, INC.; *U.S. Private*, pg. 3608
SENTRY EQUIPMENT CORP; *U.S. Private*, pg. 3610
SERCEL-GRC—See CGG; *Int'l*, pg. 1432
SEVERE SERVICE SPECIALISTS INC.—See Clearlake Capital Group, L.P.; *U.S. Private*, pg. 937
SHAANXI HAIFENG ENERGY AUTOMATION CO., LTD.—See Endress+Hauser (International) Holding AG; *Int'l*, pg. 2409
SHANGHAI DAHUA-CHINO INSTRUMENT CO., LTD.—See CHINO Corporation; *Int'l*, pg. 1571
SHANGHAI GUANZHI INDUSTRIAL AUTOMATION CO., LTD.—See CSG Smart Science & Technology Co., Ltd.; *Int'l*, pg. 1865
SHANGHAI YONGQIAN ELECTRICAL AND MECHANICAL CO., LTD.—See CSG Smart Science & Technology Co., Ltd.; *Int'l*, pg. 1865
SIERRA INSTRUMENTS INC.; *U.S. Private*, pg. 3647
SIGMASYS CORP.—See inTEST Corporation; *U.S. Public*, pg. 1159
SIMTRONICS AS—See 3M Company; *U.S. Public*, pg. 8
SIMTRONICS SAS—See 3M Company; *U.S. Public*, pg. 8
SINGAWAY FLUIDCONTROLS PTE LTD.—See Darco Water Technologies Limited; *Int'l*, pg. 1972
SINMED B.V.—See Roper Technologies, Inc.; *U.S. Public*, pg. 1813
S-IU - COR - COMINVESTMENT AG—See Endress+Hauser (International) Holding AG; *Int'l*, pg. 2409
SIXNET, LLC—See HMS Networks AB; *Int'l*, pg. 3433
SMARTEC SA—See Nova Ventures Group Corp.; *U.S. Private*, pg. 2966
SMARTSENSE—See Digi International Inc.; *U.S. Public*, pg. 662
SMD MARINE ELECTRONICS NAMIBIA (PTY) LTD—See Grupo Arbulu S.L.; *Int'l*, pg. 3120
SMITH ENGINEERING INC.—See Xylem Inc.; *U.S. Public*, pg. 2394
SOLARTRON ANALYTICAL—See AMETEK, Inc.; *U.S. Public*, pg. 118
SOUTHERN TRIALS (PTY) LTD.—See Thermo Fisher Scientific Inc.; *U.S. Public*, pg. 2147
SPECAC INC.—See Ampersand Management LLC; *U.S. Private*, pg. 265
SPECTRO ANALYTICAL INSTRUMENTS (ASIA-PACIFIC) LTD.—See AMETEK, Inc.; *U.S. Public*, pg. 118
SSD DRIVES LTD.—See Parker Hannifin Corporation; *U.S. Public*, pg. 1644
STANDARD FOR TRADING CO.—See Endress+Hauser (International) Holding AG; *Int'l*, pg. 2409
STEAG SCR-TECH, INC.—See Energy Capital Partners Management, LP; *U.S. Private*, pg. 1394
STERLING, INC.—See Harbour Group Industries, Inc.; *U.S. Private*, pg. 1860
STI CONTROLS, L.P.—See AMETEK, Inc.; *U.S. Public*, pg. 121
STRESS-TEK, INC.—See Vishay Precision Group, Inc.; *U.S. Public*, pg. 2303
SUPERIOR EQUIPMENT PTY LTD.—See Alamo Group Inc.; *U.S. Public*, pg. 71
TAG ENVIRONMENTAL INC.—See Leggett & Platt, Incorporated; *U.S. Public*, pg. 1303
TAI YU & CO., LTD.—See CHINO Corporation; *Int'l*, pg. 1571
TAYLOR HOBSON LTD.—See AMETEK, Inc.; *U.S. Public*, pg. 122
TAYLOR-WHARTON AMERICA INC.—See Air Water Inc.; *Int'l*, pg. 241
TECHNOCONTACT S.A.—See TransDigm Group Incorporated; *U.S. Public*, pg. 2181
TEKRAN INSTRUMENTS CORPORATION—See TSI Incorporated; *U.S. Private*, pg. 4253
TEKSCAN, INC.—See Artemis Capital Partners Management Co., LLC; *U.S. Private*, pg. 341
TEKTRONIX, INC.—See Fortive Corporation; *U.S. Public*, pg. 872
TELEDYNE ISCO—See Teledyne Technologies Incorporated; *U.S. Public*, pg. 1994
TELEMAC, S.A.—See Nova Ventures Group Corp.; *U.S. Private*, pg. 2966
TESEQ COMPANY LTD.—See AMETEK, Inc.; *U.S. Public*, pg. 119
TESEQ GMBH—See AMETEK, Inc.; *U.S. Public*, pg. 119
TESEQ (TAIWAN) LTD.—See AMETEK, Inc.; *U.S. Public*, pg. 119
TEST DEVICES INC.—See Durr AG; *Int'l*, pg. 2233
THERMO CIDTEC INC.—See Thermo Fisher Scientific Inc.; *U.S. Public*, pg. 2152
THERMO ELECTRIC COMPANY, INC.; *U.S. Private*, pg. 4142
THERMO ELECTRON INDUSTRIES—See Thermo Fisher Scientific Inc.; *U.S. Public*, pg. 2152
THERMO ELECTRON WEIGHING & INSPECTION LIMITED—See Thermo Fisher Scientific Inc.; *U.S. Public*, pg. 2152
THERMO FIBERGEN INC.—See Kadant Inc.; *U.S. Public*, pg. 1212

THERMO FISHER SCIENTIFIC BETEILIGUNGSVERWALTUNGS GMBH—See Thermo Fisher Scientific Inc.; *U.S. Public*, pg. 2153
THERMO FISHER SCIENTIFIC B.V.—See Thermo Fisher Scientific Inc.; *U.S. Public*, pg. 2154
THERMO FISHER SCIENTIFIC (CHINA) CO., LTD.—See Thermo Fisher Scientific Inc.; *U.S. Public*, pg. 2153
THERMO FISHER SCIENTIFIC (ECUBLENS) SARL—See Thermo Fisher Scientific Inc.; *U.S. Public*, pg. 2153
THERMO FISHER SCIENTIFIC INDIA PVT LTD—See Thermo Fisher Scientific Inc.; *U.S. Public*, pg. 2153
THERMO FISHER SCIENTIFIC IT SERVICES GMBH—See Thermo Fisher Scientific Inc.; *U.S. Public*, pg. 2154
THERMO FISHER SCIENTIFIC (PRAHA) S.R.O.—See Thermo Fisher Scientific Inc.; *U.S. Public*, pg. 2153
THERMO FISHER SCIENTIFIC SL—See Thermo Fisher Scientific Inc.; *U.S. Public*, pg. 2154
THERMO FISHER SCIENTIFIC WISSENSCHAFTLICHE GERATE GMBH—See Thermo Fisher Scientific Inc.; *U.S. Public*, pg. 2153
THERMO GAMMA-METRICS LLC—See Thermo Fisher Scientific Inc.; *U.S. Public*, pg. 2154
THERMO HYPERSIL-KEYSTONE LLC—See Thermo Fisher Scientific Inc.; *U.S. Public*, pg. 2154
THERMO NESLAB LLC—See Thermo Fisher Scientific Inc.; *U.S. Public*, pg. 2154
THERMON U.K. LTD.—See Thermon Group Holdings, Inc.; *U.S. Public*, pg. 2155
THERMO RADIOMETRIE LIMITED—See Thermo Fisher Scientific Inc.; *U.S. Public*, pg. 2154
THERMO RAMSEY ITALIA S.R.L.—See Thermo Fisher Scientific Inc.; *U.S. Public*, pg. 2154
THERMO SHANDON INC.—See Thermo Fisher Scientific Inc.; *U.S. Public*, pg. 2154
THWING-ALBERT NETHERLANDS—See Thwing-Albert Instrument Company; *U.S. Private*, pg. 4166
TIGER OPTICS LLC; *U.S. Private*, pg. 4170
TITAN INDUSTRIES INCORPORATED; *U.S. Private*, pg. 4177
TOPAS GMBH—See DZ BANK AG Deutsche Zentral-Genossenschaftsbank; *Int'l*, pg. 2245
TRAFFIC & PARKING CONTROL CO., INC.; *U.S. Private*, pg. 4203
TRANSNORM SYSTEM GMBH—See Honeywell International Inc.; *U.S. Public*, pg. 1052
TRIAD CONTROL SYSTEMS INC.—See The Newtron Group Inc.; *U.S. Private*, pg. 4084
TRI-SEN SYSTEMS CORPORATION—See China Automation Group Limited; *Int'l*, pg. 1483
TRIUMPH ACTUATION SYSTEMS-VALENCIA, LLC—See Triumph Group, Inc.; *U.S. Public*, pg. 2196
TX TECHNOLOGY CORP.—See EXX Inc.; *U.S. Private*, pg. 1453
ULTRA ELECTRONICS, NUCLEAR SENSORS & PROCESS INSTRUMENTATION—See Advent International Corporation; *U.S. Public*, pg. 100
UNITED CONTROLS GROUP, INC.—See Roper Technologies, Inc.; *U.S. Public*, pg. 1814
UNITED ELECTRIC CONTROLS COMPANY INC.; *U.S. Private*, pg. 4291
UNITED TECHNOLOGIES ELECTRONIC CONTROLS, INC.—See Carrier Global Corporation; *U.S. Public*, pg. 441
UNIVERSAL FLOW MONITORS, INC.—See Arcline Investment Management LP; *U.S. Private*, pg. 313
USON LP—See Roper Technologies, Inc.; *U.S. Public*, pg. 1814
VACUUM INSTRUMENT CORP.—See Valero Capital Partners LLC; *U.S. Private*, pg. 4331
VALCO INSTRUMENTS CO., INC.; *U.S. Private*, pg. 4330
VALCOM CO., LTD.—See Eagle Industry Co., Ltd.; *Int'l*, pg. 2266
VAL.CO SRL—See GHM Messtechnik GmbH; *Int'l*, pg. 2959
VALVULAS, ACCESORIOS Y MAQUINARIAS S.A.C.—See Emerson Electric Co.; *U.S. Public*, pg. 752
VALVULAS, ACCESORIOS Y MAQUINARIAS S.A.C.—See Emerson Electric Co.; *U.S. Public*, pg. 752
VBI LTD—See Parker Hannifin Corporation; *U.S. Public*, pg. 1643
VEEDER-ROOT COMPANY—See Vontier Corporation; *U.S. Public*, pg. 2309
VEGA AMERICAS, INC.—See Grieshaber Holding GmbH; *Int'l*, pg. 3083
VEGA-CONTROLS LTD.—See Grieshaber Holding GmbH; *Int'l*, pg. 3083
VEGA GRIESHABER KG—See Grieshaber Holding GmbH; *Int'l*, pg. 3083
VISHAY MEASUREMENTS GROUP (U.K.) LTD.—See Vishay Intertechnology, Inc.; *U.S. Public*, pg. 2303
VITEC, INC.; *U.S. Private*, pg. 4405
VTI INSTRUMENTS PRIVATE LIMITED—See AMETEK, Inc.; *U.S. Public*, pg. 122
WABASH TECHNOLOGIES MEXICO S. DE R.L. DE C.V.—See Sensata Technologies Holding plc; *U.S. Public*, pg. 1866
WALK-ON PRODUCTS, INC.—See Leggett & Platt, Incorporated; *U.S. Public*, pg. 1304

WALTER HERZOG GMBH—See Roper Technologies, Inc.; *U.S. Public*, pg. 1812
WATLOW RICHMOND—See Tinicum Enterprises, Inc.; *U.S. Private*, pg. 4175
W.E. ANDERSON DIV.—See Arcline Investment Management LP; *U.S. Private*, pg. 313
WEATHERFORD KSP CO., LTD.—See Weatherford International plc; *U.S. Public*, pg. 2340
WEISS INSTRUMENTS, INC.—See Arcline Investment Management LP; *U.S. Private*, pg. 313
WESTERN DIGITAL TAIWAN CO., LTD.—See Western Digital Corporation; *U.S. Public*, pg. 2355
WEVADA NV—See Iep Invest SA; *U.S. Public*, pg. 3597
WILCOM, INC.; *U.S. Private*, pg. 4518
WINLAND ELECTRONICS, INC.; *U.S. Private*, pg. 4542
WOODWARD POLAND SP. Z O.O.—See Woodward, Inc.; *U.S. Public*, pg. 2378
WTK-ELEKTRONIK GMBH—See Trimble, Inc.; *U.S. Public*, pg. 2190
WUNDER-BAR INTERNATIONAL, INC.—See The Middleby Corporation; *U.S. Public*, pg. 2115
WUXI KEDI AUTOMATION EQUIPMENT CO., LTD.—See Endress+Hauser (International) Holding AG; *Int'l*, pg. 2409
XOMETRY EUROPE GMBH—See Xometry, Inc.; *U.S. Public*, pg. 2391
XOMETRY, INC.; *U.S. Public*, pg. 2391
XOMETRY UK LTD.—See Xometry, Inc.; *U.S. Public*, pg. 2391
YANTAI CSG ZHENGXIN ELECTRIC TECHNOLOGY CO., LTD.—See CSG Smart Science & Technology Co., Ltd.; *Int'l*, pg. 1865
YSI INTEGRATED SYSTEMS & SERVICES—See Xylem Inc.; *U.S. Public*, pg. 2395
ZHEJIANG HELIHUA TECHNOLOGY CO., LTD.—See Endress+Hauser (International) Holding AG; *Int'l*, pg. 2409
ZHUZHOU HUASHENG TECHNOLOGY CO., LTD.—See Endress+Hauser (International) Holding AG; *Int'l*, pg. 2409
ZOLO TECHNOLOGIES—See Pinnacle West Capital Corporation; *U.S. Public*, pg. 1692
ZTEC INSTRUMENTS, INC.—See Teradyne, Inc.; *U.S. Public*, pg. 2018

334514 — TOTALIZING FLUID METER AND COUNTING DEVICE MANUFACTURING

2D FLUIDICS PTY LTD—See First Graphene Limited; *Int'l*, pg. 2684
ACCUDYNAMICS LLC—See Halma plc; *Int'l*, pg. 3231
ADVANCED CONTROLS (M) SDN. BHD—See Advanced Holdings Ltd.; *Int'l*, pg. 159
ADVANTEST KOREA CO., LTD.—See Advantest Corporation; *Int'l*, pg. 166
ADVANTEST (SUZHOU) CO., LTD.—See Advantest Corporation; *Int'l*, pg. 165
ALBER CORP.—See Vertiv Holdings Co; *U.S. Public*, pg. 2288
ALICAT BV—See Halma plc; *Int'l*, pg. 3230
AMEKAI METER (XIAMEN) CO.,LTD.—See AMETEK, Inc.; *U.S. Public*, pg. 120
AMETEK AIRTECHNOLOGY GROUP LTD.—See AMETEK, Inc.; *U.S. Public*, pg. 116
AMETEK CERAMICS, INC.—See AMETEK, Inc.; *U.S. Public*, pg. 116
AMETEK CTS GERMANY GMBH—See AMETEK, Inc.; *U.S. Public*, pg. 120
AMETEK HSA, INC.—See AMETEK, Inc.; *U.S. Public*, pg. 117
AMETEK SCP, INC.—See AMETEK, Inc.; *U.S. Public*, pg. 119
AMETEK S.R.L.—See AMETEK, Inc.; *U.S. Public*, pg. 119
ANALYTICAL TECHNOLOGY, INC.—See Badger Meter, Inc.; *U.S. Public*, pg. 263
APATOR KFAP SP. Z O.O.—See Apator S.A.; *Int'l*, pg. 501
APATOR TELEMETRIA SP. Z O.O.—See Apator S.A.; *Int'l*, pg. 501
APPLIED GEOMECHANICS INC—See CARBO Ceramics Inc.; *U.S. Public*, pg. 748
ASSA ABLOY SICHERHEITSTECHNIK GMBH—See ASSA ABLOY AB; *Int'l*, pg. 636
ATRM HOLDINGS, INC.—See Star Equity Holdings, Inc.; *U.S. Public*, pg. 1937
AUTO METER PRODUCTS, INC.—See Promus Holdings, LLC; *U.S. Public*, pg. 3284
A.Y.M. INC.—See A.Y. McDonald Manufacturing Co.; *U.S. Private*, pg. 29
AZBIL KIMMON CO., LTD.—See Azbil Corporation; *Int'l*, pg. 777
AZBIL KYOTO CO., LTD.—See Azbil Corporation; *Int'l*, pg. 777
BADGER METER DE MEXICO, SA DE CV—See Badger Meter, Inc.; *U.S. Public*, pg. 263
BADGER METER, INC.; *U.S. Public*, pg. 263
BADGER METER SLOVAKIA—See Badger Meter, Inc.; *U.S. Public*, pg. 263

N.A.I.C.S. INDEX

334515 — INSTRUMENT MANUFACT...

BADGER METER SWISS AG—See Badger Meter, Inc.; *U.S. Public*, pg. 263
BEIJING CONST INSTRUMENTS TECHNOLOGY INC.; *Int'l*, pg. 948
BIDWELL INDUSTRIAL GROUP, INC.; *U.S. Private*, pg. 551
BLUE-WHITE INDUSTRIES LTD; *U.S. Private*, pg. 596
BLU-RAY DIV.—See Bidwell Industrial Group, Inc.; *U.S. Private*, pg. 551
BOSE B.V.—See Bose Corporation; *U.S. Private*, pg. 619
CHENGDU ANDISOON MEASURE CO., LTD.—See Houpu Clean Energy Group Co., Ltd; *Int'l*, pg. 3490
THE CHISHOLM CORPORATION—See INSCO, Inc.; *U.S. Private*, pg. 2085
CI TECH COMPONENTS AG—See Giesecke & Devrient GmbH; *Int'l*, pg. 2969
CITIZEN T.I.C. CO., LTD.—See Citizen Watch Co., Ltd.; *Int'l*, pg. 1624
COMPUTIME LIMITED—See Computime Group Limited; *Int'l*, pg. 1760
CURTIS INSTRUMENTS INC.; *U.S. Private*, pg. 1126
CYTEL (SHANGHAI) LTD.—See ASSA ABLOY AB; *Int'l*, pg. 640
DANAHER CONTROLS—See Danaher Corporation; *U.S. Public*, pg. 625
DANAHER INDUSTRIAL CONTROLS—See Danaher Corporation; *U.S. Public*, pg. 626
DESIGNATRONICS, INC.; *U.S. Private*, pg. 1214
DEUBLIN AUSTRIA GMBH—See Hoerbiger Holding AG; *Int'l*, pg. 3439
DIEHL METERING AB—See Diehl Stiftung & Co. KG; *Int'l*, pg. 2115
DIEHL METERING LLC—See Diehl Stiftung & Co. KG; *Int'l*, pg. 2115
DIEHL METERING S.L.—See Diehl Stiftung & Co. KG; *Int'l*, pg. 2115
D&K ENGINEERING, INC.—See The Burke Porter Group; *U.S. Private*, pg. 4003
DURECOM CO., LTD.—See Hancom, Inc.; *Int'l*, pg. 3242
ELSTER AMCO WATER, LLC—See Honeywell International Inc.; *U.S. Public*, pg. 1048
ELSTER METERING PTY LTD.—See Honeywell International Inc.; *U.S. Public*, pg. 1048
ELSTER SOLUTIONS LLC—See Honeywell International Inc.; *U.S. Public*, pg. 1048
ELSTER WATER METERING B.V.—See Honeywell International Inc.; *U.S. Public*, pg. 1048
ELSTER WATER METERING HOLDINGS LIMITED—See Honeywell International Inc.; *U.S. Public*, pg. 1048
ELSTER WATER METERING LTD.—See Honeywell International Inc.; *U.S. Public*, pg. 1048
EMERSON AIR COMFORT PRODUCTS—See Emerson Electric Co.; *U.S. Public*, pg. 744
ENDRESS+HAUSER POLSKA SP. Z O.O.—See Endress+Hauser (International) Holding AG; *Int'l*, pg. 2407
FARIA BEEDE INSTRUMENTS, INC.; *U.S. Private*, pg. 1474
FARO TECHNOLOGY POLSKA SP. Z O.O.—See FARO Technologies, Inc.; *U.S. Public*, pg. 823
FAURE HERMAN SAS—See BNP Paribas SA; *Int'l*, pg. 1083
FLOW INSTRUMENTS & ENGINEERING GMBH—See Chart Industries, Inc.; *U.S. Public*, pg. 481
FLOW ITALIA S.R.L.—See AIP, LLC; *U.S. Private*, pg. 137
FLOW JAPAN CORPORATION - NAGOYA—See AIP, LLC; *U.S. Private*, pg. 137
FLOW JAPAN CORPORATION—See AIP, LLC; *U.S. Private*, pg. 137
FLOW LATINO AMERICANA INDUSTRIA E COMERCIO LTDA.—See AIP, LLC; *U.S. Private*, pg. 137
FLOW UK LIMITED—See AIP, LLC; *U.S. Private*, pg. 137
FOX THERMAL INSTRUMENTS, INC.—See Harbour Group Industries, Inc.; *U.S. Private*, pg. 1860
GENERAL DEVICES CO. INC.; *U.S. Private*, pg. 1664
GOLDCARD SMART GROUP CO., LTD.; *Int'l*, pg. 3027
GRACO OHIO INC.—See Graco, Inc.; *U.S. Public*, pg. 953
HAIMO TECHNOLOGIES GROUP CORP.; *Int'l*, pg. 3211
HAREL MALLAC ENGINEERING LTD—See Harel Mallac & Co. Ltd.; *Int'l*, pg. 3274
HAYS FLUID CONTROLS—See Romac Industries, Inc.; *U.S. Private*, pg. 3475
HOLLEY METERING LTD.—See Holley Holding, Ltd.; *Int'l*, pg. 3451
HUIZHONG INSTRUMENTATION CO., LTD.; *Int'l*, pg. 3527
INTERNATIONAL LIGHT TECHNOLOGIES, INC.—See Halma plc; *Int'l*, pg. 3232
INTEST CORPORATION; *U.S. Public*, pg. 1158
ISTA POLSKA SP.Z.O.O.—See CK Asset Holdings Limited; *Int'l*, pg. 1636
ITRON LIQUID MEASUREMENT—See Itron, Inc.; *U.S. Public*, pg. 1176
KESSLER-ELLIS PRODUCTS CO. INC.; *U.S. Private*, pg. 2291
K-TECHNOLOGIES, INC.; *U.S. Private*, pg. 2251
LIQUID CONTROLS, INC.—See IDEX Corp; *U.S. Public*, pg. 1091
MAGNAGRIP—See Bidwell Industrial Group, Inc.; *U.S. Private*, pg. 551

MCCROMETER INC.—See Danaher Corporation; *U.S. Public*, pg. 628
MCT WORLDWIDE LLC—See Cohu, Inc.; *U.S. Public*, pg. 530
MICRO MOTION INC.—See Emerson Electric Co.; *U.S. Public*, pg. 750
MIDWEST METER INC.—See FEI, Inc; *U.S. Private*, pg. 1493
MOOG AUSTRALIA PTY. LTD.—See Moog Inc.; *U.S. Public*, pg. 1470
MOOG CONTROLS CORP.-PHILIPPINES—See Moog Inc.; *U.S. Public*, pg. 1470
MOOG CONTROLS HONG KONG LTD.—See Moog Inc.; *U.S. Public*, pg. 1470
MOOG GMBH—See Moog Inc.; *U.S. Public*, pg. 1470
MOOG JAPAN LTD.—See Moog Inc.; *U.S. Public*, pg. 1470
MOOG KOREA LTD.—See Moog Inc.; *U.S. Public*, pg. 1470
MUELLER MIDDLE EAST (FZE)—See Mueller Water Products, Inc.; *U.S. Public*, pg. 1486
MULLEN TESTERS—See Standex International; *U.S. Public*, pg. 1930
NEPTUNE TECHNOLOGY GROUP (CANADA) LIMITED—See Roper Technologies, Inc.; *U.S. Public*, pg. 1812
OVERHOFF TECHNOLOGY CORPORATION—See US Nuclear Corp.; *U.S. Public*, pg. 2267
PALL CORPORATION—See Danaher Corporation; *U.S. Public*, pg. 629
PALL DO BRASIL LTDA.—See Danaher Corporation; *U.S. Public*, pg. 630
PARKEON, INC.—See Astorg Partners S.A.S.; *Int'l*, pg. 657
PARKER HANNIFIN GMBH & CO. KG ELECTROMECHANICAL AUTOMATION—See Parker Hannifin Corporation; *U.S. Public*, pg. 1644
PARKING FACILITIES LTD.—See Hill & Smith PLC; *Int'l*, pg. 3392
PARKTRON MALAYSIA SDH BHD—See Chung-Hsin Electric & Machinery Manufacturing Corp.; *Int'l*, pg. 1597
PG DRIVES TECHNOLOGY INC.—See Curtiss-Wright Corporation; *U.S. Public*, pg. 612
POWER-DYNE—See Bidwell Industrial Group, Inc.; *U.S. Private*, pg. 551
POWRTEC INTERNATIONAL CORP.; *U.S. Private*, pg. 3240
PRESTON KINETIC—See DynamicSignals LLC; *U.S. Private*, pg. 1299
P.T. FUJI DHARMA ELECTRIC—See Fuji Electric Co., Ltd.; *Int'l*, pg. 2812
QUANTUM DATA INC.—See Teledyne Technologies Incorporated; *U.S. Public*, pg. 1994
RADIOMETRICS CORPORATION; *U.S. Private*, pg. 3344
RAPID PRINT—See Bidwell Industrial Group, Inc.; *U.S. Private*, pg. 551
READING ALLOYS, INC.—See Palladium Equity Partners, LLC; *U.S. Private*, pg. 3078
ROUCHON INDUSTRIES, INC.; *U.S. Public*, pg. 1815
SEALTRON ACQUISITION CORP.—See AMETEK, Inc.; *U.S. Public*, pg. 116
SENSUS METERING SYSTEMS INC.—See Xylem Inc.; *U.S. Public*, pg. 2395
SINGER VALVE (TAICANG) CO., LTD.—See Mueller Water Products, Inc.; *U.S. Public*, pg. 1485
SOLIDSTATE CONTROLS, INC. DE ARGENTINA S.R.L.—See AMETEK, Inc.; *U.S. Public*, pg. 121
SPX FLOW TECHNOLOGY ROSISTA GMBH—See Lone Star Funds; *U.S. Private*, pg. 2486
STERLING INSTRUMENT DIV.—See Designatronics, Inc.; *U.S. Private*, pg. 1214
STOCK DRIVE PRODUCTS DIV.—See Designatronics, Inc.; *U.S. Private*, pg. 1214
TANCY INSTRUMENT GROUP CO., LTD.—See Goldcard Smart Group Co., Ltd.; *Int'l*, pg. 3027
TECHNO DIV.—See Designatronics, Inc.; *U.S. Private*, pg. 1214
THERMO ELECTRON CORPORATION PROCESS INSTRUMENTS—See Thermo Fisher Scientific Inc.; *U.S. Public*, pg. 2152
THERMO ELECTRON LIMITED—See Thermo Fisher Scientific Inc.; *U.S. Public*, pg. 2152
TRANSCAT, INC.; *U.S. Public*, pg. 2179
TRANSICOIL LLC—See TransDigm Group Incorporated; *U.S. Public*, pg. 2183
TRIMBLE, INC.; *U.S. Public*, pg. 2189
TRIMBLE NAVIGATION LTD.—See Trimble, Inc.; *U.S. Public*, pg. 2192
TRIMBLE RAILWAY LIMITED—See Trimble, Inc.; *U.S. Public*, pg. 2192
TRIMBLE SOLUTIONS INDIA PVT. LTD.—See Trimble, Inc.; *U.S. Public*, pg. 2193
TRIMBLE SOLUTIONS OY—See Trimble, Inc.; *U.S. Public*, pg. 2193
VONTIER CORPORATION; *U.S. Public*, pg. 2308
VORTEK INSTRUMENTS, LLC—See Azbil Corporation; *U.S. Public*, pg. 777
WESTERN SKY INDUSTRIES LLC—See TransDigm Group Incorporated; *U.S. Public*, pg. 2183
WIRELESS TELECOM GROUP, INC.—See Artemis Capital Partners Management Co., LLC; *U.S. Private*, pg. 340

ZHEJIANG TANCY ULTRASONIC TECHNOLOGY CO., LTD.—See Goldcard Smart Group Co., Ltd.; *Int'l*, pg. 3027

334515 — INSTRUMENT MANUFACTURING FOR MEASURING AND TESTING ELECTRICITY AND ELECTRICAL SIGNALS

3M COMPANY - SANTA CRUZ—See 3M Company; *U.S. Public*, pg. 5
AAI CORP. - AUTOMATED TEST EQUIPMENT—See Textron Inc.; *U.S. Public*, pg. 2029
ABM ELECTRICAL POWER SOLUTIONS, LLC—See ABM Industries, Inc.; *U.S. Public*, pg. 25
ACCELONIX B.V.—See Accelonix Limited; *Int'l*, pg. 81
ACCELONIX LIMITED; *Int'l*, pg. 81
ACCELONIX SARL—See Accelonix Limited; *Int'l*, pg. 81
ACTARIS PTY LTD—See Itron, Inc.; *U.S. Public*, pg. 1175
ACTIA-AIXIA—See Actia Group SA; *Int'l*, pg. 118
A&D CO., LTD.; *Int'l*, pg. 18
ADLINK TECHNOLOGY SINGAPORE PTE. LTD.—See AD-LINK Technology, Inc.; *Int'l*, pg. 151
ADOR POWERTRON LTD.—See Ador Welding Ltd; *Int'l*, pg. 152
ADVANTEST PHILIPPINES, INC.—See Advantest Corporation; *Int'l*, pg. 165
AEROFLEX AVCOMM—See Advent International Corporation; *U.S. Private*, pg. 99
AEROFLEX WICHITA, INC.—See Viavi Solutions Inc.; *U.S. Public*, pg. 2295
AFIS, S.A.—See Energizer Holdings, Inc.; *U.S. Public*, pg. 760
AGILENT TECHNOLOGIES DEUTSCHLAND ALPHA GMBH—See Agilent Technologies, Inc.; *U.S. Public*, pg. 61
AGILENT TECHNOLOGIES EUROPE B.V.—See Agilent Technologies, Inc.; *U.S. Public*, pg. 60
AGILENT TECHNOLOGIES WORLD TRADE, INC.—See Agilent Technologies, Inc.; *U.S. Public*, pg. 61
AGRIDENT GMBH—See Merck & Co., Inc.; *U.S. Public*, pg. 1415
ALIO INDUSTRIES, LLC—See Allient Inc.; *U.S. Public*, pg. 80
ALLIANCE FAMILY OF COMPANIES, LLC—See Ancor Holdings, L.P.; *U.S. Private*, pg. 274
AMALGAMATED ELECTRONIC CORPORATION LIMITED—See The Carlyle Group Inc.; *U.S. Public*, pg. 2045
AMERICAN INNOVATIONS, LTD.—See HM International; *U.S. Private*, pg. 1954
AMETEK DENMARK—See AMETEK, Inc.; *U.S. Public*, pg. 116
AMPLO S.A.; *Int'l*, pg. 436
ANALOG DEVICES AUSTRALIA PTY. LTD.—See Analog Devices, Inc.; *U.S. Public*, pg. 134
ANALOG DEVICES K.K.—See Analog Devices, Inc.; *U.S. Public*, pg. 135
ANALOG DEVICES TAIWAN, LTD.—See Analog Devices, Inc.; *U.S. Public*, pg. 135
ANALOGIC CORPORATION—See Altaris Capital Partners, LLC; *U.S. Private*, pg. 205
ANALYSIS & MEASUREMENT SERVICES CORPORATION; *U.S. Private*, pg. 271
ANGELS INSTRUMENTATION, INC.—See Transcat, Inc.; *U.S. Public*, pg. 2179
ANRITSU A/S—See Anritsu Corporation; *Int'l*, pg. 475
ANRITSU CUSTOMER SUPPORT CO., LTD.—See Anritsu Corporation; *Int'l*, pg. 475
ANRITSU ELECTRONICA, LTDA.—See Anritsu Corporation; *Int'l*, pg. 475
ANRITSU ELECTRONICS LTD—See Anritsu Corporation; *Int'l*, pg. 475
ANRITSU PTE. LTD—See Anritsu Corporation; *Int'l*, pg. 476
ANRITSU PTY. LTD—See Anritsu Corporation; *Int'l*, pg. 476
ANRITSU S.A—See Anritsu Corporation; *Int'l*, pg. 476
APATOR CONTROL SP. Z O.O.—See Apator S.A.; *Int'l*, pg. 501
APEGELEC INDUSTRIES—See Hiolle Industries S.A.; *Int'l*, pg. 3401
ARMATURE DNS 2000 INC.; *Int'l*, pg. 574
ARNOLD MAGNETIC TECHNOLOGIES AG—See Compass Diversified Holdings; *U.S. Public*, pg. 559
ARTIZA (SHANGHAI) SOFTWARE DEVELOPMENT CO., LTD.—See Artiza Networks, Inc.; *Int'l*, pg. 585
ASHLY AUDIO INC—See DCC plc; *Int'l*, pg. 1990
ASSOCIATED RESEARCH INC.—See Ikonix Group, Inc.; *U.S. Private*, pg. 2041
ASTRONICS TEST SYSTEMS INC.—See Astronics Corporation; *U.S. Public*, pg. 217
AUDIO PRECISION, INC.—See Battery Ventures, L.P.; *U.S. Private*, pg. 488
AUREA ENERGY SOLUTIONS, INC.—See ESW Capital, LLC; *U.S. Private*, pg. 1429
AUROS TECHNOLOGY CO., LTD.; *Int'l*, pg. 714
AVERNA TECHNOLOGIES INC.; *Int'l*, pg. 739
AVERNA TEST SYSTEMS INC.—See Averna Technologies Inc.; *Int'l*, pg. 739

334515 — INSTRUMENT MANUFACT...

AVTRON AEROSPACE, INC.—See Odyssey Investment Partners, LLC; *U.S. Private*, pg. 2994
AXIOM TEST EQUIPMENT, INC.—See Transcat, Inc.; *U.S. Public*, pg. 2179
BALLARD TECHNOLOGY, INC.—See Astronics Corporation; *U.S. Public*, pg. 217
BAUMER BOURDON-HAENNI S.A.S.; *Int'l*, pg. 895
BEIJING AEROSPACE SHENZHOU INTELLIGENT EQUIPMENT TECHNOLOGY CO., LTD.; *Int'l*, pg. 945
BEIJING ZHONGCHUANG TELECOM TEST CO., LTD.—See Beijing Xinwei Technology Group Co., Ltd.; *Int'l*, pg. 961
BIOLIDICS LIMITED; *Int'l*, pg. 1038
BIOTECTOR ANALYTICAL SYSTEMS LTD—See Danaher Corporation; *U.S. Public*, pg. 625
BIOTREND CEVRE VE ENERJI YATIRIMLARI A.S.; *Int'l*, pg. 1043
BIRD TECHNOLOGIES GROUP INC.; *U.S. Private*, pg. 564
BOONTON ELECTRONICS CORP.—See Artemis Capital Partners Management Co., LLC; *U.S. Private*, pg. 341
BOSCH LIMITED; *Int'l*, pg. 1116
BOURNS, INC.; *U.S. Private*, pg. 624
BP SOLAR ESPANA, S.A.U.—See BP plc; *Int'l*, pg. 1128
B.R.A.H.M.S. GMBH—See Thermo Fisher Scientific Inc.; *U.S. Public*, pg. 2154
CADEX ELECTRONICS INC.; *Int'l*, pg. 1248
CALIFORNIA INSTRUMENTS CORPORATION—See AMETEK, Inc.; *U.S. Public*, pg. 118
CANON ADVANCED TECHNOLOGIES TAIWAN, INC.—See Canon Inc.; *Int'l*, pg. 1295
CAPELLA MICROSYSTEMS, INC.—See Vishay Intertechnology, Inc.; *U.S. Public*, pg. 2302
CARLO GAVAZZI (CANADA) INC.—See Carlo Gavazzi Holding AG; *Int'l*, pg. 1338
CEM GMBH—See CEM Corporation; *U.S. Private*, pg. 808
CEM MICROWAVE TECHNOLOGY LTD.—See CEM Corporation; *U.S. Private*, pg. 808
CEM S.R.L.—See CEM Corporation; *U.S. Private*, pg. 808
CERULEAN SHANGHAI COMPANY LTD.—See Coesia S.p.A.; *Int'l*, pg. 1689
CHINA AUTO ELECTRONICS GROUP LIMITED; *Int'l*, pg. 1483
CHINO INSTRUMENTATION (KUNSHAN) CO., LTD.—See CHINO Corporation; *Int'l*, pg. 1570
CHROMA ATE INC.; *Int'l*, pg. 1587
CIRCUIT CHECK INC.—See Merit Capital Partners; *U.S. Private*, pg. 2674
CLASSIC INSTRUMENTS; *U.S. Private*, pg. 916
COBHAM SIGNAL & CONTROL SOLUTIONS—See Advent International Corporation; *U.S. Private*, pg. 99
COMBA TELECOM INC.—See Comba Telecom Systems Holdings Limited; *Int'l*, pg. 1708
COOPER (CHINA) CO., LTD.—See Eaton Corporation plc; *Int'l*, pg. 2277
COREPILE S.A.—See Energizer Holdings, Inc.; *U.S. Public*, pg. 760
CRESTCHIC LIMITED—See Crestchic PLC; *Int'l*, pg. 1841
CSG SMART SCIENCE & TECHNOLOGY CO., LTD.; *Int'l*, pg. 1864
C-TECH INDUSTRIES, LLC—See Group Thermote & Vanhalst; *Int'l*, pg. 3089
CUES, INC.—See SPX Technologies, Inc.; *U.S. Public*, pg. 1921
DAGE JAPAN CO., LTD.—See Nordson Corporation; *U.S. Public*, pg. 1532
DALEKOVOD EMU D.O.O.—See Dalekovod d.d.; *Int'l*, pg. 1951
DANUVIUS EOOD—See Caisse de Depot et Placement du Quebec; *Int'l*, pg. 1255
DELTA DESIGN, INC.—See Cohu, Inc.; *U.S. Public*, pg. 529
DENSO MTEC CORPORATION—See Denso Corporation; *Int'l*, pg. 2032
DIAMED G.M.B.H.—See Bio-Rad Laboratories, Inc.; *U.S. Public*, pg. 333
DIGALOG SYSTEMS INC.; *U.S. Private*, pg. 1229
DIONEX BRASIL INSTRUMENTOS CIENTIFICOS LTDA—See Thermo Fisher Scientific Inc.; *U.S. Public*, pg. 2146
DIONEX HOLDING GMBH—See Thermo Fisher Scientific Inc.; *U.S. Public*, pg. 2146
DIONEX SINGAPORE PTE LTD.—See Thermo Fisher Scientific Inc.; *U.S. Public*, pg. 2146
DIONEX SWEDEN AB—See Thermo Fisher Scientific Inc.; *U.S. Public*, pg. 2146
DIT-MCO INTERNATIONAL—See Commerce Bancshares, Inc.; *U.S. Public*, pg. 544
DOBLE ENGINEERING COMPANY—See ESCO Technologies, Inc.; *U.S. Public*, pg. 793
DOMAT CONTROL SYSTEM S.R.O.—See CEZ, a.s.; *Int'l*, pg. 1427
DOMAT CONTROL SYSTEM S.R.O.—See CEZ, a.s.; *Int'l*, pg. 1427
DOMETIC GERMANY MPS GMBH—See Dometic Group AB; *Int'l*, pg. 2160
DONG A ELTEK CO., LTD.; *Int'l*, pg. 2163
DONGHUA TESTING TECHNOLOGY CO., LTD.; *Int'l*, pg. 2167

D&V ELECTRONICS LTD—See Motorcar Parts of America, Inc.; *U.S. Public*, pg. 1477
D&V ELECTRONIC TECHNOLOGY (SHANGHAI) CO., LTD.—See Motorcar Parts of America, Inc.; *U.S. Public*, pg. 1477
DYNISCO S.R.L.—See Roper Technologies, Inc.; *U.S. Public*, pg. 1811
EATON CORP. - ELECTRICAL SECTOR, POWER QUALITY USA—See Eaton Corporation plc; *Int'l*, pg. 2279
EATON INDUSTRIES (CANADA) COMPANY—See Eaton Corporation plc; *Int'l*, pg. 2281
EATON POWER QUALITY COMPANY—See Eaton Corporation plc; *Int'l*, pg. 2279
ECE INDUSTRIES LIMITED - METER DIVISION—See ECE Industries Limited; *Int'l*, pg. 2288
ECOBAT S.R.O.—See Energizer Holdings, Inc.; *U.S. Public*, pg. 761
ECOMAL CESKA REPUBLIKA S.R.O.—See Vishay Intertechnology, Inc.; *U.S. Public*, pg. 2302
ECOMAL EUROPE GMBH—See Vishay Intertechnology, Inc.; *U.S. Public*, pg. 2302
ECOMAL IBERIA S.A.U.—See Vishay Intertechnology, Inc.; *U.S. Public*, pg. 2302
ECOMAL SWEDEN AB—See Vishay Intertechnology, Inc.; *U.S. Public*, pg. 2302
ECO-METERING—See ENGIE SA; *Int'l*, pg. 2429
EDUCATED DESIGN & DEVELOPMENT, INC.; *U.S. Private*, pg. 1338
EDWARDS VACUUM, LLC—See Atlas Copco AB; *Int'l*, pg. 682
EICO INC.; *U.S. Private*, pg. 1346
ELDOLED B.V.—See Acuity Brands, Inc.; *U.S. Public*, pg. 37
ELECTROMAGNETICA S.A.; *Int'l*, pg. 2353
ELECTRO-METRICS CORPORATION; *U.S. Private*, pg. 1354
ELEFIRST SCIENCE AND TECHNOLOGY CO., LTD.; *Int'l*, pg. 2355
ELSPEC ENGINEERING INDIA PVT. LTD.—See Elspec Engineering Ltd.; *Int'l*, pg. 2370
ELSPEC ENGINEERING LTD.; *Int'l*, pg. 2370
ELSPEC NORTH AMERICA, INC.—See Elspec Engineering Ltd.; *Int'l*, pg. 2370
ELSPEC PORTUGAL LDA.—See Elspec Engineering Ltd.; *Int'l*, pg. 2370
ENCORE ELECTRONICS, INC.—See Allan R. Nelson Engineering (1997) Inc.; *Int'l*, pg. 332
ENDRESS+HAUSER GES.M.B.H.—See Endress+Hauser (International) Holding AG; *Int'l*, pg. 2407
ENDRESS+HAUSER (SLOVENIJA) D.O.O.—See Endress+Hauser (International) Holding AG; *Int'l*, pg. 2406
ENDRESS+HAUSER (THAILAND) LTD.—See Endress+Hauser (International) Holding AG; *Int'l*, pg. 2406
ENERGIZER AUSTRALIA PTY. LTD.—See Energizer Holdings, Inc.; *U.S. Public*, pg. 761
ENERGIZER CZECH SPOL.SR.O.—See Energizer Holdings, Inc.; *U.S. Public*, pg. 761
ENERGIZER DO BRASIL LTDA.—See Energizer Holdings, Inc.; *U.S. Public*, pg. 761
ENERGIZER GROUP BELGIUM N.V.—See Energizer Holdings, Inc.; *U.S. Public*, pg. 761
ENERGIZER GROUP POLSKA SP. ZO.O—See Energizer Holdings, Inc.; *U.S. Public*, pg. 761
ENERGIZER GROUP PORTUGAL UNIPESSOAL, LDA.—See Edgewell Personal Care Company; *U.S. Public*, pg. 718
ENERGIZER GROUP VENEZUELA C.A.—See Edgewell Personal Care Company; *U.S. Public*, pg. 718
ENERGIZER ITALY S.R.L.—See Energizer Holdings, Inc.; *U.S. Public*, pg. 761
ENERGIZER LLC—See Edgewell Personal Care Company; *U.S. Public*, pg. 718
ENERGIZER PHILIPPINES, INC.—See Energizer Holdings, Inc.; *U.S. Public*, pg. 761
ENERGIZER SA—See Energizer Holdings, Inc.; *U.S. Public*, pg. 761
ENERGIZER (SOUTH AFRICA) LTD.—See Energizer Holdings, Inc.; *U.S. Public*, pg. 761
ENERGIZER (THAILAND) LIMITED—See Energizer Holdings, Inc.; *U.S. Public*, pg. 761
ENPLAS NICHING TECHNOLOGY CORPORATION—See ENPLAS CORPORATION; *Int'l*, pg. 2445
ENSINGER SPECIAL POLYMERS, INC.—See Ensinger GmbH; *Int'l*, pg. 2448
ERECTION ELECTROMECHANICS TESTING JSC; *Int'l*, pg. 2490
ETS-LINDGREN INC.—See ESCO Technologies, Inc.; *U.S. Public*, pg. 794
EVEREADY BATTERY COMPANY, INC.—See Energizer Holdings, Inc.; *U.S. Public*, pg. 761
EVEREADY ECUADOR C.A.—See Energizer Holdings, Inc.; *U.S. Public*, pg. 761
EVERETT CHARLES TECHNOLOGIES LLC—See Cohu, Inc.; *U.S. Public*, pg. 530
EVERETT CHARLES TEST FIXTURE DIVISION—See Cohu, Inc.; *U.S. Public*, pg. 530

EVER READY LIMITED—See Energizer Holdings, Inc.; *U.S. Public*, pg. 761
EXFO AMERICA INC.—See EXFO Inc.; *Int'l*, pg. 2584
EXFO ASIA PACIFIC PTE LTD.—See EXFO Inc.; *Int'l*, pg. 2584
EXFO ASIA PACIFIC PTE. LTD.—See EXFO Inc.; *Int'l*, pg. 2584
EXFO ASIA PACIFIC PTE. LTD.—See EXFO Inc.; *Int'l*, pg. 2584
EXFO EUROPE LTD.—See EXFO Inc.; *Int'l*, pg. 2584
EXFO INC.; *Int'l*, pg. 2584
EXFO INDIA—See EXFO Inc.; *Int'l*, pg. 2584
EXFO JAPAN—See EXFO Inc.; *Int'l*, pg. 2584
EXFO NAVTEL PRODUCT GROUP—See EXFO Inc.; *Int'l*, pg. 2584
FAFNIR GMBH—See Vontier Corporation; *U.S. Public*, pg. 2308
FEI SANTA BARBARA—See Thermo Fisher Scientific Inc.; *U.S. Public*, pg. 2147
FINNKUMU OY—See Harju Elekter AS; *Int'l*, pg. 3277
FISHER SCIENTIFIC SPRL—See Thermo Fisher Scientific Inc.; *U.S. Public*, pg. 2148
FLUKE CORPORATION—See Fortive Corporation; *U.S. Public*, pg. 870
FLUKE DEUTSCHLAND GMBH—See Fortive Corporation; *U.S. Public*, pg. 870
FLUKE NETWORKS INC.—See Fortive Corporation; *U.S. Public*, pg. 870
FREEDOM COMMUNICATION TECHNOLOGIES, INC.—See Astronics Corporation; *U.S. Public*, pg. 217
FUJIAN NEBULA ELECTRONICS CO., LTD.; *Int'l*, pg. 2819
FUJI ELECTRIC METER CO., LTD.—See Fuji Electric Co., Ltd.; *Int'l*, pg. 2811
GANZ METER COMPANY LTD.—See Itron, Inc.; *U.S. Public*, pg. 1175
GEFRAN FRANCE S.A.—See Gefran S.p.A.; *Int'l*, pg. 2912
GEFRAN UK LTD.—See Gefran S.p.A.; *Int'l*, pg. 2912
GEORGIA-PACIFIC PLYWOOD PLANT—See Koch Industries, Inc.; *U.S. Private*, pg. 2328
GEOVISION INC.; *Int'l*, pg. 2942
GEVEA AB—See Addtech AB; *Int'l*, pg. 133
GIGA SOLUTION TECH. CO., LTD.—See Ardentec Corporation; *Int'l*, pg. 554
GIGA-TRONICS INSTRUMENTS—See Ault Alliance, Inc.; *U.S. Public*, pg. 227
GOLDEN ALTOS CORPORATION—See Eico Inc.; *U.S. Private*, pg. 1346
GOLDEN PALM PETROLEUM SERVICES COMPANY W.L.L.—See Endress+Hauser (International) Holding AG; *Int'l*, pg. 2408
GOOD WILL INSTRUMENT EURO B.V.—See Good Will Instrument Co., Ltd.; *Int'l*, pg. 3039
GOOD WILL INSTRUMENT KOREA CO., LTD.—See Good Will Instrument Co., Ltd.; *Int'l*, pg. 3039
GOOD WILL INSTRUMENT (SEA) SDN. BHD.—See Good Will Instrument Co., Ltd.; *Int'l*, pg. 3039
GOTTFERT WERKSTOFF-PRUFMASCHINEN GMBH; *Int'l*, pg. 3044
GREKA ENERGY, CALIFORNIA—See Greka Energy Corporation; *U.S. Private*, pg. 1783
GRESHAM WORLDWIDE, INC.—See Ault Alliance, Inc.; *U.S. Public*, pg. 227
GUANGZHOU KINTE INDUSTRIAL CO., LTD.—See China National Electric Apparatus Research Institute Co., Ltd.; *Int'l*, pg. 1531
GULF COAST POWER & CONTROL OF LOUISIANA LLC—See CSE Global Ltd.; *Int'l*, pg. 1864
GW INSTEK INDIA LLP—See Good Will Instrument Co., Ltd.; *Int'l*, pg. 3039
HANGZHOU CHANG CHUAN TECHNOLOGY CO., LTD.; *Int'l*, pg. 3246
HANGZHOU INNOVER TECHNOLOGY CO., LTD.; *Int'l*, pg. 3248
HANGZHOU PAX ELECTRONIC TECHNOLOGY LIMITED—See Hi Sun Technology (China) Limited; *Int'l*, pg. 3380
HANGZHOU PREVAIL OPTOELECTRONIC EQUIPMENT CO., LTD.; *Int'l*, pg. 3249
HANGZHOU SUNRISE TECHNOLOGY COMPANY LIMITED; *Int'l*, pg. 3250
HATHAWAY SYSTEMS CORPORATION—See Allient Inc.; *U.S. Public*, pg. 80
HB SOLUTION CO., LTD.; *Int'l*, pg. 3295
HEATEFLEX CORPORATION; *U.S. Private*, pg. 1901
HEMOCUE AUSTRALIA PTY. LTD.—See Danaher Corporation; *U.S. Public*, pg. 630
HEMOCUE GMBH—See Danaher Corporation; *U.S. Public*, pg. 630
HEMOCUE, INC.—See Danaher Corporation; *U.S. Public*, pg. 630
HEMOCUE OY—See Danaher Corporation; *U.S. Public*, pg. 630
HGS-LITO KFT.—See Hella GmbH & Co. KGaA; *Int'l*, pg. 3332
HID GLOBAL CORPORATION—See ASSA ABLOY AB; *Int'l*, pg. 637
HIKAM ELECTRONICA DE MEXICO, S.A.DE C.V.—See Hirakawa Hewtech Corp.; *Int'l*, pg. 3403

N.A.I.C.S. INDEX

334515 — INSTRUMENT MANUFACT...

HIKAM TECNOLOGIA DE SINALOA, S.A.DE C.V.—See Hirakawa Hewtech Corp.; *Int'l*, pg. 3403
HIOKI ENGINEERING SERVICE CORPORATION—See HIOKI E.E. Corporation; *Int'l*, pg. 3401
HIOKI FOREST PLAZA CORPORATION—See HIOKI E.E. Corporation; *Int'l*, pg. 3401
HIOKI KOREA CO., LTD.—See HIOKI E.E. Corporation; *Int'l*, pg. 3401
HIOKI (SHANGHAI) MEASUREMENT TECHNOLOGIES CO., LTD.—See HIOKI E.E. Corporation; *Int'l*, pg. 3401
HIOKI (SHANGHAI) MEASURING INSTRUMENTS CO., LTD.—See HIOKI E.E. Corporation; *Int'l*, pg. 3401
HIOKI (SHANGHAI) TECHNOLOGY DEVELOPMENT CO., LTD.—See HIOKI E.E. Corporation; *Int'l*, pg. 3401
HIOKI SINGAPORE PTE. LTD.—See HIOKI E.E. Corporation; *Int'l*, pg. 3401
HIOKI USA CORPORATION—See HIOKI E.E. Corporation; *Int'l*, pg. 3401
HIPOTRONICS, INC.—See Hubbell Incorporated; *U.S. Public*, pg. 1066
HOKKAIDO ELECTRIC METERS INDUSTRY—See Hokkaido Electric Power Co., Inc.; *Int'l*, pg. 3443
HOLZWORTH INSTRUMENTATION, INC.—See Artemis Capital Partners Management Co., LLC; *U.S. Private*, pg. 341
HUAFENG TEST & CONTROL TECHNOLOGY (TIANJIN) CO., LTD.—See Beijing Huafeng Test & Control Technology Co., Ltd.; *Int'l*, pg. 952
HYDROGENICS TEST SYSTEMS—See Cummins Inc.; *U.S. Public*, pg. 607
ICOS VISION SYSTEMS CORPORATION N.V.—See KLA Corporation; *U.S. Public*, pg. 1267
ICOS VISION SYSTEMS LTD.—See KLA Corporation; *U.S. Public*, pg. 1268
ICOS VISION SYSTEMS NV—See KLA Corporation; *U.S. Public*, pg. 1268
ICOS VISION SYSTEMS (SHENZHEN) CO. LTD.—See KLA Corporation; *U.S. Public*, pg. 1267
IDEAL INDUSTRIES INC; *U.S. Private*, pg. 2036
IGB AUTOMOTIVE LTD.—See Lear Corporation; *U.S. Public*, pg. 1297
IGB AUTOMOTIVE VIETNAM CO., LTD.—See Lear Corporation; *U.S. Public*, pg. 1297
IMPERIAL MACHINE & TOOL CO.—See Kaiser Aluminum Corporation; *U.S. Public*, pg. 1213
IMPORT, BUILDING & TRADING CO., LTD.—See CHINO Corporation; *Int'l*, pg. 1571
INDUSTRIAL SALES & SERVICE-GC S.R.L.—See Endress+Hauser (International) Holding AG; *Int'l*, pg. 2408
INSTEK AMERICA CORP.—See Good Will Instrument Co., Ltd.; *Int'l*, pg. 3039
INSTEK ELECTRONIC (SHANGHAI) CO., LTD.—See Good Will Instrument Co., Ltd.; *Int'l*, pg. 3039
INSTRUMENT TRANSFORMER EQUIPMENT CORPORATION—See Falfurrias Capital Partners, LP; *U.S. Private*, pg. 1467
IRIS INSTRUMENTS SA—See Bureau de Recherches Geologiques et Miniere; *Int'l*, pg. 1221
ISTA BRASIL SERVICOS DE ENERGIA LTDA.—See CK Asset Holdings Limited; *Int'l*, pg. 1635
ISTA CESKA REPUBLICA S.R.O.—See CK Asset Holdings Limited; *Int'l*, pg. 1635
ISTA CIS—See CK Asset Holdings Limited; *Int'l*, pg. 1635
ISTA DANMARK A/S—See CK Asset Holdings Limited; *Int'l*, pg. 1635
ISTA DEUTSCHLAND GMBH—See CK Asset Holdings Limited; *Int'l*, pg. 1635
ISTA ENERGY SOLUTIONS LIMITED—See CK Asset Holdings Limited; *Int'l*, pg. 1635
ISTA ENERJI HIZMETLERI TIC. LTD. STI.—See CK Asset Holdings Limited; *Int'l*, pg. 1636
ISTA INTERNATIONAL GMBH—See CK Asset Holdings Limited; *Int'l*, pg. 1635
ISTA ITALIA S.R.L.—See CK Asset Holdings Limited; *Int'l*, pg. 1636
ISTA LUXEMBURG GMBH—See CK Asset Holdings Limited; *Int'l*, pg. 1636
ISTA MAGYARORSZAG MERESTECHNIKA SZERVIZ KFT.—See CK Asset Holdings Limited; *Int'l*, pg. 1636
ISTA MEASUREMENT TECHNOLOGY SERVICES (BEIJING) CO., LTD.—See CK Asset Holdings Limited; *Int'l*, pg. 1636
ISTA METERING SERVICES ESPANA, S.A.—See CK Asset Holdings Limited; *Int'l*, pg. 1636
ISTA MIDDLE EAST FZE—See CK Asset Holdings Limited; *Int'l*, pg. 1636
ISTA NEDERLAND B.V.—See CK Asset Holdings Limited; *Int'l*, pg. 1636
ISTA NORGE AS—See CK Asset Holdings Limited; *Int'l*, pg. 1636
ISTA OSTERREICH GMBH—See CK Asset Holdings Limited; *Int'l*, pg. 1636
ISTA ROMANIA SRL—See CK Asset Holdings Limited; *Int'l*, pg. 1636
ISTA RUS O.O.O.—See CK Asset Holdings Limited; *Int'l*, pg. 1636

ISTA SLOVAKIA S.R.O.—See CK Asset Holdings Limited; *Int'l*, pg. 1636
ISTA SWISS AG—See CK Asset Holdings Limited; *Int'l*, pg. 1636
ITRON JAPAN CO., LTD.—See Itron, Inc.; *U.S. Public*, pg. 1176
ITRON METERING SOLUTIONS UK LTD—See Itron, Inc.; *U.S. Public*, pg. 1176
ITRON NEDERLAND B.V.—See Itron, Inc.; *U.S. Public*, pg. 1176
ITRON PORTUGAL, UNIPESSOAL, LDA.—See Itron, Inc.; *U.S. Public*, pg. 1176
ITRON SPAIN SLU—See Itron, Inc.; *U.S. Public*, pg. 1176
ITRON UNTERSTUTZUNGSKASSE GMBH—See Itron, Inc.; *U.S. Public*, pg. 1176
IXIA—See Keysight Technologies, Inc.; *U.S. Public*, pg. 1227
JIANGSU WANLONG AUTOMATION EQUIPMENT CO., LTD.—See Endress+Hauser (International) Holding AG; *Int'l*, pg. 2408
KLA CORPORATION; *U.S. Public*, pg. 1267
KLA-TENCOR CHINA CORPORATION—See KLA Corporation; *U.S. Public*, pg. 1268
KLA-TENCOR CORP. - TEXAS-FINLE DIVISION—See KLA Corporation; *U.S. Public*, pg. 1268
KLA-TENCOR GMBH—See KLA Corporation; *U.S. Public*, pg. 1268
KLA-TENCOR ITALY S.R.L.—See KLA Corporation; *U.S. Public*, pg. 1268
KLA-TENCOR MIE GMBH—See KLA Corporation; *U.S. Public*, pg. 1268
KLA-TENCOR MIE INDIA PRIVATE LIMITED—See KLA Corporation; *U.S. Public*, pg. 1268
KLA-TENCOR (SINGAPORE) PTE. LTD.—See KLA Corporation; *U.S. Public*, pg. 1268
LADE PROFESIONAL S.A.—See Fortive Corporation; *U.S. Public*, pg. 872
LANDTEC NORTH AMERICA, INC.—See Graco, Inc.; *U.S. Public*, pg. 954
LASER PROJECTION TECHNOLOGIES, INC.—See FARO Technologies, Inc.; *U.S. Public*, pg. 823
LECROY LIGHTSPEED CORPORATION—See Teledyne Technologies Incorporated; *U.S. Public*, pg. 1994
LEVITON INTEGRATED METERING SYSTEMS, INC.—See Leviton Manufacturing Company, Inc.; *U.S. Private*, pg. 2436
LITEPOINT EUROPE A/S—See Teradyne, Inc.; *U.S. Public*, pg. 2018
MARVIN TEST SOLUTIONS, INC.—See Marvin Engineering Company, Inc.; *U.S. Private*, pg. 2598
MAXIMA TECHNOLOGIES & SYSTEMS LLC—See Enerpac Tool Group Corp.; *U.S. Public*, pg. 766
MEIYO ELECTRIC CO., LTD.—See CHINO Corporation; *Int'l*, pg. 1571
METRIC INDUSTRIAL AB—See Addtech AB; *Int'l*, pg. 134
METRIX INSTRUMENT CO., LP—See Roper Technologies, Inc.; *U.S. Public*, pg. 1812
MILBANK MANUFACTURING COMPANY INC.; *U.S. Private*, pg. 2726
MULTITEST GMBH—See Cohu, Inc.; *U.S. Public*, pg. 530
NARVA ELEKTRIJAAMAD AS—See Eesti Energia AS; *Int'l*, pg. 2317
NEARFIELD SYSTEMS, INC.—See AMETEK, Inc.; *U.S. Public*, pg. 121
NEOLOGY, INC.—See Avery Dennison Corporation; *U.S. Public*, pg. 245
NEWPORT ELECTRONICS B.V.—See Arcline Investment Management LP; *U.S. Private*, pg. 314
NORDNETZ GMBH—See E.ON SE; *Int'l*, pg. 2258
NORTH ATLANTIC INDUSTRIES INC; *U.S. Private*, pg. 2942
OBERLAND STROMNETZ GMBH & CO. KG—See E.ON SE; *Int'l*, pg. 2258
OMEGA ENGINEERING GMBH—See Arcline Investment Management LP; *U.S. Private*, pg. 314
OMEGA ENGINEERING LTD.—See Arcline Investment Management LP; *U.S. Private*, pg. 314
OPTRICON GMBH—See Biosynex SA; *Int'l*, pg. 1042
OPUS FORMENBAU GMBH & CO. KG—See AdCapital AG; *U.S. Private*, pg. 126
ORIENTEC CO., LTD.—See A&D Co., Ltd.; *Int'l*, pg. 19
PACIFIC INSTRUMENTS, INC.—See Vishay Precision Group, Inc.; *U.S. Public*, pg. 2303
PCORE ELECTRIC COMPANY, INC.—See Hubbell Incorporated; *U.S. Public*, pg. 1067
PEARPOINT, INC.—See SPX Technologies, Inc.; *U.S. Public*, pg. 1921
PE ENERGY LIMITED—See Endress+Hauser (International) Holding AG; *Int'l*, pg. 2408
PHADIA AS—See Thermo Fisher Scientific Inc.; *U.S. Public*, pg. 2153
PHASE MATRIX, INC.—See National Instruments Corporation; *U.S. Private*, pg. 2858
PICOSPIN, LLC—See Thermo Fisher Scientific Inc.; *U.S. Public*, pg. 2155
POHIVORK OU—See Eesti Energia AS; *Int'l*, pg. 2318
POYRY INFRA GMBH—See AFRY AB; *Int'l*, pg. 195
PREDICTIVE SERVICE, LLC—See Align Capital Partners, LLC; *U.S. Private*, pg. 167

PROZESS UND MASCHINEN AUTOMATION GMBH—See Danaher Corporation; *U.S. Public*, pg. 630
QINGDAO GMB AUTOMOTIVE CO., LTD—See GMB Corp.; *Int'l*, pg. 3012
QINGDAO GMB MACHINERY PRODUCT CO., LTD.—See GMB Corp.; *Int'l*, pg. 3012
QUALITROL COMPANY LLC—See Fortive Corporation; *U.S. Public*, pg. 871
RADIODETECTION CANADA LTD.—See SPX Technologies, Inc.; *U.S. Public*, pg. 1921
REBA ORGANIZACJA ODZYSKU S.A.—See Edgewell Personal Care Company; *U.S. Public*, pg. 718
RE'LEM PUBLIC BENEFIT COMPANY—See Energizer Holdings, Inc.; *U.S. Public*, pg. 761
RFL ELECTRONICS, INC.—See Hubbell Incorporated; *U.S. Public*, pg. 1067
ROCTEST LTD.—See Nova Ventures Group Corp.; *U.S. Private*, pg. 2966
ROD-L ELECTRONICS INC.; *U.S. Private*, pg. 3469
ROI-ET GREEN CO. LTD—See EGAT Public Company Limited; *Int'l*, pg. 2322
RONAN ENGINEERING COMPANY; *U.S. Private*, pg. 3477
ROYCE INSTRUMENTS, INC.—See V-Tek Incorporated; *U.S. Private*, pg. 4328
S.A. ISTA N.V.—See CK Asset Holdings Limited; *Int'l*, pg. 1635
SANTAK ELECTRONICS (SHENZHEN) CO., LTD.—See Eaton Corporation plc; *Int'l*, pg. 2282
SATIC, INC.; *U.S. Private*, pg. 3553
SCHLUMBERGER—See Schlumberger Limited; *U.S. Public*, pg. 1844
SCHWEITZER ENGINEERING LABORATORIES INC.; *U.S. Private*, pg. 3573
SEMTECH CANADA CORPORATION—See Semtech Corporation; *U.S. Public*, pg. 1864
SENCORE, INC.—See The Riverside Company; *U.S. Private*, pg. 4110
SIGNUM SYSTEMS CORP.—See IAR Systems Group AB; *Int'l*, pg. 3569
SOLID STATE MEASUREMENTS INC.; *U.S. Private*, pg. 3709
SONEL TEST & MEASUREMENT, INC.; *U.S. Private*, pg. 3712
SOUTHERN DATA SOLUTIONS, INC.—See Spire Capital Partners, LLC; *U.S. Private*, pg. 3757
SPECTRAL DYNAMICS, INC.; *U.S. Private*, pg. 3751
STERILIN LIMITED—See Thermo Fisher Scientific Inc.; *U.S. Public*, pg. 2152
TANGKO PRIMA PT—See CHINO Corporation; *Int'l*, pg. 1571
TECHNO TEST S.R.L.—See Endress+Hauser (International) Holding AG; *Int'l*, pg. 2409
TEGAM, INC.—See Advanced Energy Industries, Inc.; *U.S. Public*, pg. 47
TELEDYNE LECROY (BEIJING) TRADING CO., LTD.—See Teledyne Technologies Incorporated; *U.S. Public*, pg. 1994
TELEDYNE LECROY, INC.—See Teledyne Technologies Incorporated; *U.S. Public*, pg. 1994
TEL-INSTRUMENT ELECTRONICS CORP.; *U.S. Public*, pg. 1991
TEMPER ENERGY INTERNATIONAL, SOCIEDAD LIMITADA—See Boer Power Holdings Limited; *Int'l*, pg. 1099
TEMPO COMMUNICATIONS, INC.—See Emerson Electric Co.; *U.S. Public*, pg. 742
TEMPO COMMUNICATIONS, INC.—See Emerson Electric Co.; *U.S. Public*, pg. 750
TERADYNE GMBH—See Teradyne, Inc.; *U.S. Public*, pg. 2018
TERADYNE, INC.-ASSEMBLY TEST DIVISION—See Teradyne, Inc.; *U.S. Public*, pg. 2018
TERADYNE, INC.; *U.S. Public*, pg. 2017
TERADYNE KOREA LTD.—See Teradyne, Inc.; *U.S. Public*, pg. 2018
TERADYNE (SHANGHAI) CO., LTD—See Teradyne, Inc.; *U.S. Public*, pg. 2018
TERADYNE TAIWAN LTD.—See Teradyne, Inc.; *U.S. Public*, pg. 2018
TESTAR ELECTRONIC CORPORATION—See Chroma ATE Inc.; *Int'l*, pg. 1588
TESTEQUITY LLC—See Distribution Solutions Group, Inc.; *U.S. Public*, pg. 669
TEXIO TECHNOLOGY CORPORATION—See Good Will Instrument Co., Ltd.; *Int'l*, pg. 3039
THAI GMB INDUSTRY CO., LTD—See GMB Corp.; *Int'l*, pg. 3012
THERAGENICS CORPORATION—See Juniper Investment Company, LLC; *U.S. Private*, pg. 2244
THERMO FISHER SCIENTIFIC BIOPRODUCTION PTE. LTD.—See Thermo Fisher Scientific Inc.; *U.S. Public*, pg. 2153
THERMO FISHER SCIENTIFIC LIFE INVESTMENTS III S.A.R.L.—See Thermo Fisher Scientific Inc.; *U.S. Public*, pg. 2154
THERMO SCIENTIFIC PORTABLE ANALYTICAL INSTRUMENTS INC—See Thermo Fisher Scientific Inc.; *U.S. Public*, pg. 2154

334515 — INSTRUMENT MANUFACT...

TOHOKU ANRITSU CO., LTD.—See Anritsu Corporation; *Int'l*, pg. 476
TRIGLA LTD.—See Endress+Hauser (International) Holding AG; *Int'l*, pg. 2409
TTT-CUBED, INC.—See HEICO Corporation; *U.S. Public*, pg. 1021
UCT FLUID DELIVERY SOLUTIONS S.R.O.—See Ultra Clean Holdings, Inc.; *U.S. Public*, pg. 2223
VAF INSTRUMENTS B.V.—See Aalberts N.V.; *Int'l*, pg. 36
VIATRAN CORPORATION—See Roper Technologies, Inc.; *U.S. Public*, pg. 1814
VISHAY HIREL SYSTEMS ASIA LIMITED—See Vishay Intertechnology, Inc.; *U.S. Public*, pg. 2303
VISHAY HIREL SYSTEMS LLC—See Vishay Intertechnology, Inc.; *U.S. Public*, pg. 2303
VISHAY POLYTECH CO. LTD.—See Vishay Intertechnology, Inc.; *U.S. Public*, pg. 2303
VITREK CORPORATION—See Branford Castle, Inc.; *U.S. Private*, pg. 639
VLSI STANDARDS, INC.—See KLA Corporation; *U.S. Public*, pg. 1269
VTI INSTRUMENTS CORPORATION—See AMETEK, Inc.; *U.S. Public*, pg. 122
WAEKON CORP.—See Crawford United Corporation; *U.S. Public*, pg. 592
WENZEL ASSOCIATES, INC.—See Arcline Investment Management LP; *U.S. Private*, pg. 313
WIDE CORPORATION—See AIFUL Corporation; *Int'l*, pg. 232
WPI-BOSTON DIVISION, INC.—See Eaton Corporation plc; *Int'l*, pg. 2282
XEBEC CORPORATION; *U.S. Private*, pg. 4581
YAO OFFICE & PLANT—See GMB Corp.; *Int'l*, pg. 3012

334516 — ANALYTICAL LABORATORY INSTRUMENT MANUFACTURING

1ST DETECT CORPORATION—See Astrotech Corporation; *U.S. Public*, pg. 218
AB SCIEX LP—See Danaher Corporation; *U.S. Public*, pg. 623
AC ANALYTICAL CONTROLS B.V.—See Roper Technologies, Inc.; *U.S. Public*, pg. 1810
ACCURATE POLY SERVICES APS—See Mettler-Toledo International, Inc.; *U.S. Public*, pg. 1432
ACCURI CYTOMETERS, INC.—See Becton, Dickinson & Company; *U.S. Public*, pg. 288
ACOUNS NIGERIA LTD.—See HORIBA Ltd; *Int'l*, pg. 3474
ADVANCED FIBER RESOURCES (ZHUHAI) LTD; *Int'l*, pg. 159
ADVANCED SENSORS LIMITED—See Roper Technologies, Inc.; *U.S. Public*, pg. 1810
ADVANTEST LABORATORIES LTD—See Advantest Corporation; *Int'l*, pg. 166
AFORE OY—See AEM Holdings Ltd.; *Int'l*, pg. 175
AGAR SCIENTIFIC LIMITED; *Int'l*, pg. 200
AGENA BIOSCIENCE, INC.—See Mesa Laboratories, Inc.; *U.S. Public*, pg. 1426
AGLAB, INC.—See Astrotech Corporation; *U.S. Public*, pg. 218
AHN BIOTECHNOLOGIE GMBH—See Harvard Bioscience, Inc.; *U.S. Public*, pg. 987
ALADDIN SEPARATION TECHNOLOGIES, INC.; *U.S. Public*, pg. 70
ALIGNED GENETICS, INC.; *Int'l*, pg. 327
ALTAMIRA INSTRUMENTS, INC.—See SCIENTIFIC INDUSTRIES, INC.; *U.S. Public*, pg. 1849
ALVOG S.A.—See HORIBA Ltd; *Int'l*, pg. 3474
ALVTECHNOLOGIES PHILIPPINES INC.—See HORIBA Ltd; *Int'l*, pg. 3474
ANALYTICAL DEVELOPMENT COMPANY LIMITED—See Halma plc; *Int'l*, pg. 3230
ANALYTIK JENA AG—See Endress+Hauser (International) Holding AG; *Int'l*, pg. 2405
ANALYTIK JENA SHANGHAI INSTRUMENTS CO. LTD.—See Endress+Hauser (International) Holding AG; *Int'l*, pg. 2405
ANASYS INSTRUMENTS CORP.—See Bruker Corporation; *U.S. Public*, pg. 404
ANDROS INCORPORATED—See Advanced Energy Industries, Inc.; *U.S. Public*, pg. 47
ANHUI WANYI SCIENCE & TECHNOLOGY CO., LTD.; *Int'l*, pg. 470
ANPLE LABORATORY TECHNOLOGIES (SHANGHAI) INC.—See Focused Photonics (Hangzhou), Inc.; *Int'l*, pg. 2720
ANTON PAAR AUSTRALIA PTY LTD—See Anton Paar GmbH; *Int'l*, pg. 484
ANTON PAAR AUSTRIA GMBH—See Anton Paar GmbH; *Int'l*, pg. 484
ANTON PAAR BENELUX BVBA—See Anton Paar GmbH; *Int'l*, pg. 484
ANTON PAAR BRASIL LTDA.—See Anton Paar GmbH; *Int'l*, pg. 484
ANTON PAAR CANADA INC.—See Anton Paar GmbH; *Int'l*, pg. 484
ANTON PAAR COLOMBIA S.A.S.—See Anton Paar GmbH; *Int'l*, pg. 484
ANTON PAAR CROATIA D.O.O.—See Anton Paar GmbH; *Int'l*, pg. 484
ANTON PAAR CZECH REPUBLIC S.R.O.—See Anton Paar GmbH; *Int'l*, pg. 484
ANTON PAAR FRANCE S.A.S.—See Anton Paar GmbH; *Int'l*, pg. 484
ANTON PAAR GERMANY GMBH—See Anton Paar GmbH; *Int'l*, pg. 484
ANTON PAAR GMBH; *Int'l*, pg. 484
ANTON PAAR HUNGARY KFT—See Anton Paar GmbH; *Int'l*, pg. 484
ANTON PAAR INDIA PVT. LTD.—See Anton Paar GmbH; *Int'l*, pg. 484
ANTON PAAR IRELAND LTD.—See Anton Paar GmbH; *Int'l*, pg. 484
ANTON PAAR ITALIA S.R.L.—See Anton Paar GmbH; *Int'l*, pg. 484
ANTON PAAR JAPAN K.K.—See Anton Paar GmbH; *Int'l*, pg. 484
ANTON PAAR KOREA LTD.—See Anton Paar GmbH; *Int'l*, pg. 484
ANTON PAAR LTD.—See Anton Paar GmbH; *Int'l*, pg. 484
ANTON PAAR MALAYSIA SDN BHD—See Anton Paar GmbH; *Int'l*, pg. 484
ANTON PAAR NEW ZEALAND LIMITED—See Anton Paar GmbH; *Int'l*, pg. 485
ANTON PAAR NORDIC AB—See Anton Paar GmbH; *Int'l*, pg. 485
ANTON PAAR OLCUM ALETLERI TICARET LTD. STI.—See Anton Paar GmbH; *Int'l*, pg. 485
ANTON PAAR OPTOTEC GMBH—See Anton Paar GmbH; *Int'l*, pg. 485
ANTON PAAR POLAND SP.Z.O.O.—See Anton Paar GmbH; *Int'l*, pg. 485
ANTON PAAR PROVETEC GMBH—See Anton Paar GmbH; *Int'l*, pg. 485
ANTON PAAR QUANTATEC INC.—See Anton Paar GmbH; *Int'l*, pg. 485
ANTON PAAR SHANGHAI TRADING CO., LTD.—See Anton Paar GmbH; *Int'l*, pg. 485
ANTON PAAR SHAPETEC BA D.O.O.—See Anton Paar GmbH; *Int'l*, pg. 485
ANTON PAAR SINGAPORE PTE LTD.—See Anton Paar GmbH; *Int'l*, pg. 485
ANTON PAAR SLOVAKIA S.R.O.—See Anton Paar GmbH; *Int'l*, pg. 485
ANTON PAAR SOUTHERN AFRICA (PTY) LTD—See Anton Paar GmbH; *Int'l*, pg. 485
ANTON PAAR SPAIN S.L.U.—See Anton Paar GmbH; *Int'l*, pg. 485
ANTON PAAR SWITZERLAND AG—See Anton Paar GmbH; *Int'l*, pg. 485
ANTON PAAR TAIWAN CO. LTD.—See Anton Paar GmbH; *Int'l*, pg. 485
ANTON PAAR (THAILAND) LTD.—See Anton Paar GmbH; *Int'l*, pg. 484
ANTON PAAR TRITEC SA—See Anton Paar GmbH; *Int'l*, pg. 485
APPLIED IMAGING INTERNATIONAL LTD.—See Danaher Corporation; *U.S. Public*, pg. 624
APPLIED PHYSICS TECHNOLOGIES, INC.—See Hitachi, Ltd.; *Int'l*, pg. 3412
AQUAFINE GMBH—See Danaher Corporation; *U.S. Public*, pg. 624
ARKRAY, INC.; *Int'l*, pg. 571
ARRAYIT CORP.; *U.S. Public*, pg. 194
ARTEMA MEDICAL AB—See Getinge AB; *Int'l*, pg. 2951
ARUN TECHNOLOGY LTD.—See Focused Photonics (Hangzhou), Inc.; *Int'l*, pg. 2720
ASAHI KASEI BIOPROCESS, INC.—See Asahi Kasei Corporation; *Int'l*, pg. 595
ASIA VITAL COMPONENTS CO., LTD. - AVC TAIPEI FACTORY—See Asia Vital Components Co., Ltd.; *Int'l*, pg. 616
ASPIRA WOMEN'S HEALTH INC.; *U.S. Public*, pg. 213
ASSOCIATED ENVIRONMENTAL SYSTEMS; *U.S. Private*, pg. 355
ASTA CO LTD; *Int'l*, pg. 651
ATTARD & CO. LTD.; *Int'l*, pg. 696
AUTOGENOMICS, INC.—See Prescient Medicine Holdings LLC; *U.S. Public*, pg. 3253
AXESS CORPORATION; *U.S. Private*, pg. 412
AZPECT PHOTONICS AB; *Int'l*, pg. 781
BASELINE-MOCON, INC.—See AMETEK, Inc.; *U.S. Public*, pg. 120
BC TECHNICAL, INC.—See Alpha Source, Inc.; *U.S. Private*, pg. 199
BECKMAN COULTER BIYOMEDIKAL URUNLER SANAYI VE TICARET LIMITED SIRKETI—See Danaher Corporation; *U.S. Public*, pg. 624
BECKMAN COULTER ESPANA, S.A.—See Danaher Corporation; *U.S. Public*, pg. 624
BECKMAN COULTER, INC.—See Danaher Corporation; *U.S. Public*, pg. 624
BECKMAN COULTER LABORATORY SYSTEMS (SUZHOU) CO. LTD.—See Danaher Corporation; *U.S. Public*, pg. 624
BECKMAN COULTER MAGYARORSZAG KFT—See Danaher Corporation; *U.S. Public*, pg. 625
BECKMAN COULTER MISHIMA K.K.—See Danaher Corporation; *U.S. Public*, pg. 625
BECKMAN COULTER PUERTO RICO INC.—See Danaher Corporation; *U.S. Public*, pg. 625
BECKMAN COULTER SINGAPORE PTE. LTD.—See Danaher Corporation; *U.S. Public*, pg. 625
BECKMAN COULTER SOUTH AFRICA (PROPRIETARY) LIMITED—See Danaher Corporation; *U.S. Public*, pg. 625
BECKMAN COULTER SRL—See Danaher Corporation; *U.S. Public*, pg. 625
BECKMAN COULTER TAIWAN INC.—See Danaher Corporation; *U.S. Public*, pg. 625
BEIJING LABTECH INSTRUMENTS CO., LTD.; *Int'l*, pg. 954
BEIJING TITAN INSTRUMENT CO., LTD.—See Focused Photonics (Hangzhou), Inc.; *Int'l*, pg. 2720
BELLINGHAM & STANLEY, INC.—See Xylem Inc.; *U.S. Public*, pg. 2395
BELLINGHAM & STANLEY, LTD.—See Xylem Inc.; *U.S. Public*, pg. 2395
BEMCO INC.; *U.S. Private*, pg. 522
BERGMAN AS—See Addtech AB; *Int'l*, pg. 132
BIOCARE EUROPE S.R.L.—See FUJIFILM Holdings Corporation; *Int'l*, pg. 2821
BIOCHROM US, INC.—See Harvard Bioscience, Inc.; *U.S. Public*, pg. 987
BIOLINKER S.A.—See Abbott Laboratories; *U.S. Public*, pg. 19
BIOLIN SCIENTIFIC AB—See AddLife AB; *Int'l*, pg. 129
BIOLIN SCIENTIFIC LIMITED—See AddLife AB; *Int'l*, pg. 129
BIOLIN SCIENTIFIC OY—See AddLife AB; *Int'l*, pg. 129
BIOMETRA GMBH—See Endress+Hauser (International) Holding AG; *Int'l*, pg. 2405
BIOMETRICS LTD—See Bio-Rad Laboratories, Inc.; *U.S. Public*, pg. 333
BIONANO GENOMICS, INC.; *U.S. Public*, pg. 338
BIO-RAD ABD SEROTEC GMBH—See Bio-Rad Laboratories, Inc.; *U.S. Public*, pg. 332
BIO-RAD ABD SEROTEC LTD—See Bio-Rad Laboratories, Inc.; *U.S. Public*, pg. 332
BIO-RAD HAIFA LTD.—See Bio-Rad Laboratories, Inc.; *U.S. Public*, pg. 332
BIO-RAD KOREA LIMITED—See Bio-Rad Laboratories, Inc.; *U.S. Public*, pg. 332
BIO-RAD LABORATORIES AB—See Bio-Rad Laboratories, Inc.; *U.S. Public*, pg. 333
BIO-RAD LABORATORIES-APARELHOS E REAGENTES PARA LABORATORIOS, LDA—See Bio-Rad Laboratories, Inc.; *U.S. Public*, pg. 333
BIO-RAD LABORATORIES (CANADA) LTD.—See Bio-Rad Laboratories, Inc.; *U.S. Public*, pg. 332
BIO-RAD LABORATORIES EUROPE LIMITED—See Bio-Rad Laboratories, Inc.; *U.S. Public*, pg. 333
BIO-RAD LABORATORIES, GES.M.B.H.—See Bio-Rad Laboratories, Inc.; *U.S. Public*, pg. 333
BIO-RAD LABORATORIES GMBH—See Bio-Rad Laboratories, Inc.; *U.S. Public*, pg. 333
BIO-RAD LABORATORIES, INC.; *U.S. Public*, pg. 332
BIO-RAD LABORATORIES, INC.—See Bio-Rad Laboratories, Inc.; *U.S. Public*, pg. 333
BIO-RAD LABORATORIES (INDIA) PVT. LTD.—See Bio-Rad Laboratories, Inc.; *U.S. Public*, pg. 332
BIO-RAD LABORATORIES K.K.—See Bio-Rad Laboratories, Inc.; *U.S. Public*, pg. 333
BIO-RAD LABORATORIES LIMITED—See Bio-Rad Laboratories, Inc.; *U.S. Public*, pg. 333
BIO-RAD LABORATORIES LTD.—See Bio-Rad Laboratories, Inc.; *U.S. Public*, pg. 333
BIO-RAD LABORATORIES M E.P.E.—See Bio-Rad Laboratories, Inc.; *U.S. Public*, pg. 333
BIO-RAD LABORATORIES PTY. LIMITED—See Bio-Rad Laboratories, Inc.; *U.S. Public*, pg. 333
BIO-RAD LABORATORIES S.A.—See Bio-Rad Laboratories, Inc.; *U.S. Public*, pg. 333
BIO-RAD LABORATORIES (SHANGHAI) CO., LTD.—See Bio-Rad Laboratories, Inc.; *U.S. Public*, pg. 332
BIO-RAD LABORATORIES (SINGAPORE) PTE. LIMITED—See Bio-Rad Laboratories, Inc.; *U.S. Public*, pg. 333
BIO-RAD LABORATORIES S.R.L.—See Bio-Rad Laboratories, Inc.; *U.S. Public*, pg. 333
BIO-RAD LABORATORII OOO—See Bio-Rad Laboratories, Inc.; *U.S. Public*, pg. 333
BIO-RAD LABORATORIOS BRASIL LTDA.—See Bio-Rad Laboratories, Inc.; *U.S. Public*, pg. 333
BIO-RAD LTD.—See Bio-Rad Laboratories, Inc.; *U.S. Public*, pg. 333
BIO-RAD MEDICAL DIAGNOSTICS GMBH—See Biotest AG; *Int'l*, pg. 1043
BIO-RAD POLSKA SP. Z O.O.—See Bio-Rad Laboratories, Inc.; *U.S. Public*, pg. 333

N.A.I.C.S. INDEX
334516 — ANALYTICAL LABORATO...

BIO RAD S.A.—See Bio-Rad Laboratories, Inc.; *U.S. Public*, pg. 332
BIO-RAD SPOL. SR.O—See Bio-Rad Laboratories, Inc.; *U.S. Public*, pg. 333
BIO-RAD VERDOT—See Bio-Rad Laboratories, Inc.; *U.S. Public*, pg. 332
BIOSIGMA S.R.L.—See Dominique Dutscher SAS; *Int'l*, pg. 2161
BIOSURPLUS, INC.—See Copia Scientific, Inc.; *U.S. Private*, pg. 1044
BIOTEK INSTRUMENTS, INC.—See Agilent Technologies, Inc.; *U.S. Public*, pg. 61
BIOTEK INSTRUMENTS (I) PVT. LTD.—See Agilent Technologies, Inc.; *U.S. Public*, pg. 61
BIO VIEW LTD.; *Int'l*, pg. 1035
BISCAYNE ENGINEERING COMPANY, INC.—See Atwell, LLC; *U.S. Private*, pg. 384
BOEKEL INDUSTRIES INC.; *U.S. Private*, pg. 608
BROOKFIELD ENGINEERING LABORATORIES, INC.—See AMETEK, Inc.; *U.S. Public*, pg. 120
BROOKFIELD VISCOMETERS, LTD.—See AMETEK, Inc.; *U.S. Public*, pg. 120
BROOKS LIFE SCIENCE SYSTEMS—See Azenta, Inc.; *U.S. Public*, pg. 257
BRUKER AUSTRIA GMBH—See Bruker Corporation; *U.S. Public*, pg. 404
BRUKER AXS ANALYTICAL INSTRUMENTS PVT. LTD.—See Bruker Corporation; *U.S. Public*, pg. 404
BRUKER AXS GMBH—See Bruker Corporation; *U.S. Public*, pg. 404
BRUKER AXS HANDHELD INC.—See Bruker Corporation; *U.S. Public*, pg. 404
BRUKER AXS K.K.—See Bruker Corporation; *U.S. Public*, pg. 404
BRUKER AXS NORDIC AB—See Bruker Corporation; *U.S. Public*, pg. 404
BRUKER AXS PTE LTD—See Bruker Corporation; *U.S. Public*, pg. 404
BRUKER BELGIUM SA/NV—See Bruker Corporation; *U.S. Public*, pg. 404
BRUKER BIOSCIENCES KOREA CO., LTD.—See Bruker Corporation; *U.S. Public*, pg. 404
BRUKER BIOSPIN AG—See Bruker Corporation; *U.S. Public*, pg. 404
BRUKER BIOSPIN CORPORATION—See Bruker Corporation; *U.S. Public*, pg. 404
BRUKER BIOSPIN INTERNATIONAL AG - THAILAND OFFICE—See Bruker Corporation; *U.S. Public*, pg. 404
BRUKER BIOSPIN K.K.—See Bruker Corporation; *U.S. Public*, pg. 404
BRUKER BIOSPIN KOREA CO. LTD.—See Bruker Corporation; *U.S. Public*, pg. 405
BRUKER BIOSPIN MRI GMBH—See Bruker Corporation; *U.S. Public*, pg. 405
BRUKER BIOSPIN MRI INC.—See Bruker Corporation; *U.S. Public*, pg. 405
BRUKER BIOSPIN PTE. LTD.—See Bruker Corporation; *U.S. Public*, pg. 404
BRUKER BIOSPIN S.A. / N.V.—See Bruker Corporation; *U.S. Public*, pg. 405
BRUKER BIOSPIN S.A.—See Bruker Corporation; *U.S. Public*, pg. 405
BRUKER BIOSPIN SCANDINAVIA AB—See Bruker Corporation; *U.S. Public*, pg. 405
BRUKER CHEMICAL & APPLIED MARKETS—See Bruker Corporation; *U.S. Public*, pg. 405
BRUKER CORPORATION; *U.S. Public*, pg. 403
BRUKER DALTONICS INC.—See Bruker Corporation; *U.S. Public*, pg. 405
BRUKER DALTONICS, INC.—See Bruker Corporation; *U.S. Public*, pg. 405
BRUKER DALTONICS K.K.—See Bruker Corporation; *U.S. Public*, pg. 405
BRUKER DALTONICS LTD.—See Bruker Corporation; *U.S. Public*, pg. 405
BRUKER DALTONICS LTD.—See Bruker Corporation; *U.S. Public*, pg. 405
BRUKER DALTONICS PTE. LTD.—See Bruker Corporation; *U.S. Public*, pg. 405
BRUKER DALTONICS PTY LTD.—See Bruker Corporation; *U.S. Public*, pg. 405
BRUKER DALTONICS SCANDINAVIA AB—See Bruker Corporation; *U.S. Public*, pg. 405
BRUKER DALTONICS SCANDINAVIA AB—See Bruker Corporation; *U.S. Public*, pg. 405
BRUKER DALTONICS SPRL/BVBA—See Bruker Corporation; *U.S. Public*, pg. 405
BRUKER DALTONICS S.R.L.—See Bruker Corporation; *U.S. Public*, pg. 405
BRUKER DALTONICS S.R.O.—See Bruker Corporation; *U.S. Public*, pg. 405
BRUKER DALTONIK GMBH—See Bruker Corporation; *U.S. Public*, pg. 405
BRUKER DALTONIK GMBH—See Bruker Corporation; *U.S. Public*, pg. 405
BRUKER DO BRASIL LTDA.—See Bruker Corporation; *U.S. Public*, pg. 404

BRUKER ELEMENTAL GMBH—See Bruker Corporation; *U.S. Public*, pg. 404
BRUKER ESPANOLA S.A.—See Bruker Corporation; *U.S. Public*, pg. 405
BRUKER FRANCE S.A.S—See Bruker Corporation; *U.S. Public*, pg. 405
BRUKER INDIA SCIENTIFIC PVT. LTD.—See Bruker Corporation; *U.S. Public*, pg. 405
BRUKER ITALIA S.R.L.—See Bruker Corporation; *U.S. Public*, pg. 405
BRUKER KOREA CO., LTD.—See Bruker Corporation; *U.S. Public*, pg. 406
BRUKER (MALAYSIA) SDN BHD—See Bruker Corporation; *U.S. Public*, pg. 404
BRUKER MEXICANA, S.A. DE C.V.—See Bruker Corporation; *U.S. Public*, pg. 404
BRUKER NANO GMBH—See Bruker Corporation; *U.S. Public*, pg. 404
BRUKER NANO, INC.—See Bruker Corporation; *U.S. Public*, pg. 404
BRUKER NANO, INC.—See Bruker Corporation; *U.S. Public*, pg. 404
BRUKER NEDERLAND B.V.—See Bruker Corporation; *U.S. Public*, pg. 405
BRUKER OPTICS AB—See Bruker Corporation; *U.S. Public*, pg. 405
BRUKER OPTICS GMBH—See Bruker Corporation; *U.S. Public*, pg. 405
BRUKER OPTICS INC.—See Bruker Corporation; *U.S. Public*, pg. 406
BRUKER OPTICS K.K.—See Bruker Corporation; *U.S. Public*, pg. 406
BRUKER OPTICS LTD—See Bruker Corporation; *U.S. Public*, pg. 406
BRUKER OPTICS TAIWAN LTD.—See Bruker Corporation; *U.S. Public*, pg. 406
BRUKER OPTICS UKRAINE—See Bruker Corporation; *U.S. Public*, pg. 406
BRUKER OPTIK ASIA PACIFIC LIMITED—See Bruker Corporation; *U.S. Public*, pg. 406
BRUKER OPTIK GMBH—See Bruker Corporation; *U.S. Public*, pg. 406
BRUKER OPTIQUE SA—See Bruker Corporation; *U.S. Public*, pg. 406
BRUKER PHYSIK GMBH—See Bruker Corporation; *U.S. Public*, pg. 405
BRUKER POLSKA SP. Z O.O.—See Bruker Corporation; *U.S. Public*, pg. 406
BRUKER PORTUGAL UNIPESSOAL LDA—See Bruker Corporation; *U.S. Public*, pg. 406
BRUKER PTY. LTD.—See Bruker Corporation; *U.S. Public*, pg. 405
BRUKER SCIENTIFIC ISRAEL LTD.—See Bruker Corporation; *U.S. Public*, pg. 406
BRUKER SOUTH AFRICA PTY LTD.—See Bruker Corporation; *U.S. Public*, pg. 404
BRUKER SWITZERLAND AG—See Bruker Corporation; *U.S. Public*, pg. 406
BRUKER TAIWAN CO. LTD.—See Bruker Corporation; *U.S. Public*, pg. 406
BTX—See Harvard Bioscience, Inc.; *U.S. Public*, pg. 987
BUEHLER GMBH—See Illinois Tool Works Inc.; *U.S. Public*, pg. 1102
BUEHLER, LTD.—See Illinois Tool Works Inc.; *U.S. Public*, pg. 1102
BUEHLER—See Illinois Tool Works Inc.; *U.S. Public*, pg. 1102
BUSINESS INTERNATIONAL GROUP LLC—See HORIBA Ltd; *Int'l*, pg. 3475
CAL-BAY INTERNATIONAL, INC.; *U.S. Public*, pg. 421
CALIBRATION TECHNOLOGY LTD.—See Eppendorf AG; *Int'l*, pg. 2464
CALIPER LIFE SCIENCES, INC.—See Revvity, Inc.; *U.S. Public*, pg. 1793
CALYPTE BIOMEDICAL CORPORATION; *U.S. Private*, pg. 725
CAMECA INSTRUMENTS, INC.—See AMETEK, Inc.; *U.S. Public*, pg. 117
CAMECA S.A.S.—See AMETEK, Inc.; *U.S. Public*, pg. 117
CARL ZEISS PTY. LTD.—See Carl-Zeiss-Stiftung; *Int'l*, pg. 1335
CEM CORPORATION; *U.S. Private*, pg. 808
CEM JAPAN K.K.—See CEM Corporation; *U.S. Private*, pg. 808
CEM MICROWAVE TECHNOLOGY (IRELAND) LTD.—See CEM Corporation; *U.S. Private*, pg. 808
CEM MU WAVES S.A.S.—See CEM Corporation; *U.S. Private*, pg. 808
CENTRAL LABO EUROPE SAS—See Bio-Rad Laboratories, Inc.; *U.S. Public*, pg. 333
CEPHEID—See Danaher Corporation; *U.S. Public*, pg. 625
CEZANNE S.A.S.—See Thermo Fisher Scientific Inc.; *U.S. Public*, pg. 2145
CHEMIMAGE CORP.; *U.S. Private*, pg. 871
CHEMOMETEC A/S; *Int'l*, pg. 1463
THE CHEMOURS COMPANY FC, LLC—See The Chemours Company; *U.S. Public*, pg. 2059

CHROMA TECHNOLOGY CORPORATION; *U.S. Private*, pg. 892
CIANFLONE SCIENTIFIC LLC—See Main Line Equity Partners, LLC; *U.S. Private*, pg. 2551
CJ DO BRASIL LTDA.—See CJ Corporation; *Int'l*, pg. 1633
CLINTRAK PHARMACEUTICAL SERVICES, LLC—See Thermo Fisher Scientific Inc.; *U.S. Public*, pg. 2145
CLMO TECHNOLOGY SDN BHD—See Thermo Fisher Scientific Inc.; *U.S. Public*, pg. 2146
CMS RESEARCH CORPORATION—See Xylem Inc.; *U.S. Public*, pg. 2395
COHERENT, INC.—See Coherent Corp.; *U.S. Public*, pg. 526
COMBIMATRIX CORPORATION—See Invitae Corporation; *U.S. Public*, pg. 1165
CONCEPTOS E INSTRUMENTOS S.A. DE C.V.—See HORIBA Ltd; *Int'l*, pg. 3475
CONNECTAMERICA.COM, LLC; *U.S. Private*, pg. 1015
COPIA SCIENTIFIC, INC.; *U.S. Private*, pg. 1044
CORNING LIFE SCIENCES (WUJIANG) CO., LTD.—See Corning Incorporated; *U.S. Public*, pg. 578
COULBOURN INSTRUMENTS, LLC—See Harvard Bioscience, Inc.; *U.S. Public*, pg. 987
COVARIS, INC.—See Revvity, Inc.; *U.S. Public*, pg. 1794
CTC LABORATORY SYSTEMS CORPORATION—See Abbott Laboratories; *U.S. Public*, pg. 20
CUSTOMARRAY, INC.—See GenScript Biotech Corporation; *Int'l*, pg. 2927
CYBRDI, INC.; *U.S. Private*, pg. 1134
CYTOPEIA, INC.—See Becton, Dickinson & Company; *U.S. Public*, pg. 289
DAGE PRECISION INDUSTRIES, INC.—See Nordson Corporation; *U.S. Public*, pg. 1532
DAIHAN SCIENTIFIC CO., LTD.; *Int'l*, pg. 1926
DAKILA TRADING CORPORATION—See HORIBA Ltd; *Int'l*, pg. 3475
D'AMICO SISTEMAS S.A.—See Waters Corporation; *U.S. Public*, pg. 2334
DATACOLOR BELGIUM BVBA—See Datacolor AG; *Int'l*, pg. 1977
DATACOLOR COLOR TECHNOLOGIES TRADING & SERVICE COMPANY LLC—See Datacolor AG; *Int'l*, pg. 1977
DATACOLOR GMBH—See Datacolor AG; *Int'l*, pg. 1977
DATACOLOR INTERNATIONAL FRANCE SAS—See Datacolor AG; *Int'l*, pg. 1977
DATACOLOR INTERNATIONAL LTD.—See Datacolor AG; *Int'l*, pg. 1977
DATACOLOR SOLUTIONS PRIVATE LTD.—See Datacolor AG; *Int'l*, pg. 1977
DATACOLOR TRADING (SHANGHAI) CO., LTD.—See Datacolor AG; *Int'l*, pg. 1977
DATACOLOR VIETNAM CO., LTD.—See Datacolor AG; *Int'l*, pg. 1977
DELTA INSTRUMENTS B.V.—See Revvity, Inc.; *U.S. Public*, pg. 1795
DENTON VACUUM INC.; *U.S. Private*, pg. 1206
DENVILLE SCIENTIFIC, INC.—See Harvard Bioscience, Inc.; *U.S. Public*, pg. 987
DIAGNOSTICA STAGO, INC.—See Diagnostica Stago S.A.S.; *Int'l*, pg. 2103
DIAGNOSTICA STAGO S.A.S.; *Int'l*, pg. 2103
DIAGNOSTICO Y ASISTENCIA MEDICA S.A. I.P.S. DINAMICA—See Grupo de Inversiones Suramericana S.A.; *Int'l*, pg. 3125
DIAGNOSTIC SYSTEMS GMBH—See HORIBA Ltd; *Int'l*, pg. 3475
DIAMED AG—See Bio-Rad Laboratories, Inc.; *U.S. Public*, pg. 334
DIAMED BENELUX, N.V.—See Bio-Rad Laboratories, Inc.; *U.S. Public*, pg. 333
DIAMED DIAGNOSTIKA DEUTSCHLAND G.M.B.H.—See Bio-Rad Laboratories, Inc.; *U.S. Public*, pg. 333
DIAMED FENNICA OY—See Bio-Rad Laboratories, Inc.; *U.S. Public*, pg. 333
DIAMED FRANCE S.A.—See Bio-Rad Laboratories, Inc.; *U.S. Public*, pg. 334
DIAMED (G.B.) LIMITED—See Bio-Rad Laboratories, Inc.; *U.S. Public*, pg. 333
DIAMED LATINO AMERICA S.A.—See Bio-Rad Laboratories, Inc.; *U.S. Public*, pg. 334
DIAMED OSTERREICH GMBH—See Bio-Rad Laboratories, Inc.; *U.S. Public*, pg. 334
DIAMED (SCHWEIZ) G.M.B.H.—See Bio-Rad Laboratories, Inc.; *U.S. Public*, pg. 333
DIAS DE SOUSA S.A.—See HORIBA Ltd; *Int'l*, pg. 3475
DIBA INDUSTRIES LTD.—See Halma plc; *Int'l*, pg. 3231
DIGILAB, INC.; *U.S. Private*, pg. 1229
DIONEX AUSTRIA GMBH—See Thermo Fisher Scientific Inc.; *U.S. Public*, pg. 2146
DIONEX (CHINA) ANALYTICAL LTD—See Thermo Fisher Scientific Inc.; *U.S. Public*, pg. 2146
DIONEX CHINA LTD.—See Thermo Fisher Scientific Inc.; *U.S. Public*, pg. 2146
DIONEX DENMARK A/S—See Thermo Fisher Scientific Inc.; *U.S. Public*, pg. 2146
DIONEX INDIA PVT. LTD.—See Thermo Fisher Scientific Inc.; *U.S. Public*, pg. 2146

334516 — ANALYTICAL LABORATO...

DIONEX IRELAND LIMITED—See Thermo Fisher Scientific Inc.; *U.S. Public*, pg. 2146
DIONEX KOREA LTD.—See Thermo Fisher Scientific Inc.; *U.S. Public*, pg. 2146
DIONEX PTY LTD—See Thermo Fisher Scientific Inc.; *U.S. Public*, pg. 2146
DIONEX SOFTRON GMBH—See Thermo Fisher Scientific Inc.; *U.S. Public*, pg. 2146
DIONEX S.P.A.—See Thermo Fisher Scientific Inc.; *U.S. Public*, pg. 2146
DIONEX TAIWAN LTD.—See Thermo Fisher Scientific Inc.; *U.S. Public*, pg. 2146
THE DOW CHEMICAL COMPANY - RUSSELLVILLE—See Dow Inc.; *U.S. Public*, pg. 686
DYNAMIC TECHNOLOGY SUPPLIES COMPANY LTD.; *Int'l*, pg. 2241
DYNEX TECHNOLOGIES, INC.—See Telegraph Hill Partners Management Company, LLC; *U.S. Private*, pg. 3960
DYNISCO SHANGHAI SENSOR AND INSTRUMENT CO., LTD.—See Roper Technologies, Inc.; *U.S. Public*, pg. 1811
ECKERT & ZIEGLER ISOTOPE PRODUCTS, INC.—See Eckert & Ziegler Strahlen- und Medizintechnik AG; *Int'l*, pg. 2290
ECOCHEM N.V.—See Thermo Fisher Scientific Inc.; *U.S. Public*, pg. 2146
EDAX—See AMETEK, Inc.; *U.S. Public*, pg. 117
EDGE BIOSYSTEMS, INC.—See StoneCalibre, LLC; *U.S. Private*, pg. 3828
EKF DIAGNOSTICS HOLDINGS PLC; *Int'l*, pg. 2338
ELDAN ELECTRONIC CO. LTD.; *Int'l*, pg. 2346
ELECTRON MICROSCOPY SCIENCES, INC.—See The Graham Group, Inc.; *U.S. Private*, pg. 4037
ELE INTERNATIONAL, INC—See Danaher Corporation; *U.S. Public*, pg. 626
ELE INTERNATIONAL—See Danaher Corporation; *U.S. Public*, pg. 626
ELITECHGROUP MOLECULAR DIAGNOSTICS—See Bruker Corporation; *U.S. Public*, pg. 406
EMPOWER MATERIALS, INC.—See Axess Corporation; *U.S. Private*, pg. 412
EPPENDORF CHINA LTD.—See Eppendorf AG; *Int'l*, pg. 2464
EPPENDORF IBERICA S.L.—See Eppendorf AG; *Int'l*, pg. 2464
EPPENDORF NORGE AS—See Eppendorf AG; *Int'l*, pg. 2464
EPPENDORF NORTH AMERICA, INC.—See Eppendorf AG; *Int'l*, pg. 2464
EPPENDORF RUSSIA OOO—See Eppendorf AG; *Int'l*, pg. 2464
EPPENDORF SCIENTIFIC, INC.—See Eppendorf AG; *Int'l*, pg. 2464
EQUINLAB SAC—See HORIBA Ltd; *Int'l*, pg. 3475
EQUIPOS Y LABORATORIO DE COLOMBIA SAS—See HORIBA Ltd; *Int'l*, pg. 3475
ERIE SCIENTIFIC LLC—See Thermo Fisher Scientific Inc.; *U.S. Public*, pg. 2146
ESPEC EUROPE GMBH—See ESPEC Corp.; *Int'l*, pg. 2505
ESPEC TEST TECHNOLOGY (SHANGHAI) CO., LTD.—See ESPEC Corp.; *Int'l*, pg. 2505
ETG ENTWICKLUNGS- UND TECHNOLOGIE GESELLSCHAFT MBH—See Endress+Hauser (International) Holding AG; *Int'l*, pg. 2405
EUREKA WATER PROBES; *U.S. Private*, pg. 1433
EUROFINS A/S—See Eurofins Scientific S.E.; *Int'l*, pg. 2536
EUROFINS DANMARK A/S—See Eurofins Scientific S.E.; *Int'l*, pg. 2539
EUROFINS MILJO A/S—See Eurofins Scientific S.E.; *Int'l*, pg. 2546
EUROFINS MILJO LUFT A/S—See Eurofins Scientific S.E.; *Int'l*, pg. 2546
EUROFINS TESTING A/S—See Eurofins Scientific S.E.; *Int'l*, pg. 2549
EUROIMMUN DIAGNOSTICS ESPANA, S.L.U.—See Revvity, Inc.; *U.S. Public*, pg. 1794
EUROIMMUN FRANCE SAS—See Revvity, Inc.; *U.S. Public*, pg. 1794
EUROIMMUN ITALIA DIAGNOSTICA MEDICA S.R.L.—See Revvity, Inc.; *U.S. Public*, pg. 1794
EUROIMMUN MEDICAL DIAGNOSTICS CANADA INC.—See Revvity, Inc.; *U.S. Public*, pg. 1794
EUROIMMUN MEDICAL DIAGNOSTICS (CHINA) CO., LTD—See Revvity, Inc.; *U.S. Public*, pg. 1794
EUROIMMUN MEDICAL LABORATORY DIAGNOSTICS SOUTH AFRICA (PTY) LTD.—See Revvity, Inc.; *U.S. Public*, pg. 1794
EUROIMMUN POLSKA SPOLKA Z O.O.—See Revvity, Inc.; *U.S. Public*, pg. 1794
EUROIMMUN PORTUGAL UNIPESSOAL LDA.—See Revvity, Inc.; *U.S. Public*, pg. 1794
EUROIMMUN SCHWEIZ AG—See Revvity, Inc.; *U.S. Public*, pg. 1794
EUROIMMUN (SOUTH EAST ASIA) PTE LTD—See Revvity, Inc.; *U.S. Public*, pg. 1794
EUROIMMUN UK LTD.—See Revvity, Inc.; *U.S. Public*, pg. 1794
EUTECH INSTRUMENTS PTE LTD.—See Thermo Fisher Scientific Inc.; *U.S. Public*, pg. 2146

EXERGEN CORPORATION; *U.S. Private*, pg. 1448
FEI CZECH REPUBLIC S.R.O.—See Thermo Fisher Scientific Inc.; *U.S. Public*, pg. 2146
FEI ITALIA S.R.L.—See Thermo Fisher Scientific Inc.; *U.S. Public*, pg. 2147
FEI TECHNOLOGY DE MEXICO S.A. DE C.V.—See Thermo Fisher Scientific Inc.; *U.S. Public*, pg. 2147
FENWAL, INC.—See Fresenius SE & Co. KGaA; *Int'l*, pg. 2777
FIBERLOCK TECHNOLOGIES, INC.—See Audax Group, Limited Partnership; *U.S. Private*, pg. 388
FINESSE SOLUTIONS, INC.—See Thermo Fisher Scientific Inc.; *U.S. Public*, pg. 2147
FISHER BIOSERVICES INC.—See Thermo Fisher Scientific Inc.; *U.S. Public*, pg. 2147
FISHER SCIENTIFIC (AUSTRIA) GMBH—See Thermo Fisher Scientific Inc.; *U.S. Public*, pg. 2147
FISHER SCIENTIFIC BIOTECH LINE A/S—See Thermo Fisher Scientific Inc.; *U.S. Public*, pg. 2147
FISHER SCIENTIFIC OY—See Thermo Fisher Scientific Inc.; *U.S. Public*, pg. 2148
FISHER SCIENTIFIC PTE. LTD.—See Thermo Fisher Scientific Inc.; *U.S. Public*, pg. 2148
FISHER SCIENTIFIC S.L.—See Thermo Fisher Scientific Inc.; *U.S. Public*, pg. 2148
FISO TECHNOLOGIES, INC.—See Nova Ventures Group Corp.; *U.S. Private*, pg. 2966
FKA GSI US, INC.—See Harvard Bioscience, Inc.; *U.S. Public*, pg. 987
FLEX TECHNOLOGIES INC. - POLYFLEX DIVISION—See Flex Technologies Inc.; *U.S. Private*, pg. 1543
FLEXTRA LAB KFT.—See Bruker Corporation; *U.S. Public*, pg. 406
FLOM INC.—See GL Sciences Inc.; *Int'l*, pg. 2986
FLORIDA RADIOLOGY IMAGING; *U.S. Private*, pg. 1550
FLUIDIGM EUROPE, B.V.—See Standard BioTools Inc.; *U.S. Public*, pg. 1928
FLUIDIGM FRANCE SARL—See Standard BioTools Inc.; *U.S. Public*, pg. 1928
FLUXION BIOSCIENCES INC.—See Cell Microsystems, Inc.; *U.S. Private*, pg. 807
FOSS ANALYTICAL A/S—See Foss A/S; *Int'l*, pg. 2748
FOSS JAPAN LTD.—See Foss A/S; *Int'l*, pg. 2749
FOSS KOREA LTD.—See Foss A/S; *Int'l*, pg. 2749
FOSS PACIFIC (NZ) LTD.—See Foss A/S; *Int'l*, pg. 2749
FOSS PACIFIC PTY. LTD.—See Foss A/S; *Int'l*, pg. 2749
FOXX LIFE SCIENCES, LLC; *U.S. Private*, pg. 1585
FRONTIER ANALYTICAL LABORATORY—See Montrose Environmental Corp.; *U.S. Private*, pg. 2777
FTI FLOW TECHNOLOGY, INC.—See Roper Technologies, Inc.; *U.S. Public*, pg. 1811
GALVANIC APPLIED SCIENCES USA INC—See Galvanic Applied Sciences Inc.; *Int'l*, pg. 2876
GATAN, INC.—See AMETEK, Inc.; *U.S. Public*, pg. 120
GATAN, INC.—See AMETEK, Inc.; *U.S. Public*, pg. 120
GBC SCIENTIFIC EQUIPMENT PTY LTD.; *Int'l*, pg. 2893
GEA DIESSEL GMBH—See GEA Group Aktiengesellschaft; *Int'l*, pg. 2898
GEA NIRO SOAVI NORTH AMERICA INC—See GEA Group Aktiengesellschaft; *Int'l*, pg. 2903
GE HEALTHCARE BIO-SCIENCES AB—See GE HealthCare Technologies Inc.; *U.S. Public*, pg. 909
GELSIGHT, INC.; *U.S. Private*, pg. 1657
GENETIX CORP.—See Danaher Corporation; *U.S. Public*, pg. 627
GENIA PHOTONICS INC.; *Int'l*, pg. 2923
GILSON, INC.; *U.S. Private*, pg. 1701
GL SCIENCES B.V.—See GL Sciences Inc.; *Int'l*, pg. 2986
GL SCIENCES INC.; *Int'l*, pg. 2986
GRACE DAVISON DISCOVERY SCIENCES—See Standard Industries Holdings Inc.; *U.S. Private*, pg. 3779
GRAMEDICA LTD.—See ADDvise Group AB; *Int'l*, pg. 136
GULF SCIENTIFIC CORPORATION—See Waters Corporation; *U.S. Public*, pg. 2334
HACH COMPANY—See Danaher Corporation; *U.S. Public*, pg. 627
HACH INTERNATIONAL FOREIGN SALES CO., INC.—See Danaher Corporation; *U.S. Public*, pg. 627
HAEMONETICS ASIA, INC.—See Haemonetics Corporation; *U.S. Public*, pg. 979
HAEMONETICS CZ, SPOL.S.R.O—See Haemonetics Corporation; *U.S. Public*, pg. 979
HAEMONETICS FRANCE S.A.R.L.—See Haemonetics Corporation; *U.S. Public*, pg. 979
HAEMONETICS, GMBH—See Haemonetics Corporation; *U.S. Public*, pg. 979
HAEMONETICS ITALIA, S.R.L.—See Haemonetics Corporation; *U.S. Public*, pg. 979
HAEMONETICS JAPAN CO., LTD.—See Haemonetics Corporation; *U.S. Public*, pg. 979
HAEMONETICS LTD.—See Haemonetics Corporation; *U.S. Public*, pg. 979
HAEMONETICS MEDICAL DEVICES (SHANGHAI) TRADING CO., LTD.—See Haemonetics Corporation; *U.S. Public*, pg. 979
HAEMONETICS SCANDINAVIA AB—See Haemonetics Corporation; *U.S. Public*, pg. 979

HAMILTON BONADUZ AG—See Hamilton Co., Inc.; *U.S. Private*, pg. 1847
HAMILTON CO., INC.; *U.S. Private*, pg. 1847
HARVARD BIOSCIENCE, INC.; *U.S. Public*, pg. 987
HEMOPLAST JSC; *Int'l*, pg. 3341
HENGMEI OPTOELECTRONIC CORPORATION—See Cheng Mei Materials Technology Corporation; *Int'l*, pg. 1466
HENRY TROEMNER LLC—See Mettler-Toledo International, Inc.; *U.S. Public*, pg. 1432
HETTICH LABINSTRUMENT AB—See ADDvise Group AB; *Int'l*, pg. 136
HIGH SIERRA ELECTRONICS, INC.—See Onerain, Inc.; *U.S. Private*, pg. 3025
HITACHI HIGH-TECH ANALYTICAL SCIENCE AMERICA, INC.—See Hitachi, Ltd.; *Int'l*, pg. 3418
HITACHI HIGH-TECH ANALYTICAL SCIENCE FINLAND OY—See Hitachi, Ltd.; *Int'l*, pg. 3418
HITACHI HIGH-TECH ANALYTICAL SCIENCE GMBH—See Hitachi, Ltd.; *Int'l*, pg. 3418
HITACHI HIGH-TECH ANALYTICAL SCIENCE LIMITED—See Hitachi, Ltd.; *Int'l*, pg. 3418
HITACHI HIGH-TECH ANALYTICAL SCIENCE SHANGHAI CO., LTD.—See Hitachi, Ltd.; *Int'l*, pg. 3418
HITACHI HIGH-TECH FINE SYSTEMS CORPORATION—See Hitachi, Ltd.; *Int'l*, pg. 3418
HITACHI HIGH-TECH INDIA PRIVATE LIMITED—See Hitachi, Ltd.; *Int'l*, pg. 3418
HITACHI HIGH-TECH IPC (MALAYSIA) SDN. BHD.—See Hitachi, Ltd.; *Int'l*, pg. 3418
HITACHI HIGH-TECH ISRAEL, LTD.—See Hitachi, Ltd.; *Int'l*, pg. 3418
HITACHI HIGH-TECH KYUSHU CORPORATION—See Hitachi, Ltd.; *Int'l*, pg. 3418
HITACHI HIGH-TECH MANUFACTURING & SERVICE CORPORATION—See Hitachi, Ltd.; *Int'l*, pg. 3418
HITACHI HIGH-TECH RUS LIMITED LIABILITY COMPANY—See Hitachi, Ltd.; *Int'l*, pg. 3418
HITACHI HIGH-TECH SCIENCE AMERICA, INC.—See Hitachi, Ltd.; *Int'l*, pg. 3418
HITACHI HIGH-TECH STEEL DO BRASIL LTDA.—See Hitachi, Ltd.; *Int'l*, pg. 3418
HITACHI HIGH-TECH SUPPORT CORPORATION—See Hitachi, Ltd.; *Int'l*, pg. 3418
HOFFMAN ENGINEERING CORPORATION—See HWH Investments Limited; *Int'l*, pg. 3543
HORACIO ICAZA Y CIA, S.A.—See HORIBA Ltd; *Int'l*, pg. 3477
HORIBA EUROPE GMBH—See HORIBA Ltd; *Int'l*, pg. 3477
HORIBA EUROPE GMBH—See HORIBA Ltd; *Int'l*, pg. 3477
HORIBA JOBIN YVON GMBH - RAMAN DIVISION—See HORIBA Ltd; *Int'l*, pg. 3476
HORIBA JOBIN YVON IBH LTD.—See HORIBA Ltd; *Int'l*, pg. 3476
HORIBA JOBIN YVON LTD.—See HORIBA Ltd; *Int'l*, pg. 3476
HORIBA JOBIN YVON S.A.S. - RAMAN DIVISION—See HORIBA Ltd; *Int'l*, pg. 3476
HORIBA JOBIN YVON S.A.S.—See HORIBA Ltd; *Int'l*, pg. 3476
HORIBA JOBIN YVON S.A.S. - THIN FILM DIVISION—See HORIBA Ltd; *Int'l*, pg. 3476
HORIBA SCIENTIFIC—See HORIBA Ltd; *Int'l*, pg. 3476
HUGO SACHS ELEKTRONIK-HARVARD APPARATUS GMBH—See Harvard Bioscience, Inc.; *U.S. Public*, pg. 987
ICHINEN JIKCO CO., LTD.—See Ichinen Holdings Co., Ltd.; *Int'l*, pg. 3580
ICHINEN JIKCO POLYMER CO., LTD.—See Ichinen Holdings Co., Ltd.; *Int'l*, pg. 3580
ICHINEN JIKCO TEC CO., LTD.—See Ichinen Holdings Co., Ltd.; *Int'l*, pg. 3580
ICON ANALYTICAL EQUIPMENT PVT. LTD.; *Int'l*, pg. 3583
ILLUMINA, INC.-HAYWARD—See Illumina, Inc.; *U.S. Public*, pg. 1112
ILLUMINA, INC.; *U.S. Public*, pg. 1111
ILLUMINA KOREA LTD.—See Illumina, Inc.; *U.S. Public*, pg. 1112
ILMVAC GMBH; *Int'l*, pg. 3615
ILX LIGHTWAVE CORPORATION—See MKS Instruments, Inc.; *U.S. Public*, pg. 1453
IMMUNOTECH SAS—See Danaher Corporation; *U.S. Public*, pg. 627
INCOATEC GMBH—See Bruker Corporation; *U.S. Public*, pg. 404
INFRARED INTEGRATED SYSTEMS LTD.—See Fortive Corporation; *U.S. Public*, pg. 871
INSTRULABQ CIA. LTDA.—See HORIBA Ltd; *Int'l*, pg. 3477
INTEGENX INC.—See Thermo Fisher Scientific Inc.; *U.S. Public*, pg. 2148
INTELITOOL, INC.—See Phipps & Bird, Inc.; *U.S. Private*, pg. 3172
INTERNATIONAL DIAGNOSTIC SYSTEMS INC.—See Neogen Corporation; *U.S. Public*, pg. 1505
INTERNATIONAL FLAVORS & FRAGRANCES I.F.F. (ITALIA) S.R.L.—See International Flavors & Fragrances Inc.; *U.S. Public*, pg. 1153

N.A.I.C.S. INDEX

334516 — ANALYTICAL LABORATO...

IONSENSE, INC.—See Bruker Corporation; *U.S. Public*, pg. 407
IRIS DIAGNOSTICS FRANCE S.A.—See Danaher Corporation; *U.S. Public*, pg. 625
IRIS DIAGNOSTICS (UK) LTD.—See Danaher Corporation; *U.S. Public*, pg. 625
IRIS INTERNATIONAL, INC.—See Danaher Corporation; *U.S. Public*, pg. 625
ITRON FRANCE S.A.S.—See Itron, Inc.; *U.S. Public*, pg. 1176
ITW TEST & MEASUREMENT ITALIA SRL—See Illinois Tool Works Inc.; *U.S. Public*, pg. 1108
JAPAN ANALYST CORPORATION—See LECO Corporation; *U.S. Private*, pg. 2410
JS INDUSTRIAL S.A.C.—See HORIBA Ltd; *Int'l*, pg. 3477
KAIKA SAS—See HORIBA Ltd; *Int'l*, pg. 3477
KASAI SAS—See HORIBA Ltd; *Int'l*, pg. 3477
KLA-TENCOR MASSACHUSETTS—See KLA Corporation; *U.S. Public*, pg. 1268
LABCYTE, INC.—See Danaher Corporation; *U.S. Public*, pg. 624
LABROBOT PRODUCTS AB—See Addtech AB; *Int'l*, pg. 134
LACHAT INSTRUMENTS—See Danaher Corporation; *U.S. Public*, pg. 628
LAMBDA RESEARCH OPTICS, INC.; *U.S. Private*, pg. 2379
LECO AFRICA (PTY.) LTD.—See LECO Corporation; *U.S. Private*, pg. 2410
LECO ARGENTINA S.A.—See LECO Corporation; *U.S. Private*, pg. 2410
LECO AUSTRALIA PTY. LTD.—See LECO Corporation; *U.S. Private*, pg. 2410
LECO CORPORATION; *U.S. Private*, pg. 2410
LECO CORPORATION SVENSKA AB—See LECO Corporation; *U.S. Private*, pg. 2410
LECO EUROPE B.V.—See LECO Corporation; *U.S. Private*, pg. 2410
LECO FRANCE—See LECO Corporation; *U.S. Private*, pg. 2410
LECO INSTRUMENTE GMBH—See LECO Corporation; *U.S. Private*, pg. 2410
LECO INSTRUMENTE PLZEN S.R.O.—See LECO Corporation; *U.S. Private*, pg. 2410
LECO INSTRUMENTOS LTDA.—See LECO Corporation; *U.S. Private*, pg. 2410
LECO INSTRUMENTOS S.L.—See LECO Corporation; *U.S. Private*, pg. 2410
LECO INSTRUMENTS HONG KONG LTD.—See LECO Corporation; *U.S. Private*, pg. 2410
LECO INSTRUMENTS LTD.—See LECO Corporation; *U.S. Private*, pg. 2410
LECO INSTRUMENTS (M) SDN. BHD.—See LECO Corporation; *U.S. Private*, pg. 2410
LECO INSTRUMENTS S.A.—See LECO Corporation; *U.S. Private*, pg. 2410
LECO INSTRUMENTS TAIWAN LTD.—See LECO Corporation; *U.S. Private*, pg. 2410
LECO INSTRUMENTS (THAILAND) LTD.—See LECO Corporation; *U.S. Private*, pg. 2410
LECO INSTRUMENTS UK LTD.—See LECO Corporation; *U.S. Private*, pg. 2410
LECO ITALY, S.R.L.—See LECO Corporation; *U.S. Private*, pg. 2410
LECO JAPAN CORPORATION—See LECO Corporation; *U.S. Private*, pg. 2410
LECO KOREA CO. LTD.—See LECO Corporation; *U.S. Private*, pg. 2410
LECO MEXICO S.A. DE C.V.—See LECO Corporation; *U.S. Private*, pg. 2410
LECO POLSKA SP. Z O.O.—See LECO Corporation; *U.S. Private*, pg. 2410
LECO TECHNOLOGIES-PHILIPPINE MARKETING CORPORATION—See LECO Corporation; *U.S. Private*, pg. 2410
LECO (VIETNAM) CO., LTD.—See LECO Corporation; *U.S. Private*, pg. 2410
LEICA MICROSYSTEMS B.V.—See Danaher Corporation; *U.S. Public*, pg. 628
LEICA MICROSYSTEMS CAMBRIDGE LIMITED—See Danaher Corporation; *U.S. Public*, pg. 628
LEICA MICROSYSTEMS GMBH—See Danaher Corporation; *U.S. Public*, pg. 628
LEICA MICROSYSTEMS, INC.—See Danaher Corporation; *U.S. Public*, pg. 628
LEICA MICROSYSTEMS (SEA) PTE LTD—See Danaher Corporation; *U.S. Public*, pg. 628
LEICA MIKROSYSTEME (AUSTRIA) GMBH—See Danaher Corporation; *U.S. Public*, pg. 628
LGC PROMOCHEM INDIA PRIVATE LTD.—See Thermo Fisher Scientific Inc.; *U.S. Public*, pg. 2146
LIFE TECHNOLOGIES CLINICAL SERVICES LAB, INC.—See Thermo Fisher Scientific Inc.; *U.S. Public*, pg. 2149
LIFE TECHNOLOGIES EUROPE B.V. - NEDERLAENDERNA FILIAL SVERIGE - SWEDEN—See Thermo Fisher Scientific Inc.; *U.S. Public*, pg. 2149

LUMENIS—See Boston Scientific Corporation; *U.S. Public*, pg. 375
MALIKA FARM LLP—See HORIBA Ltd; *Int'l*, pg. 3477
MEDTOX DIAGNOSTICS, INC.—See Laboratory Corporation of America Holdings; *U.S. Public*, pg. 1287
MEE INC.—See Avex Inc.; *Int'l*, pg. 740
MELIBOKUS INDUSTRIE-ELEKTRONIK GMBH—See Mettler-Toledo International, Inc.; *U.S. Public*, pg. 1432
MESLO LTD.—See HORIBA Ltd; *Int'l*, pg. 3477
METTLER-TOLEDO AG-ANALYTICAL INSTRUMENTS—See Mettler-Toledo International, Inc.; *U.S. Public*, pg. 1432
METTLER-TOLEDO AUTOCHEM, INC.—See Mettler-Toledo International, Inc.; *U.S. Public*, pg. 1432
METTLER-TOLEDO CARGOSCAN AS—See Mettler-Toledo International, Inc.; *U.S. Public*, pg. 1432
METTLER-TOLEDO (CHANGZHOU) PRECISION INSTRUMENTS LTD.—See Mettler-Toledo International, Inc.; *U.S. Public*, pg. 1432
METTLER-TOLEDO (HK) LTD.—See Mettler-Toledo International, Inc.; *U.S. Public*, pg. 1432
METTLER-TOLEDO INC.—See Mettler-Toledo International, Inc.; *U.S. Public*, pg. 1432
METTLER-TOLEDO INDIA PRIVATE LIMITED—See Mettler-Toledo International, Inc.; *U.S. Public*, pg. 1432
METTLER-TOLEDO INTERNATIONAL, INC.; *U.S. Public*, pg. 1432
METTLER-TOLEDO INTERNATIONAL TRADING (SHANGHAI) CO., LTD.—See Mettler-Toledo International, Inc.; *U.S. Public*, pg. 1432
METTLER-TOLEDO (KOREA) LTD.—See Mettler-Toledo International, Inc.; *U.S. Public*, pg. 1432
METTLER-TOLEDO (M) SDN. BHD.—See Mettler-Toledo International, Inc.; *U.S. Public*, pg. 1432
METTLER-TOLEDO ONLINE GMBH—See Mettler-Toledo International, Inc.; *U.S. Public*, pg. 1433
METTLER-TOLEDO PRODUCT INSPECTION B.V.—See Mettler-Toledo International, Inc.; *U.S. Public*, pg. 1433
METTLER-TOLEDO SAFELINE LIMITED—See Mettler-Toledo International, Inc.; *U.S. Public*, pg. 1433
METTLER-TOLEDO SAFELINE X-RAY LIMITED—See Mettler-Toledo International, Inc.; *U.S. Public*, pg. 1433
METTLER-TOLEDO SPOL. S.R.O.—See Mettler-Toledo International, Inc.; *U.S. Public*, pg. 1433
METTLER-TOLEDO S.R.O.—See Mettler-Toledo International, Inc.; *U.S. Public*, pg. 1433
METTLER-TOLEDO TECHNOLOGIES (CHINA) CO., LTD.—See Mettler-Toledo International, Inc.; *U.S. Public*, pg. 1433
METTLER-TOLEDO (THAILAND) LTD.—See Mettler-Toledo International, Inc.; *U.S. Public*, pg. 1432
METTLER-TOLEDO THORNTON INC.—See Mettler-Toledo International, Inc.; *U.S. Public*, pg. 1433
METTLER-TOLEDO TR OLCUM ALETLERI TICARET SATIS VS SERVIS HIZMETLERI ANONIM SIRKETI—See Mettler-Toledo International, Inc.; *U.S. Public*, pg. 1433
METTLER-TOLEDO (XINJIANG) ELECTRONIC SCALE LTD.—See Mettler-Toledo International, Inc.; *U.S. Public*, pg. 1432
MICROGENICS GMBH—See Thermo Fisher Scientific Inc.; *U.S. Public*, pg. 2149
MICROMASS UK LIMITED—See Waters Corporation; *U.S. Public*, pg. 2334
MICROMERITICS CHINA—See Micromeritics Instrument Corporation, Inc.; *U.S. Private*, pg. 2703
MICROMERITICS FRANCE S.A.—See Micromeritics Instrument Corporation, Inc.; *U.S. Private*, pg. 2703
MICROMERITICS GERMANY GMBH—See Micromeritics Instrument Corporation, Inc.; *U.S. Private*, pg. 2704
MICROMERITICS INSTRUMENT CORPORATION, INC.; *U.S. Private*, pg. 2703
MICROMERITICS ITALY SRL—See Micromeritics Instrument Corporation, Inc.; *U.S. Private*, pg. 2704
MICROMERITICS JAPAN, G.K.—See Micromeritics Instrument Corporation, Inc.; *U.S. Private*, pg. 2704
MICROMERITICS NV/SA—See Micromeritics Instrument Corporation, Inc.; *U.S. Private*, pg. 2704
MICROMERITICS U.K. LTD.—See Micromeritics Instrument Corporation, Inc.; *U.S. Private*, pg. 2704
MICROMETICS COMERCIO E REPRESENTACOES LTDA—See Micromeritics Instrument Corporation, Inc.; *U.S. Private*, pg. 2704
MICROM INTERNATIONAL GMBH—See Thermo Fisher Scientific Inc.; *U.S. Public*, pg. 2149
MICRO TYPING SYSTEMS, INC.—See Johnson & Johnson; *U.S. Public*, pg. 1200
MIDLAND PRECISION EQUIPMENT CO LTD—See Waters Corporation; *U.S. Public*, pg. 2335
MOLECULAR DEVICES CORPORATION DOWNINGTOWN—See Danaher Corporation; *U.S. Public*, pg. 628
MOLECULAR DEVICES GMBH—See Danaher Corporation; *U.S. Public*, pg. 628
MOLECULAR DEVICES LLC—See Danaher Corporation; *U.S. Public*, pg. 628
MOLECULAR DEVICES LTD.—See Danaher Corporation; *U.S. Public*, pg. 628

MOLECULAR DIMENSIONS INC.—See StoneCalibre, LLC; *U.S. Private*, pg. 3827
MOLECULAR DIMENSIONS LTD.—See StoneCalibre, LLC; *U.S. Private*, pg. 3827
MONTANA INSTRUMENTS CORPORATION—See Atlas Copco AB; *Int'l*, pg. 683
MUANALYSIS INC.—See Grafoid, Inc.; *Int'l*, pg. 3050
NALGE NUNC INTERNATIONAL CORPORATION—See Thermo Fisher Scientific Inc.; *U.S. Public*, pg. 2149
NANOMECHANICS INC.—See KLA Corporation; *U.S. Public*, pg. 1268
NANOTECHNOLOGY CENTRE OF COMPOSITES LLC—See Aksa Akrilik Kimya Sanayii A.S.; *Int'l*, pg. 264
NATUS MEDICAL INCORPORATED—See ArchiMed SAS; *Int'l*, pg. 548
NATUS NEUROLOGY INC. - GRASS PRODUCTS—See ArchiMed SAS; *Int'l*, pg. 549
NBS BIOLOGICALS LIMITED—See BBI Life Sciences Corporation; *Int'l*, pg. 920
NEW BRUNSWICK SCIENTIFIC CO., INC.—See Eppendorf AG; *Int'l*, pg. 2464
NEXUS ANALYTICS SDN BHD—See HORIBA Ltd; *Int'l*, pg. 3477
NEXUS BIOSYSTEMS NIHON K.K.—See Azenta, Inc.; *U.S. Public*, pg. 258
NORDSON CORP. - UV CURING DIVISION—See Nordson Corporation; *U.S. Public*, pg. 1533
NOVA BIOMEDICAL CORPORATION; *U.S. Private*, pg. 2965
NOVODIRECT GMBH—See Thermo Fisher Scientific Inc.; *U.S. Public*, pg. 2148
NUAIRE INC.—See Kewaunee Scientific Corporation; *U.S. Public*, pg. 1225
NUCSAFE, INC.—See OSI Systems, Inc.; *U.S. Public*, pg. 1621
NU INSTRUMENTS LIMITED—See AMETEK, Inc.; *U.S. Public*, pg. 118
OCEAN INSIGHT, INC.—See Halma plc; *Int'l*, pg. 3232
OHAUS DE MEXICO S.A. DE C.V.—See Mettler-Toledo International, Inc.; *U.S. Public*, pg. 1433
OHAUS EUROPE GMBH—See Mettler-Toledo International, Inc.; *U.S. Public*, pg. 1433
OHAUS INDOCHINA LIMITED—See Mettler-Toledo International, Inc.; *U.S. Public*, pg. 1433
OHAUS INSTRUMENTS (SHANGHAI) CO. LTD.—See Mettler-Toledo International, Inc.; *U.S. Public*, pg. 1433
O.I. CORPORATION—See Xylem Inc.; *U.S. Public*, pg. 2395
OMNI INTERNATIONAL, INC.—See Revvity, Inc.; *U.S. Public*, pg. 1794
ONE LAMBDA, INC—See Thermo Fisher Scientific Inc.; *U.S. Public*, pg. 2149
OPTI MEDICAL SYSTEMS, INC.—See IDEXX Laboratories, Inc.; *U.S. Public*, pg. 1093
OTOMETRICS A/S—See ArchiMed SAS; *Int'l*, pg. 549
OXOID A/S—See Thermo Fisher Scientific Inc.; *U.S. Public*, pg. 2149
OXOID BRAZIL LTDA—See Thermo Fisher Scientific Inc.; *U.S. Public*, pg. 2150
OXOID CZ S.R.O.—See Thermo Fisher Scientific Inc.; *U.S. Public*, pg. 2150
OXOID LIMITED—See Thermo Fisher Scientific Inc.; *U.S. Public*, pg. 2150
OYO GEOSPACE CHINA—See GEOSPACE TECHNOLOGIES CORPORATION; *U.S. Public*, pg. 934
OZMEN TIBBI LABORATUAR TESHISLERI A.S.—See Revvity, Inc.; *U.S. Public*, pg. 1794
PACIFIC BIOSCIENCES OF CALIFORNIA, INC.; *U.S. Public*, pg. 1631
PALINTEST LIMITED—See Halma plc; *Int'l*, pg. 3232
PANZHIHUA TOLEDO ELECTRONIC SCALE LTD.—See Mettler-Toledo International, Inc.; *U.S. Public*, pg. 1433
PARAYTEC LIMITED—See Braveheart Investment Group Plc; *Int'l*, pg. 1141
PARR INSTRUMENT COMPANY; *U.S. Private*, pg. 3099
PERKINELMER BIOSIGNAL, INC.—See Revvity, Inc.; *U.S. Public*, pg. 1794
PERKINELMER CHEMAGEN TECHNOLOGIE GMBH—See Revvity, Inc.; *U.S. Public*, pg. 1795
PERKINELMER DANMARK A/S—See Revvity, Inc.; *U.S. Public*, pg. 1794
PERKIN ELMER DE MEXICO, S.A.—See Revvity, Inc.; *U.S. Public*, pg. 1794
PERKINELMER ESPANA, S.L.—See Revvity, Inc.; *U.S. Public*, pg. 1794
PERKINELMER FINLAND OY—See Revvity, Inc.; *U.S. Public*, pg. 1794
PERKINELMER HEALTH SCIENCES CANADA INC.—See Revvity, Inc.; *U.S. Public*, pg. 1794
PERKINELMER HEALTH SCIENCES, INC.—See Revvity, Inc.; *U.S. Public*, pg. 1794
PERKINELMER (HONG KONG) LTD.—See Revvity, Inc.; *U.S. Public*, pg. 1794
PERKINELMER INSTRUMENTS (SHANGHAI) CO. LTD.—See Revvity, Inc.; *U.S. Public*, pg. 1795
PERKINELMER JAPAN CO. LTD.—See Revvity, Inc.; *U.S. Public*, pg. 1795
PERKINELMER NEDERLAND B.V.—See Revvity, Inc.; *U.S. Public*, pg. 1795

334516 — ANALYTICAL LABORATO...

PERKINELMER PTY. LTD.—See Revvity, Inc.; *U.S. Public,* pg. 1795
PERKINELMER SINGAPORE PTE LTD.—See Revvity, Inc.; *U.S. Public,* pg. 1795
PERKINELMER TAIWAN CORPORATION—See Revvity, Inc.; *U.S. Public,* pg. 1795
PERKINELMER VERTRIEBS GMBH—See Revvity, Inc.; *U.S. Public,* pg. 1795
PERMA PURE INC. LLC—See Halma plc; *Int'l,* pg. 3232
PERTEN INSTRUMENTS AB—See Revvity, Inc.; *U.S. Public,* pg. 1795
PERTEN INSTRUMENTS FRANCE SASU—See Revvity, Inc.; *U.S. Public,* pg. 1795
PERTEN INSTRUMENTS, INC.—See Revvity, Inc.; *U.S. Public,* pg. 1795
PERTEN INSTRUMENTS OF AUSTRALIA PTY LTD—See Revvity, Inc.; *U.S. Public,* pg. 1795
PETROLEUM ANALYZER COMPANY—See Roper Technologies, Inc.; *U.S. Public,* pg. 1812
PHADIA SOCIEDAD UNIPESSOAL LDA.—See Thermo Fisher Scientific Inc.; *U.S. Public,* pg. 2153
PHARMACONTROL ELECTRONIC GMBH—See Mettler-Toledo International, Inc.; *U.S. Public,* pg. 1433
PHOTON MACHINES INC; *U.S. Private,* pg. 3174
PLD FINLAND OY—See Addtech AB; *Int'l,* pg. 134
POINTE SCIENTIFIC, INC.—See MedTest DX, Inc.; *U.S. Private,* pg. 2659
POLYMEDCO, INC.; *U.S. Private,* pg. 3225
PRECIPIO, INC.; *U.S. Public,* pg. 1713
PRESSURE BIOSCIENCES, INC.; *U.S. Public,* pg. 1716
PROTEINSIMPLE LTD.—See Bio-Techne Corporation; *U.S. Public,* pg. 334
PROTEINSIMPLE—See Bio-Techne Corporation; *U.S. Public,* pg. 334
PSIVIDA SECURITIES CORPORATION—See EyePoint Pharmaceuticals, Inc.; *U.S. Public,* pg. 817
P.T. JOHNSON & JOHNSON INDONESIA—See Kenvue Inc.; *U.S. Public,* pg. 1224
P.T. KROMTEKINDO UTAMA—See Waters Corporation; *U.S. Public,* pg. 2335
QUALMARK CORPORATION—See ESPEC Corp.; *Int'l,* pg. 2505
QUANTUM DESIGN INC; *U.S. Private,* pg. 3323
QUEST INTEGRATED, LLC; *U.S. Private,* pg. 3325
RADIOMETER AMERICA INC.—See Danaher Corporation; *U.S. Public,* pg. 630
RADIOMETER A/S—See Danaher Corporation; *U.S. Public,* pg. 630
RADIOMETER LIMITED—See Danaher Corporation; *U.S. Public,* pg. 630
RAINDANCE TECHNOLOGIES, INC.—See Bio-Rad Laboratories, Inc.; *U.S. Public,* pg. 334
REDLAKE INC.—See Roper Technologies, Inc.; *U.S. Public,* pg. 1813
REDOX SRL—See Waters Corporation; *U.S. Public,* pg. 2335
REFLECT SCIENTIFIC, INC.; *U.S. Public,* pg. 1771
REMEL INC.—See Thermo Fisher Scientific Inc.; *U.S. Public,* pg. 2151
RESEARCH INSTRUMENTS SDN BHD—See Waters Corporation; *U.S. Public,* pg. 2335
REVVITY, INC.; *U.S. Public,* pg. 1793
ROFIN-BAASEL KOREA CO., LTD.—See Coherent Corp.; *U.S. Public,* pg. 527
ROPER BRASIL COMERCIO E PROMOCAO DE PRODUCTOS E SERVICOS LTDA—See Roper Technologies, Inc.; *U.S. Public,* pg. 1813
ROPER ENGINEERING S.R.O.—See Roper Technologies, Inc.; *U.S. Public,* pg. 1813
ROPER INDUSTRIES LIMITED—See Roper Technologies, Inc.; *U.S. Public,* pg. 1813
ROPER MIDDLE EAST LTD.—See Roper Technologies, Inc.; *U.S. Public,* pg. 1813
SANTA BARBARA INFRARED, INC.—See HEICO Corporation; *U.S. Public,* pg. 1020
SCIENTIFIC BIOTECH SPECIALTIES INC.—See HORIBA Ltd; *Int'l,* pg. 3478
SCIENTIFIC INDUSTRIES, INC.; *U.S. Public,* pg. 1848
SCIENTIFIC INSTRUMENTS, INC.; *U.S. Private,* pg. 3574
SCIENTIFIC INSTRUMENTS S.A. DE C.V.—See HORIBA Ltd; *Int'l,* pg. 3478
SCIENTIFIC SYSTEMS INC.—See Teledyne Technologies Incorporated; *U.S. Public,* pg. 1994
SCILABWARE LTD.—See OEP Capital Advisors, L.P.; *U.S. Private,* pg. 2999
SELCI S.A. DE C.V.—See HORIBA Ltd; *Int'l,* pg. 3478
SENDX MEDICAL, INC.—See Danaher Corporation; *U.S. Public,* pg. 631
SENECO SRL—See ESPEC Corp.; *Int'l,* pg. 2505
SENSIT TECHNOLOGIES LLC—See Halma plc; *Int'l,* pg. 3232
SENSLAB GMBH—See EKF Diagnostics Holdings PLC; *Int'l,* pg. 2338
SEPARATION TECHNOLOGY, INC.—See EKF Diagnostics Holdings PLC; *Int'l,* pg. 2338
SEQUENOM, INC.—See Laboratory Corporation of America Holdings; *U.S. Public,* pg. 1287

SHISAS TRADING CONCERN PVT. LTD.—See HORIBA Ltd; *Int'l,* pg. 3478
SICA MEDICION SA DE CV—See HORIBA Ltd; *Int'l,* pg. 3478
SIGMATECH INC.—See HORIBA Ltd; *Int'l,* pg. 3478
SITHIPORN ASSOCIATES CO., LTD.—See Waters Corporation; *U.S. Public,* pg. 2335
SOMALOGIC, INC.—See Standard BioTools Inc.; *U.S. Public,* pg. 1928
SOMALOGIC OPERATING CO., INC.—See Standard BioTools Inc.; *U.S. Public,* pg. 1929
SONAR OY—See ADDvise Group AB; *Int'l,* pg. 136
SONOSCAN (EUROPE) LTD.—See Nordson Corporation; *U.S. Public,* pg. 1534
SPACE ELECTRONICS, LLC—See L Squared Capital Management LP; *U.S. Private,* pg. 2362
SPECIALIZED FOR ADVANCED SYSTEMS & CHEMICALS—See Waters Corporation; *U.S. Public,* pg. 2335
SPECTRASENSORS, INC.—See Endress+Hauser (International) Holding AG; *Int'l,* pg. 2407
SPECTRECOLOGY, LLC—See Salvo Technologies, Inc.; *U.S. Private,* pg. 3535
SPECTRO ANALYTICAL INSTRUMENTS GMBH—See AMETEK, Inc.; *U.S. Public,* pg. 118
SPECTRO SCIENTIFIC INC.—See AMETEK, Inc.; *U.S. Public,* pg. 122
SPRINGS FABRICATION, INC. - ADVANCED TECHNOLOGY GROUP—See Springs Fabrication, Inc.; *U.S. Private,* pg. 3764
S&S INGENIERIA S.A.S.—See HORIBA Ltd; *Int'l,* pg. 3478
STARLAB FRANCE S.A.R.L.—See Eppendorf AG; *Int'l,* pg. 2464
STARLAB INTERNATIONAL GMBH—See Eppendorf AG; *Int'l,* pg. 2464
STARLAB S.R.L.—See Eppendorf AG; *Int'l,* pg. 2464
STARLAB (UK) LIMITED—See Eppendorf AG; *Int'l,* pg. 2464
STATSPIN, INC.—See Danaher Corporation; *U.S. Public,* pg. 625
STEINEL VERTRIEB GMBH—See ADCURAM Group AG; *Int'l,* pg. 128
STERLITECH CORPORATION; *U.S. Private,* pg. 3807
STOELTING CO.; *U.S. Private,* pg. 3815
STRUERS A/S—See Roper Technologies, Inc.; *U.S. Public,* pg. 1813
STRUERS GMBH—See Roper Technologies, Inc.; *U.S. Public,* pg. 1813
STRUERS INC.—See Roper Technologies, Inc.; *U.S. Public,* pg. 1813
STRUERS LTD.—See Roper Technologies, Inc.; *U.S. Public,* pg. 1813
STRUERS SARL—See Roper Technologies, Inc.; *U.S. Public,* pg. 1813
SUMITOMO EATON NOVA CORPORATION—See Axcelis Technologies, Inc.; *U.S. Public,* pg. 255
SUZHOU ANTAI AIR TECH CO., LTD.—See AIRTECH JAPAN, LTD.; *Int'l,* pg. 249
TA INSTRUMENTS JAPAN—See Waters Corporation; *U.S. Public,* pg. 2335
TA INSTRUMENTS LTD.—See Waters Corporation; *U.S. Public,* pg. 2335
TA INSTRUMENTS-WATERS LLC—See Waters Corporation; *U.S. Public,* pg. 2335
TA INSTRUMENTS - WATERS TECHNOLOGIES (SHANGHAI) LIMITED—See Waters Corporation; *U.S. Public,* pg. 2335
TECHNI-LAB SARL—See HORIBA Ltd; *Int'l,* pg. 3478
TECNICA DEL FUTURO S.A.—See HORIBA Ltd; *Int'l,* pg. 3478
TECRA INTERNATIONAL PTY. LTD.—See 3M Company; *U.S. Public,* pg. 5
TELEDYNE CETAC TECHNOLOGIES—See Teledyne Technologies Incorporated; *U.S. Public,* pg. 1994
TELEDYNE LEEMAN LABS—See Teledyne Technologies Incorporated; *U.S. Public,* pg. 1994
TELEDYNE TEKMAR—See Teledyne Technologies Incorporated; *U.S. Public,* pg. 1995
TELSTAR INSTRUMAT, S.L.—See Azbil Corporation; *Int'l,* pg. 777
TEMPTRONIC GMBH—See inTEST Corporation; *U.S. Public,* pg. 1159
TESCOR, INC.; *U.S. Private,* pg. 3973
THERMO ELECTRON A/S—See Thermo Fisher Scientific Inc.; *U.S. Public,* pg. 2152
THERMO ELECTRON LABORATORY EQUIPMENT LLC—See Thermo Fisher Scientific Inc.; *U.S. Public,* pg. 2152
THERMO ELECTRON S.A.—See Thermo Fisher Scientific Inc.; *U.S. Public,* pg. 2152
THERMO FAST U.K. LIMITED—See Thermo Fisher Scientific Inc.; *U.S. Public,* pg. 2152
THERMO FISHER SCIENTIFIC BRASIL SERVICOS DE LOGISTICA LTDA—See Thermo Fisher Scientific Inc.; *U.S. Public,* pg. 2147
THERMO FISHER SCIENTIFIC (BREMEN) GMBH—See Thermo Fisher Scientific Inc.; *U.S. Public,* pg. 2153
THERMO FISHER SCIENTIFIC BRNO S.R.O.—See Thermo Fisher Scientific Inc.; *U.S. Public,* pg. 2153

CORPORATE AFFILIATIONS

THERMO FISHER SCIENTIFIC - FRANKLIN BRANCH—See Thermo Fisher Scientific Inc.; *U.S. Public,* pg. 2153
THERMO FISHER SCIENTIFIC GENEART GMBH—See Thermo Fisher Scientific Inc.; *U.S. Public,* pg. 2149
THERMO FISHER SCIENTIFIC GMBH—See Thermo Fisher Scientific Inc.; *U.S. Public,* pg. 2153
THERMO FISHER SCIENTIFIC INC. - CELLOMICS—See Thermo Fisher Scientific Inc.; *U.S. Public,* pg. 2154
THERMO FISHER SCIENTIFIC INC.; *U.S. Public,* pg. 2145
THERMO FISHER SCIENTIFIC INDIA PVT LTD—See Thermo Fisher Scientific Inc.; *U.S. Public,* pg. 2154
THERMO FISHER SCIENTIFIC INFORMATICS—See Thermo Fisher Scientific Inc.; *U.S. Public,* pg. 2153
THERMO FISHER SCIENTIFIC - LAB VISION IHC SYSTEM SOLUTIONS—See Thermo Fisher Scientific Inc.; *U.S. Public,* pg. 2153
THERMO FISHER SCIENTIFIC - MATRIX LIQUID HANDLING PRODUCTS—See Thermo Fisher Scientific Inc.; *U.S. Public,* pg. 2153
THERMO FISHER SCIENTIFIC MEXICO CITY, S. DE R.L. DE C.V.—See Thermo Fisher Scientific Inc.; *U.S. Public,* pg. 2154
THERMO FISHER SCIENTIFIC - NERL CLINICAL DIAGNOSTICS—See Thermo Fisher Scientific Inc.; *U.S. Public,* pg. 2153
THERMO FISHER SCIENTIFIC - NEWINGTON BRANCH—See Thermo Fisher Scientific Inc.; *U.S. Public,* pg. 2153
THERMO FISHER SCIENTIFIC - PITTSBURGH BRANCH—See Thermo Fisher Scientific Inc.; *U.S. Public,* pg. 2153
THERMO FISHER SCIENTIFIC - SAN DIEGO BRANCH—See Thermo Fisher Scientific Inc.; *U.S. Public,* pg. 2153
THERMO FISHER SCIENTIFIC—See Thermo Fisher Scientific Inc.; *U.S. Public,* pg. 2152
THERMO FISHER SCIENTIFIC—See Thermo Fisher Scientific Inc.; *U.S. Public,* pg. 2153
THERMO FISHER SCIENTIFIC—See Thermo Fisher Scientific Inc.; *U.S. Public,* pg. 2153
THERMO FISHER SCIENTIFIC (THAILAND) CO., LTD.—See Thermo Fisher Scientific Inc.; *U.S. Public,* pg. 2149
THERMOGENESIS HOLDINGS, INC.—See Boyalife Group; *Int'l,* pg. 1124
THORLABS, INC.; *U.S. Private,* pg. 4162
TRANSCORE COMMERCIAL SERVICES, LLC—See Roper Technologies, Inc.; *U.S. Public,* pg. 1814
TREK DIAGNOSTIC SYSTEMS LTD.—See Thermo Fisher Scientific Inc.; *U.S. Public,* pg. 2155
ULTRATECH, INC.—See Veeco Instruments Inc.; *U.S. Public,* pg. 2276
UNITED DIAGNOSTICS, INC.—See Thermo Fisher Scientific Inc.; *U.S. Public,* pg. 2155
UNIVERSAL ANALYZERS INC.—See AMETEK, Inc.; *U.S. Public,* pg. 118
UVP, LLC—See Endress+Hauser (International) Holding AG; *Int'l,* pg. 2405
VERACITY NETWORK INC.; *U.S. Private,* pg. 4359
VIDRIERIA Y REACTIVOS, S.A. DE C.V.—See HORIBA Ltd; *Int'l,* pg. 3478
WATER QUALITY GMBH—See Danaher Corporation; *U.S. Public,* pg. 632
WATERS AG—See Waters Corporation; *U.S. Public,* pg. 2335
WATERS ANALYTICAL INSTRUMENTS SDN BHD—See Waters Corporation; *U.S. Public,* pg. 2335
WATERS AS—See Waters Corporation; *U.S. Public,* pg. 2335
WATERS A/S—See Waters Corporation; *U.S. Public,* pg. 2335
WATERS AUSTRALIA PTY. LTD.—See Waters Corporation; *U.S. Public,* pg. 2335
WATERS CHINA LTD.—See Waters Corporation; *U.S. Public,* pg. 2335
WATERS CHROMATOGRAPHY B.V.—See Waters Corporation; *U.S. Public,* pg. 2335
WATERS CHROMATOGRAPHY EUROPE BV—See Waters Corporation; *U.S. Public,* pg. 2335
WATERS CHROMATOGRAPHY IRELAND LTD.—See Waters Corporation; *U.S. Public,* pg. 2335
WATERS CORPORATION; *U.S. Public,* pg. 2334
WATERS GES.M.B.H—See Waters Corporation; *U.S. Public,* pg. 2335
WATERS GMBH—See Waters Corporation; *U.S. Public,* pg. 2335
WATERS INDIA PVT LTD.—See Waters Corporation; *U.S. Public,* pg. 2335
WATERS KFT.—See Waters Corporation; *U.S. Public,* pg. 2335
WATERS KOREA LIMITED—See Waters Corporation; *U.S. Public,* pg. 2335
WATERS LIMITED—See Waters Corporation; *U.S. Public,* pg. 2335
WATERS LTD.—See Waters Corporation; *U.S. Public,* pg. 2335

N.A.I.C.S. INDEX

WATERS NV—See Waters Corporation; *U.S. Public*, pg. 2335
WATERS PACIFIC PTE LTD—See Waters Corporation; *U.S. Public*, pg. 2335
WATERS S.A. DE C.V.—See Waters Corporation; *U.S. Public*, pg. 2335
WATERS S.A.S.—See Waters Corporation; *U.S. Public*, pg. 2335
WATERS SPA—See Waters Corporation; *U.S. Public*, pg. 2336
WATERS SP Z.O.O—See Waters Corporation; *U.S. Public*, pg. 2335
WATERS SVERIGE AB—See Waters Corporation; *U.S. Public*, pg. 2335
WATERS (TC) ISRAEL LIMITED—See Waters Corporation; *U.S. Public*, pg. 2335
WATERS TECHNOLOGIES CORPORATION—See Waters Corporation; *U.S. Public*, pg. 2335
WATERS TECHNOLOGIES DO BRASIL LTDA.—See Waters Corporation; *U.S. Public*, pg. 2336
WEATHERFORD PRODUCTION OPTIMIZATION—See Weatherford International plc; *U.S. Public*, pg. 2341
WHATMAN INTERNATIONAL LTD.—See GE HealthCare Technologies Inc.; *U.S. Public*, pg. 909
WHEATON INDUSTRIES, INC.—See OEP Capital Advisors, L.P.; *U.S. Private*, pg. 2999
WILKS ENTERPRISE INC.—See AMETEK, Inc.; *U.S. Public*, pg. 122
XCELAERO CORP.—See Bascom Hunter Technologies Inc.; *U.S. Private*, pg. 484
XEI SCIENTIFIC, INC.; *U.S. Private*, pg. 4581
XYLEM INC. - ANALYTICS—See Xylem Inc.; *U.S. Public*, pg. 2395
YSI INCORPORATED—See Xylem Inc.; *U.S. Public*, pg. 2395
Y-Z SYSTEMS INC.—See BC Partners LLP; *Int'l*, pg. 922
Y-Z SYSTEMS INC.—See The Carlyle Group Inc.; *U.S. Public*, pg. 2044
Z.A.O. LECO CENTER MOSCOW—See LECO Corporation; *U.S. Private*, pg. 2410

334517 — IRRADIATION APPARATUS MANUFACTURING

ADVANCED MEDICAL SYSTEMS INC.—See ATC Group, Inc.; *U.S. Private*, pg. 365
AIRBOSS DEFENSE GROUP, LLC—See AirBoss of America Corp.; *Int'l*, pg. 241
AMERICAN SCIENCE AND ENGINEERING, INC.—See OSI Systems, Inc.; *U.S. Public*, pg. 1621
BROWN'S MEDICAL IMAGING, LLC—See Atlantic Street Capital Management LLC; *U.S. Private*, pg. 374
BRUKER AXS, INC.—See Bruker Corporation; *U.S. Public*, pg. 404
BRUKER JV ISRAEL LTD.—See Bruker Corporation; *U.S. Public*, pg. 405
BRUKER JV UK LTD.—See Bruker Corporation; *U.S. Public*, pg. 405
BRUKER LTD.—See Bruker Corporation; *U.S. Public*, pg. 405
BRUKER SCIENTIFIC LLC—See Bruker Corporation; *U.S. Public*, pg. 406
CAPNIA, INC.—See Soleno Therapeutics, Inc.; *U.S. Public*, pg. 1900
CLAYMOUNT HIGH VOLTAGE TECHNOLOGIES (BEIJING) CO. LTD.—See Varex Imaging Corporation; *U.S. Public*, pg. 2275
CLAYMOUNT SWITZERLAND AG—See Varex Imaging Corporation; *U.S. Public*, pg. 2275
COHERENT CRYSTAL ASSOCIATES—See Coherent Corp.; *U.S. Public*, pg. 527
COHERENT (DEUTSCHLAND) GMBH—See Coherent Corp.; *U.S. Public*, pg. 526
COHERENT FRANCE—See Coherent Corp.; *U.S. Public*, pg. 527
COHERENT LASERSYSTEMS GMBH & CO. KG—See Coherent Corp.; *U.S. Public*, pg. 527
COHERENT (U.K.) LTD.—See Coherent Corp.; *U.S. Public*, pg. 527
CUATTRO MEDICAL, LLC—See Cuattro, LLC; *U.S. Private*, pg. 1119
CYNOSURE, LLC—See Clayton, Dubilier & Rice, LLC; *U.S. Private*, pg. 922
DENT-X CORPORATION—See SMK Imaging, LLC; *U.S. Private*, pg. 3698
DETECTION TECHNOLOGY S.A.S.—See Detection Technology Oyj; *Int'l*, pg. 2048
DIRECT CONVERSION GMBH—See Varex Imaging Corporation, *U.S. Public*, pg. 2275
DIRECT RADIOGRAPHY CORP.—See Hologic, Inc.; *U.S. Public*, pg. 1044
DRTECH CORPORATION - DRTECH KOREA FACTORY—See DRTECH Corporation; *Int'l*, pg. 2206
DT ELECTRONIC TECHNOLOGY (WUXI) CO., LTD.—See Detection Technology Oyj; *Int'l*, pg. 2047
EAGLE PRODUCT INSPECTION LIMITED—See Mettler-Toledo International, Inc.; *U.S. Public*, pg. 1432

THE ELLISON CO. INC.; *U.S. Private*, pg. 4025
FLUKE BIOMEDICAL—See Fortive Corporation; *U.S. Public*, pg. 870
GADSDEN PROPERTIES, INC.; *U.S. Public*, pg. 894
GE MEDICAL SYSTEMS GLOBAL TECHNOLOGY COMPANY, LLC—See GE HealthCare Technologies Inc.; *U.S. Public*, pg. 909
GENDEX DENTAL SYSTEMS—See Danaher Corporation; *U.S. Public*, pg. 627
GENORAY CO., LTD.; *Int'l*, pg. 2925
HAIN LIFESCIENCE UK LTD.—See Bruker Corporation; *U.S. Public*, pg. 406
HESKA IMAGING US, LLC—See Mars, Incorporated; *U.S. Private*, pg. 2588
INEL SAS—See Thermo Fisher Scientific Inc.; *U.S. Public*, pg. 2148
IRRADIATION SOLUTIONS INC.—See A Brown Company, Inc.; *Int'l*, pg. 17
JORDAN VALLEY SEMICONDUCTORS UK, LTD.—See Bruker Corporation; *U.S. Public*, pg. 406
KOLLMORGEN ELECTRO-OPTICAL—See L3Harris Technologies, Inc.; *U.S. Public*, pg. 1281
LAMBDA PHYSIK JAPAN CO., LTD.—See Coherent Corp.; *U.S. Public*, pg. 527
LUMENIS (HK) LIMITED—See Boston Scientific Corporation; *U.S. Public*, pg. 375
MASIMO CORPORATION; *U.S. Public*, pg. 1392
NXSTAGE MEDICAL, INC.—See Fresenius Medical Care AG; *Int'l*, pg. 2776
OSI SYSTEMS, INC.; *U.S. Public*, pg. 1621
QSA GLOBAL INC.—See Illinois Tool Works Inc.; *U.S. Public*, pg. 1110
RAPISCAN SYSTEMS LTD.—See OSI Systems, Inc.; *U.S. Public*, pg. 1622
SENSUS HEALTHCARE, INC.; *U.S. Public*, pg. 1868
TOMOTHERAPY INCORPORATED—See Accuray Incorporated; *U.S. Public*, pg. 33
UNFORS RAYSAFE AB—See Fortive Corporation; *U.S. Public*, pg. 872
UNIFORS RAYSAFE AB—See Fortive Corporation; *U.S. Public*, pg. 872
VAREX IMAGING AMERICAS CORPORATION—See Varex Imaging Corporation; *U.S. Public*, pg. 2275
VAREX IMAGING EQUIPMENT (CHINA) CO., LTD.—See Varex Imaging Corporation; *U.S. Public*, pg. 2275
VAREX IMAGING ITALIA SRL—See Varex Imaging Corporation; *U.S. Public*, pg. 2275
VAREX IMAGING JAPAN, K.K.—See Varex Imaging Corporation; *U.S. Public*, pg. 2275
VAREX IMAGING PHILIPPINES, INC.—See Varex Imaging Corporation; *U.S. Public*, pg. 2275
WIPRO GE HEALTHCARE PRIVATE LIMITED—See General Electric Company; *U.S. Public*, pg. 920
YOUNG MICROBRUSH IRELAND, LTD.—See The Jordan Company, L.P.; *U.S. Private*, pg. 4063
YXLON INTERNATIONAL GMBH—See Comet Holding AG; *Int'l*, pg. 1711

334519 — OTHER MEASURING AND CONTROLLING DEVICE MANUFACTURING

AANDERAA DATA INSTRUMENTS AS—See Xylem Inc.; *U.S. Public*, pg. 2395
AANDERAA DATA INSTRUMENTS INC.—See Xylem Inc.; *U.S. Public*, pg. 2395
ABB INC.—See ABB Ltd.; *Int'l*, pg. 51
AB DYNAMICS EUROPE GMBH—See AB Dynamics plc; *Int'l*, pg. 39
ACOEM AB—See ACOEM Group; *Int'l*, pg. 107
ADMET, INC.; *U.S. Private*, pg. 80
ADVANCED ENERGY INDUSTRIES GMBH—See Advanced Energy Industries, Inc.; *U.S. Public*, pg. 47
ADVANCED ENERGY INDUSTRIES, INC., SHANGHAI—See Advanced Energy Industries, Inc.; *U.S. Public*, pg. 47
ADVANCED ENERGY INDUSTRIES UK LTD.—See Advanced Energy Industries, Inc.; *U.S. Public*, pg. 47
ADVANCED ENERGY JAPAN K.K.—See Advanced Energy Industries, Inc.; *U.S. Public*, pg. 47
ADVANCED ENERGY TAIWAN, LTD.—See Advanced Energy Industries, Inc.; *U.S. Public*, pg. 47
ADVANCED MEASUREMENT TECHNOLOGY, INC.—See AMETEK, Inc.; *U.S. Public*, pg. 118
ADVANCED MICRO INSTRUMENTS, INC.—See Enpro Inc.; *U.S. Public*, pg. 774
ADVANTEST CORPORATION; *Int'l*, pg. 165
AEMULUS CORPORATION SDN. BHD. - SAN RAMON BRANCH—See Aemulus Holdings Berhad; *Int'l*, pg. 176
AEMULUS CORPORATION SDN. BHD.—See Aemulus Holdings Berhad; *Int'l*, pg. 175
AERA KOREA LTD.—See Advanced Energy Industries, Inc.; *U.S. Public*, pg. 47
AGILENT TECHNOLOGIES AUSTRALIA PTY LTD—See Agilent Technologies, Inc.; *U.S. Public*, pg. 60
AGILENT TECHNOLOGIES BELGIUM S.A./N.V.—See Agilent Technologies, Inc.; *U.S. Public*, pg. 60
AGILENT TECHNOLOGIES BRASIL LTDA—See Agilent

Technologies, Inc.; *U.S. Public*, pg. 60
AGILENT TECHNOLOGIES CANADA INC.—See Agilent Technologies, Inc.; *U.S. Public*, pg. 60
AGILENT TECHNOLOGIES DEUTSCHLAND GMBH—See Agilent Technologies, Inc.; *U.S. Public*, pg. 61
AGILENT TECHNOLOGIES DEUTSCHLAND HOLDING GMBH—See Agilent Technologies, Inc.; *U.S. Public*, pg. 60
AGILENT TECHNOLOGIES FRANCE SAS—See Agilent Technologies, Inc.; *U.S. Public*, pg. 61
AGILENT TECHNOLOGIES INTERNATIONAL SARL—See Agilent Technologies, Inc.; *U.S. Public*, pg. 61
AGILENT TECHNOLOGIES IRELAND FINANCE LIMITED—See Agilent Technologies, Inc.; *U.S. Public*, pg. 61
AGILENT TECHNOLOGIES IRELAND LTD.—See Agilent Technologies, Inc.; *U.S. Public*, pg. 61
AGILENT TECHNOLOGIES ITALIA S.P.A.—See Agilent Technologies, Inc.; *U.S. Public*, pg. 61
AGILENT TECHNOLOGIES JAPAN, LTD.—See Agilent Technologies, Inc.; *U.S. Public*, pg. 61
AGILENT TECHNOLOGIES (MALAYSIA) SDN. BHD.—See Agilent Technologies, Inc.; *U.S. Public*, pg. 60
AGILENT TECHNOLOGIES MEXICO, S.DE R.L. DE C.V.—See Agilent Technologies, Inc.; *U.S. Public*, pg. 61
AGILENT TECHNOLOGIES SINGAPORE PTE. LTD.—See Agilent Technologies, Inc.; *U.S. Public*, pg. 61
AGILENT TECHNOLOGIES SINGAPORE VISION OPERATION PTE LTD.—See Agilent Technologies, Inc.; *U.S. Public*, pg. 61
AGILENT TECHNOLOGIES SWEDEN HOLDING AB—See Agilent Technologies, Inc.; *U.S. Public*, pg. 61
AGILENT TECHNOLOGIES TAIWAN LTD.—See Agilent Technologies, Inc.; *U.S. Public*, pg. 61
AGR BANGKOK LTD—See Clayton, Dubilier & Rice, LLC; *U.S. Private*, pg. 924
AGR INTERNATIONAL, INC.—See Clayton, Dubilier & Rice, LLC; *U.S. Private*, pg. 924
ALABAMA SPECIALTY PRODUCTS, INC.; *U.S. Private*, pg. 148
ALBANY INTERNATIONAL CANADA CORP.—See Albany International Corp.; *U.S. Public*, pg. 72
ALCOHOL COUNTERMEASURE SYSTEMS CORP.; *Int'l*, pg. 302
ALFRED DUNHILL LIMITED—See Compagnie Financiere Richemont S.A.; *Int'l*, pg. 1740
ALLIENT INC.; *U.S. Public*, pg. 80
ALL SENSORS ASIA PACIFIC K.K.—See Amphenol Corporation; *U.S. Public*, pg. 126
ALL WEATHER INC.; *U.S. Private*, pg. 173
ALVARADO MANUFACTURING CO. INC.—See dormakaba Holding AG; *Int'l*, pg. 2177
AMANO CINCINNATI, INC.—See Amano Corporation; *Int'l*, pg. 410
AMANO CORPORATION—See Amano Corporation; *Int'l*, pg. 410
AMANO ELECTRONICS EUROPE, N.V.—See Amano Corporation; *Int'l*, pg. 410
AMETEK GERMANY GMBH—See AMETEK, Inc.; *U.S. Public*, pg. 120
AMETEK MEASUREMENT & CALIBRATION TECHNOLOGIES—See AMETEK, Inc.; *U.S. Public*, pg. 117
AMPAC PTY LIMITED—See Halma plc; *Int'l*, pg. 3230
ANAMET INC.; *U.S. Private*, pg. 271
ANDERSON POWER PRODUCTS—See IDEAL Industries Inc; *U.S. Private*, pg. 2036
ANRITSU AB—See Anritsu Corporation; *Int'l*, pg. 475
ANRITSU (CHINA) CO., LTD.—See Anritsu Corporation; *Int'l*, pg. 475
ANRITSU COMPANY, INC.—See Anritsu Corporation; *Int'l*, pg. 475
ANRITSU COMPANY LIMITED—See Anritsu Corporation; *Int'l*, pg. 475
ANRITSU CORPORATION; *Int'l*, pg. 475
ANRITSU EMEA GMBH—See Anritsu Corporation; *Int'l*, pg. 475
ANRITSU INDIA PRIVATE LIMITED—See Anritsu Corporation; *Int'l*, pg. 475
ANRITSU INDUSTRIAL SOLUTIONS (SHANGHAI) CO., LTD.—See Anritsu Corporation; *Int'l*, pg. 475
ANRITSU INFIVIS B.V.—See Anritsu Corporation; *Int'l*, pg. 475
ANRITSU INFIVIS INC.—See Anritsu Corporation; *Int'l*, pg. 475
ANRITSU INFIVIS LTD.—See Anritsu Corporation; *Int'l*, pg. 475
ANRITSU INFIVIS (THAILAND) CO., LTD.—See Anritsu Corporation; *Int'l*, pg. 476
ANRITSU KOUSAN CO., LTD.—See Anritsu Corporation; *Int'l*, pg. 475
ANRITSU PHILIPPINES, INC.—See Anritsu Corporation; *Int'l*, pg. 476
ANRITSU SOLUTIONS SK, S.R.O.—See Anritsu Corporation; *Int'l*, pg. 476
ANSELL COMMERCIAL MEXICO S.A. DE C.V.—See Ansell Limited; *Int'l*, pg. 478
APOLLO AMERICA INC.—See Halma plc; *Int'l*, pg. 3231

334519 — OTHER MEASURING AND...

APPLANIX CORPORATION—See Trimble, Inc.; *U.S. Public*, pg. 2190
APPLIED TECHNOLOGIES ASSOCIATES; *U.S. Private*, pg. 299
AQL SRL—See El.En. S.p.A.; *Int'l*, pg. 2341
ARMITRON WATCH DIVISION—See E. Gluck Corp.; *U.S. Private*, pg. 1304
ARVIN MOTION CONTROL LIMITED—See Cummins Inc.; *U.S. Public*, pg. 608
ASAIS S.A.S.—See Itron, Inc; *U.S. Public*, pg. 1175
ASSOCIATED SPRING-ASIA PTE. LTD.—See OEP Capital Advisors, L.P.; *U.S. Private*, pg. 2998
ASSOCIATED SPRING MEXICO, S.A.—See OEP Capital Advisors, L.P.; *U.S. Private*, pg. 2998
ASSOCIATED SPRING (U.K.) LTD.—See OEP Capital Advisors, L.P.; *U.S. Private*, pg. 2998
AT TECHMAC CO., LTD.—See Anritsu Corporation; *Int'l*, pg. 475
AUXITROL S.A.—See TransDigm Group Incorporated; *U.S. Public*, pg. 2180
AXON ENTERPRISE, INC.; *U.S. Public*, pg. 255
AZBIL NORTH AMERICA, INC.—See Azbil Corporation; *Int'l*, pg. 777
AZIMUTH SYSTEMS, INC.—See Anritsu Corporation; *Int'l*, pg. 476
BACHARACH INC.—See FFL Partners, LLC; *U.S. Private*, pg. 1500
BAKER HUGHES DIGITAL SOLUTIONS GMBH—See Baker Hughes Company; *U.S. Public*, pg. 264
BALANCE TECHNOLOGY INC.; *U.S. Private*, pg. 457
BAMATEC AG—See Baumann Federn AG; *Int'l*, pg. 895
BARKSDALE, INC.—See Crane NXT, Co.; *U.S. Public*, pg. 589
BARTEC AB—See Charterhouse Capital Partners LLP; *Int'l*, pg. 1455
BARTEC BELGIUM NV/SA—See Charterhouse Capital Partners LLP; *Int'l*, pg. 1455
BARTEC ELEKTROTECHNIK GMBH—See Charterhouse Capital Partners LLP; *Int'l*, pg. 1455
BARTEC ENGINEERING + SERVICES AG—See Charterhouse Capital Partners LLP; *Int'l*, pg. 1455
BARTEC GMBH—See Charterhouse Capital Partners LLP; *Int'l*, pg. 1455
BARTEC HUNGARY KFT.—See Charterhouse Capital Partners LLP; *Int'l*, pg. 1455
BARTEC NEDERLAND B.V.—See Charterhouse Capital Partners LLP; *Int'l*, pg. 1455
BARTEC POLSKA SP. Z O.O.—See Charterhouse Capital Partners LLP; *Int'l*, pg. 1455
BARTEC S.A.R.L.—See Charterhouse Capital Partners LLP; *Int'l*, pg. 1455
BARTEC S.A.—See Charterhouse Capital Partners LLP; *Int'l*, pg. 1455
BARTEC S.R.L.—See Charterhouse Capital Partners LLP; *Int'l*, pg. 1455
BARTEC S.R.O.—See Charterhouse Capital Partners LLP; *Int'l*, pg. 1455
BARTEC UK LTD.—See Charterhouse Capital Partners LLP; *Int'l*, pg. 1455
BARTEC VARNOST, D.O.O.—See Charterhouse Capital Partners LLP; *Int'l*, pg. 1455
BASF CATALYSTS (GUILIN) CO. LTD.—See BASF SE; *Int'l*, pg. 875
BAUMANN FEDERN AG; *Int'l*, pg. 895
BAUME & MERCIER S.A.—See Compagnie Financiere Richemont S.A.; *Int'l*, pg. 1740
BAYERISCHE MASINDUSTRIE A. KELLER GMBH; *Int'l*, pg. 910
BEEDE ELECTRICAL INSTRUMENT CO, INC.—See Faria Beede Instruments, Inc.; *U.S. Private*, pg. 1474
BEIJING CONSEN AUTOMATION CONTROL COMPANY LIMITED—See China Automation Group Limited; *Int'l*, pg. 1483
BEIJING PRECISE INSTRUMENTS CO., LTD.—See China BPIC Surveying Instruments AG; *Int'l*, pg. 1487
BEIJING SAILHERO ZHONGRUN SCIENCE AND TECHNOLOGY CO., LTD.—See Hebei Sailhero Environmental Protection High-Tech Co., Ltd.; *Int'l*, pg. 3306
BENTLY NEVADA, AUSTRALIA PTY. LTD.—See General Electric Company; *U.S. Public*, pg. 919
BILFINGER GERBER GMBH—See Bilfinger SE; *Int'l*, pg. 1027
BIONICS INSTRUMENT CO., LTD.—See DKK-TOA Corporation; *Int'l*, pg. 2139
BLACKLINE SAFETY EUROPE LTD.—See Blackline Safety Corp.; *Int'l*, pg. 1061
BLANCETT—See Badger Meter, Inc.; *U.S. Public*, pg. 263
BORG INDAK INC.; *U.S. Private*, pg. 618
BOSCH INSPECTION TECHNOLOGY GMBH—See CVC Capital Partners SICAV-FIS S.A.; *Int'l*, pg. 1884
BOSCH INSPECTION TECHNOLOGY INC.—See CVC Capital Partners SICAV-FIS S.A.; *Int'l*, pg. 1884
BOSCH INSPECTION TECHNOLOGY (SHANGHAI) CO., LTD.—See CVC Capital Partners SICAV-FIS S.A.; *Int'l*, pg. 1884
BOSCH PACKAGING TECHNOLOGY K.K.—See CVC Capital Partners SICAV-FIS S.A.; *Int'l*, pg. 1884
BRANSON ULTRASONICS (SHANGHAI) CO., LTD.—See Emerson Electric Co.; *U.S. Public*, pg. 742
BRASCITI INDUSTRIA E COMERCIO DE RELOGIOS DA AMAZONIA, S.A.—See Citizen Watch Co., Ltd.; *Int'l*, pg. 1623
BREITLING S.A.—See CVC Capital Partners SICAV-FIS S.A.; *Int'l*, pg. 1882
BROOKS INSTRUMENT K.K.—See Illinois Tool Works Inc.; *U.S. Public*, pg. 1102
BROOKS INSTRUMENT, LLC—See Illinois Tool Works Inc.; *U.S. Public*, pg. 1102
BROOKS UTILITY PRODUCTS GROUP—See Bertram Capital Management, LLC; *U.S. Private*, pg. 540
BROOKS UTILITY PRODUCTS GROUP—See Crimson Investment; *U.S. Private*, pg. 1100
BRUKER DETECTION CORPORATION—See Bruker Corporation; *U.S. Public*, pg. 406
BULOVA CORPORATION—See Citizen Watch Co., Ltd.; *Int'l*, pg. 1623
BULOVA DE MEXICO, SRL—See Citizen Watch Co., Ltd.; *Int'l*, pg. 1623
CABLECRAFT MOTION CONTROLS LLC—See Torque Capital Group, LLC; *U.S. Private*, pg. 4189
CABLECRAFT MOTION CONTROLS LLC—See Torque Capital Group, LLC; *U.S. Private*, pg. 4189
CAMBRIDGE VISCOSITY, INC—See Roper Technologies, Inc.; *U.S. Public*, pg. 1810
CAPINTEC INC.—See Mirion Technologies, Inc.; *U.S. Public*, pg. 1450
CAREL INDUSTRIES S.P.A.; *Int'l*, pg. 1324
CARTIER INTERNATIONAL SA GENEVE—See Compagnie Financiere Richemont S.A.; *Int'l*, pg. 1741
CARTIER SA—See Compagnie Financiere Richemont S.A.; *Int'l*, pg. 1741
CASIO KOREA CO., LTD.—See Casio Computer Co., Ltd.; *Int'l*, pg. 1353
CASIO TAIWAN CO., LTD.—See Casio Computer Co., Ltd.; *Int'l*, pg. 1353
CATAPULT GROUP INTERNATIONAL LTD.; *Int'l*, pg. 1358
CENTRIX CONTROL SOLUTIONS LIMITED PARTNERSHIP—See Endress+Hauser (International) Holding AG; *Int'l*, pg. 2405
CENTRO INC.; *U.S. Private*, pg. 830
CHELSEA CLOCK CO., INC.; *U.S. Private*, pg. 870
CHING CHAN OPTICAL TECHNOLOGY CO., LTD.; *Int'l*, pg. 1569
CIPHERLAB CO., LTD.; *Int'l*, pg. 1616
CITIZEN BUSINESS EXPERT CO., LTD.—See Citizen Watch Co., Ltd.; *Int'l*, pg. 1623
CITIZEN ELECTRONICS CO., LTD.—See Citizen Watch Co., Ltd.; *Int'l*, pg. 1623
CITIZEN FINEDEVICE CO., LTD.—See Citizen Watch Co., Ltd.; *Int'l*, pg. 1623
CITIZEN MACHINERY ASIA CO., LTD.—See Citizen Watch Co., Ltd.; *Int'l*, pg. 1624
CITIZEN TECHNO CO., LTD.—See Citizen Watch Co., Ltd.; *Int'l*, pg. 1624
CITIZEN TOKOROZAWA WORKS—See Citizen Watch Co., Ltd.; *Int'l*, pg. 1624
CITIZEN WATCH (CHINA) CO., LTD.—See Citizen Watch Co., Ltd.; *Int'l*, pg. 1624
CITIZEN WATCH CO. OF CANADA, LTD.—See Citizen Watch Co., Ltd.; *Int'l*, pg. 1624
CITIZEN WATCH DO BRASIL S.A.—See Citizen Watch Co., Ltd.; *Int'l*, pg. 1625
CITIZEN WATCHES GULF CO.—See Citizen Watch Co., Ltd.; *Int'l*, pg. 1625
CITIZEN WATCHES (INDIA) PVT. LTD.—See Citizen Watch Co., Ltd.; *Int'l*, pg. 1625
CITIZEN WATCHES (MALAYSIA) SDN. BHD.—See Citizen Watch Co., Ltd.; *Int'l*, pg. 1625
CITIZEN WATCHES (N.Z.) LTD.—See Citizen Watch Co., Ltd.; *Int'l*, pg. 1625
CITIZEN WATCH ESPANA S.A.—See Citizen Watch Co., Ltd.; *Int'l*, pg. 1624
CITIZEN WATCH MANUFACTURING CO., LTD—See Citizen Watch Co., Ltd.; *Int'l*, pg. 1625
CITIZEN WATCH (SWITZERLAND) AG—See Citizen Watch Co., Ltd.; *Int'l*, pg. 1624
CITIZEN YUBARII CO., LTD.—See Citizen Watch Co., Ltd.; *Int'l*, pg. 1624
CLEAN DIESEL TECHNOLOGIES LIMITED—See CDTi Advanced Materials, Inc.; *U.S. Public*, pg. 462
CLEVELAND ROLL FORMING ENVIRONMENTAL DIVISION, INC.—See Fuel Tech, Inc.; *U.S. Public*, pg. 891
CLORIUS CONTROLS A/S—See Aalberts N.V.; *Int'l*, pg. 33
CMC INDUSTRIAL ELECTRONICS USA, INC.—See Ag Growth International Inc.; *U.S. Public*, pg. 198
CMI, INC.—See MPD, Inc.; *U.S. Private*, pg. 2803
COMPANIA CHILENA DE MEDICION S.A.—See Itron, Inc.; *U.S. Public*, pg. 1175
CONTREL TECHNOLOGY CO., LTD.; *Int'l*, pg. 1785
CONTROL DEVELOPMENT INC.—See Revvity, Inc.; *U.S. Public*, pg. 1794
CONTROL PRODUCTS, INC.—See Emerson Electric Co.; *U.S. Public*, pg. 743
COOPER ENVIRONMENTAL SERVICES, LLC—See Hebei Sailhero Environmental Protection High-Tech Co., Ltd.; *Int'l*, pg. 3306
CORETRONIC MEMS CORPORATION—See Coretronic Corporation; *Int'l*, pg. 1800
CORUM DEUTSCHLAND GMBH—See Citychamp Watch & Jewellery Group Limited; *Int'l*, pg. 1628
CORUM ITALIA SRL—See Citychamp Watch & Jewellery Group Limited; *Int'l*, pg. 1628
CORUM WATCHES S.A.R.L.; *Int'l*, pg. 1808
CREAFORM INC.—See AMETEK, Inc.; *U.S. Public*, pg. 120
CROSSBOW TECHNOLOGY, INC.—See Moog Inc.; *U.S. Public*, pg. 1469
CRYSTAL ENGINEERING CORPORATION—See AMETEK, Inc.; *U.S. Public*, pg. 117
CTS - NORDIC AKTIEBOLAG—See Elliott Management Corporation; *U.S. Private*, pg. 1367
CTS - NORDIC AKTIEBOLAG—See Veritas Capital Fund Management, LLC; *U.S. Private*, pg. 4361
CUBIC TRANSPORTATION SYSTEMS (AUSTRALIA) PTY. LIMITED—See Elliott Management Corporation; *U.S. Private*, pg. 1368
CUBIC TRANSPORTATION SYSTEMS (AUSTRALIA) PTY. LIMITED—See Veritas Capital Fund Management, LLC; *U.S. Private*, pg. 4362
CUBIC TRANSPORTATION SYSTEMS (DEUTSCHLAND) GMBH—See Elliott Management Corporation; *U.S. Private*, pg. 1367
CUBIC TRANSPORTATION SYSTEMS (DEUTSCHLAND) GMBH—See Veritas Capital Fund Management, LLC; *U.S. Private*, pg. 4361
CUBIC TRANSPORTATION SYSTEMS, INC.-EAST—See Elliott Management Corporation; *U.S. Private*, pg. 1368
CUBIC TRANSPORTATION SYSTEMS, INC.-EAST—See Veritas Capital Fund Management, LLC; *U.S. Private*, pg. 4362
CUBIC TRANSPORTATION SYSTEMS, INC.-MANUFACTURING CENTER—See Elliott Management Corporation; *U.S. Private*, pg. 1368
CUBIC TRANSPORTATION SYSTEMS, INC.-MANUFACTURING CENTER—See Veritas Capital Fund Management, LLC; *U.S. Private*, pg. 4362
CUBIC TRANSPORTATION SYSTEMS, INC.—See Elliott Management Corporation; *U.S. Private*, pg. 1368
CUBIC TRANSPORTATION SYSTEMS, INC.—See Veritas Capital Fund Management, LLC; *U.S. Private*, pg. 4362
CUBIC TRANSPORTATION SYSTEMS LIMITED—See Elliott Management Corporation; *U.S. Private*, pg. 1367
CUBIC TRANSPORTATION SYSTEMS LIMITED—See Veritas Capital Fund Management, LLC; *U.S. Private*, pg. 4361
CURTISS-WRIGHT CONTROLS, INC.—See Curtiss-Wright Corporation; *U.S. Public*, pg. 611
CYBEROPTICS CORPORATION—See Nordson Corporation; *U.S. Public*, pg. 1532
CZAH POMIAR SP. Z O.O.—See Aplisens S.A.; *Int'l*, pg. 515
DAGE HOLDINGS LIMITED—See Nordson Corporation; *U.S. Public*, pg. 1532
DAIICHI JITSUGYO VISWILL CO., LTD.—See Daiichi Jitsugyo Co. Ltd.; *Int'l*, pg. 1927
DAILY INSTRUMENTS INC.; *U.S. Private*, pg. 1145
DANSENSOR ESPANA, S.L.—See AMETEK, Inc.; *U.S. Public*, pg. 120
DATADOT TECHNOLOGY LTD; *Int'l*, pg. 1977
DAVCO TECHNOLOGY, LLC—See Penske Corporation; *U.S. Private*, pg. 3138
DE GRISOGONO SA—See DAMAC Group; *Int'l*, pg. 1955
DELPHIAN CORPORATION—See American Gas & Chemical Co., Ltd.; *U.S. Private*, pg. 235
DELPHI DELCO ELECTRONICS OPERATIONS DELNOSA, S.A. DE C.V.—See Aptiv PLC; *Int'l*, pg. 524
DELTA OHM S.R.L.—See GHM Messtechnik GmbH; *Int'l*, pg. 2959
DESIGN ANALYSIS ASSOCIATES, INC.—See Xylem Inc.; *U.S. Public*, pg. 2395
DESIGNATRONICS, INC. - ADVANCED ANTIVIBRATION COMPONENTS DIVISION—See Designatronics, Inc.; *U.S. Private*, pg. 1214
DETEX CORPORATION; *U.S. Private*, pg. 1216
DIAPAC LTD.—See Mistras Group, Inc.; *U.S. Public*, pg. 1451
DICKEY-JOHN CORPORATION—See Churchill Equity, Inc.; *U.S. Private*, pg. 895
DILAX FRANCE SAS—See DZ BANK AG Deutsche Zentral-Genossenschaftsbank; *Int'l*, pg. 2244
DILAX INTELCOM AG—See DZ BANK AG Deutsche Zentral-Genossenschaftsbank; *Int'l*, pg. 2244
DILAX INTELCOM IBERICA S.L.U.—See DZ BANK AG Deutsche Zentral-Genossenschaftsbank; *Int'l*, pg. 2244
DILAX SYSTEMS INC.—See DZ BANK AG Deutsche Zentral-Genossenschaftsbank; *Int'l*, pg. 2244
DILAX SYSTEMS UK LTD.—See DZ BANK AG Deutsche Zentral-Genossenschaftsbank; *Int'l*, pg. 2244
DISCO ASSOCIATES INC.—See Graybar Electric Company, Inc.; *U.S. Private*, pg. 1760
DISCOVERY TECHNOLOGY INTERNATIONAL, INC.; *U.S. Private*, pg. 1238
DRAGER MSI GMBH—See Draegerwerk AG & Co. KGaA; *Int'l*, pg. 2197
DRAGER SAFETY AG & CO. KGAA—See Draegerwerk AG & Co. KGaA; *Int'l*, pg. 2197

N.A.I.C.S. INDEX

334519 — OTHER MEASURING AND...

DRI ADVANCED TEST SYSTEMS INC.—See AB Dynamics plc; *Int'l*, pg. 39
DRONESHIELD LIMITED; *Int'l*, pg. 2206
DURHAM GEO SLOPE INDICATOR—See Durham Geo-Enterprises Incorporated; *U.S. Private*, pg. 1293
DYNALCO CONTROLS CORPORATION—See Crane NXT, Co.; *U.S. Public*, pg. 589
DYNAMIC CONTROLS, LTD.—See Allient Inc.; *U.S. Public*, pg. 80
DYNAMIC MICROSTEPPERS LIMITED; *Int'l*, pg. 2240
DYNAMIC SYSTEMS, INC.—See Vishay Precision Group, Inc.; *U.S. Public*, pg. 2303
DYNE SYSTEMS, INC.—See Taylor Dynamometer, Inc.; *U.S. Private*, pg. 3939
DYNISCO INSTRUMENTS LTD—See Roper Technologies, Inc.; *U.S. Public*, pg. 1811
DYNISCO SPOL, SRO—See Roper Technologies, Inc.; *U.S. Public*, pg. 1811
DYNOJET RESEARCH, INC.—See Irving Place Capital Management, L.P.; *U.S. Private*, pg. 2141
DYNOJET RESEARCH, INC.—See New Value Capital LLC; *U.S. Private*, pg. 2907
EACCESS LLC—See Elliott Management Corporation; *U.S. Private*, pg. 1368
EACCESS LLC—See Veritas Capital Fund Management, LLC; *U.S. Private*, pg. 4362
EASTERN INDUSTRIES—See Precision Punch Corporation; *U.S. Private*, pg. 3246
EBARA JITSUGYO POWER CO., LTD.—See Ebara Jitsugyo Co., Ltd.; *Int'l*, pg. 2284
ECKERT & ZIEGLER NUCLITEC GMBH—See Eckert & Ziegler Strahlen- und Medizintechnik AG; *Int'l*, pg. 2290
ECOLAB ENGINEERING GMBH—See Ecolab Inc.; *U.S. Public*, pg. 713
EDAP GMBH—See EDAP TMS S.A.; *Int'l*, pg. 2304
EDMUNDS MANUFACTURING COMPANY; *U.S. Private*, pg. 1338
E. GLUCK CORP.; *U.S. Private*, pg. 1304
EKS FRANCE; *Int'l*, pg. 2339
ELECTRIC TIME CO., INC.; *U.S. Private*, pg. 1352
ELECTROCRAFT MICHIGAN, INC.—See Delany Capital Management Corp.; *U.S. Private*, pg. 1194
ELECTRO STATIC TECHNOLOGY—See Illinois Tool Works Inc.; *U.S. Public*, pg. 1103
ELSTER CANADIAN METER COMPANY, LLC—See Honeywell International Inc.; *U.S. Public*, pg. 1047
ELSTER GMBH—See Honeywell International Inc.; *U.S. Public*, pg. 1047
ELSTER-INSTROMET A/S—See Honeywell International Inc.; *U.S. Public*, pg. 1048
ELSTER INSTROMET GMBH—See Honeywell International Inc.; *U.S. Public*, pg. 1048
ELSTER INSTROMET PRODUCTION GMBH—See Honeywell International Inc.; *U.S. Public*, pg. 1048
ELSTER-INSTROMET VERTRIEBSGESELLSCHAFT M.B.H.—See Honeywell International Inc.; *U.S. Public*, pg. 1048
ELSTER S.R.L.—See Honeywell International Inc.; *U.S. Public*, pg. 1048
EMERSON BEIJING INSTRUMENT CO. LTD.—See Emerson Electric Co.; *U.S. Public*, pg. 743
EMERSON MACHINERY HEALTH MANAGEMENT COMPANY—See Emerson Electric Co.; *U.S. Public*, pg. 746
EMERSON PROCESS MANAGEMENT JAPAN LTD.—See Emerson Electric Co.; *U.S. Public*, pg. 747
EMERSON PROCESS MANAGEMENT SHARED SERVICES LIMITED—See Emerson Electric Co.; *U.S. Public*, pg. 747
EMPEROR WATCH & JEWELLERY (HK) COMPANY LIMITED—See Emperor Watch & Jewellery Limited; *Int'l*, pg. 2386
EMZA VISUAL SENSE LTD.—See Synaptics Incorporated; *U.S. Public*, pg. 1969
ENERGY RECOMMERCE INC.—See Texas Instruments Incorporated; *U.S. Public*, pg. 2025
ENGELMANN SENSOR GMBH—See DPE Deutsche Private Equity GmbH; *Int'l*, pg. 2187
ENGINE CONTROL SYSTEMS EUROPE AB—See CDTi Advanced Materials, Inc.; *U.S. Public*, pg. 462
ENGINE CONTROL SYSTEMS LIMITED—See CDTi Advanced Materials, Inc.; *U.S. Public*, pg. 462
ENGINE CONTROL SYSTEMS LTD.—See CDTi Advanced Materials, Inc.; *U.S. Public*, pg. 462
ENGINE MONITOR, INC.—See MiddleGround Management, LP; *U.S. Private*, pg. 2712
ENVICONTROL-ENVITEC N.V.; *Int'l*, pg. 2453
E-PLEX LTD.; *Int'l*, pg. 2249
EPPENDORF UK LTD.—See Eppendorf AG; *Int'l*, pg. 2464
EPSILON LANDAUER DOZIMETRI TEKNOLOJILERI SANAYI VE TICARET A.S.—See Bozlu Holding; *Int'l*, pg. 1125
EPSILON LANDAUER DOZIMETRI TEKNOLOJILERI SANAYI VE TICARET A.S.—See Fortive Corporation; *U.S. Public*, pg. 871
EST GROUP, INC.—See Curtiss-Wright Corporation; *U.S. Public*, pg. 612

ETERNA AG—See Citychamp Watch & Jewellery Group Limited; *Int'l*, pg. 1629
ETS-LINDGREN, L.P.—See ESCO Technologies, Inc.; *U.S. Public*, pg. 793
EURO-PHYSICAL ACOUSTICS S.A.—See Mistras Group, Inc.; *U.S. Public*, pg. 1451
EXAKTIME, INC.; *U.S. Private*, pg. 1445
EXPRESS DIAGNOSTICS INT'L, INC.—See W.H.P.M., Inc.; *U.S. Private*, pg. 4420
FARIA BEEDE INSTRUMENTS, INC.; *U.S. Private*, pg. 1474
FARO DEUTSCHLAND HOLDING GMBH—See FARO Technologies, Inc.; *U.S. Public*, pg. 823
FARO SHANGHAI CO, LTD—See FARO Technologies, Inc.; *U.S. Public*, pg. 823
FARO TECHNOLOGIES, INC.; *U.S. Public*, pg. 823
FARO UK—See FARO Technologies, Inc.; *U.S. Public*, pg. 823
FAST & FLUID MANAGEMENT S.R.L.—See IDEX Corp; *U.S. Public*, pg. 1090
FAVITE INC.; *Int'l*, pg. 2623
FEEDBACK INSTRUMENTS LIMITED—See Aurelius Equity Opportunities SE & Co. KGaA; *Int'l*, pg. 709
FIELD CONTROLS LLC—See The Heico Companies, L.L.C.; *U.S. Private*, pg. 4050
FILMETRICS, INC.—See KLA Corporation; *U.S. Public*, pg. 1267
FISHER RESEARCH LABORATORY, INC.—See Cohu, Inc.; *U.S. Public*, pg. 530
FIYTA PRECISION TECHNOLOGY CO., LTD.; *Int'l*, pg. 2696
FLEXIM AMERICAS CORPORATION—See Emerson Electric Co.; *U.S. Public*, pg. 749
FLEXIM AUSTRALIA PTY. LTD.—See Emerson Electric Co.; *U.S. Public*, pg. 749
FLEXIM FLEXIBLE INDUSTRIEMESSTECHNIK GMBH—See Emerson Electric Co.; *U.S. Public*, pg. 749
FLEXIM FLOW INDIA PVT. LTD.—See Emerson Electric Co.; *U.S. Public*, pg. 749
FLEXIM FRANCE S.A.S.—See Emerson Electric Co.; *U.S. Public*, pg. 749
FLEXIM INSTRUMENTS ASIA PTE. LTD.—See Emerson Electric Co.; *U.S. Public*, pg. 749
FLEXIM INSTRUMENTS BENELUX B.V.—See Emerson Electric Co.; *U.S. Public*, pg. 749
FLEXIM INSTRUMENTS UK LTD.—See Emerson Electric Co.; *U.S. Public*, pg. 749
FLEXIM JAPAN LTD.—See Emerson Electric Co.; *U.S. Public*, pg. 749
FLEXIM S.A.—See Emerson Electric Co.; *U.S. Public*, pg. 749
FLUKE AUSTRALIA PTY LTD—See Fortive Corporation; *U.S. Public*, pg. 870
FLUKE AUSTRIA GMBH—See Fortive Corporation; *U.S. Public*, pg. 870
FLUKE PROCESS INSTRUMENTS GMBH—See Fortive Corporation; *U.S. Public*, pg. 870
FLUKE PROCESS INSTRUMENTS JAPAN—See Fortive Corporation; *U.S. Public*, pg. 870
FOCE INDIA LIMITED; *Int'l*, pg. 2718
FORMEX WATCH S.A.; *Int'l*, pg. 2734
FORMEX WATCH USA—See Formex Watch S.A.; *Int'l*, pg. 2734
FOSS A/S; *Int'l*, pg. 2748
FOSS BELGIUM B.V.—See Foss A/S; *Int'l*, pg. 2748
FOSS BENELUX B.V.—See Foss A/S; *Int'l*, pg. 2748
FOSS ESPANA S.A.—See Foss A/S; *Int'l*, pg. 2748
FOSS FRANCE S.A.S.—See Foss A/S; *Int'l*, pg. 2748
FOSS GMBH—See Foss A/S; *Int'l*, pg. 2749
FOSS ITALIA S.P.A.—See Foss A/S; *Int'l*, pg. 2749
FOSS UK LTD.—See Foss A/S; *Int'l*, pg. 2749
FRONTONE GMBH—See Bridgepoint Group Plc; *Int'l*, pg. 1155
FROUDE HOFMANN LTD.—See HWH Investments Limited; *Int'l*, pg. 3543
FUGRO LADS CORPORATION PTY LTD.—See Fugro N.V.; *Int'l*, pg. 2806
FUNEHIKI SEIMITSU CO., LTD.—See Citizen Watch Co., Ltd.; *Int'l*, pg. 1625
FUTABA CORPORATION OF AMERICA—See Futaba Corporation; *Int'l*, pg. 2850
GAD ENVIRONMENTAL TECHNOLOGY CO., LTD.; *Int'l*, pg. 2868
GAMMEX RMI INC.; *U.S. Private*, pg. 1641
GE ENERGY GERMANY—See General Electric Company; *U.S. Public*, pg. 919
GELAN DETECTIESYSTEMEN B.V.—See Mettler-Toledo International, Inc.; *U.S. Public*, pg. 1432
GEMS SENSORS INC.—See Fortive Corporation; *U.S. Public*, pg. 870
GENEVA WATCH GROUP; *U.S. Private*, pg. 1670
GENTEX CORPORATION; *U.S. Private*, pg. 1679
GE OIL & GAS, INC. - TWINSBURG—See General Electric Company; *U.S. Public*, pg. 919
GEOPHEX LTD.—See Geotech Ltd.; *Int'l*, pg. 2941
GEOSPACE TECHNOLOGIES CORPORATION; *U.S. Public*, pg. 934
GEOTIK SP. Z O.O.—See Arcus S.A.; *Int'l*, pg. 553

GHM MESSTECHNIK GMBH - STANDORT IMTRON—See GHM Messtechnik GmbH; *Int'l*, pg. 2959
GIMATIC AUTOMATION ENGINEERING (CHANGSHU) CO., LTD.—See Barnes Group Inc.; *U.S. Public*, pg. 277
GIMATIC S.R.L.—See Barnes Group Inc.; *U.S. Public*, pg. 277
GLEASON - M&M PRECISION SYSTEMS CORPORATION—See Gleason Corporation; *U.S. Private*, pg. 1708
GMH PRUFTECHNIK GMBH—See Georgsmarienhutte Holding GmbH; *Int'l*, pg. 2940
GOLDLINE CONTROLS, INC.—See CCMP Capital Advisors, LP; *U.S. Public*, pg. 800
GOLDLINE CONTROLS, INC.—See MSD Capital, L.P.; *U.S. Private*, pg. 2807
GOODRINGTON CO., LTD.—See Citizen Watch Co., Ltd.; *Int'l*, pg. 1625
GRAPHIC PACKAGING INTERNATIONAL AUSTRALIA PTY LIMITED—See Graphic Packaging Holding Company; *U.S. Public*, pg. 958
GRAPHO METRONIC MESS- UND REGELTECHNIK GMBH—See AIP, LLC; *U.S. Private*, pg. 134
GROVELEY DETECTION LIMITED—See Emerson Electric Co.; *U.S. Public*, pg. 747
GUANGDONG HIGH DREAM INTELLECTUALIZED MACHINERY CO., LTD.; *Int'l*, pg. 3155
GUANGZHOU FIVE GOAT WATCH CO., LIMITED—See Citychamp Watch & Jewellery Group Limited; *Int'l*, pg. 1629
GUDEL CONTROLS GMBH—See Gudel Group AG; *Int'l*, pg. 3171
H2SCAN CORPORATION; *U.S. Private*, pg. 1837
HANLA IMS CO., LTD.; *Int'l*, pg. 3256
HANSON SYSTEMS, LLC—See Crestview Partners, L.P.; *U.S. Private*, pg. 1098
HANWEI ELECTRONICS GROUP CORPORATION; *Int'l*, pg. 3264
HARCO LABORATORIES INC.—See TransDigm Group Incorporated; *U.S. Public*, pg. 2182
HARTEST PRECISION INSTRUMENTS INDIA PRIVATE LIMITED—See Checkit plc; *Int'l*, pg. 1459
HARTEST PRECISION INSTRUMENTS LIMITED—See Checkit plc; *Int'l*, pg. 1459
HEATH CONSULTANTS INCORPORATED - CENTRAL DIVISON—See Heath Consultants Incorporated; *U.S. Private*, pg. 1902
HEATH CONSULTANTS INCORPORATED - NORTHEAST DIVISON—See Heath Consultants Incorporated; *U.S. Private*, pg. 1902
HEATH CONSULTANTS INCORPORATED - SOUTHEAST DIVISION—See Heath Consultants Incorporated; *U.S. Private*, pg. 1902
HEATH CONSULTANTS INCORPORATED - WESTERN DIVISION—See Heath Consultants Incorporated; *U.S. Private*, pg. 1902
HEIWA TOKEI MANUFACTURING CO., LTD.—See Citizen Watch Co., Ltd.; *Int'l*, pg. 1625
HEMA DIAGNOSTIC SYSTEMS, LLC—See Generex Biotechnology Corporation; *U.S. Public*, pg. 930
HERAEUS ELECTRO-NITE INTERNATIONAL N.V.—See Heraeus Holding GmbH; *Int'l*, pg. 3357
HERALD ELECTRONICS LIMITED—See Herald Holdings Limited; *Int'l*, pg. 3358
HERGA TECHNOLOGY LIMITED—See discoverIE Group plc; *Int'l*, pg. 2133
HEXAGON DIGITAL WAVE, LLC—See Hexagon Composites ASA; *Int'l*, pg. 3370
HEXAGON MEASUREMENT TECHNOLOGIES—See Hexagon AB; *Int'l*, pg. 3367
HEXAGON METROLOGY FRANCE S.A.—See Hexagon AB; *Int'l*, pg. 3367
HEXAGON METROLOGY GMBH—See Hexagon AB; *Int'l*, pg. 3367
HEXAGON METROLOGY NORDIC AB—See Hexagon AB; *Int'l*, pg. 3367
HEXAGON METROLOGY SERVICES LTD.—See Hexagon AB; *Int'l*, pg. 3367
HIGHWAY TOLL ADMINISTRATION, LLC—See Platinum Equity, LLC; *U.S. Private*, pg. 3203
HI-MECHA CO., LTD.—See Citizen Watch Co., Ltd.; *Int'l*, pg. 1625
HIOKI EUROPE GMBH—See HIOKI E.E. Corporation; *Int'l*, pg. 3401
HIOKI INDIA ENGINEERING PRIVATE LIMITED—See HIOKI E.E. Corporation; *Int'l*, pg. 3401
HIOKI TAIWAN CO., LTD.—See HIOKI E.E. Corporation; *Int'l*, pg. 3401
HOFMANN PRUFTECHNIK GMBH—See HWH Investments Limited; *Int'l*, pg. 3610
HONEYWELL AEROSPACE YEOVIL—See Honeywell International Inc.; *U.S. Public*, pg. 1047
HONEYWELL ANALYTICS INSTRUMENTATION—See Honeywell International Inc.; *U.S. Public*, pg. 1048
HONEYWELL ASCA INC.—See Honeywell International Inc.; *U.S. Public*, pg. 1051
HORIBA ABX DIAGNOSTICS THAILAND LTD.—See HORIBA Ltd; *Int'l*, pg. 3475
HORIBA ABX SP. Z O.O.—See HORIBA Ltd; *Int'l*, pg. 3476

334519 — OTHER MEASURING AND...

HORIBA ADVANCED TECHNO CO., LTD.—See HORIBA Ltd; *Int'l*, pg. 3476
HORIBA AUTOMOTIVE TEST SYSTEMS LTD.—See HORIBA Ltd; *Int'l*, pg. 3476
HORIBA EUROPE AUTOMATION DIVISION GMBH—See HORIBA Ltd; *Int'l*, pg. 3476
HORIBA EUROPE GMBH - LEICHLINGEN FACILITY—See HORIBA Ltd; *Int'l*, pg. 3476
HORIBA EUROPE GMBH—See HORIBA Ltd; *Int'l*, pg. 3476
HORIBA FRANCE SARL—See HORIBA Ltd; *Int'l*, pg. 3476
HORIBA GMBH—See HORIBA Ltd; *Int'l*, pg. 3476
HORIBA INSTRUMENTS INC.- ANN ARBOR FACILITY—See HORIBA Ltd; *Int'l*, pg. 3476
HORIBA INSTRUMENTS INC. - IRVINE FACILITY—See HORIBA Ltd; *Int'l*, pg. 3476
HORIBA INSTRUMENTS INC. - TEMPE FACILITY—See HORIBA Ltd; *Int'l*, pg. 3476
HORIBA INSTRUMENTS INC. - TROY FACILITY—See HORIBA Ltd; *Int'l*, pg. 3476
HORIBA INSTRUMENTS (SHANGHAI) CO., LTD.—See HORIBA Ltd; *Int'l*, pg. 3476
HORIBA TECHNO SERVICE CO., LTD.—See HORIBA Ltd; *Int'l*, pg. 3476
HORIBA TEST AUTOMATION LTD.—See HORIBA Ltd; *Int'l*, pg. 3477
HUMBOLDT MANUFACTURING CO. INC.; *U.S. Private*, pg. 2007
HUNAN AIRBLUER ENVIRONMENTAL PROTECTION TECHNOLOGY CO., LTD.; *Int'l*, pg. 3531
HWM-WATER LIMITED—See Halma plc; *Int'l*, pg. 3231
HYDAC SOFTWARE GMBH—See Hydac International GmbH; *Int'l*, pg. 3545
HYDRAULICS INTERNATIONAL, INC.; *U.S. Private*, pg. 2017
HYDREKA ENOVEO SAS—See Halma plc; *Int'l*, pg. 3232
HYDREKA S.A.—See Halma plc; *Int'l*, pg. 3232
HYVISION SYSTEM INC.; *Int'l*, pg. 3561
HYVISION TECHNOLOGY INC.—See HyVISION SYSTEM INC.; *Int'l*, pg. 3561
HYVISION VINA COMPANY LIMITED—See HyVISION SYSTEM INC.; *Int'l*, pg. 3561
I.D. SYSTEMS (UK) LTD—See PowerFleet, Inc.; *U.S. Public*, pg. 1706
IGE ENERGY SERVICES (UK) LTD—See General Electric Company; *U.S. Public*, pg. 919
IKEGPS GROUP LIMITED; *Int'l*, pg. 3610
ILLUMINA SHANGHAI (TRADING) CO., LTD.—See Illumina, Inc.; *U.S. Public*, pg. 1112
INDUSTRIAL SCIENTIFIC ASIA-PACIFIC—See Fortive Corporation; *U.S. Public*, pg. 871
INDUSTRIAL SCIENTIFIC CORPORATION—See Fortive Corporation; *U.S. Public*, pg. 871
INDUSTRIAL SCIENTIFIC DEUTSCHLAND GMBH—See Fortive Corporation; *U.S. Public*, pg. 871
INE TECHNOLOGIES SDN BHD—See Al Jaber Group; *Int'l*, pg. 280
INPIPE GMBH—See Halma plc; *Int'l*, pg. 3232
INSTRON BRASIL EQUIPAMENTOS CIENTIFICOS LTDA.—See Illinois Tool Works Inc.; *U.S. Public*, pg. 1108
INSTRON CORPORATION—See Illinois Tool Works Inc.; *U.S. Public*, pg. 1108
INSTRON INDUSTRIAL PRODUCTS GROUP—See Illinois Tool Works Inc.; *U.S. Public*, pg. 1108
INTEGRATED DYNAMICS ENGINEERING GMBH—See Aalberts N.V.; *Int'l*, pg. 34
INTELLIVIEW TECHNOLOGIES INC.—See Enbridge Inc.; *Int'l*, pg. 2397
INTERNATIONAL WATCH CO. AG—See Compagnie Financiere Richemont S.A.; *Int'l*, pg. 1741
INTERSTATES CONTROL SYSTEMS, INC.—See Harbor Group Inc; *U.S. Public*, pg. 1859
INTOXIMETERS INC.; *U.S. Private*, pg. 2129
INTRAGRAIN TECHNOLOGIES INC.—See Calian Group Ltd.; *Int'l*, pg. 1264
ION GEOPHYSICAL CORPORATION; *U.S. Public*, pg. 1166
IPS METEOSTAR, INC.—See Danaher Corporation; *U.S. Public*, pg. 627
IRIS ID SYSTEMS INC.; *U.S. Private*, pg. 2138
ISRA VISION PARSYTEC INC—See Atlas Copco AB; *Int'l*, pg. 683
ITRON ARGENTINA S.A.—See Itron, Inc.; *U.S. Public*, pg. 1176
ITRON BV—See Itron, Inc.; *U.S. Public*, pg. 1176
ITRON GMBH—See Itron, Inc.; *U.S. Public*, pg. 1176
ITRON ITALIA SPA—See Itron, Inc.; *U.S. Public*, pg. 1176
ITRON METERING SYSTEMS (CHONGQING) CO., LTD.—See Itron, Inc.; *U.S. Public*, pg. 1176
ITRON METERING SYSTEMS (SUZHOU) CO., LTD.—See Itron, Inc.; *U.S. Public*, pg. 1176
ITRON SISTEMAS DE MEDICAO LDA.—See Itron, Inc.; *U.S. Public*, pg. 1176
ITRON SOLUCIONES DE MEDIDA ESPANA SL—See Itron, Inc.; *U.S. Public*, pg. 1176
ITRON SOLUCOES PARA ENERGIA E AGUA LTDA.—See Itron, Inc.; *U.S. Public*, pg. 1176
ITRON UKRAINE—See Itron, Inc.; *U.S. Public*, pg. 1176
ITRON US GAS, LLC—See Itron, Inc.; *U.S. Public*, pg. 1176

ITRON ZAHLER & SYSTEMTECHNIK GMBH—See Itron, Inc.; *U.S. Public*, pg. 1176
IXTHUS INSTRUMENTATION LIMITED—See discoverIE Group plc; *Int'l*, pg. 2133
JOHN DEERE ELECTRONIC SOLUTIONS, INC.—See Deere & Company; *U.S. Public*, pg. 647
KAUKO GMBH—See Aspo Oyj; *Int'l*, pg. 631
KENNAMETAL INFRASTRUCTURE GMBH—See Kennametal Inc.; *U.S. Public*, pg. 1222
KENNAMETAL WIDIA PRODUKTIONS GMBH & CO. KG—See Kennametal Inc.; *U.S. Public*, pg. 1222
KHN SOLUTIONS LLC; *U.S. Private*, pg. 2301
KINETICS NOISE CONTROL, INC.—See KPS Capital Partners, LP; *U.S. Private*, pg. 2347
KIRBY LESTER, LLC—See Levine Leichtman Capital Partners, LLC; *U.S. Private*, pg. 2435
KULITE ITALIA, SRL—See Kulite Semiconductor Products, Inc.; *U.S. Private*, pg. 2357
KULITE SEMI-CONDUCTOR, GMBH—See Kulite Semiconductor Products, Inc.; *U.S. Private*, pg. 2357
KULITE SEMICONDUCTOR PRODUCTS, INC.; *U.S. Private*, pg. 2357
KULITE SENSORS CHINA, INC.—See Kulite Semiconductor Products, Inc.; *U.S. Private*, pg. 2357
KULITE SENSORS, LTD.—See Kulite Semiconductor Products, Inc.; *U.S. Private*, pg. 2357
LAFAYETTE INSTRUMENT COMPANY, INC.—See Branford Castle, Inc.; *U.S. Private*, pg. 639
LANSMONT CORP.—See Battery Ventures, L.P.; *U.S. Private*, pg. 488
LASER TECHNOLOGY, INC.; *U.S. Private*, pg. 2395
LEICA GEOSYSTEMS, INC. - COSTA MESA—See Hexagon AB; *Int'l*, pg. 3368
LEICA GEOSYSTEMS, INC.—See Hexagon AB; *Int'l*, pg. 3368
LESMAN INSTRUMENT COMPANY—See The Stephens Group, LLC; *U.S. Private*, pg. 4121
LEVEL 1, INC.—See ICU Medical, Inc.; *U.S. Public*, pg. 1087
LINK ENGINEERING COMPANY; *U.S. Private*, pg. 2461
LIQUID CRYSTAL RESOURCES; *U.S. Private*, pg. 2465
LIVORSI MARINE INC.—See Contran Corporation; *U.S. Private*, pg. 1033
L&J TECHNOLOGIES; *U.S. Private*, pg. 2362
LOMA SYSTEMS BV—See Illinois Tool Works Inc.; *U.S. Public*, pg. 1109
LUDLUM MEASUREMENTS INC.; *U.S. Private*, pg. 2512
MAGNA-LASTIC DEVICES—See Methode Electronics, Inc.; *U.S. Public*, pg. 1428
MAGNESCALE CO., LTD.—See DMG MORI Co., Ltd.; *Int'l*, pg. 2145
MAGNETEK, INC.—See Columbus McKinnon Corporation; *U.S. Public*, pg. 536
MAGNETEK MINING—See Columbus McKinnon Corporation; *U.S. Public*, pg. 536
MAGNETIC ANALYSIS CORPORATION; *U.S. Private*, pg. 2547
MAHR AG—See Carl Mahr Holding GmbH; *Int'l*, pg. 1333
MAHR AUSTRIA GMBH—See Carl Mahr Holding GmbH; *Int'l*, pg. 1333
MANUFACTURE JAEGER-LECOULTRE SA—See Compagnie Financiere Richemont S.A.; *Int'l*, pg. 1741
MANUFACTURE ROGER DUBUIS SA—See Compagnie Financiere Richemont S.A.; *Int'l*, pg. 1741
MARKTEC CORPORATION—See Alconix Corporation; *Int'l*, pg. 302
MARSH BELLOFRAM SHANGHAI TRADING CO. LTD.—See Desco Corporation; *U.S. Private*, pg. 1211
MATEC APPLIED SCIENCES—See Matec Instrument Companies, Inc.; *U.S. Private*, pg. 2609
MATEC INSTRUMENTS NDT—See Matec Instrument Companies, Inc.; *U.S. Private*, pg. 2609
MCDONNELL & MILLER DIVISION—See Xylem Inc.; *U.S. Public*, pg. 2396
MEASUREMENT INNOVATIONS CORP.; *U.S. Private*, pg. 2648
MEDICOMP, INC.—See United Therapeutics Corporation; *U.S. Public*, pg. 2238
MEDIDORES INTERNACIONALES ROCHESTER S.A. DE C.V.—See Gas Equipment Company, Inc.; *U.S. Private*, pg. 1647
MEDISERV SP. ZOO—See ResMed Inc.; *U.S. Public*, pg. 1790
MEGGITT (ORANGE COUNTY), INC.—See Amphenol Corporation; *U.S. Public*, pg. 131
MEGGITT PLC - KVISTGAARD FACILITY—See Parker Hannifin Corporation; *U.S. Public*, pg. 1642
MEGGITT (SENSOREX) SAS—See Parker Hannifin Corporation; *U.S. Public*, pg. 1641
MERCURY INSTRUMENTS LLC—See Honeywell International Inc.; *U.S. Public*, pg. 1049
METCO SERVICES, LTD.—See Emerson Electric Co.; *U.S. Public*, pg. 748
METERTEK SDN BHD—See Itron, Inc.; *U.S. Public*, pg. 1176
METTLER-TOLEDO AB—See Mettler-Toledo International, Inc.; *U.S. Public*, pg. 1432
METTLER-TOLEDO LOGISTIK GMBH—See Mettler-Toledo International, Inc.; *U.S. Public*, pg. 1433

METTLER-TOLEDO SAE—See Mettler-Toledo International, Inc.; *U.S. Public*, pg. 1433
METTLER-TOLEDO (SCHWEIZ) GMBH—See Mettler-Toledo International, Inc.; *U.S. Public*, pg. 1432
METTLER-TOLEDO (S) PTE LTD.—See Mettler-Toledo International, Inc.; *U.S. Public*, pg. 1432
MH INSTRUMENT OU—See Endress+Hauser (International) Holding AG; *Int'l*, pg. 2408
MICRO MOTION INC.—See Emerson Electric Co.; *U.S. Public*, pg. 750
MIDWEST ENERGY EMISSIONS CORP.; *U.S. Public*, pg. 1445
MINELAB DE MEXICO SA DE CV—See Codan Limited; *Int'l*, pg. 1688
MINI-CAM LIMITED—See Halma plc; *Int'l*, pg. 3232
MIRATECH CORP.—See Argonaut Private Equity, LLC; *U.S. Private*, pg. 321
MIRION TECHNOLOGIES (CANBERRA BNLS) NV/SA—See Mirion Technologies, Inc.; *U.S. Public*, pg. 1450
MIRION TECHNOLOGIES (CANBERRA) SAS—See Mirion Technologies, Inc.; *U.S. Public*, pg. 1450
MIRION TECHNOLOGIES (CONAX NUCLEAR), INC.—See Mirion Technologies, Inc.; *U.S. Public*, pg. 1450
MISFIT, INC.—See Axon Enterprise, Inc.; *U.S. Public*, pg. 256
MISTRAS CAMBRIDGE—See Mistras Group, Inc.; *U.S. Public*, pg. 1451
MISTRAS CANADA, INC.—See Mistras Group, Inc.; *U.S. Public*, pg. 1451
MISTRAS GROUP B.V.—See Mistras Group, Inc.; *U.S. Public*, pg. 1451
MISTRAS GROUP GMBH—See Mistras Group, Inc.; *U.S. Public*, pg. 1451
MISTRAS GROUP HELLAS A.B.E.E.—See Mistras Group, Inc.; *U.S. Public*, pg. 1451
MISTRAS GROUP, INC.; *U.S. Public*, pg. 1451
MISTRAS GROUP SAS—See Mistras Group, Inc.; *U.S. Public*, pg. 1451
MISTRAS HELLAS A.B.E.E.—See Mistras Group, Inc.; *U.S. Public*, pg. 1451
MISTRAS METALTEC INC.—See Mistras Group, Inc.; *U.S. Public*, pg. 1451
MOBREY AB—See Emerson Electric Co.; *U.S. Public*, pg. 748
MOBREY MEASUREMENT LTD.—See Emerson Electric Co.; *U.S. Public*, pg. 748
MOCON, INC.—See AMETEK, Inc.; *U.S. Public*, pg. 120
MONTBLANC DEUTSCHLAND GMBH—See Compagnie Financiere Richemont S.A.; *Int'l*, pg. 1741
MONTBLANC ITALIA SRL—See Compagnie Financiere Richemont S.A.; *Int'l*, pg. 1741
MONTBLANC-SIMPLO GMBH—See Compagnie Financiere Richemont S.A.; *Int'l*, pg. 1741
MONTBLANC SUISSE SA—See Compagnie Financiere Richemont S.A.; *Int'l*, pg. 1741
MONTRES CORUM S.A.R.L.—See Citychamp Watch & Jewellery Group Limited; *Int'l*, pg. 1629
MOOG B.V.—See Moog Inc.; *U.S. Public*, pg. 1470
MOOG LUXEMBOURG—See Moog Inc.; *U.S. Public*, pg. 1471
MOST CROWN INDUSTRIES LTD.—See Citizen Watch Co., Ltd.; *Int'l*, pg. 1625
MOTION ANALYSIS CORPORATION; *U.S. Private*, pg. 2795
MOTOR CONTROLS, INC.; *U.S. Private*, pg. 2797
MPD COMPONENTS—See MPD, Inc.; *U.S. Private*, pg. 2803
MPD, INC.; *U.S. Private*, pg. 2803
MPH INDUSTRIES, INC.—See MPD, Inc.; *U.S. Private*, pg. 2803
MRP S.A.—See TPG Capital, L.P.; *U.S. Public*, pg. 2174
MTI INSTRUMENTS INC.—See Branford Castle, Inc.; *U.S. Private*, pg. 639
MTS SENSORS TECHNOLOGY K.K.—See Amphenol Corporation; *U.S. Public*, pg. 131
MTS SENSOR TECHNOLOGIE GMBH AND CO. KG—See Amphenol Corporation; *U.S. Public*, pg. 131
MTS SENSOR TECHNOLOGIE UND VERWALTUNGS-GMBH—See Amphenol Corporation; *U.S. Public*, pg. 131
MTS SENSOR TECHNOLOGY CORP—See Amphenol Corporation; *U.S. Public*, pg. 131
MTS SYSTEMS CORPORATION—See Amphenol Corporation; *U.S. Public*, pg. 130
MTS SYSTEMS LTD.—See Amphenol Corporation; *U.S. Public*, pg. 131
MUELLER CANADA LTD. - ECHOLOGICS DIVISION—See Mueller Water Products, Inc.; *U.S. Public*, pg. 1485
NAPCO, INC.—See Thermo Fisher Scientific Inc.; *U.S. Public*, pg. 2149
NARDA SAFETY TEST SOLUTIONS GMBH—See L3Harris Technologies, Inc.; *U.S. Public*, pg. 1284
NARDA SAFETY TEST SOLUTIONS S.R.L.—See L3Harris Technologies, Inc.; *U.S. Public*, pg. 1284
NATIONAL INSTRUMENTS ASIA MINOR OLCUM CI-HAZLARI TICARET LIMITED SIRKETI—See National Instruments Corporation; *U.S. Private*, pg. 2857

N.A.I.C.S. INDEX
334519 — OTHER MEASURING AND...

NDT DO BRASIL LTD.—See Mistras Group, Inc.; *U.S. Public*, pg. 1451
NDT SYSTEMS, INC.; *U.S. Private*, pg. 2876
NET SAFETY MONITORING INC.—See Emerson Electric Co.; *U.S. Public*, pg. 750
NEUMANN SYSTEMS GROUP, INC.; *U.S. Private*, pg. 2890
NEWAGE TESTING INSTRUMENTS, INC.—See AMETEK, Inc.; *U.S. Public*, pg. 117
NEW SYSTEM S.R.L.—See KLA Corporation; *U.S. Public*, pg. 1268
NIHON AIRPAX CO., LTD.—See Sensata Technologies Holding plc; *U.S. Public*, pg. 1866
NIPPON PHYSICAL ACOUSTICS LTD.—See Mistras Group, Inc.; *U.S. Public*, pg. 1451
NOOKA INC.; *U.S. Private*, pg. 2934
NORBAR TORQUE TOOLS (AUSTRALIA) PTY. LTD.—See Snap-on Incorporated; *U.S. Public*, pg. 1898
NOR-CAL PRODUCTS ASIA PACIFIC PTE. LTD.—See Dr. Ing. K. Busch GmbH; *Int'l*, pg. 2193
NOR-CAL PRODUCTS KOREA CO., LTD.—See Dr. Ing. K. Busch GmbH; *Int'l*, pg. 2193
NORTH STAR IMAGING, INC.—See Illinois Tool Works Inc.; *U.S. Public*, pg. 1109
NOVEL ENVIRONMENTAL TECHNOLOGIES LTD.—See Emerson Electric Co.; *U.S. Public*, pg. 750
OBSHESTWO S OGRANIZENNOI OTWETSTWENNOS-TJU MOOG—See Moog Inc.; *U.S. Public*, pg. 1470
OLDHAM SAS—See Teledyne Technologies Incorporated; *U.S. Public*, pg. 1992
OLDHAM WINTER GMBH—See Teledyne Technologies Incorporated; *U.S. Public*, pg. 1992
OMEGADYNE, INC.—See Arcline Investment Management LP; *U.S. Private*, pg. 315
ONICON INCORPORATED—See Harbour Group Industries, Inc.; *U.S. Private*, pg. 1860
OOO "BARTEC RUS"—See Charterhouse Capital Partners LLP; *Int'l*, pg. 1455
OOO "BARTEC SB"—See Charterhouse Capital Partners LLP; *Int'l*, pg. 1455
ORBITA CORPORATION; *U.S. Private*, pg. 3038
OROLIA SA—See Eurazeo SE; *Int'l*, pg. 2528
OSCILLOQUARTZ S.A.—See ADTRAN Holdings, Inc.; *U.S. Public*, pg. 44
PARKER HANNIFIN ELECTRONIC SYSTEMS DIV.—See Parker Hannifin Corporation; *U.S. Public*, pg. 1648
PARKER HANNIFIN HYDRAULICS DIVISION, BRAZIL—See Parker Hannifin Corporation; *U.S. Public*, pg. 1647
PARKER HANNIFIN ITALY SRL SUCURSAL EN ESPANA—See Parker Hannifin Corporation; *U.S. Public*, pg. 1648
PARKER SALES (IRELAND) LIMITED—See Parker Hannifin Corporation; *U.S. Public*, pg. 1649
PAR TECHNOLOGY CORPORATION; *U.S. Public*, pg. 1636
PCB SYNOTECH GMBH—See Amphenol Corporation; *U.S. Public*, pg. 131
PERCEPTRON DO BRASIL LTDA.—See Atlas Copco AB; *Int'l*, pg. 680
PERCEPTRON ITALIA, S.R.L—See Atlas Copco AB; *Int'l*, pg. 680
PERCEPTRON METROLOGY UK LTD.—See Atlas Copco AB; *Int'l*, pg. 680
PERCEPTRON NON CONTACT METROLOGY SOLUTIONS PVT LTD.—See Atlas Copco AB; *Int'l*, pg. 680
PERCEPTRON TRADING (SHANGHAI) CO., LTD.—See Atlas Copco AB; *Int'l*, pg. 680
PETERSON SPRING-KINGSVILLE PLANT—See MiddleGround Management, LP; *U.S. Private*, pg. 2712
PETERSON SPRING-WINDSOR PLANT—See MiddleGround Management, LP; *U.S. Private*, pg. 2712
PFEIFFER VACUUM BENELUX B. V.—See Dr. Ing. K. Busch GmbH; *Int'l*, pg. 2193
PFEIFFER VACUUM SINGAPORE PTE. LTD.—See Dr. Ing. K. Busch GmbH; *Int'l*, pg. 2194
PFEIFFER VACUUM TAIWAN CORPORATION LTD.—See Dr. Ing. K. Busch GmbH; *Int'l*, pg. 2194
PHOTON CONTROL INC.—See MKS Instruments, Inc.; *U.S. Public*, pg. 1453
PHYSICAL ACOUSTICS B.V.—See Mistras Group, Inc.; *U.S. Public*, pg. 1451
PHYSICAL ACOUSTICS CORP.—See Mistras Group, Inc.; *U.S. Public*, pg. 1451
PHYSICAL ACOUSTICS SOUTH AMERICA LTDA.—See Mistras Group, Inc.; *U.S. Public*, pg. 1451
PIAGET S.A.—See Compagnie Financiere Richemont S.A.; *Int'l*, pg. 1741
PITNEY BOWES INC.; *U.S. Public*, pg. 1604
PITNEY BOWES OF CANADA LTD.—See Pitney Bowes Inc.; *U.S. Public*, pg. 1695
POSITEK LIMITED—See discoverIE Group plc; *Int'l*, pg. 2133
POWER TEST, INC.; *U.S. Private*, pg. 3239
PRECISION SAMPLERS INC.—See Standard Laboratories Inc.; *U.S. Private*, pg. 3780
PREFERRED UTILITIES MANUFACTURING CORPORATION—See PUMC Holding Corporation; *U.S. Private*, pg. 3303

PRESSCO TECHNOLOGY INC.; *U.S. Private*, pg. 3255
PROCONTROL AG—See Moog Inc.; *U.S. Public*, pg. 1471
PRUFTECHNIK DIETER BUSCH GMBH—See Fortive Corporation; *U.S. Public*, pg. 870
PSM INSTRUMENTATION LTD.—See Alfa Laval AB; *Int'l*, pg. 312
PT. HIOKI ELECTRIC INSTRUMENT—See HIOKI E.E. Corporation; *Int'l*, pg. 3401
PYXIS TECHNOLOGIES, LLC; *U.S. Private*, pg. 3311
QUANTA SYSTEM S.P.A.—See El.En. S.p.A.; *Int'l*, pg. 2342
QUEST CONTROLS, INC.; *U.S. Private*, pg. 3325
RADIATION MONITORING DEVICES, INC.—See Dynasil Corporation of America; *U.S. Public*, pg. 1300
RANDOLPH COMPANY; *U.S. Private*, pg. 3354
RAPISCAN SYSTEMS OY—See OSI Systems, Inc.; *U.S. Public*, pg. 1622
RAYMOND & LAE ENGINEERING, INC.—See May River Capital, LLC; *U.S. Private*, pg. 2620
RAYTEK CHINA COMPANY—See Fortive Corporation; *U.S. Public*, pg. 870
REJ CO., LTD.—See AIDA Engineering, Ltd.; *Int'l*, pg. 231
RESMED TAIWAN CO., LTD—See ResMed Inc.; *U.S. Public*, pg. 1791
RESORTES Y PRODUCTOS METALICOS S.A.-QUERETARO PLANT—See MiddleGround Management, LP; *U.S. Private*, pg. 2712
RICHEMONT ASIA PACIFIC LIMITED—See Compagnie Financiere Richemont S.A.; *Int'l*, pg. 1741
RICHEMONT DE MEXICO SA DE CV—See Compagnie Financiere Richemont S.A.; *Int'l*, pg. 1741
RICHEMONT HOLDINGS (UK) LIMITED—See Compagnie Financiere Richemont S.A.; *Int'l*, pg. 1741
RICHEMONT IBERIA SL—See Compagnie Financiere Richemont S.A.; *Int'l*, pg. 1741
RICHEMONT NORTHERN EUROPE GMBH—See Compagnie Financiere Richemont S.A.; *Int'l*, pg. 1741
RICHEMONT SUISSE SA—See Compagnie Financiere Richemont S.A.; *Int'l*, pg. 1741
RIDGEWAY FURNITURE COMPANY—See Howard Miller Company; *U.S. Private*, pg. 1995
ROBERTSON FUEL SYSTEMS, LLC—See HEICO Corporation; *U.S. Public*, pg. 1020
ROCCA S.P.A.—See Damiani S.p.A.; *Int'l*, pg. 1957
ROCHESTER GAUGES INTERNATIONAL—See Gas Equipment Company, Inc.; *U.S. Private*, pg. 1647
RONAN ENGINEERING COMPANY, MEASUREMENTS DIVISION—See Ronan Engineering Company; *U.S. Private*, pg. 3477
ROSSWEINER ARMATUREN UND MESSGERATE GMBH & CO OHG—See Aalberts N.V.; *Int'l*, pg. 35
ROTARY WATCHES LIMITED—See Citychamp Watch & Jewellery Group Limited; *Int'l*, pg. 1629
SARCLAD NORTH AMERICA LP—See The Heico Companies, L.L.C.; *U.S. Private*, pg. 4051
SCANJET ASIA PACIFIC PTE. LTD.—See Alfa Laval AB; *Int'l*, pg. 312
SCIENTECH, INC.; *U.S. Private*, pg. 3574
SCIENTIFIC DUST COLLECTORS—See Venturedyne, Ltd.; *U.S. Private*, pg. 4358
SCOTT TECHNOLOGIES, INC.—See 3M Company; *U.S. Public*, pg. 8
SEA-BIRD ELECTRONICS, INC.; *U.S. Private*, pg. 3583
SEFELEC SAS—See Eaton Corporation plc; *Int'l*, pg. 2282
SEJONG-AMC CORPORATION CO. LTD.—See Honeywell International Inc.; *U.S. Public*, pg. 1048
SENSATA TECHNOLOGIES, INC.—See Sensata Technologies Holding plc; *U.S. Public*, pg. 1866
SENSATA TECHNOLOGIES POWER CONTROLS—See Sensata Technologies Holding plc; *U.S. Public*, pg. 1866
SENSOREX CORPORATION—See Halma plc; *Int'l*, pg. 3232
SERCEL CANADA LTD—See CGG; *Int'l*, pg. 1432
SERCEL ENGLAND LTD—See CGG; *Int'l*, pg. 1432
SERCEL, INC.—See CGG; *Int'l*, pg. 1432
SETRA SYSTEMS, INC.—See Fortive Corporation; *U.S. Public*, pg. 870
SEWA GMBH—See Itron, Inc.; *U.S. Public*, pg. 1176
SHADIN, LP—See Gardner Standard LLC; *U.S. Private*, pg. 1644
SHIANG PAO PRECISION CO., LTD.—See Citizen Watch Co., Ltd.; *Int'l*, pg. 1625
SHOCKWATCH, INC.—See Harbour Group Industries, INC.; *U.S. Private*, pg. 1861
SIERRA MONITOR CORPORATION—See MSA Safety Incorporated; *U.S. Public*, pg. 1482
SIGNAL ADVANCE, INC.; *U.S. Public*, pg. 1878
SIMPLEX WILFER GMBH & CO.—See Aalberts N.V.; *Int'l*, pg 35
SMITHS MEDICAL—See ICU Medical, Inc.; *U.S. Public*, pg. 1087
SNAP-ON CLIMATE SOLUTIONS S.R.L.—See Snap-on Incorporated; *U.S. Public*, pg. 1898
SOLARTRON METROLOGY LTD.—See AMETEK, Inc.; *U.S. Public*, pg. 118
SOLMETRIC CORP.—See Fortive Corporation; *U.S. Public*, pg. 870
SOLUNA HOLDINGS, INC.; *U.S. Public*, pg. 1901
SONICS & MATERIALS, INC.-EUROPEAN OFFICE—See Sonics & Materials, Inc.; *U.S. Private*, pg. 3713

SONOSCAN INC.—See Nordson Corporation; *U.S. Public*, pg. 1534
SONTEK/YSI, INC.—See Xylem Inc.; *U.S. Public*, pg. 2395
SOR (EUROPE) LTD.—See SOR, Inc.; *U.S. Private*, pg. 3715
SOURIAU JAPAN K.K.—See TransDigm Group Incorporated; *U.S. Public*, pg. 2181
SPECAC LIMITED—See Ampersand Management LLC; *U.S. Private*, pg. 265
SPECTAIRE INC.—See Spectaire Holdings Inc.; *U.S. Public*, pg. 1915
SPECTREX, INC.—See Emerson Electric Co.; *U.S. Public*, pg. 747
SPECTRUM TECHNOLOGIES, INC.; *U.S. Private*, pg. 3753
SSE DO BRASIL LTDA—See Allied Universal Manager LLC; *U.S. Private*, pg. 190
SSI TECHNOLOGIES S.R.O—See Amphenol Corporation; *U.S. Public*, pg. 132
STANDARD IMAGING, INC.; *U.S. Private*, pg. 3779
SUN NUCLEAR CORPORATION—See Mirion Technologies, Inc.; *U.S. Public*, pg. 1450
SUNSET LABORATORY, INC.—See Hebei Sailhero Environmental Protection High-Tech Co., Ltd.; *Int'l*, pg. 3306
SUPERFLOW TECHNOLOGIES GROUP; *U.S. Private*, pg. 3875
SUTRON CORPORATION—See Danaher Corporation; *U.S. Public*, pg. 627
SW AUTOMATIK AB—See Addtech AB; *Int'l*, pg. 135
SWISS WATCH INTERNATIONAL INC.; *U.S. Private*, pg. 3894
TAIYUAN DAHAO YIDA ELECTRONIC CO., LTD.—See Beijing Dahao Technology Corporation Limited; *Int'l*, pg. 948
THE TASI GROUP; *U.S. Private*, pg. 4126
TAYLOR DYNAMOMETER, INC.; *U.S. Private*, pg. 3939
TAYLOR HOBSON HOLDINGS LTD.—See AMETEK, Inc.; *U.S. Public*, pg. 118
TAYLOR PRECISION PRODUCTS, INC. - LAS CRUCES—See Lifetime Brands, Inc.; *U.S. Public*, pg. 1313
TAYLOR PRECISION PRODUCTS, INC.—See Lifetime Brands, Inc.; *U.S. Public*, pg. 1313
TECHNOLOGY FOR ENERGY CORPORATION; *U.S. Private*, pg. 3955
TECNATOM S.A.—See Enel S.p.A.; *Int'l*, pg. 2414
TEK-AIR SYSTEMS, INC.—See Desco Corporation; *U.S. Private*, pg. 1211
TEKTRONIX INDIA PRIVATE LIMITED—See Fortive Corporation; *U.S. Public*, pg. 872
TEKTRONIX JAPAN, LTD.—See Fortive Corporation; *U.S. Public*, pg. 872
TEKTRONIX SAS—See Fortive Corporation; *U.S. Public*, pg. 872
TEKTRONIX SOUTHEAST ASIA PTE LTD—See Fortive Corporation; *U.S. Public*, pg. 872
TEKTRONIX UK LTD.—See Fortive Corporation; *U.S. Public*, pg. 872
TELEDYNE INSTRUMENTS, INC.—See Teledyne Technologies Incorporated; *U.S. Public*, pg. 1993
TELEDYNE LECROY, INC. - PROTOCOL SOLUTIONS GROUP—See Teledyne Technologies Incorporated; *U.S. Public*, pg. 1994
TELEDYNE MONITOR LABS, INC.—See Teledyne Technologies Incorporated; *U.S. Public*, pg. 1994
TELOG INSTRUMENTS, INC.—See Trimble, Inc.; *U.S. Public*, pg. 2191
TENSILKUT ENGINEERING—See Sieburg International, Inc.; *U.S. Private*, pg. 3646
TENSILKUT INTL. CORP.—See Sieburg International, Inc.; *U.S. Private*, pg. 3646
TENSITRON, INC.—See Main Line Equity Partners, LLC; *U.S. Private*, pg. 2551
TESTEK, LLC—See Odyssey Investment Partners, LLC; *U.S. Private*, pg. 2995
TESTING MACHINES INC.; *U.S. Private*, pg. 3973
THERMO FISHER ISRAEL LTD.—See Thermo Fisher Scientific Inc.; *U.S. Public*, pg. 2149
THERMO FISHER SCIENTIFIC - WILMINGTON BRANCH—See Thermo Fisher Scientific Inc.; *U.S. Public*, pg. 2153
THERMOGRAPHICS, INC.—See Liquid Crystal Resources; *U.S. Private*, pg. 2465
THIELMANN ENERGIETECHNIK GMBH—See Itron, Inc.; *U.S. Public*, pg. 1176
THWING-ALBERT INSTRUMENT COMPANY; *U.S. Private*, pg. 4166
TIBERSOFT CORPORATION; *U.S. Private*, pg. 4167
T.I.C.-CITIZEN CO., LTD.—See Citizen Watch Co., Ltd.; *Int'l*, pg. 1625
TINIUS OLSEN, INC.; *U.S. Private*, pg. 4175
TOLTEQ GROUP, LLC—See NOV, Inc.; *U.S. Public*, pg. 1546
TRACKPOINT SYSTEMS LLC—See Genstar Capital, LLC; *U.S. Private*, pg. 1676
TRANSMATION (CANADA) LTD.—See Transcat, Inc.; *U.S. Public*, pg. 2179
TRANSONIC ASIA INC.—See Measurement Innovations

334519 — OTHER MEASURING AND...

Corp.; *U.S. Private*, pg. 2648
TRANSONIC EUROPE B.V.—See Measurement Innovations Corp.; *U.S. Private*, pg. 2648
TRANSONIC JAPAN INC.—See Measurement Innovations Corp.; *U.S. Private*, pg. 2648
TRANSONIC SYSTEMS INC.—See Measurement Innovations Corp.; *U.S. Private*, pg. 2648
TRIMBLE SOLUTIONS SWEDEN AB—See Trimble, Inc.; *U.S. Public*, pg. 2193
TRI-TECH SOLUTIONS, INC.—See 5th Gear Technologies Concepts, Inc.; *U.S. Private*, pg. 16
TSI AB—See TSI Incorporated; *U.S. Private*, pg. 4253
TSI FRANCE, INC.—See TSI Incorporated; *U.S. Private*, pg. 4253
TSI INCORPORATED; *U.S. Private*, pg. 4253
TYDEN GROUP INC.—See Bertram Capital Management, LLC; *U.S. Private*, pg. 540
TYDEN GROUP INC.—See Crimson Investment; *U.S. Private*, pg. 1100
ULTRA ELECTRONICS COMMAND & CONTROL SYSTEMS—See Advent International Corporation; *U.S. Private*, pg. 101
ULTRA ELECTRONICS CONTROLS DIVISION—See Advent International Corporation; *U.S. Private*, pg. 101
UNIVERSAL GENEVE S.A—See CVC Capital Partners SICAV-FIS S.A.; *Int'l*, pg. 1883
UNIVERSAL SENSORS, INC.—See China Automotive Systems, Inc.; *Int'l*, pg. 1484
VACHERON AND CONSTANTIN S.A.—See Compagnie Financiere Richemont S.A.; *Int'l*, pg. 1741
VAN CLEEF & ARPELS SA—See Compagnie Financiere Richemont S.A.; *Int'l*, pg. 1741
VARIOHM HOLDINGS LIMITED—See discoverIE Group plc; *Int'l*, pg. 2134
VENTURE MEASUREMENT COMPANY LLC—See Fortive Corporation; *U.S. Public*, pg. 872
VERMONT CLOCK COMPANY; *U.S. Private*, pg. 4367
VIBRACOUSTIC NORTH AMERICA LP—See Freudenberg SE; *Int'l*, pg. 2791
VIBRA-METRICS, INC.—See Mistras Group, Inc.; *U.S. Public*, pg. 1451
VIC LEAK DETECTION, AIR LEAK TESTING DIVISION—See Valero Capital Partners LLC; *U.S. Private*, pg. 4331
VIEW MICRO-METROLOGY, INC.—See Quality Vision International Inc.; *U.S. Private*, pg. 3321
VISHAY MICRO-MEASUREMENT—See Vishay Intertechnology, Inc.; *U.S. Public*, pg. 2303
WALOP LTD.—See Citizen Watch Co., Ltd.; *Int'l*, pg. 1625
WATCHFINDER.CO.UK LIMITED—See Compagnie Financiere Richemont S.A.; *Int'l*, pg. 1741
WATSON INDUSTRIES, INC.; *U.S. Private*, pg. 4455
WESTLOCK CONTROLS LIMITED—See Crane NXT, Co.; *U.S. Public*, pg. 589
WESTON AEROSPACE LTD.—See TransDigm Group Incorporated; *U.S. Public*, pg. 2180
WHITE'S ELECTRONICS (UK) LTD—See White's Electronics; *U.S. Private*, pg. 4510
WHITE'S OF LONG ISLAND, INC.—See White's Electronics; *U.S. Private*, pg. 4510
WILLIS AERONAUTICAL SERVICES, INC.—See Willis Lease Finance Corporation; *U.S. Public*, pg. 2371
WILLIS LEASE SINGAPORE PTE. LTD.—See Willis Lease Finance Corporation; *U.S. Public*, pg. 2372
W.N. BEST—See PUMC Holding Corporation; *U.S. Private*, pg. 3303
WUXI CRITICAL MECHANICAL COMPONENTS—See TechPrecision Corporation; *U.S. Public*, pg. 1988
YESTECH, INC.—See Nordson Corporation; *U.S. Public*, pg. 1535
YOKOGAWA ANALYTICAL SYSTEMS, INC.—See Agilent Technologies, Inc.; *U.S. Public*, pg. 62
ZETEC, INC.—See Roper Technologies, Inc.; *U.S. Public*, pg. 1814
ZHEJIANG DAHAO TECHNOLOGY CO., LTD.—See Beijing Dahao Technology Corporation Limited; *Int'l*, pg. 948
ZHUHAI ROSSINI WATCH INDUSTRY LIMITED—See Citychamp Watch & Jewellery Group Limited; *Int'l*, pg. 1629

334610 — MANUFACTURING AND REPRODUCING MAGNETIC AND OPTICAL MEDIA

3PILLAR GLOBAL, INC.; *U.S. Private*, pg. 14
4IG NYRT.; *Int'l*, pg. 12
AATRIX SOFTWARE, INC.—See HgCapital Trust plc; *Int'l*, pg. 3377
ACCELRYS, INC.—See Dassault Systemes S.A.; *Int'l*, pg. 1974
ACCESS SEOUL CO. LTD—See Access Co., Ltd.; *Int'l*, pg. 88
ACOUSOFT INFORMATISERING BV; *Int'l*, pg. 108
ADOBE SYSTEMS INC. - SAN FRANCISCO—See Adobe Inc.; *U.S. Public*, pg. 42
AD OPT TECHNOLOGIES INC.—See IBS Software Private Limited; *Int'l*, pg. 3577
ADVANCED UTILITY SYSTEMS CORPORATION—See Constellation Software Inc.; *Int'l*, pg. 1773
AEXIS NEDERLAND—See Aexis N.V.; *Int'l*, pg. 183
AGNITE EDUCATION LIMITED; *Int'l*, pg. 212
ALLIED VAUGHN - CHICAGO—See Allied Vaughn Inc.; *U.S. Private*, pg. 191
ALLIED VAUGHN—See Allied Vaughn Inc.; *U.S. Private*, pg. 191
ALL RIGHT SOFTWARE INC.—See EPS Holdings, Inc.; *Int'l*, pg. 2465
ALTOY SAVUNMA SANAYI VE HAVACILIK ANONIM SIRKETI—See AeroVironment, Inc.; *U.S. Public*, pg. 53
AMERICAN MEDIA INTERNATIONAL LTD.; *U.S. Private*, pg. 241
AMERICAN SOFTWARE, INC.; *U.S. Public*, pg. 109
AMPEX GREAT BRITAIN LTD.—See Ampex Corporation; *U.S. Private*, pg. 266
ANJANI ETECH SOLUTIONS, INC.; *U.S. Private*, pg. 284
ANSOFT CORPORATION—See ANSYS, Inc.; *U.S. Public*, pg. 138
AQ1 SYSTEMS PTY. LTD.—See Aktieselskabet Schouw & Co.; *Int'l*, pg. 265
AQUILA GROUP HOLDINGS LIMITED—See Siris Capital Group, LLC; *U.S. Private*, pg. 3673
ARTECH DIGITAL ENTERTAINMENTS, INC.—See BCE Inc.; *Int'l*, pg. 927
ARVATO DIGITAL—See Bertelsmann SE & Co. KGaA; *Int'l*, pg. 990
ASPHERE INNOVATIONS PUBLIC COMPANY LIMITED; *Int'l*, pg. 629
ASSUREWEB LIMITED—See Aviva plc; *Int'l*, pg. 745
ASTEA FRANCE—See EQT AB; *Int'l*, pg. 2477
ASTEA INTERNATIONAL, INC.—See EQT AB; *Int'l*, pg. 2477
ASTEA ISRAEL LTD.—See EQT AB; *Int'l*, pg. 2477
ASTEA SERVICE & DISTRIBUTION SYSTEMS, BV—See EQT AB; *Int'l*, pg. 2477
A TO ZMEDIA; *U.S. Private*, pg. 19
ATTUNITY (HONG KONG) LTD.—See Thoma Bravo, L.P.; *U.S. Private*, pg. 4152
ATTUNITY INC.—See Thoma Bravo, L.P.; *U.S. Private*, pg. 4152
ATTUNITY (UK) LIMITED—See Thoma Bravo, L.P.; *U.S. Private*, pg. 4152
AUDIO-DIGEST FOUNDATION; *U.S. Private*, pg. 391
AVALANCHE SEARCH MARKETING INC.; *Int'l*, pg. 734
AXWAY—See Axway Software SA; *Int'l*, pg. 772
BACKSTAGEPLAY INC.; *Int'l*, pg. 795
BAODING LUCKY INNOVATIVE MATERIALS CO., LTD.; *Int'l*, pg. 855
BAVARIA SONOR MUSIKVERLAG UND MERCHANDISING GMBH—See Bavaria Film GmbH; *Int'l*, pg. 899
BIO-RAD LABORATORIES, INC. - SPECTROSCOPY PRODUCTS—See Bio-Rad Laboratories, Inc.; *U.S. Public*, pg. 333
BIS DIGITAL, INC.; *U.S. Private*, pg. 565
BISON OPTICAL DISC INC.; *U.S. Private*, pg. 566
BLUJAY SOLUTIONS LTD.—See Francisco Partners Management, LP; *U.S. Private*, pg. 1589
BMC SOFTWARE ASIA PACIFIC PTE. LTD.—See KKR & Co., Inc.; *U.S. Public*, pg. 1240
BMC SOFTWARE ASIA SDN BHD—See KKR & Co. Inc.; *U.S. Public*, pg. 1240
BMC SOFTWARE A/S—See KKR & Co. Inc.; *U.S. Public*, pg. 1239
BMC SOFTWARE (AUSTRALIA) PTY. LTD.—See KKR & Co. Inc.; *U.S. Public*, pg. 1239
BMC SOFTWARE (AUSTRALIA) PTY. LTD.—See KKR & Co. Inc.; *U.S. Public*, pg. 1239
BMC SOFTWARE BELGIUM NV—See KKR & Co. Inc.; *U.S. Public*, pg. 1240
BMC SOFTWARE CANADA, INC.—See KKR & Co. Inc.; *U.S. Public*, pg. 1240
BMC SOFTWARE CANADA—See KKR & Co. Inc.; *U.S. Public*, pg. 1240
BMC SOFTWARE (CHINA) LIMITED—See KKR & Co. Inc.; *U.S. Public*, pg. 1239
BMC SOFTWARE DE ARGENTINA S.A.—See KKR & Co. Inc.; *U.S. Public*, pg. 1240
BMC SOFTWARE DO BRASIL LTDA.—See KKR & Co. Inc.; *U.S. Public*, pg. 1240
BMC SOFTWARE FRANCE SAS—See KKR & Co. Inc.; *U.S. Public*, pg. 1240
BMC SOFTWARE GMBH—See KKR & Co. Inc.; *U.S. Public*, pg. 1240
BMC SOFTWARE GMBH—See KKR & Co. Inc.; *U.S. Public*, pg. 1240
BMC SOFTWARE GMBH—See KKR & Co. Inc.; *U.S. Public*, pg. 1240
BMC SOFTWARE GMBH—See KKR & Co. Inc.; *U.S. Public*, pg. 1240
BMC SOFTWARE GMBH—See KKR & Co. Inc.; *U.S. Public*, pg. 1240
BMC SOFTWARE (HONG KONG) LIMITED—See KKR & Co. Inc.; *U.S. Public*, pg. 1239
BMC SOFTWARE K.K.—See KKR & Co. Inc.; *U.S. Public*, pg. 1240
BMC SOFTWARE KOREA, LTD.—See KKR & Co. Inc.; *U.S. Public*, pg. 1240
BMC SOFTWARE LIMITED—See KKR & Co. Inc.; *U.S. Public*, pg. 1240
BMC SOFTWARE S.A.—See KKR & Co. Inc.; *U.S. Public*, pg. 1240
BMC SOFTWARE S.A.—See KKR & Co. Inc.; *U.S. Public*, pg. 1240
BMC SOFTWARE S.R.L.—See KKR & Co. Inc.; *U.S. Public*, pg. 1240
BMC SOFTWARE S.R.L.—See KKR & Co. Inc.; *U.S. Public*, pg. 1240
BOOKS ON TAPE, INC.—See Bertelsmann SE & Co. KGaA; *Int'l*, pg. 991
BOSTON TECHNOLOGIES, INC.; *U.S. Private*, pg. 622
BRENDAN TECHNOLOGIES, INC.; *U.S. Private*, pg. 645
BRILLIANCE PUBLISHING, INC—See Amazon.com, Inc.; *U.S. Public*, pg. 90
BRILLIANT DIGITAL ENTERTAINMENT, INC.; *U.S. Private*, pg. 654
BROADVISION, INC.—See ESW Capital, LLC; *U.S. Private*, pg. 1429
CAPCOM CO., LTD.; *Int'l*, pg. 1302
CA TECHNOLOGIES PRIVATE LTD.—See Broadcom Inc.; *U.S. Public*, pg. 389
CCA ENGINEERING SIMULATION SOFTWARE (SHANGHAI) CO.,LTD—See FUJISOFT INCORPORATED; *Int'l*, pg. 2830
CEO IMAGING SYSTEMS, INC.—See Intellinetics, Inc.; *U.S. Public*, pg. 1140
CGI NEDERLAND B.V. - ARNHEM—See CGI Inc.; *Int'l*, pg. 1434
CGI NEDERLAND B.V.—See CGI Inc.; *Int'l*, pg. 1434
CHENGDU GALAXY MAGNET CO., LTD.; *Int'l*, pg. 1467
CHRISTIE GROUP PLC; *Int'l*, pg. 1586
CHUAN HUAT RESOURCES BERHAD; *Int'l*, pg. 1589
CINE MAGNETICS, INC.; *U.S. Private*, pg. 898
CINE MAGNETICS VIDEO & DIGITAL LABORATORIES—See Cine Magnetics, Inc.; *U.S. Private*, pg. 898
CITRIX SYSTEMS, INC.—See Elliott Management Corporation; *U.S. Private*, pg. 1366
CITRIX SYSTEMS, INC.—See Vista Equity Partners, LLC; *U.S. Private*, pg. 4395
CLARABRIDGE, INC.—See Canada Pension Plan Investment Board; *Int'l*, pg. 1281
CLARABRIDGE, INC.—See Silver Lake Group, LLC; *U.S. Private*, pg. 3655
CLINIX MEDICAL INFORMATION SERVICES LLC; *U.S. Private*, pg. 944
COMMVAULT SYSTEMS BELGIUM BVBA—See CommVault Systems, Inc.; *U.S. Public*, pg. 559
COMMVAULT SYSTEMS IBERIA SRL—See CommVault Systems, Inc.; *U.S. Public*, pg. 559
COMPUTER ASSOCIATES INTERNATIONAL GMBH—See Broadcom Inc.; *U.S. Public*, pg. 389
COMPUTER ASSOCIATES INTERNATIONAL LIMITED—See Broadcom Inc.; *U.S. Public*, pg. 389
COMPUTER ASSOCIATES JAPAN, LTD.—See Broadcom Inc.; *U.S. Public*, pg. 389
COMPUTER ASSOCIATES KOREA LTD.—See Broadcom Inc.; *U.S. Public*, pg. 389
COMPUTER ASSOCIATES MIDDLE EAST—See Broadcom Inc.; *U.S. Public*, pg. 389
COMPUTER ASSOCIATES MIDDLE EAST—See Broadcom Inc.; *U.S. Public*, pg. 389
COMPUTER ASSOCIATES PTY. LTD.—See Broadcom Inc.; *U.S. Public*, pg. 390
COMPUTER SYSTEMS COMPANY, INC.—See Thoma Bravo, L.P.; *U.S. Private*, pg. 4148
COMTRADE GMBH—See ComTrade Group B.V.; *Int'l*, pg. 1762
COMTRADE SOFTWARE SOLUTIONS LIMITED—See ComTrade Group B.V.; *Int'l*, pg. 1762
COMTRADE USA WEST, INC.—See ComTrade Group B.V.; *Int'l*, pg. 1762
CONDUANT CORPORATION; *U.S. Private*, pg. 1012
CONSTELLATION HOMEBUILDER SYSTEMS INC.—See Constellation Software Inc.; *Int'l*, pg. 1772
CONSTELLATION JUSTICE SYSTEMS INC.—See Constellation Software Inc.; *Int'l*, pg. 1775
COREL COMPANY—See KKR & Co. Inc.; *U.S. Public*, pg. 1243
COREL CORPORATION—See KKR & Co. Inc.; *U.S. Public*, pg. 1243
COREL USA—See KKR & Co. Inc.; *U.S. Public*, pg. 1243
CRESCO, LTD.; *Int'l*, pg. 1840
CRITERION SOFTWARE LTD.—See Electronic Arts Inc.; *U.S. Public*, pg. 724
THE CSC GROUP OF MICHIGAN—See Thoma Bravo, L.P.; *U.S. Private*, pg. 4148
CTP DIGITAL SERVICES PTY LTD—See Caxton and CTP Publishers and Printers Ltd.; *Int'l*, pg. 1363
CYBERNET CAE SYSTEMS (SHANGHAI) CO.,LTD—See FUJISOFT INCORPORATED; *Int'l*, pg. 2830
DAIDO ELECTRONICS CO., LTD.—See Daido Steel Co., Ltd.; *Int'l*, pg. 1922
DASSAULT SYSTEMES ENOVIA CORP.—See Dassault Systemes S.A.; *Int'l*, pg. 1974

DASSAULT SYSTEMES PROVENCE—See Dassault Systemes S.A.; *Int'l*, pg. 1975
DATA APPLICATIONS CO., LTD.; *Int'l*, pg. 1975
DATADIRECT TECHNOLOGIES LTD.—See Progress Software Corporation; *U.S. Public*, pg. 1725
DATADIRECT TECHNOLOGIES NV—See Progress Software Corporation; *U.S. Public*, pg. 1725
DATA I/O GMBH—See Data I/O Corporation; *U.S. Public*, pg. 635
DATATRAK INTERNATIONAL, INC.; *U.S. Public*, pg. 635
DATAWATCH INTERNATIONAL LIMITED—See Altair Engineering, Inc.; *U.S. Public*, pg. 86
DEEP WEB TECHNOLOGIES—See AMPLYFI Ltd; *Int'l*, pg. 436
DELMIA GMBH—See Dassault Systemes S.A.; *Int'l*, pg. 1975
DEXERIALS (SHENZHEN) CORPORATION—See Development Bank of Japan, Inc.; *Int'l*, pg. 2087
DEXERIALS (SUZHOU) CO., LTD.—See Development Bank of Japan, Inc.; *Int'l*, pg. 2087
DEXTER MAGNETIC TECHNOLOGIES, INC. - SYOSSET—See Tinicum Enterprises, Inc.; *U.S. Private*, pg. 4174
DEXTON BUSINESS SOLUTIONS; *Int'l*, pg. 2093
DEXXON BELGIUM S.A.—See Dexxon Groupe SA; *Int'l*, pg. 2093
DEXXON ITALIA SPA—See Dexxon Groupe SA; *Int'l*, pg. 2093
DIEBOLD SOFTWARE SOLUTIONS, INC.—See Diebold Nixdorf, Inc.; *U.S. Public*, pg. 661
DISCTRONICS TEXAS INC.; *U.S. Private*, pg. 1238
DISKFAKTORY.COM—See Innovative Diversified Technologies Inc.; *U.S. Private*, pg. 2082
DMD DATA SYSTEMS, INC.; *U.S. Private*, pg. 1248
DRS DATA SERVICES LIMITED—See DRS Data & Research Services Plc; *Int'l*, pg. 2206
DS DEUTSCHLAND GMBH—See Dassault Systemes S.A.; *Int'l*, pg. 1974
D-TECH OPTOELECTRONICS INC.—See GCS Holdings, Inc.; *Int'l*, pg. 2895
EARTH-PANDA ADVANCE MAGNETIC MATERIAL CO., LTD.; *Int'l*, pg. 2268
EASYSOFT-SOFTWARE E SISTEMAS SA—See 3i Group plc; *Int'l*, pg. 8
EGAIN CORPORATION; *U.S. Public*, pg. 721
ELECTRONIC ARTS (CANADA), INC.—See Electronic Arts Inc.; *U.S. Public*, pg. 724
ELECTRONIC ARTS GMBH—See Electronic Arts Inc.; *U.S. Public*, pg. 724
ELECTRONIC ARTS SOFTWARE S.L.—See Electronic Arts Inc.; *U.S. Public*, pg. 724
ELECTRONIC ARTS UK LTD.—See Electronic Arts Inc.; *U.S. Public*, pg. 724
ELEKTA IMPAC SOFTWARE—See Elekta AB; *Int'l*, pg. 2356
ELEKTRA RECORDS—See Access Industries, Inc.; *U.S. Private*, pg. 52
EMPHASYS SOFTWARE INC.—See Constellation Software Inc.; *Int'l*, pg. 1772
EMTEC MAGNETICS IBERICA S.A.—See Dexxon Groupe SA; *Int'l*, pg. 2093
EMTEC MAGNETICS POLSKA SP. Z.O.O.—See Dexxon Groupe SA; *Int'l*, pg. 2093
EMTEC MAGNETICS (SCHWEIZ) GMBH—See Dexxon Groupe SA; *Int'l*, pg. 2093
ENROUTE EMERGENCY SYSTEMS—See Koch Industries, Inc.; *U.S. Private*, pg. 2330
ENTERPRISE SOLUTIONS REALIZED; *U.S. Private*, pg. 1404
ENXNET, INC.; *U.S. Private*, pg. 1410
EPICOR SOFTWARE (ASIA) PTE LTD.—See Clayton, Dubilier & Rice, LLC; *U.S. Private*, pg. 922
EPICOR SOFTWARE (BEIJING) COMPANY, LTD.—See Clayton, Dubilier & Rice, LLC; *U.S. Private*, pg. 922
EPICOR SOFTWARE CORPORATION—See Clayton, Dubilier & Rice, LLC; *U.S. Private*, pg. 922
EPICOR SOFTWARE CPRUS LTD.—See Clayton, Dubilier & Rice, LLC; *U.S. Private*, pg. 922
EPICOR SOFTWARE CZECH S.R.O—See Clayton, Dubilier & Rice, LLC; *U.S. Private*, pg. 922
EPICOR SOFTWARE DEUTSCHLAND GMBH—See Clayton, Dubilier & Rice, LLC; *U.S. Private*, pg. 922
EPICOR SOFTWARE ESTONIA OU—See Clayton, Dubilier & Rice, LLC; *U.S. Private*, pg. 922
EPICOR SOFTWARE FINLAND OY—See Clayton, Dubilier & Rice, LLC; *U.S. Private*, pg. 922
EPICOR SOFTWARE HUNGARY KFT—See Clayton, Dubilier & Rice, LLC; *U.S. Private*, pg. 922
EPICOR SOFTWARE ITALIA S.R.I.—See Clayton, Dubilier & Rice, LLC; *U.S. Private*, pg. 922
EPICOR SOFTWARE JAPAN K.K.—See Clayton, Dubilier & Rice, LLC; *U.S. Private*, pg. 922
EPICOR SOFTWARE LATVIJA SIA—See Clayton, Dubilier & Rice, LLC; *U.S. Private*, pg. 922
EPICOR SOFTWARE (M) SDN BHD—See Clayton, Dubilier & Rice, LLC; *U.S. Private*, pg. 922
EPICOR SOFTWARE (NORTH ASIA) LTD.—See Clayton, Dubilier & Rice, LLC; *U.S. Private*, pg. 922
EPICOR SOFTWARE POLAND SP. Z O.O.—See Clayton, Dubilier & Rice, LLC; *U.S. Private*, pg. 922

EPICOR SOFTWARE (SEA) PTE LTD.—See Clayton, Dubilier & Rice, LLC; *U.S. Private*, pg. 922
EPICOR SOFTWARE (SHANGHAI) CO., LTD.—See Clayton, Dubilier & Rice, LLC; *U.S. Private*, pg. 922
EPICOR SOFTWARE SLOVAKIA, S.R.O.—See Clayton, Dubilier & Rice, LLC; *U.S. Private*, pg. 923
EPICOR SOFTWARE SRL—See Clayton, Dubilier & Rice, LLC; *U.S. Private*, pg. 922
EPICOR SOFTWARE UK LTD.—See Clayton, Dubilier & Rice, LLC; *U.S. Private*, pg. 923
ESCHOLAR, LLC—See Constellation Software Inc.; *Int'l*, pg. 1774
ESI GROUP S.A.—See Keysight Technologies, Inc.; *U.S. Public*, pg. 1226
ESI SOFTWARE PVT. LTD—See Keysight Technologies, Inc.; *U.S. Public*, pg. 1226
ESTSOFT CORP; *Int'l*, pg. 2519
E-TRIAL CO., LTD.—See EPS Holdings, Inc.; *Int'l*, pg. 2465
EUROVIDEO BILDPROGRAMM GMBH—See Bavaria Film GmbH; *Int'l*, pg. 899
EXPERIAN TALLYMAN—See Experian plc; *Int'l*, pg. 2587
EXTENSIONENGINE LLC; *U.S. Private*, pg. 1452
EXTENSIONENGINE—See ExtensionEngine LLC; *U.S. Private*, pg. 1452
EXTERRO, INC.—See Leeds Equity Partners, LLC; *U.S. Private*, pg. 2414
FINMATICA S.P.A.; *Int'l*, pg. 2675
FIRST STATE COMPUTING PTY LTD.—See BT Group plc; *Int'l*, pg. 1203
FLEXIINTERNATIONAL SOFTWARE, INC.; *U.S. Public*, pg. 853
FORCEPOINT S.C. PTY LTD—See Francisco Partners Management, LP; *U.S. Private*, pg. 1590
FUJI ELECTRIC (MALAYSIA) SDN. BHD.—See Fuji Electric Co., Ltd.; *Int'l*, pg. 2811
FUJIFILM MANUFACTURING USA, INC.—See FUJIFILM Holdings Corporation; *Int'l*, pg. 2823
FUJIFILM MEDIA CREST CO., LTD.—See FUJIFILM Holdings Corporation; *Int'l*, pg. 2824
FUJIFILM MEDIA MANUFACTURING CO., LTD.—See FUJIFILM Holdings Corporation; *Int'l*, pg. 2824
FUJIFILM OPTICS PHILIPPINES INC.—See FUJIFILM Holdings Corporation; *Int'l*, pg. 2824
FUJIFILM PRESENTEC CO., LTD.—See FUJIFILM Holdings Corporation; *Int'l*, pg. 2824
FUJIFILM RECORDING MEDIA GMBH—See FUJIFILM Holdings Corporation; *Int'l*, pg. 2822
FUJIFILM RECORDING MEDIA ITALIA S.R.L—See FUJIFILM Holdings Corporation; *Int'l*, pg. 2822
FULL PERSPECTIVE VIDEO SERVICES INC.; *U.S. Private*, pg. 1621
FUSION TRADE HK LIMITED—See Fusion Trade, Inc.; *U.S. Private*, pg. 1626
GENSYM B.V.—See ESW Capital, LLC; *U.S. Private*, pg. 1430
GENSYM CORPORATION—See ESW Capital, LLC; *U.S. Private*, pg. 1430
GIESECKE Y DEVRIENT CURRENCY TECHNOLOGY DE MEXICO, S.A. DE C.V.—See Giesecke & Devrient GmbH; *Int'l*, pg. 2969
GMO GAMEPOT INC.—See GMO Internet Group, Inc.; *Int'l*, pg. 3013
GOLDENTECH COMPUTER TECHNOLOGY (SUZHOU) CO.,LTD.—See CAC Corporation; *Int'l*, pg. 1247
GRESHAM TECHNOLOGIES PLC—See Symphony Technology Group, LLC; *U.S. Private*, pg. 3900
GSE SYSTEMS, INC.; *U.S. Public*, pg. 973
HANWHA AEROSPACE CO., LTD.—See Hanwha Group; *Int'l*, pg. 3264
HOLLYWOOD RECORDS INC.—See The Walt Disney Company; *U.S. Public*, pg. 2138
HOMENEMA TECHNOLOGY INCORPORATION; *Int'l*, pg. 3455
HOYA CORPORATION; *Int'l*, pg. 3494
ICIMS, INC.; *U.S. Private*, pg. 2031
I & K SYSTEME GMBH—See Frankfurter Sparkasse; *Int'l*, pg. 2761
IMAGE ENTERTAINMENT, INC.—See AMC Networks Inc.; *U.S. Public*, pg. 92
IMMERSION CORPORATION; *U.S. Public*, pg. 1112
INCREDIBLE TECHNOLOGIES, INC.; *U.S. Private*, pg. 2054
INDUSTRIAL AND FINANCIAL SYSTEMS, IFS AB—See EQT AB; *Int'l*, pg. 2477
INFINITE SOFTWARE SOLUTIONS, INC.—See Fortive Corporation; *U.S. Public*, pg. 871
INFOR BV—See Koch Industries, Inc.; *U.S. Private*, pg. 2330
INFOR GLOBAL SOLUTIONS - BANGKOK—See Koch Industries, Inc.; *U.S. Private*, pg. 2330
INFOR GLOBAL SOLUTIONS - BIRMINGHAM—See Koch Industries, Inc.; *U.S. Private*, pg. 2330
INFOR GLOBAL SOLUTIONS - BUENOS AIRES—See Koch Industries, Inc.; *U.S. Private*, pg. 2330
INFOR GLOBAL SOLUTIONS - CAPELLE AAN DEN IJSSEL—See Koch Industries, Inc.; *U.S. Private*, pg. 2330

INFOR GLOBAL SOLUTIONS - GUANGZHOU—See Koch Industries, Inc.; *U.S. Private*, pg. 2330
INFOR GLOBAL SOLUTIONS - HONG KONG—See Koch Industries, Inc.; *U.S. Private*, pg. 2330
INFOR GLOBAL SOLUTIONS - MUNICH—See Koch Industries, Inc.; *U.S. Private*, pg. 2330
INFOR GLOBAL SOLUTIONS - SANTIAGO—See Koch Industries, Inc.; *U.S. Private*, pg. 2330
INFOR GLOBAL SOLUTIONS - SINGAPORE—See Koch Industries, Inc.; *U.S. Private*, pg. 2330
INFOR GLOBAL SOLUTIONS - SYDNEY—See Koch Industries, Inc.; *U.S. Private*, pg. 2330
INFOWAY SOFTWARE; *U.S. Private*, pg. 2074
INOVERIS, LLC—See Comvest Group Holdings LLC; *U.S. Private*, pg. 1007
INTERGRAPH (AUSTRIA) GMBH—See Hexagon AB; *Int'l*, pg. 3368
INTERGRAPH BELGIUM NV/SA—See Hexagon AB; *Int'l*, pg. 3368
INTERGRAPH CORP. (N.Z.) LIMITED—See Hexagon AB; *Int'l*, pg. 3368
INTERGRAPH DANMARK A/S—See Hexagon AB; *Int'l*, pg. 3368
INTERGRAPH DEUTSCHLAND GMBH—See Hexagon AB; *Int'l*, pg. 3368
INTERGRAPH FRANCE S.A.—See Hexagon AB; *Int'l*, pg. 3369
INTERGRAPH (INDIA) PRIVATE LTD.—See Hexagon AB; *Int'l*, pg. 3368
INTERGRAPH (SHENZHEN) COMPANY LTD.—See Hexagon AB; *Int'l*, pg. 3368
INTERGRAPH SYSTEMS (SHENZHEN) CO. LTD—See Hexagon AB; *Int'l*, pg. 3369
INTERLINK ELECTRONICS, INC.; *U.S. Public*, pg. 1144
INTUITIVE WEB SOLUTIONS, L.L.C.; *U.S. Private*, pg. 2130
IREM SOFTWARE ENGINEERING INC.—See EIZO Corporation; *Int'l*, pg. 2337
JDA SOFTWARE ITALY S.R.L.—See New Mountain Capital, LLC; *U.S. Private*, pg. 2902
JONAS SOFTWARE LTD.—See Constellation Software Inc.; *Int'l*, pg. 1773
KERRIDGE COMMERCIAL SYSTEMS (KSH) LIMITED—See KKR & Co. Inc.; *U.S. Public*, pg. 1256
KEWILL BELGIUM NV—See Francisco Partners Management, LP; *U.S. Private*, pg. 1589
KEWILL BV—See Francisco Partners Management, LP; *U.S. Private*, pg. 1589
KEWILL CO., LTD.—See Francisco Partners Management, LP; *U.S. Private*, pg. 1589
KEWILL GMBH—See Francisco Partners Management, LP; *U.S. Private*, pg. 1589
KEWILL LIMITED—See Francisco Partners Management, LP; *U.S. Private*, pg. 1589
KEWILL PTE LTD—See Francisco Partners Management, LP; *U.S. Private*, pg. 1589
KING SYSTEMS CORPORATION—See Ambu A/S; *Int'l*, pg. 416
LABOR RELATIONS INSTITUTE, INC.; *U.S. Private*, pg. 2370
LOCKHEED MARTIN CANADA—See Lockheed Martin Corporation; *U.S. Public*, pg. 1338
MACRO 4 AG—See UNICOM Global, Inc.; *U.S. Private*, pg. 4281
MACRO 4 (BENELUX) NV/SA—See UNICOM Global, Inc.; *U.S. Private*, pg. 4281
MACRO 4 (FRANCE) SARL—See UNICOM Global, Inc.; *U.S. Private*, pg. 4281
MACRO 4 GMBH—See UNICOM Global, Inc.; *U.S. Private*, pg. 4281
MACRO 4 INC.—See UNICOM Global, Inc.; *U.S. Private*, pg. 4281
MACRO 4 LTD.—See UNICOM Global, Inc.; *U.S. Private*, pg. 4281
MAD CATZ, INC.—See Mad Catz Interactive Inc.; *U.S. Private*, pg. 2539
MAGNET APPLICATIONS INC.—See Bunting Magnetics Co.; *U.S. Private*, pg. 686
MAMUT AB—See Cinven Limited; *Int'l*, pg. 1616
MAMUT AB—See HgCapital Trust plc; *Int'l*, pg. 3377
MAMUT AB—See KKR & Co. Inc.; *U.S. Public*, pg. 1266
MANAGEMENT AND ENGINEERING TECHNOLOGIES INTERNATIONAL, INC.; *U.S. Private*, pg. 2560
MARCO 4 SRL—See UNICOM Global, Inc.; *U.S. Private*, pg. 4281
MARK STEVENS INDUSTRIES INC.; *U.S. Private*, pg. 2578
MATRA PRODUCTS—See International Business Machines Corporation; *U.S. Public*, pg. 1149
METACOM INC.; *U.S. Private*, pg. 2679
MICROSOFT D.O.O., LJUBLJANA—See Microsoft Corporation; *U.S. Public*, pg. 1440
MICROSOFT DYNAMICS DANMARK—See Microsoft Corporation; *U.S. Public*, pg. 1439
MICROSOFT GULF FZ LLC—See Microsoft Corporation; *U.S. Public*, pg. 1440
MICROSOFT (MALAYSIA) SDN. BHD.—See Microsoft Corporation; *U.S. Public*, pg. 1439
MICROSOFT NEW ZEALAND LIMITED—See Microsoft

Corporation; *U.S. Public*, pg. 1441
MICROSOFT PHILIPPINES, INC.—See Microsoft Corporation; *U.S. Public*, pg. 1441
MICROSOFT PTY. LIMITED—See Microsoft Corporation; *U.S. Public*, pg. 1441
MICROSOFT RUSSIA—See Microsoft Corporation; *U.S. Public*, pg. 1440
MICROSOFT SOUTH AFRICA—See Microsoft Corporation; *U.S. Public*, pg. 1440
MICROSOFT S.R.O.—See Microsoft Corporation; *U.S. Public*, pg. 1440
MICROSOFT TAIWAN CORPORATION—See Microsoft Corporation; *U.S. Public*, pg. 1441
MICROSOFT (THAILAND) LIMITED—See Microsoft Corporation; *U.S. Public*, pg. 1439
MICROSOFT VENEZUELA S.A.—See Microsoft Corporation; *U.S. Public*, pg. 1441
MICROSTRATEGY, INC.; *U.S. Public*, pg. 1443
MISYS INTERNATIONAL BANKING SYSTEMS LIMITED—See Vista Equity Partners, LLC; *U.S. Private*, pg. 4397
MISYS RETAIL BANKING SYSTEMS LTD—See Vista Equity Partners, LLC; *U.S. Private*, pg. 4397
MISYS RISK MANAGEMENT SYSTEMS LTD—See Vista Equity Partners, LLC; *U.S. Private*, pg. 4397
MODERN VIDEOFILM, INC.—See Point.360; *U.S. Public*, pg. 1700
MODUSLINK INTERNATIONAL—See Steel Connect, Inc.; *U.S. Public*, pg. 1941
MORITEX ASIA PACIFIC PTE., LTD.—See Cognex Corporation; *U.S. Public*, pg. 523
MORRIS BUSINESS MEDIA, LLC—See Shivers Trading & Operating Company; *U.S. Private*, pg. 3638
MS GOVERN—See Constellation Software Inc.; *Int'l*, pg. 1774
NAGRASTAR, LLC—See EchoStar Corporation; *U.S. Public*, pg. 711
NATIONAL INSTRUMENTS CHINA CORPORATION—See National Instruments Corporation; *U.S. Private*, pg. 2857
NATIONAL INSTRUMENTS CORPORATION DENMARK—See National Instruments Corporation; *U.S. Private*, pg. 2857
NATIONAL INSTRUMENTS CORPORATION FRANCE—See National Instruments Corporation; *U.S. Private*, pg. 2857
NATIONAL INSTRUMENTS CORPORATION GERMANY—See National Instruments Corporation; *U.S. Private*, pg. 2857
NATIONAL INSTRUMENTS CORPORATION ITALY—See National Instruments Corporation; *U.S. Private*, pg. 2857
NATIONAL INSTRUMENTS CORPORATION JAPAN—See National Instruments Corporation; *U.S. Private*, pg. 2857
NATIONAL INSTRUMENTS CORPORATION SINGAPORE—See National Instruments Corporation; *U.S. Private*, pg. 2857
NATIONAL INSTRUMENTS CORPORATION SPAIN—See National Instruments Corporation; *U.S. Private*, pg. 2857
NATIONAL INSTRUMENTS CORPORATION (UK) LIMITED—See National Instruments Corporation; *U.S. Private*, pg. 2857
NATIONAL INSTRUMENTS TAIWAN CORPORATION—See National Instruments Corporation; *U.S. Private*, pg. 2857
NAXOS DIGITAL SERVICES LIMITED—See HNH International Ltd.; *Int'l*, pg. 3434
NAXOS OF AMERICA INC.—See HNH International Ltd.; *Int'l*, pg. 3434
NETSOL TECHNOLOGIES EUROPE LTD.—See NetSol Technologies, Inc.; *U.S. Public*, pg. 1509
NETSOL TECHNOLOGIES LTD. (CHINA)—See NetSol Technologies, Inc.; *U.S. Public*, pg. 1509
NETSOL TECHNOLOGIES LTD.—See NetSol Technologies, Inc.; *U.S. Public*, pg. 1509
NETSOL TECHNOLOGIES LTD.—See NetSol Technologies, Inc.; *U.S. Public*, pg. 1509
NETSTEPS; *U.S. Private*, pg. 2888
NEXSAN TECHNOLOGIES CANADA INC—See Nexsan Corporation; *U.S. Private*, pg. 2919
NEXSAN TECHNOLOGIES INCORPORATED—See Nexsan Corporation; *U.S. Private*, pg. 2919
NEXSAN TECHNOLOGIES LIMITED—See Nexsan Corporation; *U.S. Private*, pg. 2919
NEXTDOCS CORPORATION; *U.S. Private*, pg. 2920
NORVAX, INC.—See Centerbridge Partners, L.P.; *U.S. Private*, pg. 815
NOVACCESS GLOBAL INC.; *U.S. Public*, pg. 1547
NUANCE COMMUNICATIONS, INC.—See Microsoft Corporation; *U.S. Public*, pg. 1441
NVIDIA LTD.—See NVIDIA Corporation; *U.S. Public*, pg. 1558
OFFICE BUSINESS SYSTEMS, INC.—See BIS Digital, Inc.; *U.S. Private*, pg. 565
OPENWAVE SYSTEMS BRASIL LTDA—See Forest Investments, Inc.; *U.S. Private*, pg. 1567
OPENWAVE SYSTEMS JAPAN KK—See Forest Investments, Inc.; *U.S. Private*, pg. 1567
ORACLE ARGENTINA S.A.—See Oracle Corporation; *U.S. Public*, pg. 1611

ORACLE BELGIUM BVBA—See Oracle Corporation; *U.S. Public*, pg. 1612
ORACLE (CHINA) SOFTWARE SYSTEMS CO., LTD.-SHANGHAI—See Oracle Corporation; *U.S. Public*, pg. 1611
ORACLE (CHINA) SOFTWARE SYSTEMS CO., LTD.—See Oracle Corporation; *U.S. Public*, pg. 1611
ORACLE COLOMBIA LIMITADA—See Oracle Corporation; *U.S. Public*, pg. 1611
ORACLE CORPORATION (AUSTRALIA) PTY. LTD.—See Oracle Corporation; *U.S. Public*, pg. 1611
ORACLE CORPORATION JAPAN—See Oracle Corporation; *U.S. Public*, pg. 1612
ORACLE CORPORATION MALAYSIA SDN. BHD.—See Oracle Corporation; *U.S. Public*, pg. 1612
ORACLE CORPORATION (PHILIPPINES), INC.—See Oracle Corporation; *U.S. Public*, pg. 1612
ORACLE CORPORATION SINGAPORE PTE LTD—See Oracle Corporation; *U.S. Public*, pg. 1611
ORACLE CORPORATION (THAILAND) COMPANY LTD.—See Oracle Corporation; *U.S. Public*, pg. 1612
ORACLE CORPORATION U.K. LTD.—See Oracle Corporation; *U.S. Public*, pg. 1612
ORACLE DE CENTRO AMERICA S.A.—See Oracle Corporation; *U.S. Public*, pg. 1612
ORACLE DE MEXICO, S.A. DE C.V.—See Oracle Corporation; *U.S. Public*, pg. 1613
ORACLE DENMARK APS—See Oracle Corporation; *U.S. Public*, pg. 1612
ORACLE DEUTSCHLAND B.V. & CO. KG—See Oracle Corporation; *U.S. Public*, pg. 1612
ORACLE DE VENEZUELA, S.A.—See Oracle Corporation; *U.S. Public*, pg. 1613
ORACLE DO BRASIL SISTEMAS LIMITADA—See Oracle Corporation; *U.S. Public*, pg. 1613
ORACLE EGYPT LTD.—See Oracle Corporation; *U.S. Public*, pg. 1612
ORACLE EMEA LIMITED—See Oracle Corporation; *U.S. Public*, pg. 1612
ORACLE FINLAND OY—See Oracle Corporation; *U.S. Public*, pg. 1612
ORACLE FRANCE S.A.S.—See Oracle Corporation; *U.S. Public*, pg. 1613
ORACLE HELLAS, S.A.—See Oracle Corporation; *U.S. Public*, pg. 1613
ORACLE HONG KONG LIMITED—See Oracle Corporation; *U.S. Public*, pg. 1612
ORACLE IBERICA SA—See Oracle Corporation; *U.S. Public*, pg. 1613
ORACLE INDIA PRIVATE LIMITED—See Oracle Corporation; *U.S. Public*, pg. 1612
ORACLE ITALIA S.R.L.—See Oracle Corporation; *U.S. Public*, pg. 1613
ORACLE KOREA LTD.—See Oracle Corporation; *U.S. Public*, pg. 1612
ORACLE NEDERLAND B.V.—See Oracle Corporation; *U.S. Public*, pg. 1613
ORACLE NORGE A/S—See Oracle Corporation; *U.S. Public*, pg. 1613
ORACLE NUMETRIX CO.—See Oracle Corporation; *U.S. Public*, pg. 1613
ORACLE POLSKA SP.Z.O.O.—See Oracle Corporation; *U.S. Public*, pg. 1613
ORACLE PORTUGAL-SISTEMAS DE INFORMACAO LDA.—See Oracle Corporation; *U.S. Public*, pg. 1613
ORACLE SOFTWARE D.O.O.—See Oracle Corporation; *U.S. Public*, pg. 1613
ORACLE SOFTWARE (SCHWEIZ) AG—See Oracle Corporation; *U.S. Public*, pg. 1613
ORACLE SVENSKA AB—See Oracle Corporation; *U.S. Public*, pg. 1613
ORACLE SVENSKA AB—See Oracle Corporation; *U.S. Public*, pg. 1613
ORACLE TAIWAN, LLC—See Oracle Corporation; *U.S. Public*, pg. 1612
PARAMETRIC TECH BRASIL LTDA.—See PTC Inc.; *U.S. Public*, pg. 1734
PARAMETRIC TECHNOLOGY EUROPE B.V.—See PTC Inc.; *U.S. Public*, pg. 1735
PARAMETRIC TECHNOLOGY GMBH SINDELFINGEN—See PTC Inc.; *U.S. Public*, pg. 1735
PARAMETRIC TECHNOLOGY GMBH—See PTC Inc.; *U.S. Public*, pg. 1735
PARAMETRIC TECHNOLOGY (HONG KONG) LIMITED—See PTC Inc.; *U.S. Public*, pg. 1734
PARAMETRIC TECHNOLOGY S.A.—See PTC Inc.; *U.S. Public*, pg. 1735
PARAMETRIC TECHNOLOGY (SCHWEIZ) AG—See PTC Inc.; *U.S. Public*, pg. 1735
PARAMETRIC TECHNOLOGY (UK) LTD.—See PTC Inc.; *U.S. Public*, pg. 1735
PARLAY ENTERTAINMENT—See Backstageplay Inc.; *Int'l*, pg. 795
PELADON SOFTWARE INC.—See The Software Construction Co. Inc.; *U.S. Private*, pg. 4119
PEOPLEADMIN, INC.—See Vista Equity Partners, LLC; *U.S. Private*, pg. 4399
PHILIPPINE COMPUTER ASSOCIATES INTERNATIONAL,

INC.—See Broadcom Inc.; *U.S. Public*, pg. 390
PHOENIX AMERICA, INC.—See discoverIE Group plc; *Int'l*, pg. 2133
PHOENIX TECHNOLOGIES KK—See Marlin Equity Partners, LLC; *U.S. Private*, pg. 2585
PHOENIX TECHNOLOGIES (KOREA) LTD.—See Marlin Equity Partners, LLC; *U.S. Private*, pg. 2584
PHOENIX TECHNOLOGIES (TAIWAN) LTD.—See Marlin Equity Partners, LLC; *U.S. Private*, pg. 2584
PITNEY BOWES SOFTWARE AUSTRALIA PTY. LTD.—See Pitney Bowes Inc.; *U.S. Public*, pg. 1695
PITNEY BOWES SOFTWARE EUROPE LIMITED—See Pitney Bowes Inc.; *U.S. Public*, pg. 1695
PLANT DESIGN ENGINEERS SDN BHD—See I Squared Capital Advisors (US) LLC; *U.S. Private*, pg. 2023
PLAXO, INC.—See Comcast Corporation; *U.S. Public*, pg. 541
POINT.360-HIGHLAND—See Point.360; *U.S. Public*, pg. 1700
PRECISE MEDIA AND FULL SERVICE; *U.S. Private*, pg. 3244
PRISM ENGINEERING LLC—See Court Square Capital Partners, L.P.; *U.S. Private*, pg. 1069
PROMOSUITE—See Banyan Software, Inc.; *U.S. Private*, pg. 470
PTC (CANADA) INC.—See PTC Inc.; *U.S. Public*, pg. 1734
QAD BILGISAYER YAZILIM LTD.—See Thoma Bravo, L.P.; *U.S. Private*, pg. 4151
QAD EUROPE LDA.—See Thoma Bravo, L.P.; *U.S. Private*, pg. 4151
QUANTEGY INC.; *U.S. Private*, pg. 3322
QUARKXPRESS PUBLISHING R&D (INDIA) PVT. LTD.—See Parallax Capital Partners, LLC; *U.S. Private*, pg. 3092
RAINBO RECORD MANUFACTURING CORP; *U.S. Private*, pg. 3347
RED PLANET JAPAN, INC.—See Evolution Capital Management LLC; *U.S. Private*, pg. 1443
RESOLUTION, INC.; *U.S. Private*, pg. 3406
RETALIX LTD.—See NCR Voyix Corporation.; *U.S. Public*, pg. 1502
ROADRUNNER RECORDS INC.; *U.S. Private*, pg. 3453
ROCKBOX LTD.—See iHeartMedia, Inc.; *U.S. Public*, pg. 1096
ROCKWELL SOFTWARE, INC.—See Rockwell Automation, Inc.; *U.S. Public*, pg. 1807
RTI, INC.—See DRI Corporation; *U.S. Private*, pg. 1277
SABA SOFTWARE, INC.—See Clearlake Capital Group, L.P.; *U.S. Private*, pg. 934
SAG SOFTWARE SYSTEMS AG—See Silver Lake Group, LLC; *U.S. Private*, pg. 3659
SAG SOFTWARE SYSTEMS SA—See Silver Lake Group, LLC; *U.S. Private*, pg. 3659
SAGUARO ROAD RECORDS, INC.—See Mosaic Media Investment Partners LLC; *U.S. Private*, pg. 2792
SALESFORCE SYSTEMS SPAIN, S.L.—See Salesforce, Inc.; *U.S. Public*, pg. 1837
SALIENT SYSTEMS, INC.—See L.B. Foster Company; *U.S. Public*, pg. 1278
SAS INSTITUTE AB—See SAS Institute Inc.; *U.S. Private*, pg. 3551
SAS INSTITUTE AG—See SAS Institute Inc.; *U.S. Private*, pg. 3551
SAS INSTITUTE A/S—See SAS Institute Inc.; *U.S. Private*, pg. 3551
SAS INSTITUTE A/S—See SAS Institute Inc.; *U.S. Private*, pg. 3551
SAS INSTITUTE AUSTRALIA PTY. LTD.—See SAS Institute Inc.; *U.S. Private*, pg. 3551
SAS INSTITUTE B.V.—See SAS Institute Inc.; *U.S. Private*, pg. 3551
SAS INSTITUTE (CANADA), INC.—See SAS Institute Inc.; *U.S. Private*, pg. 3551
SAS INSTITUTE GMBH—See SAS Institute Inc.; *U.S. Private*, pg. 3551
SAS INSTITUTE JAPAN LTD.—See SAS Institute Inc.; *U.S. Private*, pg. 3551
SAS INSTITUTE LTD.—See SAS Institute Inc.; *U.S. Private*, pg. 3551
SAS INSTITUTE LTD.—See SAS Institute Inc.; *U.S. Private*, pg. 3551
SAS INSTITUTE N.V.—See SAS Institute Inc.; *U.S. Private*, pg. 3551
SAS INSTITUTE (NZ) LTD.—See SAS Institute Inc.; *U.S. Private*, pg. 3551
SAS INSTITUTE OY—See SAS Institute Inc.; *U.S. Private*, pg. 3551
SAS INSTITUTE PTE. LTD.—See SAS Institute Inc.; *U.S. Private*, pg. 3552
SAS INSTITUTE S.A.U.—See SAS Institute Inc.; *U.S. Private*, pg. 3552
SAS INSTITUTE SDN. BHD.—See SAS Institute Inc.; *U.S. Private*, pg. 3552
SAS INSTITUTE—See SAS Institute Inc.; *U.S. Private*, pg. 3551
SAS INSTITUTE SRL—See SAS Institute Inc.; *U.S. Private*, pg. 3552

N.A.I.C.S. INDEX

335132 — RESIDENTIAL ELECTRI...

SAS INSTITUTE TAIWAN LTD.—See SAS Institute Inc.; *U.S. Private,* pg. 3552
SAS SOFTWARE KOREA LTD.—See SAS Institute Inc.; *U.S. Private,* pg. 3552
SAS SOFTWARE, LTD.—See SAS Institute Inc.; *U.S. Private,* pg. 3552
SCIENCE SYSTEMS (SPACE) LIMITED—See CGI Inc.; *Int'l,* pg. 1434
SCIENTIFIC MAGNETICS LIMITED—See Avingtrans plc; *Int'l,* pg. 744
SCIENTIGO, INC.; *U.S. Private,* pg. 3574
SECUSTACK GMBH—See Giesecke & Devrient GmbH; *Int'l,* pg. 2970
SEEQUENT LIMITED—See Bentley Systems, Inc.; *U.S. Public,* pg. 297
SENTEK GLOBAL INCORPORATED; *U.S. Private,* pg. 3608
SHANGHAI FOCI FIBER OPTIC COMMUNICATIONS, INC.—See Foci Fiber Optic Communications, Inc.; *Int'l,* pg. 2718
SHAREFILE LLC—See Elliott Management Corporation; *U.S. Private,* pg. 1367
SHAREFILE LLC—See Vista Equity Partners, LLC; *U.S. Private,* pg. 4396
THE SINGING MACHINE COMPANY, INC.; *U.S. Public,* pg. 2130
SINOCOM JAPAN CORPORATION—See Glory Sun Financial Group Limited; *Int'l,* pg. 3011
SISTEMAS ORACLE DE CHILE, S.A.—See Oracle Corporation; *U.S. Public,* pg. 1613
SKILLSOFT ASIA PACIFIC PTY. LIMITED—See Charterhouse Capital Partners LLP; *Int'l,* pg. 1456
SKILLSOFT CANADA LIMITED—See Charterhouse Capital Partners LLP; *Int'l,* pg. 1456
SKILLSOFT DEUTSCHLAND GMBH—See Charterhouse Capital Partners LLP; *Int'l,* pg. 1456
SKILLSOFT - EMEA HEADQUARTERS—See Charterhouse Capital Partners LLP; *Int'l,* pg. 1456
SKILLSOFT IRELAND LIMITED—See Charterhouse Capital Partners LLP; *Int'l,* pg. 1456
SKILLSOFT UK LIMITED—See Charterhouse Capital Partners LLP; *Int'l,* pg. 1456
SMARTEAM CORP—See Dassault Systemes S.A.; *Int'l,* pg. 1975
SMITH MICRO SOFTWARE, INC.; *U.S. Public,* pg. 1896
SMM, LTD.—See Graham Holdings Company; *U.S. Public,* pg. 956
SOFTWARE AG INTERNATIONAL INC—See Silver Lake Group, LLC; *U.S. Private,* pg. 3660
SOFTWARE AG ITALIA S.P.A.—See Silver Lake Group, LLC; *U.S. Private,* pg. 3660
SOFTWARE AG (SHENZHEN) CO LTD—See Silver Lake Group, LLC; *U.S. Private,* pg. 3659
SOFTWARE AG SOUTH AFRICA (PTY) LTD—See Silver Lake Group, LLC; *U.S. Private,* pg. 3660
SPANG POWER ELECTRONICS—See Spang & Company; *U.S. Private,* pg. 3745
STANTON MAGNETICS, INC.—See Gibson Brands, Inc.; *U.S. Private,* pg. 1696
STEEL CITY PRODUCTS, INC.—See Sterling Infrastructure, Inc.; *U.S. Public,* pg. 1947
SUMMIT CD MANUFACTURE PTE LTD—See Centurion Corporation Limited; *Int'l,* pg. 1417
SUMMIT CREATIONS PTE. LTD.—See Centurion Corporation Limited; *Int'l,* pg. 1417
SUMMIT HI-TECH PTE LTD—See Centurion Corporation Limited; *Int'l,* pg. 1417
SUMMIT TECHNOLOGY AUSTRALIA PTY LTD—See Centurion Corporation Limited; *Int'l,* pg. 1417
SUNLIGHT ROMANIA S.R.L. FILIALA—See Hellenic Telecommunications Organization S.A.; *Int'l,* pg. 3333
SYMANTEC GMBH—See Gen Digital Inc.; *U.S. Public,* pg. 911
SYMANTEC INTERNATIONAL LTD.—See Gen Digital Inc.; *U.S. Public,* pg. 911
SYMANTEC JAPAN, INC.—See Gen Digital Inc.; *U.S. Public,* pg. 911
SYMANTEC LTD.—See Gen Digital Inc.; *U.S. Public,* pg. 911
SYMANTEC—See Gen Digital Inc.; *U.S. Public,* pg. 910
SYMANTEC SRL—See Gen Digital Inc.; *U.S. Public,* pg. 911
SYMANTEC (UK) LTD.—See Gen Digital Inc.; *U.S. Public,* pg. 910
SYNPLICITY, LLC—See Synopsys, Inc.; *U.S. Public,* pg. 1971
SYRINX CONSULTING CORPORATION—See New Heritage Capital LLC; *U.S. Private,* pg. 2896
TECHRADIUM, INC.; *U.S. Private,* pg. 3956
TELEDATA INFORMATICS LTD.—See Agnite Education Limited; *Int'l,* pg. 212
THQ INC.; *U.S. Private,* pg. 4163
TIPPETT STUDIO, INC; *U.S. Private,* pg. 4175
TOP OPTO TEC CO., LTD.—See Ability Opto-Electronics Technology Co., Ltd.; *Int'l,* pg. 61
TRANSTRACK INTERNATIONAL B.V.—See Giesecke & Devrient GmbH; *Int'l,* pg. 2970
TSUTAYA STORES HOLDINGS CO., LTD—See Culture Convenience Club Co., Ltd.; *Int'l,* pg. 1877

T-SYSTEMS DEBIS SYSTEMHAUS—See Deutsche Telekom AG; *Int'l,* pg. 2085
TURNBERRY SOLUTIONS, INC; *U.S. Private,* pg. 4260
ULEAD SYSTEMS GMBH—See KKR & Co. Inc.; *U.S. Public,* pg. 1243
ULEAD SYSTEMS K.K.—See KKR & Co. Inc.; *U.S. Public,* pg. 1243
THE ULTIMATE SOFTWARE GROUP, INC.—See Hellman & Friedman LLC; *U.S. Private,* pg. 1911
ULTRA ELECTRONICS AIRPORT SYSTEMS—See Advent International Corporation; *U.S. Private,* pg. 100
UNISYS FRANCE—See Unisys Corporation; *U.S. Public,* pg. 2228
UNIVERSAL MIND; *U.S. Private,* pg. 4305
US DATAWORKS, INC.—See Checkalt, LLC; *U.S. Private,* pg. 869
VERBATIM CORPORATION—See CMC Magnetics Corporation; *Int'l,* pg. 1669
VERIDOS AMERICA INC—See Giesecke & Devrient GmbH; *Int'l,* pg. 2970
VINCULUM JAPAN CORPORATION—See FUJISOFT INCORPORATED; *Int'l,* pg. 2830
VITRIA TECHNOLOGY, INC.—See Innovation Technology Group; *U.S. Private,* pg. 2081
VTC VIDEO SERVICES—See Visual Technologies Corp.; *U.S. Private,* pg. 4404
WARNER MUSIC AUSTRALIA PTY LTD—See Access Industries, Inc.; *U.S. Private,* pg. 52
WAVEDANCER, INC.; *U.S. Public,* pg. 2338
WORKS24 CORPORATION; *U.S. Private,* pg. 4564
X-RITE EUROPE AG—See Danaher Corporation; *U.S. Public,* pg. 632
X-RITE GMBH—See Danaher Corporation; *U.S. Public,* pg. 632
ZOMAX CANADA COMPANY—See Comvest Group Holdings LLC; *U.S. Private,* pg. 1007
ZOMAX, INCORPORATED—See Comvest Group Holdings LLC; *U.S. Private,* pg. 1007
ZOMAX LIMITED—See Comvest Group Holdings LLC; *U.S. Private,* pg. 1008

335131 — RESIDENTIAL ELECTRIC LIGHTING FIXTURE MANUFACTURING

ACUITY BRANDS, INC.; *U.S. Public,* pg. 36
ACUITY BRANDS LIGHTING MEXICO, S. DE R.L. DE C.V.—See Acuity Brands, Inc.; *U.S. Public,* pg. 37
ADELPHIA LAMP & SHADE INC.; *U.S. Private,* pg. 77
ADVANCED LIGHTING TECHNOLOGIES AUSTRALIA, INC.—See Saratoga Partners L.P.; *U.S. Private,* pg. 3549
AFX INC.; *U.S. Private,* pg. 124
AMERICAN DE ROSA LAMPARTS, LLC—See Resilience Capital Partners, LLC; *U.S. Private,* pg. 3405
ANETA BELYSNING AB—See Byggma ASA; *Int'l,* pg. 1235
ANHUI COREACH TECHNOLOGY CO., LTD.; *Int'l,* pg. 467
ANSELL ELECTRICAL PRODUCTS LIMITED—See ENDO Lighting Corporation; *Int'l,* pg. 2404
ANSELL (SALES & DISTRIBUTION) LIMITED—See ENDO Lighting Corporation; *Int'l,* pg. 2404
APL ENGINEERED MATERIALS, INC.—See Saratoga Partners L.P.; *U.S. Private,* pg. 3549
A. SCHONBEK & CO.; *U.S. Private,* pg. 23
ATLAS LIGHTING PRODUCTS, INC.—See LSI Industries Inc.; *U.S. Public,* pg. 1344
BEIJING HONGFA ELECTROACOUSTIC RELAY CO., LTD.—See Hongfa Technology Co Ltd; *Int'l,* pg. 3470
BLUMBERG INDUSTRIES INC.; *U.S. Private,* pg. 599
BORMAN LIGHTING S.R.L.—See Dexelance S.p.A.; *Int'l,* pg. 2092
BRIGHTLITE NOMINEES PROPRIETARY LIMITED; *Int'l,* pg. 1163
CAPSTONE INDUSTRIES, INC.—See Capstone Companies, Inc.; *U.S. Public,* pg. 432
CHINA ELECTRIC MFG. CORPORATION; *Int'l,* pg. 1499
CHIP GOAL ELECTRONICS CORP.—See Fortune Oriental Company Limited; *Int'l,* pg. 2744
CLENERGY (XIAMEN) TECHNOLOGY CO., LTD.; *Int'l,* pg. 1657
CONTRAST LIGHTING M.L. INC.; *Int'l,* pg. 1785
CONVERT ITALIA S.P.A.—See Valmont Industries, Inc.; *U.S. Public,* pg. 2273
DAVEX AUSTRALIA PTY LTD—See Ekuiti Nasional Berhad; *Int'l,* pg. 2340
DGS RETAIL, INC.—See San Francisco Equity Partners; *U.S. Private,* pg. 3540
DISCOUNTLIGHTINGSALE.COM—See Butler's Electric Supply; *U.S. Private,* pg. 697
ELECTRIX, INC.—See Light Fantastic Realty, Inc.; *U.S. Private,* pg. 2452
EMESS DESIGN GROUP LLC—See Edg/Sw Holdings LLC; *U.S. Private,* pg. 1333
ENDO LIGHTING (THAILAND) PUBLIC COMPANY LTD.—See ENDO Lighting Corporation; *Int'l,* pg. 2404
EVERLIGHT INTELLIGENCE TECHNOLOGY CO., LTD.—See Everlight Electronics Co., Ltd.; *Int'l,* pg. 2567

FAGERHULTS BELYSNING AB—See Fagerhult Group AB; *Int'l,* pg. 2602
FAGERHULTS BELYSNING SVERIGE AB—See Fagerhult Group AB; *Int'l,* pg. 2602
FAMOSTAR EMERGENCY LIGHTING B.V.—See F.W. Thorpe plc; *Int'l,* pg. 2597
FLEXALIGHTING NORTH AMERICA LTD.—See Dexelance S.p.A.; *Int'l,* pg. 2092
FREDERICK COOPER LLC; *U.S. Private,* pg. 1601
FREDRICK RAMOND INCORPORATED; *U.S. Private,* pg. 1602
FURNLITE, INC.; *U.S. Private,* pg. 1624
GERARD LIGHTING (NZ) LIMITED—See Bain Capital, LP; *U.S. Private,* pg. 439
GERARD LIGHTING PTY LTD—See Bain Capital, LP; *U.S. Private,* pg. 439
GREAT LAKES ENERGY TECHNOLOGIES, LLC—See Orion Energy Systems, Inc.; *U.S. Public,* pg. 1618
GUANGDONG DP CO., LTD.; *Int'l,* pg. 3154
HAND HELD PRODUCTS, INC—See Honeywell International Inc.; *U.S. Public,* pg. 1047
HAVELL'S SYLVANIA (GERMANY) GMBH—See Havell's India Ltd.; *Int'l,* pg. 3286
HAVELL'S SYLVANIA NETHERLANDS B.V.—See Havell's India Ltd.; *Int'l,* pg. 3286
HERNER GLAS - BERND HOFFBAUER GMBH; *Int'l,* pg. 3363
HONGFA ITALY S.R.L.—See Hongfa Technology Co Ltd; *Int'l,* pg. 3470
HUNTER DOUGLAS KADAN S.R.O.—See 3G Capital Partners L.P.; *U.S. Private,* pg. 12
INTERMATIC, INC.; *U.S. Private,* pg. 2112
JIMCO LAMP & MANUFACTURING, CO.—See Kohlberg & Company, LLC; *U.S. Private,* pg. 2338
JOHN RICHARD INCORPORATED; *U.S. Private,* pg. 2224
JUNO LIGHTING, LLC—See Acuity Brands, Inc.; *U.S. Public,* pg. 37
KOCH & LOWY, INC.; *U.S. Private,* pg. 2326
LIFESPAN BRANDS, LLC—See The Bank of New York Mellon Corporation; *U.S. Public,* pg. 2037
LIGHTING CORPORATION PTY LTD—See Bain Capital, LP; *U.S. Private,* pg. 439
LIGHTS OF AMERICA, INC.; *U.S. Private,* pg. 2453
LION INDUSTRIES INC.; *U.S. Private,* pg. 2464
LITENORDIC AB—See DistIT AB; *Int'l,* pg. 2136
LSI MIDWEST LIGHTING INC—See LSI Industries Inc.; *U.S. Public,* pg. 1344
MARIO INDUSTRIES OF VIRGINIA; *U.S. Private,* pg. 2576
MLE S.R.L.—See 3F Filippi SpA; *Int'l,* pg. 7
MOONLIGHTING PTY LIMITED—See Bain Capital, LP; *U.S. Private,* pg. 439
MOVOMECH AB—See Amplex AB; *Int'l,* pg. 434
NORWELL MANUFACTURING CO., INC.; *U.S. Private,* pg. 2964
PARTYLITE GIFTS, LTD.—See The Carlyle Group Inc.; *U.S. Public,* pg. 2052
PARTYLITE OY—See The Carlyle Group Inc.; *U.S. Public,* pg. 2052
PARTYLITE UK LTD—See The Carlyle Group Inc.; *U.S. Public,* pg. 2052
PIERLITE AUSTRALIA PTY LIMITED—See Bain Capital, LP; *U.S. Private,* pg. 439
PRESCOLITE INC.—See Hubbell Incorporated; *U.S. Public,* pg. 1067
PROGRESS LIGHTING INC.—See Hubbell Incorporated; *U.S. Public,* pg. 1067
QUOIZEL INC.—See Sycamore Partners Management, LP; *U.S. Private,* pg. 3896
ROBERT ABBEY INC.; *U.S. Private,* pg. 3457
SCAN LAMPS AS—See Byggma ASA; *Int'l,* pg. 1235
SEAGULL LIGHTING PRODUCTS INC.; *U.S. Private,* pg. 3584
SHANGHAI HONGFA ELECTROACOUSTIC CO., LTD.—See Hongfa Technology Co Ltd; *Int'l,* pg. 3470
SICHUAN HONGFA RELAY CO., LTD.—See Hongfa Technology Co Ltd; *Int'l,* pg. 3470
SLI FRANCE S.A.—See Havell's India Ltd.; *Int'l,* pg. 3286
SUGG LIGHTING LIMITED—See F.W. Thorpe plc; *Int'l,* pg. 2597
SUNNEX EQUIPMENT AB—See Amplex AB; *Int'l,* pg. 434
SYLVANIA N.V.—See Havell's India Ltd.; *Int'l,* pg. 3286
THORLUX LIGHTING LIMITED—See F.W. Thorpe plc; *Int'l,* pg. 2597
VENTURE LIGHTING EUROPE LTD.—See Saratoga Partners L.P.; *U.S. Private,* pg. 3549
VENTURE LIGHTING INTERNATIONAL FZE—See Saratoga Partners L.P.; *U.S. Private,* pg. 3550
VENTURE LIGHTING INTERNATIONAL, INC.—See Saratoga Partners L.P.; *U.S. Private,* pg. 3549
VENTURE LIGHTING SOUTH AFRICA (PTY.) LTD.—See Saratoga Partners L.P.; *U.S. Private,* pg. 3550
WESTINGHOUSE LIGHTING CORPORATION; *U.S. Private,* pg. 4498
ZENARO LIGHTING GMBH—See Everlight Electronics Co., Ltd.; *Int'l,* pg. 2568

335132 — COMMERCIAL, INDUSTRIAL, AND

335132 — RESIDENTIAL ELECTRI...

INSTITUTIONAL ELECTRIC LIGHTING FIXTURE MANUFACTURING

9850-333 CANADA INC.—See Fagerhult Group AB; *Int'l*, pg. 2601
A.A.G. STUCCHI ASIA PACIFIC LTD.—See A.A.G. STUCCHI s.r.l.; *Int'l*, pg. 22
A.A.G. STUCCHI NORTH AMERICA, INC.—See A.A.G. STUCCHI s.r.l.; *Int'l*, pg. 22
A.A.G. STUCCHI SHANGHAI LTD.—See A.A.G. STUCCHI s.r.l.; *Int'l*, pg. 22
A.A.G. STUCCHI S.R.L.; *Int'l*, pg. 22
ACCORD INDUSTRIES LLC; *U.S. Private*, pg. 53
ACHAT-VERRE AFLOX S.A.—See A.A.G. STUCCHI s.r.l.; *Int'l*, pg. 22
ACUITY BRANDS LIGHTING CANADA, INC.—See Acuity Brands, Inc.; *U.S. Public*, pg. 37
ACUITY BRANDS LIGHTING, INC.—See Acuity Brands, Inc.; *U.S. Public*, pg. 37
ADB STAGELIGHT S.A.S.U.—See ams AG; *Int'l*, pg. 438
ADOLF SCHUCH GMBH; *Int'l*, pg. 152
ADVANCED LIGHTING CONCEPTS, LLC—See Pfingsten Partners, LLC; *U.S. Private*, pg. 3164
ADVIK OPTOELECTRONICS LIMITED—See Advik Capital Ltd; *Int'l*, pg. 168
AGM AUTOMOTIVE, LLC—See Flex Ltd.; *Int'l*, pg. 2702
A.L.P. EUROPE LTD.—See A.A.G. STUCCHI s.r.l.; *Int'l*, pg. 22
ALP LIGHTING & CEILING PRODUCTS, INC.; *U.S. Private*, pg. 196
AMERICAN LOUVER COMPANY; *U.S. Private*, pg. 240
AMERLUX, LLC—See Delta Electronics, Inc.; *Int'l*, pg. 2017
AMPLE TECHNOLOGY CO. LTD.—See A.A.G. STUCCHI s.r.l.; *Int'l*, pg. 22
AMTECH LIGHTING SERVICES—See WESCO International, Inc.; *U.S. Public*, pg. 2352
ANOMET INC.—See A.A.G. STUCCHI s.r.l.; *Int'l*, pg. 22
ARCONA INTERNATIONAL (PTY) LTD—See A.A.G. STUCCHI s.r.l.; *Int'l*, pg. 22
ARTITALIA GROUP INC.; *Int'l*, pg. 585
ASSOCIATED LIGHTING REPRESENTATIVES, INC.; *U.S. Private*, pg. 356
ATELJE LYKTAN AB—See Fagerhult Group AB; *Int'l*, pg. 2601
AURA LIGHT AB—See FSN Capital Partners AS; *Int'l*, pg. 2798
AURA LIGHT INTERNATIONAL AB—See FSN Capital Partners AS; *Int'l*, pg. 2798
AUSTUBE PTY LIMITED—See Bain Capital, LP; *U.S. Private*, pg. 439
AUTOLITE (INDIA) LIMITED; *Int'l*, pg. 728
AZZ ELECTRICAL/INDUSTRIAL PRODUCTS—See AZZ, Inc.; *U.S. Public*, pg. 258
AZZ R-A-L—See AZZ, Inc.; *U.S. Public*, pg. 258
BALLAST WISE; *U.S. Private*, pg. 461
BEACON INTERNATIONAL LIMITED—See Beacon Lighting Group Ltd; *Int'l*, pg. 932
BEGHELLI ELPLAST A.S.—See Beghelli S.p.A.; *Int'l*, pg. 941
BORID ENERGY (M) SDN BHD—See Hup Soon Global Corporation Limited; *Int'l*, pg. 3538
BOULD OPPORTUNITIES PLC; *Int'l*, pg. 1119
BOYD LIGHTING; *U.S. Private*, pg. 627
BRIGHT VIEW TECHNOLOGIES CORPORATION—See Tredegar Corporation; *U.S. Public*, pg. 2187
BRILLANTE ILUMINACION SA DE CV—See A.A.G. STUCCHI s.r.l.; *Int'l*, pg. 22
CAIRO ELECRTRICAL GROUP—See A.A.G. STUCCHI s.r.l.; *Int'l*, pg. 22
CALLEJA LTD.—See A.A.G. STUCCHI s.r.l.; *Int'l*, pg. 22
CARLO GAVAZZI AUTOMATION (CHINA) CO LTD—See Carlo Gavazzi Holding AG; *Int'l*, pg. 1338
CEAG NOTLICHTSYSTEME GMBH—See Eaton Corporation plc; *Int'l*, pg. 2278
CHINA SILVER TECHNOLOGY HOLDINGS LIMITED; *Int'l*, pg. 1551
CIRALIGHT GLOBAL, INC.; *U.S. Private*, pg. 899
CLAY PAKY S.P.A.—See ams AG; *Int'l*, pg. 438
CLEEN ENERGY AG; *Int'l*, pg. 1657
COMERCIAL TECNILUZ DE CHILE LTDA.—See A.A.G. STUCCHI s.r.l.; *Int'l*, pg. 22
COMPACT LIGHTING LIMITED—See F.W. Thorpe plc; *Int'l*, pg. 2597
COMPAGNIE D'APPAREILS ELECTRIQUES PEERLESS LIMITEE; *Int'l*, pg. 1722
COMPOLUX SPOL. S.R.O.—See A.A.G. STUCCHI s.r.l.; *Int'l*, pg. 22
CONSERVATION TECHNOLOGY, LTD.—See E&A Industries, Inc.; *U.S. Private*, pg. 1301
COOPER FINANCE USA, INC.—See Eaton Corporation plc; *Int'l*, pg. 2278
CRAFTMADE INTERNATIONAL, INC.; *U.S. Private*, pg. 1082
C. RIBAS DE SOUSA LDA—See A.A.G. STUCCHI s.r.l.; *Int'l*, pg. 22
CURRENT LIGHTING SOLUTIONS, LLC—See AIP, LLC; *U.S. Private*, pg. 134

DAEYANG ELECTRIC CO., LTD.; *Int'l*, pg. 1911
DAVEX (MALAYSIA) SDN. BHD.—See Ekuiti Nasional Berhad; *Int'l*, pg. 2340
DAVEX SINGAPORE PTE LTD—See Ekuiti Nasional Berhad; *Int'l*, pg. 2340
DAZOR MANUFACTURING CORP.; *U.S. Private*, pg. 1178
DESIGNPLAN LIGHTING LTD—See Fagerhult Group AB; *Int'l*, pg. 2602
DIAPA S.L.—See A.A.G. STUCCHI s.r.l.; *Int'l*, pg. 22
DIMCO PLC; *Int'l*, pg. 2125
DONGGUAN KINGSUN OPTOELECTRONIC CO., LTD.; *Int'l*, pg. 2167
EAGLE LIGHTING (AUSTRALIA) PTY LTD—See Fagerhult Group AB; *Int'l*, pg. 2602
ELECTRONIC THEATRE CONTROLS ASIA—See Electronic Theatre Controls, Inc.; *U.S. Private*, pg. 1356
ELECTRONIC THEATRE CONTROLS GMBH—See Electronic Theatre Controls, Inc.; *U.S. Private*, pg. 1356
ELECTRONIC THEATRE CONTROLS LTD.—See Electronic Theatre Controls, Inc.; *U.S. Private*, pg. 1356
ELECTROZEMPER S.A.—See F.W. Thorpe plc; *Int'l*, pg. 2597
ELENCO LIGHTING AB—See Fagerhult Group AB; *Int'l*, pg. 2602
ELINA TEJARAT KAVIR TRADING COMPANY—See A.A.G. STUCCHI s.r.l.; *Int'l*, pg. 22
ELLIS & COMPANY LTD.—See A.A.G. STUCCHI s.r.l.; *Int'l*, pg. 23
ENDO LIGHTING CORPORATION; *Int'l*, pg. 2404
ENERGY FOCUS, INC.; *U.S. Public*, pg. 762
ENVIRONMENTAL LIGHTING CONCEPTS, INC.; *U.S. Private*, pg. 1408
EON ELECTRIC LTD.; *Int'l*, pg. 2457
EPOCH CHEMTRONICS CORP.; *Int'l*, pg. 2463
EROPED TRADING LTD.—See A.A.G. STUCCHI s.r.l.; *Int'l*, pg. 22
EVOLUTION LIGHTING LLC—See Boyne Capital Management, LLC; *U.S. Private*, pg. 628
EXCELITAS NOBLELIGHT GMBH—See AEA Investors LP; *U.S. Private*, pg. 113
EXELED HOLDINGS, INC.; *U.S. Private*, pg. 1448
FAGERHULT LIGHTING LTD—See Fagerhult Group AB; *Int'l*, pg. 2602
FAGERHULT LIGHTING LTD—See Fagerhult Group AB; *Int'l*, pg. 2602
FAGERHULT (NZ) LTD—See Fagerhult Group AB; *Int'l*, pg. 2602
FAGERHULT RETAIL AB—See Fagerhult Group AB; *Int'l*, pg. 2602
FAGERHULT S.R.O—See Fagerhult Group AB; *Int'l*, pg. 2602
FEELUX CO., LTD.; *Int'l*, pg. 2632
FINELITE INC.; *U.S. Private*, pg. 1509
FIREFLY LIGHTING DESIGN LTD.—See Firefly Point of View Ltd.; *Int'l*, pg. 2679
FIRST LINE TECHNOLOGY, LLC; *U.S. Private*, pg. 1520
FORUM, INC.—See AIP, LLC; *U.S. Private*, pg. 134
FUTURE ENERGY SOLUTIONS; *U.S. Private*, pg. 1626
F.W. THORPE PLC; *Int'l*, pg. 2597
GAVITA INTERNATIONAL B.V.—See The Scotts Miracle-Gro Company; *U.S. Public*, pg. 2126
GENERAC MOBILE PRODUCTS S.R.L—See Generac Holdings Inc.; *U.S. Public*, pg. 912
GENERAL LED, INC.—See The CapStreet Group LLC; *U.S. Private*, pg. 4004
GENERATION BRANDS LLC—See AEA Investors LP; *U.S. Private*, pg. 114
GHIRARDELLI ALBERTO—See A.A.G. STUCCHI s.r.l.; *Int'l*, pg. 23
GREENPOWER INTERNATIONAL GROUP LIMITED; *U.S. Private*, pg. 1779
GUANGDONG PAK CORPORATION CO. LTD.; *Int'l*, pg. 3158
HADCO CORPORATION—See Sanmina Corporation; *U.S. Public*, pg. 1840
HARISON TOSHIBA LIGHTING CORP.; *Int'l*, pg. 3277
HAVELL'S SYLVANIA-CONCORD:MARLIN—See Havell's India Ltd.; *Int'l*, pg. 3286
HAVELLS SYLVANIA DUBAI FZCO—See Havell's India Ltd.; *Int'l*, pg. 3286
HAVELLS SYLVANIA LIGHTING FRANCE SAS—See Havell's India Ltd.; *Int'l*, pg. 3286
HENGDIAN GROUP TOSPO LIGHTING CO LTD; *Int'l*, pg. 3346
HEP GMBH—See HEP Tech Co., Ltd.; *Int'l*, pg. 3356
H.E. WILLIAMS, INC.; *U.S. Private*, pg. 1826
HINKLEY LIGHTING INC.; *U.S. Private*, pg. 1949
HOLOPHANE LIGHTING LTD.—See Acuity Brands, Inc.; *U.S. Public*, pg. 37
HOLOPHANE, S.A. DE C.V.—See Acuity Brands, Inc.; *U.S. Public*, pg. 37
HOLUX LIGHTING SYSTEM CO. LTD.—See A.A.G. STUCCHI s.r.l.; *Int'l*, pg. 23
HONEYWELL AIRPORT SYSTEM—See Honeywell International Inc.; *U.S. Public*, pg. 1047
HUBBELL WIRING DEVICE-KELLEMS—See Hubbell Incorporated; *U.S. Public*, pg. 1067

I. & B. AGISTRIOTIS SA—See A.A.G. STUCCHI s.r.l.; *Int'l*, pg. 23
IGUZZINI ILLUMINAZIONE SCHWEIZ AG—See Fagerhult Group AB; *Int'l*, pg. 2602
IGUZZINI ILLUMINAZIONE UK LTD.—See Fagerhult Group AB; *Int'l*, pg. 2602
IGUZZINI LIGHTING USA, LTD.—See Fagerhult Group AB; *Int'l*, pg. 2602
IGUZZINI LIGHTING WLL—See Fagerhult Group AB; *Int'l*, pg. 2602
IGUZZINI MIDDLE EAST FZE—See Fagerhult Group AB; *Int'l*, pg. 2602
IGUZZINI S.E.A. PTE. LTD.—See Fagerhult Group AB; *Int'l*, pg. 2602
ILIGHT TECHNOLOGIES; *U.S. Private*, pg. 2041
INDUSTRIAL LIGHTING PRODUCTS, LLC—See Harbour Group Industries, Inc.; *U.S. Private*, pg. 1860
INGAL EPS—See Valmont Industries, Inc.; *U.S. Public*, pg. 2273
INTENSE LIGHTING, LLC—See Leviton Manufacturing Company, Inc.; *U.S. Private*, pg. 2436
ISOLITE CORPORATION; *U.S. Private*, pg. 2146
ITUS—See A.A.G. STUCCHI s.r.l.; *Int'l*, pg. 23
I-VALO OY—See Fagerhult Group AB; *Int'l*, pg. 2602
J. W. DIDADO ELECTRIC, LLC—See Quanta Services, Inc.; *U.S. Public*, pg. 1751
KAPMAN ELEKTRIK VE ELEKTRONIK TIC. A.S.—See A.A.G. STUCCHI s.r.l.; *Int'l*, pg. 23
KELLY SERVICES CANADA, LTD.—See Kelly Services, Inc.; *U.S. Public*, pg. 1219
KENRY HOME IMPROVEMENT NETWORK, INC.; *U.S. Private*, pg. 2287
KOEHLER LIGHTING PRODUCTS—See Berkshire Hathaway Inc.; *U.S. Public*, pg. 310
LBL LIGHTING LLC—See AEA Investors LP; *U.S. Private*, pg. 114
THE L.C. DOANE COMPANY; *U.S. Private*, pg. 4067
LED SOURCE, LLC; *U.S. Private*, pg. 2410
LIGHT ENGINE DESIGN CORP.; *U.S. Public*, pg. 1315
LIGHT EXPRESSIONS—See Shaw Electric Inc.; *U.S. Private*, pg. 3628
LIGHT FANTASTIC REALTY, INC.; *U.S. Private*, pg. 2452
LIGHTING AUSTRALIA PTY. LTD.—See A.A.G. STUCCHI s.r.l.; *Int'l*, pg. 23
LIGHTOPIA LLC—See L2 Capital Partners; *U.S. Private*, pg. 2367
LIGHT SOURCE SOLUTIONS NEW ZEALAND LIMITED—See Beacon Lighting Group Ltd; *Int'l*, pg. 932
LINEAR LIGHTING CORPORATION; *U.S. Private*, pg. 2460
LITECONTROL CORPORATION; *U.S. Private*, pg. 2467
LITELAB CORP.; *U.S. Private*, pg. 2467
LITE TECH INDUSTRIES LLC—See Dubai Investments PJSC; *Int'l*, pg. 2219
LSI LIGHTRON INC.—See LSI Industries Inc.; *U.S. Public*, pg. 1344
LTS LICHT & LEUCHTEN GMBH—See Fagerhult Group AB; *Int'l*, pg. 2602
LUCCHI LTDA.—See A.A.G. STUCCHI s.r.l.; *Int'l*, pg. 23
LUMASTREAM, INC.; *U.S. Private*, pg. 2513
LUMEX LIGHTING LTD.—See A.A.G. STUCCHI s.r.l.; *Int'l*, pg. 23
LUMINATOR HOLDING LP—See Audax Group, Limited Partnership; *U.S. Private*, pg. 389
LUMITEX INC.; *U.S. Private*, pg. 2514
LUSIVE DECOR; *U.S. Private*, pg. 2516
LUXTRON SISTEMS FZCO—See A.A.G. STUCCHI s.r.l.; *Int'l*, pg. 23
MABELEK SIGNLIGHT—See A.A.G. STUCCHI s.r.l.; *Int'l*, pg. 23
MARK LIGHTING FIXTURE CO., INC.—See Acuity Brands, Inc.; *U.S. Public*, pg. 37
MOUNTING SYSTEMS GMBH—See Kawa Capital Management, Inc.; *U.S. Private*, pg. 2266
NARVA POLSKA SP. Z.O.O.—See A.A.G. STUCCHI s.r.l.; *Int'l*, pg. 23
ONE SOURCE ASSOCIATES, INC.; *U.S. Private*, pg. 3023
ORION ENERGY SYSTEMS, INC.; *U.S. Public*, pg. 1617
OSRAM, A.S.—See ams AG; *Int'l*, pg. 440
OSRAM AUSTRALIA PTY. LTD.—See ams AG; *Int'l*, pg. 440
OSRAM GMBH—See ams AG; *Int'l*, pg. 439
OSRAM, LDA.—See ams AG; *Int'l*, pg. 440
OSRAM LICHT AG—See ams AG; *Int'l*, pg. 438
OSRAM LIGHTING MIDDLE EAST FZE—See ams AG; *Int'l*, pg. 439
OSRAM LIGHTING S.A.S.U.—See ams AG; *Int'l*, pg. 439
OSRAM LIGHTING S.L.—See ams AG; *Int'l*, pg. 439
OSRAM S.P.A.—See ams AG; *Int'l*, pg. 439
OSRAM TEKNOLOJILERI TICARET ANONIM SIRKETI—See ams AG; *Int'l*, pg. 439
PAN-ISLAND INDUSTRIAL(S) PTE LTD.—See A.A.G. STUCCHI s.r.l.; *Int'l*, pg. 23
PAYPAL NEDERLANDS B.V.—See PayPal Holdings, Inc.; *U.S. Public*, pg. 1656
PEERLESS LIGHTING CORP.—See Acuity Brands, Inc.; *U.S. Public*, pg. 37
PERKASIE INDUSTRIES CORPORATION; *U.S. Private*, pg. 3151
PETREL LIMITED—See Chamberlain plc; *Int'l*, pg. 1439

N.A.I.C.S. INDEX

335139 — ELECTRIC LAMP BULB ...

PHOENIX PRODUCTS COMPANY, INC.—See JMC Capital Partners LLC; *U.S. Private*, pg. 2215
POINT ELECTRIC—See Swivelier Co., Inc.; *U.S. Private*, pg. 3894
PORTLAND LIGHTING LIMITED—See F.W. Thorpe plc; *Int'l*, pg. 2597
POWERSECURE LIGHTING—See The Southern Company; *U.S. Public*, pg. 2131
PPO-ELEKTRONIIKKA OY—See A.A.G. STUCCHI s.r.l.; *Int'l*, pg. 23
PRIMA LIGHTING CORPORATION; *U.S. Private*, pg. 3260
PROGRESSIVE LIGHTING, INC. (NORTH CAROLINA)—See Hubbell Incorporated; *U.S. Public*, pg. 1067
PROMARK INTERNATIONAL INC.; *U.S. Private*, pg. 3282
PRUDENTIAL LIGHTING CORP; *U.S. Private*, pg. 3296
RBI SOLAR BRAZIL LTDA—See Gibraltar Industries, Inc.; *U.S. Public*, pg. 936
RENOVA LIGHTING SYSTEMS, INC.; *U.S. Private*, pg. 3399
RUUD LIGHTING, INC.—See Wolfspeed, Inc.; *U.S. Public*, pg. 2377
SAINT-GOBAIN ECOPHON CZ S.R.O.—See Compagnie de Saint-Gobain SA; *Int'l*, pg. 1733
SCHULLER GMBH—See Berkshire Hathaway Inc.; *U.S. Public*, pg. 316
S-G API BV—See Compagnie de Saint-Gobain SA; *Int'l*, pg. 1725
SHAMANJWALI METALS PVT. LTD.—See A.A.G. STUCCHI s.r.l.; *Int'l*, pg. 23
SHANGHAI IGUZZINI TRADING CO., LTD.,—See Fagerhult Group AB; *Int'l*, pg. 2602
SIMKAR CORPORATION; *U.S. Private*, pg. 3665
SOFIT-LUX LTD.—See A.A.G. STUCCHI s.r.l.; *Int'l*, pg. 23
SOLAIS LIGHTING, INC.—See The Southern Company; *U.S. Public*, pg. 2131
SOLITE EUROPE LTD—See F.W. Thorpe plc; *Int'l*, pg. 2597
SOYUZ-SVET LTD.—See A.A.G. STUCCHI s.r.l.; *Int'l*, pg. 23
SPECTRO LUME INC.; *U.S. Private*, pg. 3752
SPECTRONICS CORPORATION; *U.S. Private*, pg. 3752
SPI LIGHTING INC.; *U.S. Private*, pg. 3756
STRONG TECHNICAL SERVICES, INC.—See Kingsway Financial Services Inc.; *U.S. Public*, pg. 1234
SV LIGHTING—See Revolution Lighting Technologies, Inc.; *U.S. Public*, pg. 1793
SWIVELIER CO., INC.; *U.S. Private*, pg. 3894
SYLVANIA LIGHTING SERVICES CORP.—See WESCO International, Inc.; *U.S. Public*, pg. 2352
TARGETTI-MLE S.A.—See 3F Filippi SpA; *Int'l*, pg. 7
TARGETTI POULSEN POLAND SP. Z O.O.—See 3F Filippi SpA; *Int'l*, pg. 7
TECHNOLAMP—See A.A.G. STUCCHI s.r.l.; *Int'l*, pg. 23
TECNILUZ S.A.—See A.A.G. STUCCHI s.r.l.; *Int'l*, pg. 23
TERTIUM S.P.R.L.—See A.A.G. STUCCHI s.r.l.; *Int'l*, pg. 23
THORKILD LARSEN A/S—See A.A.G. STUCCHI s.r.l.; *Int'l*, pg. 23
THORLUX LIGHTING—See F.W. Thorpe plc; *Int'l*, pg. 2597
TIVOLI, LLC—See 3F Filippi SpA; *Int'l*, pg. 7
TLS PRODUCTIONS, INC.—See Hibino Corporation; *Int'l*, pg. 3383
TRACER PRODUCTS—See Spectronics Corporation; *U.S. Private*, pg. 3752
U.S. LIGHTING TECH—See U.S. Energy Technologies, Inc.; *U.S. Private*, pg. 4270
VALMONT COMPOSITE STRUCTURES, INC.—See Valmont Industries, Inc.; *U.S. Public*, pg. 2274
VANPEE AB—See A.A.G. STUCCHI s.r.l.; *Int'l*, pg. 23
VANPEE NORGE AS—See A.A.G. STUCCHI s.r.l.; *Int'l*, pg. 23
VICTOR PRODUCTS LIMITED—See Federal Signal Corporation; *U.S. Public*, pg. 826
VISIONEERING CORP—See Leviton Manufacturing Company, Inc.; *U.S. Public*, pg. 2437
WACO N.V.—See Fagerhult Group AB; *Int'l*, pg. 2602
W. GEUKEN B.V.—See A.A.G. STUCCHI s.r.l.; *Int'l*, pg. 23
WHITECROFT LIGHTING LTD—See Fagerhult Group AB; *Int'l*, pg. 2602
WIPAC LIMITED—See Carclo plc; *Int'l*, pg. 1321
ZENO ZANINI GMBH—See A.A.G. STUCCHI s.r.l.; *Int'l*, pg. 23

335139 — ELECTRIC LAMP BULB AND OTHER LIGHTING EQUIPMENT MANUFACTURING

3F FILIPPI SPA; *Int'l*, pg. 7
ACR ELECTRONICS, INC.—See The Jordan Company, L.P.; *U.S. Private*, pg. 4059
ADVA-LITE INC.—See Camsing Global, LLC; *U.S. Private*, pg. 732
ADVANCED LIGHTING TECHNOLOGIES ASIA PTE LTD.—See Saratoga Partners L.P.; *U.S. Private*, pg. 3549
ALADIN GMBH—See Dr. Honle AG; *Int'l*, pg. 2192
AL HASSAN LIGHTING & FANS INDUSTRIES LLC—See Al Hassan Engineering Company S.A.O.G.; *Int'l*, pg. 279
ALOFT CO., LTD.—See Daikoku Denki Co., Ltd.; *Int'l*, pg. 1037
AMGLO KEMLITE LABORATORIES INC.; *U.S. Private*, pg. 262
APEX INTEC CO., LTD.; *Int'l*, pg. 511
AQUA SIGNAL GMBH; *Int'l*, pg. 527
ARCHITECTURAL AREA LIGHTING/MOLDCAST CO.—See Hubbell Incorporated; *U.S. Public*, pg. 1066
ARLIGHT AYDINLATMA A.S.—See Fagerhult Group AB; *Int'l*, pg. 2601
ARRAY LIGHTING—See Revolution Lighting Technologies, Inc.; *U.S. Public*, pg. 1793
ASTRONICS CORPORATION; *U.S. Public*, pg. 217
ASTRONICS CUSTOM CONTROLS CONCEPTS INC.—See Astronics Corporation; *U.S. Public*, pg. 217
ATG UV TECHNOLOGY LIMITED—See Xylem Inc.; *U.S. Public*, pg. 2393
AUER LIGHTING GMBH—See Saratoga Partners L.P.; *U.S. Private*, pg. 3549
AVIX, INC.; *Int'l*, pg. 746
BANGLADESH LAMPS LIMITED; *Int'l*, pg. 836
BARCO N.V.; *Int'l*, pg. 863
BEGHELLI CANADA INC.—See Beghelli S.p.A.; *Int'l*, pg. 941
BEGHELLI CHINA CO., LTD.—See Beghelli S.p.A.; *Int'l*, pg. 941
BEGHELLI DE MEXICO, S.A. DE C.V.—See Beghelli S.p.A.; *Int'l*, pg. 941
BEGHELLI HUNGARY KFT.—See Beghelli S.p.A.; *Int'l*, pg. 941
BEGHELLI POLSKA SP. Z O.O.—See Beghelli S.p.A.; *Int'l*, pg. 941
BEGHELLI PRAEZISA GMBH—See Beghelli S.p.A.; *Int'l*, pg. 941
BEL OPTRONIC DEVICES LTD.—See Bharat Electronics Limited; *Int'l*, pg. 1011
BERSON MILIEUTECHNIEK B.V.—See Halma plc; *Int'l*, pg. 3232
BEST LIGHTING PRODUCTS, INC.—See Harlow Aerostructures, LLC; *U.S. Private*, pg. 1865
BIG BEAM EMERGENCY SYSTEMS, INC.; *U.S. Private*, pg. 552
BIRCHWOOD LIGHTING, INC.—See Leviton Manufacturing Company, Inc.; *U.S. Private*, pg. 2436
BJB GMBH & CO. KG; *Int'l*, pg. 1053
BOOM POWER ELECTRONICS (SU ZHOU) CO. LTD.—See Coretronic Corporation; *Int'l*, pg. 1800
BOWENS INTERNATIONAL LTD.—See Aurelius Equity Opportunities SE & Co. KGaA; *Int'l*, pg. 708
BRIDGELUX, INC.—See China Electronics Corporation; *Int'l*, pg. 1499
BRIGHTTECH INC.—See Danaher Corporation; *U.S. Public*, pg. 625
BRINKMANN CORP.; *U.S. Private*, pg. 655
CALIFORNIA LIGHTING SALES INCORPORATED; *U.S. Private*, pg. 719
CAPSTONE COMPANIES, INC.; *U.S. Public*, pg. 432
CARLISLE ENERGY SERVICES, INC.—See Carlisle Companies Incorporated; *U.S. Public*, pg. 436
CASUAL LAMPS OF CALIFORNIA, INC.; *U.S. Private*, pg. 786
CENTRAL INDUSTRIES, INC.—See Tyson Foods, Inc.; *U.S. Public*, pg. 2209
CENTRALITE SYSTEMS, INC.—See eZLO, Inc.; *U.S. Private*, pg. 1454
CHALMIT LIGHTING LIMITED—See Hubbell Incorporated; *U.S. Public*, pg. 1066
CHANGZHOU XINGYU AUTOMOTIVE LIGHTING SYSTEM CO., LTD.; *Int'l*, pg. 1446
CHINA INTELLIGENT LIGHTING AND ELECTRONICS, INC.; *Int'l*, pg. 1510
CHINA TIANRUI AUTOMOTIVE INTERIORS CO., LTD.; *Int'l*, pg. 1559
THE CHRISTMAS LIGHT CO.; *U.S. Private*, pg. 4009
CITY THEATRICAL, INC.—See Pfingsten Partners, LLC; *U.S. Private*, pg. 3164
CML INNOVATIVE TECHNOLOGIES, GMBH & CO. KG—See Grupo Antolin-Irausa, S.A.; *Int'l*, pg. 3119
CML INNOVATIVE TECHNOLOGIES, LTD.—See Grupo Antolin-Irausa, S.A.; *Int'l*, pg. 3119
CML INNOVATIVE TECHNOLOGIES, S.A.S.—See Grupo Antolin-Irausa, S.A.; *Int'l*, pg. 3119
CML INNOVATIVE TECHNOLOGIES—See Havell's India Ltd.; *Int'l*, pg. 3286
CML INNOVATIVE TECHNOLOGIES, S.R.O.—See Grupo Antolin-Irausa, S.A.; *Int'l*, pg. 3119
CML TECHNOLOGIES, GMBH & CO. KG—See Grupo Antolin-Irausa, S.A.; *Int'l*, pg. 3119
CNLIGHT CO., LTD.; *Int'l*, pg. 1677
COLORLIGHT AB—See Amplex AB; *Int'l*, pg. 434
COLORSTARS GROUP; *Int'l*, pg. 1704
COOPER LIGHTING & SAFETY LTD—See Eaton Corporation plc; *Int'l*, pg. 2278
COREP FRANCE SARL—See Corep Lighting group; *Int'l*, pg. 1799
COREP IBERICA, LDA—See Corep Lighting group; *Int'l*, pg. 1799
COREP LIGHTING GROUP; *Int'l*, pg. 1799
COREP LIGHTING INDIA (P) LTD.—See Corep Lighting group; *Int'l*, pg. 1799
CORETRONIC (GUANGZHOU) CO., LTD.—See Coretronic Corporation; *Int'l*, pg. 1800
CORETRONIC (NANJING) CO., LTD.—See Coretronic Corporation; *Int'l*, pg. 1800
CORETRONIC (NINGBO) CO., LTD.—See Coretronic Corporation; *Int'l*, pg. 1800
CREE LED LIGHTING SOLUTIONS, INC.—See Wolfspeed, Inc.; *U.S. Public*, pg. 2377
CYALUME TECHNOLOGIES, INC.—See Cadre Holdings, Inc.; *U.S. Public*, pg. 419
CYALUME TECHNOLOGIES S.A.S.—See Cadre Holdings, Inc.; *U.S. Public*, pg. 419
CYBERLUX CORPORATION; *U.S. Public*, pg. 617
D3 LED, LLC—See Southpaw Sports & Entertainment, Inc.; *U.S. Private*, pg. 3737
DAEYANG ELECTRIC CO., LTD. - LIGHTING DIVISON—See Daeyang Electric Co., Ltd.; *Int'l*, pg. 1911
DAVEX ENGINEERING (M) SDN BHD—See Ekuiti Nasional Berhad; *Int'l*, pg. 2340
DESIGNERS FOUNTAIN; *U.S. Private*, pg. 1215
DHANASHREE ELECTRONICS LIMITED; *Int'l*, pg. 2098
DIGAGOGO VENTURES CORP.; *U.S. Private*, pg. 1229
DP OSRAM UKRAINE—See ams AG; *Int'l*, pg. 438
DR. MACH GMBH & CO. KG; *Int'l*, pg. 2194
DUAL LITE MANUFACTURING INC.—See Hubbell Incorporated; *U.S. Public*, pg. 1066
DULHUNTY POWER (AUST) PTY LIMITED—See Energy Technologies Limited; *Int'l*, pg. 2423
DULHUNTY POWER (THAILAND) LIMITED—See Energy Technologies Limited; *Int'l*, pg. 2423
DURALAMP S.P.A—See 3F Filippi SpA; *Int'l*, pg. 7
DURO DE MEXICO, S.A. DE C.V.; *Int'l*, pg. 2228
ECO-SHIFT POWER CORP.; *Int'l*, pg. 2293
ELECTROLINE LTD—See Amplex AB; *Int'l*, pg. 434
ELECTRONIC THEATRE CONTROLS, INC.; *U.S. Private*, pg. 1356
ELETTRONICA CIMONE SRL—See Beghelli S.p.A.; *Int'l*, pg. 941
ELITE CORE ENTERPRISES LTD.; *U.S. Private*, pg. 1360
EL NASSER ELECTRIC & ELECTRONIC APPARATUS CO.—See Chemical Industries Holding Company; *Int'l*, pg. 1461
ELTOSCH GRAFIX ASIA—See Dr. Honle AG; *Int'l*, pg. 2192
ELTOSCH-GRAFIX GMBH—See Dr. Honle AG; *Int'l*, pg. 2192
EMPCO-LITE INC.—See Elgin Molded Plastics Inc.; *U.S. Private*, pg. 1359
ENERGIE LLC—See ExeLED Holdings, Inc.; *U.S. Private*, pg. 1448
ENERGY DESIGN SERVICE SYSTEMS; *U.S. Private*, pg. 1395
ENPLAS CORPORATION - LED BUSINESS DIVISION—See ENPLAS CORPORATION; *Int'l*, pg. 2445
EPISTAR CORPORATION—See Ennostar Inc.; *Int'l*, pg. 2443
EUROLUX (PTY) LTD—See ARB HOLDINGS LIMITED; *Int'l*, pg. 536
EXCELITAS TECHNOLOGIES SHENZHEN CO., LTD.—See AEA Investors LP; *U.S. Private*, pg. 113
FAGERHULT LIGHTING SYSTEM (SUZHOU) CO. LTD.—See Fagerhult Group AB; *Int'l*, pg. 2602
FISHER PIERCE OUTDOOR LIGHTING CONTROLS—See Electro Switch Corporation; *U.S. Private*, pg. 1354
FLASH TECHNOLOGY, LLC—See SPX Technologies, Inc.; *U.S. Public*, pg. 1921
FOCUS LIGHTING & FIXTURES PTE. LTD.—See Focus Lighting & Fixtures Limited; *Int'l*, pg. 2719
FORESTIER SA—See Corep Lighting group; *Int'l*, pg. 1799
FOSHAN ELECTRICAL & LIGHTING CO., LTD.; *Int'l*, pg. 2748
FUJI LIGHTING AND TECHNOLOGY, INC.—See Fuji Media Holdings, Inc.; *Int'l*, pg. 2813
GENERAC MOBILE PRODUCTS UK LTD—See Generac Holdings Inc.; *U.S. Public*, pg. 912
GENERATION ALPHA, INC.; *U.S. Public*, pg. 929
GEUMVIT CORP.; *Int'l*, pg. 2954
GLOBAL LIGHTING TECHNOLOGIES, INC.—See Global Lighting Technologies Inc.; *Int'l*, pg. 2998
GMC POWERLINES (PTY) LTD—See ARB HOLDINGS LIMITED; *Int'l*, pg. 537
GUANGZHOU FORDA SIGNAL EQUIPMENT CO. LTD.—See Hongli Zhihui Group Co., Ltd.; *Int'l*, pg. 3471
HAI CHEUNG TRADING CO.—See Daeyang Electric Co., Ltd.; *Int'l*, pg. 1911
HAMAMATSU PHOTONICS (CHINA) CO., LTD.—See Hamamatsu Photonics K.K.; *Int'l*, pg. 3235
HAMAMATSU PHOTONICS TAIWAN CO., LTD.—See Hamamatsu Photonics K.K.; *Int'l*, pg. 3235
HAMMOND ELECTRONICS PTY. LIMITED—See Hammond Manufacturing Co. Ltd.; *Int'l*, pg. 3238
HAMSAR DIVERSCO INC.—See Methode Electronics, Inc.; *U.S. Public*, pg. 1428
HANOVIA LIMITED—See Halma plc; *Int'l*, pg. 3232
HAN'S LASER TECHNOLOGY INDUSTRY GROUP CO., LTD.; *Int'l*, pg. 3240
HARRIS HOLDINGS INC.; *U.S. Private*, pg. 1869

335139 — ELECTRIC LAMP BULB ...

HAVELLS SYLVANIA ARGENTINA S.A.—See Havell's India Ltd.; *Int'l*, pg. 3286
HAVELLS SYLVANIA BRASIL ILUMINACAO LTDA.—See Havell's India Ltd.; *Int'l*, pg. 3286
HELIOSPECTRA AB; *Int'l*, pg. 3330
HELIOSPECTRA INC.—See Heliospectra AB; *Int'l*, pg. 3330
HELVAR OY AB—See Helvar Merca Oy AB; *Int'l*, pg. 3339
HERAEUS AMBA LTD.—See Heraeus Holding GmbH; *Int'l*, pg. 3357
HERAEUS NOBLELIGHT ANALYTICS LTD.—See AEA Investors LP; *U.S. Private*, pg. 113
HH FLUORESCENT PARTS INCORPORATED; *U.S. Private*, pg. 1931
HIDIRECT—See Saratoga Partners L.P.; *U.S. Private*, pg. 3549
HIGH END SYSTEMS, INC.—See Electronic Theatre Controls, Inc.; *U.S. Private*, pg. 1356
HI-TECH GEARS LTD; *Int'l*, pg. 3381
HOENLE UV TECHNOLOGY (SHANGHAI) TRADING LTD.—See Dr. Honle AG; *Int'l*, pg. 2192
HONGKONG GREAT INTERNATIONAL ENTERPRISE CO., LIMITED—See Daeyang Electric Co., Ltd.; *Int'l*, pg. 1911
HONLE UV FRANCE S.A.R.L.—See Dr. Honle AG; *Int'l*, pg. 2192
HORMEN CE A.S.—See CEZ, a.s.; *Int'l*, pg. 1428
HOWARD LIGHTING PRODUCTS—See Howard Industries, Inc.; *U.S. Private*, pg. 1995
HUGHEY & PHILLIPS, LLC; *U.S. Private*, pg. 2004
IKIO LIGHTING LIMITED; *Int'l*, pg. 3610
IL SCIENCE CO., LTD.; *Int'l*, pg. 3613
INOVUS SOLAR, INC.—See SolarOne Solutions, Inc.; *U.S. Private*, pg. 3708
IOTA ENGINEERING, L.L.C.—See Acuity Brands, Inc.; *U.S. Public*, pg. 37
KAUFEL GMBH & CO. KG—See ABB Ltd.; *Int'l*, pg. 52
KD LAMP CO—See ATC Group, Inc.; *U.S. Private*, pg. 365
KICHLER LIGHTING LLC—See Kingswood Capital Management LLC; *U.S. Private*, pg. 2312
KIM LIGHTING—See Hubbell Incorporated; *U.S. Public*, pg. 1067
KOEHLER-BRIGHT STAR, INC.—See Berkshire Hathaway Inc.; *U.S. Public*, pg. 310
KONCEPT TECHNOLOGIES INC; *U.S. Private*, pg. 2342
KUNSHAN ENDO LIGHTING CO., LTD.—See ENDO Lighting Corporation; *Int'l*, pg. 2405
KURT VERSEN, INC.—See Hubbell Incorporated; *U.S. Public*, pg. 1067
LEADERS INTERNATIONAL UK LTD—See Daeyang Electric Co., Ltd.; *Int'l*, pg. 1911
LED ENGIN, INC.—See ams AG; *Int'l*, pg. 438
LED LINEAR GMBH—See Fagerhult Group AB; *Int'l*, pg. 2602
LED LINEAR UK LTD.—See Fagerhult Group AB; *Int'l*, pg. 2602
LED LINEAR USA INC.—See Fagerhult Group AB; *Int'l*, pg. 2602
LEDNOVATION, INC.; *U.S. Private*, pg. 2411
LEVITON/LES—See Leviton Manufacturing Company, Inc.; *U.S. Private*, pg. 2437
LIGHTING INNOVATIONS AFRICA (PTY) LTD.—See Fagerhult Group AB; *Int'l*, pg. 2602
LIGHTING SCIENCE GROUP CORPORATION; *U.S. Private*, pg. 2453
LIGHTRONICS B.V.—See F.W. Thorpe plc; *Int'l*, pg. 2597
LIGHTSOURCES, INC.; *U.S. Private*, pg. 2453
LIGHTWEDGE LLC; *U.S. Private*, pg. 2454
LITHONIA LIGHTING—See Acuity Brands, Inc.; *U.S. Public*, pg. 37
LSI INDUSTRIES INC.; *U.S. Public*, pg. 1344
LUMIFICIENT CORPORATION—See Revolution Lighting Technologies, Inc.; *U.S. Public*, pg. 1793
LUMINESCENT SYSTEMS CANADA, INC.—See Astronics Corporation; *U.S. Public*, pg. 217
LUMINESCENT SYSTEMS, INC.—See Astronics Corporation; *U.S. Public*, pg. 217
LUMITEC LLC—See Genstar Capital, LLC; *U.S. Private*, pg. 1676
MALLATITE LTD—See Hill & Smith PLC; *Int'l*, pg. 3392
MANAIRCO, INC.—See Hughey & Phillips, LLC; *U.S. Private*, pg. 2004
METALITE AVIATION LIGHTING—See HWH Investments Limited; *Int'l*, pg. 3543
METROSPEC TECHNOLOGY LLC; *U.S. Private*, pg. 2691
MITRONIC GMBH—See Dr. Honle AG; *Int'l*, pg. 2192
MOLE-RICHARDSON CO.; *U.S. Private*, pg. 2767
M&O PARTNERS A/S—See Daeyang Electric Co., Ltd.; *Int'l*, pg. 1911
M/S GULF DYNAMIC SWITCHGEAR CO. LTD—See Dubai Investments PJSC; *Int'l*, pg. 2219
MSI SSL; *U.S. Private*, pg. 2815
MUSCO CORPORATION; *U.S. Private*, pg. 2817
MYERS POWER PRODUCTS, INC.; *U.S. Private*, pg. 2824
NANO PRECISION (SUZHOU) CO., LTD.—See Coretronic Corporation; *Int'l*, pg. 1800
NATIONAL ENERGY & LIGHT, LLC; *U.S. Private*, pg. 2853
NEXXUS LIGHTING-POOL & SPA—See Revolution Lighting Technologies, Inc.; *U.S. Public*, pg. 1793
NORLUX; *U.S. Private*, pg. 2938

OAO OSRAM—See ams AG; *Int'l*, pg. 438
OFFSHOREMARINE TRADING LLC—See Daeyang Electric Co., Ltd.; *Int'l*, pg. 1911
ORYON TECHNOLOGIES, INC.; *U.S. Private*, pg. 3046
OSRAM AB—See ams AG; *Int'l*, pg. 438
OSRAM AMPUL TICARET A.S.—See ams AG; *Int'l*, pg. 438
OSRAM ARGENTINA S.A.C.I.—See ams AG; *Int'l*, pg. 438
OSRAM ASIA PACIFIC LTD. (OAPAC)—See ams AG; *Int'l*, pg. 438
OSRAM A/S—See ams AG; *Int'l*, pg. 438
OSRAM AS—See ams AG; *Int'l*, pg. 438
OSRAM AUTOMOTIVE LAMPS PRIVATE LIMITED—See ams AG; *Int'l*, pg. 439
OSRAM BENELUX B.V.—See ams AG; *Int'l*, pg. 439
OSRAM CESKA REPUBLIKA S.R.O.—See ams AG; *Int'l*, pg. 439
OSRAM CHILE LTDA.—See ams AG; *Int'l*, pg. 439
OSRAM CHINA LIGHTING LTD.—See ams AG; *Int'l*, pg. 439
OSRAM DE COLOMBIA ILUMINACIONES S.A.—See ams AG; *Int'l*, pg. 439
OSRAM DEL ECUADOR S.A.—See ams AG; *Int'l*, pg. 440
OSRAM DE MEXICO S.A. DE C.V.—See ams AG; *Int'l*, pg. 440
OSRAM DE PERU S.A.C.—See ams AG; *Int'l*, pg. 439
OSRAM DO BRASIL COMPANHIA DE LAMPADAS ELETRICAS S.A.—See ams AG; *Int'l*, pg. 440
OSRAM DO BRASIL LAMPADAS ELETRICAS LTDA.—See ams AG; *Int'l*, pg. 440
OSRAM D.O.O.—See ams AG; *Int'l*, pg. 439
OSRAM D.O.O.—See ams AG; *Int'l*, pg. 439
OSRAM D.O.O—See ams AG; *Int'l*, pg. 439
OSRAM EMPRESA DE APARELHAGEM ELECTRICA LDA.—See ams AG; *Int'l*, pg. 439
OSRAM EOOD—See ams AG; *Int'l*, pg. 439
OSRAM KOREA CO. LTD.—See ams AG; *Int'l*, pg. 439
OSRAM LIGHTING CONTROL SYSTEMS LTD.—See ams AG; *Int'l*, pg. 439
OSRAM LTD.—See ams AG; *Int'l*, pg. 439
OSRAM LTD.—See ams AG; *Int'l*, pg. 440
OSRAM (MALAYSIA) SDN. BHD.—See ams AG; *Int'l*, pg. 438
OSRAM-MELCO TOSHIBA LIGHTING LTD.—See ams AG; *Int'l*, pg. 440
OSRAM MIDDLE EAST FZE—See ams AG; *Int'l*, pg. 439
OSRAM OPTO SEMICONDUCTORS ASIA LTD.—See ams AG; *Int'l*, pg. 439
OSRAM OPTO SEMICONDUCTORS GMBH—See ams AG; *Int'l*, pg. 439
OSRAM OPTO SEMICONDUCTORS (MALAYSIA) SDN BHD—See ams AG; *Int'l*, pg. 439
OSRAM PTE. LTD.—See ams AG; *Int'l*, pg. 439
OSRAM (PTY.) LTD.—See ams AG; *Int'l*, pg. 438
OSRAM ROMANIA S.R.L.—See ams AG; *Int'l*, pg. 439
OSRAM S.A. DE C.V.—See ams AG; *Int'l*, pg. 439
OSRAM S.A.—See ams AG; *Int'l*, pg. 439
OSRAM S.A.S.—See ams AG; *Int'l*, pg. 439
OSRAM SOCIETA RIUNITE OSRAM-EDISON-CLERICI S.P.A.—See ams AG; *Int'l*, pg. 440
OSRAM SP. Z O.O.—See ams AG; *Int'l*, pg. 439
OSRAM SYLVANIA, INC.—See ams AG; *Int'l*, pg. 440
OSRAM SYLVANIA LTD.—See ams AG; *Int'l*, pg. 440
OSRAM TAIWAN COMPANY LTD.—See ams AG; *Int'l*, pg. 439
OXXIIUS SA—See BNP Paribas SA; *Int'l*, pg. 1089
OY OSRAM AB—See ams AG; *Int'l*, pg. 438
PACIFIC COAST LIGHTING INC.; *U.S. Private*, pg. 3066
PELCO PRODUCTS, INC.; *U.S. Private*, pg. 3130
PELICAN PRODUCTS, INC.—See Platinum Equity, LLC; *U.S. Private*, pg. 3207
PHOENIX ELECTRIC CO., LTD.—See Helios Techno Holding Co., Ltd.; *Int'l*, pg. 3330
PLUS LIGHT TECH FZE—See Focus Lighting & Fixtures Limited; *Int'l*, pg. 2719
POINT LIGHTING CORPORATION; *U.S. Private*, pg. 3222
PRECISION SOLAR CONTROLS INC.—See New Enterprise Stone & Lime Co., Inc.; *U.S. Private*, pg. 2895
PRIME SYSTEMS, INC.; *U.S. Private*, pg. 3262
PRINTCONCEPT UV-SYSTEME GMBH—See Dr. Honle AG; *Int'l*, pg. 2192
PROGRESS LIGHTING—See Hubbell Incorporated; *U.S. Public*, pg. 1066
PT. EXCELITAS TECHNOLOGIES BATAM—See AEA Investors LP; *U.S. Private*, pg. 113
P.T. OSRAM INDONESIA—See ams AG; *Int'l*, pg. 440
PURERAY CORPORATION; *U.S. Public*, pg. 1738
QUALITE SPORTS LIGHTING, LLC—See Worth Investment Group, LLC; *U.S. Private*, pg. 4570
RAESCH QUARZ (GERMANY) GMBH—See Dr. Honle AG; *Int'l*, pg. 2192
RAESCH QUARZ (MALTA) LTD.—See Dr. Honle AG; *Int'l*, pg. 2192
REJUVENATION INC.—See Williams-Sonoma, Inc.; *U.S. Public*, pg. 2371
RELUME TECHNOLOGIES, INC.—See Revolution Lighting Technologies, Inc.; *U.S. Public*, pg. 1793
RENEWABLE ENERGY & POWER, INC.; *U.S. Public*, pg. 1783

RIG-A-LITE PARTNERSHIP, LTD.—See AZZ, Inc.; *U.S. Public*, pg. 260
ROC-OFF PRODUCTIONS, INC.—See Mountain Productions, Inc.; *U.S. Private*, pg. 2799
ROGERS CORP. - DUREL DIVISION—See Rogers Corporation; *U.S. Public*, pg. 1808
ROLL & HILL, LLC; *U.S. Private*, pg. 3474
SABIK LTD.—See SPX Technologies, Inc.; *U.S. Public*, pg. 1921
SABIK OU—See SPX Technologies, Inc.; *U.S. Public*, pg. 1921
SABIK OY—See SPX Technologies, Inc.; *U.S. Public*, pg. 1922
SABIK PRIVATE LIMITED—See SPX Technologies, Inc.; *U.S. Public*, pg. 1922
SAVANT TECHNOLOGIES, LLC—See Savant Systems, Inc.; *U.S. Private*, pg. 3556
SAVWATT USA, INC.; *U.S. Public*, pg. 3557
SEA GULL LIGHTING PRODUCTS, LLC—See AEA Investors LP; *U.S. Private*, pg. 114
SELC IRELAND LTD.—See Itron, Inc.; *U.S. Public*, pg. 1176
SHANGHAI KNOW-HOW TECHNOLOGIES CO., LTD.—See Daeyang Electric Co., Ltd.; *Int'l*, pg. 1911
SILVAIR, INC.; *U.S. Public*, pg. 1880
SINHOO GROUP CO., LTD.—See Daeyang Electric Co., Ltd.; *Int'l*, pg. 1911
SITECO NORWAY AS—See ams AG; *Int'l*, pg. 440
SITECO POLAND SP. Z O.O.—See ams AG; *Int'l*, pg. 440
SITECO UK LIMITED—See ams AG; *Int'l*, pg. 440
SOLARONE SOLUTIONS, INC.; *U.S. Private*, pg. 3708
SOL, INC.—See Carmanah Technologies Corporation; *Int'l*, pg. 1341
SOUTHPAW SPORTS & ENTERTAINMENT, INC.; *U.S. Private*, pg. 3737
SPRING CITY ELECTRICAL MFG. CO., INC; *U.S. Private*, pg. 3763
STAKE FASTENER COMPANY—See Dupree, Inc.; *U.S. Private*, pg. 1291
STREAMLIGHT INC.; *U.S. Private*, pg. 3838
SUNRISE TECHNOLOGIES, INC.—See Electro Switch Corporation; *U.S. Private*, pg. 1354
SUREFIRE, LLC; *U.S. Private*, pg. 3883
TAKAOKA ELECTRONICS CO., LTD.—See Hamamatsu Photonics K.K.; *Int'l*, pg. 3235
TARGETTI SANKEY S.P.A.—See 3F Filippi SpA; *Int'l*, pg. 7
TARSIER LTD.; *U.S. Public*, pg. 1982
TEHOMET OY—See Valmont Industries, Inc.; *U.S. Public*, pg. 2274
TRAXON TECHNOLOGIES EUROPE GMBH—See ams AG; *Int'l*, pg. 440
TRAXON TECHNOLOGIES LLC—See ams AG; *Int'l*, pg. 440
TRAXON TECHNOLOGIES LTD.—See ams AG; *Int'l*, pg. 440
TRIDENT INDUSTRI AB—See AdderaCare AB; *Int'l*, pg. 128
TROJAN TECHNOLOGIES, INC.—See Danaher Corporation; *U.S. Public*, pg. 631
TROJANUV TECHNOLGIES LIMITED—See Danaher Corporation; *U.S. Public*, pg. 631
TRT LIGHTING LIMITED—See F.W. Thorpe plc; *Int'l*, pg. 2597
ULTA-LIT TECHNOLOGIES INC.; *U.S. Private*, pg. 4277
UNILUX, INC.; *U.S. Private*, pg. 4283
US LED, LTD.; *U.S. Private*, pg. 4319
US POLE LIGHTING CO.; *U.S. Private*, pg. 4319
UV-TECHNIK SPEZIALLAMPEN GMBH—See Dr. Honle AG; *Int'l*, pg. 2192
VALMONT FRANCE S.A.—See Valmont Industries, Inc.; *U.S. Public*, pg. 2274
VALMONT INDUSTRIA E COMERCIO, LTDA.—See Valmont Industries, Inc.; *U.S. Public*, pg. 2274
VALMONT INDUSTRIES HOLLAND B.V.—See Valmont Industries, Inc.; *U.S. Public*, pg. 2274
VALMONT NEWMARK, INC.—See Valmont Industries, Inc.; *U.S. Public*, pg. 2274
VALMONT STAINTON LTD.—See Valmont Industries, Inc.; *U.S. Public*, pg. 2274
VEKO LIGHTSYSTEMS GMBH—See Fagerhult Group AB; *Int'l*, pg. 2602
VEKO LIGHTSYSTEMS INTERNATIONAL B.V.—See Fagerhult Group AB; *Int'l*, pg. 2602
VEKO LIGHTSYSTEMS S.L.—See Fagerhult Group AB; *Int'l*, pg. 2602
VICTOR INDUSTRIAL EQUIPMENT (PTY) LTD.—See Federal Signal Corporation; *U.S. Public*, pg. 826
VU1 CORPORATION; *U.S. Public*, pg. 2313
WE-EF HELVETICA SA—See Fagerhult Group AB; *Int'l*, pg. 2602
WE-EF LEUCHTEN GMBH—See Fagerhult Group AB; *Int'l*, pg. 2602
WE-EF LIGHTING CO. LTD.—See Fagerhult Group AB; *Int'l*, pg. 2602
WE-EF LIGHTING LTD.—See Fagerhult Group AB; *Int'l*, pg. 2602
WE-EF LIGHTING PTY. LTD.—See Fagerhult Group AB; *Int'l*, pg. 2602
WE-EF LIGHTING USA LLC—See Fagerhult Group AB; *Int'l*, pg. 2602

335210 — SMALL ELECTRICAL APPLIANCE MANUFACTURING

WESTERN PHOTOMETRIC LABORATORIES—See Dupree, Inc.; *U.S. Private*, pg. 1291
WIRELESS ENVIRONMENT, LLC; *U.S. Private*, pg. 4547
WYATT TECHNOLOGY CORPORATION—See Waters Corporation; *U.S. Public*, pg. 2336
YOUNG LIGHTING (SUZHOU) CORPORATION—See Coretronic Corporation; *Int'l*, pg. 1800
ZANIBONI LIGHTING, LLC; *U.S. Private*, pg. 4597
ZEVOTEK, INC.; *U.S. Private*, pg. 4603

335210 — SMALL ELECTRICAL APPLIANCE MANUFACTURING

AERUS LLC; *U.S. Private*, pg. 120
AESCULAP AG & CO. KG—See B. Braun Melsungen AG; *Int'l*, pg. 785
AIR KING—See Lasko Products, LLC; *U.S. Private*, pg. 2395
ALLAN ELECTRIC MFG., LIMITED—See Allan International Holdings Limited; *Int'l*, pg. 332
ALLAN INTERNATIONAL HOLDINGS LIMITED; *Int'l*, pg. 332
AMANO AGENCY CORP.—See Amano Corporation; *Int'l*, pg. 410
AMANO MUSASHI ELECTRIC CORPORATION—See Amano Corporation; *Int'l*, pg. 411
A. O. SMITH WATER FZE—See A. O. Smith Corporation; *U.S. Public*, pg. 11
APERAM ALLOYS RESCAL SAS—See Aperam SA; *Int'l*, pg. 508
APP ENGINEERING SDN BHD—See APP Systems Services Pte. Ltd.; *Int'l*, pg. 519
APP SYSTEMS SERVICES (THAILAND) CO. LTD.—See APP Systems Services Pte. Ltd.; *Int'l*, pg. 519
ATLAS ELECTRICA, S.A.—See Controladora Mabe S.A. de C.V.; *Int'l*, pg. 1785
BAUKNECHT AG—See Whirlpool Corporation; *U.S. Public*, pg. 2367
BIALETTI INDUSTRIE S.P.A.; *Int'l*, pg. 1017
BISSELL AUSTRALIA PTY LTD—See Bissell Homecare, Inc.; *U.S. Private*, pg. 566
BISSELL HOMECARE, INC.; *U.S. Private*, pg. 566
BISSELL HOMECARE (OVERSEAS) INC.—See Bissell Homecare, Inc.; *U.S. Private*, pg. 566
BRAUN GMBH—See The Procter & Gamble Company; *U.S. Public*, pg. 2124
BUD COMERCIO DE ELETRODOMESTICOS LTDA.—See Whirlpool Corporation; *U.S. Public*, pg. 2368
BUNN-O-MATIC CORP. OF CANADA LTD.—See Bunn-O-Matic Corporation; *U.S. Private*, pg. 685
CANDY HOOVER PORTUGAL, LTDA.—See Haier Smart Home Co., Ltd.; *Int'l*, pg. 3210
CAROS CO., LTD.; *Int'l*, pg. 1342
CASABLANCA FAN COMPANY—See Griffon Corporation; *U.S. Public*, pg. 969
CER A.D.; *Int'l*, pg. 1420
CHINA OVERSEAS NUOXIN INTERNATIONAL HOLDINGS LIMITED; *Int'l*, pg. 1539
CISCO TECHNOLOGY SERVICES (DALIAN) CO. LTD.—See Cisco Systems, Inc.; *U.S. Public*, pg. 499
CLAYTON DE FRANCE, S.A.R.L.—See Clayton Industries Co.; *U.S. Private*, pg. 918
CLAYTON DE MEXICO, S.A DE C.V.—See Clayton Industries Co.; *U.S. Private*, pg. 918
CLAYTON DEUTSCHLAND GMBH—See Clayton Industries Co.; *U.S. Private*, pg. 918
CLAYTON NEDERLAND B.V.—See Clayton Industries Co.; *U.S. Private*, pg. 918
CLAYTON OF BELGIUM N.V.—See Clayton Industries Co.; *U.S. Private*, pg. 918
CLAYTON SCANDINAVIA A/S—See Clayton Industries Co.; *U.S. Private*, pg. 918
CLAYTON THERMAL PRODUCTS, LTD.—See Clayton Industries Co.; *U.S. Private*, pg. 918
COKO-WERK GMBH & CO. KG; *Int'l*, pg. 1696
CONAIR CONSUMER APPLIANCES DIVISION—See American Securities LLC; *U.S. Private*, pg. 247
CONAIR CONSUMER PRODUCTS INC.—See American Securities LLC; *U.S. Private*, pg. 248
CONAIR CORPORATION—See American Securities LLC; *U.S. Private*, pg. 247
CONCORDIA COFFEE COMPANY, INC.—See The Middleby Corporation; *U.S. Public*, pg. 2113
CREATIVE TECHNOLOGIES CORP.; *U.S. Private*, pg. 1090
CREM INTERNATIONAL AB—See Ali Holding S.r.l; *Int'l*, pg. 322
CREM INTERNATIONAL GMBH—See Ali Holding S.r.l; *Int'l*, pg. 322
CREM INTERNATIONAL (SHANGHAI) CO., LTD.—See Ali Holding S.r.l; *Int'l*, pg. 322
CREM INTERNATIONAL SPAIN, S.L.—See Ali Holding S.r.l; *Int'l*, pg. 322
CREM INTERNATIONAL UK LTD.—See Ali Holding S.r.l; *Int'l*, pg. 322
CROMPTON GREAVES CONSUMER ELECTRICALS LIMITED; *Int'l*, pg. 1853
CUCKOO HOLDINGS CO., LTD.; *Int'l*, pg. 1876

DONGGUAN YIHEDA AUTOMATION CO., LTD.; *Int'l*, pg. 2167
DREEBIT GMBH—See Dr. Ing. K. Busch GmbH; *Int'l*, pg. 2193
DYSON INC.—See Dyson Ltd.; *Int'l*, pg. 2243
DYSON LTD.; *Int'l*, pg. 2243
EDWARDS KOREA LTD.—See Atlas Copco AB; *Int'l*, pg. 682
EDWARDS TECHNOLOGIES SINGAPORE PTE. LTD.—See Atlas Copco AB; *Int'l*, pg. 682
ELECTROARGES SA; *Int'l*, pg. 2353
ELECTROLUX CEE G.M.B.H.—See AB Electrolux; *Int'l*, pg. 39
ELECTROLUX CENTRAL VACUUM SYSTEMS—See Bissell Homecare, Inc.; *U.S. Private*, pg. 566
ELECTROLUX DEUTSCHLAND GMBH—See AB Electrolux; *Int'l*, pg. 39
ELECTROLUX FLOOR CARE AND SMALL APPLIANCES AB—See AB Electrolux; *Int'l*, pg. 40
ELECTROLUX HAUSGERATE G.M.B.H.—See AB Electrolux; *Int'l*, pg. 40
THE ELTRON CO.—See The Eltron Company; *U.S. Private*, pg. 4025
EMERSON AUTOMATION SOLUTIONS AS—See Emerson Electric Co.; *U.S. Public*, pg. 743
EMERSON AUTOMATION SOLUTIONS FINAL CONTROL ITALIA S.R.L.—See Emerson Electric Co.; *U.S. Public*, pg. 743
EMERSON AUTOMATION SOLUTIONS IRELAND LIMITED—See Emerson Electric Co.; *U.S. Public*, pg. 743
EMERSON AUTOMATION SOLUTIONS UK LIMITED—See Emerson Electric Co.; *U.S. Public*, pg. 743
EMERSON CLIMATE TECHNOLOGIES - SOLUTIONS (SUZHOU) CO., LTD.—See Emerson Electric Co.; *U.S. Public*, pg. 743
EMERSON CLIMATE TECHNOLOGIES (SUZHOU) CO., LTD.—See Emerson Electric Co.; *U.S. Public*, pg. 743
EMERSON EGYPT LLC—See Emerson Electric Co.; *U.S. Public*, pg. 744
EMERSON ELECTRIC DE MEXICO S.A. DE C.V.—See Emerson Electric Co.; *U.S. Public*, pg. 745
EMERSON PROCESS MANAGEMENT CO., LTD.—See Emerson Electric Co.; *U.S. Public*, pg. 745
EMERSON PROFESSIONAL TOOLS AG—See Emerson Electric Co.; *U.S. Public*, pg. 749
ENEV-AIR GMBH—See CENTROTEC SE; *Int'l*, pg. 1414
EOS SAUNATECHNIK GMBH—See Harvia Oyj; *Int'l*, pg. 3281
EURO-PRO CORPORATION; *Int'l*, pg. 2532
EVROPEYSKAYA ELEKTROTEKHNICA PJSC; *Int'l*, pg. 2574
GECKOSYSTEMS INTL. CORP.; *U.S. Public*, pg. 909
GILLETTE SAFETY RAZOR COMPANY—See The Procter & Gamble Company; *U.S. Public*, pg. 2124
GILLETTE UK LTD.—See The Procter & Gamble Company; *U.S. Public*, pg. 2124
GLASS IDROMASSAGGIO SRL—See Masco Corporation; *U.S. Public*, pg. 1391
GORENJE GULF FZE—See Hisense Co., Ltd.; *Int'l*, pg. 3407
GORENJE ISTANBUL LTD.—See Hisense Co., Ltd.; *Int'l*, pg. 3407
GORENJE SKANDINAVIEN A/S—See Hisense Co., Ltd.; *Int'l*, pg. 3407
GORENJE TIKI D.O.O.—See Hisense Co., Ltd.; *Int'l*, pg. 3407
GRAFTECH GERMANY GMBH—See Brookfield Corporation; *Int'l*, pg. 1187
GRAFTECH IBERICA S.L.—See Brookfield Corporation; *Int'l*, pg. 1187
GRAFTECH S.P.A.—See Brookfield Corporation; *Int'l*, pg. 1187
GRAFTECH SWITZERLAND S.A.—See Brookfield Corporation; *Int'l*, pg. 1187
GRAFTECH UK LIMITED—See Brookfield Corporation; *Int'l*, pg. 1187
GREENLEE TOOLS, INC.—See Emerson Electric Co.; *U.S. Public*, pg. 750
GUANGDONG NEDFON AIR SYSTEM CO., LTD.; *Int'l*, pg. 3158
GUANGZHOU KINTE DESHENG INTELLIGENT EQUIPMENT CO., LTD.—See China National Electric Apparatus Research Institute Co., Ltd.; *Int'l*, pg. 1531
HAATZ INC.; *Int'l*, pg. 3201
HAMILTON BEACH BRANDS, INC.—See Hamilton Beach Brands Holding Company; *U.S. Public*, pg. 981
HAMILTON BEACH/PROCTOR SILEX, INC.—See Hamilton Beach Brands Holding Company; *U.S. Public*, pg. 981
HANGZHOU WEIGUANG ELECTRONIC CO., LTD.; *Int'l*, pg. 3251
HANITA COATINGS USA, INC.—See Avery Dennison Corporation; *U.S. Public*, pg. 244
HARVIA OYJ; *Int'l*, pg. 3281
HELEN OF TROY CONSUMER PRODUCTS DIVISION—See Helen of Troy Limited; *Int'l*, pg. 3328
HELEN OF TROY LIMITED; *Int'l*, pg. 3328
HELEN OF TROY PROFESSIONAL SALON DIVISION—See Helen of Troy Limited; *Int'l*, pg. 3329

HERTIG HAUSTECHNIK AG—See BKW AG; *Int'l*, pg. 1055
HERTLI & BERTSCHY AG, ELEKTRISCHE ANLAGEN—See BKW AG; *Int'l*, pg. 1055
HMI INDUSTRIES INC.; *Int'l*, pg. 1955
HOBART UK LIMITED—See Illinois Tool Works Inc.; *U.S. Public*, pg. 1104
HOKUDEN LIFE SYSTEM—See Hokkaido Electric Power Co., Inc.; *Int'l*, pg. 3443
HOT (UK) LIMITED—See Helen of Troy Limited; *Int'l*, pg. 3328
HUARUI ELECTRICAL APPLIANCE CO.,LTD; *Int'l*, pg. 3514
HUBBELL LIGHTING - PROGRESS LIGHTING DIVISION—See Hubbell Incorporated; *U.S. Public*, pg. 1066
HUBEI CUBIC-RUIYI INSTRUMENT CO., LTD.—See Cubic Sensor & Instrument Co., Ltd.; *Int'l*, pg. 1875
HUNTER FAN COMPANY—See Griffon Corporation; *U.S. Public*, pg. 969
INELECTRO SA—See BKW AG; *Int'l*, pg. 1055
INMATION BNX B.V.—See Emerson Electric Co.; *U.S. Public*, pg. 752
INSTANTRON CO., INC.; *U.S. Private*, pg. 2092
ISP ELECTRO SOLUTIONS AG—See BKW AG; *Int'l*, pg. 1055
ISPIRE TECHNOLOGY INC.; *U.S. Public*, pg. 1174
IWM AG—See BKW AG; *Int'l*, pg. 1055
KAZ, INC.—See Helen of Troy Limited; *Int'l*, pg. 3329
KENWOOD LIMITED—See De'Longhi S.p.A.; *Int'l*, pg. 1997
KENWOOD MANUFACTURING GMBH—See De'Longhi S.p.A.; *Int'l*, pg. 1997
KINETIC SEAS INCORPORATED; *U.S. Public*, pg. 1234
KIRBY WORLD HEADQUARTERS—See Berkshire Hathaway Inc.; *U.S. Public*, pg. 300
KLAFS GMBH & CO. KG—See Kohler Company; *U.S. Private*, pg. 2339
KLAUKE FRANCE SARL—See Emerson Electric Co.; *U.S. Public*, pg. 750
KNAUF AMF INTERIORS HELLAS LTD.—See Gebr. Knauf KG; *Int'l*, pg. 2906
K-TEC INCORPORATED; *U.S. Private*, pg. 2251
KUNSHAN SUNWILL ELECTRIC APPLIANCES CO., LTD.—See Guangdong Sunwill Precising Plastic Co., Ltd.; *Int'l*, pg. 3160
LASKO PRODUCTS, LLC; *U.S. Private*, pg. 2395
LINCAT GROUP PLC—See The Middleby Corporation; *U.S. Public*, pg. 2114
LINDSAY MANUFACTURING INC.; *U.S. Private*, pg. 2460
LL BUILDING PRODUCTS, INC.—See GAF Materials Corporation; *U.S. Private*, pg. 1633
LYNX HOLDCO INC—See The Middleby Corporation; *U.S. Public*, pg. 2114
THE METAL WARE CORP.; *U.S. Public*, pg. 4078
METAL WARE—See The Metal Ware Corp.; *U.S. Private*, pg. 4078
NESCO AMERICAN HARVEST INC.—See The Metal Ware Corp.; *U.S. Private*, pg. 4078
NH TECHNOLOGY GMBH—See C C P Contact Probes Co., Ltd.; *Int'l*, pg. 1237
NU SKIN EASTERN EUROPE KFT—See Nu Skin Enterprises, Inc.; *U.S. Public*, pg. 1552
PFEIFFER VACUUM GMBH—See Dr. Ing. K. Busch GmbH; *Int'l*, pg. 2194
PLASTAKET MANUFACTURING COMPANY INC.; *U.S. Private*, pg. 3198
POLYPIPE LIMITED - POLYPIPE VENTILATION DIVISION—See Genuit Group plc; *Int'l*, pg. 2930
PV VACUUM ENGINEERING PTE LTD—See Darco Water Technologies Limited; *Int'l*, pg. 1972
REGAL WARE, INC.; *U.S. Private*, pg. 3386
ROTOVAC CORPORATION; *U.S. Private*, pg. 3487
RPP, LLC—See Emerson Electric Co.; *U.S. Public*, pg. 751
RUSSELL HOBBS LIMITED—See Spectrum Brands Holdings, Inc.; *U.S. Public*, pg. 1916
SALTON AUSTRALIA PTY LTD.—See Spectrum Brands Holdings, Inc.; *U.S. Public*, pg. 1916
SAMSON BRANDS LLC; *U.S. Private*, pg. 3538
SHARKNINJA CO., LTD.—See SharkNinja, Inc.; *U.S. Public*, pg. 1873
SKUTTLE INDOOR AIR QUALITY PRODUCTS; *U.S. Private*, pg. 3683
SPECIALTY ENTERPRISES CO., INC.; *U.S. Private*, pg. 3749
SPENGLER GMBH & CO. KG—See Ali Holding S.r.l; *Int'l*, pg. 323
SPRINGFIELD WIRE INC.; *U.S. Private*, pg. 3764
STREAM ENVIRONMENT SDN. BHD.—See AWC Berhad; *Int'l*, pg. 752
TACONY MANUFACTURING—See Tacony Corporation; *U.S. Private*, pg. 3921
TOP THERMO MFG. (MALAYSIA) SDN. BHD—See Thermos L.L.C.; *U.S. Private*, pg. 4143
TRISTAR ENTERPRISES, LLC; *U.S. Private*, pg. 4238
VAPIR INC.—See Home Bistro, Inc.; *U.S. Public*, pg. 1046
VERTU SECURITY LIMITED—See Emerson Electric Co.; *U.S. Public*, pg. 752
VW WIN CENTURY INC.—See Ameritek Ventures; *U.S. Public*, pg. 115

335210 — SMALL ELECTRICAL AP...

WHIRLPOOL CANADA LP—See Whirlpool Corporation; *U.S. Public*, pg. 2367
WHIRLPOOL CORPORATION; *U.S. Public*, pg. 2366
WHIRLPOOL IRELAND LIMITED—See Whirlpool Corporation; *U.S. Public*, pg. 2368
WHIRLPOOL LATVIA S.I.A.—See Whirlpool Corporation; *U.S. Public*, pg. 2368
WHIRLPOOL MAROC SARL—See Whirlpool Corporation; *U.S. Public*, pg. 2368
WHIRLPOOL NORDIC AB—See Whirlpool Corporation; *U.S. Public*, pg. 2368
WHIRLPOOL OSTERREICH GMBH—See Whirlpool Corporation; *U.S. Public*, pg. 2368
WHIRLPOOL SOUTHEAST ASIA PTE—See Whirlpool Corporation; *U.S. Public*, pg. 2368
WUHAN SUNWILL ELECTRIC CO., LTD.—See Guangdong Sunwill Precising Plastic Co., Ltd.; *Int'l*, pg. 3160

335220 — MAJOR HOUSEHOLD APPLIANCE MANUFACTURING

AB ELECTROLUX; *Int'l*, pg. 39
ACC COMPRESSORS SPA—See Guangzhou Wanbao Group Co., Ltd.; *Int'l*, pg. 3168
AGA MARVEL (USA)—See The Middleby Corporation; *U.S. Public*, pg. 2114
AGA RANGEMASTER LIMITED—See The Middleby Corporation; *U.S. Public*, pg. 2114
AIRFORCE S.P.A.—See Elica S.p.A.; *Int'l*, pg. 2360
AIRLUX ELECTRICAL CO., LTD.; *Int'l*, pg. 248
AIRMATE (CAYMAN) INTERNATIONAL CO. LIMITED; *Int'l*, pg. 248
ALHASAWI FACTORIES FOR WATER HEATERS W.L.L.—See Al-Hasawi Industrial Group; *Int'l*, pg. 285
AL-HASAWI INDUSTRIAL GROUP; *Int'l*, pg. 285
ALI COMENDA S.A.—See Ali Holding S.r.l; *Int'l*, pg. 320
ALTRUM—See Amsoil Inc; *U.S. Private*, pg. 267
AMERICAN DRYER, LLC—See Zurn Elkay Water Solutions Corporation; *U.S. Public*, pg. 2412
AMF BAKE-TECH—See Markel Group Inc.; *U.S. Public*, pg. 1368
AMICA INTERNATIONAL GMBH—See Amica S.A.; *Int'l*, pg. 427
AMICA S.A.; *Int'l*, pg. 427
ANAHEIM MANUFACTURING COMPANY—See Western Industries, Inc.; *U.S. Private*, pg. 4494
A. O. SMITH VIETNAM COMPANY LIMITED—See A. O. Smith Corporation; *U.S. Public*, pg. 11
APCOM INC. - COOKEVILLE PLANT—See A. O. Smith Corporation; *U.S. Public*, pg. 11
ARIAFINA CO. LTD.—See Elica S.p.A.; *Int'l*, pg. 2361
ARROW HOME GROUP CO., LTD.; *Int'l*, pg. 579
ARZUM ELEKTRIKLI EV ALETLERI SANAYI VE TICARET A.S.; *Int'l*, pg. 589
ATAG BELGIE NV—See Hisense Co., Ltd.; *Int'l*, pg. 3407
A&T HAUSGERATE AG—See AB Electrolux; *Int'l*, pg. 40
AUCMA CO., LTD.; *Int'l*, pg. 699
AU OPTRONICS CORPORATION JAPAN—See AUO Corporation; *Int'l*, pg. 706
AUPU HOME STYLE CORPORATION LTD.; *Int'l*, pg. 706
BALMUDA, INC.; *Int'l*, pg. 810
BARBEQUES GALORE, INC.—See Grand Hall Enterprise Company Ltd.; *Int'l*, pg. 3055
BAUKNECHT HAUSGERATE GMBH—See Whirlpool Corporation; *U.S. Public*, pg. 2367
BAYMAK MAKINA SAN.VE TIC.A.S.—See BDR Thermea Group B.V.; *Int'l*, pg. 930
BEIJING ER SHANG-FUKUSHIMA MACHINERY ELECTRIC CO., LTD—See Fukushima Galilei Co. Ltd.; *Int'l*, pg. 2840
BEIJING LIVEN TECHNOLOGY CO., LTD.; *Int'l*, pg. 954
BERNINA SCHWEIZ AG; *Int'l*, pg. 989
BIMAR S.R.L.—See Garofalo Health Care SpA; *Int'l*, pg. 2886
BINATONE TELECOM PLC—See Binatone Electronics International Ltd.; *Int'l*, pg. 1033
BPL LIMITED; *Int'l*, pg. 1132
BRADLEY CORPORATION - FIXTURES DIVISION—See Watts Water Technologies, Inc.; *U.S. Public*, pg. 2337
BRASMOTOR S.A.—See Whirlpool Corporation; *U.S. Public*, pg. 2368
BREVILLE GROUP LIMITED; *Int'l*, pg. 1150
BRODOMERKUR DD; *Int'l*, pg. 1173
BUTANE INDUSTRIAL COMPANY; *Int'l*, pg. 1229
B&W GROUP (SCHWEIZ) GMBH—See Masimo Corporation; *U.S. Public*, pg. 1392
CAMPING GAZ CS S.R.O.—See Newell Brands Inc.; *U.S. Public*, pg. 1513
CAMPING GAZ (DEUTSCHLAND) GMBH—See Newell Brands Inc.; *U.S. Public*, pg. 1515
CANDY DOMESTIC APPLIANCES LIMITED—See Haier Smart Home Co., Ltd.; *Int'l*, pg. 3210
CANDY HOOVER ELECTRODOMESTICOS SA—See Haier Smart Home Co., Ltd.; *Int'l*, pg. 3210
CANDY HOOVER GROUP S.R.L. - BRUGHERIO PLANT—See Haier Smart Home Co., Ltd.; *Int'l*, pg. 3210

CANDY HOOVER GROUP S.R.L.—See Haier Smart Home Co., Ltd.; *Int'l*, pg. 3209
CHAMPION INDUSTRIES, INC.—See Ali Holding S.r.l; *Int'l*, pg. 321
CHANGHONG MEILING CO.,LTD.; *Int'l*, pg. 1443
CHAR-BROIL, LLC—See W.C. Bradley Co.; *U.S. Private*, pg. 4419
CHENGDU RAINBOW APPLIANCE (GROUP) SHARES CO., LTD.; *Int'l*, pg. 1468
CMA DISHMACHINES—See Ali Holding S.r.l; *Int'l*, pg. 320
COLUMBIAN HOME PRODUCTS; *U.S. Private*, pg. 978
COMENDA ALI SPA.—See Ali Holding S.r.l; *Int'l*, pg. 321
COMPANIA PROCTER & GAMBLE MEXICO, S. DE R.L. DE C.V.—See The Procter & Gamble Company; *U.S. Public*, pg. 2120
CONAIR CORPORATION - WARING DIVISION—See American Securities LLC; *U.S. Private*, pg. 248
CONAIR FAR EAST LIMITED—See American Securities LLC; *U.S. Private*, pg. 248
CONCEPCION DURABLES INC.—See Concepcion Industrial Corporation; *Int'l*, pg. 1764
CONTROLADORA MABE S.A. DE C.V.; *Int'l*, pg. 1785
COWAY CO., LTD.; *Int'l*, pg. 1821
CRUCIAL VACUUM; *U.S. Private*, pg. 1113
DAIKOKUYA HOLDINGS CO., LTD.; *Int'l*, pg. 1937
DANBY PRODUCTS LTD.; *Int'l*, pg. 1958
DEER CONSUMER PRODUCTS, INC.; *Int'l*, pg. 2003
DELIA INC.; *U.S. Private*, pg. 1197
DIHR ALI S.P.A.—See Ali Holding S.r.l; *Int'l*, pg. 321
DIPL. ING. FUST AG—See Coop-Gruppe Genossenschaft; *Int'l*, pg. 1790
DIXONS B.V.—See KKR & Co. Inc.; *U.S. Public*, pg. 1261
DIXON TECHNOLOGIES (INDIA) LIMITED; *Int'l*, pg. 2138
DOMETIC GERMANY GMBH—See Dometic Group AB; *Int'l*, pg. 2160
DOMETIC GMBH—See Dometic Group AB; *Int'l*, pg. 2160
DOMETIC UK AWNINGS LTD.—See Dometic Group AB; *Int'l*, pg. 2160
DOMETIC UK BLIND SYSTEMS LTD.—See Dometic Group AB; *Int'l*, pg. 2160
DUTRO COMPANY; *U.S. Private*, pg. 1295
DYNAMIC COOKING SYSTEMS, INC.—See Haier Smart Home Co., Ltd.; *Int'l*, pg. 3210
ECOSMART US, LLC—See The Riverside Company; *U.S. Private*, pg. 4108
EEMAX—See The Riverside Company; *U.S. Private*, pg. 4108
ELEC-TECH INTERNATIONAL CO., LTD.; *Int'l*, pg. 2347
ELECTROLUX ARGENTINA S.A.—See AB Electrolux; *Int'l*, pg. 39
ELECTROLUX AUSTRIA GMBH—See AB Electrolux; *Int'l*, pg. 39
ELECTROLUX BELGIUM N.V.—See AB Electrolux; *Int'l*, pg. 39
ELECTROLUX DE COLOMBIA S.A.—See AB Electrolux; *Int'l*, pg. 41
ELECTROLUX DEL PERU S.A.—See AB Electrolux; *Int'l*, pg. 41
ELECTROLUX DO BRASIL SA—See AB Electrolux; *Int'l*, pg. 39
ELECTROLUX ESPANA S.A.—See AB Electrolux; *Int'l*, pg. 39
ELECTROLUX (FAR EAST) LTD.—See AB Electrolux; *Int'l*, pg. 39
ELECTROLUX FILTER AB—See AB Electrolux; *Int'l*, pg. 40
ELECTROLUX FRANCE S.A.—See AB Electrolux; *Int'l*, pg. 40
ELECTROLUX HAUSGERATE GMBH—See AB Electrolux; *Int'l*, pg. 40
ELECTROLUX HOLDING AG—See AB Electrolux; *Int'l*, pg. 40
ELECTROLUX HOME CARE PRODUCTS CANADA—See Bissell Homecare, Inc.; *U.S. Private*, pg. 566
ELECTROLUX HOME PRODUCTS CORPORATION N.V.—See AB Electrolux; *Int'l*, pg. 40
ELECTROLUX HOME PRODUCTS ESPANA S.A.—See AB Electrolux; *Int'l*, pg. 40
ELECTROLUX HOME PRODUCTS, INC. - ANDERSON—See Bissell Homecare, Inc.; *U.S. Private*, pg. 566
ELECTROLUX HOME PRODUCTS, INC. - SAINT CLOUD—See Bissell Homecare, Inc.; *U.S. Private*, pg. 566
ELECTROLUX HOME PRODUCTS, INC.—See Bissell Homecare, Inc.; *U.S. Private*, pg. 566
ELECTROLUX HOME PRODUCTS, INC. - WEBSTER CITY—See Bissell Homecare, Inc.; *U.S. Private*, pg. 566
ELECTROLUX HOME PRODUCTS (NEDERLAND) B.V.—See AB Electrolux; *Int'l*, pg. 40
ELECTROLUX HOME PRODUCTS PTY. LTD.—See AB Electrolux; *Int'l*, pg. 40
ELECTROLUX HOME PRODUCTS UK—See AB Electrolux; *Int'l*, pg. 41
ELECTROLUX ITALIA S.P.A.—See AB Electrolux; *Int'l*, pg. 40
ELECTROLUX-JUNO KUCHENTECHNIK GMBH—See AB Electrolux; *Int'l*, pg. 41
ELECTROLUX LDA—See AB Electrolux; *Int'l*, pg. 40

ELECTROLUX LEHEL HUTOGEPGYAR KFT—See AB Electrolux; *Int'l*, pg. 40
ELECTROLUX (NZ) LIMITED—See AB Electrolux; *Int'l*, pg. 39
ELECTROLUX PHILLIPPINES, INC.—See AB Electrolux; *Int'l*, pg. 40
ELECTROLUX PLC—See AB Electrolux; *Int'l*, pg. 41
ELECTROLUX POLAND SPOLKA Z.O.O.—See AB Electrolux; *Int'l*, pg. 40
ELECTROLUX PROFESSIONAL GMBH—See AB Electrolux; *Int'l*, pg. 40
ELECTROLUX PROFESSIONAL LTD—See AB Electrolux; *Int'l*, pg. 40
ELECTROLUX PROFESSIONAL OY—See AB Electrolux; *Int'l*, pg. 41
ELECTROLUX PROFESSIONAL S.P.A.—See AB Electrolux; *Int'l*, pg. 40
ELECTROLUX PROFESSIONNEL SAS—See AB Electrolux; *Int'l*, pg. 40
ELECTROLUX PTY. LTD.—See AB Electrolux; *Int'l*, pg. 40
ELECTROLUX ROMANIA SA—See AB Electrolux; *Int'l*, pg. 40
ELECTROLUX S.E.A. PRIVATE LTD.—See AB Electrolux; *Int'l*, pg. 40
ELECTROLUX SLOVAKIA S.R.O. O.Z.—See AB Electrolux; *Int'l*, pg. 41
ELECTROLUX THAILAND CO. LTD.—See AB Electrolux; *Int'l*, pg. 41
ELECTROLUX UKRAINE LLC—See AB Electrolux; *Int'l*, pg. 41
ELICA FRANCE S.A.S.—See Elica S.p.A.; *Int'l*, pg. 2361
ELICA PB WHIRLPOOL KITCHEN APPLIANCES PRIVATE LIMITED—See Whirlpool Corporation; *U.S. Public*, pg. 2367
ELICA S.P.A.; *Int'l*, pg. 2360
ELICA TRADING LLC—See Elica S.p.A.; *Int'l*, pg. 2361
ELITE SEWING MACHINE MFG. CO., LTD.—See AISIN Corporation; *Int'l*, pg. 253
EPRO N.V.—See Greenheart Group Limited; *Int'l*, pg. 3075
EVAC NORTH AMERICA INC.—See Bridgepoint Group Plc; *Int'l*, pg. 1153
EVO AMERICA, LLC—See The Middleby Corporation; *U.S. Public*, pg. 2113
FAGORBRANDT SAS—See Elco Limited; *Int'l*, pg. 2345
FARCENT ENTERPRICE CO., LTD. - GUANYIN FACTORY—See Farcent Enterprice Co., Ltd.; *Int'l*, pg. 2618
FIME—See Elica S.p.A.; *Int'l*, pg. 2361
FISHER & PAYKEL APPLIANCES HOLDINGS LTD.—See Haier Smart Home Co., Ltd.; *Int'l*, pg. 3210
FISHER & PAYKEL APPLIANCES (THAILAND) CO., LTD.—See Haier Smart Home Co., Ltd.; *Int'l*, pg. 3210
FOCUS PRODUCTS GROUP INTERNATIONAL, LLC—See Centre Lane Partners, LLC; *U.S. Private*, pg. 827
FORCE 10 MANUFACTURING CORPORATION—See ENO S.A.S.; *Int'l*, pg. 2444
FOR LIFE PRODUCTS, LLC—See Spectrum Brands Holdings, Inc.; *U.S. Public*, pg. 1915
FUJIAN SNOWMAN CO., LTD.; *Int'l*, pg. 2819
FUKUSHIMA GALILEI CO. LTD.; *Int'l*, pg. 2840
FUKUSHIMA GALILEI (H.K.) CO., LTD.—See Fukushima Galilei Co. Ltd.; *Int'l*, pg. 2840
FUKUSHIMA GALILEI MALAYSIA SDN. BHD.—See Fukushima Galilei Co. Ltd.; *Int'l*, pg. 2840
FUKUSHIMA GALILEI MYANMAR CO. LTD.—See Fukushima Galilei Co. Ltd.; *Int'l*, pg. 2841
FUKUSHIMA GALILEI PHILIPPINE CORPORATION—See Fukushima Galilei Co. Ltd.; *Int'l*, pg. 2841
FUKUSHIMA GALILEI (SHANGHAI) CO., LTD.—See Fukushima Galilei Co. Ltd.; *Int'l*, pg. 2840
FUKUSHIMA GALILEI SINGAPORE PTE. LTD.—See Fukushima Galilei Co. Ltd.; *Int'l*, pg. 2841
FUKUSHIMA GALILEI TAIWAN CO., LTD.—See Fukushima Galilei Co. Ltd.; *Int'l*, pg. 2841
FUKUSHIMA GALILEI (THAILAND)CO., LTD.—See Fukushima Galilei Co. Ltd.; *Int'l*, pg. 2840
FUKUSHIMA GALILEI VIETNAM CO. LTD.—See Fukushima Galilei Co. Ltd.; *Int'l*, pg. 2841
FUKUSHIMA INDUSTRIES CORPORATION - OKAYAMA FACTORY—See Fukushima Galilei Co. Ltd.; *Int'l*, pg. 2841
FUKUSHIMA INDUSTRIES CORPORATION - SHIGA FACTORY—See Fukushima Galilei Co. Ltd.; *Int'l*, pg. 2841
FUKUSHIMA INTERNATIONAL (CAMBODIA) CO., LTD.—See Fukushima Galilei Co. Ltd.; *Int'l*, pg. 2841
FUKUSHIMA INTERNATIONAL KOREA CORPORATION—See Fukushima Galilei Co. Ltd.; *Int'l*, pg. 2841
FUKUSIMA INTERNATIONAL (H.K.) CO., LIMITED—See Fukushima Galilei Co. Ltd.; *Int'l*, pg. 2841
FUKUSHIMA INTERNATIONAL (SHANGHAI) CO., LTD—See Fukushima Galilei Co. Ltd.; *Int'l*, pg. 2841
FUKUSIMA INTERNATIONAL (SINGAPORE) PTE., LTD.—See Fukushima Galilei Co. Ltd.; *Int'l*, pg. 2841
FUNAI SERVICE CORPORATION—See Funai Electric Co., Ltd.; *Int'l*, pg. 2844

335220 — MAJOR HOUSEHOLD APP...

GALILEI (THAILAND) CO., LTD.—See Fukushima Galilei Co. Ltd.; *Int'l*, pg. 2841
GENERAL ELECTRIC CANADA COMPANY—See General Electric Company; *U.S. Public*, pg. 918
GE PACIFIC PTE. LTD.—See General Electric Company; *U.S. Public*, pg. 917
GERHARD HAAS KG; *Int'l*, pg. 2942
GHG REDUCTION TECHNOLOGIES PRIVATE LIMITED—See EKI Energy Services Limited; *Int'l*, pg. 2338
GOLDEN SON LIMITED; *Int'l*, pg. 3032
GORENJE APARATI ZA DOMACINSTVO D.O.O.—See Hisense Co., Ltd.; *Int'l*, pg. 3407
GORENJE AUSTRIA HANDELSGESELLCHAFT MBH—See Hisense Co., Ltd.; *Int'l*, pg. 3407
GORENJE BUDAPEST KFT—See Hisense Co., Ltd.; *Int'l*, pg. 3407
GORENJE, D.D.—See Hisense Co., Ltd.; *Int'l*, pg. 3407
GORENJE D.O.O.—See Hisense Co., Ltd.; *Int'l*, pg. 3407
GORENJE ESPANA S.L.—See Hisense Co., Ltd.; *Int'l*, pg. 3407
GORENJE FRANCE S.A.S.—See Hisense Co., Ltd.; *Int'l*, pg. 3407
GORENJE KAZAKHSTAN TOO—See Hisense Co., Ltd.; *Int'l*, pg. 3407
GORENJE KORTING ITALIA S.R.L.—See Hisense Co., Ltd.; *Int'l*, pg. 3407
GORENJE SKOPJE D.O.O.—See Hisense Co., Ltd.; *Int'l*, pg. 3407
GORENJE SLOVAKIA S.R.O.—See Hisense Co., Ltd.; *Int'l*, pg. 3407
GORENJE ZAGREB D.O.O.—See Hisense Co., Ltd.; *Int'l*, pg. 3407
GRAM A/S—See Amica S.A.; *Int'l*, pg. 427
GRAM COMMERCIAL NUF—See Hoshizaki Corporation; *Int'l*, pg. 3483
GRAM COMMERCIAL—See Hoshizaki Corporation; *Int'l*, pg. 3483
GRAND HALL ENTERPRISE COMPANY LTD.; *Int'l*, pg. 3055
GREE ELECTRIC APPLIANCES, INC. OF ZHUHAI; *Int'l*, pg. 3068
GREE HOUSEHOLD ELECTRIC APPLIANCES CO., LTD.—See Gree Group Co., Ltd.; *Int'l*, pg. 3069
GUANGDONG CHANT GROUP CO., LTD.; *Int'l*, pg. 3153
GUANGDONG GALANZ GROUP CO., LTD.; *Int'l*, pg. 3154
GUANGDONG HOMA APPLIANCES CO., LTD.; *Int'l*, pg. 3155
GUANGDONG REAL-DESIGN INTELLIGENT TECHNOLOGY CO., LTD.; *Int'l*, pg. 3159
GUANGDONG SHUNNA ELECTRIC CO., LTD.; *Int'l*, pg. 3160
GUANGDONG VANWARD NEW ELECTRIC CO., LTD.; *Int'l*, pg. 3161
GUANGDONG XINBAO ELECTRICAL APPLIANCES HOLDINGS CO., LTD.; *Int'l*, pg. 3162
HAIER ELECTRONICS GROUP CO., LTD.—See Haier Smart Home Co., Ltd.; *Int'l*, pg. 3210
HAIER US APPLIANCE SOLUTIONS, INC.—See Haier Smart Home Co., Ltd.; *Int'l*, pg. 3210
HANGZHOU ROBAM APPLIANCES CO., LTD.; *Int'l*, pg. 3250
HAWKINS COOKERS LIMITED; *Int'l*, pg. 3289
HENAN XINFEI ELECTRIC CO., LTD.—See Hong Leong Investment Holdings Pte. Ltd.; *Int'l*, pg. 3469
HINDWARE HOME INNOVATION LIMITED; *Int'l*, pg. 3400
HISENSE KELON ELECTRICAL HOLDINGS CO., LTD.—See Hisense Co., Ltd.; *Int'l*, pg. 3407
HISENSE-WHIRLPOOL (ZHEJIANG) ELECTRIC APPLIANCES CO., LTD.—See Hisense Co., Ltd.; *Int'l*, pg. 3408
HISENSE-WHIRLPOOL (ZHEJIANG) ELECTRIC APPLIANCES CO., LTD.—See Whirlpool Corporation; *U.S. Public*, pg. 2367
HITACHI APPLIANCES TECHNO SERVICE, LTD.—See Hitachi, Ltd.; *Int'l*, pg. 3414
HITACHI CONSUMER ELECTRONICS CO., LTD. - YOKOHAMA WORKS—See Hitachi, Ltd.; *Int'l*, pg. 3416
HITACHI CONSUMER MARKETING (CHINA) LTD.—See Hitachi, Ltd.; *Int'l*, pg. 3416
HITACHI CONSUMER PRODUCTS (THAILAND), LTD.—See Hitachi, Ltd.; *Int'l*, pg. 3416
HITACHI EUROPE A.B. (GREECE)—See Hitachi, Ltd.; *Int'l*, pg. 3417
HITACHI INDIA PVT. LTD.—See Hitachi, Ltd.; *Int'l*, pg. 3419
HITACHI PLANT SERVICES CO., LTD.—See Hitachi, Ltd.; *Int'l*, pg. 3420
HOA PHAT HOME APPLIANCES JSC—See Hoa Phat Group Joint Stock Company; *Int'l*, pg. 3435
HOA PHAT REFRIGERATION ENGINEERING CO., LTD.—See Hoa Phat Group Joint Stock Company; *Int'l*, pg. 3435
HOBART FOOD EQUIPMENT GROUP CANADA—See Illinois Tool Works Inc.; *U.S. Public*, pg. 1103
THE HOLLAND COMPANY, INC.; *U.S. Private*, pg. 4054
HOMEWAY GMBH—See Hexatronic Group AB; *Int'l*, pg. 3371
HOOVER LTD.—See Haier Smart Home Co., Ltd.; *Int'l*, pg. 3210

HOSHIZAKI SHANGHAI CO., LTD.—See Hoshizaki Corporation; *Int'l*, pg. 3484
HOSHIZAKI TOHOKU K.K.—See Hoshizaki Corporation; *Int'l*, pg. 3484
HUSQVARNA OUTDOOR PRODUCTS - NASHVILLE—See Husqvarna AB; *Int'l*, pg. 3539
IHLAS EV ALETLERI IMALAT SANAYI VE TICARET A.S.; *Int'l*, pg. 3606
IL JIN ELECTRONICS (INDIA) PRIVATE LIMITED—See Amber Enterprises India Limited; *Int'l*, pg. 414
IMPACT PRODUCTS, LLC—See Genuine Parts Company; *U.S. Public*, pg. 932
IMTRON GMBH—See Ceconomy AG; *Int'l*, pg. 1373
INDESIT COMPANY BEYAZ ESYA PAZARLAMA A.S.—See Whirlpool Corporation; *U.S. Public*, pg. 2367
INDESIT COMPANY BULGARIA LTD.—See Whirlpool Corporation; *U.S. Public*, pg. 2367
INDESIT COMPANY MAGYARORSZAG KFT—See Whirlpool Corporation; *U.S. Public*, pg. 2367
INDESIT COMPANY POLSKA SP. Z O.O.—See Whirlpool Corporation; *U.S. Public*, pg. 2367
INDESIT COMPANY S.P.A.—See Whirlpool Corporation; *U.S. Public*, pg. 2367
IN-SINK-ERATOR—See Whirlpool Corporation; *U.S. Public*, pg. 2367
INTIRION CORP.—See Danby Products Ltd.; *Int'l*, pg. 1958
J&E HALL INTERNATIONAL LTD.—See Daikin Industries, Ltd.; *Int'l*, pg. 1935
JOHN BEAN TECHNOLOGIES AB—See John Bean Technologies Corporation; *U.S. Public*, pg. 1191
KITCHENAID—See Whirlpool Corporation; *U.S. Public*, pg. 2367
KOLEKTOR LIV D.O.O.—See Fluidmaster, Inc.; *U.S. Private*, pg. 1552
LA CORNUE SAS—See The Middleby Corporation; *U.S. Public*, pg. 2114
LA CORNUE SAS—See The Middleby Corporation; *U.S. Public*, pg. 2114
LA CORNUE SAS—See The Middleby Corporation; *U.S. Public*, pg. 2114
LA CORNUE SAS—See The Middleby Corporation; *U.S. Public*, pg. 2114
LA CORNUE SAS—See The Middleby Corporation; *U.S. Public*, pg. 2114
LIBERTY MEXICANA S.A. DE C.V.—See AISIN Corporation; *Int'l*, pg. 253
LLM APPLIANCES LIMITED—See Crompton Greaves Consumer Electricals Limited; *Int'l*, pg. 1853
LOCHINVAR LIMITED—See A. O. Smith Corporation; *U.S. Public*, pg. 12
LYNX GRILLS, INC.—See The Middleby Corporation; *U.S. Public*, pg. 2114
MASTERBUILT MANUFACTURING, LLC—See The Middleby Corporation; *U.S. Public*, pg. 2114
MENSCHICK TROCKENSYSTEME GMBH—See Heidelberger Druckmaschinen AG; *Int'l*, pg. 3322
MORA MORAVIA S R.O.—See Hisense Co., Ltd.; *Int'l*, pg. 3407
MYOB HONG KONG LIMITED—See Bain Capital, LP; *U.S. Private*, pg. 442
NESTOR CO., LTD—See Hoshizaki Corporation; *Int'l*, pg. 3484
NEWELL BRANDS DE COLOMBIA S.A.S.—See Newell Brands Inc.; *U.S. Public*, pg. 1514
NEWELL BRANDS DE PERU, S.A.C.—See Newell Brands Inc.; *U.S. Public*, pg. 1514
NORCOLD—See The Dyson-Kissner-Moran Corporation; *U.S. Private*, pg. 4024
OPERIO GROUP, LLC; *U.S. Private*, pg. 3032
OY ELECTROLUX AB—See AB Electrolux; *Int'l*, pg. 41
PIONEER TECHNOLOGY (DONGGUAN) CO., LTD.—See EQT AB; *Int'l*, pg. 2471
PROCTER & GAMBLE AMIENS S.A.S.—See The Procter & Gamble Company; *U.S. Public*, pg. 2121
PROCTER & GAMBLE OVERSEAS INDIA B.V.—See The Procter & Gamble Company; *U.S. Public*, pg. 2123
PT. FUKUSHIMA INTERNATIONAL INDONESIA—See Fukushima Galilei Co. Ltd.; *Int'l*, pg. 2841
PT. MERDIS INTERNATIONAL—See Bain Capital, LP; *U.S. Private*, pg. 449
QUALITY CRAFT LTD—See Collins Co., Ltd.; *Int'l*, pg. 1702
READING STOVE COMPANY—See Reading Anthracite Company; *U.S. Private*, pg. 3366
REGAL WARE, INC.—See Regal Ware, Inc.; *U.S. Private*, pg. 3386
R.H. PETERSON CO.; *U.S. Private*, pg. 3336
RJ BRANDS LLC; *U.S. Private*, pg. 3449
ROBAM MALAYSIA SDN BHD—See Hangzhou Robam Appliances Co., Ltd.; *Int'l*, pg. 3250
ROPER CORPORATION—See Haier Smart Home Co., Ltd.; *Int'l*, pg. 3210
ROSINOX SAS—See Ali Holding S.r.l.; *Int'l*, pg. 321
RUSSELL HOBBS FOOD EQUIPMENT LIMITED—See Blue Point Capital Partners, LLC; *U.S. Private*, pg. 590
R.W. DISTRIBUTORS—See Rena-Ware Distributors Inc.; *U.S. Private*, pg. 3397
SALADMASTER—See Regal Ware, Inc.; *U.S. Private*, pg. 3386
SAMHA HOME APPLIANCE SPA—See Cevital S.p.A.; *Int'l*, pg. 1425

SCANDINAVIAN APPLIANCES A.S—See Frigoglass S.A.I.C.; *Int'l*, pg. 2792
SHARKNINJA OPERATING LLC—See SharkNinja, Inc.; *U.S. Public*, pg. 1873
SHARP (PHILS.) CORPORATION—See Hon Hai Precision Industry Co., Ltd.; *Int'l*, pg. 3457
SINGER (SRI LANKA) PLC—See Hayleys PLC; *Int'l*, pg. 3292
SMOKE'N PIT CORPORATION—See Brinkmann Corp.; *U.S. Private*, pg. 655
SODASTREAM AUSTRALIA PTY. LTD.—See PepsiCo, Inc.; *U.S. Public*, pg. 1672
SODASTREAM USA, INC.—See PepsiCo, Inc.; *U.S. Public*, pg. 1672
SONNEX INVESTMENTS (PTY.) LTD.—See Barloworld Ltd.; *Int'l*, pg. 866
SPECTRUM BRANDS AUSTRIA GMBH—See Spectrum Brands Holdings, Inc.; *U.S. Public*, pg. 1915
SPECTRUM BRANDS BENELUX B.V.—See Spectrum Brands Holdings, Inc.; *U.S. Public*, pg. 1916
STATE INDUSTRIES, LLC; *U.S. Private*, pg. 3792
STIERLEN GMBH—See Ali Holding S.r.l.; *Int'l*, pg. 321
SUB-ZERO FREEZER CO., INC.; *U.S. Private*, pg. 3847
SUMMERSET PROFESSIONAL GRILLS; *U.S. Private*, pg. 3853
SUNBEAM AMERICAS HOLDINGS, LLC—See Newell Brands Inc.; *U.S. Public*, pg. 1515
SUNBEAM CORPORATION PTY LTD—See Newell Brands Inc.; *U.S. Public*, pg. 1515
SUNBEAM PRODUCTS, INC.—See Newell Brands Inc.; *U.S. Public*, pg. 1515
TAIWAN FUKUSIMA INTERNATIONAL CO., LTD—See Fukushima Galilei Co. Ltd.; *Int'l*, pg. 2841
THAI AUTOMOTIVE & APPLIANCES LTD.—See IFB Industries Limited; *Int'l*, pg. 3598
THETFORD CORPORATION—See The Dyson-Kissner-Moran Corporation; *U.S. Private*, pg. 4024
TRAEGER PELLET GRILLS LLC; *U.S. Private*, pg. 4203
TURBOCHEF TECHNOLOGIES, INC.—See The Middleby Corporation; *U.S. Public*, pg. 2115
U-LINE CORPORATION—See The Middleby Corporation; *U.S. Public*, pg. 2115
USINES DE ROSIERES S.A.S.—See Haier Smart Home Co., Ltd.; *Int'l*, pg. 3210
VIKING RANGE LLC—See The Middleby Corporation; *U.S. Public*, pg. 2115
VITA-MIX CORPORATION; *U.S. Private*, pg. 4405
VULCAN-HART—See Illinois Tool Works Inc.; *U.S. Public*, pg. 1111
WARING PRODUCTS, INC.—See American Securities LLC; *U.S. Private*, pg. 248
WATERFORD STANLEY LTD.—See The Middleby Corporation; *U.S. Public*, pg. 2114
W.C. BRADLEY CO.; *U.S. Private*, pg. 4419
WEBER-STEPHEN PRODUCTS LLC—See BDT Capital Partners, LLC; *U.S. Private*, pg. 503
WELBILT ASIA PACIFIC PRIVATE LIMITED—See Ali Holding S.r.l; *Int'l*, pg. 323
WELBILT M.E. - FZE—See Ali Holding S.r.l; *Int'l*, pg. 323
WEXIODISK AB—See Ali Holding S.r.l.; *Int'l*, pg. 322
WHIRLPOOL ASIA INC.—See Whirlpool Corporation; *U.S. Public*, pg. 2367
WHIRLPOOL CORP. - CLYDE—See Whirlpool Corporation; *U.S. Public*, pg. 2367
WHIRLPOOL CORP. - EVANSVILLE—See Whirlpool Corporation; *U.S. Public*, pg. 2367
WHIRLPOOL CORP. - FINDLAY—See Whirlpool Corporation; *U.S. Public*, pg. 2367
WHIRLPOOL CORP. - FORT SMITH—See Whirlpool Corporation; *U.S. Public*, pg. 2367
WHIRLPOOL CORP. - MARION—See Whirlpool Corporation; *U.S. Public*, pg. 2367
WHIRLPOOL DO BRASIL LTDA.—See Whirlpool Corporation; *U.S. Public*, pg. 2368
WHIRLPOOL EUROPE B.V.—See Whirlpool Corporation; *U.S. Public*, pg. 2367
WHIRLPOOL EUROPE COORDINATION CENTER—See Whirlpool Corporation; *U.S. Public*, pg. 2367
WHIRLPOOL EUROPE OPERATIONS CENTER—See Whirlpool Corporation; *U.S. Public*, pg. 2367
WHIRLPOOL FRANCE SAS—See Whirlpool Corporation; *U.S. Public*, pg. 2367
WHIRLPOOL HELLAS SA—See Whirlpool Corporation; *U.S. Public*, pg. 2367
WHIRLPOOL HOME APPLIANCE (SHANGHAI) CO., LTD.—See Whirlpool Corporation; *U.S. Public*, pg. 2367
WHIRLPOOL (HONG KONG) LTD.—See Whirlpool Corporation; *U.S. Public*, pg. 2367
WHIRLPOOL INTERNACIONAL S. DE R.L. DE C.V.—See Whirlpool Corporation; *U.S. Public*, pg. 2368
WHIRLPOOL IRELAND—See Whirlpool Corporation; *U.S. Public*, pg. 2368
WHIRLPOOL MEXICO, S.A. DE C.V.—See Whirlpool Corporation; *U.S. Public*, pg. 2368
WHIRLPOOL NORDIC AB—See Whirlpool Corporation; *U.S. Public*, pg. 2368
WHIRLPOOL NORDIC OY—See Whirlpool Corporation; *U.S. Public*, pg. 2368

335220 — MAJOR HOUSEHOLD APP...

WHIRLPOOL OF INDIA LIMITED—See Whirlpool Corporation; *U.S. Public*, pg. 2368
WHIRLPOOL S.A.—See Whirlpool Corporation; *U.S. Public*, pg. 2368
WHIRLPOOL SLOVAKIA SPOL. S.R.O.—See Whirlpool Corporation; *U.S. Public*, pg. 2368

335311 — POWER, DISTRIBUTION, AND SPECIALTY TRANSFORMER MANUFACTURING

ABB AB—See ABB Ltd.; *Int'l*, pg. 49
ABB AUTOMATION EOOD—See ABB Ltd.; *Int'l*, pg. 50
ABB BULGARIA EOOD—See ABB Ltd.; *Int'l*, pg. 50
ABB (CHINA) LTD.—See ABB Ltd.; *Int'l*, pg. 49
ABB HEFEI TRANSFORMER CO. LTD.—See ABB Ltd.; *Int'l*, pg. 49
ABB HOLDING A.S.—See ABB Ltd.; *Int'l*, pg. 51
ABB HOLDINGS PTE. LTD.—See ABB Ltd.; *Int'l*, pg. 51
ABB INC. - ANALYTICAL & ADVANCED SOLUTIONS—See ABB Ltd.; *Int'l*, pg. 51
ABB INC. - AUTOMATION TECHNOLOGIES DRIVES & MOTORS—See ABB Ltd.; *Int'l*, pg. 51
ABB INC. - POWER SYSTEMS—See ABB Ltd.; *Int'l*, pg. 51
ABB INC. - POWER TECHNOLOGIES MEDIUM VOLTAGE—See ABB Ltd.; *Int'l*, pg. 51
ABB INC.—See ABB Ltd.; *Int'l*, pg. 51
ABB INC.—See ABB Ltd.; *Int'l*, pg. 51
ABB K.K.—See ABB Ltd.; *Int'l*, pg. 52
ABB LIMITED—See ABB Ltd.; *Int'l*, pg. 53
ABB LTD.—See ABB Ltd.; *Int'l*, pg. 53
ABB LTD.—See ABB Ltd.; *Int'l*, pg. 53
ABB LTD.—See ABB Ltd.; *Int'l*, pg. 53
ABB OY—See ABB Ltd.; *Int'l*, pg. 53
ABB POWER TECHNOLOGIES AB—See ABB Ltd.; *Int'l*, pg. 49
ABB ROMANIA—See ABB Ltd.; *Int'l*, pg. 53
ABB S.A.—See ABB Ltd.; *Int'l*, pg. 54
ABB SECHERON LTD.—See ABB Ltd.; *Int'l*, pg. 54
ABB SP. Z O.O.—See ABB Ltd.; *Int'l*, pg. 55
ABB S.R.O.—See ABB Ltd.; *Int'l*, pg. 55
ABB S.R.O.—See ABB Ltd.; *Int'l*, pg. 55
ABB STRIEBEL & JOHN GMBH—See ABB Ltd.; *Int'l*, pg. 55
ABB SWITZERLAND LTD., MICAFIL—See ABB Ltd.; *Int'l*, pg. 54
ABB SWITZERLAND LTD - POWER ELECTRONICS—See ABB Ltd.; *Int'l*, pg. 54
ABB SWITZERLAND LTD - POWER SYSTEMS—See ABB Ltd.; *Int'l*, pg. 54
ABB TECHNOLOGIES LTD.—See ABB Ltd.; *Int'l*, pg. 55
ABB TRANSFORMERS S.A.E.—See ABB Ltd.; *Int'l*, pg. 55
ABB ZHONGSHAN TRANSFORMER COMPANY LTD.—See ABB Ltd.; *Int'l*, pg. 49
ACME ELECTRIC LLC—See Hubbell Incorporated; *U.S. Public*, pg. 1066
ACTIVE ENERGY LIMITED—See Active Energy Group plc; *Int'l*, pg. 120
AEI—See Ashmore Group plc; *Int'l*, pg. 608
AFP TRANSFORMERS, INC.—See United Capital Corp.; *U.S. Private*, pg. 4288
AGC MULTI MATERIAL AMERICA, INC.—See AGC Inc.; *Int'l*, pg. 202
AICHI ELECTRIC CO., LTD.; *Int'l*, pg. 229
AICHI ELECTRIC POWER PRODUCTS DIVISION—See Aichi Electric Co., Ltd.; *Int'l*, pg. 229
AICHI KINZOKU KOGYO CO., LTD.—See Aichi Electric Co., Ltd.; *Int'l*, pg. 229
AIKOKIKI MFG. CO., LTD.—See Aichi Electric Co., Ltd.; *Int'l*, pg. 229
AIREX, LLC—See Allient Inc.; *U.S. Public*, pg. 80
ALFA TRANSFORMERS LTD.; *Int'l*, pg. 312
ALLTOP TECHNOLOGY CO., LTD.; *Int'l*, pg. 361
ALPHA TECHNOLOGIES, INC.—See EnerSys; *U.S. Public*, pg. 767
ALPHA TECHNOLOGIES LTD.—See EnerSys; *U.S. Public*, pg. 767
ALPIQ AG—See Alpiq Holding AG; *Int'l*, pg. 372
ALTAIR ENGINEERING ISRAEL LTD.—See Altair Engineering, Inc.; *U.S. Public*, pg. 86
ALTAWEST GROUP; *Int'l*, pg. 388
AMBA ENTERPRISES LTD.; *Int'l*, pg. 413
AMTECH DRIVES, INC.—See Amtech Electronics India Limited; *Int'l*, pg. 441
AMTECH POWER LIMITED—See Amtech Electronics India Limited; *Int'l*, pg. 441
APPLIED KILOVOLTS LIMITED—See L3Harris Technologies, Inc.; *U.S. Public*, pg. 1280
AQ ELECTRIC SUZHOU CO., LTD.—See AQ Group AB; *Int'l*, pg. 526
AQ TRAFOTEK AS—See AQ Group AB; *Int'l*, pg. 526
AQ TRAFOTEK OY—See AQ Group AB; *Int'l*, pg. 526
ASEA BROWN BOVERI, S.A.—See ABB Ltd.; *Int'l*, pg. 55
ASEA BROWN BOVERI, S.A.—See ABB Ltd.; *Int'l*, pg. 55
ASEA BROWN BOVERI, S.A.—See ABB Ltd.; *Int'l*, pg. 55
ASIA POWER CORPORATION LIMITED; *Int'l*, pg. 615
ASTEC CUSTOM POWER (SINGAPORE) PTE LTD.—See Advanced Energy Industries, Inc.; *U.S. Public*, pg. 47
ASTEC EUROPE LIMITED—See Advanced Energy Industries, Inc.; *U.S. Public*, pg. 47
ASTEC POWER PHILIPPINES, INC.—See Advanced Energy Industries, Inc.; *U.S. Public*, pg. 47
ASTRONICS ADVANCED ELECTRONIC SYSTEMS CORP.—See Astronics Corporation; *U.S. Public*, pg. 217
ATCO POWER LTD.—See ATCO Ltd.; *Int'l*, pg. 666
AVIENT (THAILAND) CO., LTD.—See Avient Corporation; *U.S. Public*, pg. 246
AVIONIC INSTRUMENTS INC.—See TransDigm Group Incorporated; *U.S. Public*, pg. 2182
BAODING SIFANG SANYI ELECTRIC CO., LTD.—See Beijing Sifang Automation Co., Ltd.; *Int'l*, pg. 957
BASLER ELECTRIC COMPANY; *U.S. Private*, pg. 485
BEHLMAN ELECTRONICS, INC.—See Orbit International Corp.; *U.S. Public*, pg. 1614
BEIJING CREATIVE DISTRIBUTION AUTOMATION CO., LTD.; *Int'l*, pg. 948
BEIJING HEZONG SCIENCE & TECHNOLOGY CO., LTD.; *Int'l*, pg. 951
BEIJING LI CONTEMPORARY AMPEREX TECHNOLOGY LIMITED—See Contemporary Amperex Technology Co., Ltd.; *Int'l*, pg. 1779
BEIJING SIFANG AUTOMATION CO., LTD.; *Int'l*, pg. 957
BELA VISTA GERACAO DE ENERGIA S.A.—See Companhia Paranaense de Energia; *Int'l*, pg. 1747
BENTLY NEVADA CANADA LTD.—See General Electric Company; *U.S. Public*, pg. 919
BENTLY NEVADA CANADA LTD.—See General Electric Company; *U.S. Public*, pg. 919
BENTLY NEVADA, INC.—See General Electric Company; *U.S. Public*, pg. 919
BETA TRANSFORMER TECHNOLOGY CORPORATION—See TransDigm Group Incorporated; *U.S. Public*, pg. 2182
BHEL ELECTRICAL MACHINES LIMITED—See Bharat Heavy Electricals Limited; *Int'l*, pg. 1011
BILPOWER LIMITED; *Int'l*, pg. 1031
BING ENERGY INTERNATIONAL, LLC; *U.S. Private*, pg. 560
BODE KOREA CO. LTD.—See The Carlyle Group Inc.; *U.S. Public*, pg. 2053
BOMAY ELECTRIC INDUSTRIES CO.—See STABILIS SOLUTIONS, INC.; *U.S. Public*, pg. 1924
BOSUNG POWER TECHNOLOGY CO., LTD.; *Int'l*, pg. 1118
B PLUS L TECHNOLOGIES INC.; *U.S. Private*, pg. 417
C&D TECHNOLOGIES DYNASTY DIVISION—See KPS Capital Partners, LP; *U.S. Private*, pg. 2347
CECEP ENVIRONMENTAL PROTECTION CO., LTD.; *Int'l*, pg. 1372
CEEPOWER CO., LTD.; *Int'l*, pg. 1388
CENTRAL MOLONEY INC.—See Wind Point Advisors LLC; *U.S. Private*, pg. 4534
CG ELECTRIC SYSTEMS HUNGARY ZRT—See Avantha Group; *Int'l*, pg. 735
CG HOLDINGS BELGIUM NV—See Avantha Group; *Int'l*, pg. 735
CG POWER AND INDUSTRIAL SOLUTIONS LTD.—See Avantha Group; *Int'l*, pg. 735
CG POWER SYSTEMS CANADA INC.—See Avantha Group; *Int'l*, pg. 736
CHENGDU TIANJIAN TECHNOLOGY CO., LTD.; *Int'l*, pg. 1469
CHINA STEEL PRECISION METALS KUNSHAN CO., LTD.—See China Steel Corporation; *Int'l*, pg. 1555
CHINA XD ELECTRICITY CO., LTD.; *Int'l*, pg. 1563
CHLORIDE POWER PROTECTION AUSTRALIA—See Vertiv Holdings Co; *U.S. Public*, pg. 2288
CITY WINDMILLS LTD.; *Int'l*, pg. 1628
CLEAN ENERGY PATHWAYS, INC.; *U.S. Public*, pg. 508
CLORE AUTOMOTIVE LLC; *U.S. Private*, pg. 946
CLORE AUTOMOTIVE - SOLAR DIV.—See Clore Automotive LLC; *U.S. Private*, pg. 946
CLYDE BERGEMANN FOREST S.A.—See Clyde Blowers Capital IM LLP; *Int'l*, pg. 1665
CNPV SOLAR POWER S.A.; *Int'l*, pg. 1678
COIL-TRAN LLC—See discoverIE Group plc; *Int'l*, pg. 2133
CONSTRUCTION ELECTRICAL PRODUCTS, LLC—See Southwire Company, LLC; *U.S. Private*, pg. 3742
CONTEMPORARY AMPEREX TECHNOLOGY GMBH—See Contemporary Amperex Technology Co., Ltd.; *Int'l*, pg. 1779
CONTEMPORARY AMPEREX TECHNOLOGY THURINGIA GMBH—See Contemporary Amperex Technology Co., Ltd.; *Int'l*, pg. 1779
CONTEMPORARY AMPEREX TECHNOLOGY USA INC.—See Contemporary Amperex Technology Co., Ltd.; *Int'l*, pg. 1779
CONTROL TRANSFORMER CORP.—See Park-Ohio Holdings Corp.; *U.S. Public*, pg. 1639
COOPER INDUSTRIES JAPAN K.K.—See Eaton Corporation plc; *U.S. Public*, pg. 2277
COOPER POWER SYSTEMS, LLC - WAUKESHA (EAST NORTH STREET) PLANT—See Eaton Corporation plc; *Int'l*, pg. 2278
COSEL ASIA LTD.—See COSEL Co., Ltd.; *Int'l*, pg. 1810
COSEL EUROPE GMBH—See COSEL Co., Ltd.; *Int'l*, pg. 1810
COSEL (SHANGHAI) ELECTRONICS CO., LTD.—See COSEL Co., Ltd.; *Int'l*, pg. 1810
DALEKOVOD D.D. - VELIKA GORICA FACTORY—See Dalekovod d.d.; *Int'l*, pg. 1950
DANDONG XINTAI ELECTRIC COMPANY LIMITED; *Int'l*, pg. 1959
DATA DEVICE CORPORATION—See TransDigm Group Incorporated; *U.S. Public*, pg. 2182
DATANG INTERNATIONAL POWER GENERATION CO., LTD.—See China Datang Corporation; *Int'l*, pg. 1497
DELTA ELECTRONICS (KOREA), INC.—See Delta Electronics, Inc.; *Int'l*, pg. 2017
DELTA ELECTRONICS (WUHU) CO., LTD.—See Delta Electronics, Inc.; *Int'l*, pg. 2017
DELTA STAR INC.; *U.S. Private*, pg. 1202
DELTA STAR WEST—See Delta Star Inc.; *U.S. Private*, pg. 1202
DELTA TRANSFORMERS INC.—See Hammond Power Solutions Inc.; *Int'l*, pg. 3239
DELTA VIDEO DISPLAY SYSTEM (WUJIANG) LTD.—See Delta Electronics, Inc.; *Int'l*, pg. 2017
DITEK CORPORATION; *U.S. Private*, pg. 1240
DOMINOVAS ENERGY CORPORATION; *U.S. Public*, pg. 675
D.P. EATON ELECTRIC—See Eaton Corporation plc; *Int'l*, pg. 2279
DULHUNTY POWER (NZ) LIMITED—See Energy Technologies Limited; *Int'l*, pg. 2423
DYNAPOWER COMPANY, LLC—See Sensata Technologies Holding plc; *U.S. Public*, pg. 1865
EAST GROUP CO., LTD.; *Int'l*, pg. 2270
EESTI ENERGIA AS; *Int'l*, pg. 2317
EGAT PUBLIC COMPANY LIMITED; *Int'l*, pg. 2322
EGBERT CORP.—See Materion Corporation; *U.S. Public*, pg. 1395
EGUANA TECHNOLOGIES INC.; *Int'l*, pg. 2326
ELECTRICAL EQUIPMENT JOINT STOCK COMPANY; *Int'l*, pg. 2349
ELECTRIC RESEARCH & MANUFACTURING COOPERATIVE, INC. (ERMCO)—See Arkansas Electric Cooperatives, Inc.; *U.S. Private*, pg. 325
ELECTRO-MECHANICAL CORPORATION—See Graycliff Partners LP; *U.S. Private*, pg. 1760
ELTEK AS—See Delta Electronics, Inc.; *Int'l*, pg. 2017
ELTEK DEUTSCHLAND GMBH—See Delta Electronics, Inc.; *Int'l*, pg. 2017
ELTEK ENERGY INTERNATIONAL DE MEXICO S. DE R.L. DE C.V.—See Delta Electronics, Inc.; *Int'l*, pg. 2017
ELTEK ENERGY TECHNOLOGY LTD.—See Delta Electronics, Inc.; *Int'l*, pg. 2017
ELTEK POWER FRANCE SAS—See Delta Electronics, Inc.; *Int'l*, pg. 2017
ELTEK POWER (UK) LTD.—See Delta Electronics, Inc.; *Int'l*, pg. 2017
ELTEK SISTEMAS DE ENERGIA INDUSTRIA E COMERCIO S.A.—See Delta Electronics, Inc.; *Int'l*, pg. 2017
ELTEK S.R.O.—See Delta Electronics, Inc.; *Int'l*, pg. 2017
EMERSON ELECTRONIC CONNECTOR AND COMPONENTS, S.A. DE C.V.—See Emerson Electric Co.; *U.S. Public*, pg. 745
EMERSON NETWORK POWER, LDA—See Vertiv Holdings Co; *Int'l*, pg. 2288
EMERSON NETWORK POWER—See Vertiv Holdings Co; *U.S. Public*, pg. 2288
ENA AICHI ELECTRIC CO., LTD.—See Aichi Electric Co., Ltd.; *Int'l*, pg. 229
ENGIE EPS S.A.—See ENGIE SA; *Int'l*, pg. 2429
ENTECH SOLAR, INC.; *U.S. Private*, pg. 1402
ENVIPCO SLOVAKIA S.R.O.—See Envipco Holding N.V.; *Int'l*, pg. 2453
FEELUX LIGHTING CO., LTD.—See FEELUX Co., Ltd.; *Int'l*, pg. 2632
FIBON ELECTRIC (M) SDN. BHD.—See Fibon Berhad; *Int'l*, pg. 2652
FORTUNE ELECTRIC CO., LTD. - POWER DIVISION—See Fortune Electric Co., Ltd.; *Int'l*, pg. 2743
FORTUNE ELECTRIC (WUHAN) LTD.—See Fortune Electric Co., Ltd.; *Int'l*, pg. 2743
FRANCE FILIERES PLASTIQUES S.A.S.—See Greiner Holding AG; *Int'l*, pg. 3078
FREEDOM POWER SYSTEMS, INC.—See Vicor Corporation; *U.S. Public*, pg. 2296
FRIEDHELM LOH STIFTUNG & CO. KG; *Int'l*, pg. 2791
FUJI TUSCO CO., LTD.—See Fuji Electric Co., Ltd.; *Int'l*, pg. 2812
GEC DURHAM INDUSTRIES, INC.—See Durham Co.; *U.S. Private*, pg. 1293
GEFCO, INC.—See Astec Industries, Inc.; *U.S. Public*, pg. 216
GE GRID SOLUTIONS PTE. LTD.—See General Electric Company; *U.S. Public*, pg. 918
GEI GLOBAL ENERGY CORP.; *U.S. Private*, pg. 1655
GERSAN ELEKTRIK TICARET VE SANAYI AS; *Int'l*, pg. 2945
GE T&D INDIA LTD.—See General Electric Company; *U.S. Public*, pg. 917
GIFU AICHI ELECTRIC CO., LTD.—See Aichi Electric Co., Ltd.; *Int'l*, pg. 229
GLOBTEK, INC.; *U.S. Private*, pg. 1720

335312 — MOTOR AND GENERATOR...

GOTION HIGH-TECH CO., LTD.; *Int'l*, pg. 3043
GPN GMBH—See Greiner Holding AG; *Int'l*, pg. 3079
GRAND TRANSFORMERS INC.—See Blackford Capital LLC; *U.S. Private*, pg. 574
GREINER EXTRUSION TECHNOLOGY (SHANGHAI) CO., LTD.—See Greiner Holding AG; *Int'l*, pg. 3079
GREINER TOOL.TEC GMBH—See Greiner Holding AG; *Int'l*, pg. 3079
GRID SOLUTIONS SAS—See General Electric Company; *U.S. Public*, pg. 917
GRID SOLUTIONS S.P.A—See General Electric Company; *U.S. Public*, pg. 918
GUIZHOU TAIYONG-CHANGZHENG TECHNOLOGY CO., LTD.; *Int'l*, pg. 3175
GUODIAN TECHNOLOGY & ENVIRONMENT GROUP CORPORATION LIMITED; *Int'l*, pg. 3186
HANGZHOU STAR SHUAIER ELECTRIC APPLIANCE CO., LTD.; *Int'l*, pg. 3250
HANGZHOU ZHONGHENG ELECTRIC CO., LTD.; *Int'l*, pg. 3251
HARBIN JIUZHOU GROUP CO., LTD.; *Int'l*, pg. 3270
HEBEI TIANWEI HUARI ELECTRIC CO., LTD.—See Advanced Technology & Materials Co., Ltd.; *Int'l*, pg. 162
HEXING ELECTRICAL CO LTD; *Int'l*, pg. 3371
HICO AMERICA SALES & TECHNOLOGY, INC.—See Hyosung Corporation; *Int'l*, pg. 3551
HICONICS ECO-ENERGY TECHNOLOGY CO., LTD.; *Int'l*, pg. 3384
HIREL SYSTEMS LLC—See Vishay Intertechnology, Inc.; *U.S. Public*, pg. 2302
HITACHI CANADA LTD. - CALGARY POWER AND INDUSTRY DIVISION—See Hitachi, Ltd.; *Int'l*, pg. 3415
HITACHI QIANDIAN (HANGZHOU) TRANSFORMER CO., LTD.—See Hitachi, Ltd.; *Int'l*, pg. 3419
HITACHI SOE ELECTRIC & MACHINERY CO., LTD.—See Hitachi, Ltd.; *Int'l*, pg. 3421
HITACHI T&D SYSTEMS SAUDI ARABIA, LTD.—See Hitachi, Ltd.; *Int'l*, pg. 3422
HOWARD INDUSTRIES, INC.; *U.S. Private*, pg. 1995
HOWARD INDUSTRIES—See Howard Industries, Inc.; *U.S. Private*, pg. 1995
HUNTERDON TRANSFORMER CO. INC.; *U.S. Private*, pg. 2010
HYUNDAI POWER TRANSFORMERS USA INC.—See Hyundai Electric & Energy Systems Co., Ltd.; *Int'l*, pg. 3556
IDEAL POWER INC.; *U.S. Public*, pg. 1088
INDIANA-KENTUCKY ELECTRIC CORPORATION—See American Electric Power Company, Inc.; *U.S. Public*, pg. 99
INNOSPEC RUSS OOO—See Innospec Inc.; *U.S. Public*, pg. 1125
INTELLIPOWER, INC.—See AMETEK, Inc.; *U.S. Public*, pg. 120
INTERMAGNETICS SRL—See ABB Ltd.; *Int'l*, pg. 54
JAPAN POWER BRAKES—See Carlisle Companies Incorporated; *U.S. Public*, pg. 437
JBT NETHERLANDS B.V.—See John Bean Technologies Corporation; *U.S. Public*, pg. 1191
JEFFERSON ELECTRIC INC.—See Guggenheim Partners, LLC; *U.S. Private*, pg. 1812
JIANGSU SUNEL TRANSFORMER CO., LTD.—See Guodian Nanjing Automation Co., Ltd.; *Int'l*, pg. 3186
JOHN BEAN TECHNOLOGIES SPAIN S.L.U.—See John Bean Technologies Corporation; *U.S. Public*, pg. 1192
KANJANADIT PALM OIL CO., LTD.—See Energy Absolute Public Company Limited; *Int'l*, pg. 2422
KENTUCKY ASSOCIATION OF ELECTRIC COOPERATIVES, INC.; *U.S. Private*, pg. 2288
KEPCO INC.; *U.S. Private*, pg. 2290
KOTOBUKI KOGYO CO., LTD.—See Aichi Electric Co., Ltd.; *Int'l*, pg. 229
KUHLMAN ELECTRIC CORPORATION—See ABB Ltd.; *Int'l*, pg. 52
L-3 SPD ELECTRICAL SYSTEMS, INC.—See L3Harris Technologies, Inc.; *U.S. Public*, pg. 1283
LEVITON SRL DE C.V.—See Leviton Manufacturing Company, Inc.; *U.S. Private*, pg. 2437
LIGHT SERVICOS DE ELETRICIDADE S.A.—See Companhia Energetica de Minas Gerais - CEMIG; *Int'l*, pg. 1747
LTI POWER SYSTEMS, INC.; *U.S. Private*, pg. 2509
L.V. CONTROL MANUFACTURING LIMITED—See Exchange Income Corporation; *Int'l*, pg. 2579
MADDOX INDUSTRIAL TRANSFORMER, LLC; *U.S. Private*, pg. 2539
MAG-CON ENGINEERING—See Badger Magnetics, Inc.; *U.S. Private*, pg. 424
MAGNETIKA, INC.—See Magnetika, Inc.; *U.S. Private*, pg 2547
MANHATTAN TOY EUROPE LIMITED—See Crown Crafts, Inc.; *U.S. Public*, pg. 596
MARSH BELLOFRAM CORPORATION—See Desco Corporation; *U.S. Private*, pg. 1211
MARSH BELLOFRAM—See Desco Corporation; *U.S. Private*, pg. 1211
MATERION MICROELECTRONICS & SERVICES—See Materion Corporation; *U.S. Public*, pg. 1396
MDS CO. LTD.—See CMIC Holdings Co., Ltd.; *Int'l*, pg. 1670
MEGATRAN INDUSTRIES INC.—See American Superconductor Corporation; *U.S. Public*, pg. 110
MERAMEC INSTRUMENT TRANSFORMER COMPANY—See Hubbell Incorporated; *U.S. Public*, pg. 1067
MICRON INDUSTRIES CORP.—See Hammond Power Solutions, Inc.; *U.S. Private*, pg. 1850
MILLUX B.V.—See IDEX Corp; *U.S. Public*, pg. 1091
MINNTRONIX, INC.—See Standex International; *U.S. Public*, pg. 1930
MISSION CRITICAL GROUP; *U.S. Private*, pg. 2747
MTE CORPORATION—See Steel Partners Holdings L.P.; *U.S. Public*, pg. 1943
NAGANO AICHI ELECTRIC CO., LTD.—See Aichi Electric Co., Ltd.; *Int'l*, pg. 229
NANJING CBAK NEW ENERGY TECHNOLOGY CO., LTD.—See CBAK Energy Technology, Inc.; *Int'l*, pg. 1364
NC NETWORK, INC.—See Di-Nikko Engineering Co., Ltd.; *Int'l*, pg. 2101
NEELTRAN, INC.—See American Superconductor Corporation; *U.S. Public*, pg. 110
NEWAVA TECHNOLOGY, INC.; *U.S. Private*, pg. 2913
N.G. GILBERT CORPORATION—See The Townsend Corporation; *U.S. Private*, pg. 4127
NIAGARA TRANSFORMER CORP.; *U.S. Private*, pg. 2924
NORTH HILLS SIGNAL PROCESSING CORP.—See TransDigm Group Incorporated; *U.S. Public*, pg. 2183
NORTHLAKE ENGINEERING, INC.—See Standex International; *U.S. Public*, pg. 1930
NUSCALE POWER, LLC—See Fluor Corporation; *U.S. Public*, pg. 859
NWL TRANSFORMERS INC.—See American Superconductor Corporation; *U.S. Public*, pg. 110
ORMAT INDUSTRIES LTD.—See Ormat Technologies, Inc.; *U.S. Public*, pg. 1618
OSAKA FUSE CO., LTD.—See Daihen Corporation; *Int'l*, pg. 1926
PAUWELS TRANSFORMERS N.V.—See Electrical Industries Company; *Int'l*, pg. 2349
PENNSYLVANIA TRANSFORMER TECHNOLOGY INC.—See Quanta Services, Inc.; *U.S. Public*, pg. 1752
PIPELINE RENEWAL TECHNOLOGIES LIMITED LIABILITY COMPANY—See IDEX Corp; *U.S. Public*, pg. 1091
POWELL ESCO COMPANY—See Powell Industries, Inc.; *U.S. Public*, pg. 1705
POWERGRID SOLUTIONS LLC—See AZZ, Inc.; *U.S. Public*, pg. 259
POWER PARAGON—See L3Harris Technologies, Inc.; *U.S. Public*, pg. 1283
POWER QUALITY INTERNATIONAL, INC.; *U.S. Private*, pg. 3238
POWER TECH SYSTEMS PTY LTD—See Byte Power Group Limited; *Int'l*, pg. 1237
RHOMBUS ENERGY SOLUTIONS, INC.—See BorgWarner Inc.; *U.S. Public*, pg. 371
RICHARDSON ELECTRONIQUE SAS—See Richardson Electronics, Ltd.; *U.S. Public*, pg. 1798
SAUDI POWER TRANSFORMER COMPANY LIMITED—See Electrical Industries Company; *Int'l*, pg. 2350
SAUDI TRANSFORMER COMPANY LIMITED—See Electrical Industries Company; *Int'l*, pg. 2350
SHALLBETTER, INC.; *U.S. Private*, pg. 3623
SHANGHAI FUJI ELECTRIC TRANSFORMER CO., LTD.—See Fuji Electric Co., Ltd.; *Int'l*, pg. 2813
SHIHEN TECHNICAL CORPORATION—See Daihen Corporation; *Int'l*, pg. 1927
SHIROTORI AICHI ELEC CO., LTD.—See Aichi Electric Co., Ltd.; *Int'l*, pg. 229
SIEMENS MANUFACTURING CO., INC.; *U.S. Private*, pg. 3646
SMARR EMC; *U.S. Private*, pg. 3690
SNC MANUFACTURING COMPANY, INC.—See Allient Inc.; *U.S. Public*, pg. 80
SOJO ELECTRIC CO., LTD.—See Beijing Sojo Electric Company Limited; *Int'l*, pg. 957
SOLUFIP S.A.S.—See Greiner Holding AG; *Int'l*, pg. 3079
SPECTRUM POWER MANAGEMENT SYSTEMS—See Allient Inc.; *U.S. Public*, pg. 80
SPX TRANSFORMER SOLUTIONS, INC. - GOLDSBORO—See SPX Technologies, Inc.; *U.S. Public*, pg. 1921
SPX TRANSFORMER SOLUTIONS, INC.—See SPX Technologies, Inc.; *U.S. Public*, pg. 1921
STARKSTROM-GERATEBAU GMBH—See BC Partners LLP; *Int'l*, pg. 925
STRIEBEL & JOHN GMBH & CO. KG—See ABB Ltd.; *Int'l*, pg. 50
SUNBELT SOLOMON SERVICES, LLC—See Trilantic Capital Management L.P.; *U.S. Private*, pg. 4231
SUNHYDROGEN, INC.; *U.S. Public*, pg. 1964
SUNVALLEY SOLAR, INC.; *U.S. Public*, pg. 1966
SUNWORKS, INC.; *U.S. Public*, pg. 1966
SUPERIOR ELECTRIC HOLDING GROUP LLC—See Fortive Corporation; *U.S. Public*, pg. 872
T.A. PELSUE COMPANY; *U.S. Private*, pg. 3911
TARAPUR TRANSFORMERS LIMITED—See Bilpower Limited; *Int'l*, pg. 1031
TOCHIGI ELECTRONICS INDUSTRY CO., LTD.—See Di-Nikko Engineering Co., Ltd.; *Int'l*, pg. 2101
TRASFOR SA—See ABB Ltd.; *Int'l*, pg. 56
TRINITY UTILITY STRUCTURES, LLC—See Trinity Industries, Inc.; *U.S. Public*, pg. 2194
TURBIGAS SOLAR S.A.—See Fugro N.V.; *Int'l*, pg. 2808
UAB XIRGO GLOBAL—See Sensata Technologies Holding plc; *U.S. Public*, pg. 1866
UK GRID SOLUTIONS LIMITED—See General Electric Company; *U.S. Public*, pg. 918
UNIBUS, INC.—See Powell Industries, Inc.; *U.S. Public*, pg. 1705
UNION TRADING COMPANY—See Belhasa Group of Companies; *Int'l*, pg. 964
UNITED TRANSFORMERS ELECTRIC COMPANY—See Bawan Company; *Int'l*, pg. 900
UNITED UTILITY SERVICES, LLC—See Bernhard Capital Partners Management, LP; *U.S. Private*, pg. 537
VACON DRIVES & CONTROLS PVT. LTD.—See Danfoss A/S; *Int'l*, pg. 1961
VERTIV GROUP CORPORATION—See Vertiv Holdings Co; *U.S. Public*, pg. 2288
VIRGINIA TRANSFORMER CORP.; *U.S. Private*, pg. 4388
VISHAY SPECTROL—See Vishay Intertechnology, Inc.; *U.S. Public*, pg. 2303
WARNER POWER CONVERSION, LLC—See Blackford Capital LLC; *U.S. Private*, pg. 574
WESTERN AUTOMATION RESEARCH & DEVELOPMENT LIMITED—See Littelfuse, Inc.; *U.S. Public*, pg. 1327
WESTERN POWER DISTRIBUTION—See PPL Corporation; *U.S. Public*, pg. 1712
WINDGEN ENERGY, INC.; *U.S. Public*, pg. 2372
WIST ENTERPRISES, INC.—See The Jordan Company, L.P.; *U.S. Private*, pg. 4063
ZETTLER MAGNETICS, INC.—See Zettler Components, Inc.; *U.S. Public*, pg. 4603
ZHEJIANG CHINT ELECTRICS CO., LTD.—See Chint Group Corporation; *Int'l*, pg. 1571

335312 — MOTOR AND GENERATOR MANUFACTURING

2 H ENERGY S.A.S.—See CNH Industrial N.V.; *Int'l*, pg. 1674
ABB ELECTRICAL MACHINES LTD.—See ABB Ltd.; *Int'l*, pg. 49
ABB GENERATORS LTD.—See ABB Ltd.; *Int'l*, pg. 49
ABB INC. - POWER TECHNOLOGIES COMPONENTS FACTORY—See ABB Ltd.; *Int'l*, pg. 51
ABB LIMITED—See ABB Ltd.; *Int'l*, pg. 51
ABB LTD.—See ABB Ltd.; *Int'l*, pg. 53
ABB MOTORS AND MECHANICAL INC.—See ABB Ltd.; *Int'l*, pg. 51
ABB SHANGHAI MOTORS CO. LTD.—See ABB Ltd.; *Int'l*, pg. 49
ACUVI AB; *Int'l*, pg. 121
A-DRIVE TECHNOLOGY GMBH; *Int'l*, pg. 19
ADS/TRANSICOIL CORP.—See TransDigm Group Incorporated; *U.S. Public*, pg. 2182
ADTEC PLASMA TECHNOLOGY KOREA CO., LTD.—See Adtec Plasma Technology Co., Ltd.; *Int'l*, pg. 154
ADTEC PLASMA TECHNOLOGY TAIWAN LTD.—See Adtec Plasma Technology Co., Ltd.; *Int'l*, pg. 154
AGC MANUFACTURING SERVICES INC—See Gentor, S.A. de C.V.; *Int'l*, pg. 2929
AGGREKO ANGOLA LDA.—See I Squared Capital Advisors (US) LLC; *U.S. Private*, pg. 2020
AGGREKO CANADA INC.—See I Squared Capital Advisors (US) LLC; *U.S. Private*, pg. 2020
AGGREKO CHILE LIMITADA—See I Squared Capital Advisors (US) LLC; *U.S. Private*, pg. 2020
AGGREKO DE VENEZUELA C.A.—See I Squared Capital Advisors (US) LLC; *U.S. Private*, pg. 2021
AGGREKO ENERGY RENTAL SOLUTIONS INC.—See I Squared Capital Advisors (US) LLC; *U.S. Private*, pg. 2021
AGGREKO ENERGY RENTAL SOUTH AFRICA (PROPRIETARY) LIMITED—See I Squared Capital Advisors (US) LLC; *U.S. Private*, pg. 2021
AGGREKO ENERGY RENTALS PANAMA SA—See I Squared Capital Advisors (US) LLC; *U.S. Private*, pg. 2021
AGGREKO EURASIA LLC—See I Squared Capital Advisors (US) LLC; *U.S. Private*, pg. 2021
AGGREKO FINLAND OY—See I Squared Capital Advisors (US) LLC; *U.S. Private*, pg. 2021
AGGREKO GENERATOR RENTALS (PNG) LIMITED—See I Squared Capital Advisors (US) LLC; *U.S. Private*, pg. 2021
AGGREKO IBERIA SA—See I Squared Capital Advisors (US) LLC; *U.S. Private*, pg. 2021
AGGREKO ITALIA S.R.L.—See I Squared Capital Advisors (US) LLC; *U.S. Private*, pg. 2021
AGGREKO JAPAN LIMITED—See I Squared Capital Advisors (US) LLC; *U.S. Private*, pg. 2021
AGGREKO KENYA ENERGY RENTALS LIMITED—See I

335312 — MOTOR AND GENERATOR...

Squared Capital Advisors (US) LLC; *U.S. Private*, pg. 2021
AGGREKO MYANMAR CO. LIMITED—See I Squared Capital Advisors (US) LLC; *U.S. Private*, pg. 2021
AGGREKO NAMIBIA ENERGY RENTALS (PTY) LTD.—See I Squared Capital Advisors (US) LLC; *U.S. Private*, pg. 2021
AGGREKO NORWAY AS—See I Squared Capital Advisors (US) LLC; *U.S. Private*, pg. 2021
AGGREKO (NZ) LIMITED—See I Squared Capital Advisors (US) LLC; *U.S. Private*, pg. 2020
AGGREKO PLC—See I Squared Capital Advisors (US) LLC; *U.S. Private*, pg. 2020
AGGREKO POLSKA SPOLKA ZORGANICZANA—See I Squared Capital Advisors (US) LLC; *U.S. Private*, pg. 2021
AGGREKO SOUTH EAST EUROPE S.R.L.—See I Squared Capital Advisors (US) LLC; *U.S. Private*, pg. 2021
AGGREKO SOUTH KOREA LIMITED—See I Squared Capital Advisors (US) LLC; *U.S. Private*, pg. 2021
AGGREKO (THAILAND) LIMITED—See I Squared Capital Advisors (US) LLC; *U.S. Private*, pg. 2020
AICHI ELECTRIC & ELECTRONIC PRODUCTS DIVISION—See Aichi Electric Co., Ltd.; *Int'l*, pg. 229
AI TECHNOLOGY GROUP, INC.; *U.S. Public*, pg. 63
AJ POWER LIMITED; *Int'l*, pg. 255
ALSTOM S.A.; *Int'l*, pg. 379
ALSTOM TRANSPORT B.V.—See Alstom S.A.; *Int'l*, pg. 381
ALTAMONT HOTEL ASSOCIATES LP—See Edison International; *U.S. Public*, pg. 719
AMERICAN GENTOR CORPORATION—See Gentor, S.A. de C.V.; *Int'l*, pg. 2929
AMERICAN SUPERCONDUCTOR CORPORATION; *U.S. Public*, pg. 110
AMETEK ELECTROMECHANICAL GROUP—See AMETEK, Inc.; *U.S. Public*, pg. 116
AMETEK FLOORCARE SPECIALTY MOTORS DIVISION—See AMETEK, Inc.; *U.S. Public*, pg. 116
AMETEK GMBH—See AMETEK, Inc.; *U.S. Public*, pg. 119
AMETEK, INC.; *U.S. Public*, pg. 116
AMETEK ITALIA—See AMETEK, Inc.; *U.S. Public*, pg. 119
AMETEK LAMB ELECTRIC DIVISION—See AMETEK, Inc.; *U.S. Public*, pg. 116
AMETEK SPECIALTY METAL PRODUCTS DIVISION—See AMETEK, Inc.; *U.S. Public*, pg. 116
AMETEK U.S. GAUGE—See AMETEK, Inc.; *U.S. Public*, pg. 118
AMETEK VEHICULAR INFSTRUMENTATION SYSTEMS—See AMETEK, Inc.; *U.S. Public*, pg. 118
ANKARSRUM MOTORS AB—See Duroc AB; *Int'l*, pg. 2229
ANKARSRUM UNIVERSAL MOTORS AB—See Duroc AB; *Int'l*, pg. 2229
APPLETON GROUP CANADA, LTD.—See Emerson Electric Co.; *U.S. Public*, pg. 740
ASMO NORTH CAROLINA, INC.—See Denso Corporation; *Int'l*, pg. 2028
AUSTRALIA BALDOR PTY LTD—See ABB Ltd.; *Int'l*, pg. 51
AUTOMATIC SYSTEMS (BELGIUM) SA—See Financiere de L'Odet; *Int'l*, pg. 2665
AUTOMATIC SYSTEMS EQUIPMENT UK LTD—See Financiere de L'Odet; *Int'l*, pg. 2665
AUTOMATIC SYSTEMS ESPANOLA SA—See Financiere de L'Odet; *Int'l*, pg. 2665
BABCOCK POWER UK LTD.—See Babcock Power, Inc.; *U.S. Private*, pg. 422
BABCOCK WANSON CALDEIRAS LDA—See CNIM Constructions Industrielles de la Mediterranee SA; *Int'l*, pg. 1677
BALDOR ELECTRIC CANADA INC.—See ABB Ltd.; *Int'l*, pg. 51
BALDOR ELECTRIC COMPANY DE MEXICO S.A. DE C.V.—See ABB Ltd.; *Int'l*, pg. 51
BALDOR ELECTRIC COMPANY, MANUFACTURING FACILITY—See ABB Ltd.; *Int'l*, pg. 51
BALDOR ELECTRIC COMPANY—See ABB Ltd.; *Int'l*, pg. 51
BALDOR ELECTRIC SWITZERLAND AG—See ABB Ltd.; *Int'l*, pg. 51
BALDOR PANAMA S.A.—See ABB Ltd.; *Int'l*, pg. 51
BALLARD POWER SYSTEMS EUROPE A/S—See Ballard Power Systems, Inc.; *Int'l*, pg. 809
BEIJING B. J. ELECTRIC MOTOR CO., LTD.—See Beijing Jingcheng Machinery Electric Holding Co., Ltd.; *Int'l*, pg. 952
BEIJING B.J. ELECTRIC MOTOR CO., LTD.—See Beijing Jingcheng Machinery Electric Holding Co., Ltd.; *Int'l*, pg. 953
BEI PRECISION SYSTEMS & SPACE COMPANY, INC.—See Arcline Investment Management LP; *U.S. Private*, pg. 313
BERKMANNS ANTRIEBE GMBH—See Groschopp AG; *Int'l*, pg. 3088
BESEL S.A.—See Cantoni Motor S.A.; *Int'l*, pg. 1299
BEVI CHINA—See Addtech AB; *Int'l*, pg. 132
BEVI EST OU—See Addtech AB; *Int'l*, pg. 132
BEVI FINLAND OY—See Addtech AB; *Int'l*, pg. 132
BEVI NORD AB—See Addtech AB; *Int'l*, pg. 132
BEVI NORGE AS—See Addtech AB; *Int'l*, pg. 132

BEVI TEKNIK & SERVICE AB—See Addtech AB; *Int'l*, pg. 132
BEVI UAB—See Addtech AB; *Int'l*, pg. 132
BIRDY FUEL CELLS LLC—See Abalance Corporation Ltd.; *Int'l*, pg. 48
BODINE ELECTRIC COMPANY; *U.S. Private*, pg. 608
BOMBARDIER TRANSPORTATION AB—See Alstom S.A.; *Int'l*, pg. 382
BOULDER CREEK APARTMENTS LP—See Edison International; *U.S. Public*, pg. 719
BOWMAN POWER GROUP LTD; *Int'l*, pg. 1124
BRIGGS & STRATTON POWER PRODUCTS GROUP, LLC—See Briggs & Stratton Corporation; *U.S. Private*, pg. 651
BRUSH ELECTRICAL MACHINES LTD.—See OEP Capital Advisors, L.P.; *U.S. Private*, pg. 2998
BUEHLER MOTOR INC.; *U.S. Private*, pg. 680
CAF POWER & AUTOMATION, S.L.U.—See Construcciones y Auxiliar de Ferrocarriles S.A.; *Int'l*, pg. 1776
CALNETIX TECHNOLOGIES, LLC.; *U.S. Private*, pg. 723
CALUMET ARMATURE & ELECTRIC, LLC—See IES Holdings, Inc.; *U.S. Public*, pg. 1094
CANON PRECISION INC.—See Canon Inc.; *Int'l*, pg. 1296
CANTONI MOTOR S.A.; *Int'l*, pg. 1299
CAPTIVA ENERGY SOLUTIONS PRIVATE LIMITED—See Generac Holdings Inc.; *U.S. Public*, pg. 912
CAREEN, INC.; *U.S. Private*, pg. 752
CARTER MOTOR COMPANY; *U.S. Private*, pg. 776
CATERPILLAR ENERGY SOLUTIONS INC.—See Caterpillar, Inc.; *U.S. Public*, pg. 450
CATERPILLAR MOTOREN (GUANGDONG) CO. LTD.—See Caterpillar, Inc.; *U.S. Public*, pg. 451
CATERPILLAR (NEWBERRY) LLC—See Caterpillar, Inc.; *U.S. Public*, pg. 449
CATERPILLAR (NI) LIMITED—See Caterpillar, Inc.; *U.S. Public*, pg. 449
CELMA S.A.—See Cantoni Motor S.A.; *Int'l*, pg. 1299
CEZ ENERGO, S.R.O.—See CEZ, a.s.; *Int'l*, pg. 1426
CHANGZHOU REGAL-BELOIT SINYA MOTOR CO. LTD.—See Regal Rexnord Corporation; *U.S. Public*, pg. 1773
CHANGZHOU XIANGMING INTELLIGENT DRIVE SYSTEM CORPORATION; *Int'l*, pg. 1446
CHARGEMASTER LIMITED—See BP plc; *Int'l*, pg. 1131
CHINA ELECTRIC MOTOR, INC.; *Int'l*, pg. 1499
CITIZEN CHIBA PRECISION CO., LTD.—See Citizen Watch Co., Ltd.; *Int'l*, pg. 1623
CMG ELECTRIC MOTORS (ASIA PACIFIC) PTE LTD.—See CMG Pty. Ltd.; *Int'l*, pg. 1669
CMG ELECTRIC MOTORS (MALAYSIA) SDN. BHD.—See Regal Rexnord Corporation; *U.S. Public*, pg. 1773
CMG ELECTRIC MOTORS (NZ) LIMITED—See Regal Rexnord Corporation; *U.S. Public*, pg. 1773
CMG ELECTRIC MOTORS SOUTH AFRICA (PTY) LTD.—See CMG Pty. Ltd.; *Int'l*, pg. 1670
CMG PTY. LTD.; *Int'l*, pg. 1669
CONVEL S.R.L.—See Antares Vision SpA; *Int'l*, pg. 482
CUMMINS BLR LLC—See Cummins Inc.; *U.S. Public*, pg. 605
CUMMINS FILTRATION INTERNATIONAL CORP.—See Cummins Inc.; *U.S. Public*, pg. 605
CUMMINS GENERATOR TECHNOLOGIES CO., LTD.—See Cummins Inc.; *U.S. Public*, pg. 606
CUMMINS GENERATOR TECHNOLOGIES GMBH—See Cummins Inc.; *U.S. Public*, pg. 606
CUMMINS GENERATOR TECHNOLOGIES MEXICO S DE R.L. DE C.V.—See Cummins Inc.; *U.S. Public*, pg. 606
CUMMINS GENERATOR TECHNOLOGIES NORWAY—See Cummins Inc.; *U.S. Public*, pg. 606
CUMMINS GENERATOR TECHNOLOGIES ROMANIA S.A.—See Cummins Inc.; *U.S. Public*, pg. 606
CUMMINS GENERATOR TECHNOLOGIES SPAIN S.A.—See Cummins Inc.; *U.S. Public*, pg. 606
CUMMINS POWER GENERATION—See Cummins Inc.; *U.S. Public*, pg. 606
CUMMINS SOUTH AFRICA (PTY.) LTD.—See Cummins Inc.; *U.S. Public*, pg. 607
CUMMINS TECHNOLOGIES INDIA LIMITED—See Cummins Inc.; *U.S. Public*, pg. 607
CYPRESS COVE ASSOCIATES—See Edison International; *U.S. Public*, pg. 719
DANAHER MOTION COMPANY—See Danaher Corporation; *U.S. Public*, pg. 626
DANAHER MOTION—See Danaher Corporation; *U.S. Public*, pg. 626
DAYTON-PHOENIX GROUP INC.; *U.S. Private*, pg. 1178
DCM MANUFACTURING, INC.—See Dreison International, Inc.; *U.S. Private*, pg. 1276
DEEP SEA ELECTRONICS INDIA PRIVATE LIMITED—See Generac Holdings Inc.; *U.S. Public*, pg. 912
DEEP SEA ELECTRONICS INDIA PTE. LTD.—See Caledonia Investments plc; *Int'l*, pg. 1262
DELTA ELECTRONICS (SWITZERLAND) AG—See Delta Electronics, Inc.; *Int'l*, pg. 2016
DELTA ENERGY SYSTEMS (FRANCE) S.A.—See Delta Electronics, Inc.; *Int'l*, pg. 2016
DELTA ENERGY SYSTEMS (SWEDEN) AB—See Delta Electronics, Inc.; *Int'l*, pg. 2017

CORPORATE AFFILIATIONS

DENSO MAQUINAS ROTANTES DO BRASIL LTDA.—See Denso Corporation; *Int'l*, pg. 2029
DENYO CO., LTD.; *Int'l*, pg. 2040
DENYO MANUFACTURING CORPORATION—See Denyo Co., Ltd.; *Int'l*, pg. 2040
DENYO VIETNAM CO., LTD.—See Denyo Co., Ltd.; *Int'l*, pg. 2040
DEUBLIN DE MEXICO—See Hoerbiger Holding AG; *Int'l*, pg. 3439
DL WINDY ACRES, LLC—See Constellation Energy Corporation; *U.S. Public*, pg. 572
DUMORE CORPORATION - DUMORE MOTORS UNIT—See Ilion Capital Partners; *U.S. Private*, pg. 2041
DUMORE CORPORATION—See Ilion Capital Partners; *U.S. Private*, pg. 2041
DYNACERT INC.; *Int'l*, pg. 2239
DYNAMIC SYSTEMS HOLDINGS, INC.; *Int'l*, pg. 2241
DYNA RECHI (JIUJIANG) CO., LTD.—See China Steel Corporation; *Int'l*, pg. 1555
DZI AN MECHANOELECTRIC JSC; *Int'l*, pg. 2245
EATON CORP. - INDUSTRIAL CONTROLS—See Eaton Corporation plc; *Int'l*, pg. 2280
EC FANS & DRIVES, LLC—See Epec Engineered Technologies; *U.S. Private*, pg. 1412
EEI POWER CORP.—See EEI Corporation; *Int'l*, pg. 2317
ELCO DE COLOMBIA SAS—See Regal Rexnord Corporation; *U.S. Public*, pg. 1773
ELCO E-TRADE SRL—See Regal Rexnord Corporation; *U.S. Public*, pg. 1773
ELCO MOTORS ASIA PTE LIMITED—See Regal Rexnord Corporation; *U.S. Public*, pg. 1773
ELECTRIC MOTOR & CONTRACTING CO., INC.; *U.S. Private*, pg. 1352
ELECTRIC TORQUE MACHINES, INC.—See Graco, Inc.; *U.S. Public*, pg. 953
ELECTROCRAFT ARKANSAS, INC.—See Delany Capital Management Corp.; *U.S. Private*, pg. 1194
ELECTROCRAFT, INC.—See Delany Capital Management Corp.; *U.S. Private*, pg. 1194
ELECTROCRAFT NEW HAMPSHIRE, INC.—See Delany Capital Management Corp.; *U.S. Private*, pg. 1194
ELECTROID CO—See Valcor Engineering Corporation; *U.S. Private*, pg. 4330
ELECTROPUTERE S.A.; *Int'l*, pg. 2354
ELENSYS CO., LTD.; *Int'l*, pg. 2359
ELSA SOLUTIONS SPA; *Int'l*, pg. 2370
EMERSON ASIA PACIFIC PRIVATE LIMITED—See Emerson Electric Co.; *U.S. Public*, pg. 747
EMERSON AUTOMATION SOLUTIONS INTELLIGENT PLATFORMS PRIVATE LIMITED—See Emerson Electric Co.; *U.S. Public*, pg. 749
EMERSON ELECTRIC CO. - HUMBOLDT—See Emerson Electric Co.; *U.S. Public*, pg. 744
EMERSON ELECTRIC CO.; *U.S. Public*, pg. 740
EMERSON PACIFIC PTE. LTD.—See Emerson Electric Co.; *U.S. Public*, pg. 746
EMERSON VENEZUELA C.A.—See Emerson Electric Co.; *U.S. Public*, pg. 749
EMIT S.A.—See Cantoni Motor S.A.; *Int'l*, pg. 1299
EW HOF ANTR. U. SYSTEME GMBH—See AdCapital AG; *Int'l*, pg. 126
FARADYNE MOTORS LLC—See Xylem Inc.; *U.S. Public*, pg. 2394
FASCO MOTORS THAILAND LTD.—See Regal Rexnord Corporation; *U.S. Public*, pg. 1773
FRANKLIN ELECTRIC EUROPA, GMBH—See Franklin Electric Co., Inc.; *U.S. Public*, pg. 878
FUCHI ELECTRONICS CO., LTD.—See Fujitsu Limited; *Int'l*, pg. 2832
FUJI ELECTRIC MOTOR (DALIAN) CO., LTD.—See Fuji Electric Co., Ltd.; *Int'l*, pg. 2811
FUJI MICRO CO., LTD.—See Advanex Inc.; *Int'l*, pg. 163
GE AVIATION CZECH S.R.O.—See General Electric Company; *U.S. Public*, pg. 918
GE AVIATION SYSTEMS LLC - CLEARWATER—See General Electric Company; *U.S. Public*, pg. 918
GE CANADA—See General Electric Company; *U.S. Public*, pg. 919
GE JENBACHER GMBH—See General Electric Company; *U.S. Public*, pg. 917
GENERAC POWER SYSTEMS, INC. - OSHKOSH PLANT—See Generac Holdings Inc.; *U.S. Public*, pg. 912
GENERAC POWER SYSTEMS, INC.—See Generac Holdings Inc.; *U.S. Public*, pg. 912
GENERAC SERVICES, INC.—See Generac Holdings Inc.; *U.S. Public*, pg. 912
GENERAL DYNAMICS GLOBAL IMAGING TECHNOLOGIES, INC. - CULLMAN—See General Dynamics Corporation; *U.S. Public*, pg. 915
GENERAL ELECTRIC DEUTSCHLAND HOLDING GMBH—See General Electric Company; *U.S. Public*, pg. 920
GENERAL ELECTRIC (SWITZERLAND) GMBH—See General Electric Company; *U.S. Public*, pg. 918
GENTOR, S.A. DE C.V.; *Int'l*, pg. 2929
GE VIETNAM CO. LIMITED—See General Electric Company; *U.S. Public*, pg. 918

N.A.I.C.S. INDEX

335312 — MOTOR AND GENERATOR...

GLOBE MOTORS PORTUGAL LDA.—See Allient Inc.; *U.S. Public*, pg. 80
GLOBE MOTORS—See Allient Inc.; *U.S. Public*, pg. 80
GNC ENERGY CO., LTD.; *Int'l*, pg. 3016
GOLDEN TRIANGLE GENERATORS LIMITED—See I Squared Capital Advisors (US) LLC; *U.S. Private*, pg. 2021
GROSCHOPP AG; *Int'l*, pg. 3088
GROSCHOPP, INC., *U.S. Private*, pg. 1792
GULF ELECTROQUIP LTD.; *U.S. Private*, pg. 1816
HANKSCRAFT INC.; *U.S. Private*, pg. 1854
HANNON COMPANY; *U.S. Private*, pg. 1855
HANSEN CORPORATION—See Delany Capital Management Corp.; *U.S. Private*, pg. 1194
HEASON TECHNOLOGY LIMITED—See discoverIE Group plc; *Int'l*, pg. 2133
THE HINES GROUP, INC.; *U.S. Private*, pg. 4053
HITACHI INDUSTRIAL TECHNOLOGY (THAILAND), LTD.—See Hitachi, Ltd.; *Int'l*, pg. 3419
HITCHINER MANUFACTURING COMPANY INC. - FERROUS DIVISION—See Hitchiner Manufacturing Company Inc.; *U.S. Private*, pg. 1953
HONDA INDIA POWER PRODUCTS LIMITED—See Honda Motor Co., Ltd.; *Int'l*, pg. 3461
HOUSTON MOTOR & CONTROL, INC., *U.S. Private*, pg. 1993
HYDRO-QUEBEC INDUSTECH INC—See Hydro-Quebec; *Int'l*, pg. 3547
HYUNDAI HEAVY INDUSTRIES CO., LTD.—See Hyundai Electric & Energy Systems Co., Ltd.; *Int'l*, pg. 3556
ICC INTELLIGENT PLATFORMS GMBH—See Emerson Electric Co.; *U.S. Public*, pg. 749
IDEAL ELECTRIC COMPANY—See Gulf Electroquip Ltd.; *U.S. Private*, pg. 1816
INTERZON AB—See Absolent Air Care Group AB; *Int'l*, pg. 70
JAKEL, INCORPORATED—See Regal Rexnord Corporation; *U.S. Public*, pg. 1773
JOHNSON OUTDOORS INC.-MARINE ELECTRONICS GROUP—See Johnson Outdoors Inc.; *U.S. Public*, pg. 1201
KENCOIL INC.; *U.S. Private*, pg. 2283
KIRKWOOD HOLDING, INC.; *U.S. Private*, pg. 2315
KPH HOLDINGS, LLC—See Dreison International, Inc.; *U.S. Private*, pg. 1276
MAGNETEK ELEVATORS—See Columbus McKinnon Corporation; *U.S. Public*, pg. 536
MAGNETEK (UK) LTD.—See Columbus McKinnon Corporation; *U.S. Public*, pg. 536
MAMCO CORPORATION; *U.S. Private*, pg. 2559
MARATHON ELECTRIC FAR EAST PTE LTD.—See Regal Rexnord Corporation; *U.S. Public*, pg. 1773
MARELLI ASIA PACIFIC SDN BHD—See The Carlyle Group Inc.; *U.S. Public*, pg. 2049
MARELLI CENTRAL EUROPE GMBH—See The Carlyle Group Inc.; *U.S. Public*, pg. 2049
MARELLI ELECTRICAL MACHINES SOUTH AFRICA (PTY) LTD.—See The Carlyle Group Inc.; *U.S. Public*, pg. 2049
MARELLI MOTORI S.P.A.—See The Carlyle Group Inc.; *U.S. Public*, pg. 2049
MARELLI UK LTD.—See The Carlyle Group Inc.; *U.S. Public*, pg. 2049
MARELLI USA, INC.—See The Carlyle Group Inc.; *U.S. Public*, pg. 2049
MCMILLAN ELECTRIC COMPANY; *U.S. Private*, pg. 2642
MICROVAST POWER SYSTEMS CO., LTD.—See Microvast Holdings, Inc.; *U.S. Public*, pg. 1444
MILBANK MANUFACTURING COMPANY INC.—See Milbank Manufacturing Company Inc.; *U.S. Private*, pg. 2726
MOLON MOTOR & COIL CORPORATION; *U.S. Private*, pg. 2767
MOOG BRNO S.R.O.—See Moog Inc.; *U.S. Public*, pg. 1470
MOOG CONTROLS LTD.—See Moog Inc.; *U.S. Public*, pg. 1470
MOOG EM SOLUTIONS (INDIA) PRIVATE LIMITED—See Moog Inc.; *U.S. Public*, pg. 1470
MOOG IRELAND LTD.—See Moog Inc.; *U.S. Public*, pg. 1470
MORRILL MOTORS, INC.1946—See Regal Rexnord Corporation; *U.S. Public*, pg. 1773
MORRILL MOTORS (JIAXING) CO., LTD.—See Regal Rexnord Corporation; *U.S. Public*, pg. 1773
MOTOR PRODUCTS CORPORATION—See Allient Inc.; *U.S. Public*, pg. 80
MOUNTZ TORQUE LIMITED—See Snap-on Incorporated; *U.S. Public*, pg. 1897
MUIRHEAD AEROSPACE—See AMETEK, Inc.; *U.S. Public*, pg. 117
MWM BENELUX B.V.—See Caterpillar, Inc.; *U.S. Public*, pg. 452
NAMMO (U.K.) LIMITED—See Moog Inc.; *U.S. Public*, pg. 1470
NEOMAX ENGINEERING CO., LTD.—See Hitachi, Ltd.; *Int'l*, pg. 3423
NEWAVE ENERGY AG—See ABB Ltd.; *Int'l*, pg. 54
NEWAVE ITALIA SRL—See ABB Ltd.; *Int'l*, pg. 55
NIDEC INDUSTRIAL AUTOMATION USA LLC—See Emerson Electric Co.; *U.S. Public*, pg. 750
NIKKI DENSO INTERNATIONAL KOREA CO., LTD.—See CKD Corporation; *Int'l*, pg. 1639
NORD GEAR PTE LTD—See Getriebebau NORD GmbH & Co. KG; *Int'l*, pg. 2953
NUGEN HOLDINGS, INC.; *U.S. Private*, pg. 2972
OHIO ELECTRIC MOTORS INC.—See HBD Industries, Inc.; *U.S. Public*, pg. 1887
OTTOMOTORES DO BRASIL ENERGIA LTDA.—See Generac Holdings Inc.; *U.S. Public*, pg. 912
OTTOMOTORES S.A. DE C.V.—See Generac Holdings Inc.; *U.S. Public*, pg. 912
OWENSBORO MANUFACTURING LLC—See The Hines Group, Inc.; *U.S. Private*, pg. 4053
PEERLESS ELECTRIC—See HBD Industries, Inc.; *U.S. Private*, pg. 1887
PINNACLE CENTRAL COMPANY, INC.—See Source Capital, LLC; *U.S. Private*, pg. 3718
PITTMAN—See AMETEK, Inc.; *U.S. Public*, pg. 116
POLAR POWER, INC.; *U.S. Public*, pg. 1700
PORTESCAP CO., LTD.—See Regal Rexnord Corporation; *U.S. Public*, pg. 1772
PORTESCAP INDIA PRIVATE LIMITED—See Danaher Corporation; *U.S. Public*, pg. 626
PORTESCAP SA—See Danaher Corporation; *U.S. Public*, pg. 626
POWERTEC INDUSTRIAL MOTORS—See HBD Industries, Inc.; *U.S. Private*, pg. 1887
PRAMAC ASIA PTE LTD—See Generac Holdings Inc.; *U.S. Public*, pg. 912
PRAMAC CARIBE SRL—See Generac Holdings Inc.; *U.S. Public*, pg. 912
PRAMAC EUROPE SAS—See Generac Holdings Inc.; *U.S. Public*, pg. 912
PRAMAC FU LEE FOSHAN POWER EQUIPMENT LTD—See Generac Holdings Inc.; *U.S. Public*, pg. 912
PRAMAC GMBH—See Generac Holdings Inc.; *U.S. Public*, pg. 912
PRAMAC IBERICA S.A.U.—See Generac Holdings Inc.; *U.S. Public*, pg. 912
PRAMAC RUS LTD—See Generac Holdings Inc.; *U.S. Public*, pg. 912
PRAMAC SP. Z.O.O.—See Generac Holdings Inc.; *U.S. Public*, pg. 912
PRAMAC STORAGE SYSTEMS GMBH—See Generac Holdings Inc.; *U.S. Public*, pg. 912
PRAMAC UK LIMITED—See Generac Holdings Inc.; *U.S. Public*, pg. 913
PR AUSTRALIA PTY LTD—See Generac Holdings Inc.; *U.S. Public*, pg. 912
PR INDUSTRIAL S.R.L.—See Generac Holdings Inc.; *U.S. Public*, pg. 912
PR MIDDLE EAST FZE—See Generac Holdings Inc.; *U.S. Public*, pg. 912
PSEG GLOBAL LLC—See Public Service Enterprise Group Incorporated; *U.S. Public*, pg. 1736
P.T. DEIN PRIMA GENERATOR—See Denyo Co., Ltd.; *Int'l*, pg. 2040
Q-FREE ASA—See Guardian Capital Group Limited; *Int'l*, pg. 3170
QUAD TECHNICAL SERVICES (PTY) LIMITED—See enX Group Limited; *Int'l*, pg. 2456
RBC MANUFACTURING CORPORATION—See Regal Rexnord Corporation; *U.S. Public*, pg. 1773
RECHI REFRIGERATION (DONGGUAN) CO., LTD.—See China Steel Corporation; *Int'l*, pg. 1556
REGAL BELOIT AMERICA, INC.—See Regal Rexnord Corporation; *U.S. Public*, pg. 1773
REGAL BELOIT CANADA, AN ALBERTA LIMITED PARTNERSHIP—See Regal Rexnord Corporation; *U.S. Public*, pg. 1773
REGAL BELOIT ISRAEL—See CMG Pty. Ltd.; *Int'l*, pg. 1670
REGAL REXNORD CORPORATION; *U.S. Public*, pg. 1771
REULAND ELECTRIC COMPANY - ENGINEERING SERVICES DIVISION—See Reuland Electric Company; *U.S. Private*, pg. 3412
REULAND ELECTRIC COMPANY - FOUNDRY DIVISION—See Reuland Electric Company; *U.S. Private*, pg. 3412
REULAND ELECTRIC COMPANY; *U.S. Private*, pg. 3412
RITTENHOUSE SCHOOL LP—See Edison International; *U.S. Public*, pg. 719
ROCKWELL AUTOMATION SOFT SWITCHING TECHNOLOGIES—See Rockwell Automation, Inc.; *U.S. Public*, pg. 1806
ROTOR B.V.—See Regal Rexnord Corporation; *U.S. Public*, pg. 1773
ROTOR U.K. LIMITED—See Regal Rexnord Corporation; *U.S. Public*, pg. 1773
ROXEL FRANCE—See Airbus SE; *Int'l*, pg. 247
ROXEL FRANCE—See BAE Systems plc; *Int'l*, pg. 798
SCHNEIDER ELECTRIC MOTION USA, INC.—See Novanta Inc.; *U.S. Public*, pg. 1548
THE SCOTT MOTORS COMPANY—See Jordan Industries, Inc.; *U.S. Private*, pg. 2235
SC PRAMAC GENERATORS S.R.L.—See Generac Holdings Inc.; *U.S. Public*, pg. 913
SDMO GENERATING SETS INC.—See Kohler Company; *U.S. Private*, pg. 2340
SDMO GMBH—See Kohler Company; *U.S. Private*, pg. 2340
SDMO INDUSTRIES IBERICA—See Kohler Company; *U.S. Private*, pg. 2340
SDMO INDUSTRIES—See Kohler Company; *U.S. Private*, pg. 2340
SDMO NV/SA—See Kohler Company; *U.S. Private*, pg. 2340
SHANGHAI MARATHON GEXIN ELECTRIC CO. LTD.—See Regal Rexnord Corporation; *U.S. Public*, pg. 1773
SHMERLING-SYNCHRO ENERGY ENGINEERING LTD.—See 2G Energy AG; *Int'l*, pg. 5
SIKA INTERPLANT SYSTEMS LTD.—See Danaher Corporation; *U.S. Public*, pg. 626
SINOTRANS & CSC SHIPBUILDING INDUSTRY CORPORATION - CHINA CHANGJIANG NATIONAL SHIPPING GROUP MOTOR FACTORY—See China Merchants Group Limited; *Int'l*, pg. 1521
SKURKA AEROSPACE INC.—See TransDigm Group Incorporated; *U.S. Public*, pg. 2183
SNTECH, INC.; *U.S. Private*, pg. 3701
SRC POWER SYSTEMS INC.—See SRC Holdings Corporation; *U.S. Private*, pg. 3767
STERLING ELECTRIC, INC.; *U.S. Private*, pg. 3805
STREETSCOOTER GMBH—See Deutsche Post AG; *Int'l*, pg. 2082
SUNRISE VIEW WIND FARM, LLC—See Edison International; *U.S. Public*, pg. 719
SWIGER COIL SYSTEMS - A WABTEC COMPANY—See Westinghouse Air Brake Technologies Corporation; *U.S. Public*, pg. 2359
TAYLOR POWER SYSTEMS, INC.; *U.S. Private*, pg. 3940
TECUMSEH PRODUCTS COMPANY-PARIS DIVISION—See Atlas Holdings, LLC; *U.S. Private*, pg. 378
TECUMSEH PRODUCTS COMPANY-PARIS DIVISION—See Mueller Industries, Inc.; *U.S. Public*, pg. 1485
TEREX LIGHT CONSTRUCTION—See Terex Corporation; *U.S. Public*, pg. 2019
THINGAP, INC.—See Allient Inc.; *U.S. Public*, pg. 81
TIOGA GARDENS LP—See Edison International; *U.S. Public*, pg. 719
TM4 INC.—See Hydro-Quebec; *Int'l*, pg. 3547
TOLEDO COMMUTATOR CO.—See Kirkwood Holding, Inc.; *U.S. Private*, pg. 2315
TORIN INDUSTRIES (MALAYSIA) SDN. BHD.—See Regal Rexnord Corporation; *U.S. Public*, pg. 1773
TRADEWINDS POWER CORP.—See Southeast Diesel Corp.; *U.S. Private*, pg. 3725
TRULITE, INC.; *U.S. Public*, pg. 2201
TURBOMACH NETHERLANDS B.V.—See Caterpillar, Inc.; *U.S. Public*, pg. 454
UNICO CHINA AUTOMATION CO. LTD.—See Regal Rexnord Corporation; *U.S. Public*, pg. 1774
UNICO JAPAN CO. LTD.—See Regal Rexnord Corporation; *U.S. Public*, pg. 1774
UNICOVEN C. A.—See Regal Rexnord Corporation; *U.S. Public*, pg. 1774
UNIVERSAL POWER NORDIC AB—See Duc Long Gia Lai Group JSC; *Int'l*, pg. 2222
U.S. ELECTRICAL MOTORS—See Emerson Electric Co.; *U.S. Public*, pg. 752
VACON AB—See Danfoss A/S; *Int'l*, pg. 1961
VACON BENELUX B.V.—See Danfoss A/S; *Int'l*, pg. 1961
VACON BENELUX N.V./S.A.—See Danfoss A/S; *Int'l*, pg. 1961
VACON DRIVES A/S—See Danfoss A/S; *Int'l*, pg. 1961
VACON DRIVES UK LTD.—See Danfoss A/S; *Int'l*, pg. 1961
VACON GMBH—See Danfoss A/S; *Int'l*, pg. 1962
VACON PACIFIC PTY LTD—See Danfoss A/S; *Int'l*, pg. 1962
VACON S.P.A.—See Danfoss A/S; *Int'l*, pg. 1962
VENTURETEC ROTATING SYSTEMS GMBH—See Berndorf AG; *Int'l*, pg. 987
VGWATT ENERGY CO., LTD.—See Billion Electric Co., Ltd.; *Int'l*, pg. 1031
VISTA PROPERTIES LLC—See Edison International; *U.S. Public*, pg. 719
VOLTREK, LLC—See Orion Energy Systems, Inc.; *U.S. Public*, pg. 1618
WATAIR INC.; *U.S. Private*, pg. 4451
WATERPURE INTERNATIONAL, INC.; *U.S. Private*, pg. 4454
WESTCHESTER PLASTICS—See AMETEK, Inc.; *U.S. Public*, pg. 119
WESTERBEKE CORPORATION; *U.S. Private*, pg. 4490
WESTERN HYDRO LLC—See Franklin Electric Co., Inc.; *U.S. Public*, pg. 879
WINBEL CO., LTD.—See Harmonic Drive Systems Inc.; *Int'l*, pg. 3277
WINCO INC—See Winco Generators; *U.S. Private*, pg. 4533
WOODWARD COMERCIO DE SISTEMAS DE CONTROLE E PROTECAO ELECTRICA LTDA.—See Woodward, Inc.; *U.S. Public*, pg. 2378
WOODWARD (JAPAN) LTD.—See Woodward, Inc.; *U.S. Public*, pg. 2377

335312 — MOTOR AND GENERATOR...

WOODWARD NEDERLAND B.V.—See Woodward, Inc.; *U.S. Public*, pg. 2378

335313 — SWITCHGEAR AND SWITCHBOARD APPARATUS MANUFACTURING

ABB AG—See ABB Ltd.; *Int'l*, pg. 50
ABB BEIJING SWITCHGEAR LIMITED—See ABB Ltd.; *Int'l*, pg. 50
ABB B.V.—See ABB Ltd.; *Int'l*, pg. 50
ABB CALOR EMAG MITTELSPANNUNG GMBH—See ABB Ltd.; *Int'l*, pg. 50
ABB HIGH VOLTAGE SWITCHGEAR (XIAMEN) COMPANY LTD.—See ABB Ltd.; *Int'l*, pg. 49
ABB HOLDINGS SDN. BHD.—See ABB Ltd.; *Int'l*, pg. 53
ABB INDIA LTD.—See ABB Ltd.; *Int'l*, pg. 52
ABB LTD.—See ABB Ltd.; *Int'l*, pg. 53
ABB SACE LIMITADA—See ABB Ltd.; *Int'l*, pg. 53
ABB SACE S.P.A.—See ABB Ltd.; *Int'l*, pg. 54
ABB S.A.—See ABB Ltd.; *Int'l*, pg. 53
ABB S.A.S.—See ABB Ltd.; *Int'l*, pg. 54
ABB S.P.A.—See ABB Ltd.; *Int'l*, pg. 54
ABB STOTZ-KONTAKT S.A.—See ABB Ltd.; *Int'l*, pg. 56
ABB SWITZERLAND LTD - CMC LOW VOLTAGE PRODUCTS—See ABB Ltd.; *Int'l*, pg. 54
ABB TIANJIN SWITCHGEAR CO., LTD.—See ABB Ltd.; *Int'l*, pg. 49
ABB XIAMEN LOW VOLTAGE EQUIPMENT CO. LTD.—See ABB Ltd.; *Int'l*, pg. 49
ABB XINHUI LOW VOLTAGE SWITCHGEAR CO. LTD.—See ABB Ltd.; *Int'l*, pg. 55
AL-AHLEIA SWITCHGEAR COMPANY K.S.C.C.; *Int'l*, pg. 284
ALLIS ELECTRIC (S) PTE. LTD.—See Allis Electric Co., Ltd.; *Int'l*, pg. 359
AMARA RAJA POWER SYSTEMS LIMITED—See Amara Raja Energy & Mobility Limited; *Int'l*, pg. 411
ANCOM LOGISTICS BERHAD; *Int'l*, pg. 449
ANHUI SINONET & XINLONG SCIENCE & TECHNOLOGY CO., LTD.; *Int'l*, pg. 469
ANORD MARDIX (IRELAND) LTD.—See Flex Ltd.; *Int'l*, pg. 2702
ANORD MARDIX (UK) LIMITED—See Flex Ltd.; *Int'l*, pg. 2702
APATOR METRIX S.A—See Apator S.A.; *Int'l*, pg. 501
APATOR S.A.; *Int'l*, pg. 501
ASCOMATION PTY. LTD.—See Emerson Electric Co.; *U.S. Public*, pg. 741
ASCOVAL INDUSTRIA E COMMERCIO LTDA.—See Emerson Electric Co.; *U.S. Public*, pg. 741
ASEA BROWN BOVERI INC.—See ABB Ltd.; *Int'l*, pg. 55
ATR INDUSTRIE-ELEKTRONIK GMBH—See G. Siempelkamp GmbH & Co. KG; *Int'l*, pg. 2864
AZZ CALVERT—See AZZ, Inc.; *U.S. Public*, pg. 258
AZZ CENTRAL ELECTRIC—See AZZ, Inc.; *U.S. Public*, pg. 258
AZZ CGIT—See AZZ, Inc.; *U.S. Public*, pg. 258
AZZ ENCLOSURE SYSTEMS LLC—See AZZ, Inc.; *U.S. Public*, pg. 258
BEIJING RI JIA POWER SUPPLY CO., LTD.—See GS Yuasa Corporation; *Int'l*, pg. 3143
BEIJING SOJO ELECTRIC COMPANY LIMITED; *Int'l*, pg. 957
BENFIELD CONTROL & POWER SYSTEMS, INC.—See H.H. Benfield Electric Supply Company Inc.; *U.S. Private*, pg. 1826
BOER POWER HOLDINGS LIMITED; *Int'l*, pg. 1099
BOER (SHANGHAI) SWITCH APPARATUS CO., LTD.—See Boer Power Holdings Limited; *Int'l*, pg. 1099
BREAKERS UNLIMITED INC.; *U.S. Private*, pg. 642
BRIDEX AUSTRALIA PTY. LIMITED—See Fuji Electric Co., Ltd.; *Int'l*, pg. 2812
BRIDEX SINGAPORE PTE LTD.—See Fuji Electric Co., Ltd.; *Int'l*, pg. 2812
BRIGHTEN SWITCHBOARD BUILDERS (M) SDN BHD—See Fuji Electric Co., Ltd.; *Int'l*, pg. 2812
BUSBAR SYSTEMS (INDIA) LIMITED—See Godrej & Boyce Mfg. Co. Ltd.; *Int'l*, pg. 3020
CARLING TECHNOLOGIES INC.; *U.S. Private*, pg. 764
CARLO GAVAZZI PARTICIPATION DANMARK A/S—See Carlo Gavazzi Holding AG; *Int'l*, pg. 1339
CATERPILLAR SWITCHGEAR AMERICAS LLC—See Caterpillar, Inc.; *U.S. Public*, pg. 452
CENTRAL ELECTRIC COMPANY—See AZZ, Inc.; *U.S. Public*, pg. 259
CENTRAL ELECTRIC MANUFACTURING COMPANY—See AZZ, Inc.; *U.S. Public*, pg. 259
CENTRAL PANEL, INC.—See Ajax Electric Co.; *U.S. Private*, pg. 143
CHEIL ELECTRIC CO., LTD.; *Int'l*, pg. 1460
CHICAGO SWITCHBOARD CO., INC.—See Greenbriar Equity Group, L.P.; *U.S. Private*, pg. 1776
CHICONY POWER TECHNOLOGY (THAILAND) CO., LTD.—See Chicony Electronics, Co., Ltd.; *Int'l*, pg. 1476
CHUNG - HSIN POWER SYSTEMS (JIANGSU) CORP.—See Chung-Hsin Electric & Machinery Manufacturing Corp.; *Int'l*, pg. 1597

CINCH CONNECTIVITY SOLUTIONS LTD—See Bel Fuse Inc.; *U.S. Public*, pg. 293
C&K COMPONENTS, INC.—See Littelfuse, Inc.; *U.S. Public*, pg. 1326
COMMERCE CONTROLS INC.; *U.S. Private*, pg. 982
COMUS INTERNATIONAL INC.; *U.S. Private*, pg. 1006
COOPER BUSSMANN, LLC—See Eaton Corporation plc; *Int'l*, pg. 2279
COOPER CAPRI S.A.S.—See Eaton Corporation plc; *Int'l*, pg. 2277
COOPER POWER SYSTEMS, LLC - SOUTH MILWAUKEE PLANT—See Eaton Corporation plc; *Int'l*, pg. 2278
COSEL CO., LTD.; *Int'l*, pg. 1810
CRAIG & DERRICOTT LTD.—See Addtech AB; *Int'l*, pg. 132
CUBIC MODULSYSTEM A/S—See Rockwell Automation, Inc.; *U.S. Public*, pg. 1805
CUSTOM CONTROL SENSORS, INC.; *U.S. Private*, pg. 1128
CYNERGY3 COMPONENTS LLC—See Sensata Technologies Holding plc; *U.S. Public*, pg. 1865
CYNERGY3 COMPONENTS LTD.—See Sensata Technologies Holding plc; *U.S. Public*, pg. 1865
DIGITRAN—See Electro Switch Corporation; *U.S. Private*, pg. 1353
DPS TELECOM; *U.S. Private*, pg. 1271
EATON ELECTRICAL CANADA—See Eaton Corporation plc; *Int'l*, pg. 2279
EATON HOLDING INVESTMENTS GMBH & CO. KG—See Eaton Corporation plc; *Int'l*, pg. 2281
ELECTRIC CONNECTOR TECHNOLOGY CO., LTD.; *Int'l*, pg. 2348
ELECTRONICS STAMPING CORP.; *U.S. Private*, pg. 1356
ELECTRO SWITCH CORPORATION; *U.S. Private*, pg. 1353
ELECTROSWITCH ELECTRONIC PRODUCTS—See Electro Switch Corporation; *U.S. Private*, pg. 1353
ELECTROSWITCH SWITCHES & RELAYS—See Electro Switch Corporation; *U.S. Private*, pg. 1354
ELECTROTEL S.A.; *Int'l*, pg. 2354
ELEKTRON COMPONENTS CORPORATION—See Checkit plc; *Int'l*, pg. 1459
ELEKTRON COMPONENTS LTD.—See Checkit plc; *Int'l*, pg. 1459
EMTEQ EUROPE GMBH—See RTX Corporation; *U.S. Public*, pg. 1822
ENVIROMETRIC PROCESS CONTROLS; *U.S. Private*, pg. 1407
EPG CONTROLS, INC.; *U.S. Private*, pg. 1412
ESCO DRIVES & AUTOMATION N.V.—See Esco Financial & Engineering Company S.A/N.V.; *Int'l*, pg. 2501
ETI ELB S.R.O.—See Andlinger & Company, Inc.; *U.S. Private*, pg. 278
FORTUNE ELECTRIC CO., LTD. - SWITCHGEAR DIVISION—See Fortune Electric Co., Ltd.; *Int'l*, pg. 2743
FUJI ELECTRIC DALIAN CO., LTD.—See Fuji Electric Co., Ltd.; *Int'l*, pg. 2811
FUJI-HAYA ELECTRIC CORP. OF THE PHILIPPINES—See Fuji Electric Co., Ltd.; *Int'l*, pg. 2812
FUJI SMBE ELECTRIC PTE LTD—See Fuji Electric Co., Ltd.; *Int'l*, pg. 2812
FUJI SMBE INDUSTRIES PTE LTD—See Fuji Electric Co., Ltd.; *Int'l*, pg. 2812
FUJI SMBE PTE. LTD.—See Fuji Electric Co., Ltd.; *Int'l*, pg. 2812
FUJI SMBE SYSTEMS PTE LTD—See Fuji Electric Co., Ltd.; *Int'l*, pg. 2812
FUJI SMBE TECHNOLOGY PTE LTD—See Fuji Electric Co., Ltd.; *Int'l*, pg. 2812
FUJITSU COMPONENT LIMITED; *Int'l*, pg. 2832
FUJITSU (SINGAPORE) PTE. LTD.—See Fujitsu Limited; *Int'l*, pg. 2833
GRAYHILL INC.; *U.S. Private*, pg. 1761
GRIFFIN TECHNOLOGY, INC.—See Incipio, LLC; *U.S. Private*, pg. 2053
GUANGZHOU BAIYUN ELECTRIC EQUIPMENT CO., LTD.; *Int'l*, pg. 3164
G&W CANADA CORPORATION—See G&W Electric Company; *U.S. Private*, pg. 1629
G&W ELECTRIC COMPANY; *U.S. Private*, pg. 1629
HIROSE ELECTRIC CO., LTD.; *Int'l*, pg. 3405
HIROSE ELECTRIC UK LTD.—See Hirose Electric Co., Ltd.; *Int'l*, pg. 3405
HIROSE KOREA CO. LTD.—See Hirose Electric Co., Ltd.; *Int'l*, pg. 3405
HITACHI HVB, INC.—See Hitachi, Ltd.; *Int'l*, pg. 3414
HITACHI T&D SYSTEMS ASIA PTE. LTD.—See Hitachi, Ltd.; *Int'l*, pg. 3422
HONEYWELL SENSING & CONTROL—See Honeywell International Inc.; *U.S. Public*, pg. 1050
HPL ELECTRIC & POWER LIMITED; *Int'l*, pg. 3501
HYUNDAI ELECTRIC & ENERGY SYSTEMS CO., LTD.; *Int'l*, pg. 3556
IDEAL ANDERSON ASIA PACIFIC LTD.—See IDEAL Industries Inc; *U.S. Private*, pg. 2036
IE SOLUTION SERVICE CO., LTD.—See Hitachi, Ltd.; *Int'l*, pg. 3423
INDICON CORP.; *U.S. Private*, pg. 2063
INDUSTRIAL SOLUTIONS, INC.; *U.S. Private*, pg. 2068

INERTIA ENGINEERING & MACHINE WORKS, INC.—See Centerbridge Partners, L.P.; *U.S. Private*, pg. 815
THE INTERNATIONAL ELECTRICAL PRODUCTS COMPANY (TIEPCO)—See Al-Tuwairqi Group; *Int'l*, pg. 289
ITW SWITCHES—See Illinois Tool Works Inc.; *U.S. Public*, pg. 1107
JEWELL INSTRUMENTS, LLC; *U.S. Private*, pg. 2205
JIANGSU CHUNG - HSIN PRECISION MACHINERY CO., LTD.—See Chung-Hsin Electric & Machinery Manufacturing Corp.; *Int'l*, pg. 1597
JOSLYN HI-VOLTAGE COMPANY, LLC—See ABB Ltd.; *Int'l*, pg. 52
KASA INDUSTRIAL CONTROLS INC.; *U.S. Private*, pg. 2263
KAYCEE IND. LTD.—See CMS Computers Ltd.; *Int'l*, pg. 1672
KEYSTONE ELECTRICAL MANUFACTURING COMPANY; *U.S. Private*, pg. 2296
KORRY ELECTRONICS CO.—See TransDigm Group Incorporated; *U.S. Public*, pg. 2181
L-3 COMMUNICATIONS WESTWOOD CORPORATION-NMP DIVISION—See L3Harris Technologies, Inc.; *U.S. Public*, pg. 1283
LIEBERT CORPORATION—See Vertiv Holdings Co; *U.S. Public*, pg. 2289
LITTELFUSE ASIA SALES B.V.—See Littelfuse, Inc.; *U.S. Public*, pg. 1327
LITTELFUSE, INC.; *U.S. Public*, pg. 1326
LITTELFUSE ITALY S.R.L.—See Littelfuse, Inc.; *U.S. Public*, pg. 1327
LITTELFUSE TRIAD, INC.—See Littelfuse, Inc.; *U.S. Public*, pg. 1327
MALTON ELECTRIC CO.; *U.S. Private*, pg. 2558
MARATHON SPECIAL PRODUCTS CORP.—See Regal Rexnord Corporation; *U.S. Public*, pg. 1773
MARTEC LIMITED—See Amphenol Corporation; *U.S. Public*, pg. 131
MARWELL CORPORATION; *U.S. Private*, pg. 2598
MECHANICAL PRODUCTS INC.; *U.S. Private*, pg. 2649
METEROLOGY DATA PRIVATE LIMITED—See Brookfield Corporation; *Int'l*, pg. 1178
METEROLOGY DATA PRIVATE LIMITED—See Elliott Management Corporation; *U.S. Private*, pg. 1371
METHODE ELECTRONICS FAR EAST PTE., LTD.—See Methode Electronics, Inc.; *U.S. Public*, pg. 1428
METHODE ELECTRONICS MALTA LTD.—See Methode Electronics, Inc.; *U.S. Public*, pg. 1428
M&G ELECTRONICS CORP.; *U.S. Private*, pg. 2524
M&I ELECTRIC INDUSTRIES, INC.—See STABILIS SOLUTIONS, INC.; *U.S. Public*, pg. 1924
MITSUBISHI ELECTRIC POWER PRODUCTS, INC.—See Hyosung Heavy Industries Corp.; *Int'l*, pg. 3552
MOTOR CITY ELECTRIC CO., INC.; *U.S. Private*, pg. 2796
MOTOR CITY ELECTRIC TECHNOLOGY—See Motor City Electric Co., Inc.; *U.S. Private*, pg. 2796
NELSON-MILLER, INC.; *U.S. Private*, pg. 2884
NEXT10, INC.; *U.S. Public*, pg. 1525
PANELMATIC INC.; *U.S. Private*, pg. 3086
POINT EIGHT POWER INC.—See Mission Critical Group; *U.S. Private*, pg. 2747
POWELL ELECTRICAL SYSTEMS, INC.—See Powell Industries, Inc.; *U.S. Public*, pg. 1705
POWELL (UK) LIMITED—See Powell Industries, Inc.; *U.S. Public*, pg. 1705
POWER ELECTRONICS, INC.—See AZZ, Inc.; *U.S. Public*, pg. 259
PREFORMED LINE PRODUCTS (AUSTRALIA) PTY LTD.—See Preformed Line Products Company; *U.S. Public*, pg. 1714
PROFESSIONAL POWER PRODUCTS, INC.—See Power Solutions International, Inc.; *U.S. Public*, pg. 1705
PT. HITACHI POWER SYSTEMS INDONESIA—See Hitachi, Ltd.; *Int'l*, pg. 3424
S&C ELECTRIC CANADA LTD.—See S&C Electric Company; *U.S. Private*, pg. 3512
S&C ELECTRIC COMPANY; *U.S. Private*, pg. 3512
S&C ELECTRIC DO BRASIL LIMITADA—See S&C Electric Company; *U.S. Private*, pg. 3513
S&C ELECTRIC (SUZHOU) CO. LTD.—See S&C Electric Company; *U.S. Private*, pg. 3512
SHANGHAI FUJI ELECTRIC SWITCHGEAR CO., LTD.—See Fuji Electric Co., Ltd.; *Int'l*, pg. 2813
SMB BRIGHTEN SWITCHBOARD ENGINEERING SDN. BHD.—See Fuji Electric Co., Ltd.; *Int'l*, pg. 2812
SMB HARWAL ELECTRIC PTY. LTD.—See Fuji Electric Co., Ltd.; *Int'l*, pg. 2812
SMB MACQUARIE ELECTRIC PTY LTD—See Fuji Electric Co., Ltd.; *Int'l*, pg. 2812
SMB SWITCHGEAR & ENGINEERING SDN BHD—See Fuji Electric Co., Ltd.; *Int'l*, pg. 2812
SMC ELECTRICAL PRODUCTS INC.; *U.S. Private*, pg. 3693
S&S POWER SWITCHGEAR LIMITED—See Hamilton & Company Limited; *Int'l*, pg. 3237
STACOSWITCH, INC.—See Components Corporation of America, Inc.; *U.S. Private*, pg. 1002
STONERIDGE NORDIC AB—See Stoneridge, Inc.; *U.S. Public*, pg. 1951

N.A.I.C.S. INDEX

335314 — RELAY AND INDUSTRIA...

SUNLIGHT ELECTRICAL PTE LTD—See Chint Group Corporation; *Int'l*, pg. 1571
SWITCHGEAR AB—See Addtech AB; *Int'l*, pg. 135
TABELEC FORCE ET COMMANDES S.A.—See Burkhalter Holding AG; *Int'l*, pg. 1226
TECSIT S.R.L.—See CAD IT S.p.A.; *Int'l*, pg. 1247
TEXAS INSTRUMENTS INCORPORATED - PLUG & POWER—See Texas Instruments Incorporated; *U.S. Public*, pg. 2026
TII NETWORK TECHNOLOGIES, INC.—See Kelta, Inc.; *U.S. Private*, pg. 2281
TRP CONNECTOR B.V.—See Bel Fuse Inc.; *U.S. Public*, pg. 293
TRP CONNECTOR LIMITED—See Bel Fuse Inc.; *U.S. Public*, pg. 293
VANGUARD INSTRUMENTS CO., INC.—See ESCO Technologies, Inc.; *U.S. Public*, pg. 793
WESSEX ADVANCED SWITCHING PRODUCTS LIMITED—See RTX Corporation; *U.S. Public*, pg. 1822
WILMORE ELECTRONICS COMPANY; *U.S. Private*, pg. 4529
YANGZHOU SAC SWITCHGEAR CO., LTD.—See ABB Ltd.; *Int'l*, pg. 49
ZAO DANFOSS—See Danfoss A/S; *Int'l*, pg. 1962
ZHENJIANG DAQO EATON ELECTRICAL SYSTEMS COMPANY LIMITED—See Eaton Corporation plc; *Int'l*, pg. 2281

335314 — RELAY AND INDUSTRIAL CONTROL MANUFACTURING

ABB INC.—See ABB Ltd.; *Int'l*, pg. 51
ABB INC. - SSAC—See ABB Ltd.; *Int'l*, pg. 51
ADAMS RITE AEROSPACE INC.—See TransDigm Group Incorporated; *U.S. Public*, pg. 2181
ADTEK FUJI CO., LTD.—See Fuji Corporation; *Int'l*, pg. 2809
ADVANCED AUTOMATION GROUP, LLC; *U.S. Private*, pg. 87
ADVANTECH TECHNOLOGY (CHINA) COMPANY LTD.—See Advantech Co., Ltd.; *Int'l*, pg. 165
AFAG AUTOMATION TECHNOLOGY (SHANGHAO) CO., LTD.—See Emerson Electric Co.; *U.S. Public*, pg. 740
AIRTAC INTERNATIONAL GROUP; *Int'l*, pg. 248
AIRTEC PNEUMATIC ENGINEERING BV—See AIRTEC Pneumatic GmbH; *Int'l*, pg. 249
AISIN ELECTRONICS, INC.—See AISIN Corporation; *Int'l*, pg. 252
AMERICAN TELETIMER CORP.; *U.S. Private*, pg. 257
AMETEK AUTOMATION & PROCESS TECHNOLOGIES—See AMETEK, Inc.; *U.S. Public*, pg. 117
AMETEK HDR POWER SYSTEMS, INC.—See AMETEK, Inc.; *U.S. Public*, pg. 119
ANIMATICS CORP.—See Moog Inc.; *U.S. Public*, pg. 1470
ASCENSION TECHNOLOGY CORPORATION—See Roper Technologies, Inc.; *U.S. Public*, pg. 1810
ASM FRANCE S.A.R.L.—See ASM INTERNATIONAL N.V.; *Int'l*, pg. 626
ASSA ABLOY MEXICO, S.A DE CV.—See ASSA ABLOY AB; *Int'l*, pg. 636
AURO IMPEX & CHEMICALS LIMITED; *Int'l*, pg. 711
AUTOMATIC TIMING & CONTROLS—See Desco Corporation; *U.S. Private*, pg. 1211
AUTONOMOUS ELECTRIC MOBILITY PVT. LTD.—See Digilife Technologies Limited; *Int'l*, pg. 2119
BANNER ENGINEERING CORP.; *U.S. Private*, pg. 469
BECKWITH ELECTRIC CO. INC.; *U.S. Private*, pg. 511
BEIJING ROSEMOUNT FAR EAST INSTRUMENT CO., LTD.—See Emerson Electric Co.; *U.S. Public*, pg. 742
BENSHAW INC.—See Regal Rexnord Corporation; *U.S. Public*, pg. 1772
BETA RAVEN INC.—See Gilbert Global Equity Partners; *U.S. Private*, pg. 1698
BOMAC INC.; *U.S. Private*, pg. 611
BORGWARNER GATESHEAD LIMITED—See BorgWarner Inc.; *U.S. Public*, pg. 369
BORGWARNER THERMAL SYSTEMS INC.—See BorgWarner Inc.; *U.S. Public*, pg. 370
BRITECH, INC.—See Cerberus Capital Management, L.P.; *U.S. Private*, pg. 838
BURGESS-AARDING—See CECO Environmental Corp.; *U.S. Public*, pg. 464
BUSI GROUP S.R.L.; *Int'l*, pg. 1228
BWI EAGLE, INC.—See Harbour Group Industries, Inc.; *U.S. Private*, pg. 1860
CALDARO—See Addtech AB; *Int'l*, pg. 132
CARGOTEC ACT B.V.—See Cargotec Corporation; *Int'l*, pg. 1326
CATTRON HOLDINGS, INC.—See Harbour Group Industries, Inc.; *U.S. Private*, pg. 1860
CDI ELECTRONICS LLC—See Dometic Group AB; *Int'l*, pg. 2160
CETAM AUTOMATISMES—See Hiolle Industries S.A.; *Int'l*, pg. 3401
CHANGZHOU SHENLI ELECTRICAL MACHINE INC; *Int'l*, pg. 1445

CHENGDU CARBON MATERIAL CO., LTD.—See Fangda Carbon New Material Co., Ltd.; *Int'l*, pg. 2613
CHICHIBU FUJI CO., LTD.—See Fuji Electric Co., Ltd.; *Int'l*, pg. 2810
CHIKUMA TSUSHIN INDUSTRY CO., LTD.—See FUJITSU COMPONENT LIMITED; *Int'l*, pg. 2832
CLASS 1—See IDEC Corp; *U.S. Public*, pg. 1090
CLT ENGINEERING SDN. BHD.—See Genetec Technology Berhad; *Int'l*, pg. 2922
COMPRESSOR CONTROLS (BEIJING) CORPORATION LTD.—See Roper Technologies, Inc.; *U.S. Public*, pg. 1811
COMPRESSOR CONTROLS CORPORATION B.V.—See Roper Technologies, Inc.; *U.S. Public*, pg. 1811
COMPRESSOR CONTROLS CORPORATION—See Roper Technologies, Inc.; *U.S. Public*, pg. 1810
COMPRESSOR CONTROLS CORPORATION S.R.L.—See Roper Technologies, Inc.; *U.S. Public*, pg. 1811
COMPRESSOR CONTROLS PTY. LTD.—See Roper Technologies, Inc.; *U.S. Public*, pg. 1811
CONET TAIWAN CO., LTD.—See IDEC Corporation; *Int'l*, pg. 3589
CONNOR-WINFIELD CORP.; *U.S. Private*, pg. 1018
CONTROL CHIEF CORP.—See Control Chief Holdings, Inc.; *U.S. Private*, pg. 1034
CONTROL CHIEF HOLDINGS, INC.; *U.S. Private*, pg. 1034
CONTROLS & ELECTRIC PTE. LTD.—See Boustead Singapore Limited; *Int'l*, pg. 1120
CONTROLTEK INC.—See Centre Lane Partners, LLC; *U.S. Private*, pg. 827
COOPER POWER SYSTEMS, LLC - MINNEAPOLIS PLANT—See Eaton Corporation plc; *Int'l*, pg. 2278
COPERION K-TRON FRANCE S.A.R.L.—See Hillenbrand, Inc.; *U.S. Public*, pg. 1036
COPPERLOGIC, LTD.—See Eaton Corporation plc; *Int'l*, pg. 2279
CORBY INDUSTRIES, INC.; *U.S. Private*, pg. 1047
COSMO ELECTRONICS CORP. - YILAN PLANT—See Cosmo Electronics Corporation; *Int'l*, pg. 1811
COTO TECHNOLOGY, INC.—See The Dyson-Kissner-Moran Corporation; *U.S. Private*, pg. 4024
CRUISE MUNICH GMBH—See General Motors Company; *Int'l*, pg. 923
CRYDOM, INC.—See Sensata Technologies Holding plc; *U.S. Public*, pg. 1866
CRYDOM SSR LIMITED—See Sensata Technologies Holding plc; *U.S. Public*, pg. 1866
CSE-CONTROLS S.R.O.—See CSE Global Ltd.; *Int'l*, pg. 1863
CSE CORPORATION; *U.S. Private*, pg. 1116
DANFOSS ELECTRONIC DRIVES—See Danfoss A/S; *Int'l*, pg. 1960
DANFOSS GRAHAM—See Danfoss A/S; *Int'l*, pg. 1960
DASCAN INDUSTRIAL CONTROLS; *Int'l*, pg. 1973
DATACOM SYSTEMS INC.; *U.S. Private*, pg. 1165
DELTA ELECTRONICS COMPONENTS (DONGGUAN) CO., LTD.—See Delta Electronics, Inc.; *Int'l*, pg. 2017
DELTROL CORP.; *U.S. Private*, pg. 1202
DEVAR, INC.; *U.S. Private*, pg. 1217
DISPLAYLINK CORP.—See Synaptics Incorporated; *U.S. Public*, pg. 1969
DOEDIJNS CONTROLS B.V.—See IK Investment Partners Limited; *Int'l*, pg. 3609
DY INNOVATE CORPORATION—See DY Corporation; *Int'l*, pg. 2237
EAO FAR EAST LTD.—See EAO AG; *Int'l*, pg. 2267
EAO LIMITED—See EAO AG; *Int'l*, pg. 2267
EATON ELECTRICAL S.A.—See Eaton Corporation plc; *Int'l*, pg. 2279
EECO—See Transico Incorporated; *U.S. Private*, pg. 4208
ELCON INC.; *U.S. Private*, pg. 1350
ELECTRICAL POWER PRODUCTS INC—See Electro Management Corporation; *U.S. Private*, pg. 1353
ELECTRONIC DESIGN, INC.—See Fulham & Co., Inc.; *U.S. Private*, pg. 1620
ELECTROPRIVOD LTD.; *Int'l*, pg. 2354
EMERSON FLOW CONTROLS—See Emerson Electric Co.; *U.S. Public*, pg. 744
EMERSON PROCESS MANAGEMENT POWER & WATER SOLUTIONS—See Emerson Electric Co.; *U.S. Public*, pg. 747
EMX CONTROLS INC.; *U.S. Private*, pg. 1389
ENERCON ENGINEERING INC.; *U.S. Private*, pg. 1392
ENGINEERED SOLUTIONS L.P.—See Enerpac Tool Group Corp.; *U.S. Public*, pg. 765
ENVIONEER CO., LTD.; *Int'l*, pg. 2453
ESCO FINANCIAL & ENGINEERING COMPANY S.A/N.V.; *Int'l*, pg. 2501
ETO MAGNETIC CORP.—See ETO GRUPPE Beteiligungen GmbH; *Int'l*, pg. 2524
ETRATECH ASIA-PACIFIC ELECTRONICS (SHENZHEN) LTD.—See Gentherm Incorporated; *U.S. Public*, pg. 931
ETRATECH ASIA-PACIFIC LIMITED—See Gentherm Incorporated; *U.S. Public*, pg. 931
EVANS ENTERPRISES, INC.; *U.S. Private*, pg. 1435
EVER LUMIN INCORPORATION—See Contrel Technology Co., Ltd.; *Int'l*, pg. 1785
EVERVISION ELECTRONICS CO., LTD.—See Everlight Electronics Co., Ltd.; *Int'l*, pg. 2567
EVOC INTELLIGENT TECHNOLOGY COMPANY LIMITED; *Int'l*, pg. 2572
EVT TECHNOLOGY CO., LTD.—See Chroma ATE Inc.; *Int'l*, pg. 1588
FANUC BULGARIA CORPORATION—See FANUC Corporation; *Int'l*, pg. 2614
FANUC CORPORATION; *Int'l*, pg. 2614
FANUC EUROPE GMBH—See FANUC Corporation; *Int'l*, pg. 2614
FANUC FA ITALIA S.R.L.—See FANUC Corporation; *Int'l*, pg. 2614
FANUC FRANCE S.A.—See FANUC Corporation; *Int'l*, pg. 2614
FANUC GERMANY SERVICE GMBH—See FANUC Corporation; *Int'l*, pg. 2614
FANUC IBERIA S.L.U.—See FANUC Corporation; *Int'l*, pg. 2614
FANUC MECHATRONICS (MALAYSIA) SDN. BHD.—See FANUC Corporation; *Int'l*, pg. 2615
FANUC PHILIPPINES CORPORATION—See FANUC Corporation; *Int'l*, pg. 2614
FANUC ROBOTICS EUROPE S.A.—See FANUC Corporation; *Int'l*, pg. 2614
FANUC SINGAPORE PTE. LTD.—See FANUC Corporation; *Int'l*, pg. 2615
FANUC TAIWAN LIMITED—See FANUC Corporation; *Int'l*, pg. 2615
FANUC TURKEY LTD.—See FANUC Corporation; *Int'l*, pg. 2615
FANUC U.K. LIMITED—See FANUC Corporation; *Int'l*, pg. 2615
FESTO AG—See Festo AG & Co. KG; *Int'l*, pg. 2647
FIDIA CO.—See FIDIA S.p.A.; *Int'l*, pg. 2654
FIREYE, INC.—See Carrier Global Corporation; *U.S. Public*, pg. 440
FLO-TORK INC.—See Moog Inc.; *U.S. Public*, pg. 1469
FREY AG—See Doppelmayr Group; *Int'l*, pg. 2175
FUJI ELECTRIC (CHANGSHU) CO., LTD.—See Fuji Electric Co., Ltd.; *Int'l*, pg. 2811
FUJI ELECTRIC F-TECH CO., LTD.—See Fuji Electric Co., Ltd.; *Int'l*, pg. 2811
GASTON COUNTY DYEING MACHINE COMPANY; *U.S. Private*, pg. 1649
GAVIAL ENGINEERING & MANUFACTURING; *U.S. Private*, pg. 1652
GE MULTILIN—See General Electric Company; *U.S. Public*, pg. 918
GENERAL DYNAMICS GLOBAL IMAGING TECHNOLOGIES, INC. - SAN DIEGO—See General Dynamics Corporation; *U.S. Public*, pg. 915
GENTEC; *U.S. Private*, pg. 2928
GHM MESSTECHNIK GMBH; *Int'l*, pg. 2959
GIGAVAC, LLC—See Sensata Technologies Holding plc; *U.S. Public*, pg. 1865
GLENDINNING MARINE PRODUCTS, INC.—See Orscheln Group; *U.S. Private*, pg. 3045
GOLDENFLASH ELECTRONICS CO., LTD.—See EDOM Technology Co., Ltd.; *Int'l*, pg. 2313
GUARDIAN CONTROLS LTD.; *Int'l*, pg. 3170
HAMLIN ELECTRONICS EUROPE LTD.—See Littelfuse, Inc.; *U.S. Public*, pg. 1327
HASELHOFER FEINMECHANIK GMBH—See AUMA Riester GmbH & Co. KG; *Int'l*, pg. 705
HID ASIA PACIFIC LTD.—See ASSA ABLOY AB; *Int'l*, pg. 637
HID CORPORATION LTD.—See ASSA ABLOY AB; *Int'l*, pg. 637
HI-LEX AMERICA, INC.—See Hi-Lex Corporation; *Int'l*, pg. 3380
HI-LEX CORPORATION; *Int'l*, pg. 3380
HITACHI INFORMATION CONTROL SYSTEMS EUROPE LTD.—See Hitachi, Ltd.; *Int'l*, pg. 3419
HONEYWELL (CHINA) CO., LTD.—See Honeywell International Inc.; *U.S. Public*, pg. 1047
HONGFA AMERICA, INC.—See Hongfa Technology Co Ltd; *Int'l*, pg. 3470
HONGFA ELECTROACOUSTIC (HONGKONG) CO., LTD.—See Hongfa Technology Co Ltd; *Int'l*, pg. 3470
HONGFA EUROPE GMBH—See Hongfa Technology Co Ltd; *Int'l*, pg. 3470
HONGFA TECHNOLOGY CO LTD; *Int'l*, pg. 3470
HORNER INDUSTRIAL GROUP; *U.S. Private*, pg. 1983
HOSIDEN WAKAYAMA CORPORATION—See Hosiden Corporation; *Int'l*, pg. 3484
HUAZHANG TECHNOLOGY HOLDING LIMITED; *Int'l*, pg. 3516
HUBBELL INDUSTRIAL CONTROLS, INC.—See Hubbell Incorporated; *U.S. Public*, pg. 1000
HURLETRON INC.—See Altair Corporation; *U.S. Public*, pg. 86
IDEC CORPORATION - FUKUSAKI PLANT—See IDEC Corporation; *Int'l*, pg. 3589
IDEC CORPORATION - KYOTO PLANT—See IDEC Corporation; *Int'l*, pg. 3589
IDEC CORPORATION; *Int'l*, pg. 3589
IDEC CORPORATION - TAKINO PLANT—See IDEC Corporation; *Int'l*, pg. 3589

335314 — RELAY AND INDUSTRIA...

IDEC CORPORATION - TSUKUBA PLANT—See IDEC Corporation; *Int'l*, pg. 3589
IDEC IZUMI SUZHOU CO., LTD.—See IDEC Corporation; *Int'l*, pg. 3590
IDEC IZUMI TAIWAN CORPORATION—See IDEC Corporation; *Int'l*, pg. 3590
IMC MAGNETICS CORP.—See Curtiss-Wright Corporation; *U.S. Public*, pg. 611
INDAK MANUFACTURING CORP.; *U.S. Private*, pg. 2054
INTERNATIONAL CONTROLS & MEASUREMENTS CORP.; *U.S. Private*, pg. 2116
INTERNATIONAL GOVERNOR SERVICES, LLC—See BlackRock, Inc.; *U.S. Public*, pg. 346
INTERNATIONAL GOVERNOR SERVICES, LLC—See Blackstone Inc.; *U.S. Public*, pg. 358
INTERNATIONAL GOVERNOR SERVICES, LLC—See Cascade Investment LLC; *U.S. Private*, pg. 780
ITERIS, INC.—See Almaviva S.p.A.; *Int'l*, pg. 363
ITT INDUSTRIES INC.—See ITT Inc.; *U.S. Public*, pg. 1178
IXYS INTEGRATED CIRCUITS DIVISION INC.—See Littelfuse, Inc.; *U.S. Public*, pg. 1327
JOSLYN CLARK CONTROLS, INC.—See Danaher Corporation; *U.S. Public*, pg. 627
KAHLER AUTOMATION CORPORATION; *U.S. Private*, pg. 2254
KG TECHNOLOGIES, INC.; *U.S. Private*, pg. 2301
KMC CONTROLS; *U.S. Private*, pg. 2321
KOREA FANUC CORPORATION—See FANUC Corporation; *Int'l*, pg. 2615
LAB-VENT CONTROLS A/S—See AddLife AB; *Int'l*, pg. 129
LAIRD CONTROLS UK LIMITED—See DuPont de Nemours, Inc.; *U.S. Public*, pg. 693
LEACH INTERNATIONAL CORPORATION—See TransDigm Group Incorporated; *U.S. Public*, pg. 2181
LEADSHINE AMERICA INC.—See China Leadshine Technology Co., Ltd.; *Int'l*, pg. 1514
LICOS TRUCKTEC GMBH—See Concentric AB; *Int'l*, pg. 1764
LINTOTT CONTROL SYSTEMS LIMITED—See Galliford Try Holdings plc; *Int'l*, pg. 2874
MAGNETROL ENVIRONMENTAL, L.P.—See AMETEK, Inc.; *U.S. Public*, pg. 121
MAGNUS PRECISION MANUFACTURING INC.—See Floturn Inc.; *U.S. Private*, pg. 1551
MAHR METERING SYSTEMS GMBH—See Carl Mahr Holding GmbH; *Int'l*, pg. 1333
MANTEK—See NCH Corporation; *U.S. Private*, pg. 2875
MANUFACTURING RESOURCE GROUP, INC.—See Cerberus Capital Management, L.P.; *U.S. Private*, pg. 838
MAPLE SYSTEMS, INC.; *U.S. Private*, pg. 2568
MASON INDUSTRIES; *U.S. Private*, pg. 2602
MERTIK MAXITROL GMBH & CO., KG—See Maxitrol Company; *U.S. Private*, pg. 2619
MIYAZAKI FUJITSU COMPONENTS LIMITED—See FUJITSU COMPONENT LIMITED; *Int'l*, pg. 2832
MODI AIRCRETE PRIVATE LIMITED—See Digilife Technologies Limited; *Int'l*, pg. 2119
MOLEX AUTOMOTIVE—See Koch Industries, Inc.; *U.S. Private*, pg. 2334
MOOG READING LIMITED—See Moog Inc.; *U.S. Public*, pg. 1470
MOTORTRONICS, INC.—See Standard Motor Products, Inc.; *U.S. Public*, pg. 1929
O.E.M. CONTROLS, INC., *U.S. Private*, pg. 2981
OHMITE MANUFACTURING COMPANY; *U.S. Private*, pg. 3005
ORTLINGHAUS-WERKE GMBH—See Brd. Klee A/S; *Int'l*, pg. 1143
PACIFIC MAGNETICS INC.—See Careen, Inc.; *U.S. Private*, pg. 752
PACIFIC PRECISION LABORATORIES, INC.; *U.S. Private*, pg. 3070
PARKER HANNIFIN ARGENTINA SAIC—See Parker Hannifin Corporation; *U.S. Public*, pg. 1644
PARKER HANNIFIN COMPUMOTOR CORP.—See Parker Hannifin Corporation; *U.S. Public*, pg. 1644
PARKER VANSCO ELECTRONIC CONTROLS DIVISION—See Parker Hannifin Corporation; *U.S. Public*, pg. 1647
PECO INSPX; *U.S. Private*, pg. 3127
PEERLESS MANUFACTURING CO.—See CECO Environmental Corp.; *U.S. Public*, pg. 464
PG DRIVES TECHNOLOGY LTD.—See Curtiss-Wright Corporation; *U.S. Public*, pg. 612
THE PHILLIPPINES THERMOPOWER CLIMATE CONTROL CORPORATION—See Hongfa Technology Co Ltd; *Int'l*, pg. 3470
PINE INSTRUMENT COMPANY; *U.S. Private*, pg. 3182
PIVOTAL SYSTEMS CORPORATION; *U.S. Private*, pg. 3192
PIVOT INTERNATIONAL, INC.; *U.S. Private*, pg. 3192
PMSR ELECTRO SI AUTOMATIZARE S.R.L.—See Christof Holding AG; *Int'l*, pg. 1587
POWELL ELECTRICAL MANUFACTURING COMPANY—See Powell Industries, Inc.; *U.S. Public*, pg. 1705
PROXIMITY CONTROLS CORP.—See Arcline Investment Management LP; *U.S. Private*, pg. 313

PT.HI-LEX PARTS INDONESIA—See Hi-Lex Corporation; *Int'l*, pg. 3381
THE RAILWAY ENGINEERING COMPANY LIMITED—See Hitachi, Ltd.; *Int'l*, pg. 3417
RETZLAFF INCORPORATED; *U.S. Private*, pg. 3412
RMS MORS SMITT—See Westinghouse Air Brake Technologies Corporation; *U.S. Public*, pg. 2359
ROCKWELL AUTOMATION AUSTRALIA LTD.—See Rockwell Automation, Inc.; *U.S. Public*, pg. 1805
ROCKWELL AUTOMATION DE MEXICO, S.A. DE C.V.—See Rockwell Automation, Inc.; *U.S. Public*, pg. 1806
ROCKWELL AUTOMATION DO BRASIL LTDA.—See Rockwell Automation, Inc.; *U.S. Public*, pg. 1806
ROCKWELL AUTOMATION (PHILIPPINES) INC.—See Rockwell Automation, Inc.; *U.S. Public*, pg. 1805
ROCKWELL AUTOMATION S.A./N.V.—See Rockwell Automation, Inc.; *U.S. Public*, pg. 1806
ROCKWELL AUTOMATION SOUTHEAST ASIA PTE. LTD.—See Rockwell Automation, Inc.; *U.S. Public*, pg. 1806
ROCKWELL AUTOMATION SP. Z.O.O.—See Rockwell Automation, Inc.; *U.S. Public*, pg. 1806
ROCKWELL AUTOMATION SWITZERLAND GMBH—See Rockwell Automation, Inc.; *U.S. Public*, pg. 1806
ROCKWELL COLLINS CANADA INC.—See RTX Corporation; *U.S. Public*, pg. 1823
ROCKWELL COLOMBIA S.A—See Rockwell Automation, Inc.; *U.S. Public*, pg. 1806
ROCKWELL OTOMASYON TICARET A.S.—See Rockwell Automation, Inc.; *U.S. Public*, pg. 1807
R. R. FLOODY COMPANY, INC.—See Applied Industrial Technologies, Inc.; *U.S. Public*, pg. 171
SAMINCO, INC.; *U.S. Private*, pg. 3537
S&C ELECTRIC COMPANY-AUTOMATION SYSTEMS—See S&C Electric Company; *U.S. Private*, pg. 3513
SENSATA TECHNOLOGIES DOMINICANA, S.R.L.—See Sensata Technologies Holding plc; *U.S. Public*, pg. 1865
SENYUN PRECISION OPTICAL CO., LTD.—See Giga-Byte Technology Co., Ltd.; *Int'l*, pg. 2971
SEVCON SAS—See BorgWarner Inc.; *U.S. Public*, pg. 370
SIPOS AKTORIK GMBH—See AUMA Riester GmbH & Co. KG; *Int'l*, pg. 705
SOR, INC.; *U.S. Private*, pg. 3715
S.S.I. TECHNOLOGIES INC.; *U.S. Private*, pg. 3519
STROMAG DESSAU GMBH—See Regal Rexnord Corporation; *U.S. Public*, pg. 1772
STROMAG GMBH—See Regal Rexnord Corporation; *U.S. Public*, pg. 1772
SWELEX AB—See Addtech AB; *Int'l*, pg. 135
SYSTEMS MACHINE AUTOMATION COMPONENTS; *U.S. Private*, pg. 3907
TAICANG CONET ELECTRONICS CO., LTD.—See IDEC Corporation; *Int'l*, pg. 3590
TATUNG-FANUC ROBOTICS COMPANY—See FANUC Corporation; *Int'l*, pg. 2615
TDI ADVANCED CONVERSION PRODUCTS—See TDI Power Systems; *U.S. Private*, pg. 3944
TEAMTECHNIK AUTOMATION GMBH—See Durr AG; *Int'l*, pg. 2233
TEAMTECHNIK MASCHINEN UND ANLAGEN GMBH—See Durr AG; *Int'l*, pg. 2233
TIANJIN XINDAFENG IMPORT AND EXPORT TRADE CO. LTD.—See GCH Technology Co., Ltd.; *Int'l*, pg. 2895
TRANSICO INCORPORATED; *U.S. Private*, pg. 4208
TURCK INC.; *U.S. Private*, pg. 4259
ULTRA ELECTRONICS MEASUREMENT SYSTEMS, INC.—See Advent International Corporation; *U.S. Private*, pg. 101
UNICO, INC.—See Regal Rexnord Corporation; *U.S. Public*, pg. 1774
VALCOR ENGINEERING CORPORATION; *U.S. Private*, pg. 4330
WARD LEONARD CT LLC—See Arcline Investment Management LP; *U.S. Private*, pg. 313
WELDING TECHNOLOGY CORPORATION; *U.S. Private*, pg. 4474
WESTCON—See Desco Corporation; *U.S. Public*, pg. 1211
WOODWARD GMBH—See Woodward, Inc.; *U.S. Public*, pg. 2378
XIAMEN HONGFA ELECTROACOUSTIC SCIENCE & TECHNOLOGY CO., LTD.—See Hongfa Technology Co Ltd; *Int'l*, pg. 3470
ZHEJIANG AICHI MECHANICAL & ELECTRICAL CO., LTD.—See Aichi Steel Corporation; *Int'l*, pg. 230
ZONEX INC—See Trolex Corp.; *U.S. Private*, pg. 4241

335910 — BATTERY MANUFACTURING

ABATEL AB—See Addtech AB; *Int'l*, pg. 131
ABLE NEW ENERGY CO., LTD—See Ultralife Corporation; *U.S. Public*, pg. 2224
ABM FUJIYA BERHAD; *Int'l*, pg. 63
ABSL POWER SOLUTIONS LTD.—See EnerSys; *U.S. Public*, pg. 767

ACCUTRONICS, LTD.—See Ultralife Corporation; *U.S. Public*, pg. 2224
ACME AEROSPACE, INC.—See TransDigm Group Incorporated; *U.S. Public*, pg. 2181
ACUMULADORES INDUSTRIALES ENERSYS SA—See EnerSys; *U.S. Public*, pg. 766
ADVANCED LITHIUM ELECTROCHEMISTRY (HK) CO., LIMITED—See Advanced Lithium Electrochemistry (KY) Co., Ltd.; *Int'l*, pg. 160
ADVANCED LITHIUM ELECTROCHEMISTRY (KY) CO., LTD.; *Int'l*, pg. 160
AEG POWER SOLUTIONS, S.L.—See 3W Power S.A.; *Int'l*, pg. 160
AGM BATTERIES LTD—See GS Yuasa Corporation; *Int'l*, pg. 3143
ALELION ENERGY SYSTEMS AB; *Int'l*, pg. 306
ALPHA ALTERNATIVE ENERGY INC.—See EnerSys; *U.S. Public*, pg. 767
ALPHA-EN CORPORATION; *U.S. Public*, pg. 82
ALPHA INNOVATIONS MEXICO S DE R.L. DE C.V.—See EnerSys; *U.S. Public*, pg. 767
ALPHA TECH ENERGY SOLUTIONS INDIA PRIVATE LIMITED—See EnerSys; *U.S. Public*, pg. 767
ALPHA TECHNOLOGIES ASIA LTD.—See EnerSys; *U.S. Public*, pg. 767
ALPHA TECHNOLOGIES PTY. LTD.—See EnerSys; *U.S. Public*, pg. 767
ALPHA TECHNOLOGIES SERVICES, INC.—See EnerSys; *U.S. Public*, pg. 768
AMARON BATTERIES (P) LTD.—See Amara Raja Energy & Mobility Limited; *Int'l*, pg. 411
AMITA TECHNOLOGIES INC.—See Energy Absolute Public Company Limited; *Int'l*, pg. 2422
AMITA TECHNOLOGY (THAILAND) CO., LTD.—See Energy Absolute Public Company Limited; *Int'l*, pg. 2422
AMPRIUS TECHNOLOGIES, INC.; *U.S. Public*, pg. 133
ANHUI YUANCHEN ENVIRONMENTAL PROTECTION SCIENCE & TECHNOLOGY CO., LTD.; *Int'l*, pg. 470
A-PRO CO., LTD.; *Int'l*, pg. 20
ASCENTRON, INC.—See Crestview Partners, L.P.; *U.S. Private*, pg. 1098
ASIA PACIFIC DIVISION PTE LTD.—See Hankook & Company Co., Ltd.; *Int'l*, pg. 3253
ASSOCIATED BATTERY MANUFACTURERS (CEYLON) LIMITED—See EXIDE INDUSTRIES LIMITED; *Int'l*, pg. 2585
ATLAS BATTERY LTD.—See Atlas Group of Companies; *Int'l*, pg. 685
ATLAS BATTERY LTD.—See GS Yuasa Corporation; *Int'l*, pg. 3143
ATLASBX CO., LTD.—See Hankook Tire & Technology Co.,Ltd.; *Int'l*, pg. 3253
ATON GREEN STORAGE S.P.A.; *Int'l*, pg. 689
AXION POWER INTERNATIONAL, INC.; *U.S. Public*, pg. 255
BAK BATTERY CANADA LTD.—See BAK International Ltd.; *Int'l*, pg. 804
BAK BATTERY LTD.—See BAK International Ltd.; *Int'l*, pg. 804
BAK BATTERY (SHENZHEN) CO., LTD.—See BAK International Ltd.; *Int'l*, pg. 804
BAK INTERNATIONAL LTD.; *Int'l*, pg. 804
BAOTOU FDK CO., LTD.—See Fujitsu Limited; *Int'l*, pg. 2832
BATTERIAS HAWKER DE MEXICO S. DE R.L. DE C.V.—See EnerSys; *U.S. Public*, pg. 766
BATTERIUNION AB—See Addtech AB; *Int'l*, pg. 132
BATTERY POWER INTERNATIONAL PTE LTD.—See EnerSys; *U.S. Public*, pg. 766
BEIJING EASPRING MATERIAL TECHNOLOGY CO., LTD.; *Int'l*, pg. 949
BESTEC POWER ELECTRONICS CO., LTD.; *Int'l*, pg. 1000
BLUESKY.ENERGY GMBH; *Int'l*, pg. 1074
BLUE SOLUTIONS S.A.—See Financiere de L'Odet; *Int'l*, pg. 2666
BRAILLE BATTERIES UK—See Braille Energy Systems Inc.; *Int'l*, pg. 1136
BRAILLE BATTERY INC.—See Braille Energy Systems Inc.; *Int'l*, pg. 1136
BRAMMERTZ INGENIEROS S.A.—See Hydac International GmbH; *Int'l*, pg. 3544
BRIGHT STAR, INC.—See Berkshire Hathaway Inc.; *U.S. Public*, pg. 310
BULLDOG BATTERY CORPORATION; *U.S. Private*, pg. 1211
BYD AMERICA CORPORATION—See BYD Company Limited; *Int'l*, pg. 1234
BYD COMPANY LIMITED - HUIZHOU PLANT 2—See BYD Company Limited; *Int'l*, pg. 1234
BYD COMPANY LIMITED; *Int'l*, pg. 1234
BYD (H.K.) CO., LIMITED—See BYD Company Limited; *Int'l*, pg. 1234
CALB GROUP CO., LTD.; *Int'l*, pg. 1261
CALDYNE AUTOMATICS LIMITED—See EXIDE INDUSTRIES LIMITED; *Int'l*, pg. 2585
CAMEL GROUP CO., LTD.; *Int'l*, pg. 1270
CAMEL POWER TRADING SDN. BHD.—See Camel Group Co., Ltd.; *Int'l*, pg. 1270

N.A.I.C.S. INDEX

335910 — BATTERY MANUFACTURI...

CAMX POWER LLC—See TIAX LLC; *U.S. Private*, pg. 4166
CBAK ENERGY TECHNOLOGY, INC.; *Int'l*, pg. 1364
CELGARD KOREA, LTD.—See Asahi Kasei Corporation; *Int'l*, pg. 596
CELGARD, LLC—See Asahi Kasei Corporation; *Int'l*, pg. 596
CELLTECH ENERGY SYSTEMS AB—See Addtech AB; *Int'l*, pg. 132
CELLTECH-HARRING A/S—See Addtech AB; *Int'l*, pg. 132
CELLTECH OY—See Addtech AB; *Int'l*, pg. 132
CENTURY YUASA BATTERIES (NZ) LTD—See GS Yuasa Corporation; *Int'l*, pg. 3143
CENTURY YUASA BATTERIES PTY LTD—See GS Yuasa Corporation; *Int'l*, pg. 3143
CHANGS ASCENDING ENTERPRISE CO., LTD.; *Int'l*, pg. 1444
CHANGSHA LYRUN NEW MATERIAL CO., LTD—See Hunan Corun New Energy Co., Ltd.; *Int'l*, pg. 3531
CHAOWEI POWER HOLDINGS LIMITED; *Int'l*, pg. 1447
CHAOWEI POWER (HONG KONG) LIMITED—See Chaowei Power Holdings Limited; *Int'l*, pg. 1447
CHEE YUEN PLASTIC PRODUCTS (HUIZHOU) COMPANY LIMITED - BATTERY FACTORY—See China Aerospace International Holdings Limited; *Int'l*, pg. 1481
CHENG UEI PRECISION INDUSTRY CO., LTD.; *Int'l*, pg. 1466
CHINA RITAR POWER CORP.; *Int'l*, pg. 1549
CHINA SHIPBUILDING INDUSTRY GROUP POWER CO., LTD.; *Int'l*, pg. 1551
CHINA TMK BATTERY SYSTEMS INC.; *Int'l*, pg. 1559
CHLORIDE ZIMBABWE (PRIVATE) LIMITED—See Amalgamated Regional Trading (ART) Holdings Ltd.; *Int'l*, pg. 409
CHONGQING VDL ELECTRONICS CO., LTD.; *Int'l*, pg. 1581
CHONGQING WANLI NEW ENERGY CO., LTD.; *Int'l*, pg. 1581
CLARIOS INTERNATIONAL INC.; *U.S. Public*, pg. 507
CLARIOS VARTA HANNOVER GMBH—See Brookfield Corporation; *Int'l*, pg. 1175
CLARIOS VARTA HANNOVER GMBH—See Caisse de Depot et Placement du Quebec; *Int'l*, pg. 1254
CNGR ADVANCED MATERIAL CO., LTD.; *Int'l*, pg. 1674
CODA HOLDINGS, INC.; *U.S. Private*, pg. 959
COMPACT POWER SYSTEMS, LLC—See E&S International Enterprises Inc.; *U.S. Private*, pg. 1301
COMPREHENSIVE MULTIPLE PROJECTS COMPANY PLC; *Int'l*, pg. 1754
CONCORDE BATTERY CORP; *U.S. Private*, pg. 1010
CONTEMPORARY AMPEREX TECHNOLOGY CO., LTD.; *Int'l*, pg. 1779
CONTEMPORARY AMPEREX TECHNOLOGY JAPAN KK—See Contemporary Amperex Technology Co., Ltd.; *Int'l*, pg. 1779
COSLIGHT TECHNOLOGY INTERNATIONAL GROUP LIMITED - CHANGDU COSLIGHT LI-MIN PHARMACEUTICAL FACTORY—See Coslight Technology International Group Limited; *Int'l*, pg. 1810
COSLIGHT TECHNOLOGY INTERNATIONAL GROUP LIMITED; *Int'l*, pg. 1810
COURTESY GARAGE LIMITED - TROPICAL BATTERY DIVISION—See Goddard Enterprises Limited; *Int'l*, pg. 3018
CROWN BATTERY MANUFACTURING CO. INC.; *U.S. Private*, pg. 1110
CTEK AB; *Int'l*, pg. 1870
CYG SUNRI CO., LTD.—See ChangYuan Group Ltd.; *Int'l*, pg. 1444
DARAMIC, LLC—See Asahi Kasei Corporation; *Int'l*, pg. 597
DARAMIC S.A.S.—See Asahi Kasei Corporation; *Int'l*, pg. 597
DARAMIC SEPARADORES DE BATERIAS LTDA.—See Asahi Kasei Corporation; *Int'l*, pg. 597
DARAMIC TIANJIN PE SEPARATOR CO., LTD.—See Asahi Kasei Corporation; *Int'l*, pg. 597
DARAMIC XIANGYANG BATTERY SEPARATOR CO., LTD.—See Asahi Kasei Corporation; *Int'l*, pg. 597
DELKOR CORP. LTD.—See Brookfield Corporation; *Int'l*, pg. 1175
DELKOR CORP. LTD.—See Caisse de Depot et Placement du Quebec; *Int'l*, pg. 1254
DIEHL & EAGLEPICHER GMBH—See GTCR LLC; *U.S. Private*, pg. 1805
DONGGUAN CHAO BA BATTERIES CO., LTD.—See Gold Peak Technology Group Limited; *Int'l*, pg. 3025
DOOSAN FUEL CELL CO LTD.; *U.S. Private*, pg. 1262
DRAGONFLY ENERGY HOLDINGS CORP.; *U.S. Public*, pg. 687
DRY CELL & STORAGE BATTERY JSC, *Int'l*, pg. 2226
DYNAPACK INTERNATIONAL TECHNOLOGY CORPORATION; *Int'l*, pg. 2242
DYNAPACK (SUCHOU) CO., LTD.—See Dynapack International Technology Corporation; *Int'l*, pg. 2242
EAGLEPICHER TECHNOLOGIES, LLC—See GTCR LLC; *U.S. Private*, pg. 1805
EAST PENN MANUFACTURING CO., INC.; *U.S. Private*, pg. 1317
ECOPILHAS LDA.—See Energizer Holdings, Inc.; *U.S. Public*, pg. 761

ECOPRO BM CO., LTD.; *Int'l*, pg. 2299
ECOULT—See East Penn Manufacturing Co., Inc.; *U.S. Private*, pg. 1317
EC POWER, LLC; *U.S. Private*, pg. 1326
EDGEWELL PERSONAL CARE ITALY S.P.A.—See Edgewell Personal Care Company; *U.S. Public*, pg. 718
EH EUROPE GMBH—See EnerSys; *U.S. Public*, pg. 766
ELECTOCHEM SOLUTIONS, INC.—See Integer Holdings Corporation; *U.S. Public*, pg. 1134
ELECTRIC FUEL BATTERY CORPORATION—See Greenbriar Equity Group, L.P.; *U.S. Private*, pg. 1775
ELECTROCHEM SOLUTIONS, INC. - BEAVERTON DESIGN & DEVELOPMENT CENTER—See Integer Holdings Corporation; *U.S. Public*, pg. 1134
ELECTROVAYA COMPANY—See Electrovaya Inc.; *Int'l*, pg. 2355
ELECTROVAYA CORP.,—See Electrovaya Inc.; *Int'l*, pg. 2355
ELECTROVAYA INC.; *Int'l*, pg. 2355
ELECTROVAYA USA INC.—See Electrovaya Inc.; *Int'l*, pg. 2355
ELENTEC CO,. LTD.; *Int'l*, pg. 2359
ELEXCEL CORPORATION—See DKS Co. Ltd.; *Int'l*, pg. 2140
ENABLE IPC CORP.; *U.S. Public*, pg. 754
ENDLESS CHARGE, INC.; *U.S. Private*, pg. 1391
ENDURANCE MOTIVE SA; *Int'l*, pg. 2410
ENERGIZER ARGENTINA S.A.—See Energizer Holdings, Inc.; *U.S. Public*, pg. 761
ENERGIZER BATTERY, INC.—See Energizer Holdings, Inc.; *U.S. Public*, pg. 761
ENERGIZER BATTERY MANUFACTURING, INC.—See Energizer Holdings, Inc.; *U.S. Public*, pg. 761
ENERGIZER GROUP AUSTRIA HANDELS GMBH—See Edgewell Personal Care Company; *U.S. Public*, pg. 718
ENERGIZER GROUP SWEDEN AB—See Energizer Holdings, Inc.; *U.S. Public*, pg. 761
ENERGIZER HELLAS A.E.—See Energizer Holdings, Inc.; *U.S. Public*, pg. 761
ENERGIZER HONG KONG LIMITED—See Edgewell Personal Care Company; *U.S. Public*, pg. 718
ENERGIZER IRELAND LIMITED—See Energizer Holdings, Inc.; *U.S. Public*, pg. 761
ENERGIZER KOREA LTD.—See Energizer Holdings, Inc.; *U.S. Public*, pg. 761
ENERGIZER MALAYSIA SDN. BHD.—See Energizer Holdings, Inc.; *U.S. Public*, pg. 761
ENERGIZER MIDDLE EAST AND AFRICA LIMITED—See Energizer Holdings, Inc.; *U.S. Public*, pg. 761
ENERGIZER NZ LIMITED—See Energizer Holdings, Inc.; *U.S. Public*, pg. 761
ENERGIZER PUERTO RICO, INC.—See Edgewell Personal Care Company; *U.S. Public*, pg. 718
ENERGIZER-SCHICK TAIWAN LTD.—See Edgewell Personal Care Company; *U.S. Public*, pg. 718
ENERGIZER SINGAPORE PTE. LTD.—See Energizer Holdings, Inc.; *U.S. Public*, pg. 761
ENERGY LEADER BATTERIES INDIA PRIVATE LTD.—See EnerSys; *U.S. Public*, pg. 767
ENERSYS AB—See EnerSys; *U.S. Public*, pg. 766
ENERSYS AD—See EnerSys; *U.S. Public*, pg. 766
ENERSYS ADVANCED SYSTEMS INC.—See EnerSys; *U.S. Public*, pg. 767
ENERSYS AE—See EnerSys; *U.S. Public*, pg. 766
ENERSYS BVBA—See EnerSys; *U.S. Public*, pg. 767
ENERSYS BV—See EnerSys; *U.S. Public*, pg. 766
ENERSYS CANADA INC.—See EnerSys; *U.S. Public*, pg. 767
ENERSYS DELAWARE INC.—See EnerSys; *U.S. Public*, pg. 767
ENERSYS DE MEXICO II, S DE R.L. DE CV—See EnerSys; *U.S. Public*, pg. 767
ENERSYS DE MEXICO, S.A. DE CV—See EnerSys; *U.S. Public*, pg. 767
ENERSYS ENERGY PRODUCTS INC.—See EnerSys; *U.S. Public*, pg. 767
ENERSYS EUROPE OY—See EnerSys; *U.S. Public*, pg. 766
ENERSYS HUNGARIA KFT.—See EnerSys; *U.S. Public*, pg. 767
ENERSYS INDIA BATTERIES PRIVATE LTD.—See EnerSys; *U.S. Public*, pg. 767
ENERSYS LTD.—See EnerSys; *U.S. Public*, pg. 766
ENERSYS MALAYSIA SDN BHD—See EnerSys; *U.S. Public*, pg. 767
ENERSYS MEXICO MANAGEMENT LLC—See EnerSys; *U.S. Public*, pg. 767
ENERSYS MOTIVE POWER—See EnerSys; *U.S. Public*, pg. 767
ENERSYS RESERVE POWER PTE. LTD.—See EnerSys; *U.S. Public*, pg. 767
ENERSYS S.A.R.L.—See EnerSys; *U.S. Public*, pg. 767
ENERSYS; *U.S. Public*, pg. 766
ENERSYS SOUTH EAST ASIA PTE. LTD.—See EnerSys; *U.S. Public*, pg. 767
ENERSYS SPRL—See EnerSys; *U.S. Public*, pg. 767
ENERSYS S.R.L.—See EnerSys; *U.S. Public*, pg. 767
ENERSYS S.R.O.—See EnerSys; *U.S. Public*, pg. 767

ENERSYS, S.R.O.—See EnerSys; *U.S. Public*, pg. 767
ENERSYSTEM ARGENTINA S.A.—See EnerSys; *U.S. Public*, pg. 767
ENERSYSTEM DO BRAZIL LTDA.—See EnerSys; *U.S. Public*, pg. 767
ENSER CORPORATION—See EnerSys; *U.S. Public*, pg. 767
ERICOM TELEKOMUNIKASYON VE ENERJI TEKNOLOJILERI A.S.; *Int'l*, pg. 2493
E. SCHNAPP & CO. WORKS LTD.; *Int'l*, pg. 2250
ESPEX BATTERIES LIMITED—See EXIDE INDUSTRIES LIMITED; *Int'l*, pg. 2585
EVE ENERGY CO., LTD. - JINGMEN FACTORY—See EVE Energy Co., Ltd.; *Int'l*, pg. 2561
EVE ENERGY CO., LTD.; *Int'l*, pg. 2561
EVE ENERGY CO., LTD. - XIKENG FACTORY—See EVE Energy Co., Ltd.; *Int'l*, pg. 2561
EVE ENERGY CO., LTD. - ZHONGKAI FACTORY—See EVE Energy Co., Ltd.; *Int'l*, pg. 2561
EVE ENERGY NORTH AMERICA CORPORATION—See EVE Energy Co., Ltd.; *Int'l*, pg. 2561
EVE GERMANY GMBH—See EVE Energy Co., Ltd.; *Int'l*, pg. 2561
EVE HYPERPOWER BATTERIES INC.—See EVE Energy Co., Ltd.; *Int'l*, pg. 2561
EVE INNOVATION ENERGY CO., LTD.—See EVE Energy Co., Ltd.; *Int'l*, pg. 2561
EVEREADY DE MEXICO S.A. DE C.V.—See Energizer Holdings, Inc.; *U.S. Public*, pg. 761
EVEREADY EAST AFRICA PLC; *Int'l*, pg. 2563
EVEREADY INDUSTRIES INDIA LTD; *Int'l*, pg. 2563
EXIDE INDUSTRIES LIMITED; *Int'l*, pg. 2584
EXIDE PAKISTAN LIMITED—See Vertiv Holdings Co; *U.S. Public*, pg. 2289
EXIDE SINGAPORE PTE LIMITED—See Exide Technologies, LLC; *U.S. Private*, pg. 1448
EXIDE SLOVAKIA S.R.O.—See Exide Technologies, LLC; *U.S. Private*, pg. 1448
EXIDE TECHNOLOGIES AB—See Exide Technologies, LLC; *U.S. Private*, pg. 1449
EXIDE TECHNOLOGIES AS—See Exide Technologies, LLC; *U.S. Private*, pg. 1449
EXIDE TECHNOLOGIES GMBH—See Exide Technologies, LLC; *U.S. Private*, pg. 1448
EXIDE TECHNOLOGIES, LLC; *U.S. Private*, pg. 1448
EXIDE TECHNOLOGIES OY—See Exide Technologies, LLC; *U.S. Private*, pg. 1449
EXIDE TECHNOLOGIES RECYCLING S.L.—See Exide Technologies, LLC; *U.S. Private*, pg. 1449
EXIDE TECHNOLOGIES SAS—See Exide Technologies, LLC; *U.S. Private*, pg. 1449
EXIDE TECHNOLOGIES (SHANGHAI) COMPANY LIMITED—See Exide Technologies, LLC; *U.S. Private*, pg. 1449
EXPION360 INC.; *U.S. Public*, pg. 812
EXPONENTIAL POWER, INC.—See High Road Capital Partners, LLC; *U.S. Private*, pg. 1936
FABBRICA ITALIANA ACCUMULATORI MOTOCARRI MONTECCHIO IBERICA S.A.—See Fiamm S.p.A.; *Int'l*, pg. 2650
FAIRFIELD SOLUTIONS LIMITED—See Addtech AB; *Int'l*, pg. 133
FDK ENERGY CO., LTD.—See Fujitsu Limited; *Int'l*, pg. 2832
FDK SINGAPORE PTE. LTD.—See Fujitsu Limited; *Int'l*, pg. 2832
FDK TOTTORI CO., LTD.—See Fujitsu Limited; *Int'l*, pg. 2832
FDK TWICELL CO.,LTD.—See Fujitsu Limited; *Int'l*, pg. 2832
FEDCO ELECTRONICS, INC.; *U.S. Private*, pg. 1486
FEIDONG GOTION NEW MATERIAL CO., LTD.—See Gotion High-tech Co., Ltd.; *Int'l*, pg. 3044
FIAMM ENERGY TECHNOLOGY (FRANCE) S.A.R.L.—See Fiamm S.p.A.; *Int'l*, pg. 2650
FIAMM ENERGY TECHNOLOGY S.P.A.—See Fiamm S.p.A.; *Int'l*, pg. 2650
FIAMM ENERGY TECHNOLOGY (USA) LLC—See Fiamm S.p.A.; *Int'l*, pg. 2650
FIAMM ENERGY TECHNOLOGY (WUHAN) CO., LTD.—See Fiamm S.p.A.; *Int'l*, pg. 2650
FIAMM-GS S.P.A.—See Fiamm S.p.A.; *Int'l*, pg. 2650
FIAMM-GS S.P.A.—See GS Yuasa Corporation; *Int'l*, pg. 3143
FIAMM MALAYSIA SDN. BHD.—See Fiamm S.p.A.; *Int'l*, pg. 2650
FIAMM S.P.A.; *Int'l*, pg. 2650
FIAMM UK LIMITED—See Fiamm S.p.A.; *Int'l*, pg. 2650
FIREFLY ENERGY, INC.; *U.S. Private*, pg. 1611
FLUX POWER HOLDINGS, INC.; *U.S. Public*, pg. 860
FORSEE POWER SAS; *Int'l*, pg. 2737
FREYR BATTERY SA; *Int'l*, pg. 2791
FUJIAN NANPING NANFU BATTERY CO., LTD.—See CDH China Management Company Limited; *Int'l*, pg. 1370
FUTAVIS GMBH—See DEUTZ AG; *Int'l*, pg. 2086
GELION PLC; *Int'l*, pg. 2913
GEM (WUXI) ENERGY MATERIALS CO., LTD.—See GEM Co., Ltd.; *Int'l*, pg. 2914

N.A.I.C.S. Index

335910 — BATTERY MANUFACTURI... CORPORATE AFFILIATIONS

GLOBAL BATTERY CO., LTD—See GS Yuasa Corporation; *Int'l*, pg. 3143
GOGORO INC.; *Int'l*, pg. 3022
GOLDEN POWER GROUP HOLDINGS LTD.; *Int'l*, pg. 3031
GOLD PEAK INDUSTRIES (TAIWAN) LTD.—See Gold Peak Technology Group Limited; *Int'l*, pg. 3025
GP BATTERIES (CHINA) LTD.—See Gold Peak Technology Group Limited; *Int'l*, pg. 3025
GP BATTERIES INTERNATIONAL LIMITED—See Gold Peak Technology Group Limited; *Int'l*, pg. 3025
GP BATTERIES (MALAYSIA) SDN. BHD—See Gold Peak Technology Group Limited; *Int'l*, pg. 3025
GP BATTERIES (SHENZHEN) CO., LTD.—See Gold Peak Technology Group Limited; *Int'l*, pg. 3025
GP BATTERIES (VIETNAM) LIMITED LIABILITY COMPANY—See Gold Peak Technology Group Limited; *Int'l*, pg. 3025
GP BATTERY MARKETING (HK) LTD.—See Gold Peak Technology Group Limited; *Int'l*, pg. 3025
GP BATTERY MARKETING (TAIWAN) LTD.—See Gold Peak Technology Group Limited; *Int'l*, pg. 3025
GP BATTERY (POLAND) SP. Z.O.O—See Gold Peak Technology Group Limited; *Int'l*, pg. 3025
GP ELECTRONICS (HUIZHOU) CO., LTD.—See Gold Peak Technology Group Limited; *Int'l*, pg. 3025
GP INDUSTRIES LIMITED—See Gold Peak Technology Group Limited; *Int'l*, pg. 3025
GREAT POWER (ZHUHAI) BATTERY CO., LTD.—See Guangzhou Great Power Energy & Technology Co., Ltd.; *Int'l*, pg. 3165
GS BATTERY (CHINA) CO., LTD.—See GS Yuasa Corporation; *Int'l*, pg. 3143
GS BATTERY TAIWAN CO., LTD.—See GS Yuasa Corporation; *Int'l*, pg. 3143
GS BATTERY (U.S.A.) INC.—See GS Yuasa Corporation; *Int'l*, pg. 3143
GS BATTERY VIETNAM CO., LTD.—See GS Yuasa Corporation; *Int'l*, pg. 3143
GS KASEI KOGYO CO., LTD.—See GS Yuasa Corporation; *Int'l*, pg. 3143
GS YUASA BATTERY LTD.—See GS Yuasa Corporation; *Int'l*, pg. 3143
GS YUASA BATTERY SINGAPORE CO., PTE. LTD.—See GS Yuasa Corporation; *Int'l*, pg. 3143
GS YUASA LITHIUM POWER, INC—See GS Yuasa Corporation; *Int'l*, pg. 3143
GS YUASA TECHNOLOGY LTD.—See GS Yuasa Corporation; *Int'l*, pg. 3143
GUANGDONG RUIQING CONTEMPORARY AMPEREX TECHNOLOGY LIMITED—See Contemporary Amperex Technology Co., Ltd.; *Int'l*, pg. 1779
GUANGZHOU GREAT POWER ENERGY & TECHNOLOGY CO., LTD.; *Int'l*, pg. 3165
HANKOOK & COMPANY CO., LTD.; *Int'l*, pg. 3253
HA NOI BATTERY JOINT STOCK COMPANY; *Int'l*, pg. 3201
HANSABATTERY OY—See Addtech AB; *Int'l*, pg. 131
HARBIN COSLIGHT POWER CO., LTD.—See Coslight Technology International Group Limited; *Int'l*, pg. 1810
HARBIN COSLIGHT STORAGE BATTERY COMPANY LIMITED—See Coslight Technology International Group Limited; *Int'l*, pg. 1810
HARBIN ZHONGQIANG POWER-TECH CO., LTD.—See Advanced Battery Technologies, Inc.; *U.S. Private*, pg. 88
HAWKER GMBH—See EnerSys; *U.S. Public*, pg. 767
HAWKER POWERSOURCE, INC.—See EnerSys; *U.S. Public*, pg. 767
HBL GERMANY GMBH—See HBL Power Systems Ltd.; *Int'l*, pg. 3296
HBL HONG KONG LTD.—See HBL Power Systems Ltd.; *Int'l*, pg. 3296
HBL POWER SYSTEMS LTD.; *Int'l*, pg. 3296
HENAN GREAT POWER ENERGY CO., LTD.—See Guangzhou Great Power Energy & Technology Co., Ltd.; *Int'l*, pg. 3165
HENAN GREAT POWER ENERGY & TECHNOLOGY CO., LTD.—See Guangzhou Great Power Energy & Technology Co., Ltd.; *Int'l*, pg. 3165
HIGHPOWER INTERNATIONAL, INC.; *Int'l*, pg. 3388
HITACHI CHEMICAL STORAGE BATTERY (THAILAND) PLC.; *Int'l*, pg. 3410
HITACHI STORAGE BATTERY (THAILAND) CO., LTD.—See Hitachi, Ltd.; *Int'l*, pg. 3421
HONBRIDGE HOLDINGS LTD.; *Int'l*, pg. 3459
HONG KONG HIGHPOWER INTERNATIONAL CO., LTD.—See Highpower International, Inc.; *Int'l*, pg. 3388
HONG KONG HIGHPOWER TECHNOLOGY CO., LTD.—See Highpower International, Inc.; *Int'l*, pg. 3388
HUBEI CAMEL SPECIAL POWER SUPPLY COMPANY—See Camel Group Co., Ltd.; *Int'l*, pg. 1270
HUNAN CORUN NEW ENERGY CO., LTD.; *Int'l*, pg. 3531
HUNAN YUNENG NEW ENERGY BATTERY MATERIAL CO., LTD.; *Int'l*, pg. 3534
HYBRID KINETIC GROUP LIMITED; *Int'l*, pg. 3544
ICCNEXERGY, INC. - ESCONDIDO—See KRG Capital Management, L.P.; *U.S. Private*, pg. 2351
ICCNEXERGY, INC.—See KRG Capital Management, L.P.; *U.S. Private*, pg. 2351
ICON ENERGY SYSTEM (SHENZHEN) CO., LTD.—See Highpower International, Inc.; *Int'l*, pg. 3388
IDEA POWER LIMITED—See Eveready Industries India Ltd; *Int'l*, pg. 2563
IE TECHNOLOGIES PTE LTD.—See EnerSys; *U.S. Public*, pg. 767
INDUSTRIAL - UNIROSS BATTERIES (PTY) LTD.—See Eveready Industries India Ltd; *Int'l*, pg. 2563
INFINITE GROUP, INC.; *U.S. Public*, pg. 1117
INTERSTATE BATTERY SYSTEM OF AMERICA INC.; *U.S. Private*, pg. 2123
INVENTUS POWER, INC.—See KRG Capital Management, L.P.; *U.S. Private*, pg. 2351
ION-3 CORPORATION; *U.S. Private*, pg. 2134
JIANGSU CONTEMPORARY AMPEREX TECHNOLOGY LIMITED—See Contemporary Amperex Technology Co., Ltd.; *Int'l*, pg. 1779
JOHNSON CONTROLS AUTOBATTERIE GMBH—See Brookfield Corporation; *Int'l*, pg. 1175
JOHNSON CONTROLS AUTOBATTERIE GMBH—See Caisse de Depot et Placement du Quebec; *Int'l*, pg. 1254
JOHNSON CONTROLS BATTERIE AG—See Brookfield Corporation; *Int'l*, pg. 1175
JOHNSON CONTROLS BATTERIE AG—See Caisse de Depot et Placement du Quebec; *Int'l*, pg. 1254
JOHNSON CONTROLS BATTERIES LTD.—See Brookfield Corporation; *Int'l*, pg. 1175
JOHNSON CONTROLS BATTERIES LTD.—See Caisse de Depot et Placement du Quebec; *Int'l*, pg. 1254
JOHNSON CONTROLS BATTERY GROUP, LLC—See Brookfield Corporation; *Int'l*, pg. 1175
JOHNSON CONTROLS BATTERY GROUP, LLC—See Caisse de Depot et Placement du Quebec; *Int'l*, pg. 1254
K2 ENERGY SOLUTIONS, INC.; *U.S. Private*, pg. 2253
KORE POWER, INC.; *U.S. Private*, pg. 2343
LAXAPANA BATTERIES PLC.—See E.B. Creasy & Company PLC; *Int'l*, pg. 2251
LECLANCHE GMBH—See Oakridge Global Energy Solutions, Inc.; *U.S. Public*, pg. 1560
LECLANCHE SA—See Oakridge Global Energy Solutions, Inc.; *U.S. Public*, pg. 1560
THE LION ELECTRIC CO.—See Applied Intuition, Inc.; *U.S. Private*, pg. 299
MARATHONNORCO AEROSPACE, INC.—See TransDigm Group Incorporated; *U.S. Public*, pg. 2182
MATHEWS ASSOCIATES, INC.; *U.S. Private*, pg. 2611
MISSION CRITICAL ELECTRONICS, LLC—See Windjammer Capital Investors, LLC; *U.S. Private*, pg. 4538
MK BATTERY—See East Penn Manufacturing Co., Inc.; *U.S. Private*, pg. 1317
MTI MICROFUEL CELLS INC.—See Soluna Holdings, Inc.; *U.S. Public*, pg. 1901
NATIONAL PLASTICS COMPANY—See Chemical Industries Holding Company; *Int'l*, pg. 1462
NEOVOLTA, INC.; *U.S. Public*, pg. 1506
NEW ENERGY SYSTEMS GROUP; *U.S. Private*, pg. 2893
NINGBO GP ENERGY CO., LTD.—See Gold Peak Technology Group Limited; *Int'l*, pg. 3025
NORDIC BATTERY AB—See Addtech AB; *Int'l*, pg. 134
NORDIC BATTERY AS—See Addtech AB; *Int'l*, pg. 134
NORTHSTAR BATTERY CO. LLC—See Altor Equity Partners AB; *Int'l*, pg. 395
NORTHSTAR BATTERY DMCC—See EnerSys; *U.S. Public*, pg. 767
N.V. DURACELL BATTERIES, S.A.—See The Procter & Gamble Company; *U.S. Public*, pg. 2124
NXU INC.; *U.S. Public*, pg. 1558
OAKRIDGE GLOBAL ENERGY SOLUTIONS, INC.; *U.S. Public*, pg. 1560
OPTIMA BATTERIES, INC.—See Brookfield Corporation; *Int'l*, pg. 1175
OPTIMA BATTERIES, INC.—See Caisse de Depot et Placement du Quebec; *Int'l*, pg. 1254
OUTBACK POWER TECHNOLOGIES, INC.—See EnerSys; *U.S. Public*, pg. 767
OVONIC BATTERY COMPANY, INC.—See BASF SE; *Int'l*, pg. 876
PALOS VERDES BUILDING CORP.; *U.S. Private*, pg. 3082
POLYPORE K.K.—See Asahi Kasei Corporation; *Int'l*, pg. 596
POLYPORE (SHANGHAI) MEMBRANE PRODUCTS CO., LTD.—See Asahi Kasei Corporation; *Int'l*, pg. 597
POWERSAFE ACUMULADORES INDUSTRIALIS UNIPESSOAL, LDA.—See EnerSys; *U.S. Public*, pg. 766
PROGRESSIVE TECHNOLOGIES, INC.—See Universal Power Group, Inc.; *U.S. Private*, pg. 4306
PT FDK INDONESIA—See Fujitsu Limited; *Int'l*, pg. 2833
PT. GS BATTERY INC.—See GS Yuasa Corporation; *Int'l*, pg. 3143
PT. YUASA BATTERY INDONESIA—See GS Yuasa Corporation; *Int'l*, pg. 3143
QINGHAI CONTEMPORARY AMPEREX TECHNOLOGY LIMITED—See Contemporary Amperex Technology Co., Ltd.; *Int'l*, pg. 1779
QUANTUMSPHERE, INC.; *U.S. Public*, pg. 1754
RAY-O-VAC DE MEXICO, S.A. DE C.V.—See Energizer Holdings, Inc.; *U.S. Public*, pg. 761
RAYOVAC (UK) LIMITED—See Energizer Holdings, Inc.; *U.S. Public*, pg. 761
ROVCAL, INC.—See Energizer Holdings, Inc.; *U.S. Public*, pg. 761
ROV GERMAN LIMITED GMBH—See Energizer Holdings, Inc.; *U.S. Public*, pg. 761
RUITING CONTEMPORARY AMPEREX TECHNOLOGY (SHANGHAI) LIMITED—See Contemporary Amperex Technology Co., Ltd.; *Int'l*, pg. 1779
RUSSELL HOBBS DEUTSCHLAND GMBH—See Spectrum Brands Holdings, Inc.; *U.S. Public*, pg. 1916
SENEC AUSTRALIA PTY. LTD.—See EnBW Energie Baden-Wurttemberg AG; *Int'l*, pg. 2400
SES AI CORPORATION; *U.S. Public*, pg. 1872
SHANDONG HUARI BATTERY CO., LTD.—See GS Yuasa Corporation; *Int'l*, pg. 3143
SHANGHAI BI BA BATTERIES CO. LTD.—See Gold Peak Technology Group Limited; *Int'l*, pg. 3026
SHANGHAI BYD COMPANY LIMITED—See BYD Company Limited; *Int'l*, pg. 1234
SHANGHAI JINJIANG BATTERY CO. LTD.—See Gold Peak Technology Group Limited; *Int'l*, pg. 3026
SHANGHAI SINO-IC MICROELECTRONICS COMPANY LIMITED—See Coslight Technology International Group Limited; *Int'l*, pg. 1810
SHENYANG NORTHEAST STORAGE BATTERY LTD.—See Coslight Technology International Group Limited; *Int'l*, pg. 1810
SHENZHEN COSLIGHT SOFTWARE CO., LTD.—See Coslight Technology International Group Limited; *Int'l*, pg. 1810
SHENZHEN HIGHPOWER TECHNOLOGY CO., LTD.—See Highpower International, Inc.; *Int'l*, pg. 3388
SHENZHEN LEXEL BATTERY CO., LTD.—See Coslight Technology International Group Limited; *Int'l*, pg. 1810
SHENZHEN NATIONAL ENGINEERING RESEARCH CENTER OF ADVANCED ENERGY STORAGE MATERIAL CO., LTD.—See Hunan Corun New Energy Co., Ltd.; *Int'l*, pg. 3531
SHENZHEN SYLVA ELECTROCHEMICAL LTD.—See Gold Peak Technology Group Limited; *Int'l*, pg. 3026
SICHUAN CONTEMPORARY AMPEREX TECHNOLOGY LIMITED—See Contemporary Amperex Technology Co., Ltd.; *Int'l*, pg. 1779
SITETEL SHANGHAI CO. LTD.—See EnerSys; *U.S. Public*, pg. 767
SITETEL SWEDEN AB—See EnerSys; *U.S. Public*, pg. 767
SMART BATTERY SOLUTIONS GMBH—See Gimv NV; *Int'l*, pg. 2976
SOLARIS POWER CELLS, INC.; *U.S. Private*, pg. 3707
SOLIDION TECHNOLOGY INC.; *U.S. Public*, pg. 1901
SOVEMA GLOBAL SERVICES INC.—See ANDRITZ AG; *Int'l*, pg. 456
SPEAR POWER SYSTEMS AS—See Sensata Technologies Holding plc; *U.S. Public*, pg. 1866
SPEAR POWER SYSTEMS, LLC—See Sensata Technologies Holding plc; *U.S. Public*, pg. 1866
SPECTRUM BRANDS BRASIL INDUSTRIA E COMERCIO DE BENS DE CONSUMO LTDA—See Spectrum Brands Holdings, Inc.; *U.S. Public*, pg. 1916
SPECTRUM BRANDS, INC. - FENNIMORE PLANT—See Spectrum Brands Holdings, Inc.; *U.S. Public*, pg. 1916
SPECTRUM BRANDS NEW ZEALAND LTD.—See Spectrum Brands Holdings, Inc.; *U.S. Public*, pg. 1916
SPECTRUM BRANDS POLAND SP. Z.O.O.—See Spectrum Brands Holdings, Inc.; *U.S. Public*, pg. 1916
THE STANDARD BATTERIES LIMITED—See EXIDE INDUSTRIES LIMITED; *Int'l*, pg. 2585
SUNGRID SOLUTIONS, INC.—See Hull Street Energy, LLC; *U.S. Private*, pg. 2005
SUNLABZ LLC—See Aterian, Inc.; *U.S. Public*, pg. 221
SYLVA INDUSTRIES LIMITED—See Gold Peak Technology Group Limited; *Int'l*, pg. 3026
SYSTEMATIC POWER SOLUTIONS, LLC; *U.S. Private*, pg. 3907
TAIWAN YUASA BATTERY CO., LTD.—See GS Yuasa Corporation; *Int'l*, pg. 3143
TEMPORAL POWER LTD.—See Enbridge Inc.; *Int'l*, pg. 2397
T.G. BATTERY CO. (CHINA) LTD.—See Gold Peak Technology Group Limited; *Int'l*, pg. 3026
TIANJIN COSLIGHT ELECTRICAL BICYCLE CO., LTD—See Coslight Technology International Group Limited; *Int'l*, pg. 1810
TIANJIN YUASA BATTERIES CO., LTD.—See GS Yuasa Corporation; *Int'l*, pg. 3143
TNR TECHNICAL, INC.; *U.S. Public*, pg. 2161
TRIAD PRO INNOVATORS, INC.; *U.S. Public*, pg. 2189
TROJAN BATTERY COMPANY—See KPS Capital Partners, LP; *U.S. Private*, pg. 2347
TROPICAL BATTERY COMPANY LIMITED; *U.S. Public*, pg. 2198
TROPICAL BATTERY USA, LLC.—See Tropical Battery Company Limited; *U.S. Public*, pg. 2198
ULTRALIFE BATTERIES INDIA PRIVATE LIMITED—See Ultralife Corporation; *U.S. Public*, pg. 2224
ULTRALIFE BATTERIES (UK) LTD.—See Ultralife Corporation; *U.S. Public*, pg. 2224

N.A.I.C.S. INDEX

335921 — FIBER OPTIC CABLE M...

ULTRALIFE CORPORATION; *U.S. Public*, pg. 2224
UNIROSS BATTERIES HK LTD.—See Eveready Industries India Ltd; *Int'l*, pg. 2563
UNIROSS BATTERIES SAS—See Eveready Industries India Ltd; *Int'l*, pg. 2563
UNIROSS SA—See Eveready Industries India Ltd; *Int'l*, pg. 2563
VALENCE TECHNOLOGY, INC.; *U.S. Private*, pg. 4331
VARTA BATERIE SPOL. S.R.O.—See Global Equity Partners Beteiligungs-Management AG; *Int'l*, pg. 2996
VARTA BATTERIE GES. M.B.H.—See Global Equity Partners Beteiligungs-Management AG; *Int'l*, pg. 2996
VARTA B.V.—See Global Equity Partners Beteiligungs-Management AG; *Int'l*, pg. 2996
VARTA CONSUMER BATTERIES GMBH & CO. KGAA—See Global Equity Partners Beteiligungs-Management AG; *Int'l*, pg. 2996
VARTA CONSUMER BATTERIES ITALIA, S.R.L.—See Energizer Holdings, Inc.; *U.S. Public*, pg. 761
VARTA HUNGARIA KERESKEDELMI ES SZOLGALTATO KFT.—See Global Equity Partners Beteiligungs-Management AG; *Int'l*, pg. 2996
VARTA LTD.—See Global Equity Partners Beteiligungs-Management AG; *Int'l*, pg. 2996
VARTA MICROBATTERY GMBH—See Global Equity Partners Beteiligungs-Management AG; *Int'l*, pg. 2996
VARTA MICROBATTERY, INC.—See Global Equity Partners Beteiligungs-Management AG; *Int'l*, pg. 2996
VARTA MICROBATTERY PTE. LTD.—See Global Equity Partners Beteiligungs-Management AG; *Int'l*, pg. 2996
VARTA PILLERI TICARET LIMITED SIRKETI—See Global Equity Partners Beteiligungs-Management AG; *Int'l*, pg. 2996
VARTA S.A.—See Global Equity Partners Beteiligungs-Management AG; *Int'l*, pg. 2996
VARTA STORAGE GMBH—See Global Equity Partners Beteiligungs-Management AG; *Int'l*, pg. 2996
VERSA POWER SYSTEMS, INC.—See FuelCell Energy, Inc.; *U.S. Public*, pg. 891
VERSA POWER SYSTEMS, LTD.—See FuelCell Energy, Inc.; *U.S. Public*, pg. 891
WILDCAT DISCOVERY TECHNOLOGIES INC.; *U.S. Private*, pg. 4519
XALT ENERGY, LLC—See Freudenberg SE; *Int'l*, pg. 2788
YANBIAN COSLIGHT STORAGE BATTERY LTD.—See Coslight Technology International Group Limited; *Int'l*, pg. 1810
YIYANG CORUN BATTERY CO., LTD—See Hunan Corun New Energy Co., Ltd.; *Int'l*, pg. 3532
YUASA BATTERY (EAST AFRICA) LTD.—See GS Yuasa Corporation; *Int'l*, pg. 3143
YUASA BATTERY EUROPE LTD.—See GS Yuasa Corporation; *Int'l*, pg. 3143
YUASA BATTERY (MALAYSIA) SDN. BHD. - MANUFACTURING PLANT—See GS Yuasa Corporation; *Int'l*, pg. 3143
YUASA BATTERY (MALAYSIA) SDN. BHD.—See GS Yuasa Corporation; *Int'l*, pg. 3143
YUASA BATTERY (SHUNDE) CO., LTD.—See GS Yuasa Corporation; *Int'l*, pg. 3143
YUASA POWER SYSTEMS (M) SDN BHD—See GS Yuasa Corporation; *Int'l*, pg. 3143
YUASA (TIANJIN) TECHNOLOGY LTD.—See GS Yuasa Corporation; *Int'l*, pg. 3143
ZAO "SPECTRUM BRANDS" RUSSIA—See Spectrum Brands Holdings, Inc.; *U.S. Public*, pg. 1917
ZENTRIC, INC.; *U.S. Private*, pg. 4601
ZHEJIANG CHAOWEI CHUANGYUAN INDUSTRIAL CO., LTD.—See Chaowei Power Holdings Limited; *Int'l*, pg. 1447
ZHEJIANG HUAYOU COBALT CO., LTD.—See Huayou Cobalt Co., Ltd.; *Int'l*, pg. 3516
ZHONGSHAN UNIROSS INDUSTRY CO. LIMITED—See Eveready Industries India Ltd; *Int'l*, pg. 2563
ZHUHAI COSLIGHT BATTERY CO., LTD.—See Coslight Technology International Group Limited; *Int'l*, pg. 1810
ZHUHAI COSLIGHT ELECTRIC TECHNOLOGY CO., LTD.—See Coslight Technology International Group Limited; *Int'l*, pg. 1810

335921 — FIBER OPTIC CABLE MANUFACTURING

2CONNECT BV; *Int'l*, pg. 4
ACCELINK TECHNOLOGIES CO., LTD.; *Int'l*, pg. 80
ACK CONTROLS INC.—See Chuo Spring Co., Ltd.; *Int'l*, pg. 1599
ACL CABLES PLC - FACTORY—See ACL Cables PLC; *Int'l*, pg. 106
ADTRAN NETWORKS SE—See ADTRAN Holdings, Inc.; *U.S. Public*, pg. 44
AEG POWER SOLUTIONS SPOL. S.R.O.—See 3W Power S.A.; *Int'l*, pg. 10
AFL TELECOMMUNICATIONS EUROPE LTD.—See Fujikura Ltd.; *Int'l*, pg. 2827
AFL TELECOMMUNICATIONS LLC—See Fujikura Ltd.; *Int'l*, pg. 2827
AFL TELECOMMUNICATIONS—See Fujikura Ltd.; *Int'l*, pg. 2827
AKSH OPTIFIBRE LIMITED; *Int'l*, pg. 264
AMATA NETWORK COMPANY LIMITED—See Advanced Info Service Plc; *Int'l*, pg. 159
AMERICA FUJIKURA LTD.—See Fujikura Ltd.; *Int'l*, pg. 2827
AMERICAN INSULATED WIRE CORP.—See Leviton Manufacturing Company, Inc.; *U.S. Private*, pg. 2436
AMERITEK VENTURES; *U.S. Public*, pg. 115
AMPHENOL AIR LB NORTH AMERICA, INC.—See Amphenol Corporation; *U.S. Public*, pg. 128
AMPHENOL CABLES ON DEMAND CORP.—See Amphenol Corporation; *U.S. Public*, pg. 127
AMPHENOL INTERCONNECT PRODUCTS CORPORATION—See Amphenol Corporation; *U.S. Public*, pg. 128
AMPHENOL TURKEY BAGLANTI COZUMLERI LIMITED SIRKETI—See Amphenol Corporation; *U.S. Public*, pg. 129
ANIXTER EUROFIN B.V.—See WESCO International, Inc.; *U.S. Public*, pg. 2350
AOFR PTY. LTD.—See Aegis Lightwave, Inc.; *U.S. Private*, pg. 116
APPLIED OPTICAL SYSTEMS, INC.—See Optical Cable Corporation; *U.S. Public*, pg. 1609
APPOINTECH, INC.—See ADTRAN Holdings, Inc.; *U.S. Public*, pg. 44
ARAB CABLES COMPANY—See El Sewedy Electric Company; *Int'l*, pg. 2341
AUSTRALIA PACIFIC ELECTRIC CABLES PTY., LTD.—See Asia Pacific Wire & Cable Corporation Limited; *Int'l*, pg. 614
AZENN SA; *Int'l*, pg. 778
BEFUT GLOBAL, INC.; *Int'l*, pg. 940
BELDEN, INC. - KENTUCKY PLANT—See Belden, Inc.; *U.S. Public*, pg. 294
BELDEN WIRE & CABLE COMPANY LLC—See Belden, Inc.; *U.S. Public*, pg. 294
BERK-TEK FIBER OPTIC DIVISION—See Leviton Manufacturing Company, Inc.; *U.S. Private*, pg. 2436
BIRLA CABLE LTD.—See Birla Corporation Ltd.; *Int'l*, pg. 1047
BIZLINK ELOCAB LTD.—See BizLink Holding Inc.; *Int'l*, pg. 1053
BIZLINK INDUSTRY CZECH S.R.O.—See BizLink Holding Inc.; *Int'l*, pg. 1053
BIZLINK SILITHERM S.R.L.—See BizLink Holding Inc.; *Int'l*, pg. 1053
BIZLINK SPECIAL CABLES GERMANY GMBH—See BizLink Holding Inc.; *Int'l*, pg. 1053
BLACK BOX NETWORK SERVICES—See Black Box Limited; *Int'l*, pg. 1057
CABLE DEVICES INCORPORATED—See CommScope Holding Company, Inc.; *U.S. Public*, pg. 548
CABLEWHOLESALE.COM; *U.S. Private*, pg. 711
CABLEX METAL MATERIAL (ANFU) CO., LTD.—See Copartner Technology Corporation; *Int'l*, pg. 1792
CASSIDY TECHNOLOGIES—See Alarmax Distributors Inc.; *U.S. Private*, pg. 150
CENTRIC SOLUTIONS LLC—See Optical Cable Corporation; *U.S. Public*, pg. 1609
CHELSEA GREEN PUBLISHING COMPANY; *U.S. Private*, pg. 870
CHENGDU SANDIAN CABLES CO., LTD.—See Goldcup Electric Apparatus Co., Ltd.; *Int'l*, pg. 3027
CHINA FIBER OPTIC NETWORK SYSTEM GROUP LTD.; *Int'l*, pg. 1502
CHINA U-TON FUTURE SPACE INDUSTRIAL GROUP HOLDINGS LTD.; *Int'l*, pg. 1561
CITYFIBRE INFRASTRUCTURE HOLDINGS LIMITED—See Antin Infrastructure Partners SAS; *Int'l*, pg. 483
C&M CORPORATION; *U.S. Private*, pg. 703
CMI LIMITED—See MPD, Inc.; *U.S. Private*, pg. 2803
COADNA (HK) LIMITED—See Coherent Corp.; *U.S. Public*, pg. 526
COAXIAL COMPONENTS CORP.; *U.S. Private*, pg. 957
COMMITTEE FOR ECONOMIC DEVELOPMENT—See The Conference Board, Inc.; *U.S. Private*, pg. 4014
COMMSCOPE ASIA (SUZHOU) TECHNOLOGIES CO., LTD.—See CommScope Holding Company, Inc.; *U.S. Public*, pg. 549
COMMSCOPE NEVADA, LLC—See CommScope Holding Company, Inc.; *U.S. Public*, pg. 549
COMPULINK CABLE ASSEMBLIES, INC.; *U.S. Private*, pg. 1004
COPARTNER TECHNOLOGY CORPORATION; *Int'l*, pg. 1792
CORDS CABLE INDUSTRIES LTD.; *Int'l*, pg. 1796
CORE CABLE CORPORATION—See CableWholesale.Com; *U.S. Private*, pg. 711
CORNING OPTICAL COMMUNICATIONS LLC—See Corning Incorporated; *U.S. Public*, pg. 578
CORNING OPTICAL COMMUNICATIONS LLC—See Corning Incorporated; *U.S. Public*, pg. 578
CORNING OPTICAL COMMUNICATIONS POLSKA SP. Z O.O.—See Corning Incorporated; *U.S. Public*, pg. 578
CORNING OPTICAL COMMUNICATIONS PTY. LTD.—See Corning Incorporated; *U.S. Public*, pg. 578
CORNING OPTICAL FIBER CABLE (CHENGDU) CO., LTD.—See Corning Incorporated; *U.S. Public*, pg. 578
CORNING SPECIALTY MATERIALS, INC.—See Corning Incorporated; *U.S. Public*, pg. 578
C TECHNOLOGIES, INC.—See Repligen Corporation; *U.S. Public*, pg. 1784
CTNETWORKS CO., LTD.; *Int'l*, pg. 1872
CUSTOM COMPUTER CABLES; *U.S. Private*, pg. 1128
DAVID ELECTRONICS CO., LTD.—See Chant Sincere Co., Ltd.; *Int'l*, pg. 1446
DECA CABLES INC.; *Int'l*, pg. 1999
DIAMOND USA INC.—See Diamond SA; *Int'l*, pg. 2105
DOPPELMAYR SCANDINAVIA AB—See Doppelmayr Group; *Int'l*, pg. 2174
EMCORE FIBER OPTICS, INC.—See EMCORE Corporation; *U.S. Public*, pg. 739
EMPIRE DISTRICT INDUSTRIES, INC.—See Algonquin Power & Utilities Corp.; *Int'l*, pg. 319
ENCOMPASS DIGITAL MEDIA—See Encompass Digital Media; *U.S. Private*, pg. 1390
ENPLAS CORPORATION - PLASTIC OPTICS DIVISION—See ENPLAS CORPORATION; *Int'l*, pg. 2445
EPAN INDUSTRIES PTE LTD—See Asia Pacific Wire & Cable Corporation Limited; *Int'l*, pg. 614
EZCONN CZECH A.S.—See Ezconn Corporation; *Int'l*, pg. 2593
FIBERCORE, LTD.—See Bridgepoint Group Plc; *Int'l*, pg. 1155
FIBERDYNE LABS INC.; *U.S. Private*, pg. 1502
FIBERGUIDE INDUSTRIES INC.—See Koch Industries, Inc.; *U.S. Private*, pg. 2333
FIBERLABS INC.; *Int'l*, pg. 2652
FIBER SYSTEMS INTERNATIONAL, INC.—See Amphenol Corporation; *U.S. Public*, pg. 128
FOCAL TECHNOLOGIES CORPORATION—See Moog Inc.; *U.S. Public*, pg. 1471
FOCI FIBER OPTIC COMMUNICATIONS, INC.; *Int'l*, pg. 2718
FTS USA, LLC—See Littlejohn & Co., LLC; *U.S. Private*, pg. 2472
FTS USA, LLC—See New Mountain Capital, LLC; *U.S. Private*, pg. 2903
FUJIAN NANPING SUN CABLE CO., LTD.; *Int'l*, pg. 2819
FUJIKURA EUROPE LTD. - DDK CONNECTOR DIVISION—See Fujikura Ltd.; *Int'l*, pg. 2828
FUJIKURA EUROPE LTD. - FIBRE OPTICS DIVISION—See Fujikura Ltd.; *Int'l*, pg. 2828
FUJIKURA EUROPE LTD. - PLANT & INFRASTRUCTURE CABLES DIVISION—See Fujikura Ltd.; *Int'l*, pg. 2828
FUJIKURA EUROPE LTD.—See Fujikura Ltd.; *Int'l*, pg. 2828
FUJIKURA FIBER-HOME OPTO-ELECTRONICS MATERIAL TECHNOLOGY CO., LTD.—See Fujikura Ltd.; *Int'l*, pg. 2828
FUJIKURA FIBER OPTICS VIETNAM LTD.—See Fujikura Ltd.; *Int'l*, pg. 2828
FUJIKURA HIGH OPT CO., LTD.—See Fujikura Ltd.; *Int'l*, pg. 2828
FUJIKURA LTD.—See Fujikura Ltd.; *Int'l*, pg. 2828
FUJIKURA SHANGHAI OPTICAL COMPONENTS CO., LTD.—See Fujikura Ltd.; *Int'l*, pg. 2828
FUJIKURA SHOJI CO., LTD.—See Fujikura Ltd.; *Int'l*, pg. 2829
FUJIKURA SOLUTIONS LTD.—See Fujikura Ltd.; *Int'l*, pg. 2829
FUJIOKA-CHUHATSU CO., LTD.—See Chuo Spring Co., Ltd.; *Int'l*, pg. 1599
FULGOR S.A.—See CENERGY HOLDINGS SA; *Int'l*, pg. 1401
FUNK UND TECHNIK GMBH—See Morgan Stanley; *U.S. Public*, pg. 1473
FUTONG GROUP CO., LTD. - CHENGDU PLANT—See Futong Group Co., Ltd.; *Int'l*, pg. 2852
FUTONG GROUP CO., LTD. - SHENZHEN PLANT—See Futong Group Co., Ltd.; *Int'l*, pg. 2852
FUTONG GROUP CO., LTD. - TIANJIN PLANT—See Futong Group Co., Ltd.; *Int'l*, pg. 2852
FUTONG GROUP (HONG KONG) CO., LTD.—See Futong Group Co., Ltd.; *Int'l*, pg. 2852
FUZHOU PHOTOP OPTICS CO., LTD.—See Coherent Corp.; *U.S. Public*, pg. 528
GAMAKABEL PLC; *Int'l*, pg. 2876
GC&E SYSTEMS GROUP, INC.; *U.S. Private*, pg. 1653
GCL ENERGY TECHNOLOGY CO., LTD.; *Int'l*, pg. 2895
GIFU-CHUHATSU CO., LTD.—See Chuo Spring Co., Ltd.; *Int'l*, pg. 1599
GIGACLEAR PLC; *Int'l*, pg. 2971
GLOBE TEXTILES (INDIA) LTD.; *Int'l*, pg. 3006
GOLD CUP ELECTRIC HENGYANG CABLES CO., LTD.—See Goldcup Electric Apparatus Co., Ltd.; *Int'l*, pg. 3027
GOULD TECHNOLOGY LLC—See Gooch & Housego PLC; *Int'l*, pg. 3038
GRAND-TEK TECHNOLOGY CO., LTD.; *Int'l*, pg. 3057
GUIDELINE GEO AB; *Int'l*, pg. 3173

335921 — FIBER OPTIC CABLE M...

GULF CABLE & ELECTRICAL INDUSTRIES CO. K.S.C.; *Int'l*, pg. 3179
HABIA CABLE AB—See Beijer Alma AB; *Int'l*, pg. 942
HABIA CABLE ASIA LTD—See Beijer Alma AB; *Int'l*, pg. 942
HABIA CABLE CS TECHNOLOGY AB—See Beijer Alma AB; *Int'l*, pg. 942
HABIA CABLE INDIA LTD—See Beijer Alma AB; *Int'l*, pg. 942
HABIA CABLE NORDIC AB—See Beijer Alma AB; *Int'l*, pg. 942
HABIA CABLE PRODUCTION AB—See Beijer Alma AB; *Int'l*, pg. 942
HABIA CABLE SP.Z.O.O—See Beijer Alma AB; *Int'l*, pg. 943
HENDRIX MARMON UTILITY LLC—See Berkshire Hathaway Inc.; *U.S. Public*, pg. 310
HENGTONG OPTIC-ELECTRIC CO., LTD.; *Int'l*, pg. 3347
HEXATRONIC CABLES & INTERCONNECT AB—See Hexatronic Group AB; *Int'l*, pg. 3370
HEXATRONIC CANADA INC—See Hexatronic Group AB; *Int'l*, pg. 3370
HEXATRONIC GMBH—See Hexatronic Group AB; *Int'l*, pg. 3371
HEXATRONIC GROUP AB; *Int'l*, pg. 3370
HEXATRONIC SECURITY & SURVEILLANCE AB—See Hexatronic Group AB; *Int'l*, pg. 3371
HEXATRONIC UK LTD.—See Hexatronic Group AB; *Int'l*, pg. 3371
HIGH TECHNOLOGY SYSTEMS LTD.; *Int'l*, pg. 3386
HOLD KEY ELECTRIC WIRE & CABLE, CO. LTD.; *Int'l*, pg. 3449
HUBEI KAILE SCIENCE & TECHNOLOGY CO., LTD.; *Int'l*, pg. 3518
HUBER + SUHNER AG; *Int'l*, pg. 3519
HUNAN DEVELOPMENT GROUP CO., LTD.; *Int'l*, pg. 3532
HUNAN VALIN CABLE CO., LTD.; *Int'l*, pg. 3534
INTEGRA NETWORKS INC.; *U.S. Private*, pg. 2098
INTEGRATED PHOTONICS, INC.—See Coherent Corp.; *U.S. Public*, pg. 529
IPG FIBERTECH S.R.L.—See IPG Photonics Corporation; *U.S. Public*, pg. 1167
IPG IRE-POLUS—See IPG Photonics Corporation; *U.S. Public*, pg. 1167
IPG LASER GMBH—See IPG Photonics Corporation; *U.S. Public*, pg. 1167
IPG PHOTONICS (INDIA) PVT. LTD.—See IPG Photonics Corporation; *U.S. Public*, pg. 1167
IPG PHOTONICS (UK) LTD.—See IPG Photonics Corporation; *U.S. Public*, pg. 1167
IPITEK; *U.S. Private*, pg. 2136
JIANGXI FOCI FIBER OPTIC COMMUNICATION, INC.—See Foci Fiber Optic Communications, Inc.; *Int'l*, pg. 2718
JIA XIN NEW MATERIALS (ANFU) CO., LTD.—See Copartner Technology Corporation; *Int'l*, pg. 1793
KRA INTERNATIONAL, LLC—See Patrick Industries, Inc.; *U.S. Public*, pg. 1652
LEONI CABLE INC—See EnBW Energie Baden-Wurttemberg AG; *Int'l*, pg. 2399
LINXIT LLC—See Amphenol Corporation; *U.S. Public*, pg. 130
MACKIN TECHNOLOGIES; *U.S. Private*, pg. 2537
MEGLADON MANUFACTURING GROUP—See TyRex Group, Ltd.; *U.S. Private*, pg. 4269
METRO FIBERNET, LLC—See Keystone Group, L.P.; *U.S. Private*, pg. 2299
MOLEX FIBER OPTICS—See Koch Industries, Inc.; *U.S. Private*, pg. 2335
NESTOR CABLES LTD.—See Clearfield, Inc.; *U.S. Public*, pg. 512
NOISE FIBER—See Fujikura Ltd.; *Int'l*, pg. 2827
NUFERN INC.—See Coherent Corp.; *U.S. Public*, pg. 527
OMERIN USA, INC. - QS TECHNOLOGIES DIVISION—See Groupe OMERIN; *Int'l*, pg. 3109
OPTERNA AM, INC.—See Belden, Inc.; *U.S. Public*, pg. 294
OPTERNA EUROPE LIMITED—See Belden, Inc.; *U.S. Public*, pg. 294
OPTERNA TECHNOLOGY LIMITED—See Belden, Inc.; *U.S. Public*, pg. 294
OPTERNA TRADING—See Belden, Inc.; *U.S. Public*, pg. 294
OPTERNUS GMBH—See Hexatronic Group AB; *Int'l*, pg. 3371
OPTICAL CABLE CORPORATION; *U.S. Public*, pg. 1609
OPTIWORK, INC.—See BizLink Holding Inc.; *Int'l*, pg. 1053
OPTIWORKS, INC.—See BizLink Holding Inc.; *Int'l*, pg. 1053
OPTOKON CO. LTD.—See Methode Electronics, Inc.; *U.S. Public*, pg. 1429
PPC BROADBAND, INC.—See Belden, Inc.; *U.S. Public*, pg. 294
PROXIMION AB—See Hexatronic Group AB; *Int'l*, pg. 3371
PT FUJIKURA INDONESIA—See Fujikura Ltd.; *Int'l*, pg. 2829
PT.HI-LEX INDONESIA—See Hi-Lex Corporation; *Int'l*, pg. 3381
REVOLUTION LIGHTING TECHNOLOGIES, INC.; *U.S. Public*, pg. 1793
RIPLEY EUROPE LIMITED—See Hubbell Incorporated; *U.S. Public*, pg. 1067
RIYADH CABLES GROUP OF COMPANIES—See A.K. Al-Muhaidib & Sons Group of Companies; *Int'l*, pg. 24
RUTAB AB—See Addtech AB; *Int'l*, pg. 135
SAUDI MODERN COMPANY FOR CABLES INDUSTRY LTD.—See A.K. Al-Muhaidib & Sons Group of Companies; *Int'l*, pg. 24
SAUDI MODERN COMPANY FOR METALS, CABLES AND PLASTIC INDUSTRY LTD.—See A.K. Al-Muhaidib & Sons Group of Companies; *Int'l*, pg. 24
SEI OPTICAL FIBER AND CABLE (SHENZHEN) CO., LTD.—See Futong Group Co., Ltd.; *Int'l*, pg. 2852
SHANDONG PACIFIC FIBER OPTICS CABLE CO., LTD.—See Asia Pacific Wire & Cable Corporation Limited; *Int'l*, pg. 614
SHANDONG PACIFIC RUBBER CABLE CO., LTD.—See Asia Pacific Wire & Cable Corporation Limited; *Int'l*, pg. 614
SHANGHAI FOCI FIBER OPTIC COMMUNICATION EQUIPMENTS, INC.—See Foci Fiber Optic Communications, Inc.; *Int'l*, pg. 2718
SHENZHEN SHIJIA OPTICAL CABLE TECHNOLOGY CO., LTD.—See Henan Shijia Photons Technology Co., Ltd.; *Int'l*, pg. 3343
SHINSHIRO CABLE, LTD.—See Fujikura Ltd.; *Int'l*, pg. 2829
SIGMA CABLE CO. (PTE) LTD.—See Asia Pacific Wire & Cable Corporation Limited; *Int'l*, pg. 614
SIGMA-EPAN INTERNATIONAL PTE., LTD.—See Asia Pacific Wire & Cable Corporation Limited; *Int'l*, pg. 614
SIS SPEEDY INDUSTRIAL SUPPLIES SDN. BHD.—See BizLink Holding Inc.; *Int'l*, pg. 1053
SMD, INC.; *U.S. Private*, pg. 3693
SOURCE PHOTONICS, INC.; *U.S. Private*, pg. 3718
SOUTHWIRE CANADA COMPANY—See Southwire Company, LLC; *U.S. Private*, pg. 3742
STEALTHCOM SOLUTIONS INC.; *U.S. Private*, pg. 3795
THE STOCK COMPANY MOSKABEL-FUJIKURA—See Fujikura Ltd.; *Int'l*, pg. 2829
SUZUKI GIKEN CO., LTD.—See Fujikura Ltd.; *Int'l*, pg. 2829
SYNERGY CABLES GMBH—See The Alpine Group, Inc.; *U.S. Private*, pg. 3984
TECH OPTICS FIRST COMPANY LTD.—See Hexatronic Group AB; *Int'l*, pg. 3371
TECH OPTICS LTD.—See Hexatronic Group AB; *Int'l*, pg. 3371
TEKAB CO. LTD.—See GIBCA Limited; *Int'l*, pg. 2963
TELEDYNE REYNOLDS UK—See Teledyne Technologies Incorporated; *U.S. Public*, pg. 1995
TIANJIN CHUHATSU HUAGUAN MACHINERY CO., LTD.—See Chuo Spring Co., Ltd.; *Int'l*, pg. 1599
TII FIBER OPTICS, INC.—See Kelta, Inc.; *U.S. Private*, pg. 2281
TIMES FIBER CANADA LTD.—See Amphenol Corporation; *U.S. Public*, pg. 132
TOGO CABLE CO., LTD.—See Chuo Spring Co., Ltd.; *Int'l*, pg. 1599
TRANSTECH OPTICAL COMMUNICATION CO., LTD.—See Futong Group Co., Ltd.; *Int'l*, pg. 2852
TSK (KOREA) CO., LTD—See Hi-Lex Corporation; *Int'l*, pg. 3381
UNITI FIBER—See Uniti Group Inc.; *U.S. Public*, pg. 2253
US CONEC LTD.—See Fujikura Ltd.; *Int'l*, pg. 2829
VERRILLON, INC.—See Fujikura Ltd.; *Int'l*, pg. 2827
VIAVI SOLUTIONS DO BRASIL LTDA.—See Viavi Solutions Inc.; *U.S. Public*, pg. 2295
VIAVI SOLUTIONS GMBH—See Viavi Solutions Inc.; *U.S. Public*, pg. 2295
VIAVI SOLUTIONS (SHENZHEN) CO., LTD.—See Viavi Solutions Inc.; *U.S. Public*, pg. 2295
VIAVI SOLUTIONS (SUZHOU) CO., LTD.—See Viavi Solutions Inc.; *U.S. Public*, pg. 2295
W. L. GORE & ASSOCIATES DE MEXICO, S. DE R.L DE C.V.—See W.L. Gore & Associates, Inc.; *U.S. Private*, pg. 4421
W.L. GORE & ASSOCIATES, INC.; *U.S. Private*, pg. 4421
W. L. GORE & ASSOCIATES (UK) LTD.—See W.L. Gore & Associates, Inc.; *U.S. Private*, pg. 4421
WUHAN ACCELINK POLYTRON TECHNOLOGIES INC—See Accelink Technologies Co., Ltd.; *Int'l*, pg. 80
YANGTZE OPTICAL FIBRE & CABLE JOINT STOCK LIMITED COMPANY—See China Telecommunications Corporation; *Int'l*, pg. 1558
YANTAI TSK CABLE SYSTEM CO., LTD—See Hi-Lex Corporation; *Int'l*, pg. 3381
ZHONGSHAN FOCI FIBER OPTIC COMMUNICATIONS, INC.—See Foci Fiber Optic Communications, Inc.; *Int'l*, pg. 2718
ZHU HAI OPLINK COMMUNICATIONS, INC—See Koch Industries, Inc.; *U.S. Private*, pg. 2335

335929 — OTHER COMMUNICATION AND ENERGY WIRE MANUFACTURING

ACL CABLES PLC; *Int'l*, pg. 106
ACL PLASTIC PLC; *Int'l*, pg. 107
ADAPTAFLEX LIMITED—See ABB Ltd.; *Int'l*, pg. 52
ALCHEMIST CORPORATION LIMITED; *Int'l*, pg. 300
ALFA NETWORK INC—See Accton Technology Corporation; *Int'l*, pg. 93
ALLWIN TELECOMMUNICATION CO., LTD.; *Int'l*, pg. 361
ALLWORX CORP.—See Windstream Holdings, Inc.; *U.S. Public*, pg. 2373
AMPHENOL FINLAND OY—See Amphenol Corporation; *U.S. Public*, pg. 127
AMPHENOL LTW TECHNOLOGY CO., LTD—See Amphenol Corporation; *U.S. Public*, pg. 128
AMPHENOL RF—See Amphenol Corporation; *U.S. Public*, pg. 128
ANIXTER INC. - WAUKESHA—See WESCO International, Inc.; *U.S. Public*, pg. 2350
APEX ENGINEERS (INDIA) PRIVATE LIMITED—See Cadsys (India) Ltd.; *Int'l*, pg. 1248
ARRIS BROADBAND SOLUTIONS, LTD.—See CommScope Holding Company, Inc.; *U.S. Public*, pg. 548
ARRIS COMMUNICATIONS IRELAND LIMITED—See CommScope Holding Company, Inc.; *U.S. Public*, pg. 548
ARRIS ENTERPRISES, INC.—See CommScope Holding Company, Inc.; *U.S. Public*, pg. 548
ARRIS FRANCE S.A.S.—See CommScope Holding Company, Inc.; *U.S. Public*, pg. 548
ARRIS SOLUTIONS U.K., LTD.—See CommScope Holding Company, Inc.; *U.S. Public*, pg. 548
ARRIS SWEDEN A.B.—See CommScope Holding Company, Inc.; *U.S. Public*, pg. 548
ARRIS TAIWAN, LTD.—See CommScope Holding Company, Inc.; *U.S. Public*, pg. 548
ARRIS TECHNOLOGY (SHENZHEN) CO., LTD.—See CommScope Holding Company, Inc.; *U.S. Public*, pg. 548
ASTA CONDUCTORS CO., LTD.—See Global Equity Partners Beteiligungs-Management AG; *Int'l*, pg. 2996
ASTA ELEKTRODRAHT GMBH & CO KG—See Global Equity Partners Beteiligungs-Management AG; *Int'l*, pg. 2996
ATR HOLDINGS LTD—See Centurion Group Ltd; *Int'l*, pg. 1417
AVSL INDUSTRIES LTD.; *Int'l*, pg. 750
BAOSHENG SCIENCE & TECHNOLOGY INNOVATION CO., LTD; *Int'l*, pg. 856
BAY ASSOCIATES WIRE TECHNOLOGIES INC.—See MJM Holdings Inc.; *U.S. Private*, pg. 2753
BC POWER CONTROLS LTD.; *Int'l*, pg. 925
BELDEN AB—See Belden, Inc.; *U.S. Public*, pg. 293
BELDEN CDT EUROPEAN SHARED SERVICES B.V.—See Belden, Inc.; *U.S. Public*, pg. 293
BELDEN DEUTSCHLAND GMBH—See Belden, Inc.; *U.S. Public*, pg. 293
BELDEN-DUNA KABEL KFT—See Belden, Inc.; *U.S. Public*, pg. 294
BELDEN EUROPE B.V.—See Belden, Inc.; *U.S. Public*, pg. 293
BERK-TEK LLC—See Leviton Manufacturing Company, Inc.; *U.S. Public*, pg. 2436
CABLENA DO BRASIL LTDA—See Grupo Carso, S.A.B. de C.V.; *Int'l*, pg. 3123
CABLENA, S.A.—See Grupo Carso, S.A.B. de C.V.; *Int'l*, pg. 3123
CABLES UNLIMITED, INC.—See RF Industries, Ltd.; *U.S. Public*, pg. 1796
CAFCA LIMITED; *Int'l*, pg. 1249
CANARE CORPORATION OF AMERICA—See Canare Electric Co., Ltd.; *Int'l*, pg. 1288
CANARE ELECTRIC CO., LTD.; *Int'l*, pg. 1288
CANARE FRANCE SAS—See Canare Electric Co., Ltd.; *Int'l*, pg. 1288
CENTURION GROUP LTD; *Int'l*, pg. 1417
CHAROUNG THAI WIRE & CABLE PUBLIC CO. LTD.—See Asia Pacific Wire & Cable Corporation Limited; *Int'l*, pg. 614
CHINA WIRE & CABLE CO., LTD.; *Int'l*, pg. 1563
CNIM BABCOCK POLSKA SP. Z.O.O—See CNIM Constructions Industrielles de la Mediterranee SA; *Int'l*, pg. 1677
COMMSCOPE, INC. OF NORTH CAROLINA—See CommScope Holding Company, Inc.; *U.S. Public*, pg. 549
COMMSCOPE INTERNATIONAL HOLDINGS, LLC—See CommScope Holding Company, Inc.; *U.S. Public*, pg. 549
COMMSCOPE OPTICAL TECHNOLOGIES, INC.—See CommScope Holding Company, Inc.; *U.S. Public*, pg. 549
COMPOTRON GMBH—See discoverIE Group plc; *Int'l*, pg. 2133
CONDUCTORES Y CABLES DEL PERU S.A.C.; *Int'l*, pg. 1766
CORNING OPTICAL COMMUNICATIONS GERMANY—See Corning Incorporated; *U.S. Public*, pg. 578
CTL MANUFACTURING—See Avnet, Inc.; *U.S. Public*, pg. 250
DAH SAN ELECTRIC WIRE & CABLE CO., LTD.; *Int'l*, pg. 1912
DE REGT MARINE CABLES BV—See CGG; *Int'l*, pg. 1432
DONGGUAN FUQIANG ELECTRONICS CO., LTD.—See Cheng Eui Precision Industry Co., Ltd.; *Int'l*, pg. 1465
DONGGUAN NISTAR TRANSMITTING TECHNOLOGY CO., INC—See Baosheng Science & Technology Innovation Co., Ltd; *Int'l*, pg. 856

N.A.I.C.S. INDEX

335931 — CURRENT-CARRYING WI...

DYNAMIC CABLES LIMITED; *Int'l*, pg. 2240
EAST AFRICAN CABLES LIMITED; *Int'l*, pg. 2269
ECOCAB CO., LTD.; *Int'l*, pg. 2294
ECOPRO HN CO., LTD.; *Int'l*, pg. 2299
EITA TECHNOLOGIES (MALAYSIA) SDN. BHD.—See Eita Resources Berhad; *Int'l*, pg. 2336
ELEKTRISOLA INC.—See Elektrisola Dr. Gerd Schildbach GmbH & Co. KG; *Int'l*, pg. 2356
EL SEWEDY ELECTRIC COMPANY; *Int'l*, pg. 2341
EMPIRE WIRE & SUPPLY, LLC—See Audax Group, Limited Partnership; *U.S. Private*, pg. 387
FAR EAST INTERGERATION TECHNOLOGY CO., LTD.—See Far East Smarter Energy Co., Ltd.; *Int'l*, pg. 2617
FCI COMPOSITE INSULATOR LTD.—See Benji Invest Kft.; *Int'l*, pg. 974
FEDERAL SCREW WORKS ROMULUS DIVISION—See Federal Screw Works; *U.S. Public*, pg. 826
FINOLEX CABLES LTD.—See Finolex Group; *Int'l*, pg. 2676
FOXLINK AUTOMOTIVE TECHNOLOGY CO., LTD.—See Cheng Eui Precision Industry Co., Ltd.; *Int'l*, pg. 1465
FOXLINK AUTOMOTIVE TECHNOLOGY (KUNSHAN) CO., LTD.—See Cheng Eui Precision Industry Co., Ltd.; *Int'l*, pg. 1465
FUGANG ELECTRIC (KUNSHAN) CO., LTD.—See Cheng Eui Precision Industry Co., Ltd.; *Int'l*, pg. 1465
FUGANG ELECTRIC (MAANSHAN) CO., LTD.—See Cheng Eui Precision Industry Co., Ltd.; *Int'l*, pg. 1465
FUGANG ELECTRIC (NAN CHANG) CO., LTD.—See Cheng Eui Precision Industry Co., Ltd.; *Int'l*, pg. 1465
FUGANG ELECTRIC (XUZHOU) CO., LTD.—See Cheng Eui Precision Industry Co., Ltd.; *Int'l*, pg. 1465
FUGANG ELECTRONIC (DONG GUAN) CO., LTD.—See Cheng Eui Precision Industry Co., Ltd.; *Int'l*, pg. 1465
GAON CABLE CO., LTD.; *Int'l*, pg. 2882
GARRETTCOM INDIA PVT. LTD.—See Belden, Inc.; *U.S. Public*, pg. 294
GENERAL INSTRUMENT CORPORATION INDIA PRIVATE LIMITED—See CommScope Holding Company, Inc.; *U.S. Public*, pg. 548
GLORYTEK (YANCHENG) CO., LTD.—See Cheng Eui Precision Industry Co., Ltd.; *Int'l*, pg. 1465
GOLKONDA ENGINEERING ENTERPRISES LIMITED; *Int'l*, pg. 3036
GREAT LAKES WIRE & CABLE, INC.; *U.S. Private*, pg. 1765
GUANGZHOU RISING MICRO ELECTRONICS CO., LTD.—See Guangdong Rising Assets Management Co., Ltd.; *Int'l*, pg. 3159
HARBIN COSLIGHT ELECTRIC WIRE & CABLE CO., LTD.—See Coslight Technology International Group Limited; *Int'l*, pg. 1810
HAYES INDUSTRIES, LTD.—See Enerpac Tool Group Corp.; *U.S. Public*, pg. 765
HELLERMANNTYTON AB—See Aptiv PLC; *Int'l*, pg. 525
HELLERMANNTYTON AS—See Aptiv PLC; *Int'l*, pg. 525
HELLERMANNTYTON B.V.—See Aptiv PLC; *Int'l*, pg. 525
HELLERMANNTYTON CORPORATION—See Aptiv PLC; *Int'l*, pg. 525
HELLERMANNTYTON DATA LTD.—See Aptiv PLC; *Int'l*, pg. 525
HELLERMANNTYTON GMBH—See Aptiv PLC; *Int'l*, pg. 525
HELLERMANNTYTON INDIA PVT. LTD.—See Aptiv PLC; *Int'l*, pg. 526
HELLERMANNTYTON LTD. - PLYMOUTH—See Aptiv PLC; *Int'l*, pg. 526
HELLERMANNTYTON PTE LTD.—See Aptiv PLC; *Int'l*, pg. 526
HELLERMANNTYTON S.A.S.—See Aptiv PLC; *Int'l*, pg. 526
HENAN SHIJIA PHOTONS TECHNOLOGY CO., LTD.; *Int'l*, pg. 3343
HEW-KABEL GMBH & CO. KG—See HEW-KABEL Holding GmbH; *Int'l*, pg. 3367
HIGH-TEK HARNESS ENTERPRISE CO., LTD.; *Int'l*, pg. 3386
ICA MIDWEST, INC.—See Amphenol Corporation; *U.S. Public*, pg. 130
IES COMMUNICATIONS, LLC—See IES Holdings, Inc.; *U.S. Public*, pg. 1094
INTERNATIONAL WIRE GROUP-HIGH PERFORMANCE CONDUCTORS—See Atlas Holdings, LLC; *U.S. Private*, pg. 376
JOH. PENGG AG—See Berndorf AG; *Int'l*, pg. 987
MALESELA TAIHAN ELECTRIC CABLE (PTY) LTD.—See Community Investment Holdings (Pty) Ltd.; *Int'l*, pg. 1721
MANUFACTURED ASSEMBLIES CORPORATION; *U.S. Private*, pg. 2567
MICOS TELCOM S.R.O.—See Preformed Line Products Company; *U.S. Public*, pg. 1714
NEW AGE TECHNOLOGIES, INC.—See Insight Equity Holdings LLC; *U.S. Private*, pg. 2086
NEW ENGLAND WIRE TECHNOLOGIES—See MJM Holdings Inc.; *U.S. Private*, pg. 2753
NEW FAR EAST CABLE CO., LTD.—See Far East Smarter Energy Co., Ltd.; *Int'l*, pg. 2617
ONANON INC.—See Amphenol Corporation; *U.S. Public*, pg. 132

OPTICOMM CORPORATION—See EMCORE Corporation; *U.S. Public*, pg. 739
PORT GMBH—See Belden, Inc.; *U.S. Public*, pg. 294
P.T. HO WAH GENTING—See Ho Wah Genting Berhad; *Int'l*, pg. 3435
REA MAGNET WIRE COMPANY, INC.; *U.S. Private*, pg. 3365
RFS TECHNOLOGIES, INC.—See Amphenol Corporation; *U.S. Public*, pg. 132
SAUDI MODERN COMPANY FOR SPECIAL ELECTRIC WIRE & CABLES INDUSTRY LTD.—See A.K. Al-Muhaidib & Sons Group of Companies; *Int'l*, pg. 24
SAUDI MODERN COMPANY FOR TELEPHONE CABLE INDUSTRY LTD.—See A.K. Al-Muhaidib & Sons Group of Companies; *Int'l*, pg. 24
SERVICE WIRE CO.—See Arthur's Enterprises, Inc.; *U.S. Private*, pg. 342
SRC HAVERHILL—See Aptiv PLC; *Int'l*, pg. 526
STANDARD WIRE & CABLE CO.; *U.S. Private*, pg. 3782
STANDARD WIRE & CABLE CO.—See Standard Wire & Cable Co.; *U.S. Private*, pg. 3782
STUDIO A INC.—See Cheng Eui Precision Industry Co., Ltd.; *Int'l*, pg. 1465
STUDIO A TECHNOLOGY LIMITED—See Cheng Eui Precision Industry Co., Ltd.; *Int'l*, pg. 1465
TIMES FIBER COMMUNICATIONS, INC.—See Amphenol Corporation; *U.S. Public*, pg. 132
TONICHI KYOUSAN CABLE, LTD.—See Hitachi, Ltd.; *Int'l*, pg. 3424
TPCW MEXICO, S. DE R.L. DE C.V.—See Amphenol Corporation; *U.S. Public*, pg. 132
TRILOGY COMMUNICATIONS, INC.; *U.S. Private*, pg. 4232
UNLIMITED SERVICES OF WISCONSIN, INC.; *U.S. Private*, pg. 4310
WAHAH ELECTRIC SUPPLY COMPANY OF SAUDI ARABIA LIMITED—See Electrical Industries Company; *Int'l*, pg. 2350
WALSIN LIWHA CORP.—See Corner Growth Acquisition Corp.; *U.S. Public*, pg. 577
WEI HAI FU KANG ELECTRIC CO., LTD.—See Cheng Eui Precision Industry Co., Ltd.; *Int'l*, pg. 1465
WIRE PRODUCTS LTD—See Aga Khan Development Network; *Int'l*, pg. 199
YAGI ANTENNA INC—See KKR & Co. Inc.; *U.S. Public*, pg. 1258
THE ZIPPERTUBING COMPANY - ZT AUTOMOTIVE DIVISION—See The Zippertubing Company; *U.S. Private*, pg. 4140
ZIPPERTUBING (JAPAN), LTD.—See The Zippertubing Company; *U.S. Private*, pg. 4140

335931 — CURRENT-CARRYING WIRING DEVICE MANUFACTURING

AEG POWER SOLUTIONS B.V.—See 3W Power S.A.; *Int'l*, pg. 10
AEG POWER SOLUTIONS GMBH—See 3W Power S.A.; *Int'l*, pg. 10
AEG POWER SOLUTIONS INC.—See 3W Power S.A.; *Int'l*, pg. 10
AEG POWER SOLUTIONS LTD.—See 3W Power S.A.; *Int'l*, pg. 10
AEG POWER SOLUTIONS USA, INC.—See 3W Power S.A.; *Int'l*, pg. 10
AERO-ELECTRIC CONNECTOR INC.; *U.S. Private*, pg. 118
AHOKU ELECTRONIC COMPANY; *U.S. Private*, pg. 225
ALAMBRADOS AUTOMOTRICES, S.A. DE C.V.—See General Motors Company; *U.S. Public*, pg. 923
AMPHENOL RF ASIA LIMITED—See Amphenol Corporation; *U.S. Public*, pg. 128
AMPHENOL SHOUH MIN INDUSTRY (SHENZHEN) COMPANY—See Amphenol Corporation; *U.S. Public*, pg. 128
APRESA - PLP SPAIN, S. A.—See Preformed Line Products Company; *U.S. Public*, pg. 1714
AQ WIRING SYSTEMS S.A. DE C.V.—See AQ Group AB; *Int'l*, pg. 527
AQ WIRING SYSTEMS SP.Z.O.O.—See AQ Group AB; *Int'l*, pg. 527
AQ WIRING SYSTEMS UAB—See AQ Group AB; *Int'l*, pg. 527
ARK-LES CONNECTORS—See Milestone Partners Ltd.; *U.S. Private*, pg. 2729
AUTOSPLICE INC.; *U.S. Private*, pg. 401
BAMBACH WIRES & CABLES PTY LTD—See Energy Technologies Limited; *Int'l*, pg. 2423
BARKSDALE GMBH—See Crane NXT, Co.; *U.S. Public*, pg. 589
BEIJING PLP CONDUCTOR LINE PRODUCTS, LTD.—See Preformed Line Products Company; *U.S. Public*, pg. 1714
BEIJING SEPR REFRACORIES CO., LTD.—See Compagnie de Saint-Gobain SA; *Int'l*, pg. 1722
BIZLINK TECHNOLOGY (SLOVAKIA) S.R.O.—See BizLink Holding Inc.; *Int'l*, pg. 1053
BLUE SEA SYSTEMS—See Brunswick Corporation; *U.S. Public*, pg. 408

BRYANT ELECTRIC COMPANY—See Hubbell Incorporated; *U.S. Public*, pg. 1066
BURNDY CANADA INC.—See Hubbell Incorporated; *U.S. Public*, pg. 1066
CALCULAGRAPH CO.; *U.S. Private*, pg. 716
CARLISLE INTERCONNECT TECHNOLOGIES—See Amphenol Corporation; *U.S. Public*, pg. 129
CARLISLE MEXICO, S.A. DE C.V.—See Carlisle Companies Incorporated; *U.S. Public*, pg. 436
CEMBRE AS—See CEMBRE S.p.A.; *Int'l*, pg. 1396
CEMBRE ESPANA SL—See CEMBRE S.p.A.; *Int'l*, pg. 1396
CEMBRE GMBH—See CEMBRE S.p.A.; *Int'l*, pg. 1396
CEMBRE INC.—See CEMBRE S.p.A.; *Int'l*, pg. 1396
CEMBRE LTD.—See CEMBRE S.p.A.; *Int'l*, pg. 1396
CEMBRE SARL—See CEMBRE S.p.A.; *Int'l*, pg. 1396
CEMBRE S.P.A.; *Int'l*, pg. 1396
CHANGLAN TECHNOLOGY GROUP CO., LTD; *Int'l*, pg. 1443
CHANGSHU GUORUI TECHNOLOGY CO., LTD.; *Int'l*, pg. 1444
CHANGZHOU AMPHENOL FUYANG COMMUNICATION EQUIPMENT COMPANY LIMITED—See Amphenol Corporation; *U.S. Public*, pg. 129
COBRA WATERTECH (PROPRIETARY) LIMITED—See DISTRIBUTION AND WAREHOUSING NETWORK LIMITED; *Int'l*, pg. 2136
COLE HERSEE COMPANY—See Littelfuse, Inc.; *U.S. Public*, pg. 1326
COMPULINK CABLE ASSEMBLIES OF FLORIDA INC.—See ITT Inc.; *U.S. Public*, pg. 1179
CONNECTOR MANUFACTURING COMPANY; *U.S. Private*, pg. 1016
CONTROL PRODUCTS, INC.—See Calculagraph Co.; *U.S. Private*, pg. 716
CORNING GILBERT INC.—See Corning Incorporated; *U.S. Public*, pg. 578
DAITO-TEC CO., LTD.—See Daitron Co., Ltd.; *Int'l*, pg. 1944
DEKKO TECHNICAL CENTER—See Graham Holdings Company; *U.S. Public*, pg. 955
DERINGER-NEY INC; *U.S. Private*, pg. 1209
EASTER-OWENS ELECTRIC COMPANY—See Crusoe Energy Systems LLC; *U.S. Private*, pg. 1114
EASY HEAT, INC.—See Emerson Electric Co.; *U.S. Public*, pg. 740
EASY HEAT, INC.—See Emerson Electric Co.; *U.S. Public*, pg. 740
EGS ELECTRIC GROUP CANADA LTD.—See Emerson Electric Co.; *U.S. Public*, pg. 740
ELECSYS DIVISION—See DCX-CHOL Enterprises, Inc.; *U.S. Private*, pg. 1180
ELECTRIC MOTION COMPANY INC.; *U.S. Private*, pg. 1352
ELECTRO ADAPTER; *U.S. Private*, pg. 1353
ELEKTROKOPPAR AB—See IK Investment Partners Limited; *Int'l*, pg. 3609
ELKAY ELECTRICAL—See ABB Ltd.; *Int'l*, pg. 52
ELKOK A.D.; *Int'l*, pg. 2364
ERICSON MANUFACTURING CO.; *U.S. Private*, pg. 1420
FARGO ASSEMBLY COMPANY—See Cerberus Capital Management, L.P.; *U.S. Private*, pg. 838
FEDERAL SIGNAL SAFETY & SECURITY SYSTEMS GROUP—See Federal Signal Corporation; *U.S. Public*, pg. 826
FIRST SOURCE ELECTRONICS, LLC—See Woodson Equity LLC; *U.S. Private*, pg. 4560
FLUKE BIOMEDICAL—See Cardinal Health, Inc.; *U.S. Public*, pg. 434
FOXLINK INTERNATIONAL INC—See Cheng Eui Precision Industry Co., Ltd.; *Int'l*, pg. 1465
FRIEDRICH GOHRINGER ELEKTROTECHNIK GMBH—See Amphenol Corporation; *U.S. Public*, pg. 130
FUJIKURA ASIA LTD. - DDK CONNECTOR DIVISION—See Fujikura Ltd.; *Int'l*, pg. 2827
FUJIKURA AUTOMOTIVE (THAILAND) LTD.—See Fujikura Ltd.; *Int'l*, pg. 2827
FUJIKURA HENGTONG AERIAL CABLE SYSTEM LTD.—See Fujikura Ltd.; *Int'l*, pg. 2828
GEIST MANUFACTURING INC.—See PCE, Inc.; *U.S. Private*, pg. 3120
GLENAIR INC.; *U.S. Private*, pg. 1709
GOLDCUP ELECTRIC APPARATUS CO., LTD.; *Int'l*, pg. 3027
GROUP DEKKO - NORTH WEBSTER—See Graham Holdings Company; *U.S. Public*, pg. 955
HABIA KABEL GMBH—See HEW-KABEL Holding GmbH; *Int'l*, pg. 3367
HABIA KABEL PRODUKTIONS GMBH & CO.KG—See Beijer Alma AB; *Int'l*, pg. 949
HARMER & SIMMONS—See 3W Power S.A.; *Int'l*, pg. 10
HELLERMANNTYTON CO., LTD.—See Aptiv PLC; *Int'l*, pg. 525
HENAN TONG-DA CABLE CO., LTD.; *Int'l*, pg. 3343
HENKEL + GERLACH GMBH & CO. KG; *Int'l*, pg. 3348
HEWTECH PHILIPPINES CORP.—See Hirakawa Hewtech Corp.; *Int'l*, pg. 3403
HEWTECH (SHENZHEN) ELECTRONICS CO., LTD.—See Hirakawa Hewtech Corp.; *Int'l*, pg. 3403

335931 — CURRENT-CARRYING WI...

HEWTECH (THAILAND) CO., LTD.—See Hirakawa Hewtech Corp.; *Int'l*, pg. 3403
HIRAKAWA HEWTECH CORP. - FUKUSHIMA FACTORY—See Hirakawa Hewtech Corp.; *Int'l*, pg. 3403
HIRAKAWA HEWTECH CORP. - KOGA GENERAL R&D PLANT—See Hirakawa Hewtech Corp.; *Int'l*, pg. 3403
HIRAKAWA HEWTECH CORP. - MONOU FACTORY—See Hirakawa Hewtech Corp.; *Int'l*, pg. 3403
HIRAKAWA HEWTECH CORP. - NIIGATA FACTORY—See Hirakawa Hewtech Corp.; *Int'l*, pg. 3403
HIRAKAWA HEWTECH CORP.; *Int'l*, pg. 3402
HOMAC MANUFACTURING COMPANY INC.; *U.S. Private*, pg. 1969
HOSIDEN CORPORATION; *Int'l*, pg. 3484
HOTRON PRECISION ELECTRONIC (FUQING) CO., LTD.—See Hotron Precision Electronic Industrial Co. Ltd.; *Int'l*, pg. 3489
HOTRON PRECISION ELECTRONIC (SUZHOU) CO., LTD.—See Hotron Precision Electronic Industrial Co. Ltd.; *Int'l*, pg. 3489
HST CO, LTD.—See Hirose Electric Co., Ltd.; *Int'l*, pg. 3405
HUBBELL CARIBE LTD—See Hubbell Incorporated; *U.S. Public*, pg. 1066
HUBBELL ELECTRICAL PRODUCTS—See AIP, LLC; *U.S. Private*, pg. 134
HUBBELL POWER SYSTEMS, INC. - CENTRALIA—See Hubbell Incorporated; *U.S. Public*, pg. 1067
HUBBELL WIRING SYSTEMS—See Hubbell Incorporated; *U.S. Public*, pg. 1067
INDEPENDENT PROTECTION COMPANY; *U.S. Private*, pg. 2061
INNOVATIVE TECHNOLOGY, INC.—See Eaton Corporation plc; *U.S. Public*, pg. 2282
INTERPOWER CORPORATION; *U.S. Private*, pg. 2123
IREX GROUP LTD.—See TyRex Group, Ltd.; *U.S. Private*, pg. 4269
ISCA (PROPRIETARY) LIMITED—See DISTRIBUTION AND WAREHOUSING NETWORK LIMITED; *Int'l*, pg. 2136
JUDCO MANUFACTURING INC.; *U.S. Private*, pg. 2242
KEMLON PRODUCTS & DEVELOPMENT CO.; *U.S. Private*, pg. 2281
LEVITON MANUFACTURING COMPANY, INC. - PLANT 05—See Leviton Manufacturing Company, Inc.; *U.S. Private*, pg. 2436
LEVITON MANUFACTURING OF CANADA LTD.—See Leviton Manufacturing Company, Inc.; *U.S. Private*, pg. 2436
LEVITON—See Leviton Manufacturing Company, Inc.; *U.S. Private*, pg. 2436
LUNA TECHNOLOGIES, INC,—See Luna Innovations Incorporated; *U.S. Public*, pg. 1348
MEYER WIRE & CABLE COMPANY, LLC; *U.S. Private*, pg. 2693
MINNESOTA WIRE & CABLE COMPANY; *U.S. Private*, pg. 2744
MOLEX, INC. - TAMPA BAY OPERATIONS—See Koch Industries, Inc.; *U.S. Private*, pg. 2335
MPM S.R.L.—See Koch Industries, Inc.; *U.S. Private*, pg. 2335
OPTICAL CABLE CORP. - ASHEVILLE—See Optical Cable Corporation; *U.S. Public*, pg. 1609
PANCON CONNECTORS—See Milestone Partners Ltd.; *U.S. Private*, pg. 2729
PANDUIT AUST. PTY. LTD.—See Panduit Corp.; *U.S. Private*, pg. 3086
PANDUIT CANADA CORP.—See Panduit Corp.; *U.S. Private*, pg. 3085
PANDUIT CORP. JAPAN BRANCH—See Panduit Corp.; *U.S. Private*, pg. 3086
PANDUIT EUROPE LTD.—See Panduit Corp.; *U.S. Private*, pg. 3085
PANDUIT EUROPE LTD.—See Panduit Corp.; *U.S. Private*, pg. 3085
PANDUIT GMBH—See Panduit Corp.; *U.S. Private*, pg. 3086
PANDUIT HONG KONG—See Panduit Corp.; *U.S. Private*, pg. 3086
PANDUIT KOREA LTD.—See Panduit Corp.; *U.S. Private*, pg. 3086
PANDUIT LIMITED—See Panduit Corp.; *U.S. Private*, pg. 3085
PANDUIT MEXICO S. EN N.C.—See Panduit Corp.; *U.S. Private*, pg. 3086
PANDUIT NEDERLAND—See Panduit Corp.; *U.S. Private*, pg. 3086
PANDUIT SINGAPORE PTE. LTD.—See Panduit Corp.; *U.S. Private*, pg. 3086
PARKER HANNIFIN FLUID CONNECTORS & SEAL GROUP—See Parker Hannifin Corporation; *U.S. Public*, pg. 1649
PLP PRODUTOS PARA LINHAS PROFORMADOS LTDA.—See Preformed Line Products Company; *U.S. Public*, pg. 1714
POLARIS SALES, CO., INC.—See Odyssey Investment Partners, LLC; *U.S. Private*, pg. 2995
POWERMITE AFRICA (PTY) LTD. - AMPCO DIVISION—See Hudaco Industries Limited; *Int'l*, pg. 3521

PREFORMED LINE PRODUCTS (SOUTH AFRICA) PTY. LTD.—See Preformed Line Products Company; *U.S. Public*, pg. 1714
QUICK CABLE CANADA LIMITED—See Tonka Bay Equity Partners LLC; *U.S. Private*, pg. 4185
QUICK CABLE CORPORATION—See Tonka Bay Equity Partners LLC; *U.S. Private*, pg. 4185
SANMINA CORPORATION—See Sanmina Corporation; *U.S. Public*, pg. 1840
SEBEREX GROUP LTD.—See TyRex Group, Ltd.; *U.S. Private*, pg. 4269
SEFCOR INC.—See Aubrey Silvey Enterprises Inc.; *U.S. Private*, pg. 385
SENSOR SYSTEMS, LLC; *U.S. Private*, pg. 3608
SEPURA PLC—See Hytera Communications Corporation Limited; *Int'l*, pg. 3555
SOLARBOS—See Gibraltar Industries, Inc.; *U.S. Public*, pg. 936
STATE TOOL & MANUFACTURING CO.; *U.S. Private*, pg. 3793
THERMON INDUSTRIES, INC.—See Thermon Group Holdings, Inc.; *U.S. Public*, pg. 2155
THOMAS & BETTS CARIBE, INC.—See ABB Ltd.; *Int'l*, pg. 52
TOWER MANUFACTURING CORPORATION; *U.S. Private*, pg. 4194
TRYSTAR, LLC; *U.S. Private*, pg. 4252
TYREX ENGINEERING GROUP—See TyRex Group, Ltd.; *U.S. Private*, pg. 4269
TYREX GROUP, LTD.; *U.S. Private*, pg. 4269
UNITED METALS COMPANY—See El Sewedy Electric Company; *Int'l*, pg. 2341
WHITNEY BLAKE CO., INC.; *U.S. Private*, pg. 4513
WIRING DEVICE-KELLEMS—See Hubbell Incorporated; *U.S. Public*, pg. 1067
W. L. GORE & ASSOCIATES (KOREA), LTD.—See W.L. Gore & Associates, Inc.; *U.S. Private*, pg. 4421

335932 — NONCURRENT-CARRYING WIRING DEVICE MANUFACTURING

AIREY-THOMPSON COMPANY INC.; *U.S. Private*, pg. 141
ALLIED TUBE & CONDUIT CORPORATION—See Clayton, Dubilier & Rice, LLC; *U.S. Private*, pg. 919
AMETEK CANADA, LLC—See AMETEK, Inc.; *U.S. Public*, pg. 116
ANAMET CANADA, INC.—See Anamet Inc.; *U.S. Private*, pg. 271
APPLETON GROUP - SOUTH MILWAUKEE—See Emerson Electric Co.; *U.S. Public*, pg. 740
APPLETON GROUP - STEPHENVILLE—See Emerson Electric Co.; *U.S. Public*, pg. 740
ARLINGTON INDUSTRIES INC.; *U.S. Private*, pg. 329
BRIDGEPORT FITTINGS, INC.—See Odyssey Investment Partners, LLC; *U.S. Private*, pg. 2995
CAPROCK ENCLOSURES, LLC—See NN, Inc.; *U.S. Public*, pg. 1531
DARE PRODUCTS INCORPORATED; *U.S. Private*, pg. 1159
DURA-LINE HOLDINGS, INC.—See Grupo Empresarial Kaluz S.A. de C.V.; *Int'l*, pg. 3127
DURHAM CO.; *Int'l*, pg. 1293
GEWISS S.P.A.—See Gewiss S.p.A.; *Int'l*, pg. 2955
GOSPELL DIGITAL TECHNOLOGY CO., LTD.; *Int'l*, pg. 3043
HUBBELL CANADA—See Hubbell Incorporated; *U.S. Public*, pg. 1066
IDI CARIBE, INC.—See Industrial Dielectrics Holdings, Inc.; *U.S. Private*, pg. 2065
ITW INSULATION SYSTEMS MALAYSIA SDN BHD—See Illinois Tool Works Inc.; *U.S. Public*, pg. 1106
KAF-TECH—See Clayton, Dubilier & Rice, LLC; *U.S. Private*, pg. 919
KILLARK ELECTRIC—See Hubbell Incorporated; *U.S. Public*, pg. 1067
LOCKWOOD INDUSTRIES INC.—See Arsenal Capital Management LP; *U.S. Private*, pg. 338
MIDWEST ELECTRIC PRODUCTS INC.—See General Electric Company; *U.S. Public*, pg. 919
MINERALLAC CO.; *U.S. Private*, pg. 2741
MONTI INCORPORATED; *U.S. Private*, pg. 2777
MULBERRY METAL PRODUCTS, INC.; *U.S. Private*, pg. 2811
O'BRIEN CORPORATION—See AMETEK, Inc.; *U.S. Public*, pg. 118
PANDUIT CORP.; *U.S. Private*, pg. 3085
PREFORMED LINE PRODUCTS CANADA LTD.—See Preformed Line Products Company; *U.S. Public*, pg. 1714
QUEEN CITY PLASTICS, INC.—See Clayton, Dubilier & Rice, LLC; *U.S. Private*, pg. 920
RACOO, INC.—See Hubbell Incorporated; *U.S. Public*, pg. 1067
SAGE ELECTRIC CORPORATION; *U.S. Private*, pg. 3526
SALISBURY ELECTRICAL SAFETY L.L.C.—See Honeywell International Inc.; *U.S. Public*, pg. 1052
SHERMAN + REILLY, INC.—See Emerson Electric Co.; *U.S. Public*, pg. 741

SHERMAN + REILLY, INC.—See Emerson Electric Co.; *U.S. Public*, pg. 750
STACK ELECTRONICS; *U.S. Private*, pg. 3774
SUPERIOR TECHNICAL CERAMICS CORP.—See Artemis Capital Partners Management Co., LLC; *U.S. Private*, pg. 341
TANGSHAN HIGH VOLTAGE PORCELAIN INSULATOR WORKS CO., LTD.—See BBMG Corporation; *Int'l*, pg. 921
UNITED FIBERGLASS OF AMERICA, INC.—See Hill & Smith PLC; *Int'l*, pg. 3392
THE WIEGMANN COMPANY—See Hubbell Incorporated; *U.S. Public*, pg. 1067

335991 — CARBON AND GRAPHITE PRODUCT MANUFACTURING

AERO INVENTORY (CANADA) INC—See Aero Inventory plc; *Int'l*, pg. 180
APPLIED GRAPHENE MATERIALS PLC; *Int'l*, pg. 521
ASBURY CARBONS, INC. - GRAPHITOS MEXICANOS DE ASBURY DIVISION—See Great Mill Rock LLC; *U.S. Private*, pg. 1765
ASBURY CARBONS, INC.—See Great Mill Rock LLC; *U.S. Private*, pg. 1765
ASBURY CARBONS, INC. - SOUTHWESTERN GRAPHITE DIVISION—See Great Mill Rock LLC; *U.S. Private*, pg. 1765
ASBURY GRAPHITE MILLS, INC. - ASBURY PLANT—See Great Mill Rock LLC; *U.S. Private*, pg. 1766
ASBURY GRAPHITE MILLS, INC. - KITTANNING PLANT—See Great Mill Rock LLC; *U.S. Private*, pg. 1766
ASBURY LOUISIANA, INC.—See Great Mill Rock LLC; *U.S. Private*, pg. 1766
ASBURY WILKINSON, INC. - BURLINGTON PLANT—See Great Mill Rock LLC; *U.S. Private*, pg. 1766
ATELIERS HUBERT GERKEN S.A.—See Westinghouse Air Brake Technologies Corporation; *U.S. Public*, pg. 2357
BERGEN CARBON SOLUTIONS AS; *Int'l*, pg. 979
BOGALA GRAPHITE LANKA PLC—See AMG Critical Materials N.V.; *Int'l*, pg. 425
BOOSTHEAT SAS; *Int'l*, pg. 1111
BRANWELL GRAPHITE LTD.—See AMG Critical Materials N.V.; *Int'l*, pg. 425
BRENNTAG SE; *Int'l*, pg. 1146
CABOT NORIT AMERICAS, INC.—See Cabot Corporation; *U.S. Public*, pg. 417
CABOT NORIT NEDERLAND B.V.—See Cabot Corporation; *U.S. Public*, pg. 417
CAMCO INTERNATIONAL GROUP INCORPORATED; *U.S. Private*, pg. 727
CARBEX AB—See Addtech AB; *Int'l*, pg. 132
CELESTIAL GREEN VENTURES PLC; *Int'l*, pg. 1392
CFOAM LLC—See CFOAM Limited; *Int'l*, pg. 1430
CHENGDU RONGGUANG CARBON CO., LTD.—See Fangda Carbon New Material Co., Ltd.; *Int'l*, pg. 2613
CHINA CARBON GRAPHITE GROUP, INC.; *U.S. Public*, pg. 489
CHINA GRAPHITE GROUP LIMITED; *Int'l*, pg. 1505
COMPOSITE RESOURCES, INC.; *U.S. Private*, pg. 1002
CTC GMBH—See Airbus SE; *Int'l*, pg. 242
CZ-CARBON PRODCUTS S.R.O.—See Westinghouse Air Brake Technologies Corporation; *U.S. Public*, pg. 2357
DCX SYSTEMS LIMITED; *Int'l*, pg. 1993
DECAVO LLC—See HEICO Corporation; *U.S. Public*, pg. 1019
DIRECTA PLUS PLC; *Int'l*, pg. 2130
DOWAKSA SWITZERLAND GMBH—See Aksa Akrilik Kimya Sanayii A.S.; *Int'l*, pg. 264
DOWAKSA USA LLC—See Aksa Akrilik Kimya Sanayii A.S.; *Int'l*, pg. 264
EDELGRAPHIT GMBH—See AMG Critical Materials N.V.; *Int'l*, pg. 425
ELEKTROKARBON A.S.—See HTC holding a.s.; *Int'l*, pg. 3508
ELKEM ASA-CARBON DIVISION—See China National Chemical Corporation; *Int'l*, pg. 1527
ELLWOOD ENGINEERED CASTING CO—See Ellwood Group, Inc.; *U.S. Private*, pg. 1375
ELRING KLINGER MEXICO, S.A. DE C.V.—See ElringKlinger AG; *Int'l*, pg. 2369
FANGDA CARBON NEW MATERIAL CO., LTD.; *Int'l*, pg. 2613
FIBER MATERIALS, INC.—See Edgewater Capital Partners, L.P.; *U.S. Private*, pg. 1334
FIRST GRAPHENE (UK) LTD.—See First Graphene Limited; *Int'l*, pg. 2684
FUJIAN YUANLI ACTIVE CARBON CO., LTD; *Int'l*, pg. 2820
FUJI CARBON MANUFACTURING CO.—See Alconix Corporation; *Int'l*, pg. 302
FUSHUN CARBON CO., LTD.—See Fangda Carbon New Material Co., Ltd.; *Int'l*, pg. 2613
GATAN U.K. LIMITED—See Roper Technologies, Inc.; *U.S. Public*, pg. 1811
GLOBAL LI-ION GRAPHITE CORP.; *Int'l*, pg. 2998

GOLD TIP, LLC—See Vista Outdoor Inc.; *U.S. Public*, pg. 2305
GRAFOID, INC.; *Int'l*, pg. 3050
GRAFTECH BRASIL PARTICIPACOES LTDA.—See Brookfield Corporation; *Int'l*, pg. 1187
GRAFTECH FRANCE S.N.C.—See Brookfield Corporation; *Int'l*, pg. 1187
GRAFTECH INTERNATIONAL LTD.—See Brookfield Corporation; *Int'l*, pg. 1187
GRAFTECH RUS LLC—See Brookfield Corporation; *Int'l*, pg. 1187
GRAFTECH SOUTH AFRICA (PTY) LTD.—See Brookfield Corporation; *Int'l*, pg. 1187
GRAFTECH USA LLC—See Brookfield Corporation; *Int'l*, pg. 1187
GRAPHENE CORPORATION—See Elcora Advanced Materials Corp.; *Int'l*, pg. 2346
GRAPHENE MANUFACTURING GROUP LTD.; *Int'l*, pg. 3060
GRAPHITE CORP.; *U.S. Private*, pg. 1758
GRAPHITE COVA GMBH—See Graphite India Ltd; *Int'l*, pg. 3061
GRAPHITE INDIA LTD - GLASS REINFORCED PLASTIC (GRP) PIPES AND TANKS DIVISION—See Graphite India Ltd; *Int'l*, pg. 3061
GRAPHITE INDIA LTD - IMPERVIOUS GRAPHITE EQUIPMENT DIVISION—See Graphite India Ltd; *Int'l*, pg. 3061
GRAPHITE INDIA LTD; *Int'l*, pg. 3061
GRAPHITE METALLIZING CORPORATION; *U.S. Private*, pg. 1758
GRAPHITE SALES, INC.; *U.S. Private*, pg. 1758
GRAPHIT KROPFMUHL AG—See AMG Critical Materials N.V.; *Int'l*, pg. 426
GROUPE BERKEM SA; *Int'l*, pg. 3092
HAYDALE CERAMIC TECHNOLOGIES, LLC—See Haydale Graphene Industries plc; *Int'l*, pg. 3290
HEG LIMITED; *Int'l*, pg. 3308
HELWIG CARBON PRODUCTS DE MEXICO, S. DE R.L. DE C.V.—See Helwig Carbon Products, Inc.; *U.S. Private*, pg. 1912
HELWIG CARBON PRODUCTS, INC.; *U.S. Private*, pg. 1912
HELWIG CARBON PRODUCTS OF CANADA, INC.—See Helwig Carbon Products, Inc.; *U.S. Private*, pg. 1913
HEXCEL COMPOSITES SASU—See Hexcel Corporation; *U.S. Public*, pg. 1032
HEXCEL HOLDING GMBH—See Hexcel Corporation; *U.S. Public*, pg. 1033
HEXCEL REINFORCEMENTS SASU—See Hexcel Corporation; *U.S. Public*, pg. 1033
HEXCEL REINFORCEMENTS UK LIMITED—See Hexcel Corporation; *U.S. Public*, pg. 1033
HIMADRI SPECIALTY CHEMICAL LTD.; *Int'l*, pg. 3396
HORISONT ENERGI AS; *Int'l*, pg. 3478
IBIDEN CO., LTD. - AOYANAGI PLANT—See Ibiden Co., Ltd.; *Int'l*, pg. 3575
IBIDEN CO., LTD. - KINUURA PLANT—See Ibiden Co., Ltd.; *Int'l*, pg. 3575
IBIDEN GRAPHITE CO., LTD.—See Ibiden Co., Ltd.; *Int'l*, pg. 3575
IBIDEN GRAPHITE KOREA CO., LTD.—See Ibiden Co., Ltd.; *Int'l*, pg. 3575
IMAGESAT INTERNATIONAL (ISI) LTD.; *Int'l*, pg. 3618
KBR, INC.; *U.S. Private*, pg. 2268
KYNOL EUROPA GMBH—See Gun Ei Chemical Industry Co., Ltd.; *Int'l*, pg. 3183
L.G. GRAPHITE S.R.L.—See Ibiden Co., Ltd.; *Int'l*, pg. 3576
METAULLICS SYSTEMS CO. LP - SANBORN—See Pyrotek Incorporated; *U.S. Private*, pg. 3310
METAULLICS SYSTEMS CO. LP - SOLON—See Pyrotek Incorporated; *U.S. Private*, pg. 3311
MOLL ENGINEERING GMBH—See Ensinger GmbH; *Int'l*, pg. 2448
MWI, INC.—See KBR, Inc.; *U.S. Private*, pg. 2268
PANTRAC GMBH—See Westinghouse Air Brake Technologies Corporation; *U.S. Public*, pg. 2359
PARK AEROSPACE TECHNOLOGIES ASIA PTE. LTD.—See Park Aerospace Corporation; *U.S. Public*, pg. 1637
POCO GRAPHITE INC.—See Entegris, Inc.; *U.S. Public*, pg. 777
POWERPLAN OPERATIONS ANZ PTY. LTD.—See Roper Technologies, Inc.; *U.S. Public*, pg. 1812
POWERPLAN OPERATIONS LTD.—See Roper Technologies, Inc.; *U.S. Public*, pg. 1812
ROCK WEST COMPOSITES, INC.; *U.S. Private*, pg. 3465
SERACHEM CO., LTD.—See Hitachi Zosen Corporation; *Int'l*, pg. 3412
SGL AUTOMOTIVE CARBON FIBERS GMBH & CO. KG—See Bayerische Motoren Werke Aktiengesellschaft; *Int'l*, pg. 913
SHANGHAI GRAFTECH TRADING CO., LTD.—See Brookfield Corporation; *Int'l*, pg. 1187
S&P POLSKA SP. Z.O.O.—See Simpson Manufacturing Company, Inc.; *U.S. Public*, pg. 1883
S&P REINFORCEMENT FRANCE—See Simpson Manufacturing Company, Inc.; *U.S. Public*, pg. 1883
S&P REINFORCEMENT SPAIN, S.L.—See Simpson Manufacturing Company, Inc.; *U.S. Public*, pg. 1883
TAKUMI PRECISION CO., LTD.—See Hurco Companies, Inc.; *U.S. Public*, pg. 1076
ULANQAB DARSEN GRAPHITE NEW MATERIALS CO., LTD.—See Anhui Tatfook Technology Co., Ltd; *Int'l*, pg. 469
WATER STAR, INC.—See Tennant Company; *U.S. Public*, pg. 2016
WENGLON SP. Z O.O.—See Ensinger GmbH; *Int'l*, pg. 2448
XG SCIENCES, INC.; *U.S. Private*, pg. 4581

335999 — ALL OTHER MISCELLANEOUS ELECTRICAL EQUIPMENT AND COMPONENT MANUFACTURING

3M HEALTHCARE GERMANY GMBH—See 3M Company; *U.S. Public*, pg. 6
3SIXTY GROUP LLC; *U.S. Private*, pg. 14
3W POWER S.P.A.—See 3W Power S.A.; *Int'l*, pg. 10
A&A ELECTRICAL DISTRIBUTORS LTD.—See Dewhurst Group plc; *Int'l*, pg. 2091
AAPICO FORGING PUBLIC CO., LTD.—See AAPICO Hitech plc; *Int'l*, pg. 37
ABB A/S—See ABB Ltd.; *Int'l*, pg. 49
ABB AUTOMATION PRODUCTS GMBH—See ABB Ltd.; *Int'l*, pg. 50
ABB AVANGARD AD—See ABB Ltd.; *Int'l*, pg. 50
ABB BAILEY JAPAN LIMITED—See ABB Ltd.; *Int'l*, pg. 52
ABB BEIJING DRIVE SYSTEMS CO. LTD.—See ABB Ltd.; *Int'l*, pg. 49
ABB BUSINESS SERVICES SP. Z O.O.—See ABB Ltd.; *Int'l*, pg. 50
ABB (CHINA) INVESTMENT LIMITED—See ABB Ltd.; *Int'l*, pg. 49
ABB ELEKTRIK SANAYI A.S.—See ABB Ltd.; *Int'l*, pg. 51
ABB ELETRIFICACAO LTDA.—See ABB Ltd.; *Int'l*, pg. 50
ABB FRANCE SAS—See ABB Ltd.; *Int'l*, pg. 51
ABB INC.—See ABB Ltd.; *Int'l*, pg. 51
ABB INDUSTRIAL SOLUTIONS (BIELSKO-BIALA) SP. Z O.O.—See ABB Ltd.; *Int'l*, pg. 52
ABB INDUSTRIAL SOLUTIONS (KLODZKO) SP.Z O.O.—See ABB Ltd.; *Int'l*, pg. 52
ABB LV INSTALLATION MATERIALS CO. LTD.—See ABB Ltd.; *Int'l*, pg. 52
ABB MEXICO S.A. DE C.V—See ABB Ltd.; *Int'l*, pg. 53
ABB SCHWEIZ AG—See ABB Ltd.; *Int'l*, pg. 54
ABB STOTZ-KONTAKT GMBH—See ABB Ltd.; *Int'l*, pg. 50
ABB SWITZERLAND LTD - HIGH VOLTAGE PRODUCTS—See ABB Ltd.; *Int'l*, pg. 54
ABB SWITZERLAND LTD - MINERALS & PRINTING—See ABB Ltd.; *Int'l*, pg. 54
ABB TURBO SYSTEMS (HONG KONG) LIMITED—See ABB Ltd.; *Int'l*, pg. 49
ABDULLA FOUAD IMPALLOY LTD. CO.—See Abdulla Fouad Holding Co.; *Int'l*, pg. 58
ABLEREX ELECTRONICS CO., LTD.; *Int'l*, pg. 63
ABLESTIK MALAYSIA—See Henkel AG & Co. KGaA; *Int'l*, pg. 3353
AB PRECISION (POOLE) LIMITED—See HWH Investments Limited; *Int'l*, pg. 3543
ACBEL ELECTRONIC (DONG GUAN) CO., LTD.—See AcBel Polytech Inc.; *Int'l*, pg. 78
ACBEL POLYTECH JAPAN INC.—See AcBel Polytech Inc.; *Int'l*, pg. 78
ACBEL POLYTECH (UK) CO. LTD.—See AcBel Polytech Inc.; *Int'l*, pg. 78
AC&C COMPANIES, INC.—See Brance Krachy Company, Inc.; *U.S. Private*, pg. 635
ACCOTEST TECHNOLOGY (MALAYSIA) SDN. BHD.—See Beijing Huafeng Test & Control Technology Co., Ltd.; *Int'l*, pg. 952
ACCSYS TECHNOLOGY, INC.—See Hitachi, Ltd.; *Int'l*, pg. 3413
ACTA S.P.A.; *Int'l*, pg. 117
ACTEL ELECTRONIC (DONG GUAN) CO., LTD.—See AcBel Polytech Inc.; *Int'l*, pg. 78
ACTIA S.A.—See Actia Group SA; *Int'l*, pg. 118
ACTOM (PTY) LTD.; *Int'l*, pg. 120
ACUMENTRICS CORPORATION; *U.S. Private*, pg. 71
ADCAPITAL AG; *Int'l*, pg. 126
ADDTECH AB; *Int'l*, pg. 131
ADI-GARDINER LIMITED—See Honeywell International Inc.; *U.S. Public*, pg. 1046
ADIGO DRIVES AB—See Addtech AB; *Int'l*, pg. 131
ADTEC PLASMA TECHNOLOGY CO., LTD.; *Int'l*, pg. 154
ADVANCED PNEUMATICS CO., INC.—See Hartfiel Automation; *U.S. Private*, pg. 1873
ADVANCED PROTECTION TECHNOLOGIES, INC.; *U.S. Private*, pg. 92
ADVANEX (CHANGZHOU) INC.—See Advanex Inc.; *Int'l*, pg. 163
ADVANEX CZECH REPUBLIC S.R.O.—See Advanex Inc.; *Int'l*, pg. 163
ADVANEX (DALIAN) INC.—See Advanex Inc.; *Int'l*, pg. 163
ADVANEX DE MEXICO S. DE R.L. DE C.V.—See Advanex Inc.; *Int'l*, pg. 163
ADVANEX DEUTSCHLAND GMBH—See Advanex Inc.; *Int'l*, pg. 163
ADVANEX (DONGGUAN) INC.—See Advanex Inc.; *Int'l*, pg. 163
ADVANEX (INDIA) PRIVATE LIMITED—See Advanex Inc.; *Int'l*, pg. 163
ADVANEX (SINGAPORE) PTE. LTD.—See Advanex Inc.; *Int'l*, pg. 163
ADVANEX (VIETNAM) LTD.—See Advanex Inc.; *Int'l*, pg. 163
ADVANTEST TAIWAN, INC.—See Advantest Corporation; *Int'l*, pg. 166
AEC INTERNATIONAL S.R.L.—See Allis Electric Co., Ltd.; *Int'l*, pg. 359
AEGIS ENERGY SERVICES, LLC—See Electricite de France S.A.; *Int'l*, pg. 2350
AEGIS POWER SYSTEMS, INC.; *U.S. Private*, pg. 116
AEG POWER SOLUTIONS ARAM. KFT—See 3W Power S.A.; *Int'l*, pg. 10
AEG POWER SOLUTIONS CO.—See 3W Power S.A.; *Int'l*, pg. 10
AEG POWER SOLUTIONS MIDDLE EAST—See 3W Power S.A.; *Int'l*, pg. 10
AEG POWER SOLUTIONS (RUSSIA) LLC—See 3W Power S.A.; *Int'l*, pg. 10
AERO DESIGN, INC.—See HEICO Corporation; *U.S. Public*, pg. 1019
AEROVOX CORP.—See Buckingham Capital, LLC; *U.S. Private*, pg. 677
AFFILIATED DISTRIBUTORS INC.; *U.S. Private*, pg. 121
AFTERMARKET CONTROLS CORPORATION—See Superior Capital Partners LLC; *U.S. Private*, pg. 3876
AGVA SINGAPORE PTE LTD—See AGVA Corporation Limited; *Int'l*, pg. 222
AICHI EUROPE GMBH—See Aichi Steel Corporation; *Int'l*, pg. 230
AICHI MAGFINE CZECH S.R.O—See Aichi Steel Corporation; *Int'l*, pg. 230
AI HOLDINGS CORP.; *Int'l*, pg. 227
AIRTOUCH SOLAR LTD; *Int'l*, pg. 249
AISIN MACHINE TECH CO. LTD.—See AISIN Corporation; *Int'l*, pg. 252
AKAI PROFESSIONAL, L.P.—See inMusic, LLC; *U.S. Private*, pg. 2080
AKWEL; *Int'l*, pg. 267
ALASKA INSTRUMENT COMPANY, LLC.—See The Aleut Corporation; *U.S. Private*, pg. 3984
ALBEO TECHNOLOGIES INC.; *U.S. Private*, pg. 152
ALEEES AU PTY. LTD.—See Advanced Lithium Electrochemistry (KY) Co., Ltd.; *Int'l*, pg. 160
ALEEES EU SARL—See Advanced Lithium Electrochemistry (KY) Co., Ltd.; *Int'l*, pg. 160
ALEEES UK, LTD.—See Advanced Lithium Electrochemistry (KY) Co., Ltd.; *Int'l*, pg. 160
ALENT JAPAN COMPANY—See Element Solutions Inc.; *U.S. Public*, pg. 726
ALFEN ELKAMO OY AB—See Alfen N.V.; *Int'l*, pg. 315
ALLANSON INTERNATIONAL INC.; *Int'l*, pg. 333
ALLIED MOULDED ENCLOSURE PRODUCTS (INDIA) PVT LTD.—See Allied Moulded Products Inc.; *U.S. Private*, pg. 187
ALLIED MOULDED PRODUCTS INC.; *U.S. Private*, pg. 187
AL-OMRAN INDUSTRIAL TRADING CO.; *Int'l*, pg. 287
ALPHANAM JOINT STOCK COMPANY; *Int'l*, pg. 370
ALPHA TECHNOLOGIES GMBH—See Roper Technologies, Inc.; *U.S. Public*, pg. 1810
ALPHA TECHNOLOGIES S.A.—See EnerSys; *U.S. Public*, pg. 767
ALPS GREEN DEVICES CO., LTD.—See Alps Alpine Co., Ltd.; *Int'l*, pg. 375
ALSTOM FERROVIARIA S.P.A. - MODUGNO—See Alstom S.A.; *Int'l*, pg. 381
ALTUS SISTEMAS DE AUTOMACAO S.A.; *Int'l*, pg. 399
ALUAR ALUMINIO ARGENTINO; *Int'l*, pg. 400
ALUMIFUEL POWER INTERNATIONAL, INC.—See ALUMIFUEL POWER CORPORATION; *U.S. Public*, pg. 89
AMARA RAJA ENERGY & MOBILITY LIMITED; *Int'l*, pg. 411
AMBIENTE 2000 SRL—See Falck S.p.A.; *Int'l*, pg. 2610
AMERICAN AVIONIC TECHNOLOGIES CORPORATION—See RTX Corporation; *U.S. Public*, pg. 1822
AMERICAN RADIONIC CO. INC.—See Vladmir, Ltd.; *U.S. Private*, pg. 4407
AMETEK CTS EUROPE GMBH—See AMETEK, Inc.; *U.S. Public*, pg. 116
AMETEK SOLID STATE CONTROLS—See AMETEK, Inc.; *U.S. Public*, pg. 118
AMPHENOL EEC, INC.—See Amphenol Corporation; *U.S. Public*, pg. 120
AMTEL SECURITY SYSTEMS, INC.; *U.S. Private*, pg. 268
ANALYT DE CENTROAMERICA SA—See HORIBA Ltd; *Int'l*, pg. 3474
ANDRITZ VIETNAM COMPANY LIMITED—See ANDRITZ AG; *Int'l*, pg. 455
ANHUI CABLE CO., LTD.—See Far East Smarter Energy Co., Ltd.; *Int'l*, pg. 2617

335999 — ALL OTHER MISCELLAN...

ANHUI TONGFENG ELECTRONICS CO., LTD.; *Int'l*, pg. 469
ANIXTER AUSTRIA GMBH—See WESCO International, Inc.; *U.S. Public*, pg. 2350
ANNAR DIAGNOSTICA IMPORT SAS—See HORIBA Ltd; *Int'l*, pg. 3474
ANTARES VISION ASIA PACIFIC LIMITED—See Antares Vision SpA; *Int'l*, pg. 482
ANTARES VISION DO BRASIL—See Antares Vision SpA; *Int'l*, pg. 482
ANTARES VISION FRANCE SAS—See Antares Vision SpA; *Int'l*, pg. 482
ANTARES VISION INDIA PRIVATE LIMITED—See Antares Vision SpA; *Int'l*, pg. 482
ANTARES VISION NORTH AMERICA LLC—See Antares Vision SpA; *Int'l*, pg. 482
ANTARES VISION RUS OOO—See Antares Vision SpA; *Int'l*, pg. 482
APLAB LIMITED; *Int'l*, pg. 515
APOLLO GESELLSCHAFT FUR MELDETECHNOLOGIE MBH—See Halma plc; *Int'l*, pg. 3230
APPLIED ENERGY SOLUTIONS; *U.S. Private*, pg. 298
APPLIED MATERIALS TAIWAN, LTD.—See Applied Materials, Inc.; *U.S. Public*, pg. 172
APS ENERGIA CAUCASUS LTD.—See APS Energia SA; *Int'l*, pg. 522
APS ENERGIA CZECH S.R.O.—See APS Energia SA; *Int'l*, pg. 522
APS ENERGIA SA; *Int'l*, pg. 522
APS ENERGIA TURK ELEKTRIK SANAYI VE TICARET LTD.—See APS Energia SA; *Int'l*, pg. 522
AQ MAGNETICA ITALY S.R.L.—See AQ Group AB; *Int'l*, pg. 526
AQ MAGNIT AD—See AQ Group AB; *Int'l*, pg. 526
AQ TRAFO AB—See AQ Group AB; *Int'l*, pg. 526
AQUION ENERGY LLC—See bluesky.energy Gmbh; *Int'l*, pg. 1074
ARAB ELECTRICAL INDUSTRIES; *Int'l*, pg. 530
ARBOR-CROWLEY, LLC—See AZZ, Inc.; *U.S. Public*, pg. 259
ARCOS INDUSTRIES LLC; *U.S. Private*, pg. 315
ARI. BATTERJEE & BROS COMPANY—See HORIBA Ltd; *Int'l*, pg. 3475
ARPA INDUSTRIALE S.P.A.—See Averbuch Formica Center Ltd.; *Int'l*, pg. 739
ARTECH POWER & TRADING LTD.; *Int'l*, pg. 581
ASAHI DENSHI CO., LTD.—See Hokuriku Electric Industry Co., Ltd.; *Int'l*, pg. 3444
ASCLEPION LASER TECHNOLOGIES GMBH—See El.En. S.p.A.; *Int'l*, pg. 2341
ASEA BROWN BOVERI S.A.—See ABB Ltd.; *Int'l*, pg. 54
AS ENERGOFIRMA JAUDA; *Int'l*, pg. 590
ASIAN INSULATORS PUBLIC COMPANY LIMITED; *Int'l*, pg. 618
ASSA ABLOY (ZHONGSHAN) SECURITY TECHNOLOGY COMPANY LIMITED—See ASSA ABLOY AB; *Int'l*, pg. 633
A STAR ELECTRIC COMPANY; *U.S. Private*, pg. 19
ASTRODYNE CORPORATION—See Tinicum Enterprises, Inc.; *U.S. Private*, pg. 4173
ATECH OEM, INC.; *Int'l*, pg. 667
ATI AIRTEST TECHNOLOGIES INC.; *Int'l*, pg. 670
AT INDIA AUTO PARTS PVT. LTD.—See AISIN Corporation; *Int'l*, pg. 253
ATLAS COPCO ARGENTINA S.A.C.I.—See Atlas Copco AB; *Int'l*, pg. 677
ATLAS COPCO BALTIC SIA—See Atlas Copco AB; *Int'l*, pg. 677
ATLAS COPCO (CHINA) INVESTMENT CO., LTD.—See Atlas Copco AB; *Int'l*, pg. 677
ATLAS COPCO FINANCE DAC—See Atlas Copco AB; *Int'l*, pg. 678
ATLAS COPCO INDUSTRIAL TECHNIQUE AB—See Atlas Copco AB; *Int'l*, pg. 679
ATLAS COPCO IRAQ LLC—See Atlas Copco AB; *Int'l*, pg. 679
ATLAS COPCO SERVICES MIDDLE EAST OMC—See Atlas Copco AB; *Int'l*, pg. 680
ATLAS COPCO SERVICES MIDDLE EAST SPC—See Atlas Copco AB; *Int'l*, pg. 680
ATS AUTOMATION ASIA (TIANJIN) CO., LTD.—See ATS Corporation; *Int'l*, pg. 695
ATTABOX INDUSTRIAL ENCLOSURES—See Robroy Industries Inc.; *U.S. Private*, pg. 3463
AUSTRALIAN LIFT COMPONENTS PTY. LTD.—See Dewhurst Group plc; *Int'l*, pg. 2091
AUTHID.AI; *U.S. Public*, pg. 228
AUTOFEED CORPORATION; *Int'l*, pg. 726
AVALAN WIRELESS SYSTEMS, INC.—See Dover Corporation; *U.S. Public*, pg. 678
AV BRECONRIDGE LIMITED—See Sanmina Corporation; *U.S. Public*, pg. 1840
AVIC JONHON OPTRONIC TECHNOLOGY CO., LTD.—See Aviation Industry Corporation of China; *Int'l*, pg. 741
AVIVA INDUSTRIES LIMITED; *Int'l*, pg. 745
AXIS ELECTRONICS LIMITED—See Cicor Technologies Ltd.; *Int'l*, pg. 1603

AZZ, INC.; *U.S. Public*, pg. 258
AZZ TRADING (SHANGHAI) CO., LTD—See AZZ, Inc.; *U.S. Public*, pg. 259
BABCOCK BORSIG STEINMULLER CZ S.R.O.—See Bilfinger SE; *Int'l*, pg. 1027
BAFANG ELECTRIC SUZHOU CO., LTD.; *Int'l*, pg. 799
BAJAJ ELECTRICALS LIMITED—See Bajaj Auto Ltd.; *Int'l*, pg. 804
BAKHTAR CABLE; *Int'l*, pg. 805
BALLARD POWER SYSTEMS, INC.; *Int'l*, pg. 809
BARCO COLOMBIA SAS—See Barco N.V.; *Int'l*, pg. 863
BARCO FREDRIKSTAD AS—See Barco N.V.; *Int'l*, pg. 863
BARCO SERVICES OOO—See Barco N.V.; *Int'l*, pg. 863
BASLER ELECTRIC (SUZHOU) CO., LTD—See Basler Electric Company; *U.S. Public*, pg. 485
BASSI S.R.L.—See BorgWarner Inc.; *U.S. Public*, pg. 369
BAUBLYS LASER GMBH—See Han's Laser Technology Industry Group Co., Ltd.; *Int'l*, pg. 3240
BAUER FOUNDATIONS AUSTRALIA PTY LTD.—See BAUER Aktiengesellschaft; *Int'l*, pg. 891
BAY TEK GAMES, INC.; *U.S. Public*, pg. 495
BEAR ELECTRIC APPLIANCE CO., LTD.; *Int'l*, pg. 933
BEGHELLI INC.—See Beghelli S.p.A.; *Int'l*, pg. 941
BEIJING BEETCH INC.; *Int'l*, pg. 946
BEIJING DINGHAN TECHNOLOGY GROUP CO., LTD.; *Int'l*, pg. 948
BEIJING DYNAMIC POWER CO., LTD.; *Int'l*, pg. 948
BEIJING HONGGAO CREATIVE CONSTRUCTION DESIGN CO., LTD.; *Int'l*, pg. 951
BEIJING TONGFANG MICROELECTRONICS CO., LTD.—See Guangdong Leadyo IC Testing Co., Ltd.; *Int'l*, pg. 3158
BELDEN HIRSCHMANN SOLUTIONS (SHANGHAI) COMPANY LIMITED—See Belden, Inc.; *U.S. Public*, pg. 293
BELDEN POLIRON INDUSTRIA E COMERCIO DE CABOS ESPECIAIS LTDA.—See Belden, Inc.; *U.S. Public*, pg. 294
BELDEN SOLUTIONS ASIA LIMITED—See Belden, Inc.; *U.S. Public*, pg. 294
BEL POWER INC.—See Bel Fuse Inc.; *U.S. Public*, pg. 292
BEL POWER SOLUTIONS GMBH—See Bel Fuse Inc.; *U.S. Public*, pg. 293
BEL POWER SOLUTIONS IRELAND LIMITED—See Bel Fuse Inc.; *U.S. Public*, pg. 293
BEL POWER SOLUTIONS S.R.O.—See Bel Fuse Inc.; *U.S. Public*, pg. 293
BENCHMARK ELECTRONICS NETHERLANDS HOLDING B.V.—See Benchmark Electronics, Inc.; *U.S. Public*, pg. 295
BEOGRADMONTAZA A.D.; *Int'l*, pg. 978
BESAM AUTOMATIC DOOR SYSTEMS TRADING CO. LTD.—See ASSA ABLOY AB; *Int'l*, pg. 634
BESAM ENTRANCE SOLUTIONS INC—See ASSA ABLOY AB; *Int'l*, pg. 634
BEST & CROMPTON ENGG. LTD.; *Int'l*, pg. 998
BEVING ELEKTRONIK AB—See Addtech AB; *Int'l*, pg. 132
BHARAT BIJLEE LTD - DRIVES DIVISION—See Bharat Bijlee Ltd; *Int'l*, pg. 1010
BHARAT FIH LIMITED—See Hon Hai Precision Industry Co., Ltd.; *Int'l*, pg. 3456
BIG INNOVATION COMPANY LTD.—See Hon Hai Precision Industry Co., Ltd.; *Int'l*, pg. 3456
BILLION WATTS TECHNOLOGIES CO., LTD.—See Billion Electric Co., Ltd.; *Int'l*, pg. 1031
BIOSIGMA C.A.—See HORIBA Ltd; *Int'l*, pg. 3475
BLADERANGER LTD.; *Int'l*, pg. 1062
BLUE OAK ENERGY, INC.—See TRC Companies, Inc.; *U.S. Private*, pg. 4215
BLUESTAR SECUTECH INC.; *Int'l*, pg. 1074
BODE ENERGY EQUIPMENT CO., LTD.; *Int'l*, pg. 1097
BOE TECHNOLOGY GROUP CO., LTD.; *Int'l*, pg. 1099
BOMBARDIER TRANSPORTATION PORTUGAL, S.A.—See Alstom S.A.; *Int'l*, pg. 383
BOSE LTD.—See Bose Corporation; *U.S. Private*, pg. 620
BRAIME ELEVATOR COMPONENTS LIMITED—See Braime Group Plc; *Int'l*, pg. 1136
BRANSON ULTRASONICS CORPORATION—See Emerson Electric Co.; *U.S. Public*, pg. 750
BRECKNELL WILLIS & CO., LIMITED—See Westinghouse Air Brake Technologies Corporation; *U.S. Public*, pg. 2358
BRECKNELL WILLIS (TAIWAN) CO., LIMITED—See Westinghouse Air Brake Technologies Corporation; *U.S. Public*, pg. 2358
BSL ELECTRONICS & TECHNOLOGIES SDN. BHD.—See BSL Corporation Berhad; *Int'l*, pg. 1202
BURKHALTER HOLDING AG; *Int'l*, pg. 1224
BURNDY DO BRASIL INDUSTRIA, COMERCIO, IMPORTACAO E EXPORTACAO DE CONECTORES LTDA.—See Hubbell Incorporated; *U.S. Public*, pg. 1066
BURNDY PRODUCTS MEXICO, S.A. DE C.V.—See Hubbell Incorporated; *U.S. Public*, pg. 1066
BUSCH-JAEGER ELEKTRO GMBH—See ABB Ltd.; *Int'l*, pg. 50
CABLECRAFT LIMITED—See Diploma PLC; *Int'l*, pg. 2128
THE CALVERT COMPANY—See AZZ, Inc.; *U.S. Public*, pg. 260

CORPORATE AFFILIATIONS

CAPXON INTERNATIONAL ELECTRONIC CO LTD; *Int'l*, pg. 1318
CARPEVIGO HOLDING AG; *Int'l*, pg. 1343
CASS PAK INDUSTRIES LIMITED; *Int'l*, pg. 1354
CASTLES TECHNOLOGY CO., LTD; *Int'l*, pg. 1357
CATCHER TECHNOLOGY CO., LTD.; *Int'l*, pg. 1359
CC HYDROSONICS LTD.—See Crest Group Inc.; *U.S. Private*, pg. 1095
CCT MARKETING LIMITED—See CCT Fortis Holdings Limited; *Int'l*, pg. 1369
CCX CORPORATION; *U.S. Private*, pg. 801
C&D TECHNOLOGIES, INC.—See KPS Capital Partners, LP; *U.S. Private*, pg. 2347
CELLTECH ABATEL AB—See Addtech AB; *Int'l*, pg. 132
CELLTECH AS—See Addtech AB; *Int'l*, pg. 132
C-ENERGY BOHEMIA SRO—See Carpaterra Capital Partners sro; *Int'l*, pg. 1343
CENTRALION INDUSTRIAL INC.—See Eaton Corporation plc; *Int'l*, pg. 2277
CERES POWER LIMITED—See Ceres Power Holdings plc; *Int'l*, pg. 1422
THE CHAMBERLAIN GROUP, LLC—See The Duchossois Group, Inc.; *U.S. Private*, pg. 4023
CHANGGAO ELECTRIC GROUP CO., LTD.; *Int'l*, pg. 1443
CHANGZHOU KAIDI ELECTRICAL, INC.; *Int'l*, pg. 1445
CHASE CORPORATION—See KKR & Co. Inc.; *U.S. Public*, pg. 1242
CHECON, LLC—See Trent Capital Partners, LLC; *U.S. Private*, pg. 4218
CHEM ENERGY SA (PTY) LTD.—See Chung-Hsin Electric & Machinery Manufacturing Corp.; *Int'l*, pg. 1597
CHENGDU TANGYUAN ELECTRIC CO., LTD.; *Int'l*, pg. 1469
CHENGDU XGIMI TECHNOLOGY CO., LTD.; *Int'l*, pg. 1469
CHERRY ELECTRONICS (HONG KONG) CO., LTD.—See Cherry SE; *Int'l*, pg. 1472
CHERRY TECHNOLOGIES, INC.—See Peterson Farms, Inc.; *U.S. Private*, pg. 3160
CHINA LEADSHINE TECHNOLOGY CO., LTD.; *Int'l*, pg. 1514
CHINA NATIONAL AERO-TECHNOLOGY GUANGZHOU COMPANY LIMITED—See AVIC International Holdings Limited; *Int'l*, pg. 742
CHINA NATIONAL ELECTRIC APPARATUS RESEARCH INSTITUTE CO., LTD.; *Int'l*, pg. 1531
CHINA SUNERGY CO., LTD.; *Int'l*, pg. 1556
CHLORIDE BATTERIES S E ASIA PTE LIMITED—See EXIDE INDUSTRIES LIMITED; *Int'l*, pg. 2585
CHLORIDE ESPANA, S.A.U.—See Vertiv Holdings Co; *U.S. Public*, pg. 2288
CHLORIDE ITALIA—See Vertiv Holdings Co; *U.S. Public*, pg. 2288
CHLORIDE POWER SYSTEMS & SOLUTIONS LIMITED—See EXIDE INDUSTRIES LIMITED; *Int'l*, pg. 2585
CHUBU SEIKI CO., LTD.—See Chubu Electric Power Co., Inc.; *Int'l*, pg. 1593
CHUNG-HSIN ELECTRIC & MACHINERY MANUFACTURING CORP.; *Int'l*, pg. 1597
CHUNG-HSIN PRECISION MACHINERY CO., LTD.—See Chung-Hsin Electric & Machinery Manufacturing Corp.; *Int'l*, pg. 1597
CHUNGHWA PRECISION TEST TECH. CO., LTD—See Chunghwa Telecom Co., Ltd.; *Int'l*, pg. 1598
CHUO SEISAKUSHO LTD.; *Int'l*, pg. 1598
CICOR DIGITAL ELEKTRONIK GMBH—See Cicor Technologies Ltd.; *Int'l*, pg. 1603
CIMARRON ENERGY, INC.—See Turnbridge Capital, LLC; *U.S. Private*, pg. 4260
CITIZEN SYSTEMS (JIANGMEN) CO., LTD.—See Citizen Watch Co., Ltd.; *Int'l*, pg. 1624
CKD INDIA PRIVATE LIMITED—See CKD Corporation; *Int'l*, pg. 1639
CLASSIC COMPONENTS FRANCE—See Classic Components Corp.; *U.S. Private*, pg. 916
CNPV DONGYING SOLAR POWER COMPANY LIMITED,—See CNPV Solar Power S.A.; *Int'l*, pg. 1678
COGNEX MALAYSIA SDN. BHD.—See Cognex Corporation; *U.S. Public*, pg. 523
COGNEX VISION THAILAND LIMITED—See Cognex Corporation; *U.S. Public*, pg. 523
COHERENT SINGAPORE PTE LTD.—See Coherent Corp.; *U.S. Public*, pg. 527
COIN ACCEPTORS EUROPE LIMITED—See Coin Acceptors, Inc.; *U.S. Private*, pg. 964
COIN ACCEPTORS GMBH—See Coin Acceptors, Inc.; *U.S. Private*, pg. 964
COIN ACCEPTORS, INC.—See Coin Acceptors, Inc.; *U.S. Private*, pg. 964
COIN ACCEPTORS PTY LTD—See Coin Acceptors, Inc.; *U.S. Private*, pg. 964
COLEMAN JAPAN CO., LTD.—See Newell Brands Inc.; *U.S. Public*, pg. 1515
COLE-PARMER INSTRUMENT CO. LTD.—See GTCR LLC; *U.S. Private*, pg. 1804
COMPTROL INCORPORATED; *U.S. Private*, pg. 1003
COMPX WATERLOO—See Contran Corporation; *U.S. Private*, pg. 1033

N.A.I.C.S. INDEX

335999 — ALL OTHER MISCELLAN...

COMTECH EF DATA PTE. LTD.—See Comtech Telecommunications Corp.; *U.S. Public*, pg. 562
CONDUCTIX INC.—See CVC Capital Partners SICAV-FIS S.A.; *Int'l*, pg. 1887
CONDUCTIX-WAMPFLER PTY LTD—See CVC Capital Partners SICAV-FIS S.A.; *Int'l*, pg. 1887
CONECT BUSINESS PARK SA; *Int'l*, pg. 1767
CONNECTOR CASTINGS INC.; *U.S. Private*, pg. 1016
CONTINENTAL CONTROLS LIMITED; *Int'l*, pg. 1783
CONTINUUM ELECTRO-OPTICS, INC.—See Amplitude Technologies SA; *Int'l*, pg. 436
CONTROL LASER CORPORATION—See Han's Laser Technology Industry Group Co., Ltd.; *Int'l*, pg. 3240
CONTROLLED POWER COMPANY; *U.S. Private*, pg. 1034
CONTROL MICRO SYSTEMS, INC.—See Laser Photonics Corporation; *U.S. Public*, pg. 1294
CONVERGENCE PARTNERS, INC.; *U.S. Private*, pg. 1035
COOPER B-LINE, INC.—See Eaton Corporation plc; *Int'l*, pg. 2277
COOPER CROUSE-HINDS GMBH—See Eaton Corporation plc; *Int'l*, pg. 2277
COOPER CROUSE-HINDS, LLC—See Eaton Corporation plc; *Int'l*, pg. 2277
COOPER CROUSE-HINDS MTL, INC.—See Eaton Corporation plc; *Int'l*, pg. 2278
COOPER POWER SYSTEMS, LLC - FAYETTEVILLE PLANT—See Eaton Corporation plc; *Int'l*, pg. 2278
COOPER POWER SYSTEMS, LLC - OLEAN PLANT—See Eaton Corporation plc; *Int'l*, pg. 2278
COOPER POWER SYSTEMS, LLC - PEWAUKEE PLANT—See Eaton Corporation plc; *Int'l*, pg. 2278
COOPER POWER SYSTEMS, LLC - TAOYUAN PLANT—See Eaton Corporation plc; *Int'l*, pg. 2278
COOPER SECURITE S.A.S.—See Eaton Corporation plc; *Int'l*, pg. 2279
COORSTEK, INC. - COORSTEK NEW HAMPSHIRE FACILITY—See CoorsTek, Inc.; *U.S. Private*, pg. 1043
COSEMI TECHNOLOGIES INC.—See Mobix Labs, Inc.; *U.S. Public*, pg. 1454
COSMO ELECTRONICS TECHNOLOGY (KUN SHAN)CO., LTD.—See Cosmo Electronics Corporation; *Int'l*, pg. 1811
CREATIVE & INNOVATIVE SYSTEM CO., LTD.—See CIS Co., Ltd.; *Int'l*, pg. 1618
CREST ULTRASONICS SHANGHAI LTD.—See Crest Group Inc.; *U.S. Private*, pg. 1095
CREST ULTRASONICS (THAILAND) LTD.—See Crest Group Inc.; *U.S. Private*, pg. 1095
CROMPTON CONTROLS LTD.; *Int'l*, pg. 1853
CROWN ADVANCED MATERIAL CO., LTD.; *Int'l*, pg. 1857
CUBIC DEFENCE UK LTD—See Elliott Management Corporation; *U.S. Public*, pg. 1367
CUBIC DEFENCE UK LTD—See Veritas Capital Fund Management, LLC; *U.S. Private*, pg. 4361
CUMSA CORP.—See Avis Industrial Corporation; *U.S. Private*, pg. 407
CURRENT POWER SOLUTIONS, INC.—See Patterson-UTI Energy, Inc.; *U.S. Public*, pg. 1654
CUSITECH, LLC; *U.S. Private*, pg. 1127
CYBERPOWER SYSTEMS GMBH—See CyberPower Systems, Inc.; *Int'l*, pg. 1893
CYBERPOWER SYSTEMS, INC.; *Int'l*, pg. 1893
CYBER POWER SYSTEMS S.A. DE C.V.—See CyberPower Systems, Inc.; *Int'l*, pg. 1893
CYBERPOWER SYSTEMS (USA), INC.—See CyberPower Systems, Inc.; *Int'l*, pg. 1893
CYG CONSULTING AND ENGINEERING CO., LTD.—See ChangYuan Group Ltd.; *Int'l*, pg. 1444
CYG CONTRON CO., LTD.—See ChangYuan Group Ltd.; *Int'l*, pg. 1444
CYG ELECTRIC CO., LTD.—See ChangYuan Group Ltd.; *Int'l*, pg. 1444
CYG FLYWHEEL CO., LTD.—See ChangYuan Group Ltd.; *Int'l*, pg. 1444
DAITO ELECTRON CO., LTD. - MACHIDA FACTORY—See Daitron Co., Ltd.; *Int'l*, pg. 1944
DALIAN HITACHI MACHINERY & EQUIPMENT CO. LTD.—See Hitachi, Ltd.; *Int'l*, pg. 3412
DANEN TECHNOLOGY CORPORATION; *Int'l*, pg. 1959
DATALOGIC S.P.A.; *Int'l*, pg. 1978
DB CONTROL CORP.—See HEICO Corporation; *U.S. Public*, pg. 1021
DEBFLEX SA; *Int'l*, pg. 1998
DEEPWATER CORROSION SERVICES, INC.; *U.S. Private*, pg. 1190
DEEPWATER EU LIMITED—See Deepwater Corrosion Services, Inc.; *U.S. Private*, pg. 1190
DELFINGEN US-NEW YORK, INC.—See Delfingen Industry, S.A.; *Int'l*, pg. 2012
DELTA ELECTRONICS (DONGGUAN) CO., LTD.—See Delta Electronics, Inc.; *Int'l*, pg. 2016
DELTA ELECTRONICS (JIANGSU) LTD.—See Delta Electronics, Inc.; *Int'l*, pg. 2017
DELTA ELECTRONICS (NETHERLANDS) B.V.—See Delta Electronics, Inc.; *Int'l*, pg. 2017
DELTA ELECTRONICS (POLAND) SP. Z.O.O.—See Delta Electronics, Inc.; *Int'l*, pg. 2016
DELTA ELECTRONICS POWER (DONGGUAN) CO., LTD.—See Delta Electronics, Inc.; *Int'l*, pg. 2017
DELTA ELECTRONICS (SHANGHAI) CO., LTD.—See Delta Electronics, Inc.; *Int'l*, pg. 2016
DELTA ELECTRONICS SOLUTIONS (SPAIN) SLU—See Delta Electronics, Inc.; *Int'l*, pg. 2016
DELTA ENERGY SYSTEMS (ITALY) S.R.L.—See Delta Electronics, Inc.; *Int'l*, pg. 2017
DELTA GREENTECH (BRASIL) S.A.—See Delta Electronics, Inc.; *Int'l*, pg. 2017
DELTA PLUS GROUP; *Int'l*, pg. 2019
DELTA PLUS MAGYARORSZAG KFT—See Delta Plus Group; *Int'l*, pg. 2020
DELTA PLUS MIDDLE EAST FZE—See Delta Plus Group; *Int'l*, pg. 2020
DELTA PLUS PERU SAC—See Delta Plus Group; *Int'l*, pg. 2020
DELTA PLUS ROMANIA SRL—See Delta Plus Group; *Int'l*, pg. 2020
DELTA-THERM CORPORATION—See Groupe Ouellet Canada Inc.; *Int'l*, pg. 3109
DELTON CABLES LIMITED - DHARUHERA WORKS—See Delton Cables Limited; *Int'l*, pg. 2022
DELTON CABLES LIMITED - FARIDABAD WORKS—See Delton Cables Limited; *Int'l*, pg. 2022
DELTON CABLES LIMITED - NEW DELHI WORKS—See Delton Cables Limited; *Int'l*, pg. 2022
DEMCO POWER CO., LTD.—See Demco Public Company Limited; *Int'l*, pg. 2025
DEMESNE ELECTRICAL SALES LIMITED; *Int'l*, pg. 2025
DEMMEL AG; *Int'l*, pg. 2025
DENSO WISETECH CORPORATION—See Denso Corporation; *Int'l*, pg. 2032
DESCO INDUSTRIES INC.; *U.S. Private*, pg. 1211
DESERT STATES ELECTRICAL SALES—See McGee Co.; *U.S. Private*, pg. 2634
DESIGN SECURITY INC.—See Detex Corporation; *U.S. Private*, pg. 1216
DETROIT ELECTRIC CO., LTD.—See Far East Smarter Energy Co., Ltd.; *Int'l*, pg. 2617
DEWHURST GROUP PLC; *Int'l*, pg. 2091
DEWHURST (HONG KONG) LTD—See Dewhurst Group plc; *Int'l*, pg. 2091
DEWHURST (HUNGARY) KFT—See Dewhurst Group plc; *Int'l*, pg. 2091
DEWHURST UK MANUFACTURING LTD—See Dewhurst Group plc; *Int'l*, pg. 2091
DIANGUANG EXPLOSION-PROOF TECHNOLOGY CO., LTD.; *Int'l*, pg. 2106
DIGITAL POWER CORPORATION—See Ault Alliance, Inc.; *U.S. Public*, pg. 227
DITEC ENTREMATIC CANADA INC.—See ASSA ABLOY AB; *Int'l*, pg. 639
DKSH LAOS COMPANY LIMITED—See HORIBA Ltd.; *Int'l*, pg. 3475
DOBLE POWERTEST LIMITED—See ESCO Technologies, Inc.; *U.S. Public*, pg. 793
DONGGUAN CHAOYE PRECISION EQUIPMENT CO., LTD.—See Funeng Oriental Equipment Technology Co., Ltd.; *Int'l*, pg. 2846
DONGYANG E&P INC.; *Int'l*, pg. 2171
DPSS LASERS, INC.—See The Jordan Company, L.P.; *U.S. Private*, pg. 4060
DRAGONWAVE-X CANADA, INC.—See COMSovereign Holding Corp.; *U.S. Public*, pg. 562
DRAKE & SCULL INTERNATIONAL L.L.C—See Drake & Scull International PJSC; *Int'l*, pg. 2200
DX ANTENNA CO., LTD.—See Elecom Co., Ltd.; *Int'l*, pg. 2348
DYNAMIC MANUFACTURING SOLUTIONS, LLC—See Ultra Clean Holdings, Inc.; *U.S. Public*, pg. 2223
DYNASOUND, INC.—See AMETEK, Inc.; *U.S. Public*, pg. 119
E2IP TECHNOLOGIES; *Int'l*, pg. 2261
EAO AG; *Int'l*, pg. 2267
EAO (GUANGZHOU) LIMITED—See EAO AG; *Int'l*, pg. 2267
EAO JAPAN CO. LTD.—See EAO AG; *Int'l*, pg. 2267
EATON CORP. - ELECTRICAL SECTOR, AMERICAS—See Eaton Corporation plc; *Int'l*, pg. 2279
EATON ELECTRICAL LTD.—See Eaton Corporation plc; *Int'l*, pg. 2281
EATON ELECTRICAL, S.A.—See Eaton Corporation plc; *Int'l*, pg. 2280
EATON ELECTRIC SALES S.A.S.—See Eaton Corporation plc; *Int'l*, pg. 2281
EATON ELECTRIC SIA—See Eaton Corporation plc; *Int'l*, pg. 2280
EATON FILTRATION (SHANGHAI) CO. LTD.—See Eaton Corporation plc; *Int'l*, pg. 2280
EATON HOLEC AB—See Eaton Corporation plc; *Int'l*, pg. 2280
EATON INDUSTRIES PRIVATE LIMITED—See Eaton Corporation plc; *Int'l*, pg. 2281
EATON MEDC LIMITED—See Eaton Corporation plc; *Int'l*, pg. 2281
EATON POWER QUALITY OY—See Eaton Corporation plc; *Int'l*, pg. 2281
EB TECH CO., LTD; *Int'l*, pg. 2282
ECHO ELECTRONICS COMPANY LIMITED—See Echo International Holdings Group Limited; *Int'l*, pg. 2289
ECHO INTERNATIONAL HOLDINGS GROUP LIMITED; *Int'l*, pg. 2289
ECI SCREEN PRINT INC.—See J.N. White Associates, Inc.; *U.S. Private*, pg. 2169
ECU ELECTRONIC INDUSTRY CO., LTD.—See Anhui Sun-Create Electronics Co., Ltd.; *Int'l*, pg. 469
EDVENSWA ENTERPRISES LIMITED; *Int'l*, pg. 2316
EDWARDS GROUP LIMITED—See Atlas Copco AB; *Int'l*, pg. 682
EGING PHOTOVOLTAIC TECHNOLOGY CO., LTD.; *Int'l*, pg. 2324
EHWA TECHNOLOGIES INFORMATION CO. LTD.; *Int'l*, pg. 2328
EINHELL COLOMBIA S.A.S.—See Einhell Germany AG; *Int'l*, pg. 2333
EINHELL NORDIC APS—See Einhell Germany AG; *Int'l*, pg. 2333
EINHELL OSTERREICH GESELLSCHAFT MBH—See Einhell Germany AG; *Int'l*, pg. 2333
EINHELL PORTUGAL - COMERCIO INT., LDA.—See Einhell Germany AG; *Int'l*, pg. 2333
EINHELL SAS—See Einhell Germany AG; *Int'l*, pg. 2333
EINHELL SAS—See Einhell Germany AG; *Int'l*, pg. 2333
E.I.S. ELECTRONICS GMBH—See Littelfuse, Inc.; *U.S. Public*, pg. 1326
ELCO CONTRACTING & SERVICES (1973) LTD.—See Elco Limited; *Int'l*, pg. 2345
ELDEC ELECTRONICS LTD.—See Crane NXT, Co.; *U.S. Public*, pg. 591
ELECTRICAL INDUSTRIES COMPANY; *Int'l*, pg. 2349
ELECTRI-CORD MANUFACTURING CO.; *U.S. Private*, pg. 1352
ELECTRIC UTILITY SUPPLY CO.—See Rural Electric Supply Cooperative Inc.; *U.S. Private*, pg. 3504
ELECTROAPARATAJ S.A.; *Int'l*, pg. 2353
ELECTRO COMPOSITES (2008) ULC—See Hubbell Incorporated; *U.S. Public*, pg. 1067
ELECTRODYNAMICS INC—See L3Harris Technologies, Inc.; *U.S. Public*, pg. 1281
ELECTROFILM MFG. CO.; *U.S. Private*, pg. 1354
ELECTROLUX OUTDOOR PRODUCTS A/S—See AB Electrolux; *Int'l*, pg. 40
ELECTRO MAGNETIC MARINE EXPLORATION TECHNOLOGIES (EMMET) ZAO—See Fugro N.V.; *Int'l*, pg. 2805
ELECTROMECH TECHNOLOGIES—See TransDigm Group Incorporated; *U.S. Public*, pg. 2182
ELECTRONICS INTEGRATION TECHNOLOGY, INC.—See Technology Dynamics, Inc.; *U.S. Private*, pg. 3955
ELECTRO SCIENTIFIC INDUSTRIES JAPAN CO., LTD.—See MKS Instruments, Inc.; *U.S. Public*, pg. 1452
ELEKTROBIT TECHNOLOGIES OY—See Bittium Oyj; *Int'l*, pg. 1050
ELENTEC INDIA TECHNOLOGIES PVT. LTD. - CHARGER FACTORY—See Elentec co., Ltd.; *Int'l*, pg. 2359
ELENTEC INDIA TECHNOLOGIES PVT. LTD.—See Elentec co., Ltd.; *Int'l*, pg. 2359
ELMA HANS SCHMIDBAUER GMBH & CO. KG; *Int'l*, pg. 2367
ELMA SCHMIDBAUER SUISSE AG—See Elma Hans Schmidbauer GmbH & Co. KG; *Int'l*, pg. 2367
ELMEK ELEKTROMEKANIK SANAYI VE TICARET ANONIM SIRKETI AS—See ABB Ltd.; *Int'l*, pg. 51
ELOF HANSSON AB; *Int'l*, pg. 2368
ELPO AD; *Int'l*, pg. 2369
ELPRO INTERNATIONAL LTD.; *Int'l*, pg. 2369
ELRING ITALIA S.R.L.—See ElringKlinger AG; *Int'l*, pg. 2369
ELRINGKLINGER SWITZERLAND AG—See ElringKlinger AG; *Int'l*, pg. 2370
ELSYSTEM I PERSTORP AB—See Addtech AB; *Int'l*, pg. 133
ELTECH SOLUTIONS A/S—See Addtech AB; *Int'l*, pg. 133
ELTRAF, A.S.—See CEZ, a.s.; *Int'l*, pg. 1428
ELVEX CORPORATION—See Delta Plus Group; *Int'l*, pg. 2020
EMCO INDUSTRIES LIMITED; *Int'l*, pg. 2376
EMD TECHNOLOGIES INCORPORATED—See HEICO Corporation; *U.S. Public*, pg. 1020
EMEK USA INC.—See Emek Elektrik Endustrisi A.S.; *Int'l*, pg. 2377
EMERSON & CUMING—See Henkel AG & Co. KGaA; *Int'l*, pg. 3353
EMERSON NETWORK POWER AUSTRALIA PTY. LTD.—See Vertiv Holdings Co; *U.S. Public*, pg. 2288
EMERSON NETWORK POWER LTD.—See Vertiv Holdings Co; *U.S. Public*, pg. 2288
EMERSON NETWORK POWER (MALAYSIA) SDN. BHD.—See Vertiv Holdings Co; *U.S. Public*, pg. 2288
EMERSON S.R.L.—See Emerson Electric Co.; *U.S. Public*, pg. 745
EMERSON TECHNOLOGIES GMBH & CO. OHG—See Emerson Electric Co.; *U.S. Public*, pg. 749
ENEOS CELLTECH CO., LTD.—See ENEOS Holdings, Inc.; *Int'l*, pg. 2415
ENGEMA LIGNES—See Ackermans & van Haaren NV; *Int'l*, pg. 105

335999 — ALL OTHER MISCELLAN...

ENGINUITY COMMUNICATIONS CORPORATION; *U.S. Private*, pg. 1399
ENGLISH ROAD HOLDINGS, LLC—See Hubbell Incorporated; *U.S. Public*, pg. 1066
ENGTEK PRECISION PHILIPPINES, INC.—See Giovanni Agnelli B.V.; *Int'l*, pg. 2978
ENOL SA—See HORIBA Ltd; *Int'l*, pg. 3475
ENOVATE MEDICAL, LLC—See The Sterling Group, L.P.; *U.S. Private*, pg. 4122
ENPLAS TESCO, INC.—See ENPLAS CORPORATION; *Int'l*, pg. 2445
ERL PHASE POWER TECHNOLOGIES LTD.—See Easun Reyrolle Ltd; *Int'l*, pg. 2275
ESACONTROL SRL—See FOS S.p.A.; *Int'l*, pg. 2748
ESCO ANTRIEBSTECHNIK GMBH—See Esco Financial & Engineering Company S.A/N.V.; *Int'l*, pg. 2502
E.S. ELECTRI-CORD S. DE R.L. DE C.V.—See Electri-Cord Manufacturing Co.; *U.S. Private*, pg. 1352
ESI KOREA CO. LTD.—See MKS Instruments, Inc.; *U.S. Public*, pg. 1452
ESI TAIWAN—See MKS Instruments, Inc.; *U.S. Public*, pg. 1452
ESO NORD EST—See Emerson Electric Co.; *U.S. Public*, pg. 743
ESO NORMANDIE—See Emerson Electric Co.; *U.S. Public*, pg. 743
ESSAR LAB MATE PVT LTD—See HORIBA Ltd; *Int'l*, pg. 3475
ETA-POWER EUROPE LTD.—See Eta Electric Industry Co., Ltd.; *Int'l*, pg. 2519
ETA-USA INC.—See Eta Electric Industry Co., Ltd.; *Int'l*, pg. 2519
ETI B—See Andlinger & Company, Inc.; *U.S. Private*, pg. 278
ETI DE GMBH—See Andlinger & Company, Inc.; *U.S. Private*, pg. 278
ETI SARAJEVO D.O.O.—See Andlinger & Company, Inc.; *U.S. Private*, pg. 278
EXAKTERA LLC—See Union Park Capital; *U.S. Private*, pg. 4284
EXCELLIANCE MOS CORP.; *Int'l*, pg. 2578
EXCELSYS TECHNOLOGIES LTD.—See Advanced Energy Industries, Inc.; *U.S. Public*, pg. 47
FAKHROO INTERNATIONAL TRADING AGENCIES CO.—See Einhell Germany AG; *Int'l*, pg. 2333
FANDA SCIENTIFIC FZ-LLC—See HORIBA Ltd; *Int'l*, pg. 3475
FANUC INDIA PRIVATE LIMITED—See FANUC Corporation; *Int'l*, pg. 2615
FAR EAST CABLE CO., LTD.—See Far East Smarter Energy Co., Ltd.; *Int'l*, pg. 2617
FAR EAST MATERIAL TRADING CENTER CO., LTD.—See Far East Smarter Energy Co., Ltd.; *Int'l*, pg. 2617
FAR EAST SMARTER ENERGY CO., LTD.; *Int'l*, pg. 2617
FARGO ASSEMBLY OF MISSISSIPPI, LLC—See Cerberus Capital Management, L.P.; *U.S. Private*, pg. 838
FARGO ASSEMBLY OF PA, INC.—See Cerberus Capital Management, L.P.; *U.S. Private*, pg. 838
FARGO MFG. COMPANY, INC.—See Hubbell Incorporated; *U.S. Public*, pg. 1066
FAST FUSION LLC; *U.S. Private*, pg. 1482
FEEI CHERNG DEVELOP TECHNOLOGY CO., LTD.; *Int'l*, pg. 2632
FENIX INDUSTRIA DE ELETRONICOS LTDA.—See Hon Hai Precision Industry Co., Ltd.; *Int'l*, pg. 3456
FERROTEC-NORD CORPORATION—See Ferrotec Holdings Corporation; *Int'l*, pg. 2643
FIELEX S.A.—See Einhell Germany AG; *Int'l*, pg. 2333
FIH MEXICO INDUSTRY S.A. DE C.V.—See Hon Hai Precision Industry Co., Ltd.; *Int'l*, pg. 3456
FISHER ROSEMOUNT TEMPERATURE B.V.—See Emerson Electric Co.; *U.S. Public*, pg. 745
THE FIXTURE COMPANY—See Dewhurst Group plc; *Int'l*, pg. 2091
FLAT GLASS GROUP CO., LTD.; *Int'l*, pg. 2698
FLEX LTD.; *Int'l*, pg. 2701
FLEXTRONICS DESIGN KOREA LTD.—See Flex Ltd.; *Int'l*, pg. 2702
FLEXTRONICS ENCLOSURE (ZHUHAI) CO., LTD—See Flex Ltd.; *Int'l*, pg. 2702
FLEXTRONICS INTERNATIONAL (UK) LTD—See Flex Ltd.; *Int'l*, pg. 2702
FLEXTRONICS PLASTICS (ZHUHAI) CO., LTD—See Flex Ltd.; *Int'l*, pg. 2704
FLEXTRONICS TECHNOLOGIES MEXICO, S.DE R.L. DE C.V.—See Flex Ltd.; *Int'l*, pg. 2704
FLITEBOARD PTY LIMITED—See Brunswick Corporation; *U.S. Public*, pg. 408
FLUKE SOUTH EAST ASIA PTE. LTD.—See Fortive Corporation; *U.S. Public*, pg. 870
FLUKE (SWITZERLAND) GMBH—See Fortive Corporation; *U.S. Public*, pg. 870
FLYNN & REYNOLDS AGENCY INC.; *U.S. Private*, pg. 1553
FORMOSA PROSONIC JAPAN CO. LTD.—See Formosa Prosonic Industries Berhad; *Int'l*, pg. 2736
FOSTER ELECTRIC (BAC NINH) CO., LTD.—See Foster Electric Co., Ltd.; *Int'l*, pg. 2749
FOSTER ELECTRIC PENANG SDN. BHD.—See Foster Electric Co., Ltd.; *Int'l*, pg. 2749
FOXCONN BAJA CALIFORNIA S.A. DE C.V.—See Hon Hai Precision Industry Co., Ltd.; *Int'l*, pg. 3456
FOXCONN SLOVAKIA, SPOL. S R.O.—See Hon Hai Precision Industry Co., Ltd.; *Int'l*, pg. 3456
FRANCEL S.A.—See Emerson Electric Co.; *U.S. Public*, pg. 749
FROMEX, S.A. DE C.V.—See Emerson Electric Co.; *U.S. Public*, pg. 749
F-R TECNOLOGIAS DE FLUJO, S.A. DE C.V.—See Emerson Electric Co.; *U.S. Public*, pg. 749
FUDA ALLOY MATERIALS CO., LTD.; *Int'l*, pg. 2804
FUELCELL ENERGY, INC.- EASTERN REGION—See FuelCell Energy, Inc.; *U.S. Public*, pg. 891
FUELCELL ENERGY, INC.- MANUFACTURING—See FuelCell Energy, Inc.; *U.S. Public*, pg. 891
FUJIAN MINHANG ELECTRONICS CO., LTD.; *Int'l*, pg. 2819
FUJI ELECTRIC CONSUL NEOWATT PRIVATE LIMITED—See Fuji Electric Co., Ltd.; *Int'l*, pg. 2811
FUJI ELECTRIC EUROPE GMBH—See Fuji Electric Co., Ltd.; *Int'l*, pg. 2811
FUJI ELECTRIC FA (ASIA) CO., LTD.—See Fuji Electric Co., Ltd.; *Int'l*, pg. 2811
FUJI ELECTRIC FA COMPONENTS & SYSTEMS CO., LTD.—See Fuji Electric Co., Ltd.; *Int'l*, pg. 2811
FUJI ELECTRIC FA KOREA CO., LTD.—See Fuji Electric Co., Ltd.; *Int'l*, pg. 2811
FUJI ELECTRIC FA TAIWAN CO., LTD.—See Fuji Electric Co., Ltd.; *Int'l*, pg. 2811
FUJI ELECTRIC MANUFACTURING (THAILAND) CO., LTD.—See Fuji Electric Co., Ltd.; *Int'l*, pg. 2811
FUJI ELECTRIC (SHENZHEN) CO., LTD—See Fuji Electric Co., Ltd.; *Int'l*, pg. 2811
FUJI GEMCO PRIVATE LIMITED—See Fuji Electric Co., Ltd.; *Int'l*, pg. 2812
FUJIKURA AUTOMOTIVE GUANGZHOU CO., LTD.—See Fujikura Ltd.; *Int'l*, pg. 2827
FUJIKURA DIA CABLE LTD.—See Fujikura Ltd.; *Int'l*, pg. 2828
FUJI SEMEC INC.—See Fuji Electric Co., Ltd.; *Int'l*, pg. 2812
FUJITSU COMPUTER PRODUCTS OF VIETNAM, INC.—See Fujitsu Limited; *Int'l*, pg. 2834
FULLSHARE HOLDINGS LIMITED; *Int'l*, pg. 2842
FUNAI ELECTRIC CEBU, INC.—See Funai Electric Co., Ltd.; *Int'l*, pg. 2844
FUNAI ELECTRIC PHILIPPINES INC.—See Funai Electric Co., Ltd.; *Int'l*, pg. 2844
FUNAI ELECTRIC R&D (SHENZHEN) CO., LTD.—See Funai Electric Co., Ltd.; *Int'l*, pg. 2844
FUNAI GENERAL SERVICE CO., LTD.—See Funai Electric Co., Ltd.; *Int'l*, pg. 2844
FUNAI TRADING CORP.—See Funai Electric Co., Ltd.; *Int'l*, pg. 2845
FUSHI INTERNATIONAL (DALIAN) BIMETALLIC CABLE CO., LTD.—See Fushi Copperweld, Inc.; *Int'l*, pg. 2849
FUTRONIC GMBH—See Bucher Industries AG; *Int'l*, pg. 1209
FUTURE GRAPHICS LLC; *U.S. Private*, pg. 1627
F.W. WEBB COMPANY - WEBB BIO-PHARM DIVISION—See F.W. Webb Company; *U.S. Private*, pg. 1457
GAI-TRONICS CORPORATION—See Hubbell Incorporated; *U.S. Public*, pg. 1066
GAI-TRONICS S.R.L.—See Hubbell Incorporated; *U.S. Public*, pg. 1066
GANBARO SRL—See HORIBA Ltd; *Int'l*, pg. 3475
GARO AS—See Garo AB; *Int'l*, pg. 2885
GASPOROX AB; *Int'l*, pg. 2888
GEBRUDER EBERHARD GMBH & CO. KG; *Int'l*, pg. 2909
GE HUNGARY CO. LTD.—See General Electric Company; *U.S. Public*, pg. 917
GEMEINSCHAFTSKERNKRAFTWERK GROHNDE GMBH—See E.ON SE; *Int'l*, pg. 2253
GEMEINSCHAFTSKRAFTWERK KIEL GMBH—See E.ON SE; *Int'l*, pg. 2253
GENER8, LLC—See Sverica Capital Management LP; *U.S. Private*, pg. 3888
GENTHERM GLOBAL POWER TECHNOLOGIES—See Gentherm Incorporated; *U.S. Public*, pg. 931
GERARD PERRIER INDUSTRIE S.A.; *Int'l*, pg. 2942
GETRIEBEBAU NORD GMBH & CO. KG; *Int'l*, pg. 2953
GEWISS S.P.A.; *Int'l*, pg. 2955
G.G. DANDEKAR PROPERTIES LTD.; *Int'l*, pg. 2865
G G ENGINEERING LIMITED; *Int'l*, pg. 2861
GHISALBA S.P.A.; *Int'l*, pg. 2959
GILL INDUSTRIES, INC.—See PowerSphyr Inc.; *U.S. Private*, pg. 3240
GINLONG TECHNOLOGIES CO., LTD.; *Int'l*, pg. 2977
GKN AEROSPACE CINCINNATI INC—See GKN plc; *Int'l*, pg. 2984
G.K.POWER PRODUCTS CO., LTD.—See Gunkul Engineering Co., Ltd.; *Int'l*, pg. 3183
GLEASON REEL CORPORATION—See Hubbell Incorporated; *U.S. Public*, pg. 1066
GLENAIR UK LTD.—See Glenair Inc.; *U.S. Private*, pg. 1709
GLOBAL PV SPECIALISTS; *U.S. Private*, pg. 1717

GRACE ITALY S.R.L.—See Standard Industries Holdings Inc.; *U.S. Private*, pg. 3780
GRAND PLASTIC TECHNOLOGY CORP.; *Int'l*, pg. 3056
GRAPHENE & SOLAR TECHNOLOGIES LTD; *U.S. Public*, pg. 958
GRAYBAR INTERNATIONAL, INC.—See Graybar Electric Company, Inc.; *U.S. Public*, pg. 1760
GR CONSULTING, INC.—See gremz, Inc.; *Int'l*, pg. 3080
GROUP DEKKO, INC.—See Graham Holdings Company; *U.S. Public*, pg. 955
GRUPO ANTOLIN MICHIGAN—See Grupo Antolin-Irausa, S.A.; *Int'l*, pg. 3119
GS-ELEKTROANLAGENMONTAGE GMBH; *Int'l*, pg. 3143
GUANGDONG FAILONG CRYSTAL TECHNOLOGY CO., LTD.; *Int'l*, pg. 3154
GUANGZHOU LINGNAN CABLE LTD.—See Guangzhou Zhiguang Electric Co., Ltd.; *Int'l*, pg. 3168
GUANGZHOU TONGDA AUTO ELECTRIC CO., LTD.; *Int'l*, pg. 3168
GUANGZHOU ZHIGUANG ELECTRIC CO., LTD.; *Int'l*, pg. 3168
GUANGZHOU ZHIGUANG ELECTRIC LTD.—See Guangzhou Zhiguang Electric Co., Ltd.; *Int'l*, pg. 3168
GUANGZHOU ZHIGUANG ENERGY SAVING CO., LTD.—See Guangzhou Zhiguang Electric Co., Ltd.; *Int'l*, pg. 3168
GUODIAN NANJING AUTOMATION CO., LTD.; *Int'l*, pg. 3186
GUYSON INTERNATIONAL LIMITED - HOSE & COUPLINGS DIVISION—See Guyson International Limited; *Int'l*, pg. 3189
H2 POWER TECH, LLC—See Chung-Hsin Electric & Machinery Manufacturing Corp.; *Int'l*, pg. 1597
HACH LANGE FRANCE S.A.S.—See Danaher Corporation; *U.S. Public*, pg. 627
HACH LANGE SPAIN S.L.—See Danaher Corporation; *U.S. Public*, pg. 627
HACH LANGE S.R.L.—See Danaher Corporation; *U.S. Public*, pg. 627
HAEMONETICS JAPAN GK—See Haemonetics Corporation; *U.S. Public*, pg. 979
HAEMONETICS SINGAPORE PTE. LTD.—See Haemonetics Corporation; *U.S. Public*, pg. 979
HAINAN JINPAN SMART TECHNOLOGY CO., LTD.; *Int'l*, pg. 3212
HALMA INDIA PRIVATE LTD.—See Halma plc; *Int'l*, pg. 3232
HANCHETT ENTRY SYSTEMS INC.—See ASSA ABLOY AB; *Int'l*, pg. 639
HANGZHOU CABLE CO., LTD.; *Int'l*, pg. 3246
HANGZHOU DAHE THERMO-MAGNETICS CO., LTD. - TE DIVISION—See Ferrotec Holdings Corporation; *Int'l*, pg. 2643
HANGZHOU HUAGUANG ADVANCED WELDING MATERIALS CO., LTD.; *Int'l*, pg. 3248
HANGZHOU KELIN ELECTRIC CO., LTD.; *Int'l*, pg. 3249
HANGZHOU XILI INTELLIGENT TECHNOLOGY CO., LTD.; *Int'l*, pg. 3251
HANGZHOU ZHIGUANG YICHUANG TECHNOLOGIES LTD.—See Guangzhou Zhiguang Electric Co., Ltd.; *Int'l*, pg. 3168
HANS EINHELL UKRAINE TOV—See Einhell Germany AG; *Int'l*, pg. 2333
HANWHA Q CELLS GMBH—See Hanwha Group; *Int'l*, pg. 3265
HARBIN BOILER COMPANY LIMITED—See Harbin Electric Corporation; *Int'l*, pg. 3270
HARBIN COSLIGHT SWITCH COMPANY LIMITED—See Coslight Technology International Group Limited; *Int'l*, pg. 1810
HARBIN ELECTRIC (H.E) CORPORATION—See Harbin Electric Corporation; *Int'l*, pg. 3270
HARBIN ELECTRIC INTERNATIONAL CO., LTD.—See Harbin Electric Corporation; *Int'l*, pg. 3270
HARBIN ELECTRIC MACHINERY CO., LTD.—See Harbin Electric Corporation; *Int'l*, pg. 3270
HARBINGER TECHNOLOGY CORP.—See Cub Elecparts Inc.; *Int'l*, pg. 1875
HARVARD MARITIME LIMITED—See Harvard International Ltd.; *Int'l*, pg. 3280
HAVELL'S INDIA LTD. - ALWAR WORKS—See Havell's India Ltd.; *Int'l*, pg. 3286
HAVELL'S INDIA LTD. - FARIDABAD WORKS—See Havell's India Ltd.; *Int'l*, pg. 3286
HAVELL'S INDIA LTD. - HARIDWAR WORKS—See Havell's India Ltd.; *Int'l*, pg. 3286
HAVELL'S INDIA LTD.; *Int'l*, pg. 3285
HAVELLS SYLVANIA BELGIUM B.V.B.A.—See Havell's India Ltd.; *Int'l*, pg. 3286
HAVELLS SYLVANIA COLOMBIA S.A.—See Havell's India Ltd.; *Int'l*, pg. 3286
HAVELLS SYLVANIA COSTA RICA S.A.—See Havell's India Ltd.; *Int'l*, pg. 3286
HAVELLS SYLVANIA EUROPE LTD—See Havell's India Ltd.; *Int'l*, pg. 3286
HAVELLS SYLVANIA FIXTURES UK LTD.—See Havell's India Ltd.; *Int'l*, pg. 3286
HAVELLS SYLVANIA FRANCE S.A.S.—See Havell's India Ltd.; *Int'l*, pg. 3286

N.A.I.C.S. INDEX

335999 — ALL OTHER MISCELLAN...

HAVELLS SYLVANIA GREECE A.E.E.E.—See Havell's India Ltd.; *Int'l*, pg. 3286
HAVELLS SYLVANIA (GUANGZHOU) ENTERPRISE LTD—See Havell's India Ltd.; *Int'l*, pg. 3286
HAVELLS SYLVANIA GUATEMALA S.A.—See Havell's India Ltd.; *Int'l*, pg. 3286
HAVELLS SYLVANIA ITALY S.P.A.—See Havell's India Ltd.; *Int'l*, pg. 3286
HAVELLS SYLVANIA N.V.—See Havell's India Ltd.; *Int'l*, pg. 3286
HAVELLS SYLVANIA SPAIN S.A.—See Havell's India Ltd.; *Int'l*, pg. 3286
HAVELLS SYLVANIA SWEDEN A.B.—See Havell's India Ltd.; *Int'l*, pg. 3286
HAVELLS SYLVANIA SWITZERLAND A.G.—See Havell's India Ltd.; *Int'l*, pg. 3286
HAVELLS SYLVANIA TUNISIA S.A.R.L.—See Havell's India Ltd.; *Int'l*, pg. 3286
HAVELLS SYLVANIA UK LTD.—See Havell's India Ltd.; *Int'l*, pg. 3286
HAVELLS SYLVANIA VENEZUELA C.A.—See Havell's India Ltd.; *Int'l*, pg. 3286
HAWKE ASIA PACIFIC PTE. LTD.—See Hubbell Incorporated; *U.S. Public*, pg. 1066
HAYDON KERK MOTION SOLUTIONS, INC.-HAYDON PRODUCTS DIVISION—See AMETEK, Inc.; *U.S. Public*, pg. 116
H. BENTZ ELECTRONICS LTD.—See ESPEC Corp.; *Int'l*, pg. 2505
HEINRICH KOPP GMBH—See Alfanar Trading Co.; *Int'l*, pg. 315
HENAN SENYUAN ELECTRIC CO., LTD.; *Int'l*, pg. 3343
HENKEL ABLESTIK KOREA LTD.—See Henkel AG & Co. KGaA; *Int'l*, pg. 3353
HERMANN SCHWELLING MASCHINENBAU GMBH & CO. KG; *Int'l*, pg. 3362
HIMACHAL ENERGY PRIVATE LIMITED—See HPL Electric & Power Limited; *Int'l*, pg. 3501
HIROSE ELECTRIC CO., LTD., EUROPEAN BRANCH—See Hirose Electric Co., Ltd.; *Int'l*, pg. 3405
HITACHI ENGINEERING & SERVICES CO., LTD.—See Hitachi, Ltd.; *Int'l*, pg. 3417
HITACHI HI-REL POWER ELECTRONICS PVT. LTD.—See Hitachi, Ltd.; *Int'l*, pg. 3417
HITACHI IBARAKI TECHNICAL SERVICE LTD.—See Hitachi, Ltd.; *Int'l*, pg. 3419
HITACHI INDUSTRIAL PRODUCTS, LTD.—See Hitachi, Ltd.; *Int'l*, pg. 3419
HITACHI INDUSTRY & CONTROL SOLUTIONS, LTD.—See Hitachi, Ltd.; *Int'l*, pg. 3419
HITEC POWER PROTECTION B.V.—See Air Water Inc.; *Int'l*, pg. 240
HITEK POWER LTD. U.K.—See Advanced Energy Industries, Inc.; *U.S. Public*, pg. 47
HITZINGER UK LIMITED—See Dr. Aichhorn GmbH; *Int'l*, pg. 2190
HLI SOLUTIONS, INC.—See AIP, LLC; *U.S. Private*, pg. 134
HOKURIKU TELECOMMUNICATION NETWORK CO., INC.—See Hokuriku Electric Power Co.; *Int'l*, pg. 3445
HOME AUTOMATION, INC.—See Leviton Manufacturing Company, Inc.; *U.S. Private*, pg. 2436
HONEYWELL ACCESS—See Honeywell International Inc.; *U.S. Public*, pg. 1049
HONEYWELL AVIONICS SYSTEMS LIMITED—See Honeywell International Inc.; *U.S. Public*, pg. 1051
HONEYWELL GLOBAL TRACKING—See Honeywell International Inc.; *U.S. Public*, pg. 1047
HOSIDEN ELECTRONICS (SHENZHEN) CO., LTD.—See Hosiden Corporation; *Int'l*, pg. 3484
HOSIDEN SERVICE CORPORATION—See Hosiden Corporation; *Int'l*, pg. 3484
HOSIDEN (SHANGHAI) CO., LTD.—See Hosiden Corporation; *Int'l*, pg. 3484
HOSIDEN TECHNOLOGY (QINGDAO) CO., LTD.—See Hosiden Corporation; *Int'l*, pg. 3484
HOSOKAWA POLYMER SYSTEMS—See Hosokawa Micron Corporation; *Int'l*, pg. 3486
HSW GMBH; *Int'l*, pg. 3507
HUBBELL DE MEXICO, S.A. DE C.V.—See Hubbell Incorporated; *U.S. Public*, pg. 1067
HUBBELL INCORPORATED; *U.S. Public*, pg. 1066
HUBBELL LIMITED—See Hubbell Incorporated; *U.S. Public*, pg. 1066
HUBBELL POWER SYSTEMS, INC.—See Hubbell Incorporated; *U.S. Public*, pg. 1067
HUBBELL-TAIAN CO., LTD.—See Hubbell Incorporated; *U.S. Public*, pg. 1067
HUIZHOU JECKSON ELECTRIC COMPANY LIMITED—See China Aerospace International Holdings Limited; *Int'l*, pg. 1481
HUNAN ZHONGKE ELECTRIC CO., LTD.; *Int'l*, pg. 3534
HUNTER MANUFACTURING COMPANY—See Metalmark Capital Holdings LLC; *U.S. Private*, pg. 2681
HUNTSMAN ADVANCED MATERIALS (DEUTSCHLAND) GMBH—See Huntsman Corporation; *U.S. Public*, pg. 1072
HUNT VALVE - ACTUATOR DIVISION—See Arcline Investment Management LP; *U.S. Private*, pg. 313

HYDRA-ELECTRIC COMPANY—See Loar Group, Inc.; *U.S. Private*, pg. 2477
HYDROGENICS CORPORATION—See Cummins Inc.; *U.S. Public*, pg. 607
HYPERCHARGE NETWORKS CORP.; *Int'l*, pg. 3553
I AM SMART TECHNOLOGY, INC.; *U.S. Private*, pg. 2020
ICT INTEGRATED CIRCUIT TESTING GMBH—See Applied Materials, Inc.; *U.S. Public*, pg. 172
IDENTOGO—See Advent International Corporation; *U.S. Private*, pg. 102
IDX INC.—See Adtec Plasma Technology Co., Ltd.; *Int'l*, pg. 154
IHI CHARGING SYSTEMS INTERNATIONAL S.P.A.—See IHI Corporation; *Int'l*, pg. 3604
IKHAIRI & ALJENABI TRADING CO.—See Einhell Germany AG; *Int'l*, pg. 2333
IMASEN ENGINEERING CORPORATION—See Imasen Electric Industrial Co., Ltd.; *Int'l*, pg. 3620
INCO INDUSTRIAL COMPONENTS 'S-GRAVENHAGE B.V.—See ION Geophysical Corporation; *U.S. Public*, pg. 1166
INDUSTRIAL CAPACITORS (WREXHAM) LIMITED—See BorgWarner Inc.; *U.S. Public*, pg. 369
INDUSTRIAL HARNESS CO.—See Cerberus Capital Management, L.P.; *U.S. Private*, pg. 838
INFOSCITEX CORPORATION—See DCS Corporation; *U.S. Private*, pg. 1180
INI POWER SYSTEMS, INC.—See The Dewey Electronics Corporation; *U.S. Public*, pg. 2067
INNOVASOURCE LLC—See Energizer Holdings, Inc.; *U.S. Public*, pg. 761
INNOVATIVE AUTOMATION AND CONTROLS, INC.—See Airline Hydraulics Corporation; *U.S. Private*, pg. 141
INNOVATIVE LASER TECHNOLOGIES, INC.—See IPG Photonics Corporation; *U.S. Public*, pg. 1167
INNOVERSA MOBILE SOLUTIONS GP LTD.—See Quanta Services, Inc.; *U.S. Public*, pg. 1751
INPRIA CORPORATION; *U.S. Private*, pg. 2084
INSTITUTE FOR INTERNATIONAL PRODUCT SAFETY GMBH—See Eaton Corporation plc; *Int'l*, pg. 2282
INTEGRA ENCLOSURES, INC.; *U.S. Private*, pg. 2098
INTERMETRO INDUSTRIES B.V.—See Emerson Electric Co.; *U.S. Public*, pg. 750
INTRATONE UK LTD.—See Cogelec SA; *Int'l*, pg. 1694
INVISIBLE FENCE, INC.—See Radio Systems Corporation; *U.S. Private*, pg. 3344
IN VITRO TECHNOLOGIES PTY. LTD.—See HORIBA Ltd; *Int'l*, pg. 3477
I/O MARINE SYSTEMS LIMITED—See ION Geophysical Corporation; *U.S. Public*, pg. 1166
ION GEOPHYSICAL CIS LLC—See ION Geophysical Corporation; *U.S. Public*, pg. 1166
IPVIDEO CORPORATION—See Motorola Solutions, Inc.; *U.S. Public*, pg. 1477
IRISS-ASIA PTY LTD—See IRISS, Inc.; *U.S. Private*, pg. 2139
IRISS, INC.; *U.S. Private*, pg. 2139
IRISS, LTD.—See IRISS, Inc.; *U.S. Private*, pg. 2139
I-SHENG ELECTRIC WIRE & CABLE CO., LTD.; *Int'l*, pg. 3564
I-SHENG JAPAN CO., LTD.—See I-Sheng Electric Wire & Cable Co., Ltd.; *Int'l*, pg. 3565
ISOMET CORPORATION; *U.S. Private*, pg. 2146
ISONAS, INC.—See Allegion Public Limited Company; *U.S. Public*, pg. 335
ITALCLEM S.P.A.—See Arab Electrical Industries; *Int'l*, pg. 530
ITALTRACTOR ITM S.P.A.—See Titan International, Inc.; *U.S. Public*, pg. 2160
ITW APPLIANCE COMPONENTS D.O.O.—See Illinois Tool Works Inc.; *U.S. Public*, pg. 1104
JANAM TECHNOLOGIES LLC—See ASSA ABLOY AB; *Int'l*, pg. 637
JET STREAM INTERNATIONAL; *U.S. Private*, pg. 2204
JIANGSU XIANGYUAN ELECTRIC EQUIPMENT CO., LTD.—See Hubbell Incorporated; *U.S. Public*, pg. 1067
KAMIC AB—See Amplex AB; *Int'l*, pg. 434
KAUFFMAN ENGINEERING, INC.—See Monomoy Capital Partners LLC; *U.S. Private*, pg. 2772
K CONTROLS LIMITED—See Emerson Electric Co.; *U.S. Public*, pg. 747
KEITHLEY INSTRUMENTS, LLC—See Fortive Corporation; *U.S. Public*, pg. 872
KERI SYSTEMS INC.; *U.S. Private*, pg. 2290
KERNKRAFTWERK BROKDORF GMBH—See E.ON SE; *Int'l*, pg. 2254
KERNKRAFTWERK UNTERWESER GMBH—See E.ON SE; *Int'l*, pg. 2254
KING RESOURCES, INC.; *U.S. Public*, pg. 1234
KLAUKE UK LIMITED—See Emerson Electric Co.; *U.S. Public*, pg. 750
KLN ULTRASCHALL AG—See Crest Group Inc.; *U.S. Private*, pg. 1096
KLN ULTRASONICS (SHANGHAI) CO., LTD.—See Crest Group Inc.; *U.S. Private*, pg. 1096
KNURR AG & CO. GRUNDBESITZ OHG—See Vertiv Holdings Co; *U.S. Public*, pg. 2289
KNURR ELECTRONICS GMBH & CO. GRUNDBESITZ

OHG—See Vertiv Holdings Co; *U.S. Public*, pg. 2289
KURT J. LESKER COMPANY; *U.S. Private*, pg. 2357
KURZ-KASCH, INC.—See Monomoy Capital Partners LLC; *U.S. Private*, pg. 2772
L-3 COMMUNICATIONS ADVANCED LASER SYSTEMS TECHNOLOGY INC—See L3Harris Technologies, Inc.; *U.S. Public*, pg. 1281
L-3 COMMUNICATIONS MAGNET-MOTOR GMBH—See L3Harris Technologies, Inc.; *U.S. Public*, pg. 1282
L-3 COMMUNICATIONS MARIPRO INC—See L3Harris Technologies, Inc.; *U.S. Public*, pg. 1282
LABBIOTECH LTD.—See HORIBA Ltd; *Int'l*, pg. 3477
LABORATORIOS ARSAL SA DE CV—See HORIBA Ltd; *Int'l*, pg. 3477
LA MARCHE MANUFACTURING COMPANY; *U.S. Private*, pg. 2369
L AND C WINDSOR CABLES LTD.—See Leggett & Platt, Incorporated; *U.S. Public*, pg. 1302
LARON, INC.—See Genstar Capital, LLC; *U.S. Private*, pg. 1678
LASER ENERGETICS, INC.; *U.S. Public*, pg. 1293
LAVABAU LLC—See Einhell Germany AG; *Int'l*, pg. 2333
LDR MEDICAL S.A.S.—See Zimmer Biomet Holdings, Inc.; *U.S. Public*, pg. 2406
LEAD BY SALES, LLC; *U.S. Public*, pg. 2405
LEAR CORPORATION ROMANIA S.R.L.—See Lear Corporation; *U.S. Public*, pg. 1297
L'EBENOID S.A.—See ABB Ltd.; *Int'l*, pg. 54
LEE+CHO TRADING CO.—See Einhell Germany AG; *Int'l*, pg. 2334
LEGEND CORPORATION LIMITED—See Adamantem Capital Management Pty Limited; *Int'l*, pg. 123
LEVITON MANUFACTURING/SOUTHERN DEVICES—See Leviton Manufacturing Company, Inc.; *U.S. Private*, pg. 2436
LEX PRODUCTS CORP.; *U.S. Private*, pg. 2440
LIFT MATERIALS AUSTRALIA—See Dewhurst Group plc; *Int'l*, pg. 2091
LIFTSTORE LTD.—See Dewhurst Group plc; *Int'l*, pg. 2091
LIND ELECTRONICS, INC.—See Main Street Capital Corporation; *U.S. Public*, pg. 1354
LINEAR SPACE TECHNOLOGY, LLC—See MACOM Technology Solutions Holdings, Inc.; *U.S. Public*, pg. 1352
LITHIUM BALANCE A/S—See Sensata Technologies Holding plc; *U.S. Public*, pg. 1865
LLC BELDEN RUS—See Belden, Inc.; *U.S. Public*, pg. 294
LOW VOLTAGE PTY LTD—See Bapcor Limited; *Int'l*, pg. 857
L&P SOMAPPA COMFORT SYSTEMS (INDIA) PRIVATE LIMITED—See Leggett & Platt, Incorporated; *U.S. Public*, pg. 1302
M2M COMMUNICATIONS; *U.S. Private*, pg. 2530
MAC ELECTRIC INC.; *U.S. Private*, pg. 2531
MAGNETIC METALS CORP.—See Indel, Inc.; *U.S. Private*, pg. 2055
MAHR GMBH—See Carl Mahr Holding GmbH; *Int'l*, pg. 1333
MAINCO INVESTMENTS INC.; *U.S. Private*, pg. 2552
MAINPOWER HELLAS LTD.—See Eguana Technologies Inc.; *Int'l*, pg. 2326
MAJORPOWER CORPORATION; *U.S. Private*, pg. 2555
MANDELLI SISTEMI S.P.A.—See Gruppo Riello Sistemi S.p.A.; *Int'l*, pg. 3141
MARKEM-IMAJE LTD.—See Dover Corporation; *U.S. Public*, pg. 680
MARTIN WALTER ULTRASONICS AG—See Crest Group Inc.; *U.S. Private*, pg. 1096
MASTER APPLIANCE CORP.; *U.S. Private*, pg. 2607
MASTERGUARD GMBH—See Emerson Electric Co.; *U.S. Public*, pg. 750
MATCOR, INC.—See Brand Industrial Services, Inc.; *U.S. Private*, pg. 636
MAXAL INTERNATIONAL, INC.—See Illinois Tool Works Inc.; *U.S. Public*, pg. 1109
MAXITROL COMPANY - BLISSFIELD DIVISION—See Maxitrol Company; *U.S. Private*, pg. 2619
MAXTEK COMPONENTS CORPORATION—See Fortive Corporation; *U.S. Public*, pg. 871
MAXXESS SYSTEMS EUROPE, LTD.—See MAXxess Systems, Inc.; *U.S. Private*, pg. 2620
MAXXESS SYSTEMS, INC.; *U.S. Private*, pg. 2620
MCTEC B.V.—See Merit Medical Systems, Inc.; *U.S. Public*, pg. 1425
MEDISELL RWANDA LTD.—See HORIBA Ltd; *Int'l*, pg. 3477
MEDISELL UG LTD.—See HORIBA Ltd; *Int'l*, pg. 3477
MELTRONIX, INC.; *U.S. Public*, pg. 1414
MERCURY DEFENSE SYSTEMS, INC.—See Mercury Systems, Inc.; *U.S. Public*, pg. 1422
MERCURY INTELLIGENCE SYSTEMS, INC.—See Mercury Systems, Inc.; *U.S. Public*, pg. 1422
MERITEX TECHNOLOGY (SUZHOU) CO. LTD.—See Illinois Tool Works Inc.; *U.S. Public*, pg. 1109
METHODE ELECTRONICS INTERNATIONAL GMBH—See Methode Electronics, Inc.; *U.S. Public*, pg. 1428
MICROMO ELECTRONICS, INC.—See Dr. Fritz Faulhaber GmbH & Co. KG; *Int'l*, pg. 2191
MICROSEMI CORP. - POWER MANAGEMENT GROUP—See Microchip Technology Incorporated; *U.S. Public*, pg. 1436

335999 — ALL OTHER MISCELLAN...

MID-EASTERN INDUSTRIES, INC.—See Technology Dynamics, Inc.; *U.S. Private*, pg. 3955
MIDWEST PRODUCTS & ENGINEERING, INC.; *U.S. Private*, pg. 2722
MILBANK MANUFACTURING COMPANY INC. - CONCORDIA FACILITY—See Milbank Manufacturing Company Inc.; *U.S. Private*, pg. 2726
MIRION TECHNOLOGIES (IST) CORPORATION—See Mirion Technologies, Inc.; *U.S. Public*, pg. 1450
MITEL NETWORKS LTD.—See Searchlight Capital Partners, L.P.; *U.S. Private*, pg. 3589
MK ELECTRIC LIMITED—See Honeywell International Inc.; *U.S. Public*, pg. 1049
MKS ION SYSTEMS—See MKS Instruments, Inc.; *U.S. Public*, pg. 1453
MKS TAIWAN TECHNOLOGY LTD.—See MKS Instruments, Inc.; *U.S. Public*, pg. 1453
M.L.S. HOLICE SPOL. S.R.O.—See Emerson Electric Co.; *U.S. Public*, pg. 750
MMG INDIA PVT LTD—See Delta Manufacturing Ltd; *Int'l*, pg. 2019
MOBREY LIMITED—See Emerson Electric Co.; *U.S. Public*, pg. 750
MOLEX CANADA LIMITED—See Koch Industries, Inc.; *U.S. Private*, pg. 2335
MONITOR DYNAMICS LLC—See Evergreen Fire Alarms, LLC; *U.S. Private*, pg. 1439
MOOG REKOFA GMBH—See Moog Inc.; *U.S. Public*, pg. 1470
MORSE WATCHMANS INC.; *U.S. Private*, pg. 2791
MOTION ENGINEERING INCORPORATED—See Regal Rexnord Corporation; *U.S. Public*, pg. 1772
MR&D INSTITUTE S.R.L.—See Gewiss S.p.A.; *Int'l*, pg. 2955
MTL ITALIA SRL—See Eaton Corporation plc; *Int'l*, pg. 2282
MULTITON ELEKTRONIK GMBH—See Champion Technology Holdings Ltd; *Int'l*, pg. 1440
MUYLE ELECTRO-MACHINERY SA—See Emerson Electric Co.; *U.S. Public*, pg. 750
MYERS POWER PRODUCTS, INC.—See Myers Power Products, Inc.; *U.S. Private*, pg. 2824
NAECO LLC; *U.S. Private*, pg. 2830
NANJING PUTIAN TELEGE INTELLIGENT BUILDING LTD.—See Chengdu SIWI Science and Technology Company Limited; *Int'l*, pg. 1469
NANOCOMP TECHNOLOGIES, INC.—See Huntsman Corporation; *U.S. Public*, pg. 1075
NAPIER TURBOCHARGERS AUSTRALIA PTY LTD.—See Westinghouse Air Brake Technologies Corporation; *U.S. Public*, pg. 2358
NATIONAL ELECTROSTATICS CORPORATION; *U.S. Private*, pg. 2853
NATIONAL SECURITY SYSTEMS INC.; *U.S. Private*, pg. 2863
NAVITAR, INC.—See AMETEK, Inc.; *U.S. Public*, pg. 121
NEF POWER (TAIZHOU) CO., LTD.—See Central Development Holdings Ltd.; *Int'l*, pg. 1406
NEGELE MESSTECHNIK GMBH—See Danaher Corporation; *U.S. Public*, pg. 628
NEOPTIX CANADA LP—See Fortive Corporation; *U.S. Public*, pg. 871
NEWAVE ESPANA S.A.—See ABB Ltd.; *Int'l*, pg. 55
NEWAVE FINLAND OY—See ABB Ltd.; *Int'l*, pg. 55
NEWAVE OSTERREICH GMBH—See ABB Ltd.; *Int'l*, pg. 55
NEWAVE S.A.—See ABB Ltd.; *Int'l*, pg. 55
NEWAVE SOUTH AMERICA ELETTROELETTRONICA LTDA—See ABB Ltd.; *Int'l*, pg. 55
NEWAVE UPS SYSTEMS BV—See ABB Ltd.; *Int'l*, pg. 55
NEWAVE USV SYSTEME GMBH—See ABB Ltd.; *Int'l*, pg. 55
NEWLY WEDS FOODS ASIA PACIFIC—See Newly Weds Foods, Inc.; *U.S. Private*, pg. 2915
NEWPORT CORP. - SPECTRA-PHYSICS DIVISION—See MKS Instruments, Inc.; *U.S. Public*, pg. 1453
NEXJEN SYSTEMS—See Averna Technologies Inc.; *Int'l*, pg. 739
NICHINAN CO., LTD.—See Hakuten Corporation; *Int'l*, pg. 3222
NICO TECHNOS CO., LTD.—See Hitachi, Ltd.; *Int'l*, pg. 3423
NKP POWER SOLAR CO., LTD.—See Gunkul Engineering Co., Ltd.; *Int'l*, pg. 3184
NOISELESS ACCOUSTICS OY—See Teledyne Technologies Incorporated; *U.S. Public*, pg. 1992
NORTHROP GRUMMAN ELECTRONIC SYSTEMS—See Northrop Grumman Corporation; *U.S. Public*, pg. 1540
NORTHWEST POWER, INC.—See Vicor Corporation; *U.S. Public*, pg. 2296
NOVA INTEGRATION SOLUTIONS, INC.—See Technology Dynamics, Inc.; *U.S. Private*, pg. 3955
NOVANTA HOLDINGS BV—See Novanta Inc.; *U.S. Public*, pg. 1548
NOVANTA JAPAN CORPORATION—See Novanta Inc.; *U.S. Public*, pg. 1548
NOVITA TECHNOLOGIES, INC.—See ams AG; *Int'l*, pg. 438
NRD, LLC—See BAM Enterprises, Inc.; *U.S. Private*, pg. 463
NSI-MI UK LIMITED—See AMETEK, Inc.; *U.S. Public*, pg. 121

NUVANT SYSTEMS INC.—See A3 Global, LLC; *U.S. Private*, pg. 29
NUVONYX INCORPORATED—See Coherent Corp.; *U.S. Public*, pg. 527
NXEDGE, INC.—See Trive Capital Inc.; *U.S. Private*, pg. 4240
OBERTHUR TECHNOLOGIES ROMANIA S.R.L.—See Advent International Corporation; *U.S. Private*, pg. 103
OCCIDENTAL DEVELOPMENT GROUP, INC.; *U.S. Private*, pg. 2988
OCEANGEO B.V.—See ION Geophysical Corporation; *U.S. Public*, pg. 1166
OHE INDUSTRIES LLC—See Cerberus Capital Management, L.P.; *U.S. Private*, pg. 838
OHIO MAGNETICS, INC. - STEARNS MAGNETICS DIVISION—See HBD Industries, Inc.; *U.S. Private*, pg. 1887
OLEDWORKS LLC; *U.S. Private*, pg. 3010
O.M.T OFFICINA MECCANICA TARTARINI S.R.L.—See Emerson Electric Co.; *U.S. Public*, pg. 750
ONLINE ENGINEERING GMBH—See ELMOS Semiconductor AG; *Int'l*, pg. 2368
OOO APS ENERGIA RUS—See APS Energia SA; *Int'l*, pg. 523
OOO ASTRA - 77—See HORIBA Ltd; *Int'l*, pg. 3477
OOO THERMON CIS—See Thermon Group Holdings, Inc.; *U.S. Public*, pg. 2155
OPTICAL CONNECTIVITY LLC—See Huber + Suhner AG; *Int'l*, pg. 3519
OPTOENERGY, INC.—See Fujikura Ltd.; *Int'l*, pg. 2829
OPTOFIDELITY LTD.—See ChangYuan Group Ltd.; *Int'l*, pg. 1445
OSC, A.S.—See CEZ, a.s.; *Int'l*, pg. 1428
OSRAM SALES EOOD—See ams AG; *Int'l*, pg. 439
OTT HYDROMET GMBH—See Danaher Corporation; *U.S. Public*, pg. 629
OZITO INDUSTRIES PTY. LTD.—See Einhell Germany AG; *Int'l*, pg. 2334
OZTEK CORP.—See Trystar, LLC; *U.S. Private*, pg. 4252
PACE EUROPE, LTD.—See PACE Inc.; *U.S. Private*, pg. 3063
PACIFIC SCIENTIFIC ENERGETIC MATERIALS COMPANY (CALIFORNIA) LLC—See Fortive Corporation; *U.S. Public*, pg. 871
PACSCI MOTION CONTROL, INC.—See Fortive Corporation; *U.S. Public*, pg. 871
PALAS GMBH—See Brockhaus Private Equity GmbH; *Int'l*, pg. 1172
PAOLICELLI & ASSOCIATES, INC.—See One Source Associates, Inc.; *U.S. Private*, pg. 3023
PARKER-MCCRORY MANUFACTURING CO.; *U.S. Private*, pg. 3098
PATCO ELECTRONICS, INC.—See Southwire Company, LLC; *U.S. Private*, pg. 3742
PC ELECTRIC GMBH—See Berndorf AG; *Int'l*, pg. 987
PERCEPTICS, LLC; *U.S. Private*, pg. 3146
PHOENIX SOLUTIONS CO.; *U.S. Private*, pg. 3173
PIEZO MOTION CORP.; *U.S. Private*, pg. 3179
PIONEER CORPORATION - KAWAGOE PLANT—See EQT AB; *Int'l*, pg. 2470
PITTSBURGH ELECTRIC ENGINES, INC.—See Watt Fuel Cell Corp.; *U.S. Public*, pg. 4456
PLANT POWER & CONTROL SYSTEMS, LLC—See IES Holdings, Inc.; *U.S. Public*, pg. 1094
PLEXUS DEUTSCHLAND GMBH—See Plexus Corp.; *U.S. Public*, pg. 1698
PLEXUS (HANGZHOU) CO., LTD.—See Plexus Corp.; *U.S. Public*, pg. 1698
PLEXUS SERVICES RO S.R.L.—See Plexus Corp.; *U.S. Public*, pg. 1699
PMC SCIENCE-TECH INDUSTRIES (NANJING) CO LTD—See PMC Capital Partners, LLC; *U.S. Private*, pg. 3217
POLYOIL LTD.—See Emerson Electric Co.; *U.S. Public*, pg. 751
POWERBOX INTERNATIONAL AB—See COSEL Co., Ltd.; *Int'l*, pg. 1810
POWER DISTRIBUTION, INC.—See Eaton Corporation plc; *Int'l*, pg. 2282
POWERMITE AFRICA (PTY) LTD.—See Hudaco Industries Limited; *Int'l*, pg. 3521
POWER SYSTEMS TECHNOLOGIES FAR EAST LIMITED—See Flex Ltd.; *Int'l*, pg. 2704
POWERVAR INC.—See AMETEK, Inc.; *U.S. Public*, pg. 118
PRECISE CIRCUITS INC.—See Daburn Electronics & Cable Corp.; *U.S. Private*, pg. 1144
PRECISION COIL AND ROTOR—See Jay Industrial Repair, Inc.; *U.S. Private*, pg. 2191
PRESONUS AUDIO ELECTRONICS, INC.; *U.S. Private*, pg. 3255
PROCESS SENSING TECHNOLOGIES LTD.—See Battery Ventures, L.P.; *U.S. Private*, pg. 489
PROOF RESEARCH, INC.; *U.S. Private*, pg. 3284
PROPHOTONIX—See Union Park Capital; *U.S. Private*, pg. 4285
PROPHOTONIX—See Union Park Capital; *U.S. Private*, pg. 4285

PROTEAM, INC.—See Emerson Electric Co.; *U.S. Public*, pg. 751
PT. ADVANEX PRECISION INDONESIA—See Advanex Inc.; *Int'l*, pg. 163
PT DANFOSS INDONESIA—See Danfoss A/S; *Int'l*, pg. 1961
PUCARO ELEKTRO-ISOLIERSTOFFE GMBH—See ABB Ltd.; *Int'l*, pg. 50
PULSTEKNIK AB—See Addtech AB; *Int'l*, pg. 134
PURCELL MURRAY COMPANY INC.; *U.S. Private*, pg. 3304
QMS CO., LTD.—See ENPLAS CORPORATION; *Int'l*, pg. 2445
QUALITY EQUIPMENT DISTRIBUTORS INC.; *U.S. Private*, pg. 3318
RADCHROM ANALITICA LTDA.—See HORIBA Ltd; *Int'l*, pg. 3478
RADIO SYSTEMS CORPORATION; *U.S. Private*, pg. 3344
RAFI GMBH & CO. KG—See Brookfield Corporation; *Int'l*, pg. 1182
RAPPORT, INC.; *U.S. Private*, pg. 3356
REDAPT ENGINEERING COMPANY LIMITED—See Eaton Corporation plc; *Int'l*, pg. 2279
REMOTEC, INC.—See Northrop Grumman Corporation; *U.S. Public*, pg. 1540
RESA POWER, LLC—See Blue Sea Capital Management LLC; *U.S. Private*, pg. 592
REUEL, INC.—See Hubbell Incorporated; *U.S. Public*, pg. 1067
RHOMBUS ENERGY SOLUTIONS, INC. - HIGH POWER ENERGY GROUP—See BorgWarner Inc.; *U.S. Public*, pg. 371
RICHMOND EEI LTD—See Chemring Group PLC; *Int'l*, pg. 1463
RIDGE TOOL GMBH—See Emerson Electric Co.; *U.S. Public*, pg. 752
ROBOX SPA—See EFORT Intelligent Equipment Co., Ltd.; *Int'l*, pg. 2321
ROBROY INDUSTRIES INC.; *U.S. Private*, pg. 3463
ROCKFORD SPECIALTIES CO.—See Generation Growth Capital, Inc.; *U.S. Private*, pg. 1668
ROCKWELL COMMERCIAL HOLDINGS, LTD.—See Rockwell Automation, Inc.; *U.S. Public*, pg. 1806
ROLLWAY BEARING N.V.—See Emerson Electric Co.; *U.S. Public*, pg. 752
ROSEMOUNT CHINA INC.—See Emerson Electric Co.; *U.S. Public*, pg. 747
ROSEMOUNT TANK GAUGING NORTH AMERICA, INC.—See Emerson Electric Co.; *U.S. Public*, pg. 747
ROXAR ASA—See Emerson Electric Co.; *U.S. Public*, pg. 752
ROYAL DIE & STAMPING CO., INC.—See Eaton Corporation plc; *Int'l*, pg. 2282
RUDOLPH TECHNOLOGIES, INC. - INSPECTION SYSTEMS—See Onto Innovation Inc.; *U.S. Public*, pg. 1605
SAFLOK—See dormakaba Holding AG; *Int'l*, pg. 2177
SAMIR TRADING & MARKETING - CJSC—See HORIBA Ltd; *Int'l*, pg. 3478
SANMINA-SCI ENCLOSURE SYSTEMS OY—See Sanmina Corporation; *U.S. Public*, pg. 1840
SANMINA-SCI HOLDING GMBH & CO. KG—See Sanmina Corporation; *U.S. Public*, pg. 1840
SANMINA-SCI (SHENZHEN) LIMITED—See Sanmina Corporation; *U.S. Public*, pg. 1840
SANTON CIRCUIT BREAKER SERVICES B.V.—See discoverIE Group plc; *Int'l*, pg. 2133
SANTON GMBH—See discoverIE Group plc; *Int'l*, pg. 2133
SANTON INTERNATIONAL B.V.—See discoverIE Group plc; *Int'l*, pg. 2133
SANTON SWITCHGEAR LIMITED—See discoverIE Group plc; *Int'l*, pg. 2133
SARELEM—See Altawest Group; *Int'l*, pg. 388
SATMATIC OY—See Harju Elekter AS; *Int'l*, pg. 3277
SCHALTBAU ASIA PACIFIC LTD.—See The Carlyle Group Inc.; *U.S. Public*, pg. 2053
SCHALTBAU INDIA PVT. LTD.—See The Carlyle Group Inc.; *U.S. Public*, pg. 2053
SCHUMACHER ELECTRIC CORPORATION—See Ripple Industries LLC; *U.S. Private*, pg. 3439
SCIAKY, INC.—See Phillips Service Industries, Inc. (PSI); *U.S. Private*, pg. 3171
S.C. RETRASIB S.A. SIBIU—See BC Partners LLP; *Int'l*, pg. 925
SEACOR CAPACITORS—See Electrocube Incorporated; *U.S. Public*, pg. 1354
SEIREL AUTOMATION EN—See Gerard Perrier Industrie S.A.; *Int'l*, pg. 2942
SEMELEC SAS—See Eaton Corporation plc; *Int'l*, pg. 2282
SENEC GMBH—See EnBW Energie Baden-Wurttemberg AG; *Int'l*, pg. 2400
SENSATA TECHNOLOGIES, INC. - DIMENSIONS—See Sensata Technologies Holding plc; *U.S. Public*, pg. 1866
SEOULEAGUER CO., LTD.—See ES Cube Co., Ltd.; *Int'l*, pg. 3250
SEPPIM CARAIBES SA—See HORIBA Ltd; *Int'l*, pg. 3478
SERA—See Gerard Perrier Industrie S.A.; *Int'l*, pg. 2942

335999 — ALL OTHER MISCELLAN...

SERIOUS INTEGRATED, INC.—See e2ip Technologies; *Int'l*, pg. 2261
SHANE INDUSTRIES, INC.—See Corning Incorporated; *U.S. Public*, pg. 579
SHANGHAI ABB POWER TRANSMISSION CO., LTD—See ABB Ltd.; *Int'l*, pg. 51
SHANGHAI AOWEI TECHNOLOGY DEVELOPMENT CO., LTD.—See Chengdu Xinzhu Road & Bridge Machinery Co., Ltd.; *Int'l*, pg. 1469
SHANGHAI ELECTRICAL APPARATUS RESEARCH INSTITUTE SWITCH APPARATUS CO., LTD.—See Boer Power Holdings Limited; *Int'l*, pg. 1099
SHANGHAI ELECTRIC FUJI ELECTRIC POWER TECHNOLOGY (WUXI) CO., LTD.—See Fuji Electric Co., Ltd.; *Int'l*, pg. 2812
SHANGHAI SHENHE THERMO-MAGNETICS CO., LTD. - TE DIVISION—See Ferrotec Holdings Corporation; *Int'l*, pg. 2643
SHANGHAI SHILU INSTRUMENT CO. LTD.—See Danaher Corporation; *U.S. Public*, pg. 631
SHENYANG SCHALTBAU ELECTRICAL CORPORATION LTD.—See The Carlyle Group Inc.; *U.S. Public*, pg. 2053
SHIMAL SERVICE MMC—See Einhell Germany AG; *Int'l*, pg. 2334
SHOALS TECHNOLOGIES GROUP, INC.; *U.S. Public*, pg. 1875
SHURE ASIA LIMITED—See Shure Incorporated; *U.S. Private*, pg. 3644
SIAM ASAHI TECHNOGLASS CO., LTD.—See AGC Inc.; *Int'l*, pg. 204
SICAME SA—See Equistone Partners Europe Limited; *Int'l*, pg. 2487
SIMCO-ION, INDUSTRIAL GROUP—See Illinois Tool Works Inc.; *U.S. Public*, pg. 1110
SIMCO JAPAN INC.—See Illinois Tool Works Inc.; *U.S. Public*, pg. 1110
SIMCO (NEDERLAND) B.V.—See Illinois Tool Works Inc.; *U.S. Public*, pg. 1110
SIMED CIA LTDA—See HORIBA Ltd; *Int'l*, pg. 3478
SIMED PERU S.A.C.—See HORIBA Ltd; *Int'l*, pg. 3478
SISTEMAS RADIANTES F. MOYANO, S.A.—See ACS, Actividades de Construccion y Servicios, S.A.; *Int'l*, pg. 116
SKYX PLATFORMS CORP.; *U.S. Public*, pg. 1893
SL POWER ELECTRONICS CORPORATION—See Advanced Energy Industries, Inc.; *U.S. Public*, pg. 47
S&L SEALING SOLUTIONS PRIVATE LIMITED—See Einhell Germany AG; *Int'l*, pg. 2334
SMITHS MEDICAL NEDERLAND B.V.—See ICU Medical, Inc.; *U.S. Public*, pg. 1087
SOCIETE ZEGHONDY POUR LE COMMERCE S.A.R.L.—See Einhell Germany AG; *Int'l*, pg. 2334
SOLARIS LASER S.A.—See Dover Corporation; *U.S. Public*, pg. 682
SONICS & MATERIALS, INC.; *U.S. Private*, pg. 3713
SONIX, INC.—See Danaher Corporation; *U.S. Public*, pg. 631
SONO-TEK CLEANING SYSTEMS, INC.—See Sono-Tek Corporation; *U.S. Public*, pg. 1904
SOTEB—See Gerard Perrier Industrie S.A.; *Int'l*, pg. 2942
SPECTRA-PHYSICS AB—See Thermo Fisher Scientific Inc.; *U.S. Public*, pg. 2152
SPELLMAN HIGH VOLTAGE ELECTRONICS CORPORATION; *U.S. Private*, pg. 3754
SPELLMAN HIGH VOLTAGE ELECTRONICS CORP. - VALHALLA—See Spellman High Voltage Electronics Corporation; *U.S. Private*, pg. 3754
SPI INSTRUMENT LTD.—See Einhell Germany AG; *Int'l*, pg. 2334
SPRINGER MAGRATH COMPANY—See Frandsen Corporation; *U.S. Private*, pg. 1593
SSB WIND SYSTEMS GMBH & CO. KG—See Emerson Electric Co.; *U.S. Public*, pg. 752
STANDEX ELECTRONICS (UK) LIMITED—See Standex International; *U.S. Public*, pg. 1931
STANELCO RF TECHNOLOGIES LIMITED—See Biome Technologies plc; *Int'l*, pg. 1039
STEMMANN-TECHNIK GMBH—See Westinghouse Air Brake Technologies Corporation; *U.S. Public*, pg. 2358
STEMMANN TECHNIK NETHERLANDS BV—See Westinghouse Air Brake Technologies Corporation; *U.S. Public*, pg. 2358
STMEM, A.S.—See CEZ, a.s.; *Int'l*, pg. 1428
STRAN TECHNOLOGIES INC.—See Corning Incorporated; *U.S. Public*, pg. 579
SUALAB CO., LTD.—See Cognex Corporation; *U.S. Public*, pg. 523
SUALAB (SUZHOU) CO., LTD.—See Cognex Corporation; *U.S. Public*, pg. 523
SUMILAB S.A.—See HORIBA Ltd; *Int'l*, pg. 3478
SUMMIT ELECTRIC SUPPLY COMPANY - MARINE DIVISION—See Summit Electric Supply Company; *U.S. Private*, pg. 3854
SUN FAIR ELECTRIC WIRE & CABLE (HK) COMPANY LIMITED—See Century Energy International Holdings Limited; *Int'l*, pg. 1418
SUNLIGHT SWITCHGEAR SDN. BHD.—See Chint Group Corporation; *Int'l*, pg. 1571

SUPERFLEX, LTD.—See Alexander Forbes Group Holdings Limited; *Int'l*, pg. 307
SUSTAINABLE ENERGY EUROPA SL—See Eguana Technologies Inc.; *Int'l*, pg. 2327
SUSTAINABLE ENERGY SYSTEMS INC—See Eguana Technologies, Inc.; *Int'l*, pg. 2327
SUZUKA FUJI XEROX CO., LTD.—See FUJIFILM Holdings Corporation; *Int'l*, pg. 2826
SYSTEM PLAST GMBH—See Emerson Electric Co.; *U.S. Public*, pg. 752
SYSTEM PLAST S.R.L.—See Emerson Electric Co.; *U.S. Public*, pg. 752
T4 SCIENCE SA—See Eurazeo SE; *Int'l*, pg. 2528
TACOMA ELECTRIC SUPPLY, INC.; *U.S. Private*, pg. 3921
TAOGLAS LTD.—See The Graham Group, Inc.; *U.S. Private*, pg. 4037
TECHFLEX PACKAGING, LLC—See H.I.G. Capital, LLC; *U.S. Private*, pg. 1834
TECHNO CHUBU CO., LTD.—See Chubu Electric Power Co., Inc.; *Int'l*, pg. 1593
TECHNOLOGY DESIGN LIMITED.—See Oceaneering International, Inc.; *U.S. Public*, pg. 1563
TECOMEC S.R.L.—See Emak S.p.A.; *Int'l*, pg. 2373
TEILSA SERVICIOS, S.L.—See Emerson Electric Co.; *U.S. Public*, pg. 752
TEKDATA INTERCONNECTIONS LIMITED—See Avnet, Inc.; *U.S. Public*, pg. 254
TELEDYNE E2V SEMICONDUCTORS SAS—See Teledyne Technologies Incorporated; *U.S. Public*, pg. 1995
TELEGESIS (UK) LIMITED—See Silicon Laboratories Inc.; *U.S. Public*, pg. 1880
TESCOM EUROPE GMBH & CO. KG—See Emerson Electric Co.; *U.S. Public*, pg. 752
TESCOM EUROPE MANAGEMENT GMBH—See Emerson Electric Co.; *U.S. Public*, pg. 752
TEUTECH INDUSTRIES INC.—See Hi-Tech Gears Ltd; *Int'l*, pg. 3381
THERM-O-DISC EUROPE B.V.—See Emerson Electric Co.; *U.S. Public*, pg. 745
THERMO KEVEX X-RAY INC.—See Thermo Fisher Scientific Inc.; *U.S. Public*, pg. 2154
THERMON EUROPE B.V.—See Thermon Group Holdings, Inc.; *U.S. Public*, pg. 2155
THERMON HEAT TRACERS PVT. LTD.—See Thermon Group Holdings, Inc.; *U.S. Public*, pg. 2155
THERMON MANUFACTURING COMPANY—See Thermon Group Holdings, Inc.; *U.S. Public*, pg. 2155
THERMON MIDDLE EAST, WLL—See Thermon Group Holdings, Inc.; *U.S. Public*, pg. 2155
THERMON SOLUCOES DE AQUECIMENTO LTDA.—See Thermon Group Holdings, Inc.; *U.S. Public*, pg. 2155
THERMON SOUTH AFRICA PTY. LTD.—See Thermon Group Holdings, Inc.; *U.S. Public*, pg. 2155
THOMAS & BETTS POWER SOLUTIONS, LLC—See ABB Ltd.; *Int'l*, pg. 52
TIME ERA SDN. BHD.—See Eden Inc. Berhad; *Int'l*, pg. 2306
TINITRON, INC.; *U.S. Private*, pg. 4175
TLX TECHNOLOGIES, LLC; *U.S. Private*, pg. 4179
TOHOKU FUJIKURA LTD.—See Fujikura Ltd.; *Int'l*, pg. 2829
TOO APS ENERGIA KAZAKHSTAN—See APS Energia SA; *Int'l*, pg. 523
TOOLS ACT COMPANY LIMITED—See Einhell Germany AG; *Int'l*, pg. 2334
TORQ CORPORATION; *U.S. Private*, pg. 4189
TOTALTRAX, INC.—See Pharos Capital Group, LLC; *U.S. Private*, pg. 3166
TRACKER LTD.—See General Atlantic Service Company, L.P.; *U.S. Private*, pg. 1661
TRC HONDURAS S.A. DE C.V.—See Southwire Company, LLC; *U.S. Private*, pg. 3742
TREBOL MAQUINARIA Y SUMINISTROS S.A.—See Emak S.p.A.; *Int'l*, pg. 2373
TRINOS VAKUUM-SYSTEME GMBH—See Dr. Ing. K. Busch GmbH; *Int'l*, pg. 2194
TRITIUM DCFC LIMITED—See Exicom Tele-Systems Limited; *Int'l*, pg. 2584
TROIS VIETNAM CO., LTD.—See Di-Nikko Engineering Co., Ltd.; *Int'l*, pg. 2101
TTIK INC.; *U.S. Private*, pg. 4255
TULSAT-ATLANTA LLC—See Leveling 8, Inc.; *U.S. Private*, pg. 2434
TUROTEST MEDIDORES LTDA.—See Enerpac Tool Group Corp.; *U.S. Public*, pg. 766
TYM MEDICAL—See HORIBA Ltd; *Int'l*, pg. 3478
ULC ROBOTICS, INC.—See SPX Technologies, Inc.; *U.S. Public*, pg. 1922
ULTRA ELECTRONICS LIMITED—See Advent International Corporation; *U.S Private*, pg. 101
ULTRA ELECTRONICS PRECISION AIR SYSTEMS INC—See Advent International Corporation; *U.S. Private*, pg. 101
ULTRAVOLT, INC.—See Advanced Energy Industries, Inc.; *U.S. Public*, pg. 48
ULUSOY ELEKTRIK IMALAT TAAHHUT VE TICARET A.S.—See Eaton Corporation plc; *Int'l*, pg. 2282
UNIVERSAL HOME EXPERTS; *U.S. Private*, pg. 4305

USA SWITCH INC.—See Superior Capital Partners LLC; *U.S. Private*, pg. 3876
U-SYSTEMS, INC.—See GE HealthCare Technologies Inc.; *U.S. Public*, pg. 909
UTHE JAPAN CO., LTD.—See Crest Group Inc.; *U.S. Private*, pg. 1096
UTHE SINGAPORE PTE LTD—See Crest Group Inc.; *U.S. Private*, pg. 1096
UV-TECHNIK INTERNATIONAL LTD.—See Dr. Honle AG; *Int'l*, pg. 2192
VAC MAGNETICS LLC—See Ara Partners Group; *U.S. Private*, pg. 306
VALIANT GLOBAL DEFENSE SERVICES INC.—See Valiant Integrated Services LLC; *U.S. Private*, pg. 4331
VALLIN BALTIC AS—See Addtech AB; *Int'l*, pg. 135
VARIOHM-EUROSENSOR LIMITED—See discoverIE Group plc; *Int'l*, pg. 2134
VARNAVAS HADJIPANAYIS LIMITED—See HORIBA Ltd; *Int'l*, pg. 3478
VEETHREE ELECTRONICS & MARINE LLC; *U.S. Private*, pg. 4353
VEEX, INC; *U.S. Private*, pg. 4353
VELOXION INC.; *U.S. Private*, pg. 4355
VENT-ALARM CORPORATION; *U.S. Private*, pg. 4357
VERSATILE POWER, INC.—See Advanced Energy Industries, Inc.; *U.S. Public*, pg. 48
VESNA TRADING PLC—See Einhell Germany AG; *Int'l*, pg. 2334
VIA OPTRONICS GMBH—See Ayala Corporation; *Int'l*, pg. 774
VICOR JAPAN COMPANY, LTD.—See Vicor Corporation; *U.S. Public*, pg. 2296
VIDEO KING GAMING SYSTEMS, LLC - MANUFACTURING DIVISION—See Video King Gaming Systems, LLC; *U.S. Private*, pg. 4380
VISHAY INTERTECHNOLOGY, INC.; *U.S. Public*, pg. 2302
VISHAY MEASUREMENTS GROUP FRANCE S.A.S.—See Vishay Precision Group, Inc.; *U.S. Public*, pg. 2303
VISHAY MEASUREMENTS GROUP UK LTD.—See Vishay Precision Group, Inc.; *U.S. Public*, pg. 2304
VISHAY PRECISION GROUP, INC.; *U.S. Public*, pg. 2303
VOLTA, LLC—See CSE Global Ltd.; *Int'l*, pg. 1864
VPT, INC.—See HEICO Corporation; *U.S. Public*, pg. 1021
WAGNER INDUSTRIAL ELECTRIC, INC.—See MDU Resources Group, Inc.; *U.S. Public*, pg. 1411
WARNER POWER, LLC—See Blackford Capital LLC; *U.S. Private*, pg. 574
WATER BLAST MANUFACTURING LP—See Exchange Income Corporation; *Int'l*, pg. 2579
WATTEREDGE LLC—See Southwire Company, LLC; *U.S. Private*, pg. 3742
WD MEDIA (SINGAPORE) PTE. LTD.—See Western Digital Corporation; *U.S. Public*, pg. 2355
WESTERN DIGITAL IRELAND, LTD.—See Western Digital Corporation; *U.S. Public*, pg. 2355
WESTERN DIGITAL (MALAYSIA) SDN. BHD.—See Western Digital Corporation; *U.S. Public*, pg. 2355
WIEGAND S.A. DE C.V.—See Emerson Electric Co.; *U.S. Public*, pg. 752
WINDROCK, INC.—See ChampionX Corporation; *U.S. Public*, pg. 478
WI-TRON, INC.; *U.S. Public*, pg. 2369
WM ARGENTINA SA—See HORIBA Ltd; *Int'l*, pg. 3478
WOODHEAD CONNECTIVITY S.A.S.U.—See Koch Industries, Inc.; *U.S. Private*, pg. 2335
WOODHEAD DE MEXICO S.A. DE C.V.—See Koch Industries, Inc.; *U.S. Private*, pg. 2335
WOODWARD CIS LIMITED LIABILITY COMPANY—See Woodward, Inc.; *U.S. Public*, pg. 2378
WOODWARD, INC.; *U.S. Public*, pg. 2377
WOODWARD INC.—See Woodward, Inc.; *U.S. Public*, pg. 2378
WORLD AM, INC.; *U.S. Public*, pg. 2379
W TECHNOLOGIES CORP.; *U.S. Public*, pg. 2315
WUHAN TIANHE TECHNOLOGY CO., LTD.—See Guodian Nanjing Automation Co., Ltd.; *Int'l*, pg. 3186
WUXI FUJI ELECTRIC FA CO., LTD.—See Fuji Electric Co., Ltd.; *Int'l*, pg. 2813
WUXI RONGZHI ELECTRONICS CO., LTD.—See Di-Nikko Engineering Co., Ltd.; *Int'l*, pg. 2101
XEONICS CO., LTD.—See Aroot Co., Ltd.; *Int'l*, pg. 577
XIAMEN FDK CORPORATION—See Fujitsu Limited; *Int'l*, pg. 2833
XICOM TECHNOLOGY EUROPE, LTD.—See Comtech Telecommunications Corp.; *U.S. Public*, pg. 563
XYLEM ANALYTICS FRANCE S.A.S.—See Xylem Inc.; *U.S. Public*, pg. 2395
XYLEM WATER SOLUTIONS MALAYSIA SDN. BHD.—See Xylem Inc.; *U.S. Public*, pg. 2397
XYLEM WATER SOLUTIONS UK HOLDINGS LIMITED—See Xylem Inc.; *U.S. Public*, pg. 2397
YANGZHOU YOUNGTEK ELECTRONICS LTD.—See Harvatek Corporation; *Int'l*, pg. 3280
YOUNG & CHAMPAGNE ELECTRICAL SALES INC.; *U.S. Private*, pg. 4592
YUJI SUGAI—See Hitachi, Ltd.; *Int'l*, pg. 3419
ZETEC FRANCE—See Roper Technologies, Inc.; *U.S. Public*, pg. 1814

335999 — ALL OTHER MISCELLAN...

ZETEC (SHANGHAI) CO., LTD.—See Roper Technologies, Inc.; *U.S. Public*, pg. 1814
ZHEJIANG FUDAR ALLOY MATERIALS TECHNOLOGY CO., LTD.—See Fuda Alloy Materials Co., Ltd.; *Int'l*, pg. 2804
ZHENGZHOU SENYUAN NEW ENERGY TECHNOLOGY CO., LTD.—See HENAN SENYUAN ELECTRIC CO., LTD.; *Int'l*, pg. 3343
ZHENZHOU SENYUAN NEW ENERGY TECHNOLOGY CO., LTD.—See HENAN SENYUAN ELECTRIC CO., LTD.; *Int'l*, pg. 3343
ZHUHAI CHERRY ELECTRONICS CO., LTD.—See Cherry SE; *Int'l*, pg. 1472
ZHUHAI KELI ELECTRONIC CO., LTD.—See China Keli Electric Company Ltd.; *Int'l*, pg. 1514
ZICOM PRIVATE LTD.—See Daikin Industries, Ltd.; *Int'l*, pg. 1937

336110 — AUTOMOBILE AND LIGHT DUTY MOTOR VEHICLE MANUFACTURING

ACCUBUILT ACQUISITION HOLDINGS INC.; *U.S. Private*, pg. 54
ACCUBUILT INC.—See Accubuilt Acquisition Holdings Inc.; *U.S. Private*, pg. 54
ACCURIDE WHEELS EUROPE & ASIA GMBH—See Crestview Partners, L.P.; *U.S. Private*, pg. 1097
ACSUD; *Int'l*, pg. 117
ADVANTAGE CHEVROLET OF BOLINGBROOK, INC.—See General Motors Company; *U.S. Public*, pg. 923
AFTERMARKET (UK) LIMITED—See General Motors Company; *U.S. Public*, pg. 927
AHLSTROM-MUNKSJO FILTRATION LLC—See Ahlstrom Capital Oy; *Int'l*, pg. 224
AHLSTROM-MUNKSJO FILTRATION LLC—See Bain Capital, LP; *U.S. Private*, pg. 429
AIRBAGS INTERNATIONAL LTD.—See Autoliv, Inc.; *Int'l*, pg. 728
A-JIN INDUSTRY CO.,LTD; *Int'l*, pg. 19
ALLGEIER ENGINEERING GMBH—See Allgeier SE; *Int'l*, pg. 336
ALPINE ARMORING INC.; *U.S. Private*, pg. 200
AMERITRANS BUS, INC.—See ABC Bus Companies, Inc.; *U.S. Private*, pg. 35
ANHUI ANKAI AUTOMOBILE CO., LTD.—See Anhui Jianghuai Automobile Group Corp., Ltd.; *Int'l*, pg. 468
ANHUI CHANGFENG YANGZI AUTOMOBILE MANUFACTURING, CO., LTD.—See Changfeng (Group) Co., Ltd.; *Int'l*, pg. 1443
ANHUI JIANGHUAI AUTOMOBILE GROUP CORP., LTD.; *Int'l*, pg. 468
ANTELOPE VALLEY CHEVROLET, INC.—See General Motors Company; *U.S. Public*, pg. 923
APPROACH (UK) LIMITED—See General Motors Company; *U.S. Public*, pg. 927
ARCIMOTO, INC.; *U.S. Public*, pg. 186
ARMORED AUTOGROUP AUSTRALIA PTY LTD—See Energizer Holdings, Inc.; *U.S. Public*, pg. 760
ARMORED AUTOGROUP CANADA ULC—See Energizer Holdings, Inc.; *U.S. Public*, pg. 760
ARMORED AUTOGROUP PARENT, INC.—See Spectrum Brands Holdings, Inc.; *U.S. Public*, pg. 1915
ARMORED AUTO (UK) LP—See Energizer Holdings, Inc.; *U.S. Public*, pg. 760
ASHOK LEYLAND LTD.—See Hinduja Group Ltd.; *Int'l*, pg. 3398
AS RIGAS AUTOELEKTROAPARATU RUPNICA; *Int'l*, pg. 591
ASTON MARTIN LAGONDA LIMITED—See Efad Real Estate Company; *Int'l*, pg. 2318
ATIEVA, INC.—See Lucid Group, Inc.; *U.S. Public*, pg. 1345
ATLANTIC AUTOMOBILES SAS—See General Motors Company; *U.S. Public*, pg. 927
AUTOALLIANCE INTERNATIONAL INC.—See Ford Motor Company; *U.S. Public*, pg. 864
AUTO-BERNER KOUVOLA—See Berner Oy; *Int'l*, pg. 988
AUTO-BERNER—See Berner Oy; *Int'l*, pg. 988
AUTO FORNEBU AS—See General Motors Company; *U.S. Public*, pg. 926
AUTOLIV ASIA PACIFIC—See Autoliv, Inc.; *Int'l*, pg. 728
AUTOLIV ELECTRONICS SAS, ROUEN—See Autoliv, Inc.; *Int'l*, pg. 728
AUTOLIV GMBH, BRAUNSCHWEIG—See Autoliv, Inc.; *Int'l*, pg. 728
AUTOLIV GMBH, WERK SUD—See Autoliv, Inc.; *Int'l*, pg. 728
AUTOLIV ISODELTA—See Autoliv, Inc.; *Int'l*, pg. 729
AUTOLIV ITALIA SPA—See Autoliv, Inc.; *Int'l*, pg. 729
AUTOLIV IZUMI PHILIPPINES, INC.—See Autoliv, Inc.; *Int'l*, pg. 729
AUTOLIV JAPAN KK—See Autoliv, Inc.; *Int'l*, pg. 729
AUTOLIV KK—See Autoliv, Inc.; *Int'l*, pg. 729
AUTOLIV QB, INC.—See Autoliv, Inc.; *Int'l*, pg. 729
AUTOLIV ROMANIA S.A.—See Autoliv, Inc.; *Int'l*, pg. 729
AUTOLIV SICHERHEITSTECHNIK GMBH, WERK OST—See Autoliv, Inc.; *Int'l*, pg. 729

AUTOMAG GMBH—See Bayerische Motoren Werke Aktiengesellschaft; *Int'l*, pg. 910
AUTOMOBILES CHATENET; *Int'l*, pg. 730
AUTOMOTIVE CORPORATION (MALAYSIA) SDN BHD—See DRB-HICOM Berhad; *Int'l*, pg. 2201
AUTO PINS INDIA LTD.; *Int'l*, pg. 725
AUTO RECYCLE AKITA CO., LTD.—See Dowa Holdings Co., Ltd.; *Int'l*, pg. 2182
AUTOVISION (SCOTLAND) LIMITED—See General Motors Company; *U.S. Public*, pg. 927
AVIA ASHOK LEYLAND MOTORS S.R.O—See Hinduja Group Ltd.; *Int'l*, pg. 3398
AVTOTEHNA VIS D.O.O.—See Avtotehna, d.d.; *Int'l*, pg. 751
BAIC MOTOR CORPORATION LTD.—See Beijing Automotive Industry Holding Co., Ltd.; *Int'l*, pg. 945
BALQON CORPORATION; *U.S. Public*, pg. 462
BAODING DONGLI MACHINERY CO., LTD.; *Int'l*, pg. 855
BARLOWORLD AUTOMOTIVE (PTY) LIMITED—See Barloworld Ltd.; *Int'l*, pg. 866
BAYERISCHE MOTOREN WERKE AKTIENGESELLSCHAFT - BERLIN PLANT—See Bayerische Motoren Werke Aktiengesellschaft; *Int'l*, pg. 912
BAYERISCHE MOTOREN WERKE AKTIENGESELLSCHAFT - LEIPZIG PLANT—See Bayerische Motoren Werke Aktiengesellschaft; *Int'l*, pg. 912
BAYERISCHE MOTOREN WERKE AKTIENGESELLSCHAFT - MUNICH PLANT—See Bayerische Motoren Werke Aktiengesellschaft; *Int'l*, pg. 912
BAYERISCHE MOTOREN WERKE AKTIENGESELLSCHAFT; *Int'l*, pg. 910
BAYERISCHE MOTOREN WERKE AKTIENGESELLSCHAFT - WACKERSDORF PLANT—See Bayerische Motoren Werke Aktiengesellschaft; *Int'l*, pg. 912
BBS KRAFTFAHRZEUGTECHNIK AG; *Int'l*, pg. 921
BEIJING AUTOMOTIVE INDUSTRY HOLDING CO., LTD.; *Int'l*, pg. 945
BEIJINGWEST INDUSTRIES INTERNATIONAL LIMITED; *Int'l*, pg. 962
BEIQI FOTON MOTOR COMPANY LTD.; *Int'l*, pg. 962
BELLEVUE-S, LLC—See Lithia Motors, Inc.; *U.S. Public*, pg. 1321
BELLEVUE-T, LLC—See Lithia Motors, Inc.; *U.S. Public*, pg. 1321
BENTELER AUTOMOTIVE BELGIUM N.V.—See Benteler International AG; *Int'l*, pg. 976
BENTELER AUTOMOTIVE (CHANGSHU) COMPANY LIMITED—See Benteler International AG; *Int'l*, pg. 976
BENTELER AUTOMOTIVE (CHONGQING) CO. LTD.—See Benteler International AG; *Int'l*, pg. 976
BENTELER AUTOMOTIVE RUMBURK S.R.O.—See Benteler International AG; *Int'l*, pg. 976
BENTELER AUTOMOTIVE SAS—See Benteler International AG; *Int'l*, pg. 976
BENTELER AUTOMOTIVE (SHANGHAI) CO., LTD.—See Benteler International AG; *Int'l*, pg. 976
BENTELER AUTOMOTIVE SK S.R.O.—See Benteler International AG; *Int'l*, pg. 976
BENTELER AUTOMOTIVE SOUTH AFRICA (PTY) LTD.—See Benteler International AG; *Int'l*, pg. 975
BENTELER AUTOMOTIVE UK LTD.—See Benteler International AG; *Int'l*, pg. 976
BENTELER AUTOTECHNIKA KFT—See Benteler International AG; *Int'l*, pg. 976
BENTELER CAPP AUTOMOTIVE SYSTEM (CHANGCHUN) CO., LTD.—See Benteler International AG; *Int'l*, pg. 976
BENTELER CR S.R.O.—See Benteler International AG; *Int'l*, pg. 976
BENTELER ESPANA S.A.—See Benteler International AG; *Int'l*, pg. 977
BENTELER GOSHEN, INC.—See Benteler International AG; *Int'l*, pg. 977
BENTELER-INDUSTRIA DE COMPONENTES PARA AUTOMOVEIS LDA.—See Benteler International AG; *Int'l*, pg. 977
BENTELER J.I.T. DOUAI S.A.S.—See Benteler International AG; *Int'l*, pg. 977
BENTELER JIT DUSSELDORF GMBH & CO. KG—See Benteler International AG; *Int'l*, pg. 977
BENTELER JIT PAMPLONA, S.L.U.—See Benteler International AG; *Int'l*, pg. 976
BENTELER JIT VITORIA, S.L.U.—See Benteler International AG; *Int'l*, pg. 976
BENTELER PALENCIA S.L.—See Benteler International AG; *Int'l*, pg. 977
BENTELER SISTEMAS AUTOMOTIVOS LTDA.—See Benteler International AG; *Int'l*, pg. 977
BERJAYA CHINA MOTOR SDN BHD—See Berjaya Corporation Berhad; *Int'l*, pg. 982
BMW AUSTRALIA FINANCE LTD.—See Bayerische Motoren Werke Aktiengesellschaft; *Int'l*, pg. 911
BMW BRILLIANCE AUTOMOTIVE LTD.—See Bayerische Motoren Werke Aktiengesellschaft; *Int'l*, pg. 911
BMW BRILLIANCE AUTOMOTIVE LTD.—See Brilliance China Automotive Holdings Limited; *Int'l*, pg. 1163
BMW CAR IT GMBH—See Bayerische Motoren Werke Aktiengesellschaft; *Int'l*, pg. 911
BMW DANMARK A/S—See Bayerische Motoren Werke Aktiengesellschaft; *Int'l*, pg. 911

BMW DE ARGENTINA S.A.—See Bayerische Motoren Werke Aktiengesellschaft; *Int'l*, pg. 910
BMW FINANCE S.N.C.—See Bayerische Motoren Werke Aktiengesellschaft; *Int'l*, pg. 911
BMW FINANCIAL SERVICES (IRELAND) DAC—See Bayerische Motoren Werke Aktiengesellschaft; *Int'l*, pg. 911
BMW FINANCIAL SERVICES KOREA CO. LTD.—See Bayerische Motoren Werke Aktiengesellschaft; *Int'l*, pg. 911
BMW FINANCIAL SERVICES SINGAPORE PTE. LTD.—See Bayerische Motoren Werke Aktiengesellschaft; *Int'l*, pg. 911
BMW FINANCIAL SERVICES (SOUTH AFRICA) (PTY) LTD.—See Bayerische Motoren Werke Aktiengesellschaft; *Int'l*, pg. 911
BMW INDIA FINANCIAL SERVICES PRIVATE LTD.—See Bayerische Motoren Werke Aktiengesellschaft; *Int'l*, pg. 911
BMW INDIA PRIVATE LIMITED—See Bayerische Motoren Werke Aktiengesellschaft; *Int'l*, pg. 911
BMW KOREA CO. LTD.—See Bayerische Motoren Werke Aktiengesellschaft; *Int'l*, pg. 911
BMW KUNDENBETREUUNG—See Bayerische Motoren Werke Aktiengesellschaft; *Int'l*, pg. 911
BMW MALAYSIA SDN BHD—See Bayerische Motoren Werke Aktiengesellschaft; *Int'l*, pg. 912
BMW MALTA LTD.—See Bayerische Motoren Werke Aktiengesellschaft; *Int'l*, pg. 912
BMW-MANUFACTURING CO., LLC—See Bayerische Motoren Werke Aktiengesellschaft; *Int'l*, pg. 912
BMW MANUFACTURING (THAILAND) CO., LTD.—See Bayerische Motoren Werke Aktiengesellschaft; *Int'l*, pg. 912
BMW MASCHINENFABRIK SPANDAU GMBH—See Bayerische Motoren Werke Aktiengesellschaft; *Int'l*, pg. 912
BMW MOTOREN GES.M.B.H.—See Bayerische Motoren Werke Aktiengesellschaft; *Int'l*, pg. 911
BMW NORGE AS—See Bayerische Motoren Werke Aktiengesellschaft; *Int'l*, pg. 912
BMW NORTHERN EUROPE AB—See Bayerische Motoren Werke Aktiengesellschaft; *Int'l*, pg. 912
BMW PORTUGAL LDA—See Bayerische Motoren Werke Aktiengesellschaft; *Int'l*, pg. 912
BMW SA/NV—See Bayerische Motoren Werke Aktiengesellschaft; *Int'l*, pg. 912
BMW (SCHWEIZ) AG—See Bayerische Motoren Werke Aktiengesellschaft; *Int'l*, pg. 910
BMW SLOVENSKA REPUBLIKA S.R.O.—See Bayerische Motoren Werke Aktiengesellschaft; *Int'l*, pg. 912
BMW (SOUTH AFRICA) PTY. LTD. - ROSSLYN PLANT—See Bayerische Motoren Werke Aktiengesellschaft; *Int'l*, pg. 911
BMW (SOUTH AFRICA) PTY. LTD.—See Bayerische Motoren Werke Aktiengesellschaft; *Int'l*, pg. 910
BMW SVERIGE AB—See Bayerische Motoren Werke Aktiengesellschaft; *Int'l*, pg. 912
BMW SYDNEY PTY. LTD.—See Bayerische Motoren Werke Aktiengesellschaft; *Int'l*, pg. 912
BMW (THAILAND) CO. LTD.—See Bayerische Motoren Werke Aktiengesellschaft; *Int'l*, pg. 911
BOON KOON VEHICLES INDUSTRIES SDN BHD—See Chin Hin Group Berhad; *Int'l*, pg. 1480
BRANDISH LIMITED—See General Motors Company; *U.S. Public*, pg. 927
BRITAIN CHEVROLET, INC.—See General Motors Company; *U.S. Public*, pg. 923
BUCHER-GUYER AG MUNICIPAL VEHICLES—See Bucher Industries AG; *Int'l*, pg. 1208
BUCHER-GUYER AG—See Bucher Industries AG; *Int'l*, pg. 1208
BUCHER MUNICIPAL AG—See Bucher Industries AG; *Int'l*, pg. 1208
BUCHER-SCHOERLING GMBH—See Bucher Industries AG; *Int'l*, pg. 1208
BYD EUROPEAN B.V.—See BYD Company Limited; *Int'l*, pg. 1234
BYD MOTORS PERU S.A.C.—See BYD Company Limited; *Int'l*, pg. 1234
CAB EAST LLC—See Ford Motor Company; *U.S. Public*, pg. 865
CABOT COACH BUILDER INC.; *U.S. Private*, pg. 711
CANOO INC.; *U.S. Public*, pg. 430
CARMAX LIMITED—See ANSA McAl Limited; *Int'l*, pg. 477
CHAMPION CHEVROLET, PONTIAC, BUICK, INC.—See General Motors Company; *U.S. Public*, pg. 923
CHANGZHOU TENGLONG AUTO PARTS CO., LTD.; *Int'l*, pg. 1445
CHARLATTE MANUTENTION—See FAYAT SAS; *Int'l*, pg. 2625
CHENBRO EUROPE B.V.—See Chenbro Micom Co., Ltd.; *Int'l*, pg. 1465
CHENBRO MICOM (SHENZHEN) CO., LTD.—See Chenbro Micom Co., Ltd.; *Int'l*, pg. 1465
CHERY AUTOMOBILE CO., LTD.; *Int'l*, pg. 1472
CHEVROLET AUSTRIA GMBH—See General Motors Company; *U.S. Public*, pg. 927
CHEVROLET CENTRAL AND EASTERN EUROPE—See General Motors Company; *U.S. Public*, pg. 926
CHEVROLET DEUTSCHLAND GMBH—See General Mo-

N.A.I.C.S. INDEX

336110 — AUTOMOBILE AND LIGH...

tors Company; *U.S. Public*, pg. 926
CHEVROLET ESPANA, S.A.—See General Motors Company; *U.S. Public*, pg. 927
CHEVROLET ITALIA S.P.A.—See General Motors Company; *U.S. Public*, pg. 926
CHEVROLET PORTUGAL, LDA.—See General Motors Company; *U.S. Public*, pg. 927
CHEVROLET SALES (THAILAND) LIMITED—See General Motors Company; *U.S. Public*, pg. 923
CHEVROLET SOCIEDAD ANONIMA DE AHORRO PARA FINES DETERMINADOS—See General Motors Company; *U.S. Public*, pg. 923
CHEVROLET UK LIMITED LTD—See General Motors Company; *U.S. Public*, pg. 927
CHINA FAW GROUP CORPORATION; *Int'l*, pg. 1501
CHINA FAW GROUP IMPORT & EXPORT CORPORATION—See China FAW Group Corporation; *Int'l*, pg. 1501
CHINA FINEBLANKING TECHNOLOGY CO., LTD.; *Int'l*, pg. 1503
CHINA MOTOR CORPORATION - HSIN-CHU PLANT—See China Motor Corporation; *Int'l*, pg. 1525
CHINA MOTOR CORPORATION - YANG-MEI PLANT—See China Motor Corporation; *Int'l*, pg. 1525
CHINA MOTOR CORPORATION - YU-SHIH PLANT—See China Motor Corporation; *Int'l*, pg. 1525
CHINA SOUTH INDUSTRIES GROUP CORPORATION; *Int'l*, pg. 1552
CHONGQING CHANGAN AUTOMOBILE COMPANY LTD.; *Int'l*, pg. 1579
CHONGQING CHANGAN SUZUKI AUTOMOBILE CO., LTD.—See Chongqing Changan Automobile Company Ltd.; *Int'l*, pg. 1579
CHUZHOU DUOLI AUTOMOTIVE TECHNOLOGY CO., LTD.; *Int'l*, pg. 1600
CIMC JIDONG (QINHUANGDAO) VEHICLES MANUFACTURE CO., LTD.—See China International Marine Containers (Group) Co., Ltd.; *Int'l*, pg. 1511
CLASSIC INTERNATIONAL ARMORING—See Classic Limousine Inc.; *U.S. Private*, pg. 916
CLASSIC LIMOUSINE INC.; *U.S. Private*, pg. 916
CLASSIC MOTORS LTD—See ANSA McAL Limited; *Int'l*, pg. 477
CMC INVESTMENT JOINT STOCK COMPANY; *Int'l*, pg. 1669
CNH AMERICA - NEW HOLLAND—See CNH Industrial N.V.; *Int'l*, pg. 1674
COCLISA S.A. DE C.V.—See Hahn & Company; *Int'l*, pg. 3208
COMINIX U.S.A., INC.—See Cominix Co., Ltd.; *Int'l*, pg. 1714
CONSORCIO NACIONAL FORD LTDA.—See Ford Motor Company; *U.S. Public*, pg. 864
CONTROL PRINT LTD.; *Int'l*, pg. 1785
COROMAL CARAVANS PTY LTD—See Fleetwood Limited; *Int'l*, pg. 2699
CRASH AVOIDANCE METRICS PARTNERSHIPS—See General Motors Company; *U.S. Public*, pg. 923
CRESTLINE COACH LTD.—See Caisse de Depot et Placement du Quebec; *Int'l*, pg. 1254
CRESTLINE COACH LTD.—See Clearspring Capital Partners; *Int'l*, pg. 1657
CRYOMAX COOLING SYSTEM CORP.; *Int'l*, pg. 1860
CUB ELECPARTS INC. - SHANGHAI FACILITY—See Cub Elecparts Inc.; *Int'l*, pg. 1875
CULTURAL INVESTMENT HOLDINGS CO., LTD.; *Int'l*, pg. 1877
CXJ GROUP CO., LIMITED; *Int'l*, pg. 1891
DABRYAN COACH BUILDERS INC.—See Accubuilt Acquisition Holdings Inc.; *U.S. Private*, pg. 54
DAEDONG GEAR CO., LTD.; *Int'l*, pg. 1906
DAEWOO MOTOR SALES CORPORATION; *Int'l*, pg. 1910
DARON MOTORS LLC—See Lithia Motors, Inc.; *U.S. Public*, pg. 1322
DASA CNC (WEIHAI) CO., LTD.—See Abpro Bio Co., Ltd.; *Int'l*, pg. 67
DCH BLOOMFIELD LLC—See Lithia Motors, Inc.; *U.S. Public*, pg. 1322
DCH FREEHOLD LLC—See Lithia Motors, Inc.; *U.S. Public*, pg. 1322
DCH MONTCLAIR LLC—See Lithia Motors, Inc.; *U.S. Public*, pg. 1322
DCM ENGINEERING LIMITED—See DCM Limited; *Int'l*, pg. 1992
DEJANA TRUCK & UTILITY EQUIPMENT CO., INC.—See Douglas Dynamics, Inc.; *U.S. Public*, pg. 677
DEMARAIS INDUSTRIES; *Int'l*, pg. 2025
DENSO TOOL AND DIE (THAILAND) CO., LTD.—See Denso Corporation; *Int'l*, pg. 2032
DETROIT TRUCK MANUFACTURING, LLC—See AIP, LLC; *U.S. Private*, pg. 135
DEUTA-WERKE GMBH; *Int'l*, pg. 2049
DEWAN FAROOQUE MOTORS LIMITED; *Int'l*, pg. 2091
DHSTEEL; *Int'l*, pg. 2100
DIAMONDBACK AUTOMOTIVE ACCESSORIES INC.; *U.S. Private*, pg. 1224
DIAMONDBACK TRUCK COVERS—See DiamondBack Automotive Accessories Inc.; *U.S. Private*, pg. 1224

DINUBA AUTO CENTER, INC.—See General Motors Company; *U.S. Public*, pg. 924
DNIPROVAGONMASH JSC; *Int'l*, pg. 2148
DONGFENG AUTOMOBILE CO., LTD.—See Dongfeng Motor Corporation; *Int'l*, pg. 2166
DONGFENG ELECTRIC VEHICLE CO., LTD.—See Dongfeng Motor Corporation; *Int'l*, pg. 2166
DONGFENG MOTOR CORPORATION; *Int'l*, pg. 2166
DONGFENG MOTOR GROUP CO. LTD.—See Dongfeng Motor Corporation; *Int'l*, pg. 2166
DONGFENG PEUGEOT CITROEN AUTOMOBILE COMPANY LTD.—See Dongfeng Motor Corporation; *Int'l*, pg. 2166
DONGHEE CZECH S.R.O.—See DH Holdings Co., Ltd.; *Int'l*, pg. 2097
DONGWON METAL CO., LTD.; *Int'l*, pg. 2171
DRB-HICOM BERHAD; *Int'l*, pg. 2201
DRB-HICOM COMMERCIAL VEHICLES SDN. BHD.—See DRB-HICOM Berhad; *Int'l*, pg. 2201
DRIVENOW BELGIUM S.P.R.L.—See Bayerische Motoren Werke Aktiengesellschaft; *Int'l*, pg. 912
DRIVENOW ITALY S.R.L.—See Bayerische Motoren Werke Aktiengesellschaft; *Int'l*, pg. 912
DUAL CO. LTD; *Int'l*, pg. 2217
DUNCAN ENGINEERING LIMITED; *Int'l*, pg. 2225
DYNAMIC SPECIALTY VEHICLES LTD.; *Int'l*, pg. 2241
EAGLE COACH COMPANY—See J.B. Poindexter & Co., Inc.; *U.S. Private*, pg. 2158
EARTH STAHL & ALLOYS LTD.; *Int'l*, pg. 2268
EDAG ENGINEERING AB—See ATON GmbH; *Int'l*, pg. 688
EDAG ENGINEERING GMBH—See ATON GmbH; *Int'l*, pg. 688
EDAG PRODUCTION SOLUTIONS GMBH & CO. KG—See ATON GmbH; *Int'l*, pg. 689
EFLEETS CORPORATION; *U.S. Private*, pg. 1343
EICHER MOTORS LIMITED; *Int'l*, pg. 2328
ELASTO S.A.—See General Motors Company; *U.S. Public*, pg. 924
THE ELECTRIC CAR COMPANY; *U.S. Private*, pg. 4025
ELEKTRONISCHE FAHRWERKSYSTEME GMBH—See Adecco Group AG; *Int'l*, pg. 140
ELIO MOTORS, INC; *U.S. Public*, pg. 734
EMG HOLDINGS LTD; *Int'l*, pg. 2380
E-N-G MOBILE SYSTEMS, INC.—See PositiveID Corporation; *U.S. Private*, pg. 3233
E.SOLUTIONS GMBH—See Continental Aktiengesellschaft; *Int'l*, pg. 1783
ESTRIMA S.P.A.; *Int'l*, pg. 2519
EURO TRUCK & BUS (MALAYSIA) SDN BHD—See DRB-HICOM Berhad; *Int'l*, pg. 2201
EXECUTIVE COACH BUILDERS INC.; *U.S. Private*, pg. 1447
FAMOS D.D.; *Int'l*, pg. 2612
FAURECIA BLOC AVANT—See FORVIA SE; *Int'l*, pg. 2746
FAW-EASTERN EUROPE LLC—See China FAW Group Corporation; *Int'l*, pg. 1502
FAWER AUTOMOTIVE PARTS LIMITED COMPANY; *Int'l*, pg. 2623
FAW JIEFANG GROUP CO., LTD.—See China FAW Group Corporation; *Int'l*, pg. 1502
FAWORIT-AUTO COMPANY—See China FAW Group Corporation; *Int'l*, pg. 1502
FAW TRUCK MANUFACTURERS SA (PTY) LTD—See China FAW Group Corporation; *Int'l*, pg. 1502
FAW-VOLKSWAGEN AUTOMOTIVE CO., LTD.—See China FAW Group Corporation; *Int'l*, pg. 1502
FEC CHAIN CORPORATION—See Chuo Spring Co., Ltd.; *Int'l*, pg. 1599
FEDERAL COACH COMPANY—See J.B. Poindexter & Co., Inc.; *U.S. Private*, pg. 2158
FEDERAL COACH, LLC—See J.B. Poindexter & Co., Inc.; *U.S. Private*, pg. 2158
FEDERAL-MOGUL FRICTION PRODUCTS A.S.—See Apollo Global Management, Inc.; *U.S. Public*, pg. 161
FEDERAL-MOGUL FRICTION PRODUCTS—See Apollo Global Management, Inc.; *U.S. Public*, pg. 161
FEDERAL-MOGUL PTY. LTD.—See Apollo Global Management, Inc.; *U.S. Public*, pg. 161
FEDERAL-MOGUL S.A.—See Apollo Global Management, Inc.; *U.S. Public*, pg. 161
FERRARI SOUTH WEST EUROPE S.A.R.L.—See Ferrari N.V.; *Int'l*, pg. 2639
FERRARI S.P.A.—See Ferrari N.V.; *Int'l*, pg. 2639
FILTRAUTO S.A.—See Compagnia Finanziaria de Benedetti S.p.A.; *Int'l*, pg. 1722
FLEXIDER S.P.A.—See Anamet Inc.; *U.S. Private*, pg. 272
FORCE MOTORS LIMITED; *Int'l*, pg. 2730
FORD BANK GMBH—See Ford Motor Company; *U.S. Public*, pg. 864
FORD ESPANA S.A.—See Ford Motor Company; *U.S. Public*, pg. 865
FORD ESSEX ENGINE PLANT—See Ford Motor Company; *U.S. Public*, pg. 865
FORD FRANCE—See Ford Motor Company; *U.S. Public*, pg. 865
FORD INDIA PRIVATE LIMITED—See Ford Motor Company; *U.S. Public*, pg. 865

FORD ITALIA S.P.A.—See Ford Motor Company; *U.S. Public*, pg. 865
FORD LIO HO MOTOR CO., LTD.—See Ford Motor Company; *U.S. Public*, pg. 865
FORD LUSITANA—See Ford Motor Company; *U.S. Public*, pg. 865
FORD MOTOR AUSTRIA—See Ford Motor Company; *U.S. Public*, pg. 865
FORD MOTOR BELGIUM N.V.—See Ford Motor Company; *U.S. Public*, pg. 865
FORD MOTOR COMPANY LIMITED—See Ford Motor Company; *U.S. Public*, pg. 865
FORD MOTOR COMPANY OF AUSTRALIA LIMITED—See Ford Motor Company; *U.S. Public*, pg. 865
FORD MOTOR COMPANY; *U.S. Public*, pg. 864
FORD MOTOR JAPAN LTD.—See Ford Motor Company; *U.S. Public*, pg. 866
FORD MOTOR LAND DEVELOPMENT CORPORATION—See Ford Motor Company; *U.S. Public*, pg. 866
FORD MOTOR NORGE A/S—See Ford Motor Company; *U.S. Public*, pg. 865
FORD MOTOR SERVICE COMPANY—See Ford Motor Company; *U.S. Public*, pg. 866
FORD NEDERLAND B.V.—See Ford Motor Company; *U.S. Public*, pg. 866
FORD OTOMOTIV SANAYI A.S.—See Ford Motor Company; *U.S. Public*, pg. 866
FORD ROMANIA S.A.—See Ford Motor Company; *U.S. Public*, pg. 864
FORD SALES & SERVICE (THAILAND) CO., LTD.—See Ford Motor Company; *U.S. Public*, pg. 866
FORD-WERKE GMBH—See Ford Motor Company; *U.S. Public*, pg. 866
FOREZ BENNES; *Int'l*, pg. 2732
FOXTRON VEHICLE TECHNOLOGIES CO., LTD.—See Hon Hai Precision Industry Co., Ltd.; *Int'l*, pg. 3457
FPT INDUSTRIAL S.P.A.—See CNH Industrial N.V.; *Int'l*, pg. 1675
FRAPPA; *Int'l*, pg. 2764
FREDERICKTOWN CHEVROLET CO., INC.—See General Motors Company; *U.S. Public*, pg. 924
FRONTLINE COMMUNICATIONS—See Oshkosh Corporation; *U.S. Public*, pg. 1621
FULLY EQUIPPED LIMITED—See Amotiv Limited; *Int'l*, pg. 431
FUXIN DARE AUTOMOTIVE PARTS CO., LTD.; *Int'l*, pg. 2858
GAC CHANGFENG MOTOR CO., LTD.—See Guangzhou Automobile Industry Group Co., Ltd.; *Int'l*, pg. 3164
GAFFOGLIO FAMILY METALCRAFTERS INC.; *U.S. Private*, pg. 1634
GANSU CIMC HUAJUN VEHICLE CO., LTD.—See China International Marine Containers (Group) Co., Ltd.; *Int'l*, pg. 1511
GAZ GROUP MANAGEMENT COMPANY LLC; *Int'l*, pg. 2891
GB POLO BUS MANUFACTURING COMPANY—See Ghabbour Auto S.A.E.; *Int'l*, pg. 2958
GENERAL MOTORS ASSET MANAGEMENT CORPORATION—See General Motors Company; *U.S. Public*, pg. 924
GENERAL MOTORS AUSTRIA GMBH—See General Motors Company; *U.S. Public*, pg. 927
GENERAL MOTORS BELGIUM N.V.—See General Motors Company; *U.S. Public*, pg. 927
GENERAL MOTORS BENELUX—See General Motors Company; *U.S. Public*, pg. 927
GENERAL MOTORS CHILE S.A., INDUSTRIA AUTOMOTRIZ—See General Motors Company; *U.S. Public*, pg. 924
GENERAL MOTORS COLMOTORES, S.A.—See General Motors Company; *U.S. Public*, pg. 924
GENERAL MOTORS COMPANY; *U.S. Public*, pg. 923
GENERAL MOTORS CONTINENTAL—See General Motors Company; *U.S. Public*, pg. 927
GENERAL MOTORS DE ARGENTINA S.R.L.—See General Motors Company; *U.S. Public*, pg. 925
GENERAL MOTORS DE MEXICO, S.A. DE C.V.—See General Motors Company; *U.S. Public*, pg. 925
GENERAL MOTORS DE PORTUGAL, SOCIEDADE ANONIMA—See General Motors Company; *U.S. Public*, pg. 927
GENERAL MOTORS DO BRASIL LTDA.—See General Motors Company; *U.S. Public*, pg. 925
GENERAL MOTORS ESPANA S.L.—See General Motors Company; *U.S. Public*, pg. 927
GENERAL MOTORS EUROPE HOLDINGS, S.L.—See General Motors Company; *U.S. Public*, pg. 927
GENERAL MOTORS FRANCE AUTOMOBILES S.A.—See General Motors Company; *U.S. Public*, pg. 927
GENERAL MOTORS HELLAS S.A.—See General Motors Company; *U.S. Public*, pg. 927
GENERAL MOTORS HOLDINGS LLC—See General Motors Company; *U.S. Public*, pg. 925
GENERAL MOTORS INDIA PRIVATE LIMITED—See General Motors Company; *U.S. Public*, pg. 925
GENERAL MOTORS INTERNATIONAL HOLDINGS,

336110 — AUTOMOBILE AND LIGH...   CORPORATE AFFILIATIONS

INC.—See General Motors Company; *U.S. Public*, pg. 925
GENERAL MOTORS MANUFACTURING POLAND SP. Z O.O.—See General Motors Company; *U.S. Public*, pg. 927
GENERAL MOTORS NEDERLAND B.V.—See General Motors Company; *U.S. Public*, pg. 927
GENERAL MOTORS OF CANADA COMPANY—See General Motors Company; *U.S. Public*, pg. 925
GENERAL MOTORS PERU S.A.—See General Motors Company; *U.S. Public*, pg. 925
GENERAL MOTORS POLAND SPOLKA, Z O. O.—See General Motors Company; *U.S. Public*, pg. 927
GENERAL MOTORS PORTUGAL LDA.—See General Motors Company; *U.S. Public*, pg. 927
GENERAL MOTORS POWERTRAIN - GERMANY GMBH—See General Motors Company; *U.S. Public*, pg. 927
GENERAL MOTORS POWERTRAIN (THAILAND) LIMITED—See General Motors Company; *U.S. Public*, pg. 925
GENERAL SALES COMPANY OF WEST CHESTER, INC.—See General Motors Company; *U.S. Public*, pg. 925
GHABBOUR AUTO S.A.E.; *Int'l*, pg. 2958
GHANDHARA AUTOMOBILES LIMITED—See Bibojee Services Private Limited; *Int'l*, pg. 1018
GLOBAL AUTOMOTIVE SYSTEMS LLC—See Patriarch Partners, LLC; *U.S. Private*, pg. 3109
GLOBAL ELECTRIC MOTORCARS LLC—See Polaris, Inc.; *U.S. Public*, pg. 1700
GLOBAL TEK FABRICATION CO., LTD.; *Int'l*, pg. 3001
GM CAMI ASSEMBLY—See General Motors Company; *U.S. Public*, pg. 925
GM COMPONENTS HOLDINGS, LLC—See General Motors Company; *U.S. Public*, pg. 924
GM CRUISE HOLDINGS LLC—See General Motors Company; *U.S. Public*, pg. 924
GM DAEWOO AUTO & TECHNOLOGY CO.—See General Motors Company; *U.S. Public*, pg. 924
GM GLOBAL TECHNOLOGY OPERATIONS LLC—See General Motors Company; *U.S. Public*, pg. 924
GM HOLDEN LTD.—See General Motors Company; *U.S. Public*, pg. 924
GM TECHNICAL CENTER KOREA, LTD.—See General Motors Company; *U.S. Public*, pg. 924
GM (UK) PENSION TRUSTEES LIMITED—See General Motors Company; *U.S. Public*, pg. 928
GRAMMER INDUSTRIES, LLC—See Grammer AG; *Int'l*, pg. 3053
GRANDE FORD TRUCK SALES, INC.—See Cavender Auto Group; *U.S. Private*, pg. 795
GREAT WALL MOTOR COMPANY LIMITED; *Int'l*, pg. 3065
GREEN AUTOMOTIVE COMPANY; *U.S. Private*, pg. 1771
GREENPOWER MOTOR COMPANY, INC.—See GreenPower Motor Company Inc.; *Int'l*, pg. 3076
GRENZEBACH MACHINERY (JIASHAN) LTD.—See Grenzebach Maschinenbau GmbH; *Int'l*, pg. 3082
GROHMANN USA, INC.—See Tesla, Inc.; *U.S. Public*, pg. 2021
GROUPE FMC FRANCE SAS—See Ford Motor Company; *U.S. Public*, pg. 866
G-TEKT CORPORATION; *Int'l*, pg. 2863
GUANGDONG TOPSTAR TECHNOLOGY CO., LTD.; *Int'l*, pg. 3161
GUANGZHOU AUTOMOBILE GROUP COMPANY LIMITED—See Guangzhou Automobile Industry Group Co., Ltd.; *Int'l*, pg. 3164
GUANGZHOU AUTOMOBILE INDUSTRY GROUP CO., LTD.; *Int'l*, pg. 3164
GUIDANCE AUTOMATION LIMITED—See Matthews International Corporation; *U.S. Public*, pg. 1399
HAGGLUNDS VEHICLE GMBH—See BAE Systems plc; *Int'l*, pg. 798
HAIMA AUTOMOBILE CO., LTD.; *Int'l*, pg. 3211
HAVAL MOTORS AUSTRALIA PTY. LTD.—See Great Wall Motor Company Limited; *Int'l*, pg. 3066
HAVAL MOTORS SOUTH AFRICA PROPRIETARY LIMITED—See Great Wall Motor Company Limited; *Int'l*, pg. 3066
HAYASHI TELEMPU CO., LTD.; *Int'l*, pg. 3289
HEIL FARID EUROPEAN COMPANY LIMITED—See Terex Corporation; *U.S. Public*, pg. 2019
HELLA AUTOMOTIVE SALES, INC.—See Hella GmbH & Co. KGaA; *Int'l*, pg. 3331
HENRY FORD & SONS LTD—See Ford Motor Company; *U.S. Public*, pg. 865
HER CHEE INDUSTRIAL CO., LTD.; *Int'l*, pg. 3356
HICOM AUTOMOTIVE MANUFACTURERS (MALAYSIA) SDN BHD—See DRB-HICOM Berhad; *Int'l*, pg. 2201
HIM TEKNOFORGE LIMITED; *Int'l*, pg. 3396
HINDUSTAN MOTORS LIMITED; *Int'l*, pg. 3400
HIP CORPORATION; *Int'l*, pg. 3402
HI SHARP ELECTRONICS CO., LTD.; *Int'l*, pg. 3379
HME, INC.—See Valley Truck Parts, Inc.; *U.S. Private*, pg. 4335
HOLZINDUSTRIE BRUCHSAL GMBH—See Draexlmaier Gruppe; *Int'l*, pg. 2198

HONDA ACCESS EUROPE N.V.—See Honda Motor Co., Ltd.; *Int'l*, pg. 3460
HONDA ATLAS CARS PAKISTAN LTD.—See Atlas Group of Companies; *Int'l*, pg. 685
HONDA ATLAS CARS PAKISTAN LTD.—See Honda Motor Co., Ltd.; *Int'l*, pg. 3460
HONDA AUSTRIA G.M.B.H.—See Honda Motor Co., Ltd.; *Int'l*, pg. 3460
HONDA AUTO BODY CO., LTD.—See Honda Motor Co., Ltd.; *Int'l*, pg. 3460
HONDA AUTOMOVEIS DO BRASIL LTDA.—See Honda Motor Co., Ltd.; *Int'l*, pg. 3460
HONDA CARS PHILIPPINES INC.—See Honda Motor Co., Ltd.; *Int'l*, pg. 3461
HONDA FRANCE S.A.S.—See Honda Motor Co., Ltd.; *Int'l*, pg. 3461
HONDA MALAYSIA SDN BHD—See Honda Motor Co., Ltd.; *Int'l*, pg. 3461
HONDA MANUFACTURING OF ALABAMA, LLC—See Honda Motor Co., Ltd.; *Int'l*, pg. 3461
HONDA MOTOR CO., LTD. - KUMAMOTO FACTORY—See Honda Motor Co., Ltd.; *Int'l*, pg. 3461
HONDA MOTOR CO., LTD.; *Int'l*, pg. 3459
HONDA MOTOR CO., LTD.—See Honda Motor Co., Ltd.; *Int'l*, pg. 3461
HONDA MOTOR CO., LTD.—See Honda Motor Co., Ltd.; *Int'l*, pg. 3461
HONDA MOTOR CO., LTD. - SUZUKA FACTORY—See Honda Motor Co., Ltd.; *Int'l*, pg. 3461
HONDA NEW ZEALAND LTD.—See Honda Motor Co., Ltd.; *Int'l*, pg. 3462
HONDA OF AMERICA MANUFACTURING, INC.—See Honda Motor Co., Ltd.; *Int'l*, pg. 3460
HONDA OF CANADA MFG.—See Honda Motor Co., Ltd.; *Int'l*, pg. 3463
HONDA OF SOUTH CAROLINA MANUFACTURING—See Honda Motor Co., Ltd.; *Int'l*, pg. 3463
HONDA OF THE U.K. MANUFACTURING LIMITED—See Honda Motor Co., Ltd.; *Int'l*, pg. 3463
HONDA R&D EUROPE (DEUTSCHLAND) GMBH—See Honda Motor Co., Ltd.; *Int'l*, pg. 3462
HONDA SIEL CARS INDIA LTD.—See Honda Motor Co., Ltd.; *Int'l*, pg. 3462
HONDA (SUISSE) S.A.—See Honda Motor Co., Ltd.; *Int'l*, pg. 3460
HONDA TAIWAN MOTOR CO., LTD.—See Honda Motor Co., Ltd.; *Int'l*, pg. 3462
HONDA TURKIYE A.S.—See Honda Motor Co., Ltd.; *Int'l*, pg. 3463
HONDA VIETNAM CO., LTD.—See Honda Motor Co., Ltd.; *Int'l*, pg. 3463
H-ONE CO. LTD. - KORIYAMA FACTORY—See H-One Co., Ltd.; *Int'l*, pg. 3194
H-ONE PARTS SRIRACHA CO., LTD.—See H-One Co., Ltd.; *Int'l*, pg. 3194
HONEYWELL KOREA, LTD.—See Honeywell International Inc.; *U.S. Public*, pg. 1051
HULME SUPERCARS LIMITED; *Int'l*, pg. 3528
HWA AG; *Int'l*, pg. 3541
HWASHIN CO., LTD.; *Int'l*, pg. 3542
HWASHIN CO., LTD.—See Hwashin Co., Ltd.; *Int'l*, pg. 3543
HWASHIN PRECISION INDUSTRY CO., LTD.—See Hwashin Co., Ltd.; *Int'l*, pg. 3543
HYULIM A-TECH CO. LTD; *Int'l*, pg. 3555
HYUNDAI AMERICA TECHNICAL CENTER, INC.—See Hyundai Motor Company; *Int'l*, pg. 3559
HYUNDAI KEFICO CORPORATION—See Hyundai Motor Company; *Int'l*, pg. 3559
HYUNDAI MOBIS CO., LTD.; *Int'l*, pg. 3558
HYUNDAI MOTOR COMPANY; *Int'l*, pg. 3558
HYUNDAI MOTOR DETROIT—See Hyundai Motor Company; *Int'l*, pg. 3559
HYUNDAI MOTOR INDIA LTD.—See Hyundai Motor Company; *Int'l*, pg. 3559
HYUNDAI MOTOR MANUFACTURING ALABAMA, LLC—See Hyundai Motor Company; *Int'l*, pg. 3559
HYUNDAI MOTOR TOKYO—See Hyundai Motor Company; *Int'l*, pg. 3559
HYUNDAI MOTOR U.K. LTD—See Hyundai Motor Company; *Int'l*, pg. 3559
IAG HOLDINGS INC.; *U.S. Private*, pg. 2027
IGARASHI MOTORS INDIA LIMITED; *Int'l*, pg. 3601
IMPERIAL DAIHATSU (PTY) LIMITED—See Dubai World Corporation; *Int'l*, pg. 2221
INDUS MOTOR COMPANY LIMITED—See House of Habib; *Int'l*, pg. 3491
INTERNATIONAL ARMORING CORP.—See IAG Holdings Inc.; *U.S. Private*, pg. 2027
IRISBUS IVECO - ANNONAY PLANT—See CNH Industrial N.V.; *Int'l*, pg. 1675
IRISBUS IVECO - VALLE UFITA PLANT—See CNH Industrial N.V.; *Int'l*, pg. 1675
ISUZU TRUCK SOUTH AFRICA (PTY.) LIMITED—See General Motors Company; *U.S. Public*, pg. 926
IVECO CZECH REPUBLIC A.S.—See CNH Industrial N.V.; *Int'l*, pg. 1675
IVECO MAGIRUS AG—See CNH Industrial N.V.; *Int'l*, pg. 1675

IVECO RETAIL LIMITED—See CNH Industrial N.V.; *Int'l*, pg. 1675
IVECO (SCHWEIZ) AG—See CNH Industrial N.V.; *Int'l*, pg. 1675
IVECO SLOVAKIA, S.R.O.—See CNH Industrial N.V.; *Int'l*, pg. 1676
JACKSON-T, LLC—See Lithia Motors, Inc.; *U.S. Public*, pg. 1323
J.B. POINDEXTER & CO., INC.; *U.S. Private*, pg. 2158
JEFFERSON INDUSTRIES CORPORATION; *U.S. Private*, pg. 2198
JEFFERY (WANDSWORTH) LIMITED—See General Motors Company; *U.S. Public*, pg. 928
JINGZHOU HENGLONG AUTOMOTIVE PARTS CO., LTD.—See China Automotive Systems, Inc.; *Int'l*, pg. 1484
JMT AUTO LIMITED—See Amtek Auto Limited; *Int'l*, pg. 441
JS FOLSOM AUTOMOTIVE, INC.—See General Motors Company; *U.S. Public*, pg. 925
JURGENS CI (PTY) LIMITED—See Dubai World Corporation; *Int'l*, pg. 2221
KAUTEX TEXTRON GMBH & CO. KG—See Textron Inc.; *U.S. Public*, pg. 2028
KEYSTONE RV COMPANY—See Thor Industries, Inc.; *U.S. Public*, pg. 2156
KOMOS CO.,LTD.—See Ecoplastic Corporation; *Int'l*, pg. 2299
KRONPRINZ GMBH—See Crestview Partners, L.P.; *U.S. Private*, pg. 1097
KRYSTAL INFINITY LLC; *U.S. Private*, pg. 2354
KTH LEESBURG PRODUCTS, LLC—See H-One Co., Ltd.; *Int'l*, pg. 3194
LISA DRAXLMAIER AUTOPART ROMANIA SRL—See Draexlmaier Gruppe; *Int'l*, pg. 2198
LITHIA MMF, INC.—See Lithia Motors, Inc.; *U.S. Public*, pg. 1324
LITHIA MOON-S, LLC—See Lithia Motors, Inc.; *U.S. Public*, pg. 1324
LITHIA MOON-V, LLC—See Lithia Motors, Inc.; *U.S. Public*, pg. 1324
LIVBAG SAS—See Autoliv, Inc.; *Int'l*, pg. 730
LIVEWIRE GROUP, INC.; *U.S. Public*, pg. 1333
LORDSTOWN MOTORS CORP.; *U.S. Public*, pg. 1342
L&P AUTOMOTIVE EUROPE HEADQUARTERS GMBH—See Leggett & Platt, Incorporated; *U.S. Public*, pg. 1302
LUOYANG LINYU AUTOMOBILE CO., LTD—See China International Marine Containers (Group) Co., Ltd.; *Int'l*, pg. 1512
MACK REMANUFACTURING CENTER—See AB Volvo; *Int'l*, pg. 45
MAGNETI MARELLI AFTERMARKET SP. Z O.O.—See KKR & Co. Inc.; *U.S. Public*, pg. 1260
MAHARASHTRA SCOOTERS LIMITED—See Bajaj Auto Ltd.; *Int'l*, pg. 804
MARELLI NORTH CAROLINA USA LLC—See KKR & Co. Inc.; *U.S. Public*, pg. 1261
MARSHALL OF IPSWICH LIMITED—See General Motors Company; *U.S. Public*, pg. 928
MARSHALL OF PETERBOROUGH LIMITED—See General Motors Company; *U.S. Public*, pg. 928
MAXWELL TECHNOLOGIES GMBH—See Tesla, Inc.; *U.S. Public*, pg. 2021
MBF INDUSTRIES, INC.; *U.S. Private*, pg. 2624
MCENEARNEY MOTORS LIMITED—See ANSA McAL Limited; *Int'l*, pg. 477
MEDIX SPECIALTY VEHICLES, INC.—See Caisse de Depot et Placement du Quebec; *Int'l*, pg. 1254
MEDIX SPECIALTY VEHICLES, INC.—See Clearspring Capital Partners; *Int'l*, pg. 1657
MEDTEC AMBULANCE CORP.—See Oshkosh Corporation; *U.S. Public*, pg. 1621
METAL CASTING TECHNOLOGY, INC.—See General Motors Company; *U.S. Public*, pg. 926
METTS CORPORATION—See Honda Motor Co., Ltd.; *Int'l*, pg. 3463
MILSCO DE MEXICO S. DE R.L. DE C.V.—See Jason Industries, Inc.; *U.S. Private*, pg. 2190
MINI GEORGIAN—See Georgian International Limited; *Int'l*, pg. 2939
MOBILE INDUSTRIAL ROBOTS A/S—See Teradyne, Inc.; *U.S. Public*, pg. 2018
MOBILE INDUSTRIAL ROBOTS GMBH—See Teradyne, Inc.; *U.S. Public*, pg. 2018
MOBILE INDUSTRIAL ROBOTS, INC.—See Teradyne, Inc.; *U.S. Public*, pg. 2018
MOBILE INDUSTRIAL ROBOTS PTE. LTD.—See Teradyne, Inc.; *U.S. Public*, pg. 2018
MOTORBODIES LUTON LIMITED—See General Motors Company; *U.S. Public*, pg. 928
M.P.M. INTERNATIONAL OIL COMPANY B.V.—See LKQ Corporation; *U.S. Public*, pg. 1335
MUNJAL AUTO INDUSTRIES LIMITED—See Hero Corp.; *Int'l*, pg. 3364
MURKETTS OF CAMBRIDGE LIMITED—See EMG Holdings Ltd; *Int'l*, pg. 2380
MYANMAR FAW INTL.—See China FAW Group Corporation; *Int'l*, pg. 1502

N.A.I.C.S. INDEX

336120 — HEAVY DUTY TRUCK MA...

NANJING DALUGE HIGH-TECH CO., LTD—See Beijing Zhong Ke San Huan High-tech Co., Ltd.; *Int'l*, pg. 961
NANJING HONGGUANG AUTOLIV LTD.—See Autoliv, Inc.; *Int'l*, pg. 730
NEMO MOTORS CORP.; *U.S. Private*, pg. 2884
NEW PRIDE CORPORATION; *U.S. Public*, pg. 1512
NIKOLA CORP.; *U.S. Public*, pg. 1529
NMI DURBAN SOUTH MOTORS (PTY) LTD.—See Barloworld Ltd.; *Int'l*, pg. 866
NOBO AUTOMOTIVE SYSTEMS GERMANY GMBH—See Great Wall Motor Company Limited; *Int'l*, pg. 3066
NORMA A/S—See Autoliv, Inc.; *Int'l*, pg. 730
NORTH AMERICAN NEW CARS, INC.—See General Motors Company; *U.S. Public*, pg. 926
NOVA BUS INCORPORATED—See AB Volvo; *Int'l*, pg. 43
NOW MOTOR RETAILING LIMITED—See General Motors Company; *U.S. Public*, pg. 928
ONSTAR, LLC—See General Motors Company; *U.S. Public*, pg. 926
OOO BENTELER AUTOMOTIVE—See Benteler International AG; *Int'l*, pg. 977
OOO IVECO RUSSIA—See CNH Industrial N.V.; *Int'l*, pg. 1676
ORANGE MOTORS B.V.—See General Motors Company; *U.S. Public*, pg. 927
OY BMW SUOMI AB—See Bayerische Motoren Werke Aktiengesellschaft; *Int'l*, pg. 912
PARK LANE LTD.—See Bayerische Motoren Werke Aktiengesellschaft; *Int'l*, pg. 913
PATRIOT CHEVROLET, INC.—See General Motors Company; *U.S. Public*, pg. 928
PEARL (CRAWLEY) LIMITED—See General Motors Company; *U.S. Public*, pg. 928
PHIROZE SETHNA PRIVATE LIMITED—See Chembond Chemicals Ltd; *Int'l*, pg. 1461
PISTON AUTOMOTIVE—See Piston Group, LLC; *U.S. Private*, pg. 3190
PL CUSTOM BODY & EQUIPMENT CO.; *U.S. Private*, pg. 3194
POLARIS, INC.; *U.S. Public*, pg. 1700
PRECICION TRIM, INC.; *U.S. Public*, pg. 1713
PROCESS AUTOMATION SOLUTIONS GMBH—See ATS Corporation; *Int'l*, pg. 695
PROMAK PRES OTOMASYON MAK. SAN. VE TIC. LTD.—See P/A Industries, Inc.; *U.S. Private*, pg. 3061
PROSTEP AG—See General Motors Company; *U.S. Public*, pg. 927
PROTERRA, INC.—See Proterra, Inc.; *U.S. Public*, pg. 1729
PT BMW INDONESIA—See Bayerische Motoren Werke Aktiengesellschaft; *Int'l*, pg. 913
P.T. BYD MOTOR INDONESIA—See BYD Company Limited; *Int'l*, pg. 1234
PT.H-ONE GOHI PRIMA AUTO TECHNOLOGIES INDONESIA—See H-One Co., Ltd.; *Int'l*, pg. 3194
PULLMAFLEX BENELUX N.V.—See Leggett & Platt, Incorporated; *U.S. Public*, pg. 1303
PYROTECHNIC PROCESSING FACILITY—See Autoliv, Inc.; *Int'l*, pg. 729
REEVE (DERBY) LIMITED—See General Motors Company; *U.S. Public*, pg. 928
RENTON CADILLAC PONTIAC GMC, INC.—See General Motors Company; *U.S. Public*, pg. 928
ROAD RESCUE USA, INC.—See AIP, LLC; *U.S. Private*, pg. 135
RONGCHENG HAWTAI AUTOMOBILE CO., LTD.—See Hawtai Motor Group Limited; *Int'l*, pg. 3289
RONN MOTOR GROUP, INC.; *U.S. Public*, pg. 3478
ROSSAREDS FASTIGHETS AB—See AB Volvo; *Int'l*, pg. 42
ROUSH PERFORMANCE PRODUCTS, INC.—See Roush Enterprises, Inc.; *U.S. Private*, pg. 3484
RUCKER LYPSA S.L.U.—See ATON GmbH; *Int'l*, pg. 689
SAIC GM WULING AUTOMOBILE COMPANY LIMITED—See General Motors Company; *U.S. Public*, pg. 928
SALEEN AUTOMOTIVE, INC.; *U.S. Private*, pg. 3531
SAYAMA MANUFACTURING FACILITY—See Honda Motor Co., Ltd.; *Int'l*, pg. 3464
SCAM SPA—See Certina Holding AG; *Int'l*, pg. 1423
SCHUKRA BERNDORF GES.M.B.H.—See Leggett & Platt, Incorporated; *U.S. Public*, pg. 1302
SERVICE TEAM INC.; *U.S. Public*, pg. 1872
SEWARD (WESSEX) LIMITED—See General Motors Company; *U.S. Public*, pg. 928
SHANGHAI BENTELER HUIZHONG AUTOMOTIVE COMPANY LTD.—See Benteler International AG; *Int'l*, pg. 977
SHANGHAI CIMC SPECIAL VEHICLE CO., LTD.—See China International Marine Containers (Group) Co., Ltd.; *Int'l*, pg. 1610
SHANGHAI GENERAL MOTORS CORPORATION LTD.—See General Motors Company; *U.S. Public*, pg. 929
SHANGHAI GM (SHENYANG) NORSOM MOTORS CO. LTD.—See General Motors Company; *U.S. Public*, pg. 929
SHANGHAI ONSTAR TELEMATICS CO. LTD.—See General Motors Company; *U.S. Public*, pg. 929
SHELBY AMERICAN INC.; *U.S. Public*, pg. 1874
SHENYANG BRILLIANCE JINBEI AUTOMOBILE CO., LTD.—See Brilliance China Automotive Holdings Limited; *Int'l*, pg. 1163
SHIRAM AUTOMALL INDIA LIMITED—See CarTrade Tech Ltd.; *Int'l*, pg. 1348
SOGEMI SRL—See Clariane SE; *Int'l*, pg. 1644
SONY HONDA MOBILITY INC.—See Honda Motor Co., Ltd.; *Int'l*, pg. 3464
SOUTHERN (MERTHYR) LIMITED—See General Motors Company; *U.S. Public*, pg. 927
SPICER OFF-HIGHWAY BELGIUM N.V.—See Dana Incorporated; *U.S. Public*, pg. 623
SPYKER OF CHINA LTD.—See China Automobile Trading Co., Ltd.; *Int'l*, pg. 1484
SQUARE ONE ARMORING SERVICES CO.; *U.S. Private*, pg. 3766
STRATTEC DE MEXICO S.A. DE C.V.—See Strattec Security Corporation; *U.S. Public*, pg. 1954
SUMMIT SHOWA MANUFACTURING CO., LTD.—See Hitachi Astemo, Ltd.; *Int'l*, pg. 3410
SWINDON PRESSINGS LIMITED—See Bayerische Motoren Werke Aktiengesellschaft; *Int'l*, pg. 913
SYSTEM ENHANCEMENT RESOURCES & TECHNOLOGIES SDN. BHD.—See Destini Berhad; *Int'l*, pg. 2046
TAMP AUTO PARTS INDUSTRIAL CO., LTD.—See Hitachi, Ltd.; *Int'l*, pg. 3424
TEMSA GLOBAL SANAYI VE TICARET A.S. - ADANA PLANT—See Haci Omer Sabanci Holding A.S.; *Int'l*, pg. 3204
TEMSA GLOBAL SANAYI VE TICARET A.S.—See Haci Omer Sabanci Holding A.S.; *Int'l*, pg. 3204
TERRA INVENTIONS CORP.; *U.S. Public*, pg. 3970
TESLA AUTOMATION GMBH—See Tesla, Inc.; *U.S. Public*, pg. 2021
TESLA CANADA LP—See Tesla, Inc.; *U.S. Public*, pg. 2021
TESLA CZECH REPUBLIC S.R.O.—See Tesla, Inc.; *U.S. Public*, pg. 2021
TESLA FRANCE S.A.R.L.—See Tesla, Inc.; *U.S. Public*, pg. 2021
TESLA HUNGARY KFT.—See Tesla, Inc.; *U.S. Public*, pg. 2021
TESLA, INC.; *U.S. Public*, pg. 2021
TESLA ITALY S.R.L.—See Tesla, Inc.; *U.S. Public*, pg. 2021
TESLA MOTORS AUSTRIA GMBH—See Tesla, Inc.; *U.S. Public*, pg. 2021
TESLA MOTORS ICELAND EHF.—See Tesla, Inc.; *U.S. Public*, pg. 2021
TESLA MOTORS UT, INC.—See Tesla, Inc.; *U.S. Public*, pg. 2021
TESLA POLAND SP. Z O.O.—See Tesla, Inc.; *U.S. Public*, pg. 2021
TESLA SWITZERLAND GMBH—See Tesla, Inc.; *U.S. Public*, pg. 2021
TISHOMINGO ACQUISITION, LLC—See Federal Signal Corporation; *U.S. Public*, pg. 826
TODD WENZEL BUICK GMC OF DAVISON, INC.—See General Motors Company; *U.S. Public*, pg. 929
TOYOFLEX CEBU CORPORATION—See Asahi Intecc Co., Ltd.; *Int'l*, pg. 594
TOYOFLEX CORPORATION—See Asahi Intecc Co., Ltd.; *Int'l*, pg. 594
TOYO SANGYO CO., LTD.—See Daido Steel Co., Ltd.; *Int'l*, pg. 1923
TOYOTA TURKIYE MOTORLU ARACLAR A.S.—See Abdul Latif Jameel Group of Companies; *Int'l*, pg. 58
TRANSPORTATION DESIGN & MANUFACTURING CO.; *U.S. Private*, pg. 4211
TTG EQUIPMENT, LLC; *U.S. Private*, pg. 4254
UAB IVECO CAPITAL BALTIC—See CNH Industrial N.V.; *Int'l*, pg. 1676
UBENCH INTERNATIONAL NV—See BASF SE; *Int'l*, pg. 885
UNION MOTORS CAR SALES S.R.L.—See General Motors Company; *U.S. Public*, pg. 929
UNITED STATES COACHWORKS INC.; *U.S. Private*, pg. 4298
UNITED STATES COUNCIL FOR AUTOMOTIVE RESEARCH LLC—See General Motors Company; *U.S. Public*, pg. 929
UNIVERSAL MOTORS ISRAEL LTD.—See General Motors Company; *U.S. Public*, pg. 929
VAUXHALL MOTORS LIMITED—See General Motors Company; *U.S. Public*, pg. 927
VIA MOTORS INC.—See Ideanomics, Inc.; *U.S. Public*, pg. 1088
VICKERS (LAKESIDE) LIMITED—See General Motors Company; *U.S. Public*, pg. 928
VISION INDUSTRIES CORP.; *U.S. Private*, pg. 4391
VOLVE CAR NORWAY A.S.—See GKN plc; *Int'l*, pg. 2986
VOLVO BUS AUSTRALIA—See AB Volvo; *Int'l*, pg. 43
VOLVO BUS HONG KONG LIMITED—See AB Volvo; *Int'l*, pg. 43
VOLVO BUSSAR AB—See AB Volvo; *Int'l*, pg. 43
VOLVO BUSSER DANMARK A/S—See AB Volvo; *Int'l*, pg. 43
VOLVO CARS S.L—See AB Volvo; *Int'l*, pg. 42
VOLVO (CHINA) INVESTMENT CO. LTD—See AB Volvo; *Int'l*, pg. 42
VOLVO DO BRASIL VEICULOS LTDA.—See AB Volvo; *Int'l*, pg. 47
VOLVO ESPANA, S.A.U.—See AB Volvo; *Int'l*, pg. 42
VOLVO GROUP AUTOMOTIVE TICARET, LTD—See AB Volvo; *Int'l*, pg. 44
VOLVO ITALIA SPA—See AB Volvo; *Int'l*, pg. 45
VOLVO NORGE A/S—See AB Volvo; *Int'l*, pg. 46
VOLVO PENTA FRANCE S.A.—See AB Volvo; *Int'l*, pg. 42
VOLVO PENTA NORDEN AB—See AB Volvo; *Int'l*, pg. 42
VOLVO TECHNOLOGY TRANSFER AB—See AB Volvo; *Int'l*, pg. 45
VOLVO TRUCKS (DEUTSCHLAND) GMBH—See AB Volvo; *Int'l*, pg. 46
VOLVO TRUCKS FINLAND—See AB Volvo; *Int'l*, pg. 46
VOLVO TRUCKS INDIA PVT LTD—See AB Volvo; *Int'l*, pg. 47
VOLVO TRUCKS INDONESIA—See AB Volvo; *Int'l*, pg. 47
VOLVO TRUCKS LITHUANIA—See AB Volvo; *Int'l*, pg. 46
VOLVO TRUCKS POLAND—See AB Volvo; *Int'l*, pg. 46
VOLVO TRUCKS REGION CENTRAL EUROPE GMBH—See AB Volvo; *Int'l*, pg. 47
VOLVO TRUCKS SAUDI ARABIA—See AB Volvo; *Int'l*, pg. 46
VULCO DEVELOPPEMENT—See The Goodyear Tire & Rubber Company; *U.S. Public*, pg. 2085
WHEATCROFT (WORKSOP) LIMITED—See General Motors Company; *U.S. Public*, pg. 928
WHEELS INDIA LIMITED—See Titan International, Inc.; *U.S. Public*, pg. 2160
WHITMORE'S OF EDENBRIDGE LIMITED—See General Motors Company; *U.S. Public*, pg. 928
WINNEBAGO OF INDIANA, LLC—See Winnebago Industries, Inc.; *U.S. Public*, pg. 2374
WORKHORSE GROUP INC.; *U.S. Public*, pg. 2379
WUHU BENTELER-POSCO AUTOMOTIVE CO., LTD.—See Benteler International AG; *Int'l*, pg. 977
WUHU CIMC RUIJIANG AUTOMOBILE CO LTD—See China International Marine Containers (Group) Co., Ltd.; *Int'l*, pg. 1512
XINFA AIRPORT EQUIPMENT LTD.—See China International Marine Containers (Group) Co., Ltd.; *Int'l*, pg. 1512
YACHIYO INDUSTRY CO., LTD. - YOKKAICHI FACTORY—See Honda Motor Co., Ltd.; *Int'l*, pg. 3464
ZHEJIANG YOUNGMAN LOTUS AUTOMOBILE CO., LTD.—See China Youngman Automobile Group Co., Ltd.; *Int'l*, pg. 1565
ZMC AMERICA, INC.—See FuelPositive Corporation; *Int'l*, pg. 2804

336120 — HEAVY DUTY TRUCK MANUFACTURING

AB VOLVO - VOLVO DE MEXICO AUTOBUSES DIVISION—See AB Volvo; *Int'l*, pg. 42
ALLEGIANCE TRUCKS, LLC; *U.S. Private*, pg. 176
ALL ROADS COMPANY; *U.S. Private*, pg. 171
AMERICAN LAFRANCE LLC—See Patriarch Partners, LLC; *U.S. Private*, pg. 3109
ANSHAN SENYUAN ROAD & BRIDGE CO., LTD.; *Int'l*, pg. 479
AUDUBON MANUFACTURING CORPORATION—See Oshkosh Corporation; *U.S. Public*, pg. 1620
AUTOKRAZ HOLDING CO.; *Int'l*, pg. 727
BATTISTELLA ADMINISTRACAO E PARTICIPACOES S.A.; *Int'l*, pg. 890
BRADVIN TRAILER SALES LTD.; *Int'l*, pg. 1134
BROCE MANUFACTURING CO. INC.; *U.S. Private*, pg. 660
BUCHER SCHORLING AG—See Bucher Industries AG; *Int'l*, pg. 1207
BUCHER SCHORLING KOREA LTD—See Bucher Industries AG; *Int'l*, pg. 1207
CAPARO MODULAR SYSTEMS LTD.—See Caparo Group Ltd.; *Int'l*, pg. 1302
CHAMPION BUS, INC.—See AIP, LLC; *U.S. Private*, pg. 135
CHO THAVEE PUBLIC COMPANY LIMITED; *Int'l*, pg. 1576
CHTC KAMA CO., LTD.—See China Hi-Tech Group Co., Ltd.; *Int'l*, pg. 1507
CIMC VEHICLE (GUANGXI) CO., LTD.—See China International Marine Containers (Group) Co., Ltd.; *Int'l*, pg. 1511
CNMY TRUCKS SDN BHD—See Chin Hin Group Berhad; *Int'l*, pg. 1480
COMMERCIAL BABCOCK INC.—See J.B. Poindexter & Co., Inc.; *U.S. Private*, pg. 2158
DAF CAMINHOES BRASIL INDUSTRIA LTDA.—See PACCAR Inc.; *U.S. Public*, pg. 1630
DAF TRUCKS FRANCE, S.A.R.L.—See PACCAR Inc.; *U.S. Public*, pg. 1630
DAF TRUCKS FRANCE, S.A.R.L.—See PACCAR Inc.; *U.S. Public*, pg. 1630
DAF TRUCKS LTD.—See PACCAR Inc.; *U.S. Public*, pg. 1630
DAF TRUCKS POLSKA SP.Z.O.O.—See PACCAR Inc.; *U.S. Public*, pg. 1630
DAF TRUCKS VLAANDEREN N.V.—See PACCAR Inc.; *U.S. Public*, pg. 1630
DAF VEHICULOS INDUSTRIALES S.A.—See PACCAR Inc.; *U.S. Public*, pg. 1630

336120 — HEAVY DUTY TRUCK MA...

DIAMOND COACH CORPORATION; *U.S. Private*, pg. 1223
DNEPROVAGONMASH LTD.—See Dniprovagonmash JSC; *Int'l*, pg. 2148
DODGE INDUSTRIES INC.; *U.S. Private*, pg. 1252
ELDORADO NATIONAL (CALIFORNIA), INC.—See AIP, LLC; *U.S. Private*, pg. 135
ELDORADO NATIONAL (KANSAS), INC.—See AIP, LLC; *U.S. Private*, pg. 135
ELGIN SWEEPER COMPANY—See Federal Signal Corporation; *U.S. Public*, pg. 826
ENPLUS CO., LTD.; *Int'l*, pg. 2445
FAP - KORPORACIJA A.D.; *Int'l*, pg. 2615
FERRARA FIRE APPARATUS INC.—See AIP, LLC; *U.S. Private*, pg. 135
FLORIDA TRUCK GROUP; *U.S. Private*, pg. 1550
FORD MOTOR COMPANY OF CANADA, LIMITED—See Ford Motor Company; *U.S. Public*, pg. 865
FRONTIER TRUCK GEAR; *U.S. Private*, pg. 1616
FTF KRAZ—See AutoKrAZ Holding Co.; *Int'l*, pg. 727
GARSITE PROGRESS LLC—See AFI Partners LLC; *U.S. Private*, pg. 123
GEESINK B.V.—See Geesink Group B.V.; *Int'l*, pg. 2911
GOSHEN COACH, INC.—See AIP, LLC; *U.S. Private*, pg. 135
HITACHI CONSTRUCTION TRUCK MANUFACTURING, LTD.—See Hitachi, Ltd.; *Int'l*, pg. 3416
IKARBUS A.D.; *Int'l*, pg. 3610
IOWA CONTRACT FABRICATORS,INC.—See Oshkosh Corporation; *U.S. Public*, pg. 1620
IVECO MAGIRUS FIREFIGHTING CAMIVA S.A.S.—See CNH Industrial N.V.; *Int'l*, pg. 1675
IVECO S.P.A.—See CNH Industrial N.V.; *Int'l*, pg. 1675
IVECO TRUCKS AUSTRALIA LTD—See CNH Industrial N.V.; *Int'l*, pg. 1676
KENWORTH MEXICANA, S.A. DE C.V.—See PACCAR Inc.; *U.S. Public*, pg. 1630
KENWORTH TRUCK CO.—See PACCAR Inc.; *U.S. Public*, pg. 1630
THE KNAPHEIDE MANUFACTURING COMPANY; *U.S. Private*, pg. 4065
KOCKUMS INDUSTRIES (AUSTRALIA) PTY LTD—See Arrowcrest Group Pty. Ltd.; *Int'l*, pg. 580
KOVATCH MOBILE EQUIPMENT CORP.—See AIP, LLC; *U.S. Private*, pg. 135
LAG TRAILERS N.V.—See China International Marine Containers (Group) Co., Ltd.; *Int'l*, pg. 1512
LEYLAND TRUCKS LIMITED—See PACCAR Inc.; *U.S. Public*, pg. 1630
MACK CANADA, INC.—See AB Volvo; *Int'l*, pg. 45
MACK TRUCKS AUSTRALIA PTY. LTD.—See AB Volvo; *Int'l*, pg. 45
MACK TRUCKS, INC.—See AB Volvo; *Int'l*, pg. 45
MACK TRUCKS-MACUNGIE ASSEMBLY—See AB Volvo; *Int'l*, pg. 45
MAGIRUS CAMIVA S.A.S.—See CNH Industrial N.V.; *Int'l*, pg. 1676
MAGIRUS LOHR GMBH—See CNH Industrial N.V.; *Int'l*, pg. 1676
MEDICAL COACHES INCORPORATED; *U.S. Private*, pg. 2654
NAVISTAR, INC.—See FreightCar America, Inc.; *U.S. Public*, pg. 885
NMHG MEXICO S.A. DE C.V.—See Hyster-Yale Materials Handling, Inc.; *U.S. Public*, pg. 1080
OSHKOSH AIRPORT PRODUCTS, LLC—See Oshkosh Corporation; *U.S. Public*, pg. 1621
OSHKOSH CORPORATION; *U.S. Public*, pg. 1619
OSHKOSH EUROPE B.V.—See Oshkosh Corporation; *U.S. Public*, pg. 1621
OSHKOSH SPECIALTY VEHICLES—See Oshkosh Corporation; *U.S. Public*, pg. 1621
PACCAR AUSTRALIA PTY. LTD.—See PACCAR Inc.; *U.S. Public*, pg. 1630
PACCAR FINANCIAL EUROPE B.V.—See PACCAR Inc.; *U.S. Public*, pg. 1630
PACCAR FINANCIAL MEXICO—See PACCAR Inc.; *U.S. Public*, pg. 1631
PACCAR GLOBAL SALES—See PACCAR Inc.; *U.S. Public*, pg. 1631
PACCAR INC.; *U.S. Public*, pg. 1630
PACCAR MEXICO, S.A. DE C.V.—See PACCAR Inc.; *U.S. Public*, pg. 1631
PACCAR OF CANADA LTD.—See PACCAR Inc.; *U.S. Public*, pg. 1631
PACCAR PARTS U.K. LIMITED—See PACCAR Inc.; *U.S. Public*, pg. 1631
PACCAR SALES NORTH AMERICA, INC.—See PACCAR Inc.; *U.S. Public*, pg. 1631
PACCAR TRUCKS U.K. LTD.—See PACCAR Inc.; *U.S. Public*, pg. 1631
PACLEASE MEXICANA, S.A. DE C.V.—See PACCAR Inc.; *U.S. Public*, pg. 1631
PATSY'S BUS SALES & SERVICE—See Patsy's, Inc.; *U.S. Private*, pg. 3111
PETERBILT OF CANADA—See PACCAR Inc.; *U.S. Public*, pg. 1631
PIERCE MANUFACTURING, INC.—See Oshkosh Corporation; *U.S. Public*, pg. 1621

POWER TOWERS NETHERLANDS BV—See Oshkosh Corporation; *U.S. Public*, pg. 1621
RAVO B.V.—See Federal Signal Corporation; *U.S. Public*, pg. 826
RENAULT TRUCKS ITALIA SPA—See AB Volvo; *Int'l*, pg. 45
RENAULT TRUCKS S.A.S.—See AB Volvo; *Int'l*, pg. 45
ROLL-N-LOCK CORP.—See CCMP Capital Advisors, LP; *U.S. Private*, pg. 801
ROLL-N-LOCK CORP.—See TA Associates, Inc.; *U.S. Private*, pg. 3919
SEAGRAVE FIRE APPARATUS, LLC—See FB Capital Partners, L.P.; *U.S. Private*, pg. 1485
SMITH ELECTRIC VEHICLES CORP.; *U.S. Private*, pg. 3694
SMITH ELECTRIC VEHICLES EUROPE LIMITED—See Smith Electric Vehicles Corp.; *U.S. Private*, pg. 3694
SOUTHWEST PRODUCTS CORPORATION; *U.S. Private*, pg. 3740
SUNRISE BEACH CORPORATION—See The Day & Zimmermann Group, Inc.; *U.S. Private*, pg. 4019
THE SUTPHEN CORPORATION; *U.S. Private*, pg. 4125
THOMAS REGOUT INTERNATIONAL B.V.—See Brd. Klee A/S; *Int'l*, pg. 1143
TRINITY SPECIALTY PRODUCTS, INC.—See Trinity Industries, Inc.; *U.S. Public*, pg. 2194
UD TRUCKS JAPAN CO., LTD.—See AB Volvo; *Int'l*, pg. 45
UD TRUCKS SOUTH AFRICA (PTY) LTD.—See AB Volvo; *Int'l*, pg. 46
VELOCITY VEHICLE GROUP; *U.S. Private*, pg. 4354
VFS LT, UAB—See AB Volvo; *Int'l*, pg. 44
VOLVALB SH.P.K—See AB Volvo; *Int'l*, pg. 42
VOLVO BULGARIA LTD.—See AB Volvo; *Int'l*, pg. 42
VOLVO CONSTRUCTION EQUIPMENT INTERNATIONAL AB—See AB Volvo; *Int'l*, pg. 43
VOLVO DANMARK A/S—See AB Volvo; *Int'l*, pg. 43
VOLVO EUROPA TRUCK N.V.—See AB Volvo; *Int'l*, pg. 46
VOLVO GROUP CANADA INC.—See AB Volvo; *Int'l*, pg. 44
VOLVO GROUP UK LTD—See AB Volvo; *Int'l*, pg. 46
VOLVO INDIA PRIVATE LTD.—See AB Volvo; *Int'l*, pg. 46
VOLVO LASTVAGNAR AB—See AB Volvo; *Int'l*, pg. 45
VOLVO LASTVAGNAR SVERIGE AB—See AB Volvo; *Int'l*, pg. 46
VOLVO (SOUTHERN AFRICA) PTY LTD—See AB Volvo; *Int'l*, pg. 42
VOLVO TRUCK & BUS BOTSWANA PTY. LTD.—See AB Volvo; *Int'l*, pg. 46
VOLVO TRUCK CENTER SWEDEN AB—See AB Volvo; *Int'l*, pg. 46
VOLVO TRUCK CZECH S.R.O.—See AB Volvo; *Int'l*, pg. 46
VOLVO TRUCKS BULGARIA EOOD—See AB Volvo; *Int'l*, pg. 46
VOLVO TRUCKS ESPANA, S.A.—See AB Volvo; *Int'l*, pg. 47
VOLVO TRUCKS ESTONIA—See AB Volvo; *Int'l*, pg. 46
VOLVO TRUCKS NETHERLANDS—See AB Volvo; *Int'l*, pg. 46
VOLVO TRUCKS NIGERIA—See AB Volvo; *Int'l*, pg. 46
VOLVO TRUCKS NORTH AMERICA, INC.—See AB Volvo; *Int'l*, pg. 47
VOLVO TRUCKS RUSSIA—See AB Volvo; *Int'l*, pg. 46
VOLVO TRUCKS (SCHWEIZ) AG—See AB Volvo; *Int'l*, pg. 46
VOLVO TRUCKS SWEDEN AB—See AB Volvo; *Int'l*, pg. 47
VOLVO TRUCKS THAILAND—See AB Volvo; *Int'l*, pg. 47
VPL LIMITED—See AB Volvo; *Int'l*, pg. 46
YALE FORDERTECHNIK HANDELSGESELLSCHAFT MBH—See Hyster-Yale Materials Handling, Inc.; *U.S. Public*, pg. 1080

336211 — MOTOR VEHICLE BODY MANUFACTURING

AA CATER TRUCK MANUFACTURING COMPANY, INC.; *U.S. Private*, pg. 29
ABLE MANUFACTURING AND ASSEMBLY LLC; *U.S. Private*, pg. 39
ACCURIDE CORPORATION—See Crestview Partners, L.P.; *U.S. Private*, pg. 1097
ACTION FABRICATION & TRUCK EQUIPMENT, INC.—See J.B. Poindexter & Co., Inc.; *U.S. Private*, pg. 2159
AEROSUN CORPORATION; *Int'l*, pg. 182
AEV - AMERICAN EMERGENCY VEHICLES—See AIP, LLC; *U.S. Private*, pg. 135
ALTRA S.P.A.—See CNH Industrial N.V.; *Int'l*, pg. 1675
AM GENERAL AFTERMARKET FULFILLMENT AND TRAINING CENTER—See MacAndrews & Forbes Incorporated; *U.S. Private*, pg. 2531
AM GENERAL AFTERMARKET FULFILLMENT AND TRAINING CENTER—See The Renco Group Inc.; *U.S. Private*, pg. 4104
AM GENERAL TECHNOLOGY AND ENGINEERING CENTER—See MacAndrews & Forbes Incorporated; *U.S. Private*, pg. 2531
AM GENERAL TECHNOLOGY AND ENGINEERING CENTER—See The Renco Group Inc.; *U.S. Private*, pg. 4104
ANTENNENTECHNIK ABB BAD BLANKENBURG GMBH—See Huizhou Desay SV Automotive Co., Ltd.; *Int'l*, pg. 3527
ARCQUS GMBH—See ManpowerGroup Inc.; *U.S. Public*, pg. 1357
ASPEN EQUIPMENT COMPANY INC.—See The Manitowoc Company, Inc.; *U.S. Public*, pg. 2111
AUTECH CORPORATION - GYEONGJU FACTORY—See Autech Corporation; *Int'l*, pg. 724
AUTECH CORPORATION; *Int'l*, pg. 724
AUTECH CORPORATION - YESAN FACTORY—See Autech Corporation; *Int'l*, pg. 724
AUTOCAM CORPORATION, INC.—See NN, Inc.; *U.S. Public*, pg. 1530
AUTOLIV CANKOR OTOMOTIV EMNIYET SISTEMLERI SANAYI VE TICARET A.S.—See Autoliv, Inc.; *Int'l*, pg. 728
AUTOLIV (CHINA) ELECTRONICS CO., LTD.—See Autoliv, Inc.; *Int'l*, pg. 728
AUTOLIV (SHANGHAI) MANAGEMENT CO., LTD.—See Autoliv, Inc.; *Int'l*, pg. 728
AVP ENGINEERING (M) SDN. BHD.—See CB Industrial Product Holding Berhad; *Int'l*, pg. 1364
AVTODOM OAO; *Int'l*, pg. 751
BOGDAN CORPORATION; *Int'l*, pg. 1100
BRAND FX BODY COMPANY; *U.S. Private*, pg. 635
BRANDFX BODY COMPANY—See Stonebridge Partners, LLC; *U.S. Private*, pg. 3827
BRAUN INDUSTRIES, INC.—See Caisse de Depot et Placement du Quebec; *Int'l*, pg. 1254
BRAUN INDUSTRIES, INC.—See Clearspring Capital Partners; *Int'l*, pg. 1657
BURG CARROSSERIE B.V.—See China International Marine Containers (Group) Co., Ltd.; *Int'l*, pg. 1511
CARUSO GMBH—See LKQ Corporation; *U.S. Public*, pg. 1334
CASECO TRUCK BODY; *U.S. Private*, pg. 782
CENTIGON BRAZIL—See Capital People S.A.; *Int'l*, pg. 1312
CENTIGON COLOMBIA—See Capital People S.A.; *Int'l*, pg. 1312
CENTIGON—See Capital People S.A.; *Int'l*, pg. 1312
CHINA AUTOMOTIVE SYSTEMS, INC.; *Int'l*, pg. 1484
CHINA ENGINE CORPORATION—See China Motor Corporation; *Int'l*, pg. 1525
CHINA MOTOR CORPORATION; *Int'l*, pg. 1524
CLARION TECHNOLOGIES, INC. - AMES—See Clarion Technologies, Inc.; *U.S. Private*, pg. 911
CLARION TECHNOLOGIES, INC. - ANDERSON—See Clarion Technologies, Inc.; *U.S. Private*, pg. 911
CLARION TECHNOLOGIES, INC. - CALEDONIA—See Clarion Technologies, Inc.; *U.S. Private*, pg. 911
CLARION TECHNOLOGIES, INC. - GREENVILLE—See Clarion Technologies, Inc.; *U.S. Private*, pg. 911
CLARION TECHNOLOGIES, INC.; *U.S. Private*, pg. 911
CME GORUP BERHAD; *Int'l*, pg. 1669
COLLINS BUS CORPORATION—See Berkshire Hathaway Inc.; *U.S. Public*, pg. 305
COTTRELL, INC.—See Markel Group Inc.; *U.S. Public*, pg. 1367
CRANE CARRIER COMPANY—See Platinum Equity, LLC; *U.S. Private*, pg. 3209
CROATIA-TEHNICKI PREGLEDI D.O.O.—See Adris Grupa d.d.; *Int'l*, pg. 153
CRYSTEEL MANUFACTURING, INC.—See Federal Signal Corporation; *U.S. Public*, pg. 826
CT&T CO., LTD.; *Int'l*, pg. 1868
CURTIS TRACTOR CAB, INC.; *U.S. Private*, pg. 1127
CUSTOM BUS AUSTRALIA PTY. LTD.—See Allegro Funds Pty. Ltd.; *Int'l*, pg. 336
DAF TRUCKS N.V.—See PACCAR Inc.; *U.S. Public*, pg. 1630
DANZER CORPORATION—See Obsidian Enterprises, Inc.; *U.S. Private*, pg. 2988
DANZER INDUSTRIES, INC.—See Obsidian Enterprises, Inc.; *U.S. Private*, pg. 2988
DEMERS, MANUFACTURIER D'AMBULANCES INC.—See Caisse de Depot et Placement du Quebec; *Int'l*, pg. 1254
DEMERS, MANUFACTURIER D'AMBULANCES INC.—See Clearspring Capital Partners; *Int'l*, pg. 1657
DON-BUR (BODIES & TRAILERS) LTD; *Int'l*, pg. 2162
DONGHEE RUS LLC—See DH Holdings Co., Ltd.; *Int'l*, pg. 2097
DONGHEE SLOVAKIA S.R.O.—See DH Holdings Co., Ltd.; *Int'l*, pg. 2097
DORAL-HY, LLC—See Lithia Motors, Inc.; *U.S. Public*, pg. 1322
DPH HOLDINGS CORPORATION—See Aptiv PLC; *Int'l*, pg. 524
DRIVERGE VEHICLE INNOVATIONS, LLC.; *U.S. Private*, pg. 1278
ELECTRAMECCANICA VEHICLES CORP.—See XOS, INC.; *U.S. Public*, pg. 2391
E-ONE, INC.—See AIP, LLC; *U.S. Private*, pg. 135
EON MOTORS GROUP SA; *Int'l*, pg. 2458
ESENTTIA MASTERBATCH LTDA.—See Ecopetrol S.A.; *Int'l*, pg. 2299
FORTRESS RESOURCES, LLC—See The Shyft Group, Inc.; *U.S. Public*, pg. 2130

N.A.I.C.S. INDEX

336212 — TRUCK TRAILER MANUF...

FRANKLIN PRECISION INDUSTRY, INC.—See Aisan Industry Co., Ltd.; *Int'l*, pg. 250
FRAUENTHAL AUTOMOTIVE COMPONENTS GMBH—See Frauenthal Holding AG; *Int'l*, pg. 2767
FUTABA MANUFACTURING U.K. LTD.—See Futaba Industrial Co., Ltd.; *Int'l*, pg. 2851
FUTABA SUMI CORP.—See Futaba Industrial Co., Ltd.; *Int'l*, pg. 2851
GEMILANG INTERNATIONAL LIMITED; *Int'l*, pg. 2916
GENERAL BODY MANUFACTURING COMPANY—See J.B. Poindexter & Co., Inc.; *U.S. Private*, pg. 2159
GENERAL DYNAMICS OTS (NICEVILLE), INC.—See General Dynamics Corporation; *U.S. Public*, pg. 915
GENERAL DYNAMICS OTS (PENNSYLVANIA), INC.—See General Dynamics Corporation; *U.S. Public*, pg. 915
GENERAL DYNAMICS UNITED KINGDOM LIMITED—See General Dynamics Corporation; *U.S. Public*, pg. 916
GODWIN MANUFACTURING COMPANY INC.—See The Godwin Group; *U.S. Private*, pg. 4033
G-ONE AUTO PARTS DE MEXICO, S.A. DE C.V.—See H-One Co., Ltd.; *Int'l*, pg. 3194
GOSHI-THANGLONG AUTO-PARTS CO., LTD.—See Honda Motor Co., Ltd.; *Int'l*, pg. 3464
GREAT LAKES AUTO AUCTION, INC.; *U.S. Private*, pg. 1764
GREAT WALL INDIA RESEARCH & DEVELOPMENT PRIVATE LIMITED—See Great Wall Motor Company Limited; *Int'l*, pg. 3066
GREENPOWER MOTOR COMPANY INC.; *Int'l*, pg. 3076
GUANGZHOU JINZHONG AUTO PARTS MANUFACTURING CO., LTD.; *Int'l*, pg. 3166
GUYOUNG TECH. CO., LTD; *Int'l*, pg. 3189
HALCORE GROUP, INC.—See AIP, LLC; *U.S. Private*, pg. 135
HALDEX ANAND INDIA LTD.—See Haldex AB; *Int'l*, pg. 3228
HANGZHOU YUEXI BUS MANUFACTURE CO., LTD.—See Coslight Technology International Group Limited; *Int'l*, pg. 1810
HANGZHOU ZHENGQIANG CORPORATION LIMITED; *Int'l*, pg. 3251
HANMA TECHNOLOGY GROUP CO., LTD.; *Int'l*, pg. 3256
HAULGAUGE, INC.—See LCI Industries; *U.S. Public*, pg. 1295
THE HEIL CO. - ALABAMA—See Terex Corporation; *U.S. Public*, pg. 2019
THE HEIL CO. - MISSISSIPPI—See Terex Corporation; *U.S. Public*, pg. 2019
HENDRICKSON MEXICANA—See The Boler Company; *U.S. Private*, pg. 3996
HERRAJES Y ACABADOS METALICOS, S.A. DE C.V.—See KPS Capital Partners, LP; *U.S. Private*, pg. 2347
HK BATTERY TECHNOLOGY, INC.; *U.S. Public*, pg. 1042
HONDA FOUNDRY CO., LTD.—See Honda Motor Co., Ltd.; *Int'l*, pg. 3461
HUNAN BYNAV TECHNOLOGY CO., LTD.—See Duolun Technology Co., Ltd.; *Int'l*, pg. 2227
IC BUS, LLC—See FreightCar America, Inc.; *U.S. Public*, pg. 885
JASPER TANK LTD—See Exchange Income Corporation; *Int'l*, pg. 2579
JERR-DAN CORPORATION—See Oshkosh Corporation; *U.S. Public*, pg. 1620
JLG PROPERTIES AUSTRALIA PTY LIMITED—See Oshkosh Corporation; *U.S. Public*, pg. 1620
JOHNSON TRUCK BODIES, INC.—See Henry Crown & Company; *U.S. Private*, pg. 1917
KAFFENBARGER TRUCK EQUIPMENT CO.; *U.S. Private*, pg. 2254
KIMBLE CHASSIS COMPANY—See Hines Corporation; *U.S. Private*, pg. 1949
LEADER EMERGENCY VEHICLES—See AIP, LLC; *U.S. Private*, pg. 135
LEAR CORPORATION BELGIUM CVA—See Lear Corporation; *U.S. Public*, pg. 1297
LEAR CORPORATION CHANGCHUN AUTOMOTIVE INTERIOR SYSTEMS CO., LTD.—See Lear Corporation; *U.S. Public*, pg. 1297
LEAR CORPORATION (SHANGHAI) LIMITED—See Lear Corporation; *U.S. Public*, pg. 1297
LEAR CORPORATION (UK) LIMITED—See Lear Corporation; *U.S. Public*, pg. 1297
LEAR EUROPEAN HOLDING S.L.—See Lear Corporation; *U.S. Public*, pg. 1297
LEAR NORTH EUROPEAN OPERATIONS GMBH—See Lear Corporation; *U.S. Public*, pg. 1297
LEAR SHANGHAI AUTOMOTIVE METALS CO., LTD.—See Lear Corporation; *U.S. Public*, pg. 1297
LEASESERVICE PARTNER B.V.—See LKQ Corporation; *U.S. Public*, pg. 1335
LIFE LINE EMERGENCY VEHICLES, INC.; *U.S. Private*, pg. 2448
LODAL, INC.; *U.S. Private*, pg. 2479
MACDONALD JOHNSTON LTD.—See Bucher Industries AG; *Int'l*, pg. 1208
MANITEX SABRE, INC.—See Super Steel LLC; *U.S. Private*, pg. 3875

MARMON-HERRINGTON—See Berkshire Hathaway Inc.; *U.S. Public*, pg. 310
M BILAR GROUP AB—See Bilia AB; *Int'l*, pg. 1029
MCLAUGHLIN BODY CO.; *U.S. Private*, pg. 2640
MCNEILUS COMPANIES, INC.—See Oshkosh Corporation; *U.S. Public*, pg. 1620
MCNEILUS TRUCK & MANUFACTURING, INC.—See Oshkosh Corporation; *U.S. Public*, pg. 1621
MERKAVIM TRANSPORTATION TECHNOLOGIES LTD.—See AB Volvo; *Int'l*, pg. 42
M.H. EBY INC.; *U.S. Private*, pg. 2529
MICKEY TRUCK BODIES INC.; *U.S. Private*, pg. 2701
MILLER INDUSTRIES, INC.; *U.S. Public*, pg. 1446
MISHAWAKA MANUFACTURING CAMPUS—See MacAndrews & Forbes Incorporated; *U.S. Private*, pg. 2532
MISHAWAKA MANUFACTURING CAMPUS—See The Renco Group Inc.; *U.S. Private*, pg. 4104
MORGAN CORPORATION—See J.B. Poindexter & Co., Inc.; *U.S. Private*, pg. 2158
MORGAN OLSON CORPORATION—See J.B. Poindexter & Co., Inc.; *U.S. Private*, pg. 2158
MORGAN TRUCK BODY, LLC—See J.B. Poindexter & Co., Inc.; *U.S. Private*, pg. 2158
N.C.S. PYROTECHNIE ET TECHNOLOGIES SAS—See Autoliv, Inc.; *Int'l*, pg. 730
NORTHEND TRUCK EQUIPMENT, LLC—See Federal Signal Corporation; *U.S. Public*, pg. 826
NOVARES GROUP SA—See Equistone Partners Europe Limited; *Int'l*, pg. 2486
OLCI ENGINEERING S.R.L.—See EFORT Intelligent Equipment Co., Ltd.; *Int'l*, pg. 2321
OPENLANE BELGIUM N.V.—See OPENLANE, Inc.; *U.S. Public*, pg. 1607
OPENLANE DEUTSCHLAND GMBH—See OPENLANE, Inc.; *U.S. Public*, pg. 1607
OPENLANE EUROPE N.V.—See OPENLANE, Inc.; *U.S. Public*, pg. 1607
OPENLANE FRANCE S.A.S.—See OPENLANE, Inc.; *U.S. Public*, pg. 1607
OPENLANE NEDERLAND B.V.—See OPENLANE, Inc.; *U.S. Public*, pg. 1607
OPTARE GROUP LTD—See Hinduja Group Ltd.; *Int'l*, pg. 3398
OSHKOSH COMMERCIAL (BEIJING) CO., LIMITED—See Oshkosh Corporation; *U.S. Public*, pg. 1621
OSHKOSH DEFENSE CANADA INCORPORATED—See Oshkosh Corporation; *U.S. Public*, pg. 1621
OSHKOSH-JLG (SINGAPORE) TECHNOLOGY EQUIPMENT PRIVATE LIMITED—See Oshkosh Corporation; *U.S. Public*, pg. 1621
OX BODIES, INC.—See Federal Signal Corporation; *U.S. Public*, pg. 826
PLASTAL INDUSTRI AB—See Insight Equity Holdings LLC; *U.S. Private*, pg. 2086
POLARIS INDUSTRIES LTD.—See Polaris, Inc.; *U.S. Public*, pg. 1700
PRIDE BODIES LTD—See Westinghouse Air Brake Technologies Corporation; *U.S. Public*, pg. 2359
PRIMORDIAL, INC.—See Polaris, Inc.; *U.S. Public*, pg. 1701
PROTOMASTER RIEDEL & CO. GMBH—See Gesco AG; *Int'l*, pg. 2945
PT. YACHIYO TRIMITRA INDONESIA—See Honda Motor Co., Ltd.; *Int'l*, pg. 3464
QH AUTO PARTS INDUSTRIES INC.—See H-One Co., Ltd.; *Int'l*, pg. 3194
QUALITY COLLISION GROUP, LLC—See Susquehanna International Group, LLP; *U.S. Private*, pg. 3885
QUANTUM FUEL SYSTEMS TECHNOLOGIES WORLDWIDE, INC.; *U.S. Public*, pg. 1754
RAWSON-KOENIG, INC.; *U.S. Private*, pg. 3358
READING TRUCK BODY, INC.—See J.B. Poindexter & Co., Inc.; *U.S. Private*, pg. 2159
REV AMBULANCE GROUP ORLANDO, INC.—See AIP, LLC; *U.S. Private*, pg. 135
REV GROUP, INC.—See AIP, LLC; *U.S. Private*, pg. 134
RILEY TECHNOLOGIES, LLC; *U.S. Private*, pg. 3437
RKI, INC.; *U.S. Public*, pg. 3450
ROADWORKS MANUFACTURING, INC.—See CCMP Capital Advisors, LP; *U.S. Private*, pg. 801
ROADWORKS MANUFACTURING, INC.—See TA Associates, Inc.; *U.S. Private*, pg. 3919
RUGBY MANUFACTURING COMPANY—See Federal Signal Corporation; *U.S. Public*, pg. 826
SCRANTON MANUFACTURING COMPANY INC.; *U.S. Private*, pg. 3579
SHANGHAI LEAR AUTOMOTIVE SYSTEMS CO., LTD.—See Lear Corporation; *U.S. Public*, pg. 1298
SIAM GOSHI MANUFACTURING CO., LTD.—See Honda Motor Co., Ltd.; *Int'l*, pg. 3464
SILENT DRIVE, INC.—See Brookfield Corporation; *Int'l*, pg. 1176
SKYMAN AUTO CHASSIS (WUHU) CO., LTD—See Chongqing Skyman Industry (Group) Co., Ltd.; *Int'l*, pg. 1581
SOMERSET WELDING & STEEL, INC.—See Riggs Industries, Inc.; *U.S. Private*, pg. 3435
SUPREME CORPORATION OF TEXAS—See WABASH NATIONAL CORPORATION; *U.S. Public*, pg. 2320

SUPREME INDUSTRIES, INC.—See WABASH NATIONAL CORPORATION; *U.S. Public*, pg. 2320
SUPREME MID-ATLANTIC CORPORATION—See WABASH NATIONAL CORPORATION; *U.S. Public*, pg. 2320
SUPREME TRUCK BODIES OF CALIFORNIA, INC.—See WABASH NATIONAL CORPORATION; *U.S. Public*, pg. 2320
SUPREME UPFIT SOLUTIONS & SERVICE, INC.—See WABASH NATIONAL CORPORATION; *U.S. Public*, pg. 2320
TACLE AUTOMOTIVE INDIA PRIVATE LIMITED—See Lear Corporation; *U.S. Public*, pg. 1298
TAICANG VAN OERLE ALBERTON SHENDA SPECIAL TYPE TEXTILE PRODUCTS CO., LTD.—See Autoliv, Inc.; *Int'l*, pg. 730
TESLA MOTORS AUSTRALIA, PTY LTD—See Tesla, Inc.; *U.S. Public*, pg. 2021
TETON OUTFITTERS, LLC—See Polaris, Inc.; *U.S. Public*, pg. 1701
TRUCK UTILITIES, INC.—See Custom Truck One Source, Inc.; *U.S. Public*, pg. 612
UD TRUCKS CORPORATION—See AB Volvo; *Int'l*, pg. 45
UEMURA TEC CO., LTD.—See Honda Motor Co., Ltd.; *Int'l*, pg. 3464
US YACHIYO, INC.—See Honda Motor Co., Ltd.; *Int'l*, pg. 3464
UTILIMASTER HOLDINGS, INC.—See The Shyft Group, Inc.; *U.S. Public*, pg. 2130
VAPOR BUS INTERNATIONAL—See Westinghouse Air Brake Technologies Corporation; *U.S. Public*, pg. 2359
VARI-FORM CORPORATION—See Crowne Group LLC; *U.S. Private*, pg. 1112
VOLVO TRUCK CORPORATION—See AB Volvo; *Int'l*, pg. 45
WABASH TECHNOLOGIES DE MEXICO TECHNOLOGIES S. DE R.L. DE C.V.—See Sensata Technologies Holding plc; *U.S. Public*, pg. 1866
WH AUTO PARTS INDUSTRIES INC.—See H-One Co., Ltd.; *Int'l*, pg. 3194
WILLIAMS CONTROLS, INC.—See Curtiss-Wright Corporation; *U.S. Public*, pg. 612
WOLVERINE PRESS (CHANGSHU) CO. LTD.—See ITT Inc.; *U.S. Public*, pg. 1179
XOS, INC.; *U.S. Public*, pg. 2391
YACHIYO DO BRASIL INDUSTRIA E COMERCIO DE PECAS LTDA.—See Honda Motor Co., Ltd.; *Int'l*, pg. 3464
YACHIYO GERMANY GMBH—See Honda Motor Co., Ltd.; *Int'l*, pg. 3464
YACHIYO INDIA MANUFACTURING PRIVATE LTD.—See Honda Motor Co., Ltd.; *Int'l*, pg. 3464
YACHIYO INDUSTRY CO., LTD. - SUZUKA PLANT—See Honda Motor Co., Ltd.; *Int'l*, pg. 3464
YACHIYO MANUFACTURING OF AMERICA, LLC—See Honda Motor Co., Ltd.; *Int'l*, pg. 3464

336212 — TRUCK TRAILER MANUFACTURING

ARNES WELDING LTD.; *Int'l*, pg. 576
ARS INTERNATIONAL PRIVATE LIMITED—See Accuracy Shipping Limited; *Int'l*, pg. 94
BIG TEX TRAILER MANUFACTURING, INC.—See Bain Capital, LP; *U.S. Private*, pg. 436
CIMC INTERMODAL EQUIPMENT LLC—See CIMC Vehicle (Group) Co., Ltd.; *Int'l*, pg. 1608
CIMC VEHICLE EUROPE GMBH—See CIMC Vehicle (Group) Co., Ltd.; *Int'l*, pg. 1608
CIMC VEHICLE (GROUP) CO., LTD.; *Int'l*, pg. 1608
COMMERCIAL VEHICLE PRODUCTS DIVISION—See Phillips Industries; *U.S. Private*, pg. 3171
CONTRACT MANUFACTURER, L.L.C.—See Bain Capital, LP; *U.S. Private*, pg. 436
DAKOTA MANUFACTURING CO. INC.; *U.S. Private*, pg. 1147
DAKOTA TRAILER MANUFACTURING, INC.—See Henry Crown & Company; *U.S. Private*, pg. 1918
DEALERS TRUCK EQUIPMENT CO. INC.; *U.S. Private*, pg. 1182
DEXTER GROUP HOLDINGS LLC—See General Atlantic Service Company, L.P.; *U.S. Private*, pg. 1663
DEXTER GROUP HOLDINGS LLC—See Stone Point Capital LLC; *U.S. Private*, pg. 3825
DOONAN SPECIALIZED TRAILER, LLC; *U.S. Private*, pg. 1261
EUROPART I SVERIGE AB—See Alpha Associes Conseil SAS; *Int'l*, pg. 366
EXISS ALUMINUM TRAILERS INC.; *U.S. Private*, pg. 1449
FELLING TRAILERS, INC.; *U.S. Private*, pg. 1494
FONTAINE TRAILER COMPANY—See Berkshire Hathaway Inc.; *U.S. Public*, pg. 310
FOREIGN TRADE FIRM KRAZ LLC—See AutoKrAZ Holding Co.; *Int'l*, pg. 727
FPT - POWERTRAIN TECHNOLOGIES FRANCE S.A.—See CNH Industrial N.V.; *Int'l*, pg. 1675
GENERAL ENGINES COMPANY INC.; *U.S. Private*, pg. 1664

336212 — TRUCK TRAILER MANUF...

GLOBE TRAILERS OF FLORIDA, INC.; *U.S. Private*, pg. 1720
GOLDEN GAIT TRAILERS, LLC—See Redwood Capital Investments, LLC; *U.S. Private*, pg. 3380
GREAT DANE TRAILERS—See Henry Crown & Company; *U.S. Private*, pg. 1917
GREAT DANE TRAILERS—See Henry Crown & Company; *U.S. Private*, pg. 1917
GREAT DANE TRAILERS TENNESSEE, INC.—See Henry Crown & Company; *U.S. Private*, pg. 1917
HALE TRAILER BRAKE & WHEEL; *U.S. Private*, pg. 1842
HAULMARK INDUSTRIES INC.; *U.S. Private*, pg. 1880
HEIL TRAILER INTERNATIONAL, CO.—See AIP, LLC; *U.S. Private*, pg. 134
HEIL TRAILER INTERNATIONAL, CO. - TEXAS—See AIP, LLC; *U.S. Private*, pg. 134
HENDRICKSON ASIA PACIFIC PTY. LTD.—See The Boler Company; *U.S. Private*, pg. 3996
HENDRICKSON CHINA - JINAN PLANT—See The Boler Company; *U.S. Private*, pg. 3996
HENDRICKSON CHINA—See The Boler Company; *U.S. Private*, pg. 3996
HENDRICKSON INDIA—See The Boler Company; *U.S. Private*, pg. 3996
HENDRICKSON JAPAN GK—See The Boler Company; *U.S. Private*, pg. 3996
H&H TRAILER, LLC; *U.S. Private*, pg. 1823
INTECH TRAILERS, INC.; *U.S. Private*, pg. 2097
ITI TRAILERS & TRUCK BODIES, INC.; *U.S. Private*, pg. 2149
KANDI KOUNTRY EXPRESS, LTD.—See Monroe Truck Equipment, Inc.; *U.S. Private*, pg. 2774
KENTUCKY MANUFACTURING CO.; *U.S. Private*, pg. 2288
KENTUCKY TRAILER TECHNOLOGIES—See Berkshire Hathaway Inc.; *U.S. Public*, pg. 299
LARSON CABLE TRAILERS, INC.—See Felling Trailers, Inc.; *U.S. Private*, pg. 1494
LGS INDUSTRIES, INC.; *U.S. Private*, pg. 2441
LIANGSHAN CIMC DONGYUE VEHICLES CO., LTD.—See CIMC Vehicle (Group) Co., Ltd.; *Int'l*, pg. 1608
LIANGSHAN DONGYUE CIMC VEHICLE CO., LTD.—See China International Marine Containers (Group) Co., Ltd.; *Int'l*, pg. 1512
LOAD KING, LLC—See Utility One Source L.P.; *U.S. Private*, pg. 4326
LUOYANG CIMC LINGYU AUTOMOBILE CO., LTD.—See China International Marine Containers (Group) Co., Ltd.; *Int'l*, pg. 1512
MCT INDUSTRIES INCORPORATED; *U.S. Private*, pg. 2644
MUV-ALL TRAILER COMPANY; *U.S. Private*, pg. 2820
NU VAN TECHNOLOGY INC.; *U.S. Private*, pg. 2971
PACE AMERICAN ENTERPRISES INC.-FITZGERALD—See LGS Industries, Inc.; *U.S. Private*, pg. 2441
PACE AMERICAN ENTERPRISES INC.—See LGS Industries, Inc.; *U.S. Private*, pg. 2441
PACE AMERICAN ENTERPRISES INC.-SPRINGVILLE—See LGS Industries, Inc.; *U.S. Private*, pg. 2441
PETERSON INDUSTRIES LLC; *U.S. Private*, pg. 3160
QINGDAO CIMC REEFER TRAILER CO., LTD.—See CIMC Vehicle (Group) Co., Ltd.; *Int'l*, pg. 1608
R. C. TWAY COMPANY, LLC—See Berkshire Hathaway Inc.; *U.S. Public*, pg. 298
SALFORD GROUP, INC.—See GenNx360 Capital Partners, L.P.; *U.S. Private*, pg. 1672
SHENZHEN CIMC TIANDA AIRPORT EQUIPMENT CO., LTD.—See China International Marine Containers (Group) Co., Ltd.; *Int'l*, pg. 1512
SOMERSET WELDING AND STEEL, INC. - J&J TRUCK BODIES & TRAILERS DIVISION—See Riggs Industries, Inc.; *U.S. Private*, pg. 3435
SOMERSET WELDING AND STEEL, INC. - J&J TRUCK EQUIPMENT DIVISION—See Riggs Industries, Inc.; *U.S. Private*, pg. 3435
STAHL/SCOTT FETZER COMPANY—See Berkshire Hathaway Inc.; *U.S. Public*, pg. 300
STI HOLDINGS INC.—See Seaboard Corporation; *U.S. Public*, pg. 1850
STOUGHTON TRAILERS, INC.; *U.S. Private*, pg. 3832
STRICK CORPORATION; *U.S. Private*, pg. 3839
STRICK CORPORATION—See Strick Corporation; *U.S. Private*, pg. 3839
TALBERT MANUFACTURING INC.; *U.S. Private*, pg. 3925
TEXTRAIL, INC. - HOUSTON—See Bain Capital, LP; *U.S. Private*, pg. 436
TEXTRAIL, INC. - IDAHO—See Bain Capital, LP; *U.S. Private*, pg. 436
TEXTRAIL, INC. - ODESSA—See Bain Capital, LP; *U.S. Private*, pg. 436
THOMPSON TRACTOR COMPANY - THOMPSON TRUCK SOURCE DIVISION—See Thompson Tractor Company; *U.S. Private*, pg. 4162
TIMPTE INDUSTRIES INC.; *U.S. Private*, pg. 4173
TITAN INTERTRACTOR GMBH—See Titan International, Inc.; *U.S. Public*, pg. 2160
TRAIL-EZE TRAILERS—See Dakota Manufacturing Co. Inc.; *U.S. Private*, pg. 1147
TRAIL KING INDUSTRIES, INC.—See Henry Crown & Company; *U.S. Private*, pg. 1918
TRAMEC LLC—See MacLean-Fogg Company; *U.S. Private*, pg. 2537
TRANSCRAFT CORPORATION—See WABASH NATIONAL CORPORATION; *U.S. Public*, pg. 2320
TRAVIS BODY AND TRAILER, INC.—See Federal Signal Corporation; *U.S. Public*, pg. 826
TRUDELL TRAILERS OF GRAND RAPIDS, INC.; *U.S. Private*, pg. 4247
UNIVERSAL TRAILER CORPORATION—See Corporate Partners LLC; *U.S. Private*, pg. 1055
UTILITY TRAILER MANUFACTURING COMPANY, LLC; *U.S. Private*, pg. 4326
VANGUARD NATIONAL TRAILER CORPORATION—See China International Marine Containers (Group) Co., Ltd.; *Int'l*, pg. 1512
VANTAGE TRAILERS INC.; *U.S. Private*, pg. 4345
WABASH NATIONAL CORPORATION; *U.S. Public*, pg. 2320
WABASH NATIONAL, L.P.—See WABASH NATIONAL CORPORATION; *U.S. Public*, pg. 2320
WABASH NATIONAL SERVICES, L.P.—See WABASH NATIONAL CORPORATION; *U.S. Public*, pg. 2320
WELLS INDUSTRIES—See Corporate Partners LLC; *U.S. Private*, pg. 1055
WESTERN TRAILER CO.; *U.S. Private*, pg. 4497
WILSON TRAILER COMPANY INC.; *U.S. Private*, pg. 4531
XL SPECIALIZED TRAILERS, INC.—See Caparo Group Ltd.; *Int'l*, pg. 1302
YANGZHOU CIMC TONG HUA SPECIAL VEHICLES CO., LTD.—See China International Marine Containers (Group) Co., Ltd.; *Int'l*, pg. 1512
YANGZHOU CIMC TONGHUA TANK EQUIPMENT CO., LTD.—See CIMC Vehicle (Group) Co., Ltd.; *Int'l*, pg. 1608
ZIEMAN MANUFACTURING COMPANY—See LCI Industries; *U.S. Public*, pg. 1295

336213 — MOTOR HOME MANUFACTURING

BURSTNER GMBH & CO. KG—See Thor Industries, Inc.; *U.S. Public*, pg. 2156
CAPRON GMBH—See Thor Industries, Inc.; *U.S. Public*, pg. 2156
CHARIOT VANS INC.; *U.S. Private*, pg. 850
CLACKAMAS ULTIMATE AIRSTREAMS, LLC—See Lithia Motors, Inc.; *U.S. Public*, pg. 1321
COACH HOUSE, INC.; *U.S. Private*, pg. 953
COACHMEN RECREATIONAL VEHICLE COMPANY—See Berkshire Hathaway Inc.; *U.S. Public*, pg. 305
DETHLEFFS FRANCE S.A.R.L.—See Thor Industries, Inc.; *U.S. Public*, pg. 2156
DETHLEFFS GMBH & CO. KG—See Thor Industries, Inc.; *U.S. Public*, pg. 2156
ERWIN HYMER CENTER BAD WALDSEE GMBH—See Thor Industries, Inc.; *U.S. Public*, pg. 2156
ERWIN HYMER CENTER STUTTGART GMBH—See Thor Industries, Inc.; *U.S. Public*, pg. 2156
ERWIN HYMER GROUP SE—See Thor Industries, Inc.; *U.S. Public*, pg. 2156
ETRUSCO GMBH—See Thor Industries, Inc.; *U.S. Public*, pg. 2156
EXPLORER VAN COMPANY; *U.S. Private*, pg. 1450
FORETRAVEL INC.; *U.S. Private*, pg. 1567
GOLDSCHMITT TECHMOBIL GMBH—See Thor Industries, Inc.; *U.S. Public*, pg. 2156
GULF STREAM COACH INC.; *U.S. Private*, pg. 1817
LMC CARAVAN GMBH & CO. KG—See Thor Industries, Inc.; *U.S. Public*, pg. 2156
MARATHON COACH, INC.; *U.S. Private*, pg. 2570
NIESMANN+ BISCHOFF GMBH—See Thor Industries, Inc.; *U.S. Public*, pg. 2157
REV RECREATION GROUP, INC.—See AIP, LLC; *U.S. Private*, pg. 135
THOR MOTOR COACH, INC.—See Thor Industries, Inc.; *U.S. Public*, pg. 2157
TIFFIN MOTOR HOMES, INC.—See Thor Industries, Inc.; *U.S. Public*, pg. 2157
WINNEBAGO INDUSTRIES, INC.; *U.S. Public*, pg. 2374

336214 — TRAVEL TRAILER AND CAMPER MANUFACTURING

AIRSTREAM, INC.—See Thor Industries, Inc.; *U.S. Public*, pg. 2156
ANCHOR INDUSTRIES, INC. - LEISURE POOLS FACTORY—See Anchor Industries, Inc.; *U.S. Private*, pg. 273
ARGO MANAGEMENT GROUP, LLC—See Kingsway Financial Services Inc.; *U.S. Public*, pg. 1234
BRIERTY LTD.; *Int'l*, pg. 1160
BRP-ROTAX GMBH & CO. KG—See Bain Capital, LP; *U.S. Private*, pg. 431
CARRY-ON TRAILER, INC.—See Bain Capital, LP; *U.S. Private*, pg. 436
CASITA ENTERPRISES, INC.; *U.S. Private*, pg. 783
CHARIOT EAGLE, LLC—See Cavco Industries, Inc.; *U.S. Public*, pg. 455
CIMARRON TRAILERS, INC.—See Folience, Inc.; *U.S. Private*, pg. 1559
CIRCLE J TRAILERS LIMITED—See Bain Capital, LP; *U.S. Private*, pg. 436
COACHMEN RECREATIONAL VEHICLE COMPANY OF GEORGIA—See Berkshire Hathaway Inc.; *U.S. Public*, pg. 305
CORTES CAMPERS, LLC—See US Lighting Group, Inc.; *U.S. Public*, pg. 2266
CRUISER RV, LLC—See Thor Industries, Inc.; *U.S. Public*, pg. 2156
DUTCHMEN MANUFACTURING, INC.—See Thor Industries, Inc.; *U.S. Public*, pg. 2156
DUTCHMEN MANUFACTURING, INC.—See Thor Industries, Inc.; *U.S. Public*, pg. 2156
ES CUBE CO., LTD.; *Int'l*, pg. 2500
EVELAND'S INC.; *U.S. Private*, pg. 1436
EVERGREEN RECREATIONAL VEHICLES, LLC; *U.S. Private*, pg. 1440
EXISS ALUMINUM TRAILERS, INC—See Corporate Partners LLC; *U.S. Private*, pg. 1055
EZ LOADER BOAT TRAILERS, INC.; *U.S. Private*, pg. 1454
EZ LOADER CUSTOM BOAT TRAILERS, INC.—See EZ Loader Boat Trailers, Inc.; *U.S. Private*, pg. 1454
FEATHERLITE, INC.—See Corporate Partners LLC; *U.S. Private*, pg. 1055
FLEETWOOD LIMITED; *Int'l*, pg. 2699
FLOE INTERNATIONAL, INC.; *U.S. Private*, pg. 1546
FOREST RIVER, INC.—See Berkshire Hathaway Inc.; *U.S. Public*, pg. 305
GRAND DESIGN RV, LLC—See Winnebago Industries, Inc.; *U.S. Public*, pg. 2374
HMIN, INC.—See Corporate Partners LLC; *U.S. Private*, pg. 1055
HYUNDAI TRANSLEAD, INC.—See Hyundai Motor Company; *Int'l*, pg. 3559
JAYCO INC.—See Thor Industries, Inc.; *U.S. Public*, pg. 2156
JOHNSON OUTDOORS VERTRIEBSGESELLSCHAFT GMBH—See Johnson Outdoors Inc.; *U.S. Public*, pg. 1201
JOHNSON OUTDOORS WATERCRAFT LTD.—See Johnson Outdoors Inc.; *U.S. Public*, pg. 1201
KARAVAN TRAILERS INC.; *U.S. Private*, pg. 2262
KNAUS TABBERT GMBH—See H.T.P. Investments BV; *Int'l*, pg. 3196
KODIAK PRODUCTS CO., INC.—See Brookfield Corporation; *Int'l*, pg. 1176
KZRV, L.P.—See Thor Industries, Inc.; *U.S. Public*, pg. 2156
LANCE CAMPER MANUFACTURING CORPORATION—See AIP, LLC; *U.S. Private*, pg. 135
MIDWEST INDUSTRIES, INC.; *U.S. Private*, pg. 2722
MORELO REISEMOBILE GMBH—See H.T.P. Investments BV; *Int'l*, pg. 3196
MYCO TRAILERS, LLC—See Propst Properties, LLC; *U.S. Private*, pg. 3286
NEWMAR CORPORATION—See Winnebago Industries, Inc.; *U.S. Public*, pg. 2374
NORTHWOOD HOMES INCORPORATED—See Northwood Investment Corporation; *U.S. Private*, pg. 2963
NORTHWOOD INVESTMENT CORPORATION; *U.S. Private*, pg. 2963
NORTHWOOD MANUFACTURING, INC.—See Northwood Investment Corporation; *U.S. Private*, pg. 2963
NU-WA INDUSTRIES, INC.; *U.S. Private*, pg. 2971
PJ TRAILERS INC.; *U.S. Private*, pg. 3193
SCUBAPRO AG—See Johnson Outdoors Inc.; *U.S. Public*, pg. 1201
SCUBAPRO ASIA, LTD.—See Johnson Outdoors Inc.; *U.S. Public*, pg. 1201
SCUBAPRO ESPANA, S.A.—See Johnson Outdoors Inc.; *U.S. Public*, pg. 1201
SCUBAPRO EUROPE BENELUX, S.A.—See Johnson Outdoors Inc.; *U.S. Public*, pg. 1201
SCUBAPRO EUROPE S.R.L.—See Johnson Outdoors Inc.; *U.S. Public*, pg. 1201
SCUBAPRO ITALY S.R.L.—See Johnson Outdoors Inc.; *U.S. Public*, pg. 1201
SCUBAPRO-UWATEC AUSTRALIA PTY. LTD.—See Johnson Outdoors Inc.; *U.S. Public*, pg. 1201
SOONER TRAILER MANUFACTURING COMPANY—See Corporate Partners LLC; *U.S. Private*, pg. 1055
SUPERIOR COMPANIES-MANUFACTURING DIVISION—See Superior Companies Inc.; *U.S. Private*, pg. 3876
THOR INDUSTRIES, INC.; *U.S. Public*, pg. 2156
TRITON CORP.; *U.S. Private*, pg. 4239
VANLEIGH RV, INC.—See Thor Industries, Inc.; *U.S. Public*, pg. 2157
VIKING RECREATIONAL VEHICLES LLC—See Berkshire Hathaway Inc.; *U.S. Public*, pg. 305
WS ACQUISITION, LLC—See Guardian Capital Partners, LLC; *U.S. Private*, pg. 1810

336310 — MOTOR VEHICLE GASOLINE ENGINE AND ENGINE PARTS MANUFACTURING

ABB TURBO SYSTEMS LTD—See ABB Ltd.; *Int'l*, pg. 54
AC S.A.; *Int'l*, pg. 74
AERIES ENTERPRISES, LLC; *U.S. Private*, pg. 117
AGCO POWER OY—See AGCO Corporation; *U.S. Public*, pg. 59
AISAN INDUSTRY CO., LTD - ANJO PLANT—See Aisan Industry Co., Ltd.; *Int'l*, pg. 250
ALTUM PRECISION CO., LTD.—See Giovanni Agnelli B.V.; *Int'l*, pg. 2978
AMBAC INTERNATIONAL CORPORATION; *U.S. Private*, pg. 217
AMETEK LAMB MOTORES DE MEXICO, S. DE R.L. DE C.V.—See AMETEK, Inc.; *U.S. Public*, pg. 119
AMS POLYMERS LTD.; *Int'l*, pg. 440
ANAND I-POWER LIMITED—See Apollo Global Management, Inc.; *U.S. Public*, pg. 160
ASC INDUSTRIES INC.—See Crowne Group LLC; *U.S. Private*, pg. 1112
AURRIGO INTERNATIONAL PLC; *Int'l*, pg. 714
AUTOFORM TOOL & MANUFACTURING, LLC—See Park-Ohio Holdings Corp.; *U.S. Public*, pg. 1639
AUTOVENTIL A.D.; *Int'l*, pg. 732
AVL FRANCE S.A.—See AVL List GmbH; *Int'l*, pg. 748
AVL LIST GMBH; *Int'l*, pg. 748
AVL POWERTRAIN ENGINEERING, INC.—See AVL List GmbH; *Int'l*, pg. 748
BI-PHASE TECHNOLOGIES, LLC—See Power Solutions International, Inc.; *U.S. Public*, pg. 1705
BMW HAMS HALL MOTOREN GMBH—See Bayerische Motoren Werke Aktiengesellschaft; *Int'l*, pg. 911
BMW (UK) LTD. - HAMS HALL PLANT—See Bayerische Motoren Werke Aktiengesellschaft; *Int'l*, pg. 911
BOHAI AUTOMOTIVE SYSTEMS CO., LTD.; *Int'l*, pg. 1100
CASTEC KOREA CO., LTD.; *Int'l*, pg. 1355
CATERPILLAR REMANUFACTURE FRANKLIN—See Caterpillar, Inc.; *U.S. Public*, pg. 452
CAYMAN ENGLEY INDUSTRIAL CO., LTD.; *Int'l*, pg. 1363
CDTI ADVANCED MATERIALS, INC.; *U.S. Public*, pg. 461
CELINA ALUMINUM PRECISION TECHNOLOGY INC.—See Honda Motor Co., Ltd.; *Int'l*, pg. 3461
CHANGCHUN ELRINGKLINGER LTD.—See ElringKlinger AG; *Int'l*, pg. 2369
CHONGQING LIFAN INDUSTRY (GROUP) IMP. & EXP. CO., LTD.; *Int'l*, pg. 1580
CHONGQING MACHINERY & ELECTRIC CO., LTD.—See Chongqing Machinery & Electronics Holding (Group) Co., Ltd.; *Int'l*, pg. 1580
CHONGQING QIN'AN M&E PLC.; *Int'l*, pg. 1580
CLEAN TRANSPORTATION GROUP, INC.; *Int'l*, pg. 1654
CLEARSIGN TECHNOLOGIES CORP.; *U.S. Public*, pg. 513
COMPETITION CAMS INC.; *U.S. Private*, pg. 1000
CONNEXIONONE CORP.; *U.S. Public*, pg. 568
CT AUTOMOTIVE GROUP PLC; *Int'l*, pg. 1868
C.T.I. TRAFFIC INDUSTRIES CO., LTD.; *Int'l*, pg. 1244
CUMMINS AFRICA MIDDLE EAST (PTY.) LTD.—See Cummins Inc.; *U.S. Public*, pg. 605
CUMMINS AUSTRIA GMBH—See Cummins Inc.; *U.S. Public*, pg. 605
CUMMINS INDIA LIMITED—See Cummins Inc.; *U.S. Public*, pg. 606
CUMMINS MERCRUISER DIESEL MARINE LLC—See Cummins Inc.; *U.S. Public*, pg. 606
CUMMINS WESTPORT INC.—See Cummins Inc.; *U.S. Public*, pg. 607
DAISHINSEIKI CO., LTD.—See Denso Corporation; *Int'l*, pg. 2028
DAROS PISTON RINGS AB—See Apollo Global Management, Inc.; *U.S. Public*, pg. 160
DELPHI ENERGY & ENGINE MANAGEMENT SYSTEMS—See Aptiv PLC; *Int'l*, pg. 525
DENSO HARYANA PVT. LTD.—See Denso Corporation; *Int'l*, pg. 2029
DENSO MANUFACTURING KITAKYUSHU CO.,LTD.—See Denso Corporation; *Int'l*, pg. 2029
DENSO PRESS TECH CO., LTD.—See Denso Corporation; *Int'l*, pg. 2032
DENSO TEN TECHNOSEPTA LIMITED—See Denso Corporation; *Int'l*, pg. 2030
DEUTZ AG; *Int'l*, pg. 2085
DEUTZ AUSTRALIA (PTY.) LTD.—See DEUTZ AG; *Int'l*, pg. 2086
DEUTZ ITALY S.R.L.—See DEUTZ AG; *Int'l*, pg. 2086
DEUTZ ROMANIA S.R.L.—See DEUTZ AG; *Int'l*, pg. 2086
DEUTZ SPAIN S.A.—See DEUTZ AG; *Int'l*, pg. 2086
DONGYANG TECH CO., LTD.—See Dongyang Piston Co., Ltd.; *Int'l*, pg. 2172
DRUZHBA AD; *Int'l*, pg. 2206
EATON CORP. - VEHICLE GROUP, BELMOND PLANT—See Eaton Corporation plc; *Int'l*, pg. 2280
EATON CORP. - VEHICLE GROUP, KEARNEY PLANT—See Eaton Corporation plc; *Int'l*, pg. 2280
ELRINGKLINGER AG; *Int'l*, pg. 2369
ELRINGKLINGER CHINA, LTD.—See ElringKlinger AG; *Int'l*, pg. 2369
ELRINGKLINGER CHONGQING LTD.—See ElringKlinger AG; *Int'l*, pg. 2369
ELRINGKLINGER ITALIA SRL—See ElringKlinger AG; *Int'l*, pg. 2369
ELRINGKLINGER KUNSTSTOFFTECHNIK GMBH—See ElringKlinger AG; *Int'l*, pg. 2369
ELRINGKLINGER SOUTH AFRICA (PTY) LTD.—See ElringKlinger AG; *Int'l*, pg. 2370
ELRINGKLINGER TR OTOMOTIV SANAYI VE TICARET A.S.—See ElringKlinger AG; *Int'l*, pg. 2370
ELRINGKLINGER USA, INC.—See ElringKlinger AG; *Int'l*, pg. 2370
EMERSON PROCESS MANAGEMENT-VALVE AUTOMATION—See Emerson Electric Co.; *U.S. Public*, pg. 746
ENERPULSE TECHNOLOGIES, INC.; *U.S. Private*, pg. 1396
ENGINE REBUILDERS, INC.—See Reviva Inc.; *U.S. Private*, pg. 3416
ENOVATION CONTROLS, LLC; *U.S. Private*, pg. 1401
ERIKS MIDWEST—See LKCM Headwater Investments; *U.S. Private*, pg. 2475
FEDERAL-MOGUL BURSCHEID GMBH—See Apollo Global Management, Inc.; *U.S. Public*, pg. 160
FEDERAL-MOGUL GOETZE (INDIA) LTD—See Apollo Global Management, Inc.; *U.S. Public*, pg. 161
FEDERAL-MOGUL IZMIT PISTON VE PIM URETIM TESISLERI A.S.—See Apollo Global Management, Inc.; *U.S. Public*, pg. 162
FEDERAL-MOGUL PISTON RINGS, INC.—See Apollo Global Management, Inc.; *U.S. Public*, pg. 161
FEDERAL MOGUL POWERTRAIN OTOMOTIV ANONIM SIRKETI—See Apollo Global Management, Inc.; *U.S. Public*, pg. 160
FEDERAL-MOGUL TP PISTON RINGS GMBH—See Apollo Global Management, Inc.; *U.S. Public*, pg. 161
FEY LAMELLENRINGE GMBH & CO. KG; *Int'l*, pg. 2649
FORGED PRODUCTS, INC.—See Reserve Group Management Company; *U.S. Private*, pg. 3404
FPC HOLDINGS, INC.—See Kelso & Company, L.P.; *U.S. Private*, pg. 2279
FPC HOLDINGS, INC.—See Warburg Pincus LLC; *U.S. Private*, pg. 4437
FRAUENTHAL POWERTRAIN MANAGEMENT GMBH & CO. KG—See Frauenthal Holding AG; *Int'l*, pg. 2767
FRENOS HIDRAULICOS AUTOMOTRICES, S.A. DE C.V.—See Apollo Global Management, Inc.; *U.S. Public*, pg. 162
FUJI OOZX INC.; *Int'l*, pg. 2816
FUJI VALVE (GUANGDONG) CORPORATION—See Daido Steel Co., Ltd.; *Int'l*, pg. 1923
GAJRA BEVEL GEARS LIMITED; *Int'l*, pg. 2869
GARNER REBUILT WATER PUMPS INCORPORATED; *U.S. Private*, pg. 1645
GGB AUSTRIA GMBH—See The Timken Company; *U.S. Public*, pg. 2132
GGB BEARING TECHNOLOGY (SUZHOU) CO., LTD.—See Enpro Inc.; *U.S. Public*, pg. 774
GGB BRASIL INDUSTRIA DE MANCAIS E COMPONENTES LTDA.—See The Timken Company; *U.S. Public*, pg. 2132
GGB FRANCE E.U.R.L.—See Enpro Inc.; *U.S. Public*, pg. 774
GUD FILTERS PTY. LTD.; *Int'l*, pg. 3171
GUILN FUDA ALFING LARGE CRANKSAFT CO., LTD.—See Guiln Fuda Co., Ltd.; *Int'l*, pg. 3173
HAMADEN P.S CO., LTD.—See Denso Corporation; *Int'l*, pg. 2032
HAMANAKODENSO CO., LTD.—See Denso Corporation; *Int'l*, pg. 2032
HAMPTON HYDRAULICS LLC—See Ligon Industries LLC; *U.S. Private*, pg. 2455
HANGZHOU RADICAL ENERGY SAVING TECHNOLOGY CO., LTD.; *Int'l*, pg. 3249
HANGZHOU XZB TECH CO.,LTD; *Int'l*, pg. 3251
HAO YONG AUTOMOTIVE CONTROLS LTD.; *Int'l*, pg. 3268
HARBIN DONGAN AUTO ENGINE CO., LTD.; *Int'l*, pg. 3270
HASTINGS EAST MANUFACTURING CO., LTD.—See RFE Investment Partners; *U.S. Private*, pg. 3419
HEFEI CHANG QING MACHINERY CO., LTD.; *Int'l*, pg. 3307
HELIO PRECISION PRODUCTS INC.; *U.S. Private*, pg. 1906
HIRATA CORPORATION - KANSAI PLANT—See Hirata Corporation; *Int'l*, pg. 3403
HIRATA CORPORATION - KANTO PLANT—See Hirata Corporation; *Int'l*, pg. 3403
HIRATA CORPORATION - KUMAMOTO PLANT—See Hirata Corporation; *Int'l*, pg. 3403
HIRATA CORPORATION - KUSUNO PLANT—See Hirata Corporation; *Int'l*, pg. 3403
HIRATA ENGINEERING EUROPE GMBH—See Hirata Corporation; *Int'l*, pg. 3403
HIRATA ENGINEERING (THAILAND) CO., LTD.—See Hirata Corporation; *Int'l*, pg. 3403
HIRATA FA ENGINEERING (M) SDN. BHD.—See Hirata Corporation; *Int'l*, pg. 3403
HIRATA FIELD ENGINEERING CO., LTD.—See Hirata Corporation; *Int'l*, pg. 3403
HIRATA MECHANICAL EQUIPMENT SALES (SHANGHAI) CO., LTD.—See Hirata Corporation; *Int'l*, pg. 3404
HOLLEY PERFORMANCE PRODUCTS INC.—See Holley Inc.; *U.S. Public*, pg. 1044
HUNAN OIL PUMP CO., LTD.; *Int'l*, pg. 3533
HUNAN TYEN MACHINERY CO., LTD.; *Int'l*, pg. 3534
HYDRO FITTING MANUFACTURING CORP.—See KKR & Co. Inc.; *U.S. Public*, pg. 1262
HYDRO-GEAR EUROPE BVBA—See Danfoss A/S; *Int'l*, pg. 1960
HYDRO-GEAR, INC.—See Danfoss A/S; *Int'l*, pg. 1960
HYUNDAI WIA AUTOMOTIVE ENGINE (SHANDONG) COMPANY—See Hyundai Motor Company; *Int'l*, pg. 3560
INERGY AUTOMOTIVE SYSTEMS (BELGIUM) N.V.—See Burelle S.A.; *Int'l*, pg. 1222
INERGY AUTOMOTIVE SYSTEMS S.A.—See Burelle S.A.; *Int'l*, pg. 1222
INERGY AUTOMOTIVE SYSTEMS U.K. LTD.—See Burelle S.A.; *Int'l*, pg. 1222
INLAND POWER GROUP, INC.; *U.S. Private*, pg. 2079
INTERSTATE DIESEL SERVICE, INC.; *U.S. Private*, pg. 2124
JASPER ENGINE EXCHANGE INC.—See Jasper Engine & Transmission Exchange Inc.; *U.S. Private*, pg. 2190
JASPER ENGINE & TRANSMISSION EXCHANGE INC.; *U.S. Private*, pg. 2190
JFK RINGS GMBH—See Apollo Global Management, Inc.; *U.S. Public*, pg. 162
JILIN DAHUA MACHINE MANUFACTURING CO., LTD.—See China North Industries Group Corporation; *Int'l*, pg. 1536
KEIHIN AUTO PARTS (PHILIPPINES) CORP.—See Hitachi Astemo, Ltd.; *Int'l*, pg. 3408
KEIHIN CORPORATION - KAKUDA 1ST PLANT—See Hitachi Astemo, Ltd.; *Int'l*, pg. 3409
KEIHIN CORPORATION - KAKUDA 2ND PLANT—See Hitachi Astemo, Ltd.; *Int'l*, pg. 3409
KEIHIN CORPORATION - MARUMORI PLANT—See Hitachi Astemo, Ltd.; *Int'l*, pg. 3409
KEIHIN MICHIGAN MANUFACTURING, LLC—See Hitachi Astemo, Ltd.; *Int'l*, pg. 3409
KEIHIN NORTH AMERICA, INC.—See Hitachi Astemo, Ltd.; *Int'l*, pg. 3409
K & H TRUCK PLAZA INC.—See Majors Management, LLC; *U.S. Private*, pg. 2555
KOYA CORP.—See Hirata Corporation; *Int'l*, pg. 3404
KYOSAN DENKI CO., LTD - YUKI PLANT—See Denso Corporation; *Int'l*, pg. 2032
MAHLE ARGENTINA S.A.—See Food Empire Holdings Limited; *Int'l*, pg. 2727
MAHLE ENGINE COMPONENTS (CHONGQING) CO., LTD.—See Food Empire Holdings Limited; *Int'l*, pg. 2727
MAHLE ENGINE COMPONENTS (NANJING) CO., LTD.—See Food Empire Holdings Limited; *Int'l*, pg. 2727
MAHLE ENGINE COMPONENTS (THAILAND) CO., LTD.—See Food Empire Holdings Limited; *Int'l*, pg. 2727
MAHLE ENGINE COMPONENTS (YINGKOU) CO., LTD.—See Food Empire Holdings Limited; *Int'l*, pg. 2727
MAHLE FILTER SYSTEMS NORTH AMERICA, INC.—See Food Empire Holdings Limited; *Int'l*, pg. 2727
MAHLE FILTER SYSTEMS PHILIPPINES CORPORATION—See Food Empire Holdings Limited; *Int'l*, pg. 2727
MAHLE GUANGZHOU FILTER SYSTEMS CO., LTD.—See Food Empire Holdings Limited; *Int'l*, pg. 2727
MAHLE INTERNATIONAL GMBH—See Food Empire Holdings Limited; *Int'l*, pg. 2727
MAHLE POWERTRAIN GMBH—See Food Empire Holdings Limited; *Int'l*, pg. 2727
MAHLE SHANGHAI FILTER SYSTEMS CO., LTD.—See Food Empire Holdings Limited; *Int'l*, pg. 2727
MAHLE SIAM FILTER SYSTEMS CO., LTD.—See Food Empire Holdings Limited; *Int'l*, pg. 2727
MAHLE TRADING (SHANGHAI) CO., LTD.—See Food Empire Holdings Limited; *Int'l*, pg. 2727
MAILENDER, INC.—See Bain Capital, LP; *U.S. Private*, pg. 441
MEDI1ONE MEDICAL GMBH—See Fresenius SE & Co. KGaA; *Int'l*, pg. 2780
MELLING TOOL COMPANY INC. - MELLING ENGINE PARTS DIVISION—See Melling Tool Company Inc.; *U.S. Private*, pg. 2662
MELLING TOOL COMPANY INC. - MELLING SELECT PERFORMANCE DIVISION—See Melling Tool Company Inc.; *U.S. Private*, pg. 2662
MELLING TOOL COMPANY INC.; *U.S. Private*, pg. 2662
MELLING TOOL COMPANY INC—See Melling Tool Company Inc.; *U.S. Private*, pg. 2662
METALDYNE PERFORMANCE GROUP INC.—See American Axle & Manufacturing Holdings, Inc.; *U.S. Public*, pg. 96
MIRENCO, INC.; *U.S. Private*, pg. 2746

336310 — MOTOR VEHICLE GASOL...

MOTOR COMPONENTS, LLC—See BAM Enterprises, Inc.; *U.S. Private,* pg. 463
MOTORES JOHN DEERE S.A. DE C.V.—See Deere & Company; *U.S. Public,* pg. 647
MTC ENGINEERING, LLC; *U.S. Private,* pg. 2808
MWM AUSTRIA GMBH—See Caterpillar, Inc.; *U.S. Public,* pg. 452
MWM INTERNATIONAL INDUSTRIA DE MOTORES DA AMERICA DO SUL LTDA.—See FreightCar America, Inc.; *U.S. Public,* pg. 885
NANTONG SHENGYI PRECISION MACHINERY CO., LTD.—See Chung-Hsin Electric & Machinery Manufacturing Corp.; *Int'l,* pg. 1597
NASU SEIKI MFG. CO., LTD.—See Hitachi Astemo, Ltd.; *Int'l,* pg. 3409
NDC CO., LTD.—See Daido Metal Corporation; *Int'l,* pg. 1922
NICO PRECISION CO., INC.—See IHI Corporation; *Int'l,* pg. 3606
NIIGATA POWER SYSTEMS CO., LTD.—See IHI Corporation; *Int'l,* pg. 3606
NORTHSTAR POWER LLC—See Brandt Holdings Company; *U.S. Private,* pg. 639
OEM REMANUFACTURING COMPANY INC.—See Finning International Inc.; *Int'l,* pg. 2676
OMNITEK ENGINEERING CORP.; *U.S. Public,* pg. 1600
ORIENS CO., LTD.—See Dongyang Piston Co., Ltd.; *Int'l,* pg. 2172
PARK-OHIO INDUSTRIES, INC. - OHIO CRANKSHAFT DIVISION—See Park-Ohio Holdings Corp.; *U.S. Public,* pg. 1640
PENN POWER GROUP, LLC; *U.S. Private,* pg. 3134
POWERTRAIN INTEGRATION LLC—See Power Solutions International, Inc.; *U.S. Public,* pg. 1705
PURE POWER TECHNOLOGIES, LLC; *U.S. Private,* pg. 3305
RACE WINNING BRANDS, INC.—See MiddleGround Management, LP; *U.S. Private,* pg. 2712
RIVIAN AUTOMOTIVE, INC.; *U.S. Public,* pg. 1801
ROTOBLOCK CORPORATION; *U.S. Private,* pg. 3487
RWG GERMANY GMBH—See Arcline Investment Management LP; *U.S. Private,* pg. 314
SALVADORI SPINOTTI S.R.L.—See AMSTED Industries Incorporated; *U.S. Private,* pg. 268
SAUER-DANFOSS AS—See Danfoss A/S; *Int'l,* pg. 1960
SENERTEC-CENTER GMBH—See 2G Energy AG; *Int'l,* pg. 5
SIERRA INTERNATIONAL LLC—See Dometic Group AB; *Int'l,* pg. 2160
SPECIALTY ENGINE COMPONENTS L.L.C.; *U.S. Private,* pg. 3749
SRC AUTOMOTIVE, INC.—See SRC Holdings Corporation; *U.S. Private,* pg. 3767
STURDY CORPORATION; *U.S. Private,* pg. 3844
SUPERTURBO TECHNOLOGIES—See Woodward, Inc.; *U.S. Public,* pg. 2377
TAIHEI TECHNOS CO., LTD.—See Hirata Corporation; *Int'l,* pg. 3404
TAIWAN HIRATA CORPORATION—See Hirata Corporation; *Int'l,* pg. 3404
TODAYSURE MATTHEWS LIMITED—See Matthews International Corporation; *U.S. Public,* pg. 1401
TRINITY INC.—See Hirata Corporation; *Int'l,* pg. 3404
TURBODYNE TECHNOLOGIES, INC.; *U.S. Private,* pg. 4259
UNITED ENGINE & MACHINE COMPANY; *U.S. Private,* pg. 4291
USA ZAMA INC.—See Andreas Stihl AG & Co.; *Int'l,* pg. 451
U.S. ENERGY INITIATIVES CORPORATION; *U.S. Public,* pg. 2213
U.S. ENGINE VALVE CORPORATION—See Eaton Corporation plc; *Int'l,* pg. 2280
VCST INDUSTRIAL PRODUCTS BVBA—See Gimv NV; *Int'l,* pg. 2976
VETUS N.V.—See AAC Capital Partners Holding B.V.; *Int'l,* pg. 30
VM MOTORI S.P.A.—See General Motors Company; *U.S. Public,* pg. 929
VOLVO TRUCK SLOVAK, S.R.O.—See AB Volvo; *Int'l,* pg. 46
WALKER PRODUCTS INC.; *U.S. Private,* pg. 4429
WENDENG DONGYANG PISTON CO., LTD.—See Dongyang Piston Co., Ltd.; *Int'l,* pg. 2172
WILCOX PAPER LLC—See Central National Gottesman Inc.; *U.S. Private,* pg. 823
XINYANG BURGESS-NORTON YINGUANG PISTON PIN CO., LTD.—See AMSTED Industries Incorporated; *U.S. Private,* pg. 268
ZENITH FUEL SYSTEMS LLC—See Aeries Enterprises, LLC; *U.S. Private,* pg. 117
ZI KALTUMFORMUNG GMBH—See Heckler AG; *Int'l,* pg. 3307

336320 — MOTOR VEHICLE ELECTRICAL AND ELECTRONIC EQUIPMENT MANUFACTURING

A3 GLOBAL, LLC; *U.S. Private,* pg. 29
AAC ENTERPRISES LLC; *U.S. Private,* pg. 30
ABSOLUTE ASSEMBLY CO., LTD.—See Energy Absolute Public Company Limited; *Int'l,* pg. 2422
ACCELERATED SYSTEMS, INC.; *Int'l,* pg. 80
ACTIA CHINA AUTOMOTIVE ELECTRONICS CO., LTD—See Actia Group SA; *Int'l,* pg. 118
ACTIA DE MEXICO S.A. DE C.V.—See Actia Group SA; *Int'l,* pg. 118
ACTIA GROUP SA - COLOMIERS DIVISION—See Actia Group SA; *Int'l,* pg. 118
ACTUANT GMBH—See Enerpac Tool Group Corp.; *U.S. Public,* pg. 765
ACTUANT OPERATIONS UK LTD.—See Enerpac Tool Group Corp.; *U.S. Public,* pg. 765
ADESA US AUCTION, LLC—See Carvana Co.; *U.S. Public,* pg. 445
ADVANCED TECHNOLOGY CORP.—See ATC Group, Inc.; *U.S. Private,* pg. 365
ADVANTICO GMBH—See Compagnie Generale des Etablissements Michelin SCA; *Int'l,* pg. 1741
AEL SISTEMAS S.A.—See Elbit Systems Limited; *Int'l,* pg. 2344
A.F.W CO., LTD.; *Int'l,* pg. 23
AIMFLEX BERHAD; *Int'l,* pg. 233
AISAN INDUSTRY CZECH S.R.O.—See Aisan Industry Co., Ltd.; *Int'l,* pg. 250
ALBUQUERQUE ANUSA, LLC—See AutoNation, Inc.; *U.S. Public,* pg. 232
ANTAYA TECHNOLOGIES CORPORATION—See Aptiv PLC; *Int'l,* pg. 524
ARROW SAFETY DEVICE COMPANY; *U.S. Private,* pg. 336
ATC GROUP, INC.; *U.S. Private,* pg. 365
ATC LIGHTING & PLASTICS INC.—See ATC Group, Inc.; *U.S. Private,* pg. 365
ATIVA S.P.A.—See Argo Finanziaria S.p.A.; *Int'l,* pg. 561
AURA SYSTEMS, INC.; *U.S. Public,* pg. 227
AUSMA MOTORENREVISIE B.V.—See DEUTZ AG; *Int'l,* pg. 2085
AUTOLITE MANUFACTURING LIMITED—See Autolite (India) Limited; *Int'l,* pg. 728
AUTOLIV ELECTRONICS AB—See Autoliv, Inc.; *Int'l,* pg. 728
AUTOLIV ELECTRONICS AB—See Autoliv, Inc.; *Int'l,* pg. 728
AUTOLIV ELECTRONICS AMERICA—See Autoliv, Inc.; *Int'l,* pg. 729
AUTOTRONIC CONTROLS CORPORATION—See Z Capital Group, LLC; *U.S. Private,* pg. 4595
BAL SEAL ASIA, LTD.—See Arcline Investment Management LP; *U.S. Private,* pg. 314
BAL SEAL ENGINEERING EUROPE BV—See Arcline Investment Management LP; *U.S. Private,* pg. 314
BASTA FRANCE; *Int'l,* pg. 888
BERGSTROM INC.; *U.S. Private,* pg. 531
BOLTON CONDUCTIVE SYSTEMS, LLC—See Stoneridge, Inc.; *U.S. Public,* pg. 1951
BORGWARNER AUTOMOTIVE SYSTEMS SINGAPORE INVESTMENTS PTE. LTD.—See Aptiv PLC; *Int'l,* pg. 524
BORGWARNER BERU SYSTEMS KANDEL GMBH—See BorgWarner Inc.; *U.S. Public,* pg. 369
BORGWARNER EMISSIONS SYSTEMS LTDA.—See BorgWarner Inc.; *U.S. Public,* pg. 369
BORGWARNER EMISSIONS SYSTEMS PORTUGAL UNIPESSOAL LDA.—See BorgWarner Inc.; *U.S. Public,* pg. 369
BORGWARNER EMISSIONS TALEGAON PRIVATE LIMITED—See BorgWarner Inc.; *U.S. Public,* pg. 369
BORGWARNER MORSE SYSTEMS INDIA PRIVATE LIMITED—See BorgWarner Inc.; *U.S. Public,* pg. 370
BORGWARNER MORSE SYSTEMS ITALY S.R.L.—See BorgWarner Inc.; *U.S. Public,* pg. 370
BORGWARNER PDS BRASIL PRODUTOS AUTOMOTIVOS LTDA.—See BorgWarner Inc.; *U.S. Public,* pg. 370
BORGWARNER PDS (CHANGNYEONG) INC.—See BorgWarner Inc.; *U.S. Public,* pg. 370
BORGWARNER PDS (OCHANG) INC.—See BorgWarner Inc.; *U.S. Public,* pg. 370
BORGWARNER SOUTHBOROUGH INC.—See BorgWarner Inc.; *U.S. Public,* pg. 370
BORGWARNER SYSTEMS LUGO S.R.L.—See BorgWarner Inc.; *U.S. Public,* pg. 370
BRITAX PMG LIMITED—See Ecco Safety Group; *U.S. Private,* pg. 1326
BROSE BEIJING AUTOMOTIVE SYSTEMS CO., LTD.—See Brose Fahrzeugteile GmbH & Co. KG; *Int'l,* pg. 1195
BROSE CHINA CO., LTD.—See Brose Fahrzeugteile GmbH & Co. KG; *Int'l,* pg. 1195
BROSE CHONGQING AUTOMOTIVE SYSTEMS CO., LTD.—See Brose Fahrzeugteile GmbH & Co. KG; *Int'l,* pg. 1195
BROSE DELLOYD AUTOMOTIVE CO., LTD.—See Brose Fahrzeugteile GmbH & Co. KG; *Int'l,* pg. 1195
BROSE HUNGARY AUTOMOTIVE KFT.—See Brose Fahrzeugteile GmbH & Co. KG; *Int'l,* pg. 1195
BROSE JEFFERSON, INC.—See Brose Fahrzeugteile GmbH & Co. KG; *Int'l,* pg. 1195
BROSE WUHAN AUTOMOTIVE SYSTEMS CO., LTD.—See Brose Fahrzeugteile GmbH & Co. KG; *Int'l,* pg. 1196
BRUCE AEROSPACE, INC.—See TransDigm Group Incorporated; *U.S. Public,* pg. 2182
BX SHINSEI SEIKI CO., LTD.—See Bunka Shutter Co., Ltd.; *Int'l,* pg. 1216
BYD AUSTRALIA PTY. LTD.—See BYD Company Limited; *Int'l,* pg. 1234
BYD CHILE S.P.A.—See BYD Company Limited; *Int'l,* pg. 1234
BYD KOREA COMPANY LTD.—See BYD Company Limited; *Int'l,* pg. 1234
BYD MALAYSIA SDN. BHD.—See BYD Company Limited; *Int'l,* pg. 1234
BYD MOTORS INC.—See BYD Company Limited; *Int'l,* pg. 1234
CABOT ADVANCED BATTERY MATERIALS (TIANJIN) CO., LTD.—See Cabot Corporation; *U.S. Public,* pg. 416
CANTEGA TECHNOLOGIES INC.—See Hubbell Incorporated; *U.S. Public,* pg. 1066
CASCO IMOS ITALIA S.P.A.—See Veritas Capital Fund Management, LLC; *U.S. Private,* pg. 4364
CASCO PRODUCTS CORPORATION—See The Jordan Company, L.P.; *U.S. Private,* pg. 4060
CEDS INC.—See Apollo Global Management, Inc.; *U.S. Public,* pg. 160
C.E. NIEHOFF & CO.; *U.S. Private,* pg. 706
CENTRAL AUTO PARTS (SHANGHAI) CO., LTD.—See Motorcar Parts of America, Inc.; *U.S. Public,* pg. 1477
CHARLESTON ANUSA, LLC—See AutoNation, Inc.; *U.S. Public,* pg. 234
CHIYODA INTEGRE (SHANGHAI) CO.—See Chiyoda Integre Co., Ltd.; *Int'l,* pg. 1575
CHONGQING HUF AUTOMOTIVE SYSTEMS CO., LTD.—See Huf Hulsbeck & Furst GmbH & Co. KG; *Int'l,* pg. 3523
CHONGQING QINGZHU MACHINERY MANUFACTURING CO., LTD.—See Chengdu Haoneng Technology Co., Ltd.; *Int'l,* pg. 1468
CLEAN MOTION AB; *Int'l,* pg. 1654
COLORADO SPRINGS ANUSA, LLC—See AutoNation, Inc.; *U.S. Public,* pg. 234
COMAIR ROTRON SHANGHAI FAN CO., LTD.—See Gentherm Incorporated; *U.S. Public,* pg. 931
COMET SOLUTIONS TAIWAN LTD.—See Comet Holding AG; *Int'l,* pg. 1710
COMPETITION SYSTEMS, INCORPORATED—See Z Capital Group, LLC; *U.S. Private,* pg. 4595
CONSUMER SAFETY TECHNOLOGY, LLC—See Welsh, Carson, Anderson & Stowe; *U.S. Private,* pg. 4480
CONTINENTAL AUTOMOTIVE ELECTRONICS LLC.—See Continental Aktiengesellschaft; *Int'l,* pg. 1781
CONTINENTAL AUTOMOTIVE FRANCE SAS—See Continental Aktiengesellschaft; *Int'l,* pg. 1781
CONTINENTAL AUTOMOTIVE SYSTEMS CZECH REPUBLIC S.R.O.—See Continental Aktiengesellschaft; *Int'l,* pg. 1781
CONTINENTAL AUTOMOTIVE SYSTEMS, INC—See Continental Aktiengesellschaft; *Int'l,* pg. 1782
CONTINENTAL AUTOMOTIVE SYSTEMS (SHANGHAI) CO., LTD—See Continental Aktiengesellschaft; *Int'l,* pg. 1781
CONTINENTAL MECHANICAL COMPONENTS GERMANY GMBH—See Continental Aktiengesellschaft; *Int'l,* pg. 1782
CONTOUR ELECTRONICS ASIA LIMITED—See discoverIE Group plc; *Int'l,* pg. 2133
CONTOUR ELECTRONICS LIMITED—See discoverIE Group plc; *Int'l,* pg. 2133
COROPLAST HARNESS TECHNOLOGY (KUNSHAN) CO., LTD.—See Coroplast Fritz Muller GmbH und Co. KG; *Int'l,* pg. 1802
COROPLAST HARNESS TECHNOLOGY (MIANYANG) CO., LTD.—See Coroplast Fritz Muller GmbH und Co. KG; *Int'l,* pg. 1802
COROPLAST HARNESS TECHNOLOGY (TAICANG) CO., LTD.—See Coroplast Fritz Muller GmbH und Co. KG; *Int'l,* pg. 1802
CTS CORPORATION - AUTOMOTIVE PRODUCTS—See CTS Corporation; *U.S. Public,* pg. 603
CTS ELECTRONICS MANUFACTURING SOLUTIONS—See Benchmark Electronics, Inc.; *U.S. Public,* pg. 296
CUB ELECPARTS INC.; *Int'l,* pg. 1875
DAEDONG DOOR INC.—See Hi-Lex Corporation; *Int'l,* pg. 3380
DAIDO METAL CO., LTD.—See Daido Metal Corporation; *Int'l,* pg. 1921
DELPHI AUTOMOTIVE SYSTEMS LIMITED SIRKETI—See Aptiv PLC; *Int'l,* pg. 524
DELPHI AUTOMOTIVE SYSTEMS - PORTUGAL S.A.—See Aptiv PLC; *Int'l,* pg. 524
DELPHI AUTOMOTIVE SYSTEMS SWEDEN AB—See Aptiv PLC; *Int'l,* pg. 524
DELPHI DEUTSCHLAND GMBH—See Aptiv PLC; *Int'l,* pg. 525

N.A.I.C.S. INDEX

336320 — MOTOR VEHICLE ELECT...

DELPHI ELECTRONICS & SAFETY—See Aptiv PLC; *Int'l*, pg. 524
DELPHI ELECTRONICS (SUZHOU) CO. LTD.—See Aptiv PLC; *Int'l*, pg. 524
DELPHI ITALIA AUTOMOTIVE SYSTEMS S.R.L.—See Aptiv PLC; *Int'l*, pg. 525
DELPHI SLOVENSKO S.R.O.—See Aptiv PLC; *Int'l*, pg. 525
DELPHI—See Aptiv PLC; *Int'l*, pg. 524
DELPHI TECHNICAL CENTRE LUXEMBOURG—See Aptiv PLC; *Int'l*, pg. 525
DELTA TECHNOLOGIES PLC; *Int'l*, pg. 2020
DENSO TEN AMERICA LIMITED - LOS ANGELES—See Denso Corporation; *Int'l*, pg. 2030
DENSO TEN ELECTRONICS (WUXI) LIMITED—See Denso Corporation; *Int'l*, pg. 2030
DENSO TEN ESPANA, S.A.—See Denso Corporation; *Int'l*, pg. 2030
DENSO TEN LIMITED - NAKATSUGAWA PLANT—See Denso Corporation; *Int'l*, pg. 2030
DENSO TEN LIMITED—See Denso Corporation; *Int'l*, pg. 2030
DENSO TEN PHILIPPINES CORPORATION—See Denso Corporation; *Int'l*, pg. 2030
DENSO TEN (THAILAND) LIMITED—See Denso Corporation; *Int'l*, pg. 2030
DENSO TEN (THAILAND) LIMITED—See Denso Corporation; *Int'l*, pg. 2030
DENVER 104 ANUSA, LLC—See AutoNation, Inc.; *U.S. Public*, pg. 234
DEUTZ AUSTRIA GMBH—See DEUTZ AG; *Int'l*, pg. 2086
DEUTZ BELGIUM N.V.—See DEUTZ AG; *Int'l*, pg. 2086
DEUTZ NETHERLANDS B.V.—See DEUTZ AG; *Int'l*, pg. 2086
DIAMOND ELECTRIC MFG. CO., LTD.; *Int'l*, pg. 2105
DIEHL AVIATION GILCHING GMBH—See Diehl Stiftung & Co. KG; *Int'l*, pg. 2114
DIEHL CONNECTIVITY SOLUTIONS GMBH—See Diehl Stiftung & Co. KG; *Int'l*, pg. 2115
DIEHL RETROFIT MISSILE SYSTEME GMBH—See Diehl Stiftung & Co. KG; *Int'l*, pg. 2115
DMC DIGITAL MOTOR CONTROL GMBH—See Addtech AB; *Int'l*, pg. 132
DOCK-N-LOCK LLC; *U.S. Private*, pg. 1251
EAO BENELUX B.V.—See EAO AG; *Int'l*, pg. 2267
EAO LUMITAS GMBH—See EAO AG; *Int'l*, pg. 2267
EAO SVENSKA AB—See EAO AG; *Int'l*, pg. 2267
EAO VERKAUF (SCHWEIZ) AG—See EAO AG; *Int'l*, pg. 2267
EARTH INFINITY CO., LTD.; *Int'l*, pg. 2268
EBRAINS, INC.; *Int'l*, pg. 2286
EDGE PRODUCTS; *U.S. Private*, pg. 1334
ELAMEX, S.A. DE C.V.—See Accel, S.A.B. de C.V.; *Int'l*, pg. 79
E-LEAD ELECTRONIC (THAILAND) CO., LTD.—See E-Lead Electronic Co., Ltd.; *Int'l*, pg. 2248
ELECTRIC FUEL INFRASTRUCTURE SWEDEN 2 AB—See DistIT AB; *Int'l*, pg. 2136
ELECTRIC LAST MILE SOLUTIONS, INC.—See Mullen Automotive, Inc.; *U.S. Public*, pg. 1486
ELECTRIC POWER TECHNOLOGY LIMITED; *Int'l*, pg. 2349
ELHIM ISKRA JSC; *Int'l*, pg. 2360
ELLWEE AB; *Int'l*, pg. 2367
ELRINGKLINGER KOREA CO., LTD.—See ElringKlinger AG; *Int'l*, pg. 2369
ELUON INS CO., LTD.—See ELUON Corporation; *Int'l*, pg. 2371
EMD LOCOMOTIVE COMPANY DE MEXICO, S.A. DE C.V.—See Caterpillar, Inc.; *U.S. Public*, pg. 452
EMERSON CLIMATE TECHNOLOGIES GMBH—See Emerson Electric Co.; *U.S. Public*, pg. 743
ENDRESS HAUSER A.S.—See Endress+Hauser (International) Holding AG; *Int'l*, pg. 2406
ENERPAC CO. LTD.—See Enerpac Tool Group Corp.; *U.S. Public*, pg. 765
ENERPAC HEAVY LIFTING TECHNOLOGY BV—See Enerpac Tool Group Corp.; *U.S. Public*, pg. 765
ENICS RAAHE OY—See Ahlstrom Capital Oy; *Int'l*, pg. 225
ENVIROTECH DRIVE SYSTEMS, INC.—See Envirotech Vehicles, Inc.; *U.S. Public*, pg. 781
ENVIROTECH VEHICLES, INC.; *U.S. Public*, pg. 781
EPIROC FVT INC.—See Epiroc AB; *Int'l*, pg. 2462
EPSILOR-ELECTRIC FUEL LIMITED—See Greenbriar Equity Group, L.P.; *U.S. Private*, pg. 1775
EQUIPMAKE LIMITED—See Equipmake Holdings PLC; *Int'l*, pg. 2485
EVPU A.G.; *Int'l*, pg. 2673
FIAMM S.P.A. - AVEZZANO PLANT—See Fiamm S.p.A.; *Int'l*, pg. 2650
FIAMM TECHNOLOGIES INC.—See Fiamm S.p.A.; *Int'l*, pg. 2650
FLIGHT SYSTEMS DETROIT—See Flight Systems, Inc.; *U.S. Public*, pg. 1545
FOMM CORPORATION—See Banpu Power PCL; *Int'l*, pg. 851
FORD CREDIT PORTUGAL—See Ford Motor Company; *U.S. Public*, pg. 866

FORZA X1, INC.—See Twin Vee PowerCats Co.; *U.S. Public*, pg. 2207
FRANKLIN ELECTRIC CO., INC.; *U.S. Public*, pg. 878
FRANKL & KIRCHNER GMBH & CO KG; *Int'l*, pg. 2761
F.TECH R&D NORTH AMERICA INC—See F-Tech Inc.; *Int'l*, pg. 2595
FUELCELL ENERGY, INC.; *U.S. Public*, pg. 891
FUJIKURA AUTOMOTIVE ASIA LTD.—See Fujikura Ltd.; *Int'l*, pg. 2827
FUJIKURA AUTOMOTIVE CZECH REPUBLIC, S.R.O.—See Fujikura Ltd.; *Int'l*, pg. 2827
FUJIKURA AUTOMOTIVE DO BRAZIL LTDA.—See Fujikura Ltd.; *Int'l*, pg. 2828
FUJIKURA AUTOMOTIVE EUROPE GMBH—See Fujikura Ltd.; *Int'l*, pg. 2827
FUJIKURA AUTOMOTIVE EUROPE S.A.U.—See Fujikura Ltd.; *Int'l*, pg. 2827
FUJIKURA AUTOMOTIVE MEXICO PUEBLA, S.A. DE C.V.—See Fujikura Ltd.; *Int'l*, pg. 2828
FUJIKURA AUTOMOTIVE MEXICO QUERETARO, S.A. DE C.V.—See Fujikura Ltd.; *Int'l*, pg. 2828
FUJIKURA AUTOMOTIVE MEXICO SALAMANCA, S.A. DE C.V.—See Fujikura Ltd.; *Int'l*, pg. 2828
FUJIKURA AUTOMOTIVE MEXICO S. DE R.L. DE C.V.—See Fujikura Ltd.; *Int'l*, pg. 2828
FUJIKURA AUTOMOTIVE MLD S.R.L.—See Fujikura Ltd.; *Int'l*, pg. 2828
FUJIKURA AUTOMOTIVE MOROCCO KENITRA, S.A.S.—See Fujikura Ltd.; *Int'l*, pg. 2828
FUJIKURA AUTOMOTIVE MOROCCO TANGIER, S.A.S.—See Fujikura Ltd.; *Int'l*, pg. 2828
FUJIKURA AUTOMOTIVE PARAGUAY S.A.—See Fujikura Ltd.; *Int'l*, pg. 2828
FUJIKURA AUTOMOTIVE ROMANIA S.R.L.—See Fujikura Ltd.; *Int'l*, pg. 2828
FUJIKURA AUTOMOTIVE UKRAINE LVIV, LLC—See Fujikura Ltd.; *Int'l*, pg. 2828
FUJIKURA CABOS PARA ENERGIA E TELECOMUNICACOES LTDA.—See Fujikura Ltd.; *Int'l*, pg. 2828
FUJIKURA KOREA AUTOMOTIVE LTD.—See Fujikura Ltd.; *Int'l*, pg. 2828
FUTURUM A.D.; *Int'l*, pg. 2858
GBLT CORP.; *Int'l*, pg. 2893
G.C. DUKE EQUIPMENT LTD; *Int'l*, pg. 2865
GEBR. BODE GMBH & CO. KG—See The Carlyle Group Inc.; *U.S. Public*, pg. 2053
GEFRAN SIEI ELECTRIC (SHANGHAI) PTE LTD—See Gefran S.p.A.; *Int'l*, pg. 2912
GENTHERM EUROPE GMBH—See Gentherm Incorporated; *U.S. Public*, pg. 931
GIANT ELECTRIC VEHICLE (KUNSHAN) CO., LTD.—See Giant Manufacturing Co., Ltd.; *Int'l*, pg. 2961
GLOBAL POLE TRUSION GROUP CORP.; *U.S. Public*, pg. 945
GOODALL MFG. LLC; *U.S. Private*, pg. 1738
GOUPIL INDUSTRIE S.A.—See Polaris, Inc.; *U.S. Public*, pg. 1700
GRAKON, LLC—See Methode Electronics, Inc.; *U.S. Public*, pg. 1428
GREATEK ELECTRONICS INC. - TOUFEN PLANT—See Greatek Electronics Inc.; *Int'l*, pg. 3067
GREENJACKET INC.—See Hubbell Incorporated; *U.S. Public*, pg. 1066
GREEN MOBILITY INNOVATIONS LIMITED—See CN Innovations Holdings Limited; *Int'l*, pg. 1673
GREIFFENBERGER AG; *Int'l*, pg. 3078
GROTE INDUSTRIES DE MEXICO, S.A. DE C.V.—See Grote Industries, Inc.; *U.S. Private*, pg. 1793
GROTE INDUSTRIES, INC.; *U.S. Private*, pg. 1792
GSS ENERGY LTD.; *Int'l*, pg. 3150
GUIZHOU GUIHANG AOTOMOTIVE COMPONENTS CO., LTD.; *Int'l*, pg. 3174
HAOSEN RUNBO INTELLIGENT MANUFACTURING CHANGZHOU CO., LTD.—See Dalian Haosen Equipment Manufacturing Co., Ltd.; *Int'l*, pg. 1952
HARBIN ELECTRIC GROUP JIAMUSI ELECTRIC MACHINE CO., LTD.; *Int'l*, pg. 3270
HEADS UP TECHNOLOGIES, INC.—See JLL Partners, LLC; *U.S. Private*, pg. 2212
HELLA FAST FORWARD SHANGHAI CO., LTD.—See Hella GmbH & Co. KGaA; *Int'l*, pg. 3332
HELLA INDIA AUTOMOTIVE PRIVATE LIMITITED—See Hella GmbH & Co. KGaA; *Int'l*, pg. 3332
HELLA INDIA LIGHTING LTD.; *Int'l*, pg. 3333
HELLERMANNTYTON AUSTRALIA PTY LTD—See Aptiv PLC; *Int'l*, pg. 525
HIDRIA AET D.O.O.—See Hidria d.o.o.; *Int'l*, pg. 3384
HIDRIA BAUSCH GMBH—See Hidria d.o.o.; *Int'l*, pg. 3384
HIDRIA BAUSCH KFT—See Hidria d.o.o.; *Int'l*, pg. 3384
HIDRIA GIF GMBH—See Hidria d.o.o.; *Int'l*, pg. 3384
HIDRIA IMP KLIMA D.O.O.—See Hidria d.o.o.; *Int'l*, pg. 3384
HIDRIA ROTOMATIKA D.O.O.—See Hidria d.o.o.; *Int'l*, pg. 3384
HIKAM AMERICA, INC.—See Hirakawa Hewtech Corp.; *Int'l*, pg. 3403
HI-LEX CZECH, S.R.O.—See Hi-Lex Corporation; *Int'l*, pg. 3380
HI-LEX RUS LLC—See Hi-Lex Corporation; *Int'l*, pg. 3381

HI-LEX SERBIA D.O.O.—See Hi-Lex Corporation; *Int'l*, pg. 3381
HITACHI ASIA (VIETNAM) COMPANY LIMITED—See Hitachi, Ltd.; *Int'l*, pg. 3414
HITACHI AUTOMOTIVE PRODUCTS (SUZHOU) LTD.—See Hitachi Astemo, Ltd.; *Int'l*, pg. 3408
HITACHI AUTOMOTIVE SYSTEMS CHONBURI LTD.—See Hitachi, Ltd.; *Int'l*, pg. 3415
HITACHI AUTOMOTIVE SYSTEMS ESPELKAMP GMBH—See Hitachi, Ltd.; *Int'l*, pg. 3415
HITACHI AUTOMOTIVE SYSTEMS EUROPE GMBH - DUSSELDORF—See Hitachi Astemo, Ltd.; *Int'l*, pg. 3408
HITACHI AUTOMOTIVE SYSTEMS KORAT, LTD.—See Hitachi, Ltd.; *Int'l*, pg. 3415
HITACHI AUTOMOTIVE SYSTEMS PUNE (INDIA) PVT. LTD.—See Hitachi, Ltd.; *Int'l*, pg. 3415
HITACHI CABLE (JOHOR) SDN. BHD.—See Hitachi, Ltd.; *Int'l*, pg. 3415
HITACHI (CHINA) RESEARCH & DEVELOPMENT CORPORATION—See Hitachi, Ltd.; *Int'l*, pg. 3413
HITACHI HIGHLY AUTOMOTIVE PRODUCTS (SHANGHAI) LTD.—See Hitachi Astemo, Ltd.; *Int'l*, pg. 3408
HITACHI HIGH-TECH MEXICO, S.A. DE C.V.—See Hitachi, Ltd.; *Int'l*, pg. 3418
HONDA AUSTRALIA M. & P.E. PTY. LTD.—See Honda Motor Co., Ltd.; *Int'l*, pg. 3460
HONEYWELL GARRETT S.A.—See Garrett Motion Inc.; *Int'l*, pg. 2886
HUF PORTUGUESA, LDA.—See Huf Hulsbeck & Furst GmbH & Co. KG; *Int'l*, pg. 3523
HUIZHOU FORYOU INDUSTRIES CO., LTD.—See Foryou Corporation; *Int'l*, pg. 2747
HUIZHOU GP WIRING TECHNOLOGY LTD.—See Gold Peak Technology Group Limited; *Int'l*, pg. 3025
HYDROKIT; *Int'l*, pg. 3548
IFAD AUTOS LTD.; *Int'l*, pg. 3598
IMP HOLDINGS LLC—See Patrick Industries, Inc.; *U.S. Public*, pg. 1652
INDUSTREA MINING TECHNOLOGY PTY LTD—See General Electric Company; *U.S. Public*, pg. 920
INDUSTRIAL HARNESS COMPANY; *U.S. Private*, pg. 2066
INGENICO TELESINCRO—See Apollo Global Management, Inc.; *U.S. Public*, pg. 151
INGRASYS TECHNOLOGY INC.—See Hon Hai Precision Industry Co., Ltd.; *Int'l*, pg. 3457
INNOVATIVE LIGHTING, INC.; *U.S. Private*, pg. 2082
INTERFLEX DATENSYSTEME GMBH & CO. KG—See Ingersoll Rand Inc.; *U.S. Public*, pg. 1121
ISSPRO INC.; *U.S. Private*, pg. 2147
JINXIN COMPANY—See China National Railway Signal & Communication Corp.; *Int'l*, pg. 1534
JULIAN ELECTRIC INC.; *U.S. Private*, pg. 2243
J.W. SPEAKER CORPORATION; *U.S. Private*, pg. 2172
K3 WORKS GMBH—See Gentherm Incorporated; *U.S. Public*, pg. 932
KEIHIN CORPORATION - KAKUDA 3RD PLANT—See Hitachi Astemo, Ltd.; *Int'l*, pg. 3409
LEAR CORPORATION CZECH REPUBLIC S.R.O.—See Lear Corporation; *U.S. Public*, pg. 1297
LEAR CORPORATION GMBH & CO. KG—See Lear Corporation; *U.S. Public*, pg. 1297
LITTELFUSE DO BRASIL—See Littelfuse, Inc.; *U.S. Public*, pg. 1327
LITTELFUSE HK LTD.—See Littelfuse, Inc.; *U.S. Public*, pg. 1327
LITTELFUSE JAPAN LLC—See Littelfuse, Inc.; *U.S. Public*, pg. 1327
MAGNUM CORPORATION; *U.S. Private*, pg. 2548
MAHLE AFTERMARKET DEUTSCHLAND GMBH—See Food Empire Holdings Limited; *Int'l*, pg. 2727
MAINCON CORPORATION—See Datavan International Corp.; *Int'l*, pg. 1981
MARADYNE CORPORATION - POW-R-QUIK DIVISION—See Dreison International, Inc.; *U.S. Private*, pg. 1276
MARADYNE CORPORATION—See Dreison International, Inc.; *U.S. Private*, pg. 1276
MAXZONE VEHICLE LIGHTING INC.; *U.S. Private*, pg. 2620
MECHATRONICS CONTROLS SYSTEMS YANGZHOU CO., LTD.—See Addtech AB; *Int'l*, pg. 134
MILLENWORKS—See Textron Inc.; *U.S. Public*, pg. 2029
MINDA STONERIDGE INSTRUMENTS LIMITED—See Stoneridge, Inc.; *U.S. Public*, pg. 1951
MINE MOBILITY CORPORATION CO., LTD.—See Energy Absolute Public Company Limited; *Int'l*, pg. 2422
MOBILE CONTROL SYSTEMS SA—See Addtech AB; *Int'l*, pg. 134
MODERN ROBOTICS INC.—See Doolight Corporation; *U.S. Public*, pg. 377
MOTOR APPLIANCE CORPORATION; *U.S. Private*, pg. 2796
MOTOR CENTER AUSTRIA GMBH—See DEUTZ AG; *Int'l*, pg. 2086
MR. GASKET MALLORY PRODUCTS DIVISION—See Mr. Gasket Company; *U.S. Private*, pg. 2805
MTC MICRO TECH COMPONENTS GMBH—See discoverIE Group plc; *Int'l*, pg. 2133

336320 — MOTOR VEHICLE ELECT...

MUELLER ELECTRIC COMPANY; *U.S. Private*, pg. 2810
MVR PRODUCTS PTE. LIMITED—See Motorcar Parts of America, Inc.; *U.S. Public*, pg. 1477
NANJING HUASHI ELECTRONIC SCIENTIFIC COMPANY LIMITED—See China Automation Group Limited; *Int'l*, pg. 1483
NIR-OR ISRAEL LTD.—See Imco Industries Ltd.; *Int'l*, pg. 3623
OSRAM CONTINENTAL GMBH—See ams AG; *Int'l*, pg. 439
PEKM KABELTECHNIK S.R.O.—See Commercial Vehicle Group, Inc.; *U.S. Public*, pg. 547
PERCEPTRON (EUROPE) GMBH—See Atlas Copco AB; *Int'l*, pg. 680
PERTRONIX, LLC—See Charger Investment Partners LP; *U.S. Private*, pg. 850
PERUSAHAAN OTOMOBIL NASIONAL SDN. BHD.—See DRB-HICOM Berhad; *Int'l*, pg. 2202
PETERSON MANUFACTURING COMPANY INC.; *U.S. Private*, pg. 3160
PHOENIX AVONDALE ANUSA, LLC—See AutoNation, Inc.; *U.S. Public*, pg. 237
PIONEER MANUFACTURING (THAILAND) CO., LTD.—See EQT AB; *Int'l*, pg. 2471
PIONEER RUS LIMITED LIABILITY COMPANY—See EQT AB; *Int'l*, pg. 2471
PIONEER TECHNOLOGY (SHANGHAI) CO., LTD.—See EQT AB; *Int'l*, pg. 2471
PLANO ANUSA, LLC—See AutoNation, Inc.; *U.S. Public*, pg. 237
POTENZA TECHNOLOGY LIMITED—See CNH Industrial N.V.; *Int'l*, pg. 1676
POWER EFFICIENCY CORPORATION; *U.S. Private*, pg. 3238
PURE TRANSIT TECHNOLOGIES, INC.; *U.S. Private*, pg. 3306
PYLON MANUFACTURING CORPORATION—See Wellspring Capital Management LLC; *U.S. Private*, pg. 4477
RACEPAK, LLC—See Z Capital Group, LLC; *U.S. Private*, pg. 4595
RAVEN DO BRASIL PARTICIPACOES E SERVICOS TECHNICOS LTDA—See CNH Industrial N.V.; *Int'l*, pg. 1676
RAWICKA FABRYKA WYPOSAZENIA WAGONOW SP.Z.O.O.—See The Carlyle Group Inc.; *U.S. Public*, pg. 2053
RED DOT CORPORATION; *U.S. Private*, pg. 3374
REMY POWER PRODUCTS, LLC—See Torque Capital Group, LLC; *U.S. Private*, pg. 4189
RINEHART MOTION SYSTEMS LLC—See BorgWarner Inc.; *U.S. Public*, pg. 371
RIVIAN AUTOMOTIVE CANADA, INC.—See Rivian Automotive, Inc.; *U.S. Public*, pg. 1801
RUZHOU XINTAI SOLAR POWER TECHNOLOGICAL DEVELOPMENT CO.,LTD.—See HENAN SENYUAN ELECTRIC CO., LTD.; *Int'l*, pg. 3343
SCHALTBAU TRANSPORTATION UK LTD.—See The Carlyle Group Inc.; *U.S. Public*, pg. 2053
SCHRADER ELECTRONICS LIMITED—See Sensata Technologies Holding plc; *U.S. Public*, pg. 1866
SEA LINK INTERNATIONAL IRB, INC.—See New Water Capital, L.P.; *U.S. Private*, pg. 2908
SECURICO CO., LTD.—See Howa Machinery, Ltd.; *Int'l*, pg. 3493
SELCO AS—See Littelfuse, Inc.; *U.S. Public*, pg. 1327
SENSORS EUROPE GMBH—See Sensors, Inc.; *U.S. Private*, pg. 3608
SERCEL SINGAPORE PTE LTD—See CGG; *Int'l*, pg. 1432
SEVCON JAPAN KK—See BorgWarner Inc.; *U.S. Public*, pg. 370
SHANGHAI BROSE AUTOMOTIVE COMPONENTS CO., LTD.—See Brose Fahrzeugteile GmbH & Co. KG; *Int'l*, pg. 1196
SHANGHAI BROSE ELECTRIC MOTORS CO., LTD.—See Brose Fahrzeugteile GmbH & Co. KG; *Int'l*, pg. 1196
SHANGHAI HU GONG AUTO-ELECTRIC CO., LTD.—See China Security Co., Ltd.; *Int'l*, pg. 1550
SHENYANG RAILWAY SIGNAL CO., LTD.—See China National Railway Signal & Communication Corp.; *Int'l*, pg. 1534
SHINSUNG PACKARD COMPANY, LTD.—See General Motors Company; *U.S. Public*, pg. 929
SIEI DRIVES TECHNOLOGY CO., LTD.—See Gefran S.p.A.; *Int'l*, pg. 2912
SNA EUROPE—See Snap-on Incorporated; *U.S. Public*, pg. 1898
SPACE S.R.L.—See Dover Corporation; *U.S. Public*, pg. 682
STANDARD MOTOR PRODUCTS (HONG KONG) LTD.—See Standard Motor Products, Inc.; *U.S. Public*, pg. 1929
STANDARD MOTOR PRODUCTS-MISHAWAKA—See Standard Motor Products, Inc.; *U.S. Public*, pg. 1929
STAR WHEELS ELECTRONIC SDN. BHD.—See GUH Holdings Berhad; *Int'l*, pg. 3173
STONERIDGE CONTROL DEVICES, INC.—See Standard Motor Products, Inc.; *U.S. Public*, pg. 1929
STONERIDGE ELECTRONICS AB—See Stoneridge, Inc.; *U.S. Public*, pg. 1951
STONERIDGE ELECTRONICS AB—See Stoneridge, Inc.; *U.S. Public*, pg. 1951
STONERIDGE ELECTRONICS AB—See Stoneridge, Inc.; *U.S. Public*, pg. 1951
STONERIDGE ELECTRONICS AB—See Stoneridge, Inc.; *U.S. Public*, pg. 1951
STONERIDGE, INC.; *U.S. Public*, pg. 1951
STS GROUP AG—See Adler Plastic SpA; *Int'l*, pg. 150
SUZHOU HIDRIA DIESEL COLD START TECHNOLOGIES CO., LTD.—See Hidria d.o.o.; *Int'l*, pg. 3384
TAIWAN CUMMINS SALES & SERVICES CO. LTD.—See Cummins Inc.; *U.S. Public*, pg. 609
TECNIQ, INC.; *U.S. Private*, pg. 3957
TED DE MEXICO S.A. DE C.V.—See Stoneridge, Inc.; *U.S. Public*, pg. 1951
TEK INDIA - PRODUCTRONICS—See Hanmi Semiconductor Co., Ltd.; *Int'l*, pg. 3256
TENNECO, INC.—See Apollo Global Management, Inc.; *U.S. Public*, pg. 160
TEW ENGINEERING LIMITED—See L.B. Foster Company; *U.S. Public*, pg. 1279
TIANJIN ASMO AUTOMOTIVE SMALL MOTOR CO., LTD.—See Denso Corporation; *Int'l*, pg. 2033
TIANJIN DENSO ENGINE ELECTRICAL PRODUCTS CO., LTD—See Denso Corporation; *Int'l*, pg. 2033
TOKICO (THAILAND) LTD.—See Hitachi Astemo, Ltd.; *Int'l*, pg. 3410
TRUCK-LITE CO., LLC—See Genstar Capital, LLC; *U.S. Private*, pg. 1676
TRUCK-LITE EUROPE LTD.—See Genstar Capital, LLC; *U.S. Private*, pg. 1677
TWINVISION—See Audax Group, Limited Partnership; *U.S. Private*, pg. 389
ULTRA ELECTRONICS PMES—See Advent International Corporation; *U.S. Private*, pg. 101
UNIMAX ELECTRONICS INCORPORATION—See ASUSTeK Computer Inc.; *Int'l*, pg. 664
UNITED ELECTRIC WIRE (KUNSHAN) CO., LTD.—See Copartner Technology Corporation; *Int'l*, pg. 1793
UNITY MANUFACTURING COMPANY; *U.S. Private*, pg. 4303
VANNER, INC.—See Havis, Inc.; *U.S. Private*, pg. 1881
VERIZON CONNECT INC.—See Verizon Communications Inc.; *U.S. Public*, pg. 2286
VERIZON NETWORKFLEET, INC.—See Verizon Communications Inc.; *U.S. Public*, pg. 2286
VIGNAL SYSTEMS SA—See Eurazeo SE; *Int'l*, pg. 2530
VISTEON CORPORATION; *U.S. Public*, pg. 2305
VOLCON, INC.; *U.S. Public*, pg. 2308
VRDT CORPORATION; *U.S. Public*, pg. 4415
WAI GLOBAL—See Wetherill Associates Inc.; *U.S. Private*, pg. 4502
WELDON TECHNOLOGIES INC.—See IDEX Corp; *U.S. Public*, pg. 1089
WESCO DISTRIBUTION CANADA LP—See WESCO International, Inc.; *U.S. Public*, pg. 2351
WESLEY CHAPEL ANUSA, LLC—See AutoNation, Inc.; *U.S. Public*, pg. 238
WHELEN ENGINEERING COMPANY, INC.; *U.S. Private*, pg. 4506
W.H. MCADAMS COMPANY; *U.S. Private*, pg. 4420
WILLIAMS CONTROLS EUROPE GMBH—See Curtiss-Wright Corporation; *U.S. Public*, pg. 612
WILLIAMS CONTROLS INDIA PRIVATE LIMITED—See Curtiss-Wright Corporation; *U.S. Public*, pg. 612
WOLFANGEL GMBH—See G. Siempelkamp GmbH & Co. KG; *Int'l*, pg. 2865
WUXI IHI TURBO CO., LTD.—See IHI Corporation; *Int'l*, pg. 3606
XENIA MANUFACTURING INC.; *U.S. Private*, pg. 4581
XSEMI CORPORATION—See Hon Hai Precision Industry Co., Ltd.; *Int'l*, pg. 3459
YXLON (BEIJING) X-RAY EQUIPMENT TRADING CO. LTD.—See Comet Holding AG; *Int'l*, pg. 1711
ZETA AUTOMOTIVE LIMITED—See Deutsche Bahn AG; *Int'l*, pg. 2055
ZHUHAI KAIBANG MOTOR MANUFACTURE CO., LTD.—See Gree Electric Appliances, Inc. of Zhuhai; *Int'l*, pg. 3069
ZHUHAI LUCKYSTAR ELECTRONICS CO., LTD.—See China Security Co., Ltd.; *Int'l*, pg. 1550

336330 — MOTOR VEHICLE STEERING AND SUSPENSION COMPONENTS (EXCEPT SPRING) MANUFACTURING

AAPICO AGUEDA, S.A.—See AAPICO Hitech plc; *Int'l*, pg. 37
AAPICO HITECH AUTOMATION COMPANY LIMITED—See AAPICO Hitech plc; *Int'l*, pg. 37
AAPICO MAIA, S.A.—See AAPICO Hitech plc; *Int'l*, pg. 37
ABC TECHNOLOGIES HOLDINGS INC.—See Apollo Global Management, Inc.; *U.S. Public*, pg. 146
ADD INDUSTRY (ZHEJIANG) CORPORATION LIMITED; *Int'l*, pg. 128
ADLER PELZER HOLDING GMBH—See Adler Plastic SpA; *Int'l*, pg. 150
ADVANTAGE AVIATION TECHNOLOGIES, INC.; *U.S. Private*, pg. 93

AISIN KIKO CO., LTD.—See AISIN Corporation; *Int'l*, pg. 252
AISIN SEIKI CO., LTD. - MACHINERY & EQUIPMENT PLANT—See AISIN Corporation; *Int'l*, pg. 253
AMERICAN SHOWA, INC.—See Hitachi Astemo, Ltd.; *Int'l*, pg. 3409
APM-TS B.V.—See APM Automotive Holdings Berhad; *Int'l*, pg. 516
ATCO PRODUCTS, INC.—See Blue Point Capital Partners, LLC; *U.S. Private*, pg. 591
AUTOLIV JAPAN LTD. - ATSUGI FACILITY—See Autoliv, Inc.; *Int'l*, pg. 729
AUTOLIV STEERING WHEELS S.R.L. DE C.V.—See Autoliv, Inc.; *Int'l*, pg. 730
AUTOLIV THAILAND LIMITED—See Autoliv, Inc.; *Int'l*, pg. 730
AUTOVENTURE MANDO SDN. BHD.—See Globaltec Formation Berhad; *Int'l*, pg. 3004
BAODING GREAT MACHINERY COMPANY LIMITED—See Great Wall Motor Company Limited; *Int'l*, pg. 3065
BISHOP STEERING TECHNOLOGY PTY LTD—See Georgsmarienhutte Holding GmbH; *Int'l*, pg. 2940
CARRARO NORTH AMERICA INC.—See FLY Srl; *Int'l*, pg. 2715
CHENGDU NINGJIANG SHOWA AUTOPARTS CO., LTD.—See Hitachi Astemo, Ltd.; *Int'l*, pg. 3409
CHONGQING CAFF AUTOMOTIVE BRAKING & STEERING SYSTEM CO., LTD.—See Chongqing Machinery & Electronics Holding (Group) Co., Ltd.; *Int'l*, pg. 1580
COMPONENTES VENEZOLANOS DE DIRECCION, S.A.—See Apollo Global Management, Inc.; *U.S. Public*, pg. 160
CONTITECH FLUID KOREA LTD.—See Continental Aktiengesellschaft; *Int'l*, pg. 1781
CONTITECH VIBRATION CONTROL GMBH—See Continental Aktiengesellschaft; *Int'l*, pg. 1781
DAYOU PLUS CO., LTD.; *Int'l*, pg. 1985
DELPHI AFTERMARKET AMERICA DO SUL—See Aptiv PLC; *Int'l*, pg. 524
DIHAG HOLDING GMBH; *Int'l*, pg. 2124
DITAS DOGAN YEDEK PARCA IMALAT VE TEKNIK A.S.; *Int'l*, pg. 2137
EIGENBRODT AB—See Axel Johnson Gruppen AB; *Int'l*, pg. 763
EL FORGE LTD - APPUR DIVISION—See El Forge Ltd; *Int'l*, pg. 2340
EL FORGE LTD - HOSUR DIVISION—See El Forge Ltd; *Int'l*, pg. 2341
ENDURANCE TECHNOLOGIES LIMITED—See Affirma Capital Limited; *Int'l*, pg. 187
FAD A.D. GORNJI MILANOVAC; *Int'l*, pg. 2601
FIAMM ASIA PACIFIC PTE LTD.—See Fiamm S.p.A.; *Int'l*, pg. 2650
FIAMM AUTOMOTIVE CZECH A.S.—See Fiamm S.p.A.; *Int'l*, pg. 2650
FIAMM AUTOTECH CO., LTD—See Fiamm S.p.A.; *Int'l*, pg. 2650
FIAMM ENERGY LLC—See Fiamm S.p.A.; *Int'l*, pg. 2650
FIAMM FRANCE SARL—See Fiamm S.p.A.; *Int'l*, pg. 2650
FIAMM LATIN AMERICA LTDA.—See Fiamm S.p.A.; *Int'l*, pg. 2650
FIAMM SLOVAKIA S.R.O—See Fiamm S.p.A.; *Int'l*, pg. 2650
FIAMM SONICK S.A.—See Fiamm S.p.A.; *Int'l*, pg. 2650
FOX FACTORY GMBH—See Fox Factory Holding Corp.; *U.S. Public*, pg. 877
FOX FACTORY HOLDING CORP.; *U.S. Public*, pg. 877
GABRIEL INDIA LTD; *Int'l*, pg. 2867
GENERAL MOTORS CANADA COMPONENTS DIV.—See General Motors Company; *U.S. Public*, pg. 925
GKN DRIVELINE LTD.—See GKN plc; *Int'l*, pg. 2984
GKN SERVICE INTERNATIONAL GMBH—See GKN plc; *Int'l*, pg. 2985
G.S. AUTO INTERNATIONAL LTD.; *Int'l*, pg. 2866
GUANGZHOU SHOWA AUTOPARTS CO., LTD.—See Hitachi Astemo, Ltd.; *Int'l*, pg. 3409
GUDEL SUMER SAS—See Gudel Group AG; *Int'l*, pg. 3171
HAPPY FORGING LIMITED; *Int'l*, pg. 3269
HARIG CRANKSHAFTS LIMITED; *Int'l*, pg. 3275
HARTA PACKAGING INDUSTRIES (CAMBODIA) LIMITED—See HPI Resources Berhad; *Int'l*, pg. 3500
HITACHI AUTOMOTIVE SYSTEMS AMERICAS, INC. - BEREA PLANT—See Hitachi Astemo, Ltd.; *Int'l*, pg. 3408
HITACHI AUTOMOTIVE SYSTEMS AMERICAS, INC. - GEORGIA PLANT—See Hitachi Astemo, Ltd.; *Int'l*, pg. 3408
HOGEBUILT, INC.—See Berkshire Hathaway Inc.; *U.S. Public*, pg. 310
HORSTMAN DEFENCE SYSTEMS LIMITED—See HWH Investments Limited; *Int'l*, pg. 3543
HSI AUTOMOTIVES LTD.—See Hwaseung Industries Co., Ltd.; *Int'l*, pg. 3542
HWH CORP.; *U.S. Private*, pg. 2015
IGB AUTOMOTRIZ S. DE R.L. DE C.V.—See Lear Corporation; *Int'l*, pg. 1297
INPOWER LLC; *U.S. Private*, pg. 2084
ITW AUTOMOTIVE PRODUCTS GMBH—See Illinois Tool Works Inc.; *U.S. Public*, pg. 1104
ITW AUTOMOTIVE PRODUCTS MEXICO, S. DE R.L. DE C.V.—See Illinois Tool Works Inc.; *U.S. Public*, pg. 1104

N.A.I.C.S. INDEX

336340 — MOTOR VEHICLE BRAKE...

JINGZHOU HENGSHENG AUTOMOTIVE SYSTEM CO., LTD.—See China Automotive Systems, Inc.; *Int'l*, pg. 1484
KONI NA LLC—See ITT Inc.; *U.S. Public*, pg. 1178
MARELLI EUROPE S.P.A.—See KKR & Co. Inc.; *U.S. Public*, pg. 1260
METALLVERARBEITUNG OSTALB GMBH—See Georgsmarienhutte Holding GmbH; *Int'l*, pg. 2940
METALOCAUCHO, S.L.—See Westinghouse Air Brake Technologies Corporation; *U.S. Public*, pg. 2358
MID WEST FABRICATING COMPANY, INC.; *U.S. Private*, pg. 2706
MVO USA INC.—See Georgsmarienhutte Holding GmbH; *Int'l*, pg. 2940
NEMAK WERNIGERODE GMBH—See ALFA, S.A.B. de C.V.; *Int'l*, pg. 313
NEXTEER AUTOMOTIVE GROUP LTD.—See Aviation Industry Corporation of China; *Int'l*, pg. 742
OJI PACKAGING (CAMBODIA) CO., LTD.—See HPI Resources Berhad; *Int'l*, pg. 3501
OJITEX HARTA PACKAGING (SIHANOUKVILLE) LIMITED—See HPI Resources Berhad; *Int'l*, pg. 3501
POWERS & SONS, LLC - MONTPELIER—See Letts Industries, Inc.; *U.S. Private*, pg. 2433
POWERS & SONS, LLC—See Letts Industries, Inc.; *U.S. Private*, pg. 2433
PRESSWERK KREFELD GMBH & CO. KG—See HANNOVER Finanz GmbH; *Int'l*, pg. 3257
PROREKA (M) SDN. BHD.—See Globaltec Formation Berhad; *Int'l*, pg. 3004
P.T. SHOWA INDONESIA MANUFACTURING—See Hitachi Astemo, Ltd.; *Int'l*, pg. 3409
REVIVA INC.; *U.S. Private*, pg. 3416
ROCKFORD ACROMATIC PRODUCT CO.—See Aircraft Gear Corporation; *U.S. Private*, pg. 140
R+S TECHNIK GMBH—See Matthews International Corporation; *U.S. Public*, pg. 1400
SANDSTORM MOTOR VEHICLES MANUFACTURING LLC—See Alpha Dhabi Holding PJSC; *Int'l*, pg. 368
SEASTAR SOLUTIONS - PRIME LINE INDUSTRIAL CONTROLS—See Dometic Group AB; *Int'l*, pg. 2160
SHASHI JIULONG POWER STEERING GEARS CO., LTD.—See China Automotive Systems, Inc.; *Int'l*, pg. 1484
SHIMNIT UTSCH INDIA PVT. LTD.—See Erich Utsch AG; *Int'l*, pg. 2493
SHOWA AUTOPARTS MEXICO, S.A. DE C.V.—See Hitachi Astemo, Ltd.; *Int'l*, pg. 3410
SHOWA AUTOPARTS (THAILAND) CO., LTD.—See Hitachi Astemo, Ltd.; *Int'l*, pg. 3410
SHOWA AUTO-PARTS VIETNAM CO., LTD.—See Hitachi Astemo, Ltd.; *Int'l*, pg. 3410
SHOWA CANADA INC.—See Hitachi Astemo, Ltd.; *Int'l*, pg. 3410
SHOWA CORPORATION - GOTEMBA NO.1 PLANT—See Hitachi Astemo, Ltd.; *Int'l*, pg. 3410
SHOWA CORPORATION - GOTEMBA NO.2 PLANT—See Hitachi Astemo, Ltd.; *Int'l*, pg. 3410
SHOWA CORPORATION - NAGOYA PLANT—See Hitachi Astemo, Ltd.; *Int'l*, pg. 3410
SHOWA CORPORATION—See Hitachi Astemo, Ltd.; *Int'l*, pg. 3409
SHOWA INDIA PVT. LTD.—See Hitachi Astemo, Ltd.; *Int'l*, pg. 3410
SHOWA UK LTD.—See Hitachi Astemo, Ltd.; *Int'l*, pg. 3410
ST USA HOLDING CORP.—See Fox Factory Holding Corp.; *U.S. Public*, pg. 877
THAL ENGINEERING—See House of Habib; *Int'l*, pg. 3491

336340 — MOTOR VEHICLE BRAKE SYSTEM MANUFACTURING

ADVANCED BRAKING PTY LTD—See Advanced Braking Technology Ltd.; *Int'l*, pg. 157
ADVANCED BRAKING TECHNOLOGY LTD.; *Int'l*, pg. 157
ADVICS CO., LTD.—See AISIN Corporation; *Int'l*, pg. 251
ADVICS MANUFACTURING INDIANA, L.L.C.—See AISIN Corporation; *Int'l*, pg. 251
ADVICS MANUFACTURING OHIO, INC.—See AISIN Corporation; *Int'l*, pg. 251
ADVICS NORTH AMERICA, INC.—See AISIN Corporation; *Int'l*, pg. 251
AERO SEKUR S.P.A.—See Hunting Plc; *Int'l*, pg. 3536
AISIN ASIA PTE. LTD.—See AISIN Corporation; *Int'l*, pg. 252
AISIN (AUSTRALIA) PTY. LTD.—See AISIN Corporation; *Int'l*, pg. 252
AISIN MEXICANA S.A. DE C.V.—See AISIN Corporation; *Int'l*, pg. 253
AISIN SEIKI CO., LTD. - HANDA PLANT—See AISIN Corporation; *Int'l*, pg. 253
AKEBONO ADVANCED ENGINEERING CO., LTD.—See Akebono Brake Industry Co., Ltd.; *Int'l*, pg. 261
AKEBONO ADVANCED ENGINEERING (UK) LTD.—See Akebono Brake Industry Co., Ltd.; *Int'l*, pg. 261
AKEBONO BRAKE ASTRA VIETNAM CO., LTD.—See Akebono Brake Industry Co., Ltd.; *Int'l*, pg. 261
AKEBONO BRAKE - CLARKSVILLE PLANT—See Akebono Brake Industry Co., Ltd.; *Int'l*, pg. 261
AKEBONO BRAKE CORPORATION—See Akebono Brake Industry Co., Ltd.; *Int'l*, pg. 261
AKEBONO BRAKE - ELIZABETHTOWN PLANT—See Akebono Brake Industry Co., Ltd.; *Int'l*, pg. 261
AKEBONO BRAKE FUKUSHIMA MANUFACTURING CO., LTD.—See Akebono Brake Industry Co., Ltd.; *Int'l*, pg. 261
AKEBONO BRAKE INDUSTRY CO., LTD.; *Int'l*, pg. 261
AKEBONO BRAKE IWATSUKI MANUFACTURING CO., LTD.—See Akebono Brake Industry Co., Ltd.; *Int'l*, pg. 261
AKEBONO BRAKE MEXICO S.A. DE C.V.—See Akebono Brake Industry Co., Ltd.; *Int'l*, pg. 261
AKEBONO BRAKE SANYO MANUFACTURING CO., LTD.—See Akebono Brake Industry Co., Ltd.; *Int'l*, pg. 261
AKEBONO BRAKE SLOVAKIA S.R.O.—See Akebono Brake Industry Co., Ltd.; *Int'l*, pg. 261
AKEBONO BRAKE YAMAGATA MANUFACTURING CO., LTD.—See Akebono Brake Industry Co., Ltd.; *Int'l*, pg. 261
AKEBONO CORPORATION (GUANGZHOU)—See Akebono Brake Industry Co., Ltd.; *Int'l*, pg. 262
AKEBONO CORPORATION—See Akebono Brake Industry Co., Ltd.; *Int'l*, pg. 262
AKEBONO CORPORATION (SUZHOU)—See Akebono Brake Industry Co., Ltd.; *Int'l*, pg. 262
AKEBONO EUROPE S.A.S (ARRAS)—See Akebono Brake Industry Co., Ltd.; *Int'l*, pg. 262
A&M CASTING (THAILAND) CO., LTD.—See Akebono Brake Industry Co., Ltd.; *Int'l*, pg. 261
ANG INDUSTRIES LIMITED; *Int'l*, pg. 459
APC AUTOMOTIVE TECHNOLOGIES, LLC—See Audax Group, Limited Partnership; *U.S. Private*, pg. 386
APC AUTOMOTIVE TECHNOLOGIES, LLC—See Harvest Partners L.P.; *U.S. Private*, pg. 1876
APEC LIMITED—See Blackstone Inc.; *U.S. Public*, pg. 359
ARVINMERITOR B.V.—See Cummins Inc.; *U.S. Public*, pg. 608
ARVINMERITOR HEAVY VEHICLE SYSTEMS ESPANIA S.A.—See Cummins Inc.; *U.S. Public*, pg. 608
AS BRAKE SYSTEMS, INC.—See AISIN Corporation; *Int'l*, pg. 252
ASIMCO MEILIAN BRAKING SYSTEM (LANGFANG) CO., LTD.—See Bain Capital, LP; *U.S. Private*, pg. 428
ASK TECHNICA CORPORATION—See A&A Material Corporation; *Int'l*, pg. 18
AUSCO PRODUCTS, INC.; *U.S. Private*, pg. 395
AUTOLIV ARGENTINA S.A.—See Autoliv, Inc.; *Int'l*, pg. 728
AUTOLIV AUSTRALIA PTY. LTD.—See Autoliv, Inc.; *Int'l*, pg. 728
AUTOLIV (CHANGCHUN) MAWHUNG VEHICLE SAFETY SYSTEMS CO., LTD.—See Autoliv, Inc.; *Int'l*, pg. 728
AUTOLIV DEVELOPMENT AB—See Autoliv, Inc.; *Int'l*, pg. 728
AUTOLIV ELECTRONICS CANADA, INC.—See Autoliv, Inc.; *Int'l*, pg. 729
AUTOLIV FRANCE, GOURNAY—See Autoliv, Inc.; *Int'l*, pg. 728
AUTOLIV MANDO CORPORATION—See Autoliv, Inc.; *Int'l*, pg. 729
AUTOLIV NORTH AMERICA—See Autoliv, Inc.; *Int'l*, pg. 729
AUTOLIV SOUTHERN AFRICA (PTY) LTD.—See Autoliv, Inc.; *Int'l*, pg. 729
AUTOMODULAR ASSEMBLIES, INC.—See HLS Therapeutics, Inc.; *Int'l*, pg. 3431
BALATACILAR - BALATACILIK SANAYI VE TICARET A.S.; *Int'l*, pg. 806
BANDO BELT MANUFACTURING(TURKEY), INC.—See Bando Chemical Industries, Ltd.; *Int'l*, pg. 830
BANDO MANUFACTURING (THAILAND) LTD.—See Bando Chemical Industries, Ltd.; *Int'l*, pg. 830
BANDO MANUFACTURING (VIETNAM) CO., LTD.—See Bando Chemical Industries, Ltd.; *Int'l*, pg. 830
BANDO SAKATA, LTD.—See Bando Chemical Industries, Ltd.; *Int'l*, pg. 830
BEIJING BEIMO HIGH-TECH FRICTIONAL MATERIAL CO., LTD.; *Int'l*, pg. 946
BEIJING HECHENG R&A VEHICLE PARTS CO., LTD—See Hwaseung Industries, Ltd.; *Int'l*, pg. 3542
BELHASA MOTORS COMPANY—See Belhasa Group of Companies; *Int'l*, pg. 964
BRAKE PARTS INC LLC—See Torque Capital Group, LLC; *U.S. Private*, pg. 4189
BRAKES AUTO (INDIA) LIMITED; *Int'l*, pg. 1137
BREMBO NORTH AMERICA, INC.—See Brembo S.p.A.; *Int'l*, pg. 1145
BREMBO NORTH AMERICA, INC.—See Brembo S.p.A.; *Int'l*, pg. 1145
BREMBO RASSINI S.A. DE C.V.—See Brembo S.p.A.; *Int'l*, pg. 1145
BREMBO SGL CARBON CERAMIC BRAKES S.P.A.—See Brembo S.p.A.; *Int'l*, pg. 1145
BREMBO S.P.A.; *Int'l*, pg. 1144
BROSE FAHRZEUGTEILE GMBH & CO. KG; *Int'l*, pg. 1195
CARLISLE BRAKE & FRICTION, INC.—See Lone Star Funds; *U.S. Private*, pg. 2485
CARLISLE INDUSTRIAL BRAKE & FRICTION—See Carlisle Companies Incorporated; *U.S. Public*, pg. 436
CARPLASTIC S.A. DE C.V.—See Visteon Corporation; *U.S. Public*, pg. 2305
CGE MINAS INDUSTRIA E COMERCIO DE ARTEFATOS PLASTICOS LTDA.; *Int'l*, pg. 1431
CGE SOCIEDADE FABRICADORA DE PECAS PLASTICAS LTDA.—See CGE Minas Industria E Comercio de Artefatos Plasticos Ltda.; *Int'l*, pg. 1431
CHANGSHU KDAC CO., LTD.—See Aptiv PLC; *Int'l*, pg. 525
CITIC AUTOMOBILE CO., LTD.—See CITIC Group Corporation; *Int'l*, pg. 1619
COMPA S.A.; *Int'l*, pg. 1721
COMPONENTES DE VEHICULOS DE GALICIA S.A.—See FORVIA SE; *Int'l*, pg. 2745
CONTINENTAL CHASSIS & SAFETY DIVISION—See Continental Aktiengesellschaft; *Int'l*, pg. 1782
CONTINENTAL TEMIC ELECTRONICS PHILIPPINES INC.—See Continental Aktiengesellschaft; *Int'l*, pg. 1783
CONTINENTAL TEVES INC.—See Continental Aktiengesellschaft; *Int'l*, pg. 1783
CONTINENTAL TEVES PORTUGAL SISTEMAS DE TRAVAGEM LDA—See Continental Aktiengesellschaft; *Int'l*, pg. 1783
CONTINENTAL TEVES UK LTD.—See Continental Aktiengesellschaft; *Int'l*, pg. 1783
CUMMINS FILTRATION—See Cummins Inc.; *U.S. Public*, pg. 606
DAEWOO AUTOMOTIVE COMPONENTS, LTD.—See General Motors Company; *U.S. Public*, pg. 924
DAYCO CANADA CORP.—See Dayco LLC; *U.S. Private*, pg. 1177
DAYCO EUROPE AUTOMOTIVE—See Dayco LLC; *U.S. Private*, pg. 1177
DELPHI SISTEMAS DE ENERGIA, S.A. DE C.V.—See Aptiv PLC; *Int'l*, pg. 525
DELPHI—See Aptiv PLC; *Int'l*, pg. 524
DHB-COMPONENTES AUTOMOTIVOS, S.A.—See General Motors Company; *U.S. Public*, pg. 924
DIGRAPH TRANSPORT SUPPLIES LIMITED—See LKQ Corporation; *U.S. Public*, pg. 1334
DISC BRAKES AUSTRALIA PTY LTD—See Amotiv Limited; *Int'l*, pg. 431
D PLAST-EFTEC A.S.—See EMS-Chemie Holding AG; *Int'l*, pg. 2393
DURA AUTOMOTIVE—See MiddleGround Management, LP; *U.S. Private*, pg. 2711
EATON CORP. - AIRFLEX—See Eaton Corporation plc; *Int'l*, pg. 2279
EATON CORP. - SUPERCHARGERS—See Eaton Corporation plc; *Int'l*, pg. 2280
EATON TRUCK COMPONENTS (PTY.) LIMITED—See Eaton Corporation plc; *Int'l*, pg. 2280
EXEDY CORPORATION; *Int'l*, pg. 2580
FAURECIA AUTOMOTIVE ESPANIA—See FORVIA SE; *Int'l*, pg. 2746
FAURECIA AUTOMOTIVE ESPANIA—See FORVIA SE; *Int'l*, pg. 2746
FAURECIA AUTOMOTIVE ESPANIA—See FORVIA SE; *Int'l*, pg. 2746
FAURECIA AUTOMOTIVE INDUSTRIE—See FORVIA SE; *Int'l*, pg. 2746
FAURECIA AUTOMOTIVE INDUSTRIE—See FORVIA SE; *Int'l*, pg. 2746
FAURECIA AUTOMOTIVE INDUSTRIE—See FORVIA SE; *Int'l*, pg. 2746
FAURECIA INDUSTRIE N.V.—See FORVIA SE; *Int'l*, pg. 2746
FAURECIA INDUSTRIE—See FORVIA SE; *Int'l*, pg. 2746
FAURECIA INTERIEUR INDUSTRIE—See FORVIA SE; *Int'l*, pg. 2746
FAURECIA INTERIOR SYSTEMS—See FORVIA SE; *Int'l*, pg. 2746
FAURECIA PORTUGAL—See FORVIA SE; *Int'l*, pg. 2747
FEDERAL-MOGUL OPERATIONS ITALY S.R.L.—See Apollo Global Management, Inc.; *U.S. Public*, pg. 161
FORD VIETNAM LIMITED—See Ford Motor Company; *U.S. Public*, pg. 866
FRAS-LE S.A. - ALABAMA FACILITY—See Fras-le S.A.; *Int'l*, pg. 2765
FRAS-LE S.A.; *Int'l*, pg. 2764
GENERAL MOTORS CANADA ENGINE DIV.—See General Motors Company; *U.S. Public*, pg. 925
GENERAL MOTORS CANADA TRANSMISSION DIV.—See General Motors Company; *U.S. Public*, pg. 925
GENERAL MOTORS DEL ECUADOR S.A.—See General Motors Company; *U.S. Public*, pg. 924
GENTEX MIRRORS LTD.—See Gentex Corporation; *U.S. Public*, pg. 901
GEORG FISCHER FAHRZEUGTECHNIK AG—See Georg Fischer AG; *Int'l*, pg. 2935
GKN AUTOSTRUCTURES LTD.—See GKN plc; *Int'l*, pg. 2984
GKN DRIVELINE SINGAPORE PTE LTD—See GKN plc; *Int'l*, pg. 2984
GKN SHEEPBRIDGE STOKES LTD.—See GKN plc; *Int'l*, pg. 2985
GKN VISCODRIVE GMBH—See GKN plc; *Int'l*, pg. 2985

336340 — MOTOR VEHICLE BRAKE...

GKN WALTERSCHEID GMBH—See OEP Capital Advisors, L.P.; *U.S. Private*, pg. 2999
GKN WHEELS, LTD.—See GKN plc; *Int'l*, pg. 2986
GRUPO CONDUMEX, S. A. DE C. V.—See Grupo Carso, S.A.B. de C.V.; *Int'l*, pg. 3123
GUNITE CORPORATION—See Crestview Partners, L.P.; *U.S. Private*, pg. 1098
HALDEX AB; *Int'l*, pg. 3228
HALDEX BRAKE PRODUCTS AB—See Haldex AB; *Int'l*, pg. 3228
HALDEX BRAKE PRODUCTS CORPORATION - LITTLE ROCK PLANT—See Haldex AB; *Int'l*, pg. 3228
HALDEX BRAKE PRODUCTS PTY. LTD.—See Haldex AB; *Int'l*, pg. 3228
HALDEX DO BRASIL INDUSTRIA E COMERCIO LTDA.—See Haldex AB; *Int'l*, pg. 3228
HALDEX INDIA LIMITED—See Haldex AB; *Int'l*, pg. 3228
HALDEX PRODUCTS DE MEXICO S.A. DE C.V.—See Haldex AB; *Int'l*, pg. 3228
HECHENG VEHICLE PARTS (TAICANG) CO., LTD.—See Hwaseung Industries Co., Ltd.; *Int'l*, pg. 3542
HERCULES ENGINE COMPONENTS LLC; *U.S. Private*, pg. 1921
HLS THERAPEUTICS, INC.; *Int'l*, pg. 3431
HOSEI BRAKE INDUSTRY CO., LTD. - OKAZAKI FACTORY—See AISIN Corporation; *Int'l*, pg. 253
HOSEI BRAKE INDUSTRY CO., LTD.—See AISIN Corporation; *Int'l*, pg. 253
HOSEI BRAKE INDUSTRY CO., LTD. - TAKAHAMA FACTORY—See AISIN Corporation; *Int'l*, pg. 253
HS AUTOMOTIVE ALABAMA INC.—See Hwaseung Industries Co., Ltd.; *Int'l*, pg. 3542
HWASEUNG (H.K) LTD.—See Hwaseung Industries Co., Ltd.; *Int'l*, pg. 3542
HWASEUNG INDUSTRIES CO., LTD. - DONGGUAN FACTORY—See Hwaseung Industries Co., Ltd.; *Int'l*, pg. 3542
HWASEUNG (SHANGHAI) INT'L TRADE CO., LTD.—See Hwaseung Industries Co., Ltd.; *Int'l*, pg. 3542
HWASEUNG T&C CO., LTD.—See Hwaseung Industries Co., Ltd.; *Int'l*, pg. 3542
IMRA EUROPE S.A.—See AISIN Corporation; *Int'l*, pg. 253
INDIAN HEAD INDUSTRIES, INC.; *U.S. Private*, pg. 2061
INTERNATIONAL BRAKE INDUSTRIES, INC.—See Wellspring Capital Management LLC; *U.S. Private*, pg. 4477
ITT FLUID TECHNOLOGY ASIA PTE LTD.—See ITT Inc.; *U.S. Public*, pg. 1178
KINUGAWA BRAKE PARTS CO., LTD.—See Development Bank of Japan, Inc.; *Int'l*, pg. 2088
MANDO CORPORATION - IKSAN DIVISION—See Halla Group; *Int'l*, pg. 3230
MANDO CORPORATION - WONJU DIVISION—See Halla Group; *Int'l*, pg. 3230
MEGGITT INDIA PVT LTD—See Parker Hannifin Corporation; *U.S. Public*, pg. 1642
MERITOR AUTOMOTIVE B.V.—See Cummins Inc.; *U.S. Public*, pg. 608
MERITOR BRAKE HOLDINGS, INC.—See Cummins Inc.; *U.S. Public*, pg. 608
MERITOR HEAVY VEHICLE SYSTEMS CAMERI SPA—See Cummins Inc.; *U.S. Public*, pg. 608
MERITOR HVS INDIA LTD.—See Cummins Inc.; *U.S. Public*, pg. 608
MERITOR, INC.—See Cummins Inc.; *U.S. Public*, pg. 609
MERITOR LIGHT VEHICLE TECHNOLOGY, LLC—See Cummins Inc.; *U.S. Public*, pg. 608
MERITOR LVS ZHENJIANG CO. LTD.—See Cummins Inc.; *U.S. Public*, pg. 608
MERITOR SUSPENSION SYSTEMS COMPANY—See Cummins Inc.; *U.S. Public*, pg. 609
MGM BRAKES DIVISION—See Indian Head Industries, Inc.; *U.S. Private*, pg. 2061
MODINE PONTEVICO S.R.L.—See Modine Manufacturing Company; *U.S. Public*, pg. 1455
NEW PACIFIC INDUSTRY CO., LTD.—See Cheng Shin Rubber (Xiamen) Ind., Ltd.; *Int'l*, pg. 1466
NISSIN BRAKE DE MEXICO,S.A. DE C.V.—See Honda Motor Co., Ltd.; *Int'l*, pg. 3463
NISSIN BRAKE DO BRASIL LTDA—See Honda Motor Co., Ltd.; *Int'l*, pg. 3463
NISSIN BRAKE GEORGIA INC.—See Honda Motor Co., Ltd.; *Int'l*, pg. 3463
NISSIN BRAKE INDIA PVT. LTD.—See Honda Motor Co., Ltd.; *Int'l*, pg. 3463
NISSIN BRAKE OHIO, INC.—See Honda Motor Co., Ltd.; *Int'l*, pg. 3463
NISSIN BRAKE PHILIPPINES CORPORATION—See Honda Motor Co., Ltd.; *Int'l*, pg. 3463
NISSIN BRAKE REALTY PHILIPPINES CORPORATION—See Honda Motor Co., Ltd.; *Int'l*, pg. 3463
NISSIN BRAKE (THAILAND) CO., LTD.—See Honda Motor Co., Ltd.; *Int'l*, pg. 3463
NISSIN BRAKE VIETNAM CO.—See Honda Motor Co., Ltd.; *Int'l*, pg. 3463
NISSIN KOGYO CO., LTD. - NAOETSU PLANT—See Honda Motor Co., Ltd.; *Int'l*, pg. 3463
NISSIN KOGYO CO., LTD.—See Honda Motor Co., Ltd.; *Int'l*, pg. 3463
NISSIN KOGYO CO., LTD. - TOBU PLANT—See Honda Motor Co., Ltd.; *Int'l*, pg. 3463
NISSIN R&D ASIA CO., LTD—See Honda Motor Co., Ltd.; *Int'l*, pg. 3463
NISSIN R&D EUROPE, S.L.U.—See Honda Motor Co., Ltd.; *Int'l*, pg. 3463
ORUM OY AB—See Helvar Merca Oy AB; *Int'l*, pg. 3339
OWENS CORNING - OEM SOLUTIONS GROUP—See Owens Corning; *U.S. Public*, pg. 928
PACKARD ELECTRIC DIVISION MEXICAN OPERATIONS—See General Motors Company; *U.S. Public*, pg. 928
PARKER HANNIFIN AUSTRALIA PTY. LTD.—See Parker Hannifin Corporation; *U.S. Public*, pg. 1644
PENGELUARAN GETAH BANDO (MALAYSIA) SDN. BHD.—See Bando Chemical Industries, Ltd.; *Int'l*, pg. 830
PERFORMANCE FRICTION CORP.; *U.S. Private*, pg. 3149
PREVOST CAR, INC.—See AB Volvo; *Int'l*, pg. 43
PRIOR REMANUFACTURING, INC.—See The Brenlin Group, LLC; *U.S. Private*, pg. 4000
PT. AKEBONO BRAKE ASTRA INDONESIA—See Akebono Brake Industry Co., Ltd.; *Int'l*, pg. 262
P.T. AUTOLIV INDONESIA—See Autoliv, Inc.; *Int'l*, pg. 730
P.T. CHEMCO HARAPAN NUSANTARA—See Honda Motor Co., Ltd.; *Int'l*, pg. 3463
PT TECH, LLC—See The Timken Company; *U.S. Public*, pg. 2133
QBR BRAKE, INC.; *U.S. Private*, pg. 3312
REULAND ELECTRIC COMPANY - BRAKE DIVISION—See Reuland Electric Company; *U.S. Private*, pg. 3412
ROCKWELL AUTOMATION DE MEXICO, S.A. DE C.V.—See Rockwell Automation, Inc.; *U.S. Public*, pg. 1806
ROCKWELL AUTOMATION S.A.—See Rockwell Automation, Inc.; *U.S. Public*, pg. 1806
SAI AUTOMOTIVE ALLIBERT S.A.—See FORVIA SE; *Int'l*, pg. 2747
SAI AUTOMOTIVE DO BRASIL LTDA.—See FORVIA SE; *Int'l*, pg. 2747
SAI AUTOMOTIVE WASHINGTON LTD.—See FORVIA SE; *Int'l*, pg. 2747
SEALCO AIR CONTROLS INC.; *U.S. Private*, pg. 3585
SHANDONG NISSIN INDUSTRY CO., LTD.—See Honda Motor Co., Ltd.; *Int'l*, pg. 3463
SIAM AISIN CO., LTD.—See AISIN Corporation; *Int'l*, pg. 254
SIMRAX BV—See Freudenberg SE; *Int'l*, pg. 2790
STEMCO CREWSON, LLC—See Enpro Inc.; *U.S. Public*, pg. 775
TANGSHAN AISIN GEAR CO., LTD.—See AISIN Corporation; *Int'l*, pg. 254
TECHNOVA, INC.—See AISIN Corporation; *Int'l*, pg. 254
TENNECO AUTOMOTIVE EUROPE, LTD.—See Apollo Global Management, Inc.; *U.S. Public*, pg. 162
TIANJIN AISIN AUTOMOBILE PARTS CO., LTD.—See AISIN Corporation; *Int'l*, pg. 254
TI AUTOMOTIVE LIMITED—See Bain Capital, LP; *U.S. Private*, pg. 447
TRAMEC SLOAN, LLC.—See MacLean-Fogg Company; *U.S. Private*, pg. 2537
TWIFLEX LTD.—See Regal Rexnord Corporation; *U.S. Public*, pg. 1772
UAP, INC. (CADEL DIV.)—See Genuine Parts Company; *U.S. Public*, pg. 932
U.S. AUTOMOTIVE MANUFACTURING, INC.; *U.S. Public*, pg. 2212
VICKERS SYSTEMS SBPD—See Eaton Corporation plc; *Int'l*, pg. 2281
VOLVO PARTS CORPORATION—See AB Volvo; *Int'l*, pg. 46
WARNER ELECTRIC, INC.—See Regal Rexnord Corporation; *U.S. Public*, pg. 1772
WOLVERINE ADVANCED MATERIALS GMBH—See ITT Inc.; *U.S. Public*, pg. 1179
XYLEM WATER SOLUTIONS AUSTRALIA LIMITED—See Xylem Inc.; *U.S. Public*, pg. 2396
XYLEM WATER SOLUTIONS DEUTSCHLAND GMBH—See Xylem Inc.; *U.S. Public*, pg. 2397
XYLEM WATER SOLUTIONS FRANCE SAS—See Xylem Inc.; *U.S. Public*, pg. 2397
XYLEM WATER SOLUTIONS IRELAND LTD.—See Xylem Inc.; *U.S. Public*, pg. 2397
XYLEM WATER SOLUTIONS ITALIA S.R.L.—See Xylem Inc.; *U.S. Public*, pg. 2397
XYLEM WATER SOLUTIONS MAGYARORSZAG KFT.—See Xylem Inc.; *U.S. Public*, pg. 2397
XYLEM WATER SOLUTIONS POLSKA SP. Z. O. O.—See Xylem Inc.; *U.S. Public*, pg. 2397
XYLEM WATER SOLUTIONS (SHENYANG) CO. LTD.—See Xylem Inc.; *U.S. Public*, pg. 2396
YAZAKI SABANCI OTOMOTIV KABLO DONANIMI SAN. VE TIC. A.S.—See Haci Omer Sabanci Holding A.S.; *Int'l*, pg. 3204
ZHONGSHAN NISSIN INDUSTRY CO., LTD.—See Honda Motor Co., Ltd.; *Int'l*, pg. 3463

336350 — MOTOR VEHICLE TRANSMISSION AND POWER TRAIN PARTS MANUFACTURING

AISIN AW INDUSTRIES CO., LTD.—See AISIN Corporation; *Int'l*, pg. 252
AISIN DRIVETRAIN, INC.—See AISIN Corporation; *Int'l*, pg. 252
AISIN SEIKI CO., LTD. - OGAWA PLANT—See AISIN Corporation; *Int'l*, pg. 253
AKWEL SWEDEN AB—See AKWEL; *Int'l*, pg. 267
AKWEL WUHAN AUTO PARTS CO., LTD.—See AKWEL; *Int'l*, pg. 267
ALINABAL HOLDINGS CORPORATION; *U.S. Private*, pg. 168
ALLISON TRANSMISSION, INC.—See Allison Transmission Holdings, Inc.; *U.S. Public*, pg. 81
ALLISON TRANSMISSION JAPAN CO., LTD.—See Allison Transmission Holdings, Inc.; *U.S. Public*, pg. 81
ALMA PRODUCTS COMPANY—See Blue Point Capital Partners, LLC; *U.S. Private*, pg. 591
ALTO PRODUCTS CORP.; *U.S. Private*, pg. 210
AMERICAN AXLE & MANUFACTURING DE MEXICO S. DE R.L. DE C.V.—See American Axle & Manufacturing Holdings, Inc.; *U.S. Public*, pg. 96
ANDEN (THAILAND) CO., LTD.—See Denso Corporation; *Int'l*, pg. 2028
ARIS INTERNATIONAL LIMITED—See BRCCA Services Private Limited; *Int'l*, pg. 1143
AUBURN GEAR, INC.—See North River Capital LLC; *U.S. Private*, pg. 2946
AUTOLIV POLAND SP.ZO.O.—See Autoliv, Inc.; *Int'l*, pg. 729
AUTOTECH ENGINEERING; *U.S. Private*, pg. 401
AW NORTH CAROLINA, INC.—See AISIN Corporation; *Int'l*, pg. 252
AW TRANSMISSION ENGINEERING U.S.A., INC.—See AISIN Corporation; *Int'l*, pg. 252
AXLETECH INTERNATIONAL, LLC—See Cummins Inc.; *U.S. Public*, pg. 608
AXLETECH INTERNATIONAL SAS—See Cummins Inc.; *U.S. Public*, pg. 608
BEML BRASIL INDUSTRIAL LTDA—See BEML Limited; *Int'l*, pg. 969
BEML LIMITED - HYDRAULICS & POWERLINE (H&P) DIVISION—See BEML Limited; *Int'l*, pg. 969
BHARAT GEARS LIMITED; *Int'l*, pg. 1011
BONDIOLI & PAVESI-FRANCE S.A.—See Bondioli & Pavesi S.p.A.; *Int'l*, pg. 1106
BONDIOLI & PAVESI GMBH DEUTSCHLAND—See Bondioli & Pavesi S.p.A.; *Int'l*, pg. 1106
BONDIOLI & PAVESI S.P.A.; *Int'l*, pg. 1105
BONDIOLI Y PAVESI IBERICA S.A.—See Bondioli & Pavesi S.p.A.; *Int'l*, pg. 1106
BORG-WARNER AUTOMOTIVE TAIWAN CO., LTD.—See Enstar Group Limited; *Int'l*, pg. 2448
BORGWARNER CANADA INC.—See BorgWarner Inc.; *U.S. Public*, pg. 369
BORGWARNER DRIVETRAIN DE MEXICO S.A. DE C.V.—See BorgWarner Inc.; *U.S. Public*, pg. 370
BORGWARNER DRIVETRAIN ENGINEERING GMBH—See BorgWarner Inc.; *U.S. Public*, pg. 370
BORGWARNER DRIVETRAIN MANAGEMENT SERVICES DE MEXICO S.A. DE C.V.—See BorgWarner Inc.; *U.S. Public*, pg. 369
BORGWARNER EMISSIONS SYSTEMS OF MICHIGAN INC.—See BorgWarner Inc.; *U.S. Public*, pg. 369
BORGWARNER MORSE SYSTEMS JAPAN K.K.—See BorgWarner Inc.; *U.S. Public*, pg. 370
BORGWARNER MORSE TEC, LLC—See Enstar Group Limited; *Int'l*, pg. 2448
BORGWARNER MORSE TEC MEXICO, S.A. DE C.V.—See Enstar Group Limited; *Int'l*, pg. 2448
BORGWARNER (THAILAND) LIMITED—See BorgWarner Inc.; *U.S. Public*, pg. 369
BORGWARNER TRANSMISSION SYSTEMS ARNSTADT GMBH—See BorgWarner Inc.; *U.S. Public*, pg. 370
BORGWARNER TRANSMISSION SYSTEMS GMBH—See BorgWarner Inc.; *U.S. Public*, pg. 370
BORGWARNER TRANSMISSION SYSTEMS INC.—See BorgWarner Inc.; *U.S. Public*, pg. 370
BORGWARNER TRANSMISSION SYSTEMS KOREA LTD.—See BorgWarner Inc.; *U.S. Public*, pg. 370
BORGWARNER TRANSMISSION SYSTEMS MONACO S.A.M.—See BorgWarner Inc.; *U.S. Public*, pg. 370
BORGWARNER TRANSMISSION SYSTEMS TULLE S.A.S.—See BorgWarner Inc.; *U.S. Public*, pg. 371
BORGWARNER TURBO SYSTEMS ALKATRESZGYARTO KFT.—See BorgWarner Inc.; *U.S. Public*, pg. 371
BORGWARNER VERTRIEBS UND VERWALTUNGS GMBH—See BorgWarner Inc.; *U.S. Public*, pg. 370
BRD. KLEE A/S; *Int'l*, pg. 1143
BREVINI POWER TRANSMISSION REDUKTOR SANAYI VE TICARED LIMITED SIRTEKI—See Dana Incorporated; *U.S. Public*, pg. 622
CAF CHILE, S.A.—See Construcciones y Auxiliar de Ferrocarriles S.A.; *Int'l*, pg. 1776

N.A.I.C.S. INDEX

CANG BAO TIAN XIA INTERNATIONAL ART TRADE CENTER, INC.; *Int'l*, pg. 1291
CARLISLE SPECIALTY PRODUCTS GROUP—See Carlisle Companies Incorporated; *U.S. Public*, pg. 436
CEEKAY DAIKIN LTD. - AURANGABAD PLANT—See Exedy Corporation; *Int'l*, pg. 2581
CERTIFIED POWER INC. - DRIVELINE DIVISION—See Brinkmere Capital Partners LLC; *U.S. Private*, pg. 655
CHANGCHUN YIDONG CLUTCH CO., LTD.; *Int'l*, pg. 1443
CHARKHESHGAR CO.; *Int'l*, pg. 1450
CHENGDU HAONENG TECHNOLOGY CO., LTD.; *Int'l*, pg. 1467
CHENGDU XILING POWER SCIENCE & TECHNOLOGY INCORPORATED COMPANY; *Int'l*, pg. 1469
CIE AUTOMOTIVE S.A.; *Int'l*, pg. 1603
CLOYES GEAR & PRODUCTS, INC.—See MidOcean Partners, LLP; *U.S. Private*, pg. 2716
COMPONENTA CORPORATION; *Int'l*, pg. 1753
CUMMINS JAPAN LTD.—See Cummins Inc.; *U.S. Public*, pg. 606
DAEHO MACHINERY IND. CO., LTD.—See DAE-IL Corporation; *Int'l*, pg. 1905
DAEIL AUTOMOTIVE PARTS CO., LTD.—See DAE-IL Corporation; *Int'l*, pg. 1905
DAE-IL CORPORATION-DUDONG 2 PLANT—See DAE-IL Corporation; *Int'l*, pg. 1905
DAE-IL CORPORATION-HEAVY MACHINERY PLANT—See DAE-IL Corporation; *Int'l*, pg. 1905
DAE-IL CORPORATION; *Int'l*, pg. 1905
DAE-IL CORPORATION-UNYANG PLANT—See DAE-IL Corporation; *Int'l*, pg. 1905
DAEIL INNOTECH CORPORATION—See DAE-IL Corporation; *Int'l*, pg. 1905
DAE-IL USA, INC.—See DAE-IL Corporation; *Int'l*, pg. 1905
DANA MOTION SYSTEMS ITALIA S.R.L.—See Dana Incorporated; *U.S. Public*, pg. 622
DANA OFF-HIGHWAY PRODUCTS—See Dana Incorporated; *U.S. Public*, pg. 622
DANA POWER TRANSMISSION FRANCE—See Dana Incorporated; *U.S. Public*, pg. 622
DANA SAC AUSTRALIA PTY. LTD.—See Dana Incorporated; *U.S. Public*, pg. 622
DANA SAC NORWAY AS—See Dana Incorporated; *U.S. Public*, pg. 622
DANA SAC SOUTH AFRICA (PTY) LTD.—See Dana Incorporated; *U.S. Public*, pg. 622
DANA SAC UK LIMITED—See Dana Incorporated; *U.S. Public*, pg. 622
DELPHI PACKARD ELECTRIC SYSTEMS—See Aptiv PLC; *Int'l*, pg. 525
DEXTER AXLE COMPANY—See Brookfield Corporation; *Int'l*, pg. 1175
DEXTER AXLE DIVISION - ALBION—See Brookfield Corporation; *Int'l*, pg. 1175
DEXTER AXLE DIVISION - ELKHART—See Brookfield Corporation; *Int'l*, pg. 1175
DEXTER AXLE DIVISION - EL RENO—See Brookfield Corporation; *Int'l*, pg. 1175
DEXTER AXLE DIVISION - MONTICELLO—See Brookfield Corporation; *Int'l*, pg. 1175
DYNAX AMERICA CORPORATION—See Exedy Corporation; *Int'l*, pg. 2580
EATON CORP. - TRANSMISSIONS—See Eaton Corporation plc; *Int'l*, pg. 2280
EATON INVESTMENTS CO., LTD.—See Eaton Corporation plc; *Int'l*, pg. 2281
EGERSUND ICELAND EHF—See Egersund Group AS; *Int'l*, pg. 2323
FEDERAL-MOGUL LLC—See Apollo Global Management, Inc.; *U.S. Public*, pg. 161
FILTRAN LLC—See Madison Industries Holdings LLC; *U.S. Private*, pg. 2543
FRICTION PRODUCTS CO.—See Lone Star Funds; *U.S. Private*, pg. 2485
FUJIAN SANMING GEAR CASE CO., LTD.—See Fujian Longxi Bearing (Group) Corporation Limited; *Int'l*, pg. 2818
GD EUROPEAN LAND SYSTEMS - STEYR GMBH—See General Dynamics Corporation; *U.S. Public*, pg. 913
GENERAL DYNAMICS EUROPEAN LAND SYSTEMS - MOWAG GMBH—See General Dynamics Corporation; *U.S. Public*, pg. 914
G. G. AUTOMOTIVE GEARS LIMITED; *Int'l*, pg. 2864
GKN AYRA SERVICIO SA—See GKN plc; *Int'l*, pg. 2984
GKN DRIVELINE ARNAGE—See GKN plc; *Int'l*, pg. 2984
GKN DRIVELINE BIRMINGHAM - ERDINGTON PLANT—See GKN plc; *Int'l*, pg. 2984
GKN DRIVELINE FIRENZE SPA—See GKN plc; *Int'l*, pg. 2984
GKN DRIVELINE NORTH AMERICA INC.—See GKN plc; *Int'l*, pg. 2984
GKN DRIVELINE OFFENBACH—See GKN plc; *Int'l*, pg. 2984
GKN DRIVELINE VIGO—See GKN plc; *Int'l*, pg. 2985
GKN DRIVELINE ZUMAIA—See GKN plc; *Int'l*, pg. 2985
GKN FLORANGE SARL—See GKN plc; *Int'l*, pg. 2985
GKN GELENKWELLENWERK KAISERSLAUTERN GMBH—See GKN plc; *Int'l*, pg. 2985

GKN WALTERSCHEID INC.—See OEP Capital Advisors, L.P.; *U.S. Private*, pg. 2999
GNA AXLES LIMITED; *Int'l*, pg. 3016
GRAHAM MOTORS AND CONTROLS; *U.S. Private*, pg. 1751
GSP LATIN AMERICA LTD.—See GSP Automotive Group Wenzhou Co., Ltd.; *Int'l*, pg. 3150
GUANGZHOU NITTAN VALVE CO. LTD.—See Eaton Corporation plc; *Int'l*, pg. 2281
HAISUNG TPC CO., LTD.; *Int'l*, pg. 3217
HANGZHOU HAVECO AUTOMOTIVE TRANSMISSION CO., LTD.—See Hangzhou Advance Gearbox Group Co., Ltd.; *Int'l*, pg. 3246
HGEARS AG; *Int'l*, pg. 3378
HILITE GERMANY GMBH—See Aviation Industry Corporation of China; *Int'l*, pg. 742
HILITE GERMANY GMBH—See Aviation Industry Corporation of China; *Int'l*, pg. 742
HILITE INTERNATIONAL, INC. - WHITEHALL—See Aviation Industry Corporation of China; *Int'l*, pg. 742
HONDA FRANCE MANUFACTURING S.A.S—See Honda Motor Co., Ltd.; *Int'l*, pg. 3461
HONDA PARTS MFG. CORP.—See Honda Motor Co., Ltd.; *Int'l*, pg. 3462
HONDA PRECISION PARTS OF GEORGIA, LLC—See Honda Motor Co., Ltd.; *Int'l*, pg. 3462
HOPIUM S.A.; *Int'l*, pg. 3473
HORTON INC.; *U.S. Private*, pg. 1984
IGAM LLC—See Grupo Financiero Galicia S.A.; *Int'l*, pg. 3129
IMT CORPORATION—See Mission Essential Personnel, LLC; *U.S. Private*, pg. 2747
INDIANA TOOL & DIE CO. INC.—See Jasper Engine & Transmission Exchange Inc.; *U.S. Private*, pg. 2190
JERNBERG SALES, LLC—See American Axle & Manufacturing Holdings, Inc.; *U.S. Public*, pg. 96
JINXI AXLE CO., LTD.—See China North Industries Group Corporation; *Int'l*, pg. 1535
JOHN DEERE COFFEYVILLE WORKS INC—See Deere & Company; *U.S. Public*, pg. 646
JOHNSON POWER LTD.; *U.S. Private*, pg. 2228
JUNGWON MACHINERY IND. CO., LTD.—See DAE-IL Corporation; *Int'l*, pg. 1905
KANETA KOGYO CO., LTD.—See Honda Motor Co., Ltd.; *Int'l*, pg. 3463
LEEDY MANUFACTURING CO. INC.; *U.S. Private*, pg. 2415
LM GEAR COMPANY, INC.—See Anderson-Cook Inc.; *U.S. Private*, pg. 278
MANUAL TRANSMISSIONS OF MUNCIE—See General Motors Company; *U.S. Public*, pg. 926
MAX-TORQUE LTD.—See Schlumberger Limited; *U.S. Public*, pg. 1844
MCT REMAN LTD.—See Hasgo Group Ltd.; *Int'l*, pg. 3283
MERITOR HVS—See Cummins Inc.; *U.S. Public*, pg. 608
METALDYNE, LLC—See American Axle & Manufacturing Holdings, Inc.; *U.S. Public*, pg. 96
MILL-LOG EQUIPMENT CO., INC.—See Palmer Johnson Enterprises, Inc.; *U.S. Private*, pg. 3081
MILL-LOG WILSON EQUIPMENT LTD.—See Palmer Johnson Enterprises, Inc.; *U.S. Private*, pg. 3081
MUHR UND BENDER KG—See Brd. Klee A/S; *Int'l*, pg. 1143
NEAPCO COMPONENTS, LLC—See Neapco Holdings, LLC; *U.S. Private*, pg. 2877
NEAPCO DRIVELINES, LLC—See Neapco Holdings, LLC; *U.S. Private*, pg. 2877
NEAPCO EUROPE GMBH—See Neapco Holdings, LLC; *U.S. Private*, pg. 2877
NEAPCO EUROPE SP. Z O.O.—See Neapco Holdings, LLC; *U.S. Private*, pg. 2877
NSK-WARNER KABUSHIKI KAISHA—See BorgWarner Inc.; *U.S. Public*, pg. 371
NSK-WARNER (SHANGHAI) CO., LTD.—See BorgWarner Inc.; *U.S. Public*, pg. 371
PCB LOAD & TORQUE, INC.—See Amphenol Corporation; *U.S. Public*, pg. 131
PERFECTION CLUTCH—See Berkshire Hathaway Inc.; *U.S. Public*, pg. 310
P.T. BANDO INDONESIA—See Bando Chemical Industries, Ltd.; *Int'l*, pg. 830
PT. SHOWA AUTOPARTS INDONESIA—See Hitachi Astemo, Ltd.; *Int'l*, pg. 3409
PUNCH POWERGLIDE STRASBOURG SAS—See Iep Invest SA; *Int'l*, pg. 3597
QIJIANG GEAR TRANSMISSION CO., LTD.—See Chongqing Machinery & Electronics Holding (Group) Co., Ltd.; *Int'l*, pg. 1580
RBC BEARINGS POLSKA SP. Z O.O.—See RBC Bearings Incorporated; *U.S. Public*, pg. 1766
R. CUSHMAN & ASSOCIATES, INC.—See Stone River Capital Partners, LLC; *U.S. Private*, pg. 3826
R. CUSHMAN & ASSOCIATES, INC.—See Wynnchurch Capital, L.P.; *U.S. Private*, pg. 4577
R.H. SHEPPARD CO., INC.—See Balmoral Funds LLC; *U.S. Private*, pg. 461
SEAL AFTERMARKET PRODUCTS LLC; *U.S. Private*, pg. 3584

SHOWA AUTOPARTS WUHAN CO., LTD.—See Hitachi Astemo, Ltd.; *Int'l*, pg. 3410
SHOWA CORPORATION - HADANO PLANT—See Hitachi Astemo, Ltd.; *Int'l*, pg. 3410
SMITH POWER PRODUCTS INC.; *U.S. Private*, pg. 3695
SONNAX INDUSTRIES, INC.; *U.S. Private*, pg. 3714
TAIWAN PYROLYSIS & ENERGY REGENERATION CORP.—See Hota Industrial Mfg. Co., Ltd.; *Int'l*, pg. 3487
TEAM INDUSTRIES BAGLEY-AUDUBON, INC.—See TEAM Industries, Inc.; *U.S. Private*, pg. 3949
TORSION CONTROL PRODUCTS, INC.—See The Timken Company; *U.S. Public*, pg. 2134
TRANSPORTATION POWER, INC.—See Cummins Inc.; *U.S. Public*, pg. 609
TRUCK ENTERPRISES, INC.—See Doggett Equipment Services, Inc.; *U.S. Private*, pg. 1253
TWIN DISC (FAR EAST) LTD.—See Twin Disc, Incorporated; *U.S. Public*, pg. 2206
TWIN DISC, INCORPORATED; *U.S. Public*, pg. 2206
TWIN DISC (PACIFIC) PTY. LTD.—See Twin Disc, Incorporated; *U.S. Public*, pg. 2207
UNIDRIVE PTY. LTD.—See GKN plc; *Int'l*, pg. 2986
USM DE MEXICO, S. DE R.L. DE C.V.—See Wynnchurch Capital, L.P.; *U.S. Private*, pg. 4578
VENOM PRODUCTS, LLC; *U.S. Public*, pg. 4356
VOLVO TRUCK CORPORATION POWERTRAIN DIVISION ENGINE—See AB Volvo; *Int'l*, pg. 46
WRIGHTSPEED, INC.—See Firsthand Capital Management, Inc.; *U.S. Private*, pg. 1532
XL HYBRIDS, INC.—See The Shyft Group, Inc.; *U.S. Public*, pg. 2130
XTRAC, INC.—See MiddleGround Management, LP; *U.S. Private*, pg. 2713
XTRAC LIMITED—See MiddleGround Management, LP; *U.S. Private*, pg. 2713
ZHANGZHOU JINCHI AUTOMOBILE PARTS CO., LTD.—See Fujian Longxi Bearing (Group) Corporation Limited; *Int'l*, pg. 2818

336360 — MOTOR VEHICLE SEATING AND INTERIOR TRIM MANUFACTURING

ADIENT AUTOMOTIVE ARGENTINA S.R.L.—See Adient plc; *Int'l*, pg. 148
ADIENT AUTOMOTIVE ROMANIA S.R.L.—See Adient plc; *Int'l*, pg. 148
ADIENT BELGIUM BVBA—See Adient plc; *Int'l*, pg. 148
ADIENT BOR S.R.O.—See Adient plc; *Int'l*, pg. 148
ADIENT CLANTON INC.—See Adient plc; *Int'l*, pg. 148
ADIENT ELDON INC.—See Adient plc; *Int'l*, pg. 148
ADIENT INDIA PRIVATE LIMITED—See Adient plc; *Int'l*, pg. 148
ADIENT LTD. & CO. KG.—See Adient plc; *Int'l*, pg. 148
ADIENT NOVO MESTO, PROIZVODNJA AVTOMOBILSKIH SEDEZEV, D.O.O.—See Adient plc; *Int'l*, pg. 148
ADIENT PLC; *Int'l*, pg. 148
ADIENT POLAND SP. Z O.O.—See Adient plc; *Int'l*, pg. 148
ADIENT SAARLOUIS LTD. & CO. KG.—See Adient plc; *Int'l*, pg. 148
ADIENT SEATING CANADA LP.—See Adient plc; *Int'l*, pg. 148
ADIENT SEATING D.O.O.—See Adient plc; *Int'l*, pg. 148
ADIENT SOUTH AFRICA (PTY) LTD.—See Adient plc; *Int'l*, pg. 148
ADIENT SWEDEN AB—See Adient plc; *Int'l*, pg. 148
ADIENT (THAILAND) CO., LTD.—See Adient plc; *Int'l*, pg. 148
ADIENT US LLC—See Adient plc; *Int'l*, pg. 148
AEROSPACE LIGHTING CORPORATION—See RTX Corporation; *U.S. Public*, pg. 1822
AMSAFE COMMERCIAL PRODUCTS—See TransDigm Group Incorporated; *U.S. Public*, pg. 2182
AMSAFE DEFENSE—See TransDigm Group Incorporated; *U.S. Public*, pg. 2182
AMSAFE GLOBAL SERVICES (PRIVATE) LIMITED—See TransDigm Group Incorporated; *U.S. Public*, pg. 2182
AMSAFE KUNSHAN—See TransDigm Group Incorporated; *U.S. Public*, pg. 2182
AMTEX INC.—See Hayashi Telempu Co., Ltd.; *Int'l*, pg. 3289
APM DELTA SEATING SYSTEMS SDN. BHD.—See APM Automotive Holdings Berhad; *Int'l*, pg. 516
APM TACHI-S SEATING SYSTEMS SDN. BHD.—See APM Automotive Holdings Berhad; *Int'l*, pg. 516
ASHIMORI INDIA PRIVATE LIMITED—See Ashimori Industry Co., Ltd.; *Int'l*, pg. 607
ASHIMORI INDUSTRIA DE MEXICO, S.A. DE C.V.—See Ashimori Industry Co., Ltd.; *Int'l*, pg. 607
ASHIMORI INDUSTRY YAMAGUCHI CO., LTD.—See Ashimori Industry Co., Ltd.; *Int'l*, pg. 607
ASHIMORI KOREA CO., LTD.—See Ashimori Industry Co., Ltd.; *Int'l*, pg. 607
ASHIMORI TECHNOLOGY (WUXI) CO., LTD.—See Ashimori Industry Co., Ltd.; *Int'l*, pg. 607
ASHIMORI (THAILAND) CO., LTD.—See Ashimori Industry Co., Ltd.; *Int'l*, pg. 607
AUNDE BRAZIL S.A.—See AUNDE Achter & Ebels GmbH; *Int'l*, pg. 705

336360 — MOTOR VEHICLE SEATI...

AUTOLIV BKI S.A.—See Autoliv, Inc.; *Int'l*, pg. 728
AUTOLIV B.V. & CO. KG, WERK NORD—See Autoliv, Inc.; *Int'l*, pg. 728
AUTOLIV CANKOR—See Autoliv, Inc.; *Int'l*, pg. 728
AUTOLIV DE MEXICO S.A. DE C.V.—See Autoliv, Inc.; *Int'l*, pg. 730
AUTOLIV DO BRASIL—See Autoliv, Inc.; *Int'l*, pg. 730
AUTOLIV FRANCE—See Autoliv, Inc.; *Int'l*, pg. 728
AUTOLIV HIROTAKO SDN. BHD.—See Autoliv, Inc.; *Int'l*, pg. 728
AUTOLIV JAPAN LTD. - FUJISAWA FACILITY—See Autoliv, Inc.; *Int'l*, pg. 729
AUTOLIV KLE S.A.—See Autoliv, Inc.; *Int'l*, pg. 729
AUTOLIV NORTH AMERICA AIRBAG MODULE FACILITY—See Autoliv, Inc.; *Int'l*, pg. 729
AUTOLIV NORTH AMERICA SEAT BELT FACILITY—See Autoliv, Inc.; *Int'l*, pg. 729
AUTOLIV POLAND RESTRAINT SYSTEMS—See Autoliv, Inc.; *Int'l*, pg. 729
AUTOLIV SPRING DYNAMICS—See Autoliv, Inc.; *Int'l*, pg. 730
AUTONEUM BELGIUM N.V.—See Autoneum Holding Ltd.; *Int'l*, pg. 731
AUTONEUM CANADA LTD.—See Autoneum Holding Ltd.; *Int'l*, pg. 731
AUTONEUM (CHONGQING) SOUND-PROOF PARTS CO. LTD.—See Autoneum Holding Ltd.; *Int'l*, pg. 731
AUTONEUM CZ S.R.O.—See Autoneum Holding Ltd.; *Int'l*, pg. 731
AUTONEUM FELTEX (PTY) LTD.—See Autoneum Holding Ltd.; *Int'l*, pg. 731
AUTONEUM FRANCE S.A.S.U.—See Autoneum Holding Ltd.; *Int'l*, pg. 731
AUTONEUM GERMANY GMBH—See Autoneum Holding Ltd.; *Int'l*, pg. 731
AUTONEUM GREAT BRITAIN LTD. - HECKMONDWIKE—See Autoneum Holding Ltd.; *Int'l*, pg. 731
AUTONEUM GREAT BRITAIN LTD.—See Autoneum Holding Ltd.; *Int'l*, pg. 731
AUTONEUM HOLDING LTD.; *Int'l*, pg. 731
AUTONEUM MANAGEMENT AG—See Autoneum Holding Ltd.; *Int'l*, pg. 731
AUTONEUM NETHERLANDS B.V.—See Autoneum Holding Ltd.; *Int'l*, pg. 731
AUTONEUM POLAND SP. Z.O.O.—See Autoneum Holding Ltd.; *Int'l*, pg. 731
AUTONEUM PORTUGAL LDA.—See Autoneum Holding Ltd.; *Int'l*, pg. 731
AUTONEUM SPAIN NORTHWEST S.L.U.—See Autoneum Holding Ltd.; *Int'l*, pg. 731
AUTONEUM SPAIN S.A.U.—See Autoneum Holding Ltd.; *Int'l*, pg. 731
AUTONEUM SWITZERLAND AG—See Autoneum Holding Ltd.; *Int'l*, pg. 731
AUTO PARTS MANUFACTURERS CO. SDN. BHD.—See APM Automotive Holdings Berhad; *Int'l*, pg. 516
B/E AEROSPACE (GERMANY) GMBH—See RTX Corporation; *U.S. Public*, pg. 1822
B/E AEROSPACE, INC.—See RTX Corporation; *U.S. Public*, pg. 1822
BE AEROSPACE (NETHERLANDS) B.V.—See RTX Corporation; *U.S. Public*, pg. 1822
BEAMS INDUSTRIES, INC.—See TransDigm Group Incorporated; *U.S. Public*, pg. 2182
BEIJING ADIENT AUTOMOTIVE COMPONENTS CO., LTD.—See Adient plc; *Int'l*, pg. 148
BEST SEATING SYSTEMS GMBH—See Addtech AB; *Int'l*, pg. 132
BHARAT SEATS LIMITED; *Int'l*, pg. 1011
BIRLA CORPORATION LTD. - AUTOTRIM DIVISION I—See Birla Corporation Ltd.; *Int'l*, pg. 1047
BOMBARDIER TRANSPORTATION (CHINA) LTD.—See Alstom S.A.; *Int'l*, pg. 382
BORGERS SE & CO. KGAA—See Autoneum Holding Ltd.; *Int'l*, pg. 731
THE C.E. WHITE CO.—See Hickory Springs Manufacturing Company; *U.S. Private*, pg. 1933
CHINA AUTOMOTIVE INTERIOR DECORATION HOLDINGS LIMITED; *Int'l*, pg. 1484
CHUOH LINEN SUPPLY CO., LTD.—See Central Japan Railway Company; *Int'l*, pg. 1408
CNI ENTERPRISES, INC.—See Clearlake Capital Group, L.P.; *U.S. Private*, pg. 934
COMMERCIAL VEHICLE GROUP, INC.; *U.S. Public*, pg. 547
CONTINENTAL INTERIOR DIVISION—See Continental Aktiengesellschaft; *Int'l*, pg. 1782
CVG - ALABAMA—See Commercial Vehicle Group, Inc.; *U.S. Public*, pg. 547
CVS HOLDINGS, INC.—See Commercial Vehicle Group, Inc.; *U.S. Public*, pg. 547
CYBEX RETAIL GMBH—See Goodbaby International Holdings Limited; *Int'l*, pg. 3039
DAEWON KANG UP CO., LTD.; *Int'l*, pg. 1910
DAEWON SANUP CO., LTD.; *Int'l*, pg. 1910
DAGRO EISSMANN AUTOMOTIVE GMBH—See Eissmann Automotive Deutschland GmbH; *Int'l*, pg. 2336

DAICEL SAFETY SYSTEMS, INC.—See Daicel Corporation; *Int'l*, pg. 1919
DAYTON BAG & BURLAP CO.; *U.S. Private*, pg. 1177
DELLOYD INDUSTRIES (M) SDN BHD—See Delloyd Ventures Sdn Bhd; *Int'l*, pg. 2014
DUAL CO. LTD - DUAL ASAN PLANT—See DUAL Co. Ltd; *Int'l*, pg. 2217
DUAL CO. LTD - DUAL BANWOUL PLANT—See DUAL Co. Ltd; *Int'l*, pg. 2217
DUAL CO. LTD - DUAL GANGHWA PLANT—See DUAL Co. Ltd; *Int'l*, pg. 2217
DUAL CO. LTD - DUAL ULSAN PLANT—See DUAL Co. Ltd; *Int'l*, pg. 2217
DUAL MOOLSAN CO., LTD—See DUAL Co. Ltd; *Int'l*, pg. 2217
EISSMANN COTESA GMBH—See Eissmann Automotive Deutschland GmbH; *Int'l*, pg. 2336
EISSMANN INDIVIDUAL GMBH—See Eissmann Automotive Deutschland GmbH; *Int'l*, pg. 2336
EWON COMFORTECH CO., LTD. - JEONGUP FACTORY—See Ewon Comfortech Co., Ltd.; *Int'l*, pg. 2576
EWON COMFORTECH CO., LTD. - JIANGYANG FACTORY—See Ewon Comfortech Co., Ltd.; *Int'l*, pg. 2576
EWON COMFORTECH CO., LTD.; *Int'l*, pg. 2576
EWON COMFORTECH CO., LTD. - TURKEY FACTORY—See Ewon Comfortech Co., Ltd.; *Int'l*, pg. 2576
FAURECIA AUTOMOTIVE GMBH—See FORVIA SE; *Int'l*, pg. 2746
FAURECIA AUTOMOTIVE SEATING B.V.—See FORVIA SE; *Int'l*, pg. 2746
FAURECIA AUTOMOTIVE SEATING, INC—See FORVIA SE; *Int'l*, pg. 2747
FAURECIA AUTOSITZE GMBH—See FORVIA SE; *Int'l*, pg. 2746
FAURECIA FOTELE SAMOCHODOWE SP. ZO.O—See FORVIA SE; *Int'l*, pg. 2746
FAURECIA (GUANGZHOU) AUTOMOTIVE SYSTEMS CO., LTD—See FORVIA SE; *Int'l*, pg. 2745
FAURECIA (SHANGHAI) AUTOMOTIVE SYSTEMS CO., LTD—See FORVIA SE; *Int'l*, pg. 2745
FAURECIA (SHANGHAI) MANAGEMENT COMPANY, LTD—See FORVIA SE; *Int'l*, pg. 2745
FAURECIA (WUHAN) AUTOMOTIVE SEATING CO., LTD—See FORVIA SE; *Int'l*, pg. 2745
FAURECIA (WUXI) SEATING COMPONENTS CO., LTD—See FORVIA SE; *Int'l*, pg. 2746
FISCHER AMERICA INC.—See fischerwerke GmbH & Co. KG; *Int'l*, pg. 2692
FISCHER AUTOMOTIVE SYSTEMS GMBH & CO. KG—See fischerwerke GmbH & Co. KG; *Int'l*, pg. 2692
FLEX-O-LATORS, INCORPORATED—See Leggett & Platt, Incorporated; *U.S. Public*, pg. 1302
FLEXSTEEL DUBUQUE DIVISION—See Flexsteel Industries, Inc.; *U.S. Public*, pg. 853
FLEXSTEEL METAL DIVISION—See Flexsteel Industries, Inc.; *U.S. Public*, pg. 853
FUTURIS AUTOMOTIVE INTERIORS (AUSTRALIA) PTY. LTD.—See Clearlake Capital Group, L.P.; *U.S. Private*, pg. 934
GENIUS SOLUTIONS ENGINEERING CORPORATION—See Standex International; *U.S. Public*, pg. 1930
GRACO UK & IRELAND—See Newell Brands Inc.; *U.S. Public*, pg. 1514
GRAMAG LLC; *U.S. Private*, pg. 1752
GRA-MAG TRUCK INTERIOR SYSTEMS LLC—See Grammer AG; *Int'l*, pg. 3053
GRAMMER AD—See Grammer AG; *Int'l*, pg. 3053
GRAMMER AG; *Int'l*, pg. 3053
GRAMMER ARGENTINA S.A.—See Grammer AG; *Int'l*, pg. 3053
GRAMMER AUTOMOTIVE CZ S.R.O.—See Grammer AG; *Int'l*, pg. 3053
GRAMMER AUTOMOTIVE ESPANOLA S.A.—See Grammer AG; *Int'l*, pg. 3053
GRAMMER AUTOMOTIVE METALL GMBH—See Grammer AG; *Int'l*, pg. 3053
GRAMMER AUTOMOTIVE PUEBLA S.A. DE C.V.—See Grammer AG; *Int'l*, pg. 3053
GRAMMER AUTOMOTIVE SLOVENIJA D.O.O.—See Grammer AG; *Int'l*, pg. 3053
GRAMMER CZ S.R.O.—See Grammer AG; *Int'l*, pg. 3053
GRAMMER DO BRASIL LTDA.—See Grammer AG; *Int'l*, pg. 3053
GRAMMER ELECTRONICS N.V.—See Grammer AG; *Int'l*, pg. 3053
GRAMMER FRANCE SARL—See Grammer AG; *Int'l*, pg. 3053
GRAMMER INC.—See Grammer AG; *Int'l*, pg. 3053
GRAMMER INTERIOR (BEIJING) CO., LTD.—See Grammer AG; *Int'l*, pg. 3053
GRAMMER INTERIOR (CHANGCHUN) CO. LTD.—See Grammer AG; *Int'l*, pg. 3053
GRAMMER INTERIOR (SHANGHAI) CO. LTD..—See Grammer AG; *Int'l*, pg. 3053

GRAMMER INTERIOR (TIANJIN) CO. LTD.—See Grammer AG; *Int'l*, pg. 3053
GRAMMER JAPAN LTD.—See Grammer AG; *Int'l*, pg. 3053
GRAMMER KOLTUK SISTEMLERI SANAYI VE TICARET A.S.—See Grammer AG; *Int'l*, pg. 3053
GRAMMER MEXICANA S.A. DE C.V.—See Grammer AG; *Int'l*, pg. 3053
GRAMMER SEATING (JIANGSU) CO., LTD.—See Grammer AG; *Int'l*, pg. 3053
GRAMMER SEATING (SHAANXI) CO., LTD.—See Grammer AG; *Int'l*, pg. 3053
GRAMMER SEATING SYSTEMS LTD.—See Grammer AG; *Int'l*, pg. 3053
GRAMMER SYSTEM D.O.O.—See Grammer AG; *Int'l*, pg. 3053
GRAMMER TECHNICAL COMPONENTS GMBH—See Grammer AG; *Int'l*, pg. 3053
GRAMMER WACKERSDORF GMBH—See Grammer AG; *Int'l*, pg. 3053
GRUPO ANTOLIN-IRAUSA, S.A.; *Int'l*, pg. 3119
GUANGDONG TIANAN NEW MATERIAL CO., LTD.; *Int'l*, pg. 3161
GUANGZHOU IMASEN ELECTRIC INDUSTRIAL CO., LTD.—See Imasen Electric Industrial Co., Ltd.; *Int'l*, pg. 3620
HAINAN DRINDA NEW ENERGY TECHNOLOGY CO., LTD.; *Int'l*, pg. 3212
HFI INC., *U.S. Private*, pg. 1928
HOERBIGER AUTOMOTIVE KOMFORTSYSTEME GMBH—See Hoerbiger Holding AG; *Int'l*, pg. 3440
HOOVER UNIVERSAL, INC.—See Adient plc; *Int'l*, pg. 148
HUIZHOU DESAY SV AUTOMOTIVE CO., LTD.; *Int'l*, pg. 3527
HYUNDAI INDUSTRIAL CO., LTD.; *Int'l*, pg. 3557
HYUNDAI MSEAT CO., LTD.—See Hyundai Motor Company; *Int'l*, pg. 3559
IAC GROUP B.V.B.A.—See Invesco Ltd.; *U.S. Public*, pg. 1164
IAC GROUP S.L.—See Invesco Ltd.; *U.S. Public*, pg. 1164
IKUYO CO., LTD.; *Int'l*, pg. 3612
IMASEN BUCYRUS TECHNOLOGY INC.—See Imasen Electric Industrial Co., Ltd.; *Int'l*, pg. 3620
IMASEN ELECTRIC INDUSTRIAL CO., LTD.; *Int'l*, pg. 3620
IMASEN ELECTRIC & MACHINERY CO., LTD.—See Imasen Electric Industrial Co., Ltd.; *Int'l*, pg. 3620
IMASEN MANUFACTURING (THAILAND) CO., LTD.—See Imasen Electric Industrial Co., Ltd.; *Int'l*, pg. 3620
IMASEN PHILIPPINE MANUFACTURING CORPORATION—See Imasen Electric Industrial Co., Ltd.; *Int'l*, pg. 3620
INTERNATIONAL AUTOMOTIVE COMPONENTS GROUP EUROPE—See Invesco Ltd.; *U.S. Public*, pg. 1164
INTERNATIONAL AUTOMOTIVE COMPONENTS GROUP, LLC—See Invesco Ltd.; *U.S. Public*, pg. 1164
IP BELGIAN SERVICES COMPANY SPRL—See International Paper Company; *U.S. Public*, pg. 1155
IRVIN AUTOMOTIVE PRODUCTS INC.—See Piston Group, LLC; *U.S. Private*, pg. 3190
JOHNSON CONTROLS AUTOMOTIVE SYSTEMS KK—See Adient plc; *Int'l*, pg. 148
JOHNSON CONTROLS, INC. - MURFREESBORO PLANT—See Adient plc; *Int'l*, pg. 148
KAB SEATING AB—See Commercial Vehicle Group, Inc.; *U.S. Public*, pg. 547
KAB SEATING LIMITED—See Commercial Vehicle Group, Inc.; *U.S. Public*, pg. 547
KAB SEATING PTY. LTD.—See Commercial Vehicle Group, Inc.; *U.S. Public*, pg. 547
KAB SEATING SA—See Commercial Vehicle Group, Inc.; *U.S. Public*, pg. 547
LEAR AUTOMOTIVE INDIA PRIVATE LIMITED—See Lear Corporation; *U.S. Public*, pg. 1297
LEAR CORPORATION ITALIA S.R.L.—See Lear Corporation; *U.S. Public*, pg. 1297
LEAR CORPORATION SEATING FRANCE SAS—See Lear Corporation; *U.S. Public*, pg. 1297
LEAR CORPORATION; *U.S. Public*, pg. 1296
MCCONNELL SEATS AUSTRALIA PTY. LTD.—See APM Automotive Holdings Berhad; *Int'l*, pg. 516
MEI-AN AUTOLIV CO., LTD.—See Autoliv, Inc.; *Int'l*, pg. 730
MILSCO DE MEXICO, S.A. DE C.V.—See Jason Industries, Inc.; *U.S. Private*, pg. 2189
MILSCO EUROPE—See Jason Industries, Inc.; *U.S. Private*, pg. 2189
MILSCO MANUFACTURING COMPANY - JACKSON—See Jason Industries, Inc.; *U.S. Private*, pg. 2189
MILSCO MANUFACTURING COMPANY—See Jason Industries, Inc.; *U.S. Private*, pg. 2189
NHK SEATING OF AMERICA, INC.—See Lear Corporation; *U.S. Public*, pg. 1297
OTACO SEATING CO., LTD.—See American Seating Company; *U.S. Private*, pg. 247
POLYDESIGN SYSTEMS S.A.R.L.—See Exco Technologies Limited; *Int'l*, pg. 2580
RACE COMPLETIONS LTD—See Causeway Aero Group Ltd.; *Int'l*, pg. 1361
RECARO AUTOMOTIVE SEATING GMBH—See Adient plc; *Int'l*, pg. 148

336390 — OTHER MOTOR VEHICLE...

RECARO NORTH AMERICA, INC.—See Adient plc; *Int'l*, pg. 148
SAGE AUTOMOTIVE INTERIORS, LTD.—See Asahi Kasei Corporation; *Int'l*, pg. 597
SAL AUTOMOTIVE LIMITED—See b4S Solutions Pvt Ltd.; *Int'l*, pg. 791
SCHUKRA OF NORTH AMERICA LTD.—See Leggett & Platt, Incorporated; *U.S. Public*, pg. 1303
SEARS MANUFACTURING COMPANY; *U.S. Private*, pg. 3591
SELLNER HOLDING GMBH—See CBR Management GmbH; *Int'l*, pg. 1366
SIMCO INDUSTRIES, INC.—See UFP Technologies, Inc.; *U.S. Public*, pg. 2221
SITTAB INC.—See Addtech AB; *Int'l*, pg. 135
SITTAB STOL AB—See Addtech AB; *Int'l*, pg. 135
SPRAGUE DEVICES, INC.—See Commercial Vehicle Group, Inc.; *U.S. Public*, pg. 547
TAKATA GLOBAL GROUP; *U.S. Private*, pg. 3925
TECHNOTRIM DE MEXICO, S. DE R.L. DE C.V.—See Adient plc; *Int'l*, pg. 148
TIANJIN RIETER NITTOKU AUTOMOTIVE SOUNDPROOF CO. LTD—See Autoneum Holding Ltd.; *Int'l*, pg. 731
TOLEDO MOLDING CZ S.R.O.—See Grammer AG; *Int'l*, pg. 3053
TRANSIT SOLUTIONS PROPRIETARY LIMITED—See Fortive Corporation; *U.S. Public*, pg. 872
TRIMSOL SP. Z O.O.—See DUAL Co. Ltd; *Int'l*, pg. 2217
ULTRA SEATING COMPANY—See VSE Corporation; *U.S. Public*, pg. 2313
VALLEY ENTERPRISES, INC.—See Gemini Group, Inc.; *U.S. Private*, pg. 1658
VOA CANADA—See Autoliv, Inc.; *Int'l*, pg. 730
WIELAND DESIGNS INC.; *U.S. Private*, pg. 4516
THE WISE CO. INC.; *U.S. Private*, pg. 4138

336370 — MOTOR VEHICLE METAL STAMPING

ACEMCO INCORPORATED; *U.S. Private*, pg. 58
ADVANCE ENGINEERING COMPANY; *U.S. Private*, pg. 83
ADVANCE ENGINEERING COMPANY—See Advance Engineering Company; *U.S. Private*, pg. 83
AGRIAUTO STAMPING COMPANY (PVT.) LTD.—See House of Habib; *Int'l*, pg. 3491
AGS AUTOMOTIVE SYSTEMS; *Int'l*, pg. 221
AIDA GERMANY GMBH—See AIDA Engineering, Ltd.; *Int'l*, pg. 231
AIDA GREATER ASIA PTE. LTD.—See AIDA Engineering, Ltd.; *Int'l*, pg. 231
A.J. ROSE MANUFACTURING CO. INC.; *U.S. Private*, pg. 26
ALLIED PRECISION MANUFACTURING (M) SDN. BHD.—See Allied Technologies Ltd.; *Int'l*, pg. 358
AMERICAN TRIM - CULLMAN—See American Trim LLC; *U.S. Private*, pg. 257
AMI MANCHESTER, LLC; *U.S. Private*, pg. 263
ANAMET EUROPE B.V.—See Anamet Inc.; *U.S. Private*, pg. 271
ANCHOR DIE TECHNOLOGIES—See Anchor Manufacturing Group, Inc.; *U.S. Private*, pg. 273
ANCHOR MANUFACTURING GROUP, INC.; *U.S. Private*, pg. 273
ART TECHNOLOGIES, INC.—See The C. M. Paula Company; *U.S. Private*, pg. 4003
AUTO-VEHICLE PARTS LLC—See GHK Capital Partners LP; *U.S. Private*, pg. 1690
BEUTLER NOVA AG—See ANDRITZ AG; *Int'l*, pg. 456
BIANTE PTY LIMITED—See Hancock & Gore Ltd.; *Int'l*, pg. 3242
BURKLAND INC.—See Wolverine Capital Partners LLC; *U.S. Private*, pg. 4555
CHALLENGE MANUFACTURING COMPANY; *U.S. Private*, pg. 845
CHANGCHUN ENGLEY AUTOMOBILE INDUSTRY CO., LTD.—See Cayman Engley Industrial Co., Ltd.; *Int'l*, pg. 1363
CIE UDALBIDE, S.A.U.—See Cie Automotive S.A.; *Int'l*, pg. 1604
CIE UNITOOLS PRESS CZ, A.S.—See Cie Automotive S.A.; *Int'l*, pg. 1604
CONNOR MANUFACTURING SERVICE (ASIA) PTE LTD.—See Amphenol Corporation; *U.S. Public*, pg. 130
CONNOR MANUFACTURING SERVICES (JB) SDN. BHD.—See Amphenol Corporation; *U.S. Public*, pg. 130
CONNOR MANUFACTURING SERVICES (KUSHAN) CO., LTD.—See Amphenol Corporation; *U.S. Public*, pg. 130
CONNOR MANUFACTURING (SUZHOU) CO., LTD.—See Amphenol Corporation; *U.S. Public*, pg. 130
CONNOR METAL STAMPING DE MEXICO S. DE R.L. DE C.V.—See Amphenol Corporation; *U.S. Public*, pg. 130
DEFIANCE METAL PRODUCTS CO.—See Mayville Engineering Company, Inc.; *U.S. Public*, pg. 1403
DEFIANCE METAL PRODUCTS OF ARKANSAS INC.—See Mayville Engineering Company, Inc.; *U.S. Public*, pg. 1403
DOWDING INDUSTRIES, INC.; *U.S. Private*, pg. 1268

ELECTROL CO.—See Innovative Manufacturing Solutions Corp.; *U.S. Private*, pg. 2082
ELRINGKLINGER AUTOMOTIVE MANUFACTURING, INC.—See ElringKlinger AG; *Int'l*, pg. 2369
F.C.C. CO., LTD.; *Int'l*, pg. 2596
F.E.G. DE QUERETARO S.A. DE C.V—See F-Tech Inc.; *Int'l*, pg. 2595
FENDERS N'MORE, LLC—See Brookfield Corporation; *Int'l*, pg. 1176
FINDLAY PRODUCTS CORP.—See Midway Products Group, Inc.; *U.S. Private*, pg. 2719
FLEETWOOD METAL INDUSTRIES, INC.—See Cleveland-Cliffs, Inc.; *U.S. Public*, pg. 514
FLORIDA PRODUCTION ENGINEERING INC.—See Ernie Green Industries, Inc.; *U.S. Private*, pg. 1422
THE GERSTENSLAGER COMPANY—See Worthington Industries, Inc.; *U.S. Public*, pg. 2383
GESTAMP ALABAMA, INC.—See Acek Desarrollo y Gestion Industrial SL; *Int'l*, pg. 97
GESTAMP AUTOMACION S.A.—See Acek Desarrollo y Gestion Industrial SL; *Int'l*, pg. 96
GESTAMP NORTH AMERICA, INC.—See Acek Desarrollo y Gestion Industrial SL; *Int'l*, pg. 97
GHSP, INC.—See JSJ Corporation; *U.S. Private*, pg. 2241
GILL INDUSTRIES INC.; *U.S. Private*, pg. 1700
GILL QUERETARO S DE RL DE CV—See Gill Industries Inc.; *U.S. Private*, pg. 1700
GNUTTI CARLO INDIA LTD—See Gnutti Carlo S.p.A.; *Int'l*, pg. 3017
GNUTTI CARLO SWEDEN AB KUNGSOR FACILITY—See Gnutti Carlo S.p.A.; *Int'l*, pg. 3017
GNUTTI CARLO UK LTD—See Gnutti Carlo S.p.A.; *Int'l*, pg. 3017
GNUTTI CARLO (WUXI) ENGINE COMPONENTS CO., LTD.—See Gnutti Carlo S.p.A.; *Int'l*, pg. 3017
GRANT INDUSTRIES INCORPORATED; *U.S. Private*, pg. 1756
HANWHA ADVANCED MATERIALS ALABAMA LLC—See Hanwha Group; *Int'l*, pg. 3264
HANWHA ADVANCED MATERIALS (BEIJING) CO., LTD.—See Hanwha Group; *Int'l*, pg. 3264
HANWHA ADVANCED MATERIALS (SHANGHAI) CO., LTD.—See Hanwha Group; *Int'l*, pg. 3264
HATCH STAMPING COMPANY INC.; *U.S. Private*, pg. 1879
H-ONE CO. LTD. - KAMEYAMA FACTORY—See H-One Co., Ltd.; *Int'l*, pg. 3194
H-ONE CO. LTD. - MAEBASHI FACTORY—See H-One Co., Ltd.; *Int'l*, pg. 3194
H-ONE INDIA PVT. LTD—See H-One Co., Ltd.; *Int'l*, pg. 3194
HUDSON INDUSTRIES, INC.—See Midway Products Group, Inc.; *U.S. Private*, pg. 2719
HWASHIN TECH CO., LTD.; *Int'l*, pg. 3543
JEFFERSON BLANKING INC.—See Shiloh Industries, Inc.; *U.S. Private*, pg. 3636
JSJ CORPORATION; *U.S. Private*, pg. 2241
LAKEPARK INDUSTRIES, INC.—See Midway Products Group, Inc.; *U.S. Private*, pg. 2719
LAKEPARK INDUSTRIES OF INDIANA, INC.—See Midway Products Group, Inc.; *U.S. Private*, pg. 2719
LJUNGHALL S.R.O.—See Gnutti Carlo S.p.A.; *Int'l*, pg. 3017
LOGGHE STAMPING COMPANY; *U.S. Private*, pg. 2481
L&W, INC.—See KPS Capital Partners, LP; *U.S. Private*, pg. 2346
MANUFACTURAS CIFUNSA, S.A. DE C.V.—See Grupo Industrial Saltillo S.A. de C.V.; *Int'l*, pg. 3130
MANUFACTURERS PRODUCTS COMPANY; *U.S. Private*, pg. 2567
MEANS INDUSTRIES, INC.—See AMSTED Industries Incorporated; *U.S. Private*, pg. 268
MELLING PRODUCTS CORPORATION—See Melling Tool Company Inc.; *U.S. Private*, pg. 2662
MERCURY PRODUCTS CORP.; *U.S. Private*, pg. 2671
METALLFABRIKEN LJUNGHALL AB—See Gnutti Carlo S.p.A.; *Int'l*, pg. 3017
METALURGICA NAKAYONE, LTDA.—See Cie Automotive S.A.; *Int'l*, pg. 1604
MOTOR CITY STAMPING, INC.; *U.S. Private*, pg. 2797
MPI INTERNATIONAL, INC.—See MW Universal Inc.; *U.S. Private*, pg. 2822
MTD TECHNOLOGIES INC.; *U.S. Private*, pg. 2809
MT STAHL HANDELSGESELLSCHAFT GMBH—See Financiere SNOP Dunois SA; *Int'l*, pg. 2669
NORTHERN STAMPING INC.; *U.S. Private*, pg. 2954
OAKLEY INDUSTRIES INC.; *U.S. Private*, pg. 2985
THE OAKWOOD GROUP; *U.S. Private*, pg. 4088
P&A INDUSTRIES, INC.—See Midway Products Group, Inc.; *U.S. Private*, pg. 2719
PRECISION RESOURCE INC. - MEXICO DIVISION—See Precision Resource Inc.; *U.S. Private*, pg. 3246
PRIDGEON & CLAY, INC.; *U.S. Private*, pg. 3260
PRODUCTION PRODUCTS, INC.—See Midway Products Group, Inc.; *U.S. Private*, pg. 2719
PROGRESSIVE STAMPING, INC.—See Midway Products Group, Inc.; *U.S. Private*, pg. 2719
P.T. AISIN INDONESIA—See AISIN Corporation; *Int'l*, pg. 253
Q3 STAMPED METAL; *U.S. Private*, pg. 3312

QUALITY METALCRAFT, INC.—See HMK Enterprises, Inc.; *U.S. Private*, pg. 1955
RALCO INDUSTRIES, INC.; *U.S. Private*, pg. 3349
ROL-TECH-FORT LORAMIE—See ROL Manufacturing of America Inc.; *U.S. Private*, pg. 3473
SAE-HWASHIN CO., LTD.—See Hwashin Tech Co., Ltd.; *Int'l*, pg. 3543
SALINE METAL SYSTEMS—See Patriarch Partners, LLC; *U.S. Private*, pg. 3109
SCHULER IBERICA S.A.U.—See ANDRITZ AG; *Int'l*, pg. 456
SELECT ENGINEERED PRODUCTS—See Select International Corp.; *U.S. Private*, pg. 3600
SELECT INDUSTRIES CORP—See Select International Corp.; *U.S. Private*, pg. 3600
SELECT INTERNATIONAL CORP.; *U.S. Private*, pg. 3600
SEOJIN INDUSTRIAL - ANSAN—See KPS Capital Partners, LP; *U.S. Private*, pg. 2347
SFI OF TENNESSEE, L.L.C.; *U.S. Private*, pg. 3621
SHILOH INDUSTRIES INC., DICKSON MANUFACTURING DIVISION—See Shiloh Industries, Inc.; *U.S. Private*, pg. 3636
SPARTANBURG STEEL PRODUCTS, INC.—See Reserve Group Management Company; *U.S. Private*, pg. 3404
SSP INDUSTRIAL GROUP, INC.; *U.S. Private*, pg. 3769
STAMCO INDUSTRIES INC.; *U.S. Private*, pg. 3776
STANCO METAL PRODUCTS, INC.; *U.S. Private*, pg. 3777
STEEL PARTS MANUFACTURING, INC.—See Monomoy Capital Partners LLC; *U.S. Private*, pg. 2772
THE SU-DAN CORPORATION; *U.S. Private*, pg. 4124
TOWER AUTOMOTIVE HOLDING GMBH—See Financiere SNOP Dunois SA; *Int'l*, pg. 2669
TOWER AUTOMOTIVE INDIA PVT. LTD.—See KPS Capital Partners, LP; *U.S. Private*, pg. 2347
TOWER AUTOMOTIVE JAPAN CO., LTD.—See KPS Capital Partners, LP; *U.S. Private*, pg. 2347
TOWER AUTOMOTIVE MELFI, S.R.L.—See Financiere SNOP Dunois SA; *Int'l*, pg. 2669
TOWER AUTOMOTIVE POLSKA SP. ZO.O.—See Financiere SNOP Dunois SA; *Int'l*, pg. 2669
TOWER AUTOMOTIVE PRESSWERK ZWICKAU GMBH—See Financiere SNOP Dunois SA; *Int'l*, pg. 2669
TOWER AUTOMOTIVE S.A.—See Financiere SNOP Dunois SA; *Int'l*, pg. 2669
TOWER AUTOMOTIVE SPAIN SL—See Financiere SNOP Dunois SA; *Int'l*, pg. 2669
TOWER AUTOMOTIVE S.R.L.—See Financiere SNOP Dunois SA; *Int'l*, pg. 2669
TOWER AUTOMOTIVE SUD S.R.L.—See Financiere SNOP Dunois SA; *Int'l*, pg. 2669
TOWER AUTOMOTIVE UMFORMTECHNICK GMBH—See Financiere SNOP Dunois SA; *Int'l*, pg. 2669
TOWER GOLDEN RING - CHANGCHUN—See KPS Capital Partners, LP; *U.S. Private*, pg. 2347
TOWER INTERNATIONAL, INC.—See KPS Capital Partners, LP; *U.S. Private*, pg. 2346
TRANS-MATIC MFG.; *U.S. Private*, pg. 4206
TWB COMPANY, LLC—See Worthington Industries, Inc.; *U.S. Public*, pg. 2382
VENTRA ANGOLA, LLC—See Flex-N-Gate Corporation; *U.S. Private*, pg. 1543
VENTRA IONIA MAIN, LLC—See Flex-N-Gate Corporation; *U.S. Private*, pg. 1543
WESTFALIA METAL COMPONENTS SHANGHAI CO. LTD.—See Heitkamp & Thumann KG; *Int'l*, pg. 3326
WESTFALIA METALLSCHLAUCHTECHNIK GMBH & CO. KG—See Heitkamp & Thumann KG; *Int'l*, pg. 3327
WESTFALIA PRESSTECHNIK GMBH & CO. KG—See Heitkamp & Thumann KG; *Int'l*, pg. 3327
WICO METAL PRODUCTS CO., INC.; *U.S. Private*, pg. 4516
WITMER PUBLIC SAFETY GROUP, INC.; *U.S. Private*, pg. 4551
WRENA LLC—See Angstrom Usa, Llc.; *U.S. Private*, pg. 283
YAREMA DIE & ENGINEERING CO.; *U.S. Private*, pg. 4586
YUTAKA GIKEN CO., LTD.—See Honda Motor Co., Ltd.; *Int'l*, pg. 3465

336390 — OTHER MOTOR VEHICLE PARTS MANUFACTURING

3G YATIRIM VE GAYRIMENKUL TICARET A.S.—See Autoliv, Inc.; *Int'l*, pg. 728
4 WAY SUSPENSION PRODUCTS PTY. LTD.—See Eastern Polymer Group Public Company Limited; *Int'l*, pg. 2273
AAA SALES & ENGINEERING, INC. - ANGOLA—See Industrial Opportunity Partners, LLC; *U.S. Private*, pg. 2067
AADI AUSTRALIA PTY LTD—See Bapcor Limited; *Int'l*, pg. 857
AAM DO BRASIL LTDA.—See American Axle & Manufacturing Holdings, Inc.; *U.S. Public*, pg. 96
AAPICO AMATA CO., LTD.—See AAPICO Hitech plc; *Int'l*, pg. 37
AAPICO ELECTRONICS COMPANY LIMITED—See AAPICO Hitech plc; *Int'l*, pg. 37
AAPICO ENGINEERING COMPANY LIMITED—See AAPICO Hitech plc; *Int'l*, pg. 37

336390 — OTHER MOTOR VEHICLE... CORPORATE AFFILIATIONS

AAPICO HITECH PLC - PLUAKDAENG FACTORY—See AAPICO Hitech plc; *Int'l*, pg. 37
AAPICO HITECH PLC; *Int'l*, pg. 36
AAPICO INVESTMENT PTE. LTD.—See AAPICO Hitech plc; *Int'l*, pg. 37
AAPICO ITS COMPANY LIMITED—See AAPICO Hitech plc; *Int'l*, pg. 37
AAPICO LEMTECH (THAILAND) COMPANY LIMITED—See AAPICO Hitech plc; *Int'l*, pg. 37
AAPICO MITSUIKE (THAILAND) COMPANY LIMITED—See AAPICO Hitech plc; *Int'l*, pg. 37
AAPICO PRECISION COMPANY LIMITED—See AAPICO Hitech plc; *Int'l*, pg. 37
AAPICO SHANGHAI CO., LTD.—See AAPICO Hitech plc; *Int'l*, pg. 37
AAPICO STRUCTURAL PRODUCTS CO., LTD.—See AAPICO Hitech plc; *Int'l*, pg. 37
AAPICO TRAINING CENTER COMPANY LIMITED—See AAPICO Hitech plc; *Int'l*, pg. 37
AAPICO VENTURE COMPANY LIMITED—See AAPICO Hitech plc; *Int'l*, pg. 37
THE ACCESS WORKS, INC.—See Fleet Engineers, Inc.; *U.S. Private*, pg. 1541
ACCURIDE CANADA, INC.—See Crestview Partners, L.P.; *U.S. Private*, pg. 1097
ACCURIDE DE MEXICO, S.A. DE C.V.—See Crestview Partners, L.P.; *U.S. Private*, pg. 1098
ACCURIDE ERIE, L.P.—See Crestview Partners, L.P.; *U.S. Private*, pg. 1097
ACCURIDE HENDERSON LIMITED LIABILITY COMPANY—See Crestview Partners, L.P.; *U.S. Private*, pg. 1097
ACTIA GROUP SA - ACTIA TUNISIE DIVISION—See Actia Group SA; *Int'l*, pg. 118
ACTIA GROUP SA - CIPI ACTIA DIVISION—See Actia Group SA; *Int'l*, pg. 118
ACTIA IME GMBH—See Actia Group SA; *Int'l*, pg. 118
ACTIA INDIA PVT LTD—See Actia Group SA; *Int'l*, pg. 118
ACTIA ITALIA SRL—See Actia Group SA; *Int'l*, pg. 118
ACTIA NORDIC AB—See Actia Group SA; *Int'l*, pg. 118
ACTIA (UK) LIMITED—See Actia Group SA; *Int'l*, pg. 118
ACTIVE EXHAUST CORP.; *Int'l*, pg. 120
ACTUATOR COMPONENTS GMBH & CO. KG—See Eagle Industry Co., Ltd.; *Int'l*, pg. 2265
ADELL CORPORATION—See Kinderhook Industries, LLC; *U.S. Private*, pg. 2306
AD PLASTIK TISZA KFT.—See AD Plastik d.d.; *Int'l*, pg. 122
ADRAL, MATRICERIA Y PUESTA A PUNTO, S.L.—See Acek Desarrollo y Gestion Industrial SL; *Int'l*, pg. 96
ADVAL TECH DO BRASIL INDUSTRIA DE AUTOPECAS LTDA.—See Adval Tech Holding AG; *Int'l*, pg. 155
ADVAL TECH (HUNGARY) PLANT 2 KFT.—See Adval Tech Holding AG; *Int'l*, pg. 155
ADVAL TECH (SWITZERLAND) AG—See Adval Tech Holding AG; *Int'l*, pg. 155
ADVAL TECH US INC.—See Adval Tech Holding AG; *Int'l*, pg. 155
ADVANCED COMFORT SYSTEMS FRANCE, S.A.S.—See Cie Automotive S.A.; *Int'l*, pg. 1603
ADVANCED COMFORT SYSTEMS IBERICA, S.L.U.—See Cie Automotive S.A.; *Int'l*, pg. 1603
ADVANCED COMFORT SYSTEMS ROMANIA, S.R.L.—See Cie Automotive S.A.; *Int'l*, pg. 1603
ADVANCED COMFORT SYSTEMS SHANGHAI CO. LTD.—See Cie Automotive S.A.; *Int'l*, pg. 1604
ADVANCED FILTRATION SYSTEMS, INC.—See Caterpillar, Inc.; *U.S. Public*, pg. 449
ADVANCED FILTRATION SYSTEMS, INC.—See Donaldson Company, Inc.; *U.S. Public*, pg. 675
AEP NVH OPCO, LLC—See Angeles Equity Partners, LLC; *U.S. Private*, pg. 281
AER MANUFACTURING, INC.; *U.S. Private*, pg. 117
AEROKLAS ASIA PACIFIC GROUP PTY. LTD.—See Eastern Polymer Group Public Company Limited; *Int'l*, pg. 2273
AEROKLAS (SHANGHAI) CO., LTD.—See Eastern Polymer Group Public Company Limited; *Int'l*, pg. 2273
AEROMOTIVE, INC.—See The Roadster Shop; *U.S. Private*, pg. 4111
A ERP COMPANY LIMITED—See AAPICO Hitech plc; *Int'l*, pg. 37
AEVA, INC.—See Aeva Technologies, Inc.; *U.S. Public*, pg. 53
AEVA TECHNOLOGIES, INC.; *U.S. Public*, pg. 53
AGC FLAT GLASS (THAILAND) PUBLIC CO., LTD. - CHON BURI FACTORY—See AGC Inc.; *Int'l*, pg. 202
AGRIAUTO INDUSTRIES LTD—See House of Habib; *Int'l*, pg. 3491
AGRIGOLD—See Groupe Limagrain Holding SA; *Int'l*, pg. 3107
AGS AUTOMOTIVE SYSTEMS - CAMBRIDGE PLANT—See AGS Automotive Systems; *Int'l*, pg. 221
AGS AUTOMOTIVE SYSTEMS - OSHAWA PLANT—See AGS Automotive Systems; *Int'l*, pg. 221
AGS AUTOMOTIVE SYSTEMS - STERLING HEIGHTS PLANT—See AGS Automotive Systems; *Int'l*, pg. 221
AGS AUTOMOTIVE SYSTEMS - WINDSOR PLANT—See AGS Automotive Systems; *Int'l*, pg. 221

AIA CO., LTD. - AIA II PLANT—See Ecoplastic Corporation; *Int'l*, pg. 2299
AICHI FORGE USA, INC.—See Aichi Steel Corporation; *Int'l*, pg. 230
AICHI GIKEN CO., LTD.—See AISIN Corporation; *Int'l*, pg. 252
AIKITEC CO., LTD.—See Honda Motor Co., Ltd.; *Int'l*, pg. 3459
AIRBORNE ENGINES LTD.—See M International Inc.; *U.S. Private*, pg. 2523
AISAN AUTOPARTES MEXICO, S.A. DE C.V.—See Aisan Industry Co., Ltd.; *Int'l*, pg. 250
AISAN COMPUTER SERVICES CORP.—See Aisan Industry Co., Ltd.; *Int'l*, pg. 250
AISAN (FHOSHAN) AUTO PARTS CO., LTD—See Aisan Industry Co., Ltd.; *Int'l*, pg. 250
AISAN (FOSHAN) AUTO PARTS CO., LTD.—See Aisan Industry Co., Ltd.; *Int'l*, pg. 250
AISAN INDUSTRY CO., LTD.; *Int'l*, pg. 250
AISAN INDUSTRY CO., LTD. - TOYOTA PLANT—See Aisan Industry Co., Ltd.; *Int'l*, pg. 250
AISAN INDUSTRY INDIA PVT. LTD.—See Aisan Industry Co., Ltd.; *Int'l*, pg. 250
AISAN INDUSTRY KENTUCKY, LLC—See Aisan Industry Co., Ltd.; *Int'l*, pg. 250
AISAN INDUSTRY LOUNY S.R.O.—See Aisan Industry Co., Ltd.; *Int'l*, pg. 250
AISAN KUMAMOTO CO., LTD.—See Aisan Industry Co., Ltd.; *Int'l*, pg. 250
AISAN (TIANJIN) AUTO PARTS CO., LTD—See Aisan Industry Co., Ltd.; *Int'l*, pg. 250
AISIN AI (THAILAND) CO., LTD.—See AISIN Corporation; *Int'l*, pg. 251
AISIN ASIA PACIFIC CO., LTD—See AISIN Corporation; *Int'l*, pg. 251
AISIN CANADA, INC—See AISIN Corporation; *Int'l*, pg. 251
AISIN CHEMICAL INDIANA, LLC—See AISIN Corporation; *Int'l*, pg. 252
AISIN CHEMICAL (THAILAND) CO., LTD.—See AISIN Corporation; *Int'l*, pg. 251
AISIN CORPORATION; *Int'l*, pg. 251
AISIN EUROPE MANUFACTURING CZECH S. R. O.—See AISIN Corporation; *Int'l*, pg. 251
AISIN KYUSHU CO., LTD.—See AISIN Corporation; *Int'l*, pg. 252
AISIN METALTECH CO., LTD.—See AISIN Corporation; *Int'l*, pg. 252
AISIN MFG. AGUASCALIENTES, S. A. DE C.V.—See AISIN Corporation; *Int'l*, pg. 252
AISIN OTOMOTIV PARCALARI SANAYI VE TICARET A. S.—See AISIN Corporation; *Int'l*, pg. 252
AISIN SEIKI CO., LTD. - ANJO PLANT—See AISIN Corporation; *Int'l*, pg. 253
AISIN SEIKI CO., LTD. - KINUURA PLANT—See AISIN Corporation; *Int'l*, pg. 253
AISIN SEIKI CO., LTD. - SHINKAWA PLANT—See AISIN Corporation; *Int'l*, pg. 253
AISIN SEIKI CO., LTD. - SHINTOYO PLANT—See AISIN Corporation; *Int'l*, pg. 253
AISIN SIN'EI CO., LTD.—See AISIN Corporation; *Int'l*, pg. 252
AISIN TOHOKU CO., LTD.—See AISIN Corporation; *Int'l*, pg. 253
AISIN USA MANUFACTURING INC.—See AISIN Corporation; *Int'l*, pg. 252
AJIN USA LLC—See DAEWOO ELECTRONIC COMPONENTS Co., Ltd.; *Int'l*, pg. 1910
AKASOL AG—See BorgWarner Inc.; *U.S. Public*, pg. 369
AKKA CZECH REPUBLIC S.R.O.—See Adecco Group AG; *Int'l*, pg. 139
AK SPECIALTY VEHICLES B.V.—See Oshkosh Corporation; *U.S. Public*, pg. 1620
AKWEL AUTOMOTIVE PUNE INDIA PRIVATE LIMITED—See AKWEL; *Int'l*, pg. 268
AKWEL BURSA TURKEY OTOMOTIVE A.S—See AKWEL; *Int'l*, pg. 268
AKWEL CADILLAC USA INC.—See AKWEL; *Int'l*, pg. 268
AKWEL CHONGQING AUTO PARTS CO, LTD—See AKWEL; *Int'l*, pg. 268
AKWEL CORDOBA ARGENTINA SA—See AKWEL; *Int'l*, pg. 268
AKWEL EL JADIDA MOROCCO SARL—See AKWEL; *Int'l*, pg. 268
AKWEL GERMANY SERVICES GMBH—See AKWEL; *Int'l*, pg. 268
AKWEL JAPAN SERVICES CO.—See AKWEL; *Int'l*, pg. 268
AKWEL JUNDIAI BRAZIL LTDA.—See AKWEL; *Int'l*, pg. 268
AKWEL MATEUR TUNISIA SARL—See AKWEL; *Int'l*, pg. 268
AKWEL NINGBO CHINA CO, LTD—See AKWEL; *Int'l*, pg. 268
AKWEL ORIZABA MEXICO SA DE C.V.—See AKWEL; *Int'l*, pg. 268
AKWEL PAREDES DE COURA (PORTUGAL) UNIPESSOAL LDA—See AKWEL; *Int'l*, pg. 268
AKWEL RUDNIK CZECH REPUBLIC A.S—See AKWEL; *Int'l*, pg. 268

AKWEL SANT JUST SPAIN S.L.—See AKWEL; *Int'l*, pg. 268
AKWEL SWEDEN AB—See AKWEL; *Int'l*, pg. 268
AKWEL TIMISOARA ROMANIA SRL—See AKWEL; *Int'l*, pg. 268
AKWEL TONDELA (PORTUGAL), LDA—See AKWEL; *Int'l*, pg. 268
AKWEL USA INC.—See AKWEL; *Int'l*, pg. 268
AKWEL VANNES FRANCE S.A.S—See AKWEL; *Int'l*, pg. 268
AKWEL VIGO SPAIN S.L—See AKWEL; *Int'l*, pg. 268
ALBAR INDUSTRIES, INC.; *U.S. Private*, pg. 152
ALBION AUTOMOTIVE LIMITED—See American Axle & Manufacturing Holdings, Inc.; *U.S. Public*, pg. 96
ALBONAIR GMBH—See Hinduja Group Ltd.; *Int'l*, pg. 3398
ALBONAIR (INDIA) PRIVATE LIMITED—See Hinduja Group Ltd.; *Int'l*, pg. 3398
ALCASTING LEGUTIANO, S.L.U.—See Cie Automotive S.A.; *Int'l*, pg. 1604
ALLIANCE COACH INC.—See Lazydays Holdings, Inc.; *U.S. Public*, pg. 1294
ALLIGATOR DIESEL PERFORMANCE LLC; *U.S. Private*, pg. 192
ALLOMATIC PRODUCTS COMPANY—See Sun Capital Partners, Inc.; *U.S. Private*, pg. 3860
ALLSAFE JAPAN LTD.—See Ashimori Industry Co., Ltd.; *Int'l*, pg. 607
ALLSAFE JAPAN LTD. - TOHOKU PLANT—See Ashimori Industry Co., Ltd.; *Int'l*, pg. 607
ALPHA CORPORATION - GUMMA PLANT—See ALPHA Corporation; *Int'l*, pg. 367
ALPHA TECHNOLOGY CORPORATION—See ALPHA Corporation; *Int'l*, pg. 367
ALTUR S.A.; *Int'l*, pg. 399
ALURECY, S.A.U.—See Cie Automotive S.A.; *Int'l*, pg. 1604
AMCOR INDUSTRIES, INC.—See Clearlake Capital Group, L.P.; *U.S. Private*, pg. 937
AMERICAN AXLE & MANUFACTURING, INC.—See American Axle & Manufacturing Holdings, Inc.; *U.S. Public*, pg. 96
AMERICAN CABLE COMPANY INC.; *U.S. Private*, pg. 226
AMERICAN CRANE & TRACTOR PARTS INCORPORATED—See GB Ricambi S.p.A.; *Int'l*, pg. 2893
AMERICAN INDUSTRIAL MANUFACTURING SERVICES, INC.—See Denso Corporation; *Int'l*, pg. 2028
AMOTECH CO., LTD. - MOTOR DIVISION—See Amotech Co Ltd; *Int'l*, pg. 431
AMTEK AUTO LIMITED; *Int'l*, pg. 441
AMTEK DEUTSCHLAND GMBH—See Amtek Auto Limited; *Int'l*, pg. 441
AMTEK GERMANY HOLDING GMBH & CO. KG—See Amtek Auto Limited; *Int'l*, pg. 441
AMTEK INVESTMENTS U.K. LIMITED—See Amtek Auto Limited; *Int'l*, pg. 441
AMTEK TRANSPORTATION SYSTEMS LIMITED—See Amtek Auto Limited; *Int'l*, pg. 441
ANGELL-DEMMEL EUROPE GMBH—See Demmel AG; *Int'l*, pg. 2025
ANGELL-DEMMEL NORTH AMERICA CORPORATION—See American Trim LLC; *U.S. Private*, pg. 257
ANGELL-DEMMEL NORTH AMERICA—See American Trim LLC; *U.S. Private*, pg. 257
ANSA MOTORS GUYANA INC.—See ANSA McAL Limited; *Int'l*, pg. 477
ANTAYA TECHNOLOGIES CORPORATION (ZHUHAI) LTD.—See Aptiv PLC; *Int'l*, pg. 524
ANTONOV AUTOMOTIVE TECHNOLOGIES B.V.—See Antonov plc; *Int'l*, pg. 485
ANTONOV AUTOMOTIVE TECHNOLOGIES LTD—See Antonov plc; *Int'l*, pg. 485
ANTONOV PLC; *Int'l*, pg. 485
ANVL, INC.—See Vista Equity Partners, LLC; *U.S. Private*, pg. 4395
AP EMISSIONS TECHNOLOGIES, LLC; *U.S. Private*, pg. 290
APICS CO., LTD.—See Futaba Industrial Co., Ltd.; *Int'l*, pg. 2851
APINES INC.—See Denso Corporation; *Int'l*, pg. 2028
APM AUTO COMPONENTS (VIETNAM) CO. LTD.—See APM Automotive Holdings Berhad; *Int'l*, pg. 516
APM AUTO PARTS MARKETING (MALAYSIA) SDN. BHD.—See APM Automotive Holdings Berhad; *Int'l*, pg. 516
APM AUTO SAFETY SYSTEMS SDN. BHD.—See APM Automotive Holdings Berhad; *Int'l*, pg. 516
APM-COACHAIR SDN. BHD.—See APM Automotive Holdings Berhad; *Int'l*, pg. 516
APM SEATINGS SDN. BHD.—See APM Automotive Holdings Berhad; *Int'l*, pg. 516
APM SHOCK ABSORBERS SDN. BHD.—See APM Automotive Holdings Berhad; *Int'l*, pg. 516
APM SPRINGS SDN. BHD.—See APM Automotive Holdings Berhad; *Int'l*, pg. 516
AP RACING LTD.—See Brembo S.p.A.; *Int'l*, pg. 1144
APTIV SAFETY & MOBILITY SERVICES SINGAPORE PTE. LTD—See Aptiv PLC; *Int'l*, pg. 524
A RAYMOND AUTOMOTIVE FASTENERS (ZHENJIANG)

N.A.I.C.S. INDEX
336390 — OTHER MOTOR VEHICLE...

CO., LTD.—See A. Raymond & Cie SCS; *Int'l*, pg. 21
A RAYMOND BAGLANTI ELEMANLARI LTD. STI—See A. Raymond & Cie SCS; *Int'l*, pg. 21
A RAYMOND BRASIL LTDA—See A. Raymond & Cie SCS; *Int'l*, pg. 22
A RAYMOND FASTENERS INDIA PRIVATE LIMITED—See A. Raymond & Cie SCS; *Int'l*, pg. 22
A. RAYMOND GMBH & CO. KG—See A. Raymond & Cie SCS; *Int'l*, pg. 22
A. RAYMOND JABLONEC S.R.O.—See A. Raymond & Cie SCS; *Int'l*, pg. 22
A. RAYMOND JAPAN CO., LTD.—See A. Raymond & Cie SCS; *Int'l*, pg. 21
A. RAYMOND - PACIFIC SIGHT LTD—See A. Raymond & Cie SCS; *Int'l*, pg. 21
A. RAYMOND RUS LLC—See A. Raymond & Cie SCS; *Int'l*, pg. 22
A. RAYMOND SINGAPORE PTE. LTD.—See A. Raymond & Cie SCS; *Int'l*, pg. 22
A.RAYMOND SLOVAKIA, S.R.O.—See A. Raymond & Cie SCS; *Int'l*, pg. 22
A RAYMOND TECNIACERO SAU—See A. Raymond & Cie SCS; *Int'l*, pg. 21
A. RAYMOND TINNERMAN AUTOMOTIVE INC.—See A. Raymond & Cie SCS; *Int'l*, pg. 22
A. RAYMOND TINNERMAN AUTOMOTIVE MEXICO S. DE R.L. DE C.V.—See A. Raymond & Cie SCS; *Int'l*, pg. 22
ARAYMOND TINNERMAN INDUSTRIAL INC.—See A. Raymond & Cie SCS; *Int'l*, pg. 22
A.RAYMOND TINNERMAN MANUFACTURING HAMILTON, INC.—See A. Raymond & Cie SCS; *Int'l*, pg. 22
ARB CORPORATION LIMITED; *Int'l*, pg. 536
A.R.E. ACCESSORIES, LLC; *U.S. Private*, pg. 27
ARLINGTON RACK & PACKAGING CO.; *U.S. Private*, pg. 329
ARMSTRONG HYDRAULICS SOUTH AFRICA (PTY.) LTD.—See Apollo Global Management, Inc.; *U.S. Public*, pg. 160
ARVIN EUROPEAN HOLDINGS (UK) LIMITED—See Cummins Inc.; *U.S. Public*, pg. 608
ARVINMERITOR CV AFTERMARKET GMBH—See Cummins Inc.; *U.S. Public*, pg. 608
ARVINMERITOR CVS (SHANGHAI) CO., LTD.—See Cummins Inc.; *U.S. Public*, pg. 608
ARVINMERITOR LIGHT VEHICLE AFTERMARKET GROUP—See Cummins Inc.; *U.S. Public*, pg. 608
ARVINMERITOR LIGHT VEHICLE SYSTEMS-FRANCE—See Cummins Inc.; *U.S. Public*, pg. 608
ARVINMERITOR SWEDEN AB—See Cummins Inc.; *U.S. Public*, pg. 608
ASAHI MANUFACTURING CO., LTD.—See Denso Corporation; *Int'l*, pg. 2028
ASAMA COLDWATER MFG.—See Honda Motor Co., Ltd.; *Int'l*, pg. 3460
ASHIMORI ENGINEERING CO., LTD.—See Ashimori Industry Co., Ltd.; *Int'l*, pg. 607
ASHIMORI INDUSTRY CO., LTD. - FUKUI PLANT—See Ashimori Industry Co., Ltd.; *Int'l*, pg. 607
ASHIMORI INDUSTRY CO., LTD. - HAMAMATSU PLANT—See Ashimori Industry Co., Ltd.; *Int'l*, pg. 607
ASHIMORI INDUSTRY CO., LTD. - SASAYAMA PLANT—See Ashimori Industry Co., Ltd.; *Int'l*, pg. 607
ASHIMORI INDUSTRY CO., LTD.; *Int'l*, pg. 607
ASIA KELMET CO., LTD.—See Daido Metal Corporation; *Int'l*, pg. 1921
ASIMCO TECHNOLOGIES LIMITED—See Bain Capital, LP; *U.S. Private*, pg. 428
ASIMCO TIANWEI FUEL INJECTION EQUIPMENT STOCK CO., LTD.—See Bain Capital, LP; *U.S. Private*, pg. 428
ASKOLL EVA SPA; *Int'l*, pg. 625
ASMO CO., LTD—See Denso Corporation; *Int'l*, pg. 2028
ASMO CZECH S.R.O.—See Denso Corporation; *Int'l*, pg. 2028
ASMO GREENVILLE OF NORTH CAROLINA, INC.—See Denso Corporation; *Int'l*, pg. 2028
AS NORMA—See Autoliv, Inc.; *Int'l*, pg. 728
ASSEMBLIES ON TIME, INC.—See Crestview Partners, L.P.; *U.S. Private*, pg. 1098
ATLAS ENGINEERING LIMITED—See Atlas Group of Companies; *Int'l*, pg. 685
ATTC MANUFACTURING, INC.—See AISIN Corporation; *Int'l*, pg. 253
ATUL GREEN AUTOMOTIVE PRIVATE LIMITED—See Atul Auto Ltd.; *Int'l*, pg. 697
AUNDE CORPORATION—See AUNDE Achter & Ebels GmbH; *Int'l*, pg. 705
AUNDE KULMBACH GMBH—See AUNDE Achter & Ebels GmbH; *Int'l*, pg. 705
AUNDE S.A.—See AUNDE Achter & Ebels GmbH; *Int'l*, pg. 705
AUSTEM CO., LTD.; *Int'l*, pg. 716
AUSTIN TRI-HAWK AUTOMOTIVE, INC.—See G-TEKT Corporation; *Int'l*, pg. 2863
AUTINS AB—See Autins Group plc; *Int'l*, pg. 724
AUTINS GMBH—See Autins Group plc; *Int'l*, pg. 724
AUTINS LIMITED—See Autins Group plc; *Int'l*, pg. 724
AUTINS TECHNICAL CENTRE LIMITED—See Autins Group plc; *Int'l*, pg. 724

AUTOCAM CORPORATION—See NN, Inc.; *U.S. Public*, pg. 1530
AUTOCOM COMPONENTES AUTOMOTIVOS DO BRASIL LTDA.—See Cie Automotive S.A.; *Int'l*, pg. 1604
AUTOFORJAS, LTDA.—See Cie Automotive S.A.; *Int'l*, pg. 1604
AUTOLINE DESIGN SOFTWARE LIMITED—See Autoline Industries Limited; *Int'l*, pg. 727
AUTOLINE INDUSTRIES LIMITED - BHOSARI UNIT III—See Autoline Industries Limited; *Int'l*, pg. 728
AUTOLINE INDUSTRIES LIMITED - BHOSARI UNIT II—See Autoline Industries Limited; *Int'l*, pg. 727
AUTOLINE INDUSTRIES LIMITED - BHOSARI UNIT I—See Autoline Industries Limited; *Int'l*, pg. 727
AUTOLINE INDUSTRIES LIMITED - CHAKAN UNIT III—See Autoline Industries Limited; *Int'l*, pg. 728
AUTOLINE INDUSTRIES LIMITED - CHAKAN UNIT I—See Autoline Industries Limited; *Int'l*, pg. 728
AUTOLINE INDUSTRIES LIMITED; *Int'l*, pg. 727
AUTOLIV AB—See Autoliv, Inc.; *Int'l*, pg. 728
AUTOLIV ASP B.V.—See Autoliv, Inc.; *Int'l*, pg. 728
AUTOLIV CANADA, INC.—See Autoliv, Inc.; *Int'l*, pg. 729
AUTOLIV CORPORATION—See Autoliv, Inc.; *Int'l*, pg. 728
AUTOLIV HIROTAKO SAFETY SDN. BHD.—See Autoliv, Inc.; *Int'l*, pg. 729
AUTOLIV HIROTAKO SRS SDN. BHD.—See Autoliv, Inc.; *Int'l*, pg. 729
AUTOLIV INITIATORS—See Autoliv, Inc.; *Int'l*, pg. 729
AUTOLIV MEKAN AB—See Autoliv, Inc.; *Int'l*, pg. 728
AUTOLIV NORTH AMERICA, AMERICAN TECHNICAL CENTER—See Autoliv, Inc.; *Int'l*, pg. 729
AUTOLIV NORTH AMERICA STEERING WHEEL FACILITY—See Autoliv, Inc.; *Int'l*, pg. 729
AUTOLIV SAFETY TECHNOLOGY—See Autoliv, Inc.; *Int'l*, pg. 729
AUTOMAXI INTERNATIONAL—See Accent Equity Partners AB; *Int'l*, pg. 81
AUTOMETAL SBC INJECAO E PINTURA DE PLASTICOS LTDA.—See Cie Automotive S.A.; *Int'l*, pg. 1604
AUTOMOTIVE AXLES LIMITED—See Cummins Inc.; *U.S. Public*, pg. 608
AUTOMOTIVE COMPONENTS EUROPE S.A.—See Grupo Industrial Saltillo S.A. de C.V.; *Int'l*, pg. 3130
AUTOMOTIVE SOLUTIONS GROUP LIMITED—See AMA Group Limited; *Int'l*, pg. 403
AUTONEUM ERKURT OTOMOTIV AS—See Autoneum Holding Ltd.; *Int'l*, pg. 731
AUTONEUM INDIA PVT. LTD.—See Autoneum Holding Ltd.; *Int'l*, pg. 731
AUTONEUM KOREA LTD.—See Autoneum Holding Ltd.; *Int'l*, pg. 731
AUTONEUM MEXICO OPERATIONS, S.A. DE C.V.—See Autoneum Holding Ltd.; *Int'l*, pg. 731
AUTONEUM MEXICO, S. DE R.L. DE C.V.—See Autoneum Holding Ltd.; *Int'l*, pg. 731
AUTONEUM NITTOKU (GUANGZHOU) SOUND-PROOF CO. LTD.—See Autoneum Holding Ltd.; *Int'l*, pg. 731
AUTONEUM NITTOKU SOUND PROOF PRODUCTS INDIA PVT. LTD.—See Autoneum Holding Ltd.; *Int'l*, pg. 731
AUTONEUM NORTH AMERICA, INC. - AIKEN—See Autoneum Holding Ltd.; *Int'l*, pg. 731
AUTONEUM NORTH AMERICA, INC. - BLOOMSBURG—See Autoneum Holding Ltd.; *Int'l*, pg. 731
AUTONEUM NORTH AMERICA, INC.—See Autoneum Holding Ltd.; *Int'l*, pg. 731
AUTONEUM RUS LLC—See Autoneum Holding Ltd.; *Int'l*, pg. 731
AUTONEUM (SHANGHAI) MANAGEMENT CO. LTD.—See Autoneum Holding Ltd.; *Int'l*, pg. 731
AUTONEUM TECHNOLOGIES AG—See Autoneum Holding Ltd.; *Int'l*, pg. 731
AUTO PARTS ALLIANCE (CHINA) LTD.—See G-TEKT Corporation; *Int'l*, pg. 2863
AUTOSTRADA EKSPLOATACJA SA—See Groupe Egis S.A.; *Int'l*, pg. 3102
AUTOV CORPORATION BERHAD—See Globaltec Formation Berhad; *Int'l*, pg. 3004
AUTOVENTURE CORPORATION SDN. BHD.—See Globaltec Formation Berhad; *Int'l*, pg. 3004
AVA CEE SP. Z O.O.—See Enterex International Limited; *Int'l*, pg. 2451
AVK TOOLING A/S—See AVK Holding A/S; *Int'l*, pg. 747
AVM, INC.—See Cummins Inc.; *U.S. Public*, pg. 608
AW EUROPE S.A.—See AISIN Corporation; *Int'l*, pg. 252
AW-I S CO., LTD.—See AISIN Corporation; *Int'l*, pg. 252
AXIS-TEC PTE. LTD.—See Ellipsiz Ltd.; *Int'l*, pg. 2366
AY MANUFACTURING LTD.—See Honda Motor Co., Ltd.; *Int'l*, pg. 3464
AZIA AVTO JSC; *Int'l*, pg. 778
BAD DAWG ACCESSORIES, LLC—See The Toro Company; *U.S. Public*, pg. 2134
BAE SYSTEMS TVS INC.—See BAE Systems plc; *Int'l*, pg. 797
BAIER & KOPPEL GMBH & CO. KG—See The Timken Company; *U.S. Public*, pg. 2132
BAKER TECHNOLOGY LIMITED; *Int'l*, pg. 805

BALDWIN FILTERS, INC.—See Parker Hannifin Corporation; *U.S. Public*, pg. 1640
BALUCHISTAN WHEELS LIMITED; *Int'l*, pg. 812
BARKER MANUFACTURING CO; *U.S. Private*, pg. 475
BAUMANN SPRINGS LEON S. DE R.L. DEC. V.—See Baumann Federn AG; *Int'l*, pg. 895
BAUMOT GROUP AG; *Int'l*, pg. 895
BBB INDUSTRIES LLC—See Clearlake Capital Group, L.P.; *U.S. Private*, pg. 933
BBS OF AMERICA, INC.—See BBS Kraftfahrzeugtechnik AG; *Int'l*, pg. 921
BD DIESEL PERFORMANCE; *Int'l*, pg. 929
BEIJING HWASHIN AUTOMOBILE PARTS CO., LTD.—See Hwashin Co., Ltd.; *Int'l*, pg. 3543
BEIJING HYUNDAI MOBIS AUTOMOTIVE PARTS CO., LTD.—See Hyundai MOBIS Co., Ltd.; *Int'l*, pg. 3558
BEIJING WANYUAN-HENNIGES SEALING SYSTEMS CO., LTD—See China Energine International (Holdings) Limited; *Int'l*, pg. 1500
BEIJING WKW AUTOMOTIVE PARTS CO., LTD.; *Int'l*, pg. 960
BEKA-LUBE GMBH—See The Timken Company; *U.S. Public*, pg. 2132
BEKA-LUBE N.V.—See The Timken Company; *U.S. Public*, pg. 2132
BENDA SUNKWANG IND. CO., LTD.; *Int'l*, pg. 970
BERGER KAROSSERIE- UND FAHRZEUGBAU GMBH; *Int'l*, pg. 979
BERU EICHENAUER GMBH—See BorgWarner Inc.; *U.S. Public*, pg. 369
BESTOP, INC.—See Kinderhook Industries, LLC; *U.S. Private*, pg. 2306
BETRACO STAHL VERTRIEBS GMBH—See Georgsmarienhutte Holding GmbH; *Int'l*, pg. 2940
BF1SYSTEMS LTD.—See BF1 Motorsport Holdings Ltd.; *Int'l*, pg. 1006
BGE ELEKTROTECHNIK GMBH; *Int'l*, pg. 1007
BHATIA BROTHERS GROUP - BHATIA BROTHERS-AUTOMOTIVE DIVISION—See Bhatia Brothers Group; *Int'l*, pg. 1013
BLUDOT INC.—See 3 Rivers Capital, LLC; *U.S. Private*, pg. 7
BMW FAHRZEUGTECHNIK GMBH—See Bayerische Motoren Werke Aktiengesellschaft; *Int'l*, pg. 911
BON-AIRE INDUSTRIES INC.; *U.S. Private*, pg. 613
BORBET ALABAMA INC.—See BORBET GmbH; *Int'l*, pg. 1112
BORBET AUSTRIA GMBH—See BORBET GmbH; *Int'l*, pg. 1112
BORBET GMBH; *Int'l*, pg. 1112
BORG AUTOMOTIVE A/S—See Aktieselskabet Schouw & Co.; *Int'l*, pg. 265
BORG AUTOMOTIVE REMAN SPAIN S.L.U.—See Aktieselskabet Schouw & Co.; *Int'l*, pg. 265
BORG AUTOMOTIVE SPAIN S.L.U.—See Aktieselskabet Schouw & Co.; *Int'l*, pg. 265
BORG AUTOMOTIVE SP.Z.O.O—See Aktieselskabet Schouw & Co.; *Int'l*, pg. 265
BORG AUTOMOTIVE UK LTD.—See Aktieselskabet Schouw & Co.; *Int'l*, pg. 265
BORGWARNER ARDEN LLC—See BorgWarner Inc.; *U.S. Public*, pg. 369
BORGWARNER AUTOMOTIVE COMPONENTS (NINGBO) CO., LTD.—See BorgWarner Inc.; *U.S. Public*, pg. 369
BORGWARNER BERU SYSTEMS GMBH—See BorgWarner Inc.; *U.S. Public*, pg. 369
BORGWARNER BRASIL, LTDA.—See BorgWarner Inc.; *U.S. Public*, pg. 369
BORGWARNER CHUNGJU LTD.—See BorgWarner Inc.; *U.S. Public*, pg. 369
BORGWARNER COOLING SYSTEMS GMBH—See BorgWarner Inc.; *U.S. Public*, pg. 370
BORGWARNER COOLING SYSTEMS (INDIA) PRIVATE LIMITED—See BorgWarner Inc.; *U.S. Public*, pg. 370
BORGWARNER COOLING SYSTEMS KOREA, INC.—See BorgWarner Inc.; *U.S. Public*, pg. 370
BORGWARNER EMISSIONS SYSTEMS SPAIN S.L.—See BorgWarner Inc.; *U.S. Public*, pg. 369
BORGWARNER EMOBILITY POLAND SP. Z O.O.—See BorgWarner Inc.; *U.S. Public*, pg. 371
BORGWARNER KFT.—See BorgWarner Inc.; *U.S. Public*, pg. 369
BORGWARNER LIMITED—See BorgWarner Inc.; *U.S. Public*, pg. 371
BORGWARNER MORSE TEC JAPAN K.K.—See Enstar Group Limited; *Int'l*, pg. 2448
BORGWARNER MORSE TEC KOREA LTD.—See Enstar Group Limited; *Int'l*, pg. 2448
BORGWARNER NEW ENERGY (XIANGYANG) CO., LTD.—See BorgWarner Inc.; *U.S. Public*, pg. 370
BORGWARNER NOBLESVILLE LLC—See BorgWarner Inc.; *U.S. Public*, pg. 370
BORGWARNER OCHANG INC.—See BorgWarner Inc.; *U.S. Public*, pg. 370
BORGWARNER PDS BEIJING CO. LTD.—See BorgWarner Inc.; *U.S. Public*, pg. 370
BORGWARNER PDS (USA) INC.—See BorgWarner Inc.; *U.S. Public*, pg. 370

BORGWARNER POWDERED METALS INC.—See Borg-Warner Inc.; *U.S. Public*, pg. 370
BORGWARNER PYONGTAEK LLC—See BorgWarner Inc.; *U.S. Public*, pg. 370
BORGWARNER REYNOSA S DE R.L. DE C.VL—See Borg-Warner Inc.; *U.S. Public*, pg. 370
BORGWARNER SALTILLO S. DE R.L. DE C.V.—See Borg-Warner Inc.; *U.S. Public*, pg. 370
BORGWARNER SHENGLONG (NINGBO) CO. LTD.—See BorgWarner Inc.; *U.S. Public*, pg. 370
BORGWARNER SLP S. DE R.L. DE C.V.—See BorgWarner Inc.; *U.S. Public*, pg. 370
BORGWARNER STUTTGART GMBH—See BorgWarner Inc.; *U.S. Public*, pg. 370
BORGWARNER TURBO & EMISSIONS SYSTEMS FRANCE S.A.S.—See BorgWarner Inc.; *U.S. Public*, pg. 371
BORGWARNER TURBO SYSTEMS ENGINEERING GMBH—See BorgWarner Inc.; *U.S. Public*, pg. 371
BORGWARNER TURBO SYSTEMS GMBH—See BorgWarner Inc.; *U.S. Public*, pg. 371
BORGWARNER TURBO SYSTEMS INC.—See BorgWarner Inc.; *U.S. Public*, pg. 371
BORUSAN YATIRIM VE PAZARLAMA AS; *Int'l*, pg. 1115
BOSAL AFRICA (PTY) LTD.—See Bosal International NV; *Int'l*, pg. 1116
BOSAL INTERNATIONAL - GEORGIA—See Bosal International NV; *Int'l*, pg. 1116
BOSAL INTERNATIONAL NORTH AMERICA—See Bosal International NV; *Int'l*, pg. 1116
BOSAL INTERNATIONAL NV; *Int'l*, pg. 1116
BOSAL MEXICO AM—See Bosal International NV; *Int'l*, pg. 1116
BOSAL NEDERLAND BV—See Bosal International NV; *Int'l*, pg. 1116
BOSAL USA, INC.—See Bosal International NV; *Int'l*, pg. 1116
BOWA-ELECTRONIC GMBH & CO. KG; *Int'l*, pg. 1123
BRITAX PSV WYPERS LTD.—See Ecco Safety Group; *U.S. Private*, pg. 1326
BROMFORD INDUSTRIES LIMITED - LEICESTER FACILITY—See Bromford Industries Limited; *Int'l*, pg. 1173
BROSE BRATISLAVA, SPOL. S R.O.—See Brose Fahrzeugteile GmbH & Co. KG; *Int'l*, pg. 1195
BROSE CANADA INC—See Brose Fahrzeugteile GmbH & Co. KG; *Int'l*, pg. 1195
BROSE CHANGCHUN AUTOMOTIVE SYSTEMS CO., LTD—See Brose Fahrzeugteile GmbH & Co. KG; *Int'l*, pg. 1195
BROSE CHICAGO, INC.—See Brose Fahrzeugteile GmbH & Co. KG; *Int'l*, pg. 1195
BROSE CZ SPOL. S R.O.—See Brose Fahrzeugteile GmbH & Co. KG; *Int'l*, pg. 1195
BROSE DO BRASIL LTDA.—See Brose Fahrzeugteile GmbH & Co. KG; *Int'l*, pg. 1196
BROSE FRANCE S.A.S.—See Brose Fahrzeugteile GmbH & Co. KG; *Int'l*, pg. 1195
BROSE GENT BVBA—See Brose Fahrzeugteile GmbH & Co. KG; *Int'l*, pg. 1195
BROSE KOREA LTD.—See Brose Fahrzeugteile GmbH & Co. KG; *Int'l*, pg. 1195
BROSE LIMITED—See Brose Fahrzeugteile GmbH & Co. KG; *Int'l*, pg. 1195
BROSE MEXICO, S.A. DE C.V.—See Brose Fahrzeugteile GmbH & Co. KG; *Int'l*, pg. 1195
BROSE NORTH AMERICA, INC.—See Brose Fahrzeugteile GmbH & Co. KG; *Int'l*, pg. 1195
BROSE S. A.—See Brose Fahrzeugteile GmbH & Co. KG; *Int'l*, pg. 1195
BROSE SHANGHAI AUTOMOTIVE SYSTEMS CO., LTD.—See Brose Fahrzeugteile GmbH & Co. KG; *Int'l*, pg. 1195
BROSE SISTEMAS DE FECHADURAS PARA AUTOMOVEIS, UNIPESSOAL LDA—See Brose Fahrzeugteile GmbH & Co. KG; *Int'l*, pg. 1196
BROSE SWEDEN AB—See Brose Fahrzeugteile GmbH & Co. KG; *Int'l*, pg. 1196
BROSE TUSCALOOSA, INC.—See Brose Fahrzeugteile GmbH & Co. KG; *Int'l*, pg. 1195
BROWN & WATSON INTERNATIONAL PTY LTD—See Amotiv Limited; *Int'l*, pg. 431
BUCHER AUTOMATION AG—See Bucher Industries AG; *Int'l*, pg. 1206
BUCHER AUTOMATION TETTNANG GMBH—See Bucher Industries AG; *Int'l*, pg. 1206
BUCHER MUNICIPAL S.A.S.—See Bucher Industries AG; *Int'l*, pg. 1207
BUNKER CORPORATION; *U.S. Private*, pg. 685
BWI CZECH REPUBLIC S.R.O.—See BeijingWest Industries International Limited; *Int'l*, pg. 962
BYD E-MOTORS ECUADOR S.A—See BYD Company Limited; *Int'l*, pg. 1234
BYD MOTOR COLOMBIA SAS—See BYD Company Limited; *Int'l*, pg. 1234
CADILLAC PRODUCTS, INC.; *U.S. Private*, pg. 713
CARADO GMBH—See Thor Industries, Inc.; *U.S. Public*, pg. 2156

CARBODY S.A.S.—See BAVARIA Industries Group AG; *Int'l*, pg. 899
CARDINGTON YUTAKA TECHNOLOGIES INC.—See Honda Motor Co., Ltd.; *Int'l*, pg. 3460
CARDONE INDUSTRIES, INC.; *U.S. Private*, pg. 751
CARL ZEISS INNOVATIONSZENTRUM FUR MESSTECHNIK GMBH—See Carl-Zeiss-Stiftung; *Int'l*, pg. 1334
CAR MATE MFG. CO., LTD.; *Int'l*, pg. 1319
CAR MATE USA, INC.—See Car Mate Mfg. Co., Ltd.; *Int'l*, pg. 1319
CAR-O-LINER COMPANY USA—See Snap-on Incorporated; *U.S. Public*, pg. 1897
CAR PARTS INDUSTRIES BELGIUM SA—See Aktieselskabet Schouw & Co.; *Int'l*, pg. 265
CARRARO QINGDAO LTD.—See FLY Srl; *Int'l*, pg. 2715
CAR SOUND MAGNAFLOW; *U.S. Private*, pg. 747
CARTER INDUSTRIES INC.—See Adrian Steel Company Inc.; *U.S. Private*, pg. 82
CARWOOD (BDS) MOTOR UNIT LTD—See Carwood Motor Units Ltd; *Int'l*, pg. 1349
CARWOOD MOTOR UNITS LTD - OLLERTON FACTORY—See Carwood Motor Units Ltd; *Int'l*, pg. 1349
CARWOOD MOTOR UNITS LTD; *Int'l*, pg. 1349
CASCO IMOS ITALIA S.R.L.—See Amphenol Corporation; *U.S. Public*, pg. 129
CBC INGS AMERICA INC.—See CBC Co., Ltd.; *Int'l*, pg. 1365
C. COWLES & CO.; *U.S. Private*, pg. 705
C&C TRUCKS CO., LTD.—See China International Marine Containers (Group) Co., Ltd.; *Int'l*, pg. 1511
CDTI—See CDTi Advanced Materials, Inc.; *U.S. Public*, pg. 462
CEMM-MEX, S.A. DE C.V.—See Amphenol Corporation; *U.S. Public*, pg. 129
CENTEK INDUSTRIES INC—See Atlantic Gasket Corp.; *U.S. Private*, pg. 373
CENTER LINE WHEELS, INC.; *U.S. Private*, pg. 811
CENTRAL AUTOMOTIVE PRODUCTS LTD.; *Int'l*, pg. 1404
CENTRAL MOTEK CO., LTD.; *Int'l*, pg. 1408
CENTRAL MOTOR WHEEL OF AMERICA; *U.S. Private*, pg. 822
CENTRAL STATES BUS SALES INC. - ARKANSAS FACILITY—See Central States Bus Sales Inc.; *U.S. Private*, pg. 825
CENTRAL STATES BUS SALES INC. - ILLINOIS FACILITY—See Central States Bus Sales Inc.; *U.S. Private*, pg. 825
CENTRAL STATES BUS SALES INC. - TENNESSEE FACILITY—See Central States Bus Sales Inc.; *U.S. Private*, pg. 825
CENTRO TECNICO HERRAMENTAL, S.A. DE C.V.—See Aptiv PLC; *Int'l*, pg. 524
CEPTON, INC.; *U.S. Public*, pg. 475
CEQUENT CONSUMER PRODUCTS, INC.—See Crowne Group LLC; *U.S. Private*, pg. 1112
CEQUENT PERFORMANCE PRODUCTS, INC.—See Crowne Group LLC; *U.S. Private*, pg. 1112
CEVO MOBILITY CO., LTD.—See CAMMSYS Co., LTD; *Int'l*, pg. 1273
CHALLENGER DOOR, LLC—See LCI Industries; *U.S. Public*, pg. 1295
CHANGCHUN CECK AUTO. PARTS CO., LTD.—See China Steel Corporation; *Int'l*, pg. 1555
CHANGCHUN FAWAY AUTOMOBILE COMPONENTS CO., LTD.—See China FAW Group Corporation; *Int'l*, pg. 1501
CHANGCHUN HELLA AUTOMOTIVE LIGHTING LTD.—See Hella GmbH & Co. KGaA; *Int'l*, pg. 3331
CHANGCHUN HI-LEX AUTO CABLE CO. LTD.—See Hi-Lex Corporation; *Int'l*, pg. 3380
CHANGCHUN VISTEON FAWAY AUTOMOTIVE ELECTRONICS CO., LTD.—See Visteon Corporation; *U.S. Public*, pg. 2305
CHANG HEART CORP.—See HKS CO., LTD.; *Int'l*, pg. 3429
CHANGZHOU TENGXING AUTO ACCESSORIES MANUFACTURING CO., LTD.—See Changzhou Tenglong Auto Parts Co., Ltd.; *Int'l*, pg. 1445
CHARTER AUTOMOTIVE—See Charter Manufacturing Company, Inc.; *U.S. Private*, pg. 858
CHASYS CO., LTD; *Int'l*, pg. 1457
CHENGDU JOUAV AUTOMATION TECHNOLOGY CO., LTD.; *Int'l*, pg. 1468
CHEVROLET EURO PARTS CENTER B.V.—See General Motors Company; *U.S. Public*, pg. 927
CHIAN HSING FORGING INDUSTRIAL CO., LTD.; *Int'l*, pg. 1476
CHIAN HSING (HUAI'AN) AUTO PARTS CO., LTD.—See Chian Hsing Forging Industrial Co., Ltd.; *Int'l*, pg. 1476
CHIAN HSING (TAICANG) METAL PRODUCTS CO., LTD.—See Chian Hsing Forging Industrial Co., Ltd.; *Int'l*, pg. 1476
CHINA AUTO SYSTEM TECHNOLOGIES LIMITED; *Int'l*, pg. 1483
CHINA DALIAN CFM PRECISION TOOLING CO., LTD.—See CFM Holdings Limited; *Int'l*, pg. 1430
CHINA METAL PRODUCTS CO., LTD.; *Int'l*, pg. 1523
CHINA RAILWAY MATERIALS COMPANY LIMITED—See China FAW Group Corporation; *Int'l*, pg. 1502
CHIN HIN GROUP PROPERTY BERHAD—See Chin Hin Group Berhad; *Int'l*, pg. 1480
CHONGQING CHANGTENG AUTO PARTS MANUFACTURING CO., LTD.—See Changzhou Tenglong Auto Parts Co., Ltd.; *Int'l*, pg. 1445
CHONGQING HI-LEX CONTROL CABLE SYSTEM CO LTD.—See Hi-Lex Corporation; *Int'l*, pg. 3380
CHONGQING SKYMAN INDUSTRY (GROUP) CO., LTD.; *Int'l*, pg. 1581
CHS-CORSICA—See CHS INC.; *U.S. Public*, pg. 492
CHUHATSU NORTH AMERICA, INC.—See Chuo Spring Co., Ltd.; *Int'l*, pg. 1599
CHUHATSU-TECHNO CO., LTD.—See Chuo Spring Co., Ltd.; *Int'l*, pg. 1599
CHUN YU METAL PRODUCTS CO., LTD.—See Chun Yu Works & Co., Ltd.; *Int'l*, pg. 1596
C.I.A.P. S.P.A.—See Honda Motor Co., Ltd.; *Int'l*, pg. 3460
CIE AUTOMOTIVE PARTS (SHANGHAI) CO., LTD.—See Cie Automotive S.A.; *Int'l*, pg. 1604
CIE AUTOMOTIVE, USA INC.—See Cie Automotive S.A.; *Int'l*, pg. 1604
CIE CELAYA, S.A.P.I. DE C.V.—See Cie Automotive S.A.; *Int'l*, pg. 1604
CIE COMPIEGNE, S.A.S.—See Cie Automotive S.A.; *Int'l*, pg. 1604
CIE DEUTSCHLAND, GMBH—See Cie Automotive S.A.; *Int'l*, pg. 1604
CIE FORJAS MINAS, LTDA.—See Cie Automotive S.A.; *Int'l*, pg. 1604
CIE GALFOR, S.A.U.—See Cie Automotive S.A.; *Int'l*, pg. 1604
CIE MECAUTO, S.A.U.—See Cie Automotive S.A.; *Int'l*, pg. 1604
CIE METAL CZ, S.R.O.—See Cie Automotive S.A.; *Int'l*, pg. 1604
CIE PLASTICOS MEXICO, S.A. DE C.V.—See Cie Automotive S.A.; *Int'l*, pg. 1604
CIE PLASTY CZ, S.R.O.—See Cie Automotive S.A.; *Int'l*, pg. 1604
CIE STRATIS-TRATAMENTOS, LTDA.—See Cie Automotive S.A.; *Int'l*, pg. 1604
CIE ZDANICE, S.R.O.—See Cie Automotive S.A.; *Int'l*, pg. 1604
CIMC VEHICLE (LIAONING) CO., LTD.—See China International Marine Containers (Group) Co., Ltd.; *Int'l*, pg. 1511
CLUTCH AUTO LIMITED; *Int'l*, pg. 1664
COBB TUNING PRODUCTS, LLC—See Promus Holdings, LLC; *U.S. Private*, pg. 3284
COFLE DO BRASIL LTDA.—See Cofle SpA; *Int'l*, pg. 1693
COFLE TK OTOMOTIV AS—See Cofle SpA; *Int'l*, pg. 1693
COMPONENTA WIRSBO AB—See Componenta Corporation; *Int'l*, pg. 1753
COMPONENTE AUTO S.A.; *Int'l*, pg. 1753
COMPONENTES AUTOMOTIVOS TAUBATE, LTDA.—See Cie Automotive S.A.; *Int'l*, pg. 1604
COMPONENTES DE AUTOMOCION RECYTEC, S.L.U.—See Cie Automotive S.A.; *Int'l*, pg. 1604
COMPONENTES DE DIRECCION RECYLAN, S.L.U.—See Cie Automotive S.A.; *Int'l*, pg. 1604
COMSTAR AUTOMOTIVE TECHNOLOGIES PVT LTD—See Blackstone Inc.; *U.S. Public*, pg. 360
CONSORCIO INDUSTRIAL MEXICANO DE AUTOPARTES S. DE R.L. DE C.V.—See Lear Corporation; *U.S. Public*, pg. 1296
CONTINENTAL AKTIENGESELLSCHAFT; *Int'l*, pg. 1780
CONTINENTAL AUTOMOTIVE AUSTRIA GMBH—See Continental Aktiengesellschaft; *Int'l*, pg. 1781
CONTINENTAL AUTOMOTIVE CANADA, INC.—See Continental Aktiengesellschaft; *Int'l*, pg. 1781
CONTINENTAL AUTOMOTIVE COMPONENTS (INDIA) PRIVATE LTD.—See Continental Aktiengesellschaft; *Int'l*, pg. 1781
CONTINENTAL AUTOMOTIVE COMPONENTS MALAYSIA SDN. BHD.—See Continental Aktiengesellschaft; *Int'l*, pg. 1782
CONTINENTAL AUTOMOTIVE CZECH REPUBLIC S.R.O.—See Continental Aktiengesellschaft; *Int'l*, pg. 1782
CONTINENTAL AUTOMOTIVE GMBH—See Continental Aktiengesellschaft; *Int'l*, pg. 1782
CONTINENTAL AUTOMOTIVE GMBH—See Continental Aktiengesellschaft; *Int'l*, pg. 1782
CONTINENTAL AUTOMOTIVE GMBH—See Continental Aktiengesellschaft; *Int'l*, pg. 1782
CONTINENTAL AUTOMOTIVE JAPAN KK—See Continental Aktiengesellschaft; *Int'l*, pg. 1781
CONTINENTAL AUTOMOTIVE PTE. LTD.—See Continental Aktiengesellschaft; *Int'l*, pg. 1782
CONTINENTAL AUTOMOTIVE S.A. DE C.V—See Continental Aktiengesellschaft; *Int'l*, pg. 1781
CONTINENTAL AUTOMOTIVE SPAIN S.A.—See Continental Aktiengesellschaft; *Int'l*, pg. 1781
CONTINENTAL AUTOMOTIVE SPAIN, S.A.—See Continental Aktiengesellschaft; *Int'l*, pg. 1782
CONTINENTAL AUTOMOTIVE SWITZERLAND AG—See Continental Aktiengesellschaft; *Int'l*, pg. 1782
CONTINENTAL AUTOMOTIVE SYSTEMS MANAGEMENT

336390 — OTHER MOTOR VEHICLE...

CO., LTD—See Continental Aktiengesellschaft; *Int'l*, pg. 1781
CONTINENTAL AUTOMOTIVE SYSTEMS US, INC.—See Continental Aktiengesellschaft; *Int'l*, pg. 1781
CONTINENTAL AUTOMOTIVE SYSTEMS US, INC.—See Continental Aktiengesellschaft; *Int'l*, pg. 1781
CONTINENTAL AUTOMOTIVE SYSTEMS US, INC.—See Continental Aktiengesellschaft; *Int'l*, pg. 1782
CONTINENTAL AUTOMOTIVE SYSTEMS US, INC.—See Continental Aktiengesellschaft; *Int'l*, pg. 1782
CONTINENTAL AUTOMOTIVE TRADING NEDERLAND B.V.—See Continental Aktiengesellschaft; *Int'l*, pg. 1782
CONTINENTAL AUTOMOTIVE TRADING UK LTD.—See Continental Aktiengesellschaft; *Int'l*, pg. 1782
CONTINENTAL BENELUX S.A.—See Continental Aktiengesellschaft; *Int'l*, pg. 1782
CONTINENTAL BRASIL INDUSTRIA AUTOMOTIVA LTDA.—See Continental Aktiengesellschaft; *Int'l*, pg. 1782
CONTINENTAL BRASIL INDUSTRIA AUTOMOTIVA LTDA.—See Continental Aktiengesellschaft; *Int'l*, pg. 1782
CONTINENTAL PTY. LTD. - MELBOURNE PLANT—See Continental Aktiengesellschaft; *Int'l*, pg. 1782
CONTINENTAL PTY LTD—See Continental Aktiengesellschaft; *Int'l*, pg. 1782
CONTINENTAL SAFETY ENGINEERING INTERNATIONAL GMBH—See Continental Aktiengesellschaft; *Int'l*, pg. 1782
CONTINENTAL TRADING GMBH—See Continental Aktiengesellschaft; *Int'l*, pg. 1782
CONTINENTAL VDO AUTOMOTIVE, S.A.—See Continental Aktiengesellschaft; *Int'l*, pg. 1782
CONTITECH CONTINENTAL SUISSE S.A.—See Continental Aktiengesellschaft; *Int'l*, pg. 1780
CONTITECH FLUID MONTERREY SERVICIOS, S.A. DE C.V.—See Continental Aktiengesellschaft; *Int'l*, pg. 1780
CONTITECH FLUID SHANGHAI CO., LTD.—See Continental Aktiengesellschaft; *Int'l*, pg. 1781
CONTITECH NORTH AMERICA, INC.—See Continental Aktiengesellschaft; *Int'l*, pg. 1780
CONTITECH ROMANIA S.R.L.—See Continental Aktiengesellschaft; *Int'l*, pg. 1781
CONTITECH SCANDINAVIA AB—See Continental Aktiengesellschaft; *Int'l*, pg. 1780
CONTI TEMIC MICROELECTONICS GMBH—See Continental Aktiengesellschaft; *Int'l*, pg. 1782
CONTROLLED ENVIRONMENT SYSTEMS, LLC; *U.S. Private*, pg. 1034
CONTROL-TEC, LLC—See Aptiv PLC; *Int'l*, pg. 524
COOL MAX AUTO PARTS CO., LTD.—See Cryomax Cooling System Corp.; *Int'l*, pg. 1860
COOL TECHNOLOGIES, INC.; *U.S. Public*, pg. 573
COOPER-STANDARD AUTOMOTIVE CANADA LIMITED—See Cooper-Standard Holdings Inc.; *U.S. Public*, pg. 574
COOPER-STANDARD AUTOMOTIVE CESKA REPUBLIKA S.R.O.—See Cooper-Standard Holdings Inc.; *U.S. Public*, pg. 574
COOPER-STANDARD AUTOMOTIVE DE MEXICO S.A. DE C.V.—See Cooper-Standard Holdings Inc.; *U.S. Public*, pg. 574
COOPER-STANDARD AUTOMOTIVE FLUID SYSTEMS DE MEXICO, S. DE R.L. DE C.V.—See Cooper-Standard Holdings Inc.; *U.S. Public*, pg. 574
COOPER-STANDARD AUTOMOTIVE INC.—See Cooper-Standard Holdings Inc.; *U.S. Public*, pg. 574
COOPER-STANDARD AUTOMOTIVE INTERNATIONAL HOLDINGS B.V.—See Cooper-Standard Holdings Inc.; *U.S. Public*, pg. 574
COOPER-STANDARD AUTOMOTIVE ITALY SPA—See Cooper-Standard Holdings Inc.; *U.S. Public*, pg. 574
COOPER STANDARD AUTOMOTIVE JAPAN K.K.—See Cooper-Standard Holdings Inc.; *U.S. Public*, pg. 574
COOPER-STANDARD AUTOMOTIVE PIOTRKOW SP ZOO—See Cooper-Standard Holdings Inc.; *U.S. Public*, pg. 574
COOPER-STANDARD AUTOMOTIVE SERVICES, S.A. DE C.V.—See Cooper-Standard Holdings Inc.; *U.S. Public*, pg. 574
COOPER STANDARD FRANCE SAS—See Cooper-Standard Holdings Inc.; *U.S. Public*, pg. 573
COOPER-STANDARD ROCKFORD INC.—See Cooper-Standard Holdings Inc.; *U.S. Public*, pg. 574
COPPER CORE LTD.; *Int'l*, pg. 1793
CORNING (SHANGHAI) CO., LTD.—See Corning Incorporated; *U.S. Public*, pg. 578
COUNTRY COACH CORPORATION; *U.S. Private*, pg. 1066
COUPLED PRODUCTS, INC.—See Dana Incorporated; *U.S. Public*, pg. 622
CPI HOLDINGS, LLC—See Cash Technologies, Inc.; *U.S. Private*, pg. 782
CSF POLAND Z O.O.—See Cooper-Standard Holdings Inc.; *U.S. Public*, pg. 573
CUBTEK INC.—See Cub Elecparts Inc.; *Int'l*, pg. 1875
CUMMINS CZECH REPUBLIC S.R.O.—See Cummins Inc.; *U.S. Public*, pg. 605

CUMMINS FILTRATION—See Cummins Inc.; *U.S. Public*, pg. 606
CUMMINS SALES AND SERVICE PRIVATE LIMITED—See Cummins Inc.; *U.S. Public*, pg. 607
CURT MANUFACTURING LLC—See LCI Industries; *U.S. Public*, pg. 1295
CUSTOM FIBERGLASS MANUFACTURING CO. INC.; *U.S. Private*, pg. 1128
CVG SPRAGUE DEVICES, LLC—See Commercial Vehicle Group, Inc.; *U.S. Public*, pg. 547
CVG SPRAGUE DIVISION—See Commercial Vehicle Group, Inc.; *U.S. Public*, pg. 547
CVG - VONORE—See Commercial Vehicle Group, Inc.; *U.S. Public*, pg. 547
CWB AUTOMOTIVE ELECTRONICS (TAICANG) CO., LTD.—See CWB Automotive Electronics Co., Ltd.; *Int'l*, pg. 1890
CYSORE SA DE CV—See 2G Energy AG; *Int'l*, pg. 5
DACCO, INC.—See Blue Point Capital Partners, LLC; *U.S. Private*, pg. 591
DAD CO., LTD.; *Int'l*, pg. 1904
DAE DONG HI-LEX INC—See Hi-Lex Corporation; *Int'l*, pg. 3380
DAE DONG SYSTEM CO., LTD.—See Hi-Lex Corporation; *Int'l*, pg. 3380
DAFINE ENGINEERING OU—See Addtech AB; *Int'l*, pg. 132
DA HUI LIMITED; *Int'l*, pg. 1901
DAICEL SAFETY SYSTEMS AMERICA LLC—See Daicel Corporation; *Int'l*, pg. 1918
DAICEL SAFETY SYSTEMS EUROPE SP.Z.O.O—See Daicel Corporation; *Int'l*, pg. 1919
DAICEL SAFETY SYSTEMS (THAILAND) CO.,LTD.—See Daicel Corporation; *Int'l*, pg. 1919
DAICEL SAFETY TECHNOLOGIES (THAILAND) CO., LTD.—See Daicel Corporation; *Int'l*, pg. 1919
DAIDO METAL KOTOR AD—See Daido Metal Corporation; *Int'l*, pg. 1921
DAIDO PLAIN BEARINGS CO., LTD.—See Daido Metal Corporation; *Int'l*, pg. 1921
DAIDO PRECISION METAL (SUZHOU) CO., LTD.—See Daido Metal Corporation; *Int'l*, pg. 1921
DAIFUKU (CHINA) AUTOMATION CO., LTD.—See Daifuku Co., Ltd.; *Int'l*, pg. 1925
DAK CO., LTD—See Dongwon Metal Co., Ltd.; *Int'l*, pg. 2171
DANA AUSTRALIA PTY. LTD.—See Dana Incorporated; *U.S. Public*, pg. 622
DANA AUSTRIA GMBH—See Dana Incorporated; *U.S. Public*, pg. 622
DANA AUTOMOCION, S.A.—See Dana Incorporated; *U.S. Public*, pg. 622
DANA AUTOMOTIVE AFTERMARKET, INC.—See Dana Incorporated; *U.S. Public*, pg. 622
DANA BELGIUM BVBA—See Dana Incorporated; *U.S. Public*, pg. 622
DANA BELGIUM NV—See Dana Incorporated; *U.S. Public*, pg. 622
DANA CANADA CORPORATION—See Dana Incorporated; *U.S. Public*, pg. 622
DANA DE MEXICO CORPORACION, S. DE R.L. DE C.V.—See Dana Incorporated; *U.S. Public*, pg. 623
DANA HEAVY VEHICLE TECHNOLOGIES & SYSTEMS—See Dana Incorporated; *U.S. Public*, pg. 622
DANA HOLDING GMBH—See Dana Incorporated; *U.S. Public*, pg. 622
DANA OFF-HIGHWAY PRODUCTS—See Dana Incorporated; *U.S. Public*, pg. 622
DANA SAC BENELUX B.V.—See Dana Incorporated; *U.S. Public*, pg. 622
DANA SAC MEXICO, S.A. DE C.V.—See Dana Incorporated; *U.S. Public*, pg. 622
DANA SAN LUIS S.A.—See Dana Incorporated; *U.S. Public*, pg. 623
DANA TM4 INC.—See Dana Incorporated; *U.S. Public*, pg. 623
DANA TM4 ITALIA S.R.L.—See Dana Incorporated; *U.S. Public*, pg. 623
DANA TM4 UK—See Dana Incorporated; *U.S. Public*, pg. 623
DANA TORQUE TECHNOLOGY—See Dana Incorporated; *U.S. Public*, pg. 623
DATALINER AB; *Int'l*, pg. 1978
DAYCO PRODUCTS LLC—See Dayco LLC; *U.S. Private*, pg. 1177
DAYTON SUPERIOR PRODUCTS CO., INC.; *U.S. Private*, pg. 1178
DEE ENGINEERING INC.; *U.S. Private*, pg. 1189
DEE ZEE, INC.; *U.S. Private*, pg. 1189
DELPHI AUTOMOTIVE LLP—See Aptiv PLC; *Int'l*, pg. 524
DELPHI AUTOMOTIVE SYSTEMS DO BRASIL LTDA.—See Aptiv PLC; *Int'l*, pg. 524
DELPHI AUTOMOTIVE SYSTEMS (THAILAND) LTD.—See Aptiv PLC; *Int'l*, pg. 524
DELPHI CABLEADOS, S.A. DE C.V.—See Aptiv PLC; *Int'l*, pg. 525
DELPHI CHINA LLC—See Aptiv PLC; *Int'l*, pg. 524
DELPHI CONNECTION SYSTEMS BELGIUM NV—See Aptiv PLC; *Int'l*, pg. 525

DELPHI CONNECTION SYSTEMS JAPAN LTD.—See Aptiv PLC; *Int'l*, pg. 525
DELPHI CONNECTION SYSTEMS MEXICO S. DE R.L. DE C.V.—See Aptiv PLC; *Int'l*, pg. 525
DELPHI CONNECTION SYSTEMS NANTONG LTD.—See Aptiv PLC; *Int'l*, pg. 525
DELPHI PACKARD TANGER SA—See Aptiv PLC; *Int'l*, pg. 524
DELPHI POLAND S.A.—See Aptiv PLC; *Int'l*, pg. 525
DEL WEST ENGINEERING INC.; *U.S. Private*, pg. 1193
DENAT 2007, S.L.U.—See Cie Automotive S.A.; *Int'l*, pg. 1604
DENSO AIR SYSTEMS YASAKA CORPORATION—See Denso Corporation; *Int'l*, pg. 2029
DENSO AUTOMOTIVE SYSTEMS AUSTRALIA PTY. LTD.—See Denso Corporation; *Int'l*, pg. 2029
DENSO (CHANGZHOU) FUEL INJECTION SYSTEM CO., LTD.—See Denso Corporation; *Int'l*, pg. 2028
DENSO CORPORATION; *Int'l*, pg. 2028
DENSO DO BRASIL LTDA.—See Denso Corporation; *Int'l*, pg. 2029
DENSO (GUANGZHOU NANSHA) CO., LTD.—See Denso Corporation; *Int'l*, pg. 2028
DENSO INDUSTRIAL DA AMAZONIA LTDA.—See Denso Corporation; *Int'l*, pg. 2031
DENSO INTERNATIONAL EUROPE B.V.—See Denso Corporation; *Int'l*, pg. 2029
DENSO KIKO CO., LTD.—See Denso Corporation; *Int'l*, pg. 2029
DENSO MANUFACTURING ARGENTINA S.A.—See Denso Corporation; *Int'l*, pg. 2029
DENSO MANUFACTURING ARKANSAS, INC.—See Denso Corporation; *Int'l*, pg. 2031
DENSO MANUFACTURING CANADA, INC—See Denso Corporation; *Int'l*, pg. 2029
DENSO MANUFACTURING MICHIGAN, INC.—See Denso Corporation; *Int'l*, pg. 2031
DENSO MANUFACTURING MIDLANDS LTD.—See Denso Corporation; *Int'l*, pg. 2031
DENSO MANUFACTURING TENNESSEE, INC.—See Denso Corporation; *Int'l*, pg. 2029
DENSO MANUFACTURING UK LTD.—See Denso Corporation; *Int'l*, pg. 2031
DENSO MARSTON LTD.—See Denso Corporation; *Int'l*, pg. 2031
DENSO MEXICO S.A. DE C.V—See Denso Corporation; *Int'l*, pg. 2030
DENSO MIYAZAKI, INC.—See Denso Corporation; *Int'l*, pg. 2032
DENSO OTOMOTIV PARCALARI SANAYI ANONIM SIRKET—See Denso Corporation; *Int'l*, pg. 2030
DENSO OTOMOTIV PARCALARI SANAYI A.S.—See Denso Corporation; *Int'l*, pg. 2031
DENSO PREAS CO., LTD.—See Denso Corporation; *Int'l*, pg. 2030
DENSO PS CORPORATION - HONGSEONG FACTORY—See Denso Corporation; *Int'l*, pg. 2030
DENSO PS CORPORATION—See Denso Corporation; *Int'l*, pg. 2030
DENSO REMANI CORPORATION—See Denso Corporation; *Int'l*, pg. 2030
DENSO TAIWAN CORP.—See Denso Corporation; *Int'l*, pg. 2030
DENSO TAIYO CO., LTD.—See Denso Corporation; *Int'l*, pg. 2030
DENSO TEN MINDA INDIA PRIVATE LIMITED—See Denso Corporation; *Int'l*, pg. 2030
DENSO (THAILAND) CO., LTD - WELLGROW PLANT—See Denso Corporation; *Int'l*, pg. 2028
DENSO THERMAL SYSTEMS PUNE PVT. LTD.—See Denso Corporation; *Int'l*, pg. 2030
DENSO THERMAL SYSTEMS SPA—See Denso Corporation; *Int'l*, pg. 2031
DENSO (TIANJIN) THERMAL PRODUCTS CO., LTD.—See Denso Corporation; *Int'l*, pg. 2028
DENSO WIPER SYSTEMS, INC.—See Denso Corporation; *Int'l*, pg. 2032
DENSO WIRELESS SYSTEMS AMERICA, INC.—See Denso Corporation; *Int'l*, pg. 2031
DFF CORP.—See CORE Industrial Partners, LLC; *U.S. Private*, pg. 1048
DFS DRAXLMAIER FAHRZEUGSYSTEME GMBH—See Draexlmaier Gruppe; *Int'l*, pg. 2198
DGENX CO., LTD. - GUNSAN PLANT—See Dgenx Co., Ltd.; *Int'l*, pg. 2096
DGENX CO., LTD.; *Int'l*, pg. 2096
D&H CO., LTD.—See Aisan Industry Co., Ltd.; *Int'l*, pg. 250
DIESEL RADIATOR CO.; *U.S. Private*, pg. 1229
DIGRAPH TRANSPORT SUPPLIES (TELFORD) LIMITED—See LKQ Corporation; *U.S. Public*, pg. 1334
DIVGI TORQTRANSFER SYSTEMS—See BorgWarner Inc.; *U.S. Public*, pg. 370
DN AUTOMOTIVE GERMANY GMBH—See DN Automotive Corporation; *Int'l*, pg. 2147
DN AUTOMOTIVE VMS LIMITED—See DN Automotive Corporation; *Int'l*, pg. 2147
DONALDSON CO., INC.—See Donaldson Company, Inc.; *U.S. Public*, pg. 675

336390 — OTHER MOTOR VEHICLE...

DONG AH TIRE & RUBBER CO., LTD. - BUKJEONG PLANT—See DN Automotive Corporation; *Int'l*, pg. 2147
DONGFENG ELECTRONIC TECHNOLOGY CO., LTD.; *Int'l*, pg. 2166
DONGFENG HONDA AUTOMOBILE CO., LTD.—See Honda Motor Co., Ltd.; *Int'l*, pg. 3460
DONGSUNG METAL CO., LTD.—See Daido Metal Corporation; *Int'l*, pg. 1921
DONGWON AUTOPART TECHNOLOGY ALABAMA L.L.C—See Dongwon Metal Co., Ltd.; *Int'l*, pg. 2171
DONGWON METAL CO., LTD. - ASAN PLANT—See Dongwon Metal Co., Ltd.; *Int'l*, pg. 2171
DONGWON METAL CO., LTD. - KYUNGSAN PLANT—See Dongwon Metal Co., Ltd.; *Int'l*, pg. 2171
DORMAN PRODUCTS, INC.; *U.S. Public*, pg. 677
DOUBLE E COMPANY, LLC—See River Associates Investments, LLC; *U.S. Private*, pg. 3443
DOUGLAS DYNAMICS, INC.; *U.S. Public*, pg. 677
DPECO CO., LTD.; *Int'l*, pg. 2188
DRAEXLMAIER AUTOMOTIVE OF AMERICA, LLC—See Draexlmaier Gruppe; *Int'l*, pg. 2198
DRAEXLMAIER AUTOMOTIVE SYSTEMS (THAILAND) CO., LTD.—See Draexlmaier Gruppe; *Int'l*, pg. 2198
DRAEXLMAIER (SHENYANG) AUTOMOTIVE COMPONENTS CO., LTD.—See Draexlmaier Gruppe; *Int'l*, pg. 2198
DRONE USA, LLC—See Bantec, Inc.; *U.S. Public*, pg. 275
DST INDUSTRIES, INC.; *U.S. Private*, pg. 1282
DTR VMS ITALY S.R.L.—See DN Automotive Corporation; *Int'l*, pg. 2147
DTR VMS ITALY S.R.L.—See KKR & Co. Inc.; *U.S. Public*, pg. 1260
DUCKYANG INDUSTRY CO., LTD.; *Int'l*, pg. 2223
DURA AUTOMOTIVE SYSTEMS, INC.—See MiddleGround Management, LP; *U.S. Private*, pg. 2711
DURAMETAL, S.A.—See Cie Automotive S.A.; *Int'l*, pg. 1604
DURR INC.—See Durr AG; *Int'l*, pg. 2231
DY AUTO CORPORATION—See DY Corporation; *Int'l*, pg. 2237
DYMOS CZECH REPUBLIC S.R.O—See Hyundai Motor Company; *Int'l*, pg. 3558
DYNA-MIG MFG. OF STRATFORD INC.—See F-Tech Inc.; *Int'l*, pg. 2595
DYNAX CORPORATION—See Exedy Corporation; *Int'l*, pg. 2580
DYNAX INDUSTRY (SHANGHAI) CO., LTD.—See Exedy Corporation; *Int'l*, pg. 2580
EATON AUTOMOTIVE COMPONENTS SPOLKA Z O.O.—See Eaton Corporation plc; *Int'l*, pg. 2279
EATON AUTOMOTIVE G.M.B.H.—See Eaton Corporation plc; *Int'l*, pg. 2279
EATON AUTOMOTIVE SYSTEMS SPOLKA Z O.O.—See Eaton Corporation plc; *Int'l*, pg. 2279
EATON CORP. - ENGINE AIR MANAGEMENT—See Eaton Corporation plc; *Int'l*, pg. 2280
EATON CORP. - VEHICLE GROUP, AUTOMOTIVE DIVISION—See Eaton Corporation plc; *Int'l*, pg. 2280
EATON CORP. - VEHICLE GROUP—See Eaton Corporation plc; *Int'l*, pg. 2280
EATON CORP. - VEHICLE GROUP, TRUCK DIVISION—See Eaton Corporation plc; *Int'l*, pg. 2280
ECCO SAFETY GROUP; *U.S. Private*, pg. 1326
ECONTROLS GROUP, INC.—See Genisys Controls, LLC; *U.S. Private*, pg. 1671
ECS INDUSTRIAL COMPUTER CO., LTD.—See Elitegroup Computer Systems Co., Ltd.; *Int'l*, pg. 2363
EDAG ENGINEERING POLSKA SP.Z.O.O.—See ATON GmbH; *Int'l*, pg. 688
EDAG ITALIA S.R.L.—See ATON GmbH; *Int'l*, pg. 689
EDAG NETHERLANDS B.V.—See ATON GmbH; *Int'l*, pg. 689
EDELBROCK CORPORATION; *U.S. Private*, pg. 1332
EDSCHA AAPICO AUTOMOTIVE CO., LTD.—See Acek Desarrollo y Gestion Industrial SL; *Int'l*, pg. 96
EDSCHA PHA LTD.—See Acek Desarrollo y Gestion Industrial SL; *Int'l*, pg. 96
EGANA 2, S.L.—See Cie Automotive S.A.; *Int'l*, pg. 1604
EGE ENDUSTRI VE TICARET AS; *Int'l*, pg. 2322
EINHELL DENMARK APS—See Einhell Germany AG; *Int'l*, pg. 2333
EINHELL NORWAY AS—See Einhell Germany AG; *Int'l*, pg. 2333
EISSMANN AUTOMOTIVE DETROIT DEVELOPMENT, LLC—See Eissmann Automotive Deutschland GmbH; *Int'l*, pg. 2336
EISSMANN AUTOMOTIVE DEUTSCHLAND GMBH; *Int'l*, pg. 2336
EISSMANN AUTOMOTIVE SLOVENSKO S.R.O—See Eissmann Automotive Deutschland GmbH; *Int'l*, pg. 2336
EKASER, S.A. DE C.V.—See ElringKlinger AG; *Int'l*, pg. 2369
ELBAR INDUSTRIAL LIMITED; *Int'l*, pg. 2344
ELECTRICAL REBUILDERS SALES INC.; *U.S. Private*, pg. 1353
ELECTROPRECIZIA S.A.; *Int'l*, pg. 2354
ELECTROTHERM INDIA LTD - ELECTRIC VEHICLE DIVISION—See Electrotherm India Ltd; *Int'l*, pg. 2354

ELESYS NORTH AMERICA INC.—See Honda Motor Co., Ltd.; *Int'l*, pg. 3460
ELGIN INDUSTRIES INC.; *U.S. Private*, pg. 1359
ELICA GROUP POLSKA—See Elica S.p.A.; *Int'l*, pg. 2361
ELLWOOD CRANKSHAFT & MACHINE COMPANY, LLC—See Ellwood Group, Inc.; *U.S. Private*, pg. 1375
ELRINGKLINGER CANADA, INC.—See ElringKlinger AG; *Int'l*, pg. 2369
ELRINGKLINGER HOLDING USA, INC.—See ElringKlinger AG; *Int'l*, pg. 2369
ELRINGKLINGER TEXAS, LLC—See ElringKlinger AG; *Int'l*, pg. 2370
EMBED LIMITED—See Littelfuse, Inc.; *U.S. Public*, pg. 1326
ENDO FORGING (THAILAND) CO. LTD.—See Endo Manufacturing Co., Ltd.; *Int'l*, pg. 2405
ENERGY 1 CORP.; *U.S. Private*, pg. 1393
ENHANCED MANUFACTURING SOLUTIONS, LLC—See American Computer Development, Inc.; *U.S. Private*, pg. 228
ENKEI AMERICA INC.; *U.S. Private*, pg. 1400
ENTERPRISE VENTURES CORPORATION—See Concurrent Technologies Corporation; *U.S. Private*, pg. 1011
ENVIROTEST CORP.—See Searchlight Capital Partners, L.P.; *U.S. Private*, pg. 3590
EQUOS RESEARCH CO., LTD.—See AISIN Corporation; *Int'l*, pg. 253
ERICH JAEGER GMBH + CO. KG—See AdCapital AG; *Int'l*, pg. 126
ERICH JAEGER MEXICO, S. DE R.L.—See AdCapital AG; *Int'l*, pg. 126
ERICH JAEGER U.S.A. INC.—See AdCapital AG; *Int'l*, pg. 126
ERLING HAUG AS—See Axel Johnson Gruppen AB; *Int'l*, pg. 764
ERLSON PRECISION COMPONENTS LIMITED—See GIL Investments Ltd.; *Int'l*, pg. 2973
ERNIE GREEN INDUSTRIES, INC.; *U.S. Private*, pg. 1422
ESMO CORPORATION; *Int'l*, pg. 2504
ETO GRUPPE BETEILIGUNGEN GMBH; *Int'l*, pg. 2524
EUREKA DESIGN PUBLIC COMPANY LIMITED; *Int'l*, pg. 2530
EUROKONTOR S.R.O.—See BERGER Holding GmbH; *Int'l*, pg. 979
EUROWHEEL BVBA—See Compagnie Generale des Etablissements Michelin SCA; *Int'l*, pg. 1742
EXCO AUTOMOTIVE SOLUTIONS L.P.—See Exco Technologies Limited; *Int'l*, pg. 2580
EXEDY AMERICA CORPORATION—See Exedy Corporation; *Int'l*, pg. 2581
EXEDY AUSTRALIA PTY. LTD.—See Exedy Corporation; *Int'l*, pg. 2581
EXEDY BEIJING CO., LTD.—See Exedy Corporation; *Int'l*, pg. 2581
EXEDY CASTING CO., LTD.—See Exedy Corporation; *Int'l*, pg. 2580
EXEDY CLUTCH EUROPE LTD.—See Exedy Corporation; *Int'l*, pg. 2581
EXEDY CLUTCH INDIA PVT. LTD.—See Exedy Corporation; *Int'l*, pg. 2581
EXEDY CORPORATION - KAWAGOE PLANT—See Exedy Corporation; *Int'l*, pg. 2581
EXEDY CORPORATION - UENO DIVISION—See Exedy Corporation; *Int'l*, pg. 2581
EXEDY DYNAX EUROPE LTD.—See Exedy Corporation; *Int'l*, pg. 2581
EXEDY DYNAX MEXICO, S.A. DE C.V.—See Exedy Corporation; *Int'l*, pg. 2581
EXEDY DYNAX SHANGHAI CO., LTD.—See Exedy Corporation; *Int'l*, pg. 2581
EXEDY ELECTRIC FACILITIES CO., LTD.—See Exedy Corporation; *Int'l*, pg. 2581
EXEDY ENGINEERING ASIA CO., LTD.—See Exedy Corporation; *Int'l*, pg. 2581
EXEDY FUKUSHIMA CO., LTD.—See Exedy Corporation; *Int'l*, pg. 2581
EXEDY HIROSHIMA CO., LTD.—See Exedy Corporation; *Int'l*, pg. 2580
EXEDY KYOTO CO., LTD.—See Exedy Corporation; *Int'l*, pg. 2580
EXEDY LATIN AMERICA S.A.—See Exedy Corporation; *Int'l*, pg. 2581
EXEDY MEXICO AFTERMARKET SALES, S.A. DE C.V.—See Exedy Corporation; *Int'l*, pg. 2581
EXEDY NARA CO., LTD.—See Exedy Corporation; *Int'l*, pg. 2581
EXEDY POIPET CO., LTD.—See Exedy Corporation; *Int'l*, pg. 2581
EXEDY PRECISION CO., LTD.—See Exedy Corporation; *Int'l*, pg. 2580
EXEDY SB HYOGO CO., LTD.—See Exedy Corporation; *Int'l*, pg. 2581
EXEDY SINGAPORE PTE. LTD.—See Exedy Corporation; *Int'l*, pg. 2581
EXEDY SUN CO., LTD.—See Exedy Corporation; *Int'l*, pg. 2580
EXTANG CORPORATION—See Kinderhook Industries, LLC; *U.S. Private*, pg. 2307
EZEN TECH CO., LTD.; *Int'l*, pg. 2594

FABCO AUTOMOTIVE CORPORATION—See Stone River Capital Partners, LLC; *U.S. Private*, pg. 3826
FABCO AUTOMOTIVE CORPORATION—See Wynnchurch Capital, L.P.; *U.S. Private*, pg. 4577
FABRICA BRASILEIRA DE FREIOS S.A.—See Haldex AB; *Int'l*, pg. 3228
FABRYCA OSI NAPEDOWYCH S.A.—See FLY Srl; *Int'l*, pg. 2715
FAIVELEY TRANSPORT NOWE GMBH—See Westinghouse Air Brake Technologies Corporation; *U.S. Public*, pg. 2357
FAIVELEY TRANSPORT PLZEN S.R.O.—See Westinghouse Air Brake Technologies Corporation; *U.S. Public*, pg. 2357
FARMINGTONS HOLDING GMBH; *Int'l*, pg. 2619
FATRASTYLING INC.—See Autobacs Seven Co., Ltd.; *Int'l*, pg. 726
FAURECIA ABGASTECHNIK GMBH—See FORVIA SE; *Int'l*, pg. 2746
FAURECIA ASIENTOS PARA AUTOMOVIL ESPANA, S.A.—See FORVIA SE; *Int'l*, pg. 2746
FAURECIA AUTOMOTIVE ESPANA, S.L.—See FORVIA SE; *Int'l*, pg. 2746
FAURECIA AUTOMOTIVE EXTERIORS ESPANA, S.A.—See FORVIA SE; *Int'l*, pg. 2746
FAURECIA (CHANGCHUN) AUTOMOTIVE SYSTEMS CO., LTD—See FORVIA SE; *Int'l*, pg. 2745
FAURECIA EMISSIONS CONTROL TECHNOLOGIES, (CHONGQING) CO., LTD—See FORVIA SE; *Int'l*, pg. 2746
FAURECIA EMISSIONS CONTROL TECHNOLOGIES, CORDOBA SA—See FORVIA SE; *Int'l*, pg. 2746
FAURECIA EMISSIONS CONTROL TECHNOLOGIES DEVELOPMENT (SHANGHAI) COMPANY LTD—See FORVIA SE; *Int'l*, pg. 2746
FAURECIA EMISSIONS CONTROL TECHNOLOGIES, FINNENTROP GMBH—See FORVIA SE; *Int'l*, pg. 2746
FAURECIA EMISSIONS CONTROL TECHNOLOGIES, GERMANY GMBH—See FORVIA SE; *Int'l*, pg. 2746
FAURECIA EMISSIONS CONTROL TECHNOLOGIES, MLADA BOLESLAV, S.R.O.—See FORVIA SE; *Int'l*, pg. 2746
FAURECIA EMISSIONS CONTROL TECHNOLOGIES, NETHERLANDS B.V.—See FORVIA SE; *Int'l*, pg. 2746
FAURECIA EMISSIONS CONTROL TECHNOLOGIES, NOVAFERRA GMBH—See FORVIA SE; *Int'l*, pg. 2746
FAURECIA EMISSIONS CONTROL TECHNOLOGIES, PAMPELONA, S.L.—See FORVIA SE; *Int'l*, pg. 2746
FAURECIA EMISSIONS CONTROL TECHNOLOGIES, (SHANGHAI) CO., LTD—See FORVIA SE; *Int'l*, pg. 2746
FAURECIA EMISSIONS CONTROL TECHNOLOGIES—See FORVIA SE; *Int'l*, pg. 2747
FAURECIA EMISSIONS CONTROL TECHNOLOGIES SPARTANBURG, INC.—See FORVIA SE; *Int'l*, pg. 2747
FAURECIA EMISSIONS CONTROL TECHNOLOGIES USA LLC—See FORVIA SE; *Int'l*, pg. 2747
FAURECIA EXHAUST SYSTEMS, INC.—See FORVIA SE; *Int'l*, pg. 2747
FAURECIA EXHAUST SYSTEMS SOUTH AFRICA LTD—See FORVIA SE; *Int'l*, pg. 2746
FAURECIA INTERIOR SYSTEMS BOHEMIA S.R.O.—See FORVIA SE; *Int'l*, pg. 2746
FAURECIA INTERIOR SYSTEMS ESPANA, S.A.—See FORVIA SE; *Int'l*, pg. 2746
FAURECIA INTERIOR SYSTEMS SOUTH AFRICA (PTY) LTD—See FORVIA SE; *Int'l*, pg. 2746
FAURECIA JAPAN K.K.—See FORVIA SE; *Int'l*, pg. 2747
FAURECIA KUNSTSTOFFE AUTOMOBILSYSTEME GMBH—See FORVIA SE; *Int'l*, pg. 2747
FAURECIA (QINGDAO) EXHAUST SYSTEMS CO, LTD—See FORVIA SE; *Int'l*, pg. 2745
FAURECIA - SISTEMAS DE ESCAPE PORTUGAL, LDA—See FORVIA SE; *Int'l*, pg. 2746
FAURECIA SYSTEMES D'ECHAPPEMENT—See FORVIA SE; *Int'l*, pg. 2747
FAURECIA (WUHU) EXHAUST SYSTEMS CO, LTD—See FORVIA SE; *Int'l*, pg. 2746
F.C.C. (ADAMS), LLC—See F.C.C. Co., Ltd.; *Int'l*, pg. 2596
FCC DO BRASIL LTDA.—See F.C.C. Co., Ltd.; *Int'l*, pg. 2596
FCC (INDIANA), INC.—See F.C.C. Co., Ltd.; *Int'l*, pg. 2596
FCC (NORTH AMERICA), INC.—See F.C.C. Co., Ltd.; *Int'l*, pg. 2596
FCC (TAIWAN) CO., LTD.—See F.C.C. Co., Ltd.; *Int'l*, pg. 2596
FEDERAL-MOGUL FRICTION PRODUCTS—See Apollo Global Management, Inc.; *U.S. Public*, pg. 161
FEDERAL-MOGUL FRICTION PRODUCTS (THAILAND) LTD—See Apollo Global Management, Inc.; *U.S. Public*, pg. 161
FEDERAL-MOGUL GORZYCE SA—See Apollo Global Management, Inc.; *U.S. Public*, pg. 161
FEDERAL-MOGUL HUNGARY KFT.—See Apollo Global Management, Inc.; *U.S. Public*, pg. 161
FEDERAL-MOGUL POWERTRAIN, LLC—See Apollo Global Management, Inc.; *U.S. Public*, pg. 161
FEDERAL-MOGUL SINTERTECH, SAS—See Apollo Global Management, Inc.; *U.S. Public*, pg. 162
FEDERAL-MOGUL TECHNOLOGY LIMITED—See Apollo

N.A.I.C.S. INDEX 336390 — OTHER MOTOR VEHICLE...

Global Management, Inc.; *U.S. Public*, pg: 162
FEDERAL-MOGUL VALVE TRAIN INTERNATIONAL LLC—See Apollo Global Management, Inc.; *U.S. Public*, pg. 162
FIELD SYSTEMS DESIGNS HOLDINGS PLC; *Int'l*, pg. 2655
FIEM INDUSTRIES LTD.; *Int'l*, pg. 2659
FILTRAUTO DO BRASIL LTDA.—See Compagnia Finanziaria de Benedetti S.p.A.; *Int'l*, pg. 1722
FILTRAUTO SLOVENIJA—See Compagnia Finanziaria de Benedetti S.p.A.; *Int'l*, pg. 1722
FILTROS PARTMO S.A.S.—See Donaldson Company, Inc.; *U.S. Public*, pg. 676
FINE BLANKING & TOOL CO., LTD.; *Int'l*, pg. 2673
FIRESTONE INDUSTRIAL PRODUCTS COMPANY-DYERSBURG—See Bridgestone Corporation; *Int'l*, pg. 1156
FIRST BRANDS GROUP, LLC—See Crowne Group LLC; *U.S. Public*, pg. 1112
FISHER & COMPANY INCORPORATED; *U.S. Private*, pg. 1533
FLEET ENGINEERS, INC.; *U.S. Private*, pg. 1541
FLEETLINE PRODUCTS—See Berkshire Hathaway Inc.; *U.S. Public*, pg. 310
FLEX-N-GATE CORPORATION; *U.S. Private*, pg. 1543
FLINT CO., LTD.—See F.C.C. Co., Ltd.; *Int'l*, pg. 2596
FLOWMASTER INC.; *U.S. Private*, pg. 1552
FLUDICON GMBH—See General Motors Company; *U.S. Public*, pg. 926
FOOSUNG PRECISION IND. CO., LTD. - BEIJING FACTORY—See Foosung Co., Ltd.; *Int'l*, pg. 2728
FOOSUNG PRECISION IND. CO., LTD. - GAJAE-RI FACTORY—See Foosung Co., Ltd.; *Int'l*, pg. 2728
FOOSUNG PRECISION IND. CO., LTD. - MUNMAK FACTORY—See Foosung Co., Ltd.; *Int'l*, pg. 2728
FOOSUNG PRECISION IND. CO., LTD. - NINGBO FPI FACTORY—See Foosung Co., Ltd.; *Int'l*, pg. 2728
FOOSUNG PRECISION IND. CO., LTD. - SUZHOU FACTORY—See Foosung Co., Ltd.; *Int'l*, pg. 2728
FORD CREDIT ITALIA SPA—See Ford Motor Company; *U.S. Public*, pg. 866
FORD MOTOR COMPANY (AUSTRIA) GMBH—See Ford Motor Company; *U.S. Public*, pg. 865
FORJAS DE CELAYA, S.A. DE C.V.—See Cie Automotive S.A.; *Int'l*, pg. 1604
FORMEX INDUSTRIES (PROPRIETARY) LIMITED—See E Media Holdings Limited; *Int'l*, pg. 2246
FORTE NOORD-WEST-EUROPA B.V.—See Illinois Tool Works Inc.; *U.S. Public*, pg. 1103
FORTUNE PARTS INDUSTRY PUBLIC COMPANY LIMITED; *Int'l*, pg. 2744
FORVIA SE; *Int'l*, pg. 2745
FOUR SEASONS - A DIVISION OF STANDARD MOTOR PRODUCTS, INC.—See Standard Motor Products, Inc.; *U.S. Public*, pg. 1929
F&P AMERICA MFG., INC.—See F-Tech Inc.; *Int'l*, pg. 2595
F&P GEORGIA MFG., INC.—See F-Tech Inc.; *Int'l*, pg. 2595
F.P.I. FERRARA PROMOZIONE INDUSTRIALE SRL; *Int'l*, pg. 2597
F&P MFG. DE MEXICO, S.A. DE C.V.—See F-Tech Inc.; *Int'l*, pg. 2595
F&P MFG. INC.—See F-Tech Inc.; *Int'l*, pg. 2595
FPT MOTORENFORSCHUNG AG—See CNH Industrial N.V.; *Int'l*, pg. 1675
FRAUENTHAL AUTOMOTIVE AZAMBUJA, UNIPESSOAL, LDA.—See Frauenthal Holding AG; *Int'l*, pg. 2767
FRAUENTHAL AUTOMOTIVE ELTERLEIN GMBH—See Frauenthal Holding AG; *Int'l*, pg. 2767
FRAUENTHAL GNOTEC CHINA CO. LTD.—See Frauenthal Holding AG; *Int'l*, pg. 2767
FRAUENTHAL GNOTEC SLOVAKIA S.R.O.—See Frauenthal Holding AG; *Int'l*, pg. 2767
FRAUENTHAL HOLDING AG; *Int'l*, pg. 2767
FRED JONES ENTERPRISES; *U.S. Private*, pg. 1601
FREUDENBERG FILTRATION TECHNOLOGIES (AUST) PTY. LTD.—See Freudenberg SE; *Int'l*, pg. 2786
FREUDENBERG FILTRATION TECHNOLOGIES (PTY) LTD.—See Freudenberg SE; *Int'l*, pg. 2786
FRIC-ROT S.A.I.C.—See Apollo Global Management, Inc.; *U.S. Public*, pg. 162
FRIEDRICH BOYSEN GMBH & CO. KG; *Int'l*, pg. 2792
F-TECH AUTOMOTIVE COMPONENTS PVT. LTD.—See F-Tech Inc.; *Int'l*, pg. 2595
F-TECH INC. - KAMEYAMA PLANT—See F-Tech Inc.; *Int'l*, pg. 2595
F-TECH INC - KUKI PLANT—See F-Tech Inc.; *Int'l*, pg. 2595
F-TECH INC.; *Int'l*, pg. 2595
F-TECH PHILIPPINES MFG., INC.—See F-Tech Inc.; *Int'l*, pg. 2595
F-TECH R&D (GUANGZHOU) INC.—See F-Tech Inc.; *Int'l*, pg. 2595
F-TECH R&D PHILIPPINES INC—See F-Tech Inc.; *Int'l*, pg. 2595
F-TECH WUHAN INC.—See F-Tech Inc.; *Int'l*, pg. 2595
F-TECH ZHONGSHAN INC.—See F-Tech Inc.; *Int'l*, pg. 2595
FUJI PRESS CO. LTD.—See Alconix Corporation; *Int'l*, pg. 302

FUJI SEATS (MALAYSIA) SDN. BHD.—See APM Automotive Holdings Berhad; *Int'l*, pg. 516
FUKOKU INDIA PRIVATE LIMITED—See Fukoku Co., Ltd.; *Int'l*, pg. 2839
FUKOKU KOREA CO., LTD. - BORYEONG PLANT—See Fukoku Co., Ltd.; *Int'l*, pg. 2839
FUKOKU KOREA CO., LTD.—See Fukoku Co., Ltd.; *Int'l*, pg. 2839
FUKOKU VIETNAM CO., LTD.—See Fukoku Co., Ltd.; *Int'l*, pg. 2839
FUTABA CZECH, S.R.O.—See Futaba Industrial Co., Ltd.; *Int'l*, pg. 2851
FUTABA GENERAL CO., LTD.—See Futaba Industrial Co., Ltd.; *Int'l*, pg. 2851
FUTABA HIRAIZUMI CO., LTD.—See Futaba Industrial Co., Ltd.; *Int'l*, pg. 2851
FUTABA INDIANA OF AMERICA CORP.—See Futaba Industrial Co., Ltd.; *Int'l*, pg. 2851
FUTABA INDUSTRIAL CO., LTD. - CHIRYU PLANT—See Futaba Industrial Co., Ltd.; *Int'l*, pg. 2851
FUTABA INDUSTRIAL CO., LTD. - KOTA PLANT—See Futaba Industrial Co., Ltd.; *Int'l*, pg. 2851
FUTABA INDUSTRIAL CO., LTD. - MIDORI PLANT—See Futaba Industrial Co., Ltd.; *Int'l*, pg. 2851
FUTABA INDUSTRIAL CO., LTD. - MUTSUMI PLANT—See Futaba Industrial Co., Ltd.; *Int'l*, pg. 2851
FUTABA INDUSTRIAL CO., LTD.; *Int'l*, pg. 2851
FUTABA INDUSTRIAL CO., LTD. - TAHARA PLANT—See Futaba Industrial Co., Ltd.; *Int'l*, pg. 2851
FUTABA INDUSTRIAL CO., LTD. - TAKAHASHI PLANT—See Futaba Industrial Co., Ltd.; *Int'l*, pg. 2851
FUTABA INDUSTRIAL GUJARAT PRIVATE LIMITED—See Futaba Industrial Co., Ltd.; *Int'l*, pg. 2851
FUTABA INDUSTRIAL U.K. LTD.—See Futaba Industrial Co., Ltd.; *Int'l*, pg. 2851
FUTABA KYUSYU CO., LTD. - MIYATA PLANT—See Futaba Industrial Co., Ltd.; *Int'l*, pg. 2851
FUTABA KYUSYU CO., LTD. - NOGATA PLANT—See Futaba Industrial Co., Ltd.; *Int'l*, pg. 2851
FUTABA KYUSYU CO., LTD.—See Futaba Industrial Co., Ltd.; *Int'l*, pg. 2851
FUTABA TENNECO U.K. LIMITED—See Apollo Global Management, Inc.; *U.S. Public*, pg. 162
FUTABA TENNECO U.K. LIMITED—See Futaba Corporation; *Int'l*, pg. 2850
FYSAM AUTO DECORATIVE GMBH—See Fuyao Glass Industry Group Co., Ltd.; *Int'l*, pg. 2858
GABRIEL EUROPE—See Cummins Inc.; *U.S. Public*, pg. 608
GAMEKO FABRICACION DE COMPONENTES, S.A.—See Cie Automotive S.A.; *Int'l*, pg. 1604
GARRETT MOTION INC.; *Int'l*, pg. 2886
GB RICAMBI S.P.A.; *Int'l*, pg. 2893
GENTEX CORPORATION; *U.S. Public*, pg. 931
GENTEX (SHANGHAI) ELECTRONIC TECHNOLOGY CO., INC.—See Gentex Corporation; *U.S. Public*, pg. 931
GENTHERM INCORPORATED; *U.S. Public*, pg. 931
GEORG FISCHER AUTOMOTIVE (KUNSHAN) CO., LTD.—See Georg Fischer AG; *Int'l*, pg. 2935
GESTAMP AUTOMOCION S.A. - GESTAMP BAIRES-ESCOBAR (I, II) PLANT—See Acek Desarrollo y Gestion Industrial SL; *Int'l*, pg. 96
GESTAMP AUTOMOCION S.A. - GESTAMP BEYCELIK (I, II) PLANT—See Acek Desarrollo y Gestion Industrial SL; *Int'l*, pg. 96
GESTAMP AUTOMOCION S.A. - GESTAMP GRAVATAI PLANT—See Acek Desarrollo y Gestion Industrial SL; *Int'l*, pg. 96
GESTAMP AUTOMOCION S.A. - GESTAMP GRIWE HAYNRODE PLANT—See Acek Desarrollo y Gestion Industrial SL; *Int'l*, pg. 96
GESTAMP AUTOMOCION S.A. - GESTAMP LLANELLI PLANT—See Acek Desarrollo y Gestion Industrial SL; *Int'l*, pg. 96
GESTAMP AUTOMOCION S.A. - GESTAMP NILUFER TURKEY PLANT—See Acek Desarrollo y Gestion Industrial SL; *Int'l*, pg. 96
GESTAMP AUTOMOCION S.A. - GESTAMP PARANA PLANT—See Acek Desarrollo y Gestion Industrial SL; *Int'l*, pg. 96
GESTAMP AUTOMOCION S.A. - GESTAMP SANTA ISABEL PLANT—See Acek Desarrollo y Gestion Industrial SL; *Int'l*, pg. 96
GESTAMP AUTOMOCION S.A. - GESTAMP SANTPEDOR PLANT—See Acek Desarrollo y Gestion Industrial SL; *Int'l*, pg. 96
GESTAMP AUTOMOCION S.A. - GESTAMP TAUBATE PLANT—See Acek Desarrollo y Gestion Industrial SL; *Int'l*, pg. 96
GESTAMP AUTOMOCION S.A. - GESTAMP WROCLAW PLANT—See Acek Desarrollo y Gestion Industrial SL; *Int'l*, pg. 96
GESTAMP AUTOMOCION S.A. - GMF OTOMOTIV PLANT—See Acek Desarrollo y Gestion Industrial SL; *Int'l*, pg. 96
GESTAMP AUTOMOCION S.A. - LOIRE SAFE PLANT—See Acek Desarrollo y Gestion Industrial SL; *Int'l*, pg. 96

GESTAMP AUTOMOCION S.A. -SOFEDIT LE THEIL PLANT—See Acek Desarrollo y Gestion Industrial SL; *Int'l*, pg. 96
GESTAMP AUTOMOCION S.A. - SOFEDIT SERMAISES PLANT—See Acek Desarrollo y Gestion Industrial SL; *Int'l*, pg. 96
GESTAMP AUTOMOCION S.A. - SOFEDIT ST. ROMAIN PLANT—See Acek Desarrollo y Gestion Industrial SL; *Int'l*, pg. 96
GESTAMP GALVANIZADOS, S.A.—See Acek Desarrollo y Gestion Industrial SL; *Int'l*, pg. 97
GESTAMP INGENIERIA EUROPA SUR, S.L.—See Acek Desarrollo y Gestion Industrial SL; *Int'l*, pg. 97
GESTAMP TALLENT, LTD.—See Acek Desarrollo y Gestion Industrial SL; *Int'l*, pg. 97
GESTAMP UMFORMTECHNIK GMBH—See Acek Desarrollo y Gestion Industrial SL; *Int'l*, pg. 97
GETRAG FORD TRANSMISSIONS GMBH - BORDEAUX PLANT—See Ford Motor Company; *U.S. Public*, pg. 866
GETRAG FORD TRANSMISSIONS GMBH - COLOGNE-MERKENICH—See Ford Motor Company; *U.S. Public*, pg. 866
GETRAG FORD TRANSMISSIONS GMBH - HALEWOOD PLANT—See Ford Motor Company; *U.S. Public*, pg. 866
GETRAG FORD TRANSMISSIONS SLOVAKIA SRO—See Ford Motor Company; *U.S. Public*, pg. 866
GHANADHARA INDUSTRIES LTD.—See Bibojee Services Private Limited; *Int'l*, pg. 1018
GKN AMERICA CORP—See GKN plc; *Int'l*, pg. 2984
GKN ARMSTRONG WHEELS INC—See GKN plc; *Int'l*, pg. 2984
GKN DRIVELINE BOWLING GREEN INC—See GKN plc; *Int'l*, pg. 2984
GKN DRIVELINE CELAYA SA DE CV—See GKN plc; *Int'l*, pg. 2984
GKN DRIVELINE DEUTSCHLAND GMBH—See GKN plc; *Int'l*, pg. 2984
GKN DRIVELINE INTERNATIONAL GMBH—See GKN plc; *Int'l*, pg. 2984
GKN DRIVELINE KOPING AB—See GKN plc; *Int'l*, pg. 2984
GKN DRIVELINE KOPING AB—See GKN plc; *Int'l*, pg. 2984
GKN DRIVELINE NEWTON LLC—See GKN plc; *Int'l*, pg. 2984
GKN DRIVELINE POLSKA SP. Z O.O.—See GKN plc; *Int'l*, pg. 2985
GKN DRIVELINE SA—See GKN plc; *Int'l*, pg. 2984
GKN DRIVELINE SERVICE SCANDINAVIA AB—See GKN plc; *Int'l*, pg. 2984
GKN DRIVELINE SLOVENIJA D.O.O.—See GKN plc; *Int'l*, pg. 2985
GKN ESKISEHIR AUTOMOTIVE PRODUCTS MANUFACTURE AND SALES A.S.—See GKN plc; *Int'l*, pg. 2985
GKN INDUSTRIES LTD—See GKN plc; *Int'l*, pg. 2985
GKN LAND SYSTEMS LTD—See GKN plc; *Int'l*, pg. 2985
GKN NORTH AMERICA SERVICES INC.—See GKN plc; *Int'l*, pg. 2985
GKN PLC; *Int'l*, pg. 2983
GKN ROCKFORD, INC.—See GKN plc; *Int'l*, pg. 2985
GKN SINTER METALS INC.—See GKN plc; *Int'l*, pg. 2985
GKN WHEELS NAGBOL A/S—See GKN plc; *Int'l*, pg. 2986
G-KT DO BRASIL LTDA.—See G-TEKT Corporation; *Int'l*, pg. 2863
GLOBAL PMX CO., LTD.; *Int'l*, pg. 3000
GMB CORP.; *Int'l*, pg. 3012
GMB KOREA CORP.—See GMB Corp.; *Int'l*, pg. 3012
GME AEROSPACE INDUSTRIA DE MATERIAL COMPOSTO S.A.—See EFORT Intelligent Equipment Co., Ltd.; *Int'l*, pg. 2321
GM POWERTRAIN GROUP—See General Motors Company; *U.S. Public*, pg. 924
GOLDE AUBURN HILLS, LLC—See Cie Automotive S.A.; *Int'l*, pg. 1604
GOLDE CHANGCHUN CO., LTD.—See Cie Automotive S.A.; *Int'l*, pg. 1604
GOLDE LOZORNO, SPOL, S.R.O.—See Cie Automotive S.A.; *Int'l*, pg. 1604
GOLDE ORADEA, SRL—See Cie Automotive S.A.; *Int'l*, pg. 1604
GOLDE SHANDONG CO., LTD.—See Cie Automotive S.A.; *Int'l*, pg. 1604
GOLDE SHANGHAI CO., LTD.—See Cie Automotive S.A.; *Int'l*, pg. 1604
GOLDE TIANJIN CO., LTD.—See Cie Automotive S.A.; *Int'l*, pg. 1604
GOLDE WUHAN CO., LTD.—See Cie Automotive S.A.; *Int'l*, pg. 1604
GONVARRI GALICIA, S.A.—See Corporacion Gestamp SL; *Int'l*, pg. 1804
GONVAUTO, S.A.—See Corporacion Gestamp SL; *Int'l*, pg. 1804
GOODYEAR GERMANY GMBH—See The Goodyear Tire & Rubber Company; *U.S. Public*, pg. 2084
GORDON-DARBY SYSTEMS, INC.—See Searchlight Capital Partners, L.P.; *U.S. Private*, pg. 3590
GRAMMER INTERIOR COMPONENTS GMBH—See Grammer AG; *Int'l*, pg. 3053
GREAT LAKES ASSEMBLIES, LLC—See TAG Holdings, LLC; *U.S. Private*, pg. 3922

336390 — OTHER MOTOR VEHICLE...

GREEN POINT COMPRESSOR SERVICES & PARTS SDN. BHD.—See Far East Group Limited; *Int'l*, pg. 2616
GREINER PERFOAM GMBH—See Greiner Holding AG; *Int'l*, pg. 3079
GRIFFIN THERMAL PRODUCTS INC.; *U.S. Private*, pg. 1788
GROCLIN KARPATY SP. Z O.O.—See Groclin S.A.; *Int'l*, pg. 3087
GROCLIN SEATING GMBH—See Groclin S.A.; *Int'l*, pg. 3087
GROCLIN SERVICE SP. Z O.O.—See Groclin S.A.; *Int'l*, pg. 3087
GROTE ELECTRONICS—See Grote Industries, Inc.; *U.S. Private*, pg. 1793
GROTE INDUSTRIES, CO.—See Grote Industries, Inc.; *U.S. Private*, pg. 1793
GROTE INDUSTRIES EUROPE GMBH—See Grote Industries, Inc.; *U.S. Private*, pg. 1793
GROTE (SHANGHAI) CO., LTD—See Grote Industries, Inc.; *U.S. Private*, pg. 1793
GRUPO ANTOLIN-ARAGUSA, S.A.U.—See Grupo Antolin-Irausa, S.A.; *Int'l*, pg. 3119
GRUPO ANTOLIN-ARA SL—See Grupo Antolin-Irausa, S.A.; *Int'l*, pg. 3119
GRUPO ANTOLIN-ARDASA, S.A.U.—See Grupo Antolin-Irausa, S.A.; *Int'l*, pg. 3119
GRUPO ANTOLIN-AUTOTRIM, S.A.U.—See Grupo Antolin-Irausa, S.A.; *Int'l*, pg. 3119
GRUPO ANTOLIN-BOHEMIA AS—See Grupo Antolin-Irausa, S.A.; *Int'l*, pg. 3119
GRUPO ANTOLIN-BRATISLAVA, S.R.O.—See Grupo Antolin-Irausa, S.A.; *Int'l*, pg. 3119
GRUPO ANTOLIN-DAPSA, S.A.U.—See Grupo Antolin-Irausa, S.A.; *Int'l*, pg. 3119
GRUPO ANTOLIN IGA SAS—See Grupo Antolin-Irausa, S.A.; *Int'l*, pg. 3119
GRUPO ANTOLIN-ILLINOIS, INC.—See Grupo Antolin-Irausa, S.A.; *Int'l*, pg. 3120
GRUPO ANTOLIN-ITALIA, S.R.L—See Grupo Antolin-Irausa, S.A.; *Int'l*, pg. 3119
GRUPO ANTOLIN-JAPAN, CO.—See Grupo Antolin-Irausa, S.A.; *Int'l*, pg. 3119
GRUPO ANTOLIN-JARNY, S.A.S.—See Grupo Antolin-Irausa, S.A.; *Int'l*, pg. 3119
GRUPO ANTOLIN KENTUCKY, INC.—See Grupo Antolin-Irausa, S.A.; *Int'l*, pg. 3119
GRUPO ANTOLIN-KOREA, L.L.C.—See Grupo Antolin-Irausa, S.A.; *Int'l*, pg. 3119
GRUPO ANTOLIN-LOGISTIK DEUTSCHLAND GMBH—See Grupo Antolin-Irausa, S.A.; *Int'l*, pg. 3120
GRUPO ANTOLIN LOIRE SAS—See Grupo Antolin-Irausa, S.A.; *Int'l*, pg. 3119
GRUPO ANTOLIN-MAGNESIO, S.L.U.—See Grupo Antolin-Irausa, S.A.; *Int'l*, pg. 3120
GRUPO ANTOLIN MATORELL, S.A.U.—See Grupo Antolin-Irausa, S.A.; *Int'l*, pg. 3119
GRUPO ANTOLIN-MICHIGAN, INC.—See Grupo Antolin-Irausa, S.A.; *Int'l*, pg. 3120
GRUPO ANTOLIN-MISSOURI, LLC—See Grupo Antolin-Irausa, S.A.; *Int'l*, pg. 3120
GRUPO ANTOLIN-NAVARRA, S.A.U.—See Grupo Antolin-Irausa, S.A.; *Int'l*, pg. 3120
GRUPO ANTOLIN-NORTH AMERICA, INC.—See Grupo Antolin-Irausa, S.A.; *Int'l*, pg. 3120
GRUPO ANTOLIN-OSTRAVA, S.R.O.—See Grupo Antolin-Irausa, S.A.; *Int'l*, pg. 3120
GRUPO ANTOLIN-PLASBUR, S.A.U.—See Grupo Antolin-Irausa, S.A.; *Int'l*, pg. 3120
GRUPO ANTOLIN-RYA, S.A.U.—See Grupo Antolin-Irausa, S.A.; *Int'l*, pg. 3120
GRUPO ANTOLIN-SALTILLO, S. DE R.L.DE C.V.—See Grupo Antolin-Irausa, S.A.; *Int'l*, pg. 3120
GRUPO ANTOLIN SILAO SA DE CV—See Grupo Antolin-Irausa, S.A.; *Int'l*, pg. 3119
GRUPO ANTOLIN-SOUTH AFRICA, LTD.—See Grupo Antolin-Irausa, S.A.; *Int'l*, pg. 3120
GRUPO ANTOLIN-TURNOV, S.R.O.—See Grupo Antolin-Irausa, S.A.; *Int'l*, pg. 3120
GRUPO ANTOLIN-VALPLAS, S.A.U.—See Grupo Antolin-Irausa, S.A.; *Int'l*, pg. 3120
GRUPO ANTOLIN-VIGO, S.L.U.—See Grupo Antolin-Irausa, S.A.; *Int'l*, pg. 3120
GRUPO ANTOLIN VOSGES—See Grupo Antolin-Irausa, S.A.; *Int'l*, pg. 3119
GRUPO COMPONENTES VILANOVA, S.L.—See Cie Automotive S.A.; *Int'l*, pg. 1604
GRUPO VISTEON, S. DE R.L. DE C.V.—See Visteon Corporation; *U.S. Public*, pg. 2305
GSF CAR PARTS LIMITED—See LKQ Corporation; *U.S. Public*, pg. 1336
GSP AUTOMOTIVE GROUP WENZHOU CO., LTD.; *Int'l*, pg. 3150
GSP EUROPE GMBH—See GSP Automotive Group Wenzhou Co., Ltd.; *Int'l*, pg. 3150
GSP NANJING CO., LTD.—See GSP Automotive Group Wenzhou Co., Ltd.; *Int'l*, pg. 3150
GSP N.A.—See GSP Automotive Group Wenzhou Co., Ltd.; *Int'l*, pg. 3150

G-TEKT CO., LTD. - GUNMA PLANT—See G-TEKT Corporation; *Int'l*, pg. 2863
G-TEKT CO., LTD. - HAMURA PLANT—See G-TEKT Corporation; *Int'l*, pg. 2863
G-TEKT CO., LTD. - SAITAMA PLANT—See G-TEKT Corporation; *Int'l*, pg. 2863
G-TEKT CO., LTD. - SHIGA PLANT—See G-TEKT Corporation; *Int'l*, pg. 2863
G-TEKT CO., LTD. - TOCHIGI PLANT—See G-TEKT Corporation; *Int'l*, pg. 2863
G-TEKT (DEUTSCHLAND) GMBH—See G-TEKT Corporation; *Int'l*, pg. 2863
G-TEKT EASTERN CO., LTD.—See G-TEKT Corporation; *Int'l*, pg. 2863
G-TEKT (THAILAND) CO., LTD.—See G-TEKT Corporation; *Int'l*, pg. 2863
GT TECHNOLOGIES, INC.—See Industrial Opportunity Partners, LLC; *U.S. Private*, pg. 2067
GUANAJUATO GEAR & AXLE DE MEXICO S. DE R.L. DE C.V.—See American Axle & Manufacturing Holdings, Inc.; *U.S. Public*, pg. 96
GUANGDONG CHUANGFU METAL MANUFACTURING CO., LTD.—See Alconix Corporation; *Int'l*, pg. 302
GUANGDONG DCENTI AUTO-PARTS STOCK LIMITED COMPANY; *Int'l*, pg. 3153
GUANGDONG HI LEX CABLE SYSTEM CO, LTD.—See Hi-Lex Corporation; *Int'l*, pg. 3380
GUANGDONG ZHAOQING L&V CO. LTD.—See Leggett & Platt, Incorporated; *U.S. Public*, pg. 1302
GUANGZHOU ANTOLIN AUTO-PARTS CO., LTD.—See Grupo Antolin-Irausa, S.A.; *Int'l*, pg. 3120
GUANGZHOU AUTOMOBILE GROUP COMPONENT CO., LTD.—See Guangzhou Automobile Industry Group Co., Ltd.; *Int'l*, pg. 3164
GUANGZHOU DENSO CO., LTD.—See Denso Corporation; *Int'l*, pg. 2032
GUANGZHOU GUANGYUE ASSETS MANAGEMENT CO., LTD.—See Guangzhou Automobile Industry Group Co., Ltd.; *Int'l*, pg. 3164
GUANGZHOU HITACHI UNISIA AUTOMOTIVE PARTS CO., LTD.—See Hitachi Astemo, Ltd.; *Int'l*, pg. 3408
GUILFORD MILLS AUTOMOTIVE (CZECH REPUBLIC) LIMITED—See Lear Corporation; *U.S. Public*, pg. 1296
GUI ZHOU TYRE CO., LTD.; *Int'l*, pg. 3173
GURIT COMPOSITE COMPONENTS LIMITED—See Gurit Holding AG; *Int'l*, pg. 3188
HAARTZ GMBH—See The Haartz Corporation; *U.S. Private*, pg. 4041
HALDEX AIR MANAGEMENT—See Haldex AB; *Int'l*, pg. 3228
HALDEX BRAKE PRODUCTS CORPORATION—See Haldex AB; *Int'l*, pg. 3228
HALDEX BRAKE PRODUCTS GMBH—See Haldex AB; *Int'l*, pg. 3228
HALDEX DO BRASIL IND. E COMERCIO LTDA.—See Haldex AB; *Int'l*, pg. 3228
HALDEX ESPANA S.A.—See Haldex AB; *Int'l*, pg. 3228
HALDEX EUROPE SAS—See Haldex AB; *Int'l*, pg. 3228
HALDEX HUNGARY KFT—See Haldex AB; *Int'l*, pg. 3228
HALDEX INTERNATIONAL TRADING (SHANGHAI) CO., LTD.—See Haldex AB; *Int'l*, pg. 3228
HALDEX ITALIA SRL.—See Haldex AB; *Int'l*, pg. 3228
HALDEX KOREA LTD.—See Haldex AB; *Int'l*, pg. 3228
HALDEX LIMITED—See Haldex AB; *Int'l*, pg. 3228
HALDEX NV—See Haldex AB; *Int'l*, pg. 3228
HALDEX RUSSIA OOO—See Haldex AB; *Int'l*, pg. 3228
HALDEX VEHICLE PRODUCTS (SUZHOU) CO. LTD.—See Haldex AB; *Int'l*, pg. 3228
HALDEX WIEN GES.M.B.H.—See Haldex AB; *Int'l*, pg. 3228
HANDS CORPORATION LTD. - HANDS 1 PLANT—See Hands Corporation Ltd.; *Int'l*, pg. 3243
HANDS CORPORATION LTD. - HANDS 2 PLANT—See Hands Corporation Ltd.; *Int'l*, pg. 3243
HANDS CORPORATION LTD. - HANDS 3 PLANT—See Hands Corporation Ltd.; *Int'l*, pg. 3243
HANDS CORPORATION LTD. - HANDS 5 PLANT—See Hands Corporation Ltd.; *Int'l*, pg. 3243
HANDS CORPORATION LTD. - HANDS 6 PLANT—See Hands Corporation Ltd.; *Int'l*, pg. 3243
HANDS CORPORATION LTD. - HANDS MECHANIC PLANT—See Hands Corporation Ltd.; *Int'l*, pg. 3243
HANDS CORPORATION LTD. - HANDS THUMB PLANT—See Hands Corporation Ltd.; *Int'l*, pg. 3243
HANDS CORPORATION LTD.; *Int'l*, pg. 3243
HANGZHOU HI-LEX CABLE SYSTEMS CO., LTD.—See Hi-Lex Corporation; *Int'l*, pg. 3380
HANIL FORGING INDUSTRIAL CO., LTD. - JINCHEON FACTORY—See Hanil Forging Industrial Co., Ltd.; *Int'l*, pg. 3252
HANIL FORGING INDUSTRIAL CO., LTD.; *Int'l*, pg. 3252
HANIL FORGING INDUSTRIAL CO., LTD. - THAILAND FACTORY—See Hanil Forging Industrial Co., Ltd.; *Int'l*, pg. 3252
HANJUNGNCS CO., LTD.; *Int'l*, pg. 3253
HANON CLIMATE SYSTEMS INDIA PRIVATE LIMITED—See Hahn & Company; *Int'l*, pg. 3208
HANON SYSTEMS ALABAMA CORP.—See Hahn & Company; *Int'l*, pg. 3208

HANON SYSTEMS (BEIJING) CO., LTD.—See Hahn & Company; *Int'l*, pg. 3208
HANON SYSTEMS CANADA, INC.—See Hahn & Company; *Int'l*, pg. 3208
HANON SYSTEMS PORTUGAL, S.A.—See Hahn & Company; *Int'l*, pg. 3208
HANON SYSTEMS—See Hahn & Company; *Int'l*, pg. 3207
HANON SYSTEMS (THAILAND) CO. LTD.—See Hahn & Company; *Int'l*, pg. 3208
HANSEN INTERNATIONAL INC.—See Marsh & McLennan Companies, Inc.; *U.S. Public*, pg. 1376
HARBIN VITI ELECTRONICS CO., LTD.; *Int'l*, pg. 3271
HASTINGS MANUFACTURING COMPANY—See RFE Investment Partners; *U.S. Private*, pg. 3419
HAYASHI CANADA INC.—See Hayashi Telempu Co., Ltd.; *Int'l*, pg. 3289
HAYASHI TELEMPU CO., LTD. - HAMAMATSU PLANT—See Hayashi Telempu Co., Ltd.; *Int'l*, pg. 3289
HAYASHI TELEMPU CO., LTD. - MAIN PLANT—See Hayashi Telempu Co., Ltd.; *Int'l*, pg. 3289
HAYASHI TELEMPU CO., LTD. - MIZUSHIMA PLANT—See Hayashi Telempu Co., Ltd.; *Int'l*, pg. 3289
HAYASHI TELEMPU CO., LTD. - NAGOYA PLANT—See Hayashi Telempu Co., Ltd.; *Int'l*, pg. 3289
HAYASHI TELEMPU CO., LTD. - TOYOHASHI PLANT—See Hayashi Telempu Co., Ltd.; *Int'l*, pg. 3289
HAYASHI TELEMPU NORTH AMERICA CORPORATION - ALABAMA PLANT—See Hayashi Telempu Co., Ltd.; *Int'l*, pg. 3289
HAYASHI TELEMPU NORTH AMERICA CORPORATION - KENTUCKY PLANT—See Hayashi Telempu Co., Ltd.; *Int'l*, pg. 3289
HAYASHI TELEMPU NORTH AMERICA CORPORATION - OHIO PLANT—See Hayashi Telempu Co., Ltd.; *Int'l*, pg. 3290
HAYASHI TELEMPU NORTH AMERICA CORPORATION—See Hayashi Telempu Co., Ltd.; *Int'l*, pg. 3289
HAYATELE KANTO CO., LTD.—See Hayashi Telempu Co., Ltd.; *Int'l*, pg. 3290
HAYATELE KYUSHU K.K.—See Hayashi Telempu Co., Ltd.; *Int'l*, pg. 3290
HAYATELE TOUHOKU CO., LTD.—See Hayashi Telempu Co., Ltd.; *Int'l*, pg. 3290
HAYDEN AUTOMOTIVE—See Standard Motor Products, Inc.; *U.S. Public*, pg. 1929
HBPO GMBH—See Burelle S.A.; *Int'l*, pg. 1222
HC QUERETARO S.A. DE C.V.—See Hitachi, Ltd.; *Int'l*, pg. 3413
HEARTLAND AUTOMOTIVE LLC.; *U.S. Private*, pg. 1899
HECKETHORN MANUFACTURING COMPANY, INC.—See The Rosewood Corporation; *U.S. Private*, pg. 4112
HEILONGJIANG FUJIN KAMA VEHICLE WHEEL MANUFACTURING CO., LTD.—See China Hi-Tech Group Corporation; *Int'l*, pg. 1508
HELLA CHANGCHUN TOOLING CO., LTD.—See Hella GmbH & Co. KGaA; *Int'l*, pg. 3331
HELLA ELECTRONICS ENGINEERING GMBH—See Hella GmbH & Co. KGaA; *Int'l*, pg. 3331
HELLA FAHRZEUGKOMPONENTEN GMBH—See Hella GmbH & Co. KGaA; *Int'l*, pg. 3331
HELLA GUTMANN ANLAGENVERMIETUNG GMBH—See Hella GmbH & Co. KGaA; *Int'l*, pg. 3332
HELLA GUTMANN HOLDING GMBH—See Hella GmbH & Co. KGaA; *Int'l*, pg. 3332
HELLA GUTMANN SOLUTIONS A/S—See Hella GmbH & Co. KGaA; *Int'l*, pg. 3332
HELLA GUTMANN SOLUTIONS INTERNATIONAL AG—See Hella GmbH & Co. KGaA; *Int'l*, pg. 3332
HELLA INNENLEUCHTEN-SYSTEME GMBH—See Hella GmbH & Co. KGaA; *Int'l*, pg. 3332
HELLA KGAA HUECK & CO. - NELLINGEN PLANT—See Hella GmbH & Co. KGaA; *Int'l*, pg. 3332
HELLA KGAA HUECK & CO. - PLANT 4—See Hella GmbH & Co. KGaA; *Int'l*, pg. 3332
HELLA KGAA HUECK & CO. - PLANT 5—See Hella GmbH & Co. KGaA; *Int'l*, pg. 3332
HELLA-NEW ZEALAND LIMITED—See Hella GmbH & Co. KGaA; *Int'l*, pg. 3332
HELLA SATURNUS SLOVENIJA D.O.O.—See Hella GmbH & Co. KGaA; *Int'l*, pg. 3332
HELLA SHANGHAI ELECTRONICS CO., LTD.—See Hella GmbH & Co. KGaA; *Int'l*, pg. 3332
HELLA WERKZEUG TECHNOLOGIEZENTRUM GMBH—See Hella GmbH & Co. KGaA; *Int'l*, pg. 3332
HELLA (XIAMEN) AUTOMOTIVE ELECTRONICS CO. LTD.—See Hella GmbH & Co. KGaA; *Int'l*, pg. 3331
HELLERMANNTYTON ESPANA SL—See Aptiv PLC; *Int'l*, pg. 525
HELLERMANNTYTON SP. Z.O.O.—See Aptiv PLC; *Int'l*, pg. 526
HELLO PAL INTERNATIONAL, INC.; *Int'l*, pg. 3337
HENDRICKSON AUSTRIA GMBH—See The Boler Company; *U.S. Private*, pg. 3996
HENDRICKSON AUXILIARY AXLE SYSTEMS—See The Boler Company; *U.S. Private*, pg. 3996
HENDRICKSON BUMPER & TRIM—See The Boler Company; *U.S. Private*, pg. 3996

336390 — OTHER MOTOR VEHICLE...

HENDRICKSON CANADA—See The Boler Company; *U.S. Private*, pg. 3996
HENDRICKSON COMMERCIAL VEHICLE SYSTEMS UK—See The Boler Company; *U.S. Private*, pg. 3996
HENDRICKSON FRANCE S.A.S.—See The Boler Company; *U.S. Private*, pg. 3996
HENDRICKSON INTERNATIONAL CORPORATION—See The Boler Company; *U.S. Private*, pg. 3996
HENDRICKSON ROMANIA—See The Boler Company; *U.S. Private*, pg. 3996
HENDRICKSON TRUCK COMMERCIAL VEHICLE SYSTEMS—See The Boler Company; *U.S. Private*, pg. 3996
HENGLONG USA CORPORATION—See China Automotive Systems, Inc.; *Int'l*, pg. 1484
HENKEL LOCTITE-KID GMBH—See Henkel AG & Co. KGaA; *Int'l*, pg. 3351
HENMAN ENGINEERING & MACHINE INC.—See JD Norman Industries, Inc.; *U.S. Private*, pg. 2195
HENNESSY INDUSTRIES, LLC—See Vontier Corporation; *U.S. Public*, pg. 2309
HERAEUS CATALYSTS (DANYANG) CO. LTD.—See Heraeus Holding GmbH; *Int'l*, pg. 3357
HERMES ABRASIVES (SHANGHAI) CO., LTD.—See Hermes Schleifmittel GmbH & Co. KG; *Int'l*, pg. 3363
HESCO PARTS CORPORATION; *U.S. Private*, pg. 1927
HGEARS (SUZHOU) CO., LTD.—See hGears AG; *Int'l*, pg. 3378
HI-LEX AUTO PARTS SPAIN, S.L.—See Hi-Lex Corporation; *Int'l*, pg. 3380
HI-LEX CONTROLS, INC.—See Hi-Lex Corporation; *Int'l*, pg. 3380
HI LEX DO BRASIL LTDA.—See Hi-Lex Corporation; *Int'l*, pg. 3380
HI-LEX EUROPE GMBH—See Hi-Lex Corporation; *Int'l*, pg. 3380
HI-LEX HUNGARY CABLE SYSTEM MANUFACTURING LLC—See Hi-Lex Corporation; *Int'l*, pg. 3380
HI-LEX ITALY S.P.A.—See Hi-Lex Corporation; *Int'l*, pg. 3380
HI-LEX MIYAGI, INC.—See Hi-Lex Corporation; *Int'l*, pg. 3380
HI-LEX SAITAMA, INC.—See Hi-Lex Corporation; *Int'l*, pg. 3381
HI-LEX SHIMANE, INC.—See Hi-Lex Corporation; *Int'l*, pg. 3381
HI-LEX VIETNAM CO., LTD—See Hi-Lex Corporation; *Int'l*, pg. 3380
HINDUSTAN HARDY LIMITED; *Int'l*, pg. 3400
HI-POWER LIMITED—See Flowtech Fluidpower plc; *Int'l*, pg. 2709
HITACHI AUTOMOTIVE SYSTEMS AMERICAS, INC.—See Hitachi Astemo, Ltd.; *Int'l*, pg. 3408
HITACHI AUTOMOTIVE SYSTEMS ASIA, LTD.—See Hitachi Astemo, Ltd.; *Int'l*, pg. 3408
HITACHI AUTOMOTIVE SYSTEMS (CHINA) LTD.—See Hitachi Astemo, Ltd.; *Int'l*, pg. 3408
HITACHI AUTOMOTIVE SYSTEMS EUROPE (FRANCE)—See Hitachi Astemo, Ltd.; *Int'l*, pg. 3408
HITACHI AUTOMOTIVE SYSTEMS EUROPE GMBH—See Hitachi Astemo, Ltd.; *Int'l*, pg. 3408
HITACHI AUTOMOTIVE SYSTEMS EUROPE LTD.—See Hitachi Astemo, Ltd.; *Int'l*, pg. 3408
HKS CO., LTD.; *Int'l*, pg. 3429
HKS EUROPE, LTD.—See HKS CO., LTD.; *Int'l*, pg. 3429
HL MANDO CO., LTD—See Halla Group; *Int'l*, pg. 3229
HODYON L.P.—See Fallbrook Technologies Inc.; *U.S. Private*, pg. 1467
HOERBIGER PENZBERG GMBH—See Hoerbiger Holding AG; *Int'l*, pg. 3440
HOERBIGER SYNCHRONTECHNIK GMBH & CO. KG—See Hoerbiger Holding AG; *Int'l*, pg. 3440
HO LEONG TRACTORS SDN. BHD.—See Hoe Leong Corporation Ltd.; *Int'l*, pg. 3439
HONDA ACCESS CORPORATION—See Honda Motor Co., Ltd.; *Int'l*, pg. 3460
HONDA ATLAS POWER PRODUCT (PRIVATE) LTD.—See Honda Motor Co., Ltd.; *Int'l*, pg. 3460
HONDA AUTOMOBILE (CHINA) CO., LTD—See Guangzhou Automobile Industry Group Co., Ltd.; *Int'l*, pg. 3164
HONDA DEVELOPMENT & MANUFACTURING OF AMERICA, LLC—See Honda Motor Co., Ltd.; *Int'l*, pg. 3461
HONDA ENGINEERING CHINA CO., LTD.—See Honda Motor Co., Ltd.; *Int'l*, pg. 3461
HONDA GULF FZE—See Honda Motor Co., Ltd.; *Int'l*, pg. 3461
HONDA LOGISTIC CENTER AUSTRIA G.M.B.H.—See Honda Motor Co., Ltd.; *Int'l*, pg. 3461
HONDA LOGISTIC CENTRE (U.K.) LTD.—See Honda Motor Co., Ltd.; *Int'l*, pg. 3461
HONDA MANUFACTURING OF INDIANA, LLC—See Honda Motor Co., Ltd.; *Int'l*, pg. 3461
HONDA MOTOR CO., LTD. - HAMAMATSU HOSOE FACTORY—See Honda Motor Co., Ltd.; *Int'l*, pg. 3461
HONDA SALES OPERATIONS JAPAN CO., LTD.—See Honda Motor Co., Ltd.; *Int'l*, pg. 3462

HONDA SOUTH AMERICA LTDA.—See Honda Motor Co., Ltd.; *Int'l*, pg. 3462
HONDA TRADING (CHINA) CO., LTD.—See Honda Motor Co., Ltd.; *Int'l*, pg. 3462
HONDA TRADING DE MEXICO S.A. DE C.V.—See Honda Motor Co., Ltd.; *Int'l*, pg. 3463
HONDA TRADING DO BRASIL LTDA.—See Honda Motor Co., Ltd.; *Int'l*, pg. 3463
HONDA TRADING EUROPE LTD.—See Honda Motor Co., Ltd.; *Int'l*, pg. 3462
HONDA TRADING (GUANGZHOU) CO., LTD.—See Honda Motor Co., Ltd.; *Int'l*, pg. 3462
HONDA TRADING (SOUTH CHINA) CO., LTD.—See Honda Motor Co., Ltd.; *Int'l*, pg. 3462
HONDA TRANSMISSION MANUFACTURING OF AMERICA, INC.—See Honda Motor Co., Ltd.; *Int'l*, pg. 3463
H-ONE CO. LTD. - KARASUYAMA PLANT—See H-One Co., Ltd.; *Int'l*, pg. 3194
H-ONE CO., LTD.; *Int'l*, pg. 3194
H-ONE PARTS (THAILAND) CO., LTD.—See H-One Co., Ltd.; *Int'l*, pg. 3194
HONEYWELL AUTOMOTIVE PARTS SERVICES (SHANGHAI) CO., LTD.—See Garrett Motion Inc.; *Int'l*, pg. 2886
HORIBA TECHNOLOGY (SUZHOU) CO.,LTD.—See HORIBA Ltd; *Int'l*, pg. 3476
HORMANN VEHICLE ENGINEERING GMBH—See Hormann Holding GmbH & Co. KG; *Int'l*, pg. 3480
HOR TECHNOLOGIE GMBH—See DZ BANK AG Deutsche Zentral-Genossenschaftsbank; *Int'l*, pg. 2244
HORTON MEXICO, S. DE RL DE CV—See Horton Inc.; *U.S. Private*, pg. 1984
HOTA INDUSTRIAL MFG. CO., LTD.; *Int'l*, pg. 3487
HOWCO DISTRIBUTING CO.—See Bantec, Inc.; *U.S. Public*, pg. 275
HUADA AUTOMOTIVE TECHNOLOGY CO.,LTD.; *Int'l*, pg. 3511
HUF ELECTRONICS DUSSELDORF GMBH—See Huf Hulsbeck & Furst GmbH & Co. KG; *Int'l*, pg. 3523
HUF ESPANA S.A.—See Huf Hulsbeck & Furst GmbH & Co. KG; *Int'l*, pg. 3523
HUF HULSBECK & FURST GMBH & CO. KG; *Int'l*, pg. 3523
HUF INDIA PRIVATE LIMITED—See Huf Hulsbeck & Furst GmbH & Co. KG; *Int'l*, pg. 3523
HUF NORTH AMERICA AUTOMOTIVE PARTS MANUFACTURING CORP.; *U.S. Private*, pg. 2002
HUKA B.V.—See AdderaCare AB; *Int'l*, pg. 128
HUNTER DEUTSCHLAND GMBH—See Hunter Engineering Company; *U.S. Private*, pg. 2010
HUNTER ENGINEERING COMPANY; *U.S. Private*, pg. 2009
HUNTSMAN GOMET S.R.L.—See Huntsman Corporation; *U.S. Public*, pg. 1072
HURON INC.—See Seven Mile Capital Partners, LLC; *U.S. Private*, pg. 3618
HUTCHENS INDUSTRIES INC.; *U.S. Private*, pg. 2014
HWAJIN CO., LTD.; *Int'l*, pg. 3542
HWASEUNG R&A CO., LTD.; *Int'l*, pg. 3542
HWASHIN AMERICA CORP.—See Hwashin Co., Ltd.; *Int'l*, pg. 3543
HWASHIN AUTOMOTIVE INDIA PVT., LTD.—See Hwashin Co., Ltd.; *Int'l*, pg. 3543
HWASHIN BRASIL CORP.—See Hwashin Co., Ltd.; *Int'l*, pg. 3543
HYBTRONICS MICROSYSTEMS, S.A.; *Int'l*, pg. 3544
HYDRAULICS & TRANSMISSIONS LIMITED—See Flowtech Fluidpower plc; *Int'l*, pg. 2709
HYUNDAI IHL CO., LTD.—See Hyundai MOBIS Co., Ltd.; *Int'l*, pg. 3558
HYUNDAI INDUSTRIAL CO., LTD. - ASAN PLANT—See Hyundai Industrial Co., Ltd.; *Int'l*, pg. 3557
HYUNDAI INDUSTRIAL CO., LTD. - BEIJING PLANT—See Hyundai Industrial Co., Ltd.; *Int'l*, pg. 3557
HYUNDAI MNSOFT, INC.—See Hyundai Motor Company; *Int'l*, pg. 3559
HYUNDAI MOBIS CO., LTD. - ANYANG FACTORY—See Hyundai MOBIS Co., Ltd.; *Int'l*, pg. 3558
HYUNDAI MOBIS CO., LTD. - ASAN FACTORY—See Hyundai MOBIS Co., Ltd.; *Int'l*, pg. 3558
HYUNDAI MOBIS CO., LTD. - CHANGWON FACTORY—See Hyundai MOBIS Co., Ltd.; *Int'l*, pg. 3558
HYUNDAI MOBIS CO., LTD. - CHEONAN IP FACTORY—See Hyundai MOBIS Co., Ltd.; *Int'l*, pg. 3558
HYUNDAI MOBIS CO., LTD. - CHUNGJU FACTORY—See Hyundai MOBIS Co., Ltd.; *Int'l*, pg. 3558
HYUNDAI MOBIS CO., LTD. - GIMCHEON FACTORY—See Hyundai MOBIS Co., Ltd.; *Int'l*, pg. 3558
HYUNDAI MOBIS CO., LTD. - GWANGJU FACTORY—See Hyundai MOBIS Co., Ltd.; *Int'l*, pg. 3558
HYUNDAI MOBIS CO., LTD. - IHWA FACTORY—See Hyundai MOBIS Co., Ltd.; *Int'l*, pg. 3558
HYUNDAI MOBIS CO., LTD. - JINCHEON FACTORY—See Hyundai MOBIS Co., Ltd.; *Int'l*, pg. 3558
HYUNDAI MOBIS CO., LTD. - POSEUNG FACTORY—See Hyundai MOBIS Co., Ltd.; *Int'l*, pg. 3558

HYUNDAI MOBIS CO., LTD. - SEOSAN FACTORY—See Hyundai MOBIS Co., Ltd.; *Int'l*, pg. 3558
HYUNDAI MOBIS CO., LTD. - YEOMPO-DONG FACTORY—See Hyundai MOBIS Co., Ltd.; *Int'l*, pg. 3558
HYUNDAI MOTOR GROUP (CHINA) LTD.—See Hyundai Motor Company; *Int'l*, pg. 3559
HYUNDAI MOTOR (SHANGHAI) CO., LTD.—See Hyundai MOBIS Co., Ltd.; *Int'l*, pg. 3558
HYUNDAI PARTECS INC.—See Hyundai Motor Company; *Int'l*, pg. 3559
HYUNDAI ROTEM COMPANY - DANGJIN PLANT—See Hyundai Motor Company; *Int'l*, pg. 3560
HYUNDAI TRANSYS—See Hyundai Motor Company; *Int'l*, pg. 3560
HYUNDAI WIA CORPORATION—See Hyundai Motor Company; *Int'l*, pg. 3560
HYUNDAI WIA CORPORATION - ULSAN PLANT 2—See Hyundai Motor Company; *Int'l*, pg. 3560
HYUNDAI-WIA INDIA PVT LTD—See Hyundai Motor Company; *Int'l*, pg. 3560
HYUNDAM SLOVAKIA S.R.O.—See Aisan Industry Co., Ltd.; *Int'l*, pg. 250
HYUNDAM TECH CO., LTD.—See Aisan Industry Co., Ltd.; *Int'l*, pg. 250
HYUNDAM (ZHANGJIAGANG) AUTOMOBILE PARTS CO., LTD.—See Aisan Industry Co., Ltd.; *Int'l*, pg. 250
IAC MENDON, LLC—See Invesco Ltd.; *U.S. Public*, pg. 1164
IBIDEN FINE CERAMICS (SUZHOU) CO., LTD.—See Ibiden Co., Ltd.; *Int'l*, pg. 3575
IDEAL CLAMP PRODUCTS, INC.-BROWNSVILLE—See TruArc Partners, L.P.; *U.S. Private*, pg. 4245
IEA INCORPORATED; *U.S. Private*, pg. 2038
IFB AUTOMOTIVE PRIVATE LIMITED—See IFB Industries Limited; *Int'l*, pg. 3598
IGARASHI ELECTRIC WORKS (ZHUHAI) LTD.—See Igarashi Motors India Limited; *Int'l*, pg. 3601
IGARASHI MOTOREN GMBH—See Igarashi Motors India Limited; *Int'l*, pg. 3601
IHI TURBO AMERICA CO.—See IHI Corporation; *Int'l*, pg. 3604
IINO (FOSHAN) TECHNOLOGY CO., LTD.—See Daido Metal Corporation; *Int'l*, pg. 1921
ILJI TECHNOLOGY CO., LTD.; *Int'l*, pg. 3614
IMRA MATERIAL R&D CO., LTD.—See AISIN Corporation; *Int'l*, pg. 253
INDUSTRIA DE EJES Y TRANSMISSIONES S.A.—See Dana Incorporated; *U.S. Public*, pg. 623
INDUSTRIAL AIR INC.—See Limbach Holdings, Inc.; *U.S. Public*, pg. 1316
INDUSTRIAL FERRO DISTRIBUIDORA, S.A.—See Corporacion Gestamp SL; *Int'l*, pg. 1804
INDUSTRIAS AMAYA TELLERIA, S.A.U.—See Cie Automotive S.A.; *Int'l*, pg. 1604
INERGY AUTOMOTIVE SYSTEMS ARGENTINA S.A.—See Burelle S.A.; *Int'l*, pg. 1222
INGENIERIA Y CONSTRUCCION DE MATRICES, S.A.—See Acek Desarrollo y Gestion Industrial SL; *Int'l*, pg. 98
INGRESS ENERGY SDN. BHD.—See G Capital Berhad; *Int'l*, pg. 2861
INTERFACE SOLUTIONS CO., LTD.—See Daido Kogyo Co., Ltd.; *Int'l*, pg. 1922
INTERKAT KATALYSATOREN GMBH—See Baumot Group AG; *Int'l*, pg. 895
INTERMOBIL OTOMOTIV MUMESSILLIK VE TICARET A.S.—See Hella GmbH & Co. KGaA; *Int'l*, pg. 3332
INTERNATIONAL AUTOMOTIVE COMPONENTS GROUP NORTH AMERICA INC.—See Invesco Ltd.; *U.S. Public*, pg. 1164
INTERNATIONAL AUTOMOTIVE COMPONENTS GROUP, S.A.—See Invesco Ltd.; *U.S. Public*, pg. 1164
INTERNATIONAL PRODUCT DEVELOPMENT CO., INC.; *U.S. Private*, pg. 2119
INTERTEC SYSTEMS, LLC—See Adient plc; *Int'l*, pg. 148
INTERTRIM, LTDA.—See Grupo Antolin-Irausa, S.A.; *Int'l*, pg. 3120
INYECTAMETAL, S.A.—See Cie Automotive S.A.; *Int'l*, pg. 1604
ISRI GMBH—See AUNDE Achter & Ebels GmbH; *Int'l*, pg. 705
ISRINGHAUSEN GMBH & CO. KG—See AUNDE Achter & Ebels GmbH; *Int'l*, pg. 705
ISRINGHAUSEN, INC.—See AUNDE Achter & Ebels GmbH; *Int'l*, pg. 706
ISRINGHAUSEN INDUSTRIAL LTDA.—See AUNDE Achter & Ebels GmbH; *Int'l*, pg. 706
ISRINGHAUSEN OF SOUTH AFRICA (PTY) LTD.—See AUNDE Achter & Ebels GmbH; *Int'l*, pg. 706
ISRINGHAUSEN QUERETARO S.A. DE C.V.—See AUNDE Achter & Ebels GmbH; *Int'l*, pg. 706
ISRINGHAUSEN SPAIN S.L.U.—See AUNDE Achter & Ebels GmbH; *Int'l*, pg. 706
ISS AMERICA, INC.—See Daido Metal Corporation; *Int'l*, pg. 1922
ISS MEXICO MANUFACTURING, S.A. DE C.V.—See Daido Metal Corporation; *Int'l*, pg. 1922

336390 — OTHER MOTOR VEHICLE...

ISUZU SERVICE CENTER SDN. BHD.—See DRB-HICOM Berhad; *Int'l*, pg. 2201.
ITM MINING PTY. LTD.—See Titan International, Inc.; *U.S. Public*, pg. 2160
ITT INDUSTRIES INC.—See ITT Inc.; *U.S. Public*, pg. 1178
ITW DELFAST DO BRASIL LTDA.—See Illinois Tool Works Inc.; *U.S. Public*, pg. 1105
ITW EF&C SELB GMBH—See Illinois Tool Works Inc.; *U.S. Public*, pg. 1105
I YUAN PRECISION INDUSTRIAL CO., LTD.; *Int'l*, pg. 3562
JACOBS (SUZHOU) VEHICLE SYSTEMS CO., LTD—See Cummins Inc.; *U.S. Public*, pg. 608
JAEGER FRANCE SARL—See AdCapital AG; *Int'l*, pg. 126
JANESVILLE DE MEXICO, S.A. DE C.V. - CELAYA PLANT—See Jason Industries, Inc.; *U.S. Private*, pg. 2189
JANESVILLE DE MEXICO, S.A. DE C.V.—See Jason Industries, Inc.; *U.S. Private*, pg. 2189
JARDIM SISTEMAS AUTOMOTIVOS E INDUSTRIAIS, S.A.—See Cie Automotive S.A.; *Int'l*, pg. 1604
JASON INCORPORATED - BATTLE CREEK PLANT—See Jason Industries, Inc.; *U.S. Private*, pg. 2189
JASON INCORPORATED - COLUMBUS PLANT—See Jason Industries, Inc.; *U.S. Private*, pg. 2189
JASON INCORPORATED - OLD FORT PLANT—See Jason Industries, Inc.; *U.S. Private*, pg. 2189
JD NORMAN INDUSTRIES-WINDSOR PLANT—See JD Norman Industries, Inc.; *U.S. Private*, pg. 2195
JECO CO., LTD.—See Denso Corporation; *Int'l*, pg. 2032
JEFFERSON ELORA CORPORATION—See G-TEKT Corporation; *Int'l*, pg. 2864
JEFFERSON INDUSTRIES CORPORATION—See G-TEKT Corporation; *Int'l*, pg. 2863
JEFFERSON SOUTHERN CORPORATION—See G-TEKT Corporation; *Int'l*, pg. 2864
JIANGSU DAEDONG DOOR INC.—See Hi-Lex Corporation; *Int'l*, pg. 3381
JIANGSU DAE DONG HI-LEX INC.—See Hi-Lex Corporation; *Int'l*, pg. 3381
JIANGSU DAIFUKU RIXIN AUTOMATION CO., LTD.—See Daifuku Co., Ltd.; *Int'l*, pg. 1926
JIANGSU FLEXIBLE AUTO PARTS CO., LTD.—See Changzhou Tenglong Auto Parts Co., Ltd.; *Int'l*, pg. 1445
JIANGSU MOBIS AUTOMOTIVE PARTS CO., LTD.—See Hyundai MOBIS Co., Ltd.; *Int'l*, pg. 3558
JINXI INDUSTRIES GROUP CO., LTD.—See China North Industries Group Corporation; *Int'l*, pg. 1535
JOHN BOYD ENTERPRISES INC.; *U.S. Private*, pg. 2220
JOHN CHUBB INSTRUMENTATION LTD.—See DEKRA e.V.; *Int'l*, pg. 2009
JOST-WERKE GMBH—See Cinven Limited; *Int'l*, pg. 1612
JVIS MANUFACTURING—See JVIS USA LLC; *U.S. Private*, pg. 2246
JVIS USA LLC; *U.S. Private*, pg. 2246
KALIDA MANUFACTURING, INC.—See H-One Co., Ltd.; *Int'l*, pg. 3194
KEIHIN AUTO PARTS (THAILAND) CO., LTD.—See Hitachi Astemo, Ltd.; *Int'l*, pg. 3408
KEIHIN CAROLINA SYSTEM TECHNOLOGY, LLC—See Hitachi Astemo, Ltd.; *Int'l*, pg. 3409
KEIHIN CORPORATION—See Hitachi Astemo, Ltd.; *Int'l*, pg. 3408
KEIHIN DE MEXICO, S.A. DE C.V.—See Hitachi, Ltd.; *Int'l*, pg. 3423
KEIHIN FIE PVT LTD—See Hitachi Astemo, Ltd.; *Int'l*, pg. 3409
KEIHIN IPT MFG., LLC—See Hitachi Astemo, Ltd.; *Int'l*, pg. 3409
KEIHIN (THAILAND) CO., LTD.—See Hitachi Astemo, Ltd.; *Int'l*, pg. 3408
KEIHIN WATARI CO., LTD.—See Hitachi Astemo, Ltd.; *Int'l*, pg. 3409
KENDON CORPORATION—See Cox Enterprises, Inc.; *U.S. Private*, pg. 1075
KEYKERT USA, INC.—See China North Industries Group Corporation; *Int'l*, pg. 1535
KIEKERT AG—See China North Industries Group Corporation; *Int'l*, pg. 1535
KIEKERT CS S.R.O.—See China North Industries Group Corporation; *Int'l*, pg. 1536
KINEDYNE CANADA LIMITED—See Kinedyne Corporation; *U.S. Private*, pg. 2307
KINEDYNE CORPORATION; *U.S. Private*, pg. 2307
KINETICS LTD.—See Elbit Systems Limited; *Int'l*, pg. 2345
KIYA CORPORATION—See HOWA Corporation; *Int'l*, pg. 3492
K'MAC CO., LTD.—See Alconix Corporation; *Int'l*, pg. 302
K&N ENGINEERING INC.; *U.S. Private*, pg. 2250
KOREA DELPHI AUTOMOTIVE SYSTEMS CORPORATION—See Aptiv PLC; *U.S. Public*, pg. 525
KOTOBUKI INDUSTRY CO., LTD.—See AISIN Corporation; *Int'l*, pg. 253
KP HOLDINGS LLC; *U.S. Private*, pg. 2345
KTH PARTS INDUSTRIES INC.; *U.S. Private*, pg. 2355
KTH SHELBURNE MFG., INC.—See Honda Motor Co., Ltd.; *Int'l*, pg. 3463
KWM BEACH MANUFACTURING CO INC; *U.S. Private*, pg. 2359

KYOSAN DENKI AMERICA, INC.—See Denso Corporation; *Int'l*, pg. 2032
KYOSAN DENKI CO., LTD. - PLANT 2—See Denso Corporation; *Int'l*, pg. 2032
KYUSHU ALPHA CO., LTD.—See ALPHA Corporation; *Int'l*, pg. 367
KYUSHU F.C.C. CO., LTD.—See F.C.C. Co., Ltd.; *Int'l*, pg. 2596
KYUSHU SHIROKI CO., LTD.—See AISIN Corporation; *Int'l*, pg. 253
L-3 COMMUNICATIONS COMBAT PROPULSION SYSTEMS—See L3Harris Technologies, Inc.; *U.S. Public*, pg. 1282
LAFRANCE CORPORATION - BENMATT INDUSTRIES DIVISION—See LaFrance Corporation; *U.S. Private*, pg. 2373
LEAR AUTOMOTIVE MOROCCO SAS—See Lear Corporation; *U.S. Public*, pg. 1297
LEAR CORPORATION HUNGARY AUTOMOTIVE MANUFACTURING KFT.—See Lear Corporation; *U.S. Public*, pg. 1297
LEAR CORPORATION POLAND II SP. Z O.O.—See Lear Corporation; *U.S. Public*, pg. 1297
LEAR CORPORATION PORTUGAL - COMPONENTES PARA AUTOMOVEIS S.A.—See Lear Corporation; *U.S. Public*, pg. 1297
LEAR CORPORATION SEATING FRANCE FEIGNIES SAS—See Lear Corporation; *U.S. Public*, pg. 1297
LEAR TEKNIK OTO YAN SANAYI LTD. SIRKET—See Lear Corporation; *U.S. Public*, pg. 1297
LESJOFORS AUTOMOTIVE LTD.—See Beijer Alma AB; *Int'l*, pg. 943
LIFESAFER, INC; *U.S. Private*, pg. 2451
LIGHTNING EMOTORS, INC.; *U.S. Public*, pg. 1315
LINK MANUFACTURING LTD.; *U.S. Private*, pg. 2461
LIUZHOU LONGRUN AUTO PARTS MANUFACTURING CO., LTD.—See Changzhou Tenglong Auto Parts Co., Ltd.; *Int'l*, pg. 1445
L&M RADIATOR INCORPORATED—See Westinghouse Air Brake Technologies Corporation; *U.S. Public*, pg. 2358
LORAIN COUNTY AUTOMOTIVE SYSTEMS INC.—See P&C Group, Inc.; *U.S. Private*, pg. 3059
LUND INTERNATIONAL HOLDING COMPANY—See CCMP Capital Advisors, LP; *U.S. Private*, pg. 801
LUND INTERNATIONAL HOLDING COMPANY—See TA Associates, Inc.; *U.S. Private*, pg. 3919
LUVERNE TRUCK EQUIPMENT INC.—See LCI Industries; *U.S. Public*, pg. 1295
MACHINE TOOL & GEAR, INC.—See Cie Automotive S.A.; *Int'l*, pg. 1604
MAE MASCHINEN- UND APPARATEBAU GOTZEN GMBH—See Gesco AG; *Int'l*, pg. 2945
MAGNETI MARELLI AUTOMOTIVE COMPONENTS (WUHU) CO. LTD.—See KKR & Co. Inc.; *U.S. Public*, pg. 1260
MAGNETI MARELLI EXHAUST SYSTEMS POLSKA SP. Z O.O.—See KKR & Co. Inc.; *U.S. Public*, pg. 1260
MAGNETI MARELLI FRANCE S.A.S.—See KKR & Co. Inc.; *U.S. Public*, pg. 1261
MAGNETI MARELLI JAPAN K.K.—See KKR & Co. Inc.; *U.S. Public*, pg. 1261
MAGNETI MARELLI POWERTRAIN (SHANGHAI) CO. LTD.—See KKR & Co. Inc.; *U.S. Public*, pg. 1261
MAGNETI MARELLI POWERTRAIN SLOVAKIA S.R.O.—See KKR & Co. Inc.; *U.S. Public*, pg. 1261
MAGNETI MARELLI SLOVAKIA S.R.O.—See KKR & Co. Inc.; *U.S. Public*, pg. 1261
MAGNETI MARELLI SUSPENSION SYSTEMS BIELSKO SP. Z.O.O.—See KKR & Co. Inc.; *U.S. Public*, pg. 1261
MAGNETO EQUIPMENT, INC.—See Ilion Capital Partners; *U.S. Private*, pg. 2041
MAHLE COMPONENTE DE MOTOR SRL—See Food Empire Holdings Limited; *Int'l*, pg. 2727
MANDO BROSE CORPORATION—See Brose Fahrzeugteile GmbH & Co. KG; *Int'l*, pg. 1196
MANGINO CHEVROLET, INC.—See General Motors Company; *U.S. Public*, pg. 925
MAQUINADOS DE PRECISION DE MEXICO S. DE R.L. DE C.V.—See Cie Automotive S.A.; *Int'l*, pg. 1604
MARADYNE CORPORATION - SUPERTRAPP INDUSTRIAL MUFFLERS DIVISION—See Dreison International, Inc.; *U.S. Private*, pg. 1276
MARELLI CORPORATION—See KKR & Co. Inc.; *U.S. Public*, pg. 1260
MARELLI NORTH AMERICA, INC.—See KKR & Co. Inc.; *U.S. Public*, pg. 1260
MARELLI TENNESSEE USA LLC—See KKR & Co. Inc.; *U.S. Public*, pg. 1261
MARION FLUID POWER DIVISION OF MARADYNE CORP—See Dreison International, Inc.; *U.S. Private*, pg. 1276
MAR SK, S.R.O.—See Cie Automotive S.A.; *Int'l*, pg. 1604
MARTIN WELLS INDUSTRIES; *U.S. Private*, pg. 2596
MASTSYSTEM INTERNATIONAL OY—See Advent International Corporation; *U.S. Private*, pg. 100
MAVAL INDUSTRIES LLC—See Torque Capital Group, LLC; *U.S. Private*, pg. 4189

MAVIC S.A.S.—See ANTA Sports Products Limited; *Int'l*, pg. 480
MAXEY TRAILERS MFG., INC.; *U.S. Private*, pg. 2618
MCGOVERN AUTO GROUP CORP SERVICES, INC.; *U.S. Private*, pg. 2635
MCKECHNIE VEHICLE COMPONENTS—See MVC Holdings LLC; *U.S. Private*, pg. 2821
MEDALLION INSTRUMENTATION SYSTEMS LLC.; *U.S. Private*, pg. 2650
MEFRO RADERWERK RONNEBURG GMBH—See Crestview Partners, L.P.; *U.S. Private*, pg. 1097
MEFRO WHEELS FRANCE S.A.S.—See Crestview Partners, L.P.; *U.S. Private*, pg. 1098
MEFRO WHEELS PANAMERICA S.A.—See Crestview Partners, L.P.; *U.S. Private*, pg. 1098
MEFRO WHEELS RUSSIA PLANT TOGLIATTI OOO—See Crestview Partners, L.P.; *U.S. Private*, pg. 1098
MEFRO WHEELS TURKEY JANT SANAYI A.S.—See Crestview Partners, L.P.; *U.S. Private*, pg. 1097
MELETT LIMITED—See Westinghouse Air Brake Technologies Corporation; *U.S. Public*, pg. 2358
MERITOR AFTERMARKET SWITZERLAND AG—See Cummins Inc.; *U.S. Public*, pg. 608
MERITOR HEAVY VEHICLE SYSTEMS, LLC—See Cummins Inc.; *U.S. Public*, pg. 608
MERITOR HOLDINGS NETHERLANDS B.V.—See Cummins Inc.; *U.S. Public*, pg. 609
MERITOR, INC.—See Cummins Inc.; *U.S. Public*, pg. 608
MERITOR JAPAN K.K.—See Cummins Inc.; *U.S. Public*, pg. 609
MERITOR MANAGEMENT CORP.—See Cummins Inc.; *U.S. Public*, pg. 609
MERITOR MEXICANA, S.A. DE C.V.—See Cummins Inc.; *U.S. Public*, pg. 609
METALDYNE INTERNATIONAL (UK) LTD.—See American Axle & Manufacturing Holdings, Inc.; *U.S. Public*, pg. 97
METALDYNE SINTERED COMPONENTS, INC. - ST. MARYS—See American Axle & Manufacturing Holdings, Inc.; *U.S. Public*, pg. 97
METALDYNE SINTERFORGED PRODUCTS, LLC—See American Axle & Manufacturing Holdings, Inc.; *U.S. Public*, pg. 97
METALSA, S.A. DE C.V.—See Grupo Proeza, S.A.P.I. de C.V.; *Int'l*, pg. 3134
METAVATION, LLC—See MW Universal Inc.; *U.S. Private*, pg. 2822
METRA ELECTRONICS CORPORATION; *U.S. Private*, pg. 2684
METZELER AUTOMOTIVE PROFILE SYSTEMS GMBH—See Cooper-Standard Holdings Inc.; *U.S. Public*, pg. 574
MEYER PRODUCTS LLC—See Aebi Schmidt Holding AG; *Int'l*, pg. 170
MGI COUTIER UK LTD.—See AKWEL; *Int'l*, pg. 268
MICHELIN AUSTRALIA PTY LTD—See Compagnie Generale des Etablissements Michelin SCA; *Int'l*, pg. 1743
MICHELIN MALAYSIA SDN. BHD.—See Compagnie Generale des Etablissements Michelin SCA; *Int'l*, pg. 1744
MICHIGAN WHEEL OPERATIONS, LLC—See The Anderson Group, LLC; *U.S. Public*, pg. 3986
MILE MARKER INTERNATIONAL INC.; *U.S. Private*, pg. 2727
MIYAZAKI ASMO CO., LTD.—See Denso Corporation; *Int'l*, pg. 2032
MOBIS ALABAMA, LLC—See Hyundai MOBIS Co., Ltd.; *Int'l*, pg. 3558
MOBIS AUTOMOTIVE CZECH S.R.O.—See Hyundai MOBIS Co., Ltd.; *Int'l*, pg. 3558
MOBIS GEORGIA LLC—See Hyundai MOBIS Co., Ltd.; *Int'l*, pg. 3558
MOBIS INDIA, LTD.—See Hyundai MOBIS Co., Ltd.; *Int'l*, pg. 3558
MOBIS NORTH AMERICA, LLC—See Hyundai MOBIS Co., Ltd.; *Int'l*, pg. 3558
MOBIS PARTS AMERICA, LLC—See Hyundai MOBIS Co., Ltd.; *Int'l*, pg. 3558
MOBIS PARTS AUSTRALIA PTY. LTD.—See Hyundai MOBIS Co., Ltd.; *Int'l*, pg. 3558
MOBIS PARTS CANADA CORPORATION—See Hyundai MOBIS Co., Ltd.; *Int'l*, pg. 3558
MOBIS PARTS EUROPE B.V.—See Hyundai MOBIS Co., Ltd.; *Int'l*, pg. 3558
MOBIS PARTS MIAMI, LLC—See Hyundai MOBIS Co., Ltd.; *Int'l*, pg. 3558
MOBIS PARTS MIDDLE EAST FZE—See Hyundai MOBIS Co., Ltd.; *Int'l*, pg. 3558
MOBIS SLOVAKIA S.R.O.—See Hyundai MOBIS Co., Ltd.; *Int'l*, pg. 3558
MODINE AUTOMOBILTECHNIK GMBH—See Modine Manufacturing Company; *U.S. Public*, pg. 1455
MODINE EUROPE GMBH—See Modine Manufacturing Company; *U.S. Public*, pg. 1455
MODINE HUNGARIA KFT.—See Modine Manufacturing Company; *U.S. Public*, pg. 1455
MODINE MANUFACTURING COMPANY; *U.S. Public*, pg. 1454
MODINE NEUENKIRCHEN GMBH—See Modine Manufacturing Company; *U.S. Public*, pg. 1455

N.A.I.C.S. INDEX
336390 — OTHER MOTOR VEHICLE...

MONROE AUSTRALIA PTY. LIMITED—See Apollo Global Management, Inc.; *U.S. Public*, pg. 162

MONT BLANC INDUSTRI AB—See Accent Equity Partners AB; *Int'l*, pg. 81

MOROSO PERFORMANCE PRODUCTS, INC.; *U.S. Private*, pg. 2786

MORSE TEC EUROPE S.R.L.—See Enstar Group Limited; *Int'l*, pg. 2448

MOULAGES PLASTIQUES INDUSTRIELS DE L'ESSONNE SARL—See HEICO Corporation; *U.S. Public*, pg. 1020

MOVE, INC.—See Base Intelligence, Inc; *U.S. Private*, pg. 484

MR. GASKET COMPANY; *U.S. Private*, pg. 2805

MR. GASKET INC.—See Mr. Gasket Company; *U.S. Private*, pg. 2805

MUELLES Y BALLESTAS HISPANI-ALEMANAS S.A.—See The Boler Company; *U.S. Private*, pg. 3996

MUNJAL SHOWA LIMITED—See Hero Corp.; *Int'l*, pg. 3364

MUNJAL SHOWA LIMITED—See Hitachi Astemo, Ltd.; *Int'l*, pg. 3409

MUSTANG DYNAMOMETER, CHINA—See Mustang Dynamometer; *U.S. Private*, pg. 2819

MUSTANG MOTORCYCLE PRODUCTS, LLC—See LDR Growth Partners; *U.S. Private*, pg. 2404

NAGANO JECO CO., LTD.—See Denso Corporation; *Int'l*, pg. 2032

NAM YANG METALS CO., LTD.—See Hitachi, Ltd.; *Int'l*, pg. 3423

NANJING CRYOMAX AUTO PARTS CO., LTD.—See Cryomax Cooling System Corp.; *U.S. Private*, pg. 1860

NANTONG KINEDYNE LIMITED—See Kinedyne Corporation; *U.S. Private*, pg. 2307

NANYANG CIJAN AUTO SHOCK ABSORBER CO., LTD.—See China First Capital Group Limited; *Int'l*, pg. 1503

NEC SCHOTT COMPONENTS CORPORATION—See Carl-Zeiss-Stiftung; *Int'l*, pg. 1336

NELSON GLOBAL PRODUCTS, INC. - BLACK RIVER FALLS MANUFACTURING FACILITY—See Wind Point Advisors LLC; *U.S. Private*, pg. 4534

NELSON GLOBAL PRODUCTS, INC.—See Wind Point Advisors LLC; *U.S. Private*, pg. 4534

NEMAK WISCONSIN-TAYLOR FACILITY—See ALFA, S.A.B. de C.V.; *Int'l*, pg. 313

NEPAL HYDRO & ELECTRIC LIMITED—See Butwal Power Company Limited; *Int'l*, pg. 1229

NEUMAYER TEKFOR AUTOMOTIVE BRASIL LTDA.—See Amtek Auto Limited; *Int'l*, pg. 441

NEUMAYER TEKFOR SCHMOLLN GMBH—See Amtek Auto Limited; *Int'l*, pg. 441

NICHIALLOY CO., LTD.—See Aisan Industry Co., Ltd.; *Int'l*, pg. 251

NINGBO FUERDA SMARTECH CO., LTD. - MELVINDALE BRANCH—See Beijing WKW Automotive Parts Co., Ltd.; *Int'l*, pg. 960

NINGBO FUERDA SMARTECH CO., LTD.—See Beijing WKW Automotive Parts Co., Ltd.; *Int'l*, pg. 960

NIPPON RETARDER SYSTEM CO., LTD.—See Exedy Corporation; *Int'l*, pg. 2581

NIPPON WIPER BLADE CO., LTD.—See Denso Corporation; *Int'l*, pg. 2032

NISSIN BRAKE EUROPE, S.L.U—See Honda Motor Co., Ltd.; *Int'l*, pg. 3463

NORTH AMERICAN ASSEMBLIES, LLC—See TAG Holdings, LLC; *U.S. Private*, pg. 3922

NORTHERN TECHNICAL, L.L.C.—See Donaldson Company, Inc.; *U.S. Public*, pg. 676

NORTH LINGYUN INDUSTRIAL GROUP CO., LTD.—See China North Industries Group Corporation; *Int'l*, pg. 1535

NOVA BUS CORPORATION—See AB Volvo; *Int'l*, pg. 42

NOVA RECYD, S.A.U.—See Cie Automotive S.A.; *Int'l*, pg. 1605

NRF BVBA—See Banco Products (I) Ltd.; *Int'l*, pg. 824

NRF FRANCE SAS—See Banco Products (I) Ltd.; *Int'l*, pg. 824

NRF HANDELSGES. GMBH—See Banco Products (I) Ltd.; *Int'l*, pg. 824

NUGAR, S.A. DE C.V.—See Cie Automotive S.A.; *Int'l*, pg. 1605

NUMECA INDIA SOFTWARE PRIVATE LIMITED—See Cadence Design Systems, Inc.; *U.S. Public*, pg. 419

OCTAGON AUTOMOTIVE, LLC—See Octagon Holdings, LLC; *U.S. Private*, pg. 2992

OE PLUS, LTD.—See Motorcar Parts of America, Inc.; *U.S. Public*, pg. 1477

OHBA SEIKEN CO. LTD.—See Alconix Corporation; *Int'l*, pg. 302

OKAYAMA EAGLE CO., LTD.—See Eagle Industry Co., Ltd.; *Int'l*, pg. 2266

O.L.C.I. ENGINEERING INDIA PRIVATE LIMITED—See EFORT Intelligent Equipment Co., Ltd.; *Int'l*, pg. 2321

OME IRON CASTING CO., LTD.—See Harmonic Drive Systems Inc.; *Int'l*, pg. 3277

OMIX-ADA, INC.—See CCMP Capital Advisors, LP; *U.S. Private*, pg. 801

OMIX-ADA, INC.—See TA Associates, Inc.; *U.S. Private*, pg. 3919

OMNIMATICS SDN. BHD.—See APM Automotive Holdings Berhad; *Int'l*, pg. 516

OOO EDAG PRODUCTION SOLUTIONS RU—See ATON GmbH; *Int'l*, pg. 689

OPTIMA BATTERIES AB—See Brookfield Corporation; *Int'l*, pg. 1175

OPTIMA BATTERIES AB—See Caisse de Depot et Placement du Quebec; *Int'l*, pg. 1254

OPTIMAL AG & CO. KG—See LKQ Corporation; *U.S. Public*, pg. 1336

OPTIMAL POLSKA SP. Z O.O.—See LKQ Corporation; *U.S. Public*, pg. 1336

OPUS GROUP AB—See Searchlight Capital Partners, L.P.; *U.S. Private*, pg. 3590

OPUS INSPECTION (PVT) LTD.—See Searchlight Capital Partners, L.P.; *U.S. Private*, pg. 3590

OPUS INSPECTION SA—See Searchlight Capital Partners, L.P.; *U.S. Private*, pg. 3590

ORBELAN PLASTICOS, S.A.—See Cie Automotive S.A.; *Int'l*, pg. 1605

ORIENTAL ASSEMBLERS SDN. BHD.—See Berjaya Assets Berhad; *Int'l*, pg. 982

PACCAR PARTS—See PACCAR Inc.; *U.S. Public*, pg. 1631

PACCAR WINCH INC.—See The Black Phoenix Group; *U.S. Private*, pg. 3995

PACIFIC CENTURY MOTORS—See Aviation Industry Corporation of China; *Int'l*, pg. 742

P/A GMBH—See P/A Industries, Inc.; *U.S. Private*, pg. 3061

PAI INDUSTRIES INC.; *U.S. Private*, pg. 3075

PARKER HANNIFIN PNEUMATIC DIVISION NORTH AMERICA WATTS FLUIDAIR—See Parker Hannifin Corporation; *U.S. Public*, pg. 1644

PARKER HANNIFIN WATTS FLUID AIR—See Parker Hannifin Corporation; *U.S. Public*, pg. 1643

PEER CHAIN COMPANY; *U.S. Private*, pg. 3128

PELLEGRINO DISTRIBUIDORA AUTOPECAS LTDA.—See The Cypress Group LLC; *U.S. Private*, pg. 4017

PEPS-JV (KEDAH) SDN. BHD.—See EP Manufacturing Bhd.; *Int'l*, pg. 2458

PERFECT EQUIPMENT CO., LLC - MURFREESBORO—See Berwind Corporation; *U.S. Private*, pg. 541

PERFECT EQUIPMENT CO., LLC - MURFREESBORO—See Berwind Corporation; *U.S. Private*, pg. 541

PERFECT EQUIPMENT CO., LLC - SNUGL MANUFACTURING DIVISION—See Berwind Corporation; *U.S. Private*, pg. 541

PERFECT EQUIPMENT CO., LLC - SNUGL MANUFACTURING DIVISION—See Berwind Corporation; *U.S. Private*, pg. 541

PERFECT EQUIPMENT COMPANY, LLC—See Berwind Corporation; *U.S. Private*, pg. 541

PERFECT EQUIPMENT COMPANY, LLC—See Berwind Corporation; *U.S. Private*, pg. 541

PERFECT EQUIPMENT COMPANY, LLC—See Berwind Corporation; *U.S. Private*, pg. 541

PERFECT EQUIPMENT COMPANY, LLC—See Berwind Corporation; *U.S. Private*, pg. 541

PHILIPPINE AUTO COMPONENTS, INC.—See Denso Corporation; *Int'l*, pg. 2032

PHILLIPS INDUSTRIES; *U.S. Private*, pg. 3171

PHILLIPS & TEMRO INDUSTRIES, INC.—See Harbour Group Industries, Inc.; *U.S. Private*, pg. 1860

PHN INDUSTRY SDN. BHD.—See DRB-HICOM Berhad; *Int'l*, pg. 2202

THE PIERCE CO., INC.—See Avis Industrial Corporation; *U.S. Private*, pg. 408

PIEZAS Y RODAJES SA—See Titan International, Inc.; *U.S. Public*, pg. 2160

PINTURA, ESTAMPADO Y MONTAJE, S.A.P.I. DE C.V.—See Cie Automotive S.A.; *Int'l*, pg. 1605

PLEWS, INC.; *U.S. Private*, pg. 3214

POLYCHARGE AMERICA, INC.—See BorgWarner Inc.; *U.S. Public*, pg. 371

PORTER ENGINEERED SYSTEMS INC—See KP Holdings LLC; *U.S. Private*, pg. 2345

POWERBRACE CORPORATION—See Miner Enterprises, Inc.; *U.S. Private*, pg. 2741

POWERFLOW, INC.—See Kinderhook Industries, LLC; *U.S. Private*, pg. 2306

POWER STOP LLC; *U.S. Private*, pg. 3239

PRECISE MACHINE COMPANY INC.—See George T. Schmidt, Inc.; *U.S. Private*, pg. 1683

PREMIER HAZARD LTD.—See Ecco Safety Group; *U.S. Private*, pg. 1326

PRESSURE SYSTEMS INTERNATIONAL, INC.—See Genstar Capital, LLC; *U.S. Private*, pg. 1676

PRIME WHEEL CORPORATION; *U.S. Private*, pg. 3262

PRITEX LIMITED—See Compagnie de Saint-Gobain SA; *Int'l*, pg. 1725

PROAIR, LLC—See KODA Enterprises Group, LLC; *U.S. Private*, pg. 2335

PROLIANCE INTERNATIONAL, INC.; *U.S. Public*, pg. 1726

PRORETA SP. Z O.O.—See Figene Capital SA; *Int'l*, pg. 2661

PRO-TECH INDUSTRIES INC.; *U.S. Private*, pg. 3271

PSC METALS MASSILLON, LLC—See Icahn Enterprises L.P.; *U.S. Public*, pg. 1085

PSM FASTENERS (HONG KONG) LTD.—See Bulten AB; *Int'l*, pg. 1214

P.T. AISAN NASMOCO INDUSTRI—See Aisan Industry Co., Ltd.; *Int'l*, pg. 251

PT. EXEDY MANUFACTURING INDONESIA—See Exedy Corporation; *Int'l*, pg. 2581

PT. EXEDY PRIMA INDONESIA—See Exedy Corporation; *Int'l*, pg. 2581

PT. F.TECH INDONESIA—See F-Tech Inc.; *Int'l*, pg. 2595

PT. HAMADEN INDONESIA MANUFACTURING—See Denso Corporation; *Int'l*, pg. 2032

PT. HI-LEX CIREBON—See Hi-Lex Corporation; *Int'l*, pg. 3381

PT. HI-LEX INDONESIA CIKARANG FACTORY—See Hi-Lex Corporation; *Int'l*, pg. 3381

P.T. HONDA PRECISION PARTS MANUFACTURING—See Honda Motor Co., Ltd.; *Int'l*, pg. 3464

P.T. HONDA TRADING INDONESIA—See Honda Motor Co., Ltd.; *Int'l*, pg. 3463

PT MICHELIN INDONESIA—See Compagnie Generale des Etablissements Michelin SCA; *Int'l*, pg. 1745

P.T. MOLTEN ALUMINIUM PRODUCER INDONESIA—See Honda Motor Co., Ltd.; *Int'l*, pg. 3463

PT MULTISTRADA ARAH SARANA TBK.—See Compagnie Generale des Etablissements Michelin SCA; *Int'l*, pg. 1745

QINGDAO CIMC ECO - EQUIPMENT CO., LTD.—See China International Marine Containers (Group) Co., Ltd.; *Int'l*, pg. 1512

QUALICO PRECISION PRODUCTS, LLC—See Orscheln Group; *U.S. Private*, pg. 3045

QUALITOR, INC.—See Wellspring Capital Management LLC; *U.S. Private*, pg. 4477

QUALITY/CENTURY HOLDINGS CORPORATION—See Brookfield Corporation; *U.S. Public*, pg. 1176

QUANZHOU FENSUN AUTOMOBILE PARTS CO., LTD.—See China Automobile Parts Holdings Limited; *Int'l*, pg. 1484

RADIADORES VISCONDE S/A—See Modine Manufacturing Company; *U.S. Public*, pg. 1455

RADIATORS AUSTRALIA (2000) PTY. LTD.—See APM Automotive Holdings Berhad; *Int'l*, pg. 516

RALLY MANUFACTURING, INC.; *U.S. Private*, pg. 3350

RAM-BUL LLC—See Bulten AB; *Int'l*, pg. 1215

RANAS BILFJADRAR AB—See Axel Johnson Gruppen AB; *Int'l*, pg. 765

RANDALL MANUFACTURING, LLC—See The Sterling Group, L.P.; *U.S. Private*, pg. 4123

RAVAGLIOLI DEUTSCHLAND GMBH—See Dover Corporation; *U.S. Public*, pg. 682

RAVAGLIOLI S.P.A.—See Dover Corporation; *U.S. Public*, pg. 682

RAV EQUIPOS ESPANA, S.L.—See Dover Corporation; *U.S. Public*, pg. 682

RAV FRANCE—See Dover Corporation; *U.S. Public*, pg. 682

RAYBESTOS POWERTRAIN, LLC—See Sun Capital Partners, Inc.; *U.S. Private*, pg. 3860

RCO ENGINEERING INC.; *U.S. Private*, pg. 3362

RCTS AUTOWORX INC.—See HKS CO., LTD.; *Int'l*, pg. 3429

READYLIFT SUSPENSION, INC.—See Clearlake Capital Group, L.P.; *U.S. Private*, pg. 938

RECYDE, S.A.U.—See Cie Automotive S.A.; *Int'l*, pg. 1605

RELIABLE TOOL & MACHINE CO.; *U.S. Private*, pg. 3394

RENCOL TOLERANCE RINGS LTD.—See Compagnie de Saint-Gobain SA; *Int'l*, pg. 1725

REPAIR & MAINTENANCE PLANS LIMITED—See Cambria Automobiles plc; *U.S. Private*, pg. 1269

RETERRA CO., LTD—See F-Tech Inc.; *Int'l*, pg. 2595

RG BROSE AUTOMOTIVE COMPONENTS (PTY.) LTD.—See Brose Fahrzeugteile GmbH & Co. KG; *Int'l*, pg. 1196

RHENOY ONDERDELEN B.V.—See LKQ Corporation; *U.S. Public*, pg. 1336

RIKER PRODUCTS, INC.; *U.S. Private*, pg. 3436

ROCHESTER GEAR, INC.—See Cie Automotive S.A.; *Int'l*, pg. 1604

ROCKWELL AMERICAN—See Questor Management Company, LLC; *U.S. Private*, pg. 3326

ROCKWOOD & CO. INC.—See Rockwood Holding Company Inc.; *U.S. Private*, pg. 3468

ROH WHEELS AUSTRALIA—See Arrowcrest Group Pty. Ltd.; *Int'l*, pg. 580

ROMEO POWER, INC.—See Nikola Corp.; *U.S. Public*, pg. 1529

ROSTRA PRECISION CONTROLS, INC.—See Superior Capital Partners LLC; *U.S. Private*, pg. 3876

ROUSH MANUFACTURING, INC.—See Roush Enterprises, Inc.; *U.S. Private*, pg. 3489

RUGGED LINER INC.; *U.S. Private*, pg. 3502

RUSSIAN MACHINES CORPORATION—See Basic Element Company; *Int'l*, pg. 886

RYCO GROUP PTY LIMITED—See Amotiv Limited; *Int'l*, pg. 431

SAFETY COMPONENTS FABRIC TECHNOLOGIES, INC.—See Platinum Equity, LLC; *U.S. Private*, pg. 3203

336390 — OTHER MOTOR VEHICLE...

SAFETY SOLUTIONS, INC.—See Carousel Capital Partners; *U.S. Private*, pg. 770
SAGE AUTOMOTIVE INTERIORS, INC. - ABBEVILLE PLANT—See Asahi Kasei Corporation; *Int'l*, pg. 597
SAGE AUTOMOTIVE INTERIORS, INC. - GAYLEY PLANT—See Asahi Kasei Corporation; *Int'l*, pg. 597
SAGE AUTOMOTIVE INTERIORS, INC. - SHARON PLANT—See Asahi Kasei Corporation; *Int'l*, pg. 597
SAGE AUTOMOTIVE INTERIORS, INC.—See Asahi Kasei Corporation; *Int'l*, pg. 597
SAGE BRASIL INTERIORS AUTOMOTIVOS INDUSTRIA E COMERCIO, LTDA.—See Asahi Kasei Corporation; *Int'l*, pg. 597
SAINT-GOBAIN AUTOVER DEUTSCHLAND GMBH—See Compagnie de Saint-Gobain SA; *Int'l*, pg. 1736
SAINT-GOBAIN SEKURIT CR SPOL S.R.O.—See Compagnie de Saint-Gobain SA; *Int'l*, pg. 1736
SAKTHI AUTO COMPONENT LIMITED—See AAPICO Hitech plc; *Int'l*, pg. 37
SAMHAN CO. LTD.—See CR Holdings Co., Ltd.; *Int'l*, pg. 1827
SANKYO RADIATOR CO., LTD.—See Denso Corporation; *Int'l*, pg. 2033
SAUER-DANFOSS-DAIKIN LTD.—See Danfoss A/S; *Int'l*, pg. 1961
SAUER-DANFOSS-DAIKIN MOBILE HYDRAULICS (SHANGHAI) CO., LTD.—See Danfoss A/S; *Int'l*, pg. 1961
SAUER-DANFOSS-DAIKIN PTE. LTD.—See Danfoss A/S; *Int'l*, pg. 1961
SAUER-DANFOSS (SHANGHAI) CO. LTD.—See Danfoss A/S; *Int'l*, pg. 1960
SAUER-DANFOSS (US) COMPANY—See Danfoss A/S; *Int'l*, pg. 1960
SAVE-A-LOAD, INC.—See Fleet Engineers, Inc.; *U.S. Private*, pg. 1541
SC CIE MATRICON, S.A.—See Cie Automotive S.A.; *Int'l*, pg. 1605
SCHENCK ROTEC CORPORATION—See Durr AG; *Int'l*, pg. 2233
SCHENCK USA CORP.—See Durr AG; *Int'l*, pg. 2233
SCHUMAG AG—See Hangzhou Meibah Precision Machinery Co., Ltd.; *Int'l*, pg. 3249
SCHUMAG ROMANIA S.R.L.—See Hangzhou Meibah Precision Machinery Co., Ltd.; *Int'l*, pg. 3249
SCS FRIGETTE—See Hickman Investments Inc.; *U.S. Private*, pg. 1933
SECURITY CHAIN COMPANY—See The Carlyle Group Inc.; *U.S. Public*, pg. 2055
SENSE TECHNOLOGIES INC.; *U.S. Public*, pg. 1866
SEOHANWARNER TURBO SYSTEMS, LTD.—See BorgWarner Inc.; *U.S. Public*, pg. 371
SEOJIN INDUSTRIAL CO., LTD.—See Ecoplastic Corporation; *Int'l*, pg. 2299
SHANDONG KANGTAI CHASYS AUTOMOBILE PARTS CO., LTD—See CHASYS Co., Ltd; *Int'l*, pg. 1457
SHANGHAI BORGWARNER AUTOMOTIVE (GROUP) CO., LTD.—See BorgWarner Inc.; *U.S. Public*, pg. 371
SHANGHAI FUTAILONG AUTO TECH CO., LTD.—See Beijing WKW Automotive Parts Co., Ltd.; *Int'l*, pg. 960
SHANGHAI FUYULONG AUTO TECH CO., LTD.—See Beijing WKW Automotive Parts Co., Ltd.; *Int'l*, pg. 960
SHANGHAI HUF AUTOMOTIVE LOCK CO., LTD.—See Huf Hulsbeck & Furst GmbH & Co. KG; *Int'l*, pg. 3523
SHANGHAI SHOWA AUTO PARTS CO., LTD.—See Hitachi Astemo, Ltd.; *Int'l*, pg. 3409
SHENYANG JINBEI HENGLONG AUTOMOTIVE STEERING SYSTEM CO., LTD.—See China Automotive Systems, Inc.; *Int'l*, pg. 1484
SHIMANE EAGLE CO., LTD.—See Eagle Industry Co., Ltd.; *Int'l*, pg. 2266
SHIMIZU INDUSTRY CO., LTD—See Denso Corporation; *Int'l*, pg. 2032
SHIROKI CORPORATION—See AISIN Corporation; *Int'l*, pg. 253
SHIROKI-GA, LLC—See AISIN Corporation; *Int'l*, pg. 253
SHIROKI-GT, LLC—See AISIN Corporation; *Int'l*, pg. 254
SHIROKI NORTH AMERICA, INC.—See AISIN Corporation; *Int'l*, pg. 253
SHOWA DO BRAZIL LTDA.—See Hitachi Astemo, Ltd.; *Int'l*, pg. 3410
SHOWA INDUSTRIA E COMERCIO LTDA.—See Hitachi Astemo, Ltd.; *Int'l*, pg. 3410
SHOWA KYUSHU CORPORATION—See Hitachi Astemo, Ltd.; *Int'l*, pg. 3410
SIAM HITACHI AUTOMOTIVE PRODUCTS LTD.—See Hitachi, Ltd.; *Int'l*, pg. 3424
SIMPSON PERFORMANCE PRODUCTS INC.—See Carousel Capital Partners; *U.S. Private*, pg. 770
SINFA CABLES SARL—See AKWEL; *Int'l*, pg. 268
SISTEMAS ELECTRICOS Y CONMUTADORES, S.A. DE C.V.—See Aptiv PLC; *Int'l*, pg. 525
SISTEMAS KINEDYNE, S.A. DE C.V.—See Kinedyne Corporation; *U.S. Private*, pg. 2307
SMEAL SFA, LLC—See AIP, LLC; *U.S. Private*, pg. 135
SMP FOUR SEASONS DE MEXICO, S. DE R.L. DE C.V.—See Standard Motor Products, Inc.; *U.S. Public*, pg. 1929

SMP POLAND SP. Z O.O.—See Standard Motor Products, Inc.; *U.S. Public*, pg. 1929
SOFTRIDE, INC.—See Allsop, Inc.; *U.S. Private*, pg. 193
SOGEFI FILTRATION ARGENTINA S.A.—See Compagnia Finanziaria de Benedetti S.p.A.; *Int'l*, pg. 1722
SOGEFI S.P.A.—See Compagnia Finanziaria de Benedetti S.p.A.; *Int'l*, pg. 1722
SOMASCHINI AUTOMOTIVE, SRL—See Cie Automotive S.A.; *Int'l*, pg. 1605
SOUTHERN FELT COMPANY, INC.—See Lydall, Inc.; *U.S. Public*, pg. 1350
SPALDING AUTOMOTIVE INC.; *U.S. Private*, pg. 3744
SPAREX (TRACTOR ACCESSORIES) LIMITED—See AGCO Corporation; *U.S. Public*, pg. 59
SPARTAN MOWERS, LLC—See The Toro Company; *U.S. Public*, pg. 2135
SPECIAL DEVICES JAPAN LTD.—See Daicel Corporation; *Int'l*, pg. 1920
SPECIAL DEVICES (THAILAND) CO., LTD.—See Daicel Corporation; *Int'l*, pg. 1920
SPORTECH, LLC—See Monomoy Capital Partners LLC; *U.S. Private*, pg. 2772
SPRIG & TRANSPORT NEEDS MANUFACTURING CO—See Chemical Industries Holding Company; *Int'l*, pg. 1462
SRC POWER SYSTEMS—See SRC Holdings Corporation; *U.S. Private*, pg. 3767
STANADYNE CORPORATION—See Kohlberg & Company, LLC; *U.S. Private*, pg. 2339
STANDARD MOTOR PRODUCTS GREENVILLE DIV—See Standard Motor Products, Inc.; *U.S. Public*, pg. 1929
STANDARD MOTOR PRODUCTS, INC.; *U.S. Public*, pg. 1929
STANT CORP.—See H.I.G. Capital, LLC; *U.S. Private*, pg. 1831
STEMCO INC.—See Enpro Inc.; *U.S. Public*, pg. 775
STEMCO KAISER—See Enpro Inc.; *U.S. Public*, pg. 775
ST HITEC LTD.—See HKS CO., LTD.; *Int'l*, pg. 3429
STIGAB OY—See Addtech AB; *Int'l*, pg. 135
STRATTEC SECURITY CORPORATION; *U.S. Public*, pg. 1954
STS ACOUSTICS S.P.A.—See Adler Plastic SpA; *Int'l*, pg. 150
SUAB CO., LTD.—See Denso Corporation; *Int'l*, pg. 2032
SUDRAD GMBH RADTECHNIK—See Crestview Partners, L.P.; *U.S. Private*, pg. 1097
SUJAN BARRE THOMAS AVS PRIVATE LIMITED—See Cooper-Standard Holdings Inc.; *U.S. Public*, pg. 574
SUMIDEN HYOSUNG STEEL CORD (THAILAND) CO., LTD.—See Hyosung Corporation; *Int'l*, pg. 3552
SUN MEDICAL TECHNOLOGY RESEARCH CORP—See Hi-Lex Corporation; *Int'l*, pg. 3381
SUPERIOR INDUSTRIES DE MEXICO, S.A. DE C.V.—See SUPERIOR INDUSTRIES INTERNATIONAL INC; *U.S. Public*, pg. 1967
SUPERIOR INDUSTRIES INTERNATIONAL INC; *U.S. Public*, pg. 1966
SUPERIOR INDUSTRIES INTERNATIONAL KANSAS, LLC—See SUPERIOR INDUSTRIES INTERNATIONAL INC; *U.S. Public*, pg. 1967
SUPERIOR INDUSTRIES INTERNATIONAL MICHIGAN, LLC—See SUPERIOR INDUSTRIES INTERNATIONAL INC; *U.S. Public*, pg. 1967
SUPERTRAPP INDUSTRIES, INC.—See Dreison International, Inc.; *U.S. Private*, pg. 1276
SUSPA GMBH—See Andlinger & Company, Inc.; *U.S. Private*, pg. 279
SUSPA NANJING CO. LTD.—See Andlinger & Company, Inc.; *U.S. Private*, pg. 279
SVENSK AIRBAG AB—See Autoliv, Inc.; *Int'l*, pg. 728
SWELL-MARUI (GUANGZHOU) AUTOMOBILE PARTS CO., LTD.—See Guangdong Hongtu Technology (Holdings) Co., Ltd.; *Int'l*, pg. 3156
SWENSON SPREADER LLC—See Aebi Schmidt Holding AG; *Int'l*, pg. 170
SYPRIS TECHNOLOGIES, INC.—See Sypris Solutions, Inc.; *U.S. Public*, pg. 1972
SYPRIS TECHNOLOGIES TOLUCA, S.A. DE C.V.—See Sypris Solutions, Inc.; *U.S. Public*, pg. 1972
SYSTECH CHILE LTDA.—See Searchlight Capital Partners, L.P.; *U.S. Private*, pg. 3590
SYSTECH PERUANA SRL—See Searchlight Capital Partners, L.P.; *U.S. Private*, pg. 3590
SZ DESIGN SRL—See Autoline Industries Limited; *Int'l*, pg. 728
TABO OTOMOTIV AS—See Cofle SpA; *Int'l*, pg. 1693
TAIWAN KEIHHIN CARBURETOR CO., LTD. - CHING-SHUI FACTORY—See Hitachi Astemo, Ltd.; *Int'l*, pg. 3409
TAIWAN KEIHHIN CARBURETOR CO., LTD.—See Hitachi Astemo, Ltd.; *Int'l*, pg. 3409
TAIWAY INDUSTRY CO., LTD.—See Dana Incorporated; *U.S. Public*, pg. 623
TAIWAY INDUSTRY CO., LTD.—See GKN plc; *Int'l*, pg. 2986
TAKAOKA LIOHO (TIANJIN) INDUSTRIES CO., LTD.—See AISIN Corporation; *Int'l*, pg. 253
TALESOL S.A.—See Dana Incorporated; *U.S. Public*, pg. 623
TANGSHAN AISIN AUTOMOTIVE PARTS CO., LTD—See AISIN Corporation; *Int'l*, pg. 254
TASHEELAT AUTOMOTIVE COMPANY WLL—See Bahrain Commercial Facilities Company BSC; *Int'l*, pg. 800
TAYLOR MADE SYSTEMS - INDIANA FACILITY—See LCI Industries; *U.S. Public*, pg. 1295
TBMECA POLAND SP. Z O.O.—See Denso Corporation; *Int'l*, pg. 2029
TBMECA POLAND SP. Z O.O.—See Equistone Partners Europe Limited; *Int'l*, pg. 2487
TECHNISCH SERVICE CENTRUM RHENOY B.V.—See LKQ Corporation; *U.S. Public*, pg. 1336
TECNOLOGIA MODIFICADA, S.A. DE C.V.—See Caterpillar, Inc.; *U.S. Public*, pg. 454
TEKFOR INC—See Amtek Auto Limited; *Int'l*, pg. 441
TEMSA EUROPE NV—See Haci Omer Sabanci Holding A.S.; *Int'l*, pg. 3204
TENNECO AUTOMOTIVE DEUTSCHLAND GMBH—See Apollo Global Management, Inc.; *U.S. Public*, pg. 162
TENNECO AUTOMOTIVE EASTERN EUROPE SP. ZO.O.—See Apollo Global Management, Inc.; *U.S. Public*, pg. 162
TENNECO AUTOMOTIVE EUROPE COORDINATION CENTER BVBA—See Apollo Global Management, Inc.; *U.S. Public*, pg. 162
TENNECO AUTOMOTIVE HOLDINGS SOUTH AFRICA PTY. LTD—See Apollo Global Management, Inc.; *U.S. Public*, pg. 163
TENNECO AUTOMOTIVE PORT ELIZABETH (PTY) LIMITED—See Apollo Global Management, Inc.; *U.S. Public*, pg. 163
TENNECO AUTOMOTIVE SVERIGE A.B.—See Apollo Global Management, Inc.; *U.S. Public*, pg. 163
TENNECO MARZOCCHI ASIA LTD.—See Apollo Global Management, Inc.; *U.S. Public*, pg. 163
TENNECO MARZOCCHI S.R.L.—See Apollo Global Management, Inc.; *U.S. Public*, pg. 163
TENNECO ZWICKAU GMBH—See Apollo Global Management, Inc.; *U.S. Public*, pg. 163
TEXTRON VERWALTUNGS-GMBH—See Textron Inc.; *U.S. Public*, pg. 2028
THERM AIR AUSTRALIA PTY. LTD.—See Elders Limited; *Int'l*, pg. 2346
THYSSENKRUPP TAILORED BLANKS (WUHAN) LTD.—See Advent International Corporation; *U.S. Private*, pg. 107
THYSSENKRUPP TAILORED BLANKS (WUHAN) LTD.—See Cinven Limited; *Int'l*, pg. 1615
TIANJIN DENSO AIR-CONDITIONER CO., LTD.—See Denso Corporation; *Int'l*, pg. 2033
TIANJIN FAWER DENSO AIR-CONDITIONER CO., LTD.—See Denso Corporation; *Int'l*, pg. 2033
TIANJIN FAW TOYOTA MOTOR CO., LTD.—See China FAW Group Corporation; *Int'l*, pg. 1502
TIANJIN MOBIS AUTOMOTIVE PARTS CO., LTD.—See Hyundai MOBIS Co., Ltd.; *Int'l*, pg. 3558
TIANJIN TENGLONG UNITED AUTO PARTS CO., LTD.—See Changzhou Tenglong Auto Parts Co., Ltd.; *Int'l*, pg. 1445
TISZA AUTOMOTIVE KFT—See AD Plastik d.d.; *Int'l*, pg. 122
TITAN ASIA JANT SANAYI VE TICARET A.S.—See Titan International, Inc.; *U.S. Public*, pg. 2160
TITAN EUROPE PLC—See Titan International, Inc.; *U.S. Public*, pg. 2160
TITAN WHEEL CORPORATION OF VIRGINIA—See Titan International, Inc.; *U.S. Public*, pg. 2160
TK CARBURETTOR CO. LTD.—See Aisan Industry Co., Ltd.; *Int'l*, pg. 251
TONAMINO KOGYO CO., LTD.—See AISIN Corporation; *Int'l*, pg. 254
TORRE AUTOMOTIVE (PTY) LIMITED—See Apex Partners Proprietary Limited; *Int'l*, pg. 512
TORRE AUTOMOTIVE (PTY) LIMITED—See TRG Management LP; *U.S. Private*, pg. 4220
TOYO SPRING INDUSTRIAL CO., LTD.—See Carlit Co., Ltd.; *Int'l*, pg. 1338
TRANSEJES TRANSMISSIONES HOMOCINETICAS DE COLUMBIA S.A.—See Dana Incorporated; *U.S. Public*, pg. 623
TRANSFORMACIONES METALURGICAS NORMA, S.A.—See Cie Automotive S.A.; *Int'l*, pg. 1605
TRANSMISIONES Y EQUIPOS MECANICOS, S.A. DE C.V.—See Grupo Kuo, S.A.B. de C.V.; *Int'l*, pg. 3131
TRANSWHEEL CORPORATION; *U.S. Private*, pg. 4211
TRELLEBORGVIBRACOUSTIC—See Freudenberg SE; *Int'l*, pg. 2790
TRIANGLE SUSPENSION SYSTEMS, INC.—See Berkshire Hathaway Inc.; *U.S. Public*, pg. 310
TRICO COMPONENTES S.A. DE C.V.—See Crowne Group LLC; *U.S. Private*, pg. 1112
TRICO LATINOAMERICANA DO BRASIL LTDA—See Crowne Group LLC; *U.S. Private*, pg. 1112
TRICO LATINOAMERICANA SA—See Crowne Group LLC; *U.S. Private*, pg. 1112
TRICO LIMITED—See Crowne Group LLC; *U.S. Private*, pg. 1112
TRICO PTY. LIMITED—See Crowne Group LLC; *U.S. Private*, pg. 1112

N.A.I.C.S. INDEX

336411 — AIRCRAFT MANUFACTUR...

TRIM PARTS, INC.—See Dubin Clark & Company, Inc.; *U.S. Private*, pg. 1283

TRIM SYSTEMS OPERATING CORP.—See Commercial Vehicle Group, Inc.; *U.S. Public*, pg. 547

TRISTONE FLOWTECH GERMANY GMBH—See BAVARIA Industries Group AG; *Int'l*, pg. 899

TRUCK HERO, INC.—See CCMP Capital Advisors, LP; *U.S. Private*, pg. 801

TRUCK HERO, INC.—See TA Associates, Inc.; *U.S. Private*, pg. 3919

TSUKIBOSHI MANUFACTURING CO., LTD.—See Daido Kogyo Co., Ltd.; *Int'l*, pg. 1921

TSUSHIMA DIE-ENGINEERING CORP.—See Honda Motor Co., Ltd.; *Int'l*, pg. 3464

TUBULAR METAL SYSTEMS—See Patriarch Partners, LLC; *U.S. Private*, pg. 3109

TUNGALOY FRICTION MATERIAL VIETNAM LTD.—See Honda Motor Co., Ltd.; *Int'l*, pg. 3463

TURBO ENERGY PRIVATE LTD.—See BorgWarner Inc.; *U.S. Public*, pg. 371

TVH AUSTRALIA PTY LTD—See Group Thermote & Vanhalst; *Int'l*, pg. 3090

TVH DEUTSCHLAND GMBH—See Group Thermote & Vanhalst; *Int'l*, pg. 3090

TVH FRANCE SASU—See Group Thermote & Vanhalst; *Int'l*, pg. 3090

TVH INDIA PRIVATE LTD.—See Group Thermote & Vanhalst; *Int'l*, pg. 3090

TVH MIDDLE EAST FZE—See Group Thermote & Vanhalst; *Int'l*, pg. 3090

TVH PARTS MEXICO S. DE R.L. DE C.V.—See Group Thermote & Vanhalst; *Int'l*, pg. 3090

TVH TRADING (XIAMEN) CO. LTD.—See Group Thermote & Vanhalst; *Int'l*, pg. 3090

T&WA, INC.—See The Goodyear Tire & Rubber Company; *U.S. Public*, pg. 2084

TWINTEC TECHNOLOGIE GMBH—See Baumot Group AG; *Int'l*, pg. 895

UCANDO GMBH—See Hella GmbH & Co. KGaA; *Int'l*, pg. 3333

UGN DE MEXICO, S. DE R.L. DE C.V.—See Autoneum Holding Ltd.; *Int'l*, pg. 731

UGN, INC.—See Autoneum Holding Ltd.; *Int'l*, pg. 731

UKM FAHRZEUGTEILE GMBH—See CMP Capital Management-Partners GmbH; *Int'l*, pg. 1672

ULSAN ENGINEERING CO.,LTD.—See Honda Motor Co., Ltd.; *Int'l*, pg. 3464

ULTRA WHEEL COMPANY INC.; *U.S. Private*, pg. 4277

UNEEK 4X4 AUSTRALIA PTY LTD—See Amotiv Limited; *Int'l*, pg. 431

UNIVERSAL AIR TOOL COMPANY LIMITED—See ShoreView Industries, LLC; *U.S. Private*, pg. 3642

U.S. MANUFACTURING CORPORATION—See Wynnchurch Capital, L.P.; *U.S. Private*, pg. 4578

VCST AUTOMOTIVE COMPONENTS (CHANGZHOU) CO, LTD.—See Gimv NV; *Int'l*, pg. 2976

VCST AUTOMOTIVE PRODUCTION ALBA SRL—See Gimv NV; *Int'l*, pg. 2976

VCST DE MEXICO S. DE R.L. DE C.V.—See Gimv NV; *Int'l*, pg. 2976

VCST REICHENBACH GMBH—See Gimv NV; *Int'l*, pg. 2976

VELVAC INCORPORATED—See The Eastern Company; *U.S. Public*, pg. 2069

VENCHURS PACKAGING, INC.; *U.S. Private*, pg. 4356

VENTRA LLC GRAND RAPIDS PLANT 5—See Flex-N-Gate Corporation; *U.S. Private*, pg. 1543

VENTREX AUTOMOTIVE GMBH—See Aalberts N.V.; *Int'l*, pg. 36

VETH PROPULSION B.V.—See Twin Disc, Incorporated; *U.S. Public*, pg. 2207

VIAM MANUFACTURING, INC.—See Freudenberg SE; *Int'l*, pg. 2790

VISTA-PRO AUTOMOTIVE, LLC—See Wynnchurch Capital, L.P.; *U.S. Private*, pg. 4578

VISTEON ASIA PACIFIC, INC.—See Visteon Corporation; *U.S. Public*, pg. 2305

VISTEON AUTOMOTIVE ELECTRONICS (THAILAND) LIMITED—See Visteon Corporation; *U.S. Public*, pg. 2305

VISTEON AUTOMOTIVE SYSTEMS INDIA PRIVATE LTD.—See Hahn & Company; *Int'l*, pg. 3208

VISTEON-AUTOPAL S.R.O.—See Visteon Corporation; *U.S. Public*, pg. 2306

VISTEON ELECTRONICS KOREA LTD.—See Visteon Corporation; *U.S. Public*, pg. 2306

VISTEON INTERIOR SYSTEMS ITALIA S.P.A.—See Cerberus Capital Management, L.P.; *U.S. Private*, pg. 839

VISTEON PORTUGUESA, LTD.—See Visteon Corporation; *U.S. Public*, pg. 2306

VISTEON S.A.—See Visteon Corporation; *U.S. Public*, pg. 2306

VOLVO HRVATSKA D.O.O.—See AB Volvo; *Int'l*, pg. 45

VOLVO-PENTA NORTH AMERICA, INC.—See AB Volvo; *Int'l*, pg. 42

VOLVO PENTA SVERIGE—See AB Volvo; *Int'l*, pg. 42

VOLVO POWERTRAIN AB—See AB Volvo; *Int'l*, pg. 45

WAECO GERMANY WSE GMBH—See Dometic Group AB; *Int'l*, pg. 2160

WAI EUROPE B.V.—See Wetherill Associates Inc.; *U.S. Private*, pg. 4502

WALKER AUSTRALIA PTY. LIMITED—See Apollo Global Management, Inc.; *U.S. Public*, pg. 163

WALKER DANMARK APS.—See Apollo Global Management, Inc.; *U.S. Public*, pg. 163

WARN AUTOMOTIVE, LLC—See Dover Corporation; *U.S. Public*, pg. 683

WARN INDUSTRIES, INC.—See Dover Corporation; *U.S. Public*, pg. 680

WATSON & CHALIN HOLDING CORP.; *U.S. Private*, pg. 4455

WATSON & CHALIN MANUFACTURING, INC.—See Watson & Chalin Holding Corp.; *U.S. Private*, pg. 4455

WEBASTO DONGHEE CO., LTD.—See DH Holdings Co., Ltd.; *Int'l*, pg. 2097

WEBB WHEEL PRODUCTS INC.; *U.S. Private*, pg. 4464

WEBER AUTOMOTIVE GMBH—See Ardian SAS; *Int'l*, pg. 556

WESTBORN SERVICE CENTER, INC.—See Cooper-Standard Holdings Inc.; *U.S. Public*, pg. 574

W.E.T. AUTOMOTIVE SYSTEMS (CHINA) LIMITED—See Gentherm Incorporated; *U.S. Public*, pg. 931

WETHERILL ASSOCIATES INC. - MONTREAL DIVISION—See Wetherill Associates Inc.; *U.S. Private*, pg. 4502

WETHERILL ASSOCIATES INC. - TORONTO DIVISION—See Wetherill Associates Inc.; *U.S. Private*, pg. 4502

WETHERILL ASSOCIATES INC. - WAIGLOBAL SHANGHAI DIVISION—See Wetherill Associates Inc.; *U.S. Private*, pg. 4502

W.E.T. SISTEMAS AUTOMOTRICES, S.A. DE C.V.—See Gentherm Incorporated; *U.S. Public*, pg. 931

WHIRLAWAY CORPORATION—See NN, Inc.; *U.S. Public*, pg. 1531

WILLIAMS CONTROLS INDUSTRIES, INC.—See Curtiss-Wright Corporation; *U.S. Public*, pg. 612

WORTHINGTON INDUSTRIES ENGINEERED CABS, INC.—See Angeles Equity Partners, LLC; *U.S. Private*, pg. 282

WORTHINGTON INDUSTRIES ENGINEERED CABS, LLC—See Angeles Equity Partners, LLC; *U.S. Private*, pg. 282

WUHAN AUTO PARTS ALLIANCE (CHINA) CO., LTD.—See G-TEKT Corporation; *Int'l*, pg. 2864

WUHAN FUBOHE AUTO PARTS CO., LTD.—See Hanwa Co., Ltd.; *Int'l*, pg. 3263

WUHAN TENGLONG UNITED AUTO ACCESSORIES MANUFACTURING CO., LTD.—See Changzhou Tenglong Auto Parts Co., Ltd.; *Int'l*, pg. 1445

WUHU TENGLONG AUTO PARTS CO., LTD.—See Changzhou Tenglong Auto Parts Co., Ltd.; *Int'l*, pg. 1445

WUXI HOTA PRECISION GEAR CO., LTD.—See Hota Industrial Mfg. Co., Ltd.; *Int'l*, pg. 3487

WUXI LEGGETT & PLATT-HUAGUANG AUTOMOBILE PARTS CO. LTD.—See Leggett & Platt, Incorporated; *U.S. Public*, pg. 1304

WUXI MOBIS AUTOMOTIVE PARTS CO., LTD.—See Hyundai MOBIS Co., Ltd.; *Int'l*, pg. 3558

WUXI NR-FREUDENBERG OILSEAL CO., LTD.—See Freudenberg SE; *Int'l*, pg. 2791

XCLUTCHUSA, INC.—See Amotiv Limited; *Int'l*, pg. 431

XIAMEN DA JUN ACCURATE INDUSTRIAL CO., LTD.—See Changzhou Tenglong Auto Parts Co., Ltd.; *Int'l*, pg. 1445

XPEL B.V.—See XPEL, Inc.; *U.S. Public*, pg. 2391

XPEL CANADA CORP.—See XPEL, Inc.; *U.S. Public*, pg. 2391

XPEL DE MEXICO S. DE R.L. DE C.V.—See XPEL, Inc.; *U.S. Public*, pg. 2391

XPEL, INC.; *U.S. Public*, pg. 2391

XPEL LTD.—See XPEL, Inc.; *U.S. Public*, pg. 2391

YACHIYO INDUSTRY CO., LTD. - KASHIWABARA PLANT—See Honda Motor Co., Ltd.; *Int'l*, pg. 3464

YACHIYO INDUSTRY CO., LTD.—See Honda Motor Co., Ltd.; *Int'l*, pg. 3464

YACHIYO MEXICO MANUFACTURING S.A. DE C.V.—See Honda Motor Co., Ltd.; *Int'l*, pg. 3464

YACHIYO OF AMERICA INC.—See Honda Motor Co., Ltd.; *Int'l*, pg. 3464

YACHIYO WUHAN MANUFACTURING CO., LTD.—See Honda Motor Co., Ltd.; *Int'l*, pg. 3464

YACHIYO ZHONGSHAN MANUFACTURING CO., LTD.—See Honda Motor Co., Ltd.; *Int'l*, pg. 3464

YAMADA SEISAKUSHO CO., LTD.—See Honda Motor Co., Ltd.; *Int'l*, pg. 3465

YAMAGATA CLUTCH CO., LTD.—See AISIN Corporation; *Int'l*, pg. 254

YANAGAWA SEIKI CO., LTD.—See Honda Motor Co., Ltd.; *Int'l*, pg. 3465

YANTAI FUYAN MOULD CO., LTD.—See F-Tech Inc.; *Int'l*, pg. 2595

YANTAI HUF AUTOMOTIVE LOCK CO., LTD.—See Huf Hulsbeck & Furst GmbH & Co. KG; *Int'l*, pg. 3523

YASAKA GAC CO., LTD.—See Denso Corporation; *Int'l*, pg. 2033

YAT YUE INDUSTRIAL CO. (HK) LTD.—See Igarashi Motors India Limited; *Int'l*, pg. 3601

YCK (THAILAND) CO., LTD.—See AISIN Corporation; *Int'l*, pg. 254

YING KOU ABE HARNESS CO., LTD.—See Air Water Inc.; *Int'l*, pg. 241

YONEZAWA ELECTRIC WIRE CO., LTD.—See Fujikura Ltd.; *Int'l*, pg. 2829

YS TECH (THAILAND) CO., LTD.—See Honda Motor Co., Ltd.; *Int'l*, pg. 3465

ZAO NORMA-OSVAR—See Autoliv, Inc.; *Int'l*, pg. 730

ZENN MOTOR COMPANY LIMITED—See FuelPositive Corporation; *Int'l*, pg. 2804

ZHANJIANG DENI CARBURETOR CO., LTD—See Hitachi Astemo, Ltd.; *Int'l*, pg. 3409

ZHEJIANG HENGDIAN TOSPO IMP.&EXP. CO. LTD.—See Hengdian Group TOSPO Lighting Co Ltd; *Int'l*, pg. 3346

ZHEJIANG RICHLEO ENVIRONMETTAL TECHNOLOGY CO., LTD.—See Changzhou Tenglong Auto Parts Co., Ltd.; *Int'l*, pg. 1445

336411 — AIRCRAFT MANUFACTURING

AAI AEROSONDE PTY LTD.—See Textron Inc.; *U.S. Public*, pg. 2029

ADANI AEROSPACE & DEFENCE LIMITED—See Adani Enterprises Limited; *Int'l*, pg. 124

AERCAP B.V.—See AerCap Holdings N.V.; *Int'l*, pg. 179

AERCAP DUTCH AIRCRAFT LEASING B.V.—See AerCap Holdings N.V.; *Int'l*, pg. 179

AERCAP IRELAND LIMITED—See AerCap Holdings N.V.; *Int'l*, pg. 179

AERCAP NETHERLANDS B.V.—See AerCap Holdings N.V.; *Int'l*, pg. 179

AERCAP USA, INC.—See AerCap Holdings N.V.; *Int'l*, pg. 179

AERFI GROUP LIMITED—See AerCap Holdings N.V.; *Int'l*, pg. 179

AEROMETALS INC.; *U.S. Private*, pg. 119

AEROSPACE INDUSTRIAL DEVELOPMENT CORPORATION; *Int'l*, pg. 181

AEROSTAR INTERNATIONAL, INC.—See TCOM, L.P.; *U.S. Private*, pg. 3943

AEROVIRONMENT, INC.; *U.S. Public*, pg. 52

AERWINS INC—See AERWINS Technologies Inc.; *Int'l*, pg. 182

AERWINS TECHNOLOGIES INC.; *Int'l*, pg. 182

AIRBUS AMERICAS, INC.—See Airbus SE; *Int'l*, pg. 244

AIRBUS DEFENCE & SPACE GMBH—See Airbus SE; *Int'l*, pg. 242

AIRBUS DEFENCE & SPACE LIMITED—See Airbus SE; *Int'l*, pg. 243

AIRBUS DEFENCE & SPACE S.A.—See Airbus SE; *Int'l*, pg. 243

AIRBUS DEUTSCHLAND GMBH—See Airbus SE; *Int'l*, pg. 244

AIRBUS DS OPTRONICS GMBH—See Airbus SE; *Int'l*, pg. 242

AIRBUS HELICOPTERS CANADA—See Airbus SE; *Int'l*, pg. 243

AIRBUS HELICOPTERS DEUTSCHLAND GMBH—See Airbus SE; *Int'l*, pg. 243

AIRBUS HELICOPTERS, INC.—See Airbus SE; *Int'l*, pg. 243

AIRBUS HELICOPTERS S.A.S.—See Airbus SE; *Int'l*, pg. 243

AIRBUS OPERATIONS GMBH—See Airbus SE; *Int'l*, pg. 244

AIRBUS OPERATIONS LTD.—See Airbus SE; *Int'l*, pg. 244

AIRBUS S.A.S.—See Airbus SE; *Int'l*, pg. 244

AIRBUS SE; *Int'l*, pg. 241

AIRCRAFT RESEARCH ASSOCIATION LIMITED—See BAE Systems plc; *Int'l*, pg. 796

AIR PARTS & SUPPLY CO.—See VSE Corporation; *U.S. Public*, pg. 2312

AIRSCREW LIMITED—See AMETEK, Inc.; *U.S. Public*, pg. 117

AMERICAN BLIMP CORP.—See Van Wagner Communications, LLC; *U.S. Private*, pg. 4341

AMPHENOL BORISCH TECHNOLOGIES, INC—See Amphenol Corporation; *U.S. Public*, pg. 126

APOLLO AEROSPACE COMPONENTS LIMITED—See Park-Ohio Holdings Corp.; *U.S. Public*, pg. 1638

ASI INNOVATION SAS; *Int'l*, pg. 609

ATHOS AERONAUTIQUE—See Assystem S.A.; *Int'l*, pg. 651

AURORA FLIGHT SCIENCES CORPORATION—See The Boeing Company; *U.S. Public*, pg. 2039

AUSTRALIAN AEROSPACE LIMITED—See Airbus SE; *Int'l*, pg. 243

AVCO CORPORATION—See Textron Inc.; *U.S. Public*, pg. 2028

AVIALL NEW ZEALAND—See The Boeing Company; *U.S. Public*, pg. 2039

AVIALL PTE LTD—See The Boeing Company; *U.S. Public*, pg. 2039

AVIATION INDUSTRY CORPORATION OF CHINA; *Int'l*, pg. 741

AVIC HELICOPTER CO., LTD.—See Aviation Industry Corporation of China; *Int'l*, pg. 741

336411 — AIRCRAFT MANUFACTUR...

AVICHINA INDUSTRY & TECHNOLOGY CO., LTD.—See Aviation Industry Corporation of China; *Int'l*, pg. 741
AVIOANE CRAIOVA S.A.; *Int'l*, pg. 744
AVIONIC DESIGN GMBH—See Deutsche Lufthansa AG; *Int'l*, pg. 2066
AVIONS DE TRANSPORT REGIONAL—See Airbus SE; *Int'l*, pg. 246
BAE SYSTEMS-FLIGHT SYSTEMS—See BAE Systems plc; *Int'l*, pg. 797
BAE SYSTEMS—See BAE Systems plc; *Int'l*, pg. 796
BAE SYSTEMS—See BAE Systems plc; *Int'l*, pg. 796
BASLER TURBO CONVERSIONS, LLC.; *U.S. Private*, pg. 485
BEECHCRAFT CORPORATION—See Textron Inc.; *U.S. Public*, pg. 2028
BEIJING EMERGING EASTERN AVIATION EQUIPMENT CO., LTD.; *Int'l*, pg. 949
BELL HELICOPTER INDIA INC.—See Textron Inc.; *U.S. Public*, pg. 2028
BELL HELICOPTER MIAMI INC.—See Textron Inc.; *U.S. Public*, pg. 2028
BELL HELICOPTER TEXTRON CANADA LIMITED—See Textron Inc.; *U.S. Public*, pg. 2028
BELL HELICOPTER TEXTRON, INC.—See Textron Inc.; *U.S. Public*, pg. 2028
BLUE FORCE TECHNOLOGIES, INC.—See Anduril Industries, Inc.; *U.S. Private*, pg. 280
B-N GROUP LIMITED; *Int'l*, pg. 785
BOEING CANADA OPERATIONS LTD.—See The Boeing Company; *U.S. Public*, pg. 2040
THE BOEING CO. - 777 PROGRAM—See The Boeing Company; *U.S. Public*, pg. 2039
THE BOEING CO. - HELICOPTER DIVISION—See The Boeing Company; *U.S. Public*, pg. 2039
BOEING COMMERCIAL AIRPLANE GROUP - EVERETT—See The Boeing Company; *U.S. Public*, pg. 2039
BOEING COMMERCIAL AIRPLANE GROUP - SEATTLE—See The Boeing Company; *U.S. Public*, pg. 2039
BOEING COMMERCIAL AIRPLANE GROUP—See The Boeing Company; *U.S. Public*, pg. 2039
THE BOEING CO. - RIDLEY PARK—See The Boeing Company; *U.S. Public*, pg. 2041
THE BOEING CO. - SEATTLE—See The Boeing Company; *U.S. Public*, pg. 2041
BOEING DEFENCE AUSTRALIA LTD—See The Boeing Company; *U.S. Public*, pg. 2040
BOEING DEFENCE UK LIMITED—See The Boeing Company; *U.S. Public*, pg. 2041
BOEING DEFENSE, SPACE & SECURITY GROUP—See The Boeing Company; *U.S. Public*, pg. 2039
BOEING DEUTSCHLAND GMBH—See The Boeing Company; *U.S. Public*, pg. 2040
BOEING INTELLECTUAL PROPERTY LICENSING COMPANY—See The Boeing Company; *U.S. Public*, pg. 2040
BOEING MILITARY AIRCRAFT DIVISION—See The Boeing Company; *U.S. Public*, pg. 2039
BOEING NETHERLANDS B.V.—See The Boeing Company; *U.S. Public*, pg. 2040
BOEING NEVADA, INC.—See The Boeing Company; *U.S. Public*, pg. 2041
BOEING SINGAPORE TRAINING AND FLIGHT SERVICES PTE. LTD.—See The Boeing Company; *U.S. Public*, pg. 2040
BOMBARDIER AEROSPACE—See Bombardier Inc.; *Int'l*, pg. 1103
BOMBARDIER AEROSPACE—See Bombardier Inc.; *Int'l*, pg. 1103
BOMBARDIER INC.; *Int'l*, pg. 1103
BOMBARDIER - LEARJET—See Bombardier Inc.; *Int'l*, pg. 1103
BRISTOW CARIBBEAN LTD.—See Bristow Group, Inc.; *U.S. Public*, pg. 387
BRITTEN-NORMAN INC—See B-N Group Limited; *Int'l*, pg. 785
BRITTEN-NORMAN PTY LTD—See B-N Group Limited; *Int'l*, pg. 785
BUTLER NATIONAL CORPORATION; *U.S. Public*, pg. 413
CAMERON BALLOONS LTD.; *Int'l*, pg. 1271
CAMERON BALLOONS U.S.—See Cameron Balloons Ltd.; *Int'l*, pg. 1271
CARBON BY DESIGN, L.P.—See HEICO Corporation; *U.S. Public*, pg. 1019
CENTRA INDUSTRIES INC.—See Berkshire Hathaway Inc.; *U.S. Public*, pg. 314
CESSNA AIRCRAFT COMPANY—See Textron Inc.; *U.S. Public*, pg. 2028
CHONGQING AEROSPACE NEW CENTURY SATELLITE APPLICATION TECHNOLOGY CO., LTD.—See Aerosun Corporation; *Int'l*, pg. 182
CIRRUS DESIGN CORPORATION—See Aviation Industry Corporation of China; *Int'l*, pg. 741
C&L AVIATION SERVICES—See C&L Aerospace Pty Ltd.; *Int'l*, pg. 1239
C-MAP/COMMERCIAL, LTD.—See The Boeing Company; *U.S. Public*, pg. 2041

COMPOSITE ENGINEERING, INC.—See Kratos Defense & Security Solutions, Inc.; *U.S. Public*, pg. 1276
COMSOVEREIGN HOLDING CORP.; *U.S. Public*, pg. 562
CONSTRUCCIONES AERONAUTICAS, S.A.—See Airbus SE; *Int'l*, pg. 246
CORSE COMPOSITES AERONAUTIQUE—See Groupe Industriel Marcel Dassault S.A.; *Int'l*, pg. 3104
CT AEROSPACE LLC—See VSE Corporation; *U.S. Public*, pg. 2313
DASSAULT ASSURANCES COURTAGE—See Groupe Industriel Marcel Dassault S.A.; *Int'l*, pg. 3104
DASSAULT AVIATION POITIERS—See Groupe Industriel Marcel Dassault S.A.; *Int'l*, pg. 3105
DASSAULT AVIATION SAINT-CLOUD—See Groupe Industriel Marcel Dassault S.A.; *Int'l*, pg. 3105
DASSAULT AVIATION—See Groupe Industriel Marcel Dassault S.A.; *Int'l*, pg. 3104
DASSAULT AVIATION—See Groupe Industriel Marcel Dassault S.A.; *Int'l*, pg. 3104
DASSAULT FALCON SERVICE—See Groupe Industriel Marcel Dassault S.A.; *Int'l*, pg. 3105
DERICHEBOURG ATIS AERONAUTIQUE SAS—See Derichebourg S.A.; *Int'l*, pg. 2042
DIAMOND AIRBORNE SENSING GMBH—See Diamond Aircraft Industries Gmbh; *Int'l*, pg. 2105
DIAMOND AIRCRAFT INDUSTRIES GMBH; *Int'l*, pg. 2105
DIVISION EQUIPEMENTS DASSAULT (DED)—See Groupe Industriel Marcel Dassault S.A.; *Int'l*, pg. 3105
DRAGANFLY, INC.; *Int'l*, pg. 2199
DRAKEN INTERNATIONAL INC.; *U.S. Private*, pg. 1272
DRONE SERVICES USA, INC.; *U.S. Private*, pg. 1279
DRONEUP LLC; *U.S. Private*, pg. 1279
EAGLE AERIAL SYSTEMS, INC.—See AgEagle Aerial Systems Inc.; *U.S. Public*, pg. 60
EBV EXPLOSIVES ENVIRONMENTAL COMPANY—See EQT AB; *Int'l*, pg. 2467
ECLIPSE AEROSPACE, INC.; *U.S. Private*, pg. 1328
EMBENTION SISTEMAS INTELIGENTES, S.A.; *Int'l*, pg. 2375
EMBRAER CHINA—See Embraer S.A.; *Int'l*, pg. 2375
EMBRAER EXECUTIVE AIRCRAFT, INC.—See Embraer S.A.; *Int'l*, pg. 2375
EMBRAER EXECUTIVE JET SERVICES, LLC—See Embraer S.A.; *Int'l*, pg. 2375
EMBRAER S.A.; *Int'l*, pg. 2375
EMBRAER SERVICES, INC.—See Embraer S.A.; *Int'l*, pg. 2375
EMIVEST AEROSPACE CORPORATION—See Emirates Investment & Development Company PSC; *Int'l*, pg. 2381
THE ENSTROM HELICOPTER CORP.—See Chongqing Helicopter Investment Co. Ltd.; *Int'l*, pg. 1579
ERICKSON INCORPORATED; *U.S. Private*, pg. 1419
ETABLISSEMENT D'ARGONAY—See Groupe Industriel Marcel Dassault S.A.; *Int'l*, pg. 3105
ETABLISSEMENT DE MARTIGNAS—See Groupe Industriel Marcel Dassault S.A.; *Int'l*, pg. 3105
ETABLISSEMENT DE MERIGNAC—See Groupe Industriel Marcel Dassault S.A.; *Int'l*, pg. 3105
ETABLISSEMENT D'ISTRES—See Groupe Industriel Marcel Dassault S.A.; *Int'l*, pg. 3105
EUROCOPTER CHILE SA—See Airbus SE; *Int'l*, pg. 243
EUROCOPTER DE MEXICO S.A.—See Airbus SE; *Int'l*, pg. 244
EUROCOPTER ESPANA SA—See Airbus SE; *Int'l*, pg. 244
EUROCOPTER JAPAN CO.—See Airbus SE; *Int'l*, pg. 244
EUROCOPTER PHILIPPINES INC.—See Airbus SE; *Int'l*, pg. 244
EUROCOPTER SOUTH EAST ASIA PTE. LTD.—See Airbus SE; *Int'l*, pg. 244
EUROCOPTER SOUTHERN AFRICA PTY. LTD.—See Airbus SE; *Int'l*, pg. 244
EUROCOPTER VOSTOK—See Airbus SE; *Int'l*, pg. 243
EUROFIGHTER GMBH—See Airbus SE; *Int'l*, pg. 247
EVIATION AIRCRAFT LTD.; *Int'l*, pg. 2570
FORCE PROTECTION, INC.—See General Dynamics Corporation; *U.S. Public*, pg. 914
FORREST MACHINING INC.—See DVSM LLC; *U.S. Private*, pg. 1295
FUTURE MOBILITY SOLUTIONS; *Int'l*, pg. 2856
GENERAL ATOMICS AERONAUTICAL SYSTEMS INC.—See General Atomics; *U.S. Private*, pg. 1663
GENERAL DYNAMICS AEROSPACE GROUP—See General Dynamics Corporation; *U.S. Public*, pg. 913
GENERAL DYNAMICS COMMERCIAL CYBER SERVICES, LLC—See General Dynamics Corporation; *U.S. Public*, pg. 914
GENERAL DYNAMICS GLOBAL IMAGING TECHNOLOGIES, INC.—See General Dynamics Corporation; *U.S. Public*, pg. 915
GENERAL DYNAMICS LAND SYSTEMS - CANADA CORPORATION—See General Dynamics Corporation; *U.S. Public*, pg. 915
GENERAL DYNAMICS MISSION SYSTEMS ASIA-PACIFIC SDN. BHD.—See General Dynamics Corporation; *U.S. Public*, pg. 915
GENERAL DYNAMICS ROBOTIC SYSTEMS—See General Dynamics Corporation; *U.S. Public*, pg. 914
GENERAL DYNAMICS SATELLITE COMMUNICATION SERVICES, INC.—See General Dynamics Corporation; *U.S. Public*, pg. 915

GENERAL DYNAMICS SHARED RESOURCES, INC.—See General Dynamics Corporation; *U.S. Public*, pg. 915
GENERAL DYNAMICS WORLDWIDE HOLDINGS, INC.—See General Dynamics Corporation; *U.S. Public*, pg. 916
GENERAL ELECTRIC COMPANY POLSKA SP. Z O.O.—See General Electric Company; *U.S. Public*, pg. 920
GIMATIC UK LIMITED—See Barnes Group Inc.; *U.S. Public*, pg. 277
GOERTEK ROBOTICS CO., LTD.—See GoerTek Inc.; *Int'l*, pg. 3021
GROEN BROTHERS AVIATION, INC.; *U.S. Private*, pg. 1791
GULFSTREAM AEROSPACE CORPORATION OF TEXAS—See General Dynamics Corporation; *U.S. Public*, pg. 916
GULFSTREAM AEROSPACE CORPORATION—See General Dynamics Corporation; *U.S. Public*, pg. 913
GULFSTREAM AEROSPACE SERVICES CORPORATION—See General Dynamics Corporation; *U.S. Public*, pg. 916
GULFSTREAM - CALIFORNIA, INC.—See General Dynamics Corporation; *U.S. Public*, pg. 916
GUSTAV KLAUKE GMBH—See Emerson Electric Co.; *U.S. Public*, pg. 750
HANSAMATRIX AS; *Int'l*, pg. 3259
HAWKER BEECHCRAFT GLOBAL CUSTOMER SUPPORT, LLC—See Textron Inc.; *U.S. Public*, pg. 2028
HAWKER PACIFIC AIRSERVICES LIMITED—See General Dynamics Corporation; *U.S. Public*, pg. 916
HELIBRAS—See Airbus SE; *Int'l*, pg. 244
HELI-LYNX HELICOPTER SERVICES INC.; *Int'l*, pg. 3329
HELI-TECH, INC.—See Bristow Group, Inc.; *U.S. Public*, pg. 388
HENSOLDT AUSTRALIA PTY LTD—See HENSOLDT AG; *Int'l*, pg. 3355
HENSOLDT DO BRASIL SEGURANCA E DEFESA ELECTRONICA E OPTICA LTDA—See HENSOLDT AG; *Int'l*, pg. 3355
HENSOLDT FRANCE S.A.S.—See HENSOLDT AG; *Int'l*, pg. 3355
HENSOLDT OPTRONICS GMBH—See HENSOLDT AG; *Int'l*, pg. 3355
HENSOLDT OPTRONICS (PTY) LTD.—See HENSOLDT AG; *Int'l*, pg. 3355
HENSOLDT PRIVATE LTD.—See HENSOLDT AG; *Int'l*, pg. 3355
HENSOLDT SENSORS GMBH—See HENSOLDT AG; *Int'l*, pg. 3355
HENSOLDT SINGAPORE PTE LTD—See HENSOLDT AG; *Int'l*, pg. 3355
HINDUSTAN AERONAUTICS LIMITED; *Int'l*, pg. 3399
HIZEAERO CO.,LTD.; *Int'l*, pg. 3427
HONEYWELL ANALYTICS ASIA PACIFIC CO., LTD.—See Honeywell International Inc.; *U.S. Public*, pg. 1047
HONEYWELL INTERNATIONAL SDN. BHD.—See Honeywell International Inc.; *U.S. Public*, pg. 1051
HOWMET S.A.S.—See Howmet Aerospace Inc.; *U.S. Public*, pg. 1061
IAR SA; *Int'l*, pg. 3569
IDEAFORGE TECHNOLOGY LIMITED; *Int'l*, pg. 3588
IMAG GROUP, INC.; *U.S. Private*, pg. 2044
INGENIA-CAT S.L.—See Novanta Inc.; *U.S. Public*, pg. 1548
INSITU, INC.—See The Boeing Company; *U.S. Public*, pg. 2040
INVENTORY LOCATOR SERVICE, LLC—See The Boeing Company; *U.S. Public*, pg. 2041
JEPPESEN (CANADA), LTD.—See The Boeing Company; *U.S. Public*, pg. 2039
JEPPESEN DATAPLAN, INC.—See The Boeing Company; *U.S. Public*, pg. 2039
JEPPESEN POLAND SPOLKA Z OGRANICZONA ODPOWIEDZIALNOSCIA—See The Boeing Company; *U.S. Public*, pg. 2039
JEPPESEN SYSTEMS AB—See The Boeing Company; *U.S. Public*, pg. 2039
JET AVIATION AG—See General Dynamics Corporation; *U.S. Public*, pg. 916
JET RESOURCE, INC.—See Chemed Corporation; *U.S. Public*, pg. 484
JOBY AERO, INC.—See Joby Aviation, Inc.; *U.S. Public*, pg. 1190
L-3 UNMANNED SYSTEMS—See L3Harris Technologies, Inc.; *U.S. Public*, pg. 1283
LATECOERE SA—See Searchlight Capital Partners, L.P.; *U.S. Private*, pg. 3588
LETOV S.R.O.—See Searchlight Capital Partners, L.P.; *U.S. Private*, pg. 3588
LOCKHEED MARTIN AERONAUTICS COMPANY—See Lockheed Martin Corporation; *U.S. Public*, pg. 1337
LOCKHEED MARTIN AERONAUTICS COMPANY—See Lockheed Martin Corporation; *U.S. Public*, pg. 1338
LOCKHEED MARTIN GLOBAL, INC. - BELGIUM OFFICE—See Lockheed Martin Corporation; *U.S. Public*, pg. 1338

LOCKHEED MARTIN GLOBAL, INC. - TURKEY OFFICE—See Lockheed Martin Corporation; *U.S. Public*, pg. 1338
LOCKHEED MARTIN INTERNATIONAL S.A.—See Lockheed Martin Corporation; *U.S. Public*, pg. 1338
LOCKHEED MARTIN INVESTMENTS INC.—See Lockheed Martin Corporation; *U.S. Public*, pg. 1338
LOCKHEED MARTIN MISSILES & FIRE CONTROL—See Lockheed Martin Corporation; *U.S. Public*, pg. 1338
LOCKHEED MARTIN SPACE SYSTEMS COMPANY—See Lockheed Martin Corporation; *U.S. Public*, pg. 1338
LOCKHEED MARTIN SPACE SYSTEMS CO. - SUNNYVALE—See Lockheed Martin Corporation; *U.S. Public*, pg. 1339
LUFTHANSA BOMBARDIER AVIATION SERVICES GMBH—See Bombardier Inc.; *Int'l*, pg. 1104
MD HELICOPTERS, INC.—See MB Global Advisers, LLC; *U.S. Private*, pg. 2623
MD HELICOPTERS, INC.—See MBIA Inc.; *U.S. Public*, pg. 1403
MEGGITT AVIONICS—See Parker Hannifin Corporation; *U.S. Public*, pg. 1642
MEGGITT (BALTIMORE) INC.—See Parker Hannifin Corporation; *U.S. Public*, pg. 1641
METRO MACHINE CORP.—See General Dynamics Corporation; *U.S. Public*, pg. 916
MOLLER INTERNATIONAL, INC.; *U.S. Private*, pg. 2767
MONTANA AVIATION RESEARCH COMPANY—See The Boeing Company; *U.S. Public*, pg. 2041
MOONEY AIRPLANE COMPANY, INC.—See Mooney Aerospace Group, Ltd.; *U.S. Private*, pg. 2779
NEXEYA CANADA INC.—See HENSOLDT AG; *Int'l*, pg. 3356
NEXEYA USA INC.—See HENSOLDT AG; *Int'l*, pg. 3356
NORTHROP GRUMMAN AEROSPACE SYSTEMS-SAN DIEGO—See Northrop Grumman Corporation; *U.S. Public*, pg. 1540
NOVA SMART SOLUTIONS, INC.; *U.S. Private*, pg. 2966
OGMA - INDUSTRIA AERONAUTICA DE PORTUGAL S.A.—See Embraer S.A.; *Int'l*, pg. 2375
OOO GIMATIC RUS—See Barnes Group Inc.; *U.S. Public*, pg. 277
OPTO-ELECTRONICS INC.—See Textron Inc.; *U.S. Public*, pg. 2028
PANAVIA AIRCRAFT GMBH—See Airbus SE; *Int'l*, pg. 247
PANAVIA AIRCRAFT GMBH—See BAE Systems plc; *Int'l*, pg. 798
PENSER MAITRISER TECHNICITE LOGISTIQUE - P.M.T.L S.A.S.—See HENSOLDT AG; *Int'l*, pg. 3356
PIPER AIRCRAFT, INC.; *U.S. Private*, pg. 3189
PREMIUM AEROTEC SRL - BRASOV PLANT—See Airbus SE; *Int'l*, pg. 243
PULSE AEROSPACE, LLC—See AeroVironment, Inc.; *U.S. Public*, pg. 53
QUEST AIRCRAFT COMPANY, LLC—See DAHER Group; *Int'l*, pg. 1913
RANSOMES JACOBSEN FRANCE S.A.S.—See Textron Inc.; *U.S. Public*, pg. 2028
ROBINSON HELICOPTER COMPANY; *U.S. Private*, pg. 3462
ROCKWELL AUTOMATION EUROPEAN HEADQUARTERS S.A./N.V.—See Rockwell Automation, Inc.; *U.S. Public*, pg. 1806
ROCKWELL AUTOMATION LTD.—See Rockwell Automation, Inc.; *U.S. Public*, pg. 1806
ROCKWELL AUTOMATION S.A.—See Rockwell Automation, Inc.; *U.S. Public*, pg. 1806
ROCKWELL AUTOMATION S.R.L.—See Rockwell Automation, Inc.; *U.S. Public*, pg. 1806
ROCKWELL AUTOMATION THAI CO. LTD.—See Rockwell Automation, Inc.; *U.S. Public*, pg. 1806
SECA (SOCIETE D'EXPLOITATION ET DE CONSTRUCTION AERONAUTIQUES)—See Airbus SE; *Int'l*, pg. 246
SECBAT-BREGUET ATLANTIC—See Groupe Industriel Marcel Dassault S.A.; *Int'l*, pg. 3105
SENSEFLY SA—See AgEagle Aerial Systems Inc.; *U.S. Public*, pg. 60
SEPECAT—See Groupe Industriel Marcel Dassault S.A.; *Int'l*, pg. 3105
SILVERLIGHT AVIATION, LLC—See 808 Renewable Energy Corp.; *U.S. Public*, pg. 9
SIMFRONT SIMULATION SYSTEMS CORPORATION—See Calian Group Ltd.; *Int'l*, pg. 1264
SKY AIRCRAFT—See GECI International SA; *Int'l*, pg. 2909
SKY SAPIENCE LTD.—See COMSovereign Holding Corp.; *U.S. Public*, pg. 562
SPRECHER & SCHUH, INC.—See Rockwell Automation, Inc.; *U.S. Public*, pg. 1807
TEXTRON AVIATION DEFENSE LLC—See Textron Inc.; *U.S. Public*, pg. 2029
TEXTRON CAPITAL B.V.—See Textron Inc.; *U.S. Public*, pg. 2029
TEXTRON SYSTEMS AUSTRALIA PTY LTD—See Textron Inc.; *U.S. Public*, pg. 2029
THIRD ELEMENT AVIATION GMBH—See Hamburger Hafen und Logistik AG; *Int'l*, pg. 3237
THRUSH AIRCRAFT, INC., *U.S. Private*, pg. 4165
TOULOUSE LOCATION S.A.R.L.—See AerCap Holdings N.V.; *Int'l*, pg. 179
TRANSTAR METALS LIMITED—See A. M. Castle & Co.; *U.S. Public*, pg. 11
TRIUMPH AEROSPACE SYSTEMS GROUP, LLC—See Triumph Group, Inc.; *U.S. Public*, pg. 2196
TYONEK SERVICES OVERHAUL FACILITY-STENNIS, LLC—See The Tyonek Native Corporation; *U.S. Private*, pg. 4128
UAS DRONE CORP.; *U.S. Public*, pg. 2217
UNIVERSITY SWAGING CORPORATION—See Berkshire Hathaway Inc.; *U.S. Public*, pg. 315
UTCL INVESTMENTS B.V.—See RTX Corporation; *U.S. Public*, pg. 1825
VSE AVIATION, INC.—See VSE Corporation; *U.S. Public*, pg. 2313
WESTERN AVIATION PRODUCTS LLC—See World Kinect Corporation; *U.S. Public*, pg. 2381
XEOS SP. Z O.O.—See Deutsche Lufthansa AG; *Int'l*, pg. 2071

336412 — AIRCRAFT ENGINE AND ENGINE PARTS MANUFACTURING

AAA AIRCRAFT SUPPLY, LLC—See The Boeing Company; *U.S. Public*, pg. 2040
AAR AIRCRAFT & ENGINE SALES & LEASING—See AAR Corp.; *U.S. Public*, pg. 12
AAR CORP. - AVIATION SUPPLY CHAIN—See AAR Corp.; *U.S. Public*, pg. 13
AAR CORP.; *U.S. Public*, pg. 12
AAR INTERNATIONAL (FRANCE) S.A.R.L.—See AAR Corp.; *U.S. Public*, pg. 13
AB VOLVO PENTA ITALIA S.P.A.—See AB Volvo; *Int'l*, pg. 42
AC&A ENTERPRISES LLC—See AE Industrial Partners, LP; *U.S. Private*, pg. 111
ADCOLE MARYLAND AEROSPACE, LLC—See Redwire Corporation; *U.S. Public*, pg. 1771
ADVANCED THERMAL SCIENCES TAIWAN CORP.—See RTX Corporation; *U.S. Public*, pg. 1822
AECC AERO SCIENCE & TECHNOLOGY CO., LTD.; *Int'l*, pg. 171
AECC AVIATION POWER CO., LTD.; *Int'l*, pg. 171
AECC SHANGHAI COMMERCIAL AIRCRAFT ENGINE MANUFACTURING CO.; *Int'l*, pg. 171
AERO COMPONENTS, LLC—See P4G Capital Management, LLC; *U.S. Private*, pg. 3062
AEROTECH GMBH—See Aerotech World Trade Corp.; *U.S. Private*, pg. 120
AEROTECH HOLLAND B.V.—See Aerotech World Trade Corp.; *U.S. Private*, pg. 120
AEROTECH WORLD TRADE CO., LTD.—See Aerotech World Trade Corp.; *U.S. Private*, pg. 120
AEROTECH WORLD TRADE LTD.—See Aerotech World Trade Corp.; *U.S. Private*, pg. 120
AERO WIN TECHNOLOGY CORPORATION; *Int'l*, pg. 180
AEROWORKS (ASIA) LTD.—See HEICO Corporation; *U.S. Public*, pg. 1019
AERSALE AVIATION, LTD.—See Leonard Green & Partners, L.P.; *U.S. Private*, pg. 2424
AERSALE SINGAPORE—See Leonard Green & Partners, L.P.; *U.S. Private*, pg. 2424
AIR COOLED MOTORS—See Danbury AeroSpace, Inc.; *U.S. Private*, pg. 1152
AIRCRAFT PRECISION PRODUCTS, INC.; *U.S. Private*, pg. 140
AIRFOIL TECHNOLOGIES INTERNATIONAL SINGAPORE PTE LTD.—See General Electric Company; *U.S. Public*, pg. 918
AMERICAN AIRCRAFT PARTS MANUFACTURING CO.; *U.S. Private*, pg. 222
ARCHER AVIATION INC.; *U.S. Public*, pg. 180
ARCHER AVIATION OPERATING CORP.—See Archer Aviation Inc.; *U.S. Public*, pg. 180
ARCTURUS UAV, INC.—See AeroVironment, Inc.; *U.S. Public*, pg. 53
ARROW GEAR COMPANY; *U.S. Private*, pg. 335
ASHOT ASHKELON INDUSTRIES LTD.—See First Israel Mezzanine Investors; *Int'l*, pg. 2685
ASIAN SURFACE TECHNOLOGIES PTE. LTD.—See The Carlyle Group Inc.; *U.S. Public*, pg. 2054
ATLANTIC PRECISION, INC.—See Berkshire Hathaway Inc.; *U.S. Public*, pg. 313
THE ATLAS GROUP; *U.S. Private*, pg. 3990
AUSTRO ENGINE GMBH—See Diamond Aircraft Industries Gmbh; *Int'l*, pg. 2105
AVIATION, POWER & MARINE, INC.—See Pfingsten Partners, LLC; *U.S. Private*, pg. 3164
AVIC XIAN AIRCRAFT INDUSTRY GROUP COMPANY LTD.—See Aviation Industry Corporation of China; *Int'l*, pg. 741
AVIQUIPO DE PORTUGAL, LTDA—See Aerotech World Trade Corp.; *U.S. Private*, pg. 120
BARNES AEROSPACE - LANSING—See Barnes Group Inc.; *U.S. Public*, pg. 276
BARNES AEROSPACE—See Barnes Group Inc.; *U.S. Public*, pg. 276
BARRETT TURBINE ENGINE COMPANY—See BlackRock, Inc.; *U.S. Public*, pg. 346
BARRETT TURBINE ENGINE COMPANY—See Blackstone Inc.; *U.S. Public*, pg. 358
BARRETT TURBINE ENGINE COMPANY—See Cascade Investment LLC; *U.S. Private*, pg. 780
BEACON INDUSTRIES, INC.; *U.S. Private*, pg. 504
BET SHEMESH ENGINES LTD.—See Bet Shemesh Engines Holdings (1997) Ltd.; *Int'l*, pg. 1001
B.H. AIRCRAFT CO., INC.; *U.S. Private*, pg. 420
BN AEROCOMPONENTS LTD—See B-N Group Limited; *Int'l*, pg. 785
BN AEROSYSTEMS LTD—See B-N Group Limited; *Int'l*, pg. 785
BN AVIATION LTD—See B-N Group Limited; *Int'l*, pg. 785
BN DEFENCE LTD—See B-N Group Limited; *Int'l*, pg. 785
THE BOEING COMPANY; *U.S. Public*, pg. 2038
BOEING WINNIPEG—See The Boeing Company; *U.S. Public*, pg. 2041
BRITISH POLAR ENGINES LIMITED—See Associated British Engineering plc; *Int'l*, pg. 648
BRITTEN-NORMAN AIRCRAFT LTD—See B-N Group Limited; *Int'l*, pg. 785
BROMFORD TECHNOLOGIES - ALCESTER FACILITY—See Bromford Industries Limited; *Int'l*, pg. 1173
BROWN & SHARPE QIANSHAO—See Hexagon AB; *Int'l*, pg. 3367
BUDNEY INDUSTRIES; *U.S. Private*, pg. 679
BULLERBEKAMPAREN AB—See Christian Berner Tech Trade AB; *Int'l*, pg. 1586
CAR-GRAPH INC.; *U.S. Private*, pg. 748
C BLADE S.P.A. MANUFACTURING & FORGING—See SIFCO Industries, Inc.; *U.S. Public*, pg. 1877
CFAN INC—See General Electric Company; *U.S. Public*, pg. 918
CHAMPION AEROSPACE INC.—See TransDigm Group Incorporated; *U.S. Public*, pg. 2182
CHROMALLOY GAS TURBINE FRANCE—See Veritas Capital Fund Management, LLC; *U.S. Private*, pg. 4364
CHROMALLOY GAS TURBINE LLC - MIDDLETOWN—See Veritas Capital Fund Management, LLC; *U.S. Private*, pg. 4364
CHROMALLOY GAS TURBINE LLC—See Veritas Capital Fund Management, LLC; *U.S. Private*, pg. 4364
CHROMALLOY HOLLAND B.V.—See Veritas Capital Fund Management, LLC; *U.S. Private*, pg. 4364
CHROMALLOY S.A. DE C.V.—See Veritas Capital Fund Management, LLC; *U.S. Private*, pg. 4364
CHROMALLOY THAILAND CO. LTD.—See Veritas Capital Fund Management, LLC; *U.S. Private*, pg. 4364
CHROMALLOY UNITED KINGDOM LTD.—See Veritas Capital Fund Management, LLC; *U.S. Private*, pg. 4364
CIRCOR PUMPING TECHNOLOGIES—See KKR & Co. Inc.; *U.S. Public*, pg. 1242
CLOUD GLOBAL LTD.; *Int'l*, pg. 1662
COLLINS AEROSPACE - RIVERSIDE—See RTX Corporation; *U.S. Public*, pg. 1821
COLLINS AEROSPACE - SAN MARCOS—See RTX Corporation; *U.S. Public*, pg. 1821
COMBAT ADVANCED PROPULSION, LLC—See L3Harris Technologies, Inc.; *U.S. Public*, pg. 1281
CONTINENTAL MOTORS, INC.—See Aviation Industry Corporation of China; *Int'l*, pg. 741
CORRY MANUFACTURING COMPANY; *U.S. Private*, pg. 1059
CRANFIELD AEROSPACE SOLUTIONS LIMITED; *Int'l*, pg. 1828
CURTISS-WRIGHT FLIGHT SYSTEMS, INC.—See Curtiss-Wright Corporation; *U.S. Public*, pg. 611
DAHER GROUP; *Int'l*, pg. 1913
DAIHATSU BRIGGS & STRATTON CO., LTD.—See Briggs & Stratton Corporation; *U.S. Public*, pg. 651
DALLAS AIRMOTIVE, INC. - DALLAS FACILITY—See BlackRock, Inc.; *U.S. Public*, pg. 346
DALLAS AIRMOTIVE, INC. - DALLAS FACILITY—See Blackstone Inc.; *U.S. Public*, pg. 358
DALLAS AIRMOTIVE, INC. - DALLAS FACILITY—See Cascade Investment LLC; *U.S. Private*, pg. 780
DALLAS AIRMOTIVE, INC.—See BlackRock, Inc.; *U.S. Public*, pg. 346
DALLAS AIRMOTIVE, INC.—See Blackstone Inc.; *U.S. Public*, pg. 358
DALLAS AIRMOTIVE, INC.—See Cascade Investment LLC; *U.S. Private*, pg. 780
DANVILLE METAL STAMPING CO. INC.; *U.S. Private*, pg. 1158
DIVERSIFIED AERO SERVICES, INC.; *U.S. Private*, pg. 1241
DK TURBINES, LLC—See Kalitta Air, LLC; *U.S. Private*, pg. 2257
DYNAMIC PRECISION GROUP—See AeroEquity Partners, LLC; *U.S. Private*, pg. 118
DYNAMIC PRECISION GROUP—See The Carlyle Group Inc.; *U.S. Public*, pg. 2046
EBP AB—See AB Volvo; *Int'l*, pg. 42
EDAC AERO ROTATING COMPONENTS—See Hanwha Group; *Int'l*, pg. 3264

336412 — AIRCRAFT ENGINE AND...

ELECTRO-METHODS, INC.; *U.S. Private*, pg. 1354
EMBEE PROCESSING, LLC—See All Metals Processing of Orange County, LLC; *U.S. Private*, pg. 171
ENCORE AVIATION LLC; *U.S. Private*, pg. 1390
ENGINE COMPONENTS, INC.—See Danbury AeroSpace, Inc.; *U.S. Private*, pg. 1152
FABRICATIONS MECANIQUES DE L'ATLANTIQUE SA—See General Electric Company; *U.S. Public*, pg. 918
FASTENER DISTRIBUTION HOLDINGS LLC—See Audax Group, Limited Partnership; *U.S. Private*, pg. 387
FIRST RENT A CAR AB—See AB Volvo; *Int'l*, pg. 42
FLEXENERGY GREEN SOLUTIONS, INC.; *U.S. Public*, pg. 852
FLORIDA AERO PRECISION INC.—See Meyer Tool Inc.; *U.S. Private*, pg. 2693
FLOW AEROSPACE—See AIP, LLC; *U.S. Private*, pg. 133
FRANKE INDUSTRIE AG—See Artemis Holding AG; *Int'l*, pg. 582
FRANKE MANAGEMENT AG—See Artemis Holding AG; *Int'l*, pg. 582
GCE INDUSTRIES, INC.—See Dubai Holding LLC; *Int'l*, pg. 2218
GE AIRCRAFT ENGINES UK—See General Electric Company; *U.S. Public*, pg. 918
GE AVIATION SYSTEMS LLC—See General Electric Company; *U.S. Public*, pg. 918
GE AVIO S.R.L.—See General Electric Company; *U.S. Public*, pg. 919
GE CALEDONIAN LIMITED—See General Electric Company; *U.S. Public*, pg. 916
GECAS ASSET MANAGEMENT SERVICES—See General Electric Company; *U.S. Public*, pg. 920
GECI SOUTH AFRICA PTY LTD—See GECI International SA; *Int'l*, pg. 2909
GE ENERGY PRODUCTS FRANCE SNC—See General Electric Company; *U.S. Public*, pg. 917
GE EVERGREEN ENGINE SERVICES CORPORATION—See General Electric Company; *U.S. Public*, pg. 917
GKN AEROSPACE CHEM-TRONICS, INC.—See GKN plc; *Int'l*, pg. 2984
GKN AEROSPACE ENGINE PRODUCTS—See GKN plc; *Int'l*, pg. 2984
HARTZELL ENGINE TECHNOLOGIES LLC—See Arcline Investment Management LP; *U.S. Private*, pg. 313
HEICO AEROSPACE CORPORATION—See HEICO Corporation; *U.S. Public*, pg. 1019
HEROUX-DEVTEK INC.; *Int'l*, pg. 3364
HONDA AERO, INC.—See Honda Motor Co., Ltd.; *Int'l*, pg. 3460
HONEYWELL AEROSPACE GMBH—See Honeywell International Inc.; *U.S. Public*, pg. 1047
HONEYWELL AEROSPACE - HOUSTON, AIR CENTER BOULEVARD—See Honeywell International Inc.; *U.S. Public*, pg. 1047
HONEYWELL COMMERCIAL ELECTRONIC SYSTEMS—See Honeywell International Inc.; *U.S. Public*, pg. 1047
HONEYWELL LIMITED—See Honeywell International Inc.; *U.S. Public*, pg. 1051
HOWMET LAVAL CASTING LTD.—See Howmet Aerospace Inc.; *U.S. Public*, pg. 1061
HOWMET LIMITED—See Howmet Aerospace Inc.; *U.S. Public*, pg. 1061
HPE S.P.A.—See Barnes Group Inc.; *U.S. Public*, pg. 277
H+S AVIATION LIMITED—See BlackRock, Inc.; *U.S. Public*, pg. 346
H+S AVIATION LIMITED—See Blackstone Inc.; *U.S. Public*, pg. 358
H+S AVIATION LIMITED—See Cascade Investment LLC; *U.S. Public*, pg. 780
IAE INTERNATIONAL AERO ENGINES AG—See RTX Corporation; *U.S. Public*, pg. 1823
IHI ENGINEERING AUSTRALIA PTY. LTD.—See IHI Corporation; *Int'l*, pg. 3604
IHI EUROPE LTD.—See IHI Corporation; *Int'l*, pg. 3604
IHI OXYFUEL AUSTRALIA PTY.LTD.—See IHI Corporation; *Int'l*, pg. 3604
INNOVENT—See Standex International; *U.S. Public*, pg. 1930
INTEGRATED ENERGY TECHNOLOGIES, INC.—See Dubai Holding LLC; *Int'l*, pg. 2218
INTERNATIONAL AERO ENGINES AG—See RTX Corporation; *U.S. Public*, pg. 1823
INTERNATIONAL MOTION CONTROL, INC.—See ITT Inc.; *U.S. Public*, pg. 1178
ISCAR BLADES LTD.—See IDB Development Corporation Ltd.; *Int'l*, pg. 3588
ITT ENIDINE INC.—See ITT Inc.; *U.S. Public*, pg. 1178
JBT AEROTECH CORPORATION—See Oshkosh Corporation; *U.S. Public*, pg. 1620
JET AVIATION GROUP—See General Dynamics Corporation; *U.S. Public*, pg. 913
JET AVION CORPORATION—See HEICO Corporation; *U.S. Public*, pg. 1019
JOHNSON TECHNOLOGY—See General Electric Company; *U.S. Public*, pg. 919

KERNS MANUFACTURING CORP.; *U.S. Private*, pg. 2291
KK PRECISION, INC.—See River Associates Investments, LLC; *U.S. Private*, pg. 3443
L-3 COMMUNICATIONS INTEGRATED SYSTEMS GROUP—See L3Harris Technologies, Inc.; *U.S. Public*, pg. 1282
LEVIATE AIR GROUP; *U.S. Private*, pg. 2435
LOCKHEED MARTIN AEROPARTS, INC.—See Lockheed Martin Corporation; *U.S. Public*, pg. 1337
LORD CORP. - ERIE—See Parker Hannifin Corporation; *U.S. Public*, pg. 1641
L&P AEROSPACE ACQUISITION COMPANY, LLC—See Leggett & Platt, Incorporated; *U.S. Public*, pg. 1302
LPI CORPORATION—See HEICO Corporation; *U.S. Public*, pg. 1019
MB AEROSPACE LIMITED—See Barnes Group Inc.; *U.S. Public*, pg. 277
MB AEROSPACE WARREN, LLC—See Barnes Group Inc.; *U.S. Public*, pg. 277
MBDA FRANCE SAS—See Airbus SE; *Int'l*, pg. 247
MBDA FRANCE SAS—See BAE Systems plc; *Int'l*, pg. 798
MB WESTFIELD, INC.—See Insight Equity Holdings LLC; *U.S. Private*, pg. 2086
MCTURBINE, INC.—See Textron Inc.; *U.S. Public*, pg. 2029
MECO, INC.—See Dubai Holding LLC; *Int'l*, pg. 2218
MEYER TOOL INC.; *U.S. Private*, pg. 2692
MORRIS GROUP, INC. - MORRIS TURBINE GROUP DIVISION—See Morris Group, Inc.; *U.S. Private*, pg. 2787
NORTHROP GRUMMAN ELECTRONIC SYSTEMS—See Northrop Grumman Corporation; *U.S. Public*, pg. 1540
NUMET MACHINING TECHNIQUES, LLC—See Arlington Capital Partners LLC; *U.S. Private*, pg. 328
OCAM JSC—See Hiolle Industries S.A.; *Int'l*, pg. 3401
ODYNE CORP.; *U.S. Private*, pg. 2993
OHB DIGITAL SOLUTIONS GMBH—See Hiscox Ltd.; *Int'l*, pg. 3407
PARADIGM PRECISION BURNLEY LTD—See General Electric Company; *U.S. Public*, pg. 919
PARADIGM PRECISION - MALDEN—See AeroEquity Partners, LLC; *U.S. Private*, pg. 118
PARADIGM PRECISION - MALDEN—See The Carlyle Group Inc.; *U.S. Public*, pg. 2046
PARADIGM PRECISION - TEMPE—See AeroEquity Partners, LLC; *U.S. Private*, pg. 118
PARADIGM PRECISION - TEMPE—See The Carlyle Group Inc.; *U.S. Public*, pg. 2046
PARADIGM PRECISION - TUNIS—See AeroEquity Partners, LLC; *U.S. Private*, pg. 119
PARADIGM PRECISION - TUNIS—See The Carlyle Group Inc.; *U.S. Public*, pg. 2046
PCX AEROSYSTEMS - MANCHESTER LLC—See Greenbriar Equity Group, L.P.; *U.S. Private*, pg. 1776
PFW AEROSPACE GMBH—See Airbus SE; *Int'l*, pg. 244
PRATT & WHITNEY AUTO-AIR COMPOSITES, INC.—See RTX Corporation; *U.S. Public*, pg. 1823
PRATT & WHITNEY CANADA CORP.—See RTX Corporation; *U.S. Public*, pg. 1823
PRATT & WHITNEY CANADA LEASING, LIMITED PARTNERSHIP—See RTX Corporation; *U.S. Public*, pg. 1823
PRATT & WHITNEY MILITARY AFTERMARKET SERVICES, INC.—See RTX Corporation; *U.S. Public*, pg. 1823
PRATT & WHITNEY PSD INC.—See RTX Corporation; *U.S. Public*, pg. 1823
PRATT & WHITNEY RZESZOW S.A.—See RTX Corporation; *U.S. Public*, pg. 1824
PRATT & WHITNEY SERVICES PTE LTD—See RTX Corporation; *U.S. Public*, pg. 1824
PRATT & WHITNEY—See RTX Corporation; *U.S. Public*, pg. 1823
PRECISION AIRMOTIVE LLC—See Aeries Enterprises, LLC; *U.S. Private*, pg. 117
PRECISION ENGINES, LLC—See Aeries Enterprises, LLC; *U.S. Private*, pg. 117
PRIAMUS SYSTEM TECHNOLOGIES AG—See Barnes Group Inc.; *U.S. Public*, pg. 277
PRIAMUS SYSTEM TECHNOLOGIES GMBH—See Barnes Group Inc.; *U.S. Public*, pg. 277
RADIUS AEROSPACE UK LTD.—See Arlington Capital Partners LLC; *U.S. Private*, pg. 328
RANGER AIR AVIATION LTD.—See JLL Partners, LLC; *U.S. Private*, pg. 2212
SEQUA CORP. - PRECOAT METALS DIVISION—See AZZ, Inc.; *U.S. Public*, pg. 260
SIFCO INDUSTRIES, INC.; *U.S. Public*, pg. 1877
SOUTHEASTERN TECHNOLOGY, INC.—See NN, Inc.; *U.S. Public*, pg. 1530
STANDARDAERO—See The Carlyle Group Inc.; *U.S. Public*, pg. 2054
STAR AVIATION, INC.—See Amphenol Corporation; *U.S. Public*, pg. 129
STERLING ENGINEERING CORPORATION—See Air Industries Group; *U.S. Public*, pg. 64
STORK H & E TURBO BLADING; *U.S. Private*, pg. 3831
STRATEGIC INDUSTRIES, LLC; *U.S. Private*, pg. 3835
SUPERIOR AIR PARTS INC.; *U.S. Private*, pg. 3875

TAT TECHNOLOGIES LTD.—See First Israel Mezzanine Investors Ltd.; *Int'l*, pg. 2685
TELL TOOL, INC.—See Arlington Capital Partners LLC; *U.S. Private*, pg. 327
TETHERS UNLIMITED, INC.—See Amergint Technologies, Inc.; *U.S. Private*, pg. 219
TEXTRON INTERNATIONAL MEXICO, S DE RL DE CV—See Textron Inc.; *U.S. Public*, pg. 2029
TEXTRON LYCOMING—See Textron Inc.; *U.S. Public*, pg. 2029
THERM, INC.; *U.S. Private*, pg. 4142
TIMKEN AEROSPACE TRANSMISSIONS, LLC—See The Timken Company; *U.S. Public*, pg. 2133
TRIBUS AEROSPACE LLC—See Shorehill Capital LLC; *U.S. Private*, pg. 3641
TRIUMPH ACTUATION SYSTEMS - ISLE OF MAN, LTD.—See Triumph Group, Inc.; *U.S. Public*, pg. 2196
TRIUMPH AEROSTRUCTURES - TULSA, LLC—See Triumph Group, Inc.; *U.S. Public*, pg. 2196
TRIUMPH ENGINE CONTROL SYSTEMS, LLC—See Triumph Group, Inc.; *U.S. Public*, pg. 2197
TRIUMPH ENGINEERING SERVICES, INC.—See Triumph Group, Inc.; *U.S. Public*, pg. 2197
TRIUMPH FABRICATIONS-SAN DIEGO, INC.—See Arlington Capital Partners LLC; *U.S. Private*, pg. 328
TRIUMPH GEAR SYSTEMS, INC.—See Triumph Group, Inc.; *U.S. Public*, pg. 2196
TRIUMPH INSULATION SYSTEMS—See Triumph Group, Inc.; *U.S. Public*, pg. 2197
TRIUMPH STRUCTURES-KANSAS CITY, INC.—See Triumph Group, Inc.; *U.S. Public*, pg. 2197
TRIUMPH STRUCTURES-LONG ISLAND, LLC—See Triumph Group, Inc.; *U.S. Public*, pg. 2197
TURBINE AVIATION, INC.; *U.S. Public*, pg. 2205
TURBINE KINETICS, INC.—See HEICO Corporation; *U.S. Public*, pg. 1020
TURBINE REPAIR SERVICES GLOBAL IRELAND LTD—See The Carlyle Group Inc.; *U.S. Public*, pg. 2054
TURBOCHROME LTD.—See First Israel Mezzanine Investors Ltd.; *Int'l*, pg. 2685
TURBOCOMBUSTOR KFT.—See AeroEquity Partners, LLC; *U.S. Private*, pg. 119
TURBOCOMBUSTOR KFT.—See The Carlyle Group Inc.; *U.S. Public*, pg. 2046
TURBOCOMBUSTOR TECHNOLOGY, INC.—See AeroEquity Partners, LLC; *U.S. Private*, pg. 119
TURBOCOMBUSTOR TECHNOLOGY, INC.—See The Carlyle Group Inc.; *U.S. Public*, pg. 2046
T&W FORGE, LLC—See SIFCO Industries, Inc.; *U.S. Public*, pg. 1877
TWG EUROPE LIMITED—See Assurant, Inc.; *U.S. Public*, pg. 215
UAV ENGINES LTD.—See Elbit Systems Limited; *Int'l*, pg. 2345
UCA HOLDINGS INC.; *U.S. Private*, pg. 4273
UNISON ENGINE COMPONENTS—See General Electric Company; *U.S. Public*, pg. 919
UNISON ENGINE COMPONENTS—See General Electric Company; *U.S. Public*, pg. 919
UNISON INDUSTRIES, LLC—See General Electric Company; *U.S. Public*, pg. 919
UNISON INDUSTRIES LLC—See General Electric Company; *U.S. Public*, pg. 919
UNISON INDUSTRIES LLC—See General Electric Company; *U.S. Public*, pg. 919
UNISON INDUSTRIES, LLC—See General Electric Company; *U.S. Public*, pg. 919
UNISON INDUSTRIES—See General Electric Company; *U.S. Public*, pg. 919
UNITED TOOL & DIE COMPANY; *U.S. Private*, pg. 4301
U.S. AIRMOTIVE GSE; *U.S. Private*, pg. 4269
UTC AEROSPACE SYSTEMS - AEROSTRUCTURES, COLOMIERS—See RTX Corporation; *U.S. Public*, pg. 1821
UTC AEROSPACE SYSTEMS - AEROSTRUCTURES, HAMBURG—See RTX Corporation; *U.S. Public*, pg. 1821
UTICA CORPORATION—See UCA Holdings Inc.; *U.S. Private*, pg. 4273
VOLVO AERO CORPORATION—See GKN plc; *Int'l*, pg. 2986
VOLVO AERO ENGINE SERVICES AB—See GKN plc; *Int'l*, pg. 2986
VOLVO AERO ENGINE SERVICES ARBOGA AB—See GKN plc; *Int'l*, pg. 2986
VOLVO AERO TURBINES (UK) LTD.—See GKN plc; *Int'l*, pg. 2986
VOLVO ARTICULATED HAULERS AB—See AB Volvo; *Int'l*, pg. 43
VOLVO BUS POLAND CO.—See AB Volvo; *Int'l*, pg. 43
VOLVO BUSSE DEUTSCHLAND GMBH—See AB Volvo; *Int'l*, pg. 43
VOLVO CARS AUSTRIA GMBH—See AB Volvo; *Int'l*, pg. 43
VOLVO CONSTRUCTION EQUIPMENT AUSTRALIA PTY. LTD.—See AB Volvo; *Int'l*, pg. 43
VOLVO CONSTRUCTION EQUIPMENT CABS AB—See AB Volvo; *Int'l*, pg. 43
VOLVO CONSTRUCTION EQUIPMENT COMPONENTS

N.A.I.C.S. INDEX

336413 — OTHER AIRCRAFT PART...

AB—See AB Volvo; *Int'l*, pg. 43
VOLVO CONSTRUCTION EQUIPMENT CUSTOMER SUPPORT AB—See AB Volvo; *Int'l*, pg. 43
VOLVO CONSTRUCTION EQUIPMENT EAST ASIA (PTE.) LTD.—See AB Volvo; *Int'l*, pg. 43
VOLVO CONSTRUCTION EQUIPMENT EUROPE HOLDING GMBH—See AB Volvo; *Int'l*, pg. 43
VOLVO CONSTRUCTION EQUIPMENT EUROPE SAS—See AB Volvo; *Int'l*, pg. 43
VOLVO CONSTRUCTION EQUIPMENT LTD.—See AB Volvo; *Int'l*, pg. 43
VOLVO CONSTRUCTION EQUIPMENT NORTH AMERICA, INC.—See AB Volvo; *Int'l*, pg. 43
VOLVO DEUTSCHLAND GMBH—See AB Volvo; *Int'l*, pg. 43
VOLVO DO BRASIL VEICULOS LTDA.—See AB Volvo; *Int'l*, pg. 47
VOLVO EQUIPAMENTOS DE CONSTRUCAO LTDA.—See AB Volvo; *Int'l*, pg. 43
VOLVO GROUP MEXICO—See AB Volvo; *Int'l*, pg. 44
VOLVO GROUP REPRESENTATION—See AB Volvo; *Int'l*, pg. 44
VOLVO HOLDING DANMARK A/S—See AB Volvo; *Int'l*, pg. 44
VOLVO INFORMATION TECHNOLOGY AB—See AB Volvo; *Int'l*, pg. 45
VOLVO INTERNATIONAL HOLDING BV—See AB Volvo; *Int'l*, pg. 45
VOLVO KUORMA-JA LINJA-AUTOT OY AB—See AB Volvo; *Int'l*, pg. 46
VOLVO LASTVOGNE DANMARK A/S—See AB Volvo; *Int'l*, pg. 46
VOLVO PENTA CENTRAL EUROPE GMBH—See AB Volvo; *Int'l*, pg. 42
VOLVO PENTA DO BRASIL LTDA.—See AB Volvo; *Int'l*, pg. 42
VOLVO-SAFFLE AB—See AB Volvo; *Int'l*, pg. 43
VOLVO TRUCK AUSTRALIA PTY. LTD.—See AB Volvo; *Int'l*, pg. 46
VOLVO TRUCK & BUS (THAILAND) CO. LTD.—See AB Volvo; *Int'l*, pg. 46
VOLVO TRUCK EN BUS NEDERLAND B.V.—See AB Volvo; *Int'l*, pg. 46
VOLVO TRUCK LATVIA SIA—See AB Volvo; *Int'l*, pg. 46
VOLVO TRUCKS BELGIUM N.V.—See AB Volvo; *Int'l*, pg. 47
VOLVO TRUCKS DE MEXICO S.A. DE C.V.—See AB Volvo; *Int'l*, pg. 47
VOLVO TRUCK—See AB Volvo; *Int'l*, pg. 46
VOLVO WHEEL LOADERS AB—See AB Volvo; *Int'l*, pg. 43
WELDED RING PRODUCTS CO., INC.; *U.S. Private*, pg. 4474
WHITCRAFT LLC—See Greenbriar Equity Group, L.P.; *U.S. Private*, pg. 1776
WILLIAMS INTERNATIONAL; *U.S. Private*, pg. 4526
WOODWARD CONTROLS, INC.—See Woodward, Inc.; *U.S. Public*, pg. 2378
WOODWARD INTERNATIONAL, INC. - PRESTWICK PLANT—See Woodward, Inc.; *U.S. Public*, pg. 2378

336413 — OTHER AIRCRAFT PARTS AND AUXILIARY EQUIPMENT MANUFACTURING

3P MANUFACTURING, INC.—See Highland Capital Management, L.P.; *U.S. Private*, pg. 1938
AAI CORPORATION—See Textron Inc.; *U.S. Public*, pg. 2029
ABLE AEROSPACE SERVICES, INC.—See Textron Inc.; *U.S. Public*, pg. 2028
ACE CLEARWATER ENTERPRISES; *U.S. Private*, pg. 56
ACOUSTICFAB, LLC—See ITT Inc.; *U.S. Public*, pg. 1177
AE GROUP MATERIALS INC.—See AE Industrial Partners, LP; *U.S. Private*, pg. 111
AERNNOVA AEROSPACE CORPORATION S.A.—See TowerBrook Capital Partners, L.P.; *U.S. Private*, pg. 4194
AEROCISION, LLC—See Arlington Capital Partners LLC; *U.S. Private*, pg. 327
AEROLIA S.A.S. - MEAULTE FACILITY—See Airbus SE; *Int'l*, pg. 246
AEROLIA S.A.S. - SAINT-NAZAIRE FACILITY—See Airbus SE; *Int'l*, pg. 246
AEROLIA S.A.S.—See Airbus SE; *Int'l*, pg. 246
AEROLIA S.A.S. - TOULOUSE FACILITY—See Airbus SE; *Int'l*, pg. 246
AERO SHADE TECHNOLOGIES, INC.; *U.S. Private*, pg. 118
AERO SIMULATION, INC.; *U.S. Private*, pg. 118
AEROSONIC CORPORATION—See TransDigm Group Incorporated; *U.S. Public*, pg. 2181
AEROSPACE DYNAMICS INTERNATIONAL INC.—See Berkshire Hathaway Inc.; *U.S. Public*, pg. 313
AEROSPACE HOLDINGS, INC.—See Harlow Aerostructures, LLC; *U.S. Private*, pg. 1865
AEROSPACE SYSTEMS & COMPONENTS INC.—See Great Plains Ventures, Inc.; *U.S. Private*, pg. 1767
AEROSPACE TECHNOLOGY OF KOREA, INC.; *Int'l*, pg. 181
AEROSPARES 2000 LIMITED—See Acorn Growth Companies, LC; *U.S. Private*, pg. 63
AEROX AVIATION OXYGEN SYSTEMS, LLC—See O2 Aero Acquisitions LLC; *U.S. Private*, pg. 2981
AGC ACQUISITION LLC—See Loar Group, Inc.; *U.S. Private*, pg. 2477
AIRBUS DEFENCE & SPACE GMBH - CASSIDIAN DIVISION—See Airbus SE; *Int'l*, pg. 242
AIRBUS HELICOPTERS ESPANA, S. A.—See Airbus SE; *Int'l*, pg. 243
AIRBUS OPERATIONS SAS—See Airbus SE; *Int'l*, pg. 244
AIRBUS OPERATIONS, S.L.—See Airbus SE; *Int'l*, pg. 244
AIRBUS UK—See Airbus SE; *Int'l*, pg. 244
AIRCO INDUSTRIES, INC.—See Firan Technology Group Corporation; *Int'l*, pg. 2678
AIR COMM CORPORATION - ADDISON—See Arcline Investment Management LP; *U.S. Private*, pg. 312
AIR COST CONTROL PTE. LTD.—See HEICO Corporation; *U.S. Public*, pg. 1019
AIR COST CONTROL US, LLC—See HEICO Corporation; *U.S. Public*, pg. 1019
AIRCRAFT APPLIANCES & EQUIPMENT LIMITED—See J.F. Lehman & Company, Inc.; *U.S. Private*, pg. 2162
AIRCRAFT BELTS, INC.—See Hicks Holdings, LLC; *U.S. Private*, pg. 1934
AIRCRAFT BELTS, INC.—See The Riverside Company; *U.S. Private*, pg. 4108
AIRCRAFT BELTS, INC.—See Weinberg Capital Group, Inc.; *U.S. Private*, pg. 4471
AIRCRAFT BRAKING SYSTEMS CORPORATION—See Parker Hannifin Corporation; *U.S. Public*, pg. 1642
AIRCRAFT GEAR CORPORATION; *U.S. Private*, pg. 140
AIRDYNE AEROSPACE INC.; *U.S. Private*, pg. 140
AIRDYNE R&D INC.—See Airdyne Aerospace Inc.; *U.S. Private*, pg. 141
AIR FRANCE KLM COMPONENT SERVICES CO. LTD.—See Air France-KLM S.A.; *Int'l*, pg. 236
AIR INDUSTRIES MACHINING CORPORATION—See Air Industries Group; *U.S. Public*, pg. 64
AIR-LOCK INCORPORATED—See David Clark Company Incorporated; *U.S. Private*, pg. 1169
AIRPORT SYSTEMS UTAH-GROUND EQUIPMENT—See Oshkosh Corporation; *U.S. Public*, pg. 1620
AIR PRECISION SAS—See Advent International Corporation; *U.S. Private*, pg. 99
AIRTECH INTERNATIONAL INC.; *U.S. Private*, pg. 142
ALBANY ENGINEERED COMPOSITES - SALT LAKE CITY—See Albany International Corp.; *U.S. Public*, pg. 72
ALKAN SAS; *Int'l*, pg. 330
ALLEN AIRCRAFT PRODUCTS, INC.; *U.S. Private*, pg. 178
AMERICAN PANEL CORPORATION—See Mercury Systems, Inc.; *U.S. Public*, pg. 1422
AMRO FABRICATING CORPORATION; *U.S. Private*, pg. 266
AMSAFE AVIATION (CHONGQING), LTD.—See TransDigm Group Incorporated; *U.S. Public*, pg. 2181
AMSAFE BRIDPORT NITTAMBUWA—See TransDigm Group Incorporated; *U.S. Public*, pg. 2182
AMSAFE-C SAFE, INC.—See TransDigm Group Incorporated; *U.S. Public*, pg. 2182
AMSAFE, INC.—See TransDigm Group Incorporated; *U.S. Public*, pg. 2181
ANA MOTOR SERVICE CO., LTD.—See ANA Holdings Inc.; *Int'l*, pg. 444
APACHE ENTERPRISES, INC.—See Sowell & Co., Inc.; *U.S. Private*, pg. 3743
APEX COMPOSITES INC.—See Apex Engineering Inc.; *U.S. Private*, pg. 292
APEX ENGINEERING INC.; *U.S. Private*, pg. 292
APPH AVIATION SERVICES LTD.—See Heroux-Devtek Inc.; *Int'l*, pg. 3364
APPH (BOLTON) LTD.—See Heroux-Devtek Inc.; *Int'l*, pg. 3364
APPH LTD.—See Heroux-Devtek Inc.; *Int'l*, pg. 3364
APPH NOTTINGHAM LTD.—See Heroux-Devtek Inc.; *Int'l*, pg. 3364
APPH WICHITA, INC.—See Heroux-Devtek Inc.; *Int'l*, pg. 3364
APPLIED AVIONICS, INC.; *U.S. Private*, pg. 298
ARKWIN INDUSTRIES, INC.—See TransDigm Group Incorporated; *U.S. Public*, pg. 2182
ARMY FLEET SUPPORT LLC—See L3Harris Technologies, Inc.; *U.S. Public*, pg. 1280
ARNPRIOR AEROSPACE INC.—See Consolidated Industries, Inc.; *U.S. Private*, pg. 1021
ARVAN INC.—See Churchill Equity, Inc.; *U.S. Private*, pg. 894
ASCENT AEROSPACE—See AIP, LLC; *U.S. Private*, pg. 133
ASCO AEROSPACE CANADA LTD.—See ASCO Industries NV/SA; *Int'l*, pg. 602
ASCO AEROSPACE DO BRASIL—See ASCO Industries NV/SA; *Int'l*, pg. 602
ASCO AEROSPACE USA, LLC—See ASCO Industries NV/SA; *Int'l*, pg. 602
ASCO DEUTSCHLAND GMBH—See ASCO Industries NV/SA; *Int'l*, pg. 602
ASCO INDUSTRIES NV/SA; *Int'l*, pg. 602
ASI AVIATION, INC.; *U.S. Private*, pg. 350
ASSOCIATED AIRCRAFT COMPANY LLC; *U.S. Private*, pg. 354
ASSOCIATED AIRCRAFT MANUFACTURING & SALES, INC.; *U.S. Private*, pg. 354
ASTRONICS CONNECTIVITY SYSTEMS & CERTIFICATION CORP.—See Astronics Corporation; *U.S. Public*, pg. 217
ASTRO SPAR, INC.—See Arlington Capital Partners LLC; *U.S. Private*, pg. 327
ATELIERS TOFER SAS—See Figeac-Aero SA; *Int'l*, pg. 2660
ATS JAPAN KABUSHIKI KAISHA—See RTX Corporation; *U.S. Public*, pg. 1822
AUSTRALIAN AVIONICS PTY. LTD.—See General Dynamics Corporation; *U.S. Public*, pg. 913
AUVERGNE AERONAUTIQUE SAS—See Figeac-Aero SA; *Int'l*, pg. 2660
AVCORP INDUSTRIES, INC.—See Searchlight Capital Partners, L.P.; *U.S. Private*, pg. 3588
AVIALL AUSTRALIA PTY. LTD.—See The Boeing Company; *U.S. Public*, pg. 2039
AVIATION MANUFACTURING GROUP, LLC—See Loar Group, Inc.; *U.S. Private*, pg. 2477
AVIATION PARTNERS, INC.—See Washington Corporations; *U.S. Private*, pg. 4446
AVIATION TECHNOLOGIES, INC.—See TransDigm Group Incorporated; *U.S. Public*, pg. 2182
AVIMAC PTE. LTD.—See Frencken Group Limited; *Int'l*, pg. 2772
AVIOR INTEGRATED PRODUCTS—See Searchlight Capital Partners, L.P.; *U.S. Private*, pg. 3588
AVIOSUPPORT, INC.—See Avio Global, Inc.; *U.S. Private*, pg. 407
BAE SYSTEMS-APPLIED TECHNOLOGIES—See BAE Systems plc; *Int'l*, pg. 797
BAE SYSTEMS C-ITS AB—See BAE Systems plc; *Int'l*, pg. 796
BAE SYSTEMS HAGGLUNDS AB—See BAE Systems plc; *Int'l*, pg. 796
BAE SYSTEMS, INC.—See BAE Systems plc; *Int'l*, pg. 796
BAE SYSTEMS (MALAYSIA) SDN BHD—See BAE Systems plc; *Int'l*, pg. 796
BAE SYSTEMS-PLATFORM SOLUTIONS—See BAE Systems plc; *Int'l*, pg. 798
BARON GROUP LLC; *U.S. Private*, pg. 478
BATTERY SHOP, LLC—See HEICO Corporation; *U.S. Public*, pg. 1019
BE AEROSPACE HOLDINGS (UK) LIMITED—See RTX Corporation; *U.S. Public*, pg. 1822
B/E AEROSPACE MACHINED PRODUCTS, INC.—See RTX Corporation; *U.S. Public*, pg. 1822
B/E AEROSPACE SYSTEMS GMBH—See RTX Corporation; *U.S. Public*, pg. 1822
BEIJING ANDAWELL SCIENCE & TECHNOLOGY CO., LTD.; *Int'l*, pg. 945
BEIJING HENGYU DATACOM AVIATION EQUIPMENT CO., LTD.; *Int'l*, pg. 951
BELL HELICOPTER ASIA (PTE) LTD.—See Textron Inc.; *U.S. Public*, pg. 2028
BELL HELICOPTER SUPPLY CENTER N.V.—See Textron Inc.; *U.S. Public*, pg. 2028
BHW (COMPONENTS) LIMITED—See a2e Venture Catalysts Limited; *Int'l*, pg. 30
BLR AEROSPACE, LLC—See Ducommun Incorporated; *U.S. Public*, pg. 689
BODYCOTE THERMAL PROCESSING CANADA, INC.—See Bodycote plc; *Int'l*, pg. 1098
BOEING AEROSTRUCTURES AUSTRALIA PTY LTD.—See The Boeing Company; *U.S. Public*, pg. 2040
THE BOEING CO. - OAK RIDGE—See The Boeing Company; *U.S. Public*, pg. 2040
BOEING DISTRIBUTION, INC.—See The Boeing Company; *U.S. Public*, pg. 2039
BOEING DISTRIBUTION SERVICES GMBH—See The Boeing Company; *U.S. Public*, pg. 2040
BOEING DISTRIBUTION SERVICES II LIMITED—See The Boeing Company; *U.S. Public*, pg. 2040
BOEING DISTRIBUTION SERVICES INC.—See The Boeing Company; *U.S. Public*, pg. 2040
BOEING DISTRIBUTION SERVICES INC.—See The Boeing Company; *U.S. Public*, pg. 2040
BOEING DISTRIBUTION SERVICES - TOULOUSE—See The Boeing Company; *U.S. Public*, pg. 2040
BOEING JAPAN CO., LTD.—See The Boeing Company; *U.S. Public*, pg. 2040
BREEZE-EASTERN LLC—See TransDigm Group Incorporated; *U.S. Public*, pg. 2182
BRIDGEN AEROSPACE, LLC—See Bridger Aerospace Group Holdings, Inc.; *U.S. Public*, pg. 382
BRIDGESTONE AIRCRAFT TIRE COMPANY (CHINA) LIMITED—See Bridgestone Corporation; *Int'l*, pg. 1156
BRIDPORT ERIE AVIATION, INC.—See TransDigm Group Incorporated; *U.S. Public*, pg. 2182
BRITTAIN MACHINE, INC.—See Berkshire Hathaway Inc.; *U.S. Public*, pg. 313
BROAD REACH ENGINEERING COMPANY—See Moog Inc.; *U.S. Public*, pg. 1470

336413 — OTHER AIRCRAFT PART...

BROWN AEROSPACE MFG, SYSTEMS, LLC—See AIP, LLC; *U.S. Private,* pg. 133
BRUNTONS AERO PRODUCTS LIMITED—See Carclo plc; *Int'l,* pg. 1321
BUCHER AEROSPACE CORP.—See Bucher Leichtbau AG; *Int'l,* pg. 1209
BUCHER INTERIORS GMBH—See Bucher Leichtbau AG; *Int'l,* pg. 1209
BUCHER LEICHTBAU AG; *Int'l,* pg. 1209
CADENCE AEROSPACE, LLC—See Arlington Capital Partners LLC; *U.S. Private,* pg. 327
CANYON ENGINEERING PRODUCTS, INC.—See ESCO Technologies, Inc.; *U.S. Public,* pg. 793
CARLETON TECHNOLOGIES INC.—See Eaton Corporation plc; *Int'l,* pg. 2277
CARLYLE AVIATION PARTNERS LLC—See The Carlyle Group Inc.; *U.S. Public,* pg. 2045
CAV AEROSPACE LTD.—See Heritage Group Ltd.; *Int'l,* pg. 3361
CAVOTEC DABICO UK LTD.—See Cavotec SA; *Int'l,* pg. 1362
CAVOTEC DABICO US INC.—See Cavotec SA; *Int'l,* pg. 1362
CAVOTEC REALTY ITALIA SRL—See Cavotec SA; *Int'l,* pg. 1363
CEF INDUSTRIES, LLC—See TransDigm Group Incorporated; *U.S. Public,* pg. 2182
CERTIFIED AVIATION SERVICES, LLC; *U.S. Private,* pg. 841
CESKA ZBROJOVKA A.S.—See Colt CZ Group SE; *Int'l,* pg. 1705
CFN PRECISION LTD.; *Int'l,* pg. 1430
CHELTON ANTENNAS SA—See Advent International Corporation; *U.S. Public,* pg. 99
CHENGDU ALD AVIATION MANUFACTURING CORPORATION; *Int'l,* pg. 1467
CHURCHILL NAVIGATION INC.—See Helinet Aviation Services LLC; *U.S. Private,* pg. 1906
CIRCOMP GMBH—See Albany International Corp.; *U.S. Public,* pg. 72
CIRCOR MAROC SARL A.U.—See KKR & Co. Inc.; *U.S. Public,* pg. 1242
CIVITANAVI SYSTEMS SPA; *Int'l,* pg. 1630
COBHAM ADVANCED ELECTRONIC SOLUTIONS INC.—See Advent International Corporation; *U.S. Private,* pg. 99
COBHAM (INDIA) PVT LIMITED—See Advent International Corporation; *U.S. Private,* pg. 99
COBHAM MISSION SYSTEMS WIMBORNE LIMITED—See Eaton Corporation plc; *Int'l,* pg. 2277
COLLINS AEROSPACE – ACTUATION SYSTEMS—See RTX Corporation; *U.S. Public,* pg. 1821
COLLINS AEROSPACE – AIR MANAGEMENT SYSTEMS—See RTX Corporation; *U.S. Public,* pg. 1821
COLLINS AEROSPACE - ISR SYSTEMS—See RTX Corporation; *U.S. Public,* pg. 1821
COLLINS AEROSPACE - LANDING GEAR—See RTX Corporation; *U.S. Public,* pg. 1821
COLLINS AEROSPACE - WHEELS & BRAKES—See RTX Corporation; *U.S. Public,* pg. 1821
COMPOSITES AQUITAINE S.A.—See Airbus SE; *Int'l,* pg. 246
COMPOSITES ATLANTIC LIMITED—See Airbus SE; *Int'l,* pg. 245
COMPUTADORAS, REDES E INGENIERIA SA—See Airbus SE; *Int'l,* pg. 245
CONAX FLORIDA CORPORATION—See Advent International Corporation; *U.S. Private,* pg. 99
CORMER GROUP INDUSTRIES, INC.; *Int'l,* pg. 1801
COX & COMPANY, INC.; *U.S. Private,* pg. 1074
CPI AEROSTRUCTURES, INC.; *U.S. Public,* pg. 588
CRANE LEAR ROMEC CORP.—See Crane NXT, Co.; *U.S. Public,* pg. 589
CROMPTON TECHNOLOGY GROUP LIMITED—See RTX Corporation; *U.S. Public,* pg. 1821
CSI AEROSPACE, INC.—See HEICO Corporation; *U.S. Public,* pg. 1019
CT GROUP LIMITED—See RTX Corporation; *U.S. Public,* pg. 1821
CTL AEROSPACE INC.; *U.S. Private,* pg. 1118
CTRM AERO COMPOSITES SDN. BHD.—See DRB-HICOM Berhad; *Int'l,* pg. 2201
CTRM COMPOSITES ENGINEERING SDN. BHD.—See DRB-HICOM Berhad; *Int'l,* pg. 2201
CTT SYSTEMS AB; *Int'l,* pg. 1874
CYCLONE MFG. INC.; *Int'l,* pg. 1894
DACO INSTRUMENT COMPANY—See Alinabal Holdings Corporation; *U.S. Private,* pg. 168
DANISH AEROTECH A/S; *Int'l,* pg. 1963
DART AEROSPACE LTD.—See TransDigm Group Incorporated; *U.S. Public,* pg. 2180
DASSAULT AVIATION SA – ARGONAY FACILITY—See Groupe Industriel Marcel Dassault S.A.; *Int'l,* pg. 3105
DEC TECHNOLOGIES, INC.—See HEICO Corporation; *U.S. Public,* pg. 1019
DELAVAN LIMITED—See R.W. Beckett Corporation; *U.S. Private,* pg. 3340

DELTA MATERIAL SERVICES, LLC—See Delta Air Lines, Inc.; *U.S. Public,* pg. 651
DESTINI BERHAD; *Int'l,* pg. 2046
DUCOMMUN AEROSTRUCTURES INC.—See Ducommun Incorporated; *U.S. Public,* pg. 690
DUCOMMUN AEROSTRUCTURES, LLC—See Ducommun Incorporated; *U.S. Public,* pg. 690
DUCOMMUN AEROSTRUCTURES—See Ducommun Incorporated; *U.S. Public,* pg. 690
DUCOMMUN INCORPORATED; *U.S. Public,* pg. 689
DUKES AEROSPACE, INC.—See TransDigm Group Incorporated; *U.S. Public,* pg. 2182
DUTCH SPACE B.V.—See Airbus SE; *Int'l,* pg. 245
DYNAMIC CONTROLS HS, INC.—See RTX Corporation; *U.S. Public,* pg. 1821
EADS CANADA, INC.—See Airbus SE; *Int'l,* pg. 245
EADS COMPOSITES ATLANTIC LIMITED—See Airbus SE; *Int'l,* pg. 245
EADS FRANCE S.A.S.—See Airbus SE; *Int'l,* pg. 246
EAGLE ENGINEERING AEROSPACE CO., LTD.—See Eagle Industry Co., Ltd.; *Int'l,* pg. 2265
EARTH & AEROSPACE MANUFACTURING IND. CO. LTD; *Int'l,* pg. 2267
EATON AEROSPACE LLC - FUEL SYSTEMS DIVISION, CLEVELAND—See Eaton Corporation plc; *Int'l,* pg. 2279
EATON AEROSPACE LLC - HYDRAULIC SYSTEMS DIVISION, LOS ANGELES—See Eaton Corporation plc; *Int'l,* pg. 2279
EATON LIMITED - FUEL & MOTION CONTROL SYSTEMS DIVISION—See Eaton Corporation plc; *Int'l,* pg. 2279
ELBIT SYSTEMS CYCLONE LTD.—See Elbit Systems Limited; *Int'l,* pg. 2344
ELBIT SYSTEMS OF AUSTRALIA PTY LTD.—See Elbit Systems Limited; *Int'l,* pg. 2345
ENGINEERED ARRESTING SYSTEMS CORPORATION—See Curtiss-Wright Corporation; *U.S. Public,* pg. 612
ENGINEERED FABRICS CORPORATION—See Parker Hannifin Corporation; *U.S. Public,* pg. 1642
ESNA - TEXAS—See KKR & Co. Inc.; *U.S. Public,* pg. 1262
ESTERLINE ENGINEERED MATERIALS—See TransDigm Group Incorporated; *U.S. Public,* pg. 2180
ESTERLINE SERVICES CHINA LTD.—See TransDigm Group Incorporated; *U.S. Public,* pg. 2180
EXACTA AEROSPACE, INC.—See Berkshire Hathaway Inc.; *U.S. Public,* pg. 314
EXOTIC METALS FORMING COMPANY LLC.; *U.S. Private,* pg. 1449
FABER ENTERPRISES, INC.; *U.S. Private,* pg. 1458
FACC AG; *Int'l,* pg. 2600
FAIVELEY TRANSPORT N.S.F—See Westinghouse Air Brake Technologies Corporation; *U.S. Public,* pg. 2357
FGA NORTH AMERICA INC.—See Figeac-Aero SA; *Int'l,* pg. 2660
FIGEAC AERO AUXERRE SASU—See Figeac-Aero SA; *Int'l,* pg. 2660
FIRESTONE INDUSTRIAL PRODUCTS DE COSTA RICA, S.A.—See Bridgestone Corporation; *Int'l,* pg. 1156
FIRESTONE INDUSTRIAL PRODUCTS POLAND SP. Z O.O.—See Bridgestone Corporation; *Int'l,* pg. 1156
FIRST AVIATION SERVICES INC.—See First Equity Group, Inc.; *U.S. Private,* pg. 1517
FLANAGAN BROTHERS, INC.—See Hanwha Group; *Int'l,* pg. 3264
FLEET CANADA INC.; *Int'l,* pg. 2698
FLIGHT REFUELLING LIMITED—See Advent International Corporation; *U.S. Private,* pg. 99
FLUGZEUG-UNION SUD GMBH—See Airbus SE; *Int'l,* pg. 242
FLUID POWER, INC.—See O2 Aero Acquisitions LLC; *U.S. Private,* pg. 2981
FMI, INC.—See AE Industrial Partners, LP; *U.S. Private,* pg. 112
FOKKER AEROSTRUCTURES B.V. - HOOGEVEEN—See GKN plc; *Int'l,* pg. 2983
FRASCA INTERNATIONAL INC.; *U.S. Private,* pg. 1599
FTG AEROSPACE INC.—See Firan Technology Group Corporation; *Int'l,* pg. 2678
GE AVIATION SYSTEMS GROUP LIMITED—See General Electric Company; *U.S. Public,* pg. 919
GE AVIATION SYSTEMS LIMITED—See General Electric Company; *U.S. Public,* pg. 918
GE AVIATION SYSTEMS LTD. - SOUTHAMPTON—See General Electric Company; *U.S. Public,* pg. 918
GE ENGINE SERVICES, LLC—See General Electric Company; *U.S. Public,* pg. 916
GEMCOR II, LLC—See AIP, LLC; *U.S. Private,* pg. 133
GKN AEROSPACE AEROSTRUCTURES NORTH AMERICA—See GKN plc; *Int'l,* pg. 2983
GKN AEROSPACE ALABAMA—See GKN plc; *Int'l,* pg. 2983
GKN AEROSPACE BANDY MACHINING INC—See GKN plc; *Int'l,* pg. 2984
GKN AEROSPACE - MONITOR, INC.—See GKN plc; *Int'l,* pg. 2983
GKN AEROSPACE NEW ENGLAND INC—See GKN plc; *Int'l,* pg. 2984
GKN AEROSPACE NORTH AMERICA INC—See GKN plc; *Int'l,* pg. 2984

CORPORATE AFFILIATIONS

GKN AEROSPACE SERVICES LTD—See GKN plc; *Int'l,* pg. 2984
GKN AEROSPACE TRANSPARENCY SYSTEMS INC—See GKN plc; *Int'l,* pg. 2984
GKN FOKKER AEROSPACE—See GKN plc; *Int'l,* pg. 2983
GKN WESTLAND AEROSPACE INC—See GKN plc; *Int'l,* pg. 2986
GLOBAL GROUND SUPPORT LLC—See Air T, Inc.; *U.S. Public,* pg. 67
GOGO BUSINESS AVIATION, LLC—See Gogo Inc.; *U.S. Public,* pg. 949
GOODRICH AEROSPACE EUROPE GMBH—See RTX Corporation; *U.S. Public,* pg. 1821
GOODRICH LIGHTING SYSTEMS GMBH & CO. KG—See RTX Corporation; *U.S. Public,* pg. 1821
GROUPAERO MEXICO—See Harlow Aerostructures, LLC; *U.S. Private,* pg. 1865
G.S. PRECISION, INC.—See AE Industrial Partners, LP; *U.S. Private,* pg. 112
GUANGLIAN AVIATION INDUSTRY CO., LTD.; *Int'l,* pg. 3162
HAAS GROUP AUSTRALIA PTY LIMITED—See Platinum Equity, LLC; *U.S. Private,* pg. 3210
HARCOSEMCO LLC—See TransDigm Group Incorporated; *U.S. Public,* pg. 2181
HARLOW AEROSTRUCTURES, LLC; *U.S. Private,* pg. 1865
HARTZELL PROPELLER INC.—See Tailwind Technologies Inc.; *U.S. Private,* pg. 3924
HDI LANDING GEAR USA, INC.—See Heroux-Devtek Inc.; *Int'l,* pg. 3364
HEFEI JIANGHANG AIRCRAFT EQUIPMENT CO., LTD.; *Int'l,* pg. 3307
HEICO AEROSPACE PARTS CORP.—See HEICO Corporation; *U.S. Public,* pg. 1019
HEICO PARTS GROUP, INC.—See HEICO Corporation; *U.S. Public,* pg. 1019
HELICOMB INTERNATIONAL, INC.—See Berkshire Hathaway Inc.; *U.S. Public,* pg. 314
HELIQWEST AVIATION INC; *Int'l,* pg. 3331
HEROUX-DEVTEK - LONGUEUIL PLANT—See Heroux-Devtek Inc.; *Int'l,* pg. 3364
HEROUX-DEVTEK - SCARBOROUGH PLANT—See Heroux-Devtek Inc.; *Int'l,* pg. 3364
HEXCEL COMPOSITES GMBH—See Hexcel Corporation; *U.S. Public,* pg. 1032
HOLMBERG GMBH & CO. KG; *Int'l,* pg. 3452
HONDA AIRCRAFT COMPANY, LLC—See Honda Motor Co., Ltd.; *Int'l,* pg. 3460
HONEYWELL AEROSPACE - BOYNE CITY—See Honeywell International Inc.; *U.S. Public,* pg. 1047
HONEYWELL AEROSPACE - MOORESTOWN—See Honeywell International Inc.; *U.S. Public,* pg. 1047
HONEYWELL AEROSPACE - TORRANCE—See Honeywell International Inc.; *U.S. Public,* pg. 1047
HONEYWELL AEROSPACE - URBANA—See Honeywell International Inc.; *U.S. Public,* pg. 1047
HONEYWELL AIRCRAFT LANDING SYSTEMS—See Honeywell International Inc.; *U.S. Public,* pg. 1047
HONEYWELL CO., LTD.—See Honeywell International Inc.; *U.S. Public,* pg. 1051
HONEYWELL DEFENSE AVIONICS SYSTEMS—See Honeywell International Inc.; *U.S. Public,* pg. 1047
HS MARSTON AEROSPACE LIMITED—See RTX Corporation; *U.S. Public,* pg. 1821
HYDRAFLOW INC.; *U.S. Private,* pg. 2017
HYDRO-AIRE INC.—See Crane NXT, Co.; *U.S. Public,* pg. 589
HYPER-TECHNOLOGIES SAS—See Advent International Corporation; *U.S. Private,* pg. 99
IDD AEROSPACE CORP.; *U.S. Private,* pg. 2035
I.M.P. AEROSPACE DIVISION—See I.M.P. Group International Inc.; *Int'l,* pg. 3566
IMPRESA AEROSPACE, LLC—See Graycliff Partners LP; *U.S. Private,* pg. 1761
INDUSTRIA DE TURBO PROPULSORES S.A.—See Bain Capital, LP; *U.S. Private,* pg. 433
INDUSTRIAL TUBE COMPANY LLC—See ITT Inc.; *U.S. Public,* pg. 1178
INET AIRPORT SYSTEMS, INC.—See Cavotec SA; *Int'l,* pg. 1363
INFINITY TRADING & SOLUTIONS; *U.S. Private,* pg. 2072
INNOVATIVE SOLUTIONS AND SUPPORT, LLC—See Innovative Solutions & Support, Inc.; *U.S. Public,* pg. 1127
ION CORPORATION; *U.S. Private,* pg. 2133
IS&S AVIATION, INC.—See Innovative Solutions & Support, Inc.; *U.S. Public,* pg. 1127
IS&S AVIATION, LLC—See Innovative Solutions & Support, Inc.; *U.S. Public,* pg. 1127
IS&S AVIATION, INC.—See Innovative Solutions & Support, Inc.; *U.S. Public,* pg. 1127
IS&S DELAWARE, INC.—See Innovative Solutions & Support, Inc.; *U.S. Public,* pg. 1127
IS&S HOLDINGS, INC.—See Innovative Solutions & Support, Inc.; *U.S. Public,* pg. 1127
J.A. REINHARDT & CO., INC.—See RTX Corporation; *U.S. Public,* pg. 1822
J&B AVIATION SERVICES INC.—See Illinois Tool Works Inc.; *U.S. Public,* pg. 1103
JBT AEROTECH-GROUND SUPPORT EQUIPMENT—See

336413 — OTHER AIRCRAFT PART...

Oshkosh Corporation; *U.S. Public*, pg. 1620
JBT AEROTECH SINGAPORE PTE. LTD.—See John Bean Technologies Corporation; *U.S. Public*, pg. 1191
JBT AEROTECH UK LIMITED—See John Bean Technologies Corporation; *U.S. Public*, pg. 1191
KAMAN AEROSPACE CORPORATION—See Arcline Investment Management LP; *U.S. Private*, pg. 314
KAMAN COMPOSITES - WICHITA, INC.—See Arcline Investment Management LP; *U.S. Private*, pg. 314
KELLY AEROSPACE INC.—See Arcline Investment Management LP; *U.S. Private*, pg. 313
K&F INDUSTRIES, INC.—See Parker Hannifin Corporation; *U.S. Public*, pg. 1642
KIDDE AEROSPACE—See RTX Corporation; *U.S. Public*, pg. 1822
KID-SYSTEME GMBH—See Airbus SE; *Int'l*, pg. 244
KILGORE FLARES—See Chemring Group PLC; *Int'l*, pg. 1463
KLUNE INDUSTRIES, INC.—See Berkshire Hathaway Inc.; *U.S. Public*, pg. 315
KOREA COMPOSITES INC.—See HANKUK CARBON Co., Ltd.; *Int'l*, pg. 3254
KUO AEROSPACE, S.A. DE C.V.—See Grupo Kuo, S.A.B. de C.V.; *Int'l*, pg. 3131
L-3 COMMUNICATIONS INTEGRATED SYSTEMS—See L3Harris Technologies, Inc.; *U.S. Public*, pg. 1282
L-3 CRESTVIEW AEROSPACE—See AIP, LLC; *U.S. Private*, pg. 133
LABEL SAS—See Advent International Corporation; *U.S. Private*, pg. 100
LEE COMPANY S.A.—See The Lee Company; *U.S. Private*, pg. 4068
LEE HYDRAULISCHE MINIATURKOMPONENTEN—See The Lee Company; *U.S. Private*, pg. 4068
LEE SRL—See The Lee Company; *U.S. Private*, pg. 4068
LIGHTNING DIVERSION SYSTEMS, INC.—See Ducommun Incorporated; *U.S. Public*, pg. 690
LIMCO AIREPAIR INC.—See First Israel Mezzanine Investors Ltd.; *Int'l*, pg. 2685
LIMCO-PIEDMONT INC.—See First Israel Mezzanine Investors Ltd.; *Int'l*, pg. 2685
LOAR GROUP, INC.; *U.S. Private*, pg. 2477
LOOS & COMPANY, INC. - CABLEWARE—See Loos & Company, Inc.; *U.S. Private*, pg. 2494
MARVIN ENGINEERING COMPANY, INC.; *U.S. Private*, pg. 2597
MARVIN LAND SYSTEMS—See Marvin Engineering Company, Inc.; *U.S. Private*, pg. 2598
MASON ELECTRIC CO.—See TransDigm Group Incorporated; *U.S. Public*, pg. 2181
MASS SYSTEMS AMERON GLOBAL, INC.—See AMETEK, Inc.; *U.S. Public*, pg. 117
MBDA DEUTSCHLAND GMBH—See Airbus SE; *Int'l*, pg. 247
MBDA DEUTSCHLAND GMBH—See BAE Systems plc; *Int'l*, pg. 798
M.C. GILL EUROPE, LTD.—See M.C. Gill Corporation; *U.S. Private*, pg. 2528
MCKECHNIE AEROSPACE DE, INC.—See TransDigm Group Incorporated; *U.S. Public*, pg. 2182
MECANISMOS DE MATAMORES S.A. DE C.V.—See TransDigm Group Incorporated; *U.S. Public*, pg. 2183
MEGGITT AVIONICS—See Parker Hannifin Corporation; *U.S. Public*, pg. 1642
MEGGITT CONTROL SYSTEMS - SAN DIEGO—See Parker Hannifin Corporation; *U.S. Public*, pg. 1642
MEGGITT CONTROL SYSTEMS—See Parker Hannifin Corporation; *U.S. Public*, pg. 1642
MEGGITT DEFENSE SYSTEMS—See Parker Hannifin Corporation; *U.S. Public*, pg. 1642
MEGGITT DEFENSE SYSTEMS—See Parker Hannifin Corporation; *U.S. Public*, pg. 1642
MEGGITT (FRANCE) SAS—See Parker Hannifin Corporation; *U.S. Public*, pg. 1641
MEGGITT (NEW HAMPSHIRE), INC—See Parker Hannifin Corporation; *U.S. Public*, pg. 1642
MEGGITT PLC - RUGBY FACILITY—See Parker Hannifin Corporation; *U.S. Public*, pg. 1642
MEGGITT PLC—See Parker Hannifin Corporation; *U.S. Public*, pg. 1641
MEGGITT (ROCKMART), INC.—See Parker Hannifin Corporation; *U.S. Public*, pg. 1642
MEGGITT SAFETY SYSTEMS, INC.—See Parker Hannifin Corporation; *U.S. Public*, pg. 1642
MEGGITT-USA, INC.—See Parker Hannifin Corporation; *U.S. Public*, pg. 1642
MEREX AIRCRAFT COMPANY, INCORPORATED—See Merex Holding Corporation; *U.S. Private*, pg. 2672
MID-CONTINENT INSTRUMENT CO., INC.; *U.S. Private*, pg. 2708
MOELLER MFG. COMPANY, LLC.—See AE Industrial Partners, LP; *U.S. Private*, pg. 112
MONTANA TECH COMPONENTS AG—See Global Equity Partners Beteiligungs-Management AG; *Int'l*, pg. 2996
MOOG MOTION CONTROLS PVT. LTD.—See Moog Inc.; *U.S. Public*, pg. 1470
MOOG SINGAPORE PTE LTD.—See Moog Inc.; *U.S. Public*, pg. 1470

MOOG WOLVERHAMPTON LIMITED—See Moog Inc.; *U.S. Public*, pg. 1470
MSA AIRCRAFT PRODUCTS, INC.—See Aero Shade Technologies, Inc.; *U.S. Private*, pg. 118
NANOSPACE AB—See GomSpace Group AB; *Int'l*, pg. 3037
NASCO AIRCRAFT BRAKE INC.—See Parker Hannifin Corporation; *U.S. Public*, pg. 1642
NASSAU TOOL WORKS, INC.—See Air Industries Group; *U.S. Public*, pg. 64
NC DYNAMICS INC.—See Harlow Aerostructures, LLC; *U.S. Private*, pg. 1865
NEILL AIRCRAFT COMPANY; *U.S. Private*, pg. 2882
NOBLES MANUFACTURING, INC.—See The Graham Group, Inc.; *U.S. Private*, pg. 4037
NORANCO INC. - DEER VALLEY DIVISION—See Berkshire Hathaway Inc.; *U.S. Public*, pg. 314
NORANCO INC.—See Berkshire Hathaway Inc.; *U.S. Public*, pg. 314
NORDAM EUROPE LIMITED—See General Dynamics Corporation; *U.S. Public*, pg. 913
THE NORDAM GROUP, INC.—See General Dynamics Corporation; *U.S. Public*, pg. 913
THE NORDAM GROUP, INC.—See General Dynamics Corporation; *U.S. Public*, pg. 913
NORDAM SINGAPORE PTE LTD—See General Dynamics Corporation; *U.S. Public*, pg. 913
NORTHSTAR AEROSPACE - CHICAGO—See Wynnchurch Capital, L.P.; *U.S. Private*, pg. 4577
NORTHSTAR AEROSPACE, INC.—See Wynnchurch Capital, L.P.; *U.S. Private*, pg. 4577
NORTHSTAR AEROSPACE - MILTON—See Wynnchurch Capital, L.P.; *U.S. Private*, pg. 4577
NORTHSTAR AEROSPACE - PHOENIX—See Wynnchurch Capital, L.P.; *U.S. Private*, pg. 4577
NORTHSTAR AEROSPACE - WINDSOR—See Wynnchurch Capital, L.P.; *U.S. Private*, pg. 4577
NORTHSTAR MACHINE & TOOL CO., INC.; *U.S. Private*, pg. 2958
NORTHWEST METALCRAFT, INC.—See Metalcraft Industries, Inc.; *U.S. Private*, pg. 2680
NSI, INC.—See RTX Corporation; *U.S. Public*, pg. 1823
OPTICAL DISPLAY ENGINEERING LLC—See HEICO Corporation; *U.S. Public*, pg. 1020
OREGON AERO, INC.; *U.S. Private*, pg. 3039
PACIFIC AEROSPACE & ELECTRONICS, INC. - BONDED METALS—See TransDigm Group Incorporated; *U.S. Public*, pg. 2181
PARADIGM AEROSPACE CORPORATION—See Metro Aviation, Inc.; *U.S. Private*, pg. 2685
PARAVION TECHNOLOGIES INC.—See TransDigm Group Incorporated; *U.S. Public*, pg. 2181
PARKER HANNIFIN CONTROL SYSTEMS DIV.—See Parker Hannifin Corporation; *U.S. Public*, pg. 1648
PARKER CONTROLS SYSTEMS DIVISION—See Parker Hannifin Corporation; *U.S. Public*, pg. 1648
PARKER FLUID CONNECTORS DE MEXICO—See Parker Hannifin Corporation; *U.S. Public*, pg. 1645
PARKER HANNIFIN CORPORATION, AIRBORNE DIVISION—See Parker Hannifin Corporation; *U.S. Public*, pg. 1648
PARKER HANNIFIN CUSTOMER SUPPORT COMMERCIAL DIVISION—See Parker Hannifin Corporation; *U.S. Public*, pg. 1648
PARKER HANNIFIN HYDRAULIC ACCUMULATOR DIVISION—See Parker Hannifin Corporation; *U.S. Public*, pg. 1647
PARKER HANNIFIN HYDRAULICS SYSTEMS DIVISION—See Parker Hannifin Corporation; *U.S. Public*, pg. 1649
PARKER HANNIFIN MALAYSIA SDN. BHD—See Parker Hannifin Corporation; *U.S. Public*, pg. 1648
PARKER HANNIFIN SEAL GROUP—See Parker Hannifin Corporation; *U.S. Public*, pg. 1648
PAS TECHNOLOGIES INC.—See The Carlyle Group Inc.; *U.S. Public*, pg. 2054
PCC AEROSTRUCTURES AUBURN—See Berkshire Hathaway Inc.; *U.S. Public*, pg. 314
PCC AEROSTRUCTURES DORVAL INC.—See Berkshire Hathaway Inc.; *U.S. Public*, pg. 314
PCC STRUCTURALS, INC.—See Berkshire Hathaway Inc.; *U.S. Public*, pg. 314
PCX AEROSTRUCTURES, LLC—See Greenbriar Equity Group, L.P.; *U.S. Private*, pg. 1776
PECO, INC.—See Astronics Corporation; *U.S. Public*, pg. 217
PEERLESS AEROSPACE FASTENER CORP.—See Diploma PLC; *Int'l*, pg. 2129
PERFORMANCE PLASTICS INC.—See Rock West Composites, Inc.; *U.S. Private*, pg. 3465
PHOENIX COATING RESOURCES, INC.—See Compagnie de Saint-Gobain SA; *Int'l*, pg. 1732
PIEDMONT AVIATION COMPONENT SERVICES LLC—See First Israel Mezzanine Investors Ltd.; *Int'l*, pg. 2685
PIONEER AEROSPACE CORPORATION—See Space Exploration Technologies Corp.; *U.S. Private*, pg. 3744
P.L. PORTER CONTROLS, INC.—See Crane NXT, Co.; *U.S. Public*, pg. 589

PNEUDRAULICS, INC.—See TransDigm Group Incorporated; *U.S. Public*, pg. 2183
PRECISION AEROSPACE CORP.; *U.S. Private*, pg. 3244
PRECISION COMPONENTS INTL. INC.—See RTX Corporation; *U.S. Public*, pg. 1824
PRECISION MACHINE WORKS, INC.—See Arlington Capital Partners LLC; *U.S. Private*, pg. 327
PREMIUM AEROTEC GMBH - AUGSBURG PLANT—See Airbus SE; *Int'l*, pg. 243
PREMIUM AEROTEC GMBH - BREMEN PLANT—See Airbus SE; *Int'l*, pg. 243
PREMIUM AEROTEC GMBH - NORDENHAM PLANT—See Airbus SE; *Int'l*, pg. 243
PREMIUM AEROTEC GMBH—See Airbus SE; *Int'l*, pg. 243
PREMIUM AEROTEC GMBH - VAREL PLANT—See Airbus SE; *Int'l*, pg. 243
PREMIUM AEROTEC SRL—See Airbus SE; *Int'l*, pg. 243
PRESCOTT AEROSPACE, INC.; *U.S. Private*, pg. 3254
PROFILECOMP GMBH—See Albany International Corp.; *U.S. Public*, pg. 72
PROGRESSIVE INCORPORATED—See Berkshire Hathaway Inc.; *U.S. Public*, pg. 314
PTI TECHNOLOGIES INC.—See ESCO Technologies, Inc.; *U.S. Public*, pg. 794
QUALISEAL TECHNOLOGY, LLC—See Enpro Inc.; *U.S. Public*, pg. 775
QUALITY TURNING INC.; *U.S. Private*, pg. 3321
QUERETARO S DE RL DE CV—See Parker Hannifin Corporation; *U.S. Public*, pg. 1642
QWEST AIR PARTS, INC.—See Leonard Green & Partners, L.P.; *U.S. Private*, pg. 2424
RADIANT POWER CORP.—See HEICO Corporation; *U.S. Public*, pg. 1020
RAFAUT SA—See HLD Associes SA; *Int'l*, pg. 3431
RAISBECK ENGINEERING, INC.—See Acorn Growth Companies, LC; *U.S. Private*, pg. 63
RANGE GENERATION NEXT, LLC—See RTX Corporation; *U.S. Public*, pg. 1824
RATIER-FIGEAC SA—See RTX Corporation; *U.S. Public*, pg. 1821
REGENT AEROSPACE CORPORATION; *U.S. Private*, pg. 3387
REINHOLD INDUSTRIES INC.—See HEICO Corporation; *U.S. Public*, pg. 1021
REMEC DEFENSE & SPACE, INC—See Advent International Corporation; *U.S. Private*, pg. 99
ROCKWELL COLLINS UK LIMITED—See RTX Corporation; *U.S. Public*, pg. 1823
ROGERSON AIRCRAFT CONTROLS—See Rogerson Aircraft Corporation; *U.S. Private*, pg. 3472
ROGERSON AIRCRAFT CORPORATION; *U.S. Private*, pg. 3472
ROHR, INC.—See RTX Corporation; *U.S. Public*, pg. 1821
SAINT GOBAIN PERFORMANCE PLASTICS CORPORATION—See Compagnie de Saint-Gobain SA; *Int'l*, pg. 1731
SATAIR A/S—See Airbus SE; *Int'l*, pg. 244
SCHENCK ITALIA S.R.L.—See Durr AG; *Int'l*, pg. 2233
SEAL DYNAMICS LIMITED—See HEICO Corporation; *U.S. Public*, pg. 1021
SECURAPLANE TECHNOLOGIES INC.—See Parker Hannifin Corporation; *U.S. Public*, pg. 1643
SELECTAERO—See Applied Avionics, Inc.; *U.S. Private*, pg. 298
SENTRY AEROSPACE CORP.—See Acorn Growth Companies, LC; *U.S. Private*, pg. 63
SHOWA AIRCRAFT INDUSTRY CO., LTD.—See Bain Capital, LP; *U.S. Private*, pg. 444
SIERRACIN CORPORATION—See PPG Industries, Inc.; *U.S. Public*, pg. 1707
SIERRA NEVADA CORPORATION; *U.S. Private*, pg. 3647
SILVER WINGS AEROSPACE, INC.—See HEICO Corporation; *U.S. Public*, pg. 1021
SKANDIA, INC.—See TransDigm Group Incorporated; *U.S. Public*, pg. 2183
SKYTRONICS, INC.—See Phillips Service Industries, Inc. (PSI); *U.S. Private*, pg. 3171
SMS S.A.S.—See Advent International Corporation; *U.S. Private*, pg. 100
SN AUVERGNE AERONAUTIQUE SAS—See Figeac-Aero SA; *Int'l*, pg. 2661
SPACE-LOK, INC.—See KKR & Co. Inc.; *U.S. Public*, pg. 1262
SPECIALIST TECHNOLOGIES LTD.—See ALA SpA; *Int'l*, pg. 289
SPECTRALUX CORPORATION—See Avio Global, Inc.; *U.S. Private*, pg. 407
SR TECHNICS UK LIMITED—See Hainan Traffic Administration Holding Co., Ltd.; *Int'l*, pg. 3216
STADCO—See Harlow Aerostructures, LLC; *U.S. Private*, pg. 1865
STEALTH AEROSPACE, INC.—See Audax Group, Limited Partnership; *U.S. Private*, pg. 388
S-TEC CORPORATION—See Advent International Corporation; *U.S. Private*, pg. 100
STEVENS MANUFACTURING COMPANY INCORPORATED—See Essex Industries, Inc.; *U.S. Private*, pg. 1428

336413 — OTHER AIRCRAFT PART...

STI FRANCE SAS—See Arbonia AG; *Int'l*, pg. 538
STYLES LOGISTICS, INC.—See Carl Marks & Co., Inc.; *U.S. Private*, pg. 763
SUN COUNTRY INDUSTRIES LLC—See McNally Industries, LLC; *U.S. Private*, pg. 2643
SUNGEAR, INC.—See Hicks Holdings, LLC; *U.S. Private*, pg. 1934
SUNGEAR, INC.—See The Riverside Company; *U.S. Private*, pg. 4108
SUNGEAR, INC.—See Weinberg Capital Group, Inc.; *U.S. Private*, pg. 4471
SURVIRN ENGINEERING LTD.—See Harlow Aerostructures, LLC; *U.S. Private*, pg. 1865
SWISS TEKNIK LLC; *U.S. Private*, pg. 3894
SYSTEMS 3, INC.—See Gallant Capital Partners, LLC; *U.S. Private*, pg. 1639
TDW-GESELLSCHAFT FUR VERTEIDIGUNGSTECHNISCHE WIRKSYSTEME GMBH—See Airbus SE; *Int'l*, pg. 247
TDW-GESELLSCHAFT FUR VERTEIDIGUNGSTECHNISCHE WIRKSYSTEME GMBH—See BAE Systems plc; *Int'l*, pg. 798
TEAM SA—See Advent International Corporation; *U.S. Private*, pg. 100
TECH MANUFACTURING, LLC—See Onward Capital LLC; *U.S. Private*, pg. 3028
TECH MANUFACTURING, LLC—See Thompson Street Capital Manager LLC; *U.S. Private*, pg. 4161
TECT AEROSPACE, INC.—See UCA Holdings Inc.; *U.S. Private*, pg. 4273
TECT AEROSPACE—See Stony Point Group, Inc.; *U.S. Private*, pg. 3830
TECT AEROSPACE—See Stony Point Group, Inc.; *U.S. Private*, pg. 3830
TELAIR INTERNATIONAL GMBH—See TransDigm Group Incorporated; *U.S. Public*, pg. 2183
TEMIS S.R.L.—See Avio S.p.A.; *Int'l*, pg. 744
TEXAS AIR COMPOSITES, INC.—See JLL Partners, LLC; *U.S. Private*, pg. 2212
TEXAS PNEUMATIC SYSTEMS, INC.—See JLL Partners, LLC; *U.S. Private*, pg. 2212
TEXSTARS LLC—See PPG Industries, Inc.; *U.S. Public*, pg. 1710
THERMAL SOLUTIONS LLC—See RTX Corporation; *U.S. Public*, pg. 1822
TOFER EUROPE SOLUTIONS SRL—See Figeac-Aero SA; *Int'l*, pg. 2661
TRANSDIGM INC.—See TransDigm Group Incorporated; *U.S. Public*, pg. 2181
TRANSICOIL (MALAYSIA) SENDIRIAN BERHAD—See TransDigm Group Incorporated; *U.S. Public*, pg. 2183
TRANS-PACIFIC AEROSPACE COMPANY, INC.; *U.S. Public*, pg. 2179
TRIUMPH ACTUATION SYSTEMS-UK, LTD. - CHELTENHAM—See Triumph Group, Inc.; *U.S. Public*, pg. 2196
TRIUMPH ACTUATION SYSTEMS-YAKIMA, LLC—See Triumph Group, Inc.; *U.S. Public*, pg. 2196
TRIUMPH AIRBORNE STRUCTURES, LLC—See Triumph Group, Inc.; *U.S. Public*, pg. 2197
TRIUMPH COMPOSITE SYSTEMS, INC.—See Triumph Group, Inc.; *U.S. Public*, pg. 2196
TRIUMPH CONTROLS, LLC—See Triumph Group, Inc.; *U.S. Public*, pg. 2196
TRIUMPH CONTROLS-UK, LTD.—See Triumph Group, Inc.; *U.S. Public*, pg. 2196
TRIUMPH GEAR SYSTEMS-MACOMB, INC.—See Triumph Group, Inc.; *U.S. Public*, pg. 2196
TRIUMPH GROUP -MEXICO S. DE R.L. DE C.V.—See Triumph Group, Inc.; *U.S. Public*, pg. 2197
TRIUMPH INSULATION SYSTEMS, LLC—See Triumph Group, Inc.; *U.S. Public*, pg. 2196
TRIUMPH STRUCTURES-EAST TEXAS, INC.—See Triumph Group, Inc.; *U.S. Public*, pg. 2196
TRIUMPH THERMAL SYSTEMS, LLC—See Triumph Group, Inc.; *U.S. Public*, pg. 2196
TRONAIR, INC.—See Golden Gate Capital Management II, LLC; *U.S. Private*, pg. 1732
TRUIMPH ACCESSORY SERVICES—See Triumph Group, Inc.; *U.S. Public*, pg. 2197
TULIP DEVELOPMENT LABORATORY, INC.—See Orbit International Corp.; *U.S. Public*, pg. 1615
TURBINE CONTROLS, LLC—See VSE Corporation; *U.S. Public*, pg. 2313
TURBINE ENGINE COMPONENTS TEXTRON, INC.—See UCA Holdings Inc.; *U.S. Private*, pg. 4273
TURBO-UNION LTD.—See Airbus SE; *Int'l*, pg. 243
TWC AVIATION, INC.; *U.S. Private*, pg. 4263
TWIN COMMANDER AIRCRAFT LLC—See Hicks Holdings, LLC; *U.S. Private*, pg. 1934
TWIN COMMANDER AIRCRAFT LLC—See The Riverside Company; *U.S. Private*, pg. 4108
TWIN COMMANDER AIRCRAFT LLC—See Weinberg Capital Group, Inc.; *U.S. Private*, pg. 4471
UAV FACTORY LTD.—See AE Industrial Partners, LP; *U.S. Private*, pg. 112
UAV FACTORY USA LLC—See AE Industrial Partners, LP; *U.S. Private*, pg. 112

UNIVERSAL AEROSPACE CO., INC.—See Strength Capital Partners, LLC; *U.S. Private*, pg. 3839
U.S. AEROSPACE, INC.; *U.S. Public*, pg. 2212
UTC AEROSPACE SYSTEMS - ACTUATION SYSTEMS, BUC—See RTX Corporation; *U.S. Public*, pg. 1821
UTC AEROSPACE SYSTEMS - LANDING GEAR, OAKVILLE—See RTX Corporation; *U.S. Public*, pg. 1821
UTC (US) LTD.—See RTX Corporation; *U.S. Public*, pg. 1825
VALLEY TOOL & MANUFACTURING, INC.—See Harlow Aerostructures, LLC; *U.S. Private*, pg. 1865
VECTOR AEROSPACE FRANCE—See The Carlyle Group Inc.; *U.S. Public*, pg. 2054
VISIONEERING INC.; *U.S. Private*, pg. 4392
WALDEN'S MACHINE LLC—See Berkshire Hathaway Inc.; *U.S. Public*, pg. 314
WASI, INC.—See The Atlas Group; *U.S. Private*, pg. 3990
WENCOR, LLC—See HEICO Corporation; *U.S. Public*, pg. 1021
WHIPPANY ACTUATION SYSTEMS, LLC—See TransDigm Group Incorporated; *U.S. Public*, pg. 2183
WIPAIRE INC.; *U.S. Private*, pg. 4546
W. L. GORE & ASSOCIATES SCANDINAVIA AB—See W.L. Gore & Associates, Inc.; *U.S. Private*, pg. 4421
W. L. GORE & ASSOCIATI S.R.L.—See W.L. Gore & Associates, Inc.; *U.S. Private*, pg. 4421
WOODWARD HRT, INC.—See Woodward, Inc.; *U.S. Public*, pg. 2378
WOODWARD, INC. - DUARTE—See Woodward, Inc.; *U.S. Public*, pg. 2378
WORLD AEROSPACE CORPORATION; *U.S. Private*, pg. 4564
WORTHINGTON AVIATION PARTS, INC.—See Churchill Equity, Inc.; *U.S. Private*, pg. 895
XCOR AEROSPACE, INC.; *U.S. Private*, pg. 4580
ZENITH CORPORATION—See KKR & Co. Inc.; *U.S. Public*, pg. 1242
ZIM FLUGSITZE GMBH—See Aurelius Equity Opportunities SE & Co. KGaA; *Int'l*, pg. 710

336414 — GUIDED MISSILE AND SPACE VEHICLE MANUFACTURING

AIRBUS DEFENCE AND SPACE LIMITED—See Airbus SE; *Int'l*, pg. 245
ASTROTECH CORPORATION; *U.S. Public*, pg. 218
ATK LAUNCH SYSTEMS INC.—See Northrop Grumman Corporation; *U.S. Public*, pg. 1540
BAE SYSTEMS PERFORMANCE BASED SOLUTIONS—See BAE Systems plc; *Int'l*, pg. 797
BOEING LAUNCH SERVICES, INC.—See The Boeing Company; *U.S. Public*, pg. 2041
DIEHL AEROSPACE GMBH—See Diehl Stiftung & Co. KG; *Int'l*, pg. 2114
DIEHL AEROSPACE GMBH—See Diehl Stiftung & Co. KG; *Int'l*, pg. 2114
E'PRIME AEROSPACE CORPORATION; *U.S. Private*, pg. 1302
EUROSAM—See Airbus SE; *Int'l*, pg. 247
EUROSAM—See BAE Systems plc; *Int'l*, pg. 798
GENERAL DYNAMICS CORPORATION; *U.S. Public*, pg. 913
LOCKHEED MARTIN ADVANCED PROJECTS—See Lockheed Martin Corporation; *U.S. Public*, pg. 1337
LOCKHEED MARTIN AUSTRALIA PTY. LIMITED—See Lockheed Martin Corporation; *U.S. Public*, pg. 1338
LOCKHEED MARTIN GOVERNMENT ELECTRONIC SYSTEMS—See Lockheed Martin Corporation; *U.S. Public*, pg. 1338
LOCKHEED MARTIN MARITIME SYSTEMS & SENSORS—See Lockheed Martin Corporation; *U.S. Public*, pg. 1338
LOCKHEED MARTIN MARITIME SYSTEMS & SENSORS—See Lockheed Martin Corporation; *U.S. Public*, pg. 1338
LOCKHEED MARTIN NAVAL & ELECTRONIC SYSTEMS—See Lockheed Martin Corporation; *U.S. Public*, pg. 1338
MBDA ITALIA SPA—See Airbus SE; *Int'l*, pg. 247
MBDA ITALIA SPA—See BAE Systems plc; *Int'l*, pg. 798
MBDA UK LTD.—See Airbus SE; *Int'l*, pg. 247
MBDA UK LTD.—See BAE Systems plc; *Int'l*, pg. 798
MBDA UK—See Airbus SE; *Int'l*, pg. 247
MBDA UK—See BAE Systems plc; *Int'l*, pg. 798
MILLENNIUM SPACE SYSTEMS, INC.—See The Boeing Company; *U.S. Public*, pg. 2041
RAYTHEON MISSILE SYSTEMS—See RTX Corporation; *U.S. Public*, pg. 1824
ROCKET LAB USA, INC.; *U.S. Public*, pg. 1804
SHL NEW ZEALAND LIMITED—See Exponent Private Equity LLP; *Int'l*, pg. 2589
SPACE EXPLORATION TECHNOLOGIES CORP.; *U.S. Private*, pg. 3744
SPACE VECTOR CORPORATION; *U.S. Private*, pg. 3744
WORLD SURVEILLANCE GROUP INC.; *U.S. Public*, pg. 4567

336415 — GUIDED MISSILE AND SPACE VEHICLE PROPULSION UNIT AND PROPULSION UNIT PARTS MANUFACTURING

AEROJET ORDNANCE TENNESSEE, INC.—See L3Harris Technologies, Inc.; *U.S. Public*, pg. 1279
AEROJET ROCKETDYNE HOLDINGS, INC.—See L3Harris Technologies, Inc.; *U.S. Public*, pg. 1279
AEROJET ROCKETDYNE, INC. - CAMDEN—See L3Harris Technologies, Inc.; *U.S. Public*, pg. 1279
AEROJET ROCKETDYNE, INC. - GAINESVILLE—See L3Harris Technologies, Inc.; *U.S. Public*, pg. 1279
AEROJET ROCKETDYNE, INC.—See L3Harris Technologies, Inc.; *U.S. Public*, pg. 1279
AEROJET ROCKETDYNE OF DE, INC.—See L3Harris Technologies, Inc.; *U.S. Public*, pg. 1279
AIRBUS SAFRAN LAUNCHERS SAS—See Airbus SE; *Int'l*, pg. 245
ATK AEROSPACE GROUP—See Northrop Grumman Corporation; *U.S. Public*, pg. 1540
ATK MISSLE SYSTEMS—See Northrop Grumman Corporation; *U.S. Public*, pg. 1540
AVIO S.P.A.; *Int'l*, pg. 744
BAE SYSTEMS ARMAMENT SYSTEMS DIVISION—See BAE Systems plc; *Int'l*, pg. 797
BAYERN-CHEMIE GESELLSCHAFT FUR FLUGCHEMISCHE ANTRIEBE MBH—See Airbus SE; *Int'l*, pg. 247
BAYERN-CHEMIE GESELLSCHAFT FUR FLUGCHEMISCHE ANTRIEBE MBH—See BAE Systems plc; *Int'l*, pg. 798
THE BOEING CO. - ANAHEIM—See The Boeing Company; *U.S. Public*, pg. 2040
BRADFORD ENGINEERING B.V.—See Moog Inc.; *U.S. Public*, pg. 1470
KARMAN MISSILE & SPACE SYSTEMS COMPANY—See Trive Capital Inc.; *U.S. Private*, pg. 4240
PRIMUS AEROSPACE, INC.—See Angeles Equity Partners, LLC; *U.S. Private*, pg. 282
ROXEL S.A.S.—See Airbus SE; *Int'l*, pg. 247
ROXEL S.A.S.—See BAE Systems plc; *Int'l*, pg. 798
TRIUMPH ACTUATION SYSTEMS-CONNECTICUT, LLC—See Triumph Group, Inc.; *U.S. Public*, pg. 2196

336419 — OTHER GUIDED MISSILE AND SPACE VEHICLE PARTS AND AUXILIARY EQUIPMENT MANUFACTURING

APPLIED AEROSPACE STRUCTURES, CORP.—See Greenbriar Equity Group, L.P.; *U.S. Private*, pg. 1775
ASTRA SPACE, INC.; *U.S. Private*, pg. 361
CAE AUSTRALIA PTY LTD.—See CAE Inc.; *Int'l*, pg. 1248
COI CERAMICS, INC.—See Northrop Grumman Corporation; *U.S. Public*, pg. 1541
COLLINS AEROSPACE - ELECTRIC SYSTEMS—See RTX Corporation; *U.S. Public*, pg. 1821
DAHER INDUSTRY & DEFENCE—See DAHER Group; *Int'l*, pg. 1913
DEW ENGINEERING AND DEVELOPMENT ULO—See CoorsTek, Inc.; *U.S. Private*, pg. 1044
EUROPEAN SPACE PROPULSION LIMITED—See L3Harris Technologies, Inc.; *U.S. Public*, pg. 1279
GRESHAM HOLDINGS, INC.—See Ault Alliance, Inc.; *U.S. Public*, pg. 227
HAMILTON SUNDSTRAND SPACE SYSTEMS INTERNATIONAL, INC.—See RTX Corporation; *U.S. Public*, pg. 1821
HEMERIA SASU; *Int'l*, pg. 3341
HONEYWELL SPACE SYSTEMS—See Honeywell International Inc.; *U.S. Public*, pg. 1047
KAMAN PRECISION PRODUCTS, INC. - MIDDLETOWN—See Arcline Investment Management LP; *U.S. Private*, pg. 314
KAMAN PRECISION PRODUCTS, INC.—See Arcline Investment Management LP; *U.S. Private*, pg. 314
KPSS GOVERNMENT SOLUTIONS, INC.—See Kratos Defense & Security Solutions, Inc.; *U.S. Public*, pg. 1276
KRATOS SPACE & MISSILE DEFENSE SYSTEMS, INC.—See Kratos Defense & Security Solutions, Inc.; *U.S. Public*, pg. 1276
METALCRAFT TECHNOLOGIES, INC.—See Madison Dearborn Partners, LLC; *U.S. Private*, pg. 2540
MICROCOSM, INC.; *U.S. Private*, pg. 2703
PLANETARY SYSTEMS CORP.—See Rocket Lab USA, Inc.; *U.S. Public*, pg. 1804
SAYRES & ASSOCIATES, LLC—See Broadtree Partners, Inc.; *U.S. Private*, pg. 659
SCI TECHNOLOGY, INC.—See Sanmina Corporation; *U.S. Public*, pg. 1840

336510 — RAILROAD ROLLING STOCK MANUFACTURING

ACF INDUSTRIES LLC; *U.S. Private*, pg. 58
ACIERIES DE PLOERMEL—See AMSTED Industries Incorporated; *U.S. Private*, pg. 267

N.A.I.C.S. INDEX

336510 — RAILROAD ROLLING ST...

AERO TRANSPORTATION PRODUCTS, INC—See Westinghouse Air Brake Technologies Corporation; *U.S. Public*, pg. 2357
A&K RAILROAD MATERIALS INC. - KANSAS CITY MFG FACILITY—See A&K Railroad Materials Inc.; *U.S. Private*, pg. 20
ALCO VENTURES INC.; *Int'l*, pg. 301
ALNA SHARYO CO., LTD.—See Hankyu Hanshin Holdings Inc.; *Int'l*, pg. 3254
ALSTOM ALGERIE SOCIETE PAR ACTIONS—See Alstom S.A.; *Int'l*, pg. 379
ALSTOM BALTICS SIA—See Alstom S.A.; *Int'l*, pg. 379
ALSTOM CZECH REPUBLIC A.S.—See Alstom S.A.; *Int'l*, pg. 379
ALSTOM DANMARK A/S—See Alstom S.A.; *Int'l*, pg. 380
ALSTOM FERROVIARIA PORTUGAL, S.A.—See Alstom S.A.; *Int'l*, pg. 379
ALSTOM FERROVIARIA S.P.A. - BOLOGNA—See Alstom S.A.; *Int'l*, pg. 381
ALSTOM FERROVIARIA S.P.A.—See Alstom S.A.; *Int'l*, pg. 381
ALSTOM HUNGARY KFT.—See Alstom S.A.; *Int'l*, pg. 379
ALSTOM ISRAEL LTD.—See Alstom S.A.; *Int'l*, pg. 379
ALSTOM KAZAKHSTAN LLP—See Alstom S.A.; *Int'l*, pg. 379
ALSTOM LOKOMOTIVEN SERVICE GMBH—See Alstom S.A.; *Int'l*, pg. 380
ALSTOM NETHERLANDS B.V.—See Alstom S.A.; *Int'l*, pg. 379
ALSTOM PANAMA, S.A.—See Alstom S.A.; *Int'l*, pg. 379
ALSTOM POLSKA SPOLKA AKCYJNA—See Alstom S.A.; *Int'l*, pg. 379
ALSTOM PROYECTOS DE TRANSPORTE, SRL—See Alstom S.A.; *Int'l*, pg. 379
ALSTOM SERVICES ITALIA S.P.A.—See Alstom S.A.; *Int'l*, pg. 379
ALSTOM (SHARED SERVICES) PHILIPPINES, INC.—See Alstom S.A.; *Int'l*, pg. 380
ALSTOM SIGNALLING, LIMITED LIABILITY COMPANY—See Alstom S.A.; *Int'l*, pg. 379
ALSTOM TRANSPORT AB—See Alstom S.A.; *Int'l*, pg. 381
ALSTOM TRANSPORTATION COLOMBIA S.A.S.—See Alstom S.A.; *Int'l*, pg. 380
ALSTOM TRANSPORTATION GERMANY GMBH—See Alstom S.A.; *Int'l*, pg. 380
ALSTOM TRANSPORTATION INC—See Alstom S.A.; *Int'l*, pg. 381
ALSTOM TRANSPORT AUSTRIA GMBH—See Alstom S.A.; *Int'l*, pg. 379
ALSTOM TRANSPORT BELGIUM—See Alstom S.A.; *Int'l*, pg. 380
ALSTOM TRANSPORT BV—See Alstom S.A.; *Int'l*, pg. 381
ALSTOM TRANSPORT DEUTSCHLAND GMBH—See Alstom S.A.; *Int'l*, pg. 380
ALSTOM TRANSPORTE SA DE CV—See Alstom S.A.; *Int'l*, pg. 381
ALSTOM TRANSPORTE SA—See Alstom S.A.; *Int'l*, pg. 380
ALSTOM TRANSPORT NEW ZEALAND LTD—See Alstom S.A.; *Int'l*, pg. 381
ALSTOM TRANSPORT SYSTEMS (MALAYSIA) SDN. BHD.—See Alstom S.A.; *Int'l*, pg. 380
ALSTOM UBUNYE (PTY) LTD.—See Alstom S.A.; *Int'l*, pg. 381
AMERICAN HYDRAULICS—See The Greenbrier Companies, Inc.; *U.S. Public*, pg. 2086
AMERICAN INDUSTRIES, INC—See Stone Canyon Industries, LLC; *U.S. Private*, pg. 3817
AMERICAN & OHIO LOCOMOTIVE CRANE CO.—See ERS Industries Inc.; *U.S. Private*, pg. 1423
AMERICAN RAILCAR INDUSTRIES, INC—See ITE Management L.P.; *U.S. Private*, pg. 2149
AMERICAN STEEL FOUNDRIES—See AMSTED Industries Incorporated; *U.S. Private*, pg. 267
AMSTED RAIL COMPANY, INC. - ASF KEYSTONE—See AMSTED Industries Incorporated; *U.S. Private*, pg. 267
ARI LONGTRAIN, INC.—See ITE Management L.P.; *U.S. Private*, pg. 2149
A. STUCKI COMPANY—See Stone Canyon Industries, LLC; *U.S. Private*, pg. 3817
AUSTBRECK PTY LIMITED—See Westinghouse Air Brake Technologies Corporation; *U.S. Public*, pg. 2358
AUSTBRECK PTY., LTD.—See Westinghouse Air Brake Technologies Corporation; *U.S. Public*, pg. 2357
AXTONE GMBH—See ITT Inc.; *U.S. Public*, pg. 1177
BEIJING TIANYISHANGJIA NEW MATERIAL CORP., LTD.; *Int'l*, pg. 958
BEIJING TIEKE SHOUGANG RAILWAY-TECHNOLOGY CO., LTD.; *Int'l*, pg. 068
BEML LIMITED - EARTH MOVING DIVISION—See BEML Limited; *Int'l*, pg. 969
BEML LIMITED - ENGINE DIVISION—See BEML Limited; *Int'l*, pg. 969
BETHEL AUTOMOTIVE SAFETY SYSTEMS CO., LTD.; *Int'l*, pg. 1002
BOMBARDIER TRANSPORTATION BELGIUM—See Alstom S.A.; *Int'l*, pg. 382
BOMBARDIER TRANSPORTATION CANADA—See Alstom S.A.; *Int'l*, pg. 382

BOMBARDIER TRANSPORTATION DENMARK A/S—See Alstom S.A.; *Int'l*, pg. 382
BOMBARDIER TRANSPORTATION GMBH—See Alstom S.A.; *Int'l*, pg. 381
BOMBARDIER TRANSPORTATION (HOLDINGS) UK LTD.—See Alstom S.A.; *Int'l*, pg. 382
BOMBARDIER TRANSPORTATION (HOLDINGS) USA INC.—See Alstom S.A.; *Int'l*, pg. 382
BOMBARDIER TRANSPORTATION HUNGARY KFT.—See Alstom S.A.; *Int'l*, pg. 382
BOMBARDIER TRANSPORTATION KOREA LTD.—See Alstom S.A.; *Int'l*, pg. 382
BOMBARDIER TRANSPORTATION (PROPULSION & CONTROLS) GERMANY GMBH—See Alstom S.A.; *Int'l*, pg. 382
BOMBARDIER TRANSPORTATION (RAIL ENGINEERING) POLSKA SP. Z O.O—See Alstom S.A.; *Int'l*, pg. 382
BOMBARDIER TRANSPORTATION (ROLLING STOCK) UK LTD.—See Alstom S.A.; *Int'l*, pg. 382
BOMBARDIER TRANSPORT FRANCE S.A.S. - SERVICES DIVISION—See Alstom S.A.; *Int'l*, pg. 382
BOMBARDIER TRANSPORT FRANCE S.A.S.—See Alstom S.A.; *Int'l*, pg. 381
BONATRANS GROUP A.S.; *Int'l*, pg. 1105
BRENCO, INC.—See AMSTED Industries Incorporated; *U.S. Private*, pg. 268
CAF ARGELIA EURL—See Construcciones y Auxiliar de Ferrocarriles S.A.; *Int'l*, pg. 1776
CAF BRASIL INDUSTRIA E COMERCIO, S.A.—See Construcciones y Auxiliar de Ferrocarriles S.A.; *Int'l*, pg. 1776
CAF DEUTSCHLAND GMBH—See Construcciones y Auxiliar de Ferrocarriles S.A.; *Int'l*, pg. 1776
CAF HUNGARY KFT.—See Construcciones y Auxiliar de Ferrocarriles S.A.; *Int'l*, pg. 1776
CAF INDIA PRIVATE LIMITED—See Construcciones y Auxiliar de Ferrocarriles S.A.; *Int'l*, pg. 1776
CAF ISRAEL RAILS LTD.—See Construcciones y Auxiliar de Ferrocarriles S.A.; *Int'l*, pg. 1776
CAF RAIL AUSTRALIA PTY LTD—See Construcciones y Auxiliar de Ferrocarriles S.A.; *Int'l*, pg. 1776
CAF RAIL UK LIMITED—See Construcciones y Auxiliar de Ferrocarriles S.A.; *Int'l*, pg. 1776
CENTER D'ESSAIS FERROVIAIRES SA—See Alstom S.A.; *Int'l*, pg. 383
CHINA RAILWAY LIUYUAN GROUP CO., LTD.—See China Railway Group Limited; *Int'l*, pg. 1543
CIESSE S.P.A.—See LCI Industries; *U.S. Public*, pg. 1295
CLARK FILTER, INC.—See Parker Hannifin Corporation; *U.S. Public*, pg. 1641
CMC ALAMO VICTORIA—See Commercial Metals Company; *U.S. Public*, pg. 546
COFREN S.A.S.—See Westinghouse Air Brake Technologies Corporation; *U.S. Public*, pg. 2357
COMMUTER TRANSPORT ENGINEERING (PTY) LTD.; *Int'l*, pg. 1721
CONSTRUCCIONES Y AUXILIAR DE FERROCARRILES S.A.; *Int'l*, pg. 1776
CRRC CHANGCHUN RAILWAY VEHICLE CO., LTD.—See CRRC Corporation Limited; *Int'l*, pg. 1858
CRRC CORPORATION LIMITED; *Int'l*, pg. 1858
CRRC DALIAN R&D CO., LTD.—See CRRC Corporation Limited; *Int'l*, pg. 1858
CRRC DATONG CO., LTD.—See CRRC Corporation Limited; *Int'l*, pg. 1858
CRRC NANJING PUZHEN CO., LTD.—See CRRC Corporation Limited; *Int'l*, pg. 1858
CRRC QINGDAO SIFANG CO., LTD.—See CRRC Corporation Limited; *Int'l*, pg. 1858
CRRC SIFANG CO., LTD.—See CRRC Corporation Limited; *Int'l*, pg. 1858
CRRC TANGSHAN CO., LTD.—See CRRC Corporation Limited; *Int'l*, pg. 1858
CRRC YANGTZE GROUP, LTD.—See CRRC Corporation Limited; *Int'l*, pg. 1858
CRRC ZHUZHOU INSTITUTE CO., LTD.—See CRRC Corporation Limited; *Int'l*, pg. 1858
CRRC ZIYANG CO., LTD.—See CRRC Corporation Limited; *Int'l*, pg. 1858
CRSC RESEARCH & DESIGN INSTITUTE GROUP CO., LTD.—See China Railway Signal & Communication Corporation Ltd.; *Int'l*, pg. 1544
CSR FEB. 7TH ROLLING STOCK CO., LTD—See CRRC Corporation Limited; *Int'l*, pg. 1858
CSR MEISHAN ROLLING STOCK CO., LTD—See CRRC Corporation Limited; *Int'l*, pg. 1858
CSR ZIYANG LOCOMOTIVE CO., LTD—See CRRC Corporation Limited; *Int'l*, pg. 1858
CWA CONSTRUCTIONS SA—See Doppelmayr Group; *Int'l*, pg. 2174
DALIAN CIMC RAILWAY EQUIPMENT CO., LTD.—See China International Marine Containers (Group) Co., Ltd.; *Int'l*, pg. 1511
DAWONSYS CO., LTD. - GIMCHEON FACTORY—See Dawonsys Co., Ltd.; *Int'l*, pg. 1984
DCD-DORBYL ROLLING STOCK DIVISION—See DCD-Dorbyl (Pty) Ltd.; *Int'l*, pg. 1991
DUROX COMPANY—See Westinghouse Air Brake Technologies Corporation; *U.S. Public*, pg. 2357

EBENEZER RAILCAR SERVICES—See ERS Industries Inc.; *U.S. Private*, pg. 1423
ELECTROPUTERE VFU PASCANI S.A.; *Int'l*, pg. 2354
ELECTROVOZ KURASTYRU ZAUYTY LLP—See Alstom S.A.; *Int'l*, pg. 383
ELH WBN WAGGONBAU NIESKY GMBH—See Budamar Logistics AS; *Int'l*, pg. 1210
ELLCON-NATIONAL INC.; *U.S. Private*, pg. 1363
EUROTEM DEMIRYOLU ARACLARI SAN. VE TIC A.S.—See Hyundai Motor Company; *Int'l*, pg. 3559
FAIVELEY TRANSPORT AUSTRALIA LTD.—See Westinghouse Air Brake Technologies Corporation; *U.S. Public*, pg. 2357
FAIVELEY TRANSPORT FAR EAST LTD—See Westinghouse Air Brake Technologies Corporation; *U.S. Public*, pg. 2357
FAIVELEY TRANSPORT KOREA LTD.—See Westinghouse Air Brake Technologies Corporation; *U.S. Public*, pg. 2357
FAIVELEY TRANSPORT NORDIC AB—See Westinghouse Air Brake Technologies Corporation; *U.S. Public*, pg. 2357
FAIVELEY TRANSPORT S.A.—See Westinghouse Air Brake Technologies Corporation; *U.S. Public*, pg. 2357
FAIVELEY TRANSPORT TOURS—See Westinghouse Air Brake Technologies Corporation; *U.S. Public*, pg. 2358
FAIVELEY TRANSPORT WITTEN GMBH—See Westinghouse Air Brake Technologies Corporation; *U.S. Public*, pg. 2357
FERIFOS SA—See Ermewa Interservices Sarl; *Int'l*, pg. 2494
FREIGHTCAR AMERICA, INC.; *U.S. Public*, pg. 885
FREIGHTCAR ROANOKE, LLC—See FreightCar America, Inc.; *U.S. Public*, pg. 885
FREIGHT CAR SERVICES, INC.—See FreightCar America, Inc.; *U.S. Public*, pg. 885
G&B SPECIALTIES, INC.—See Westinghouse Air Brake Technologies Corporation; *U.S. Public*, pg. 2358
GEISMAR S.A. - COLMAR FACTORY—See Geismar S.A.; *Int'l*, pg. 2912
GEISMAR S.A.; *Int'l*, pg. 2912
GE TRANSPORTATION RAIL—See General Electric Company; *U.S. Public*, pg. 920
THE GREENBRIER COMPANIES, INC.; *U.S. Public*, pg. 2085
GREENBRIER GERMANY GMBH—See The Greenbrier Companies, Inc.; *U.S. Public*, pg. 2085
GUNDERSON - GIMSA S. A. DE C.V.—See The Greenbrier Companies, Inc.; *U.S. Public*, pg. 2086
GUNDERSON RAIL SERVICES, LLC—See The Greenbrier Companies, Inc.; *U.S. Public*, pg. 2086
GUTEHOFFNUNGSHUTTE RADSATZ GMBH—See Bonatrans Group a.s.; *Int'l*, pg. 1105
HARSCO RAIL—See Enviri Corporation; *U.S. Public*, pg. 781
HITACHI RAIL STS AUSTRALIA PTY LTD—See Hitachi, Ltd.; *Int'l*, pg. 3421
HYUNDAI ROTEM COMPANY - CHANGWON PLANT—See Hyundai Motor Company; *Int'l*, pg. 3560
HYUNDAI ROTEM COMPANY—See Hyundai Motor Company; *Int'l*, pg. 3559
INDEPENDENT DRAFT GEAR CO.—See Stone Canyon Industries, LLC; *U.S. Private*, pg. 3817
INTRANS ENGINEERING LIMITED—See Westinghouse Air Brake Technologies Corporation; *U.S. Public*, pg. 2358
JAIX LEASING COMPANY—See FreightCar America, Inc.; *U.S. Public*, pg. 885
JAPAN TRANSPORT ENGINEERING COMPANY—See East Japan Railway Company; *Int'l*, pg. 2270
JOHNSTOWN AMERICA, LLC—See FreightCar America, Inc.; *U.S. Public*, pg. 885
L.B. FOSTER RAIL TECHNOLOGIES (UK) LTD.—See L.B. Foster Company; *U.S. Public*, pg. 1278
LUBRITECH PERU S.A.C.—See Enovis Corporation; *U.S. Public*, pg. 773
MARMON INDUSTRIAL PRODUCTS—See Berkshire Hathaway Inc.; *U.S. Public*, pg. 310
MASTRAK SDN BHD—See Heidelberg Materials AG; *Int'l*, pg. 3315
MERIDIAN RAIL ACQUISITION CORP.—See The Greenbrier Companies, Inc.; *U.S. Public*, pg. 2086
MILLER FELPAX CORPORATION; *U.S. Private*, pg. 2734
MINDSEED CORPORATION; *U.S. Private*, pg. 2741
MINER ENTERPRISES, INC.; *U.S. Private*, pg. 2741
MODERN TRACK MACHINERY, LTD.—See Geismar S.A.; *Int'l*, pg. 2912
MOTIVE EQUIPMENT, INC.—See Westinghouse Air Brake Technologies Corporation; *U.S. Public*, pg. 2358
MOTIVEPOWER, INC.—See Westinghouse Air Brake Technologies Corporation; *U.S. Public*, pg. 2358
MZT HEPOS POLSKA SP. ZO.O—See Westinghouse Air Brake Technologies Corporation; *U.S. Public*, pg. 2358
NATIONAL RAILWAY EQUIPMENT COMPANY; *U.S. Private*, pg. 2861
NORDCO, INC.—See Greenbriar Equity Group, L.P.; *U.S. Private*, pg. 1776
NORTH AMERICAN TECHNOLOGIES GROUP, INC. (NAMC); *U.S. Private*, pg. 2941

336510 — RAILROAD ROLLING ST...

PINTSCH B.V.—See The Carlyle Group Inc.; *U.S. Public*, pg. 2053
PINTSCH GMBH—See The Carlyle Group Inc.; *U.S. Public*, pg. 2053
PINTSCH TIEFENBACH US INC.—See The Carlyle Group Inc.; *U.S. Public*, pg. 2053
QINGDAO KAMAX BUFFER EQUIPMENT COMPANY LTD.—See ITT Inc.; *U.S. Public*, pg. 1178
RAILS COMPANY; *U.S. Private*, pg. 3346
RAILTECH INTERNATIONAL—See CVC Capital Partners SICAV-FIS S.A.; *Int'l*, pg. 1887
RAYVAG VAGON SANAYI VE TICARET A.S.—See The Greenbrier Companies, Inc.; *U.S. Public*, pg. 2086
RESCAR INC.; *U.S. Private*, pg. 3403
ROTEM USA CORPORATION—See Hyundai Motor Company; *Int'l*, pg. 3560
SAFETY RAILWAY SERVICE—See Commercial Metals Company; *U.S. Public*, pg. 547
SALCO PRODUCTS INC.—See Stone Canyon Industries, LLC; *U.S. Private*, pg. 3817
SCHALTBAU AUSTRIA GMBH—See The Carlyle Group Inc.; *U.S. Public*, pg. 2053
SCHALTBAU FRANCE S.A.S.—See The Carlyle Group Inc.; *U.S. Public*, pg. 2053
SCHALTBAU NORTH AMERICA INC.—See The Carlyle Group Inc.; *U.S. Public*, pg. 2053
SCT EUROPE LTD.—See Westinghouse Air Brake Technologies Corporation; *U.S. Public*, pg. 2359
SKELTON CANADA INC.—See Andlauer Healthcare Group, Inc.; *Int'l*, pg. 451
SOLARIS AUSTRIA GMBH—See Construcciones y Auxiliar de Ferrocarriles S.A.; *Int'l*, pg. 1777
SOLARIS BUS & COACH LATVIA LTD.—See Construcciones y Auxiliar de Ferrocarriles S.A.; *Int'l*, pg. 1777
SOLARIS BUS & COACH ROMANIA S.R.L.—See Construcciones y Auxiliar de Ferrocarriles S.A.; *Int'l*, pg. 1777
SOLARIS BUS & COACH, SP. Z O.O.—See Construcciones y Auxiliar de Ferrocarriles S.A.; *Int'l*, pg. 1777
SOLARIS BUS IBERICA, S.L.U.—See Construcciones y Auxiliar de Ferrocarriles S.A.; *Int'l*, pg. 1777
SOLARIS CZECH SPOL. S.R.O.—See Construcciones y Auxiliar de Ferrocarriles S.A.; *Int'l*, pg. 1777
SOLARIS FRANCE S.A.R.L.—See Construcciones y Auxiliar de Ferrocarriles S.A.; *Int'l*, pg. 1777
SOLARIS ITALIA S.R.L.—See Construcciones y Auxiliar de Ferrocarriles S.A.; *Int'l*, pg. 1777
SOLARIS NORGE AS—See Construcciones y Auxiliar de Ferrocarriles S.A.; *Int'l*, pg. 1777
SOLARIS SVERIGE AB—See Construcciones y Auxiliar de Ferrocarriles S.A.; *Int'l*, pg. 1777
SPII S.P.A.—See The Carlyle Group Inc.; *U.S. Public*, pg. 2053
STEMMANN POLSKA SP ZOO—See Westinghouse Air Brake Technologies Corporation; *U.S. Public*, pg. 2359
STEMMANN TECHNIK NEDERLAND BV—See Westinghouse Air Brake Technologies Corporation; *U.S. Public*, pg. 2359
STORK RAILWAY SERVICES—See Fluor Corporation; *U.S. Public*, pg. 860
STUCKI DE MEXICO S DE RL DE C.V.—See Stone Canyon Industries, LLC; *U.S. Private*, pg. 3817
TAIYUAN RAILWAY ROLLING STOCK CO., LTD.—See CRRC Corporation Limited; *Int'l*, pg. 1859
TRACKMOBILE, INC.—See Berkshire Hathaway Inc.; *U.S. Public*, pg. 311
TRENES DE NAVARRA, S.A.U.—See Construcciones y Auxiliar de Ferrocarriles S.A.; *Int'l*, pg. 1777
TRINITY RAIL GROUP, LLC—See Trinity Industries, Inc.; *U.S. Public*, pg. 2194
TRS STAFFING SOLUTIONS BELGIUM B.V.—See Fluor Corporation; *U.S. Public*, pg. 860
TRS STAFFING SOLUTIONS GMBH—See Fluor Corporation; *U.S. Public*, pg. 860
UNION TANK CAR COMPANY—See Berkshire Hathaway Inc.; *U.S. Public*, pg. 311
UNITRAC RAILROAD MATERIALS, INC.—See Westinghouse Air Brake Technologies Corporation; *U.S. Public*, pg. 2359
VAPOR RAIL KAPI SISTEMLERI TICARET VE HIZMETLERI LIMITED SIRKETI—See Westinghouse Air Brake Technologies Corporation; *U.S. Public*, pg. 2359
VMV PADUCAHBILT—See National Railway Equipment Company; *U.S. Private*, pg. 2861
WABTEC ASSEMBLY SERVICES S. DE R.L. DE C.V.—See Westinghouse Air Brake Technologies Corporation; *U.S. Public*, pg. 2359
WABTEC BRASIL FABRICACOA MANUTENCAO DE EQUIPAMENTOS FERROVIAROS LTDA—See Westinghouse Air Brake Technologies Corporation; *U.S. Public*, pg. 2359
WABTEC CANADA, INC.—See Westinghouse Air Brake Technologies Corporation; *U.S. Public*, pg. 2359
WABTEC MZT AD SKOPJE—See Westinghouse Air Brake Technologies Corporation; *U.S. Public*, pg. 2359
WABTEC RAIL SCOTLAND LIMITED—See Westinghouse Air Brake Technologies Corporation; *U.S. Public*, pg. 2359
WABTEC RAILWAY ELECTRONICS CORPORATION—See Westinghouse Air Brake Technologies Corporation; *U.S. Public*, pg. 2360
WABTEC SERVICIOS ADMINISTRATIVOS, S.A. DE C.V.—See Westinghouse Air Brake Technologies Corporation; *U.S. Public*, pg. 2360
WABTEC SOUTH AFRICA PROPRIETARY LIMITED—See Westinghouse Air Brake Technologies Corporation; *U.S. Public*, pg. 2360
WAGONYSWIDNICA S.A.—See The Greenbrier Companies, Inc.; *U.S. Public*, pg. 2086
WAGONYSWIDNICA SP. Z O.O.—See The Greenbrier Companies, Inc.; *U.S. Public*, pg. 2086
WESTCODE INC.; *U.S. Private*, pg. 4489
WESTINGHOUSE AIR BRAKE TECHNOLOGIES CORPORATION; *U.S. Public*, pg. 2356
WORKHORSE RAIL, LLC—See Westinghouse Air Brake Technologies Corporation; *U.S. Public*, pg. 2360

336611 — SHIP BUILDING AND REPAIRING

2X1 HOLDING CAPE MIDIA SHIPYARD; *Int'l*, pg. 5
ABU DHABI MARINE OPERATING COMPANY—See Abu Dhabi National Oil Company; *Int'l*, pg. 72
ABU DHABI SHIP BUILDING PJSC; *Int'l*, pg. 73
ALAM MARITIM (M) SDN. BHD.—See Alam Maritim Resources Berhad; *Int'l*, pg. 290
ALANG MARINE LTD.; *Int'l*, pg. 290
ALGOMA CENTRAL CORPORATION - FRASER MARINE & INDUSTRIAL DIVISION—See Algoma Central Corporation; *Int'l*, pg. 318
AL LARSON BOAT SHOP, INC.; *U.S. Private*, pg. 147
ALLSHIPS LTD.; *Int'l*, pg. 360
AMELS—See Damen Shipyards Group; *Int'l*, pg. 1956
APPLEDORE SHIPBUILDERS (2004) LIMITED—See Babcock International Group PLC; *Int'l*, pg. 792
ARAB HEAVY INDUSTRIES P.J.S.C; *Int'l*, pg. 530
ARAB SHIPBUILDING & REPAIR YARD CO.; *Int'l*, pg. 531
ART MARINE LLC—See Abraaj Capital Limited; *Int'l*, pg. 67
ASC PTY. LTD.; *Int'l*, pg. 600
ASIAN SEALAND OFFSHORE & MARINE PTE. LTD.—See Beng Kuang Marine Limited; *Int'l*, pg. 973
ASIC ENGINEERING SDN BHD—See Beng Kuang Marine Limited; *Int'l*, pg. 973
ASI SERVICES, INC.—See The Progressive Corporation; *U.S. Public*, pg. 2124
ASL MARINE HOLDINGS LTD; *Int'l*, pg. 625
ASMAR; *Int'l*, pg. 627
ATLANTIC MARITIME GROUP FZE—See Atlantic Navigation Holdings (Singapore) Limited; *Int'l*, pg. 675
AUSTAL LIMITED; *Int'l*, pg. 716
AVIC WEIHAI SHIPYARD CO., LTD.—See AVIC International Holdings Limited; *Int'l*, pg. 742
AZIMUT-BENETTI S.P.A.; *Int'l*, pg. 780
AZOREAN-AQUATIC TECHNOLOGIES SA; *Int'l*, pg. 781
BABCOCK ENGINEERING SERVICES LTD.—See Babcock International Group PLC; *Int'l*, pg. 792
BABCOCK MARINE—See Babcock International Group PLC; *Int'l*, pg. 792
BAE SYSTEMS APPLIED INTELLIGENCE & SECURITY—See BAE Systems plc; *Int'l*, pg. 796
BAE SYSTEMS HAWAII SHIPYARDS—See BAE Systems plc; *Int'l*, pg. 797
BAE SYSTEMS NORFOLK SHIP REPAIR—See BAE Systems plc; *Int'l*, pg. 797
BAE SYSTEMS SAN DIEGO SHIP REPAIR—See BAE Systems plc; *Int'l*, pg. 797
BAE SYSTEMS SHIP REPAIR—See BAE Systems plc; *Int'l*, pg. 797
BAE SYSTEMS—See Puglia Engineering Inc.; *U.S. Private*, pg. 3303
BAE SYSTEMS SOUTHEAST SHIPYARDS ALABAMA, LLC—See BAE Systems plc; *Int'l*, pg. 797
BAE SYSTEMS SOUTHEAST SHIPYARDS AMHC INC.—See BAE Systems plc; *Int'l*, pg. 797
BAE SYSTEMS SOUTHEAST SHIPYARDS JACKSONVILLE, LLC—See BAE Systems plc; *Int'l*, pg. 797
BAHRAIN SHIP REPAIR AND ENGINEERING COMPANY; *Int'l*, pg. 800
BAKER ENGINEERING PTE. LTD.—See Baker Technology Limited; *Int'l*, pg. 805
BATH IRON WORKS CORPORATION—See General Dynamics Corporation; *U.S. Public*, pg. 915
BAY SHIPBUILDING CO.—See Fincantieri S.p.A.; *Int'l*, pg. 2671
BENG KUANG MARINE LIMITED; *Int'l*, pg. 973
BERGEN GROUP KIMEK AS—See Endur ASA; *Int'l*, pg. 2409
BERGEN GROUP KIMEK OFFSHORE AS—See Endur ASA; *Int'l*, pg. 2409
BHARATI DEFENCE AND INFRASTRUCTURE LIMITED; *Int'l*, pg. 1011
BLOHM + VOSS B.V & CO. KG—See Fr. Lurssen Werft GmbH & Co. KG; *Int'l*, pg. 2758
BLRT GRUPP AS; *Int'l*, pg. 1065
BOGO CO., LTD.—See Daeyang Electric Co., Ltd.; *Int'l*, pg. 1911
BOLLINGER ALGIERS LLC—See Bollinger Shipyards, Inc.; *U.S. Private*, pg. 611
BOLLINGER AMELIA REPAIR, LLC—See Bollinger Shipyards, Inc.; *U.S. Private*, pg. 611
BOLLINGER FOURCHON, LLC—See Bollinger Shipyards, Inc.; *U.S. Private*, pg. 611
BOLLINGER MARINE FABRICATORS, LLC—See Bollinger Shipyards, Inc.; *U.S. Private*, pg. 611
BOLLINGER MORGAN CITY, LLC—See Bollinger Shipyards, Inc.; *U.S. Private*, pg. 611
BOLLINGER QUICK REPAIR—See Bollinger Shipyards, Inc.; *U.S. Private*, pg. 611
BOLLINGER RGS—See Bollinger Shipyards, Inc.; *U.S. Private*, pg. 611
BOLLINGER SHIPYARD LOCKPORT, LLC—See Bollinger Shipyards, Inc.; *U.S. Private*, pg. 611
BOLLINGER SHIPYARDS, INC.; *U.S. Private*, pg. 610
BOLLINGER TEXAS CITY, LP—See Bollinger Shipyards, Inc.; *U.S. Private*, pg. 611
BURCKHARDT COMPRESSION (ITALIA) S.R.L.—See Burckhardt Compression Holding AG; *Int'l*, pg. 1220
CAMBER TECHNICAL SERVICES LLC—See Huntington Ingalls Industries, Inc.; *U.S. Public*, pg. 1072
CASCADE GENERAL INC.—See Stellex Capital Management LP; *U.S. Private*, pg. 3800
CASCADE GENERAL INC.—See The Carlyle Group Inc.; *U.S. Public*, pg. 2056
CATTLE LINE TWO PTE. LTD.—See Beng Kuang Marine Limited; *Int'l*, pg. 973
C&C MARINE MAINTENANCE COMPANY—See Blue Danube Incorporated; *U.S. Private*, pg. 588
CFF FLUID CONTROL LIMITED; *Int'l*, pg. 1429
CHANTIER DAVIE CANADA INC.—See Davie Yards ASA; *Int'l*, pg. 1984
CHANTIER NAVAL DE MARSEILLE SAS—See Carnival Corporation; *U.S. Public*, pg. 438
CHANTIERS DE L'ATLANTIQUE SA; *Int'l*, pg. 1447
CHANTIERS DE L'ATLANTIQUE SERVICES—See Chantiers de l'Atlantique SA; *Int'l*, pg. 1447
CHANTIERS JEANNEAU SA—See Beneteau S.A.; *Int'l*, pg. 972
CHINA CSSC HOLDINGS LIMITED—See China State Shipbuilding Corporation; *Int'l*, pg. 1554
CHINA OCEAN INDUSTRY GROUP LIMITED; *Int'l*, pg. 1536
CHINA SHIPBUILDING INDUSTRY COMPANY LIMITED; *Int'l*, pg. 1551
CHINA SHIPBUILDING MANSION SCIENCE RESEARCH CENTER COMPANY LIMITED—See China Shipbuilding Industry Company Limited; *Int'l*, pg. 1551
CHINA SHIP DESIGN & RESEARCH CENTRE CO., LTD.—See China Shipbuilding Industry Company Limited; *Int'l*, pg. 1551
CHINA SHIPPING INVESTMENT CO., LTD—See China COSCO Shipping Corporation Limited; *Int'l*, pg. 1492
CHINA STATE SHIPBUILDING CORPORATION; *Int'l*, pg. 1554
CLEVELAND SHIP REPAIR COMPANY—See Fincantieri S.p.A.; *Int'l*, pg. 2671
COCHIN SHIPYARD LIMITED; *Int'l*, pg. 1686
COLOMBO DOCKYARD PLC; *Int'l*, pg. 1702
COLONNAS SHIPYARD INCORPORATED; *U.S. Private*, pg. 1710
COMMODORE FINANCIAL CORP.—See MARCO Global Inc.; *U.S. Private*, pg. 2572
CONRAD ALUMINUM, L.L.C.—See Conrad Industries, Inc.; *U.S. Public*, pg. 569
CONRAD INDUSTRIES, INC.; *U.S. Public*, pg. 569
CONRAD SHIPYARD, L.L.C.—See Conrad Industries, Inc.; *U.S. Public*, pg. 569
CONSOLIDATED LAUNCHER TECHNOLOGY, INC.—See Oceaneering International, Inc.; *U.S. Public*, pg. 1562
CONTINENTAL MARITIME OF SAN DIEGO, INC.—See Huntington Ingalls Industries, Inc.; *U.S. Public*, pg. 1072
CONVERDYN—See General Atomics; *U.S. Private*, pg. 1663
COSCO MARINE ENGINEERING (SINGAPORE) PTE LTD.—See China COSCO Shipping Corporation Limited; *Int'l*, pg. 1492
COSCO (SHANGHAI) SHIPYARD CO., LTD—See China COSCO Shipping Corporation Limited; *Int'l*, pg. 1492
COSCO SHIPPING LINES (PTY) LTD—See China COSCO Shipping Corporation Limited; *Int'l*, pg. 1494
CRC-EVANS OFFSHORE, LTD.—See Stanley Black & Decker, Inc.; *U.S. Public*, pg. 1932
CSBC CORP. TAIWAN; *Int'l*, pg. 1862
CSSC OFFSHORE & MARINE ENGINEERING COMPANY LTD.; *Int'l*, pg. 1867
DALIAN DALI STEEL WORKS CO., LTD.—See Hitachi Zosen Corporation; *Int'l*, pg. 3410
DALIAN MARINE DIESEL CO., LTD.—See China Shipbuilding Industry Company Limited; *Int'l*, pg. 1551
DALIAN SHIPBUILDING INDUSTRY CO., LTD.—See China Shipbuilding Industry Company Limited; *Int'l*, pg. 1551
DAMEN DREDGING EQUIPMENT BV—See Damen Shipyards Group; *Int'l*, pg. 1956
DAMEN ENGINEERING GDANSK SP. Z O. O.—See Damen Shipyards Group; *Int'l*, pg. 1956

N.A.I.C.S. INDEX

336611 — SHIP BUILDING AND R...

DAMEN MARINE COMPONENTS BV—See Damen Shipyards Group; *Int'l*, pg. 1956
DAMEN OSKARSHAMNSVARVET SWEDEN AB—See Damen Shipyards Group; *Int'l*, pg. 1956
DAMEN SERVICES BRISBANE PTY LTD—See Damen Shipyards Group; *Int'l*, pg. 1956
DAMEN SHIPREPAIR BREST S.A.S.—See Damen Shipyards Group; *Int'l*, pg. 1956
DAMEN SHIPREPAIR DUNKERQUE—See Damen Shipyards Group; *Int'l*, pg. 1956
DAMEN SHIPREPAIR—See Damen Shipyards Group; *Int'l*, pg. 1956
DAMEN SHIPREPAIR VLISSINGEN B.V.—See Damen Shipyards Group; *Int'l*, pg. 1956
DAMEN SHIPYARDS BERGUM—See Damen Shipyards Group; *Int'l*, pg. 1956
DAMEN SHIPYARDS CAPE TOWN (PTY) LTD.—See Damen Shipyards Group; *Int'l*, pg. 1956
DAMEN SHIPYARDS DEN HELDER B.V.—See Damen Shipyards Group; *Int'l*, pg. 1956
DAMEN SHIPYARDS GALATI—See Damen Shipyards Group; *Int'l*, pg. 1956
DAMEN SHIPYARDS GDYNIA S.A.—See Damen Shipyards Group; *Int'l*, pg. 1956
DAMEN SHIPYARDS GROUP; *Int'l*, pg. 1956
DAMEN SHIPYARDS HARDINXVELD BV—See Damen Shipyards Group; *Int'l*, pg. 1956
DAMEN SHIPYARDS SINGAPORE PTE LTD—See Damen Shipyards Group; *Int'l*, pg. 1956
DAMEN SHIPYARDS YICHANG—See Damen Shipyards Group; *Int'l*, pg. 1956
DAMEN TRADING (SUZHOU) CO., LTD.—See Damen Shipyards Group; *Int'l*, pg. 1956
DAMEN YICHANG SHIPYARD LTD—See Damen Shipyards Group; *Int'l*, pg. 1956
DAMEX SHIPBUILDING & ENGINEERING—See Damen Shipyards Group; *Int'l*, pg. 1956
DAVIE YARDS ASA; *Int'l*, pg. 1984
DB INTERMODAL SERVICES GMBH—See Deutsche Bahn AG; *Int'l*, pg. 2050
DDW OFFSHORE AS—See Akastor ASA; *Int'l*, pg. 260
DEEP OCEAN ENGINEERING INC.—See Vortex Marine Construction; *U.S. Private*, pg. 4413
DELTAMARIN LTD.—See China Merchants Group Limited; *Int'l*, pg. 1520
DELTAMARIN SP.Z O.O.—See China Merchants Group Limited; *Int'l*, pg. 1520
DETYENS SHIPYARDS INC.; *U.S. Private*, pg. 1217
DEVONPORT ROYAL DOCKYARD LIMITED—See Babcock International Group PLC; *Int'l*, pg. 792
DIVERSIFIED GROUP LLC; *U.S. Private*, pg. 1242
DIV GRUPA DOO; *Int'l*, pg. 2137
DONGDO SHIP REPAIR CO. LTD—See Dong Do Marine Joint Stock Company; *Int'l*, pg. 2163
DORMAC PTY. LTD.; *Int'l*, pg. 2177
DREW MARINE USA, INC.—See Court Square Capital Partners, L.P.; *U.S. Private*, pg. 1068
DRYDOCKS WORLD LLC—See Dubai World Corporation; *Int'l*, pg. 2222
DSEC CO., LTD.; *Int'l*, pg. 2209
EASTERN SHIPBUILDING GROUP, INC.; *U.S. Private*, pg. 1321
ECRC; *Int'l*, pg. 2301
EEI CONSTRUCTION & MARINE CORP.—See EEI Corporation; *Int'l*, pg. 2317
EGERSUND HEROY AS—See Egersund Group AS; *Int'l*, pg. 2323
ELECTRIC BOAT CORPORATION—See General Dynamics Corporation; *U.S. Public*, pg. 915
ELECTROCOM, INC.—See General Dynamics Corporation; *U.S. Public*, pg. 913
EVERETT SHIPYARD, INC.—See Stellex Capital Management LP; *U.S. Private*, pg. 3800
EVERETT SHIPYARD, INC.—See The Carlyle Group Inc.; *U.S. Public*, pg. 2056
EZION HOLDINGS LIMITED; *Int'l*, pg. 2594
FINCANTIERI MARINE GROUP, LLC—See Fincantieri S.p.A.; *Int'l*, pg. 2671
FINCANTIERI S.P.A.; *Int'l*, pg. 2671
FIRST WAVE MARINE INC.; *U.S. Private*, pg. 1530
FR. LURSSEN WERFT GMBH & CO. KG; *Int'l*, pg. 2758
GB YACHTS PTE. LTD.—See Grand Banks Yachts Limited; *Int'l*, pg. 3054
GENERAL DYNAMICS LAND SYSTEMS CUSTOMER SERVICE & SUPPORT COMPANY—See General Dynamics Corporation; *U.S. Public*, pg. 915
GENERAL DYNAMICS MARINE SYSTEMS, INC.—See General Dynamics Corporation; *U.S. Public*, pg. 915
GEORGE G. SHARP INC.; *U.S. Private*, pg. 1682
GERUSTBAU MUEHLHAN GMBH—See Brand Industrial Services, Inc.; *U.S. Private*, pg. 636
GIBUNCO GROUP LIMITED; *Int'l*, pg. 2963
GODO SENPAKU KOGYO CO., LTD.—See Iino Kaiun Kaisha Ltd.; *Int'l*, pg. 3608
GOTAVERKEN ARENDAL AB; *Int'l*, pg. 3043
GOTAVERKEN CITYVARVET AB—See Damen Shipyards Group; *Int'l*, pg. 1956
GRAND BAHAMA SHIP YARD LIMITED—See Carnival Corporation; *U.S. Public*, pg. 438
GRAND BANKS YACHTS AUSTRALIA PTY LTD—See Grand Banks Yachts Limited; *Int'l*, pg. 3054
GRUPO BOLUDA; *Int'l*, pg. 3123
GUANGZHOU WENCHONG SHIPYARD CO., LTD.—See CSSC Offshore & Marine Engineering Company Ltd.; *Int'l*, pg. 1868
GULF COPPER & MANUFACTURING CORP; *U.S. Private*, pg. 1816
GULF DEVELOPMENT CORPORATION—See Abdulla Ahmed Nass Group WLL; *Int'l*, pg. 58
GULF ISLAND SHIPYARDS, LLC—See Gulf Island Fabrication, Inc.; *U.S. Public*, pg. 975
GULF MARINE REPAIR CORPORATION; *U.S. Private*, pg. 1816
GUNDERSON MARINE LLC; *U.S. Private*, pg. 1818
GURIT—See Gurit Holding AG; *Int'l*, pg. 3187
HALSNOY DOKK AS; *Int'l*, pg. 3233
HANJIN HEAVY INDUSTRIES & CONSTRUCTION CO., LTD. - DADAEPO FACTORY—See Hanjin Heavy Industries & Construction Co., Ltd.; *Int'l*, pg. 3252
HANJIN HEAVY INDUSTRIES & CONSTRUCTION CO., LTD. - ULSAN FACTORY—See HJ Shipbuilding & Construction Company, Ltd.; *Int'l*, pg. 3428
HANJIN HEAVY INDUSTRIES & CONSTRUCTION CO., LTD. - YULDO FACTORY—See Hanjin Heavy Industries & Construction Co., Ltd.; *Int'l*, pg. 3252
HANJIN HEAVY INDUSTRIES & CONSTRUCTION CO., LTD. - YULDO FACTORY—See HJ Shipbuilding & Construction Company, Ltd.; *Int'l*, pg. 3428
HANWHA OCEAN CO., LTD.; *Int'l*, pg. 3266
HANYUAN TECHNICAL SERVICE CENTER GMBH—See China COSCO Shipping Corporation Limited; *Int'l*, pg. 1494
HAVEN AUTOMATION INDUSTRIES (S) PTE. LTD.—See Hanwha Group; *Int'l*, pg. 3264
HAVEN AUTOMATION INDUSTRIES (S) PTE. LTD.—See Hanwha Ocean Co., Ltd.; *Int'l*, pg. 3266
HEAVY ENGINEERING INDUSTRIES & SHIPBUILDING CO. K.S.C. - INDUSTRIAL CONTRACTS DIVISION—See Heavy Engineering Industries & Shipbuilding Co. K.S.C.; *Int'l*, pg. 3305
HEAVY ENGINEERING INDUSTRIES & SHIPBUILDING CO. K.S.C.; *Int'l*, pg. 3305
HHIC-HONG KONG LTD.—See Hanjin Heavy Industries & Construction Co., Ltd.; *Int'l*, pg. 3252
HHIC-PHIL INC.—See Cerberus Capital Management, L.P.; *U.S. Private*, pg. 838
HITACHI ZOSEN CORPORATION; *Int'l*, pg. 3410
HITACHI ZOSEN DIESEL & ENGINEERING CO., LTD.—See Hitachi Zosen Corporation; *Int'l*, pg. 3410
HITACHI ZOSEN ENGINEERING SINGAPORE (PTE.) LTD.—See Hitachi Zosen Corporation; *Int'l*, pg. 3410
HITACHI ZOSEN EUROPE LTD.—See Hitachi Zosen Corporation; *Int'l*, pg. 3410
HITACHI ZOSEN EUROPE LTD.—See Hitachi Zosen Corporation; *Int'l*, pg. 3411
HITACHI ZOSEN SERVICES (MALAYSIA) SDN. BHD.—See Hitachi Zosen Corporation; *Int'l*, pg. 3411
HONGKONG SALVAGE & TOWAGE—See CK Hutchison Holdings Limited; *Int'l*, pg. 1637
THE HONG KONG SHIPYARD LIMITED—See Henderson Land Development Co. Ltd.; *Int'l*, pg. 3345
HOP HING MARINE INDUSTRIAL (HONG KONG) LIMITED—See China COSCO Shipping Corporation Limited; *Int'l*, pg. 1494
HSBC SHIPPING SERVICES LTD.—See HSBC Holdings plc; *Int'l*, pg. 3507
HUD GROUP—See CK Hutchison Holdings Limited; *Int'l*, pg. 1637
HUNTINGTON INGALLS INDUSTRIES, INC.; *U.S. Public*, pg. 1071
HVCC HAMBURG VESSEL COORDINATION CENTER GMBH—See Hamburger Hafen und Logistik AG; *Int'l*, pg. 3236
HYUNDAI FINANCIAL LEASING CO., LTD.—See Hyundai Heavy Industries Co., Ltd.; *Int'l*, pg. 3557
HYUNDAI HEAVY INDUSTRIES CO., LTD.; *Int'l*, pg. 3557
HYUNDAI HEAVY INDUSTRIES FRANCE SAS—See Hyundai Heavy Industries Co., Ltd.; *Int'l*, pg. 3557
HYUNDAI KHOROL AGRO LTD.—See Hyundai Heavy Industries Co., Ltd.; *Int'l*, pg. 3557
HYUNDAI MIPO DOCKYARD CO., LTD.—See Hyundai Heavy Industries Co., Ltd.; *Int'l*, pg. 3557
HYUNDAI SHIPBUILDING—See Hyundai Heavy Industries Co., Ltd.; *Int'l*, pg. 3557
IDS AUSTRALASIA PTY. LTD.—See Fincantieri S.p.A.; *Int'l*, pg. 2671
IDS KOREA CO. LTD.—See Fincantieri S.p.A.; *Int'l*, pg. 2671
IKM KRAN & LOFTETEKNIKK AS—See IKM Gruppen AS; *Int'l*, pg. 3611
IKM MEKANISKE KRISTIANSAND AS—See IKM Gruppen AS; *Int'l*, pg. 3611
IMCS MARINE (SHANGHAI) CO., LTD.—See IHI Corporation; *Int'l*, pg. 3605
INDAL TECHNOLOGIES INC.—See Curtiss-Wright Corporation; *U.S. Public*, pg. 611
INGALLS SHIPBUILDING, INC.—See Huntington Ingalls Industries, Inc.; *U.S. Public*, pg. 1072
INVINCIBLE BOAT COMPANY—See EagleTree Capital, LP; *U.S. Private*, pg. 1311
JAMES MARINE INC.; *U.S. Private*, pg. 2184
JAMESTOWN METAL MARINE SALES, INC.; *U.S. Private*, pg. 2186
JAPAN MARINE UNITED CORPORATION—See IHI Corporation; *Int'l*, pg. 3605
KERNEY SERVICE GROUP INC.; *U.S. Private*, pg. 2291
KEY WEST BOATS INC.; *U.S. Private*, pg. 2294
KIRBY OFFSHORE MARINE HAWAII, LLC—See Kirby Corporation; *U.S. Public*, pg. 1236
KOREA SHIPBUILDING & OFFSHORE ENGINEERING CO., LTD.—See Hyundai Heavy Industries Co., Ltd.; *Int'l*, pg. 3557
KREUZ SHIPBUILDING & ENGINEERING PTE LTD—See Headland Capital Partners Limited; *Int'l*, pg. 3301
LAKEN SHIPPING CORPORATION SMT (USA) INC.—See Algoma Central Corporation; *Int'l*, pg. 318
LLOYD WERFT BREMERHAVEN GMBH—See Genting Hong Kong Limited; *Int'l*, pg. 2929
MAASKANT SHIPYARDS BV—See Damen Shipyards Group; *Int'l*, pg. 1956
MARCO GLOBAL INC.; *U.S. Private*, pg. 2571
MARCO SEATTLE, INC.—See MARCO Global Inc.; *U.S. Private*, pg. 2572
MARINE HYDRAULICS INTERNATIONAL, INC.—See Stellex Capital Management LP; *U.S. Private*, pg. 3800
MARINE HYDRAULICS INTERNATIONAL, INC.—See The Carlyle Group Inc.; *U.S. Public*, pg. 2056
MARINE INDUSTRIES NORTHWEST, INC.—See Stellex Capital Management LP; *U.S. Private*, pg. 3800
MARINE INDUSTRIES NORTHWEST, INC.—See The Carlyle Group Inc.; *U.S. Public*, pg. 2056
MARINE SYSTEMS, INC.—See Kirby Corporation; *U.S. Public*, pg. 1235
MARINE SYSTEMS, INC.—See Kirby Corporation; *U.S. Public*, pg. 1235
MARINETTE MARINE CORPORATION—See Fincantieri S.p.A.; *Int'l*, pg. 2671
MARISCO LTD.; *U.S. Private*, pg. 2576
MEP ACQUISITION CORP—See Patrick Industries, Inc.; *U.S. Public*, pg. 1652
MIKE'S INC.; *U.S. Private*, pg. 2726
MISSISSIPPI MARINE CORPORATION; *U.S. Private*, pg. 2748
MOBILE SHIPBUILDING & REPAIR INC.—See Parker Towing Company, Inc.; *U.S. Private*, pg. 3097
MONTE CARLO YACHT SPA—See Beneteau S.A.; *Int'l*, pg. 972
MORAN SHIPYARD CORPORATION—See Moran Towing Corporation; *U.S. Private*, pg. 2781
MULDOON MARINE SERVICES, INC.—See GenNx360 Capital Partners, L.P.; *U.S. Private*, pg. 1672
MV WERFTEN ROSTOCK GMBH—See Genting Hong Kong Limited; *Int'l*, pg. 2929
MV WERFTEN STRALSUND GMBH—See Genting Hong Kong Limited; *Int'l*, pg. 2929
MV WERFTEN WISMAR GMBH—See OEP Capital Advisors, L.P.; *U.S. Private*, pg. 3000
NAIAD DYNAMICS HOLLAND, BV—See Naiad Maritime Group, Inc.; *U.S. Private*, pg. 2831
NAIAD DYNAMICS UK, LTD.—See Naiad Maritime Group, Inc.; *U.S. Private*, pg. 2831
NAIAD MARITIME GROUP, INC.; *U.S. Private*, pg. 2831
NASSCO HOLDINGS INCORPORATED—See General Dynamics Corporation; *U.S. Public*, pg. 915
NASSCO-NORFOLK—See General Dynamics Corporation; *U.S. Public*, pg. 915
NEW ORLEANS SHIP YARD—See Archer-Daniels-Midland Company; *U.S. Public*, pg. 185
NEWPORT NEWS SHIPBUILDING AND DRY DOCK COMPANY—See Huntington Ingalls Industries, Inc.; *U.S. Public*, pg. 1072
NICHOLS BROTHERS BOAT BUILDERS; *U.S. Private*, pg. 2925
NORDEN TANKERS & BULKERS DO BRAZIL LTDA—See Dampskibsselskabet NORDEN A/S; *Int'l*, pg. 1957
NORDIC TUGS INC.; *U.S. Private*, pg. 2937
NORDSEEWERKE EMDEN SHIPYARD GMBH—See Beaufort Capital GmbH; *Int'l*, pg. 934
NORTH FLORIDA SHIPYARDS INC. - MAYPORT FACILITY—See North Florida Shipyards Inc.; *U.S. Private*, pg. 2945
NORWALK COVE MARINA, INC.—See Rex Marine Center, Inc.; *U.S. Private*, pg. 3417
NSP MARITIME LINK INC.—See Emera, Inc.; *Int'l*, pg. 2377
NTI LTD.—See Daeyang Electric Co., Ltd.; *Int'l*, pg. 1911
OCEANEERING ROTATOR AS—See Oceaneering International, Inc.; *U.S. Public*, pg. 1562
OCEAN SHIPHOLDINGS, INC.; *U.S. Private*, pg. 2990
ODENSE STEEL SHIPYARD LTD.—See A.P. Moller-Maersk A/S; *Int'l*, pg. 27
ORANGE SHIPBUILDING COMPANY, INC.—See Conrad Industries, Inc.; *U.S. Public*, pg. 569
PACIFIC SHIP REPAIR & FABRICATION; *U.S. Private*, pg. 3070
PALM BEACH MOTOR YACHT CO. PTY. LTD.—See Grand

3765

336611 — SHIP BUILDING AND R...

Banks Yachts Limited; *Int'l*, pg. 3054
PENGUIN INTERNATIONAL LIMITED—See Dymon Asia Capital (Singapore) Pte. Ltd; *Int'l*, pg. 2238
PENGUIN SHIPYARD INTERNATIONAL PTE LTD—See Dymon Asia Capital (Singapore) Pte. Ltd; *Int'l*, pg. 2238
PHILLY SHIPYARD, INC.—See Aker ASA; *Int'l*, pg. 262
PIH LTD.—See Stanley Black & Decker, Inc.; *U.S. Public*, pg. 1933
PIH SERVICES ME LTD.—See Stanley Black & Decker, Inc.; *U.S. Public*, pg. 1933
PLANACO SA—See Folli Follie S.A.; *Int'l*, pg. 2721
PT. ASL SHIPYARD INDONESIA—See ASL Marine Holdings Ltd; *Int'l*, pg. 625
PT. NEXELITE CP INDONESIA—See Beng Kuang Marine Limited; *Int'l*, pg. 973
PT. NEXUS ENGINEERING INDONESIA—See Beng Kuang Marine Limited; *Int'l*, pg. 973
QINGDAO BEIHAI SHIPBUILDING HEAVY INDUSTRY CO., LTD.—See China Shipbuilding Industry Company Limited; *Int'l*, pg. 1551
RIVERHAWK FAST SEA FRAMES, LLC; *U.S. Private*, pg. 3444
ROB INT S.R.L.—See Fincantieri S.p.A.; *Int'l*, pg. 2671
ROSYTH ROYAL DOCKYARD LIMITED—See Babcock International Group PLC; *Int'l*, pg. 793
RYBOVICH BOAT COMPANY LLC—See Sun Communities, Inc.; *U.S. Public*, pg. 1963
SAMHWA TRADING CO., LTD.—See Daeyang Electric Co., Ltd.; *Int'l*, pg. 1911
SAMWOO HEAVY INDUSTRIES CO., LTD.—See Hanwha Ocean Co., Ltd.; *Int'l*, pg. 3266
SAUNDERS YACHTWORKS; *U.S. Private*, pg. 3554
SC WESTERN SHIPYARD—See BLRT Grupp AS; *Int'l*, pg. 1066
SEALEGS INTERNATIONAL LIMITED—See Future Mobility Solutions; *Int'l*, pg. 2857
SHANHAIGUAN SHIPBUILDING INDUSTRY CO., LTD.—See China Shipbuilding Industry Company Limited; *Int'l*, pg. 1551
SHINHAN MACHINERY CO., LTD.—See Hanwha Ocean Co., Ltd.; *Int'l*, pg. 3267
SHIPDOCK B.V.—See Damen Shipyards Group; *Int'l*, pg. 1956
SHM SIESTA KEY, LLC—See Sun Communities, Inc.; *U.S. Public*, pg. 1962
S. J. DELPHIA SP Z.O.O.—See Beneteau S.A; *Int'l*, pg. 973
STANFORD MARINE GROUP—See Abraaj Capital Limited; *Int'l*, pg. 67
SUBSEA GLOBAL SOLUTIONS LLC—See GenNx360 Capital Partners, L.P.; *U.S. Private*, pg. 1672
SUNDIAL MARINE TUG & BARGE WORKS INC—See Tidewater Holdings, Inc.; *U.S. Private*, pg. 4168
TECHNOLOGIE TWORZYW SZTUCNYCH SPOL. ZOO.—See Aurelius Equity Opportunities SE & Co. KGaA; *Int'l*, pg. 709
THYSSENKRUPP MARINE SYSTEMS GMBH—See OEP Capital Advisors, L.P.; *U.S. Private*, pg. 3000
TIANJIN XINGANG SHIPBUILDING HEAVY INDUSTRY CO., LTD.—See China Shipbuilding Industry Company Limited; *Int'l*, pg. 1551
TIMOLOR LEROUX ET LOTZ SAS—See Altawest Group; *Int'l*, pg. 388
TREADWELL CORPORATION; *U.S. Private*, pg. 4216
TURKU REPAIR YARD LTD—See BLRT Grupp AS; *Int'l*, pg. 1066
TURNBULL LLC; *U.S. Private*, pg. 4260
UAB WESTERN BALTIJA SHIPBUILDING—See BLRT Grupp AS; *Int'l*, pg. 1066
U.M.C. INTERNATIONAL PLC—See Ackermans & van Haaren NV; *Int'l*, pg. 106
UNDERSEA SOLUTIONS CORPORATION—See Huntington Ingalls Industries, Inc.; *U.S. Public*, pg. 1072
UNIVERSAL ENSCO, INC.—See PMC Capital Partners, LLC; *U.S. Private*, pg. 3218
UNIVERSAL SHIPBUILDING CORPORATION—See Hitachi Zosen Corporation; *Int'l*, pg. 3412
US JOINER LLC - GULF COAST—See J.F. Lehman & Company, Inc.; *U.S. Private*, pg. 2164
US JOINER, LLC—See J.F. Lehman & Company, Inc.; *U.S. Private*, pg. 2164
VANCOUVER DRYDOCK COMPANY LTD.—See Washington Corporations; *U.S. Private*, pg. 4446
VANCOUVER SHIPYARDS CO. LTD.—See Washington Corporations; *U.S. Private*, pg. 4447
VARD BRAILA SA—See Fincantieri S.p.A.; *Int'l*, pg. 2671
VARD BRATTVAAG AS—See Fincantieri S.p.A.; *Int'l*, pg. 2671
VARD ELECTRO BRAZIL (INSTALACOES ELETRICAS) LTDA.—See Fincantieri S.p.A.; *Int'l*, pg. 2671
VARD HOLDINGS LIMITED—See Fincantieri S.p.A.; *Int'l*, pg. 2671
VARD MARINE GDANSK SP. Z O.O.—See Fincantieri S.p.A.; *Int'l*, pg. 2672
VARD MARINE INC.—See Fincantieri S.p.A.; *Int'l*, pg. 2672
VARD NITEROI SA—See Fincantieri S.p.A.; *Int'l*, pg. 2672
VARD PROMAR SA—See Fincantieri S.p.A.; *Int'l*, pg. 2672
VARD TULCEA SA—See Fincantieri S.p.A.; *Int'l*, pg. 2672
VARD VUNG TAU LTD.—See Fincantieri S.p.A.; *Int'l*, pg. 2672
VERTEX RSI—See General Dynamics Corporation; *U.S. Public*, pg. 916
VICTORIA SHIPYARDS CO. LTD.—See Washington Corporations; *U.S. Private*, pg. 4447
VIGOR ALASKA SHIP & DRYDOCK INC.—See Stellex Capital Management LP; *U.S. Private*, pg. 3800
VIGOR ALASKA SHIP & DRYDOCK INC.—See The Carlyle Group Inc.; *U.S. Public*, pg. 2056
VIGOR MACHINE LLC—See Stellex Capital Management LP; *U.S. Private*, pg. 3800
VIGOR MACHINE LLC—See The Carlyle Group Inc.; *U.S. Public*, pg. 2056
VIGOR SHIPYARDS—See Stellex Capital Management LP; *U.S. Private*, pg. 3801
VIGOR SHIPYARDS—See The Carlyle Group Inc.; *U.S. Public*, pg. 2056
VOLVO PENTA UK LIMITED—See AB Volvo; *Int'l*, pg. 42
VT HALTER MARINE, INC—See Bollinger Shipyards, Inc.; *U.S. Private*, pg. 611
WESTERN EXPLORATION, LLC—See Western Exploration Inc.; *U.S. Public*, pg. 2356
WHITE LAKE DOCK & DREDGE, INC.—See J.F. Lehman & Company, Inc.; *U.S. Private*, pg. 2163
WUCHANG SHIPBUILDING INDUSTRY CO., LTD.—See China Shipbuilding Industry Company Limited; *Int'l*, pg. 1551
YANTAI CIMC RAFFLES SHIP CO., LTD.—See China International Marine Containers (Group) Co., Ltd.; *Int'l*, pg. 1513
YIYANG ZHONGHAI SHIPYARD CO, LTD—See China National Chemical Corporation; *Int'l*, pg. 1530
YUAN HUA TECHNICAL & SUPPLY CORPORATION—See China COSCO Shipping Corporation Limited; *Int'l*, pg. 1492
YUANTONG MARINE SERVICE CO. LIMITED—See China COSCO Shipping Corporation Limited; *Int'l*, pg. 1492
YUANTONG MARINE TRADE (SHANGHAI) CO. LIMITED—See China COSCO Shipping Corporation Limited; *Int'l*, pg. 1492
ZHOUSHAN NIPPON PUSNES SHIP MACHINERY CO., LTD.—See Hitachi Zosen Corporation; *Int'l*, pg. 3412

336612 — BOAT BUILDING

ALEXANDER MARINE CO., LTD.; *Int'l*, pg. 307
ALICAT WORKBOATS LIMITED—See HAL Trust N.V.; *Int'l*, pg. 3226
ALL AMERICAN MARINE, INC.—See Bryton Marine Group; *Int'l*, pg. 1201
ALUMACRAFT BOAT COMPANY—See Bain Capital, LP; *U.S. Private*, pg. 430
ALUMACRAFT BOAT COMPANY—See Bain Capital, LP; *U.S. Private*, pg. 431
ALUMA-WELD INC.; *U.S. Private*, pg. 211
AMERICAN CUSTOM YACHTS, INC.; *U.S. Private*, pg. 229
ANNAPOLIS INFLATABLES—See Fawcett Marine Supplies LLC; *U.S. Private*, pg. 1484
BABCOCK INTERNATIONAL GROUP—See Babcock International Group PLC; *Int'l*, pg. 792
BAJA MARINE, INC.—See American Marine Holdings, LLC; *U.S. Private*, pg. 240
BENETEAU S.A; *Int'l*, pg. 972
BERING MARINE CORPORATION—See Lynden Incorporated; *U.S. Private*, pg. 2521
BOMBARDIER MOTOR CORPORATION OF AMERICA—See Bain Capital, LP; *U.S. Private*, pg. 431
BOMBARDIER RECREATIONAL PRODUCTS INC.—See Bain Capital, LP; *U.S. Private*, pg. 431
BOSTON WHALER, INC.—See Brunswick Corporation; *U.S. Public*, pg. 407
BRUNSWICK BOAT GROUP—See Brunswick Corporation; *U.S. Public*, pg. 407
BRUNSWICK COMMERCIAL & GOVERNMENT PRODUCTS, INC.—See Brunswick Corporation; *U.S. Public*, pg. 407
BRUNSWICK CORPORATION; *U.S. Public*, pg. 407
BRUNSWICK LEISURE BOAT COMPANY, LLC—See Brunswick Corporation; *U.S. Public*, pg. 407
BRYANT BOATS, INC.—See Correct Craft, Inc.; *U.S. Private*, pg. 1058
CAMPION MARINE INC.; *Int'l*, pg. 1275
CATALINA YACHTS, INC.; *U.S. Private*, pg. 786
CATANA GROUP SA; *Int'l*, pg. 1358
CATHERWOOD TOWING LTD.; *Int'l*, pg. 1361
CHANTIER CATANA; *Int'l*, pg. 1446
CHANTIERS AMEL S.A.; *Int'l*, pg. 1446
CHAPARRAL BOATS, INC.—See Marine Products Corporation; *U.S. Public*, pg. 1366
CHRIS-CRAFT CORPORATION; *U.S. Private*, pg. 890
CHRISTENSEN SHIPYARDS LTD.; *U.S. Private*, pg. 890
CIGARETTE RACING TEAM, LLC—See Lionheart Capital, LLC; *U.S. Private*, pg. 2464
CLEARWATER MARINE INC.; *U.S. Private*, pg. 939
COBALT BOATS, LLC—See Malibu Boats, Inc.; *U.S. Public*, pg. 1355

CONFLUENCE WATERSPORTS CO. INC.; *U.S. Private*, pg. 1013
CONSTRUCTION NAVALE BORDEAUX SA—See Beneteau S.A; *Int'l*, pg. 972
CONVER B.V.—See Alamo Group Inc.; *U.S. Public*, pg. 71
CORRECT CRAFT, INC.; *U.S. Private*, pg. 1058
CRESTLINER, INC.—See Brunswick Corporation; *U.S. Public*, pg. 407
CREST MARINE, LLC—See MasterCraft Boat Holdings, Inc.; *U.S. Public*, pg. 1395
DAKOTA CREEK INDUSTRIES, INC.; *U.S. Private*, pg. 1147
DAMEN SHIPYARDS KOZLE SP Z.O.O.—See Damen Shipyards Group; *Int'l*, pg. 1956
DAVIS BOAT WORKS INC.; *U.S. Private*, pg. 1173
DELTA MARINE INDUSTRIES, INC.; *U.S. Private*, pg. 1201
DERECKTOR GUNNELL INC.; *U.S. Private*, pg. 1209
DESTINI MARINE SAFETY SOLUTIONS LTD.—See Destini Berhad; *Int'l*, pg. 2046
DONZI MARINE CORPORATION—See American Marine Holdings, LLC; *U.S. Private*, pg. 240
DPC MASCHINEN VERTRIEB GMBH—See Alamo Group Inc.; *U.S. Public*, pg. 71
EBBTIDE CORPORATION; *U.S. Private*, pg. 1323
ELIMINATOR CUSTOM BOATS INC.; *U.S. Private*, pg. 1360
FINELINE INDUSTRIES INC.; *U.S. Private*, pg. 1509
THE FISHING HOLDINGS, LLC—See The Great American Outdoors Group LLC; *U.S. Private*, pg. 4038
FOUNTAINE PAJOT SA; *Int'l*, pg. 2754
FOUNTAIN POWERBOATS, INC.—See American Marine Holdings, LLC; *U.S. Private*, pg. 240
FOUR WINNS, LLC—See Beneteau S.A; *Int'l*, pg. 973
FUSION X MARINE, LLC—See US Lighting Group, Inc.; *U.S. Public*, pg. 2266
FUTURE MOBILITY SOLUTIONS LTD; *Int'l*, pg. 2857
GLASTRON, LLC—See Beneteau S.A; *Int'l*, pg. 973
GRADY-WHITE BOATS, INC.; *U.S. Private*, pg. 1750
GRAND BANKS YACHTS LIMITED; *Int'l*, pg. 3054
GRAND BANKS YACHTS, LTD.—See Grand Banks Yachts Limited; *Int'l*, pg. 3054
GRAND BANKS YACHTS SDN. BHD.—See Grand Banks Yachts Limited; *Int'l*, pg. 3054
HANN ENTERPRISES, INC.; *U.S. Private*, pg. 1854
HANSEYACHTS AG—See Aurelius Equity Opportunities SE & Co. KGaA; *Int'l*, pg. 708
HATTERAS YACHTS—See Brunswick Corporation; *U.S. Public*, pg. 407
HEWES MANUFACTURING CO.—See Maverick Boat Co. Inc.; *U.S. Private*, pg. 2615
HLB INC.; *Int'l*, pg. 3430
HOBIE CAT COMPANY; *U.S. Private*, pg. 1958
HODGDON YACHTS, INC.; *U.S. Private*, pg. 1959
HYDROID EUROPE—See Huntington Ingalls Industries, Inc.; *U.S. Public*, pg. 1072
HYLAS YACHTS INC.; *U.S. Private*, pg. 2019
INHA WORKS LTD.—See Fiskars Oyj Abp; *Int'l*, pg. 2694
JIM SMITH BOATS, INC.; *U.S. Private*, pg. 2209
JOHNSON OUTDOORS WATERCRAFT INC.—See Johnson Outdoors Inc.; *U.S. Public*, pg. 1201
JUPITER MARINE INTERNATIONAL HOLDINGS, INC.; *U.S. Public*, pg. 1211
KCS INTERNATIONAL, INC.—See MarineMax, Inc.; *U.S. Public*, pg. 1366
LAND & SEA, INC.—See Power Test, Inc.; *U.S. Private*, pg. 3239
LARSON BOATS LLC—See Polaris, Inc.; *U.S. Public*, pg. 1700
LASERPERFORMANCE (EUROPE) LIMITED—See Full Moon Holdings Limited; *Int'l*, pg. 2842
LAZZARA YACHT CORP.; *U.S. Private*, pg. 2403
LOWE BOATS—See Brunswick Corporation; *U.S. Public*, pg. 407
LUND BOAT COMPANY—See Brunswick Corporation; *U.S. Public*, pg. 407
MALIBU BOATS HOLDINGS, LLC—See Malibu Boats, Inc.; *U.S. Public*, pg. 1356
MALIBU BOATS, INC.; *U.S. Public*, pg. 1355
MALIBU BOATS PTY LTD.—See Malibu Boats, Inc.; *U.S. Public*, pg. 1356
MARINE ACCESSORIES EUROPE B.V.—See Patrick Industries, Inc.; *U.S. Public*, pg. 1652
MARINE ADVANCED ROBOTICS, INC.—See Ocean Power Technologies, Inc.; *U.S. Public*, pg. 1562
MARINE PRODUCTS CORPORATION; *U.S. Public*, pg. 1366
MARINE TRADING INTERNATIONAL, INC.—See Miller Yacht Sales, Inc.; *U.S. Private*, pg. 2736
MARQUIS-LARSON BOAT GROUP; *U.S. Private*, pg. 2588
MASTERCRAFT BOAT COMPANY, LLC—See MasterCraft Boat Holdings, Inc.; *U.S. Public*, pg. 1395
MAVERICK BOAT CO. INC.; *U.S. Private*, pg. 2615
MCCLENDON RESOURCES INC.; *U.S. Private*, pg. 2628
MECHANICAL INDUSTRIES, LLC; *U.S. Private*, pg. 2648
NAUTIC STAR, LLC—See MasterCraft Boat Holdings, Inc.; *U.S. Public*, pg. 1395
NORTHWEST BOATS INDUSTRIES, INC.—See Renaissance Marine Group, Inc.; *U.S. Private*, pg. 3397

N.A.I.C.S. INDEX

336991 — MOTORCYCLE, BICYCLE...

OLD TOWN CANOE CO.—See Johnson Outdoors Inc.; *U.S. Public*, pg. 1201
OSTRODA YACHT SP. Z O.O.—See Beneteau S.A; *Int'l*, pg. 972
OYSTER MARINE LTD.—See H.T.P. Investments BV; *Int'l*, pg. 3196
OYSTER YACHTS LTD.—See H.T.P. Investments BV; *Int'l*, pg. 3196
OYSTER YACHTS SOUTHAMPTON—See H.T.P. Investments BV; *Int'l*, pg. 3196
PALM BEACH TOWERS—See Viking Yacht Company; *U.S. Private*, pg. 4383
PERKO WORLDWIDE CORP.; *U.S. Private*, pg. 3152
PONTOON BOAT, LLC; *U.S. Private*, pg. 3227
PRINCECRAFT BOATS, INC.—See Brunswick Corporation; *U.S. Public*, pg. 407
PRO-LINE BOATS—See American Marine Holdings, LLC; *U.S. Private*, pg. 240
QUARTER MOON INC.—See Full Moon Holdings Limited; *Int'l*, pg. 2842
REC BOAT HOLDINGS, LLC—See Beneteau S.A; *Int'l*, pg. 972
RECONCRAFT; *U.S. Private*, pg. 3371
REGAL MARINE INDUSTRIES, INC.; *U.S. Private*, pg. 3385
RENAISSANCE MARINE GROUP, INC.; *U.S. Private*, pg. 3397
RIVERVIEW MARINA INC.; *U.S. Private*, pg. 3448
S2 YACHTS, INC.; *U.S. Private*, pg. 3519
SABRE YACHTS; *U.S. Private*, pg. 3521
SAFETY & SURVIVAL SYSTEMS INTERNATIONAL LTD.; *U.S. Private*, pg. 3524
SEAARK MARINE INC.—See McClendon Resources Inc.; *U.S. Private*, pg. 2628
SEABRING MARINE INDUSTRIES INC.; *U.S. Private*, pg. 3583
SEAFOX BOAT COMPANY INC.; *U.S. Private*, pg. 3584
SEA RAY BOATS, INC.—See Brunswick Corporation; *U.S. Public*, pg. 407
SEI MANUFACTURING, INC.—See Patrick Industries, Inc.; *U.S. Public*, pg. 1653
SHIPBUILDERS OF WISCONSIN, INC.; *U.S. Private*, pg. 3637
SILVER SHIPS, INC.; *U.S. Private*, pg. 3662
SKIER'S CHOICE INC.; *U.S. Private*, pg. 3682
SMOKER CRAFT INC.; *U.S. Private*, pg. 3698
SVENDSEN'S BOAT WORKS, INC.—See Bay Ship & Yacht Co; *U.S. Private*, pg. 494
TECHNO FIBRE AUSTRALIA PTY. LTD.—See Destini Berhad; *Int'l*, pg. 2047
TECHNO FIBRE MIDDLE EAST MARINE SERVICES FZE—See Destini Berhad; *Int'l*, pg. 2047
TECHNO FIBRE (S) PTE. LTD.—See Destini Berhad; *Int'l*, pg. 2046
TEXTRON MARINE & LAND SYSTEMS—See Textron Inc.; *U.S. Public*, pg. 2029
TRACKER MARINE GROUP LLC—See The Great American Outdoors Group LLC; *U.S. Private*, pg. 4038
TRACY INTERNATIONAL—See Chem-Tainer Industries, Inc.; *U.S. Private*, pg. 871
TRINITY YACHTS, LLC; *U.S. Private*, pg. 4236
TRITON SUBMARINES, LLC; *U.S. Private*, pg. 4239
TWIN VEE POWERCATS CO.; *U.S. Public*, pg. 2207
VANGUARDE PTE. LTD.—See Destini Berhad; *Int'l*, pg. 2047
VICTORY MARINE HOLDINGS CORP.; *U.S. Public*, pg. 2296
VIKING YACHT COMPANY; *U.S. Private*, pg. 4382
WELLCRAFT, LLC—See Beneteau S.A; *Int'l*, pg. 973
WILLARD MARINE, INC.—See Future Mobility Solutions Ltd.; *Int'l*, pg. 2857
ZODIAC HURRICANE TECHNOLOGIES INC.—See The Carlyle Group Inc.; *U.S. Public*, pg. 2057
ZODIAC OF NORTH AMERICA, INC.—See The Carlyle Group Inc.; *U.S. Public*, pg. 2057

336991 — MOTORCYCLE, BICYCLE, AND PARTS MANUFACTURING

2WHEELBIKES.COM; *U.S. Private*, pg. 7
ACCELL ASIA LTD.—See Accell Group N.V.; *Int'l*, pg. 80
ACCELL BISIKLET SANAYI VE TICARET A.S.—See Accell Group N.V.; *Int'l*, pg. 80
ACCELL GERMANY GMBH—See Accell Group N.V.; *Int'l*, pg. 80
ACCELL GROUP N.V.; *Int'l*, pg. 80
ACCELL HUNLAND KFT—See Accell Group N.V.; *Int'l*, pg. 80
ACCELL IT B.V.—See Accell Group N.V.; *Int'l*, pg. 80
ACCELL NEDERLAND B.V.—See Accell Group N.V.; *Int'l*, pg. 80
AEON MOTOR CO., LTD.; *Int'l*, pg. 179
AHRESTY PRETECH CORPORATION—See Ahresty Corporation; *Int'l*, pg. 226
ALTON SPORTS CO., LTD. - CHINA PLANT—See Alton Sports Co., Ltd.; *Int'l*, pg. 394
ALTON SPORTS CO., LTD.; *Int'l*, pg. 394
ALTON SPORTS CO., LTD. - YANGJU PLANT—See Alton Sports Co., Ltd.; *Int'l*, pg. 394
THE AMERICAN BICYCLE GROUP LLC; *U.S. Private*, pg. 3985
ANSWER PRODUCTS, INC.—See LDI Ltd., LLC; *U.S. Private*, pg. 2404
APT MOTO VOX GROUP, INC.; *U.S. Public*, pg. 174
ASIAN AUTOPARTS CO., LTD.—See Honda Motor Co., Ltd.; *Int'l*, pg. 3460
ATC VENTURE GROUP INC.; *U.S. Private*, pg. 365
ATLAS CYCLES (HARYANA) LTD.; *Int'l*, pg. 685
ATLAS DID (PRIVATE) LTD.—See Daido Kogyo Co., Ltd.; *Int'l*, pg. 1920
ATLAS HONDA LIMITED—See Atlas Group of Companies; *Int'l*, pg. 685
ATLAS HONDA LIMITED—See Honda Motor Co., Ltd.; *Int'l*, pg. 3460
THE BABY JOGGER COMPANY—See Newell Brands Inc.; *U.S. Public*, pg. 1515
BAJAJ AUTO LTD. - AKURDI PLANT—See Bajaj Auto Ltd.; *Int'l*, pg. 803
BAJAJ AUTO LTD.; *Int'l*, pg. 803
BAJAJ AUTO LTD. - WALUJ PLANT—See Bajaj Auto Ltd.; *Int'l*, pg. 804
BANGLADESH HONDA PRIVATE LIMITED—See Honda Motor Co., Ltd.; *Int'l*, pg. 3460
BATAVUS B.V.—See Accell Group N.V.; *Int'l*, pg. 80
BIANCHI CAFE & CYCLES SVERIGE AB—See Grimaldi Industri AB; *Int'l*, pg. 3085
BIANCHI U.S.A., INC.; *U.S. Private*, pg. 550
BOON SIEW HONDA SDN. BHD.—See Honda Motor Co., Ltd.; *Int'l*, pg. 3460
BRASSEUR S.A.—See Accell Group N.V.; *Int'l*, pg. 80
BRIDGESTONE CYCLE CO., LTD. - AGEO PLANT—See Bridgestone Corporation; *Int'l*, pg. 1158
BRIDGESTONE CYCLE CO., LTD. - ASAHI PLANT—See Bridgestone Corporation; *Int'l*, pg. 1158
BRIDGESTONE CYCLE CO., LTD.—See Bridgestone Corporation; *Int'l*, pg. 1158
BURKE INC.; *U.S. Private*, pg. 688
CANNONDALE BICYCLE CORPORATION—See Dorel Industries, Inc.; *Int'l*, pg. 2176
CANNONDALE JAPAN KK—See Dorel Industries, Inc.; *Int'l*, pg. 2176
CETC ACOUSTIC-OPTIC-ELECTRONIC TECHNOLOGY INC.; *Int'l*, pg. 1424
COMET DISTRIBUCIONES COMMERCIALES S.L.—See Accell Group N.V.; *Int'l*, pg. 80
CORBIN PACIFIC INCORPORATED; *U.S. Private*, pg. 1047
CURTISS MOTORCYCLE COMPANY, INC.; *U.S. Public*, pg. 611
CUSTOM CHROME INCORPORATED—See Global Motor Sport Group, Inc.; *U.S. Private*, pg. 1716
CYCLE SERVICES NORDIC APS—See Accell Group N.V.; *Int'l*, pg. 80
CYCLES FRANCE-LOIRE S.A.S.—See Accell Group N.V.; *Int'l*, pg. 80
CYCLES LAPIERRE S.A.—See Accell Group N.V.; *Int'l*, pg. 80
CYCLES MERCIER FRANCE-LOIRE S.A.—See Accell Group N.V.; *Int'l*, pg. 80
CYCLEUROPE AB—See Grimaldi Industri AB; *Int'l*, pg. 3086
CYCLEUROPE SVERIGE AB—See Grimaldi Industri AB; *Int'l*, pg. 3086
CYCLING SPORTS GROUP INC.—See Dorel Industries, Inc.; *Int'l*, pg. 2176
DAELIM MOTOR CO., LTD.—See Daelim Industrial Co., Ltd.; *Int'l*, pg. 1908
DAIDO SITTIPOL CO., LTD.—See Daido Kogyo Co., Ltd.; *Int'l*, pg. 1920
DAIWA CYCLE CO., LTD.; *Int'l*, pg. 1944
DAYTONA CORPORATION; *Int'l*, pg. 1985
DENSOTRIM CO., LTD.—See Denso Corporation; *Int'l*, pg. 2031
DIA-FRAG INDUSTRIA E COMERCIO DE MOTOPECAS LTDA.—See Westinghouse Air Brake Technologies Corporation; *U.S. Public*, pg. 2357
DID MALAYSIA SDN. BHD.—See Daido Kogyo Co., Ltd.; *Int'l*, pg. 1920
DOREL SUISSE SARL—See Dorel Industries, Inc.; *Int'l*, pg. 2176
DUTCH ID B.V.—See ASR Nederland N.V.; *Int'l*, pg. 632
ELLSWORTH HANDCRAFTED BICYCLES, INC.—See BST NanoCarbon LLC; *U.S. Private*, pg. 675
EMPIRE DIVERSIFIED ENERGY, INC.; *U.S. Public*, pg. 753
ENERGICA MOTOR COMPANY S.P.A.—See Ideanomics, Inc.; *U.S. Public*, pg. 1088
ENGINES ENGINEERING S.R.L.; *Int'l*, pg. 2435
ENVE COMPOSITES LLC—See ANTA Sports Products Limited; *Int'l*, pg. 480
ERAAYA LIFESPACES LIMITED; *Int'l*, pg. 2488
EURO-CYCLES SA; *Int'l*, pg. 2531
E. WIENER BIKE PARTS GMBH—See Accell Group N.V.; *Int'l*, pg. 80
F.C.C. (TAIWAN) CO., LTD.—See F.C.C. Co., Ltd.; *Int'l*, pg. 2596
FIV E. BIANCHI S.P.A.—See Grimaldi Industri AB; *Int'l*, pg. 3086
FLAGSHIP CO., LTD.—See Capcom Co., Ltd.; *Int'l*, pg. 1302
GARIA INC.—See Platinum Equity, LLC; *U.S. Private*, pg. 3202
GHANI AUTOMOBILE INDUSTRIES LIMITED; *Int'l*, pg. 2958
GIANT BELGIUM N.V.—See Giant Manufacturing Co., Ltd.; *Int'l*, pg. 2961
GIANT BENELUX B.V.—See Giant Manufacturing Co., Ltd.; *Int'l*, pg. 2961
GIANT BICYCLE CANADA, INC.—See Giant Manufacturing Co., Ltd.; *Int'l*, pg. 2961
GIANT BICYCLE CO. LTD.—See Giant Manufacturing Co., Ltd.; *Int'l*, pg. 2961
GIANT BICYCLE DE MEXICO S DE R.L. DE C.V.—See Giant Manufacturing Co., Ltd.; *Int'l*, pg. 2961
GIANT BICYCLE INC.—See Giant Manufacturing Co., Ltd.; *Int'l*, pg. 2961
GIANT BIKE CO., LTD.—See Giant Manufacturing Co., Ltd.; *Int'l*, pg. 2961
GIANT (CHINA) CO. LTD.—See Giant Manufacturing Co., Ltd.; *Int'l*, pg. 2961
GIANT EUROPE MANUFACTURING B.V.—See Giant Manufacturing Co., Ltd.; *Int'l*, pg. 2961
GIANT FRANCE S.A.R.L.—See Giant Manufacturing Co., Ltd.; *Int'l*, pg. 2961
GIANT MANUFACTURING CO., LTD.; *Int'l*, pg. 2961
GIANT MANUFACTURING HUNGARY LTD.—See Giant Manufacturing Co., Ltd.; *Int'l*, pg. 2961
GIANT MEXICO S. DE R.L. DE C.V.—See Giant Manufacturing Co., Ltd.; *Int'l*, pg. 2961
GIANT POLSKA SP. Z O.O. UL.—See Giant Manufacturing Co., Ltd.; *Int'l*, pg. 2961
GIANT SALES COMPANY LTD.—See Giant Manufacturing Co., Ltd.; *Int'l*, pg. 2961
GIANT VIETNAM MANUFACTURING COMPANY LIMITED—See Giant Manufacturing Co., Ltd.; *Int'l*, pg. 2961
GLOBAL MOTOR SPORT GROUP, INC.; *U.S. Private*, pg. 1716
GOSHI GIKEN CO., LTD.—See Honda Motor Co., Ltd.; *Int'l*, pg. 3464
GOSHI INDIA AUTO PARTS PRIVATE LTD.—See Honda Motor Co., Ltd.; *Int'l*, pg. 3464
GOSHI PHILIPPINES, INC.—See Honda Motor Co., Ltd.; *Int'l*, pg. 3464
GREENTRANS CORPORATION—See China Motor Corporation; *Int'l*, pg. 1525
GUANGZHOU MOTORS GROUP COMPANY—See Guangzhou Automobile Industry Group Co., Ltd.; *Int'l*, pg. 3164
HAMAMATSU MANUFACTURING FACILITY—See Honda Motor Co., Ltd.; *Int'l*, pg. 3460
HARLEY-DAVIDSON BENELUX B.V.—See Harley-Davidson, Inc.; *U.S. Public*, pg. 984
HARLEY-DAVIDSON CENTRAL AND EASTERN EUROPE S.R.O.—See Harley-Davidson, Inc.; *U.S. Public*, pg. 985
HARLEY-DAVIDSON ESPANA S.L.—See Harley-Davidson, Inc.; *U.S. Public*, pg. 985
HARLEY-DAVIDSON FINANCIAL SERVICES EUROPE LTD.—See Harley-Davidson, Inc.; *U.S. Public*, pg. 985
HARLEY-DAVIDSON FINANCIAL SERVICES, INC.—See Harley-Davidson, Inc.; *U.S. Public*, pg. 985
HARLEY-DAVIDSON GMBH—See Harley-Davidson, Inc.; *U.S. Public*, pg. 985
HARLEY-DAVIDSON HOLDING CO., INC.—See Harley-Davidson, Inc.; *U.S. Public*, pg. 985
HARLEY-DAVIDSON, INC.; *U.S. Public*, pg. 984
HARLEY-DAVIDSON ITALIA S.R.L.—See Harley-Davidson, Inc.; *U.S. Public*, pg. 985
HARLEY-DAVIDSON MOTOR COMPANY, INC.—See Harley-Davidson, Inc.; *U.S. Public*, pg. 985
HARLEY-DAVIDSON RETAIL, INC.—See Harley-Davidson, Inc.; *U.S. Public*, pg. 985
HARLEY-DAVIDSON SWITZERLAND GMBH—See Harley-Davidson, Inc.; *U.S. Public*, pg. 985
HASBRO UK LTD—See Hasbro, Inc.; *U.S. Public*, pg. 988
HASC, LLC—See Harley-Davidson, Inc.; *U.S. Public*, pg. 985
HAWLEY, LLC; *U.S. Private*, pg. 1883
H-D GROUP LLC—See Harley-Davidson, Inc.; *U.S. Public*, pg. 984
H-D U.S.A., LLC—See Harley-Davidson, Inc.; *U.S. Public*, pg. 984
HERO ECO LIMITED—See Hero Corp.; *Int'l*, pg. 3363
HERO MOTOCORP LTD.—See Hero Corp.; *Int'l*, pg. 3363
HI-LEX CABLE SYSTEM CO.,LTD.—See Hi-Lex Corporation; *Int'l*, pg. 3380
HL CORP - HANDLEBAR DIVISION—See HL CORP; *Int'l*, pg. 3429
HL CORP (HONG KONG) LIMITED—See HL CORP; *Int'l*, pg. 3429
HL CORP (TAICANG)—See HL CORP; *Int'l*, pg. 3429
HONDA DEL PERU S.A.—See Honda Motor Co., Ltd.; *Int'l*, pg. 3461
HONDA ITALIA INDUSTRIALE S.P.A.—See Honda Motor Co., Ltd.; *Int'l*, pg. 3461
HONDA MOTORCYCLE & SCOOTER INDIA PVT. LTD.—See Honda Motor Co., Ltd.; *Int'l*, pg. 3462

336991 — MOTORCYCLE, BICYCLE...

HONDA PHILIPPINES INC.—See Honda Motor Co., Ltd.; *Int'l*, pg. 3462
HOTLINES EUROPE LTD.—See The American Bicycle Group LLC; *U.S. Private*, pg. 3985
HOVDING SVERIGE AB; *Int'l*, pg. 3492
HUFFY BICYCLE COMPANY—See Huffy Corporation; *U.S. Private*, pg. 2003
HWA FONG RUBBER (THAILAND) PUBLIC COMPANY LIMITED—See Hwa Fong Rubber Industry Co., Ltd.; *Int'l*, pg. 3541
IUVO INDUSTRY CO., LTD.—See Dyaco International Inc.; *Int'l*, pg. 2238
JAYBRAKE, LLC—See Dreison International, Inc.; *U.S. Private*, pg. 1276
KABIRDASS MOTOR COMPANY LTD—See BEST CAST IT LTD; *Int'l*, pg. 998
KINUTA FLOWER AUCTION CO., LTD.—See Aucnet Inc.; *Int'l*, pg. 700
KOGA B.V.—See Accell Group N.V.; *Int'l*, pg. 80
KUMAMOTO MANUFACTURING FACILITY—See Honda Motor Co., Ltd.; *Int'l*, pg. 3463
LEHMAN TRIKES USA, INC.; *U.S. Private*, pg. 2419
MAJESTIC AUTO LTD.—See Hero Corp.; *Int'l*, pg. 3363
MARKLAND INDUSTRIES INC.; *U.S. Private*, pg. 2582
MASSIMO GROUP; *U.S. Public*, pg. 1392
MATTEL S.R.L.—See Mattel, Inc.; *U.S. Public*, pg. 1399
MONARK EXERCISE AB—See Grimaldi Industri AB; *Int'l*, pg. 3086
MONSTER SCOOTER PARTS; *U.S. Private*, pg. 2774
MONTESA HONDA SPAIN—See Honda Motor Co., Ltd.; *Int'l*, pg. 3463
MONVO HONDA BA AMAZONIA LTDA.—See Honda Motor Co., Ltd.; *Int'l*, pg. 3463
MOTOSIKAL DAN ENJIN NASIONAL SDN. BHD.—See DRB-HICOM Berhad; *Int'l*, pg. 2202
NINER BIKES; *U.S. Private*, pg. 2928
OZOP ENERGY SOLUTIONS, INC.; *U.S. Public*, pg. 1629
PACIFIC CYCLE INC.—See Dorel Industries, Inc.; *Int'l*, pg. 2176
PANTHER MOTOR GROUP INC.; *U.S. Private*, pg. 3087
PERF-FORM PRODUCTS, INC.; *U.S. Private*, pg. 3148
POLARIS BRITAIN LIMITED—See Polaris, Inc.; *U.S. Public*, pg. 1700
POLARIS FINLAND OY—See Polaris, Inc.; *U.S. Public*, pg. 1700
POLARIS FRANCE S.A.—See Polaris, Inc.; *U.S. Public*, pg. 1700
POLARIS INDUSTRIES OF CANADA—See Polaris, Inc.; *U.S. Public*, pg. 1700
POLARIS NORWAY AS—See Polaris, Inc.; *U.S. Public*, pg. 1701
POLARIS SALES AUSTRALIA PTY LTD.—See Polaris, Inc.; *U.S. Public*, pg. 1701
POLARIS SCANDINAVIA AB—See Polaris, Inc.; *U.S. Public*, pg. 1701
PT. BAJAJ AUTO INDONESIA—See Bajaj Auto Ltd.; *Int'l*, pg. 804
PT DAYTONA AZIA—See DAYTONA CORPORATION; *Int'l*, pg. 1985
QUINTANA ROO BICYCLES INC.—See The American Bicycle Group LLC; *U.S. Private*, pg. 3985
RALEIGH CYCLE CO. LTD—See Accell Group N.V.; *Int'l*, pg. 81
RALEIGH UK LTD—See Accell Group N.V.; *Int'l*, pg. 81
REKLUSE MOTOR SPORTS, INC.—See MiddleGround Management, LP; *U.S. Private*, pg. 2712
REYNOLDS CYCLING, LLC—See MacLean-Fogg Company; *U.S. Private*, pg. 2537
SARIS CYCLING GROUP, INC.—See C&A Marketing, Inc.; *U.S. Private*, pg. 702
SENA MOTORS LTD.—See Honda Motor Co., Ltd.; *Int'l*, pg. 3464
SHARK S.A.—See Groupe BPCE; *Int'l*, pg. 3095
SHIVAM AUTOTECH LTD.—See Hero Corp.; *Int'l*, pg. 3364
SHOWA REGIONAL CENTER (THAILAND) CO., LTD.—See Hitachi Astemo, Ltd.; *Int'l*, pg. 3410
SIMPLON FAHRRAD GMBH—See HANNOVER Finanz GmbH; *Int'l*, pg. 3257
SPARTA B.V.—See Accell Group N.V.; *Int'l*, pg. 81
SPECIALIZED BICYCLE COMPONENTS; *U.S. Private*, pg. 3748
SRAM, LLC - COLORADO DEVELOPMENT CENTER—See SRAM International Corporation; *U.S. Private*, pg. 3767
SRAM, LLC—See SRAM International Corporation; *U.S. Private*, pg. 3767
SRAM - TAIWAN—See SRAM International Corporation; *U.S. Private*, pg. 3767
STACYC, INC.—See Harley-Davidson, Inc.; *U.S. Public*, pg. 985
T3 MOTION, INC.; *U.S. Private*, pg. 3913
THAI HONDA MANUFACTURING CO., LTD.—See Honda Motor Co., Ltd.; *Int'l*, pg. 3464
TOMOS D.O.O.—See Hidria d.o.o.; *Int'l*, pg. 3384
TREK BICYCLE CORPORATION; *U.S. Private*, pg. 4217
TRELOCK GMBH—See Allegion Public Limited Company; *Int'l*, pg. 335
TRI-CHEM, INC.; *U.S. Private*, pg. 4221
ULTIMATE RACK, INC.; *U.S. Private*, pg. 4277

ULTIMATE SUPPORT SYSTEMS INC.; *U.S. Private*, pg. 4277
VICTORY MOTORCYCLES AUSTRALIA PTY LTD—See Polaris, Inc.; *U.S. Public*, pg. 1701
XTREME GREEN ELECTRIC VEHICLES INC.; *U.S. Private*, pg. 4583
Y INTERNATIONAL CO., LTD.—See The Riverside Company; *U.S. Private*, pg. 4110
ZAP; *U.S. Public*, pg. 2401

336992 — MILITARY ARMORED VEHICLE, TANK, AND TANK COMPONENT MANUFACTURING

ACHIDATEX NAZARETH ELITE (1977) LTD—See DEFENSE INDUSTRIES INTERNATIONAL, INC.; *Int'l*, pg. 2004
AMERICAN OVERSEAS MARINE CORPORATION—See General Dynamics Corporation; *U.S. Public*, pg. 915
AM GENERAL LLC—See MacAndrews & Forbes Incorporated; *U.S. Private*, pg. 2531
AM GENERAL LLC—See The Renco Group Inc.; *U.S. Private*, pg. 4104
ATK SPACE SYSTEMS INC.—See Northrop Grumman Corporation; *U.S. Public*, pg. 1540
BAE SYSTEMS GROUND SYSTEMS DIVISION—See BAE Systems plc; *Int'l*, pg. 797
BAE SYSTEMS LAND & ARMAMENTS INC.—See BAE Systems plc; *Int'l*, pg. 797
BAE SYSTEMS OMC—See BAE Systems plc; *Int'l*, pg. 796
BAE SYSTEMS—See BAE Systems plc; *Int'l*, pg. 796
BAE SYSTEMS STEEL PRODUCTS DIVISION—See BAE Systems plc; *Int'l*, pg. 797
BEIJING NORTH VEHICLE GROUP CORPORATION—See China North Industries Group Corporation; *Int'l*, pg. 1535
BHARAT DYNAMICS LIMITED; *Int'l*, pg. 1010
BINAS D.D.; *Int'l*, pg. 1033
CB-HDT HOLDINGS INC.—See Charlesbank Capital Partners, LLC; *U.S. Private*, pg. 855
CHESS DYNAMICS LIMITED—See Cohort plc; *Int'l*, pg. 1695
COORSTEK ARMOR SOLUTIONS, INC.—See CoorsTek, Inc.; *U.S. Private*, pg. 1043
DEFENSE VENTURE GROUP LTD.—See J.F. Lehman & Company, Inc.; *U.S. Private*, pg. 2163
DIEHL REMSCHEID GMBH & CO—See Diehl Stiftung & Co. KG; *Int'l*, pg. 2115
DIMO CORP.—See Acorn Growth Companies, LC; *U.S. Private*, pg. 63
DISTRIBUTION CONTROL SYSTEMS CARIBE, INC.—See ESCO Technologies, Inc.; *U.S. Public*, pg. 793
EURO-SHELTER SA—See GIAT Industries S.A.; *Int'l*, pg. 2962
FLYER DEFENSE, LLC—See Marvin Engineering Company, Inc.; *U.S. Private*, pg. 2598
FRAMECO AB—See Addtech AB; *Int'l*, pg. 133
GD ARABIA LTD—See General Dynamics Corporation; *U.S. Public*, pg. 913
GENERAL DYNAMICS COMBAT SYSTEMS GROUP—See General Dynamics Corporation; *U.S. Public*, pg. 913
GENERAL DYNAMICS EUROPEAN LAND SYSTEMS - AUSTRIA GMBH—See General Dynamics Corporation; *U.S. Public*, pg. 914
GENERAL DYNAMICS EUROPEAN LAND SYSTEMS - BRIDGE SYSTEMS GMBH—See General Dynamics Corporation; *U.S. Public*, pg. 914
GENERAL DYNAMICS EUROPEAN LAND SYSTEMS - DEUTSCHLAND GMBH—See General Dynamics Corporation; *U.S. Public*, pg. 914
GENERAL DYNAMICS EUROPEAN LAND SYSTEMS - FWW GMBH—See General Dynamics Corporation; *U.S. Public*, pg. 914
GENERAL DYNAMICS EUROPEAN LAND SYSTEMS GMBH—See General Dynamics Corporation; *U.S. Public*, pg. 914
GENERAL DYNAMICS EUROPEAN LAND SYSTEMS-STEYR—See General Dynamics Corporation; *U.S. Public*, pg. 914
GENERAL DYNAMICS LAND SYSTEMS INC.—See General Dynamics Corporation; *U.S. Public*, pg. 914
GENERAL DYNAMICS ORDNANCE AND TACTICAL SYSTEMS - SIMUNITION OPERATIONS, INC.—See General Dynamics Corporation; *U.S. Public*, pg. 915
GENERAL DYNAMICS OTS (DRI), INC.—See General Dynamics Corporation; *U.S. Public*, pg. 914
GENERAL DYNAMICS-OTS, INC.—See General Dynamics Corporation; *U.S. Public*, pg. 916
GLOBAL SUPPLY SOLUTIONS LLC; *U.S. Private*, pg. 1718
HARDWIRE LLC; *U.S. Private*, pg. 1864
HOWE & HOWE TECHNOLOGIES, INC.—See Textron Inc.; *U.S. Public*, pg. 2029
HUBEI JIANGSHAN HEAVY INDUSTRIES CO., LTD.—See China North Industries Group Corporation; *Int'l*, pg. 1535
IMCO INDUSTRIES LTD.; *Int'l*, pg. 3623
INDIGEN ARMOR, INC.—See J.F. Lehman & Company, Inc.; *U.S. Private*, pg. 2163

INRCORE, LLC—See The Jordan Company, L.P.; *U.S. Private*, pg. 4063
ITALTRACTOR ITM SPA—See Titan International, Inc.; *U.S. Public*, pg. 2160
IVECO DEFENCE VEHICLES SPA—See CNH Industrial N.V.; *Int'l*, pg. 1675
JOSEPH ASH LTD—See Hill & Smith PLC; *Int'l*, pg. 3391
LIAOSHEN INDUSTRIAL GROUP CO., LTD.—See China North Industries Group Corporation; *Int'l*, pg. 1535
MDT ARMOR CORPORATION—See Greenbriar Equity Group, L.P.; *U.S. Private*, pg. 1775
MEGGITT DEFENSE SYSTEMS, INC.—See Parker Hannifin Corporation; *U.S. Public*, pg. 1642
MOWAG GMBH—See General Dynamics Corporation; *U.S. Public*, pg. 914
NAVISTAR DEFENSE, LLC—See FreightCar America, Inc.; *U.S. Public*, pg. 885
NBC-SYS SAS—See GIAT Industries S.A.; *Int'l*, pg. 2962
NEXTER ROBOTICS—See GIAT Industries S.A.; *Int'l*, pg. 2962
OPTSYS SAS—See GIAT Industries S.A.; *Int'l*, pg. 2962
PATTONAIR—See Platinum Equity, LLC; *U.S. Private*, pg. 3207
PROTECTIVE PRODUCTS ENTERPRISES, INC.—See Sun Capital Partners, Inc.; *U.S. Private*, pg. 3860
SANTA BARBARA SISTEMAS S.A.—See General Dynamics Corporation; *U.S. Public*, pg. 914
SEEMANN COMPOSITES, INC.; *U.S. Public*, pg. 3598
SIOUX MANUFACTURING CORP.; *U.S. Private*, pg. 3671
TEN CATE ADVANCED ARMOUR DANMARK A/S—See ABN AMRO Group N.V.; *Int'l*, pg. 64
TEN CATE ADVANCED ARMOUR DANMARK A/S—See Gilde Buy Out Partners B.V.; *Int'l*, pg. 2974
TENCATE ADVANCED ARMOUR SASU—See ABN AMRO Group N.V.; *Int'l*, pg. 64
TENCATE ADVANCED ARMOUR SASU—See Gilde Buy Out Partners B.V.; *Int'l*, pg. 2974
TEN CATE ADVANCED ARMOUR UK LIMITED—See ABN AMRO Group N.V.; *Int'l*, pg. 64
TEN CATE ADVANCED ARMOUR UK LIMITED—See Gilde Buy Out Partners B.V.; *Int'l*, pg. 2974

336999 — ALL OTHER TRANSPORTATION EQUIPMENT MANUFACTURING

ADVANCED TRANSIT DYNAMICS, INC.—See Enpro Inc.; *U.S. Public*, pg. 775
AERO FASTENER CO., INC.; *U.S. Private*, pg. 118
AIXAM LUSITANA SOCIEDAD DE COMERCIALIZACAE DE AUTOMOVEIS, S.A.—See Polaris, Inc.; *U.S. Public*, pg. 1700
AIXAM-MEGA IBERICA, S.L.—See Polaris, Inc.; *U.S. Public*, pg. 1700
AIXAM MEGA ITALIA S.R.L.—See Polaris, Inc.; *U.S. Public*, pg. 1700
AIXAM MEGA NEDERLAND BV—See Polaris, Inc.; *U.S. Public*, pg. 1700
AIXAM MEGA S.A.S.—See Polaris, Inc.; *U.S. Public*, pg. 1700
ALBEMARLE MANAGEMENT (SHANGHAI) CO., LTD.—See Albemarle Corporation; *U.S. Public*, pg. 73
ALBERT ZIEGLER GMBH—See China International Marine Containers (Group) Co., Ltd.; *Int'l*, pg. 1510
ARCTIC CAT ESPANA S.L.—See Textron Inc.; *U.S. Public*, pg. 2028
ARCTIC CAT INC.—See Textron Inc.; *U.S. Public*, pg. 2028
ARDCO/TRAVERSE LIFT—See The Heico Companies, L.L.C.; *U.S. Private*, pg. 4050
ASTON MARTIN JAPAN GK—See Aston Martin Lagonda Global Holdings Plc; *Int'l*, pg. 655
AURRIGO PTE. LTD.—See Aurrigo International Plc; *Int'l*, pg. 714
AUTOMATIC EQUIPMENT MANUFACTURING CO.; *U.S. Private*, pg. 399
BECORIT GMBH—See Westinghouse Air Brake Technologies Corporation; *U.S. Public*, pg. 2357
BEIJING E-HUALU INFORMATION TECHNOLOGY CO., LTD.; *Int'l*, pg. 948
BEIJING JIAXUN FEIHONG ELECTRICAL CO., LTD.; *Int'l*, pg. 952
BOASSO GLOBAL, INC.—See KKR & Co. Inc.; *U.S. Public*, pg. 1241
BOMBARDIER EUROPEAN INVESTMENTS, S.L.—See Bombardier Inc.; *Int'l*, pg. 1104
BOMBARDIER MOTOR CORPORATION OF AMERICA—See Bain Capital, LP; *U.S. Private*, pg. 431
BOMBARDIER RECREATIONAL PRODUCTS, INC.—See Bain Capital, LP; *U.S. Private*, pg. 431
BOMBARDIER TRANSPORTATION BRASIL LTDA.—See Alstom S.A.; *Int'l*, pg. 382
BOMBARDIER TRANSPORTATION NORWAY AS—See Alstom S.A.; *Int'l*, pg. 382
BOMBARDIER TRANSPORTATION (OBSLUGA KLIENTA) POLSKA SP. Z.O.O.—See Alstom S.A.; *Int'l*, pg. 382
BOMBARDIER TRANSPORTATION POLSKA SP. Z.O.Q.—See Alstom S.A.; *Int'l*, pg. 383

BRP - FINLAND OY—See Bain Capital, LP; *U.S. Private*, pg. 431
BRP INC.—See Bain Capital, LP; *U.S. Private*, pg. 430
BRP US INC. - OUTBOARD ENGINE DIVISION—See Bain Capital, LP; *U.S. Private*, pg. 431
CAMEC PTY LTD—See Fleetwood Limited; *Int'l*, pg. 2699
CARDWELL WESTINGHOUSE CO.—See Westinghouse Air Brake Technologies Corporation; *U.S. Public*, pg. 2357
CEI EQUIPMENT COMPANY LLC—See Berkshire Hathaway Inc.; *U.S. Public*, pg. 299
CENTURY MATERIALS INC—See Nesbitt Investment Company; *U.S. Private*, pg. 2886
CEQUENT PERFORMANCE PRODUCTS - TRAILER DIVISION—See Crowne Group LLC; *U.S. Private*, pg. 1112
CHENGDU YUNDA TECHNOLOGY CO., LTD.; *Int'l*, pg. 1470
CIMC TRAILER POLAND SP. Z O.O.—See CIMC Vehicle (Group) Co., Ltd.; *Int'l*, pg. 1608
CIMC VEHICLE AUSTRALIA PTY LTD—See China International Marine Containers (Group) Co., Ltd.; *Int'l*, pg. 1511
CIMC VEHICLES SOUTH AFRICA (PTY) LTD.—See CIMC Vehicle (Group) Co., Ltd.; *Int'l*, pg. 1608
CLUB CAR, LLC—See Platinum Equity, LLC; *U.S. Private*, pg. 3202
CNR DALIAN LOCOMOTIVE RESEARCH INSTITUTE CO., LTD.—See CRRC Corporation Limited; *Int'l*, pg. 1858
COFREN S.R.L.—See Westinghouse Air Brake Technologies Corporation; *U.S. Public*, pg. 2357
COLUMBIA PARCAR CORP.—See Nordic Group of Companies, Ltd.; *U.S. Private*, pg. 2936
CONSOL MARINE TERMINALS LLC—See CONSOL Energy Inc.; *U.S. Public*, pg. 569
CRAFTSMAN EUROPE B.V.—See Craftsman Automation Limited; *Int'l*, pg. 1827
CRUISE CAR INC.; *U.S. Private*, pg. 1114
CS WIND CANADA INC.—See CS Wind Corporation; *Int'l*, pg. 1861
CS WIND CHINA CO., LTD.—See CS Wind Corporation; *Int'l*, pg. 1861
CS WIND MALAYSIA SDN. BHD.—See CS Wind Corporation; *Int'l*, pg. 1861
CS WIND TAIWAN LTD.—See CS Wind Corporation; *Int'l*, pg. 1861
CS WIND TURKEY IMALATI ENERJI VE CELIK SAN. TIC. A.S.—See CS Wind Corporation; *Int'l*, pg. 1861
CS WIND UK LIMITED—See CS Wind Corporation; *Int'l*, pg. 1861
CS WIND VIETNAM CO., LTD.—See CS Wind Corporation; *Int'l*, pg. 1861
DISCOUNT RAMPS.COM, LLC—See Rotunda Capital Partners LLC; *U.S. Private*, pg. 3488
DOPPELMAYR BRASIL SISTEMAS DE TRANSPORTE LTDA.—See Doppelmayr Group; *Int'l*, pg. 2174
DOPPELMAYR CABLE CAR GMBH—See Doppelmayr Group; *Int'l*, pg. 2174
DOPPELMAYR CHILE HOLDING SPA—See Doppelmayr Group; *Int'l*, pg. 2174
DOPPELMAYR COLOMBIA S.A.S.—See Doppelmayr Group; *Int'l*, pg. 2174
DOPPELMAYR INDIA PRIVATE LIMITED—See Doppelmayr Group; *Int'l*, pg. 2174
DOPPELMAYR MEXICO S.A. DE C.V.—See Doppelmayr Group; *Int'l*, pg. 2174
DOPPELMAYR PANAMA CORP.—See Doppelmayr Group; *Int'l*, pg. 2174
DOPPELMAYR PERU S.A.C.—See Doppelmayr Group; *Int'l*, pg. 2174
DOPPELMAYR PORTUGAL UNIPESSOLA, LDA.—See Doppelmayr Group; *Int'l*, pg. 2174
DOPPELMAYR SKIOALYFTUR EHF—See Doppelmayr Group; *Int'l*, pg. 2174
DOPPELMAYR SOUTH CAUCASUS—See Doppelmayr Group; *Int'l*, pg. 2174
DOPPELMAYR TURKEY ASANSOR TELEFERIK VE KABLOLU TASIYICI SISTEMLER INS. TAAH. LTD. STI.—See Doppelmayr Group; *Int'l*, pg. 2175
DOPPELMAYR USA, INC—See Doppelmayr Group; *Int'l*, pg. 2175
DOPPELMAYR VIETNAM CO. LTD.—See Doppelmayr Group; *Int'l*, pg. 2175
EGYPTIAN VEHICLES MANUFACTURING CO. S.A.E.—See Ghabbour Auto S.A.E.; *Int'l*, pg. 2958
E-Z-GO TEXTRON—See Textron Inc.; *U.S. Public*, pg. 2028
FAIVELEY TRANSPORT CZECH A.S—See Westinghouse Air Brake Technologies Corporation; *U.S. Public*, pg. 2357
F.I.P, PTY LTD—See Westinghouse Air Brake Technologies Corporation; *U.S. Public*, pg. 2357
FLEXQUBE EUROPE AB—See FlexQube AB; *Int'l*, pg. 2705
FLEXQUBE GMBH—See FlexQube AB; *Int'l*, pg. 2705
FLEXQUBE INC.—See FlexQube AB; *Int'l*, pg. 2705
FORD MOTOR COMPANY OF SOUTHERN AFRICA (PTY) LIMITED—See Ford Motor Company; *U.S. Public*, pg. 865
FOREST RIVER BUS, LLC—See Berkshire Hathaway Inc.; *U.S. Public*, pg. 305
FSP PTE LTD.—See Fujitec Co., Ltd.; *Int'l*, pg. 2831

FUJITEC SHANGHAI SOURCING CENTER CO., LTD.—See Fujitec Co., Ltd.; *Int'l*, pg. 2831
FUJITEC SHANGHAI TECHNOLOGIES CO., LTD.—See Fujitec Co., Ltd.; *Int'l*, pg. 2831
GARAVENTA SA—See Doppelmayr Group; *Int'l*, pg. 2175
GB IMPEX (PVT.) LIMITED—See Doppelmayr Group; *Int'l*, pg. 2175
GEMBALLA HOLDING SE; *Int'l*, pg. 2915
GENERAL DYNAMICS EUROPEAN LAND SYSTEMS - CZECH S.R.O.—See General Dynamics Corporation; *U.S. Public*, pg. 914
GE SWEDEN HOLDINGS AB—See General Electric Company; *U.S. Public*, pg. 919
GKN OFFHIGHWAY SYSTEMS LTD.—See GKN plc; *Int'l*, pg. 2985
GUJARAT APOLLO INDUSTRIES LIMITED; *Int'l*, pg. 3175
GURIT (ASIA PACIFIC) LTD.—See Gurit Holding AG; *Int'l*, pg. 3187
HIAB GERMANY GMBH—See Cargotec Corporation; *Int'l*, pg. 1328
HIND RECTIFIERS LIMITED; *Int'l*, pg. 3397
HITACHI RAIL EUROPE LTD.—See Hitachi, Ltd.; *Int'l*, pg. 3417
HORIZON GLOBAL CORPORATION—See Crowne Group LLC; *U.S. Private*, pg. 1112
HUAYU-COOPER STANDARD SEALING SYSTEMS CO., LTD.—See Cooper-Standard Holdings Inc.; *U.S. Public*, pg. 574
INVERSIONES DOPPELMAYR DE VENEZUELA C.A.—See Doppelmayr Group; *Int'l*, pg. 2175
KALMAR HEBEFAHRZEUGE HANDELSGESMBH—See Cargotec Corporation; *Int'l*, pg. 1327
LAG SERVICE POLSKA SP. Z O.O.—See CIMC Vehicle (Group) Co., Ltd.; *Int'l*, pg. 1608
LOGISNEXT HANDLING SYSTEM CORPORATION—See Hitachi Zosen Corporation; *Int'l*, pg. 3411
LTW INTRALOGISTICS GMBH—See Doppelmayr Group; *Int'l*, pg. 2175
MARMON TRANSPORTATION SERVICES & ENGINEERED PRODUCTS—See Berkshire Hathaway Inc.; *U.S. Public*, pg. 311
MARSHALL LETHLEAN INDUSTRIES PTY LTD—See China International Marine Containers (Group) Co., Ltd.; *Int'l*, pg. 1512
MICROPHOR—See Westinghouse Air Brake Technologies Corporation; *U.S. Public*, pg. 2358
MOBITEC BRASIL LTDA—See Audax Group, Limited Partnership; *U.S. Private*, pg. 389
MOBITEC GMBH—See Audax Group, Limited Partnership; *U.S. Private*, pg. 389
MOTIS BRANDS, INC.—See Prospect Hill Growth Partners, L.P.; *U.S. Private*, pg. 3288
NANTONG CIMC SPECIAL TRANSPORTATION EQUIPMENT MANUFACTURE CO., LTD.—See China International Marine Containers (Group) Co., Ltd.; *Int'l*, pg. 1512
NEW SOUTH EQUIPMENT MATS; *U.S. Private*, pg. 2906
NIVEL PARTS & MANUFACTURING COMPANY, LLC—See Morgan Stanley; *U.S. Public*, pg. 1474
NORWICH AERO PRODUCTS, INC.—See TransDigm Group Incorporated; *U.S. Public*, pg. 2180
OOZX TECHNO INC.—See Fuji Oozx Inc.; *Int'l*, pg. 2816
PATCO INDUSTRIES, INC.; *U.S. Private*, pg. 3105
PIONEER FRICTION LIMITED—See Westinghouse Air Brake Technologies Corporation; *U.S. Public*, pg. 2359
POLARIS DIRECT INC.—See Polaris, Inc.; *U.S. Public*, pg. 1700
POLARIS INDUSTRIES MANUFACTURING LLC—See Polaris, Inc.; *U.S. Public*, pg. 1700
POLARIS SALES INC.—See Polaris, Inc.; *U.S. Public*, pg. 1701
PROJECT 2000 S.R.L.—See LCI Industries; *U.S. Public*, pg. 1296
PT HANS R. JOST—See Doppelmayr Group; *Int'l*, pg. 2175
QINGDAO CIMC SPECIAL VEHICLE CO., LTD.—See CIMC Vehicle (Group) Co., Ltd.; *Int'l*, pg. 1608
RAILROAD FRICTION PRODUCTS CORPORATION—See Westinghouse Air Brake Technologies Corporation; *U.S. Public*, pg. 2359
RICH MARK ENGINEERING LIMITED.—See Fujitec Co., Ltd.; *Int'l*, pg. 2831
SCHAEFER EQUIPMENT, INC.—See Westinghouse Air Brake Technologies Corporation; *U.S. Public*, pg. 2359
SDC TRAILERS LTD.—See CIMC Vehicle (Group) Co., Ltd.; *Int'l*, pg. 1608
SEASUCKER; *U.S. Private*, pg. 3591
SHENZHEN CIMC WOOD CO., LTD.—See China International Marine Containers (Group) Co., Ltd.; *Int'l*, pg. 1512
SHOREPOWER TECHNOLOGIES, INC.; *U.S. Public*, pg. 1875
SHOWA ADOMINISTRACAO, SERVICOS E COMERCIO LTDA—See Hitachi Astemo, Ltd.; *Int'l*, pg. 3410
SHOWA DO BRASIL LTDA.—See Hitachi Astemo, Ltd.; *Int'l*, pg. 3410
SHOWA (GUANGZHOU) AUTO PARTS R&D CO., LTD.—See Hitachi Astemo, Ltd.; *Int'l*, pg. 3409
SIA BUCHER SCHOERLING BALTIC SA—See Bucher Industries AG; *Int'l*, pg. 1208

SNAP-ON EQUIPMENT GMBH—See Snap-on Incorporated; *U.S. Public*, pg. 1898
SNAP-ON EQUIPMENT INC.—See Snap-on Incorporated; *U.S. Public*, pg. 1898
SPECIAL METHODS & ENGINEERING TECHNIQUES SDN BHD—See Doppelmayr Group; *Int'l*, pg. 2175
STANDARD CAR TRUCK COMPANY—See Westinghouse Air Brake Technologies Corporation; *U.S. Public*, pg. 2359
TAP MANUFACTURING, LLC—See Polaris, Inc.; *U.S. Public*, pg. 1701
TAP WORLDWIDE, LLC—See Polaris, Inc.; *U.S. Public*, pg. 1701
TITAN FRANCE SAS—See Titan International, Inc.; *U.S. Public*, pg. 2160
TITAN ITALIA SPA—See Titan International, Inc.; *U.S. Public*, pg. 2160
TOC JIT INTERNATIONAL SERV S.R.L.—See Doppelmayr Group; *Int'l*, pg. 2175
TRANSTECH OF SC, INC.—See Westinghouse Air Brake Technologies Corporation; *U.S. Public*, pg. 2358
TRANSTEX LLC; *U.S. Private*, pg. 4211
TSUZUKI MANUFACTURING CO., LTD.—See Honda Motor Co., Ltd.; *Int'l*, pg. 3464
TTS HUA HAI AB—See Cargotec Corporation; *Int'l*, pg. 1329
TTS HUA HAI SHIPS EQUIPMENT CO., LTD.—See Cargotec Corporation; *Int'l*, pg. 1329
TTS MARINE AB—See Cargotec Corporation; *Int'l*, pg. 1329
TTS MARINE GMBH—See Cargotec Corporation; *Int'l*, pg. 1329
TTS MARINE S.R.L—See Cargotec Corporation; *Int'l*, pg. 1329
ULTIMATE SPORTS INC.; *U.S. Public*, pg. 2223
VAPOR EUROPE S.R.L.—See Westinghouse Air Brake Technologies Corporation; *U.S. Public*, pg. 2359
VAPOR RICON EUROPE LTD.—See Westinghouse Air Brake Technologies Corporation; *U.S. Public*, pg. 2359
VICTORY GROUND SUPPORT EQUIPMENT; *U.S. Private*, pg. 4378
VMS AIRCRAFT COMPANY, INC.—See ADDEV Material SAS; *Int'l*, pg. 128
WABCO LOCOMOTIVE—See Westinghouse Air Brake Technologies Corporation; *U.S. Public*, pg. 2359
WABTEC DE MEXICO, S. DE R.L. DE C.V.—See Westinghouse Air Brake Technologies Corporation; *U.S. Public*, pg. 2360
WABTEC PASSENGER TRANSIT—See Westinghouse Air Brake Technologies Corporation; *U.S. Public*, pg. 2359
WABTEC RAILWAY ELECTRONICS CORPORATION—See Westinghouse Air Brake Technologies Corporation; *U.S. Public*, pg. 2360
WILLIAMS GRAND PRIX ENGINEERING LIMITED—See Dorilton Capital Advisors LLC; *U.S. Private*, pg. 1263
WUXI TEXTRON SPECIALIZED VEHICLES CO., LTD.—See Textron Inc.; *U.S. Public*, pg. 2029
XINHUI CIMC SPECIAL TRANSPORTATION EQUIPMENT CO., LTD.—See China International Marine Containers (Group) Co., Ltd.; *Int'l*, pg. 1512

337110 — WOOD KITCHEN CABINET AND COUNTERTOP MANUFACTURING

ABC CABINETRY—See Bain Capital, LP; *U.S. Private*, pg. 450
AC PRODUCTS, INC.—See AIP, LLC; *U.S. Private*, pg. 133
AFG SCHWEIZ AG—See Arbonia AG; *Int'l*, pg. 537
ALLIKRISTE LLC; *U.S. Private*, pg. 192
ARAN WORLD S.R.L.—See Masco Corporation; *U.S. Public*, pg. 1391
ARMOIRES FABRITEC LTEE.-COOKSHIRE—See Armoires Fabritec Ltee.; *Int'l*, pg. 574
ARMOIRES FABRITEC LTEE.; *Int'l*, pg. 574
ARROWWOOD CABINETRY, INC.; *U.S. Private*, pg. 336
AYA KITCHENS & BATHS, LTD.; *Int'l*, pg. 773
BALLERINA-KUCHEN H.-E. ELLERSIEK GMBH; *Int'l*, pg. 809
BERTCH CABINET MANUFACTURING INC.; *U.S. Private*, pg. 539
BINA WAREHOUSE SDN. BHD.; *Int'l*, pg. 1033
BRANDOM CABINETS; *U.S. Private*, pg. 638
BRENTWOOD CORP.—See Quanex Building Products Corp.; *U.S. Public*, pg. 1750
BUSY BEE CABINETS, INC.; *U.S. Private*, pg. 696
CABINETRY BY KARMAN—See Wellborn Cabinet, Inc.; *U.S. Private*, pg. 4474
CANAC KITCHENS—See Kohler Company; *U.S. Private*, pg. 2339
CANDELL KITCHEN & BATH CABINETRY; *U.S. Private*, pg. 749
C & C RESOURCES INC.—See Callidus Capital Corporation; *Int'l*, pg. 1265
COPPES-NAPANEE CO.; *U.S. Private*, pg. 1045
COUNTERTOPS INC.; *U.S. Private*, pg. 1066
CRESTWOOD INC.; *U.S. Private*, pg. 1099
CRYSTAL CABINET WORKS, INC.; *U.S. Private*, pg. 1115
CUCINA BELLA S.A.; *Int'l*, pg. 1876
CUSTOM WOOD PRODUCTS INC.; *U.S. Private*, pg. 1130

N.A.I.C.S. Index

337110 — WOOD KITCHEN CABINE... CORPORATE AFFILIATIONS

DE PERE CABINET, INC.—See HCI Equity Management, L.P.; *U.S. Private*, pg. 1889
DESLAURIER CUSTOM CABINETS INC.; *Int'l*, pg. 2045
DEWILS INDUSTRIES; *U.S. Private*, pg. 1219
DIRECT CABINET SALES INC.—See Express Kitchens; *U.S. Private*, pg. 1451
DISTINCTIVE KITCHENS & BATHS, INC.—See The Sterling Group, L.P.; *U.S. Private*, pg. 4122
DUNCAN CREEK INC.—See Mason Companies, Inc.; *U.S. Private*, pg. 2602
DUTCH MADE; *U.S. Private*, pg. 1294
DYNASTY MODULAR FURNITURES PRIVATE LIMITED—See Dhabriya Polywood Limited; *Int'l*, pg. 2097
EBENISTERIE ST-URBAIN LTEE; *Int'l*, pg. 2284
EURO-RITE CABINETS LTD.—See Ebenisterie St-Urbain Ltee; *Int'l*, pg. 2285
EXECUTIVE CABINETRY,LLC; *U.S. Private*, pg. 1447
EXM MANUFACTURING LTD.; *Int'l*, pg. 2585
EXPRESS KITCHENS; *U.S. Private*, pg. 1451
FLOFORM COUNTERTOPS; *Int'l*, pg. 2707
FLOORABLE, LLC—See Live Ventures Incorporated; *U.S. Public*, pg. 1332
GARLAND WOODWORKS, INC.—See Prengler Products Corporation; *U.S. Private*, pg. 3252
GRANDVIEW PRODUCTS CO.; *U.S. Private*, pg. 1754
GREENELL CORP.; *U.S. Private*, pg. 1777
GREENLAM RUS LLC—See Greenlam Industries Limited; *Int'l*, pg. 3075
GROUPE VIAL SA; *Int'l*, pg. 3112
GUILDMASTER, INC.; *U.S. Private*, pg. 1814
HAAS CABINET CO. INC.; *U.S. Private*, pg. 1837
HABITAT; *Int'l*, pg. 3203
HAMPTON DISTRIBUTING CO.; *U.S. Private*, pg. 1851
HOWDEN JOINERY GROUP PLC; *Int'l*, pg. 3494
INFINITY DESIGN LLC—See CNC Associates NY Inc.; *U.S. Private*, pg. 952
KILLION INDUSTRIES INC.; *U.S. Private*, pg. 2304
KITCHEN KOMPACT, INC.; *U.S. Private*, pg. 2316
KITCHEN SUPPLIERS INCORPORATED; *U.S. Private*, pg. 2316
KITH KITCHENS, LLC—See Pfingsten Partners, LLC; *U.S. Private*, pg. 3164
KITH KITCHENS, LLC—See Promus Holdings, LLC; *U.S. Private*, pg. 3284
KRAFTMAID CABINETRY, INC.—See AIP, LLC; *U.S. Private*, pg. 133
KRAFTMAID CABINETRY—See AIP, LLC; *U.S. Private*, pg. 133
KYLE'S CUSTOM WOOD SHOP, INC.—See 1847 Holdings LLC; *U.S. Public*, pg. 2
LAMI WOOD PRODUCTS CORPORATION; *U.S. Private*, pg. 2380
LEEDO MANUFACTURING CO.; *U.S. Private*, pg. 2414
LESCARE KITCHENS INC.; *U.S. Private*, pg. 2432
MAAX BATH INC.—See American Bath Group; *U.S. Private*, pg. 224
MANTLE WHITE CABINET GROUP, INC.—See Mantle White Partnership; *U.S. Private*, pg. 2567
MANTLE WHITE PARTNERSHIP; *U.S. Private*, pg. 2567
MARSH FURNITURE COMPANY; *U.S. Private*, pg. 2591
MASCO BUILDER CABINET GROUP-MERILLAT, ATKINS PANEL PLANT—See AIP, LLC; *U.S. Private*, pg. 133
MASCO BUILDER CABINET GROUP-MERILLAT, JACKSON PLANT—See AIP, LLC; *U.S. Private*, pg. 133
MASCO BUILDER CABINET GROUP-MERILLAT, LAS VEGAS PLANT—See AIP, LLC; *U.S. Private*, pg. 133
MASCO BUILDER CABINET GROUP-MERILLAT, MOUNT JACKSON PLANT—See AIP, LLC; *U.S. Private*, pg. 133
MASCO CABINETRY, LLC—See AIP, LLC; *U.S. Private*, pg. 133
MASCO CORPORATION LIMITED—See Masco Corporation; *U.S. Public*, pg. 1391
MASCO RETAIL CABINET GROUP, LLC—See Masco Corporation; *U.S. Public*, pg. 1391
MASISA USA, INC.—See GrupoNueva S.A.; *Int'l*, pg. 3140
MASTERBRAND CABINET NHB INDUSTRIES LTD.—See MasterBrand, Inc.; *U.S. Public*, pg. 1394
MASTERBRAND CABINETS LLC - DECORA CABINETS—See MasterBrand, Inc.; *U.S. Public*, pg. 1394
MASTERBRAND CABINETS LLC—See MasterBrand, Inc.; *U.S. Public*, pg. 1394
MASTERCRAFT CABINETS, INC.—See Zurn Elkay Water Solutions Corporation; *U.S. Public*, pg. 2412
MASTERCRAFT INDUSTRIES, INC.; *U.S. Private*, pg. 2608
MEDALLION CABINETRY—See Zurn Elkay Water Solutions Corporation; *U.S. Public*, pg. 2412
METRO DOORS LTD.—See ASSA ABLOY AB; *Int'l*, pg. 638
MID-AMERICA CABINETS INC.; *U.S. Private*, pg. 2707
MID CONTINENT CABINETRY INC.—See MasterBrand, Inc.; *U.S. Public*, pg. 1394
MIDDLEBURY HARDWOOD PRODUCTS—See Patrick Industries, Inc.; *U.S. Public*, pg. 1653
MILLER MULTIPLEX DISPLAY FIXTURE CO.—See Miller Manufacturing, Inc.; *U.S. Private*, pg. 2735
MODERN WOODCRAFTS LLC; *U.S. Private*, pg. 2763
MOORES FURNITURE GROUP LTD.—See Masco Corporation; *U.S. Public*, pg. 1391
MOUSER CUSTOM CABINETRY LLC—See Pfingsten Partners, LLC; *U.S. Private*, pg. 3164
MOUSER CUSTOM CABINETRY LLC—See Promus Holdings, LLC; *U.S. Private*, pg. 3284
NEWELL RUBBERMAID JAPAN LTD.—See Newell Brands Inc.; *U.S. Public*, pg. 1514
NORCRAFT CANADA CORPORATION—See MasterBrand, Inc.; *U.S. Public*, pg. 1394
NORCRAFT COMPANIES, L.P.—See MasterBrand, Inc.; *U.S. Public*, pg. 1394
NORTHERN CONTOURS INC.—See Northern Contours Holding Corp.; *U.S. Private*, pg. 2952
THE O'BRIEN GROUP LIMITED—See Fletcher Building Limited; *Int'l*, pg. 2701
OLDCASTLE SURFACES, INC.—See CRH plc; *Int'l*, pg. 1848
OMEGA CABINETS, LTD.—See MasterBrand, Inc.; *U.S. Public*, pg. 1394
PACE INDUSTRIES INC.; *U.S. Private*, pg. 3063
PANELFOLD INC.; *U.S. Private*, pg. 3086
PATRICK INDUSTRIES, INC.; *U.S. Public*, pg. 1652
PLAIN 'N FANCY KITCHENS INC.; *U.S. Private*, pg. 3194
PRECISION COUNTERTOPS INC.; *U.S. Private*, pg. 3244
PRENGLER PRODUCTS CORPORATION; *U.S. Private*, pg. 3252
PROFILE CABINET & DESIGN; *U.S. Private*, pg. 3276
QUALITY CUSTOM CABINETRY INC.; *U.S. Private*, pg. 3318
REBORN CABINETS, INC.—See Audax Group, Limited Partnership; *U.S. Private*, pg. 389
REPUBLIC INDUSTRIES INC.; *U.S. Private*, pg. 3402
REPUBLIC NATIONAL CABINET CORPORATION—See The Cypress Group LLC; *U.S. Private*, pg. 4017
RIVERWOODS MILL, INC.; *U.S. Private*, pg. 3448
ROYAL INDUSTRIES, INC.; *U.S. Private*, pg. 3492
RTA CABINET STORE; *U.S. Private*, pg. 3498
SCHOTT VTF SAS—See Carl-Zeiss-Stiftung; *Int'l*, pg. 1337
SHAMROCK CABINET & FIXTURE CORP.; *U.S. Private*, pg. 3624
SHERIDAN FABRICATIONS LIMITED—See Howden Joinery Group Plc; *Int'l*, pg. 3494
SIMS-LOHMAN, INC.; *U.S. Private*, pg. 3669
SLEEK INTERNATIONAL PRIVATE LIMITED—See Asian Paints Limited; *Int'l*, pg. 619
SMART, LLC—See Blackbaud, Inc.; *U.S. Public*, pg. 341
SORRY ROBOTS LLC; *U.S. Private*, pg. 3716
SPECIAL PROJECTS DIVISION LLC—See BUILD LLC; *U.S. Private*, pg. 681
STARMARK CABINETRY—See MasterBrand, Inc.; *U.S. Public*, pg. 1394
SURFACE TECHNOLOGIES, INC.—See Facility Concepts Inc.; *U.S. Private*, pg. 1459
TEDD WOOD, INC.—See Executive Cabinetry,LLC; *U.S. Private*, pg. 1447
TENNSCO CORPORATION - PLANT 2—See Tennsco Corporation; *U.S. Private*, pg. 3968
TMLC SAFES, S.A. DE C.V.—See Fortune Brands Innovations, Inc.; *U.S. Public*, pg. 873
TOP MASTER, INC.—See O2 Investment Partners, LLC; *U.S. Private*, pg. 2982
TOP MASTER, INC.—See Oakland Standard Co., LLC; *U.S. Private*, pg. 2985
TRI-STAR CABINET & TOP CO.; *U.S. Private*, pg. 4223
UNITED CABINET COMPANY, LLC; *U.S. Private*, pg. 4288
VALLEY CABINET INC.; *U.S. Private*, pg. 4332
VICTORIA & ALBERT PRODUCTS PROPRIETARY LIMITED—See Fortune Brands Innovations, Inc.; *U.S. Public*, pg. 873
VT INDUSTRIES, INC.; *U.S. Private*, pg. 4415
VTI OF TEXAS INC.—See VT Industries, Inc.; *U.S. Private*, pg. 4415
V-T WEST INC.—See VT Industries, Inc.; *U.S. Private*, pg. 4415
WALZCRAFT INDUSTRIES INC.; *U.S. Private*, pg. 4435
WELLBORN CABINET, INC.; *U.S. Private*, pg. 4474
WELLBORN HOLDINGS INC.—See Wellborn Cabinet, Inc.; *U.S. Private*, pg. 4475
WESTMARK PRODUCTS, INC.; *U.S. Private*, pg. 4499
WEST-REEVES INC.; *U.S. Private*, pg. 4488
WILSONART AUSTRALIA PTY LTD—See AICA Kogyo Company, Limited; *Int'l*, pg. 229
WILSONART INTERNATIONAL, INC.—See Clayton, Dubilier & Rice, LLC; *U.S. Private*, pg. 930
WILSONART LLC - BOSTON—See Clayton, Dubilier & Rice, LLC; *U.S. Private*, pg. 930
WILSONART LLC—See Clayton, Dubilier & Rice, LLC; *U.S. Private*, pg. 930
WILSONART (SHANGHAI) CO., LTD.—See AICA Kogyo Company, Limited; *Int'l*, pg. 229
WILSONART (THAILAND) COMPANY LIMITED—See AICA Kogyo Company, Limited; *Int'l*, pg. 229
WM OHS INC.; *U.S. Private*, pg. 4552
THE WOLF ORGANIZATION, LLC; *U.S. Private*, pg. 4138
WOODCRAFTERS HOME PRODUCTS, LLC—See MasterBrand, Inc.; *U.S. Public*, pg. 1394
WOODCRAFT INDUSTRIES, INC.—See Quanex Building Products Corp.; *U.S. Public*, pg. 1750
WOODHARBOR MOLDING & MILLWORKS, INC.—See HCI Equity Management, L.P.; *U.S. Private*, pg. 1889
WOOD-MODE INCORPORATED; *U.S. Private*, pg. 4557
XEY CORP. EMPRESARIAL, S.L.—See Masco Corporation; *U.S. Public*, pg. 1391
YORKTOWNE, INC.—See Zurn Elkay Water Solutions Corporation; *U.S. Public*, pg. 2412
ZUHNE LLC; *U.S. Private*, pg. 4610

337121 — UPHOLSTERED HOUSEHOLD FURNITURE MANUFACTURING

AFG IMMOBILIEN AG—See Arbonia AG; *Int'l*, pg. 537
AIRMATE CHINA INTERNATIONAL LIMITED—See Airmate (Cayman) International Co. Limited; *Int'l*, pg. 248
AIRMATE E-COMMERCE (SHENZHEN) CO., LTD.—See Airmate (Cayman) International Co. Limited; *Int'l*, pg. 248
AIRMATE ELECTRICAL APPLIANCES (JIUJIANG) CO., LIMITED—See Airmate (Cayman) International Co. Limited; *Int'l*, pg. 248
AIRMATE INTERNATIONAL HOLDINGS LIMITED—See Airmate (Cayman) International Co. Limited; *Int'l*, pg. 248
THE ALAN WHITE COMPANY INC.; *U.S. Private*, pg. 3983
AMERICAN FURNITURE MANUFACTURING, INC.; *U.S. Private*, pg. 234
AMERICAN LEATHER OPERATIONS, LLC—See Heartwood Partners, LLC; *U.S. Private*, pg. 1901
ARTE DE MEXICO INCORPORATED; *U.S. Private*, pg. 340
A-ZENITH HOME FURNISHINGS CO., LTD.; *Int'l*, pg. 21
BASELINE SPORTS, INC.; *U.S. Private*, pg. 484
BASSETT FURNITURE CO.—See Bassett Furniture Industries, Incorporated; *U.S. Public*, pg. 279
BASSETT UPHOLSTERY DIVISION—See Bassett Furniture Industries, Incorporated; *U.S. Public*, pg. 279
BAUHAUS FURNITURE GROUP, LLC; *U.S. Private*, pg. 490
BEST CHAIRS INC.; *U.S. Private*, pg. 542
BLU DOT DESIGN & MANUFACTURING, INC.; *U.S. Private*, pg. 585
BRADINGTON-YOUNG LLC—See Hooker Furnishings Corporation; *U.S. Public*, pg. 1052
BRIGHOLME INTERIORS GROUP; *Int'l*, pg. 1161
BROOKLINE FURNITURE CO. LLC—See Heartwood Partners, LLC; *U.S. Private*, pg. 1901
CARLTON MANUFACTURING, INC.; *U.S. Private*, pg. 765
CARSONS INCORPORATED; *U.S. Private*, pg. 774
CARTER FURNITURE—See Tomlinson/Erwin-Lambeth, Inc.; *U.S. Private*, pg. 4184
CASSINA S.P.A.—See Haworth, Inc.; *U.S. Private*, pg. 1883
CENTURY FURNITURE INDUSTRIES—See CV Industries Inc.; *U.S. Private*, pg. 1132
CLASSIC LEATHER, INC.; *U.S. Private*, pg. 916
CLAUDE GABLE CO. INC.; *U.S. Private*, pg. 917
CLAYTON-MARCUS COMPANY, INC.—See Sun Capital Partners, Inc.; *U.S. Private*, pg. 3860
CLEVELAND CHAIR COMPANY—See Jackson Furniture Industries; *U.S. Private*, pg. 2176
COLLINS & HAYES FURNITURE LTD.—See Airsprung Group PLC; *Int'l*, pg. 248
COMPANIAS CIC SA; *Int'l*, pg. 1749
CORDAROY'S ORIGINALS, INC.; *U.S. Private*, pg. 1047
CRAFTMASTER FURNITURE CORP.; *U.S. Private*, pg. 1082
DESIGN STUDIO (HUIZHOU) HOME FURNISHING CO., LTD.—See Design Studio Group Ltd.; *Int'l*, pg. 2045
DFS FURNITURE LTD.; *Int'l*, pg. 2096
DIRECTIONAL FURNITURE—See Tomlinson/Erwin-Lambeth, Inc.; *U.S. Private*, pg. 4184
DISTINCTIVE DESIGNS FURNITURE, INC.; *Int'l*, pg. 2135
DMI SOURCING COMPANY, LLC—See Flexsteel Industries, Inc.; *U.S. Public*, pg. 853
DOGTAS KELEBEK MOBILYA SANAYI VE TICARET A.S.; *Int'l*, pg. 2154
DS FURNITURE MANUFACTURER SDN BHD—See Design Studio Group Ltd.; *Int'l*, pg. 2045
EIDAI VIETNAM CO., LTD.—See Eidai Co., Ltd.; *Int'l*, pg. 2328
E.J. VICTOR INC.; *U.S. Private*, pg. 1306
ENGERS KERAMIK GMBH & CO. KG—See Eczacibasi Holding A.S.; *Int'l*, pg. 2301
ENGLAND, INC.—See La-Z-Boy Incorporated; *U.S. Public*, pg. 1285
ETHAN ALLEN GLOBAL, INC.—See Ethan Allen Interiors Inc.; *U.S. Public*, pg. 797
ETHAN ALLEN INTERNATIONAL, BVBA—See Ethan Allen Interiors Inc.; *U.S. Public*, pg. 797
ETHAN ALLEN RETAIL, INC.—See Ethan Allen Interiors Inc.; *U.S. Public*, pg. 797
EUROSPAN HOLDINGS BERHAD; *Int'l*, pg. 2558
FAIRFIELD CHAIR COMPANY; *U.S. Private*, pg. 1463
FERDINAND LUSCH GMBH & CO. KG; *Int'l*, pg. 2637
FERGUSON COPELAND LLC—See Eighteen Seventy Corporation; *U.S. Private*, pg. 1347
FLEXSTEEL COMMERCIAL SEATING DIVISION—See Flexsteel Industries, Inc.; *U.S. Public*, pg. 853
FLEXSTEEL DUBLIN DIVISION—See Flexsteel Industries, Inc.; *U.S. Public*, pg. 853

337122 — NONUPHOLSTERED WOOD...

FLEXSTEEL INDUSTRIES, INC.; *U.S. Public*, pg. 853
FLEXSTEEL LANCASTER DIVISION—See Flexsteel Industries, Inc.; *U.S. Public*, pg. 853
FLEXSTEEL NEW PARIS DIVISION—See Flexsteel Industries, Inc.; *U.S. Public*, pg. 853
FOREMOST GROUPS, INC.; *U.S. Private*, pg. 1565
FOREMOST INTERNATIONAL LTD.—See Foremost Groups, Inc.; *U.S. Private*, pg. 1566
FRANKLIN CORPORATION; *U.S. Private*, pg. 1596
GRACE HOME FASHIONS LLC—See GHCL Limited; *Int'l*, pg. 2959
GRIBETZ INTERNATIONAL, INC.—See Leggett & Platt, Incorporated; *U.S. Public*, pg. 1302
HANCOCK & MOORE INC.; *U.S. Private*, pg. 1852
HANKOOK FURNITURE CO., LTD.; *Int'l*, pg. 3253
HEVEAPAC SDN. BHD.—See HeveaBoard Berhad; *Int'l*, pg. 3367
HICKORY CHAIR COMPANY—See Heritage Home Group, LLC; *U.S. Private*, pg. 1924
HILL CRAFT FURNITURE CO.; *U.S. Private*, pg. 1945
HOMERITZ CORPORATION BERHAD; *Int'l*, pg. 3455
HUGHES FURNITURE INDUSTRIES INC.; *U.S. Private*, pg. 2003
HWS COMPANY INC.—See Sherrill Furniture Company Inc.; *U.S. Private*, pg. 3634
INDIANA CHAIR FRAME—See Leggett & Platt, Incorporated; *U.S. Public*, pg. 1302
INTERIOR CRAFTS INC.; *U.S. Private*, pg. 2111
INTERLUDE HOME, INC.; *U.S. Private*, pg. 2112
ISENHOUR FURNITURE COMPANY; *U.S. Private*, pg. 2143
JACK CARTWRIGHT, INC.—See Boss Design Ltd.; *Int'l*, pg. 1117
JACKSON FURNITURE INDUSTRIES; *U.S. Private*, pg. 2176
JAMES MARTIN SIGNATURE VANITIES, LLC—See Ferguson plc; *Int'l*, pg. 2638
KAY UPHOSTERY; *U.S. Private*, pg. 2266
KINCAID FURNITURE COMPANY, INC.—See La-Z-Boy Incorporated; *U.S. Public*, pg. 1285
KINCAID UPHOLSTERY—See La-Z-Boy Incorporated; *U.S. Public*, pg. 1285
KING HICKORY FURNITURE COMPANY INC.; *U.S. Private*, pg. 2309
KLAUSSNER FURNITURE INDUSTRIES, INC.—See Monomoy Capital Partners LLC; *U.S. Private*, pg. 2772
KLOTE INTERNATIONAL CORP.; *U.S. Private*, pg. 2320
KRAVET CANADA—See Kravet, Inc.; *U.S. Private*, pg. 2350
KRAVET, INC.; *U.S. Private*, pg. 2350
KROEHLER FURNITURE MANUFACTURING COMPANY, INC.—See Schottenstein Stores Corporation; *U.S. Private*, pg. 3569
LABRUM AB—See ADDvise Group AB; *Int'l*, pg. 136
LANCER INC.—See Getinge AB; *Int'l*, pg. 2951
LANE FURNITURE INDUSTRIES—See Heritage Home Group, LLC; *U.S. Private*, pg. 1924
LANEVENTURE—See Heritage Home Group, LLC; *U.S. Private*, pg. 1924
LAZAR INDUSTRIES LLC; *U.S. Private*, pg. 2402
LA-Z-BOY INCORPORATED; *U.S. Public*, pg. 1284
LA-Z-BOY RESIDENTIAL—See La-Z-Boy Incorporated; *U.S. Public*, pg. 1285
LA-Z-BOY SOUTH—See La-Z-Boy Incorporated; *U.S. Public*, pg. 1285
LA-Z-BOY TENNESSEE—See La-Z-Boy Incorporated; *U.S. Public*, pg. 1285
LA-Z-BOY WEST—See La-Z-Boy Incorporated; *U.S. Public*, pg. 1285
LEE INDUSTRIES INC.; *U.S. Private*, pg. 2413
LEGGETT & PLATT INTERNATIONAL DEVELOPMENT CO.—See Leggett & Platt, Incorporated; *U.S. Public*, pg. 1303
LEWIS MITTMAN INC.; *U.S. Private*, pg. 2439
THE LOVESAC COMPANY; *U.S. Public*, pg. 2109
L&P INTERNATIONAL HOLDINGS COMPANY—See Leggett & Platt, Incorporated; *U.S. Public*, pg. 1302
L&P PROPERTY MANAGEMENT COMPANY—See Leggett & Platt, Incorporated; *U.S. Public*, pg. 1302
LZB FURNITURE GALLERIES OF ST. LOUIS, INC.—See La-Z-Boy Incorporated; *U.S. Public*, pg. 1285
MCCREARY MODERN INC.; *U.S. Private*, pg. 2631
MICHAEL THOMAS FURNITURE INC.; *U.S. Private*, pg. 2698
MIKROCOZE INC.; *U.S. Private*, pg. 2726
MITCHELL GOLD & BOB WILLIAMS—See Wafra Investment Advisory Group, Inc.; *U.S. Private*, pg. 4425
NAJARIAN FURNITURE COMPANY; *U.S. Private*, pg. 2831
NORTHFIELD METAL PRODUCTS LTD.—See Leggett & Platt, Incorporated; *U.S. Public*, pg. 1303
NORWALK CUSTOM ORDER FURNITURE; *U.S. Private*, pg. 2964
THE PEARSON COMPANY—See Heritage Home Group, LLC; *U.S. Private*, pg. 1924
PFC FURNITURE INDUSTRIES; *U.S. Private*, pg. 3164
POLTRONA FRAU S.P.A.—See Haworth, Inc.; *U.S. Private*, pg. 1883
PT. EIDAI INDUSTRIES INDONESIA—See Eidai Co., Ltd.; *Int'l*, pg. 2328
PUUR NV—See Colruyt Group N.V.; *Int'l*, pg. 1705

ROWE FURNITURE—See Sun Capital Partners, Inc.; *U.S. Private*, pg. 3860
SABA ITALIA S.R.L.—See Dexelance S.p.A.; *Int'l*, pg. 2092
SAM MOORE FURNITURE LLC—See Hooker Furnishings Corporation; *U.S. Public*, pg. 1052
SCREEN SOLUTIONS LTD.—See Gabriel Holding A/S; *Int'l*, pg. 2867
SEBEL FURNITURE HOLDINGS PTY LTD—See GWA Group Limited; *Int'l*, pg. 3190
SHERRILL FURNITURE COMPANY INC.; *U.S. Private*, pg. 3634
SOUTHERN FURNITURE COMPANY OF CONOVER INC.; *U.S. Private*, pg. 3732
SOUTHERN MOTION, INC.—See Gainline Capital Partners LP; *U.S. Private*, pg. 1635
SOUTHWOOD FURNITURE CORP.; *U.S. Private*, pg. 3742
STANFORD FURNITURE CORP.—See Gabriella White LLC; *U.S. Private*, pg. 1632
STEELCASE AG—See Steelcase Inc.; *U.S. Public*, pg. 1944
STEELCASE FURNITURE (DONGGUAN) COMPANY LIMITED—See Steelcase Inc.; *U.S. Public*, pg. 1944
STEELCASE S.A.—See Steelcase Inc.; *U.S. Public*, pg. 1944
STYLE-LINE FURNITURE INC.; *U.S. Private*, pg. 3846
TCL MANUFACTURING LTD.—See Fortune Brands Innovations, Inc.; *U.S. Public*, pg. 873
THERAPEDIC ASSOCIATES, INC.; *U.S. Private*, pg. 4142
TOMLINSON/ERWIN-LAMBETH, INC.; *U.S. Private*, pg. 4183
TRADITION HILTON HEAD, LLC—See Hilton Grand Vacations Inc.; *U.S. Public*, pg. 1040
TURRI S.R.L.—See Dexelance S.p.A.; *Int'l*, pg. 2092
UNITED FURNITURE INDUSTRIES; *U.S. Private*, pg. 4292
VANGUARD FURNITURE CO. INC.; *U.S. Private*, pg. 4343
VI-SPRING LTD.—See Flex Equipos de Descanso SA; *Int'l*, pg. 2701
WAON DEVELOPMENT LIMITED—See Airmate (Cayman) International Co. Limited; *Int'l*, pg. 248
WEIMAN—See Interlude Home, Inc.; *U.S. Private*, pg. 2112
WEIWU TECHNOLOGY (FOSHAN CITY) CO., LTD.—See Airmate (Cayman) International Co. Limited; *Int'l*, pg. 248
WOODHAVEN FURNITURE INDUSTRIES—See Aaron's Company, Inc.; *U.S. Public*, pg. 13
ZAPAROH S.P.Z O.O.—See Frasers Group plc; *Int'l*, pg. 2765

337122 — NONUPHOLSTERED WOOD HOUSEHOLD FURNITURE MANUFACTURING

ACCENT FURNITURE, INC.—See The Bedroom Store; *U.S. Private*, pg. 3992
ACEBED CO. LTD.; *Int'l*, pg. 95
AKIN COMPLETE FURNITURE; *U.S. Private*, pg. 145
AMERIWOOD INDUSTRIES, INC.—See Dorel Industries, Inc.; *Int'l*, pg. 2176
ARTHUR LAUER, INC.; *U.S. Private*, pg. 342
ASHLEY FURNITURE INDUSTRIES, INC.; *U.S. Private*, pg. 350
BAKER KNAPP & TUBBS INC.—See Kohler Company; *U.S. Private*, pg. 2339
BALTA FLOORCOVERING YER DOS, EMELERI SAN.VE TIC A.S.—See Balta Group NV; *Int'l*, pg. 811
BALTA ORIENT TEKSTIL SANAYI VE TICARET A.S.—See Balta Group NV; *Int'l*, pg. 812
BALTA USA, INC.—See Balta Group NV; *Int'l*, pg. 812
BASSETT FURNITURE INDUSTRIES, INCORPORATED; *U.S. Public*, pg. 279
BAUSMAN & COMPANY, INC.; *U.S. Private*, pg. 490
BDU NY, LLC—See Bassett Furniture Industries, Incorporated; *U.S. Public*, pg. 279
BERNHARDT FURNITURE COMPANY; *U.S. Private*, pg. 537
BLACK RED WHITE SA; *Int'l*, pg. 1059
THE BRICK SLIP BUSINESS LIMITED—See Brickability Group plc; *Int'l*, pg. 1151
BROYHILL FURNITURE INDUSTRIES, INC.—See Heritage Home Group, LLC; *U.S. Private*, pg. 1924
BUTTERFLY LIVING LLC—See Kids2, Inc.; *U.S. Private*, pg. 2303
CAROLINA BUSINESS FURNITURE, LLC; *U.S. Private*, pg. 767
CAROUSEL DESIGNS LLC—See Crown Crafts, Inc.; *U.S. Public*, pg. 596
CARPENTER TAN DEVELOPMENT COMPANY LIMITED—See Carpenter Tan Holdings Limited; *Int'l*, pg. 1343
CEFLA S.C. - MADRID PLANT—See Cefla S.C.; *Int'l*, pg. 1389
CEFLA S.C. - PARIS PLANT—See Cefla S.C.; *Int'l*, pg. 1389
CEFLA SOC. COOP. A R.L.—See Cefla S.C.; *Int'l*, pg. 1389
CHEREPOVETS PLYWOOD & FURNITURE PLANT, JSC; *Int'l*, pg. 1471
CHILD CRAFT INDUSTRIES, INC.; *U.S. Private*, pg. 882
CHROMCRAFT CORPORATION—See Sport Haley Holdings, Inc.; *U.S. Private*, pg. 3760
CHROMCRAFT REVINGTON, INC.—See Sport Haley Holdings, Inc.; *U.S. Private*, pg. 3760

CISCO BROS. CORP.; *U.S. Private*, pg. 900
CLIVE CHRISTIAN FURNITURE LIMITED; *Int'l*, pg. 1660
COCALO, INC.—See TG Valentine, LLC; *U.S. Private*, pg. 3979
CRAMCO INC.; *U.S. Private*, pg. 1084
CRAWFORD FURNITURE MANUFACTURING CORPORATION; *U.S. Private*, pg. 1086
CRESENT ENTERPRISES INC.; *U.S. Private*, pg. 1094
DESSIN/FOURNIR, INC.; *U.S. Private*, pg. 1215
DMI FURNITURE, INC.—See Flexsteel Industries, Inc.; *U.S. Public*, pg. 853
DOREL FRANCE S.A.—See Dorel Industries, Inc.; *Int'l*, pg. 2176
DUBOIS WOOD PRODUCTS INC.; *U.S. Private*, pg. 1283
DUNAV A.D.; *Int'l*, pg. 2225
EAST COAST FURNITECH PUBLIC COMPANY LIMITED; *Int'l*, pg. 2269
ELDIAR FURNITURE MANUFACTURING AND DECORATION L.L.C.—See Depa PLC; *Int'l*, pg. 2041
ELLO FURNITURE MANUFACTURING CO.; *U.S. Private*, pg. 1374
ENEX CO., LTD.; *Int'l*, pg. 2425
ENVIRONMENT FURNITURE, INC.—See Cisco Bros. Corp.; *U.S. Private*, pg. 900
EPI S.A.; *Int'l*, pg. 2460
ETC, ENVIRONMENTAL TEEN CONCEPTS—See Child Craft Industries, Inc.; *U.S. Private*, pg. 882
ETHAN ALLEN INTERIORS INC.; *U.S. Public*, pg. 797
FANCHER CHAIR CO. INC.—See Fancher Industries Inc.; *U.S. Private*, pg. 1472
FANCHER INDUSTRIES INC.; *U.S. Private*, pg. 1472
FEDERAL INTERNATIONAL HOLDINGS BERHAD; *Int'l*, pg. 2630
FILOMARKET S.R.L.—See Cefla S.C.; *Int'l*, pg. 1390
FUJIAN ZHANGPING KIMURA FORESTRY PRODUCTS CO., LTD.—See China Environmental Technology & Bioenergy Holdings Limited; *Int'l*, pg. 1500
GENERAL MILLS—See General Mills, Inc.; *U.S. Public*, pg. 921
GILBERT MARTIN WOODWORKING COMPANY, INC.; *U.S. Private*, pg. 1699
GOOD COMPANIES; *U.S. Private*, pg. 1737
GROUPE DUTAILIER INC.; *Int'l*, pg. 3102
GUANGZHOU HOLIKE CREATIVE HOME CO., LTD.; *Int'l*, pg. 3166
HANSSEM CO., LTD. - ANSAN PLANT 1—See Hanssem Co., Ltd.; *Int'l*, pg. 3261
HANSSEM CO., LTD. - ANSAN PLANT 2—See Hanssem Co., Ltd.; *Int'l*, pg. 3261
HANSSEM CO., LTD. - ANSAN PLANT 3—See Hanssem Co., Ltd.; *Int'l*, pg. 3261
HANSSEM CO., LTD. - SIHEUNG PLANT 1—See Hanssem Co., Ltd.; *Int'l*, pg. 3261
HANSSEM CO., LTD. - SIHEUNG PLANT 2—See Hanssem Co., Ltd.; *Int'l*, pg. 3261
HANSSEM CO., LTD.; *Int'l*, pg. 3261
HANSSEM CORPORATION - NEW JERSEY PLANT 2—See Hanssem Co., Ltd.; *Int'l*, pg. 3261
HANSSEM INC.—See Hanssem Co., Ltd.; *Int'l*, pg. 3261
HANSSEM (SHANGHAI) HOME FURNISHINGS CO., LTD.—See Hanssem Co., Ltd.; *Int'l*, pg. 3261
HARDEN FURNITURE INC.; *U.S. Private*, pg. 1862
HARDEN MANUFACTURING CORP.—See Linsalata Capital Partners, Inc.; *U.S. Private*, pg. 2463
HEKMAN FURNITURE COMPANY—See Howard Miller Company; *U.S. Private*, pg. 1995
HENREDON FURNITURE INDUSTRIES, INC.—See Heritage Home Group, LLC; *U.S. Private*, pg. 1924
HERITAGE BABY PRODUCTS LLC; *U.S. Private*, pg. 1922
HIGDON FURNITURE CO.; *U.S. Private*, pg. 1934
HI-LO INDUSTRIES INC.; *U.S. Private*, pg. 1932
HITCHCOCK CHAIR COMPANY LTD.; *U.S. Private*, pg. 1952
HOOKER FURNISHINGS CORPORATION; *U.S. Public*, pg. 1052
HUISEN HOUSEHOLD INTERNATIONAL GROUP LIMITED; *Int'l*, pg. 3526
HUNTLEIGH RENRAY LTD.—See Getinge AB; *Int'l*, pg. 2949
IDM HOME FURNISHINGS, INC.; *U.S. Private*, pg. 2038
INTERCON INC.; *U.S. Private*, pg. 2109
JOHNSTON-TOMBIGBEE FURNITURE MFG. CO.—See Lounora Industries Inc.; *U.S. Private*, pg. 2500
THE KARGES FURNITURE COMPANY, INC.; *U.S. Private*, pg. 4064
KINDEL FURNITURE COMPANY; *U.S. Private*, pg. 2306
LAFUMA MOBILIER SAS—See Calida Holding AG; *Int'l*, pg. 1264
LEGGETT & PLATT INDUSTRY (HUIZHOU) CO LTD—See Leggett & Platt, Incorporated; *U.S. Public*, pg. 1303
LEGGETT & PLATT (TAIZHOU) CO. LTD.—See Leggett & Platt, Incorporated; *U.S. Public*, pg. 1302
MARK WILKINSON FURNITURE LIMITED—See Canburg Limited; *Int'l*, pg. 1288
MCGUIRE FAMILY FURNITURE MAKERS; *U.S. Private*, pg. 2636
MERRY GARDEN (US) INC.—See China Environmental Technology & Bioenergy Holdings Limited; *Int'l*, pg. 1500

337122 — NONUPHOLSTERED WOOD...

MIKHAIL DARAFEEV INC.; *U.S. Private*, pg. 2726
MOBEL INCORPORATED; *U.S. Private*, pg. 2756
NICHOLS & STONE CO.—See L. & J.G. Stickley Inc.; *U.S. Private*, pg. 2364
NORDIC CARE AB—See Humana AB; *Int'l*, pg. 3530
NOVA LIFESTYLE, INC.; *U.S. Public*, pg. 1547
ORLEANS FURNITURE INC.; *U.S. Private*, pg. 3044
PETERS-REVINGTON CORP.—See Sport Haley Holdings, Inc.; *U.S. Private*, pg. 3760
PILLOW KINGDOM INC.—See Funiture Row LLC; *U.S. Private*, pg. 1623
PROGRESSIVE FURNITURE INC.; *U.S. Private*, pg. 3279
RICHARDSON INDUSTRIES, INC.; *U.S. Private*, pg. 3429
RIFAS UAB—See Harju Elekter AS; *Int'l*, pg. 3277
RIVERSIDE FURNITURE CORPORATION; *U.S. Private*, pg. 3445
ROCHELLE FURNITURE—See The Lightning Group, Inc.; *U.S. Private*, pg. 4070
THE ROMWEBER COMPANY; *U.S. Private*, pg. 4112
RUSH INDUSTRIES INC.; *U.S. Private*, pg. 3505
SAMUEL LAWRENCE FURNITURE—See Hooker Furnishings Corporation; *U.S. Public*, pg. 1052
SANDBERG FURNITURE MANUFACTURING CO.; *U.S. Private*, pg. 3543
SLEEPSAFE BEDS, LLC; *U.S. Private*, pg. 3688
SMALLBONE & CO (DEVIZES) LIMITED—See Canburg Limited; *Int'l*, pg. 1288
STAKMORE, INC.; *U.S. Private*, pg. 3776
STANDARD FURNITURE MANUFACTURING COMPANY INC.; *U.S. Private*, pg. 3778
STEIN WORLD OPERATING CO.—See ELK Group International, Inc.; *U.S. Private*, pg. 1362
TOKYO BED CO., LTD.—See FRANCE BED HOLDINGS CO. LTD.; *Int'l*, pg. 2759
TOYAMA JUKI CO., LTD.—See Daiken Corporation; *Int'l*, pg. 1931
TRENDWOOD INC.; *U.S. Private*, pg. 4218
VAUGHAN-BASSETT FURNITURE COMPANY INC.; *U.S. Private*, pg. 4348
VIRCO-CONWAY DIVISION—See VIRCO MFG. CORPORATION; *U.S. Public*, pg. 2299
WEBB FURNITURE ENTERPRISES INC.; *U.S. Private*, pg. 4464
WELLBORN FOREST PRODUCTS, INC.—See HCI Equity Management, L.P.; *U.S. Private*, pg. 1889
WESTERN DOVETAIL, INC.; *U.S. Private*, pg. 4492
WHALEN FURNITURE MANUFACTURING; *U.S. Private*, pg. 4503
WHITE LOTUS HOME; *U.S. Private*, pg. 4509
WHITEWOOD INDUSTRIES, INC.; *U.S. Private*, pg. 4512
WHITTIER WOOD PRODUCTS CO.; *U.S. Private*, pg. 4514
THE WINDWARD DESIGN GROUP, INC.; *U.S. Private*, pg. 4137

337126 — HOUSEHOLD FURNITURE (EXCEPT WOOD AND UPHOLSTERED) MANUFACTURING

5K YUZEY TEKNOLOJILERI A.S.—See Gentas AS; *Int'l*, pg. 2928
901D, LLC—See Curtiss-Wright Corporation; *U.S. Public*, pg. 611
AETHERTEK TECHNOLOGY CO., LTD.; *Int'l*, pg. 183
AIRSPRUNG FURNITURE LIMITED—See Airsprung Group PLC; *Int'l*, pg. 248
ALBER USA, LLC—See Invacare Corporation; *U.S. Private*, pg. 2130
ALNOX S.R.O.; *Int'l*, pg. 365
ALPHASON DESIGNS LIMITED—See Dorel Industries, Inc.; *Int'l*, pg. 2176
AMERICAN LOCKER COMPANY, INC.—See American Locker Group Incorporated; *U.S. Private*, pg. 240
AMISCO INDUSTRIES LTD.—See Gestion Martin Poitras Inc; *Int'l*, pg. 2946
ANTECO SA; *Int'l*, pg. 482
APIX INTERNATIONAL CO., LTD.—See Denkyo Group Holdings Co.,Ltd.; *Int'l*, pg. 2028
ASSOCIATED RACK CORPORATION; *U.S. Private*, pg. 357
BELL'O INTERNATIONAL CORP.—See Z Capital Group, LLC; *U.S. Private*, pg. 4595
BENICIA FOUNDRY & IRON WORKS INC.; *U.S. Private*, pg. 526
BENNER-NAWMAN INC.; *U.S. Private*, pg. 526
BURLINGTON BASKET CO.; *U.S. Private*, pg. 688
CARLISLE CORPORATION—See Carlisle Companies Incorporated; *U.S. Public*, pg. 436
CASUAL LIVING WORLD WIDE—See Littlejohn & Co., LLC; *U.S. Private*, pg. 2470
CESIMEX S.R.L.—See Grup Simex S.R.L.; *Int'l*, pg. 3115
CHENGDU QUSHUI SCIENCE & TECHNOLOGY CO., LTD.; *Int'l*, pg. 1468
CHINA BAOFENG (INTERNATIONAL) LTD.; *Int'l*, pg. 1485
CKF, INC.; *Int'l*, pg. 1639
CLEANUP CAREER SERVICE CO., LTD.—See Cleanup Corporation; *Int'l*, pg. 1656
CLEANUP CORPORATION - CRETE FACTORY—See Cleanup Corporation; *Int'l*, pg. 1656
CLEANUP CORPORATION - KASHIMA FACTORY—See Cleanup Corporation; *Int'l*, pg. 1656
CLEANUP CORPORATION - KASHIMA SYSTEM FACTORY—See Cleanup Corporation; *Int'l*, pg. 1656
CLEANUP CORPORATION - PROJECT SALES DIVISION—See Cleanup Corporation; *Int'l*, pg. 1656
CLEANUP CORPORATION; *Int'l*, pg. 1656
CLEANUP CORPORATION - YOTSUKURA FACTORY—See Cleanup Corporation; *Int'l*, pg. 1656
CLEANUP CORPORATION - YUMOTO FACTORY—See Cleanup Corporation; *Int'l*, pg. 1656
CLEANUP OKAYAMA INDUSTRIAL CO., LTD.—See Cleanup Corporation; *Int'l*, pg. 1656
CLEANUP OKAYAMA INDUSTRIAL CO., LTD. - TSUYAMA FACTORY—See Cleanup Corporation; *Int'l*, pg. 1656
CLEANUP STEEL PROCESSING CO., LTD.—See Cleanup Corporation; *Int'l*, pg. 1656
CLEANUP TECHNO SERVICE CO., LTD.—See Cleanup Corporation; *Int'l*, pg. 1656
COLEBROOK BOSSON SAUNDERS, LTD.—See Miller-Knoll, Inc.; *U.S. Public*, pg. 1446
CORSICAN FURNITURE, INC.; *U.S. Private*, pg. 1060
CREATIVE LEATHER FURNITURE INC.; *U.S. Private*, pg. 1089
CROSSWINDS FURNITURE COMPANY; *U.S. Private*, pg. 1108
DAKE OEM FURNITURE—See JSJ Corporation; *U.S. Private*, pg. 2241
DELTA DESIGNS LTD.—See Gilde Equity Management (GEM) Benelux Holding B.V.; *Int'l*, pg. 2975
DEXION COMMERCIAL (NEW ZEALAND) LIMITED—See Amotiv Limited; *Int'l*, pg. 431
DIONO, INC.; *U.S. Private*, pg. 1234
DOREL HOME FURNISHINGS, INC.—See Dorel Industries, Inc.; *Int'l*, pg. 2176
DWYER KITCHENS—See Dwyer Products Corporation; *U.S. Private*, pg. 1296
DWYER PRODUCTS CORPORATION; *U.S. Private*, pg. 1296
DYNASPAN FURNITURE SDN. BHD.—See Eurospan Holdings Berhad; *Int'l*, pg. 2558
ELICAMEX—See Elica S.p.A.; *Int'l*, pg. 2361
ELITE STORAGE SOLUTIONS INC.—See Nucor Corporation; *U.S. Public*, pg. 1553
EL RAN FURNITURE; *Int'l*, pg. 2341
ENGINEERED PRODUCTS LLC—See Gower Corporation; *Int'l*, pg. 1747
EVENFLO COMPANY, INC.—See Goodbaby International Holdings Limited; *Int'l*, pg. 3039
EXEL COMPOSITES (AUSTRALIA) PTY LTD—See Exel Composites Oyj; *Int'l*, pg. 2581
FALCON-BELMONT—See Whippoorwill Associates, Inc.; *U.S. Private*, pg. 4507
FASHION BED GROUP—See Leggett & Platt, Incorporated; *U.S. Public*, pg. 1302
FERMOB SA; *Int'l*, pg. 2639
FLANDERS INDUSTRIES, INC.; *U.S. Private*, pg. 1540
FORIS CORPORATION—See Haseko Corporation; *Int'l*, pg. 3283
FRAZIER INDUSTRIAL COMPANY INC.; *U.S. Private*, pg. 1600
FREDMAN BROS. FURNITURE COMPANY INC.; *U.S. Private*, pg. 1602
GABRIELLA WHITE LLC; *U.S. Private*, pg. 1632
GENMAR YAPI URUNLERI A.S.—See Gentas AS; *Int'l*, pg. 2928
GENSUN CASUAL LIVING; *U.S. Private*, pg. 1679
GLOBAL STEEL PRODUCTS CORPORATION—See ITR Industries Inc.; *U.S. Private*, pg. 2150
GOLDENHOME LIVING CO., LTD.; *Int'l*, pg. 3033
GROCLIN S.A.; *Int'l*, pg. 3087
GROUPE BERMEX INC.; *U.S. Private*, pg. 3092
GRUP SIMEX S.R.L.; *Int'l*, pg. 3115
GUANGDONG PIANO CUSTOMIZED FURNITURE CO., LTD.; *Int'l*, pg. 3158
THE GUTMANN COMPANY—See Elica S.p.A.; *Int'l*, pg. 2361
HAMILTON & SPILL LTD; *Int'l*, pg. 3237
HANDY STORE FIXTURES, INC.; *U.S. Private*, pg. 1853
HAR AS—See MillerKnoll; *U.S. Public*, pg. 1447
HARTMANN & FORBES; *U.S. Private*, pg. 1874
HAUTECOEUR FRANCE; *Int'l*, pg. 3285
HAY APS—See MillerKnoll; *U.S. Public*, pg. 1447
HAY INTERNATIONAL DE GMBH B.V.—See MillerKnoll, Inc.; *U.S. Public*, pg. 1447
HEARTHSTONE ENTERPRISES, INC.; *U.S. Private*, pg. 1899
H&H INDUSTRIAL CORPORATION; *U.S. Private*, pg. 1823
HIKARI FURNITURE CO., LTD.; *Int'l*, pg. 3389
HILLSDALE FURNITURE LLC—See Brookside International Incorporated; *U.S. Private*, pg. 665
HOMECREST OUTDOOR LIVING LLC; *U.S. Private*, pg. 1973
HOMEEASE INDUSTRIAL CO. LTD.; *Int'l*, pg. 3455
HUFCOR INCORPORATED—See OpenGate Capital Management, LLC; *U.S. Private*, pg. 3030
IGS STORE FIXTURES INC.; *U.S. Private*, pg. 2040
JACK-POST CORPORATION; *U.S. Private*, pg. 2175
JARDEN CORP.—See Newell Brands Inc.; *U.S. Public*, pg. 1515
JBC TECHNOLOGIES, INC.; *U.S. Private*, pg. 2193
KESSLER INDUSTRIES INC.; *U.S. Private*, pg. 2291
KNICKERBOCKER PARTITION CORPORATION; *U.S. Private*, pg. 2322
LEGGETT & PLATT - AMCO DIVISION—See Leggett & Platt, Incorporated; *U.S. Public*, pg. 1303
LEGGETT & PLATT, INC. - CHICAGO—See Leggett & Platt, Incorporated; *U.S. Public*, pg. 1303
LEGGETT & PLATT RESIDENCIAL, S. DE R.L. DE C.V.—See Leggett & Platt, Incorporated; *U.S. Public*, pg. 1303
LIGO PRODUCTS INC.; *U.S. Private*, pg. 2455
LLOYD/FLANDERS INDUSTRIES, INC.—See Flanders Industries, Inc.; *U.S. Private*, pg. 1540
LOZIER CORPORATION; *U.S. Private*, pg. 2506
MADIX INC.; *U.S. Private*, pg. 2544
MAGNECORP, INC.; *U.S. Private*, pg. 2547
MAITLAND-SMITH CEBU, INC.—See Heritage Home Group, LLC; *U.S. Public*, pg. 1924
MANTUA MANUFACTURING CO. INC.; *U.S. Private*, pg. 2567
MASCO CORPORATION; *U.S. Public*, pg. 1389
THE MCGUIRE FURNITURE COMPANY—See Kohler Company; *U.S. Private*, pg. 2340
MEADOWCRAFT, INC.; *U.S. Private*, pg. 2647
MEG—See Hirsh Industries, Inc.; *U.S. Private*, pg. 1951
MIDWEST WOODWORKING & FIXTURE CORP.; *U.S. Private*, pg. 2724
MINSON CORPORATION; *U.S. Private*, pg. 2744
MULTICENTER S.R.L.—See Einhell Germany AG; *Int'l*, pg. 2334
MURPHY BED CO., INC.; *U.S. Private*, pg. 2815
NAUGHTONE MANUFACTURING LTD.—See MillerKnoll, Inc.; *U.S. Public*, pg. 1447
NORD SIMEX S.R.L.—See Grup Simex S.R.L.; *Int'l*, pg. 3115
NOVUM MEDICAL PRODUCTS, INC.; *U.S. Private*, pg. 2968
PASLODE FASTENERS (SHANGHAI) CO., LTD.—See Illinois Tool Works Inc.; *U.S. Public*, pg. 1110
PI INC.; *U.S. Private*, pg. 3175
PJH GROUP LTD.—See Globe Union Industrial Corp.; *Int'l*, pg. 3007
POINT P—See Compagnie de Saint-Gobain SA; *Int'l*, pg. 1724
PREMIER METAL PRODUCTS CO.—See Pepco Manufacturing Company; *U.S. Private*, pg. 3143
PREMIUM SERVICE BRANDS LLC—See Susquehanna International Group, LLP; *U.S. Private*, pg. 3885
RAPID RACK INDUSTRIES INC.; *U.S. Private*, pg. 3356
REEVE STORE EQUIPMENT COMPANY; *U.S. Private*, pg. 3383
RICHARD SCHULTZ DESIGN, LLC—See MillerKnoll, Inc.; *U.S. Public*, pg. 1447
RIDG-U-RAK, INC.; *U.S. Private*, pg. 3432
RIO BRANDS, INC.—See Guardian Capital Partners, LLC; *U.S. Private*, pg. 1810
ROBERN, INC.—See Kohler Company; *U.S. Private*, pg. 2340
ROBERT LIGHTON FURNITURE, INC.; *U.S. Private*, pg. 3458
SAMSON PRODUCTS INC.—See Activar, Inc.; *U.S. Private*, pg. 68
SANDUSKY CABINETS INC.; *U.S. Private*, pg. 3545
SCUBAPRO/UWATEC FRANCE S.A.—See Johnson Outdoors Inc.; *U.S. Public*, pg. 1201
SHENYANG CLEANBIZ CO., LTD.—See Cleanup Corporation; *Int'l*, pg. 1656
SIMEX PLUS S.R.L.—See Grup Simex S.R.L.; *Int'l*, pg. 3115
SINGER INDUSTRIES (CEYLON) PLC—See Hayleys PLC; *Int'l*, pg. 3292
SMITH BROTHERS OF BERNE INC.; *U.S. Private*, pg. 3694
SOURCE OUTDOOR CORP.; *U.S. Private*, pg. 3718
SPECTRUM BRANDS CANADA, INC.—See Spectrum Brands Holdings, Inc.; *U.S. Public*, pg. 1916
STORE KRAFT MANUFACTURING CO; *U.S. Private*, pg. 3831
SWAIM INC.; *U.S. Private*, pg. 3889
SYCAMORE SYSTEMS, INC.—See Lyon & Dittrich Holding Company; *U.S. Private*, pg. 2522
T&D METAL PRODUCTS LLC; *U.S. Private*, pg. 3909
TECHNA CO. LTD.—See Hitachi, Ltd.; *Int'l*, pg. 3424
TELESCOPE CASUAL FURNITURE INC.; *U.S. Private*, pg. 3961
TIER-RACK CORPORATION; *U.S. Private*, pg. 4169
TRANSOLID, INC.—See TRM Inc.; *U.S. Private*, pg. 4241
TRIANGLE SYSTEMS INC.; *U.S. Private*, pg. 4226
TROPITONE FURNITURE COMPANY, INC.—See Littlejohn & Co., LLC; *U.S. Private*, pg. 2470
TS-LEAR AUTOMOTIVE (MALAYSIA) SDN. BHD.—See Lear Corporation; *U.S. Public*, pg. 1298
TVILUM—See Masco Corporation; *U.S. Public*, pg. 1391
UNIVERSAL DISPLAY & FIXTURES COMPANY INC.; *U.S. Private*, pg. 4304
UNIWEB INC.; *U.S. Private*, pg. 4310

N.A.I.C.S. INDEX

VIFAH MANUFACTURING COMPANY; *U.S. Private*, pg. 4381
VIKING METAL CABINET CO.—See Krueger International, Inc.; *U.S. Private*, pg. 2353
WESLEY ALLEN INC.; *U.S. Private*, pg. 4482
WESTERN PACIFIC STORAGE SYSTEMS INC.; *U.S. Private*, pg. 4495
WILLIAMSBURG FURNITURE INC.—See Patrick Industries, Inc.; *U.S. Public*, pg. 1653
WIRE WELD USA INC.; *U.S. Private*, pg. 4546
YINGKOU EBARA CO., LTD.—See Ebara Corporation; *Int'l*, pg. 2284

337127 — INSTITUTIONAL FURNITURE MANUFACTURING

ADDEN FURNITURE INC.; *U.S. Private*, pg. 77
ADELPHI PAPER HANGINGS LLC; *U.S. Private*, pg. 77
ALEXANDER SERVICES, LLC; *U.S. Private*, pg. 164
ARTCOBELL CORPORATION—See CounterPoint Capital Partners, LLC; *U.S. Private*, pg. 1066
ARTCO-BELL CORPORATION—See CounterPoint Capital Partners, LLC; *U.S. Private*, pg. 1066
BAKER COMPANY INC.; *U.S. Private*, pg. 455
BANGKOK DEC-CON PUBLIC COMPANY LIMITED; *Int'l*, pg. 833
BELVEDERE, LLC; *U.S. Private*, pg. 521
BLOCKHOUSE COMPANY, INC.; *U.S. Private*, pg. 583
BRODA ENTERPRISES, INC.—See Sorenson Capital Partners; *U.S. Private*, pg. 3715
BULL HEAD PRODUCTS INC.—See Ilustrato Pictures International Inc.; *Int'l*, pg. 3616
CAPSA SOLUTIONS LLC—See Levine Leichtman Capital Partners, LLC; *U.S. Private*, pg. 2435
CARROLL HEALTHCARE, INC.—See Invacare Corporation; *U.S. Private*, pg. 2130
CHAMPION MANUFACTURING, INC.—See DW Management Services, LLC; *Int'l*, pg. 2236
CHURCH CHAIR INDUSTRIES, INC.; *U.S. Private*, pg. 894
COMMERCIAL FURNITURE GROUP, INC. - FALCON PRODUCTS DIVISION—See Whippoorwill Associates, Inc.; *U.S. Private*, pg. 4506
COMMERCIAL FURNITURE GROUP, INC.—See Whippoorwill Associates, Inc.; *U.S. Private*, pg. 4506
DANT CLAYTON CORPORATION; *U.S. Private*, pg. 1157
DAUPHIN ESPANA S.A.—See Dauphin HumanDesign Group GmbH & Co. KG; *Int'l*, pg. 1983
DAUPHIN FRANCE S. A.—See Dauphin HumanDesign Group GmbH & Co. KG; *Int'l*, pg. 1983
DAUPHIN HUMANDESIGN AG—See Dauphin HumanDesign Group GmbH & Co. KG; *Int'l*, pg. 1983
DAUPHIN HUMANDESIGN BELGIUM NV/SA—See Dauphin HumanDesign Group GmbH & Co. KG; *Int'l*, pg. 1983
DAUPHIN HUMANDESIGN B.V.—See Dauphin HumanDesign Group GmbH & Co. KG; *Int'l*, pg. 1983
DAUPHIN ITALIA—See Dauphin HumanDesign Group GmbH & Co. KG; *Int'l*, pg. 1983
DAUPHIN OFFICE SEATING S.A. (PTY) LTD.—See Dauphin HumanDesign Group GmbH & Co. KG; *Int'l*, pg. 1983
DAUPHIN-RIM POLSKA SP. Z O.O.—See Dauphin HumanDesign Group GmbH & Co. KG; *Int'l*, pg. 1983
DAUPHIN SCANDINAVIA A/S—See Dauphin HumanDesign Group GmbH & Co. KG; *Int'l*, pg. 1983
DAUPHIN (SEA) PTE. LTD.—See Dauphin HumanDesign Group GmbH & Co. KG; *Int'l*, pg. 1982
DESIGN CONTEMPO INC.; *U.S. Private*, pg. 1213
DESIGN STUDIO GROUP LTD.; *Int'l*, pg. 2045
DIVERSIFIED WOODCRAFTS, INC.—See JBC Holding Co.; *U.S. Private*, pg. 2193
EARTHLITE, LLC—See Branford Castle, Inc.; *U.S. Private*, pg. 639
EPOXYN PRODUCTS LLC—See OpenGate Capital Management, LLC; *U.S. Private*, pg. 3030
ESA MCINTOSH LIMITED—See Havelock Europa PLC; *Int'l*, pg. 3287
FEDERAL FURNITURE (1982) SDN BHD—See Federal International Holdings Berhad; *Int'l*, pg. 2630
FELLFAB CORPORATION—See FELLFAB Limited; *Int'l*, pg. 2633
FIXTURES FURNITURE—See JSJ Corporation; *U.S. Private*, pg. 2241
FLY SRL; *Int'l*, pg. 2715
FOLDCRAFT COMPANY; *U.S. Private*, pg. 1557
FORBES INDUSTRIES, INC.—See Winsford II Corporation; *U.S. Private*, pg. 4543
GASSER CHAIR COMPANY INC.; *U.S. Private*, pg. 1648
GENERAL WOODWORKING INC.; *U.S. Private*, pg. 1668
GIBCA FURNITURE INDUSTRIES CO. LTD.—See GIBCA Limited; *Int'l*, pg. 2962
GMI COMPANIES, INC.; *U.S. Private*, pg. 1722
GT GRANDSTANDS, INC.—See Court Square Capital Partners, L.P.; *U.S. Private*, pg. 1070
HAMILTON SCIENTIFIC LLC—See OpenGate Capital Management, LLC; *U.S. Private*, pg. 3030

HAUSMANN INDUSTRIES, INC.—See Dynatronics Corporation; *U.S. Public*, pg. 700
HERMAN MILLER (AUSTRALIA) PTY., LTD.—See MillerKnoll, Inc.; *U.S. Public*, pg. 1447
HILL-ROM SERVICIOS S DE RL DE CV—See Baxter International Inc.; *U.S. Public*, pg. 283
HOA PHAT FURNITURE JSC—See Hoa Phat Group Joint Stock Company; *Int'l*, pg. 3435
HOWE A/S—See Whippoorwill Associates, Inc.; *U.S. Private*, pg. 4507
HUNT COUNTRY FURNITURE INC.; *U.S. Private*, pg. 2009
HUSSEY SEATING CO.; *U.S. Private*, pg. 2014
IMPERIAL WOODWORKS, INC.; *U.S. Private*, pg. 2049
IRWIN SEATING COMPANY INC.; *U.S. Private*, pg. 2142
IRWIN TELESCOPIC SEATING—See Irwin Seating Company Inc.; *U.S. Private*, pg. 2142
JBI, INC.; *U.S. Private*, pg. 2193
JL FURNISHINGS LLC; *U.S. Private*, pg. 2211
KEWAUNEE LABWAY ASIA PTE. LTD.—See Kewaunee Scientific Corporation; *U.S. Public*, pg. 1224
KEWAUNEE LABWAY INDIA PVT. LTD.—See Kewaunee Scientific Corporation; *U.S. Public*, pg. 1225
KEWAUNEE SCIENTIFIC CORPORATION INDIA PVT. LTD.—See Kewaunee Scientific Corporation; *U.S. Public*, pg. 1224
KEWAUNEE SCIENTIFIC CORPORATION; *U.S. Public*, pg. 1224
KNOLL, INC.—See MillerKnoll, Inc.; *U.S. Public*, pg. 1447
KNURR TECHNICAL FURNITURE GMBH—See Vertiv Holdings Co; *U.S. Public*, pg. 2289
LAB CRAFTERS INC.—See Huron Capital Partners LLC; *U.S. Private*, pg. 2012
LANDSCAPE FORMS, INC.; *U.S. Private*, pg. 2387
LEONARD PETERSON & CO., INC.; *U.S. Private*, pg. 2430
LISTA AG—See GreatStar Group Co., Ltd.; *Int'l*, pg. 3068
LISTA INTERNATIONAL CORPORATION—See Stanley Black & Decker, Inc.; *U.S. Public*, pg. 1935
LSI CORPORATION OF AMERICA, INC.—See Stevens Industries, Inc.; *U.S. Private*, pg. 3809
MAGIKITCH'N, INC.—See The Middleby Corporation; *U.S. Public*, pg. 2113
MODUFORM, INC.; *U.S. Private*, pg. 2763
NEMSCHOFF CHAIRS, INC.—See MillerKnoll, Inc.; *U.S. Public*, pg. 1447
NEMSCHOFF, INC.—See MillerKnoll, Inc.; *U.S. Public*, pg. 1447
NEW 24, INC—See Pinnacle Exhibits, Inc.; *U.S. Private*, pg. 3185
NYCOM INC.; *U.S. Private*, pg. 2976
PALMER SNYDER FURNITURE CO.; *U.S. Private*, pg. 3081
PANEL SPECIALISTS INC.—See Markel Group Inc.; *U.S. Public*, pg. 1369
PHONET & JOHNSON—See Whippoorwill Associates, Inc.; *U.S. Private*, pg. 4507
POLYVISION CORPORATION—See Industrial Opportunity Partners, LLC; *U.S. Private*, pg. 2067
POSH OFFICE SYSTEMS (HK) LTD.—See MillerKnoll, Inc.; *U.S. Public*, pg. 1447
RODET SAS—See Fermob SA; *Int'l*, pg. 2639
ROL-AWAY TRUCK MANUFACTURING CO. INC.—See The Cutler Corporation; *U.S. Private*, pg. 4017
SAGUS INTERNATIONAL LLC; *U.S. Private*, pg. 3528
SAUDER MANUFACTURING COMPANY—See Sauder Woodworking Co.; *U.S. Private*, pg. 3554
SAUDER WOODWORKING CO.; *U.S. Private*, pg. 3554
SCHOLAR CRAFT PRODUCTS, INC.; *U.S. Private*, pg. 3567
SCHROER MANUFACTURING COMPANY—See Midmark Corporation; *U.S. Private*, pg. 2716
SEATS INCORPORATED—See Nordic Group of Companies, Ltd.; *U.S. Private*, pg. 2937
SEBEL FURNITURE LTD.—See Krueger International, Inc.; *U.S. Private*, pg. 2353
SHAFER COMMERCIAL SEATING INC.; *U.S. Private*, pg. 3623
SHELBY WILLIAMS INDUSTRIES, INC.—See Whippoorwill Associates, Inc.; *U.S. Private*, pg. 4507
SHELDON LABORATORY SYSTEMS INC.—See MISSCO Contract Sales; *U.S. Private*, pg. 2747
SICO INCORPORATED; *U.S. Private*, pg. 3645
SICO JAPAN INC.—See Sico Incorporated; *U.S. Private*, pg. 3645
SICO NORTH AMERICA INC.—See Sico Incorporated; *U.S. Private*, pg. 3645
SMITH SYSTEM MANUFACTURING COMPANY—See Steelcase Inc.; *U.S. Public*, pg. 1944
SPACESAVER CORPORATION—See Krueger International, Inc.; *U.S. Private*, pg. 2353
SPECTRUM INDUSTRIES, INC.; *U.S. Private*, pg. 3753
STEELCASE HEALTH—See Steelcase Inc.; *U.S. Public*, pg. 1944
STREET FURNITURE (NSW) PTY LTD.—See iHeartMedia, Inc.; *U.S. Public*, pg. 1096
SYNSOR CORPORATION; *U.S. Private*, pg. 3904
TEACHERBOARDS (1985) LIMITED—See Havelock Europa PLC; *Int'l*, pg. 3287
TECHNOLOGICAL LABORATORY FURNITURE MANUFACTURER (LABTEC)—See Dubai Investments PJSC; *Int'l*, pg. 2219
TRENDLINE OFFICE INTERIORS LTD.—See Dauphin HumanDesign Group GmbH & Co. KG; *Int'l*, pg. 1983
UNITED METAL FABRICATORS, INC.; *U.S. Private*, pg. 4294
UNIVERSAL MANUFACTURING COMPANY; *U.S. Private*, pg. 4305
VERSARE SOLUTIONS, LLC—See WILsquare Capital LLC; *U.S. Private*, pg. 4532
VIP CINEMA, LLC; *U.S. Private*, pg. 4386
VIRCO MFG. CORPORATION; *U.S. Public*, pg. 2299
W.C. HELLER & CO.; *U.S. Private*, pg. 4419
WORDEN COMPANY; *U.S. Private*, pg. 4563

337211 — WOOD OFFICE FURNITURE MANUFACTURING

AC FURNITURE CO. INC.; *U.S. Private*, pg. 45
AF STEELCASE S.A.—See Steelcase Inc.; *U.S. Public*, pg. 1944
AIRBORNE—See FIMOPART Group; *Int'l*, pg. 2664
ALAN NUTTALL LTD.; *Int'l*, pg. 290
AL QURAISHI FURNITURE CORP.—See Ali Zaid Al-Quraishi & Brothers Co.; *Int'l*, pg. 323
BALATON BUTOR KFT.—See Fotex Holding SE; *Int'l*, pg. 2752
BIG CAMERA CORPORATION PCL; *Int'l*, pg. 1021
BOSS OFFICE PRODUCTS; *U.S. Private*, pg. 620
BRIMAR WOOD INNOVATIONS, INC.; *U.S. Private*, pg. 654
BUROSITZMOBELFABRIK FRIEDRICH- W. DAUPHIN GMBH & CO. KG—See Dauphin HumanDesign Group GmbH & Co. KG; *Int'l*, pg. 1982
CCN INTERNATIONAL INC.; *U.S. Private*, pg. 801
CLESTRA HAUSERMAN KOREA—See Clestra Hauserman S.A.; *Int'l*, pg. 1658
COALESSE—See Steelcase Inc.; *U.S. Public*, pg. 1944
CREATIVE OFFICE PAVILION LLC; *U.S. Private*, pg. 1089
DAI CHAU JSC; *Int'l*, pg. 1913
DAR/RAN FURNITURE INDUSTRIES; *U.S. Private*, pg. 1158
DATES WEISER FURNITURE CORP.—See MillerKnoll, Inc.; *U.S. Public*, pg. 1447
DAVID-EDWARD COMPANY LTD.; *U.S. Private*, pg. 1171
DAVIS FURNITURE, INC.; *U.S. Private*, pg. 1173
DECOR-REST FURNITURE LTD.; *Int'l*, pg. 2001
DELAGRAVE SA; *Int'l*, pg. 2010
DESIGN OPTIONS; *U.S. Private*, pg. 1214
EURO HOLDINGS BERHAD; *Int'l*, pg. 2531
FABRYKI MEBLI FORTE S.A.; *Int'l*, pg. 2600
FALCON DE JUAREZ, S.A. DE C.V.— See Whippoorwill Associates, Inc.; *U.S. Private*, pg. 4506
F.E. HALE MANUFACTURING COMPANY; *U.S. Private*, pg. 1456
FRANK CHERVAN INC.; *U.S. Private*, pg. 1594
FULLY, LLC—See MillerKnoll, Inc.; *U.S. Public*, pg. 1447
GEIGER INTERNATIONAL—See MillerKnoll, Inc.; *U.S. Public*, pg. 1447
GPODS, INC.; *U.S. Private*, pg. 1748
GROUPE LACASSE INC.; *Int'l*, pg. 3105
THE GUNLOCKE COMPANY—See HNI Corporation; *U.S. Public*, pg. 1043
HAMILTON SORTER, INC—See H.S. Morgan Limited Partnership; *U.S. Private*, pg. 1836
HARKEL OFFICE FURNITURE LTD.; *Int'l*, pg. 3277
HAWORTH HONG KONG LTD.—See Haworth, Inc.; *U.S. Private*, pg. 1883
HERMAN MILLER, LTD.—See MillerKnoll, Inc.; *U.S. Public*, pg. 1447
HERMAN MILLER MEXICO S.A. DE C.V.-MONTERREY—See MillerKnoll, Inc.; *U.S. Public*, pg. 1447
HERMAN MILLER MEXICO S.A. DE C.V.—See MillerKnoll, Inc.; *U.S. Public*, pg. 1447
HH RUSEAU, LLC—See MillerKnoll, Inc.; *U.S. Public*, pg. 1447
HICKORY BUSINESS FURNITURE—See HNI Corporation; *U.S. Public*, pg. 1043
HIGH POINT FURNITURE INDUSTRIES; *U.S. Private*, pg. 1936
HUMANSCALE CORPORATION; *U.S. Private*, pg. 2006
INDIANA FURNITURE INDUSTRIES, INC.; *U.S. Private*, pg. 2062
JASPER SEATING CO., INC., JSI DIVISION—See Jasper Seating Co., Inc.; *U.S. Private*, pg. 2190
JASPER SEATING CO., INC.; *U.S. Private*, pg. 2190
JASPER SEATING COMPANY—See Jasper Seating Co., Inc.; *U.S. Private*, pg. 2190
JOFCO INC.; *U.S. Private*, pg. 2219
JSJ FURNITURE CORPORATION—See JSJ Corporation; *U.S. Private*, pg. 2241
J SQUARED INC.; *U.S. Private*, pg. 2153
KIMBALL FURNITURE GROUP, LLC—See HNI Corporation; *U.S. Public*, pg. 1043
KIMBALL INTERNATIONAL, INC.—See HNI Corporation; *U.S. Public*, pg. 1043

337211 — WOOD OFFICE FURNITU...

KIMBALL OFFICE, INC. - BORDEN—See HNI Corporation; *U.S. Public*, pg. 1043
KIMBALL OFFICE, INC. - JASPER, 15TH STREET—See HNI Corporation; *U.S. Public*, pg. 1043
KIMBALL OFFICE, INC. - JASPER, CHERRY STREET—See HNI Corporation; *U.S. Public*, pg. 1043
KIMBALL OFFICE, INC. - POST FALLS—See HNI Corporation; *U.S. Public*, pg. 1043
KIMBALL OFFICE, INC. - SALEM—See HNI Corporation; *U.S. Public*, pg. 1043
KNURR LTDA.—See Vertiv Holdings Co; *U.S. Public*, pg. 2289
KOALA STUDIOS—See Tacony Corporation; *U.S. Private*, pg. 3921
KRUEGER INTERNATIONAL, INC.; *U.S. Private*, pg. 2353
LEGGETT & PLATT (GUANGZHOU) CO. LTD.—See Leggett & Platt, Incorporated; *U.S. Public*, pg. 1302
MARTIN UNIVERSAL DESIGN, INC.; *U.S. Private*, pg. 2596
MILLERKNOLL, INC.; *U.S. Public*, pg. 1446
MODULAR MANUFACTURING HOLDINGS; *U.S. Private*, pg. 2763
MONTBLEAU & ASSOCIATES INC; *U.S. Private*, pg. 2775
MUUTO A/S—See MillerKnoll, Inc.; *U.S. Public*, pg. 1447
NATIONAL OFFICE FURNITURE, INC. - FORDSVILLE—See HNI Corporation; *U.S. Public*, pg. 1043
NATIONAL OFFICE FURNITURE, INC. - JASPER, 11TH AVE—See HNI Corporation; *U.S. Public*, pg. 1043
NATIONAL OFFICE FURNITURE, INC. - SANTA CLAUS—See HNI Corporation; *U.S. Public*, pg. 1043
NEW MAVERICK DESK INC.—See H.S. Morgan Limited Partnership; *U.S. Private*, pg. 1836
NIENKAMPER FURNITURE & ACCESSORIES INC.—See ICF Group; *U.S. Private*, pg. 2031
NOVA SOLUTIONS INC.; *U.S. Private*, pg. 2966
OFFICEMAX CANADA—See The ODP Corporation; *U.S. Public*, pg. 2117
PAOLI LLC—See HNI Corporation; *U.S. Public*, pg. 1043
POLYREY BENELUX—See International Paper Company; *U.S. Public*, pg. 1157
RETAIL FIXTURE, LLC.; *U.S. Private*, pg. 3411
SAUDER RTA—See Sauder Woodworking Co.; *U.S. Private*, pg. 3554
SEBEL FURNITURE LIMITED (NZ)—See Krueger International, Inc.; *U.S. Private*, pg. 2353
SPINNEYBECK LIMITED—See MillerKnoll, Inc.; *U.S. Public*, pg. 1447
STEELCASE CZECH REPUBLIC S.R.O.—See Steelcase Inc.; *U.S. Public*, pg. 1944
STEELCASE DE MEXICO, S. DE R.L. DE C.V.—See Steelcase Inc.; *U.S. Public*, pg. 1944
STEELCASE WERNDL AG—See Steelcase Inc.; *U.S. Public*, pg. 1944
STEVENS INDUSTRIES, INC.; *U.S. Private*, pg. 3809
STONE CREEK FURNITURE INC.; *U.S. Private*, pg. 3818
STYLINE INDUSTRIES INC.; *U.S. Private*, pg. 3846
TUOHY FURNITURE CORPORATION; *U.S. Private*, pg. 4258
VIA, INC.—See Groupe Lacasse Inc.; *Int'l*, pg. 3105
WATSON FURNITURE GROUP, INC.; *U.S. Private*, pg. 4455
WYNNDEL BOX AND LUMBER CO. LTD.—See Canfor Corporation; *Int'l*, pg. 1291

337212 — CUSTOM ARCHITECTURAL WOODWORK AND MILLWORK MANUFACTURING

AMSTORE CORPORATION; *U.S. Private*, pg. 268
ARIZONA LEATHER COMPANY INC.; *U.S. Private*, pg. 324
ARRAY MARKETING GROUP INC.; *Int'l*, pg. 578
ASIAN PACIFIC TIMBER MARKETING PTY LTD; *Int'l*, pg. 618
ATELIER D'OEUVRES DE FORGE—See Ateliers Perrault Freres; *Int'l*, pg. 668
ATELIERS FERIGNAC SA—See Ateliers Perrault Freres; *Int'l*, pg. 668
ATELIERS PERRAULT FRERES; *Int'l*, pg. 668
BALS HONG KONG LIMITED—See BALS CORPORATION; *Int'l*, pg. 811
BIESSE MANUFACTURING CO. PVT. LTD.—See Biesse S.p.A.; *Int'l*, pg. 1020
BIGFORK CUSTOM WOODWORKS—See Martel Construction, Inc.; *U.S. Private*, pg. 2593
BISHOP FIXTURE AND MILLWORK; *U.S. Private*, pg. 565
BODEN STORE FIXTURES INC.; *U.S. Private*, pg. 608
BOISERIES RAYMOND INC; *Int'l*, pg. 1101
CONSTRUCTION SPECIALTIES AUSTRALIA PTY. LTD.—See Construction Specialties, Inc.; *U.S. Private*, pg. 1024
C/S CONSTRUCTION SPECIALTIES (MALAYSIA) SDN BHD—See Construction Specialties, Inc.; *U.S. Private*, pg. 1024
DAIKEN CO., LTD.; *Int'l*, pg. 1930
DAIKEN INDUSTRIES (NINGBO) CORPORATION—See Daiken Corporation; *Int'l*, pg. 1931
DAMI LLC—See Aaron's Company, Inc.; *U.S. Public*, pg. 13

DIC INTERIOR CO., LTD.—See DIC Corporation; *Int'l*, pg. 2108
DONG YI RI SHENG HOME DECORATION GROUP COMPANY LIMITED; *Int'l*, pg. 2164
ELIPTICON WOOD PRODUCTS, INC.; *U.S. Private*, pg. 1360
THE ENKEBOLL COMPANY; *U.S. Private*, pg. 4026
FIBRE-CROWN MANUFACTURING, INC.; *Int'l*, pg. 2653
FOREIGN TRADERS, INC.; *U.S. Private*, pg. 1565
GARMAN CABINET & MILLWORK, INC.; *U.S. Private*, pg. 1645
GARTNER STEEL AND GLASS GMBH—See Atlas Holdings, LLC; *U.S. Private*, pg. 377
GENESIS PRODUCTS, INC.; *U.S. Private*, pg. 1670
GILBERT DISPLAY INC.; *U.S. Private*, pg. 1698
GLOBAL TECH DESIGN PTE LTD.—See Atlas Holdings, LLC; *U.S. Private*, pg. 377
GOEBEL FIXTURE CO.; *U.S. Private*, pg. 1725
GOLDEN PHAROS BERHAD; *Int'l*, pg. 3030
GRAND EFFECTS, INC.—See The Carlyle Group Inc.; *U.S. Public*, pg. 2057
GREENLAM AMERICA, INC.—See Greenply Industries Limited; *Int'l*, pg. 3076
HARBOR INDUSTRIES INC.; *U.S. Private*, pg. 1859
HOLLMAN INC.; *U.S. Private*, pg. 1966
HUAHUI EDUCATION GROUP INC.; *Int'l*, pg. 3512
HUALI INDUSTRIES CO LTD; *Int'l*, pg. 3513
HUNTER DOUGLAS ALU - COIL OPERATIONS—See 3G Capital Partners L.P.; *U.S. Private*, pg. 11
HUNTER DOUGLAS ARCHITECTURAL PRODUCTS (BEIJING) CO., LTD.—See 3G Capital Partners L.P.; *U.S. Private*, pg. 11
HUNTER DOUGLAS ARCHITECTURAL PRODUCTS (CHINA) CO., LTD.—See 3G Capital Partners L.P.; *U.S. Private*, pg. 11
HUNTER DOUGLAS ARCHITECTURAL PRODUCTS (SHENZHEN) CO., LTD.—See 3G Capital Partners L.P.; *U.S. Private*, pg. 11
HUNTER DOUGLAS ARCHITECTURAL PRODUCTS XIAMEN—See 3G Capital Partners L.P.; *U.S. Private*, pg. 11
HUNTER DOUGLAS ARCHITECTURAL PROJECTS NL—See 3G Capital Partners L.P.; *U.S. Private*, pg. 11
HUNTER DOUGLAS ARCHITEKTUR-SYSTEME GMBH—See 3G Capital Partners L.P.; *U.S. Private*, pg. 11
HUNTER DOUGLAS ARGENTINA SA—See 3G Capital Partners L.P.; *U.S. Private*, pg. 11
HUNTER DOUGLAS BELGIUM ARCHITECTURAL PRODUCTS—See 3G Capital Partners L.P.; *U.S. Private*, pg. 11
HUNTER DOUGLAS BELGIUM N.V.—See 3G Capital Partners L.P.; *U.S. Private*, pg. 11
HUNTER DOUGLAS BENELUX—See 3G Capital Partners L.P.; *U.S. Private*, pg. 11
HUNTER DOUGLAS BULGARIA LTD—See 3G Capital Partners L.P.; *U.S. Private*, pg. 11
HUNTER DOUGLAS COMPONENTS—See 3G Capital Partners L.P.; *U.S. Private*, pg. 12
HUNTER DOUGLAS CROATIA—See 3G Capital Partners L.P.; *U.S. Private*, pg. 12
HUNTER DOUGLAS - CUSTOM SHUTTER DIVISION—See 3G Capital Partners L.P.; *U.S. Private*, pg. 13
HUNTER DOUGLAS CZECHIA NA—See 3G Capital Partners L.P.; *U.S. Private*, pg. 12
HUNTER DOUGLAS CZECHIA (SLOVAKIA) S.R.O.—See 3G Capital Partners L.P.; *U.S. Private*, pg. 12
HUNTER DOUGLAS ESPANA S.A—See 3G Capital Partners L.P.; *U.S. Private*, pg. 12
HUNTER DOUGLAS EUROPE—See 3G Capital Partners L.P.; *U.S. Private*, pg. 12
HUNTER DOUGLAS - HORIZONTAL BLINDS DIVISION—See 3G Capital Partners L.P.; *U.S. Private*, pg. 13
HUNTER DOUGLAS HUNGARY LTD—See 3G Capital Partners L.P.; *U.S. Private*, pg. 12
HUNTER DOUGLAS ITALY—See 3G Capital Partners L.P.; *U.S. Private*, pg. 12
HUNTER DOUGLAS LATINA AMERICA—See 3G Capital Partners L.P.; *U.S. Private*, pg. 12
HUNTER DOUGLAS (MALAYSIA) SDN. BHD.—See 3G Capital Partners L.P.; *U.S. Private*, pg. 11
HUNTER DOUGLAS MEXICO S.A. DE C.V.—See 3G Capital Partners L.P.; *U.S. Private*, pg. 12
HUNTER DOUGLAS MIDDLE EAST FZE—See 3G Capital Partners L.P.; *U.S. Private*, pg. 12
HUNTER DOUGLAS POLSKA SP. Z.O.O.—See 3G Capital Partners L.P.; *U.S. Private*, pg. 12
HUNTER DOUGLAS PRODUKTION GMBH—See 3G Capital Partners L.P.; *U.S. Private*, pg. 12
HUNTER DOUGLAS ROMANIA SRL—See 3G Capital Partners L.P.; *U.S. Private*, pg. 12
HUNTER DOUGLAS SERBIA—See 3G Capital Partners L.P.; *U.S. Private*, pg. 12
HUNTER DOUGLAS (THAILAND) CO LTD—See 3G Capital Partners L.P.; *U.S. Private*, pg. 11

HUNTER DOUGLAS TURKEY—See 3G Capital Partners L.P.; *U.S. Private*, pg. 12
HUNTER DOUGLAS VENEZUELA SA—See 3G Capital Partners L.P.; *U.S. Private*, pg. 12
HUNTER DOUGLAS - WINDOW DESIGNS DIVISION—See 3G Capital Partners L.P.; *U.S. Private*, pg. 13
IMPERIAL WOODWORKING COMPANY; *U.S. Private*, pg. 2049
IMPRESSIONS MARKETING GROUP INC; *U.S. Private*, pg. 2050
INAMI DAIKEN PRODUCTS CORPORATION—See Daiken Corporation; *Int'l*, pg. 1931
INNOVATIVE DISPLAYWORKS, INC.—See Oxford Financial Group Ltd.; *U.S. Private*, pg. 3057
INTERIOR ENVIRONMENTS, INC.; *U.S. Private*, pg. 2111
INTERMETRO DE MEXICO, S. DE R.L. DE C.V.—See Emerson Electric Co.; *U.S. Public*, pg. 750
JAHABOW INDUSTRIES INC.; *U.S. Private*, pg. 2182
JASCO INDUSTRIES INC.; *U.S. Private*, pg. 2189
JLE MANUFACTURING, INC.; *U.S. Private*, pg. 2212
JOSEF GARTNER & CO. UK LTD—See Atlas Holdings, LLC; *U.S. Private*, pg. 377
JOSEF GARTNER CURTAIN WALL (SUZHOU) CO. LTD—See Atlas Holdings, LLC; *U.S. Private*, pg. 377
LEIDEN CABINET CO.; *U.S. Private*, pg. 2419
L. & J.G. STICKLEY INC.; *U.S. Private*, pg. 2364
LYNDAN, INC.; *U.S. Private*, pg. 2521
MASS MEDICAL STORAGE, LLC—See Levine Leichtman Capital Partners, LLC; *U.S. Private*, pg. 2435
MILLER MANUFACTURING, INC.; *U.S. Private*, pg. 2735
MILL-RITE WOODWORKING COMPANY, INC.; *U.S. Private*, pg. 2730
MURASPEC DECORATIVE SOLUTIONS LIMITED—See a2e Venture Catalysts Limited; *Int'l*, pg. 30
PACIFIC COLUMNS, INC.; *U.S. Private*, pg. 3066
PANEL PROCESSING, INC.; *U.S. Private*, pg. 3086
PERMASTEELISA ESPANA S.A.U—See Atlas Holdings, LLC; *U.S. Private*, pg. 377
PERMASTEELISA FRANCE S.A.S.—See Atlas Holdings, LLC; *U.S. Private*, pg. 377
PERMASTEELISA IMPIANTI S.R.L.- FCC PLANTERM DIVISION—See Atlas Holdings, LLC; *U.S. Private*, pg. 377
PERMASTEELISA (INDIA) PRIVATE LIMITED—See Atlas Holdings, LLC; *U.S. Private*, pg. 378
PERMASTEELISA INTERIORS S.R.L.—See Atlas Holdings, LLC; *U.S. Private*, pg. 377
PERMASTEELISA IRELAND LTD.—See Atlas Holdings, LLC; *U.S. Private*, pg. 377
PERMASTEELISA TAIWAN LTD.—See Atlas Holdings, LLC; *U.S. Public*, pg. 378
PERMASTEELISA UK LTD.—See Atlas Holdings, LLC; *U.S. Private*, pg. 378
PERMASTEELISA (VICTORIA) PTY LTD.—See Atlas Holdings, LLC; *U.S. Private*, pg. 377
PHOENIX RETAIL GROUP; *U.S. Private*, pg. 3173
SCHELDEBOUW B.V.—See Atlas Holdings, LLC; *U.S. Private*, pg. 378
SPECIALTY WOOD MANUFACTURING INC.—See Bargreen-Ellingson Inc.; *U.S. Private*, pg. 474
STAINLESS METALCRAFT (CHATTERIS) LIMITED—See Avingtrans plc; *Int'l*, pg. 744
STRUCTURAL CONCEPTS CORPORATION—See Mason Wells, Inc.; *U.S. Private*, pg. 2602
T.J. HALE COMPANY INC.; *U.S. Private*, pg. 3912
ULTRAFRAME (UK) LTD.—See Epwin Group Plc; *Int'l*, pg. 2466
WADDELL DISPLAY CASES—See GMi Companies, Inc.; *U.S. Private*, pg. 1722
WALTER E. SMITHE FURNITURE INC.; *U.S. Private*, pg. 4433
WISCONSIN BUILT INC.; *U.S. Private*, pg. 4548

337214 — OFFICE FURNITURE (EXCEPT WOOD) MANUFACTURING

ABCO OFFICE FURNITURE—See JSJ Corporation; *U.S. Private*, pg. 2241
AFFORDABLE INTERIOR SYSTEMS, INC.—See Audax Group, Limited Partnership; *U.S. Private*, pg. 386
ALEXIS MANUFACTURING CO.—See Roll & Hill, LLC; *U.S. Private*, pg. 3474
ALLSTEEL INC.—See HNI Corporation; *U.S. Public*, pg. 1042
AMERICAN SEATING COMPANY; *U.S. Private*, pg. 247
ARGOSY CONSOLE, INC.; *U.S. Private*, pg. 322
ASPA BENELUX B.V.—See HAL Trust N.V.; *Int'l*, pg. 3223
AURORA OFFICE FURNITURE CO., LTD.—See Aurora Corporation; *Int'l*, pg. 713
BAKER MANUFACTURING COMPANY, INC.; *U.S. Private*, pg. 456
BEATTIES BASICS OFFICE PRODUCTS—See Beatties Basics; *Int'l*, pg. 933
BEATTIES BASICS; *Int'l*, pg. 933
BEIJING BBMG TIANTAN FURNITURE CO., LTD.—See BBMG Corporation; *Int'l*, pg. 920
BENE GMBH; *Int'l*, pg. 972

N.A.I.C.S. INDEX

BEOENTERIJER A.D.; *Int'l*, pg. 978
BEYOND THE OFFICE DOOR, LLC; *U.S. Private*, pg. 548
BKM OFFICEWORKS; *U.S. Private*, pg. 569
BOSS DESIGN LTD.; *Int'l*, pg. 1117
BP ERGO LIMITED—See HNI Corporation; *U.S. Public*, pg. 1042
BRODART CO. - CONTRACT FURNITURE DIVISION—See Brodart Co.; *U.S. Private*, pg. 661
BROWNBUILT PTY LIMITED—See Arrowcrest Group Pty. Ltd.; *Int'l*, pg. 580
BRYAST-D JSC; *Int'l*, pg. 1201
CHUO MALLEABLE IRON CO., LTD.; *Int'l*, pg. 1598
COALESSE—See Steelcase Inc.; *U.S. Public*, pg. 1944
COLEBROOK BOSSON SAUNDERS, PTY. LTD.—See MillerKnoll, Inc.; *U.S. Public*, pg. 1447
CONTRACT RESOURCE GROUP LLC—See HNI Corporation; *U.S. Public*, pg. 1043
DAIICHI SOGYO CO. LTD.; *Int'l*, pg. 1930
DROMEAS S.A; *Int'l*, pg. 2205
DUOBACK CO., LTD; *Int'l*, pg. 2227
ENGINEERED DATA PRODUCTS, LLC; *U.S. Private*, pg. 1398
ERCO INTERIEURBOUW B.V.; *Int'l*, pg. 2489
EURO CHAIRS MANUFACTURER (M) SDN BHD.—See Euro Holdings Berhad; *Int'l*, pg. 2531
EURO SPACE INDUSTRIES (M) SDN BHD—See Euro Holdings Berhad; *Int'l*, pg. 2531
EXEMPLIS LLC; *U.S. Private*, pg. 1448
FALCON-SOPRON BUTOR KFT.; *Int'l*, pg. 2610
FELLOWES IBERICA S.L.—See Fellowes, Inc.; *U.S. Private*, pg. 1494
FIRE KING SECURITY GROUP; *U.S. Private*, pg. 1511
FURSYS, INC.; *Int'l*, pg. 2846
GEORGIA CORRECTIONAL INDUSTRIES; *U.S. Private*, pg. 1684
GLOBAL INDUSTRIES INC.; *U.S. Private*, pg. 1714
GODREJ (MALAYSIA) SDN. BHD.—See Godrej & Boyce Mfg. Co. Ltd.; *Int'l*, pg. 3020
GODREJ (SINGAPORE) PTE. LTD.—See Godrej & Boyce Mfg. Co. Ltd.; *Int'l*, pg. 3020
GODREJ (VIETNAM) CO. LTD.—See Godrej & Boyce Mfg. Co. Ltd.; *Int'l*, pg. 3020
GPC INTERNATIONAL, INC.; *U.S. Private*, pg. 1748
GRENDENE ITALY S.R.L.—See Grendene S.A.; *Int'l*, pg. 3080
HALI BUROMOBEL GMBH; *Int'l*, pg. 3229
HARTER—See JSJ Corporation; *U.S. Private*, pg. 2241
HAWORTH BUROEINRICHTUNGEN GMBH—See Haworth, Inc.; *U.S. Private*, pg. 1883
HAWORTH FRANCE—See Haworth, Inc.; *U.S. Private*, pg. 1883
HAWORTH GMBH—See Haworth, Inc.; *U.S. Private*, pg. 1883
HAWORTH, INC.; *U.S. Private*, pg. 1883
HAWORTH PORTUGAL—See Haworth, Inc.; *U.S. Private*, pg. 1883
HAWORTH U.K. LTD.—See Haworth, Inc.; *U.S. Private*, pg. 1883
HENGLIN HOME FURNISHINGS CO., LTD.; *Int'l*, pg. 3346
HERMAN MILLER ASIA (PTE.) LTD.—See MillerKnoll, Inc.; *U.S. Public*, pg. 1447
HERMAN MILLER CANADA—See MillerKnoll, Inc.; *U.S. Public*, pg. 1447
HERMAN MILLER FURNITURE (INDIA) PVT. LTD.—See MillerKnoll, Inc.; *U.S. Public*, pg. 1447
HERMAN MILLER ITALIA S.P.A.—See MillerKnoll, Inc.; *U.S. Public*, pg. 1447
HERMAN MILLER JAPAN, LTD.—See MillerKnoll, Inc.; *U.S. Public*, pg. 1447
HIRSH INDUSTRIES DOVER DIVISION—See Hirsh Industries, Inc.; *U.S. Private*, pg. 1951
HIRSH INDUSTRIES, INC.; *U.S. Private*, pg. 1951
HIRSH INDUSTRIES LLC—See Hirsh Industries, Inc.; *U.S. Private*, pg. 1951
HNI ASIA L.L.C.—See HNI Corporation; *U.S. Public*, pg. 1043
HNI ASIA TECHNOLOGY SERVICES (SHENZHEN) LIMITED—See HNI Corporation; *U.S. Public*, pg. 1043
HNI CORPORATION; *U.S. Public*, pg. 1042
HNI OFFICE INDIA LTD.—See HNI Corporation; *U.S. Public*, pg. 1043
THE HON COMPANY, LLC—See HNI Corporation; *U.S. Public*, pg. 1043
THE HON CO.—See HNI Corporation; *U.S. Public*, pg. 1043
HOWE FURNITURE CORPORATION—See Whippoorwill Associates, Inc.; *U.S. Private*, pg. 4507
INVINCIBLE OFFICE FURNITURE; *U.S. Private*, pg. 2133
JETER SYSTEMS—See H.S. Morgan Limited Partnership; *U.S. Private*, pg. 1835
KINTEC-SOLUTION GMBH—See Leggett & Platt, Incorporated; *U.S. Public*, pg. 1302
KI (UK) LTD.—See Krueger International, Inc.; *U.S. Private*, pg. 2353
KNOLL INTERNATIONAL S.A.—See MillerKnoll, Inc.; *U.S. Public*, pg. 1447
KNOLL INTERNATIONAL S.A.—See MillerKnoll, Inc.; *U.S. Public*, pg. 1447

KNOLL INTERNATIONAL U.K. LTD.—See MillerKnoll, Inc.; *U.S. Public*, pg. 1447
KONINKLIJKE AHREND N.V.—See HAL Trust N.V.; *Int'l*, pg. 3223
LEGGETT & PLATT OFFICE COMPONENTS INTERNATIONAL S.R.L.—See Leggett & Platt, Incorporated; *U.S. Public*, pg. 1303
LEGGETT & PLATT OFFICE COMPONENTS, LLC—See Leggett & Platt, Incorporated; *U.S. Public*, pg. 1303
LUXOR CORP.—See EBSCO Industries, Inc.; *U.S. Private*, pg. 1325
THE MARVEL GROUP, INC.; *U.S. Private*, pg. 4075
MAYLINE COMPANY, LLC—See Liberty Diversified International Inc.; *U.S. Private*, pg. 2444
MERCHANTS OFFICE FURNITURE COMPANY; *U.S. Private*, pg. 2670
MERCURY MANUFACTURING CO. LTD.—See Godrej & Boyce Mfg. Co. Ltd.; *Int'l*, pg. 3021
MICHIGAN TUBE SWAGERS SEATING; *U.S. Private*, pg. 2701
MIDWEST FOLDING PRODUCTS—See Sagus International LLC; *U.S. Private*, pg. 3528
MITY ENTERPRISES, INC.—See Sorenson Capital Partners; *U.S. Private*, pg. 3715
MODERNFOLD, INC.—See dormakaba Holding AG; *Int'l*, pg. 2179
NEUTRAL POSTURE, INC.; *U.S. Private*, pg. 2891
OFFICE MASTER INC.; *U.S. Private*, pg. 3001
OFM, LLC—See HNI Corporation; *U.S. Public*, pg. 1043
PEAR, LLC—See Merchants Office Furniture Company; *U.S. Private*, pg. 2670
POLYVISION CORPORATION-BEAVERTON—See Industrial Opportunity Partners, LLC; *U.S. Private*, pg. 2067
PRESSEL VERSAND GMBH—See Sycamore Partners Management, LP; *U.S. Private*, pg. 3897
RECONDITIONED SYSTEMS, INC.; *U.S. Public*, pg. 1769
RICHARDS-WILCOX, INC.; *U.S. Private*, pg. 3429
ROSEMOUNT OFFICE SYSTEMS LLC—See Hillcrest Capital Partners LP; *U.S. Private*, pg. 1946
RUSS BASSETT CORP; *U.S. Private*, pg. 3505
SCHUKRA GERATEBAU GMBH—See Leggett & Platt, Incorporated; *U.S. Public*, pg. 1303
SENTRYSAFE—See Sentry Group, Inc.; *U.S. Private*, pg. 3610
SMEAD EUROPE BV—See Smead Manufacturing Company; *U.S. Private*, pg. 3693
STAPLES AUSTRIA GMBH—See Sycamore Partners Management, LP; *U.S. Private*, pg. 3897
STAPLES NORDIC AS—See Sycamore Partners Management, LP; *U.S. Private*, pg. 3898
STEELCASE CANADA LIMITED—See Steelcase Inc.; *U.S. Public*, pg. 1944
STEELCASE INC.; *U.S. Public*, pg. 1943
STEELCASE INC.—See Steelcase Inc.; *U.S. Public*, pg. 1944
STEELCASE JAPAN, K.K.—See Steelcase Inc.; *U.S. Public*, pg. 1944
STEELCASE SAS—See Steelcase Inc.; *U.S. Public*, pg. 1944
TAB CANADA—See H.S. Morgan Limited Partnership; *U.S. Private*, pg. 1835
TAB PRODUCTS EUROPE B.V.—See H.S. Morgan Limited Partnership; *U.S. Private*, pg. 1835
TECHO, A. S.—See HAL Trust N.V.; *Int'l*, pg. 3223
TENNSCO CORPORATION; *U.S. Private*, pg. 3968
TRANSCO UNION OFFICE; *U.S. Private*, pg. 4207
TRENDWAY CORPORATION—See Fellowes, Inc.; *U.S. Private*, pg. 1494
TURNSTONE—See Steelcase Inc.; *U.S. Public*, pg. 1944
VECTA—See Steelcase Inc.; *U.S. Public*, pg. 1944
WILSON OFFICE INTERIORS LLC—See HNI Corporation; *U.S. Public*, pg. 1043
WORKSTREAM INC.—See H.S. Morgan Limited Partnership; *U.S. Private*, pg. 1836

337215 — SHOWCASE, PARTITION, SHELVING, AND LOCKER MANUFACTURING

ACCESS DISPLAY GROUP INC.; *U.S. Private*, pg. 51
ACIAL SAS—See Blackstone Inc.; *U.S. Public*, pg. 348
AMERICAN DREW—See La-Z-Boy Incorporated; *U.S. Public*, pg. 1285
AMERICAN LOCKER GROUP INCORPORATED; *U.S. Private*, pg. 240
AMERICAN LOCKER SECURITY SYSTEMS, INC.—See American Locker Group Incorporated; *U.S. Private*, pg. 240
ARCHBOLD CONTAINER CORPORATION—See Green Bay Packaging Inc.; *U.S. Private*, pg. 1771
ARRAY MARKETING GROUP INC. - ARRAY BRADFORD FIXTURE DIVISION—See Array Marketing Group Inc.; *Int'l*, pg. 578
ARTISTIC FRAME CO., INC.; *U.S. Private*, pg. 343
AVERYS SA—See Blackstone Inc.; *U.S. Public*, pg. 348
BARTON STORAGE SYSTEMS LTD.; *Int'l*, pg. 870
BEST LOCKERS, LLC—See ASSA ABLOY AB; *Int'l*, pg. 640
BRUYNZEEL STORAGE SYSTEMS B.V.—See Gilde Equity

Management (GEM) Benelux Partners B.V.; *Int'l*, pg. 2975
CEFLA ARREDAMENTI GROUP—See Cefla S.C.; *Int'l*, pg. 1389
CLEMCO-ELITE STANDARD SYSTEMS LLC—See Reeve Store Equipment Company; *U.S. Private*, pg. 3384
CLESTRA HAUSERMAN S.A.; *Int'l*, pg. 1658
CLESTRA HAUSERMAN SWITZERLAND—See Clestra Hauserman S.A.; *Int'l*, pg. 1658
COMANY INC.; *Int'l*, pg. 1707
CONSTRUCTOR DANMARK A/S—See Corporacion Gestamp SL; *Int'l*, pg. 1804
CONSTRUCTOR DEXION FRANCE SARL—See Corporacion Gestamp SL; *Int'l*, pg. 1804
CONSTRUCTOR NORGE AS—See Corporacion Gestamp SL; *Int'l*, pg. 1804
CONSTRUCTOR SVERIGE AB—See Corporacion Gestamp SL; *Int'l*, pg. 1804
CORPORATE DISPLAY SPECIALTIES, INC.; *U.S. Private*, pg. 1054
CORSAIR DISPLAY SYSTEMS, LLC—See The Vollrath Company LLC; *U.S. Private*, pg. 4132
CSR FRICKER CEILING SYSTEMS QLD—See CSR Limited; *Int'l*, pg. 1867
CSR FRICKER CEILING SYSTEMS—See CSR Limited; *Int'l*, pg. 1867
D3, LLC—See Ardian SAS; *Int'l*, pg. 555
DEXION (AUSTRALIA) PTY. LTD.—See Corporacion Gestamp SL; *Int'l*, pg. 1804
DEXION COMINO LTD.—See Corporacion Gestamp SL; *Int'l*, pg. 1804
DEXION GMBH—See Corporacion Gestamp SL; *Int'l*, pg. 1804
DEXION KFT.—See Corporacion Gestamp SL; *Int'l*, pg. 1804
DEXION NV—See Corporacion Gestamp SL; *Int'l*, pg. 1804
DEXION S.R.O.—See Corporacion Gestamp SL; *Int'l*, pg. 1804
DIAM DISPLAY (CHINA) CO., LTD.—See Ardian SAS; *Int'l*, pg. 555
DISPLAY TECHNOLOGIES, LLC—See Berkshire Hathaway Inc.; *U.S. Public*, pg. 309
DISPLAY WAYS LTD.—See Foga System International AB; *Int'l*, pg. 2720
DORMA HUEPPE PTY. LTD.—See dormakaba Holding AG; *Int'l*, pg. 2177
DORMA HUPPE ASIA SDN. BHD.—See dormakaba Holding AG; *Int'l*, pg. 2177
DORMAKABA LUXEMBOURG S.A.—See dormakaba Holding AG; *Int'l*, pg. 2179
EBSCO INDUSTRIES, INC. - VULCAN INDUSTRIES DIVISION—See EBSCO Industries, Inc.; *U.S. Private*, pg. 1325
EDEN INDUSTRIES (UK) LIMITED—See Berkshire Hathaway Inc.; *U.S. Public*, pg. 311
EDSAL MANUFACTURING COMPANY, INC.—See Monomoy Capital Partners LLC; *U.S. Private*, pg. 2772
EQUIPTO, INC.—See Consolidated Storage Companies, Inc.; *U.S. Private*, pg. 1022
EUROFOGA S.L.—See Foga System International AB; *Int'l*, pg. 2720
EVENTWORKS INC.; *U.S. Private*, pg. 1437
FLORENCE CORPORATION—See Gibraltar Industries, Inc.; *U.S. Public*, pg. 936
FOGA BENELUX B.V.—See Foga System International AB; *Int'l*, pg. 2720
FOGA INTERIJERE D.O.O.—See Foga System International AB; *Int'l*, pg. 2720
FOGA POLEN SP. Z O.O.—See Foga System International AB; *Int'l*, pg. 2720
FOGA SYSTEM CORPORATION—See Foga System International AB; *Int'l*, pg. 2720
FOGA SYSTEM FRANCE S.A.R.L.—See Foga System International AB; *Int'l*, pg. 2720
FOGA SYSTEM GMBH—See Foga System International AB; *Int'l*, pg. 2720
FOGA SYSTEM INTERNATIONAL AB; *Int'l*, pg. 2720
FOGA SYSTEM SCANDINAVIA AB—See Foga System International AB; *Int'l*, pg. 2721
FRANCEBED SALES CO., LTD.—See FRANCE BED HOLDINGS CO. LTD.; *Int'l*, pg. 2759
HARTMANN TRESORE FRANCE S.A.R.L.—See HARTMANN TRESORE AG; *Int'l*, pg. 3280
HARTMANN TRESORE ITALIA SRL—See HARTMANN TRESORE AG; *Int'l*, pg. 3280
HARTMANN TRESORE MIDDLE EAST LLC—See HARTMANN TRESORE AG; *Int'l*, pg. 3280
HARTMANN TRESORE POLSKA SP. Z O.O.—See HARTMANN TRESORE AG; *Int'l*, pg. 3280
HARTMANN TRESORE SCHWEIZ AG—See HARTMANN TRESORE AG; *Int'l*, pg. 3280
HUNGSEO INDUSTRIAL CO., LTD.—See Foga System International AB; *Int'l*, pg. 2721
I JIANG INDUSTRIAL CO., LTD.; *Int'l*, pg. 3562
INSIGHT MERCHANDISING, INC.; *U.S. Private*, pg. 2086
JAMESTOWN ENTERTAINMENT; *U.S. Private*, pg. 2186
JSI STORE FIXTURES, INC.—See LSI Industries Inc.; *U.S. Public*, pg. 1344
KNAPE & VOGT MANUFACTURING COMPANY—See

337215 — SHOWCASE, PARTITION...

Wind Point Advisors LLC; *U.S. Private*, pg. 4534
LAUREL STEEL LIMITED—See Nucor Corporation; *U.S. Public*, pg. 1553
LEADER METAL INDUSTRY CO., LTD.—See Berkshire Hathaway Inc.; *U.S. Public*, pg. 311
LIST INDUSTRIES, INC.; *U.S. Private*, pg. 2466
LOZIER CORPORATION - SCOTTSBORO PLANT 1—See Lozier Corporation; *U.S. Private*, pg. 2506
LOZIER CORPORATION - SCOTTSBORO PLANT 2—See Lozier Corporation; *U.S. Private*, pg. 2506
METALUX—See Groupe SFPI SA; *Int'l*, pg. 3111
MG DESIGN ASSOCIATES CORP.; *U.S. Private*, pg. 2693
M. LAVINE DESIGN WORKSHOP; *U.S. Private*, pg. 2526
MUEBLES FINO BUENO S.A.—See Good Companies; *U.S. Private*, pg. 1737
NORKING ALUMINIUM LTD.—See Foga System International AB; *Int'l*, pg. 2721
PAN-OSTON CO.—See Houchens Industries, Inc.; *U.S. Private*, pg. 1990
PENCO PRODUCTS, INC.—See Summa Holdings, Inc.; *U.S. Private*, pg. 3852
POTTER INTERIOR SYSTEMS LTD.—See CSR Limited; *Int'l*, pg. 1867
PRESENCE FROM INNOVATION, LLC; *U.S. Private*, pg. 3254
RADIOSHACK STORE FIXTURES—See RS Legacy Corporation; *U.S. Private*, pg. 3496
READY METAL MANUFACTURING COMPANY; *U.S. Private*, pg. 3367
RELEC ELECTRONICS LTD.—See Ault Alliance, Inc.; *U.S. Public*, pg. 227
REPUBLIC STORAGE SYSTEMS, LLC—See Independence Capital Partners, LLC; *U.S. Private*, pg. 2057
RICHARDSON'S FURNITURE EMPORIUM—See Richardson Industries, Inc.; *U.S. Private*, pg. 3429
SAAR-LAGER-UND PROFILTECHNIK GMBH—See Blackstone Inc.; *U.S. Public*, pg. 348
SCRANTON PRODUCTS INC.—See The AZEK Company Inc.; *U.S. Public*, pg. 2035
SCREENFLEX PORTABLE PARTITION, LLC—See WILsquare Capital LLC; *U.S. Private*, pg. 4532
SECURITY MANUFACTURING CORP—See American Locker Group Incorporated; *U.S. Private*, pg. 240
SHANGHAI STOW STORAGE EQUIPMENT CO. LTD.—See Blackstone Inc.; *U.S. Public*, pg. 348
SHELFGENIE; *U.S. Private*, pg. 3631
SILVESTRI STUDIO INC.; *U.S. Private*, pg. 3664
SKYFOLD INC.—See dormakaba Holding AG; *Int'l*, pg. 2178
SPACESAVER STORAGE SOLUTIONS LLC; *U.S. Private*, pg. 3744
SPARTAN SHOWCASE, INC.—See Leggett & Platt, Incorporated; *U.S. Public*, pg. 1303
STANDARD DEPO VE RAF SISTEMLERI A.S.—See Blackstone Inc.; *U.S. Public*, pg. 348
STOW AUSTRIA GMBH—See Blackstone Inc.; *U.S. Public*, pg. 348
STOW CESKA REPUBLIKA S.R.O—See Blackstone Inc.; *U.S. Public*, pg. 348
STOW DEUTSCHLAND GMBH—See Blackstone Inc.; *U.S. Public*, pg. 348
STOW FRANCE S.A.S—See Blackstone Inc.; *U.S. Public*, pg. 348
STOW INTERNATIONAL NV—See Blackstone Inc.; *U.S. Public*, pg. 348
STOW NEDERLAND BV—See Blackstone Inc.; *U.S. Public*, pg. 348
STOW POLSKA SP. Z O.O.—See Blackstone Inc.; *U.S. Public*, pg. 348
SUPERMARKET SOURCE, INC.; *U.S. Private*, pg. 3881
THOMASVILLE FURNITURE INDUSTRIES, INC.—See Heritage Home Group, LLC; *U.S. Private*, pg. 1924
TONG LUNG METAL INDUSTRY CO., LTD.—See Stanley Black & Decker, Inc.; *U.S. Public*, pg. 1936
TRIAD MANUFACTURING, INC.; *U.S. Private*, pg. 4225
VOYAGER INC.; *U.S. Private*, pg. 4414
WENGER CORPORATION; *U.S. Private*, pg. 4481

337910 — MATTRESS MANUFACTURING

ACEBED CO. LTD. - GUANGZHOU FACTORY—See Acebed Co. Ltd.; *Int'l*, pg. 95
ACEBED CO. LTD. - YEOJU FACTORY—See Acebed Co. Ltd.; *Int'l*, pg. 95
AIRSPRUNG GROUP PLC; *Int'l*, pg. 248
AMF SUPPORT SURFACES INC.; *U.S. Private*, pg. 262
AW INDUSTRIES, INC.; *U.S. Private*, pg. 410
BANNER MATTRESS COMPANY; *U.S. Private*, pg. 469
BEKAERT (AUSTRALIA) PTY. LTD.—See Franz Haniel & Cie. GmbH; *Int'l*, pg. 2762
BEMCO ASSOCIATES, INC.; *U.S. Private*, pg. 522
BETTZEIT GMBH; *Int'l*, pg. 1004
BIOTECH MEDICAL, INC.—See Suarez Corporation Industries; *U.S. Private*, pg. 3846
BOYD FLOTATION, INC—See The Bedroom Store; *U.S. Private*, pg. 3992
BROOKLYN BEDDING LLC—See Cerberus Capital Management, L.P.; *U.S. Private*, pg. 837
BURLINGTON MATTRESS CO. LLC—See Tempur Sealy International, Inc.; *U.S. Public*, pg. 1999
CAMPBELL SLEEP, LLC—See Mattress Direct, Inc.; *U.S. Private*, pg. 2614
CASPER SLEEP INC.; *U.S. Public*, pg. 446
CHANGZHOU TIANSHENG NEW MATERIALS CO., LTD.; *Int'l*, pg. 1445
CHITTENDEN & EASTMAN CO.; *U.S. Private*, pg. 887
CLARE BEDDING MFG. CO.; *U.S. Private*, pg. 910
COMFORTAIRE CORPORATION—See Sleep Number Corporation; *U.S. Public*, pg. 1894
CONTINENTAL SILVERLINE PRODUCTS INC.—See Restonic Mattress Corporation; *U.S. Private*, pg. 3409
CORSICANA BEDDING, LLC; *U.S. Private*, pg. 1060
CULP FABRICS (SHANGHAI) CO., LTD.—See Culp, Inc.; *U.S. Public*, pg. 604
DAN-FOAM APS—See Tempur Sealy International, Inc.; *U.S. Public*, pg. 1999
DBC INTERNATIONAL B.V.—See Beter Bed Holding N.V.; *Int'l*, pg. 1002
DEFINITIVE REST MATTRESS COMPANY; *U.S. Private*, pg. 1191
DE RUCCI HEALTHY SLEEP CO., LTD.; *Int'l*, pg. 1997
DIXIE BEDDING CORPORATION; *U.S. Private*, pg. 1244
DOMENECH HERMANOS S.A.U—See Beaulieu International Group NV; *Int'l*, pg. 934
DORMAEL SLAAPKAMERS B.V.—See Beter Bed Holding N.V.; *Int'l*, pg. 1002
DREAM PRODUCTS SDN. BHD.—See FACB Industries Incorporated Berhad; *Int'l*, pg. 2600
DUNLOPILLO DEUTSCHLAND GMBH—See Bettzeit GmbH; *Int'l*, pg. 1004
DYNASTY CONSOLIDATED INDUSTRIES INCORPORATED; *U.S. Private*, pg. 1300
EAGAN PRODUCTS, LLC—See Leggett & Platt, Incorporated; *U.S. Public*, pg. 1302
EASTERN SLEEP PRODUCTS COMPANY INC.; *U.S. Private*, pg. 1321
EJE (HONG KONG) HOLDINGS LIMITED; *Int'l*, pg. 2337
E.S. KLUFT & CO.—See Flex Equipos de Descanso SA; *Int'l*, pg. 2701
EUROFOAM S.R.L.—See Greiner Holding AG; *Int'l*, pg. 3078
EUROPEAN HOUSE OF BEDS AB—See Herkules Capital AS; *Int'l*, pg. 3362
EVERTON MATTRESS FACTORY, INC.—See Restonic Mattress Corporation; *U.S. Private*, pg. 3409
EVE SLEEP PLC; *Int'l*, pg. 2561
FACTORY DIRECT INC.—See Mathis Bros. Furniture Co. Inc.; *U.S. Private*, pg. 2611
FIBRE STAR (M) SDN.BHD.—See HHRG Berhad; *Int'l*, pg. 3379
FLEX EQUIPOS DE DESCANSO SA; *Int'l*, pg. 2701
HEALTHCARE CO., LTD.; *Int'l*, pg. 3304
HELIX SLEEP, INC.—See Cerberus Capital Management, L.P.; *U.S. Private*, pg. 838
HIGHLAND FABRICATORS INC.—See Hickory Springs Manufacturing Company; *U.S. Private*, pg. 1933
HUNTLEIGH TECHNOLOGY (ENGINEERING) LTD—See Getinge AB; *Int'l*, pg. 2949
IBC GROUP INC.; *U.S. Private*, pg. 2028
INNOVATIVE MATTRESS SOLUTIONS, LLC—See Tempur Sealy International, Inc.; *U.S. Public*, pg. 1999
INTELLIBED, LLC—See Purple Innovation, Inc.; *U.S. Public*, pg. 1738
INTERNATIONAL BEDDING CORP.—See IBC Group Inc.; *U.S. Private*, pg. 2028
INTERNATIONAL BEDDING CORP.—See IBC Group Inc.; *U.S. Private*, pg. 2028
INTERNATIONAL BEDDING CORP.—See IBC Group Inc.; *U.S. Private*, pg. 2028
INTERNATIONAL BEDDING CORP.—See IBC Group Inc.; *U.S. Private*, pg. 2028
JACKSON MATTRESS COMPANY LLC; *U.S. Private*, pg. 2177
JAMISON BEDDING, INC.—See Solstice Sleep Products, Inc.; *U.S. Private*, pg. 3710
JOHNSON CITY BEDDING COMPANY—See Restonic Mattress Corporation; *U.S. Private*, pg. 3409
KING KOIL LICENSING COMPANY INC.; *U.S. Private*, pg. 2309
LEGGETT & PLATT COMPONENTS EUROPE LIMITED—See Leggett & Platt, Incorporated; *U.S. Public*, pg. 1303
LEGGETT & PLATT FRANCE S.A.S.—See Leggett & Platt, Incorporated; *U.S. Public*, pg. 1303
LEGGETT & PLATT INTERNATIONAL SERVICE CORPORATION—See Leggett & Platt, Incorporated; *U.S. Public*, pg. 1303
LEGGETT & PLATT (JIAXING) CO. LTD.—See Leggett & Platt, Incorporated; *U.S. Public*, pg. 1302
MADAD PTY. LTD.—See Dyer Holdings Pty. Ltd.; *Int'l*, pg. 2238
MAGGIES ENTERPRISES INC.; *U.S. Private*, pg. 2545
MARSPRING CORPORATION; *U.S. Private*, pg. 2593
MATTRESS DIRECT, INC.; *U.S. Private*, pg. 2614
MCKINNEY BEDDING COMPANY—See Restonic Mattress Corporation; *U.S. Private*, pg. 3409
MCROSKEY MATTRESS COMPANY—See Pleasant Mattress Co., Inc.; *U.S. Private*, pg. 3213
MPI, INC.—See Leggett & Platt, Incorporated; *U.S. Public*, pg. 1303
NEVEON HOLDING GMBH—See Greiner Holding AG; *Int'l*, pg. 3079
NORTHWEST BEDDING CO.; *U.S. Private*, pg. 2959
OHIO-SEALY MATTRESS MANUFACTURING - FORT WORTH—See Tempur Sealy International, Inc.; *U.S. Public*, pg. 1999
OREGON MATTRESS COMPANY—See Restonic Mattress Corporation; *U.S. Private*, pg. 3409
THE ORIGINAL MATTRESS FACTORY; *U.S. Private*, pg. 4089
OROTEX BELGIUM NV—See Beaulieu International Group NV; *Int'l*, pg. 934
PARK PLACE CORPORATION; *U.S. Private*, pg. 3096
PLEASANT MATTRESS CO., INC.; *U.S. Private*, pg. 3213
RESTONIC MATTRESS CORPORATION - RESTONIC BRITISH COLUMBIA FACTORY—See Restonic Mattress Corporation; *U.S. Private*, pg. 3409
RESTONIC MATTRESS CORPORATION - RESTONIC CARIBBEAN FACTORY—See Restonic Mattress Corporation; *U.S. Private*, pg. 3409
RESTONIC MATTRESS CORPORATION - RESTONIC DOMINICAN REPUBLIC FACTORY—See Restonic Mattress Corporation; *U.S. Private*, pg. 3409
RESTONIC MATTRESS CORPORATION - RESTONIC ECUADOR FACTORY—See Restonic Mattress Corporation; *U.S. Private*, pg. 3409
RESTONIC MATTRESS CORPORATION - RESTONIC MIDDLE EAST FACTORY—See Restonic Mattress Corporation; *U.S. Private*, pg. 3409
RESTONIC MATTRESS CORPORATION - RESTONIG OF INDIA FACTORY—See Restonic Mattress Corporation; *U.S. Private*, pg. 3409
RESTONIC MATTRESS CORPORATION - RESTONIC OF KOREA FACTORY—See Restonic Mattress Corporation; *U.S. Private*, pg. 3409
RESTONIC MATTRESS CORPORATION - RESTONIC QUEBEC FACTORY—See Restonic Mattress Corporation; *U.S. Private*, pg. 3409
RESTONIC MATTRESS CORPORATION; *U.S. Private*, pg. 3409
RICHARDS QUALITY BEDDING, INC.; *U.S. Private*, pg. 3429
ROYAL BEDDING COMPANY INC.; *U.S. Private*, pg. 3491
SAATVA, INC.; *U.S. Private*, pg. 3520
SAVVY REST INC.; *U.S. Private*, pg. 3557
SEALY ASIA (HONG KONG) LTD—See Dyer Holdings Pty. Ltd.; *Int'l*, pg. 2238
SEALY ASIA (HONG KONG) LTD—See Tempur Sealy International, Inc.; *U.S. Public*, pg. 1999
SEALY CANADA, LTD.—See Tempur Sealy International, Inc.; *U.S. Public*, pg. 1999
SEALY COMPONENTS GROUP - COLORADO SPRINGS—See Tempur Sealy International, Inc.; *U.S. Public*, pg. 1999
SEALY COMPONENTS GROUP - DELANO—See Tempur Sealy International, Inc.; *U.S. Public*, pg. 2000
SEALY CORPORATION—See Tempur Sealy International, Inc.; *U.S. Public*, pg. 1999
SEALY MATTRESS COMPANY OF ALBANY, INC.—See Tempur Sealy International, Inc.; *U.S. Public*, pg. 2000
SEALY MATTRESS COMPANY OF ILLINOIS—See Tempur Sealy International, Inc.; *U.S. Public*, pg. 2000
SEALY MATTRESS COMPANY OF KANSAS CITY, INC.—See Tempur Sealy International, Inc.; *U.S. Public*, pg. 2000
SEALY MATTRESS COMPANY OF PUERTO RICO—See Tempur Sealy International, Inc.; *U.S. Public*, pg. 2000
SEALY MATTRESS COMPANY—See Tempur Sealy International, Inc.; *U.S. Public*, pg. 2000
SEALY MATTRESS CORPORATION—See Tempur Sealy International, Inc.; *U.S. Public*, pg. 2000
SEALY OF MARYLAND AND VIRGINIA, INC.—See Tempur Sealy International, Inc.; *U.S. Public*, pg. 2000
SEALY OF MINNESOTA, INC.—See Tempur Sealy International, Inc.; *U.S. Public*, pg. 2000
SEALY STEARNS & FOSTER MANUFACTURING - ATLANTA—See Tempur Sealy International, Inc.; *U.S. Public*, pg. 2000
SEALY STEARNS & FOSTER MANUFACTURING - HOUSTON—See Tempur Sealy International, Inc.; *U.S. Public*, pg. 2000
SEALY STEARNS & FOSTER MANUFACTURING - ORLANDO—See Tempur Sealy International, Inc.; *U.S. Public*, pg. 2000
SEALY TECHNOLOGY LLC—See Tempur Sealy International, Inc.; *U.S. Public*, pg. 2000
SERTA, INC.—See Ares Management Corporation; *U.S. Public*, pg. 190
SERTA MATTRESS COMPANY—See Ares Management Corporation; *U.S. Public*, pg. 190
SERTA MATTRESS COMPANY—See Ares Management Corporation; *U.S. Public*, pg. 190
SILENTNIGHT GROUP LIMITED - SEALY UK

N.A.I.C.S. INDEX

339112 — SURGICAL AND MEDICA...

DIVISION—See H.I.G. Capital, LLC; *U.S. Private*, pg. 1828
SILENTNIGHT GROUP LIMITED—See H.I.G. Capital, LLC; *U.S. Private*, pg. 1828
SIMMONS COMPANY—See Ares Management Corporation; *U.S. Public*, pg. 190
SLEEP HAVEN, INC.—See Restonic Mattress Corporation; *U.S. Private*, pg. 3409
SLEEP NUMBER CORPORATION; *U.S. Public*, pg. 1894
SLEEP PRODUCTS, INC.—See Restonic Mattress Corporation; *U.S. Private*, pg. 3409
SLEEP-RITE INDUSTRIES, INC.—See Restonic Mattress Corporation; *U.S. Private*, pg. 3409
STEVENS MATTRESS MFG., INC.—See Restonic Mattress Corporation; *U.S. Private*, pg. 3409
STEVENS MATTRESS OF IOWA, INC.—See Restonic Mattress Corporation; *U.S. Private*, pg. 3409
STYLUTION INT'L CORP.—See Restonic Mattress Corporation; *U.S. Private*, pg. 3409
STYLUTION INT'L CORP.—See Restonic Mattress Corporation; *U.S. Private*, pg. 3409
STYLUTION JAPAN INC.—See Restonic Mattress Corporation; *U.S. Private*, pg. 3409
SWAMP MATS INC—See Dexterra Group Inc.; *Int'l*, pg. 2093
SYMBOL MATTRESS OF NEW ENGLAND INC.—See Eastern Sleep Products Company Inc.; *U.S. Private*, pg. 1321
SYMBOL MATTRESS OF WISCONSIN, INC.—See Eastern Sleep Products Company Inc.; *U.S. Private*, pg. 1321
TEMPO INDUSTRIES INC.; *U.S. Private*, pg. 3964
TEMPUR AUSTRALIA PTY. LTD.—See Tempur Sealy International, Inc.; *U.S. Public*, pg. 2000
TEMPUR BENELUX B.V.—See Tempur Sealy International, Inc.; *U.S. Public*, pg. 2000
TEMPUR DANMARK A/S—See Tempur Sealy International, Inc.; *U.S. Public*, pg. 2000
TEMPUR DEUTSCHLAND GMBH—See Tempur Sealy International, Inc.; *U.S. Public*, pg. 2000
TEMPUR FRANCE SARL—See Tempur Sealy International, Inc.; *U.S. Public*, pg. 2000
TEMPUR NORGE AS—See Tempur Sealy International, Inc.; *U.S. Public*, pg. 2000
TEMPUR-PEDIC AMERICA, LLC—See Tempur Sealy International, Inc.; *U.S. Public*, pg. 2000
TEMPUR PRODUCTION USA, LLC—See Tempur Sealy International, Inc.; *U.S. Public*, pg. 2000
TEMPUR SCHWEIZ AG—See Tempur Sealy International, Inc.; *U.S. Public*, pg. 2000
TEMPUR SEALY DEUTSCHLAND GMBH—See Tempur Sealy International, Inc.; *U.S. Public*, pg. 2000
TEMPUR SEALY ESPANA S.A.—See Tempur Sealy International, Inc.; *U.S. Public*, pg. 2000
TEMPUR SEALY FRANCE SAS—See Tempur Sealy International, Inc.; *U.S. Public*, pg. 2000
TEMPUR SEALY INTERNATIONAL, INC.; *U.S. Public*, pg. 1999
TEMPUR SINGAPORE PTE LTD.—See Tempur Sealy International, Inc.; *U.S. Public*, pg. 2000
TEMPUR SUOMI OY—See Tempur Sealy International, Inc.; *U.S. Public*, pg. 2000
TEMPUR SVERIGE AB—See Tempur Sealy International, Inc.; *U.S. Public*, pg. 2000
TEMPUR UK LIMITED—See Tempur Sealy International, Inc.; *U.S. Public*, pg. 2000
THERAPEDIC ASSOCIATES, INC. - THE BED FACTORY—See Therapedic Associates, Inc.; *U.S. Private*, pg. 4142
THER-A-PEDIC MIDWEST INC.; *U.S. Private*, pg. 4142
TUALATIN SLEEP PRODUCTS INC.; *U.S. Private*, pg. 4255
VIRTUS INC.—See DCC plc; *Int'l*, pg. 1991
WHITE CROSS SLEEP PRODUCTS—See Eastern Sleep Products Company Inc.; *U.S. Private*, pg. 1321

337920 — BLIND AND SHADE MANUFACTURING

3 DAY BLINDS LLC; *U.S. Private*, pg. 7
AEROSPACE TECHNOLOGIES GROUP, INC.; *U.S. Private*, pg. 119
APOLLO SUNGUARD SYSTEMS, INC.; *U.S. Private*, pg. 295
AUSTRALIAN WINDOW FURNISHINGS (NSW) PTY. LTD.—See 3G Capital Partners L.P.; *U.S. Private*, pg. 12
BEAUTI-VUE PRODUCTS CORP.; *U.S. Private*, pg. 508
BLINDS TO GO (CANADA) INC.—See Blinds To Go Inc.; *U.S. Private*, pg. 581
BLIND SUPPLY, LLC; *U.S. Private*, pg. 581
COMFORTEX CORPORATION—See 3G Capital Partners L.P.; *U.S. Private*, pg. 13
DECORA S.A.; *Int'l*, pg. 2001
DONGHIA INC.—See Kravet, Inc.; *U.S. Private*, pg. 2350
DURAL LEEDS PTY. LTD.—See 3G Capital Partners L.P.; *U.S. Private*, pg. 12
GARDINIA HOME DECOR GMBH; *Int'l*, pg. 2884
HT WINDOW FASHIONS; *U.S. Private*, pg. 1999
HUNTER DOUGLAS CANADA, INC.—See 3G Capital Partners L.P.; *U.S. Private*, pg. 11
HUNTER DOUGLAS CATALUNA SL—See 3G Capital Partners L.P.; *U.S. Private*, pg. 12
HUNTER DOUGLAS C.I.S.—See 3G Capital Partners L.P.; *U.S. Private*, pg. 11
HUNTER DOUGLAS DO BRAZIL LTDA.—See 3G Capital Partners L.P.; *U.S. Private*, pg. 12
HUNTER DOUGLAS ENTWICKLUNGSGESELLSCHAFT MBH—See 3G Capital Partners L.P.; *U.S. Private*, pg. 12
HUNTER DOUGLAS FABRICATION—See 3G Capital Partners L.P.; *U.S. Private*, pg. 13
HUNTER DOUGLAS FASHIONS INC.—See 3G Capital Partners L.P.; *U.S. Private*, pg. 13
HUNTER DOUGLAS, INC.—See 3G Capital Partners L.P.; *U.S. Private*, pg. 13
HUNTER DOUGLAS LIMITED—See 3G Capital Partners L.P.; *U.S. Private*, pg. 12
HUNTER DOUGLAS PANAMA SA—See 3G Capital Partners L.P.; *U.S. Private*, pg. 12
HUNTER DOUGLAS PERU S.A.C—See 3G Capital Partners L.P.; *U.S. Private*, pg. 12
HUNTER DOUGLAS (SCHWEIZ) GMBH—See 3G Capital Partners L.P.; *U.S. Private*, pg. 11
HUNTER DOUGLAS SINGAPORE PTE. LTD.—See 3G Capital Partners L.P.; *U.S. Private*, pg. 12
HUNTER DOUGLAS VERTICALS—See 3G Capital Partners L.P.; *U.S. Private*, pg. 13
HUNTER DOUGLAS WINDOW FASHIONS, INC.—See 3G Capital Partners L.P.; *U.S. Private*, pg. 13
KAWNEER UK LIMITED—See Howmet Aerospace Inc.; *U.S. Public*, pg. 1062
KENNEY MANUFACTURING COMPANY; *U.S. Private*, pg. 2286
LAFAYETTE VENETIAN BLIND INC.; *U.S. Private*, pg. 2372
LEVOLOR, INC.—See 3G Capital Partners L.P.; *U.S. Private*, pg. 13
LEVOLOR KIRSCH WINDOW FASHIONS—See 3G Capital Partners L.P.; *U.S. Private*, pg. 13
MILLER MANUFACTURING, INC.; *U.S. Private*, pg. 2735
NEXT DAY BLINDS CORPORATION; *U.S. Private*, pg. 2919
PHASE II PRODUCTS INC.; *U.S. Private*, pg. 3166
ROYAL WINDOWS INC.; *U.S. Private*, pg. 3494
SELECTIVE ENTERPRISES INC.; *U.S. Private*, pg. 3601
SHADE-O-MATIC LTD.—See 3G Capital Partners L.P.; *U.S. Private*, pg. 13
SKAGFIELD CORPORATION; *U.S. Private*, pg. 3680
SPRINGS WINDOW FASHIONS LLC—See AEA Investors LP; *U.S. Private*, pg. 115
SPRINGS WINDOW FASHIONS LLC—See British Columbia Investment Management Corp.; *Int'l*, pg. 1169
VENETIAN BLIND & FLOOR; *U.S. Private*, pg. 4356
VISTA PRODUCTS INC.; *U.S. Private*, pg. 4403
WEBBSHADE, INC.—See InPro Corporation; *U.S. Private*, pg. 2085

339112 — SURGICAL AND MEDICAL INSTRUMENT MANUFACTURING

3B SCIENTIFIC GMBH—See J.H. Whitney & Co., LLC; *U.S. Private*, pg. 2166
3DIEMME SRL—See Zimmer Biomet Holdings, Inc.; *U.S. Public*, pg. 2405
3-D MATRIX EMEA B.V.—See 3-D Matrix, Ltd.; *Int'l*, pg. 6
3-D MATRIX, LTD.; *Int'l*, pg. 6
3-D MATRIX MEDICAL TECHNOLOGY, LTD.—See 3-D Matrix, Ltd.; *Int'l*, pg. 6
3-D MATRIX MEDICAL TECHNOLOGY PTY LTD—See 3-D Matrix, Ltd.; *Int'l*, pg. 6
3-D MATRIX UK LTD.—See 3-D Matrix, Ltd.; *Int'l*, pg. 6
3M HEALTH CARE—See Solventum Corporation; *U.S. Public*, pg. 1901
908 DEVICES INC.; *U.S. Public*, pg. 10
AA MEDICAL STORE, INC.—See Shore Capital Partners, LLC; *U.S. Private*, pg. 3641
ABALAT S.A. DE C.V.—See HORIBA Ltd; *Int'l*, pg. 3474
ABAXIS HOLDING GMBH—See Zoetis, Inc.; *U.S. Public*, pg. 2409
ABAXIS, INC.—See Zoetis, Inc.; *U.S. Public*, pg. 2409
ABBOTT AG—See Abbott Laboratories; *U.S. Public*, pg. 14
ABBOTT AUTOMATION SOLUTIONS GMBH—See Abbott Laboratories; *U.S. Public*, pg. 14
ABBOTT CIENTIFICA, S.A.—See Abbott Laboratories; *U.S. Public*, pg. 14
ABBOTT DIAGNOSTICOS RAPIDOS S.A.—See Abbott Laboratories; *U.S. Public*, pg. 14
ABBOTT DIAGNOSTICS GMBH—See Abbott Laboratories; *U.S. Public*, pg. 14
ABBOTT DIAGNOSTICS MEDICAL CO., LTD.—See Abbott Laboratories; *U.S. Public*, pg. 14
ABBOTT DIAGNOSTICS SCARBOROUGH, INC.—See Abbott Laboratories; *U.S. Public*, pg. 14
ABBOTT DIAGNOSTICS—See Abbott Laboratories; *U.S. Public*, pg. 14
ABBOTT HEALTHCARE CONNECTIONS LIMITED—See Abbott Laboratories; *U.S. Public*, pg. 15
ABBOTT HEALTHCARE COSTA RICA, S.A.—See Abbott Laboratories; *U.S. Public*, pg. 15
ABBOTT HEMATOLOGY- DIAGNOSTICS DIVISION—See Abbott Laboratories; *U.S. Public*, pg. 14
ABBOTT LABORATORIES LIMITED - DIAGNOSTIC DIVISION—See Abbott Laboratories; *U.S. Public*, pg. 16
ABBOTT LABORATORIES LIMITED—See Abbott Laboratories; *U.S. Public*, pg. 16
ABBOTT MEDICAL AUSTRIA GES.M.B.H.—See Abbott Laboratories; *U.S. Public*, pg. 16
ABBOTT MEDICAL ESPANA, S.A.—See Abbott Laboratories; *U.S. Public*, pg. 17
ABBOTT MEDICAL FRANCE SAS—See Abbott Laboratories; *U.S. Public*, pg. 17
ABBOTT MEDICAL ITALIA S.P.A.—See Abbott Laboratories; *U.S. Public*, pg. 17
ABBOTT MEDICAL (MALAYSIA) SDN. BHD.—See Abbott Laboratories; *U.S. Public*, pg. 16
ABBOTT MEDICAL SPOLKA Z OGRANICZONA ODPOWIEDZIALNOSCIA—See Abbott Laboratories; *U.S. Public*, pg. 17
ABBOTT NUTRITION LIMITED—See Abbott Laboratories; *U.S. Public*, pg. 16
ABBOTT POINT OF CARE CANADA LTD.—See Abbott Laboratories; *U.S. Public*, pg. 14
ABBOTT POINT OF CARE, INC.—See Abbott Laboratories; *U.S. Public*, pg. 14
ABBOTT RAPID DIAGNOSTICS ARGENTINA S.A.—See Abbott Laboratories; *U.S. Public*, pg. 17
ABBOTT RAPID DIAGNOSTICS HEALTHCARE, S.L.—See Abbott Laboratories; *U.S. Public*, pg. 17
ABBOTT RAPID DIAGNOSTICS HEALTH CORP.—See Abbott Laboratories; *U.S. Public*, pg. 17
ABBOTT RAPID DIAGNOSTICS LIMITED—See Abbott Laboratories; *U.S. Public*, pg. 18
ABBOTT RAPID DIAGNOSTICS MEDICAL—See Abbott Laboratories; *U.S. Public*, pg. 17
ABBOTT RAPID DIAGNOSTICS (PTY) LTD.—See Abbott Laboratories; *U.S. Public*, pg. 17
ABBOTT SA/NV—See Abbott Laboratories; *U.S. Public*, pg. 18
ABBOTT SAUDI ARABIA TRADING COMPANY—See Abbott Laboratories; *U.S. Public*, pg. 18
ABBOTT (SHANGHAI) DIAGNOSTICS SALES CO., LTD.—See Abbott Laboratories; *U.S. Public*, pg. 14
ABBOTT TOXICOLOGY LIMITED—See Abbott Laboratories; *U.S. Public*, pg. 18
ABBOTT VASCULAR DEUTSCHLAND GMBH—See Abbott Laboratories; *U.S. Public*, pg. 18
ABBOTT VASCULAR DEVICES (2) LIMITED—See Abbott Laboratories; *U.S. Public*, pg. 14
ABBOTT VASCULAR DEVICES HOLLAND B.V.—See Abbott Laboratories; *U.S. Public*, pg. 14
ABBOTT VASCULAR DEVICES IRELAND LIMITED—See Abbott Laboratories; *U.S. Public*, pg. 14
ABBOTT VASCULAR DEVICES LIMITED—See Abbott Laboratories; *U.S. Public*, pg. 14
ABBOTT VASCULAR INTERNATIONAL BVBA—See Abbott Laboratories; *U.S. Public*, pg. 14
ABBOTT VASCULAR JAPAN CO., LTD—See Abbott Laboratories; *U.S. Public*, pg. 18
ABBOTT VASCULAR NETHERLANDS B.V.—See Abbott Laboratories; *U.S. Public*, pg. 18
ABCAM (HONG KONG) LIMITED—See Danaher Corporation; *U.S. Public*, pg. 623
ABCAM SINGAPORE PTE. LIMITED—See Danaher Corporation; *U.S. Public*, pg. 624
ABIOMED EUROPE—See Johnson & Johnson; *U.S. Public*, pg. 1193
ABIOMED, INC.—See Johnson & Johnson; *U.S. Public*, pg. 1193
ABIOMED R&D, INC.—See Johnson & Johnson; *U.S. Public*, pg. 1193
ABI ORTHOTIC/PROSTHETIC LABORATORIES, LTD.—See Patient Square Capital, L.P.; *U.S. Private*, pg. 3107
ACARIX AB; *Int'l*, pg. 78
ACARIX USA INC.—See Acarix AB; *Int'l*, pg. 78
ACCELERATE DIAGNOSTICS, INC.; *U.S. Public*, pg. 32
ACCESS BIO, INC.; *U.S. Public*, pg. 32
ACCESS CLOSURE, INC.—See Cardinal Health, Inc.; *U.S. Public*, pg. 433
ACCESS POINT TECHNOLOGIES, LLC—See Wasatch Advantage Group, LLC; *U.S. Private*, pg. 4445
ACCLARENT, INC.—See Integra LifeSciences Holdings Corporation; *U.S. Public*, pg. 1135
ACCUMED CORPORATION—See Lear Corporation; *U.S. Public*, pg. 1296
ACCURAY EUROPE SAS—See Accuray Incorporated; *U.S. Public*, pg. 33
ACCURAY INCORPORATED; *U.S. Public*, pg. 33
ACCURAY JAPAN K.K.—See Accuray Incorporated; *U.S. Public*, pg. 33
ACELITY L.P. INC.; *U.S. Private*, pg. 57
ACELL, INC.—See Integra LifeSciences Holdings Corporation; *U.S. Public*, pg. 1135
ACIST MEDICAL SYSTEMS, INC.—See Bracco S.p.A.; *Int'l*, pg. 1134
ACUMED IBERICA S.L.—See Berkshire Hathaway Inc.; *U.S. Public*, pg. 308
ACUTUS MEDICAL, N.V.—See Acutus Medical, Inc.; *U.S. Public*, pg. 37

339112 — SURGICAL AND MEDICA...

ADDVISE TILLQUIST AB—See ADDvise Group AB; *Int'l*, pg. 136
ADHERIUM LIMITED; *Int'l*, pg. 145
AD ME TECH CO., LTD.; *Int'l*, pg. 122
ADVANCED COOLING THERAPY, INC.—See Haemonetics Corporation; *U.S. Public*, pg. 979
ADVANCED LIFE SCIENCE INSTITUTE, INC.—See H.U. Group Holdings, Inc.; *Int'l*, pg. 3196
ADVANCED LIQUID LOGIC, INC.; *U.S. Private*, pg. 90
ADVANCED MEDICAL SOLUTIONS ISRAEL (SEALANTIS) LIMITED—See Advanced Medical Solutions Group plc; *Int'l*, pg. 161
ADVANCED PROSTHETICS CENTER, LLC—See Patient Square Capital, L.P.; *U.S. Private*, pg. 3107
ADVANCED PROSTHETICS & ORTHOTICS, L.L.C.—See Patient Square Capital, L.P.; *U.S. Private*, pg. 3106
ADVANCED SYSTEMS COMPANY LLC—See ASBISc Enterprises Plc; *Int'l*, pg. 600
A&D VIETNAM LIMITED—See A&D Co., Ltd.; *Int'l*, pg. 19
ADYNXX, INC.; *U.S. Public*, pg. 50
AEGEA MEDICAL INC.—See The Cooper Companies, Inc.; *U.S. Public*, pg. 2066
AESCULAP CHIFA SP. Z OO.—See B. Braun Melsungen AG; *Int'l*, pg. 785
AESCULAP S.A.—See B. Braun Melsungen AG; *Int'l*, pg. 785
AESCULAP SUHL GMBH—See B. Braun Melsungen AG; *Int'l*, pg. 785
AETHLON MEDICAL, INC.; *U.S. Public*, pg. 53
AFFINITY MEDICAL TECHNOLOGIES, LLC—See Koch Industries, Inc.; *U.S. Private*, pg. 2333
AFFLUENT MEDICAL SAS; *Int'l*, pg. 188
AGFA-GEVAERT S.A.—See Agfa-Gevaert N.V.; *Int'l*, pg. 208
AIOBIO CO., LTD.; *Int'l*, pg. 234
AIR FILTRATION MANAGEMENT INC.—See Medical Technology Associates, LLC; *U.S. Private*, pg. 2656
AIR WATER LINK INC.—See Air Water Inc.; *Int'l*, pg. 239
AITHENUTRIGENE CO.; *Int'l*, pg. 254
ALASKA SURGERY CENTER LIMITED PARTNERSHIP—See HCA Healthcare, Inc.; *U.S. Public*, pg. 990
ALCON OPHTHALMIKA GMBH—See Alcon Inc.; *Int'l*, pg. 302
ALERE AB—See Abbott Laboratories; *U.S. Public*, pg. 18
ALERE COLOMBIA S.A.—See Abbott Laboratories; *U.S. Public*, pg. 18
ALERE SAN DIEGO, INC.—See Abbott Laboratories; *U.S. Public*, pg. 19
ALERE TECHNOLOGIES AS—See Abbott Laboratories; *U.S. Public*, pg. 19
ALFA-WASSERMANN INC.—See Alfa-Wassermann S.p.A.; *Int'l*, pg. 314
ALGAM DRUGS & CHEMICALS CO., LTD.—See HORIBA Ltd; *Int'l*, pg. 3474
ALIGN TECHNOLOGY, INC.; *U.S. Public*, pg. 77
ALIGN TECHNOLOGY SWITZERLAND GMBH—See Align Technology, Inc.; *U.S. Public*, pg. 77
ALLEGRA ORTHOPAEDICS LTD.; *Int'l*, pg. 336
ALL EIGHTS (M) SDN BHD—See HORIBA Ltd; *Int'l*, pg. 3474
ALLEN MEDICAL SYSTEMS, INC.—See Baxter International Inc.; *U.S. Public*, pg. 282
ALLGENS MEDICAL TECHNOLOGY CO., LTD.; *Int'l*, pg. 338
ALLIANCE BIOTECH & ANALYTICAL LTD.—See HORIBA Ltd; *Int'l*, pg. 3474
ALLIANT HEALTHCARE PRODUCTS; *U.S. Private*, pg. 185
ALLIED MEDICAL, LLC—See Flexicare (Group) Limited; *Int'l*, pg. 2705
ALLIUM MEDICAL SOLUTIONS LTD.; *Int'l*, pg. 359
ALLMED MEDICAL PRODUCTS CO., LTD.; *Int'l*, pg. 359
ALMO-ERZEUGNISSE E. BUSCH GMBH—See B. Braun Melsungen AG; *Int'l*, pg. 786
ALPAX COMERCIO DE PRODS.—See HORIBA Ltd; *Int'l*, pg. 3474
ALPHA-BIO TEC LTD.—See Danaher Corporation; *U.S. Public*, pg. 628
ALPHA IMAGING, INC.—See Radon Medical Imaging Corp.; *U.S. Private*, pg. 3345
ALPHA TAU MEDICAL LTD.; *Int'l*, pg. 370
ALPHATEC SPINE, INC.—See Alphatec Holdings, Inc.; *U.S. Public*, pg. 84
ALPS SOUTH LLC; *U.S. Private*, pg. 202
ALTECO MEDICAL AB; *Int'l*, pg. 389
ALTO DEVELOPMENT CORPORATION—See Zimmer Biomet Holdings, Inc.; *U.S. Public*, pg. 2405
AMATECH CORPORATION—See Baxter International Inc.; *U.S. Public*, pg. 282
AMBICOM HOLDINGS, INC.; *U.S. Private*, pg. 217
AMBICOM, INC.—See AmbiCom Holdings, Inc.; *U.S. Private*, pg. 217
AMBU FRANCE S.A.R.L.—See Ambu A/S; *Int'l*, pg. 416
AMBU INDIA PRIVATE LIMITED—See Ambu A/S; *Int'l*, pg. 416
AMBU KK—See Ambu A/S; *Int'l*, pg. 416
AMBU LLC—See Ambu A/S; *Int'l*, pg. 416

AMBU MEXICO OPERATIONS S. A. DE C. V.—See Ambu A/S; *Int'l*, pg. 416
AMBU NEW ZEALAND PTY. LTD.—See Ambu A/S; *Int'l*, pg. 416
AMBU NORDIC A/S—See Ambu A/S; *Int'l*, pg. 416
AMBU SALES & SERVICES SDN. BHD.—See Ambu A/S; *Int'l*, pg. 416
AMENDIA, INC.—See Kohlberg & Company, LLC; *U.S. Private*, pg. 2337
AMERICAN MEDICAL SYSTEMS FRANCE S.A.S—See Endo International plc; *Int'l*, pg. 2404
AMERICAN MEDICAL SYSTEMS HOLDINGS, INC.—See Endo International plc; *Int'l*, pg. 2404
AMERICAN MEDICAL SYSTEMS IBERICA S.L.—See Endo International plc; *Int'l*, pg. 2404
AMPLIFON FRANCE SA—See Amplifon S.p.A.; *Int'l*, pg. 435
AMPLIFON MIDDLE EAST SA—See Amplifon S.p.A.; *Int'l*, pg. 435
AMPLIFON S.P.A.; *Int'l*, pg. 435
AMTRION GMBH—See Gesco AG; *Int'l*, pg. 2945
ANGIODYNAMICS, INC.; *U.S. Public*, pg. 136
ANGIODYNAMICS NETHERLANDS B. V.—See AngioDynamics, Inc.; *U.S. Public*, pg. 137
ANGIODYNAMICS UK LIMITED—See AngioDynamics, Inc.; *U.S. Public*, pg. 137
ANHUI HONGYU WUZHOU MEDICAL MANUFACTURER CO., LTD.; *Int'l*, pg. 468
ANIMAS LLC—See Johnson & Johnson; *U.S. Public*, pg. 1194
ANODYNE MEDICAL DEVICE, INC.—See Baxter International Inc.; *U.S. Public*, pg. 282
THE ANSPACH EFFORT, LLC—See Johnson & Johnson; *U.S. Public*, pg. 1200
ANTARES PHARMA, INC.—See Halozyme Therapeutics, Inc.; *U.S. Public*, pg. 981
ANT NEURO B.V.; *Int'l*, pg. 479
ANULEX TECHNOLOGIES, INC.; *U.S. Private*, pg. 289
ANYMEDI CO., LTD.; *Int'l*, pg. 487
AOI MEDICAL, INC.; *U.S. Private*, pg. 289
APERIO TECHNOLOGIES, INC.—See Danaher Corporation; *U.S. Public*, pg. 628
APOLLO ENDOSURGERY UK LTD.—See Boston Scientific Corporation; *U.S. Public*, pg. 373
APOLLO ENDOSURGERY US, INC.—See Boston Scientific Corporation; *U.S. Public*, pg. 373
APOPLEX MEDICAL TECHNOLOGIES GMBH—See Geratherm Medical AG; *Int'l*, pg. 2942
APPLIED MEDICAL CORPORATION; *U.S. Private*, pg. 299
APT MEDICAL, INC.; *Int'l*, pg. 523
APYX MEDICAL CORPORATION; *U.S. Public*, pg. 175
ARAB MEDICAL & SCIENTIFIC ALLIANCE CO.—See HORIBA Ltd; *Int'l*, pg. 3474
ARCH MEDICAL SOLUTIONS CORP—See The Jordan Company, L.P.; *U.S. Private*, pg. 4060
ARCH THERAPEUTICS, INC.; *U.S. Public*, pg. 180
ARCOA GHANA LTD.—See HORIBA Ltd; *Int'l*, pg. 3474
ARCROYAL UNLIMITED—See Owens & Minor, Inc.; *U.S. Public*, pg. 1625
THE ARISTOTLE CORPORATION—See Geneve Holdings Corp.; *U.S. Private*, pg. 1671
ARJOHUNTLEIGH GMBH—See Getinge AB; *Int'l*, pg. 2948
ARLAB S.A.—See Biotronik GmbH & Co.; *Int'l*, pg. 1044
ARTHREX CALIFORNIA INC.—See Arthrex, Inc.; *U.S. Private*, pg. 341
ARTHREX DANMARK A/S—See Arthrex, Inc.; *U.S. Private*, pg. 341
ARTHREX DO BRAZIL—See Arthrex, Inc.; *U.S. Private*, pg. 341
ARTHREX ESPANA & PORTUGAL—See Arthrex, Inc.; *U.S. Private*, pg. 341
ARTHREX GESMBH—See Arthrex, Inc.; *U.S. Private*, pg. 341
ARTHREX, INC.; *U.S. Private*, pg. 341
ARTHREX KOREA—See Arthrex, Inc.; *U.S. Private*, pg. 341
ARTHREX LTD.—See Arthrex, Inc.; *U.S. Private*, pg. 341
ARTHREX MEDIZINISCHE INSTRUMENTE GMBH—See Arthrex, Inc.; *U.S. Private*, pg. 341
ARTHREX MEXICO, S.A. DE C.V.—See Arthrex, Inc.; *U.S. Private*, pg. 341
ARTHREX NEDERLAND B.V.—See Arthrex, Inc.; *U.S. Private*, pg. 341
ARTHREX S.A.S.—See Arthrex, Inc.; *U.S. Private*, pg. 341
ARTHREX SVERIGE AB—See Arthrex, Inc.; *U.S. Private*, pg. 341
ARTHREX SWISS AG—See Arthrex, Inc.; *U.S. Private*, pg. 341
ASAHI INTECC CO., LTD.; *Int'l*, pg. 594
ASAHI INTECC EUROPE B.V.—See Asahi Intecc Co., Ltd.; *Int'l*, pg. 594
ASAHI INTECC GMA CO., LTD.—See Asahi Intecc Co., Ltd.; *Int'l*, pg. 594
ASAHI INTECC HANOI CO., LTD.—See Asahi Intecc Co., Ltd.; *Int'l*, pg. 594
ASAHI INTECC J-SALES, INC.—See Asahi Intecc Co., Ltd.; *Int'l*, pg. 594
ASAHI INTECC LATIN PROMACAO DE VENDAS LTDA.—See Asahi Intecc Co., Ltd.; *Int'l*, pg. 594
ASAHI INTECC SCIENTIFIC (BEIJING) CO., LTD.—See Asahi Intecc Co., Ltd.; *Int'l*, pg. 594

ASAHI INTECC THAILAND CO., LTD.—See Asahi Intecc Co., Ltd.; *Int'l*, pg. 594
ASAHI INTECC USA, INC.—See Asahi Intecc Co., Ltd.; *Int'l*, pg. 594
ASAHI KASEI MEDICAL CO., LTD.—See Asahi Kasei Corporation; *Int'l*, pg. 595
ASAHI SURGICAL ROBOTICS CO., LTD.—See Asahi Intecc Co., Ltd.; *Int'l*, pg. 594
ASCENSION ORTHOPEDICS, LTD.—See Integra LifeSciences Holdings Corporation; *U.S. Public*, pg. 1135
ASICO LLC—See Audax Group, Limited Partnership; *U.S. Private*, pg. 388
ASPEN MEDICAL EUROPE LIMITED—See Baxter International Inc.; *U.S. Public*, pg. 283
ASPEN MEDICAL EUROPE LIMITED (UK)—See Baxter International Inc.; *U.S. Public*, pg. 283
ASPEN SURGICAL PRODUCTS, INC.—See Audax Group, Limited Partnership; *U.S. Private*, pg. 386
ASPEN SURGICAL PUERTO RICO CORP.—See Audax Group, Limited Partnership; *U.S. Private*, pg. 386
ASTER PHARMACIES GROUP LLC—See Aster DM Healthcare Ltd.; *Int'l*, pg. 654
ASTHMATX, INC.—See Boston Scientific Corporation; *U.S. Public*, pg. 373
ATLANTIC COASTAL ELECTRONICS; *U.S. Private*, pg. 372
ATOS MEDICAL S.A.S.—See Coloplast A/S; *Int'l*, pg. 1703
ATRICURE EUROPE, B.V.—See AtriCure, Inc.; *U.S. Public*, pg. 225
ATRICURE, INC.; *U.S. Public*, pg. 225
ATRITECH, INC.—See Boston Scientific Corporation; *U.S. Public*, pg. 373
ATRIUM MEDICAL CORPORATION—See Getinge AB; *Int'l*, pg. 2951
AT SINGAPORE (GLOBAL) PTE. LTD.—See Agilent Technologies, Inc.; *U.S. Public*, pg. 60
ATTANA AB; *Int'l*, pg. 696
AUBREY GROUP, INC.—See Elbit Systems Limited; *Int'l*, pg. 2344
AURIS HEALTH, INC.—See Johnson & Johnson; *U.S. Public*, pg. 1194
AURORA SPINE CORPORATION; *U.S. Public*, pg. 228
AUSTOFIX GROUP LIMITED; *Int'l*, pg. 718
AUSTRALIAN BIOTECHNOLOGIES PTY. LTD.—See EBOS Group Limited; *Int'l*, pg. 2285
AUTEL INTELLIGENT TECHNOLOGY CORP., LTD.; *Int'l*, pg. 724
AUTONOMIX MEDICAL, INC.; *U.S. Public*, pg. 238
AVALIGN CASES & TRAYS—See Arlington Capital Partners LLC; *U.S. Private*, pg. 327
AVALIGN TECHNOLOGIES, INC.—See Arlington Capital Partners LLC; *U.S. Private*, pg. 327
AVALON LABORATORIES LLC—See Nordson Corporation; *U.S. Public*, pg. 1532
AVANOS MEDICAL AUSTRALIA PTY LTD.—See Avanos Medical, Inc.; *U.S. Public*, pg. 241
AVANOS MEDICAL DEUTSCHLAND GMBH—See Avanos Medical, Inc.; *U.S. Public*, pg. 241
AVANOS MEDICAL SINGAPORE PTE. LTD.—See Avanos Medical, Inc.; *U.S. Public*, pg. 241
AVANT DIAGNOSTICS, INC.—See Theralink Technologies, Inc.; *U.S. Public*, pg. 2144
AVANTOR PERFORMANCE MATERIALS INDIA LIMITED—See Avantor, Inc.; *U.S. Public*, pg. 241
AVANTOR PERFORMANCE MATERIALS KOREA LIMITED—See Avantor, Inc.; *U.S. Public*, pg. 241
AVANTOR PERFORMANCE MATERIALS TAIWAN CO., LTD.—See Avantor, Inc.; *U.S. Public*, pg. 241
AVANTOR VWR (SHANGHAI) CO., LTD.—See Avantor, Inc.; *U.S. Public*, pg. 242
AVID MEDICAL, INC.—See Owens & Minor, Inc.; *U.S. Public*, pg. 1625
AVINGER, INC.; *U.S. Public*, pg. 248
AVITUS ORTHOPAEDICS, INC.—See Zimmer Biomet Holdings, Inc.; *U.S. Public*, pg. 2405
AVNET EMBEDDED (FREIBURG) GMBH—See Avnet, Inc.; *U.S. Public*, pg. 251
AVRA SURGICAL ROBOTICS, INC.; *U.S. Private*, pg. 410
AWARENESS TECHNOLOGY INC.; *U.S. Public*, pg. 410
AXIS-SHIELD AS—See Abbott Laboratories; *U.S. Public*, pg. 19
AXIS-SHIELD DIAGNOSTICS LIMITED—See Abbott Laboratories; *U.S. Public*, pg. 19
AXON LAB AG—See HORIBA Ltd; *Int'l*, pg. 3475
AXON LAB GMBH—See HORIBA Ltd; *Int'l*, pg. 3475
AXON LAB D.O.O—See HORIBA Ltd; *Int'l*, pg. 3475
AXON LAB SPOL. S R.O.—See HORIBA Ltd; *Int'l*, pg. 3475
AZENTA SINGAPORE PTE. LTD.—See Azenta, Inc.; *U.S. Public*, pg. 257
AZENTA (TIANJIN) BIOTECHNOLOGY CO., LTD.—See Azenta, Inc.; *U.S. Public*, pg. 257
BAETA CORP.; *U.S. Private*, pg. 425
BALT EXTRUSION SAS—See Bridgepoint Group Plc; *Int'l*, pg. 1154
BARD ACCESS SYSTEMS, INC.—See Becton, Dickinson & Company; *U.S. Public*, pg. 290

N.A.I.C.S. INDEX

339112 — SURGICAL AND MEDICA...

BARD BENELUX N.V.—See Becton, Dickinson & Company; *U.S. Public*, pg. 290
BARD CANADA INC.—See Becton, Dickinson & Company; *U.S. Public*, pg. 290
BARD COLOMBIA S.A.S.—See Becton, Dickinson & Company; *U.S. Public*, pg. 290
BARD CZECH REPUBLIC S.R.O.—See Becton, Dickinson & Company; *U.S. Public*, pg. 290
BARD FRANCE S.A.S.—See Becton, Dickinson & Company; *U.S. Public*, pg. 290
BARD HELLAS S.A.—See Becton, Dickinson & Company; *U.S. Public*, pg. 290
BARD KOREA LIMITED—See Becton, Dickinson & Company; *U.S. Public*, pg. 291
BARD LIMITED—See Becton, Dickinson & Company; *U.S. Public*, pg. 291
BARD MEDICA S.A.—See Becton, Dickinson & Company; *U.S. Public*, pg. 291
BARD PACIFIC HEALTH CARE COMPANY LTD.—See Becton, Dickinson & Company; *U.S. Public*, pg. 291
BARD PERIPHERAL VASCULAR, INC.—See Becton, Dickinson & Company; *U.S. Public*, pg. 291
BARD POLAND SP. Z.O.O.—See Becton, Dickinson & Company; *U.S. Public*, pg. 291
BARD SINGAPORE PRIVATE LIMITED—See Becton, Dickinson & Company; *U.S. Public*, pg. 291
BARD SWEDEN AB—See Becton, Dickinson & Company; *U.S. Public*, pg. 291
BARKEY CORPORATION—See Azenta, Inc.; *U.S. Public*, pg. 257
BARKEY GMBH & CO. KG—See Azenta, Inc.; *U.S. Public*, pg. 257
BARRON PRECISION INSTRUMENTS, LLC—See GTCR LLC; *U.S. Private*, pg. 1804
BAUMER S.A. - MOGI MIRIM FACTORY—See Baumer S.A.; *Int'l*, pg. 895
BAUMER S.A.; *Int'l*, pg. 895
BAUSCH & LOMB SAGLIK VE OPTIK URUNLERITIC A.S.—See Bausch Health Companies Inc.; *Int'l*, pg. 896
BAUSCH & LOMB SURGICAL KOREA—See Bausch Health Companies Inc.; *Int'l*, pg. 896
BAUSCH & LOMB (THAILAND) LTD.—See Bausch Health Companies Inc.; *Int'l*, pg. 896
BAXTER HEALTHCARE CORPORATION—See Baxter International Inc.; *U.S. Public*, pg. 280
BAXTER MANUFACTURING SP Z O.O.—See Baxter International Inc.; *U.S. Public*, pg. 281
BAXTER MEDICATION DELIVERY—See Baxter International Inc.; *U.S. Public*, pg. 281
BAXTER POLSKA SP. Z.O.O.—See Baxter International Inc.; *U.S. Public*, pg. 281
BAXTER S.A.—See Baxter International Inc.; *U.S. Public*, pg. 281
BAYER OU—See Bayer Aktiengesellschaft; *Int'l*, pg. 905
B. BRAUN ADRIA D.O.O.—See B. Braun Melsungen AG; *Int'l*, pg. 786
B. BRAUN AVITUM SAXONIA GMBH—See B. Braun Melsungen AG; *Int'l*, pg. 786
B. BRAUN GERMANY GMBH & CO. KG—See B. Braun Melsungen AG; *Int'l*, pg. 786
B. BRAUN INTERVENTIONAL SYSTEMS INC.—See B. Braun Melsungen AG; *Int'l*, pg. 787
B.BRAUN TAIWAN CO. LTD.—See B. Braun Melsungen AG; *Int'l*, pg. 787
BBS-BIOACTIVE BONE SUBSTITUTES PLC; *Int'l*, pg. 921
BD BIOSCIENCES DISCOVERY LABWARE—See Becton, Dickinson & Company; *U.S. Public*, pg. 289
BD BIOSCIENCES PHARMINGEN—See Becton, Dickinson & Company; *U.S. Public*, pg. 289
BD DIAGNOSTIC SYSTEMS—See Becton, Dickinson & Company; *U.S. Public*, pg. 288
BD PREANALYTICAL—See Becton, Dickinson & Company; *U.S. Public*, pg. 288
BD SWITZERLAND SARL—See Becton, Dickinson & Company; *U.S. Public*, pg. 290
BEBO HEALTH SA; *Int'l*, pg. 936
BECTON DICKINSON AKTIEBOLAG—See Becton, Dickinson & Company; *U.S. Public*, pg. 289
BECTON DICKINSON BIOSCIENCES, SYSTEMS AND REAGENTS INC.—See Becton, Dickinson & Company; *U.S. Public*, pg. 289
BECTON, DICKINSON B.V.—See Becton, Dickinson & Company; *U.S. Public*, pg. 289
BECTON, DICKINSON & COMPANY - PUERTO RICO—See Becton, Dickinson & Company; *U.S. Public*, pg. 290
BECTON, DICKINSON & COMPANY; *U.S. Public*, pg. 288
BECTON, DICKINSON DE MEXICO, S.A. DE C.V.—See Becton, Dickinson & Company; *U.S. Public*, pg. 290
BECTON DICKINSON DISPENSING FRANCE SAS—See Becton, Dickinson & Company; *U.S. Public*, pg. 289
BECTON, DICKINSON DISPENSING SPAIN S.L.U.—See Becton, Dickinson & Company; *U.S. Public*, pg. 289
BECTON DICKINSON DISPENSING UK LTD.—See Becton, Dickinson & Company; *U.S. Public*, pg. 289
BECTON DICKINSON FRANCE S.A.S.—See Becton, Dickinson & Company; *U.S. Public*, pg. 289
BECTON DICKINSON GMBH—See Becton, Dickinson & Company; *U.S. Public*, pg. 289

BECTON DICKINSON HUNGARY KFT.—See Becton, Dickinson & Company; *U.S. Public*, pg. 289
BECTON DICKINSON INDIA PRIVATE LIMITED—See Becton, Dickinson & Company; *U.S. Public*, pg. 289
BECTON, DICKINSON INDUSTRIAS CIRURGICAS, LTDA.—See Becton, Dickinson & Company; *U.S. Public*, pg. 290
BECTON DICKINSON INFUSION THERAPY AB—See Becton, Dickinson & Company; *U.S. Public*, pg. 289
BECTON DICKINSON INFUSION THERAPY GMBH—See Becton, Dickinson & Company; *U.S. Public*, pg. 289
BECTON DICKINSON INFUSION THERAPY AB—See Becton, Dickinson & Company; *U.S. Public*, pg. 289
BECTON DICKINSON INSULIN SYRINGE, LTD.—See Becton, Dickinson & Company; *U.S. Public*, pg. 289
BECTON, DICKINSON ITALIA S.P.A.—See Becton, Dickinson & Company; *U.S. Public*, pg. 290
BECTON DICKINSON KOREA LTD.—See Becton, Dickinson & Company; *U.S. Public*, pg. 289
BECTON DICKINSON MEDICAL DEVICES CO. SHANGHAI LTD.—See Becton, Dickinson & Company; *U.S. Public*, pg. 290
BECTON DICKINSON MEDICAL PRODUCTS PTE. LTD.—See Becton, Dickinson & Company; *U.S. Public*, pg. 290
BECTON DICKINSON MEDICAL—See Becton, Dickinson & Company; *U.S. Public*, pg. 289
BECTON DICKINSON MEDICAL—See Becton, Dickinson & Company; *U.S. Public*, pg. 290
BECTON DICKINSON MEDICAL (S) PTE LTD.—See Becton, Dickinson & Company; *U.S. Public*, pg. 290
BECTON, DICKINSON MEDICAL SURGICAL—See Becton, Dickinson & Company; *U.S. Public*, pg. 290
BECTON DICKINSON NORWAY AS—See Becton, Dickinson & Company; *U.S. Public*, pg. 290
BECTON DICKINSON OY—See Becton, Dickinson & Company; *U.S. Public*, pg. 289
BECTON DICKINSON PAKISTAN (PVT) LTD.—See Becton, Dickinson & Company; *U.S. Public*, pg. 290
BECTON DICKINSON POLSKA SP.Z.O.O.—See Becton, Dickinson & Company; *U.S. Public*, pg. 290
BECTON DICKINSON ROWA GERMANY GMBH—See Becton, Dickinson & Company; *U.S. Public*, pg. 290
BECTON DICKINSON ROWA ITALY SRL—See Becton, Dickinson & Company; *U.S. Public*, pg. 290
BECTON DICKINSON, S.A.—See Becton, Dickinson & Company; *U.S. Public*, pg. 290
BECTON DICKINSON SDN. BHD.—See Becton, Dickinson & Company; *U.S. Public*, pg. 290
BECTON DICKINSON U.K. LIMITED—See Becton, Dickinson & Company; *U.S. Public*, pg. 290
BECTON DICKINSON VERWALTUNGS GMBH—See Becton, Dickinson & Company; *U.S. Public*, pg. 290
BE HEALTH SPA—See Health Biosciences SpA; *Int'l*, pg. 3303
BEIJING 3-D MATRIX INVESTMENT CONSULTING, LTD.—See 3-D Matrix, Ltd.; *Int'l*, pg. 6
BEIJING BALANCE MEDICAL TECHNOLOGY CO., LTD.; *Int'l*, pg. 946
BEIJING BOHUI INNOVATION BIOTECHNOLOGY GROUP CO., LTD.; *Int'l*, pg. 946
BEIJING CHUNLIZHENGDA MEDICAL INSTRUMENTS CO., LTD.; *Int'l*, pg. 947
BEIJING DT ELECTRONIC TECHNOLOGY CO., LTD.—See Detection Technology Oyj; *Int'l*, pg. 2047
BEIJING FUKUDA DENSHI MEDICAL INSTRUMENTS CO., LTD.—See Fukuda Denshi Co., Ltd.; *Int'l*, pg. 2839
BEIJING HOTGEN BIOTECH CO., LTD.; *Int'l*, pg. 951
BEIJING MONTAGNE MEDICAL DEVICE CO. LTD.—See Zimmer Biomet Holdings, Inc.; *U.S. Public*, pg. 2405
BEIJING SUCCEEDER TECHNOLOGY, INC.; *Int'l*, pg. 958
BEIJING TCT MEDICAL TECHNOLOGY CO., LTD.—See Hologic, Inc.; *U.S. Public*, pg. 1044
BEIJING TIANXINFU MEDICAL APPLIANCE CO., LTD.—See China Biologic Products Holdings, Inc.; *Int'l*, pg. 1486
BEIJING TINAVI MEDICAL TECHNOLOGIES CO., LTD.; *Int'l*, pg. 958
BEIJING WANDONG MEDICAL TECHNOLOGY CO., LTD.; *Int'l*, pg. 960
BELL24-CELL PRODUCT, INC.—See CMIC Holdings Co., Ltd.; *Int'l*, pg. 1670
BELLUSCURA PLC; *Int'l*, pg. 967
BENQ MATERIAL (WUHU) CO. LTD.—See BenQ Materials Corp.; *Int'l*, pg. 975
BENQ MEDICAL TECHNOLOGY CORP.; *Int'l*, pg. 975
BENTEKK GMBH—See Draegerwerk AG & Co. KGaA; *Int'l*, pg. 2198
BERKELEY ADVANCED BIOMATERIALS, INC.—See GNI Group Ltd.; *Int'l*, pg. 3017
BERKLEY MEDICAL RESOURCES INC.; *U.S. Private*, pg. 533
BERKLEY MEDICAL RESOURCES INC.—See Berkley Medical Resources Inc.; *U.S. Private*, pg. 533
BEST NOMOS RADIATION ONCOLOGY—See Best Medical International, Inc.; *U.S. Public*, pg. 543
B. GRIMM & CO. R.O.P.—See B. Grimm Group; *Int'l*, pg. 788

B. GRIMM HEALTHCARE CO., LTD.—See B. Grimm Group; *Int'l*, pg. 788
BIGFOOT BIOMEDICAL, INC.—See Abbott Laboratories; *U.S. Public*, pg. 19
BIMINI TECHNOLOGIES, LLC; *U.S. Private*, pg. 560
BIOCARTIS US INC.—See Biocartis Group NV; *Int'l*, pg. 1036
BIOCHECK, INC.—See OriGene Technologies, Inc.; *U.S. Private*, pg. 3042
BIOCOMPOSITES LTD.—See TA Associates, Inc.; *U.S. Private*, pg. 3914
BIODERM INC.; *U.S. Private*, pg. 561
BIO-DETEK, INC.—See Asahi Kasei Corporation; *Int'l*, pg. 597
BIODEX MEDICAL SYSTEMS, INC.—See Mirion Technologies, Inc.; *U.S. Public*, pg. 1450
BIODYNE CO., LTD.; *Int'l*, pg. 1037
BIOEUROPE GMBH—See Biomerica, Inc.; *U.S. Public*, pg. 337
BIOGENETICS CO.,LTD. - CHINA FACTORY—See Billions Co., Ltd.; *Int'l*, pg. 1031
BIOGENETICS CO.,LTD. - JEUNGPYOUNG FACTORY—See Billions Co., Ltd.; *Int'l*, pg. 1031
BIOLASE EUROPE GMBH—See BIOLASE, Inc.; *U.S. Public*, pg. 337
BIOMARK DIAGNOSTICS INC.; *Int'l*, pg. 1039
BIOMARKETING SERVICES (M) SDN BHD—See HORIBA Ltd; *Int'l*, pg. 3475
BIOMED DIAGNOSTICS, INC.—See Diagnostic Consulting Network, Inc.; *U.S. Private*, pg. 1222
BIOMET 3I AUSTRALIA PTY. LTD.—See Zimmer Biomet Holdings, Inc.; *U.S. Public*, pg. 2405
BIOMET ARGENTINA SA—See Zimmer Biomet Holdings, Inc.; *U.S. Public*, pg. 2405
BIOMET AUSTRALIA PTY. LTD.—See Zimmer Biomet Holdings, Inc.; *U.S. Public*, pg. 2405
BIOMET BIOLOGICS, LLC—See Zimmer Biomet Holdings, Inc.; *U.S. Public*, pg. 2405
BIOMET CEMENTING TECHNOLOGIES AB—See Zimmer Biomet Holdings, Inc.; *U.S. Public*, pg. 2405
BIOMET DEUTSCHLAND GMBH—See Zimmer Biomet Holdings, Inc.; *U.S. Public*, pg. 2405
BIOMET FAIR LAWN LLC—See Zimmer Biomet Holdings, Inc.; *U.S. Public*, pg. 2406
BIOMET, INC.—See Zimmer Biomet Holdings, Inc.; *U.S. Public*, pg. 2406
BIOMETRIC ALBANIA SH.P.K.—See HORIBA Ltd; *Int'l*, pg. 3475
BIO-METRICS, LIMITED—See Bio-Rad Laboratories, Inc.; *U.S. Public*, pg. 332
BIOMET SPAIN ORTHOPAEDICS, S.L.—See Zimmer Biomet Holdings, Inc.; *U.S. Public*, pg. 2405
BIOMET SPORTS MEDICINE, LLC—See Zimmer Biomet Holdings, Inc.; *U.S. Public*, pg. 2406
BIOMET UK LIMITED—See Zimmer Biomet Holdings, Inc.; *U.S. Public*, pg. 2405
BIOMET UK LIMITED - SWINDON—See Zimmer Biomet Holdings, Inc.; *U.S. Public*, pg. 2405
BIOMIMIX, INC.; *U.S. Public*, pg. 338
BIONIK LABORATORIES CORP.; *Int'l*, pg. 1040
BIONIME CORPORATION; *Int'l*, pg. 1040
BIONIME (MALAYSIA) SDN. BHD.—See Bionime Corporation; *Int'l*, pg. 1040
BIONORDIKA BERGMAN AS—See AddLife AB; *Int'l*, pg. 129
BIONOSTICS INC.—See Bio-Techne Corporation; *U.S. Public*, pg. 334
BIOPHAN TECHNOLOGIES, INC.; *U.S. Public*, pg. 338
BIOPSY SCIENCES, LLC; *U.S. Private*, pg. 562
BIO-RAD LABORATORIES, INC. - CLINICAL DIAGNOSTICS—See Bio-Rad Laboratories, Inc.; *U.S. Public*, pg. 333
BIOSENSORS INTERNATIONAL GROUP, LTD.; *Int'l*, pg. 1041
BIOSENSORS INTERNATIONAL PTE LTD—See Biosensors International Group, Ltd.; *Int'l*, pg. 1041
BIOSENSORS INTERNATIONAL USA—See Biosensors International Group, Ltd.; *Int'l*, pg. 1041
BIOSENSORS INTERVENTIONAL TECHNOLOGIES PTE LTD—See Biosensors International Group, Ltd.; *Int'l*, pg. 1041
BIO-SERVICES CONGO SARL—See HORIBA Ltd; *Int'l*, pg. 3475
BIOSIGN TECHNOLOGIES INC.; *Int'l*, pg. 1042
BIOSPHERE MEDICAL EMEA & INDIA—See Merit Medical Systems, Inc.; *U.S. Public*, pg. 1425
BIOSPHERE MEDICAL, INC.—See Merit Medical Systems, Inc.; *U.S. Public*, pg. 1425
BIOSYNERGIE SARL—See HORIBA Ltd; *Int'l*, pg. 3475
BIOTRONIK ARGENTINA S.R.L.—See Biotronik GmbH & Co.; *Int'l*, pg. 1044
BIOTRONIK KAZAKHSTAN GMBH—See Biotronik GmbH & Co.; *Int'l*, pg. 1044
BIOTRONIK PORTUGAL UNIPESSOAL LDA.—See Biotronik GmbH & Co.; *Int'l*, pg. 1044
BIOTRONIK (THAILAND) CO., LTD.—See Biotronik GmbH & Co.; *Int'l*, pg. 1044
BIOVAIL TECHNOLOGIES LTD.—See Bausch Health Companies Inc.; *Int'l*, pg. 898

339112 — SURGICAL AND MEDICA...

BIOVENTUS COOPERATIEF U.A.—See Bioventus Inc.; *U.S. Public*, pg. 339
BIOVICA INC.—See Biovica International AB; *Int'l*, pg. 1045
BISTOS CO., LTD.; *Int'l*, pg. 1049
BK MEDICAL APS—See Altaris Capital Partners, LLC; *U.S. Private*, pg. 205
BK MEDICAL MEDIZINISCHE SYSTEME GMBH—See Altaris Capital Partners, LLC; *U.S. Private*, pg. 205
B-K MEDICAL SYSTEMS, INC.—See Altaris Capital Partners, LLC; *U.S. Private*, pg. 205
BLOCKADE MEDICAL LLC—See Bridgepoint Group Plc; *Int'l*, pg. 1154
BLUEDOT MEDICAL, INC.; *U.S. Private*, pg. 596
BMC MEDICAL CO., LTD.; *Int'l*, pg. 1076
B MEDICAL SYSTEMS INDIA PRIVATE LIMITED—See Azenta, Inc.; *U.S. Public*, pg. 257
B MEDICAL SYSTEMS NORTH AMERICA LLC—See Azenta, Inc.; *U.S. Public*, pg. 257
B MEDICAL SYSTEMS S.A.R.L.—See Azenta, Inc.; *U.S. Public*, pg. 257
BODITECH MED, INC.; *Int'l*, pg. 1097
BOSTON SCIENTIFIC CARDIAC DIAGNOSTICS, INC.—See Boston Scientific Corporation; *U.S. Public*, pg. 374
BOSTON SCIENTIFIC CLONMEL (CRM)—See Boston Scientific Corporation; *U.S. Public*, pg. 374
BOSTON SCIENTIFIC CORPORATION; *U.S. Public*, pg. 373
BOSTON SCIENTIFIC DEL CARRIBE, INC.—See Boston Scientific Corporation; *U.S. Public*, pg. 375
BOSTON SCIENTIFIC - FREMONT—See Boston Scientific Corporation; *U.S. Public*, pg. 374
BOSTON SCIENTIFIC - MAPLE GROVE—See Boston Scientific Corporation; *U.S. Public*, pg. 374
BOSTON SCIENTIFIC NEDERLAND B.V.—See Boston Scientific Corporation; *U.S. Public*, pg. 374
BOSTON SCIENTIFIC NEUROMODULATION CORPORATION—See Boston Scientific Corporation; *U.S. Public*, pg. 374
BOSTON SCIENTIFIC - PLYMOUTH TECHNOLOGY CENTER—See Boston Scientific Corporation; *U.S. Public*, pg. 374
BOSTON SCIENTIFIC - SAN JOSE—See Boston Scientific Corporation; *U.S. Public*, pg. 374
BOSTON SCIENTIFIC (SOUTH AFRICA) PROPRIETARY LIMITED—See Boston Scientific Corporation; *U.S. Public*, pg. 374
BOSTON SCIENTIFIC - SPENCER—See Boston Scientific Corporation; *U.S. Public*, pg. 374
BOSTON SCIENTIFIC (THAILAND) LTD.—See Boston Scientific Corporation; *U.S. Public*, pg. 374
BOULE DIAGNOSTICS AB; *Int'l*, pg. 1119
BOULE MEDICAL LLC—See Boule Diagnostics AB; *Int'l*, pg. 1119
BOVIE CANADA ULC—See Apyx Medical Corporation; *U.S. Public*, pg. 175
BPL MEDICAL TECHNOLOGIES PRIVATE LTD.—See The Goldman Sachs Group, Inc.; *U.S. Public*, pg. 2076
BRAIN POWER INC.; *U.S. Private*, pg. 634
BRAINSWAY LTD.; *Int'l*, pg. 1137
BRASTER S.A.; *Int'l*, pg. 1140
BREATHHEALTH CORPORATION—See Astrotech Corporation; *U.S. Public*, pg. 218
BREG, INC.—See Water Street Healthcare Partners, LLC; *U.S. Private*, pg. 4452
BRESSLERGROUP, INC.—See Trinity Hunt Management, L.P.; *U.S. Private*, pg. 4234
THE BREWER COMPANY; *U.S. Private*, pg. 4000
BRIDGER BIOMED, INC.—See Becton, Dickinson & Company; *U.S. Public*, pg. 291
BRIGHTGENE BIO-MEDICAL TECHNOLOGY CO., LTD.; *Int'l*, pg. 1162
BROOKHAVEN MEDICAL, INC.; *U.S. Private*, pg. 663
BROWNMED, INC.; *U.S. Private*, pg. 669
BSD MEDICAL CORPORATION—See Scion Medical Technologies, LLC; *U.S. Private*, pg. 3574
BUKWANG MEDICAL INC.—See Bukwang Pharmaceutical Co., Ltd.; *Int'l*, pg. 1213
CADENCE, INC.—See Kohlberg & Company, LLC; *U.S. Private*, pg. 2337
CAINA TECHNOLOGY CO., LTD.; *Int'l*, pg. 1252
CALTH INC.; *Int'l*, pg. 1266
CAMBUS TEORANTA LTD.—See Freudenberg SE; *Int'l*, pg. 2782
CANADIAN HOSPITAL SPECIALTIES LIMITED; *Int'l*, pg. 1283
CANNABIX TECHNOLOGIES INC.; *Int'l*, pg. 1292
CANNGROS APS—See DanCann Pharma A/S; *Int'l*, pg. 1958
CANNORDIC A/S—See CS Medica A/S; *Int'l*, pg. 1861
CANON ITS MEDICAL INC.—See Canon Inc.; *Int'l*, pg. 1296
CANON MEDICAL SYSTEMS CORPORATION—See Canon Inc.; *Int'l*, pg. 1296
CANON MEDICAL SYSTEMS EUROPE B.V.—See Canon Inc.; *Int'l*, pg. 1296
CANON MEDICAL SYSTEMS USA, INC.—See Canon Inc.; *Int'l*, pg. 1296
CARDIAC SCIENCE HOLDINGS UK LTD.—See Asahi Kasei Corporation; *Int'l*, pg. 597
CARDIAC SCIENCE INTERNATIONAL A/S—See Asahi Kasei Corporation; *Int'l*, pg. 597
CARDINAL HEALTH CANADA 437, INC.—See Cardinal Health, Inc.; *U.S. Public*, pg. 433
CARDINAL HEALTH CANADA, INC.—See Cardinal Health, Inc.; *U.S. Public*, pg. 433
CARDINAL HEALTH KOREA LIMITED—See Cardinal Health, Inc.; *U.S. Public*, pg. 433
CARDINAL HEALTH RADIATION MANAGEMENT SERVICES—See Cardinal Health, Inc.; *U.S. Public*, pg. 433
CARDIODX, INC.; *U.S. Private*, pg. 751
CARDIONOVUM GMBH—See Grand Pharmaceutical Group Limited; *Int'l*, pg. 3056
CARDIVA MEDICAL, INC.—See Haemonetics Corporation; *U.S. Public*, pg. 979
CAREDX, INC.; *U.S. Public*, pg. 435
CAREFUSION CORPORATION—See Becton, Dickinson & Company; *U.S. Public*, pg. 291
CAREFUSION DENMARK 329 A/S—See Becton, Dickinson & Company; *U.S. Public*, pg. 291
CAREFUSION FRANCE 309 S.A.S.—See Becton, Dickinson & Company; *U.S. Public*, pg. 291
CAREFUSION GERMANY 318 GMBH—See Becton, Dickinson & Company; *U.S. Public*, pg. 291
CAREFUSION GERMANY 326 GMBH—See Becton, Dickinson & Company; *U.S. Public*, pg. 291
CAREFUSION ISRAEL 330 LTD.—See Becton, Dickinson & Company; *U.S. Public*, pg. 291
CAREFUSION ITALY 311 S.R.L.—See Becton, Dickinson & Company; *U.S. Public*, pg. 291
CAREFUSION ITALY 327 S.R.L.—See Becton, Dickinson & Company; *U.S. Public*, pg. 291
CAREFUSION MEXICO 215 SA DE CV—See Becton, Dickinson & Company; *U.S. Public*, pg. 291
CAREFUSION SOLUTIONS, LLC—See Becton, Dickinson & Company; *U.S. Public*, pg. 291
CAREFUSION U.K. 306 LIMITED—See Becton, Dickinson & Company; *U.S. Public*, pg. 292
CAREMILE CO., LTD.; *Int'l*, pg. 1324
CARERAY DIGITAL MEDICAL TECHNOLOGY CO., LTD.; *Int'l*, pg. 1325
CARESTREAM MEDICAL LTD.; *Int'l*, pg. 1325
CARIBBEAN DIAGNOSTICS LTD.—See HORIBA Ltd; *Int'l*, pg. 3475
CARL ZEISS CANADA LTD.—See Carl-Zeiss-Stiftung; *Int'l*, pg. 1333
CARL ZEISS CO., LTD.—See Carl-Zeiss-Stiftung; *Int'l*, pg. 1334
CARL ZEISS MEDITEC FRANCE S.A.S.—See Carl-Zeiss-Stiftung; *Int'l*, pg. 1334
CARL ZEISS MEDITEC PRODUCTION, LLC—See Carl-Zeiss-Stiftung; *Int'l*, pg. 1334
CARL ZEISS MEDITEC SAS—See Carl-Zeiss-Stiftung; *Int'l*, pg. 1334
CARL ZEISS MICROSCOPY, LLC—See Carl-Zeiss-Stiftung; *Int'l*, pg. 1335
CARL ZEISS PTY LTD—See Carl-Zeiss-Stiftung; *Int'l*, pg. 1334
CARL ZEISS TEKNOLOJI COZUMLERI TICARET LIMITED SIRKETI—See Carl-Zeiss-Stiftung; *Int'l*, pg. 1335
CARL ZEISS VIETNAM COMPANY LIMITED—See Carl-Zeiss-Stiftung; *Int'l*, pg. 1335
CARMAT SAS; *Int'l*, pg. 1341
CARSTENS INC.; *U.S. Private*, pg. 774
CATHETER RESEARCH, INC.—See ATL Technology, Inc.; *U.S. Private*, pg. 369
CATHETER RESEARCH, INC.—See Wasatch Advantage Group, LLC; *U.S. Private*, pg. 4445
CAYENNE MEDICAL, INC.—See Zimmer Biomet Holdings, Inc.; *U.S. Public*, pg. 2406
CELLAVISION AB; *Int'l*, pg. 1392
CELLCURA ASA—See Dag Dvergsten AS; *Int'l*, pg. 1912
CELLCYTE GENETICS CORPORATION; *U.S. Private*, pg. 807
CELLSOURCE CO., LTD.; *Int'l*, pg. 1394
CENSIS TECHNOLOGIES, INC.—See Fortive Corporation; *U.S. Public*, pg. 870
CENTRAL CIRCLE CO.—See HORIBA Ltd; *Int'l*, pg. 3475
CENTRO DE CONSTRUCCION DE CARDIOESTIMULADORES DEL URUGUAY SA—See Integer Holdings Corporation; *U.S. Public*, pg. 1135
CENTURION MEDICAL PRODUCTS CORPORATION—See Medline Industries, LP; *U.S. Private*, pg. 2657
CHEETAH MEDICAL (ISRAEL), LTD.—See Baxter International Inc.; *U.S. Public*, pg. 281
CHEETAH MEDICAL (UK) LIMITED—See Baxter International Inc.; *U.S. Public*, pg. 281
CHEMBIO DIAGNOSTICS GMBH—See Biosynex SA; *Int'l*, pg. 1042
CHEMBIO DIAGNOSTICS, INC.—See Biosynex SA; *Int'l*, pg. 1042
CHEMBIO DIAGNOSTIC SYSTEMS, INC.—See Biosynex SA; *Int'l*, pg. 1042
CHEMCLIN DIAGNOSTICS CO., LTD.; *Int'l*, pg. 1461
CHIMIN HEALTH MANAGEMENT CO., LTD.; *Int'l*, pg. 1479

CHINA MEDICAL TECHNOLOGIES, INC.; *Int'l*, pg. 1518
CHINA NATIONAL MEDICAL EQUIPMENT INDUSTRY CORPORATION—See China National Pharmaceutical Group Corporation; *Int'l*, pg. 1533
CHIRANA T. INJECTA, A.S.; *Int'l*, pg. 1573
CHI SHENG PHARMA & BIOTECH CO., LTD.; *Int'l*, pg. 1475
CHISON DEUTSCHLAND GMBH—See Chison Medical Technologies Co., Ltd.; *Int'l*, pg. 1574
CHISON MEDICAL TECHNOLOGIES CO., LTD.; *Int'l*, pg. 1574
CHITOGENX INC; *Int'l*, pg. 1574
CHOICE SPINE, LLC—See Altus Capital Partners, Inc.; *U.S. Private*, pg. 211
CHROMOGENEX TECHNOLOGIES LTD.; *Int'l*, pg. 1588
CINEOPTIC A.D.; *Int'l*, pg. 1610
CIRTEC MEDICAL, LLC—See 3i Group plc; *Int'l*, pg. 8
CIVCO MEDICAL INSTRUMENTS CO., INC.—See Roper Technologies, Inc.; *U.S. Public*, pg. 1810
CLARET MEDICAL, INC.—See Boston Scientific Corporation; *U.S. Public*, pg. 375
CLASSYS INC.; *Int'l*, pg. 1653
CLEARPOINT NEURO, INC.; *U.S. Public*, pg. 512
CLEARSTREAM TECHNOLOGIES GROUP LIMITED—See Becton, Dickinson & Company; *U.S. Public*, pg. 291
CLEARSTREAM TECHNOLOGIES LIMITED—See Becton, Dickinson & Company; *U.S. Public*, pg. 291
CLINICAL DESIGN TECHNOLOGIES LTD.; *Int'l*, pg. 1659
CLINICAL GENOMICS PTY. LTD.; *Int'l*, pg. 1659
CLINICAL LASERTHERMIA SYSTEMS AB; *Int'l*, pg. 1659
CLOUDTAG INC.; *Int'l*, pg. 1662
CME AMERICA LLC—See Becton, Dickinson & Company; *U.S. Public*, pg. 291
CMICS MEDICAL ELECTRONIC INSTRUMENT CO., LTD.—See China National Pharmaceutical Group Corporation; *Int'l*, pg. 1533
CMS GMBH—See Elekta AB; *Int'l*, pg. 2355
CMS JAPAN K.K.—See Elekta AB; *Int'l*, pg. 2355
COCHLEAR AUSTRIA GMBH—See Cochlear Limited; *Int'l*, pg. 1686
COCHLEAR COLOMBIA SAS—See Cochlear Limited; *Int'l*, pg. 1687
COCHLEAR ITALIA SRL—See Cochlear Limited; *Int'l*, pg. 1687
COCHLEAR LATINOAMERICA S.A.—See Cochlear Limited; *Int'l*, pg. 1687
COCHLEAR LIMITED; *Int'l*, pg. 1686
COCHLEAR MEDICAL DEVICE (BEIJING) CO., LTD.—See Cochlear Limited; *Int'l*, pg. 1687
COCHLEAR MEXICO SA DE CV—See Cochlear Limited; *Int'l*, pg. 1687
COCHLEAR MIDDLE EAST FZ-LLC—See Cochlear Limited; *Int'l*, pg. 1687
COCHLEAR NORWAY AS—See Cochlear Limited; *Int'l*, pg. 1687
CODMAN NEUROVASCULAR INC.—See Johnson & Johnson; *U.S. Public*, pg. 1194
CO.DON AG; *Int'l*, pg. 1680
COEUR, INC.—See Illinois Tool Works Inc.; *U.S. Public*, pg. 1102
COEUR MEDICAL PRODUCTS, S. DE R.L. DE C.V.—See Illinois Tool Works Inc.; *U.S. Public*, pg. 1102
COFOE MEDICAL TECHNOLOGY CO., LTD.; *Int'l*, pg. 1693
COHEREX MEDICAL, INC.—See Johnson & Johnson; *U.S. Public*, pg. 1194
COLOPLAST (CHINA) MEDICAL DEVICES LTD.—See Coloplast A/S; *Int'l*, pg. 1703
COLOPLAST CORP.—See Coloplast A/S; *Int'l*, pg. 1703
COLOPLAST CROATIA—See Coloplast A/S; *Int'l*, pg. 1703
COLOPLAST CZECH REPUBLIC—See Coloplast A/S; *Int'l*, pg. 1703
COLOPLAST GREECE—See Coloplast A/S; *Int'l*, pg. 1703
COLOPLAST (HONG KONG) LTD.—See Coloplast A/S; *Int'l*, pg. 1703
COLOPLAST (INDIA) PRIVATE LIMITED—See Coloplast A/S; *Int'l*, pg. 1703
COLOPLAST KOREA LIMITED—See Coloplast A/S; *Int'l*, pg. 1703
COLOPLAST OY—See Coloplast A/S; *Int'l*, pg. 1703
COLOPLAST PORTUGAL LDA.—See Coloplast A/S; *Int'l*, pg. 1703
COLOPLAST SLOVAKIA—See Coloplast A/S; *Int'l*, pg. 1704
COLOPLAST SLOVENIA—See Coloplast A/S; *Int'l*, pg. 1704
COLOPLAST SPAIN—See Coloplast A/S; *Int'l*, pg. 1704
COMPRESSION THERAPY CONCEPTS, INC.—See Zimmer Biomet Holdings, Inc.; *U.S. Public*, pg. 2406
CONCEPTUS, INC.—See Bayer Aktiengesellschaft; *Int'l*, pg. 905
CONFIRM BIOSCIENCES, INC.—See Clinical Reference Laboratory, Inc.; *U.S. Private*, pg. 944
CONFLUENT MEDICAL TECHNOLOGIES, INC.—See TPG Capital, L.P.; *U.S. Public*, pg. 2169
CONFORMIS, INC.—See restor3d, Inc.; *U.S. Private*, pg. 3409
CONMED EUROPE BV—See CONMED Corporation; *U.S. Public*, pg. 567
CONNECTYX TECHNOLOGIES HOLDINGS GROUP, INC.; *U.S. Public*, pg. 568

339112 — SURGICAL AND MEDICA...

CONVATEC ARGENTINA SRL—See ConvaTec Group PLC; *Int'l*, pg. 1786

CONVATEC (AUSTRALIA) PTY LIMITED—See ConvaTec Group PLC; *Int'l*, pg. 1786

CONVATEC BELGIUM BVBA—See ConvaTec Group PLC; *Int'l*, pg. 1786

CONVATEC CANADA LIMITED—See ConvaTec Group PLC; *Int'l*, pg. 1786

CONVATEC CESKA REPUBLIKA S.R.O.—See ConvaTec Group PLC; *Int'l*, pg. 1786

CONVATEC CHINA LIMITED—See ConvaTec Group PLC; *Int'l*, pg. 1786

CONVATEC DENMARK A/S—See ConvaTec Group PLC; *Int'l*, pg. 1786

CONVATEC DOMINICAN REPUBLIC INC.—See ConvaTec Group PLC; *Int'l*, pg. 1786

CONVATEC GROUP PLC; *Int'l*, pg. 1786

CONVATEC HELLAS MEDICAL PRODUCTS S.A.—See ConvaTec Group PLC; *Int'l*, pg. 1786

CONVATEC HONG KONG LIMITED—See ConvaTec Group PLC; *Int'l*, pg. 1786

CONVATEC INDIA PRIVATE LIMITED—See ConvaTec Group PLC; *Int'l*, pg. 1786

CONVATEC ITALIA S.R.L.—See ConvaTec Group PLC; *Int'l*, pg. 1786

CONVATEC JAPAN KK—See ConvaTec Group PLC; *Int'l*, pg. 1786

CONVATEC KOREA, LTD.—See ConvaTec Group PLC; *Int'l*, pg. 1786

CONVATEC LIMITED—See ConvaTec Group PLC; *Int'l*, pg. 1786

CONVATEC LTD.—See Avista Capital Partners, L.P.; *U.S. Private*, pg. 408

CONVATEC MALAYSIA SDN BHD—See ConvaTec Group PLC; *Int'l*, pg. 1786

CONVATEC MIDDLE EAST & AFRICA LLC—See ConvaTec Group PLC; *Int'l*, pg. 1786

CONVATEC NEDERLAND B.V.—See ConvaTec Group PLC; *Int'l*, pg. 1786

CONVATEC NORWAY AS—See ConvaTec Group PLC; *Int'l*, pg. 1786

CONVATEC PERU S.A.C.—See ConvaTec Group PLC; *Int'l*, pg. 1786

CONVATEC POLSKA SP. Z O.O.—See ConvaTec Group PLC; *Int'l*, pg. 1786

CONVATEC SAGLIK URUNLERI LIMITED SIRKETI—See ConvaTec Group PLC; *Int'l*, pg. 1786

CONVATEC (SINGAPORE) PTE LIMITED—See ConvaTec Group PLC; *Int'l*, pg. 1786

CONVATEC SOUTH AFRICA (PTY) LIMITED—See ConvaTec Group PLC; *Int'l*, pg. 1786

CONVATEC (SWEDEN) AB—See ConvaTec Group PLC; *Int'l*, pg. 1786

CONVATEC TECHNOLOGIES INC.—See ConvaTec Group PLC; *Int'l*, pg. 1786

CONVATEC (THAILAND) CO. LIMITED—See ConvaTec Group PLC; *Int'l*, pg. 1786

COOK (CANADA) INC.—See Cook Group Incorporated; *U.S. Private*, pg. 1037

COOK INCORPORATED—See Cook Group Incorporated; *U.S. Private*, pg. 1037

COOK IRELAND LTD.—See Cook Group Incorporated; *U.S. Private*, pg. 1037

COOLSYSTEMS, INC.—See Avanos Medical, Inc.; *U.S. Public*, pg. 241

COOPER-ATKINS CORPORATION—See Emerson Electric Co.; *U.S. Public*, pg. 742

CORDIS EUROPA NV—See Johnson & Johnson; *U.S. Public*, pg. 1194

CORDIS LLC—See Johnson & Johnson; *U.S. Public*, pg. 1194

CORENTEC CO., LTD.; *Int'l*, pg. 1799

CORETRONIC DISPLAY SOLUTION CORPORATION—See Coretronic Corporation; *Int'l*, pg. 1800

CORPAK MEDSYSTEMS, INC.—See Avanos Medical, Inc.; *U.S. Public*, pg. 241

CORZA MEDICAL INC.—See GTCR LLC; *U.S. Private*, pg. 1804

COVALON TECHNOLOGIES INC.—See Covalon Technologies Ltd.; *Int'l*, pg. 1820

CP MEDICAL—See Juniper Investment Company, LLC; *U.S. Private*, pg. 2244

C-RAD INCORPORATED—See C-RAD AB; *Int'l*, pg. 1239

CRANIAL TECHNOLOGIES, INC.—See Eurazeo SE; *Int'l*, pg. 2528

C. R. BARD GMBH—See Becton, Dickinson & Company; *U.S. Public*, pg. 291

C.R. BARD, INC.—See Becton, Dickinson & Company; *U.S. Public*, pg. 290

C.R. BARD, INC.—See Becton, Dickinson & Company; *U.S. Public*, pg. 291

CREO MEDICAL LIMITED—See Creo Medical Group PLC; *Int'l*, pg. 1839

CROSSJECT SA; *Int'l*, pg. 1856

CRYOFOCUS MEDTECH (SHANGHAI) CO., LTD.; *Int'l*, pg. 1859

CRYSTAL BIOTECH—See Matec Instrument Companies, Inc.; *U.S. Private*, pg. 2609

CS MEDICA A/S; *Int'l*, pg. 1861

CU MEDICAL SYSTEMS INC.; *Int'l*, pg. 1875

CURIA NEW MEXICO, LLC—See GTCR LLC; *U.S. Private*, pg. 1805

CURIA NEW MEXICO, LLC—See The Carlyle Group Inc.; *U.S. Public*, pg. 2046

CURIOX BIOSYSTEMS CO., LTD.; *Int'l*, pg. 1878

CVM DIAGNOSTICO VETERINARIO, S.L.—See Mars, Incorporated; *U.S. Private*, pg. 2588

CVR MEDICAL CORP.; *Int'l*, pg. 1889

CVRX, INC.; *U.S. Public*, pg. 613

CYBERDYNE INC.; *Int'l*, pg. 1892

CYCLOMEDICA EUROPE LIMITED—See Cyclopharm Limited; *Int'l*, pg. 1894

CYCLOMEDICA GERMANY GMBH—See Cyclopharm Limited; *Int'l*, pg. 1894

CYCLOMEDICA NORDIC AB—See Cyclopharm Limited; *Int'l*, pg. 1894

CYG MEDITECH TECHNOLOGY CO., LTD.—See ChangYuan Group Ltd.; *Int'l*, pg. 1444

CYNOSURE GMBH—See El.En. S.p.A.; *Int'l*, pg. 2341

CYNOSURE KK—See El.En. S.p.A.; *Int'l*, pg. 2341

CYTOGNOS SPAIN S.L.U.—See Becton, Dickinson & Company; *U.S. Public*, pg. 292

CYTOSORBENTS CORPORATION; *U.S. Public*, pg. 618

CYTOTOOLS AG; *Int'l*, pg. 1898

CYTYC PRENATAL PRODUCTS CORP.—See Hologic, Inc.; *U.S. Public*, pg. 1044

DAIKEN MEDICAL CO., LTD.; *Int'l*, pg. 1931

DANISCO AUSTRIA GMBH—See International Flavors & Fragrances Inc.; *U.S. Public*, pg. 1151

DARIOHEALTH CORP.; *U.S. Public*, pg. 633

DASCO HOME MEDICAL EQUIPMENT; *U.S. Private*, pg. 1161

DATA SCIENCES INTERNATIONAL—See Harvard Bioscience, Inc.; *U.S. Public*, pg. 987

DAYS HEALTHCARE U.K. LIMITED—See Madison Dearborn Partners, LLC; *U.S. Private*, pg. 2542

DE DIETRICH SINGAPORE (PTE) LTD.—See De Dietrich Process Systems S.A.; *Int'l*, pg. 1995

DE DIETRICH SOUTH AFRICA (PTY) LTD.—See De Dietrich Process Systems S.A.; *Int'l*, pg. 1995

DEKA LASERTECHNOLOGIE GMBH—See El.En. S.p.A.; *Int'l*, pg. 2342

DEKA MEDICAL INC—See El.En. S.p.A.; *Int'l*, pg. 2342

DEKA M.E.L.A. SRL—See El.En. S.p.A.; *Int'l*, pg. 2342

DEKA TECHNOLOGIES LASER SARL—See El.En. S.p.A.; *Int'l*, pg. 2342

DELCATH SYSTEMS, INC.; *U.S. Public*, pg. 648

DELSTAR INTERNATIONAL, LIMITED—See Mativ Holdings, Inc.; *U.S. Public*, pg. 1396

DELTAMED S.A.—See ArchiMed SAS; *Int'l*, pg. 548

DELTEX MEDICAL ESPANA—See Deltex Medical Group plc; *Int'l*, pg. 2020

DELTEX MEDICAL GROUP PLC; *Int'l*, pg. 2020

DELTEX MEDICAL LIMITED—See Deltex Medical Group plc; *Int'l*, pg. 2020

DELTEX MEDICAL SC INC.—See Deltex Medical Group plc; *Int'l*, pg. 2021

DENTAPLY PROSTHETICS AUSTRIA GMBH—See DENTSPLY SIRONA Inc.; *U.S. Public*, pg. 654

DENTIS CO., LTD.; *Int'l*, pg. 2033

DENTSPLY IMPLANTS TURKEY A.S.—See DENTSPLY SIRONA Inc.; *U.S. Public*, pg. 654

DENTSPLY SIRONA BENELUX B.V.—See DENTSPLY SIRONA Inc.; *U.S. Public*, pg. 654

DENTSPLY SIRONA IMPLANTS NORWAY—See DENTSPLY SIRONA Inc.; *U.S. Public*, pg. 654

DENTSPLY SIRONA - NORWAY—See DENTSPLY SIRONA Inc.; *U.S. Public*, pg. 654

DEPUY INTERNATIONAL LIMITED—See Johnson & Johnson; *U.S. Public*, pg. 1195

DEPUY (IRELAND) LIMITED—See Johnson & Johnson; *U.S. Public*, pg. 1195

DEPUY MITEK, INC.—See Johnson & Johnson; *U.S. Public*, pg. 1195

DEPUY ORTHOPEDIE S.A.—See Johnson & Johnson; *U.S. Public*, pg. 1195

DEPUY SPINE, INC.—See Johnson & Johnson; *U.S. Public*, pg. 1195

DEPUY SPINE SARL—See Johnson & Johnson; *U.S. Public*, pg. 1195

DEPUY SYNTHES PRODUCTS, INC.—See Johnson & Johnson; *U.S. Public*, pg. 1195

DERMA SCIENCES, INC.—See Integra LifeSciences Holdings Corporation; *U.S. Public*, pg. 1135

DERMTECH, LLC; *U.S. Private*, pg. 1210

DERMTECH OPERATIONS, INC.—See DermTech, LLC; *U.S. Private*, pg. 1210

DEROYAL INDUSTRIES INC.; *U.S. Private*, pg. 1210

DETECTION TECHNOLOGY, INC.—See Detection Technology Oyj; *Int'l*, pg. 2048

DETECTION TECHNOLOGY OYJ; *Int'l*, pg. 2047

DEVAX, INC.—See Biosensors International Group, Ltd.; *Int'l*, pg. 1041

DEVICOR MEDICAL PRODUCTS, INC.—See Danaher Corporation; *U.S. Public*, pg. 628

DEXCOM INC; *U.S. Public*, pg. 657

DIAGENODE CO., LTD.—See Hologic, Inc.; *U.S. Public*, pg. 1044

DIAGENODE SA—See Hologic, Inc.; *U.S. Public*, pg. 1044

DIAGENODE SPA—See Hologic, Inc.; *U.S. Public*, pg. 1044

DIAGNOSTIC MEDICAL SYSTEMS S.A.; *Int'l*, pg. 2103

DIAGNOSTIX LTD.—See Thermo Fisher Scientific Inc.; *U.S. Public*, pg. 2148

DIAMEDIC IMPORT—See HORIBA Ltd; *Int'l*, pg. 3475

DIATEC SARL—See HORIBA Ltd; *Int'l*, pg. 3475

DIBA INDUSTRIES, INC.—See Halma plc; *Int'l*, pg. 3231

DIDRICK MEDICAL, INC.; *U.S. Public*, pg. 1228

DIFCO LABORATORIES INCORPORATED—See Becton, Dickinson & Company; *U.S. Public*, pg. 292

DIGITAL ENDOSCOPY GMBH—See Hoya Corporation; *Int'l*, pg. 3496

DIGNITANA INC.—See Dignitana AB; *Int'l*, pg. 2124

DILWORTH HEARING LTD.—See Amplifon S.p.A.; *Int'l*, pg. 435

DIOPSYS, INC.—See LumiThera, Inc.; *U.S. Private*, pg. 2514

DIRECT MEDICAL SUPPLY, LLC—See KKR & Co. Inc.; *U.S. Public*, pg. 1249

DJO FRANCE, S.A.S.—See Enovis Corporation; *U.S. Public*, pg. 772

DJ ORTHOPEDICS DE MEXICO SA DE CV—See Enovis Corporation; *U.S. Public*, pg. 772

DJ ORTHOPEDICS DEUTSCHLAND—See Enovis Corporation; *U.S. Public*, pg. 772

DJO SURGICAL—See Enovis Corporation; *U.S. Public*, pg. 772

DJO UK LTD.—See Enovis Corporation; *U.S. Public*, pg. 772

DNA ELECTRONICS LTD.—See Genting Berhad; *Int'l*, pg. 2928

DOMS APS—See Vontier Corporation; *U.S. Public*, pg. 2308

DONATELLE PLASTICS, INC.—See DuPont de Nemours, Inc.; *U.S. Public*, pg. 692

D.O.R.C. DUTCH OPHTHALMIC RESEARCH CENTER (INTERNATIONAL) B.V.—See Carl-Zeiss-Stiftung; *Int'l*, pg. 1333

DORNIER MEDTECH EUROPE GMBH—See Airbus SE; *U.S. Public*, pg. 242

DORSAVI LTD; *Int'l*, pg. 2179

DRAEGER ARABIA CO. LTD.—See Draegerwerk AG & Co. KGaA; *Int'l*, pg. 2196

DRAEGER AUSTRALIA PTY. LTD.—See Draegerwerk AG & Co. KGaA; *Int'l*, pg. 2196

DRAEGER, INC.—See Draegerwerk AG & Co. KGaA; *Int'l*, pg. 2197

DRAEGER IRELAND LTD.—See Draegerwerk AG & Co. KGaA; *Int'l*, pg. 2196

DRAEGER ITALIA S.P.A.—See Draegerwerk AG & Co. KGaA; *Int'l*, pg. 2196

DRAEGER KOREA CO., LTD.—See Draegerwerk AG & Co. KGaA; *Int'l*, pg. 2196

DRAEGER MALAYSIA SDN. BHD.—See Draegerwerk AG & Co. KGaA; *Int'l*, pg. 2196

DRAEGER MAROC SARLAU—See Draegerwerk AG & Co. KGaA; *Int'l*, pg. 2196

DRAEGER MEDICAL TAIWAN LTD.—See Draegerwerk AG & Co. KGaA; *Int'l*, pg. 2196

DRAEGER MEDICAL (THAILAND) LTD.—See Draegerwerk AG & Co. KGaA; *Int'l*, pg. 2196

DRAEGER MEDICAL UK LTD.—See Draegerwerk AG & Co. KGaA; *Int'l*, pg. 2196

DRAEGER MEDIKAL TICARET VE SERVIS ANONIM SIRKETI—See Draegerwerk AG & Co. KGaA; *Int'l*, pg. 2196

DRAEGER MYANMAR LIMITED—See Draegerwerk AG & Co. KGaA; *Int'l*, pg. 2196

DRAEGER NEW ZEALAND LIMITED—See Draegerwerk AG & Co. KGaA; *Int'l*, pg. 2196

DRAEGER PHILIPPINES CORPORATION—See Draegerwerk AG & Co. KGaA; *Int'l*, pg. 2197

DRAEGER SAFETY KORUNMA TEKNOLOJILERI ANONIM SIRKETI—See Draegerwerk AG & Co. KGaA; *Int'l*, pg. 2197

DRAEGER SAFETY UK LTD.—See Draegerwerk AG & Co. KGaA; *Int'l*, pg. 2197

DRAEGER SINGAPORE PTE LTD.—See Draegerwerk AG & Co. KGaA; *Int'l*, pg. 2197

DRAEGER TEHNIKA D.O.O.—See Draegerwerk AG & Co. KGaA; *Int'l*, pg. 2197

DRAEGER VIETNAM CO., LTD.—See Draegerwerk AG & Co. KGaA; *Int'l*, pg. 2197

DRAGER ARGENTINA SA—See Draegerwerk AG & Co. KGaA; *Int'l*, pg. 2198

DRAGER DO BRASIL LTDA.—See Draegerwerk AG & Co. KGaA; *Int'l*, pg. 2198

DRAGER GEBAUDE UND SERVICE GMBH—See Draegerwerk AG & Co. KGaA; *Int'l*, pg. 2197

DRAGER MEDICAL ANSY GMBH—See Draegerwerk AG & Co. KGaA; *Int'l*, pg. 2197

DRAGER MEDICAL CROATIA D.O.O.—See Draegerwerk AG & Co. KGaA; *Int'l*, pg. 2197

DRAGER MEDICAL DEUTSCHLAND GMBH—See Draegerwerk AG & Co. KGaA; *Int'l*, pg. 2197

339112 — SURGICAL AND MEDICA...

DRAGER MEDICAL HISPANIA SA—See Draegerwerk AG & Co. KGaA; *Int'l*, pg. 2197
DRAGER MEDICAL HUNGARY KFT.—See Draegerwerk AG & Co. KGaA; *Int'l*, pg. 2197
DRAGER NEDERLAND B.V.—See Draegerwerk AG & Co. KGaA; *Int'l*, pg. 2197
DRAGER NORGE AS—See Draegerwerk AG & Co. KGaA; *Int'l*, pg. 2197
DRAGER SAFETY D.O.O.—See Draegerwerk AG & Co. KGaA; *Int'l*, pg. 2198
DRAGER SAFETY HISPANIA SA—See Draegerwerk AG & Co. KGaA; *Int'l*, pg. 2197
DRAGER SAFETY HUNGARIA KFT.—See Draegerwerk AG & Co. KGaA; *Int'l*, pg. 2198
DRAGER SLOVENIJA D.O.O.—See Draegerwerk AG & Co. KGaA; *Int'l*, pg. 2198
DRAGER SLOVENSKO S.R.O.—See Draegerwerk AG & Co. KGaA; *Int'l*, pg. 2198
DRAGER SOUTH AFRICA (PTY) LTD.—See Draegerwerk AG & Co. KGaA; *Int'l*, pg. 2198
DRAGER TGM GMBH—See Draegerwerk AG & Co. KGaA; *Int'l*, pg. 2198
DRAVON MEDICAL, INC.; *U.S. Private*, pg. 1272
DRGEM CORP.; *Int'l*, pg. 2204
DT ELECTRONIC MANUFACTURING (BEIJING) CO., LTD.—See Detection Technology Oyj; *Int'l*, pg. 2047
DTF (H.K.) LTD.—See Detection Technology Oyj; *Int'l*, pg. 2048
DUNE MEDICAL DEVICES—See Dilon Technologies LLC; *U.S. Private*, pg. 1232
DUTCH OPHTHALMIC USA, INC.—See Carl-Zeiss-Stiftung; *Int'l*, pg. 1333
DVX, INC.; *Int'l*, pg. 2236
DX & VX CO.; *Int'l*, pg. 2237
DYN DIAGNOSTICS LTD.—See HORIBA Ltd; *Int'l*, pg. 3475
EBI PATIENT CARE, INC.—See Zimmer Biomet Holdings, Inc.; *U.S. Public*, pg. 2406
ECA MEDICAL INSTRUMENTS—See LongueVue Capital, LLC; *U.S. Private*, pg. 2493
ECHO THERAPEUTICS, INC.; *U.S. Public*, pg. 710
ECKERT & ZIEGLER BEBIG DO BRASIL LTDA.—See Eckert & Ziegler Strahlen- und Medizintechnik AG; *Int'l*, pg. 2290
ECKERT & ZIEGLER BEBIG LTD.—See Eckert & Ziegler Strahlen- und Medizintechnik AG; *Int'l*, pg. 2290
ECKERT & ZIEGLER BEBIG SARL—See Eckert & Ziegler Strahlen- und Medizintechnik AG; *Int'l*, pg. 2290
ECKERT & ZIEGLER BEBIG S.A.—See Eckert & Ziegler Strahlen- und Medizintechnik AG; *Int'l*, pg. 2290
ECKERT & ZIEGLER F-CON DEUTSCHLAND GMBH—See Eckert & Ziegler Strahlen- und Medizintechnik AG; *Int'l*, pg. 2290
ECKERT & ZIEGLER F-CON EUROPE GMBH—See Eckert & Ziegler Strahlen- und Medizintechnik AG; *Int'l*, pg. 2290
ECKERT & ZIEGLER IBERIA S.L.—See Eckert & Ziegler Strahlen- und Medizintechnik AG; *Int'l*, pg. 2290
ECKERT & ZIEGLER ITALIA S.R.L.—See Eckert & Ziegler Strahlen- und Medizintechnik AG; *Int'l*, pg. 2290
ECKERT & ZIEGLER UMWELTDIENSTE GMBH—See Eckert & Ziegler Strahlen- und Medizintechnik AG; *Int'l*, pg. 2290
EDAP TECHNOMED CO. LTD.—See EDAP TMS S.A.; *Int'l*, pg. 2304
EDAP TECHNOMED ITALIA SRL—See EDAP TMS S.A.; *Int'l*, pg. 2304
EDAP TECHNOMED (M) SDN BHD—See EDAP TMS S.A.; *Int'l*, pg. 2304
EDAP TECHNOMED SDN BHD—See EDAP TMS S.A.; *Int'l*, pg. 2304
EDAP TMS GMBH—See EDAP TMS S.A.; *Int'l*, pg. 2304
EDWARDS LIFESCIENCES AG—See Edwards Lifesciences Corporation; *U.S. Public*, pg. 720
EDWARDS LIFESCIENCES CORPORATION OF PUERTO RICO—See Edwards Lifesciences Corporation; *U.S. Public*, pg. 720
EDWARDS LIFESCIENCES DR—See Edwards Lifesciences Corporation; *U.S. Public*, pg. 720
EDWARDS LIFESCIENCES (MALAYSIA) SDN. BHD.—See Edwards Lifesciences Corporation; *U.S. Public*, pg. 720
EDWARDS LIFESCIENCES—See Edwards Lifesciences Corporation; *U.S. Public*, pg. 720
EHS LENS PHILIPPINES, INC.—See Hoya Corporation; *Int'l*, pg. 3494
EKSO BIONICS (EMEA)—See Ekso Bionics Holdings, Inc.; *U.S. Public*, pg. 722
EKSO BIONICS HOLDINGS, INC.; *U.S. Public*, pg. 722
ELASTIC THERAPY, LLC—See Enovis Corporation; *U.S. Public*, pg. 772
ELBIT MEDICAL TECHNOLOGIES LTD.; *Int'l*, pg. 2344
ELECTRICAL GEODESICS, INC.—See Telegraph Hill Partners Management Company, LLC; *U.S. Private*, pg. 3960
ELECTRO MEDICAL INSTRUMENTS BV—See Amplifon S.p.A.; *Int'l*, pg. 435
ELECTROMED, INC.; *U.S. Public*, pg. 723
ELEKTA AB; *Int'l*, pg. 2355
ELEKTA BMEI (BEIJING) MEDICAL EQUIPMENT CO., LTD—See Elekta AB; *Int'l*, pg. 2355
ELEKTA B.V.—See Elekta AB; *Int'l*, pg. 2355

ELEKTA GMBH—See Elekta AB; *Int'l*, pg. 2355
ELEKTA / IMPAC MEDICAL SYSTEMS, INC.—See Elekta AB; *Int'l*, pg. 2355
ELEKTA INC.—See Elekta AB; *Int'l*, pg. 2355
ELEKTA INSTRUMENT AB—See Elekta AB; *Int'l*, pg. 2355
ELEKTA INSTRUMENT (SHANGHAI) LTD—See Elekta AB; *Int'l*, pg. 2355
ELEKTA LIMITED—See Elekta AB; *Int'l*, pg. 2355
ELEKTA MEDICAL S.A.—See Elekta AB; *Int'l*, pg. 2355
ELEKTA MEDICAL SYSTEMS INDIA PVT. LTD.—See Elekta AB; *Int'l*, pg. 2355
ELEKTA NEUROMAG OY—See Elekta AB; *Int'l*, pg. 2356
ELEKTA PTY. LTD.—See Elekta AB; *Int'l*, pg. 2356
ELEKTA (PTY) LTD (SOUTHERN AFRICA)—See Elekta AB; *Int'l*, pg. 2355
ELEKTA SA—See Elekta AB; *Int'l*, pg. 2356
ELI LILLY (M) SDN. BHD.—See Eli Lilly & Company; *U.S. Public*, pg. 732
ELI LILLY Y COMPANIA DE VENEZUELA, S.A.—See Eli Lilly & Company; *U.S. Public*, pg. 733
ELITECHGROUP INC.—See Bruker Corporation; *U.S. Public*, pg. 406
ELK CORPORATION—See Canon Inc.; *Int'l*, pg. 1296
ELLMAN INTERNATIONAL, LLC—See Clayton, Dubilier & Rice, LLC; *U.S. Private*, pg. 922
ELOS MEDTECH AB—See TA Associates, Inc.; *U.S. Private*, pg. 3918
ELOS MEDTECH PINOL A/S—See TA Associates, Inc.; *U.S. Private*, pg. 3918
ELOS MEDTECH TIANJIN CO. LTD.—See TA Associates, Inc.; *U.S. Private*, pg. 3918
ELOS MEDTECH TIMMERSDALA AB—See TA Associates, Inc.; *U.S. Private*, pg. 3918
EMBLA SYSTEMS LLC—See ArchiMed SAS; *Int'l*, pg. 548
EMBRYOTECH LABS INC.—See Astorg Partners S.A.S.; *Int'l*, pg. 656
E MED FUTURE, INC.; *U.S. Public*, pg. 701
EMERALD MEDICAL SERVICES PTE. LTD.—See IntriCon Corporation; *U.S. Public*, pg. 1159
EMERGENT PROTECTIVE PRODUCTS USA INC—See Emergent BioSolutions Inc.; *U.S. Public*, pg. 740
EMSOR, SOCIEDAD DE RESPONSABILIDAD LIMITADA—See Hologic, Inc.; *U.S. Public*, pg. 1044
EMVISION MEDICAL DEVICES LTD.; *Int'l*, pg. 2395
ENCISION INC.; *U.S. Public*, pg. 754
ENDOGENE LTD.; *Int'l*, pg. 2405
ENDOLOGIX, INC.; *U.S. Private*, pg. 1392
ENDOSCOPIC TECHNOLOGIES, LLC—See AtriCure, Inc.; *U.S. Public*, pg. 225
ENDOSOLUTIONS, INC.—See Integra LifeSciences Holdings Corporation; *U.S. Public*, pg. 1135
ENDO-THERAPEUTICS, INC.; *U.S. Private*, pg. 1392
ENDYMED LTD.; *Int'l*, pg. 2410
ENICOR GMBH—See Haemonetics Corporation; *U.S. Public*, pg. 979
ENOVA ILLUMINATION, LLC; *U.S. Private*, pg. 1401
ENVIZION MEDICAL LTD.; *Int'l*, pg. 2456
EOFLOW CO., LTD.; *Int'l*, pg. 2457
EONE DIAGNOMICS GENOME CENTER CO., LTD.; *Int'l*, pg. 2458
EOS IMAGE, INC.—See Alphatec Holdings, Inc.; *U.S. Public*, pg. 84
EOS IMAGING CANADA—See Alphatec Holdings, Inc.; *U.S. Public*, pg. 84
EOS IMAGING GMBH—See Alphatec Holdings, Inc.; *U.S. Public*, pg. 84
EOS IMAGING INC.—See Alphatec Holdings, Inc.; *U.S. Public*, pg. 84
EOS IMAGING S.A.—See Alphatec Holdings, Inc.; *U.S. Public*, pg. 84
EPIPROCARE GMBH; *Int'l*, pg. 2460
EPISURF MEDICAL AB; *Int'l*, pg. 2463
EPPENDORF AG; *Int'l*, pg. 2463
EPPENDORF INDIA LTD.—See Eppendorf AG; *Int'l*, pg. 2464
EPPENDORF ZENTRIFUGEN GMBH—See Eppendorf AG; *Int'l*, pg. 2464
EPS EKISHIN CO., LTD.—See EPS Holdings, Inc.; *Int'l*, pg. 2465
EPTAM PRECISION SOLUTIONS—See Frazier & Company, Inc.; *U.S. Private*, pg. 1599
ERGO-FLEX TECHNOLOGIES, LLC; *U.S. Private*, pg. 1417
ERWEKA GMBH; *Int'l*, pg. 2500
ESS GMBH—See Masco Corporation; *U.S. Public*, pg. 1390
ESTILL MEDICAL TECHNOLOGIES, INC.; *U.S. Private*, pg. 1429
ETHICON ENDO-SURGERY (EUROPE) GMBH—See Johnson & Johnson; *U.S. Public*, pg. 1196
ETHICON ENDO-SURGERY INC—See Johnson & Johnson; *U.S. Public*, pg. 1195
ETHICON GMBH—See Johnson & Johnson; *U.S. Public*, pg. 1196
ETHICON, INC.—See Johnson & Johnson; *U.S. Public*, pg. 1196
ETS-LINDGREN GMBH—See ESCO Technologies, Inc.; *U.S. Public*, pg. 794
EUROCHARM HOLDINGS CO., LTD.; *Int'l*, pg. 2533

EUROFINS BACTIMM BV—See Eurofins Scientific S.E.; *Int'l*, pg. 2538
EUROFINS LIFECODEXX GMBH—See Eurofins Scientific S.E.; *Int'l*, pg. 2545
EUROFINS MATERIALS SCIENCE NETHERLANDS BV—See Eurofins Scientific S.E.; *Int'l*, pg. 2546
EUROTEC B.V.—See ConvaTec Group PLC; *Int'l*, pg. 1786
EUROTEC GMBH—See ConvaTec Group PLC; *Int'l*, pg. 1786
EVOME MEDICAL TECHNOLOGIES INC.; *U.S. Public*, pg. 804
EWELLNESS HEALTHCARE CORPORATION; *U.S. Public*, pg. 805
EXACTECH, INC.—See TPG Capital, L.P.; *U.S. Public*, pg. 2173
EXACTECH INTERNATIONAL OPERATION AG—See TPG Capital, L.P.; *U.S. Public*, pg. 2173
EXCELLUS TECHNOLOGIES, INC.—See J.H. Whitney & Co., LLC; *U.S. Private*, pg. 2166
EXCELSIOR MEDICAL CORPORATION—See ICU Medical, Inc.; *U.S. Public*, pg. 1087
EXCEL TECH CORP.—See ArchiMed SAS; *Int'l*, pg. 548
EXCEL TECH LTD.—See ArchiMed SAS; *Int'l*, pg. 548
EXIMO MEDICAL, LTD.—See AngioDynamics, Inc.; *U.S. Public*, pg. 137
EYEBRIGHT MEDICAL TECHNOLOGY BEIJING CO., LTD.; *Int'l*, pg. 2592
EYELOGIC SYSTEMS INC.; *Int'l*, pg. 2593
FACET TECHNOLOGIES, LLC—See Tower Three Partners, LLC; *U.S. Private*, pg. 4194
FAITH PROSTHETIC-ORTHOTIC SERVICES, INC.—See Patient Square Capital, L.P.; *U.S. Private*, pg. 3107
FARM DESIGN, INC.—See Flex Ltd.; *Int'l*, pg. 2703
FAXITRON BIOPTICS, LLC—See Hologic, Inc.; *U.S. Public*, pg. 1044
FCI OPHTHALMICS INC.—See Carl-Zeiss-Stiftung; *Int'l*, pg. 1336
FEEDBACK PLC; *Int'l*, pg. 2631
FENWAL CONTROLS OF JAPAN,LTD.; *Int'l*, pg. 2634
FIBERTECH CO., LTD.—See Fujikura Ltd.; *Int'l*, pg. 2827
FILMECC CO., LTD.—See Asahi Intecc Co., Ltd.; *Int'l*, pg. 594
FILTERTEK DO BRASIL INDUSTRIA E COMERCIO LTDA.—See Illinois Tool Works Inc.; *U.S. Public*, pg. 1103
FIRMA AMBU, S.L.—See Ambu A/S; *Int'l*, pg. 416
FISHER & PAYKEL HEALTHCARE AB—See Fisher & Paykel Healthcare Corporation Limited; *Int'l*, pg. 2693
FISHER & PAYKEL HEALTHCARE CORPORATION LIMITED; *Int'l*, pg. 2692
FISHER & PAYKEL HEALTHCARE GMBH & CO. KG—See Fisher & Paykel Healthcare Corporation Limited; *Int'l*, pg. 2693
FISHER & PAYKEL HEALTHCARE (GUANGZHOU) LIMITED—See Fisher & Paykel Healthcare Corporation Limited; *Int'l*, pg. 2692
FISHER & PAYKEL HEALTHCARE INC.—See Fisher & Paykel Healthcare Corporation Limited; *Int'l*, pg. 2693
FISHER & PAYKEL HEALTHCARE K.K.—See Fisher & Paykel Healthcare Corporation Limited; *Int'l*, pg. 2693
FISHER & PAYKEL HEALTHCARE LIMITED—See Fisher & Paykel Healthcare Corporation Limited; *Int'l*, pg. 2693
FISHER & PAYKEL HEALTHCARE LIMITED—See Fisher & Paykel Healthcare Corporation Limited; *Int'l*, pg. 2693
FISHER & PAYKEL HEALTHCARE PTY. LIMITED—See Fisher & Paykel Healthcare Corporation Limited; *Int'l*, pg. 2693
FISHER & PAYKEL HEALTHCARE S.A. DE C.V.—See Fisher & Paykel Healthcare Corporation Limited; *Int'l*, pg. 2693
FISHER & PAYKEL HEALTHCARE SAS—See Fisher & Paykel Healthcare Corporation Limited; *Int'l*, pg. 2693
FISHER PAYKEL SAGLIK URUNLERI TICARET LIMITED SIRKETI—See Fisher & Paykel Healthcare Corporation Limited; *Int'l*, pg. 2693
FLAGSHIP GLOBAL CORPORATION; *Int'l*, pg. 2697
FLEXICARE MEDICAL LTD.—See Flexicare (Group) Limited; *Int'l*, pg. 2704
FMI HANSA MEDICAL PRODUCTS, LLC; *U.S. Private*, pg. 1554
FRANTZ MEDICAL GROUP; *U.S. Private*, pg. 1598
FRESENIUS MEDICAL CARE DEUTSCHLAND GMBH—See Fresenius Medical Care AG; *Int'l*, pg. 2775
FRESENIUS MEDICAL CARE DEUTSCHLAND GMBH—See Fresenius Medical Care AG; *Int'l*, pg. 2775
FRESENIUS MEDICAL CARE ITALIA S.P.A.—See Fresenius Medical Care AG; *Int'l*, pg. 2775
FRESENIUS MEDICAL CARE KOREA LTD.—See Fresenius Medical Care AG; *Int'l*, pg. 2775
FRESENIUS MEDICAL CARE LTDA.—See Fresenius Medical Care AG; *Int'l*, pg. 2775
FRESENIUS MEDICAL CARE MEXICO S.A.—See Fresenius Medical Care AG; *Int'l*, pg. 2775
FREUDENBERG MEDICAL EUROPE GMBH—See Freudenberg SE; *Int'l*, pg. 2787
FREUDENBERG MEDICAL SRL—See Freudenberg SE; *Int'l*, pg. 2787
FUJIFILM HOLDINGS AMERICA CORPORATION—See

N.A.I.C.S. INDEX

339112 — SURGICAL AND MEDICA...

FUJIFILM Holdings Corporation; *Int'l*, pg. 2824
FUJIFILM MEDICAL SOLUTIONS CO., LTD.—See FUJIFILM Holdings Corporation; *Int'l*, pg. 2824
FUJIFILM TOYAMA CHEMICAL CO., LTD.—See FUJIFILM Holdings Corporation; *Int'l*, pg. 2825
FUJIREBIO CHINA CO., LTD.—See H.U. Group Holdings, Inc.; *Int'l*, pg. 3196
FUJIREBIO EUROPE N.V.—See H.U. Group Holdings, Inc.; *Int'l*, pg. 3196
FUJIREBIO FRANCE SARL—See H.U. Group Holdings, Inc.; *Int'l*, pg. 3196
FUJIREBIO GERMANY GMBH—See H.U. Group Holdings, Inc.; *Int'l*, pg. 3196
FUJIREBIO HOLDINGS, INC.—See H.U. Group Holdings, Inc.; *Int'l*, pg. 3196
FUJIREBIO IBERIA SL—See H.U. Group Holdings, Inc.; *Int'l*, pg. 3196
FUJIREBIO ITALIA S.R.L.—See H.U. Group Holdings, Inc.; *Int'l*, pg. 3196
FUJIREBIO US, INC.—See H.U. Group Holdings, Inc.; *Int'l*, pg. 3196
FUJISOFT TISSUE ENGINEERING CO., LTD.—See FUJISOFT INCORPORATED; *Int'l*, pg. 2830
FUKUDA ASIA PACIFIC PTE. LTD.—See Fukuda Denshi Co., Ltd.; *Int'l*, pg. 2839
FUKUDA DENSHI CO., LTD.; *Int'l*, pg. 2839
FUKUDA DENSHI UK LTD.—See Fukuda Denshi Co., Ltd.; *Int'l*, pg. 2839
FUKUDA DENSHI USA, INC.—See Fukuda Denshi Co., Ltd.; *Int'l*, pg. 2840
FUMOUZE DIAGNOSTICS—See Church & Dwight Co., Inc.; *U.S. Public*, pg. 493
FUSO TEIYAKU (QINGDAO) CO., LTD.—See Fuso Chemical Co., Ltd.; *Int'l*, pg. 2850
FUTUREMATRIX INTERVENTIONAL, INC.—See Brookhaven Medical, Inc.; *U.S. Private*, pg. 663
GAES COLOMBIA SAS—See Amplifon S.p.A.; *Int'l*, pg. 435
GALATEA SURGICAL, INC.—See Becton, Dickinson & Company; *U.S. Public*, pg. 292
GALEMED CORPORATION; *Int'l*, pg. 2872
GALT MEDICAL CORP.—See Juniper Investment Company, LLC; *U.S. Private*, pg. 2244
GAMBRO DIALYSATOREN GMBH—See Baxter International Inc.; *U.S. Public*, pg. 282
GAMBRO INC.—See Baxter International Inc.; *U.S. Public*, pg. 281
GATT TECHNOLOGIES B.V.—See Johnson & Johnson; *U.S. Public*, pg. 1196
GAUDLITZ PRECISION S.R.O.—See H&R KGaA; *Int'l*, pg. 3193
GCE GROUP AB—See Enovis Corporation; *U.S. Public*, pg. 772
GCE INDIA LTD.—See Enovis Corporation; *U.S. Public*, pg. 772
GCX CORPORATION—See Audax Group, Limited Partnership; *U.S. Private*, pg. 388
GE HEALTHCARE FINLAND OY—See GE HealthCare Technologies Inc.; *U.S. Public*, pg. 909
GEMMEL RX; *U.S. Private*, pg. 1658
GEM S.R.L.; *Int'l*, pg. 2915
GENCURIX, INC.; *Int'l*, pg. 2917
GENEJET BIOTECH CO., LTD.—See BenQ Materials Corp.; *Int'l*, pg. 975
GENERA BIOSYSTEMS LIMITED; *Int'l*, pg. 2917
GENESYSTEM CO., LTD.; *Int'l*, pg. 2922
GENKO ITALIA SRL; *Int'l*, pg. 2924
GENORAY AMERICA INC.—See Genoray Co., Ltd.; *Int'l*, pg. 2925
GENORAY EU GMBH—See Genoray Co., Ltd.; *Int'l*, pg. 2925
GENORAY JAPAN, K.K.—See Genoray Co., Ltd.; *Int'l*, pg. 2925
GENOVEL ORTHOPEDICS, INC.—See INNOVATE Corp.; *U.S. Public*, pg. 1126
GEN-PROBE DENMARK APS—See Hologic, Inc.; *U.S. Public*, pg. 1044
GEN-PROBE PRODESSE, INC.—See Hologic, Inc.; *U.S. Public*, pg. 1044
GEN-PROBE SWEDEN AB—See Hologic, Inc.; *U.S. Public*, pg. 1045
GERATHERM MEDICAL AG; *Int'l*, pg. 2942
GERATHERM RESPIRATORY GMBH—See Geratherm Medical AG; *Int'l*, pg. 2942
GERMFREE LABORATORIES INC.; *U.S. Private*, pg. 1687
GERRESHEIMER BUNDE GMBH—See Gerresheimer AG; *Int'l*, pg. 2943
GERRESHEIMER ITEM GMBH—See Gerresheimer AG; *Int'l*, pg. 2943
GERRESHEIMER SISTEMAS PLASTICOS MEDICINAIS SAO PAULO LTDA.—See Gerresheimer AG; *Int'l*, pg. 2944
GETINGE ARJO A/S—See Getinge AB; *Int'l*, pg. 2949
GETINGE DANMARK A/S—See Getinge AB; *Int'l*, pg. 2949
GETINGE SKARHAMN AB—See Getinge AB; *Int'l*, pg. 2950
GETINGE SOURCING LLC—See Getinge AB; *Int'l*, pg. 2950
GI DYNAMICS, INC.; *U.S. Private*, pg. 1691
GLAUKOS CORPORATION; *U.S. Public*, pg. 939

GLAUKOS GERMANY GMBH—See Glaukos Corporation; *U.S. Public*, pg. 940
GLAXOSMITHKLINE CONSUMER HEALTHCARE AB—See GSK plc; *Int'l*, pg. 3147
GLAXOSMITHKLINE CONSUMER HEALTHCARE AUSTRALIA PTY LTD—See GSK plc; *Int'l*, pg. 3147
GLAXOSMITHKLINE CONSUMER HEALTHCARE COLOMBIA SAS—See GSK plc; *Int'l*, pg. 3147
GLAXOSMITHKLINE CONSUMER HEALTHCARE CZECH REPUBLIC S.R.O.—See GSK plc; *Int'l*, pg. 3147
GLAXOSMITHKLINE CONSUMER HEALTHCARE FINLAND OY—See GSK plc; *Int'l*, pg. 3147
GLAXOSMITHKLINE CONSUMER HEALTHCARE KOREA CO., LTD.—See GSK plc; *Int'l*, pg. 3147
GLAXOSMITHKLINE CONSUMER HEALTHCARE PAKISTAN LIMITED—See GSK plc; *Int'l*, pg. 3147
GLAXOSMITHKLINE CONSUMER HEALTHCARE S.A.—See GSK plc; *Int'l*, pg. 3147
GLAXOSMITHKLINE CONSUMER HEALTHCARE SLOVAKIA S. R. O.—See GSK plc; *Int'l*, pg. 3147
GLAXOSMITHKLINE CONSUMER HEALTHCARE (THAILAND) LIMITED—See GSK plc; *Int'l*, pg. 3147
GLAXOSMITHKLINE-CONSUMER HUNGARY LIMITED LIABILITY COMPANY—See GSK plc; *Int'l*, pg. 3149
GLAXOSMITHKLINE CONSUMER NIGERIA PLC—See GSK plc; *Int'l*, pg. 3147
GLAXOSMITHKLINE GUATEMALA S.A.—See GSK plc; *Int'l*, pg. 3147
GLAXOSMITHKLINE HEALTHCARE AO—See GSK plc; *Int'l*, pg. 3147
GLAXOSMITHKLINE HONDURAS S.A.—See GSK plc; *Int'l*, pg. 3147
GLAXOSMITHKLINE LIETUVA UAB—See GSK plc; *Int'l*, pg. 3148
GLAXOSMITHKLINE SINGLE MEMBER A.E.B.E.—See GSK plc; *Int'l*, pg. 3149
GLAXOSMITHKLINE TUNISIA S.A.R.L.—See GSK plc; *Int'l*, pg. 3149
GLOBAL HEALTH TECHNOLOGIES, INC.; *U.S. Private*, pg. 1714
GLOBUS MEDICAL AUSTRALIA PTY LIMITED—See Globus Medical, Inc.; *U.S. Public*, pg. 947
GLOBUS MEDICAL AUSTRIA GMBH—See Globus Medical, Inc.; *U.S. Public*, pg. 947
GLOBUS MEDICAL BRASIL LTDA.—See Globus Medical, Inc.; *U.S. Public*, pg. 947
GLOBUS MEDICAL, INC.; *U.S. Public*, pg. 946
GLOBUS MEDICAL SOUTH AFRICA PTY LIMITED—See Globus Medical, Inc.; *U.S. Public*, pg. 947
GMO MEDICAL RESERVATIONS TECHNOLOGY CO., LTD.—See GMO Internet Group, Inc.; *Int'l*, pg. 3014
GN RESOUND A/S—See GN Store Nord A/S; *Int'l*, pg. 3016
GN RESOUND ITALIA SRL—See GN Store Nord A/S; *Int'l*, pg. 3016
GOLDEN ALLY LIFETECH GROUP, INC.; *U.S. Public*, pg. 950
GOLDEN MEDITECH HOLDINGS LIMITED; *Int'l*, pg. 3030
GRANDHOPE BIOTECH CO., LTD.; *Int'l*, pg. 3058
GRANDHOPE BIOTECH (SHANGHAI) CO., LTD—See Grandhope Biotech Co., Ltd.; *Int'l*, pg. 3058
GRASEBY MEDICAL IRELAND LTD.—See ICU Medical, Inc.; *U.S. Public*, pg. 1087
GREAT BASIN SCIENTIFIC, INC.; *U.S. Private*, pg. 1762
GREATBATCH LTD. - PLYMOUTH PLANT—See Integer Holdings Corporation; *U.S. Public*, pg. 1135
GREATBATCH LTD.—See Integer Holdings Corporation; *U.S. Public*, pg. 1134
GREATBATCH MCSO, S. DE R.L. DE C.V—See Integer Holdings Corporation; *U.S. Public*, pg. 1135
GREATBATCH MEDICAL SA—See Integer Holdings Corporation; *U.S. Public*, pg. 1135
GREATBATCH MEDICAL SAS—See Integer Holdings Corporation; *U.S. Public*, pg. 1135
GRIFOLS CANADA LTD.—See Grifols, S.A.; *Int'l*, pg. 3084
GSK BUSINESS SERVICE CENTRE SDN BHD—See GSK plc; *Int'l*, pg. 3145
GSK CH KAZAKHSTAN LLP—See GSK plc; *Int'l*, pg. 3145
GSK CONSUMER HEALTHCARE LEVICE, S.R.O.—See GSK plc; *Int'l*, pg. 3145
GSK CONSUMER HEALTHCARE TRINIDAD & TOBAGO LIMITED—See GSK plc; *Int'l*, pg. 3145
GSK D.O.O.—See GSK plc; *Int'l*, pg. 3145
GSK KAZAKHSTAN LLP—See GSK plc; *Int'l*, pg. 3145
GSK VACCINES GMBH—See GSK plc; *Int'l*, pg. 3145
GSK VACCINES INSTITUTE FOR GLOBAL HEALTH S.R.L.—See GSK plc; *Int'l*, pg. 3145
GTG WELLNESS CO., LTD.; *Int'l*, pg. 3151
GUANGDONG BIOLIGHT MEDITECH CO., LTD.; *Int'l*, pg. 3153
GUANGZHOU LBP MEDICINE SCIENCE & TECHNOLOGY CO., LTD.; *Int'l*, pg. 3166
GUERBET COLOMBIA S.A.S.—See Guerbet SA; *Int'l*, pg. 3172
GUERBET KOREA LTD.—See Guerbet SA; *Int'l*, pg. 3172
GUERBET POLAND SP. Z O.O.—See Guerbet SA; *Int'l*, pg. 3172
GUIDANT EUROPE SA/NV—See Boston Scientific Corporation; *U.S. Public*, pg. 374

GUIDED THERAPEUTICS, INC.; *U.S. Public*, pg. 974
GYROS PROTEIN TECHNOLOGIES AB—See Mesa Laboratories, Inc.; *U.S. Public*, pg. 1426
HADER SA—See Fagron NV; *Int'l*, pg. 2603
HAEMONETICS BELGIUM N.V.—See Haemonetics Corporation; *U.S. Public*, pg. 979
HAEMONETICS CANADA, LTD.—See Haemonetics Corporation; *U.S. Public*, pg. 979
HAEMONETICS CORPORATION; *U.S. Public*, pg. 979
HAEMONETICS HONG KONG LTD.—See Haemonetics Corporation; *U.S. Public*, pg. 979
HAEMONETICS HOSPITALAR EIRELI—See Haemonetics Corporation; *U.S. Public*, pg. 979
HAEMONETICS MANUFACTURING, INC.—See Haemonetics Corporation; *U.S. Public*, pg. 979
HANGZHOU ALLTEST BIOTECH CO., LTD.; *Int'l*, pg. 3246
HANGZHOU ANOW MICROFILTRATION CO., LTD.—See Entegris, Inc.; *U.S. Public*, pg. 777
HANS BIOMED CORPORATION; *Int'l*, pg. 3258
HANSEN MEDICAL, INC.—See Johnson & Johnson; *U.S. Public*, pg. 1194
HANSEN MEDICAL UK LTD.—See Johnson & Johnson; *U.S. Public*, pg. 1194
HARMAC MEDICAL PRODUCTS INC.; *U.S. Private*, pg. 1865
HARTFORD GREAT HEALTH CORP.; *U.S. Public*, pg. 986
HARVARD BIOSCIENCE (SHANGHAI) CO. LTD.—See Harvard Bioscience, Inc.; *U.S. Public*, pg. 987
HEALIOS K.K.; *Int'l*, pg. 3302
HEALTH PHARMA SPA—See Health Biosciences SpA; *Int'l*, pg. 3303
HEALTHWELL MEDICAL INC.—See CU Medical Systems Inc.; *Int'l*, pg. 1875
HEARTSINE TECHNOLOGIES, LLC—See Stryker Corporation; *U.S. Public*, pg. 1955
HEIDELBERG ENGINEERING GMBH—See EssilorLuxottica SA; *Int'l*, pg. 2514
HELENA LABORATORIES CORPORATION; *U.S. Private*, pg. 1906
HELIUS MEDICAL TECHNOLOGIES, INC.; *U.S. Public*, pg. 1024
HEPAHOPE, INC.; *U.S. Private*, pg. 1920
HI-CLEARANCE, INC.; *Int'l*, pg. 3380
HILL-ROM AB—See Baxter International Inc.; *U.S. Public*, pg. 282
HILL-ROM AUSTRIA GMBH—See Baxter International Inc.; *U.S. Public*, pg. 282
HILL-ROM COMERCIALIZADOR A DE MEXICO S DE RL DE CV—See Baxter International Inc.; *U.S. Public*, pg. 283
HILL-ROM DTC, INC.—See Baxter International Inc.; *U.S. Public*, pg. 283
HILL-ROM GMBH—See Baxter International Inc.; *U.S. Public*, pg. 283
HILL-ROM, INC.—See Baxter International Inc.; *U.S. Public*, pg. 282
HILL-ROM JAPAN KK—See Baxter International Inc.; *U.S. Public*, pg. 283
HILL-ROM LOGISTICS, LLC—See Baxter International Inc.; *U.S. Public*, pg. 283
HILL-ROM MANUFACTURING, INC.—See Baxter International Inc.; *U.S. Public*, pg. 283
HILL-ROM PTY, LTD—See Baxter International Inc.; *U.S. Public*, pg. 283
HILL-ROM SARL—See Baxter International Inc.; *U.S. Public*, pg. 283
HILL-ROM SERVICES PTE, LTD.—See Baxter International Inc.; *U.S. Public*, pg. 283
HILL-ROM SHANGHAI LTD.—See Baxter International Inc.; *U.S. Public*, pg. 283
HILL-ROM SOCIEDADE UNIPESSOAL, LDA A PORTUGUESE CORPORATION—See Baxter International Inc.; *U.S. Public*, pg. 283
HILL-ROM SOCIEDADE UNIPESSOAL, LDA—See Baxter International Inc.; *U.S. Public*, pg. 283
HILL-ROM SPRL—See Baxter International Inc.; *U.S. Public*, pg. 283
HILL-ROM TURKEY MEDIKAL URUNLER DAGITIM VE TICARET LIMITED SIRKETI—See Baxter International Inc.; *U.S. Public*, pg. 283
HILL-ROM UK (HOLDINGS) LTD.—See Baxter International Inc.; *U.S. Public*, pg. 283
HIRONIC CO., LTD.; *Int'l*, pg. 3405
HISSAB LASANTECH SAS—See HORIBA Ltd; *Int'l*, pg. 3477
HI-TECH INSTRUMENTS SDN BHD—See HORIBA Ltd; *Int'l*, pg. 3477
HNE MEDICAL SA—See Getinge AB; *Int'l*, pg. 2948
HOB BIOTECH GROUP CORP., LTD.; *Int'l*, pg. 3436
HOHNER MASCHINENBAU GMBH; *Int'l*, pg. 3442
HOLDCO NUVO GROUP D.G LTD.; *U.S. Public*, pg. 1044
HOLLISTER DO BRASIL LTDA—See Hollister Incorporated; *U.S. Private*, pg. 1966
HOLOGIC ASIA PACIFIC LIMITED—See Hologic, Inc.; *U.S. Public*, pg. 1045
HOLOGIC (AUSTRALIA) PTY LIMITED—See Hologic, Inc.; *U.S. Public*, pg. 1045

339112 — SURGICAL AND MEDICA...   CORPORATE AFFILIATIONS

HOLOGIC DEUTSCHLAND GMBH—See Hologic, Inc.; *U.S. Public*, pg. 1045
HOLOGIC FRANCE, SARL—See Hologic, Inc.; *U.S. Public*, pg. 1045
HOLOGIC FRANCE S.A.—See Hologic, Inc.; *U.S. Public*, pg. 1045
HOLOGIC HITEC-IMAGING GMBH—See Hologic, Inc.; *U.S. Public*, pg. 1045
HOLOGIC IBERIA, S.L.—See Hologic, Inc.; *U.S. Public*, pg. 1045
HOLOGIC, INC.; *U.S. Public*, pg. 1044
HOLOGIC JAPAN, INC.—See Hologic, Inc.; *U.S. Public*, pg. 1045
HOLOGIC NETHERLANDS B.V.—See Hologic, Inc.; *U.S. Public*, pg. 1045
HOLOGIC SUISSE SA—See Hologic, Inc.; *U.S. Public*, pg. 1045
HOLOGIC SURGICAL PRODUCTS COSTA RICA S.A.—See Hologic, Inc.; *U.S. Public*, pg. 1045
HOLOGIC SWEDEN AB—See Hologic, Inc.; *U.S. Public*, pg. 1045
HOMEDICS USA LLC; *U.S. Private*, pg. 1973
HONEYWELL SAFETY PRODUCTS USA, INC.—See Honeywell International Inc.; *U.S. Public*, pg. 1048
HORIBA PRECISION INSTRUMENTS (BEIJING) CO., LTD.—See HORIBA Ltd; *Int'l*, pg. 3477
HOYA GLASS DISK VIETNAM II LTD.—See Hoya Corporation; *Int'l*, pg. 3495
HOYA GLASS DISK VIETNAM LTD.—See Hoya Corporation; *Int'l*, pg. 3495
HOYA HEALTHCARE (SHANGHAI) CO., LTD.—See Hoya Corporation; *Int'l*, pg. 3495
HOYA LAMPHUN LTD.—See Hoya Corporation; *Int'l*, pg. 3497
HOYA LAOS CO., LTD.—See Hoya Corporation; *Int'l*, pg. 3497
HOYA LENS MANUFACTURING HUNGARY PRIVATE CO.—See Hoya Corporation; *Int'l*, pg. 3497
HOYA LENS RUSSIA LLC—See Hoya Corporation; *Int'l*, pg. 3498
HOYA MEDICAL DEVICE CONSULTING CO., LTD.—See Hoya Corporation; *Int'l*, pg. 3498
HOYA MEDICAL INDIA PVT, LTD.—See Hoya Corporation; *Int'l*, pg. 3498
HOYA MEMORY DISK TECHNOLOGIES LTD.—See Hoya Corporation; *Int'l*, pg. 3498
HOYA SURGICAL OPTICS, INC.—See Hoya Corporation; *Int'l*, pg. 3497
HOYA TURKEY OPTIK LENS SAN. VE TIC. A.S.—See Hoya Corporation; *Int'l*, pg. 3498
HPIL HOLDING; *U.S. Public*, pg. 1065
H.U. CELLS, INC.—See H.U. Group Holdings, Inc.; *Int'l*, pg. 3197
HUIHENG MEDICAL, INC.; *Int'l*, pg. 3526
HUMAN METABOLOME TECHNOLOGIES INC.; *Int'l*, pg. 3529
HUNAN APT MEDICAL INC.—See APT Medical, Inc.; *Int'l*, pg. 523
HUNTLEIGH TECHNOLOGY LTD—See Getinge AB; *Int'l*, pg. 2949
HUVITZ CO., LTD.; *Int'l*, pg. 3540
HYALTECH LTD.—See Carl-Zeiss-Stiftung; *Int'l*, pg. 1336
HYPERTENSION DIAGNOSTICS, INC.; *U.S. Public*, pg. 1079
I.CERAM; *Int'l*, pg. 3565
ICONOVO AB; *Int'l*, pg. 3586
ICU MEDICAL AUSTRALIA PTY LIMITED—See ICU Medical, Inc.; *U.S. Public*, pg. 1087
ICU MEDICAL, INC.; *U.S. Public*, pg. 1086
ICU MEDICAL (UTAH), INC.—See ICU Medical, Inc.; *U.S. Public*, pg. 1087
IDEX BIOMETRICS UK LTD.—See IDEX Biometrics ASA; *Int'l*, pg. 3592
IDEX HEATH & SCIENCE GMBH—See IDEX Corp; *U.S. Public*, pg. 1090
I-FLOW, LLC—See Kimberly-Clark Corporation; *U.S. Public*, pg. 1229
ILLUMINA K.K.—See Illumina, Inc.; *U.S. Public*, pg. 1112
ILLUMINA MIDDLE EAST FZE—See Illumina, Inc.; *U.S. Public*, pg. 1112
ILLUMINA SINGAPORE PTE. LTD.—See Illumina, Inc.; *U.S. Public*, pg. 1112
ILLUMINOSS MEDICAL, INC.—See HealthpointCapital, LLC; *U.S. Private*, pg. 1897
ILOODA CO., LTD.; *Int'l*, pg. 3616
ILS SERVICES SWITZERLAND LTD.—See Integra LifeSciences Holdings Corporation; *U.S. Public*, pg. 1135
IMA AUTOMATION USA, INC.—See I.M.A. Industria Macchine Automatiche S.p.A.; *Int'l*, pg. 3565
IMAGE PROTECT, INC.; *U.S. Public*, pg. 1112
IMAGING DYNAMICS COMPANY LTD.; *Int'l*, pg. 3619
IMA MEDTECH SWITZERLAND SA—See I.M.A. Industria Macchine Automatiche S.p.A.; *Int'l*, pg. 3565
I.M.D. INTERNATIONAL MEDICAL DEVICES S.P.A.; *Int'l*, pg. 3564
IM-MEDICO SVENSKA AB—See ADDvise Group AB; *Int'l*, pg. 136

IMMUNETICS, INC.—See Revvity, Inc.; *U.S. Public*, pg. 1794
IMMUNOLAB CLINICAL DIAGNOSTICS GMBH—See Eurofins Scientific S.E.; *Int'l*, pg. 2550
IMMUNOLAB GMBH—See Eurofins Scientific S.E.; *Int'l*, pg. 2550
IMMUNOSTICS, INC.—See Boditech Med, Inc.; *Int'l*, pg. 1097
IMPLANTABLE PROVIDER GROUP—See TPG Capital, L.P.; *U.S. Public*, pg. 2176
IMPLANT DIRECT SYBRON MANUFACTUING LLC—See Danaher Corporation; *U.S. Public*, pg. 627
IMRIS INC.; *U.S. Public*, pg. 1114
INFUSE MEDICAL; *U.S. Private*, pg. 2075
INFUSYSTEM HOLDINGS, INC.; *U.S. Public*, pg. 1118
INGEN TECHNOLOGIES, INC.; *U.S. Public*, pg. 1118
INNOGENETICS DIAGNOSTICA IBERIA, S.L.—See H.U. Group Holdings, Inc.; *Int'l*, pg. 3196
INNOGENETICS, INC.—See H.U. Group Holdings, Inc.; *Int'l*, pg. 3196
INNOGENETICS SARL—See H.U. Group Holdings, Inc.; *Int'l*, pg. 3196
INNOGENETICS S.R.L.—See H.U. Group Holdings, Inc.; *Int'l*, pg. 3196
INNOVATION TEAM SWEDEN AB—See Etteplan Oyj; *Int'l*, pg. 2525
INNOVEREN SCIENTIFIC, INC.; *U.S. Public*, pg. 1127
INNOVIA ST CO., LTD.—See Hoya Corporation; *Int'l*, pg. 3498
INOGEN, INC.; *U.S. Public*, pg. 1128
INOLIFE TECHNOLOGIES INC.; *U.S. Private*, pg. 2084
INOVIO PHARMACEUTICALS, INC.; *U.S. Public*, pg. 1128
INOVO, INC.—See Medical Depot, Inc.; *U.S. Private*, pg. 2655
INSTITUTE OF BIO-MEDICAL AND WELFARE ENGINEERING CO., LTD—See Core Corporation; *Int'l*, pg. 1797
INSTITUTO EM DIAGNOSTICO MOLECULAR THERANOSTICA LTDA—See H.U. Group Holdings, Inc.; *Int'l*, pg. 3196
INSTRUMED INTERNATIONAL, INC.—See Arlington Capital Partners LLC; *U.S. Private*, pg. 327
INSULET CORPORATION; *U.S. Public*, pg. 1134
INTEGRA GMBH—See Integra LifeSciences Holdings Corporation; *U.S. Public*, pg. 1135
INTEGRA LIFESCIENCES CORPORATION—See Integra LifeSciences Holdings Corporation; *U.S. Public*, pg. 1135
INTEGRA LIFESCIENCES SERVICES (FRANCE) SAS—See Integra LifeSciences Holdings Corporation; *U.S. Public*, pg. 1135
INTEGRA LS (BENELUX) NV—See Integra LifeSciences Holdings Corporation; *U.S. Public*, pg. 1135
INTEGRA LUXTEC, INC.—See Integra LifeSciences Holdings Corporation; *U.S. Public*, pg. 1136
INTEGRA NEUROSCIENCES LIMITED—See Integra LifeSciences Holdings Corporation; *U.S. Public*, pg. 1136
INTELLIGENT HEARING SYSTEMS CORP.; *U.S. Private*, pg. 2105
INTER BUSINESS'91 LTD.—See HORIBA Ltd; *Int'l*, pg. 3477
INTERLINK PRODUCTS INTERNATIONAL, INC.; *U.S. Public*, pg. 1144
INTERMED NUCLEAR MEDICINE, INC.—See Cressey & Company, LP; *U.S. Private*, pg. 1095
INTERMED NUCLEAR MEDICINE, INC.—See Health Enterprise Partners LLC; *U.S. Private*, pg. 1893
INTERNATIONAL LIFE SCIENCES LLC; *U.S. Private*, pg. 2118
INTERPLEX MEDICAL, LLC—See Blackstone Inc.; *U.S. Public*, pg. 355
INTUITIVE SURGICAL DEUTSCHLAND GMBH—See Intuitive Surgical, Inc.; *U.S. Public*, pg. 1160
INTUITIVE SURGICAL GK—See Intuitive Surgical, Inc.; *U.S. Public*, pg. 1160
INTUITIVE SURGICAL, INC.; *U.S. Public*, pg. 1160
INTUITIVE SURGICAL KOREA LIMITED—See Intuitive Surgical, Inc.; *U.S. Public*, pg. 1160
INTUITIVE SURGICAL MEDICAL DEVICE SCIENCE & TECHNOLOGY (SHANGHAI) CO., LTD.—See Intuitive Surgical, Inc.; *U.S. Public*, pg. 1160
INTUITIVE SURGICAL, SARL—See Intuitive Surgical, Inc.; *U.S. Public*, pg. 1160
INVACARE CORPORATION; *U.S. Private*, pg. 2130
INVETECH PTY. LTD.—See Fortive Corporation; *U.S. Public*, pg. 871
INVIVO THERAPEUTICS HOLDINGS CORP,; *U.S. Public*, pg. 1166
INVO BIOSCIENCE, INC.; *U.S. Public*, pg. 1166
INVUITY, INC.—See Stryker Corporation; *U.S. Public*, pg. 1955
IRIDEX S.A.—See IRIDEX Corporation; *U.S. Public*, pg. 1171
I-SENS INC. - SONGDO FACTORY—See i-SENS Inc.; *Int'l*, pg. 3564
I-SENS INC.; *Int'l*, pg. 3564
I-SENS INC. - WONJU FACTORY—See i-SENS Inc.; *Int'l*, pg. 3564
ISORAY MEDICAL, INC.—See Perspective Therapeutics, Inc.; *U.S. Public*, pg. 1678

ITS SCIENCE & MEDICAL PTE. LTD.—See HORIBA Ltd; *Int'l*, pg. 3477
ITW MEDICAL PRODUCTS INC—See Illinois Tool Works Inc.; *U.S. Public*, pg. 1106
IVERMEDI LTD.—See HORIBA Ltd; *Int'l*, pg. 3477
IVY SPORTS MEDICINE, LLC—See Stryker Corporation; *U.S. Public*, pg. 1956
IZI MEDICAL PRODUCTS, LLC—See Halma plc; *Int'l*, pg. 3232
JAPAN TISSUE ENGINEERING CO., LTD.—See FUJIFILM Holdings Corporation; *Int'l*, pg. 2826
JARIT GMBH—See Integra LifeSciences Holdings Corporation; *U.S. Public*, pg. 1136
JEISYS MEDICAL INC.—See ArchiMed SAS; *Int'l*, pg. 548
JMAR, LLC; *U.S. Private*, pg. 2214
JOERNS HEALTHCARE, LLC; *U.S. Private*, pg. 2219
JOHNSON & JOHNSON AB—See Johnson & Johnson; *U.S. Public*, pg. 1198
JOHNSON & JOHNSON (CHINA) LTD.—See Johnson & Johnson; *U.S. Public*, pg. 1198
JOHNSON & JOHNSON DE COLOMBIA S.A.—See Kenvue Inc.; *U.S. Public*, pg. 1224
JOHNSON & JOHNSON DE VENEZUELA, S.A.—See Johnson & Johnson; *U.S. Public*, pg. 1199
JOHNSON & JOHNSON HELLAS S.A.—See Johnson & Johnson; *U.S. Public*, pg. 1198
JOHNSON & JOHNSON (HONG KONG) LIMITED—See Johnson & Johnson; *U.S. Public*, pg. 1198
JOHNSON & JOHNSON INC.—See Kenvue Inc.; *U.S. Public*, pg. 1224
JOHNSON & JOHNSON PACIFIC PTY. LTD.—See Kenvue Inc.; *U.S. Public*, pg. 1224
JOHNSON & JOHNSON (PHILIPPINES), INC.—See Johnson & Johnson; *U.S. Public*, pg. 1198
JOHNSON & JOHNSON PROFESSIONAL CO. (P.R.) INC.—See Johnson & Johnson; *U.S. Public*, pg. 1199
JOHNSON & JOHNSON, S.A. DE C.V.—See Kenvue Inc.; *U.S. Public*, pg. 1224
JOHNSON & JOHNSON SDN. BHD.—See Johnson & Johnson; *U.S. Public*, pg. 1199
JOHNSON & JOHNSON S.P.A.—See Johnson & Johnson; *U.S. Public*, pg. 1199
JOHNSON & JOHNSON SURGICAL VISION, INC.—See Johnson & Johnson; *U.S. Public*, pg. 1199
JOLIFE AB—See Stryker Corporation; *U.S. Public*, pg. 1956
J.O. PHARMA CO., LTD.—See Earth Corporation; *Int'l*, pg. 2268
JTECH MEDICAL INDUSTRIES, INC.—See ADDvise Group AB; *Int'l*, pg. 136
JV ZEISS-BELOMO OOO—See Carl-Zeiss-Stiftung; *Int'l*, pg. 1336
JW ICU MEDICAL LIMITED—See Biosensors International Group, Ltd.; *Int'l*, pg. 1041
KALTENBACH & VOIGT GMBH—See Danaher Corporation; *U.S. Public*, pg. 627
KATALYST SURGICAL, LLC—See Carl-Zeiss-Stiftung; *Int'l*, pg. 1334
KAVTEK SOFTWARE CORP; *U.S. Public*, pg. 1215
KCI AUSTRALIA PTY. LTD.—See 3M Company; *U.S. Public*, pg. 7
KCI AUSTRIA GMBH—See 3M Company; *U.S. Public*, pg. 7
KCI CLINIC SPAIN S.L.—See 3M Company; *U.S. Public*, pg. 7
KCI EUROPE HOLDING B.V.—See 3M Company; *U.S. Public*, pg. 8
KCI KK—See 3M Company; *U.S. Public*, pg. 7
KCI MEDICAL AB—See 3M Company; *U.S. Public*, pg. 7
KCI MEDICAL APS—See 3M Company; *U.S. Public*, pg. 7
KCI MEDICAL ASIA PTE, LTD.—See 3M Company; *U.S. Public*, pg. 7
KCI MEDICAL B.V.—See 3M Company; *U.S. Public*, pg. 7
KCI MEDICAL CANADA, INC.—See 3M Company; *U.S. Public*, pg. 7
KCI MEDICAL GMBH—See 3M Company; *U.S. Public*, pg. 7
KCI MEDICAL LTD.—See 3M Company; *U.S. Public*, pg. 8
KCI MEDICAL SOUTH AFRICA PTY. LTD.—See 3M Company; *U.S. Public*, pg. 8
KCI MEDICAL S.R.L.—See 3M Company; *U.S. Public*, pg. 8
KCI MEDIZINPRODUCKTE GMBH—See 3M Company; *U.S. Public*, pg. 8
KCI USA, INC.—See 3M Company; *U.S. Public*, pg. 8
KD SCIENTIFIC, INC.—See Harvard Bioscience, Inc.; *U.S. Public*, pg. 987
KEELER LIMITED—See Halma plc; *Int'l*, pg. 3232
KEIS GROUP—See HORIBA Ltd; *Int'l*, pg. 3477
KEYSTONE DENTAL AB—See Keystone Dental, Inc.; *U.S. Private*, pg. 2296
KEYSTONE DENTAL GMBH—See Keystone Dental, Inc.; *U.S. Private*, pg. 2296
KEYSTONE DENTAL S.A.S.—See Keystone Dental, Inc.; *U.S. Private*, pg. 2296
KEYSTONE DENTAL SPA—See Keystone Dental, Inc.; *U.S. Private*, pg. 2296
KIMBERLY-CLARK BALLARD MEDICAL—See Kimberly-Clark Corporation; *U.S. Public*, pg. 1230
KIMBERLY-CLARK HEALTH CARE INC.—See Kimberly-Clark Corporation; *U.S. Public*, pg. 1230

339112 — SURGICAL AND MEDICA...

KINETIC CONCEPTS, INC.—See 3M Company; *U.S. Public*, pg. 7
KMA HOLDING, INC.; *U.S. Public*, pg. 1269
KOLIGO THERAPEUTICS, INC.—See Orgenesis Inc.; *U.S. Public*, pg. 1617
KOLLMORGEN EUROPE GMBH—See Regal Rexnord Corporation; *U.S. Public*, pg. 1772
KORU MEDICAL SYSTEMS, INC.; *U.S. Public*, pg. 1275
LA ADA DE ACUNA, S. DE R.L. DE C.V.—See Kimberly-Clark Corporation; *U.S. Public*, pg. 1231
LABORATOIRE KCI MEDICAL—See 3M Company; *U.S. Public*, pg. 8
LABORATOIRES CONVATEC SAS—See ConvaTec Group PLC; *Int'l*, pg. 1786
LABOR-ZENTRAL.CH AG—See IDEXX Laboratories, Inc.; *U.S. Public*, pg. 1093
LAKE REGION MANUFACTURING, INC.—See Integer Holdings Corporation; *U.S. Public*, pg. 1135
LAKE REGION MEDICAL, INC.—See Integer Holdings Corporation; *U.S. Public*, pg. 1135
LAKE REGION MEDICAL LTD—See Integer Holdings Corporation; *U.S. Public*, pg. 1135
LAKE REGION MEDICAL - TRENTON—See Integer Holdings Corporation; *U.S. Public*, pg. 1135
LANGER INSTRUMENTS CORPORATION—See Halma plc; *Int'l*, pg. 3232
LANTHEUS MEDICAL IMAGING, INC.—See Avista Capital Partners, L.P.; *U.S. Private*, pg. 408
LASER DIAGNOSTIC TECHNOLOGIES—See Carl-Zeiss-Stiftung; *Int'l*, pg. 1334
LASIT USA INC.—See El.En. S.p.A.; *Int'l*, pg. 2342
LDR HOLDING CORPORATION—See Zimmer Biomet Holdings, Inc.; *U.S. Public*, pg. 2406
LEICA BIOSYSTEMS NEWCASTLE LIMITED—See Danaher Corporation; *U.S. Public*, pg. 628
LEICA BIOSYSTEMS NUSSLOCH GMBH—See Danaher Corporation; *U.S. Public*, pg. 628
LEICA MICROSYSTEMS IR GMBH—See Danaher Corporation; *U.S. Public*, pg. 628
LEICA MICROSYSTEMS KK—See Danaher Corporation; *U.S. Public*, pg. 628
LEICA MICROSYSTEMS LIMITED—See Danaher Corporation; *U.S. Public*, pg. 628
LEICA MIKROSYSTEME VERTRIEB GMBH—See Danaher Corporation; *U.S. Public*, pg. 628
LEMAITRE VASCULAR GK—See LeMaitre Vascular, Inc.; *U.S. Public*, pg. 1304
LEMAITRE VASCULAR GMBH—See LeMaitre Vascular, Inc.; *U.S. Public*, pg. 1304
LEMAITRE VASCULAR, INC.; *U.S. Public*, pg. 1304
LEMAITRE VASCULAR, LTD—See LeMaitre Vascular, Inc.; *U.S. Public*, pg. 1305
LESO INDUSTRIAL SRL—See HORIBA Ltd; *Int'l*, pg. 3477
LI-COR, INC.—See Battery Ventures, L.P.; *U.S. Private*, pg. 489
LIFEGLOBAL GROUP LLC—See The Cooper Companies, Inc.; *U.S. Public*, pg. 2066
LIFELINE BIOTECHNOLOGIES, INC.; *U.S. Public*, pg. 1312
LIFELOC TECHNOLOGIES, INC.; *U.S. Public*, pg. 1312
LIFESCAN CANADA LTD.—See Platinum Equity, LLC; *U.S. Private*, pg. 3205
LIFESCAN, LLC—See Platinum Equity, LLC; *U.S. Private*, pg. 3205
LIFE SCIENCE OUTSOURCING, INC.—See Public Pension Capital, LLC; *U.S. Private*, pg. 3300
LIFE-TECH INC.; *U.S. Private*, pg. 2449
LIGHTHOUSE IMAGING LLC—See Precision Optics Corporation, Inc.; *U.S. Public*, pg. 1713
LIKO AB—See Baxter International Inc.; *U.S. Public*, pg. 282
LIMA AUSTRIA GMBH—See Enovis Corporation; *U.S. Public*, pg. 773
LIMACORPORATE S.P.A.—See Enovis Corporation; *U.S. Public*, pg. 773
LIMA CZ S.R.O.—See Enovis Corporation; *U.S. Public*, pg. 773
LIMA DEUTSCHLAND GMBH—See Enovis Corporation; *U.S. Public*, pg. 773
LIMA IMPLANTES PORTUGAL S.U. LDA—See Enovis Corporation; *U.S. Public*, pg. 773
LIMA JAPAN KK—See Enovis Corporation; *U.S. Public*, pg. 773
LIMA O.I. D.O.O. ORTOPEDIJA—See Enovis Corporation; *U.S. Public*, pg. 773
LIMA ORTHOPAEDICS UK LTD.—See Enovis Corporation; *U.S. Public*, pg. 773
LIMA POLSKA SP. Z O.O.—See Enovis Corporation; *U.S. Public*, pg. 773
LIMA SWEDEN S.R.O.—See Enovis Corporation; *U.S. Public*, pg. 773
LIMA SWITZERLAND S.A.—See Enovis Corporation; *U.S. Public*, pg. 773
LIMITED LIABILITY COMPANY FISHER & PAYKEL HEALTHCARE—See Fisher & Paykel Healthcare Corporation; *Int'l*, pg. 2693
LIMITED LIABILITY COMPANY "ABBOTT UKRAINE"—See Abbott Laboratories; *U.S. Public*, pg. 20

LINEARX, INC.—See Applied DNA Sciences, Inc.; *U.S. Public*, pg. 170
LINVATEC CORPORATION—See CONMED Corporation; *U.S. Public*, pg. 567
LINVATEC U.K. LTD.—See CONMED Corporation; *U.S. Public*, pg. 567
LITECURE LLC—See Enovis Corporation; *U.S. Public*, pg. 773
LITOS GMBH—See DZ BANK AG Deutsche Zentral-Genossenschaftsbank; *Int'l*, pg. 2244
LIVE MICROSYSTEMS, INC.; *U.S. Public*, pg. 1327
LMA UROLOGY B.V.—See Teleflex Incorporated; *U.S. Public*, pg. 1996
LMA UROLOGY SUISSE SA—See Teleflex Incorporated; *U.S. Public*, pg. 1996
LMT MEDICAL SYSTEMS GMBH—See Geratherm Medical AG; *Int'l*, pg. 2942
LOMA VISTA MEDICAL, INC.—See Becton, Dickinson & Company; *U.S. Public*, pg. 291
LRE MEDICAL GMBH—See TransDigm Group Incorporated; *U.S. Public*, pg. 2180
LUCID, INC.; *U.S. Public*, pg. 1345
LUCIRA HEALTH, INC.; *U.S. Public*, pg. 1345
LUMENIS LTD.—See Boston Scientific Corporation; *U.S. Public*, pg. 375
LUMENIS (UK), LTD.—See Boston Scientific Corporation; *U.S. Public*, pg. 375
LUTONIX, INC.—See Becton, Dickinson & Company; *U.S. Public*, pg. 291
LUTRONIC CORPORATION—See Hahn & Company; *Int'l*, pg. 3208
LUTRONIC MEDICAL SYSTEMS GERMANY GMBH—See Hahn & Company; *Int'l*, pg. 3208
MAGSTIM, INC.—See Telegraph Hill Partners Management Company, LLC; *U.S. Private*, pg. 3960
MANGAR INDUSTRIES INC.; *U.S. Private*, pg. 2563
MANUS MEDICAL, LLC—See Aplary Medical, Inc.; *U.S. Private*, pg. 294
MAQUET & ALM BELGIQUE N.V.—See Getinge AB; *Int'l*, pg. 2951
MAQUET AUSTRALIA PTY LTD—See Getinge AB; *Int'l*, pg. 2951
MAQUET BELGIUM NV—See Getinge AB; *Int'l*, pg. 2951
MAQUET CARDIOPULMONARY AG—See Getinge AB; *Int'l*, pg. 2951
MAQUET CARDIOPULMONARY DO BRASIL. IND. E COM S.A.—See Getinge AB; *Int'l*, pg. 2951
MAQUET CARDIOVASCULAR GMBH—See Getinge AB; *Int'l*, pg. 2951
MAQUET CRITICAL CARE AB—See Getinge AB; *Int'l*, pg. 2951
MAQUET DENMARK A/S—See Getinge AB; *Int'l*, pg. 2951
MAQUET DO BRASIL EQUIPAMENTOS. MEDICOS LTDA.—See Getinge AB; *Int'l*, pg. 2952
MAQUET FINLAND OY—See Getinge AB; *Int'l*, pg. 2951
MAQUET GMBH & CO. KG—See Getinge AB; *Int'l*, pg. 2951
MAQUET HONG KONG LTD.—See Getinge AB; *Int'l*, pg. 2952
MAQUET HOSPITAL SOLUTIONS GMBH.—See Getinge AB; *Int'l*, pg. 2952
MAQUET IRELAND LTD—See Getinge AB; *Int'l*, pg. 2952
MAQUET ITALIA S.P.A.—See Getinge AB; *Int'l*, pg. 2951
MAQUET JAPAN KK—See Getinge AB; *Int'l*, pg. 2952
MAQUET LLC—See Getinge AB; *Int'l*, pg. 2952
MAQUET LTD—See Getinge AB; *Int'l*, pg. 2952
MAQUET MEDICAL INDIA PVT LTD—See Getinge AB; *Int'l*, pg. 2952
MAQUET MEDICAL KOREA CO. LTD.—See Getinge AB; *Int'l*, pg. 2952
MAQUET MEDIZINTECHNIK VERTRIEB UND SERVICE GMBH-O.S—See Getinge AB; *Int'l*, pg. 2952
MAQUET MEXICANA, S.DE R.L.DE CV—See Getinge AB; *Int'l*, pg. 2952
MAQUET MIDDLE EAST FZ-LLC—See Getinge AB; *Int'l*, pg. 2952
MAQUET NETHERLANDS B.V.—See Getinge AB; *Int'l*, pg. 2952
MAQUET POLAND SP.Z.O.O—See Getinge AB; *Int'l*, pg. 2952
MAQUET PORTUGAL LDA—See Getinge AB; *Int'l*, pg. 2952
MAQUET SOUTH EAST ASIA LTD—See Getinge AB; *Int'l*, pg. 2952
MAQUET SPAIN S.L.U.—See Getinge AB; *Int'l*, pg. 2952
MAQUET (SUZHOU) CO. LTD.—See Getinge AB; *Int'l*, pg. 2951
MAQUET VERTRIEB UND SERVICE. DEUTSCHLAND GMBH—See Getinge AB; *Int'l*, pg. 2952
MARCH PLASMA SYSTEMS, INC. - FLORIDA PCB LAB & CONTRACT SERVICES—See Nordson Corporation; *U.S. Public*, pg. 1533
MARCH PLASMA SYSTEMS, INC.—See Nordson Corporation; *U.S. Public*, pg. 1533
MARK TWO ENGINEERING, INC.—See CORE Industrial Partners, LLC; *U.S. Private*, pg. 1048
MAROX CORP.—See Argosy Capital Group, LLC; *U.S. Private*, pg. 321
MASIMO AMERICAS, INC.—See Masimo Corporation; *U.S. Public*, pg. 1392

MASIMO EUROPE LIMITED, SUCURSAL EN ESPANA—See Masimo Corporation; *U.S. Public*, pg. 1392
MASIMO GULF, LLC—See Masimo Corporation; *U.S. Public*, pg. 1392
MASIMO INTERNATIONAL SARL - DUBAI, U.A.E.—See Masimo Corporation; *U.S. Public*, pg. 1392
MASIMO MEDIKAL URUNLER TICARET LIMITED SIRKETI ISTANBUL SUBESI—See Masimo Corporation; *U.S. Public*, pg. 1392
MASIMO SWEDEN AB—See Masimo Corporation; *U.S. Public*, pg. 1392
MATHYS AG—See Enovis Corporation; *U.S. Public*, pg. 773
MAYS CHEMICAL COMPANY - MAYS LIFE SCIENCES DIVISON—See Mays Chemical Company; *U.S. Private*, pg. 2623
MEDAES LIMITED—See Atlas Copco AB; *Int'l*, pg. 681
MEDBIO, INC; *U.S. Private*, pg. 2650
MEDCONX, INC.—See ATL Technology, Inc.; *U.S. Private*, pg. 370
MEDCORE AB—See EQT AB; *Int'l*, pg. 2478
MEDENTIS MEDICAL GMBH—See Henry Schein, Inc.; *U.S. Public*, pg. 1027
MEDICAL AUSTRALIA LIMITED—See ICU Medical, Inc.; *U.S. Public*, pg. 1087
MEDICAL CITY SURGERY CENTER SOUTHLAKE, LLC—See HCA Healthcare, Inc.; *U.S. Public*, pg. 1002
MEDICAL DEVICES INTERNATIONAL LLC—See Johnson & Johnson; *U.S. Public*, pg. 1199
MEDICALEX SARL—See HORIBA Ltd; *Int'l*, pg. 3477
MEDICAL INSTRUMENT DEVELOPMENT (MID) LABS, INC.—See Hoya Corporation; *Int'l*, pg. 3498
MEDICAL INTELLIGENCE MEDIZINTECHNIK GMBH—See 3C-Carbon Group AG; *Int'l*, pg. 7
MEDICAL SERVICE GMBH—See Teleflex Incorporated; *U.S. Public*, pg. 1996
MEDICAL TECHNOLOGIES OF GEORGIA, INC.—See HR Pharmaceuticals, Inc.; *U.S. Private*, pg. 1998
MEDICEL AG—See Halma plc; *Int'l*, pg. 3232
MEDIFOCUS, INC.; *U.S. Public*, pg. 1412
MEDIN TECHNOLOGIES, INC.—See Seven Point Equity Partners, LLC; *U.S. Private*, pg. 3619
MEDISIZE OY—See Flexicare (Group) Limited; *Int'l*, pg. 2705
MEDISIZE SCHWEIZ AG—See Flexicare (Group) Limited; *Int'l*, pg. 2705
MEDITE CANCER DIAGNOSTICS INC.; *U.S. Public*, pg. 1413
MEDIVANCE, INC.—See Becton, Dickinson & Company; *U.S. Public*, pg. 291
MEDLINE INTERNATIONAL BELGIUM BVBA—See Medline Industries, LP; *U.S. Private*, pg. 2658
MEDLINE INTERNATIONAL DENMARK APS—See Medline Industries, LP; *U.S. Private*, pg. 2658
MEDLINE INTERNATIONAL IBERIA S.L.U—See Medline Industries, LP; *U.S. Private*, pg. 2658
MEDLINE INTERNATIONAL NETHERLANDS BV—See Medline Industries, LP; *U.S. Private*, pg. 2658
MEDLINE INTERNATIONAL SWITZERLAND SARL—See Medline Industries, LP; *U.S. Private*, pg. 2658
MEDLINE INTERNATIONAL TWO AUSTRALIA PTY LTD—See Medline Industries, LP; *U.S. Private*, pg. 2658
MEDOVATIONS, INC.; *U.S. Private*, pg. 2658
MEDRON, INC—See New Mountain Capital, LLC; *U.S. Private*, pg. 2902
MEDSIGN INTERNATIONAL CORPORATION; *U.S. Private*, pg. 2658
MEDSOURCE TECHNOLOGIES, LLC—See Integer Holdings Corporation; *U.S. Public*, pg. 1135
MEDTECH SA—See Zimmer Biomet Holdings, Inc.; *U.S. Public*, pg. 2406
MEDTEC, INC.—See Roper Technologies, Inc.; *U.S. Public*, pg. 1812
MEDTRONIC XOMED, INC.—See Integra LifeSciences Holdings Corporation; *U.S. Public*, pg. 1136
MEDVENTURE TECHNOLOGY CORPORATION—See Freudenberg SE; *Int'l*, pg. 2789
MEDYSSEY CO LTD—See DONG WHA PHARM CO., LTD.; *Int'l*, pg. 2164
MEGADYNE MEDICAL PRODUCTS INC.—See Johnson & Johnson; *U.S. Public*, pg. 1196
MENTOR B.V.—See Johnson & Johnson; *U.S. Public*, pg. 1199
MENTOR TEXAS L.P.—See Johnson & Johnson; *U.S. Public*, pg. 1199
MERIDIAN BIOSCIENCE CORPORATION—See Meridian Bioscience Inc.; *U.S. Public*, pg. 1424
MERIDIAN BIOSCIENCE ISRAEL HOLDING LTD.—See Meridian Bioscience Inc.; *U.S. Public*, pg. 1424
MERIDIAN MEDICAL TECHNOLOGIES, INC.—See Altaris Capital Partners, LLC; *U.S. Private*, pg. 206
MERIDIAN MEDICAL TECHNOLOGIES WESTPORT—See Altaris Capital Partners, LLC; *U.S. Private*, pg. 206
MERIT MEDICAL DENMARK A/S—See Merit Medical Systems, Inc.; *U.S. Public*, pg. 1425
MERIT MEDICAL IRELAND, LIMITED—See Merit Medical Systems, Inc.; *U.S. Public*, pg. 1425

339112 — SURGICAL AND MEDICA...

MERIT MEDICAL NEDERLAND B.V.—See Merit Medical Systems, Inc.; *U.S. Public*, pg. 1425
MERIT MEDICAL NORWAY AS—See Merit Medical Systems, Inc.; *U.S. Public*, pg. 1425
MESA LABORATORIES, INC. - NORTH BAY BIOSCIENCE—See Mesa Laboratories, Inc.; *U.S. Public*, pg. 1426
MESM, LLC—See Avantor, Inc.; *U.S. Public*, pg. 242
METRON INSTRUMENTS D.O.O.—See HORIBA Ltd; *Int'l*, pg. 3477
MHT OPTIC RESEARCH AG—See DENTSPLY SIRONA Inc.; *U.S. Public*, pg. 655
MHT S.R.L.—See DENTSPLY SIRONA Inc.; *U.S. Public*, pg. 655
MICK RADIO-NUCLEAR INSTRUMENT, INC.—See Eckert & Ziegler Strahlen- und Medizintechnik AG; *Int'l*, pg. 2290
MICROAIRE SURGICAL INSTRUMENTS INC.—See Berkshire Hathaway Inc.; *U.S. Public*, pg. 308
MICROGENICS CORPORATION—See Thermo Fisher Scientific Inc.; *U.S. Public*, pg. 2149
MICROLINE B.V.—See Hoya Corporation; *Int'l*, pg. 3498
MICROLINE SURGICAL INC.—See Hoya Corporation; *Int'l*, pg. 3497
MICROLUMEN, INC.; *U.S. Private*, pg. 2703
MICROSON S.A.—See Amplifon S.p.A.; *Int'l*, pg. 435
MICRO STAMPING CORP. - FLORIDA FACILITY—See Micro Stamping Corp.; *U.S. Private*, pg. 2702
MICROTEST LABORATORIES, INC.—See Ampersand Management LLC; *U.S. Private*, pg. 265
MIDMARK ANIMAL HEALTH—See Midmark Corporation; *U.S. Private*, pg. 2716
MIDMARK CORPORATION; *U.S. Private*, pg. 2716
MILESTONE EDUCATION LLC—See Milestone Scientific Inc.; *U.S. Public*, pg. 1446
MIMEDX GROUP, INC.; *U.S. Public*, pg. 1448
MISAWA MEDICAL INDUSTRY CO., LTD.—See Air Water Inc.; *Int'l*, pg. 240
MISONIX, INC.—See Bioventus Inc.; *U.S. Public*, pg. 339
MMAR MEDICAL GROUP, INC.—See Patient Square Capital, L.P.; *U.S. Private*, pg. 3107
MOBIDIAG UK LTD.—See Hologic, Inc.; *U.S. Public*, pg. 1045
MOBIUS IMAGING, LLC—See Stryker Corporation; *U.S. Public*, pg. 1956
MODULAR MEDICAL, INC.; *U.S. Public*, pg. 1456
MOLDED RUBBER & PLASTIC CORPORATION; *U.S. Private*, pg. 2766
MOLLER MEDICAL GMBH—See CENTROTEC SE; *Int'l*, pg. 1414
MONROE WHEELCHAIR, INC.—See AEA Investors LP; *U.S. Private*, pg. 116
MOOG MEDICAL DEVICES GROUP—See Moog Inc.; *U.S. Public*, pg. 1470
MOOG MEDICAL DEVICES GROUP—See Moog Inc.; *U.S. Public*, pg. 1470
MOVANO INC.; *U.S. Public*, pg. 1480
MP BIOMEDICALS, LLC—See CECEP Environmental Protection Co., Ltd.; *Int'l*, pg. 1372
MUREX BIOTECH SOUTH AFRICA—See Abbott Laboratories; *U.S. Public*, pg. 20
MYOMO, INC.; *U.S. Public*, pg. 1488
NALU MEDICAL, INC.; *U.S. Public*, pg. 1490
NANOMR, INC.—See Genting Berhad; *Int'l*, pg. 2928
NASHVILLE RECORDS, INC.; *U.S. Public*, pg. 1492
NATIONAL SURGICAL PTY LTD—See EBOS Group Limited; *Int'l*, pg. 2285
NATUS EUROPE GMBH—See ArchiMed SAS; *Int'l*, pg. 548
NATUS MEDICAL DENMARK APS—See ArchiMed SAS; *Int'l*, pg. 548
NEMAURA MEDICAL INC.; *U.S. Public*, pg. 1505
NEOMEDICS, INC.—See Orthofix Medical Inc.; *U.S. Public*, pg. 1619
NEOMED, INC.—See Avanos Medical, Inc.; *U.S. Public*, pg. 241
NEOMEND, INC.—See Becton, Dickinson & Company; *U.S. Public*, pg. 291
NEOTRACT, INC.—See Teleflex Incorporated; *U.S. Public*, pg. 1995
NEOVASC MEDICAL INC.—See Johnson & Johnson; *U.S. Public*, pg. 1200
NEPHROS, INC.; *U.S. Public*, pg. 1506
NEURAVI LIMITED—See Johnson & Johnson; *U.S. Public*, pg. 1200
NEUROMETRIX, INC.; *U.S. Public*, pg. 1510
NEURONETICS, INC.; *U.S. Public*, pg. 1510
NEVRO CORP.; *U.S. Public*, pg. 1511
NEW DAY DIAGNOSTICS LLC; *U.S. Private*, pg. 2893
NEWDEAL SAS—See Integra LifeSciences Holdings Corporation; *U.S. Public*, pg. 1136
NEXALIN TECHNOLOGY, INC.; *U.S. Public*, pg. 1521
NEXCELOM BIOSCIENCE LLC—See Revvity, Inc.; *U.S. Public*, pg. 1794
NEXGEL, INC.; *U.S. Public*, pg. 1522
NEXTPHASE MEDICAL DEVICES LLC—See Kidd & Company LLC; *U.S. Private*, pg. 2302
NEXUS CMF, L.L.C.—See Crocker Ventures LLC; *U.S. Private*, pg. 1102

NINE POINT MEDICAL—See Corning Incorporated; *U.S. Public*, pg. 579
NINGBO SENSCURE BIOTECHNOLOGY CO., LTD.—See Cryofocus Medtech (Shanghai) Co., Ltd.; *Int'l*, pg. 1859
NIPRO MEDICAL CORPORATION—See HORIBA Ltd; *Int'l*, pg. 3477
NIPRO MEDICAL CORPORATION—See HORIBA Ltd; *Int'l*, pg. 3477
NOBEL BIOCARE COMMERCIAL (SHANGHAI) CO. LTD.—See Danaher Corporation; *U.S. Public*, pg. 629
NOBEL BIOCARE INDIA PVT. LTD.—See Danaher Corporation; *U.S. Public*, pg. 629
NOBEL BIOCARE NEDERLAND BV—See Danaher Corporation; *U.S. Public*, pg. 629
NOBEL BIOCARE SOUTH AFRICA (PTY) LTD—See Danaher Corporation; *U.S. Public*, pg. 629
NONINVASIVE MEDICAL TECHNOLOGIES, INC.; *U.S. Private*, pg. 2934
NORCES EQUIPAMIENTO CIENTIFICO SRL—See HORIBA Ltd; *Int'l*, pg. 3477
NORDSON MEDICAL—See Nordson Corporation; *U.S. Public*, pg. 1534
NORWOOD MEDICAL; *U.S. Private*, pg. 2964
NOVABONE PRODUCTS, LLC—See Halma plc; *Int'l*, pg. 3232
NOVASALUD S.A.—See Abbott Laboratories; *U.S. Public*, pg. 20
NOVASTEP SAS—See Enovis Corporation; *U.S. Public*, pg. 773
NOVASYTE, LLC—See IQVIA Holdings Inc.; *U.S. Public*, pg. 1170
NOVAVISION, INC.—See Vycor Medical, Inc.; *U.S. Public*, pg. 2315
NSPIRE HEALTH GMBH—See nSpire Health, Inc.; *U.S. Private*, pg. 2970
NSPIRE HEALTH, INC.; *U.S. Private*, pg. 2970
NSPIRE HEALTH LTD.—See nSpire Health, Inc.; *U.S. Private*, pg. 2970
NUCLETRON ASIA PACIFIC LTD.—See Elekta AB; *Int'l*, pg. 2356
NUCLETRON A/S—See Elekta AB; *Int'l*, pg. 2356
NUCLETRON B.V.—See Elekta AB; *Int'l*, pg. 2356
NUCLETRON CANADA INC.—See Elekta AB; *Int'l*, pg. 2356
NUCLETRON POLAND SP Z.O.O.—See Elekta AB; *Int'l*, pg. 2356
NUCLETRON PTY. LTD.—See Elekta AB; *Int'l*, pg. 2356
NUCLETRON SAS—See Elekta AB; *Int'l*, pg. 2356
NUCLETRON UK LTD.—See Elekta AB; *Int'l*, pg. 2356
NUVASIVE CLINICAL SERVICES MONITORING, INC.—See Globus Medical, Inc.; *U.S. Public*, pg. 947
NUVASIVE SPECIALIZED ORTHOPEDICS, INC.—See Globus Medical, Inc.; *U.S. Public*, pg. 947
NUVASIVE UK LIMITED—See Globus Medical, Inc.; *U.S. Public*, pg. 947
NUVERA MEDICAL, INC.—See Johnson & Johnson; *U.S. Public*, pg. 1194
NUVO GROUP LTD.—See Holdco Nuvo Group D.G Ltd.; *U.S. Public*, pg. 1044
NUWELLIS, INC.; *U.S. Public*, pg. 1556
NYPRO INC.—See Jabil Inc.; *U.S. Public*, pg. 1181
OBERG MEDICAL—See Oberg Industries Corp.; *U.S. Private*, pg. 2987
OBTECH MEDICAL AG—See Johnson & Johnson; *U.S. Public*, pg. 1200
OCUGEN, INC.; *U.S. Public*, pg. 1563
OEC MEDICAL SYSTEMS, INC.—See GE HealthCare Technologies Inc.; *U.S. Public*, pg. 909
OHIO MEDICAL CORP.—See Barings BDC, Inc.; *U.S. Public*, pg. 276
OLAREGEN THERAPEUTIX, INC.—See Generex Biotechnology Corporation; *U.S. Public*, pg. 930
QMNI MOTION, INC.—See Water Street Healthcare Partners, LLC; *U.S. Private*, pg. 4452
OMNIPHARMA S.A.L.—See HORIBA Ltd; *Int'l*, pg. 3477
ONCOLOGIX TECH, INC.; *U.S. Public*, pg. 3019
ONCORAL PHARMA APS—See Ascelia Pharma AB; *Int'l*, pg. 601
ONCOSEC MEDICAL INCORPORATED; *U.S. Public*, pg. 1601
ON-X LIFE TECHNOLOGIES, INC.—See Artivion, Inc.; *U.S. Public*, pg. 208
ONYX HEALTHCARE EUROPE B.V.—See ASUSTeK Computer Inc.; *Int'l*, pg. 664
ONYX MEDICAL LLC—See TA Associates, Inc.; *U.S. Private*, pg. 3918
OOO OPTEC—See Carl-Zeiss-Stiftung; *Int'l*, pg. 1336
OPTIMA NEUROSCIENCE—See Tucker-Davis Technologies, Inc.; *U.S. Private*, pg. 4256
OPTI MEDICAL, INC.—See IDEXX Laboratories, Inc.; *U.S. Public*, pg. 1093
OPTIMEDI SP. Z O.O.—See Carl-Zeiss-Stiftung; *Int'l*, pg. 1336
OPTOMED SAS—See Mars, Incorporated; *U.S. Private*, pg. 2588
OPTOTAL HOYA LIMITADA—See Hoya Corporation; *Int'l*, pg. 3498
ORCHARD VALE NATURALS INC.—See EastWest Bioscience, Inc.; *Int'l*, pg. 2275

ORGANOVO HOLDINGS, INC.; *U.S. Public*, pg. 1616
ORMCO BV—See Danaher Corporation; *U.S. Public*, pg. 629
ORPHAMED INC.—See Bausch Health Companies Inc.; *Int'l*, pg. 897
ORPHEUS MEDICAL GMBH—See Intuitive Surgical, Inc.; *U.S. Public*, pg. 1160
ORPHEUS MEDICAL LTD.—See Intuitive Surgical, Inc.; *U.S. Public*, pg. 1160
ORPHEUS MEDICAL USA INC.—See Intuitive Surgical, Inc.; *U.S. Public*, pg. 1161
THE ORTHODONTIC STORE, INC.—See The Jordan Company, L.P.; *U.S. Private*, pg. 4063
ORTHOFIX AUSTRALIA PTY LIMITED—See Orthofix Medical Inc.; *U.S. Public*, pg. 1619
ORTHOFIX DO BRASIL LTDA.—See Orthofix Medical Inc.; *U.S. Public*, pg. 1619
ORTHOFIX GMBH—See Orthofix Medical Inc.; *U.S. Public*, pg. 1619
ORTHOFIX SPINE G.M.B.H.—See Orthofix Medical Inc.; *U.S. Public*, pg. 1619
ORTHOFIX SPORTS MEDICINE BREG, INC. - MANUFACTURING FACILITY—See Orthofix Medical Inc.; *U.S. Public*, pg. 1619
ORTHOFIX S.R.L.—See Orthofix Medical Inc.; *U.S. Public*, pg. 1619
ORTHOMED MEDIZINTECHNIK GMBH—See Enovis Corporation; *U.S. Public*, pg. 773
ORTHOSONICS LTD.—See Orthofix Medical Inc.; *U.S. Public*, pg. 1619
ORTHOSPACE, LTD.—See Stryker Corporation; *U.S. Public*, pg. 1956
ORTHOVITA, INC.—See Stryker Corporation; *U.S. Public*, pg. 1956
ORTHOVITA—See Stryker Corporation; *U.S. Public*, pg. 1956
OSCOR INC.; *U.S. Private*, pg. 3047
OSPREY MEDICAL INC.; *U.S. Public*, pg. 1622
OSTEOMED CORPORATION—See Berkshire Hathaway Inc.; *U.S. Public*, pg. 308
OSTEOMETER MEDITECH, INC.—See OSI Systems, Inc.; *U.S. Public*, pg. 1621
OTSUKA MEDICAL DEVICES CO., LTD.—See Earth Corporation; *Int'l*, pg. 2268
PALIWAL DIAGNOSTICS PRIVATE LIMITED—See Dr. Lal PathLabs Ltd.; *Int'l*, pg. 2194
PALL BIOMEDICAL, INC.—See Danaher Corporation; *U.S. Public*, pg. 629
PALODEX HOLDING OY—See Danaher Corporation; *U.S. Public*, pg. 630
PALOMAR MEDICAL PRODUCTS, LLC—See Clayton, Dubilier & Rice, LLC; *U.S. Private*, pg. 922
PANSEND, LLC—See INNOVATE Corp.; *U.S. Public*, pg. 1126
PAPYRO-TEX A/S—See ConvaTec Group PLC; *Int'l*, pg. 1786
PARADIGM MEDICAL INDUSTRIES, INC.; *U.S. Public*, pg. 1636
PARAGON MEDICAL, DEVICE (CHANGZHOU) CO., LTD.—See AMETEK, Inc.; *U.S. Public*, pg. 121
PARAGON MEDICAL EUROPE SARL—See AMETEK, Inc.; *U.S. Public*, pg. 121
PARAGON MEDICAL INTERNATIONAL, INC.—See AMETEK, Inc.; *U.S. Public*, pg. 121
PARAGON SIECHNICE SP. Z O.O.—See AMETEK, Inc.; *U.S. Public*, pg. 121
PARCUS MEDICAL, LLC—See Anika Therapeutics, Inc.; *U.S. Public*, pg. 137
PARKELL INC.—See Carl Bennet AB; *Int'l*, pg. 1332
PARTICLE SIZING SYSTEMS, LLC—See Entegris, Inc.; *U.S. Public*, pg. 777
PATH-TEC; *U.S. Private*, pg. 3105
PATIENTKEEPER, INC.—See HCA Healthcare, Inc.; *U.S. Public*, pg. 1006
PATIENTS PENDING LTD.—See Abbott Laboratories; *U.S. Public*, pg. 20
PAVMED INC.; *U.S. Public*, pg. 1655
PDC EUROPE SPRL—See Brady Corporation; *U.S. Public*, pg. 379
PDP HOLDINGS, INC.—See Stone Point Capital LLC; *U.S. Private*, pg. 3821
PENLON LIMITED—See The Goldman Sachs Group, Inc.; *U.S. Public*, pg. 2076
PENTAX MEDICAL RUS LLC—See Hoya Corporation; *Int'l*, pg. 3498
PENTAX MEDICAL SINGAPORE PTE. LTD.—See Hoya Corporation; *Int'l*, pg. 3495
PENTAX MEDICAL—See Hoya Corporation; *Int'l*, pg. 3495
PENUMBRA, INC.; *U.S. Public*, pg. 1666
PETERS SURGICAL SASU—See Eurazeo SE; *Int'l*, pg. 2529
PHADIA AB—See Thermo Fisher Scientific Inc.; *U.S. Public*, pg. 2147
PHADIA US INC.—See Thermo Fisher Scientific Inc.; *U.S. Public*, pg. 2148
PHARMASMART INTERNATIONAL INC; *U.S. Private*, pg. 3165
PHARMATEK PMC S.R.L.—See Fine Foods & Pharmaceu-

N.A.I.C.S. INDEX

339112 — SURGICAL AND MEDICA...

ticals N.T.M. S.p.A.; *Int'l*, pg. 2673
PLASMABIOTICS S.A.S.—See Hoya Corporation; *Int'l*, pg. 3498
PLASTICWELD SYSTEMS INC.—See Forsyth Capital Investors LLC; *U.S. Private*, pg. 1574
PLC MEDICAL SYSTEMS, INC.; *U.S. Private*, pg. 3213
POLYZEN, LLC—See Altaris Capital Partners, LLC; *U.S. Private*, pg. 206
PORTLYN, LLC—See Integer Holdings Corporation; *U.S. Public*, pg. 1135
PRECISION DYNAMICS CORPORATION—See Brady Corporation; *U.S. Public*, pg. 379
PRECISION EDGE SURGICAL PRODUCTS COMPANY INC.—See Berkshire Hathaway Inc.; *U.S. Public*, pg. 308
PRECISION ENGINEERED PRODUCTS, LLC—See NN, Inc.; *U.S. Public*, pg. 1531
PRECISION VASCULAR SYSTEMS, INC.—See Boston Scientific Corporation; *U.S. Public*, pg. 375
PRESCIENT MEDICAL, INC.; *U.S. Private*, pg. 3253
PRESCOTT'S, INC.—See Atlantic Street Capital Management LLC; *U.S. Private*, pg. 374
PRESTIGE MEDICAL IMAGING LLC—See Atlantic Street Capital Management LLC; *U.S. Private*, pg. 374
PRIDE MOBILITY PRODUCTS CORP. - QUANTUM REHAB DIVISION—See Pride Mobility Products Corp.; *U.S. Private*, pg. 3259
PROCEPT BIOROBOTICS CORPORATION; *U.S. Public*, pg. 1723
PRODUCTOS AEREOS, S.A. DE C.V.—See Teleflex Incorporated; *U.S. Public*, pg. 1995
PRODUCTOS BARD DE MEXICO S.A. DE C.V.—See Becton, Dickinson & Company; *U.S. Public*, pg. 291
PROPPER MANUFACTURING COMPANY, INC.; *U.S. Private*, pg. 3286
PROSEMEDIC S.A.C.—See UnitedHealth Group Incorporated; *U.S. Public*, pg. 2249
PROSOMNUS, INC.; *U.S. Public*, pg. 1728
PSI HEALTH SOLUTIONS, INC.; *U.S. Private*, pg. 3297
PT. ABBOTT INDONESIA—See Abbott Laboratories; *U.S. Public*, pg. 20
PT. ABBOTT PRODUCTS INDONESIA—See Abbott Laboratories; *U.S. Public*, pg. 20
PT ALERE HEALTH—See Abbott Laboratories; *U.S. Public*, pg. 19
P.T. APT MEDICAL INDONESIA—See APT Medical, Inc.; *Int'l*, pg. 523
PT DRAEGERINDO JAYA—See Draegerwerk AG & Co. KGaA; *Int'l*, pg. 2198
PT DRAEGER MEDICAL INDONESIA—See Draegerwerk AG & Co. KGaA; *Int'l*, pg. 2198
PT GLAXO WELLCOME INDONESIA—See GSK plc; *Int'l*, pg. 3149
PT GSK CONSUMER HEALTHCARE INDONESIA—See GSK plc; *Int'l*, pg. 3149
PT. HOYA LENS INDONESIA—See Hoya Corporation; *Int'l*, pg. 3498
PULMATRIX OPERATING COMPANY—See Pulmatrix, Inc.; *U.S. Public*, pg. 1736
PULMONX AUSTRALIA PTY LTD—See Pulmonx Corporation; *U.S. Public*, pg. 1736
PULMONX CORPORATION; *U.S. Public*, pg. 1736
PULMONX INTERNATIONAL SARL—See Pulmonx Corporation; *U.S. Public*, pg. 1736
PULSAR VASCULAR, INC.—See Johnson & Johnson; *U.S. Public*, pg. 1195
PULSION MEDICAL SYSTEMS SE—See Getinge AB; *Int'l*, pg. 2952
PULS MEDICAL DEVICES AS LC—See Becton, Dickinson & Company; *U.S. Public*, pg. 292
PURAGRAFT, LLC—See The Jordan Company, L.P.; *U.S. Private*, pg. 4063
PURE HEALTH PRODUCTS, LLC—See Can B Corp.; *U.S. Public*, pg. 428
PURE LAB TECH LTD.—See HORIBA Ltd; *Int'l*, pg. 3478
PUREWICK CORPORATION—See Becton, Dickinson & Company; *U.S. Public*, pg. 292
PURSUIT VASCULAR, INC.—See ICU Medical, Inc.; *U.S. Public*, pg. 1087
Q-MED AB—See Abu Dhabi Investment Authority; *Int'l*, pg. 71
Q-MED AB—See EQT Corporation; *U.S. Public*, pg. 785
Q-MED INTERNATIONAL LTD—See Abu Dhabi Investment Authority; *Int'l*, pg. 71
Q-MED INTERNATIONAL LTD—See EQT Corporation; *U.S. Public*, pg. 785
Q-MED POLSKA SP. Z.O.O—See Abu Dhabi Investment Authority; *Int'l*, pg. 72
Q-MED POLSKA SP. Z.O.O—See EQT Corporation; *U.S. Public*, pg. 785
QOSINA CORP.; *U.S. Private*, pg. 3313
QUANTRX BIOMEDICAL CORP.; *U.S. Public*, pg. 1753
QUANTUM DIAGNOSTICOS LTDA—See Abbott Laboratories; *U.S. Public*, pg. 18
QUANTUM OPS, INC.—See Enovis Corporation; *U.S. Public*, pg. 773
QUASAR BIO TECH LLC; *U.S. Private*, pg. 3324
QUEST MEDICAL, INC.—See Nordson Corporation; *U.S. Public*, pg. 1532

RADIOMETER DANMARK A/S—See Danaher Corporation; *U.S. Public*, pg. 630
RADIOMETER MEDICAL A/S—See Danaher Corporation; *U.S. Public*, pg. 630
RADIOMETER PACIFIC PTY. LTD.—See Danaher Corporation; *U.S. Public*, pg. 631
RADIOMETER SOUTH AFRICA—See Danaher Corporation; *U.S. Public*, pg. 631
RAL DIAGNOSTICS SAS—See CellaVision AB; *Int'l*, pg. 1392
RALEIGH ADHESIVE COATINGS LIMITED—See Advanced Medical Solutions Group plc; *Int'l*, pg. 161
RAPID PATHOGEN SCREENING, INC.; *U.S. Private*, pg. 3356
REBOUND THERAPEUTICS CORPORATION—See Integra LifeSciences Holdings Corporation; *U.S. Public*, pg. 1136
REFOCUS GROUP, INC.; *U.S. Public*, pg. 1771
RELIEVANT MEDSYSTEMS INC.—See Boston Scientific Corporation; *U.S. Public*, pg. 375
REMSLEEP HOLDINGS, INC.; *U.S. Public*, pg. 1782
RENOVACARE, INC.; *U.S. Public*, pg. 1783
RESHAPE LIFESCIENCES INC.; *U.S. Public*, pg. 1789
RESHAPE LIFESCIENCES INC.—See ReShape Lifesciences Inc.; *U.S. Public*, pg. 1789
RESMED DEUTSCHLAND GMBH—See ResMed Inc.; *U.S. Public*, pg. 1791
RESMED FINLAND OY—See ResMed Inc.; *U.S. Public*, pg. 1791
RESMED HOLDINGS LTD.—See ResMed Inc.; *U.S. Public*, pg. 1791
RESMED INC.; *U.S. Public*, pg. 1790
RESMED KK—See ResMed Inc.; *U.S. Public*, pg. 1791
RESMED NEW ZEALAND LIMITED—See ResMed Inc.; *U.S. Public*, pg. 1791
RESMED SAS—See ResMed Inc.; *U.S. Public*, pg. 1791
RESMED SCHWEIZ AG—See ResMed Inc.; *U.S. Public*, pg. 1791
RESMED SWEDEN AB—See ResMed Inc.; *U.S. Public*, pg. 1791
RESMED (UK) LIMITED—See ResMed Inc.; *U.S. Public*, pg. 1791
RESPIRATORY SUPPORT PRODUCTS INC.—See ICU Medical, Inc.; *U.S. Public*, pg. 1087
RESPONSE BIOMEDICAL CORP.—See OrbiMed Advisors LLC; *U.S. Private*, pg. 3038
RESTOR3D, INC.; *U.S. Private*, pg. 3409
RETINALGENIX TECHNOLOGIES INC.—See Sanovas, Inc.; *U.S. Private*, pg. 3546
RETRACTABLE TECHNOLOGIES, INC.; *U.S. Public*, pg. 1792
REVOLUTIONS MEDICAL CORPORATION; *U.S. Private*, pg. 3417
RHEIN MEDICAL, INC.—See Audax Group, Limited Partnership; *U.S. Private*, pg. 388
RHYTHMLINK INTERNATIONAL, LLC—See The Graham Group, Inc.; *U.S. Private*, pg. 4037
ROBUTEC AG—See Halma plc; *Int'l*, pg. 3232
ROXWOOD MEDICAL, INC.—See Boston Scientific Corporation; *U.S. Public*, pg. 374
R.P. KINCHELOE COMPANY INC.; *U.S. Private*, pg. 3339
RPM CO., LTD.—See Bain Capital, LP; *U.S. Private*, pg. 435
RUSCH URUGUAY LTDA—See Teleflex Incorporated; *U.S. Public*, pg. 1996
S4J MANUFACTURING SERVICES, INC.; *U.S. Private*, pg. 3519
S.A. CEBELOR—See Axel Johnson Gruppen AB; *Int'l*, pg. 765
SADRA MEDICAL, INC.—See Boston Scientific Corporation; *U.S. Public*, pg. 375
SAFEAIR AG—See Stryker Corporation; *U.S. Public*, pg. 1956
SAFETY SYRINGES INC.—See Becton, Dickinson & Company; *U.S. Public*, pg. 292
SALTER LABS—See RoundTable Healthcare Management, Inc.; *U.S. Private*, pg. 3489
SALVIN DENTAL SPECIALTIES, INC.—See The Jordan Company, L.P.; *U.S. Private*, pg. 4063
SAMSARA VISION, INC.; *U.S. Private*, pg. 3538
SANAVITA MEDICAL, LLC—See Compagnie Generale des Etablissements Michelin SCA; *Int'l*, pg. 1745
SANDHILL SCIENTIFIC, INC.—See Medovations, Inc.; *U.S. Private*, pg. 2658
SANGHAMITRA HOSPITALS PRIVATE LIMITED—See Aster DM Healthcare Ltd.; *Int'l*, pg. 654
SANUWAVE HEALTH, INC.; *U.S. Public*, pg. 1841
SATELIT PRODUTOS PARA LABORATORIOS LTDA—See HORIBA Ltd; *Int'l*, pg. 3478
SAUDI MAIS COMPANY FOR MEDICAL PRODUCTS—See Arab Supply & Trading Co.; *Int'l*, pg. 532
SAVYON LTD.—See Gamida for Life B.V.; *Int'l*, pg. 2878
S.C. GENKO MED GROUP S.A.—See Genko Italia srl; *Int'l*, pg. 2924
SCHLEIFRING MEDICAL SYSTEMS, LLC—See GE HealthCare Technologies Inc.; *U.S. Public*, pg. 909
SCHOELLY, INC.—See Intuitive Surgical, Inc.; *U.S. Public*, pg. 1161
SCHULKE & MAYR GMBH—See EQT AB; *Int'l*, pg. 2479
SCHULKE & MAYR UK LTD—See EQT AB; *Int'l*, pg. 2479

SCIENTIFIC MEDICAL SYSTEMS CORP.—See Daxor Corporation; *U.S. Public*, pg. 644
SCION MEDICAL TECHNOLOGIES, LLC; *U.S. Private*, pg. 3574
SEASTAR MEDICAL HOLDING CORPORATION; *U.S. Public*, pg. 1855
SEBIA, INC.—See Caisse de Depot et Placement du Quebec; *Int'l*, pg. 1255
SEBIA, INC.—See CVC Capital Partners SICAV-FIS S.A.; *Int'l*, pg. 1884
SEBIA SA—See Caisse de Depot et Placement du Quebec; *Int'l*, pg. 1255
SEBIA SA—See CVC Capital Partners SICAV-FIS S.A.; *Int'l*, pg. 1884
THE SECANT GROUP, LLC—See Compagnie Generale des Etablissements Michelin SCA; *Int'l*, pg. 1745
SECHRIST INDUSTRIES, INC.—See The Jordan Company, L.P.; *U.S. Private*, pg. 4062
S.E.G-WAY ORTHOPAEDICS, INC.—See Trice Medical, Inc; *U.S. Private*, pg. 4228
SEISA MEDICAL, INC.—See Genstar Capital, LLC; *U.S. Private*, pg. 1679
SEMLER SCIENTIFIC, INC.; *U.S. Public*, pg. 1863
SENSILE MEDICAL AG—See Gerresheimer AG; *Int'l*, pg. 2944
SENTINELLE MEDICAL USA INC.—See Hologic, Inc.; *U.S. Public*, pg. 1045
SENTREHEART, INC.—See AtriCure, Inc.; *U.S. Public*, pg. 225
SENTRY MEDICAL PTY. LTD.—See EBOS Group Limited; *Int'l*, pg. 2285
SETEMA LTD.—See HORIBA Ltd; *Int'l*, pg. 3478
SG MEDICAL PTE LTD—See ResMed Inc.; *U.S. Public*, pg. 1791
SHANGHAI DONGPENG SAFETY CO., LTD.—See Air Water Inc.; *Int'l*, pg. 240
SHANGHAI HONGTONG INDUSTRIAL CO., LTD.—See APT Medical, Inc.; *Int'l*, pg. 523
SHANGHAI HUVITZ CO., LTD.—See Huvitz Co., Ltd.; *Int'l*, pg. 3541
SHARKLET TECHNOLOGIES, INC.; *U.S. Private*, pg. 3626
SHARPS TECHNOLOGY, INC.; *U.S. Public*, pg. 1874
SHENNAN CIRCUITS CO., LTD.—See AVIC International Holdings Limited; *Int'l*, pg. 742
SHINA CORPORATION—See CNL Strategic Capital Management LLC; *U.S. Private*, pg. 952
SICAT VERWALTUNGS GMBH—See DENTSPLY SIRONA Inc.; *U.S. Public*, pg. 655
SIENTRA, INC.; *U.S. Public*, pg. 1876
SINTX TECHNOLOGIES, INC.; *U.S. Public*, pg. 1888
SIRONA DENTAL A/S—See DENTSPLY SIRONA Inc.; *U.S. Public*, pg. 655
SISTEMAS ANALITICOS S.A.—See HORIBA Ltd; *Int'l*, pg. 3478
SISTEMAS INTEGRALES DE MEDICINA, S.A.—See Hoya Corporation; *Int'l*, pg. 3495
SIS-TER S.P.A.—See Fresenius Medical Care AG; *Int'l*, pg. 2775
SKELETAL KINETICS LLC—See Berkshire Hathaway Inc.; *U.S. Public*, pg. 308
SKLAR CORPORATION; *U.S. Private*, pg. 3683
SLEM MEDICAL SARL—See HORIBA Ltd; *Int'l*, pg. 3478
SMA'LIA MEDICAL GROUP—See HORIBA Ltd; *Int'l*, pg. 3478
SMALL BONE INNOVATIONS, INC.—See Stryker Corporation; *U.S. Public*, pg. 1956
SMITHS MEDICAL FRANCE S.A.—See ICU Medical, Inc.; *U.S. Public*, pg. 1087
SMITHS MEDICAL INSTRUMENT (ZHEJIANG) CO., LTD.—See ICU Medical, Inc.; *U.S. Public*, pg. 1087
SMITHS MEDICAL LIMITED—See ICU Medical, Inc.; *U.S. Public*, pg. 1087
SMITHS MEDICAL MD, INC.—See ICU Medical, Inc.; *U.S. Public*, pg. 1087
SMITHS MEDICAL PM INC.—See ICU Medical, Inc.; *U.S. Public*, pg. 1087
SMITHS MEDICAL—See ICU Medical, Inc.; *U.S. Public*, pg. 1087
SMITHS MEDICAL—See ICU Medical, Inc.; *U.S. Public*, pg. 1087
SMIT MOBILE EQUIPMENT B.V.—See Berkshire Hathaway Inc.; *U.S. Public*, pg. 299
SOBR SAFE, INC.; *U.S. Public*, pg. 1899
SOLAR LASER SYSTEMS JSC—See HORIBA Ltd; *Int'l*, pg. 3478
SOLMETEX, LLC—See Avista Capital Partners, L.P.; *U.S. Private*, pg. 409
SOLOS ENDOSCOPY, INC.—See American Medical Group LLC; *U.S. Private*, pg. 241
SOLUCIONES TECNOLOGICAS AVANZADAS LTDA.—See HORIBA Ltd; *Int'l*, pg. 3478
SOLVENTUM CORPORATION; *U.S. Public*, pg. 1901
SOMATEX MEDICAL TECHNOLOGIES GMBH—See Hologic, Inc.; *U.S. Public*, pg. 1045
SOMEDIB SARL—See HORIBA Ltd; *Int'l*, pg. 3478
SONDE HEALTH, INC.—See PureTech Health plc; *U.S. Public*, pg. 1738

339112 — SURGICAL AND MEDICA... **CORPORATE AFFILIATIONS**

SONIC INNOVATIONS PTY LTD.—See Demant A/S; *Int'l*, pg. 2024
SONOMED, INC.—See Escalon Medical Corp.; *U.S. Public*, pg. 793
SONUS USA INC.—See Amplifon S.p.A.; *Int'l*, pg. 435
SOPHION BIOSCIENCE A/S—See AddLife AB; *Int'l*, pg. 129
SOTERA WIRELESS, INC.; *U.S. Private*, pg. 3716
SOUTH SHORE MEDICAL SUPPLY, INC.—See ConvaTec Group PLC; *Int'l*, pg. 1786
SPACELABS HEALTHCARE, INC.—See OSI Systems, Inc.; *U.S. Public*, pg. 1622
SPECIALIZED LEASING, INC.; *U.S. Private*, pg. 3749
SPECIALTY RENAL PRODUCTS, INC.—See Nephros, Inc.; *U.S. Public*, pg. 1506
SPECIALTY SURGICAL INSTRUMENTATION, INC.—See Audax Group, Limited Partnership; *U.S. Private*, pg. 386
SPECTRUM MANUFACTURING, INC.—See Integer Holdings Corporation; *U.S. Public*, pg. 1135
SPINAL ELEMENTS, INC.—See Kohlberg & Company, LLC; *U.S. Private*, pg. 2337
SPINAL KINETICS, LLC—See Orthofix Medical Inc.; *U.S. Public*, pg. 1619
SPINEMEDICA, LLC—See MiMedx Group, Inc.; *U.S. Public*, pg. 1448
STAAR JAPAN INC—See STAAR Surgical Co.; *U.S. Public*, pg. 1924
STAAR SURGICAL CHINA CO., LTD.—See STAAR Surgical Co.; *U.S. Public*, pg. 1924
STATCORP MEDICAL—See OSI Systems, Inc.; *U.S. Public*, pg. 1621
STATIC SYSTEMS GROUP LIMITED—See Halma plc; *Int'l*, pg. 3233
STATSURE DIAGNOSTIC SYSTEMS, INC.; *U.S. Public*, pg. 1941
STERIMEDIX LIMITED—See Bausch Health Companies Inc.; *Int'l*, pg. 897
STIHLER ELECTRONIC GMBH—See Gentherm Incorporated; *U.S. Public*, pg. 932
ST. JUDE MEDICAL BRASIL, LTDA.—See Abbott Laboratories; *U.S. Public*, pg. 21
ST. JUDE MEDICAL, LLC—See Abbott Laboratories; *U.S. Public*, pg. 20
STRATA SKIN SCIENCES, INC.; *U.S. Public*, pg. 1953
STRUKMYER, LLC; *U.S. Private*, pg. 3842
STRYKER AB—See Stryker Corporation; *U.S. Public*, pg. 1956
STRYKER B.V.—See Stryker Corporation; *U.S. Public*, pg. 1956
STRYKER CANADA INC.—See Stryker Corporation; *U.S. Public*, pg. 1956
STRYKER CORPORATION; *U.S. Public*, pg. 1955
STRYKER FRANCE S.A-LEIBINGER MEDSURG DIVISION—See Stryker Corporation; *U.S. Public*, pg. 1956
STRYKER FRANCE SAS—See Stryker Corporation; *U.S. Public*, pg. 1956
STRYKER GMBH & CO. KG—See Stryker Corporation; *U.S. Public*, pg. 1956
STRYKER GMBH—See Stryker Corporation; *U.S. Public*, pg. 1956
STRYKER HOLDINGS BV—See Stryker Corporation; *U.S. Public*, pg. 1957
STRYKER IBERIA, S.L.—See Stryker Corporation; *U.S. Public*, pg. 1957
STRYKER INSTRUMENTS IRELAND LIMITED—See Stryker Corporation; *U.S. Public*, pg. 1957
STRYKER JAPAN K.K.—See Stryker Corporation; *U.S. Public*, pg. 1957
STRYKER KOREA LTD.—See Stryker Corporation; *U.S. Public*, pg. 1957
STRYKER LEIBINGER GMBH & CO. KG—See Stryker Corporation; *U.S. Public*, pg. 1957
STRYKER MEXICO, S.A. DE C.V.—See Stryker Corporation; *U.S. Public*, pg. 1957
STRYKER NETHERLANDS BV—See Stryker Corporation; *U.S. Public*, pg. 1957
STRYKER NEW ZEALAND LIMITED—See Stryker Corporation; *U.S. Public*, pg. 1957
STRYKER OSTEONICS ROMANIA S.R.L.—See Stryker Corporation; *U.S. Public*, pg. 1957
STRYKER PACIFIC LIMITED—See Stryker Corporation; *U.S. Public*, pg. 1957
STRYKER POLSKA SP. ZO.O.—See Stryker Corporation; *U.S. Public*, pg. 1957
STRYKER PORTUGAL PRODUTOS MEDICOS, LDA—See Stryker Corporation; *U.S. Public*, pg. 1957
STRYKER PUERTO RICO, LTD—See Stryker Corporation; *U.S. Public*, pg. 1957
STRYKER SUSTAINABILITY SOLUTIONS, INC.—See Stryker Corporation; *U.S. Public*, pg. 1957
STRYKER UK LTD.—See Stryker Corporation; *U.S. Public*, pg. 1957
STS MEDICAL GROUP SARL—See Monitor Clipper Partners, LLC; *U.S. Private*, pg. 2771
SUBURBAN SURGICAL CO.; *U.S. Private*, pg. 3848
SUMMIT MEDICAL, INC.—See The Graham Group, Inc.; *U.S. Private*, pg. 4037

SUNSET HEALTHCARE SOLUTIONS; *U.S. Private*, pg. 3871
SUNTECH MEDICAL DEVICES (SHENZHEN) CO. LTD.—See Halma plc; *Int'l*, pg. 3233
SURGICAL APPLIANCE INDUSTRIES, INC. - PCP-CHAMPION DIVISION—See Surgical Appliance Industries, Inc.; *U.S. Private*, pg. 3884
SURGICAL SPECIALTIES CORPORATION—See GTCR LLC; *U.S. Private*, pg. 1804
SURGIQUEST, INC.—See CONMED Corporation; *U.S. Public*, pg. 567
SURMODICS MD, LLC—See SurModics, Inc.; *U.S. Public*, pg. 1967
SUTUREX & RENODEX S.A.S.—See B. Braun Melsungen AG; *Int'l*, pg. 788
SYMBIENT PRODUCT DEVELOPMENT, LLC—See Sverica Capital Management LP; *U.S. Private*, pg. 3888
SYMETIS SA—See Boston Scientific Corporation; *U.S. Public*, pg. 375
SYNBIOTICS LTD.—See Ambalal Sarabhai Enterprises Ltd.; *Int'l*, pg. 413
SYNECTIC ENGINEERING, INC.—See Mack Molding Company Inc.; *U.S. Private*, pg. 2536
SYNERGY MEDICAL BRG INC.—See Becton, Dickinson & Company; *U.S. Public*, pg. 292
SYNERGY MEDICAL EUROPE LTD.—See Becton, Dickinson & Company; *U.S. Public*, pg. 292
SYNOVIS MICRO COMPANIES ALLIANCE, INC.—See Baxter International Inc.; *U.S. Public*, pg. 281
SYNTHES USA, LLC—See Johnson & Johnson; *U.S. Public*, pg. 1200
SYNVASIVE TECHNOLOGY, INC.—See Zimmer Biomet Holdings, Inc.; *U.S. Public*, pg. 2406
TANDEM DIABETES CANADA—See Tandem Diabetes Care, Inc.; *U.S. Public*, pg. 1980
TANDEM DIABETES CARE, INC.; *U.S. Public*, pg. 1980
TCM BIOSCIENCES, INC.—See BL PharmTech Corp; *Int'l*, pg. 1056
TECH GROUP GRAND RAPIDS, INC.—See West Pharmaceutical Services, Inc.; *U.S. Public*, pg. 2352
TECH GROUP TEMPE—See West Pharmaceutical Services, Inc.; *U.S. Public*, pg. 2352
TECHNISCAN, INC.; *U.S. Private*, pg. 3954
TECOMET INC.—See Charlesbank Capital Partners, LLC; *U.S. Private*, pg. 856
TEDAN SURGICAL INNOVATIONS, INC—See Halma plc; *Int'l*, pg. 3233
TEI BIOSCIENCES INC—See Integra LifeSciences Holdings Corporation; *U.S. Public*, pg. 1136
TEKNA INC.—See Arendals Fossekompani ASA; *Int'l*, pg. 559
TELEFLEX MEDICAL ASIA PTE LTD.—See Teleflex Incorporated; *U.S. Public*, pg. 1996
TELEFLEX MEDICAL BV—See Teleflex Incorporated; *U.S. Public*, pg. 1996
TELEFLEX MEDICAL DE MEXICO, S. DE R.L. DE C.V.—See Teleflex Incorporated; *U.S. Public*, pg. 1996
TELEFLEX MEDICAL EDC BVBA—See Teleflex Incorporated; *U.S. Public*, pg. 1996
TELEFLEX MEDICAL EUROPE LIMITED—See Teleflex Incorporated; *U.S. Public*, pg. 1996
TELEFLEX MEDICAL GROUP—See Teleflex Incorporated; *U.S. Public*, pg. 1995
TELEFLEX MEDICAL INCORPORATED—See Teleflex Incorporated; *U.S. Public*, pg. 1996
TEMAMED MEDIZINTECHNISCHE DIENSTLEISTUNGS GMBH—See Fresenius SE & Co. KGaA; *Int'l*, pg. 2781
TEMPTIME CORP.—See Zebra Technologies Corporation; *U.S. Public*, pg. 2401
TENON MEDICAL, INC.; *U.S. Public*, pg. 2016
TFX GROUP LIMITED—See Teleflex Incorporated; *U.S. Public*, pg. 1995
TFX MEDICAL OEM—See Teleflex Incorporated; *U.S. Public*, pg. 1996
TFX MEDICAL WIRE PRODUCTS, INC.—See Teleflex Incorporated; *U.S. Public*, pg. 1996
TGX MEDICAL SYSTEMS, LLC—See Integra LifeSciences Holdings Corporation; *U.S. Public*, pg. 1136
THERANOSTIC MEDIZINTECHNIK GMBH—See Elekta AB; *Int'l*, pg. 2356
THERICS, INC.—See Tredegar Corporation; *U.S. Public*, pg. 2187
THERMO FISHER SCIENTIFIC AUSTRALIA PTY LTD—See Thermo Fisher Scientific Inc.; *U.S. Public*, pg. 2153
THERMO FISHER SCIENTIFIC NEW ZEALAND LTD—See Thermo Fisher Scientific Inc.; *U.S. Public*, pg. 2154
THERMOTEK, INC.—See Havencrest Capital Management, LLC; *U.S. Private*, pg. 1880
THEROX, INC.—See Asahi Kasei Corporation; *Int'l*, pg. 597
THOMAS MEDICAL PRODUCTS, INC.—See Merit Medical Systems, Inc.; *U.S. Public*, pg. 1425
THRIFTY PAYLESS, INC.—See New Rite Aid, LLC; *U.S. Private*, pg. 2906
TMJ SOLUTIONS, LLC—See Stryker Corporation; *U.S. Public*, pg. 1957
TNF PHARMACEUTICALS, INC; *U.S. Public*, pg. 2161
TORAX MEDICAL, INC.—See Johnson & Johnson; *U.S. Public*, pg. 1196

TOTIPOTENTRX CELL THERAPY PVT LTD.—See Boyalife Group; *Int'l*, pg. 1124
TRANSGENOMIC LTD.—See Precipio, Inc.; *U.S. Public*, pg. 1713
TRANSMEDICS, INC.; *U.S. Private*, pg. 4209
TRANSONIC SCISENSE INC—See Measurement Innovations Corp.; *U.S. Private*, pg. 2648
TRAUMAFX SOLUTIONS, INC.—See CNL Strategic Capital Management LLC; *U.S. Private*, pg. 952
TRAUSON (CHINA) MEDICAL INSTRUMENT COMPANY LIMITED—See Stryker Corporation; *U.S. Public*, pg. 1957
TRIA BEAUTY, INC.; *U.S. Private*, pg. 4225
TRILINK BIOTECHNOLOGIES, INC.—See Maravai Life-Sciences Holdings, Inc.; *U.S. Public*, pg. 1364
TRILLIANT SURGICAL, LTD.—See Enovis Corporation; *U.S. Public*, pg. 772
TRIOLAB AB—See AddLife AB; *Int'l*, pg. 130
TRIOLAB OY—See HORIBA Ltd; *Int'l*, pg. 3478
TRIPATH IMAGING, INC.—See Becton, Dickinson & Company; *U.S. Public*, pg. 288
TRIVASCULAR GERMANY GMBH—See Endologix, Inc.; *U.S. Private*, pg. 1392
TRUE HEALTHCARE (THAILAND) CO., LTD.—See Berjaya Corporation Berhad; *Int'l*, pg. 984
TRUMPF MEDICAL SYSTEMS LTD.—See Baxter International Inc.; *U.S. Public*, pg. 283
TRUMPF MEDIZINSYSTEMS OSTERREICH GMBH—See Baxter International Inc.; *U.S. Public*, pg. 282
TRU TECH SYSTEMS INC.—See Star Cutter Company; *U.S. Private*, pg. 3784
TUCKER-DAVIS TECHNOLOGIES, INC.; *U.S. Private*, pg. 4256
TUMBLE FORMS INC.—See Patterson Companies, Inc.; *U.S. Public*, pg. 1654
ULTIMED, INC.—See CNL Strategic Capital Management LLC; *U.S. Private*, pg. 952
ULTRA CLEAN SYSTEMS INC.—See Getinge AB; *Int'l*, pg. 2952
ULTROID TECHNOLOGIES, INC.; *U.S. Private*, pg. 4278
UMANA MEDICAL TECHNOLOGIES LTD.—See GPI S.p.A.; *Int'l*, pg. 3046
UNILIFE CORPORATION; *U.S. Private*, pg. 4283
UNILIFE MEDICAL SOLUTIONS, INC.—See Unilife Corporation; *U.S. Private*, pg. 4283
UNION PLASTIC SA—See Groupe OMERIN; *Int'l*, pg. 3109
UNITED HEALTH PRODUCTS, INC.; *U.S. Public*, pg. 2231
USA SCIENTIFIC, INC.—See Eppendorf AG; *Int'l*, pg. 2465
UTAH MEDICAL PRODUCTS LTD.—See Utah Medical Products, Inc.; *U.S. Public*, pg. 2267
VAN HOPPLYNUS OPHTALM SA—See Fagron NV; *Int'l*, pg. 2603
VASAMED, INC.; *U.S. Public*, pg. 2276
VASCULAR SOLUTIONS, INC.—See Teleflex Incorporated; *U.S. Public*, pg. 1996
VECTOR LABORATORIES, INC.—See Thompson Street Capital Manager LLC; *U.S. Private*, pg. 4161
VECTURA DELIVERY DEVICES LTD.—See Philip Morris International Inc.; *U.S. Public*, pg. 1688
VEDANTA BIOSCIENCES, INC.—See PureTech Health plc; *U.S. Public*, pg. 1738
VENCLOSE, INC.—See Becton, Dickinson & Company; *U.S. Public*, pg. 292
VENITI, INC.—See Boston Scientific Corporation; *U.S. Public*, pg. 375
VENTION MEDICAL, INC. - GRAND RAPIDS—See Viant Medical, LLC; *U.S. Private*, pg. 4375
VENTION MEDICAL, INC. - WEST HAVEN—See Viant Medical, LLC; *U.S. Private*, pg. 4375
VENUSA DE MEXICO, S.A. DE C.V.—See Integer Holdings Corporation; *U.S. Public*, pg. 1135
VENUSA, LTD.—See Integer Holdings Corporation; *U.S. Public*, pg. 1135
VERANEX; *U.S. Private*, pg. 4359
VERIDEX, LLC—See Johnson & Johnson; *U.S. Public*, pg. 1200
VERITEQ CORPORATION; *U.S. Private*, pg. 4366
VERNAY EUROPA B.V.—See Vernay Laboratories, Inc.; *U.S. Private*, pg. 4368
VEXIM SA—See Stryker Corporation; *U.S. Public*, pg. 1958
VIANT COLLEGEVILLE, LLC—See Integer Holdings Corporation; *U.S. Public*, pg. 1135
VIANT MEDICAL, LLC; *U.S. Private*, pg. 4375
VIATAR CTC SOLUTIONS INC.; *U.S. Public*, pg. 2292
VICARIOUS SURGICAL INC.; *U.S. Public*, pg. 2295
VICOR TECHNOLOGIES, INC.; *U.S. Private*, pg. 4377
VIDEOJET TECHNOLOGIES S.A.S.—See Danaher Corporation; *U.S. Public*, pg. 632
VIDEOMED S.R.L.—See Baxter International Inc.; *U.S. Public*, pg. 283
VILEX IN TENNESSEE, INC.—See OrthoPediatrics Corp.; *U.S. Public*, pg. 1619
VILTECHMEDA UAB—See Moog Inc.; *U.S. Public*, pg. 1471
VIROTECH DIAGNOSTICS GMBH—See Eurofins Scientific S.E.; *Int'l*, pg. 2552
VISION CARE COMPANY—See Hoya Corporation; *Int'l*, pg. 3498
VI SOLE FZC—See HORIBA Ltd; *Int'l*, pg. 3478

N.A.I.C.S. INDEX

339113 — SURGICAL APPLIANCE ...

VITTA SCIENTIFIC - TECHNICAL COMPANY—See HORIBA Ltd; *Int'l*, pg. 3478
VIVANI MEDICAL, INC.; *U.S. Public*, pg. 2307
VIVEVE MEDICAL INC.; *U.S. Public*, pg. 2307
VWR INTERNATIONAL AS—See Avantor, Inc.; *U.S. Public*, pg. 242
VWR INTERNATIONAL A/S—See Avantor, Inc.; *U.S. Public*, pg. 242
VWR INTERNATIONAL LIMITADA—See Avantor, Inc.; *U.S. Public*, pg. 242
VWR INTERNATIONAL LTD.—See Avantor, Inc.; *U.S. Public*, pg. 242
VWR LAB PRODUCTS PRIVATE LIMITED—See Avantor, Inc.; *U.S. Public*, pg. 242
VWR NA SERVICES, LTD.—See Avantor, Inc.; *U.S. Public*, pg. 242
VWR SINGAPORE PTE. LTD.—See Avantor, Inc.; *U.S. Public*, pg. 242
VYAIRE MEDICAL, INC.—See Apax Partners LLP; *Int'l*, pg. 507
VYAIRE MEDICAL, INC.—See Becton, Dickinson & Company; *U.S. Public*, pg. 292
VYAIRE MEDICAL—See Apax Partners LLP; *Int'l*, pg. 507
VYAIRE MEDICAL—See Apax Partners LLP; *Int'l*, pg. 507
VYAIRE MEDICAL—See Becton, Dickinson & Company; *U.S. Public*, pg. 292
VYAIRE MEDICAL—See Becton, Dickinson & Company; *U.S. Public*, pg. 292
VYCOR MEDICAL, INC.; *U.S. Public*, pg. 2315
W.A. BAUM COMPANY, INC.; *U.S. Private*, pg. 4418
WALK VASCULAR, LLC—See Abbott Laboratories; *U.S. Public*, pg. 21
WALLACH SURGICAL DEVICES, INC.; *U.S. Private*, pg. 4431
WEARABLE HEALTH SOLUTIONS, INC.; *U.S. Public*, pg. 2339
WELCH ALLYN AUSTRALIA (PTY) LIMITED—See Baxter International Inc.; *U.S. Public*, pg. 284
WELCH ALLYN BEAVERTON DEVELOPMENT AND TECHNOLOGY CENTER—See Baxter International Inc.; *U.S. Public*, pg. 284
WELCH ALLYN B.V.—See Baxter International Inc.; *U.S. Public*, pg. 284
WELCH ALLYN, INC.—See Baxter International Inc.; *U.S. Public*, pg. 284
WELCH ALLYN JAPAN K.K.—See Baxter International Inc.; *U.S. Public*, pg. 284
WELCH ALLYN LTD.—See Baxter International Inc.; *U.S. Public*, pg. 284
WELCH ALLYN SERVICE GMBH—See Baxter International Inc.; *U.S. Public*, pg. 284
WELCH ALLYN SINGAPORE PTE. LTD.—See Baxter International Inc.; *U.S. Public*, pg. 284
WELCH ALLYN (U.K.) LTD.—See Baxter International Inc.; *U.S. Public*, pg. 284
WELLMETRIX, LLC—See Zivo Bioscience, Inc.; *U.S. Public*, pg. 2409
WELLSPECT B.V.—See DENTSPLY SIRONA Inc.; *U.S. Public*, pg. 655
WELLSPECT HEALTHCARE NORWAY—See DENTSPLY SIRONA Inc.; *U.S. Public*, pg. 656
WELLSPECT LTD.—See DENTSPLY SIRONA Inc.; *U.S. Public*, pg. 656
WESTERN METALS CORP.; *U.S. Public*, pg. 2356
WHEELCHAIR ADL SOLUTIONS CORPORATION; *U.S. Private*, pg. 4505
W.H.P.M., INC.; *U.S. Private*, pg. 4420
WIDEX A/S—See EQT AB; *Int'l*, pg. 2480
WILLIAM A. COOK AUSTRALIA PTY. LTD.—See Cook Group Incorporated; *U.S. Private*, pg. 1037
WILLIAM COOK EUROPE APS—See Cook Group Incorporated; *U.S. Private*, pg. 1037
WILMINGTON MEDICAL SUPPLY, INC.—See ConvaTec Group PLC; *Int'l*, pg. 1786
WIRUTEC RUSCH MEDICAL VERTRIEBS GMBH—See Teleflex Incorporated; *U.S. Public*, pg. 1996
WM NETHERLANDS C.V.—See Stryker Corporation; *U.S. Public*, pg. 1958
WOLFE-TORY MEDICAL, INC.—See Teleflex Incorporated; *U.S. Public*, pg. 1996
WONDFO USA CO., LTD.—See Guangzhou Wondfo Biotech Co., Ltd.; *Int'l*, pg. 3168
XERIDIEM MEDICAL DEVICES, INC.—See Kohlberg & Company, LLC; *U.S. Private*, pg. 2338
XHALE, INC.; *U.S. Private*, pg. 4581
XL PRECISION TECHNOLOGIES, LTD.—See QHP Capital, L.P.; *U.S. Private*, pg. 3313
X-SPINE SYSTEMS, INC.—See Xtant Medical Holdings, Inc.; *U.S. Public*, pg. 2393
XSTREAM SYSTEMS, INC.—See Veracity Network Inc.; *U.S. Private*, pg. 4359
X TECHNOLOGIES INC.—See Abbott Laboratories; *U.S. Public*, pg. 21
YALITECH SPA—See HORIBA Ltd; *Int'l*, pg. 3478
YOUNG MICROBRUSH INTERNATIONAL, LLC—See The Jordan Company, L.P.; *U.S. Private*, pg. 4063
ZAO CONVATEC—See ConvaTec Group PLC; *Int'l*, pg. 1786
ZAVATION MEDICAL PRODUCTS, LLC—See Gemspring Capital Management, LLC; *U.S. Private*, pg. 1659
ZELTIQ AESTHETICS, INC.—See AbbVie Inc.; *U.S. Public*, pg. 24
ZELTIQ LIMITED—See AbbVie Inc.; *U.S. Public*, pg. 24
ZEUS SCIENTIFIC, INC.—See Caisse de Depot et Placement du Quebec; *Int'l*, pg. 1255
ZEUS SCIENTIFIC, INC.—See CVC Capital Partners SICAV-FIS S.A.; *Int'l*, pg. 1884
ZHUHAI S.E.Z. VIDEOJET ELECTRONICS LTD.—See Danaher Corporation; *U.S. Public*, pg. 632
ZIEHM IMAGING AUSTRIA GMBH—See ATON GmbH; *Int'l*, pg. 689
ZIEHM IMAGING SPAIN S.L.U.—See ATON GmbH; *Int'l*, pg. 689
ZIEHM IMAGING SRL—See ATON GmbH; *Int'l*, pg. 689
ZIMMER BIOMET CMF & THORACIC, LLC—See Zimmer Biomet Holdings, Inc.; *U.S. Public*, pg. 2407
ZIMMER BIOMET DENTAL K.K.—See Zimmer Biomet Holdings, Inc.; *U.S. Public*, pg. 2407
ZIMMER BIOMET NEW ZEALAND COMPANY—See Zimmer Biomet Holdings, Inc.; *U.S. Public*, pg. 2407
ZIMMER BIOMET SPAIN S.L.—See Zimmer Biomet Holdings, Inc.; *U.S. Public*, pg. 2407
ZIMMER BIOMET SPINE, LLC—See H.I.G. Capital, LLC; *U.S. Private*, pg. 1834
ZIMMER BIOMET UK LTD.—See Zimmer Biomet Holdings, Inc.; *U.S. Public*, pg. 2407
ZIMMER MANUFACTURING B.V.—See Zimmer Biomet Holdings, Inc.; *U.S. Public*, pg. 2407
ZIMMER SURGICAL, INC.—See Zimmer Biomet Holdings, Inc.; *U.S. Public*, pg. 2407
ZIMVIE INC.; *U.S. Public*, pg. 2408
ZOLL INTERNATIONAL HOLDING BV—See Asahi Kasei Corporation; *Int'l*, pg. 597
ZOLL MEDICAL AUSTRALIA PTY. LTD.—See Asahi Kasei Corporation; *Int'l*, pg. 597
ZOLL MEDICAL CANADA, INC.—See Asahi Kasei Corporation; *Int'l*, pg. 597
ZOLL MEDICAL DEUTSCHLAND (GMBH)—See Asahi Kasei Corporation; *Int'l*, pg. 598
ZOLL MEDICAL FRANCE S.A.—See Asahi Kasei Corporation; *Int'l*, pg. 598
ZOLL MEDICAL NEW ZEALAND PTY. LTD.—See Asahi Kasei Corporation; *Int'l*, pg. 598
ZOLL MEDICAL U.K. LTD.—See Asahi Kasei Corporation; *Int'l*, pg. 598
ZYNEX NEURODIAGNOSTICS, INC.—See ZYNEX, INC.; *U.S. Public*, pg. 2414

339113 — SURGICAL APPLIANCE AND SUPPLIES MANUFACTURING

3M (SCHWEITZ) GMBH—See 3M Company; *U.S. Public*, pg. 5
3 SIGMA CORP.—See Brixey & Meyer, Inc.; *U.S. Private*, pg. 658
4TITUDE LTD.—See Azenta, Inc.; *U.S. Public*, pg. 257
ACCUTRON, INC.—See Foxtronics EMS; *U.S. Private*, pg. 1585
ACME UNITED CORPORATION; *U.S. Public*, pg. 35
ACUITY SURGICAL DEVICES, LLC; *U.S. Private*, pg. 71
ACUMED LLC—See Berkshire Hathaway Inc.; *U.S. Public*, pg. 308
ACUMED LTD.—See Berkshire Hathaway Inc.; *U.S. Public*, pg. 308
ADESHWAR MEDITEX LIMITED; *Int'l*, pg. 144
ADVANCED MEDICAL SOLUTIONS LTD.—See Advanced Medical Solutions Group plc; *Int'l*, pg. 161
ADVANCED O & P SOLUTIONS, L.L.C.—See Patient Square Capital, L.P.; *U.S. Private*, pg. 3106
ADVANCED STERILIZATION PRODUCTS, INC.—See Johnson & Johnson; *U.S. Public*, pg. 1195
AIMEDIC MMT CO., LTD.—See Bando Chemical Industries, Ltd.; *Int'l*, pg. 830
AK MEDICAL HOLDINGS LIMITED; *Int'l*, pg. 259
ALBAHEALTH, LLC—See Encompass Group LLC; *U.S. Private*, pg. 1390
ALLERGAN AUSTRALIA (PTY.) LTD.—See AbbVie Inc.; *U.S. Public*, pg. 22
ALLERGAN FRANCE S.A.S.—See AbbVie Inc.; *U.S. Public*, pg. 23
ALLERGAN LIMITED—See AbbVie Inc.; *U.S. Public*, pg. 23
ALLERGAN PHARMACEUTICALS (IRELAND) LTD., INC.—See AbbVie Inc.; *U.S. Public*, pg. 23
ALLERGAN PRODUTOS FARMACEUTICOS, LTDA.—See AbbVie Inc.; *U.S. Public*, pg. 23
ALLERGAN S.A.U.—See AbbVie Inc.; *U.S. Public*, pg. 23
ALLERGAN S.P.A.—See AbbVie Inc.; *U.S. Public*, pg. 23
ALPHA BIOTEC LTD.—See Danaher Corporation; *U.S. Public*, pg. 634
ALPHA PRO TECH-NOGALES—See Alpha Pro Tech, Ltd.; *Int'l*, pg. 369
AMERICAN MEDICAL SYSTEMS, INC.—See Endo International plc; *Int'l*, pg. 2404
AMERICH CORPORATION; *U.S. Private*, pg. 259
AMERON PROTECTIVE LININGS CO—See NOV, Inc.; *U.S. Public*, pg. 1544
ANDWIN CORPORATION; *U.S. Private*, pg. 281
ANSELL CANADA INC.—See Ansell Limited; *Int'l*, pg. 478
ANSELL HEALTHCARE JAPAN CO. LTD.—See Ansell Limited; *Int'l*, pg. 478
ANSELL SANDEL MEDICAL SOLUTIONS LLC—See Ansell Limited; *Int'l*, pg. 478
APPLE HOMECARE MEDICAL SUPPLY, LLC—See InTandem Capital Partners, LLC; *U.S. Private*, pg. 2097
APPLIED RAPID TECHNOLOGIES CORP.—See Obsidian Solutions Group LLC; *U.S. Private*, pg. 2988
ARAN BIOMEDICAL TEORANTA LTD.—See Integer Holdings Corporation; *U.S. Public*, pg. 1134
ARIZANT DEUTSCHLAND GMBH—See 3M Company; *U.S. Public*, pg. 8
ARIZANT FRANCE SAS—See 3M Company; *U.S. Public*, pg. 8
ARIZANT, INC.—See 3M Company; *U.S. Public*, pg. 8
ARIZANT INTERNATIONAL CORPORATION—See 3M Company; *U.S. Public*, pg. 8
ARIZANT OSTERREICH GMBH—See 3M Company; *U.S. Public*, pg. 8
ARIZANT UK LIMITED—See 3M Company; *U.S. Public*, pg. 8
ARJO AUSTRIA GMBH—See Getinge AB; *Int'l*, pg. 2947
ARJO EQUIPEMENTS HOSPITALIERS S.A.—See Getinge AB; *Int'l*, pg. 2947
ARJO FAR EAST LTD.—See Getinge AB; *Int'l*, pg. 2947
ARJO HOSPITAL EQUIPMENT AB—See Getinge AB; *Int'l*, pg. 2947
ARJO HOSPITAL EQUIPMENT PTY LTD.—See Getinge AB; *Int'l*, pg. 2948
ARJO HOSPITAL EQUIPMENT S.R.O.—See Getinge AB; *Int'l*, pg. 2948
ARJOHUNTLEIGH NEDERLAND B.V.—See Getinge AB; *Int'l*, pg. 2948
ARJOHUNTLEIGH UK—See Getinge AB; *Int'l*, pg. 2948
ARJO ITALIA S.P.A.—See Getinge AB; *Int'l*, pg. 2948
ARJO SPAIN S.A.—See Getinge AB; *Int'l*, pg. 2948
A.R. MEDICOM INC. HEALTHCARE (SHANGHAI) LTD.—See A.R. Medicom Inc.; *Int'l*, pg. 28
ARROW INTERVENTIONAL, INC.—See Teleflex Incorporated; *U.S. Public*, pg. 1995
ARSEUS MEDICAL NV; *Int'l*, pg. 580
ARTEGRAFT INC—See LeMaitre Vascular, Inc.; *U.S. Public*, pg. 1304
ARTHROSURFACE INCORPORATED—See Anika Therapeutics, Inc.; *U.S. Public*, pg. 137
ARTISENT, LLC—See Gentex Corporation; *U.S. Private*, pg. 1679
ARTIVION, INC.; *U.S. Public*, pg. 208
ASPRESEG SAS—See Delta Plus Group; *Int'l*, pg. 2019
ASTEK GROUP PLC; *Int'l*, pg. 651
ATOS MEDICAL APS—See Coloplast A/S; *Int'l*, pg. 1703
ATOS MEDICAL AUSTRIA GMBH—See Coloplast A/S; *Int'l*, pg. 1703
ATOS MEDICAL B.V.B.A.—See Coloplast A/S; *Int'l*, pg. 1703
ATOS MEDICAL B.V.—See Coloplast A/S; *Int'l*, pg. 1703
ATOS MEDICAL CANADA INC.—See Coloplast A/S; *Int'l*, pg. 1703
ATOS MEDICAL GMBH—See Coloplast A/S; *Int'l*, pg. 1703
ATOS MEDICAL INC.—See Coloplast A/S; *Int'l*, pg. 1703
ATOS MEDICAL PTY. LTD.—See Coloplast A/S; *Int'l*, pg. 1703
ATOS MEDICAL S.R.L.—See Coloplast A/S; *Int'l*, pg. 1703
AT SURGICAL COMPANY, INC.; *U.S. Private*, pg. 363
AUSTOFIX SURGICAL PTY LTD—See Austofix Group Limited; *Int'l*, pg. 718
AVERY DENNISON BELGIE BVBA—See Avery Dennison Corporation; *U.S. Public*, pg. 243
AVON PROTECTION SYSTEMS, INC.—See Avon Protection plc; *Int'l*, pg. 750
AXONICS, INC.; *U.S. Public*, pg. 256
AXYGEN, INC.—See Corning Incorporated; *U.S. Public*, pg. 578
BACKJOY ORTHOTICS, LLC; *U.S. Private*, pg. 423
BARD DEVICES, INC.—See Becton, Dickinson & Company; *U.S. Public*, pg. 290
BARD MEDICAL DIVISION—See Becton, Dickinson & Company; *U.S. Public*, pg. 291
BARRIERSAFE SOLUTIONS INTERNATIONAL INC.—See Ansell Limited; *Int'l*, pg. 478
BASF CATALYSTS GERMANY GMBH—See BASF SE; *Int'l*, pg. 875
BAUSCH & LOMB AUSTRALIA PTY. LTD.—See Bausch Health Companies Inc.; *Int'l*, pg. 896
BAUSCH & LOMB B.V.—See Bausch Health Companies Inc.; *Int'l*, pg. 896
BAUSCH & LOMB ESPANA S.A.—See Bausch Health Companies Inc.; *Int'l*, pg. 896
BAUSCH & LOMB IOM S.P.A.—See Bausch Health Companies Inc.; *Int'l*, pg. 896
BAUSCH & LOMB MEXICO S.A. DE C.V.—See Bausch Health Companies Inc.; *Int'l*, pg. 896
BAUSCH & LOMB (S) PTE LTD.—See Bausch Health Companies Inc.; *Int'l*, pg. 896
BAUSCH & LOMB SURGICAL CORP.—See Bausch Health Companies Inc.; *Int'l*, pg. 896

339113 — SURGICAL APPLIANCE ...

BAUSCH & LOMB SWISS AG—See Bausch Health Companies Inc.; *Int'l*, pg. 897
BAUSCH & LOMB TAIWAN LTD.—See Bausch Health Companies Inc.; *Int'l*, pg. 896
BAXA CORPORATION—See Baxter International Inc.; *U.S. Public*, pg. 280
BAYLIS MEDICAL CO. INC.—See Boston Scientific Corporation; *U.S. Public*, pg. 374
BD HOLDING S. DE R.L. DE C.V.—See Becton, Dickinson & Company; *U.S. Public*, pg. 288
BD KIESTRA BV—See Becton, Dickinson & Company; *U.S. Public*, pg. 288
BECTON DICKINSON ASIA LIMITED—See Becton, Dickinson & Company; *U.S. Public*, pg. 289
BECTON DICKINSON CANADA INC.—See Becton, Dickinson & Company; *U.S. Public*, pg. 289
BECTON, DICKINSON & COMPANY, LTD.—See Becton, Dickinson & Company; *U.S. Public*, pg. 290
BECTON DICKINSON INFUSION THERAPY A/S—See Becton, Dickinson & Company; *U.S. Public*, pg. 289
BECTON DICKINSON INFUSION THERAPY B.V.—See Becton, Dickinson & Company; *U.S. Public*, pg. 289
BECTON DICKINSON INFUSION THERAPY HOLDINGS UK LIMITED—See Becton, Dickinson & Company; *U.S. Public*, pg. 289
BECTON DICKINSON INFUSION THERAPY SYSTEMS INC., S.A. DE C.V.—See Becton, Dickinson & Company; *U.S. Public*, pg. 289
BECTON DICKINSON LTD.—See Becton, Dickinson & Company; *U.S. Public*, pg. 289
BECTON DICKINSON MANAGEMENT GMBH & CO. KG—See Becton, Dickinson & Company; *U.S. Public*, pg. 289
BECTON DICKINSON (ROYSTON) LIMITED—See Becton, Dickinson & Company; *U.S. Public*, pg. 288
BECTON DICKINSON SWEDEN HOLDINGS AB—See Becton, Dickinson & Company; *U.S. Public*, pg. 290
BELTONE ELECTRONICS OF CANADA LTD.—See GN Store Nord A/S; *Int'l*, pg. 3016
BERCHTOLD ASIA SDN BHD—See Stryker Corporation; *U.S. Public*, pg. 1955
BERCHTOLD CHINA LTD—See Stryker Corporation; *U.S. Public*, pg. 1955
BERCHTOLD CONSULTING GMBH—See Stryker Corporation; *U.S. Public*, pg. 1955
BERCHTOLD ESPANA S.L.—See Stryker Corporation; *U.S. Public*, pg. 1955
BERCHTOLD ITALIA SRL—See Stryker Corporation; *U.S. Public*, pg. 1955
BERCHTOLD JAPAN KK—See Stryker Corporation; *U.S. Public*, pg. 1955
BERCHTOLD PACIFIC PTY—See Stryker Corporation; *U.S. Public*, pg. 1955
BERCHTOLD UK LIMITED—See Stryker Corporation; *U.S. Public*, pg. 1955
BERTHEAS & CIE—See Cheynet S.A.S; *Int'l*, pg. 1474
BIOMEDICAL ENTERPRISES, INC.—See Johnson & Johnson; *U.S. Public*, pg. 1195
BIOMET 3I CANADA, INC.—See Zimmer Biomet Holdings, Inc.; *U.S. Public*, pg. 2405
BIOMET 3I DE BRASIL LTDA.—See Zimmer Biomet Holdings, Inc.; *U.S. Public*, pg. 2405
BIOMET 3I FRANCE SAS—See Zimmer Biomet Holdings, Inc.; *U.S. Public*, pg. 2405
BIOMET 3I NETHERLANDS B.V.—See Zimmer Biomet Holdings, Inc.; *U.S. Public*, pg. 2405
BIOMET AUSTRIA GMBH—See Zimmer Biomet Holdings, Inc.; *U.S. Public*, pg. 2405
BIOMET CHILE SA—See Zimmer Biomet Holdings, Inc.; *U.S. Public*, pg. 2405
BIOMET CHINA CO., LTD.—See Zimmer Biomet Holdings, Inc.; *U.S. Public*, pg. 2405
BIOMET EL SALVADOR SA DE CV—See Zimmer Biomet Holdings, Inc.; *U.S. Public*, pg. 2405
BIOMET FRANCE SARL—See Zimmer Biomet Holdings, Inc.; *U.S. Public*, pg. 2405
BIOMET GLOBAL SUPPLY CHAIN CENTER B.V.—See Zimmer Biomet Holdings, Inc.; *U.S. Public*, pg. 2406
BIOMET HELLAS SA—See Zimmer Biomet Holdings, Inc.; *U.S. Public*, pg. 2406
BIOMET MEXICO S.A. DE C.V.—See Zimmer Biomet Holdings, Inc.; *U.S. Public*, pg. 2406
BIOMET ORTHOPAEDIC INDIA PRIVATE LIMITED—See Zimmer Biomet Holdings, Inc.; *U.S. Public*, pg. 2406
BIOMET ORTHOPAEDICS SWITZERLAND GMBH—See Zimmer Biomet Holdings, Inc.; *U.S. Public*, pg. 2406
BIOMET ORTHOPEDICS PUERTO RICO, INC.—See Zimmer Biomet Holdings, Inc.; *U.S. Public*, pg. 2406
BIOMET TRAUMA, LLC—See Zimmer Biomet Holdings, Inc.; *U.S. Public*, pg. 2406
BIOSTORAGE TECHNOLOGIES ASIA PACIFIC PTE. LTD.—See Azenta, Inc.; *U.S. Public*, pg. 257
BIOSTORAGE TECHNOLOGIES GMBH—See Azenta, Inc.; *U.S. Public*, pg. 257
BIOTRONIK GMBH & CO.—See Biotronik GmbH & Co.; *Int'l*, pg. 1044
BIOTRONIK GMBH & CO. VERTRIEBS KG—See Biotronik GmbH & Co.; *Int'l*, pg. 1044

BIRD & CRONIN, LLC—See Dynatronics Corporation; *U.S. Public*, pg. 700
BLAKE H BROWN INC.; *U.S. Private*, pg. 578
BL INDUSTRIA OTICA, LTDA.—See Bausch Health Companies Inc.; *Int'l*, pg. 896
B.L.J. COMPANY LTD.—See Bausch Health Companies Inc.; *Int'l*, pg. 896
BODYGUARD WORKWEAR LIMITED—See Bunzl plc; *Int'l*, pg. 1217
BOSTON BRACE INTERNATIONAL, INC.—See OrthoPediatrics Corp.; *U.S. Public*, pg. 1619
BOSTON ENDO-SURGICAL TECHNOLOGIES LLC—See NN, Inc.; *U.S. Public*, pg. 1531
BRICON AG—See CENTROTEC SE; *Int'l*, pg. 1414
BRIVANT LIMITED—See Integer Holdings Corporation; *U.S. Public*, pg. 1134
BURLINGTON MEDICAL LLC—See Fox Three Partners LLC; *U.S. Private*, pg. 1585
BURLINGTON MEDICAL LLC—See Peninsula Capital Partners LLC; *U.S. Private*, pg. 3133
CANCER DIAGNOSTICS, INC.; *U.S. Private*, pg. 733
CARDINAL HEALTH MALAYSIA 211 SDN. BHD.—See Cardinal Health, Inc.; *U.S. Public*, pg. 433
CAREPLUS (M) SDN BHD—See Ansell Limited; *Int'l*, pg. 478
CARTIKA MEDICAL—See Teleflex Incorporated; *U.S. Public*, pg. 1996
CAS MEDICAL SYSTEMS, INC.—See Edwards Lifesciences Corporation; *U.S. Public*, pg. 720
CATHETER PRECISION, INC.; *U.S. Public*, pg. 454
CENTENIAL SURGICAL SUTURE LTD.; *Int'l*, pg. 1402
CHANGZHOU BIOMET MEDICAL DEVICES CO. LTD.—See Zimmer Biomet Holdings, Inc.; *U.S. Public*, pg. 2406
CHATTANOOGA GROUP—See Enovis Corporation; *U.S. Public*, pg. 772
CHEMLAND INDUSTRIES, INC.—See Lakeland Industries, Inc.; *U.S. Public*, pg. 1288
CHISON USA INC.—See Chison Medical Technologies Co., Ltd.; *Int'l*, pg. 1574
CITATION PLASTICS CO.—See West Pharmaceutical Services, Inc.; *U.S. Public*, pg. 2352
CLEANSPACE TECHNOLOGY PTY LIMITED—See Cleanspace Holdings Limited; *Int'l*, pg. 1655
COLOPLAST II PORTUGAL, UNIPESSOAL LDA.—See Coloplast A/S; *Int'l*, pg. 1703
COLOPLAST MANUFACTURING US, LLC—See Coloplast A/S; *Int'l*, pg. 1703
COLOPLAST OOO—See Coloplast A/S; *Int'l*, pg. 1703
COMFOOR BV—See Amplifon S.p.A.; *Int'l*, pg. 435
COMPANIA CHILENA DE FOSFOROS S.A.; *Int'l*, pg. 1748
CONSTRONICS INFRA LIMITED; *Int'l*, pg. 1776
CONTEMPORARY PRODUCTS, LLC—See Bidwell Industrial Group, Inc.; *U.S. Private*, pg. 551
CORE MOLDING TECHNOLOGIES, INC.; *U.S. Public*, pg. 576
CORE PRODUCTS INTERNATIONAL, INC.; *U.S. Private*, pg. 1049
CORNING S.A.—See Corning Incorporated; *U.S. Public*, pg. 578
CREAGH MEDICAL LIMITED—See SurModics, Inc.; *U.S. Public*, pg. 1967
CREO MEDICAL GROUP PLC; *Int'l*, pg. 1838
CUREXO INC.; *Int'l*, pg. 1878
CYNOSURE GMBH—See Clayton, Dubilier & Rice, LLC; *U.S. Private*, pg. 922
CYTYC SURGICAL PRODUCTS II, LLC—See Hologic, Inc.; *U.S. Public*, pg. 1044
DALE MEDICAL PRODUCTS INC.; *U.S. Private*, pg. 1149
DALIAN FREE TRADE ZONE NICHIURA TRADING CO. LTD.—See Azearth Corporation; *Int'l*, pg. 778
DANAMECO MEDICAL JOINT STOCK CORPORATION; *Int'l*, pg. 1958
DAVOL INC.—See Becton, Dickinson & Company; *U.S. Public*, pg. 291
DC SAFETY SALES, INC.—See Dubilier & Company, Inc.; *U.S. Private*, pg. 1283
.DECIMAL, INC; *U.S. Private*, pg. 1
DEGIL SAFETY PRODUCTS, INC.—See Delta Plus Group; *Int'l*, pg. 2019
DELTA PLUS CENTROAMERICA S.A.—See Delta Plus Group; *Int'l*, pg. 2019
DELTA PLUS CHINA CO., LTD.—See Delta Plus Group; *Int'l*, pg. 2019
DELTA PLUS IBERIA S.A.U.—See Delta Plus Group; *Int'l*, pg. 2020
DELTA PLUS PERSONEL GIYIM VE IS GUVENLIGI EKIPMANLARI SANAYI VE TICARET LIMITED SIRKET—See Delta Plus Group; *Int'l*, pg. 2020
DELTA PLUS PHILIPPINES, INC.—See Delta Plus Group; *Int'l*, pg. 2020
DELTA PLUS RUSSIE OOO—See Delta Plus Group; *Int'l*, pg. 2020
DELTA PLUS SAS—See Delta Plus Group; *Int'l*, pg. 2020
DENTIUM USA INC.—See Dentium Co., Ltd; *Int'l*, pg. 2033
DEPUY ORTHOPAEDICS, INC.—See Johnson & Johnson; *U.S. Public*, pg. 1195
DIAVERUM S.A.—See Bridgepoint Group Plc; *Int'l*, pg. 1153

DJO ASIA-PACIFIC LTD.—See Enovis Corporation; *U.S. Public*, pg. 772
DJO CANADA INC.—See Enovis Corporation; *U.S. Public*, pg. 772
DJO GLOBAL, INC.—See Enovis Corporation; *U.S. Public*, pg. 772
DJO IBERICA PRODUCTOS ORTOPEDICOS S.L.—See Enovis Corporation; *U.S. Public*, pg. 772
DJO ITALIA SRL—See Enovis Corporation; *U.S. Public*, pg. 772
DJO NORDIC AB—See Enovis Corporation; *U.S. Public*, pg. 772
DJO ORTHOPAEDIC SOUTH AFRICA PTY. LTD.—See Enovis Corporation; *U.S. Public*, pg. 772
DNA GENOTEK INC.—See OraSure Technologies, Inc.; *U.S. Public*, pg. 1614
DNA HOLDINGS CORPORATION; *Int'l*, pg. 2147
DOUBLE MEDICAL TECHNOLOGY INC.; *Int'l*, pg. 2181
DRAEGER MEDICAL BULGARIA EOOD—See Draegerwerk AG & Co. KGaA; *Int'l*, pg. 2196
DRAEGER OOO—See Draegerwerk AG & Co. KGaA; *Int'l*, pg. 2196
DRAGER AUSTRIA GMBH—See Draegerwerk AG & Co. KGaA; *Int'l*, pg. 2197
DRAGER DANMARK A/S—See Draegerwerk AG & Co. KGaA; *Int'l*, pg. 2197
DRAGER FRANCE SAS—See Draegerwerk AG & Co. KGaA; *Int'l*, pg. 2197
DRAGER MEDICAL BELGIUM NV—See Draegerwerk AG & Co. KGaA; *Int'l*, pg. 2197
DRAGER MEDICAL ROMANIA SRL—See Draegerwerk AG & Co. KGaA; *Int'l*, pg. 2197
DRAGER PORTUGAL, LDA.—See Draegerwerk AG & Co. KGaA; *Int'l*, pg. 2197
DRAGER SAFETY ROMANIA SRL—See Draegerwerk AG & Co. KGaA; *Int'l*, pg. 2198
DRAGER SCHWEIZ AG—See Draegerwerk AG & Co. KGaA; *Int'l*, pg. 2198
DRAGER SVERIGE AB—See Draegerwerk AG & Co. KGaA; *Int'l*, pg. 2198
DURSTMULLER GMBH—See Arcure; *Int'l*, pg. 552
DVS EQUIPAMENTOS DE PROTECAO INDIVIDUAL LTDA.—See Bunzl plc; *Int'l*, pg. 1218
EAGLE VISION, INC.—See Audax Group, Limited Partnership; *U.S. Private*, pg. 388
E.D. BULLARD COMPANY; *U.S. Private*, pg. 1305
EDWARDS LIFESCIENCES ASSET MANAGEMENT CORPORATION—See Edwards Lifesciences Corporation; *U.S. Public*, pg. 720
EDWARDS LIFESCIENCES (SINGAPORE) PTE LTD—See Edwards Lifesciences Corporation; *U.S. Public*, pg. 720
EES, S.A. DE C.V.—See Johnson & Johnson; *U.S. Public*, pg. 1195
ELECTRIC MOBILITY CORPORATION; *U.S. Private*, pg. 1352
ELEKTA LIMITED—See Elekta AB; *Int'l*, pg. 2355
EMERGENCY ESSENTIALS INC.; *U.S. Private*, pg. 1380
ENVVENO MEDICAL CORPORATION; *U.S. Public*, pg. 782
ESSILOR CANADA LTD.—See EssilorLuxottica SA; *Int'l*, pg. 2512
ETHICON ENDO-SURGERY, LLC—See Johnson & Johnson; *U.S. Public*, pg. 1196
ETHICON, INC.—See Johnson & Johnson; *U.S. Public*, pg. 1195
ETHICON, INC.—See Johnson & Johnson; *U.S. Public*, pg. 1196
ETHICON IRELAND LIMITED—See Johnson & Johnson; *U.S. Public*, pg. 1196
ETHICON SAS—See Johnson & Johnson; *U.S. Public*, pg. 1196
EUROMED, INC.—See Mativ Holdings, Inc.; *U.S. Public*, pg. 1396
EUROMEDIS GROUPE SA; *Int'l*, pg. 2554
EXACTECH DEUTSCHLAND GMBH—See TPG Capital, L.P.; *U.S. Public*, pg. 2173
EXACTECH FRANCE SAS—See TPG Capital, L.P.; *U.S. Public*, pg. 2173
EXACTECH (UK) LTD.—See TPG Capital, L.P.; *U.S. Public*, pg. 2173
FARU, S.L.U.—See Bunzl plc; *Int'l*, pg. 1218
FEMASYS INC.; *U.S. Public*, pg. 829
FERNO-WASHINGTON INC.; *U.S. Private*, pg. 1497
FILLAUER EUROPE AB—See Patient Square Capital, L.P.; *U.S. Private*, pg. 3107
FILLAUER LLC—See Patient Square Capital, L.P.; *U.S. Private*, pg. 3107
FINESSE MEDICAL LTD.—See Avery Dennison Corporation; *U.S. Public*, pg. 244
FIRST AID ONLY INC.—See Acme United Corporation; *U.S. Public*, pg. 35
FORUS S.A.; *Int'l*, pg. 2744
FREEDOM DESIGNS, INC.—See Invacare Corporation; *U.S. Public*, pg. 2130
GAMIDA SA—See Gamida for Life B.V.; *Int'l*, pg. 2878
GENERAL BANDAGES, INC.; *U.S. Private*, pg. 1664
GENEWEL CO., LTD.—See Dongsung Chemical Co., Ltd.; *Int'l*, pg. 2170
GERRESHEIMER MEDICAL PLASTIC SYSTEMS DONG-

N.A.I.C.S. INDEX

339113 — SURGICAL APPLIANCE ...

GUAN CO. LTD.—See Gerresheimer AG; *Int'l*, pg. 2943
GETINGE D.S.E. NV—See Getinge AB; *Int'l*, pg. 2949
GETINGE FINLAND OY—See Getinge AB; *Int'l*, pg. 2949
GETINGE IBERICA S.L.—See Getinge AB; *Int'l*, pg. 2950
GETINGE SOUTH AFRICA (PTY) LTD.—See Getinge AB; *Int'l*, pg. 2950
GETINGE STERILIZATION AB—See Getinge AB; *Int'l*, pg. 2950
GETINGE SVERIGE AB—See Getinge AB; *Int'l*, pg. 2950
GETINGE USA, INC.—See Getinge AB; *Int'l*, pg. 2951
GIIB HOLDINGS BERHAD; *Int'l*, pg. 2972
GLOBUS MEDICAL BRAZIL LDTA.—See Globus Medical, Inc.; *U.S. Public*, pg. 947
HAEMONETICS PUERTO RICO, LLC—See Haemonetics Corporation; *U.S. Public*, pg. 979
HALKEY-ROBERTS CORPORATION—See Nordson Corporation; *U.S. Public*, pg. 1532
HANCOM LIFECARE INC.; *Int'l*, pg. 3242
HANGER FABRICATION NETWORK LLC—See Patient Square Capital, L.P.; *U.S. Private*, pg. 3107
HANSEN MEDICAL DEUTSCHLAND GMBH—See Johnson & Johnson; *U.S. Public*, pg. 1194
HANS HEPP GMBH & CO. KG; *Int'l*, pg. 3259
HARRY J. LAWALL & SON; *U.S. Private*, pg. 1871
HARVARD APPARATUS REGENERATIVE TECHNOLOGY, INC.; *U.S. Public*, pg. 987
HEBEI YONGLE TAPE CO., LTD.—See Avery Dennison Corporation; *U.S. Public*, pg. 244
HELIX MEDICAL LLC - BALDWIN PARK—See Freudenberg SE; *Int'l*, pg. 2789
HELIX MEDICAL LLC—See Freudenberg SE; *Int'l*, pg. 2789
HEXTAR HEALTHCARE BERHAD—See Hextar Global Berhad; *Int'l*, pg. 3373
H&H MEDICAL CORPORATION—See Water Street Healthcare Partners, LLC; *U.S. Private*, pg. 4452
HILL-ROM - CHARLESTON—See Baxter International Inc.; *U.S. Public*, pg. 283
HILL-ROM COMPANY, INC.—See Baxter International Inc.; *U.S. Public*, pg. 283
HL CORP - MEDICAL EQUIPMENT DIVISION—See HL CORP; *Int'l*, pg. 3429
HOLLISTER INCORPORATED; *U.S. Private*, pg. 1965
HOLLISTER MEDICAL INDIA PRIVATE LIMITED—See Hollister Incorporated; *U.S. Private*, pg. 1965
HOLLISTER S.A. DE C.V.—See Hollister Incorporated; *U.S. Private*, pg. 1965
HOLLISTER ULC—See Hollister Incorporated; *U.S. Private*, pg. 1966
HOME WELLNESS, INC.—See AdaptHealth Corp.; *U.S. Public*, pg. 38
HONEYWELL SAFETY PRODUCTS AUSTRALIA PTY LTD—See Honeywell International Inc.; *U.S. Public*, pg. 1049
HONEYWELL SAFETY PRODUCTS HEARING PROTECTION, LLC—See Honeywell International Inc.; *U.S. Public*, pg. 1049
HORSAM AB; *Int'l*, pg. 3482
HOSHIIRYO-SANKI CO., LTD.; *Int'l*, pg. 3482
HOSMER-DORRANCE CORPORATION—See Patient Square Capital, L.P.; *U.S. Private*, pg. 3107
HOSPIDANA A/S—See AddLife AB; *Int'l*, pg. 129
HOVEROUND CORP.—See Jordan Industries, Inc.; *U.S. Private*, pg. 2235
HOWMEDICA OSTEONICS CORP.—See Stryker Corporation; *U.S. Public*, pg. 1955
HUDSON RESPIRATORY CARE TECATE, S. DE R.L. DE C.V.—See Teleflex Incorporated; *U.S. Public*, pg. 1996
HUVEXEL CO LTD; *Int'l*, pg. 3540
ICOR AB—See Teleflex Incorporated; *U.S. Public*, pg. 1995
INEL INC.—See Thermo Fisher Scientific Inc.; *U.S. Public*, pg. 2148
INSTRUMEDICS, LLC—See Stryker Corporation; *U.S. Public*, pg. 1955
INTEGRA LIFESCIENCES ITALY S.R.L.—See Integra LifeSciences Holdings Corporation; *U.S. Public*, pg. 1135
INTERMED ULTRASOUND—See Cressey & Company, LP; *U.S. Private*, pg. 1095
INTERMED ULTRASOUND—See Health Enterprise Partners LLC; *U.S. Private*, pg. 1893
INTERVASCULAR SARL.—See Getinge AB; *Int'l*, pg. 2951
INVACARE CONTINUING CARE, INC.—See Invacare Corporation; *U.S. Private*, pg. 2130
INVACARE FRANCE OPERATIONS SAS—See Invacare Corporation; *U.S. Private*, pg. 2130
INVACARE LTD.—See Invacare Corporation; *U.S. Private*, pg. 2131
INVACARE VERWALTUNGS GMBH—See Invacare Corporation; *U.S. Private*, pg. 2131
JACKSON PRODUCTS, INC.—See Kimberly-Clark Corporation; *U.S. Public*, pg. 1264
JANSSEN-CILAG AB—See Johnson & Johnson; *U.S. Public*, pg. 1197
JANSSEN-CILAG, C.A.—See Johnson & Johnson; *U.S. Public*, pg. 1197
JERRY MEDICAL EQUIPMENT (SHANGHAI) CO., LTD.—See Cofoe Medical Technology Co., Ltd.; *Int'l*, pg. 1693

J.M.R. MEDICAL, INC.—See AdaptHealth Corp.; *U.S. Public*, pg. 39
JOHNSON & JOHNSON HELLAS COMMERCIAL & INDUSTRIAL S.A.—See Kenvue Inc.; *U.S. Public*, pg. 1224
JOHNSON & JOHNSON INDIA LTD.—See Johnson & Johnson; *U.S. Public*, pg. 1198
JOHNSON & JOHNSON VISION CARE (IRELAND) LIMITED—See Johnson & Johnson; *U.S. Public*, pg. 1199
JRI ORTHOPAEDICS LIMITED—See AK Medical Holdings Limited; *Int'l*, pg. 259
KELVIN MEDICAL, INC.; *U.S. Public*, pg. 1220
LABCONCO CORPORATION; *U.S. Private*, pg. 2370
LABTECH INTERIORS LLC—See Dubai Investments PJSC; *Int'l*, pg. 2219
LAKELAND INDUSTRIES, INC.; *U.S. Public*, pg. 1288
LAKE REGION MEDICAL LIMITED—See Integer Holdings Corporation; *U.S. Public*, pg. 1135
LANCER HOLLAND B.V.—See Getinge AB; *Int'l*, pg. 2949
LANCER S.N.C.—See Getinge AB; *Int'l*, pg. 2949
LEGACY OXYGEN & HOME CARE EQUIPMENT, LLC—See Quipt Home Medical Corp.; *U.S. Public*, pg. 1757
LEICA BIOSYSTEMS RICHMOND, INC.—See Danaher Corporation; *U.S. Public*, pg. 628
LEMAITRE MEDICAL TECHNOLOGY (SHANGHAI) CO., LTD.—See LeMaitre Vascular, Inc.; *U.S. Public*, pg. 1304
LEMAITRE VASCULAR AS—See LeMaitre Vascular, Inc.; *U.S. Public*, pg. 1304
LEMAITRE VASCULAR PTY LTD—See LeMaitre Vascular, Inc.; *U.S. Public*, pg. 1305
LEMAITRE VASCULAR SWITZERLAND GMBH—See LeMaitre Vascular, Inc.; *U.S. Public*, pg. 1305
LEMAITRE VASCULAR ULC—See LeMaitre Vascular, Inc.; *U.S. Public*, pg. 1305
LEXAGENE HOLDINGS INC.; *U.S. Private*, pg. 2440
LIENTEH TECHNOLOGY SDN. BHD.—See Eonmetall Group Berhad; *Int'l*, pg. 2458
LIFESAVING SYSTEMS CORP.—See Arcline Investment Management LP; *U.S. Private*, pg. 315
LIFESCAN PRODUCTS, LLC—See Johnson & Johnson; *U.S. Public*, pg. 1199
LIFESCAN SCOTLAND LIMITED—See Johnson & Johnson; *U.S. Public*, pg. 1199
LIFE WEAR TECHNOLOGIES, INC.—See Modular Thermal Technologies, LLC; *U.S. Private*, pg. 2763
LILY MEDICAL CORPORATION—See Audix Corporation; *Int'l*, pg. 702
LIMA SK S.R.O.—See Enovis Corporation; *U.S. Public*, pg. 773
LINVATEC KOREA LTD.—See CONMED Corporation; *U.S. Public*, pg. 567
LUXOTTICA AUSTRALIA PTY. LTD.—See EssilorLuxottica SA; *Int'l*, pg. 2515
LUXOTTICA MEXICO SA DE C.V.—See EssilorLuxottica SA; *Int'l*, pg. 2515
LUXOTTICA—See EssilorLuxottica SA; *Int'l*, pg. 2515
LUXOTTICA (SWITZERLAND) A.G.—See EssilorLuxottica SA; *Int'l*, pg. 2515
MAKO SURGICAL CORP.—See Stryker Corporation; *U.S. Public*, pg. 1955
MAQUET CARDIOVASCULAR LLC—See Getinge AB; *Int'l*, pg. 2951
MAQUET SA—See Getinge AB; *Int'l*, pg. 2951
MASTERCLEAN TECHNOLOGIES (M) SDN BHD—See Careplus Group Berhad; *Int'l*, pg. 1325
MATHYS ORTHOPADIE GMBH—See Enovis Corporation; *U.S. Public*, pg. 773
MATHYS ORTHOPAEDICS BV—See Enovis Corporation; *U.S. Public*, pg. 773
MATHYS ORTHOPAEDICS LTD.—See Enovis Corporation; *U.S. Public*, pg. 773
MATHYS ORTHOPAEDICS PTY. LTD.—See Enovis Corporation; *U.S. Public*, pg. 773
MATHYS ORTHOPEDIE SAS—See Enovis Corporation; *U.S. Public*, pg. 773
MATHYS ORTOPEDIA SRL—See Enovis Corporation; *U.S. Public*, pg. 773
MDT INT'L SA—See Holy Stone Enterprise Co., Ltd.; *Int'l*, pg. 3454
MEDBLOC, INC.—See Invacare Corporation; *U.S. Private*, pg. 2131
MED-ENG, LLC—See Kanders & Company, Inc.; *U.S. Private*, pg. 2259
MED-ENG SYSTEMS INC.—See Kanders & Company, Inc.; *U.S. Private*, pg. 2259
MEDICAL ACTION INDUSTRIES INC.—See Owens & Minor, Inc.; *U.S. Public*, pg. 1625
MEDICAL DEPOT, INC.; *U.S. Private*, pg. 2654
MEDIQ/PRN LIFE SUPPORT SYSTEMS, LLC—See Baxter International Inc.; *U.S. Public*, pg. 283
MEDISIZE B.V.—See Flexicare (Group) Limited; *Int'l*, pg. 2705
MEDI-TECH INTERNATIONAL CORPORATION—See MarketLab, Inc.; *U.S. Private*, pg. 2581
MEDITECHNIK GMBH—See Getinge AB; *Int'l*, pg. 2952
MEDLINE ACCUCARE DIVISION—See Medline Industries, LP; *U.S. Private*, pg. 2657

MEDLINE INDUSTRIES, LP; *U.S. Private*, pg. 2657
MEDLINE INDUSTRIES LTD.—See Medline Industries, LP; *U.S. Private*, pg. 2658
MEDLINE MEDCREST DIVISION—See Medline Industries, LP; *U.S. Private*, pg. 2658
MEDSOLL CYPRUS LTD—See Biotronik GmbH & Co.; *Int'l*, pg. 1044
MEDTECH SURGICAL, INC.—See Zimmer Biomet Holdings, Inc.; *U.S. Public*, pg. 2406
MED X CHANGE INC.—See Novanta Inc.; *U.S. Public*, pg. 1548
MEMOMETAL UK LIMITED—See Stryker Corporation; *U.S. Public*, pg. 1956
MENTOR CORPORATION—See Johnson & Johnson; *U.S. Public*, pg. 1196
MENTOR MEDICAL SYSTEMS B.V.—See Johnson & Johnson; *U.S. Public*, pg. 1196
MENTOR TEXAS—See Johnson & Johnson; *U.S. Public*, pg. 1196
MENTOR WORLDWIDE LLC—See Johnson & Johnson; *U.S. Public*, pg. 1199
MERIT MEDICAL CANADA LTD.—See Merit Medical Systems, Inc.; *U.S. Public*, pg. 1425
MERIT MEDICAL SYSTEMS, INC.; *U.S. Public*, pg. 1424
MESA CANADA, INC.—See Mesa Laboratories, Inc.; *U.S. Public*, pg. 1426
MESA FRANCE SAS—See Mesa Laboratories, Inc.; *U.S. Public*, pg. 1426
MESA GERMANY GMBH—See Mesa Laboratories, Inc.; *U.S. Public*, pg. 1426
MICROTEK MEDICAL BV—See Ecolab Inc.; *U.S. Public*, pg. 715
MILESTONE MEDICAL INC.—See Milestone Scientific Inc.; *U.S. Public*, pg. 1446
MILESTONE SCIENTIFIC INC.; *U.S. Public*, pg. 1446
MODULAR THERMAL TECHNOLOGIES, LLC; *U.S. Private*, pg. 2763
MOTION CONCEPTS, L.P.—See Invacare Corporation; *U.S. Private*, pg. 2131
MUN (AUSTRALIA) PTY LIMITED—See Hartalega Holdings Berhad; *Int'l*, pg. 3279
MUN GLOBAL SDN. BHD.—See Hartalega Holdings Berhad; *Int'l*, pg. 3279
MUN HEALTH PRODUCT (INDIA) PVT LTD—See Hartalega Holdings Berhad; *Int'l*, pg. 3279
MUSTANG SURVIVAL, INC.—See Wing Inflatables, Inc.; *U.S. Private*, pg. 4541
MUSTANG SURVIVAL MFG, INC.—See Wing Inflatables, Inc.; *U.S. Private*, pg. 4541
NATUS MANUFACTURING IRELAND, LTD.—See ArchiMed SAS; *Int'l*, pg. 548
NAVILYST MEDICAL, INC. - NEW YORK—See AngioDynamics, Inc.; *U.S. Public*, pg. 137
NAVILYST MEDICAL, INC.—See AngioDynamics, Inc.; *U.S. Public*, pg. 137
NEMARIS, INC.—See Globus Medical, Inc.; *U.S. Public*, pg. 947
NEOPREX LIMITED—See Hayleys PLC; *Int'l*, pg. 3291
NEW ENGLAND CATHETER CORP.—See MJM Holdings Inc.; *U.S. Private*, pg. 2753
NICHIURA TRADING (SHANGHAI) CO., LTD.—See Azearth Corporation; *Int'l*, pg. 778
NITRITEX LIMITED—See Ansell Limited; *Int'l*, pg. 478
NITRITEX (M) SDN. BHD.—See Ansell Limited; *Int'l*, pg. 478
NKC BOCA RATON, LLC—See Fresenius Medical Care AG; *Int'l*, pg. 2776
NORMEDIX, LLC—See SurModics, Inc.; *U.S. Public*, pg. 1967
NORSE CROWN CO. (M) SDN. BHD.—See Ferd AS; *Int'l*, pg. 2636
NORTH AMERICAN RESCUE, LLC—See Henry Schein, Inc.; *U.S. Public*, pg. 1027
NORTHERN CROSS, LTD.—See Barancorp, Ltd.; *U.S. Private*, pg. 471
NOW DISTRIBUTION INDIA PRIVATE LIMITED—See DNOW Inc.; *U.S. Public*, pg. 671
NUVASIVE, INC.—See Globus Medical, Inc.; *U.S. Public*, pg. 947
NUVASIVE ITALIA S.R.L.—See Globus Medical, Inc.; *U.S. Public*, pg. 947
NXSTAGE BOSTON NORTH, LLC—See Fresenius Medical Care AG; *Int'l*, pg. 2776
NXSTAGE OAK BROOK, LLC—See Fresenius Medical Care AG; *Int'l*, pg. 2777
NXSTAGE ORLANDO NORTH, LLC—See Fresenius Medical Care AG; *Int'l*, pg. 2777
ONTARIO GLOVE & SAFETY, INC.—See Delta Plus Group; *Int'l*, pg. 2020
OPS-CORE INC.—See Gentex Corporation; *U.S. Private*, pg. 1679
OPTODEV, INC.—See EssilorLuxottica SA; *Int'l*, pg. 2512
ORTHO DEVELOPMENT CORPORATION; *U.S. Private*, pg. 3045
ORTHOFIX AG—See Orthofix Medical Inc.; *U.S. Public*, pg. 1619
ORTHOFIX INC.—See Orthofix Medical Inc.; *U.S. Public*, pg. 1619
ORTHOFIX MEDICAL INC.; *U.S. Public*, pg. 1619

339113 — SURGICAL APPLIANCE ...

ORTHOPEDIATRICS CORP.; *U.S. Public,* pg. 1619
ORTHOPEDIC BIOMET CENTROAMERICANA SA—See Zimmer Biomet Holdings, Inc.; *U.S. Public,* pg. 2406
OSHITARI LABORATORY, INC.—See Freudenberg SE; *Int'l,* pg. 2790
OTS CORPORATION—See Patient Square Capital, L.P.; *U.S. Private,* pg. 3107
PAC-KIT SAFETY EQUIPMENT—See Acme United Corporation; *U.S. Public,* pg. 35
PASTEL GLOVE SDN. BHD.—See Enviro-Hub Holdings Ltd.; *Int'l,* pg. 2454
PC GROUP, INC.; *U.S. Private,* pg. 3119
PEGASUS HEALTH GROUP PTY. LTD.—See H&G High Conviction Limited; *Int'l,* pg. 3191
PERIOPTIX, INC.—See Centre Partners Management LLC; *U.S. Private,* pg. 828
PERIOPTIX, INC.—See Mill Street Partners LLC; *U.S. Private,* pg. 828
PERPETUAL MOTION ENTERPRISES LIMITED—See Invacare Corporation; *U.S. Private,* pg. 2131
PERSONNA AMERICAN SAFETY RAZOR COMPANY—See Edgewell Personal Care Company; *U.S. Public,* pg. 718
PHIPPS & BIRD, INC.; *U.S. Private,* pg. 3171
PIVOT MEDICAL, INC.—See Stryker Corporation; *U.S. Public,* pg. 1956
POINT BLANK BODY ARMOR INC.—See JLL Partners, LLC; *U.S. Private,* pg. 2213
PRIDE MOBILITY PRODUCTS AUSTRALIA PTY. LTD.—See Pride Mobility Products Corp.; *U.S. Private,* pg. 3259
PRIDE MOBILITY PRODUCTS CORP.; *U.S. Private,* pg. 3259
PRIMEMEDICAL SUPPLY COMPANY; *U.S. Private,* pg. 3263
PROTECTIVE APPAREL CORPORATION OF AMERICA—See JLL Partners, LLC; *U.S. Private,* pg. 2213
QINGDAO NESCO MEDICAL CO., LTD.—See Alfresa Holdings Corporation; *Int'l,* pg. 317
Q-MED MEXICO S.A DE C.V.—See Abu Dhabi Investment Authority; *Int'l,* pg. 71
Q-MED MEXICO S.A DE C.V.—See EQT Corporation; *U.S. Public,* pg. 785
QUALLION, LLC—See EnerSys; *U.S. Public,* pg. 767
RANPAK PTE. LTD.—See Ranpak Holdings Corp.; *U.S. Public,* pg. 1763
RAPID FIRE MARKETING, INC.; *U.S. Private,* pg. 3355
REPRESENTACIONES ZIMMER INC., S. DE R.L. DE C.V.—See Zimmer Biomet Holdings, Inc.; *U.S. Public,* pg. 2406
RESORBA MEDICAL GMBH—See Advanced Medical Solutions Group plc; *Int'l,* pg. 161
RESORBA OOO—See Advanced Medical Solutions Group plc; *Int'l,* pg. 161
RESORBA S.R.O.—See Advanced Medical Solutions Group plc; *Int'l,* pg. 161
REVA MEDICAL, INC.; *U.S. Private,* pg. 3413
RICHARD-ALLAN SCIENTIFIC COMPANY—See Thermo Fisher Scientific Inc.; *U.S. Public,* pg. 2152
RITTER D.O.O.—See Avantor, Inc.; *U.S. Public,* pg. 242
ROSCOE MEDICAL, INC.—See Tenex Capital Management, L.P.; *U.S. Private,* pg. 3966
RUBBERCARE PROTECTION PRODUCTS SDN BHD—See Careplus Group Berhad; *Int'l,* pg. 1325
RUSCH AUSTRIA GMBH—See Teleflex Incorporated; *U.S. Public,* pg. 1995
SAFEOP SURGICAL, INC.—See Alphatec Holdings, Inc.; *U.S. Public,* pg. 84
SAFETY SOLUTIONS U.K. LIMITED—See Carrier Global Corporation; *U.S. Public,* pg. 444
SAGE PRODUCTS, LLC—See Stryker Corporation; *U.S. Public,* pg. 1956
SALK, INC.; *U.S. Private,* pg. 3533
SAM MEDICAL PRODUCTS; *U.S. Private,* pg. 3535
SANARA MEDTECH INC.; *U.S. Public,* pg. 1839
SANTA ROSA LEAD PRODUCTS INC.—See Metalico Inc.; *U.S. Private,* pg. 2681
SBS ENTERPRISES INC.; *U.S. Private,* pg. 3560
SCHOLL'S WELLNESS CO.—See Yellow Wood Partners LLC; *U.S. Public,* pg. 4587
SCHULKE & MAYR BELGIUM NV—See EQT AB; *Int'l,* pg. 2479
SCHULKE & MAYR BENELUX BV—See EQT AB; *Int'l,* pg. 2479
SCHULKE & MAYR GES.M.B.H—See EQT AB; *Int'l,* pg. 2479
SCHULKE & MAYR ITALIA S.R.L.—See EQT AB; *Int'l,* pg. 2479
SCIENTIFIC & MEDICAL SUPPLIES CO. (SMS)—See Agilent Technologies, Inc.; *U.S. Public,* pg. 62
SCOTT HEALTH & SAFETY LIMITED—See 3M Company; *U.S. Public,* pg. 8
SEABROOK INTERNATIONAL, LLC—See The Jordan Company, L.P.; *U.S. Private,* pg. 4060
SEASPINE HOLDINGS CORPORATION; *U.S. Private,* pg. 3591
SEASPINE, INC.—See SeaSpine Holdings Corporation; *U.S. Private,* pg. 3591
SHASTA ORTHOTIC PROSTHETIC SERVICE, INC.—See Patient Square Capital, L.P.; *U.S. Private,* pg. 3107
SHEERVISION INC.; *U.S. Private,* pg. 3630
SHOCKWAVE MEDICAL, INC.—See Johnson & Johnson; *U.S. Public,* pg. 1200
SILK ROAD MEDICAL, INC.—See Boston Scientific Corporation; *U.S. Public,* pg. 375
SIMICON GMBH—See Mesa Laboratories, Inc.; *U.S. Public,* pg. 1426
SMITHS MEDICAL ASD INC.—See ICU Medical, Inc.; *U.S. Public,* pg. 1087
SOLARA MEDICAL SUPPLIES, LLC—See AdaptHealth Corp.; *U.S. Public,* pg. 39
SPEETEC IMPLANTATE GMBH—See Enovis Corporation; *U.S. Public,* pg. 773
SPINEEX, INC.; *U.S. Private,* pg. 3757
SPY INC.—See Alvarez & Marsal, Inc.; *U.S. Private,* pg. 212
SRP ENVIRONMENTAL LLC; *U.S. Private,* pg. 3768
SS WHITE MEDICAL PRODUCTS—See S.S. White Technologies Inc.; *U.S. Private,* pg. 3518
STAAR SURGICAL CO.; *U.S. Public,* pg. 1924
STEALTH COMPOSITES, LLC—See Patient Square Capital, L.P.; *U.S. Private,* pg. 3107
STERILMED, INC.—See Johnson & Johnson; *U.S. Public,* pg. 1200
STOKVIS TAPES BENELUX B.V.—See Illinois Tool Works Inc.; *U.S. Public,* pg. 1110
STRYKER ENDOSCOPY—See Stryker Corporation; *U.S. Public,* pg. 1956
STRYKER GRUNDSTUCKS GMBH & CO KG—See Stryker Corporation; *U.S. Public,* pg. 1956
STRYKER (SHANGHAI) HEALTHCARE PRODUCTS CO., LTD.—See Stryker Corporation; *U.S. Public,* pg. 1956
STRYKER SPINE—See Stryker Corporation; *U.S. Public,* pg. 1957
STRYKER (THAILAND) LIMITED—See Stryker Corporation; *U.S. Public,* pg. 1956
SUMMIT MEDICAL LIMITED—See Apposite Capital LLP; *Int'l,* pg. 522
SUNRISE MEDICAL INC.—See Vestar Capital Partners, LLC; *U.S. Private,* pg. 4372
SUNRISE MEDICAL INC.—See Vestar Capital Partners, LLC; *U.S. Private,* pg. 4372
SUNRISE MEDICAL MOBILITY PRODUCTS—See Vestar Capital Partners, LLC; *U.S. Private,* pg. 4372
SUNRISE SPAIN (URIBARRI)—See Vestar Capital Partners, LLC; *U.S. Private,* pg. 4372
SURGICAL APPLIANCE INDUSTRIES, INC.; *U.S. Private,* pg. 3884
SURGICAL PRODUCT SOLUTIONS LLC—See Shore Capital Partners, LLC; *U.S. Private,* pg. 3641
SYNCARDIA SYSTEMS LLC—See Hunniwell Lake Ventures LLC; *U.S. Private,* pg. 2008
SYNDAVER LABS INC.; *U.S. Private,* pg. 3903
SYNOVIS LIFE TECHNOLOGIES, INC.—See Baxter International Inc.; *U.S. Public,* pg. 281
SYNTHES AUSTRALIA PTY LTD—See Johnson & Johnson; *U.S. Public,* pg. 1200
SYNTHES (CANADA) LTD.—See Johnson & Johnson; *U.S. Public,* pg. 1200
SYNTHES, INC.—See Johnson & Johnson; *U.S. Public,* pg. 1195
SYNTHES PRODUKTIONS GMBH—See Johnson & Johnson; *U.S. Public,* pg. 1200
SYNTHES (SHANGHAI) MEDICAL TRADING CO., LTD.—See Johnson & Johnson; *U.S. Public,* pg. 1200
SYNTHES (SUZHOU) MEDICAL CO., LTD.—See Johnson & Johnson; *U.S. Public,* pg. 1200
SYNTHES TUTTLINGEN GMBH—See Johnson & Johnson; *U.S. Public,* pg. 1200
TECH GROUP EUROPE LIMITED—See West Pharmaceutical Services, Inc.; *U.S. Public,* pg. 2352
TECHNICAL TEXTILE SERVICES LIMITED—See Ecolab Inc.; *U.S. Public,* pg. 716
TELEFLEX GRUNDSTUCKS GMBH & CO. KG—See Teleflex Incorporated; *U.S. Public,* pg. 1995
TELEFLEX INCORPORATED - LIMERICK—See Teleflex Incorporated; *U.S. Public,* pg. 1995
TELEFLEX INCORPORATED; *U.S. Public,* pg. 1995
TELEFLEX MEDICAL IBERIA S.A.—See Teleflex Incorporated; *U.S. Public,* pg. 1996
TELEFLEX MEDICAL PRIVATE LIMITED—See Teleflex Incorporated; *U.S. Public,* pg. 1996
TELEFLEX MEDICAL SAS—See Teleflex Incorporated; *U.S. Public,* pg. 1996
TELEFLEX MEDICAL S.R.L.—See Teleflex Incorporated; *U.S. Public,* pg. 1996
TELEFLEX MEDICAL, S.R.O.—See Teleflex Incorporated; *U.S. Public,* pg. 1996
TELEFLEX MEDICAL TUTTLINGEN GMBH—See Teleflex Incorporated; *U.S. Public,* pg. 1996
TELEFLEX SWISS HOLDING GMBH—See Teleflex Incorporated; *U.S. Public,* pg. 1996
THELONG AIRTECH JOINT STOCK COMPANY—See AIRTECH JAPAN, LTD.; *Int'l,* pg. 249
THERMO FISHER DIAGNOSTICS, SOCIEDADE UNIPESSOAL LDA—See Thermo Fisher Scientific Inc.; *U.S. Public,* pg. 2153
THERMO FISHER SCIENTIFIC - CONSOLIDATED TECHNOLOGIES—See Thermo Fisher Scientific Inc.; *U.S. Public,* pg. 2153
THERMO FISHER SCIENTIFIC - MOLECULAR BIOPRODUCTS—See Thermo Fisher Scientific Inc.; *U.S. Public,* pg. 2153
T.K INDIA PRIVATE LIMITED—See Teleflex Incorporated; *U.S. Public,* pg. 1995
TRIVASCULAR, INC.—See Endologix, Inc.; *U.S. Private,* pg. 1392
TRONEX INTERNATIONAL INC.; *U.S. Private,* pg. 4241
TRUFORM ORTHOTICS & PROSTHETICS—See Surgical Appliance Industries, Inc.; *U.S. Private,* pg. 3884
TRUMPF MEDIZINSYSTEMS OSTERREICH GMBH—See Baxter International Inc.; *U.S. Public,* pg. 282
TUTTNAUER LTD.—See Fortissimo Capital Management Ltd.; *Int'l,* pg. 2740
TVA MEDICAL, INC.—See Becton, Dickinson & Company; *U.S. Public,* pg. 292
UNITED SEATING & MOBILITY LLC—See AEA Investors LP; *U.S. Private,* pg. 116
UNIVERSITY OF MIAMI TISSUE BANK—See Vivex Biomedical, Inc.; *U.S. Private,* pg. 4406
US ORTHOTICS AND PROSTHETICS, INC.—See Patient Square Capital, L.P.; *U.S. Private,* pg. 3107
UTAH MEDICAL PRODUCTS, INC.; *U.S. Public,* pg. 2267
UTC FIRE & SECURITY CANADA—See Carrier Global Corporation; *U.S. Public,* pg. 441
VERTIC INTERNATIONAL, SA—See Delta Plus Group; *Int'l,* pg. 2020
VERTIC NEDERLAND BV—See Delta Plus Group; *Int'l,* pg. 2020
VISION QUEST INDUSTRIES INCORPORATED; *U.S. Private,* pg. 4391
WESTMED, INC.—See HCA Healthcare, Inc.; *U.S. Public,* pg. 1011
WEST PHARMACEUTICAL PACKAGING (CHINA) COMPANY LTD.—See West Pharmaceutical Services, Inc.; *U.S. Public,* pg. 2353
WEST PHARMACEUTICAL PACKAGING INDIA PRIVATE LIMITED—See West Pharmaceutical Services, Inc.; *U.S. Public,* pg. 2353
WEST PHARMACEUTICAL SERVICES COLOMBIA S.A.—See West Pharmaceutical Services, Inc.; *U.S. Public,* pg. 2353
WEST PHARMACEUTICAL SERVICES HISPANIA S.A.—See West Pharmaceutical Services, Inc.; *U.S. Public,* pg. 2353
WEST PHARMACEUTICAL SERVICES, INC.; *U.S. Public,* pg. 2352
WEST PHARMACEUTICAL SERVICES NORMANDIE SAS—See West Pharmaceutical Services, Inc.; *U.S. Public,* pg. 2353
WEST PHARMACEUTICAL SERVICES OF DELAWARE, INC.—See West Pharmaceutical Services, Inc.; *U.S. Public,* pg. 2353
WEST PHARMACEUTICAL SERVICES OF FLORIDA, INC.—See West Pharmaceutical Services, Inc.; *U.S. Public,* pg. 2353
WEST PHARMACEUTICAL SERVICES VERWALTUNGS GMBH—See West Pharmaceutical Services, Inc.; *U.S. Public,* pg. 2353
WILLOWWOOD GLOBAL LLC—See DW Management Services, LLC; *Int'l,* pg. 2236
WRIGHT & FILIPPIS INC.; *U.S. Private,* pg. 4572
ZHEJIANG BIOMET MEDICAL PRODUCTS CO. LTD.—See Zimmer Biomet Holdings, Inc.; *U.S. Public,* pg. 2406
ZIMMER AUSTRIA GMBH—See Zimmer Biomet Holdings, Inc.; *U.S. Public,* pg. 2406
ZIMMER BIOMET DEUTSCHLAND GMBH—See Zimmer Biomet Holdings, Inc.; *U.S. Public,* pg. 2407
ZIMMER BIOMET ITALIA SRL—See Zimmer Biomet Holdings, Inc.; *U.S. Public,* pg. 2407
ZIMMER BIOMET NEDERLAND B.V.—See Zimmer Biomet Holdings, Inc.; *U.S. Public,* pg. 2407
ZIMMER BIOMET PORTUGAL UNIPESSOAL, LDA—See Zimmer Biomet Holdings, Inc.; *U.S. Public,* pg. 2407
ZIMMER BIOMET SPINE—See H.I.G. Capital, LLC; *U.S. Private,* pg. 1834
ZIMMER CEP USA, INC.—See Zimmer Biomet Holdings, Inc.; *U.S. Public,* pg. 2407
ZIMMER DENTAL CHILE SPA—See Zimmer Biomet Holdings, Inc.; *U.S. Public,* pg. 2407
ZIMMER GMBH—See Zimmer Biomet Holdings, Inc.; *U.S. Public,* pg. 2407
ZIMMER, INC.—See Zimmer Biomet Holdings, Inc.; *U.S. Public,* pg. 2408
ZIMMER INDIA PRIVATE LTD.—See Zimmer Biomet Holdings, Inc.; *U.S. Public,* pg. 2407
ZIMMER SURGICAL—See Zimmer Biomet Holdings, Inc.; *U.S. Public,* pg. 2407
ZIMMER US, INC.—See Zimmer Biomet Holdings, Inc.; *U.S. Public,* pg. 2407

339114 — DENTAL EQUIPMENT AND SUP-

N.A.I.C.S. INDEX

339114 — DENTAL EQUIPMENT AN...

PLIES MANUFACTURING

3M ESPE—See Solventum Corporation; *U.S. Public*, pg. 1901
3M IMTEC CORPORATION—See Solventum Corporation; *U.S. Public*, pg. 1901
3M UNITEK CORPORATION—See Solventum Corporation; *U.S. Public*, pg. 1901
ABC ORTHODONTICS SA; *Int'l*, pg. 57
A-DEC, INC.; *U.S. Private*, pg. 22
ADENTATEC GMBH—See Elementis plc; *Int'l*, pg. 2358
AIR TECHNIQUES, INC.; *U.S. Private*, pg. 139
AIR TECHNIQUES, INC. - WESTERN FACILITY—See Air Techniques, Inc.; *U.S. Private*, pg. 140
ALIGN TECHNOLOGY, B.V.—See Align Technology, Inc.; *U.S. Public*, pg. 77
ALPHA PROTECH ENGINEERED PRODUCTS, INC.—See Alpha Pro Tech, Ltd.; *Int'l*, pg. 369
AMANN GIRRBACH AG—See Capvis AG; *Int'l*, pg. 1318
AMANN GIRRBACH AMERICA INC.—See Capvis AG; *Int'l*, pg. 1318
AMANN GIRRBACH ASIA PTE. LTD.—See Capvis AG; *Int'l*, pg. 1318
AMANN GIRRBACH BRASIL LTDA.—See Capvis AG; *Int'l*, pg. 1318
AMANN GIRRBACH CHINA CO., LTD.—See Capvis AG; *Int'l*, pg. 1318
AMANN GIRRBACH GMBH—See Capvis AG; *Int'l*, pg. 1318
APOLLO ENDOSURGERY COSTA RICA S.R.L.—See Boston Scientific Corporation; *U.S. Public*, pg. 373
ARIBEX, INC.—See Danaher Corporation; *U.S. Public*, pg. 628
ARJOHUNTLEIGH CANADA INC.—See Getinge AB; *Int'l*, pg. 2948
A.R. MEDICOM INC.; *Int'l*, pg. 28
ARSEUS DENTAL NEDERLAND B.V.—See Fagron NV; *Int'l*, pg. 2603
ASTEK INNOVATIONS LTD.—See The Jordan Company, L.P.; *U.S. Private*, pg. 4063
BIOHORIZONS, INC.—See Henry Schein, Inc.; *U.S. Public*, pg. 1025
BIOLASE, INC.; *U.S. Public*, pg. 337
BIOMET 3I, LLC—See Zimmer Biomet Holdings, Inc.; *U.S. Public*, pg. 2405
BIOTROL INTERNATIONAL—See The Jordan Company, L.P.; *U.S. Private*, pg. 4063
BOYD INDUSTRIES, INC.—See Salt Creek Capital Management, LLC; *U.S. Private*, pg. 3533
BRASSELER CANADA, INC.—See Carousel Capital Partners; *U.S. Private*, pg. 769
BUFFALO DENTAL MANUFACTURING CO., INC.; *U.S. Private*, pg. 680
CAP CITY DENTAL LAB, LLC; *U.S. Private*, pg. 737
CEFLA DENTAL GROUP—See Cefla S.C.; *Int'l*, pg. 1389
CI MEDICAL CO., LTD.; *Int'l*, pg. 1601
CLEARCORRECT, INC.; *U.S. Private*, pg. 932
COLTENE/WHALEDENT AG—See COLTENE Holding AG; *Int'l*, pg. 1705
COLTENE/WHALEDENT GMBH + CO. KG—See COLTENE Holding AG; *Int'l*, pg. 1705
COLTENE/WHALEDENT INC.—See COLTENE Holding AG; *Int'l*, pg. 1706
COLTENE/WHALEDENT LTD—See COLTENE Holding AG; *Int'l*, pg. 1706
COLTENE/WHALEDENT S.A.R.L.—See COLTENE Holding AG; *Int'l*, pg. 1706
COLUMBIA DENTOFORM CORPORATION—See The DentalEZ Group; *U.S. Private*, pg. 4020
DANVILLE MATERIALS, LLC—See BC Partners LLP; *Int'l*, pg. 925
DENKEN-HIGHDENTAL CO., LTD.—See Air Water Inc.; *Int'l*, pg. 240
DEN-MAT HOLDINGS, LLC—See Centre Partners Management LLC; *U.S. Private*, pg. 828
DEN-MAT HOLDINGS, LLC—See Mill Street Partners LLC; *U.S. Private*, pg. 2730
DENTAL BURS USA; *U.S. Private*, pg. 1206
DENTAL EQUIPMENT, LLC—See Danaher Corporation; *U.S. Public*, pg. 626
THE DENTALEZ GROUP; *U.S. Private*, pg. 4020
DENTALIA KFT—See COLTENE Holding AG; *Int'l*, pg. 1706
DENTAL IMAGING TECHNOLOGIES CORPORATION—See Danaher Corporation; *U.S. Public*, pg. 626
DENTAS CO., LTD.; *Int'l*, pg. 2033
DENTATUS AB; *Int'l*, pg. 2033
DENTSABLE, INC.; *U.S. Private*, pg. 1207
DENTSPLY ARGENTINA—See DENTSPLY SIRONA Inc.; *U.S. Public*, pg. 654
DENTSPLY GERMANY INVESTMENTS GMBH—See DENTSPLY SIRONA Inc.; *U.S. Public*, pg. 654
DENTSPLY IH AB—See DENTSPLY SIRONA Inc.; *U.S. Public*, pg. 654
DENTSPLY IH AB—See DENTSPLY SIRONA Inc.; *U.S. Public*, pg. 654
DENTSPLY IH AB—See DENTSPLY SIRONA Inc.; *U.S. Public*, pg. 654

DENTSPLY IH AB—See DENTSPLY SIRONA Inc.; *U.S. Public*, pg. 654
DENTSPLY IH GMBH—See DENTSPLY SIRONA Inc.; *U.S. Public*, pg. 654
DENTSPLY IH INC—See DENTSPLY SIRONA Inc.; *U.S. Public*, pg. 654
DENTSPLY IH S.A.—See DENTSPLY SIRONA Inc.; *U.S. Public*, pg. 655
DENTSPLY IMPLANTS MANUFACTURING GMBH—See DENTSPLY SIRONA Inc.; *U.S. Public*, pg. 654
DENTSPLY IMPLANTS TAIWAN CO, LTD.—See DENTSPLY SIRONA Inc.; *U.S. Public*, pg. 654
DENTSPLY INDIA PVT. LTD.—See DENTSPLY SIRONA Inc.; *U.S. Public*, pg. 654
DENTSPLY LIMITED—See DENTSPLY SIRONA Inc.; *U.S. Public*, pg. 654
DENTSPLY MEXICO, S.A. DE C.V.—See DENTSPLY SIRONA Inc.; *U.S. Public*, pg. 654
DENTSPLY (SINGAPORE) PTE. LTD.—See DENTSPLY SIRONA Inc.; *U.S. Public*, pg. 654
DENTSPLY SIRONA ENDODONTICS—See DENTSPLY SIRONA Inc.; *U.S. Public*, pg. 655
DENTSPLY SIRONA INC. - PREVENTIVE DIVISION—See DENTSPLY SIRONA Inc.; *U.S. Public*, pg. 654
DENTSPLY SIRONA INC. - RESTORATIVE—See DENTSPLY SIRONA Inc.; *U.S. Public*, pg. 654
DENTSPLY SIRONA K.K.—See DENTSPLY SIRONA Inc.; *U.S. Public*, pg. 654
DIA DENTAL AESTHETICS INTERNATIONAL INC.; *Int'l*, pg. 2101
DIATECH INC.—See COLTENE Holding AG; *Int'l*, pg. 1706
DIO CORPORATION; *Int'l*, pg. 2127
DIO IMPLANT AUSTRALIA PTY LTD.—See DIO Corporation; *Int'l*, pg. 2127
DOXA AB; *Int'l*, pg. 2187
ELEVATE ORAL CARE, LLC; *U.S. Private*, pg. 1358
EUROTEC DENTAL GMBH—See Fagron NV; *Int'l*, pg. 2603
FONA DENTAL S.R.O.—See DENTSPLY SIRONA Inc.; *U.S. Public*, pg. 655
FONA S.R.L.—See DENTSPLY SIRONA Inc.; *U.S. Public*, pg. 655
GABA INTERNATIONAL AG—See Colgate-Palmolive Company; *U.S. Public*, pg. 532
GAC DEUTSCHLAND GMBH—See DENTSPLY SIRONA Inc.; *U.S. Public*, pg. 655
GC AMERICA, INC.—See GC Corporation; *Int'l*, pg. 2894
GC CORPORATION; *Int'l*, pg. 2894
GETINGE AUSTRALIA PTY LTD.—See Getinge AB; *Int'l*, pg. 2949
GETINGE DISINFECTION AB—See Getinge AB; *Int'l*, pg. 2949
GETINGE FRANCE SAS—See Getinge AB; *Int'l*, pg. 2949
GETINGE POLAND SP. Z.O.O.—See Getinge AB; *Int'l*, pg. 2950
GETINGE USA, INC. - FLORIDA—See Getinge AB; *Int'l*, pg. 2951
G&H ORTHODONTICS—See The Riverside Company; *U.S. Private*, pg. 4108
GILLETTE GRUPPE DEUTSCHLAND GMBH & CO.OHG—See The Procter & Gamble Company; *U.S. Public*, pg. 2124
GLAXOSMITHKLINE ORAL CARE PLANT (IRELAND)—See GSK plc; *Int'l*, pg. 3148
HARRY J. BOSWORTH COMPANY; *U.S. Private*, pg. 1871
HENRY SCHEIN, INC. - LIVERMORE, CA—See Henry Schein, Inc.; *U.S. Public*, pg. 1026
HENRY SCHEIN, INC. - SOLON—See Henry Schein, Inc.; *U.S. Public*, pg. 1026
HU-FRIEDY MFG. CO., LLC—See Peak Rock Capital LLC; *U.S. Private*, pg. 3124
IMAGING SCIENCES INTERNATIONAL LLC—See Danaher Corporation; *U.S. Public*, pg. 627
IMPLADENT, LTD.—See Avista Capital Partners, L.P.; *U.S. Private*, pg. 409
IMPLANT DIRECT SYBRON INTERNATIONAL LLC—See Danaher Corporation; *U.S. Public*, pg. 627
INFINIDENT SERVICES GMBH—See DENTSPLY SIRONA Inc.; *U.S. Public*, pg. 655
INTEGRATED MEDIA SOLUTIONS; *U.S. Private*, pg. 2100
INTER-MED, INC.—See Behrman Brothers Management Corp.; *U.S. Private*, pg. 515
JELRUS INTERNATIONAL—See Air Techniques, Inc.; *U.S. Private*, pg. 140
KAVO DENTAL GMBH—See Danaher Corporation; *U.S. Public*, pg. 627
KAVO DENTAL LTD.—See Danaher Corporation; *U.S. Public*, pg. 627
KAVO DENTAL TECHNOLOGIES, LLC—See Danaher Corporation; *U.S. Public*, pg. 627
KAVO DO BRASIL INDUSTRIA E COMERCIO LTDA.—See Danaher Corporation; *U.S. Public*, pg. 627
KERR CORPORATION—See Danaher Corporation; *U.S. Public*, pg. 628
KERR GMBH—See Danaher Corporation; *U.S. Public*, pg. 628
KERR ITALIA S.R.L.—See Danaher Corporation; *U.S. Public*, pg. 628
KEYSTONE DENTAL, INC.; *U.S. Private*, pg. 2296

LANCER ORTHODONTICS INC.; *U.S. Public*, pg. 1292
LLC DENTSPLY RUSSIA—See DENTSPLY SIRONA Inc.; *U.S. Public*, pg. 655
LORNAMEAD, INC.; *U.S. Private*, pg. 2495
MATRX BY MIDMARK—See Midmark Corporation; *U.S. Private*, pg. 2716
MEDICAL 3 IMPORTACION SERVICE IBERICA S.L.—See DENTSPLY SIRONA Inc.; *U.S. Public*, pg. 655
MIDWAY DENTAL SUPPLY, INC.—See Henry Schein, Inc.; *U.S. Public*, pg. 1027
NAPP PHARMACEUTICALS LTD.—See Purdue Pharma LP; *U.S. Private*, pg. 3305
NEXTDENT B.V.—See 3D Systems Corporation; *U.S. Public*, pg. 4
NOBEL BIOCARE AB—See Danaher Corporation; *U.S. Public*, pg. 628
NOBEL BIOCARE HOLDING AG—See Danaher Corporation; *U.S. Public*, pg. 628
NOBEL BIOCARE PROCERA K.K.—See Danaher Corporation; *U.S. Public*, pg. 629
ORAMETRIX, INC.—See DENTSPLY SIRONA Inc.; *U.S. Public*, pg. 655
ORMCO CORPORATION—See Danaher Corporation; *U.S. Public*, pg. 631
ORTHODENTAL INTERNATIONAL, INC.—See DENTSPLY SIRONA Inc.; *U.S. Public*, pg. 655
PALODEX GROUP OY—See Danaher Corporation; *U.S. Public*, pg. 630
PENTRON CORPORATION; *U.S. Private*, pg. 3140
PERI-DENT LTD.—See Platinum Equity, LLC; *U.S. Private*, pg. 3205
PREAT CORP.—See The Jordan Company, L.P.; *U.S. Private*, pg. 4063
PREST, LLC—See Danaher Corporation; *U.S. Public*, pg. 630
PRIMA DENTAL GROUP—See Darby Group Companies, Inc.; *U.S. Private*, pg. 1158
PRIMUS STERILIZER COMPANY, LLC—See Chalmers Group of Companies; *Int'l*, pg. 1439
QR S.R.L.—See Cefla S.C.; *Int'l*, pg. 1390
RMO INC.; *U.S. Private*, pg. 3452
ROBLING MEDICAL, INC.—See SV Health Investors, LLP; *U.S. Private*, pg. 3888
SAFCO DENTAL SUPPLY LLC—See The PNC Financial Services Group, Inc.; *U.S. Public*, pg. 2120
SDC CANADA INC.—See SmileDirectClub, Inc.; *U.S. Public*, pg. 1896
SERVIMED TECNICOS, S.L.U.—See Henry Schein, Inc.; *U.S. Public*, pg. 1027
SHOWA YAKUHIN KAKO CO., LTD.—See GC Corporation; *Int'l*, pg. 2894
SIRONA DENTAL, INC.—See DENTSPLY SIRONA Inc.; *U.S. Public*, pg. 655
SIRONA DENTAL LIMITED SIRKETI—See DENTSPLY SIRONA Inc.; *U.S. Public*, pg. 655
SIRONA DENTAL SYSTEMS GMBH—See DENTSPLY SIRONA Inc.; *U.S. Public*, pg. 655
SIRONA DENTAL SYSTEMS, INC.—See DENTSPLY SIRONA Inc.; *U.S. Public*, pg. 655
SIRONA DENTAL SYSTEMS LTD.—See DENTSPLY SIRONA Inc.; *U.S. Public*, pg. 655
SIRONA DENTAL SYSTEMS O.O.O.—See DENTSPLY SIRONA Inc.; *U.S. Public*, pg. 655
SIRONA DENTAL SYSTEMS S.R.L.—See DENTSPLY SIRONA Inc.; *U.S. Public*, pg. 655
SIRONA DENTAL SYSTEMS TRADING (SHANGHAI) CO. LTD—See DENTSPLY SIRONA Inc.; *U.S. Public*, pg. 655
SIRONA TECHNOLOGIE GMBH & CO. KG—See DENTSPLY SIRONA Inc.; *U.S. Public*, pg. 655
SPOFADENTAL A.S.—See Danaher Corporation; *U.S. Public*, pg. 631
SYBRON CANADA LP—See Danaher Corporation; *U.S. Public*, pg. 631
SYBRON DENTAL SPECIALTIES, INC.—See Danaher Corporation; *U.S. Public*, pg. 631
TDV DENTAL LTDA.—See Septodont Inc.; *U.S. Private*, pg. 3612
TIDI PRODUCTS LLC—See The Jordan Company, L.P.; *U.S. Private*, pg. 4062
TP ORTHODONTICS INC.; *U.S. Public*, pg. 4199
VERTEX-DENTAL B.V.—See 3D Systems Corporation; *U.S. Public*, pg. 4
VIPI INDUSTRIA, COMERCIO, EXPORTACAO E IMPORTACAO DE PRODUTOS ODONTOLOGICOS LTDA.—See DENTSPLY SIRONA Inc.; *U.S. Public*, pg. 655
WASATCH PRODUCT DEVELOPMENT, LLC—See Nu Skin Enterprises, Inc.; *U.S. Public*, pg. 1552
WATER PIK, INC.—See Church & Dwight Co., Inc.; *U.S. Public*, pg. 493
WELLSPECT HEALTHCARE AB—See DENTSPLY SIRONA Inc.; *U.S. Public*, pg. 655
WELLSPECT HEALTHCARE GMBH—See DENTSPLY SIRONA Inc.; *U.S. Public*, pg. 656
WHIP-MIX CORPORATION; *U.S. Private*, pg. 4506
WHITE SMILE GLOBAL, INC.; *U.S. Private*, pg. 4510
XO CARE THE NETHERLANDS BV—See Fagron NV; *Int'l*, pg. 2604

339114 — DENTAL EQUIPMENT AN...

YOUNG DENTAL MANUFACTURING I, LLC—See The Jordan Company, L.P.; *U.S. Private*, pg. 4063
YOUNG'S L&S DENTAL SUPPLIES LTD.—See Danaher Corporation; *U.S. Public*, pg. 632
ZEST ANCHORS LLC—See BC Partners LLP; *Int'l*, pg. 925
ZHERMACK GMBH—See DENTSPLY SIRONA Inc.; *U.S. Public*, pg. 656
ZHERMACK S.P.A.—See DENTSPLY SIRONA Inc.; *U.S. Public*, pg. 654
ZHERMAPOL SP ZOO—See DENTSPLY SIRONA Inc.; *U.S. Public*, pg. 656
ZIMMER DENTAL DO BRASIL PARTICIPACOES LTDA.—See Zimmer Biomet Holdings, Inc.; *U.S. Public*, pg. 2407
ZIMMER DENTAL SAS—See Zimmer Biomet Holdings, Inc.; *U.S. Public*, pg. 2407

339115 — OPHTHALMIC GOODS MANUFACTURING

4CARE GMBH—See EssilorLuxottica SA; *Int'l*, pg. 2515
ACTIO OPTICAL CORP.—See Hoya Corporation; *Int'l*, pg. 3494
AEARO TECHNOLOGIES LLC—See 3M Company; *U.S. Public*, pg. 8
ALCON INC.; *Int'l*, pg. 302
ALDEN OPTICAL LABORATORIES, INC.—See Bausch Health Companies Inc.; *Int'l*, pg. 896
ANDREA INTERNATIONAL—See American International Industries Company; *U.S. Private*, pg. 238
APEX OPTICAL COMPANY INC.—See EssilorLuxottica SA; *Int'l*, pg. 2513
ARGENT OPTICAL MANUFACTORY LIMITED—See Arts Optical International Holdings Ltd; *Int'l*, pg. 585
ARTS OPTICAL COMPANY LIMITED—See Arts Optical International Holdings Ltd; *Int'l*, pg. 585
ARTS STUDIO LIMITED—See Arts Optical International Holdings Ltd; *Int'l*, pg. 585
ASIA OPTICAL CO., INC.; *Int'l*, pg. 613
ATRION LEASING COMPANY LLC—See Nordson Corporation; *U.S. Public*, pg. 1532
BAUR OPTIK GMBH RAIN—See Fielmann Group AG; *Int'l*, pg. 2656
BAUSCH & LOMB INCORPORATED—See Bausch Health Companies Inc.; *Int'l*, pg. 896
BAUSCH & LOMB INDIA PRIVATE LIMITED—See Bausch Health Companies Inc.; *Int'l*, pg. 896
BAUSCH & LOMB INSTRUMENTS—See Bausch Health Companies Inc.; *Int'l*, pg. 896
BAUSCH & LOMB MALAYSIA SDN BHD - SURGICAL DIVISION—See Bausch Health Companies Inc.; *Int'l*, pg. 896
BAUSCH & LOMB NORDIC AKTIEBOLAG—See Bausch Health Companies Inc.; *Int'l*, pg. 896
BAUSCH & LOMB POLSKA SP. Z.O.O.—See Bausch Health Companies Inc.; *Int'l*, pg. 896
BBGR SKANDINAVISKA AB—See EssilorLuxottica SA; *Int'l*, pg. 2512
BEAVER-VISITEC INTERNATIONAL, INC.—See TPG Capital, L.P.; *U.S. Public*, pg. 2169
BEIJING BAUSCH & LOMB EYECARE COMPANY, LTD.—See Bausch Health Companies Inc.; *Int'l*, pg. 897
BEST HEALTH, INC.; *U.S. Private*, pg. 542
BEST MEDICAL CO., LTD.—See Hulic Co., Ltd.; *Int'l*, pg. 3528
BIOPTIGEN, INC.—See Danaher Corporation; *U.S. Public*, pg. 628
BNL EUROLENS SA—See EssilorLuxottica SA; *Int'l*, pg. 2512
BOOTS OPTICIANS LTD—See Walgreens Boots Alliance, Inc.; *U.S. Public*, pg. 2323
BORN BRILLEN OPTIK GMBH & CO. OHG—See Fielmann Group AG; *Int'l*, pg. 2656
BRILLEN MULLER GMBH & CO. OHG—See Fielmann Group AG; *Int'l*, pg. 2656
CAPLIN STERILES LIMITED—See Caplin Point Laboratories Limited; *Int'l*, pg. 1315
CARL ZEISS AS—See Carl-Zeiss-Stiftung; *Int'l*, pg. 1334
CARL ZEISS SPORTS OPTICS, LLC—See Carl-Zeiss-Stiftung; *Int'l*, pg. 1334
CARL ZEISS VISION INC.—See Carl-Zeiss-Stiftung; *Int'l*, pg. 1335
CARL ZEISS VISION INC.—See EQT AB; *Int'l*, pg. 2473
CLASSIC OPTICAL LABORATORIES, INC.—See EssilorLuxottica SA; *Int'l*, pg. 2513
COBURN TECHNOLOGIES, INC.; *U.S. Private*, pg. 958
CONTINENTAL SALES COMPANY OF AMERICA, LTD.; *U.S. Private*, pg. 1031
COOPERVISION CL KFT—See The Cooper Companies, Inc.; *U.S. Public*, pg. 2066
COOPERVISION, INC.—See The Cooper Companies, Inc.; *U.S. Public*, pg. 2066
COOPERVISION NORDIC AB—See The Cooper Companies, Inc.; *U.S. Public*, pg. 2066
COSTA DEL MAR, INC.—See EssilorLuxottica SA; *Int'l*, pg. 2513

CSC LABORATORIES, INC.—See EssilorLuxottica SA; *Int'l*, pg. 2513
DAICEL PROSPERITY (CHINA) LTD.—See Daicel Corporation; *Int'l*, pg. 1919
DANKER LABORATORIES INC.; *U.S. Private*, pg. 1157
DE RIGO D.A.CH. GMBH—See De Rigo S.p.A.; *Int'l*, pg. 1996
DE RIGO HONG KONG LTD.—See De Rigo S.p.A.; *Int'l*, pg. 1997
DE RIGO REM INC.—See De Rigo S.p.A.; *Int'l*, pg. 1997
DE RIGO S.P.A.; *Int'l*, pg. 1996
DE RIGO UK LTD—See De Rigo S.p.A.; *Int'l*, pg. 1997
DE RIGO VE SESA GRUP GOZLUK SAN VE TIC AS—See De Rigo S.p.A.; *Int'l*, pg. 1997
DE RIGO VISION S.P.A.—See De Rigo S.p.A.; *Int'l*, pg. 1997
DISPENSERS OPTICAL SERVICE CORPORATION; *U.S. Private*, pg. 1238
DUNLAW OPTICAL LABORATORIES INC.—See EssilorLuxottica SA; *Int'l*, pg. 2513
ELEGANCE OPTICAL MANUFACTORY LIMITED—See Elegance Optical International Holdings Ltd.; *Int'l*, pg. 2355
ESSILOR DANMARK A.S.—See EssilorLuxottica SA; *Int'l*, pg. 2512
ESSILOR POLONIA SP. Z O.O—See EssilorLuxottica SA; *Int'l*, pg. 2513
ESSILOR S.A.—See EssilorLuxottica SA; *Int'l*, pg. 2513
EYECONCEPT LIMITED—See Arts Optical International Holdings Ltd; *Int'l*, pg. 586
FGX CANADA CORP—See EssilorLuxottica SA; *Int'l*, pg. 2514
FIELMANN AG & CO. AM HAUPTMARKT OHG—See Fielmann Group AG; *Int'l*, pg. 2658
FIELMANN AG & CO. BERLIN-HELLERSDORF OHG—See Fielmann Group AG; *Int'l*, pg. 2656
FIELMANN AG & CO. BRACKWEDE KG—See Fielmann Group AG; *Int'l*, pg. 2656
FIELMANN AG & CO. CITY-ARKADEN KG—See Fielmann Group AG; *Int'l*, pg. 2656
FIELMANN AG & CO. CITY GALERIE OHG—See Fielmann Group AG; *Int'l*, pg. 2656
FIELMANN AG & CO. EBERTPLATZ KG—See Fielmann Group AG; *Int'l*, pg. 2656
FIELMANN AG & CO. EKZ HAMBURGER STRABE KG—See Fielmann Group AG; *Int'l*, pg. 2656
FIELMANN AG & CO. EKZ MILANEO OHG—See Fielmann Group AG; *Int'l*, pg. 2656
FIELMANN AG & CO. ELBERFELD OHG—See Fielmann Group AG; *Int'l*, pg. 2656
FIELMANN AG & CO. FORUM MITTELRHEIN OHG—See Fielmann Group AG; *Int'l*, pg. 2656
FIELMANN AG & CO. FRIEDRICHSHAGEN OHG—See Fielmann Group AG; *Int'l*, pg. 2656
FIELMANN AG & CO. FRIEDRICHSHAIN OHG—See Fielmann Group AG; *Int'l*, pg. 2656
FIELMANN AG & CO. GESUNDBRUNNEN-CENTER KG—See Fielmann Group AG; *Int'l*, pg. 2656
FIELMANN AG & CO. GLACIS-GALERIE OHG—See Fielmann Group AG; *Int'l*, pg. 2656
FIELMANN AG & CO. GROPIUS PASSAGEN OHG—See Fielmann Group AG; *Int'l*, pg. 2656
FIELMANN AG & CO. HARBURG SAND OHG—See Fielmann Group AG; *Int'l*, pg. 2656
FIELMANN AG & CO. HESSEN-CENTER OHG—See Fielmann Group AG; *Int'l*, pg. 2656
FIELMANN AG & CO. IM ALEXA KG—See Fielmann Group AG; *Int'l*, pg. 2658
FIELMANN AG & CO. IM ALSTERTALEINKAUFSZENTRUM OHG—See Fielmann Group AG; *Int'l*, pg. 2658
FIELMANN AG & CO. IM ELBEEINKAUFSZENTRUM OHG—See Fielmann Group AG; *Int'l*, pg. 2658
FIELMANN AG & CO. JAHNPLATZ KG—See Fielmann Group AG; *Int'l*, pg. 2656
FIELMANN AG & CO. KONTAKTLINSEN-SERVICE KG—See Fielmann Group AG; *Int'l*, pg. 2657
FIELMANN AG & CO. KREUZBERG KG—See Fielmann Group AG; *Int'l*, pg. 2657
FIELMANN AG & CO. LEIPZIGER STRASSE OHG—See Fielmann Group AG; *Int'l*, pg. 2657
FIELMANN AG & CO. LEOPOLDSTRASSE OHG—See Fielmann Group AG; *Int'l*, pg. 2657
FIELMANN AG & CO. LINDEN-CENTER KG—See Fielmann Group AG; *Int'l*, pg. 2657
FIELMANN AG & CO. MARKISCHES ZENTRUM KGB—See Fielmann Group AG; *Int'l*, pg. 2657
FIELMANN AG & CO. MARZAHN OHG—See Fielmann Group AG; *Int'l*, pg. 2657
FIELMANN AG & CO. MOABIT KG—See Fielmann Group AG; *Int'l*, pg. 2657
FIELMANN AG & CO. NEUKOLLN KG—See Fielmann Group AG; *Int'l*, pg. 2657
FIELMANN AG & CO. OBERNSTRASSE OHG—See Fielmann Group AG; *Int'l*, pg. 2657
FIELMANN AG & CO. OHG MUNCHEN OEZ—See Fielmann Group AG; *Int'l*, pg. 2658
FIELMANN AG & CO. OHG—See Fielmann Group AG; *Int'l*, pg. 2657
FIELMANN AG & CO. OTHMARSCHEN OHG—See Fielmann Group AG; *Int'l*, pg. 2657

FIELMANN AG & CO. PANKOW OHG—See Fielmann Group AG; *Int'l*, pg. 2657
FIELMANN AG & CO. PFERDEMARKT OHG—See Fielmann Group AG; *Int'l*, pg. 2657
FIELMANN AG & CO. PRENZLAUER BERG OHG—See Fielmann Group AG; *Int'l*, pg. 2657
FIELMANN AG & CO. RAHLSTEDT OHG—See Fielmann Group AG; *Int'l*, pg. 2657
FIELMANN AG & CO. RATHAUS OHG—See Fielmann Group AG; *Int'l*, pg. 2657
FIELMANN AG & CO. RHEIN-GALERIE KG—See Fielmann Group AG; *Int'l*, pg. 2657
FIELMANN AG & CO. SCHONEWEIDE OHG—See Fielmann Group AG; *Int'l*, pg. 2657
FIELMANN AG & CO. SPANDAU OHG—See Fielmann Group AG; *Int'l*, pg. 2657
FIELMANN AG & CO. STEGLITZ OHG—See Fielmann Group AG; *Int'l*, pg. 2657
FIELMANN AG & CO. TEMPELHOF OHG—See Fielmann Group AG; *Int'l*, pg. 2657
FIELMANN AG & CO. TREPTOW KG—See Fielmann Group AG; *Int'l*, pg. 2658
FIELMANN AG & CO. WANDSBEK OHG—See Fielmann Group AG; *Int'l*, pg. 2658
FIELMANN AG & CO. WEISSENSEE KG—See Fielmann Group AG; *Int'l*, pg. 2658
FIELMANN AG & CO. WESERPARK OHG—See Fielmann Group AG; *Int'l*, pg. 2658
FIELMANN AG & CO. WESTEND KG—See Fielmann Group AG; *Int'l*, pg. 2658
FIELMANN AG & CO. WILMERSDORF KG—See Fielmann Group AG; *Int'l*, pg. 2658
FIELMANN AG & CO. ZENTRUM KG—See Fielmann Group AG; *Int'l*, pg. 2658
FIELMANN AUGENOPTIK AG—See Fielmann Group AG; *Int'l*, pg. 2658
FIELMANN FARMSEN FIELMANN GMBH & CO. KG—See Fielmann Group AG; *Int'l*, pg. 2659
FIELMANN GMBH—See Fielmann Group AG; *Int'l*, pg. 2658
FIELMANN MODEBRILLEN RATHENOW AG & CO. KG—See Fielmann Group AG; *Int'l*, pg. 2658
FIELMANN VENTURES GMBH—See Fielmann Group AG; *Int'l*, pg. 2658
FORMOSA OPTICAL TECHNOLOGY CO., LTD.; *Int'l*, pg. 2735
FRANCE CHIRURGIE INSTRUMENTATION (F.C.I.) SAS—See Carl-Zeiss-Stiftung; *Int'l*, pg. 1336
GENTEX OPTICS, INC.—See EssilorLuxottica SA; *Int'l*, pg. 2514
GINKO INTERNATIONAL CO., LTD.; *Int'l*, pg. 2977
GROUPE VISION OPTIQUE—See EssilorLuxottica SA; *Int'l*, pg. 2514
GUJARAT MEDITECH LTD; *Int'l*, pg. 3176
HANS ANDERS NEDERLAND B.V.—See 3i Group plc; *Int'l*, pg. 9
HAWS MANUFACTURING PTE. LTD.—See Haws Corporation; *U.S. Private*, pg. 1884
HET HUIS OPTICIENS—See CVC Capital Partners SICAV-FIS S.A.; *Int'l*, pg. 1886
THE HILSINGER COMPANY PARENT, LLC—See Windjammer Capital Investors, LLC; *U.S. Private*, pg. 4538
HOLMARC OPTO-MECHATRONICS LTD.; *Int'l*, pg. 3452
HONEYWELL SAFETY PRODUCTS RESPIRATORY PROTECTION USA, LLC—See Honeywell International Inc.; *U.S. Public*, pg. 1049
HORIZON OPTICAL COMPANY LTD—See EssilorLuxottica SA; *Int'l*, pg. 2515
HOYA CORPORATION - SAN DIEGO FACILITY—See Hoya Corporation; *Int'l*, pg. 3497
HOYA LENS AUSTRALIA PTY. LTD.—See Hoya Corporation; *Int'l*, pg. 3495
HOYA LENS U.K. LIMITED—See Hoya Corporation; *Int'l*, pg. 3496
HOYA OPTICAL LABORATORIES—See Hoya Corporation; *Int'l*, pg. 3497
HOYA OPTICAL LABORATORIES—See Hoya Corporation; *Int'l*, pg. 3497
HOYA VISION CARE COMPANY - SEATTLE FACILITY—See Hoya Corporation; *Int'l*, pg. 3497
HOYA VISION CARE COMPANY—See Hoya Corporation; *Int'l*, pg. 3497
HOYA VISION CARE NORTH AMERICA INC.—See Hoya Corporation; *Int'l*, pg. 3497
ICARE INDUSTRIES, INC.; *U.S. Private*, pg. 2029
IDEX OPTICAL TECHNOLOGIES B.V.—See IDEX Corp; *U.S. Public*, pg. 1091
INFIELD SAFETY UK, LTD.—See EssilorLuxottica SA; *Int'l*, pg. 2515
INTEGRATED LENS TECHNOLOGY PTE LTD—See EssilorLuxottica SA; *Int'l*, pg. 2515
IRIDIAN SPECTRAL TECHNOLOGIES, LTD.—See IDEX Corp; *U.S. Public*, pg. 1091
JIANGSU HORIEN CONTACT LENS CO., LTD.—See Ginko international Co., Ltd.; *Int'l*, pg. 2977
JOHNSON & JOHNSON VISION CARE, INC.—See Johnson & Johnson; *U.S. Public*, pg. 1199
KATZ & KLEIN—See EssilorLuxottica SA; *Int'l*, pg. 2513

N.A.I.C.S. INDEX

339910 — JEWELRY AND SILVERW...

K & W OPTICAL LTD.—See EssilorLuxottica SA; *Int'l*, pg. 2515
LENSCLEAN, INC.—See Radians, Inc.; *U.S. Private*, pg. 3343
MICROSURGICAL TECHNOLOGY, INC.—See Halma plc; *Int'l*, pg. 3232
M.I.S.S. OPHTHALMICS LIMITED—See Bausch Health Companies Inc.; *Int'l*, pg. 897
MOC ACQUISITION CORPORATION—See EssilorLuxottica SA; *Int'l*, pg. 2514
NATIONAL OPTRONICS INC.; *U.S. Private*, pg. 2860
NEA OPTICAL LLC—See EssilorLuxottica SA; *Int'l*, pg. 2513
OAKLEY, INC.—See EssilorLuxottica SA; *Int'l*, pg. 2515
OMEGA OPTICAL CO. LP; *U.S. Private*, pg. 3015
OPTEGO VISION USA INC.—See Windjammer Capital Investors, LLC; *U.S. Private*, pg. 4538
OPTICAL DIMENSION INC—See EssilorLuxottica SA; *Int'l*, pg. 2514
OPTICAL ONE INC—See EssilorLuxottica SA; *Int'l*, pg. 2513
OPTIK HORGER GMBH & CO. OHG—See Fielmann Group AG; *Int'l*, pg. 2659
OPTIK SCHUPPIN GMBH & CO. OHG—See Fielmann Group AG; *Int'l*, pg. 2659
OPTIQUE DE L'ESTRIE INC—See EssilorLuxottica SA; *Int'l*, pg. 2516
PARAGON VISION SCIENCES, INC.—See The Cooper Companies, Inc.; *U.S. Public*, pg. 2066
PARMELEE INDUSTRIES, INC.—See Bunzl plc; *Int'l*, pg. 1219
PARMELEE LIMITED—See Bunzl plc; *Int'l*, pg. 1219
PLASTINAX AUSTRAL LIMITEE—See ENL Limited; *Int'l*, pg. 2441
PLASTINAX MADAGASCAR LTD.—See ENL Limited; *Int'l*, pg. 2441
PLASTINTCO INTERNATIONAL LTD.—See ENL Limited; *Int'l*, pg. 2441
PROFESSIONAL OPHTHALMIC LABORATORIES, INC.—See EssilorLuxottica SA; *Int'l*, pg. 2514
PRO-OPTIK AG—See Fielmann Group AG; *Int'l*, pg. 2659
PT BAUSCH & LOMB INDONESIA—See Bausch Health Companies Inc.; *Int'l*, pg. 897
RATHENOWER OPTISCHE WERKE GMBH—See Fielmann Group AG; *Int'l*, pg. 2659
RAYBAN SUN OPTICS INDIA LIMITED—See EssilorLuxottica SA; *Int'l*, pg. 2515
RD CHERRY, INC.—See EssilorLuxottica SA; *Int'l*, pg. 2514
RITE-STYLE OPTICAL CO; *U.S. Private*, pg. 3442
RODENSTOCK GMBH—See Compass Advisers Group LLC; *U.S. Private*, pg. 999
ROKKU DESIGNSTUDIO GMBH—See Fielmann Group AG; *Int'l*, pg. 2659
RUPP & HUBRACH OPTIK GMBH—See EssilorLuxottica SA; *Int'l*, pg. 2516
SATISLOH GMBH—See EssilorLuxottica SA; *Int'l*, pg. 2516
SELECT OPTICAL, INC.—See EssilorLuxottica SA; *Int'l*, pg. 2513
SELLSTROM MANUFACTURING CO.; *U.S. Private*, pg. 3603
SHENZHEN AINEAR CORNEA ENGINEERING COMPANY LIMITED—See China Regenerative Medicine International Co., Ltd; *Int'l*, pg. 1547
SIGNATURE EYEWEAR, INC.; *U.S. Public*, pg. 1878
SIGNET ARMORLITE CANADA, INC—See EssilorLuxottica SA; *Int'l*, pg. 2516
SIGNET ARMORLITE (HOLLAND) BV—See EssilorLuxottica SA; *Int'l*, pg. 2516
SIGNET ARMORLITE, INC.—See EssilorLuxottica SA; *Int'l*, pg. 2514
SPECIAL OPTICS, INC.—See AMETEK, Inc.; *U.S. Public*, pg. 121
SPECTRUM OPHTHALMOLOGY LTD.—See AddLife AB; *Int'l*, pg. 130
STAAR SURGICAL PTE. LTD.—See STAAR Surgical Co.; *U.S. Public*, pg. 1924
STEINER INDUSTRIES, INC.—See Bunzl plc; *Int'l*, pg. 1218
STEPPER FRANCE—See Arts Optical International Holdings Ltd; *Int'l*, pg. 586
SUNRIDGE INTERNATIONAL, INC.; *U.S. Public*, pg. 1965
SYNERGEYES UK LTD.—See The Cooper Companies, Inc.; *U.S. Public*, pg. 2066
TRANSITIONS OPTICAL, INC.—See EssilorLuxottica SA; *Int'l*, pg. 2514
UNILENS VISION INC.—See Bausch Health Companies Inc.; *Int'l*, pg. 897
VIP OPTICAL LABORATORIES, INC.—See EssilorLuxottica SA; *Int'l*, pg. 2514
VISIONAID, INC.—See Radians, Inc.; *U.S. Private*, pg. 3343
VISIONEERING TECHNOLOGIES, INC.; *U.S. Public*, pg. 2304
VOLK OPTICAL INC.—See Halma plc; *Int'l*, pg. 3233
WALMAN OPTICAL COMPANY; *U.S. Private*, pg. 4431
WARBY PARKER INC.; *U.S. Public*, pg. 2325
WINCHESTER OPTICAL COMPANY; *U.S. Private*, pg. 4533
X-CEL CONTACTS—See Walman Optical Company; *U.S. Private*, pg. 4432
YOUNGER MFG. CO.; *U.S. Private*, pg. 4594

339116 — DENTAL LABORATORIES

AFFORDABLE CARE, INC.—See Berkshire Partners LLC; *U.S. Private*, pg. 534
AMERICAN DENTAL PARTNERS, INC.—See JLL Partners, LLC; *U.S. Private*, pg. 2212
BIOTECH DENTAL PROSTHETICS, INC.—See Cerberus Capital Management, L.P.; *U.S. Private*, pg. 839
BONADENT DENTAL LABORATORIES; *U.S. Private*, pg. 613
CORNERSTONE DENTAL LABORATORIES, LLC; *U.S. Private*, pg. 1052
DDS LAB, LLC—See RoundTable Healthcare Management, Inc.; *U.S. Private*, pg. 3489
DECARE OPERATIONS IRELAND, LIMITED—See Elevance Health, Inc.; *U.S. Public*, pg. 729
DENTAL HEALTH MANAGEMENT SOLUTIONS (DHMS); *U.S. Private*, pg. 1206
DENTAL SALON; *U.S. Private*, pg. 1206
DENTCARE DELIVERY SYSTEMS, INC.; *U.S. Private*, pg. 1206
DENTIUM CO., LTD; *Int'l*, pg. 2033
FIRST DENTAL HEALTH; *U.S. Private*, pg. 1517
HENRY SCHEIN, INC. - BUFFALO, NY—See Henry Schein, Inc.; *U.S. Public*, pg. 1026
HENRY SCHEIN, INC. - TAMPA, FL—See Henry Schein, Inc.; *U.S. Public*, pg. 1026
JASLOW DENTAL LABORATORY, INC.—See Cornerstone Dental Laboratories, LLC; *U.S. Private*, pg. 1052
KELLER LABORATORIES INC.—See Cerberus Capital Management, L.P.; *U.S. Private*, pg. 839
LUMINO DENTAL LIMITED—See BGH Capital Pty Ltd; *Int'l*, pg. 1008
MAVERICK DENTAL, LLC; *U.S. Private*, pg. 2616
MEDICO INTERNATIONAL INC.; *U.S. Private*, pg. 2656
NDX ALBENSI—See Cerberus Capital Management, L.P.; *U.S. Private*, pg. 839
OJSYS, INC.; *U.S. Public*, pg. 1566
SENIOR DENTAL CARE LLC—See Serent Capital Management Company, LLC; *U.S. Private*, pg. 3613
SMILEBUILDERZ; *U.S. Private*, pg. 3693
SPECIALISTKLINIKEN FOR DENTALA IMPLANTAT KB—See Apax Partners LLP; *Int'l*, pg. 502
ZFX GMBH—See Zimmer Biomet Holdings, Inc.; *U.S. Public*, pg. 2406

339910 — JEWELRY AND SILVERWARE MANUFACTURING

ABBEYCREST THAILAND LTD.—See Brown & Newirth Ltd.; *Int'l*, pg. 1198
ADAMAS ONE CORP.; *U.S. Public*, pg. 37
ADRIENNE DESIGNS INC.; *U.S. Private*, pg. 82
AKERUE INDUSTRIES, LLC; *U.S. Private*, pg. 145
ALEXA'S ANGELS, INC.; *U.S. Private*, pg. 163
ALEXIS BITTAR, LLC—See Brooks Brothers, Inc.; *U.S. Private*, pg. 664
ALEXX, INC.; *U.S. Private*, pg. 164
ALMAST OJSC; *Int'l*, pg. 363
ANTICA DITTA MARCHISIO S.P.A.; *Int'l*, pg. 483
ANTWERP DIAMOND DISTRIBUTORS INC.; *U.S. Private*, pg. 289
APOLLO FUTURE MOBILITY GROUP LIMITED; *Int'l*, pg. 517
ARCULUS HOLDINGS, L.L.C.—See CompoSecure, Inc.; *U.S. Public*, pg. 561
ARIAN SILVER MEXICO S.A. DE C.V.MEXICO—See Alien Metals Ltd.; *Int'l*, pg. 327
ASAHI DIAMOND INDUSTRIAL CO. LTD. - CHIBA TSURUMAI FACTORY—See Asahi Diamond Industrial Co. Ltd.; *Int'l*, pg. 592
ASAHI DIAMOND INDUSTRIAL CO. LTD. - MIE FACTORY—See Asahi Diamond Industrial Co. Ltd.; *Int'l*, pg. 592
ASAHI DIAMOND INDUSTRIAL CO. LTD.; *Int'l*, pg. 592
ASAHI DIAMOND INDUSTRIAL CO. LTD. - TAMAGAWA FACTORY—See Asahi Diamond Industrial Co. Ltd.; *Int'l*, pg. 592
ASHAPURI GOLD ORNAMENT LTD.; *Int'l*, pg. 606
ASIAN STAR COMPANY LIMITED (USA)—See Asian Star Company Ltd; *Int'l*, pg. 619
ASIAN STAR COMPANY LTD; *Int'l*, pg. 619
ASPREY; *Int'l*, pg. 632
ATASAY KUYUMCULUK; *Int'l*, pg. 666
ATLAS JEWELLERY INDIA LIMITED; *Int'l*, pg. 686
AUDEMARS PIGUET & CIE; *Int'l*, pg. 700
AUDEMARS PIGUET DEUTSCHLAND—See Audemars Piguet & Cie; *Int'l*, pg. 701
AUDEMARS PIGUET FRANCE—See Audemars Piguet & Cie; *Int'l*, pg. 701
AUDEMARS PIGUET ITALIA S.P.A.—See Audemars Piguet & Cie; *Int'l*, pg. 701
AUDEMARS PIGUET (NORTH AMERICA)—See Audemars Piguet & Cie; *Int'l*, pg. 701
AUDEMARS PIGUET (SUISSE) S.A.—See Audemars Piguet & Cie; *Int'l*, pg. 701
AURAFIN LLC—See Berkshire Hathaway Inc.; *U.S. Public*, pg. 316
AURAFIN OROAMERICA—See Berkshire Hathaway Inc.; *U.S. Public*, pg. 316
AURORA DESIGN PUBLIC COMPANY LIMITED; *Int'l*, pg. 713
AVERY DENNISON RETAIL BRANDING & INFORMATION SOLUTIONS - FAIR LAWN—See Avery Dennison Corporation; *U.S. Public*, pg. 243
A&Z HAYWARD, INC.—See Allison Reed Group, Inc.; *U.S. Private*, pg. 192
BANARAS BEADS LIMITED; *Int'l*, pg. 814
BAZAR GROUP INC.; *U.S. Private*, pg. 497
BEIJING FOPE JEWELRY & ARTS, LTD—See Fope S.R.L.; *Int'l*, pg. 2728
BHAKTI GEMS & JEWELLERY LIMITED; *Int'l*, pg. 1010
BIJOU BRIGITTE MODISCHE ACCESSOIRES AG; *Int'l*, pg. 1022
BIRKS GROUP INC.; *Int'l*, pg. 1047
BOILLAT LES BOIS S.A.—See Citychamp Watch & Jewellery Group Limited; *Int'l*, pg. 1628
BOMBSHELL ACCESSORIES INC.; *U.S. Private*, pg. 612
BONITAS INTERNATIONAL LLC; *U.S. Private*, pg. 614
BREUNING GMBH; *Int'l*, pg. 1150
BREUNING INC.—See Breuning GmbH; *Int'l*, pg. 1150
BRIJU S.A.; *Int'l*, pg. 1163
BROWN & NEWIRTH LTD.; *Int'l*, pg. 1198
BRUCE FOX INC.; *U.S. Private*, pg. 671
BUCCELLATI HOLDING ITALIA S.P.A.—See Compagnie Financiere Richemont S.A.; *Int'l*, pg. 1741
BULGARIAN MINT EAD—See Bulgarian National Bank; *Int'l*, pg. 1213
CAROLEE LLC—See Brooks Brothers, Inc.; *U.S. Private*, pg. 664
CENTER INTERNATIONAL GROUP CO LTD; *Int'l*, pg. 1402
CHARISMA MANUFACTURING COMPANY INC.—See Charisma Brands, LLC; *U.S. Private*, pg. 850
CHARLESANDCOLVARD.COM, LLC—See Charles & Colvard Ltd; *U.S. Public*, pg. 479
CHARLES & COLVARD DIRECT, LLC—See Charles & Colvard Ltd; *U.S. Public*, pg. 479
CHARLES & COLVARD LTD; *U.S. Public*, pg. 479
CHIBOUGAMAU DRILLING LTD; *Int'l*, pg. 1476
CHOPARD DEUTSCHLAND GMBH—See Chopard & Cie S.A.; *Int'l*, pg. 1582
CHOW SANG SANG HOLDINGS INTERNATIONAL LIMITED; *Int'l*, pg. 1584
CITIZEN (CHINA) PRECISION MACHINERY CO., LTD.—See Citizen Watch Co., Ltd.; *Int'l*, pg. 1623
CITIZEN CUSTOMER SERVICE CO., LTD.—See Citizen Watch Co., Ltd.; *Int'l*, pg. 1623
CITIZEN DE MEXICO, S.A. DE C.V.—See Citizen Watch Co., Ltd.; *Int'l*, pg. 1625
CITIZEN FINEDEVICE PHILIPPINES CORP.—See Citizen Watch Co., Ltd.; *Int'l*, pg. 1623
CITIZEN JEWELRY CO., LTD.—See Citizen Watch Co., Ltd.; *Int'l*, pg. 1623
CITIZEN LOGISTICS SERVICE CO., LTD.—See Citizen Watch Co., Ltd.; *Int'l*, pg. 1623
CITIZEN MACHINERY SERVICE CO., LTD.—See Citizen Watch Co., Ltd.; *Int'l*, pg. 1624
CITIZEN MACHINERY VIETNAM CO.—See Citizen Watch Co., Ltd.; *Int'l*, pg. 1624
CITIZEN RETAIL PLANNING., LTD.—See Citizen Watch Co., Ltd.; *Int'l*, pg. 1624
CITIZEN (SHANGHAI) TRADING CO., LTD.—See Citizen Watch Co., Ltd.; *Int'l*, pg. 1623
CITIZEN SYSTEMS (DONGGUAN) CO., LTD.—See Citizen Watch Co., Ltd.; *Int'l*, pg. 1624
CITIZEN SYSTEMS (H.K.) LTD.—See Citizen Watch Co., Ltd.; *Int'l*, pg. 1624
CITIZEN WATCH IBERICA S.A.U.—See Citizen Watch Co., Ltd.; *Int'l*, pg. 1624
CITIZEN WATCH MANUFACTURING (THAILAND) CO., LTD.—See Citizen Watch Co., Ltd.; *Int'l*, pg. 1625
CITIZEN WATCH UNITED KINGDOM, LTD.—See Citizen Watch Co., Ltd.; *Int'l*, pg. 1625
CITYCHAMP WATCH & JEWELLERY GROUP LIMITED; *Int'l*, pg. 1628
CIVIS MANUFACTURING LTD.—See Citizen Watch Co., Ltd.; *Int'l*, pg. 1625
C.J. (UK) LIMITED—See Continental Holdings Limited; *Int'l*, pg. 1784
CJ USA LLC—See Continental Holdings Limited; *Int'l*, pg. 1784
CLYDE DUNEIER INC.; *U.S. Private*, pg. 949
C. MAHENDRA EXPORTS LTD. - DIAMOND FACTORY—See C. Mahendra Exports Ltd.; *Int'l*, pg. 1240
COLEMAN COMPANY; *U.S. Private*, pg. 967
COLETTE MALOUF INC.; *U.S. Private*, pg. 967
COMBINE INTERNATIONAL INC.; *U.S. Private*, pg. 980
COMMEMORATIVE BRANDS, INC.—See Fenway Partners, LLC; *U.S. Private*, pg. 1495
CONTINENTAL JEWELLERY (JIANGMEN) CO., LTD.—See Continental Holdings Limited; *Int'l*, pg. 1784
CROSSFOR CO., LTD.; *Int'l*, pg. 1856

339910 — JEWELRY AND SILVERW...

CROSSFOR HK LIMITED—See Crossfor Co., Ltd.; *Int'l*, pg. 1856
DANECRAFT INC.—See American Exchange Group; *U.S. Private*, pg. 232
DARLENE JEWELRY MANUFACTURING COMPANY; *U.S. Private*, pg. 1159
DE BEERS JEWELLERS JAPAN K.K.—See Anglo American PLC; *Int'l*, pg. 462
DE BEERS PLC.—See Anglo American PLC; *Int'l*, pg. 462
DEEP DIAMOND INDIA LIMITED; *Int'l*, pg. 2002
DEGEM BERHAD; *Int'l*, pg. 2004
DEV LABTECH VENTURE LTD.; *Int'l*, pg. 2086
DIAGOLD DESIGNS LIMITED—See Goldiam International Limited; *Int'l*, pg. 3033
DIAMOND COMPANY OF ARMENIA; *Int'l*, pg. 2105
DIAMOND TECHNOLOGY ENTERPRISES, INC.; *U.S. Private*, pg. 1224
DICKSON'S, INC.—See Templeton Coal Company, Inc.; *U.S. Private*, pg. 3963
DR CORPORATION LIMITED; *Int'l*, pg. 2189
ELEMENT SIX ABRASIVES HOLDINGS LIMITED—See Anglo American PLC; *Int'l*, pg. 462
ELEMENT SIX LIMITED—See Anglo American PLC; *Int'l*, pg. 462
ELEMENT SIX LIMITED—See Anglo American PLC; *Int'l*, pg. 462
ELEMENT SIX TECHNOLOGIES LIMITED—See Anglo American PLC; *Int'l*, pg. 462
ELEMENT SIX TECHNOLOGIES (OR) CORP.—See Anglo American PLC; *Int'l*, pg. 462
ELEMENT SIX TECHNOLOGIES US CORPORATION—See Anglo American PLC; *Int'l*, pg. 462
ELEMENT SIX TRADING (SHANGHAI) CO., LTD.—See Anglo American PLC; *Int'l*, pg. 462
ELEMENT SIX (UK) LIMITED—See Anglo American PLC; *Int'l*, pg. 462
EMPIRE SILVER CO., INC.—See Lifetime Brands, Inc.; *U.S. Public*, pg. 1313
ERNEST BOREL S.A.—See Citychamp Watch & Jewellery Group Limited; *Int'l*, pg. 1629
ERWIN PEARL INC.; *U.S. Private*, pg. 1424
ESTELLE HOLDINGS CO., LTD.; *Int'l*, pg. 2517
EURO COSMETIC S.P.A.—See Fine Foods & Pharmaceuticals N.T.M. S.p.A.; *Int'l*, pg. 2673
FINDINGS INC.—See Berkshire Hathaway Inc.; *U.S. Public*, pg. 316
FITAIHI HOLDING GROUP; *Int'l*, pg. 2695
FOPE S.R.L.; *Int'l*, pg. 2728
FOSSIL ACCESSORIES SOUTH AFRICA PTY LTD—See Fossil Group, Inc.; *U.S. Public*, pg. 874
FOVEA JEWELRY HOLDINGS LTD.; *U.S. Public*, pg. 875
FRANCE TOURISME IMMOBILIER SA; *Int'l*, pg. 2759
FREDERICK GOLDMAN INC.; *U.S. Private*, pg. 1602
FREDERIQUE CONSTANT HOLDING S.A.—See Citizen Watch Co., Ltd.; *Int'l*, pg. 1625
FUQI INTERNATIONAL, INC.; *Int'l*, pg. 2846
FURUYA ECO-FRONT TECHNOLOGY CO., LTD.—See Furuya Metal Co., Ltd.; *Int'l*, pg. 2848
GALANTAS IRISH GOLD LIMITED—See Galantas Gold Corporation; *Int'l*, pg. 2870
GAUTAM GEMS LIMITED; *Int'l*, pg. 2891
GEMVARA, INC.—See Berkshire Hathaway Inc.; *U.S. Public*, pg. 316
GEMZ CORP.; *U.S. Public*, pg. 910
GIORGIO VISCONTI S.P.A.; *Int'l*, pg. 2978
GISMONDI 1754 S.P.A.; *Int'l*, pg. 2979
GODINGER SILVER ART CO. LTD.; *U.S. Private*, pg. 1724
GOENKA DIAMOND AND JEWELS LIMITED; *Int'l*, pg. 3021
GOLD CRAFT JEWELRY CORP.; *U.S. Private*, pg. 1727
GOLDFINE MANUFACTURERS PUBLIC COMPANY LIMITED; *Int'l*, pg. 3033
GOLDIAM INTERNATIONAL LIMITED; *Int'l*, pg. 3033
GOLDIAM JEWELLERY LIMITED—See Goldiam International Limited; *Int'l*, pg. 3033
GOLDIAM USA, INC.—See Goldiam International Limited; *Int'l*, pg. 3033
GOLKUNDA DIAMONDS & JEWELLERY LIMITED; *Int'l*, pg. 3036
GRAFF DIAMONDS INTERNATIONAL LTD.; *Int'l*, pg. 3050
GUANGDONG CHJ INDUSTRY CO., LTD.; *Int'l*, pg. 3153
GUANGZHOU MOST CROWN ELECTRONICS LIMITED—See Citizen Watch Co., Ltd.; *Int'l*, pg. 1625
GUANGZHOU NOBLE JEWELRY LIMITED—See Central Development Holdings Ltd.; *Int'l*, pg. 1406
GUANGZHOU SINOBLE JEWELRY LIMITED—See Central Development Holdings Ltd.; *Int'l*, pg. 1406
GUNTHER GRANT, INC.; *U.S. Public*, pg. 975
HALLMARK INTERNATIONAL—See Hallmark Cards, Inc.; *U.S. Private*, pg. 1844
HANVEY GROUP HOLDINGS LTD.; *Int'l*, pg. 3261
HEARTS ON FIRE COMPANY LLC—See Chow Tai Fook Enterprises Limited; *Int'l*, pg. 1584
HERFF JONES, INC. - JEWELRY—See Bain Capital, LP; *U.S. Private*, pg. 452
HERFF JONES, INC.—See Bain Capital, LP; *U.S. Private*, pg. 451
H. STERN COM & IND., S.A.; *Int'l*, pg. 3195

IIDGR (UK) LIMITED—See Anglo American PLC; *Int'l*, pg. 462
IMPERIAL-DELTAH, INC.; *U.S. Private*, pg. 2050
INTERNATIONAL INSPIRATIONS; *U.S. Private*, pg. 2118
ITSHOT.COM; *U.S. Private*, pg. 2150
JAMES AVERY CRAFTSMAN INC.; *U.S. Private*, pg. 2183
JAY JEMS INC.; *U.S. Private*, pg. 2192
JETBLACK CORP.; *U.S. Public*, pg. 1189
JIANG XING ELECTRONICS LTD.—See Citizen Watch Co., Ltd.; *Int'l*, pg. 1625
JOHN ATENCIO GOLDSMITH, LTD.; *U.S. Private*, pg. 2220
JOHN C. NORDT CO., INC.—See Berkshire Hathaway Inc.; *U.S. Public*, pg. 316
JR LICENSING, LLC—See XCel Brands, Inc.; *U.S. Public*, pg. 2385
KABANA INC.; *U.S. Private*, pg. 2253
KEEGAN RESOURCES (GHANA) LIMITED—See Galiano Gold Inc.; *Int'l*, pg. 2873
KENDRA SCOTT DESIGN, INC.; *U.S. Private*, pg. 2283
K&M ASSOCIATES—See American Biltrite Inc.; *U.S. Public*, pg. 98
KREMENTZ & COMPANY; *U.S. Private*, pg. 2351
LAGOS INC.; *U.S. Private*, pg. 2373
LANA UNLIMITED COMPANY; *U.S. Private*, pg. 2381
LANDAU DIRECT; *U.S. Private*, pg. 2384
LIGHTBOX JEWELRY INC.—See Anglo American PLC; *Int'l*, pg. 462
LINKS (LONDON) LIMITED—See Folli Follie S.A.; *Int'l*, pg. 2721
LOREN INDUSTRIES INC.; *U.S. Private*, pg. 2495
LUCID CZECH REPUBLIC S.R.O.—See Cint Group AB; *Int'l*, pg. 1611
MAN SANG INTERNATIONAL LIMITED—See China Metro-Rural Holdings Limited; *Int'l*, pg. 1524
MANUFACTURE LA JOUX-PERRET S.A.—See Citizen Watch Co., Ltd.; *Int'l*, pg. 1625
M.A. REICH & CO., INC.—See Jay Jems Inc.; *U.S. Private*, pg. 2192
THE MARFO COMPANY INC.; *U.S. Private*, pg. 4074
MARTIN FLYER INC.; *U.S. Private*, pg. 2595
MASTER CROWN ELECTRONICS (WUZHOU) LTD.—See Citizen Watch Co., Ltd.; *Int'l*, pg. 1625
MASTERS OF DESIGN, INC.—See Bain Capital, LP; *U.S. Private*, pg. 452
MAX KAHAN INC.; *U.S. Private*, pg. 2617
MEDALLIC ART COMPANY, LTD.; *U.S. Private*, pg. 2650
MEESHAA INC.; *U.S. Private*, pg. 2659
MEL BERNIE & COMPANY INC.; *U.S. Private*, pg. 2661
METAL MARKETPLACE INTERNATIONAL; *U.S. Private*, pg. 2680
M. FABRIKANT & SONS, INC.; *U.S. Private*, pg. 2526
MICHAEL ANTHONY JEWELERS, INC.—See Berkshire Hathaway Inc.; *U.S. Public*, pg. 316
MINERA PLATTE RIVER GOLD S.A. DE RL DE C.V.—See Americas Gold and Silver Corporation; *Int'l*, pg. 423
MOISSANITEOUTLET.COM, LLC—See Charles & Colvard Ltd; *U.S. Public*, pg. 479
MONTANA SILVERSMITHS, INC.—See Thompson Street Capital Manager LLC; *U.S. Private*, pg. 4161
MOUAWAD INTERNATIONAL GOLD JEWELLERY COMPANY—See Mondera.com; *U.S. Private*, pg. 2769
NIESSING (AUSTRALIA) PTY. LTD.—See Aspial Corporation Limited; *Int'l*, pg. 630
NIESSING (HONG KONG) LIMITED—See Aspial Corporation Limited; *Int'l*, pg. 630
NIESSING MANUFAKTUR GMBH & CO. KG—See Aspial Corporation Limited; *Int'l*, pg. 630
NOVELL ENTERPRISES, INC.—See Continental Holdings Limited; *Int'l*, pg. 1784
O.C. TANNER COMPANY INC.; *U.S. Private*, pg. 2981
OSCAR HEYMAN & BROTHERS, INC.; *U.S. Private*, pg. 3046
PAUL WINSTON FINE JEWELRY GROUP; *U.S. Private*, pg. 3113
PEYOTE BIRD DESIGNS; *U.S. Private*, pg. 3164
PLAINVILLE STOCK COMPANY, INC.; *U.S. Private*, pg. 3195
POBJOY MINT LTD.—See Derek Pobjoy Investments Ltd.; *Int'l*, pg. 2041
QUELOZ SA—See Diethelm Keller Holding Limited; *Int'l*, pg. 2117
REINFORCING SERVICES, INC.—See AZZ, Inc.; *U.S. Public*, pg. 260
RENA-WARE DISTRIBUTORS INC.; *U.S. Private*, pg. 3397
RICHLINE GROUP, INC.—See Berkshire Hathaway Inc.; *U.S. Public*, pg. 316
RIDDLES GROUP, INC.; *U.S. Private*, pg. 3431
ROCCA INTERNATIONAL S.A.—See Damiani S.p.A.; *Int'l*, pg. 1957
ROIZIN REFINING CO. INC.; *U.S. Private*, pg. 3473
ROMAN RESEARCH, INC.; *U.S. Private*, pg. 3476
R.S. OWENS & COMPANY; *U.S. Private*, pg. 3339
SALVADORE TOOL & FINDINGS, INC.; *U.S. Private*, pg. 3535
SCHAAP & CITROEN—See KKR & Co. Inc.; *U.S. Public*, pg. 1261
SCIO DIAMOND TECHNOLOGY CORP.—See Adamas One Corp.; *U.S. Public*, pg. 37

SHANGHAI NOBLE CONCEPTS JEWELRY LIMITED—See Central Development Holdings Ltd.; *Int'l*, pg. 1406
SHENZHEN FUQI JEWELRY CO., LTD.—See Fuqi International, Inc.; *Int'l*, pg. 2846
STELLA & DOT LLC; *U.S. Private*, pg. 3799
STULLER, INC.; *U.S. Private*, pg. 3844
SUNCITI PVD (JIANGMEN) LTD.—See Citizen Watch Co., Ltd.; *Int'l*, pg. 1625
SUNSTONE IMPORTS INC.; *U.S. Private*, pg. 3873
TALISMAN COMPANY—See Terryberry Company LLC; *U.S. Private*, pg. 3972
TROPAR MFG. CO., INC.; *U.S. Private*, pg. 4242
TROPAR MFG. CO., INC.—See Tropar Mfg. Co., Inc.; *U.S. Private*, pg. 4242
TRU-EDGE GRINDING INC.—See MSC Industrial Direct Co., Inc.; *U.S. Public*, pg. 1483
TWO'S COMPANY INC.; *U.S. Private*, pg. 4267
UNCAS (HK) COMPANY LTD.—See Uncas Manufacturing Company; *U.S. Private*, pg. 4279
UNCAS MANUFACTURING COMPANY; *U.S. Private*, pg. 4279
VETTA JEWELRY INC.; *U.S. Private*, pg. 4374
VINDICATOR SILVER LEAD MINING CO.; *U.S. Public*, pg. 2298
THE VOLLRATH COMPANY LLC; *U.S. Private*, pg. 4132
WEST COAST FOUNDRY, INC.; *U.S. Private*, pg. 4484
WIEGAND CUSTOM WATCH, LLC; *U.S. Private*, pg. 4516
W.J. HAGERTY & SONS CANADA LTD.—See W.J. Hagerty & Sons, Ltd., Inc.; *U.S. Private*, pg. 4421
W.R. COBB COMPANY; *U.S. Private*, pg. 4422
YA OTTA PINATA—See Thomas H. Lee Partners, L.P.; *U.S. Private*, pg. 4156
YUEN SANG WATCH INDUSTRIES LIMITED—See Chuang's Consortium International Limited; *Int'l*, pg. 1590
YURMAN DESIGN, INC.; *U.S. Private*, pg. 4595

339920 — SPORTING AND ATHLETIC GOODS MANUFACTURING

361 DEGREES INTERNATIONAL LIMITED; *Int'l*, pg. 6
A2I SA—See Airesis S.A.; *Int'l*, pg. 247
ABEO SAS; *Int'l*, pg. 59
ABU AB—See Sycamore Partners Management, LP; *U.S. Private*, pg. 3896
ACCENT GROUP LIMITED; *Int'l*, pg. 81
ACTIONSPORTGAMES A/S; *Int'l*, pg. 119
ACTION TARGET, INC.; *U.S. Private*, pg. 68
ACUSHNET CANADA INC.—See FILA Holdings Corporation; *Int'l*, pg. 2662
ACUSHNET COMPANY—See FILA Holdings Corporation; *Int'l*, pg. 2662
ACUSHNET EUROPE LTD.—See FILA Holdings Corporation; *Int'l*, pg. 2662
ACUSHNET GMBH—See FILA Holdings Corporation; *Int'l*, pg. 2662
ACUSHNET HOLDINGS CORP.—See FILA Holdings Corporation; *Int'l*, pg. 2662
ACUSHNET KOREA CO., LTD.—See FILA Holdings Corporation; *Int'l*, pg. 2662
ACUSHNET NEDERLAND B.V.—See FILA Holdings Corporation; *Int'l*, pg. 2662
ACUSHNET SVERIGE AB—See FILA Holdings Corporation; *Int'l*, pg. 2662
ADAMS USA ATHLETICS INC.; *U.S. Private*, pg. 75
ADIDAS AG; *Int'l*, pg. 145
ADIDAS BELGIUM N.V.—See adidas AG; *Int'l*, pg. 146
ADIDAS (CHINA) LTD.—See adidas AG; *Int'l*, pg. 146
ADIDAS ESPANA S.A.—See adidas AG; *Int'l*, pg. 146
ADIDAS INDUSTRIAL, S.A. DE C.V.—See adidas AG; *Int'l*, pg. 147
ADIDAS INTERNATIONAL B.V.—See adidas AG; *Int'l*, pg. 147
ADIDAS ITALY S.P.A.—See adidas AG; *Int'l*, pg. 147
ADIDAS KOREA LTD.—See adidas AG; *Int'l*, pg. 147
ADIDAS NEW ZEALAND LIMITED—See adidas AG; *Int'l*, pg. 147
ADIDAS SPORTS (CHINA) CO. LTD.—See adidas AG; *Int'l*, pg. 146
ADIDAS TAIWAN LIMITED—See adidas AG; *Int'l*, pg. 147
ADING BULGARIA EOOD—See Ading AD; *Int'l*, pg. 149
ADING D.O.O.—See Ading AD; *Int'l*, pg. 149
ADOLPH KIEFER & ASSOCIATES, INC.; *U.S. Private*, pg. 81
ADVANCED INTERNATIONAL MULTITECH CO., LTD.; *Int'l*, pg. 160
AIPS TECHNOLOGY CO., LTD.—See Giant Manufacturing Co., Ltd.; *Int'l*, pg. 2961
AKADEMA, INC.; *U.S. Private*, pg. 144
ALIVE CO., LTD.—See AB&Company Co., Ltd.; *Int'l*, pg. 47
ALPEN CO., LTD.; *Int'l*, pg. 366
ALPINA BH, D.O.O.—See Alpina, d.d.; *Int'l*, pg. 371
ALPINA BROMY, D.O.O.—See Alpina, d.d.; *Int'l*, pg. 371
ALPINA CRO, D.O.O.—See Alpina, d.d.; *Int'l*, pg. 371
ALPINA SIRO, S.R.L.—See Alpina, d.d.; *Int'l*, pg. 371
ALPINA SPORTS CORP.—See Alpina, d.d.; *Int'l*, pg. 371
ALPINA YUG, D.O.O.—See Alpina, d.d.; *Int'l*, pg. 371
ALTAIR INTERNATIONAL CORP.; *U.S. Public*, pg. 86

N.A.I.C.S. INDEX

339920 — SPORTING AND ATHLET...

AMERICAN ATHLETIC INC.—See Berkshire Hathaway Inc.; *U.S. Public*, pg. 305
AMERICAN GOLF OF ATLANTA—See Drive Shack Inc.; *U.S. Public*, pg. 688
AMERICAN HERITAGE BILLIARDS, LLC—See Escalade, Incorporated; *U.S. Public*, pg. 793
AMERICAN OUTDOOR BRANDS, INC.; *U.S. Public*, pg. 108
AMERICAN SOCCER COMPANY, INC.—See Brand Velocity Partners; *U.S. Private*, pg. 637
AMERICAN UNDERWATER PRODUCTS; *U.S. Private*, pg. 257
AMER SPORT OY—See ANTA Sports Products Limited; *Int'l*, pg. 479
AMER SPORTS AUSTRALIA PTY. LTD.—See ANTA Sports Products Limited; *Int'l*, pg. 481
AMER SPORTS COMPANY—See ANTA Sports Products Limited; *Int'l*, pg. 480
AMER SPORTS CORPORATION—See ANTA Sports Products Limited; *Int'l*, pg. 479
AMERSPORTS CZECH REPUBLIC—See ANTA Sports Products Limited; *Int'l*, pg. 480
AMER SPORTS DEUTSCHLAND GMBH—See ANTA Sports Products Limited; *Int'l*, pg. 480
AMER SPORTS FRANCE—See ANTA Sports Products Limited; *Int'l*, pg. 480
AMER SPORTS KOREA LTD.—See ANTA Sports Products Limited; *Int'l*, pg. 481
AMER SPORTS LATIN AMERICA—See ANTA Sports Products Limited; *Int'l*, pg. 480
AMER SPORTS SPAIN S.A—See ANTA Sports Products Limited; *Int'l*, pg. 481
AMER SPORTS SUOMI OY—See ANTA Sports Products Limited; *Int'l*, pg. 480
AMER SPORTS SVERIGE AB—See ANTA Sports Products Limited; *Int'l*, pg. 480
AMER SPORTS TAIWAN—See ANTA Sports Products Limited; *Int'l*, pg. 481
AMER SPORTS WINTER & OUTDOOR COMPANY—See ANTA Sports Products Limited; *Int'l*, pg. 480
AMRON INTERNATIONAL INC.; *U.S. Private*, pg. 266
ANVIL HOLDINGS, INC.—See Gildan Activewear Inc.; *Int'l*, pg. 2973
ASESORIA DEPORTIVA ESPECIALIZADA, S.A. DE C.V.—See ANTA Sports Products Limited; *Int'l*, pg. 480
ASICS APPAREL INDUSTRY CORP.—See ASICS Corporation; *Int'l*, pg. 620
ASICS ASIA PTE. LTD.—See ASICS Corporation; *Int'l*, pg. 620
ASICS AUSTRIA GMBH—See ASICS Corporation; *Int'l*, pg. 620
ASICS CANADA CORPORATION—See ASICS Corporation; *Int'l*, pg. 620
ASICS CHINA TRADING CO., LTD.—See ASICS Corporation; *Int'l*, pg. 620
ASICS CORPORATION; *Int'l*, pg. 620
ASICS DENMARK A/S—See ASICS Corporation; *Int'l*, pg. 620
ASICS DEUTSCHLAND GMBH—See ASICS Corporation; *Int'l*, pg. 620
ASICS EUROPE B.V.—See ASICS Corporation; *Int'l*, pg. 620
ASICS FRANCE S.A.S.—See ASICS Corporation; *Int'l*, pg. 620
ASICS HONG KONG LIMITED—See ASICS Corporation; *Int'l*, pg. 620
ASICS IBERIA S.L.—See ASICS Corporation; *Int'l*, pg. 621
ASICS INDIA PRIVATE LIMITED—See ASICS Corporation; *Int'l*, pg. 621
ASICS ITALIA S.R.L.—See ASICS Corporation; *Int'l*, pg. 621
ASICS KOREA CORPORATION—See ASICS Corporation; *Int'l*, pg. 621
ASICS MALAYSIA SDN. BHD.—See ASICS Corporation; *Int'l*, pg. 621
ASICS MIDDLE EAST TRADING LLC—See ASICS Corporation; *Int'l*, pg. 621
ASICS NORGE AS—See ASICS Corporation; *Int'l*, pg. 621
ASICS OCEANIA PTY. LTD.—See ASICS Corporation; *Int'l*, pg. 621
ASICS POLSKA SP.ZO.O.—See ASICS Corporation; *Int'l*, pg. 621
ASICS SOURCING (VIETNAM) CO., LTD.—See ASICS Corporation; *Int'l*, pg. 621
ASICS SOUTH AFRICA PTY. LTD.—See ASICS Corporation; *Int'l*, pg. 621
ASICS SPORTS COMPLEX CORP.—See ASICS Corporation; *Int'l*, pg. 621
ASICS SPORTS MEXICO, S.A. DE C.V.—See ASICS Corporation; *Int'l*, pg. 621
ASICS SVERIGE AB—See ASICS Corporation; *Int'l*, pg. 621
ASICS TAIWAN CORPORATION—See ASICS Corporation; *Int'l*, pg. 621
ASICS THAILAND CO., LTD.—See ASICS Corporation; *Int'l*, pg. 621
ASICS TRYUS SERVICE CORP.—See ASICS Corporation; *Int'l*, pg. 621
ASICS UK LIMITED—See ASICS Corporation; *Int'l*, pg. 621
ASOLO NORTH AMERICA INC.—See Asolo S.p.A.; *Int'l*, pg. 628

ASOLO S.P.A.; *Int'l*, pg. 628
ATHLETICA INC.; *U.S. Private*, pg. 368
ATHLETIC TRAINING EQUIPMENT COMPANY, INC.—See ANTA Sports Products Limited; *Int'l*, pg. 481
ATOMIC AUSTRIA GMBH—See ANTA Sports Products Limited; *Int'l*, pg. 480
ATOMIC SPORTS CANADA—See ANTA Sports Products Limited; *Int'l*, pg. 480
AVON INFLATABLES LTD.—See The Carlyle Group Inc.; *U.S. Public*, pg. 2057
BAIKSAN CO., LTD.; *Int'l*, pg. 802
BALANCED BODY, INC.; *U.S. Private*, pg. 457
BALI LEATHERS INC.; *U.S. Private*, pg. 459
BANGKOK ATHLETIC CO., LTD.—See Bangkok Rubber Public Co., Ltd.; *Int'l*, pg. 835
BASS PRO SHOPS, INC.—See The Great American Outdoors Group LLC; *U.S. Private*, pg. 4037
BATTENFELD TECHNOLOGIES, INC.—See Smith & Wesson Brands, Inc.; *U.S. Public*, pg. 1896
BCI BURKE COMPANY CO—See The Halifax Group LLC; *U.S. Private*, pg. 4042
BEAR ARCHERY, INC.—See Escalade, Incorporated; *U.S. Public*, pg. 793
BEE STINGER, LLC—See Vista Outdoor Inc.; *U.S. Public*, pg. 2304
BEIJING GOLDWIN CO., LTD.—See Goldwin, Inc.; *Int'l*, pg. 3035
BELL RACING USA, LLC—See Vista Outdoor Inc.; *U.S. Public*, pg. 2304
BELL SPORTS, INC.—See Vista Outdoor Inc.; *U.S. Public*, pg. 2304
BERNARD ATHLETIC KNIT LTD.; *Int'l*, pg. 986
BESTWAY AUSTRALIA PTY. LTD.—See Bestway Global Holding Inc.; *Int'l*, pg. 1001
BESTWAY CENTRAL & SOUTH AMERICA LTDA.—See Bestway Global Holding Inc.; *Int'l*, pg. 1001
BESTWAY DEUTSCHLAND GMBH—See Bestway Global Holding Inc.; *Int'l*, pg. 1001
BESTWAY EASTERN EUROPE SP. Z O.O.—See Bestway Global Holding Inc.; *Int'l*, pg. 1001
BESTWAY FRANCE S.R.L.—See Bestway Global Holding Inc.; *Int'l*, pg. 1001
BESTWAY (HONG KONG) INTERNATIONAL LIMITED—See Bestway Global Holding Inc.; *Int'l*, pg. 1001
BESTWAY ITALY S.R.L.—See Bestway Global Holding Inc.; *Int'l*, pg. 1001
BIEM.L .FDLKK GARMENT CO., LTD.; *Int'l*, pg. 1020
BIG SKY CARVERS INC.—See Thompson Street Capital Manager LLC; *U.S. Private*, pg. 4161
BIGTOYS, INC.—See Court Square Capital Partners, L.P.; *U.S. Private*, pg. 1069
BLACK DIAMOND EQUIPMENT AG—See Clarus Corporation; *U.S. Public*, pg. 508
BLACK DIAMOND EQUIPMENT LTD.—See Clarus Corporation; *U.S. Public*, pg. 508
BLU3, INC.—See Brownie's Marine Group, Inc.; *U.S. Public*, pg. 403
BLUE FALLS MANUFACTURING LTD.; *Int'l*, pg. 1068
BLYTH S.R.O.—See Bunzl plc; *Int'l*, pg. 1217
BOATECHNOLOGY GMBH—See Compass Diversified Holdings; *U.S. Public*, pg. 559
BOA TECHNOLOGY INC.—See Compass Diversified Holdings; *U.S. Public*, pg. 560
BOA TECHNOLOGY JAPAN INC.—See Compass Diversified Holdings; *U.S. Public*, pg. 559
BOA TECHNOLOGY KOREA INC.—See Compass Diversified Holdings; *U.S. Public*, pg. 559
BOA TECHNOLOGY (SHENZEN) LTD.—See Compass Diversified Holdings; *U.S. Public*, pg. 559
BODY ACTION ENTERPRISE CO., LTD.; *Int'l*, pg. 1097
BODY GLOVE INTERNATIONAL, LLC—See Marquee Brands LLC; *U.S. Private*, pg. 2586
BONNY WORLDWIDE LIMITED; *Int'l*, pg. 1109
BRAVO SPORTS CORPORATION—See Transom Capital Group, LLC; *U.S. Private*, pg. 4209
BRG SPORTS MEXICO, S.A. DE C.V.—See Fenway Partners, LLC; *U.S. Private*, pg. 1495
BRIDGESTONE GOLF, INC.—See Bridgestone Corporation; *Int'l*, pg. 1159
BRIDGESTONE SPORTS CO., LTD.—See Bridgestone Corporation; *Int'l*, pg. 1159
BRINE, INC.—See New Balance Athletic Shoe, Inc.; *U.S. Private*, pg. 2892
BROWNIE'S MARINE GROUP, INC.; *U.S. Public*, pg. 403
BROWNING INTERNATIONAL S.A.—See Herstal, S.A.; *Int'l*, pg. 3364
BRUNSWICK BOWLING & BILLIARDS CORPORATION—See Brunswick Corporation; *U.S. Public*, pg. 407
BRUNSWICK INTERNATIONAL GMBH—See Brunswick Corporation; *U.S. Public*, pg. 407
BSN SPORTS, LLC—See Bain Capital, LP; *U.S. Private*, pg. 451
BURTON SNOWBOARD COMPANY; *U.S. Private*, pg. 693
CALLAWAY GOLF EUROPE LTD.—See Topgolf Callaway Brands Corp.; *U.S. Public*, pg. 2164
CALLAWAY GOLF KABUSHIKI KAISHA—See Topgolf Callaway Brands Corp.; *U.S. Public*, pg. 2164

CALLAWAY GOLF KOREA LTD.—See Topgolf Callaway Brands Corp.; *U.S. Public*, pg. 2164
CALLAWAY GOLF MALAYSIA SDN. BHD.—See Topgolf Callaway Brands Corp.; *U.S. Public*, pg. 2164
CALLAWAY GOLF SALES COMPANY—See Topgolf Callaway Brands Corp.; *U.S. Public*, pg. 2164
CALLAWAY GOLF SOUTH PACIFIC PTY LTD.—See Topgolf Callaway Brands Corp.; *U.S. Public*, pg. 2164
CAMBUCI S.A.; *Int'l*, pg. 1270
CAMELBAK PRODUCTS LLC—See Vista Outdoor Inc.; *U.S. Public*, pg. 2305
CANTERBURY OF NEW ZEALAND JAPAN INC.—See Goldwin, Inc.; *Int'l*, pg. 3035
CARDIO FITNESS GMBH & CO. KG—See Dyaco International Inc.; *Int'l*, pg. 2237
CARRON NET COMPANY, INC.; *U.S. Private*, pg. 774
CHINA SPORTS INTERNATIONAL CO., LTD.—See China Sports Industry Group Co., Ltd.; *Int'l*, pg. 1553
CHINA SPORTS MANAGEMENT GROUP CO., LTD.—See China Sports Industry Group Co., Ltd.; *Int'l*, pg. 1553
CLARUS CORPORATION; *U.S. Public*, pg. 507
COAST CUTLERY COMPANY; *U.S. Private*, pg. 954
THE COLEMAN COMPANY, INC.—See Newell Brands Inc.; *U.S. Public*, pg. 1515
COLUMBIA CASCADE COMPANY; *U.S. Private*, pg. 976
COLUMBIA SPORTSWEAR ASIA PACIFIC SARL—See Columbia Sportswear Company; *U.S. Public*, pg. 535
COMERCIAL UDRA, S.A.U.—See Grupo Empresarial San Jose, S.A.; *Int'l*, pg. 3128
CONNELLY BILLIARD MANUFACTURING; *U.S. Private*, pg. 1017
CONNELLY SKIS, INC.; *U.S. Private*, pg. 1017
CONVERSE KOREA LLC—See NIKE, Inc.; *U.S. Public*, pg. 1528
CORE HEALTH & FITNESS LLC; *U.S. Private*, pg. 1048
COSCO (INDIA) LIMITED; *Int'l*, pg. 1809
C P S SHAPERS LIMITED; *Int'l*, pg. 1238
CRAVATEX LTD.; *Int'l*, pg. 1828
CREATIVE PLAYTHINGS LTD.; *U.S. Private*, pg. 1090
CREME LURE CO., INC.; *U.S. Private*, pg. 1092
CRESCENT MOON SNOWSHOES, INC.—See Dunn-Rite Products, Inc.; *U.S. Private*, pg. 1290
CROAKIES; *U.S. Private*, pg. 1102
CROSMAN CORPORATION—See Bruckmann, Rosser, Sherrill & Co., LLC; *U.S. Private*, pg. 671
CUMMINS DISTRIBUTION HOLDCO INC.—See Cummins Inc.; *U.S. Public*, pg. 605
CYBEX INTERNATIONAL, INC.—See KPS Capital Partners, LP; *U.S. Private*, pg. 2347
CYCLING SPORTS GROUP AUSTRALIA PTY LTD—See Dorel Industries, Inc.; *Int'l*, pg. 2176
CYCLING SPORTS GROUP EUROPE B.V—See Dorel Industries, Inc.; *Int'l*, pg. 2176
DACOR CORPORATION—See Head B.V.; *Int'l*, pg. 3300
DAIWA FRANCE S.A.S.—See Globeride, Inc.; *Int'l*, pg. 3007
DA KINE HAWAII INC.; *U.S. Private*, pg. 1143
DATREK PROFESSIONAL BAGS, INC.; *U.S. Private*, pg. 1167
DD'S DELUXE ROD HOLDER, INC.; *Int'l*, pg. 1993
DETROIT RED WINGS, INC.—See Ilitch Holdings, Inc.; *U.S. Private*, pg. 2041
DICE SPORT & CASUAL WEAR S.A.E.; *Int'l*, pg. 2111
DJO BENELUX B.V.B.A.—See Enovis Corporation; *U.S. Public*, pg. 772
DJO GLOBAL SWITZERLAND SARL—See Enovis Corporation; *U.S. Public*, pg. 772
DO OUTDOORS, LLC—See BDT Capital Partners, LLC; *U.S. Private*, pg. 503
DOREL GERMANY GMBH—See Dorel Industries, Inc.; *Int'l*, pg. 2176
D SPORTS MERCHANDISING INC.—See Dentsu Group Inc.; *Int'l*, pg. 2034
DUNLOP SLAZENGER GROUP LTD.; *Int'l*, pg. 2227
DUNN-RITE PRODUCTS, INC.; *U.S. Private*, pg. 1290
DYACO CANADA INC.—See Dyaco International Inc.; *Int'l*, pg. 2238
DYACO EUROPE GMBH—See Dyaco International Inc.; *Int'l*, pg. 2238
DYACO GERMANY GMBH—See Dyaco International Inc.; *Int'l*, pg. 2238
DYACO INTERNATIONAL INC. - MAIN FACTORY—See Dyaco International Inc.; *Int'l*, pg. 2238
DYACO INTERNATIONAL INC.; *Int'l*, pg. 2237
DYACO (SHANGHAI) TRADING CO., LTD.—See Dyaco International Inc.; *Int'l*, pg. 2238
EASTBAY FOOT LOCKER.COM—See Foot Locker, Inc.; *U.S. Public*, pg. 863
EASTON BASEBALL/SOFTBALL INC. See Fairfax Financial Holdings Limited; *Int'l*, pg. 2605
EBONITE INTERNATIONAL INCORPORATED; *U.S. Private*, pg. 1324
EBSCO INDUSTRIES, INC. - PRADCO FISHING DIVISION—See EBSCO Industries, Inc.; *U.S. Private*, pg. 1325
ELEMENT SKATEBOARDS, INC.—See Leonard Green & Partners, L.P.; *U.S. Public*, pg. 2424
ELEVATION, INC.; *U.S. Private*, pg. 1358

339920 — SPORTING AND ATHLET...

ENDLESS POOLS, INC.—See Masco Corporation; *U.S. Public*, pg. 1392
ENDO THAI CO.LTD.—See Endo Manufacturing Co., Ltd.; *Int'l*, pg. 2405
EPON GOLF CORPORATION—See Endo Manufacturing Co., Ltd.; *Int'l*, pg. 2405
EPPINGER MANUFACTURING CO.; *U.S. Private*, pg. 1414
ERIMA GMBH; *Int'l*, pg. 2493
ESCALADE, INCORPORATED; *U.S. Public*, pg. 793
ESCALADE SPORTS PLAYGROUND, INC.—See Escalade, Incorporated; *U.S. Public*, pg. 793
EUROPOOL ITALIA S.R.L.—See The Carlyle Group Inc.; *U.S. Public*, pg. 2057
EUROZONE BRANDS LIMITED—See Colan Totte.Co., Ltd.; *Int'l*, pg. 1697
EVERLAST CLIMBING INDUSTRIES, INC.—See Court Square Capital Partners, L.P.; *U.S. Private*, pg. 1069
EVERLAST WORLDWIDE, INC.—See Frasers Group plc; *Int'l*, pg. 2765
FABRY INDUSTRIES SARANAC WORLD OF GLOVES; *U.S. Private*, pg. 1459
FAIRPLAY CORPORATION—See Trans-Lux Corporation; *U.S. Public*, pg. 2179
FALCON POWER CO., LTD.; *Int'l*, pg. 2611
FERADYNE OUTDOORS LLC—See TruArc Partners, L.P.; *U.S. Private*, pg. 4245
FIELD LOGIC, INC.—See TruArc Partners, L.P.; *U.S. Private*, pg. 4245
FILA ARGENTINA S.A.—See FILA Holdings Corporation; *Int'l*, pg. 2662
FILA CANADA, INC.—See FILA Holdings Corporation; *Int'l*, pg. 2662
FILA EUROPE S.P.A.—See FILA Holdings Corporation; *Int'l*, pg. 2662
FILA FRANCE S.A.—See FILA Holdings Corporation; *Int'l*, pg. 2662
FILA SPORT (HONG KONG) LIMITED—See FILA Holdings Corporation; *Int'l*, pg. 2662
FILA UK LIMITED—See FILA Holdings Corporation; *Int'l*, pg. 2662
FITBIT, INC.—See Alphabet Inc.; *U.S. Public*, pg. 83
FITNESS CUBED INC.; *U.S. Private*, pg. 1536
FLAMBEAU, INC. - FLAMBEAU OUTDOORS DIVISION—See Nordic Group of Companies, Ltd.; *U.S. Private*, pg. 2937
FLITEBOARD EUROPE B.V.—See Brunswick Corporation; *U.S. Public*, pg. 408
FLITE HOCKEY; *Int'l*, pg. 2706
FOUNDER SPORT GROUP—See Platinum Equity, LLC; *U.S. Private*, pg. 3207
FOX POOL CORPORATION—See Wexco Incorporated; *U.S. Private*, pg. 4502
FRANKLIN SPORTS, INC.; *U.S. Private*, pg. 1598
FRANKLIN SPORTS, INC. - UNIFORCE TACTICAL DIVISION—See Franklin Sports, Inc.; *U.S. Private*, pg. 1598
FREENOTES HARMONY PARK, INC.—See Court Square Capital Partners, L.P.; *U.S. Private*, pg. 1069
FUJIKURA COMPOSITE AMERICA, INC.—See Fujikura Composites Inc.; *Int'l*, pg. 2826
FURUNO NORGE AS—See Furuno Electric Co., Ltd.; *Int'l*, pg. 2848
FUTBOL CLUB BARCELONA MERCHANDISING, S.L.—See NIKE, Inc.; *U.S. Public*, pg. 1528
GAMMA SPORTS; *U.S. Private*, pg. 1640
GARED HOLDINGS, LLC—See Gen Cap America, Inc.; *U.S. Private*, pg. 1660
GARED SPORTS—See Gen Cap America, Inc.; *U.S. Private*, pg. 1660
GEAR AID, INC.; *U.S. Private*, pg. 1654
GENCO BULGARIA LTD—See FOURLIS HOLDINGS S.A.; *Int'l*, pg. 2755
GIANT UK LTD.—See Giant Manufacturing Co., Ltd.; *Int'l*, pg. 2961
GILL ATHLETICS, INC.—See Litania Sports Group, Inc.; *U.S. Private*, pg. 2467
GLASS PRO INC.; *U.S. Private*, pg. 1706
GLOBERIDE, INC.; *Int'l*, pg. 3007
GOALSETTER SYSTEMS, INC.—See Escalade, Incorporated; *U.S. Public*, pg. 793
GOC (PAK) LIMITED; *Int'l*, pg. 3018
GOLDWIN CHINA,LTD.—See Goldwin, Inc.; *Int'l*, pg. 3035
GOLDWIN ITALIA SRL—See Goldwin, Inc.; *Int'l*, pg. 3035
GOLDWIN KOREA CORPORATION—See Goldwin, Inc.; *Int'l*, pg. 3035
GOLDWIN SAI GON VIETNAM CO., LTD.—See Goldwin, Inc.; *Int'l*, pg. 3035
GOLF GALAXY GOLFWORKS, INC.—See Dick's Sporting Goods, Inc.; *U.S. Public*, pg. 659
GRAPHITE DESIGN INC.; *Int'l*, pg. 3061
GROUPE ROSSIGNOL CANADA INC.—See Altor Equity Partners AB; *Int'l*, pg. 396
HAKERS ENTERPRISE CO., LTD.; *Int'l*, pg. 3219
HAMPIDJAN HF; *Int'l*, pg. 3239
HEAD B.V.; *Int'l*, pg. 3300
HEAD/PENN RACQUET SPORTS—See Head B.V.; *Int'l*, pg. 3300
HEARTLINE FITNESS SYSTEMS; *U.S. Private*, pg. 1901

HILLERICH & BRADSBY CO., INC.; *U.S. Private*, pg. 1946
HI-TEC SPORTS PLC; *Int'l*, pg. 3381
HL CORP; *Int'l*, pg. 3429
HL CORP - SPORTING GOODS AND FITNESS DIVISION—See HL CORP; *Int'l*, pg. 3429
HL CORP (USA) , INC.—See HL CORP; *Int'l*, pg. 3429
HOIST FITNESS SYSTEMS INC.; *U.S. Private*, pg. 1961
HONMA GOLF LIMITED; *Int'l*, pg. 3471
HONMA GOLF U.S., LTD.—See Honma Golf Limited; *Int'l*, pg. 3472
HUALI INDUSTRIAL GROUP COMPANY LIMITED; *Int'l*, pg. 3512
HUFFY CORPORATION; *U.S. Private*, pg. 2003
HUGGER MUGGER YOGA PRODUCTS LLC; *U.S. Private*, pg. 2003
HUNTERS SPECIALTIES, INC.—See Peak Rock Capital LLC; *U.S. Private*, pg. 3124
HURLEY AUSTRALIA PTY. LTD.—See Bluestar Alliance LLC; *U.S. Private*, pg. 598
HYPERFORM, INC.—See Patrick Industries, Inc.; *U.S. Public*, pg. 1652
ICON HEALTH & FITNESS, INC.; *U.S. Private*, pg. 2032
IMPERIAL POOLS, INC.; *U.S. Private*, pg. 2049
INDIAN INDUSTRIES, INC.—See Escalade, Incorporated; *U.S. Public*, pg. 793
IN MOCEAN GROUP LLC; *U.S. Private*, pg. 2052
INNOVATIVE DESIGNS, INC.; *U.S. Public*, pg. 1126
INTEGRAL DESIGNS—See Bantam Capital Corp.; *Int'l*, pg. 855
INTERFAB INC.; *U.S. Private*, pg. 2110
JANSPORT APPAREL CORP.—See V. F. Corporation; *U.S. Public*, pg. 2269
JIANG SU ASICS CO., LTD.—See ASICS Corporation; *Int'l*, pg. 621
JOHNSON OUTDOORS DIVING—See Johnson Outdoors Inc.; *U.S. Public*, pg. 1201
JOHNSON OUTDOORS FRANCE—See Johnson Outdoors Inc.; *U.S. Public*, pg. 1201
JOHNSON OUTDOORS GEAR LLC—See Johnson Outdoors Inc.; *U.S. Public*, pg. 1201
JOHNSON OUTDOORS INC.; *U.S. Public*, pg. 1200
K-2 SPORTS, LLC—See Kohlberg & Company, LLC; *U.S. Private*, pg. 2338
KARSTEN MANUFACTURING CORPORATION; *U.S. Private*, pg. 2263
KENT SPORTING GOODS COMPANY; *U.S. Private*, pg. 2288
KISSMARK JAPAN CO., LTD.—See Alpen Co., Ltd.; *Int'l*, pg. 366
KOLPIN OUTDOORS, INC.—See Polaris, Inc.; *U.S. Public*, pg. 1700
KURT MANUFACTURING CO. INC. - KURT KINETIC DIVISION—See Kurt Manufacturing Co. Inc.; *U.S. Private*, pg. 2358
KWIK TEK INC.—See Falconhead Capital, LLC; *U.S. Private*, pg. 1467
LAFUMA SA—See Calida Holding AG; *Int'l*, pg. 1264
LANDSCAPE STRUCTURES INC.; *U.S. Private*, pg. 2387
L.A. STEELCRAFT PRODUCTS CO.—See Hindman Manufacturing Co.; *U.S. Private*, pg. 1948
LAUNCH TECHNOLOGIES CO., LTD.—See Advanced International Multitech Co., Ltd.; *Int'l*, pg. 160
LEISURE BAY DISTRIBUTING CO. INC.—See Leisure Bay Industries, Inc.; *U.S. Private*, pg. 2420
LEISURE BAY INDUSTRIES, INC.; *U.S. Private*, pg. 2420
LIFE FITNESS EUROPE GMBH—See KPS Capital Partners, LP; *U.S. Private*, pg. 2347
LIFE FITNESS, INC.—See KPS Capital Partners, LP; *U.S. Private*, pg. 2347
LIFE FITNESS (U.K.) LIMITED—See KPS Capital Partners, LP; *U.S. Private*, pg. 2347
LIFETIME PRODUCTS INC.; *U.S. Private*, pg. 2451
LITANIA SPORTS GROUP, INC.; *U.S. Private*, pg. 2467
LOGAN OUTDOOR PRODUCTS, LLC—See Vista Outdoor Inc.; *U.S. Public*, pg. 2305
LUDOPARC S.A.—See Burelle S.A.; *Int'l*, pg. 1222
MACGREGOR GOLF ASIA LTD.—See Hellman & Friedman LLC; *U.S. Public*, pg. 1907
MACNEILL ENGINEERING CO., INC.—See Centre Partners Management LLC; *U.S. Private*, pg. 828
MADSHUS A/S—See Kohlberg & Company, LLC; *U.S. Private*, pg. 2338
MAIER SPORTS GMBH & CO. KG—See Findos Investor GmbH; *Int'l*, pg. 2673
MAMMUT SPORTS GROUP AG—See Bystronic AG; *Int'l*, pg. 1236
MARES AMERICA—See Head B.V.; *Int'l*, pg. 3300
MARES—See Head B.V.; *Int'l*, pg. 3300
MARUCCI SPORTS, LLC—See Fox Factory Holding Corp.; *U.S. Public*, pg. 877
MATHEWS INC.; *U.S. Private*, pg. 2611
MAXI MILIAAN B.V.—See Dorel Industries, Inc.; *Int'l*, pg. 2176
MEDI-DYNE HEALTHCARE PRODUCTS LTD.; *U.S. Private*, pg. 2651
MERVIN MANUFACTURING, INC.—See Extreme Holdings, Inc.; *U.S. Private*, pg. 1452
MINI-GOLF, INC.; *U.S. Private*, pg. 2742

MIRACLE RECREATION EQUIPMENT COMPANY—See Littlejohn & Co., LLC; *U.S. Private*, pg. 2471
MISTER TWISTER, L.L.C.—See Sheldons' Inc.; *U.S. Private*, pg. 3631
MOTION WATER SPORTS INC.; *U.S. Private*, pg. 2796
MUELLER JAPAN—See Mueller Sports Medicine, Inc.; *U.S. Private*, pg. 2810
MUSTANG SURVIVAL CORP.—See Wing Inflatables, Inc.; *U.S. Private*, pg. 4541
MYLAPS ASIA PACIFIC LTY LTD—See HAL Trust N.V.; *Int'l*, pg. 3224
NATARE CORPORATION; *U.S. Private*, pg. 2838
NAUTILUS COMMERCIAL FITNESS—See Core Health & Fitness LLC; *U.S. Private*, pg. 1048
NEW ARCHERY PRODUCTS, INC.—See Bruckmann, Rosser, Sherrill & Co., LLC; *U.S. Private*, pg. 671
NEWRON SPORT; *U.S. Public*, pg. 1518
NICKLAUS GOLF EQUIPMENT COMPANY, L.C.—See Nicklaus Companies, LLC; *U.S. Private*, pg. 2926
NIKE DE CHILE LTDA.—See NIKE, Inc.; *U.S. Public*, pg. 1529
NIKE DO BRASIL COMERCIO E PARTICIPACOES LTDA.—See NIKE, Inc.; *U.S. Public*, pg. 1529
NIKE FINLAND OY—See NIKE, Inc.; *U.S. Public*, pg. 1529
NIKE, INC.; *U.S. Public*, pg. 1529
NIKE POLAND SP.ZO.O—See NIKE, Inc.; *U.S. Public*, pg. 1529
NIKE RETAIL ISRAEL LTD.—See NIKE, Inc.; *U.S. Public*, pg. 1529
NISHI ATHLETIC GOODS CO., LTD.—See ASICS Corporation; *Int'l*, pg. 621
O'BRIEN INTERNATIONAL, INC.—See Motion Water Sports Inc.; *U.S. Private*, pg. 2796
OLHAUSEN BILLIARD MFG, INC.; *U.S. Private*, pg. 3010
ONFIELD APPAREL GROUP LLC—See Leonard Green & Partners, L.P.; *U.S. Private*, pg. 2424
ORU KAYAK INC.; *U.S. Private*, pg. 3045
THE ORVIS COMPANY—See The Orvis Company, Inc.; *U.S. Private*, pg. 4089
PARSONS XTREME GOLF, LLC; *U.S. Private*, pg. 3100
PELOTON INTERACTIVE, INC.; *U.S. Public*, pg. 1661
PENNANT SPORTS INC.; *U.S. Private*, pg. 3135
PENN FISHING TACKLE MANUFACTURING COMPANY—See Sycamore Partners Management, LP; *U.S. Private*, pg. 3896
PERFORMANCE SPORTS SYSTEMS, INC.—See Gen Cap America, Inc.; *U.S. Private*, pg. 1660
PERFORMANCE STRENGTH DESIGNS, INC.; *U.S. Private*, pg. 3150
PERFORM GROUP, LLC - ALPHA FACTOR DIVISION—See Perform Group, LLC; *U.S. Private*, pg. 3148
PLASTIC RESEARCH AND DEVELOPMENT CORPORATION—See EBSCO Industries, Inc.; *U.S. Private*, pg. 1325
PLAYCORE, INC.—See Court Square Capital Partners, L.P.; *U.S. Private*, pg. 1069
PLAYCORE WISCONSIN, INC.—See Court Square Capital Partners, L.P.; *U.S. Private*, pg. 1069
PLAY & PARK STRUCTURES—See Court Square Capital Partners, L.P.; *U.S. Private*, pg. 1069
PLAYPOWER CANADA—See Littlejohn & Co., LLC; *U.S. Private*, pg. 2471
PLAYPOWER, INC.—See Littlejohn & Co., LLC; *U.S. Private*, pg. 2471
PLAYPOWER LT FARMINGTON, INC.—See Littlejohn & Co., LLC; *U.S. Private*, pg. 2471
PLAYWORLD SYSTEMS, INC.—See Littlejohn & Co., LLC; *U.S. Private*, pg. 2471
PORTER ATHLETIC EQUIPMENT COMPANY—See Litania Sports Group, Inc.; *U.S. Private*, pg. 2467
PRECISION SHOOTING EQUIPMENT INC.; *U.S. Private*, pg. 3246
PRECOR, INC.—See Peloton Interactive, Inc.; *U.S. Public*, pg. 1661
PRIMOS HUNTING—See Vista Outdoor Inc.; *U.S. Public*, pg. 2304
PRINCE GOLF; *U.S. Private*, pg. 3264
PROMAXIMA MANUFACTURING LTD; *U.S. Private*, pg. 3282
PURE FISHING, INC.—See Sycamore Partners Management, LP; *U.S. Private*, pg. 3896
QUBICAAMF WORLDWIDE, LLC—See Bowlero Corp; *U.S. Public*, pg. 376
RAWLINGS SPORTING GOODS CO., INC.—See Major League Baseball; *U.S. Private*, pg. 2555
RAWLINGS SPORTING GOODS CO., INC.—See The Seidler Company, LLC; *U.S. Private*, pg. 4116
RECREATION CREATIONS, LLC—See Worth Investment Group, LLC; *U.S. Private*, pg. 4570
REEBOK-CCM HOCKEY AB—See adidas AG; *Int'l*, pg. 147
REEBOK-CCM HOCKEY GMBH—See Leonard Green & Partners, L.P.; *U.S. Private*, pg. 2425
REEBOK-CCM HOCKEY, INC.—See Leonard Green & Partners, L.P.; *U.S. Private*, pg. 2425
REEBOK PRODUTOS ESPORTIVOS BRASIL LTDA.—See Leonard Green & Partners, L.P.; *U.S. Private*, pg. 2424
REVOLUTION MANUFACTURING, LLC; *U.S. Private*, pg. 3416

N.A.I.C.S. INDEX

RIDDELL SPORTS GROUP, INC.—See Fenway Partners, LLC; *U.S. Private*, pg. 1495
RIO PRODUCTS INTL., INC.—See Joshua Green Corporation; *U.S. Private*, pg. 2237
RODEDAWG INTERNATIONAL INDUSTRIES, INC.; *U.S. Public*, pg. 1807
ROSSIGNOL GMBH—See Altor Equity Partners AB; *Int'l*, pg. 396
ROSSIGNOL LANGE SRL—See Altor Equity Partners AB; *Int'l*, pg. 396
ROSSIGNOL OSTERREICH GMBH—See Altor Equity Partners AB; *Int'l*, pg. 396
ROSSIGNOL SCI SARL—See Altor Equity Partners AB; *Int'l*, pg. 396
ROSSIGNOL SKI COMPANY, INC.—See Altor Equity Partners AB; *Int'l*, pg. 396
ROSSIGNOL SKI DEUTSCHLAND GMBH—See Altor Equity Partners AB; *Int'l*, pg. 396
RUSSELL BRANDS, LLC—See Berkshire Hathaway Inc.; *U.S. Public*, pg. 305
SACKS PARENTE GOLF, INC.; *U.S. Public*, pg. 1834
SAGE MANUFACTURING CORPORATION—See Joshua Green Corporation; *U.S. Private*, pg. 2237
SALOMON & BONFIRE SNOWBOARDING, INC.—See ANTA Sports Products Limited; *Int'l*, pg. 481
SALOMON S.A.—See ANTA Sports Products Limited; *Int'l*, pg. 480
SAVAGE ARMS (CANADA) INC.—See Vista Outdoor Inc.; *U.S. Public*, pg. 2305
SCHUTT SPORTS—See Platinum Equity, LLC; *U.S. Private*, pg. 3208
SCHUYLKILL VALLEY SPORTS; *U.S. Private*, pg. 3571
SCIFIT SYSTEMS, INC.—See Brunswick Corporation; *U.S. Public*, pg. 408
SCUBAPRO ASIA PACIFIC LTD.—See Johnson Outdoors Inc.; *U.S. Public*, pg. 1201
SCUBAPRO-UWATEC FRANCE S.A.—See Johnson Outdoors Inc.; *U.S. Public*, pg. 1201
SECTOR 9, INC.—See Transom Capital Group, LLC; *U.S. Private*, pg. 4209
SEEKER ROD COMPANY—See Parrish Enterprises, Ltd.; *U.S. Private*, pg. 3100
SHAKESPEARE (AUSTRALIA) PTY. LTD.—See One Rock Capital Partners, LLC; *U.S. Private*, pg. 3023
SHAKESPEARE CO., LLC - MONOFILAMENT DIVISION—See One Rock Capital Partners, LLC; *U.S. Private*, pg. 3023
SHAKESPEARE COMPANY, LLC—See One Rock Capital Partners, LLC; *U.S. Private*, pg. 3023
SHAKESPEARE MONOFILAMENT U.K. LTD.—See One Rock Capital Partners, LLC; *U.S. Private*, pg. 3023
SHANGHAI GOLDWIN CO., LTD.—See Goldwin, Inc.; *Int'l*, pg. 3035
SHANGHAI HUI YU FINE CHEMICALS CO., LTD.—See Headway Advanced Materials Inc.; *Int'l*, pg. 3302
SHELDONS' INC.; *U.S. Private*, pg. 3631
SHOCK DOCTOR, INC.—See Wells Fargo & Company; *U.S. Public*, pg. 2344
SIMULATED ENVIRONMENT CONCEPTS, INC.; *U.S. Public*, pg. 1884
SKIS DYNASTAR S.A.S.—See Altor Equity Partners AB; *Int'l*, pg. 396
SKIS ROSSIGNOL DE ESPANA S.A.—See Altor Equity Partners AB; *Int'l*, pg. 396
SKIS ROSSIGNOL S.A.S.—See Altor Equity Partners AB; *Int'l*, pg. 396
SLINGER BAG AMERICAS, INC.—See CONNEXA SPORTS TECHNOLOGIES INC.; *U.S. Public*, pg. 568
SNOWBOARD DACHSTEIN TAUERN GMBH—See Zumiez Incorporated; *U.S. Public*, pg. 2411
SNOW PEAK INC.—See Bain Capital, LP; *U.S. Private*, pg. 436
SOFT PLAY, LLC—See Littlejohn & Co., LLC; *U.S. Private*, pg. 2471
SOLOFLEX, INC.; *U.S. Private*, pg. 3709
SPALDING—See Berkshire Hathaway Inc.; *U.S. Public*, pg. 305
SP COMPANY, INC.—See BDT Capital Partners, LLC; *U.S. Private*, pg. 503
SPECTRUM PRODUCTS LLC—See Court Square Capital Partners, L.P.; *U.S. Private*, pg. 1070
SPLASH SUPERPOOLS LTD.—See Ecomembrane S.p.A.; *Int'l*, pg. 2296
SPORT HALEY HOLDINGS, INC.; *U.S. Private*, pg. 3760
SPORT MASKA INC.—See Birch Hill Equity Partners Management Inc.; *Int'l*, pg. 1046
S.R. SMITH, LLC—See Champlain Capital Management LLC; *U.S. Private*, pg. 847
S&S ACTIVEWEAR LLC—See Clayton, Dubilier & Rice, LLC; *U.S. Private*, pg. 926
SSI INTERNATIONAL GMBH—See Head B.V.; *Int'l*, pg. 3300
STANDARD MERCHANDISING CO.; *U.S. Private*, pg. 3781
STAR MANUFACTURING, L.L.C.—See Sheldons' Inc.; *U.S. Private*, pg. 3631
STAR TRAC - IRVINE—See Core Health & Fitness LLC; *U.S. Private*, pg. 1048

STIGA SPORTS AB—See Escalade, Incorporated; *U.S. Public*, pg. 793
STRIKE KING LURE CO.—See BDT Capital Partners, LLC; *U.S. Private*, pg. 503
STUART SPORTS SPECIALTIES, INC.; *U.S. Private*, pg. 3843
STX, LLC—See Wm T. Burnett & Co.; *U.S. Private*, pg. 4552
SUGOI PERFORMANCE APPAREL LIMITED PARTNERSHIP—See Dorel Industries, Inc.; *U.S. Private*, pg. 2176
SUN MOUNTAIN SPORTS INC.—See Solace Capital Partners, LLC; *U.S. Private*, pg. 3706
SUUNTO OY—See ANTA Sports Products Limited; *Int'l*, pg. 481
SWIMWEAR ANYWHERE, INC.; *U.S. Private*, pg. 3893
SWING KINGDOM LLC—See PennSpring Capital, LLC; *U.S. Private*, pg. 3136
SWIX SPORT AS—See Ferd AS; *Int'l*, pg. 2636
TAYLOR MADE GOLF COMPANY, INC.; *U.S. Private*, pg. 3940
T&C SURF DESIGNS—See T&C Holding Ltd; *U.S. Private*, pg. 3909
TEAM WENDY, LLC—See Dan T. Moore Co.; *U.S. Private*, pg. 1151
TEXTRONICS, INC.—See adidas AG; *Int'l*, pg. 146
TOO ALFAR—See Ading AD; *Int'l*, pg. 149
TOPGOLF CALLAWAY BRANDS CORP.; *U.S. Public*, pg. 2164
TOTAL STRENGTH AND SPEED—See Performance Strength Designs, Inc.; *U.S. Private*, pg. 3150
TOUR HOCKEY, INC.—See Roller Derby Skate Corp.; *U.S. Private*, pg. 3474
TOV ALPINA UA—See Alpina, d.d.; *Int'l*, pg. 371
TRAVIS MATHEW RETAIL, LLC—See Topgolf Callaway Brands Corp.; *U.S. Public*, pg. 2164
TRUE FITNESS TECHNOLOGY INC.; *U.S. Private*, pg. 4247
TRUE TEMPER SPORTS, INC.; *U.S. Private*, pg. 4248
TRU-FIRE CORP.—See TruArc Partners, L.P.; *U.S. Private*, pg. 4245
TUBBS SNOWSHOE COMPANY—See Kohlberg & Company, LLC; *U.S. Private*, pg. 2338
TUNTURI-HELLBERG OY LTD.—See Accell Group N.V.; *Int'l*, pg. 81
TYPHOON INTERNATIONAL LIMITED—See Safety & Survival Systems International Ltd.; *U.S. Private*, pg. 3524
UMBRO LTD.—See Iconix Acquisition LLC; *U.S. Private*, pg. 2033
UNDER ARMOUR EUROPE B.V.—See Under Armour, Inc.; *U.S. Public*, pg. 2225
UST MAMIYA; *U.S. Private*, pg. 4324
UWATEC AG—See Johnson Outdoors Inc.; *U.S. Public*, pg. 1201
VEEZEE, INC—See Leonard Green & Partners, L.P.; *U.S. Private*, pg. 2424
VICTORY TAILGATE, LLC—See Escalade, Incorporated; *U.S. Public*, pg. 793
WATER GREMLIN COMPANY; *U.S. Private*, pg. 4451
WEDCOR HOLDINGS, INC.—See Escalade, Incorporated; *U.S. Public*, pg. 793
WHITE FLYER TARGETS, LLC—See Wynnchurch Capital, L.P.; *U.S. Private*, pg. 4578
WILD THINGS, LLC—See Blue Point Capital Partners, LLC; *U.S. Private*, pg. 590
WILSON BRAZIL—See ANTA Sports Products Limited; *Int'l*, pg. 481
WILSON SPORTING GOODS CO. DE MEXICO—See ANTA Sports Products Limited; *Int'l*, pg. 481
WILSON SPORTING GOODS CO.—See ANTA Sports Products Limited; *Int'l*, pg. 481
WILSON SPORTING GOODS CO.—See ANTA Sports Products Limited; *Int'l*, pg. 481
THE WORTH COMPANY; *U.S. Private*, pg. 4139
WORTH INC.—See Major League Baseball; *U.S. Private*, pg. 2555
WORTH INC.—See The Seidler Company, LLC; *U.S. Private*, pg. 4116
WRIGHT & MCGILL CO.; *U.S. Private*, pg. 4572
WUXI JAPANA SPORTS GOODS CO., LTD.—See Alpen Co., Ltd.; *Int'l*, pg. 366
XFIT BRANDS, INC.; *U.S. Public*, pg. 2391
YAKIMA BAIT CO.; *U.S. Private*, pg. 4584
YORK BARBELL COMPANY, INC.; *U.S. Private*, pg. 4590
ZAO AMER SPORTS—See ANTA Sports Products Limited; *Int'l*, pg. 480
ZODIAC OF NORTH AMERICA, INC. - RECREATIONAL MARINE DIVISION—See The Carlyle Group Inc.; *U.S. Public*, pg. 2057
ZODIAC POOL CARE SOUTH AFRICA PTY. LTD.—See The Carlyle Group Inc.; *U.S. Public*, pg. 2057
ZODIAC POOL DEUTSCHLAND GMBH—See The Carlyle Group Inc.; *U.S. Public*, pg. 2057
ZOGICS, LLC; *U.S. Private*, pg. 4607

339930 — DOLL, TOY, AND GAME MANUFACTURING

600 RACING INC.—See Sonic Financial Corporation; *U.S. Private*, pg. 3713
ACTIVISION PUBLISHING, INC.—See Microsoft Corporation; *U.S. Public*, pg. 1438
ALEXANDER DOLL COMPANY, INC.—See Kahn-Lucas-Lancaster Inc.; *U.S. Private*, pg. 2254
ALEX PANLINE USA, INC.—See Propel Equity Partners, LLC; *U.S. Private*, pg. 3284
ALPHA ANIMATION & CULTURE CO., LTD. - CHENGHAI FACTORY—See Alpha Group Co., Ltd.; *Int'l*, pg. 368
ALPHA GROUP CO., LTD.; *Int'l*, pg. 368
ALVIMAR GLOBAL INC.; *U.S. Private*, pg. 214
AMERICAN PLASTIC TOYS INC.; *U.S. Private*, pg. 244
AMLOID CORPORATION; *U.S. Private*, pg. 264
APRICA CHILDCARE INSTITUTE-APRICA IKUJI KENKYUSH KABUSHIKI KAISHA—See Newell Brands Inc.; *U.S. Public*, pg. 1513
APRICA CHILDREN'S PRODUCTS KK—See Newell Brands Inc.; *U.S. Public*, pg. 1513
AS COMPANY S.A.; *Int'l*, pg. 589
A.S. DESIGN LIMITED—See JAKKS Pacific, Inc.; *U.S. Public*, pg. 1186
AS KIDS TOYS S.R.L.—See AS COMPANY S.A.; *Int'l*, pg. 589
ASS/ SPIELKARTENFABRIK ALTENBURG GMBH—See Cartamundi N.V.; *Int'l*, pg. 1347
ASTRO GAMING, INC.—See Logitech International S.A.; *U.S. Public*, pg. 1341
AURORA WORLD CORPORATION; *Int'l*, pg. 714
BABYEARTH; *U.S. Private*, pg. 422
BABY TULA POLAND—See Compass Diversified Holdings; *U.S. Public*, pg. 559
BACKYARD LEISURE HOLDINGS, INC.—See Aterian Investment Management, L.P.; *U.S. Private*, pg. 366
BANBAO CO., LTD.; *Int'l*, pg. 814
BANDAI CO., LTD.—See BANDAI NAMCO Holdings Inc.; *Int'l*, pg. 828
BANPRESTO (H.K.) LTD.—See BANDAI NAMCO Holdings Inc.; *Int'l*, pg. 829
BASIC FUN, INC.; *U.S. Private*, pg. 485
B. DAZZLE, INC.; *U.S. Private*, pg. 419
BEGINAGAIN, INC.; *U.S. Private*, pg. 514
BENESSE HONG KONG CO., LTD.—See EQT AB; *Int'l*, pg. 2467
BENJAMIN TOYS (HK) LTD.—See Benjamin Toys Ltd.; *Int'l*, pg. 974
BENJAMIN TOYS LTD.; *Int'l*, pg. 974
BEVERLY HILLS TEDDY BEAR COMPANY; *U.S. Private*, pg. 547
BIG FISH GAMES, INC.—See Aristocrat Leisure Limited; *Int'l*, pg. 566
BIG TREE GROUP, INC.; *U.S. Private*, pg. 554
BLACKALL ASSOCIATES INC.; *U.S. Private*, pg. 573
BLATT BILLIARDS CORP.; *U.S. Private*, pg. 579
B. LITTLE & COMPANY INC.; *U.S. Private*, pg. 419
BLITZWAY CO., LTD.; *Int'l*, pg. 1064
BRIARPATCH INC.—See University Games Corporation; *U.S. Private*, pg. 4307
BUFFALO GAMES, LLC—See Mason Wells, Inc.; *U.S. Private*, pg. 2602
BUSHIROAD INTERNATIONAL PTE. LTD.—See Bushiroad, Inc.; *Int'l*, pg. 1227
BUSHIROAD USA INC.—See Bushiroad, Inc.; *Int'l*, pg. 1227
BUZZTIME ENTERTAINMENT, INC—See Eterna Therapeutics Inc.; *U.S. Public*, pg. 797
CAPCOM ASIA CO., LTD.—See Capcom Co., Ltd.; *Int'l*, pg. 1302
CAPCOM ENTERTAINMENT KOREA CO., LTD.—See Capcom Co., Ltd.; *Int'l*, pg. 1302
CAPTRON CO., LTD.—See Capcom Co., Ltd.; *Int'l*, pg. 1302
CARROM CO.—See The Lightning Group, LLC; *U.S. Private*, pg. 924
CARTA MUNDI ASIA PACIFIC PTE. LTD.—See Cartamundi N.V.; *Int'l*, pg. 1347
CARTAMUNDI N.V.; *Int'l*, pg. 1347
CASDON LIMITED; *Int'l*, pg. 1351
CASDON TOYS LTD.—See Casdon Limited; *Int'l*, pg. 1351
CCP CO., LTD.—See BANDAI NAMCO Holdings Inc.; *Int'l*, pg. 829
CEACO INC.; *U.S. Private*, pg. 803
CE EUROPE LTD.—See Capcom Co., Ltd.; *Int'l*, pg. 1302
CEPIA, LLC; *U.S. Private*, pg. 835
CESAR SA; *Int'l*, pg. 1424
CHARIOT CARRIERS INC.; *Int'l*, pg. 1450
C&H TOYS (SUZHOU) CO , LTD—See Dream International Ltd; *Int'l*, pg. 2202
COLORLIGHT CLOUD B.V.—See Colorlight Cloud Tech Ltd., *Int'l*, pg. 1704
COMBI CORPORATION; *Int'l*, pg. 1708
COMMONWEALTH TOY & NOVELTY COMPANY; *U.S. Private*, pg. 987
CUDDLE CLONES LLC—See D2C Stores Inc.; *U.S. Private*, pg. 1143
CYBERGUN SA; *Int'l*, pg. 1893
CYBEX GMBH—See Goodbaby International Holdings Limited; *Int'l*, pg. 3039
DECIPHER INC.—See EQT AB; *Int'l*, pg. 2475

339930 — DOLL, TOY, AND GAME...

DELTA EDUCATION, LLC—See School Specialty, Inc.; *U.S. Public*, pg. 1848
DIMENSIONS HOLDINGS LLC—See GTCR LLC; *U.S. Private*, pg. 1806
DISGUISE INC.—See JAKKS Pacific, Inc.; *U.S. Public*, pg. 1186
DISNEY INTERACTIVE STUDIOS—See The Walt Disney Company; *U.S. Public*, pg. 2138
DOLLY INC.; *U.S. Private*, pg. 1254
DOREL BELGIUM SA—See Dorel Industries, Inc.; *Int'l*, pg. 2176
DOREL HISPANIA SA—See Dorel Industries, Inc.; *Int'l*, pg. 2176
DOREL ITALIA SPA—See Dorel Industries, Inc.; *Int'l*, pg. 2176
DREAM INKO CO., LTD.—See Dream International Ltd; *Int'l*, pg. 2202
DREAM INTERNATIONAL LTD; *Int'l*, pg. 2202
DREAM INTERNATIONAL USA, INC—See Dream International Ltd; *Int'l*, pg. 2202
EASTER UNLIMITED INC.; *U.S. Private*, pg. 1319
EDARON INC.; *U.S. Private*, pg. 1332
EEBOO CORPORATION; *U.S. Private*, pg. 1343
EPOCH CO. LTD.; *Int'l*, pg. 2463
ERGOBABY EUROPE GMBH—See Compass Diversified Holdings; *U.S. Public*, pg. 560
ESTES-COX CORP.—See Hobbico, Inc.; *U.S. Private*, pg. 1958
EXX INC.; *U.S. Private*, pg. 1453
FABRICAS AGRUPADAS DE MUNECAS DE ONIL, S.A.—See Giochi Preziosi S.p.A.; *Int'l*, pg. 2977
FANTASY FLIGHT GAMES; *U.S. Private*, pg. 1472
FISCHERTECHNIK GMBH—See fischerwerke GmbH & Co. KG; *Int'l*, pg. 2692
FLAMBEAU INC.—See Nordic Group of Companies, Ltd.; *U.S. Private*, pg. 2936
FORTUNET, INC.—See AMCON Distributing Company; *U.S. Public*, pg. 93
FUNKO GAMES, LLC—See Funko Inc.; *U.S. Public*, pg. 893
GAMES WORKSHOP GROUP PLC; *Int'l*, pg. 2877
GAMES WORKSHOP LIMITED—See Games Workshop Group PLC; *Int'l*, pg. 2877
GAMEWRIGHT—See Ceaco Inc.; *U.S. Private*, pg. 804
GAMING PARTNERS INTERNATIONAL CORPORATION—See Angel Holdings Godo Kaisha; *Int'l*, pg. 459
GAMING PARTNERS INTERNATIONAL—See Angel Holdings Godo Kaisha; *Int'l*, pg. 459
GEBR. MARKLIN & CIE. GMBH; *Int'l*, pg. 2909
GEOBRA BRANDSTATTER GMBH & CO. KG; *Int'l*, pg. 2932
GEORG SCHARDT KG; *Int'l*, pg. 2938
GIANTMICROBES INC.; *U.S. Private*, pg. 1695
GIANTMICROBES UK LIMITED—See Giantmicrobes Inc.; *U.S. Private*, pg. 1695
GO FLY A KITE—See JAKKS Pacific, Inc.; *U.S. Public*, pg. 1186
GO-GO BABYZ, CORP.; *U.S. Private*, pg. 1723
THE GOLDBERGER COMPANY, LLC; *U.S. Private*, pg. 4034
GOLDLOK HOLDINGS (GUANGDONG) CO., LTD.; *Int'l*, pg. 3034
GOODBABY CHINA COMMERCIAL CO., LTD—See Goodbaby International Holdings Limited; *Int'l*, pg. 3039
GOODBABY (HONG KONG) LIMITED—See Goodbaby International Holdings Limited; *Int'l*, pg. 3039
GOODBABY INTERNATIONAL HOLDINGS LIMITED; *Int'l*, pg. 3039
GOODBABY JAPAN CO., LTD.—See Goodbaby International Holdings Limited; *Int'l*, pg. 3039
GPI—See Angel Holdings Godo Kaisha; *Int'l*, pg. 459
GRAVITY CO., LTD.; *Int'l*, pg. 3062
GUANGDONG QUNXING TOYS JOINT-STOCK CO., LTD.; *Int'l*, pg. 3159
GUANGZHOU WAHLAP TECHNOLOGY CORPORATION LIMITED; *Int'l*, pg. 3168
HAIXIN TOYS CO., LTD.—See Haixin Group Company Ltd.; *Int'l*, pg. 3219
HANS ENG CO., LTD.; *Int'l*, pg. 3259
HANUNG TOYS AND TEXTILES LIMITED; *Int'l*, pg. 3261
HAPPINET CORPORATION; *Int'l*, pg. 3269
HASBRO AUSTRALIA—See Hasbro, Inc.; *U.S. Public*, pg. 987
HASBRO BRADLEY FAR EAST LTD.—See Hasbro, Inc.; *U.S. Public*, pg. 987
HASBRO CANADA CORPORATION—See Hasbro, Inc.; *U.S. Public*, pg. 988
HASBRO DE MEXICO S.R.L. DE C.V.—See Hasbro, Inc.; *U.S. Public*, pg. 988
HASBRO FRANCE—See Hasbro, Inc.; *U.S. Public*, pg. 988
HASBRO, INC.; *U.S. Public*, pg. 987
HEINRICH GEUTHER KINDERMOBEL UND -GERATE GMBH & CO. KG; *Int'l*, pg. 3324
HENRY GORDY INTERNATIONAL INC.—See EXX Inc.; *U.S. Private*, pg. 1453
HERALD METAL AND PLASTIC WORKS LIMITED—See Herald Holdings Limited; *Int'l*, pg. 3358
IMPERIAL TOY CORPORATION; *U.S. Private*, pg. 2049

IRON MOUNTAIN FORGE CORPORATION—See MGA Entertainment, Inc.; *U.S. Private*, pg. 2694
JAKKS PACIFIC GERMANY GMBH—See JAKKS Pacific, Inc.; *U.S. Public*, pg. 1186
JAKKS PACIFIC, INC.; *U.S. Public*, pg. 1186
JAKKS PACIFIC (UK) LTD.—See JAKKS Pacific, Inc.; *U.S. Public*, pg. 1186
JAPAN CARD PRODUCTS CO., LTD—See Cartamundi N.V.; *Int'l*, pg. 1348
JA-RU INC.; *U.S. Private*, pg. 2172
JA-RU INC.—See JA-RU Inc.; *U.S. Private*, pg. 2172
JAZWARES, INC.—See Berkshire Hathaway Inc.; *U.S. Public*, pg. 298
JOYTECH EUROPE LIMITED—See Take-Two Interactive Software, Inc.; *U.S. Public*, pg. 1979
JUST PLAY PRODUCTS, LLC; *U.S. Private*, pg. 2245
KIDDESIGNS, INC.—See SDI Technologies, Inc.; *U.S. Private*, pg. 3581
KID GALAXY INC.—See China Healthwise Holdings Limited; *Int'l*, pg. 1507
KIDKRAFT INC.—See MidOcean Partners, LLP; *U.S. Private*, pg. 2717
KIDROBOT INC.—See National Entertainment Collectibles Association, Inc; *U.S. Private*, pg. 2853
KIDS ONLY, INC.—See JAKKS Pacific, Inc.; *U.S. Public*, pg. 1187
KOALA KARE PRODUCTS—See Bobrick Washroom Equipment, Inc.; *U.S. Private*, pg. 607
KOLCRAFT ENTERPRISES, INC.; *U.S. Private*, pg. 2341
THE KYJEN COMPANY, LLC—See Prospect Hill Growth Partners, L.P.; *U.S. Private*, pg. 3288
LIONEL LLC; *U.S. Private*, pg. 2464
THE LITTLE TIKES COMPANY—See MGA Entertainment, Inc.; *U.S. Private*, pg. 2694
MAGIC CABIN—See Evergreen Enterprises, Inc.; *U.S. Private*, pg. 1439
MAG-NIF INC.; *U.S. Private*, pg. 2545
MATTEL ESPANA, S.A.—See Mattel, Inc.; *U.S. Public*, pg. 1398
MATTEL EUROPA BV—See Mattel, Inc.; *U.S. Public*, pg. 1398
MATTEL GAMES/PUZZLES—See Mattel, Inc.; *U.S. Public*, pg. 1398
MATTEL GMBH—See Mattel, Inc.; *U.S. Public*, pg. 1398
MATTEL HOLDING, INC.—See Mattel, Inc.; *U.S. Public*, pg. 1399
MATTEL, INC.; *U.S. Public*, pg. 1398
MATTEL (MALAYSIA) SDN. BHD.—See Mattel, Inc.; *U.S. Public*, pg. 1398
MATTEL PTY. LTD.—See Mattel, Inc.; *U.S. Public*, pg. 1399
MATTEL TOYS (H.K.) LTD.—See Mattel, Inc.; *U.S. Public*, pg. 1399
MAUI TOYS, INC.—See JAKKS Pacific, Inc.; *U.S. Public*, pg. 1187
MCFARLANE TOYS—See TMP International, Inc.; *U.S. Private*, pg. 4179
MEGA BRANDS AMERICA INC.—See Mattel, Inc.; *U.S. Public*, pg. 1398
MEGA BRANDS INC.—See Mattel, Inc.; *U.S. Public*, pg. 1398
MEGA BRANDS SPAIN & PORTUGAL SRL—See Mattel, Inc.; *U.S. Public*, pg. 1398
MEGA BRANDS UNITED KINGDOM LTD.—See Mattel, Inc.; *U.S. Public*, pg. 1398
MEGAHOUSE CORPORATION—See BANDAI NAMCO Holdings Inc.; *Int'l*, pg. 829
MGA ZAPF CREATION GMBH—See MGA Entertainment, Inc.; *U.S. Private*, pg. 2694
MIDNIGHT GAMING CORP.; *U.S. Private*, pg. 2716
MIDWAY AMUSEMENT GAMES LLC—See Midway Games Inc.; *U.S. Private*, pg. 2718
MILLION DOLLAR BABY; *U.S. Private*, pg. 2737
MINDWARE, INC.—See Berkshire Hathaway Inc.; *U.S. Public*, pg. 313
MONAHAN PRODUCTS, LLC—See The Seidler Company, LLC; *U.S. Private*, pg. 4116
NATIONAL ENTERTAINMENT COLLECTIBLES ASSOCIATION, INC; *U.S. Private*, pg. 2853
NEO CYON INC.—See Gravity Co., Ltd.; *Int'l*, pg. 3062
NINGBO COMBI BABY GOODS CO., LTD—See Combi Corporation; *Int'l*, pg. 1708
NINJA JUMP INC.; *U.S. Private*, pg. 2928
THE OHIO ART COMPANY, INC.; *U.S. Public*, pg. 2118
ORIGINAL APPALACHIAN ARTWORKS, INC.; *U.S. Private*, pg. 3042
PLAYAGS, INC.; *U.S. Public*, pg. 1697
PLAYMOBIL MALTA LTD—See Geobra Brandstatter GmbH & Co. KG; *Int'l*, pg. 2932
PLEX CO., LTD.—See BANDAI NAMCO Holdings Inc.; *Int'l*, pg. 829
PL FINLAND OY—See Proto Labs, Inc.; *U.S. Public*, pg. 1729
POOF-SLINKY, LLC—See Propel Equity Partners, LLC; *U.S. Private*, pg. 3284
PRIMA TOY & LEISURE GROUP (PTY) LTD.—See E Media Holdings Limited; *Int'l*, pg. 3358
PT BOYAA INTERACTIVE INDONESIA—See Boyaa Interactive International Ltd; *Int'l*, pg. 1124

RADIO FLYER INC.; *U.S. Private*, pg. 3343
REEVES INTERNATIONAL, INC.; *U.S. Private*, pg. 3384
REEVES INTERNATIONAL, INC.—See Reeves International, Inc.; *U.S. Private*, pg. 3384
RELIABLE TOY CORPORATION—See Allied Plastic Skylight; *Int'l*, pg. 358
REVELL GMBH—See Carrera Revell of Americas, Inc.; *U.S. Private*, pg. 771
REVELL, INC.—See Hobbico, Inc.; *U.S. Private*, pg. 1958
SASSY, INC.—See Angelcare Holding Inc.; *Int'l*, pg. 459
SEEDS CO., LTD.—See BANDAI NAMCO Holdings Inc.; *Int'l*, pg. 829
SENTINEL INTERNATIONAL CO. LIMITED—See Amuse Group Holding Ltd.; *Int'l*, pg. 442
SPIELKARTENFABRIK ALTENBURG GMBH—See Cartamundi N.V.; *Int'l*, pg. 1348
SRM ENTERTAINMENT, INC.; *U.S. Public*, pg. 1922
STEVEN TOYS—See EXX Inc.; *U.S. Private*, pg. 1453
SUMMIT PRODUCTS, LLC—See Propel Equity Partners, LLC; *U.S. Private*, pg. 3285
TELEGAMES INC.; *U.S. Private*, pg. 3960
TEUTONIA KINDERWAGENFABRIK GMBH—See Newell Brands Inc.; *U.S. Public*, pg. 1515
THORLEY INDUSTRIES LLC—See The Seidler Company, LLC; *U.S. Private*, pg. 4116
THQ ENTERTAINMENT GMBH—See THQ Inc.; *U.S. Private*, pg. 4163
TMP INTERNATIONAL, INC.; *U.S. Private*, pg. 4179
TODD MCFARLANE ENTERTAINMENT—See TMP International, Inc.; *U.S. Private*, pg. 4179
TODD MCFARLANE PRODUCTIONS—See TMP International, Inc.; *U.S. Private*, pg. 4179
TONNER DOLL COMPANY, INC.; *U.S. Private*, pg. 4185
TURN KEY DESIGN B.V.—See Goodbaby International Holdings Limited; *Int'l*, pg. 3039
THE UNITED STATES PLAYING CARD COMPANY—See Cartamundi N.V.; *Int'l*, pg. 1348
UNIVERSITY GAMES AUSTRALIA—See University Games Corporation; *U.S. Private*, pg. 4307
UNIVERSITY GAMES CORPORATION; *U.S. Private*, pg. 4307
UNIVERSITY GAMES EUROPE B.V.—See University Games Corporation; *U.S. Private*, pg. 4307
UNIVERSITY GAMES UK LTD.—See University Games Corporation; *U.S. Private*, pg. 4308
USPC HOLDING, INC.—See Newell Brands Inc.; *U.S. Public*, pg. 1515
VALLEY CASTING, INC.; *U.S. Private*, pg. 4333
THE VERMONT TEDDY BEAR COMPANY—See The Mustang Group, LLC; *U.S. Private*, pg. 4081
VIDEO KING GAMING SYSTEMS, LLC; *U.S. Private*, pg. 4380
WARNER BROS. INTERACTIVE ENTERTAINMENT INC.—See Warner Bros. Discovery, Inc.; *U.S. Public*, pg. 2328
WHAM-O, INC.; *U.S. Private*, pg. 4503
WINNING MOVES GAMES, INC.; *U.S. Private*, pg. 4542
WIZARDS OF THE COAST, LLC—See Hasbro, Inc.; *U.S. Public*, pg. 988
WIZ CO., LTD.—See BANDAI NAMCO Holdings Inc.; *Int'l*, pg. 829
THE WORLD OF MINIATURE BEARS, INC.; *U.S. Private*, pg. 4139
XBOX GAME STUDIOS—See Microsoft Corporation; *U.S. Public*, pg. 1440
XBOX—See Microsoft Corporation; *U.S. Public*, pg. 1440
ZAPF CREATION (U.K.) LTD.—See MGA Entertainment, Inc.; *U.S. Private*, pg. 2694
ZOBMONDO!! ENTERTAINMENT LLC; *U.S. Private*, pg. 4607

339940 — OFFICE SUPPLIES (EXCEPT PAPER) MANUFACTURING

ABLEREX CORPORATION—See Ablerex Electronics Co., Ltd.; *Int'l*, pg. 63
ABLEREX ELECTRONICS (THAILAND) CO., LTD.—See Ablerex Electronics Co., Ltd.; *Int'l*, pg. 63
ABLEREX LATAM CORPORATION—See Ablerex Electronics Co., Ltd.; *Int'l*, pg. 63
ACCO BRANDS NEW ZEALAND LIMITED—See ACCO Brands Corporation; *U.S. Public*, pg. 32
ALEXANDER STAMPS & COIN LTD.; *Int'l*, pg. 307
ALLTEC GMBH—See Danaher Corporation; *U.S. Public*, pg. 632
AMANO BUSINESS CREDIT—See Amano Corporation; *Int'l*, pg. 411
AMERICAN MARKING SYSTEMS, INC.; *U.S. Private*, pg. 241
ART & FRAME DIRECT INC.; *U.S. Private*, pg. 339
A.T. CROSS COMPANY—See Transom Capital Group, LLC; *U.S. Private*, pg. 4209
AUBEX CORPORATION; *Int'l*, pg. 698
AVERY DENNISON RBIS PTY LTD—See Avery Dennison Corporation; *U.S. Public*, pg. 243
AVERY DENNISON R.I.S. FRANCE S. A. S.—See Avery Dennison Corporation; *U.S. Public*, pg. 243

339950 — SIGN MANUFACTURING

A.W. FABER-CASTELL ARGENTINA S.A.—See Faber-Castell AG; *Int'l*, pg. 2598
A.W. FABER-CASTELL (AUST.) PTY. LTD.—See Faber-Castell AG; *Int'l*, pg. 2598
A.W. FABER-CASTELL DE MEXICO SA DE CV—See Faber-Castell AG; *Int'l*, pg. 2599
A.W. FABER-CASTELL GES.M.B.H.—See Faber-Castell AG; *Int'l*, pg. 2599
A.W. FABER-CASTELL GUANGZHOU STATIONERY CO., LTD.—See Faber-Castell AG; *Int'l*, pg. 2599
A.W. FABER-CASTELL (H.K.) LTD.—See Faber-Castell AG; *Int'l*, pg. 2598
A.W. FABER-CASTELL (INDIA) LTD.—See Faber-Castell AG; *Int'l*, pg. 2598
A.W. FABER-CASTELL ITALIA S.R.L.—See Faber-Castell AG; *Int'l*, pg. 2599
A.W. FABER-CASTELL (M) SDN. BHD.—See Faber-Castell AG; *Int'l*, pg. 2598
A.W. FABER-CASTELL NORDIC APS—See Faber-Castell AG; *Int'l*, pg. 2599
A.W. FABER-CASTELL (NZ) LTD.—See Faber-Castell AG; *Int'l*, pg. 2598
A.W. FABER-CASTELL PERUANA S.A.—See Faber-Castell AG; *Int'l*, pg. 2599
A.W. FABER-CASTELL S.A.R.L.—See Faber-Castell AG; *Int'l*, pg. 2599
A.W. FABER-CASTELL S.A.—See Faber-Castell AG; *Int'l*, pg. 2599
A.W. FABER-CASTELL SCHWEIZ AG—See Faber-Castell AG; *Int'l*, pg. 2599
A.W. FABER-CASTELL SPOL. S RO.—See Faber-Castell AG; *Int'l*, pg. 2599
A.W. FABER-CASTELL USA INC—See Faber-Castell AG; *Int'l*, pg. 2599
A.W. FABER-CASTELL VERTRIEB GMBH—See Faber-Castell AG; *Int'l*, pg. 2599
BADGER AIR BRUSH COMPANY; *U.S. Private*, pg. 424
BARRINGTON GROUP LTD.; *U.S. Private*, pg. 480
BAUMGARTEN STAMP CO.—See American Marking Systems, Inc.; *U.S. Private*, pg. 241
BERGER PAINTS PAKISTAN LIMITED; *Int'l*, pg. 980
BERLACK GMBH—See Burelle S.A.; *Int'l*, pg. 1223
COSCO INDUSTRIES, INC.—See Taylor Corporation; *U.S. Private*, pg. 3938
C&P MICROSYSTEMS, LLC—See Colter & Peterson Inc.; *U.S. Private*, pg. 976
CRAYOLA CANADA—See Hallmark Cards, Inc.; *U.S. Private*, pg. 1844
CRAYOLA LLC—See Hallmark Cards, Inc.; *U.S. Private*, pg. 1844
CRESCENT EUROPE GMBH—See Potomac Corporation; *U.S. Private*, pg. 3235
DAEWOONG VIETNAM CO., LTD.—See Daewoong Pharmaceutical Co., Ltd.; *Int'l*, pg. 1911
DIAGRAPH MARKING & STENCILING PRODUCTS GROUP—See Illinois Tool Works Inc.; *U.S. Public*, pg. 1102
DIAGRAPH—See Illinois Tool Works Inc.; *U.S. Public*, pg. 1102
DIXON TICONDEROGA COMPANY—See F.I.L.A. - Fabbrica Italiana Lapis ed Affini S.p.A.; *Int'l*, pg. 2596
DIXON TICONDEROGA DE MEXICO, S.A. DE C.V.—See F.I.L.A. - Fabbrica Italiana Lapis ed Affini S.p.A.; *Int'l*, pg. 2596
DIXON TICONDEROGA INC.—See F.I.L.A. - Fabbrica Italiana Lapis ed Affini S.p.A.; *Int'l*, pg. 2596
DNP IMAGINGCOMM AMERICA CORPORATION—See Dai Nippon Printing Co., Ltd.; *Int'l*, pg. 1914
DNP IMAGINGCOMM AMERICA CORPORATION—See Dai Nippon Printing Co., Ltd.; *Int'l*, pg. 1914
DRI MARK PRODUCTS, INC.; *U.S. Private*, pg. 1277
D.T.C. INDUSTRIES PUBLIC COMPANY LIMITED; *Int'l*, pg. 1901
DURO ART INDUSTRIES, INC.; *U.S. Private*, pg. 1293
DYNIC (UK) LTD.—See Dynic Corporation; *Int'l*, pg. 2242
DYNIC USA CORPORATION—See Dynic Corporation; *Int'l*, pg. 2243
EDDING ARGENTINA SA—See Edding AG; *Int'l*, pg. 2304
EDDING BENELUX BV—See Edding AG; *Int'l*, pg. 2304
EDDING COLOMBIA SAS—See Edding AG; *Int'l*, pg. 2304
EDDING FRANCE SAS—See Edding AG; *Int'l*, pg. 2304
EDDING HELLAS LTD.—See Edding AG; *Int'l*, pg. 2304
EDDING OFIS VE KIRTASIYE—See Edding AG; *Int'l*, pg. 2304
EDDING UK LTD.—See Edding AG; *Int'l*, pg. 2304
EDDING VERTRIEB GMBH—See Edding AG; *Int'l*, pg. 2304
ESSELTE SRO—See ACCO Brands Corporation; *U.S. Public*, pg. 33
ESSELTE UK LTD.—See ACCO Brands Corporation; *U.S. Public*, pg. 33
EVERSHARP LTD—See Amalgamated Regional Trading (ART) Holdings Ltd.; *Int'l*, pg. 409
FABER-CASTELL AG; *Int'l*, pg. 2598
FABER-CASTELL- CHILE S.A.—See Faber-Castell AG; *Int'l*, pg. 2599
FABER-CASTELL VERTRIEB GMBH—See Faber-Castell AG; *Int'l*, pg. 2599

FELLOWES LEONARDI S.P.A—See Fellowes, Inc.; *U.S. Private*, pg. 1494
F.I.L.A. - FABBRICA ITALIANA LAPIS ED AFFINI S.P.A.; *Int'l*, pg. 2596
FUJICOPIAN CO., LTD.; *Int'l*, pg. 2820
FUJI XEROX FAR EAST LIMITED—See FUJIFILM Holdings Corporation; *Int'l*, pg. 2825
FUJI XEROX INTERFIELD CO., LTD.—See FUJIFILM Holdings Corporation; *Int'l*, pg. 2825
GENERAL PENCIL COMPANY; *U.S. Private*, pg. 1666
GESTETNER OF CEYLON PLC; *Int'l*, pg. 2946
GUANGZHOU EMHART FASTENING SYSTEM CO., LTD.—See Stanley Black & Decker, Inc.; *U.S. Public*, pg. 1932
HARRISBURG STAMP CO.—See American Marking Systems, Inc.; *U.S. Private*, pg. 241
HC BRANDS; *U.S. Private*, pg. 1888
IDENTITY GROUP HOLDINGS CORP.—See Ancor Holdings, L.P.; *U.S. Private*, pg. 275
IDENTITY GROUP HOLDINGS CORP.—See Merit Capital Partners; *U.S. Private*, pg. 2674
IDENTITY GROUP HOLDINGS CORP.—See The PNC Financial Services Group, Inc.; *U.S. Public*, pg. 2119
IMAJE NORDIC AB—See Dover Corporation; *U.S. Public*, pg. 680
INFASTECH FASTENING SYSTEMS (WUXI) LIMITED—See Stanley Black & Decker, Inc.; *U.S. Public*, pg. 1932
INTERNATIONAL IMAGING MATERIALS, INC.—See ACON Investments, LLC; *U.S. Private*, pg. 62
KORECTYPE CORPORATION—See Ko-Rec-Type Corp.; *U.S. Private*, pg. 2325
KO-REC-TYPE CORP.; *U.S. Private*, pg. 2325
LASER IMAGE PLUS IMAGING PRODUCTS, INC.—See Magnum Print Solutions, Inc.; *U.S. Private*, pg. 2549
LEGAMASTER BVBA—See Edding AG; *Int'l*, pg. 2304
LEGAMASTER INTERNATIONAL BV—See Edding AG; *Int'l*, pg. 2304
LISTO CORPORATION INC.; *U.S. Private*, pg. 2467
MARKEM-IMAJE AG—See Dover Corporation; *U.S. Public*, pg. 680
MARKEM-IMAJE A/S—See Dover Corporation; *U.S. Public*, pg. 680
MARKEM-IMAJE AS—See Dover Corporation; *U.S. Public*, pg. 680
MARKEM-IMAJE BV—See Dover Corporation; *U.S. Public*, pg. 680
MARKEM-IMAJE CO., LTD.—See Dover Corporation; *U.S. Public*, pg. 680
MARKEM-IMAJE GMBH - AUSTRIA—See Dover Corporation; *U.S. Public*, pg. 680
MARKEM-IMAJE GMBH—See Dover Corporation; *U.S. Public*, pg. 680
MARKEM-IMAJE (HONG KONG) LIMITED—See Dover Corporation; *U.S. Public*, pg. 680
MARKEM-IMAJE INC.—See Dover Corporation; *U.S. Public*, pg. 680
MARKEM-IMAJE INDIA PRIVATE LIMITED—See Dover Corporation; *U.S. Public*, pg. 680
MARKEM-IMAJE K.K.—See Dover Corporation; *U.S. Public*, pg. 680
MARKEM-IMAJE LLC—See Dover Corporation; *U.S. Public*, pg. 680
MARKEM-IMAJE OY—See Dover Corporation; *U.S. Public*, pg. 680
MARKEM-IMAJE PTE. LTD.—See Dover Corporation; *U.S. Public*, pg. 680
MARKEM-IMAJE PTY LTD.—See Dover Corporation; *U.S. Public*, pg. 680
MARKEM-IMAJE S.A. DE C.V.—See Dover Corporation; *U.S. Public*, pg. 680
MARKEM-IMAJE SAS—See Dover Corporation; *U.S. Public*, pg. 680
MARKEM-IMAJE SPAIN S.A.—See Dover Corporation; *U.S. Public*, pg. 680
MARKEM-IMAJE S.R.L A SOCIO UNICO—See Dover Corporation; *U.S. Public*, pg. 680
MARKEM-IMAJE (TAIWAN) LTD.—See Dover Corporation; *U.S. Public*, pg. 680
MARKEM-IMAJE UNIPESSOAL, LDA—See Dover Corporation; *U.S. Public*, pg. 680
MARKEM-IMAJE USA—See Dover Corporation; *U.S. Public*, pg. 680
MARTIN/F. WEBER COMPANY—See Martin Universal Design, Inc.; *U.S. Private*, pg. 2596
MARTIN YALE INDUSTRIES, LLC—See Escalade, Incorporated; *U.S. Public*, pg. 793
MATTHEWS CANADA LTD.—See Matthews International Corporation; *U.S. Public*, pg. 1400
MATTHEWS INTERNATIONAL CORP. - MARKING PRODUCTS—See Matthews International Corporation; *U.S. Public*, pg. 1400
MEURAL, INC.—See NETGEAR, Inc.; *U.S. Public*, pg. 1508
MONTBLANC INTERNATIONAL BV—See Compagnie Financiere Richemont S.A.; *Int'l*, pg. 1741
MUSEUM QUALITY DISCOUNT FRAMING; *U.S. Private*, pg. 2817
NATIONAL PEN CO., LLC—See Cimpress plc; *Int'l*, pg. 1609

NORTHWEST FRAMING; *U.S. Private*, pg. 2960
NORWOOD MARKING SYSTEMS—See Illinois Tool Works Inc.; *U.S. Public*, pg. 1109
OMAS SRL—See Apollo Future Mobility Group Limited; *Int'l*, pg. 517
PANNIER CORPORATION; *U.S. Private*, pg. 3087
PATERSON STAMP WORKS—See American Marking Systems, Inc.; *U.S. Private*, pg. 241
PENCOA; *U.S. Private*, pg. 3132
PITNEY BOWES TECHNOLOGY CENTER—See Pitney Bowes Inc.; *U.S. Public*, pg. 1695
PLAID ENTERPRISES, INC.—See The Dyson-Kissner-Moran Corporation; *U.S. Private*, pg. 4024
PRINTRON ENGRAVERS INC.; *U.S. Private*, pg. 3266
PT. FABER-CASTELL INTERNATIONAL INDONESIA—See Faber-Castell AG; *Int'l*, pg. 2599
QUAKER CITY STAMP & STENCIL—See American Marking Systems, Inc.; *U.S. Private*, pg. 241
SANFORD L.P.—See Newell Brands Inc.; *U.S. Public*, pg. 1514
SCHWAAB INC.; *U.S. Private*, pg. 3571
SHEAFFER PEN & ART SUPPLY CO.—See Transom Capital Group, LLC; *U.S. Private*, pg. 4209
SICO ASIA PTE LTD.—See Sico Incorporated; *U.S. Private*, pg. 3645
SICO EUROPE LIMITED—See Sico Incorporated; *U.S. Private*, pg. 3645
SICO SOUTH PACIFIC—See Sico Incorporated; *U.S. Private*, pg. 3645
SMART TECHNOLOGIES (GB) LIMITED—See Hon Hai Precision Industry Co., Ltd.; *Int'l*, pg. 3457
SMART TECHNOLOGIES (MIDDLE EAST) FZE—See Hon Hai Precision Industry Co., Ltd.; *Int'l*, pg. 3457
SPELLBINDERS PAPER ARTS LLC; *U.S. Private*, pg. 3754
STAMPIN UP INC.; *U.S. Private*, pg. 3777
STRIDE, INC.; *U.S. Private*, pg. 3840
SUNG SAN COMPANY, LTD.—See General Motors Company; *U.S. Public*, pg. 929
TARA MATERIALS INC.; *U.S. Private*, pg. 3933
THERMOPATCH CORPORATION; *U.S. Private*, pg. 4143
TODAYTEC CANADA INC.—See Hangzhou Todaytec Digital Co., Ltd.; *Int'l*, pg. 3251
TODAYTEC INDIA PRIVATE LIMITED—See Hangzhou Todaytec Digital Co., Ltd.; *Int'l*, pg. 3251
TODAYTEC INDUSTRIA DE CODIGOS DE BARRAS LTDA.—See Hangzhou Todaytec Digital Co., Ltd.; *Int'l*, pg. 3251
US FLEET TRACKING CORP.; *U.S. Private*, pg. 4318
UTRECHT MANUFACTURING CORP.—See Dick Blick Holdings Inc.; *U.S. Private*, pg. 1225
V.D. LEDERMANN & CO. GMBH—See Edding AG; *Int'l*, pg. 2304
WATERMAN S.A.S.—See Newell Brands Inc.; *U.S. Public*, pg. 1515
WEBER ETIKETTEN BV—See Weber Packaging Solutions, Inc.; *U.S. Private*, pg. 4465
WEBER ETIKET VE ETIKETLEME SISTEMLERI SAN VE TIC LTD. STI.—See Weber Packaging Solutions, Inc.; *U.S. Private*, pg. 4465
WEBER LABELLING & CODING LTD.—See Weber Packaging Solutions, Inc.; *U.S. Private*, pg. 4465
WEBER MARKING SYSTEMS CANADA LTD.—See Weber Packaging Solutions, Inc.; *U.S. Private*, pg. 4465
WEBER MARKING SYSTEMS GMBH—See Weber Packaging Solutions, Inc.; *U.S. Private*, pg. 4465
WEBER MARKING SYSTEMS LTD.—See Weber Packaging Solutions, Inc.; *U.S. Private*, pg. 4465
WEBER MARKING SYSTEMS NV/SA—See Weber Packaging Solutions, Inc.; *U.S. Private*, pg. 4465
XEROX CORP.—See Xerox Holdings Corporation; *U.S. Public*, pg. 2390
XEROX CORP.—See Xerox Holdings Corporation; *U.S. Public*, pg. 2390

339950 — SIGN MANUFACTURING

2/90 SIGN SYSTEMS INC.; *U.S. Private*, pg. 4
ACCUFORM MANUFACTURING, INC.; *U.S. Private*, pg. 54
THE AD ART COMPANY; *U.S. Private*, pg. 3981
ADCORP SIGN SYSTEMS, LLC—See Darrell's Sign Company; *U.S. Private*, pg. 1159
AFFINITY DISPLAY & EXPOSITION; *U.S. Private*, pg. 122
ALLEN INDUSTRIES INC.; *U.S. Private*, pg. 179
AMD INDUSTRIES, INC.; *U.S. Private*, pg. 218
ANZA INC.—See Holien Inc.; *U.S. Private*, pg. 1963
APCO GRAPHICS INC.; *U.S. Private*, pg. 290
APOLLO SIGN & MILLWORK LTD.; *Int'l*, pg. 518
AQUASIGN—See Ecolab Inc.; *U.S. Public*, pg. 712
ARABIAN NEON W.L.L.—See Dadabhai Group; *Int'l*, pg. 1904
ART GUILD INC.; *U.S. Private*, pg. 339
BARLO PLASTICS CO. INC.; *U.S. Private*, pg. 476
BENCHMARC DISPLAY INC.; *U.S. Private*, pg. 523
BLANC INDUSTRIES, INC.; *U.S. Private*, pg. 579
BRADY AB—See Brady Corporation; *U.S. Public*, pg. 378
BRADY AUSTRALIA PTY. LTD.—See Brady Corporation; *U.S. Public*, pg. 378

339950 — SIGN MANUFACTURING

BRADY (BEIJING) CO. LTD.—See Brady Corporation; *U.S. Public*, pg. 378
BRADY CORPORATION ASIA PTE. LTD.—See Brady Corporation; *U.S. Public*, pg. 378
BRADY CORPORATION LTD.—See Brady Corporation; *U.S. Public*, pg. 378
BRADY CORPORATION LTD.—See Brady Corporation; *U.S. Public*, pg. 378
BRADY CORPORATION; *U.S. Public*, pg. 378
BRADY ITALIA, S.R.L.—See Brady Corporation; *U.S. Public*, pg. 378
BRADY TECHNOLOGY SDN. BHD.—See Brady Corporation; *U.S. Public*, pg. 379
CAPITAL ARCHITECTURAL SIGNS, INC.—See Facility Solutions Group, Inc.; *U.S. Private*, pg. 1460
CHANDLER SIGNS, LP; *U.S. Private*, pg. 848
CHARLESTON INDUSTRIES INC—See Carlisle Companies Incorporated; *U.S. Public*, pg. 437
COLOR-AD, INC.; *U.S. Private*, pg. 973
COMPLIANCESIGNS.COM; *U.S. Private*, pg. 1001
CREATIVE SIGN DESIGNS; *U.S. Private*, pg. 1090
CUMMINGS RESOURCES LLC—See Prophet Equity L.P.; *U.S. Private*, pg. 3286
DAKTRONICS AUSTRALIA PTY LTD.—See Daktronics, Inc.; *U.S. Public*, pg. 620
DAKTRONICS, INC.; *U.S. Public*, pg. 620
DEE SIGN COMPANY - ANAHEIM FACILITY—See Dee Sign Company; *U.S. Private*, pg. 1189
DEE SIGN COMPANY - LOS ANGELES FACILITY—See Dee Sign Company; *U.S. Private*, pg. 1189
DEE SIGN COMPANY - OAKLAND FACILITY—See Dee Sign Company; *U.S. Private*, pg. 1189
DEE SIGN COMPANY - SAN DIEGO FACILITY—See Dee Sign Company; *U.S. Private*, pg. 1189
DEE SIGN COMPANY; *U.S. Private*, pg. 1189
DELPHI DISPLAY SYSTEMS INC.—See Toast, Inc.; *U.S. Public*, pg. 2161
DIVERSEID PRODUCTS OF FLORIDA LLC; *U.S. Private*, pg. 1241
DOWNING DISPLAYS INC.; *U.S. Private*, pg. 1269
EASTERN METAL OF ELMIRA INC.; *U.S. Private*, pg. 1320
EBSCO INDUSTRIES, INC. - STEWART SIGNS DIVISION—See EBSCO Industries, Inc.; *U.S. Private*, pg. 1325
EBSCO SIGNS & DISPLAYS—See EBSCO Industries, Inc.; *U.S. Private*, pg. 1325
ECOMPANYSTORE, INC.; *U.S. Private*, pg. 1329
EMEDCO INC.—See Brady Corporation; *U.S. Public*, pg. 379
EVERBRITE LACROSSE—See Everbrite, LLC; *U.S. Private*, pg. 1437
EVERBRITE, LLC; *U.S. Private*, pg. 1437
EXHIBITOR SOURCE BY SKYLINE; *U.S. Private*, pg. 1448
EXPRESS A BUTTON, INC.; *U.S. Private*, pg. 1451
FAIRMONT SIGN COMPANY; *U.S. Private*, pg. 1464
FALLON LUMINOUS PRODUCTS CORPORATION; *U.S. Private*, pg. 1468
FALLON VISUAL PRODUCTS CORP.—See Fallon Luminous Products Corporation; *U.S. Private*, pg. 1468
FELLERS, INC.; *U.S. Private*, pg. 1494
FIELDFLEX BENELUX—See Ardian SAS; *Int'l*, pg. 555
FIELDFLEX EUROPE SAS—See Ardian SAS; *Int'l*, pg. 555
FLUORESCO SERVICES LLC—See Everbrite, LLC; *U.S. Private*, pg. 1437
FORMETCO, INC.; *U.S. Private*, pg. 1571
FRANK MAYER & ASSOCIATES INC.; *U.S. Private*, pg. 1595
GEIGER BROTHERS; *U.S. Private*, pg. 1655
GEORGE LAY SIGNS, INC.—See Miracle Signs, Inc.; *U.S. Private*, pg. 2745
GEORGE PATTON ASSOCIATES, INC.—See Franz Haniel & Cie. GmbH; *Int'l*, pg. 2763
GERBER SCIENTIFIC, INC. - GERBER SCIENTIFIC PRODUCTS GROUP—See Vector Capital Management, L.P.; *U.S. Private*, pg. 4350
GHN—See Everbrite, LLC; *U.S. Private*, pg. 1437
GMPC; *U.S. Private*, pg. 1723
GORDON SIGN CO.—See Lincolnshire Management, Inc.; *U.S. Private*, pg. 2459
GREEN BAY PACKAGING INC. - BAIRD DISPLAY DIVISION—See Green Bay Packaging Inc.; *U.S. Private*, pg. 1771
GRIMCO INC.; *U.S. Private*, pg. 1789
HADLEY EXHIBITS INC.; *U.S. Private*, pg. 1839
HALL SIGNS, INC.; *U.S. Private*, pg. 1843
HAMILTON EXHIBITS LLC; *U.S. Private*, pg. 1847
HANGZHOU MULTI-COLOR OPTOELECTRICAL CO., LTD.—See Hangzhou Silan Microelectronics Co., Ltd.; *Int'l*, pg. 3250
H.B. STUBBS COMPANY; *U.S. Private*, pg. 1825
HOLIEN INC.; *U.S. Private*, pg. 1963
ICON IDENTITY SOLUTIONS, INC.—See MC Group; *U.S. Private*, pg. 2625
IDL WORLDWIDE, INC.—See Matthews International Corporation; *U.S. Public*, pg. 1399
IKONSIGN ETCH—See Terawulf Inc.; *U.S. Public*, pg. 2018
ILLINI INC.—See Neil International Inc.; *U.S. Private*, pg. 2882

IMAGO GROUP; *Int'l*, pg. 3619
IMAGO NORTH AMERICA—See IMAGO Group; *Int'l*, pg. 3619
INTERSTATE HIGHWAY SIGN CORP; *U.S. Private*, pg. 2125
INTERWEST SAFETY SUPPLY INC.; *U.S. Private*, pg. 2128
J.M. STEWART CORPORATION—See EBSCO Industries, Inc.; *U.S. Private*, pg. 1325
THE KAY COMPANY, INC.; *U.S. Private*, pg. 4064
KENDAL KING GROUP; *U.S. Private*, pg. 2283
KIEFFER & CO., INC.; *U.S. Private*, pg. 2303
KMK INDUSTRIES, INC.—See Exhibit Systems, Inc.; *U.S. Private*, pg. 1448
KROY SIGN SYSTEMS, LLC—See Pubco Corporation; *U.S. Private*, pg. 3298
LIDDELL BROTHERS, INC.—See Trilantic Capital Management L.P.; *U.S. Private*, pg. 4231
LSI RETAIL GRAPHICS INC.—See LSI Industries Inc.; *U.S. Public*, pg. 1344
LYLE SIGNS INC.; *U.S. Private*, pg. 2520
MALTBIE, INC.; *U.S. Private*, pg. 2558
MARKMASTER, INC.; *U.S. Private*, pg. 2582
MC SIGN COMPANY—See Arcapita Group Holdings Limited; *Int'l*, pg. 542
MDI FRANCE SA—See MDI Worldwide; *U.S. Private*, pg. 2646
MDI WORLDWIDE; *U.S. Private*, pg. 2646
MECHTRONICS CORPORATION; *U.S. Private*, pg. 2649
MEDIA GRAPHICS INC.; *U.S. Private*, pg. 2652
MEGAPLAS, S.A.—See Fomento de Construcciones y Contratas, S.A.; *Int'l*, pg. 2723
METAL ART OF CALIFORNIA, INC.; *U.S. Private*, pg. 2679
MONTROY SIGN & GRAPHIC PRODUCTS—See JDW Management Co.; *U.S. Private*, pg. 2196
MOSS INC.—See EagleTree Capital, LP; *U.S. Private*, pg. 1312
MOUNT VERNON NEON—See Everbrite, LLC; *U.S. Private*, pg. 1437
NATIONAL BANNER COMPANY, INC.; *U.S. Private*, pg. 2848
NATIONAL MARKER COMPANY—See The Riverside Company; *U.S. Private*, pg. 4109
NIMLOK COMPANY; *U.S. Private*, pg. 2928
NIPPON BRADY K.K.—See Brady Corporation; *U.S. Public*, pg. 379
NORTH AMERICAN SIGNS INC.; *U.S. Private*, pg. 2941
NW SIGN INDUSTRIES INC.; *U.S. Private*, pg. 2975
OMAHA NEON SIGN CO. INC.; *U.S. Private*, pg. 3014
PANNIER CORPORATION - PANNIER GRAPHICS DIVISION—See Pannier Corporation; *U.S. Private*, pg. 3087
PERSONA INC.—See Holien Inc.; *U.S. Private*, pg. 1963
PHILADELPHIA SIGN COMPANY - LITTLETON PLANT—See Philadelphia Sign Company; *U.S. Private*, pg. 3169
PHILADELPHIA SIGN COMPANY; *U.S. Private*, pg. 3169
PHILIP PAYNE LIMITED—See F.W. Thorpe plc; *Int'l*, pg. 2597
POBLOCKI SIGN COMPANY, LLC; *U.S. Private*, pg. 3219
POSTERLOID CORPORATION—See Visual Graphics Systems, Inc.; *U.S. Private*, pg. 4404
POST-UP STAND, INC.—See Franz Haniel & Cie. GmbH; *Int'l*, pg. 2763
PUBLIC IMAGERY; *U.S. Private*, pg. 3299
QUICK POINT INCORPORATED; *U.S. Private*, pg. 3326
QUICK SIGN LLC—See Al Shafar Group; *Int'l*, pg. 282
QUIKEY MANUFACTURING CO. INC.; *U.S. Private*, pg. 3327
RAINIER INDUSTRIES, LTD.; *U.S. Private*, pg. 3348
RAPID DISPLAYS - UNION CITY—See Gemspring Capital Management, LLC; *U.S. Private*, pg. 1659
R.D. NIVEN & ASSOCIATES LTD.; *U.S. Private*, pg. 3335
ROURA CEVASA, S.A.—See ACS, Actividades de Construccion y Servicios, S.A.; *Int'l*, pg. 116
SAFETY SIGNS INC.—See Gilvin-Terrill Inc.; *U.S. Private*, pg. 1701
SETON AUSTRALIA PTY. LTD.—See Brady Corporation; *U.S. Public*, pg. 378
SIGN-A-RAMA; *U.S. Private*, pg. 3649
SIGNATURE S.A.—See Burelle S.A.; *Int'l*, pg. 1223
SIGN PARROT, LLC; *U.S. Private*, pg. 3649
SIGNTECH ELECTRICAL ADVERTISING; *U.S. Private*, pg. 3651
SIGNTRONIX; *U.S. Private*, pg. 3651
SIGN ZONE LLC—See HarbourVest Partners, LLC; *U.S. Private*, pg. 1861
SIGN ZONE LLC—See Pfingsten Partners, LLC; *U.S. Private*, pg. 3164
SKYLINE DISPLAYS INC.; *U.S. Private*, pg. 3685
SKYSERVICE, INC.—See Skyline Displays Inc.; *U.S. Private*, pg. 3685
SMARTSIGN.COM LLC; *U.S. Private*, pg. 3692
SUNCOAST SIGN SHOP, INC.; *U.S. Private*, pg. 3866
SWISSPLAKAT AG—See APG/SGA SA; *Int'l*, pg. 513
TECNICAS E IMAGEN CORPORATIVA, S.L.—See ACS, Actividades de Construccion y Servicios, S.A.; *Int'l*, pg. 116

THOMAS SIGN & AWNING CO., INC.; *U.S. Private*, pg. 4158
TRAFFIC MANAGEMENT PRODUCTS LTD.—See Dewhurst Group plc; *Int'l*, pg. 2091
TRANS-LUX COCTEAU CORPORATION—See Trans-Lux Corporation; *U.S. Public*, pg. 2179
TRANS-LUX PTY. LTD.—See Trans-Lux Corporation; *U.S. Public*, pg. 2179
TRANS WORLD MARKETING CORP.; *U.S. Private*, pg. 4205
TRICOR GROUPE S.A.—See Brady Corporation; *U.S. Public*, pg. 379
TUBE ART DISPLAYS INC.; *U.S. Private*, pg. 4255
UNIFIED RESOURCES IN DISPLAY; *U.S. Private*, pg. 4283
USCUTTER INC.; *U.S. Private*, pg. 4322
US SIGNS, INC.—See FM Facility Maintenance, LLC; *U.S. Private*, pg. 1553
VISTA SYSTEM, LLC; *U.S. Private*, pg. 4403
VISUAL GRAPHICS SYSTEMS, INC.; *U.S. Private*, pg. 4404
VIVID INK INC.; *U.S. Private*, pg. 4406
VULCAN, INC. - VULCAN TECHNOLOGY CENTER DIVISION—See Vulcan, Inc.; *U.S. Private*, pg. 4416
WALTON SIGNAGE CORPORATION; *U.S. Private*, pg. 4435
WATCHFIRE SIGNS, LLC—See H.I.G. Capital, LLC; *U.S. Private*, pg. 1834
WESTERN REMAC, INC.—See Trilantic Capital Management L.P.; *U.S. Private*, pg. 4231
W.H.B. DO BRASIL LTDA.—See Brady Corporation; *U.S. Public*, pg. 379
W.H. BRADY, NV—See Brady Corporation; *U.S. Public*, pg. 379
W.H. BRADY S. DE R.L. DE C.V.—See Brady Corporation; *U.S. Public*, pg. 379
WILSON-HURD MANUFACTURING CO., INC.—See Nelson-Miller, Inc.; *U.S. Private*, pg. 2884
YOUNG ELECTRIC SIGN CO. - BOISE—See Young Electric Sign Company; *U.S. Private*, pg. 4593
YOUNG ELECTRIC SIGN CO. - DENVER—See Young Electric Sign Company; *U.S. Private*, pg. 4593
YOUNG ELECTRIC SIGN CO. - LAS VEGAS—See Young Electric Sign Company; *U.S. Private*, pg. 4593
YOUNG ELECTRIC SIGN COMPANY; *U.S. Private*, pg. 4593
YOUNG ELECTRIC SIGN CO. - RENO—See Young Electric Sign Company; *U.S. Private*, pg. 4593
YOUNG ELECTRIC SIGN CO. - SALT LAKE CITY—See Young Electric Sign Company; *U.S. Private*, pg. 4593

339991 — GASKET, PACKING, AND SEALING DEVICE MANUFACTURING

AA GASKETS PTY LTD—See Amotiv Limited; *Int'l*, pg. 431
ADHEREX GROUP—See Akoya Capital LLC; *U.S. Private*, pg. 146
AESSEAL INC.—See AESSEAL Plc; *Int'l*, pg. 182
AESSEAL INDIA PRIVATE LIMITED—See AESSEAL Plc; *Int'l*, pg. 182
AESSEAL PTY LTD—See AESSEAL Plc; *Int'l*, pg. 182
AGS FLEXITALLIC, INC.—See Bridgepoint Group Plc; *Int'l*, pg. 1154
ALTECH SHANGHAI CO., LTD.—See Altech Co., Ltd.; *Int'l*, pg. 388
A.R. THOMSON GROUP; *Int'l*, pg. 28
ASTROSEAL PRODUCTS MFG CORPORATION—See HEICO Corporation; *U.S. Public*, pg. 1019
THE AUBURN MANUFACTURING COMPANY; *U.S. Private*, pg. 3990
A.W. CHESTERTON CO. LTD.—See A.W. Chesterton Company; *U.S. Private*, pg. 28
A.W. CHESTERTON COMPANY; *U.S. Private*, pg. 28
BANCO PRODUCTS (I) LTD.; *Int'l*, pg. 824
BANKS BROS. CORPORATION; *U.S. Private*, pg. 468
BEMIS PACKAGING MEXICO, S.A. DE C.V.—See Amcor plc; *Int'l*, pg. 418
BENDER GMBH—See Berry Global Group, Inc; *U.S. Public*, pg. 322
BETECH A/S—See Addtech AB; *Int'l*, pg. 132
BURGMANN DALIAN CO., LTD.—See Freudenberg SE; *Int'l*, pg. 2783
BURGMANN SEALING MATERIALS CO., LTD. CIXI—See Freudenberg SE; *Int'l*, pg. 2783
BURGMANN SHANGHAI CO., LTD.—See Freudenberg SE; *Int'l*, pg. 2783
CALDWELL INDUSTRIES INC.; *U.S. Private*, pg. 716
CALEX EXPRESS INC—See Calex Logistics Corp.; *U.S. Private*, pg. 717
CATHY SEAL PTE. LTD.—See Erria A/S; *Int'l*, pg. 2497
CDI ENERGY PRODUCTS, INC.—See Compagnie Generale des Etablissements Michelin SCA; *Int'l*, pg. 1745
CGR PRODUCTS INC.; *U.S. Private*, pg. 844
CGR VALLEY PRODUCTS INCORPORATED; *U.S. Private*, pg. 844
CGS TECHNOLOGIES, INC.—See System Integrators, L.L.C.; *U.S. Private*, pg. 3906
CHEEYUEN ELECTRONICS TECHNOLOGY (HUIZHOU)

CO., LTD.—See China Aerospace International Holdings Limited; *Int'l*, pg. 1481
CHESTERTON CR S.R.O.—See A.W. Chesterton Company; *U.S. Private*, pg. 28
CHESTERTON HUNGARY KFT—See A.W. Chesterton Company; *U.S. Private*, pg. 28
CHESTERTON INTERNATIONAL GMBH—See A.W. Chesterton Company; *U.S. Private*, pg. 28
CHESTERTON MEXICANA S.A. DE C.V.—See A.W. Chesterton Company; *U.S. Private*, pg. 28
CHESTERTON NINGBO SEALING TECHNOLOGY CO. LTD—See A.W. Chesterton Company; *U.S. Private*, pg. 28
CHESTERTON POLSKA SP.ZO.O—See A.W. Chesterton Company; *U.S. Private*, pg. 28
CHESTERTON ROMA SRL—See A.W. Chesterton Company; *U.S. Private*, pg. 28
CHESTERTON SLOVAKIA S.R.O.—See A.W. Chesterton Company; *U.S. Private*, pg. 28
CHICAGO-WILCOX MFG. COMPANY, INC.; *U.S. Private*, pg. 879
CHOMERICS DIVISION-EUROPE—See Parker Hannifin Corporation; *U.S. Public*, pg. 1648
CORESA S.A.; *Int'l*, pg. 1799
CORROSION CONTROL CORPORATION—See Enpro Inc.; *U.S. Public*, pg. 774
COVENTRY GROUP (NZ) LIMITED—See Coventry Group Limited; *Int'l*, pg. 1821
DANA INC. - PARIS PLANT—See Dana Incorporated; *U.S. Public*, pg. 622
DANA SEALING PRODUCTS—See Dana Incorporated; *U.S. Public*, pg. 623
DICHTUNGSPARTNER HAMBURG GMBH; *Int'l*, pg. 2111
DIPACO, INC.—See Diesel Forward, Inc.; *U.S. Private*, pg. 1228
DMR SEALS LIMITED—See Diploma PLC; *Int'l*, pg. 2128
DONGGUAN COSMOS PLASTICS PRODUCTS COMPANY LTD—See Cosmos Machinery Enterprises Limited; *Int'l*, pg. 1813
DPH (SOUTH AFRICA) INDUSTRIAL, MINING & AUTOMOTIVE SUPPLIES (PTY) LTD—See Dichtungspartner Hamburg GmbH; *Int'l*, pg. 2111
EAGLEBURGMANN AUSTRALASIA PTY. LTD.—See Eagle Industry Co., Ltd.; *Int'l*, pg. 2265
EAGLEBURGMANN AUSTRALASIA PTY. LTD.—See Freudenberg SE; *Int'l*, pg. 2783
EAGLEBURGMANN AUSTRIA GMBH—See Freudenberg SE; *Int'l*, pg. 2783
EAGLEBURGMANN BELGIUM BVBA—See Freudenberg SE; *Int'l*, pg. 2783
EAGLEBURGMANN BREDAN S.R.O.—See Freudenberg SE; *Int'l*, pg. 2783
EAGLEBURGMANN BT S.P.A—See Freudenberg SE; *Int'l*, pg. 2783
EAGLEBURGMANN CANADA INC.—See Freudenberg SE; *Int'l*, pg. 2783
EAGLEBURGMANN DE VENEZUELA, C.A.—See Freudenberg SE; *Int'l*, pg. 2784
EAGLEBURGMANN DO BRASIL VEDACOES INDUSTRIAS LTDA.—See Freudenberg SE; *Int'l*, pg. 2784
EAGLEBURGMANN ENDUSTRIYEL SIZDIRMALIK SANAYI VE TICARET LTD. STI.—See Freudenberg SE; *Int'l*, pg. 2783
EAGLEBURGMANN ESPEY GMBH—See Freudenberg SE; *Int'l*, pg. 2783
EAGLEBURGMANN FRANCE S.A.S.—See Freudenberg SE; *Int'l*, pg. 2783
EAGLEBURGMANN GERMANY GMBH & CO. KG—See Freudenberg SE; *Int'l*, pg. 2783
EAGLEBURGMANN HUNGARIA KFT.—See Freudenberg SE; *Int'l*, pg. 2784
EAGLEBURGMANN IBERICA S. A.—See Freudenberg SE; *Int'l*, pg. 2784
EAGLEBURGMANN INDIA PVT. LTD.—See Eagle Industry Co., Ltd.; *Int'l*, pg. 2265
EAGLEBURGMANN INDIA PVT. LTD. — See Eagle Industry Co., Ltd.; *Int'l*, pg. 2265
EAGLEBURGMANN INDIA PVT. LTD.—See Freudenberg SE; *Int'l*, pg. 2784
EAGLEBURGMANN INDIA PVT. LTD.—See Freudenberg SE; *Int'l*, pg. 2784
EAGLEBURGMANN INDUSTRIES RUSSIA—See Freudenberg SE; *Int'l*, pg. 2784
EAGLEBURGMANN INDUSTRIES UK LP—See Freudenberg SE; *Int'l*, pg. 2784
EAGLEBURGMANN ITALIA S.R.L.—See Freudenberg SE; *Int'l*, pg. 2704
EAGLEBURGMANN KE PTE. LTD.—See Freudenberg SE; *Int'l*, pg. 2784
EAGLEBURGMANN KE PVT. LTD.—See Freudenberg SE; *Int'l*, pg. 2784
EAGLEBURGMANN KOREA LTD.—See Freudenberg SE; *Int'l*, pg. 2784
EAGLEBURGMANN (MALAYSIA) SDN BHD—See Freudenberg SE; *Int'l*, pg. 2783
EAGLEBURGMANN MEXICO S.A. DE C.V.—See Freudenberg SE; *Int'l*, pg. 2784

EAGLEBURGMANN MIDDLE EAST FZE—See Freudenberg SE; *Int'l*, pg. 2784
EAGLEBURGMANN NETHERLANDS B.V.—See Freudenberg SE; *Int'l*, pg. 2784
EAGLEBURGMANN NEW ZEALAND, LTD.—See Eagle Industry Co., Ltd.; *Int'l*, pg. 2265
EAGLEBURGMANN NEW ZEALAND, LTD.—See Freudenberg SE; *Int'l*, pg. 2784
EAGLEBURGMANN NORWAY A/S—See Freudenberg SE; *Int'l*, pg. 2784
EAGLEBURGMANN OOO—See Freudenberg SE; *Int'l*, pg. 2784
EAGLEBURGMANN PHILIPPINES INC.—See Freudenberg SE; *Int'l*, pg. 2784
EAGLEBURGMANN PRODUCTION CENTER JUDENBURG GMBH—See Freudenberg SE; *Int'l*, pg. 2784
EAGLEBURGMANN RO SRL—See Freudenberg SE; *Int'l*, pg. 2784
EAGLEBURGMANN SEALS SOUTH AFRICA (PTY) LTD.—See Freudenberg SE; *Int'l*, pg. 2784
EAGLEBURGMANN SWEDEN AB—See Freudenberg SE; *Int'l*, pg. 2784
EAGLEBURGMANN SWEDEN AB—See Freudenberg SE; *Int'l*, pg. 2784
EAGLEBURGMANN (SWITZERLAND) AG—See Freudenberg SE; *Int'l*, pg. 2783
EAGLEBURGMANN (THAILAND) CO., LTD.—See Freudenberg SE; *Int'l*, pg. 2783
EAGLE INDUSTRY CO., LTD. - OKAYAMA FACTORY—See Eagle Industry Co., Ltd.; *Int'l*, pg. 2265
EAGLE NEW ZEALAND LIMITED—See Eagle Industry Co., Ltd.; *Int'l*, pg. 2265
ECOPACK, D.O.O.—See Comet Umetni brusi in nekovine, d.d.; *Int'l*, pg. 1711
EFTEC SHROFF INDIA LIMITED—See EMS-Chemie Holding AG; *Int'l*, pg. 2394
EGC CRITICAL COMPONENTS—See Compagnie Generale des Etablissements Michelin SCA; *Int'l*, pg. 1745
ELRING KLINGER DO BRASIL LTDA.—See ElringKlinger AG; *Int'l*, pg. 2369
ELRING KLINGER (GREAT BRITAIN) LTD.—See ElringKlinger AG; *Int'l*, pg. 2369
ENPRO INC.; *U.S. Public*, pg. 2111
E&R ENGINEERING CORP.; *Int'l*, pg. 2247
ERIKS WEST, INC.—See LKCM Headwater Investments; *U.S. Private*, pg. 2475
ERIKS WEST—See LKCM Headwater Investments; *U.S. Private*, pg. 2475
EVERSEAL GASKET, INC.; *U.S. Private*, pg. 1440
FEDERAL-MOGUL CORP. - FRANKFORT—See Apollo Global Management, Inc.; *U.S. Public*, pg. 161
FEDERAL-MOGUL CORP. - SKOKIE—See Apollo Global Management, Inc.; *U.S. Public*, pg. 161
FEDERAL-MOGUL CORP. - SUMMERTON—See Apollo Global Management, Inc.; *U.S. Public*, pg. 161
FEDERAL-MOGUL DUTCH HOLDINGS INC.—See Apollo Global Management, Inc.; *U.S. Public*, pg. 160
FEDERAL-MOGUL FRICTION PRODUCTS—See Apollo Global Management, Inc.; *U.S. Public*, pg. 161
FEDERAL-MOGUL GLOBAL INC.—See Apollo Global Management, Inc.; *U.S. Public*, pg. 161
FEDERAL-MOGUL UK HOLDINGS INC.—See Apollo Global Management, Inc.; *U.S. Public*, pg. 162
FELT PRODUCTS MANUFACTURING CO.—See Apollo Global Management, Inc.; *U.S. Public*, pg. 162
FERROTEC HOLDINGS CORPORATION; *Int'l*, pg. 2642
FERROTEC (USA) CORPORATION—See Ferrotec Holdings Corporation; *Int'l*, pg. 2643
THE FLEXITALLIC GROUP, INC.—See Bridgepoint Group Plc; *Int'l*, pg. 1154
FLEXITALLIC LP—See Bridgepoint Group Plc; *Int'l*, pg. 1154
FLEXITALLIC LTD.—See Bridgepoint Group Plc; *Int'l*, pg. 1154
FLOW DRY TECHNOLOGY LTD—See Brittany Stamping, LLC; *U.S. Private*, pg. 657
FLOWSERVE CORP.—See Flowserve Corporation; *U.S. Public*, pg. 855
FLOWSERVE SANMAR LTD.—See Flowserve Corporation; *U.S. Public*, pg. 856
FM INTERNATIONAL, LLC—See Apollo Global Management, Inc.; *U.S. Public*, pg. 160
FOREST CITY TECHNOLOGIES INC.; *U.S. Private*, pg. 1566
FOTAFLEX LTD.—See Forges Tardieu Ltd; *Int'l*, pg. 2733
FRANKEN PLASTIKS GMBH—See Enpro Inc.; *U.S. Public*, pg. 775
FREUDENBERG DICHTUNGS- UND SCHWINGUNGSTECHNIK GMBH & CO. KG—See Freudenberg SE; *Int'l*, pg. 2786
FREUDENBERG JOINTS ELASTOMERES SAS—See Freudenberg SE; *Int'l*, pg. 2787
FREUDENBERG-NOK DE MEXICO—See Freudenberg SE; *Int'l*, pg. 2789
FREUDENBERG-NOK GENERAL PARTNERSHIP—See Freudenberg SE; *Int'l*, pg. 2788
FREUDENBERG NOK-RUBBER PRODUCTS—See Freudenberg SE; *Int'l*, pg. 2788
FREUDENBERG NOK-RUBBER PRODUCTS—See Freudenberg SE; *Int'l*, pg. 2788

FREUDENBERG NOK—See Freudenberg SE; *Int'l*, pg. 2788
FREUDENBERG NOK—See Freudenberg SE; *Int'l*, pg. 2788
FREUDENBERG NOK—See Freudenberg SE; *Int'l*, pg. 2788
FREUDENBERG OIL & GAS, LLC—See Freudenberg SE; *Int'l*, pg. 2787
FREUDENBERG SEALING TECHNOLOGIES AG—See Freudenberg SE; *Int'l*, pg. 2788
FREUDENBERG SEALING TECHNOLOGIES GMBH & CO. KG—See Freudenberg SE; *Int'l*, pg. 2788
FREUDENBERG SEALING TECHNOLOGIES SAS—See Freudenberg SE; *Int'l*, pg. 2788
FREUDENBERG SIMRIT SAS—See Freudenberg SE; *Int'l*, pg. 2788
FUJI SEAL EUROPE LTD.—See Fuji Seal International, Inc.; *Int'l*, pg. 2816
FUJI SEAL INTERNATIONAL, INC.; *Int'l*, pg. 2816
GALLAGHER FLUID SEALS INC.; *U.S. Private*, pg. 1638
GARLOCK GMBH—See Enpro Inc.; *U.S. Public*, pg. 775
GARLOCK (GREAT BRITAIN) LIMITED—See Enpro Inc.; *U.S. Public*, pg. 774
GARLOCK SEALING TECHNOLOGIES (SHANGHAI) CO., LTD.—See Enpro Inc.; *U.S. Public*, pg. 775
GARLOCK SEALING TECHNOLOGIES—See Enpro Inc.; *U.S. Public*, pg. 775
GENERAL RUBBER CO.—See Minnesota Flexible Corp.; *U.S. Private*, pg. 2743
GILLETTE AUSTRALIA PTY. LTD.—See The Procter & Gamble Company; *U.S. Public*, pg. 2120
GILLETTE PAKISTAN LIMITED—See The Procter & Gamble Company; *U.S. Public*, pg. 2124
GISLAVED GUMMI LANKA (PVT) LTD.—See HEXPOL AB; *Int'l*, pg. 3371
GISLAVED GUMMI (QINGDAO) CO., LTD.—See HEXPOL AB; *Int'l*, pg. 3371
GLASSEAL PRODUCTS—See AMETEK, Inc.; *U.S. Public*, pg. 116
GREENE, TWEED & CO.; *U.S. Private*, pg. 1777
GUANGDONG HONGWAN SUPPLY CHAIN TECHNOLOGY CO., LTD.—See Huali Industries Co Ltd; *Int'l*, pg. 3513
HALLITE (FRANCE) LIMITED—See Compagnie Generale des Etablissements Michelin SCA; *Int'l*, pg. 1745
HALLITE ITALIA SRL—See Compagnie Generale des Etablissements Michelin SCA; *Int'l*, pg. 1745
HALLITE SEALS (CANADA) LIMITED—See Compagnie Generale des Etablissements Michelin SCA; *Int'l*, pg. 1745
HALLITE SEALS INTERNATIONAL LTD—See Compagnie Generale des Etablissements Michelin SCA; *Int'l*, pg. 1745
HALLITE SEALS INTERNATIONAL LTD—See Compagnie Generale des Etablissements Michelin SCA; *Int'l*, pg. 1745
HAMON CORPORATION—See Hamon & Cie S.A.; *Int'l*, pg. 3239
HANGZHOU YOUNGSUN INTELLIGENT EQUIPMENT CO., LTD.; *Int'l*, pg. 3251
HENNIGES AUTOMOTIVE INC. - GOMEZ PALACIO—See Aviation Industry Corporation of China; *Int'l*, pg. 742
HENNIGES AUTOMOTIVE INC. - GUADALAJARA—See Aviation Industry Corporation of China; *Int'l*, pg. 742
HENNIGES AUTOMOTIVE, INC. - NEW HAVEN—See Aviation Industry Corporation of China; *Int'l*, pg. 742
HENNIGES AUTOMOTIVE, INC. - OAKVILLE—See Aviation Industry Corporation of China; *Int'l*, pg. 742
HENNIGES AUTOMOTIVE, INC. - REIDSVILLE PLANT—See Aviation Industry Corporation of China; *Int'l*, pg. 742
HENNIGES AUTOMOTIVE, INC.—See Aviation Industry Corporation of China; *Int'l*, pg. 742
HENNIGES AUTOMOTIVE INC. - TORREON—See Aviation Industry Corporation of China; *Int'l*, pg. 742
HUDACO INDUSTRIES LIMITED - ANGUS HAWKEN DIVISION—See Hudaco Industries Limited; *Int'l*, pg. 3521
ILPEA INDUSTRIES, INC.—See Ilpea Inc.; *U.S. Private*, pg. 2043
INDUSTRIAL GASKET INC.; *U.S. Private*, pg. 2066
INTERFACE PERFORMANCE MATERIALS, INC.—See Lydall, Inc.; *U.S. Public*, pg. 1349
INTERFACE PERFORMANCE MATERIALS INDIA, LLP—See Lydall, Inc.; *U.S. Public*, pg. 1349
INTERFACE SEALING SOLUTIONS—See Lydall, Inc.; *U.S. Public*, pg. 1349
JETSEAL, INC.—See HEICO Corporation; *U.S. Public*, pg. 1021
KINUGAWA KORIYAMA CO., LTD.—See Development Bank of Japan, Inc.; *Int'l*, pg. 2088
KINUGAWA OITA CO., LTD.—See Development Bank of Japan, Inc.; *Int'l*, pg. 2088
KUBO TECH AG—See Diploma PLC; *Int'l*, pg. 2128
KUBO TECH GMBH—See Diploma PLC; *Int'l*, pg. 2128
LAMONS GASKET COMPANY—See TriMas Corporation; *U.S. Public*, pg. 2189

339991 — GASKET, PACKING, AN...

LARSTAN INDUSTRIES, INC.—See Banks Bros. Corporation; *U.S. Private,* pg. 468
L&L PRODUCTS, INC.; *U.S. Private,* pg. 2363
LONESTAR FASTENERS EUROPE LIMITED—See Trinity Hunt Management, L.P.; *U.S. Private,* pg. 4235
LONE STAR FASTENERS, L.P.—See Trinity Hunt Management, L.P.; *U.S. Private,* pg. 4235
LONE STAR LEEDS LIMITED—See Trinity Hunt Management, L.P.; *U.S. Private,* pg. 4235
MCD GASKETS INC.—See Alfa Laval AB; *Int'l,* pg. 312
MERIDIAN ADHESIVES GROUP LLC—See Arsenal Capital Management LP; *U.S. Private,* pg. 339
MERKEL NOK-FREUDENBERG CO. LTD.—See Freudenberg SE; *Int'l,* pg. 2789
M SEALS A/S—See Diploma PLC; *Int'l,* pg. 2129
M SEALS UK LIMITED—See Diploma PLC; *Int'l,* pg. 2129
MT SEALING TECHNOLOGY INC—See Burckhardt Compression Holding AG; *Int'l,* pg. 1221
MUELLER DIE CUT SOLUTIONS, INC.—See Sur-Seal, Inc.; *U.S. Private,* pg. 3883
NIANTIC SEAL INC.—See INSCO, Inc.; *U.S. Private,* pg. 2085
NOVOTEMA SPA—See IDEX Corp; *U.S. Public,* pg. 1091
NZ GASKETS LIMITED—See Amotiv Limited; *Int'l,* pg. 431
PALMETTO INC.—See Greene, Tweed & Co.; *U.S. Private,* pg. 1777
PARKER AEROSPACE—See Parker Hannifin Corporation; *U.S. Public,* pg. 1643
PARKER HANNIFIN ADVANCED PRODUCTS COMPANY—See Parker Hannifin Corporation; *U.S. Public,* pg. 1648
PARKER HANNIFIN COMPOSITE SEALING SYSTEMS DIVISION—See Parker Hannifin Corporation; *U.S. Public,* pg. 1643
PARKER HANNIFIN POWER TRAIN DIVISION—See Parker Hannifin Corporation; *U.S. Public,* pg. 1643
PARKER SEALS—See Parker Hannifin Corporation; *U.S. Public,* pg. 1649
PELICAN WORLDWIDE; *U.S. Private,* pg. 3131
P&G SOUTH AFRICAN TRADING (PTY.) LTD.—See The Procter & Gamble Company; *U.S. Public,* pg. 2121
PILLAR TECHNOLOGIES—See Illinois Tool Works Inc.; *U.S. Public,* pg. 1110
PLASTOMER TECHNOLOGIES—See Enpro Inc.; *U.S. Public,* pg. 775
PPE, LLC—See IDEX Corp; *U.S. Public,* pg. 1091
PRECIX INC.; *U.S. Private,* pg. 3247
PROCTER & GAMBLE EGYPT—See The Procter & Gamble Company; *U.S. Public,* pg. 2121
P.T. EAGLEBURGMANN INDONESIA—See Eagle Industry Co., Ltd.; *Int'l,* pg. 2266
P.T. EAGLEBURGMANN INDONESIA—See Freudenberg SE; *Int'l,* pg. 2784
P.T. EAGLE INDUSTRY INDONESIA—See Eagle Industry Co., Ltd.; *Int'l,* pg. 2266
PYROTEK HIGH-TEMPERATURE INDUSTRIAL PRODUCTS INC—See Pyrotek Incorporated; *U.S. Private,* pg. 3311
REINZ-DICHTUNGS-GMBH & CO KG—See Dana Incorporated; *U.S. Public,* pg. 623
ROL MANUFACTURING OF AMERICA INC.; *U.S. Private,* pg. 3473
ROPLAN AB—See IDEX Corp; *U.S. Public,* pg. 1091
ROPLAN INC.—See IDEX Corp; *U.S. Public,* pg. 1091
ROPLAN LTD—See IDEX Corp; *U.S. Public,* pg. 1091
ROPLAN MACHINERY (NINGBO) CO., LTD.—See IDEX Corp; *U.S. Public,* pg. 1092
RUBBERLITE INC.; *U.S. Private,* pg. 3499
SCHLEGEL BVBA—See Quanex Building Products Corp.; *U.S. Public,* pg. 1749
SCHLEGEL FAR EAST LTD—See Quanex Building Products Corp.; *U.S. Public,* pg. 1749
SCHLEGEL GERMANY GMBH—See Quanex Building Products Corp.; *U.S. Public,* pg. 1749
SCHLEGEL PTY LTD—See Quanex Building Products Corp.; *U.S. Public,* pg. 1749
SCHLEGEL SRL—See Quanex Building Products Corp.; *U.S. Public,* pg. 1750
SCHLEGEL TALIANA SL—See Quanex Building Products Corp.; *U.S. Public,* pg. 1750
SCHLEGEL (UK) LIMITED—See Quanex Building Products Corp.; *U.S. Public,* pg. 1750
SEALING DEVICES INC.; *U.S. Private,* pg. 3585
SEALING EQUIPMENT PRODUCTS COMPANY, INC.; *U.S. Private,* pg. 3585
SEAL SCIENCE, INC.—See Arcline Investment Management LP; *U.S. Private,* pg. 314
SELIG SEALING PRODUCTS, INC.—See Henry Crown & Company; *U.S. Private,* pg. 1918
SIGMA FREUDENBERG NOK PVT. LTD. - 2 PLANT—See Freudenberg SE; *Int'l,* pg. 2790
SIGMA FREUDENBERG NOK PVT. LTD.—See Freudenberg SE; *Int'l,* pg. 2790
SIMRIT SERVICE CENTER DENMARK EAGLEBURGMANN KE A/S—See Freudenberg SE; *Int'l,* pg. 2790
SPECIFICATION RUBBER PRODUCTS INC.—See American Cast Iron Pipe Company; *U.S. Private,* pg. 226
STEIN SEAL COMPANY; *U.S. Private,* pg. 3798
SUMMIT INDUSTRIES, INC.; *U.S. Private,* pg. 3854
SUNBELT ASPHALT SURFACES, INC—See Construction Partners, Inc.; *U.S. Public,* pg. 572
SURE-SEAL LLC—See CSW Industrials, Inc.; *U.S. Public,* pg. 601
SUR-SEAL LLC; *U.S. Private,* pg. 3883
SYSTEM INTEGRATORS, L.L.C.; *U.S. Private,* pg. 3906
TECHNETICS GROUP DAYTONA, INC.—See Enpro Inc.; *U.S. Public,* pg. 775
TECHNETICS GROUP LLC—See Enpro Inc.; *U.S. Public,* pg. 775
TECHNETICS GROUP SINGAPORE PTE. LTD.—See Enpro Inc.; *U.S. Public,* pg. 775
TEKNA SEAL LLC—See Aptiv PLC; *Int'l,* pg. 526
TF VICTOR, S.A. DE C.V.—See Grupo Kuo, S.A.B. de C.V.; *Int'l,* pg. 2129
T&N DE MEXICO SA DE CV—See Apollo Global Management, Inc.; *U.S. Public,* pg. 162
TOTALSEAL GROUP AUSTRALIA PTY LIMITED—See Diploma PLC; *Int'l,* pg. 2129
TRINITY INDUSTRIES—See Trinity Industries, Inc.; *U.S. Public,* pg. 2194
TROSTEL LTD.—See HEXPOL AB; *Int'l,* pg. 3372
UNIQUE FABRICATING, INC.—See Taglich Private Equity LLC; *U.S. Private,* pg. 3922
UTEX INDUSTRIES INC.—See Riverstone Holdings LLC; *U.S. Private,* pg. 3448
VESTPAK AS—See Freudenberg SE; *Int'l,* pg. 2791
VIBRACOUST AG—See Freudenberg SE; *Int'l,* pg. 2791
VIBRACOUSTIC JAPAN KK—See Freudenberg SE; *Int'l,* pg. 2791
VSP TECHNOLOGIES, INC.—See Diploma PLC; *Int'l,* pg. 2129
WEST PHARMACEUTICAL SERVICES, INC. - CLEARWATER—See West Pharmaceutical Services, Inc.; *U.S. Public,* pg. 2353
WOLVERINE ADVANCED MATERIALS GMBH—See GTCR LLC; *U.S. Private,* pg. 1805
WOLVERINE ADVANCED MATERIALS, LLC—See ITT Inc.; *U.S. Public,* pg. 1179
WUXI MCD GASKET CO., LTD.—See Alfa Laval AB; *Int'l,* pg. 312
ZATKOFF SEALS & PACKINGS; *U.S. Private,* pg. 4598
ZERO INTERNATIONAL, INC.—See Allegion Public Limited Company; *Int'l,* pg. 335

339992 — MUSICAL INSTRUMENT MANUFACTURING

ALLEN INTEGRATED ASSEMBLIES—See Allen Organ Company; *U.S. Private,* pg. 179
ALLEN ORGAN COMPANY; *U.S. Private,* pg. 179
ARMADILLO ENTERPRISES, INC.; *U.S. Private,* pg. 329
AUG. LAUKHUFF GMBH & CO. KG; *Int'l,* pg. 702
AVEDIS ZILDJIAN COMPANY INC.; *U.S. Private,* pg. 405
AXL MUSICAL INSTRUMENTS CO., LTD., CORP.; *U.S. Private,* pg. 414
BALDWIN PIANO, INC.—See Gibson Brands, Inc.; *U.S. Private,* pg. 1696
BATALPHA BOBACH GMBH; *Int'l,* pg. 889
BBE SOUND INC.; *U.S. Private,* pg. 498
BOSTON PIANO GMBH—See Paulson & Co. Inc.; *U.S. Private,* pg. 3114
BUFFET CRAMPON DEUTSCHLAND GMBH—See Fondations Capital SA; *Int'l,* pg. 2725
BUFFET CRAMPON S.A.S.—See Fondations Capital SA; *Int'l,* pg. 2725
CARVIN CORP.; *U.S. Private,* pg. 777
C.F. MARTIN & CO., INC.; *U.S. Private,* pg. 707
CONN-SELMER, INC.—See Paulson & Co. Inc.; *U.S. Private,* pg. 3114
D'ADDARIO & COMPANY, INC.; *U.S. Private,* pg. 1138
DEAN MARKLEY STRINGS, INC.; *U.S. Private,* pg. 1184
DIGITAL PROJECTION LTD.—See Delta Electronics, Inc.; *Int'l,* pg. 2018
E-MU SYSTEMS, INC—See Creative Technology Ltd.; *Int'l,* pg. 1833
THE EPIPHONE COMPANY—See Gibson Brands, Inc.; *U.S. Private,* pg. 1696
ERNIE BALL INC.; *U.S. Private,* pg. 1422
EXACT CO. LTD.—See GMM Grammy Public Company Limited; *Int'l,* pg. 3012
FENDER MUSICAL INSTRUMENTS CORPORATION—See TPG Capital, L.P.; *U.S. Public,* pg. 2173
FERNANDES CO., LTD.; *Int'l,* pg. 2639
FOCUSRITE AUDIO ENGINEERING LTD.—See Focusrite plc; *Int'l,* pg. 2720
FROCH ENTERPRISE CO., LTD.; *Int'l,* pg. 2794
GHS CORP.; *U.S. Private,* pg. 1691
GIBSON ACOUSTIC—See Gibson Brands, Inc.; *U.S. Private,* pg. 1696
GIBSON BRANDS, INC.; *U.S. Private,* pg. 1696
GIBSON CUSTOM, ART & HISTORIC—See Gibson Brands, Inc.; *U.S. Private,* pg. 1696
GIBSON GEAR—See Gibson Brands, Inc.; *U.S. Private,* pg. 1696
G&L MUSIC SALES INC.—See BBE Sound Inc.; *U.S. Private,* pg. 498
GODIN GUITARS; *Int'l,* pg. 3020
GREENHOE, INC.—See Schilke Music Products, Inc.; *U.S. Private,* pg. 3565
GUANGZHOU HOSHINO GAKKI MFG. CO., LTD.—See Hoshino Gakki Co., Ltd.; *Int'l,* pg. 3483
GUANGZHOU PEARL RIVER PIANO GROUP CO., LTD.; *Int'l,* pg. 3167
GUILD GUITARS—See TPG Capital, L.P.; *U.S. Public,* pg. 2173
HAILUN PIANO CO., LTD.; *Int'l,* pg. 3211
HANPIN ELECTRON CO., LTD.; *Int'l,* pg. 3258
HENRI SELMER PARIS—See Argos Wityu S.A.; *Int'l,* pg. 563
HOSHINO GAKKI CO., LTD. - AKATSUKI FACTORY—See Hoshino Gakki Co., Ltd.; *Int'l,* pg. 3483
HOSHINO GAKKI CO., LTD.; *Int'l,* pg. 3483
JAM INDUSTRIES LTD.—See DCC plc; *Int'l,* pg. 1990
KLUGE KLAVIATUREN GMBH—See Paulson & Co. Inc.; *U.S. Private,* pg. 3114
LUDWIG/MUSSER PERCUSSION INSTRUMENTS—See Paulson & Co. Inc.; *U.S. Private,* pg. 3114
MUSSER—See Paulson & Co. Inc.; *U.S. Private,* pg. 3114
NYPRO LIMITED—See Jabil Inc.; *U.S. Public,* pg. 1182
THE O.S. KELLY COMPANY—See Paulson & Co. Inc.; *U.S. Private,* pg. 3114
OVATION INSTRUMENTS—See Arcline Investment Management LP; *U.S. Private,* pg. 314
PAUL REED SMITH GUITARS; *U.S. Private,* pg. 3113
QRS MUSIC TECHNOLOGY, INC.; *U.S. Public,* pg. 1744
REMO INC.; *U.S. Private,* pg. 3396
RICKENBACKER INTERNATIONAL CORPORATION; *U.S. Private,* pg. 3431
RICO INTERNATIONAL—See D'Addario & Company, Inc.; *U.S. Private,* pg. 1138
SCHILKE MUSIC PRODUCTS, INC.; *U.S. Private,* pg. 3565
SEQUENTIAL LLC—See Focusrite plc; *Int'l,* pg. 2720
STEINWAY HAUS DUSSELDORF GMBH—See Paulson & Co. Inc.; *U.S. Private,* pg. 3114
STEINWAY MUSICAL INSTRUMENTS, INC.—See Paulson & Co. Inc.; *U.S. Private,* pg. 3114
STEINWAY & SONS—See Paulson & Co. Inc.; *U.S. Private,* pg. 3114
ST. LOUIS MUSIC, INC.—See U.S. Band & Orchestra Supplies, Inc.; *U.S. Private,* pg. 4270
SUPER-SENSITIVE MUSICAL STRING CO.; *U.S. Private,* pg. 3875
TAYLOR-LISTUG INC.; *U.S. Private,* pg. 3941
U.S. BAND & ORCHESTRA SUPPLIES, INC.; *U.S. Private,* pg. 4270
U.S. MUSIC CORPORATION—See DCC plc; *Int'l,* pg. 1990
VINCENT BACH CO.—See Paulson & Co. Inc.; *U.S. Private,* pg. 3114
VINCENT BACH INTERNATIONAL, LTD.—See Paulson & Co. Inc.; *U.S. Private,* pg. 3114
VOYAGE-AIR GUITAR, INC.; *U.S. Private,* pg. 4414

339993 — FASTENER, BUTTON, NEEDLE, AND PIN MANUFACTURING

AFFORDABLEBUTTONS.COM; *U.S. Private,* pg. 123
AMSTED RPS—See AMSTED Industries Incorporated; *U.S. Private,* pg. 267
ARCONIC FASTENING SYSTEMS & RINGS-AUSTRALIA PTY. LTD.—See Howmet Aerospace Inc.; *U.S. Public,* pg. 1061
ARCONIC GLOBAL FASTENERS LIMITED - TELFORD—See Howmet Aerospace Inc.; *U.S. Public,* pg. 1062
ATECT CORPORATION; *Int'l,* pg. 667
BARNHART INDUSTRIES, INC.; *U.S. Private,* pg. 478
BRUNNER MANUFACTURING CO. INC.; *U.S. Private,* pg. 672
C&C METAL PRODUCTS CORP; *U.S. Private,* pg. 702
CHINA APEX GROUP LIMITED; *Int'l,* pg. 1482
CHIN WELL HOLDINGS BERHAD; *Int'l,* pg. 1480
COVENTRY GROUP LIMITED ARTIA DIVISION—See Coventry Group Limited; *Int'l,* pg. 1821
COVENTRY GROUP LIMITED HYLTON PARKER FASTENERS DIVISION—See Coventry Group Limited; *Int'l,* pg. 1821
DAKOTA ENGINEERING, INC.—See Mursix Corporation; *U.S. Private,* pg. 2816
DEEPAK FASTENERS (AUSTRALIA) PTY LTD.—See Deepak Fasteners Limited; *Int'l,* pg. 2002
DUNLAP INDUSTRIES INC.; *U.S. Private,* pg. 1290
EDWIN B. STIMPSON COMPANY, INC.; *U.S. Private,* pg. 1342
EMSIG MANUFACTURING CORP.; *U.S. Private,* pg. 1388
ENDRIES INTERNATIONAL, INC.—See MSD Capital, L.P.; *U.S. Private,* pg. 2807
FASTENER INDUSTRIES INC.; *U.S. Private,* pg. 1482
FIBAM COMPANHIA INDUSTRIAL; *Int'l,* pg. 2651
FUJIAN SBS ZIPPER SCIENCE & TECHNOLOGY CO., LTD.; *Int'l,* pg. 2819
FUXING CHINA GROUP LIMITED; *Int'l,* pg. 2858

N.A.I.C.S. INDEX

339999 — ALL OTHER MISCELLAN...

GIST, INC.; *U.S. Private*, pg. 1703
GLOBAL SM TECH LIMITED; *Int'l*, pg. 3001
HANDY BUTTON MACHINE COMPANY—See The Handy/Kenlin Group; *U.S. Private*, pg. 4043
THE HANDY/KENLIN GROUP; *U.S. Private*, pg. 4042
THE HILLMAN GROUP, INC.—See Hillman Solutions Corp.; *U.S. Public*, pg. 1038
IMAM BUTTON INDUSTRIES LTD.; *Int'l*, pg. 3619
ITW BUILDEX—See Illinois Tool Works Inc.; *U.S. Public*, pg. 1104
ITW CONSTRUCTION PRODUCTS (SINGAPORE) PTE. LTD.—See Illinois Tool Works Inc.; *U.S. Public*, pg. 1105
ITW CONSTRUCTION PRODUCTS—See Illinois Tool Works Inc.; *U.S. Public*, pg. 1105
ITW CONSTRUCTION PRODUCTS UK—See Illinois Tool Works Inc.; *U.S. Public*, pg. 1105
ITW DEVCON JAPAN—See Illinois Tool Works Inc.; *U.S. Public*, pg. 1105
ITW ESPANA, S.A.—See Illinois Tool Works Inc.; *U.S. Public*, pg. 1105
ITW FASTEX—See Illinois Tool Works Inc.; *U.S. Public*, pg. 1105
ITW LIMITED—See Illinois Tool Works Inc.; *U.S. Public*, pg. 1106
ITW SHAKEPROOF GROUP—See Illinois Tool Works Inc.; *U.S. Public*, pg. 1107
ITW SHAKEPROOF—See Illinois Tool Works Inc.; *U.S. Public*, pg. 1107
KEE (GUANGDONG) GARMENT ACCESSORIES LIMITED—See China Apex Group Limited; *Int'l*, pg. 1483
KEE (JINGMEN) GARMENT ACCESSORIES LIMITED—See China Apex Group Limited; *Int'l*, pg. 1483
KEE (ZHEJIANG) GARMENT ACCESSORIES LIMITED—See China Apex Group Limited; *Int'l*, pg. 1483
KEE ZIPPERS CORPORATION LIMITED—See China Apex Group Limited; *Int'l*, pg. 1483
KVT-FASTENING, ZWEIGNIEDERLASSUNG DER BOSSARD AG—See Bossard Holding AG; *Int'l*, pg. 1117
LINDSTROM METRIC, LLC—See Nautic Partners, LLC; *U.S. Private*, pg. 2871
MACHIN & EWIN PTY. LTD.—See Valmont Industries, Inc.; *U.S. Public*, pg. 2273
MACLEAN MAYNARD LLC—See MacLean-Fogg Company; *U.S. Private*, pg. 2537
MNP AEROSPACE, LLC.—See MNP Corporation; *U.S. Private*, pg. 2756
MNP CORPORATION - MNP PLANT II—See MNP Corporation; *U.S. Private*, pg. 2756
MNP CORPORATION - MNP PLANT I—See MNP Corporation; *U.S. Private*, pg. 2756
MOTOR CITY INDUSTRIAL LLC—See Kian Capital Partners, LLC; *U.S. Private*, pg. 2302
MOTOR CITY INDUSTRIAL LLC—See Oakland Standard Co., LLC; *U.S. Private*, pg. 2985
ND INDUSTRIES INC. - EASTERN FASTENER PROCESSING DIVISION—See H.B. Fuller Company; *U.S. Public*, pg. 978
ND INDUSTRIES INC. - SOUTHEASTERN FASTENER PROCESSING DIVISION—See H.B. Fuller Company; *U.S. Public*, pg. 978
ND INDUSTRIES INC. - SOUTHWESTERN FASTENER PROCESSING DIVISION—See H.B. Fuller Company; *U.S. Public*, pg. 978
NELSON STUD WELDING, INC.—See Dubai Holding LLC; *Int'l*, pg. 2218
NIPPON POP RIVETS & FASTENERS LTD.—See Stanley Black & Decker, Inc.; *U.S. Public*, pg. 1934
NISSEI SEIKO CO., LTD.—See Daido Steel Co., Ltd.; *Int'l*, pg. 1923
OHIO NUT & BOLT CO—See Fastener Industries Inc.; *U.S. Private*, pg. 1482
OPTIMAS OE SOLUTIONS, LLC—See AIP, LLC; *U.S. Private*, pg. 134
PAM FASTENING TECHNOLOGY, INC.—See Steel Partners Holdings L.P.; *U.S. Public*, pg. 1943
PASLODE—See Illinois Tool Works Inc.; *U.S. Public*, pg. 1110
PAULIN INDUSTRIES INC.—See Hillman Solutions Corp.; *U.S. Public*, pg. 1038
PCC DISTRIBUTION JAPAN K. K.—See Berkshire Hathaway Inc.; *U.S. Public*, pg. 315
PINPROS; *U.S. Private*, pg. 3186
POWER INDUSTRIES LTD.—See Stanley Black & Decker, Inc.; *U.S. Public*, pg. 1934
PRECISION TURNED COMPONENTS—See Groov-Pin Corporation; *U.S. Private*, pg. 1792
PREMIER FASTENERS PTY LIMITED—See DFL Holdings Pty Ltd; *Int'l*, pg. 2095
REPUBLIC FASTENER PRODUCTS CORP.; *U.S. Private*, pg. 3402
SCOLDING LOCKS CORP.; *U.S. Private*, pg. 3575
SCOVILL FASTENERS INC.—See The Gores Group, LLC; *U.S. Private*, pg. 4035
SEMCO TOOL & MANUFACTURING CO., INC.—See The Cly-Del Manufacturing Company; *U.S. Private*, pg. 4011
SHANGHAI EMHART FASTENING SYSTEMS LTD.—See Stanley Black & Decker, Inc.; *U.S. Public*, pg. 1934
SIMPSON STRONG-TIE (QUIK DRIVE FACTORY)—See Simpson Manufacturing Company, Inc.; *U.S. Public*, pg. 1883
SOUTHCO, INC.—See South Chester Tube Company; *U.S. Private*, pg. 3721
SPEEDTECH INTERNATIONAL, INC.; *U.S. Private*, pg. 3754
SPIROL INDUSTRIES, LTD.—See Spirol International Corporation; *U.S. Private*, pg. 3758
SPIROL INDUSTRIES, LTD.—See Spirol International Corporation; *U.S. Private*, pg. 3758
SPIROL SAS—See Spirol International Corporation; *U.S. Private*, pg. 3758
TAG FASTENERS SDN. BHD.—See Illinois Tool Works Inc.; *U.S. Public*, pg. 1111
TAG-IT PACIFIC (HK) LTD—See Talon International, Inc.; *U.S. Public*, pg. 1980
THO-RO PRODUCTS, INC.—See Eagle Button Co., Inc.; *U.S. Private*, pg. 1308
TOLEETO FASTENERS INTERNATIONAL, INC.—See SpeedTech International, Inc.; *U.S. Private*, pg. 3754
WATERBURY STYLE, INC.—See Custom Metal Crafters, Inc.; *U.S. Private*, pg. 1129
WPS, INC.; *U.S. Private*, pg. 4571

339994 — BROOM, BRUSH, AND MOP MANUFACTURING

ABTEX LLC—See The Malish Corp.; *U.S. Private*, pg. 4074
A.H.I. INVESTMENT INC.; *U.S. Private*, pg. 26
AMERICAN BRUSH COMPANY INC.—See A.H.I. Investment Inc.; *U.S. Private*, pg. 26
ANDERSON PRODUCTS, INC.—See Weiler Corporation; *U.S. Private*, pg. 4471
BBC CO., LTD.; *Int'l*, pg. 920
BRUSH RESEARCH MANUFACTURING COMPANY; *U.S. Private*, pg. 673
BUILD A SIGN LLC—See Cimpress plc; *Int'l*, pg. 1609
BUTLER HOME PRODUCTS, INC.; *U.S. Private*, pg. 697
COLGATE-PALMOLIVE EESKA REPUBLIKA SPOL. S R.O.—See Colgate-Palmolive Company; *U.S. Public*, pg. 532
DTM PACKAGING, LLC—See Granite Equity Partners LLC; *U.S. Private*, pg. 1755
DUPONT FILAMENTS EUROPE, B.V.—See Celanese Corporation; *U.S. Public*, pg. 465
ELTA MD, INC.—See Colgate-Palmolive Company; *U.S. Public*, pg. 532
FOAMPRO MANUFACTURING, INC.; *U.S. Private*, pg. 1556
FREUDENBERG HOUSEHOLD PRODUCTS LP—See Freudenberg SE; *Int'l*, pg. 2787
GOLDEN STAR INC.; *U.S. Private*, pg. 1733
GORDON BRUSH MFG CO, INC.; *U.S. Private*, pg. 1742
HARPER BRUSH WORKS INCORPORATED—See Griffon Corporation; *U.S. Public*, pg. 969
IMPACT FULFILLMENT SERVICES, LLC—See IFS Holdings, LLC; *U.S. Private*, pg. 2039
KWS MANUFACTURING COMPANY, LTD.—See Kadant Inc.; *U.S. Public*, pg. 1212
THE LIBMAN COMPANY; *U.S. Private*, pg. 4069
LINZER PRODUCTS CORP.; *U.S. Private*, pg. 2463
THE MALISH CORP.; *U.S. Private*, pg. 4074
MICHIGAN BRUSH MANUFACTURING COMPANY, INC.—See Gordon Brush Mfg Co, Inc.; *U.S. Private*, pg. 1742
MILL-ROSE COMPANY; *U.S. Private*, pg. 2730
OLD DOMINION BRUSH COMPANY, INC.—See Alamo Group Inc.; *U.S. Public*, pg. 71
POLYCLEAN INNOVATIONS, LLC; *U.S. Private*, pg. 3225
QUICKIE MANUFACTURING CORPORATION—See Newell Brands Inc.; *U.S. Public*, pg. 1514
SEALEZE—See Jason Industries, Inc.; *U.S. Private*, pg. 2190
SUNBELT MODULAR, INC.—See Littlejohn & Co., LLC; *U.S. Private*, pg. 2471
UNITED ROTARY BRUSH CORPORATION EASTERN DIVISION—See United Rotary Brush Corporation; *U.S. Private*, pg. 4296
UNITED ROTARY BRUSH CORPORATION OF CANADA—See United Rotary Brush Corporation; *U.S. Private*, pg. 4296
UNITED ROTARY BRUSH CORPORATION; *U.S. Private*, pg. 4296
UNITED ROTARY BRUSH—See United Rotary Brush Corporation; *U.S. Private*, pg. 4296
UNITED ROTARY BRUSH—See United Rotary Brush Corporation; *U.S. Private*, pg. 4296
WEILER CORPORATION; *U.S. Private*, pg. 4471
THE WOOSTER BRUSH COMPANY; *U.S. Private*, pg. 4139

339995 — BURIAL CASKET MANUFACTURING

AURORA CASKET COMPANY, LLC—See Matthews International Corporation; *U.S. Public*, pg. 1399
BATESVILLE CASKET UK LIMITED—See Hillenbrand, Inc.; *U.S. Public*, pg. 1035
BROWN-SERVICE FUNERAL HOMES CO. INC.—See Globe Life Inc.; *U.S. Public*, pg. 946
CASKET SHELLS, INC.; *U.S. Private*, pg. 783
CLARK GRAVE VAULT COMPANY; *U.S. Private*, pg. 913
THE FORT MILLER SERVICE CORP.—See The Fort Miller Group Inc.; *U.S. Private*, pg. 4030
FREEMAN METAL PRODUCTS INC.—See Matthews International Corporation; *U.S. Public*, pg. 1399
HILLENBRAND, INC.; *U.S. Public*, pg. 1035
J.M. HUTTON & CO., INC.; *U.S. Private*, pg. 2169
SOUTHERN HERITAGE CASKET CO.—See Matthews International Corporation; *U.S. Public*, pg. 1399
SUHOR INDUSTRIES INC.; *U.S. Private*, pg. 3850
UNGRICHT GMBH + CO KG—See Matthews International Corporation; *U.S. Public*, pg. 1400
YORK CASKET DEVELOPMENT COMPANY, INC.—See Matthews International Corporation; *U.S. Public*, pg. 1401

339999 — ALL OTHER MISCELLANEOUS MANUFACTURING

3M DEUTSCHLAND GMBH - SEPARATION AND PURIFICATION SCIENCES DIVISION—See 3M Company; *U.S. Public*, pg. 5
3M DEUTSCHLAND GMBH—See 3M Company; *U.S. Public*, pg. 5
3M FALL PROTECTION BUSINESS—See 3M Company; *U.S. Public*, pg. 5
3M HUNGARIA KFT.—See 3M Company; *U.S. Public*, pg. 6
9-BLOCK CO., LTD.—See EAT&HOLDINGS Co.,Ltd; *Int'l*, pg. 2277
ABFAR COMPANY (PUBLIC JOINT STOCK); *Int'l*, pg. 60
ACME PLASTICS, INC.; *U.S. Private*, pg. 61
ACTION FABRICATORS, INC.—See The Goldman Sachs Group, Inc.; *U.S. Public*, pg. 2080
ADERANS PHILIPPINES, INC.—See Aderans Co., Ltd.; *Int'l*, pg. 133
ADIRONDACK SCENIC, INC.; *U.S. Private*, pg. 79
ADOS PAKISTAN LIMITED; *Int'l*, pg. 152
A.D. USLUGA; *Int'l*, pg. 23
ADVANCED MEDICAL SOLUTIONS (PLYMOUTH) LTD.—See Advanced Medical Solutions Group plc; *Int'l*, pg. 161
ADVANCED SCIENTIFICS, INC.—See Thermo Fisher Scientific Inc.; *U.S. Public*, pg. 2145
AFG GROUP NIJMEGEN B.V.; *Int'l*, pg. 188
AIRBORNE SYSTEMS NORTH AMERICA INC.—See TransDigm Group Incorporated; *U.S. Public*, pg. 2181
AIRBORNE SYSTEMS NORTH AMERICA OF CA INC.—See TransDigm Group Incorporated; *U.S. Public*, pg. 2181
A.I. ROOT CO. - SAN ANTONO FACTORY—See A.I. Root Co.; *U.S. Private*, pg. 26
A.I. ROOT CO.; *U.S. Private*, pg. 26
AJKA CRYSTAL GLASS FACTORY LTD.—See Fotex Holding SE; *Int'l*, pg. 2752
A.J. PLAST PUBLIC COMPANY LIMITED; *Int'l*, pg. 24
ALAM SUBSEA PTE. LTD.—See Alam Maritim Resources Berhad; *Int'l*, pg. 290
ALBECCA INC.—See Berkshire Hathaway Inc.; *U.S. Public*, pg. 298
ALCORE BRIGANTINE SA—See M.C. Gill Corporation; *U.S. Private*, pg. 2528
ALEXANDER PLASTICS INC.; *U.S. Private*, pg. 164
ALLGREEN TIMBER PRODUCTS SDN. BHD.—See Evergreen Fibreboard Berhad; *Int'l*, pg. 2565
ALPRO A.D.; *Int'l*, pg. 375
ALUMTEK CORPORATION; *Int'l*, pg. 401
AMERICAN ACHIEVEMENT CORPORATION—See Fenway Partners, LLC; *U.S. Private*, pg. 1495
AMERICAN COVERS, INC.—See Energizer Holdings, Inc.; *U.S. Public*, pg. 760
AMPLIFON USA—See Amplifon S.p.A.; *Int'l*, pg. 435
AMT, INC.—See 3D Systems Corporation; *U.S. Public*, pg. 4
ANDIS COMPANY; *U.S. Private*, pg. 278
ANSELL PROTECTIVE SOLUTIONS AB—See Ansell Limited; *Int'l*, pg. 478
AQUAWORLD PRODUCTS—See Chem-Tainer Industries, Inc.; *U.S. Private*, pg. 871
ARABIAN CAN INDUSTRY LLC—See Al Ghurair Group; *Int'l*, pg. 277
ARGOS GESTION, S.L.U.—See RPM International Inc.; *U.S. Public*, pg. 1816
ARI UTARA SDN. BHD.—See Ajiya Berhad; *Int'l*, pg. 258
ARMOR DESIGNS, INC.; *U.S. Private*, pg. 331
ARMORTEX, INC.—See TCTCO, Inc.; *U.S. Private*, pg. 3973
AROMATIQUE INC.; *U.S. Private*, pg. 334
ARSAN TEKSTIL TICARET VE SANAYI AS; *Int'l*, pg. 580
ARTISAN DISPLAY & PACKAGING—See President Container Group, Inc.; *U.S. Private*, pg. 3254
ART LINE INC.; *U.S. Private*, pg. 340
ARTNATURE INC.; *Int'l*, pg. 585
ARTNATURE MALAYSIA SDN. BHD.—See Artnature Inc.; *Int'l*, pg. 585

339999 — ALL OTHER MISCELLAN...

ARTNATURE (SHANGHAI) INC.—See Artnature Inc.; *Int'l*, pg. 585
ARTNATURE SINGAPORE PTE. LTD.—See Artnature Inc.; *Int'l*, pg. 585
THE ART OF SHAVING - FL, LLC—See The Procter & Gamble Company; *U.S. Public*, pg. 2124
ASIA FIBER PUBLIC COMPANY LIMITED; *Int'l*, pg. 612
ASIA METAL PUBLIC COMPANY LIMITED; *Int'l*, pg. 613
ASIA PIONEER ENTERTAINMENT HOLDINGS LIMITED; *Int'l*, pg. 614
ASM INDUSTRIES INC.—See SERFILCO, Ltd.; *U.S. Private*, pg. 3613
ASP-HOLMBLAD A/S—See Gies Holding GmbH; *Int'l*, pg. 2969
AUGROS COSMETIC PACKAGING; *Int'l*, pg. 703
AVERY DENNISON OVERSEAS CORPORATION—See Avery Dennison Corporation; *U.S. Public*, pg. 243
AVICENNA TECHNOLOGY, INC.—See AMETEK, Inc.; *U.S. Public*, pg. 120
BALASORE ALLOYS LIMITED; *Int'l*, pg. 806
BALMER LAWRIE & CO. LTD.; *Int'l*, pg. 810
BAMKO, LLC—See Superior Group Of Companies, Inc.; *U.S. Public*, pg. 1966
BANDAI NAMCO AMUSEMENT AMERICA INC.—See BANDAI NAMCO Holdings Inc.; *Int'l*, pg. 829
BANSAL ROOFING PRODUCTS LIMITED; *Int'l*, pg. 854
BASF 3D PRINTING SOLUTIONS GMBH—See BASF SE; *Int'l*, pg. 871
BASF BULGARIA LTD.—See BASF SE; *Int'l*, pg. 872
BAT IBERICA, S.L.—See BAT S.p.A.; *Int'l*, pg. 888
BAT S.P.A.; *Int'l*, pg. 888
BEIJING LIER HIGH-TEMPERATURE MATERIALS CO., LTD.; *Int'l*, pg. 954
BELOVO PAPER MILL S.A.; *Int'l*, pg. 968
BERNINA INTERNATIONAL AG—See Bernina Schweiz AG; *Int'l*, pg. 989
BERSATU SAGO INDUSTRIES (MUKAH) SDN BHD—See EKA Noodles Berhad; *Int'l*, pg. 2337
BERSATU SAGO INDUSTRIES SDN BHD—See EKA Noodles Berhad; *Int'l*, pg. 2337
BRADY ETIKET VE ISARETLEME TICARET LTD. SIRKETI—See Brady Corporation; *U.S. Public*, pg. 378
BRADY KOREA LLP—See Brady Corporation; *U.S. Public*, pg. 378
BRADY TECHNOLOGIES (THAILAND) CO. LTD.—See Brady Corporation; *U.S. Public*, pg. 379
BRANDT & WALTHER GMBH; *Int'l*, pg. 1140
BSC FILTERS—See Dover Corporation; *U.S. Public*, pg. 678
BTV REAL-LEASING I GMBH—See Bank fur Tirol und Vorarlberg Ag; *Int'l*, pg. 838
THE BURKE PORTER GROUP; *U.S. Private*, pg. 4003
BUSHIROAD CREATIVE, INC.—See Bushiroad, Inc.; *Int'l*, pg. 1227
BUZTRONICS, INC.; *U.S. Private*, pg. 699
BYOTROL LIMITED; *Int'l*, pg. 1235
CALIFORNIA SCENTS, INC.—See Energizer Holdings, Inc.; *U.S. Public*, pg. 760
CANDLE-LITE—See Lancaster Colony Corporation; *U.S. Public*, pg. 1291
CANDLE WARMERS ETC. INC.; *U.S. Private*, pg. 733
CAPEWELL COMPONENTS COMPANY, LLC—See CapitalWorks, LLC; *U.S. Private*, pg. 742
CARL M LUNDH AB—See Aderans Co., Ltd.; *Int'l*, pg. 143
C-COM SATELLITE SYSTEMS INC.; *Int'l*, pg. 1239
CEAT LTD.; *Int'l*, pg. 1372
CERAMICA SAN LORENZO COLOMBIA S.A.—See Etex SA/NV; *Int'l*, pg. 2521
CERAMICA SAN LORENZO DE MEXICO S.A. DE C.V.—See Etex SA/NV; *Int'l*, pg. 2521
CERAMICA SAN LORENZO I.C.S.A—See Etex SA/NV; *Int'l*, pg. 2521
CERAMICA SAN LORENZO S.A.C.—See Grupo Lamosa S.A. de C.V.; *Int'l*, pg. 3131
CERAMICA SAN LORENZO U.S.A. INC.—See Etex SA/NV; *Int'l*, pg. 2521
CERAMTEC CZECH REPUBLIC S.R.O.—See BC Partners LLP; *Int'l*, pg. 923
CERAMTEC-ETEC GMBH—See BC Partners LLP; *Int'l*, pg. 923
CERAMTEC GMBH—See BC Partners LLP; *Int'l*, pg. 923
CERAMTEC IBERICA, INNOVATIVE CERAMIC ENGINEERING, S.L.—See BC Partners LLP; *Int'l*, pg. 923
CERAMTEC INNOVATIVE CERAMIC ENGINEERING, (M) SDN. BHD.—See BC Partners LLP; *Int'l*, pg. 923
CERAMTEC KOREA LTD., INNOVATIVE CERAMIC ENGINEERING—See BC Partners LLP; *Int'l*, pg. 923
CERAMTEC SUZHOU LTD.—See BC Partners LLP; *Int'l*, pg. 923
CERERIA SGARBI S.P.A.; *Int'l*, pg. 1422
CERTIKIN IBERICA S.L.U—See Fluidra SA; *Int'l*, pg. 2714
CERTIKIN ITALIA SPA—See Fluidra SA; *Int'l*, pg. 2714
CHARACTERS UNLIMITED INC.; *U.S. Private*, pg. 850
CHARLES INDUSTRIES, LTD.—See Amphenol Corporation; *U.S. Public*, pg. 129
CHECKERS INDUSTRIAL PRODUCTS LLC—See Audax Group, Limited Partnership; *U.S. Private*, pg. 386
CHTC FONG'S INTERNATIONAL COMPANY LIMITED—See China Hi-Tech Group Corporation; *Int'l*, pg. 1507
CIMENTS RENFORCES INDUSTRIES S.A.S.U.—See Etex SA/NV; *Int'l*, pg. 2521
CIRTRAN CORPORATION; *U.S. Public*, pg. 496
CLEAR EDGE FILTRATION SWEDEN AB—See Gilde Buy Out Partners B.V.; *Int'l*, pg. 2974
CLINE ACQUISITION CORP.—See Zurn Elkay Water Solutions Corporation; *U.S. Public*, pg. 2412
CLORACKS CORPORATION; *U.S. Public*, pg. 946
COAST SPAS MANUFACTURING INC; *Int'l*, pg. 1681
COINCO INC.; *U.S. Private*, pg. 964
COLOMER DENMARK A/S—See MacAndrews & Forbes Incorporated; *U.S. Private*, pg. 2534
COLOMER GERMANY GMBH—See MacAndrews & Forbes Incorporated; *U.S. Private*, pg. 2534
COLOMER ITALY SPA—See MacAndrews & Forbes Incorporated; *U.S. Private*, pg. 2534
COLOMER NETHERLANDS BV—See MacAndrews & Forbes Incorporated; *U.S. Private*, pg. 2534
COLOMER-PORTUGAL PRODUTOS COSMET. E PROFESIONAIS, LTDA—See MacAndrews & Forbes Incorporated; *U.S. Private*, pg. 2534
COLOMER PROFESSIONAL LTD. - LONDON—See MacAndrews & Forbes Incorporated; *U.S. Private*, pg. 2534
COLOMER PROFESSIONAL LTD.—See MacAndrews & Forbes Incorporated; *U.S. Private*, pg. 2534
COLOMER RUS CJSC—See MacAndrews & Forbes Incorporated; *U.S. Private*, pg. 2534
CONTAINMENT SOLUTIONS, INC.—See NOV, Inc.; *U.S. Public*, pg. 1544
COOPER SAFETY LTD.—See Eaton Corporation plc; *Int'l*, pg. 2278
CORONA CURTAIN MANUFACTURING CO. INC.—See Natco Products Corporation; *U.S. Private*, pg. 2838
COSCOLAB SDN. BHD.—See FCW Holdings Berhad; *Int'l*, pg. 2628
COSMO FERRITES LTD.—See Cosmo First Limited; *Int'l*, pg. 1812
CRAIG FRAMES, INC.; *U.S. Private*, pg. 1082
CRANE MERCHANDISING SYSTEMS, INC.—See Crane NXT, Co.; *U.S. Public*, pg. 591
CREATON HUNGARY KFT.—See Etex SA/NV; *Int'l*, pg. 2521
CROWN PACKAGING POLSKA SP.Z.O.O.—See Crown Holdings, Inc.; *U.S. Public*, pg. 597
CROWN PRODUCTS, LLC—See EBSCO Industries, Inc.; *U.S. Private*, pg. 1324
CR SERRATURE SPA—See Groupe SFPI SA; *Int'l*, pg. 3111
CRYOPAK CANADA - VANCOUVER PLANT—See Integreon Global; *U.S. Private*, pg. 2102
CTI INDUSTRIES—See Amphenol Corporation; *U.S. Public*, pg. 129
CULTI MILANO S.P.A.; *Int'l*, pg. 1877
CUSTOM MANUFACTURING & ENGINEERING, INC.; *U.S. Private*, pg. 1129
CYC DESIGN CORPORATION—See Aritzia, Inc.; *Int'l*, pg. 567
DADANT & SONS INC.; *U.S. Private*, pg. 1144
DAESUNG FINE TECH. CO., LTD.; *Int'l*, pg. 1909
DAIICHI KASEI CO., LTD.—See Abico Group; *Int'l*, pg. 61
DALLAS MANUFACTURING COMPANY INC.—See Brinkmann Corp.; *U.S. Private*, pg. 655
DALLI-WERKE GMBH & CO. KG; *Int'l*, pg. 1954
DATA I/O CHINA, LTD.—See Data I/O Corporation; *U.S. Public*, pg. 635
DATA I/O CORPORATION; *U.S. Public*, pg. 635
DATA I/O ELECTRONICS (SHANGHAI) CO., LTD.—See Data I/O Corporation; *U.S. Public*, pg. 635
D B INDUSTRIES, LLC—See 3M Company; *U.S. Public*, pg. 5
DELSBO CANDLE AB; *Int'l*, pg. 2015
DEMA ENGINEERING CO.; *U.S. Private*, pg. 1203
DENALI INCORPORATED—See NOV, Inc.; *U.S. Public*, pg. 1544
DENISON MAYES GROUP LTD.—See Amphenol Corporation; *U.S. Public*, pg. 130
DEPUY PRODUCTS, INC.—See Johnson & Johnson; *U.S. Public*, pg. 1195
DESHBANDHU POLYMER LIMITED; *Int'l*, pg. 2045
DEVELOPMENT ADVANCE SOLUTION CO., LTD.; *Int'l*, pg. 2087
DIAMOND GAME ENTERPRISES, INC.—See Flutter Entertainment plc; *Int'l*, pg. 2715
DIRECTED ENERGY SOLUTIONS; *U.S. Private*, pg. 1236
DMA ENTERPRISES; *U.S. Private*, pg. 1248
DOCK LEVELER MANUFACTURING; *U.S. Private*, pg. 1251
DONGBANG SHIP MACHINERY CO., LTD.; *Int'l*, pg. 2165
DONGKUK S&C CO., LTD.; *Int'l*, pg. 2168
DOREL INDUSTRIES, INC.; *Int'l*, pg. 2175
DPM FRAGRANCE—See The Thymes, LLC; *U.S. Private*, pg. 4127
DR. KURT WOLFF GMBH & CO. KG; *Int'l*, pg. 2194
DUNI OY—See Duni AB; *Int'l*, pg. 2226
DURACO SPECIALTY TAPES LLC—See OpenGate Capital Management, LLC; *U.S. Private*, pg. 3030
DURATHERM WINDOW CORPORATION—See Westny Building Products Co.; *U.S. Private*, pg. 4500
EASTAR OFFSHORE PTE. LTD.—See Alam Maritim Resources Berhad; *Int'l*, pg. 290
EBSCO INDUSTRIES, INC. - EBSCO CREATIVE CONCEPTS DIVISION—See EBSCO Industries, Inc.; *U.S. Private*, pg. 1325
EBSCO INDUSTRIES, INC. - KNIGHT & HALE DIVISION—See EBSCO Industries, Inc.; *U.S. Private*, pg. 1325
EDGETECH EUROPE GMBH—See Quanex Building Products Corp.; *U.S. Public*, pg. 1749
EDUCATIONAL INSIGHTS, INC.—See Learning Resources, Inc.; *U.S. Private*, pg. 2408
ELAUT N.V.—See Elaut International N.V.; *Int'l*, pg. 2343
ELECTRIC KHODRO SHARGH COMPANY; *Int'l*, pg. 2349
ELLIS & WATTS GLOBAL INDUSTRIES, LLC—See Berkshire Hathaway Inc.; *U.S. Public*, pg. 312
EMIL MULLER GMBH—See BC Partners LLP; *Int'l*, pg. 923
EMPIRE CANDLE COMPANY, LLC; *U.S. Private*, pg. 1384
EMSTEEL BUILDING MATERIALS PJSC; *Int'l*, pg. 2394
ENEFCO USA, INC.—See Argosy Capital Group, LLC; *U.S. Private*, pg. 321
ENGTEK INTERNATIONAL LIMITED—See Giovanni Agnelli B.V.; *Int'l*, pg. 2978
ENTAPACK PTY. LTD.—See Sealed Air Corporation; *U.S. Public*, pg. 1853
ENTERRISE CO. LTD.—See Capcom Co., Ltd.; *Int'l*, pg. 1302
ERWIN HALDER KG; *Int'l*, pg. 2500
E SYSTEMS TECHNOLOGY; *U.S. Private*, pg. 1301
ETHICON, LLC—See Johnson & Johnson; *U.S. Public*, pg. 1196
EUROPEENNE DE COUVERTURE AUTOMATIQUES, S.A.R.L.—See Fluidra SA; *Int'l*, pg. 2714
THE EVERCARE COMPANY—See Ultimate Evercare Holdings, LLC; *U.S. Private*, pg. 4277
EVERGREEN FIBREBOARD (JB) SDN. BHD.—See Evergreen Fibreboard Berhad; *Int'l*, pg. 2565
EVERGREEN HEAVY INDUSTRIAL CORP (M) BERHAD—See Evergreen Marine Corporation (Taiwan) Ltd.; *Int'l*, pg. 2566
EVERGREEN INDUSTRIES INC.; *U.S. Private*, pg. 1439
EVERGREEN PRODUCTS GROUP LIMITED; *Int'l*, pg. 2567
FAAB FABRICAUTO—See 3M Company; *U.S. Public*, pg. 6
FANTASIA ACCESSORIES LTD.; *U.S. Private*, pg. 1472
FASHY GMBH; *Int'l*, pg. 2621
FELTON INC.; *U.S. Private*, pg. 1494
FERD CORP.; *Int'l*, pg. 2637
FERROTEC S.R.L.—See Ferrotec Holdings Corporation; *Int'l*, pg. 2643
FIBRED-MARYLAND, INC.—See Arsenal Capital Management LP; *U.S. Private*, pg. 338
FIBROLITH DAMMSTOFFE GMBH—See Etex SA/NV; *Int'l*, pg. 2522
FIRE EATER A/S; *Int'l*, pg. 2678
FIRE EATER POLAND SP. Z OO—See Fire Eater A/S; *Int'l*, pg. 2678
FIRE EATER SPAIN—See Fire Eater A/S; *Int'l*, pg. 2678
FIRESTONE BUILDING PRODUCTS COMPANY, LLC - CORSICANA MANUFACTURING FACILITY—See Bridgestone Corporation; *Int'l*, pg. 1157
FIRESTONE BUILDING PRODUCTS COMPANY, LLC - FLORENCE MANUFACTURING FACILITY—See Bridgestone Corporation; *Int'l*, pg. 1157
FIRESTONE BUILDING PRODUCTS COMPANY, LLC - JACKSONVILLE MANUFACTURING FACILITY—See Bridgestone Corporation; *Int'l*, pg. 1157
FIRESTONE BUILDING PRODUCTS COMPANY, LLC - SALT LAKE CITY MANUFACTURING FACILITY—See Bridgestone Corporation; *Int'l*, pg. 1157
FIRSTFARMS A/S; *Int'l*, pg. 2688
FITTERS SDN BHD—See FITTERS Diversified Berhad; *Int'l*, pg. 2695
FLAVORS15, LLC; *U.S. Private*, pg. 1541
FLORIS OBDAM B.V.—See BAT S.p.A.; *Int'l*, pg. 889
FONON CORPORATION; *U.S. Private*, pg. 1559
FORMOPLAST PLC; *Int'l*, pg. 2734
FRAMED PICTURES ENTERPRISE INC.; *U.S. Private*, pg. 1586
FTS LEESONA, INCORPORATED; *U.S. Private*, pg. 1619
FULL CIRCLE HOME LLC; *U.S. Private*, pg. 1620
GALAXY MULTI RIDES; *U.S. Private*, pg. 1636
GALEO CONCEPT SA; *Int'l*, pg. 2872
GATEKEEPER SYSTEMS, INC.—See The Graham Group, Inc.; *U.S. Private*, pg. 4036
GCM MEDICAL & OEM, INC.—See Avista Capital Partners, L.P.; *U.S. Private*, pg. 408
GEMLINE FRAME CO. INC.; *U.S. Private*, pg. 1658
GENERAL FOAM PLASTICS CORP.; *U.S. Private*, pg. 1665
GENERAL WAX CO. INC.; *U.S. Private*, pg. 1668
GIES HOLDING GMBH; *Int'l*, pg. 2969
GIES KERZEN GMBH—See Gies Holding GmbH; *Int'l*, pg. 2969
GIES NATURA HANDELSGESELLSCHAFT MBH—See Gies Holding GmbH; *Int'l*, pg. 2969
GINNI FILAMENTS LIMITED; *Int'l*, pg. 2977
GLOBAL DRAW LIMITED—See Light & Wonder, Inc.; *U.S. Public*, pg. 1314

339999 — ALL OTHER MISCELLAN...

GLOBALTECH INDUSTRIES INC.; *U.S. Private*, pg. 1719
GLOSTER LIMITED; *Int'l*, pg. 3011
GMV INNOVATING SOLUTIONS, S.L.—See Grupo Tecnologico e Industrial GMV, S.A.; *Int'l*, pg. 3135
GODIVA LTD.—See IDEX Corp; *U.S. Public*, pg. 1090
GO GREEN GLOBAL TECHNOLOGIES CORP.; *U.S. Public*, pg. 949
GOLD STAR POWDERS UK—See Goodwin PLC; *Int'l*, pg. 3042
GOPROTO, INC.—See CORE Industrial Partners, LLC; *U.S. Private*, pg. 1048
GRAPEFRUIT USA, INC.; *U.S. Public*, pg. 958
GREAT PLAINES MODEL MANUFACTURING CO—See Hobbico, Inc.; *U.S. Private*, pg. 1958
GREENFIELDS BV—See ABN AMRO Group N.V.; *Int'l*, pg. 64
GREENFIELDS BV—See Gilde Buy Out Partners B.V.; *Int'l*, pg. 2974
GREENFIELDS SWISS AG—See ABN AMRO Group N.V.; *Int'l*, pg. 64
GREENFIELDS SWISS AG—See Gilde Buy Out Partners B.V.; *Int'l*, pg. 2974
GUARDIAN TRAFFIC SYSTEMS, LLC—See The Duchossois Group, Inc.; *U.S. Private*, pg. 4023
GUO ANDA CO., LTD.; *Int'l*, pg. 3186
GUTJAHR SYSTEMTECHNIK GMBH; *Int'l*, pg. 3189
HAEDUK POWERWAY CO., LTD.; *Int'l*, pg. 3205
HAKUGEN EARTH CO., LTD.—See Earth Corporation; *Int'l*, pg. 2268
HALOS CORPORATION—See Hanwa Co., Ltd.; *Int'l*, pg. 3262
HANWHA ADVANCED MATERIALS CO., LTD.—See Hanwha Group; *Int'l*, pg. 3264
HANZA AB; *Int'l*, pg. 3267
HENAN REBECCA HAIR PRODUCTS CO., LTD.; *Int'l*, pg. 3343
HERCULES HOISTS LIMITED—See Bajaj Auto Ltd.; *Int'l*, pg. 804
HESCO ARMOR, INC.—See CVC Capital Partners SICAV-FIS S.A.; *Int'l*, pg. 1886
HESS AUSTRIA GMBH—See Gauselmann AG; *Int'l*, pg. 2890
HESS CASH SYSTEMS GMBH & CO. KG—See Gauselmann AG; *Int'l*, pg. 2890
HESS SCHWEIZ AG—See Gauselmann AG; *Int'l*, pg. 2890
HIDROPNEVMOTEHNIKA AD; *Int'l*, pg. 3384
HIMALAYAN DISTILLERY LIMITED; *Int'l*, pg. 3396
HIREL SYSTEMS, LLC-MARSHALL—See Vishay Intertechnology, Inc.; *U.S. Public*, pg. 2302
HOBBY LOBBY MANUFACTURING—See Hob-Lob Limited Partnership; *U.S. Private*, pg. 1958
HOFFINGER INDUSTRIES, INC.; *U.S. Private*, pg. 1959
HOSTI INTERNATIONAL GMBH; *Int'l*, pg. 3486
HUBBARD SCIENTIFIC—See Geneve Holdings Corp.; *U.S. Private*, pg. 1671
HUDSON RIVER INLAY INC.—See United Vision Group Inc.; *U.S. Private*, pg. 4301
HUMANETICS INNOVATIVE SOLUTIONS, INC.—See Bridgepoint Group Plc; *Int'l*, pg. 1155
HYDRALIGN—See Butler Automatic, Inc.; *U.S. Private*, pg. 696
HYDRAULIC ELEMENTS & SYSTEMS PLC; *Int'l*, pg. 3546
HYFUSIN GROUP HOLDINGS LTD.; *Int'l*, pg. 3549
I3SYSTEM INC.; *Int'l*, pg. 3567
ICYBREEZE COOLING LLC—See Solo Brands, Inc.; *U.S. Public*, pg. 1901
IDENTA CORP.; *Int'l*, pg. 3592
IFB INDUSTRIES LIMITED; *Int'l*, pg. 3598
IMECO, INC.—See J.F. Lehman & Company, Inc.; *U.S. Private*, pg. 2163
INDUSTRIAL ACOUSTICS COMPANY, INC.—See AEA Investors LP; *U.S. Private*, pg. 114
INDUSTRIAL ACOUSTICS COMPANY, LTD.—See AEA Investors LP; *U.S. Private*, pg. 114
INDUSTRIAL COMPONENTS INC.; *U.S. Private*, pg. 2065
INGE GMBH—See DuPont de Nemours, Inc.; *U.S. Public*, pg. 694
INTEGRATED ENVIRONMENTAL TECHNOLOGIES, LTD.; *U.S. Public*, pg. 1136
INTERMAT—See Edgewater Capital Partners, L.P.; *U.S. Private*, pg. 1335
INTERNATIONAL HAIRGOODS INC.—See Aderans Co., Ltd.; *Int'l*, pg. 143
ITT HIGH PRECISION MANUFACTURED PRODUCTS (WUXI) CO., LTD.—See ITT Inc.; *U.S. Public*, pg. 1178
JAMES H. HEAL & COMPANY LIMITED—See Battery Ventures, L.P.; *U.S. Private*, pg. 489
JANSSEN-CILAG NV—See Johnson & Johnson; *U.S. Public*, pg. 1197
J&K NOVELTY, INC.; *U.S. Private*, pg. 2154
JOHNSON SYSTEM, INC.—See AGCO Corporation; *U.S. Public*, pg. 59
JTC PRISON INDUSTRIES, LLC—See Liquidity Services, Inc.; *U.S. Public*, pg. 1321
JUNE TAILOR, INC.—See WILsquare Capital LLC; *U.S. Private*, pg. 4532
KALMAR INDUSTRIES CORPORATION—See Cargotec Corporation; *Int'l*, pg. 1327

KAYWOODIE—See S.M. Frank & Co., Inc.; *U.S. Private*, pg. 3518
KEMEERA INC.—See CORE Industrial Partners, LLC; *U.S. Private*, pg. 1049
KE PROTEZIONI SOLARI SRL—See BAT S.p.A.; *Int'l*, pg. 889
KG PROCESS INNOVATIONS, S.R.O.—See Koch Industries, Inc.; *U.S. Private*, pg. 2331
K&H MANUFACTURING LLC—See Central Garden & Pet Company; *U.S. Public*, pg. 473
KICTEAM, INC.—See Argosy Capital Group, LLC; *U.S. Private*, pg. 321
KIDDE TECHNOLOGIES INC.—See RTX Corporation; *U.S. Public*, pg. 1822
KING TESTER CORPORATION—See Salt Creek Capital Management, LLC; *U.S. Private*, pg. 3533
KLEN INTERNATIONAL (74) PTY LTD.—See Avantor, Inc.; *U.S. Public*, pg. 242
KNUD NIELSEN COMPANY INC.; *U.S. Private*, pg. 2325
KOCH-ASIA PACIFIC, INC.—See Koch Industries, Inc.; *U.S. Private*, pg. 2332
KOTLOSTROENE JSCO—See Favorit Hold AD; *Int'l*, pg. 2623
KTM INDUSTRIES INC.—See TemperPack Technologies, Inc.; *U.S. Private*, pg. 3963
LA-CO INDUSTRIES EUROPE S.A.S.—See LA-CO Industries Markal Co., Inc.; *U.S. Private*, pg. 2370
LAFRANCE CORPORATION - J.A.T. CREATIVE PRODUCTS DIVISION—See LaFrance Corporation; *U.S. Private*, pg. 2373
LAMPLIGHT FARMS INCORPORATED—See W.C. Bradley Co.; *U.S. Private*, pg. 4419
LASER EXCEL, INC.; *U.S. Private*, pg. 2395
LEGS (SHANGHAI) TRADING COMPANY, LTD.—See CL Holdings Inc.; *Int'l*, pg. 1640
L'HOTELLIER—See RTX Corporation; *U.S. Public*, pg. 1822
LILJEHOLMENS STEARINFABRIKS AB—See Gies Holding GmbH; *Int'l*, pg. 2969
LODGING ACCESS SYSTEMS, LLC—See CCL Industries Inc.; *Int'l*, pg. 1367
LUVU BRANDS, INC.; *U.S. Public*, pg. 1349
M.A.C. TECHNOLOGY (M) SDN. BHD.—See Abico Group; *Int'l*, pg. 61
MARCK & ASSOCIATES, INC.; *U.S. Private*, pg. 2571
MARQUIS CORP.—See Monomoy Capital Partners LLC; *U.S. Private*, pg. 2772
MARYLAND ORTHOTICS & PROSTHETICS CO., INC.—See D&J Sales Co. LLC; *U.S. Private*, pg. 1138
MAST TECHNOLOGIES, INC.—See Arcline Investment Management LP; *U.S. Private*, pg. 314
MCM GROUP—See EBSCO Industries, Inc.; *U.S. Private*, pg. 1325
M.C.S. INDUSTRIES INC.; *U.S. Private*, pg. 2528
M CUBED TECHNOLOGIES, INC.—See Coherent Corp.; *U.S. Public*, pg. 529
MEDLINE DERMAL MANAGEMENT SYSTEMS—See Medline Industries, LP; *U.S. Private*, pg. 2657
MEGA SPIELGERATE ENTWICKLUNGS- UND VERTRIEBSGESELLSCHAFT MBH & CO. KG- See Gauselmann AG; *Int'l*, pg. 2890
MEGGITT POLYMER SOLUTIONS—See Parker Hannifin Corporation; *U.S. Public*, pg. 1641
MERCK HEALTHCARE PRODUCTS—See Merck & Co., Inc.; *U.S. Public*, pg. 1419
MICHELL BEARINGS LTD—See British Engines Ltd.; *Int'l*, pg. 1171
MIDDLE EAST MARKETING GROUP; *U.S. Private*, pg. 2711
MIDWEST COMPOSITE TECHNOLOGIES, LLC—See CORE Industrial Partners, LLC; *U.S. Private*, pg. 1049
MIDWEST PROTOTYPING LLC; *U.S. Private*, pg. 2722
MILLER MFG. CO.; *U.S. Private*, pg. 2735
MINE SAFETY APPLIANCES COMPANY, LLC—See MSA Safety Incorporated; *U.S. Public*, pg. 1482
MINE SAFETY APPLIANCES COMPANY-SAFETY PRODUCTS DIVISION—See MSA Safety Incorporated; *U.S. Public*, pg. 1482
MINE SAFETY APPLIANCES COMPANY-SAFETY PRODUCTS DIVISION—See MSA Safety Incorporated; *U.S. Public*, pg. 1482
MIREX AQUAPURE SOLUTIONS, LP—See BDT Capital Partners, LLC; *U.S. Public*, pg. 502
MSA SAFETY INCORPORATED; *U.S. Public*, pg. 1481
MUENCH-KREUZER CANDLE COMPANY; *U.S. Private*, pg. 2810
MYSTIC SCENIC STUDIOS INC.; *U.S. Private*, pg. 2826
NANAMICA INC.—See Goldwin, Inc.; *Int'l*, pg. 3035
NATIONAL STARCH & CHEMICAL (THAILAND) LTD.—See Ingredion Incorporated; *U.S. Public*, pg. 1124
NATURAL DECORATIONS, INC.; *U.S. Private*, pg. 2867
NAVAM LANKA LTD.—See Gravita India Limited; *Int'l*, pg. 3062
NEST FRAGRANCES, LLC—See Eurazeo SE; *Int'l*, pg. 2529
NEWHYDROGEN, INC.; *U.S. Public*, pg. 1515
NIELSEN & BAINBRIDGE, LLC - NIELSEN MANUFACTURING—See Sycamore Partners Management, LP; *U.S. Private*, pg. 3896

NIELSEN & BAINBRIDGE, LLC—See Sycamore Partners Management, LP; *U.S. Private*, pg. 3896
NMI HEALTH, INC.; *U.S. Private*, pg. 2931
THE NOBLE COMPANY—See Federal Process Corporation; *U.S. Private*, pg. 1489
NOMACORC, LLC—See Global Leisure Partners LLP; *Int'l*, pg. 2998
NOMACORC, LLC—See Noel Group, LLC; *U.S. Private*, pg. 2933
NORAFIN INDUSTRIES (GERMANY) GMBH—See DZ BANK AG Deutsche Zentral-Genossenschaftsbank; *Int'l*, pg. 2245
NORDLICHT GMBH—See The Carlyle Group Inc.; *U.S. Public*, pg. 2052
NORIMAX SDN. BHD.—See Eonmetall Group Berhad; *Int'l*, pg. 2458
NORLAINE INC.; *U.S. Private*, pg. 2938
NORTHERN LIGHTS ENTERPRISES, INC.—See Zippo Manufacturing Company, Inc.; *U.S. Private*, pg. 4606
OBERTHUR TECHNOLOGIES (BEIJING) CO LTD—See Advent International Corporation; *U.S. Private*, pg. 102
OBERTHUR TECHNOLOGIES COLOMBIA—See Advent International Corporation; *U.S. Private*, pg. 102
OBERTHUR TECHNOLOGIES DE MEXICO, S. DE R.L. DE C.V.—See Advent International Corporation; *U.S. Private*, pg. 103
OBERTHUR TECHNOLOGIES DENMARK A/S—See Advent International Corporation; *U.S. Private*, pg. 102
OBERTHUR TECHNOLOGIES FINLAND SEGENMARK OY—See Advent International Corporation; *U.S. Private*, pg. 102
OBERTHUR TECHNOLOGIES INC.—See Advent International Corporation; *U.S. Private*, pg. 103
OBERTHUR TECHNOLOGIES KFT—See Advent International Corporation; *U.S. Private*, pg. 103
OBERTHUR TECHNOLOGIES KK—See Advent International Corporation; *U.S. Private*, pg. 103
OBERTHUR TECHNOLOGIES KOREA INC.—See Advent International Corporation; *U.S. Private*, pg. 103
OBERTHUR TECHNOLOGIES LATVIA SIA—See Advent International Corporation; *U.S. Private*, pg. 103
OBERTHUR TECHNOLOGIES LTDA—See Advent International Corporation; *U.S. Private*, pg. 103
OBERTHUR TECHNOLOGIES LTD—See Advent International Corporation; *U.S. Private*, pg. 103
OBERTHUR TECHNOLOGIES NORWAY A/S—See Advent International Corporation; *U.S. Private*, pg. 103
OBERTHUR TECHNOLOGIES OF AMERICA CORP.—See Advent International Corporation; *U.S. Private*, pg. 103
OBERTHUR TECHNOLOGIES SOUTH AFRICA (PTY) LTD—See Advent International Corporation; *U.S. Private*, pg. 103
OBERTHUR TECHNOLOGIES SUCURSAL EM PORTUGAL—See Advent International Corporation; *U.S. Private*, pg. 103
OBERTHUR TECHNOLOGIES SWEDEN ACSC AB—See Advent International Corporation; *U.S. Private*, pg. 103
OBERTHUR TECHNOLOGIES TEKNOLOJI SANAYI VE TICARET LTD.—See Advent International Corporation; *U.S. Private*, pg. 103
OLDCASTLE LAWN & GARDEN, INC.—See CRH plc; *U.S. Private*, pg. 1846
ORANJTEK CO.; *U.S. Private*, pg. 3038
OSBORN INTERNATIONAL LTDA—See Jason Industries, Inc.; *U.S. Private*, pg. 2190
OSBORN INTERNATIONAL—See Jason Industries, Inc.; *U.S. Private*, pg. 2190
OUT INTERNATIONAL INC.—See NCH Corporation; *U.S. Private*, pg. 2876
OWENS-ILLINOIS GENERAL INC.—See O-I Glass, Inc.; *U.S. Public*, pg. 1559
PACIFIC COAST COMPOSITES, INC.—See Carl Marks & Co., Inc.; *U.S. Private*, pg. 763
PACIFIC REGISTER CO. INC—See Cottonwood Acquisitions LLC; *U.S. Private*, pg. 1064
PARAGON DECORS INC.; *U.S. Private*, pg. 3090
PARTYLITE GMBH—See The Carlyle Group Inc.; *U.S. Public*, pg. 2052
PARTYLITE HANDELSGESELLSCHAFT M.B.H.—See The Carlyle Group Inc.; *U.S. Public*, pg. 2052
PARTYLITE, INC.—See The Carlyle Group Inc.; *U.S. Public*, pg. 2052
PARTYLITE TRADING S.A.—See The Carlyle Group Inc.; *U.S. Public*, pg. 2052
PATINA-V—See Norlaine Inc.; *U.S. Private*, pg. 2938
PDC BRAZELETES Y PRODUCTOS S. DE R.L. DE C.V.—See Brady Corporation; *U.S. Public*, pg. 379
PEERLESS UMBRELLA CO., INC.; *U.S. Private*, pg. 3129
PEPROTECH, INC.—See Thermo Fisher Scientific Inc.; *U.S. Public*, pg. 2151
PLASTI-FAB, INC.; *U.S. Private*, pg. 3198
PLASTI-FAB LTD. - CROSSFIELD PLANT—See The Riverside Company; *U.S. Private*, pg. 4109
POWERCART SYSTEMS INC.—See Active Control Technology Inc.; *Int'l*, pg. 120
PRESS AND SINTER TECHNICS DE MEXICO, S.A. DE C.V.—See BC Partners LLP; *Int'l*, pg. 923

339999 — ALL OTHER MISCELLAN...

PRICE'S PATENT CANDLE LTD.—See Cereria Sgarbi S.p.A.; *Int'l*, pg. 1422
PROCTER & GAMBLE ARGENTINA SRL—See The Procter & Gamble Company; *U.S. Public*, pg. 2121
PROCTER & GAMBLE (CHINA) LTD.—See The Procter & Gamble Company; *U.S. Public*, pg. 2121
PROCTER & GAMBLE GULF FZE—See The Procter & Gamble Company; *U.S. Public*, pg. 2122
PROCTER & GAMBLE HOLDING FRANCE S.A.S.—See The Procter & Gamble Company; *U.S. Public*, pg. 2122
PROCTER & GAMBLE INDUSTRIAL E COMERCIAL LTDA.—See The Procter & Gamble Company; *U.S. Public*, pg. 2122
PROCTER & GAMBLE TUKETIM MALLARI SANAYII A.S.—See The Procter & Gamble Company; *U.S. Public*, pg. 2123
PRODUCTION RESOURCE GROUP—See The Jordan Company, L.P.; *U.S. Private*, pg. 4061
PROFILE PRODUCTS LLC—See Platte River Ventures, LLC; *U.S. Private*, pg. 3211
PROMAT AG—See Etex SA/NV; *Int'l*, pg. 2522
PROMAT AUSTRALIA PTY LTD.—See Etex SA/NV; *Int'l*, pg. 2522
PROMAT BUILDING SYSTEM PTE LTD.—See Etex SA/NV; *Int'l*, pg. 2522
PROMAT B.V.—See Etex SA/NV; *Int'l*, pg. 2522
PROMAT CHINA LTD.—See Etex SA/NV; *Int'l*, pg. 2522
PROMAT GLASGOW LTD.—See Etex SA/NV; *Int'l*, pg. 2522
PROMAT GMBH—See Etex SA/NV; *Int'l*, pg. 2522
PROMAT GMBH—See Etex SA/NV; *Int'l*, pg. 2522
PROMAT (MALAYSIA) SDN. BHD.—See Etex SA/NV; *Int'l*, pg. 2522
PROMAT S.A.S.—See Etex SA/NV; *Int'l*, pg. 2522
PROMAT SHANGAI LTD.—See Etex SA/NV; *Int'l*, pg. 2522
PROMAT S.P.A.—See Etex SA/NV; *Int'l*, pg. 2522
PROMAT S.R.O.—See Etex SA/NV; *Int'l*, pg. 2522
PROMAT TOP SP. Z O.O.—See Etex SA/NV; *Int'l*, pg. 2522
PROMAT UK LTD.—See Etex SA/NV; *Int'l*, pg. 2522
PROTEDYNE CORPORATION—See Laboratory Corporation of America Holdings; *U.S. Public*, pg. 1287
PROTO TECHNOLOGIES, INC.—See Sea Lion Corporation; *U.S. Private*, pg. 3582
PT HIJAU LESTARI RAYA FIBREBOARD—See Evergreen Fibreboard Berhad; *Int'l*, pg. 2565
PUPPET WORKSHOP INC.; *U.S. Private*, pg. 3304
PURE HEALTH SOLUTIONS, INC.—See BDT Capital Partners, LLC; *U.S. Private*, pg. 502
QUENCH USA, INC.—See BDT Capital Partners, LLC; *U.S. Private*, pg. 502
QUIRKY INC.; *U.S. Private*, pg. 3329
RADIANS, INC.; *U.S. Private*, pg. 3343
R&D ENTERPRISES, INC.—See Ruby Has LLC; *U.S. Private*, pg. 3332
RE-GRIP INC.—See Chicago Aerosol, LLC; *U.S. Private*, pg. 877
RESEARCH PRODUCTS INTERNATIONAL CORPORATION; *U.S. Private*, pg. 3404
RIOT PLATFORMS, INC.; *U.S. Public*, pg. 1799
ROSS PROMOTIONAL PRODUCTS LIMITED—See Altitude Group plc; *Int'l*, pg. 393
SAFARILAND LLC - DEFENSE TECHNOLOGY—See Kanders & Company, Inc.; *U.S. Private*, pg. 2259
SAFARILAND, LLC—See Kanders & Company, Inc.; *U.S. Private*, pg. 2259
SA FEATHER CO., INC.—See Bain Capital, LP; *U.S. Private*, pg. 452
SANOMEDICS, INC.; *U.S. Private*, pg. 3546
SANTA'S BEST CRAFT, LTD.; *U.S. Private*, pg. 3547
SANTEC HOLDINGS CORPORATION—See EXEO Group Inc.; *Int'l*, pg. 2584
SAWSTOP, LLC; *U.S. Private*, pg. 3558
SCENTSY, INC.; *U.S. Private*, pg. 3562
SEALEGS (US) CORPORATION—See Future Mobility Solutions; *Int'l*, pg. 2857
SECTOR 10, INC.; *U.S. Public*, pg. 1855
SELECTO INC.—See Axel Johnson Gruppen AB; *Int'l*, pg. 765
SERGEANT'S PET CARE PRODUCTS, INC.—See Bansk Group LLC; *U.S. Private*, pg. 469
SHANGHAI CHUN YUAN STEEL INDUSTRY CO., LTD.—See Chun Yuan Steel Industry Co., Ltd.; *Int'l*, pg. 1596
SHIROKI CORPORATION (THAILAND) LTD.—See AISIN Corporation; *Int'l*, pg. 253
SIGNCAD SYSTEMS, INC.—See Bentley Systems, Inc.; *U.S. Private*, pg. 297
SILVER SEAS SHIPPING LLC—See Belhasa Group of Companies; *Int'l*, pg. 964
SINIAT B.V.—See Etex SA/NV; *Int'l*, pg. 2522
SINIAT NV—See Etex SA/NV; *Int'l*, pg. 2522
S.M. FRANK & CO., INC.; *U.S. Private*, pg. 3518
SMITHERS-OASIS NORTH AMERICA—See Smithers-Oasis Company; *U.S. Private*, pg. 3697
SM LIGHTERS BV—See Philip Morris International Inc.; *U.S. Public*, pg. 1687
SM PHILIPPINES INC.—See Philip Morris International Inc.; *U.S. Public*, pg. 1687
SOCIEDAD INDUSTRIAL PIZARRENO S.A—See Etex SA/NV; *Int'l*, pg. 2522

SOCIEDAD INDUSTRIAL ROMERAL S.A.—See Etex SA/NV; *Int'l*, pg. 2523
SOCIEDAD INDUSTRIAL TEJAS DE CHENA S.A.—See Etex SA/NV; *Int'l*, pg. 2523
SOLARPRO HOLDING AD—See Alfa Finance Holding AD; *Int'l*, pg. 307
SOLVIX SOLUTIONS, LLC; *U.S. Private*, pg. 3711
SOUTH BEACH SMOKE LLC—See Turning Point Brands, Inc.; *U.S. Public*, pg. 2205
SOUTHERN SPARS EUROPE A/S—See Windway Capital Corp.; *U.S. Private*, pg. 4540
SOUTHERN SPARS INTERNATIONAL (PVT) LTD—See Windway Capital Corp.; *U.S. Private*, pg. 4540
SOUTHERN SPARS LTD - CAPE TOWN FACILITY—See Windway Capital Corp.; *U.S. Private*, pg. 4540
SOUTHERN SPARS LTD - RIG PRO RHODE ISLAND FACILITY—See Windway Capital Corp.; *U.S. Private*, pg. 4540
SOUTHERN SPARS LTD—See Windway Capital Corp.; *U.S. Private*, pg. 4540
STAGING CONCEPTS—See Trex Company, Inc.; *U.S. Public*, pg. 2188
STRATASYS DIRECT, INC. - BELTON PLANT—See The Lamarjean Group, Inc.; *U.S. Private*, pg. 4067
STRATASYS DIRECT, INC. - DETROIT PLANT—See The Lamarjean Group, Inc.; *U.S. Private*, pg. 4067
STRATASYS DIRECT, INC.—See The Lamarjean Group, Inc.; *U.S. Private*, pg. 4067
STRUCTURAL INDUSTRIES, INC.; *U.S. Private*, pg. 3842
STRYKER TRAUMA GMBH—See Stryker Corporation; *U.S. Public*, pg. 1957
SWEDISH MATCH INDUSTRIES AB—See Philip Morris International Inc.; *U.S. Public*, pg. 1687
SWEDISH MATCH LIGHTERS BV—See Philip Morris International Inc.; *U.S. Public*, pg. 1687
SYARIKAT BUKIT GRANITE SDN. BHD.—See AbleGroup Berhad; *Int'l*, pg. 63
T2 INTERNATIONAL LLC; *U.S. Private*, pg. 3913
TAOS - FL, LLC—See The Procter & Gamble Company; *U.S. Public*, pg. 2123
TASZ, INC.; *U.S. Private*, pg. 3935
TASZ, INC.—See TASZ, Inc.; *U.S. Private*, pg. 3935
TCP RELIABLE MANUFACTURING, INC.—See Integreon Global; *U.S. Private*, pg. 2102
TEGRAL HOLDINGS LTD.—See Etex SA/NV; *Int'l*, pg. 2523
TENCATE PROTECTIVE FABRICS HOLDING BV—See ABN AMRO Group N.V.; *Int'l*, pg. 65
TENCATE PROTECTIVE FABRICS HOLDING BV—See Gilde Buy Out Partners B.V.; *Int'l*, pg. 2975
TENCATE PROTECTIVE FABRICS USA INC.—See ABN AMRO Group N.V.; *Int'l*, pg. 65
TENCATE PROTECTIVE FABRICS USA INC.—See Gilde Buy Out Partners B.V.; *Int'l*, pg. 2975
TEXEL TECHNICAL MATERIALS, INC.—See Lydall, Inc.; *U.S. Public*, pg. 1350
TEX-TECH INDUSTRIES, INC.—See Arlington Capital Partners LLC; *U.S. Private*, pg. 328
TIANJIN JL RAILWAY TRANSPORT EQUIPMENT LTD.—See CRRC Corporation Limited; *Int'l*, pg. 1859
TIGERTURF NZ LIMITED—See ABN AMRO Group N.V.; *Int'l*, pg. 65
TIGERTURF NZ LIMITED—See Gilde Buy Out Partners B.V.; *Int'l*, pg. 2975
TIGERTURF (UK) LIMITED—See ABN AMRO Group N.V.; *Int'l*, pg. 65
TIGERTURF (UK) LIMITED—See Gilde Buy Out Partners B.V.; *Int'l*, pg. 2975
TITAN D.D.—See Groupe SFPI SA; *Int'l*, pg. 3111
TITMAN TIP TOOLS LTD—See Checkit plc; *Int'l*, pg. 1459
TRIDENT MANUFACTURING, INC.—See Clean Energy Technologies, Inc.; *U.S. Public*, pg. 508
TRI-M, INC.—See DAIICHIKOUSHO CO., LTD.; *Int'l*, pg. 1930
UAB ETERNIT BALTIC—See Etex SA/NV; *Int'l*, pg. 2523
ULTRATEC JEWELRY SUPPLIES (GUANGZHOU) LTD.—See Goodwin PLC; *Int'l*, pg. 3042
UMBELINO MONTEIRO S.A—See Groupe Bruxelles Lambert SA; *Int'l*, pg. 3100
VALERO CAPITAL PARTNERS LLC; *U.S. Private*, pg. 4331
VERNACARE LIMITED—See H.I.G. Capital, LLC; *U.S. Private*, pg. 1832
THE VERNON GRAPHICS GROUP—See The Vernon Company; *U.S. Private*, pg. 4130
VERNON PROMOTIONS—See The Vernon Company; *U.S. Private*, pg. 4130
VIDEO GAMING TECHNOLOGIES, INC.—See Aristocrat Leisure Limited; *Int'l*, pg. 566
VIDEO GAMING TECHNOLOGIES, INC. - TULSA—See Aristocrat Leisure Limited; *Int'l*, pg. 567
WAHL CLIPPER CORPORATION; *U.S. Private*, pg. 4426
WALKER EXHAUST (THAILAND) CO. LTD.—See Apollo Global Management, Inc.; *U.S. Public*, pg. 163
WALKER MAGNETICS NATIONAL, LTD.—See Alliance Holdings, Inc.; *U.S. Private*, pg. 183
WALKER NATIONAL, INC.—See Alliance Holdings, Inc.; *U.S. Private*, pg. 183
WANIT FULGURIT GMBH—See Etex SA/NV; *Int'l*, pg. 2523

CORPORATE AFFILIATIONS

WAX LYRICAL LIMITED—See The Carlyle Group Inc.; *U.S. Public*, pg. 2052
THE W.E. BASSETT COMPANY—See Levine Leichtman Capital Partners, LLC; *U.S. Public*, pg. 2436
WESTCOAST MOULDING & MILLWORK LIMITED—See E.R. Probyn Ltd.; *Int'l*, pg. 2260
WHOLESALE SUPPLIES PLUS, LLC—See Incline MGMT Corp.; *U.S. Private*, pg. 2054
WICKS UNLIMITED, INC.—See Edwin B. Stimpson Company, Inc.; *U.S. Private*, pg. 1342
WILL & BAUMER; *U.S. Private*, pg. 4521
WINDHAGER HANDELSGESMBH—See Gale Pacific Limited; *Int'l*, pg. 2872
WINTEX-DEPARTMENT VLISCO—See General Atlantic Service Company, L.P.; *U.S. Private*, pg. 1661
WOODGRAIN MILLWORK, INC. - NATURE'S DIVISION—See Woodgrain, Inc.; *U.S. Private*, pg. 4558
THE WOODSTREAM CORPORATION—See Vestar Capital Partners, LLC; *U.S. Private*, pg. 4372
WOOLRICH JAPAN INC.—See Goldwin, Inc.; *Int'l*, pg. 3035
WOONGJIN ENERGY CO., LTD.—See SunPower Corporation; *U.S. Public*, pg. 1965
WRS GROUP LTD.; *U.S. Private*, pg. 4574
YANKEE CANDLE COMPANY (EUROPE) LIMITED—See Newell Brands Inc.; *U.S. Public*, pg. 1515
THE YANKEE CANDLE COMPANY, INC.—See Newell Brands Inc.; *U.S. Public*, pg. 1515
YUASA MEMBRANE SYSTEMS CO., LTD.—See GS Yuasa Corporation; *Int'l*, pg. 3143
ZIPPO CANADA SALES, LLC—See Hyde's Distribution; *Int'l*, pg. 3546
ZIPPO ITALIA S.R.L.—See Zippo Manufacturing Company, Inc.; *U.S. Private*, pg. 4606
ZIPPO S.A.—See Zippo Manufacturing Company, Inc.; *U.S. Private*, pg. 4606

423110 — AUTOMOBILE AND OTHER MOTOR VEHICLE MERCHANT WHOLESALERS

1060038 ONTARIO LTD; *Int'l*, pg. 1
3WM UGANDA LIMITED—See Envipro Holdings Inc.; *Int'l*, pg. 2454
401 AUTO DEALERS EXCHANGE; *Int'l*, pg. 11
7. JULI MAJKE JEVROSIME 47-49 A.D.; *Int'l*, pg. 14
ABC BUS COMPANIES, INC.; *U.S. Private*, pg. 35
ABC COMPANIES INC.—See ABC Bus Companies, Inc.; *U.S. Private*, pg. 35
ABVI AYMOND BRUNEL VEHICULES INDUSTRIEL; *Int'l*, pg. 74
AB VOLVO PENTA—See AB Volvo; *Int'l*, pg. 42
ACADIA AUTO GROUP INC.; *U.S. Private*, pg. 46
ACTIVE SPORTS, INC.—See Camping World Holdings, Inc.; *U.S. Public*, pg. 427
ADESA ARKANSAS, LLC—See OPENLANE, Inc.; *U.S. Public*, pg. 1606
ADESA ATLANTA, LLC—See OPENLANE, Inc.; *U.S. Public*, pg. 1606
ADESA AUCTIONS PITTSBURGH—See OPENLANE, Inc.; *U.S. Public*, pg. 1606
ADESA COLORADO, LLC—See OPENLANE, Inc.; *U.S. Public*, pg. 1606
ADESA-GOLDEN GATE—See OPENLANE, Inc.; *U.S. Public*, pg. 1607
ADESA, INC.—See OPENLANE, Inc.; *U.S. Public*, pg. 1606
ADESA-KANSAS CITY—See OPENLANE, Inc.; *U.S. Public*, pg. 1607
ADESA PHOENIX, LLC—See OPENLANE, Inc.; *U.S. Public*, pg. 1607
ADESA-SEATTLE—See OPENLANE, Inc.; *U.S. Public*, pg. 1607
ADTRANS HINO PTY LTD—See Eagers Automotive Limited; *Int'l*, pg. 2263
ADTRANS TRUCK CENTRE PTY. LTD.—See Eagers Automotive Limited; *Int'l*, pg. 2263
AFIN SLOVAKIA S.R.O.—See CNH Industrial N.V.; *Int'l*, pg. 1674
AGROOPREMA ODZACI A.D.; *Int'l*, pg. 220
AICHI EUROPE B.V.—See Aichi Corporation; *Int'l*, pg. 229
AL-BABTAIN GROUP; *Int'l*, pg. 284
AL-FUTTAIM AUTO & MACHINERY COMPANY LLC—See AB Volvo; *Int'l*, pg. 42
AL HABTOOR MOTORS COMPANY LLC—See Al Habtoor Group LLC; *Int'l*, pg. 278
AL-HAJ FAW MOTORS PRIVATE LIMITED—See Al-Haj Group of Companies; *Int'l*, pg. 285
ALHAMRANI COMPANY FOR INVESTMENT IN TRADE LIMITED—See Alhamrani Group; *Int'l*, pg. 319
ALLENTOWN MACK SALES & SERVICE, INC.; *U.S. Private*, pg. 180
ALLSAFE JUNGFALK AUSTRALIA—See allsafe JUNGFALK GmbH & Co. KG; *Int'l*, pg. 360
ALLSAFE JUNGFALK BENELUX—See allsafe JUNGFALK GmbH & Co. KG; *Int'l*, pg. 360
ALL STAR TOYOTA—See All Star Automotive Group; *U.S. Private*, pg. 172
ALPEN SRL—See Grimaldi Industri AB; *Int'l*, pg. 3086
ALPINE AUTO BROKERS INC.; *U.S. Public*, pg. 85

423110 — AUTOMOBILE AND OTHE...

AMA GROUP LIMITED; *Int'l*, pg. 403
AMERICAN EQUIPMENT & TRAILER, INC.; *U.S. Private*, pg. 232
AMERICAN HAVAL MOTOR TECHNOLOGY, LLC—See Great Wall Motor Company Limited; *Int'l*, pg. 3065
AMERICAN HONDA MOTOR CO., INC.—See Honda Motor Co., Ltd.; *Int'l*, pg. 3459
AMERICAN TRUCK & BUS INC.; *U.S. Private*, pg. 257
AMERICA'S BODY COMPANY; *U.S. Private*, pg. 220
AMERIMARK GROUP AG; *Int'l*, pg. 423
ANADOLU ARACLAR TICARET A.S.—See AG Anadolu Grubu Holding A.S.; *Int'l*, pg. 197
ANCHORAGE SUZUKI ARCTIC CAT; *U.S. Private*, pg. 274
ANSA MOTORS LIMITED—See ANSA McAL Limited; *Int'l*, pg. 476
ARDEN TUNBRIDGE WELLS LIMITED—See Lithia Motors, Inc.; *U.S. Public*, pg. 1321
ARENA AUTO AUCTION—See Cox Enterprises, Inc.; *U.S. Private*, pg. 1076
ARIZONA AUTO AUCTION—See Cox Enterprises, Inc.; *U.S. Private*, pg. 1076
ARIZONA RV CENTERS, LLC—See Camping World Holdings, Inc.; *U.S. Public*, pg. 427
ARKANSAS KENWORTH INC.—See Murphy-Hoffman Company; *U.S. Private*, pg. 2816
ARKCORE, INC.; *Int'l*, pg. 568
AROUND THE CLOCK FREIGHTLINER GROUP LLC—See Penske Automotive Group, Inc.; *U.S. Public*, pg. 1664
ARRMA-DURANGO LTD.—See Hobbico, Inc.; *U.S. Private*, pg. 1958
ARROWHEAD EQUIPMENT INC.; *U.S. Private*, pg. 336
ASAHI CO., LTD.; *Int'l*, pg. 592
ASHOK LEYLAND (NIGERIA) LIMITED—See Hinduja Group Ltd.; *Int'l*, pg. 3398
ASSOCIATED MOTOR HOLDINGS (PTY) LIMITED—See Dubai World Corporation; *Int'l*, pg. 2221
ASTLEFORD INTERNATIONAL TRUCKS, INC.; *U.S. Private*, pg. 360
ASTON MARTIN LAGONDA OF NORTH AMERICA, INC.—See Efad Real Estate Company; *Int'l*, pg. 2318
ATKINSON TRUCK SALES INC.; *U.S. Private*, pg. 369
ATLANTA AUTO AUCTION, INC.—See Cox Enterprises, Inc.; *U.S. Private*, pg. 1076
ATLAS TERMINAL CO. INC—See Atlas World Group, Inc.; *U.S. Private*, pg. 380
AUCTION BROADCASTING CO. LLC; *U.S. Private*, pg. 385
AUDIOXTRA PTY. LTD.—See Autobacs Seven Co., Ltd.; *Int'l*, pg. 725
AUTOBACS CAR SERVICE MALAYSIA SDN. BHD.—See Autobacs Seven Co., Ltd.; *Int'l*, pg. 725
AUTOBACS FRANCE SAS—See Autobacs Seven Co., Ltd.; *Int'l*, pg. 725
AUTOBACS MANAGEMENT SERVICE CO., LTD.—See Autobacs Seven Co., Ltd.; *Int'l*, pg. 725
AUTOBACS NAGASAKI CO., LTD.—See Autobacs Seven Co., Ltd.; *Int'l*, pg. 726
AUTOGRANA A.D.; *Int'l*, pg. 726
AUTO KUCA LESKOVAC A.D.; *Int'l*, pg. 725
AUTOMAKEDONIJA A.D.; *Int'l*, pg. 730
AUTOMETAL S.A.—See Cie Automotive S.A.; *Int'l*, pg. 1604
AUTOMOTIVE ACADEMY B.V.—See LKQ Corporation; *U.S. Public*, pg. 1333
AUTO PROMINENCE (M) SDN BHD—See DRB-HICOM Berhad; *Int'l*, pg. 2201
AUTORESIDUOS S.L.U.—See Copart, Inc.; *U.S. Public*, pg. 574
AUTOSTOP LEUVEN NV—See LKQ Corporation; *U.S. Public*, pg. 1334
AUTOTRADER GROUP, INC.—See Cox Enterprises, Inc.; *U.S. Private*, pg. 1076
AVIA ASHOK LEYLAND RUS—See Hinduja Group Ltd.; *Int'l*, pg. 3398
AXIAL R/C, INC.—See Hobbico, Inc.; *U.S. Private*, pg. 1958
A-Z BUS SALES, INC.; *U.S. Private*, pg. 22
AZF AUTOMOTIVE GROUP INC.; *U.S. Private*, pg. 415
BADGER TRUCK AND AUTOMOTIVE GROUP, INC.; *U.S. Private*, pg. 424
BALTIMORE FREIGHTLINER; *U.S. Private*, pg. 462
BANCO HONDA S.A—See Honda Motor Co., Ltd.; *Int'l*, pg. 3460
BANNERS CO., LTD.; *Int'l*, pg. 851
BANNER TRUCK & TRAILER SALES, INC.; *U.S. Private*, pg. 469
BARR INTERNATIONAL INC.; *U.S. Private*, pg. 479
BAY CITIES AUTO AUCTION—See Cox Enterprises, Inc.; *U.S. Private*, pg. 1076
BELHASA TRADING & DEVELOPMENT COMPANY—See Belhasa Group of Companies; *Int'l*, pg. 964
BELLA GROUP; *U.S. Private*, pg. 519
BELL EQUIPMENT COMPANY—See Rotunda Capital Partners LLC; *U.S. Private*, pg. 3488
BERGE AUTOMOCION, SL—See Berge y Cia SA; *Int'l*, pg. 979
BERJAYA BRILLIANCE AUTO SDN BHD—See Berjaya Corporation Berhad; *Int'l*, pg. 984
BERMAZ AUTO BERHAD—See Berjaya Corporation Berhad; *Int'l*, pg. 983

BIG H AUTO AUCTION SERVICES, INC.—See Cox Enterprises, Inc.; *U.S. Private*, pg. 1076
BILL WALSH CHEVROLET—See Bill Walsh Automotive Group; *U.S. Private*, pg. 558
BING POWER ORIGIN KFT.—See BING Power Systems GmbH; *Int'l*, pg. 1033
BING POWER SYSTEMS GMBH; *Int'l*, pg. 1033
BLACK HILLS TRUCK & TRAILER INC.—See North American Truck & Trailer, Inc.; *U.S. Private*, pg. 2941
BLAINE JENSEN RV CENTERS, LLC—See Camping World Holdings, Inc.; *U.S. Public*, pg. 427
BLUECITY UK LTD.—See Financiere de L'Odet; *Int'l*, pg. 2666
BLUECUB SAS—See Financiere de L'Odet; *Int'l*, pg. 2666
BMW AUSTRALIA LTD.—See Bayerische Motoren Werke Aktiengesellschaft; *Int'l*, pg. 911
BMW AUSTRIA GESELLSCHAFT M.B.H.—See Bayerische Motoren Werke Aktiengesellschaft; *Int'l*, pg. 911
BMW CANADA INC.—See Bayerische Motoren Werke Aktiengesellschaft; *Int'l*, pg. 912
BMW CHINA AUTOMOTIVE TRADING LTD—See Bayerische Motoren Werke Aktiengesellschaft; *Int'l*, pg. 911
BMW DE MEXICO, S. A. DE C. V.—See Bayerische Motoren Werke Aktiengesellschaft; *Int'l*, pg. 912
BMW FRANCE S.A.—See Bayerische Motoren Werke Aktiengesellschaft; *Int'l*, pg. 911
BMW IBERICA S.A.—See Bayerische Motoren Werke Aktiengesellschaft; *Int'l*, pg. 911
BMW ITALIA S.P.A.—See Bayerische Motoren Werke Aktiengesellschaft; *Int'l*, pg. 911
BMW JAPAN CORP.—See Bayerische Motoren Werke Aktiengesellschaft; *Int'l*, pg. 911
BMW M GMBH GESELLSCHAFT FUR INDIVIDUELLE AUTOMOBILE—See Bayerische Motoren Werke Aktiengesellschaft; *Int'l*, pg. 912
BMW NEDERLAND B.V.—See Bayerische Motoren Werke Aktiengesellschaft; *Int'l*, pg. 911
BMW NEW ZEALAND LTD.—See Bayerische Motoren Werke Aktiengesellschaft; *Int'l*, pg. 912
BMW OF NORTH AMERICA, LLC—See Bayerische Motoren Werke Aktiengesellschaft; *Int'l*, pg. 912
BMW (UK) LTD—See Bayerische Motoren Werke Aktiengesellschaft; *Int'l*, pg. 911
BOB MAXEY FORD, INC-BOB MAXEY LINCOLN MERCURY—See Bob Maxey Ford, Inc.; *U.S. Private*, pg. 604
BODILY RV, INC.—See Camping World Holdings, Inc.; *U.S. Public*, pg. 427
BOLT MOBILITY CORP.; *U.S. Private*, pg. 611
BOMBAY CYCLE & MOTOR AGENCY LIMITED; *Int'l*, pg. 1104
BONERTS (PTY) LTD—See Combined Motor Holdings Limited; *Int'l*, pg. 1709
BOON KOON FLEET MANAGEMENT SDN BHD—See Chin Hin Group Berhad; *Int'l*, pg. 1480
BRIDGESTONE CYCLE EAST JAPAN SALES CO., LTD.—See Bridgestone Corporation; *Int'l*, pg. 1158
BRP INC.—See Bain Capital, LP; *U.S. Private*, pg. 431
BURNSIDE RV CENTERS, LLC—See Camping World Holdings, Inc.; *U.S. Public*, pg. 427
BURNS INDUSTRIAL EQUIPMENT, INC.; *U.S. Private*, pg. 691
CABLEPRICE (NZ) LTD.—See Hitachi, Ltd.; *Int'l*, pg. 3415
CAMBRIA AUTOMOTIVE COMPANIES; *U.S. Private*, pg. 726
CAMPING WORLD, INC.—See Camping World Holdings, Inc.; *U.S. Public*, pg. 427
CAMPING WORLD RV SALES, LLC—See Camping World Holdings, Inc.; *U.S. Public*, pg. 427
CAPITAL CITY AUTO AUCTION INC.; *U.S. Private*, pg. 739
CARCO INTERNATIONAL, INC.; *U.S. Private*, pg. 749
CARCOUNTRY MOTORS, INC.—See AutoNation, Inc.; *U.S. Public*, pg. 233
CARGURUS, INC.; *U.S. Public*, pg. 435
CARS GALORE LTD.; *Int'l*, pg. 1346
CENTA CORPORATION—See Zurn Elkay Water Solutions Corporation; *U.S. Public*, pg. 2413
CENTENNIAL LEASING INC.; *U.S. Private*, pg. 809
CENTIGON MEXICO—See Capital People S.A.; *Int'l*, pg. 1312
CENTIGON VENEZUELA—See Capital People S.A.; *Int'l*, pg. 1312
CENTRAL CALIFORNIA TRUCK AND TRAILER SALES, LLC—See Rush Enterprises, Inc.; *U.S. Public*, pg. 1826
CENTRAL FLORIDA AUTO AUCTION—See Cox Enterprises, Inc.; *U.S. Private*, pg. 1076
CENTRAL ILLINOIS TRUCKS, INC.; *U.S. Private*, pg. 821
CENTROCAMIONES INC.; *U.S. Private*, pg. 830
CERNI MOTOR SALES, INC.; *U.S. Private*, pg. 841
CHANGAN BERJAYA AUTO SDN BHD—See Berjaya Corporation Berhad; *Int'l*, pg. 984
CHANGCHUN RESEARCH INSTITUTE FOR MECHANICAL SCIENCE CO., LTD.—See China National Machinery Industry Corporation; *Int'l*, pg. 1531
CHARLATTE OF AMERICA—See FAYAT SAS; *Int'l*, pg. 2625
CHARLATTE (UK) LIMITED—See FAYAT SAS; *Int'l*, pg. 2625

CHARTERED MOTORS PVT LTD—See Chartered Logistics Ltd.; *Int'l*, pg. 1454
CHASTANG ENTERPRISES, INC.; *U.S. Private*, pg. 860
CHERY SOUTH AFRICA—See Chery Automobile Co., Ltd.; *Int'l*, pg. 1472
CHEVROLET OF COLUMBUS, INC.—See General Motors Company; *U.S. Public*, pg. 923
CHEVROLET SUISSE S.A.—See General Motors Company; *U.S. Public*, pg. 926
CHICAGO BUS SALES INC.—See Cook-Illinois Corp.; *U.S. Private*, pg. 1038
CHICAGO MACK SALES & SERVICES INC.; *U.S. Private*, pg. 878
CHINA AUTOMOBILE TRADING CO., LTD.; *Int'l*, pg. 1484
CHINA CMIIC ENGINEERING & CONSTRUCTION CORP.—See China National Machinery Industry Corporation; *Int'l*, pg. 1531
CHINA HARMONY AUTO HOLDING LIMITED; *Int'l*, pg. 1506
CHINA NATIONAL AUTOMATION CONTROL SYSTEM CORP.—See China National Machinery Industry Corporation; *Int'l*, pg. 1531
CHINA NATIONAL AUTOMOTIVE INDUSTRY INTERNATIONAL CORP.—See China National Machinery Industry Corporation; *Int'l*, pg. 1531
CHINA NATIONAL ERZHONG GROUP CO.—See China National Machinery Industry Corporation; *Int'l*, pg. 1531
CHINA NATIONAL GENERAL MACHINERY ENGINEERING CORP—See China National Machinery Industry Corporation; *Int'l*, pg. 1531
CHINA NATIONAL HEAVY MACHINERY CORPORATION—See China National Machinery Industry Corporation; *Int'l*, pg. 1531
CHINA NATIONAL MACHINERY & EQUIPMENT I/E CORP—See China National Machinery Industry Corporation; *Int'l*, pg. 1531
CHINA OCEAN AVIATION GROUP INCORPORATION—See China National Machinery Industry Corporation; *Int'l*, pg. 1531
CHINA PERFECT MACHINERY INDUSTRY CORP, LTD.—See China National Machinery Industry Corporation; *Int'l*, pg. 1531
CHINA SINOMACH HEAVY INDUSTRY CORPORATION LTD.—See China National Machinery Industry Corporation; *Int'l*, pg. 1531
CHONBANG AUTO CO., LTD.—See Chonbang Co., Ltd.; *Int'l*, pg. 1578
CHOWGULE INDUSTRIES PVT. LTD.—See Chowgule & Company Pvt. Ltd.; *Int'l*, pg. 1585
CITY AUTO SALES, LLC.; *U.S. Private*, pg. 905
CLARK TRUCK EQUIPMENT—See Harsh International, Inc.; *U.S. Private*, pg. 1872
CLEVELAND MACK SALES INC.; *U.S. Private*, pg. 941
COLONIAL FORD TRUCK SALES, INC.; *U.S. Private*, pg. 970
COLONIAL TRUCK SALES INC.—See Colonial Ford Truck Sales, Inc.; *U.S. Private*, pg. 971
COLORADO KENWORTH INC.—See Murphy-Hoffman Company; *U.S. Private*, pg. 2816
COLORADO-WEST EQUIPMENT INC.; *U.S. Private*, pg. 975
COMMERCE AUTO GROUP; *U.S. Private*, pg. 982
COPART OF ARKANSAS, INC.—See Copart, Inc.; *U.S. Public*, pg. 575
COPART OF CONNECTICUT, INC.—See Copart, Inc.; *U.S. Public*, pg. 575
COPART OF LOUISIANA, INC.—See Copart, Inc.; *U.S. Public*, pg. 575
COPART OF OKLAHOMA, INC.—See Copart, Inc.; *U.S. Public*, pg. 575
COPART OF WASHINGTON, INC.—See Copart, Inc.; *U.S. Public*, pg. 574
COPART SALVAGE AUTO AUCTIONS, INC.—See Copart, Inc.; *U.S. Public*, pg. 575
COPART UK LIMITED—See Copart, Inc.; *U.S. Public*, pg. 575
CORRY AUTO DEALERS EXCHANGE, INC.—See Huron Capital Partners LLC; *U.S. Private*, pg. 2012
CROSSROADS FORD TRUCK SALES INC.; *U.S. Private*, pg. 1108
CROSSROADS TRAILER SALES & SERVICE; *U.S. Private*, pg. 1108
CRTS INC.; *U.S. Private*, pg. 1113
CSM COMPANIES, INC.; *U.S. Private*, pg. 1117
C&S MOTORS, INC.; *U.S. Private*, pg. 704
CUMBERLAND INTERNATIONAL TRUCKS, INC.; *U.S. Private*, pg. 1122
CUMMINS EASTERN MARINE, INC.—See Cummins Inc.; *U.S. Public*, pg. 805
CYCLE EXPRESS, LLC—See Copart, Inc.; *U.S. Public*, pg. 575
DAF VEICOLI INDUSTRIALI S.P.A.—See PACCAR Inc.; *U.S. Public*, pg. 1630
DAIGLE & HOUGHTON INC.; *U.S. Private*, pg. 1145
DALES AUTO MART INC.; *U.S. Private*, pg. 1149
DALLAS AUTO AUCTION INC.—See Cox Enterprises, Inc.; *U.S. Private*, pg. 1076
DALLAS COPART SALVAGE AUTO AUCTIONS LP—See

3809

Copart, Inc.; *U.S. Public*, pg. 575
DANTONE INC.; *U.S. Private*, pg. 1158
DCH MAMARONECK LLC—See Lithia Motors, Inc.; *U.S. Public*, pg. 1322
DCH MOTORS LLC—See Lithia Motors, Inc.; *U.S. Public*, pg. 1322
DCH SIMI VALLEY INC.—See Lithia Motors, Inc.; *U.S. Public*, pg. 1322
DEANCO AUCTION & REAL ESTATE CO., INC.; *U.S. Private*, pg. 1185
DEFILIPPO BROS MOTORCARS AUTO SALES INC; *U.S. Private*, pg. 1191
DELEK AUTOMOTIVE SYSTEMS, LTD.—See Delek Group Ltd.; *Int'l*, pg. 2011
DELEK MOTORS LTD.—See Delek Group Ltd.; *Int'l*, pg. 2011
DELLENBACH MOTORS; *U.S. Private*, pg. 1197
DELRAY IMPORTS INC.; *U.S. Private*, pg. 1199
DENSO CHUGOKU CORPORATION—See Denso Corporation; *Int'l*, pg. 2029
DENVER AUTO AUCTION—See Cox Enterprises, Inc.; *U.S. Private*, pg. 1076
DEWAN AUTOMATIVE ENGINEERING LTD.—See Dewan Farooque Motors Limited; *Int'l*, pg. 2091
DFW CAMPER CORRAL INC.; *U.S. Private*, pg. 1220
DIRECT CHASSISLINK, INC.—See Apollo Global Management, Inc.; *U.S. Public*, pg. 150
DIRECT CHASSIS LLC—See China International Marine Containers (Group) Co., Ltd.; *Int'l*, pg. 1511
DOGUS OTOMOTIV SERVIS VE TICARET A.S.; *Int'l*, pg. 2155
DON'S TRUCK SALES INC.; *U.S. Private*, pg. 1259
DORAL-VW, LLC—See Lithia Motors, Inc.; *U.S. Public*, pg. 1322
DUNCAN FREIGHTLINER, INC.—See Lonestar Freightliner Group, Ltd.; *U.S. Private*, pg. 2489
DUSTYS CAMPER WORLD, LLC—See Camping World Holdings, Inc.; *U.S. Public*, pg. 427
EAGERS AUTOMOTIVE LIMITED; *Int'l*, pg. 2263
EBRAHIM K. KANOO COMPANY B.S.C.; *Int'l*, pg. 2286
EDAG DO BRASIL LTDA.—See ATON GmbH; *Int'l*, pg. 689
EDAG ENGINEERING CZ SPOL. S.R.O.—See ATON GmbH; *Int'l*, pg. 688
EDAG ENGINEERING & DESIGN INDIA PRIV. LTD.—See ATON GmbH; *Int'l*, pg. 688
EDAG ENGINEERING SCHWEIZ GMBH—See ATON GmbH; *Int'l*, pg. 689
EDAG ENGINEERING S.R.L.—See ATON GmbH; *Int'l*, pg. 689
EDAG HOLDING SDN. BHD.—See ATON GmbH; *Int'l*, pg. 689
EDAG HUNGARY KFT.—See ATON GmbH; *Int'l*, pg. 689
EDAG INC.—See ATON GmbH; *Int'l*, pg. 689
EDAG JAPAN CO., LTD.—See ATON GmbH; *Int'l*, pg. 689
EDAG MEXICO, S.A. DE C.V.—See ATON GmbH; *Int'l*, pg. 689
EDAG PRODUCTION SOLUTION CZ S.R.O.—See ATON GmbH; *Int'l*, pg. 689
EDAG PRODUCTION SOLUTIONS KOREA LTD.—See ATON GmbH; *Int'l*, pg. 689
EDAG TECHNOLOGIES INDIA PRIV. LTD.—See ATON GmbH; *Int'l*, pg. 689
EFFINGHAM TRUCK SALES INC.; *U.S. Private*, pg. 1343
ELLIOTT EQUIPMENT COMPANY INCORPORATED; *U.S. Private*, pg. 1364
ELLIOTT EQUIPMENT COMPANY INC.; *U.S. Private*, pg. 1364
EMIL FREY HOLDING AG; *Int'l*, pg. 2380
EMIL FREY NEDERLAND NV—See Emil Frey Holding AG; *Int'l*, pg. 2380
E.M. THARP INC.; *U.S. Private*, pg. 1306
ENKEI WHEELS (INDIA) LTD.; *Int'l*, pg. 2440
EQ INDIANA AUTO & TRUCK AUCTION INC.; *U.S. Private*, pg. 1414
EQUIPMENTFACTS LLC—See Sandhills Publishing Company; *U.S. Private*, pg. 3543
EUROCHARM INNOVATION CO., LTD.—See Eurocharm Holdings Co., Ltd.; *Int'l*, pg. 2533
EUROSPORTS GLOBAL LIMITED; *Int'l*, pg. 2558
EVERSET SA; *Int'l*, pg. 2568
E-W TRUCK & EQUIPMENT CO., INC.; *U.S. Private*, pg. 1303
EXEDY GLOBALPARTS CORPORATION—See Exedy Corporation; *Int'l*, pg. 2581
FAMILY MANAGEMENT CORPORATION; *U.S. Private*, pg. 1471
FEDERAL-MOGUL SEALING SYSTEMS GMBH—See Apollo Global Management, Inc.; *U.S. Public*, pg. 161
FEDERAL-MOGUL SHANGHAI BEARING CO., LTD.—See Apollo Global Management, Inc.; *U.S. Public*, pg. 162
FERMAN AUTOMOTIVE MANAGEMENT SERVICES, INC.; *U.S. Private*, pg. 1497
FERRARI JAPAN KK—See Ferrari N.V.; *Int'l*, pg. 2639
FERRARI NORTH AMERICA, INC.—See Ferrari N.V.; *Int'l*, pg. 2639
FIRST INDUSTRIES CORPORATION—See Velocity Vehicle Group; *U.S. Private*, pg. 4354
FLEETCO INC.; *U.S. Private*, pg. 1542

FLEET LEASE DISPOSAL INC.; *U.S. Private*, pg. 1541
FLEET TRUCK SALES, INC.—See Werner Enterprises, Inc.; *U.S. Public*, pg. 2349
FLOYD'S TRUCK CENTER, INC.; *U.S. Private*, pg. 1552
FLY-E GROUP, INC.; *U.S. Public*, pg. 860
FOLEY RV CENTER, LLC—See Camping World Holdings, Inc.; *U.S. Public*, pg. 427
FORD MOTOR COMPANY BRASIL LTDA.—See Ford Motor Company; *U.S. Public*, pg. 865
FORT WORTH VEHICLE AUCTION—See Cox Enterprises, Inc.; *U.S. Private*, pg. 1076
FOUAD ALGHANIM & SONS AUTOMOTIVE CO.—See Fouad Alghanim & Sons Group of Companies; *Int'l*, pg. 2753
FOX & JAMES INC.; *U.S. Private*, pg. 1583
FPT INDUSTRIAL ARGENTINA S.A.—See CNH Industrial N.V.; *Int'l*, pg. 1675
FREDERICKSBURG AUTO AUCTION—See Cox Enterprises, Inc.; *U.S. Private*, pg. 1076
FREIGHTLINER OF UTAH, LLC; *U.S. Private*, pg. 1608
FRESNO AUTO DEALERS AUCTION—See Cox Enterprises, Inc.; *U.S. Private*, pg. 1076
FRONTIER INTERNATIONAL TRUCKS; *U.S. Private*, pg. 1615
FUJIAN ZHANGZHOU DEVELOPMENT CO., LTD.; *Int'l*, pg. 2820
FURUKAWA ROCK DRILL EUROPE B.V.—See Furukawa Co., Ltd.; *Int'l*, pg. 2847
GENERAL GMC TRUCK SALES & SERVICE, INC.—See SF Holding Corp.; *U.S. Private*, pg. 3621
GENERAL MOTORS CHILE INDUSTRIA AUTOMOTRIZ LIMITADA—See General Motors Company; *U.S. Public*, pg. 924
GENERAL MOTORS EGYPT S.A.E.—See General Motors Company; *U.S. Public*, pg. 924
GIN-COR INDUSTRIES INC.; *U.S. Private*, pg. 2976
GOLF CART WORLD, INC.—See LPI, Inc.; *U.S. Private*, pg. 2507
GOODPASTURE MOTOR COMPANY, INC.—See Thompson Distribution Company, Inc.; *U.S. Private*, pg. 4159
GREATER CHICAGO AUTO AUCTION—See Cox Enterprises, Inc.; *U.S. Private*, pg. 1076
GROHMANN ENGINEERING TRADING (SHANGHAI) CO. LTD.—See Tesla, Inc.; *U.S. Public*, pg. 2021
GROUPE PAROT SA; *Int'l*, pg. 3109
GS&L ENTERPRISES INCORPORATED; *U.S. Private*, pg. 1800
GULF ASHLEY MOTORS LIMITED—See Hinduja Group Ltd.; *Int'l*, pg. 3398
GULF STATES TOYOTA, INC.—See The Friedkin Group, Inc.; *U.S. Private*, pg. 4031
HAKKANI MOTORS LTD.—See Hakkani Group; *Int'l*, pg. 3219
HALLA MEISTER LTD.—See Halla Group; *Int'l*, pg. 3229
HAP SENG TRUCKS DISTRIBUTION SDN. BHD.—See Hap Seng Consolidated Berhad; *Int'l*, pg. 3268
HARADA ASIA-PACIFIC LTD.—See HARADA INDUSTRY CO., LTD.; *Int'l*, pg. 3269
HARLEY-DAVIDSON AUSTRALIA PTY. LIMITED—See Harley-Davidson, Inc.; *U.S. Public*, pg. 984
HARLEY-DAVIDSON CANADA GP INC.—See Harley-Davidson, Inc.; *U.S. Public*, pg. 985
HARLEY-DAVIDSON CANADA LP—See Harley-Davidson, Inc.; *U.S. Public*, pg. 984
HARLEY-DAVIDSON DEALER SYSTEMS, INC.—See Harley-Davidson, Inc.; *U.S. Public*, pg. 984
HARLEY-DAVIDSON FINANCIAL SERVICES CANADA, INC.—See Harley-Davidson, Inc.; *U.S. Public*, pg. 985
HARLEY-DAVIDSON FRANCE SAS—See Harley-Davidson, Inc.; *U.S. Public*, pg. 985
HARLEY-DAVIDSON MOTOR COMPANY OPERATIONS, INC.—See Harley-Davidson, Inc.; *U.S. Public*, pg. 985
HARLEY-DAVIDSON (THAILAND) COMPANY LIMITED—See Harley-Davidson, Inc.; *U.S. Public*, pg. 985
HARRISON TRUCK CENTERS, INC.—See Omaha Truck Center Inc.; *U.S. Private*, pg. 3014
H-D TOMAHAWK INDUSTRIAL PARK, LLC—See Harley-Davidson, Inc.; *U.S. Public*, pg. 985
HEINRICH SCHMIDT GMBH & CO. KG; *Int'l*, pg. 3325
HELKAMA-AUTO OY; *Int'l*, pg. 3331
HENDERSON-HY, LLC—See Lithia Motors, Inc.; *U.S. Public*, pg. 1322
HENDRICKSON USA LLC—See The Boler Company; *U.S. Private*, pg. 3996
HERCEGOVINA AUTO D.D.; *Int'l*, pg. 3361
HERITAGE EQUIPMENT INC.; *U.S. Private*, pg. 1922
HEWS COMPANY LLC; *U.S. Private*, pg. 1928
HIGH LIFTER PRODUCTS, INC.—See Morgan Stanley; *U.S. Public*, pg. 1474
HILL TRUCK SALES INC.; *U.S. Private*, pg. 1945
HONDA AUTOMOVILES ESPANA S.A.—See Honda Motor Co., Ltd.; *Int'l*, pg. 3460
HONDA CANADA INC.—See Honda Motor Co., Ltd.; *Int'l*, pg. 3461
HONDA CZECH REPUBLIC LTD.—See Honda Motor Co., Ltd.; *Int'l*, pg. 3461

HONDA HUNGARY KFT.—See Honda Motor Co., Ltd.; *Int'l*, pg. 3461
HONDA KOREA CO., LTD.—See Honda Motor Co., Ltd.; *Int'l*, pg. 3461
HONDA MOTOR DE ARGENTINA S.A.—See Honda Motor Co., Ltd.; *Int'l*, pg. 3462
HONDA MOTOR DE CHILE S.A.—See Honda Motor Co., Ltd.; *Int'l*, pg. 3462
HONDA MOTOR RUS LLC—See Honda Motor Co., Ltd.; *Int'l*, pg. 3462
HONDA MOTOR SOUTHERN AFRICA (PTY.) LTD.—See Honda Motor Co., Ltd.; *Int'l*, pg. 3462
HONDA NORTH AMERICA INC.—See Honda Motor Co., Ltd.; *Int'l*, pg. 3459
HONDA POLAND LTD.—See Honda Motor Co., Ltd.; *Int'l*, pg. 3462
HONDA SLOVAKIA SPOL. S.R.O.—See Honda Motor Co., Ltd.; *Int'l*, pg. 3462
HONDA TAIWAN CO., LTD.—See Honda Motor Co., Ltd.; *Int'l*, pg. 3462
HOTAI MOTOR CO., LTD.; *Int'l*, pg. 3487
HTC VAN CENTRE LTD—See Ballyvesey Holdings Limited; *Int'l*, pg. 809
HUDACO INDUSTRIES LIMITED - BAUER GEARED MOTORS DIVISION—See Hudaco Industries Limited; *Int'l*, pg. 3521
HUNTERS TRUCK SALES & SERVICE; *U.S. Private*, pg. 2010
HUSH CRAFT LTD.—See Fugro N.V.; *Int'l*, pg. 2808
HV YORK ROAD IMPORTS, LLC—See AutoNation, Inc.; *U.S. Public*, pg. 235
HYUNDAI ASSAN OTOMOTIV SANAYI VE TICARET A.S.—See Hyundai Motor Company; *Int'l*, pg. 3558
HYUNDAI MOTOR AMERICA—See Hyundai Motor Company; *Int'l*, pg. 3559
HYUNDAI MOTOR COMPANY ITALY S.R.L.—See Hyundai Motor Company; *Int'l*, pg. 3559
HYUNDAI MOTOR JAPAN CO.—See Hyundai Motor Company; *Int'l*, pg. 3559
HYUNDAI MOTOR NORWAY AS—See Hyundai Motor Company; *Int'l*, pg. 3559
IAC GROUP AB—See Invesco Ltd.; *U.S. Public*, pg. 1164
I.A GROUP CORPORATION; *Int'l*, pg. 3565
ICE CONCEPT S.A.; *Int'l*, pg. 3579
ICHINEN AUTOS (N.Z.) LTD—See Ichinen Holdings Co., Ltd.; *Int'l*, pg. 3580
IMPERIAL SELECT ALBERTON—See Dubai World Corporation; *Int'l*, pg. 2221
INGRAM EQUIPMENT COMPANY, LLC.; *U.S. Private*, pg. 2076
INTERIORES AEREOS S.A. DE C.V.—See General Dynamics Corporation; *U.S. Public*, pg. 916
INTERNATIONAL TRANSPORTATION CORP.; *U.S. Private*, pg. 2121
INTER-STATE FORD TRUCK SALES, INC.; *U.S. Private*, pg. 2107
INTERSTATE TRUCK CENTER, LLC—See Interstate International, Inc.; *U.S. Private*, pg. 2125
I STATE TRUCK CENTER—See Interstate Companies, Inc.; *U.S. Private*, pg. 2124
IVECO FRANCE S.A.—See CNH Industrial N.V.; *Int'l*, pg. 1675
JACK DOHENY SUPPLIES, INC.; *U.S. Private*, pg. 2173
JACK L. SLAGLE FIRE EQUIPMENT SUPPLY CO.; *U.S. Private*, pg. 2174
J.H. BARKAU & SONS INC.; *U.S. Private*, pg. 2165
JILCO EQUIPMENT LEASING CO., INC.; *U.S. Private*, pg. 2208
JIM HAWK GROUP INC.; *U.S. Private*, pg. 2209
JM FAMILY ENTERPRISES INC.; *U.S. Private*, pg. 2213
JX ENTERPRISES INC.; *U.S. Private*, pg. 2247
KALAMAZOO TRUCK SALES INC.; *U.S. Private*, pg. 2257
KANSAS CITY PETERBILT INC.; *U.S. Private*, pg. 2260
KENWORTH NORTHWEST, INC.; *U.S. Private*, pg. 2289
KENWORTH OF CINCINNATI INC.; *U.S. Private*, pg. 2289
KENWORTH OF ST. LOUIS INC.; *U.S. Private*, pg. 2289
KENWORTH SALES COMPANY, INC.; *U.S. Private*, pg. 2289
KIA HELLAS S.A.—See AUTOHELLAS S.A.; *Int'l*, pg. 727
KUMAMOTO AUTOBACS INC.—See Autobacs Seven Co., Ltd.; *Int'l*, pg. 726
LAKELAND AUTO AUCTION—See Cox Enterprises, Inc.; *U.S. Private*, pg. 1076
LAMBRETTA SOUTH INCORPORATED; *U.S. Private*, pg. 2380
LANCASTER EQUIPMENT CORPORATION—See Leuner Inc.; *U.S. Private*, pg. 2433
LAS CRUCES AUTOMOTIVE GROUP, INC.—See General Motors Company; *U.S. Public*, pg. 926
LAUDERDALE-MIAMI AUTO AUCTION INC.—See Cox Enterprises, Inc.; *U.S. Private*, pg. 1076
LEADER TRAILER, LLC.—See International Industries, Inc.; *U.S. Private*, pg. 2117
LEONARD BUS SALES INC.; *U.S. Private*, pg. 2423
LEUNER INC.; *U.S. Private*, pg. 2433
LITHIA JEF, INC.—See Lithia Motors, Inc.; *U.S. Public*, pg. 1324

N.A.I.C.S. INDEX

423110 — AUTOMOBILE AND OTHE...

LITHIA MONROEVILLE-F, LLC—See Lithia Motors, Inc.; *U.S. Public*, pg. 1324
LITHIA OF BENNINGTON - 1, LLC—See Lithia Motors, Inc.; *U.S. Public*, pg. 1325
LITHIA OF CASPER, LLC—See Lithia Motors, Inc.; *U.S. Public*, pg. 1325
LITHIA OF CLEAR LAKE, LLC—See Lithia Motors, Inc.; *U.S. Public*, pg. 1325
LITHIA OF CONCORD II, INC.—See Lithia Motors, Inc.; *U.S. Public*, pg. 1325
LITHIA OF CONCORD I, INC.—See Lithia Motors, Inc.; *U.S. Public*, pg. 1325
LITHIA OF PORTLAND, LLC—See Lithia Motors, Inc.; *U.S. Public*, pg. 1325
LITHIA OF UTICA-1, LLC—See Lithia Motors, Inc.; *U.S. Public*, pg. 1325
LITHIA OF YORKVILLE-1, LLC—See Lithia Motors, Inc.; *U.S. Public*, pg. 1325
LITHIA OF YORKVILLE-3, LLC—See Lithia Motors, Inc.; *U.S. Public*, pg. 1325
LITHIA PARAMUS-M, LLC—See Lithia Motors, Inc.; *U.S. Public*, pg. 1324
LITHIA RAMSEY-B, LLC—See Lithia Motors, Inc.; *U.S. Public*, pg. 1324
LITHIA RAMSEY-L, LLC—See Lithia Motors, Inc.; *U.S. Public*, pg. 1324
LITHIA RAMSEY-M, LLC—See Lithia Motors, Inc.; *U.S. Public*, pg. 1324
LITHIA UNIONTOWN-C, LLC—See Lithia Motors, Inc.; *U.S. Public*, pg. 1325
LKQ SK S.R.O.—See LKQ Corporation; *U.S. Public*, pg. 1335
LONGHORN INTERNATIONAL TRUCKS; *U.S. Private*, pg. 2492
LOS ANGELES TRUCK CENTERS LLC—See Velocity Vehicle Group; *U.S. Private*, pg. 4354
LOU BACHRODT FREIGHTLINER; *U.S. Private*, pg. 2498
LOUISIANA'S FIRST CHOICE AUTO AUCTION LLC—See E Automotive Inc.; *Int'l*, pg. 2245
MACK HARVEY SALES & SERVICE; *U.S. Private*, pg. 2536
MACK MCBRIDE SALES INC.; *U.S. Private*, pg. 2536
MAN AUTOMOTIVE IMPORTS (NZ) LTD—See Penske Automotive Group, Inc.; *U.S. Public*, pg. 1666
MANCINO HOLDINGS INC.; *U.S. Private*, pg. 2562
MANEY INTERNATIONAL INC.; *U.S. Private*, pg. 2563
MANHEIM ALBANY—See Cox Enterprises, Inc.; *U.S. Private*, pg. 1076
MANHEIM AUCTIONS, INC.—See Cox Enterprises, Inc.; *U.S. Private*, pg. 1076
MANHEIM BALTIMORE-WASHINGTON—See Cox Enterprises, Inc.; *U.S. Private*, pg. 1076
MANHEIM CINCINNATI—See Cox Enterprises, Inc.; *U.S. Private*, pg. 1076
MANHEIM DARLINGTON—See Cox Enterprises, Inc.; *U.S. Private*, pg. 1076
MANHEIM GEORGIA—See Cox Enterprises, Inc.; *U.S. Private*, pg. 1076
MANHEIM IMPERIAL FLORIDA—See Cox Enterprises, Inc.; *U.S. Private*, pg. 1077
MANHEIM METRO DALLAS—See Cox Enterprises, Inc.; *U.S. Private*, pg. 1077
MANHEIM NEW ENGLAND—See Cox Enterprises, Inc.; *U.S. Private*, pg. 1077
MANHEIM NEW JERSEY—See Cox Enterprises, Inc.; *U.S. Private*, pg. 1077
MANHEIM NEW MEXICO—See Cox Enterprises, Inc.; *U.S. Private*, pg. 1077
MANHEIM OHIO—See Cox Enterprises, Inc.; *U.S. Private*, pg. 1077
MANHEIM ORLANDO—See Cox Enterprises, Inc.; *U.S. Private*, pg. 1077
MANHEIM PHILADELPHIA—See Cox Enterprises, Inc.; *U.S. Private*, pg. 1077
MANHEIM PORTLAND—See Cox Enterprises, Inc.; *U.S. Private*, pg. 1077
MANHEIM SAN ANTONIO—See Cox Enterprises, Inc.; *U.S. Private*, pg. 1077
MANHEIM SEATTLE—See Cox Enterprises, Inc.; *U.S. Private*, pg. 1077
MANHEIM'S THE MOTOR CITY AUTO AUCTION—See Cox Enterprises, Inc.; *U.S. Private*, pg. 1077
MANNING ENTERPRISES INC.; *U.S. Private*, pg. 2565
MANNING EQUIPMENT, LLC—See Manning Enterprises Inc.; *U.S. Private*, pg. 2565
MANNING TRUCK MODIFICATION—See Manning Enterprises Inc.; *U.S. Private*, pg. 2565
MARKET LOGISTICS INC.; *U.S. Private*, pg. 2579
MARSHALLS HOLDING CO.; *U.S. Private*, pg. 2593
MARTINS PETERBILT INC.; *U.S. Private*, pg. 2597
MATTHEWS BUSES INC.—See The Matthews Group Inc.; *U.S. Private*, pg. 4076
THE MATTHEWS GROUP INC.; *U.S. Private*, pg. 4076
MEMPHIS EQUIPMENT COMPANY; *U.S. Private*, pg. 2664
METRO MILWAUKEE AUTO AUCTION—See Cox Enterprises, Inc.; *U.S. Private*, pg. 1077
MG ABLE MOTORS COMPANY LIMITED—See AAPICO Hitech plc; *Int'l*, pg. 37
MHC FINANCIAL SERVICES—See Murphy-Hoffman Company; *U.S. Private*, pg. 2816
MID STATES UTILITY TRAILER SALES, INC.; *U.S. Private*, pg. 2706
MID-STATE TRUCK SERVICE INC.; *U.S. Private*, pg. 2709
MIDVALE TRUCK SALES & SERVICE INC.; *U.S. Private*, pg. 2718
MIDWAY FORD TRUCK CENTER INC.; *U.S. Private*, pg. 2718
MIDWEST BUS SALES INC.; *U.S. Private*, pg. 2720
MID WESTERN AUTOMOTIVE LLC; *U.S. Private*, pg. 2706
MIDWEST TRAILER SALES INC.; *U.S. Private*, pg. 2723
MIDWEST TRANSIT EQUIPMENT, INC.; *U.S. Private*, pg. 2723
MIKE REICHENBACH CHEVROLET, INC.—See General Motors Company; *U.S. Public*, pg. 926
MINN-DAK INC.; *U.S. Private*, pg. 2742
MINNEAPOLIS AUTO AUCTION—See Cox Enterprises, Inc.; *U.S. Private*, pg. 1077
MISSISSIPPI AUTO AUCTION INC.—See Cox Enterprises, Inc.; *U.S. Private*, pg. 1077
MIZUMA RAILWAY CO., LTD.—See Gourmet Kineya Co., Ltd.; *Int'l*, pg. 3044
M&K TRAILER CENTERS—See M & K Truck & Trailer, LLC; *U.S. Private*, pg. 2523
M & K TRUCK & TRAILER, LLC; *U.S. Private*, pg. 2523
MMC AUTOMOVILES ESPANA, S.A.—See Berge y Cia SA; *Int'l*, pg. 979
MOMENTUM VOLKSWAGEN OF JERSEY VILLAGE; *U.S. Private*, pg. 2768
MORTON AUTO AUCTION INC.; *U.S. Private*, pg. 2791
MOTORS AUCTION GROUP, INC.—See Copart, Inc.; *U.S. Public*, pg. 575
MOTOR TRUCK EQUIPMENT COMPANY; *U.S. Private*, pg. 2797
MOUNTAIN STATE AUTO AUCTION INC.; *U.S. Private*, pg. 2799
MOVEIX INC.—See SeriesOne, LLC; *U.S. Private*, pg. 3613
MURPHY-HOFFMAN COMPANY; *U.S. Private*, pg. 2816
MURRAYS FORD INC.; *U.S. Private*, pg. 2816
MYERS DIESEL & EQUIPMENT; *U.S. Private*, pg. 2824
NATIONAL MOTOR COMPANY W.L.L.—See Bahrain Commercial Facilities Company BSC; *Int'l*, pg. 800
NAVISTAR CANADA, INC.—See FreightCar America, Inc.; *U.S. Public*, pg. 885
NEELY COBLE COMPANY, INC.—See Velocity Vehicle Group; *U.S. Private*, pg. 4355
NELSON FORD-LINCOLN-MERCURY, INC.; *U.S. Private*, pg. 2883
NELSON LEASING INC.; *U.S. Private*, pg. 2883
NEWBURGH AUTO AUCTION—See Cox Enterprises, Inc.; *U.S. Private*, pg. 1077
NEW CASTLE CHEVROLET, INC.—See General Motors Company; *U.S. Public*, pg. 926
NEW ENGLAND TRUCK SALES & SERVICES INC.; *U.S. Private*, pg. 2895
NEXV SYNERGY SDN. BHD.—See Careplus Group Berhad; *Int'l*, pg. 1325
NICOLE RACING JAPAN, LLC—See Penske Automotive Group, Inc.; *U.S. Public*, pg. 1665
NORCAL KENWORTH - ANDERSON—See SSMB Pacific Holding Company, Inc.; *U.S. Private*, pg. 3769
NORCAL KENWORTH - SACRAMENTO—See SSMB Pacific Holding Company, Inc.; *U.S. Private*, pg. 3769
NORCAL KENWORTH - SAN LEANDRO—See SSMB Pacific Holding Company, Inc.; *U.S. Private*, pg. 3769
NORTH AMERICAN TRUCK & TRAILER, INC.; *U.S. Private*, pg. 2941
NORTH MISSOURI TIRE, INC; *U.S. Private*, pg. 2946
NORTHWEST EQUIPMENT SALES INC.; *U.S. Private*, pg. 2960
NORWALK AUTO AUCTION; *U.S. Private*, pg. 2964
O'BRIEN AUTOMOTIVE TEAM; *U.S. Private*, pg. 2977
O'HALLORAN INTERNATIONAL INC.; *U.S. Private*, pg. 2978
OMAHA AUTO AUCTION—See Cox Enterprises, Inc.; *U.S. Private*, pg. 1077
OPENLANE ITALIA S.R.L.—See OPENLANE, Inc.; *U.S. Public*, pg. 1607
OPENLANE REMARKETING LIMITED—See OPENLANE, Inc.; *U.S. Public*, pg. 1607
OPENLANE SUBASTAS ESPANA, S.L.—See OPENLANE, Inc.; *U.S. Public*, pg. 1607
OVERMYER & ASSOCIATES INC.; *U.S. Private*, pg. 3053
OZARK KENWORTH INC.—See Murphy-Hoffman Company; *U.S. Private*, pg. 2816
PACCAR ENGINE COMPANY—See PACCAR Inc.; *U.S. Public*, pg. 1630
PACKER CITY INTERNATIONAL TRUCKS INC.; *U.S. Private*, pg. 3073
PAR, INC.—See OPENLANE, Inc.; *U.S. Public*, pg. 1607
PATSON INC.; *U.S. Private*, pg. 3111
PAUL WURTH IHI CO., LTD.—See IHI Corporation; *Int'l*, pg. 3606
PEACH STATE FORD TRUCK SALES, INC.; *U.S. Private*, pg. 3123
PERFORMANCE AUTOMOTIVE NETWORK; *U.S. Private*, pg. 3148
PETERBILT OF ONTARIO INC.—See Brandt Industries Ltd.; *Int'l*, pg. 1140
PETERBILT OF WISCONSIN INC—See JX Enterprises Inc.; *U.S. Private*, pg. 2247
THE PETERBILT STORE - KNOXVILLE—See The Pete Store, LLC; *U.S. Private*, pg. 4093
PITTSBURGH MACK SALES & SERVICE INC.—See Allentown Mack Sales & Service, Inc.; *U.S. Private*, pg. 180
PORTER TRUCK SALES INC.; *U.S. Private*, pg. 3232
POWERLOCK INTERNATIONAL CORP.; *U.S. Public*, pg. 1706
PRAIRIE INTERNATIONAL TRUCKS; *U.S. Private*, pg. 3242
PRESTIGE MOTORS, INC.; *U.S. Private*, pg. 3256
PROTON MOTORS (THAILAND) LIMITED—See DRB-HICOM Berhad; *Int'l*, pg. 2202
PROVENCE DISTRIBUTION SERVICES S.A.R.L.—See CNH Industrial N.V.; *Int'l*, pg. 1675
Q-TRONIC B.V.—See Addtech AB; *Int'l*, pg. 134
QUAD-CITY PETERBILT INC.; *U.S. Private*, pg. 3315
QUALITY TRUCK CARE CENTER INC.; *U.S. Private*, pg. 3321
QUIETKAT, INC.—See Vista Outdoor Inc.; *U.S. Public*, pg. 2305
RADFORD AUTO AUCTION; *U.S. Private*, pg. 3342
RALEIGH TRACTOR & TRUCK COMPANY; *U.S. Private*, pg. 3350
RECAMBIA—See Berge y Cia SA; *Int'l*, pg. 979
REDDING FREIGHTLINER LLC; *U.S. Private*, pg. 3377
REED NISSAN; *U.S. Private*, pg. 3382
REGIONAL INTERNATIONAL CORP.; *U.S. Private*, pg. 3388
REGIONS ASSET COMPANY—See Regions Financial Corporation; *U.S. Public*, pg. 1776
RICHMOND FORD; *U.S. Private*, pg. 3430
RIHM MOTOR COMPANY; *U.S. Private*, pg. 3436
RIVER VALLEY TRUCK CENTERS; *U.S. Private*, pg. 3444
ROCKFORD TRUCK SALES INC.—See William Charles, Ltd.; *U.S. Private*, pg. 4522
ROCKWELL AUTOMATION ARGENTINA S.A.—See Rockwell Automation, Inc.; *U.S. Public*, pg. 1805
RODY TRUCK CENTER OF MIAMI, INC.; *U.S. Private*, pg. 3470
ROHRER ENTERPRISES, INC.; *U.S. Private*, pg. 3473
RUSH TRUCK CENTER OF ALBUQUERQUE, INC.—See Rush Enterprises, Inc.; *U.S. Public*, pg. 1826
RUSH TRUCK CENTERS - KANSAS CITY—See Rush Enterprises, Inc.; *U.S. Public*, pg. 1826
RUSH TRUCK CENTERS - LOWELL—See Rush Enterprises, Inc.; *U.S. Public*, pg. 1826
RUSH TRUCK CENTERS - MEMPHIS—See Rush Enterprises, Inc.; *U.S. Public*, pg. 1826
RUSH TRUCK CENTERS - NORTH LITTLE ROCK—See Rush Enterprises, Inc.; *U.S. Public*, pg. 1826
RUSH TRUCK CENTERS OF COLORADO INC.—See Rush Enterprises, Inc.; *U.S. Public*, pg. 1826
RUSH TRUCK CENTERS OF GEORGIA, INC.—See Rush Enterprises, Inc.; *U.S. Public*, pg. 1826
RUSH TRUCK CENTERS OF IDAHO, INC.—See Rush Enterprises, Inc.; *U.S. Public*, pg. 1826
RUSH TRUCK CENTERS OF ILLINOIS, INC.—See Rush Enterprises, Inc.; *U.S. Public*, pg. 1826
RUSH TRUCK CENTERS OF KENTUCKY, INC.—See Rush Enterprises, Inc.; *U.S. Public*, pg. 1827
RUSH TRUCK CENTERS OF NEVADA, INC.—See Rush Enterprises, Inc.; *U.S. Public*, pg. 1827
RUSH TRUCK CENTERS OF OHIO, INC.—See Rush Enterprises, Inc.; *U.S. Public*, pg. 1827
RUSH TRUCK CENTERS OF OREGON, INC.—See Rush Enterprises, Inc.; *U.S. Public*, pg. 1827
RUSH TRUCK CENTERS OF TENNESSEE, INC.—See Rush Enterprises, Inc.; *U.S. Public*, pg. 1827
RUSH TRUCK CENTERS OF UTAH, INC.—See Rush Enterprises, Inc.; *U.S. Public*, pg. 1827
RUSH TRUCK LEASING-JACKSONVILLE—See Rush Enterprises, Inc.; *U.S. Public*, pg. 1827
RWC INTERNATIONAL LTD.; *U.S. Private*, pg. 3508
SAI TYSONS CORNER H, LLC—See Graham Holdings Company; *U.S. Public*, pg. 956
SALEM-V, LLC—See Lithia Motors, Inc.; *U.S. Public*, pg. 1326
SANTA MONICA FORD COMPANY; *U.S. Private*, pg. 3547
SANTEX TRUCK CENTER LTD.; *U.S. Private*, pg. 3548
SC HONDA TRADING ROMANIA SRL—See Honda Motor Co., Ltd.; *Int'l*, pg. 3464
SCHOOL BUS SALES COMPANY; *U.S. Private*, pg. 3568
SCHOOL LINES, INC.—See Girardin Blue Bird Company; *Int'l*, pg. 2979
SEMI-TRAILER SALES & LEASING; *U.S. Private*, pg. 3603
SHANGHAI HUANGPU BAOZEN AUTOMOBILE SALES CO., LTD—See China Yongda Automobiles Services Holdings Limited; *Int'l*, pg. 1564
SHANGHAI YONGDA AUTOMOBILE PUXI SALES AND SERVICES CO., LTD.—See China Yongda Automobiles Services Holdings Limited; *Int'l*, pg. 1564
SHARLENE REALTY LLC—See Lithia Motors, Inc.; *U.S. Public*, pg. 1326

423110 — AUTOMOBILE AND OTHE...

SHEEHAN MACK SALES AND EQUIPMENT INC.; *U.S. Private*, pg. 3629
SHIPLEY MOTOR EQUIPMENT COMPANY—See Bruckner Truck Sales, Inc.; *U.S. Private*, pg. 671
SIAM AUTOBACS CO., LTD.—See Autobacs Seven Co., Ltd.; *Int'l*, pg. 726
SILL TERHAR MOTORS, INC; *U.S. Private*, pg. 3653
SILVER STATE INTERNATIONAL—See Interstate International, Inc.; *U.S. Private*, pg. 2125
SINOMACH AUTOMOBILE CO., LTD.—See China National Machinery Industry Corporation; *Int'l*, pg. 1531
SINOMACH CAPITAL MANAGEMENT CORPORATION—See China National Machinery Industry Corporation; *Int'l*, pg. 1531
SINOMACH PRECISION INDUSTRY CO., LTD.—See China National Machinery Industry Corporation; *Int'l*, pg. 1531
SIOUX CITY TRUCK & TRAILER—See North American Truck & Trailer, Inc.; *U.S. Private*, pg. 2941
SIOUX FALLS AUTO AUCTION, INC.—See OPENLANE, Inc.; *U.S. Public*, pg. 1607
SKYLINE AUTO EXCHANGE—See Cox Enterprises, Inc.; *U.S. Private*, pg. 1077
SMP AUTOMOTIVE DE MEXICO, S.A. DE C.V.—See Standard Motor Products, Inc.; *U.S. Public*, pg. 1929
SODI AUTOMOTIVE SPA—See Cevital S.p.A.; *Int'l*, pg. 1425
SOUTHEAST TOYOTA DISTRIBUTORS, LLC—See JM Family Enterprises Inc.; *U.S. Private*, pg. 2214
SOUTHERN AUTO SALES INC.; *U.S. Private*, pg. 3729
SOUTHWEST PROFESSIONAL VEHICLES; *U.S. Private*, pg. 3740
SOUTHWEST RV CENTERS, LLC—See Camping World Holdings, Inc.; *U.S. Public*, pg. 428
SPAREX LTD.—See AGCO Corporation; *U.S. Public*, pg. 59
ST. CLOUD TRUCK SALES INC.; *U.S. Private*, pg. 3771
ST. LOUIS AUTO AUCTION—See Cox Enterprises, Inc.; *U.S. Private*, pg. 1077
ST. PETE AUTO AUCTION—See Cox Enterprises, Inc.; *U.S. Private*, pg. 1077
SUMEC CORPORATION LIMITED—See China National Machinery Industry Corporation; *Int'l*, pg. 1531
SUNSET AUTO COMPANY INC.; *U.S. Private*, pg. 3871
SYTNER GROUP LIMITED—See Penske Automotive Group, Inc.; *U.S. Public*, pg. 1666
TEAM MOTO PTY. LTD.—See Archer Capital Pty. Ltd.; *Int'l*, pg. 547
TEC EQUIPMENT, INC.; *U.S. Private*, pg. 3951
TEN-8 FIRE EQUIPMENT INC.; *U.S. Private*, pg. 3964
TESLA NORWAY AS—See Tesla, Inc.; *U.S. Public*, pg. 2021
TEXAS LONE STAR AUTO AUCTION LUBBOCK—See Huron Capital Partners LLC; *U.S. Private*, pg. 2012
TNT EQUIPMENT SALES & RENTALS, LLC—See Utility One Source L.P.; *U.S. Private*, pg. 4326
TOM JOHNSON CAMPING CENTER CHARLOTTE, INC.—See Camping World Holdings, Inc.; *U.S. Public*, pg. 428
TOWER AUTOMOTIVE MEXICO, S.DE R.L. DE C.V.—See KPS Capital Partners, LP; *U.S. Private*, pg. 2347
TOYOTA NIGERIA LIMITED—See Elizade Nigeria Limited; *Int'l*, pg. 2363
TRADITION CHEVROLET BUICK, INC.—See General Motors Company; *U.S. Public*, pg. 929
TRAFFORD VAN CENTRE LTD—See Ballyvesey Holdings Limited; *Int'l*, pg. 809
TRAILERS DIRECT—See Bain Capital, LP; *U.S. Private*, pg. 436
TRANSPORTATION EQUIPMENT SALES CORP. (TESCO); *U.S. Private*, pg. 4211
TRANSWORLD INFORMATION SYSTEMS—See Agnite Education Limited; *Int'l*, pg. 212
TRIAD FREIGHTLINER OF GREENSBORO INC.; *U.S. Private*, pg. 4225
TRI-COUNTY INTERNATIONAL TRUCKS INC.—See C&S Motors, Inc.; *U.S. Private*, pg. 704
TRIPLE CITIES ACQUISITION LLC; *U.S. Private*, pg. 4236
TRI-STATE AUCTION CO., INC.—See OPENLANE, Inc.; *U.S. Public*, pg. 1607
TRI-STATE AUTO AUCTION LLC; *U.S. Private*, pg. 4223
TRI-STATE LEASING—See Tri-State Truck Center, Inc.; *U.S. Private*, pg. 4224
TRI-STATE TRUCK CENTER, INC.; *U.S. Private*, pg. 4224
TRUCK CITY OF GARY INC.; *U.S. Private*, pg. 4246
TRUCK COUNTRY INC.; *U.S. Private*, pg. 4246
TRUCK SALES & SERVICE INC. - MANSFIELD—See Midvale Truck Sales & Service Inc.; *U.S. Private*, pg. 2718
TRUCK SALES & SERVICE INC.; *U.S. Private*, pg. 4246
TRUCKS & PARTS OF TAMPA INC.; *U.S. Private*, pg. 4246
TRUCK TRAILER & EQUIPMENT INC.; *U.S. Private*, pg. 4246
TRUECAR, INC.; *U.S. Public*, pg. 2199
TURN5, INC.; *U.S. Private*, pg. 4260
TWIN BRIDGES TRUCK CITY INC.; *U.S. Private*, pg. 4264
UCO EQUIPMENT, LLC—See Utility One Source L.P.; *U.S. Private*, pg. 4326
UD TRUCKS NORTH AMERICA, INC.—See AB Volvo; *Int'l*, pg. 46

UTAH AUTO AUCTION—See Cox Enterprises, Inc.; *U.S. Private*, pg. 1077
UTICA GENERAL TRUCK CO. INC.; *U.S. Private*, pg. 4325
UTILITY FLEET SALES, LTD.—See Utility One Source L.P.; *U.S. Private*, pg. 4326
UTILITY TRAILER SALES OF COLORADO LLC; *U.S. Private*, pg. 4327
UTILITY TRAILER SALES OF NEW JERSEY, INC.—See Atlantic Utility Trailer Sales, Inc.; *U.S. Private*, pg. 375
UTILITY TRI-STATE INC.; *U.S. Private*, pg. 4327
VANGUARD TRUCK CENTER OF ST. LOUIS—See SF Holding Corp.; *U.S. Private*, pg. 3621
VANGUARD TRUCK CENTERS, LLC—See SF Holding Corp.; *U.S. Private*, pg. 3621
VB2, INC.—See Copart, Inc.; *U.S. Public*, pg. 575
VENTA GLOBAL, INC.; *U.S. Private*, pg. 4357
VIETNAM PRECISION INDUSTRIAL NO.1 CO., LTD.—See Eurocharm Holdings Co., Ltd.; *Int'l*, pg. 2583
VOLVO BUS NEDERLAND B.V.—See AB Volvo; *Int'l*, pg. 43
VOLVO GROUP AUSTRALIA PTY LTD—See AB Volvo; *Int'l*, pg. 44
VOLVO PENTA BENELUX B.V.—See AB Volvo; *Int'l*, pg. 42
VOLVO PERU S.A.—See AB Volvo; *Int'l*, pg. 42
VOLVO TRUCKS AUSTRIA GMBH—See AB Volvo; *Int'l*, pg. 47
VOLVO TRUCKS IRAN—See AB Volvo; *Int'l*, pg. 46
VOLVO TRUCKS MACEDONIA—See AB Volvo; *Int'l*, pg. 46
VOLVO TRUCKS PHILIPPINES—See AB Volvo; *Int'l*, pg. 47
VOLVO TRUCKS (SUISSE) SA—See AB Volvo; *Int'l*, pg. 47
VOLVO TRUCKS SYRIA—See AB Volvo; *Int'l*, pg. 46
WABASH NATIONAL TRAILER CENTERS, INC.—See WABASH NATIONAL CORPORATION; *U.S. Public*, pg. 2320
WATKINS AUTOMOTIVE GROUP; *U.S. Private*, pg. 4455
WESTERN BUS SALES INC.; *U.S. Private*, pg. 4491
WESTERN MOTORS LLC—See Al Fahim Group; *Int'l*, pg. 277
WESTERN STAR TRUCKS AUSTRALIA PTY. LTD.—See Penske Automotive Group, Inc.; *U.S. Public*, pg. 1666
WESTFALL GMC TRUCK INC.—See Nextran Corporation; *U.S. Private*, pg. 2921
WEST PALM BEACH AUTO AUCTION—See Cox Enterprises, Inc.; *U.S. Private*, pg. 1077
WEST VIRGINIA-OHIO MOTOR SALES; *U.S. Private*, pg. 4488
WHEELER RV LAS VEGAS, LLC—See Camping World Holdings, Inc.; *U.S. Public*, pg. 428
WHITED FORD TRUCK CENTER; *U.S. Private*, pg. 4511
WICHITA KENWORTH INC.; *U.S. Private*, pg. 4515
WOODPECKER TRUCK & EQUIPMENT INCORPORATED; *U.S. Private*, pg. 4559
WORLDPAC, INC.—See The Carlyle Group Inc.; *U.S. Public*, pg. 2057
WORLDWIDE EQUIPMENT, INC.; *U.S. Private*, pg. 4569
YANCEY BUS SALES & SERVICE, LLC—See Yancey Bros. Co.; *U.S. Private*, pg. 4585
YOUNG'S TRUCK CENTER INC.; *U.S. Private*, pg. 4593
ZACHERL MOTOR TRUCK SALES; *U.S. Private*, pg. 4596
ZHEJIANG AICHI INDUSTRIAL MACHINERY CO., LTD.—See Aichi Corporation; *Int'l*, pg. 229

423120 — MOTOR VEHICLE SUPPLIES AND NEW PARTS MERCHANT WHOLESALERS

1211863 ONTARIO INC.; *Int'l*, pg. 2
129157 CANADA INC; *Int'l*, pg. 2
1-800-RADIATOR & A/C—See Roark Capital Group Inc.; *U.S. Private*, pg. 3454
A-1 TRUCK PARTS—See Auto-Wares, LLC; *U.S. Private*, pg. 398
AA WHEEL & TRUCK SUPPLY INC.; *U.S. Private*, pg. 30
ABC AUTO PARTS LTD.; *U.S. Private*, pg. 35
ABRO DISTRIBUTION SERVICE LLC—See ABRO Industries, Inc.; *U.S. Private*, pg. 40
ACCELL SUISSE AG—See Accell Group N.V.; *Int'l*, pg. 80
A.C. NELSEN ENTERPRISES INC.; *U.S. Private*, pg. 24
ACTIA CORPORATION—See Actia Group SA; *Int'l*, pg. 118
ACTIA MULLER (UK) LTD.—See Actia Group SA; *Int'l*, pg. 118
ACTIA NEDERLAND BV—See Actia Group SA; *Int'l*, pg. 118
ACTIA-POLSKA SP. Z O.O.—See Actia Group SA; *Int'l*, pg. 118
ADLER PLASTIC SPA; *Int'l*, pg. 150
ADSCOM CORPORATION—See Adrian Steel Company Inc.; *U.S. Private*, pg. 82
ADVANCE AUTO PARTS—See Advance Auto Parts, Inc.; *U.S. Public*, pg. 44
ADVANCE E-SERVICE SOLUTIONS, INC.—See Advance Auto Parts, Inc.; *U.S. Public*, pg. 44
ADVICS ASIA PACIFIC CO., LTD.—See AISIN Corporation; *Int'l*, pg. 251
AEROFIL INC—See Absolent Air Care Group AB; *Int'l*, pg. 70
AFRITOOL (PTY) LTD.—See Honda Motor Co., Ltd.; *Int'l*, pg. 3459
AGC AUTOMOTIVE CALIFORNIA, INC.—See AGC Inc.; *Int'l*, pg. 200

AGC AUTOMOTIVE FOSHAN CO., LTD—See AGC Inc.; *Int'l*, pg. 201
AGC AUTOMOTIVE (THAILAND) CO., LTD.—See AGC Inc.; *Int'l*, pg. 201
AIRTEX PRODUCTS, LP—See Crowne Group LLC; *U.S. Private*, pg. 1112
AISAN CORPORATION ASIA PACIFIC LIMITED—See Aisan Industry Co., Ltd.; *Int'l*, pg. 250
AISAN SALES INDIA PVT. LTD.—See Aisan Industry Co., Ltd.; *Int'l*, pg. 250
AISIN WORLD CORP. OF AMERICA—See AISIN Corporation; *Int'l*, pg. 252
AKEBONO BRAKE EUROPE N.V.—See Akebono Brake Industry Co., Ltd.; *Int'l*, pg. 261
AKEBONO BRAKE (THAILAND) CO., LTD.—See Akebono Brake Industry Co., Ltd.; *Int'l*, pg. 261
AKEBONO EUROPE GMBH—See Akebono Brake Industry Co., Ltd.; *Int'l*, pg. 262
AKEBONO EUROPE S.A.S (GONESSE)—See Akebono Brake Industry Co., Ltd.; *Int'l*, pg. 262
AL-AHLEIA SWITCHGEAR COMPANY K.S.C.C. - UNIT - 4—See Al-Ahleia Switchgear Company K.S.C.C.; *Int'l*, pg. 284
AL-AHLEIA SWITCHGEAR COMPANY K.S.C.C. - UNIT - 5—See Al-Ahleia Switchgear Company K.S.C.C.; *Int'l*, pg. 284
AL-AHLEIA SWITCHGEAR COMPANY K.S.C.C. - UNIT - 6—See Al-Ahleia Switchgear Company K.S.C.C.; *Int'l*, pg. 284
ALBERT KEMPERLE INC.; *U.S. Private*, pg. 153
ALBERT KEMPERLE OF FLORIDA, LLC—See Albert Kemperle Inc.; *U.S. Private*, pg. 153
ALBION AUTOMOTIVE (HOLDINGS) LIMITED—See American Axle & Manufacturing Holdings, Inc.; *U.S. Public*, pg. 96
ALBONAIR AUTOMOTIVE TECHNOLOGY CO. LTD.—See Hinduja Group Ltd.; *Int'l*, pg. 3398
ALEXANDER AUTOMOTIVE GROUP; *U.S. Private*, pg. 163
ALFA PAINTS B.V.—See LKQ Corporation; *U.S. Public*, pg. 1333
AL-FUTTAIM MOTORS COMPANY LLC—See Al-Futtaim Private Company LLC; *Int'l*, pg. 285
ALHAMRANI UNITED COMPANY—See Alhamrani Group; *Int'l*, pg. 319
ALL AMERICAN GLASS DISTRIBUTORS INC.; *U.S. Private*, pg. 169
ALLEY-CASSETTY COMPANIES - ALLEY-CASSETTY TRUCK CENTER DIVISION—See Alley-Cassetty Companies; *U.S. Private*, pg. 181
ALLIANCE TRUCK AND EQUIPMENT, LLC; *U.S. Private*, pg. 184
ALLIED MANUFACTURING INC.; *U.S. Private*, pg. 186
ALLPIKE AUTOS PTY LTD—See Eagers Automotive Limited; *Int'l*, pg. 2263
ALL STAR AUTO LIGHTS, INC.—See Atlantic Street Capital Management LLC; *U.S. Private*, pg. 374
ALL STAR AUTOMOTIVE PRODUCTS; *U.S. Private*, pg. 172
ALPHA (GUANGZHOU) AUTOMOTIVEPARTS CO., LTD.—See ALPHA Corporation; *Int'l*, pg. 367
ALPHA HOUSING HARDWARE (THAILAND) CO., LTD.—See ALPHA Corporation; *Int'l*, pg. 367
ALPHA INDUSTRY QUERETARO, S.A. DE C.V.—See ALPHA Corporation; *Int'l*, pg. 367
ALPHA INDUSTRY (THAILAND) CO., LTD.—See ALPHA Corporation; *Int'l*, pg. 367
ALTROM CANADA CORP.—See Genuine Parts Company; *U.S. Public*, pg. 932
AMALFE BROS INC.; *U.S. Private*, pg. 215
AMERICAN BATTERY CO. INC.; *U.S. Private*, pg. 224
AMERICAN EAGLE WHEEL CORP.; *U.S. Private*, pg. 231
AMERLING COMPANY; *U.S. Private*, pg. 261
AMIGO TRUCK & EQUIPMENT, LLC.; *U.S. Private*, pg. 263
ANDERSON AUTO PARTS CO. INC.; *U.S. Private*, pg. 276
ANGEL WAREHOUSE INC.; *U.S. Private*, pg. 281
ANHUI EDSCHA AUTOMOTIVE PARTS, CO. LTD.—See Corporacion Gestamp SL; *Int'l*, pg. 1804
A.P. FORD PTY LTD—See Eagers Automotive Limited; *Int'l*, pg. 2263
API INTERNATIONAL INC.; *U.S. Private*, pg. 294
APM AUTO COMPONENTS (USA) INC.—See APM Automotive Holdings Berhad; *Int'l*, pg. 516
APM AUTO PARTS MARKETING SDN. BHD.—See APM Automotive Holdings Berhad; *Int'l*, pg. 516
A.P. MOTORS (NO.2) PTY LTD—See Eagers Automotive Limited; *Int'l*, pg. 2263
A.P. MOTORS (NO.3) PTY LTD—See Eagers Automotive Limited; *Int'l*, pg. 2263
APOLLORETAILING CO., LTD.—See Idemitsu Kosan Co., Ltd.; *Int'l*, pg. 3590
APPLICA SERVICIOS DE MEXICO, S. DE R.L. DE C.V.—See Spectrum Brands Holdings, Inc.; *U.S. Public*, pg. 1916
ARAYMOND INDUSTRIAL—See A. Raymond & Cie SCS; *Int'l*, pg. 22
A RAYMOND ITALIANA S.R.L—See A. Raymond & Cie SCS; *Int'l*, pg. 21

N.A.I.C.S. INDEX

423120 — MOTOR VEHICLE SUPPL...

A. RAYMOND KOREA CO. LTD.—See A. Raymond & Cie SCS; *Int'l*, pg. 22
A. RAYMOND LTD.—See A. Raymond & Cie SCS; *Int'l*, pg. 22
ARAZU INCORPORATED; *Int'l*, pg. 536
ARCH AUTO PARTS CORP.—See Blue Point Capital Partners, LLC; *U.S. Private*, pg. 590
ARIES AUTOMOTIVE ACCESSORIES, INC.—See LCI Industries; *U.S. Public*, pg. 1295
ARKANSAS TRAILER MANUFACTURING CO., INC.; *U.S. Private*, pg. 326
ARNOLD MOTOR SUPPLY, LLP; *U.S. Private*, pg. 333
AROS DEL PACIFICO S.A.C.—See Titan International, Inc.; *U.S. Public*, pg. 2160
ARROWHEAD ELECTRICAL PRODUCTS, INC.—See The Riverside Company; *U.S. Private*, pg. 4107
ASCO NUMATICS (INDIA) PRIVATE LIMITED—See Emerson Electric Co.; *U.S. Public*, pg. 740
AS DOMZALE MOTO CENTER D.O.O.—See Honda Motor Co., Ltd.; *Int'l*, pg. 3459
ASIMCO INTERNATIONAL INC.—See Bain Capital, LP; *U.S. Private*, pg. 428
ASSOCIATED AUTO PARTS; *U.S. Private*, pg. 354
ATLANTA POWERTRAIN & HYDRAULICS, INC.—See Force America Inc.; *U.S. Private*, pg. 1563
ATLANTIC FILTER CORP.—See A. O. Smith Corporation; *U.S. Public*, pg. 11
ATLANTIC INTERNATIONAL DISTRIBUTORS, INC.—See The Riverside Company; *U.S. Private*, pg. 4108
ATLAS WORLDWIDE GENERAL TRADING LLC—See Atlas Group of Companies; *Int'l*, pg. 685
AUCNET SALES AND SUPPORT INC.—See Aucnet Inc.; *Int'l*, pg. 700
AUNDE FRANCE SA—See AUNDE Achter & Ebels GmbH; *Int'l*, pg. 705
AUNDE KFT—See AUNDE Achter & Ebels GmbH; *Int'l*, pg. 705
AUNDE MEXICO S.A. DE C.V.—See AUNDE Achter & Ebels GmbH; *Int'l*, pg. 705
AUNDE POLAND SP. Z O.O.—See AUNDE Achter & Ebels GmbH; *Int'l*, pg. 705
AUSTRAL PTY LTD—See Eagers Automotive Limited; *Int'l*, pg. 2263
AUTOBODY SUPPLY COMPANY, INC.—See LKQ Corporation; *U.S. Public*, pg. 1336
AUTO BODY TOOLMART; *U.S. Private*, pg. 396
AUTOHAUS ARIZONA, INC.; *U.S. Private*, pg. 398
AUTO IMPEX JOINT STOCK COMPANY; *Int'l*, pg. 724
AUTOLIV (CHINA) STEERING WHEEL CO., LTD.—See Autoliv, Inc.; *Int'l*, pg. 728
AUTOLIV NORTH AMERICA SERVICE PARTS FACILITY—See Autoliv, Inc.; *Int'l*, pg. 729
AUTOMESTER DANMARK APS—See Hella GmbH & Co. KGaA; *Int'l*, pg. 3331
AUTOMOTIVE AFTER MARKET INC.; *U.S. Private*, pg. 400
AUTOMOTIVE DISTRIBUTORS CO., INC.; *U.S. Private*, pg. 400
AUTOMOTIVE HARD PARTS INC.; *U.S. Private*, pg. 400
AUTOMOTIVE IMPORTING MANUFACTURING, INC.; *U.S. Private*, pg. 400
AUTOMOTIVE MANUFACTURING & SUPPLY CO.; *U.S. Private*, pg. 400
AUTOMOTIVE PARTS DISTRIBUTION INTERNATIONAL, LLC.—See Enterex International Limited; *Int'l*, pg. 2451
AUTOMOTIVE PARTS EXPRESS INC.; *U.S. Private*, pg. 400
AUTOMOTIVE PARTS HEADQUARTERS, INC.; *U.S. Private*, pg. 400
AUTOMOTIVE SUPPLY ASSOCIATES, INC.; *U.S. Private*, pg. 401
AUTOMOTIVE WAREHOUSE, INC.—See Advance Auto Parts, Inc.; *U.S. Public*, pg. 45
AUTO NETWORKS INTERNATIONAL CORPORATION; *Int'l*, pg. 725
AUTO PAINT—See Auto-Wares, LLC; *U.S. Private*, pg. 398
AUTOPAL INC—See Autolite (India) Limited; *Int'l*, pg. 728
AUTO PARTNER SA; *Int'l*, pg. 725
AUTOPARTS ARMETAL S.A.—See Fras-le S.A.; *Int'l*, pg. 2765
AUTO PARTS COMPANY; *U.S. Private*, pg. 397
AUTO PARTS WAREHOUSE INC.; *U.S. Private*, pg. 397
AUTO PERFORMANCE, INC.—See Auto-Wares, LLC; *U.S. Private*, pg. 398
AUTO SUPPLY COMPANY INC.; *U.S. Private*, pg. 397
AUTOTECH ENGINEERING DEUTSCHLAND, GMBH—See Acek Desarrollo y Gestion Industrial SL; *Int'l*, pg. 96
AUTO TODO MEXICANA S.A. DE C.V.—See Genuine Parts Company; *U.S. Public*, pg. 932
AUTOVATIVE TECHNOLOGIES, INC.; *U.S. Private*, pg. 401
AUTO-WARES, LLC; *U.S. Private*, pg. 398
AUTO-WARES OE—See Auto-Wares, LLC; *U.S. Private*, pg. 398
AUTO-WARES TOOLS, INC.—See Auto-Wares, LLC; *U.S. Private*, pg. 398
AUTOWAVE CO., LTD.; *Int'l*, pg. 732
AUTOZONE RETAIL AND DISTRIBUTION (PTY) LTD—See TRG Management LP; *U.S. Private*, pg. 4219

AVA BENELUX B.V.—See Enterex International Limited; *Int'l*, pg. 2450
AVA COOLING UK LIMITED—See Enterex International Limited; *Int'l*, pg. 2450
AVA DANMARK A/S—See Enterex International Limited; *Int'l*, pg. 2450
AVA ITALIA S.R.L.—See Enterex International Limited; *Int'l*, pg. 2451
AVA KUHLERCENTER AUSTRIA GMBH—See Enterex International Limited; *Int'l*, pg. 2451
AVA MORADIA SAS—See Enterex International Limited; *Int'l*, pg. 2451
AXIOM AUTOMOTIVE TECHNOLOGIES, INC.—See Blue Point Capital Partners, LLC; *U.S. Private*, pg. 590
AXLETECH DO BRASIL SISTEMAS AUTOMOTIVOS LTDA.—See Cummins Inc.; *U.S. Public*, pg. 608
BANDO (SHANGHAI) MANAGEMENT CO., LTD.—See Bando Chemical Industries, Ltd.; *Int'l*, pg. 830
BARLOWORLD SOUTH AFRICA (PTY) LIMITED—See Barloworld Ltd.; *Int'l*, pg. 866
BARRAULT; *Int'l*, pg. 868
BARRON MOTOR INC.; *U.S. Private*, pg. 480
BATTERY SPECIALISTS, INC.—See Auto-Wares, LLC; *U.S. Private*, pg. 398
BATTERY SYSTEMS LLC; *U.S. Private*, pg. 488
BEAM MACK SALES & SERVICE, INC.; *U.S. Private*, pg. 506
BEHARRY AUTOMOTIVE LIMITED—See Edward B. Beharry & Co. Ltd.; *Int'l*, pg. 2316
BEIFANG HELLA AUTOMOTIVE LIGHTING LTD.—See Hella GmbH & Co. KGaA; *Int'l*, pg. 3331
BENNETT AUTO SUPPLY INC.; *U.S. Private*, pg. 527
BERU ITALIA S.R.L.—See BorgWarner Inc.; *U.S. Public*, pg. 369
BERU MEXICO S.A. DE C.V.—See BorgWarner Inc.; *U.S. Public*, pg. 369
BH PARTNERS, LLC—See Platinum Equity, LLC; *U.S. Private*, pg. 3209
B&I AUTO SUPPLIES INC.; *U.S. Private*, pg. 418
BIERHAKE GMBH & CO. KG; *Int'l*, pg. 1020
BIKE24 GMBH—See Bike24 Holding AG; *Int'l*, pg. 1023
BIKEEXCHANGE AUSTRALIA PTY. LTD.—See BikeExchange Limited; *Int'l*, pg. 1023
BIKEEXCHANGE COLOMBIA S.A.S.—See BikeExchange Limited; *Int'l*, pg. 1023
BIKEEXCHANGE DE VERTRIEBS GMBH—See BikeExchange Limited; *Int'l*, pg. 1023
BILL BUCKLE AUTOS PTY LTD—See Eagers Automotive Limited; *Int'l*, pg. 2264
BILL BUCKLE HOLDINGS PTY LTD—See Eagers Automotive Limited; *Int'l*, pg. 2264
BISHOP INTERNATIONAL, INC.; *U.S. Private*, pg. 565
BLACKCIRCLES.COM LIMITED—See Compagnie Generale des Etablissements Michelin SCA; *Int'l*, pg. 1741
BLAISE OF COLOR—See LKQ Corporation; *U.S. Public*, pg. 1336
BOLZONI AURAMO AB—See Hyster-Yale Materials Handling, Inc.; *U.S. Public*, pg. 1080
BOLZONI AURAMO POLSKA SP ZOO—See Hyster-Yale Materials Handling, Inc.; *U.S. Public*, pg. 1080
BOLZONI AURAMO S.A.R.L.—See Hyster-Yale Materials Handling, Inc.; *U.S. Public*, pg. 1080
BOLZONI AURAMO S.L.—See Hyster-Yale Materials Handling, Inc.; *U.S. Public*, pg. 1080
BOND AUTO PARTS INC.; *U.S. Private*, pg. 613
BOON KOON SERVICES & PARTS SDN BHD—See Chin Hin Group Berhad; *Int'l*, pg. 1480
BOOST CONTROLLED PERFORMANCE INC.—See HKS CO., LTD.; *Int'l*, pg. 3429
BORBET SOLINGEN GMBH—See BORBET GmbH; *Int'l*, pg. 1112
BORBET SOUTH AFRICA (PTY) LTD.—See BORBET GmbH; *Int'l*, pg. 1112
BORBET THURINGEN GMBH—See BORBET GmbH; *Int'l*, pg. 1112
BORBET VERTRIEBS GMBH—See BORBET GmbH; *Int'l*, pg. 1112
BORGWARNER AFTERMARKET EUROPE GMBH—See BorgWarner Inc.; *U.S. Public*, pg. 369
BORGWARNER ESSLINGEN GMBH—See BorgWarner Inc.; *U.S. Public*, pg. 369
BORGWARNER FRANCE S.A.S.—See BorgWarner Inc.; *U.S. Public*, pg. 369
BORGWARNER HEIDELBERG II RE GMBH & CO. KG—See BorgWarner Inc.; *U.S. Public*, pg. 369
BORGWARNER IT SERVICES EUROPE GMBH—See BorgWarner Inc.; *U.S. Public*, pg. 369
BORGWARNER LUDWIGSBURG GMBH—See BorgWarner Inc.; *U.S. Public*, pg. 369
BORGWARNER OROSZLANY KFT.—See BorgWarner Inc.; *U.S. Public*, pg. 370
BORGWARNER SWEDEN AB—See BorgWarner Inc.; *U.S. Public*, pg. 370
BORGWARNER TORQTRANSFER SYSTEMS AB—See BorgWarner Inc.; *U.S. Public*, pg. 370
BORGWARNER TRALEE LTD.—See BorgWarner Inc.; *U.S. Public*, pg. 370

BORGWARNER TTS, S. DE R.L. DE C.V.—See BorgWarner Inc.; *U.S. Public*, pg. 370
BORGWARNER TURBO SYSTEMS POLAND SP.Z.O.O—See BorgWarner Inc.; *U.S. Public*, pg. 371
BORGWARNER WREXHAM LIMITED—See BorgWarner Inc.; *U.S. Public*, pg. 371
BOSAL AUTOMOTIVE & INDUSTRIAL COMPONENTS LTD—See Bosal International NV; *Int'l*, pg. 1116
BOSAL GERMANY GMBH—See Bosal International NV; *Int'l*, pg. 1116
BOSAL IRELAND LTD—See Bosal International NV; *Int'l*, pg. 1116
BOSAL MIMAYSAN A.S.—See Bosal International NV; *Int'l*, pg. 1116
BOS HOMOGENISERS B.V.—See GEA Group Aktiengesellschaft; *Int'l*, pg. 2897
BOURNS, INC. - AUTOMOTIVE DIVISION—See Bourns, Inc.; *U.S. Private*, pg. 624
BRAAS COMPANY—See Genuine Parts Company; *U.S. Public*, pg. 933
BRAKE & TRANSMISSION NZ LIMITED—See Bapcor Limited; *Int'l*, pg. 857
BREMBO JAPAN CO. LTD.—See Brembo S.p.A.; *Int'l*, pg. 1145
BREMBO SCANDINAVIA A.B.—See Brembo S.p.A.; *Int'l*, pg. 1145
BREVINI FLUID POWER UK LIMITED—See Dana Incorporated; *U.S. Public*, pg. 621
BREVINI INDIA LTD—See Dana Incorporated; *U.S. Public*, pg. 621
BRITAX AUTOMOTIVE EQUIPMENT PTY—See Ecco Safety Group; *U.S. Private*, pg. 1326
BRITAX AUTOZUBEHOR GMBH—See Ecco Safety Group; *U.S. Private*, pg. 1326
BRITAX SIGNALISATION SAS—See Ecco Safety Group; *U.S. Private*, pg. 1326
BROPFS CORPORATION; *U.S. Private*, pg. 665
BROSE AUNDE FAHRZEUGISTZE GMBH—See Brose Fahrzeugteile GmbH & Co. KG; *Int'l*, pg. 1195
BROSE AUTOMOTIVE LA SUZE S.A.S.—See Brose Fahrzeugteile GmbH & Co. KG; *Int'l*, pg. 1195
BROSE BELVIDERE INC.—See Brose Fahrzeugteile GmbH & Co. KG; *Int'l*, pg. 1195
BROSE FAHRZEUGTEILE GMBH—See Brose Fahrzeugteile GmbH & Co. KG; *Int'l*, pg. 1195
BROSE GUANGZHOU AUTOMOTIVE SYSTEMS CO., LTD.—See Brose Fahrzeugteile GmbH & Co. KG; *Int'l*, pg. 1195
BROSE INDIA AUTOMOTIVE SYSTEMS PVT LTD.—See Brose Fahrzeugteile GmbH & Co. KG; *Int'l*, pg. 1195
BROSE ITALIA S.R.L.—See Brose Fahrzeugteile GmbH & Co. KG; *Int'l*, pg. 1195
BROSE JAPAN LTD.—See Brose Fahrzeugteile GmbH & Co. KG; *Int'l*, pg. 1195
BROSE MELFI AUTOMOTIVE S.R.L.—See Brose Fahrzeugteile GmbH & Co. KG; *Int'l*, pg. 1195
BROSE NEW BOSTON, INC.—See Brose Fahrzeugteile GmbH & Co. KG; *Int'l*, pg. 1195
BROSE PRIEVIDZA SPOL. S.R.O.—See Brose Fahrzeugteile GmbH & Co. KG; *Int'l*, pg. 1195
BROSE PUEBLA, S.A. DE C.V.—See Brose Fahrzeugteile GmbH & Co. KG; *Int'l*, pg. 1195
BROSE QUERETARO S.A. DE C.V.—See Brose Fahrzeugteile GmbH & Co. KG; *Int'l*, pg. 1195
BROSE RUSSLAND LLC—See Brose Fahrzeugteile GmbH & Co. KG; *Int'l*, pg. 1195
BROSE SCHLIESSSYSTEME GMBH & CO., KG—See Brose Fahrzeugteile GmbH & Co. KG; *Int'l*, pg. 1195
BROSE SHENYANG AUTOMOTIVE SYSTEMS CO., LTD.—See Brose Fahrzeugteile GmbH & Co. KG; *Int'l*, pg. 1195
BROSE SPARTANBURG, INC.—See Brose Fahrzeugteile GmbH & Co. KG; *Int'l*, pg. 1196
BROSE TAICANG AUTOMOTIVE SYSTEMS CO., LTD.—See Brose Fahrzeugteile GmbH & Co. KG; *Int'l*, pg. 1196
BROSE (THAILAND) CO., LTD.—See Brose Fahrzeugteile GmbH & Co. KG; *Int'l*, pg. 1195
BROSE TOGLIATTI AUTOMOTIVE LLC—See Brose Fahrzeugteile GmbH & Co. KG; *Int'l*, pg. 1196
BROWN BROTHERS DISTRIBUTION LIMITED—See Brown Brothers Harriman & Co.; *U.S. Private*, pg. 666
BUDGE INDUSTRIES INC.; *U.S. Private*, pg. 679
BUTLER INDUSTRIES INC.; *U.S. Private*, pg. 697
CAL-STATE AUTO PARTS, INC.; *U.S. Private*, pg. 715
CAPCO GUANGZHOU, LTD.—See Central Automotive Products Ltd.; *Int'l*, pg. 1404
CAPCO (MALAYSIA) SDN. BHD.—See Central Automotive Products Ltd.; *Int'l*, pg. 1404
CAPCO MIDDLE EAST FZCO—See Central Automotive Products Ltd.; *Int'l*, pg. 1404
CAR & GENERAL (TANZANIA) LIMITED—See Car & General (Kenya) Limited; *Int'l*, pg. 1319
CAR & GENERAL (UGANDA) LIMITED—See Car & General (Kenya) Limited; *Int'l*, pg. 1319
CARMAX CO., LTD.—See Hotai Motor Co., Ltd.; *Int'l*, pg. 3487

423120 — MOTOR VEHICLE SUPPL...

CAROLINA RIM & WHEEL COMPANY; *U.S. Private*, pg. 768
CAR-O-LINER (BEIJING) CO., LTD.—See Snap-on Incorporated; *U.S. Public*, pg. 1897
CAR-O-LINER INDIA PRIVATE LIMITED—See Snap-on Incorporated; *U.S. Public*, pg. 1897
CAR-O-LINER MEA (FZE)—See Snap-on Incorporated; *U.S. Public*, pg. 1897
CAR-O-LINER NORGE AS—See Snap-on Incorporated; *U.S. Public*, pg. 1897
CAR-O-LINER SAS—See Snap-on Incorporated; *U.S. Public*, pg. 1897
CAR-O-LINER S.R.L.—See Snap-on Incorporated; *U.S. Public*, pg. 1897
CAR-O-LINER (THAILAND) CO., LTD.—See Snap-on Incorporated; *U.S. Public*, pg. 1897
CAR-O-LINER (UK) LIMITED—See Snap-on Incorporated; *U.S. Public*, pg. 1897
CARPARTS.COM, INC.; *U.S. Public*, pg. 438
CARPARTS DISTRIBUTION CENTER; *U.S. Private*, pg. 770
CAR PARTS WAREHOUSE INC.; *U.S. Private*, pg. 747
CARQUEST AUTO PARTS OF ANDERSON—See Advance Auto Parts, Inc.; *U.S. Public*, pg. 45
CARQUEST AUTO PARTS OF GRAND FORKS—See Advance Auto Parts, Inc.; *U.S. Public*, pg. 45
CARQUEST AUTO PARTS—See Advance Auto Parts, Inc.; *U.S. Public*, pg. 45
CARQUEST CORPORATION—See Advance Auto Parts, Inc.; *U.S. Public*, pg. 45
CARQUEST DISTRIBUTION CENTER - ALABAMA—See Advance Auto Parts, Inc.; *U.S. Public*, pg. 45
CARQUEST DISTRIBUTION CENTER - CALIFORNIA—See Advance Auto Parts, Inc.; *U.S. Public*, pg. 45
CARQUEST DISTRIBUTION CENTER - MICHIGAN—See Advance Auto Parts, Inc.; *U.S. Public*, pg. 45
CARQUEST DISTRIBUTION CENTER - MICHIGAN—See Advance Auto Parts, Inc.; *U.S. Public*, pg. 45
CARQUEST DISTRIBUTION CENTER - MINNESOTA—See Advance Auto Parts, Inc.; *U.S. Public*, pg. 45
CARQUEST DISTRIBUTION CENTER - MISSOURI—See Advance Auto Parts, Inc.; *U.S. Public*, pg. 45
CARQUEST DISTRIBUTION CENTER - MONTANA—See Advance Auto Parts, Inc.; *U.S. Public*, pg. 45
CARQUEST DISTRIBUTION CENTER- NEW YORK—See Advance Auto Parts, Inc.; *U.S. Public*, pg. 45
CARQUEST DISTRIBUTION CENTER - NORTH CAROLINA—See Advance Auto Parts, Inc.; *U.S. Public*, pg. 45
CARQUEST DISTRIBUTION CENTER - NORTH CAROLINA—See Advance Auto Parts, Inc.; *U.S. Public*, pg. 45
CARQUEST DISTRIBUTION CENTER - TENNESSEE—See Advance Auto Parts, Inc.; *U.S. Public*, pg. 45
CARQUEST DISTRIBUTION CENTER - TEXAS—See Advance Auto Parts, Inc.; *U.S. Public*, pg. 45
CARQUEST DISTRIBUTION CENTER - TEXAS—See Advance Auto Parts, Inc.; *U.S. Public*, pg. 45
CARQUEST DISTRIBUTION CENTER - WASHINGTON—See Advance Auto Parts, Inc.; *U.S. Public*, pg. 45
CARQUEST DISTRIBUTION CENTER - WISCONSIN—See Advance Auto Parts, Inc.; *U.S. Public*, pg. 45
CARQUEST-MEMPHIS—See Advance Auto Parts, Inc.; *U.S. Public*, pg. 45
CARQUEST—See Advance Auto Parts, Inc.; *U.S. Public*, pg. 45
CARQUEST—See Advance Auto Parts, Inc.; *U.S. Public*, pg. 45
CARQUEST—See Advance Auto Parts, Inc.; *U.S. Public*, pg. 45
CARQUEST—See Advance Auto Parts, Inc.; *U.S. Public*, pg. 45
CARRUS TECHNOLOGIES INC.—See KKR & Co. Inc.; *U.S. Public*, pg. 1267
CARWOOD (HK) LIMITED—See Carwood Motor Units Ltd; *Int'l*, pg. 1349
CENTRALE TECHNIQUE D'APPROVISIONNEMENT INDUSTRIEL; *Int'l*, pg. 1411
CENTRAL MOTORS & EQUIPMENT LLC—See Al Fahim Group; *Int'l*, pg. 277
CERTIFIT, INC.; *U.S. Private*, pg. 842
CG AUTOMOTIVE GROUP, INC.; *U.S. Private*, pg. 844
CHALKS TRUCK PARTS, INC.; *U.S. Private*, pg. 845
CHANGAN MINSHENG APLL LOGISTICS CO., LTD.; *Int'l*, pg. 1442
CHANGSHA FUTABA AUTO PARTS CO., LTD.—See Futaba Industrial Co., Ltd.; *Int'l*, pg. 2851
CHANGSHU MONO HIROSAWA AUTOMOTIVE TRIM CO., LTD.—See Hiroca Holdings Ltd.; *Int'l*, pg. 3404
CHLODNICE NISSENS POLSKA SP.ZO.O,—See Standard Motor Products, Inc.; *U.S. Public*, pg. 1929
CHONGQING FUTABA AUTO PARTS CO., LTD.—See Futaba Industrial Co., Ltd.; *Int'l*, pg. 2851
CHUNG YUAN DAIDO CO., LTD.—See Daido Metal Corporation; *Int'l*, pg. 1921

CHUNG YUAN DAIDO (GUANGZHOU) CO., LTD.—See Daido Metal Corporation; *Int'l*, pg. 1921
CITY AUTOMOTIVE GROUP PTY LTD—See Eagers Automotive Limited; *Int'l*, pg. 2264
CLAUS ETTENSBERGER CORPORATION; *U.S. Private*, pg. 917
CLOYES DYNAGEAR MEXICANA S. DE R.L. DE C.V.—See MidOcean Partners, LLP; *U.S. Private*, pg. 2716
CLOYES DYNAGEAR MEXICANA S. DE R.L. DE C.V.—See MidOcean Partners, LLP; *U.S. Private*, pg. 2716
CLOYES DYNAGEAR MEXICANA S. DE R.L. DE C.V.—See MidOcean Partners, LLP; *U.S. Private*, pg. 2716
C & M AUTO PARTS, INC.—See Blue Point Capital Partners, LLC; *U.S. Private*, pg. 590
COFC LOGISTICS, LLC; *U.S. Private*, pg. 960
COLD AIR DISTRIBUTORS WAREHOUSE OF FLORIDA INC.—See TPH Acquisition, LLLP; *U.S. Private*, pg. 4200
COLONIAL AUTO SUPPLY CO.; *U.S. Private*, pg. 970
COLORADO BRAKE & SUPPLY INC.—See North American Truck & Trailer, Inc.; *U.S. Private*, pg. 2941
COLUMBUS TRUCK AND EQUIPMENT CO. INC.; *U.S. Private*, pg. 979
COMAT AUTO SA; *Int'l*, pg. 1707
COMPETITION PRODUCTS, INC.; *U.S. Private*, pg. 1000
COMPETITION SPECIALTIES INC.; *U.S. Private*, pg. 1000
COMSTAR AUTOMOTIVE LLC USA—See Blackstone Inc.; *U.S. Public*, pg. 360
CONCHO SUPPLY INC.; *U.S. Private*, pg. 1009
CONTINENTAL AUTOMOTIVE (THAILAND) CO. LTD—See Continental Aktiengesellschaft; *Int'l*, pg. 1781
CONTINENTAL AUTOMOTIVE TRADING S.R.L.—See Continental Aktiengesellschaft; *Int'l*, pg. 1782
CONTINENTAL BATTERY COMPANY—See H.I.G. Capital, LLC; *U.S. Private*, pg. 1829
CONTINENTAL TEVES AG & CO. OHG—See Continental Aktiengesellschaft; *Int'l*, pg. 1783
CONTINENTAL TEVES HUNGARY KFT.—See Continental Aktiengesellschaft; *Int'l*, pg. 1783
CONTINENTAL TRADING UK LTD.—See Continental Aktiengesellschaft; *Int'l*, pg. 1783
CONTITECH POWER TRANSMISSION SYSTEM (SHANGHAI) CO., LTD.—See Continental Aktiengesellschaft; *Int'l*, pg. 1780
COOPER-STANDARD AUTOMOTIVE (CHANGCHUN) CO., LTD.—See Cooper-Standard Holdings Inc.; *U.S. Public*, pg. 574
COOPER-STANDARD AUTOMOTIVE (DEUTSCHLAND) GMBH—See Cooper-Standard Holdings Inc.; *U.S. Public*, pg. 574
COOPER STANDARD AUTOMOTIVE FRANCE S.A.S.—See Cooper-Standard Holdings Inc.; *U.S. Public*, pg. 574
COOPER-STANDARD AUTOMOTIVE FRANCE S.A.S.—See Cooper-Standard Holdings Inc.; *U.S. Public*, pg. 574
COOPER-STANDARD CHONGQING AUTOMOTIVE CO., LTD.—See Cooper-Standard Holdings Inc.; *U.S. Public*, pg. 574
COOPER STANDARD SEALING (GUANGZOU) CO. LTD.—See Cooper-Standard Holdings Inc.; *U.S. Public*, pg. 573
COOPER-STANDARD SEALING (SHENYANG) CO. LTD.—See Cooper-Standard Holdings Inc.; *U.S. Public*, pg. 574
COOPER STANDARD SRBIJA DOO SREMSKA MITROVICA—See Cooper-Standard Holdings Inc.; *U.S. Public*, pg. 573
COPART DEUTSCHLAND GMBH—See Copart, Inc.; *U.S. Public*, pg. 575
COPART UAE AUCTIONS LLC—See Copart, Inc.; *U.S. Public*, pg. 575
CORPORACION UPWARDS 98 S.A.—See Brembo S.p.A.; *Int'l*, pg. 1145
CORTECO LTD.—See Freudenberg SE; *Int'l*, pg. 2783
CORTECO SAS—See Freudenberg SE; *Int'l*, pg. 2783
CORTECO S.R.L.—See Freudenberg SE; *Int'l*, pg. 2783
CORTECO USA—See Freudenberg SE; *Int'l*, pg. 2783
COSMOS INTERNATIONAL, INC.; *U.S. Private*, pg. 1062
COVINGTON HEAVY DUTY PARTS; *U.S. Private*, pg. 1073
CRAFT CO., LTD.—See Diamondback Energy, Inc.; *U.S. Public*, pg. 658
CRASHED TOYS LLC—See Copart, Inc.; *U.S. Public*, pg. 575
CROW-BURLINGAME CO. INC.—See Replacement Parts Inc.; *U.S. Private*, pg. 3401
CROW-BURLINGAME CO. INC.—See Replacement Parts Inc.; *U.S. Private*, pg. 3401
CROW BURLINGAME OF CONWAY INC.—See Replacement Parts Inc.; *U.S. Private*, pg. 3401
CROWN AUTOMOTIVE SALES CO. INC.; *U.S. Private*, pg. 1110
CRP DE MEXICO S.A. DE C.V.—See CRP Industries Inc.; *U.S. Private*, pg. 1113
CRP INDUSTRIES INC.; *U.S. Private*, pg. 1113
CRW PARTS INC.; *U.S. Private*, pg. 1114
CRYSTEEL TRUCK EQUIPMENT, INC.; *U.S. Private*, pg. 1116

CSF POLAND SP. Z O.O.—See Cooper-Standard Holdings Inc.; *U.S. Public*, pg. 573
CUMMINS ARGENTINA-SERVICIOS MINEROS S.A.—See Cummins Inc.; *U.S. Public*, pg. 605
CUMMINS BRIDGEWAY, LLC - HILLIARD—See Cummins Inc.; *U.S. Public*, pg. 605
CUMMINS C&G LIMITED—See Car & General (Kenya) Limited; *Int'l*, pg. 1319
CUMMINS EASTERN CANADA LP—See Cummins Inc.; *U.S. Public*, pg. 605
CUMMINS EMISSION SOLUTIONS INC.—See Cummins Inc.; *U.S. Public*, pg. 605
CUMMINS ENERGY SOLUTIONS BUSINESS IBERIA—See Cummins Inc.; *U.S. Public*, pg. 605
CUMMINS FUEL SYSTEMS (WUHAN) CO. LTD.—See Cummins Inc.; *U.S. Public*, pg. 606
CUMMINS GENERATOR TECHNOLOGIES ITALY SRL—See Cummins Inc.; *U.S. Public*, pg. 606
CUMMINS GENERATOR TECHNOLOGIES SINGAPORE PTE LTD.—See Cummins Inc.; *U.S. Public*, pg. 606
CUMMINS NIGERIA LTD.—See Cummins Inc.; *U.S. Public*, pg. 606
CUMMINS POWER GENERATION (U.K.) LIMITED—See Cummins Inc.; *U.S. Public*, pg. 606
CUMMINS SOUTH PACIFIC PTY. LIMITED—See Cummins Inc.; *U.S. Public*, pg. 607
CUMMINS SPAIN, S.L.—See Cummins Inc.; *U.S. Public*, pg. 607
CUMMINS SWEDEN AB—See Cummins Inc.; *U.S. Public*, pg. 607
CUMMINS ZAMBIA LTD.—See Cummins Inc.; *U.S. Public*, pg. 607
CUMMINS ZIMBABWE PVT. LTD.—See Cummins Inc.; *U.S. Public*, pg. 607
CURRENT MOTOR CORPORATION; *Int'l*, pg. 1879
CUSTOM ACCESSORIES INC.; *U.S. Private*, pg. 1127
CV PRODUCTS, INC.; *U.S. Private*, pg. 1132
CVTECH-AAB INC.—See Brookfield Corporation; *Int'l*, pg. 1181
CYTON INDUSTRIES INC.; *U.S. Private*, pg. 1136
DACCO DETROIT OF OHIO, INC.—See Blue Point Capital Partners, LLC; *U.S. Private*, pg. 591
DAICEL SAFETY SYSTEMS INDIA PVT. LTD.—See Daicel Corporation; *Int'l*, pg. 1919
DAIDO METAL EUROPE GMBH—See Daido Metal Corporation; *Int'l*, pg. 1921
DAIDO METAL MEXICO SALES, S.A. DE C.V.—See Daido Metal Corporation; *Int'l*, pg. 1921
DAIFUKU DE MEXICO, S.A. DE C.V.—See Daifuku Co., Ltd.; *Int'l*, pg. 1926
DAKOTALAND AUTOGLASS INC.—See West Edge Partners, LLC; *U.S. Private*, pg. 4485
DALLAS WHEELS & ACCESSORIES INC.—See Ultra Wheel Company Inc.; *U.S. Private*, pg. 4277
DANA INDIA TECHNICAL CENTRE PVT. LTD.—See Dana Incorporated; *U.S. Public*, pg. 622
DANCOMECH HOLDINGS BERHAD; *Int'l*, pg. 1958
D-AUTO SUISSE SA—See Dogus Holding AS; *Int'l*, pg. 2154
DEE DRAXLMAIER ELEKTRIK-UND ELEKTRONIKSYSTEME GMBH—See Draexlmaier Gruppe; *Int'l*, pg. 2198
DELEGARD TOOL COMPANY INC; *U.S. Private*, pg. 1196
DELFINGEN AUTOMOTIVE PARTS (WUHAN) CO., LTD.—See Delfingen Industry, S.A.; *Int'l*, pg. 2012
DELFINGEN BR-SAO PAULO LTDA—See Delfingen Industry, S.A.; *Int'l*, pg. 2012
DELFINGEN HN-CORTES—See Delfingen Industry, S.A.; *Int'l*, pg. 2012
DELFINGEN INDIA PRIVATE LIMITED—See Delfingen Industry, S.A.; *Int'l*, pg. 2012
DELFINGEN MA-CASABLANCA SARL—See Delfingen Industry, S.A.; *Int'l*, pg. 2012
DELFINGEN MA-TANGER SARL—See Delfingen Industry, S.A.; *Int'l*, pg. 2012
DELFINGEN MX-COAHUILA SRL—See Delfingen Industry, S.A.; *Int'l*, pg. 2012
DELFINGEN PH-FILIPINAS, INC—See Delfingen Industry, S.A.; *Int'l*, pg. 2012
DELFINGEN PT-PORTO S.A.—See Delfingen Industry, S.A.; *Int'l*, pg. 2012
DELFINGEN RO-TRANSILVANIA S.R.L.—See Delfingen Industry, S.A.; *Int'l*, pg. 2012
DELFINGEN RO-VALAHIA S.R.L.—See Delfingen Industry, S.A.; *Int'l*, pg. 2012
DELFINGEN SK-NITRA S.R.O.—See Delfingen Industry, S.A.; *Int'l*, pg. 2012
DELFINGEN TN-TUNIS—See Delfingen Industry, S.A.; *Int'l*, pg. 2012
DELFINGEN TR-MARMARA PLASTIK SAN. VE DIS TIC. LTD. STI.—See Delfingen Industry, S.A.; *Int'l*, pg. 2012
DELFINGEN US-TEXAS LP—See Delfingen Industry, S.A.; *Int'l*, pg. 2012
DELPHI ALAMBRADOS AUTOMOTRICES, S.A. DE C.V.—See Aptiv PLC; *Int'l*, pg. 524
DELPHI ENERGY CHASSIS SYSTEMS—See Aptiv PLC; *Int'l*, pg. 524
DELPHI PACKARD ESPANA, SL—See Aptiv PLC; *Int'l*, pg. 525

N.A.I.C.S. INDEX

423120 — MOTOR VEHICLE SUPPL...

DELPHI PRODUCT & SERVICE SOLUTIONS—See Aptiv PLC; *Int'l*, pg. 524
DELPHI THERMAL HUNGARY KFT—See Aptiv PLC; *Int'l*, pg. 525
DENSO AUTOMOTIVE DEUTSCHLAND GMBH—See Denso Corporation; *Int'l*, pg. 2031
DENSO (CHINA) INVESTMENT CO., LTD.—See Denso Corporation; *Int'l*, pg. 2028
DENSO EUROPE B.V.—See Denso Corporation; *Int'l*, pg. 2031
DENSO INTERNATIONAL AMERICA—See Denso Corporation; *Int'l*, pg. 2031
DENSO INTERNATIONAL INDIA PVT. LTD.—See Denso Corporation; *Int'l*, pg. 2029
DENSO INTERNATIONAL UK LTD.—See Denso Corporation; *Int'l*, pg. 2029
DENSO MANUFACTURING ITALIA SPA—See Denso Corporation; *Int'l*, pg. 2031
DENSO SALES CALIFORNIA, INC.—See Denso Corporation; *Int'l*, pg. 2032
DENSO SALES CANADA, INC.—See Denso Corporation; *Int'l*, pg. 2030
DENSO SALES FRANCE S.A.R.L.—See Denso Corporation; *Int'l*, pg. 2030
DENSO SALES ITALIA SRL—See Denso Corporation; *Int'l*, pg. 2031
DENSO SALES RUS L.L.C.—See Denso Corporation; *Int'l*, pg. 2030
DENSO SALES SWEDEN AB—See Denso Corporation; *Int'l*, pg. 2031
DENSO SALES UK LTD.—See Denso Corporation; *Int'l*, pg. 2031
DENSO TEN (CHINA) LIMITED—See Denso Corporation; *Int'l*, pg. 2030
DHOLLANDIA FRANCE; *Int'l*, pg. 2100
DIESEL DISTRIBUTORS LIMITED—See Bapcor Limited; *Int'l*, pg. 857
DIESEL ELECTRICA LDA.—See Honda Motor Co., Ltd.; *Int'l*, pg. 3460
DINARA GRADNJA A.D.; *Int'l*, pg. 2126
DIS DRAXLMAIER INDUSTRIAL SOLUTIONS GMBH—See Draexlmaier Gruppe; *Int'l*, pg. 2198
DISTRIBUIDORA CUMMINS CENTROAMERICA COSTA RICA, S.DE R.L.—See Cummins Inc.; *U.S. Public*, pg. 607
DISTRIBUIDORA CUMMINS CENTROAMERICA EL SALVADOR, S.DE R.L.—See Cummins Inc.; *U.S. Public*, pg. 607
DISTRIBUIDORA CUMMINS CENTROAMERICA HONDURAS, S.DE R.L.—See Cummins Inc.; *U.S. Public*, pg. 607
DISTRIBUIDORA CUMMINS DE PANAMA, S. DE R.L.—See Cummins Inc.; *U.S. Public*, pg. 607
DISTRIBUTORS WAREHOUSE INC.; *U.S. Private*, pg. 1239
DIXIE ELECTRIC, INC.—See Motorcar Parts of America, Inc.; *U.S. Public*, pg. 1477
DMA HOLDINGS, INC.; *U.S. Private*, pg. 1248
DMS KOREA CO., LTD.—See Daido Metal Corporation; *Int'l*, pg. 1921
DOEDIJNS AUTOMOTIVE B.V.—See IK Investment Partners Limited; *Int'l*, pg. 3609
DOGUS OTO PAZARLAMA VE TICARET A.S.—See Dogus Holding AS; *Int'l*, pg. 2154
DONGFENG BROSE AUTOMOTIVE SYSTEM CO., LTD.—See Brose Fahrzeugteile GmbH & Co. KG; *Int'l*, pg. 1196
DONGGUAN FUTABA METAL PRODUCTS CO., LTD.—See Futaba Industrial Co., Ltd.; *Int'l*, pg. 2851
DONG GUAN HIROSAWA AUTOMOTIVE TRIM CO., LTD.—See Hiroca Holdings Ltd.; *Int'l*, pg. 3404
DONGGUAN TAICA HIROSAWA TECHNOLOGIES CO., LTD.—See Hiroca Holdings Ltd.; *Int'l*, pg. 3404
DONGYANG PISTON CO., LTD.; *Int'l*, pg. 2171
DOORS AKADEMI EGITIM VE DANISMANLIK HIZMETLERI A.S.—See Dogus Holding AS; *Int'l*, pg. 2154
DREYCO INC.; *U.S. Private*, pg. 1276
DRIVE TRAIN INDUSTRIES, INC.; *U.S. Private*, pg. 1278
DRIVE VAUXHALL BRISTOL—See DRIVE Motor Retail Limited; *Int'l*, pg. 2204
DSI AUTOMOTIVE PRODUCTS—See DSI, Inc.; *U.S. Private*, pg. 1281
DSI, INC.; *U.S. Private*, pg. 1281
DUAL BORGSTENA TEXTILE PORTUGAL UNIPESSOAL, LDA.—See DUAL Co. Ltd; *Int'l*, pg. 2217
DUNCAN SYSTEMS INC.—See LCI Industries; *U.S. Public*, pg. 1295
D&W DIESEL INC., *U.S. Private*, pg. 1138
DYNACRAFT—See PACCAR Inc.; *U.S. Public*, pg. 1630
DYNACRAFT—See PACCAR Inc.; *U.S. Public*, pg. 1630
DYNA METAL CO., LTD.—See Daido Metal Corporation; *Int'l*, pg. 1921
DYSONS INC.; *U.S. Private*, pg. 1300
EAGERS RETAIL PTY LTD—See Eagers Automotive Limited; *Int'l*, pg. 2264
EAGLE-I HOLDINGS PLC; *Int'l*, pg. 2266
E.A.L MAN HIN & SONS LTD.—See Honda Motor Co., Ltd.; *Int'l*, pg. 3460

EAST MANUFACTURING CORP.—See Fultra SAPI de CV; *Int'l*, pg. 2843
EBRAHIM K. KANOO COMPANY B.S.C. - KANOO AUTOMOTIVE EQUIPMENT DIVISION—See Ebrahim K. Kanoo Company B.S.C.; *Int'l*, pg. 2286
EDMONTON KENWORTH LTD. - KENWORTH FORT MCMURRAY DIVISION—See Edmonton Kenworth Ltd.; *Int'l*, pg. 2313
ED PERRY AUTO PARTS COMPANY, INC.; *U.S. Private*, pg. 1331
EDSCHA AUTOMOTIVE HAUZENBERG GMBH—See Acek Desarrollo y Gestion Industrial SL; *Int'l*, pg. 96
EDSCHA AUTOMOTIVE HENGERSBERG GMBH—See Acek Desarrollo y Gestion Industrial SL; *Int'l*, pg. 96
EDSCHA AUTOMOTIVE MICHIGIAN INC.—See Acek Desarrollo y Gestion Industrial SL; *Int'l*, pg. 96
EDSCHA BRIEY, S.A.S.—See Acek Desarrollo y Gestion Industrial SL; *Int'l*, pg. 96
EDSCHA BURGOS, S.A.—See Acek Desarrollo y Gestion Industrial SL; *Int'l*, pg. 96
EDSCHA DO BRASIL, LTDA.—See Acek Desarrollo y Gestion Industrial SL; *Int'l*, pg. 96
EDSCHA ENGINEERING FRANCE S.A.S—See Acek Desarrollo y Gestion Industrial SL; *Int'l*, pg. 96
EDSCHA ENGINEERING, GMBH.—See Acek Desarrollo y Gestion Industrial SL; *Int'l*, pg. 96
EDSCHA HRADEC S.R.O.—See Acek Desarrollo y Gestion Industrial SL; *Int'l*, pg. 96
EDSCHA SANTANDER, S.L.—See Acek Desarrollo y Gestion Industrial SL; *Int'l*, pg. 96
EDSCHA VELKY MEDER S.R.O.—See Acek Desarrollo y Gestion Industrial SL; *Int'l*, pg. 96
EFTEC (CHANGSHU) AUTOMOTIVE MATERIALS LIMITED—See EMS-Chemie Holding AG; *Int'l*, pg. 2393
EFTEC (CHANGSHU) ENGINEERING CO., LTD.—See EMS-Chemie Holding AG; *Int'l*, pg. 2393
EFTEC (CZECH REPUBLIC) A.S.—See EMS-Chemie Holding AG; *Int'l*, pg. 2393
EFTEC (ELABUGA) OOO—See EMS-Chemie Holding AG; *Int'l*, pg. 2393
EFTEC MEXICO S.A. DE C.V.—See EMS-Chemie Holding AG; *Int'l*, pg. 2393
EFTEC (NIZHNIY NOVGOROD) OOO—See EMS-Chemie Holding AG; *Int'l*, pg. 2393
EFTEC NORTH AMERICA, L.L.C.—See EMS-Chemie Holding AG; *Int'l*, pg. 2393
EHW (SEYCHELLES) LTD.—See Honda Motor Co., Ltd.; *Int'l*, pg. 3460
EIGENBRODT WIDNI BALTIC OU—See Axel Johnson Gruppen AB; *Int'l*, pg. 763
EIGENBRODT WIDNI OY—See Axel Johnson Gruppen AB; *Int'l*, pg. 763
EIS DE MEXICO—See Genuine Parts Company; *U.S. Public*, pg. 932
EISENWERK ERLA GMBH—See Dynamatic Technologies Limited; *Int'l*, pg. 2239
EISSMANN AUTOMOTIVE CESKA REPUBLIKA S.R.O.—See Eissmann Automotive Deutschland GmbH; *Int'l*, pg. 2336
EISSMANN AUTOMOTIVE DE MEXICO S.A. DE C.V.—See Eissmann Automotive Deutschland GmbH; *Int'l*, pg. 2336
EISSMANN AUTOMOTIVE HUNGARIA KFT.—See Eissmann Automotive Deutschland GmbH; *Int'l*, pg. 2336
EISSMANN AUTOMOTIVE NORTH AMERICA, INC.—See Eissmann Automotive Deutschland GmbH; *Int'l*, pg. 2336
E&L BATTERY & IGNITION CO.—See Hahn Automotive Warehouse, Inc.; *U.S. Private*, pg. 1840
ELECTRA HELLA'S S.A.—See Hella GmbH & Co. KGaA; *Int'l*, pg. 3331
ELEKTRO-DYNAMO AB—See Axel Johnson Gruppen AB; *Int'l*, pg. 763
ELRINGKLINGER AUTOMOTIVE COMPONENTS (INDIA) PVT. LTD.—See ElringKlinger AG; *Int'l*, pg. 2369
ELTRAK S.A.; *Int'l*, pg. 2371
EMPI, INC.—See Enovis Corporation; *U.S. Public*, pg. 772
ENERGY POWER SYSTEMS AUSTRALIA PTY. LTD.; *Int'l*, pg. 2423
ENGINE & PERFORMANCE WAREHOUSE, INC.—See National Auto Parts Warehouse, LLC; *U.S. Private*, pg. 2847
ENGINETECH INC.; *U.S. Private*, pg. 1399
ENTEREX AMERICA LLC—See Enterex International Limited; *Int'l*, pg. 2451
ENTEREX EUROPE HOLDING B.V.—See Enterex International Limited; *Int'l*, pg. 2451
ENVIA SYSTEMS, INC.—See General Motors Company; *U.S. Public*, pg. 924
EPIC VENTURES SDN. BHD.—See Amverton Berhad; *Int'l*, pg. 442
EP POLYMERS (M) SDN BHD—See EP Manufacturing Bhd.; *Int'l*, pg. 2458
ESCO COUPLINGS (JINAN) LTD—See Esco Financial & Engineering Company S.A/N.V.; *Int'l*, pg. 2501
EUROPE ONLINE TRADE EAD; *Int'l*, pg. 2555
EUROTRONICS SISTEMAS DE SEGURIDAD S.A.U.—See Emerson Electric Co.; *U.S. Public*, pg. 749
EXACT SYSTEMS CZECH REPUBLIC S.R.O.—See CVI Dom Maklerski sp. z o.o.; *Int'l*, pg. 1889

EXACT SYSTEMS GMBH—See CVI Dom Maklerski sp. z o.o.; *Int'l*, pg. 1889
EXACT SYSTEMS SLOVAKIA S.R.O.—See CVI Dom Maklerski sp. z o.o.; *Int'l*, pg. 1889
EXEDY CHONGQING CO., LTD.—See Exedy Corporation; *Int'l*, pg. 2581
EXEDY-DYNAX AMERICA CORPORATION—See Exedy Corporation; *Int'l*, pg. 2581
EXEDY FRICTION MATERIAL CO.,LTD.—See Exedy Corporation; *Int'l*, pg. 2581
EXEDY GUANGZHOU CO., LTD.—See Exedy Corporation; *Int'l*, pg. 2581
EXEDY INDIA LTD.—See Exedy Corporation; *Int'l*, pg. 2581
EXEDY (MALAYSIA) SDN.BHD.—See Exedy Corporation; *Int'l*, pg. 2580
EXEDY MIDDLE EAST FZCO—See Exedy Corporation; *Int'l*, pg. 2581
EXEDY NEW ZEALAND LTD.—See Exedy Corporation; *Int'l*, pg. 2580
EXEDY (SHANGHAI) CO., LTD.—See Exedy Corporation; *Int'l*, pg. 2580
EXEDY (THAILAND) CO., LTD.—See Exedy Corporation; *Int'l*, pg. 2580
EXEDY TRADING CO., LTD.—See Exedy Corporation; *Int'l*, pg. 2580
EXEDY VIETNAM CO.,LTD.—See Exedy Corporation; *Int'l*, pg. 2581
THE EXPEDITER, LLC—See Brookfield Corporation; *Int'l*, pg. 1176
FAB FOURS, INC.; *U.S. Private*, pg. 1458
FAST PRO INC.—See Fast Undercar Inc.; *U.S. Private*, pg. 1482
FAST UNDERCAR INC.; *U.S. Private*, pg. 1482
FAURECIA - ASSENTOS DE AUTOMOVEL, LIMITADA—See FORVIA SE; *Int'l*, pg. 2746
FAURECIA AST LUXEMBOURG S.A.—See FORVIA SE; *Int'l*, pg. 2746
FAURECIA EXHAUST MEXICANA, S.A. DE C.V.—See FORVIA SE; *Int'l*, pg. 2746
FAURECIA INTERIOR SYSTEMS SALC ESPANA, S.L.—See FORVIA SE; *Int'l*, pg. 2747
FAURECIA INTERIOR SYSTEMS—See FORVIA SE; *Int'l*, pg. 2747
FAURECIA INTERIOR SYSTEMS THAILAND CO., LTD.—See FORVIA SE; *Int'l*, pg. 2747
FEDERAL-MOGUL AFTERMARKET GMBH—See Apollo Global Management, Inc.; *U.S. Public*, pg. 160
FEDERAL-MOGUL ANAND SEALINGS INDIA LIMITED—See Apollo Global Management, Inc.; *U.S. Public*, pg. 160
FEDERAL-MOGUL BEARINGS INDIA LIMITED—See Apollo Global Management, Inc.; *U.S. Public*, pg. 160
FEDERAL-MOGUL CONTROLLED POWER LIMITED—See Apollo Global Management, Inc.; *U.S. Public*, pg. 160
FEDERAL-MOGUL MOTORPARTS (SINGAPORE) PTE. LTD.—See Apollo Global Management, Inc.; *U.S. Public*, pg. 161
FERRARIS PISTON SERVICE LTD.—See Blackstone Inc.; *U.S. Public*, pg. 360
FIC AMERICA CORP.—See Futaba Industrial Co., Ltd.; *Int'l*, pg. 2851
FICHOU SAS; *Int'l*, pg. 2653
FINANCIERE FAURECIA—See FORVIA SE; *Int'l*, pg. 2747
FINLEY INDUSTRIES INC.; *U.S. Private*, pg. 1510
FIO AUTOMOTIVE CANADA CORP.—See Futaba Industrial Co., Ltd.; *Int'l*, pg. 2851
FISHER AUTO PARTS INC.; *U.S. Private*, pg. 1534
FLEET ACQUISITIONS LLC; *U.S. Private*, pg. 1541
FLEET PARTS & SERVICE, INC.—See Boyne Capital Management, LLC; *U.S. Private*, pg. 629
FLEETPRIDE, INC.—See American Securities LLC; *U.S. Private*, pg. 248
FLEETPRIDE - NORTHEAST—See American Securities LLC; *U.S. Private*, pg. 248
FLEETPRIDE - SOUTHEAST—See American Securities LLC; *U.S. Private*, pg. 248
FLEETPRIDE - WESTERN/CENTRAL—See American Securities LLC; *U.S. Private*, pg. 248
FMI AUTOMOTIVE COMPONENTS LTD.—See Futaba Industrial Co., Ltd.; *Int'l*, pg. 2851
FORD COMPONENT SALES, L.L.C.—See Ford Motor Company; *U.S. Public*, pg. 865
FOREIGN PARTS SPECIALISTS—See Auto-Wares, LLC; *U.S. Private*, pg. 398
FORT PNEUS; *Int'l*, pg. 2737
FPS DISTRIBUTION LIMITED—See Blackstone Inc.; *U.S. Public*, pg. 360
FRAS-LE ATTICA AUTOMOTIVE (PTY) LTD.—See Fras-le S.A.; *Int'l*, pg. 2765
FRAS-LE ANDINA COMERCIO Y REPRESENTACIONES LTDA.—See Fras-le S.A.; *Int'l*, pg. 2765
FRAS-LE ARGENTINA S.A.—See Fras-le S.A.; *Int'l*, pg. 2765
FRAS-LE EUROPE HANDELSGESELLSCHAFT MBH—See Fras-le S.A.; *Int'l*, pg. 2765
FRAS-LE FRICTION MATERIALS (PINGHU) CO., LTD—See Fras-le S.A.; *Int'l*, pg. 2765

3815

423120 — MOTOR VEHICLE SUPPL...

FRAS-LE MEXICO, S. DE R.L. DE C.V.—See Fras-le S.A.; *Int'l*, pg. 2765
FRAS-LE MIDDLE EAST—See Fras-le S.A.; *Int'l*, pg. 2765
FRAS-LE NORTH AMERICA INC.—See Fras-le S.A.; *Int'l*, pg. 2765
FREEDOM TRUCK CENTERS INC.; *U.S. Private*, pg. 1604
FRENCH-ELLISON TRUCK CENTER INC.; *U.S. Private*, pg. 1609
FREUDENBERG FILTRATION TECHNOLOGIES FINLAND OY—See Freudenberg SE; *Int'l*, pg. 2786
FREUDENBERG FILTRATION TECHNOLOGIES INDIA PRIVATE LIMITED—See Freudenberg SE; *Int'l*, pg. 2786
FREUDENBERG FILTRATION TECHNOLOGIES LP—See Freudenberg SE; *Int'l*, pg. 2786
FREUDENBERG FILTRATION TECHNOLOGIES OOO—See Freudenberg SE; *Int'l*, pg. 2786
FREUDENBERG FILTRATION TECHNOLOGIES SAS—See Freudenberg SE; *Int'l*, pg. 2786
FREUDENBERG FILTRATION TECHNOLOGIES SLOVENSKO, S.R.O.—See Freudenberg SE; *Int'l*, pg. 2786
FREUDENBERG FILTRATION TECHNOLOGIES UK LIMITED—See Freudenberg SE; *Int'l*, pg. 2786
FREUDENBERG-NOK DE QUERETARO, S.A. DE C.V.—See Freudenberg SE; *Int'l*, pg. 2789
FROUDE HOFMANN, INC.—See HWH Investments Limited; *Int'l*, pg. 3543
FRUITAGE INTERNATIONAL CO., LTD—See Enterex International Limited; *Int'l*, pg. 2451
FRUITAGE INTERNATIONAL CO., LTD.—See Enterex International Limited; *Int'l*, pg. 2451
FS TRUCKS GMBH—See AGRAVIS Raiffeisen AG; *Int'l*, pg. 215
FULL LINE EXHAUST INC.; *U.S. Private*, pg. 1620
FULL SERVICE AUTO PARTS OF SAN ANTONIO; *U.S. Private*, pg. 1621
FUTABA CHANGZHOU ENGINEERING & MARKETING CO., LTD.—See Futaba Industrial Co., Ltd.; *Int'l*, pg. 2851
FUTABA INDUSTRIAL TEXAS CORP.—See Futaba Industrial Co., Ltd.; *Int'l*, pg. 2851
FUTABA NORTH AMERICA ENGINEERING & MARKETING CO.—See Futaba Industrial Co., Ltd.; *Int'l*, pg. 2851
FUTURIS AUTOMOTIVE INTERIORS TRADING (SHANGHAI) CO. LTD.—See Clearlake Capital Group, L.P.; *U.S. Private*, pg. 934
FUYAO AUTOMOTIVE NORTH AMERICA, INC.—See Fuyao Glass Industry Group Co., Ltd.; *Int'l*, pg. 2858
G-7 MOTORS CO., LTD.—See G-7 HOLDINGS Inc.; *Int'l*, pg. 2862
G7 RETAIL MALAYSIA SDN. BHD.—See G-7 HOLDINGS Inc.; *Int'l*, pg. 2862
GAMMA SOLUTIONS S.A.—See G7 Entreprises; *Int'l*, pg. 2867
GB 500 SATELLITE INC.; *U.S. Private*, pg. 1653
GEARCHIEF EISSMANN AUTOMOTIVE PARTS CO., LTD—See Eissmann Automotive Deutschland GmbH; *Int'l*, pg. 2336
GEARHEAD ENGINES INC.—See LKQ Corporation; *U.S. Public*, pg. 1334
GEAR-O-RAMA SUPPLY LTD.; *Int'l*, pg. 2904
GENERAL MOTORS OVERSEAS DISTRIBUTION LLC—See General Motors Company; *U.S. Public*, pg. 925
GENERAL PARTS, INC.—See Advance Auto Parts, Inc.; *U.S. Public*, pg. 45
GENERAL PARTS INTERNATIONAL, INC.—See Advance Auto Parts, Inc.; *U.S. Public*, pg. 44
GENERAL TRAILER PARTS LLC; *U.S. Private*, pg. 1667
GENERAL TRUCK EQUIPMENT & TRAILER SALES; *U.S. Private*, pg. 1667
GENERAL TRUCK PARTS & EQUIPMENT CO.; *U.S. Private*, pg. 1667
GENERATOR SOURCE, LLC—See Regent Square Capital, LLC; *U.S. Private*, pg. 3387
GENTHERM DE MEXICO S.A. DE C.V—See Gentherm Incorporated; *U.S. Public*, pg. 932
GENUINE PARTS COMPANY EASTERN DIVISION—See Genuine Parts Company; *U.S. Public*, pg. 932
GENUINE PARTS COMPANY MOUNTAIN & WESTERN DIVISION—See Genuine Parts Company; *U.S. Public*, pg. 932
GENUINE PARTS COMPANY - U.S. AUTOMOTIVE PARTS GROUP—See Genuine Parts Company; *U.S. Public*, pg. 932
GERMAN AUTOMOBILES LIMITED—See G.A. Holdings Limited; *Int'l*, pg. 2865
GERRY'S TRUCK CENTRE LTD.; *Int'l*, pg. 2945
GESTAMP ABRERA, S.A.—See Acek Desarrollo y Gestion Industrial SL; *Int'l*, pg. 96
GESTAMP AGUAS CALIENTES, S.A. DE C.V.—See Acek Desarrollo y Gestion Industrial SL; *Int'l*, pg. 96
GESTAMP ARAGON, S.A.—See Acek Desarrollo y Gestion Industrial SL; *Int'l*, pg. 96
GESTAMP AUTOCOMPONENTS (DONGGUAN),CO. LTD.—See Acek Desarrollo y Gestion Industrial SL; *Int'l*, pg. 96
GESTAMP AUTOCOMPONENTS (SHENYANG), CO. LTD.—See Acek Desarrollo y Gestion Industrial SL; *Int'l*, pg. 96
GESTAMP AUTOMOTIVE CHENNAI PRIVATE LIMITED—See Acek Desarrollo y Gestion Industrial SL; *Int'l*, pg. 96
GESTAMP AUTOMOTIVE INDIA PRIVATE LTD.—See Acek Desarrollo y Gestion Industrial SL; *Int'l*, pg. 97
GESTAMP AVEIRO, S.A.—See Acek Desarrollo y Gestion Industrial SL; *Int'l*, pg. 97
GESTAMP BAIRES, S.A—See Acek Desarrollo y Gestion Industrial SL; *Int'l*, pg. 97
GESTAMP BIZKAIA, S.A.—See Acek Desarrollo y Gestion Industrial SL; *Int'l*, pg. 97
GESTAMP CERVEIRA, LDA.—See Acek Desarrollo y Gestion Industrial SL; *Int'l*, pg. 97
GESTAMP CHATTANOOGA, LLC.—See Acek Desarrollo y Gestion Industrial SL; *Int'l*, pg. 97
GESTAMP CORDOBA, S.A.—See Acek Desarrollo y Gestion Industrial SL; *Int'l*, pg. 97
GESTAMP EDSCHA JAPAN CO., LTD.—See Acek Desarrollo y Gestion Industrial SL; *Int'l*, pg. 97
GESTAMP ESMAR, S.A.—See Acek Desarrollo y Gestion Industrial SL; *Int'l*, pg. 97
GESTAMP GRIWE WESTERBURG, GMBH—See Acek Desarrollo y Gestion Industrial SL; *Int'l*, pg. 97
GESTAMP HARDTECH, A.B.—See Acek Desarrollo y Gestion Industrial SL; *Int'l*, pg. 97
GESTAMP HUNGARIA, KFT.—See Acek Desarrollo y Gestion Industrial SL; *Int'l*, pg. 97
GESTAMP KARTEK CO, LTD.—See Acek Desarrollo y Gestion Industrial SL; *Int'l*, pg. 97
GESTAMP LEVANTE, S.A.—See Acek Desarrollo y Gestion Industrial SL; *Int'l*, pg. 97
GESTAMP LINARES, S.A.—See Acek Desarrollo y Gestion Industrial SL; *Int'l*, pg. 97
GESTAMP LOUNY, S.R.O.—See Acek Desarrollo y Gestion Industrial SL; *Int'l*, pg. 97
GESTAMP MANUFACTURING AUTOCHASIS, S.L.—See Acek Desarrollo y Gestion Industrial SL; *Int'l*, pg. 97
GESTAMP MASON, LLC.—See Acek Desarrollo y Gestion Industrial SL; *Int'l*, pg. 97
GESTAMP METAL FORMING (CHONGQING) CO., LTD.—See Acek Desarrollo y Gestion Industrial SL; *Int'l*, pg. 97
GESTAMP METAL FORMING (WUHAN), LTD.—See Acek Desarrollo y Gestion Industrial SL; *Int'l*, pg. 97
GESTAMP NAVARRA, S.A.—See Acek Desarrollo y Gestion Industrial SL; *Int'l*, pg. 97
GESTAMP NORTH EUROPE SERVICES, S.L—See Acek Desarrollo y Gestion Industrial SL; *Int'l*, pg. 97
GESTAMP NOURY S.A.S.—See Acek Desarrollo y Gestion Industrial SL; *Int'l*, pg. 97
GESTAMP PALENCIA, S.A.—See Acek Desarrollo y Gestion Industrial SL; *Int'l*, pg. 97
GESTAMP POLSKA SP. Z.O.O.—See Acek Desarrollo y Gestion Industrial SL; *Int'l*, pg. 97
GESTAMP PORTUGAL LTDA.—See Corporacion Gestamp SL; *Int'l*, pg. 1804
GESTAMP PRISMA S.A.S—See Acek Desarrollo y Gestion Industrial SL; *Int'l*, pg. 97
GESTAMP PUEBLA, S.A. DE C.V.—See Acek Desarrollo y Gestion Industrial SL; *Int'l*, pg. 97
GESTAMP RENEWABLES—See Corporacion Gestamp SL; *Int'l*, pg. 1804
GESTAMP RONCHAMP, S.A.S.—See Acek Desarrollo y Gestion Industrial SL; *Int'l*, pg. 97
GESTAMP SEVERSTAL KALUGA, LLC.—See Acek Desarrollo y Gestion Industrial SL; *Int'l*, pg. 97
GESTAMP SEVERSTAL VSEVOLOZHSK LLC.—See Acek Desarrollo y Gestion Industrial SL; *Int'l*, pg. 97
GESTAMP SOLBLANK NAVARRA, S.L.U—See Acek Desarrollo y Gestion Industrial SL; *Int'l*, pg. 97
GESTAMP SOLBLANK, S.A.—See Acek Desarrollo y Gestion Industrial SL; *Int'l*, pg. 97
GESTAMP SOUTH CAROLINA, LLC.—See Acek Desarrollo y Gestion Industrial SL; *Int'l*, pg. 97
GESTAMP TOGLIATTI, LLC.—See Acek Desarrollo y Gestion Industrial SL; *Int'l*, pg. 97
GESTAMP TOLEDO, S.A.—See Acek Desarrollo y Gestion Industrial SL; *Int'l*, pg. 97
GESTAMP TOLUCA, S.A. DE C. V.—See Acek Desarrollo y Gestion Industrial SL; *Int'l*, pg. 97
GESTAMP TOOL HARDENING, S.L.—See Acek Desarrollo y Gestion Industrial SL; *Int'l*, pg. 97
GESTAMP VENDAS NOVAS, LDA.—See Acek Desarrollo y Gestion Industrial SL; *Int'l*, pg. 97
GESTAMP VIGO, S.A.—See Acek Desarrollo y Gestion Industrial SL; *Int'l*, pg. 97
GESTAMP WASHINGTON, UK LTD.—See Acek Desarrollo y Gestion Industrial SL; *Int'l*, pg. 98
GESTAMP WEST VIRGINIA LLC.—See Acek Desarrollo y Gestion Industrial SL; *Int'l*, pg. 97
GGM PUEBLA, S.A. DE C.V.—See Acek Desarrollo y Gestion Industrial SL; *Int'l*, pg. 96
GHI AUTOMOTIVE SERVICES INC.; *U.S. Private*, pg. 1690
GIANT KOREA CO., LTD.—See Giant Manufacturing Co., Ltd.; *Int'l*, pg. 2961
GILBARCO ITALIA S.R.L.—See Vontier Corporation; *U.S. Public*, pg. 2309
GILBARCO VEEDER-ROOT SOLUCOES INDUSTRIA E COMERCIO LTDA.—See Vontier Corporation; *U.S. Public*, pg. 2309
GKN DRIVELINE BRUNECK AG—See GKN plc; *Int'l*, pg. 2984
GKN DRIVELINE JAPAN LTD—See GKN plc; *Int'l*, pg. 2984
GKN DRIVELINE JTEKT MANUFACTURING LTD—See GKN plc; *Int'l*, pg. 2984
GKN DRIVELINE KOREA LTD—See GKN plc; *Int'l*, pg. 2984
GKN DRIVELINE (THAILAND) LTD—See GKN plc; *Int'l*, pg. 2984
GKN DRIVELINE URUGUAY SA—See GKN plc; *Int'l*, pg. 2985
GKN DRIVELINE VILLAGRAN SA DE CV—See GKN plc; *Int'l*, pg. 2985
GKN GLENCO SA—See GKN plc; *Int'l*, pg. 2985
GKN SERVICE AUSTRIA GMBH—See GKN plc; *Int'l*, pg. 2985
GKN SERVICE BENELUX BV—See GKN plc; *Int'l*, pg. 2985
GKN WALTERSSCHEID AS—See GKN plc; *Int'l*, pg. 2986
GLAENZER-SEURRE NV/SA—See GKN plc; *Int'l*, pg. 2986
GLEASON INDUSTRIAL PRODUCTS INC.—See Gleason Corporation; *U.S. Private*, pg. 1708
GLOBAL TRADE ALLIANCE INC.—See LKQ Corporation; *U.S. Public*, pg. 1334
GM PHILIPPINES, INC.—See General Motors Company; *U.S. Public*, pg. 924
GONVAUTO ASTURIAS, S.L.—See Corporacion Gestamp SL; *Int'l*, pg. 1804
GOODSPEED CO., LTD.; *Int'l*, pg. 3041
GOODYEAR DUNLOP TIRES SVERIGE AB—See The Goodyear Tire & Rubber Company; *U.S. Public*, pg. 2084
GORDON AUTO BODY PARTS CO., LTD.; *Int'l*, pg. 3042
GRAFFMANS INC.; *U.S. Private*, pg. 1750
GREINER PERFOAM GMBH—See Greiner Holding AG; *Int'l*, pg. 3079
GREINER PERFOAM SPOL. S R.O.—See Greiner Holding AG; *Int'l*, pg. 3079
GRIFFITHS EQUIPMENT LIMITED—See Amotiv Limited; *Int'l*, pg. 431
GROUPAUTO UK & IRELAND LTD.—See Blackstone Inc.; *U.S. Public*, pg. 360
GRUPO ANTOLIN-LOUISIANA, INC.—See Grupo Antolin-Irausa, S.A.; *Int'l*, pg. 3119
GRUPO ANTOLIN-PUNE PVT, LTD.—See Grupo Antolin-Irausa, S.A.; *Int'l*, pg. 3120
GRUPO BRAVO—See Corpfin Capital SA; *Int'l*, pg. 1802
GUANGZHOU AUTOMOBILE GROUP BUSINESS CO., LTD.—See Guangzhou Automobile Industry Group Co., Ltd.; *Int'l*, pg. 3164
GUANGZHOU FUTABA AUTO PARTS CO., LTD.—See Futaba Industrial Co., Ltd.; *Int'l*, pg. 2851
GUELPH TOOL SALES INC.—See Guelph Tool Inc.; *Int'l*, pg. 3172
HAHN AUTOMOTIVE WAREHOUSE, INC.; *U.S. Private*, pg. 1840
HALDEX INT TRADING CO LTD—See Haldex AB; *Int'l*, pg. 3228
HALDEX LIMITED—See Haldex AB; *Int'l*, pg. 3228
HALDEX SP. Z.O.O.—See Haldex AB; *Int'l*, pg. 3228
HALLA MEISTER SHANGHAI TRADING CO., LTD.—See Halla Group; *Int'l*, pg. 3229
HANSON DISTRIBUTING COMPANY; *U.S. Private*, pg. 1856
HARRIS BATTERY CO. INC.; *U.S. Private*, pg. 1869
HAVANA AUTO PARTS INC.; *U.S. Private*, pg. 1880
HAWE FINLAND OY—See HAWE Hydraulik SE; *Int'l*, pg. 3288
HAWE HIDRAULICA, S.L.U.—See HAWE Hydraulik SE; *Int'l*, pg. 3288
HAWE HIDRAVLIKA D.O.O.—See HAWE Hydraulik SE; *Int'l*, pg. 3288
HAWE HOLDING GMBH—See HAWE Hydraulik SE; *Int'l*, pg. 3288
HAWE-HYDRATEC AG—See HAWE Hydraulik SE; *Int'l*, pg. 3288
HAWE HYDRAULICS AUSTRALIA PTY LTD—See HAWE Hydraulik SE; *Int'l*, pg. 3288
HAWE HYDRAULICS PVT. LTD.—See HAWE Hydraulik SE; *Int'l*, pg. 3288
HAWE HYDRAULIK SINGAPORE PTE. LTD.—See HAWE Hydraulik SE; *Int'l*, pg. 3288
HAWE ITALIANA S.R.L.—See HAWE Hydraulik SE; *Int'l*, pg. 3288
HAWE JAPAN LTD.—See HAWE Hydraulik SE; *Int'l*, pg. 3288
HAWE KOREA CO., LTD.—See HAWE Hydraulik SE; *Int'l*, pg. 3288
HAWE OIL-HYDRAULIC TECHNOLOGY (SHANGHAI) CO., LTD.—See HAWE Hydraulik SE; *Int'l*, pg. 3288
HAWE OSTERREICH GMBH—See HAWE Hydraulik SE; *Int'l*, pg. 3288
HAWE-OTELEC S.A.S.—See HAWE Hydraulik SE; *Int'l*, pg. 3288
HAYNES INTERNATIONAL, AG—See Acerinox, S.A.; *Int'l*, pg. 100

N.A.I.C.S. INDEX

423120 — MOTOR VEHICLE SUPPL...

HECKLER ROMANIA S.R.L.—See Heckler AG; *Int'l*, pg. 3307
HEDAHLS INC.; *U.S. Private*, pg. 1903
HELLA ASIA SINGAPORE PTE. LTD.—See Hella GmbH & Co. KGaA; *Int'l*, pg. 3331
HELLA A/S—See Hella GmbH & Co. KGaA; *Int'l*, pg. 3331
HELLA AUSTRALIA PTY LTD.—See Hella GmbH & Co. KGaA; *Int'l*, pg. 3331
HELLA AUTOTECHNIK NOVA S.R.O.—See Hella GmbH & Co. KGaA; *Int'l*, pg. 3331
HELLA-BEKTO INDUSTRIES D.O.O.—See Hella GmbH & Co. KGaA; *Int'l*, pg. 3332
HELLA CENTRO CORPORATIVO MEXICO S.A. DE C.V.—See Hella GmbH & Co. KGaA; *Int'l*, pg. 3331
HELLA CORPORATE CENTER (CHINA) CO., LTD.—See Hella GmbH & Co. KGaA; *Int'l*, pg. 3331
HELLA CORPORATE CENTER USA, INC.—See Hella GmbH & Co. KGaA; *Int'l*, pg. 3332
HELLA CZ. S.R.O.—See Hella GmbH & Co. KGaA; *Int'l*, pg. 3331
HELLA DISTRIBUTION GMBH—See Hella GmbH & Co. KGaA; *Int'l*, pg. 3331
HELLA DO BRAZIL AUTOMOTIVE LTDA.—See Hella GmbH & Co. KGaA; *Int'l*, pg. 3332
HELLA ENGINEERING FRANCE S.A.S.—See Hella GmbH & Co. KGaA; *Int'l*, pg. 3331
HELLA FAHRZEUGTEILE AUSTRIA GMBH—See Hella GmbH & Co. KGaA; *Int'l*, pg. 3331
HELLA FINANCE NEDERLAND—See Hella GmbH & Co. KGaA; *Int'l*, pg. 3332
HELLA GMBH & CO. KGaA; *Int'l*, pg. 3331
HELLA HANDEL AUSTRIA GMBH—See Hella GmbH & Co. KGaA; *Int'l*, pg. 3332
HELLA HUNGARIA KFT.—See Hella GmbH & Co. KGaA; *Int'l*, pg. 3332
HELLA INC—See Hella GmbH & Co. KGaA; *Int'l*, pg. 3332
HELLA INDIA AUTOMOTIVE PRIVATE LIMITED—See Hella GmbH & Co. KGaA; *Int'l*, pg. 3332
HELLA INDUPERM A/S—See Hella GmbH & Co. KGaA; *Int'l*, pg. 3332
HELLA INNENLEUCHTEN-SYSTEME BRATISLAVA, S.R.O.—See Hella GmbH & Co. KGaA; *Int'l*, pg. 3332
HELLA IRELAND LIMITED—See Hella GmbH & Co. KGaA; *Int'l*, pg. 3332
HELLA JAPAN INC.—See Hella GmbH & Co. KGaA; *Int'l*, pg. 3332
HELLA KOREA INC.—See Hella GmbH & Co. KGaA; *Int'l*, pg. 3332
HELLA LIGHTING FINLAND OY—See Hella GmbH & Co. KGaA; *Int'l*, pg. 3332
HELLA MIDDLE EAST FZE—See Hella GmbH & Co. KGaA; *Int'l*, pg. 3332
HELLA MINING LLC—See Hella GmbH & Co. KGaA; *Int'l*, pg. 3332
HELLANOR AS—See Aurelius Equity Opportunities SE & Co. KGaA; *Int'l*, pg. 708
HELLA POLSKA SP. Z O.O.—See Hella GmbH & Co. KGaA; *Int'l*, pg. 3332
HELLA ROMANIA S.R.L.—See Hella GmbH & Co. KGaA; *Int'l*, pg. 3332
HELLA S.A.—See Hella GmbH & Co. KGaA; *Int'l*, pg. 3332
HELLA S.A.S.—See Hella GmbH & Co. KGaA; *Int'l*, pg. 3332
HELLA SLOVAKIA FRONT-LIGHTING S.R.O.—See Hella GmbH & Co. KGaA; *Int'l*, pg. 3332
HELLA SLOVAKIA SIGNAL-LIGHTING S.R.O.—See Hella GmbH & Co. KGaA; *Int'l*, pg. 3332
HELLA S.P.A.—See Hella GmbH & Co. KGaA; *Int'l*, pg. 3332
HELLA TRADING (SHANGHAI) CO., LTD.—See Hella GmbH & Co. KGaA; *Int'l*, pg. 3332
HELLA UK HOLDINGS LIMITED—See Hella GmbH & Co. KGaA; *Int'l*, pg. 3332
HELLA VIETNAM COMPANY LIMITED—See Hella GmbH & Co. KGaA; *Int'l*, pg. 3332
HELLA (XIAMEN) ELECTRONIC DEVICE CO., LTD.—See Hella GmbH & Co. KGaA; *Int'l*, pg. 3331
HENGST ASIA PACIFIC PTE. LTD.—See Hengst SE & Co. KG; *Int'l*, pg. 3347
HENGST FILTER SYSTEMS (KUNSHAN) CO., LTD.—See Hengst SE & Co. KG; *Int'l*, pg. 3347
HENGST INDUSTRIA DE FILTROS LTDA.—See Hengst SE & Co. KG; *Int'l*, pg. 3347
HENGST-LUMAN INDIA PVT. LTD.—See Hengst SE & Co. KG; *Int'l*, pg. 3347
HENGST POLAND SP. Z O.O.—See Hengst SE & Co. KG; *Int'l*, pg. 3347
HENGST SE & CO. KG - BERLIN PLANT—See Hengst SE & Co. KG; *Int'l*, pg. 3347
HENGST SE & CO. KG - NORDWALDE PLANT—See Hengst SE & Co. KG; *Int'l*, pg. 3347
HENKELHAUSEN GMBH & CO. KG; *Int'l*, pg. 3354
HESCO PARTS—See Hesco Parts Corporation; *U.S. Private*, pg. 1927
H&H SPAS & TRUCK COVERS—See Harrell Hall Enterprises Inc.; *U.S. Private*, pg. 1868
HICKMAN INVESTMENTS INC.; *U.S. Private*, pg. 1933
HI-LEX MEXICANA S.A. DE C.V.—See Hi-Lex Corporation; *U.S. Private*, pg. 3380
HIRSCHMANN & LUMBERG AUTOMATION USA—See Belden, Inc.; *U.S. Public*, pg. 294
HITACHI AUTOMOTIVE SYSTEMS AMERICAS, INC. - ALLEN PARK—See Hitachi Astemo, Ltd.; *Int'l*, pg. 3408
HITACHI AUTOMOTIVE SYSTEMS AMERICAS, INC. - FARMINGTON HILLS—See Hitachi Astemo, Ltd.; *Int'l*, pg. 3408
HITACHI AUTOMOTIVE SYSTEMS AMERICAS, INC. - LOS ANGELES—See Hitachi Astemo, Ltd.; *Int'l*, pg. 3408
HITACHI AUTOMOTIVE SYSTEMS (S) PTE LTD.—See Hitachi Astemo, Ltd.; *Int'l*, pg. 3408
HKS (SHANGHAI) TRADING CO., LTD—See HKS CO., LTD.; *Int'l*, pg. 3429
HKS (THAILAND) CO., LTD.—See HKS CO., LTD.; *Int'l*, pg. 3429
HNTI LIMITED—See Northern Technologies International Corporation; *U.S. Public*, pg. 1538
HOEKSTRA TRUCK EQUIPMENT COMPANY INC.; *U.S. Private*, pg. 1959
HOFFMAN BROS AUTO ELECTRIC; *U.S. Private*, pg. 1960
HONDA CENTRE (2010) PVT. LTD.—See Honda Motor Co., Ltd.; *Int'l*, pg. 3461
HONDA INTERNATIONAL TRADING CO. (H.I.T.)—See Honda Motor Co., Ltd.; *Int'l*, pg. 3459
HONDA MALMO—See Honda Motor Co., Ltd.; *Int'l*, pg. 3461
HONDA MOTOR (CHINA) CO., LTD.—See Honda Motor Co., Ltd.; *Int'l*, pg. 3461
HONDA MOTOR (CHINA) INVESTMENT CO., LTD.—See Honda Motor Co., Ltd.; *Int'l*, pg. 3461
HONDA PERFORMANCE DEVELOPMENT—See Honda Motor Co., Ltd.; *Int'l*, pg. 3462
HONDA TRADING AMERICA CORP.—See Honda Motor Co., Ltd.; *Int'l*, pg. 3462
HONDA TRADING ASIA CO., LTD.—See Honda Motor Co., Ltd.; *Int'l*, pg. 3462
HONDA UGANDA LTD.—See Honda Motor Co., Ltd.; *Int'l*, pg. 3463
HORIBA AUTOMOTIVE TEST SYSTEMS INC.—See HORIBA Ltd; *Int'l*, pg. 3476
HORMANN AUTOMOTIVE GMBH—See Hormann Holding GmbH & Co. KG; *Int'l*, pg. 3480
HTC U.S.A., INC.—See HTC holding a.s.; *Int'l*, pg. 3508
HYUNDAI AUTO CANADA—See Hyundai Motor Company; *Int'l*, pg. 3559
HYUNDAI HYSCO RUS LLC—See Hyundai Motor Company; *Int'l*, pg. 3559
I-AUC INC.—See Aucnet Inc.; *Int'l*, pg. 700
IINO MANUFACTURING CO., LTD.—See Daido Metal Corporation; *Int'l*, pg. 1922
IMPAR COMERCIO E REPRESENTACOES LTDA.—See Illinois Tool Works Inc.; *U.S. Public*, pg. 1108
IMPORT PRODUCTS CO. INC.; *U.S. Private*, pg. 2050
INDUSTRIAL INTERNATIONAL TIRE COMPANY NV—See Compagnie Generale des Etablissements Michelin SCA; *Int'l*, pg. 1743
INLAD TRUCK & VAN EQUIPMENT COMPANY, INCORPORATED—See Driverge Vehicle Innovations, LLC.; *U.S. Private*, pg. 1278
INLAND TRUCK PARTS COMPANY; *U.S. Private*, pg. 2079
INSTALLER SALES & SERVICE INCORPORATED; *U.S. Private*, pg. 2092
INSTRUMENT SALES AND SERVICE; *U.S. Private*, pg. 2094
INTEC BIELENBERG GMBH & CO. KG—See Eisenmann AG; *Int'l*, pg. 2336
INTEGRATED SUPPLY NETWORK, LLC—See Freeman Spogli & Co. Incorporated; *U.S. Private*, pg. 1606
INTERAMERICAN MOTOR CORPORATION—See Parts Authority Inc.; *U.S. Private*, pg. 3103
INTERNAL ENGINE PARTS GROUP INC.; *U.S. Private*, pg. 2113
INTERSTATE BATTERY SYSTEM OF AMERICA INC.—See Interstate Battery System of America Inc.; *U.S. Private*, pg. 2124
INTERSTATE BATTERY SYSTEM OF HAWAII INC.—See Interstate Battery System of America Inc.; *U.S. Private*, pg. 2124
INTERTEC POLSKA SP.ZO.O.—See Deutsche Bahn AG; *Int'l*, pg. 2052
IOWA EXPORT-IMPORT—See Ruan Transportation; *U.S. Private*, pg. 3499
ISRINGHAUSEN AB—See AUNDE Achter & Ebels GmbH; *Int'l*, pg. 705
ISRINGHAUSEN ASSENTOS, LDA.—See AUNDE Achter & Ebels GmbH; *Int'l*, pg. 705
ISRINGHAUSEN B.V.B.A.—See AUNDE Achter & Ebels GmbH; *Int'l*, pg. 705
ISRINGHAUSEN KOLTUK SISTEMLERI LTD.—See AUNDE Achter & Ebels GmbH; *Int'l*, pg. 705
ISRINGHAUSEN MEXICO S.A.DE C.V.—See AUNDE Achter & Ebels GmbH; *Int'l*, pg. 706
ISRINGHAUSEN OTO YAN SANAYI, YEDEK PARCA VE KOLTUK SISTEMLERI SANAYI VE TICARET A.S.—See AUNDE Achter & Ebels GmbH; *Int'l*, pg. 706
ISRINGHAUSEN PTY. LTD.—See AUNDE Achter & Ebels GmbH; *Int'l*, pg. 706
ISRINGHAUSEN S.A.—See AUNDE Achter & Ebels GmbH; *Int'l*, pg. 706
ISRINGHAUSEN S.P.A.—See AUNDE Achter & Ebels GmbH; *Int'l*, pg. 706
ISRINGHAUSEN UMEA AB—See AUNDE Achter & Ebels GmbH; *Int'l*, pg. 706
IWIS-DAIDO LLC—See Daido Kogyo Co., Ltd.; *Int'l*, pg. 1921
JAGUAR FUELING SERVICES, LLC; *U.S. Private*, pg. 2182
JATA LLC; *U.S. Private*, pg. 2191
JB AUTO CORE INC.—See John Boyd Enterprises Inc.; *U.S. Private*, pg. 2220
JEAD AUTO SUPPLY INC.; *U.S. Private*, pg. 2196
JEGS AUTOMOTIVE INC.—See Greenbriar Equity Group, L.P.; *U.S. Private*, pg. 1776
JENS S. TRANSMISSIONER AB—See Axel Johnson Gruppen AB; *Int'l*, pg. 763
JERNBERG INDUSTRIES, LLC—See American Axle & Manufacturing Holdings, Inc.; *U.S. Public*, pg. 97
JERVIS WEBB CHINA CO., LTD.—See Daifuku Co., Ltd.; *Int'l*, pg. 1925
JKM FERROTECH LIMITED—See Dynamatic Technologies Limited; *Int'l*, pg. 2239
JMC EQUIPMENT LLC; *U.S. Private*, pg. 2215
JOBBERS AUTOMOTIVE WAREHOUSE; *U.S. Private*, pg. 2217
JOBBERS SERVICE OF SAN ANGELO—See Installer Sales & Service Incorporated; *U.S. Private*, pg. 2092
JOMAR INVESTMENTS, INC.; *U.S. Private*, pg. 2231
JOSAM RICHTTECKNIK GMBH—See Snap-on Incorporated; *U.S. Public*, pg. 1897
JUI LI EDSCHA BODY SYSTEMS, CO., LTD.—See Acek Desarrollo y Gestion Industrial SL; *Int'l*, pg. 96
JX NIPPON OIL & ENERGY TRADING CORPORATION—See ENEOS Holdings, Inc.; *Int'l*, pg. 2417
KAIFENG HIROYOSHI AUTOMOTIVE TRIM CO., LTD.—See Hiroca Holdings Ltd.; *Int'l*, pg. 3404
KEIHIN ASIA BANGKOK CO., LTD.—See Hitachi Astemo, Ltd.; *Int'l*, pg. 3408
KEIHIN SALES AND DEVELOPMENT EUROPE GMBH—See Hitachi Astemo, Ltd.; *Int'l*, pg. 3409
KENMAR CORPORATION; *U.S. Private*, pg. 2284
KET MARINE ASIA PTE. LTD.—See GEA Group Aktiengesellschaft; *Int'l*, pg. 2903
KET MARINE INTERNATIONAL B.V.—See GEA Group Aktiengesellschaft; *Int'l*, pg. 2903
KEYSTONE AUTOMOTIVE DISTRIBUTORS COMPANY, LLC—See LKQ Corporation; *U.S. Public*, pg. 1334
KEYSTONE AUTOMOTIVE INDUSTRIES - ATLANTA—See LKQ Corporation; *U.S. Public*, pg. 1334
KEYSTONE AUTOMOTIVE INDUSTRIES BETHLEHEM—See LKQ Corporation; *U.S. Public*, pg. 1334
KEYSTONE AUTOMOTIVE INDUSTRIES, INC.—See LKQ Corporation; *U.S. Public*, pg. 1334
KEYSTONE AUTOMOTIVE INDUSTRIES NASHVILLE—See LKQ Corporation; *U.S. Public*, pg. 1334
KEYSTONE SPRING SERVICE, INC.—See American Securities LLC; *U.S. Private*, pg. 248
KIRKS AUTOMOTIVE INC.; *U.S. Private*, pg. 2315
KNOPF AUTOMOTIVE DO BRASIL LTDA—See Knopf Automotive Parts; *U.S. Private*, pg. 2323
KNOPF AUTOMOTIVE PARTS; *U.S. Private*, pg. 2323
KOI AUTO PARTS-LOUISVILLE—See KOI Auto Parts; *U.S. Private*, pg. 2340
K-O-I ENTERPRISES INC.; *U.S. Private*, pg. 2251
KONAN KOGYO CO., LTD.—See AISIN Corporation; *Int'l*, pg. 253
KS AUTOMOTIVE INC—See Kennerley-Spratling Inc.; *U.S. Private*, pg. 2286
KSI TRADING COMPANY; *U.S. Private*, pg. 2354
K-TOOL CORPORATION MICHIGAN; *U.S. Private*, pg. 2251
KUHLMAN LLC—See BorgWarner Inc.; *U.S. Public*, pg. 371
THE KUNKEL SERVICE COMPANY INC.; *U.S. Private*, pg. 4066
KWIK AUTO BODY SUPPLIES, INC.—See LKQ Corporation; *U.S. Public*, pg. 1334
KWIKPART SDN BHD—See Hup Soon Global Corporation Limited; *Int'l*, pg. 3538
LABEL INDUSTRIES, INC.—See Sycamore Partners Management, LP; *U.S. Private*, pg. 3896
LACAVA & SOWERSBY INC.; *U.S. Private*, pg. 2371
LAKE SHORE RADIATOR INC.; *U.S. Private*, pg. 2376
LAPPEN AUTO SUPPLY CO. INC.; *U.S. Private*, pg. 2391
LEADING EDGE AUTO REFINISHES, INC.—See Wesco Group, Inc.; *U.S. Private*, pg. 4482
LEAR CORPORATION JARNY, S.A.S.—See Lear Corporation; *U.S. Public*, pg. 1297
LEAR CORPORATION PONTEVEDRA, S.A.U.—See Lear Corporation; *U.S. Public*, pg. 1297
LEAR CORPORATION VIGO, S.A.U.—See Lear Corporation; *U.S. Public*, pg. 1297
LEISURE TIME MARKETING INC.; *U.S. Private*, pg. 2420
LEMANS CORPORATION; *U.S. Private*, pg. 2420
LEWIS GLASS, INC.; *U.S. Private*, pg. 2439
LIBERTY BELL EQUIPMENT CORP.—See Sycamore Part-

423120 — MOTOR VEHICLE SUPPL...

ners Management, LP; *U.S. Private,* pg. 3896
LKQ CZ S.R.O.—See LKQ Corporation; *U.S. Public,* pg. 1335
L&L PRODUCTS EUROPE SAS—See L&L Products, Inc.; *U.S. Private,* pg. 2363
LONDON MACHINERY INC.—See Oshkosh Corporation; *U.S. Public,* pg. 1620
LONG MOTOR CORPORATION; *U.S. Private,* pg. 2491
LONNIE MCCURRY'S FOUR WHEEL DRIVE CENTER, INC.; *U.S. Private,* pg. 2493
MACHINE SERVICE INC.; *U.S. Private,* pg. 2535
MAGIC MOBILE HOMES, INC.—See Style Crest, Inc.; *U.S. Private,* pg. 3846
MAGNETI MARELLI AFTERMARKET GMBH—See KKR & Co. Inc.; *U.S. Public,* pg. 1260
MAGNETI MARELLI AFTER MARKET PARTS AND SERVICES S.P.A.—See KKR & Co. Inc.; *U.S. Public,* pg. 1260
MAGNETI MARELLI DO BRASIL INDUSTRIA E COMERCIO SA—See KKR & Co. Inc.; *U.S. Public,* pg. 1261
MAGNETI MARELLI MOTOPROPULSION FRANCE SAS—See KKR & Co. Inc.; *U.S. Public,* pg. 1261
MAGNETI MARELLI REPUESTOS S.A—See KKR & Co. Inc.; *U.S. Public,* pg. 1260
MAHLE ENGINEERING SERVICES INDIA PRIVATE LIMITED—See Food Empire Holdings Limited; *Int'l,* pg. 2727
MAHLE INDUSTRIA E COMERCIO LTDA.—See Food Empire Holdings Limited; *Int'l,* pg. 2727
MAN AUTOMOTIVE IMPORTS PTY LTD—See Penske Automotive Group, Inc.; *U.S. Public,* pg. 1666
MANGO DISTRIBUTING CO. INC.—See Home Service Oil Co. Inc.; *U.S. Private,* pg. 1972
MANUFACTURAS Y ACCESORIOS ELECTRICOS S.A.—See Hella GmbH & Co. KGaA; *Int'l,* pg. 3332
MARINEX INC.; *U.S. Private,* pg. 2576
MARMON HIGHWAY TECHNOLOGIES—See Berkshire Hathaway Inc.; *U.S. Public,* pg. 310
MATRICERIA DEUSTO, S.L.—See Acek Desarrollo y Gestion Industrial SL; *Int'l,* pg. 98
MATT MANAGEMENT INC.; *U.S. Private,* pg. 2613
MAXGEAR SP. Z O.O. SP. KOMANDYTOWA—See Auto Partner SA; *Int'l,* pg. 725
MAYS DISTRIBUTING COMPANY; *U.S. Private,* pg. 2623
MCDEVITT TRUCKS INC; *U.S. Private,* pg. 2632
MCIS SAFETY GLASS SDN. BHD.—See AGC Inc.; *Int'l,* pg. 204
MCKAY AUTO PARTS INCORPORATED; *U.S. Private,* pg. 2637
MECANOR-RUMANIA S.R.L.—See Corpfin Capital SA; *Int'l,* pg. 1802
MECAPLAST INDIA PVT. LTD.—See Equistone Partners Europe Limited; *Int'l,* pg. 2486
MECAPLAST SERBIA D.O.O.—See Equistone Partners Europe Limited; *Int'l,* pg. 2486
MECAPLAST SHANGHAI—See Equistone Partners Europe Limited; *Int'l,* pg. 2487
MECAPLAST SHENYANG CAR COMPONENTS CO., LTD.—See Equistone Partners Europe Limited; *Int'l,* pg. 2487
MECHALESS SYSTEMS GMBH—See ELMOS Semiconductor AG; *Int'l,* pg. 2368
MEDCO TOOL OF OHIO, INC.—See Sycamore Partners Management, LP; *U.S. Private,* pg. 3896
MERIDIAN RACK & PINION, INC.—See Gladstone Management Corporation; *U.S. Private,* pg. 1705
MERITOR AFTERMARKET SPAIN, S.A.—See Cummins Inc.; *U.S. Public,* pg. 608
MERITOR HUAYANG VEHICLE BRAKING COMPANY, LTD.—See Cummins Inc.; *U.S. Public,* pg. 609
MERIT WISE INTERNATIONAL LIMITED—See Enterex International Limited; *Int'l,* pg. 2451
MERLES AUTOMOTIVE SUPPLY, INC.—See Genuine Parts Company; *U.S. Public,* pg. 933
MERRILL COMPANY; *U.S. Private,* pg. 2676
METALDYNE INTERNATIONAL FRANCE SAS—See American Axle & Manufacturing Holdings, Inc.; *U.S. Public,* pg. 97
METALDYNE POWERTRAIN MEXICO, S. DE R.L. DE C.V.—See American Axle & Manufacturing Holdings, Inc.; *U.S. Public,* pg. 97
MICHIGAN JOBBER BROKER EQUIPMENT & SUPPLIES CO. INC.—See CenTra, Inc.; *U.S. Private,* pg. 818
MID AMERICA MOTORWORKS; *U.S. Private,* pg. 2705
MID-USA CYCLE PARTS INC.; *U.S. Private,* pg. 2709
MIDWAY TRUCK PARTS INC.; *U.S. Private,* pg. 2719
MIDWEST AIR TECHNOLOGIES INC.; *U.S. Private,* pg. 2719
MIDWEST MOTOR SUPPLY CO.; *U.S. Private,* pg. 2722
MIDWEST WHEEL COMPANY; *U.S. Private,* pg. 2723
MILE MARKER INC.—See Mile Marker International Inc.; *U.S. Private,* pg. 2727
MI TECHNOLOGY GROUP LTD.—See CSA Group; *Int'l,* pg. 1861
MODINE TRANSFERENCIA DE CALOR, S.A. DE C.V.—See Modine Manufacturing Company; *U.S. Public,* pg. 1455
MOHAMED A. ALHAMRANI & CO INTERTRADE CO (LTD)—See Alhamrani Group; *Int'l,* pg. 319
MONROE MOTOR PRODUCTS CORP.—See Genuine Parts Company; *U.S. Public,* pg. 933
MONROE TRUCK EQUIPMENT, INC.; *U.S. Private,* pg. 2774
MONT BLANC INDUSTRI UK LTD—See Accent Equity Partners AB; *Int'l,* pg. 81
MOOG LOUISVILLE WAREHOUSE INC.; *U.S. Private,* pg. 2778
MORGAN AUTO PARTS INC.; *U.S. Private,* pg. 2783
MOTIVE PARTS COMPANY FMP; *U.S. Private,* pg. 2796
MOTOREN STEFFENS GMBH—See Caterpillar, Inc.; *U.S. Public,* pg. 453
MUFFLER MAN SUPPLY CO; *U.S. Private,* pg. 2811
MULBERRY MOTOR PARTS INC.; *U.S. Private,* pg. 2811
MUSTANG ALLIANCES, INC.; *U.S. Private,* pg. 2819
MUTUAL WHEEL COMPANY INC.; *U.S. Private,* pg. 2820
MWM FRANCE S.A.S.—See Caterpillar, Inc.; *U.S. Public,* pg. 452
MWM LATIN AMERICA SOLUCOES ENERGETICAS LTDA.—See Caterpillar, Inc.; *U.S. Public,* pg. 453
MYGRANT GLASS COMPANY INC.; *U.S. Private,* pg. 2825
NAPCO INTERNATIONAL, INC.—See Jata LLC; *U.S. Private,* pg. 2191
NASHVILLE TRANSMISSION PARTS—See Jordan Industries, Inc.; *U.S. Private,* pg. 2235
NATIONAL AUTOMOTIVE PARTS ASSOCIATION, LLC—See Genuine Parts Company; *U.S. Public,* pg. 932
NATIONAL AUTO PARTS WAREHOUSE, LLC; *U.S. Private,* pg. 2847
NATIONAL OAK DISTRIBUTORS INC.; *U.S. Private,* pg. 2860
NATIONAL TRUCK PARTS, INC.—See Illinois Tool Works Inc.; *U.S. Public,* pg. 1109
NBC TRUCK EQUIPMENT INC.; *U.S. Private,* pg. 2874
NDC SALES CO., LTD.—See Daido Metal Corporation; *Int'l,* pg. 1922
NEAPCO DRIVELINES (SHANGHAI) CO., LTD.—See Neapco Holdings, LLC; *U.S. Private,* pg. 2877
NELSON TRUCK EQUIPMENT CO. INC.; *U.S. Private,* pg. 2883
NEOTEK CORPORATION INC.; *U.S. Private,* pg. 2885
NESTOR SALES LLC—See Sycamore Partners Management, LP; *U.S. Private,* pg. 3896
NICHOLS MOTORCYCLE SUPPLY INC.; *U.S. Private,* pg. 2925
NICKELS PERFORMANCE WAREHOUSE—See Blue Point Capital Partners, LLC; *U.S. Private,* pg. 591
NIIT C&G LIMITED—See Car & General (Kenya) Limited; *Int'l,* pg. 1319
NISSEN FRANCE—See Standard Motor Products, Inc.; *U.S. Public,* pg. 1929
NISSENS BENELUX S.A.—See Standard Motor Products, Inc.; *U.S. Public,* pg. 1929
NISSENS DEUTSCHLAND GMBH—See Standard Motor Products, Inc.; *U.S. Public,* pg. 1929
NISSENS FINLAND OY—See Standard Motor Products, Inc.; *U.S. Public,* pg. 1929
NISSENS HUNGARIA KFT.—See Standard Motor Products, Inc.; *U.S. Public,* pg. 1929
NISSENS ITALIA SRL—See Standard Motor Products, Inc.; *U.S. Public,* pg. 1929
NISSENS NORTH AMERICA, INC.—See Standard Motor Products, Inc.; *U.S. Public,* pg. 1929
NISSENS OSTERREICH G.M.B.H—See Standard Motor Products, Inc.; *U.S. Public,* pg. 1929
NISSENS SCHWEIZ AG—See Standard Motor Products, Inc.; *U.S. Public,* pg. 1929
NISSENS (SHANGHAI) AUTO PARTS TRADING CO., LTD.—See Standard Motor Products, Inc.; *U.S. Public,* pg. 1929
NISSENS SLOVAKIA S.R.O.—See Standard Motor Products, Inc.; *U.S. Public,* pg. 1929
NISSENS SVERIGE AB—See Standard Motor Products, Inc.; *U.S. Public,* pg. 1929
NISSENS (UK) LTD.—See Standard Motor Products, Inc.; *U.S. Public,* pg. 1929
NISSENS UKRAINE LTD.—See Standard Motor Products, Inc.; *U.S. Public,* pg. 1929
NOMO KULLAGER AB—See Axel Johnson Gruppen AB; *Int'l,* pg. 763
NORDGLASS DANMARK A/S—See AGC Inc.; *Int'l,* pg. 202
NORDGLASS DISTRIBUCE S.R.O.—See AGC Inc.; *Int'l,* pg. 202
NORDGLASS DISTRIBUTION GMBH—See AGC Inc.; *Int'l,* pg. 202
NORDGLASS FRANCE SARL—See AGC Inc.; *Int'l,* pg. 202
NORDGLASS SVERIGE AB—See AGC Inc.; *Int'l,* pg. 202
NORGLEN CORPORATION; *U.S. Private,* pg. 2937
NORTH AMERICAN EQUIPMENT SALES (CANADA) LTD.—See ERS Industries Inc.; *U.S. Private,* pg. 1423
NORTHERN FACTORY SALES INC.; *U.S. Private,* pg. 2952
NORTHERN INDIANA PAINT SUPPLY, INC.; *U.S. Private,* pg. 2953
NORTH SIDE IMPORTS INC.; *U.S. Private,* pg. 2947
NORTH WEST ENTERPRISES—See Caribou Corporation; *U.S. Private,* pg. 761
NORTHWEST MACK PARTS & SERVICE CO.—See Celli Enterprises Inc.; *U.S. Private,* pg. 807
NRF ESPANA S.A.—See Banco Products (I) Ltd.; *Int'l,* pg. 824
NSK-WARNER MEXICO, S.A. DE C.V.—See BorgWarner Inc.; *U.S. Public,* pg. 371
NSK-WARNER U.S.A., INC.—See BorgWarner Inc.; *U.S. Public,* pg. 371
NTP DISTRIBUTION—See LKQ Corporation; *U.S. Public,* pg. 1334
NUADI—See Arta Capital SGEIC SA; *Int'l,* pg. 580
O'DAY EQUIPMENT, INC.; *U.S. Private,* pg. 2978
OECONNECTION LLC—See Genstar Capital, LLC; *U.S. Private,* pg. 1678
OFF ROAD UNLIMITED; *U.S. Private,* pg. 3001
OHIO AUTO KOLOR, INC.; *U.S. Private,* pg. 3003
OK AUTOMOTIVE—See Automotive Parts Headquarters, Inc.; *U.S. Private,* pg. 400
OLYMPIC BRAKE SUPPLY; *U.S. Private,* pg. 3012
OLYMPIC IMPORTED PARTS CORP.; *U.S. Private,* pg. 3012
OLYMPUS IMPORTED AUTO PARTS—See Genuine Parts Company; *U.S. Public,* pg. 932
ONE STOP UNDERCAR, INC.—See Halla Group; *Int'l,* pg. 3230
OOO CONTINENTAL AUTOMOTIVE RUS—See Continental Aktiengesellschaft; *Int'l,* pg. 1783
OPTARE UK LTD—See Hinduja Group Ltd.; *Int'l,* pg. 3398
OPTIMAL BENELUX BVBA—See LKQ Corporation; *U.S. Public,* pg. 1336
OPTIMAL UK DISTRIBUTION LIMITED—See LKQ Corporation; *U.S. Public,* pg. 1336
ORSCHELN EUROPE ULC—See Orscheln Group; *U.S. Private,* pg. 3045
ORSCHELN PRODUCTS TRADING CO. LTD—See Orscheln Group; *U.S. Private,* pg. 3045
OSCAR FAH AG—See Addtech AB; *Int'l,* pg. 134
OZARK AUTOMOTIVE DISTRIBUTORS, INC.—See O'Reilly Automotive, Inc.; *U.S. Public,* pg. 1559
PACCAR PARTS MEXICO, S.A. DE C.V.—See PACCAR Inc.; *U.S. Public,* pg. 1631
PACIFIC BEST INC.; *U.S. Private,* pg. 3065
PACKARD MOTOR CAR CO. INC.; *U.S. Private,* pg. 3073
PAN-MAR CORPORATION; *U.S. Private,* pg. 3084
PARTS AUTHORITY INC.; *U.S. Private,* pg. 3103
PARTS PLUS OF NEW MEXICO INCORPORATED; *U.S. Private,* pg. 3103
PARTS WAREHOUSE INC.—See Replacement Parts Inc.; *U.S. Private,* pg. 3401
PARTS WHOLESALERS INC.; *U.S. Private,* pg. 3103
PAUL POLLRICH GMBH—See GEA Group Aktiengesellschaft; *Int'l,* pg. 2903
PAVAN U.S.A., INC.—See GEA Group Aktiengesellschaft; *Int'l,* pg. 2903
PAYLESS TIRE & EXHAUST—See Condon Oil Company, Inc.; *U.S. Private,* pg. 1012
PBE JOBBERS WAREHOUSE INC.; *U.S. Private,* pg. 3118
PBE WAREHOUSE INC.; *U.S. Private,* pg. 3118
PBE WAREHOUSE SALES INC.; *U.S. Private,* pg. 3118
PEACH STATE TRUCK CENTERS LLC; *U.S. Private,* pg. 3123
PEPS - JV (M) SDN BHD—See EP Manufacturing Bhd.; *Int'l,* pg. 2458
PERCEPTRON ASIA PACIFIC LTD.—See Atlas Copco AB; *Int'l,* pg. 680
PERCEPTRON ASIA PTE. LTD.—See Atlas Copco AB; *Int'l,* pg. 680
PERFORMANCE WAREHOUSE COMPANY, INC.—See National Auto Parts Warehouse, LLC; *U.S. Private,* pg. 2847
PERFORMANCE WAREHOUSE—See National Auto Parts Warehouse, LLC; *U.S. Private,* pg. 2847
PERFORMANCE WHOLESALE PTY. LTD.—See HKS CO., LTD.; *Int'l,* pg. 3429
PIONEER RIM AND WHEEL COMPANY; *U.S. Private,* pg. 3188
PIV DRIVES GMBH—See Dana Incorporated; *U.S. Public,* pg. 623
PLASTIC OMNIUM INDUSTRIES INC.—See Burelle S.A.; *Int'l,* pg. 1223
POWER AND SIGNAL GROUP GMBH—See Arrow Electronics, Inc.; *U.S. Public,* pg. 199
POWER GREAT LAKES, INC—See Power Solutions International, Inc.; *U.S. Public,* pg. 1705
POWER TOOLS DISTRIBUTION N.V.—See Atlas Copco AB; *Int'l,* pg. 684
PREMIER PERFORMANCE, LLC—See Heartwood Partners, LLC; *U.S. Private,* pg. 1901
PRESSAN MADENI ESYA SAN. VE TICARET A.S.—See Brose Fahrzeugteile GmbH & Co, KG; *Int'l,* pg. 1196
PRIME AUTOMOTIVE PARTS CO., INC.—See Hahn Automotive Warehouse, Inc.; *U.S. Private,* pg. 1840
PRO-CUT INTERNATIONAL LLC—See Snap-on Incorporated; *U.S. Public,* pg. 1898
PROTON PARTS CENTRE SDN BHD—See DRB-HICOM Berhad; *Int'l,* pg. 2202
PT. ADVICS INDONESIA—See AISIN Corporation; *Int'l,* pg. 251

N.A.I.C.S. INDEX

423120 — MOTOR VEHICLE SUPPL...

P.T. EXEDY MOTORCYCLE INDONESIA—See Exedy Corporation; *Int'l*, pg. 2581
PT.FUTABA INDUSTRIAL INDONESIA—See Futaba Industrial Co., Ltd.; *Int'l*, pg. 2851
PT. HONDA POWER PRODUCTS INDONESIA—See Honda Motor Co., Ltd.; *Int'l*, pg. 3464
P.T. HONDA PROSPECT MOTOR—See Honda Motor Co., Ltd.; *Int'l*, pg. 3464
P.T. KEIHIN INDONESIA—See Hitachi Astemo, Ltd.; *Int'l*, pg. 3409
PT TITAN WHEELS INDONESIA—See Titan International, Inc.; *U.S. Public*, pg. 2160
P.T. TRACKSPARE—See Hoe Leong Corporation Ltd.; *Int'l*, pg. 3439
P.T. TRI DHARMA WISESA—See Akebono Brake Industry Co., Ltd.; *Int'l*, pg. 262
PUBLIC SAFETY EQUIPMENT (SUZHOU) CO., LTD.—See Ecco Safety Group; *U.S. Private*, pg. 1326
PUNCHCRAFT MACHINING AND TOOLING, LLC—See American Axle & Manufacturing Holdings, Inc.; *U.S. Public*, pg. 97
QINGDAO DONGHWA CASTINGS CO., LTD—See Hands Corporation Ltd.; *Int'l*, pg. 3243
QUALITY TRAILER SALES CORP.—See Great Western Leasing & Sales, LLC; *U.S. Private*, pg. 1768
RACEMARK INDUSTRIES, SA—See Racemark International, LP; *U.S. Private*, pg. 3341
RADIADORES NISSEN, S.A.—See Standard Motor Products, Inc.; *U.S. Public*, pg. 1929
RAFAEL BENITEZ CARRILLO, INC.—See Applied Industrial Technologies, Inc.; *U.S. Public*, pg. 171
RAINBO OIL COMPANY; *U.S. Private*, pg. 3347
RALLYSPORT DIRECT, LLC—See Heartwood Partners, LLC; *U.S. Private*, pg. 1901
RANCH HAND, INC.—See The Kaspar Companies; *U.S. Private*, pg. 4064
RANEW'S TRUCK & EQUIPMENT CO. LLC—See ALJ Regional Holdings, Inc.; *U.S. Public*, pg. 78
RANEY'S TRUCK CENTER, INC.—See American Securities LLC; *U.S. Private*, pg. 248
RAYLOC—See Genuine Parts Company; *U.S. Public*, pg. 932
RAYSIDE TRUCK & TRAILER INC.—See J.B. Poindexter & Co., Inc.; *U.S. Private*, pg. 2159
REDNECK INC.—See Brookfield Corporation; *Int'l*, pg. 1176
REPLACEMENT PARTS INC.; *U.S. Private*, pg. 3401
REVILLE TIRE CO.; *U.S. Private*, pg. 3416
REXITE, S.A. DE C.V.—See Melling Tool Company Inc.; *U.S. Private*, pg. 2662
REYDEL AUTOMOTIVE SPAIN, S.L.U.—See Cerberus Capital Management, L.P.; *U.S. Private*, pg. 839
RH SCALES CO. INC.; *U.S. Private*, pg. 3421
RIKEN MOTOR SALES INC.—See HKS CO., LTD.; *Int'l*, pg. 3429
ROCKFORD CONSTANT VELOCITY—See Aircraft Gear Corporation; *U.S. Private*, pg. 140
ROPPEL INDUSTRIES INC.; *U.S. Private*, pg. 3480
ROWERDINK INC.; *U.S. Private*, pg. 3490
RUNMART INC.—See Aucnet Inc.; *Int'l*, pg. 700
RUSH TRUCK CENTERS OF INDIANA, INC.—See Rush Enterprises, Inc.; *U.S. Public*, pg. 1826
RUSH TRUCK CENTERS OF KANSAS, INC.—See Rush Enterprises, Inc.; *U.S. Public*, pg. 1826
RUSH TRUCK CENTERS OF MISSOURI, INC.—See Rush Enterprises, Inc.; *U.S. Public*, pg. 1827
SAB WABCO (UK) LIMITED—See Westinghouse Air Brake Technologies Corporation; *U.S. Public*, pg. 2358
SAINT-GOBAIN AUTOVER DISTRIBUTION SA—See Compagnie de Saint-Gobain SA; *Int'l*, pg. 1736
SAINT-GOBAIN AUTOVER OSTERREICH GMBH—See Compagnie de Saint-Gobain SA; *Int'l*, pg. 1727
SAINT-GOBAIN AUTOVER PORTUGAL S.A.—See Compagnie de Saint-Gobain SA; *Int'l*, pg. 1736
SAINT-GOBAIN SEKURIT INDIA LIMITED—See Compagnie de Saint-Gobain SA; *Int'l*, pg. 1736
SAN LOMA, INC.—See Platinum Equity, LLC; *U.S. Private*, pg. 3209
SAUER-DANFOSS BVBA—See Danfoss A/S; *Int'l*, pg. 1961
SAUER-DANFOSS S.A.S.—See Danfoss A/S; *Int'l*, pg. 1961
SCIENTIFIC BRAKE & EQUIPMENT CO.; *U.S. Private*, pg. 3574
SCOTTSDALE PAINT & BODY, LLC—See Penske Automotive Group, Inc.; *U.S. Public*, pg. 1666
SEATTLE AUTOMOTIVE DISTRIBUTING; *U.S. Private*, pg. 3591
SERVICE CHAMP; *U.S. Private*, pg. 3614
SERVICIOS ADMINISTRATIVOS INDUSTRIALES SA DE CV—See Apollo Global Management, Inc.; *U.S. Public*, pg. 162
SETTE ASSOCIATES INC.; *U.S. Private*, pg. 3617
SEVCON GMBH—See BorgWarner Inc.; *U.S. Public*, pg. 371
SEVCON NEW ENERGY TECHNOLOGY (HUBEI) COMPANY LIMITED—See BorgWarner Inc.; *U.S. Public*, pg. 371
SHANGHAI CUMMINS TRADING CO., LTD.—See Cummins Inc.; *U.S. Public*, pg. 609
SHANGHAI DYNAX CO., LTD.—See Exedy Corporation; *Int'l*, pg. 2581
SHANGHAI EDSCHA MACHINERY CO., LTD.—See Acek Desarrollo y Gestion Industrial SL; *Int'l*, pg. 96
SHENYANG LEAR AUTOMOTIVE SEATING AND INTERIOR SYSTEMS CO., LTD.—See Lear Corporation; *U.S. Public*, pg. 1298
SHENZHEN FUTABA METAL PRODUCTS CO., LTD.—See Futaba Industrial Co., Ltd.; *Int'l*, pg. 2851
SIDLEY TRUCK & EQUIPMENT—See R.W. Sidley, Incorporated; *U.S. Private*, pg. 3340
SIGMA DISTRIBUTING COMPANY INCORPORATED; *U.S. Private*, pg. 3648
SING HIAP HIN CO.—See HKS CO., LTD.; *Int'l*, pg. 3429
SISTEMAS ILUMINACION S.A. DE C.V.—See Hella GmbH & Co. KGaA; *Int'l*, pg. 3332
SIX ROBBLEES INC.; *U.S. Private*, pg. 3677
SIXT MOBILITY CONSULTING AG—See Banco Santander, S.A.; *Int'l*, pg. 826
SIXT MOBILITY CONSULTING AG—See Hyundai Motor Company; *Int'l*, pg. 3559
SIXT MOBILITY CONSULTING GMBH—See Banco Santander, S.A.; *Int'l*, pg. 826
SIXT MOBILITY CONSULTING GMBH—See Hyundai Motor Company; *Int'l*, pg. 3559
SIXT MOBILITY CONSULTING S.A.R.L.—See Banco Santander, S.A.; *Int'l*, pg. 826
SIXT MOBILITY CONSULTING S.A.R.L.—See Hyundai Motor Company; *Int'l*, pg. 3559
SMARTS TRUCK & TRAILER EQUIPMENT; *U.S. Private*, pg. 3692
SMITTY'S SUPPLY INC.; *U.S. Private*, pg. 3698
SMYTH AUTOMOTIVE INC.; *U.S. Private*, pg. 3699
SNAP-ON EQUIPMENT AUSTRIA GMBH—See Snap-on Incorporated; *U.S. Public*, pg. 1898
S&N PUMP AND REWIND LIMITED—See Lone Star Funds; *U.S. Private*, pg. 2486
SOONER EQUIPMENT & LEASING, INC.; *U.S. Private*, pg. 3715
SOUTHEASTERN AUTOMOTIVE WAREHOUSE; *U.S. Private*, pg. 3727
SOUTHEAST POWER SYSTEMS OF ORLANDO, INC.; *U.S. Private*, pg. 3726
SPORT TRUCK USA, INC.—See Fox Factory Holding Corp.; *U.S. Public*, pg. 877
SPRINGFIELD AUTO SUPPLY INC.; *U.S. Private*, pg. 3764
S&S AUTOMOTIVE INC.; *U.S. Private*, pg. 3513
STAG-PARKWAY, INC.; *U.S. Private*, pg. 3775
STANDARD PARTS CORPORATION; *U.S. Private*, pg. 3781
STAR ENVIROTECH, INC.—See Harbour Group Industries, Inc.; *U.S. Private*, pg. 1860
STARMANN SP. Z O.O.—See LKQ Corporation; *U.S. Public*, pg. 1336
STEEL CURTAIN INDUSTRIES, LLC; *U.S. Private*, pg. 3796
STEFFEN, INC.—See Americold Realty Trust, Inc.; *U.S. Public*, pg. 113
STEINWAY AUTO PARTS INC.—See Advance Auto Parts, Inc.; *U.S. Public*, pg. 45
STENTEN'S GOLF CART ACCESSORIES, INC.; *U.S. Private*, pg. 3801
ST. LUCIE BATTERY & TIRE INC.; *U.S. Private*, pg. 3772
STM AUTOMOTIVE; *U.S. Private*, pg. 3813
STONE WHEEL INC.; *U.S. Private*, pg. 3826
STREHL, LLC—See Knight-Swift Transportation Holdings Inc.; *U.S. Public*, pg. 1269
STURTEVANT AUTO PARTS INC.; *U.S. Private*, pg. 3845
SUNNYSIDE AUTO PARTS; *U.S. Private*, pg. 3868
SUNRISE NATIONAL DISTRIBUTORS; *U.S. Private*, pg. 3870
SUZHOU AICHI TECHNOLOGY CO., LTD.—See Aichi Electric Co., Ltd.; *Int'l*, pg. 229
SVERULL AB—See Axel Johnson Gruppen AB; *Int'l*, pg. 763
TAT HONG MACHINERY PTE LTD—See Affirma Capital Limited; *Int'l*, pg. 187
TECHNICAL CHEMICAL COMPANY INC.; *U.S. Private*, pg. 3953
TECNICOS EN LA ALTA PRODUCCION S.A. DE C.V.—See Corpfin Capital SA; *Int'l*, pg. 1802
TEXTRAIL, INC. - FITZGERALD—See Bain Capital, LP; *U.S. Private*, pg. 436
TEXTRAIL, INC. - FLORIDA—See Bain Capital, LP; *U.S. Private*, pg. 436
TEXTRAIL, INC. - GEORGIA—See Bain Capital, LP; *U.S. Private*, pg. 436
TEXTRAIL, INC.—See Bain Capital, LP; *U.S. Private*, pg. 436
THERMO KING OF INDIANA INC.; *U.S. Private*, pg. 4142
THIRLBY AUTOMOTIVE INC.; *U.S. Private*, pg. 4145
TIANJIN FUTABA SHYE CHAN MECHANICAL CO., LTD.—See Futaba Industrial Co., Ltd.; *Int'l*, pg. 2851
TIANJIN SHUANG SHYE MECHANICAL INDUSTRIAL CO., LTD.—See Futaba Industrial Co., Ltd.; *Int'l*, pg. 2851
TIDEWATER FLEET SUPPLY—See Falcon Affiliates, LLC; *U.S. Private*, pg. 1466
TITAN ITM (TIANJIN) CO. LTD.—See Titan International, Inc.; *U.S. Public*, pg. 2160
TOP RACING GROUP LTD.—See HKS CO., LTD.; *Int'l*, pg. 3429
TOYOTA MOTOR PHILIPPINES CORPORATION—See GT Capital Holdings, Inc.; *U.S. Public*, pg. 3150
TPH ACQUISITION, LLLP; *U.S. Private*, pg. 4200
TRACKSPARES (AUSTRALIA) PTY. LTD.—See Hoe Leong Corporation Ltd.; *Int'l*, pg. 3439
TRANSAXLE LLC—See Crossplane Capital Management LP; *U.S. Private*, pg. 1107
TRANSTAR INDUSTRIES, INC.—See Blue Point Capital Partners, LLC; *U.S. Private*, pg. 590
TRIMON INC.; *U.S. Private*, pg. 4232
TRI-STATE ENTERPRISES INC.; *U.S. Private*, pg. 4223
TRI-STATES AUTOMOTIVE WAREHOUSE, INC.—See Replacement Parts Inc.; *U.S. Private*, pg. 3401
TRUCK EQUIPMENT INC.; *U.S. Private*, pg. 4246
TRUCK LIGHTHOUSE; *U.S. Private*, pg. 4246
TRUCK PARTS & EQUIPMENT INC.—See American Securities LLC; *U.S. Private*, pg. 248
TUCKER-ROCKY DISTRIBUTING—See LDI Ltd., LLC; *U.S. Private*, pg. 2404
TVH AUSTRALASIA PTY LTD.—See Group Thermote & Vanhalst; *Int'l*, pg. 3090
TVH CANADA LTD—See Group Thermote & Vanhalst; *Int'l*, pg. 3090
TVH ITALIA SRL—See Group Thermote & Vanhalst; *Int'l*, pg. 3090
TVH MALAYSIA SDN. BHD.—See Group Thermote & Vanhalst; *Int'l*, pg. 3090
TVH MEXICO, S DE RL DE CV—See Group Thermote & Vanhalst; *Int'l*, pg. 3090
TVH NEW ZEALAND LTD.—See Group Thermote & Vanhalst; *Int'l*, pg. 3090
TVH NORDIC AB—See Group Thermote & Vanhalst; *Int'l*, pg. 3090
TVH PARTS SOUTH AFRICA (PTY) LTD—See Group Thermote & Vanhalst; *Int'l*, pg. 3090
TVH POLSKA SP.Z O.O.—See Group Thermote & Vanhalst; *Int'l*, pg. 3090
TVH RUS, LLC—See Group Thermote & Vanhalst; *Int'l*, pg. 3090
TVH SINGAPORE PTE LTD—See Group Thermote & Vanhalst; *Int'l*, pg. 3090
TVH TRADING CO., LTD.—See Group Thermote & Vanhalst; *Int'l*, pg. 3090
TVH YEDEK PARCA TICARET A.S.—See Group Thermote & Vanhalst; *Int'l*, pg. 3090
T.W.E. WHOLESALE, INC. OF SAN DIEGO; *U.S. Private*, pg. 3912
TWINCO AUTOMOTIVE WAREHOUSE, INC.; *U.S. Private*, pg. 4266
UCANDO SP. Z O.O.—See Hella GmbH & Co. KGaA; *Int'l*, pg. 3333
UNI-SELECT INC.—See LKQ Corporation; *U.S. Public*, pg. 1336
UNITED AUTO SUPPLY INC.; *U.S. Private*, pg. 4287
UNITED AUTO SUPPLY; *U.S. Private*, pg. 4287
UNITED CONSTRUCTION & REALTY; *U.S. Private*, pg. 4290
UNITED MARKETING INC.; *U.S. Private*, pg. 4294
UNITED TRANSMISSION EXCHANGE, INC.—See Blue Point Capital Partners, LLC; *U.S. Private*, pg. 591
UNIVERSAL AUTO BODY SUPPLY—See KSI Trading Company; *U.S. Private*, pg. 2354
UNIWHEELS AG—See SUPERIOR INDUSTRIES INTERNATIONAL INC; *U.S. Public*, pg. 1967
URIMAN INC.—See Halla Group; *Int'l*, pg. 3230
UTILITY TRAILER SALES OF BOISE; *U.S. Private*, pg. 4327
UTSCH DO BRASIL—See Erich Utsch AG; *Int'l*, pg. 2493
UTSCH INTERNATIONAL LTD.—See Erich Utsch AG; *Int'l*, pg. 2493
UTSCH TONNJES INTERNATIONAL AG—See Erich Utsch AG; *Int'l*, pg. 2493
VALEO TECHNOLOGIES LLC—See Ansell Limited; *Int'l*, pg. 478
VALLEY TRUCK PARTS, INC.; *U.S. Private*, pg. 4335
VANDER HAAG'S INC.; *U.S. Private*, pg. 4342
VAUGHAN INTERESTS INC.; *U.S. Private*, pg. 4348
VCST, INC.—See Gimv NV; *Int'l*, pg. 2976
VE COMMERCIAL VEHICLES LTD—See Eicher Motors Limited; *Int'l*, pg. 2328
VENTURE INC OF BEAUFORT; *U.S. Private*, pg. 4358
VIBRACOUSTIC CV AIR SPRINGS GMBH—See Freudenberg SE; *Int'l*, pg. 2791
VIBRACOUSTIC DE MEXICO S.A. DE C.V.—See Freudenberg SE; *Int'l*, pg. 2791
VIBRACOUSTIC DO BRASIL INDUSTRIA E COMERCIO DE ARTEFATOS DE BORRACHA LTDA.—See Freudenberg SE; *Int'l*, pg. 2791
VISION WHEEL, INC.; *U.S. Private*, pg. 4392
VISTEON ELECTRONICS BULGARIA EOOD—See Visteon Corporation; *U.S. Public*, pg. 2305
VOLVO PENTA SINGAPORE—See AB Volvo; *Int'l*, pg. 42
VTEX AMERICA INC—See Hitachi Zosen Corporation; *Int'l*, pg. 3412
V TEX SHANGHAI CO., LTD.—See Hitachi Zosen Corporation; *Int'l*, pg. 3412

423120 — MOTOR VEHICLE SUPPL... CORPORATE AFFILIATIONS

WALKER AUTOMOTIVE SUPPLY INC.; *U.S. Private*, pg. 4428
WALT'S AUTO CARE CENTERS—See Roark Capital Group Inc.; *U.S. Private*, pg. 3454
WARREN DISTRIBUTING INC.; *U.S. Private*, pg. 4443
WATU CREDIT LIMITED—See Car & General (Kenya) Limited; *Int'l*, pg. 1319
WEAVER AUTOMOTIVE, INC.—See Incline MGMT Corp.; *U.S. Private*, pg. 2054
WEAVER SALES OF SAUK CITY INC.; *U.S. Private*, pg. 4463
WELDON PARTS INC.; *U.S. Private*, pg. 4474
WELLER AUTO PARTS INC.; *U.S. Private*, pg. 4475
WELLINGTON DRIVE TECHNOLOGIES US, INC.—See AoFrio Limited; *Int'l*, pg. 487
WESTAR DISTRIBUTION, LLC.; *U.S. Private*, pg. 4488
WESTERN AUTO OF ST. THOMAS, INC.—See Advance Auto Parts, Inc.; *U.S. Public*, pg. 46
WESTERN POWER SPORTS INCORPORATED; *U.S. Private*, pg. 4496
WESTERN PRECISION AERO LLC—See RBC Bearings Incorporated; *U.S. Public*, pg. 1766
WESTERN TRUCK PARTS & EQUIPMENT COMPANY LLC—See Greenbriar Equity Group, L.P.; *U.S. Private*, pg. 1776
WESTIN AUTOMOTIVE PRODUCTS, INC.; *U.S. Private*, pg. 4498
W.E.T. AUTOMOTIVE SYSTEMS (MALTA) LIMITED—See Gentherm Incorporated; *U.S. Public*, pg. 931
WETHERILL ASSOCIATES INC.; *U.S. Private*, pg. 4502
WHEELER BROS., INC.—See VSE Corporation; *U.S. Public*, pg. 2313
WHITE BROTHERS AUTO SUPPLY, INC.—See TPH Acquisition, LLLP; *U.S. Private*, pg. 4200
WILLIAMSPORT AUTOMOTIVE, INC.—See Genuine Parts Company; *U.S. Public*, pg. 933
W.M. AUTOMOTIVE WAREHOUSE INC.; *U.S. Private*, pg. 4421
WOLVERINE ADVANCED MATERIALS LLC—See Center Rock Capital Partners, LP; *U.S. Private*, pg. 811
WOM WRECKONLINEMARKET GMBH—See Copart, Inc.; *U.S. Public*, pg. 575
WORLDPAC, CANADA, INC.—See Advance Auto Parts, Inc.; *U.S. Public*, pg. 46
WORLDWIDE AUTO PARTS, INC.—See Advance Auto Parts, Inc.; *U.S. Public*, pg. 46
WORLD WIDE PARTS & ACCESSORIES CORPORATION; *U.S. Private*, pg. 4567
WUHAN HIROYOSHI AUTOMOTIVE TRIM CO., LTD.—See Hiroca Holdings Ltd.; *Int'l*, pg. 3404
WUHAN MECAPLAST CO LTD—See Equistone Partners Europe Limited; *Int'l*, pg. 2487
XYBERNET, INC.—See Blue Hill Data Services, Inc.; *U.S. Private*, pg. 589
YANGZHOU CHUNG-MEI AUTO PARTS CO., LTD.—See Enterex International Limited; *Int'l*, pg. 2451
YANGZHOU ENTEREX INDUSTRIAL CO., LTD.—See Enterex International Limited; *Int'l*, pg. 2451
YANTAI MECAPLAST CAR COMPONENTS CO., LTD.—See Equistone Partners Europe Limited; *Int'l*, pg. 2487
YEAR ONE INC.; *U.S. Private*, pg. 4587
ZECOL INC.—See Twinco Automotive Warehouse, Inc.; *U.S. Private*, pg. 4266
ZHUMADIAN CIMC HUAJUN VEHICLE TRADING CO., LTD—See China International Marine Containers (Group) Co., Ltd.; *Int'l*, pg. 1513
ZIEBART INTERNATIONAL CORPORATION; *U.S. Private*, pg. 4603
ZIEBART JAPAN LIMITED—See Ziebart International Corporation; *U.S. Private*, pg. 4603
ZIEBART OKINAWA CO. LTD—See Ziebart International Corporation; *U.S. Private*, pg. 4603

423130 — TIRE AND TUBE MERCHANT WHOLESALERS

ADVANTAGE TRAILER COMPANY—See Wind Point Advisors LLC; *U.S. Private*, pg. 4533
ALBAN TIRE CORP.; *U.S. Private*, pg. 151
ALDEN PADFIELD INC.; *U.S. Private*, pg. 159
AL-JAZEERA TRADING FZCO.—See Al-Rakaez PLC; *Int'l*, pg. 288
ALLIED OIL & TIRE COMPANY, LLC—See AIP, LLC; *U.S. Private*, pg. 135
AMERICAN TIRE DISTRIBUTORS, INC.—See TPG Capital, L.P.; *U.S. Public*, pg. 2166
AM-PAC TIRE DISTRIBUTORS, INC.—See TPG Capital, L.P.; *U.S. Public*, pg. 2166
API, INC.; *U.S. Private*, pg. 294
APOLLO (SOUTH AFRICA) HOLDINGS (PTY) LTD.—See Apollo Tyres Ltd.; *Int'l*, pg. 518
APOLLO TYRES B.V.—See Apollo Tyres Ltd.; *Int'l*, pg. 518
APOLLO TYRES (GERMANY) GMBH—See Apollo Tyres Ltd.; *Int'l*, pg. 518
APOLLO TYRES GLOBAL R & D B.V—See Apollo Tyres Ltd.; *Int'l*, pg. 518
APOLLO TYRES HOLDINGS (SINGAPORE) PTE. LTD.—See Apollo Tyres Ltd.; *Int'l*, pg. 518
APOLLO TYRES (HUNGARY) KFT.—See Apollo Tyres Ltd.; *Int'l*, pg. 518
APOLLO TYRES (MALAYSIA) SDN BHD—See Apollo Tyres Ltd.; *Int'l*, pg. 518
APOLLO TYRES (MIDDLE EAST) FZE.—See Apollo Tyres Ltd.; *Int'l*, pg. 518
APOLLO TYRES (THAILAND) LIMITED—See Apollo Tyres Ltd.; *Int'l*, pg. 518
APOLLO TYRES (UK) PVT. LTD.—See Apollo Tyres Ltd.; *Int'l*, pg. 518
APOLLO VREDESTEIN KFT.—See Apollo Tyres Ltd.; *Int'l*, pg. 519
APOLLO VREDESTEIN SCHWEIZ AG—See Apollo Tyres Ltd.; *Int'l*, pg. 518
APPALACHIAN TIRE PRODUCTS INC.; *U.S. Private*, pg. 295
AREA WHOLESALE TIRE COMPANY, LLC; *U.S. Private*, pg. 318
ATC PVT. LTD.—See Bridgestone Corporation; *Int'l*, pg. 1155
ATI WAREHOUSE INC.; *U.S. Private*, pg. 369
ATLANTA COMMERCIAL TIRE INC.; *U.S. Private*, pg. 370
BAUER BUILT TIRE CENTER OF PERRY, IA—See Bauer Built, Inc.; *U.S. Private*, pg. 490
BECKER TIRE & TREADING INC.; *U.S. Private*, pg. 511
BEN TIRE DISTRIBUTORS LTD. INC.; *U.S. Private*, pg. 523
BEST ONE TIRE & SERVICE OF MID AMERICA, INC.; *U.S. Private*, pg. 543
BIG BRAND TIRE & SERVICE; *U.S. Private*, pg. 552
BLACKSTONE/OTR, LLC—See OTR Wheel Engineering, Inc.; *U.S. Private*, pg. 3049
BOBBY HENARD TIRE SERVICE; *U.S. Private*, pg. 606
BRIDGESTONE AMERICAS TIRE OPERATIONS, LLC - DES MOINES—See Cox Enterprises, Inc.; *U.S. Private*, pg. 1075
BRIDGESTONE AMERICAS TIRE OPERATIONS, LLC - OFF ROAD TIRE, U.S. & CANADA TIRE SALES DIVISION—See Cox Enterprises, Inc.; *U.S. Private*, pg. 1075
BRIDGESTONE AMERICAS TIRE OPERATIONS, LLC - REPLACEMENT TIRE SALES, U.S. & CANADA CONSUMER TIRE SALES DIVISION—See Cox Enterprises, Inc.; *U.S. Private*, pg. 1075
BRIDGESTONE ASIA PACIFIC PTE. LTD.—See Bridgestone Corporation; *Int'l*, pg. 1157
BRIDGESTONE AUSTRIA GMBH—See Bridgestone Corporation; *Int'l*, pg. 1158
BRIDGESTONE CHILE, S.A.—See Bridgestone Corporation; *Int'l*, pg. 1156
BRIDGESTONE (CHINA) INVESTMENT CO., LTD.—See Bridgestone Corporation; *Int'l*, pg. 1157
BRIDGESTONE IRELAND LTD.—See Bridgestone Corporation; *Int'l*, pg. 1158
BRIDGESTONE MIDDLE EAST & AFRICA FZE.—See Bridgestone Corporation; *Int'l*, pg. 1159
BRIDGESTONE OFF-THE-ROAD TIRE PERU S.A.C.—See Bridgestone Corporation; *Int'l*, pg. 1156
BRIDGESTONE (SCHWEIZ) AG—See Bridgestone Corporation; *Int'l*, pg. 1158
BRIDGESTONE SLOVAKIA S.R.O.—See Bridgestone Corporation; *Int'l*, pg. 1159
BRIDGESTONE TYRE SALES SINGAPORE PTE. LTD.—See Bridgestone Corporation; *Int'l*, pg. 1155
BRIDGESTONE TYRES (P.N.G) PTY. LTD—See Bridgestone Corporation; *Int'l*, pg. 1155
THE BURGGRAF CORPORATION; *U.S. Private*, pg. 4003
CAMSO DEUTSCHLAND GMBH—See Compagnie Generale des Etablissements Michelin SCA; *Int'l*, pg. 1741
CAMSO NEDERLAND B.V.—See Compagnie Generale des Etablissements Michelin SCA; *Int'l*, pg. 1742
CAPITAL TIRE, INC.; *U.S. Private*, pg. 742
CARBON GREEN INC.; *Int'l*, pg. 1320
CARR'S TIRE SERVICE OF HARRISONBURG; *U.S. Private*, pg. 771
CASINGS INC.; *U.S. Private*, pg. 783
COKER TIRE COMPANY; *U.S. Private*, pg. 965
COMMUNITY TIRE COMPANY INC.; *U.S. Private*, pg. 997
COMPETITION TIRE LLC; *U.S. Private*, pg. 1000
CONSTANT PRICE MONITOR LIMITED—See Halfords Group plc; *Int'l*, pg. 3229
COOPER TIRE & RUBBER COMPANY DE MEXICO S.A. DE CV—See The Goodyear Tire & Rubber Company; *U.S. Public*, pg. 2083
CROSS-DILLON TIRE INC.; *U.S. Private*, pg. 1105
CTTG INC.—See The Goodyear Tire & Rubber Company; *U.S. Public*, pg. 2082
CURRY'S AUTO SERVICE; *U.S. Private*, pg. 1126
DAN CALLAGHAN ENTERPRISES INC.; *U.S. Private*, pg. 1151
DELLOYD VENTURES SDN BHD; *Int'l*, pg. 2014
DELRAY TIRE & RETREADING INC.; *U.S. Private*, pg. 1199
DELTICOM AG; *Int'l*, pg. 2021
DE RONDE CASING INTERNATIONAL INC.; *U.S. Private*, pg. 1181
DE RONDE TIRE SUPPLY, INC.; *U.S. Private*, pg. 1181
DJR HOLDING CO.; *U.S. Private*, pg. 1247
DONALD B. RICE TIRE CO. INC.; *U.S. Private*, pg. 1259
DS CORP.—See Thor Industries, Inc.; *U.S. Public*, pg. 2156
DUNLAP & KYLE CO. INC.; *U.S. Private*, pg. 1289
EAST BAY TIRE CO.; *U.S. Private*, pg. 1315
EBRAHIM K. KANOO COMPANY B.S.C. - TYRE DIVISION—See Ebrahim K. Kanoo Company B.S.C.; *Int'l*, pg. 2286
THE EDWARD S. QUIRK CO., INC.; *U.S. Private*, pg. 4025
ELASTRAK S.A.—See ELTRAK S.A.; *Int'l*, pg. 2371
ENGLEWOOD TIRE DISTRIBUTORS, INC.; *U.S. Private*, pg. 1400
EUROMASTER AB—See Compagnie Generale des Etablissements Michelin SCA; *Int'l*, pg. 1742
EUROMASTER DANMARK A/S—See Compagnie Generale des Etablissements Michelin SCA; *Int'l*, pg. 1742
FELGTEKNIKK NORGE AS—See Bilia AB; *Int'l*, pg. 1029
FOREIGN TIRE SALES INC.; *U.S. Private*, pg. 1565
FRED ALLEN ENTERPRISES INC.; *U.S. Private*, pg. 1600
FRIEND TIRE COMPANY—See Southern Tire Mart, LLC; *U.S. Private*, pg. 3735
GALLAGHER TIRE INC.; *U.S. Private*, pg. 1638
GALLOWAY TIRE COMPANY INC.—See Farmers Cooperative Inc.; *U.S. Private*, pg. 1477
GATEWAY TIRE OF ARKANSAS INC.; *U.S. Private*, pg. 1651
GCR TIRE CENTERS—See Bridgestone Corporation; *Int'l*, pg. 1157
GITI TIRE (USA) LTD.—See Giti Tire Pte. Ltd.; *Int'l*, pg. 2979
GLENN ROBERTS TIRE & RECAPPING CO. INC.—See Appalachian Tire Products Inc.; *U.S. Private*, pg. 295
GOODYEAR DUNLOP TIRES BALTIC OU—See The Goodyear Tire & Rubber Company; *U.S. Public*, pg. 2083
GOODYEAR DUNLOP TIRES DANMARK A/S—See The Goodyear Tire & Rubber Company; *U.S. Public*, pg. 2083
GOODYEAR DUNLOP TIRES HELLAS S.A.I.C.—See The Goodyear Tire & Rubber Company; *U.S. Public*, pg. 2083
GOODYEAR DUNLOP TIRES ITALIA S.P.A.—See The Goodyear Tire & Rubber Company; *U.S. Public*, pg. 2083
GOODYEAR DUNLOP TIRES POLSKA SP Z.O.O.—See The Goodyear Tire & Rubber Company; *U.S. Public*, pg. 2083
GOODYEAR DUNLOP TIRES ROMANIA S.R.L.—See The Goodyear Tire & Rubber Company; *U.S. Public*, pg. 2083
GOODYEAR DUNLOP TIRES SLOVAKIA S.R.O.—See The Goodyear Tire & Rubber Company; *U.S. Public*, pg. 2084
GOODYEAR & DUNLOP TYRES (NZ) LIMITED—See The Goodyear Tire & Rubber Company; *U.S. Public*, pg. 2083
GOODYEAR EXPORT INC.—See The Goodyear Tire & Rubber Company; *U.S. Public*, pg. 2084
GOODYEAR JAPAN LTD.—See The Goodyear Tire & Rubber Company; *U.S. Public*, pg. 2084
GOODYEAR MARKETING & SALES SDN. BHD.—See The Goodyear Tire & Rubber Company; *U.S. Public*, pg. 2084
GOODYEAR MIDDLE EAST FZE—See The Goodyear Tire & Rubber Company; *U.S. Public*, pg. 2084
GREENBALL CORPORATION; *U.S. Private*, pg. 1774
GRL B.V.—See Govind Rubber Ltd.; *Int'l*, pg. 3044
HANKOOK REIFEN DEUTSCHLAND GMBH—See Hankook Tire & Technology Co.,Ltd.; *Int'l*, pg. 3254
HANKOOK TIRE AMERICA CORP.—See Hankook Tire & Technology Co.,Ltd.; *Int'l*, pg. 3253
HANKOOK TIRE CANADA CORP.—See Hankook Tire & Technology Co.,Ltd.; *Int'l*, pg. 3253
HANKOOK TIRE CO., LTD. - PANAMA OFFICE—See Hankook Tire & Technology Co.,Ltd.; *Int'l*, pg. 3253
HANKOOK TIRE DO BRASIL LTDA.—See Hankook Tire & Technology Co.,Ltd.; *Int'l*, pg. 3253
HANKOOK TIRE FRANCE SARL—See Hankook Tire & Technology Co.,Ltd.; *Int'l*, pg. 3254
HANKOOK TIRE ITALIA S.R.L.—See Hankook Tire & Technology Co.,Ltd.; *Int'l*, pg. 3254
HANKOOK TYRE AUSTRALIA PTY. LTD.—See Hankook Tire & Technology Co.,Ltd.; *Int'l*, pg. 3254
HANKOOK TYRE U.K. LTD.—See Hankook Tire & Technology Co.,Ltd.; *Int'l*, pg. 3254
HARRIS TIRE COMPANY; *U.S. Private*, pg. 1870
THE HERCULES TIRE & RUBBER COMPANY—See TPG Capital, L.P.; *U.S. Public*, pg. 2166
HERCULES TIRE SALES INC.; *U.S. Private*, pg. 1921
HESSELBEIN TIRE CO. INC.—See Dunlap & Kyle Co. Inc.; *U.S. Private*, pg. 1290
H&F GULF INC.; *U.S. Private*, pg. 1822
HI-Q AUTOMOTIVE (PTY) LTD—See The Goodyear Tire & Rubber Company; *U.S. Public*, pg. 2084
I&E TIRE CORP.; *U.S. Private*, pg. 2026
IHLE ANVELOPE SRL—See Compagnie Generale des Etablissements Michelin SCA; *Int'l*, pg. 1742
IHLE CZECH, S.R.O.—See Compagnie Generale des Etablissements Michelin SCA; *Int'l*, pg. 1742
IHLE PNEVMATIKE, D.O.O.—See Compagnie Generale des Etablissements Michelin SCA; *Int'l*, pg. 1743
IHLE SLOVAKIA S.R.O.—See Compagnie Generale des Etablissements Michelin SCA; *Int'l*, pg. 1742
JAVELIN SOUTHEAST CORPORATION; *U.S. Private*, pg. 2191
KAUFFMAN TIRE INC.; *U.S. Private*, pg. 2265
KAUFFMAN TIRE SERVICE OF CINCINNATI INC.—See Kauffman Tire Inc.; *U.S. Private*, pg. 2265
K&M TIRE, INC.; *U.S. Private*, pg. 2250

N.A.I.C.S. Index

N.A.I.C.S. INDEX

423140 — MOTOR VEHICLE PARTS...

KRAMER TIRE CO. INC.; *U.S. Private*, pg. 2349
K&W TIRE COMPANY INC.; *U.S. Private*, pg. 2250
LAKIN GENERAL CORPORATION; *U.S. Private*, pg. 2379
LES SCHWAB WAREHOUSE CENTER, INC.—See Les Schwab Tire Centers of Oregon, Inc.; *U.S. Private*, pg. 2432
L & S TIRE COMPANY; *U.S. Private*, pg. 2361
MASSENGILL TIRE CO. INC.; *U.S. Private*, pg. 2606
MAX-TRAC TIRE CO., INC.—See The Goodyear Tire & Rubber Company; *U.S. Public*, pg. 2083
MAXXIS INTERNATIONAL - UK PLC—See Cheng Shin Rubber (Xiamen) Ind., Ltd.; *Int'l*, pg. 1466
MAXXIS TECH CENTER EUROPE B.V.—See Cheng Shin Rubber (Xiamen) Ind., Ltd.; *Int'l*, pg. 1466
MCCARTHY TIRE AND AUTOMOTIVE CENTER—See McCarthy Tire Service Company; *U.S. Private*, pg. 2628
MICHELIN ASIA (HONG KONG) LIMITED—See Compagnie Generale des Etablissements Michelin SCA; *Int'l*, pg. 1743
MICHELIN ASIA (SINGAPORE) CO. PTE. LTD.—See Compagnie Generale des Etablissements Michelin SCA; *Int'l*, pg. 1743
MICHELIN BELUX S.A.—See Compagnie Generale des Etablissements Michelin SCA; *Int'l*, pg. 1743
MICHELIN NORDIC AB—See Compagnie Generale des Etablissements Michelin SCA; *Int'l*, pg. 1744
MILO C. COCKERHAM INC.; *U.S. Private*, pg. 2738
MOORE'S RETREAD & TIRE CO.; *U.S. Private*, pg. 2780
MOORES TIRE SALES INC.; *U.S. Private*, pg. 2780
MOUNTAIN MINING & SUPPLY COMPANY INC.—See Appalachian Tire Products Inc.; *U.S. Private*, pg. 295
MR. TIRE, INC.—See Monro, Inc.; *U.S. Public*, pg. 1465
NETIX S.R.L.—See Delticom AG; *Int'l*, pg. 2021
NIPPON GOODYEAR LTD—See The Goodyear Tire & Rubber Company; *U.S. Public*, pg. 2084
NORTHEAST WHOLESALE TIRE CORP.—See I&E Tire Corp.; *U.S. Private*, pg. 2026
NV VREDESTEIN SA—See Apollo Tyres Ltd.; *Int'l*, pg. 519
O.E. WHEELS, LLC; *U.S. Private*, pg. 2981
OREBRO BIDEMONTERING AB—See LKQ Corporation; *U.S. Public*, pg. 1336
OTOMOTIV LASTIKLERI TEVZI AS—See Continental Aktiengesellschaft; *Int'l*, pg. 1783
OTR WHEEL ENGINEERING, INC.; *U.S. Private*, pg. 3049
PACIFIC TIRE DISTRIBUTORS—See U.S. Venture, Inc.; *U.S. Private*, pg. 4272
PARMENTER, INC.; *U.S. Private*, pg. 3099
PARRISH TIRE COMPANY, INC.; *U.S. Private*, pg. 3100
PARRISH TIRE COMPANY, INC. - WHOLESALE DIVISION—See Parrish Tire Company, Inc.; *U.S. Private*, pg. 3100
PETE'S ROAD SERVICE, INC.; *U.S. Private*, pg. 3157
PETRO AMIGOS SUPPLY, INC.; *U.S. Private*, pg. 3161
PIEDMONT TRUCK TIRES INC.—See McCarthy Tire Service Company; *U.S. Private*, pg. 2628
PINCOTT SALES COMPANY INC—See Elgi Rubber Company Limited; *Int'l*, pg. 2360
PIRELLI TIRE, INC.—See China National Chemical Corporation; *Int'l*, pg. 1529
PLAINSMAN TIRE CO. INC.; *U.S. Private*, pg. 3195
PLAZA TIRE SERVICE INC.; *U.S. Private*, pg. 3213
POMP'S TIRE SERVICE INC.; *U.S. Private*, pg. 3227
PTG REIFENDRUCKREGELSYSTEME GMBH—See Compagnie Generale des Etablissements Michelin SCA; *Int'l*, pg. 1745
PURCELL TIRE COMPANY OF KENTUCKY—See Purcell Tire & Rubber Company Inc.; *U.S. Private*, pg. 3305
RACE TIRES AMERICA INC.—See Polymer Enterprises Inc.; *U.S. Private*, pg. 3226
REDBURN TIRE COMPANY; *U.S. Private*, pg. 3377
REIFEN BAIERLACHER GMBH—See The Goodyear Tire & Rubber Company; *U.S. Public*, pg. 2084
REIFENCOM GMBH—See Apollo Tyres Ltd.; *Int'l*, pg. 519
RELIABLE TIRE DISTRIBUTORS INC.; *U.S. Private*, pg. 3394
RILEY PARK TIRE SERVICES—See Indy Tire Centers, Inc.; *U.S. Private*, pg. 2069
ROLAND'S TIRE SERVICE, INC.; *U.S. Private*, pg. 3474
ROYAL TIRE INC.; *U.S. Private*, pg. 3494
SAFE-START, LLC; *U.S. Private*, pg. 3524
SMETZERS TIRE CENTER INC.; *U.S. Private*, pg. 3693
SOUTH DADE AUTOMOTIVE INC.; *U.S. Private*, pg. 3722
SOUTHSIDE TIRE CO. INC.; *U.S. Private*, pg. 3738
S&S FIRESTONE INC.; *U.S. Private*, pg. 3514
STATEWIDE TIRE DISTRIBUTORS; *U.S. Private*, pg. 3793
STEPHANIE TIRE CORP.; *U.S. Private*, pg. 3802
STEVE SHANNON TIRE COMPANY; *U.S. Private*, pg. 3808
STROUHAL'S TIRE RECAPPING PLANT INC.; *U.S. Private*, pg. 3841
SUMMIT TIRES NORTHEAST, LLC—See TPG Capital, L.P.; *U.S. Public*, pg. 2166
SUOMEN EUROMASTER OY—See Compagnie Generale des Etablissements Michelin SCA; *Int'l*, pg. 1745
SUPERIOR INDUSTRIES-SOUTHFIELD—See SUPERIOR INDUSTRIES INTERNATIONAL INC; *U.S. Public*, pg. 1967
SUPERIOR TIRE SERVICE INC.; *U.S. Private*, pg. 3880

TARAY INTERNATIONAL CORPORATION; *U.S. Private*, pg. 3933
TCI TIRE CENTERS, LLC—See Compagnie Generale des Etablissements Michelin SCA; *Int'l*, pg. 1744
TCI TIRE CENTERS—See Compagnie Generale des Etablissements Michelin SCA; *Int'l*, pg. 1744
TERRY'S TIRE TOWN INC.—See TPG Capital, L.P.; *U.S. Public*, pg. 2166
TIRECORP GMBH—See Compagnie Generale des Etablissements Michelin SCA; *Int'l*, pg. 1745
TIRE GROUP INTERNATIONAL, LLC; *U.S. Private*, pg. 4176
TIRENDO GMBH—See Delticom AG; *Int'l*, pg. 2021
THE TIRE RACK INC.; *U.S. Private*, pg. 4127
TIRESOLES OF BROWARD INC.; *U.S. Private*, pg. 4176
TIRE WHOLESALERS COMPANY, LLC—See Kingswood Capital Management LLC; *U.S. Private*, pg. 2312
TITAN DISTRIBUTION (UK) LIMITED—See Titan International, Inc.; *U.S. Public*, pg. 2160
TITAN STEEL WHEELS LIMITED—See Titan International, Inc.; *U.S. Public*, pg. 2160
TRACTION WHOLESALE CENTER; *U.S. Private*, pg. 4201
TREDIT TIRE & WHEEL COMPANY, INC.; *U.S. Private*, pg. 4216
TRENTYRE (LESOTHO) (PTY) LTD—See The Goodyear Tire & Rubber Company; *U.S. Public*, pg. 2085
TRI-JAY TIRE DISTRIBUTORS INC.; *U.S. Private*, pg. 4222
TRIPLE S TIRE CO. INC.; *U.S. Private*, pg. 4237
TYLDIN CORP.; *U.S. Private*, pg. 4267
TYRES INTERNATIONAL INC.; *U.S. Private*, pg. 4269
UNIVERSAL COOPERATIVES, INC.; *U.S. Private*, pg. 4304
THE UNIVERSAL TYRE COMPANY (DEPTFORD) LIMITED—See Halfords Group plc; *Int'l*, pg. 3229
U.S. WHOLESALE PIPE AND TUBE, INC.; *U.S. Private*, pg. 4272
VOGUE TYRE & RUBBER CO., INC.; *U.S. Private*, pg. 4409
VREDESTEIN FRANCE S.A.—See Apollo Tyres Ltd.; *Int'l*, pg. 519
VREDESTEIN GMBH—See Apollo Tyres Ltd.; *Int'l*, pg. 519
VREDESTEIN GMBH—See Apollo Tyres Ltd.; *Int'l*, pg. 519
VREDESTEIN IBERICA S.A.—See Apollo Tyres Ltd.; *Int'l*, pg. 519
VREDESTEIN NORDIC AB—See Apollo Tyres Ltd.; *Int'l*, pg. 519
WALTER J. MUELLER INC.; *U.S. Private*, pg. 4433
WHEEL PROS, LLC—See Clearlake Capital Group, L.P.; *U.S. Private*, pg. 937
WHOLESALE TIRE INC.; *U.S. Private*, pg. 4515
WINNEBAGO FLEET SERVICE, INC.—See William Charles, Ltd.; *U.S. Private*, pg. 4523

423140 — MOTOR VEHICLE PARTS (USED) MERCHANT WHOLESALERS

ABC MOTORS COMPANY LIMITED; *Int'l*, pg. 57
ACCUAIR CONTROL SYSTEMS LLC—See MidOcean Partners, LLP; *U.S. Private*, pg. 2716
A.E. SRL—See FLY Srl; *Int'l*, pg. 2715
APW INTERNATIONAL (USA), INC.—See Auto Parts Warehouse Inc.; *U.S. Private*, pg. 397
A-RELIABLE AUTO PARTS & WRECKERS, INC.—See LKQ Corporation; *U.S. Public*, pg. 1333
AUTOMOTIVE DATA SERVICES LIMITED—See LKQ Corporation; *U.S. Public*, pg. 1333
BAKER AND PRIEM BULL BARS PTY LIMITED—See Guangzhou Automobile Industry Group Co., Ltd.; *Int'l*, pg. 3164
BAPCOR RETAIL PTY. LTD.—See Bapcor Limited; *Int'l*, pg. 857
BDK USA; *U.S. Private*, pg. 500
BROTHERS AUTO SALVAGE YARD, INC.—See Stellex Capital Management LP; *U.S. Private*, pg. 3800
BUDGET AUTO PARTS U-PULL-IT, INC.—See LKQ Corporation; *U.S. Public*, pg. 1334
BUTLER TIRE COMPANY INCORPORATED; *U.S. Private*, pg. 697
COOPER STANDARD EUROPE GMBH—See Cooper-Standard Holdings Inc.; *U.S. Public*, pg. 573
CROW-BURLINGAME CO.—See Replacement Parts Inc.; *U.S. Private*, pg. 3401
DAEDONG HI-LEX OF AMERICA, INC—See Hi-Lex Corporation; *Int'l*, pg. 3380
DANA FLUID POWER DISTRIBUTION S.R.L.—See Dana Incorporated; *U.S. Public*, pg. 622
DON'S AUTOMOTIVE MALL, INC.—See Stellex Capital Management LP; *U.S. Private*, pg. 3800
EISS BROTHERS, INC.—See Stellex Capital Management LP; *U.S. Private*, pg. 3800
EURO CAR PARTS (NORTHERN IRELAND) LIMITED—See LKQ Corporation; *U.S. Public*, pg. 1334
FOUR LANE AUTO SALES; *U.S. Private*, pg. 1582
GARY'S U-PULL-IT, INC.—See Stellex Capital Management LP; *U.S. Private*, pg. 3800
GKN DRIVELINE TORQUE TECHNOLOGY (SHANGHAI) CO LTD—See GKN plc; *Int'l*, pg. 2985
GREEN OAK INVESTMENTS LLC—See Stellex Capital Management LP; *U.S. Private*, pg. 3800

HI-LEX HUNGARY KFT—See Hi-Lex Corporation; *Int'l*, pg. 3380
HONEYWELL TECHNOLOGY SOLUTIONS LAB PVT. LTD.—See Honeywell International Inc.; *U.S. Public*, pg. 1051
HORSEHEADS AUTOMOTIVE RECYCLING, INC.—See Stellex Capital Management LP; *U.S. Private*, pg. 3800
JERRY BROWN, LTD.—See Stellex Capital Management LP; *U.S. Private*, pg. 3800
LEESVILLE AUTO WRECKERS, INC.—See Stellex Capital Management LP; *U.S. Private*, pg. 3800
LKQ 1ST CHOICE AUTO PARTS, LLC—See LKQ Corporation; *U.S. Public*, pg. 1335
LKQ 250 AUTO, INC.—See LKQ Corporation; *U.S. Public*, pg. 1335
LKQ APEX AUTO PARTS, INC.—See LKQ Corporation; *U.S. Public*, pg. 1335
LKQ ATLANTA, L.P.—See LKQ Corporation; *U.S. Public*, pg. 1335
LKQ AUTO PARTS OF ORLANDO, LLC—See LKQ Corporation; *U.S. Public*, pg. 1335
LKQ BEST AUTOMOTIVE CORP.—See LKQ Corporation; *U.S. Public*, pg. 1335
LKQ CANADA AUTO PARTS INC.—See LKQ Corporation; *U.S. Public*, pg. 1335
LKQ COPHER SELF SERVICE AUTO PARTS-BRADENTON INC.—See LKQ Corporation; *U.S. Public*, pg. 1335
LKQ COPHER SELF SERVICE AUTO PARTS-ST. PETERSBURG INC.—See LKQ Corporation; *U.S. Public*, pg. 1335
LKQ CORPORATION; *U.S. Public*, pg. 1333
LKQ FOSTER AUTO PARTS, INC.—See LKQ Corporation; *U.S. Public*, pg. 1335
LKQ GORHAM AUTO PARTS CORP.—See LKQ Corporation; *U.S. Public*, pg. 1335
LKQ GREAT LAKES CORP.—See LKQ Corporation; *U.S. Public*, pg. 1335
LKQ HEAVY TRUCK-TEXAS BEST DIESEL, L.P.—See LKQ Corporation; *U.S. Public*, pg. 1335
LKQ HUNTS POINT AUTO PARTS CORP.—See LKQ Corporation; *U.S. Public*, pg. 1335
LKQ LAKENOR AUTO & TRUCK SALVAGE, INC.—See LKQ Corporation; *U.S. Public*, pg. 1335
LKQ METRO, INC.—See LKQ Corporation; *U.S. Public*, pg. 1335
LKQ OF MICHIGAN, INC.—See LKQ Corporation; *U.S. Public*, pg. 1335
LKQ OF NEVADA, INC.—See LKQ Corporation; *U.S. Public*, pg. 1335
LKQ OF TENNESSEE, INC.—See LKQ Corporation; *U.S. Public*, pg. 1335
LKQ PENN-MAR, INC.—See LKQ Corporation; *U.S. Public*, pg. 1335
LKQ PLUNKS TRUCK PARTS & EQUIPMENT-JACKSON, INC.—See LKQ Corporation; *U.S. Public*, pg. 1335
LKQ RALEIGH AUTO PARTS CORP.—See LKQ Corporation; *U.S. Public*, pg. 1335
LKQ SELF SERVICE AUTO PARTS-HOLLAND, INC.—See LKQ Corporation; *U.S. Public*, pg. 1335
LKQ SELF SERVICE AUTO PARTS-KALAMAZOO, INC.—See LKQ Corporation; *U.S. Public*, pg. 1335
LKQ SELF SERVICE AUTO PARTS-MEMPHIS LLC—See LKQ Corporation; *U.S. Public*, pg. 1335
LKQ SELF SERVICE AUTO PARTS-TULSA, INC.—See LKQ Corporation; *U.S. Public*, pg. 1335
LKQ SMART PARTS, INC.—See LKQ Corporation; *U.S. Public*, pg. 1335
LKQ SOUTHWICK LLC—See LKQ Corporation; *U.S. Public*, pg. 1335
LKQ TRIPLETT ASAP, INC.—See LKQ Corporation; *U.S. Public*, pg. 1335
LKQ U-PULL-IT AUTO DAMASCUS, INC.—See LKQ Corporation; *U.S. Public*, pg. 1335
MICHAEL AUTO PARTS, INCORPORATED—See LKQ Corporation; *U.S. Public*, pg. 1335
N-ONE RACING SDN BHD.—See HKS CO., LTD.; *Int'l*, pg. 3429
OCEAN COUNTY AUTO WRECKERS, INC.—See Stellex Capital Management LP; *U.S. Private*, pg. 3800
OREBRO BILDEMONTERING AB—See LKQ Corporation; *U.S. Public*, pg. 1336
PARTS ALLIANCE GROUP LIMITED—See LKQ Corporation; *U.S. Public*, pg. 1336
POLAR PARTS CO.—See Road Machinery & Supplies Company; *U.S. Private*, pg. 3453
POTOMAC GERMAN AUTO, INC.—See LKQ Corporation; *U.S. Public*, pg. 1336
QUALITY PARTS SUPPLY, INC.; *U.S. Private*, pg. 3320
REBUILDERS AUTOMOTIVE SUPPLY CO. INC.; *U.S. Private*, pg. 3368
SALVAGE HUNTER AUTO PARTS—See Four Lane Auto Sales; *U.S. Private*, pg. 1582
SILTIN INDUSTRIES, INC.—See Deeco Metals Corporation; *U.S. Private*, pg. 1189
STANDARD AUTO WRECKERS, INC.—See Stellex Capital Management LP; *U.S. Private*, pg. 3800
SUPERIOR INDUSTRIES AUTOMOTIVE GERMANY

423140 — MOTOR VEHICLE PARTS...

GMBH—See SUPERIOR INDUSTRIES INTERNATIONAL INC; *U.S. Public*, pg. 1967
SUPERIOR INDUSTRIES EUROPE AG—See SUPERIOR INDUSTRIES INTERNATIONAL INC; *U.S. Public*, pg. 1967
SUPERIOR INDUSTRIES LEICHTMETALLRADER GERMANY GMBH—See SUPERIOR INDUSTRIES INTERNATIONAL INC; *U.S. Public*, pg. 1967
SUPERIOR INDUSTRIES PRODUCTION GERMANY GMBH—See SUPERIOR INDUSTRIES INTERNATIONAL INC; *U.S. Public*, pg. 1967
TESLA MOTORS BELGIUM SPRL—See Tesla, Inc.; *U.S. Public*, pg. 2021
TESLA MOTORS LUXEMBOURG S.A.R.L.—See Tesla, Inc.; *U.S. Public*, pg. 2021
T.J.T., INC.; *U.S. Public*, pg. 1978
TRUCKPRO, LLC—See Platinum Equity, LLC; *U.S. Private*, pg. 3209
UAP INC.—See Genuine Parts Company; *U.S. Public*, pg. 932
VEHICLE MAINTENANCE PROGRAM, INC.; *U.S. Private*, pg. 4354
VOLVO PARTS GENT NV—See AB Volvo; *Int'l*, pg. 45
WKDA OSTERREICH GMBH—See AUTO1 Group SE; *Int'l*, pg. 725

423210 — FURNITURE MERCHANT WHOLESALERS

A AMERICA INC.; *U.S. Private*, pg. 18
ACE BED INTERNATIONAL PTE LTD.—See Acebed Co. Ltd.; *Int'l*, pg. 95
ADVANCED OFFICE ENVIRONMENTS, INC.; *U.S. Private*, pg. 91
AHB DISTRIBUTION SDN. BHD.—See AHB Holdings Berhad; *Int'l*, pg. 222
AJAX BUSINESS INTERIORS, INC.; *U.S. Private*, pg. 143
ALEXANDER-PATTERSON GROUP INC.; *U.S. Private*, pg. 164
ALFAX WHOLESALE FURNITURE INC.—See Franz Haniel & Cie. GmbH; *Int'l*, pg. 2763
ALFRED WILLIAMS & COMPANY; *U.S. Private*, pg. 166
ALL MAKES OFFICE EQUIPMENT CO.—See All Makes Office Equipment Co. Inc.; *U.S. Private*, pg. 171
ALPHA OFFICE SUPPLIES INC.; *U.S. Private*, pg. 199
AMERICAN ARCHITECTURAL DESIGN SPECIALTIES, INC.; *U.S. Private*, pg. 222
AMERICAN OFFICE EQUIPMENT CO. INC.; *U.S. Private*, pg. 242
APEX FACILITY RESOURCES, INC.; *U.S. Private*, pg. 292
ARBEE ASSOCIATES INC.; *U.S. Private*, pg. 308
ASHLEY DISTRIBUTION SERVICES, LTD.—See Ashley Furniture Industries, Inc.; *U.S. Private*, pg. 350
ASPA BELGIUM N.V.—See HAL Trust N.V.; *Int'l*, pg. 3223
ATLANTIC CORPORATE INTERIORS, INC.; *U.S. Private*, pg. 372
ATLANTIC GROUP; *U.S. Private*, pg. 373
ATMOSPHERE COMMERCIAL INTERIORS, LLC—See HNI Corporation; *U.S. Public*, pg. 1043
BABY TREND, INC.—See Alpha Group Co., Ltd.; *Int'l*, pg. 368
BEAR MATTRESS LLC—See Cerberus Capital Management, L.P.; *U.S. Private*, pg. 837
BECK TOTAL OFFICE INTERIORS; *U.S. Private*, pg. 510
BENE BELGIUM BVBA—See Bene GmbH; *Int'l*, pg. 972
BENE BRATISLAVA SPOL.S.R.O.—See Bene GmbH; *Int'l*, pg. 972
BENE BUDAPEST KFT.—See Bene GmbH; *Int'l*, pg. 972
BENE DEUTSCHLAND GMBH—See Bene GmbH; *Int'l*, pg. 972
BENE GMBH—See Bene GmbH; *Int'l*, pg. 972
BENE KYIV TOV—See Bene GmbH; *Int'l*, pg. 972
BENE LJUBLJANA D.O.O.—See Bene GmbH; *Int'l*, pg. 972
BENE OFFICE FURNITURE IRELAND LTD.—See Bene GmbH; *Int'l*, pg. 972
BENE PLC—See Bene GmbH; *Int'l*, pg. 972
BENE PRAHA SPOL.S.R.O.—See Bene GmbH; *Int'l*, pg. 972
BENE ROMANIA S.R.L.—See Bene GmbH; *Int'l*, pg. 972
BENE RUS OOO—See Bene GmbH; *Int'l*, pg. 972
BENE WARSZAWA SP. Z O.O.—See Bene GmbH; *Int'l*, pg. 972
BERNHARDT FURNITURE COMPANY - BERNHARDT HOSPITALITY DIVISION—See Bernhardt Furniture Company; *U.S. Private*, pg. 537
BERWIN INC.; *U.S. Private*, pg. 540
BETER BED B.V.—See Beter Bed Holding N.V.; *Int'l*, pg. 1002
BIZCHAIR.COM; *U.S. Private*, pg. 567
BKM OF CALIFORNIA—See bkm OfficeWorks; *U.S. Private*, pg. 569
BLANKENSHIP ASSOCIATES, INC.—See Bain Capital, LP; *U.S. Private*, pg. 431
BRODART CO. - SUPPLIES & FURNISHINGS DIVISION—See Brodart Co.; *U.S. Private*, pg. 661
BUCKO'S INC.; *U.S. Private*, pg. 678

BUNKA KOUGEI CO., LTD.—See Bunka Shutter Co., Ltd.; *Int'l*, pg. 1216
BUSINESS FURNITURE, INC.; *U.S. Private*, pg. 694
BUSINESS FURNITURE LLC; *U.S. Private*, pg. 694
BUSINESS INTERIORS INC.; *U.S. Private*, pg. 695
BUSINESS OFFICE SYSTEMS INC.; *U.S. Private*, pg. 695
CALLIGARIS S.P.A.—See Alpha Associes Conseil SAS; *Int'l*, pg. 366
CAPITOL BUSINESS INTERIORS—See Champion Industries, Inc.; *U.S. Public*, pg. 478
CAPITOL SUPPLY, INC.; *U.S. Private*, pg. 744
CAPSTONE SYSTEMS, INC.; *Int'l*, pg. 1317
CAREFREE INDUSTRIES, INC.; *U.S. Private*, pg. 753
CARITHERS WALLACE COURTENAY LLC; *U.S. Private*, pg. 761
CARPENTER BELGIUM NV—See Carpenter Co.; *U.S. Private*, pg. 770
CARROLL SEATING COMPANY INC.; *U.S. Private*, pg. 773
CASE FURNITURE & DESIGN, LLC.; *U.S. Private*, pg. 782
C BANCROFT LTD.—See Frank Key Group Limited; *Int'l*, pg. 2761
CDMM CORP.; *U.S. Private*, pg. 803
CHL BUSINESS INTERIORS, LLC; *U.S. Private*, pg. 887
CLEANUP (SHANGHAI) CO., LTD.—See Cleanup Corporation; *Int'l*, pg. 1656
CLESTRA B.V.—See Clestra Hauserman S.A.; *Int'l*, pg. 1658
CLESTRA GMBH—See Clestra Hauserman S.A.; *Int'l*, pg. 1658
CLESTRA K.K.—See Clestra Hauserman S.A.; *Int'l*, pg. 1658
CLESTRA LIMITED—See Clestra Hauserman S.A.; *Int'l*, pg. 1658
CLESTRA LIMITED—See Clestra Hauserman S.A.; *Int'l*, pg. 1658
COASTER OF AMERICA INC.; *U.S. Private*, pg. 957
COE DISTRIBUTING INC.; *U.S. Private*, pg. 960
COIN FURNITURE LIMITED—See DFS Furniture Ltd.; *Int'l*, pg. 2096
COLLINS INTERNATIONAL CO., LTD.—See Collins Co., Inc.; *Int'l*, pg. 1702
COLOR ART OFFICE INTERIORS INC.; *U.S. Private*, pg. 972
COMFORT REVOLUTION, LLC—See Tempur Sealy International, Inc.; *U.S. Public*, pg. 1999
COMMERCIAL & HOME FURNISHINGS, INC.; *U.S. Private*, pg. 982
CONRAN CONTRACTS LIMITED—See Conran Holdings Limited; *Int'l*, pg. 1769
CONTAINER MARKETING INC.; *U.S. Private*, pg. 1026
CONTINENTAL OFFICE ENVIRONMENTS; *U.S. Private*, pg. 1030
CONTRACT FURNISHERS OF HAWAII; *U.S. Private*, pg. 1032
CONTRACT FURNITURE INC.; *U.S. Private*, pg. 1032
CONTRACT OFFICE GROUP, INC.; *U.S. Private*, pg. 1032
CONTRACT PURCHASING & DESIGN INC.; *U.S. Private*, pg. 1032
COORDINATED RESOURCES, INC. OF SAN FRANCISCO; *U.S. Private*, pg. 1043
CORNER OFFICE INC.; *U.S. Private*, pg. 1051
CORPORATE BUSINESS INTERIORS, INC.; *U.S. Private*, pg. 1054
CORPORATE CONCEPTS, INC.—See PARIC Holdings, Inc.; *U.S. Private*, pg. 3094
THE CORPORATE ENVIRONMENTS GROUP; *U.S. Private*, pg. 4015
CORPORATE FACILITIES INC.; *U.S. Private*, pg. 1054
CORPORATE INTERIORS, INC.; *U.S. Private*, pg. 1055
CORPORATE INTERIORS, INC.; *U.S. Private*, pg. 1055
CORPORATE INTERIOR SYSTEMS; *U.S. Private*, pg. 1055
CORPORATE SPACES, INC.—See Corporate Business Interiors, Inc.; *U.S. Private*, pg. 1054
CORT FURNITURE RENTAL—See Berkshire Hathaway Inc.; *U.S. Public*, pg. 303
CRAFTMATIC ORGANIZATION, INC.—See Craftmatic Industries, Inc.; *U.S. Private*, pg. 1082
CREATIVE OFFICE ENVIRONMENT, LLC; *U.S. Private*, pg. 1089
CREATIVE OFFICE INTERIORS INC.; *U.S. Private*, pg. 1089
DAUPHIN HUMANDESIGN UK LIMITED—See Dauphin HumanDesign Group GmbH & Co. KG; *Int'l*, pg. 1983
DAUPHIN INDUSTRY (SCHWEIZ) UNIQ SOLUTION GMBH—See Dauphin HumanDesign Group GmbH & Co. KG; *Int'l*, pg. 1983
DAUPHIN NORTH AMERICA—See Dauphin HumanDesign Group GmbH & Co. KG; *Int'l*, pg. 1983
DBC DEUTSCHLAND GMBH—See Beter Bed Holding N.V.; *Int'l*, pg. 1002
DBI BUSINESS INTERIORS LLC; *U.S. Private*, pg. 1179
DE CLERCQ OFFICE GROUP, LTD.—See Creative Office Pavilion LLC; *U.S. Private*, pg. 1089
DESIGN CAPITAL LIMITED—See Wipro Limited; *Int'l*, pg. 2045
DESIGNER IMPORTS INTERNATIONAL; *U.S. Private*, pg. 1214
DESIGN & SUPPLY CO., INC.—See Delta Holdings, Inc.; *U.S. Private*, pg. 1200
DESKS INC.; *U.S. Private*, pg. 1215

DIAMOND BAR OUTDOORS, INC.—See Nova Lifestyle, Inc.; *U.S. Public*, pg. 1547
DICKSON INDUSTRIES, LLC; *U.S. Private*, pg. 1227
DICOR CORPORATION, INC.—See Thor Industries, Inc.; *U.S. Public*, pg. 2156
D.I. SUPPLY INC.—See Drury Inn Inc.; *U.S. Private*, pg. 1280
DJ INTERNATIONAL INCORPORATED; *U.S. Private*, pg. 1246
DOURON, INC.; *U.S. Private*, pg. 1268
DREAMLAND CORPORATION (MALAYSIA) SDN. BHD.—See FACB Industries Incorporated Berhad; *Int'l*, pg. 2600
DRIVE-O-RAMA INC.; *U.S. Private*, pg. 1278
DURAGROUP LLC; *U.S. Private*, pg. 1292
DUTAILIER LTD.—See Groupe Dutailier Inc.; *Int'l*, pg. 3102
EGGER AUSTRALASIA PTY LIMITED—See Fritz Egger GmbH & Co.; *Int'l*, pg. 2793
EGGER BALTIC UAB—See Fritz Egger GmbH & Co.; *Int'l*, pg. 2793
EGGER BESCHICHTUNGSWERK MARIENMUNSTER GMBH & CO. KG - BEVERN PLANT—See Fritz Egger GmbH & Co.; *Int'l*, pg. 2793
EGGER BESCHICHTUNGSWERK MARIENMUNSTER GMBH & CO. KG—See Fritz Egger GmbH & Co.; *Int'l*, pg. 2793
EGGER CZ S.R.O.—See Fritz Egger GmbH & Co.; *Int'l*, pg. 2793
EGGER HOLZWERKSTOFFE BRILON GMBH & CO. KG—See Fritz Egger GmbH & Co.; *Int'l*, pg. 2793
EGGER HOLZWERKSTOFFE SCHWEIZ GMBH—See Fritz Egger GmbH & Co.; *Int'l*, pg. 2793
EGGER HOLZWERKSTOFFE WISMAR GMBH & CO. KG—See Fritz Egger GmbH & Co.; *Int'l*, pg. 2793
EGGER KUNSTSTOFFE GMBH & CO. KG—See Fritz Egger GmbH & Co.; *Int'l*, pg. 2793
EGGER ORMAN URUNLERI A.S.—See Fritz Egger GmbH & Co.; *Int'l*, pg. 2793
EGGER POLSKA SP. Z O.O.—See Fritz Egger GmbH & Co.; *Int'l*, pg. 2793
EGGER PRODUCTOS DE MADERA LIMITADA—See Fritz Egger GmbH & Co.; *Int'l*, pg. 2793
EGGER RETAIL PRODUCTS FRANCE S.A.S.—See Fritz Egger GmbH & Co.; *Int'l*, pg. 2793
EGGER RETAIL PRODUCTS GMBH & CO. KG—See Fritz Egger GmbH & Co.; *Int'l*, pg. 2793
EGGER RS DOO—See Fritz Egger GmbH & Co.; *Int'l*, pg. 2793
ELK-DESA FURNITURE SDN. BHD.—See ELK-Desa Resources Bhd; *Int'l*, pg. 2364
EMMONS BUSINESS INTERIORS LLC; *U.S. Private*, pg. 1383
EMPIRE OFFICE, INC.; *U.S. Private*, pg. 1385
EMUAMERICAS, LLC.; *U.S. Private*, pg. 1388
ESPACIO LLC—See Coteminas Companhia de Tecidos Norte de Minas; *Int'l*, pg. 1817
ESPACIO LLC—See Springs Global, Inc.; *Int'l*, pg. 3764
ETHAN ALLEN OPERATIONS, INC.—See Ethan Allen Interiors Inc.; *U.S. Public*, pg. 797
EVENFLO CANADA—See Goodbaby International Holdings Limited; *Int'l*, pg. 3039
EVENFLO MEXICO S.A. DE C.V.—See Goodbaby International Holdings Limited; *Int'l*, pg. 3039
FACILITECH INC.; *U.S. Private*, pg. 1459
FACILITECH, INC.; *U.S. Private*, pg. 1459
FACILITY INTERIORS INC.; *U.S. Private*, pg. 1459
FACILITY MATRIX GROUP INC.; *U.S. Private*, pg. 1460
FACILITY SERVICES INC.—See DJ International Incorporated; *U.S. Private*, pg. 1246
FEDERAL FURNITURE (M) SDN BHD—See Federal International Holdings Berhad; *Int'l*, pg. 2630
FIRESIDE OFFICE PRODUCTS INC.; *U.S. Private*, pg. 1512
FLORIDA BUSINESS INTERIORS INC.—See Business Office Systems Inc.; *U.S. Private*, pg. 695
FLORIDA BUSINESS INTERIORS - TAMPA BAY—See Business Office Systems Inc.; *U.S. Private*, pg. 695
FORD BUSINESS MACHINES—See Ford Business Machines, Inc.; *U.S. Private*, pg. 1564
FORRER STRATEGIC BUSINESS INTERIORS INC.; *U.S. Private*, pg. 1572
FORTE RUS LTD.—See Fabryki Mebli Forte S.A.; *Int'l*, pg. 2600
FORTE UKRAINE, LTD.—See Fabryki Mebli Forte S.A.; *Int'l*, pg. 2600
FOUR HANDS, LLC; *U.S. Private*, pg. 1582
FRAENKEL COMPANY, INC.; *U.S. Private*, pg. 1586
FRANKLIN INTERIORS INC.; *U.S. Private*, pg. 1597
FREEDOM GROUP LIMITED; *Int'l*, pg. 2769
FRITZ EGGER AG—See Fritz Egger GmbH & Co.; *Int'l*, pg. 2794
FRITZ EGGER GMBH & CO. - EGGER PANNEAUX & DECORS—See Fritz Egger GmbH & Co.; *Int'l*, pg. 2794
FRITZ EGGER GMBH HUNGARY—See Fritz Egger GmbH & Co.; *Int'l*, pg. 2794
FURNITURE CONSULTANTS LLC; *U.S. Private*, pg. 1624

423220 — HOME FURNISHING MER...

FURNITURE MARKETING GROUP INC.; *U.S. Private*, pg. 1624
FURNITURE VILLAGE LIMITED; *Int'l*, pg. 2846
GABRIEL (TIANJIN) INTERNATIONAL TRADING CO. LTD.—See Gabriel Holding A/S; *Int'l*, pg. 2867
GARDENSIDE LTD.—See BIG Camera Corporation PCL; *Int'l*, pg. 1021
GENERAL OFFICE INTERIORS, INC.—See Officeworks, Inc.; *U.S. Private*, pg. 3002
GLASSWELLS LTD; *Int'l*, pg. 2989
GLOBE BUSINESS INTERIORS; *U.S. Private*, pg. 1719
G.L. SEAMAN & COMPANY-FORT WORTH—See G.L. Seaman & Company; *U.S. Private*, pg. 1631
G.L. SEAMAN & COMPANY; *U.S. Private*, pg. 1631
G-MARK, INC.—See GSI Creos Corporation; *Int'l*, pg. 3144
THE GNS GROUP, INC.; *U.S. Public*, pg. 2075
GOODMANS, INC.; *U.S. Private*, pg. 1739
HACKNEY CONTRACT FURNITURE—See The H.T. Hackney Company; *U.S. Private*, pg. 4041
HAWORTH LTD.—See Haworth, Inc.; *U.S. Private*, pg. 1883
HENRICKSEN & COMPANY INC.; *U.S. Private*, pg. 1917
HENRIKSEN-BUTLER DESIGN GROUP; *U.S. Private*, pg. 1917
HERMAN MILLER DO BRASIL, LTDA.—See MillerKnoll, Inc.; *U.S. Public*, pg. 1447
HOGUE & ASSOCIATES INC.; *U.S. Private*, pg. 1961
HOLLAND HOUSE FURNITURE—See The H.T. Hackney Company; *U.S. Private*, pg. 4041
HOLLY HUNT DO BRASIL IMPORTACAO E COMERCIO DE MOBILIARIOS LTDA—See MillerKnoll, Inc.; *U.S. Public*, pg. 1447
HOLLY HUNT ENTERPRISES, INC.—See MillerKnoll, Inc.; *U.S. Public*, pg. 1447
HOME LINE FURNITURE INDUSTRIES INC.; *U.S. Private*, pg. 1971
HUMAN TOUCH, LLC; *U.S. Private*, pg. 2006
HYUNDAI LIVART CO., LTD.—See Hyundai Department Store Co., Ltd.; *Int'l*, pg. 3556
IE CONNECT LLC—See Interior Environments, Inc.; *U.S. Private*, pg. 2111
I. KEATING FURNITURE INC.; *U.S. Private*, pg. 2026
IMERYS KILN FURNITURE HUNGARY KFT—See Groupe Bruxelles Lambert SA; *Int'l*, pg. 3100
INNOMAX CORPORATION; *U.S. Private*, pg. 2080
INSIDE SOURCE INC.; *U.S. Private*, pg. 2085
INSTA-BED, INC.—See Exxel Outdoors, Inc.; *U.S. Private*, pg. 1453
INTELLIGENT INTERIORS INC.; *U.S. Private*, pg. 2106
INTERIOR DESIGN SERVICES, INC.; *U.S. Private*, pg. 2111
INTERIOR DYNAMICS INC.; *U.S. Private*, pg. 2111
INTERIOR FUSION, LLC; *U.S. Private*, pg. 2111
INTERIOR INVESTMENTS LLC; *U.S. Private*, pg. 2111
INTERIOR SYSTEMS INC.; *U.S. Private*, pg. 2111
INTERNATIONAL CONTRACT FURNITURE; *U.S. Private*, pg. 2116
INTEX RECREATION CORP.; *U.S. Private*, pg. 2128
IOOO EGGER DREVPLIT—See Fritz Egger GmbH & Co.; *Int'l*, pg. 2794
ISPACE FURNITURE, INC.; *U.S. Private*, pg. 2146
IVGSTORES LLC; *U.S. Private*, pg. 2151
JANUS ET CIE—See Haworth, Inc.; *U.S. Private*, pg. 1883
J. WASSON ENTERPRISES INC.; *U.S. Private*, pg. 2157
KBM-HOGUE; *U.S. Private*, pg. 2268
KENTWOOD OFFICE FURNITURE INC.; *U.S. Private*, pg. 2289
KERSHNER OFFICE FURNITURE; *U.S. Private*, pg. 2291
KIMBALL HOSPITALITY, INC.—See HNI Corporation; *U.S. Public*, pg. 1043
KREISS COLLECTION ARIZONA INC.—See Kreiss Enterprises Inc.; *U.S. Private*, pg. 2350
KREISS COLLECTION COLORADO INC.—See Kreiss Enterprises Inc.; *U.S. Private*, pg. 2351
KREISS COLLECTION ILLINOIS INC.—See Kreiss Enterprises Inc.; *U.S. Private*, pg. 2351
KREISS COLLECTION NEVADA INC.—See Kreiss Enterprises Inc.; *U.S. Private*, pg. 2351
KREISS ENTERPRISES INC.; *U.S. Private*, pg. 2350
KWALU—See DuraGroup LLC; *U.S. Private*, pg. 1292
LA-Z-BOY (THAILAND) LTD.—See La-Z-Boy Incorporated; *U.S. Public*, pg. 1285
LEE JOFA, INC.—See Kravet Fabrics Inc.; *U.S. Private*, pg. 2350
LIBERTY FURNITURE INDUSTRIES INC.; *U.S. Private*, pg. 2444
LINCOLN OFFICE SUPPLY CO. INCORPORATED; *U.S. Private*, pg. 2458
LOROMAN CO. INC.—See Abbott Industries Inc.; *U.S. Private*, pg. 35
LOTH INC.—See Loth MDI, Inc.; *U.S. Private*, pg. 2497
LOTH MBI, INC.; *U.S. Private*, pg. 2497
L. POWELL COMPANY ACQUISITION CORP.; *U.S. Private*, pg. 2364
M2L INC.; *U.S. Private*, pg. 2530
MAB LTD.; *U.S. Private*, pg. 2531
MAGNA FOREMOST SDN BHD—See Owens Corning; *U.S. Public*, pg. 1627
MARNOY INTERESTS LTD.; *U.S. Private*, pg. 2586

MEADOWS OFFICE FURNITURE COMPANY INC.; *U.S. Private*, pg. 2647
MEBLE POLONIA, LTD.—See Fabryki Mebli Forte S.A.; *Int'l*, pg. 2600
MECA INC.; *U.S. Private*, pg. 2648
MEMPHIS BUSINESS INTERIORS, LLC; *U.S. Private*, pg. 2664
MG WEST COMPANY; *U.S. Private*, pg. 2694
MILLER'S OF COLUMBIA, INC.; *U.S. Private*, pg. 2736
MILLINGTON LOCKWOOD INC.; *U.S. Private*, pg. 2737
MISSCO CONTRACT SALES; *U.S. Private*, pg. 2747
MOBELVERTRIEB FORTE GMBH—See Fabryki Mebli Forte S.A.; *Int'l*, pg. 2600
MYOFFICEPRODUCTS LLC—See MyOfficeProducts LLC; *U.S. Private*, pg. 2825
NADEAU CORP.; *U.S. Private*, pg. 2830
NATIONAL BUSINESS FURNITURE INC.—See Franz Haniel & Cie. GmbH; *Int'l*, pg. 2763
NATIONAL OFFICE FURNITURE, INC.—See HNI Corporation; *U.S. Public*, pg. 1043
NEW TANGRAM, LLC; *U.S. Private*, pg. 2907
OAK HARBOUR MARKETING LIMITED; *U.S. Private*, pg. 2983
OEC BUSINESS INTERIORS, INC.; *U.S. Private*, pg. 2997
OFFICE CONCEPTS INC.; *U.S. Private*, pg. 3001
OFFICE ENVIRONMENTS INC.; *U.S. Private*, pg. 3001
OFFICE & FLOORING WORX INC.; *U.S. Private*, pg. 3001
OFFICE FURNITURE DEPOT, INC.—See Interior Fusion, LLC; *U.S. Private*, pg. 2111
OFFICE FURNITURE PARTNERSHIP; *U.S. Private*, pg. 3001
OFFICE RESOURCES INC.; *U.S. Private*, pg. 3001
OHIO DESK CO., INC.; *U.S. Private*, pg. 3004
OMNIFICS INC.; *U.S. Private*, pg. 3017
ONE KINGS LANE, INC.—See 20230930-DK-Butterfly-1, Inc.; *U.S. Private*, pg. 5
ONE WORKPLACE; *U.S. Private*, pg. 3024
ONLINE COMMERCE GROUP, LLC; *U.S. Private*, pg. 3026
OOO EGGER DREVPRODUKT GAGARIN—See Fritz Egger GmbH & Co.; *Int'l*, pg. 2794
OOO EGGER DREVPRODUKT SHUYA—See Fritz Egger GmbH & Co.; *Int'l*, pg. 2794
OPEN PLAN SYSTEMS, INC.—See The Supply Room Companies Inc.; *U.S. Private*, pg. 4125
PCL FIXTURES, INC.; *U.S. Private*, pg. 3120
PEABODY OFFICE FURNITURE CORPORATION; *U.S. Private*, pg. 3122
PEAR COMMERCIAL INTERIORS INC.; *U.S. Private*, pg. 3125
PERDUE INC.; *U.S. Private*, pg. 3147
PETER PEPPER PRODUCTS, INC.; *U.S. Private*, pg. 3159
PETRONE WORLDWIDE, INC.; *U.S. Public*, pg. 1678
PHILLIPS OFFICE SOLUTIONS, INC.—See Wells Fargo & Company; *U.S. Public*, pg. 2344
PIGOTT INC.; *U.S. Private*, pg. 3179
PIVOT INTERIORS INC.; *U.S. Private*, pg. 3192
PLANNED FURNITURE PROMOTIONS, LLC; *U.S. Private*, pg. 3196
POLIFORM USA, INC.; *U.S. Private*, pg. 3224
PRODUCTIVE BUSINESS INTERIORS—See Indiana Records Managers, Inc.; *U.S. Private*, pg. 2062
PROFESSIONAL OFFICE ENVIRONMENTS; *U.S. Private*, pg. 3275
REALTRUCK, INC.; *U.S. Private*, pg. 3369
RED THREAD SPACES LLC; *U.S. Private*, pg. 3376
RESTORATION HARDWARE CANADA, INC.—See RH; *U.S. Public*, pg. 1796
ROCKFORD BUSINESS INTERIORS INC.; *U.S. Private*, pg. 3466
ROMA PLASTIK A.S.—See Fritz Egger GmbH & Co.; *Int'l*, pg. 2794
SAFCO PRODUCTS COMPANY—See Liberty Diversified International Inc.; *U.S. Private*, pg. 2443
SALA AZABU CO., LTD.—See Hulic Co., Ltd.; *Int'l*, pg. 3528
SALEM VENT INTERNATIONAL, INC.—See Marsh & McLennan Companies, Inc.; *U.S. Public*, pg. 1376
SANGJATTEN SVERIGE AB—See Beter Bed Holding N.V.; *Int'l*, pg. 1002
SARREID, LTD.; *U.S. Private*, pg. 3550
SATURN PEST VIDEO TV HIFI ELEKTRO PHOTO COMPUTER KERESKEDELMI KFT.—See Ceconomy AG; *Int'l*, pg. 1385
SAXTON, BRADLEY, INC; *U.S. Private*, pg. 3558
SCAN DESIGN OF FLORIDA INC.; *U.S. Private*, pg. 3561
SCOTT RICE OFFICE INTERIORS; *U.S. Private*, pg. 3577
SEAL FURNITURE SYSTEMS SAN DIEGO INC.; *U.S. Private*, pg. 3584
SEALY ARGENTINA SRL—See Tempur Sealy International, Inc.; *U.S. Public*, pg. 1999
SEALY ASIA (SINGAPORE) PTE, LTD.—See Dyer Holdings Pty. Ltd.; *Int'l*, pg. 2238
SEALY ASIA (SINGAPORE) PTE, LTD.—See Tempur Sealy International, Inc.; *U.S. Public*, pg. 1999
SHANTAWOOD MANUFACTURING SDN. BHD.—See DPS Resources Berhad; *Int'l*, pg. 2189
SICO MIDDLE EAST JLT (LLC)—See Sico Incorporated; *U.S. Private*, pg. 3645
SIDEMARK; *U.S. Private*, pg. 3645

SODIMA SAS—See General Mills, Inc.; *U.S. Public*, pg. 922
SOUTH CONE HOME, INC.; *U.S. Private*, pg. 3721
SOUTHWEST SOLUTIONS GROUP; *U.S. Private*, pg. 3741
SPACE & ASSET MANAGEMENT INC.; *U.S. Private*, pg. 3743
S ROSE INC.; *U.S. Private*, pg. 3512
STABILUS; *U.S. Private*, pg. 3774
STEELCASE AUSTRALIA PTY. LTD.—See Steelcase Inc.; *U.S. Public*, pg. 1944
STEINHOFF ASIA PACIFIC LIMITED—See Freedom Group Limited; *Int'l*, pg. 2769
STOREY-KENWORTHY COMPANY; *U.S. Private*, pg. 3831
STORR OFFICE ENVIRONMENTS, INC.; *U.S. Private*, pg. 3831
STORR OFFICE ENVIRONMENTS OF FLORIDA, INC.—See Storr Office Environments, Inc.; *U.S. Private*, pg. 3832
STUDIO RTA; *U.S. Private*, pg. 3843
SUGAR STORES INC.; *U.S. Private*, pg. 3849
SUNNY DESIGN INC.; *U.S. Private*, pg. 3868
SUPPLYSOURCE INC.; *U.S. Private*, pg. 3882
SURF HARDWARE INTERNATIONAL USA INC.—See Gowing Brothers Limited; *Int'l*, pg. 3045
SYRACUSE OFFICE EQUIPMENT; *U.S. Private*, pg. 3905
SYSTEMS SOURCE, INC.; *U.S. Private*, pg. 3908
TARGET COMMERCIAL INTERIORS, INC. - GREEN BAY—See HNI Corporation; *U.S. Public*, pg. 1043
TEAMMATES COMMERCIAL INTERIORS; *U.S. Private*, pg. 3951
TEAMSON DESIGN CORP.; *U.S. Private*, pg. 3951
TEMPUR SEALY BENELUX B.V.—See Tempur Sealy International, Inc.; *U.S. Public*, pg. 2000
TEMPUR SEALY DACH GMBH—See Tempur Sealy International, Inc.; *U.S. Public*, pg. 2000
TEMPUR SEALY JAPAN YUGEN KAISHA, LTD.—See Tempur Sealy International, Inc.; *U.S. Public*, pg. 2000
TEXAS WILSON OFFICE FURNITURE & SERVICES; *U.S. Private*, pg. 3978
THOMAS INTERIOR SYSTEMS INC.; *U.S. Private*, pg. 4156
TMK A/S—See Axcel Management A/S; *Int'l*, pg. 762
TNT PARTS INC.—See Falcon Affiliates, LLC; *U.S. Private*, pg. 1466
TOV EGGER HOLZWERKSTOFFE—See Fritz Egger GmbH & Co.; *Int'l*, pg. 2794
TRADE PRODUCTS CORP; *U.S. Private*, pg. 4202
UNISOURCE SOLUTIONS INC.; *U.S. Private*, pg. 4286
UNIVERSAL INDUSTRIES LLC; *U.S. Private*, pg. 4305
UNIVERSITY AUTO RECYCLERS, INC.—See Stellex Capital Management LP; *U.S. Private*, pg. 3800
VENTE-UNIQUE.COM SA—See Cafom SA; *Int'l*, pg. 1250
VESSCO LLC; *U.S. Private*, pg. 4371
WALKER EDISON FURNITURE COMPANY LLC—See Prospect Hill Growth Partners, L.P.; *U.S. Private*, pg. 3288
THE W.B. WOOD COMPANY; *U.S. Private*, pg. 4132
WESTERN OFFICE INTERIORS INC.; *U.S. Private*, pg. 4495
WIDMER INTERIORS INC.; *U.S. Private*, pg. 4516
WILSON GROUP LTD.; *U.S. Private*, pg. 4530
WINDSOR OFFICE PRODUCTS INC.; *U.S. Private*, pg. 4539
WITTIGS OFFICE INTERIORS LTD.; *U.S. Private*, pg. 4551
WOODARD, LLC—See Craftmade International, Inc.; *U.S. Private*, pg. 1082
WORKPLACE SOLUTIONS INC.; *U.S. Private*, pg. 4564
WORKPLACE SOLUTIONS, LLC; *U.S. Private*, pg. 4564
WORKSCAPES INC.—See Workscapes Inc.; *U.S. Private*, pg. 4564
WORKSPACE DEVELOPMENT LLC; *U.S. Private*, pg. 4564
WORKSQUARED INC.; *U.S. Private*, pg. 4564
YOUNG OFFICE SOLUTIONS LLC—See HNI Corporation; *U.S. Public*, pg. 1043

423220 — HOME FURNISHING MERCHANT WHOLESALERS

A-1 HOSPITALITY PRODUCTS INC.; *U.S. Private*, pg. 21
ABSOLUTE BATHROOMS LIMITED—See Grafton Group plc; *Int'l*, pg. 3050
ACHIM IMPORTING COMPANY INC.; *U.S. Private*, pg. 59
ACOUSTICAL SPECIALTIES & SUPPLY, INC.; *U.S. Private*, pg. 64
ADAM KAEPPEL GMBH—See Dierig Holding AG; *Int'l*, pg. 2115
ADLETA CORPORATION; *U.S. Private*, pg. 80
ADVANCED M & D SALES INC.; *U.S. Private*, pg. 90
AFG SERVICES AG—See Arbonia AG; *Int'l*, pg. 537
AFRICA SWISS TRADING (PROPRIETARY) l IMITED—See DISTRIBUTION AND WAREHOUSING NETWORK LIMITED; *Int'l*, pg. 2136
AFRICA SWISS TRADING (ZAMBIA) LIMITED—See DISTRIBUTION AND WAREHOUSING NETWORK LIMITED; *Int'l*, pg. 2136
AGA JOHN ORIENTAL RUGS; *U.S. Private*, pg. 125
AJKA CRYSTAL USA—See Fotex Holding SE; *Int'l*, pg. 2752

423220 — HOME FURNISHING MER...

AKASHA CRYSTALS, INC.; *U.S. Private,* pg. 144
ALASKA HOUSEWARES INC.; *U.S. Private,* pg. 150
ALCCO CORP.—See The Belknap White Group, LLC.; *U.S. Private,* pg. 3993
ALINEA SAS; *Int'l,* pg. 329
ALL COMMERCIAL FLOORS, INC.; *U.S. Private,* pg. 170
ALL TILE INC.; *U.S. Private,* pg. 173
ALLURE HOME CREATIONS INC.; *U.S. Private,* pg. 194
ALSUWAIKET FURNITURE & HOME FURNISHING DIVISION—See AlSuwaiket Trading & Contracting Co.; *Int'l,* pg. 383
ALUCON S.R.O.—See Freudenberg SE; *Int'l,* pg. 2782
AMERICAN FURNITURE WAREHOUSE; *U.S. Private,* pg. 235
AMERICAN METAL MOULDING CORP.; *U.S. Private,* pg. 241
AMERICAN STEEL INC.; *U.S. Private,* pg. 255
AMEUBLEMENTS TANGUAY INC.—See BMTC Group Inc.; *Int'l,* pg. 1078
AMTICO USA, LLC—See Mannington Mills, Inc.; *U.S. Private,* pg. 2565
AMWAY SOUTH AFRICA—See Alticor Inc.; *U.S. Private,* pg. 209
AMWAY TURKEY LTD.—See Alticor Inc.; *U.S. Private,* pg. 209
ANDREW LAUREN CO. INC.; *U.S. Private,* pg. 279
AQUALUX PRODUCTS HOLDINGS LTD.—See Fetim B.V.; *Int'l,* pg. 2648
AQUALUX PRODUCTS LTD.—See Fetim B.V.; *Int'l,* pg. 2648
ARCHITEC HOUSEWARES; *U.S. Private,* pg. 311
ARCTIC STRUCTURES LLC; *U.S. Private,* pg. 316
ARLUN FLOOR COVERINGS INC.; *U.S. Private,* pg. 329
ARQUATI S.P.A.; *Int'l,* pg. 578
ASAHI KASEI HOME PRODUCTS CORP.—See Asahi Kasei Corporation; *Int'l,* pg. 595
A.S. CREATION (NL) B.V.—See A.S. Creation Tapeten AG; *Int'l,* pg. 28
A.S. CREATION TEXTIL GMBH—See A.S. Creation Tapeten AG; *Int'l,* pg. 28
THE ASHTON COMPANY; *U.S. Private,* pg. 3989
ATHEZZA; *Int'l,* pg. 670
ATLANTIC PROMOTIONS INC.; *Int'l,* pg. 675
AUGUSTA POINTE, LLC—See Century Communities, Inc.; *U.S. Public,* pg. 475
AUTOMATED OUTLET, INC.; *U.S. Private,* pg. 399
AVOCA HANDWEAVERS DESIGNS LIMITED—See Aramark; *U.S. Public,* pg. 178
BALTER SALES CO. INC.; *U.S. Private,* pg. 462
BALTIC LINEN COMPANY, INC.; *U.S. Private,* pg. 462
BASTIDE DIFFUSION; *Int'l,* pg. 888
BAUM BROTHERS IMPORTS INC.; *U.S. Private,* pg. 490
BEATON BROTHERS FLOORING, INC.; *U.S. Private,* pg. 507
THE BELKNAP WHITE GROUP, LLC.; *U.S. Private,* pg. 3993
BENMARK PTE. LTD.—See FJ Benjamin Holdings Ltd.; *Int'l,* pg. 2697
BETTER BATHROOMS UK LIMITED; *Int'l,* pg. 1003
BEYOND, INC.; *U.S. Public,* pg. 327
BISHOP DISTRIBUTING CO.; *U.S. Private,* pg. 565
BLAKELY PRODUCTS COMPANY—See ShoreView Industries, LLC; *U.S. Private,* pg. 3642
BLINDS TO GO INC.; *U.S. Private,* pg. 581
BOIS ET CHIFFONS INTERNATIONAL SA; *Int'l,* pg. 1101
BOKARA RUG CO., INC.; *U.S. Private,* pg. 609
BOLL & BRANCH LLC; *U.S. Private,* pg. 610
BOSTON TRADE INTERIOR SOLUTIONS—See Blackford Capital LLC; *U.S. Private,* pg. 574
BRADSHAW INTERNATIONAL, INC.; *U.S. Private,* pg. 633
BRANDON COMPANY; *U.S. Private,* pg. 638
BREWSTER WALLPAPER CORP.; *U.S. Private,* pg. 647
B.R. FUNSTEN & CO., INC.; *U.S. Private,* pg. 421
BRIAN TRADING CO. INC.; *U.S. Private,* pg. 647
BRITTANICA HOME FASHIONS INC.; *U.S. Private,* pg. 657
BUFFALO HOTEL SUPPLY COMPANY, INC.—See Lorraine Capital LLC; *U.S. Private,* pg. 2496
BUILDERS CARPET INC.; *U.S. Private,* pg. 681
BUILDING PLASTICS, INC.; *U.S. Private,* pg. 683
BURGAD AG—See Eczacibasi Holding A.S.; *Int'l,* pg. 2301
BUTLER-JOHNSON CORPORATION; *U.S. Private,* pg. 697
CAIN & BULTMAN, INC.; *U.S. Private,* pg. 714
CAMBRIDGE SILVERSMITHS LTD., INC.—See Centre Lane Partners, LLC; *U.S. Private,* pg. 827
CARPET CUSHION CO., INC.—See Hickory Springs Manufacturing Company; *U.S. Private,* pg. 1933
CARPET CUSHIONS & SUPPLIES, INC.; *U.S. Private,* pg. 770
CARTWRIGHT DISTRIBUTING, LLC—See ShoreView Industries, LLC; *U.S. Private,* pg. 3642
CASABLANCA HOME (SHENZHEN) LIMITED—See Casablanca Group Limited; *Int'l,* pg. 1349
CCA GLOBAL PARTNERS, INC. - THE FLOOR TRADER DIVISION—See CCA Global Partners, Inc.; *U.S. Private,* pg. 799
CDI INTERNATIONAL INC.; *U.S. Private,* pg. 802
CERSANIT ROMANIA SA; *Int'l,* pg. 1423
C&F ENTERPRISES, INC.; *U.S. Private,* pg. 703

CHF INDUSTRIES, INC.; *U.S. Private,* pg. 876
CHIC REPUBLIC PUBLIC COMPANY LIMITED; *Int'l,* pg. 1476
CLARENCE HOUSE, INC.—See Fabricut Inc.; *U.S. Private,* pg. 1459
CLASSIC TILE INC.; *U.S. Private,* pg. 916
CODY DIRECT CORP.—See Hanung Toys and Textiles Limited; *Int'l,* pg. 3261
COGDALL CONSTRUCTION CO.; *U.S. Private,* pg. 961
COMPANY C, INC.; *U.S. Private,* pg. 998
CONRAD IMPORTS INC.; *U.S. Private,* pg. 1019
CON-TECH LIGHTING—See E&A Industries, Inc.; *U.S. Private,* pg. 1301
COTEMINAS ARGENTINA S.A.—See Coteminas Companhia de Tecidos Norte de Minas; *Int'l,* pg. 1817
CRONIN CO.; *U.S. Private,* pg. 1103
CUSTOM DRAPERY COMPANY INC.; *U.S. Private,* pg. 1128
CUSTOM MIRRORED WALLS; *U.S. Private,* pg. 1129
CUSTOM WHOLESALE FLOORS INC.; *U.S. Private,* pg. 1130
CUTCO INTERNATIONAL INC.—See CUTCO Corporation; *U.S. Private,* pg. 1131
DALE TIFFANY INC; *U.S. Private,* pg. 1149
DALYN CORPORATION; *U.S. Private,* pg. 1150
DANESCO INC.; *Int'l,* pg. 1959
DEALERS SUPPLY COMPANY; *U.S. Private,* pg. 1182
DECOLIGHT TRADING CO. LLC—See Depa PLC; *Int'l,* pg. 2040
DEGOL BROTHERS CARPET—See The DeGol Organization; *U.S. Private,* pg. 4019
DELCO INTERNATIONAL, LTD.—See EveryWare Global, Inc.; *U.S. Private,* pg. 1441
DELTA FAUCET COMPANY MEXICO, S. DE R.L. DE C.V.—See Masco Corporation; *U.S. Public,* pg. 1390
DERR FLOORING CO. INC.; *U.S. Private,* pg. 1210
DESIGN DISTRIBUTING INC.—See William M. Bird & Company, Inc.; *U.S. Private,* pg. 4523
DHI ACQUISITION INC.; *U.S. Private,* pg. 1221
DIERIG AG—See Dierig Holding AG; *Int'l,* pg. 2115
DOMBRACHT AUSTRIA GMBH—See Aloys F. Dornbracht GmbH & Co. KG; *Int'l,* pg. 365
DON-MAR CREATIONS INC.; *U.S. Private,* pg. 1259
DORNBRACHT AMERICAS INC.—See Aloys F. Dornbracht GmbH & Co. KG; *Int'l,* pg. 365
DORNBRACHT ASIA PACIFIC LTD.—See Aloys F. Dornbracht GmbH & Co. KG; *Int'l,* pg. 365
DORNBRACHT ESPANA S.L.—See Aloys F. Dornbracht GmbH & Co. KG; *Int'l,* pg. 365
DORNBRACHT FRANCE SARL—See Aloys F. Dornbracht GmbH & Co. KG; *Int'l,* pg. 365
DORNBRACHT INDIA PRIVATE LIMITED—See Aloys F. Dornbracht GmbH & Co. KG; *Int'l,* pg. 365
DORNBRACHT INTERNATIONAL HOLDING GMBH—See Aloys F. Dornbracht GmbH & Co. KG; *Int'l,* pg. 365
DORNBRACHT ITALIA S.R.L.—See Aloys F. Dornbracht GmbH & Co. KG; *Int'l,* pg. 365
DORNBRACHT NEDERLAND BV—See Aloys F. Dornbracht GmbH & Co. KG; *Int'l,* pg. 365
DORNBRACHT NORDIC A/S—See Aloys F. Dornbracht GmbH & Co. KG; *Int'l,* pg. 365
DORNBRACHT SCHWEIZ AG—See Aloys F. Dornbracht GmbH & Co. KG; *Int'l,* pg. 365
DORNBRACHT (SHANGHAI) COMMERCIAL LTD.—See Aloys F. Dornbracht GmbH & Co. KG; *Int'l,* pg. 365
DORNBRACHT SOUTH EAST ASIA PTE LTD.—See Aloys F. Dornbracht GmbH & Co. KG; *Int'l,* pg. 365
DORNBRACHT TURKEY—See Aloys F. Dornbracht GmbH & Co. KG; *Int'l,* pg. 365
DORNBRACHT UK LTD.—See Aloys F. Dornbracht GmbH & Co. KG; *Int'l,* pg. 365
DOUGHERTY GLASS COMPANY—See Dothan Glass Co. Inc.; *U.S. Private,* pg. 1265
DUNI BETEILIGUNGSGESELLSCHAFT MBH—See Duni AB; *Int'l,* pg. 2226
DUNI EFF SP. Z O.O.—See Duni AB; *Int'l,* pg. 2226
DUSK GROUP LIMITED; *Int'l,* pg. 2234
DUST-TEX HONOLULU, INC.—See Hakuyosha Company Ltd.; *Int'l,* pg. 3222
D & W PAPER TUBE, INC.—See Sonoco Products Company; *U.S. Public,* pg. 1904
EASTSIDE FLOOR SUPPLIES, LTD.—See Eastside Floor Services Ltd.; *U.S. Private,* pg. 1322
E.J. WELCH COMPANY INC.; *U.S. Private,* pg. 1306
ELEMUS LLC—See Danto Holdings Corporation; *Int'l,* pg. 1969
ELIAS WILF CORPORATION; *U.S. Private,* pg. 1360
ELIKO EX-IMPORT INC.; *U.S. Private,* pg. 1360
ELITE COLLECTIONS, INC.; *U.S. Private,* pg. 1360
ELITE FLOORING & DESIGN INC.; *U.S. Private,* pg. 1361
ELLERY HOMESTYLES—See Trivest Partners, LP; *U.S. Private,* pg. 4240
ELTE; *Int'l,* pg. 2370
EMHART GLASS VISION GMBH—See Bucher Industries AG; *Int'l,* pg. 1209
EMSER TILE LLC; *U.S. Private,* pg. 1388
ENCOMPASS TEXTILES & INTERIORS—See Encompass Group LLC; *U.S. Private,* pg. 1390

ENERGEN OF VIRGINIA INC.; *U.S. Private,* pg. 1393
ERICKSONS FLOORING & SUPPLY CO.; *U.S. Private,* pg. 1420
EUGENE ALLARD CUISINE ET TENDANCES; *Int'l,* pg. 2526
EVEREL—See Mohawk Industries, Inc.; *U.S. Public,* pg. 1457
EVERGREEN ENTERPRISES, INC.; *U.S. Private,* pg. 1439
EVERTRADE (PTY) LTD.; *Int'l,* pg. 2569
FAGERHULT AS—See Fagerhult Group AB; *Int'l,* pg. 2602
FAGERHULT BELYSNING AS—See Fagerhult Group AB; *Int'l,* pg. 2602
FAGERHULT BV—See Fagerhult Group AB; *Int'l,* pg. 2602
FAGERHULT FRANCE—See Fagerhult Group AB; *Int'l,* pg. 2602
FAGERHULT OU—See Fagerhult Group AB; *Int'l,* pg. 2602
FAGERHULT OY—See Fagerhult Group AB; *Int'l,* pg. 2602
FAGERHULT S.L.—See Fagerhult Group AB; *Int'l,* pg. 2602
FAGERHULT SPB—See Fagerhult Group AB; *Int'l,* pg. 2602
FAGERHULT SP.Z.O.O—See Fagerhult Group AB; *Int'l,* pg. 2602
FASHIONTECH INC.; *U.S. Private,* pg. 1481
FAZE THREE LIMITED; *Int'l,* pg. 2627
FEIZY IMPORT & EXPORT COMPANY INC.; *U.S. Private,* pg. 1493
FETCO HOME DECOR INC.; *U.S. Private,* pg. 1500
THE FINIAL COMPANY—See Rowley Company, LLC; *U.S. Private,* pg. 3490
FISHER & PAYKEL APPLIANCES CANADA, INC.—See Haier Smart Home Co., Ltd.; *Int'l,* pg. 3210
FISKARS ESTONIA AS—See Fiskars Oyj Abp; *Int'l,* pg. 2694
FLEURESSE GMBH—See Dierig Holding AG; *Int'l,* pg. 2115
FLOOR KING INC.; *U.S. Private,* pg. 1546
FLOORS INC.—See The Sterling Group, L.P.; *U.S. Private,* pg. 4122
FLOORWORX AFRICA (PTY) LIMITED—See Accentuate Limited; *Int'l,* pg. 82
FLORSTAR SALES, INC.; *U.S. Private,* pg. 1551
FORESTON TRENDS, INC.; *U.S. Private,* pg. 1567
FOX RUN CRAFTSMEN; *U.S. Private,* pg. 1584
FRANZ REINKEMEIER GMBH; *Int'l,* pg. 2763
FREUDENBERG HOUSEHOLD PRODUCTS EVICI KULLANIM ARACLARI SANAYI VE TICARET A.S.—See Freudenberg SE; *Int'l,* pg. 2786
FREUDENBERG HOUSEHOLD PRODUCTS (SUZHOU) CO., LTD.—See Freudenberg SE; *Int'l,* pg. 2786
FREUDENBERG HOUSEHOLD PRODUCTS (TAIWAN) CO., LTD.—See Freudenberg SE; *Int'l,* pg. 2786
GARLAND SALES INC.; *U.S. Private,* pg. 1644
GEC SMART FURNITURE LTD.—See Global Education Communities Corp; *Int'l,* pg. 2995
GEDY IBERICA, S.A.—See Gedy S.p.A.; *Int'l,* pg. 2910
GENERAL DISTRIBUTORS INC.; *U.S. Private,* pg. 1664
G.E.T. ENTERPRISES, LLC—See Olympus Partners; *U.S. Private,* pg. 3013
GOLDENMARC (PTY) LTD.—See Bounty Brands Pty Ltd.; *Int'l,* pg. 1119
GOLDEN TADCO INTERNATIONAL CORPORATION; *U.S. Private,* pg. 1733
GOYO INTEX CO., LTD.; *Int'l,* pg. 3045
GPMI COMPANY—See Kelso & Company, L.P.; *U.S. Private,* pg. 2279
GPMI COMPANY—See Warburg Pincus LLC; *U.S. Private,* pg. 4436
GRANDMATE INDUSTRIAL COMPANY LIMITED—See China Automobile New Retail (Holdings) Limited; *Int'l,* pg. 1484
H2O (PRO) LIMITED—See E. Bon Holdings Ltd; *Int'l,* pg. 2250
HABITAT UK LTD.—See Hilco Trading, LLC; *U.S. Private,* pg. 1944
HACKNEY HOME FURNISHINGS—See The H.T. Hackney Company; *U.S. Private,* pg. 4041
HADRIAN SOLUTIONS ULC—See Zurn Elkay Water Solutions Corporation; *U.S. Public,* pg. 2413
HAMPTON FORGE, LTD.—See Centre Lane Partners, LLC; *U.S. Private,* pg. 827
HANKYU HOME STYLING CO, LTD.—See H2O Retailing Corp.; *Int'l,* pg. 3200
HANSGROHE ARMATUR SANAYI VE TICARET LIMITED SIRKETI—See Masco Corporation; *U.S. Public,* pg. 1390
HANSGROHE BRASIL METALS SANTITARIOS LTDA.—See Masco Corporation; *U.S. Public,* pg. 1390
HANSGROHE PTY LTD—See Masco Corporation; *U.S. Public,* pg. 1390
HANSGROHE SA (PTY) LTD.—See Masco Corporation; *U.S. Public,* pg. 1390
HANSGROHE S.A.U.—See Masco Corporation; *U.S. Public,* pg. 1390
HANSGROHE SE—See Masco Corporation; *U.S. Public,* pg. 1390
HEALTHBANK HOLDINGS LIMITED; *Int'l,* pg. 3303
HEMTEX AB—See ICA Gruppen AB; *Int'l,* pg. 3577
HERALD HOUSEWARE LIMITED—See Herald Holdings Limited; *Int'l,* pg. 3358
HERITAGE LACE INC.; *U.S. Private,* pg. 1924
HERREGAN DISTRIBUTORS, INC.; *U.S. Private,* pg. 1926
HFD LTD—See Headlam Group plc; *Int'l,* pg. 3301

N.A.I.C.S. INDEX

423220 — HOME FURNISHING MER...

HIGH COUNTRY LINENS INC.; *U.S. Private*, pg. 1935
HIGUERA HARDWOODS LLC; *U.S. Private*, pg. 1943
H&M HENNES & MAURITZ LP—See H&M Hennes & Mauritz AB; *Int'l*, pg. 3192
HOLIDAY CARPET & FLOOR COVERINGS; *U.S. Private*, pg. 1962
HOME DECOR HOLDING COMPANY—See Kohlberg & Company, LLC; *U.S. Private*, pg. 2338
HOME ESSENTIALS & BEYOND INC.; *U.S. Private*, pg. 1970
HOME ETC; *U.S. Private*, pg. 1970
HOME & GARDEN PARTY, LTD.; *U.S. Private*, pg. 1970
HOME PRODUCTS INTERNATIONAL, INC.—See Quaestus Holdings, LLC; *U.S. Private*, pg. 3316
HOME SHOPPING EUROPE GMBH—See Providence Equity Partners L.L.C.; *U.S. Private*, pg. 3292
HOME SOURCE INTERNATIONAL, INC.; *U.S. Private*, pg. 1972
HOSHIZAKI KITAKANTO CO LTD.—See Hoshizaki Corporation; *Int'l*, pg. 3483
HOSLEY INTERNATIONAL TRADING CORPORATION; *U.S. Private*, pg. 1985
HOT SPRING SPA AUSTRALASIA PTY LTD—See Masco Corporation; *U.S. Public*, pg. 1392
HUNTER DOUGLAS COMPONENTS—See 3G Capital Partners L.P.; *U.S. Private*, pg. 12
HUNTER DOUGLAS EUROPE B.V.—See 3G Capital Partners L.P.; *U.S. Private*, pg. 12
HUNTER DOUGLAS KOREA LIMITED—See 3G Capital Partners L.P.; *U.S. Private*, pg. 12
HUNTER DOUGLAS N.V.—See 3G Capital Partners L.P.; *U.S. Private*, pg. 11
HUNTER DOUGLAS PHILIPPINES INC—See 3G Capital Partners L.P.; *U.S. Private*, pg. 12
HUNTER DOUGLAS TAIWAN LTD.—See 3G Capital Partners L.P.; *U.S. Private*, pg. 12
HUNTER DOUGLAS VIETNAM LTD—See 3G Capital Partners L.P.; *U.S. Private*, pg. 12
HUNTER DOUGLAS WINDOW COVERING PRODUCTS (BEIJING) CO., LTD.—See 3G Capital Partners L.P.; *U.S. Private*, pg. 13
HUNTER DOUGLAS WINDOW COVERING PRODUCTS (CHINA) CO., LTD.—See 3G Capital Partners L.P.; *U.S. Private*, pg. 13
HUNTER DOUGLAS WINDOW COVERING PRODUCTS (SHANGHAI) CO., LTD.—See 3G Capital Partners L.P.; *U.S. Private*, pg. 13
HUNTER DOUGLAS WINDOW COVERING PRODUCTS (SHENZHEN) CO., LTD.—See 3G Capital Partners L.P.; *U.S. Private*, pg. 13
HUPPE INSAAT SANAYI VE TICARET A.S.—See Masco Corporation; *U.S. Public*, pg. 1391
HUPPE (SHANGHAI) CO., LTD.—See Masco Corporation; *U.S. Public*, pg. 1391
HUPPE S.L.—See Masco Corporation; *U.S. Public*, pg. 1390
HY CITE CORPORATION; *U.S. Private*, pg. 2015
IITTALA BV—See Fiskars Oyj Abp; *Int'l*, pg. 2695
IMEX GROUP CO. LTD.—See Gree Electric Appliances, Inc. of Zhuhai; *Int'l*, pg. 3069
INDES WONTEXTIL GMBH—See A.S. Creation Tapeten AG; *Int'l*, pg. 28
INTERNATIONAL DESIGN GUILD—See CCA Global Partners, Inc.; *U.S. Private*, pg. 799
INTERNATIONAL WINE ACCESSORIES, INC.—See Vintage Wine Estates, Inc.; *U.S. Public*, pg. 2298
INVENTORY LIQUIDATORS CORP.; *U.S. Private*, pg. 2131
IRON TRADE IMPORTS, INC.; *U.S. Private*, pg. 2140
JAECKLE WHOLESALE INC.; *U.S. Private*, pg. 2181
JEK CARPET INC.; *U.S. Private*, pg. 2198
JIANGSU ROYAL HOME USA, INC.; *U.S. Private*, pg. 2208
JJJ FLOOR COVERING INC.; *U.S. Private*, pg. 2211
JULISKA; *U.S. Private*, pg. 2243
KALALOU INC.; *U.S. Private*, pg. 2256
KAMIC LIGHT & SAFETY AB—See Amplex AB; *Int'l*, pg. 434
KAY BVBA—See Ecolab Inc.; *U.S. Public*, pg. 714
KEECO, LLC; *U.S. Private*, pg. 2271
KENDALL MOULDING & FRAMES, INC.; *U.S. Private*, pg. 2283
KENNY & COMPANY—See Kenny Pipe & Supply, Inc.; *U.S. Private*, pg. 2286
KIEFER SPECIALTY FLOORING, INC.; *U.S. Private*, pg. 2303
KITTRICH CORPORATION; *U.S. Private*, pg. 2316
KNIGHTSBRIDGE CARPETS LIMITED—See Bremworth Limited; *Int'l*, pg. 1145
KOECKRITZ RUGS, INC.; *U.S. Private*, pg. 2336
K PAR K—See Compagnie de Saint-Gobain SA; *Int'l*, pg. 1723
KRAVET MEXICO—See Kravet Fabrics Inc.; *U.S. Private*, pg. 2350
LANDS' END EUROPE LIMITED—See Lands' End, Inc.; *U.S. Public*, pg. 1292
LANDS' END GMBH—See Lands' End, Inc.; *U.S. Public*, pg. 1292
LETHEM-VERGEER B.V.—See Headlam Group plc; *Int'l*, pg. 3301
LEWIS HYMAN INC.; *U.S. Private*, pg. 2439

LINON HOME DECOR PRODUCTS INC.; *U.S. Private*, pg. 2462
LIPPER INTERNATIONAL INC.; *U.S. Private*, pg. 2465
LIVING ARATA CO., LTD.—See Arata Corporation; *Int'l*, pg. 536
LMS SA—See Headlam Group plc; *Int'l*, pg. 3301
LONGUST DISTRIBUTING INC.; *U.S. Private*, pg. 2493
LORRAINE HOME FASHIONS; *U.S. Private*, pg. 2496
LUNA CARPET & BLINDS CO., INC.; *U.S. Private*, pg. 2515
MAGICIAN LIFESTYLE LIMITED—See China Automobile New Retail (Holdings) Limited; *Int'l*, pg. 1484
MAITLAND-SMITH FURNITURE INDUSTRIES, INC.—See Heritage Home Group, LLC; *U.S. Private*, pg. 1924
MARIETTA DRAPERY & WINDOW COVERINGS CO., INC.; *U.S. Private*, pg. 2574
MASCO BETEILIGUNGSGESELLSCHAFT MBH—See Masco Corporation; *U.S. Public*, pg. 1390
MASDA CORPORATION; *U.S. Private*, pg. 2601
MASTERCRAFT FLOORING DISTRIBUTORS, INC.—See Gilford-Johnson Flooring LLC; *U.S. Private*, pg. 1700
MASTERS CRAFT CORPORATION; *U.S. Private*, pg. 2608
MIDWEST DESIGNER SUPPLY, INC.; *U.S. Private*, pg. 2720
MIDWEST FLOOR COVERINGS; *U.S. Private*, pg. 2721
MIDWEST HOME DISTRIBUTORS, INC.—See Skogman Construction Company of Iowa Inc.; *U.S. Private*, pg. 3683
MOMENI INC.; *U.S. Private*, pg. 2768
MR. CHRISTMAS LIMITED—See Mr. Christmas Inc.; *U.S. Private*, pg. 2805
MS DISTRIBUTORS OF TOLEDO; *U.S. Private*, pg. 2806
NEW BUFFALO CORPORATION; *U.S. Private*, pg. 2892
NEWELL PUERTO RICO, LTD.—See 3G Capital Partners L.P.; *U.S. Private*, pg. 13
NOLAND SALES CORP.; *U.S. Private*, pg. 2934
NORCON INDUSTRIES INC.; *U.S. Private*, pg. 2936
NORDIC NEST AB—See BHG Group AB; *Int'l*, pg. 1015
NOURISON RUG CORP.; *U.S. Private*, pg. 2965
NOVATECH GROUP, INC—See Garaga Inc.; *Int'l*, pg. 2883
OFFICE INTERIORS OF VIRGINIA, INC.—See Workplace Install Network, Inc.; *U.S. Private*, pg. 4564
OHIO VALLEY FLOORING—See Pabco Fluid Power Company; *U.S. Private*, pg. 3063
OI GLASSPACK GMBH & CO. KG—See O-I Glass, Inc.; *U.S. Public*, pg. 1559
OMAHA HARDWOOD LUMBER CO.; *U.S. Private*, pg. 3014
ONECOAST NETWORK CORPORATION; *U.S. Private*, pg. 3024
ONEIDA CONSUMER PRODUCTS DIVISION—See EveryWare Global, Inc.; *U.S. Private*, pg. 1441
ONEIDA FOOD SERVICE, INC.—See EveryWare Global, Inc.; *U.S. Private*, pg. 1441
ONEIDA (GUANGZHOU) FOODSERVICE CO. LTD.—See EveryWare Global, Inc.; *U.S. Private*, pg. 1441
ORREFORS KOSTA BODA, INC.—See Axcel Management A/S; *Int'l*, pg. 762
PALECEK IMPORTS INC.; *U.S. Private*, pg. 3076
PALO DURO HARDWOODS INC.; *U.S. Private*, pg. 3082
PARK B SMITH, LTD.; *U.S. Private*, pg. 3095
PEACOCK ALLEY INC.; *U.S. Private*, pg. 3123
PEKING HANDICRAFT INC.; *U.S. Private*, pg. 3130
PENTWATER CABINETRY, INC.; *U.S. Private*, pg. 3140
THE PHOENIX GRILL COMPANY—See American Performance Industries; *U.S. Private*, pg. 243
PHOENIX TEXTILE CORPORATION; *U.S. Private*, pg. 3174
PILOT HOUSEWARES (U.K.) LIMITED—See Herald Holdings Limited; *Int'l*, pg. 3358
PLOW & HEARTH, LLC—See Evergreen Enterprises, Inc.; *U.S. Private*, pg. 1439
PLY GEM PACIFIC WINDOWS CORPORATION—See Clayton, Dubilier & Rice, LLC; *U.S. Private*, pg. 921
PNS STORES, INC.—See Big Lots, Inc.; *U.S. Public*, pg. 330
THE POMEROY COLLECTION LTD.—See ELK Group International, Inc.; *U.S. Private*, pg. 1362
PRIMAT RD D.O.O.—See Honkarakenne Oyj; *Int'l*, pg. 3471
PRODUCT CONCEPTS RESIDENTIAL LLC—See Milliken & Company; *U.S. Private*, pg. 2737
PROGRESSIVE INTERNATIONAL CORP.—See Kainos Capital, LLC; *U.S. Private*, pg. 2255
PT HUNTER DOUGLAS INDONESIA—See 3G Capital Partners L.P.; *U.S. Private*, pg. 13
PT TUPPERWARE INDONESIA SERVICES—See Tupperware Brands Corporation; *U.S. Public*, pg. 2204
PUGET TECHNOLOGIES, INC.; *U.S. Public*, pg. 1736
RALPH'S MIRROR AND GLASS (PTY) LIMITED—See AG Industries Limited; *Int'l*, pg. 198
THE R.A. SIEGEL COMPANY; *U.S. Private*, pg. 4101
READER'S WHOLESALE DISTRIBUTORS INC.; *U.S. Private*, pg. 3366
REDI-CARPET, INC.—See The Home Depot, Inc.; *U.S. Public*, pg. 2089
REDI-CARPET SALES OF DALLAS; *U.S. Private*, pg. 3378
RENA WARE DE COSTA RICA, S.A.—See Rena-Ware Distributors Inc.; *U.S. Private*, pg. 3397
RENA WARE DISTRIBUTORS, C.A.—See Rena-Ware Distributors Inc.; *U.S. Private*, pg. 3397

R E W ENTERPRISES, INC.; *U.S. Private*, pg. 3331
RIEDEL CRYSTAL; *U.S. Private*, pg. 3434
RIGHT CENTURY LIMITED—See E. Bon Holdings Ltd; *Int'l*, pg. 2250
RIOBEL INC.—See Fortune Brands Innovations, Inc.; *U.S. Public*, pg. 873
THE ROBERT ALLEN GROUP, INC.—See Decor Holdings, Inc.; *U.S. Private*, pg. 1187
ROBINSON HOME PRODUCTS INC.; *U.S. Private*, pg. 3462
ROD WORKS INC.; *U.S. Private*, pg. 3469
RONCO INVENTIONS LLC; *U.S. Private*, pg. 3478
ROTH DISTRIBUTING COMPANY; *U.S. Private*, pg. 3487
SAFAVIEH CARPETS OF ISFAHAN; *U.S. Private*, pg. 3523
SALESMASTER ASSOCIATES, INC.—See Floor & Decor Holdings, Inc.; *U.S. Public*, pg. 853
SEA-PAC SALES COMPANY; *U.S. Private*, pg. 3583
SERGENIANS FLOOR COVERINGS; *U.S. Private*, pg. 3613
SHEETS & CO.; *U.S. Private*, pg. 3630
SHERLE WAGNER INTERNATIONAL; *U.S. Private*, pg. 3633
SHULER DISTRIBUTING COMPANY; *U.S. Private*, pg. 3644
SID'S CARPET BARN INC.; *U.S. Private*, pg. 3645
SITCO IMPORTING CO.; *U.S. Private*, pg. 3676
SLOAN DE MEXICO. S. DE R.L. DE C.V.—See Sloan Valve Company; *U.S. Private*, pg. 3689
SLOAN MIYASATO INC.; *U.S. Private*, pg. 3689
SLOAN VALVE COMPANY - ARICHELL TECHNOLOGIES DIVISION—See Sloan Valve Company; *U.S. Private*, pg. 3689
SOBEL WESTEX; *U.S. Private*, pg. 3702
SOUTHERN TILE DISTRIBUTORS, INC.; *U.S. Private*, pg. 3735
SOUTHERN WHOLESALE FLOORING CO.; *U.S. Private*, pg. 3735
SPRINGS BRANDS, LLC—See Coteminas Companhia de Tecidos Norte de Minas; *Int'l*, pg. 1817
S.S. DWECK & SONS INC.; *U.S. Private*, pg. 3518
STANLEY STEPHENS CO. INC.; *U.S. Private*, pg. 3783
STARK CARPET CORPORATION; *U.S. Private*, pg. 3786
STAY-LITE LIGHTING, INC.—See Orion Energy Systems, Inc.; *U.S. Public*, pg. 1618
STEPHANIE ODEGARD COLLECTION; *U.S. Private*, pg. 3802
STERLING CUT GLASS COMPANY, INC.; *U.S. Private*, pg. 3805
STORE DESIGN SERVICES—See United Natural Foods, Inc.; *U.S. Public*, pg. 2232
SUPERIOR FURNITURE SOLUTIONS, INC.—See One80 Intermediaries LLC; *U.S. Private*, pg. 3024
SURE FIT INC.—See Centre Lane Partners, LLC; *U.S. Private*, pg. 827
SURYA INC.; *U.S. Private*, pg. 3885
SWIFF-TRAIN COMPANY INC.—See The Belknap White Group, LLC; *U.S. Private*, pg. 3993
TARA PICTURE FRAMES—See Tara Materials Inc.; *U.S. Private*, pg. 3933
T&A SUPPLY CO. INC.; *U.S. Private*, pg. 3909
TAYSE INTERNATIONAL TRADING, INC.; *U.S. Private*, pg. 3941
T DISTRIBUTION; *U.S. Private*, pg. 3908
TERAGREN; *U.S. Private*, pg. 3969
THRO, LTD.—See Kohlberg & Company, LLC; *U.S. Private*, pg. 2338
T&L DISTRIBUTING COMPANY INC.; *U.S. Private*, pg. 3909
TOSHINSHOKAI CO., LTD.—See Cominix Co., Ltd.; *Int'l*, pg. 1714
TOWNECRAFT, INC.; *U.S. Private*, pg. 4198
TRADE AM INTERNATIONAL INC.; *U.S. Private*, pg. 4201
TRENDMALL GALLERY LIMITED—See e Lighting Group Holdings Limited; *Int'l*, pg. 2246
TRINITY CARPET INC.—See Trinity Carpet Brokers Inc.; *U.S. Private*, pg. 4233
TRINITY HARDWOOD DISTRIBUTORS, INC.—See Transom Capital Group, LLC; *U.S. Private*, pg. 4209
TRI-STATE WHOLESALE FLOORING, INC.—See ShoreView Industries, LLC; *U.S. Private*, pg. 3642
TRI-WEST LTD.; *U.S. Private*, pg. 4224
TRI-WEST OF HAWAII INC.—See Tri-West Ltd.; *U.S. Private*, pg. 4225
TUFENKIAN IMPORT/EXPORT VENTURES, INC.; *U.S. Private*, pg. 4257
TUPPERWARE BRANDS FOUNDATION—See Tupperware Brands Corporation; *U.S. Public*, pg. 2204
TUPPERWARE BRANDS KOREA LTD.—See Tupperware Brands Corporation; *U.S. Public*, pg. 2204
TUPPERWARE VIETNAM LLC—See Tupperware Brands Corporation; *U.S. Public*, pg. 2205
TWIN-STAR INTERNATIONAL, INC.—See Z Capital Group, LLC; *U.S. Private*, pg. 4595
UMBRA INC.; *U.S. Private*, pg. 4278
UNIQUE WHOLESALE DISTRIBUTORS, INC.; *U.S. Private*, pg. 4286
VARNELL-STRUCK & ASSOCIATES INC.; *U.S. Private*, pg. 4347

423220 — HOME FURNISHING MER...

VECTOR MARKETING CORPORATION—See CUTCO Corporation; *U.S. Private*, pg. 1131
VERTILUX LTD.; *U.S. Private*, pg. 4370
VICTORIA & ALBERT BATH, LLC—See Fortune Brands Innovations, Inc.; *U.S. Public*, pg. 873
VICTORIA & ALBERT BATHS LIMITED—See Fortune Brands Innovations, Inc.; *U.S. Public*, pg. 873
VILLAGE HEARTH & HOME DISTRIBUTION, LLC; *U.S. Private*, pg. 4383
VIRGINIA TILE COMPANY; *U.S. Private*, pg. 4388
VORTEX ENTERPRISES INCORPORATED; *U.S. Private*, pg. 4413
WANKE CASCADE DISTRIBUTION LTD.—See Buckwold Western Ltd.; *Int'l*, pg. 1210
WAUSAU TILE, INC.; *U.S. Private*, pg. 4457
WAYFAIR LLC—See Wayfair Inc.; *U.S. Public*, pg. 2338
WC DESIGNS; *U.S. Private*, pg. 4461
WC TINGLE COMPANY; *U.S. Private*, pg. 4461
W.D. MATHEWS INC.; *U.S. Private*, pg. 4419
WEBER CARPET INC.; *U.S. Private*, pg. 4465
WELL HARBOUR DEVELOPMENT LIMITED—See China Automobile New Retail (Holdings) Limited; *Int'l*, pg. 1484
WESTERN CARPET & LINOLEUM CO.; *U.S. Private*, pg. 4491
WHOLE BRIGHT INDUSTRIES (HK) LIMITED—See Dejin Resources Group Company Limited; *Int'l*, pg. 2005
WHOLESALE FLOORS, INC.—See ACON Investments, LLC; *U.S. Private*, pg. 62
WILLIAM M. BIRD & COMPANY, INC.; *U.S. Private*, pg. 4523
WILSONART ASIA LIMITED—See AICA Kogyo Company, Limited; *Int'l*, pg. 229
WILTON INDUSTRIES, INC.—See GTCR LLC; *U.S. Private*, pg. 1806
WINDOW WORLD INC.; *U.S. Private*, pg. 4538
WINSOME TRADING INC.; *U.S. Private*, pg. 4543
WISENBAKER BUILDER SERVICES LTD.; *U.S. Private*, pg. 4550
WOOD CULTURE PTE. LTD.—See Hap Seng Consolidated Berhad; *Int'l*, pg. 3268
WOOD PRO INC.; *U.S. Private*, pg. 4557
WOVEN LEGENDS INC.; *U.S. Private*, pg. 4571
WWRD AUSTRALIA PTY LIMITED—See Fiskars Oyj Abp; *Int'l*, pg. 2694
ZAK DESIGNS INC.; *U.S. Private*, pg. 4597
ZARIN FABRICS; *U.S. Private*, pg. 4598
ZIMDAR ENTERPRISES; *U.S. Private*, pg. 4605
THE ZRIKE COMPANY INC.; *U.S. Private*, pg. 4140

423310 — LUMBER, PLYWOOD, MILLWORK, AND WOOD PANEL MERCHANT WHOLESALERS

1249270 ONTARIO INC; *Int'l*, pg. 2
ABLE ROLLING STEEL DOOR, INC.—See On-Point Group, LLC; *U.S. Private*, pg. 3018
ACCESS OVERHEAD DOOR, INC.; *U.S. Private*, pg. 52
A.C. HOUSTON LUMBER COMPANY; *U.S. Private*, pg. 24
A & D SUPPLY OF OKC, INC.—See American Securities LLC; *U.S. Private*, pg. 248
AETNA PLYWOOD, INC.; *U.S. Private*, pg. 120
AGI ALUMINIUM (PTY) LIMITED—See AG Industries Limited; *Int'l*, pg. 198
AJ FOREST PRODUCTS LTD.—See E.R. Probyn Ltd.; *Int'l*, pg. 2260
AKATI IMPEX PTE. LTD.—See Dominant Enterprise Berhad; *Int'l*, pg. 2161
ALAMO FOREST PRODUCTS, INC.—See Vaughan & Sons, Inc.; *U.S. Private*, pg. 4348
ALAMO FOREST PRODUCTS; *U.S. Private*, pg. 149
ALBUQUERQUE HARDWOOD LUMBER COMPANY—See Hardwoods Distribution Inc.; *Int'l*, pg. 3273
ALEXANDER LUMBER CO., INC.; *U.S. Private*, pg. 163
ALFRED SCHELLENBERG GMBH; *Int'l*, pg. 317
ALJOMA LUMBER, INC.—See UFP Industries, Inc.; *U.S. Public*, pg. 2218
ALLEN & ALLEN COMPANY; *U.S. Private*, pg. 178
ALLEN LUMBER COMPANY INC.; *U.S. Private*, pg. 179
ALLEY-CASSETTY BRICK COLUMBIA DIV.—See Alley-Cassetty Companies; *U.S. Private*, pg. 180
ALLIANCE WHOLESALE SUPPLY, INC.—See Hendricks Holding Company, Inc.; *U.S. Private*, pg. 1914
ALLIED BUILDING PRODUCTS CORP. - FERNDALE—See Beacon Roofing Supply, Inc.; *U.S. Public*, pg. 285
ALLIED BUILDING PRODUCTS CORPORATION—See Beacon Roofing Supply, Inc.; *U.S. Public*, pg. 285
ALLSTAR BUILDING MATERIALS LTD.; *U.S. Private*, pg. 193
ALPA LUMBER INC; *Int'l*, pg. 365
ALPHA BUILDING CENTER INC.; *U.S. Private*, pg. 196
ALPINE LUMBER COMPANY INC.; *U.S. Private*, pg. 201
ALUMINIUM GLASS INDUSTRIES (MAURITIUS) LIMITED—See AG Industries Limited; *Int'l*, pg. 198
AMANDUS D. MOYER LUMBER INCORPORATED; *U.S. Private*, pg. 216
AMERHART LIMITED; *U.S. Private*, pg. 219
AMERICAN BUILDERS SUPPLY, INC. - CLERMONT—See Kodiak Building Partners LLC; *U.S. Private*, pg. 2336
AMERICAN BUILDERS SUPPLY, INC.—See Kodiak Building Partners LLC; *U.S. Private*, pg. 2336
AMERICAN FOREST PRODUCTS LLC; *U.S. Private*, pg. 234
AMERICAN LUMBER COMPANY INCORPORATED; *U.S. Private*, pg. 240
AMERICAN LUMBER COMPANY LP; *U.S. Private*, pg. 240
AMERICAN WAL-BOARD LLC—See American Securities LLC; *U.S. Private*, pg. 248
AMERICAN WOODMARK CORPORATION; *U.S. Public*, pg. 112
AMERICAN WOOD MOULDING, LLC; *U.S. Private*, pg. 258
AMERSOL, INC.—See Solar Art Window Film, Inc.; *U.S. Private*, pg. 3707
A&M SUPPLY CORP.; *U.S. Private*, pg. 20
ANCHORSTONE HOLDINGS LTD.; *Int'l*, pg. 448
ANKMAR, LLC—See E.E. Newcomer Enterprises Inc.; *U.S. Private*, pg. 1305
A.P. HUBBARD WHOLESALE LUMBER; *U.S. Private*, pg. 27
APOLLO FOREST PRODUCTS LTD; *Int'l*, pg. 517
ARCHITECTURAL DOORS INC.; *U.S. Private*, pg. 311
ARCHITECTURAL SYSTEMS INC.; *U.S. Private*, pg. 311
ARCHITECTURAL WOODS INC.; *U.S. Private*, pg. 311
ARKANSAS WHOLESALE LUMBER, LLC—See Bain Capital, LP; *U.S. Private*, pg. 451
ARLINGTON COAL & LUMBER CO. INC.; *U.S. Private*, pg. 328
ARMSTRONG FLOORING HONG KONG LIMITED—See Armstrong Flooring, Inc.; *U.S. Public*, pg. 193
ARMSTRONG FLOORING PTY. LTD.—See Armstrong Flooring, Inc.; *U.S. Public*, pg. 193
ARNOLD LUMBER COMPANY; *U.S. Private*, pg. 333
ARROW BUILDING CENTERS—See Consolidated Lumber Co.; *U.S. Private*, pg. 1021
ARROW LUMBER & HARDWARE LLC; *U.S. Private*, pg. 335
ASIA TIMBER PRODUCTS GROUP—See CVC Capital Partners SICAV-FIS S.A.; *Int'l*, pg. 1885
ASTRO BUILDINGS INC.—See Roberts Trading Corporation; *U.S. Private*, pg. 3460
A-TECH; *U.S. Private*, pg. 22
ATLANTA HARDWOOD CORPORATION; *U.S. Private*, pg. 370
AUBURN CORPORATION; *U.S. Private*, pg. 385
AURA HARDWOOD LUMBER INC.—See Hardwoods Distribution Inc.; *Int'l*, pg. 3273
AUTOMATED BUILDING COMPONENTS, INC.—See Bain Capital, LP; *U.S. Private*, pg. 450
AUTOMATISMES BATIMENT SA—See ASSA ABLOY AB; *Int'l*, pg. 638
A.W. HASTINGS & CO. INC.; *U.S. Private*, pg. 28
BADGER CORRUGATING COMPANY; *U.S. Private*, pg. 424
BAILEY LUMBER & SUPPLY CO.—See Bain Capital, LP; *U.S. Private*, pg. 450
BAILLIE LUMBER CO., INC.; *U.S. Private*, pg. 426
BANNER SUPPLY CO.; *U.S. Private*, pg. 469
BARLETTA MATERIALS & CONSTRUCTION; *U.S. Private*, pg. 476
BARR DO IT BEST LUMBER—See Barr Lumber Co. Inc.; *U.S. Private*, pg. 479
BASF WOLMAN GMBH—See BASF SE; *Int'l*, pg. 882
BATEMAN BROTHERS LUMBER CO., INC.; *U.S. Private*, pg. 486
BAYOU HOLZWERKSTOFFE GMBH; *Int'l*, pg. 914
BEARD HARDWOODS, INC; *U.S. Private*, pg. 506
BECKERLE LUMBER SUPPLY CO., INC.; *U.S. Private*, pg. 511
BEESON HARDWARE CO. INC.; *U.S. Private*, pg. 514
BEISSER LUMBER COMPANY; *U.S. Private*, pg. 516
BELAIR ROAD SUPPLY COMPANY INC.; *U.S. Private*, pg. 516
BELLETETE'S INC.; *U.S. Private*, pg. 520
BENDER LUMBER COMPANY INC.; *U.S. Private*, pg. 524
BENNETT LUMBER COMPANY; *U.S. Private*, pg. 527
BENSON LUMBER & HARDWARE INC.; *U.S. Private*, pg. 528
BENTHALL BROTHERS, INC.; *U.S. Private*, pg. 528
BEP/LYMAN, LLC—See Bain Capital, LP; *U.S. Private*, pg. 450
BERLIN LUMBER COMPANY, INC.—See Your Building Centers, Inc.; *U.S. Private*, pg. 4594
BERNARD BUILDING CENTER INC.; *U.S. Private*, pg. 535
BERRY ENTERPRISES INC.; *U.S. Private*, pg. 538
BESSE FOREST PRODUCTS GROUP, CO.—See The Hoffmann Family of Companies; *U.S. Private*, pg. 4053
BEST MATERIALS, LLC—See The Sterling Group, L.P.; *U.S. Private*, pg. 4122
BESTWAY ENTERPRISES INC.; *U.S. Private*, pg. 544
BETHEL MILLS, INC.; *U.S. Private*, pg. 545
BETHEL MILLS KITCHEN & BATH—See Bethel Mills, Inc.; *U.S. Private*, pg. 545
BETTER LIVING INC.; *U.S. Private*, pg. 546
BIG C LUMBER CO., INC.; *U.S. Private*, pg. 552
BIG LAKE LUMBER, INC.; *U.S. Private*, pg. 553
BIG L CORPORATION; *U.S. Private*, pg. 553
BILL HANKS LUMBER CO.; *U.S. Private*, pg. 557
BINGAMAN & SON LUMBER, INC.; *U.S. Private*, pg. 560
BIRCHLAND PLYWOOD-VENEER LIMITED; *Int'l*, pg. 1046
BIRMINGHAM INTERNATIONAL FOREST PRODUCTS, LLC—See Forest City Trading Group, LLC; *U.S. Private*, pg. 1566
BISON BUILDING MATERIALS LTD.—See Builders First-Source, Inc.; *U.S. Public*, pg. 409
B&J BUILDER'S SUPPLY & SERVICE; *U.S. Private*, pg. 418
BLACK LUMBER CO. INC.; *U.S. Private*, pg. 572
BLACK MILLWORK CO., INC.; *U.S. Private*, pg. 572
BLEVINS WORK SHOP INC.; *U.S. Private*, pg. 581
BLUELINX CORPORATION—See Cerberus Capital Management, L.P.; *U.S. Private*, pg. 837
BLUELINX FLORIDA LP—See Cerberus Capital Management, L.P.; *U.S. Private*, pg. 837
BLUE TRIANGLE HARDWOODS, LLC—See Baillie Lumber Co., Inc.; *U.S. Private*, pg. 426
BMC EAST, LLC—See Builders FirstSource, Inc.; *U.S. Public*, pg. 409
BMC FORESTRY CORPORATION—See Benguet Corporation; *Int'l*, pg. 974
BODDINGTON LUMBER CO; *U.S. Private*, pg. 607
BOLAND-MALONEY LUMBER COMPANY INC.—See Boland Maloney Enterprises Inc.; *U.S. Private*, pg. 610
BOLAND-MALONEY REALTY CO.—See Boland Maloney Enterprises Inc.; *U.S. Private*, pg. 610
BORKHOLDER CORPORATION; *U.S. Private*, pg. 618
BOSCUS CANADA INC; *Int'l*, pg. 1116
BOTKIN LUMBER COMPANY, INC.; *U.S. Private*, pg. 622
BOURGET BROS. BUILDING MATERIALS; *U.S. Private*, pg. 624
BOWIE-SIMS-PRANGE INC.; *U.S. Private*, pg. 625
BOWIE-SIMS-PRANGE TREATING CORP.—See Bowie-Sims-Prange Inc.; *U.S. Private*, pg. 625
BOYCE LUMBER CO.; *U.S. Private*, pg. 627
BRECKENRIDGE BUILDING CENTER, INC.—See Bain Capital, LP; *U.S. Private*, pg. 450
BRIDGER FOREST PRODUCTS—See OrePac Holding Company Inc.; *U.S. Private*, pg. 3041
BRIDGEWATER LUMBER CO—See Chelsea Lumber Company; *U.S. Private*, pg. 870
BRIDGEWATER WHOLESALERS, INC.—See Owens Corning; *U.S. Public*, pg. 1626
BRINK FOREST PRODUCTS LTD.—See Brink Group of Companies; *Int'l*, pg. 1164
BRITTINGHAM & HIXON LUMBER CO.—See Alexander Lumber Co., Inc.; *U.S. Private*, pg. 163
B.R. JOHNSON, LLC—See Regional Brands Inc.; *U.S. Public*, pg. 1775
BROWN LUMBER SALES COMPANY; *U.S. Private*, pg. 668
BROWN LUMBER & SUPPLY COMPANY; *U.S. Private*, pg. 668
BRUNSELL BROTHERS LTD.; *U.S. Private*, pg. 672
BUCHHEIT INC.; *U.S. Private*, pg. 676
BUCKEYE PACIFIC, LLC—See Forest City Trading Group, LLC; *U.S. Private*, pg. 1566
BUFORD WHITE LUMBER COMPANY; *U.S. Private*, pg. 681
BUILDERS BEST DEWITT CENTERS INC.—See Bestway Enterprises Inc.; *U.S. Private*, pg. 544
BUILDERS FENCE COMPANY INC.; *U.S. Private*, pg. 682
BUILDERS FIRSTSOURCE - FLORIDA, LLC—See Builders FirstSource, Inc.; *U.S. Public*, pg. 410
BUILDERS FIRSTSOURCE - MBS, LLC—See Builders FirstSource, Inc.; *U.S. Public*, pg. 410
BUILDERS FIRSTSOURCE OF GREENVILLE—See Builders FirstSource, Inc.; *U.S. Public*, pg. 410
BUILDERS FIRSTSOURCE OF HIGH POINT—See Builders FirstSource, Inc.; *U.S. Public*, pg. 410
BUILDERS FIRSTSOURCE OF SOUTHPORT—See Builders FirstSource, Inc.; *U.S. Public*, pg. 410
BUILDERS GYPSUM SUPPLY—See Beacon Roofing Supply, Inc.; *U.S. Public*, pg. 285
BUILDERS HARDWARE, INC.—See Wynnchurch Capital, L.P.; *U.S. Private*, pg. 4578
BUILDERS SUPPLY COMPANY INC.; *U.S. Private*, pg. 682
BUILDERS SURPLUS, INC.; *U.S. Private*, pg. 682
BUILDERS TRUSS INC; *U.S. Private*, pg. 682
THE BUILDING CENTER, INC.; *U.S. Private*, pg. 4002
BUILDING MATERIAL DISTRIBUTORS; *U.S. Private*, pg. 683
BUILDING PRODUCTS INC. OF IOWA—See Building Products Inc.; *U.S. Private*, pg. 683
BUILDING PRODUCTS INC. OF S.D.—See Building Products Inc.; *U.S. Private*, pg. 683
BUILDING SPECIALTIES COMPANY, INC.—See Platinum Equity, LLC; *U.S. Private*, pg. 3208
BURT BOULTON & HAYWOOD LTD.—See Iivari Mononen Oy; *U.S. Private*, pg. 3608
BURTON LUMBER CORP.; *U.S. Private*, pg. 693
BURTON LUMBER & HARDWARE CO.; *U.S. Private*, pg. 693
CALDWELL HARDWARE, LTD.—See ASSA ABLOY AB; *Int'l*, pg. 639

N.A.I.C.S. INDEX

423310 — LUMBER, PLYWOOD, MI...

CALIFORNIA PANEL & VENEER COMPANY; *U.S. Private*, pg. 720
CALIPER BUILDING SYSTEMS, LLC—See UFP Industries, Inc.; *U.S. Public*, pg. 2218
CANFOR JAPAN CORPORATION—See Canfor Corporation; *Int'l*, pg. 1291
CANUSA WOOD PRODUCTS LIMITED; *Int'l*, pg. 1300
CAPE COD LUMBER CO. INC.; *U.S. Private*, pg. 737
CAPITAL FOREST PRODUCTS INC.; *U.S. Private*, pg. 740
CAPITAL LUMBER COMPANY; *U.S. Private*, pg. 741
CAPITOL PLYWOOD INC.; *U.S. Private*, pg. 744
CAPITOL PLYWOOD INC.—See Capitol Plywood Inc.; *U.S. Private*, pg. 744
CARHART LUMBER COMPANY; *U.S. Private*, pg. 760
CARPENTER COMPANY OF SPOTSYLVANIA INC.—See The Lester Group Inc.; *U.S. Private*, pg. 4069
CARROLLTON WOOD PRODUCTS INC—See Magnolia Forest Products Inc.; *U.S. Private*, pg. 2548
THE CARTER-JONES LUMBER COMPANY INC.—See Carter Lumber Co.; *U.S. Private*, pg. 776
CARTER LUMBER CO. INC.—See Carter Lumber Co.; *U.S. Private*, pg. 775
CARTER LUMBER CO.; *U.S. Private*, pg. 775
CARTER LUMBER OF THE SOUTH INC.—See Carter Lumber Co.; *U.S. Private*, pg. 775
CARTER LUMBER OF VIRGINIA INC.—See Carter Lumber Co.; *U.S. Private*, pg. 775
CASCADE LUMBER COMPANY; *U.S. Private*, pg. 781
CASE SUPPLY INC.; *U.S. Private*, pg. 782
CAUSEWAY LUMBER COMPANY; *U.S. Private*, pg. 794
CECO (FLOORING) LIMITED—See Headlam Group plc; *Int'l*, pg. 3301
CEDAR CREEK - AITKIN—See Cerberus Capital Management, L.P.; *U.S. Private*, pg. 837
CEDAR CREEK LLC—See Cerberus Capital Management, L.P.; *U.S. Private*, pg. 837
CEDAR SIDING & LUMBER INC.; *U.S. Private*, pg. 805
CENTRAL FOREST PRODUCTS INC.; *U.S. Private*, pg. 821
CENTRAL HARDWOODS, INC.; *U.S. Private*, pg. 821
CENTRAL SUPPLY COMPANY; *U.S. Private*, pg. 825
CENTRAL VALLEY BUILDERS SUPPLY; *U.S. Private*, pg. 825
CENTRAL WHOLESALE SUPPLY CORPORATION; *U.S. Private*, pg. 826
CENTRAL WOODWORK, INC.; *U.S. Private*, pg. 826
CENTRAL WOODWORK OF NASHVILLE, INC.—See Central Woodwork, Inc.; *U.S. Private*, pg. 826
CERTIFIED LUMBER CORPORATION; *U.S. Private*, pg. 841
CHACE BUILDING SUPPLY OF CT, INC.; *U.S. Private*, pg. 845
CHAMPION WINDOW COMPANY OF OKLAHOMA CITY, LLC—See Champion Windows Manufacturing Inc.; *U.S. Private*, pg. 847
CHANNEL LUMBER COMPANY INC.; *U.S. Private*, pg. 848
CHARLES F. SHIELS & CO. INC.; *U.S. Private*, pg. 852
CHARLES F. VATTEROTT & CO.; *U.S. Private*, pg. 852
CHASE LUMBER & FUEL COMPANY, INC.—See Bliffert Lumber & Fuel Co. Inc.; *U.S. Private*, pg. 581
CHAS F. WILLIAMS CO. INC.; *U.S. Private*, pg. 859
C.H. CARPENTER LUMBER COMPANY; *U.S. Private*, pg. 707
CHEBOYGAN LUMBER COMPANY; *U.S. Private*, pg. 868
CHELMSFORD LUMBER COMPANY—See Arlington Coal & Lumber Co. Inc.; *U.S. Private*, pg. 329
CHELSEA LUMBER COMPANY; *U.S. Private*, pg. 870
CHEROKEE BUILDING MATERIALS INC.—See GMS Inc.; *U.S. Public*, pg. 948
CHEROKEE BUILDING MATERIALS OF OKC, INC.—See GMS Inc.; *U.S. Public*, pg. 948
CHINOOK LUMBER INC.; *U.S. Private*, pg. 886
CHRISTENSEN LUMBER, INC.—See Kodiak Building Partners LLC; *U.S. Private*, pg. 2336
CHRISTMAS LUMBER COMPANY INC.; *U.S. Private*, pg. 891
CHURCH & CHURCH INC.; *U.S. Private*, pg. 894
CITY FEED & LUMBER COMPANY INC.; *U.S. Private*, pg. 905
CITY MILL COMPANY LTD.; *U.S. Private*, pg. 906
CLASSIC AMERICAN HARDWOODS INC.; *U.S. Private*, pg. 916
CLINTONVILLE LUMBER COMPANY INC.; *U.S. Private*, pg. 945
CLOSE LUMBER; *U.S. Private*, pg. 946
CLYDE/WEST INC.—See Joshua Green Corporation; *U.S. Private*, pg. 2237
CNC ASSOCIATES NY INC.; *U.S. Private*, pg. 952
COASTAL DOOR & WINDOW INC.; *U.S. Private*, pg. 956
COAST COUNTIES GLASS INC.; *U.S. Private*, pg. 954
COEUR D'ALENE BUILDERS SUPPLY; *U.S. Private*, pg. 960
COLE HALL LUMBER CO.—See Lumber Group Inc.; *U.S. Private*, pg. 2513
COLE LUMBER COMPANY INC.; *U.S. Private*, pg. 966
COLLIER BUILDING SPECIALTIES; *U.S. Private*, pg. 968
COLLINS DOOR AND HARDWARE INC.—See DNS Capital, LLC; *U.S. Private*, pg. 1249

COLUMBUS BUILDERS SUPPLY INC.; *U.S. Private*, pg. 979
COMBIMILL REOPALU OU—See Combimill OU; *Int'l*, pg. 1708
COMMONWEALTH BUILDING MATERIALS, INC.—See GMS Inc.; *U.S. Public*, pg. 948
COMMONWEALTH PLYWOOD CO. LTD. - SEASONS FLOORING DIVISION—See Commonwealth Plywood Co. Ltd.; *Int'l*, pg. 1720
COMMONWEALTH WOOD PRESERVERS; *U.S. Private*, pg. 987
COMPLETE MILLWORK SERVICES, INC.; *U.S. Private*, pg. 1001
CONCANNON CORPORATION; *U.S. Private*, pg. 1008
CONCORD LUMBER CORP.; *U.S. Private*, pg. 1010
CONFEDERATED BUILDERS INC.; *U.S. Private*, pg. 1012
CONNECTICUT PLYWOOD CORP.; *U.S. Private*, pg. 1016
CONSOLIDATED LUMBER CO.; *U.S. Private*, pg. 1021
CONSOLIDATED SUPPLY COMPANY INC.; *U.S. Private*, pg. 1022
CONSTRUCTION MATERIALS INC.; *U.S. Private*, pg. 1024
CONSTRUCTION MATERIALS LTD.—See The Sterling Group, L.P.; *U.S. Private*, pg. 4122
CONSTRUCTION SPECIALTIES, INC.—See Construction Specialties, Inc.; *U.S. Private*, pg. 1024
CONTINENTAL TIMBER CO. INC.—See Conner Industries, Inc.; *U.S. Private*, pg. 1017
CONTINENTAL TRADING & HARDWARE INC.; *U.S. Private*, pg. 1031
COOK & BOARDMAN, LLC - SIMPSONVILLE—See Platinum Equity, LLC; *U.S. Private*, pg. 3208
COOK & BOARDMAN, LLC—See Platinum Equity, LLC; *U.S. Private*, pg. 3208
COOLEY INDUSTRIES INC.; *U.S. Private*, pg. 1039
COOPER BUILDING MATERIALS—See Cooper Communities, Inc.; *U.S. Private*, pg. 1041
COUSINEAU INC.; *U.S. Private*, pg. 1071
COVENTRY LUMBER INC.; *U.S. Private*, pg. 1072
CRAFTY BEAVER HOME CENTERS; *U.S. Private*, pg. 1082
CRANE JOHNSON LUMBER COMPANY INC.; *U.S. Private*, pg. 1085
CRAWFORD LABORATORIES, INC.—See Tennant Company; *U.S. Public*, pg. 2016
CRONLAND LUMBER CO. INC.; *U.S. Private*, pg. 1103
CROSS CREEK SALES LLC—See Baillie Lumber Co., Inc.; *U.S. Private*, pg. 426
CROSSROADS ROOFING & SUPPLY, INC.—See Beacon Roofing Supply, Inc.; *U.S. Public*, pg. 286
CROWN DOOR CORP.—See Owens Corning; *U.S. Public*, pg. 1626
CUSTOM BUILDER SUPPLY COMPANY; *U.S. Private*, pg. 1128
CUTLER DISTRIBUTION & FABRICATION—See Cutler Forest Products Inc.; *Int'l*, pg. 1881
DAIRYMAN'S SUPPLY COMPANY INC.; *U.S. Private*, pg. 1146
DAKERYN INDUSTRIES LTD.; *Int'l*, pg. 1950
DAKOTA CRAFT INC.; *U.S. Private*, pg. 1147
DALE & MAXEY, INC.; *U.S. Private*, pg. 1148
DANIELS-OLSEN BLDG PRODUCTS INC—See Midwest Hardwood Corporation; *U.S. Private*, pg. 2721
DANTZLER LUMBER & EXPORT CO., INC.; *U.S. Private*, pg. 1158
DARTMOUTH BUILDING SUPPLY INC.; *U.S. Private*, pg. 1160
DAVIDSON ENMAN LUMBER LTD.; *Int'l*, pg. 1984
DEALER IMPORTS INC.; *U.S. Private*, pg. 1182
DEAN LUMBER & SUPPLY CO.; *U.S. Private*, pg. 1184
DEERFIELD BUILDERS SUPPLY CO.; *U.S. Private*, pg. 1190
DEFORD LUMBER COMPANY INC.—See Builders FirstSource, Inc.; *U.S. Public*, pg. 410
THE DEGOL ORGANIZATION; *U.S. Private*, pg. 4019
DELSON LUMBER, LLC; *U.S. Private*, pg. 1199
DENISON-CANNON INC.; *U.S. Private*, pg. 1205
DERSIMO BV—See Headlam Group plc; *Int'l*, pg. 3301
DESCHUTES PINE SALES, INC.—See Ochoco Lumber Company; *U.S. Private*, pg. 2992
DESERT LUMBER, INC.—See Bain Capital, LP; *U.S. Private*, pg. 450
DETERING COMPANY OF HOUSTON LP; *U.S. Private*, pg. 1216
DEXTER AXLE DIVISION - FREMONT—See Brookfield Corporation; *Int'l*, pg. 1175
D.H. PACE COMPANY INC.—See E.E. Newcomer Enterprises Inc.; *U.S. Private*, pg. 1305
DIAMOND HARDWOODS & ARCHITECTURAL PRODUCTS, INC.—See Hardwoods Distribution Inc.; *Int'l*, pg. 3273
DIAMOND HILL PLYWOOD COMPANY—See The Palmer-Donavin Manufacturing Company, Inc.; *U.S. Private*, pg. 4090
DIAMOND HOME HARDWARE & GARDEN, LLC—See Kodiak Building Partners LLC; *U.S. Private*, pg. 2336
DIKSHA GREENS LTD.; *Int'l*, pg. 2125
DISDERO LUMBER CO. INC.—See Tumac Lumber Co. Inc.; *U.S. Private*, pg. 4258

DISTRIBUTOR SERVICE INC.; *U.S. Private*, pg. 1239
DITEC S.P.A.—See ASSA ABLOY AB; *Int'l*, pg. 639
DITTMAR LUMBER CORP.; *U.S. Private*, pg. 1240
DIXIE PLYWOOD AND LUMBER COMPANY; *U.S. Private*, pg. 1245
DLH POLAND SP. Z O.O.—See Grupa Grass Sp. z o.o.; *Int'l*, pg. 3116
DLH SLOVAKIA S.R.O.—See Grupa Grass Sp. z o.o.; *Int'l*, pg. 3116
DOMEXPORT INC.; *Int'l*, pg. 2161
DOORS INCORPORATED; *U.S. Private*, pg. 1262
DORMAKABA AUSTRIA GMBH—See dormakaba Holding AG; *Int'l*, pg. 2178
DOUG ASHY BUILDING MATERIALS INC.; *U.S. Private*, pg. 1266
DOUG ASHY BUILDING MATERIALS OF RAYNE INC.—See Doug Ashy Building Materials Inc.; *U.S. Private*, pg. 1266
DOUG ASHY BUILDING MATERIALS OF VILLE PLATTE INC.—See Doug Ashy Building Materials Inc.; *U.S. Private*, pg. 1266
DOWNES & READER HARDWOOD CO., INC.—See Hardwoods Distribution Inc.; *Int'l*, pg. 3273
DRAWER BOX SPECIALTIES INC.—See Renovo Capital, LLC; *U.S. Private*, pg. 3399
DRAWER BOX SPECIALTIES INC.—See The Rosewood Corporation; *U.S. Private*, pg. 4112
DU BELL LUMBER CO.; *U.S. Private*, pg. 1282
DUBLIN MILLWORK CO. INC.—See Strait & Lamp Lumber Co. Inc.; *U.S. Private*, pg. 3833
DUBUG NO 7 INC.; *U.S. Private*, pg. 1283
DUKES LUMBER CO. INC.; *U.S. Private*, pg. 1286
DUNN LUMBER COMPANY INCORPORATED; *U.S. Private*, pg. 1290
DUNN LUMBER NORTHWEST INC.—See Dunn Lumber Company Incorporated; *U.S. Private*, pg. 1290
DYKE INDUSTRY, INC.; *U.S. Private*, pg. 1296
DYKES LUMBER COMPANY INC.; *U.S. Private*, pg. 1296
EAST COAST LUMBER COMPANY INC.; *U.S. Private*, pg. 1316
EAST COAST LUMBER & SUPPLY CO. INC.; *U.S. Private*, pg. 1316
EASTERN ENGINEERED WOOD PRODUCTS; *U.S. Private*, pg. 1319
EAST HARDWOOD CO. INC.; *U.S. Private*, pg. 1316
EAST OHIO LUMBER CO. INC.; *U.S. Private*, pg. 1317
EAST SIDE LUMBERYARD SUPPLY CO.; *U.S. Private*, pg. 1317
EAST TEAK FINE HARDWOODS, INC.; *U.S. Private*, pg. 1317
EAST TEAK FINE HARDWOODS, INC.—See East Teak Fine Hardwoods, Inc.; *U.S. Private*, pg. 1317
E.C. BARTON & COMPANY; *U.S. Private*, pg. 1304
ECB BROKERAGE—See E.C. Barton & Company; *U.S. Private*, pg. 1304
E.C. COTTLE INC.; *U.S. Private*, pg. 1304
ECMD, INC.; *U.S. Private*, pg. 1328
E.D. COLLIER & SON—See Bateman Brothers Lumber Co., Inc.; *U.S. Private*, pg. 486
EDWARDS DOORS SYSTEMS LIMITED; *Int'l*, pg. 2316
EGER PROPERTIES—See Owens Corning; *U.S. Public*, pg. 1626
EGGER BENELUX GCV—See Fritz Egger GmbH & Co.; *Int'l*, pg. 2793
ELK SUPPLY COMPANY; *U.S. Private*, pg. 1363
EMERSON HARDWOOD COMPANY; *U.S. Private*, pg. 1382
EMPIRE BUILDING MATERIALS INC.; *U.S. Private*, pg. 1384
THE EMPIRE COMPANY, LLC—See Hardwoods Distribution Inc.; *Int'l*, pg. 3273
EMWOOD LUMBER CO. INC.; *U.S. Private*, pg. 1388
ENAP INC.; *U.S. Private*, pg. 1389
E.N. BEARD HARDWOOD LUMBER INC.; *U.S. Private*, pg. 1306
ENNO ROGGEMANN GMBH & CO. KG; *Int'l*, pg. 2443
ENVICOR; *U.S. Private*, pg. 1406
E.R. PROBYN EXPORT LTD.—See E.R. Probyn Ltd.; *Int'l*, pg. 2260
ESTATES WINDOWS LTD.; *U.S. Private*, pg. 1428
EVERGREEN LUMBER INC.—See Bain Capital, LP; *U.S. Private*, pg. 450
EXPO INDUSTRIES, INC.; *U.S. Private*, pg. 1450
EXTECH INDUSTRIES INC.; *U.S. Private*, pg. 1452
FABRICATORS SUPPLY COMPANY; *U.S. Private*, pg. 1459
FARGO GLASS & PAINT COMPANY; *U.S. Private*, pg. 1473
FARGO TANK & STEEL CO.—See TrueNorth Steel Inc.; *U.S. Private*, pg. 4249
FAR WEST PLYWOOD COMPANY—See Hardwoods Distribution Inc.; *Int'l*, pg. 3273
FASTEK PRODUCTS INC.—See Quanex Building Products Corp.; *U.S. Public*, pg. 1749
FAVOR WOODPANEL (THAILAND) CO., LTD.—See Dominant Enterprise Berhad; *Int'l*, pg. 2161
F.D. STERRITT LUMBER CO.; *U.S. Private*, pg. 1456
FELDMAN WOOD PRODUCTS CO. INC.; *U.S. Private*, pg. 1493

423310 — LUMBER, PLYWOOD, MI...

FENCE SUPPLY, INC.—See The Sterling Group, L.P.; *U.S. Private*, pg. 4123
FERRETERIA TESORO DEL EBANISTA; *U.S. Private*, pg. 1498
FESSENDEN HALL INCORPORATED; *U.S. Private*, pg. 1499
FIBER FUELS INC.; *U.S. Private*, pg. 1501
FIFTH AVENUE LUMBER CO., INC.—See Strait & Lamp Lumber Co. Inc.; *U.S. Private*, pg. 3833
FINMAC LUMBER LTD.; *Int'l*, pg. 2675
FIRST UNITED DOOR TECHNOLOGIES, LLC—See CapitalWorks, LLC; *U.S. Private*, pg. 742
FISCHER LUMBER CO. INC.; *U.S. Private*, pg. 1533
FLAGG INC.—See Clayton, Dubilier & Rice, LLC; *U.S. Private*, pg. 930
FLOORSCAPE LIMITED—See Mohawk Industries, Inc.; *U.S. Public*, pg. 1457
FLY TIMBER CO. INC.; *U.S. Private*, pg. 1553
FOREMANS INC.; *U.S. Private*, pg. 1565
FORESTAL ANCHILE LTDA.—See Daio Paper Corporation; *Int'l*, pg. 1940
FOREST CITY TRADING GROUP, LLC; *U.S. Private*, pg. 1566
FOREST PLYWOOD SALES INC.; *U.S. Private*, pg. 1567
FOREST PRODUCTS DISTRIBUTORS, INC.; *U.S. Private*, pg. 1567
FOREST SALES CORPORATION; *U.S. Private*, pg. 1567
FORT WORTH LUMBER COMPANY; *U.S. Private*, pg. 1575
FORT WORTH SASH AND DOOR CO.—See Fort Worth Lumber Company; *U.S. Private*, pg. 1575
FOSTER SUPPLY INC.—See Core & Main, Inc.; *U.S. Public*, pg. 576
FOX COMPANIES; *U.S. Private*, pg. 1584
FOXWORTH-GALBRAITH LUMBER COMPANY; *U.S. Private*, pg. 1585
FOXWORTH-GALBRAITH LUMBER COMPANY—See Foxworth-Galbraith Lumber Company; *U.S. Private*, pg. 1585
FRAMERICA CORPORATION; *U.S. Private*, pg. 1586
FRANCIS-SCHULZE, CO.—See Wynnchurch Capital, L.P.; *U.S. Private*, pg. 4578
FRANKLIN BUILDING SUPPLY CO. INC.; *U.S. Private*, pg. 1596
FRANK PAXTON LUMBER COMPANY; *U.S. Private*, pg. 1595
FRED C. HOLMES LUMBER COMPANY; *U.S. Private*, pg. 1600
FREUDENBERG POLITEX LTD.—See Freudenberg SE; *Int'l*, pg. 2787
FREUDENBERG POLITEX OOO—See Freudenberg SE; *Int'l*, pg. 2787
FREUDENBERG POLITEX SP. Z O.O.—See Freudenberg SE; *Int'l*, pg. 2787
FREUDENBERG SPUNWEB JAPAN COMPANY, LTD.—See Freudenberg SE; *Int'l*, pg. 2788
FRONTIER INDUSTRIES INC.; *U.S. Private*, pg. 1615
F.S. VANHOOSE & COMPANY INC.; *U.S. Private*, pg. 1457
FULLERTON LUMBER COMPANY; *U.S. Private*, pg. 1621
FULLTECH CO., LTD.; *Int'l*, pg. 2843
F.W. HONERKAMP, CO. INC.—See Hardwoods Distribution Inc.; *Int'l*, pg. 3273
F.W. KIBLER MILLING INC.; *U.S. Private*, pg. 1457
FYPON, LTD.; *U.S. Private*, pg. 1628
GANAHL LUMBER COMPANY; *U.S. Private*, pg. 1641
GARLAND CANADA INC.—See Garland Industries Inc.; *U.S. Private*, pg. 1644
THE GARLAND COMPANY UK LIMITED—See Garland Industries Inc.; *U.S. Private*, pg. 1644
GARRIS-EVANS LUMBER CO. INC.; *U.S. Private*, pg. 1645
GARVIN CONSTRUCTION PRODUCTS, INC.—See Beacon Roofing Supply, Inc.; *U.S. Public*, pg. 286
GATOR GYPSUM INC.—See GMS Inc.; *U.S. Public*, pg. 948
GBS BUILDING SUPPLY - US LBM, LLC—See Bain Capital, LP; *U.S. Private*, pg. 450
GENERAL GLASS INTERNATIONAL CORP.; *U.S. Private*, pg. 1665
GENERAL SUPPLY COMPANY; *U.S. Private*, pg. 1667
GERRETSEN BUILDING SUPPLY, CO.—See TAL Holdings LLC; *U.S. Private*, pg. 3925
GILBERT HARDWOOD CENTERS INC. OF TENNESSEE—See Gilbert Hardwoods Inc.; *U.S. Private*, pg. 1699
GILBERT HARDWOODS INC.; *U.S. Private*, pg. 1699
GILCREST/JEWETT LUMBER COMPANY—See Bain Capital, LP; *U.S. Private*, pg. 450
GILLEBAARD USA CORPORATION; *U.S. Private*, pg. 1700
GILLIES LUMBER INC.—See Alpa Lumber Inc; *Int'l*, pg. 366
GIRTMAN & ASSOCIATES—See Platinum Equity, LLC; *U.S. Private*, pg. 3208
GLEASON WOODWORK, INC.; *U.S. Private*, pg. 1708
GLENBROOK BUILDING SUPPLY, INC.—See Star Equity Holdings, Inc.; *U.S. Public*, pg. 1937
GLENORA LUMBER & BUILDING SUPPLIES LTD.; *Int'l*, pg. 2992
GLESBY BUILDING MATERIALS CO.; *U.S. Private*, pg. 1711
GMC HARDWOODS INC.; *U.S. Private*, pg. 1721
GOD A.D.; *Int'l*, pg. 3018

GOLDEN PHAROS EUROPE LTD—See Golden Pharos Berhad; *Int'l*, pg. 3030
GOLDEN STATE LUMBER INC.; *U.S. Private*, pg. 1733
GOODFELLOW INC. - MANCHESTER BRANCH—See Goodfellow Inc.; *Int'l*, pg. 3040
GOODFELLOW INC. - OLIVER LUMBER DIVISION—See Goodfellow Inc.; *Int'l*, pg. 3040
GOODFELLOW UK LTD—See Goodfellow Inc.; *Int'l*, pg. 3040
GRABOYES COMMERCIAL WINDOW COMPANY; *U.S. Private*, pg. 1748
GRANT ROAD LUMBER CO. INC.; *U.S. Private*, pg. 1756
GRAYCO, INC.; *U.S. Private*, pg. 1761
GRAY LUMBER COMPANY INC.; *U.S. Private*, pg. 1759
GREAT CENTRAL LUMBER COMPANY—See Millman Lumber Company; *U.S. Private*, pg. 2737
GREAT LAKES VENEER INC.—See Marion Plywood Corporation; *U.S. Private*, pg. 2576
GREENHEART (SURINAME) N.V.—See Greenheart Group Limited; *Int'l*, pg. 3075
GREEN PANEL PTY. LTD.—See Dominant Enterprise Berhad; *Int'l*, pg. 2161
GREENWOOD PRODUCTS, INC.—See Jewett-Cameron Trading Company Ltd.; *U.S. Public*, pg. 1190
GRESHAM-PRUETT LUMBER EXCHANGE; *U.S. Private*, pg. 1784
G.R. MITCHELL INC.; *U.S. Private*, pg. 1631
GROOM & SONS' HARDWARE & LUMBER, INC.; *U.S. Private*, pg. 1791
GROSSMANS BARGAIN OUTLET—See E.C. Barton & Company; *U.S. Private*, pg. 1304
GROUPE B.M.R. INC.; *Int'l*, pg. 3091
GROWTH THROUGH SERVICE INTERIOR SUPPLY CO. INC.; *U.S. Private*, pg. 1796
GR WOOD INC.; *U.S. Private*, pg. 1748
GUADALUPE LUMBER CO.; *U.S. Private*, pg. 1808
GULF STREAM BUILDERS SUPPLY, INC; *U.S. Private*, pg. 1817
GUMBLE BROTHERS INC.; *U.S. Private*, pg. 1818
GUNTON CORPORATION; *U.S. Private*, pg. 1819
GUTHRIE LUMBER SALES INC.; *U.S. Private*, pg. 1820
G.V. MOORE LUMBER CO., INC.; *U.S. Private*, pg. 1631
GYPSUM PRODUCTS INC.; *U.S. Private*, pg. 1821
GYPSUM WALLBOARD SUPPLY INC.—See American Securities LLC; *U.S. Private*, pg. 249
HAGER CABINETS INCORPORATED; *U.S. Private*, pg. 1839
HAGER GROUP INC.; *U.S. Private*, pg. 1839
HAGLE LUMBER COMPANY, INC.; *U.S. Private*, pg. 1840
HALL & HOUSE LUMBER CO. INC.; *U.S. Private*, pg. 1843
HAMAR-QUANDT CO. INC.; *U.S. Private*, pg. 1847
HAMMOND LUMBER COMPANY; *U.S. Private*, pg. 1850
HAMPTON AFFILIATES; *U.S. Private*, pg. 1851
HAMPTON TREE FARMS, INC.—See Hampton Affiliates; *U.S. Private*, pg. 1851
HAMSHAW LUMBER INC.; *U.S. Private*, pg. 1851
HANCOCK LUMBER COMPANY, INC.; *U.S. Private*, pg. 1852
HANKINS LUMBER COMPANY, INC.; *U.S. Private*, pg. 1853
HARBIN LUMBER COMPANY INCORPORATED; *U.S. Private*, pg. 1858
HARDMAN WHOLESALE LLC—See Hardwoods Distribution Inc.; *Int'l*, pg. 3273
HARDWOOD INDUSTRIES INC.; *U.S. Private*, pg. 1864
HARDWOODS DISTRIBUTION INC.; *Int'l*, pg. 3273
HARDWOODS INCORPORATED—See Atlanta Hardwood Corporation; *U.S. Private*, pg. 370
HARDWOODS SPECIALTY PRODUCTS US LP—See Hardwoods Distribution Inc.; *Int'l*, pg. 3273
H. ARNOLD WOOD TURNING INC.; *U.S. Private*, pg. 1824
HATCH & BAILEY COMPANY; *U.S. Private*, pg. 1879
HAWAII PLANING MILL LTD.; *U.S. Private*, pg. 1881
HAWKEYE DISTRIBUTION INC.; *U.S. Private*, pg. 1882
HAWKEYE FOREST PRODUCTS INC.; *U.S. Private*, pg. 1882
HAYNES BROTHERS LUMBER CO. LTD. PARTNER; *U.S. Private*, pg. 1885
H.C. LA MARCHE ENTERPRISES; *U.S. Private*, pg. 1825
HEADLAM BV—See Headlam Group plc; *Int'l*, pg. 3301
HEARTLAND BUILDING CENTER INC.; *U.S. Private*, pg. 1899
HEIDEGESELLASCHAFT G.M.B.H.—See Det Danske Hedeselskab; *Int'l*, pg. 2047
HEISTER HOUSE MILLWORKS, INC.; *U.S. Private*, pg. 1905
HEL VED BOLIG AS—See Honkarakenne Oyj; *Int'l*, pg. 3471
HENRIETTA BUILDING SUPPLIES, INC—See American Securities LLC; *U.S. Private*, pg. 248
HERITAGE FOREST PRODUCTS INC—See Baillie Lumber Co., Inc.; *U.S. Private*, pg. 426
HERITAGE FOREST PRODUCTS—See Baillie Lumber Co., Inc.; *U.S. Private*, pg. 426
HERRMAN LUMBER COMPANY; *U.S. Private*, pg. 1926
H&H LUMBER CO., INC.—See Bain Capital, LP; *U.S. Private*, pg. 450
HHP INC.; *U.S. Private*, pg. 1931

HIAG HANDEL AG—See Holzwerkstoff Holding AG; *Int'l*, pg. 3454
HICKMAN INDUSTRIES LIMITED—See Owens Corning; *U.S. Public*, pg. 1626
HIGH COUNTRY LUMBER INC.; *U.S. Private*, pg. 1935
HILL'S SUPPLY CO.; *U.S. Private*, pg. 1945
HINES BUILDING SUPPLY - US LBM, LLC—See Bain Capital, LP; *U.S. Private*, pg. 450
HIXSON LUMBER SALES, INC.; *U.S. Private*, pg. 1953
H.J. OLDENKAMP CO.; *U.S. Private*, pg. 1834
HLAVINKA EQUIPMENT COMPANY; *U.S. Private*, pg. 1954
HOBATEX GMBH—See AUCTUS Capital Partners AG; *Int'l*, pg. 700
HOLBROOK LUMBER COMPANY; *U.S. Private*, pg. 1961
HOLDAHL INC.; *U.S. Private*, pg. 1962
HOLDERNESS BUILDING MATERIALS, INC.—See Bain Capital, LP; *U.S. Private*, pg. 451
HOLLOW METAL SPECIALISTS, INC.—See Platinum Equity, LLC; *U.S. Private*, pg. 3208
HOLMEN TIMBER UK—See Holmen AB; *Int'l*, pg. 3453
HOLMES LUMBER & BUILDING CENTER INC.—See Carter Lumber Co.; *U.S. Private*, pg. 776
HOLT & BUGBEE COMPANY; *U.S. Private*, pg. 1968
HOLT LUMBER INC.; *U.S. Private*, pg. 1968
HOLZWERKSTOFF HOLDING AG; *Int'l*, pg. 3454
HOMAN LUMBER MART, INC.; *U.S. Private*, pg. 1970
HOME BUILDERS & SUPPLY CO. INC.; *U.S. Private*, pg. 1970
HOME LUMBER & SUPPLY CO.; *U.S. Private*, pg. 1971
HOMER T. HAYWARD LUMBER CO. INC.; *U.S. Private*, pg. 1973
HONSADOR LUMBER LLC—See Grey Mountain Partners, LLC; *U.S. Private*, pg. 1784
HOOD DISTRIBUTION MCEWEN GROUP—See Hood Industries Inc.; *U.S. Private*, pg. 1977
HOOD DISTRIBUTION—See Hood Industries Inc.; *U.S. Private*, pg. 1977
HOOVER BUILDING SUPPLY INC.—See BHHH Companies Inc.; *U.S. Private*, pg. 549
HORDENER HOLZWERK GMBH; *Int'l*, pg. 3474
HORIZON FOREST PRODUCTS LP—See Baillie Lumber Co., Inc.; *U.S. Private*, pg. 426
HORNE BUILDING SPECIALTIES; *U.S. Private*, pg. 1983
HORNER MILLWORK CORP.; *U.S. Private*, pg. 1983
HOSKIN & MUIR, INC.; *U.S. Private*, pg. 1985
HOUDARD; *Int'l*, pg. 3490
HOWDEN JOINERY LIMITED—See Howden Joinery Group Plc; *Int'l*, pg. 3494
HOWLETT LUMBER CO., INC.; *U.S. Private*, pg. 1996
H&S FOREST PRODUCTS INC.; *U.S. Private*, pg. 1824
HUGHES LUMBER COMPANY; *U.S. Private*, pg. 2003
HUMPHREY LUMBER CORPORATION; *U.S. Private*, pg. 2007
HUSTON SUPPLY CO. INC.; *U.S. Private*, pg. 2014
HUTCHISON INCORPORATED; *U.S. Private*, pg. 2014
HUTTIG BUILDING PRODUCTS, INC.—See Woodgrain, Inc.; *U.S. Private*, pg. 4558
H.W. JENKINS COMPANY; *U.S. Private*, pg. 1836
IDAHO PACIFIC LUMBER COMPANY INC.; *U.S. Private*, pg. 2035
IDAHO WESTERN, INC.—See UFP Industries, Inc.; *U.S. Public*, pg. 2219
IDEAL PRODUCTS OF DONGGUAN LTD.—See TopBuild Corp.; *U.S. Public*, pg. 2163
IHLO SALES & IMPORT CO.; *U.S. Private*, pg. 2040
IKE TRADING CO. LTD. INC.; *U.S. Private*, pg. 2041
INEX CORP.; *U.S. Private*, pg. 2070
INLAND PLYWOOD COMPANY—See Patrick Industries, Inc.; *U.S. Public*, pg. 1652
INSULATION SUPPLY COMPANY INC.; *U.S. Private*, pg. 2094
INTEGRA PACKAGING PTY LTD—See UFP Industries, Inc.; *U.S. Public*, pg. 2219
INTERIOR DISTRIBUTORS INC.; *U.S. Private*, pg. 2111
INTERMOUNTAIN WOOD PRODUCTS INC.; *U.S. Private*, pg. 2113
INTERNATIONAL BUILDING MATERIALS LLC; *U.S. Private*, pg. 2114
INTERNATIONAL PAPER COMPANY—See International Paper Company; *U.S. Public*, pg. 1156
ISAM MITCHELL & CO. INC.; *U.S. Private*, pg. 2143
IVERSON'S LUMBER COMPANY INC.—See The Schockman Lumber Company, Inc.; *U.S. Private*, pg. 4114
JACKSON LUMBER AND MILLWORK CO.; *U.S. Private*, pg. 2177
JACKSONVILLE BUILDERS SUPPLY—See East Hardwood Co. Inc.; *U.S. Private*, pg. 1316
JAECKLE MINNESOTA INC.—See Jaeckle Wholesale Inc.; *U.S. Private*, pg. 2181
JAEGER LUMBER AND SUPPLY CO. INC.; *U.S. Private*, pg. 2181
JAMES A. ANDREW INC.; *U.S. Private*, pg. 2183
JAMES LUMBER CO.; *U.S. Private*, pg. 2184
JAMES RITTER LUMBER COMPANY; *U.S. Private*, pg. 2185
J.C. SNAVELY & SONS INC.; *U.S. Private*, pg. 2160
JEWETT-CAMERON LUMBER CORPORATION—See

N.A.I.C.S. INDEX

423310 — LUMBER, PLYWOOD, MI...

Jewett-Cameron Trading Company Ltd.; *U.S. Public*, pg. 1190
JEWETT-CAMERON SEED COMPANY—See Jewett-Cameron Trading Company Ltd.; *U.S. Public*, pg. 1190
J.F. JOHNSON LUMBER COMPANY; *U.S. Private*, pg. 2162
J. GIBSON MCILVAIN COMPANY; *U.S. Private*, pg. 2156
J&H FOREST PRODUCTS; *U.S. Private*, pg. 2154
JIMMY WHITTINGTON LUMBER CO.; *U.S. Private*, pg. 2210
JIM WHITE LUMBER SALES INC.; *U.S. Private*, pg. 2210
J.M. MCCORMICK COMPANY INC.; *U.S. Private*, pg. 2169
JOHN DI NASO & SONS INC; *U.S. Private*, pg. 2221
JOHN E. QUARLES CO.; *U.S. Private*, pg. 2221
JOHN H. MYERS & SON INC.—See Bain Capital, LP; *U.S. Private*, pg. 451
JOHN'S LUMBER & HARDWARE CO.—See Builders FirstSource, Inc.; *U.S. Public*, pg. 410
JOHNSON INTERNATIONAL CO.; *U.S. Private*, pg. 2228
JOHNSON LUMBER COMPANY; *U.S. Private*, pg. 2228
JOHNSON-MANLEY LUMBER COMPANY; *U.S. Private*, pg. 2229
JONES LUMBER COMPANY—See Bain Capital, LP; *U.S. Private*, pg. 451
J.P. HART LUMBER COMPANY INC.; *U.S. Private*, pg. 2169
J.T. SHANNON LUMBER INC.; *U.S. Private*, pg. 2171
J. WRIGHT BUILDING CENTER INC.; *U.S. Private*, pg. 2157
K&A LUMBER COMPANY INC.—See Stock Building Supply; *U.S. Private*, pg. 3814
KAMCO BUILDING SUPPLY CORPORATION OF PENNSYLVANIA—See Kamco Supply Corporation; *U.S. Private*, pg. 2258
KAMCO SUPPLY CORPORATION OF NEW ENGLAND—See Kamco Supply Corporation; *U.S. Private*, pg. 2258
KAMCO SUPPLY CORPORATION; *U.S. Private*, pg. 2258
KAMCO SUPPLY CORPORATION—See GMS Inc.; *U.S. Public*, pg. 949
KANSAS LUMBER HOMESTORE INC.; *U.S. Private*, pg. 2261
KC COMPANY INC.; *U.S. Private*, pg. 2269
KEIM LUMBER COMPANY; *U.S. Private*, pg. 2274
THE KELLEHER CORPORATION; *U.S. Private*, pg. 4064
KELLER-SMITH SUPPLY, INC.; *U.S. Private*, pg. 2275
KELLOGG SUPPLY CO. INC.; *U.S. Private*, pg. 2276
KEN-API SUPPLY INC.; *U.S. Private*, pg. 2283
KENT GYPSUM SUPPLY INC.; *U.S. Private*, pg. 2287
KENTUCKY INDIANA LUMBER - US LBM, LLC—See Bain Capital, LP; *U.S. Private*, pg. 451
KETCHAM FOREST PRODUCTS, INC.; *U.S. Private*, pg. 2291
KIMAL LUMBER COMPANY—See Gulfeagle Supply, Inc.; *U.S. Private*, pg. 1817
KIMAL LUMBER COMPANY—See Gulfeagle Supply, Inc.; *U.S. Private*, pg. 1817
KIM GUAN IMPEX SDN. BHD.—See Dominant Enterprise Berhad; *Int'l*, pg. 2161
KITCHEN (PRO) LIMITED—See E. Bon Holdings Ltd; *Int'l*, pg. 2250
KLUMB LUMBER COMPANY INC. - INTERNATIONAL DIVISION—See Klumb Lumber Company Inc.; *U.S. Private*, pg. 2320
KLUMB LUMBER COMPANY INC.; *U.S. Private*, pg. 2320
KNEZ BUILDING MATERIALS CO. INC.; *U.S. Private*, pg. 2321
KOOPMAN LUMBER CO. INC.; *U.S. Private*, pg. 2343
KRAMER BROS LUMBER CO. INC.; *U.S. Private*, pg. 2349
THE KUIKEN BROTHERS COMPANY, INC.; *U.S. Private*, pg. 4066
KURATLE & JAECKER AG—See Holzwerkstoff Holding AG; *Int'l*, pg. 3454
KURTZ BROS. INC.; *U.S. Private*, pg. 2358
LA CROSSE LUMBER COMPANY; *U.S. Private*, pg. 2368
LAMPERT YARDS, INC.; *U.S. Private*, pg. 2381
LANDIS SUPPLY OF NEW JERSEY, INC.—See Hendricks Holding Company, Inc.; *U.S. Private*, pg. 1915
LANDRETH LUMBER COMPANY; *U.S. Private*, pg. 2386
LANSING BUILDING PRODUCTS, INC. - NORFOLK—See Lansing Building Products, Inc.; *U.S. Private*, pg. 2390
LANSING BUILDING PRODUCTS, INC.; *U.S. Private*, pg. 2390
LARSON MANUFACTURING COMPANY, INC.—See Fortune Brands Innovations, Inc.; *U.S. Public*, pg. 873
LAVALLEY BUILDING SUPPLY INC.; *U.S. Private*, pg. 2400
LEARNED LUMBER; *U.S. Private*, pg. 2408
LEE BUILDER MART INC.; *U.S. Private*, pg. 2411
LEE LUMBER & BUILDING MATERIAL CORP.; *U.S. Private*, pg. 2413
LENSING WHOLESALE INC.; *U.S. Private*, pg. 2422
LES MENUISERIES FRANCAISES—See Compagnie de Saint-Gobain SA; *Int'l*, pg. 1724
LEWISVILLE WOOD PRODUCTS INC.—See Magnolia Forest Products Inc.; *U.S. Private*, pg. 2548
LEZZER LUMBER—See Lezzer Lumber, Inc.; *U.S. Private*, pg. 2441
LIBERTY HARDWOODS INC.; *U.S. Private*, pg. 2444
LINCOLN LUMBER COMPANY; *U.S. Private*, pg. 2458

LINEAL VENEER INC.—See Industrial Ventilation, Inc.; *U.S. Private*, pg. 2069
LINWORTH LUMBER INC.—See Strait & Lamp Lumber Co. Inc.; *U.S. Private*, pg. 3833
L.I.S. CUSTOM DESIGNS, INC.; *U.S. Private*, pg. 2366
LONG BELL VENTURES LLC.; *U.S. Private*, pg. 2490
LONG ISLAND FIREPROOF DOOR INC.; *U.S. Private*, pg. 2490
L. THORN COMPANY INC.; *U.S. Private*, pg. 2364
LTL HOME PRODUCTS, INC.; *U.S. Private*, pg. 2509
LUMBER GROUP INC.; *U.S. Private*, pg. 2513
LUMBER INVESTORS LLC; *U.S. Private*, pg. 2513
LUMBER KING INC.; *U.S. Private*, pg. 2513
LUMBERMENS MERCHANDISING CORPORATION; *U.S. Private*, pg. 2514
LUMBER TECHNOLOGY CORPORATION; *U.S. Private*, pg. 2513
LUMMUS SUPPLY COMPANY INC.; *U.S. Private*, pg. 2514
LYF-TYM BUILDING PRODUCTS CO., INC.—See Beacon Roofing Supply, Inc.; *U.S. Public*, pg. 286
THE LYON & BILLARD CO., INC.; *U.S. Private*, pg. 4073
MACBEATH HARDWOOD COMPANY INC.; *U.S. Private*, pg. 2534
MACDONALD & OWEN VENEER & LUMBER CO., INC.; *U.S. Private*, pg. 2535
MADISON WOOD PRESERVERS INC.; *U.S. Private*, pg. 2544
MAGNOLIA FOREST PRODUCTS INC.; *U.S. Private*, pg. 2548
MAKI CORPORATION; *U.S. Private*, pg. 2556
MAKI HOME CENTER, INC.—See Maki Corporation; *U.S. Private*, pg. 2556
MANER BUILDERS SUPPLY CO.—See Bain Capital, LP; *U.S. Private*, pg. 451
MANIS LUMBER COMPANY—See Wheeler's Corporation; *U.S. Private*, pg. 4505
MANNING BUILDING SUPPLIES, INC.—See Bain Capital, LP; *U.S. Private*, pg. 451
MAPLEWOOD BUILDING SPECIALTIES; *U.S. Private*, pg. 2569
MARJAM SUPPLY COMPANY, INC.—See American Securities LLC; *U.S. Private*, pg. 249
MARLING LUMBER CO., INC.; *U.S. Private*, pg. 2585
MARQUETTE LUMBER CO. INC.; *U.S. Private*, pg. 2587
MARQUETTE LUMBERMENS WAREHOUSE—See Hager Group Inc.; *U.S. Private*, pg. 1839
MARQUETTE SAGINAW WAREHOUSE—See Hager Group Inc.; *U.S. Private*, pg. 1839
MARSH BUILDING PRODUCTS, INC.—See Leonard Green & Partners, L.P.; *U.S. Private*, pg. 2429
MARTCO LTD PARTNERSHIP—See Roy O. Martin Lumber Company, LLC; *U.S. Private*, pg. 3491
MASON FOREST PRODUCTS INC.; *U.S. Private*, pg. 2602
MASONITE CHILE S.A.—See Owens Corning; *U.S. Public*, pg. 1627
MASON'S MILL & LUMBER CO., INC.; *U.S. Private*, pg. 2602
MASSO ENTERPRISES; *U.S. Private*, pg. 2607
MCCAULEY LUMBER COMPANY INCORPORATED; *U.S. Private*, pg. 2628
MCCOY'S BUILDING SUPPLY CENTERS; *U.S. Private*, pg. 2630
MCCRAY LUMBER COMPANY - MCCRAY LUMBER & MILLWORK DIVISION—See McCray Lumber Company; *U.S. Private*, pg. 2631
MCCRAY LUMBER COMPANY; *U.S. Private*, pg. 2631
MCDONALD LUMBER CO. INC.; *U.S. Private*, pg. 2632
MDJ INCORPORATED; *U.S. Private*, pg. 2646
MEAD CLARK LUMBER COMPANY INCORPORATED; *U.S. Private*, pg. 2646
MECHANICS BUILDING MATERIAL CO.; *U.S. Private*, pg. 2649
MENARD, INC.; *U.S. Private*, pg. 2665
MENDO MILL & LUMBER CO.; *U.S. Private*, pg. 2666
THE MENTOR LUMBER & SUPPLY CO., INC.; *U.S. Private*, pg. 4078
MERICKEL LUMBER MILLS INC.; *U.S. Private*, pg. 2672
MERRILL & RING; *U.S. Private*, pg. 2676
METRO LUMBER WHOLESALE CO. INC.; *U.S. Private*, pg. 2685
METROPOLITAN CABINET DISTRIBUTORS; *U.S. Private*, pg. 2688
MEYER LAMINATES, INC.—See Compagnie de Saint-Gobain SA; *Int'l*, pg. 1730
MG BUILDING MATERIALS; *U.S. Private*, pg. 2693
MID-AM BUILDING SUPPLY.—See Hardwoods Distribution Inc.; *Int'l*, pg. 3273
MID-CITY LUMBER COMPANY LTD.; *U.S. Private*, pg. 2707
MIDDLE ATLANTIC WHOLESALE LUMBER COMPANY—See Sherwood Lumber Corporation; *U.S. Private*, pg. 3635
MIDDLETON BUILDING SUPPLY INC.; *U.S. Private*, pg. 2714
MID-SOUTH BUILDING SUPPLY CO., INC.; *U.S. Private*, pg. 2708
MID SOUTH BUILDING SUPPLY, COMMERCIAL

DIVISION—See Mid South Building Supply; *U.S. Private*, pg. 2706
MID SOUTH BUILDING SUPPLY; *U.S. Private*, pg. 2706
MID-SOUTH LUMBER AND SUPPLY; *U.S. Private*, pg. 2708
MID-SOUTH LUMBER COMPANY OF GEORGIA INC.; *U.S. Private*, pg. 2709
MID-STATE LUMBER CORP.—See Specialty Building Products, LLC; *U.S. Private*, pg. 3749
MIDWEST ALUMINUM SUPPLY INC.—See Richards Building Supply Company; *U.S. Private*, pg. 3428
MIDWEST HARDWOOD CORPORATION; *U.S. Private*, pg. 2721
MIDWEST SIDING SUPPLY INC.—See Richards Building Supply Company; *U.S. Private*, pg. 3428
MIDWEST WALNUT COMPANY; *U.S. Private*, pg. 2723
MILLENIUM MILLWORK CORP.; *U.S. Private*, pg. 2731
MILLMAN LUMBER COMPANY; *U.S. Private*, pg. 2737
MILLWORK DISTRIBUTORS INC.; *U.S. Private*, pg. 2738
MINOT BUILDERS SUPPLY ASSOCIATION; *U.S. Private*, pg. 2744
MJB WOOD GROUP INC.; *U.S. Private*, pg. 2753
M & K INDUSTRIES LIMITED, CO.—See New America Energy Corp.; *U.S. Public*, pg. 1511
MOBILE LUMBER & MILLWORK INC.; *U.S. Private*, pg. 2757
MOEHL MILLWORK INC.; *U.S. Private*, pg. 2764
MOELLERING INDUSTRIES CO. INC.; *U.S. Private*, pg. 2764
MONTALBANO LUMBER COMPANY INC.; *U.S. Private*, pg. 2774
MORGAN-WIGHTMAN SUPPLY COMPANY; *U.S. Private*, pg. 2784
MORRIS BLACK & SONS INC.; *U.S. Private*, pg. 2786
MORRIS LEVIN AND SON; *U.S. Private*, pg. 2788
MORTIMER & SON LUMBER CO. INC.; *U.S. Private*, pg. 2791
MOSCOW MILLS LUMBER COMPANY; *U.S. Private*, pg. 2792
MOSS LUMBER CO. INC.; *U.S. Private*, pg. 2794
MPC CASH-WAY LUMBER CO., INC.; *U.S. Private*, pg. 2803
MPC CASH-WAY LUMBER CO. WILLIAMSTON, INC.—See MPC Cash-Way Lumber Co., Inc.; *U.S. Private*, pg. 2803
MS CARVER LUMBER CO.; *U.S. Private*, pg. 2806
MSI BUILDING SUPPLIES INC.; *U.S. Private*, pg. 2807
MULHERIN LUMBER CO; *U.S. Private*, pg. 2811
N.A. MANS SONS INC.; *U.S. Private*, pg. 2827
NAMSCO INC.—See Charles River Laboratories International, Inc.; *U.S. Public*, pg. 480
NAPLES LUMBER & SUPPLY INC.; *U.S. Private*, pg. 2834
NASSAU SUFFOLK LUMBER & SUPPLY CORPORATION; *U.S. Private*, pg. 2837
NATIONAL DOOR SYSTEMS, LLC—See National Construction Enterprises Inc.; *U.S. Private*, pg. 2851
NATIONAL INDUSTRIAL LUMBER CO (NILCO); *U.S. Private*, pg. 2856
NATIONAL LUMBER CO.; *U.S. Private*, pg. 2859
NATIONAL WOOD PRODUCTS, INC.; *U.S. Private*, pg. 2865
NEGWER MATERIALS INCORPORATED; *U.S. Private*, pg. 2880
NELSON-YOUNG LUMBER CO.; *U.S. Private*, pg. 2884
NEWMAN LUMBER CO., INC.; *U.S. Private*, pg. 2915
NEXGEN BUILDING SUPPLY—See NexGen Building Supply; *U.S. Private*, pg. 2919
NICKERSON LUMBER COMPANY; *U.S. Private*, pg. 2926
NIEHAUS COMPANIES INC.; *U.S. Private*, pg. 2926
NIELSEN BROTHERS, INC.; *U.S. Private*, pg. 2927
NOBLE LUMBER INC.; *U.S. Private*, pg. 2933
NORCROSS COMPANY; *U.S. Private*, pg. 2936
NORTH CASCADE BUILDING MATERIALS; *U.S. Private*, pg. 2943
NORTHEAST BUILDERS SUPPLY HOME CENTER LLC; *U.S. Private*, pg. 2949
NORTHLAND CORPORATION; *U.S. Private*, pg. 2955
NORTHLAND FOREST PRODUCTS INC.; *U.S. Private*, pg. 2955
NORTHWEST BUILDING MATERIALS & SUPPLY CO.; *U.S. Private*, pg. 2959
NORTHWEST INC.; *U.S. Private*, pg. 2960
NORWOOD SASH & DOOR MANUFACTURING CO.; *U.S. Private*, pg. 2964
NYPRO ALABAMA LLC—See Jabil Inc.; *U.S. Public*, pg. 1181
OHIO VALLEY SUPPLY COMPANY; *U.S. Private*, pg. 3005
OLDHAM LUMBER CO. INC.; *U.S. Private*, pg. 3010
OLYMPIC INDUSTRIES, INC.—See Forest City Trading Group, LLC; *U.S. Private*, pg. 1566
ONGWEOWEH CORP.; *U.S. Private*, pg. 3026
ORANGE COUNTY BUILDING MATERIALS INC.; *U.S. Private*, pg. 3037
OREGON PACIFIC BUILDING PRODUCTS EXCHANGE INC.—See OrePac Holding Company Inc.; *U.S. Private*, pg. 3041
OREGON PACIFIC BUILDING PRODUCTS IDAHO INC.—See OrePac Holding Company Inc.; *U.S. Private*, pg. 3041

423310 — LUMBER, PLYWOOD, MI...

OREGON PACIFIC BUILDING PRODUCTS MAPLE INC.—See OrePac Holding Company Inc.; *U.S. Private*, pg. 3041
OREGON PACIFIC BUILDING PRODUCTS WASH. INC.—See OrePac Holding Company Inc.; *U.S. Private*, pg. 3041
OREPAC HOLDING COMPANY INC.; *U.S. Private*, pg. 3041
ORGAIN BUILDING SUPPLY COMPANY; *U.S. Private*, pg. 3041
OVERHEAD DOOR COMPANY OF ALBUQUERQUE—See E.E. Newcomer Enterprises Inc.; *U.S. Private*, pg. 1305
OVERHEAD DOOR COMPANY OF ATLANTA—See E.E. Newcomer Enterprises Inc.; *U.S. Private*, pg. 1305
OVERHEAD DOOR COMPANY OF CENTRAL ARIZONA—See E.E. Newcomer Enterprises Inc.; *U.S. Private*, pg. 1305
OVERHEAD DOOR COMPANY OF CENTRAL MISSOURI—See E.E. Newcomer Enterprises Inc.; *U.S. Private*, pg. 1305
OVERHEAD DOOR COMPANY OF SANTA FE—See E.E. Newcomer Enterprises Inc.; *U.S. Private*, pg. 1305
OVERHEAD DOOR COMPANY OF SPRINGFIELD—See E.E. Newcomer Enterprises Inc.; *U.S. Private*, pg. 1305
OVERHEAD DOOR COMPANY OF ST. LOUIS—See E.E. Newcomer Enterprises Inc.; *U.S. Private*, pg. 1305
OVERHEAD DOOR COMPANY OF THE FOUR CORNERS—See E.E. Newcomer Enterprises Inc.; *U.S. Private*, pg. 1305
OVERHEAD DOOR COMPANY OF WICHITA—See E.E. Newcomer Enterprises Inc.; *U.S. Private*, pg. 1305
OWENSVILLE SUPPLY, INC.; *U.S. Private*, pg. 3055
PACIFIC COAST SHOWCASE, INC.—See UFP Industries, Inc.; *U.S. Public*, pg. 2219
PACIFIC COAST SUPPLY, LLC - ANDERSON LUMBER DIVISION—See Pacific Coast Building Products, Inc.; *U.S. Private*, pg. 3066
PACIFIC COAST SUPPLY, LLC - P.C. WHOLESALE DIVISION—See Pacific Coast Building Products, Inc.; *U.S. Private*, pg. 3066
PACIFIC MUTUAL DOOR COMPANY—See Hardwoods Distribution Inc.; *Int'l*, pg. 3273
PACIFIC SOURCE INC.; *U.S. Private*, pg. 3070
PACIFIC STATES INDUSTRIES INCORPORATED; *U.S. Private*, pg. 3071
PAGE BROS ENTERPRISES LTD.; *U.S. Private*, pg. 3074
PALLET DIRECT, INC.; *U.S. Private*, pg. 3079
PALLET SERVICES INC.; *U.S. Private*, pg. 3079
THE PALMER-DONAVIN MANUFACTURING COMPANY, INC.; *U.S. Private*, pg. 4090
PALMERTON LUMBER CO., INC.—See Your Building Centers, Inc.; *U.S. Private*, pg. 4594
PALUMBO LUMBER & MANUFACTURING CO.; *U.S. Private*, pg. 3082
PARAGON INDUSTRIES INC.; *U.S. Private*, pg. 3091
PARKER LUMBER; *U.S. Private*, pg. 3097
THE PARKSITE GROUP; *U.S. Private*, pg. 4091
PARKSITE PLUNKETT-WEBSTER—See The Parksite Group; *U.S. Private*, pg. 4091
PARRISH & COMPANY INC.; *U.S. Private*, pg. 3099
PARR LUMBER COMPANY INC.; *U.S. Private*, pg. 3099
PATRICK LUMBER COMPANY, INC.; *U.S. Private*, pg. 3110
PELLA PRODUCTS OF KANSAS CITY; *U.S. Private*, pg. 3131
PELLA WINDOW & DOOR LLC; *U.S. Private*, pg. 3131
PELLA WINDOWS & DOORS, INC. - BOSTON; *U.S. Private*, pg. 3131
PELLA WINDOWS & DOORS, INC. - COLORADO—See Pella Corporation; *U.S. Private*, pg. 3131
PELLA WINDOWS & DOORS, INC.; *U.S. Private*, pg. 3131
PELLA WINDOWS & DOORS, INC.—See Pella Corporation; *U.S. Private*, pg. 3131
PENN WOOD PRODUCTS INC.; *U.S. Private*, pg. 3135
THE PENROD COMPANY INC.; *U.S. Private*, pg. 4093
PERFORMANCE DOOR & HARDWARE, INC.; *U.S. Private*, pg. 3149
PERGO ASIA CO. LTD.—See Mohawk Industries, Inc.; *U.S. Public*, pg. 1458
PERKINS HOME CENTER, INC.; *U.S. Private*, pg. 3151
PERKINS LUMBER CO. INC.; *U.S. Private*, pg. 3151
PETER LUMBER COMPANY; *U.S. Private*, pg. 3158
PGM PRODUCTS, LLC; *U.S. Private*, pg. 3165
PHILADELPHIA RESERVE SUPPLY COMPANY; *U.S. Private*, pg. 3169
PHILLIPS BUILDING SUPPLY OF GULFPORT; *U.S. Private*, pg. 3170
PINE TREE LUMBER CO. INC.; *U.S. Private*, pg. 3183
PIONEER MATERIALS, INC.—See GMS Inc.; *U.S. Public*, pg. 948
PLAINFIELD LUMBER COMPANY; *U.S. Private*, pg. 3194
PLATEAU FOREST PRODUCTS, LLC—See Forest City Trading Group, LLC; *U.S. Private*, pg. 1566
PLY-TRIM INC.; *U.S. Private*, pg. 3215
PLYWOOD & DOOR MANUFACTURERS; *U.S. Private*, pg. 3216
PLYWOOD & LUMBER SALES INCORPORATED; *U.S. Private*, pg. 3216
PORTAGE LUMBER COMPANY, INC.—See Bliffert Lumber & Fuel Co. Inc.; *U.S. Private*, pg. 581

PORTERS BUILDING CENTER; *U.S. Private*, pg. 3232
POTLATCH CORPORATION WOOD PRODUCTS GROUP—See PotlatchDeltic Corporation; *U.S. Public*, pg. 1704
POTTER ROEMER DIV.—See Jay R. Smith Mfg. Co.; *U.S. Private*, pg. 2192
POULIN LUMBER INC.; *U.S. Private*, pg. 3236
PRAIRIE PELLA INC.; *U.S. Private*, pg. 3243
PRECISION DOORS & HARDWARE—See Platinum Equity, LLC; *U.S. Private*, pg. 3209
PREFERRED MILLWORK ENTERPRISES INC.—See McDonough Corporation; *U.S. Private*, pg. 2632
PREMIER COOPERATIVE; *U.S. Private*, pg. 3249
PRE-MIX MARBLE TITE MANUFACTURING COMPANY; *U.S. Private*, pg. 3243
PRIMESOURCE BUILDING PRODUCTS, INC.—See Clearlake Capital Group, L.P.; *U.S. Private*, pg. 937
PRINCE CORPORATION; *U.S. Private*, pg. 3264
PRUETT FOREST PRODUCTS INC.; *U.S. Private*, pg. 3296
PW&D INC.; *U.S. Private*, pg. 3308
QUALITY PLYWOOD SPECIALTIES, INC.; *U.S. Private*, pg. 3320
QUALITY WHOLESALE BUILDING PRODUCTS INC.; *U.S. Private*, pg. 3321
QUALITY WOODS INC.; *U.S. Private*, pg. 3321
RACKHAMS LIMITED—See Headlam Group plc; *Int'l*, pg. 3301
RAFAEL LUMBER & SUPPLY COMPANY; *U.S. Private*, pg. 3345
RAILROAD DISTRIBUTION SERVICES, INC.—See Pinsly Railroad Co. Inc.; *U.S. Private*, pg. 3186
RAINTREE LUMBER SPECIALTIES LTD—See E.R. Probyn Ltd.; *Int'l*, pg. 2260
RAKS BUILDING SUPPLY INC; *U.S. Private*, pg. 3349
RANCHERS SUPPLY COMPANY, INC.; *U.S. Private*, pg. 3352
RANDALL BROTHERS INC.; *U.S. Private*, pg. 3353
RAYMOND BUILDING SUPPLY LLC—See Bain Capital, LP; *U.S. Private*, pg. 451
RAYNER & RINN-SCOTT INC.; *U.S. Private*, pg. 3359
RAYNOR BUILDING CENTER—See Neisewander Enterprises Inc.; *U.S. Private*, pg. 2882
REEL LUMBER SERVICE; *U.S. Private*, pg. 3383
REEVES HARDWARE COMPANY; *U.S. Private*, pg. 3384
REFRIGERATION SUPPLIES INC.; *U.S. Private*, pg. 3385
REICO, INC.; *U.S. Private*, pg. 3391
RELCO PRODUCTS INC.; *U.S. Private*, pg. 3393
RELIABLE WHOLESALE LUMBER INC.; *U.S. Private*, pg. 3394
RESEAU BOIS S.A.R.L.—See Owens Corning; *U.S. Public*, pg. 1627
R.E. SWEENEY COMPANY INC.; *U.S. Private*, pg. 3335
RICHARD G. JENNINGS III ENTERPRISES; *U.S. Private*, pg. 3428
RICHMOND INTERNATIONAL FOREST PRODUCTS, LLC—See Forest City Trading Group, LLC; *U.S. Private*, pg. 1566
RIDOUT LUMBER COMPANY OF BATESVILLE, LLC—See Bain Capital, LP; *U.S. Private*, pg. 451
RIDOUT LUMBER COMPANY OF JOPLIN, INC.—See Bain Capital, LP; *U.S. Private*, pg. 451
RIDOUT LUMBER CO. OF BRINKLEY, INC.—See Bain Capital, LP; *U.S. Private*, pg. 451
RIDOUT LUMBER CO. OF RUSSELLVILLE, INC.—See Bain Capital, LP; *U.S. Private*, pg. 451
RIM FOREST LUMBER, CO.; *U.S. Private*, pg. 3437
RINGS END INC.; *U.S. Private*, pg. 3438
RITTER LUMBER CO.; *U.S. Private*, pg. 3442
RIVER CITY MILLWORK, INC.—See Hardwoods Distribution Inc.; *Int'l*, pg. 3273
RIVERHEAD BUILDING SUPPLY CORP.—See Riverhead Building Supply Corp.; *U.S. Private*, pg. 3444
RIVERSIDE FOREST PRODUCTS INC.; *U.S. Private*, pg. 3445
RMA HOME SERVICES INC.; *U.S. Private*, pg. 3451
ROBCO MADEIRAS LTDA.—See Robinson Lumber & Export Company; *U.S. Private*, pg. 3462
ROBERT BOWDEN INC.; *U.S. Private*, pg. 3457
ROBERT N. KARPP CO. INC.—See GMS Inc.; *U.S. Public*, pg. 948
ROBERTS & DYBDAHL INC.—See Roberts Trading Corporation; *U.S. Private*, pg. 3460
ROBERTS TRADING CORPORATION; *U.S. Private*, pg. 3460
ROBINSON EXPORT AND IMPORT CORPORATION; *U.S. Private*, pg. 3461
ROBINSON LUMBER & EXPORT COMPANY; *U.S. Private*, pg. 3462
ROCKY CREEK LUMBER COMPANY LLC; *U.S. Private*, pg. 3464
ROCKY TOP MATERIALS, INC.—See GMS Inc.; *U.S. Public*, pg. 948
ROOF TRUSS SUPPLY INC.; *U.S. Private*, pg. 3478
ROPER BROTHERS LUMBER CO., INC.; *U.S. Private*, pg. 3480
ROSS PALLETS INC.; *U.S. Private*, pg. 3485
ROWE SUPPLY CO—See Leonard Green & Partners, L.P.; *U.S. Private*, pg. 2429

ROY O. ELDER LUMBER COMPANY INC.; *U.S. Private*, pg. 3491
R.P. WILLIAMS & SONS, INC.; *U.S. Private*, pg. 3339
RUGBY IPD CORP.—See Hardwoods Distribution Inc.; *Int'l*, pg. 3273
RUSSELL LANDS INC.; *U.S. Private*, pg. 3506
RUSSELL-MOORE LUMBER INC; *U.S. Private*, pg. 3507
RUSSIN LUMBER CORP; *U.S. Private*, pg. 3507
RW SPECIALTIES LLC—See Strength Capital Partners, LLC; *U.S. Private*, pg. 3839
SAINT CROIX VALLEY HARDWOODS INC.; *U.S. Private*, pg. 3529
SAINT-GOBAIN BUILDING DISTRIBUTION LTD.—See CVC Capital Partners SICAV-FIS S.A.; *Int'l*, pg. 1884
SALTIRE TRADE PLASTICS LIMITED—See Epwin Group Plc; *Int'l*, pg. 2466
S.A. MORMAN & COMPANY; *U.S. Private*, pg. 3515
SAMPSON LUMBER CO. INC.; *U.S. Private*, pg. 3537
SAMUEL FELDMAN LUMBER CO., INC.—See Bain Capital, LP; *U.S. Private*, pg. 451
SANFORD & HAWLEY, INC.; *U.S. Private*, pg. 3545
SAN JOAQUIN LUMBER CO.; *U.S. Private*, pg. 3541
SANXIN FACADE TECHNOLOGY LTD.—See Hainan Development Holdings Nanhai Co., Ltd.; *Int'l*, pg. 3212
SAROYAN LUMBER COMPANY INC.; *U.S. Private*, pg. 3550
SCHALLER HARDWOOD LUMBER CO.; *U.S. Private*, pg. 3563
SCHERER BROTHERS LUMBER COMPANY; *U.S. Private*, pg. 3564
SCHILLING BROS LUMBER CO., INC.; *U.S. Private*, pg. 3565
SCHMIDT BUILDERS SUPPLY INC.; *U.S. Private*, pg. 3566
THE SCHOCKMAN LUMBER COMPANY, INC.; *U.S. Private*, pg. 4114
SCHOLL FOREST INDUSTRIES INC.; *U.S. Private*, pg. 3567
SCHUCK & SONS CONSTRUCTION COMPANY, INC.; *U.S. Private*, pg. 3570
SCHUTTE LUMBER COMPANY; *U.S. Private*, pg. 3571
SCOTT LUMBER COMPANY; *U.S. Private*, pg. 3577
SCR, INC.; *U.S. Private*, pg. 3579
SEABOARD INTERNATIONAL FOREST PRODUCTS LLC—See Forest City Trading Group, LLC; *U.S. Private*, pg. 1566
SEEMAC INCORPORATED; *U.S. Private*, pg. 3598
SELF SERVE LUMBER CO.; *U.S. Private*, pg. 3602
SEPULVEDA BUILDING MATERIALS, INC.; *U.S. Private*, pg. 3612
SERVICE CONSTRUCTION SUPPLY, INC.—See Darragh Co; *U.S. Private*, pg. 1159
SERVICE TEAM INC.; *U.S. Private*, pg. 3616
SEVEN D INDUSTRIES, L.P.—See The DeGol Organization; *U.S. Private*, pg. 4019
SHEETS WHOLESALE INC.; *U.S. Private*, pg. 3630
SHELTER PRODUCTS INC.; *U.S. Private*, pg. 3631
SHERWOOD LUMBER CORPORATION; *U.S. Private*, pg. 3635
SHORT AND PAULK SUPPLY COMPANY; *U.S. Private*, pg. 3642
SILVERADO BUILDING MATERIALS; *U.S. Private*, pg. 3662
SIMMS LUMBER CO. INC.; *U.S. Private*, pg. 3666
SIND PARTICLE BOARD MILLS LTD.—See B.F. Modaraba; *Int'l*, pg. 789
SINO-MAPLE (SHANGHAI) TRADING CO., LTD.—See Emerald Plantation Holdings Limited; *Int'l*, pg. 2378
SLITERS; *U.S. Private*, pg. 3689
SMARTPLY EUROPE LIMITED—See Coillte Ltd.; *Int'l*, pg. 1696
SMITH COMPANIES OF LEXINGTON; *U.S. Private*, pg. 3694
SMITH PHILLIPS BUILDING SUPPLY; *U.S. Private*, pg. 3695
SNAVELY FOREST PRODUCTS, INC.—See MacArthur Co.; *U.S. Private*, pg. 2534
SOLID SURFACES, INC.; *U.S. Private*, pg. 3709
SOUTH ALABAMA BRICK COMPANY; *U.S. Private*, pg. 3719
SOUTH ATLANTIC FOREST PRODUCTS INC.; *U.S. Private*, pg. 3719
SOUTHEASTERN SUPPLY CO. INC.; *U.S. Private*, pg. 3729
SOUTHERN HOME & RANCH CENTER; *U.S. Private*, pg. 3732
SOUTHWEST MOULDING CO.—See Hardwoods Distribution Inc.; *Int'l*, pg. 3273
SPARTANBURG FOREST PRODUCTS INC.; *U.S. Private*, pg. 3746
SPECIALTY WOOD PRODUCTS INC.—See Tumac Lumber Co. Inc.; *U.S. Private*, pg. 4258
SPELLMAN HARDWOODS INC.; *U.S. Private*, pg. 3754
SPERRHOLZ KOCH GMBH—See Enno Roggemann GmbH & Co. KG; *Int'l*, pg. 2443
SPOROCO INC.; *U.S. Private*, pg. 3760
S&S SALES CORPORATION; *U.S. Private*, pg. 3514
STANDALE HOME CENTER—See Standale Lumber & Supply Co. Inc.; *U.S. Private*, pg. 3777

N.A.I.C.S. INDEX

STANDALE LUMBER & SUPPLY CO. INC.; *U.S. Private,* pg. 3777
STANDARD BUILDERS SUPPLY INC.; *U.S. Private,* pg. 3778
STANDARD SUPPLY & LUMBER CO.—See Bain Capital, LP; *U.S. Private,* pg. 451
STANDEX DE MEXICO S.A. DE C.V.—See Standex International; *U.S. Public,* pg. 1931
STANLEY ACCESS TECHNOLOGIES, LLC—See Allegion Public Limited Company; *Int'l,* pg. 335
STAR LUMBER & SUPPLY COMPANY, INC.; *U.S. Private,* pg. 3785
STATE LINE BUILDING SUPPLY INC.—See GMS Inc.; *U.S. Public,* pg. 948
STEINKAMP WAREHOUSES, INC.; *U.S. Private,* pg. 3798
STENERSON BROS LUMBER COMPANY; *U.S. Private,* pg. 3801
STEPHENSON LUMBER COMPANY, INC.; *U.S. Private,* pg. 3803
STERLING LUMBER COMPANY; *U.S. Private,* pg. 3806
STERLING LUMBER & INVESTMENT CO.; *U.S. Private,* pg. 3806
STILL LUMBER CO. INC.—See Spahn & Rose Lumber Co., Inc.; *U.S. Private,* pg. 3744
STINE INC.; *U.S. Private,* pg. 3812
STINE & LUMBER INC.—See Stine Inc.; *U.S. Private,* pg. 3813
STOCK BUILDING SUPPLY; *U.S. Private,* pg. 3814
STOCK BUILDING SUPPLY—See Builders FirstSource, Inc.; *U.S. Public,* pg. 409
STOCK BUILDING SUPPLY—See Builders FirstSource, Inc.; *U.S. Public,* pg. 409
STOCK BUILDING SUPPLY—See Builders FirstSource, Inc.; *U.S. Public,* pg. 409
STOCK BUILDING SUPPLY—See Builders FirstSource, Inc.; *U.S. Public,* pg. 409
STOCK BUILDING SUPPLY—See Builders FirstSource, Inc.; *U.S. Public,* pg. 409
STONE'S, INC.—See Clyde Companies Inc.; *U.S. Private,* pg. 949
STRAIT & LAMP LUMBER CO. INC.; *U.S. Private,* pg. 3833
STRATHAM TIRE INC.; *U.S. Private,* pg. 3837
STRINGFELLOW LUMBER COMPANY LLC; *U.S. Private,* pg. 3840
SUDBURY LUMBER COMPANY INC.—See Arlington Coal & Lumber Co. Inc.; *U.S. Private,* pg. 329
SULLIVAN & MANN LUMBER CO., INC.; *U.S. Private,* pg. 3851
SUNDERLAND BROTHERS COMPANY; *U.S. Private,* pg. 3866
SUN MOUNTAIN LUMBER, INC.; *U.S. Private,* pg. 3863
SUNNYVALE LUMBER INC.; *U.S. Private,* pg. 3869
SUNRISE WINDOWS LTD.—See Koch Industries, Inc.; *U.S. Private,* pg. 2332
SUPER PALLET RECYCLING CORP.; *U.S. Private,* pg. 3874
SUTHERLAND LUMBER CO.; *U.S. Private,* pg. 3886
SUWANNEE LUMBER COMPANY LLC—See Conifex Timber Inc.; *Int'l,* pg. 1768
SWIFT SUPPLY, INC.; *U.S. Private,* pg. 3893
TABOR CITY LUMBER COMPANY INCORPORATED; *U.S. Private,* pg. 3920
TAGUE LUMBER INC.; *U.S. Private,* pg. 3922
TAMPA INTERNATIONAL FOREST PRODUCTS, LLC—See Forest City Trading Group, LLC; *U.S. Private,* pg. 1566
T. BAIRD MCILVAIN CO.; *U.S. Private,* pg. 3911
TBS SPECIALTIES DIRECT INC.—See ITR Industries Inc.; *U.S. Private,* pg. 2150
TEAGUE LUMBER COMPANY INC.; *U.S. Private,* pg. 3948
TECHNIC INCORPORATED - TECHNIC ENGINEERED POWDERS DIVISION—See Technic Incorporated; *U.S. Private,* pg. 3953
THRIFTWAY INC.; *U.S. Private,* pg. 4164
T.H. ROGERS LUMBER CO.; *U.S. Private,* pg. 3912
TIBBETTS LUMBER CO., LLC; *U.S. Private,* pg. 4166
TIMBER INDUSTRIES INC.; *U.S. Private,* pg. 4171
TIMBERLINE FOREST PRODUCTS LLC; *U.S. Private,* pg. 4172
TIMBER PRODUCTS CO.—See Timber Products Company, LP; *U.S. Private,* pg. 4171
TIMSAMLEE ASSOCIATES INC.; *U.S. Private,* pg. 4173
TINDELL'S INC.; *U.S. Private,* pg. 4173
TREVDAN INC.; *U.S. Private,* pg. 4219
TRI-EXCELLENCE, INC.—See Gulfside Supply Inc.; *U.S. Private,* pg. 1817
TRIMCO MILLWORK—See Hoff Companies, Inc; *U.S. Private,* pg. 1959
TRINITY CONSTRUCTION MATERIALS, INC.—See Trinity Industries, Inc.; *U.S. Public,* pg. 2193
TRINITY CRYOGENICS, LLC—See Trinity Industries, Inc.; *U.S. Public,* pg. 2194
TRINITY FOREST INDUSTRIES INC.; *U.S. Private,* pg. 4233
TRI-STATE DISTRIBUTORS INCORPORATED; *U.S. Private,* pg. 4223
TRI-STATE FOREST PRODUCTS; *U.S. Private,* pg. 4224
TRI SUPPLY COMPANY; *U.S. Private,* pg. 4221

TRNLWS, LLC—See Trinity Industries, Inc.; *U.S. Public,* pg. 2193
TRUSSES UNLIMITED INC.; *U.S. Private,* pg. 4250
TUMAC LUMBER CO. INC.; *U.S. Private,* pg. 4258
UFP BELCHERTOWN, LLC—See UFP Industries, Inc.; *U.S. Public,* pg. 2219
UFP BERLIN, LLC—See UFP Industries, Inc.; *U.S. Public,* pg. 2219
UFP DISTRIBUTION, LLC—See UFP Industries, Inc.; *U.S. Public,* pg. 2219
UFP ELKWOOD, LLC—See UFP Industries, Inc.; *U.S. Public,* pg. 2219
UFP GRANDVIEW, LLC—See UFP Industries, Inc.; *U.S. Public,* pg. 2220
UFP HAMILTON, LLC—See UFP Industries, Inc.; *U.S. Public,* pg. 2220
UFP HILLSBORO, LLC—See UFP Industries, Inc.; *U.S. Public,* pg. 2220
UFP LODI, LLC—See UFP Industries, Inc.; *U.S. Public,* pg. 2220
UFP MCMINNVILLE, LLC—See UFP Industries, Inc.; *U.S. Public,* pg. 2220
UFP MID-ATLANTIC, LLC - LIBERTY—See UFP Industries, Inc.; *U.S. Public,* pg. 2220
UFP MORRISTOWN, LLC—See UFP Industries, Inc.; *U.S. Public,* pg. 2220
UFP NAPPANEE, LLC—See UFP Industries, Inc.; *U.S. Public,* pg. 2220
UFP SALISBURY, LLC—See UFP Industries, Inc.; *U.S. Public,* pg. 2220
UFP TAMPA, LLC—See UFP Industries, Inc.; *U.S. Public,* pg. 2220
UFP VENTURES II, INC.—See UFP Industries, Inc.; *U.S. Public,* pg. 2220
UFP WARRENS, LLC—See UFP Industries, Inc.; *U.S. Public,* pg. 2220
UFP WHITE BEAR LAKE, LLC—See UFP Industries, Inc.; *U.S. Public,* pg. 2221
UNITED PLYWOODS & LUMBER INC.; *U.S. Private,* pg. 4295
UNIVERSAL BUILDING SPECIALTIES INCORPORATED; *U.S. Private,* pg. 4304
UNIVERSAL CONSUMER PRODUCTS, INC.—See UFP Industries, Inc.; *U.S. Public,* pg. 2221
UNIVERSAL INTERLOCK CORP.; *U.S. Private,* pg. 4305
URESCO CONSTRUCTION MATERIALS INC.; *U.S. Private,* pg. 4315
USG INTERNATIONAL, LTD.—See Gebr. Knauf KG; *Int'l,* pg. 2908
US LUMBER GROUP INC.—See Specialty Building Products, LLC; *U.S. Private,* pg. 3749
VALLEY ACQUISITION CO. LLC; *U.S. Private,* pg. 4332
VALLEY BUILDING SUPPLY INC.—See Eagle Corporation; *U.S. Private,* pg. 1309
VALLEY CONSTRUCTION SUPPLY; *U.S. Private,* pg. 4333
VALLEY PALLET RECYCLERS INC.; *U.S. Private,* pg. 4335
VALUTEC GROUP AB—See Addtech AB; *Int'l,* pg. 135
VANDERMEER FOREST PRODUCTS INC.—See Cerberus Capital Management, L.P.; *U.S. Private,* pg. 837
VAN LUMBER INC.; *U.S. Private,* pg. 4340
VANPORT CANADA, CO.—See Vanport Manufacturing, Inc.; *U.S. Private,* pg. 4344
VAUGHAN FURNITURE COMPANY INC.; *U.S. Private,* pg. 4348
VAUGHAN & SONS, INC. MULTI-FAMILY SALES—See Vaughan & Sons, Inc.; *U.S. Private,* pg. 4348
VAUGHAN & SONS, INC.; *U.S. Private,* pg. 4348
VERCOR S.A—See ASSA ABLOY AB; *Int'l,* pg. 638
VIKING FOREST PRODUCTS, LLC—See Forest City Trading Group, LLC; *U.S. Private,* pg. 1566
VIKING INC.; *U.S. Private,* pg. 4382
VIRGINIA HARDWOOD CO.; *U.S. Private,* pg. 4387
VIRGINIA PELLA INC.; *U.S. Private,* pg. 4388
VON TOBEL CORPORATION; *U.S. Private,* pg. 4412
VOS WINDOW & DOOR INC.; *U.S. Private,* pg. 4413
WALBROOK MILL & LUMBER CO. INC.; *U.S. Private,* pg. 4427
WALKER LUMBER COMPANY, INC.—See Hardwoods Distribution Inc.; *Int'l,* pg. 3273
WALLBOARD, INC.—See American Securities LLC; *U.S. Private,* pg. 249
WALNUT INVESTMENT CORP.; *U.S. Private,* pg. 4432
WARNER ROBINS SUPPLY CO. INC.; *U.S. Private,* pg. 4442
WARREN BROTHERS SASH & DOOR COMPANY—See Hardwoods Distribution Inc.; *Int'l,* pg. 3273
WARREN LUMBER & MILLWORK; *U.S. Private,* pg. 4444
WARREN TRASK COMPANY INC.—See Gerrity Company Incorporated; *U.S. Private,* pg. 1687
WASHOE BUILDING SUPPLY COMPANY, INC.—See Leonard Green & Partners, L.P.; *U.S. Private,* pg. 2429
WAVERLY LUMBER & MANUFACTURING; *U.S. Private,* pg. 4458
WBH INDUSTRIES INC; *U.S. Private,* pg. 4461
WDD INC.; *U.S. Private,* pg. 4462
WEEKES FOREST PRODUCTS INC.; *U.S. Private,* pg. 4469

423320 — BRICK, STONE, AND R...

WEEKS SUPPLY—See Horton Industries, Inc.; *U.S. Private,* pg. 1984
WEISMAN HOME OUTLETS; *U.S. Private,* pg. 4472
WEST COAST LUMBER, INC.—See Building Industry Partners LLC; *U.S. Private,* pg. 683
WEST COAST MILLS INC.; *U.S. Private,* pg. 4484
THE WEST END LUMBER COMPANY; *U.S. Private,* pg. 4134
WESTERN FOREST PRODUCTS INC.; *U.S. Private,* pg. 4493
WESTERN INTERNATIONAL FOREST PRODUCTS, LLC—See Forest City Trading Group, LLC; *U.S. Private,* pg. 1566
WESTERN LUMBER CO.; *U.S. Private,* pg. 4494
WESTERN MATERIALS INC.; *U.S. Private,* pg. 4494
WESTERN PACIFIC BUILDING MATERIALS; *U.S. Private,* pg. 4495
WESTERN TIMBER PRODUCTS INC.; *U.S. Private,* pg. 4497
WEYERHAEUSER (ASIA) LIMITED—See Weyerhaeuser Company; *U.S. Public,* pg. 2365
WEYERHAEUSER INTERNATIONAL, INC.—See Weyerhaeuser Company; *U.S. Public,* pg. 2365
WEYERHAEUSER NR COMPANY—See Weyerhaeuser Company; *U.S. Public,* pg. 2365
WEYERHAEUSER POLAND SP. Z O.O.—See Weyerhaeuser Company; *U.S. Public,* pg. 2365
WEYERHAEUSER PRODUCTOS, S.A.—See Weyerhaeuser Company; *U.S. Public,* pg. 2365
W. H. CRESS COMPANY, INC.; *U.S. Private,* pg. 4418
WHEELER'S CORPORATION; *U.S. Private,* pg. 4505
WHEELER'S-NEWNAN—See Wheeler's Corporation; *U.S. Private,* pg. 4506
WHEELER'S-ROME—See Wheeler's Corporation; *U.S. Private,* pg. 4506
WHOLESALE BUILDERS SUPPLY INC.; *U.S. Private,* pg. 4514
WHOLESALE WOOD PRODUCTS—See Lumber Group Inc.; *U.S. Private,* pg. 2513
WIENER CROWLEY & ST JOHN; *U.S. Private,* pg. 4516
THE WILLAMETTE VALLEY COMPANY - WVCO WOOD PRODUCTS DIVISION—See The Willamette Valley Company; *U.S. Private,* pg. 4136
WILLIAM B. MORSE LUMBER CO.; *U.S. Private,* pg. 4522
WILLIAM BROJACK LUMBER COMPANY; *U.S. Private,* pg. 4522
WILMINGTON BUILDERS SUPPLY COMPANY INC.—See Arlington Coal & Lumber Co. Inc.; *U.S. Private,* pg. 329
WILSON LUMBER COMPANY INC.; *U.S. Private,* pg. 4531
WILSON PLYWOOD & DOOR, INC.; *U.S. Private,* pg. 4531
WINDOW WIDGETS LLP—See Owens Corning; *U.S. Public,* pg. 1627
WIRTHS LUMBER CO., INC.; *U.S. Private,* pg. 4547
WITT BUILDING MATERIAL COMPANY; *U.S. Private,* pg. 4551
W.M. CRAMER LUMBER CO. INC.; *U.S. Private,* pg. 4421
W.M. TINDER INCORPORATED; *U.S. Private,* pg. 4422
WOLVERINE HARDWOODS INC.; *U.S. Private,* pg. 4555
WOLVERINE SUPPLY INC.; *U.S. Private,* pg. 4555
WOODFORD PLYWOOD INC.; *U.S. Private,* pg. 4558
WOODGRAIN DISTRIBUTION, INC.—See Woodgrain, Inc.; *U.S. Private,* pg. 4558
WOODINVILLE LUMBER, INC.; *U.S. Private,* pg. 4558
WOODLAND FOREST PRODUCTS INC.; *U.S. Private,* pg. 4559
WOODSMAN KITCHENS & FLOORS; *U.S. Private,* pg. 4560
WOOD SOURCE, INC.—See Patrick Lumber Company, Inc.; *U.S. Private,* pg. 3110
WOOD TRADE INTERNATIONAL LLC; *U.S. Private,* pg. 4557
WORLD WOOD CO., INC.—See Baillie Lumber Co., Inc.; *U.S. Private,* pg. 426
W.S. TRIMBLE CO., INC.; *U.S. Private,* pg. 4423
WYNDHAM SUPPLIES PTE LTD—See Allgreen Properties Ltd.; *Int'l,* pg. 338
WYOMING MILLWORK CO.—See Builders FirstSource, Inc.; *U.S. Public,* pg. 410
YOUR BUILDING CENTERS, INC.; *U.S. Private,* pg. 4594
ZARSKY LUMBER CO., INC.—See Kodiak Building Partners LLC; *U.S. Private,* pg. 2336
ZIEGLER LUMBER COMPANY; *U.S. Private,* pg. 4604

423320 — BRICK, STONE, AND RELATED CONSTRUCTION MATERIAL MERCHANT WHOLESALERS

3 PAGEN HANDELSGESELLSCHAFT MBH—See Damartex SA; *Int'l,* pg. 1955
3 RIVERS MATERIALS INC—See Cumberland Materials; *U.S. Private,* pg. 1122
AALBORG CEMENT COMPANY INC.—See Cementir Holding N.V.; *Int'l,* pg. 1397
AALBORG PORTLAND FRANCE SAS—See Cementir Holding N.V.; *Int'l,* pg. 1397
AALBORG PORTLAND ISLANDI EHF—See Cementir Holding N.V.; *Int'l,* pg. 1397

423320 — BRICK, STONE, AND R...

AALBORG PORTLAND OOO—See Cementir Holding N.V.; *Int'l*, pg. 1397
AALBORG PORTLAND POLSKA SP.Z.O.O—See Cementir Holding N.V.; *Int'l*, pg. 1397
AALBORG PORTLAND US INC.—See Cementir Holding N.V.; *Int'l*, pg. 1397
ABE MATERIALS - EASTON—See Haines & Kibblehouse Inc.; *U.S. Private*, pg. 1840
ACF ENVIRONMENTAL; *U.S. Private*, pg. 58
ACTION SUPPLY CO., INC.—See Vulcan Materials Company; *U.S. Public*, pg. 2313
AEROC JAMERA OY—See Aeroc International AS; *Int'l*, pg. 180
AGC CERAMICS CO., LTD.—See AGC Inc.; *Int'l*, pg. 201
AGGREGATE INDUSTRIES MID-ATLANTIC REGION—See Holcim Ltd.; *Int'l*, pg. 3446
AGGREGATE INDUSTRIES MIDWEST REGION—See Holcim Ltd.; *Int'l*, pg. 3446
AGGREGATE INDUSTRIES NORTHEAST REGION—See Holcim Ltd.; *Int'l*, pg. 3446
AGOSTINI MARKETING—See Agostini's Limited; *Int'l*, pg. 213
AHI SUPPLY INC.; *U.S. Private*, pg. 130
ALAMO GULF COAST RAILROAD COMPANY—See Martin Marietta Materials, Inc.; *U.S. Public*, pg. 1389
AL KATHIRI HOLDING CO; *Int'l*, pg. 280
ALLEY-CASSETTY BRICK MURFREESBORO DIV.—See Alley-Cassetty Companies; *U.S. Private*, pg. 180
ALLEYTON RESOURCE COMPANY, LLC—See Summit Materials, Inc.; *U.S. Public*, pg. 1959
ALLIED BUILDING MATERIALS INC.; *U.S. Private*, pg. 185
ALL STATES ASPHALT INC.; *U.S. Private*, pg. 172
AL MUHAIDIB BUILDING MATERIALS COMPANY—See A.K. Al-Muhaidib & Sons Group of Companies; *Int'l*, pg. 24
AL-SALBOOKH TRADING COMPANY K.S.C.; *Int'l*, pg. 288
ALTAVIEW CONCRETE, LLC—See Summit Materials, Inc.; *U.S. Public*, pg. 1960
ANCHORAGE SAND & GRAVEL COMPANY, INC.—See MDU Resources Group, Inc.; *U.S. Public*, pg. 1409
ANDINO CEMENTS USA, LLC; *U.S. Private*, pg. 278
ANGELO'S SUPPLIES, INC.—See SiteOne Landscape Supply, Inc.; *U.S. Public*, pg. 1889
ARCHITECTURAL GRANITE & MARBLE, LLC—See Architectural Surfaces Group, LLC; *U.S. Private*, pg. 311
ARIZONA STONE & ARCHITECTURAL, LLC.; *U.S. Private*, pg. 325
ARIZONA TILE-ANAHEIM—See Arizona Tile Supply, Inc.; *U.S. Private*, pg. 325
ARLEY WHOLESALE INC.; *U.S. Private*, pg. 326
ARTWALK TILE, INC.; *U.S. Private*, pg. 344
ASIA HOLDINGS CO., LTD. - SEOUL REMICON PLANT—See Asia Holdings Co., Ltd.; *Int'l*, pg. 612
ASIA HOLDINGS CO., LTD. - SUWON PLANT—See Asia Holdings Co., Ltd.; *Int'l*, pg. 612
ASIA HOLDINGS CO., LTD. - YONGIN PLANT—See Asia Holdings Co., Ltd.; *Int'l*, pg. 612
ASIAN PORCELAIN SDN. BHD.—See CSH Alliance Berhad; *Int'l*, pg. 1865
ASPHALT PAVING & SUPPLY INC.—See McCormick Incorporated; *U.S. Private*, pg. 2630
ASSAS FOR CONCRETE PRODUCTS CO. LTD.; *Int'l*, pg. 641
ASSIUT ISLAMIC TRADING; *Int'l*, pg. 648
ASSOCIATED ASPHALT INC.—See Ergon, Inc.; *U.S. Private*, pg. 1418
ATKINSON MATERIALS—See Haines & Kibblehouse Inc.; *U.S. Private*, pg. 1840
ATLAS CONSTRUCTION SUPPLY INC.; *U.S. Private*, pg. 375
ATLAS CORPORATION S.R.L. - APLA DIVISION—See Atlas Corporation S.R.L.; *Int'l*, pg. 685
ATTARD & CO. INDUSTRIAL LTD.—See Attard & Co. Ltd.; *Int'l*, pg. 696
AUGUSTA READY MIX INC.; *U.S. Private*, pg. 392
BADGERLAND SUPPLY, INC.—See GMS Inc.; *U.S. Public*, pg. 947
BAKER ROCK RESOURCES—See Baker Rock Crushing Co.; *U.S. Private*, pg. 456
BARNSCO INC.—See Kodiak Building Partners LLC; *U.S. Private*, pg. 2336
BARNSCO—See Georgeco Inc.; *U.S. Private*, pg. 1684
BASF MINERALS OY—See BASF SE; *Int'l*, pg. 880
BATCHELDER & COLLINS INC.—See CRH plc; *Int'l*, pg. 486
BAUSTEINWERK BOTT - BLASBERG G.M.B.H. & CO. KOMMANDITGESELLSCHAFT—See Heidelberg Materials AG; *Int'l*, pg. 3308
BEAR RIVER ZEOLITE COMPANY—See United States Antimony Corporation; *U.S. Public*, pg. 2236
BEEHIVE BRICK & STONE—See Leonard Green & Partners, L.P.; *U.S. Private*, pg. 2429
BEIJING CULTURAL INVESTMENT HOLDINGS CO., LTD.; *Int'l*, pg. 948
BEIJING NEW BUILDING MATERIALS PUBLIC LIMITED COMPANY—See China National Building Material Group Co., Ltd.; *Int'l*, pg. 1525
THE BELDEN BRICK SALES COMPANY INC.—See The Belden Brick Company Inc.; *U.S. Private*, pg. 3993

BELDEN TRI-STATE BUILDING MATERIALS—See The Belden Brick Company Inc.; *U.S. Private*, pg. 3993
BELL SUPPLY CO.; *U.S. Private*, pg. 519
BELVIDERE SAND & GRAVEL—See Haines & Kibblehouse Inc.; *U.S. Private*, pg. 1840
BEST MASONRY & TOOL SUPPLY, INC.—See CRH plc; *Int'l*, pg. 1846
BETON BELANGER INC.—See Beton Provincial Ltee; *Int'l*, pg. 1002
BETON BRUNSWICK LTEE—See Beton Provincial Ltee; *Int'l*, pg. 1002
BETONG OST AS—See Heidelberg Materials AG; *Int'l*, pg. 3309
BETON HI-TECH INC.—See Beton Provincial Ltee; *Int'l*, pg. 1002
BETON MISTRAL LTEE—See Beton Provincial Ltee; *Int'l*, pg. 1002
BETON REGIONAL INC.—See Beton Provincial Ltee; *Int'l*, pg. 1002
BETON RIVE-NORD INC.—See Beton Provincial Ltee; *Int'l*, pg. 1002
BETONS TRIO INC.—See Beton Provincial Ltee; *Int'l*, pg. 1003
BKEP MATERIALS LLC—See Ergon, Inc.; *U.S. Private*, pg. 1418
BLACK LAB, LLC—See Covia Holdings Corporation; *U.S. Private*, pg. 1072
BLAISTEN SA—See Cencosud S.A.; *Int'l*, pg. 1400
BM VALLA EHF—See Heidelberg Materials AG; *Int'l*, pg. 3308
BODE CONCRETE, LLC—See Vulcan Materials Company; *U.S. Public*, pg. 2313
BORDER CONSTRUCTION SPECIALTIES, LLC—See The Sterling Group, L.P.; *U.S. Private*, pg. 4122
BOSIG INC.—See BOSIG Holding GmbH & Co. KG; *Int'l*, pg. 1116
BOXLEY MATERIALS COMPANY—See Summit Materials, Inc.; *U.S. Public*, pg. 1960
BRASTILE INC.; *U.S. Private*, pg. 640
BRICK-ABILITY LTD.—See Brickability Group plc; *Int'l*, pg. 1151
BRICK-LINK LIMITED—See Brickability Group plc; *Int'l*, pg. 1151
BRICKMONGERS (WESSEX) LTD.—See Brickability Group plc; *Int'l*, pg. 1151
BRICK SERVICES LIMITED—See Brickability Group plc; *Int'l*, pg. 1151
BROCK WHITE COMPANY LLC—See The Sterling Group, L.P.; *U.S. Private*, pg. 4122
BUILDERS BOX (INDIA) PVT. LTD—See BuilderSmart Public Company Limited; *Int'l*, pg. 1212
BUILDERSMART (VIETNAM) LIMITED—See BuilderSmart Public Company Limited; *Int'l*, pg. 1212
BUILDING PRODUCTS INC.; *U.S. Private*, pg. 683
BURNCO COLORADO, LLC—See Burnco Rock Products Ltd; *Int'l*, pg. 1226
BURRELL MINING PRODUCTS INC.; *U.S. Private*, pg. 691
BURRELL MINING PRODUCTS INC UTAH—See Burrell Mining Products Inc.; *U.S. Private*, pg. 691
B.V. BOUWGRONDSTOFFEN A.G.M.—See Heidelberg Materials AG; *Int'l*, pg. 3308
BYGGFAKTA DOCU AS—See Byggfakta Group Nordic HoldCo AB; *Int'l*, pg. 1234
CALCEMENTI JONICI S.R.L.—See Heidelberg Materials AG; *Int'l*, pg. 3316
CALHOUN ASPHALT COMPANY, INC.—See Vulcan Materials Company; *U.S. Public*, pg. 2313
CAMBRIDGE AGGREGATES INC.—See Heidelberg Materials AG; *Int'l*, pg. 3317
CANTERA DE ARIDOS PUIG BROCA S.A.—See CRH plc; *Int'l*, pg. 1844
CANTERA EL HOYON, S.A.—See Heidelberg Materials AG; *Int'l*, pg. 3309
CANTILLANA GMBH—See Cantillana SA/NV; *Int'l*, pg. 1299
CARLISLE CONSTRUCTION MATERIALS BV—See Carlisle Companies Incorporated; *U.S. Public*, pg. 436
CARLISLE CONSTRUCTION MATERIALS UK—See Carlisle Companies Incorporated; *U.S. Public*, pg. 436
CARL OWNBY & CO. INC.; *U.S. Private*, pg. 763
CAROLINA SAND - JOHNSONVILLE—See Summit Materials, Inc.; *U.S. Public*, pg. 1959
CASTLE BUILDING PRODUCTS LIMITED—See Heidelberg Materials AG; *Int'l*, pg. 3309
CBR INTERNATIONAL SERVICES S.A.—See Heidelberg Materials AG; *Int'l*, pg. 3309
CBR PORTLAND B.V.—See Heidelberg Materials AG; *Int'l*, pg. 3309
CEMENTO POLPAICO S.A. - MEJILLONES GRINDING PLANT—See Cemento Polpaico S.A.; *Int'l*, pg. 1397
CEMENT TRADING ACTIVITIES - COMERCIO INTERNACIONAL S.A.—See Camargo Correa S.A.; *Int'l*, pg. 1267
CEMEX AB—See CEMEX, S.A.B. de C.V.; *Int'l*, pg. 1398
CEMEX OY—See CEMEX, S.A.B. de C.V.; *Int'l*, pg. 1399
CENTEX MATERIALS LLC—See Eagle Materials Inc.; *U.S. Public*, pg. 702
CENTRAL ALLIED ENTERPRISES - MASSILLON WASHED GRAVEL DIVISION—See Central Allied Enterprises; *U.S. Private*, pg. 818

CENTRAL VALLEY CONCRETE INC.; *U.S. Private*, pg. 826
CENTRAL WASHINGTON CONCRETE; *U.S. Private*, pg. 826
CHAPARRAL MATERIALS, INC.—See GMS Inc.; *U.S. Public*, pg. 948
CHARCON LIMITED—See Holcim Ltd.; *Int'l*, pg. 3446
CHEMEMAN AUSTRALIA PTY LTD.—See Chememan Public Company Limited; *Int'l*, pg. 1461
CHEVALIER (BUILDING SUPPLIES & ENGINEERING) LIMITED—See Chevalier International Holdings Limited; *Int'l*, pg. 1473
CHINA UNITED CEMENT CORPORATION—See China National Building Material Group Co., Ltd.; *Int'l*, pg. 1525
CH. KARNCHANG (LAO) CO., LTD—See CH. Karnchang Public Company Limited; *Int'l*, pg. 1435
CIARGA - ARGAMASSAS SECAS S.A.—See Camargo Correa S.A.; *Int'l*, pg. 1267
CIESCO INC.—See Novinger Group, Inc.; *U.S. Private*, pg. 2968
CIMENTOS DE MOCAMBIQUE, S.A.—See Camargo Correa S.A.; *Int'l*, pg. 1267
CIMGABON S.A.—See Heidelberg Materials AG; *Int'l*, pg. 3310
CIMPOR TRADING, S.A.—See Camargo Correa S.A.; *Int'l*, pg. 1267
CINDERCRETE PRODUCTS LIMITED—See Heidelberg Materials AG; *Int'l*, pg. 3310
CIRKEL GMBH & CO.KG; *Int'l*, pg. 1618
CLAYTON BLOCK CO. INC.; *U.S. Private*, pg. 918
CMI STONE GROUP INC.; *U.S. Private*, pg. 951
CMS PENKUARI SDN. BHD.—See Cahya Mata Sarawak Berhad; *Int'l*, pg. 1251
COLONIAL CONCRETE COMPANY—See Vulcan Materials Company; *U.S. Public*, pg. 2314
COLONIAL MATERIALS INC.—See GMS Inc.; *U.S. Public*, pg. 948
COLONIAL MATERIALS OF FAYETTEVILLE, INC.—See GMS Inc.; *U.S. Public*, pg. 948
COLONY MATERIALS HARDSCAPE & LANDSCAPE SUPPLIES—See Haines & Kibblehouse Inc.; *U.S. Private*, pg. 1840
COLORADO BEST BLOCK, LLC—See The Quikrete Companies, LLC; *U.S. Private*, pg. 4101
COLORADO DRYWALL SUPPLY LLC; *U.S. Private*, pg. 973
COLOR STONE INTERNATIONAL INC.—See Ointon International Inc.; *U.S. Private*, pg. 3006
COMMERCIAL BUILDING MATERIALS LLC—See National Construction Enterprises Inc.; *U.S. Private*, pg. 2851
COMMERCIAL READY MIX PRODUCTS INC.; *U.S. Private*, pg. 984
COMPAGNIE DES CIMENTS BELGES SA—See Cementir Holding N.V.; *Int'l*, pg. 1397
COMPANIA MINERA POLPAICO LTD.—See Cemento Polpaico S.A.; *Int'l*, pg. 1397
CONCRETE EXPRESS INC.; *U.S. Private*, pg. 1011
CONCRETE SOLUTIONS, INC.—See Rhino Linings Corporation; *U.S. Private*, pg. 3421
CONCRETE TIE INDUSTRIES INCORPORATED; *U.S. Private*, pg. 1011
CONESTOGA CERAMIC TILE DISTRIBUTORS; *U.S. Private*, pg. 1012
CONRAD COMPANY INCORPORATED; *U.S. Private*, pg. 1019
CONRAD YELVINGTON DISTRIBUTORS, INC.—See CRH plc; *Int'l*, pg. 1847
CONSOLIDATED BRICK & BUILDING SUPPLIES INC.; *U.S. Private*, pg. 1020
CONSOLIDATED INFRASTRUCTURE GROUP LIMITED; *Int'l*, pg. 1770
CONTEMPO CERAMIC TILE CORP.; *U.S. Private*, pg. 1027
CONTIGA TINGLEV A/S—See Heidelberg Materials AG; *Int'l*, pg. 3310
CONTINENTAL FLORIDA MATERIALS, INC.—See Heidelberg Materials AG; *Int'l*, pg. 3313
CORAM MATERIALS CORP.—See Vulcan Materials Company; *U.S. Public*, pg. 2314
CORESLAB STRUCTURES (ARIZ) INC.—See Coreslab International, Inc.; *Int'l*, pg. 1799
CORESLAB STRUCTURES (KANSAS), INC.—See Coreslab International, Inc.; *Int'l*, pg. 1799
CORESLAB STRUCTURES (MIAMI) INC.—See Coreslab International, Inc.; *Int'l*, pg. 1799
CORESLAB STRUCTURES (MISSOURI) INC.—See Coreslab International, Inc.; *Int'l*, pg. 1799
COSMIC STONE & TILE DISTRIBUTORS, INC.—See Architectural Surfaces Group, LLC; *U.S. Private*, pg. 311
COWELLS ARROW BINGO—See Arrow International, Inc.; *U.S. Private*, pg. 335
COWTOWN MATERIALS, INC.—See GMS Inc.; *U.S. Public*, pg. 948
CREST BRICK SLATE & TILE LIMITED—See Brickability Group plc; *Int'l*, pg. 1151
CRH CEMENT - MISSISSAUGA PLANT—See CRH plc; *Int'l*, pg. 1843
CRH CONCRETE A/S—See CRH plc; *Int'l*, pg. 1843
CRH FRANCE DISTRIBUTION SAS—See CRH plc; *Int'l*, pg. 1843

CRH STRUCTURAL CONCRETE B.V.—See CRH plc; *Int'l*, pg. 1844
CUMBERLAND MATERIALS; *U.S. Private*, pg. 1122
DAGSBORO MATERIALS—See Haines & Kibblehouse Inc.; *U.S. Private*, pg. 1841
DALACO MATERIALS LLC; *U.S. Private*, pg. 1148
DAL-TILE OF CANADA INC—See Mohawk Industries, Inc.; *U.S. Public*, pg. 1457
DARRAGH COMPANY; *U.S. Private*, pg. 1159
D&B TILE DISTRIBUTORS; *U.S. Private*, pg. 1136
DC HALSVIK AGGREGATES AS—See Group de Cloedt SA; *Int'l*, pg. 3088
DECK'S HARDSCAPE & LANDSCAPE SUPPLIES—See Haines & Kibblehouse Inc.; *U.S. Private*, pg. 1841
DELF SAND (PTY) LIMITED—See Afrimat Limited; *Int'l*, pg. 192
DELTA GRANITE AND MARBLE INC.; *U.S. Private*, pg. 1200
DELTA GYPSUM, LLC—See Hendricks Holding Company, Inc.; *U.S. Private*, pg. 1915
DESIGN MATERIALS INCORPORATED; *U.S. Private*, pg. 1213
DESIGN SPECIALTIES, INC.—See Precision Walls, Inc.; *U.S. Private*, pg. 3247
DESIMPEL BRICK LIMITED—See Heidelberg Materials AG; *Int'l*, pg. 3310
DIENER BRICK COMPANY; *U.S. Private*, pg. 1228
DIRECT SOURCE SUPPLY, INC.—See Myers Industries, Inc.; *U.S. Public*, pg. 1488
D&I SILICA, LLC—See Atlas Energy Solutions Inc.; *U.S. Public*, pg. 224
DONGGUAN UNIVERSAL CLASSICAL MATERIAL LTD.—See China Resources Building Materials Technology Holdings Limited; *Int'l*, pg. 1548
DOUTERLOIGNE N.V.—See CRH plc; *Int'l*, pg. 1844
DRAINAGE SYSTEMS DUBLIN LIMITED—See Grafton Group plc; *Int'l*, pg. 3050
DUBROOK CONCRETE, INC.—See Vulcan Materials Company; *U.S. Public*, pg. 2314
DUFFEK SAND & GRAVEL INC.; *U.S. Private*, pg. 1284
DUSHORE CONSTRUCTION MATERIALS—See Haines & Kibblehouse Inc.; *U.S. Private*, pg. 1841
DUTCHESS QUARRY & SUPPLY CO., INC.—See Peckham Industries, Inc.; *U.S. Private*, pg. 3127
EASTERN INDUSTRIES, INC.—See New Enterprise Stone & Lime Co., Inc.; *U.S. Private*, pg. 2895
ECKLEY ASPHALT—See Haines & Kibblehouse Inc.; *U.S. Private*, pg. 1841
EDILIT S.R.L.—See Etex SA/NV; *Int'l*, pg. 2521
EGE SERAMIK AMERICA INC.—See Ege Seramik Sanayi ve Ticaret A.S.; *Int'l*, pg. 2322
EIFFAGE CONSTRUCTION MATERIEL—See Eiffage S.A.; *Int'l*, pg. 2329
ELEMENT AG—See CRH plc; *Int'l*, pg. 1844
ELLIS CONSTRUCTION SPECIALTIES; *U.S. Private*, pg. 1374
ELLIS & EASTERN COMPANY—See MDU Resources Group, Inc.; *U.S. Public*, pg. 1410
ENCHO CO., LTD.; *Int'l*, pg. 2401
EQIOM BETONS—See CRH plc; *Int'l*, pg. 1843
EQUATION RESOURCES PTE. LTD.—See DISA LIMITED; *Int'l*, pg. 2131
ERGON N.V.—See CRH plc; *Int'l*, pg. 1844
EUGENE CORPORATION; *Int'l*, pg. 2526
EUREKA MATERIALS CO—See Breedon Group plc; *Int'l*, pg. 1144
FALLUJAH FOR CONSTRUCTION MATERIALS CO.; *Int'l*, pg. 2611
FASTENAL COLOMBIA S.A.S.—See Fastenal Company; *U.S. Public*, pg. 823
FASTENAL EUROPE AB—See Fastenal Company; *U.S. Public*, pg. 823
FASTENAL EUROPE RO S.R.L.—See Fastenal Company; *U.S. Public*, pg. 824
FASTENAL (THAILAND) LTD.—See Fastenal Company; *U.S. Public*, pg. 823
FASTENAL (TIANJIN) INTERNATIONAL TRADING CO. LTD.—See Fastenal Company; *U.S. Public*, pg. 823
FAYAT MIDDLE EAST FZE—See FAYAT SAS; *Int'l*, pg. 2625
FAYAT RO SRL—See FAYAT SAS; *Int'l*, pg. 2625
FERROBETON BETON-ES VASBETONELEM GYARTO ZRT—See CRH plc; *Int'l*, pg. 1844
FERROBETON DUNAUJVAROSI BETON- ES VASBETONELEM-GYARTO ZRT—See CRH plc; *Int'l*, pg. 1844
FERROBETON ROMANIA—See CRH plc; *Int'l*, pg. 1844
FERROBETON SLOVAKIA, S.R.O.—See CRH plc; *Int'l*, pg. 1844
FERTIGBETON (FBU) GMBH—See Heidelberg Materials AG; *Int'l*, pg. 3310
FIZZANO BROTHERS CONCRETE PRODUCTS; *U.S. Private*, pg. 1538
FLORIDA SILICA SAND CO. INC.; *U.S. Private*, pg. 1550
FORMAN BUILDING SYSTEMS PTY LIMITED—See Fletcher Building Limited; *Int'l*, pg. 2700
F.S. LOPKE CONTRACTING INC.; *U.S. Private*, pg. 1457
FULLEN DOCK & WAREHOUSE INC.; *U.S. Private*, pg. 1621

GARDEN STATE TILE DISTRIBUTORS; *U.S. Private*, pg. 1643
GARKALNES GRANTS SIA—See Heidelberg Materials AG; *Int'l*, pg. 3310
GENESEE CERAMIC TILE DISTRIBUTORS; *U.S. Private*, pg. 1669
GENEVA ROCK PRODUCTS INC.—See Clyde Companies Inc.; *U.S. Private*, pg. 949
GEN-S POWER GROUP CO., LTD.; *Int'l*, pg. 2916
GEORGECO INC.; *U.S. Private*, pg. 1684
GEO. SCHOFIELD CO. INC.—See Trilantic Capital Management L.P.; *U.S. Private*, pg. 4231
GERRITY STONE INC.—See Gerrity Company Incorporated; *U.S. Private*, pg. 1687
GIBCA CRUSHING & QUARRY OPERATIONS CO. LTD.—See GIBCA Limited; *Int'l*, pg. 2962
GIBSON BENNESS INDUSTRIES PTY., LTD.—See GBI Holdings Pty., Ltd.; *Int'l*, pg. 2893
GOSFORD QUARRIES PTY. LTD.; *Int'l*, pg. 3043
GPROULX INC.; *U.S. Private*, pg. 1748
GRAYMONT LIMITED - SAINT-MARC-DES-CARRIERES FACILITY—See Graymont Limited; *Int'l*, pg. 3063
GREENVILLE READY MIX—See Martin Marietta Materials, Inc.; *U.S. Public*, pg. 1389
GULF INTERNATIONAL CHEMICALS SAOG; *Int'l*, pg. 3181
GULF TILE DISTRIBUTORS OF FLORIDA, INC.; *U.S. Private*, pg. 1817
GYPSUM SUPPLY COMPANY—See GMS Inc.; *U.S. Public*, pg. 948
GYPSUM SUPPLY CO.; *U.S. Private*, pg. 1821
HANSON AGGREGATES MID-PACIFIC, INC.—See Heidelberg Materials AG; *Int'l*, pg. 3313
HANSON AGGREGATES NEDERLAND B.V.—See Heidelberg Materials AG; *Int'l*, pg. 3311
HANSON AMALGAMATED INDUSTRIES LIMITED—See Heidelberg Materials AG; *Int'l*, pg. 3311
HANSON BUILDING MATERIALS CARTAGE SDN BHD—See Heidelberg Materials AG; *Int'l*, pg. 3311
HANSON BUILDING MATERIALS EUROPE LIMITED—See Heidelberg Materials AG; *Int'l*, pg. 3311
HANSON BUILDING MATERIALS INDUSTRIES SDN BHD—See Heidelberg Materials AG; *Int'l*, pg. 3312
HANSON BUILDING MATERIALS LIMITED—See Heidelberg Materials AG; *Int'l*, pg. 3312
HANSON BUILDING MATERIALS SERVICES SDN BHD—See Heidelberg Materials AG; *Int'l*, pg. 3312
HANSON QUARRY PRODUCTS (SEGAMAT) SDN BHD—See Heidelberg Materials AG; *Int'l*, pg. 3312
HANSON RETAIL LIMITED—See Heidelberg Materials AG; *Int'l*, pg. 3312
HANSON TIS LIMITED—See Heidelberg Materials AG; *Int'l*, pg. 3313
HAZAMA KOGYO CO., LTD.—See Hazama Ando Corporation; *Int'l*, pg. 3295
HC BETONS SIA—See Heidelberg Materials AG; *Int'l*, pg. 3310
HCT ASIA SERVICES PTE. LTD.—See Heidelberg Materials AG; *Int'l*, pg. 3311
HEIDELBERGER BETON DONAU-ILLER VERWALTUNGS-GMBH—See Heidelberg Materials AG; *Int'l*, pg. 3315
HEIDELBERGER BETON SCHWANDORF GMBH—See Heidelberg Materials AG; *Int'l*, pg. 3316
HEIDELBERGER SAND UND KIES HANDELS- UND VERTRIEBS-GMBH—See Heidelberg Materials AG; *Int'l*, pg. 3316
HENKEL BAUTECHNIK KAZAKHSTAN TOO—See Henkel AG & Co. KGaA; *Int'l*, pg. 3350
HENRY PRODUCTS INCORPORATED; *U.S. Private*, pg. 1919
HOCK HENG MARKETING (KL) SDN BHD—See DFCITY Group Berhad; *Int'l*, pg. 2094
HOCK HENG MARKETING (SOUTHERN REGION) SDN BHD—See DFCITY Group Berhad; *Int'l*, pg. 2094
HOCK HENG STONE—See DFCITY Group Berhad; *Int'l*, pg. 2094
HOHMANN & BARNARD, INC.—See Berkshire Hathaway Inc.; *U.S. Public*, pg. 312
HOLCIM BETEILIGUNGS GMBH—See Holcim Ltd.; *Int'l*, pg. 3448
HOLCIM BF+P SA—See Holcim Ltd.; *Int'l*, pg. 3447
HOLCIM KIES UND BETON AG—See Holcim Ltd.; *Int'l*, pg. 3447
HOLCIM KIES UND BETON GMBH—See Holcim Ltd.; *Int'l*, pg. 3447
HOLCIM (NEDERLAND) B.V.—See Holcim Ltd.; *Int'l*, pg. 3447
HOLCIM (NEW ZEALAND) LTD.—See Holcim Ltd.; *Int'l*, pg. 3447
HOLCIM PRECONTRAINT S.A.—See Holcim Ltd.; *Int'l*, pg. 3447
HOLCIM (REUNION) - See Holcim Ltd.; *Int'l*, pg. 3447
HOLCIM (SCHWEIZ) AG - SIGGENTHAL PLANT—See Holcim Ltd.; *Int'l*, pg. 3447
HOLCIM (SCHWEIZ) AG - UNTERVAZ PLANT—See Holcim Ltd.; *Int'l*, pg. 3447
HOLLIDAY ROCK CO., INC.; *U.S. Private*, pg. 1965

HOPKINS CONSTRUCTION (LACOMBE) LTD.; *Int'l*, pg. 3473
HORIZON STONE LLC; *U.S. Private*, pg. 1982
HUNTINGTON TILE, INC.—See PGM Products, LLC; *U.S. Private*, pg. 3165
HUTCHERSON TILE COMPANY; *U.S. Private*, pg. 2014
IBIDEN DEUTSCHLAND GMBH—See Ibiden Co., Ltd.; *Int'l*, pg. 3575
IBIDEN FRANCE S.A.S.—See Ibiden Co., Ltd.; *Int'l*, pg. 3575
IDEAL PRODUCTS OF CANADA LTD.—See TopBuild Corp.; *U.S. Public*, pg. 2163
IKTINOS MARMARON S.A.—See Iktinos Hellas SA; *Int'l*, pg. 3612
INGOLSTADTER ASPHALTMISCHWERKE GMBH & CO. KG—See H. Geiger GmbH; *Int'l*, pg. 3194
INTERMOUNTAIN CONCRETE SPCECIALTY; *U.S. Private*, pg. 2112
INTERNATIONAL GRANITE & MARBLE; *U.S. Private*, pg. 2117
INTERNATIONAL MATERIALS INC.; *U.S. Private*, pg. 2119
J.D. RUSSELL COMPANY; *U.S. Private*, pg. 2161
J.F. ALLEN COMPANY; *U.S. Private*, pg. 2162
JIMSTONE CO OF LOUISIANA, INC.—See SiteOne Landscape Supply, Inc.; *U.S. Public*, pg. 1888
J & J IMPORTS & FABRICATION, INC.; *U.S. Private*, pg. 2152
J & J MATERIALS CORP.—See SiteOne Landscape Supply, Inc.; *U.S. Public*, pg. 1888
JOBU CO., LTD.—See Godo Steel, Ltd.; *Int'l*, pg. 3020
JOHN ABELL CORPORATION; *U.S. Private*, pg. 2220
JOHN COCKBURN BUILDING SUPPLIES LIMITED—See Fletcher Building Limited; *Int'l*, pg. 2700
JOINTA GALUSHA LLC—See The D.A. Collins Construction Co., Inc.; *U.S. Private*, pg. 4017
JUN CERAMIC, INC.; *U.S. Private*, pg. 2244
JUSHI JAPAN CO., LTD.—See China Jushi Co., Ltd.; *Int'l*, pg. 1514
J W BRETT, INC.—See RPM International Inc.; *U.S. Public*, pg. 1818
KALKSANDSTEINWERK AMBERG GMBH & CO. KG—See Heidelberg Materials AG; *Int'l*, pg. 3317
KAMCO SUPPLY CORPORATION OF BOSTON—See Kamco Supply Corporation; *U.S. Private*, pg. 2258
KANSAS CITY AGGREGATE LLC—See Eagle Materials Inc.; *U.S. Public*, pg. 702
KANSAS CITY FLY ASH LLC—See Eagle Materials Inc.; *U.S. Public*, pg. 702
KASTEN MASONRY SALES INC.; *U.S. Private*, pg. 2264
KAW VALLEY COMPANIES, INC.; *U.S. Private*, pg. 2265
KCG, INC.; *U.S. Private*, pg. 2269
KELLY LIMESTONE, LLC—See Arcosa, Inc.; *U.S. Public*, pg. 186
KENT SAND & GRAVEL, L.L.C.—See Haines & Kibblehouse Inc.; *U.S. Private*, pg. 1841
KIESWERKE KIESER GMBH & CO. KG—See Heidelberg Materials AG; *Int'l*, pg. 3317
KINALAJU SUPPLY SDN. BHD.—See B.I.G. Industries Berhad; *Int'l*, pg. 790
KUHLMAN CONSTRUCTION PRODUCTS, INC.—See Kuhlman Corporation; *U.S. Private*, pg. 2356
K. WAH CONSTRUCTION MATERIALS LIMITED—See Galaxy Entertainment Group Limited; *Int'l*, pg. 2871
LABSKE STERKOPISKY A BETON S.R.O.—See Heidelberg Materials AG; *Int'l*, pg. 3318
LAFARGE BETONS CENTRALE BPE QUIMPER—See Holcim Ltd.; *Int'l*, pg. 3449
LASITER CONSTRUCTION INC.; *U.S. Private*, pg. 2395
LATTIMORE MATERIALS COMPANY, L.P.—See Holcim Ltd.; *Int'l*, pg. 3446
LAWRENCE READY MIXED CONCRETE CO.—See Boston Sand & Gravel Company; *U.S. Private*, pg. 373
LEEWARD ASPHALT, L.L.C.—See Haines & Kibblehouse Inc.; *U.S. Private*, pg. 1841
LEGRAND JOHNSON CONSTRUCTION CO.—See Summit Materials, Inc.; *U.S. Public*, pg. 1960
LEVIAT B.V.—See CRH plc; *Int'l*, pg. 1845
LEWIS & LEWIS, INC.—See Summit Materials, Inc.; *U.S. Public*, pg. 1959
LIMITED LIABILITY COMPANY HEIDELBERGBETON UKRAINE—See Heidelberg Materials AG; *Int'l*, pg. 3318
LKL ASSOCIATES INC.; *U.S. Private*, pg. 2475
LONE STAR MATERIALS, INC.—See GMS Inc.; *U.S. Public*, pg. 948
LOUISVILLE TILE DISTRIBUTORS INC.; *U.S. Private*, pg. 2500
LUMBERMEN'S BRICK & SUPPLY CO.; *U.S. Private*, pg. 2513
LYMPIKE PTY LTD—See Gebr. Knauf KG; *Int'l*, pg. 2908
LYNWOOD BUILDING MATERIALS, INC.; *U.S. Private*, pg. 2522
MAGNOLIA MARINE TRANSPORT COMPANY—See Ergon, Inc.; *U.S. Private*, pg. 1418
MAINLAND CONSTRUCTION MATERIALS ULC—See Summit Materials, Inc.; *U.S. Public*, pg. 1959
MAJESTIC STONE, INC.—See Horizon Stone LLC; *U.S. Private*, pg. 1982

423320 — BRICK, STONE, AND R...

MARAZZI JAPAN CO., LTD.—See Mohawk Industries, Inc.; *U.S. Public*, pg. 1458
MARBLE CRAFT DESIGN, INC.; *U.S. Private*, pg. 2570
MARINI FAYAT LANGFANG CHINA—See FAYAT SAS; *Int'l*, pg. 2625
MARLUX KLAPS N.V.—See CRH plc; *Int'l*, pg. 1845
MARRIOTT DRYWALL MATERIALS, INC—See American Securities LLC; *U.S. Private*, pg. 249
MARSHALL STONE, INC.—See SiteOne Landscape Supply, Inc.; *U.S. Public*, pg. 1889
MARTIN MARIETTA MATERIALS SOUTHWEST, INC.—See Martin Marietta Materials, Inc.; *U.S. Public*, pg. 1389
MATERIALS MARKETING CORP.; *U.S. Private*, pg. 2610
MAX BALZ GMBH & CO.—See H. Geiger GmbH; *Int'l*, pg. 3194
MEES DISTRIBUTORS INC.; *U.S. Private*, pg. 2659
MERIWETHER READY MIX, INC.—See Heidelberg Materials AG; *Int'l*, pg. 3318
MERRIMACK BUILDING SUPPLY, INC.—See Hendricks Holding Company, Inc.; *U.S. Private*, pg. 1915
METROPOLITAN BRICK COMPANY PTY LTD—See Brickworks Limited; *Int'l*, pg. 1152
MG BUILDING MATERIALS - TRUSS DIVISION—See MG Building Materials; *U.S. Private*, pg. 2693
MID-AMERICA TILE, INC.—See Louisville Tile Distributors Inc.; *U.S. Private*, pg. 2500
MIDWEST BLOCK & BRICK INC.; *U.S. Private*, pg. 2720
MILLER SURFACE GALLERY; *U.S. Private*, pg. 2735
MIYAKE CONCRETE ACCESSORIES, INC.—See Hawaii Planing Mill Ltd.; *U.S. Private*, pg. 1881
MODERN CONCRETE, INC.; *U.S. Private*, pg. 2760
MODIFIED CONCRETE SUPPLIERS INC.—See Hughes Group, Inc.; *U.S. Private*, pg. 2003
MODUL MARBLE & GRANITE—See Architectural Surfaces Group, LLC; *U.S. Private*, pg. 311
MORITANI S.A.—See Aiphone Co., Ltd.; *Int'l*, pg. 235
MORRIS TILE DISTRIBUTORS INC.; *U.S. Private*, pg. 2788
MS INTERNATIONAL INC.; *U.S. Private*, pg. 2806
MULTIPLE CONCRETE ACCESSORIES; *U.S. Private*, pg. 2813
NEMO TILE CO., LLC—See Saw Mill Capital LLC; *U.S. Private*, pg. 3557
NEW ENGLAND SILICA INC—See SiteOne Landscape Supply, Inc.; *U.S. Public*, pg. 1889
NEW SOUTH SUPPLY LLC; *U.S. Private*, pg. 2906
NORD-FOSEN PUKKVERK AS—See Heidelberg Materials AG; *Int'l*, pg. 3318
NORSK STEIN AS—See Heidelberg Materials AG; *Int'l*, pg. 3318
NORTHERN WHITE SAND LLC—See Eagle Materials Inc.; *U.S. Public*, pg. 702
NORTHFIELD BLOCK—See CRH plc; *Int'l*, pg. 1846
NORTH GEORGIA BRICK COMPANY INC.; *U.S. Private*, pg. 2945
NPC - CIMPOR (PTY) LIMITED—See HUAXIN CEMENT CO., LTD.; *Int'l*, pg. 3515
NU-WAY CONCRETE FORMS INC.; *U.S. Private*, pg. 2972
OINTON INTERNATIONAL INC.; *U.S. Private*, pg. 3006
OLDCASTLE APG NORTHEAST, INC.—See CRH plc; *Int'l*, pg. 1846
OLDCASTLE BUILDING ENVELOP CANADA, INC.—See CRH plc; *Int'l*, pg. 1846
OLD FORT BUILDING SUPPLY OF SOUTH BEND INC—See Hendricks Holding Company, Inc.; *U.S. Private*, pg. 1915
OLD VIRGINIA BRICK COMPANY INC.; *U.S. Private*, pg. 3009
OLEN CORPORATION—See Kokosing Construction Company, Inc.; *U.S. Private*, pg. 2341
OOO NORCEM KOLA—See Heidelberg Materials AG; *Int'l*, pg. 3318
OPA INTERNATIONAL CORPORATION - HOUSTON—See Alfa; *Int'l*, pg. 307
OPEN JOINT STOCK COMPANY GUROVO-BETON—See Heidelberg Materials AG; *Int'l*, pg. 3318
OPTIMERA A/S—See Compagnie de Saint-Gobain SA; *Int'l*, pg. 1724
PACIFIC SHORE STONES; *U.S. Private*, pg. 3070
PEAK MATERIALS, LLC—See Summit Materials, Inc.; *U.S. Public*, pg. 1959
PEBBLE TECHNOLOGY, INC.—See Graycliff Partners LP; *U.S. Private*, pg. 1761
PECKHAM ASPHALT RESALE CORP.—See Peckham Industries, Inc.; *U.S. Private*, pg. 3127
PENTAL GRANITE & MARBLE, LLC—See Architectural Surfaces Group, LLC; *U.S. Private*, pg. 311
PETER FREY GMBH—See BayWa AG; *Int'l*, pg. 918
PIKES CREEK ASPHALT & CRUSHED STONE—See Haines & Kibblehouse Inc.; *U.S. Private*, pg. 1841
PIONEER MATERIALS WEST, INC.—See GMS Inc.; *U.S. Public*, pg. 948
PIONEER OIL LLC; *U.S. Private*, pg. 3187
PITTS SAND & GRAVEL, INC.—See Smith's Greenhouses, Inc.; *U.S. Private*, pg. 3696
PLATINOVA SARL—See Einhell Germany AG; *Int'l*, pg. 2334
PLATINUM ENERGY SERVICES ULC—See Trinity Industries, Inc.; *U.S. Public*, pg. 2193
PLUMBING & DRAINAGE MERCHANTS LTD.—See Grafton Group plc; *Int'l*, pg. 3051
POLARIS TECHNOLOGIES; *U.S. Private*, pg. 3223
PORTCEMEN S.A.—See Cementos Molins S.A.; *Int'l*, pg. 1397
PORT ORCHARD SAND & GRAVEL COMPANY, INC.—See Miles Sand & Gravel Company; *U.S. Private*, pg. 2727
PREFA GRYGOV A.S.—See Heidelberg Materials AG; *Int'l*, pg. 3318
PRIME MASONRY MATERIALS; *U.S. Private*, pg. 3262
RAILWAY DISTRIBUTING INC.; *U.S. Private*, pg. 3346
RALPH CLAYTON & SONS; *U.S. Private*, pg. 3350
RED WING PROPERTIES, INC.; *U.S. Private*, pg. 3376
REVERE PRODUCTS—See Pioneer Manufacturing Company; *U.S. Private*, pg. 3187
RIO GRANDE CO.; *U.S. Private*, pg. 3438
RIVER AGGREGATES, LLC—See Sun Capital Partners, Inc.; *U.S. Private*, pg. 3861
RIVER CITY LANDSCAPE SUPPLY; *U.S. Private*, pg. 3443
ROBBINS BRICK & BLOCK INC.; *U.S. Private*, pg. 3456
ROBERT F. HENRY TILE COMPANY; *U.S. Private*, pg. 3457
ROBERT ROHLINGER GMBH—See Hornbach Holding AG & Co. KGaA; *Int'l*, pg. 3482
ROCK TRANSPORT, INC.—See Vulcan Materials Company; *U.S. Public*, pg. 2314
ROCK YARD INC—See GLM Landscape Supply, LLC; *U.S. Private*, pg. 1711
ROEWEKAMP GMBH & CO KOMMANDITGESELLSCHAFT—See Heidelberg Materials AG; *Int'l*, pg. 3319
ROEWEKAMP GMBH—See Heidelberg Materials AG; *Int'l*, pg. 3319
ROLLIN B. CHILD INCORPORATED; *U.S. Private*, pg. 3475
RT MYCOCK & SONS LIMITED—See Breedon Group plc; *Int'l*, pg. 1144
SABIA SPOL. S.R.O.—See Heidelberg Materials AG; *Int'l*, pg. 3319
SAGRAX B.V.—See Heidelberg Materials AG; *Int'l*, pg. 3319
SAGREX PRODUCTIE B.V.—See Heidelberg Materials AG; *Int'l*, pg. 3319
SALT RIVER MATERIALS GROUP; *U.S. Private*, pg. 3533
SAN ANTONIO MASONRY & TOOL SUPPLY, INC.; *U.S. Private*, pg. 3538
SAN BENITO SUPPLY INCORPORATED; *U.S. Private*, pg. 3539
SANDWERKE BIESERN GMBH—See Heidelberg Materials AG; *Int'l*, pg. 3319
SAN FERNANDO MARBLE & GRANITE; *U.S. Private*, pg. 3540
SANGHI INDUSTRIES LTD—See Adani Enterprises Limited; *Int'l*, pg. 125
SANTAFE TILE CORP.; *U.S. Private*, pg. 3548
SCORECO - VALORIZACAO DE RESIDUOS LDA—See Camargo Correa S.A.; *Int'l*, pg. 1268
SEVERN SANDS LIMITED—See Breedon Group plc; *Int'l*, pg. 1144
SHAMROCK MATERIALS INC. - SAND & GRAVEL DIVISION—See Vulcan Materials Company; *U.S. Public*, pg. 2313
SHINAM OIL CO., LTD.—See Dongjin Semichem Co., Ltd.; *Int'l*, pg. 2168
SKY SANDS (PROPRIETARY) LIMITED—See Group Five Limited; *Int'l*, pg. 3089
SMW SAND UND MORTELWERK VERWALTUNGS-GMBH—See Heidelberg Materials AG; *Int'l*, pg. 3319
SNYDER CONCRETE PRODUCTS INC.; *U.S. Private*, pg. 3701
SOUTH COAST BASALT PTY LTD—See Heidelberg Materials AG; *Int'l*, pg. 3319
SOUTH VALLEY MATERIALS, INC.—See Heidelberg Materials AG; *Int'l*, pg. 3319
SOUTHWEST BUILDING MATERIALS, LLC—See GMS Inc.; *U.S. Public*, pg. 948
SOUTHWESTERN SUPPLIERS, INC.; *U.S. Private*, pg. 3742
SOUTHWEST TRADING COMPANY; *U.S. Private*, pg. 3741
SPAULDING BRICK COMPANY INC.; *U.S. Private*, pg. 3747
SSANGYONG CEMENT (S) PTE LTD—See EnGro Corporation Limited; *Int'l*, pg. 2436
S&S INTERNATIONAL CORP; *U.S. Private*, pg. 3514
STALOTON KLINKER VERTRIEBS GMBH—See Deutsche Steinzeug Cremer & Breuer AG; *Int'l*, pg. 2083
STANDARD TILE DISTRIBUTORS OF NEW HAVEN INC.; *U.S. Private*, pg. 3782
STANLEY SVENSKA AB—See Stanley Black & Decker, Inc.; *U.S. Public*, pg. 1936
ST EDOUARD S.A.R.L.—See Heidelberg Materials AG; *Int'l*, pg. 3319
STENSTROM SAND & GRAVEL GROUP—See Stenstrom Companies Ltd.; *U.S. Private*, pg. 3801
STONE MARKETING INTERNATIONAL; *U.S. Private*, pg. 3818
STONE SOURCE LLC—See Platinum Equity, LLC; *U.S. Private*, pg. 3206
SUNSHINE SUPPLY CO., INC.; *U.S. Private*, pg. 3872
SURFACE PROJECT PTE. LTD.—See Hap Seng Consolidated Berhad; *Int'l*, pg. 3268
SURFACE STONE PTE. LTD.—See Hap Seng Consolidated Berhad; *Int'l*, pg. 3268
SWANSON BUILDING MATERIALS; *U.S. Private*, pg. 3890
SYAR CONCRETE LLC - FAIRFIELD READYMIX PLANT—See Syar Industries, Inc.; *U.S. Private*, pg. 3895
SYAR CONCRETE LLC—See Syar Industries, Inc.; *U.S. Private*, pg. 3895
SYAR INDUSTRIES, INC.; *U.S. Private*, pg. 3895
SYVERSON TILE INC.; *U.S. Private*, pg. 3908
TAHOE SAND & GRAVEL INC.—See Trilantic Capital Management L.P.; *U.S. Private*, pg. 4231
TAMARACK MATERIALS, INC.—See GMS Inc.; *U.S. Public*, pg. 948
TARMAC BUILDING PRODUCTS LIMITED—See CRH plc; *Int'l*, pg. 1848
TARMAC TRADING LIMITED—See CRH plc; *Int'l*, pg. 1848
TBG BAK S.R.O.—See Heidelberg Materials AG; *Int'l*, pg. 3320
TBG TRANSPORTBETON GMBH & CO. KG—See Heidelberg Materials AG; *Int'l*, pg. 3320
TBG WIKA-BETON VERWALTUNGS-GMBH—See Heidelberg Materials AG; *Int'l*, pg. 3320
TBM TRANSPORTBETON-GESELLSCHAFT MBH MARIENFELD & CO. KG—See Heidelberg Materials AG; *Int'l*, pg. 3320
TBM TRANSPORTBETON-GESELLSCHAFT MIT BESCHRANKTER HAFTUNG MARIENFELD—See Heidelberg Materials AG; *Int'l*, pg. 3320
T. BROWN CONSTRUCTORS, INC.; *U.S. Private*, pg. 3911
TQL TRADING LIMITED—See CEMEX, S.A.B. de C.V.; *Int'l*, pg. 1400
TEJAS MATERIALS, INC.—See GMS Inc.; *U.S. Public*, pg. 948
TERICO; *U.S. Private*, pg. 3969
TERRAFIRMA ROADWAYS LIMITED—See Newpark Resources, Inc.; *U.S. Public*, pg. 1518
TERRY MELLSOP BUILDING SUPPLIES LIMITED—See Fletcher Building Limited; *Int'l*, pg. 2701
TILE CONTRACTORS SUPPLY COMPANY; *U.S. Private*, pg. 4170
TOWN & COUNTRY LANDSCAPE SUPPLY CO.; *U.S. Private*, pg. 4196
TRAVIS TILE SALES INC.; *U.S. Private*, pg. 4214
TROWEL TRADES SUPPLY, INC.—See GMS Inc.; *U.S. Public*, pg. 949
THE TRYON GROUP INC.—See O2 Investment Partners, LLC; *U.S. Private*, pg. 2982
THE TRYON GROUP INC.—See Oakland Standard Co., LLC; *U.S. Private*, pg. 2984
TUCKER ACOUSTICAL PRODUCTS, INC.—See GMS Inc.; *U.S. Public*, pg. 948
TUCKER PAVING, INC.; *U.S. Private*, pg. 4256
TWIN CITY CONCRETE PRODUCTS CO.; *U.S. Private*, pg. 4264
UAB AEROC—See Aeroc International AS; *Int'l*, pg. 180
UK STONE DIRECT LIMITED—See Breedon Group plc; *Int'l*, pg. 1144
UNION CORRUGATING COMPANY—See Clayton, Dubilier & Rice, LLC; *U.S. Private*, pg. 921
UNITED GRANITE LLC—See CARYSIL LIMITED; *Int'l*, pg. 1349
UNITED MATERIALS, INC.—See Guggenheim Partners, LLC; *U.S. Private*, pg. 1811
USG BORAL BUILDING PRODUCTS PTY LIMITED—See Gebr. Knauf KG; *Int'l*, pg. 2908
VALENTE EQUIPMENT LEASING CORP.—See Vulcan Materials Company; *U.S. Public*, pg. 2314
VALLEY BUILDING MATERIALS—See West Coast Materials, Inc.; *U.S. Private*, pg. 4484
VALLEY SUPPLY, INC.—See Clayton, Dubilier & Rice, LLC; *U.S. Private*, pg. 930
VAN NEERBOS BELGIE N.V.—See CRH plc; *Int'l*, pg. 1849
VEMAC SRL—See Compagnie de Saint-Gobain SA; *Int'l*, pg. 1737
VERWALTUNGSGESELLSCHAFT BAUSTOFFWERKE DRESDEN MBH—See Heidelberg Materials AG; *Int'l*, pg. 3320
VIRGINIA TILE COMPANY, LLC—See Transom Capital Group, LLC; *U.S. Public*, pg. 4209
VULCAN MATERIALS CO. - HELOTES—See Vulcan Materials Company; *U.S. Public*, pg. 2314
VULCAN MATERIALS CO. - TAFT YARD—See Vulcan Materials Company; *U.S. Public*, pg. 2314
WALDO BROS. COMPANY—See Waldo Bros. Company; *U.S. Private*, pg. 4428
WALKER SAND & GRAVEL LTD. CO.—See Summit Materials, Inc.; *U.S. Public*, pg. 1960
WALKER & ZANGER, INC - MOUNT VERNON—See Walker & Zanger, Inc.; *U.S. Private*, pg. 4428
WALKER & ZANGER, INC.; *U.S. Private*, pg. 4428
WEBFORGE AUSTRALIA PTY LTD.—See Valmont Industries, Inc.; *U.S. Public*, pg. 2274
WERTHAN; *U.S. Private*, pg. 4482
WEST COAST MATERIALS, INC.; *U.S. Private*, pg. 4484
WEST END CLAYBRICK (PROPRIETARY) LIMITED—See Consolidated Infrastructure Group Limited; *Int'l*, pg. 1771

N.A.I.C.S. INDEX

423330 — ROOFING, SIDING, AN...

WESTSIDE BUILDING MATERIAL CORP.—See GMS Inc.; *U.S. Public*, pg. 949
WHITE CAP SUPPLY HOLDINGS LLC—See Clayton, Dubilier & Rice, LLC; *U.S. Private*, pg. 930
WIKA STADE GMBH U. CO. KG—See Heidelberg Materials AG; *Int'l*, pg. 3320
WILDCAT MATERIALS, INC.—See GMS Inc.; *U.S. Public*, pg. 948
XIAMEN ISO STANDARD SAND CO., LTD.—See China National Materials; *Int'l*, pg. 1532
YEOMAN POLAND SP. Z O.O.—See Holcim Ltd.; *Int'l*, pg. 3446
ZEIDLER & WIMMEL NATURSTEININDUSTRIE GMBH & CO. KG—See H. Geiger GmbH; *Int'l*, pg. 3194
ZUMPANO ENTERPRISES INC.; *U.S. Private*, pg. 4610

423330 — ROOFING, SIDING, AND INSULATION MATERIAL MERCHANT WHOLESALERS

ABCO SUPPLY, LLC—See Leonard Green & Partners, L.P.; *U.S. Private*, pg. 2428
ACORN ROOFING SUPPLY, CO.—See Leonard Green & Partners, L.P.; *U.S. Private*, pg. 2428
ADMIRAL BUILDING PRODUCTS, INC.; *U.S. Private*, pg. 81
ADVANCED BUILDING PRODUCTS, INC.—See Leonard Green & Partners, L.P.; *U.S. Private*, pg. 2428
AHI ROOFING GYARTO ES KERESKEDELMI KORLATOLT FELELOSSEGU TARASAG—See Fletcher Building Limited; *Int'l*, pg. 2699
AICHI NZ LIMITED—See Aichi Corporation; *Int'l*, pg. 229
ALL AMERICAN BUILDING PRODUCTS—See Strength Capital Partners, LLC; *U.S. Private*, pg. 3839
ALLIED BUILDING PRODUCTS CORP. - HICKORY HILLS - TRI-STATE WHOLESALE—See Beacon Roofing Supply, Inc.; *U.S. Public*, pg. 285
ALLIED BUILDING PRODUCTS CORP. - ROCKVILLE—See Beacon Roofing Supply, Inc.; *U.S. Public*, pg. 285
ALLIED INSULATION SUPPLY CO., INC.; *U.S. Private*, pg. 186
A.L.L. ROOFING MATERIALS OF SAN JOSE, LLC—See Leonard Green & Partners, L.P.; *U.S. Private*, pg. 2428
ALPHA SYSTEMS INC.; *U.S. Private*, pg. 200
AL'S ROOFING SUPPLY, INC.—See Beacon Roofing Supply, Inc.; *U.S. Public*, pg. 285
ALTRAD BALLIAUW MULTISERVICES N.V.—See Altrad Investment Authority SAS; *Int'l*, pg. 397
ALUMI - COVER AWNING CO, INC.—See Style Crest, Inc.; *U.S. Private*, pg. 3846
AMCRAFT BUILDING PRODUCTS CO., INC.—See Hendricks Holding Company, Inc.; *U.S. Private*, pg. 1914
AMERICAN BUILDERS & CONTRACTORS SUPPLY CO., INC.—See Hendricks Holding Company, Inc.; *U.S. Private*, pg. 1914
AMERICAN BUILDING & ROOFING—See Beacon Roofing Supply, Inc.; *U.S. Public*, pg. 285
AMERICAN WHOLESALERS INC.; *U.S. Private*, pg. 258
APPLICATOR SALES & SERVICE; *U.S. Private*, pg. 298
ARMADAN A/S—See Beijer Ref AB; *Int'l*, pg. 944
ASI BUILDING PRODUCTS; *U.S. Private*, pg. 350
AS PAROC—See Owens Corning; *U.S. Public*, pg. 1626
ASTINO SOUTHERN SDN. BHD.—See Astino Berhad; *Int'l*, pg. 655
ATLANTA ROOFING SUPPLY INC—See Leonard Green & Partners, L.P.; *U.S. Private*, pg. 2428
AXALTA COATING SYSTEMS BELGIUM BVBA—See Axalta Coating Systems Ltd.; *U.S. Public*, pg. 254
BAY INDUSTRIES INC.; *U.S. Private*, pg. 493
BAY INSULATION OF ARIZONA INC.—See Bay Industries Inc.; *U.S. Private*, pg. 493
BAY INSULATION OF KANSAS CITY INC—See Bay Industries Inc.; *U.S. Private*, pg. 493
BAY INSULATION OF TEXAS INC—See Bay Industries Inc.; *U.S. Private*, pg. 493
BAY INSULATION—See Bay Industries Inc.; *U.S. Private*, pg. 493
BAY INSULATION—See Bay Industries Inc.; *U.S. Private*, pg. 493
BAY INSULATION SUPPLY OF COLORADO INC.—See Bay Industries Inc.; *U.S. Private*, pg. 493
BAY INSULATION SUPPLY OF COLUMBUS—See Bay Industries Inc.; *U.S. Private*, pg. 493
BAY INSULATION SUPPLY OF MILWAUKEE—See Bay Industries Inc.; *U.S. Private*, pg. 493
BAY INSULATION SUPPLY OF NEVADA INC—See Bay Industries Inc.; *U.S. Private*, pg. 493
BAY INSULATION SUPPLY OF OHIO—See Bay Industries Inc.; *U.S. Private*, pg. 493
BAY INSULATION SUPPLY OF SAN DIEGO INC.—See Bay Industries Inc.; *U.S. Private*, pg. 493
BAY INSULATION SUPPLY OF SPOKANE—See Bay Industries Inc.; *U.S. Private*, pg. 493
BEACON ROOFING SUPPLY CANADA COMPANY—See Beacon Roofing Supply, Inc.; *U.S. Public*, pg. 285
BEACON ROOFING SUPPLY, INC. - PITTSBURGH—See Beacon Roofing Supply, Inc.; *U.S. Public*, pg. 285
BEACON ROOFING SUPPLY, INC.; *U.S. Public*, pg. 285

BEACON SALES ACQUISITION INC.; *U.S. Private*, pg. 505
BLUESCOPE LYSAGHT (BRUNEI) SDN BHD—See BlueScope Steel Limited; *Int'l*, pg. 1072
B&L WHOLESALE SUPPLY INC.; *U.S. Private*, pg. 419
B&M METALS LP; *U.S. Private*, pg. 419
BRAAS MONIER BUILDING GROUP SERVICES GMBH; *Int'l*, pg. 1133
BRADCO SUPPLY CORPORATION—See Hendricks Holding Company, Inc.; *U.S. Private*, pg. 1914
BURNHAM INSULATION SALES, INC.—See Dunes Point Capital, LLC; *U.S. Private*, pg. 1289
CALIFORNIA SHINGLE & SHAKE CO.; *U.S. Private*, pg. 720
CAMERON ASHLEY BUILDING PRODUCTS, INC.—See Pacific Avenue Capital Partners, LLC; *U.S. Private*, pg. 3065
CANNON SUPPLY, INC.—See Leonard Green & Partners, L.P.; *U.S. Private*, pg. 2429
CARDINAL BUILDING MATERIALS, INC.; *U.S. Private*, pg. 750
COMMERCIAL ROOFING SPECIALTIES INC.; *U.S. Private*, pg. 984
CONSTRUCTION MATERIALS SUPPLY, INC.—See Beacon Roofing Supply, Inc.; *U.S. Public*, pg. 285
CONSTRUCTION METALS INC.; *U.S. Private*, pg. 1024
CONTRACTORS COATING SUPPLY INC.—See Walton Industries, Inc.; *U.S. Private*, pg. 4434
COOL OR COSY PERTH—See AWN Holdings Limited; *Int'l*, pg. 753
COST ENTERPRISES INC.—See AC Holding Co.; *U.S. Private*, pg. 45
CRABTREE SIDING & SUPPLY—See Beacon Roofing Supply, Inc.; *U.S. Public*, pg. 285
CRIMSON INSULATIONS CO INC.; *U.S. Private*, pg. 1100
CROSSROADS C&I DISTRIBUTORS, INC.—See TopBuild Corp.; *U.S. Public*, pg. 2163
CUSTOM MOLDED PRODUCTS, INC.—See Tenex Capital Management, L.P.; *U.S. Private*, pg. 3966
DAICO SUPPLY COMPANY—See Hendricks Holding Company, Inc.; *U.S. Private*, pg. 1915
DAVINCI ROOFSCAPES, LLC—See Westlake Corporation; *U.S. Public*, pg. 2360
DEBEL ROOFING SUPPLY, INC.—See Leonard Green & Partners, L.P.; *U.S. Private*, pg. 2429
DEUTSCHE FOAMGLAS GMBH—See Owens Corning; *U.S. Public*, pg. 1626
D&G EQUIPMENT CO., INC.; *U.S. Private*, pg. 1137
DJ ROOFING SUPPLY INC.; *U.S. Private*, pg. 1246
DOMINION INTERIOR SUPPLY CORPORATION—See American Securities LLC; *U.S. Private*, pg. 248
EAGLE CREEK SIDING, LLC—See Bain Capital, LP; *U.S. Private*, pg. 450
EASTERN ALUMINUM SUPPLY-A RICHARDS COMPANY—See Richards Building Supply Company; *U.S. Public*, pg. 3428
EASTERN ALUMINUM SUPPLY OF VIRGINIA, A RICHARDS COMPANY—See Richards Building Supply Company; *U.S. Public*, pg. 3428
E.J. BARTELLS CO.; *U.S. Private*, pg. 1305
ELEKTROPORCELAN A.D.; *Int'l*, pg. 2357
ERIE MATERIALS INC.; *U.S. Private*, pg. 1420
ETERNIT ECUATORIANA—See Grupo Empresarial Kaluz S.A. de C.V.; *Int'l*, pg. 3127
EVERITE BUILDING PRODUCTS PTY LTD—See Group Five Limited; *Int'l*, pg. 3089
E. WICKLEIN GMBH—See Decora S.A.; *Int'l*, pg. 2001
EXPERT INSULATION OF MINNESOTA, LLC—See Installed Building Products, Inc.; *U.S. Public*, pg. 1132
FEDRUS INTERNATIONAL NV; *Int'l*, pg. 2631
FIBERLAY INC; *U.S. Private*, pg. 1502
FIBRAS FIVENGLASS SA—See Compagnie de Saint-Gobain SA; *Int'l*, pg. 1723
FIBROCEMENTOS PUDAHUEL S.A.—See Etex SA/NV; *Int'l*, pg. 2522
FILTER SALES & SERVICE INC.; *U.S. Private*, pg. 1506
FLETCHER INSULATION PTY. LIMITED—See Fletcher Building Limited; *Int'l*, pg. 2700
FLIGG HOLDING COMPANY; *U.S. Private*, pg. 1545
FLORENCE CORPORATION; *U.S. Private*, pg. 1547
FOAMGLAS (ITALIA) SRL—See Owens Corning; *U.S. Public*, pg. 1626
FOAMGLAS (NORDIC) AB—See Owens Corning; *U.S. Public*, pg. 1626
FORD WHOLESALE CO., INC. OF SAN BERNARDINO; *U.S. Private*, pg. 1565
FORD WHOLESALE CO., INC. OF SAN JOSE—See Beacon Roofing Supply, Inc.; *U.S. Public*, pg. 286
FORT WORTH ROOFING SUPPLY, LLC—See Beacon Roofing Supply, Inc.; *U.S. Public*, pg. 286
FOX BROTHERS COMPANY—See Beacon Roofing Supply, Inc.; *U.S. Public*, pg. 286
GARLOCK CHICAGO INC.—See Hines Corporation; *U.S. Private*, pg. 1949
GARLOCK EAST EQUIPMENT CO—See Hines Corporation; *U.S. Private*, pg. 1949
GARLOCK EQUIPMENT COMPANY—See Hines Corporation; *U.S. Private*, pg. 1949
GENERAL INSULATION CO. INC.; *U.S. Private*, pg. 1665

GREENVOLT NEXT PORTUGAL, LDA.—See KKR & Co. Inc.; *U.S. Public*, pg. 1252
GREINER PURTEC CZ SPOL. S.R.O.—See Greiner Holding AG; *Int'l*, pg. 3079
GULF COAST SUPPLY & MFG INC.; *U.S. Private*, pg. 1815
GULFEAGLE SUPPLY, INC.; *U.S. Private*, pg. 1817
GULFSIDE SUPPLY INC.; *U.S. Private*, pg. 1817
HANITA PACIFIC PTY LTD.—See Avery Dennison Corporation; *U.S. Public*, pg. 244
HANITATEK, LLC—See Avery Dennison Corporation; *U.S. Public*, pg. 244
HARVEY INDUSTRIES, LLC—See Clayton, Dubilier & Rice, LLC; *U.S. Private*, pg. 920
HEELY-BROWN COMPANY INC.; *U.S. Private*, pg. 1903
H. EIKENHOUT & SONS, INC.; *U.S. Private*, pg. 1824
HERITAGE WHOLESALERS INC.; *U.S. Private*, pg. 1925
H & H ROOFING SUPPLY, LLC—See Beacon Roofing Supply, Inc.; *U.S. Public*, pg. 286
HOME CONCEPT SA; *Int'l*, pg. 3454
HOMEXTERIOR BUILDING SUPPLY, INC.—See Hendricks Holding Company, Inc.; *U.S. Private*, pg. 1914
HUNTER DOUGLAS BELGIUM - HELIOSCREEN PROJECTS DIVISION—See 3G Capital Partners L.P.; *U.S. Private*, pg. 11
HUNTER DOUGLAS CHINA/HONG KONG LIMITED—See 3G Capital Partners L.P.; *U.S. Private*, pg. 12
HUNTER DOUGLAS INDIA PVT LTD.—See 3G Capital Partners L.P.; *U.S. Private*, pg. 12
HUNTER DOUGLAS SCANDINAVIA AB—See 3G Capital Partners L.P.; *U.S. Private*, pg. 12
HUNTER PANELS, LLC—See Carlisle Companies Incorporated; *U.S. Public*, pg. 436
HYDRA-MATIC PACKING COMPANY; *U.S. Private*, pg. 2017
IKO MANUFACTURING INC.—See IKO Enterprises Ltd.; *Int'l*, pg. 3612
INDUSTRIAL FIBERGLASS CORP.; *U.S. Private*, pg. 2066
INSULATION DEALERS & SUPPLY CO.; *U.S. Private*, pg. 2094
INSULATION DISTRIBUTORS, INC.—See MacArthur Co.; *U.S. Private*, pg. 2534
INSULATION WHOLESALE SUPPLY, LLC—See Installed Building Products, Inc.; *U.S. Public*, pg. 1133
INSULSPAN, LLC—See The Riverside Company; *U.S. Private*, pg. 4109
INTERNATIONAL PACKAGING PRODUCTS PVT. LTD.—See Owens Corning; *U.S. Public*, pg. 1626
INTERWRAP CORP. PVT. LTD.—See Owens Corning; *U.S. Public*, pg. 1626
IVARSSON A/S—See Etex SA/NV; *Int'l*, pg. 2522
IVARSSON SVERIGE AB—See Etex SA/NV; *Int'l*, pg. 2522
JGA BEACON—See Beacon Roofing Supply, Inc.; *U.S. Public*, pg. 286
J&L BUILDING MATERIALS INC.; *U.S. Private*, pg. 2154
J&L BUILDING MATERIALS OF DELAWARE INC.—See J&L Building Materials Inc.; *U.S. Private*, pg. 2154
JONGENEEL B.V.—See Blackstone Inc.; *U.S. Public*, pg. 356
KAYCAN LTD.—See Compagnie de Saint-Gobain SA; *Int'l*, pg. 1723
KOHL ROOFING & SIDING CO., INC.; *U.S. Private*, pg. 2337
LANZHOU CENTER STEEL STRUCTURE CO., LTD—See Center International Group Co Ltd; *Int'l*, pg. 1403
LAS VEGAS ROOFING SUPPLY, LLC—See Beacon Roofing Supply, Inc.; *U.S. Public*, pg. 286
LEAFFILTER NORTH INC.; *U.S. Private*, pg. 2407
LOUIS T. OLLESHEIMER & SON, INC.—See Leonard Green & Partners, L.P.; *U.S. Private*, pg. 2429
LUMASENSE TECHNOLOGIES A/S—See Advanced Energy Industries, Inc.; *U.S. Public*, pg. 47
LUMBERMEN'S INC.; *U.S. Private*, pg. 2513
LUMBERYARD SUPPLIERS INC.; *U.S. Private*, pg. 2514
LYDALL, INC.; *U.S. Public*, pg. 1349
MACARTHUR CO.; *U.S. Private*, pg. 2534
MACARTHUR CO.—See MacArthur Co.; *U.S. Private*, pg. 2534
MCCORMICK INSULATION SUPPLY; *U.S. Private*, pg. 2630
MEL STEVENSON & ASSOCIATES, INC.; *U.S. Private*, pg. 2661
MIDWAY SALES & DISTRIBUTING, INC.; *U.S. Private*, pg. 2719
MIDWEST ROOFING SUPPLY INC.—See Leonard Green & Partners, L.P.; *U.S. Private*, pg. 2429
MILWAUKEE INSULATION CO., INC.—See MacArthur Co.; *U.S. Private*, pg. 2534
MINNESOTA THERMAL SCIENCE, LLC—See Platinum Equity, LLC; *U.S. Public*, pg. 3207
MISSOURI PETROLEUM PRODUCTS CO., INC.—See Lionmark Inc.; *U.S. Private*, pg. 2464
MONSMA MARKETING CORPORATION; *U.S. Private*, pg. 2774
MOORE GRAHAM SALES, INC.; *U.S. Private*, pg. 2780
MUELLER ROOFING DISTRIBUTORS INC.; *U.S. Private*, pg. 2810
MULE-HIDE PRODUCTS CO., INC.—See Hendricks Holding Company, Inc.; *U.S. Private*, pg. 1915

423330 — ROOFING, SIDING, AN...

MYLES F. KELLY INC.; *U.S. Private*, pg. 2825
NATIONAL BUILDING & ROOFING SUPPLIES, INC.—See Leonard Green & Partners, L.P.; *U.S. Private*, pg. 2429
NATIONAL INSULATION, CO.—See Shook & Fletcher Insulation Co.; *U.S. Private*, pg. 3639
NORDIC WATERPROOFING AB—See Axcel Management A/S; *Int'l*, pg. 762
NORGE BUILDERS INC.; *U.S. Private*, pg. 2937
NORTH COAST COMMERCIAL ROOFING SYSTEMS—See Beacon Roofing Supply, Inc.; *U.S. Public*, pg. 286
NORTH LOUISIANA ROOFING SUPPLY; *U.S. Private*, pg. 2945
NOVIK SALES CORP.—See Clearview Capital, LLC; *U.S. Private*, pg. 939
NTIC EUROPE GMBH—See Northern Technologies International Corporation; *U.S. Public*, pg. 1538
NTIC (SHANGHAI) CO., LTD.—See Northern Technologies International Corporation; *U.S. Public*, pg. 1538
OCV CHAMBERY INTERNATIONAL—See Owens Corning; *U.S. Public*, pg. 1627
OMNIMAX INTERNATIONAL, INC.—See Omnimax Holdings, Inc.; *U.S. Private*, pg. 3017
OOI JOO KEE & BROTHERS SDN. BHD.—See Astino Berhad; *Int'l*, pg. 655
OWENS-CORNING (GUANGZHOU) FIBERGLAS CO. LTD.—See Owens Corning; *U.S. Public*, pg. 1628
PACE ROOFING SUPPLY COMPANY—See Leonard Green & Partners, L.P.; *U.S. Private*, pg. 2429
PACIFIC SUPPLY COMPANY; *U.S. Private*, pg. 3071
PACOR, INC.; *U.S. Private*, pg. 3073
PAROC OY AB—See Owens Corning; *U.S. Public*, pg. 1628
PIONEER BUILDERS SUPPLY CO.; *U.S. Private*, pg. 3186
PITTSBURGH CORNING FRANCE—See Owens Corning; *U.S. Public*, pg. 1628
PITTSBURGH CORNING GESELLSCHAFT M.B.H.—See Owens Corning; *U.S. Public*, pg. 1628
PITTSBURGH CORNING NEDERLAND B.V.—See Owens Corning; *U.S. Public*, pg. 1628
PITTSBURGH CORNING SUISSE SA—See Owens Corning; *U.S. Public*, pg. 1628
PITTSBURGH CORNING (UNITED KINGDOM) LIMITED—See Owens Corning; *U.S. Public*, pg. 1628
POINT P DEVELOPPEMENT—See Compagnie de Saint-Gobain SA; *Int'l*, pg. 1724
PREFINISHED STAINING PRODUCTS INC.—See Louisiana-Pacific Corporation; *U.S. Public*, pg. 1343
PRO ROOF STEEL MERCHANTS (PTA) PROPRIETARY LIMITED—See Andulela Investment Holdings Limited; *Int'l*, pg. 457
QUALITY ROOFING SUPPLY COMPANY INC.—See Beacon Sales Acquisition Inc.; *U.S. Private*, pg. 505
REDDING ROOFING SUPPLY INC.; *U.S. Private*, pg. 3378
RED GOAT DISPOSERS - UNITED SERVICE EQUIPMENT—See Standex International; *U.S. Public*, pg. 1930
REFLECTIX, INC.—See Sealed Air Corporation; *U.S. Public*, pg. 1854
RICHARDS BUILDING SUPPLY COMPANY; *U.S. Private*, pg. 3428
RIVERCITY WHOLESALE INC.—See Leonard Green & Partners, L.P.; *U.S. Private*, pg. 2429
ROOFERS MART, INC.; *U.S. Private*, pg. 3478
ROOFERS MART OF SOUTHERN CALIFORNIA, INC.—See Beacon Roofing Supply, Inc.; *U.S. Public*, pg. 286
ROOFERS SUPPLY INC.—See Leonard Green & Partners, L.P.; *U.S. Private*, pg. 2429
ROOFERS' SUPPLY OF GREENVILLE, INC.—See Beacon Roofing Supply, Inc.; *U.S. Public*, pg. 286
ROOFING & INSULATION SUPPLY INC.—See Beacon Roofing Supply, Inc.; *U.S. Public*, pg. 286
ROOFING SUPPLY GROUP - ALABAMA, LLC—See Beacon Roofing Supply, Inc.; *U.S. Public*, pg. 286
ROOFING SUPPLY GROUP - AUSTIN—See Beacon Roofing Supply, Inc.; *U.S. Public*, pg. 286
ROOFING SUPPLY GROUP - BAY AREA, LLC—See Beacon Roofing Supply, Inc.; *U.S. Public*, pg. 286
ROOFING SUPPLY GROUP-CINCINNATI—See Beacon Roofing Supply, Inc.; *U.S. Public*, pg. 286
ROOFING SUPPLY GROUP - CORPUS CHRISTI—See Beacon Roofing Supply, Inc.; *U.S. Public*, pg. 286
ROOFING SUPPLY GROUP - KANSAS CITY—See Beacon Roofing Supply, Inc.; *U.S. Public*, pg. 286
ROOFING SUPPLY GROUP - KENTUCKY, LLC—See Beacon Roofing Supply, Inc.; *U.S. Public*, pg. 286
ROOFING SUPPLY GROUP OF COLUMBUS, LLC—See Beacon Roofing Supply, Inc.; *U.S. Public*, pg. 286
ROOFING SUPPLY GROUP OF OKLAHOMA, LLC—See Beacon Roofing Supply, Inc.; *U.S. Public*, pg. 286
ROOFING SUPPLY GROUP OF VIRGINIA, LLC—See Beacon Roofing Supply, Inc.; *U.S. Public*, pg. 286
ROOFING SUPPLY GROUP-OMAHA—See Beacon Roofing Supply, Inc.; *U.S. Public*, pg. 286
ROOFING SUPPLY GROUP ORLANDO, LLC—See Beacon Roofing Supply, Inc.; *U.S. Public*, pg. 286
ROOFING SUPPLY GROUP - POLK COUNTY, LLC—See Beacon Roofing Supply, Inc.; *U.S. Public*, pg. 286
ROOFING SUPPLY GROUP - RALEIGH, LCC—See Beacon Roofing Supply, Inc.; *U.S. Public*, pg. 286
ROOFING SUPPLY GROUP SAN DIEGO, LLC—See Beacon Roofing Supply, Inc.; *U.S. Public*, pg. 286
ROOFING SUPPLY GROUP - TAMPA, LLC—See Beacon Roofing Supply, Inc.; *U.S. Public*, pg. 286
ROOFING SUPPLY GROUP - TUSCALOOSA, LLC—See Beacon Roofing Supply, Inc.; *U.S. Public*, pg. 286
ROOFING SUPPLY GROUP UTAH, LLC—See Beacon Roofing Supply, Inc.; *U.S. Public*, pg. 286
ROOFING SUPPLY, LLC - HOUSTON—See Beacon Roofing Supply, Inc.; *U.S. Public*, pg. 286
ROOFING SUPPLY OF ARIZONA-EAST VALLEY—See Beacon Roofing Supply, Inc.; *U.S. Public*, pg. 286
ROOFING SUPPLY OF ARIZONA, LLC—See Beacon Roofing Supply, Inc.; *U.S. Public*, pg. 287
ROOFING SUPPLY OF ARIZONA - TUCSON, LLC—See Beacon Roofing Supply, Inc.; *U.S. Public*, pg. 287
ROOFING SUPPLY OF ATLANTA, LLC—See Beacon Roofing Supply, Inc.; *U.S. Public*, pg. 287
ROOFING SUPPLY OF CHARLOTTE, LLC—See Beacon Roofing Supply, Inc.; *U.S. Public*, pg. 287
ROOFING SUPPLY OF NASHVILLE, LLC—See Beacon Roofing Supply, Inc.; *U.S. Public*, pg. 287
ROOFING SUPPLY OF NEW MEXICO, LLC—See Beacon Roofing Supply, Inc.; *U.S. Public*, pg. 287
ROOFING SUPPLY OF TENNESSEE, LLC—See Beacon Roofing Supply, Inc.; *U.S. Public*, pg. 287
ROOFING SUPPLY TRANSPORTATION, LLC—See Beacon Roofing Supply, Inc.; *U.S. Public*, pg. 286
ROOFING WHOLESALE CO., INC.; *U.S. Private*, pg. 3479
ROOFING WHOLESALE INC.; *U.S. Private*, pg. 3479
ROOFLINE SUPPLY & DELIVERY, INC.—See Leonard Green & Partners, L.P.; *U.S. Private*, pg. 2429
ROOFLINE SUPPLY—See Leonard Green & Partners, L.P.; *U.S. Private*, pg. 2429
ROSLYN SUPPLY COMPANY INC.; *U.S. Private*, pg. 3485
ROYAL BUILDING PRODUCTS (USA) INC.—See Westlake Corporation; *U.S. Public*, pg. 2360
RRS INC; *U.S. Private*, pg. 3496
RSG COLUMBIA—See Beacon Roofing Supply, Inc.; *U.S. Public*, pg. 286
RSG SPOKANE INTERMOUNTAIN SUPPLY—See Beacon Roofing Supply, Inc.; *U.S. Public*, pg. 286
SAINT-GOBAIN CONSTRUCTION PRODUCTS FINLAND—See Compagnie de Saint-Gobain SA; *Int'l*, pg. 1726
SAINT-GOBAIN DISTRIBUTION DENMARK A/S—See Compagnie de Saint-Gobain SA; *Int'l*, pg. 1733
SAINT-GOBAIN DISTRIBUTION NORDIC AB—See Compagnie de Saint-Gobain SA; *Int'l*, pg. 1733
SAINT-GOBAIN IDAPLAC, S.L.—See Compagnie de Saint-Gobain SA; *Int'l*, pg. 1728
SAINT-GOBAIN LIMITED—See Compagnie de Saint-Gobain SA; *Int'l*, pg. 1728
SAINT-GOBAIN SOLAR GARD CANADA, INC—See Compagnie de Saint-Gobain SA; *Int'l*, pg. 1730
SCHAFER GMBH—See Compagnie de Saint-Gobain SA; *Int'l*, pg. 1736
SEAL FOR LIFE INDUSTRIES, LLC—See Henkel AG & Co. KGaA; *Int'l*, pg. 3354
SG WHOLESALE ROOFING SUPPLIES; *U.S. Private*, pg. 3622
SHAFFNER-HEANEY ASSOCIATES INC.; *U.S. Private*, pg. 3623
S & H BUILDING MATERIAL CORP.—See Beacon Roofing Supply, Inc.; *U.S. Public*, pg. 287
SHOOK & FLETCHER INSULATION CO., INC.; *U.S. Private*, pg. 3639
SIDEWINDER SUPPLY, INC.—See Hendricks Holding Company, Inc.; *U.S. Private*, pg. 1915
SPECIALTY PRODUCTS & INSULATION CO.—See Dunes Point Capital, LLC; *U.S. Private*, pg. 1289
SRS DISTRIBUTION INC.— SIERRA ROOFING SUPPLY DIVISION—See Leonard Green & Partners, L.P.; *U.S. Private*, pg. 2429
SRS DISTRIBUTION INC.—See Leonard Green & Partners, L.P.; *U.S. Private*, pg. 2428
STANDARD ROOFINGS INC.—See Hendricks Holding Company, Inc.; *U.S. Private*, pg. 1915
STATEWIDE WHOLESALE, INC.—See Beacon Roofing Supply, Inc.; *U.S. Public*, pg. 287
STELLAR STRUCTURES LLC; *U.S. Private*, pg. 3799
STETSON BUILDING PRODUCTS, LLC—See The Sterling Group, L.P.; *U.S. Private*, pg. 4122
STEWART BUILDING & ROOFING SUPPLY, INC.—See Leonard Green & Partners, L.P.; *U.S. Private*, pg. 2429
STONEWAY ROOFING SUPPLY; *U.S. Private*, pg. 3830
STRUCTURAL MATERIALS CO., INC.—See Beacon Roofing Supply, Inc.; *U.S. Public*, pg. 287
SUNNILAND CORPORATION; *U.S. Private*, pg. 3868
SUPERGLASS DAMMSTOFFE GMBH—See Compagnie de Saint-Gobain SA; *Int'l*, pg. 1726
SUPERIOR DISTRIBUTION COMPANY—See Leonard Green & Partners, L.P.; *U.S. Private*, pg. 2429
TARAH ASPHALT PRODUCTS; *U.S. Private*, pg. 3933
TDA INDUSTRIES, INC.; *U.S. Private*, pg. 3944
THERM-CON, LLC—See Installed Building Products, Inc.; *U.S. Public*, pg. 1133
TREK JAPAN K.K.—See Advanced Energy Industries, Inc.; *U.S. Public*, pg. 48
UAB PAROC—See Owens Corning; *U.S. Public*, pg. 1628
UNILIN BVBA-DIVISION SYSTEMS—See Mohawk Industries, Inc.; *U.S. Public*, pg. 1458
UNITED PRODUCTS CORP.—See Beacon Roofing Supply, Inc.; *U.S. Public*, pg. 285
UNIVERSAL SUPPLY COMPANY INC.—See Bain Capital, LP; *U.S. Private*, pg. 451
VAN KEULEN BV—See Compagnie de Saint-Gobain SA; *Int'l*, pg. 1737
VERSICO, LLC—See Carlisle Companies Incorporated; *U.S. Public*, pg. 436
WAKE SUPPLY CO. INC.; *U.S. Private*, pg. 4427
WAMELING DRYWALL CORP.—See Hendricks Holding Company, Inc.; *U.S. Private*, pg. 1915
WASHINGTON CEDAR & SUPPLY CO.; *U.S. Private*, pg. 4446
WAUSAU SUPPLY COMPANY; *U.S. Private*, pg. 4457
WEATHERPANEL, INC.—See Leonard Green & Partners, L.P.; *U.S. Private*, pg. 2429
WEST END ROOFING, SIDING & WINDOWS—See Beacon Roofing Supply, Inc.; *U.S. Public*, pg. 287
WIMSATT BUILDING MATERIALS CORPORATION; *U.S. Private*, pg. 4532
WOOLF DISTRIBUTING COMPANY INC.; *U.S. Private*, pg. 4562
XAMAX INDUSTRIES, INC.; *U.S. Private*, pg. 4580

423390 — OTHER CONSTRUCTION MATERIAL MERCHANT WHOLESALERS

ABC STONE, INC.; *U.S. Private*, pg. 36
ACE ALUMINUM DISTRIBUTORS, INC.—See Hendricks Holding Company, Inc.; *U.S. Private*, pg. 1915
ADING AD; *Int'l*, pg. 149
ADSG, INC.—See Apollo Global Management, Inc.; *U.S. Public*, pg. 146
ADVANCED PAVEMENT GROUP CORP.; *U.S. Private*, pg. 91
AFRICA SWISS TRADING (MAURITIUS) LIMITED—See DISTRIBUTION AND WAREHOUSING NETWORK LIMITED; *Int'l*, pg. 2136
AGC FLAT GLASS (HONG KONG) CO., LTD.—See AGC Inc.; *Int'l*, pg. 202
AGC FLAT GLASS IBERICA S.A.—See AGC Inc.; *Int'l*, pg. 202
AGI GLASS (PTY) LIMITED—See AG Industries Limited; *Int'l*, pg. 198
AG INDUSTRIES LIMITED; *Int'l*, pg. 198
AGROSAVEZ A.D.; *Int'l*, pg. 220
AHLSELL SVERIGE AB—See Ahlsell AB; *Int'l*, pg. 223
AICA TECH KENZAI CO., LTD.—See AICA Kogyo Company, Limited; *Int'l*, pg. 228
AKERS VALJI RAVNE D.O.O.—See Ampco-Pittsburgh Corporation; *U.S. Public*, pg. 126
ALFA LAVAL EOOD—See Alfa Laval AB; *Int'l*, pg. 309
AL GHURAIR CONSTRUCTION - ALUMINUM INDIA PRIVATE LIMITED—See Al Ghurair Investment LLC; *Int'l*, pg. 278
ALL COUNTIES GLASS, INC.—See Patrick Industries, Inc.; *U.S. Public*, pg. 1652
ALLIED CONCRETE PRODUCTS INC.; *U.S. Private*, pg. 185
ALLSTATE RENT A FENCE, INC.—See American Fence Company, Inc.; *U.S. Private*, pg. 233
ALL-TEX SUPPLY INC.—See The Sterling Group, L.P.; *U.S. Private*, pg. 4122
AL-OSAIS INDUSTRIAL & STRUCTURAL SUPPLY CO.—See Al-Osais International Holding Company; *Int'l*, pg. 287
ALUMEX PLC—See Hayleys PLC; *Int'l*, pg. 3291
AMATA SUMMIT READY BUILT CO. LTD.—See Amata Corporation Public Company Limited; *Int'l*, pg. 413
AMERICAN CONSTRUCTION SOURCE, LLC—See Bain Capital, LP; *U.S. Private*, pg. 450
AMERICAN FENCE COMPANY OF ARIZONA, INC.—See American Fence Company, Inc.; *U.S. Private*, pg. 233
A. METAXIOTIS S.A.; *Int'l*, pg. 21
AMICO CANADA, INC.—See Gibraltar Industries, Inc.; *U.S. Public*, pg. 935
ARCOSA AGGREGATES GULF COAST, LLC—See Arcosa, Inc.; *U.S. Public*, pg. 186
ARCOSA AGGREGATES OHIO RIVER VALLEY, LLC—See Arcosa, Inc.; *U.S. Public*, pg. 186
ARCOSA AGGREGATES TEXAS, LLC—See Arcosa, Inc.; *U.S. Public*, pg. 186
ARCOSA AGGREGATES WEST, LLC—See Arcosa, Inc.; *U.S. Public*, pg. 186
ARCOSA, INC.; *U.S. Public*, pg. 186
ARMORCAST PRODUCTS COMPANY; *U.S. Private*, pg. 331
ASAHI KASEI GEOTECHNOLOGIES CO., LTD.—See Asahi Kasei Corporation; *Int'l*, pg. 595
ASDCO—See APi Group Corporation; *Int'l*, pg. 514

N.A.I.C.S. INDEX
423390 — OTHER CONSTRUCTION ...

AS ESPAK—See Einhell Germany AG; *Int'l*, pg. 2332
ASHAPURA MIDGULF NV—See Ashapura Minechem Limited; *Int'l*, pg. 606
ASIAHUB TRADING SDN. BHD.—See Fajarbaru Builder Group Bhd.; *Int'l*, pg. 2610
ASSOCIATED GLASS, INC.; *U.S. Private*, pg. 355
ASTRIMEX UTRECHT—See Blackstone Inc.; *U.S. Public*, pg. 356
ATIKA GMBH & CO. KG—See Altrad Investment Authority SAS; *Int'l*, pg. 397
ATLAS METAL PRODUCTS COMPANY; *U.S. Private*, pg. 379
AUTOVIA MITLA- TEHUANTEPEC, S.A. DE C.V.—See Empresas ICA S.A.B. de C.V.; *Int'l*, pg. 2390
AUTOVIA PARADORES Y SERVICIOS, S.A. DE C.V.—See Empresas ICA S.A.B. de C.V.; *Int'l*, pg. 2390
BAOSTEEL DEVELOPMENT CO., LTD.—See China Baowu Steel Group Corp., Ltd.; *Int'l*, pg. 1485
BAOSTEEL GROUP FINANCE CO., LTD.—See China Baowu Steel Group Corp., Ltd.; *Int'l*, pg. 1485
BAOSTEEL GROUP SHANGHAI ERGANG CO., LTD.—See China Baowu Steel Group Corp., Ltd.; *Int'l*, pg. 1485
BARRETT INDUSTRIES, INC.; *U.S. Private*, pg. 480
BASF CONSTRUCTION CHEMICALS ESPANA SA—See BASF SE; *Int'l*, pg. 874
BASF KASPIAN YAPI KIMYASALLARI SANAYI MEHUD MESULIYYETLI CEMIYYETI—See BASF SE; *Int'l*, pg. 880
BASF POZZOLITH LTD.—See BASF SE; *Int'l*, pg. 881
BAUKING AG—See CRH plc; *Int'l*, pg. 1843
BAYWA AG; *Int'l*, pg. 915
BAYWA R.E. PROJECTS ESPANA S.L.U.—See BayWa AG; *Int'l*, pg. 916
BAYWA R.E. SOLARSYSTEMER APS—See BayWa AG; *Int'l*, pg. 917
BAYWA R.E. SOLAR SYSTEMS S.L.U.—See BayWa AG; *Int'l*, pg. 916
B.E.A. INC.—See Halma plc; *Int'l*, pg. 3231
BEIXIN NEW BUILDING MATERIAL (GROUP) CO., LTD.—See China National Building Material Group Co., Ltd.; *Int'l*, pg. 1525
B. EN N. KNAUF EN C-ISOLAVA G.C.V.—See Gebr. Knauf KG; *Int'l*, pg. 2906
BERMULLER & CO. GMBH; *Int'l*, pg. 986
BETONG PREMIX SDN. BHD.—See Cahya Mata Sarawak Berhad; *Int'l*, pg. 1251
BLUELINX BUILDING PRODUCTS CANADA LTD.—See Cerberus Capital Management, L.P.; *U.S. Private*, pg. 837
BNBM PNG LIMITED—See China National Building Material Group Co., Ltd.; *Int'l*, pg. 1525
BORNEO GRANITE SDN. BHD.—See Cahya Mata Sarawak Berhad; *Int'l*, pg. 1251
BPB NETHERLANDS B.V.—See Compagnie de Saint-Gobain SA; *Int'l*, pg. 1725
BR BAUHANDEL AG—See CRH plc; *Int'l*, pg. 1843
BRIDGEPORT BUILDING CENTERS—See Nation's Best Holdings, LLC; *U.S. Private*, pg. 2839
BTI BEFESTIGUNGSTECHNIK GMBH & CO. KG—See Berner SE; *Int'l*, pg. 988
BUILDBASE LIMITED—See Grafton Group plc; *Int'l*, pg. 3050
BUILDERS' HARDWARE & SPECIALTY CO.—See Platinum Equity, LLC; *U.S. Private*, pg. 3208
BUILDERSMART PUBLIC COMPANY LIMITED; *Int'l*, pg. 1212
BUILDERS MATERIAL COMPANY—See E.C. Barton & Company; *U.S. Private*, pg. 1304
THE BUILDING COMPANY PROPRIETARY LIMITED—See Capitalworks Investment Partners (Pty) Ltd; *Int'l*, pg. 1314
CAMINOS Y CARRETERAS DEL MAYAB, S.A.P.I. DE C.V.—See Empresas ICA S.A.B. de C.V.; *Int'l*, pg. 2390
CAPITAL HOLDING GROUP, INC.; *U.S. Private*, pg. 740
CAPITOL BUILDING SUPPLY—See GMS Inc.; *U.S. Public*, pg. 947
CARCERI E INFRAESTRUCTURA, S.A.P.I. DE C.V.—See Empresas ICA S.A.B. de C.V.; *Int'l*, pg. 2390
CARDINAL GLASS COMPANY; *U.S. Private*, pg. 750
CARGOTEC ASIA LIMITED—See Cargotec Corporation; *Int'l*, pg. 1327
CARSTENS AB—See Holm Travaror AB; *Int'l*, pg. 3452
CEDAR RUSTIC FENCE CO.; *U.S. Private*, pg. 805
CEMATRIX (CALGARY) LTD.—See Cematrix Corporation; *Int'l*, pg. 1396
CEMENTOS DE ANDALUCIA S.L.—See Camargo Correa S.A.; *Int'l*, pg. 1267
CENTRAL GLASS INTERNATIONAL, INC.—See Central Glass Co., Ltd.; *Int'l*, pg. 1406
CENTRAL GLASS KOREA CO., LTD.—See Central Glass Co., Ltd.; *Int'l*, pg. 1406
CERAMICAS CORDILLERA S.A.—See Etex SA/NV; *Int'l*, pg. 2521
CHANDLER BUILDING SUPPLY COMPANY—See Chandler Concrete Inc.; *U.S. Private*, pg. 848
CHANDLER CONCRETE OF VIRGINIA, INC.—See Chandler Concrete Inc.; *U.S. Private*, pg. 848

CHILANGA CEMENT PLC—See HUAXIN CEMENT CO., LTD.; *Int'l*, pg. 3515
CHINA NATIONAL BUILDING MATERIAL GROUP FZE—See China National Building Material Group Co., Ltd.; *Int'l*, pg. 1525
CHINA RAILWAY LEASING CO., LTD.—See China Railway Materials Co., Ltd.; *Int'l*, pg. 1544
CHINA RAILWAY MATERIALS BEIJING COMPANY—See China Railway Materials Co., Ltd.; *Int'l*, pg. 1544
CHINA RAILWAY MATERIALS CO., LTD. - CRM HARBIN WOOD PRESERVATION FACTORY—See China Railway Materials Co., Ltd.; *Int'l*, pg. 1544
CHINA RAILWAY MATERIALS CO., LTD. - CRM LONGCHANG RAILWAY WORKS EQUIPMENT FACTORY—See China Railway Materials Co., Ltd.; *Int'l*, pg. 1544
CHINA RAILWAY MATERIALS CO., LTD.; *Int'l*, pg. 1544
CHINA RAILWAY MATERIALS DEVELOPMENT HOLDING CO., LTD.—See China Railway Materials Co., Ltd.; *Int'l*, pg. 1544
CHINA RAILWAY MATERIALS GUANGZHOU COMPANY—See China Railway Materials Co., Ltd.; *Int'l*, pg. 1544
CHINA RAILWAY MATERIALS HARBIN COMPANY—See China Railway Materials Co., Ltd.; *Int'l*, pg. 1544
CHINA RAILWAY MATERIALS IMPORT & EXPORT CO., LTD.—See China Railway Materials Co., Ltd.; *Int'l*, pg. 1544
CHINA RAILWAY MATERIALS SHANGHAI COMPANY—See China Railway Materials Co., Ltd.; *Int'l*, pg. 1544
CHINA RAILWAY MATERIALS SHENYANG COMPANY—See China Railway Materials Co., Ltd.; *Int'l*, pg. 1544
CHINA RAILWAY MATERIALS TIANJIN COMPANY—See China Railway Materials Co., Ltd.; *Int'l*, pg. 1544
CHINA RAILWAY MATERIALS WUHAN COMPANY—See China Railway Materials Co., Ltd.; *Int'l*, pg. 1544
CHINA RAILWAY MATERIAL TRADING CO., LTD.—See China Railway Materials Co., Ltd.; *Int'l*, pg. 1544
CHINA RAILWAY MODERN LOGISTIC TECHNOLOGY CO., LTD.—See China Railway Materials Co., Ltd.; *Int'l*, pg. 1544
CHINA RUNJI CEMENT, INC.; *Int'l*, pg. 1549
CHINA UNITED CEMENT GROUP CORPORATION LIMITED—See China National Building Material Group Co., Ltd.; *Int'l*, pg. 1525
CHUO DENSETSU CO., LTD.—See Hankyu Hanshin Holdings Inc.; *Int'l*, pg. 3255
CLOPAY CORPORATION—See Griffon Corporation; *U.S. Public*, pg. 969
CMS PREMIX (MIRI) SDN. BHD.—See Cahya Mata Sarawak Berhad; *Int'l*, pg. 1251
CMS RESOURCES SDN. BHD.—See Cahya Mata Sarawak Berhad; *Int'l*, pg. 1251
CMS WIRES SDN. BHD.—See Cahya Mata Sarawak Berhad; *Int'l*, pg. 1251
CNBM GERMANY GMBH.—See China National Building Material Group Co., Ltd.; *Int'l*, pg. 1525
CNBM INDIA PRIVATE LIMITED—See China National Building Material Group Co., Ltd.; *Int'l*, pg. 1525
CNBM INTERNATIONAL (JORDAN) COMPANY—See China National Building Material Group Co., Ltd.; *Int'l*, pg. 1525
CNBM IN UKRAINE, LLC.—See China National Building Material Group Co., Ltd.; *Int'l*, pg. 1525
CNBM VIETNAM COMPANY LIMITED—See China National Building Material Group Co., Ltd.; *Int'l*, pg. 1525
COASTAL CONSTRUCTION PRODUCTS, LLC—See Beacon Roofing Supply, Inc.; *U.S. Public*, pg. 285
COLN GRAVEL COMPANY LIMITED—See Heidelberg Materials AG; *Int'l*, pg. 3310
COLORADO MECHANICAL SERVICES, LLC; *U.S. Private*, pg. 974
COMAP HUNGARIA KERESKEDELMI KFT.—See Aalberts N.V.; *Int'l*, pg. 33
COMMERCE HOUSE SDN BHD—See IJM Corporation Berhad; *Int'l*, pg. 3608
COMPTOIR GENERAL DES GLACES ET PRODUITS VERRIERS—See Compagnie de Saint-Gobain SA; *Int'l*, pg. 1723
CONSERVATION RESOURCES COMPANY, INC.—See Heidelberg Materials AG; *Int'l*, pg. 3310
CONSTRUCTION DISTRIBUTION & SUPPLY COMPANY INC; *Int'l*, pg. 1777
CONSTRUCTION MATERIAL SUPPLY CO., LTD.—See CH. Karnchang Public Company Limited; *Int'l*, pg. 1435
CONSTRUCTION SITE SERVICES LLC—See Fortiline Waterworks, Inc.; *U.S. Private*, pg. 1576
CONSTRUCTION SUPPLY GROUP—See The Sterling Group, L.P.; *U.S. Private*, pg. 4122
CONTIGA AB—See Heidelberg Materials AG; *Int'l*, pg. 3310
CONTIGA AS—See Heidelberg Materials AG; *Int'l*, pg. 3310
COPAPAMERICAS LLC—See COPAP Inc.; *Int'l*, pg. 1792
COPAP EUROPE SAS—See COPAP Inc.; *Int'l*, pg. 1792
CORE & MAIN, INC.; *U.S. Public*, pg. 575
COSMUR CONSTRUCTION (LONDON) LTD; *Int'l*, pg. 1814
COURTESY GLASS INC.; *U.S. Private*, pg. 1070

CRANE DISTRIBUTION LIMITED—See Blackfriars Corp.; *U.S. Private*, pg. 575
CREATON KERA-DACH GMBH & CO. KG—See Etex SA/NV; *Int'l*, pg. 2521
CREVET PIPELINES PTY LTD—See Fletcher Building Limited; *Int'l*, pg. 2699
CRH BOUWMATEN B.V.—See CRH plc; *Int'l*, pg. 1843
CRH BOUWMATERIALENHANDEL B.V.—See CRH plc; *Int'l*, pg. 1843
CRH ILE DE FRANCE DISTRIBUTION SAS—See CRH plc; *Int'l*, pg. 1843
CRH KLINKIER SP. Z O.O.—See CRH plc; *Int'l*, pg. 1844
CRISTACOL S.A.—See PPG Industries, Inc.; *U.S. Public*, pg. 1707
CRM BEIJING TAIBO REAL ESTATE CO., LTD.—See China Railway Materials Co., Ltd.; *Int'l*, pg. 1544
CRM CHAOHU RAILWAY CEMENT CO., LTD.—See China Railway Materials Co., Ltd.; *Int'l*, pg. 1544
CRM (HONG KONG) HOLDINGS LIMITED—See China Railway Materials Co., Ltd.; *Int'l*, pg. 1544
CRM TAIYUAN RAIL SLEEPERS CO., LTD.—See China Railway Materials Co., Ltd.; *Int'l*, pg. 1544
CRM WUHAN WOOD PRESERVATION CO., LTD.—See China Railway Materials Co., Ltd.; *Int'l*, pg. 1544
CRM YINGTAN WOOD PRESERVATION CO., LTD.—See China Railway Materials Co., Ltd.; *Int'l*, pg. 1544
CRM ZHENLAI WOOD PRESERVATION CO., LTD.—See China Railway Materials Co., Ltd.; *Int'l*, pg. 1544
DAELIM TRADING CO., LTD.; *Int'l*, pg. 1908
DAIDO GROUP LTD; *Int'l*, pg. 1920
DAIDO HOME INTERNATIONAL LTD.—See Daido Group Ltd; *Int'l*, pg. 1920
DAIRYMAN'S SUPPLY COMPANY INC.—See Dairyman's Supply Company Inc.; *U.S. Private*, pg. 1146
DAITO STEEL CO., LTD.—See Daito Trust Construction Co., Ltd.; *Int'l*, pg. 1943
DANUGRAIN LAGEREI GMBH—See BayWa AG; *Int'l*, pg. 917
DARANT DISTRIBUTING CORP.; *U.S. Private*, pg. 1158
DECISION DISTRIBUTION; *U.S. Private*, pg. 1187
DEVINE CIVIL CONTRACTING PTY LTD.—See ACS, Actividades de Construccion y Servicios, S.A.; *Int'l*, pg. 113
DHC SUPPLY, LLC—See High Tide, Inc.; *Int'l*, pg. 3386
DISCOUNT FENCE SUPPLY, INC.; *U.S. Private*, pg. 1237
DKLS MARKETING SDN. BHD.—See DKLS Industries Berhad; *Int'l*, pg. 2139
D.L. BUILDING MATERIALS INC.—See GMS Inc.; *U.S. Public*, pg. 947
DOKA SCHWEIZ AG—See HIAG Immobilen Holding AG; *Int'l*, pg. 3382
DON'S BUILDING SUPPLY, L.P.—See CRH plc; *Int'l*, pg. 1847
DON'S MOBILE GLASS INC.; *U.S. Private*, pg. 1259
DRIFT SUPERSAND (PROPRIETARY) LIMITED—See Consolidated Infrastructure Group Limited; *Int'l*, pg. 1771
EASA S.A.—See Etex SA/NV; *Int'l*, pg. 2521
EASTON BLOCK & SUPPLY—See Haines & Kibblehouse Inc.; *U.S. Private*, pg. 1841
EGGER SCANDINAVIA APS—See Fritz Egger GmbH & Co.; *Int'l*, pg. 2794
EGGER (UK) LIMITED—See Fritz Egger GmbH & Co.; *Int'l*, pg. 2793
ELBE HOLDING GMBH & CO. KG—See Brd. Klee A/S; *Int'l*, pg. 1143
ELKEM JAPAN K.K.—See China National Chemical Corporation; *Int'l*, pg. 1527
ELMORE INTEREST INC.; *U.S. Private*, pg. 1376
EMERSON PROCESS MANAGEMENT POWER & WATER SOLUTIONS SP. Z.O.O.—See Emerson Electric Co.; *U.S. Public*, pg. 748
ENGINEERED PRODUCTS, INC.; *U.S. Private*, pg. 1398
ENGLER, MEIER & JUSTUS, INC.—See GMS Inc.; *U.S. Public*, pg. 947
EQUIPMENT MANAGEMENT GROUP, LLC—See Big-Rentz, Inc.; *U.S. Private*, pg. 556
ERGON POLAND SP. Z O.O.—See CRH plc; *Int'l*, pg. 1844
ERICKSON FRAMING AZ LLC—See Asahi Kasei Corporation; *Int'l*, pg. 595
ESO SUD EST SARL—See Emerson Electric Co.; *U.S. Public*, pg. 743
ESTABELECIMENTOS SCIAL DO NORTE S.A.—See Camargo Correa S.A.; *Int'l*, pg. 1268
ETERNIT KALUGA OOO—See Etex SA/NV; *Int'l*, pg. 2521
EUROPEAN OWENS CORNING FIBERGLAS SPRL—See Owens Corning; *U.S. Public*, pg. 1626
EUROPROFIL NORGE AS—See IAI Holding A/S; *Int'l*, pg. 3568
EXTENSIVE TRADING COMPANY LIMITED—See FSE Services Group Limited; *Int'l*, pg. 2798
FABRICATED GLASS SPECIALTIES; *U.S. Private*, pg. 1458
FASHION GLASS & MIRROR INC.; *U.S. Private*, pg. 1481
FASTENING & BUILDING SYSTEMS LIMITED—See Agostini's Limited; *Int'l*, pg. 213
FIBER COMPOSITES, LLC; *U.S. Private*, pg. 1501
FIBREGRID LIMITED—See RPM International Inc.; *U.S. Public*, pg. 1817

423390 — OTHER CONSTRUCTION ...

FLSMIDTH WUPPERTAL GMBH—See FLSmidth & Co. A/S; *Int'l*, pg. 2711
FORMGLAS JAPAN LTD.—See Formglas Products Ltd.; *Int'l*, pg. 2734
FORMIGONS GIRONA S.A.—See CRH plc; *Int'l*, pg. 1844
FORTILINE WATERWORKS, INC.; *U.S. Private*, pg. 1576
FOUNDATION TECHNOLOGIES, INC.; *U.S. Private*, pg. 1580
FREUDENBERG HOME & CLEANING SOLUTIONS IBERICA, S.L.U.—See Freudenberg SE; *Int'l*, pg. 2786
FREUDENBERG SEALING TECHNOLOGIES, S.L.U.—See Freudenberg SE; *Int'l*, pg. 2788
GACEM COMPANY LIMITED—See Heidelberg Materials AG; *Int'l*, pg. 3316
GAMMID GROUP PROPRIETARY LIMITED—See ARGENT INDUSTRIAL LIMITED; *Int'l*, pg. 560
GARY-HOBART ROOFING & SUPPLY COMPANY—See Leonard Green & Partners, L.P.; *U.S. Private*, pg. 2429
GEBERIT SLOVENSKO S.R.O.—See Geberit AG; *Int'l*, pg. 2905
GEBERIT TECNOLOGIA SANITARIA S.A.—See Geberit AG; *Int'l*, pg. 2905
GEORGE F. KEMPF SUPPLY CO.; *U.S. Private*, pg. 1681
GEORGIA FENCE WHOLESALE INC.; *U.S. Private*, pg. 1684
GEROQUIP INC.; *Int'l*, pg. 2943
GIGA GAS & ELECTRONIC MATERIALS COMPANY—See Central Glass Co., Ltd.; *Int'l*, pg. 1407
GILLFOR DISTRIBUTION INC.; *Int'l*, pg. 2976
GKD (BEIJING) IND. TECHNOLOGIES CO., LTD.—See GKD - Gebr. Kufferath AG; *Int'l*, pg. 2983
GKD BUISMET (PTY) LTD.—See GKD - Gebr. Kufferath AG; *Int'l*, pg. 2983
GKD INDIA LTD.—See GKD - Gebr. Kufferath AG; *Int'l*, pg. 2983
GKD LATAM S.A.—See GKD - Gebr. Kufferath AG; *Int'l*, pg. 2983
GLASBAU HAHN AMERICA LLC—See GLASBAU HAHN GmbH; *Int'l*, pg. 2988
GLASBAU JAPAN CO. LTD.—See GLASBAU HAHN GmbH; *Int'l*, pg. 2988
GLASS & DOOR INTERNATIONAL; *U.S. Private*, pg. 1706
GRANULATS OUEST - GO—See Heidelberg Materials AG; *Int'l*, pg. 3316
GRES UNIVERSAL PTE. LTD.—See Hap Seng Consolidated Berhad; *Int'l*, pg. 3268
GTS DRYWALL SUPPLY COMPANY—See GMS Inc.; *U.S. Public*, pg. 948
GUARDIAN INDUSTRIE FRANCE SAS—See Koch Industries, Inc.; *U.S. Private*, pg. 2329
GULF GLASS INDUSTRIES LLC—See GIBCA Limited; *Int'l*, pg. 2962
GYPROC A/S—See Compagnie de Saint-Gobain SA; *Int'l*, pg. 1725
GYPROC AS—See Compagnie de Saint-Gobain SA; *Int'l*, pg. 1725
GYPSUM MANAGEMENT & SUPPLY, INC.—See GMS Inc.; *U.S. Public*, pg. 947
H2X GMBH—See BayWa AG; *Int'l*, pg. 918
HAFARY BALESTIER SHOWROOM PTE. LTD.—See Hap Seng Consolidated Berhad; *Int'l*, pg. 3268
HATSUHO SHOUJI CO., LTD.; *Int'l*, pg. 3284
HBIS DUFERCO INTERNATIONAL TRADING HOLDING S.A.—See HBIS Group Co., Ltd.; *Int'l*, pg. 3296
HC MATERIALEN B.V.—See Heidelberg Materials AG; *Int'l*, pg. 3311
HC TRADING MALTA LIMITED—See Heidelberg Materials AG; *Int'l*, pg. 3311
HD SUPPLY, INC.—See The Home Depot, Inc.; *U.S. Public*, pg. 2089
HEDGES BUILDING SUPPLIES LIMITED—See Fletcher Building Limited; *Int'l*, pg. 2700
HELLA INFRA MARKET PRIVATE LIMITED; *Int'l*, pg. 3333
HEYWOOD WILLIAMS COMPONENTS LIMITED—See ASSA ABLOY AB; *Int'l*, pg. 639
HIGGINBOTHAM-BARTLETT COMPANY LTD.—See Higginbotham Bros. & Company; *U.S. Private*, pg. 1935
HIGH STANDARD, INC.—See RFE Investment Partners; *U.S. Private*, pg. 3419
HOANG PHUC MINERAL TRADING & CONSTRUCTION JSC; *Int'l*, pg. 3436
HOLCIM TRADING S.A.—See Holcim Ltd.; *Int'l*, pg. 3448
HOLDFAST TECHNOLOGIES, LLC—See The Sterling Group, L.P.; *U.S. Private*, pg. 4122
HOWA TRADING CO., LTD.—See China Baowu Steel Group Corp., Ltd.; *Int'l*, pg. 1485
HUIS CLOS SA; *Int'l*, pg. 3526
HUITEX LIMITED—See Huikwang Corp.; *Int'l*, pg. 3526
HYDRO GATE, LLC—See Mueller Water Products, Inc.; *U.S. Public*, pg. 1485
IBIDEN EUROPE B.V.—See Ibiden Co., Ltd.; *Int'l*, pg. 3575
ICS KNAUF GIPS SRL—See Gebr. Knauf KG; *Int'l*, pg. 2906
IJM (INDIA) INFRASTRUCTURE LIMITED—See IJM Corporation Berhad; *Int'l*, pg. 3608
IMMOBILIENVERMIETUNG GESELLSCHAFT M.B.H.—See BayWa AG; *Int'l*, pg. 918
THE INDUSTRIAL GROUP, LLC—See BWAB, Inc.; *U.S. Private*, pg. 700

INDUSTRY SERVICES CO INC.—See Osceola Capital Management, LLC; *U.S. Private*, pg. 3047
IN-O-VATE TECHNOLOGIES, INC.—See Bee Street Holdings LLC; *U.S. Private*, pg. 513
INTERBULK TRADING S.A.—See Heidelberg Materials AG; *Int'l*, pg. 3316
INTERTRADING S.R.L.—See Heidelberg Materials AG; *Int'l*, pg. 3316
INVERSORA LOCKEY LTDA.—See Ingersoll Rand Inc.; *U.S. Public*, pg. 1121
IOO KNAUF MARKETING—See Gebr. Knauf KG; *Int'l*, pg. 2906
ITW CONSTRUCTION PRODUCTS UK—See Illinois Tool Works Inc.; *U.S. Public*, pg. 1105
JAGO AG—See HIAG Immobilien Holding AG; *Int'l*, pg. 3382
JALMAT SUD OUEST, SA—See Altrad Investment Authority SAS; *Int'l*, pg. 398
JANSONS ASSOCIATES, INC.; *U.S. Private*, pg. 2188
J. DE SAEGHER STEENHANDEL N.V.—See CRH plc; *Int'l*, pg. 1844
JEFFERSON QUARRY, LLC—See Summit Materials, Inc.; *U.S. Public*, pg. 1959
JL INDUSTRIES, INC.—See Activar, Inc.; *U.S. Private*, pg. 68
JOHNS MANVILLE CANADA INC. - INNISFAIL—See Berkshire Hathaway Inc.; *U.S. Public*, pg. 308
JONKER BETON B.V.—See CRH plc; *Int'l*, pg. 1845
JR TOKAI CORPORATION—See Central Japan Railway Company; *Int'l*, pg. 1408
KAB ALLGLASS GMBH—See AG Industries Limited; *Int'l*, pg. 198
KAMCO SUPPLY CORPORATION OF BOSTON - KAMCO/O'CONNOR DOOR DIVISION—See Kamco Supply Corporation; *U.S. Private*, pg. 2258
KAMCO SUPPLY CORPORATION OF BOSTON - MAINE DOOR DIVISION—See Kamco Supply Corporation; *U.S. Private*, pg. 2258
KAMCO SUPPLY CORPORATION OF BOSTON - MASSACHUSETTS DOOR DIVISION—See Kamco Supply Corporation; *U.S. Private*, pg. 2258
KAMCO SUPPLY OF NJ, LLC—See Kamco Supply Corporation; *U.S. Private*, pg. 2258
KAWNEER COMPANY, INC.—See Howmet Aerospace Inc.; *U.S. Public*, pg. 1062
KBS AG—See Compagnie de Saint-Gobain SA; *Int'l*, pg. 1723
KENNA BUILDING SUPPLIES LIMITED—See Fletcher Building Limited; *Int'l*, pg. 2700
KEVIN JARVIS BUILDING SUPPLIES LIMITED—See Fletcher Building Limited; *Int'l*, pg. 2700
KING ARCHITECTURAL METALS, INC.; *U.S. Private*, pg. 2308
KIN LONG (MALAYSIA) SDN. BHD.—See Guangdong Kinlong Hardware Prdcts Co., Ltd.; *Int'l*, pg. 3157
KIRKWOOD MATERIAL SUPPLY, INC.—See SiteOne Landscape Supply, Inc.; *U.S. Public*, pg. 1889
KLEIWARENFABRIEK BUGGENUM B.V.—See CRH plc; *Int'l*, pg. 1845
KNAUF AFRICA TRADE—See Gebr. Knauf KG; *Int'l*, pg. 2906
KNAUF AMF CEILINGS LTD.—See Gebr. Knauf KG; *Int'l*, pg. 2906
KNAUF AMF D.O.O.—See Gebr. Knauf KG; *Int'l*, pg. 2906
KNAUF AMF EOOD—See Gebr. Knauf KG; *Int'l*, pg. 2906
KNAUF AMF FORROS DO BRASIL LTDA.—See Gebr. Knauf KG; *Int'l*, pg. 2906
KNAUF AMF FRANCE SARL—See Gebr. Knauf KG; *Int'l*, pg. 2906
KNAUF AMF HELLAS EPE—See Gebr. Knauf KG; *Int'l*, pg. 2906
KNAUF AMF ITALIA CONTROSOFFITTI S.R.L.—See Gebr. Knauf KG; *Int'l*, pg. 2906
KNAUF AMF KFT.—See Gebr. Knauf KG; *Int'l*, pg. 2906
KNAUF AMF PLAFONDS BVBA—See Gebr. Knauf KG; *Int'l*, pg. 2906
KNAUF AMF PLAFONDSYSTEMEN B.V.—See Gebr. Knauf KG; *Int'l*, pg. 2906
KNAUF AMF SISTEMAS DE TECHOS S.L.—See Gebr. Knauf KG; *Int'l*, pg. 2906
KNAUF AMF S.R.O.—See Gebr. Knauf KG; *Int'l*, pg. 2906
KNAUF A/S—See Gebr. Knauf KG; *Int'l*, pg. 2906
KNAUF A.S.—See Gebr. Knauf KG; *Int'l*, pg. 2906
KNAUF BATIMENT SAS—See Gebr. Knauf KG; *Int'l*, pg. 2906
KNAUF BAUPRODUKTE POLSKA SP. Z O. O.—See Gebr. Knauf KG; *Int'l*, pg. 2906
KNAUF BELCHATOW SP. Z O. O.—See Gebr. Knauf KG; *Int'l*, pg. 2906
KNAUF BRATISLAVA S.R.O.—See Gebr. Knauf KG; *Int'l*, pg. 2906
KNAUF BULGARIA EOOD—See Gebr. Knauf KG; *Int'l*, pg. 2906
KNAUF CO. LTD.—See Gebr. Knauf KG; *Int'l*, pg. 2906
KNAUF CYPRUS LIMITED—See Gebr. Knauf KG; *Int'l*, pg. 2906
KNAUF DANOGIPS A/S—See Gebr. Knauf KG; *Int'l*, pg. 2906

CORPORATE AFFILIATIONS

KNAUF DE CHILE LTDA.—See Gebr. Knauf KG; *Int'l*, pg. 2908
KNAUF DI LOTHAR KNAUF S.A.S.—See Gebr. Knauf KG; *Int'l*, pg. 2908
KNAUF DO BRASIL LTDA.—See Gebr. Knauf KG; *Int'l*, pg. 2908
KNAUF D.O.O.—See Gebr. Knauf KG; *Int'l*, pg. 2908
KNAUF EST SAS—See Gebr. Knauf KG; *Int'l*, pg. 2906
KNAUF FIBRE SAS—See Gebr. Knauf KG; *Int'l*, pg. 2906
KNAUF GYPSOPIIA ABEE—See Gebr. Knauf KG; *Int'l*, pg. 2907
KNAUF GYPSUM THAILAND LIMITED—See Gebr. Knauf KG; *Int'l*, pg. 2907
KNAUF ILE-DE-FRANCE SAS—See Gebr. Knauf KG; *Int'l*, pg. 2907
KNAUF INDUSTRIES NORD—See Gebr. Knauf KG; *Int'l*, pg. 2907
KNAUF INDUSTRIES OUEST—See Gebr. Knauf KG; *Int'l*, pg. 2907
KNAUF INDUSTRIES SP. Z O. O.—See Gebr. Knauf KG; *Int'l*, pg. 2907
KNAUF INSULATION AB—See Gebr. Knauf KG; *Int'l*, pg. 2907
KNAUF INSULATION AE—See Gebr. Knauf KG; *Int'l*, pg. 2907
KNAUF INSULATION ARTIX SAS—See Gebr. Knauf KG; *Int'l*, pg. 2907
KNAUF INSULATION A/S—See Gebr. Knauf KG; *Int'l*, pg. 2907
KNAUF INSULATION B.V.—See Gebr. Knauf KG; *Int'l*, pg. 2907
KNAUF INSULATION CO. LTD—See Gebr. Knauf KG; *Int'l*, pg. 2907
KNAUF INSULATION D.O.O.—See Gebr. Knauf KG; *Int'l*, pg. 2907
KNAUF INSULATION EOOD—See Gebr. Knauf KG; *Int'l*, pg. 2907
KNAUF INSULATION KFT.—See Gebr. Knauf KG; *Int'l*, pg. 2907
KNAUF INSULATION LANNEMEZAN SAS—See Gebr. Knauf KG; *Int'l*, pg. 2907
KNAUF INSULATION LLC—See Gebr. Knauf KG; *Int'l*, pg. 2907
KNAUF INSULATION OOO—See Gebr. Knauf KG; *Int'l*, pg. 2907
KNAUF INSULATION PTY LTD—See Gebr. Knauf KG; *Int'l*, pg. 2907
KNAUF INSULATION SAS—See Gebr. Knauf KG; *Int'l*, pg. 2907
KNAUF INSULATION S.L.—See Gebr. Knauf KG; *Int'l*, pg. 2907
KNAUF INSULATION SPA—See Gebr. Knauf KG; *Int'l*, pg. 2907
KNAUF INSULATION SPOL. S.R.O.—See Gebr. Knauf KG; *Int'l*, pg. 2907
KNAUF INSULATION SPRL—See Gebr. Knauf KG; *Int'l*, pg. 2907
KNAUF INSULATION SP. Z O. O.—See Gebr. Knauf KG; *Int'l*, pg. 2907
KNAUF ISBA SAS—See Gebr. Knauf KG; *Int'l*, pg. 2907
KNAUF JAWORZNO III SP. Z O. O.—See Gebr. Knauf KG; *Int'l*, pg. 2907
KNAUF JORDAN—See Gebr. Knauf KG; *Int'l*, pg. 2907
KNAUF KFT.—See Gebr. Knauf KG; *Int'l*, pg. 2907
KNAUF LEBANON S.A.R.L.—See Gebr. Knauf KG; *Int'l*, pg. 2907
KNAUF LISBOA GMBH—See Gebr. Knauf KG; *Int'l*, pg. 2907
KNAUF LJUBLJANA D.O.O.—See Gebr. Knauf KG; *Int'l*, pg. 2907
KNAUF LTD.—See Gebr. Knauf KG; *Int'l*, pg. 2907
KNAUF MAROKKO—See Gebr. Knauf KG; *Int'l*, pg. 2907
KNAUF NEW BUILDING MATERIAL PRODUCT CO., LTD.—See Gebr. Knauf KG; *Int'l*, pg. 2908
KNAUF NEW BUILDING MATERIAL (WUHU) CO. LTD.—See Gebr. Knauf KG; *Int'l*, pg. 2908
KNAUF OUEST SAS—See Gebr. Knauf KG; *Int'l*, pg. 2908
KNAUF OY—See Gebr. Knauf KG; *Int'l*, pg. 2908
KNAUF PFT GMBH & CO. KG—See Gebr. Knauf KG; *Int'l*, pg. 2908
KNAUF PLASTERBOARD (JIANGSU) CO., LTD.—See Gebr. Knauf KG; *Int'l*, pg. 2908
KNAUF PLASTERBOARD TIANJIN CO. LTD.—See Gebr. Knauf KG; *Int'l*, pg. 2908
KNAUF PLATRES ET CIE. S.C.S.—See Gebr. Knauf KG; *Int'l*, pg. 2908
KNAUF PLATRES SARL—See Gebr. Knauf KG; *Int'l*, pg. 2908
KNAUF PORTO GMBH—See Gebr. Knauf KG; *Int'l*, pg. 2908
KNAUF RADIKA AD—See Gebr. Knauf KG; *Int'l*, pg. 2908
KNAUF SIA—See Gebr. Knauf KG; *Int'l*, pg. 2908
KNAUF SINGAPORE PTE LTD.—See Gebr. Knauf KG; *Int'l*, pg. 2908
KNAUF SP. Z O. O.—See Gebr. Knauf KG; *Int'l*, pg. 2908
KNAUF SUD-EST SAS—See Gebr. Knauf KG; *Int'l*, pg. 2908
KNAUF SUD-OUEST SAS—See Gebr. Knauf KG; *Int'l*, pg. 2908
KNAUF SYRIA—See Gebr. Knauf KG; *Int'l*, pg. 2908

N.A.I.C.S. INDEX

423410 — PHOTOGRAPHIC EQUIPM...

KNAUF TALLINN UU—See Gebr. Knauf KG; *Int'l*, pg. 2908
KNAUF TIRANA SHPK—See Gebr. Knauf KG; *Int'l*, pg. 2908
KNAUF TRADING (SHANGHAI) CO. LTD.—See Gebr. Knauf KG; *Int'l*, pg. 2908
KNAUF UAB—See Gebr. Knauf KG; *Int'l*, pg. 2908
KOOY BAKSTEENCENTRUM B.V.—See CRH plc; *Int'l*, pg. 1845
KS INDUSTRIES, L.P.; *U.S. Private*, pg. 2354
LAMINEX GROUP PTY LIMITED—See Fletcher Building Limited; *Int'l*, pg. 2700
LASSELSBERGER-KNAUF KFT.—See Gebr. Knauf KG; *Int'l*, pg. 2908
LEAMAAT OMIKRON B.V.—See Heidelberg Materials AG; *Int'l*, pg. 3318
L.H. VOSS MATERIALS, INC.—See SiteOne Landscape Supply, Inc.; *U.S. Public*, pg. 1889
LISBON BUILDERS SUPPLY—See D.W. Dickey & Sons Inc.; *U.S. Private*, pg. 1143
LOCUST LUMBER COMPANY, INC.—See Builders FirstSource, Inc.; *U.S. Public*, pg. 410
LOUISVILLE PLATE GLASS COMPANY, INC.—See Aldora Aluminum & Glass Products, Inc.; *U.S. Private*, pg. 160
MAHALO ACQUISITION CORP.—See CRH plc; *Int'l*, pg. 1845
MAKATI OY—See Axcel Management A/S; *Int'l*, pg. 762
MANNING MANAGEMENT CORPORATION; *U.S. Private*, pg. 2565
MAX GRIGSBY CO. INC.; *U.S. Private*, pg. 2617
MEADOW BURKE—See CRH plc; *Int'l*, pg. 1845
MEGADOOR INC.—See ASSA ABLOY AB; *Int'l*, pg. 635
MESCO BUILDINGS SOLUTIONS—See Clayton, Dubilier & Rice, LLC; *U.S. Private*, pg. 921
METALES DE OLYMPIC, S. DE R. L. DE C.V.—See Olympic Steel Inc.; *U.S. Public*, pg. 1571
MGA TRADING EST.—See Al-Osais International Holding Company; *Int'l*, pg. 287
MIDWEST LUMBER MINNESOTA, INC.—See Specialty Building Products, LLC; *U.S. Private*, pg. 3749
MILLER PATTISON LIMITED—See Brookfield Corporation; *Int'l*, pg. 1188
MILLS FENCE CO. INC.; *U.S. Private*, pg. 2737
MIROITERIES DE L'OUEST ARMORIQUE—See Compagnie de Saint-Gobain SA; *Int'l*, pg. 1736
MOBILE STRUCTURES INC.; *U.S. Private*, pg. 2757
MONARCH WINDOWS & DOORS INC—See Woodgrain, Inc.; *U.S. Private*, pg. 4558
MOSTERFARM AS—See Caiano AS; *Int'l*, pg. 1252
N.C. PRODUCTS—See CRH plc; *Int'l*, pg. 1846
NEKADSATU JAYA SDN BHD—See IJM Corporation Berhad; *Int'l*, pg. 3609
N ET B KNAUF ET CIE S.C.S.—See Gebr. Knauf KG; *Int'l*, pg. 2908
NEW ZEALAND CEILING & DRYWALL SUPPLIES LIMITED—See Fletcher Building Limited; *Int'l*, pg. 2700
NEXGEN BUILDING SUPPLY; *U.S. Private*, pg. 2919
NIKKO KINZOKU CO., LTD.—See Hanwa Co., Ltd.; *Int'l*, pg. 3263
NINGBO CHAIN CHON METAL TECHNOLOGY CO., LTD.—See Chain Chon Industrial Co., Ltd.; *Int'l*, pg. 1437
NORTH STAR SURFACES, LLC—See Christ's Household of Faith; *U.S. Private*, pg. 890
NORTHSTONE (NI) LIMITED—See CRH plc; *Int'l*, pg. 1845
N.V.B. UBBENS BOUWSTOFFEN B.V.—See CRH plc; *Int'l*, pg. 1845
OOO KNAUF ARMENIA—See Gebr. Knauf KG; *Int'l*, pg. 2908
OOO KNAUF GIPS—See Gebr. Knauf KG; *Int'l*, pg. 2908
OOO KNAUF GIPS TBILISI—See Gebr. Knauf KG; *Int'l*, pg. 2908
O'STEEL BUILDINGS, INC.; *U.S. Private*, pg. 2980
OUTDOOR WORLD OF NEW ENGLAND, INC.—See Boston Sand & Gravel Company; *U.S. Public*, pg. 373
OWENS CORNING FIBERGLAS A.S. LIMITADA—See Owens Corning; *U.S. Public*, pg. 1628
OWENS CORNING FIBERGLAS FRANCE—See Owens Corning; *U.S. Public*, pg. 1628
PCI BAUPRODUKTE AG—See BASF SE; *Int'l*, pg. 884
PERFECTION STRUCTURAL COMPONENTS LLC—See Star Lumber & Supply Company, Inc.; *U.S. Private*, pg. 3785
PETROCHINA & CRM OIL MARKETING CO., LTD.—See China Railway Materials Co., Ltd.; *Int'l*, pg. 1544
PINGDINGSHAN RAIL SLEEPER COMPANY—See China Railway Materials Co., Ltd.; *Int'l*, pg. 1544
PJ&J, INC.; *U.S. Private*, pg. 3193
PLAKABETON N.V.—See CRH plc; *Int'l*, pg. 1848
PLAKA IRELAND LIMITED—See CRH plc; *Int'l*, pg. 1848
PLZENSKE STERKOPISKY S.R.O.—See Heidelberg Materials AG; *Int'l*, pg. 3319
PORTLAND CONTRACTORS SUPPLY, INC.—See Mallory Safety & Supply LLC; *U.S. Private*, pg. 2558
POWERS PRODUCTS CO.; *U.S. Private*, pg. 3240
PRECISION STRUCTURES INCORPORATED (PSI); *U.S. Private*, pg. 3247
PROMAT IBERICA S.A.—See Etex SA/NV; *Int'l*, pg. 2522
PT. CNBM INTERNATIONAL INDONESIA—See China National Building Material Group Co., Ltd.; *Int'l*, pg. 1526

QUESTER BAUSTOFFHANDEL GMBH—See CRH plc; *Int'l*, pg. 1848
RAMCAST ORNAMENTAL SUPPLY CO.; *U.S. Private*, pg. 3351
RAMCO - RELIABLE ARCHITECTURAL METALS CO.; *U.S. Private*, pg. 3351
RANGER SPECIALIZED GLASS INC.; *U.S. Private*, pg. 3355
RECYCLED AGGREGATE MATERIALS COMPANY, INC.—See Arcosa, Inc.; *U.S. Public*, pg. 186
REFOJOULE CO., LTD.—See Fukuvi Chemical Industry Co., Ltd.; *Int'l*, pg. 2841
REGUSCI S.A.—See CRH plc; *Int'l*, pg. 1848
REMACLE NV/SA.—See CRH plc; *Int'l*, pg. 1848
RIGIPS AG—See Compagnie de Saint-Gobain SA; *Int'l*, pg. 1725
RIGIPS BOSNIA—See Compagnie de Saint-Gobain SA; *Int'l*, pg. 1725
RIGIPS BULGARIA E.O.O.D.—See Compagnie de Saint-Gobain SA; *Int'l*, pg. 1725
RIGIPS CROATIA—See Compagnie de Saint-Gobain SA; *Int'l*, pg. 1725
RIHAM GENERAL TRADING & CONTR. CO. W.L.L—See Fouad Alghanim & Sons Group of Companies; *Int'l*, pg. 2753
RJD GREEN, INC.; *U.S. Public*, pg. 1801
ROLLAC SHUTTER OF TEXAS, INC.; *U.S. Private*, pg. 3474
ROLLESTON BUILDING SUPPLIES LIMITED—See Fletcher Building Limited; *Int'l*, pg. 2701
ROOFTOP SYSTEMS INC.—See Canada Pension Plan Investment Board; *Int'l*, pg. 1281
ROYAL BUILDING PRODUCTS—See Westlake Corporation; *U.S. Public*, pg. 2360
ROYAL ROOFING MATERIALS B.V.—See CRH plc; *Int'l*, pg. 1848
RPM LUX ENTERPRISES S.A.R.L.—See RPM International Inc.; *U.S. Public*, pg. 1818
SAINT-GOBAIN CONSTRUCTION PRODUCT RUSSIA INSULATION—See Compagnie de Saint-Gobain SA; *Int'l*, pg. 1726
SAINT-GOBAIN CONSTRUCTION PRODUCTS BELGIUM NV—See Compagnie de Saint-Gobain SA; *Int'l*, pg. 1726
SAINT-GOBAIN CONSTRUCTION PRODUCTS BELGIUM NV—See Compagnie de Saint-Gobain SA; *Int'l*, pg. 1726
SAINT-GOBAIN CONSTRUCTION PRODUCTS HUNGARY KFT.—See Compagnie de Saint-Gobain SA; *Int'l*, pg. 1726
SAINT-GOBAIN CONSTRUCTION PRODUCTS (MALAYSIA) SDN BHD—See Compagnie de Saint-Gobain SA; *Int'l*, pg. 1726
SAINT-GOBAIN CONSTRUCTION PRODUCTS NEDERLAND BV—See Compagnie de Saint-Gobain SA; *Int'l*, pg. 1726
SAINT-GOBAIN DISTRIBUTION THE NETHERLANDS BV—See Compagnie de Saint-Gobain SA; *Int'l*, pg. 1733
SAINT-GOBAIN EUROVEDER OPERADORA S.A. DE C.V.—See Compagnie de Saint-Gobain SA; *Int'l*, pg. 1733
SAINT-GOBAIN GYPROC BELGIUM NV—See Compagnie de Saint-Gobain SA; *Int'l*, pg. 1726
SAINT-GOBAIN QUARTZ (JINZHOU) COMPANY LTD.—See Compagnie de Saint-Gobain SA; *Int'l*, pg. 1735
SAINT GOBAIN WEBER TERRANOVA, SPOL. S.R.O.—See Compagnie de Saint-Gobain SA; *Int'l*, pg. 1726
SAUDI BASF FOR BUILDING MATERIALS CO. LTD.—See BASF SE; *Int'l*, pg. 884
SCHOTT BENELUX B.V.—See Carl-Zeiss-Stiftung; *Int'l*, pg. 1336
SEALCO ASPHALT, INC.—See Rabine Paving America, LLC; *U.S. Private*, pg. 3341
SEEGARS FENCE COMPANY INC.; *U.S. Private*, pg. 3597
SERVICIOS FORMICA DE MEXICO SA DE CV—See Fletcher Building Limited; *Int'l*, pg. 2701
SERVICIOS Y MATERIALES PARA LA CONSTRUCCION S.A.—See Camargo Correa S.A.; *Int'l*, pg. 1268
SG DISTRIBUZIONE SRL—See Compagnie de Saint-Gobain SA; *Int'l*, pg. 1724
SHANGHAI HUAGONGBAO E-COMMERCE CO., LTD.—See China Baowu Steel Group Corp., Ltd.; *Int'l*, pg. 1486
SHANGHAI MEISHAN IRON & STEEL CO., LTD.—See China Baowu Steel Group Corp., Ltd.; *Int'l*, pg. 1486
SHENZHEN SUNRAY (GROUP) CO., LTD.—See China Railway Materials Co., Ltd.; *Int'l*, pg. 1544
SIMEX, INC.—See Clayton, Dubilier & Rice, LLC; *U.S. Private*, pg. 921
SINOPEC & CRM OIL MARKETING CO., LTD.—See China Railway Materials Co., Ltd.; *Int'l*, pg. 1544
SOCIETE INTERNATIONALE ITALCEMENTI (LUXEMBOURG) S.A.—See Heidelberg Materials AG; *Int'l*, pg. 3317
SOCIETE VERRIERE FRANCAISE—See Compagnie de Saint-Gobain SA; *Int'l*, pg. 1737
SOPROVER—See Compagnie de Saint-Gobain SA; *Int'l*, pg. 1737

SOUTHEASTERN INTERNATIONAL SALES; *U.S. Private*, pg. 3728
SQUARE DEAL BUILDING SUPPLY; *U.S. Private*, pg. 3766
STAR EVENTS LIMITED—See Altrad Investment Authority SAS; *Int'l*, pg. 398
STARK GROUP A/S—See CVC Capital Partners SICAV-FIS S.A.; *Int'l*, pg. 1884
STEVEN MARSHALL BUILDING SUPPLIES LIMITED—See Fletcher Building Limited; *Int'l*, pg. 2701
STRATA MATERIALS, LLC—See Arcosa, Inc.; *U.S. Public*, pg. 186
SULLIVAN & ARMSTRONG BUILDING SUPPLIES LIMITED—See Fletcher Building Limited; *Int'l*, pg. 2701
SUNPRO CORPORATION—See Clyde Companies Inc.; *U.S. Private*, pg. 949
SURFACE MATERIALS IKI OY—See Fletcher Building Limited; *Int'l*, pg. 2701
TAIKO SHOJI LTD.—See BASF SE; *Int'l*, pg. 885
TANGSHAN SENPU MINE EQUIPMENT CO., LTD.—See China National Building Material Group Co., Ltd.; *Int'l*, pg. 1526
TECHNICAL GLASS PRODUCTS DMCC—See Allegion Public Limited Company; *Int'l*, pg. 335
TED HARPER BUILDING SUPPLIES LIMITED—See Fletcher Building Limited; *Int'l*, pg. 2701
TEXAS ELECTRIC COOPERATIVES, INC. - TEC POLE MANUFACTURING PLANT—See Texas Electric Cooperatives, Inc.; *U.S. Private*, pg. 3975
TGP CANADA ENTERPRISES, ULC—See Allegion Public Limited Company; *Int'l*, pg. 335
THB-IJM JOINT VENTURE SDN BHD—See IJM Corporation Berhad; *Int'l*, pg. 3609
THOMPSON FABRICATING LLC—See Ligon Industries LLC; *U.S. Private*, pg. 2455
TIANJIN CHAIN CHON STAINLESS STEEL CO., LTD.—See Chain Chon Industrial Co., Ltd.; *Int'l*, pg. 1437
TINSLEY GROUP - PS&W, INC.—See Olympic Steel Inc.; *U.S. Public*, pg. 1571
TOMBARI STRUCTURAL PRODUCTS, INC.—See Slate Capital Group LLC; *U.S. Private*, pg. 3687
TRANSGOODS AMERICA INC.—See China Railway Materials Co., Ltd.; *Int'l*, pg. 1544
TREBOLIT AB—See Axcel Management A/S; *Int'l*, pg. 762
TRIUMPH GEO-SYNTHETICS, INC.—See Clayton, Dubilier & Rice, LLC; *U.S. Private*, pg. 930
TRULITE GLASS & ALUMINUM SOLUTIONS, LLC - CHESWICK—See Trulite Glass & Aluminum Solutions, LLC; *U.S. Private*, pg. 4249
TUBOS Y ACTIVOS, S. DE R.L. DE C.V.—See NOV, Inc.; *U.S. Public*, pg. 1546
UFP CONSTRUCTION, LLC—See UFP Industries, Inc.; *U.S. Public*, pg. 2219
UNION BAUZENTRUM HORNBACH GMBH—See Hornbach Holding AG & Co. KGaA; *Int'l*, pg. 3482
UNIPOL HOLLAND B.V.—See CRH plc; *Int'l*, pg. 1849
UNISPAN AUSTRALIA PTY LTD—See Acrow Limited; *Int'l*, pg. 109
UNITED STATES BULLET PROOFING, INC.—See River Associates Investments, LLC; *U.S. Private*, pg. 3443
US LBM HOLDINGS, INC.—See Bain Capital, LP; *U.S. Private*, pg. 450
VALUTEC WOOD DRYERS INC.—See Addtech AB; *Int'l*, pg. 135
VETROTECH SAINT-GOBAIN POLAND SP. Z O.O.—See Compagnie de Saint-Gobain SA; *Int'l*, pg. 1737
VIRTA INC.—See Fluor Corporation; *U.S. Public*, pg. 860
VISION PRODUCTS INC—See Sampco Inc.; *U.S. Private*, pg. 3537
VIVA RAILINGS LLC; *U.S. Private*, pg. 4406
WAVIN ROMANIA S.R.L.—See Bharti Enterprises Limited; *Int'l*, pg. 1013
WESTMONT INTERIOR SUPPLY HOUSE—See GMS Inc.; *U.S. Public*, pg. 947
WIDYAN TRADING COMPANY LTD.—See Hayel Saeed Anam Group of Companies; *Int'l*, pg. 3291
WILLIAM WILSON LTD.—See Ferguson plc; *Int'l*, pg. 2638
WILSONART ENGINEERED SURFACES—See Clayton, Dubilier & Rice, LLC; *U.S. Private*, pg. 930
W MARKETING INC.—See ProBility Media Corporation; *Int'l*, pg. 1723
WOLSELEY CENTRAL AND EASTERN EUROPE AG—See Ferguson plc; *Int'l*, pg. 2638
W.S. NIELSEN CO., INC.; *U.S. Private*, pg. 4423
XM INTERNATIONAL INC.; *U.S. Private*, pg. 4581

423410 — PHOTOGRAPHIC EQUIPMENT AND SUPPLIES MERCHANT WHOLESALERS

ADOLPH GASSER INC.; *U.S. Private*, pg. 81
AGFA-GEVAERT COLOMBIA LTDA.—See Agfa-Gevaert N.V.; *Int'l*, pg. 208
AGFA-GEVAERT DE VENEZUELA S.A.—See Agfa-Gevaert N.V.; *Int'l*, pg. 208
AGFA-GEVAERT DO BRASIL LTDA.—See Agfa-Gevaert N.V.; *Int'l*, pg. 208
AGFA-GEVAERT INTERNATIONAL NV—See Agfa-Gevaert N.V.; *Int'l*, pg. 208

423410 — PHOTOGRAPHIC EQUIPM...

AGFA-GEVAERT LIMITED—See Agfa-Gevaert N.V.; *Int'l*, pg. 208
AGFA-GEVAERT LTDA.—See Agfa-Gevaert N.V.; *Int'l*, pg. 208
AGFA INDIA PRIVATE LTD.—See Agfa-Gevaert N.V.; *Int'l*, pg. 207
ALPHA CARD SYSTEMS, LLC—See Odyssey Investment Partners, LLC; *U.S. Private*, pg. 2994
AMERICAN THEATRE SUPPLY INC.—See Eastern Federal Corp.; *U.S. Private*, pg. 1319
ARC ENTERTAINMENT LLC; *U.S. Private*, pg. 309
ARGUS CAMERA COMPANY, LLC—See Impero Electronics, Inc.; *U.S. Private*, pg. 2050
ATLANTIC ZEISER LTD—See Atlantic Zeiser GmbH & Co.; *Int'l*, pg. 676
BAUSCH & LOMB FRANCE SAS—See Bausch Health Companies Inc.; *Int'l*, pg. 896
B&J PHOTO, INC.; *U.S. Private*, pg. 418
BLACKRAPID, INC.; *U.S. Private*, pg. 576
BRISTOL ID TECHNOLOGIES, INC.; *U.S. Private*, pg. 656
CAMCOR INC.; *U.S. Private*, pg. 727
CAMERA HOUSE LIMITED—See FUJIFILM Holdings Corporation; *Int'l*, pg. 2821
CANON CANADA, INC.—See Canon Inc.; *Int'l*, pg. 1297
CANON CEE GMBH—See Canon Inc.; *Int'l*, pg. 1294
CANON EUROPA N.V.—See Canon Inc.; *Int'l*, pg. 1293
CANON MARKETING VIETNAM COMPANY LIMITED—See Canon Inc.; *Int'l*, pg. 1297
CANON SLOVAKIA S.R.O.—See Canon Inc.; *Int'l*, pg. 1294
CANON USA, INC.—See Canon Inc.; *Int'l*, pg. 1297
CANTRONIC SYSTEMS INC.—See Cantronic Systems Inc.; *Int'l*, pg. 1300
CBC AMERICA CO., LTD.—See CBC Co., Ltd.; *Int'l*, pg. 1365
COMP VIEW INC.; *U.S. Private*, pg. 998
DALLMEIER ELECTRONIC UK LTD—See Dallmeier electronic GmbH & Co. KG; *Int'l*, pg. 1954
DALLMEIER ELECTRONIC USA INC.—See Dallmeier electronic GmbH & Co. KG; *Int'l*, pg. 1954
DALLMEIER INTERNATIONAL LTD.—See Dallmeier electronic GmbH & Co. KG; *Int'l*, pg. 1954
DALLMEIER INTERNATIONAL LTD.—See Dallmeier electronic GmbH & Co. KG; *Int'l*, pg. 1954
DALLMEIER ITALIA SRL—See Dallmeier electronic GmbH & Co. KG; *Int'l*, pg. 1954
DALLMEIER SWITZERLAND DIVINET GMBH—See Dallmeier electronic GmbH & Co. KG; *Int'l*, pg. 1954
DALLMEIER TURKEY NI-TI ELEKTRONIK GUVENLIK SIST SAN.TIC. LTD—See Dallmeier electronic GmbH & Co. KG; *Int'l*, pg. 1954
DAYMEN CANADA; *Int'l*, pg. 1985
DNP DENMARK A/S—See Dai Nippon Printing Co., Ltd.; *Int'l*, pg. 1914
DNP PHOTO IMAGING EUROPE SAS—See Dai Nippon Printing Co., Ltd.; *Int'l*, pg. 1915
ELANDERS ITALY S.R.L.—See Carl Bennet AB; *Int'l*, pg. 1331
FLIR GOVERNMENT SYSTEMS, INC.—See Teledyne Technologies Incorporated; *U.S. Public*, pg. 1993
FLIR SYSTEMS HOLDING AB—See Teledyne Technologies Incorporated; *U.S. Public*, pg. 1993
FOTOJOKER SP. Z O. O.—See CEWE Stiftung & Co. KGaA; *Int'l*, pg. 1425
FUJIFILM AUSTRALIA PTY. LTD.—See FUJIFILM Holdings Corporation; *Int'l*, pg. 2821
FUJIFILM CANADA INC.—See FUJIFILM Holdings Corporation; *Int'l*, pg. 2821
FUJIFILM CZ, S.R.O.—See FUJIFILM Holdings Corporation; *Int'l*, pg. 2821
FUJIFILM DIS TICARET A.S.—See FUJIFILM Holdings Corporation; *Int'l*, pg. 2821
FUJIFILM DO BRASIL LTDA.—See FUJIFILM Holdings Corporation; *Int'l*, pg. 2823
FUJIFILM ELECTRONIC IMAGING EUROPE GMBH—See FUJIFILM Holdings Corporation; *Int'l*, pg. 2821
FUJIFILM ELECTRONIC IMAGING KOREA CO., LTD.—See FUJIFILM Holdings Corporation; *Int'l*, pg. 2821
FUJIFILM E-SYSTEMS, INC.—See FUJIFILM Holdings Corporation; *Int'l*, pg. 2823
FUJIFILM EUROPE GMBH—See FUJIFILM Holdings Corporation; *Int'l*, pg. 2821
FUJIFILM EUROPE N.V.—See FUJIFILM Holdings Corporation; *Int'l*, pg. 2821
FUJIFILM HAWAII, INC.—See FUJIFILM Holdings Corporation; *Int'l*, pg. 2822
FUJIFILM HOLDINGS AUSTRALASIA PTY LTD—See FUJIFILM Holdings Corporation; *Int'l*, pg. 2824
FUJIFILM HUNGARY LTD.—See FUJIFILM Holdings Corporation; *Int'l*, pg. 2822
FUJIFILM INDIA PRIVATE LIMITED—See FUJIFILM Holdings Corporation; *Int'l*, pg. 2824
FUJIFILM IRELAND LTD.—See FUJIFILM Holdings Corporation; *Int'l*, pg. 2822
FUJIFILM ITALIA S.P.A.—See FUJIFILM Holdings Corporation; *Int'l*, pg. 2822
FUJIFILM (MALAYSIA) SDN. BHD.—See FUJIFILM Holdings Corporation; *Int'l*, pg. 2821
FUJIFILM MIDDLE EAST FZE—See FUJIFILM Holdings Corporation; *Int'l*, pg. 2822
FUJIFILM NORDIC AB—See FUJIFILM Holdings Corporation; *Int'l*, pg. 2822
FUJIFILM NORTH AMERICA CORPORATION—See FUJIFILM Holdings Corporation; *Int'l*, pg. 2822
FUJIFILM POLSKA DISTRIBUTION SPOLKA ZO.O—See FUJIFILM Holdings Corporation; *Int'l*, pg. 2822
FUJIFILM RUS LLC—See FUJIFILM Holdings Corporation; *Int'l*, pg. 2825
FUJIFILM (SINGAPORE) PTE. LTD.—See FUJIFILM Holdings Corporation; *Int'l*, pg. 2821
FUJIFILM SOUTH AFRICA (PTY) LTD.—See FUJIFILM Holdings Corporation; *Int'l*, pg. 2823
FUJIFILM UK LTD.—See FUJIFILM Holdings Corporation; *Int'l*, pg. 2823
FUJIFILM UKRAINE LLC—See FUJIFILM Holdings Corporation; *Int'l*, pg. 2823
FUJIFILM VIETNAM CO., LTD.—See FUJIFILM Holdings Corporation; *Int'l*, pg. 2823
FUJI PHOTO PRODUCTS COMPANY, LIMITED—See China-Hong Kong Photo Products Holdings Limited; *Int'l*, pg. 1568
GEOVISION JAPAN INC.—See GeoVision Inc.; *Int'l*, pg. 2942
GEOVISION TECHNOLOGY (SHANGHAI) CO., LTD.—See GeoVision Inc.; *Int'l*, pg. 2942
HAVERFORD SYSTEMS; *U.S. Private*, pg. 1880
HELIX LIMITED; *U.S. Private*, pg. 1906
HIBINO IMAGINEERING CORPORATION—See Hibino Corporation; *Int'l*, pg. 3383
HIKVISION EUROPE B.V.—See Hangzhou Hikvision Digital Technology Co., Ltd.; *Int'l*, pg. 3247
HNT (DONGGUAN) COMPANY LIMITED—See HNT Electronics Co.,Ltd; *Int'l*, pg. 3434
HNT (VINA) COMPANY LIMITED—See HNT Electronics Co.,Ltd; *Int'l*, pg. 3434
HPI INTERNATIONAL INC.; *U.S. Private*, pg. 1997
HP MARKETING CORP.—See Gepe Holding AG; *Int'l*, pg. 2942
IMAGICA CORP. OF AMERICA—See IMAGICA Corp.; *Int'l*, pg. 3618
IMAGING SPECTRUM INC.—See Photoreflect, LLC; *U.S. Private*, pg. 3174
KODAK A/S—See Eastman Kodak Company; *U.S. Public*, pg. 707
KODAK (AUSTRALASIA) PTY. LTD.—See Eastman Kodak Company; *U.S. Public*, pg. 707
KODAK (CHINA) LTD.—See Eastman Kodak Company; *U.S. Public*, pg. 707
KODAK GESELLSCHAFT M.B.H.—See Eastman Kodak Company; *U.S. Public*, pg. 707
KODAK GRAPHIC COMMUNICATIONS GMBH—See Eastman Kodak Company; *U.S. Public*, pg. 707
KODAK (JAPAN) LTD.—See Eastman Kodak Company; *U.S. Public*, pg. 707
KODAK KOREA LTD.—See Eastman Kodak Company; *U.S. Public*, pg. 707
KODAK NEW ZEALAND LIMITED—See Eastman Kodak Company; *U.S. Public*, pg. 707
KODAK NORDIC AB—See Eastman Kodak Company; *U.S. Public*, pg. 707
KODAK PHILIPPINES, LTD.—See Eastman Kodak Company; *U.S. Public*, pg. 708
KODAK SOCIETE ANONYME—See Eastman Kodak Company; *U.S. Public*, pg. 708
KODAK S.P.A.—See Eastman Kodak Company; *U.S. Public*, pg. 708
LIULI OPTOMA TECHNOLOGY CORP.—See Coretronic Corporation; *Int'l*, pg. 1800
MDA SPACE & ROBOTICS LIMITED—See Advent International Corporation; *U.S. Private*, pg. 103
METROMAP PTY. LTD.—See Aerometrex Limited; *Int'l*, pg. 181
MYANMAR INDO BEST CO., LTD.—See Berli Jucker Public Co. Ltd.; *Int'l*, pg. 985
NEIL ENTERPRISES INC—See Neil International Inc.; *U.S. Private*, pg. 2882
OPTICSPLANET, INC.; *U.S. Private*, pg. 3034
PHOTO SYSTEMS INC.; *U.S. Private*, pg. 3174
PT. FUJIFILM INDONESIA—See FUJIFILM Holdings Corporation; *Int'l*, pg. 2823
ROBERTS DISTRIBUTORS INC.; *U.S. Private*, pg. 3459
SENSORY TECHNOLOGIES, LLC—See Diversified Specialties, LLC; *U.S. Private*, pg. 1243
SIGNAL COMMUNICATIONS LIMITED—See CircuTech International Holdings Limited; *Int'l*, pg. 1618
SIQURA B.V.—See Vector Capital Management, L.P.; *U.S. Private*, pg. 4352
SUZHOU WUFANG PHOTOELECTRIC MATERIAL CO., LTD.—See Hubei W Olf Photoelectric Technology Co., Ltd.; *Int'l*, pg. 3518
TIFFEN INTERNATIONAL LTD.—See Topspin Partners, L.P.; *U.S. Private*, pg. 4188
TP-LINK CORPORATION LIMITED—See Ban Leong Technologies Limited; *Int'l*, pg. 814
USA VISION SYSTEMS INC.—See GeoVision Inc.; *Int'l*, pg. 2942
VSA, INC.; *U.S. Private*, pg. 4415
W. SCHILLER & CO., INC.; *U.S. Private*, pg. 4418
YAMANASHI RPB SUPPLY CO.—See Eastman Kodak Company; *U.S. Public*, pg. 707
ZAO FUJIFILM-RU—See FUJIFILM Holdings Corporation; *Int'l*, pg. 2823

423420 — OFFICE EQUIPMENT MERCHANT WHOLESALERS

4 OFFICE AUTOMATION LTD.; *Int'l*, pg. 10
A1 PRINTER REPAIR & SUPPLIES, INC.—See Restored Digital Solutions, LLC; *U.S. Private*, pg. 3410
AARQUE GRAPHICS NZ LTD—See Hancock & Gore Ltd.; *Int'l*, pg. 3242
ABA MORIAH CORPORATION; *U.S. Private*, pg. 33
ABDULLA FOUAD INFORMATION TECHNOLOGY CO. LTD.—See Abdulla Fouad Holding Co.; *Int'l*, pg. 58
ACCO BRANDS JAPAN K.K.—See ACCO Brands Corporation; *U.S. Public*, pg. 32
ACM TECHNOLOGIES INC.; *U.S. Private*, pg. 60
ACTIV C.S.A.; *Int'l*, pg. 119
ADVANCE BUSINESS SYSTEMS & SUPPLY COMPANY—See Oval Partners; *U.S. Private*, pg. 3052
ADVANCED IMAGING SOLUTIONS, INC.; *U.S. Private*, pg. 90
AHB TECHNOLOGY SDN. BHD.—See AHB Holdings Berhad; *Int'l*, pg. 222
ALARMTEC AS—See Allied Universal Manager LLC; *U.S. Private*, pg. 188
ALLSTATE IMAGING INC.; *U.S. Private*, pg. 193
ALPHA GROUP INC.; *Int'l*, pg. 368
ALTIMATE ND BELGIUM BVBA—See Arrow Electronics, Inc.; *U.S. Public*, pg. 195
AMANO INTERNATIONAL TRADING (SHANGHAI) CO., LTD.—See Amano Corporation; *Int'l*, pg. 410
AMANO KOREA CORPORATION—See Amano Corporation; *Int'l*, pg. 410
AMANO TIME & AIR SINGAPORE PTE. LTD.—See Amano Corporation; *Int'l*, pg. 411
AMCO UNITED HOLDING LIMITED; *Int'l*, pg. 416
APATOR GMBH—See Apator S.A.; *Int'l*, pg. 501
ARROW ECS INTERNET SECURITY, S.L.—See Arrow Electronics, Inc.; *U.S. Public*, pg. 196
ASBIS LV SIA—See ASBISc Enterprises Plc; *Int'l*, pg. 600
ASHLAND OFFICE SUPPLY, INC.; *U.S. Private*, pg. 349
ASKUL (SHANGHAI) TRADING CO., LTD.—See ASKUL Corporation; *Int'l*, pg. 625
ASMARU CORPORATION—See ASKUL Corporation; *Int'l*, pg. 625
ATLANTA OFFICE TECHNOLOGIES, INC.; *U.S. Private*, pg. 371
ATM NETWORK, INC.—See NCR Voyix Corporation.; *U.S. Public*, pg. 1501
ATM PARTS COMPANY LTD.—See discoverIE Group plc; *Int'l*, pg. 2132
ATS ASSEMBLY & TEST, INC.—See ATS Corporation; *Int'l*, pg. 695
AURORA CORP. OF AMERICA—See Aurora Corporation; *Int'l*, pg. 713
AURORA OFFICE AUTOMATION CORPORATION—See Aurora Corporation; *Int'l*, pg. 713
AURORA OFFICE AUTOMATION SALES CO., LTD.—See Aurora Corporation; *Int'l*, pg. 713
AUTOMATED IMAGING SYSTEMS, INC.—See R.J. Young Co., Inc.; *U.S. Private*, pg. 3337
AVISION LABS., INC.—See Avision Inc.; *Int'l*, pg. 744
AVISION (SUZHOU) CO., LTD.—See Avision Inc.; *Int'l*, pg. 744
BANGKOK BUSINESS EQUIPMENT AUTOMATION CO., LTD.; *Int'l*, pg. 833
BANKCARD USA MERCHANT SERVICES, INC.; *U.S. Private*, pg. 467
BAN-KOE SYSTEMS COMPANIES; *U.S. Private*, pg. 464
BASICS OFFICE PRODUCTS LTD.; *Int'l*, pg. 886
B&B OFFICE SYSTEMS, INC.; *U.S. Private*, pg. 417
BERNEY OFFICE SOLUTIONS, LLC—See Xerox Holdings Corporation; *U.S. Public*, pg. 2387
BISHOP BUSINESS EQUIPMENT CO.; *U.S. Private*, pg. 565
BIZEX CORPORATION—See ASKUL Corporation; *Int'l*, pg. 625
BLUESTONE PAYMENTS, LLC—See PCP Enterprise, L.P.; *U.S. Private*, pg. 3121
BMI IMAGING SYSTEMS INC.; *U.S. Private*, pg. 600
BOISE OFFICE EQUIPMENT, INC.—See Xerox Holdings Corporation; *U.S. Public*, pg. 2387
BOW-BOECK ENTERPRISES LLC; *U.S. Private*, pg. 625
BRASWELL OFFICE SYSTEMS INC.—See Sentinel Capital Partners, L.L.C.; *U.S. Private*, pg. 3609
BRISTOL OFFICE SUPPLY INC.—See R.J. Young Co., Inc.; *U.S. Private*, pg. 3337
BROTHER (CHINA) LTD.—See Brother Industries, Ltd.; *Int'l*, pg. 1196
BROTHER INTERNATIONAL CORPORATION (CANADA) LTD.—See Brother Industries, Ltd.; *Int'l*, pg. 1197
BROTHER INTERNATIONAL CORPORATION DE ARGEN-

N.A.I.C.S. INDEX

423420 — OFFICE EQUIPMENT ME...

TINA S.R.L.—See Brother Industries, Ltd.; *Int'l*, pg. 1197
BROTHER INTERNATIONAL CORPORATION DO BRAZIL, LTDA.—See Brother Industries, Ltd.; *Int'l*, pg. 1197
BROTHER INTERNATIONAL CORPORATION - USA—See Brother Industries, Ltd.; *Int'l*, pg. 1197
BROTHER INTERNATIONAL DE CHILE, LTDA.—See Brother Industries, Ltd.; *Int'l*, pg. 1197
BROTHER INTERNATIONAL DE MEXICO, S.A. DE C.V.—See Brother Industries, Ltd.; *Int'l*, pg. 1197
BRYDENS BUSINESS SOLUTIONS INC.—See ANSA McAL Limited; *Int'l*, pg. 476
BURTRONICS BUSINESS SYSTEMS, INC.; *U.S. Private*, pg. 693
BUSINESS EQUIPMENT UNLIMITED—See Xerox Holdings Corporation; *U.S. Public*, pg. 2387
BUSINESSMART CORPORATION—See ASKUL Corporation; *Int'l*, pg. 625
CAMERON OFFICE PRODUCTS, LLC—See Xerox Holdings Corporation; *U.S. Public*, pg. 2387
CANON ARGENTINA S.A.—See Canon Inc.; *Int'l*, pg. 1297
CANON BELGIUM N.V./S.A.—See Canon Inc.; *Int'l*, pg. 1294
CANON BRETAGNE S.A.—See Canon Inc.; *Int'l*, pg. 1294
CANON CHILE S.A.—See Canon Inc.; *Int'l*, pg. 1297
CANON (CHINA) CO., LTD.—See Canon Inc.; *Int'l*, pg. 1292
CANON CZ SPOL S.R.O.—See Canon Inc.; *Int'l*, pg. 1294
CANON DO BRASIL INDUSTRIAL E COMERCIO LIMITADA—See Canon Inc.; *Int'l*, pg. 1297
CANON EAST EUROPE VERTRIEBSGESELLSCHAFT MBH—See Canon Inc.; *Int'l*, pg. 1294
CANON GIESSEN GMBH—See Canon Inc.; *Int'l*, pg. 1294
CANON HUNGARIA KFT.—See Canon Inc.; *Int'l*, pg. 1294
CANON INDIA PVT. LTD.—See Canon Inc.; *Int'l*, pg. 1295
CANON (IRL) BUSINESS EQUIPMENT LTD.—See Canon Inc.; *Int'l*, pg. 1294
CANON MARKETING JAPAN INC.—See Canon Inc.; *Int'l*, pg. 1295
CANON MARKETING (PHILIPPINES), INC.—See Canon Inc.; *Int'l*, pg. 1295
CANON MARKETING (TAIWAN) CO., LTD.—See Canon Inc.; *Int'l*, pg. 1295
CANON MIDDLE EAST, FZ-LLC—See Canon Inc.; *Int'l*, pg. 1294
CANON NEDERLAND N.V. - 'S-HERTOGENBOSCH—See Canon Inc.; *Int'l*, pg. 1294
CANON NEDERLAND N.V.—See Canon Inc.; *Int'l*, pg. 1294
CANON NORTH-EAST OY—See Canon Inc.; *Int'l*, pg. 1294
CANON POLSKA SP. Z O.O.—See Canon Inc.; *Int'l*, pg. 1294
CANON PROFESSIONAL PRINTING—See Canon Inc.; *Int'l*, pg. 1293
CANON (SCHWEIZ) AG - GLATTBRUGG—See Canon Inc.; *Int'l*, pg. 1293
CANON SINGAPORE PTE. LTD.—See Canon Inc.; *Int'l*, pg. 1296
CANON SOLUTIONS AMERICA, INC. - BURLINGTON—See Canon Inc.; *Int'l*, pg. 1297
CANON SOLUTIONS AMERICA, INC. - GARDENA—See Canon Inc.; *Int'l*, pg. 1297
CANON SOLUTIONS AMERICA, INC. - SALT LAKE CITY—See Canon Inc.; *Int'l*, pg. 1297
CANON SOLUTIONS AMERICA, INC. - SCHAUMBURG—See Canon Inc.; *Int'l*, pg. 1297
CANON SOLUTIONS AMERICA, INC.—See Canon Inc.; *Int'l*, pg. 1297
CANON SOLUTIONS AMERICA, INC. - TRUMBULL—See Canon Inc.; *Int'l*, pg. 1297
CANON SYSTEM & SUPPORT—See Canon Inc.; *Int'l*, pg. 1296
CANON U.S.A., INC.—See Canon Inc.; *Int'l*, pg. 1296
CAROLINA OFFICE SYSTEMS, INC.—See Xerox Holdings Corporation; *U.S. Public*, pg. 2387
CAROLINA WHOLESALE OFFICE MACHINE COMPANY, INC.; *U.S. Private*, pg. 769
CARR BUSINESS SYSTEMS, INC.—See Xerox Holdings Corporation; *U.S. Public*, pg. 2387
CASH REGISTER SALES INC.; *U.S. Private*, pg. 782
CASIO AMERICA, INC.—See Casio Computer Co., Ltd.; *Int'l*, pg. 1353
CASIO, INC.—See Casio Computer Co., Ltd.; *Int'l*, pg. 1353
CDP SERVICES LLC; *U.S. Private*, pg. 803
C.D.S. OFFICE TECHNOLOGY CORP; *U.S. Private*, pg. 706
CENTRAL BUSINESS SYSTEMS INC.—See Advanced Business Methods Inc.; *U.S. Private*, pg. 88
CENTURY BUSINESS TECHNOLOGIES, INC.; *U.S. Private*, pg. 832
CEYLON LAND & EQUITY PLC; *Int'l*, pg. 1426
CHICAGO OFFICE TECHNOLOGY GROUP—See Xerox Holdings Corporation; *U.S. Public*, pg. 2389
CHIYODA INTEGRE CO. (JOHOR) SDN. BHD.—See Chiyoda Integre Co., Ltd.; *Int'l*, pg. 1575
CHIYODA INTEGRE CO. (M) SDN. BHD.—See Chiyoda Integre Co., Ltd.; *Int'l*, pg. 1575
CHIYODA INTEGRE CO. (S) PTE. LTD.—See Chiyoda Integre Co., Ltd.; *Int'l*, pg. 1575
CHIYODA INTEGRE (DALIAN) CO., LTD.—See Chiyoda Integre Co., Ltd.; *Int'l*, pg. 1575
CHIYODA INTEGRE DE BAJA CALIFORNIA, S. A. DE C.V.—See Chiyoda Integre Co., Ltd.; *Int'l*, pg. 1575
CHIYODA INTEGRE DE MEXICO, S.A. DE C.V.—See Chiyoda Integre Co., Ltd.; *Int'l*, pg. 1575
CHIYODA INTEGRE (DONG GUAN) CO., LTD.—See Chiyoda Integre Co., Ltd.; *Int'l*, pg. 1575
CHIYODA INTEGRE (GUANGZHOU) CO., LTD.—See Chiyoda Integre Co., Ltd.; *Int'l*, pg. 1575
CHIYODA INTEGRE (HK) LTD.—See Chiyoda Integre Co., Ltd.; *Int'l*, pg. 1575
CHIYODA INTEGRE (PHILIPPINES) CORPORATION—See Chiyoda Integre Co., Ltd.; *Int'l*, pg. 1575
CHIYODA INTEGRE (SHANDONG) CO., LTD.—See Chiyoda Integre Co., Ltd.; *Int'l*, pg. 1575
CHIYODA INTEGRE (SHENZHEN) CO., LTD.—See Chiyoda Integre Co., Ltd.; *Int'l*, pg. 1575
CHIYODA INTEGRE (SUZHOU) CO., LTD.—See Chiyoda Integre Co., Ltd.; *Int'l*, pg. 1575
CHIYODA INTEGRE (THAILAND) CO., LTD.—See Chiyoda Integre Co., Ltd.; *Int'l*, pg. 1575
CHIYODA INTEGRE (TIAN JIN) CO., LTD.—See Chiyoda Integre Co., Ltd.; *Int'l*, pg. 1575
CHIYODA INTEGRE VIETNAM CO., LTD.—See Chiyoda Integre Co., Ltd.; *Int'l*, pg. 1575
CHIYODA INTEGRE (ZHONG SHAN) CO., LTD.—See Chiyoda Integre Co., Ltd.; *Int'l*, pg. 1575
CITIZEN SYSTEMS AMERICA CORPORATION—See Citizen Watch Co., Ltd.; *Int'l*, pg. 1624
CLARY BUSINESS MACHINES COMPANY; *U.S. Private*, pg. 915
COLLINS DISTRIBUTING COMPANY; *U.S. Private*, pg. 969
CONCEPT GROUP (SALES) LIMITED—See Xerox Holdings Corporation; *U.S. Public*, pg. 2387
CONESTOGA BUSINESS SOLUTIONS, INC.—See Xerox Holdings Corporation; *U.S. Public*, pg. 2389
CONTINUA LIMITED—See Xerox Holdings Corporation; *U.S. Public*, pg. 2387
CONWAY OFFICE SOLUTIONS, INC.—See Xerox Holdings Corporation; *U.S. Public*, pg. 2387
COPIER BUSINESS SOLUTIONS—See Loffler Companies, Inc.; *U.S. Private*, pg. 2480
COPYCO OFFICE SOLUTIONS, INC.—See Xerox Holdings Corporation; *U.S. Public*, pg. 2387
CORPORATE DIRECT APPAREL LLC; *U.S. Private*, pg. 1054
CROWLEY MICROGRAPHICS, INC.; *U.S. Private*, pg. 1110
CTX BUSINESS SOLUTIONS, INC.—See Xerox Holdings Corporation; *U.S. Public*, pg. 2387
CULLIGAN WATER INDIANA—See BDT Capital Partners, LLC; *U.S. Private*, pg. 502
CURRENCY TECH LTD.—See Giesecke & Devrient GmbH; *Int'l*, pg. 2969
CUSTOM BUSINESS SOLUTIONS INC.; *U.S. Private*, pg. 1128
DATA BUSINESS SYSTEMS INC.; *U.S. Private*, pg. 1162
DATAFLOW BUSINESS SYSTEMS, INC.; *U.S. Private*, pg. 1165
DAVIS TYPEWRITER COMPANY, INC.—See McNally Operations LLC; *U.S. Private*, pg. 2643
DEERFIELD DISTRIBUTING INC.; *U.S. Private*, pg. 1190
DEX IMAGING, INC.—See Sycamore Partners Management, LP; *U.S. Private*, pg. 3896
DOCEO OFFICE SOLUTIONS, LLC; *U.S. Private*, pg. 1251
DOCUGRAPHICS, LLC; *U.S. Private*, pg. 1252
DOCUMENT SOLUTIONS LLC—See Modern Office Methods Inc.; *U.S. Private*, pg. 2762
DOLPHIN DEBIT ACCESS, LLC—See Euronet Worldwide, Inc.; *U.S. Public*, pg. 797
DONNELLON MCCARTHY INC.; *U.S. Private*, pg. 1261
DOSMAR OY—See Amplex AB; *Int'l*, pg. 433
DUMAC BUSINESS SYSTEMS, INC.; *U.S. Private*, pg. 1286
DUPLICATOR SALES & SERVICE INC.; *U.S. Private*, pg. 1291
DUPLO USA CORPORATION; *U.S. Private*, pg. 1291
DYNABOOK FRANCE—See Hon Hai Precision Industry Co., Ltd.; *Int'l*, pg. 3457
EASTERN MANAGED PRINT NETWORK, LLC – FAIRPORT—See Xerox Holdings Corporation; *U.S. Public*, pg. 2387
ECO SUPPLIES EUROPE AB; *Int'l*, pg. 2292
EDWARDS BUSINESS MACHINES INC.; *U.S. Private*, pg. 1341
ELAN MARKETING, INC.—See Xerox Holdings Corporation; *U.S. Public*, pg. 2387
ELECTRONIC SYSTEMS, INC.—See Xerox Holdings Corporation; *U.S. Public*, pg. 2389
E.O. JOHNSON COMPANY, INC.; *U.S. Private*, pg. 1306
ETERNAL TECHNOLOGY CORPORATION—See Eternal Materials Co., Ltd.; *Int'l*, pg. 2521
EXECUTIVE IMAGE SOLUTIONS, INC.; *U.S. Private*, pg. 1447
EXECUTIVE TECHNOLOGIES, INC.—See Wells Fargo & Company; *U.S. Public*, pg. 2344
EXERTIS (UK) LTD—See DCC plc; *Int'l*, pg. 1990
FAIRWAY MARKETING GROUP—See U.S. Bancorp; *U.S. Public*, pg. 2212
FARMER BUSINESS SYSTEMS—See Alliance Office Systems; *U.S. Private*, pg. 183
FELLOWES CANADA LTD.—See Fellowes, Inc.; *U.S. Private*, pg. 1494
FENTON'S OFFICE SOLUTIONS, INC.—See Pacific Office Automation, Inc.; *U.S. Private*, pg. 3069
FIREFLY TECHNOLOGIES; *U.S. Private*, pg. 1511
FISHER'S DOCUMENT SYSTEMS, INC.; *U.S. Private*, pg. 1534
FORD BUSINESS MACHINES, INC.; *U.S. Private*, pg. 1564
FOREMOST BUSINESS SYSTEMS, INC.—See NCR Voyix Corporation; *U.S. Public*, pg. 1502
FUJI XEROX ASIA PACIFIC PTE LTD. - INDOCHINA OPERATIONS—See FUJIFILM Holdings Corporation; *Int'l*, pg. 2825
FUJI XEROX ASIA PACIFIC PTE LTD. - MALAYSIA—See FUJIFILM Holdings Corporation; *Int'l*, pg. 2825
FUJI XEROX ASIA PACIFIC PTE LTD.—See FUJIFILM Holdings Corporation; *Int'l*, pg. 2825
FUJI XEROX AUSTRALIA PTY. LTD.—See FUJIFILM Holdings Corporation; *Int'l*, pg. 2825
FUJI XEROX (CHINA) LIMITED—See FUJIFILM Holdings Corporation; *Int'l*, pg. 2825
FUJI XEROX NEW ZEALAND LTD.—See FUJIFILM Holdings Corporation; *Int'l*, pg. 2825
FUJI XEROX SINGAPORE PTE LTD.—See FUJIFILM Holdings Corporation; *Int'l*, pg. 2826
FUTABA TECHNOLOGY LTD.—See Futaba Industrial Co., Ltd.; *Int'l*, pg. 2851
GATEWAY PRINTING & OFFICE SUPPLY, INC.; *U.S. Private*, pg. 1651
G&D AMERICA DO SUL INDUSTRIA E COMERCIO DE SMART CARDS SOCIEDADE ANONIMA—See Giesecke & Devrient GmbH; *Int'l*, pg. 2969
G&D LOMO, ZAO—See Giesecke & Devrient GmbH; *Int'l*, pg. 2969
GIESECKE & DEVRIENT 3S AB—See Giesecke & Devrient GmbH; *Int'l*, pg. 2969
GIESECKE & DEVRIENT 3S GMBH—See Giesecke & Devrient GmbH; *Int'l*, pg. 2969
GIESECKE & DEVRIENT 3S OY—See Giesecke & Devrient GmbH; *Int'l*, pg. 2969
GIESECKE & DEVRIENT AFRICA LTD.—See Giesecke & Devrient GmbH; *Int'l*, pg. 2969
GIESECKE & DEVRIENT ASIA PACIFIC BANKING SYSTEMS (SHANGHAI) CO. LTD.—See Giesecke & Devrient GmbH; *Int'l*, pg. 2969
GIESECKE & DEVRIENT ASIA PACIFIC (KOREA)—See Giesecke & Devrient GmbH; *Int'l*, pg. 2969
GIESECKE & DEVRIENT ASIA PACIFIC LTD—See Giesecke & Devrient GmbH; *Int'l*, pg. 2969
GIESECKE & DEVRIENT ASIA PTE. LTD.—See Giesecke & Devrient GmbH; *Int'l*, pg. 2969
GIESECKE & DEVRIENT AUSTRALASIA PTY. LTD.—See Giesecke & Devrient GmbH; *Int'l*, pg. 2969
GIESECKE & DEVRIENT BRASIL LTDA.—See Giesecke & Devrient GmbH; *Int'l*, pg. 2969
GIESECKE & DEVRIENT (CHINA) INFORMATION TECHNOLOGIES CO., LTD.—See Giesecke & Devrient GmbH; *Int'l*, pg. 2969
GIESECKE & DEVRIENT EGYPT SERVICES LLC—See Giesecke & Devrient GmbH; *Int'l*, pg. 2969
GIESECKE & DEVRIENT FRANCE S.A.S.—See Giesecke & Devrient GmbH; *Int'l*, pg. 2969
GIESECKE & DEVRIENT FZE—See Giesecke & Devrient GmbH; *Int'l*, pg. 2969
GIESECKE & DEVRIENT GB LTD.—See Giesecke & Devrient GmbH; *Int'l*, pg. 2969
GIESECKE & DEVRIENT INDIA PRIVATE LIMITED—See Giesecke & Devrient GmbH; *Int'l*, pg. 2969
GIESECKE & DEVRIENT ISTANBUL TICARET VE SERVIS LTD. SIRKETI—See Giesecke & Devrient GmbH; *Int'l*, pg. 2969
GIESECKE & DEVRIENT ITALIA, S.R.L.—See Giesecke & Devrient GmbH; *Int'l*, pg. 2969
GIESECKE & DEVRIENT KABUSHIKI KAISHA—See Giesecke & Devrient GmbH; *Int'l*, pg. 2969
GIESECKE & DEVRIENT MALAYSIA SDN BHD—See Giesecke & Devrient GmbH; *Int'l*, pg. 2969
GIESECKE & DEVRIENT MATSOUKIS, SECURITY PRINTING, S.A.—See Giesecke & Devrient GmbH; *Int'l*, pg. 2969
GIESECKE & DEVRIENT SLOVAKIA, S.R.O.—See Giesecke & Devrient GmbH; *Int'l*, pg. 2969
GIESECKE & DEVRIENT (SOUTHERN AFRICA) (PTY) LTD.—See Giesecke & Devrient GmbH; *Int'l*, pg. 2969
GIESECKE Y DEVRIENT DE MEXICO S.A. DE C.V.—See Giesecke & Devrient GmbH; *Int'l*, pg. 2970
GORDON FLESCH COMPANY, INC.; *U.S. Private*, pg. 1743
GRAND & TOY LIMITED—See The ODP Corporation; *U.S. Public*, pg. 2117
GRANT VICTOR; *U.S. Private*, pg. 1757
GRAPHIC ENTERPRISES INC.—See Visual Edge Technology, Inc.; *U.S. Private*, pg. 4404
GUANGZHOU KINGTELLER TECHNOLOGY CO., LTD.; *Int'l*, pg. 3166
GULF COAST OFFICE PRODUCTS, INC.; *U.S. Private*, pg. 1815

423420 — OFFICE EQUIPMENT ME...

GYD IBERICA S.A.—See Giesecke & Devrient GmbH; *Int'l*, pg. 2970
GYD LATINOAMERICANA S.A.—See Giesecke & Devrient GmbH; *Int'l*, pg. 2970
HAREL MALLAC BUREAUTIQUE LTD—See Harel Mallac & Co. Ltd.; *Int'l*, pg. 3274
HARMAN TECHNOLOGY, LTD.—See DH Private Equity Partners LLP; *Int'l*, pg. 2097
HERITAGE BUSINESS SYSTEMS, INC.—See Xerox Holdings Corporation; *U.S. Public*, pg. 2388
HITACHI TERMINAL SOLUTIONS (THAILAND) COMPANY LIMITED—See Hitachi, Ltd.; *Int'l*, pg. 3422
HOKKAIDO GLORY CO., LTD.—See GLORY Ltd.; *Int'l*, pg. 3010
HONEYWELL DEFENSE AND SPACE ELECTRONIC SYSTEMS—See Honeywell International Inc.; *U.S. Public*, pg. 1047
HUANGSHI G&D WANDA SECURITY CARD CO. LTD.—See Giesecke & Devrient GmbH; *Int'l*, pg. 2970
HUXEN CORPORATION; *Int'l*, pg. 3541
IE GROUP, INC.—See Hikari Tsushin, Inc.; *Int'l*, pg. 3390
IMAGE IV SYSTEMS INC.; *U.S. Private*, pg. 2044
IMAGE TECHNOLOGY SPECIALISTS, INC.—See Xerox Holdings Corporation; *U.S. Public*, pg. 2387
IMAGING ALLIANCE GROUP, LLC; *U.S. Private*, pg. 2046
IMAGING BUSINESS SYSTEMS (N.I.) LIMITED—See Xerox Holdings Corporation; *U.S. Public*, pg. 2387
IMAGING CONCEPTS OF NEW MEXICO, INC.—See Xerox Holdings Corporation; *U.S. Public*, pg. 2387
INDIANA BUSINESS EQUIPMENT, LLC—See Gordon Flesch Company, Inc.; *U.S. Private*, pg. 1743
INFASTECH (GUANGZHOU) LIMITED—See Stanley Black & Decker, Inc.; *U.S. Public*, pg. 1932
INFINCOM, INC.; *U.S. Private*, pg. 2070
INGRAM MICRO (CHINA) LTD—See Hainan Traffic Administration Holding Co., Ltd.; *Int'l*, pg. 3214
INGRAM MICRO DATA CAPTURE/POS DIVISION—See Hainan Traffic Administration Holding Co., Ltd.; *Int'l*, pg. 3214
INGRAM MICRO INC.—See Hainan Traffic Administration Holding Co., Ltd.; *Int'l*, pg. 3213
INGRAM MICRO - MIAMI—See Hainan Traffic Administration Holding Co., Ltd.; *Int'l*, pg. 3214
INLAND TECHNOLOGY—See Canon Inc.; *Int'l*, pg. 1293
INTERBORO SYSTEMS CORPORATION—See Hellman & Friedman LLC; *U.S. Private*, pg. 1910
IRISH BUSINESS SYSTEMS LIMITED—See Xerox Holdings Corporation; *U.S. Public*, pg. 2387
ISG SERVICES, LLC—See Xerox Holdings Corporation; *U.S. Public*, pg. 2387
JJR ENTERPRISES INC.; *U.S. Private*, pg. 2211
JOLOHA ENTERPRISES, INC.—See Word Systems, Inc.; *U.S. Private*, pg. 4563
JONES & COOK STATIONERS, INC.—See Gateway Printing & Office Supply, Inc.; *U.S. Private*, pg. 1651
JTF BUSINESS SYSTEMS; *U.S. Private*, pg. 2242
KATUN ARGENTINA S.R.L.—See General Plastic Industrial Co., Ltd.; *Int'l*, pg. 2919
KATUN BENELUX B.V.—See General Plastic Industrial Co., Ltd.; *Int'l*, pg. 2919
KATUN BRASIL COMERCIO DE SUPRIMENTOS PECAS E EQUIPAMENTOS LTDA.—See General Plastic Industrial Co., Ltd.; *Int'l*, pg. 2919
KATUN CORPORATION—See General Plastic Industrial Co., Ltd.; *Int'l*, pg. 2919
KATUN FRANCE S.A.R.L.—See General Plastic Industrial Co., Ltd.; *Int'l*, pg. 2919
KATUN GERMANY GMBH—See General Plastic Industrial Co., Ltd.; *Int'l*, pg. 2919
KATUN ITALY S.R.L.—See General Plastic Industrial Co., Ltd.; *Int'l*, pg. 2919
KATUN PORTUGAL S.A.—See General Plastic Industrial Co., Ltd.; *Int'l*, pg. 2919
KATUN SPAIN S.A.—See General Plastic Industrial Co., Ltd.; *Int'l*, pg. 2919
KATUN U.K. LTD.—See General Plastic Industrial Co., Ltd.; *Int'l*, pg. 2919
KONICA MINOLTA BUSINESS SOLUTIONS NEW ZEALAND LTD.—See FUJIFILM Holdings Corporation; *Int'l*, pg. 2825
KOPIER NET—See Perpetual Capital, LLC; *U.S. Private*, pg. 3153
KRONOS SYSTEMS LTD—See Hellman & Friedman LLC; *U.S. Private*, pg. 1910
KSOLUTIONS SPA—See Giovanni Agnelli B.V.; *Int'l*, pg. 2978
LAKE BUSINESS PRODUCTS, INC.; *U.S. Private*, pg. 2374
THE LANG COMPANY, INC.; *U.S. Private*, pg. 4067
LATOFF WAINER & COMPANY; *U.S. Private*, pg. 2397
LEWAN TECHNOLOGY—See Xerox Holdings Corporation; *U.S. Public*, pg. 2388
LIBERTY BUSINESS SYSTEMS, INC.; *U.S. Private*, pg. 2443
LIGHTHOUSE ELECTRONICS, INC., *U.S. Private*, pg. 2453
LOFFLER COMPANIES, INC., *U.S. Private*, pg. 2480
LOWERY CORPORATION; *U.S. Private*, pg. 2506
LUCAS BUSINESS SYSTEMS, INC.—See Xerox Holdings Corporation; *U.S. Public*, pg. 2388

LUTGEN & ASSOCIATES, INC.; *U.S. Private*, pg. 2516
MANUTAN LTD—See Eraser Dust, Inc.; *U.S. Private*, pg. 1417
MARTIN WHALEN OFFICE SOLUTIONS INC.; *U.S. Private*, pg. 2596
MC HOLDING GMBH & CO. KG—See Giesecke & Devrient GmbH; *Int'l*, pg. 2970
MCP OF CALIFORNIA, INC.—See Xerox Holdings Corporation; *U.S. Public*, pg. 2388
METRO SALES, INC.; *U.S. Private*, pg. 2686
MICROS-FIDELIO U.K. LTD.—See Oracle Corporation; *U.S. Public*, pg. 1612
MILLENNIUM BUSINESS SYSTEMS, LLC; *U.S. Private*, pg. 2731
MINNESOTA OFFICE TECHNOLOGY GROUP, INC.—See Xerox Holdings Corporation; *U.S. Public*, pg. 2388
MISSISSIPPI INDUSTRIES FOR THE BLIND; *U.S. Private*, pg. 2748
MODERN OFFICE METHODS INC.; *U.S. Private*, pg. 2761
M-S CASH DRAWER CORPORATION; *U.S. Private*, pg. 2526
MT BUSINESS TECHNOLOGIES, INC.—See Xerox Holdings Corporation; *U.S. Public*, pg. 2389
MURFREESBORO BUSINESS MACHINES, INC.—See Bow-Boeck Enterprises LLC; *U.S. Private*, pg. 625
NAUTILUS HYOSUNG AMERICA, INC.—See Hyosung Corporation; *Int'l*, pg. 3551
NEW AGE ELECTRONICS, INC.—See TD Synnex Corp; *U.S. Public*, pg. 1984
NMS - IMAGING; *U.S. Private*, pg. 2931
NORTH COUNTRY BUSINESS PRODUCTS; *U.S. Private*, pg. 2944
NORTHEAST COPIER SYSTEMS, LLC—See Xerox Holdings Corporation; *U.S. Public*, pg. 2388
NORTHWEST OFFICE TECHNOLOGIES INC.—See Pacific Office Automation, Inc.; *U.S. Private*, pg. 3069
OASYS, INC.; *U.S. Private*, pg. 2986
OCE-CANADA, INC.—See Canon Inc.; *Int'l*, pg. 1297
OCE-ESPANA S.A.—See Canon Inc.; *Int'l*, pg. 1294
OFFICE SYSTEMS OF VERMONT, INC.—See Visual Edge Technology, Inc.; *U.S. Private*, pg. 4404
PAPIERFABRIK LOUISENTHAL GMBH—See Giesecke & Devrient GmbH; *Int'l*, pg. 2970
PETTUS OFFICE PRODUCTS, INC.; *U.S. Private*, pg. 3163
PITNEY BOWES JAPAN—See Pitney Bowes Inc.; *U.S. Public*, pg. 1695
PITNEY BOWES LIMITED—See Pitney Bowes Inc.; *U.S. Public*, pg. 1695
PITNEY BOWES OY—See Pitney Bowes Inc.; *U.S. Public*, pg. 1695
PITNEY BOWES (SWITZERLAND) AG—See Pitney Bowes Inc.; *U.S. Public*, pg. 1694
PNA HOLDINGS MEXICO S.A. DE C.V.—See General Plastic Industrial Co., Ltd.; *Int'l*, pg. 2919
POSTRONIC AB—See Amplex AB; *Int'l*, pg. 433
PRODATA LDA.—See Brithol Michcoma Mozambique Limited; *Int'l*, pg. 1165
P.T. AMANO INDONESIA—See Amano Corporation; *Int'l*, pg. 411
PT. CHIYODA INTEGRE INDONESIA—See Chiyoda Integre Co., Ltd.; *Int'l*, pg. 1575
PT GIESECKE & DEVRIENT INDONESIA—See Giesecke & Devrient GmbH; *Int'l*, pg. 2970
QUALITY BUSINESS SYSTEMS, INC.—See Xerox Holdings Corporation; *U.S. Public*, pg. 2388
QUALSTAR SALES AND SERVICE CORPORATION—See Qualstar Corporation; *U.S. Public*, pg. 1748
RABBIT COPIERS, INC.—See Xerox Holdings Corporation; *U.S. Public*, pg. 2387
RESTORED DIGITAL SOLUTIONS, LLC; *U.S. Private*, pg. 3410
R.J. YOUNG CO., INC.; *U.S. Private*, pg. 3337
R.K. BLACK INC.; *U.S. Private*, pg. 3338
RK DIXON—See Xerox Holdings Corporation; *U.S. Public*, pg. 2389
ROCKWELL COLLINS FRANCE, S.A.S.—See RTX Corporation; *U.S. Public*, pg. 1823
ROYAL CONSUMER INFORMATION PRODUCTS INC.; *U.S. Private*, pg. 3491
SAXON BUSINESS SYSTEMS, INC.—See Xerox Holdings Corporation; *U.S. Public*, pg. 2389
SELECT BUSINESS SYSTEMS, INC.—See GoodSuite; *U.S. Private*, pg. 1740
SHAMROCK OFFICE SOLUTIONS—See Oval Partners; *U.S. Private*, pg. 3052
SHARP BUSINESS SYSTEMS OF NORTH CAROLINA—See Hon Hai Precision Industry Co., Ltd.; *Int'l*, pg. 3458
SHARP BUSINESS SYSTEMS—See Hon Hai Precision Industry Co., Ltd.; *Int'l*, pg. 3458
SHARP BUSINESS SYSTEMS - WASHINGTON—See Hon Hai Precision Industry Co., Ltd.; *Int'l*, pg. 3458
SHARP ELECTRONICS CORPORATION—See Hon Hai Precision Industry Co., Ltd.; *Int'l*, pg. 3458
SHIELDS BUSINESS SOLUTIONS INC.; *U.S. Private*, pg. 3635
SIMPLYGLOBO INC; *U.S. Private*, pg. 3668
SITRADE ITALIA S.P.A.—See GLORY Ltd.; *Int'l*, pg. 3010

CORPORATE AFFILIATIONS

SKYWAY TECHNOLOGY GROUP, INC.; *U.S. Private*, pg. 3686
SMOLTZ DISTRIBUTING, INC.—See Carolina Wholesale Office Machine Company, Inc.; *U.S. Private*, pg. 769
SOCAL OFFICE TECHNOLOGIES, INC.—See Xerox Holdings Corporation; *U.S. Public*, pg. 2388
SOLOEL CORPORATION—See ASKUL Corporation; *Int'l*, pg. 625
SOS OF TAMPA BAY, INC.; *U.S. Public*, pg. 3716
SOTIS BUSINESS EQUIPMENT LTD.; *U.S. Private*, pg. 3716
SPECTRUM IMAGING TECHNOLOGIES, INC.; *U.S. Private*, pg. 3752
SPICERS (IRELAND) LIMITED—See Heritage Group Ltd.; *Int'l*, pg. 3362
SPICERS LTD.—See Heritage Group Ltd.; *Int'l*, pg. 3361
STANDARD DUPLICATING MACHINES CORPORATION; *U.S. Private*, pg. 3778
STARGEL OFFICE SYSTEMS, INC.; *U.S. Private*, pg. 3786
STAR GRAPHICS, INC.; *U.S. Private*, pg. 3784
SUMNER GROUP INC.; *U.S. Private*, pg. 3857
SUPPLYPRO INC.; *U.S. Private*, pg. 3882
SWENSON GROUP INC.; *U.S. Private*, pg. 3892
SYSTEL BUSINESS EQUIPMENT CO. INC.; *U.S. Private*, pg. 3906
TAM BUSINESS SYSTEMS INC.; *U.S. Private*, pg. 3927
TASCOSA OFFICE MACHINES, INC.; *U.S. Private*, pg. 3934
TECHNIFAX CORPORATION; *U.S. Private*, pg. 3954
THAI FUJI XEROX CO., LTD.—See FUJIFILM Holdings Corporation; *Int'l*, pg. 2826
THERMOCOPY OF TENNESSEE INC.; *U.S. Private*, pg. 4143
TOAST, INC.; *U.S. Public*, pg. 2161
TRAVIS BUSINESS SYSTEMS INC.; *U.S. Private*, pg. 4214
TRIO SUPPLY COMPANY—See The ODP Corporation; *U.S. Public*, pg. 2118
TSAWORLD INC.; *U.S. Private*, pg. 4252
TUBELITE COMPANY INC.; *U.S. Private*, pg. 4255
TUBELITE COMPANY INC.—See Tubelite Company Inc.; *U.S. Private*, pg. 4255
TUBELITE COMPANY INC.—See Tubelite Company Inc.; *U.S. Private*, pg. 4255
TUBELITE COMPANY INC.—See Tubelite Company Inc.; *U.S. Private*, pg. 4255
TUBELITE COMPANY INC.—See Tubelite Company Inc.; *U.S. Private*, pg. 4255
TUBELITE COMPANY INC.—See Tubelite Company Inc.; *U.S. Private*, pg. 4255
UNISYS LIMITED—See Unisys Corporation; *U.S. Public*, pg. 2228
VAN AUSDALL & FARRAR INC.; *U.S. Private*, pg. 4338
VEENMAN B.V.—See Xerox Holdings Corporation; *U.S. Public*, pg. 2388
VELOX SYSTEMS, INC.—See Advanced Document Solutions, Inc.; *U.S. Private*, pg. 89
VICTOR TECHNOLOGY; *U.S. Private*, pg. 4378
VISUAL EDGE TECHNOLOGY, INC.; *U.S. Private*, pg. 4404
WILMAC BUSINESS EQUIPMENT CO, INC.; *U.S. Private*, pg. 4529
WORKWELL TECHNOLOGIES, INC.; *U.S. Private*, pg. 4564
XC TRADING HONG KONG LIMITED—See Xerox Holdings Corporation; *U.S. Public*, pg. 2388
XC TRADING SINGAPORE PTE LTD.—See Xerox Holdings Corporation; *U.S. Public*, pg. 2388
XEROX AB—See Xerox Holdings Corporation; *U.S. Public*, pg. 2388
XEROX ARGENTINA, I.C.S.A.—See Xerox Holdings Corporation; *U.S. Public*, pg. 2389
XEROX AUSTRIA GMBH—See Xerox Holdings Corporation; *U.S. Public*, pg. 2389
XEROX BURO ARACLARI TICARET VE SERVIS A.S.—See Xerox Holdings Corporation; *U.S. Public*, pg. 2389
XEROX BUSINESS EQUIPMENT LIMITED—See Xerox Holdings Corporation; *U.S. Public*, pg. 2389
XEROX BUSINESS SOLUTIONS, INC.—See Xerox Holdings Corporation; *U.S. Public*, pg. 2389
XEROX CORP.—See Xerox Holdings Corporation; *U.S. Public*, pg. 2390
XEROX CORP.—See Xerox Holdings Corporation; *U.S. Public*, pg. 2390
XEROX DE CHILE S.A.—See Xerox Holdings Corporation; *U.S. Public*, pg. 2390
XEROX DEL ECUADOR, S.A.—See Xerox Holdings Corporation; *U.S. Public*, pg. 2391
XEROX DE PANAMA SA—See Xerox Holdings Corporation; *U.S. Public*, pg. 2390
XEROX EGYPT S.A.E.—See Xerox Holdings Corporation; *U.S. Public*, pg. 2390
XEROX ESPANA, S.A.U.—See Xerox Holdings Corporation; *U.S. Public*, pg. 2390
XEROX ESPANA, THE DOCUMENT COMPANY SAU—See Xerox Holdings Corporation; *U.S. Public*, pg. 2389
XEROX FINANCE AG—See Xerox Holdings Corporation; *U.S. Public*, pg. 2389
XEROX GMBH—See Xerox Holdings Corporation; *U.S. Public*, pg. 2389

N.A.I.C.S. INDEX

XEROX MEXICANA, S.A. DE C.V.—See Xerox Holdings Corporation; *U.S. Public*, pg. 2390
XEROX OY—See Xerox Holdings Corporation; *U.S. Public*, pg. 2389
XEROX POLSKA SP ZOO—See Xerox Holdings Corporation; *U.S. Public*, pg. 2389
XEROX PORTUGAL—See Xerox Holdings Corporation; *U.S. Public*, pg. 2389
XEROX SA—See Xerox Holdings Corporation; *U.S. Public*, pg. 2389
XEROX SLOVENIA D.O.O.—See Xerox Holdings Corporation; *U.S. Public*, pg. 2390
XEROX UKRAINE—See Xerox Holdings Corporation; *U.S. Public*, pg. 2390
ZENO DIGITAL SOLUTIONS, LLC—See Visual Edge Technology, Inc.; *U.S. Private*, pg. 4404
ZOOM IMAGING SOLUTIONS, INC.; *U.S. Private*, pg. 4608

423430 — COMPUTER AND COMPUTER PERIPHERAL EQUIPMENT AND SOFTWARE MERCHANT WHOLESALERS

2000 SOFT INC.—See QXO, Inc.; *U.S. Public*, pg. 1758
3D SYSTEMS ASIA-PACIFIC PTY LTD—See 3D Systems Corporation; *U.S. Public*, pg. 4
3D SYSTEMS EUROPE LTD.—See 3D Systems Corporation; *U.S. Public*, pg. 4
3D SYSTEMS FRANCE SARL—See 3D Systems Corporation; *U.S. Public*, pg. 4
3D SYSTEMS GMBH—See 3D Systems Corporation; *U.S. Public*, pg. 4
3D SYSTEMS INDUSTRIA E COMERCIO LTDA—See 3D Systems Corporation; *U.S. Public*, pg. 4
3D SYSTEMS ITALIA S.R.L.—See 3D Systems Corporation; *U.S. Public*, pg. 4
3D SYSTEMS JAPAN K.K.—See 3D Systems Corporation; *U.S. Public*, pg. 4
3D SYSTEMS S.A.—See 3D Systems Corporation; *U.S. Public*, pg. 4
3D SYSTEMS SOFTWARE SRL—See 3D Systems Corporation; *U.S. Public*, pg. 4
505 GAMES GMBH—See Digital Bros SpA; *Int'l*, pg. 2120
505 GAMES S.R.L—See Digital Bros SpA; *Int'l*, pg. 2120
AAEON ELECTRONICS, INC.—See ASUSTeK Computer Inc.; *Int'l*, pg. 663
AAEON ELECTRONICS—See ASUSTeK Computer Inc.; *Int'l*, pg. 663
AAEON TECHNOLOGY (SUZHOU) INC.—See ASUSTeK Computer Inc.; *Int'l*, pg. 663
AAREON SOFTWARE HANDELSGESELLSCHAFT MBH—See Advent International Corporation; *U.S. Private*, pg. 96
AAREON SOFTWARE HANDELSGESELLSCHAFT MBH—See Centerbridge Partners, L.P.; *U.S. Private*, pg. 812
ABACUS 24-7 LLC; *U.S. Private*, pg. 33
ABEL WOMACK INTEGRATED HANDLING SOLUTIONS; *U.S. Private*, pg. 37
ABF DATA SYSTEMS INC.; *U.S. Private*, pg. 38
ABILITY INTERNATIONAL CO., LTD.—See Abico Group; *Int'l*, pg. 61
ABOL SOFTWARE, INC.—See Thoma Bravo, L.P.; *U.S. Private*, pg. 4153
AB S.A.; *Int'l*, pg. 41
ABTECH SYSTEMS, INC.—See Abtech Technologies, Inc.; *U.S. Private*, pg. 45
ABYSS GROUP INC; *U.S. Private*, pg. 45
ACCEO SOLUTIONS, INC. - QUEBEC—See Constellation Software Inc.; *Int'l*, pg. 1773
ACCOUNTING EQUIPMENT CORP.; *U.S. Private*, pg. 54
ACCUTECH DATA SUPPLIES INC.; *U.S. Private*, pg. 55
ACER ASIA PACIFIC SDN BHD—See Acer Incorporated; *Int'l*, pg. 98
ACER COMPUTER IBERICA, S.A.U.—See Acer Incorporated; *Int'l*, pg. 99
ACER COMPUTER INTERNATIONAL LTD.—See Acer Incorporated; *Int'l*, pg. 99
ACER COMPUTER (SHANGHAI) LTD.—See Acer Incorporated; *Int'l*, pg. 98
ACER COMPUTER (SWITZERLAND) AG—See Acer Incorporated; *Int'l*, pg. 98
ACER EUROPE SA—See Acer Incorporated; *Int'l*, pg. 99
ACER HELLAS LTD—See Acer Incorporated; *Int'l*, pg. 99
ACER UK LIMITED—See Acer Incorporated; *Int'l*, pg. 99
ACI WORLDWIDE BRASIL LTDA.—See ACI Worldwide, Inc.; *U.S. Public*, pg. 34
ACI WORLDWIDE B.V.—See ACI Worldwide, Inc.; *U.S. Public*, pg. 34
ACI WORLDWIDE CANADA, INC.—See ACI Worldwide, Inc.; *U.S. Public*, pg. 34
ACI WORLDWIDE EASTERN EUROPE DEVELOPMENT S.R.L.—See ACI Worldwide, Inc.; *U.S. Public*, pg. 34
ACI WORLDWIDE (EPS) AG—See ACI Worldwide, Inc.; *U.S. Public*, pg. 34
ACI WORLDWIDE FRANCE S.A.R.L.—See ACI Worldwide, Inc.; *U.S. Public*, pg. 34

ACI WORLDWIDE ITALIA S.R.L.—See ACI Worldwide, Inc.; *U.S. Public*, pg. 34
ACI WORLDWIDE MEXICO S.A. DE C.V.—See ACI Worldwide, Inc.; *U.S. Public*, pg. 34
ACI WORLDWIDE (PACIFIC) PTY. LTD.—See ACI Worldwide, Inc.; *U.S. Public*, pg. 34
ACI WORLDWIDE SOLUTIONS PVT. LTD.—See ACI Worldwide, Inc.; *U.S. Public*, pg. 35
ACTION EUROPE GMBH—See ACTION S.A.; *Int'l*, pg. 119
ACTION INTERNATIONAL MARKETING, INC.; *U.S. Private*, pg. 67
ACXIOM LTD.—See The Interpublic Group of Companies, Inc.; *U.S. Public*, pg. 2090
ADVANCED BUSINESS ANALYTICS (M) SDN. BHD.; *Int'l*, pg. 157
ADVANCED CLINICAL SERVICES LLC—See The Advanced Group of Companies; *U.S. Private*, pg. 3982
ADVANCED COMPUTER CONCEPTS; *U.S. Private*, pg. 88
ADVANCED DATA SYSTEMS CORP.; *U.S. Private*, pg. 89
ADVANCED INDUSTRIAL COMPUTER INC.; *U.S. Private*, pg. 90
ADVANCED MICRO DEVICES SPA—See Advanced Micro Devices, Inc.; *U.S. Public*, pg. 48
ADVANCED NETWORK SOLUTIONS; *U.S. Private*, pg. 91
ADVANTECH BRAZIL LTDA.—See Advantech Co., Ltd.; *Int'l*, pg. 164
ADVANTECH CORPORATION—See Advantech Co., Ltd.; *Int'l*, pg. 164
ADVANTECH EUROPE B.V.—See Advantech Co., Ltd.; *Int'l*, pg. 164
ADVANTECH RAISER INDIA PRIVATE LIMITED—See Advantech Co., Ltd.; *Int'l*, pg. 165
ADVANTECH TURKEY TEKNOLOJI AS—See Advantech Co., Ltd.; *Int'l*, pg. 165
ADVENT DATA LIMITED—See DCC plc; *Int'l*, pg. 1989
AGFA HEALTHCARE UK LIMITED—See Agfa-Gevaert N.V.; *Int'l*, pg. 208
AG NEOVO TECHNOLOGY B.V.—See Associated Industries China, Inc.; *Int'l*, pg. 649
AG NEOVO TECHNOLOGY CORPORATION—See Associated Industries China, Inc.; *Int'l*, pg. 649
AHEARN & SOPER INC.—See Ahearn & Soper Inc.; *Int'l*, pg. 223
ALLIED TELESYN INTERNATIONAL S.A.—See ALLIED TELESIS HOLDINGS K.K.; *Int'l*, pg. 358
ALLOT COMMUNICATIONS (ASIA PACIFIC) PTE. LTD.—See Allot Ltd.; *Int'l*, pg. 360
ALLOT COMMUNICATIONS UK LIMITED—See Allot Ltd.; *Int'l*, pg. 360
ALPHA INTERNATIONAL B.V.—See Droege Group AG; *Int'l*, pg. 2205
ALSEN MARKETING SP. Z O.O.—See AB S.A.; *Int'l*, pg. 41
ALSO A/S—See Droege Group AG; *Int'l*, pg. 2205
ALSO AS—See Droege Group AG; *Int'l*, pg. 2205
ALSO AUSTRIA GMBH—See Droege Group AG; *Int'l*, pg. 2205
ALSO DEUTSCHLAND GMBH—See Droege Group AG; *Int'l*, pg. 2205
ALSO DIGITAL B.V—See Droege Group AG; *Int'l*, pg. 2205
ALSO EESTI OU—See Droege Group AG; *Int'l*, pg. 2205
ALSO FINLAND OY—See Droege Group AG; *Int'l*, pg. 2205
ALSO FRANCE S.A.S.—See Droege Group AG; *Int'l*, pg. 2205
ALSO NEDERLAND B.V.—See Droege Group AG; *Int'l*, pg. 2205
ALSO POLSKA SP. Z O.O.—See Droege Group AG; *Int'l*, pg. 2205
ALSO SCHWEIZ AG—See Droege Group AG; *Int'l*, pg. 2205
ALTERNATIVE TECHNOLOGY SOLUTIONS; *U.S. Private*, pg. 207
ALTURNA NETWORKS N.V.—See Amphenol Corporation; *U.S. Public*, pg. 126
ALVIVA HOLDINGS LIMITED; *Int'l*, pg. 401
AMAX GLOBAL SERVICES INC.; *U.S. Private*, pg. 216
AMCC JAPAN CO. LTD.—See MACOM Technology Solutions Holdings, Inc.; *U.S. Public*, pg. 1352
AMCS CORPORATION—See Advanced Manufacturing Control Systems Ltd.; *Int'l*, pg. 160
AMCS FRANCE SAS—See Advanced Manufacturing Control Systems Ltd.; *Int'l*, pg. 160
AMCS LTD—See Advanced Manufacturing Control Systems Ltd.; *Int'l*, pg. 160
AMCS SWEDEN AB—See Advanced Manufacturing Control Systems Ltd.; *Int'l*, pg. 160
AMD INTERNATIONAL SALES & SERVICE, LTD.—See Advanced Micro Devices, Inc.; *U.S. Public*, pg. 48
AMD SOUTH AMERICA LTDA—See Advanced Micro Devices, Inc.; *U.S. Public*, pg. 48
AMERICAN BARCODE AND RFID; *U.S. Private*, pg. 224
AMERICAN BRIGHT SIGNS, INC.—See ACEP France; *Int'l*, pg. 98
AMERICAN EAGLE SYSTEMS INC.; *U.S. Private*, pg. 231
AMERICAN SUNREX CORPORATION; *U.S. Private*, pg. 256
AMERINDIA TECHNOLOGIES, INC.; *U.S. Private*, pg. 260
AMION, LLC—See Doximity, Inc.; *U.S. Public*, pg. 686
ANABELLE BITS PTY LTD.; *Int'l*, pg. 444
ANDES TECHNOLOGY USA CORPORATION—See Andes Technology Corporation; *Int'l*, pg. 450
APOLLO ENTERPRISE SOLUTIONS, INC.—See Apollo Enterprise Solutions, Ltd.; *U.S. Private*, pg. 294
APPAREL BUSINESS SYSTEMS, LLC—See TA Associates, Inc.; *U.S. Private*, pg. 3914
APPLIED COMMUNICATIONS IRELAND LIMITED—See ACI Worldwide, Inc.; *U.S. Public*, pg. 34
APPLIED MATERIALS UK LIMITED—See Applied Materials, Inc.; *U.S. Public*, pg. 172
ARBITECH; *U.S. Private*, pg. 308
ARENA BILGISAYAR SANAYI VE TICARET A.S.; *Int'l*, pg. 558
ARLINGTON COMPUTER PRODUCTS; *U.S. Private*, pg. 329
ARRAY NETWORKS, INC.; *U.S. Private*, pg. 334
ARROW ECS ANZ LIMITED—See Arrow Electronics, Inc.; *U.S. Public*, pg. 195
ARROW ECS ANZ PTY LTD—See Arrow Electronics, Inc.; *U.S. Public*, pg. 195
ARROW ECS ASIA PTE. LTD.—See Arrow Electronics, Inc.; *U.S. Public*, pg. 195
ARROW ECS B.V.—See Arrow Electronics, Inc.; *U.S. Public*, pg. 196
ARROW ECS FZCO—See Arrow Electronics, Inc.; *U.S. Public*, pg. 196
ARROW ECS GMBH—See Arrow Electronics, Inc.; *U.S. Public*, pg. 196
ARROW ECS KFT.—See Arrow Electronics, Inc.; *U.S. Public*, pg. 196
ARROW ECS LTD.—See Arrow Electronics, Inc.; *U.S. Public*, pg. 196
ARROW ECS PTY LTD.—See Arrow Electronics, Inc.; *U.S. Public*, pg. 196
ARROW ECS SPA—See Arrow Electronics, Inc.; *U.S. Public*, pg. 196
ARROW ELECTRONICS COMPONENTS—See Arrow Electronics, Inc.; *U.S. Public*, pg. 197
ARROW ELECTRONICS, LTD.—See Arrow Electronics, Inc.; *U.S. Public*, pg. 198
ARROW ENTERPRISE COMPUTING SOLUTIONS, INC.—See Arrow Electronics, Inc.; *U.S. Public*, pg. 198
ARROW VALUE RECOVERY NORWAY AS—See Arrow Electronics, Inc.; *U.S. Public*, pg. 198
ARTRONIX SDN. BHD.—See ARTRONIQ BERHAD; *Int'l*, pg. 585
ASBIS-BALTIK AS—See ASBISc Enterprises Plc; *Int'l*, pg. 600
ASBIS CA LLC—See ASBISc Enterprises Plc; *Int'l*, pg. 600
ASBISC-CR D.O.O.—See ASBISc Enterprises Plc; *Int'l*, pg. 600
ASBISC ENTERPRISES PLC; *Int'l*, pg. 600
ASBIS CZ, SPOL. S R.O.—See ASBISc Enterprises Plc; *Int'l*, pg. 600
ASBIS D.O.O.—See ASBISc Enterprises Plc; *Int'l*, pg. 600
ASBIS EUROPE BV—See ASBISc Enterprises Plc; *Int'l*, pg. 600
ASBIS HELLAS SINGLE MEMBER S.A.—See ASBISc Enterprises Plc; *Int'l*, pg. 600
ASBIS HUNGARY COMMERCIAL LTD—See ASBISc Enterprises Plc; *Int'l*, pg. 600
ASBIS KAZAKHSTAN LLP—See ASBISc Enterprises Plc; *Int'l*, pg. 600
ASBIS KYPROS LTD—See ASBISc Enterprises Plc; *Int'l*, pg. 600
ASBIS LTD.—See ASBISc Enterprises Plc; *Int'l*, pg. 600
ASBIS ME FZE—See ASBISc Enterprises Plc; *Int'l*, pg. 600
ASBIS PL SP.Z O.O.—See ASBISc Enterprises Plc; *Int'l*, pg. 600
ASBIS TR BILGISAYAR LIMITED SIRKETI—See ASBISc Enterprises Plc; *Int'l*, pg. 600
ASBIS UKRAINE LTD.—See ASBISc Enterprises Plc; *Int'l*, pg. 600
ASBIS VILNIUS UAB—See ASBISc Enterprises Plc; *Int'l*, pg. 600
ASCENDTECH, INC.; *U.S. Private*, pg. 346
THE ASCII GROUP, INC.; *U.S. Private*, pg. 3989
ASENTINEL, LLC—See Marlin Equity Partners, LLC; *U.S. Private*, pg. 2583
ASI CORPORATION; *U.S. Private*, pg. 350
ASPENTECH (SHANGHAI) CO., LTD.—See Emerson Electric Co.; *U.S. Public*, pg. 741
ASPENTECH (THAILAND) LTD.—See Emerson Electric Co.; *U.S. Public*, pg. 741
ASROCK AMERICA, INC.—See ASRock Inc.; *Int'l*, pg. 632
ASROCK EUROPE B.V.—See ASRock Inc.; *Int'l*, pg. 632
ASSET VANTAGE INC.—See Asset Vantage Systems Pvt. Ltd.; *Int'l*, pg. 642
ASTRO-MED GMBH—See AstroNova, Inc.; *U.S. Public*, pg. 218
ASUS COMPUTER GMBH—See ASUSTeK Computer Inc.; *Int'l*, pg. 663
ASUS COMPUTER INTERNATIONAL, INC.—See ASUSTeK Computer Inc.; *Int'l*, pg. 663
ATCORE SYSTEMS, LLC—See Faye Business Systems Group Inc.; *U.S. Private*, pg. 1484
ATEA AS—See Atea ASA; *Int'l*, pg. 667
ATEA A/S—See Atea ASA; *Int'l*, pg. 667
ATEA LOGISTICS AB—See Atea ASA; *Int'l*, pg. 667

423430 — COMPUTER AND COMPUT...

ATEA SVERIGE AB—See Atea ASA; *Int'l*, pg. 667
ATEN TECHNOLOGY INC.—See Aten International Co., Ltd.; *Int'l*, pg. 668
ATLANTIC.NET, INC.; *U.S. Private*, pg. 375
ATLANTIX GLOBAL SYSTEMS, LLC—See H.I.G. Capital, LLC; *U.S. Private*, pg. 1829
A&T SYSTEMS—See A&T Systems Inc.; *U.S. Private*, pg. 21
AURDEL SWEDEN AB—See DistIT AB; *Int'l*, pg. 2136
AURES USA INC—See Aures Technologies; *Int'l*, pg. 710
AUSTIN RIBBON & COMPUTER SUPPLIES, INC.—See Pivot Technology Solutions, Inc.; *U.S. Public*, pg. 1695
AUTODESK ASIA PTE. LTD.—See Autodesk, Inc.; *U.S. Public*, pg. 229
AUTODESK DE MEXICO S.A. DE C.V.—See Autodesk, Inc.; *U.S. Public*, pg. 229
AUTOENGINUITY LLC—See Searchlight Capital Partners, L.P.; *U.S. Private*, pg. 3590
AUTOSTAR SOLUTIONS, INC.—See Vista Equity Partners, LLC; *U.S. Private*, pg. 4400
AVANQUEST DEUTSCHLAND GMBH—See Claranova SA; *Int'l*, pg. 1642
AVANQUEST IBERICA S.L.—See Claranova SA; *Int'l*, pg. 1642
AVATECH OF NEBRASKA INC.—See Rand Worldwide, Inc.; *U.S. Public*, pg. 1762
AVID TECHNOLOGY (S.E. ASIA) PTE LTD—See Symphony Technology Group, LLC; *U.S. Private*, pg. 3901
AVID TECHNOLOGY S.L.—See Symphony Technology Group, LLC; *U.S. Private*, pg. 3901
AVNET ABACUS HERLEV—See TD Synnex Corp; *U.S. Public*, pg. 1985
AVNET B.V.—See Avnet, Inc.; *U.S. Public*, pg. 250
AVNET CHILE S.A.—See Avnet, Inc.; *U.S. Public*, pg. 250
AVNET COMPONENTS LTD.—See Avnet, Inc.; *U.S. Public*, pg. 250
AVNET COMPUTER SERVICE (HONG KONG) LIMITED—See Avnet, Inc.; *U.S. Public*, pg. 250
AVNET COMPUTER SERVICE (MACAU) LIMITED—See Avnet, Inc.; *U.S. Public*, pg. 250
AVNET DE MEXICO, S.A. DE C.V.—See Avnet, Inc.; *U.S. Public*, pg. 252
AVNET DO BRASIL LTDA—See Avnet, Inc.; *U.S. Public*, pg. 252
AVNET ELECTRONICS MARKETING—See Avnet, Inc.; *U.S. Public*, pg. 250
AVNET EMG ELEKTRONISCHE BAUELMENTE GMBH—See Avnet, Inc.; *U.S. Public*, pg. 250
AVNET EMG FRANCE S.A.—See Avnet, Inc.; *U.S. Public*, pg. 250
AVNET EM SP. Z.O O.—See Avnet, Inc.; *U.S. Public*, pg. 250
AVNET ENTERPRISE SOLUTIONS—See Avnet, Inc.; *U.S. Public*, pg. 251
AVNET KOPP (PTY) LIMITED—See Avnet, Inc.; *U.S. Public*, pg. 251
AVNET NORTEC A/S—See Avnet, Inc.; *U.S. Public*, pg. 252
AXI EDUCATION SOLUTIONS, LLC—See Rotunda Capital Partners LLC; *U.S. Private*, pg. 3488
AXIOM TECHNOLOGY INC—See Axiomtek Co., Ltd; *Int'l*, pg. 769
AXIOMTEK CO., LTD; *Int'l*, pg. 769
AXIOMTEK DEUTSCHLAND GMBH—See Axiomtek Co., Ltd; *Int'l*, pg. 769
AXIOMTEK (M) SDN. BHD.—See Axiomtek Co., Ltd; *Int'l*, pg. 769
AXIOMTEK TECHNOLOGY (SHEN ZHENG) CO., LTD.—See Axiomtek Co., Ltd; *Int'l*, pg. 769
AXIOMTEK (THAILAND) CO., LTD.—See Axiomtek Co., Ltd; *Int'l*, pg. 769
AXIS BUSINESS SOLUTIONS, INC.; *U.S. Private*, pg. 413
AZLAN LOGISTICS LIMITED—See TD Synnex Corp; *U.S. Public*, pg. 1985
B2B COMPUTER PRODUCTS, LLC; *U.S. Private*, pg. 421
BALDWIN AMERICAS DO BRASIL LTDA—See Forsyth Capital Investors LLC; *U.S. Private*, pg. 1573
BALDWIN GERMANY GMBH—See Forsyth Capital Investors LLC; *U.S. Private*, pg. 1573
BANCO IBM S.A.—See International Business Machines Corporation; *U.S. Public*, pg. 1145
BAN LEONG TECHNOLOGIES LIMITED; *Int'l*, pg. 813
BAN LEONG TECHNOLOGIES SDN BHD—See Ban Leong Technologies Limited; *Int'l*, pg. 814
BANQUE MAGNETIQUE SAS—See DCC plc; *Int'l*, pg. 1989
BAR CODE DIRECT, INC.—See Sole Source Capital LLC; *U.S. Private*, pg. 3708
BASS COMPUTERS INC.; *U.S. Private*, pg. 486
BAY STATE COMPUTERS INC.; *U.S. Private*, pg. 494
BECHTLE AG; *Int'l*, pg. 936
BECHTLE DIRECT NV—See Bechtle AG; *Int'l*, pg. 937
BECHTLE DIRECT S.L.U.—See Bechtle AG; *Int'l*, pg. 937
BECHTLE FINANCIAL SERVICES AG—See Bechtle AG; *Int'l*, pg. 937
BECHTLE HOSTING & OPERATIONS GMBH & CO. KG—See Bechtle AG; *Int'l*, pg. 937
BECHTLE ONSITE SERVICES GMBH—See Bechtle AG; *Int'l*, pg. 937
BEHAVIOR TECH COMPUTER (US) CORPORATION—See Behavior Tech Computer Corporation; *Int'l*, pg. 941
BEIJING CONTEC MICROELECTRONICS CORPORATION—See Daifuku Co., Ltd.; *Int'l*, pg. 1924
BEIJING DIGITAL TELECOM CO., LTD.; *Int'l*, pg. 948
BEIJING FUTONG DONGFANG TECHNOLOGY CO., LTD.—See Futong Technology Development Holdings Limited; *Int'l*, pg. 2852
BELKIN ASIA PACIFIC LIMITED—See Hon Hai Precision Industry Co., Ltd.; *Int'l*, pg. 3456
BELKIN BV—See Hon Hai Precision Industry Co., Ltd.; *Int'l*, pg. 3456
BELKIN GMBH—See Hon Hai Precision Industry Co., Ltd.; *Int'l*, pg. 3456
BELKIN INTERNATIONAL, INC.—See Hon Hai Precision Industry Co., Ltd.; *Int'l*, pg. 3456
BELKIN LIMITED—See Hon Hai Precision Industry Co., Ltd.; *Int'l*, pg. 3456
BELKIN SAS—See Hon Hai Precision Industry Co., Ltd.; *Int'l*, pg. 3456
BENQ AMERICA CORP.—See BenQ Corporation; *Int'l*, pg. 975
BENQ BENELUX—See BenQ Corporation; *Int'l*, pg. 975
BERMUDA COMPUTER SERVICES LTD.—See International Business Machines Corporation; *U.S. Public*, pg. 1145
BIOTEK INSTRUMENTS LIMITED—See Agilent Technologies, Inc.; *U.S. Public*, pg. 61
BIOTEK INSTRUMENTS TAIWAN, INC.—See Agilent Technologies, Inc.; *U.S. Public*, pg. 62
BIXOLON EUROPE GMBH—See Bixolon Co Ltd; *Int'l*, pg. 1052
BIZCOM ELECTRONICS, INC.—See Compal Electronics, Inc.; *Int'l*, pg. 1746
BLACK RIVER COMPUTER, LLC; *U.S. Private*, pg. 572
BLACKWOLF INC.; *U.S. Private*, pg. 577
BLUE CABOOSE INC.; *U.S. Private*, pg. 585
BLUE SKY ENVIRONMENTAL TECHNOLOGY (SHENZHEN) LIMITED—See Global Token Limited; *Int'l*, pg. 3001
BLUE SOLUTIONS LIMITED; *Int'l*, pg. 1069
BLUE WAVE MICRO; *U.S. Private*, pg. 594
BMB INTERNATIONAL CORP.—See Brother Industries, Ltd.; *Int'l*, pg. 1196
BMC SOFTWARE AB—See KKR & Co. Inc.; *U.S. Public*, pg. 1240
BMC SOFTWARE AS—See KKR & Co. Inc.; *U.S. Public*, pg. 1240
BMC SOFTWARE CHINA—See KKR & Co. Inc.; *U.S. Public*, pg. 1239
BMC SOFTWARE DISTRIBUTION B.V.—See KKR & Co. Inc.; *U.S. Public*, pg. 1240
BMC SOFTWARE OY—See KKR & Co. Inc.; *U.S. Public*, pg. 1240
BNL TECHNOLOGIES INC.; *U.S. Private*, pg. 602
BOUNDARY DEVICES, LLC.—See Audax Group, Limited Partnership; *U.S. Private*, pg. 388
BOXLIGHT CORPORATION; *U.S. Public*, pg. 377
BRADY ENERGY CANADA, INC.—See Brady plc; *Int'l*, pg. 1135
BRADY ENERGY US, INC.—See Brady plc; *Int'l*, pg. 1135
BRADY LLC—See Brady Corporation; *U.S. Public*, pg. 379
BRAINLAB INC.; *U.S. Private*, pg. 634
BRAINSTORMUSA LLC; *U.S. Private*, pg. 634
BRANDMUSCLE, INC.; *U.S. Private*, pg. 638
BRAND MUSCLE, INC.—See The Riverside Company; *U.S. Private*, pg. 4108
BRESSNER TECHNOLOGY GMBH—See One Stop Systems, Inc.; *U.S. Public*, pg. 1602
BURGESS COMPUTER DECISIONS, INC.; *U.S. Private*, pg. 687
BUSINESS INTEGRATORS INC.; *U.S. Private*, pg. 695
BYTE POWER PTY LTD—See Byte Power Group Limited; *Int'l*, pg. 1237
CABLESANDKITS.COM; *U.S. Private*, pg. 711
CABLEXPRESS CORPORATION—See H.I.G. Capital, LLC; *U.S. Private*, pg. 1829
CADMIN SERVICES, INC.—See Addnode Group AB; *Int'l*, pg. 131
CAKEWALK, INC.; *U.S. Private*, pg. 715
CALCOM ESI SA—See Keysight Technologies, Inc.; *U.S. Public*, pg. 1226
CAL-COMP ELECTRONICS AND COMMUNICATIONS COMPANY LIMITED—See Cal-Comp Electronics (Thailand) pcl; *Int'l*, pg. 1261
CALTECH SOFTWARE SYSTEMS, LLC—See Frontenac Company LLC; *U.S. Private*, pg. 1613
CALYPSO TECHNOLOGY DEUTSCHLAND GMBH—See Thoma Bravo, L.P.; *U.S. Private*, pg. 4146
CALYPSO TECHNOLOGY K.K.—See Thoma Bravo, L.P.; *U.S. Private*, pg. 4146
CALYPSO TECHNOLOGY LTD—See Thoma Bravo, L.P.; *U.S. Private*, pg. 4146
CALYPSO TECHNOLOGY PRIVATE LIMITED—See Thoma Bravo, L.P.; *U.S. Private*, pg. 4146
CALYPSO TECHNOLOGY PTY LTD—See Thoma Bravo, L.P.; *U.S. Private*, pg. 4146
CALYPSO TECHNOLOGY S.A.—See Thoma Bravo, L.P.; *U.S. Private*, pg. 4146
CALYX TECHNOLOGY, INC. - SALES, SUPPORT & TRAINING CENTER—See Calyx Technology, Inc.; *U.S. Private*, pg. 725
CAMOZZI APS—See Camozzi Group; *Int'l*, pg. 1273
CANON DEVELOPMENT AMERICAS, INC.—See Canon Inc.; *Int'l*, pg. 1297
CANTO SOFTWARE, INC.; *U.S. Private*, pg. 735
CAPARIO, INC.—See McKesson Corporation; *U.S. Public*, pg. 1407
CAPITAL BUSINESS SYSTEMS, INC.—See Xerox Holdings Corporation; *U.S. Public*, pg. 2387
CAPITAL IQ, INC. - CANADA BRANCH—See S&P Global Inc.; *U.S. Public*, pg. 1831
CART.COM, INC.; *U.S. Private*, pg. 775
CASEKING GMBH—See Gilde Buy Out Partners B.V.; *Int'l*, pg. 2974
CASEWISE SYSTEMS INC.; *U.S. Private*, pg. 782
CASIO EUROPE GMBH—See Casio Computer Co., Ltd.; *Int'l*, pg. 1353
CASIO INFORMATION SYSTEMS CO., LTD.—See Casio Computer Co., Ltd.; *Int'l*, pg. 1353
CATALYTIC SOFTWARE, INC.; *U.S. Private*, pg. 787
CATS CO.; *U.S. Private*, pg. 792
CCS-INC.; *U.S. Private*, pg. 801
CCT TECHNOLOGIES INC.; *U.S. Private*, pg. 801
CDE SERVICES, INC.—See Milestone Partners Ltd.; *U.S. Private*, pg. 2728
CDI COMPUTER DEALERS INC.—See Relational LLC; *U.S. Private*, pg. 3392
CDW CANADA, INC.—See CDW Corporation; *U.S. Public*, pg. 462
CDW TECHNOLOGIES, INC. - APPLETON—See CDW Corporation; *U.S. Public*, pg. 462
CDW TECHNOLOGIES, INC. - CHICAGO—See CDW Corporation; *U.S. Public*, pg. 462
CDW TECHNOLOGIES, INC. - CINCINNATI—See CDW Corporation; *U.S. Public*, pg. 462
CDW TECHNOLOGIES, INC. - CLEVELAND—See CDW Corporation; *U.S. Public*, pg. 462
CDW TECHNOLOGIES, INC. - DETROIT—See CDW Corporation; *U.S. Public*, pg. 462
CDW TECHNOLOGIES, INC. - GRAND RAPIDS—See CDW Corporation; *U.S. Public*, pg. 462
CDW TECHNOLOGIES, INC. - INDIANAPOLIS—See CDW Corporation; *U.S. Public*, pg. 462
CDW TECHNOLOGIES, INC. - MADISON—See CDW Corporation; *U.S. Public*, pg. 462
CDW TECHNOLOGIES, INC. - MILWAUKEE—See CDW Corporation; *U.S. Public*, pg. 462
CDW TECHNOLOGIES, INC. - MINNEAPOLIS—See CDW Corporation; *U.S. Public*, pg. 462
CDW TECHNOLOGIES, INC. - WAUSAU—See CDW Corporation; *U.S. Public*, pg. 462
CENTURY SOFTWARE LIMITED; *U.S. Private*, pg. 834
CGG JASON (AUSTRALIA) PTY. LTD.—See CGG; *Int'l*, pg. 1431
C+G INFORMATIONSTECHNOLOGIE GMBH; *Int'l*, pg. 1239
CGS ASIA CO., LTD.—See C&G SYSTEMS INC.; *Int'l*, pg. 1238
CHANGSHA DIGITAL CHINA COMPANY LIMITED—See Digital China Holdings Limited; *Int'l*, pg. 2121
CHECK POINT SOFTWARE TECHNOLOGIES B.V.—See Check Point Software Technologies Ltd.; *Int'l*, pg. 1458
CHECK POINT SOFTWARE TECHNOLOGIES (DENMARK) APS—See Check Point Software Technologies Ltd.; *Int'l*, pg. 1458
CHECK POINT SOFTWARE TECHNOLOGIES (RUSSIA) OOO—See Check Point Software Technologies Ltd.; *Int'l*, pg. 1458
CHEM USA CORP.—See Chung-Hsin Electric & Machinery Manufacturing Corp.; *Int'l*, pg. 1597
CHENBRO UK LTD.—See Chenbro Micom Co., Ltd.; *Int'l*, pg. 1465
CHENMING USA INC.—See Chenming Electronic Tech. Corp.; *Int'l*, pg. 1470
CHICAGO-SOFT, LTD.; *U.S. Private*, pg. 879
CHICONY ELECTRONICS JAPAN CO., LTD.—See Chicony Electronics Co., Ltd.; *Int'l*, pg. 1476
CHICONY ELECTRONICS (SU ZOU, MAINLAND CHINA III) CO., LTD.—See Chicony Electronics Co., Ltd.; *Int'l*, pg. 1476
CHIPS TECHNOLOGY GROUP LLC—See IT Solutions Consulting LLC; *U.S. Private*, pg. 2148
CHIYODA INTEGRE OF AMERICA (SAN DIEGO), INC.—See Chiyoda Integre Co., Ltd.; *Int'l*, pg. 1575
CIBOX INTERACTIVE SA; *Int'l*, pg. 1602
CIMATRON (BEIJING) TECHNOLOGY CO. LTD.—See Battery Ventures, L.P.; *U.S. Private*, pg. 488
CIMATRON GIBBS LLC—See Battery Ventures, L.P.; *U.S. Private*, pg. 488
CIMATRON LTD.—See Battery Ventures, L.P.; *U.S. Private*, pg. 488
CIMATRON TECHNOLOGIES, INC.—See Battery Ventures, L.P.; *U.S. Private*, pg. 488
CIMATRON TECHNOLOGIES INDIA PVT. LTD.—See Battery Ventures, L.P.; *U.S. Private*, pg. 488
CIRQIT DE HONDURAS S. DE R.L. DE C.V.—See HH Global Group Limited; *Int'l*, pg. 3378

N.A.I.C.S. INDEX

423430 — COMPUTER AND COMPUT...

CISCO (CHINA) INNOVATION TECHNOLOGY CO., LTD.—See Cisco Systems, Inc.; *U.S. Public*, pg. 497
CISCO (CHINA) TECHNOLOGY SERVICES CO., LTD.—See Cisco Systems, Inc.; *U.S. Public*, pg. 497
CISCO DUTCH HOLDINGS B.V.—See Cisco Systems, Inc.; *U.S. Public*, pg. 497
CISCO SYSTEMS FINANCE INTERNATIONAL UNLIMITED COMPANY—See Cisco Systems, Inc.; *U.S. Public*, pg. 498
CISCO SYSTEMS (KOREA) LIMITED—See Cisco Systems, Inc.; *U.S. Public*, pg. 497
CISCO TECHNOLOGIES (BEIJING) CO., LTD.—See Cisco Systems, Inc.; *U.S. Public*, pg. 499
CITIZEN AMERICA CORP.—See Citizen Watch Co., Ltd.; *Int'l*, pg. 1623
CLARITY COMMERCE SOLUTIONS, INC.—See Heritage Group Ltd.; *Int'l*, pg. 3361
CLARITY COMMERCE SOLUTIONS LTD.—See Heritage Group Ltd.; *Int'l*, pg. 3361
CLH INTERNATIONAL INC.; *U.S. Private*, pg. 942
CLIMB GLOBAL SOLUTIONS, INC.; *U.S. Public*, pg. 514
CLOUDLOCK, LTD.—See Cisco Systems, Inc.; *U.S. Public*, pg. 499
CLUBSYSTEMS GROUP INC.; *U.S. Private*, pg. 949
CMT HOLDINGS INC.; *U.S. Private*, pg. 951
CNE DIRECT, INC.; *U.S. Private*, pg. 952
CN NEGOCIOS, S.A.; *Int'l*, pg. 1673
CNT BRASIL SERVICOS LTDA.—See Arrow Electronics, Inc.; *U.S. Public*, pg. 198
COGNITEC SYSTEMS PTY LTD—See Cognitec Systems GmbH; *Int'l*, pg. 1695
COKEM INTERNATIONAL LTD.; *U.S. Private*, pg. 965
COLORWARE INC.; *U.S. Private*, pg. 975
COMARK, LLC; *U.S. Private*, pg. 980
COMMERCIAL & INDUSTRIAL DESIGN COMPANY INC.; *U.S. Private*, pg. 983
COMMERCIAL NETWORK SERVICES—See Beeks Financial Cloud Group Plc; *Int'l*, pg. 939
COMPAGNIE IBM FRANCE, S.A.—See International Business Machines Corporation; *U.S. Public*, pg. 1145
COMPUCON JAPAN CO. LTD—See COMPUCON S.A.; *Int'l*, pg. 1755
COMPUCON USA L.L.C.—See COMPUCON S.A.; *Int'l*, pg. 1755
COMPUTECH INTERNATIONAL INC.; *U.S. Private*, pg. 1004
COMPUTER ADD-ONS INC.; *U.S. Private*, pg. 1004
COMPUTER AIDED TECHNOLOGY INC.—See Court Square Capital Partners, L.P.; *U.S. Private*, pg. 1069
COMPUTERLINKS (AUST) PTY LTD.—See Arrow Electronics, Inc.; *U.S. Public*, pg. 198
COMPUTERLINKS DENMARK A/S—See Arrow Electronics, Inc.; *U.S. Public*, pg. 198
COMPUTERLINKS FZCO—See Arrow Electronics, Inc.; *U.S. Public*, pg. 198
COMPUTERLINKS KFT.—See Arrow Electronics, Inc.; *U.S. Public*, pg. 198
COMPUTERLINKS NORTH AMERICA INC.—See Arrow Electronics, Inc.; *U.S. Public*, pg. 198
COMPUTERLINKS SPA—See Arrow Electronics, Inc.; *U.S. Public*, pg. 198
COMPUTERLINKS SWEDEN AB—See Arrow Electronics, Inc.; *U.S. Public*, pg. 198
COMPUTER NETWORK SOLUTIONS LLC; *U.S. Private*, pg. 1005
COMPUTER PERFORMANCE INC.; *U.S. Private*, pg. 1005
COMPUTER STATIONERY INDUSTRY S.A.O.G.; *Int'l*, pg. 1760
COMPUTIZE, INC.; *U.S. Private*, pg. 1006
COMSTOR CORPORATION—See TD Synnex Corp; *U.S. Public*, pg. 1987
COMTEL CORPORATION; *U.S. Private*, pg. 1006
COMTRONIC COMPUTER INC.; *Int'l*, pg. 1762
CONCENTRIX (CANADA) LIMITED—See TD Synnex Corp; *U.S. Public*, pg. 1983
CONCENTRIX CRM SERVICES GERMANY GMBH—See TD Synnex Corp; *U.S. Public*, pg. 1983
CONCENTRIX DUISBURG GMBH—See TD Synnex Corp; *U.S. Public*, pg. 1983
CONCENTRIX DUSSELDORF GMBH—See TD Synnex Corp; *U.S. Public*, pg. 1984
CONCENTRIX FRANKFURT A. M. GMBH—See TD Synnex Corp; *U.S. Public*, pg. 1984
CONCENTRIX GERA GMBH—See TD Synnex Corp; *U.S. Public*, pg. 1984
CONCENTRIX HALLE GMBH—See TD Synnex Corp; *U.S. Public*, pg. 1984
CONCENTRIX LEIPZIG GMBH—See TD Synnex Corp; *U.S. Public*, pg. 1984
CONCENTRIX MANAGEMENT HOLDING GMBH & CO. KG—See TD Synnex Corp; *U.S. Public*, pg. 1984
CONCENTRIX MUNSTER GMBH—See TD Synnex Corp; *U.S. Public*, pg. 1984
CONCENTRIX OSNABRUCK GMBH—See TD Synnex Corp; *U.S. Public*, pg. 1984
CONCENTRIX SCHWERIN GMBH—See TD Synnex Corp; *U.S. Public*, pg. 1984
CONCENTRIX WISMAR GMBH—See TD Synnex Corp; *U.S. Public*, pg. 1984
CONCENTRIX WUPPERTAL GMBH—See TD Synnex Corp; *U.S. Public*, pg. 1984
CONGATEC AG; *Int'l*, pg. 1768
CONGATEC ASIA LTD.—See Congatec AG; *Int'l*, pg. 1768
CONGATEC AUSTRALIA PTY LTD.—See Congatec AG; *Int'l*, pg. 1768
CONGATEC CHINA TECHNOLOGY LTD.—See Congatec AG; *Int'l*, pg. 1768
CONGATEC, INC.—See Congatec AG; *Int'l*, pg. 1768
CONGATEC JAPAN K.K.—See Congatec AG; *Int'l*, pg. 1768
CONGATEC SRO—See Congatec AG; *Int'l*, pg. 1768
CONSUMER DEPOT LLC; *U.S. Private*, pg. 1025
CONTEC AMERICAS INC.—See Daifuku Co., Ltd.; *Int'l*, pg. 1924
CONTEC (SHANGHAI) CO., LTD.—See Daifuku Co., Ltd.; *Int'l*, pg. 1924
CONTEC SOLUTION CO., LTD.—See Daifuku Co., Ltd.; *Int'l*, pg. 1925
CONTINUUM LLC—See EPAM Systems, Inc.; *U.S. Public*, pg. 783
CONVENTIVE TECHNOLOGIES LTD.; *Int'l*, pg. 1787
COOPERATIVE SYSTEMS, LLC; *U.S. Private*, pg. 1043
COPYPRO INC.; *U.S. Private*, pg. 1046
CORE INDUSTRIES CO., LTD.—See Core Corporation; *Int'l*, pg. 1797
CORIDIAN TECHNOLOGIES INC.—See Sole Source Capital LLC; *U.S. Private*, pg. 3708
CORSAIR GAMING, INC.; *U.S. Public*, pg. 580
CPG INTERNATIONAL—See CPG International S.p.A.; *Int'l*, pg. 1824
CPI COMPUTER PERIPHERALS INTERNATIONAL; *Int'l*, pg. 1825
CRANEL INCORPORATED; *U.S. Private*, pg. 1085
CRAY AUSTRALIA PTY. LIMITED—See Hewlett Packard Enterprise Company; *U.S. Public*, pg. 1030
CRAY COMPUTER DEUTSCHLAND GMBH—See Hewlett Packard Enterprise Company; *U.S. Public*, pg. 1030
CRAY COMPUTER GMBH—See Hewlett Packard Enterprise Company; *U.S. Public*, pg. 1030
CRAY COMPUTER SAS—See Hewlett Packard Enterprise Company; *U.S. Public*, pg. 1030
CRAY JAPAN, INC.—See Hewlett Packard Enterprise Company; *U.S. Public*, pg. 1030
CRAYON GROUP AS; *Int'l*, pg. 1829
CRAY SUPERCOMPUTERS (INDIA) PRIVATE LIMITED—See Hewlett Packard Enterprise Company; *U.S. Public*, pg. 1031
CRAY TAIWAN, INC.—See Hewlett Packard Enterprise Company; *U.S. Public*, pg. 1031
CRAY U.K. LIMITED—See Hewlett Packard Enterprise Company; *U.S. Public*, pg. 1031
CREATEC PTY LTD—See Hancock & Gore Ltd.; *Int'l*, pg. 3242
CREATIVE LABS, INC.—See Creative Technology Ltd.; *Int'l*, pg. 1833
CS BUSINESS SYSTEMS INC.; *U.S. Private*, pg. 1116
CSS LABORATORIES INC.; *U.S. Private*, pg. 1118
CUSTOM AMERICA, INC.—See Custom SpA; *Int'l*, pg. 1880
CYBERARK SOFTWARE (UK) LIMITED—See CyberArk Software Ltd.; *Int'l*, pg. 1892
CYBERLINK USA—See CyberLink Corp.; *Int'l*, pg. 1893
CYBERPORT GMBH; *Int'l*, pg. 1893
CYBERRESEARCH INC.; *U.S. Private*, pg. 1133
DAIKO DENSHI TSUSHIN, LTD.; *Int'l*, pg. 1937
DAIWABO INFORMATION SYSTEM CO., LTD.—See Daiwabo Holdings Co., Ltd.; *Int'l*, pg. 1949
DANFORTH SYSTEMS LLC—See The Graham Group, Inc.; *U.S. Private*, pg. 4036
DASHER TECHNOLOGIES INC.; *U.S. Private*, pg. 1162
DASSAULT SYSTEMES AUSTRIA GMBH—See Dassault Systemes S.A.; *Int'l*, pg. 1974
DASSAULT SYSTEMES DELMIA CORP.—See Dassault Systemes S.A.; *Int'l*, pg. 1974
DATABIT, INC.; *U.S. Private*, pg. 1164
DATAGATE BILGISAYAR MALZEMELERI TICARET A.S.; *Int'l*, pg. 1977
DATALINE LLC; *U.S. Private*, pg. 1165
DATAPLOT GMBH; *Int'l*, pg. 1979
DATAPOINT CUSTOMER SOLUTIONS LTD.; *Int'l*, pg. 1979
DATAPOINT FRANCE—See Datapoint Customer Solutions Ltd.; *Int'l*, pg. 1979
DATAPOINT IBERICA S.A.—See Datapoint Customer Solutions Ltd.; *Int'l*, pg. 1979
DATAPOINT NEDERLAND B.V.—See Datapoint Customer Solutions Ltd.; *Int'l*, pg. 1979
DATA RESPONS AB—See Adecco Group AG; *Int'l*, pg. 139
DATA RESPONS ASA—See Adecco Group AG; *Int'l*, pg. 139
DATA RESPONS A/S—See Adecco Group AG; *Int'l*, pg. 139
DATA RESPONS NORGE AS—See Adecco Group AG; *Int'l*, pg. 139
DATA RESPONS NORGE AS—See Adecco Group AG; *Int'l*, pg. 140
DATA RESPONS NORGE AS—See Adecco Group AG; *Int'l*, pg. 140
DATA SALES CO.; *U.S. Private*, pg. 1163
DATA SOURCE MEDIA INC.; *U.S. Private*, pg. 1163
DATA SPECIALISTS, INC.—See Dairy, LLC; *U.S. Private*, pg. 1146
DATA STRATEGIES, INC.—See Integrated Solutions Group, Inc.; *U.S. Private*, pg. 2101
DATA TRANSLATION GMBH—See National Instruments Corporation; *U.S. Private*, pg. 2856
DATAWATCH ANALYTICS (SINGAPORE) PTE LTD.—See Altair Engineering, Inc.; *U.S. Public*, pg. 86
DAYMARK SOLUTIONS, INC.; *U.S. Private*, pg. 1177
DECERNO AB—See Addnode Group AB; *Int'l*, pg. 130
DEEP SURPLUS; *U.S. Private*, pg. 1189
DELL AB—See Dell Technologies Inc.; *U.S. Public*, pg. 649
DELL ASIA PACIFIC SDN.—See Dell Technologies Inc.; *U.S. Public*, pg. 649
DELL A/S—See Dell Technologies Inc.; *U.S. Public*, pg. 649
DELL A.S.—See Dell Technologies Inc.; *U.S. Public*, pg. 649
DELL AUSTRALIA PTY. LIMITED—See Dell Technologies Inc.; *U.S. Public*, pg. 649
DELL B.V.—See Dell Technologies Inc.; *U.S. Public*, pg. 649
DELL CANADA INC.—See Dell Technologies Inc.; *U.S. Public*, pg. 649
DELL (CHINA) COMPANY LIMTED—See Dell Technologies Inc.; *U.S. Public*, pg. 649
DELL COMPUTADORES DO BRASIL LTDA.—See Dell Technologies Inc.; *U.S. Public*, pg. 649
DELL COMPUTER DE CHILE LTDA—See Dell Technologies Inc.; *U.S. Public*, pg. 649
DELL COMPUTER INDIA PRIVATE LIMITED—See Dell Technologies Inc.; *U.S. Public*, pg. 649
DELL COMPUTER (PROPRIETARY) S.A.—See Dell Technologies Inc.; *U.S. Public*, pg. 649
DELL COMPUTER S.A.—See Dell Technologies Inc.; *U.S. Public*, pg. 649
DELL COMPUTER SPOL. S R O.—See Dell Technologies Inc.; *U.S. Public*, pg. 649
DELL CORPORATION LIMITED—See Dell Technologies Inc.; *U.S. Public*, pg. 649
DELL CORPORATION (THAILAND) CO., LTD.—See Dell Technologies Inc.; *U.S. Public*, pg. 649
DELL GMBH—See Dell Technologies Inc.; *U.S. Public*, pg. 649
DELL HALLE GMBH—See Dell Technologies Inc.; *U.S. Public*, pg. 649
DELL INTERNATIONAL SERVICES INDIA PRIVATE LIMITED—See Dell Technologies Inc.; *U.S. Public*, pg. 650
DELL INTERNATIONAL SERVICES PHILIPPINES INC.—See Dell Technologies Inc.; *U.S. Public*, pg. 650
DELL JAPAN INC.—See Dell Technologies Inc.; *U.S. Public*, pg. 650
DELL NEW ZEALAND LIMITED—See Dell Technologies Inc.; *U.S. Public*, pg. 650
DELL N.V.—See Dell Technologies Inc.; *U.S. Public*, pg. 650
DELL S.A.—See Dell Technologies Inc.; *U.S. Public*, pg. 650
DELL SA—See Dell Technologies Inc.; *U.S. Public*, pg. 650
DELL S.A.—See Dell Technologies Inc.; *U.S. Public*, pg. 650
DELL SINGAPORE PTE. LTD.—See Dell Technologies Inc.; *U.S. Public*, pg. 650
DELL SP.Z.O.O—See Dell Technologies Inc.; *U.S. Public*, pg. 650
DELL S.R.O.—See Dell Technologies Inc.; *U.S. Public*, pg. 650
DELTA ELECTRONICS MEXICO S.A. DE C.V.—See Delta Electronics, Inc.; *Int'l*, pg. 2018
DERIVE TECHNOLOGIES; *U.S. Private*, pg. 1209
DESPEC AFRICA EPZ LTD—See Despec Group B.V.; *Int'l*, pg. 2046
DESPEC BILGISAYAR PAZARLAMA VE TICARET A.S.; *Int'l*, pg. 2046
DESPEC DENMARK A/S—See Despec Group B.V.; *Int'l*, pg. 2046
DESPEC DOO—See Despec Group B.V.; *Int'l*, pg. 2046
DESPEC EUROPE B.V.—See Despec Group B.V.; *Int'l*, pg. 2046
DESPEC GROUP B.V.; *Int'l*, pg. 2046
DESPEC IBERIA SL.—See Despec Group B.V.; *Int'l*, pg. 2046
DESPEC JORDAN FZE—See Despec Group B.V.; *Int'l*, pg. 2046
DESPEC KENYA LTD—See Despec Group B.V.; *Int'l*, pg. 2046
DESPEC LEBANON SAL—See Despec Group B.V.; *Int'l*, pg. 2046
DESPEC MERA LTD.—See Despec Group B.V.; *Int'l*, pg. 2046
DESPEC SUPPLIES BVBA—See Despec Group B.V.; *Int'l*, pg. 2046
DESPEC SUPPLIES UTIBU A ISLANDI AS—See Despec Group B.V.; *Int'l*, pg. 2046
DESPEC SWEDEN AB—See Despec Group B.V.; *Int'l*, pg. 2046
DESPEC TANZANIA LTD—See Despec Group B.V.; *Int'l*, pg. 2046
DESPEC TURKEY A.S.—See Despec Group B.V.; *Int'l*, pg. 2046
DESPEC UGANDA LTD—See Despec Group B.V.; *Int'l*, pg. 2046

N.A.I.C.S. Index
423430 — COMPUTER AND COMPUT... CORPORATE AFFILIATIONS

DEVOTEAM TELECOM AS—See Devoteam SA; *Int'l*, pg. 2090
D&H CANADA ULC—See D&H Distributing Co., Inc.; *U.S. Private*, pg. 1137
D&H DISTRIBUTING CO., INC.; *U.S. Private*, pg. 1137
DIAMOND FLOWER INFORMATION (NL) B.V.—See DFI Inc.; *Int'l*, pg. 2095
DICKER DATA FINANCIAL SERVICES PTY LTD—See Dicker Data Limited; *Int'l*, pg. 2111
DICKER DATA LIMITED; *Int'l*, pg. 2111
DICKER DATA NEW ZEALAND LTD.—See Dicker Data Limited; *Int'l*, pg. 2111
DIEBOLD-CORP SYSTEMS SDN BHD—See Diebold Nixdorf, Inc.; *U.S. Public*, pg. 661
DIGERATI GROUP, LLC.; *U.S. Private*, pg. 1229
DIGITAL BROS FRANCE S.A.R.L.—See Digital Bros SpA; *Int'l*, pg. 2120
DIGITAL CHINA (CHINA) LIMITED—See Digital China Group Co., Ltd.; *Int'l*, pg. 2121
DIGITAL CHINA (HEFEI) COMPANY LIMITED—See Digital China Holdings Limited; *Int'l*, pg. 2121
DIGITAL CHINA (HK) LIMITED—See Digital China Holdings Limited; *Int'l*, pg. 2121
DIGITAL CHINA (ZHENGZHOU) LIMITED—See Digital China Holdings Limited; *Int'l*, pg. 2121
DIGITAL DIMENSIONS, INC.—See DASI Solutions, LLC; *U.S. Private*, pg. 1162
DIGITAL HUB PTE LTD—See Ban Leong Technologies Limited; *Int'l*, pg. 814
DIGITAL PERIPHERAL SOLUTIONS, INC.; *U.S. Private*, pg. 1230
DIMA LTDA.; *Int'l*, pg. 2125
DIP TECH LTD.—See American Securities LLC; *U.S. Private*, pg. 251
DIRECTEC CORPORATION; *U.S. Private*, pg. 1236
DISA LIMITED; *Int'l*, pg. 2131
DISTIT AB; *Int'l*, pg. 2136
DISWAY SA; *Int'l*, pg. 2137
DIVERSIFIED COMPUTER SUPPLIES; *U.S. Private*, pg. 1241
DIVIHN INTEGRATION INC.; *U.S. Private*, pg. 1244
D-LINK SYSTEMS, INC.—See D-Link Corporation, Inc.; *Int'l*, pg. 1900
DMOA CO., LTD; *Int'l*, pg. 2146
DMSS SOFTWARE LTDA.; *Int'l*, pg. 2146
DOLPHIN INTERCONNECT SOLUTIONS NA INC.—See Dolphin Interconnect Solutions AS; *Int'l*, pg. 2159
DOMINO AMJET B.V.—See Brother Industries, Ltd.; *Int'l*, pg. 1197
DOMINO AMJET IBERICA SAU—See Brother Industries, Ltd.; *Int'l*, pg. 1197
DOMINO SAS—See Brother Industries, Ltd.; *Int'l*, pg. 1197
THE DOUGLAS STEWART COMPANY INC.; *U.S. Private*, pg. 4023
DP DATA SYSTEMS LIMITED; *Int'l*, pg. 2187
DP IRAN CO.; *Int'l*, pg. 2187
DROR ORTHO-DESIGN, INC.; *U.S. Public*, pg. 688
DSC SYSTEMS (M) SDN. BHD.—See DGB Asia Berhad; *Int'l*, pg. 2096
DTC COMPUTER SUPPLIES, INC.; *U.S. Private*, pg. 1282
DU INTERNATIONAL INC.; *U.S. Private*, pg. 1282
DUNCAN-PARNELL—See Duncan-Parnell, Inc.; *U.S. Private*, pg. 1288
DUNWELL COMPUTERS OF CALIFORNIA—See PC Warehouse Investment Inc.; *U.S. Private*, pg. 3119
DUSTIN GROUP AB; *Int'l*, pg. 2235
DYNAMIC SUPPLIES PTY. LTD.; *Int'l*, pg. 2241
DYNELYTICS AG; *Int'l*, pg. 2242
EAKES INC.; *U.S. Private*, pg. 1312
EASTERN DATA, INC.; *U.S. Private*, pg. 1319
EBERTLANG DISTRIBUTION GMBH—See Harald Quandt Holding GmbH; *Int'l*, pg. 3270
EBOOK INITIATIVE JAPAN CO., LTD.; *Int'l*, pg. 2285
EBRYIT INC.; *U.S. Private*, pg. 1324
EBS ASSOCIATES, INC.—See OUT OF THE BOXTECHNOLOGY; *U.S. Private*, pg. 3051
ECONOCOM FRANCE SAS—See Econocom Group SA; *Int'l*, pg. 2297
ECONOCOM PRODUCTS & SOLUTIONS S.L.—See Econocom Group SA; *Int'l*, pg. 2297
ECONOCOM RE SA LUXEMBOURG—See Econocom Group SA; *Int'l*, pg. 2298
ECONOCOM SAS—See Econocom Group SA; *Int'l*, pg. 2298
EDAC SYSTEMS INC.; *U.S. Private*, pg. 1332
EDGEWARE COMPUTERS, INC.; *U.S. Private*, pg. 1334
EDIMAX TECHNOLOGY EUROPE B.V.—See Edimax Technology Co., Ltd.; *Int'l*, pg. 2310
EDIMAX TECHNOLOGY MEA FZE—See Edimax Technology Co., Ltd.; *Int'l*, pg. 2310
EDIMAX TECHNOLOGY POLAND SP. Z O.O.—See Edimax Technology Co., Ltd.; *Int'l*, pg. 2310
EDIMAX TECHNOLOGY (UK) LTD.—See Edimax Technology Co., Ltd.; *Int'l*, pg. 2310
EDIMENSIONAL, INC.; *U.S. Private*, pg. 1336
EDOM TRADING (SHENZHEN) LTD.—See EDOM Technology Co., Ltd.; *Int'l*, pg. 2313
EIZO GMBH—See EIZO Corporation; *Int'l*, pg. 2337
EIZO INC.—See EIZO Corporation; *Int'l*, pg. 2337
EIZO NANAO AG—See EIZO Corporation; *Int'l*, pg. 2337
ELECO PLC; *Int'l*, pg. 2347
ELECTRONIC ARTS CZECH REPUBLIC S.R.O.—See Electronic Arts Inc.; *U.S. Public*, pg. 724
ELECTRONIC ARTS HK LIMITED—See Electronic Arts Inc.; *U.S. Public*, pg. 724
ELECTRONIC ARTS ITALIA S.R.L.—See Electronic Arts Inc.; *U.S. Public*, pg. 724
ELECTRONIC ARTS POLSKA SP.Z.O.O.—See Electronic Arts Inc.; *U.S. Public*, pg. 724
ELECTRONIC ARTS PROPRIETARY LIMITED—See Electronic Arts Inc.; *U.S. Public*, pg. 724
ELEXO S.A.—See Atos SE; *Int'l*, pg. 692
ELIDATA S.R.L.—See CAD IT S.p.A.; *Int'l*, pg. 1247
ELITEGROUP COMPUTER SYSTEMS (HK) CO., LTD.—See Elitegroup Computer Systems Co., Ltd.; *Int'l*, pg. 2363
ELONEX; *Int'l*, pg. 2368
ELO TOUCH SOLUTIONS ARGENTINA SA—See Crestview Partners, L.P.; *U.S. Private*, pg. 1098
ELPIDA MEMORY (HONG KONG) CO., LTD.—See Micron Technology, Inc.; *U.S. Public*, pg. 1437
ELPIDA MEMORY (TAIWAN) CO., LTD.—See Micron Technology, Inc.; *U.S. Public*, pg. 1437
ELPIDA MEMORY (USA) INC.—See Micron Technology, Inc.; *U.S. Public*, pg. 1437
ELVA INTERNATIONAL INC.; *U.S. Public*, pg. 735
EMC COMPUTER SYSTEMS AUSTRIA GMBH—See Dell Technologies Inc.; *U.S. Public*, pg. 650
EMC COMPUTER SYSTEMS DANMARK A/S—See Dell Technologies Inc.; *U.S. Public*, pg. 650
EMC COMPUTER SYSTEMS (FE) LIMITED—See Dell Technologies Inc.; *U.S. Public*, pg. 650
EMC COMPUTER SYSTEMS FRANCE—See Dell Technologies Inc.; *U.S. Public*, pg. 650
EMC COMPUTER-SYSTEMS OY—See Dell Technologies Inc.; *U.S. Public*, pg. 651
EMC COMPUTER SYSTEMS (SOUTH ASIA) PTE LTD—See Dell Technologies Inc.; *U.S. Public*, pg. 650
EMC COMPUTER SYSTEMS SPAIN, S.A.U.—See Dell Technologies Inc.; *U.S. Public*, pg. 650
EMC CORPORATION OF CANADA—See Dell Technologies Inc.; *U.S. Public*, pg. 651
EMC CORPORATION - SANTA CLARA—See Dell Technologies Inc.; *U.S. Public*, pg. 651
EMC CZECH REPUBLIC S.R.O.—See Dell Technologies Inc.; *U.S. Public*, pg. 651
EMC DEUTSCHLAND GMBH—See Dell Technologies Inc.; *U.S. Public*, pg. 651
EMC INFORMATION SYSTEMS COLOMBIA LTDA.—See Dell Technologies Inc.; *U.S. Public*, pg. 651
EMC INFORMATION SYSTEMS N.V.—See Dell Technologies Inc.; *U.S. Public*, pg. 651
EMC INFORMATION SYSTEMS PAKISTAN (PRIVATE) LIMITED—See Dell Technologies Inc.; *U.S. Public*, pg. 651
EMC INFORMATION SYSTEMS SWEDEN AB—See Dell Technologies Inc.; *U.S. Public*, pg. 651
EMC INFORMATION SYSTEMS (THAILAND) LIMITED—See Dell Technologies Inc.; *U.S. Public*, pg. 651
E-MEDIA PLUS INC.; *U.S. Private*, pg. 1302
EMERGITECH, INC.—See Vista Equity Partners, LLC; *U.S. Private*, pg. 4395
EMERPOWSYS, S. DE R.L. DE C.V.—See Emerson Electric Co.; *U.S. Public*, pg. 743
EM QUANTUM TECHNOLOGIES, INC.; *U.S. Public*, pg. 735
EMTEX SOFTWARE, INC.—See Pitney Bowes Inc.; *U.S. Public*, pg. 1694
ENLACES COMPUTACIONALES, S. DE R.L. DE C.V.—See Avnet, Inc.; *U.S. Public*, pg. 253
ENTATECH UK LTD.; *Int'l*, pg. 2450
ENTERTAINMENT NETWORK FRONTIER INC.—See GEO Holdings Corporation; *Int'l*, pg. 2932
ENTISYS SOLUTIONS, INC.; *U.S. Private*, pg. 1405
ENVIRONMENTAL SYSTEMS RESEARCH INSTITUTE INC.; *U.S. Private*, pg. 1408
EPAM CONSULTING BV—See EPAM Systems, Inc.; *U.S. Public*, pg. 783
EPARTNERS, INC.—See ePartners, Inc.; *U.S. Private*, pg. 1411
EQUUS COMPUTER SYSTEMS, INC.—See Equus Holdings, Inc.; *U.S. Private*, pg. 1417
ERGONOMIC GROUP INC.; *U.S. Private*, pg. 1418
ERGOTRON NEDERLAND B.V.—See The Sterling Group, L.P.; *U.S. Private*, pg. 4123
ESI GMBH—See Keysight Technologies, Inc.; *U.S. Public*, pg. 1226
ESI GROUP NETHERLANDS—See Keysight Technologies, Inc.; *U.S. Public*, pg. 1226
ESI NORTH AMERICA, INC.—See Keysight Technologies, Inc.; *U.S. Public*, pg. 1226
ESI UK LIMITED—See Keysight Technologies, Inc.; *U.S. Public*, pg. 1227
ESKO-GRAPHICS GMBH—See Danaher Corporation; *U.S. Public*, pg. 626
ESPIAL (UK) LIMITED—See Enghouse Systems Limited; *Int'l*, pg. 2427
ESPO S.R.O.—See AdCapital AG; *Int'l*, pg. 126
ESPRINET S.P.A.; *Int'l*, pg. 2506
ESRI BELUX S.A.—See Environmental Systems Research Institute Inc.; *U.S. Private*, pg. 1408
ESRI BILGI SISTEMLERI MUHENDISLIK VE EGITIM, LTD.—See Environmental Systems Research Institute Inc.; *U.S. Private*, pg. 1408
ESRI BULGARIA LTD.—See Environmental Systems Research Institute Inc.; *U.S. Private*, pg. 1408
ESRI CANADA LIMITED—See Environmental Systems Research Institute Inc.; *U.S. Private*, pg. 1409
ESRI CHILE S.A.—See Environmental Systems Research Institute Inc.; *U.S. Private*, pg. 1409
ESRI CHINA (HONG KONG) LTD.—See Environmental Systems Research Institute Inc.; *U.S. Private*, pg. 1408
ESRI CHINA INFORMATION TECHNOLOGY CO. LTD—See Environmental Systems Research Institute Inc.; *U.S. Private*, pg. 1409
ESRI CIS LIMITED—See Environmental Systems Research Institute Inc.; *U.S. Private*, pg. 1408
ESRI DEUTSCHLAND GMBH—See Environmental Systems Research Institute Inc.; *U.S. Private*, pg. 1409
ESRI EASTERN AFRICA LTD.—See Environmental Systems Research Institute Inc.; *U.S. Private*, pg. 1409
ESRI FINLAND OY—See Environmental Systems Research Institute Inc.; *U.S. Private*, pg. 1409
ESRI ITALIA S.P.A.—See Environmental Systems Research Institute Inc.; *U.S. Private*, pg. 1409
ESRI JAPAN CORPORATION—See Environmental Systems Research Institute Inc.; *U.S. Private*, pg. 1409
ESRI KOREA, INC.—See Environmental Systems Research Institute Inc.; *U.S. Private*, pg. 1409
ESRI MUSCAT CO. LLC—See Environmental Systems Research Institute Inc.; *U.S. Private*, pg. 1409
ESRI NEDERLAND B.V.—See Environmental Systems Research Institute Inc.; *U.S. Private*, pg. 1409
ESRI POLSKA SP. Z O.O.—See Environmental Systems Research Institute Inc.; *U.S. Private*, pg. 1409
ESRI PORTUGAL, S.A.—See Environmental Systems Research Institute Inc.; *U.S. Private*, pg. 1409
ESRI ROMANIA S.R.L.—See Environmental Systems Research Institute Inc.; *U.S. Private*, pg. 1409
ESRI RWANDA LTD.—See Environmental Systems Research Institute Inc.; *U.S. Private*, pg. 1409
ESRI SAUDI ARABIA LTD.—See Environmental Systems Research Institute Inc.; *U.S. Private*, pg. 1409
ESRI SCHWEIZ AG—See Environmental Systems Research Institute Inc.; *U.S. Private*, pg. 1409
ESRI SENEGAL SARL—See Environmental Systems Research Institute Inc.; *U.S. Private*, pg. 1409
ESRI SOUTH AFRICA (PTY) LTD.—See Environmental Systems Research Institute Inc.; *U.S. Private*, pg. 1409
ESRI SOUTH ASIA SDN. BHD.—See Boustead Singapore Limited; *Int'l*, pg. 1120
ESRI SUISSE SA—See Environmental Systems Research Institute Inc.; *U.S. Private*, pg. 1409
ESRI SVERIGE AB—See Environmental Systems Research Institute Inc.; *U.S. Private*, pg. 1409
ESRI (THAILAND) CO., LTD.—See Environmental Systems Research Institute Inc.; *U.S. Private*, pg. 1408
ESRI (UK) LTD.—See Environmental Systems Research Institute Inc.; *U.S. Private*, pg. 1408
ESRI UKRAINE LTD.—See Environmental Systems Research Institute Inc.; *U.S. Private*, pg. 1409
ESTEREL TECHNOLOGIES GMBH—See ANSYS, Inc.; *U.S. Public*, pg. 139
ESYS TECHNOLOGIES PTE. LTD.—See Agnite Education Limited; *Int'l*, pg. 212
EURONET SERVICES—See Euronet Worldwide, Inc.; *U.S. Public*, pg. 798
EXEGY, INC.—See Marlin Equity Partners, LLC; *U.S. Private*, pg. 2584
EXELIS VIS KK—See L3Harris Technologies, Inc.; *U.S. Public*, pg. 1280
EXELIS VISUAL INFORMATION SOLUTIONS B.V.—See L3Harris Technologies, Inc.; *U.S. Public*, pg. 1280
EXELIS VISUAL INFORMATION SOLUTIONS FRANCE SARL—See L3Harris Technologies, Inc.; *U.S. Public*, pg. 1280
EXELIS VISUAL INFORMATION SOLUTIONS GMBH—See L3Harris Technologies, Inc.; *U.S. Public*, pg. 1280
EXELIS VISUAL INFORMATION SOLUTIONS SRL—See L3Harris Technologies, Inc.; *U.S. Public*, pg. 1280
EXELIS VISUAL INFORMATION SOLUTIONS UK LIMITED—See L3Harris Technologies, Inc.; *U.S. Public*, pg. 1280
EXERTIS CAPTECH AB—See DCC plc; *Int'l*, pg. 1990
EXERTIS FRANCE SAS—See DCC plc; *Int'l*, pg. 1990
EXPRESSPOINT TECHNOLOGY SERVICES, INC.; *U.S. Private*, pg. 1452
FABCO—See Fabick CAT; *U.S. Private*, pg. 1458
FAIRCOM BRAZIL, INC.—See FairCom Corporation; *U.S. Private*, pg. 1462
FAIRCOM EUROPE S.R.L.—See FairCom Corporation; *U.S. Private*, pg. 1462

N.A.I.C.S. INDEX

423430 — COMPUTER AND COMPUT...

FANTOM DRIVES—See BNL Technologies Inc.; *U.S. Private*, pg. 602

FASVER TECHNOLOGY, INC.—See Illinois Tool Works Inc.; *U.S. Public*, pg. 1103

FAULKNER & FLYNN, INC.—See Marsh & McLennan Companies, Inc.; *U.S. Public*, pg. 1375

FC VIETNAM CORPORATION—See Fujicopian Co., Ltd.; *Int'l*, pg. 2820

FIDELIO INDIA PRIVATE LTD.—See Oracle Corporation; *U.S. Public*, pg. 1612

FIDELITY NATIONAL INFORMATION SERVICES, INC. - HERNDON—See Fidelity National Infor; *U.S. Public*, pg. 832

FIELDONE CORPORATION—See ACMOS INC.; *Int'l*, pg. 107

FILIALES ASYTEL S.P.A.—See Econocom Group SA; *Int'l*, pg. 2298

FIRICH KOREA CO., LTD.—See Firich Enterprises Co., Ltd.; *Int'l*, pg. 2679

FIRICH USA INC.—See Firich Enterprises Co., Ltd.; *Int'l*, pg. 2679

FISION CORP; *U.S. Public*, pg. 851

FLECTION FRANCE SAS—See Arrow Electronics, Inc.; *U.S. Public*, pg. 199

FLECTION GERMANY GMBH—See Arrow Electronics, Inc.; *U.S. Public*, pg. 199

FLUKE EUROPE B.V.—See Fortive Corporation; *U.S. Public*, pg. 870

FLYTECH TECHNOLOGY (U.S.A.) INC.—See Flytech Technology Co., Ltd.; *Int'l*, pg. 2716

FORQUER GROUP, INC.—See MCPc Inc.; *U.S. Private*, pg. 2644

FUJI COPIAN (H.K.) LTD.—See Fujicopian Co., Ltd.; *Int'l*, pg. 2820

FUJI ELECTRIC IT SOLUTIONS CO., LTD.—See Fuji Electric Co., Ltd.; *Int'l*, pg. 2811

FUJITSU COMPUTER PRODUCTS OF AMERICA, INC.—See Fujitsu Limited; *Int'l*, pg. 2833

FUJITSU COMPUTER PRODUCTS OF AMERICA - RESEARCH & DEVELOPMENT—See Fujitsu Limited; *Int'l*, pg. 2833

FUJITSU INDIA PVT. LTD.—See Fujitsu Limited; *Int'l*, pg. 2836

FUJITSU LABORATORIES LTD.—See Fujitsu Limited; *Int'l*, pg. 2835

FUJITSU MARKETING OFFICE SERVICES LTD.—See Fujitsu Limited; *Int'l*, pg. 2835

FUJITSU PC ASIA PACIFIC PTE. LTD.—See Fujitsu Limited; *Int'l*, pg. 2835

FUJITSU PC AUSTRALIA PTY LTD—See Fujitsu Limited; *Int'l*, pg. 2835

FUJITSU TECHNOLOGY SOLUTIONS B.V.—See Fujitsu Limited; *Int'l*, pg. 2836

FULCRUM BIOMETRICS, LLC—See Fujitsu Limited; *Int'l*, pg. 2834

FUTURE COMPUTING SOLUTIONS INC.; *U.S. Private*, pg. 1626

FUTURESOFT, INC.; *U.S. Private*, pg. 1627

FUZE, INC.—See 8x8, Inc.; *U.S. Public*, pg. 10

FUZHOU DIGITAL CHINA COMPANY LIMITED—See Digital China Holdings Limited; *Int'l*, pg. 2121

GAME SERVICE S.R.L.—See Digital Bros SpA; *Int'l*, pg. 2120

GAP AG—See CapMan PLC; *Int'l*, pg. 1315

GAP AG—See Osprey Capital LLC; *U.S. Private*, pg. 3048

GDP TECHNOLOGIES, INC.—See Xerox Holdings Corporation; *U.S. Public*, pg. 2387

GEETA MONITORS PRIVATE LIMITED.—See Cerebra Integrated Technologies Ltd.; *Int'l*, pg. 1422

GENERAL MICROSYSTEMS, INC.; *U.S. Private*, pg. 1666

GENESIS TECHNOLOGIES, INC.; *U.S. Private*, pg. 1670

GENICA CORPORATION; *U.S. Private*, pg. 1671

GENIUS JONES INC.; *U.S. Private*, pg. 1671

GENIUS SYSTEMS LTD.; *Int'l*, pg. 2924

GEOMAGIC (SHANGHAI) SOFTWARE CO., LTD.—See 3D Systems Corporation; *U.S. Public*, pg. 4

GEOSCIENCE (BEIJING) LTD.—See CGG; *Int'l*, pg. 1432

GFI SOFTWARE USA, INC.—See GFI Software S.A.; *Int'l*, pg. 2957

GHA TECHNOLOGIES, INC.; *U.S. Private*, pg. 1690

GICIEL; *Int'l*, pg. 2968

GIGA-BYTE TECHNOLOGY B.V.—See Giga-Byte Technology Co., Ltd.; *Int'l*, pg. 2971

GISH INTERNATIONAL CO., LTD.; *Int'l*, pg. 2979

GLOBALMEDIA GROUP LLC; *U.S. Private*, pg. 1719

GLOBAL MEMORY PROCUREMENT CORP.; *U.S. Private*, pg. 1716

GLOBAL PRINTER SERVICES INC.; *U.S. Private*, pg. 1717

GLOBAL TECH SOLUTIONS, INC.; *U.S. Private*, pg. 1718

GLOBENET INTERNATIONAL CORPORATION; *U.S. Private*, pg. 1720

GLORY MARK ELECTRONIC LIMITED—See China United Venture Investment Limited; *Int'l*, pg. 1561

GODO KAISHA SOURCEFIRE—See Cisco Systems, Inc.; *U.S. Public*, pg. 500

GO ENGINEER, INC.—See Court Square Capital Partners, L.P.; *U.S. Private*, pg. 1069

GOTHAM TECHNOLOGY GROUP, LLC; *U.S. Private*, pg. 1745

GRANDTECH C.G.SYSTEM, INC.; *Int'l*, pg. 3058

GRANITE BUSINESS SOLUTIONS, INC.—See ePlus Inc.; *U.S. Public*, pg. 784

GRAY MATTER SYSTEMS, LLC.—See Hamilton Robinson LLC; *U.S. Private*, pg. 1848

GREAT SOUTH TEXAS CORPORATION; *U.S. Private*, pg. 1768

GREEN PACKET NETWORKS W.L.L.—See Green Packet Berhad; *Int'l*, pg. 3072

GREENTECH DENMARK APS—See Arrow Electronics, Inc.; *U.S. Public*, pg. 199

GREENTECH SWEDEN AB—See Arrow Electronics, Inc.; *U.S. Public*, pg. 199

GROUP MOBILE, INC.; *U.S. Private*, pg. 1793

G/S LEASING INC.; *U.S. Private*, pg. 1632

GTC SYSTEMS INC.; *U.S. Private*, pg. 1801

GUIDANT PARTNERS; *U.S. Private*, pg. 1813

GUILLEMOT SA—See Guillemot Corporation S.A.; *Int'l*, pg. 3174

GUILLEMOT SPAIN SL—See Guillemot Corporation S.A.; *Int'l*, pg. 3174

GULF BUSINESS MACHINES (GBM) L.L.C.—See Gulf Business Machines EC; *Int'l*, pg. 3179

GULF BUSINESS MACHINES (OMAN) CO. L.L.C.—See Gulf Business Machines EC; *Int'l*, pg. 3179

GULF BUSINESS MACHINES PERSONAL SYSTEMS DIVISION—See Gulf Business Machines EC; *Int'l*, pg. 3179

HAKRO-OOSETERBERG-NIJKERK B.V.—See TD Synnex Corp; *U.S. Public*, pg. 1986

HANIL NETWORKS CO., LTD.—See Hanil Holdings Co., Ltd; *Int'l*, pg. 3252

HANNSPREE EUROPE GMBH—See HannStar Display Corporation; *Int'l*, pg. 3258

HANSEN CORPORATION EUROPE LIMITED—See Hansen Technologies Limited; *Int'l*, pg. 3260

HANSEN CORPORATION USA LIMITED—See Hansen Technologies Limited; *Int'l*, pg. 3260

HANSEN NEW ZEALAND LIMITED—See Hansen Technologies Limited; *Int'l*, pg. 3260

HANVON TECHNOLOGY COMPANY LTD—See Hanwang Technology Co., Ltd.; *Int'l*, pg. 3264

HANVON TECHNOLOGY (DEUTSCHLAND) GMBH—See Hanwang Technology Co., Ltd.; *Int'l*, pg. 3264

HARD DOLLAR CORPORATION; *U.S. Private*, pg. 1862

HARMON.IE CORP. - BOSTON OFFICE—See Cukierman & Co. Investment House Ltd.; *Int'l*, pg. 1876

HARRIS DATA SERVICES OF WISCONSIN—See Harris Business Group Inc.; *U.S. Private*, pg. 1869

HBS SYSTEMS, INC.; *U.S. Private*, pg. 1888

HCL TECHNOLOGIES (MASS) INC.—See HCL Technologies Ltd.; *Int'l*, pg. 3298

HEALTH INTELLIGENCE COMPANY LLC—See GuideWell Mutual Holding Corporation; *U.S. Private*, pg. 1814

HEAT SOFTWARE FRANCE SAS—See Clearlake Capital Group, L.P.; *U.S. Private*, pg. 935

HEIDELBERG CHINA LTD.—See Heidelberger Druckmaschinen AG; *Int'l*, pg. 3321

HEIDELBERG DO BRASIL SISTEMAS GRAFICOS E SERVICOS LTDA—See Heidelberger Druckmaschinen AG; *Int'l*, pg. 3322

HEIDELBERGER DRUCKMASCHINEN VERTRIEB DEUTSCHLAND GMBH—See Heidelberger Druckmaschinen AG; *Int'l*, pg. 3322

HEIDELBERG FRANCE S.A.S.—See Heidelberger Druckmaschinen AG; *Int'l*, pg. 3321

HEIDELBERG GRAPHIC EQUIPMENT (SHANGHAI) CO. LTD.—See Heidelberger Druckmaschinen AG; *Int'l*, pg. 3321

HEIDELBERG GRAPHIC SYSTEMS SOUTHERN AFRICA (PTY) LTD—See Heidelberger Druckmaschinen AG; *Int'l*, pg. 3321

HEIDELBERG POLSKA SP Z.O.O.—See Heidelberger Druckmaschinen AG; *Int'l*, pg. 3321

HEIDELBERG PRINT FINANCE AMERICAS, INC—See Heidelberger Druckmaschinen AG; *Int'l*, pg. 3322

HEIDELBERG SCHWEIZ AG—See Heidelberger Druckmaschinen AG; *Int'l*, pg. 3322

HEIDELBERG SVERIGE AB—See Heidelberger Druckmaschinen AG; *Int'l*, pg. 3322

HEWLETT-PACKARD APS—See Hewlett Packard Enterprise Company; *U.S. Public*, pg. 1031

HEWLETT-PACKARD AUSTRALIA PTY. LTD.—See Hewlett Packard Enterprise Company; *U.S. Public*, pg. 1031

HEWLETT-PACKARD AUSTRALIA PTY. LTD.—See Hewlett Packard Enterprise Company; *U.S. Public*, pg. 1031

HEWLETT-PACKARD BELGIUM SPRL/BVBA—See Hewlett Packard Enterprise Company; *U.S. Public*, pg. 1031

HEWLETT PACKARD ENTERPRISE (CHINA) CO., LTD.—See Hewlett Packard Enterprise Company; *U.S. Public*, pg. 1031

HEWLETT-PACKARD FRANCE SAS—See Hewlett Packard Enterprise Company; *U.S. Public*, pg. 1031

HEWLETT-PACKARD FRANCE—See Hewlett Packard Enterprise Company; *U.S. Public*, pg. 1031

HEWLETT-PACKARD GESELLSCHAFT MBH—See Hewlett Packard Enterprise Company; *U.S. Public*, pg. 1031

HEWLETT-PACKARD GMBH—See Hewlett Packard Enterprise Company; *U.S. Public*, pg. 1031

HEWLETT-PACKARD GMBH—See Hewlett Packard Enterprise Company; *U.S. Public*, pg. 1031

HEWLETT-PACKARD GMBH—See Hewlett Packard Enterprise Company; *U.S. Public*, pg. 1031

HEWLETT-PACKARD GMBH—See Hewlett Packard Enterprise Company; *U.S. Public*, pg. 1031

HEWLETT-PACKARD GMBH—See Hewlett Packard Enterprise Company; *U.S. Public*, pg. 1031

HEWLETT-PACKARD GMBH—See Hewlett Packard Enterprise Company; *U.S. Public*, pg. 1031

HEWLETT-PACKARD HK SAR LIMITED—See Hewlett Packard Enterprise Company; *U.S. Public*, pg. 1031

HEWLETT-PACKARD (ISRAEL) LTD.—See Hewlett Packard Enterprise Company; *U.S. Public*, pg. 1031

HEWLETT-PACKARD ITALIANA S.R.L.—See Hewlett Packard Enterprise Company; *U.S. Public*, pg. 1031

HEWLETT-PACKARD JAPAN, LTD.—See Hewlett Packard Enterprise Company; *U.S. Public*, pg. 1031

HEWLETT-PACKARD LIMITED—See Hewlett Packard Enterprise Company; *U.S. Public*, pg. 1032

HEWLETT-PACKARD MIDDLE EAST FZ-LLC—See Hewlett Packard Enterprise Company; *U.S. Public*, pg. 1032

HEWLETT-PACKARD NEDERLAND B.V.—See Hewlett Packard Enterprise Company; *U.S. Public*, pg. 1032

HEWLETT-PACKARD NEW ZEALAND—See Hewlett Packard Enterprise Company; *U.S. Public*, pg. 1031

HEWLETT-PACKARD NORGE A/S—See Hewlett Packard Enterprise Company; *U.S. Public*, pg. 1032

HEWLETT-PACKARD OY—See Hewlett Packard Enterprise Company; *U.S. Public*, pg. 1032

HEWLETT-PACKARD PORTUGAL LDA—See Hewlett Packard Enterprise Company; *U.S. Public*, pg. 1032

HEWLETT-PACKARD S.A.R.L.—See Hewlett Packard Enterprise Company; *U.S. Public*, pg. 1032

HEWLETT-PACKARD (SCHWEIZ) GMBH—See Hewlett Packard Enterprise Company; *U.S. Public*, pg. 1031

HEWLETT PACKARD (SCHWEIZ) GMBH—See Hewlett Packard Enterprise Company; *U.S. Public*, pg. 1031

HEWLETT-PACKARD (SCHWEIZ) GMBH—See Hewlett Packard Enterprise Company; *U.S. Public*, pg. 1031

HEWLETT-PACKARD SINGAPORE (SALES) PTE. LTD.—See Hewlett Packard Enterprise Company; *U.S. Public*, pg. 1031

HEWLETT-PACKARD SOUTH AFRICA (PROPRIETARY) LIMITED—See Hewlett Packard Enterprise Company; *U.S. Public*, pg. 1032

HEWLETT-PACKARD S.R.O.—See Hewlett Packard Enterprise Company; *U.S. Public*, pg. 1032

HEWLETT-PACKARD SVERIGE AB—See Hewlett Packard Enterprise Company; *U.S. Public*, pg. 1032

HEWLETT-PACKARD VIETNAM LTD.—See HP Inc.; *U.S. Public*, pg. 1064

HITACHI DATA SYSTEMS CORPORATION—See Hitachi, Ltd.; *Int'l*, pg. 3413

HITACHI DATA SYSTEMS ISRAEL LTD.—See Hitachi, Ltd.; *Int'l*, pg. 3414

HITACHI EUROPE GMBH—See Hitachi, Ltd.; *Int'l*, pg. 3417

HI-TECH COMPONENT DISTRIBUTORS; *U.S. Private*, pg. 1932

HOEI SANGYO CO., LTD.; *Int'l*, pg. 3439

HOU ELECTRONICS INC.; *U.S. Private*, pg. 1989

HPC SOLUTIONS CO., LTD.—See Argo Graphics Inc.; *Int'l*, pg. 562

HPI AG; *Int'l*, pg. 3500

HP KSA LTD.—See HP Inc.; *U.S. Public*, pg. 1063

HP MIDDLE EAST HOLDINGS LIMITED COMPANY—See Helmerich & Payne, Inc.; *U.S. Public*, pg. 1063

HP TECHNOLOGY IRELAND LIMITED—See HP Inc.; *U.S. Public*, pg. 1063

HUBSPOT ASIA PTE. LTD.—See HubSpot, Inc.; *U.S. Public*, pg. 1068

HUBSPOT JAPAN K.K.—See HubSpot, Inc.; *U.S. Public*, pg. 1068

HYBMM OVERSEAS, INC.; *U.S. Private*, pg. 2016

HYPERCOM FINANCIAL TERMINALS AB—See British Columbia Investment Management Corp.; *Int'l*, pg. 1170

HYPERCOM FINANCIAL TERMINALS AB—See Francisco Partners Management, LP; *U.S. Private*, pg. 1592

HYPER INC.; *Int'l*, pg. 3553

HYUNDAI CORPORATION EUROPE GMBH—See Hyundai Corporation; *Int'l*, pg. 3555

I3-RANDALL, LLC—See i3 Verticals, Inc.; *U.S. Public*, pg. 1081

IAR SYSTEMS AB—See IAR Systems Group AB; *Int'l*, pg. 3569

IAR SYSTEMS AG—See IAR Systems Group AB; *Int'l*, pg. 3569

IAR SYSTEMS K.K.—See IAR Systems Group AB; *Int'l*, pg. 3569

IAR SYSTEMS LTD.—See IAR Systems Group AB; *Int'l*, pg. 3569

IAR SYSTEMS SOFTWARE INC.—See IAR Systems Group AB; *Int'l*, pg. 3569

IAR SYSTEMS SOFTWARE INC.—See IAR Systems Group AB; *Int'l*, pg. 3569

423430 — COMPUTER AND COMPUT... CORPORATE AFFILIATIONS

N.A.I.C.S. Index

IBASE SOLUTION CO., LTD; *Int'l*, pg. 3569
IBM ARGENTINA, S.A.—See International Business Machines Corporation; *U.S. Public*, pg. 1146
IBM AUSTRALIA LIMITED—See International Business Machines Corporation; *U.S. Public*, pg. 1146
IBM BAHAMAS LIMITED—See International Business Machines Corporation; *U.S. Public*, pg. 1146
IBM BRASIL - INDUSTRIA, MAQUINAS E SERVICOS LIMITADA—See International Business Machines Corporation; *U.S. Public*, pg. 1146
IBM BRASIL-INDUSTRIA, MAQUINAS E SERVICOS LIMITADA—See International Business Machines Corporation; *U.S. Public*, pg. 1146
IBM BULGARIA LTD.—See International Business Machines Corporation; *U.S. Public*, pg. 1146
IBM CANADA LIMITED—See International Business Machines Corporation; *U.S. Public*, pg. 1146
IBM CANADA LIMITED—See International Business Machines Corporation; *U.S. Public*, pg. 1146
IBM CANADA LIMITED—See International Business Machines Corporation; *U.S. Public*, pg. 1146
IBM CANADA LIMITED—See International Business Machines Corporation; *U.S. Public*, pg. 1146
IBM CESKA REPUBLIKA SPOL. SR.O.—See International Business Machines Corporation; *U.S. Public*, pg. 1146
IBM CHINA/HONG KONG LIMITED—See International Business Machines Corporation; *U.S. Public*, pg. 1146
IBM DANMARK A/S—See International Business Machines Corporation; *U.S. Public*, pg. 1146
IBM DE CHILE, S.A.C—See International Business Machines Corporation; *U.S. Public*, pg. 1149
IBM DE COLOMBIA, S.A.—See International Business Machines Corporation; *U.S. Public*, pg. 1149
IBM DEL ECUADOR, C.A.—See International Business Machines Corporation; *U.S. Public*, pg. 1149
IBM DEL PERU, S.A.—See International Business Machines Corporation; *U.S. Public*, pg. 1149
IBM DE MEXICO, COMERCIALIZACION Y SERVICIOS S. DE R.L. DE C.V.—See International Business Machines Corporation; *U.S. Public*, pg. 1149
IBM DE MEXICO, S. DE R.L.—See International Business Machines Corporation; *U.S. Public*, pg. 1149
IBM DEUTSCHLAND KREDITBANK GMBH—See International Business Machines Corporation; *U.S. Public*, pg. 1146
IBM DE VENEZUELA, S.A—See International Business Machines Corporation; *U.S. Public*, pg. 1149
IBM FOREIGN SALES CORPORATION—See International Business Machines Corporation; *U.S. Public*, pg. 1146
IBM FRANCE FINANCEMENT, S.A.—See International Business Machines Corporation; *U.S. Public*, pg. 1146
IBM GLOBAL FINANCING AUSTRALIA LIMITED—See International Business Machines Corporation; *U.S. Public*, pg. 1146
IBM HELLAS INFORMATION HANDLING SYSTEMS S.A.—See International Business Machines Corporation; *U.S. Public*, pg. 1147
IBM IRELAND LIMITED—See International Business Machines Corporation; *U.S. Public*, pg. 1147
IBM ISRAEL LIMITED—See International Business Machines Corporation; *U.S. Public*, pg. 1147
IBM JAMAICA—See International Business Machines Corporation; *U.S. Public*, pg. 1147
IBM JAPAN LTD—See International Business Machines Corporation; *U.S. Public*, pg. 1147
IBM KOREA, INC.—See International Business Machines Corporation; *U.S. Public*, pg. 1147
IBM MIDDLE EAST FZ-LLC—See International Business Machines Corporation; *U.S. Public*, pg. 1147
IBM NEDERLAND B.V.—See International Business Machines Corporation; *U.S. Public*, pg. 1147
IBM NETHERLANDS ANTILLES—See International Business Machines Corporation; *U.S. Public*, pg. 1147
IBM NEW ZEALAND LIMITED—See International Business Machines Corporation; *U.S. Public*, pg. 1148
IBM OESTERREICH INTERNATIONALE BUEROMASCHINEN GESELLSCHAFT M.B.H.—See International Business Machines Corporation; *U.S. Public*, pg. 1146
IBM PAKISTAN—See International Business Machines Corporation; *U.S. Public*, pg. 1148
IBM PHILIPPINES, INCORPORATED—See International Business Machines Corporation; *U.S. Public*, pg. 1148
IBM POLSKA SP.Z.O.O.—See International Business Machines Corporation; *U.S. Public*, pg. 1148
IBM SINGAPORE PTE. LTD.—See International Business Machines Corporation; *U.S. Public*, pg. 1148
IBM SURINAME—See International Business Machines Corporation; *U.S. Public*, pg. 1148
IBM THAILAND COMPANY LTD.—See International Business Machines Corporation; *U.S. Public*, pg. 1148
IBM UNITED KINGDOM FINANCIAL SERVICES LIMITED—See International Business Machines Corporation; *U.S. Public*, pg. 1148
IBM UNITED KINGDOM LTD. - GREENFORD—See International Business Machines Corporation; *U.S. Public*, pg. 1149
ICON LABORATORIES, INC.—See Francisco Partners Management, LP; *U.S. Private*, pg. 1591
ICRON TECHNOLOGIES CORPORATION—See Analog Devices, Inc.; *U.S. Public*, pg. 135
IFS PHILIPPINES INC.—See EQT AB; *Int'l*, pg. 2478
IFS SOLUTIONS ASIA PACIFIC PTE LTD—See EQT AB; *Int'l*, pg. 2478
IFS SOLUTIONS MALAYSIA SDN BHD—See EQT AB; *Int'l*, pg. 2478
IFS SOLUTIONS (THAI) LTD.—See EQT AB; *Int'l*, pg. 2478
IMACON, INC.—See Glunz & Jensen Holding A/S; *Int'l*, pg. 3011
IMX SOFTWARE GROUP PTY. LTD.—See Holley Holland Limited; *Int'l*, pg. 3451
INDEPENDENCE TECHNOLOGY, LLC—See Johnson & Johnson; *U.S. Public*, pg. 1196
INDEXCOMPUTER.COM; *U.S. Private*, pg. 2061
INDIGOVISION INC.—See Motorola Solutions, Inc.; *U.S. Public*, pg. 1478
INDISOFT LLC; *U.S. Private*, pg. 2064
INFINITE GRAPHICS INCORPORATED; *U.S. Public*, pg. 1117
INFORMATICS HOLDINGS, INC.—See Renovo Capital, LLC; *U.S. Private*, pg. 3399
INGRAM MACROTRON GMBH—See Hainan Traffic Administration Holding Co., Ltd.; *Int'l*, pg. 3214
INGRAM MARINE GROUP—See Ingram Industries, Inc.; *U.S. Private*, pg. 2077
INGRAM MICRO ASIA PACIFIC PTE. LTD—See Hainan Traffic Administration Holding Co., Ltd.; *Int'l*, pg. 3214
INGRAM MICRO A/S—See Hainan Traffic Administration Holding Co., Ltd.; *Int'l*, pg. 3215
INGRAM MICRO BILIIM SISTEMLERI A.S.—See Hainan Traffic Administration Holding Co., Ltd.; *Int'l*, pg. 3213
INGRAM MICRO BRASIL LTDA.—See Hainan Traffic Administration Holding Co., Ltd.; *Int'l*, pg. 3214
INGRAM MICRO BVBA—See Hainan Traffic Administration Holding Co., Ltd.; *Int'l*, pg. 3214
INGRAM MICRO BV—See Hainan Traffic Administration Holding Co., Ltd.; *Int'l*, pg. 3214
INGRAM MICRO DISTRIBUTION GMBH—See Hainan Traffic Administration Holding Co., Ltd.; *Int'l*, pg. 3214
INGRAM MICRO GMBH—See Hainan Traffic Administration Holding Co., Ltd.; *Int'l*, pg. 3214
INGRAM MICRO GMBH—See Hainan Traffic Administration Holding Co., Ltd.; *Int'l*, pg. 3214
INGRAM MICRO GMBH—See Hainan Traffic Administration Holding Co., Ltd.; *Int'l*, pg. 3215
INGRAM MICRO (INDIA) EXPORTS PTE LTD—See Hainan Traffic Administration Holding Co., Ltd.; *Int'l*, pg. 3214
INGRAM MICRO MALAYSIA SDN BHD—See Hainan Traffic Administration Holding Co., Ltd.; *Int'l*, pg. 3214
INGRAM MICRO MEXICO, S.A. DE C.V.—See Hainan Traffic Administration Holding Co., Ltd.; *Int'l*, pg. 3215
INGRAM MICRO MOBILITY AS—See Hainan Traffic Administration Holding Co., Ltd.; *Int'l*, pg. 3215
INGRAM MICRO (NZ) LIMITED—See Hainan Traffic Administration Holding Co., Ltd.; *Int'l*, pg. 3214
INGRAM MICRO SL—See Hainan Traffic Administration Holding Co., Ltd.; *Int'l*, pg. 3215
INGRAM MICRO (THAILAND) LTD—See Hainan Traffic Administration Holding Co., Ltd.; *Int'l*, pg. 3214
INGRAM MICRO (UK) LIMITED—See Hainan Traffic Administration Holding Co., Ltd.; *Int'l*, pg. 3214
INLAND ASSOCIATES, INC.; *U.S. Private*, pg. 2078
INSIGHT DIRECT UK LIMITED—See Insight Enterprises, Inc.; *U.S. Public*, pg. 1129
INSIGHT DIRECT USA, INC.—See Insight Enterprises, Inc.; *U.S. Public*, pg. 1130
INSIGHT ENTERPRISES BV—See Insight Enterprises, Inc.; *U.S. Public*, pg. 1130
INSIGHT ENTERPRISES, INC.—See Insight Enterprises, Inc.; *U.S. Public*, pg. 1130
INSIGHT ENTERPRISES, INC.—See Insight Enterprises, Inc.; *U.S. Public*, pg. 1130
INSIGHT ENTERPRISES NETHERLANDS BV—See Insight Enterprises, Inc.; *U.S. Public*, pg. 1130
INSIGHT NORTH AMERICA, INC.—See Insight Enterprises, Inc.; *U.S. Public*, pg. 1130
INSIGHT TECHNOLOGY SOLUTIONS PTE LTD—See Insight Enterprises, Inc.; *U.S. Public*, pg. 1130
INTEGRATED BUSINESS SOLUTIONS, INC.—See Apollo Global Management, Inc.; *U.S. Public*, pg. 146
INTEGRITY ONE TECHNOLOGIES, INC.—See Xerox Holdings Corporation; *U.S. Public*, pg. 2387
INTEL GMBH—See Intel Corporation; *U.S. Public*, pg. 1138
INTELLI-MARK TECHNOLOGIES, INC.; *U.S. Private*, pg. 2105
INTEL SWEDEN AB—See Intel Corporation; *U.S. Public*, pg. 1139
INTERLINK COMMUNICATION SYSTEMS, INC.—See Global Convergence, Inc.; *U.S. Private*, pg. 1713
INTERMEC TECHNOLOGIES CANADA ULC—See Honeywell International Inc.; *U.S. Public*, pg. 1050
INTERMEC TECHNOLOGIES DE MEXICO, S. DE R.L. DE C.V.—See Honeywell International Inc.; *U.S. Public*, pg. 1050
INTERMEC TECHNOLOGIES GMBH—See Honeywell International Inc.; *U.S. Public*, pg. 1050
INTERMEC TECHNOLOGIES S.A.S.—See Honeywell International Inc.; *U.S. Public*, pg. 1050
INTERMEC TECHNOLOGIES S.R.L.—See Honeywell International Inc.; *U.S. Public*, pg. 1050
INTERMEC TECHNOLOGIES U.K. LIMITED—See Honeywell International Inc.; *U.S. Public*, pg. 1050
INTERNATIONAL BUSINESS MACHINES A/S—See International Business Machines Corporation; *U.S. Public*, pg. 1149
INTERNATIONAL BUSINESS MACHINES AS—See International Business Machines Corporation; *U.S. Public*, pg. 1149
INTERNATIONAL BUSINESS MACHINES CORPORATION MAGYSRORSSYAGI KFT.—See International Business Machines Corporation; *U.S. Public*, pg. 1149
INTERNATIONAL BUSINESS MACHINES, S.A.—See International Business Machines Corporation; *U.S. Public*, pg. 1149
INTERNATIONAL BUSINESS MACHINES SVENSKA AB—See International Business Machines Corporation; *U.S. Public*, pg. 1149
INTERNATIONAL BUSINESS MACHINES WEST AFRICA LIMITED—See International Business Machines Corporation; *U.S. Public*, pg. 1149
INTERTECH COMPUTER PRODUCTS INC.; *U.S. Private*, pg. 2127
INVESTEDGE, INC.—See Featheringill Capital, LLC; *U.S. Private*, pg. 1486
INVESTRONICA, S.A.—See El Corte Ingles, S.A.; *Int'l*, pg. 2340
IPI GRAMMTECH, INC.; *U.S. Private*, pg. 2136
ISI-DENTSU SHANGHAI CO., LTD—See Dentsu Group Inc.; *Int'l*, pg. 2038
ISLAND COMPUTER PRODUCTS, INC.; *U.S. Private*, pg. 2145
ITC INTERMEC TECHNOLOGIES CORPORATION AS—See Honeywell International Inc.; *U.S. Public*, pg. 1050
ITOX, LLC—See DFI Inc.; *Int'l*, pg. 2095
ITW RIPPEY CORPORATION—See Illinois Tool Works Inc.; *U.S. Public*, pg. 1107
IVANTAGE HEALTH ANALYTICS, INC.—See Audax Group, Limited Partnership; *U.S. Private*, pg. 390
IVANTI GERMANY GMBH—See Clearlake Capital Group, L.P.; *U.S. Private*, pg. 935
JABIL CIRCUIT TECHNOLOGY INDIA PVT. LTD.—See Jabil Inc.; *U.S. Public*, pg. 1181
JACKIN OPTICAL MARKETING COMPANY LIMITED—See AMCO United Holding Limited; *Int'l*, pg. 416
JACK OF ALL GAMES, INC.—See TD Synnex Corp; *U.S. Public*, pg. 1984
JADAK EUROPE BV—See Novanta Inc.; *U.S. Public*, pg. 1548
JANSON COMPUTERS PLC—See DCC plc; *Int'l*, pg. 1990
JASPERSOFT GMBH—See Vista Equity Partners, LLC; *U.S. Private*, pg. 4402
JASPERSOFT LIMITED—See Vista Equity Partners, LLC; *U.S. Private*, pg. 4402
JASPERSOFT SARL—See Vista Equity Partners, LLC; *U.S. Private*, pg. 4402
JCL COMPANY LIMITED; *U.S. Private*, pg. 2195
JDL TECHNOLOGIES, INC.—See TheIPGuys.Net LLC; *U.S. Private*, pg. 4141
JD RESEARCH INC.; *U.S. Private*, pg. 2195
JRC CZECH, A.S.—See Hamaga as; *Int'l*, pg. 3235
KELSER CORPORATION; *U.S. Private*, pg. 2277
KGS ELECTRONICS; *U.S. Private*, pg. 2301
KINGDOM INC.; *U.S. Private*, pg. 2310
KST DATA INC.; *U.S. Private*, pg. 2355
KULR TECHNOLOGY GROUP, INC.; *U.S. Public*, pg. 1277
L2C, INC.—See TransUnion; *U.S. Public*, pg. 2184
LAFI LOGICIELS APPLICATION FORMATION INFORMATION S.A.S—See Droege Group AG; *Int'l*, pg. 2205
LAM RESEARCH CO., LTD.—See Lam Research Corporation; *U.S. Public*, pg. 1289
LASER PROS INTERNATIONAL CORP.; *U.S. Private*, pg. 2395
LEADMAN ELECTRONICS USA, INC.; *U.S. Private*, pg. 2406
LENOVO-ASIAINFO TECHNOLOGIES, INC—See CITIC Group Corporation; *Int'l*, pg. 1619
LEVERAGE INFORMATION SYSTEMS, INC.—See American Securities LLC; *U.S. Private*, pg. 250
LICENSE ONLINE, INC.—See TD Synnex Corp; *U.S. Public*, pg. 1984
LINK COMPUTER CORPORATION; *U.S. Private*, pg. 2461
LIQUID TECHNOLOGY INC.; *U.S. Private*, pg. 2466
LOGITECH FRANCE SAS—See Logitech International S.A.; *U.S. Public*, pg. 1341
LOGITECH HELLAS MEPE—See Logitech International S.A.; *U.S. Public*, pg. 1341
LOGITECH MIDDLE EAST FZ-LLC—See Logitech International S.A.; *U.S. Public*, pg. 1341
LOGITECH SCHWEIZ AG—See Logitech International S.A.; *U.S. Public*, pg. 1341
LOWRY COMPUTER PRODUCTS, INC.—See Lowry Holding Company Inc.; *U.S. Private*, pg. 2506
LOWRY HOLDING COMPANY INC.; *U.S. Private*, pg. 2506

N.A.I.C.S. INDEX

423430 — COMPUTER AND COMPUT...

LRI, LLC—See Xerox Holdings Corporation; *U.S. Public*, pg. 2388
LUIDIA UK LTD.—See Luidia, Inc.; *U.S. Private*, pg. 2512
MAINLINE INFORMATION SYSTEMS, INC.—See H.I.G. Capital, LLC; *U.S. Private*, pg. 1833
MA LABORATORIES, INC.; *U.S. Private*, pg. 2530
MAM SOFTWARE LTD.—See KKR & Co. Inc.; *U.S. Public*, pg. 1256
MAMUT APS—See Cinven Limited; *Int'l*, pg. 1616
MAMUT APS—See HgCapital Trust plc; *Int'l*, pg. 3377
MAMUT APS—See KKR & Co. Inc.; *U.S. Public*, pg. 1266
MAMUT NORGE AS—See Cinven Limited; *Int'l*, pg. 1616
MAMUT NORGE AS—See HgCapital Trust plc; *Int'l*, pg. 3377
MAMUT NORGE AS—See KKR & Co. Inc.; *U.S. Public*, pg. 1267
MAMUT SOFTWARE LTD.—See Cinven Limited; *Int'l*, pg. 1616
MAMUT SOFTWARE LTD.—See HgCapital Trust plc; *Int'l*, pg. 3377
MAMUT SOFTWARE LTD.—See KKR & Co. Inc.; *U.S. Public*, pg. 1267
MARK 3 SYSTEMS, INC.; *U.S. Private*, pg. 2577
MARUBUN-ARROW MEXICO, S. DE R.L. DE C.V.—See Arrow Electronics, Inc.; *U.S. Public*, pg. 199
MASS INTEGRATED SYSTEMS; *U.S. Private*, pg. 2603
M&A TECHNOLOGY, INC.; *U.S. Private*, pg. 2524
MAXELER TECHNOLOGIES, INC.—See Groq, Inc.; *U.S. Private*, pg. 1792
MAX GROUP CORPORATION; *U.S. Private*, pg. 2617
MECAS ESI S.R.O.—See Keysight Technologies, Inc.; *U.S. Public*, pg. 1227
MEDICAL INFORMATION TECHNOLOGY, INC.; *U.S. Private*, pg. 2655
MEGATREND D.O.O. SARAJEVO—See ASBISc Enterprises Plc; *Int'l*, pg. 600
MEMORY 4 LESS; *U.S. Private*, pg. 2664
MEMOSUN, INC.; *U.S. Private*, pg. 2664
MERAKI NETWORKS AUSTRALIA PTY. LTD.—See Cisco Systems, Inc.; *U.S. Public*, pg. 499
MEREDITH DIGITAL; *U.S. Private*, pg. 2671
MERIDIAN IT, INC.—See Meridian Group International, Inc.; *U.S. Private*, pg. 2673
MERIDIAN TECHNOLOGIES, INC.; *U.S. Private*, pg. 2673
METANETICS CORPORATION—See Zebra Technologies Corporation; *U.S. Public*, pg. 2401
METROLOGIC INSTRUMENTS GMBH—See Honeywell International Inc.; *U.S. Public*, pg. 1050
METROLOGIC JAPAN CO., LTD.—See Honeywell International Inc.; *U.S. Public*, pg. 1050
METROPOLITAN SALES DISTRIBUTORS INCORPORATED; *U.S. Private*, pg. 2689
MICRO 2000, INC.; *U.S. Private*, pg. 2702
MICRO ELECTRONICS, INC.; *U.S. Private*, pg. 2702
MICROLAND ELECTRONICS CORP.; *U.S. Private*, pg. 2703
MICRONET TECHNOLOGY—See BNL Technologies Inc.; *U.S. Private*, pg. 602
MICROS-FIDELIO AUSTRALIA PTY LTD.—See Oracle Corporation; *U.S. Public*, pg. 1611
MICROS-FIDELIO HONG KONG LTD.—See Oracle Corporation; *U.S. Public*, pg. 1612
MICROS-FIDELIO SWEDEN AB—See Oracle Corporation; *U.S. Public*, pg. 1613
MICRO SMART INC.; *U.S. Private*, pg. 2702
MICROSOFT OPERATIONS PTE LTD—See Microsoft Corporation; *U.S. Public*, pg. 1441
MICROTECH COMPUTERS INC.; *U.S. Private*, pg. 2704
MICROWAREHOUSE BV—See Insight Enterprises, Inc.; *U.S. Public*, pg. 1130
MIDLAND COMPUTER INC.; *U.S. Private*, pg. 2715
MIDRANGE SUPPORT & SERVICE, INC.—See CDW Corporation; *U.S. Public*, pg. 462
MINNESOTA COMPUTERS CORPORATION—See Dynamic Recycling; *U.S. Private*, pg. 1298
MITEL BELGIUM SA—See Searchlight Capital Partners, L.P.; *U.S. Public*, pg. 3589
MITEL COMMUNICATIONS FINLAND AB—See Searchlight Capital Partners, L.P.; *U.S. Private*, pg. 3589
MITEL DANMARK A/S—See Searchlight Capital Partners, L.P.; *U.S. Public*, pg. 3588
MITEL DEUTSCHLAND GMBH—See Searchlight Capital Partners, L.P.; *U.S. Public*, pg. 3589
MITEL FRANCE SAS—See Searchlight Capital Partners, L.P.; *U.S. Public*, pg. 3589
MITEL ITALIA S.P.A.—See Searchlight Capital Partners, L.P.; *U.S. Public*, pg. 3589
MITEL NORWAY AS—See Searchlight Capital Partners, L.P.; *U.S. Public*, pg. 3580
MITEL SCHWEIZ AG—See Searchlight Capital Partners, L.P.; *U.S. Public*, pg. 3589
MNJ TECHNOLOGIES DIRECT, INC.; *U.S. Private*, pg. 2755
MOBILE INTEGRATED TECHNOLOGIES, INC.—See Zebra Technologies Corporation; *U.S. Public*, pg. 2401
MOLDFLOW B.V.—See Autodesk, Inc.; *U.S. Public*, pg. 229
MOMENTUM ECM, LLC; *U.S. Private*, pg. 2768

MONCLICK S.R.L.—See Rhone Group, LLC; *U.S. Private*, pg. 3424
MRV COMMUNICATIONS, INC. - LITTLETON—See ADTRAN Holdings, Inc.; *U.S. Public*, pg. 44
MSC.SOFTWARE LTD. - BEIJING OFFICE—See Hexagon AB; *Int'l*, pg. 3369
MSI COMPUTER CORP.; *U.S. Private*, pg. 2807
MTC DIRECT; *U.S. Private*, pg. 2808
MTM TECHNOLOGIES INC.—See MTM Technologies, Inc.; *U.S. Private*, pg. 2809
MUSHKO ELECTRONICS (PVT) LIMITED—See Hewlett Packard Enterprise Company; *U.S. Public*, pg. 1031
MX CORPORATION; *U.S. Private*, pg. 2822
MYTHICS INC.—See OEP Capital Advisors, L.P.; *U.S. Private*, pg. 2999
NATIONAL CUSTOMER ENGINEERING, INC.; *U.S. Private*, pg. 2852
NEDGRAPHICS BVBA—See Constellation Software Inc.; *Int'l*, pg. 1773
NEDGRAPHICS OF TENNESSEE, INC.—See Constellation Software Inc.; *U.S. Private*, pg. 1773
NEDGRAPHICS SAS—See Constellation Software Inc.; *Int'l*, pg. 1773
NEDGRAPHICS SRL—See Constellation Software Inc.; *Int'l*, pg. 1773
NEMATRON CORPORATION—See Comark, LLC; *U.S. Private*, pg. 980
NEOMAGIC SEMICONDUCTOR INDIA PRIVATE LIMITED—See NeoMagic Corporation; *U.S. Public*, pg. 1506
NETGEAR INTERNATIONAL, INC. - SPAIN—See NETGEAR, Inc.; *U.S. Public*, pg. 1508
NETSWORK INC.; *U.S. Public*, pg. 2888
NETWORK DATA, INC.—See EQT AB; *Int'l*, pg. 2477
NETWORK HARDWARE RESALE, LLC; *U.S. Private*, pg. 2889
NEWMARKET INTERNATIONAL LTD.—See Amadeus IT Group, S.A.; *Int'l*, pg. 406
NEWMARKET INTERNATIONAL SOFTWARE PTE. LTD.—See Amadeus IT Group, S.A.; *Int'l*, pg. 406
NEW TECH COMPUTER SYSTEMS INC.—See Morris & Dickson Co., LLC; *U.S. Private*, pg. 2786
NICHOLAS DATA SERVICES, INC.—See Nicholas Financial, Inc.; *U.S. Public*, pg. 1528
NILOX—See Esprinet S.p.A.; *Int'l*, pg. 2506
NILOY INC.; *U.S. Private*, pg. 2927
NORDISK SYSTEMS INC.—See Converge Technology Solutions Corp.; *Int'l*, pg. 1787
NORTHEAST OFFICE SYSTEMS, LLC—See Xerox Holdings Corporation; *U.S. Public*, pg. 2388
NUANCE COMMUNICATIONS UK LTD.—See Microsoft Corporation; *U.S. Public*, pg. 1442
NU HORIZONS ELECTRONICS A/S—See Arrow Electronics, Inc.; *U.S. Public*, pg. 199
OCTAGON RESEARCH SOLUTIONS, INC.—See Accenture plc; *Int'l*, pg. 86
OFFICE MANAGEMENT SYSTEMS INC.; *U.S. Private*, pg. 3001
OFFSITE VISION HOLDINGS, INC.—See Gathid Ltd.; *Int'l*, pg. 2889
THE OMEGA GROUP, INC.—See Vista Equity Partners, LLC; *U.S. Public*, pg. 4395
ONESOURCE MANAGED SERVICES, LLC—See Xerox Holdings Corporation; *U.S. Public*, pg. 2388
ONIX NETWORKING, CORP.—See Tailwind Capital Group, LLC; *U.S. Private*, pg. 3924
ON-LINE COMPUTER PRODUCTS INC.; *U.S. Private*, pg. 3018
ONLINE INSIGHT INC.—See HealthTrio, LLC; *U.S. Private*, pg. 1898
OOO MITEL RUS—See Searchlight Capital Partners, L.P.; *U.S. Public*, pg. 3589
OPENEYE SCIENTIFIC SOFTWARE, INC.—See Cadence Design Systems, Inc.; *U.S. Public*, pg. 419
OPENGEAR, INC.—See Digi International Inc.; *U.S. Public*, pg. 662
OPEN SYSTEMS OF CLEVELAND, INC.; *U.S. Private*, pg. 3029
OPTOMA BENELUX B.V.—See Coretronic Corporation; *Int'l*, pg. 1800
OPTOMA ESPANA, S.L.—See Coretronic Corporation; *Int'l*, pg. 1800
OPTOMA FRANCE, S.A.S.—See Coretronic Corporation; *Int'l*, pg. 1800
ORACLE CANADA - HOSPITALITY - RICHMOND—See Oracle Corporation; *U.S. Public*, pg. 1611
ORACLE NEW ZEALAND LIMITED—See Oracle Corporation; *U.S. Public*, pg. 1613
ORACLE NEW ZEALAND LIMITED—See Oracle Corporation; *U.S. Public*, pg. 1613
ORACLE SOUTH AFRICA (PTY) LTD.—See Oracle Corporation; *U.S. Public*, pg. 1613
OTHER WORLD COMPUTING; *U.S. Public*, pg. 3049
OY DELL A.B.—See Dell Technologies Inc.; *U.S. Public*, pg. 650
PACIFIC ALLIANCE CAPITAL, INC.—See Craftsman Capital Partners, LLC; *U.S. Private*, pg. 1082

PACKARD BELL BELGIUM BVBA—See Acer Incorporated; *Int'l*, pg. 100
PACKARD BELL DEUTSCHLAND GMBH—See Acer Incorporated; *Int'l*, pg. 100
PACT-ONE SOLUTIONS, INC.—See Executech Utah, LLC; *U.S. Private*, pg. 1447
PALAMIDA, INC.—See TA Associates, Inc.; *U.S. Private*, pg. 3915
PANAMERICA COMPUTERS INC.; *U.S. Private*, pg. 3085
PARADIGM SYSTEM SOLUTIONS, INC.; *U.S. Public*, pg. 1636
PARAMETRIC TECHNOLOGY AUSTRALIA PTY. LIMITED—See PTC Inc.; *U.S. Public*, pg. 1735
PARAMETRIC TECHNOLOGY GESELLSCHAFT, M.B.H.—See PTC Inc.; *U.S. Public*, pg. 1735
PARTS NOW LLC—See CounterPoint Capital Partners, LLC; *U.S. Private*, pg. 1066
PATRIOT TECHNOLOGIES, INC.—See L3Harris Technologies, Inc.; *U.S. Public*, pg. 1284
PC CONNECTION, INC.; *U.S. Public*, pg. 1658
PC CONNECTION SALES CORPORATION—See PC Connection, Inc.; *U.S. Public*, pg. 1658
PC MALL CANADA, INC.—See Insight Enterprises, Inc.; *U.S. Public*, pg. 1130
PCM, INC.—See Insight Enterprises, Inc.; *U.S. Public*, pg. 1130
PCM TECHNOLOGY SOLUTIONS UK, LTD.—See Insight Enterprises, Inc.; *U.S. Public*, pg. 1130
PCNET INC.; *U.S. Private*, pg. 3120
PC PARTS, INC.—See GreenLoop IT, Inc.; *U.S. Private*, pg. 1779
PC PRODUCTS & SERVICES INC—See UCA Group Component Specialty Inc.; *U.S. Private*, pg. 4273
PCTEL RF SOLUTIONS INC.—See Amphenol Corporation; *U.S. Public*, pg. 132
PCU, INC.—See ITT Inc.; *U.S. Public*, pg. 1178
PC WHOLESALE CANADA—See TD Synnex Corp; *U.S. Public*, pg. 1984
PC WHOLESALE LTD.; *U.S. Private*, pg. 3119
PC ZONE COMPUTER TRADING (M) SDN. BHD.—See Harvest Miracle Capital Berhad; *Int'l*, pg. 3281
PEREMEX PTE. LTD.—See Digilife Technologies Limited; *Int'l*, pg. 2119
PERIPHERAL COMPANY, INC.—See Black River Computer, LLC; *U.S. Private*, pg. 572
PERIPHERAL DEVICES & PRODUCTS SYSTEMS INC.; *U.S. Private*, pg. 3151
PEROBOT CO., LTD.—See Hon Hai Precision Industry Co., Ltd.; *Int'l*, pg. 3457
PERSONAL COMPUTER SYSTEMS, INC.; *U.S. Private*, pg. 3155
PINNACLE BUSINESS SYSTEMS, INC.; *U.S. Private*, pg. 3184
P&I PERSONAL & INFORMATIK AG—See HgCapital Trust plc; *Int'l*, pg. 3377
P&I PERSONAL & INFORMATIK GMBH—See HgCapital Trust plc; *Int'l*, pg. 3377
P&I PERSONAL & INFORMATIK S.R.O.—See HgCapital Trust plc; *Int'l*, pg. 3377
PITSS AMERICA LLC; *U.S. Private*, pg. 3191
PRECISION DATA PRODUCTS, INC.; *U.S. Private*, pg. 3244
PRECISION GROUP INC.; *U.S. Private*, pg. 3245
PRECISIONHAWK INC.; *U.S. Private*, pg. 3247
PREMIO INCORPORATED; *U.S. Private*, pg. 3251
PRESTIGIO EUROPE SPOL. S.R.O.—See ASBISc Enterprises Plc; *Int'l*, pg. 600
THE PRINTER WORKS INC.; *U.S. Private*, pg. 4098
PRINT FINANCE VERMITTLUNG GMBH—See Heidelberger Druckmaschinen AG; *Int'l*, pg. 3322
PROCURRI CORPORATION LIMITED—See EXEO Group Inc.; *Int'l*, pg. 2583
PROCURRI LLC—See EXEO Group Inc.; *Int'l*, pg. 2583
PROCURRI UK LIMITED—See EXEO Group Inc.; *Int'l*, pg. 2583
PROFESSIONAL COMPUTER CENTER INC.; *U.S. Private*, pg. 3274
PROFESSIONAL CONTROL CORPORATION; *U.S. Private*, pg. 3274
PROGRAMMER'S PARADISE, INC.—See Climb Global Solutions, Inc.; *U.S. Public*, pg. 515
PROGRESS SOFTWARE AG—See Progress Software Corporation; *U.S. Public*, pg. 1725
PROGRESS SOFTWARE A/S—See Progress Software Corporation; *U.S. Public*, pg. 1725
PROGRESS SOFTWARE AS—See Progress Software Corporation; *U.S. Public*, pg. 1725
PROGRESS SOFTWARE B.V.—See Progress Software Corporation; *U.S. Public*, pg. 1725
PROGRESS SOFTWARE CORPORATION LIMITED—See Progress Software Corporation; *U.S. Public*, pg. 1726
PROGRESS SOFTWARE CORPORATION (S) PTE. LTD.—See Progress Software Corporation; *U.S. Public*, pg. 1726
PROGRESS SOFTWARE DO BRASIL LTDA.—See Progress Software Corporation; *U.S. Public*, pg. 1726
PROGRESS SOFTWARE GMBH—See Progress Software Corporation; *U.S. Public*, pg. 1725

PROGRESS SOFTWARE ITALY S.R.L.—See Progress Software Corporation; *U.S. Public*, pg. 1725
PROGRESS SOFTWARE LIMITED—See Progress Software Corporation; *U.S. Public*, pg. 1725
PROGRESS SOFTWARE NV—See Progress Software Corporation; *U.S. Public*, pg. 1725
PROGRESS SOFTWARE OY—See Progress Software Corporation; *U.S. Public*, pg. 1725
PROGRESS SOFTWARE PTY. LTD.—See Progress Software Corporation; *U.S. Public*, pg. 1725
PROGRESS SOFTWARE S.A.S.—See Progress Software Corporation; *U.S. Public*, pg. 1725
PROGRESS SOFTWARE S.L.—See Progress Software Corporation; *U.S. Public*, pg. 1725
PROGRESS SOFTWARE S.L.U.—See Progress Software Corporation; *U.S. Public*, pg. 1725
PROGRESS SOFTWARE SP. Z O.O.—See Progress Software Corporation; *U.S. Public*, pg. 1725
PROGRESS SOFTWARE SVENSKA AB—See Progress Software Corporation; *U.S. Public*, pg. 1725
PROJECT SHOP LAND SPA—See H.I.G. Capital, LLC; *U.S. Private*, pg. 1831
PROSTAR COMPUTER, INC.; *U.S. Private*, pg. 3289
PROSTEN TECHNOLOGY COMPANY LIMITED—See China Brilliant Global Limited; *Int'l*, pg. 1487
PSION EUROPE S.A.S.—See Zebra Technologies Corporation; *U.S. Public*, pg. 2401
PSION MOBILE GROUP, S.L.—See Zebra Technologies Corporation; *U.S. Public*, pg. 2401
PSION N.V.—See Zebra Technologies Corporation; *U.S. Public*, pg. 2401
PSION SYSTEMS INC.—See Zebra Technologies Corporation; *U.S. Public*, pg. 2401
PSION SYSTEMS INDIA PRIVATE LIMITED—See Zebra Technologies Corporation; *U.S. Public*, pg. 2401
PSION TEKLOGIX DO BRASIL LTDA—See Zebra Technologies Corporation; *U.S. Public*, pg. 2401
PT MARUBUN ARROW INDONESIA—See Arrow Electronics, Inc.; *U.S. Public*, pg. 199
P.T. ORACLE INDONESIA—See Oracle Corporation; *U.S. Public*, pg. 1612
PURE STORAGE NEW ZEALAND LIMITED—See Pure Storage, Inc.; *U.S. Public*, pg. 1738
PURE STORAGE (RUS) LIMITED LIABILITY COMPANY—See Pure Storage, Inc.; *U.S. Public*, pg. 1738
PYRAMID SYSTEMS, INC.; *U.S. Private*, pg. 3310
QUATEC AG—See Droege Group AG; *Int'l*, pg. 2205
QUOTE COMPONENTS B.V.—See TD Synnex Corp; *U.S. Public*, pg. 1986
R2 INNOVATIVE TECHNOLOGIES INC; *U.S. Private*, pg. 3340
RAHI BILGI SISTEMLERI DIS TICARET LIMITED SIRKETI—See WESCO International, Inc.; *U.S. Public*, pg. 2351
RAHI SYSTEMS EUROPE B.V.—See WESCO International, Inc.; *U.S. Public*, pg. 2351
RAHI SYSTEMS PTE. LTD.—See WESCO International, Inc.; *U.S. Public*, pg. 2351
RAMCOM INTERNATIONAL CORP.; *U.S. Private*, pg. 3351
RAND WORLDWIDE, INC.; *U.S. Public*, pg. 1762
RAYTHEON PIKEWERKS CORPORATION—See RTX Corporation; *U.S. Public*, pg. 1824
RAZER USA LTD.—See Razer Inc.; *U.S. Private*, pg. 3359
RECAB UK LTD.—See Addtech AB; *Int'l*, pg. 135
REMOTE BACKUP SYSTEMS INC.; *U.S. Private*, pg. 3396
RESCUECOM CORPORATION; *U.S. Private*, pg. 3403
RESILIENCE TECHNOLOGY CORPORATION; *U.S. Private*, pg. 3405
RESULTS TECHNOLOGY; *U.S. Private*, pg. 3410
RETALIGENT SOLUTIONS, INC.—See Mi9 Retail, Inc.; *U.S. Private*, pg. 2696
RFXCEL CORPORATION—See Antares Vision SpA; *Int'l*, pg. 482
RICHARDSON RFPD DO BRASIL LTDA—See Arrow Electronics, Inc.; *U.S. Public*, pg. 200
RIGHT SYSTEMS INC.; *U.S. Private*, pg. 3436
ROBERTSON (USA) INC.—See CGG; *Int'l*, pg. 1432
SANDISK HONG KONG LIMITED—See Western Digital Corporation; *U.S. Public*, pg. 2355
SANDISK INTERNATIONAL LIMITED—See Western Digital Corporation; *U.S. Public*, pg. 2355
SANDISK KOREA LIMITED—See Western Digital Corporation; *U.S. Public*, pg. 2355
SANDISK LIMTED—See Western Digital Corporation; *U.S. Public*, pg. 2356
SANDISK SAS—See Western Digital Corporation; *U.S. Public*, pg. 2356
SANDISK SCOTLAND LIMITED—See Western Digital Corporation; *U.S. Public*, pg. 2356
SANDISK TAIWAN LIMITED—See Western Digital Corporation; *U.S. Public*, pg. 2356
SAS INSTITUTE (PHILIPPINES), INC.—See SAS Institute Inc.; *U.S. Private*, pg. 3551
SCANSOURCE, INC.; *U.S. Public*, pg. 1843
SCANSOURCE LATIN AMERICA—See ScanSource, Inc.; *U.S. Public*, pg. 1843
SCHOLARBUYS LLC; *U.S. Private*, pg. 3567

SC NEDSENSE SRL.—See Constellation Software Inc.; *Int'l*, pg. 1773
SDV SOLUTIONS, INC.; *U.S. Private*, pg. 3582
SED INTERNATIONAL HOLDINGS, INC.; *U.S. Private*, pg. 3597
SED MAGNA (MIAMI), INC.—See SED International Holdings, Inc.; *U.S. Private*, pg. 3597
SENAO INTERNATIONAL CO., LTD.—See Chunghwa Telecom Co., Ltd.; *Int'l*, pg. 1598
SENDMAIL KK—See Thoma Bravo, L.P.; *U.S. Private*, pg. 4151
SENECA DATA DISTRIBUTORS INC.; *U.S. Private*, pg. 3606
SENSOR ECS A/S—See Addtech AB; *Int'l*, pg. 135
SERCOM DISTRIBUTION LIMITED—See DCC plc; *Int'l*, pg. 1991
SERVEX (MALAYSIA) SDN BHD—See Acer Incorporated; *Int'l*, pg. 99
SET SOLUTIONS INC.—See American Securities LLC; *U.S. Private*, pg. 250
SHANGHAI WORLDTREND INTEGRATED TECHNOLOGIES INC.—See Fortune Information Systems Corp.; *Int'l*, pg. 2743
SHENZHEN TIGER INFORMATION TECHNOLOGY DEVELOPMENT CO., LTD.—See HNA International Investment Holdings Limited; *Int'l*, pg. 3433
SHEWAS, INC.; *U.S. Private*, pg. 3635
SHF CO., LTD.—See Beauty Kadan Co., Ltd.; *Int'l*, pg. 935
SHI INTERNATIONAL CORP.; *U.S. Private*, pg. 3635
SHILOH TECHNOLOGIES, LLC—See Rock Solid UK Ltd.; *U.S. Private*, pg. 3465
SHIRO CORPORATION PTE LTD—See Aztech Group Ltd.; *Int'l*, pg. 781
SIA ALSO LATVIA—See Droege Group AG; *Int'l*, pg. 2205
SICOM SYSTEMS, INC.—See Global Payments Inc.; *U.S. Public*, pg. 944
SILICONEXPERT TECHNOLOGIES, INC.—See Arrow Electronics, Inc.; *U.S. Public*, pg. 200
SILVACO EUROPE LTD.—See Silvaco Group, Inc.; *U.S. Public*, pg. 1880
SILVACO JAPAN CO., LTD.—See Silvaco Group, Inc.; *U.S. Public*, pg. 1880
SILVACO KOREA CO. LTD.—See Silvaco Group, Inc.; *U.S. Public*, pg. 1880
SILVACO SINGAPORE PTE LTD.—See Silvaco Group, Inc.; *U.S. Public*, pg. 1880
SILVACO TAIWAN CO., LTD.—See Silvaco Group, Inc.; *U.S. Public*, pg. 1880
SIMPLY MAC, INC.—See Simply, Inc.; *U.S. Public*, pg. 1882
SIMPLY NUC, INC.; *U.S. Private*, pg. 3668
SINGAPORE CONTEC PTE. LTD.—See Daifuku Co., Ltd.; *Int'l*, pg. 1926
SINGAPORE ELECTRIC VEHICLES PTE, LTD.—See Digilife Technologies Limited; *Int'l*, pg. 2120
SINTECMEDIA DV INC.—See Francisco Partners Management, LP; *U.S. Private*, pg. 1591
SINTECMEDIA SYD PTY LTD—See Francisco Partners Management, LP; *U.S. Private*, pg. 1592
SKILLSURVEY, INC.—See iCIMS, Inc.; *U.S. Private*, pg. 2031
SKY440, INC.; *U.S. Public*, pg. 1892
SKYLINE ADVANCED TECHNOLOGY SERVICES; *U.S. Private*, pg. 3685
SKYLINE CONNECTIONS INC.; *U.S. Private*, pg. 3685
SMALL DOG ELECTRONICS; *U.S. Private*, pg. 3690
SMS DATA PRODUCTS GROUP INCORPORATED; *U.S. Private*, pg. 3698
SMS MEMORY MODULE ASSEMBLY, INC.; *U.S. Private*, pg. 3699
SOCIAL SOLUTIONS GLOBAL INC.; *U.S. Private*, pg. 3703
SOFTWARE ADVICE, INC.—See Gartner, Inc.; *U.S. Public*, pg. 907
SOFTWARE AG AUSTRALIA PTY LTD.—See Silver Lake Group, LLC; *U.S. Private*, pg. 3659
SOFTWARE AG BILGI SISTEMLERI TICARET A.S—See Silver Lake Group, LLC; *U.S. Private*, pg. 3659
SOFTWARE AG FACTORIA S.A.—See Silver Lake Group, LLC; *U.S. Private*, pg. 3659
SOFTWARE AG NEDERLAND B.V.—See Silver Lake Group, LLC; *U.S. Private*, pg. 3660
SOFTWARE AG PORTUGAL ALTA TECNOLOGIA INFORMATICA LDA—See Silver Lake Group, LLC; *U.S. Private*, pg. 3660
SOFTWARE BROKERS OF AMERICA, INC.—See INTCOMEX, Inc.; *U.S. Private*, pg. 2097
SOFTWARE INFORMATION SYSTEMS LLC—See Converge Technology Solutions Corp.; *Int'l*, pg. 1787
SOFTWARE INFORMATION SYSTEMS; *U.S. Private*, pg. 3705
SOFTWARE PACKAGING ASSOCIATES INC; *U.S. Private*, pg. 3705
SOLAR SYSTEMS & PERIPHERALS; *U.S. Private*, pg. 3707
SOLARWINDS WORLDWIDE, LLC—See Silver Lake Group, LLC; *U.S. Public*, pg. 3661
SOLARWINDS WORLDWIDE, LLC—See Thoma Bravo, L.P.; *U.S. Private*, pg. 4153
SOLUCIONES DE INTEGRACION DE NEGOCIOS S.A.—See Silver Lake Group, LLC; *U.S. Private*, pg. 3660
SONICWALL B.V.—See Dell Technologies Inc.; *U.S. Public*, pg. 650
SOURCE CODE CORPORATION—See Cerberus Capital Management, L.P.; *U.S. Private*, pg. 839
SOURCEFIRE BRASIL COMERCIO E SEGURANCA DE REDE LTDA.—See Cisco Systems, Inc.; *U.S. Public*, pg. 500
SOURCEFIRE CANADA LTD.—See Cisco Systems, Inc.; *U.S. Public*, pg. 500
SOURCEFIRE LIMITED—See Cisco Systems, Inc.; *U.S. Public*, pg. 500
SOURCEFIRE SINGAPORE PTE. LTD.—See Cisco Systems, Inc.; *U.S. Public*, pg. 500
SOURCENET DISTRIBUTION, INC.; *U.S. Private*, pg. 3718
SOUTHERN COMPUTER WAREHOUSE; *U.S. Private*, pg. 3730
SOUTHLAND TECHNOLOGY, INC.; *U.S. Private*, pg. 3737
SPACEBOUND, INC.; *U.S. Private*, pg. 3744
SPANDEX USA INC.; *U.S. Private*, pg. 3744
SPARKLE POWER INC.; *U.S. Private*, pg. 3746
SPECTRA INNOVATIONS INC.; *U.S. Private*, pg. 3751
SPSS SOUTH ASIA (PVT.) LTD.—See International Business Machines Corporation; *U.S. Public*, pg. 1148
STAPLES TECHNOLOGY SOLUTIONS—See Sycamore Partners Management, LP; *U.S. Private*, pg. 3898
STERLINGTECH, INC.—See Ampersand Management LLC; *U.S. Private*, pg. 265
STEWART OF ALABAMA, INC.—See Xerox Holdings Corporation; *U.S. Public*, pg. 2388
STORENEXT LTD.—See NCR Voyix Corporation.; *U.S. Public*, pg. 1502
STRONG WAY INTERNATIONAL LIMITED—See Golden Century International Holdings Group Limited; *Int'l*, pg. 3028
SUNLAND INTERNATIONAL, LLC—See CRU Data Security Group, LLC; *U.S. Private*, pg. 1113
SUN MICROSYSTEMS DE CHILE S.A.—See Oracle Corporation; *U.S. Public*, pg. 1611
SUN MICROSYSTEMS DE MEXICO, S.A. DE C.V.—See Oracle Corporation; *U.S. Public*, pg. 1611
SUN MICROSYSTEMS DO BRASIL INDUSTRIA E COMERCIO LTDA.—See Oracle Corporation; *U.S. Public*, pg. 1611
SUNNYTECH INC.; *U.S. Private*, pg. 3869
SUNNYTECH INC.—See Sunnytech Inc.; *U.S. Private*, pg. 3869
SUPER MICRO COMPUTER B.V.—See Super Micro Computer, Inc.; *U.S. Public*, pg. 1966
SUPERMICRO KK—See Super Micro Computer, Inc.; *U.S. Public*, pg. 1966
SUPER WAREHOUSE; *U.S. Private*, pg. 3875
SYMBOL TECHNOLOGIES CZECH REPUBLIC S.R.O.—See Zebra Technologies Corporation; *U.S. Public*, pg. 2401
SYMBOL TECHNOLOGIES HOLDINGS DO BRASIL LTDA.—See Zebra Technologies Corporation; *U.S. Public*, pg. 2401
SYNERGY GLOBAL SOLUTIONS; *U.S. Private*, pg. 3904
SYNNEX DE MEXICO, S.A. DE C.V.—See TD Synnex Corp; *U.S. Public*, pg. 1984
SYNNEX INFORMATION TECHNOLOGIES (BEIJING) LTD.—See TD Synnex Corp; *U.S. Public*, pg. 1984
SYNNEX INFOTEC CORPORATION—See TD Synnex Corp; *U.S. Public*, pg. 1984
SYSPRO IMPACT SOFTWARE INC.; *U.S. Private*, pg. 3906
SYSTEMAX MANUFACTURING CO.—See Global Industrial Company; *U.S. Public*, pg. 942
SYSTEM DESIGN ADVANTAGE LLC; *U.S. Private*, pg. 3906
SYSTEMS HARDWARE INC.; *U.S. Private*, pg. 3907
SYSTEMS MANAGEMENT PLANNING, INC. (SMP); *U.S. Private*, pg. 3908
SYSTEMS PRODUCTS INTERNATIONAL, INC.—See Kingsway Financial Services Inc.; *U.S. Public*, pg. 1235
TD SYNNEX K.K.—See TD Synnex Corp; *U.S. Public*, pg. 1985
TD TECH DATA PORTUGAL LDA—See TD Synnex Corp; *U.S. Public*, pg. 1986
TEAC DEUTSCHLAND GMBH—See Evolution Capital Management LLC; *U.S. Private*, pg. 1443
TEAC MEXICO S.A. DE C.V.—See Evolution Capital Management LLC; *U.S. Private*, pg. 1443
TEAC SYSTEM CREATE CORPORATION—See Evolution Capital Management LLC; *U.S. Private*, pg. 1443
TEAC UK LTD.—See Evolution Capital Management LLC; *U.S. Private*, pg. 1443
TECH DATA ADVANCED SOLUTIONS (ANZ) LIMITED—See TD Synnex Corp; *U.S. Public*, pg. 1985
TECH DATA ADVANCED SOLUTIONS NV—See TD Synnex Corp; *U.S. Public*, pg. 1985
TECH DATA ADVANCED SOLUTIONS (SINGAPORE) PTE. LTD.—See TD Synnex Corp; *U.S. Public*, pg. 1986
TECH DATA ADVANCED SOLUTIONS (VIETNAM) COMPANY LIMITED—See TD Synnex Corp; *U.S. Public*, pg. 1986

N.A.I.C.S. INDEX
423440 — OTHER COMMERCIAL EQ...

TECH DATA AS KFT—See TD Synnex Corp; *U.S. Public*, pg. 1985
TECH DATA AUSTRIA GMBH—See TD Synnex Corp; *U.S. Public*, pg. 1986
TECH DATA BVBA/SPRL—See TD Synnex Corp; *U.S. Public*, pg. 1987
TECH DATA COMPUTER SERVICE (HONG KONG) LIMITED—See TD Synnex Corp; *U.S. Public*, pg. 1986
TECH DATA CORPORATION—See TD Synnex Corp; *U.S. Public*, pg. 1985
TECH DATA CROATIA D.O.O.—See TD Synnex Corp; *U.S. Public*, pg. 1986
TECH DATA DENMARK APS—See TD Synnex Corp; *U.S. Public*, pg. 1986
TECH DATA DEUTSCHLAND GMBH—See TD Synnex Corp; *U.S. Public*, pg. 1986
TECH DATA DISTRIBUTION S.R.O.—See TD Synnex Corp; *U.S. Public*, pg. 1986
TECH DATA ESPANA S.L.U.—See TD Synnex Corp; *U.S. Public*, pg. 1986
TECH DATA EUROPEAN MANAGEMENT GMBH—See TD Synnex Corp; *U.S. Public*, pg. 1986
TECH DATA EUROPE GMBH—See TD Synnex Corp; *U.S. Public*, pg. 1986
TECH DATA GMBH & CO. OHG—See TD Synnex Corp; *U.S. Public*, pg. 1986
TECH DATA GMBH & CO. OHG—See TD Synnex Corp; *U.S. Public*, pg. 1986
TECH DATA LTD.—See TD Synnex Corp; *U.S. Public*, pg. 1985
TECH DATA MEXICO S. DE R. L. DE C. V.—See TD Synnex Corp; *U.S. Public*, pg. 1986
TECH DATA NEDERLAND B.V.—See TD Synnex Corp; *U.S. Public*, pg. 1985
TECH DATA NORGE AS—See TD Synnex Corp; *U.S. Public*, pg. 1987
TECH DATA OSTERREICH GMBH—See TD Synnex Corp; *U.S. Public*, pg. 1985
TECH DATA OSTERREICH GMBH—See TD Synnex Corp; *U.S. Public*, pg. 1987
TECH DATA POLSKA SP. Z.O.O.—See TD Synnex Corp; *U.S. Public*, pg. 1987
TECH DATA (SCHWEIZ) GMBH—See TD Synnex Corp; *U.S. Public*, pg. 1986
TECHDEPOT—See The ODP Corporation; *U.S. Public*, pg. 2117
TECHNICAL APPLICATIONS ASSOCIATES, INC.; *U.S. Private*, pg. 3953
TEKLA GMBH—See Trimble, Inc.; *U.S. Public*, pg. 2191
TEKLA INC.—See Trimble, Inc.; *U.S. Public*, pg. 2191
TEKLA INDIA PRIVATE LIMITED—See Trimble, Inc.; *U.S. Public*, pg. 2191
TEKLA KK—See Trimble, Inc.; *U.S. Public*, pg. 2191
TEKLA SARL—See Trimble, Inc.; *U.S. Public*, pg. 2191
TEKLA SOFTWARE AB—See Trimble, Inc.; *U.S. Public*, pg. 2191
TEKLA SOFTWARE (SHANGHAI) CO., LTD.—See Trimble, Inc.; *U.S. Public*, pg. 2191
TEKLA (UK) LTD.—See Trimble, Inc.; *U.S. Public*, pg. 2191
TEKSAVERS, INC.; *U.S. Private*, pg. 3959
TELESPREE COMMUNICATIONS—See CCUR Holdings Inc.; *U.S. Public*, pg. 461
TELREPCO INC.; *U.S. Private*, pg. 3962
TELXON CORPORATION—See Zebra Technologies Corporation; *U.S. Public*, pg. 2401
TEXAS BARCODE SYSTEMS INC.; *U.S. Private*, pg. 3974
THIRD WAVE SYSTEMS, INC.; *U.S. Private*, pg. 4145
TIGA GAMING, INC.—See Firich Enterprises Co., Ltd.; *Int'l*, pg. 2679
TIGERLOGIC FRANCE—See TigerLogic Corporation; *U.S. Private*, pg. 4170
TIGERLOGIC GERMANY GMBH—See TigerLogic Corporation; *U.S. Private*, pg. 4170
TIGERLOGIC UK, LTD.—See TigerLogic Corporation; *U.S. Private*, pg. 4170
TOPDEK, INC.; *U.S. Private*, pg. 4187
TOPS SOFTWARE, LLC; *U.S. Private*, pg. 4188
TRADETICITY SERVICE D.O.O.—See Antares Vision SpA; *Int'l*, pg. 482
TRANSFINDER CORPORATION; *U.S. Private*, pg. 4207
TRANSIM TECHNOLOGY CORPORATION—See Arrow Electronics; *U.S. Public*, pg. 200
TRANSTEC AG—See Adiuva Capital GmbH; *Int'l*, pg. 149
TRANSTEC COMPUTER AG—See Adiuva Capital GmbH; *Int'l*, pg. 149
TRANSTEC COMPUTERS LTD.—See Adiuva Capital GmbH; *Int'l*, pg. 149
TRANSTEC S.A.R.L.—See Adiuva Capital GmbH; *Int'l*, pg. 149
TRIDENT MICROSYSTEMS (FAR EAST) LTD.—See Trident Microsystems, Inc.; *U.S. Public*, pg. 4230
TRIMBLE INTERNATIONAL (SCHWEIZ) SEESTRASSE SA—See Trimble, Inc.; *U.S. Public*, pg. 2192
TRINTECH INC.—See Summit Partners, L.P.; *U.S. Private*, pg. 3856
TRINTECH UK LTD.—See Summit Partners, L.P.; *U.S. Private*, pg. 3856
TRIVIUM SYSTEMS, INC.—See Provana LLC; *U.S. Private*, pg. 3291
TROY HEALTHCARE SOLUTIONS—See Troy Group Inc.; *U.S. Private*, pg. 4243
TRUSTMARQUE SOLUTIONS LIMITED—See Capita plc; *Int'l*, pg. 1309
TTEC COMPUTER B.V.—See Adiuva Capital GmbH; *Int'l*, pg. 149
TUBELITE COMPANY INC.—See Tubelite Company Inc.; *U.S. Private*, pg. 4256
TURANLI ELEKTRONIK LTD.—See Billionton Systems Inc.; *Int'l*, pg. 1031
THE TWISTER GROUP, INC.; *U.S. Private*, pg. 4128
UAB ALSO LIETUVA—See Droege Group AG; *Int'l*, pg. 2205
UCI COMMUNICATIONS LLC—See Black Box Limited; *Int'l*, pg. 1058
UMAX TECHNOLOGIES INC.—See Hiyes International Co., Ltd.; *Int'l*, pg. 3427
UNICOM GOVERNMENT, INC.—See UNICOM Global, Inc.; *U.S. Private*, pg. 4282
UNIPLEX SOFTWARE, INC.—See CP Software Group, Inc.; *U.S. Private*, pg. 1079
UNISISTEMAS PANAMA, SA—See Hewlett Packard Enterprise Company; *U.S. Public*, pg. 1032
UNISTAR-SPARCO COMPUTERS INC.; *U.S. Private*, pg. 4287
UNISYS (SCHWEIZ) A.G.—See Unisys Corporation; *U.S. Public*, pg. 2228
UNITED BMEC PTE. LTD.—See Boustead Singapore Limited; *Int'l*, pg. 1121
UNITED SOLUTIONS, INC.—See Aktion Associates, Inc.; *U.S. Private*, pg. 147
UNITED SYSTEMS, INC.; *U.S. Private*, pg. 4300
UPPER EDGE TECHNOLOGIES, INC.; *U.S. Private*, pg. 4312
USERS INCORPORATED—See Fiserv, Inc.; *U.S. Public*, pg. 857
U.S. MICRO CORPORATION; *U.S. Private*, pg. 4271
U & S SERVICES, INC.; *U.S. Private*, pg. 4269
VARIQ CORPORATION; *U.S. Private*, pg. 4347
VELOCENT SYSTEMS, INC.—See DRW Holdings, LLC; *U.S. Private*, pg. 1280
VELOCENT SYSTEMS, INC.—See Emergence Capital Partners; *U.S. Private*, pg. 1380
VELOCENT SYSTEMS, INC.—See North Bridge Venture Management Company, Inc.; *U.S. Private*, pg. 2942
VELOCENT SYSTEMS, INC.—See Voyager Capital, LLC; *U.S. Private*, pg. 4414
VENTURE TECHNOLOGIES, INC.—See CVC Capital Partners SICAV-FIS S.A.; *Int'l*, pg. 1883
VERIFONE, S.A. DE C.V.—See British Columbia Investment Management Corp.; *Int'l*, pg. 1171
VERIFONE, S.A. DE C.V.—See Francisco Partners Management, LP; *U.S. Private*, pg. 1593
VERIFONE SYSTEMS FRANCE SAS—See British Columbia Investment Management Corp.; *Int'l*, pg. 1170
VERIFONE SYSTEMS FRANCE SAS—See Francisco Partners Management, LP; *U.S. Private*, pg. 1592
VERIFONE (U.K.) LIMITED—See British Columbia Investment Management Corp.; *Int'l*, pg. 1170
VERIFONE (U.K.) LIMITED—See Francisco Partners Management, LP; *U.S. Private*, pg. 1592
VIEWNET COMPUTER SYSTEM SDN. BHD.—See Harvest Miracle Capital Berhad; *Int'l*, pg. 3281
VIEWSONIC EUROPE LTD.—See ViewSonic Corporation; *U.S. Private*, pg. 4381
VINZEO TECHNOLOGIES S.A.U.—See Esprinet S.p.A.; *Int'l*, pg. 2506
THE VIRTUAL TRY-OUT SPACE S.L.—See Keysight Technologies, Inc.; *U.S. Public*, pg. 1227
VISHAY COMPONENTS, S.A.—See Vishay Intertechnology, Inc.; *U.S. Public*, pg. 2302
VISIBLETHREAD LTD.—See VisibleThread, LLC; *U.S. Private*, pg. 4390
VISION TECH INFORMATION TECHNOLOGY, INC.—See Acer Incorporated; *Int'l*, pg. 100
VISIONTEK PRODUCTS, LLC—See Impero Electronics, Inc.; *U.S. Private*, pg. 2050
VIZTEK; *U.S. Private*, pg. 4407
VLASIC INVESTMENTS LLC; *U.S. Private*, pg. 4407
VOYETRA TURTLE BEACH INC.—See Turtle Beach Corporation; *U.S. Public*, pg. 2205
VSI METER SERVICES, INC.—See Asplundh Tree Expert Co.; *U.S. Private*, pg. 353
VXCHNGE HOLDINGS, LLC—See The Stephens Group, LLC; *U.S. Private*, pg. 4121
WARKENTINE, INC.—See BlackRock, Inc.; *U.S. Public*, pg. 347
WASHINGTON ELECTRIC CO. INC.; *U.S. Private*, pg. 4447
WAV, INC.; *U.S. Private*, pg. 4457
WEST COAST COMPUTER EXCHANGE, *U.S. Private*, pg. 4484
WESTCON BRASIL, LTDA.—See TD Synnex Corp; *U.S. Public*, pg. 1987
WESTCON CANADA SYSTEMS (WCSI) INC.—See TD Synnex Corp; *U.S. Public*, pg. 1987
WESTCON GROUP, INC.—See TD Synnex Corp; *U.S. Public*, pg. 1987
WESTCON GROUP NORTH AMERICA, INC.—See TD Synnex Corp; *U.S. Public*, pg. 1987
WESTERN DIGITAL DRIVE ENGINEERING INC.—See Western Digital Corporation; *U.S. Public*, pg. 2355
WESTHAM TRADE COMPANY LIMITED; *U.S. Private*, pg. 4498
WHALLEY COMPUTER ASSOCIATES INC.; *U.S. Private*, pg. 4503
WIEDENBACH APPARATEBAU GMBH—See Brother Industries, Ltd.; *Int'l*, pg. 1198
WILDFLOWER INTERNATIONAL, LTD.; *U.S. Private*, pg. 4519
WIND RIVER SALES CO., INC.—See TPG Capital, L.P.; *U.S. Public*, pg. 2177
WOODFIELD GROUP INC.; *U.S. Private*, pg. 4558
WORKGROUP IT (PTY) LIMITED—See Alviva Holdings Limited; *Int'l*, pg. 402
WORLDAPP, INC.—See Diversis Capital, LLC; *U.S. Private*, pg. 1244
WORLDWIDE REBATES INC.—See Global Industrial Company; *U.S. Public*, pg. 942
WORLD WIDE TECHNOLOGY - HONG KONG SALES OFFICE—See World Wide Technology Holding Co., LLC; *U.S. Public*, pg. 4568
WOW VISION PTE LTD—See Centurion Corporation Limited; *Int'l*, pg. 1417
XBYTE TECHNOLOGIES, INC.; *U.S. Private*, pg. 4580
XEROX CANADA N.S. ULC—See Xerox Holdings Corporation; *U.S. Public*, pg. 2390
XEROX GLOBAL SERVICES GMBH—See Xerox Holdings Corporation; *U.S. Public*, pg. 2390
XEROX MAROC S.A.—See Xerox Holdings Corporation; *U.S. Public*, pg. 2390
XILINX ASIA PACIFIC PTE. LTD.—See Advanced Micro Devices, Inc.; *U.S. Public*, pg. 49
XILINX IRELAND UNLIMITED COMPANY—See Advanced Micro Devices, Inc.; *U.S. Public*, pg. 49
XPERTTECH INC.; *U.S. Private*, pg. 4582
XPLORE TECHNOLOGIES CORPORATION OF AMERICA—See Zebra Technologies Corporation; *U.S. Public*, pg. 2402
ZAO HEWLETT-PACKARD AO—See HP Inc.; *U.S. Public*, pg. 1065
ZEBRA TECHNOLOGIES ASIA PACIFIC, LLC—See Zebra Technologies Corporation; *U.S. Public*, pg. 2402
ZEBRA TECHNOLOGIES AUSTRIA GMBH—See Zebra Technologies Corporation; *U.S. Public*, pg. 2402
ZEBRA TECHNOLOGIES COLOMBIA S.A.S.—See Zebra Technologies Corporation; *U.S. Public*, pg. 2402
ZEBRA TECHNOLOGIES EUROPE LIMITED—See Zebra Technologies Corporation; *U.S. Public*, pg. 2402
ZEBRA TECHNOLOGIES EUROPE SALES COMPANY, LLC—See Zebra Technologies Corporation; *U.S. Public*, pg. 2402
ZEBRA TECHNOLOGIES GERMANY GMBH—See Zebra Technologies Corporation; *U.S. Public*, pg. 2402
ZEBRA TECHNOLOGIES (HONG KONG) LIMITED—See Zebra Technologies Corporation; *U.S. Public*, pg. 2402
ZEBRA TECHNOLOGIES ITALY S.R.L.—See Zebra Technologies Corporation; *U.S. Public*, pg. 2402
ZEBRA TECHNOLOGIES JAPAN CO. LTD.—See Zebra Technologies Corporation; *U.S. Public*, pg. 2402
ZEBRA TECHNOLOGIES KOREA YCH—See Zebra Technologies Corporation; *U.S. Public*, pg. 2402
ZEBRA TECHNOLOGIES LANKA (PRIVATE) LIMITED—See Zebra Technologies Corporation; *U.S. Public*, pg. 2402
ZEBRA TECHNOLOGIES MAGYARORSZAG KFT.—See Zebra Technologies Corporation; *U.S. Public*, pg. 2402
ZEBRA TECHNOLOGIES (NEW ZEALAND) LIMITED—See Zebra Technologies Corporation; *U.S. Public*, pg. 2402
ZIMBRA EUROPE LIMITED—See Centre Lane Partners, LLC; *U.S. Public*, pg. 827
ZT GROUP INT'L INC.; *U.S. Private*, pg. 4609

423440 — OTHER COMMERCIAL EQUIPMENT MERCHANT WHOLESALERS

17TH STREET ALD MANAGEMENT CORP.—See ForceField Energy Inc.; *U.S. Public*, pg. 1563
ABC TARGET, LLC; *U.S. Private*, pg. 36
ABRASIVE PRODUCTS & EQUIPMENT, LLC—See Ridgemont Partners Management LLC; *U.S. Private*, pg. 3432
ABSTRACT DISPLAYS, INC.; *U.S. Private*, pg. 44
ACE MART RESTAURANT SUPPLY COMPANY INC.; *U.S. Private*, pg. 57
ADAMS-BURCH, LLC—See Warburg Pincus LLC; *U.S. Private*, pg. 4440
ADDVANTAGE TECHNOLOGIES GROUP, INC.; *U.S. Public*, pg. 40
A&D ENGINEERING, INC.—See A&D Co., Ltd.; *Int'l*, pg. 18
A&D EUROPE GMBH—See A&D Co., Ltd.; *Int'l*, pg. 18
A&D INSTRUMENTS INDIA PVT. LTD.—See A&D Co., Ltd.; *Int'l*, pg. 18
A&D INSTRUMENTS LTD.—See A&D Co., Ltd.; *Int'l*, pg. 18
A&D TECHNOLOGY INC.—See A&D Co., Ltd.; *Int'l*, pg. 19

423440 — OTHER COMMERCIAL EQ...

AEBI SCHMIDT AUSTRIA GMBH—See Aebi Schmidt Holding AG; *Int'l*, pg. 170
AEBI SCHMIDT BELGIUM—See Aebi Schmidt Holding AG; *Int'l*, pg. 170
AEBI SCHMIDT IBERICA S.A.—See Aebi Schmidt Holding AG; *Int'l*, pg. 170
AEBI SCHMIDT SWEDEN AB—See Aebi Schmidt Holding AG; *Int'l*, pg. 170
AEBI SCHMIDT UK LIMITED—See Aebi Schmidt Holding AG; *Int'l*, pg. 170
AGFA SINGAPORE PTE. LTD.—See Agfa-Gevaert N.V.; *Int'l*, pg. 207
ALLPOINTS FOODSERVICE PARTS & SUPPLIES, INC.—See New Mountain Capital, LLC; *U.S. Private*, pg. 2901
ALOIS DALLMAYR AUTOMATEN-SERVICE GMBH HERXHEIM—See Alois Dallmayr KG; *Int'l*, pg. 365
ALTON INTERNATIONAL (S) PTE LTD—See Federal International (2000) Ltd; *Int'l*, pg. 2630
AMERICAN HOTEL REGISTER COMPANY; *U.S. Private*, pg. 236
AMERICAN VENDING SALES, INC.; *U.S. Private*, pg. 258
APEX COMMERCIAL KITCHEN CO—See Osceola Capital Management, LLC; *U.S. Private*, pg. 3046
APS FRANCE S.A.R.L.—See Brother Industries, Ltd.; *Int'l*, pg. 1197
AQUA CURE LIMITED (UK)—See Castik Capital S.a.r.l.; *Int'l*, pg. 1356
AQUA CURE (SCOTLAND) LIMITED—See Castik Capital S.a.r.l.; *Int'l*, pg. 1356
ARDEL STEEL; *Int'l*, pg. 554
ARIENS SPECIALTY BRANDS, LLC—See The Riverside Company; *U.S. Private*, pg. 4108
ARIZONA COMMERCIAL TRUCK SALES, LLC.; *U.S. Private*, pg. 324
ASM UNITED KINGDOM SALES B.V—See ASM INTERNATIONAL N.V.; *Int'l*, pg. 626
AS SELECTA S.R.O.—See Allianz SE; *Int'l*, pg. 343
ASSOCIATED TIME & PARKING CONTROLS, INC.; *U.S. Private*, pg. 357
A/S WODSCHOW & CO.—See The Middleby Corporation; *U.S. Public*, pg. 2113
AUTOMATION TECHNIQUES PTY. LTD.—See Graco, Inc.; *U.S. Public*, pg. 953
BARBOUR INTERNATIONAL INC.; *U.S. Private*, pg. 472
BARCODES, INC—See Odyssey Investment Partners, LLC; *U.S. Private*, pg. 2994
BARGREEN-ELLINGSON INC.; *U.S. Private*, pg. 474
BELTRAM EDGE TOOL SUPPLY CORP; *U.S. Private*, pg. 521
BEST RESTAURANT EQUIPMENT & DESIGN CO.; *U.S. Private*, pg. 543
BEST WORLD LIFESTYLE PTE LTD—See Best World International Ltd.; *Int'l*, pg. 1000
BETSON ENTERPRISES—See H. Betti Industries, Inc.; *U.S. Private*, pg. 1824
BEZAC EQUIPMENT CO.—See Johnson-Lancaster & Associates, Inc.; *U.S. Private*, pg. 2229
BIRMINGHAM VENDING COMPANY; *U.S. Private*, pg. 565
BKW ENVIRONMENTAL SERVICES, LLC—See Ridgemont Partners Management LLC; *U.S. Private*, pg. 3432
BLUE LINE DISTRIBUTING—See Ilitch Holdings, Inc.; *U.S. Private*, pg. 2042
BLUE SEAL LIMITED—See Ali Holding S.r.l; *Int'l*, pg. 321
BMSVISION LLC—See Alpha Associes Conseil SAS; *Int'l*, pg. 366
BOOMERANG COMMERCE, INC.—See Lowe's Companies, Inc.; *U.S. Public*, pg. 1343
BOS EQUIPEMENT HOTELIER; *Int'l*, pg. 1115
BRAKES CATERING EQUIPMENT—See Sysco Corporation; *U.S. Public*, pg. 1973
BRECHBUHLER SCALES INC.; *U.S. Private*, pg. 644
BREMA GROUP S.P.A—See Hoshizaki Corporation; *Int'l*, pg. 3483
BREWSTER WHOLESALER COMPANY—See The RMR Group Inc.; *U.S. Public*, pg. 2126
BUCKELEW'S FOOD SERVICE EQUIPMENT CO.; *U.S. Private*, pg. 677
BUNZL GROSSHANDEL GMBH—See Bunzl plc; *Int'l*, pg. 1217
BURFORD BAKERY SOLUTIONS LIMITED—See The Middleby Corporation; *U.S. Public*, pg. 2113
BURKETT RESTAURANT EQUIPMENT, CO.; *U.S. Private*, pg. 688
BURLODGE CANADA LTD.—See Ali Holding S.r.l.; *Int'l*, pg. 320
BURLODGE SAS—See Ali Holding S.r.l.; *Int'l*, pg. 320
BURLODGE S.R.L.—See Ali Holding S.r.l; *Int'l*, pg. 320
BURLODGE USA INC.—See Ali Holding S.r.l.; *Int'l*, pg. 320
BURMAC MACHINERY LTD.—See ANSA McAl Limited; *Int'l*, pg. 477
BUSSMANN DO BRASIL LTDA.—See Eaton Corporation plc; *Int'l*, pg. 2277
BUTTERFLY GANDHIMATHI APPLIANCES LIMITED—See Crompton Greaves Consumer Electricals Limited; *Int'l*, pg. 1853
CANADIAN LOCKER CO., LTD.—See American Locker Group Incorporated; *U.S. Private*, pg. 240

CAPITOL HARDWARE, INC.—See Leggett & Platt, Incorporated; *U.S. Public*, pg. 1301
CARLTON GROUP, INC.; *U.S. Private*, pg. 765
CAROMETEC S.L.—See KKR & Co. Inc.; *U.S. Public*, pg. 1241
CARPIGIANI DEUTSCHLAND GMBH—See Ali Holding S.r.l; *Int'l*, pg. 320
CARPIGIANI NEDERLAND—See Ali Holding S.r.l; *Int'l*, pg. 320
CARPIGIANI SOLUTIONS—See Ali Holding S.r.l; *Int'l*, pg. 321
CATERING EQUIPMENT INDUSTRY SRL—See The Middleby Corporation; *U.S. Public*, pg. 2113
CHART COOLER SERVICE COMPANY, INC.—See Chart Industries, Inc.; *U.S. Public*, pg. 481
CHART CRYOGENIC DISTRIBUTION EQUIPMENT (CHANGZHOU) COMPANY LIMITED—See Chart Industries, Inc.; *U.S. Public*, pg. 481
CLEANERS CLOSET INC.; *U.S. Private*, pg. 931
COAST LINE SUPPLY & EQUIPMENT COMPANY; *U.S. Private*, pg. 954
COMASEC ITALIA SRL—See Ansell Limited; *Int'l*, pg. 478
COMMERCIAL LAUNDRY PRODUCTS, INC.—See EVI Industries, Inc.; *U.S. Public*, pg. 803
CONERGY DEUTSCHLAND GMBH—See Kawa Capital Management, Inc.; *U.S. Private*, pg. 2266
CONERGY, INC.—See Kawa Capital Management, Inc.; *U.S. Private*, pg. 2266
COOPER (NINGBO) ELECTRIC CO., LTD.—See Eaton Corporation plc; *Int'l*, pg. 2277
COOPER YUHUA (CHANGZHOU) ELECTRIC EQUIPMENT MANUFACTURING CO., LTD.—See Eaton Corporation plc; *Int'l*, pg. 2277
CORETRAX TECHNOLOGY LIMITED—See Buckthorn Partners LLP; *Int'l*, pg. 1210
COROB BRASIL—See Graco, Inc.; *U.S. Public*, pg. 953
COROB GMBH—See Graco, Inc.; *U.S. Public*, pg. 953
COROB NORTH AMERICA, INC.—See Graco, Inc.; *U.S. Public*, pg. 953
COROB PTE. LTD.—See Graco, Inc.; *U.S. Public*, pg. 953
COROB RUS—See Graco, Inc.; *U.S. Public*, pg. 953
COROB S.A.—See Graco, Inc.; *U.S. Public*, pg. 953
COROB SCANDINAVIA AB—See Graco, Inc.; *U.S. Public*, pg. 953
COROB TRADING (SHENZHEN) LIMITED—See Graco, Inc.; *U.S. Public*, pg. 953
COURTNEY MARKETING, INC.; *U.S. Private*, pg. 1070
CRANE NATIONAL VENDORS CO., LTD.—See Crane NXT, Co.; *U.S. Public*, pg. 591
CRANE PAYMENT INNOVATIONS SRL—See Crane NXT, Co.; *U.S. Public*, pg. 591
CULINARY DEPOT, INC.; *U.S. Private*, pg. 1120
CULINEX; *U.S. Private*, pg. 1121
CURTIS RESTAURANT EQUIPMENT INC.; *U.S. Private*, pg. 1127
CUSCO FABRICATORS, LLC—See H.I.G. Capital, LLC; *U.S. Private*, pg. 1832
DALLMAYR AUTOMATEN-SERVICE GMBH—See Alois Dallmayr KG; *Int'l*, pg. 365
DANIEL M. POWERS & ASSOCIATES LTD.; *U.S. Private*, pg. 1156
THE DICKLER CORP.; *U.S. Private*, pg. 4021
DIRECT SOUTH INC.; *U.S. Private*, pg. 1235
DURAND PRODUCTS, LLC—See Lyon & Dittrich Holding Company; *U.S. Private*, pg. 2522
EATON INDUSTRIES (COLOMBIA) S.A.S.—See Eaton Corporation plc; *Int'l*, pg. 2281
EATON INDUSTRIES (EGYPT) LTD.—See Eaton Corporation plc; *Int'l*, pg. 2281
EATON INDUSTRIES EOOD—See Eaton Corporation plc; *Int'l*, pg. 2281
EATON INDUSTRIES (FRANCE) S.A.S.—See Eaton Corporation plc; *Int'l*, pg. 2281
ECOLAB (CHINA) INVESTMENT CO., LTD.—See Ecolab Inc.; *U.S. Public*, pg. 712
ECOLAB HOLDING ITALY SRL—See Ecolab Inc.; *U.S. Public*, pg. 713
ECOLAB INC.; *U.S. Public*, pg. 712
ECOLAB LIMITED—See Ecolab Inc.; *U.S. Public*, pg. 713
ECOLAB LIMITED—See Ecolab Inc.; *U.S. Public*, pg. 713
ECOLAB LIMITED—See Ecolab Inc.; *U.S. Public*, pg. 713
ECOLAB LIMITED—See Ecolab Inc.; *U.S. Public*, pg. 713
ECOLAB QUIMICA LTDA.—See Ecolab Inc.; *U.S. Public*, pg. 714
ECOLAB, S.A. DE C.V.—See Ecolab Inc.; *U.S. Public*, pg. 714
ECOLAB SRL—See Ecolab Inc.; *U.S. Public*, pg. 714
EDWARD DON & COMPANY—See Sysco Corporation; *U.S. Public*, pg. 1973
EFACEC ALGERIE EURL—See Efacec Capital, SGPS, S.A.; *Int'l*, pg. 2318
EFACEC ANGOLA, LDA.—See Efacec Capital, SGPS, S.A.; *Int'l*, pg. 2318
EFACEC ASIA PACIFICO, LTD.—See Efacec Capital, SGPS, S.A.; *Int'l*, pg. 2318
EFACEC CENTRAL EUROPE—See Efacec Capital, SGPS, S.A.; *Int'l*, pg. 2318

EFACEC CHILE, SA—See Efacec Capital, SGPS, S.A.; *Int'l*, pg. 2318
EFACEC CONTRACTING CENTRAL EUROPE GMBH—See Efacec Capital, SGPS, S.A.; *Int'l*, pg. 2318
EFACEC C&S MV COMPONENTS PVT. LTD.—See Efacec Capital, SGPS, S.A.; *Int'l*, pg. 2318
EFACEC DO BRASIL, LTDA.—See Efacec Capital, SGPS, S.A.; *Int'l*, pg. 2318
EFACEC EQUIPOS ELECTRICOS, S.L.—See Efacec Capital, SGPS, S.A.; *Int'l*, pg. 2318
EFACEC MARKETING INTERNACIONAL, SA—See Efacec Capital, SGPS, S.A.; *Int'l*, pg. 2318
EFACEC MAROC SARLAU—See Efacec Capital, SGPS, S.A.; *Int'l*, pg. 2318
ELECTRIC MOTOR REPAIR COMPANY; *U.S. Private*, pg. 1352
ELGI GULF FZE—See ELGI Equipments Limited; *Int'l*, pg. 2360
EMPIRE OPTICAL OF CALIFORNIA INC—See EssilorLuxottica SA; *Int'l*, pg. 2513
EPSILON ELECTRONICS INDUSTRY AND TRADE INC.—See Bozlu Holding; *Int'l*, pg. 1125
ESCOWA AB—See Castik Capital S.a.r.l.; *Int'l*, pg. 1356
ESE DIRECT LIMITED—See HC Slingsby PLC; *Int'l*, pg. 3297
E-SOURCE, INC.; *U.S. Private*, pg. 1303
EUROMED SWISS AG—See AddLife AB; *Int'l*, pg. 129
EVANS ELECTRIC LTD.; *Int'l*, pg. 2560
FAVORITE FOODS, INC.; *U.S. Private*, pg. 1484
FIMI ALI S.P.A.—See Ali Holding S.r.l; *Int'l*, pg. 321
FINNLIFT MATERIAALINKASITTELY OY—See Amplex AB; *Int'l*, pg. 434
FOOD EQUIPMENT REPRESENTATIVES, INC.; *U.S. Private*, pg. 1560
FOOD EQUIPMENT SERVICES CO.—See Berkshire Partners LLC; *U.S. Private*, pg. 535
FOODSERV SOLUTIONS (PTY) LTD.—See Excellerate Holdings Ltd.; *Int'l*, pg. 2578
FORBES INDUSTRIES ASIA PTE. LTD.—See Winsford II Corporation; *U.S. Private*, pg. 4543
FORTIER INC.; *U.S. Private*, pg. 1576
FRANKLIN MACHINE PRODUCTS, INC.—See New Mountain Capital, LLC; *U.S. Private*, pg. 2901
FRESH ENCOUNTER INC.; *U.S. Private*, pg. 1609
FUJIFILM DISPLAY SOLUTIONS KOREA CO., LTD.—See FUJIFILM Holdings Corporation; *Int'l*, pg. 2824
FUJIMAK (CAMBODIA) CO., LTD.—See Fujimak Corporation; *Int'l*, pg. 2829
FUJIMAK GUAM CORPORATION—See Fujimak Corporation; *Int'l*, pg. 2829
FUJIMAK HONG KONG COMPANY LIMITED—See Fujimak Corporation; *Int'l*, pg. 2829
FUJIMAK PHILIPPINES CORPORATION—See Fujimak Corporation; *Int'l*, pg. 2829
FUJIMAK SHANGHAI CORPORATION—See Fujimak Corporation; *Int'l*, pg. 2829
FUJIMAK TAIWAN CORPORATION—See Fujimak Corporation; *Int'l*, pg. 2829
FUJIMAK (THAILAND) COMPANY LIMITED—See Fujimak Corporation; *Int'l*, pg. 2829
GARRETT PAPER, INC.—See Bain Capital, LP; *U.S. Private*, pg. 440
GATEKEEPER SYSTEMS CANADA, LTD.—See The Graham Group, Inc.; *U.S. Private*, pg. 4037
GATEKEEPER SYSTEMS (HK), LTD.—See The Graham Group, Inc.; *U.S. Private*, pg. 4036
GATEKEEPER SYSTEMS UK, LTD.—See The Graham Group, Inc.; *U.S. Private*, pg. 4037
GCS SERVICE, INC.—See Ecolab Inc.; *U.S. Public*, pg. 714
GCS SERVICE, INC.—See Ecolab Inc.; *U.S. Public*, pg. 714
GLOBE FOOD EQUIPMENT COMPANY—See The Middleby Corporation; *U.S. Public*, pg. 2114
GLORY GLOBAL SOLUTIONS (HONG KONG) LTD.—See GLORY Ltd.; *Int'l*, pg. 3009
GN HEARING SRL—See GN Store Nord A/S; *Int'l*, pg. 3016
GN NETCOM AB—See GN Store Nord A/S; *Int'l*, pg. 3016
GN NETCOM BENELUX B.V.—See GN Store Nord A/S; *Int'l*, pg. 3016
GN NETCOM GMBH—See GN Store Nord A/S; *Int'l*, pg. 3016
GN NETCOM (ITALIA) S.R.L—See GN Store Nord A/S; *Int'l*, pg. 3016
GN NETCOM (UK) LTD.—See GN Store Nord A/S; *Int'l*, pg. 3016
GOLD STAR PRODUCTS; *U.S. Private*, pg. 1728
GRAND & BENEDICTS INC.; *U.S. Private*, pg. 1752
GRG INTERNATIONAL LIMITED; *Int'l*, pg. 3082
HANDY NETWORK INTERNATIONAL CO., LTD.; *Int'l*, pg. 3244
HANNAM CHAIN USA INC.; *U.S. Private*, pg. 1855
HAPPINET VENDING SERVICE CORPORATION—See Happinet Corporation; *Int'l*, pg. 3269
HEAT & CONTROL INC.—See Heat & Control, Inc.; *U.S. Private*, pg. 1901
HERITAGE FOOD SERVICE GROUP, INC.—See Windjammer Capital Investors, LLC; *U.S. Private*, pg. 4537
HEUSSER NEWEIGH METROLOGY SERVICES—See

Rice Lake Weighing Systems, Inc.; *U.S. Private*, pg. 3425
H&M WAGNER & SONS INC.; *U.S. Private*, pg. 1823
HNA STORKOKSSERVICE AB—See Bravida Holding AB; *Int'l*, pg. 1142
HOCKENBERG EQUIPMENT & SUPPLY CO., INC.; *U.S. Private*, pg. 1958
HOCKENBERGS EQUIPMENT & SUPPLY CO., INC.—See Warburg Pincus LLC; *U.S. Private*, pg. 4440
HOMAG U.K. LTD.—See Durr AG; *Int'l*, pg. 2232
HOONVED ALI SPA—See Ali Holding S.r.l.; *Int'l*, pg. 321
HOSPITALITY RESOURCES S.P.C.—See Gulf Hotels Group B.S.C.; *Int'l*, pg. 3181
HOTEL COMPANY INC.; *U.S. Private*, pg. 1989
HOTEL & RESTAURANT SUPPLY; *U.S. Private*, pg. 1989
HUBERT COMPANY—See Franz Haniel & Cie. GmbH; *Int'l*, pg. 2763
IAP WORLDWIDE SERVICES, INC.; *U.S. Private*, pg. 2027
ICON BRAZIL—See Wasserman Media Group, LLC; *U.S. Private*, pg. 4450
ICON DUBAI—See Wasserman Media Group, LLC; *U.S. Private*, pg. 4450
ICONEX SP. Z O.O.—See Amplex AB; *Int'l*, pg. 433
ICON NORTH AMERICA—See Wasserman Media Group, LLC; *U.S. Private*, pg. 4450
ICON OMAN—See Wasserman Media Group, LLC; *U.S. Private*, pg. 4450
ICON OVERLAY AND FITOUT—See Wasserman Media Group, LLC; *U.S. Private*, pg. 4450
ICON QATAR—See Wasserman Media Group, LLC; *U.S. Private*, pg. 4450
ICON RUSSIA—See Wasserman Media Group, LLC; *U.S. Private*, pg. 4450
INDON INTERNATIONAL, LLC; *U.S. Private*, pg. 2064
INSIGHT DISTRIBUTING, INC.—See Bain Capital, LP; *U.S. Private*, pg. 441
INTERNATIONAL RESTAURANT DISTRIBUTORS, INC.; *U.S. Private*, pg. 2120
INTERSTATE ELECTRIC COMPANY INCORPORATED; *U.S. Private*, pg. 2124
INTERSTATE OPTICAL CO INC—See EssilorLuxottica SA; *Int'l*, pg. 2513
J.D. HONIGBERG INTERNATIONAL, INC.; *U.S. Private*, pg. 2161
J.E.S. RESTAURANT EQUIPMENT, INC.—See Trivest Partners, LP; *U.S. Private*, pg. 4240
JETBOIL, INC.—See Johnson Outdoors Inc.; *U.S. Public*, pg. 1200
JLA LIMITED—See Cinven Limited; *Int'l*, pg. 1612
JOHNSON-LANCASTER & ASSOCIATES, INC.; *U.S. Private*, pg. 2229
KANAWHA SCALES & SYSTEMS INC.; *U.S. Private*, pg. 2259
KITTREDGE EQUIPMENT CO. INC.—See Singer Equipment Company; *U.S. Private*, pg. 3670
LACE FOODSERVICE CORPORATION; *U.S. Private*, pg. 2371
LANDAUER AUSTRALASIA PTY, LTD.—See Fortive Corporation; *U.S. Public*, pg. 871
LANDAUER EUROPE, LTD.—See Fortive Corporation; *U.S. Public*, pg. 871
LATO SUPPLY CORPORATION; *U.S. Private*, pg. 2397
LEIPURIN OY—See Aspo Oyj; *Int'l*, pg. 631
LIPPERT INCORPORATED; *U.S. Private*, pg. 2465
LLC ASH RUS.—See Aebi Schmidt Holding AG; *Int'l*, pg. 170
LOUIS WOHL & SON INC.; *U.S. Private*, pg. 2499
LYNCH MATERIAL HANDLING CO.; *U.S. Private*, pg. 2521
MADDEN COMMUNICATIONS, INC.; *U.S. Private*, pg. 2539
MARIGOLD INDUSTRIAL GLOVES IBERIA S.L.—See Ansell Limited; *Int'l*, pg. 478
MARIGOLD INDUSTRIAL GMBH—See Ansell Limited; *Int'l*, pg. 478
MARIGOLD INDUSTRIAL USA INC.—See Ansell Limited; *Int'l*, pg. 478
MARMON/KEYSTONE LLC—See Berkshire Hathaway Inc.; *U.S. Public*, pg. 309
MCCUE CORPORATION; *U.S. Private*, pg. 2631
MCGEE STORAGE & HANDLING, INC.—See Atlanta Forklifts, Inc.; *U.S. Private*, pg. 370
MEMPHIS SCALE WORKS INC.; *U.S. Private*, pg. 2665
MESSNER INC.—See Nassco, Inc.; *U.S. Private*, pg. 2837
MFS SUPPLY, INC.; *U.S. Private*, pg. 2693
MICHAEL BLACKMAN & ASSOCIATES, INC.—See The Dickler Corp.; *U.S. Private*, pg. 4021
MIDWEST DIRECT; *U.S. Private*, pg. 2720
MILL HARDWARE & FOOD SERVICE, INC.—See New Mountain Capital, LLC; *U.S. Private*, pg. 2901
MIRACLE SIGNS, INC.; *U.S. Private*, pg. 2745
MODERNFOLD/STYLES INC.; *U.S. Private*, pg. 2763
MOFFAT LTD—See Ali Holding S.r.l.; *Int'l*, pg. 321
MOFFAT PTY LTD.—See Ali Holding S.r.l.; *Int'l*, pg. 321
NALCO CAL WATER, LLC—See Ecolab Inc.; *U.S. Public*, pg. 715
NALCO CROSSBOW WATER LLC—See Ecolab Inc.; *U.S. Public*, pg. 715
NASSCO, INC.; *U.S. Private*, pg. 2837
NASS COMMERICAL—See Abdulla Ahmed Nass Group WLL; *Int'l*, pg. 58

NATIONAL OILWELL VARCO, L.P.—See NOV, Inc.; *U.S. Public*, pg. 1546
NATIONAL RESTAURANT SUPPLY COMPANY; *U.S. Private*, pg. 2862
NEMCO, INC.; *U.S. Private*, pg. 2884
N. GLANTZ & SON; *U.S. Private*, pg. 2827
NSC INTERNATIONAL DIVISION - SIEGEL DISPLAY PRODUCTS DIVISION—See EBSCO Industries, Inc.; *U.S. Private*, pg. 1325
OPSG LTD.—See EssilorLuxottica SA; *Int'l*, pg. 2515
OSHKOSH JLG (TIANJIN) EQUIPMENT TECHNOLOGY CO. LIMITED—See Oshkosh Corporation; *U.S. Public*, pg. 1620
PARAMOUNT RESTAURANT SUPPLY CORPORATION; *U.S. Private*, pg. 3093
PASCO BROKERAGE, INC.; *U.S. Private*, pg. 3104
PBI MARKET EQUIPMENT INC.; *U.S. Private*, pg. 3118
PERSONEELSVERENIGING LUFKIN COOPER TOOLS—See Bain Capital, LP; *U.S. Private*, pg. 430
PING INC.—See Karsten Manufacturing Corporation; *U.S. Private*, pg. 2263
PIONEER MARKETING CORP—See EQT AB; *Int'l*, pg. 2471
PITSCO INC.; *U.S. Private*, pg. 3191
PLATFORMAS ELEVADORAS JLG IBERICA S.L.—See Oshkosh Corporation; *U.S. Public*, pg. 1621
POSITOUCH, LLC—See Shift4 Payments, Inc.; *U.S. Public*, pg. 1875
POS PORTAL, INC.—See ScanSource, Inc.; *U.S. Public*, pg. 1843
PREMIER TECHNOLOGY INC.; *U.S. Private*, pg. 3251
PRICE-DAVIS, INC.; *U.S. Private*, pg. 3258
PRI-MA-TECH VERWALTUNGS GMBH—See Brother Industries, Ltd.; *Int'l*, pg. 1198
PRIMESOURCE FOODSERVICE EQUIPMENT; *U.S. Private*, pg. 3263
PROGRESS SOFTWARE JAPAN KK—See Progress Software Corporation; *U.S. Public*, pg. 1725
PRONOMIC AB—See Amplex AB; *Int'l*, pg. 434
PWA-PROSEP MALAYSIA—See AQUANEX, Servicio Domiciliario del Agua de EXTREMADURA SA; *Int'l*, pg. 527
PW STOELTING, L.L.C.—See The Vollrath Company LLC; *U.S. Private*, pg. 4132
QUALSERV SOLUTIONS LLC—See The Middleby Corporation; *U.S. Public*, pg. 2115
RANCILIO GROUP DEUTSCHLAND GMBH—See Ali Holding S.r.l; *Int'l*, pg. 321
RANCILIO GROUP ESPANA S.A.—See Ali Holding S.r.l; *Int'l*, pg. 321
RANCILIO GROUP NORTH AMERICA INC.—See Ali Holding S.r.l; *Int'l*, pg. 321
RANCILIO GROUP PORTUGAL LDA—See Ali Holding S.r.l; *Int'l*, pg. 321
RECO TECHNOLOGY (BVI) LIMITED—See General Interface Solution (GIS) Holding Ltd.; *Int'l*, pg. 2919
RESTAURANT SERVICES, INC.; *U.S. Private*, pg. 3408
THE RESTAURANT SOURCE—See Bargreen-Ellingson Inc.; *U.S. Private*, pg. 474
RHINO RESEARCH INDUSTRIES, LLC—See New Pendulum Corporation; *U.S. Private*, pg. 2905
ROBERTS COMPANY CANADA LIMITED—See Q.E.P. Co., Inc.; *U.S. Public*, pg. 1741
ROFSON ASSOCIATES, INC.; *U.S. Private*, pg. 3471
RONI, INC.—See Amplex AB; *Int'l*, pg. 434
RTI GLOBAL, INC.—See Hybrid Software Group PLC; *Int'l*, pg. 3544
RUSSELL T. BUNDY ASSOCIATES; *U.S. Private*, pg. 3507
R.W. SMITH & CO.—See Warburg Pincus LLC; *U.S. Private*, pg. 4440
SAM PIEVAC COMPANY INC.; *U.S. Private*, pg. 3536
SCALE SYSTEMS INC.—See B&D Industrial, Inc.; *U.S. Private*, pg. 418
SELECTA AG—See Allianz SE; *Int'l*, pg. 355
SELECTA A/S—See Allianz SE; *Int'l*, pg. 355
SELECTA BETRIEBSVERPFLEGUNGS GMBH—See Allianz SE; *Int'l*, pg. 355
SELECTA HUNGARY AUTOMATAUZEMELTETO KFT—See Allianz SE; *Int'l*, pg. 355
SELECTA PURCHASING AG—See Allianz SE; *Int'l*, pg. 355
SELECTA TMP AG—See Allianz SE; *Int'l*, pg. 355
SIGGINS COMPANY INC.; *U.S. Private*, pg. 3648
SILGAN EQUIPMENT COMPANY—See Silgan Holdings, Inc.; *U.S. Public*, pg. 1879
SINGER EQUIPMENT COMPANY; *U.S. Private*, pg. 3670
SKYLTAR & MARKEN GRUPPEN AB—See Addtech AB; *Int'l*, pg. 135
SOCAMEL UK LIMITED—See Groupe Guillin SA; *Int'l*, pg. 3104
SOCIEDADE TECNICA DE EQUIPAMENTOS E TRACTORES SA—See Barloworld Ltd.; *Int'l*, pg. 866
SPD DEVELOPMENT COMPANY LIMITED—See The Procter & Gamble Company; *U.S. Public*, pg. 2123
SPECTRUM SERVICES—See Diamond Chemical Co., Inc.; *U.S. Private*, pg. 1223
S.S. KEMP & CO., LLC—See Warburg Pincus LLC; *U.S. Private*, pg. 4440
STAFFORD-SMITH INC.; *U.S. Private*, pg. 3775
STAHLIN NON-METALLIC ENCLOSURES INC.—See Robroy Industries Inc.; *U.S. Private*, pg. 3463
STANDARD RESTAURANT EQUIPMENT COMPANY; *U.S. Private*, pg. 3781
STEELBUILDING.COM, INC.—See Clayton, Dubilier & Rice, LLC; *U.S. Private*, pg. 921
STORAGE SOLUTIONS INC.—See Merit Capital Partners; *U.S. Private*, pg. 2674
STORAGE SOLUTIONS INC.—See MFG Partners LLC; *U.S. Private*, pg. 2693
STORAGE SYSTEMS MIDWEST; *U.S. Private*, pg. 3831
STORE SUPPLY WAREHOUSE, LLC.; *U.S. Private*, pg. 3831
STREATOR INDUSTRIAL HANDLING, INC.; *U.S. Private*, pg. 3838
SUNNEX EQUIPMENT SARL—See Amplex AB; *Int'l*, pg. 435
SUZO-HAPP GROUP TECHNICAL COMPONENTS ESPANA, SAU—See ACON Investments, LLC; *U.S. Private*, pg. 63
SVEBA DAHLEN RUS. LTD.—See The Middleby Corporation; *U.S. Public*, pg. 2115
TAYLOR FREEZER OF MICHIGAN; *U.S. Private*, pg. 3940
TEMP-RITE INTERNATIONAL GMBH—See Ali Holding S.r.l.; *Int'l*, pg. 321
TEMP-RITE INTERNATIONAL KFT.—See Ali Holding S.r.l.; *Int'l*, pg. 322
THERMOS HONG KONG LTD.—See Thermos L.L.C.; *U.S. Private*, pg. 4143
T&O REFRIGERATION, INC.—See Ares Management Corporation; *U.S. Public*, pg. 189
TRIMARK MARLINN INC.—See Warburg Pincus LLC; *U.S. Private*, pg. 4440
TRIMARK SS KEMP—See Warburg Pincus LLC; *U.S. Private*, pg. 4440
TRIMARK USA LLC—See Warburg Pincus LLC; *U.S. Private*, pg. 4440
TUNDRA RESTAURANT SUPPLY, INC.—See New Mountain Capital, LLC; *U.S. Private*, pg. 2902
UAB LEIPURIN—See Aspo Oyj; *Int'l*, pg. 631
UNITED RADIO, INCORPORATED; *U.S. Private*, pg. 4296
UNITED RESTAURANT SUPPLY INC.; *U.S. Private*, pg. 4296
UNITED SCALE & ENGINEERING CORPORATION—See Transcat, Inc.; *U.S. Public*, pg. 2179
UNITED SERVICE TECHNOLOGIES, INC.—See HCI Equity Management, L.P.; *U.S. Private*, pg. 1889
U-SELECT-IT CORPORATION—See The Wittern Group; *U.S. Private*, pg. 4138
US FOODS CULINARY EQUIPMENT & SUPPLIES, LLC—See US Foods Holding Corp.; *U.S. Public*, pg. 2266
VIKING TRUCK & EQUIPMENT SALES (OH), INC.—See Oshkosh Corporation; *U.S. Public*, pg. 1621
WALBERER AUTOMATEN GMBH & CO. KG—See Gauselmann AG; *Int'l*, pg. 2890
THE WAREHOUSE STORE FIXTURE COMPANY; *U.S. Private*, pg. 4133
WATERLOGIC AMERICAS LLC—See Castik Capital S.a.r.l.; *Int'l*, pg. 1356
WATERLOGIC AUSTRALIA PTY—See Castik Capital S.a.r.l.; *Int'l*, pg. 1356
WATERLOGIC COMMERCIAL PRODUCTS, LLC—See Castik Capital S.a.r.l.; *Int'l*, pg. 1356
WATERLOGIC DANMARK AS—See Castik Capital S.a.r.l.; *Int'l*, pg. 1356
WATERLOGIC FRANCE SA—See Castik Capital S.a.r.l.; *Int'l*, pg. 1356
WATERLOGIC GMBH—See Castik Capital S.a.r.l.; *Int'l*, pg. 1356
WATERLOGIC NORGE AS—See Castik Capital S.a.r.l.; *Int'l*, pg. 1356
WELLSTREAM AUSTRALIA PTY LIMITED—See General Electric Company; *U.S. Public*, pg. 920
WENSCO MICHIGAN CORPORATION; *U.S. Private*, pg. 4481
WESTERN PACIFIC DISTRIBUTORS; *U.S. Private*, pg. 4495
WHALEY FOODSERVICE, LLC—See Berkshire Partners LLC; *U.S. Private*, pg. 535
WICHITA RESTAURANT SUPPLY CO, INC.—See Ace Mart Restaurant Supply Company Inc.; *U.S. Private*, pg. 57
WLI TRADING LTD.—See Castik Capital S.a.r.l.; *Int'l*, pg. 1356

423450 — MEDICAL, DENTAL, AND HOSPITAL EQUIPMENT AND SUPPLIES MERCHANT WHOLESALERS

000 WIDEX—See EQT AB; *Int'l*, pg. 2480
1800ENDOSCOPE.COM, LLC; *U.S. Private*, pg. 3
180 MEDICAL, INC.—See Avista Capital Partners, L.P.; *U.S. Private*, pg. 408
365 HEALTHCARE LIMITED—See Bunzl plc; *Int'l*, pg. 1216
3-D MATRIX (BEIJING) BIOTECHNOLOGY CO., LTD.—See 3-D Matrix, Ltd.; *Int'l*, pg. 6
3M HEALTH CARE LIMITED—See Solventum Corporation; *U.S. Public*, pg. 1901

3M IRELAND LTD.—See 3M Company; *U.S. Public*, pg. 6
AAH PHARMACEUTICALS LTD.—See McKesson Corporation; *U.S. Public*, pg. 1408
ABACUS DX PTY LIMITED—See Diploma PLC; *Int'l*, pg. 2128
ABAXIS EUROPE GMBH—See Zoetis, Inc.; *U.S. Public*, pg. 2409
ABAXIS UK LIMITED—See Zoetis, Inc.; *U.S. Public*, pg. 2409
ABBOTT DIAGNOSTICS—See Abbott Laboratories; *U.S. Public*, pg. 14
ABCAM LIMITED—See Danaher Corporation; *U.S. Public*, pg. 623
ABC HOME MEDICAL SUPPLY, INC.; *U.S. Private*, pg. 36
ABDULLA FOUAD MEDICAL SUPPLIES DIVISION—See Abdulla Fouad Holding Co.; *Int'l*, pg. 59
AB WIDEX—See EQT AB; *Int'l*, pg. 2480
ACARIAHEALTH PHARMACY #12, INC.—See Centene Corporation; *U.S. Public*, pg. 467
ACCESSIBLE SYSTEMS, INC.; *U.S. Private*, pg. 53
ACCURATE SURGICAL & SCIENTIFIC INSTRUMENTS CORPORATION—See Accurate Chemical & Scientific Corporation; *U.S. Private*, pg. 55
ACERTYS HEALTHCARE NV—See Gimv NV; *Int'l*, pg. 2976
ACE SURGICAL SUPPLY CO., INC.—See Henry Schein, Inc.; *U.S. Public*, pg. 1025
ACTIVSTYLE, INC—See AdaptHealth Corp.; *U.S. Public*, pg. 38
ADDVISE GROUP AB; *Int'l*, pg. 136
ADELAIDE DIGITAL HEARING SOLUTIONS PTY. LTD.—See Demant A/S; *Int'l*, pg. 2023
ADHERIUM NORTH AMERICA, INC.—See Adherium Limited; *Int'l*, pg. 145
A&D RUS CO., LTD.—See A&D Co., Ltd.; *Int'l*, pg. 18
ADS DIAGNOSTICS LIMITED; *Int'l*, pg. 153
ADVANCED MEDICAL SOLUTIONS (US) INC—See Advanced Medical Solutions Group plc; *Int'l*, pg. 161
ADVANCED PROSTHETICS OF AMERICA, INC.—See Patient Square Capital, L.P.; *U.S. Private*, pg. 3107
ADVANCED TECHNOLOGY COMPANY K.S.C.C.; *Int'l*, pg. 162
ADVANTAGE MEDICAL, INC.—See Ares Management Corporation; *U.S. Public*, pg. 188
ADVANTEST KYUSHU SYSTEMS CO., LTD—See Advantest Corporation; *Int'l*, pg. 166
AEROCARE HOME MEDICAL EQUIPMENT, INC.—See AdaptHealth Corp.; *U.S. Public*, pg. 38
AEROFLOW, INC.; *U.S. Private*, pg. 119
AESCULAP FLEXIMED GMBH—See B. Braun Melsungen AG; *Int'l*, pg. 785
AESCULAP, INC.—See B. Braun Melsungen AG; *Int'l*, pg. 785
AFFILIATED HEALTHCARE SYSTEMS, INC.—See Eastern Maine Healthcare Systems; *U.S. Private*, pg. 1320
AGFA HEALTHCARE AUSTRALIA LIMITED—See Agfa-Gevaert N.V.; *Int'l*, pg. 207
AGFA HEALTHCARE BRAZIL IMPORTACAO E SERVICOS LTDA.—See Agfa-Gevaert N.V.; *Int'l*, pg. 207
AGFA HEALTHCARE HONG KONG LTD—See Agfa-Gevaert N.V.; *Int'l*, pg. 207
AGFA HEALTHCARE IMAGING AGENTS GMBH—See Agfa-Gevaert N.V.; *Int'l*, pg. 207
AGFA HEALTHCARE NORWAY AS—See Agfa-Gevaert N.V.; *Int'l*, pg. 207
AGFA HEALTHCARE SINGAPORE PTE. LTD.—See Agfa-Gevaert N.V.; *Int'l*, pg. 207
AGFA HEALTHCARE SOUTH AFRICA PTY. LTD.—See Agfa-Gevaert N.V.; *Int'l*, pg. 207
AHEARINGAID.COM LLC; *U.S. Private*, pg. 130
AHN INTERNATIONAL LLC; *U.S. Private*, pg. 131
AIRWAY OXYGEN, INC.—See AdaptHealth Corp.; *U.S. Public*, pg. 38
AIRXPANDERS INC.; *U.S. Private*, pg. 142
AJ ROBOSCREEN GMBH—See Endress+Hauser (International) Holding AG; *Int'l*, pg. 2405
ALADDIN TEMP-RITE, LLC—See Ali Holding S.r.l; *Int'l*, pg. 320
ALCOHOL MONITORING SYSTEMS, INC.—See Riverside Partners, LLC; *U.S. Private*, pg. 3445
ALCO SALES & SERVICE CO.; *U.S. Private*, pg. 154
AL FAISALIAH MEDICAL SYSTEMS—See Al Faisaliah Group; *Int'l*, pg. 277
ALFA-WASSERMANN B.V.—See Alfa-Wassermann S.p.A.; *Int'l*, pg. 314
ALFRESA CORPORATION—See Alfresa Holdings Corporation; *Int'l*, pg. 317
ALFRESA SHINOHARA CHEMICALS CORPORATION—See Alfresa Holdings Corporation; *Int'l*, pg. 317
ALGOL DIAGNOSTICS A/S—See Algol Oy; *Int'l*, pg. 318
ALIMED, INC.; *U.S. Private*, pg. 168
ALLCARE MEDICAL SNJ CORP.—See Quadrant Management, Inc.; *U.S. Private*, pg. 3316
ALLERGON AB—See Thermo Fisher Scientific Inc.; *U.S. Public*, pg. 2145
ALLIED 100, LLC—See Ridgemont Partners Management LLC; *U.S. Private*, pg. 3433
ALLIED HOME MEDICAL, INC.; *U.S. Private*, pg. 186

ALL MED MEDICAL SUPPLY, LLC; *U.S. Private*, pg. 171
ALMEDA VENTURES LP; *Int'l*, pg. 363
ALPHA PRO TECH, LTD.; *Int'l*, pg. 369
ALPHA SOURCE, INC.; *U.S. Private*, pg. 199
ALPIC S.A.—See Delta Plus Group; *Int'l*, pg. 2019
ALPINE APS—See ArchiMed SAS; *Int'l*, pg. 548
ALPINION GUANGZHOU MEDICAL SYSTEMS CO., LTD.—See Iljin Display Co., Ltd.; *Int'l*, pg. 3614
ALPINION MEDICAL DEUTSCHLAND GMBH—See Iljin Display Co., Ltd.; *Int'l*, pg. 3614
ALPINION USA, INC.—See Iljin Display Co., Ltd.; *Int'l*, pg. 3614
AMBER DIAGNOSTICS CAMEROON SARL—See Amber Diagnostics, Inc.; *U.S. Private*, pg. 217
AMBU AUSTRALIA PTY. LTD.—See Ambu A/S; *Int'l*, pg. 416
AMBU BV—See Ambu A/S; *Int'l*, pg. 416
AMBU INC.—See Ambu A/S; *Int'l*, pg. 416
AMBU LTD.—See Ambu A/S; *Int'l*, pg. 416
AMBU S.R.L.—See Ambu A/S; *Int'l*, pg. 416
AMBU (XIAMEN) TRADING LTD.—See Ambu A/S; *Int'l*, pg. 416
AMERICAN HEALTHCARE PRODUCTS, INC.; *U.S. Private*, pg. 236
AMERICAN LABORATORIES; *U.S. Private*, pg. 239
AMERICAN MEDICAL SYSTEMS CANADA INC.—See Endo International plc; *Int'l*, pg. 2404
AMERICAN MEDICAL SYSTEMS DEUTSCHLAND GMBH—See Endo International plc; *Int'l*, pg. 2404
AMERICAN MEDICAL SYSTEMS EUROPE B.V.—See Endo International plc; *Int'l*, pg. 2404
AMERICAN MEDICAL SYSTEMS UK LIMITED—See Endo International plc; *Int'l*, pg. 2404
AMERICAN MOBILE HEALTHCARE—See AMN Healthcare Services, Inc.; *U.S. Public*, pg. 125
AMERICAN PROSTHETIC COMPONENTS, LLC—See The Jordan Company, L.P.; *U.S. Private*, pg. 4060
AMERI-QUIPT OF NORTH CAROLINA, INC.—See AdaptHealth Corp.; *U.S. Public*, pg. 38
AMES WALKER INTERNATIONAL INC.; *U.S. Private*, pg. 262
AMICO—See EssilorLuxottica SA; *Int'l*, pg. 2512
AMPLIFON BEHEER BV—See Amplifon S.p.A.; *Int'l*, pg. 435
AMPLIFON SIETECH LTD.—See Amplifon S.p.A.; *Int'l*, pg. 435
A.M.S. 2000—See BATM Advanced Communications Ltd.; *Int'l*, pg. 890
AMS - AMERICAN MEDICAL SYSTEMS DO BRASIL PRODUTOS UROLOGICOS E GINECOLOGICOS LTDA.—See Endo International plc; *Int'l*, pg. 2404
AMS MEDICAL SYSTEMS IRELAND LIMITED—See Endo International plc; *Int'l*, pg. 2404
ANACHEM LIMITED—See Mettler-Toledo International, Inc.; *U.S. Public*, pg. 1432
ANALOGIC ITALIA S.R.L.—See Altaris Capital Partners, LLC; *U.S. Private*, pg. 205
ANALYTIK JENA JAPAN CO., LTD.—See Endress+Hauser (International) Holding AG; *Int'l*, pg. 2405
ANALYTIK JENA US, INC.—See Endress+Hauser (International) Holding AG; *Int'l*, pg. 2405
ANATOMY SUPPLY PARTNERS; *U.S. Private*, pg. 272
ANGY (CHINA) MEDICAL LIMITED; *Int'l*, pg. 464
ANGY (GUANGZHOU) MEDICAL TECHNOLOGY CO., LTD.—See Angy (China) Medical Limited; *Int'l*, pg. 464
ANSHAN LISHAN DISTRICT AOXIN Q & M STOMATOLOGY POLYCLINIC CO., LTD.—See Aoxin Q & M Dental Group Limited; *Int'l*, pg. 498
ANT ASIA CO., LTD.—See ANT Neuro B.V.; *Int'l*, pg. 479
ANT NORTH AMERICA, INC.—See ANT Neuro B.V.; *Int'l*, pg. 479
AOSS MEDICAL SUPPLY, INC.; *U.S. Private*, pg. 289
APELON INC.; *U.S. Private*, pg. 291
APEX BIOTECHNOLOGY SUZHOU CORPORATION—See Apex Biotechnology Corp.; *Int'l*, pg. 509
APEX MEDICAL CORPORATION—See Tenex Capital Management, L.P.; *U.S. Private*, pg. 3966
APIARY MEDICAL, INC.; *U.S. Private*, pg. 294
A PLUS INTERNATIONAL INC.; *U.S. Private*, pg. 19
APOCELL, INC.—See Precision Medicine Group, Inc.; *U.S. Private*, pg. 3245
ARJO AB—See Getinge AB; *Int'l*, pg. 2947
ARJOHUNTLEIGH AB—See Getinge AB; *Int'l*, pg. 2948
ARJOHUNTLEIGH AG—See Getinge AB; *Int'l*, pg. 2948
ARJOHUNTLEIGH A/S—See Getinge AB; *Int'l*, pg. 2948
ARJOHUNTLEIGH HEALTHCARE INDIA PVT. LTD.—See Getinge AB; *Int'l*, pg. 2948
ARJOHUNTLEIGH HOSPITAL EQUIPMENT AB—See Getinge AB; *Int'l*, pg. 2948
ARJOHUNTLEIGH INC—See Getinge AB; *Int'l*, pg. 2948
ARJOHUNTLEIGH INTERNATIONAL AB—See Getinge AB; *Int'l*, pg. 2949
ARJOHUNTLEIGH INTERNATIONAL LTD—See Getinge AB; *Int'l*, pg. 2948
ARJOHUNTLEIGH LTD—See Getinge AB; *Int'l*, pg. 2948
ARJOHUNTLEIGH MAGOG INC—See Getinge AB; *Int'l*, pg. 2948
ARJOHUNTLEIGH MIDDLE EAST—See Getinge AB; *Int'l*, pg. 2948

ARJOHUNTLEIGH NORWAY A/S—See Getinge AB; *Int'l*, pg. 2948
ARJOHUNTLEIGH NV/SA—See Getinge AB; *Int'l*, pg. 2948
ARJOHUNTLEIGH POLSKA SP. Z.O.O.—See Getinge AB; *Int'l*, pg. 2948
ARJOHUNTLEIGH PTY LTD.—See Getinge AB; *Int'l*, pg. 2948
ARJOHUNTLEIGH SAS—See Getinge AB; *Int'l*, pg. 2948
ARJOHUNTLEIGH (SHANGHAI) MEDICAL TRADING CO. LTD—See Getinge AB; *Int'l*, pg. 2948
ARJOHUNTLEIGH SINGAPORE PTE LTD—See Getinge AB; *Int'l*, pg. 2948
ARJOHUNTLEIGH SOUTH AFRICA (PTY) LTD—See Getinge AB; *Int'l*, pg. 2948
ARJOHUNTLEIGH SPA—See Getinge AB; *Int'l*, pg. 2948
ARJOHUNTLEIGH S.R.O.—See Getinge AB; *Int'l*, pg. 2948
ARJOHUNTLEIGH UK AND IRELAND—See Getinge AB; *Int'l*, pg. 2948
ARJOHUNTLEIGH - UK—See Getinge AB; *Int'l*, pg. 2948
ARJO LTD MED. AB—See Getinge AB; *Int'l*, pg. 2948
ARJO LTD.—See Getinge AB; *Int'l*, pg. 2948
ARKRAY CO. LTD., INC.—See ARKRAY, Inc.; *Int'l*, pg. 571
ARKRAY EUROPE, B.V.—See ARKRAY, Inc.; *Int'l*, pg. 571
ARKRAY FACTORY, INC. - KUSATSU FACTORY—See ARKRAY, Inc.; *Int'l*, pg. 571
ARKRAY FACTORY, INC.—See ARKRAY, Inc.; *Int'l*, pg. 571
ARKRAY HEALTHCARE PVT. LTD.—See ARKRAY, Inc.; *Int'l*, pg. 571
ARKRAY MARKETING SHANGHAI, INC.—See ARKRAY, Inc.; *Int'l*, pg. 572
ARKRAY & PARTNERS PTE. LTD.—See ARKRAY, Inc.; *Int'l*, pg. 571
ARKRAY USA, INC.—See ARKRAY, Inc.; *Int'l*, pg. 572
A.R. MEDICOM INC. (ASIA) LTD.—See A.R. Medicom Inc.; *Int'l*, pg. 28
A.R. MEDICOM INC. (JAPAN) LTD.—See A.R. Medicom Inc.; *Int'l*, pg. 28
A.R. MEDICOM INC. (TAIWAN) LTD.—See A.R. Medicom Inc.; *Int'l*, pg. 28
ARRHYTHMIA NETWORK TECHNOLOGY SL; *Int'l*, pg. 578
ARROWHEAD MEDICAL, LLC—See Evome Medical Technologies Inc.; *U.S. Public*, pg. 805
ARSEUS HOSPITAL NV—See Arseus Medical NV; *Int'l*, pg. 580
ARTHREX BVBA—See Arthrex, Inc.; *U.S. Private*, pg. 341
ASAHI KASEI BIOPROCESS EUROPE SA/NV—See Asahi Kasei Corporation; *Int'l*, pg. 595
ASAHI KASEI MEDICAL EUROPE GMBH—See Asahi Kasei Corporation; *Int'l*, pg. 595
ASAHI KASEI MEDICAL EUROPE GMBH—See Asahi Kasei Corporation; *Int'l*, pg. 595
ASAHI KASEI MEDICAL (HANGZHOU) CO., LTD.—See Asahi Kasei Corporation; *Int'l*, pg. 595
ASAHI KASEI MEDICAL TRADING (KOREA) CO., LTD.—See Asahi Kasei Corporation; *Int'l*, pg. 595
ASAHI KASEI ZOLL MEDICAL CORP.—See Asahi Kasei Corporation; *Int'l*, pg. 596
ASCENSION ORTHOPEDICS, INC.—See Integra LifeSciences Holdings Corporation; *U.S. Public*, pg. 1135
ASSIST GMBH—See Advent International Corporation; *U.S. Private*, pg. 104
ASSISTIVE TECHNOLOGY GROUP, INC.—See Audax Group, Limited Partnership; *U.S. Private*, pg. 386
ASTRAZENECA AB, O.Z.—See AstraZeneca PLC; *Int'l*, pg. 659
ASTRAZENECA CZECH REPUBLIC—See AstraZeneca PLC; *Int'l*, pg. 659
ASTRAZENECA DOMINICAN REPUBLIC—See AstraZeneca PLC; *Int'l*, pg. 659
ASTRAZENECA KFT.—See AstraZeneca PLC; *Int'l*, pg. 660
ASTRAZENECA KK—See AstraZeneca PLC; *Int'l*, pg. 660
ASTRAZENECA OY—See AstraZeneca PLC; *Int'l*, pg. 660
ASTRAZENECA PHARMACEUTICALS (IRELAND) LTD.—See AstraZeneca PLC; *Int'l*, pg. 660
ASTRAZENECA PHARMA POLAND SP. Z.O.O.—See AstraZeneca PLC; *Int'l*, pg. 660
ASTRAZENECA ROMANIA—See AstraZeneca PLC; *Int'l*, pg. 661
ATCOR MEDICAL INC.—See CardieX Limited; *Int'l*, pg. 1321
ATRICURE HONG KONG LIMITED.—See AtriCure, Inc.; *U.S. Public*, pg. 225
ATRIUM AUSTRALIA-PACIFIC RIM PTY. LTD.—See Getinge AB; *Int'l*, pg. 2949
ATRIUM EUROPE BV—See Getinge AB; *Int'l*, pg. 2949
ATRIUM MEDICAL INDIA PVT LTD—See Getinge AB; *Int'l*, pg. 2949
AUDIONOVA DENMARK—See HAL Trust N.V.; *Int'l*, pg. 3223
AUDITECH BV—See Amplifon S.p.A.; *Int'l*, pg. 435
AUSMEDIC AUSTRALIA PTY LIMITED—See Madison Dearborn Partners, LLC; *U.S. Private*, pg. 2542
AUTOMED TECHNOLOGIES (CANADA), INC.—See Cencora, Inc.; *U.S. Public*, pg. 467
AVANOS MEDICAL, INC.; *U.S. Private*, pg. 241
AVEDRO, INC.—See Glaukos Corporation; *U.S. Public*, pg. 939

AVISION EUROPE GMBH—See Avision Inc.; *Int'l*, pg. 744
AXIOM WORLDWIDE INC.; *U.S. Private*, pg. 413
AXON LAB NV—See HORIBA Ltd; *Int'l*, pg. 3475
AZLAN SCANDINAVIA AB—See TD Synnex Corp; *U.S. Public*, pg. 1985
BACKLOGS LIMITED—See HCA Healthcare, Inc.; *U.S. Public*, pg. 991
BANGKOK CHAIN HOSPITAL PUBLIC COMPANY LIMITED; *Int'l*, pg. 833
BARNES HEALTHCARE SERVICES; *U.S. Private*, pg. 477
BARRIER FREE ACCESS, INC.—See SFM Mutual Insurance Company; *U.S. Private*, pg. 3621
BAUMERT—See Groupe Gorge S.A.; *Int'l*, pg. 3103
BAXTER AG—See Baxter International Inc.; *U.S. Public*, pg. 280
BAXTER BELGIUM SPRL—See Baxter International Inc.; *U.S. Public*, pg. 280
BAXTER DISTRIBUTION CENTER EUROPE SA—See Baxter International Inc.; *U.S. Public*, pg. 280
BAXTER HEALTHCARE CORPORATION OF PUERTO RICO—See Baxter International Inc.; *U.S. Public*, pg. 280
BAXTER HEALTHCARE GMBH—See Baxter International Inc.; *U.S. Public*, pg. 281
BAXTER LIMITED—See Baxter International Inc.; *U.S. Public*, pg. 281
BAXTER R AND D EUROPE S.C.R.L.—See Baxter International Inc.; *U.S. Public*, pg. 281
BAXTER S.A.S.—See Baxter International Inc.; *U.S. Public*, pg. 281
BAYLIS MEDICAL COMPANY INC.—See Boston Scientific Corporation; *U.S. Public*, pg. 374
B.BRAUN AESCULAP DE MEXICO S.A. DE C.V.—See B. Braun Melsungen AG; *Int'l*, pg. 786
B. BRAUN AESCULAP JAPAN CO., LTD.—See B. Braun Melsungen AG; *Int'l*, pg. 786
B.BRAUN AUSTRALIA PTY. LTD.—See B. Braun Melsungen AG; *Int'l*, pg. 787
B. BRAUN AUSTRIA GES. M.B.H.—See B. Braun Melsungen AG; *Int'l*, pg. 786
B. BRAUN AVITUM ANKARA DIYALIZ HIZMETLERI A.S.—See B. Braun Melsungen AG; *Int'l*, pg. 786
B. BRAUN AVITUM BULOVKA S.R.O.—See B. Braun Melsungen AG; *Int'l*, pg. 786
B. BRAUN AVITUM FRANCE S.A.S.—See B. Braun Melsungen AG; *Int'l*, pg. 786
B. BRAUN AVITUM IRELAND LTD.—See B. Braun Melsungen AG; *Int'l*, pg. 786
B.BRAUN AVITUM PHILIPPINES INC.—See B. Braun Melsungen AG; *Int'l*, pg. 787
B. BRAUN AVITUM S.A.S.—See B. Braun Melsungen AG; *Int'l*, pg. 786
B.BRAUN AVITUM (SHANGHAI) TRADING CO. LTD.—See B. Braun Melsungen AG; *Int'l*, pg. 787
B. BRAUN AVITUM ZVOLEN S.R.O.—See B. Braun Melsungen AG; *Int'l*, pg. 786
B. BRAUN DOMINICAN REPUBLIC INC.—See B. Braun Melsungen AG; *Int'l*, pg. 786
B. BRAUN HOSPICARE LTD.—See B. Braun Melsungen AG; *Int'l*, pg. 786
B.BRAUN KOREA CO. LTD.—See B. Braun Melsungen AG; *Int'l*, pg. 787
B. BRAUN LANKA (PRIVATE) LIMITED—See B. Braun Melsungen AG; *Int'l*, pg. 786
B. BRAUN MEDICAL AB—See B. Braun Melsungen AG; *Int'l*, pg. 786
B. BRAUN MEDICAL AG—See B. Braun Melsungen AG; *Int'l*, pg. 786
B. BRAUN MEDICAL A/S—See B. Braun Melsungen AG; *Int'l*, pg. 786
B. BRAUN MEDICAL B.V.—See B. Braun Melsungen AG; *Int'l*, pg. 786
B. BRAUN MEDICAL CENTRAL AMERICA & CARIBE, S.A. DE C.V.—See B. Braun Melsungen AG; *Int'l*, pg. 786
B.BRAUN MEDICAL (H.K.) LTD.—See B. Braun Melsungen AG; *Int'l*, pg. 787
B. BRAUN MEDICAL, INC.—See B. Braun Melsungen AG; *Int'l*, pg. 787
B. BRAUN MEDICAL (INDIA) PVT. LTD.—See B. Braun Melsungen AG; *Int'l*, pg. 786
B.BRAUN MEDICAL INDUSTRIES SDN. BHD.—See B. Braun Melsungen AG; *Int'l*, pg. 787
B. BRAUN MEDICAL LDA.—See B. Braun Melsungen AG; *Int'l*, pg. 786
B. BRAUN MEDICAL LLC—See B. Braun Melsungen AG; *Int'l*, pg. 786
B. BRAUN MEDICAL LTD.—See B. Braun Melsungen AG; *Int'l*, pg. 786
B. BRAUN MEDICAL OU—See B. Braun Melsungen AG; *Int'l*, pg. 786
B. BRAUN MEDICAL OY—See B. Braun Melsungen AG; *Int'l*, pg. 786
B. BRAUN MEDICAL PARAGUAY S.A—See B. Braun Melsungen AG; *Int'l*, pg. 786
B.BRAUN MEDICAL PERU S.A.—See B. Braun Melsungen AG; *Int'l*, pg. 787
B.BRAUN MEDICAL (PTY) LTD.—See B. Braun Melsungen AG; *Int'l*, pg. 787

B.BRAUN MEDICAL S.A.—See B. Braun Melsungen AG; *Int'l*, pg. 787
B.BRAUN MEDICAL S.A.—See B. Braun Melsungen AG; *Int'l*, pg. 787
B.BRAUN MEDICAL S.A.—See B. Braun Melsungen AG; *Int'l*, pg. 787
B. BRAUN MEDICAL SAS—See B. Braun Melsungen AG; *Int'l*, pg. 786
B. BRAUN MEDICAL SIA—See B. Braun Melsungen AG; *Int'l*, pg. 786
B.BRAUN MEDICAL SPA—See B. Braun Melsungen AG; *Int'l*, pg. 787
B.BRAUN MEDICAL SUPPLIES INC.—See B. Braun Melsungen AG; *Int'l*, pg. 787
B.BRAUN MEDICAL SUPPLIES SDN. BHD.—See B. Braun Melsungen AG; *Int'l*, pg. 787
B.BRAUN MEDICAL (SUZHOU) COMPANY LIMITED—See B. Braun Melsungen AG; *Int'l*, pg. 787
B. BRAUN MEDICAL UAB—See B. Braun Melsungen AG; *Int'l*, pg. 786
B. BRAUN MEDICAL UKRAINE LLC—See B. Braun Melsungen AG; *Int'l*, pg. 787
B. BRAUN MEDIKAL DIS TICARET A.S.—See B. Braun Melsungen AG; *Int'l*, pg. 787
B. BRAUN MILANO S.P.A.—See B. Braun Melsungen AG; *Int'l*, pg. 787
B. BRAUN NEW ZEALAND PTY LTD—See B. Braun Melsungen AG; *Int'l*, pg. 787
B. BRAUN OF CANADA, LTD.—See B. Braun Melsungen AG; *Int'l*, pg. 787
B.BRAUN PAKISTAN (PRIVATE) LTD.—See B. Braun Melsungen AG; *Int'l*, pg. 787
B. BRAUN PETZOLD GMBH—See B. Braun Melsungen AG; *Int'l*, pg. 787
B. BRAUN RSRB D.O.O.—See B. Braun Melsungen AG; *Int'l*, pg. 787
B. BRAUN SINGAPORE PTE. LTD.—See B. Braun Melsungen AG; *Int'l*, pg. 787
B. BRAUN STERILOG (BIRMINGHAM) LTD.—See B. Braun Melsungen AG; *Int'l*, pg. 787
B. BRAUN STERILOG (YORKSHIRE) LTD.—See B. Braun Melsungen AG; *Int'l*, pg. 787
B.BRAUN (THAILAND) LTD.—See B. Braun Melsungen AG; *Int'l*, pg. 787
B.BRAUN VIETNAM CO. LTD.—See B. Braun Melsungen AG; *Int'l*, pg. 787
BC MEDICARE SDN. BHD.—See BCM Alliance Berhad; *Int'l*, pg. 928
BD NORGE AS—See Becton, Dickinson & Company; *U.S. Public*, pg. 288
BEACON MEDICAL PRODUCTS LLC—See Atlas Copco AB; *Int'l*, pg. 681
BEACON RESPIRATORY SERVICES, INC.—See AdaptHealth Corp.; *U.S. Public*, pg. 38
B/E AEROSPACE INC.—See RTX Corporation; *U.S. Public*, pg. 1822
BECKMAN COULTER AUSTRALIA PTY. LTD.—See Danaher Corporation; *U.S. Public*, pg. 624
BECKMAN COULTER CANADA, INC.—See Danaher Corporation; *U.S. Public*, pg. 624
BECKMAN COULTER DE MEXICO, S.A. DE C.V.—See Danaher Corporation; *U.S. Public*, pg. 625
BECKMAN COULTER EUROCENTER S.A.—See Danaher Corporation; *U.S. Public*, pg. 624
BECKMAN COULTER FRANCE S.A—See Danaher Corporation; *U.S. Public*, pg. 624
BECKMAN COULTER GMBH—See Danaher Corporation; *U.S. Public*, pg. 624
BECKMAN COULTER INTERNATIONAL S.A.—See Danaher Corporation; *U.S. Public*, pg. 624
BECKMAN COULTER K. K.—See Danaher Corporation; *U.S. Public*, pg. 624
BECKMAN COULTER LIMITED LIABILITY COMPANY—See Danaher Corporation; *U.S. Public*, pg. 625
BECKMAN COULTER S.P.A.—See Danaher Corporation; *U.S. Public*, pg. 625
BECKMAN COULTER UNITED KINGDOM LTD.—See Danaher Corporation; *U.S. Public*, pg. 625
BECTON DICKINSON ADVANCED PEN INJECTION SYSTEMS GMBH—See Becton, Dickinson & Company; *U.S. Public*, pg. 289
BECTON DICKINSON AG—See Becton, Dickinson & Company; *U.S. Public*, pg. 289
BECTON DICKINSON ARGENTINA S.R.L.—See Becton, Dickinson & Company; *U.S. Public*, pg. 289
BECTON DICKINSON A/S—See Becton, Dickinson & Company; *U.S. Public*, pg. 289
BECTON DICKINSON AUSTRIA GMBH—See Becton, Dickinson & Company; *U.S. Public*, pg. 289
BECTON DICKINSON DE COLOMBIA LTDA.—See Becton, Dickinson & Company; *U.S. Public*, pg. 290
BECTON DICKINSON DISTRIBUTION CENTER N.V.—See Becton, Dickinson & Company; *U.S. Public*, pg. 289
BECTON DICKINSON HELLAS S.A.—See Becton, Dickinson & Company; *U.S. Public*, pg. 289
BECTON DICKINSON INFUSION THERAPY UK—See Becton, Dickinson & Company; *U.S. Public*, pg. 290

BECTON DICKINSON MEDICAL DEVICES CO. LTD. SUZHOU—See Becton, Dickinson & Company; *U.S. Public*, pg. 290
BECTON DICKINSON PHILIPPINES, INC.—See Becton, Dickinson & Company; *U.S. Public*, pg. 290
BECTON DICKINSON (PTY) LTD.—See Becton, Dickinson & Company; *U.S. Public*, pg. 288
BECTON DICKINSON (THAILAND) LIMITED—See Becton, Dickinson & Company; *U.S. Public*, pg. 288
BED TECHS, INC.—See iMedical Equipment & Services LLC; *U.S. Private*, pg. 2046
BENCO DENTAL SUPPLY CO. INC.; *U.S. Private*, pg. 524
BENEX LTD.—See Becton, Dickinson & Company; *U.S. Public*, pg. 290
BERGMANLABORA AB—See Addtech AB; *Int'l*, pg. 132
BERNAFON A/S—See Demant A/S; *Int'l*, pg. 2023
BERNAFON AUSTRALIA PTY. LTD.—See Demant A/S; *Int'l*, pg. 2023
BERNAFON IBERICA S.L.U.—See Demant A/S; *Int'l*, pg. 2023
BERNAFON NEW ZEALAND LTD.—See Demant A/S; *Int'l*, pg. 2023
BERNAFON S.R.L.—See Demant A/S; *Int'l*, pg. 2023
BESTINET HEALTHCARE SDN BHD—See G3 Global Berhad; *Int'l*, pg. 2866
BESTMED RESPIRATORY, INC.—See AdaptHealth Corp.; *U.S. Public*, pg. 38
BEST VASCULAR, INC.—See Best Medical International, Inc.; *U.S. Private*, pg. 543
BETER HOREN BV—See Amplifon S.p.A.; *Int'l*, pg. 435
BIBBINSTRUMENTS AB; *Int'l*, pg. 1017
BIG GREEN SURGICAL COMPANY PTY LIMITED—See Diploma PLC; *Int'l*, pg. 2128
BIMECO GROUP INC.; *U.S. Private*, pg. 560
THE BINDING SITE BENELUX B.V.—See Thermo Fisher Scientific Inc.; *U.S. Public*, pg. 2152
THE BINDING SITE FRANCE S.A.S.—See Thermo Fisher Scientific Inc.; *U.S. Public*, pg. 2152
THE BINDING SITE GMBH—See Thermo Fisher Scientific Inc.; *U.S. Public*, pg. 2152
THE BINDING SITE SPAIN (SPECIALIST PROTEIN COMPANY) S.L.—See Thermo Fisher Scientific Inc.; *U.S. Public*, pg. 2152
THE BINDING SITE S.R.L.—See Thermo Fisher Scientific Inc.; *U.S. Public*, pg. 2152
BIOCOMPATIBLES UK LIMITED—See Boston Scientific Corporation; *U.S. Public*, pg. 373
BIOHORIZONS CAMLOG ITALIA SRL—See Henry Schein, Inc.; *U.S. Public*, pg. 1025
BIOIASIS JSC; *Int'l*, pg. 1038
BIOMAR SP. Z.O.O.—See Aktieselskabet Schouw & Co.; *Int'l*, pg. 265
BIOMEDICA ARGENTINA S.A.—See Biotronik GmbH & Co.; *Int'l*, pg. 1044
BIOMEDICA BULGARIA OOD—See AddLife AB; *Int'l*, pg. 129
BIOMEDICA CS S.R.O.—See AddLife AB; *Int'l*, pg. 129
BIOMEDICA DIJAGNOSTIKA DOO—See AddLife AB; *Int'l*, pg. 129
BIOMEDICA HUNGARIA KFT.—See AddLife AB; *Int'l*, pg. 129
BIOMEDICA ITALIA S.R.L.—See AddLife AB; *Int'l*, pg. 129
BIOMEDICA MEDIZINPRODUKTE GMBH—See AddLife AB; *Int'l*, pg. 129
BIOMEDICA MEDIZINPRODUKTE ROMANIA SRL—See AddLife AB; *Int'l*, pg. 129
BIOMEDICA MP D.O.O.—See AddLife AB; *Int'l*, pg. 129
BIOMEDICA POLAND SP. Z O.O.—See AddLife AB; *Int'l*, pg. 129
BIOMEDICA SLOVAKITA S.R.O.—See AddLife AB; *Int'l*, pg. 129
BIOMET 3I BELGIUM N.V.—See Zimmer Biomet Holdings, Inc.; *U.S. Public*, pg. 2405
BIOMET 3I NORDIC AB—See Zimmer Biomet Holdings, Inc.; *U.S. Public*, pg. 2405
BIOQUELL ASIA PACIFIC PTE LTD—See Ecolab Inc.; *U.S. Public*, pg. 712
BIOQUELL GLOBAL LOGISTICS (IRELAND) LTD.—See Ecolab Inc.; *U.S. Public*, pg. 712
BIO-RAD PACIFIC LTD.—See Bio-Rad Laboratories, Inc.; *U.S. Public*, pg. 333
BIO-RAD SNC—See Bio-Rad Laboratories, Inc.; *U.S. Public*, pg. 333
BIO-SCIENCES LTD.—See Thermo Fisher Scientific Inc.; *U.S. Public*, pg. 2145
BIOSENSE TECHNOLOGIES PVT. LTD.—See Revvity, Inc.; *U.S. Public*, pg. 1795
BIOSENSORS B.V.—See Biosensors International Group, Ltd.; *Int'l*, pg. 1041
BIOSENSORS EUROPE SA—See Biosensors International Group, Ltd.; *Int'l*, pg. 1041
BIOSENSORS JAPAN CO., LTD.—See Biosensors International Group, Ltd.; *Int'l*, pg. 1042
BIOTEK INSTRUMENTS GMBH—See Agilent Technologies, Inc.; *U.S. Public*, pg. 61
BIOTEST HELLAS M.E.P.E.—See Biotest AG; *Int'l*, pg. 1043
BIOTEST PHARMA GMBH—See Biotest AG; *Int'l*, pg. 1043
BIOTRONIK AG—See Biotronik GmbH & Co.; *Int'l*, pg. 1044

423450 — MEDICAL, DENTAL, AN...

BIOTRONIK APS—See Biotronik GmbH & Co.; *Int'l*, pg. 1044
BIOTRONIK ASIA PACIFIC PTE LTD.—See Biotronik GmbH & Co.; *Int'l*, pg. 1044
BIOTRONIK AUSTRALIA PTY. LTD.—See Biotronik GmbH & Co.; *Int'l*, pg. 1044
BIOTRONIK BALTIJA SIA—See Biotronik GmbH & Co.; *Int'l*, pg. 1044
BIOTRONIK (BEIJING) MEDICAL DEVICES LTD.—See Biotronik GmbH & Co.; *Int'l*, pg. 1044
BIOTRONIK BELGIUM S.A.—See Biotronik GmbH & Co.; *Int'l*, pg. 1044
BIOTRONIK BIYOMEDIKAL TEKNOLOJILER LTD. STI.—See Biotronik GmbH & Co.; *Int'l*, pg. 1044
BIOTRONIK BULGARIA LTD—See Biotronik GmbH & Co.; *Int'l*, pg. 1044
BIOTRONIK CANADA INC.—See Biotronik GmbH & Co.; *Int'l*, pg. 1044
BIOTRONIK COMERCIAL MEDICA LTDA.—See Biotronik GmbH & Co.; *Int'l*, pg. 1044
BIOTRONIK D.O.O.—See Biotronik GmbH & Co.; *Int'l*, pg. 1044
BIOTRONIK FRANCE S.A.S.—See Biotronik GmbH & Co.; *Int'l*, pg. 1044
BIOTRONIK HELLAS SINGLE MEMBER LTD.—See Biotronik GmbH & Co.; *Int'l*, pg. 1044
BIOTRONIK HONG KONG LIMITED—See Biotronik GmbH & Co.; *Int'l*, pg. 1044
BIOTRONIK HUNGARIA KFT—See Biotronik GmbH & Co.; *Int'l*, pg. 1044
BIOTRONIK INC.—See Biotronik GmbH & Co.; *Int'l*, pg. 1044
BIOTRONIK ITALIA S.P.A.—See Biotronik GmbH & Co.; *Int'l*, pg. 1044
BIOTRONIK JAPAN, INC.—See Biotronik GmbH & Co.; *Int'l*, pg. 1044
BIOTRONIK KOREA CO., LTD.—See Biotronik GmbH & Co.; *Int'l*, pg. 1044
BIOTRONIK MEDICAL DEVICES INDIA PRIVATE LIMITED.—See Biotronik GmbH & Co.; *Int'l*, pg. 1044
BIOTRONIK MEDICAL DEVICES (MALAYSIA) SDN BHD—See Biotronik GmbH & Co.; *Int'l*, pg. 1044
BIOTRONIK NEDERLAND B.V.—See Biotronik GmbH & Co.; *Int'l*, pg. 1044
BIOTRONIK OY—See Biotronik GmbH & Co.; *Int'l*, pg. 1044
BIOTRONIK POLSKA SP. Z.O.O.—See Biotronik GmbH & Co.; *Int'l*, pg. 1044
BIOTRONIK PRAHA SPOL. S.R.O.—See Biotronik GmbH & Co.; *Int'l*, pg. 1044
BIOTRONIK SA (PTY) LTD.—See Biotronik GmbH & Co.; *Int'l*, pg. 1044
BIOTRONIK SCHWEIZ AG—See Biotronik GmbH & Co.; *Int'l*, pg. 1044
BIOTRONIK SLOVENSKO, S.R.O.—See Biotronik GmbH & Co.; *Int'l*, pg. 1044
BIOTRONIK UK LTD.—See Biotronik GmbH & Co.; *Int'l*, pg. 1044
BIOTRONIK VERTRIEBS-GMBH—See Biotronik GmbH & Co.; *Int'l*, pg. 1044
BIOVENTUS LLC; *U.S. Private*, pg. 563
BITTIUM BIOSIGNALS LTD.—See Bittium Oyj; *Int'l*, pg. 1050
B-K MEDICAL AB—See Altaris Capital Partners, LLC; *U.S. Private*, pg. 205
BK MEDICAL AUSTRALIA PTY LTD—See GE HealthCare Technologies Inc.; *U.S. Public*, pg. 908
BK MEDICAL AUSTRIA GMBH—See GE HealthCare Technologies Inc.; *U.S. Public*, pg. 908
BK MEDICAL FRANCE SAS—See GE HealthCare Technologies Inc.; *U.S. Public*, pg. 908
BK MEDICAL HOLDING COMPANY, INC.—See GE HealthCare Technologies Inc.; *U.S. Public*, pg. 908
BK MEDICAL ITALIA S.R.L.—See GE HealthCare Technologies Inc.; *U.S. Public*, pg. 908
BK MEDICAL SCHWEIZ GMBH—See GE HealthCare Technologies Inc.; *U.S. Public*, pg. 908
BK MEDICAL SWEDEN AB—See GE HealthCare Technologies Inc.; *U.S. Public*, pg. 908
BK MEDICAL TECHNOLOGY SHANGHAI CO., LTD.—See GE HealthCare Technologies Inc.; *U.S. Public*, pg. 908
BK MEDICAL UK LIMITED—See GE HealthCare Technologies Inc.; *U.S. Public*, pg. 908
BK ULTRASOUND LIMITED—See Altaris Capital Partners, LLC; *U.S. Private*, pg. 205
BLACK BEAR MEDICAL, INC.—See Quipt Home Medical Corp.; *U.S. Public*, pg. 1757
BLACKBURN'S PHYSICIANS PHARMACY, INC.; *U.S. Private*, pg. 573
BLAINE LABS, INC.—See Alternate Health Corp.; *Int'l*, pg. 391
BLUE BELL BIO-MEDICAL—See Kennedy Manufacturing Company; *U.S. Private*, pg. 2285
BLUE ORTHO SAS—See TPG Capital, L.P.; *U.S. Public*, pg. 2173
BMDI TUTA HEALTHCARE PTY LTD—See ICU Medical, Inc.; *U.S. Public*, pg. 1087
BMEYE B.V.—See Edwards Lifesciences Corporation; *U.S. Public*, pg. 720

BML MEDICAL WORKS, INC.—See BML, Inc.; *Int'l*, pg. 1076
BOC OPHTHALMIC INSTRUMENTS PTY LTD—See Hancock & Gore Ltd.; *Int'l*, pg. 3242
BOMI ITALIA S.P.A.—See United Parcel Service, Inc.; *U.S. Public*, pg. 2233
BOSLEY MEDICAL—See Aderans Co., Ltd.; *Int'l*, pg. 143
BOSTON SCIENTIFIC ASIA PACIFIC PTE. LTD.—See Boston Scientific Corporation; *U.S. Public*, pg. 374
BOSTON SCIENTIFIC COLOMBIA LIMITADA—See Boston Scientific Corporation; *U.S. Public*, pg. 374
BOSTON SCIENTIFIC CORK LIMITED—See Boston Scientific Corporation; *U.S. Public*, pg. 374
BOSTON SCIENTIFIC DE MEXICO, S.A. DE C.V.—See Boston Scientific Corporation; *U.S. Public*, pg. 375
BOSTON SCIENTIFIC GESELLSCHAFT M.B.H.—See Boston Scientific Corporation; *U.S. Public*, pg. 374
BOSTON SCIENTIFIC GROUP PLC—See Boston Scientific Corporation; *U.S. Public*, pg. 374
BOSTON SCIENTIFIC HONG KONG LIMITED—See Boston Scientific Corporation; *U.S. Public*, pg. 374
BOSTON SCIENTIFIC LATIN AMERICA B.V.—See Boston Scientific Corporation; *U.S. Public*, pg. 374
BOSTON SCIENTIFIC LEBANON SAL—See Boston Scientific Corporation; *U.S. Public*, pg. 374
BOSTON SCIENTIFIC MEDIZINTECHNIK GMBH—See Boston Scientific Corporation; *U.S. Public*, pg. 374
BOSTON SCIENTIFIC NEW ZEALAND LIMITED—See Boston Scientific Corporation; *U.S. Public*, pg. 374
BOSTON SCIENTIFIC NORDIC AB—See Boston Scientific Corporation; *U.S. Public*, pg. 375
BOSTON SCIENTIFIC PHILIPPINES, INC.—See Boston Scientific Corporation; *U.S. Public*, pg. 375
BOSTON SCIENTIFIC POLSKA SP. Z O.O.—See Boston Scientific Corporation; *U.S. Public*, pg. 375
BOSTON SCIENTIFIC PTY. LTD.—See Boston Scientific Corporation; *U.S. Public*, pg. 375
BOSTON SCIENTIFIC S.A.S.—See Boston Scientific Corporation; *U.S. Public*, pg. 375
BOSTON SCIENTIFIC SCIMED, INC.—See Boston Scientific Corporation; *U.S. Public*, pg. 375
BOSTON SCIENTIFIC SPA—See Boston Scientific Corporation; *U.S. Public*, pg. 375
BOSTON SCIENTIFIC SVERIGE AB—See Boston Scientific Corporation; *U.S. Public*, pg. 375
BOSTON SCIENTIFIC - VIENNA—See Boston Scientific Corporation; *U.S. Public*, pg. 374
BOUCART MEDICAL SRL—See Creo Medical Group PLC; *Int'l*, pg. 1839
BOWA INTERNATIONAL SP. Z O.O. SP. K.—See BOWA-electronic GmbH & Co. KG; *Int'l*, pg. 1123
B+P BEATMUNGSPRODUKTE GMBH—See COLTENE Holding AG; *Int'l*, pg. 1706
BRACCO IMAGING EUROPE BV—See Bracco S.p.A.; *Int'l*, pg. 1134
BRACCO IMAGING FRANCE SA—See Bracco S.p.A.; *Int'l*, pg. 1134
BRACCO IMAGING ITALIA S.R.L.—See Bracco S.p.A.; *Int'l*, pg. 1134
BRACCO IMAGING KOREA, LTD—See Bracco S.p.A.; *Int'l*, pg. 1134
BRACCO IMAGING POLSKA SP.Z.O.O.—See Bracco S.p.A.; *Int'l*, pg. 1134
BRACCO IMAGING SCANDINAVIA AB—See Bracco S.p.A.; *Int'l*, pg. 1134
BRAINCOOL AB; *Int'l*, pg. 1137
BRASSELER USA, INC.—See Carousel Capital Partners; *U.S. Private*, pg. 769
BRAUN AIDUN (SHANGHAI) TRADING CO., LTD.—See B. Braun Melsungen AG; *Int'l*, pg. 787
BRAUN MEDICAL (SHANDONG) CO., LTD.—See B. Braun Melsungen AG; *Int'l*, pg. 787
BRAUN MEDICAL (SHANGHAI) INTERNATIONAL TRADE CO., LTD.—See B. Braun Melsungen AG; *Int'l*, pg. 787
BREATHE GRACE MEDICAL SUPPLY, LLC—See AdaptHealth Corp.; *U.S. Public*, pg. 38
BREEZY POLAND SP. Z.O.O.—See ASBISc Enterprises Plc; *Int'l*, pg. 600
BRIGGS CORP.; *U.S. Private*, pg. 651
BRIGGS HEALTHCARE—See Briggs Corp.; *U.S. Private*, pg. 651
BRIGHTON SURGICENTER, LLC—See HCA Healthcare, Inc.; *U.S. Public*, pg. 991
BRUNO INDEPENDENT LIVING AIDS, INC.; *U.S. Private*, pg. 672
BUFFALO HOSPITAL SUPPLY CO., INC.; *U.S. Private*, pg. 680
BUNZL RETAIL, LLC—See Bunzl plc; *Int'l*, pg. 1217
BURKHART DENTAL SUPPLY CO. INC.; *U.S. Private*, pg. 688
BUSINESS ALIGNMENT PUBLIC COMPANY LIMITED; *Int'l*, pg. 1228
BUTLER ANIMAL HEALTH HOLDING COMPANY, LLC—See Clayton, Dubilier & Rice, LLC; *U.S. Private*, pg. 921
BUTLER ANIMAL HEALTH HOLDING COMPANY, LLC—See TPG Capital, L.P.; *U.S. Public*, pg. 2170
BUTLER ANIMAL HEALTH SUPPLY—See Clayton, Dubilier

& Rice, LLC; *U.S. Private*, pg. 921
BUTLER ANIMAL HEALTH SUPPLY—See TPG Capital, L.P.; *U.S. Public*, pg. 2170
BW SPORTS PRACTICE, LLC—See Tenet Healthcare Corporation; *U.S. Public*, pg. 2001
BYRAM HEALTHCARE CENTERS, INC.—See Owens & Minor, Inc.; *U.S. Public*, pg. 1625
BYRAM HEALTHCARE CENTERS, INC.—See Owens & Minor, Inc.; *U.S. Public*, pg. 1625
BYRAM HEALTHCARE, INC.—See Advent International Corporation; *U.S. Private*, pg. 104
CAMBRIDGE NUTRITIONAL SCIENCES LIMITED—See Cambridge Nutritional Sciences Plc; *Int'l*, pg. 1269
CAMLAB, LTD.—See StoneCalibre, LLC; *U.S. Private*, pg. 3827
CANDELA FRANCE SARL—See Apax Partners LLP; *Int'l*, pg. 506
CANDELA ITALIA S.R.L.—See Apax Partners LLP; *Int'l*, pg. 506
CANDELA LASER (DEUTSCHLAND) GMBH—See Apax Partners LLP; *Int'l*, pg. 506
CAPITAL SAFETY GROUP EMEA—See 3M Company; *U.S. Public*, pg. 8
CARDINAL HEALTH, INC. - CHICAGO—See Cardinal Health, Inc.; *U.S. Public*, pg. 434
CAREFUSION HONG KONG LIMITED—See Becton, Dickinson & Company; *U.S. Public*, pg. 291
CAREFUSION NEW ZEALAND 313 LIMITED—See Becton, Dickinson & Company; *U.S. Public*, pg. 291
CAREFUSION NORWAY 315 A/S—See Becton, Dickinson & Company; *U.S. Public*, pg. 291
CAREFUSION S.A. 319 (PROPRIETARY) LIMITED—See Becton, Dickinson & Company; *U.S. Public*, pg. 291
CARE & HEALTH LIMITED—See Hanison Construction Holdings Limited; *Int'l*, pg. 3252
CARE LINE INDUSTRIES INC.; *U.S. Private*, pg. 751
CARIBBEAN MEDICAL BROKERS, INC.; *U.S. Private*, pg. 760
CARL ZEISS, INC.—See Carl-Zeiss-Stiftung; *Int'l*, pg. 1334
CARL ZEISS (N.Z.) LTD.—See Carl-Zeiss-Stiftung; *Int'l*, pg. 1333
CARL ZEISS SDN. BHD.—See Carl-Zeiss-Stiftung; *Int'l*, pg. 1335
CAROLINA'S HOME MEDICAL EQUIPMENT, INC.; *U.S. Private*, pg. 769
CASCADE ORTHOPEDIC SUPPLY INC.; *U.S. Private*, pg. 781
CASMONT SAS—See HORIBA Ltd; *Int'l*, pg. 3475
CASSLING DIAGNOSTIC IMAGING INC.; *U.S. Private*, pg. 784
CCS MEDICAL, INC.—See CCS Medical Holdings, Inc.; *U.S. Private*, pg. 801
CDMV INC.; *Int'l*, pg. 1371
CEFLA DEUTSCHLAND GMBH—See Cefla S.C.; *Int'l*, pg. 1389
CELLAVISION CANADA INC.—See CellaVision AB; *Int'l*, pg. 1392
CELLAVISION INC.—See CellaVision AB; *Int'l*, pg. 1392
CELLAVISION JAPAN K.K.—See CellaVision AB; *Int'l*, pg. 1392
CELLCURA, INC.—See Dag Dvergsten AS; *Int'l*, pg. 1912
C.E.M. BIOTRONIK S.A.—See Biotronik GmbH & Co.; *Int'l*, pg. 1044
CEN-MED ENTERPRISES, INC.; *U.S. Private*, pg. 808
CENTAUR SERVICES LTD.—See Cencora, Inc.; *U.S. Public*, pg. 467
CENTERPULSE AUSTRALIA PTY LTD; *Int'l*, pg. 1403
CENTRAL OXYGEN INC.—See Quipt Home Medical Corp.; *U.S. Public*, pg. 1757
CENTRIC HEALTH RESOURCES, INC.—See Dohmen Co.; *U.S. Private*, pg. 1254
CENTRO AUDITIVO TELEX S.A.—See Demant A/S; *Int'l*, pg. 2023
CENTRO AUDITIVO WIDEX BRASITOM LTDA.—See EQT AB; *Int'l*, pg. 2480
CFM INFRATRADE PTE. LTD.—See CFM Holdings Limited; *Int'l*, pg. 1430
CHARTER MEDICAL, LTD.—See Compagnie Generale des Etablissements Michelin SCA; *Int'l*, pg. 1744
CHC (GUANGZHOU) MEDICAL TECHNOLOGY CO., LTD.—See CHC Healthcare Group; *Int'l*, pg. 1458
CHC HEALTHCARE GROUP; *Int'l*, pg. 1458
CHI ENTERPRISES, INC.; *U.S. Private*, pg. 876
CHINAGATE COMPANY LIMITED—See UnitedHealth Group Incorporated; *U.S. Public*, pg. 2239
CHINA MEHECO BEIJING BAITAI PHARMA CO., LTD.—See China Meheco Group Co., Ltd.; *Int'l*, pg. 1518
CHINA MEHECO BEIJING PHARMA CO., LTD.—See China Meheco Group Co., Ltd.; *Int'l*, pg. 1518
CHINA MEHECO GUANGDONG PHARMA CO., LTD.—See China Meheco Group Co., Ltd.; *Int'l*, pg. 1518
CHINA MEHECO HEILONGJIANG PHARMA CO., LTD.—See China Meheco Group Co., Ltd.; *Int'l*, pg. 1518
CHINA MEHECO HENAN PHARMA CO., LTD.—See China Meheco Group Co., Ltd.; *Int'l*, pg. 1518
CHINA MEHECO HUBEI PHARMA CO., LTD.—See China Meheco Group Co., Ltd.; *Int'l*, pg. 1518
CHINA MEHECO JIANGXI NANHUA PHARMA CO.,

N.A.I.C.S. INDEX

423450 — MEDICAL, DENTAL, AN...

LTD.—See China Meheco Group Co., Ltd.; *Int'l*, pg. 1518
CHINA MEHECO JIANGXI PHARMA CO., LTD.—See China Meheco Group Co., Ltd.; *Int'l*, pg. 1519
CHIRAL TECHNOLOGIES INC.—See Daicel Corporation; *Int'l*, pg. 1918
CIDEAS S.R.L.—See Dentium Co., Ltd; *Int'l*, pg. 2033
CITICON (HONG KONG) LIMITED—See Danaher Corporation; *U.S. Public*, pg. 625
CLARKE HEALTH CARE PRODUCTS; *U.S. Private*, pg. 914
CLAYMOUNT ASSEMBLIES PHILIPPINES, INC.—See Varex Imaging Corporation; *U.S. Public*, pg. 2275
CLEARVIEW MEDICAL INCORPORATED—See AdaptHealth Corp.; *U.S. Public*, pg. 38
CLINICHAIN BV—See ADDvise Group AB; *Int'l*, pg. 136
CLINICLANDS AB—See Henry Schein, Inc.; *U.S. Public*, pg. 1025
C-MER EYE CARE HOLDINGS LTD.; *Int'l*, pg. 1239
CMX MEDICAL IMAGING—See National Healthcare Distribution, Inc.; *U.S. Private*, pg. 2856
CNMC COMPANY, INC.—See Best Medical International, Inc.; *U.S. Private*, pg. 543
COASTAL LIFE TECHNOLOGIES, INC.—See Viant Medical, LLC; *U.S. Private*, pg. 4375
COEUR MEDICAL PRODUCTS SERVICES, S. DE R.L. DE C.V.—See Illinois Tool Works Inc.; *U.S. Public*, pg. 1102
COLLECT RX INC.—See New Capital Partners; *U.S. Private*, pg. 2892
COLOPLAST DISTRIBUTION CENTER—See Coloplast A/S; *Int'l*, pg. 1703
COLOPLAST ISRAEL—See Coloplast A/S; *Int'l*, pg. 1703
COLOR TRADING SP. Z O. O.—See ARKRAY, Inc.; *Int'l*, pg. 572
COLTENE/WHALEDENT PRIVATE LIMITED—See COLTENE Holding AG; *Int'l*, pg. 1706
COMBICARE B.V.—See Advent International Corporation; *U.S. Private*, pg. 104
COMBICARE VASTGOED B.V.—See Advent International Corporation; *U.S. Private*, pg. 104
COMET TECHNOLOGIES USA, INC. - X-RAY SYSTEMS—See Comet Holding AG; *Int'l*, pg. 1710
COMFORT MEDICAL, LLC—See Coloplast A/S; *Int'l*, pg. 1704
COMFORT MEDICAL SUPPLY LLC; *U.S. Private*, pg. 981
COMPLETE MEDICAL HOMECARE, INC.—See Advanz Pharma Corp.; *Int'l*, pg. 166
COMP-RAY, INC.—See Christie InnoMed, Inc.; *Int'l*, pg. 1587
CONCORDIA HEALTHCARE (USA) INC.—See Advanz Pharma Corp.; *Int'l*, pg. 166
CONDOR TECHNOLOGIES NV; *Int'l*, pg. 1766
CONMED CORPORATION - DENMARK—See CONMED Corporation; *U.S. Public*, pg. 567
CONMED IBERIA SL—See CONMED Corporation; *U.S. Public*, pg. 567
CONSOLIDATED NEURO SUPPLY, INC.; *U.S. Private*, pg. 1021
CONVEY HEALTH SOLUTIONS, INC.—See TPG Capital, L.P.; *U.S. Private*, pg. 2170
COOK ASIA LTD.—See Cook Group Incorporated; *U.S. Private*, pg. 1037
COOK JAPAN INCORPORATED—See Cook Group Incorporated; *U.S. Private*, pg. 1037
COOK MEDICAL EUROPE LTD.—See Cook Group Incorporated; *U.S. Private*, pg. 1037
COOK MEDICAL INCORPORATED—See Cook Group Incorporated; *U.S. Private*, pg. 1037
COOK MEDICAL (THAILAND) CO., LTD.—See Cook Group Incorporated; *U.S. Private*, pg. 1037
COOK TAIWAN LTD.—See Cook Group Incorporated; *U.S. Private*, pg. 1037
COOLEY MEDICAL EQUIPMENT, INC.—See Quipt Home Medical Corp.; *U.S. Public*, pg. 1757
CPAC, INC.—See Buckingham Capital, LLC; *U.S. Private*, pg. 678
CP GABA GMBH—See Colgate-Palmolive Company; *U.S. Public*, pg. 531
C. R. BARD NETHERLANDS SALES BV—See Becton, Dickinson & Company; *U.S. Public*, pg. 290
CREATE MEDIC DALIAN INTERNATIONAL TRADING CO., LTD.—See CREATE MEDIC CO. LTD.; *Int'l*, pg. 1832
CROSSMED S.P.A.—See Penumbra, Inc.; *U.S. Public*, pg. 1667
CROSS TECHNOLOGIES PLC—See Checkit plc; *Int'l*, pg. 1459
CROSSWELL INTERNATIONAL CORP; *U.S. Private*, pg. 1108
CURE MEDICAL & TECHNICAL SUPPLY LTD—See Eldan Electronic Co. Ltd.; *Int'l*, pg. 2346
CUTERA FRANCE SARL—See Cutera, Inc.; *U.S. Public*, pg. 613
CUTERA JAPAN KK—See Cutera, Inc.; *U.S. Public*, pg. 613
CUTERA SPAIN SL—See Cutera, Inc.; *U.S. Public*, pg. 613
CUTERA SWITZERLAND GMBH—See Cutera, Inc.; *U.S. Public*, pg. 613
CWS-BOCO IRELAND LIMITED—See Franz Haniel & Cie. GmbH; *Int'l*, pg. 2762
CYBIO NORTHERN EUROPE LTD.—See Endress+Hauser (International) Holding AG; *Int'l*, pg. 2405

CYNOSURE PORTUGAL, UNIPESSOAL, LIMITADA—See Hologic, Inc.; *U.S. Public*, pg. 1044
CYPRESS MEDICAL PRODUCTS LTD.; *U.S. Private*, pg. 1135
CYPRESS MEDIC SDN. BHD.—See BCM Alliance Berhad; *Int'l*, pg. 928
CYTOSORBENTS EUROPE GMBH—See CYTOSORBENTS CORPORATION; *U.S. Public*, pg. 618
DACH AUSTRIA MEDICAL GROUP GMBH—See AddLife AB; *Int'l*, pg. 129
D-A-CH GERMANY MEDICAL GROUP GMBH—See AddLife AB; *Int'l*, pg. 129
DACH SWITZERLAND MEDICAL GROUP GMBH—See AddLife AB; *Int'l*, pg. 129
DAKO DIAGNOSTICOS S.A.—See Agilent Technologies, Inc.; *U.S. Public*, pg. 61
DALIAN AOXIN QUANMIN STOMATOLOGY HOSPITAL CO., LTD.—See Aoxin Q & M Dental Group Limited; *Int'l*, pg. 498
DALIAN CREATE MEDICAL PRODUCTS CO., LTD.—See CREATE MEDIC CO. LTD.; *Int'l*, pg. 1832
DANISCO BRASIL LTDA.—See DuPont de Nemours, Inc.; *U.S. Public*, pg. 692
DANSAC & HOLLISTER DANMARK—See Hollister Incorporated; *U.S. Private*, pg. 1965
DANYEL BIOTECH LTD.—See Gamida for Life B.V.; *Int'l*, pg. 2878
DARBY DENTAL SUPPLY, LLC—See Darby Group Companies, Inc.; *U.S. Private*, pg. 1158
DARBY GROUP COMPANIES, INC.; *U.S. Private*, pg. 1158
DC DENTAL SUPPLIES, LLC; *U.S. Private*, pg. 1179
DD BIOLAB S.L.—See Dominique Dutscher SAS; *Int'l*, pg. 2161
DEALMED MEDICAL SUPPLIES LLC; *U.S. Private*, pg. 1182
DECISION DIAGNOSTICS CORP.; *U.S. Private*, pg. 1187
DEKA JAPAN CO. LTD.—See El.En. S.p.A.; *Int'l*, pg. 2342
DEKA LASER TECHNOLOGIES LLC—See El.En. S.p.A.; *Int'l*, pg. 2342
DELTA MEDICAL SYSTEMS INC.; *U.S. Private*, pg. 1201
DENTAL COMPLEX—See Danaher Corporation; *U.S. Public*, pg. 626
DENTAL DIAMOND CO.—See GC Corporation; *Int'l*, pg. 2894
DENTAL EQUIPMENT LIQUIDATORS, INC.; *U.S. Private*, pg. 1206
DENTAL HEALTH PRODUCTS INC.; *U.S. Private*, pg. 1206
DENTALHOLDING SP. Z.O.O.—See Dentium Co., Ltd; *Int'l*, pg. 2033
DENTAL SORRIA LTDA.—See Bunzl plc; *Int'l*, pg. 1218
DENTATUS USA, LTD.—See Dentatus AB; *Int'l*, pg. 2033
DENTISAN LTD.—See Getinge AB; *Int'l*, pg. 2949
DENTIUM BALTIC, SIA—See Dentium Co., Ltd; *Int'l*, pg. 2033
DENTIUM CHINA CO., LTD.—See Dentium Co., Ltd; *Int'l*, pg. 2033
DENTIUM-COM S.R.L—See Dentium Co., Ltd; *Int'l*, pg. 2033
DENTIUM IBERIA SL—See Dentium Co., Ltd; *Int'l*, pg. 2033
DENTIUM KFT.—See Dentium Co., Ltd; *Int'l*, pg. 2033
DENTIUM SHANGHAI CO., LTD.—See Dentium Co., Ltd; *Int'l*, pg. 2033
DENTIUM SINGAPORE PTE LTD.—See Dentium Co., Ltd; *Int'l*, pg. 2033
DENTSPLY DETREY GMBH—See DENTSPLY SIRONA Inc.; *U.S. Public*, pg. 654
DENTSPLY GAC EUROPE SAS—See DENTSPLY SIRONA Inc.; *U.S. Public*, pg. 654
DENTSPLY IH A/S—See DENTSPLY SIRONA Inc.; *U.S. Public*, pg. 654
DENTSPLY IH GMBH—See DENTSPLY SIRONA Inc.; *U.S. Public*, pg. 654
DENTSPLY IH LTD.—See DENTSPLY SIRONA Inc.; *U.S. Public*, pg. 654
DENTSPLY IH OY—See DENTSPLY SIRONA Inc.; *U.S. Public*, pg. 654
DENTSPLY SIRONA CANADA—See DENTSPLY SIRONA Inc.; *U.S. Public*, pg. 655
DENTSPLY SIRONA EUROPE GMBH—See DENTSPLY SIRONA Inc.; *U.S. Public*, pg. 655
DENTSPLY SIRONA FRANCE S.A.S.—See DENTSPLY SIRONA Inc.; *U.S. Public*, pg. 655
DENTSPLY SIRONA (PHILS.), INC.—See DENTSPLY SIRONA Inc.; *U.S. Public*, pg. 654
DENTSPLY SIRONA PTY. LTD.—See DENTSPLY SIRONA Inc.; *U.S. Public*, pg. 655
DENTSPLY SIRONA PTY. LTD.—See DENTSPLY SIRONA Inc.; *U.S. Public*, pg. 655
DENTSPLY SIRONA SWITZERLAND SARL—See DENTSPLY SIRONA Inc.; *U.S. Public*, pg. 655
DEPUY FRANCE S.A.—See Johnson & Johnson; *U.S. Public*, pg. 1195
DEPUY SYNTHES A/S—See Johnson & Johnson; *U.S. Public*, pg. 1195
DEVILBISS HEALTHCARE GMBH—See Medical Depot, Inc.; *U.S. Private*, pg. 2654
DEVILBISS HEALTHCARE LLC—See Medical Depot, Inc.; *U.S. Private*, pg. 2654

DEVILBISS HEALTHCARE LTD.—See Medical Depot, Inc.; *U.S. Private*, pg. 2654
DEVILBISS HEALTHCARE PTY LTD—See Medical Depot, Inc.; *U.S. Private*, pg. 2655
DEVILBISS HEALTHCARE S.A.S.—See Medical Depot, Inc.; *U.S. Private*, pg. 2655
DEVYSER AB—See Devyser Diagnostics AB; *Int'l*, pg. 2091
DEVYSER FRANCE S.A.S.—See Devyser Diagnostics AB; *Int'l*, pg. 2091
DEVYSER IBERIA S.L.—See Devyser Diagnostics AB; *Int'l*, pg. 2091
DEVYSER S.R.L.—See Devyser Diagnostics AB; *Int'l*, pg. 2091
DEXCOM DEUTSCHLAND GMBH—See DexCom Inc; *U.S. Public*, pg. 657
DEXCOM INTERNATIONAL LTD.—See DexCom Inc; *U.S. Public*, pg. 657
DEXCOM SUISSE GMBH—See DexCom Inc; *U.S. Public*, pg. 657
DEXCOM (UK) LIMITED—See DexCom Inc; *U.S. Public*, pg. 657
DHR HOLDING INDIA PVT. LTD.—See Danaher Corporation; *U.S. Public*, pg. 625
DIABETES MANAGEMENT & SUPPLIES LLC—See AdaptHealth Corp.; *U.S. Public*, pg. 38
DIABETES MEDICAL SUPPLY CENTER OF THE MIDLANDS—See AdaptHealth Corp.; *U.S. Public*, pg. 38
DIABETES SPECIALTY CENTER, LLC—See Advent International Corporation; *U.S. Private*, pg. 104
DIAGNOS POLAND SP. Z O O.—See Diagnos Inc.; *Int'l*, pg. 2103
DIAGNOSTIC SERVICES, INC.—See Laboratory Corporation of America Holdings; *U.S. Public*, pg. 1286
DIAMED DEUTSCHLAND GMBH—See Bio-Rad Laboratories, Inc.; *U.S. Public*, pg. 334
DIATEC AG—See Demant A/S; *Int'l*, pg. 2023
DIATEC DIAGNOSTICS GMBH—See Demant A/S; *Int'l*, pg. 2023
DIATEC SPAIN, S.L.U.—See Demant A/S; *Int'l*, pg. 2023
DIAVERUM HUNGARY—See Baxter International Inc.; *U.S. Public*, pg. 281
DIRECT DENTAL SUPPLY CO.—See Patterson Companies, Inc.; *U.S. Public*, pg. 1653
DIRECT LINK USA LLC—See Fuling Global Inc.; *Int'l*, pg. 2842
DISPOMED DIABETES SERVICE NEDERLAND—See Advent International Corporation; *U.S. Private*, pg. 104
DIXIE MEDICAL INC.; *U.S. Private*, pg. 1245
DIXON-SHANE LLC—See Amneal Pharmaceuticals, Inc.; *U.S. Public*, pg. 125
DJO, LLC—See Enovis Corporation; *U.S. Public*, pg. 772
D&J SALES CO. LLC; *U.S. Private*, pg. 1137
DNA TESTING CENTERS, CORP.; *Int'l*, pg. 2147
DNA TESTING CENTRES OF CANADA, LTD.—See DNA Testing Centers, Corp.; *Int'l*, pg. 2147
DOMINIQUE DUTSCHER SAS; *Int'l*, pg. 2161
DORNIER MEDTECH AMERICA—See Airbus SE; *Int'l*, pg. 242
DORNOCH MEDICAL SYSTEMS, INC.—See Zimmer Biomet Holdings, Inc.; *U.S. Public*, pg. 2406
DRAEGER COLOMBIA SA—See Draegerwerk AG & Co. KGaA; *Int'l*, pg. 2196
DRAEGER HONG KONG LIMITED—See Draegerwerk AG & Co. KGaA; *Int'l*, pg. 2196
DRAEGER INDIA PRIVATE LIMITED—See Draegerwerk AG & Co. KGaA; *Int'l*, pg. 2196
DRAEGER PANAMA COMERCIAL, S. DE R.L.—See Draegerwerk AG & Co. KGaA; *Int'l*, pg. 2196
DRAEGER PANAMA S. DE R.L.—See Draegerwerk AG & Co. KGaA; *Int'l*, pg. 2197
DRAEGER PERU S.A.C.—See Draegerwerk AG & Co. KGaA; *Int'l*, pg. 2197
DRAEGER SAFETY BULGARIA EOOD—See Draegerwerk AG & Co. KGaA; *Int'l*, pg. 2197
DRAEGER SAFETY EQUIPMENT (CHINA) CO., LTD.—See Draegerwerk AG & Co. KGaA; *Int'l*, pg. 2197
DRAEGER SAFETY INDIA PVT. LTD.—See Draegerwerk AG & Co. KGaA; *Int'l*, pg. 2197
DRAGER CHILE LTDA.—See Draegerwerk AG & Co. KGaA; *Int'l*, pg. 2197
DRAGER IRELAND LTD.—See Draegerwerk AG & Co. KGaA; *Int'l*, pg. 2197
DRAGER MEDICAL EQUIPMENT (SHANGHAI) CO., LTD.—See Draegerwerk AG & Co. KGaA; *Int'l*, pg. 2197
DRAGER ROMANIA SRL—See Draegerwerk AG & Co. KGaA; *Int'l*, pg. 2197
DRAGER SAFETY BELGIUM N.V.—See Draegerwerk AG & Co. KGaA; *Int'l*, pg. 2197
DRAGER SUOMI OY—See Draegerwerk AG & Co. KGaA; *Int'l*, pg. 2198
DRE INC. See Jordan Industries, Inc.; *U.S. Private*, pg. 2235
DRTECH EUROPE GMBH—See DRTECH Corporation; *Int'l*, pg. 2206
DRTECH NORTH AMERICA INC.—See DRTECH Corporation; *Int'l*, pg. 2206
DRTECH SHANGHAI CO, LTD.—See DRTECH Corporation; *Int'l*, pg. 2206

423450 — MEDICAL, DENTAL, AN...

DUKAL CORPORATION; *U.S. Private*, pg. 1285
DUPONT DEUTSCHLAND HOLDING GMBH & CO. KG—See DuPont de Nemours, Inc.; *U.S. Public*, pg. 692
DUPONT NUTRITION & BIOSCIENCES IBERICA S.L.U.—See DuPont de Nemours, Inc.; *U.S. Public*, pg. 692
DUPONT UENTROP GMBH—See DuPont de Nemours, Inc.; *U.S. Public*, pg. 693
DURA MEDICAL, INC.—See HCA Healthcare, Inc.; *U.S. Public*, pg. 995
DURAMED INC.—See Can B Corp.; *U.S. Public*, pg. 428
DURR DENTAL AG—See Air Techniques, Inc.; *U.S. Private*, pg. 140
DUTSCHER SCIENTIFIC LTD—See Dominique Dutscher SAS; *Int'l*, pg. 2161
DYNAMIC MEDICAL SYSTEMS, INC.—See Invacare Corporation; *U.S. Private*, pg. 2130
DYNAREX CORP; *U.S. Private*, pg. 1299
EBI MEDICAL SYSTEMS, LLC—See Zimmer Biomet Holdings, Inc.; *U.S. Public*, pg. 2406
EBOS GROUP LIMITED; *Int'l*, pg. 2285
ECOLOGICALLY SOUND MEDICAL SERVICES—See Federated Healthcare Supply Holdings, Inc.; *U.S. Private*, pg. 1491
EDAN INSTRUMENTS GMBH—See Edan Instruments, Inc.; *Int'l*, pg. 2303
EDAN MEDICAL INDIA PRIVATE LTD.—See Edan Instruments, Inc.; *Int'l*, pg. 2304
EDAN MEDICAL (UK) LTD.—See Edan Instruments, Inc.; *Int'l*, pg. 2304
EDAP TECHNOMED INC.—See EDAP TMS S.A.; *Int'l*, pg. 2304
EDGE SYSTEMS, LLC—See The Beauty Health Company; *U.S. Public*, pg. 2038
EDWARDS LIFESCIENCES (ASIA) PTE., LTD.—See Edwards Lifesciences Corporation; *U.S. Public*, pg. 720
EDWARDS LIFESCIENCES A/S—See Edwards Lifesciences Corporation; *U.S. Public*, pg. 720
EDWARDS LIFESCIENCES AUSTRIA GMBH—See Edwards Lifesciences Corporation; *U.S. Public*, pg. 720
EDWARDS LIFESCIENCES (CANADA) INC.—See Edwards Lifesciences Corporation; *U.S. Public*, pg. 720
EDWARDS LIFESCIENCES COMERCIO E INDUSTRIA DE PRODUTOS MEDICO-CIRURGICOS LTDA.—See Edwards Lifesciences Corporation; *U.S. Public*, pg. 720
EDWARDS LIFESCIENCES CZECH REPUBLIC S.R.O.—See Edwards Lifesciences Corporation; *U.S. Public*, pg. 720
EDWARDS LIFESCIENCES HELLAS, EPE—See Edwards Lifesciences Corporation; *U.S. Public*, pg. 720
EDWARDS LIFESCIENCES (INDIA) PRIVATE LIMITED—See Edwards Lifesciences Corporation; *U.S. Public*, pg. 720
EDWARDS LIFESCIENCES IRELAND, LIMITED—See Edwards Lifesciences Corporation; *U.S. Public*, pg. 720
EDWARDS LIFESCIENCES (ISRAEL) LTD—See Edwards Lifesciences Corporation; *U.S. Public*, pg. 720
EDWARDS LIFESCIENCES ITALIA SPA—See Edwards Lifesciences Corporation; *U.S. Public*, pg. 720
EDWARDS LIFESCIENCES (JAPAN) LIMITED—See Edwards Lifesciences Corporation; *U.S. Public*, pg. 720
EDWARDS LIFESCIENCES KOREA CO., LTD.—See Edwards Lifesciences Corporation; *U.S. Public*, pg. 720
EDWARDS LIFESCIENCES LIMITED—See Edwards Lifesciences Corporation; *U.S. Public*, pg. 720
EDWARDS LIFESCIENCES MEXICO, S.A. DE C.V.—See Edwards Lifesciences Corporation; *U.S. Public*, pg. 721
EDWARDS LIFESCIENCES NORDIC AB—See Edwards Lifesciences Corporation; *U.S. Public*, pg. 721
EDWARDS LIFESCIENCES (POLAND) LTD.—See Edwards Lifesciences Corporation; *U.S. Public*, pg. 720
EDWARDS LIFESCIENCES (PORTUGAL) COMERCIO E DISTRIBUICAO DE DISPOSITIVOS MEDICOS, LDA.—See Edwards Lifesciences Corporation; *U.S. Public*, pg. 720
EDWARDS LIFESCIENCES (PROPRIETARY) LTD—See Edwards Lifesciences Corporation; *U.S. Public*, pg. 720
EDWARDS LIFESCIENCES PTY. LIMITED—See Edwards Lifesciences Corporation; *U.S. Public*, pg. 721
EDWARDS LIFESCIENCES SALES CORPORATION—See Edwards Lifesciences Corporation; *U.S. Public*, pg. 721
EDWARDS LIFESCIENCES SALES (ISRAEL) LTD.—See Edwards Lifesciences Corporation; *U.S. Public*, pg. 721
EDWARDS LIFESCIENCES SAS—See Edwards Lifesciences Corporation; *U.S. Public*, pg. 721
EDWARDS LIFESCIENCES SERVICES GMBH—See Edwards Lifesciences Corporation; *U.S. Public*, pg. 721
EDWARDS LIFESCIENCES (SHANGHAI) MEDICAL PRODUCTS CO., LTD.—See Edwards Lifesciences Corporation; *U.S. Public*, pg. 720
EDWARDS LIFESCIENCES S.L.—See Edwards Lifesciences Corporation; *U.S. Public*, pg. 721
EDWARDS LIFESCIENCES S.P.R.L.—See Edwards Lifesciences Corporation; *U.S. Public*, pg. 721
EDWARDS LIFESCIENCES (TAIWAN) CORPORATION—See Edwards Lifesciences Corporation; *U.S. Public*, pg. 720
EDWARDS LIFESCIENCES (THAILAND) LTD.—See Edwards Lifesciences Corporation; *U.S. Public*, pg. 720
EDWARDS LIFESCIENCES WORLD TRADE (SHANGHAI) CO., LTD.—See Edwards Lifesciences Corporation; *U.S. Public*, pg. 721
EDWARDS (SHANGHAI) MEDICAL PRODUCTS CO., LTD.—See Edwards Lifesciences Corporation; *U.S. Public*, pg. 720
ELECTRA-BOX DIAGNOSTICA AB—See Addtech AB; *Int'l*, pg. 133
ELECTRA-BOX DIAGNOSTICA OY—See Addtech AB; *Int'l*, pg. 133
ELECTRO-BIOLOGY, LLC—See Zimmer Biomet Holdings, Inc.; *U.S. Public*, pg. 2406
ELEKTA ASIA LTD—See Elekta AB; *Int'l*, pg. 2355
ELEKTA KK—See Elekta AB; *Int'l*, pg. 2355
ELEKTA MEDICAL SYSTEMS COMERCIO E PRESTACAO DE SERVICOS PARA RADIOLOGIA, RADIOCIRURGIA E RADIOTERAPIA LTDA.—See Elekta AB; *Int'l*, pg. 2355
ELEKTA S.A./N.V.—See Elekta AB; *Int'l*, pg. 2356
ELEKTA S.P.A.—See Elekta AB; *Int'l*, pg. 2356
ELI LILLY JAPAN K.K.—See Eli Lilly & Company; *U.S. Public*, pg. 732
ELITE CARE INCORPORATED—See Patient Square Capital, L.P.; *U.S. Private*, pg. 3107
ELITECH FRANCE SAS—See Bruker Corporation; *U.S. Public*, pg. 406
ELITECHGROUP AUSTRALIA PTY. LTD.—See Bruker Corporation; *U.S. Public*, pg. 406
ELITECHGROUP B.V.—See Bruker Corporation; *U.S. Public*, pg. 406
ELITECHGROUP (NZ) LIMITED—See Bruker Corporation; *U.S. Public*, pg. 406
ELITECHGROUP S.P.A.—See Bruker Corporation; *U.S. Public*, pg. 406
ELITECH LTDA.—See Bruker Corporation; *U.S. Public*, pg. 406
ELITECH MICROBIO SAS—See Bruker Corporation; *U.S. Public*, pg. 406
ELITECH SA/NV—See Bruker Corporation; *U.S. Public*, pg. 406
ELITECH SR D.O.O.—See Bruker Corporation; *U.S. Public*, pg. 406
ELITECH UK LIMITED—See Bruker Corporation; *U.S. Public*, pg. 406
ELLEX DEUTSCHLAND GMBH—See Ellex Medical Lasers Limited; *Int'l*, pg. 2365
ELLEX (JAPAN) CORPORATION—See Ellex Medical Lasers Limited; *Int'l*, pg. 2365
ELLEX (USA) INC.—See Ellex Medical Lasers Limited; *Int'l*, pg. 2365
ELLIS HOME OXYGEN & MEDICAL EQUIPMENT, INC.—See AdaptHealth Corp.; *U.S. Public*, pg. 38
EMBECTA CORP.; *U.S. Public*, pg. 736
EMILY CORPORATION—See GMSS Holdings, LLC; *U.S. Private*, pg. 1723
ENDODENT INC—See COLTENE Holding AG; *Int'l*, pg. 1706
ENDOTEC, INC.—See Cellumed Co., Ltd; *Int'l*, pg. 1395
ENVIZION MEDICAL INC.; *U.S. Private*, pg. 1410
EPPENDORF ASIA PACIFIC SDN. BHD.—See Eppendorf AG; *Int'l*, pg. 2464
EPPENDORF AUSTRIA GMBH—See Eppendorf AG; *Int'l*, pg. 2464
EPPENDORF BELGIUM NV/SA—See Eppendorf AG; *Int'l*, pg. 2464
EPPENDORF CANADA LTD.—See Eppendorf AG; *Int'l*, pg. 2464
EPPENDORF CHINA LTD.—See Eppendorf AG; *Int'l*, pg. 2464
EPPENDORF CZECH & SLOVAKIA S.R.O.—See Eppendorf AG; *Int'l*, pg. 2464
EPPENDORF DO BRASIL LTDA.—See Eppendorf AG; *Int'l*, pg. 2464
EPPENDORF FRANCE S.A.R.L.—See Eppendorf AG; *Int'l*, pg. 2464
EPPENDORF KOREA LTD.—See Eppendorf AG; *Int'l*, pg. 2464
EPPENDORF MIDDLE EAST FZ-LLC—See Eppendorf AG; *Int'l*, pg. 2464
EPPENDORF POLAND SP. ZO.O.—See Eppendorf AG; *Int'l*, pg. 2464
EPPENDORF (THAILAND) CO, LTD.—See Eppendorf AG; *Int'l*, pg. 2464
EPS BIO TECHNOLOGY CORP.; *Int'l*, pg. 2465
EP TRADING CO., LTD.—See EPS Holdings, Inc.; *Int'l*, pg. 2465
ERIMED INTERNATIONAL KB—See AdderaCare AB; *Int'l*, pg. 128
ESPANORMED S.L.—See Zimmer Biomet Holdings, Inc.; *U.S. Public*, pg. 2406
ESSITY OPERATIONS WITZENHAUSEN GMBH—See Essity Aktiebolag; *Int'l*, pg. 2517
ETROPAL JSC; *Int'l*, pg. 2524
EUROBIO SCIENTIFIC SA; *Int'l*, pg. 2533
EUROCLONE S.P.A.—See AddLife AB; *Int'l*, pg. 129
THE EVANS-SHERRATT CO.; *U.S. Private*, pg. 4027
EXCELSIOR MEDICAL CO., LTD.; *Int'l*, pg. 2579
EXCELSYS TECHNOLOGIES; *U.S. Private*, pg. 1446
EXLITES HOLDINGS INTERNATIONAL, INC.; *U.S. Public*, pg. 807
EYE TECH CARE—See BNP Paribas SA; *Int'l*, pg. 1089
FAH MAI HOLDINGS GROUP INC.; *U.S. Private*, pg. 1461
FAST-AID PRODUCTS LIMITED; *Int'l*, pg. 2622
FEMCARE AUSTRALIA LTD—See Utah Medical Products, Inc.; *U.S. Public*, pg. 2267
FEMCARE GROUP LIMITED—See Utah Medical Products, Inc.; *U.S. Public*, pg. 2267
FERROSAN A/S—See Pfizer Inc.; *U.S. Public*, pg. 1679
FIBRA-SONICS (NY) INC.—See Bioventus Inc.; *U.S. Public*, pg. 339
FIRE & FLOWER HOLDINGS CORP.; *Int'l*, pg. 2678
FIRST CHOICE HOME MEDICAL EQUIPMENT, LLC—See AdaptHealth Corp.; *U.S. Public*, pg. 38
FISCHER INTERNATIONAL S.R.O.—See fischerwerke GmbH & Co. KG; *Int'l*, pg. 2692
FISHER CLINICAL SERVICES GMBH—See Thermo Fisher Scientific Inc.; *U.S. Public*, pg. 2147
FISHER & PAYKEL HEALTHCARE INDIA PRIVATE LIMITED—See Fisher & Paykel Healthcare Corporation Limited; *Int'l*, pg. 2693
FISHER & PAYKEL HEALTHCARE LIMITED—See Fisher & Paykel Healthcare Corporation Limited; *Int'l*, pg. 2693
FISHER SCIENTIFIC COMPANY—See Thermo Fisher Scientific Inc.; *U.S. Public*, pg. 2148
FISHER SCIENTIFIC KOREA LTD—See Thermo Fisher Scientific Inc.; *U.S. Public*, pg. 2148
FISHER SCIENTIFIC NORWAY AS—See Thermo Fisher Scientific Inc.; *U.S. Public*, pg. 2148
FITTERS (SARAWAK) SDN BHD—See FITTERS Diversified Berhad; *Int'l*, pg. 2695
FLEISCHHACKER GMBH & CO. KG; *Int'l*, pg. 2699
FLEXMEDICAL DISPOSABLES—See Flex Ltd.; *Int'l*, pg. 2703
FLEXMEDICAL DISPOSABLES—See Flex Ltd.; *Int'l*, pg. 2703
FLEXMEDICAL DISPOSABLES—See Flex Ltd.; *Int'l*, pg. 2703
FMC PORTUGAL, S.A.—See Fresenius Medical Care AG; *Int'l*, pg. 2774
FRANCE BED MEDICAL SERVICE CO., LTD.—See FRANCE BED HOLDINGS CO. LTD.; *Int'l*, pg. 2759
FRESENIUS HEMOCARE NETHERLANDS B.V.—See Fresenius SE & Co. KGaA; *Int'l*, pg. 2777
FRESENIUS MEDICAL CARE AUSTRALIA PTY LTD. - NEPHROCARE AUSTRALIA DIVISION—See Fresenius Medical Care AG; *Int'l*, pg. 2774
FRESENIUS MEDICAL CARE AUSTRIA GMBH—See Fresenius Medical Care AG; *Int'l*, pg. 2774
FRESENIUS MEDICAL CARE BELGIUM N.V.—See Fresenius Medical Care AG; *Int'l*, pg. 2775
FRESENIUS MEDICAL CARE CR, S.R.O.—See Fresenius Medical Care AG; *Int'l*, pg. 2775
FRESENIUS MEDICAL CARE DANMARK A/S—See Fresenius Medical Care AG; *Int'l*, pg. 2775
FRESENIUS MEDICAL CARE - DS, S.R.O.—See Fresenius Medical Care AG; *Int'l*, pg. 2775
FRESENIUS MEDICAL CARE GROUPE FRANCE S.A.S.—See Fresenius Medical Care AG; *Int'l*, pg. 2775
FRESENIUS MEDICAL CARE HONG KONG LIMITED—See Fresenius Medical Care AG; *Int'l*, pg. 2775
FRESENIUS MEDICAL CARE INDIA PRIVATE LIMITED—See Fresenius Medical Care AG; *Int'l*, pg. 2775
FRESENIUS MEDICAL CARE LEBANON S.A.R.L.—See Fresenius Medical Care AG; *Int'l*, pg. 2775
FRESENIUS MEDICAL CARE MALAYSIA SDN. BHD.—See Fresenius Medical Care AG; *Int'l*, pg. 2775
FRESENIUS MEDICAL CARE PHILIPPINES, INC.—See Fresenius Medical Care AG; *Int'l*, pg. 2775
FRESENIUS MEDICAL CARE ROMANIA SRL—See Fresenius Medical Care AG; *Int'l*, pg. 2775
FRESENIUS MEDICAL CARE TAIWAN CO., LTD.—See Fresenius Medical Care AG; *Int'l*, pg. 2775
FRESENIUS MEDIKAL HIZMETLER A.S.—See Fresenius Medical Care AG; *Int'l*, pg. 2775
FUJIFILM FILMED TIBBI CIHAZLAR PAZARLAMA VE TICARET A.S.—See FUJIFILM Holdings Corporation; *Int'l*, pg. 2822
FUJIFILM HEALTHCARE AMERICAS CORPORATION—See FUJIFILM Holdings Corporation; *Int'l*, pg. 2822
FUJIFILM MEDICAL CO., LTD.—See FUJIFILM Holdings Corporation; *Int'l*, pg. 2824
FUJIFILM MEDICAL SYSTEMS FRANCE S.A.S.—See FUJIFILM Holdings Corporation; *Int'l*, pg. 2822
FUJIFILM MYANMAR LIMITED—See FUJIFILM Holdings Corporation; *Int'l*, pg. 2824
FUJINON AUSTRALIA PTY. LTD.—See FUJIFILM Holdings Corporation; *Int'l*, pg. 2823
FUJIREBIO DIAGNOSTICS INC.—See H.U. Group Holdings, Inc.; *Int'l*, pg. 3196
FUSE MEDICAL, INC.; *U.S. Public*, pg. 893
GAIZHOU CITY AOXIN Q & M STOMATOLOGY HOSPITAL CO., LTD.—See Aoxin Q & M Dental Group Limited; *Int'l*, pg. 498
GALLAY MEDICAL & SCIENTIFIC NZ PTY LTD—See Eco-

N.A.I.C.S. INDEX

423450 — MEDICAL, DENTAL, AN...

lab Inc.; *U.S. Public*, pg. 714
GALLAY MEDICAL & SCIENTIFIC PTY LTD—See Ecolab Inc.; *U.S. Public*, pg. 714
GALLOPING HILL SURGICAL CORPORATION—See Quadrant Management, Inc.; *U.S. Private*, pg. 3316
GAMBRO A/S—See Baxter International Inc.; *U.S. Public*, pg. 281
GAMBRO DE MEXICO, S.A. DE C.V.—See Baxter International Inc.; *U.S. Public*, pg. 282
GAMBRO EXPORT—See Baxter International Inc.; *U.S. Public*, pg. 281
GAMBRO GMBH—See Baxter International Inc.; *U.S. Public*, pg. 281
GAMBRO/HOSPAL AUSTRIA GMBH—See Baxter International Inc.; *U.S. Public*, pg. 282
GAMBRO/HOSPAL SCHWEIZ AG—See Baxter International Inc.; *U.S. Public*, pg. 282
GAMBRO NORGE NUF—See Baxter International Inc.; *U.S. Public*, pg. 282
GAMBRO POLAND SP. Z O.O.—See Baxter International Inc.; *U.S. Public*, pg. 282
GAMBRO PTY. LTD. (BRISBANE)—See Baxter International Inc.; *U.S. Public*, pg. 282
GAMBRO S.A.S.—See Baxter International Inc.; *U.S. Public*, pg. 282
GAMBRO TAIWAN LTD.—See Baxter International Inc.; *U.S. Public*, pg. 282
GAMIDA LTD.—See Gamida for Life B.V.; *Int'l*, pg. 2878
GAMIDOR TECHNICAL SERVICES LTD—See Gamida for Life B.V.; *Int'l*, pg. 2878
GARG INTERNATIONAL PRIVATE LIMITED—See Garg Furnace Ltd.; *Int'l*, pg. 2884
GAUSH MEDITECH LTD.; *Int'l*, pg. 2891
GBC SCIENTIFIC EQUIPMENT DE MEXICO S.A. DE C.V.—See GBC Scientific Equipment Pty Ltd.; *Int'l*, pg. 2893
GC ADVANCED TECHNOLOGIES INC.—See GC Corporation; *Int'l*, pg. 2894
GC ASIA DENTAL PTE. LTD.—See GC Corporation; *Int'l*, pg. 2894
GC AUSTRALASIA DENTAL PTY. LTD.—See GC Corporation; *Int'l*, pg. 2894
GC AUSTRIA GMBH—See GC Corporation; *Int'l*, pg. 2894
GC DENTAL (SUZHOU) CO., LTD.—See GC Corporation; *Int'l*, pg. 2894
GC EUROPE N.V.—See GC Corporation; *Int'l*, pg. 2894
GC FRANCE S.A.S.—See GC Corporation; *Int'l*, pg. 2894
GC GERMANY GMBH—See GC Corporation; *Int'l*, pg. 2894
GC ITALIA S.R.L.—See GC Corporation; *Int'l*, pg. 2894
GC KOREA CO., LTD.—See GC Corporation; *Int'l*, pg. 2894
GC NORDIC AB—See GC Corporation; *Int'l*, pg. 2894
GC TAIWAN DENTAL CORP.—See GC Corporation; *Int'l*, pg. 2894
GC TECH. EUROPE N.V.—See GC Corporation; *Int'l*, pg. 2894
GC UNITED KINGDOM LTD.—See GC Corporation; *Int'l*, pg. 2894
GEERS HALLOKESZULEK KFT—See HAL Trust N.V.; *Int'l*, pg. 3223
GENCONN BIOTECH CO., LTD.—See Hon Hai Precision Industry Co., Ltd.; *Int'l*, pg. 3457
GENDRON INC.—See GF Health Products, Inc.; *U.S. Private*, pg. 1689
GENERAL SCIENTIFIC SAFETY EQUIPMENT CO.; *U.S. Private*, pg. 1667
GENEZONE INTERNATIONAL HEALTH MANAGEMENT LIMITED—See China Biotech Services Holdings Limited; *Int'l*, pg. 1487
GERIATRIC MEDICAL & SURGICAL SUPPLY, INC.—See GMSS Holdings, LLC; *U.S. Private*, pg. 1723
GERICARE MEDICAL SUPPLY INC.; *U.S. Private*, pg. 1686
GERMAN BRAUN MEDICAL CO., LTD.—See B. Braun Melsungen AG; *Int'l*, pg. 787
GETINGE ARJO HOLDING NETHERLANDS B.V.—See Getinge AB; *Int'l*, pg. 2949
GETINGE B.V.—See Getinge AB; *Int'l*, pg. 2949
GETINGE CANADA LTD.—See Getinge AB; *Int'l*, pg. 2949
GETINGE CZECH REPUBLIC, S.R.O.—See Getinge AB; *Int'l*, pg. 2949
GETINGE HEALTHCARE SAS—See Getinge AB; *Int'l*, pg. 2949
GETINGE HONG KONG COMPANY LTD.—See Getinge AB; *Int'l*, pg. 2950
GETINGE INDIA PVT LTD.—See Getinge AB; *Int'l*, pg. 2950
GETINGE INFECTION CONTROL AB—See Getinge AB; *Int'l*, pg. 2950
GETINGE INTERNATIONAL AB—See Getinge AB; *Int'l*, pg. 2950
GETINGE INTERNATIONAL ASIA LTD.—See Getinge AB; *Int'l*, pg. 2950
GETINGE IT-SOLUTION APS—See Getinge AB; *Int'l*, pg. 2950
GETINGE JAPAN KK—See Getinge AB; *Int'l*, pg. 2950
GETINGE KOREA CO. LTD.—See Getinge AB; *Int'l*, pg. 2950
GETINGE LA CALHENE FRANCE SA—See Getinge AB; *Int'l*, pg. 2950

GETINGE-LA CALHENE USA INC—See Getinge AB; *Int'l*, pg. 2951
GETINGE LIFE SCIENCE AMERICAS—See Getinge AB; *Int'l*, pg. 2950
GETINGE LIFE SCIENCES SAS—See Getinge AB; *Int'l*, pg. 2950
GETINGE MIDDLE EAST & AFRICA—See Getinge AB; *Int'l*, pg. 2950
GETINGE NORGE AS—See Getinge AB; *Int'l*, pg. 2950
GETINGE ODELGA GMBH—See Getinge AB; *Int'l*, pg. 2950
GETINGE PRODUCTION FRANCE SAS—See Getinge AB; *Int'l*, pg. 2950
GETINGE (SHANGHAI) TRADING CO. LTD.—See Getinge AB; *Int'l*, pg. 2949
GETINGE SINGAPORE PTE. LTD.—See Getinge AB; *Int'l*, pg. 2950
GETINGE S.P.A.—See Getinge AB; *Int'l*, pg. 2950
GETINGE (SUZHOU) CO. LTD.—See Getinge AB; *Int'l*, pg. 2949
GETINGE VERTRIEB UND SERVICE GMBH—See Getinge AB; *Int'l*, pg. 2951
G.E. WALKER, INC.; *U.S. Private*, pg. 1631
GF HEALTH PRODUCTS, INC.; *U.S. Private*, pg. 1689
GILMEDICA. S.A.—See Biotronik GmbH & Co.; *Int'l*, pg. 1044
GLAUKOS AUSTRALIA PTY LTD—See Glaukos Corporation; *U.S. Public*, pg. 940
GLAUKOS CANADA INC.—See Glaukos Corporation; *U.S. Public*, pg. 940
GLAUKOS EUROPE GMBH—See Glaukos Corporation; *U.S. Public*, pg. 940
GLAUKOS JAPAN GK—See Glaukos Corporation; *U.S. Public*, pg. 940
GLAUKOS PRODUTOS MEDICOS LTDA.—See Glaukos Corporation; *U.S. Public*, pg. 940
GLAXOSMITHKLINE—See Bora Pharmaceuticals Co., Ltd.; *Int'l*, pg. 1112
GLOBE SCIENTIFIC, INC.—See L Squared Capital Management LP; *U.S. Private*, pg. 2362
GLOBUS MEDICAL ITALY S.R.L.—See Globus Medical, Inc.; *U.S. Public*, pg. 947
GLOBUS MEDICAL JAPAN, INC.—See Globus Medical, Inc.; *U.S. Public*, pg. 947
GLOBUS MEDICAL UK LIMITED—See Globus Medical, Inc.; *U.S. Public*, pg. 947
GL SCIENCES (SHANGHAI) LIMITED—See GL Sciences Inc.; *Int'l*, pg. 2986
GMI; *U.S. Private*, pg. 1722
GN AUDIO AUSTRALIA PTY. LTD.—See GN Store Nord A/S; *Int'l*, pg. 3015
GN AUDIO (CHINA) LTD.—See GN Store Nord A/S; *Int'l*, pg. 3015
GN AUDIO FRANCE SA—See GN Store Nord A/S; *Int'l*, pg. 3015
GN AUDIO HONG KONG LIMITED—See GN Store Nord A/S; *Int'l*, pg. 3015
GN AUDIO ITALY S.R.L.—See GN Store Nord A/S; *Int'l*, pg. 3015
GN AUDIO LOGISTIC (XIAMEN) LTD.—See GN Store Nord A/S; *Int'l*, pg. 3015
GN AUDIO (SHANGHAI) CO., LTD.—See GN Store Nord A/S; *Int'l*, pg. 3015
GN AUDIO SINGAPORE PTE. LTD.—See GN Store Nord A/S; *Int'l*, pg. 3015
GN AUDIO SPAIN, S.A.—See GN Store Nord A/S; *Int'l*, pg. 3015
GN AUDIO SWEDEN AB—See GN Store Nord A/S; *Int'l*, pg. 3015
GN AUDIO UK LTD.—See GN Store Nord A/S; *Int'l*, pg. 3015
GN HEARING AUSTRALIA PTY. LTD.—See GN Store Nord A/S; *Int'l*, pg. 3015
GN HEARING AUSTRIA GMBH—See GN Store Nord A/S; *Int'l*, pg. 3015
GN HEARING CZECH REPUBLIC SPOL. S R.O.—See GN Store Nord A/S; *Int'l*, pg. 3015
GN HEARING FINLAND OY/AB—See GN Store Nord A/S; *Int'l*, pg. 3015
GOETZE DENTAL; *U.S. Private*, pg. 1726
GOLD STANDARD DIAGNOSTICS CD KASSEL GMBH—See Eurofins Scientific S.E.; *Int'l*, pg. 2550
G P MAINTENANCE SOLUTIONS, INC.—See Alexander & Baldwin, Inc.; *U.S. Public*, pg. 75
GRACE HEALTHCARE MEDICAL, INC.—See AdaptHealth Corp.; *U.S. Public*, pg. 38
GRAHAM MEDICAL TECHNOLOGIES, L.L.C.—See ADDvise Group AB; *Int'l*, pg. 136
GRATES CORPORATION; *U.S. Private*, pg. 1758
GREINER BIO-ONE BRASIL PRODUTOS MEDICOS HOSPITALARES LTDA.—See Greiner Holding AG; *Int'l*, pg. 3079
GREINER BIO-ONE B.V.—See Greiner Holding AG; *Int'l*, pg. 3079
GREINER BIO-ONE CO. LTD.—See Greiner Holding AG; *Int'l*, pg. 3079
GREINER BIO-ONE FRANCE S.A.S.—See Greiner Holding AG; *Int'l*, pg. 3079
GREINER BIO-ONE GMBH—See Greiner Holding AG; *Int'l*, pg. 3079

GREINER BIO-ONE GMBH—See Greiner Holding AG; *Int'l*, pg. 3079
GREINER BIO-ONE HUNGARY KFT.—See Greiner Holding AG; *Int'l*, pg. 3079
GREINER BIO-ONE INDIA PRIVATE LIMITED—See Greiner Holding AG; *Int'l*, pg. 3079
GREINER BIO-ONE LTD.—See Greiner Holding AG; *Int'l*, pg. 3079
GREINER BIO-ONE NORTH AMERICA, INC.—See Greiner Holding AG; *Int'l*, pg. 3079
GREINER BIO-ONE SUNS CO., LTD.—See Greiner Holding AG; *Int'l*, pg. 3079
GREINER BIO-ONE (THAILAND) LTD.—See Greiner Holding AG; *Int'l*, pg. 3079
GREINER BIO-ONE VACUETTE SCHWEIZ GMBH—See Greiner Holding AG; *Int'l*, pg. 3079
GSOURCE, LLC—See The Jordan Company, L.P.; *U.S. Private*, pg. 4060
GUANGZHOU DYNAMIC INC.—See Excelsior Medical Co., Ltd.; *Int'l*, pg. 2579
HALPRIN, INCORPORATED—See AdaptHealth Corp.; *U.S. Public*, pg. 39
HALYARD BELGIUM BVBA—See Avanos Medical, Inc.; *U.S. Public*, pg. 241
HALYARD CHINA CO., LTD.—See Avanos Medical, Inc.; *U.S. Public*, pg. 241
HALYARD DEUTSCHLAND GMBH—See Avanos Medical, Inc.; *U.S. Public*, pg. 241
HALYARD HEALTH INDIA PRIVATE LIMITED—See Avanos Medical, Inc.; *U.S. Public*, pg. 241
HALYARD NEDERLAND B.V.—See Avanos Medical, Inc.; *U.S. Public*, pg. 241
HALYARD SINGAPORE PTE. LTD.—See Avanos Medical, Inc.; *U.S. Public*, pg. 241
HAMAMATSU PHOTONICS UK LIMITED—See Hamamatsu Photonics K.K.; *Int'l*, pg. 3235
HANGER ADVANCED BIO-MECHANICS INC.—See Patient Square Capital, L.P.; *U.S. Private*, pg. 3107
HANSBIOMED CHINA, INC.—See Hans Biomed Corporation; *Int'l*, pg. 3258
HANSBIOMED USA, INC.—See Hans Biomed Corporation; *Int'l*, pg. 3258
HARDY DIAGNOSTICS; *U.S. Private*, pg. 1864
HAYLEYS LIFESCIENCES (PVT) LTD.—See Hayleys PLC; *Int'l*, pg. 3292
HEALTHFIRST CORP.; *U.S. Private*, pg. 1896
HEALTHMARK INDUSTRIES CO. INC.—See Getinge AB; *Int'l*, pg. 2951
HEALTH & NUTRITION TECHNOLOGY, INC.—See CalNutri, Inc.; *U.S. Private*, pg. 723
HEALTH PRODUCTS PLUS, INC.—See AdaptHealth Corp.; *U.S. Public*, pg. 39
HEALTH SUPPORT LIMITED—See EBOS Group Limited; *Int'l*, pg. 2285
HEALTH TECHNOLOGY RESOURCES, LLC—See Quipt Home Medical Corp.; *U.S. Public*, pg. 1757
HEARING HELP EXPRESS, INC.—See IntriCon Corporation; *U.S. Public*, pg. 1159
HEARTLAND MEDICAL CORPORATION—See AIN Holdings Inc.; *Int'l*, pg. 234
HEARTSINE TECHNOLOGIES LIMITED—See Stryker Corporation; *U.S. Public*, pg. 1955
HEIDELBERG ENGINEERING INC.—See EssilorLuxottica SA; *Int'l*, pg. 2514
HEIDELBERG ENGINEERING LTD.—See EssilorLuxottica SA; *Int'l*, pg. 2514
HEIDELBERG ENGINEERING PTY. LTD.—See EssilorLuxottica SA; *Int'l*, pg. 2514
HEMANT SURGICAL INDUSTRIES LIMITED; *Int'l*, pg. 3340
HEMASOURCE, INC.—See Ridgemont Partners Management LLC; *U.S. Private*, pg. 3433
HENRY SCHEIN ARCONA, INC.—See Henry Schein, Inc.; *U.S. Public*, pg. 1025
HENRY SCHEIN CANADA, INC.—See Henry Schein, Inc.; *U.S. Public*, pg. 1025
HENRY SCHEIN DENTAL WAREHOUSE (PTY) LTD.—See Henry Schein, Inc.; *U.S. Public*, pg. 1025
HENRY SCHEIN ESPANA, S.L.—See Henry Schein, Inc.; *U.S. Public*, pg. 1025
HENRY SCHEIN HEMAO GUANGZHOUMEDICAL DEVICE CO., LTD.—See Henry Schein, Inc.; *U.S. Public*, pg. 1025
HENRY SCHEIN HONG KONG LIMITED—See Henry Schein, Inc.; *U.S. Public*, pg. 1025
HENRY SCHEIN, INC. - ATLANTA, GA—See Henry Schein, Inc.; *U.S. Public*, pg. 1026
HENRY SCHEIN, INC. - BIRMINGHAM, AL—See Henry Schein, Inc.; *U.S. Public*, pg. 1026
HENRY SCHEIN, INC. - BOISE, ID—See Henry Schein, Inc.; *U.S. Public*, pg. 1026
HENRY SCHEIN, INC. - BOSTON, MA—See Henry Schein, Inc.; *U.S. Public*, pg. 1026
HENRY SCHEIN, INC. - CHICAGO, IL—See Henry Schein, Inc.; *U.S. Public*, pg. 1026
HENRY SCHEIN, INC. - CINCINNATI, OH—See Henry Schein, Inc.; *U.S. Public*, pg. 1026
HENRY SCHEIN, INC.-DENVER, PENNSYLVANIA—See Henry Schein, Inc.; *U.S. Public*, pg. 1026

423450 — MEDICAL, DENTAL, AN...

HENRY SCHEIN, INC. - DETROIT, MI—See Henry Schein, Inc.; *U.S. Public*, pg. 1026
HENRY SCHEIN, INC.-FLORIDA—See Henry Schein, Inc.; *U.S. Public*, pg. 1026
HENRY SCHEIN, INC. - GRAND RAPIDS, MI—See Henry Schein, Inc.; *U.S. Public*, pg. 1026
HENRY SCHEIN, INC. - GREENVILLE, SC—See Henry Schein, Inc.; *U.S. Public*, pg. 1026
HENRY SCHEIN, INC. - JACKSON, MS—See Henry Schein, Inc.; *U.S. Public*, pg. 1026
HENRY SCHEIN, INC. - LAS VEGAS, NV—See Henry Schein, Inc.; *U.S. Public*, pg. 1026
HENRY SCHEIN, INC. - MINNEAPOLIS/ST. PAUL, MN—See Henry Schein, Inc.; *U.S. Public*, pg. 1026
HENRY SCHEIN, INC.-MURRAY, UTAH—See Henry Schein, Inc.; *U.S. Public*, pg. 1027
HENRY SCHEIN, INC.-NEVADA RENO—See Henry Schein, Inc.; *U.S. Public*, pg. 1027
HENRY SCHEIN, INC.-NORTH CAROLINA—See Henry Schein, Inc.; *U.S. Public*, pg. 1027
HENRY SCHEIN, INC.-NORTH CAROLINA—See Henry Schein, Inc.; *U.S. Public*, pg. 1027
HENRY SCHEIN, INC. - OMAHA, NE—See Henry Schein, Inc.; *U.S. Public*, pg. 1026
HENRY SCHEIN, INC. - ORANGE, CA—See Henry Schein, Inc.; *U.S. Public*, pg. 1026
HENRY SCHEIN, INC. - RICHMOND, VA—See Henry Schein, Inc.; *U.S. Public*, pg. 1026
HENRY SCHEIN, INC. - SAN ANTONIO, TX—See Henry Schein, Inc.; *U.S. Public*, pg. 1026
HENRY SCHEIN, INC.; *U.S. Public*, pg. 1025
HENRY SCHEIN, INC.—See Henry Schein, Inc.; *U.S. Public*, pg. 1026
HENRY SCHEIN, INC.—See Henry Schein, Inc.; *U.S. Public*, pg. 1026
HENRY SCHEIN, INC.-TEXAS—See Henry Schein, Inc.; *U.S. Public*, pg. 1027
HENRY SCHEIN, INC.-TOLEDO, OHIO—See Henry Schein, Inc.; *U.S. Public*, pg. 1027
HENRY SCHEIN, INC. - TULSA, OK—See Henry Schein, Inc.; *U.S. Public*, pg. 1026
HENRY SCHEIN, INC. - WISCONSIN—See Henry Schein, Inc.; *U.S. Public*, pg. 1026
HENRY SCHEIN MEDICAL—See Henry Schein, Inc.; *U.S. Public*, pg. 1025
HENRY SCHEIN REGIONAL LIMITED—See Henry Schein, Inc.; *U.S. Public*, pg. 1026
HENRY SCHEIN REGIONAL PTY LTD—See Henry Schein, Inc.; *U.S. Public*, pg. 1026
HENRY SCHEIN SUNSHINE (BEIJING) MEDICAL DEVICE CO., LTD.—See Henry Schein, Inc.; *U.S. Public*, pg. 1026
HENRY SCHEIN TRADING (SHANGHAI) CO., LTD.—See Henry Schein, Inc.; *U.S. Public*, pg. 1026
HERAEUS MEDICAL COMPONENTS, INC.—See Heraeus Holding GmbH; *Int'l*, pg. 3358
HESKA IMAGING INTERNATIONAL, LLC—See Mars, Incorporated; *U.S. Private*, pg. 2588
HESSCO; *U.S. Private*, pg. 1927
HEXIS CIENTIFICA S.A.—See Danaher Corporation; *U.S. Public*, pg. 627
HIDDEN HEARING (UK) LTD.—See Demant A/S; *Int'l*, pg. 2023
HILCO EUROPE—See Windjammer Capital Investors, LLC; *U.S. Private*, pg. 4538
HILL-ROM B.V.—See Baxter International Inc.; *U.S. Public*, pg. 283
HILL-ROM CANADA, LTD.—See Baxter International Inc.; *U.S. Public*, pg. 283
HILL-ROM IBERIA S.L.—See Baxter International Inc.; *U.S. Public*, pg. 283
HILL-ROM INDUSTRIES SA—See Baxter International Inc.; *U.S. Public*, pg. 283
HILL-ROM LTD.—See Baxter International Inc.; *U.S. Public*, pg. 283
HILL-ROM, S.P.A—See Baxter International Inc.; *U.S. Public*, pg. 283
HISTOLAB PRODUCTS AB—See Algol Oy; *Int'l*, pg. 318
HITACHI HEALTHCARE AMERICAS CORPORATION—See Hitachi, Ltd.; *Int'l*, pg. 3414
HITACHI HIGH TECHNOLOGIES DO BRASIL LTDA.—See Hitachi, Ltd.; *Int'l*, pg. 3418
HITACHI MEDICAL SYSTEMS B.V.—See Hitachi, Ltd.; *Int'l*, pg. 3420
HITACHI MEDICAL SYSTEMS GMBH—See Hitachi, Ltd.; *Int'l*, pg. 3420
HITACHI MEDICAL SYSTEMS GMBH—See Hitachi, Ltd.; *Int'l*, pg. 3420
HITACHI MEDICAL SYSTEMS KFT—See Hitachi, Ltd.; *Int'l*, pg. 3420
HITACHI MEDICAL SYSTEMS N.V.—See Hitachi, Ltd.; *Int'l*, pg. 3420
HITACHI MEDICAL SYSTEMS S.A.S.—See Hitachi, Ltd.; *Int'l*, pg. 3420
HITACHI MEDICAL SYSTEMS S.L.—See Hitachi, Ltd.; *Int'l*, pg. 3420
HITACHI MEDICAL SYSTEMS (S) PTE. LTD.—See Hitachi, Ltd.; *Int'l*, pg. 3420

HITACHI SISTEMAS MEDICOS DO BRASIL LTDA.—See Hitachi, Ltd.; *Int'l*, pg. 3421
HNE HUNTLEIGH NESBIT EVANS HEALTH CARE GMBH.—See Getinge AB; *Int'l*, pg. 2951
HOLLISTER ASIA INCORPORATED—See Hollister Incorporated; *U.S. Private*, pg. 1965
HOLLISTER BELGIUM—See Hollister Incorporated; *U.S. Private*, pg. 1965
HOLLISTER B.V.—See Hollister Incorporated; *U.S. Private*, pg. 1965
HOLLISTER CO., LTD.—See Hollister Incorporated; *U.S. Private*, pg. 1965
HOLLISTER EUROPE LIMITED—See Hollister Incorporated; *U.S. Private*, pg. 1965
HOLLISTER GMBH—See Hollister Incorporated; *U.S. Private*, pg. 1965
HOLLISTER GREECE MEDICAL PRODUCTS COMMERCIAL S.A.—See Hollister Incorporated; *U.S. Private*, pg. 1965
HOLLISTER IBERICA, SA—See Hollister Incorporated; *U.S. Private*, pg. 1965
HOLLISTER INCORPORATED NIEDERLASSUNG DEUTSCHLAND—See Hollister Incorporated; *U.S. Private*, pg. 1965
HOLLISTER KFT—See Hollister Incorporated; *U.S. Private*, pg. 1965
HOLLISTER LATIN AMERICA—See Hollister Incorporated; *U.S. Private*, pg. 1965
HOLLISTER LIBERTY MEDICAL (SWITZERLAND) AG—See Hollister Incorporated; *U.S. Private*, pg. 1965
HOLLISTER LIMITED—See Hollister Incorporated; *U.S. Private*, pg. 1965
HOLLISTER LIMITED—See Hollister Incorporated; *U.S. Private*, pg. 1965
HOLLISTER LIMITED—See Hollister Incorporated; *U.S. Private*, pg. 1965
HOLLISTER NORGE—See Hollister Incorporated; *U.S. Private*, pg. 1965
HOLLISTER SCANDINAVIA INC., SUOMEN SIVULIIKE—See Hollister Incorporated; *U.S. Private*, pg. 1965
HOLLISTER—See Hollister Incorporated; *U.S. Private*, pg. 1965
HOLLISTER SOUTH AFRICA (PTY) LTD—See Hollister Incorporated; *U.S. Private*, pg. 1966
HOLLISTER S.P.A.—See Hollister Incorporated; *U.S. Private*, pg. 1965
HOLLISTER SP. ZO.O.—See Hollister Incorporated; *U.S. Private*, pg. 1966
HOLLISTER S.R.O—See Hollister Incorporated; *U.S. Private*, pg. 1966
HOLLISTER SVERIGE—See Hollister Incorporated; *U.S. Private*, pg. 1966
HOLOGIC AUSTRIA GMBH—See Hologic, Inc.; *U.S. Public*, pg. 1045
HOLOGIC MEDICOR SUISSE GMBH—See Hologic, Inc.; *U.S. Public*, pg. 1045
HOLOGIC N.V.—See Hologic, Inc.; *U.S. Public*, pg. 1045
HOLOGIC SA—See Hologic, Inc.; *U.S. Public*, pg. 1045
HOLY STONE HEALTHCARE CO., LTD.—See Holy Stone Enterprise Co., Ltd.; *Int'l*, pg. 3454
HOME CARE DELIVERED, INC.—See Beecken Petty O'Keefe & Company, LLC; *U.S. Private*, pg. 514
HOME HEALTH DEPOT, INC.; *U.S. Private*, pg. 1971
HOME MEDICAL EXPRESS, INC.—See AdaptHealth Corp.; *U.S. Public*, pg. 39
HOPITAL SERVICES SYSTEMES S.A.S.—See Illinois Tool Works Inc.; *U.S. Public*, pg. 1104
HOSPAL S.A.—See Baxter International Inc.; *U.S. Public*, pg. 282
HOSPICE SOURCE LLC—See New Mountain Capital, LLC; *U.S. Private*, pg. 2903
HOSPIRA - AUSTIN—See Pfizer Inc.; *U.S. Public*, pg. 1680
HOSPITHERA N.V.—See Viatris Inc.; *U.S. Public*, pg. 2293
HOWARD TECHNOLOGY SOLUTIONS, INC.—See Howard Industries, Inc.; *U.S. Private*, pg. 1995
HS BIO SDN. BHD.—See Hong Seng Consolidated Berhad; *Int'l*, pg. 3469
HSHS MEDICAL GROUP INC.—See Hospital Sisters Health System; *U.S. Private*, pg. 1987
HULUDAO AOXIN Q & M STOMATOLOGY HOSPITAL CO., LTD.—See Aoxin Q & M Dental Group Limited; *Int'l*, pg. 498
HULUDAO CITY AOXIN STOMATOLOGY POLYCLINIC CO., LTD.—See Aoxin Q & M Dental Group Limited; *Int'l*, pg. 498
HULUDAO LONGGANG DISTRICT AOXIN STOMATOLOGY POLYCLINIC CO., LTD.—See Aoxin Q & M Dental Group Limited; *Int'l*, pg. 498
HUMAN MEDICS CO., LTD.—See Teleflex Incorporated; *U.S. Public*, pg. 1995
HUNTLEIGH DIAGNOSTICS LTD—See Getinge AB; *Int'l*, pg. 2949
HUNTLEIGH HEALTHCARE A/S—See Getinge AB; *Int'l*, pg. 2948
HUNTLEIGH HEALTHCARE LLC—See Getinge AB; *Int'l*, pg. 2948

HUNTLEIGH NESBIT EVANS HEALTHCARE GMBH—See Getinge AB; *Int'l*, pg. 2949
HYPHENS PHARMA PHILIPPINES, INC.—See Hyphens Pharma International Limited; *Int'l*, pg. 3553
HYPHENS PHARMA SDN. BHD.—See Hyphens Pharma International Limited; *Int'l*, pg. 3553
ICT EUROPE GMBH—See Dentium Co., Ltd; *Int'l*, pg. 2033
ICT FZCO—See Dentium Co., Ltd; *Int'l*, pg. 2034
ICU MEDICAL FLEET SERVICES, LLC—See ICU Medical, Inc.; *U.S. Public*, pg. 1087
ICU MEDICAL GERMANY GMBH—See ICU Medical, Inc.; *U.S. Public*, pg. 1087
IDEV TECHNOLOGIES, INC.—See Abbott Laboratories; *U.S. Public*, pg. 20
IDEXX LABORATORIES PRIVATE LIMITED—See IDEXX Laboratories, Inc.; *U.S. Public*, pg. 1092
IHEALTHCARE, INC., *U.S. Private*, pg. 2040
ILEX BIOTECH LTD.—See Ilex Medical Ltd.; *Int'l*, pg. 3614
ILEX SOUTH AFRICA (PTY) LTD.—See Ilex Medical Ltd.; *Int'l*, pg. 3614
ILS LABORATORIES SCANDINAVIA A/S; *Int'l*, pg. 3616
IMAGING ASSOCIATES INC.; *U.S. Private*, pg. 2046
IMMUNO DIAGNOSTICS OY—See AddLife AB; *Int'l*, pg. 129
IMPLANTES Y SISTEMAS MEDICOS, INC.—See Orthofix Medical Inc.; *U.S. Public*, pg. 1619
IMPLANTIUM CO.,LTD—See Dentium Co., Ltd; *Int'l*, pg. 2033
IMPLANTIUM DE MEXICO SA DE CV—See Dentium Co., Ltd; *Int'l*, pg. 2084
IMPLANTIUM HONGKONG LTD—See Dentium Co., Ltd; *Int'l*, pg. 2033
IMPLANTIUM INDIA PVT. LTD.—See Dentium Co., Ltd; *Int'l*, pg. 2033
IMPLANTIUM MALAYSIA SDN. BHD.—See Dentium Co., Ltd; *Int'l*, pg. 2033
IMPLANTIUM & MEDICAL COMPANY SRL—See Dentium Co., Ltd; *Int'l*, pg. 2033
IMPLANTIUM UK LTD.—See Dentium Co., Ltd; *Int'l*, pg. 2033
IMPLANT SOLUTIONS, LLC—See Tenet Healthcare Corporation; *U.S. Public*, pg. 2010
IMRES B.V.—See Dubai World Corporation; *Int'l*, pg. 2221
INDUSTRIAL DRUG SERVICE DIV.—See General Scientific Safety Equipment Co.; *U.S. Private*, pg. 1667
INFOLAB INC.; *U.S. Private*, pg. 2072
INFUSION PARTNERS OF BRUNSWICK, LLC—See Option Care Health, Inc,; *U.S. Public*, pg. 1610
INFUSION PARTNERS OF MELBOURNE, LLC—See Option Care Health, Inc.; *U.S. Public*, pg. 1610
INKOZELL ZELLSTOFF-VERTRIEB GMBH—See Bunzl plc; *Int'l*, pg. 1218
INNOVATIVE MEDICAL SYSTEMS, INC.—See Ares Management Corporation; *U.S. Public*, pg. 189
INSTITUTO AUDITIVO WIDEX S.A.—See EQT AB; *Int'l*, pg. 2480
INSTRUMENTARIUM DENTAL INC.—See Danaher Corporation; *U.S. Public*, pg. 630
INTEGRA LIFESCIENCES (SHANGHAI) CO., LTD.—See Integra LifeSciences Holdings Corporation; *U.S. Public*, pg. 1135
INTEGRA YORK PA, INC.—See Integra LifeSciences Holdings Corporation; *U.S. Public*, pg. 1136
INTEPROD LLC; *U.S. Private*, pg. 2106
THE INTERMED GROUP, INC.—See Cressey & Company, LP; *U.S. Public*, pg. 1095
THE INTERMED GROUP, INC.—See Health Enterprise Partners LLC; *U.S. Private*, pg. 1893
INTERMED X-RAY, INC.—See Cressey & Company, LP; *U.S. Public*, pg. 1095
INTERMED X-RAY, INC.—See Health Enterprise Partners LLC; *U.S. Private*, pg. 1893
INTERNATIONAL MEDICAL EQUIPMENT COLLABORATIVE; *U.S. Private*, pg. 2119
INTERNATIONAL MEDICAL EQUIPMENT & SERVICE, INC.—See Richardson Electronics, Ltd.; *U.S. Public*, pg. 1797
INTERPORE CROSS INTERNATIONAL, LLC—See Zimmer Biomet Holdings, Inc.; *U.S. Public*, pg. 2406
INTER SCIENCE LTDA.—See HORIBA Ltd; *Int'l*, pg. 3477
INVACARE DEUTSCHLAND GMBH—See Invacare Corporation; *U.S. Private*, pg. 2130
INVACARE HOLDING TWO AB—See Invacare Corporation; *U.S. Private*, pg. 2131
INVACARE POIRIER SAS—See Invacare Corporation; *U.S. Private*, pg. 2131
INVACARE (PORTUGAL) II-MATERIAL ORTOPEDICO, LDA—See Invacare Corporation; *U.S. Private*, pg. 2130
IQVIA BIOTECH—See IQVIA Holdings Inc.; *U.S. Public*, pg. 1169
IQVIA BIOTECH LTD.—See IQVIA Holdings Inc.; *U.S. Public*, pg. 1169
IRB MEDICAL EQUIPMENT, LLC; *U.S. Private*, pg. 2137
IRIS THE VISUAL GROUP INC.—See Caisse de Depot et Placement du Quebec; *Int'l*, pg. 1254
IRIS THE VISUAL GROUP INC.—See FFL Partners, LLC; *U.S. Private*, pg. 1500
I-SENS USA INC.—See i-SENS Inc.; *Int'l*, pg. 3564
ISOKINETICS, INC.; *U.S. Private*, pg. 2146

423450 — MEDICAL, DENTAL, AN...

ITEM 9 LABS CORP.; *U.S. Public*, pg. 1175
IVY SPORTS MEDICINE GMBH—See Stryker Corporation; *U.S. Public*, pg. 1955
JAPAN DENTAL SUPPLY CO., LTD.—See GC Corporation; *Int'l*, pg. 2894
JINZHOU AOXIN YOUXIN DENTAL CLINIC CO., LTD.—See Aoxin Q & M Dental Group Limited; *Int'l*, pg. 498
JOHNSON & JOHNSON HEALTH CARE SYSTEMS INC.—See Johnson & Johnson; *U.S. Public*, pg. 1198
JOHNSON & JOHNSON MEDICAL B.V.—See Johnson & Johnson; *U.S. Public*, pg. 1198
JOLLY BUYER ACQUISITION GMBH—See Artivion, Inc.; *U.S. Public*, pg. 208
JORDAN RESES SUPPLY COMPANY—See First Nation Group LLC; *U.S. Private*, pg. 1521
JOTEC CARDIOVASCULAR S.L.—See Artivion, Inc.; *U.S. Public*, pg. 208
JOTEC GMBH—See Artivion, Inc.; *U.S. Public*, pg. 208
JOTEC POLSKA SP. Z.O.O—See Artivion, Inc.; *U.S. Public*, pg. 208
JOTEC SALES GMBH—See Artivion, Inc.; *U.S. Public*, pg. 208
JOTEC S.R.L.—See Artivion, Inc.; *U.S. Public*, pg. 208
JOTEC UK LTD.—See Artivion, Inc.; *U.S. Public*, pg. 208
K2M GERMANY GMBH—See Stryker Corporation; *U.S. Public*, pg. 1955
K2M UK LIMITED—See Stryker Corporation; *U.S. Public*, pg. 1955
KANE VETERINARY SUPPLIES, LTD.—See Patterson Companies, Inc.; *U.S. Public*, pg. 1654
KARDIA S.R.L.—See Asahi Intecc Co., Ltd.; *Int'l*, pg. 594
KASHIDASU CO., LTD.—See FRANCE BED HOLDINGS CO. LTD.; *Int'l*, pg. 2759
KATENA PRODUCTS, INC.—See Audax Group, Limited Partnership; *U.S. Private*, pg. 388
KDF U.S., INC.—See Air Water Inc.; *Int'l*, pg. 240
KENTUCKY MEDICAL SUPPLY, INC.—See AdaptHealth Corp.; *U.S. Public*, pg. 39
KHRYSOS INDUSTRIES, INC.—See Youngevity International Corp.; *U.S. Public*, pg. 2399
KIMBERLY-CLARK INTEGRATED SERVICES CORPORATION—See Kimberly-Clark Corporation; *U.S. Public*, pg. 1230
KING BELGIUM NV—See Bunzl plc; *Int'l*, pg. 1218
KINGSTON MEDICAL SUPPLIES (PTE.) LTD.—See Fiamma Holdings Berhad; *Int'l*, pg. 2650
KINSMEDIC SDN. BHD.—See Fiamma Holdings Berhad; *Int'l*, pg. 2650
KLM LABORATORIES, INC.; *U.S. Private*, pg. 2320
THE KMW GROUP INC.; *U.S. Private*, pg. 4065
KOL BIOMEDICAL INSTRUMENTS INC.; *U.S. Private*, pg. 2341
KOLMI-HOPEN SAS—See A.R. Medicom Inc.; *Int'l*, pg. 28
KUULOPIIRI OY—See Demant A/S; *Int'l*, pg. 2023
LABORATOIRE SERVICES INTERNATIONAL (LSI) SAS—See Thermo Fisher Scientific Inc.; *U.S. Public*, pg. 2149
LABORATORIOS B.BRAUN S.A.—See B. Braun Melsungen AG; *Int'l*, pg. 787
LAERDAL MEDICAL CORPORATION; *U.S. Private*, pg. 2372
LAGAAY MEDICAL GROUP B.V.—See B&S Group S.A.; *Int'l*, pg. 784
LAMBERT VET SUPPLY; *U.S. Private*, pg. 2380
LANDMARK HEALTHCARE, INC.; *U.S. Private*, pg. 2385
LDR BRASIL COMERCIO, IMPORTACAO E EXPORTACAO LTDA.—See Zimmer Biomet Holdings, Inc.; *U.S. Public*, pg. 2406
LDR SPINE USA, INC.—See Zimmer Biomet Holdings, Inc.; *U.S. Public*, pg. 2406
LEDISO ITALIA S.R.L.—See Demant A/S; *Int'l*, pg. 2024
LEESAR, INC.; *U.S. Private*, pg. 2415
LEICA MICROSYSTEMS CANADA—See Danaher Corporation; *U.S. Public*, pg. 628
LIBERATOR HEALTH & WELLNESS, INC.—See Becton, Dickinson & Company; *U.S. Public*, pg. 291
LIBERATOR MEDICAL SUPPLY, INC.—See Becton, Dickinson & Company; *U.S. Public*, pg. 291
LIBERTY MEDICAL NZ LIMITED—See Hollister Incorporated; *U.S. Private*, pg. 1966
LIBERTY MEDICAL PTY. LTD.—See Hollister Incorporated; *U.S. Private*, pg. 1966
LIBERTY MEDICAL (SWITZERLAND) AG—See Hollister Incorporated; *U.S. Private*, pg. 1966
LIFEGUARD MEDICAL SOLUTIONS, LLC—See Ridgemont Partners Management LLC; *U.S. Private*, pg. 3433
LIFEHEALTHCARE DISTRIBUTION PTY LTD.—See EBOS Group Limited; *Int'l*, pg. 2285
LIFEHME, INC.—See AdaptHealth Corp.; *U.S. Public*, pg. 39
LIFE PLUS SP. Z O.O.—See Aviva plc; *Int'l*, pg. 746
LIFEWAY MOBILITY, LLC—See Rockwood Equity Partners, LLC; *U.S. Private*, pg. 3468
LIFEZEN HEALTHCARE PRIVATE LIMITED—See Bal Pharma Ltd; *Int'l*, pg. 806
LILIAL S.A.S.—See Coloplast A/S; *Int'l*, pg. 1704
LIMA ORTHOPAEDICS NEW ZEALAND PTY. LTD.—See Enovis Corporation; *U.S. Public*, pg. 773

LINGUALCARE, INC.—See Solventum Corporation; *U.S. Public*, pg. 1902
LLC DENTSPLY IH—See DENTSPLY SIRONA Inc.; *U.S. Public*, pg. 655
LOFTIS HOME MEDICAL, LLC—See AdaptHealth Corp.; *U.S. Public*, pg. 39
LOGICMARK, LLC—See LogicMark, Inc.; *U.S. Public*, pg. 1340
THE LONDON OTOLOGICAL CENTRE LTD—See Amplifon S.p.A.; *Int'l*, pg. 436
LORD CORPORATION (EUROPE) LTD—See Parker Hannifin Corporation; *U.S. Public*, pg. 1641
LUMENIS HOLDINGS (HOLLAND) B.V.—See Boston Scientific Corporation; *U.S. Public*, pg. 375
LUMENIS JAPAN CO. LTD.—See Boston Scientific Corporation; *U.S. Public*, pg. 375
MADA MEDICAL PRODUCTS INC.; *U.S. Private*, pg. 2539
MADISON COUNTY MEDICAL EQUIPMENT, INC.—See AdaptHealth Corp.; *U.S. Public*, pg. 39
MAICO S.R.L.—See Demant A/S; *Int'l*, pg. 2024
MAJOR MEDICAL SUPPLY OF COLORADO SPRINGS, LLC—See AdaptHealth Corp.; *U.S. Public*, pg. 39
MAJOR MEDICAL SUPPLY OF DENVER, LLC—See AdaptHealth Corp.; *U.S. Public*, pg. 39
MAJOR MEDICAL SUPPLY OF FORT COLLINS, LLC—See AdaptHealth Corp.; *U.S. Public*, pg. 39
MANADIALISIS S.A.—See Fresenius Medical Care AG; *Int'l*, pg. 2776
MANNING JAYA TRADING (B) SDN. BHD.—See Biotronik GmbH & Co.; *Int'l*, pg. 1044
MAQUET BISTRO GMBH.—See Getinge AB; *Int'l*, pg. 2951
MAQUET CARDIOVASCULAR US SALES, LLC—See Getinge AB; *Int'l*, pg. 2951
MAQUET-DYNAMED INC—See Getinge AB; *Int'l*, pg. 2952
MAQUET (SHANGHAI) MEDICAL EQUIPMENT CO., LTD.—See Getinge AB; *Int'l*, pg. 2951
MARKETLAB, INC.; *U.S. Private*, pg. 2581
MASIMO EUROPE LTD.—See Masimo Corporation; *U.S. Public*, pg. 1392
MASIMO UK LTD—See Masimo Corporation; *U.S. Public*, pg. 1392
MAXTEC LLC—See Halma plc; *Int'l*, pg. 3232
MAXTER CATHETERS SAS—See Avanos Medical, Inc.; *U.S. Public*, pg. 241
MAYMEDIC TECHNOLOGY SDN. BHD.—See BCM Alliance Berhad; *Int'l*, pg. 928
MC2—See Dominique Dutscher SAS; *Int'l*, pg. 2161
MCFARLANE MEDICAL, INC.—See Jacsten Holdings, LLC; *U.S. Private*, pg. 2181
MCKESSON PLASMA AND BIOLOGICS, LLC—See McKesson Corporation; *U.S. Public*, pg. 1408
MCLEODD OPTICAL COMPANY INC.—See EssilorLuxottica SA; *Int'l*, pg. 2513
MDEVERYWHERE, INC.—See Marlin Equity Partners, LLC; *U.S. Private*, pg. 2584
MDS MEDICAL SOFTWARE; *U.S. Private*, pg. 2646
MEDA OY—See Viatris Inc.; *U.S. Public*, pg. 2293
MEDBRIDGE HOME MEDICAL LLC—See AdaptHealth Corp.; *U.S. Public*, pg. 39
MEDCO RESPIRATORY INSTRUMENTS INC; *U.S. Private*, pg. 2651
MEDECO SA/NV—See Advent International Corporation; *U.S. Private*, pg. 104
MEDGLUV INC; *U.S. Private*, pg. 2651
MEDICAL COMPRESSION SYSTEMS, INC.—See Zimmer Biomet Holdings, Inc.; *U.S. Public*, pg. 2406
MEDICAL DIRECT CLUB LLC; *U.S. Private*, pg. 2655
MEDICAL ENGINEERS (I) PVT. LTD.—See Everest Kanto Cylinder Limited; *Int'l*, pg. 2564
MEDICAL EQUIPMENT DISTRIBUTORS, INC.—See Roper Technologies, Inc.; *U.S. Public*, pg. 1812
MEDICAL EQUIPMENT TECHNOLOGIES, INC.—See Avista Capital Partners, L.P.; *U.S. Private*, pg. 408
MEDICAL IMAGING SYSTEMS, INC.—See Radon Medical Imaging Corp.; *U.S. Private*, pg. 3345
MEDICAL IMAGING TECHNOLOGIES, INC.; *U.S. Private*, pg. 2655
MEDICAL INDICATORS, INC.—See Progress Equity Partners, LLC; *U.S. Private*, pg. 3278
MEDICAL POSITIONING, INC.—See Rockwood Equity Partners, LLC; *U.S. Private*, pg. 3468
MEDICAL PRODUCTS INC.; *U.S. Private*, pg. 2655
MEDICAL SPECIALTIES DISTRIBUTORS LLC—See McKesson Corporation; *U.S. Public*, pg. 1408
THE MEDICAL SUPPLY DEPOT, INC.; *U.S. Private*, pg. 4077
MEDICAL TECHNOLOGIES LIMITED—See Deson Development International Holdings Ltd; *Int'l*, pg. 2045
MEDICAL TECHNOLOGY ASSOCIATES, LLC; *U.S. Private*, pg. 2656
MEDICAL ULTRASONICS LTD—See Getinge AB; *Int'l*, pg. 2952
MEDI-CHEM SYSTEMS SDN. BHD.—See Excelsior Medical Co., Ltd.; *Int'l*, pg. 2579
MEDICINA CORPORATIVA DE DIALISIS SA—See Baxter International Inc.; *U.S. Public*, pg. 284
MEDICOM HEALTHCARE B.V.—See A.R. Medicom Inc.; *Int'l*, pg. 28

MEDICOM-UKRAINE LLC—See A.R. Medicom Inc.; *Int'l*, pg. 28
MEDICOM USA, INC.—See A.R. Medicom Inc.; *Int'l*, pg. 28
MEDIFIRST SOLUTIONS, INC.; *U.S. Public*, pg. 1412
MED, INC.; *U.S. Private*, pg. 2650
MEDI-NUCLEAR CORP; *U.S. Private*, pg. 2651
MEDIPLAST AB—See AddLife AB; *Int'l*, pg. 129
MEDIPLAST A/S—See AddLife AB; *Int'l*, pg. 129
MEDIPLAST AS—See AddLife AB; *Int'l*, pg. 129
MEDIPLAST BENELUX B.V.—See AddLife AB; *Int'l*, pg. 129
MEDIPLAST GMBH—See AddLife AB; *Int'l*, pg. 130
MEDIPLAST S.R.L.—See AddLife AB; *Int'l*, pg. 130
MEDIQ DANMARK A/S—See Advent International Corporation; *U.S. Private*, pg. 104
MEDIQ DIRECT DIABETES B.V.—See Advent International Corporation; *U.S. Private*, pg. 104
MEDIQ DIREKT DIABETES GMBH—See Advent International Corporation; *U.S. Private*, pg. 104
MEDIQ DIREKT KFT.—See Advent International Corporation; *U.S. Private*, pg. 104
MEDIQ EESTI OU—See Advent International Corporation; *U.S. Private*, pg. 104
MEDIQ LIETUVA UAB—See Advent International Corporation; *U.S. Private*, pg. 104
MEDIQ MEDECO—See Advent International Corporation; *U.S. Private*, pg. 104
MEDIQ NORGE AS—See Advent International Corporation; *U.S. Private*, pg. 104
MEDIQ SUISSE AG—See Advent International Corporation; *U.S. Private*, pg. 104
MEDIQ SUOMI OY—See Advent International Corporation; *U.S. Private*, pg. 104
MEDIQ SVERIGE AB—See Advent International Corporation; *U.S. Private*, pg. 104
MEDIQ TEFA B.V.—See Advent International Corporation; *U.S. Private*, pg. 104
MEDIRECT LATINO, INC.; *U.S. Public*, pg. 1413
MEDISERV GMBH—See Asklepios Kliniken GmbH & Co. KGaA; *Int'l*, pg. 623
MEDISIZE ITALIA SRL—See Flexicare (Group) Limited; *Int'l*, pg. 2705
MEDIX I.C.S.A.—See ArchiMed SAS; *Int'l*, pg. 548
MED-LAB SUPPLY COMPANY, INC.; *U.S. Private*, pg. 2650
MEDLINE INTERNATIONAL FRANCE SAS—See Medline Industries, LP; *U.S. Private*, pg. 2658
MEDSURGE ADVANCES—See MedSurge Holdings, Inc.; *U.S. Private*, pg. 2659
MEDSURGE HOLDINGS, INC.; *U.S. Private*, pg. 2659
MEDWAY MEDICAL EQUIPMENT, LLC—See AdaptHealth Corp.; *U.S. Public*, pg. 39
MED WAY MEDICAL, INC.—See AdaptHealth Corp.; *U.S. Public*, pg. 39
MEDYSSEY USA, INC.—See DONG WHA PHARM CO., LTD.; *Int'l*, pg. 2164
MENTOR DEUTSCHLAND GMBH—See Johnson & Johnson; *U.S. Public*, pg. 1196
MENTOR MEDICAL SYSTEMS LTD.—See Johnson & Johnson; *U.S. Public*, pg. 1196
MENTOR MEDICAL SYSTEMS PTY. LTD.—See Johnson & Johnson; *U.S. Public*, pg. 1196
MERCEDES MEDICAL INC.; *U.S. Private*, pg. 2668
MERCURY ENTERPRISES, INC.; *U.S. Private*, pg. 2670
MERIDIAN BIOSCIENCE EUROPE S.R.L.—See Meridian Bioscience Inc.; *U.S. Public*, pg. 1424
MERLIN MEDICAL SUPPLY—See Laboratory Services MSO LLC; *U.S. Private*, pg. 2370
MERRITT VETERINARY SUPPLIES INC.—See Clayton, Dubilier & Rice, LLC; *U.S. Private*, pg. 921
MERRITT VETERINARY SUPPLIES INC.—See TPG Capital, L.P.; *U.S. Public*, pg. 2170
MERRY X-RAY CORPORATION; *U.S. Private*, pg. 2676
METRON MEDICAL AUSTRALIA PTY LIMITED—See Patterson Companies, Inc.; *U.S. Public*, pg. 1653
METTLER-TOLEDO D.O.O.—See Mettler-Toledo International, Inc.; *U.S. Public*, pg. 1433
MICROTEK MEDICAL, INC.—See Ecolab Inc.; *U.S. Public*, pg. 715
MICROTEK MEDICAL MALTA LIMITED—See Ecolab Inc.; *U.S. Public*, pg. 715
MID-AMERICA ISOTOPES, INC.—See Webster Equity Partners, LLC; *U.S. Private*, pg. 4467
MIDWEST HEME MANAGEMENT, INC.; *U.S. Private*, pg. 2721
MILIAN SA—See Dominique Dutscher SAS; *Int'l*, pg. 2161
MILIAN USA—See Dominique Dutscher SAS; *Int'l*, pg. 2161
MILLENNIUM MEDICAL MEDICAL PRODUCTS INC.; *U.S. Private*, pg. 2732
MILLENNIUM SURGICAL CORP—See Arlington Capital Partners LLC; *U.S. Private*, pg. 327
MILVERTON LTD.—See Alphatec Holdings, Inc.; *U.S. Public*, pg. 84
MI-MED SUPPLY CO. INC.; *U.S. Private*, pg. 2695
MINIMAX IMPLANT PTY LTD—See Dentium Co., Ltd; *Int'l*, pg. 2034
MO HA GE MOMMSEN HANDELSGESELLSCHAFT MBH—See Bunzl plc; *Int'l*, pg. 1219
MOVIANTO ESPANA SL—See Owens & Minor, Inc.; *U.S. Public*, pg. 1626

423450 — MEDICAL, DENTAL, AN...

MOVIANTO NORDIC APS—See Owens & Minor, Inc.; *U.S. Public*, pg. 1626
MOVIANTO SCHWEIZ GMBH—See Owens & Minor, Inc.; *U.S. Public*, pg. 1626
MOVIANTO SLOVENSKO SRO—See Owens & Minor, Inc.; *U.S. Public*, pg. 1626
MOVIANTO UK LTD.—See Owens & Minor, Inc.; *U.S. Public*, pg. 1626
MUF - PRO S.R.O.—See Dominique Dutscher SAS; *Int'l*, pg. 2161
MUKA METAL TICARET VE SANAYI ANONIM SIRKETI—See Stryker Corporation; *U.S. Public*, pg. 1956
M+W DENTAL GMBH—See Carl Bennet AB; *Int'l*, pg. 1332
MYCO MEDICAL; *U.S. Private*, pg. 2823
MYCONE DENTAL SUPPLY CO. INC; *U.S. Private*, pg. 2824
MYDENT INTERNATIONAL, INC.—See The Jordan Company, L.P.; *U.S. Public*, pg. 4063
NANAO AGENCY CORPORATION—See EIZO Corporation; *Int'l*, pg. 2337
NASHVILLE DENTAL INC.; *U.S. Private*, pg. 2836
NATIONAL HME, INC.—See New Mountain Capital, LLC; *U.S. Private*, pg. 2903
NATIONAL SEATING & MOBILITY, INC. - DUNBAR—See Court Square Capital Partners, L.P.; *U.S. Private*, pg. 1069
NATIONAL SEATING & MOBILITY, INC.—See Court Square Capital Partners, L.P.; *U.S. Private*, pg. 1069
NATIONAL SLEEP THERAPY; *U.S. Private*, pg. 2863
NCONTACT SURGICAL INC.—See AtriCure, Inc.; *U.S. Public*, pg. 225
NELLIX, INC.—See Endologix, Inc.; *U.S. Private*, pg. 1392
NEOFORCE GROUP INC.—See Soleno Therapeutics, Inc.; *U.S. Public*, pg. 1900
NETMED, INC.; *U.S. Public*, pg. 1509
NETWORK MEDICAL, LLC—See StateServ Medical, LLC; *U.S. Private*, pg. 3793
NEUROONE MEDICAL TECHNOLOGIES CORPORATION; *U.S. Public*, pg. 1510
NEW ENGLAND HOME MEDICAL EQUIPMENT LLC—See AdaptHealth Corp.; *U.S. Public*, pg. 39
NEWMARK MEDICAL COMPONENTS INC.—See The Platt Brothers & Company, Inc.; *U.S. Private*, pg. 4096
NIELSEN TELE MEDICAL GMBH—See Brookfield Corporation; *Int'l*, pg. 1180
NIELSEN TELE MEDICAL GMBH—See Elliott Management Corporation; *U.S. Private*, pg. 1372
NIHON COCHLEAR CO LIMITED—See Cochlear Limited; *Int'l*, pg. 1687
NIHON RINSHO, INC.—See H.U. Group Holdings, Inc.; *Int'l*, pg. 3197
NINTAMED HANDELS GMBH—See DexCom Inc; *U.S. Public*, pg. 657
NOBEL BIOCARE DANMARK A/S—See Danaher Corporation; *U.S. Public*, pg. 629
NOBEL BIOCARE DISTRIBUTION CENTER BV—See Danaher Corporation; *U.S. Public*, pg. 629
NOBEL BIOCARE MAGYARORSZAG KFT.—See Danaher Corporation; *U.S. Public*, pg. 629
NOBEL BIOCARE MEXICO S.A. DE C.V.—See Danaher Corporation; *U.S. Public*, pg. 629
NOBEL BIOCARE NORWAY AS—See Danaher Corporation; *U.S. Public*, pg. 629
NOBEL BIOCARE PORTUGAL S.A.—See Danaher Corporation; *U.S. Public*, pg. 629
NOBEL BIOCARE RUSSIA LLC—See Danaher Corporation; *U.S. Public*, pg. 629
NOBEL BIOCARE SERVICES AG—See Danaher Corporation; *U.S. Public*, pg. 629
NOBEL BIOCARE SINGAPORE PTE LTD.—See Danaher Corporation; *U.S. Public*, pg. 629
NOBEL BIOCARE SOUTH AFRICA—See Danaher Corporation; *U.S. Public*, pg. 629
NOBEL BIOCARE SUOMI OY—See Danaher Corporation; *U.S. Public*, pg. 629
NOBEL BIOCARE UAB—See Danaher Corporation; *U.S. Public*, pg. 629
NORMATEC INDUSTRIES, LP.—See Hyperice, Inc.; *U.S. Private*, pg. 2019
NORTHSIDE OXYGEN & MEDICAL EQUIPMENT—See Genesis HealthCare System; *U.S. Private*, pg. 1669
NORTHWEST GEORGIA ONCOLOGY SUPPLY; *U.S. Private*, pg. 2960
NOVA BIOMEDICAL CANADA, LTD.—See Nova Biomedical Corporation; *U.S. Private*, pg. 2965
NOVA BIOMEDICAL GMBH—See Nova Biomedical Corporation; *U.S. Private*, pg. 2965
NOVA BIOMEDICAL U.K.—See Nova Biomedical Corporation; *U.S. Private*, pg. 2965
NOVABONE PRODUCTS - INTERNATIONAL—See Halma plc; *Int'l*, pg. 3232
NUCLEAR MEDICINE PROFESSIONALS, INC.; *U.S. Private*, pg. 2972
NUTRA ESSENTIAL OTC SL—See Ascendis Health Limited; *Int'l*, pg. 601
NUTRITIONAL SUPPORT SERVICES, L.P.—See National HealthCare Corporation; *U.S. Public*, pg. 1496

NUVASIVE (AUS/NZ) PTY. LTD.—See Globus Medical, Inc.; *U.S. Public*, pg. 947
NUVASIVE GERMANY, GMBH—See Globus Medical, Inc.; *U.S. Public*, pg. 947
NUVASIVE NETHERLANDS B.V.—See Globus Medical, Inc.; *U.S. Public*, pg. 947
N.V. STRATEC MEDICAL S.A.—See Johnson & Johnson; *U.S. Public*, pg. 1195
NXC IMAGING; *U.S. Private*, pg. 2975
NYPRO HEALTHCARE BAJA INC.—See Jabil Inc.; *U.S. Public*, pg. 1181
OAASIS GROUP LIMITED—See DNOW Inc.; *U.S. Public*, pg. 671
OAKWORKS INC.; *U.S. Private*, pg. 2986
OD MEDICAL SOLUTIONS LLC—See The ODP Corporation; *U.S. Public*, pg. 2117
O'FLYNN MEDICAL LIMITED—See AddLife AB; *Int'l*, pg. 130
OLYMPIA RESPIRATORY SERVICES LLC—See AdaptHealth Corp.; *U.S. Public*, pg. 39
OMAR MEDICAL SUPPLIES, INC.; *U.S. Private*, pg. 3014
OMNIS HEALTH, LLC—See Bertram Capital Management, LLC; *U.S. Private*, pg. 540
OOO BIOTRONIK—See Biotronik GmbH & Co.; *Int'l*, pg. 1044
OOO BIOTRONIK URAL—See Biotronik GmbH & Co.; *Int'l*, pg. 1044
OOO TRUMPF MED—See Baxter International Inc.; *U.S. Public*, pg. 283
OPHTHASWISSMED PHILIPPINES INC—See EBOS Group Limited; *Int'l*, pg. 2285
OPKO CHILE, S.A.—See OPKO Health, Inc.; *U.S. Public*, pg. 1608
OPKO DIAGNOSTICS, LLC—See OPKO Health, Inc.; *U.S. Public*, pg. 1608
ORALABS, INC.—See China Precision Steel, Inc.; *Int'l*, pg. 1542
OREGON SCIENTIFIC SOUTH EAST ASIA PTE LIMITED—See IDT International Limited; *Int'l*, pg. 3597
ORTHOFIX LIMITED—See Orthofix Medical Inc.; *U.S. Public*, pg. 1619
ORTHOFIX SA—See Orthofix Medical Inc.; *U.S. Public*, pg. 1619
ORTHOFIX UK LIMITED—See Orthofix Medical Inc.; *U.S. Public*, pg. 1619
ORTHOMED S.A.S—See Apposite Capital LLP; *Int'l*, pg. 522
ORTHOSCAN, INC.—See ATON GmbH; *Int'l*, pg. 689
ORTHO TECHNOLOGY, INC.—See Henry Schein, Inc.; *U.S. Public*, pg. 1027
OTICON AB—See Demant A/S; *Int'l*, pg. 2024
OTICON AUSTRALIA PTY. LTD.—See Demant A/S; *Int'l*, pg. 2024
OTICON K.K.—See Demant A/S; *Int'l*, pg. 2024
OTICON KOREA CO. LTD.—See Demant A/S; *Int'l*, pg. 2024
OTICON MEDICAL A/S—See Demant A/S; *Int'l*, pg. 2024
OTICON NEW ZEALAND LTD.—See Demant A/S; *Int'l*, pg. 2024
OTICON POLSKA SP. Z O.O.—See Demant A/S; *Int'l*, pg. 2024
OTICON S.A.—See Demant A/S; *Int'l*, pg. 2024
OTICON SINGAPORE PTE. LTD.—See Demant A/S; *Int'l*, pg. 2024
OT-RHEIN-MAIN GMBH—See Asklepios Kliniken GmbH & Co. KGaA; *Int'l*, pg. 624
OUTPATIENT INFUSION SYSTEMS, INC.—See McKesson Corporation; *U.S. Public*, pg. 1408
OWENS & MINOR DISTRIBUTION, INC.—See Owens & Minor, Inc.; *U.S. Public*, pg. 1626
OXOID COMPANY—See Thermo Fisher Scientific Inc.; *U.S. Public*, pg. 2150
OXYGEN ONE, INC.—See AdaptHealth Corp.; *U.S. Public*, pg. 39
OY GAMBRO—See Baxter International Inc.; *U.S. Public*, pg. 282
OYSTER MEDISAFE PRIVATE LTD.—See B. Braun Melsungen AG; *Int'l*, pg. 788
PAL-MED, LLC—See AdaptHealth Corp.; *U.S. Public*, pg. 39
PALMETTO OXYGEN, LLC—See AdaptHealth Corp.; *U.S. Public*, pg. 39
PANJIN AOXIN QUANMIN STOMATOLOGY HOSPITAL CO., LTD.—See Aoxin Q & M Dental Group Limited; *Int'l*, pg. 498
PANJIN JINGCHENG Q & M STOMATOLOGY CO., LTD.—See Aoxin Q & M Dental Group Limited; *Int'l*, pg. 498
PANJIN JINSAI Q & M STOMATOLOGY CO., LTD.—See Aoxin Q & M Dental Group Limited; *Int'l*, pg. 498
PAN-MALAYAN PHARMACEUTICALS PTE LTD—See Hyphens Pharma International Limited; *Int'l*, pg. 3553
PANORAMIC RENTAL CORP.—See The Jordan Company, L.P.; *U.S. Public*, pg. 4063
PARAGON 28, INC.; *U.S. Public*, pg. 1636
PARK SURGICAL CO, INC.—See Dealmed Medical Supplies LLC; *U.S. Private*, pg. 1183
PARRISH HOME MEDICAL INC—See AdaptHealth Corp.; *U.S. Public*, pg. 39
PARTSSOURCE, INC.—See Great Hill Partners, L.P.; *U.S. Private*, pg. 1763

PATHOLOGY LAB SOLUTIONS, INC.—See Harol Brothers LLC; *U.S. Private*, pg. 1866
PATIENT-AIDS, INC.—See Quipt Home Medical Corp.; *U.S. Public*, pg. 1757
PATIENTSAFE SOLUTIONS, INC.; *U.S. Private*, pg. 3109
PATTERSON COMPANIES, INC.; *U.S. Public*, pg. 1653
PATTERSON DENTAL CANADA INC.—See Patterson Companies, Inc.; *U.S. Public*, pg. 1654
PATTERSON DENTAL—See Patterson Companies, Inc.; *U.S. Public*, pg. 1654
PATTERSON DENTAL SUPPLY, INC.—See Patterson Companies, Inc.; *U.S. Public*, pg. 1654
PATTERSON GLOBAL LIMITED—See Patterson Companies, Inc.; *U.S. Public*, pg. 1654
PATTERSON LOGISTICS SERVICES, INC.—See Patterson Companies, Inc.; *U.S. Public*, pg. 1654
PATTERSON MEDICAL CANADA, INC.—See Madison Dearborn Partners, LLC; *U.S. Private*, pg. 2542
PATTERSON OFFICE SUPPLIES, INC.—See Patterson Companies, Inc.; *U.S. Public*, pg. 1654
PATTERSON TECHNOLOGY CENTER, INC.—See Patterson Companies, Inc.; *U.S. Public*, pg. 1654
PCI PHARMA SERVICES—See Kohlberg & Company, LLC; *U.S. Private*, pg. 2339
PEAKS & PLAINS MEDICAL, INC.—See Mi-Med Supply Co. Inc.; *U.S. Private*, pg. 2696
PEARSON DENTAL SUPPLIES INC.; *U.S. Private*, pg. 3126
PENRAD TECHNOLOGIES, INC.—See HgCapital Trust plc; *Int'l*, pg. 3376
PENSALAB SA—See HORIBA Ltd; *Int'l*, pg. 3478
PENTAX MEDICAL (SHANGHAI) CO., LTD.—See Hoya Corporation; *Int'l*, pg. 3495
PENUMBRA EUROPE GMBH—See Penumbra, Inc.; *U.S. Public*, pg. 1667
PENUMBRA LATIN AMERICA DISTRIBUIDORA DE EQUIPAMENTOS E PRODUCTOS MEDICOS LTDA—See Penumbra, Inc.; *U.S. Public*, pg. 1667
PENUMBRA NEURO AUSTRALIA PTY. LTD.—See Penumbra, Inc.; *U.S. Public*, pg. 1667
PERFECT CARE INC.; *U.S. Private*, pg. 3148
PERFORMANCE HEALTH FRANCE—See Patterson Companies, Inc.; *U.S. Public*, pg. 1654
PERFORMANCE HEALTH INTERNATIONAL LIMITED—See Madison Dearborn Partners, LLC; *U.S. Private*, pg. 2542
PERFORMANCE HEALTH SUPPLY, INC.—See Madison Dearborn Partners, LLC; *U.S. Private*, pg. 2542
PERFORMANCE MEDICAL GROUP; *U.S. Private*, pg. 3149
PERKINELMER HEALTHCARE DIAGNOSTICS (SHANGHAI) CO., LTD.—See Revvity, Inc.; *U.S. Public*, pg. 1795
PERKIN-ELMER INSTRUMENTS (PHILIPPINES) CORPORATION—See Revvity, Inc.; *U.S. Public*, pg. 1794
PERKINELMER SAGLIK VE CEVRE BILIMLERI LTD.—See Revvity, Inc.; *U.S. Public*, pg. 1795
PERKINELMER SAOLYK VE CEVRE BILIMLERI LTD.—See Revvity, Inc.; *U.S. Public*, pg. 1795
PERKINELMER SOUTH AFRICA (PTY) LTD.—See Revvity, Inc.; *U.S. Public*, pg. 1795
PERTEN INSTRUMENTS GMBH—See Revvity, Inc.; *U.S. Public*, pg. 1795
PERTEN INSTRUMENTS INC.—See Revvity, Inc.; *U.S. Public*, pg. 1795
PHARMACY, INC.—See AdaptHealth Corp.; *U.S. Public*, pg. 39
PHARM-MART PHARMACY OF WARREN, INC.—See Walgreens Boots Alliance, Inc.; *U.S. Public*, pg. 2323
PHONIC EAR A/S—See Demant A/S; *Int'l*, pg. 2023
PHYSIO-CONTROL CANADA SALES LTD.—See Stryker Corporation; *U.S. Public*, pg. 1956
PHYSIO-CONTROL SINGAPORE PTE. LTD.—See Stryker Corporation; *U.S. Public*, pg. 1956
PHYSIO-CONTROL UK SALES LTD.—See Stryker Corporation; *U.S. Public*, pg. 1956
PINNACLE MEDICAL SOLUTIONS LLC—See AdaptHealth Corp.; *U.S. Public*, pg. 39
PLANET DDS, INC.—See Level Equity Management, LLC; *U.S. Private*, pg. 2434
PLURADENT AG & CO. KG—See Deutsche Mittelstandsholding GmbH; *Int'l*, pg. 2071
POLYSTAN A/S—See Getinge AB; *Int'l*, pg. 2952
PRATTVILLE MEDICAL EQUIPMENT, INC.—See AdaptHealth Corp.; *U.S. Public*, pg. 39
PRECISE DENTAL INTERNACIONAL, S.A. DE C.V.—See Integra LifeSciences Holdings Corporation; *U.S. Public*, pg. 1136
PRECISION FOR MEDICINE, INC.—See Precision Medicine Group, Inc.; *U.S. Private*, pg. 3245
PREMIERE MANUFACTURING, INC.—See Tupperware Brands Corporation; *U.S. Public*, pg. 2204
PREMIER HEALTHCARE ALLIANCE, L.P.—See Premier, Inc.; *U.S. Public*, pg. 1715
PREMIER PRODUCTS CO.; *U.S. Private*, pg. 3251
PRIDE MOBILITY PRODUCTS COMPANY—See Pride Mobility Products Corp.; *U.S. Private*, pg. 3259
PRIDE MOBILITY PRODUCTS EUROPE BV—See Pride Mobility Products Corp.; *U.S. Private*, pg. 3259
PRIDE MOBILITY PRODUCTS ITALIA S.R.L.—See Pride

Mobility Products Corp.; *U.S. Private*, pg. 3259
PRIDE MOBILITY PRODUCTS LTD.—See Pride Mobility Products Corp.; *U.S. Private*, pg. 3259
PRIDE MOBILITY PRODUCTS NEW ZEALAND LTD.—See Pride Mobility Products Corp.; *U.S. Private*, pg. 3259
PRIDE MOBILITY PRODUCTS SARL—See Pride Mobility Products Corp.; *U.S. Private*, pg. 3259
PRISM MEDICAL PRODUCTS, L.L.C.—See Henry Schein, Inc.; *U.S. Public*, pg. 1027
PROBO MEDICAL, LLC—See Avista Capital Partners, L.P.; *U.S. Private*, pg. 408
PRO-DEX, INC.; *U.S. Public*, pg. 1722
PRODITION S.A.—See Demant A/S; *Int'l*, pg. 2023
PROFESSIONAL HOSPITAL SUPPLY, INC.—See Medline Industries, LP; *U.S. Private*, pg. 2658
PROMISE MEDICAL, INC.—See AdaptHealth Corp.; *U.S. Public*, pg. 39
PRORISK S.A.S.—See Bunzl plc; *Int'l*, pg. 1219
PT. ARKRAY—See ARKRAY, Inc.; *Int'l*, pg. 572
PT. B.BRAUN MEDICAL INDONESIA—See B. Braun Melsungen AG; *Int'l*, pg. 788
PT BECTON DICKINSON INDONESIA—See Becton, Dickinson & Company; *U.S. Public*, pg. 292
PT BOSTON SCIENTIFIC INDONESIA—See Boston Scientific Corporation; *U.S. Public*, pg. 375
PT. ELO KARSA UTAMA—See BioLASCO Taiwan Co., Ltd.; *Int'l*, pg. 1038
PT. ICT WORLDWIDE INDONESIA—See Dentium Co., Ltd; *Int'l*, pg. 2034
PT INDO GENESIS MEDIKA—See Clearbridge Health Limited; *Int'l*, pg. 1656
QADOS—See Checkit plc; *Int'l*, pg. 1459
QD PHARMACEUTICALS ULC—See Viatris Inc.; *U.S. Public*, pg. 2294
Q-MED BRASIL COMERCIO E IMPORTACAO DE PRODUTOS MEDICOS LTDA—See Abu Dhabi Investment Authority; *Int'l*, pg. 71
Q-MED BRASIL COMERCIO E IMPORTACAO DE PRODUTOS MEDICOS LTDA—See EQT Corporation; *U.S. Public*, pg. 785
QUIPT HOME MEDICAL CORP.; *U.S. Public*, pg. 1757
QUIRUMED, S.L.U.—See Bunzl plc; *Int'l*, pg. 1219
RADIADYNE, LLC—See AngioDynamics, Inc.; *U.S. Public*, pg. 137
RADIOMETER IBERICA S.L.—See Danaher Corporation; *U.S. Public*, pg. 630
RADIOMETER K.K.—See Danaher Corporation; *U.S. Public*, pg. 630
RADIOMETER MEDICAL EQUIPMENT (SHANGHAI) CO. LTD.—See Danaher Corporation; *U.S. Public*, pg. 631
RADIOMETER RSCH GMBH—See Danaher Corporation; *U.S. Public*, pg. 631
R&D SYSTEMS CHINA CO., LTD.—See Bio-Techne Corporation; *U.S. Public*, pg. 334
RECIPROCAL LABS CORPORATION—See ResMed Inc.; *U.S. Public*, pg. 1790
RECOVERCARE LLC—See Joerns Healthcare, LLC; *U.S. Private*, pg. 2219
RELIABLE MEDICAL EQUIPMENT LLC—See AdaptHealth Corp.; *U.S. Public*, pg. 39
RELIABLE MEDICAL OF CONWAY, LLC—See AdaptHealth Corp.; *U.S. Public*, pg. 39
RELIANT MEDICAL SYSTEMS, INC.—See Radon Medical Imaging Corp.; *U.S. Private*, pg. 3345
REMOTE MEDICAL INTERNATIONAL, INC.; *U.S. Private*, pg. 3396
RENU MEDICAL INC.—See Getinge AB; *Int'l*, pg. 2948
REPRESENTACIONES TECHLAB S.A.C—See HORIBA Ltd; *Int'l*, pg. 3478
RESMED ASIA OPERATIONS PTY LTD—See ResMed Inc.; *U.S. Public*, pg. 1791
RESMED (BEIJING) TRADING CO., LTD.—See ResMed Inc.; *U.S. Public*, pg. 1790
RESMED GERMANY SAAS HOLDINGS GMBH—See ResMed Inc.; *U.S. Public*, pg. 1791
RESMED LTD.—See ResMed Inc.; *U.S. Public*, pg. 1791
RESMED POLSKA SP ZOO—See ResMed Inc.; *U.S. Public*, pg. 1791
RESPIRATORY HOME CARE OF BRISTOL, LLC—See AdaptHealth Corp.; *U.S. Public*, pg. 39
RESPIRATORY SERVICES OF WESTERN NEW YORK, INC.—See AdaptHealth Corp.; *U.S. Public*, pg. 39
RESPITEK MEDICAL SERVICES; *U.S. Private*, pg. 3407
RGH ENTERPRISES, INC.—See Cardinal Health, Inc.; *U.S. Public*, pg. 433
RHYTHMIA MEDICAL, INC.—See Boston Scientific Corporation; *U.S. Public*, pg. 375
RITE AID OF DELAWARE, INC.—See New Rite Aid, LLC; *U.S. Private*, pg. 2905
RITE AID OF MAINE, INC.—See New Rite Aid, LLC; *U.S. Private*, pg. 2906
RIVERPOINT MEDICAL, LLC—See Arlington Capital Partners LLC; *U.S. Private*, pg. 328
ROBERTS OXYGEN COMPANY INC.; *U.S. Private*, pg. 3460
ROCKLYN MEDICAL SUPPLY, INC.—See Mi-Med Supply Co. Inc.; *U.S. Private*, pg. 2696

ROMEDIC B.V.—See Advent International Corporation; *U.S. Private*, pg. 104
ROPOX A/S—See AddLife AB; *Int'l*, pg. 130
ROZINN ELECTRONICS, INC.—See Berkshire Hathaway Inc.; *U.S. Public*, pg. 300
RXSAFE LLC—See Illinois Tool Works Inc.; *U.S. Public*, pg. 1110
SAAD'S MEDICAL EQUIPMENT INC.—See Saad's Healthcare Services, Inc.; *U.S. Private*, pg. 3519
SAFESKIN MEDICAL & SCIENTIFIC (THAILAND) LIMITED—See Kimberly-Clark Corporation; *U.S. Public*, pg. 1231
SANARE, LLC—See Bertram Capital Management, LLC; *U.S. Private*, pg. 540
SAN JOSE SURGICAL SUPPLY INC.; *U.S. Private*, pg. 3541
SANUWAVE AG—See SANUWAVE Health, Inc.; *U.S. Public*, pg. 1841
SARL DENTIUM MAROC—See Dentium Co., Ltd; *Int'l*, pg. 2034
SAWTOOTH ORTHOTICS AND PROSTHETICS, INC.—See Patient Square Capital, L.P.; *U.S. Private*, pg. 3107
SCAN MODUL BYRUM APS—See Stanley Black & Decker, Inc.; *U.S. Public*, pg. 1934
SCHOOL HEALTH CORPORATION; *U.S. Private*, pg. 3568
SCHRYVER MEDICAL SALES & MARKETING, INC.; *U.S. Private*, pg. 3569
SCIENTIFIC SUPPLIES & TECHNOLOGY INTERNATIONAL INC.; *U.S. Private*, pg. 3574
SCM-VERBOOM—See Groupe Gorge S.A.; *Int'l*, pg. 3103
SCOPIS GMBH—See Stryker Corporation; *U.S. Public*, pg. 1956
SCRIP COMPANIES; *U.S. Private*, pg. 3579
SCRIPHESSCO; *U.S. Private*, pg. 3579
SENGEWALD KLINIKPRODUKTE GMBH—See Monitor Clipper Partners, LLC; *U.S. Private*, pg. 2771
SHANGHAI HESIDI COSMETICS COMPANY LIMITED—See China Regenerative Medicine International Co., Ltd.; *Int'l*, pg. 1547
SHARED SERVICE SYSTEMS INC.—See Nebraska Methodist Health System Inc.; *U.S. Private*, pg. 2878
SHENYANG AOXIN Q & M STOMATOLOGY HOSPITAL CO., LTD.—See Aoxin Q & M Dental Group Limited; *Int'l*, pg. 498
SHENYANG HEPING Q & M AOXIN STOMATOLOGY POLYCLINIC CO., LTD.—See Aoxin Q & M Dental Group Limited; *Int'l*, pg. 498
SHENYANG HUANGGU AOXIN DENTAL CLINIC CO., LTD.—See Aoxin Q & M Dental Group Limited; *Int'l*, pg. 498
SHENYANG MAOTAI Q & M MEDICAL EQUIPMENT CO., LTD.—See Aoxin Q & M Dental Group Limited; *Int'l*, pg. 498
SHENYANG QINGAOMEI ORAL RESTORATIVE TECHNOLOGY CO., LTD.—See Aoxin Q & M Dental Group Limited; *Int'l*, pg. 498
SHENYANG SHENHE AOXIN STOMATOLOGY POLYCLINIC CO., LTD.—See Aoxin Q & M Dental Group Limited; *Int'l*, pg. 498
SHENZHEN WORLD SURGERY MEDICAL DEVICE TECHNOLOGY CO.,LTD.—See Double Medical Technology Inc.; *Int'l*, pg. 2181
SHIELD RESTRAINT SYSTEMS, INC.—See TransDigm Group Incorporated; *U.S. Public*, pg. 2183
SHIELD RESTRAINT SYSTEMS LTD.—See TransDigm Group Incorporated; *U.S. Public*, pg. 2183
SIA MEDIQ LATVIJA—See Advent International Corporation; *U.S. Private*, pg. 104
SI-BONE DEUTSCHLAND GMBH—See SI-BONE, Inc.; *U.S. Public*, pg. 1876
SI-BONE S.R.L.—See SI-BONE, Inc.; *U.S. Public*, pg. 1876
SI-BONE UK LTD.—See SI-BONE, Inc.; *U.S. Public*, pg. 1876
SINWHA ADVANCE CO., LTD.—See HLB Life Science Co.,Ltd.; *Int'l*, pg. 3430
SIRONA DENTAL GMBH—See DENTSPLY SIRONA Inc.; *U.S. Public*, pg. 655
SIRONA DENTAL MEXICO S. DE R.L. DE C.V.—See DENTSPLY SIRONA Inc.; *U.S. Public*, pg. 655
SIRONA DENTAL SYSTEMS K.K.—See DENTSPLY SIRONA Inc.; *U.S. Public*, pg. 655
SIRONA DENTAL SYSTEMS KOREA, LTD.—See DENTSPLY SIRONA Inc.; *U.S. Public*, pg. 655
SIRONA DENTAL SYSTEMS PRIVATE LTD.—See DENTSPLY SIRONA Inc.; *U.S. Public*, pg. 655
SIRONA DENTAL SYSTEMS PTE. LTD—See DENTSPLY SIRONA Inc.; *U.S. Public*, pg. 655
SIRONA DENTAL SYSTEMS SAS—See DENTSPLY SIRONA Inc.; *U.S. Public*, pg. 655
SIRONA DENTAL SYSTEMS SOUTH AFRICA (PTY) LTD.—See DENTSPLY SIRONA Inc.; *U.S. Public*, pg. 655
SIRONA VERWALTUNGS GMBH—See DENTSPLY SIRONA Inc.; *U.S. Public*, pg. 655
SIZEWISE RENTALS, L.L.C.—See Thomas H. Lee Partners, L.P.; *U.S. Private*, pg. 4156

SKORO ENTERPRISES LLC—See AdaptHealth Corp.; *U.S. Public*, pg. 39
SKULLS UNLIMITED INTERNATIONAL, INC.; *U.S. Private*, pg. 3683
SLEEPTECH LIMITED—See ResMed Inc.; *U.S. Public*, pg. 1791
SMARTHEALTH INC.; *U.S. Private*, pg. 3692
SMARTPRACTICE.COM—See Smarthealth Inc.; *U.S. Private*, pg. 3692
SMITH & SCHAEFER INC.; *U.S. Private*, pg. 3694
SMITHS MEDICAL (BEIJING) CO., LTD.—See ICU Medical, Inc.; *U.S. Public*, pg. 1087
SMITHS MEDICAL BELGIUM N.V.—See ICU Medical, Inc.; *U.S. Public*, pg. 1087
SMITHS MEDICAL CANADA LTD.—See ICU Medical, Inc.; *U.S. Public*, pg. 1087
SMITHS MEDICAL DENMARK APS—See ICU Medical, Inc.; *U.S. Public*, pg. 1087
SMITHS MEDICAL ESPANA, S.R.L.—See ICU Medical, Inc.; *U.S. Public*, pg. 1087
SMITHS MEDICAL GROUP LIMITED—See ICU Medical, Inc.; *U.S. Public*, pg. 1087
SMITHS MEDICAL ITALIA S.R.L.—See ICU Medical, Inc.; *U.S. Public*, pg. 1087
SMITHS MEDICAL (PORTUGAL) UNIPESSOAL LDA.—See ICU Medical, Inc.; *U.S. Public*, pg. 1087
SMITHS MEDICAL SVERIGE AB—See ICU Medical, Inc.; *U.S. Public*, pg. 1087
SNAKY CREEK ENTERPRISES, LLC; *U.S. Private*, pg. 3699
SOCOMA-PERTEN SAS—See Revvity, Inc.; *U.S. Public*, pg. 1795
SOLUSCOPE INTERNATIONAL TRADING (SHANGHAI) CO., LTD.—See Ecolab Inc.; *U.S. Public*, pg. 716
SOMARO—See Bouygues S.A.; *Int'l*, pg. 1123
SOMERSET MED SERVICES, INC.—See MedCare Equipment Company, LLC; *U.S. Private*, pg. 2651
SONIC INNOVATIONS CANADA LTD.—See Demant A/S; *Int'l*, pg. 2024
SONOMA PHARMACEUTICALS NETHERLANDS B.V.—See Sonoma Pharmaceuticals, Inc.; *U.S. Public*, pg. 1909
SONOSITE LTD.—See FUJIFILM Holdings Corporation; *Int'l*, pg. 2823
SONOSITE (SHANGHAI) CO. LTD.—See FUJIFILM Holdings Corporation; *Int'l*, pg. 2823
SOUTHERN HOME RESPIRATORY & EQUIPMENT, INC.—See AdaptHealth Corp.; *U.S. Public*, pg. 39
SOUTHERN LIFE SYSTEMS, INC.—See ADDvise Group AB; *Int'l*, pg. 136
SOUTHERN PROSTHETIC SUPPLY, INC.—See Patient Square Capital, L.P.; *U.S. Private*, pg. 3107
SP ABLEWARE—See Harbour Group Industries, Inc.; *U.S. Private*, pg. 1861
SPACELABS HEALTHCARE (CANADA), INC.—See OSI Systems, Inc.; *U.S. Public*, pg. 1622
SPACELABS HEALTHCARE, LLC—See OSI Systems, Inc.; *U.S. Public*, pg. 1622
SPACELABS HEALTHCARE LTD.—See OSI Systems, Inc.; *U.S. Public*, pg. 1622
SPACELABS HEALTHCARE SAS—See OSI Systems, Inc.; *U.S. Public*, pg. 1622
SPAEQUIP, INC.; *U.S. Private*, pg. 3744
SPAIN DENTAL EXPRESS S.A.U.—See Henry Schein, Inc.; *U.S. Public*, pg. 1027
SPECIALTY CARTS, INC.—See Levine Leichtman Capital Partners, LLC; *U.S. Private*, pg. 2436
SPECTRA MEDICAL DEVICES, LLC—See QHP Capital, L.P.; *U.S. Private*, pg. 3313
SPIRO HEALTH SERVICES, LLC—See AdaptHealth Corp.; *U.S. Public*, pg. 39
SRW INDUSTRIES CORPORATION; *U.S. Private*, pg. 3768
STARMEDTEC GMBH—See Boston Scientific Corporation; *U.S. Public*, pg. 375
STATESERV MEDICAL, LLC; *U.S. Private*, pg. 3793
STATLAB MEDICAL PRODUCTS, LLC—See Audax Group, Limited Partnership; *U.S. Private*, pg. 389
STIRILAB S.R.O.—See Dominique Dutscher SAS; *Int'l*, pg. 2161
STORAGE SYSTEMS UNLIMITED, INC.—See Cme Corporation; *U.S. Private*, pg. 950
STRATEC MEDICAL LDA.—See Johnson & Johnson; *U.S. Public*, pg. 1195
STRATEC MEDICAL MEDIZINTECHNIK GMBH—See Johnson & Johnson; *U.S. Public*, pg. 1195
STRATEC MEDICAL S.P.A.—See Johnson & Johnson; *U.S. Public*, pg. 1195
STRYKER AUSTRALIA PTY. LTD.—See Stryker Corporation; *U.S. Public*, pg. 1956
STRYKER BENELUX—See Stryker Corporation; *U.S. Public*, pg. 1956
STRYKER CANADA HOLDING COMPANY—See Stryker Corporation; *U.S. Public*, pg. 1956
STRYKER INDIA PRIVATE LIMITED—See Stryker Corporation; *U.S. Public*, pg. 1957
STRYKER LEIBINGER INC.—See Stryker Corporation; *U.S. Public*, pg. 1957
STRYKER S.A.-EUROPEAN HEADQUARTERS—See

Stryker Corporation; *U.S. Public*, pg. 1957
STRYKER SINGAPORE PRIVATE LIMITED—See Stryker Corporation; *U.S. Public*, pg. 1957
SUNCOAST ORTHOTICS & PROSTHETICS, INC.—See Patient Square Capital, L.P.; *U.S. Private*, pg. 3107
SUN MEDICAL INC.; *U.S. Private*, pg. 3863
SUN-MED, LLC—See HCA Healthcare, Inc.; *U.S. Public*, pg. 1011
SUNRISE MEDICAL CANADA INC.—See Vestar Capital Partners, LLC; *U.S. Public*, pg. 4372
SUNRISE MEDICAL GMBH—See Vestar Capital Partners, LLC; *U.S. Public*, pg. 4372
SUNRISE MEDICAL LONG TERM CARE—See Vestar Capital Partners, LLC; *U.S. Private*, pg. 4372
SUNTECH MEDICAL, INC.—See Halma plc; *Int'l*, pg. 3233
SUPERIOR ECONOMIC MED PRODUCTS CO.; *U.S. Private*, pg. 3876
SUPERIOR ORTHOTICS & PROSTHETICS, LLC—See Patient Square Capital, L.P.; *U.S. Private*, pg. 3107
SURGICAL PRINCIPALS, INC.; *U.S. Private*, pg. 3884
SURGI-CARE, INC.—See Envois Corporation; *U.S. Public*, pg. 773
SUZHOU DIVA LAB. INC.—See Diva Laboratories Ltd.; *Int'l*, pg. 2137
SUZHOU SNAKE MEDICAL TECHNOLOGY CONSULTING SERVICE CO., LTD.—See B. Braun Melsungen AG; *Int'l*, pg. 788
SUZHOU VICTOR MEDICAL EQUIPMENT CO., LTD.—See Cefla S.C.; *Int'l*, pg. 1390
SWISSMED PTE. LTD.—See EBOS Group Limited; *Int'l*, pg. 2286
SWISSMED SDN. BHD.—See EBOS Group Limited; *Int'l*, pg. 2286
SYNERON CANDELA CO., LTD.—See Apax Partners LLP; *Int'l*, pg. 506
SYNERON CANDELA CORPORATION AUSTRALIA PTY LTD—See Apax Partners LLP; *Int'l*, pg. 506
SYNERON CANDELA S.A.—See Apax Partners LLP; *Int'l*, pg. 506
SYNERON CANDELA (UK) LIMITED—See Apax Partners LLP; *Int'l*, pg. 506
SYNERON MEDICAL (HK) LTD.—See Apax Partners LLP; *Int'l*, pg. 506
SYNTHES AB—See Johnson & Johnson; *U.S. Public*, pg. 1195
SYNTHES ARGENTINA S.A.—See Johnson & Johnson; *U.S. Public*, pg. 1195
SYNTHES COLOMBIA LTDA—See Johnson & Johnson; *U.S. Public*, pg. 1195
SYNTHES, GMBH - EUROPEAN HEADQUARTERS—See Johnson & Johnson; *U.S. Public*, pg. 1195
SYNTHES GMBH—See Johnson & Johnson; *U.S. Public*, pg. 1195
SYNTHES IND. COM. LTDA.—See Johnson & Johnson; *U.S. Public*, pg. 1195
SYNTHES LTD.—See Johnson & Johnson; *U.S. Public*, pg. 1195
SYNTHES MEDICAL KFT.—See Johnson & Johnson; *U.S. Public*, pg. 1195
SYNTHES S.R.O.—See Johnson & Johnson; *U.S. Public*, pg. 1195
SYNTHES STRATEC—See Johnson & Johnson; *U.S. Public*, pg. 1195
TACTICAL MEDICAL SOLUTIONS, INC.—See CNL Strategic Capital Management LLC; *U.S. Private*, pg. 952
TACTILE SYSTEMS TECHNOLOGY, INC.; *U.S. Public*, pg. 1978
T&C BIO TECHNOLOGY—See Dentium Co., Ltd; *Int'l*, pg. 2034
TDSC, INC.—See Henry Schein, Inc.; *U.S. Public*, pg. 1027
TECHNICAL PROSPECTS LLC—See NMS Capital Services, LLC; *U.S. Private*, pg. 2931
TECHNO-PATH (DISTRIBUTION) LIMITED—See Diploma PLC; *Int'l*, pg. 2129
TELEFLEX MEDICAL AUSTRALIA PTY LTD—See Teleflex Incorporated; *U.S. Public*, pg. 1995
TELEFLEX MEDICAL CANADA INC.—See Teleflex Incorporated; *U.S. Public*, pg. 1996
TELEFLEX MEDICAL COLOMBIA SAS—See Teleflex Incorporated; *U.S. Public*, pg. 1995
TELEFLEX MEDICAL GMBH—See Teleflex Incorporated; *U.S. Public*, pg. 1995
TELEFLEX MEDICAL JAPAN, LTD.—See Teleflex Incorporated; *U.S. Public*, pg. 1996
TELEFLEX MEDICAL (PROPRIETARY) LIMITED—See Teleflex Incorporated; *U.S. Public*, pg. 1996
TELEFLEX MEDICAL, S.R.O.—See Teleflex Incorporated; *U.S. Public*, pg. 1996
TENVISION, LLC—See Avista Capital Partners, L.P.; *U.S. Private*, pg. 409
TESTAR ELECTRONICS CORPORATION—See Chroma ATE Inc.; *Int'l*, pg. 1588
THERAPAK LLC—See Avantor, Inc.; *U.S. Public*, pg. 241
THERAPY SUPPORT, INC.—See New Mountain Capital, LLC; *U.S. Private*, pg. 2903
THERMO FISHER DIAGNOSTICS SAS—See Thermo Fisher Scientific Inc.; *U.S. Public*, pg. 2152
THERMO FISHER SCIENTIFIC B.V.B.A.—See Thermo Fisher Scientific Inc.; *U.S. Public*, pg. 2153
THERMO SCIENTIFIC MICROBIOLOGY PTE LTD.—See Thermo Fisher Scientific Inc.; *U.S. Public*, pg. 2154
THREE RIVERS ORTHOPEDIC & SPINE PRODUCTS, INC.; *U.S. Private*, pg. 4164
TIANJIN WEIKAI BIOENG LTD.—See China Regenerative Medicine International Co., Ltd.; *Int'l*, pg. 1547
TMS VT, LLC—See AdaptHealth Corp.; *U.S. Public*, pg. 39
TOHOKU ALFRESA CORPORATION—See Alfresa Holdings Corporation; *Int'l*, pg. 317
TOP-SERVICE FUR LINGUALTECHNIK GMBH—See Solventum Corporation; *U.S. Public*, pg. 1902
T-PLEX INDUSTRIES, INC.—See Federated Healthcare Supply Holdings, Inc.; *U.S. Private*, pg. 1491
TRANSMEDIC CHINA LTD.—See EBOS Group Limited; *Int'l*, pg. 2286
TRANSMEDIC COMPANY LTD.—See EBOS Group Limited; *Int'l*, pg. 2286
TRANSMEDIC PHILIPPINES, INC.—See EBOS Group Limited; *Int'l*, pg. 2286
TRANSMEDIC PTE. LTD.—See EBOS Group Limited; *Int'l*, pg. 2286
TRANSMEDIC (THAILAND) CO. LTD.—See EBOS Group Limited; *Int'l*, pg. 2286
TRANS-MED USA INC.; *U.S. Private*, pg. 4206
TRI-COUNTY MEDICAL & OSTOMY SUPPLIES, INC.—See Becton, Dickinson & Company; *U.S. Public*, pg. 291
TRI-STATE SURGICAL SUPPLY & EQUIPMENT LTD.; *U.S. Private*, pg. 4224
TRUE HEALTHCARE INDIA PVT. LTD.—See Berjaya Corporation Berhad; *Int'l*, pg. 985
TRUMPF MED ITALIA S.R.L.—See Baxter International Inc.; *U.S. Public*, pg. 283
TRUPHATEK (BEIJING) TRADING CO., LTD.—See Teleflex Incorporated; *U.S. Public*, pg. 1996
TRUPHATEK INTERNATIONAL LIMITED—See Teleflex Incorporated; *U.S. Public*, pg. 1996
TRUPHATEK PRODUCT RESOURCES INDIA PRIVATE LIMITED—See Teleflex Incorporated; *U.S. Public*, pg. 1996
TS ALFRESA CORPORATION—See Alfresa Holdings Corporation; *Int'l*, pg. 317
TSO3 CORPORATION—See Stryker Corporation; *U.S. Public*, pg. 1957
TSO3 INC.—See Stryker Corporation; *U.S. Public*, pg. 1957
TUFFCARE INC.; *U.S. Private*, pg. 4257
TUTTNAUER U.S.A. CO., LTD.—See Fortissimo Capital Management Ltd.; *Int'l*, pg. 2740
TWIN MED LLC—See TA Associates, Inc.; *U.S. Private*, pg. 3919
TWIN RIVERS RESPIRATORY CARE, INC.—See AdaptHealth Corp.; *U.S. Public*, pg. 39
ULTIMA RX, LLC—See UnitedHealth Group Incorporated; *U.S. Public*, pg. 2251
ULTRA-VIOLET PRODUCTS LTD.—See Endress+Hauser (International) Holding AG; *Int'l*, pg. 2405
UMECO, INC.—See Cesar Castillo, Inc.; *U.S. Private*, pg. 842
UMG / DEL MEDICAL—See United Marketing Group, Inc.; *U.S. Private*, pg. 4294
UNITECH LIMITED—See Clayton, Dubilier & Rice, LLC; *U.S. Private*, pg. 928
UNITED MARKETING GROUP, INC.; *U.S. Private*, pg. 4294
UNITRACT SYRINGE PTY LIMITED—See Unilife Corporation; *U.S. Private*, pg. 4283
UNIVERSAL MEDICAL SYSTEMS, INC.—See Merry X-Ray Corporation; *U.S. Private*, pg. 2676
USDIAGNOSTICS, INC.; *U.S. Private*, pg. 4322
US DIAGNOSTICS, INC.—See Abbott Laboratories; *U.S. Public*, pg. 19
U.S. MED-EQUIP, INC.—See Freeman Spogli & Co. Incorporated; *U.S. Private*, pg. 1606
VALTECH CARDIO, LTD.—See Edwards Lifesciences Corporation; *U.S. Public*, pg. 721
VANTAGE MEDICAL SUPPLIES, INC.—See Dealmed Medical Supplies LLC; *U.S. Private*, pg. 1183
VAREX IMAGING NEDERLAND B.V.—See Varex Imaging Corporation; *U.S. Public*, pg. 2275
VARINAK ONKOLOJI SISTEMLERI SATIS VE SERVIS A.S.—See Bozlu Holding; *Int'l*, pg. 1125
VARVAN LTDA.—See Dentium Co., Ltd; *Int'l*, pg. 2034
VAUDAUX-EPPENDORF AG—See Eppendorf AG; *Int'l*, pg. 2465
VENOSAN NORTH AMERICA, INC.—See Ames Walker International Inc.; *U.S. Private*, pg. 262
VERATHON MEDICAL (AUSTRAILIA) PTY LIMITED—See Roper Technologies, Inc.; *U.S. Public*, pg. 1814
VERNAY BRASIL LTDA—See Vernay Laboratories, Inc.; *U.S. Private*, pg. 4368
VERTEC SCIENTIFIC LTD.—See discoverIE Group plc; *Int'l*, pg. 2134
VERTIC SUISSE SARL—See Delta Plus Group; *Int'l*, pg. 2020
VERTOS MEDICAL INC.—See Stryker Corporation; *U.S. Public*, pg. 1958
VETERINARY SERVICE INC.; *U.S. Private*, pg. 4374
VEXIM ITALIA SRL—See Stryker Corporation; *U.S. Public*, pg. 1958
VEXIM SPINE SL—See Stryker Corporation; *U.S. Public*, pg. 1958
VHS GROUP, LLC; *U.S. Public*, pg. 4375
VIETNAM CREATE MEDIC CO., LTD.—See CREATE MEDIC CO. LTD.; *Int'l*, pg. 1832
VITAL IMAGES CHINA—See Canon Inc.; *Int'l*, pg. 1298
VITAL IMAGES EUROPE B.V.—See Canon, Inc.; *Int'l*, pg. 1298
VITAL IMAGES, INC.—See Canon Inc.; *Int'l*, pg. 1298
VITALMED, INC.—See Kohlberg & Company, LLC; *U.S. Private*, pg. 2338
VOLLRATH DE MEXICO S. DE R.L. DE C.V.—See The Vollrath Company LLC; *U.S. Private*, pg. 4132
V-TECH AB—See AddLife AB; *Int'l*, pg. 130
VWR INTERNATIONAL CO.—See Avantor, Inc.; *U.S. Public*, pg. 241
VWR INTERNATIONAL EUROLAB, S.L.—See Avantor, Inc.; *U.S. Public*, pg. 242
VWR INTERNATIONAL, LLC—See Avantor, Inc.; *U.S. Public*, pg. 241
WAND DENTAL , INC.—See Milestone Scientific, Inc.; *U.S. Public*, pg. 1446
WARNER & WEBSTER PTY LTD—See EBOS Group Limited; *Int'l*, pg. 2286
WASATCH ORTHOTICS & PEDORTHICS, LLC—See Patient Square Capital, L.P.; *U.S. Private*, pg. 3107
WAVE FORM SYSTEMS INC.; *U.S. Private*, pg. 4458
WECARE MEDICAL, LLC—See AdaptHealth Corp.; *U.S. Public*, pg. 39
WELCH ALLYN CANADA LTD.—See Baxter International Inc.; *U.S. Public*, pg. 284
WELCH ALLYN DE MEXICO S. DE R.L. DE C.V.—See Baxter International Inc.; *U.S. Public*, pg. 284
WELCH ALLYN MALAYSIA SDN. BHD—See Baxter International Inc.; *U.S. Public*, pg. 284
WELCH ALLYN PRODUCTOS MEDICOS S. DE R.L. DE C.V.—See Baxter International Inc.; *U.S. Public*, pg. 284
WELCH ALLYN SOUTH AFRICA PTY, LTD.—See Baxter International Inc.; *U.S. Public*, pg. 284
WELCH ALLYN SVERIGE—See Baxter International Inc.; *U.S. Public*, pg. 284
WELLSPECT HEALTHCARE - UROLOGY DIVISION—See DENTSPLY SIRONA Inc.; *U.S. Public*, pg. 655
WELLSPECT HEALTHCARE - UROLOGY DIVISION—See DENTSPLY SIRONA Inc.; *U.S. Public*, pg. 656
WESTERN QUARTZ PRODUCTS, INC.—See Forsyth Capital Investors LLC; *U.S. Private*, pg. 1573
WHEELER'S MEDICAL SUPPLY LLC—See AEA Investors LP; *U.S. Private*, pg. 116
WHITE MOUNTAIN IMAGING INC.; *U.S. Private*, pg. 4509
WHITEROCK INCORPORATION PRIVATE LIMITED—See Boustead Singapore Limited; *Int'l*, pg. 1121
WIDEX AKUSTIK OY—See EQT AB; *Int'l*, pg. 2480
WIDEX ALGERIE EURL—See EQT AB; *Int'l*, pg. 2480
WIDEX ARGENTINA SA—See EQT AB; *Int'l*, pg. 2480
WIDEX A.S.—See EQT AB; *Int'l*, pg. 2480
WIDEX AUDIFONOS S.A.—See EQT AB; *Int'l*, pg. 2480
WIDEX AUSTRALIA PTY LTD—See EQT AB; *Int'l*, pg. 2480
WIDEX CANADA LTD.—See EQT AB; *Int'l*, pg. 2480
WIDEX CHILE SPA.—See EQT AB; *Int'l*, pg. 2480
WIDEX COLOMBIA LTDA.—See EQT AB; *Int'l*, pg. 2480
WIDEX CO., LTD.—See EQT AB; *Int'l*, pg. 2480
WIDEX DOMINICANA, SRL—See EQT AB; *Int'l*, pg. 2480
WIDEX D.O.O—See EQT AB; *Int'l*, pg. 2481
WIDEX-EGYPT—See EQT AB; *Int'l*, pg. 2481
WIDEX EMIRATES HEARING CARE—See EQT AB; *Int'l*, pg. 2480
WIDEX FRANCE SAS—See EQT AB; *Int'l*, pg. 2480
WIDEX HEARING AID (SHANGHAI) CO. LTD.—See EQT AB; *Int'l*, pg. 2480
WIDEX-H KFT.—See EQT AB; *Int'l*, pg. 2481
WIDEX HORGERATE GMBH—See EQT AB; *Int'l*, pg. 2480
WIDEX INDIA PRIVATE LIMITED—See EQT AB; *Int'l*, pg. 2481
WIDEX IRELAND LTD.—See EQT AB; *Int'l*, pg. 2481
WIDEX ITALIA S.P.A—See EQT AB; *Int'l*, pg. 2481
WIDEX KOREA LTD.—See EQT AB; *Int'l*, pg. 2481
WIDEX LIBYA—See EQT AB; *Int'l*, pg. 2481
WIDEX LINE S.R.O.—See EQT AB; *Int'l*, pg. 2481
WIDEX MAROC—See EQT AB; *Int'l*, pg. 2481
WIDEX MEDICAL EQUIPMENT—See EQT AB; *Int'l*, pg. 2481
WIDEX NEW ZEALAND LTD.—See EQT AB; *Int'l*, pg. 2481
WIDEX PANAMA—See EQT AB; *Int'l*, pg. 2481
WIDEX POLSKA SP. Z.O.O.—See EQT AB; *Int'l*, pg. 2481
WIDEX - REABILITACAO AUDITIVA, LDA.—See EQT AB; *Int'l*, pg. 2480
WIDEX SINGAPORE PTE LTD—See EQT AB; *Int'l*, pg. 2481
WIDEX SLUSNI APARATI D.O.O—See EQT AB; *Int'l*, pg. 2481
WIDEX SOUTH AFRICA (PTY) LTD.—See EQT AB; *Int'l*, pg. 2481
W. L. GORE & ASSOCIATES CANADA, INC.—See W.L. Gore & Associates, Inc.; *U.S. Private*, pg. 4421
W. L. GORE & ASSOCIATES HONG KONG, LTD.—See W.L. Gore & Associates, Inc.; *U.S. Private*, pg. 4421
W. L. GORE & ASSOCIES S.A.R.L.—See W.L. Gore & Associates, Inc.; *U.S. Private*, pg. 4421

N.A.I.C.S. INDEX

423460 — OPHTHALMIC GOODS ME...

W. L. GORE Y ASOCIADOS, S.L.—See W.L. Gore & Associates, Inc.; *U.S. Private*, pg. 4421
W.O.M. WORLD OF MEDICINE ASIA LTD.—See Novanta Inc.; *U.S. Public*, pg. 1548
W.O.M. WORLD OF MEDICINE USA, INC.—See Novanta Inc.; *U.S. Public*, pg. 1548
WORLD REACH HEALTH, LLC—See Healthtech Solutions, Inc.; *U.S. Public*, pg. 1017
X-RAY INC. OF RHODE ISLAND; *U.S. Private*, pg. 4579
X-RAY OPTICAL SYSTEMS, INC.—See Danaher Corporation; *U.S. Public*, pg. 632
X-RAY VISIONS, INC.—See Atlantic Street Capital Management LLC; *U.S. Private*, pg. 374
ZAG USA, INC.—See Stanley Black & Decker, Inc.; *U.S. Public*, pg. 1936
ZENECA INTERNATIONAL LTD.—See AstraZeneca PLC; *Int'l*, pg. 661
ZHUANGHE CITY AOXIN DAWEI DENTAL CO., LTD.—See Aoxin Q & M Dental Group Limited; *Int'l*, pg. 498
ZIMMER BIOMET AUSTRIA GMBH—See Zimmer Biomet Holdings, Inc.; *U.S. Public*, pg. 2406
ZIMMER BIOMET BVBA—See Zimmer Biomet Holdings, Inc.; *U.S. Public*, pg. 2406
ZIMMER BIOMET BVBA—See Zimmer Biomet Holdings, Inc.; *U.S. Public*, pg. 2407
ZIMMER BIOMET CANADA, INC.—See Zimmer Biomet Holdings, Inc.; *U.S. Public*, pg. 2407
ZIMMER BIOMET DENMARK APS—See Zimmer Biomet Holdings, Inc.; *U.S. Public*, pg. 2407
ZIMMER BIOMET DENTAL CANADA INC.—See Zimmer Biomet Holdings, Inc.; *U.S. Public*, pg. 2407
ZIMMER BIOMET FINLAND OY—See Zimmer Biomet Holdings, Inc.; *U.S. Public*, pg. 2407
ZIMMER BIOMET FRANCE SAS—See Zimmer Biomet Holdings, Inc.; *U.S. Public*, pg. 2407
ZIMMER BIOMET GK—See Zimmer Biomet Holdings, Inc.; *U.S. Public*, pg. 2407
ZIMMER BIOMET KOREA CO., LTD.—See Zimmer Biomet Holdings, Inc.; *U.S. Public*, pg. 2407
ZIMMER BIOMET NORWAY AS—See Zimmer Biomet Holdings, Inc.; *U.S. Public*, pg. 2407
ZIMMER BIOMET POLSKA SP. Z.O.O.—See Zimmer Biomet Holdings, Inc.; *U.S. Public*, pg. 2407
ZIMMER BIOMET PTY. LTD.—See Zimmer Biomet Holdings, Inc.; *U.S. Public*, pg. 2407
ZIMMER BIOMET SOUTH AFRICA (PTY) LTD.—See Zimmer Biomet Holdings, Inc.; *U.S. Public*, pg. 2407
ZIMMER CIS LTD.—See Zimmer Biomet Holdings, Inc.; *U.S. Public*, pg. 2407
ZIMMER CZECH SRO—See Zimmer Biomet Holdings, Inc.; *U.S. Public*, pg. 2407
ZIMMER DENTAL LTD.—See Zimmer Biomet Holdings, Inc.; *U.S. Public*, pg. 2407
ZIMMER MEDICAL MALAYSIA SDN BHD—See Zimmer Biomet Holdings, Inc.; *U.S. Public*, pg. 2407
ZIMMER MEDICAL (THAILAND) CO., LTD.—See Zimmer Biomet Holdings, Inc.; *U.S. Public*, pg. 2407
ZIMMER PTE. LTD.—See Zimmer Biomet Holdings, Inc.; *U.S. Public*, pg. 2407
ZIMMER (SHANGHAI) MEDICAL INTERNATIONAL TRADING CO., LTD.—See Zimmer Biomet Holdings, Inc.; *U.S. Public*, pg. 2406
ZINSSER ANALYTIC GMBH—See Ingersoll Rand Inc.; *U.S. Public*, pg. 1120
ZINSSER NA, INC.—See Ingersoll Rand Inc.; *U.S. Public*, pg. 1120
Z-MEDICA, LLC—See Teleflex Incorporated; *U.S. Public*, pg. 1996

423460 — OPHTHALMIC GOODS MERCHANT WHOLESALERS

ABB CONCISE INC.—See ABB/Con-Cise Optical Group LLC; *U.S. Private*, pg. 34
ABB/CON-CISE OPTICAL GROUP LLC; *U.S. Private*, pg. 34
ABILITY OPTO-ELECTRONICS TECHNOLOGY CO., LTD.; *Int'l*, pg. 61
ALCADON APS—See Alcadon Group AB; *Int'l*, pg. 300
ALCADON GMBH—See Alcadon Group AB; *Int'l*, pg. 300
ALLERGAN K.K.—See AbbVie Inc.; *U.S. Public*, pg. 23
ALLERGAN S.A. DE C.V.—See AbbVie Inc.; *U.S. Public*, pg. 23
AMO (SHANGHAI) MEDICAL DEVICES TRADING CO., LTD.—See Johnson & Johnson; *U.S. Public*, pg. 1193
ATASUN OPTIK A.S.—See HAL Trust N.V.; *Int'l*, pg. 3223
AVANSTRATE TAIWAN INC.—See Hoya Corporation; *Int'l*, pg. 3495
BAUSCH & LOMB B.V.B.A.—See Bausch Health Companies Inc.; *Int'l*, pg. 896
BAUSCH & LOMB EYECARE (INDIA) PVT LTD.—See Bausch Health Companies Inc.; *Int'l*, pg. 896
BAUSCH & LOMB GESELLSCHAFT M.B.H.—See Bausch Health Companies Inc.; *Int'l*, pg. 897
BAUSCH & LOMB GREECE—See Bausch Health Companies Inc.; *Int'l*, pg. 896
BAUSCH & LOMB (HK) LTD.—See Bausch Health Companies Inc.; *Int'l*, pg. 896
BAUSCH & LOMB KOREA, CO. LTD.—See Bausch Health Companies Inc.; *Int'l*, pg. 896
BAUSCH & LOMB NORDIC AB—See Bausch Health Companies Inc.; *Int'l*, pg. 896
BAUSCH & LOMB PHILIPPINES, INC.—See Bausch Health Companies Inc.; *Int'l*, pg. 896
BAUSCH & LOMB PUERTO RICO INC.—See Bausch Health Companies Inc.; *Int'l*, pg. 896
BAUSCH & LOMB (SINGAPORE) PRIVATE LIMITED—See Bausch Health Companies Inc.; *Int'l*, pg. 896
BAUSCH & LOMB U.K. LIMITED—See Bausch Health Companies Inc.; *Int'l*, pg. 896
BOLLE AUSTRALIA PTY LTD—See Alvarez & Marsal, Inc.; *U.S. Private*, pg. 212
BOLLE BRANDS SAS—See Alvarez & Marsal, Inc.; *U.S. Private*, pg. 212
BUSHNELL OUTDOOR PRODUCTS JAPAN LIMITED—See Vista Outdoor Inc.; *U.S. Public*, pg. 2304
BUSHNELL OUTDOOR PRODUCTS SPAIN, S.A.U.—See Vista Outdoor Inc.; *U.S. Public*, pg. 2304
BUSHNELL PERFORMANCE OPTICS ASIA LIMITED—See Vista Outdoor Inc.; *U.S. Public*, pg. 2305
BUSHNELL PERFORMANCE OPTICS GERMANY GMBH—See Vista Outdoor Inc.; *U.S. Public*, pg. 2305
BUSHNELL PERFORMANCE OPTICS ITALY S.R.L.—See Vista Outdoor Inc.; *U.S. Public*, pg. 2305
BUSHNELL PERFORMANCE OPTICS MEXICO S.A. DE C.V.—See Vista Outdoor Inc.; *U.S. Public*, pg. 2305
BUSHNELL PERFORMANCE OPTICS UK LIMITED—See Vista Outdoor Inc.; *U.S. Public*, pg. 2305
CANOPTEC INC.—See EssilorLuxottica SA; *Int'l*, pg. 2512
CASCADE OPTICAL LTD.—See EssilorLuxottica SA; *Int'l*, pg. 2512
CORNING DISPLAY TECHNOLOGIES (CHONGQING) CO., LTD.—See Corning Incorporated; *U.S. Public*, pg. 578
CORNING DISPLAY TECHNOLOGIES (HEFEI) CO., LTD.—See Corning Incorporated; *U.S. Public*, pg. 578
CORNING (HAINAN) OPTICAL COMMUNICATIONS CO., LTD.—See Corning Incorporated; *U.S. Public*, pg. 578
CORNING TECHNOLOGIES INDIA PRIVATE LIMITED—See Corning Incorporated; *U.S. Public*, pg. 578
COWELL ELECTRONICS COMPANY LIMITED—See Cowell e Holdings Inc.; *Int'l*, pg. 1821
COWELL OPTIC ELECTRONICS LIMITED—See Cowell e Holdings Inc.; *Int'l*, pg. 1821
DEEPEYE CO., LTD.—See ESTsoft Corp; *Int'l*, pg. 2519
DOCTORGLASSES CHAIN CO LTD; *Int'l*, pg. 2153
EASY VISION—See EssilorLuxottica SA; *Int'l*, pg. 2512
EIS OPTICS LIMITED—See Materion Corporation; *U.S. Public*, pg. 1395
EIS OPTICS (SHANGHAI) LIMITED—See Materion Corporation; *U.S. Public*, pg. 1395
ELOA CALIFORNIA ACQUISITION CORP.—See EssilorLuxottica SA; *Int'l*, pg. 2513
ESCHENBACH OPTIK A/S—See Equistone Partners Europe Limited; *Int'l*, pg. 2486
ESCHENBACH OPTIK BV—See Equistone Partners Europe Limited; *Int'l*, pg. 2486
ESCHENBACH OPTIK GMBH—See Equistone Partners Europe Limited; *Int'l*, pg. 2486
ESCHENBACH OPTIK OF JAPAN CO. LTD.—See Equistone Partners Europe Limited; *Int'l*, pg. 2486
ESCHENBACH OPTIK POLEN SP.Z.O.O.—See Equistone Partners Europe Limited; *Int'l*, pg. 2486
ESCHENBACH OPTIK S.A.R.L.—See Equistone Partners Europe Limited; *Int'l*, pg. 2486
ESCHENBACH OPTIK S.L.—See Equistone Partners Europe Limited; *Int'l*, pg. 2486
ESCHENBACH OPTIK SPOL S.R.O.—See Equistone Partners Europe Limited; *Int'l*, pg. 2486
ESCHENBACH OPTIK S.R.L.—See Equistone Partners Europe Limited; *Int'l*, pg. 2486
ESSILOR AB—See EssilorLuxottica SA; *Int'l*, pg. 2512
ESSILOR AUSTRIA GMBH—See EssilorLuxottica SA; *Int'l*, pg. 2512
ESSILOR GROUP THE NETHERLANDS B.V—See EssilorLuxottica SA; *Int'l*, pg. 2512
ESSILOR LENS & SPECTS P LTD—See EssilorLuxottica SA; *Int'l*, pg. 2513
ESSILOR MEXICO S.A DE CV—See EssilorLuxottica SA; *Int'l*, pg. 2513
ESSILOR NORGE A.S.—See EssilorLuxottica SA; *Int'l*, pg. 2513
EUROKERA (THAILAND) LIMITED—See Corning Incorporated; *U.S. Public*, pg. 579
EYECONIC, INC.—See Vision Service Plan; *U.S. Private*, pg. 4391
EYEWEAR DESIGNS, LTD.; *U.S. Private*, pg. 1453
FGX DIRECT LLC—See EssilorLuxottica SA; *Int'l*, pg. 2514
FIELMANN AG & CO. DERENDORF OHG—See Fielmann Group AG; *Int'l*, pg. 2656
FIELMANN AG & CO. EKZ HAMBURGER STRASSE KG—See Fielmann Group AG; *Int'l*, pg. 2656
FIELMANN AG & CO. KG—See Fielmann Group AG; *Int'l*, pg. 2656
FIELMANN AG & CO. OHG CITY-GALERIE—See Fielmann Group AG; *Int'l*, pg. 2658
FIELMANN AG & CO. RIEM ARCADEN KG—See Fielmann Group AG; *Int'l*, pg. 2657
FRAMES DATA INC.—See The Wicks Group of Companies, LLC; *U.S. Private*, pg. 4135
FUJIFILM HONG KONG LIMITED—See FUJIFILM Holdings Corporation; *Int'l*, pg. 2822
FUJIFILM MEDICAL SYSTEMS USA, INC. - ENDOSCOPY DIV—See FUJIFILM Holdings Corporation; *Int'l*, pg. 2822
GENETIER SAS—See EssilorLuxottica SA; *Int'l*, pg. 2515
HELLMA (ASIA PACIFIC) PTE LTD—See Hellma GmbH & Co. KG; *Int'l*, pg. 3334
HELLMA BENELUX BVBA—See Hellma GmbH & Co. KG; *Int'l*, pg. 3334
HELLMA CANADA LIMITED—See Hellma GmbH & Co. KG; *Int'l*, pg. 3334
HELLMA-FRANCE S.A.R.L.—See Hellma GmbH & Co. KG; *Int'l*, pg. 3335
HELLMA GMBH & CO. KG; *Int'l*, pg. 3334
HELLMA ITALIA S.R.L.—See Hellma GmbH & Co. KG; *Int'l*, pg. 3334
HELLMA MATERIALS GMBH—See Hellma GmbH & Co. KG; *Int'l*, pg. 3334
HELLMA OPTIK GMBH—See Hellma GmbH & Co. KG; *Int'l*, pg. 3334
HELLMA SCHWEIZ AG—See Hellma GmbH & Co. KG; *Int'l*, pg. 3334
HELLMA UK LTD—See Hellma GmbH & Co. KG; *Int'l*, pg. 3334
HELLMA USA INC.—See Hellma GmbH & Co. KG; *Int'l*, pg. 3335
HITACHI HIGH-TECH (SHENZHEN) CO., LTD.—See Hitachi, Ltd.; *Int'l*, pg. 3418
HOLLAND OPTICAL INSTRUMENTS BV—See EssilorLuxottica SA; *Int'l*, pg. 2514
HOMER OPTICAL COMPANY, INC.—See EssilorLuxottica SA; *Int'l*, pg. 2513
HOYA CORPORATION - USA OPTICS DIVISION—See Hoya Corporation; *Int'l*, pg. 3497
HOYA HILL OPTICS SOUTH AFRICA (PTY) LTD.—See Hoya Corporation; *Int'l*, pg. 3494
HOYA LENS OF AMERICA INC.—See Hoya Corporation; *Int'l*, pg. 3496
HOYA LENS OF CHICAGO, INC.—See Hoya Corporation; *Int'l*, pg. 3497
HOYA SURGICAL OPTICS GMBH—See Hoya Corporation; *Int'l*, pg. 3496
HYDROGEL VISION CORP.—See Clerio Vision Inc.; *U.S. Private*, pg. 940
ICU EYEWEAR, INC.—See 1847 Holdings LLC; *U.S. Public*, pg. 2
II-VI JAPAN INCORPORATED—See Coherent Corp.; *U.S. Public*, pg. 528
II-VI U.K. LTD.—See Coherent Corp.; *U.S. Public*, pg. 529
INFIELD SAFETY GMBH—See EssilorLuxottica SA; *Int'l*, pg. 2515
INSIGHT OPTICAL MANUFACTURING CO.; *U.S. Private*, pg. 2086
INTERNATIONAL EYEWEAR LTD.—See Equistone Partners Europe Limited; *Int'l*, pg. 2486
ISRA VISION INDIA PRIVATE LIMITED—See Atlas Copco AB; *Int'l*, pg. 682
ISRA VISION IRAN—See Atlas Copco AB; *Int'l*, pg. 682
ISRA VISION KOREA CO. LTD.—See Atlas Copco AB; *Int'l*, pg. 682
ISRA VISION LLC—See Atlas Copco AB; *Int'l*, pg. 683
ISRA VISION TAIWAN—See Atlas Copco AB; *Int'l*, pg. 683
ITALEE OPTICS INC.; *U.S. Private*, pg. 2149
JANOS TECHNOLOGY, LLC—See Fortive Corporation; *U.S. Public*, pg. 871
JOHNSON & JOHNSON SIHHI MALZEME SANAYI VE TICARET LIMITED SIRKETI—See Johnson & Johnson; *U.S. Public*, pg. 1199
JONAS PAUL EYEWEAR, LLC; *U.S. Private*, pg. 2231
LEYBOLD OPTICS GMBH—See Buhler AG; *Int'l*, pg. 1212
LOMBART BROTHERS, INC.—See Atlantic Street Capital Management LLC; *U.S. Private*, pg. 374
LUXOTTICA BELGIUM N.V.—See EssilorLuxottica SA; *Int'l*, pg. 2515
LUXOTTICA CANADA, INC.—See EssilorLuxottica SA; *Int'l*, pg. 2515
LUXOTTICA DO BRASIL LTDA.—See EssilorLuxottica SA; *Int'l*, pg. 2515
LUXOTTICA FASHION BRILLEN VIRTIES GMBH—See EssilorLuxottica SA; *Int'l*, pg. 2515
LUXOTTICA FRANCE S.A.R.L.—See EssilorLuxottica SA; *Int'l*, pg. 2515
LUXOTTICA HELLAS AE—See EssilorLuxottica SA; *Int'l*, pg. 2515
LUXOTTICA IBERICA S.A.—See EssilorLuxottica SA; *Int'l*, pg. 2515
LUXOTTICA NEDERLAND B.V.—See EssilorLuxottica SA; *Int'l*, pg. 2515
LUXOTTICA PORTUGAL S.A.—See EssilorLuxottica SA; *Int'l*, pg. 2515
LUXOTTICA SWEDEN A.B.—See EssilorLuxottica SA; *Int'l*, pg. 2515

423460 — OPHTHALMIC GOODS ME...

LUXOTTICA U.K. LTD.—See EssilorLuxottica SA; *Int'l*, pg. 2515
LUXOTTICA VERTRIEBS GMBH—See EssilorLuxottica SA; *Int'l*, pg. 2515
MARCHON EYEWEAR, INC.—See Vision Service Plan; *U.S. Private*, pg. 4391
MARCHON HISPANIA, SL—See Vision Service Plan; *U.S. Private*, pg. 4391
MIRARI JAPAN LTD—See EssilorLuxottica SA; *Int'l*, pg. 2515
MJ OPTICAL INC.; *U.S. Private*, pg. 2752
NASSAU LENS CO., INC.; *U.S. Private*, pg. 2837
NETWORKS CENTRE LTD.—See Alcadon Group AB; *Int'l*, pg. 300
NETWORKS CENTRE (SCOTLAND) LIMITED—See Alcadon Group AB; *Int'l*, pg. 300
NEW LOOK VISION GROUP, INC.—See Caisse de Depot et Placement du Quebec; *Int'l*, pg. 1254
NEW LOOK VISION GROUP, INC.—See FFL Partners, LLC, *U.S. Private*, pg. 1500
OOGP, INC.—See EssilorLuxottica SA; *Int'l*, pg. 2514
OPTIKOS SP ZOO—See EssilorLuxottica SA; *Int'l*, pg. 2516
OPTIQUE LISON INC.—See EssilorLuxottica SA; *Int'l*, pg. 2516
OPTO-TECH SRL—See FARO Technologies, Inc.; *U.S. Public*, pg. 823
OY LUXOTTICA FINLAND AB—See EssilorLuxottica SA; *Int'l*, pg. 2515
PIONEER OPTICAL INC.—See EssilorLuxottica SA; *Int'l*, pg. 2516
PLUNKETT OPTICAL, INC.—See EssilorLuxottica SA; *Int'l*, pg. 2514
PROCORNEA NEDERLAND B.V.—See The Cooper Companies, Inc.; *U.S. Public*, pg. 2066
R & R OPTICAL LABORATORY LTD.—See EssilorLuxottica SA; *Int'l*, pg. 2516
SALEM DISTRIBUTING COMPANY INC.; *U.S. Private*, pg. 3531
SATISLOH DO BRASIL LTDA—See EssilorLuxottica SA; *Int'l*, pg. 2516
SATISLOH NORTH AMERICA INC—See EssilorLuxottica SA; *Int'l*, pg. 2514
SCHOTT (SHANGHAI) PRECISION MATERIALS & EQUIPMENT INTERNATIONAL TRADING CO., LTD.—See Carl-Zeiss-Stiftung; *Int'l*, pg. 1336
SCHOTT SINGAPORE PTE. LTD.—See Carl-Zeiss-Stiftung; *Int'l*, pg. 1337
SENTRALSLIP AS—See EssilorLuxottica SA; *Int'l*, pg. 2516
SKAGGS AND GRUBER, LTD—See EssilorLuxottica SA; *Int'l*, pg. 2516
SOLSTICE MARKETING CORP.; *U.S. Private*, pg. 3710
TELEON SURGICAL VERTRIEBS GMBH—See Gaush Meditech Ltd.; *Int'l*, pg. 2891
THAI HOYA LENS LTD.—See Hoya Corporation; *Int'l*, pg. 3496
TURA INC.—See Equistone Partners Europe Limited; *Int'l*, pg. 2486
UAB JZP OPTIKA LITUANIA—See EssilorLuxottica SA; *Int'l*, pg. 2516
VECTORVISION OCULAR HEALTH, INC.—See Guardion Health Sciences, Inc.; *U.S. Public*, pg. 973
THE WALMAN INSTRUMENT GROUP—See Walman Optical Company; *U.S. Private*, pg. 4432
WALMAN OPTICAL COMPANY - IMAGEWEAR DIVISION—See Walman Optical Company; *U.S. Private*, pg. 4432
WEBEYECARE; *U.S. Private*, pg. 4465
WHOLESALE LENS CORPORATION LIMITED—See EssilorLuxottica SA; *Int'l*, pg. 2516
WISCONSIN VISION ASSOCIATES INC.; *U.S. Private*, pg. 4549
ZHUHAI ROSSINI GLASSES INDUSTRY LIMITED—See Citychamp Watch & Jewellery Group Limited; *Int'l*, pg. 1629

423490 — OTHER PROFESSIONAL EQUIPMENT AND SUPPLIES MERCHANT WHOLESALERS

ACCESS SCIENTIFIC, LLC—See ICU Medical, Inc.; *U.S. Public*, pg. 1087
ACTIVAIDED ORTHOTICS LLC—See Elizur Corp.; *U.S. Private*, pg. 1362
A. DAIGGER & COMPANY INC.; *U.S. Private*, pg. 23
ADDTECH LIFE SCIENCE AB—See Addtech AB; *Int'l*, pg. 131
ADHEZION BIOMEDICAL, LLC—See H.B. Fuller Company; *U.S. Public*, pg. 977
AGC ASIA PACIFIC PTE., LTD.—See AGC Inc.; *Int'l*, pg. 201
AKM ASIA PTE LTD—See Fortive Corporation; *U.S. Public*, pg. 870
ALFA AESAR (CHINA) CHEMICAL CO. LTD.—See Thermo Fisher Scientific Inc.; *U.S. Public*, pg. 2145
ALLIANCE ENGINEERING INC.—See Alliance Engineering Inc.; *U.S. Private*, pg. 182
ALLIED TELESYN VERTRIEBSGESELLSCHAFT M.B.H.—See ALLIED TELESIS HOLDINGS K.K.; *Int'l*, pg. 359
ALPHA ASSEMBLY SOLUTIONS BELGIUM NV—See Element Solutions Inc.; *U.S. Public*, pg. 726
ALPHA ASSEMBLY SOLUTIONS FRANCE SAS—See Element Solutions Inc.; *U.S. Public*, pg. 726
AMERICAN EAGLE CO., INC.; *U.S. Private*, pg. 231
AMERICAN READING COMPANY; *U.S. Private*, pg. 245
AMETEK PROCESS & ANALYTICAL INSTRUMENTS DIVISION—See AMETEK, Inc.; *U.S. Public*, pg. 117
AMUZA, INC.; *U.S. Private*, pg. 269
ANTON PAAR USA, INC.—See Anton Paar GmbH; *Int'l*, pg. 485
APPLIED BIOSYSTEMS TRADING (SHANGHAI) COMPANY LTD.—See Thermo Fisher Scientific Inc.; *U.S. Public*, pg. 2145
ARCA.TECH SYSTEMS, L.L.C.—See BC Partners LLP; *Int'l*, pg. 924
ART ROBBINS INSTRUMENTS, LLC—See Argosy Capital Group, LLC; *U.S. Private*, pg. 321
AS ONE CORPORATION; *Int'l*, pg. 591
AS ONE SHANGHAI CORPORATION—See AS ONE Corporation; *Int'l*, pg. 591
AST FARMA B.V.—See EQT AB; *Int'l*, pg. 2474
ATLANTIC TACTICAL, INC.—See Kanders & Company, Inc.; *U.S. Private*, pg. 2259
AVBA HI TECH SERVICES LTD.; *Int'l*, pg. 737
AXEL JOHNSON LAB SYSTEMS A/S—See Axel Johnson Gruppen AB; *Int'l*, pg. 764
BAE SYSTEMS MOBILITY & PROTECTION SYSTEMS—See BAE Systems plc; *Int'l*, pg. 796
BECKER'S SCHOOL SUPPLIES, INC.; *U.S. Private*, pg. 511
BENVENUE MEDICAL, INC.—See Kohlberg & Company, LLC; *U.S. Private*, pg. 2337
BIO MEDIC CORPORATION; *U.S. Private*, pg. 561
BIO-RAD DENMARK APS—See Bio-Rad Laboratories, Inc.; *U.S. Public*, pg. 332
BIO-RAD LABORATORIES AG—See Bio-Rad Laboratories, Inc.; *U.S. Public*, pg. 333
BIO-RAD LABORATORIES B.V.—See Bio-Rad Laboratories, Inc.; *U.S. Public*, pg. 333
BIO-RAD LABORATORIES, INC. - LIFE SCIENCE GROUP—See Bio-Rad Laboratories, Inc.; *U.S. Public*, pg. 333
BIO-RAD SERVICES UK LIMITED—See Bio-Rad Laboratories, Inc.; *U.S. Public*, pg. 333
BIORIVER CO., LTD.—See BioLASCO Taiwan Co., Ltd.; *Int'l*, pg. 1038
BIOTEK INSTRUMENTS SAS—See Agilent Technologies, Inc.; *U.S. Public*, pg. 61
BMT GMBH LABORPRODUKTE—See Thermo Fisher Scientific Inc.; *U.S. Public*, pg. 2153
BRAINBITS LLC—See Thompson Street Capital Manager LLC; *U.S. Private*, pg. 4161
BRINKMANN INSTRUMENTS (CANADA), LTD.—See Eppendorf AG; *Int'l*, pg. 2464
BRINKMANN INSTRUMENTS, INC.—See Eppendorf AG; *Int'l*, pg. 2464
BRUKER FINANCE B.V.—See Bruker Corporation; *U.S. Public*, pg. 405
BRUKER KOREA CO. LTD.—See Bruker Corporation; *U.S. Public*, pg. 405
BRUKER MICROCT N.V.—See Bruker Corporation; *U.S. Public*, pg. 405
BRUKER OPTICS SCANDINAVIA AB—See Bruker Corporation; *U.S. Public*, pg. 406
BRUKER PTY. LTD.—See Bruker Corporation; *U.S. Public*, pg. 406
BRUKER SCIENTIFIC INSTRUMENTS HONG KONG CO., LTD.—See Bruker Corporation; *U.S. Public*, pg. 406
BRUKER SINGAPORE PTE. LTD.—See Bruker Corporation; *U.S. Public*, pg. 404
BUEHLER LTD., IRVINE—See Illinois Tool Works Inc.; *U.S. Public*, pg. 1102
CALLAWAY SAFETY EQUIPMENT CO., INC.—See Littlejohn & Co., LLC; *U.S. Private*, pg. 2472
CAPITOL SCIENTIFIC, INC.; *U.S. Private*, pg. 744
CARL ZEISS JAPAN GROUP—See Carl-Zeiss-Stiftung; *Int'l*, pg. 1334
CAROLINA BIOLOGICAL SUPPLY COMPANY; *U.S. Private*, pg. 767
CENTRAL SCIENTIFIC COMMERCE, INC.—See GSI Creos Corporation; *Int'l*, pg. 3144
CHERRY OPTICAL, INC.—See EssilorLuxottica SA; *Int'l*, pg. 2513
CHINNEY CONSTRUCTION COMPANY, LIMITED—See Chinney Alliance Group Limited; *Int'l*, pg. 1570
CHRISTIE LITES INC.; *Int'l*, pg. 1587
CLASSROOM ESSENTIALS ONLINE; *U.S. Private*, pg. 917
COHERENT GMBH—See Coherent Corp.; *U.S. Public*, pg. 527
COMCATER PTY. LTD.; *Int'l*, pg. 1709
CONERGY PTY LIMITED—See Kawa Capital Management, Inc.; *U.S. Private*, pg. 2266
CORE INFORMATICS, LLC—See Thermo Fisher Scientific Inc.; *U.S. Public*, pg. 2146

CORPORATE AFFILIATIONS

CORNING LIFE SCIENCES B.V.—See Corning Incorporated; *U.S. Public*, pg. 578
CORTECH SOLUTIONS, INC.; *U.S. Private*, pg. 1060
CPI-THE ALTERNATIVE SUPPLIER; *U.S. Private*, pg. 1080
CYRPA INTERNATIONAL SPRL—See C-RAD AB; *Int'l*, pg. 1240
DE DIETRICH PROCESS SYSTEMS AG—See De Dietrich Process Systems S.A.; *Int'l*, pg. 1995
DE DIETRICH PROCESS SYSTEMS INDIA PRIVATE LIMITED—See De Dietrich Process Systems S.A.; *Int'l*, pg. 1995
DE DIETRICH PROCESS SYSTEMS N.V.—See De Dietrich Process Systems S.A.; *Int'l*, pg. 1995
DE DIETRICH PROCESS SYSTEMS SEMUR SAS—See De Dietrich Process Systems S.A.; *Int'l*, pg. 1995
DE DIETRICH PROCESS SYSTEMS—See De Dietrich Process Systems S.A.; *Int'l*, pg. 1995
DE DIETRICH PROCESS SYSTEMS SRL.—See De Dietrich Process Systems S.A.; *Int'l*, pg. 1995
DE DIETRICH PROCESS SYSTEMS (WUXI) CO, LTD.—See De Dietrich Process Systems S.A.; *Int'l*, pg. 1995
DEHCO, INC.—See Patrick Industries, Inc.; *U.S. Public*, pg. 1652
DICOCCO FAMILY'S ST. JUDE SHOP, INC.; *U.S. Private*, pg. 1227
DIMOS; *Int'l*, pg. 2126
DIONEX BENELUX B.V.—See Thermo Fisher Scientific Inc.; *U.S. Public*, pg. 2146
DIONEX GMBH—See Thermo Fisher Scientific Inc.; *U.S. Public*, pg. 2146
DIONEX (SWITZERLAND) AG—See Thermo Fisher Scientific Inc.; *U.S. Public*, pg. 2146
DIONEX (U.K.) LTD.—See Thermo Fisher Scientific Inc.; *U.S. Public*, pg. 2146
DRAPHIX, LLC; *U.S. Private*, pg. 1272
DRG INTERNATIONAL, INC.—See OriGene Technologies, Inc.; *U.S. Private*, pg. 3042
DRILTECH GEOTECHNICAL ENGINEERING LIMITED—See Chinney Alliance Group Limited; *Int'l*, pg. 1570
DURHAM GEO-ENTERPRISES INCORPORATED; *U.S. Private*, pg. 1293
EARL DUDLEY ASSOCIATES INC.; *U.S. Private*, pg. 1312
ECLAT ENTERPRISE LTD.—See Eclat Textile Co., Ltd.; *Int'l*, pg. 2291
ELECTRA-BOX DIAGNOSTICA A/S—See Addtech AB; *Int'l*, pg. 133
ENGINEER SUPPLY, LLC—See ProClick Ventures, Inc.; *U.S. Private*, pg. 3272
ENVIRONMENTS INC.; *U.S. Private*, pg. 1409
EPPENDORF BIOTECHNOLOGY INTERNATIONAL TRADE (SHANGHAI) COMPANY LTD.—See Eppendorf AG; *Int'l*, pg. 2464
EPPENDORF CO., LTD.—See Eppendorf AG; *Int'l*, pg. 2464
EPPENDORF SOUTH PACIFIC PTY. LTD.—See Eppendorf AG; *Int'l*, pg. 2464
ESAB MIDDLE EAST LLC—See Enovis Corporation; *U.S. Public*, pg. 771
ESPEC KYUSHU CORP.—See ESPEC Corp.; *Int'l*, pg. 2505
EVOLVE LTD.—See Attard & Co. Ltd.; *Int'l*, pg. 696
EXCEL SCIENTIFIC, INC.—See Vance Street Capital LLC; *U.S. Private*, pg. 4342
EXTRACT TECHNOLOGY LIMITED—See WABASH NATIONAL CORPORATION; *U.S. Public*, pg. 2320
FEEDBACK EDUCATION, INC.—See Aurelius Equity Opportunities SE & Co. KGaA; *Int'l*, pg. 709
FEI EFA, INC.—See Thermo Fisher Scientific Inc.; *U.S. Public*, pg. 2146
FEI SAS—See Thermo Fisher Scientific Inc.; *U.S. Public*, pg. 2147
FENIE BROSSETTE; *Int'l*, pg. 2634
FETIM B.V.; *Int'l*, pg. 2648
FINANCIAL & OFFICE SYSTEMS, INC.—See Smart Source of Georgia, LLC; *U.S. Private*, pg. 3691
FISHER SCIENTIFIC RESEARCH/FISHER SAFETY—See Thermo Fisher Scientific Inc.; *U.S. Public*, pg. 2148
FITTERS (IPOH) SDN BHD—See FITTERS Diversified Berhad; *Int'l*, pg. 2695
FLINN SCIENTIFIC, INC.; *U.S. Private*, pg. 1545
FOSS NORTH AMERICA, INC.—See Foss A/S; *Int'l*, pg. 2749
FRAMES FOR AMERICA INC—See EssilorLuxottica SA; *Int'l*, pg. 2514
FREY SCIENTIFIC, INC.—See School Specialty, Inc.; *U.S. Public*, pg. 1848
FRONTIER PRECISION INC.; *U.S. Private*, pg. 1615
FUJIFILM VET SYSTEMS CO., LTD.—See FUJIFILM Holdings Corporation; *Int'l*, pg. 2825
FULL SPECTRUM GROUP, LLC—See CBRE Group, Inc.; *U.S. Public*, pg. 460
FURUNO KYUSHU HAMBAI CO., LTD.—See Furuno Electric Co., Ltd.; *Int'l*, pg. 2848
GAIA SCIENCE SDN BHD; *Int'l*, pg. 2868
GBC SCIENTIFIC EQUIPMENT USA, LLC—See GBC Scientific Equipment Pty Ltd.; *Int'l*, pg. 2893
GILSON COMPANY, INC.; *U.S. Private*, pg. 1701
GREAT VICTORY CHEMICAL INDUSTRY CO., LTD.—See

N.A.I.C.S. INDEX

423510 — METAL SERVICE CENTE...

Formosan Union Chemical Corp.; *Int'l*, pg. 2736
GRG INTERNATIONAL CORPORATION—See GRG International Limited; *Int'l*, pg. 3082
GUIDED WAVE ASIA PTE. LTD.—See Advanced Holdings Ltd.; *Int'l*, pg. 159
GUIDED WAVE EUROPE BVBA—See Advanced Holdings Ltd.; *Int'l*, pg. 159
GW VITEK CO., LTD.; *Int'l*, pg. 3190
HACKER INSTRUMENTS & INDUSTRIES INC.; *U.S. Private*, pg. 1838
HAIN LIFESCIENCES S.A. PTY. LTD.—See Bruker Corporation; *U.S. Public*, pg. 406
HAMLON PTY LTD—See Hancock & Gore Ltd.; *Int'l*, pg. 3242
HARRY J. KLOEPPEL & ASSOCIATES; *U.S. Private*, pg. 1871
HC SLINGSBY PLC; *Int'l*, pg. 3297
HEART TEST LABORATORIES, INC.; *U.S. Public*, pg. 1017
HEIDELBERGCEMENT PUMPS & TRUCKS AS—See Heidelberg Materials AG; *Int'l*, pg. 3315
HEKA ELECTRONIK DR. SCHULZE GMBH—See Harvard Bioscience, Inc.; *U.S. Public*, pg. 987
HEKA INSTRUMENTS INCORPORATED—See Harvard Bioscience, Inc.; *U.S. Public*, pg. 987
HEYE INTERNATIONAL GMBH—See Ardagh Group S.A.; *Int'l*, pg. 553
HITACHI HIGH-TECH FIELDING CORPORATION—See Hitachi, Ltd.; *Int'l*, pg. 3418
HITACHI HIGH-TECH SCIENTIFIC SOLUTIONS (BEIJING) CO., LTD.—See Hitachi, Ltd.; *Int'l*, pg. 3418
HITACHI HIGH-TECH SCIENTIFIC SOLUTIONS CO., LTD.—See Hitachi, Ltd.; *Int'l*, pg. 3418
HOLM & HALBY A/S—See Addtech AB; *Int'l*, pg. 133
HORIBA CANADA, INC.—See HORIBA Ltd; *Int'l*, pg. 3476
HORIBA (CHINA) TRADING CO., LTD.—See HORIBA Ltd; *Int'l*, pg. 3475
HORIBA ITALIA SRL—See HORIBA Ltd; *Int'l*, pg. 3476
HORIBA KOREA LTD.—See HORIBA Ltd; *Int'l*, pg. 3476
HORIBA TAIWAN, INC.—See HORIBA Ltd; *Int'l*, pg. 3476
HORIBA (THAILAND) LIMITED—See HORIBA Ltd; *Int'l*, pg. 3475
HUNTSMAN (NETHERLANDS) BV—See Huntsman Corporation; *U.S. Public*, pg. 1073
HYPERBRANCH MEDICAL TECHNOLOGY, INC.—See Stryker Corporation; *U.S. Public*, pg. 1955
IBIS BIOSCIENCES LLC—See Abbott Laboratories; *U.S. Public*, pg. 20
INDOX SERVICES INC.—See SBI Incorporated; *U.S. Private*, pg. 3560
INNOVATIVE CONTROL SYSTEMS LP; *U.S. Private*, pg. 2082
INSCIENCE SDN BHD—See HORIBA Ltd; *Int'l*, pg. 3477
INTERPATH SERVICES PTY. LTD.—See Bunzl plc; *Int'l*, pg. 1218
JAYBRO GROUP PTY. LTD.—See CHAMP Private Equity Pty. Ltd.; *Int'l*, pg. 1439
JH TECHNOLOGIES INC.; *U.S. Private*, pg. 2207
J & R MEDICAL, LLC—See ConvaTec Group PLC; *Int'l*, pg. 1786
KAPLAN COMPANIES INC.; *U.S. Private*, pg. 2261
KAPLAN EARLY LEARNING COMPANY—See Kaplan Companies Inc.; *U.S. Private*, pg. 2261
KEELER INSTRUMENTS INC.—See Halma plc; *Int'l*, pg. 3231
KIN WING FOUNDATIONS LIMITED—See Chinney Alliance Group Limited; *Int'l*, pg. 1570
KRACKELER SCIENTIFIC INC.; *U.S. Private*, pg. 2348
LAB SCIENCE SOLUTION SDN BHD—See HORIBA Ltd; *Int'l*, pg. 3477
LABWORLD (PTY) LTD.—See AFGRI Limited; *Int'l*, pg. 188
LANCER SALES USA INC—See Getinge AB; *Int'l*, pg. 2951
LANCER UK LTD—See Getinge AB; *Int'l*, pg. 2951
LASER SPECTRA SERVICES INDIA PVT. LTD.—See HORIBA Ltd; *Int'l*, pg. 3477
LEEDS PRECISION INSTRUMENTS; *U.S. Private*, pg. 2415
MACDERMID ENTHONE GMBH—See Element Solutions Inc.; *U.S. Public*, pg. 727
MACDERMID ENTHONE SP. Z.O.O.—See Element Solutions Inc.; *U.S. Public*, pg. 727
MACDERMID KFT—See Element Solutions Inc.; *U.S. Public*, pg. 727
MACDERMID PERFORMANCE SOLUTIONS ESPANOLA SA—See Element Solutions Inc.; *U.S. Public*, pg. 727
MACDERMID PERFORMANCE SOLUTIONS FRANCE S.A.S.—See Element Solutions Inc.; *U.S. Public*, pg. 727
MACDERMID PERFORMANCE SOLUTIONS JAPAN K.K.—See Element Solutions Inc.; *U.S. Public*, pg. 727
MACDERMID PERFORMANCE SOLUTIONS KIMYASAL SANAYI VE TICARET A.S.—See Element Solutions Inc.; *U.S. Public*, pg. 727
MANGAN, INC., *U.S. Private*, pg. 2563
MARSHALL TOOL & SUPPLY CORP.; *U.S. Private*, pg. 2593
MARTIN SAFETY SOLUTIONS—See MSCO Inc.; *U.S. Private*, pg. 2806
MEP INSTRUMENTS PTY LTD—See Anton Paar GmbH; *Int'l*, pg. 485
MERCURY MISSION SYSTEMS INTERNATIONAL, SA—See Mercury Systems, Inc.; *U.S. Public*, pg. 1422
MERCURY MISSION SYSTEMS SPAIN, SL—See Mercury Systems, Inc.; *U.S. Public*, pg. 1422
METTLER-TOLEDO B.V.—See Mettler-Toledo International, Inc.; *U.S. Public*, pg. 1432
METTLER-TOLEDO (CHANGZHOU) SCALE & SYSTEM LTD.—See Mettler-Toledo International, Inc.; *U.S. Public*, pg. 1432
MICRO VIDEO INSTRUMENTS INC.; *U.S. Private*, pg. 2702
MONADNOCK LIFETIME PRODUCTS, INC.—See BAE Systems plc; *Int'l*, pg. 796
MULTI CHANNEL SYSTEMS MCS GMBH—See Harvard Bioscience, Inc.; *U.S. Public*, pg. 987
NEW BRUNSWICK SCIENTIFIC B.V.—See Eppendorf AG; *Int'l*, pg. 2464
NEW BRUNSWICK SCIENTIFIC GMBH—See Eppendorf AG; *Int'l*, pg. 2464
NEW BRUNSWICK SCIENTIFIC (UK) LTD.—See Eppendorf AG; *Int'l*, pg. 2464
NION, CO.—See Bruker Corporation; *U.S. Public*, pg. 407
NORCOSTCO, INC.; *U.S. Private*, pg. 2936
OHAUS AUSTRALIA PTY. LTD.—See Mettler-Toledo International, Inc.; *U.S. Public*, pg. 1433
OMEGA OPTICAL, LLC—See Artemis Capital Partners Management Co., LLC; *U.S. Private*, pg. 341
OMNIPROCESS AB—See Addtech AB; *Int'l*, pg. 134
ORTHOCOR MEDICAL, INC.—See Caerus Corporation; *U.S. Private*, pg. 714
PACKINOX MOSCOW—See Alfa Laval AB; *Int'l*, pg. 311
PARTICULAR SCIENCES LTD.—See HORIBA Ltd; *Int'l*, pg. 3478
PATHEON API MANUFACTURING INC.—See Thermo Fisher Scientific Inc.; *U.S. Public*, pg. 2151
PATHEON BIOLOGICS B.V.—See Thermo Fisher Scientific Inc.; *U.S. Public*, pg. 2151
PATHEON KK—See Thermo Fisher Scientific Inc.; *U.S. Public*, pg. 2151
PATHEON PUERTO RICO, INC.—See Thermo Fisher Scientific Inc.; *U.S. Public*, pg. 2151
PATHEON REGENSBURG GMBH—See Thermo Fisher Scientific Inc.; *U.S. Public*, pg. 2151
PATHEON SOFTGELS B.V.—See Thermo Fisher Scientific Inc.; *U.S. Public*, pg. 2151
PATHEON SOFTGELS INC.—See Thermo Fisher Scientific Inc.; *U.S. Public*, pg. 2151
PC/NAMETAG, INC.—See CCL Industries Inc.; *Int'l*, pg. 1367
PENDUM LLC—See Marlin Equity Partners, LLC; *U.S. Private*, pg. 2584
PERFECT COMMERCE HOLDINGS, LLC.; *U.S. Private*, pg. 3148
PHOENIX TRADING INC.; *U.S. Private*, pg. 3174
PHOTON SYSTEMS, INC.—See Dow Inc.; *U.S. Public*, pg. 685
PINE ENVIRONMENTAL SERVICES, LLC—See ACON Investments, LLC; *U.S. Private*, pg. 62
PREISER SCIENTIFIC, INC.; *U.S. Private*, pg. 3248
PREMIER CONTROL TECHNOLOGIES, LTD.—See Badger Meter, Inc.; *U.S. Public*, pg. 263
PRINT-O-STAT, INC.—See Pace Resources, Inc.; *U.S. Private*, pg. 3064
PROTECH ARMORED PRODUCTS—See BAE Systems plc; *Int'l*, pg. 796
PROVET (NSW) PTY LTD.—See Clayton, Dubilier & Rice, LLC; *U.S. Private*, pg. 922
PROVET (NSW) PTY LTD.—See TPG Capital, L.P.; *U.S. Public*, pg. 2170
PROVET NZ PTY LIMITED—See Clayton, Dubilier & Rice, LLC; *U.S. Private*, pg. 922
PROVET NZ PTY LIMITED—See TPG Capital, L.P.; *U.S. Public*, pg. 2170
PROVET SA PTY LTD.—See Clayton, Dubilier & Rice, LLC; *U.S. Private*, pg. 922
PROVET SA PTY LTD.—See TPG Capital, L.P.; *U.S. Public*, pg. 2170
PROVET VICTORIA PTY LTD.—See Clayton, Dubilier & Rice, LLC; *U.S. Private*, pg. 922
PROVET VICTORIA PTY LTD.—See TPG Capital, L.P.; *U.S. Public*, pg. 2170
PROVET VMS PTY LTD.—See Clayton, Dubilier & Rice, LLC; *U.S. Private*, pg. 922
PROVET VMS PTY LTD.—See TPG Capital, L.P.; *U.S. Public*, pg. 2170
PROVET WA PTY LTD.—See Clayton, Dubilier & Rice, LLC; *U.S. Private*, pg. 922
PROVET WA PTY LTD.—See TPG Capital, L.P.; *U.S. Public*, pg. 2170
PT. BESHA ANALITIKA—See HORIBA Ltd; *Int'l*, pg. 3478
REICHERT MICROSCOPE SERVICES—See AMETEK, Inc.; *U.S. Public*, pg. 116
ROCKSTONE CO., LTD.—See Prudential Financial, Inc.; *U.S. Public*, pg. 1733
ROCTEST INC.—See Nova Ventures Group Corp.; *U.S. Private*, pg. 2966
R.S. KNAPP CO. INC.; *U.S. Private*, pg. 3339
SANTINELLI INTERNATIONAL INC.; *U.S. Private*, pg. 3548
SARL OUTILUX—See Einhell Germany AG; *Int'l*, pg. 2334
SCHLUMPF INDUSTRIEPRODUKTE GMBH—See Convum Ltd.; *Int'l*, pg. 1788
SCHUYLER HOUSE INC.—See CompuGroup Medical SE & Co. KGaA; *Int'l*, pg. 1756
SCIENCE KIT LLC; *U.S. Private*, pg. 3573
SECUROS EUROPE GMBH—See Cencora, Inc.; *U.S. Public*, pg. 467
SENTINEL SYSTEM, LLC—See Revolution Lighting Technologies, Inc.; *U.S. Public*, pg. 1793
SERA PROGNOSTICS, INC.; *U.S. Public*, pg. 1868
SHINE MEDICAL TECHNOLOGIES, LLC; *U.S. Private*, pg. 3637
SKAGGS COMPANIES, INC.; *U.S. Private*, pg. 3680
SKC GULF COAST, INC.—See SKC Inc.; *U.S. Private*, pg. 3681
SKC INC.; *U.S. Private*, pg. 3681
SKC-WEST, INC.—See SKC Inc.; *U.S. Private*, pg. 3681
SLEEPIQ LABS INC.—See Sleep Number Corporation; *U.S. Public*, pg. 1894
SOFT CHEMICAL CORP.—See Formosan Union Chemical Corp.; *Int'l*, pg. 2736
SOLSYS MEDICAL, LLC—See Bioventus Inc.; *U.S. Public*, pg. 339
STANDARD INSTRUMENTATION—See Preiser Scientific, Inc.; *U.S. Private*, pg. 3249
STEREO OPTICAL CO. INC.—See EssilorLuxottica SA; *Int'l*, pg. 2514
SUPPLIER.IO, INC.; *U.S. Private*, pg. 3882
SURPLUS CENTER—See Burden Sales Company; *U.S. Private*, pg. 686
TECHNICAL INSTRUMENTS SAN FRANCISCO; *U.S. Private*, pg. 3954
TEST INTERNATIONAL—See Schlumberger Limited; *U.S. Public*, pg. 1844
TEXAS INSTRUMENTS CHINA TRADING LIMITED—See Texas Instruments Incorporated; *U.S. Public*, pg. 2026
TEXAS SCENIC COMPANY INC.; *U.S. Private*, pg. 3977
TFS LLC—See Thermo Fisher Scientific Inc.; *U.S. Public*, pg. 2152
THERMO CRS LTD.—See Thermo Fisher Scientific Inc.; *U.S. Public*, pg. 2152
THERMO FISHER DIAGNOSTICS AB—See Thermo Fisher Scientific Inc.; *U.S. Public*, pg. 2152
THERMO FISHER DIAGNOSTICS AG—See Thermo Fisher Scientific Inc.; *U.S. Public*, pg. 2152
THERMO FISHER DIAGNOSTICS AUSTRIA GMBH—See Thermo Fisher Scientific Inc.; *U.S. Public*, pg. 2153
THERMO FISHER DIAGNOSTICS B.V.—See Thermo Fisher Scientific Inc.; *U.S. Public*, pg. 2152
THERMO FISHER DIAGNOSTICS NV—See Thermo Fisher Scientific Inc.; *U.S. Public*, pg. 2153
THERMO FISHER DIAGNOSTICS, S.L.U.—See Thermo Fisher Scientific Inc.; *U.S. Public*, pg. 2153
THERMO FISHER SCIENTIFIC (MISSISSAUGA) INC.—See Thermo Fisher Scientific Inc.; *U.S. Public*, pg. 2153
THOMA INC.; *U.S. Private*, pg. 4154
TOTAL SAFETY U.S., INC.—See Littlejohn & Co., LLC; *U.S. Private*, pg. 2472
UNITRON CUSTOMIZED SYSTEMS—See Unitron Inc.; *U.S. Private*, pg. 4302
UNITRON INC.; *U.S. Private*, pg. 4302
UNITRON LEISURE PRODS.—See Unitron Inc.; *U.S. Private*, pg. 4302
UNIVERSAL PHOTONICS, INC.; *U.S. Private*, pg. 4306
U.S. TOY CO., INC.—See Windy City Novelties, Inc.; *U.S. Private*, pg. 4540
VASHAW SCIENTIFIC INC.; *U.S. Private*, pg. 4347
VERTICO XTREME LLC—See EdiliziAcrobatica S.p.A.; *Int'l*, pg. 2310
VIRTUAL DRIVER INTERACTIVE, INC.—See Cemtrex, Inc.; *U.S. Public*, pg. 466
VISION ENGINEERING ITALIA—See Vision Engineering Inc.; *U.S. Private*, pg. 4390
VISION ENGINEERING LTD.—See Vision Engineering Inc.; *U.S. Private*, pg. 4390
VIVEVE, INC.—See Viveve Medical Inc.; *U.S. Public*, pg. 2307
VWR ADVANCED INSTRUMENTS, LLC—See Avantor, Inc.; *U.S. Public*, pg. 241
WATER TECHNOLOGIES CORPORATION—See Waters Corporation; *U.S. Public*, pg. 2335
THE WISE OPTICAL VISION GROUP; *U.S. Private*, pg. 4138
W.W. GRAINGER - JANESVILLE—See W.W. Grainger, Inc.; *U.S. Public*, pg. 2320
X-RITE LIMITED—See Danaher Corporation; *U.S. Public*, pg. 632

423510 — METAL SERVICE CENTERS AND OTHER METAL MERCHANT WHOLESALERS

101 PIPE & CASING INC.; *U.S. Private*, pg. 2
AALCO METALS LTD.—See Henley Management Company; *U.S. Private*, pg. 1916
AA PLUS TRADELINK LIMITED; *Int'l*, pg. 30
AARON FERER & SONS CO.; *U.S. Private*, pg. 32

423510 — METAL SERVICE CENTE...

ABTERRA LTD.; *Int'l,* pg. 70
AB THAI FOUNDRY SUPPLIERS CO., LTD.—See Huettenes-Albertus Chemische Werke GmbH; *Int'l,* pg. 3522
ACCENT WIRE; *U.S. Private,* pg. 50
ACE IRON & METAL—See Duggan Industries, Inc.; *U.S. Private,* pg. 1285
ACENTA STEEL LIMITED; *Int'l,* pg. 98
ACERINOX ARGENTINA, S.A.—See Acerinox, S.A.; *Int'l,* pg. 100
ACERINOX CHILE, S.A.—See Acerinox, S.A.; *Int'l,* pg. 100
ACERINOX COLOMBIA, S.A.S.—See Acerinox, S.A.; *Int'l,* pg. 100
ACERINOX FRANCE SAS—See Acerinox, S.A.; *Int'l,* pg. 100
ACERINOX METAL SANAYII VE TIKARET L.S.—See Acerinox, S.A.; *Int'l,* pg. 100
ACERINOX PACIFIC LTD.—See Acerinox, S.A.; *Int'l,* pg. 100
ACERINOX RUSSIA, L.L.C.—See Acerinox, S.A.; *Int'l,* pg. 100
ACERINOX, S.A. - VENEZUELA—See Acerinox, S.A.; *Int'l,* pg. 100
ACEROL COMERCIO E INDUSTRIA DE ACOS INOXIDAVEIS UNIPESSOAL, LTDA.—See Acerinox, S.A.; *Int'l,* pg. 100
ACEROS CHAPA INDUSTRIAL, S.L.—See BAMESA Aceros; *Int'l,* pg. 813
ACE STEEL SUPPLY, INC.—See Commercial Steel Products LLC; *U.S. Private,* pg. 984
A&C PLASTICS, INC.; *U.S. Private,* pg. 19
ACP METAL FINISHING PTE LTD—See Grand Venture Technology Limited; *Int'l,* pg. 3057
ACTION STAINLESS & ALLOYS INC.—See Olympic Steel Inc.; *U.S. Public,* pg. 1570
ACT PIPE & SUPPLY INC.; *U.S. Private,* pg. 66
ACX DO BRASIL REPRESENTACOES, LTDA.—See Acerinox, S.A.; *Int'l,* pg. 100
ADMET SA; *Int'l,* pg. 151
ADMIRAL METALS SERVICENTER COMPANY INC.—See BMH Corp.; *U.S. Private,* pg. 600
ADOR FONTECH LTD.—See Ador Welding Ltd; *Int'l,* pg. 152
ADVANCE STEEL CO.; *U.S. Private,* pg. 87
AEB INTERNATIONAL INC.; *U.S. Private,* pg. 116
AERODYNE ALLOYS LLC—See O'Neal Industries, Inc.; *U.S. Private,* pg. 2979
AGRATI GIE—See A.Agrati S.p.A.; *Int'l,* pg. 23
AK STEEL S.A.R.L.—See Cleveland-Cliffs, Inc.; *U.S. Public,* pg. 514
ALADDIN STEEL INC.; *U.S. Private,* pg. 148
ALAMEDA PIPE & SUPPLY CO., INC.—See J.D. Fields & Company Inc.; *U.S. Private,* pg. 2161
ALAMO IRON WORKS - BROWNSVILLE—See Triple-S Steel Holdings Inc.; *U.S. Private,* pg. 4237
ALAMO IRON WORKS, INC.—See Triple-S Steel Holdings Inc.; *U.S. Private,* pg. 4237
ALASKAN COPPER & BRASS COMPANY-PORTLAND—See Alco Investment Co., Inc.; *U.S. Private,* pg. 154
ALASKAN COPPER & BRASS COMPANY-SEATTLE—See Alco Investment Co., Inc.; *U.S. Private,* pg. 154
ALASKAN COPPER & BRASS COMPANY—See Alco Investment Co., Inc.; *U.S. Private,* pg. 153
ALASKAN COPPER & BRASS COMPANY—See Alco Investment Co., Inc.; *U.S. Private,* pg. 154
ALBANY STEEL INC.; *U.S. Private,* pg. 151
ALBA SE; *Int'l,* pg. 292
ALBCO SALES INC.; *U.S. Private,* pg. 152
ALBEDO CORPORATION PTE. LTD.—See China Medical (International) Group Limited; *Int'l,* pg. 1518
ALCONIX CORPORATION; *Int'l,* pg. 302
ALENT ALPHA METALS (SHANGHAI) TRADING CO. LTD—See Element Solutions Inc.; *U.S. Public,* pg. 726
ALLEGHENY PIPE & SUPPLY CO—See Winsupply, Inc.; *U.S. Private,* pg. 4545
ALLEGHENY STEEL DISTRIBUTORS, INC.—See Reliance Steel & Aluminum Co.; *U.S. Public,* pg. 1779
ALLEGHENY TECHNOLOGIES GMBH—See ATI Inc.; *U.S. Public,* pg. 221
ALLEGHENY TECHNOLOGIES INCORPORATED - SINGAPORE—See ATI Inc.; *U.S. Public,* pg. 222
ALLEGHENY TECHNOLOGIES JAPAN LTD—See ATI Inc.; *U.S. Public,* pg. 222
ALLEGHENY TECHNOLOGIES LIMITED—See ATI Inc.; *U.S. Public,* pg. 222
ALLEGHENY TECHNOLOGIES SAS—See ATI Inc.; *U.S. Public,* pg. 222
ALLIED METALLURG SOUTH AFRICA (AMETSA)—See Allied Mineral Products, Inc.; *U.S. Private,* pg. 186
ALLIED METALS CORP.; *U.S. Private,* pg. 186
ALLIED WIRE & CABLE INC.; *U.S. Private,* pg. 191
ALLIED WIRE & CABLE INC.—See Allied Wire & Cable Inc.; *U.S. Private,* pg. 191
ALL METAL SERVICES INDIA PRIVATE LIMITED—See Reliance Steel & Aluminum Co.; *U.S. Public,* pg. 1779
ALL METAL SERVICES LIMITED—See Reliance Steel & Aluminum Co.; *U.S. Public,* pg. 1779
ALL METAL SERVICES LTD.—See Reliance Steel & Aluminum Co.; *U.S. Public,* pg. 1779

ALL METAL SERVICES LTD.—See Reliance Steel & Aluminum Co.; *U.S. Public,* pg. 1779
ALL METAL SERVICES (MALAYSIA) SDN. BHD.—See Reliance Steel & Aluminum Co.; *U.S. Public,* pg. 1779
ALLOY STEEL INTERNATIONAL, INC. - MOORESVILLE BRANCH—See Alloy Steel International, Inc.; *Int'l,* pg. 360
ALLTUB UK LIMITED—See OEP Capital Advisors, L.P.; *U.S. Private,* pg. 2998
ALLTUB USA, LLC—See OEP Capital Advisors, L.P.; *U.S. Private,* pg. 2998
ALMET NEDERLAND BV—See Henley Management Company; *U.S. Private,* pg. 1916
ALMET—See Henley Management Company; *U.S. Private,* pg. 1916
ALP INDUSTRIES, INC.; *U.S. Private,* pg. 196
ALRO METAL SERVICE CENTER, BOCA RATON—See Alro Steel Corporation; *U.S. Private,* pg. 202
ALRO METALS PLUS, CLEARWATER—See Alro Steel Corporation; *U.S. Private,* pg. 202
ALRO METALS SERVICE CENTER, ORLANDO—See Alro Steel Corporation; *U.S. Private,* pg. 202
ALRO SPECIALTY METALS, CHARLOTTE—See Alro Steel Corporation; *U.S. Private,* pg. 202
ALRO SPECIALTY METALS, REDFORD—See Alro Steel Corporation; *U.S. Private,* pg. 202
ALRO STEEL CORPORATION; *U.S. Private,* pg. 202
ALRO STEEL—See Alro Steel Corporation; *U.S. Private,* pg. 202
ALRO STEEL—See Alro Steel Corporation; *U.S. Private,* pg. 202
ALUMINIUM AUSTRIA METALL QUEBEC INC—See AMAG Austria Metall AG; *Int'l,* pg. 408
ALUMINUM AND STAINLESS, INC.—See Reliance Steel & Aluminum Co.; *U.S. Public,* pg. 1779
ALUMINUM LINE PRODUCTS COMPANY; *U.S. Private,* pg. 211
AMAG ASIA PACIFIC LTD.—See AMAG Austria Metall AG; *Int'l,* pg. 407
AMAG CHINA LTD.—See AMAG Austria Metall AG; *Int'l,* pg. 407
AMAG DEUTSCHLAND GMBH—See AMAG Austria Metall AG; *Int'l,* pg. 407
AMAG FRANCE S.A.R.L.—See AMAG Austria Metall AG; *Int'l,* pg. 407
AMAG ITALIA S.R.L.—See AMAG Austria Metall AG; *Int'l,* pg. 408
AMAG ROLLING EASTERN EUROPE, S.R.O.—See AMAG Austria Metall AG; *Int'l,* pg. 408
AMAG ROLLING IBERIA S.L.—See AMAG Austria Metall AG; *Int'l,* pg. 408
AMAG UK LTD.—See AMAG Austria Metall AG; *Int'l,* pg. 408
AMAG USA CORP.—See AMAG Austria Metall AG; *Int'l,* pg. 408
AMALGAMET (SOUTH EAST ASIA) PTE LTD—See Amalgamated Metal Corporation PLC; *Int'l,* pg. 408
AMBRO SALES (PTY) LTD.—See Hudaco Industries Limited; *Int'l,* pg. 3521
A. M. CASTLE & CO. (CANADA) INC.—See A. M. Castle & Co.; *U.S. Public,* pg. 11
A. M. CASTLE & CO.; *U.S. Public,* pg. 10
A.M. CASTLE METAL MATERIALS (SHANGHAI) CO., LTD.—See A. M. Castle & Co.; *U.S. Public,* pg. 11
AMERICAN AGENCIES CO. INC.; *U.S. Private,* pg. 222
AMERICAN ALLOY STEEL INC.; *U.S. Private,* pg. 222
AMERICAN DOUGLAS METALS INC.; *U.S. Private,* pg. 230
AMERICAN EAGLE STEEL CORP.; *U.S. Private,* pg. 231
AMERICAN LIFTING PRODUCTS INC.—See ALP Industries, Inc.; *U.S. Private,* pg. 196
AMERICAN METALS CORPORATION—See Reliance Steel & Aluminum Co.; *U.S. Public,* pg. 1779
AMERICAN PILEDRIVING EQUIPMENT, INC.; *U.S. Private,* pg. 243
AMERICAN PIPING PRODUCTS INC.—See Center Rock Capital Partners, LP; *U.S. Private,* pg. 811
AMERICAN PRECAST REFRACTORIES DIVISION—See Allied Mineral Products, Inc.; *U.S. Private,* pg. 187
AMERICAN STEEL & SUPPLY INC.; *U.S. Private,* pg. 255
AMERIPIPE SUPPLY, INC.; *U.S. Private,* pg. 260
AMI METALS EUROPE SPRL—See Reliance Steel & Aluminum Co.; *U.S. Public,* pg. 1779
AMI METALS FRANCE SAS—See Reliance Steel & Aluminum Co.; *U.S. Public,* pg. 1779
AMI METALS, INC.—See Reliance Steel & Aluminum Co.; *U.S. Public,* pg. 1779
AMI METALS UK LIMITED—See Reliance Steel & Aluminum Co.; *U.S. Public,* pg. 1779
AMPCO METAL DEUTSCHLAND GMBH—See Ampco Metal SA; *Int'l,* pg. 433
AMPCO METAL (FOSHAN) CO. LTD.—See Ampco Metal SA; *Int'l,* pg. 433
AMPCO METAL, INC. - WELDING PRODUCTS DIVISION—See Ampco Metal SA; *Int'l,* pg. 433
AMPCO METAL INDIA PVT LTD—See Ampco Metal SA; *Int'l,* pg. 433
AMPCO METAL KOREA CO., LTD.—See Ampco Metal SA; *Int'l,* pg. 433

CORPORATE AFFILIATIONS

AMPCO METAL SA - AREOSPACE DIVISION—See Ampco Metal SA; *Int'l,* pg. 433
AMPCO METAL SRL—See Ampco Metal SA; *Int'l,* pg. 433
AMPCO METAL S.R.O.—See Ampco Metal SA; *Int'l,* pg. 433
AMSCO STEEL COMPANY; *U.S. Private,* pg. 267
AMSCO WEAR PRODUCTS INC.; *U.S. Private,* pg. 267
AMSTEK METAL; *U.S. Private,* pg. 268
ANGELES WELDING & MFG., INC.; *U.S. Private,* pg. 282
ANN AIK PTE LTD—See AnnAik Limited; *Int'l,* pg. 473
ANN JOO METAL (SINGAPORE) PTE. LTD.—See Ann Joo Resources Berhad; *Int'l,* pg. 473
A ONE ALFORM CO., LTD.; *Int'l,* pg. 18
AOOVAC LIMITED—See ATI Inc.; *U.S. Public,* pg. 222
APERAM STAINLESS SERVICES & SOLUTIONS FRANCE S.A.—See Aperam SA; *Int'l,* pg. 508
APERAM STAINLESS SERVICES & SOLUTIONS IBERICA SL—See Aperam SA; *Int'l,* pg. 508
APERAM STAINLESS SERVICES & SOLUTIONS INTERNATIONAL S.A.—See Aperam SA; *Int'l,* pg. 508
APERAM STAINLESS SERVICES & SOLUTIONS ITALY SRL—See Aperam SA; *Int'l,* pg. 508
APERAM STAINLESS SERVICES & SOLUTIONS POLAND SP. Z O O—See Aperam SA; *Int'l,* pg. 508
API FOILS (NEW ZEALAND) LIMITED—See Aldus Pty. Ltd.; *Int'l,* pg. 305
API FOILS PTY LIMITED—See Aldus Pty. Ltd.; *Int'l,* pg. 305
API FOILS SAS—See Aldus Pty. Ltd.; *Int'l,* pg. 305
ARCELORMITTAL DISTRIBUTION SOLUTIONS—See ArcelorMittal S.A.; *Int'l,* pg. 544
ARCELORMITTAL INTERNATIONAL LUXEMBOURG S.A.—See ArcelorMittal S.A.; *Int'l,* pg. 544
ARCELORMITTAL MINES CANADA INC.—See ArcelorMittal S.A.; *Int'l,* pg. 544
ARCELORMITTAL STEEL NORTH AMERICA—See ArcelorMittal S.A.; *Int'l,* pg. 545
ARCONIC GMBH—See Howmet Aerospace Inc.; *U.S. Public,* pg. 1062
ARCONIC INTERNATIONAL (ASIA) LIMITED—See Howmet Aerospace Inc.; *U.S. Public,* pg. 1062
ARDOUR WORLD LIMITED; *Int'l,* pg. 557
ARGENT STEEL GROUP (PTY) LTD—See ARGENT INDUSTRIAL LIMITED; *Int'l,* pg. 560
ARKU COIL SYSTEMS INC.—See ARKU Maschinenbau GmbH; *Int'l,* pg. 572
ARKU LEVELING SYSTEMS (KUNSHAN) CO., LTD.—See ARKU Maschinenbau GmbH; *Int'l,* pg. 572
ARLINGTON METALS CORPORATION; *U.S. Private,* pg. 329
ARMCO METALS HOLDINGS, INC.; *U.S. Private,* pg. 330
ARROW THOMPSON METALS, INC.—See The Thompson Companies; *U.S. Private,* pg. 4126
ARTCO GROUP INTERNATIONAL, INC.; *U.S. Private,* pg. 340
ART IRON, INC.; *U.S. Private,* pg. 340
ASAKA RIKEN CO., LTD.; *Int'l,* pg. 599
ASEEM GLOBAL LTD.; *Int'l,* pg. 605
ATA CASTING TECHNOLOGY JAPAN CO., LTD.—See Daido Metal Corporation; *Int'l,* pg. 1921
ATI STELLRAM S.A—See ATI Inc.; *U.S. Public,* pg. 221
ATLAS BRONZE; *U.S. Private,* pg. 375
ATLAS STEEL PRODUCTS CO. INC.; *U.S. Private,* pg. 380
ATLAS TUBULAR LP; *U.S. Private,* pg. 380
AURUBIS BUFFALO, INC.—See Aurubis AG; *Int'l,* pg. 714
AURUBIS SWEDEN—See Aurubis AG; *Int'l,* pg. 715
AUSTRAL WRIGHT METALS—See Fletcher Building Limited; *Int'l,* pg. 2699
AVINS INDUSTRIAL PRODUCTS CORPORATION; *U.S. Private,* pg. 407
AZCON CORP.—See Blue Tee Corporation; *U.S. Private,* pg. 594
BACVIET FURNITURE COMPANY LIMITED—See Bacviet Steel JSC; *Int'l,* pg. 795
BAKERSFIELD PIPE & SUPPLY; *U.S. Private,* pg. 457
BAL HOLDINGS INC.—See Grupo BAL; *Int'l,* pg. 3121
BALL BEVERAGE CAN EGYPT S.A.E.—See Ball Corporation; *U.S. Public,* pg. 267
BALL BEVERAGE PACKAGING FREDERICIA A/S—See Ball Corporation; *U.S. Public,* pg. 267
BALL BEVERAGE PACKAGING GELSENKIRCHEN GMBH—See Ball Corporation; *U.S. Public,* pg. 267
BALL BEVERAGE PACKAGING (INDIA) PRIVATE LIMITED—See Ball Corporation; *U.S. Public,* pg. 267
BALL BEVERAGE PACKAGING LUDESCH GMBH—See Ball Corporation; *U.S. Public,* pg. 267
BALL BEVERAGE PACKAGING MANTSALA OY—See Ball Corporation; *U.S. Public,* pg. 267
BALL BEVERAGE PACKAGING NARO-FOMINSK LLC—See Ball Corporation; *U.S. Public,* pg. 267
BALL BEVERAGE PACKAGING OSS BV—See Ball Corporation; *U.S. Public,* pg. 267
BALL BEVERAGE PACKAGING VSEVOLOZHSK LLC—See Ball Corporation; *U.S. Public,* pg. 267
BALL BEVERAGE PACKAGING WIDNAU GMBH—See Ball Corporation; *U.S. Public,* pg. 267
BALL CHILE S.A.—See Ball Corporation; *U.S. Public,* pg. 266
BALL FOUNDATION-NOT FOR PROFIT—See Ball Corporation; *U.S. Public,* pg. 266

N.A.I.C.S. INDEX

423510 — METAL SERVICE CENTE...

BALL GLOBAL BUSINESS SERVICES EUROPE AND AMEA D.O.O. BEOGRAD-NOVI BEOGRAD—See Ball Corporation; *U.S. Public*, pg. 266
BALLI KLOCKNER GMBH—See Balli Group plc; *Int'l*, pg. 809
BALLI STEEL INC—See Balli Group plc; *Int'l*, pg. 809
BALLI WEST AFRICA LIMITED—See Balli Group plc; *Int'l*, pg. 809
BAL METALS INTERNATIONAL INC—See Grupo BAL; *Int'l*, pg. 3121
BAMESA CELIK A.S.—See BAMESA Aceros; *Int'l*, pg. 813
BAMESA CELIK MURADIYE DEMIR SANAYI VE TICARET—See BAMESA Aceros; *Int'l*, pg. 813
BAMESA CELIK SERVIS S.V.T.A.S.—See BAMESA Aceros; *Int'l*, pg. 813
BAMESA FRANCE, S.A.—See BAMESA Aceros; *Int'l*, pg. 813
BAMESA OTEL, S.A.—See BAMESA Aceros; *Int'l*, pg. 813
BANNER SERVICE CORPORATION—See MiddleGround Management, LP; *U.S. Private*, pg. 2711
BARSTEEL CORP; *U.S. Private*, pg. 482
BASF METALS (SHANGHAI) CO. LTD.—See BASF SE; *Int'l*, pg. 880
BASTA HOLDINGS, CORP.; *U.S. Private*, pg. 486
B&B SURPLUS, INC.; *U.S. Private*, pg. 418
BD PRINT LIMITED—See Ball Corporation; *U.S. Public*, pg. 266
BE GROUP AB; *Int'l*, pg. 931
BE GROUP AS—See BE Group AB; *Int'l*, pg. 931
BE GROUP OY AB—See BE Group AB; *Int'l*, pg. 931
BE GROUP SIA—See BE Group AB; *Int'l*, pg. 931
BE GROUP SLOVAKIA S.R.O.—See BE Group AB; *Int'l*, pg. 931
BE GROUP SP. Z O.O.—See BE Group AB; *Int'l*, pg. 931
BE GROUP S.R.O.—See BE Group AB; *Int'l*, pg. 931
BE GROUP SVERIGE AB—See BE Group AB; *Int'l*, pg. 931
BE GROUP UAB—See BE Group AB; *Int'l*, pg. 931
BEIJING ZHONG KE SAN HUAN INTERNATIONAL TRADING COMPANY—See Beijing Zhong Ke San Huan Hightech Co., Ltd.; *Int'l*, pg. 961
BELDEN ELECTRONICS GMBH—See Belden, Inc.; *U.S. Public*, pg. 293
BELL PROCESSING INCORPORATED; *U.S. Private*, pg. 519
BENJAMIN STEEL COMPANY INC.; *U.S. Private*, pg. 526
BERGEN GROUP SKARVELAND AS—See Endur ASA; *Int'l*, pg. 2409
BERG STEEL CORP.—See UPG Enterprises LLC; *U.S. Private*, pg. 4311
BERLIN METALS LLC—See Olympic Steel Inc.; *U.S. Public*, pg. 1570
BETA STEEL—See MNP Corporation; *U.S. Private*, pg. 2756
BETINOKS TURKEY—See Acerinox, S.A.; *Int'l*, pg. 100
BFL FABRICATORS LTD.—See Bird Construction Inc.; *Int'l*, pg. 1046
BICO AKRON INC.—See The Burger Iron Company; *U.S. Private*, pg. 4003
BICO MICHIGAN INC.—See The Burger Iron Company; *U.S. Private*, pg. 4003
BICO SOUTH INC.—See The Burger Iron Company; *U.S. Private*, pg. 4003
BI METALLURGICAL SPECIALTIES, INC.—See Joint Holdings/Basic Metal Industries, Inc.; *U.S. Private*, pg. 2230
BISALLOY (THAILAND) CO LIMITED—See Bisalloy Steel Group Ltd.; *Int'l*, pg. 1048
BLACKHAWK STEEL CORP; *U.S. Private*, pg. 576
BLOCK INDUSTRIES INC.; *U.S. Private*, pg. 582
BLOOM INDUSTRIES LIMITED; *Int'l*, pg. 1065
BLUESCOPE STEEL SOUTHERN AFRICA (PTY) LTD.—See BlueScope Steel Limited; *Int'l*, pg. 1073
BMB OCEL S.R.O.—See Benteler International AG; *Int'l*, pg. 976
BMG METALS, INC.; *U.S. Private*, pg. 600
BMH CORP.; *U.S. Private*, pg. 600
BOLIDEN BERGSOE AS—See Boliden AB; *Int'l*, pg. 1102
BOLIDEN COMMERCIAL AB—See Boliden AB; *Int'l*, pg. 1102
BORRMANN METAL CENTER, INC.—See Triple-S Steel Holdings Inc.; *U.S. Private*, pg. 4237
BOURLAND & LEVERICH HOLDING COMPANY; *U.S. Private*, pg. 624
BOURLAND & LEVERICH SUPPLY CO. INC.—See Bourland & Leverich Holding Company; *U.S. Private*, pg. 624
BOWIM S.A.; *Int'l*, pg. 1124
BOYD METALS, INC.; *U.S. Private*, pg. 627
BOYD METALS OF JOPLIN, INC—See Boyd Metals, Inc.; *U.S. Private*, pg. 627
BRITANNIA REFINED METALS LIMITED—See Glencore plc; *Int'l*, pg. 2990
BRITISH METAL CORPORATION (INDIA) PTE LTD—See Amalgamated Metal Corporation PLC; *Int'l*, pg. 408
BRODRENE DAHL A/S—See Compagnie de Saint-Gobain SA; *Int'l*, pg. 1733
BROWN-CAMPBELL COMPANY; *U.S. Private*, pg. 669
BROWN METALS COMPANY; *U.S. Private*, pg. 668
BROWN-STRAUSS STEEL—See Blue Tee Corporation; *U.S. Private*, pg. 594

BUCHANAN SALES CO INC; *U.S. Private*, pg. 676
THE BURGER IRON COMPANY; *U.S. Private*, pg. 4003
BURWILL RESOURCES LIMITED—See Burwill Holdings Limited; *Int'l*, pg. 1227
BUSHWICK METALS LLC - BINGHAMTON DIVISION—See Berkshire Hathaway Inc.; *U.S. Public*, pg. 309
BUSHWICK METALS, LLC—See Berkshire Hathaway Inc.; *U.S. Public*, pg. 309
BWAY CORP. - TRENTON PLANT—See Stone Canyon Industries, LLC; *U.S. Private*, pg. 3817
CABLE CORPORATION OF INDIA LTD. - MALEGAON PLANT—See Cable Corporation of India Ltd.; *Int'l*, pg. 1246
CABLE CORPORATION OF INDIA LTD. - NASHIK PLANT—See Cable Corporation of India Ltd.; *Int'l*, pg. 1246
CALIFORNIA STEEL & ORNAMENTAL SUPPLIES, INC.; *U.S. Private*, pg. 720
CAMALLOY, INC.—See Republic Financial Corporation; *U.S. Private*, pg. 3402
CAMBRIDGE-LEE CANADA LTD.—See Cambridge-Lee Industries, Inc.; *U.S. Private*, pg. 727
CAMBRIDGE-LEE (EUROPE) LTD.—See Cambridge-Lee Industries, Inc.; *U.S. Private*, pg. 727
CAMBRIDGE-LEE INDUSTRIES, INC.; *U.S. Private*, pg. 727
CAMBRIDGE STREET METAL CO.; *U.S. Private*, pg. 727
CAMPBELL TOOL & METAL SUPPLY, INC.—See Industrial Metal Supply Company; *U.S. Private*, pg. 2067
CANADA PIPE CO. LTD.—See McWane, Inc.; *U.S. Private*, pg. 2645
CANADA PIPE CO. LTD.—See McWane, Inc.; *U.S. Private*, pg. 2645
CANADA PIPE CO. LTD.—See McWane, Inc.; *U.S. Private*, pg. 2645
CANFIELD & JOSEPH, INC.; *U.S. Private*, pg. 734
CANOX CORPORATION; *Int'l*, pg. 1298
CARGILL INC.—See Cargill, Inc.; *U.S. Private*, pg. 756
CARLISLE BRASS LIMITED—See ASSA ABLOY AB; *Int'l*, pg. 638
CARL SCHAEFER (AUSTRIA) GMBH—See Carl Schaefer GmbH & Co. KG; *Int'l*, pg. 1333
CARL SCHAEFER GMBH & CO. KG; *Int'l*, pg. 1333
CARL SCHAEFER HUNGARY KFT.—See Carl Schaefer GmbH & Co. KG; *Int'l*, pg. 1333
CARPENTER TECHNOLOGY (CANADA) LTD.—See Carpenter Technology Corporation; *U.S. Public*, pg. 439
CARPENTER TECHNOLOGY (EUROPE) S.A.—See Carpenter Technology Corporation; *U.S. Public*, pg. 439
CARPENTER TECHNOLOGY (UK) LTD.—See Carpenter Technology Corporation; *U.S. Public*, pg. 439
CASTLE METAL-PHOENIX—See A. M. Castle & Co.; *U.S. Public*, pg. 11
CASTLE METALS - CLEVELAND—See A. M. Castle & Co.; *U.S. Public*, pg. 11
CASTLE METALS FRANCE—See A. M. Castle & Co.; *U.S. Public*, pg. 11
CASTLE METALS - LOS ANGELES—See A. M. Castle & Co.; *U.S. Public*, pg. 11
CASTLE METALS UK LIMITED—See A. M. Castle & Co.; *U.S. Public*, pg. 11
CATALONE PIPE & SUPPLY CO.—See Core & Main, Inc.; *U.S. Public*, pg. 576
CELLMARK CHINA LTD—See CellMark AB; *Int'l*, pg. 1393
CELLMARK DEUTSCHLAND GMBH—See CellMark AB; *Int'l*, pg. 1393
CENTRAL STATES INDUSTRIAL SUPPLY, INC.; *U.S. Private*, pg. 825
CENTRAL STEEL & WIRE COMPANY—See Ryerson Holding Corporation; *U.S. Public*, pg. 1829
CENTRAL VIETNAM METAL CORPORATION; *Int'l*, pg. 1410
CENTURY AMERICA CORPORATION; *U.S. Private*, pg. 831
CENTURY STEEL—See Esmark Incorporated; *U.S. Private*, pg. 1426
CHAIN CHON STAINLESS STEEL SDN. BHD.—See Chain Chon Industrial Co., Ltd.; *Int'l*, pg. 1437
CHALLENGER PIPE & STEEL, LLC; *U.S. Private*, pg. 845
CHAMPIONS PIPE & SUPPLY INC.; *U.S. Private*, pg. 847
CHANG FU STAINLESS STEEL CENTER (SUZHOU) CO., LTD.—See Hanwa Co., Ltd.; *Int'l*, pg. 3261
CHAPEL STEEL CANADA, LTD.—See Reliance Steel & Aluminum Co.; *U.S. Public*, pg. 1779
CHAPEL STEEL COMPANY; *U.S. Private*, pg. 849
CHAPEL STEEL CORP.—See Reliance Steel & Aluminum Co.; *U.S. Public*, pg. 1779
CHARLES C. LEWIS COMPANY; *U.S. Private*, pg. 851
CHATHAM STEEL CORPORATION—See Reliance Steel & Aluminum Co.; *U.S. Public*, pg. 1779
CHEERGLORY TRADERS LIMITED—See China Rare Earth Resources And Technology Co., Ltd.; *Int'l*, pg. 1545
CHEMEX FOUNDRY SOLUTIONS GMBH—See Huettenes-Albertus Chemische Werke GmbH; *Int'l*, pg. 3522
CHEMUNG SUPPLY CORPORATION; *U.S. Private*, pg. 872
CHERNAN METAL INDUSTRIAL CORP.; *Int'l*, pg. 1471
CHICAGO STEEL & IRON—See Esmark Incorporated; *U.S. Private*, pg. 1426

CHICAGO TUBE & IRON CO.—See Olympic Steel Inc.; *U.S. Public*, pg. 1570
CHINA INTERNATIONAL ENGINEERING & MATERIALS CORP.—See China Rare Earth Resources And Technology Co., Ltd.; *Int'l*, pg. 1545
CHINA METAL RECYCLING (HOLDINGS) LIMITED; *Int'l*, pg. 1523
CHINA MINMETALS H.K. (HOLDING) LIMITED—See China Rare Earth Resources And Technology Co., Ltd.; *Int'l*, pg. 1545
CHINA MINMETALS NON-FERROUS METALS CO. LTD.—See China Rare Earth Resources And Technology Co., Ltd.; *Int'l*, pg. 1545
CHINA MINMETALS SOUTH AMERICA (HOLDING) LTD.—See China Rare Earth Resources And Technology Co., Ltd.; *Int'l*, pg. 1545
CHINA MINMETALS ZHUHAI IMPORT AND EXPORT TRADING CO., LTD.—See China Rare Earth Resources And Technology Co., Ltd.; *Int'l*, pg. 1545
CHINA NATIONAL METAL PRODUCTS IMP/EXP COMPANY—See China Rare Earth Resources And Technology Co., Ltd.; *Int'l*, pg. 1545
CHINA NATIONAL METALS & MINERALS IMP. & EXP. SHANGHAI PUDONG CORP.—See China Rare Earth Resources And Technology Co., Ltd.; *Int'l*, pg. 1545
CHINA NATIONAL METALS & MINERALS IMP/EXP SHENZHEN CORP.—See China Rare Earth Resources And Technology Co., Ltd.; *Int'l*, pg. 1545
CHINA NATIONAL MINERALS CO., LTD.—See China Rare Earth Resources And Technology Co., Ltd.; *Int'l*, pg. 1545
CHINA ORIENTAL SINGAPORE PTE. LTD.—See China Oriental Group Company Limited; *Int'l*, pg. 1538
CINCINNATI TOOL STEEL CO., INC.; *U.S. Private*, pg. 898
CIVES CORPORATION - NORTHERN DIVISION—See Cives Corporation; *U.S. Private*, pg. 908
CLAYTON METALS, INC.—See Reliance Steel & Aluminum Co.; *U.S. Public*, pg. 1779
CLEVELAND-CLIFFS BURNS HARBOR LLC—See Cleveland-Cliffs, Inc.; *U.S. Public*, pg. 514
CLEVELAND METAL EXCHANGE INC.—See The Mill Steel Co., Inc.; *U.S. Private*, pg. 4079
CLIFFORD METAL—See Lapham-Hickey Steel Corp.; *U.S. Private*, pg. 2391
CLINGAN STEEL INC.; *U.S. Private*, pg. 943
CMC CONSTRUCTION SERVICES INC—See Commercial Metals Company; *U.S. Public*, pg. 545
CMC CONSTRUCTION SERVICES—See Commercial Metals Company; *U.S. Public*, pg. 545
CMC EUROPE AG—See Commercial Metals Company; *U.S. Public*, pg. 545
CMC FAREAST LIMITED—See Commercial Metals Company; *U.S. Public*, pg. 545
CMC POLAND SP. Z O.O.—See Commercial Metals Company; *U.S. Public*, pg. 545
CMC REBAR—See Commercial Metals Company; *U.S. Public*, pg. 545
CMC RECEIVABLES, INC.—See Commercial Metals Company; *U.S. Public*, pg. 545
CMC STEEL DISTRIBUTION PTY LTD—See Commercial Metals Company; *U.S. Public*, pg. 545
CMC STEEL OKLAHOMA, LLC—See Commercial Metals Company; *U.S. Public*, pg. 546
COAST ALUMINUM & ARCHITECTURAL INC.; *U.S. Private*, pg. 954
COGNOR HOLDING S.A.; *Int'l*, pg. 1695
COLLATERAL FINANCE CORPORATION—See A-Mark Precious Metals, Inc.; *U.S. Public*, pg. 10
COLUMBIA NATIONAL GROUP INC; *U.S. Private*, pg. 977
COLUMBIA PIPE & SUPPLY COMPANY; *U.S. Private*, pg. 977
COLUMBUS PIPE & EQUIPMENT COMPANY; *U.S. Private*, pg. 979
COMANY INC. - MARKET DEVELOPMENT DIVISION—See Comany Inc.; *Int'l*, pg. 1707
COMAP PRAHA S.R.O.—See Aalberts N.V.; *Int'l*, pg. 33
COMBINED METALS OF CHICAGO LLC—See Cleveland-Cliffs, Inc.; *U.S. Public*, pg. 514
THE COMMERCIAL GROUP LIFTING PRODUCTS—See The Commercial Group Lifting Products; *U.S. Private*, pg. 4012
COMMERCIAL METALS COMPANY; *U.S. Public*, pg. 545
COMMERCIAL METALS (INTERNATIONAL) AG—See Commercial Metals Company; *U.S. Public*, pg. 546
COMMERCIAL METALS SF/JV COMPANY—See Commercial Metals Company; *U.S. Public*, pg. 546
COMPONENTA FRAMMESTAD AB—See Componenta Corporation; *Int'l*, pg. 1753
COMPONENTA ITALY S.R.L.—See Componenta Corporation; *Int'l*, pg. 1753
COMPONENTA NETHERLANDS B.V.—See Componenta Corporation; *Int'l*, pg. 1753
CON-DEA SUPPLY CORP.; *U.S. Private*, pg. 1008
CONESTOGA SUPPLY CORP.; *U.S. Private*, pg. 1012
CONKLIN METAL INDUSTRIES; *U.S. Private*, pg. 1014
CONNECTOR SPECIALIST INC.; *U.S. Private*, pg. 1016
CONSOLIDATED METAL PRODUCTS, INC.-EUROPE—See Consolidated Metal Products, Inc.; *U.S. Private*, pg. 1021

423510 — METAL SERVICE CENTE...

CONSOLIDATED METAL PRODUCTS, INC.-JAPAN—See Consolidated Metal Products, Inc.; *U.S. Private*, pg. 1021
CONSOLIDATED PIPE & SUPPLY COMPANY; *U.S. Private*, pg. 1021
CONSOLIDATED REINFORCEMENTS; *U.S. Private*, pg. 1022
CONSOLIDATED STEEL SERVICES, INC.; *U.S. Private*, pg. 1022
CONSUMERS PIPE & SUPPLY CO; *U.S. Private*, pg. 1026
CONTAINER TECHNOLOGY AND SUPPLY INTERNATIONAL INCORPORATED; *U.S. Private*, pg. 1027
CONTECH—See Apax Partners LLP; *Int'l*, pg. 503
CONTINENTAL CASTING, LLC; *U.S. Private*, pg. 1028
CONTRACTORS STEEL COMPANY—See UPG Enterprises LLC; *U.S. Private*, pg. 4311
COOKSEY IRON & METAL CO. INC.—See Reliance Steel & Aluminum Co.; *U.S. Public*, pg. 1779
COONER WIRE COMPANY; *U.S. Private*, pg. 1040
COPAL S.A.S.—See Ball Corporation; *U.S. Public*, pg. 267
CORPAC STEEL PRODUCTS CORP.; *U.S. Private*, pg. 1053
CORPORACION ACERINOX PERU, S.A.C.—See Acerinox, S.A.; *Int'l*, pg. 100
COSMOSTEEL (AUSTRALIA) PTY LTD—See CosmoSteel Holdings Limited; *Int'l*, pg. 1814
CPI WIRECLOTH & SCREENS, INC.; *U.S. Private*, pg. 1080
CRESTWOOD TUBULARS INC.; *U.S. Private*, pg. 1099
THE CRISPIN COMPANY; *U.S. Private*, pg. 4016
CRONILEG ROHSTOFFHANDELSGESELLSCHAFT MBH—See CRONIMET Holding GmbH; *Int'l*, pg. 1854
CRONIMET ALFA FERROLEGIERUNGEN HANDELS GMBH—See CRONIMET Holding GmbH; *Int'l*, pg. 1854
CRONIMET BASE METALS GMBH—See CRONIMET Holding GmbH; *Int'l*, pg. 1854
CRONIMET BELGIUM NV—See CRONIMET Holding GmbH; *Int'l*, pg. 1854
CRONIMET BRASIL LTDA—See CRONIMET Holding GmbH; *Int'l*, pg. 1854
CRONIMET CHINA—See CRONIMET Holding GmbH; *Int'l*, pg. 1854
CRONIMET CHROME MINING (PTY.) LTD.—See CRONIMET Holding GmbH; *Int'l*, pg. 1854
CRONIMET CORPORATION—See CRONIMET Holding GmbH; *Int'l*, pg. 1854
CRONIMET FAGERSTA AB—See CRONIMET Holding GmbH; *Int'l*, pg. 1854
CRONIMET FRANCE S.A.S.—See CRONIMET Holding GmbH; *Int'l*, pg. 1854
CRONIMET (GREAT BRITAIN) LTD.—See CRONIMET Holding GmbH; *Int'l*, pg. 1854
CRONIMET HISPANIA, S. A.—See CRONIMET Holding GmbH; *Int'l*, pg. 1854
CRONIMET (HOLLAND) B.V.—See CRONIMET Holding GmbH; *Int'l*, pg. 1854
CRONIMET INDIA METALS PVT. LTD.—See CRONIMET Holding GmbH; *Int'l*, pg. 1854
CRONIMET LATVIA SIA—See CRONIMET Holding GmbH; *Int'l*, pg. 1854
CRONIMET LEGIERUNGEN DORTMUND GMBH—See CRONIMET Holding GmbH; *Int'l*, pg. 1854
CRONIMET LONDON LTD.—See CRONIMET Holding GmbH; *Int'l*, pg. 1854
CRONIMET METAL PHILIPPINES, INC.—See CRONIMET Holding GmbH; *Int'l*, pg. 1854
CRONIMET MEXICO—See CRONIMET Holding GmbH; *Int'l*, pg. 1854
CRONIMET NOBLE ALLOYS HANDELGES. MBH—See CRONIMET Holding GmbH; *Int'l*, pg. 1854
CRONIMET NORDIC OU—See CRONIMET Holding GmbH; *Int'l*, pg. 1854
CRONIMET OSTRAVA, S.R.O—See CRONIMET Holding GmbH; *Int'l*, pg. 1854
CRONIMET PL SP. Z.O.O,—See CRONIMET Holding GmbH; *Int'l*, pg. 1854
CRONIMET RSA (PTY) LTD—See CRONIMET Holding GmbH; *Int'l*, pg. 1854
CRONIMET S.A.—See CRONIMET Holding GmbH; *Int'l*, pg. 1854
CRONIMET SHANGHAI CO., LTD.—See CRONIMET Holding GmbH; *Int'l*, pg. 1854
CRONIMET SINGAPORE PTE. LTD.—See CRONIMET Holding GmbH; *Int'l*, pg. 1855
CROWN CENTRAL HOLDINGS LIMITED—See Chu Kong Petroleum and Natural Gas Steel Pipe Holdings Limited; *Int'l*, pg. 1589
CROWN COMMERCIAL NETHERLANDS B.V.—See Crown Holdings, Inc.; *U.S. Public*, pg. 597
CROWN STEEL SALES INCORPORATED; *U.S. Private*, pg. 1112
CSGT HONG KONG LIMITED—See China Steel Corporation; *Int'l*, pg. 1555
CSGT METALS VIETNAM JOINT STOCK COMPANY—See China Steel Corporation; *Int'l*, pg. 1555
CSGT (SHENZHEN) CO., LTD.—See China Steel Corporation; *Int'l*, pg. 1555
CSGT TRADING INDIA PRIVATE LIMITED—See China Steel Corporation; *Int'l*, pg. 1555
CUMBERLAND DIVERSIFIED METALS, INC.—See Slate Capital Group LLC; *U.S. Private*, pg. 3687
CURTIS STEEL COMPANY; *U.S. Private*, pg. 1127
CYPRUS METALS COMPANY—See Freeport-McMoRan Inc.; *U.S. Public*, pg. 884
DAIDO AMISTAR(S) PTE LTD—See Daido Steel Co., Ltd.; *Int'l*, pg. 1922
DAIDO MATEX CO., LTD.—See Daido Steel Co., Ltd.; *Int'l*, pg. 1923
DAIDO PDM (THAILAND) CO., LTD.—See Daido Steel Co., Ltd.; *Int'l*, pg. 1922
DAIDO STAINLESS STEEL (DALIAN) CO., LTD.—See Daido Steel Co., Ltd.; *Int'l*, pg. 1923
DAIDO STEEL MATERIALS TECHNOLOGY SHANGHAI CO.,LTD.—See Daido Steel Co., Ltd.; *Int'l*, pg. 1923
DAIKI (FOSHAN) TRADING LTD.—See Daiki Aluminium Industry Co., Ltd.; *Int'l*, pg. 1931
DAIKI INTERNATIONAL TRADING CORPORATION—See Daiki Aluminium Industry Co., Ltd.; *Int'l*, pg. 1931
DAIRYMANS SUPPLY COMPANY INC.—See Dairyman's Supply Company Inc.; *U.S. Private*, pg. 1146
DALCO METALS, INC.; *U.S. Private*, pg. 1148
DANA KEPNER COMPANY, LLC—See Core & Main, Inc.; *U.S. Public*, pg. 576
DARCO ENTERPRISES INC.; *U.S. Private*, pg. 1158
DAWN ASSOCIATES INC.; *U.S. Private*, pg. 1175
DECKORATORS, INC.—See UFP Industries, Inc.; *U.S. Public*, pg. 2219
DEECO METALS CORPORATION; *U.S. Private*, pg. 1189
DELAWARE STEEL CO.—See MNP Corporation; *U.S. Private*, pg. 2756
DELAWARE VALLEY STEEL CO.; *U.S. Private*, pg. 1196
DELTA METAL RECYCLING (HOLDINGS) LTD.—See Daiki Aluminium Industry Co., Ltd.; *Int'l*, pg. 1931
DELTA METALS COMPANY, INC.; *U.S. Private*, pg. 1201
DELTA STEEL, L.P.—See Reliance Steel & Aluminum Co.; *U.S. Public*, pg. 1779
DEN COL SUPPLY CO; *U.S. Private*, pg. 1204
DESIGNED ALLOYS INC.; *U.S. Private*, pg. 1214
DEUTSCHE NICKEL AMERICA INC.—See Deutsche Nickel GmbH; *Int'l*, pg. 2071
DILLINGER MIDDLE EAST FZE—See AG der Dillinger Huttenwerke; *Int'l*, pg. 197
DIVERSIFIED ULBRICH OF CANADA—See Ulbrich Stainless Steel & Special Metals, Inc.; *U.S. Private*, pg. 4275
DIXIE PIPE SALES, LP; *U.S. Private*, pg. 1245
D&L SUPPLY INC.; *U.S. Private*, pg. 1138
DODSON STEEL PRODUCTS INC.; *U.S. Private*, pg. 1252
DOFASCO USA INC.—See ArcelorMittal S.A.; *Int'l*, pg. 544
DOMUS AUREA GMBH—See Carl Schaefer GmbH & Co. KG; *Int'l*, pg. 1333
DONGBU METAL CO., LTD.—See Dongbu Group; *Int'l*, pg. 2166
DONGGUAN STEEL WEALTH METAL CO., LTD.—See Golik Holdings Limited; *Int'l*, pg. 3036
DONGGUAN WIDEHOLD METAL COMPANY LIMITED—See Golik Holdings Limited; *Int'l*, pg. 3036
DORAL STEEL INC.; *U.S. Private*, pg. 1262
DOUGLAS STEEL SUPPLY CO.; *U.S. Private*, pg. 1267
DOWA NEW MATERIALS (SHANGHAI) CO., LTD.—See Dowa Holdings Co., Ltd.; *Int'l*, pg. 2183
DOWA PRECISION CO., LTD. — See Dowa Holdings Co., Ltd.; *Int'l*, pg. 2183
DOWA PRECISION (THAILAND) CO., LTD.—See Dowa Holdings Co., Ltd.; *Int'l*, pg. 2183
DROZAPOL-PROFIL S.A.; *Int'l*, pg. 2206
DSP CO., LTD.—See DHSteel; *Int'l*, pg. 2100
DSR TRADING CORP—See DSR Wire Corporation; *Int'l*, pg. 2210
DUBOSE NATIONAL ENERGY SERVICES, INC.—See Reliance Steel & Aluminum Co.; *U.S. Public*, pg. 1779
DUFERCO INTERNATIONAL TRADING HOLDING SA—See HBIS Group Co., Ltd.; *Int'l*, pg. 3295
DUFERCO STEEL INC.—See Duferco S.A.; *Int'l*, pg. 2223
DUGGAN INDUSTRIES, INC.; *U.S. Private*, pg. 1285
DURRETT SHEPPARD STEEL COMPANY, INC.—See Reliance Steel & Aluminum Co.; *U.S. Public*, pg. 1779
D & W MANUFACTURING CO., INC.; *U.S. Private*, pg. 1136
EAGLE NATIONAL STEEL LTD; *U.S. Private*, pg. 1310
EARLE M. JORGENSEN CANADA, INC.—See Reliance Steel & Aluminum Co; *U.S. Public*, pg. 1779
EARLE M. JORGENSEN CANADA, INC.—See Reliance Steel & Aluminum Co.; *U.S. Public*, pg. 1780
EARLE M. JORGENSEN CO. - HONING CENTER/TULSA—See Reliance Steel & Aluminum Co.; *U.S. Public*, pg. 1780
EARLE M. JORGENSEN COMPANY—See Reliance Steel & Aluminum Co.; *U.S. Public*, pg. 1779
EARLE M. JORGENSEN CO. SPECIALTY TUBING/ELDRIDGE—See Reliance Steel & Aluminum Co.; *U.S. Public*, pg. 1780
EASTERN INDUSTRIAL LTD., SHANGHAI—See The Eastern Company; *U.S. Public*, pg. 2069
EASTERN METAL SUPPLY INC.—See Wynnchurch Capital, L.P.; *U.S. Private*, pg. 4577
EASTERN METAL SUPPLY TEXAS INC.—See Wynnchurch Capital, L.P.; *U.S. Private*, pg. 4577
EASTERN STEEL CORP.; *U.S. Private*, pg. 1321
EASTERN STEEL SDN BHD; *Int'l*, pg. 2274

EATON STEEL CORPORATION; *U.S. Private*, pg. 1323
ECKA GRANULES GERMANY GMBH - ESSEN BEARING TECHNOLOGIES—See Palladium Equity Partners, LLC; *U.S. Private*, pg. 3078
ECKA GRANULES ITALIA SRL—See Palladium Equity Partners, LLC; *U.S. Private*, pg. 3078
ECKA GRANULES JAPAN CO. LTD.—See Palladium Equity Partners, LLC; *U.S. Private*, pg. 3078
ECKA GRANULES OF AMERICA L.P.—See Palladium Equity Partners, LLC; *U.S. Private*, pg. 3078
ED FAGAN INC.; *U.S. Private*, pg. 1331
E&E STEEL, INC.—See Rolled Steel Products Corporation; *U.S. Private*, pg. 3474
EFCO CORP.—See Wilian Holding Co., Inc.; *U.S. Private*, pg. 4520
E.F. LACROSSE SALES INC.; *U.S. Private*, pg. 1305
E. JORDAN BROOKES CO. INC.; *U.S. Private*, pg. 1304
ELASTRON S.A.; *Int'l*, pg. 2343
ELEMENTAL RESOURCE MANAGEMENT LTD.—See Elemental Holding S.A.; *Int'l*, pg. 2358
ELITE SURFACE TECHNOLOGIES PTY. LTD.; *Int'l*, pg. 2362
ELME METALL FINLAND OY—See BLRT Grupp AS; *Int'l*, pg. 1065
ELME METALL LATVIA SIA—See BLRT Grupp AS; *Int'l*, pg. 1065
ELME METALL LITHUANIA, UAB—See BLRT Grupp AS; *Int'l*, pg. 1065
ELME METALL POLAND SP. Z O.O.—See BLRT Grupp AS; *Int'l*, pg. 1065
ELME METALL RUSSIA—See BLRT Grupp AS; *Int'l*, pg. 1065
EMMEGI DEUTSCHLAND GMBH—See Cifin S.r.l.; *Int'l*, pg. 1605
EMMEGI DO BRASIL LTDA—See Cifin S.r.l.; *Int'l*, pg. 1606
EMMEGI IBERICA, S.A.—See Cifin S.r.l.; *Int'l*, pg. 1605
EMMEGI SCANDINAVIA AB—See Cifin S.r.l.; *Int'l*, pg. 1605
EMMEGI SCANDINAVIA AB—See Cifin S.r.l.; *Int'l*, pg. 1606
EMMEGI SUISSE SA—See Cifin S.r.l.; *Int'l*, pg. 1606
EMMEGI (SUZHOU) CO., LTD.—See Cifin S.r.l.; *Int'l*, pg. 1605
EMMEGI TURK—See Cifin S.r.l.; *Int'l*, pg. 1606
EMMEGI (UK) LTD.—See Cifin S.r.l.; *Int'l*, pg. 1605
EMPIRE PIPE & SUPPLY CO., INC.; *U.S. Private*, pg. 1385
ENCORE METALS, INC.—See Reliance Steel & Aluminum Co.; *U.S. Public*, pg. 1781
ENCORE METALS—See Reliance Steel & Aluminum Co.; *U.S. Public*, pg. 1781
ENERGY ALLOYS SERVICES, LLC—See Energy Alloys, LLC; *U.S. Private*, pg. 1393
ENERGY STEEL PRODUCTS, INC.—See Lone Star New Markets LP; *U.S. Private*, pg. 2489
ENERGY STEEL PRODUCTS—See Lone Star New Markets LP; *U.S. Private*, pg. 2489
ENSA STEEL INDUSTRIES LIMITED; *Int'l*, pg. 2445
ENVASES DEL ISTMO SA—See Ball Corporation; *U.S. Public*, pg. 267
ENVASES UNIVERSALES REXAM DE CENTROAMERICA SA—See Ball Corporation; *U.S. Public*, pg. 267
ERASTEEL INC.—See Eramet SA; *Int'l*, pg. 2489
ERG EDELSTAHL RECYCLING GMBH—See CRONIMET Holding GmbH; *Int'l*, pg. 1854
ERICKSON METALS CORPORATION; *U.S. Private*, pg. 1420
ESSENTRA SP. Z O.O. ODDZIAL SKIFFY—See Essentra plc; *Int'l*, pg. 2511
EUROLLS MACHINERY (SHANGHAI) CO. LTD.—See EUROLLS S.p.A.; *Int'l*, pg. 2553
EVCILER KIMYA MADENCILIK VE DEGERLI METALLER SAN.TIC A.S.—See Elemental Holding S.A.; *Int'l*, pg. 2358
EVRAZ MARKET JSC—See Evraz plc; *Int'l*, pg. 2573
EXXARO INTERNATIONAL TRADING BV—See Exxaro Resources Ltd.; *Int'l*, pg. 2592
E-Z LOK—See TCI Precision Metals, Inc.; *U.S. Private*, pg. 3942
FABRICATED PRODUCTS, INC.—See The Renco Group Inc.; *U.S. Private*, pg. 4104
FALCON STEEL INC.; *U.S. Private*, pg. 1467
FARMERS COPPER & INDUSTRIAL SUPPLY—See Four Winds Investment Corp.; *U.S. Private*, pg. 1583
FARWEST STEEL CORPORATION; *U.S. Private*, pg. 1481
FAY INDUSTRIES, INC.—See Ryerson Holding Corporation; *U.S. Public*, pg. 1829
FDK ECOTEC CO., LTD. - GIFU WORKS—See Fujitsu Limited; *Int'l*, pg. 2832
FEDERAL CASTERS CORPORATION; *U.S. Private*, pg. 1487
FEDERAL INTERNATIONAL (SHANGHAI) CO., LTD.—See Federal International (2000) Ltd; *Int'l*, pg. 2630
FEDERAL STEEL SUPPLY INC.—See Vergani & Associates, LLC; *U.S. Private*, pg. 4359
FEHR BROS INDUSTRIES INC.; *U.S. Private*, pg. 1493
FERALLOY CHARLESTON DIVISION—See Reliance Steel & Aluminum Co.; *U.S. Public*, pg. 1780
FERALLOY CORPORATION—See Reliance Steel & Aluminum Co.; *U.S. Public*, pg. 1780
FERALLOY MIDWEST (PORTAGE) DIVISION—See Reli-

N.A.I.C.S. INDEX

423510 — METAL SERVICE CENTE...

ance Steel & Aluminum Co.; *U.S. Public*, pg. 1780
FERALLOY PROCESSING COMPANY—See Reliance Steel & Aluminum Co.; *U.S. Public*, pg. 1780
FERALLOY PROCESSING COMPANY—See United States Steel Corporation; *U.S. Public*, pg. 2236
FERALLOY SOUTHERN DIVISION—See Reliance Steel & Aluminum Co.; *U.S. Public*, pg. 1780
FERALLOY ST. LOUIS DIVISION—See Reliance Steel & Aluminum Co.; *U.S. Public*, pg. 1780
FERALLOY WESTERN DIVISION—See Reliance Steel & Aluminum Co.; *U.S. Public*, pg. 1780
FERRAGON CORPORATION; *U.S. Private*, pg. 1498
FERROMETALLI SAFEM S.P.A.—See ArcelorMittal S.A.; *Int'l*, pg. 545
FIBRELITE AUSTRALIA—See Fibrelite Composites Limited.; *Int'l*, pg. 2653
FIELD INDUSTRIES LLC; *U.S. Private*, pg. 1503
FIM INOX SAS—See ERG S.p.A.; *Int'l*, pg. 2491
FLASHCO MANUFACTURING, INC.; *U.S. Private*, pg. 1540
FORD STEEL COMPANY—See North Shore Supply Company Inc.; *U.S. Private*, pg. 2947
FORD TOOL STEELS, INC.—See Ryerson Holding Corporation; *U.S. Public*, pg. 1829
FOUR WINDS INVESTMENT CORP.; *U.S. Private*, pg. 1583
FOX METALS & ALLOYS, INC.—See Reliance Steel & Aluminum Co.; *U.S. Public*, pg. 1780
F. RAMADA, ACOS E INDUSTRIAS, S.A.—See F. Ramada Investimentos, SGPS, S.A.; *Int'l*, pg. 2596
FRY STEEL COMPANY—See Reliance Steel & Aluminum Co.; *U.S. Public*, pg. 1780
FUTURE METALS, INC.—See Berkshire Hathaway Inc.; *U.S. Public*, pg. 309
THE GAGE COMPANY; *U.S. Private*, pg. 4031
GAMMA FOUNDRIES LTD.—See Victaulic Company; *U.S. Private*, pg. 4377
G.A.M. STEEL PTY. LTD.—See Commercial Metals Company; *U.S. Public*, pg. 546
GANESHA ECOVERSE LTD.; *Int'l*, pg. 2880
GATETECH TECHNOLOGY INC.—See China Motor Corporation; *Int'l*, pg. 1525
GATSTEEL INDUSTRIES INC.; *Int'l*, pg. 2889
GEBR. KEMPER UK & IRELAND LTD.—See Gebr. Kemper GmbH & Co. KG; *Int'l*, pg. 2906
GENERAL ALUMINUM MANUFACTURING COMPANY—See Park-Ohio Holdings Corp.; *U.S. Public*, pg. 1639
GENERAL PURPOSE STEEL INC.; *U.S. Private*, pg. 1667
GENERAL STEEL INC.; *U.S. Private*, pg. 1667
GENERAL SULLIVAN GROUP INC.; *U.S. Private*, pg. 1667
GEORG FISCHER SA DE CV—See Georg Fischer AG; *Int'l*, pg. 2937
GERALD METALS INC.; *U.S. Private*, pg. 1685
GERARD DANIEL WORLDWIDE, INC.—See Graycliff Partners LP; *U.S. Private*, pg. 1760
GERARD DANIEL WORLDWIDE—See Graycliff Partners LP; *U.S. Private*, pg. 1760
GFE MATERIALS TECHNOLOGY, INC.—See AMG Critical Materials N.V.; *Int'l*, pg. 426
GIANT LIGHT METAL TECHNOLOGY (MALAYSIA) SDN. BHD.—See Giant Manufacturing Co., Ltd.; *Int'l*, pg. 2961
GIBBS WIRE & STEEL COMPANY, INC.; *U.S. Private*, pg. 1695
GIBBS WIRE & STEEL COMPANY OF CANADA LTD.—See Gibbs Wire & Steel Company, Inc.; *U.S. Private*, pg. 1695
GIBBS WIRE & STEEL CO.—See Gibbs Wire & Steel Company, Inc.; *U.S. Private*, pg. 1695
GIBBS WIRE & STEEL CO.—See Gibbs Wire & Steel Company, Inc.; *U.S. Private*, pg. 1695
GIBBS WIRE & STEEL CO.—See Gibbs Wire & Steel Company, Inc.; *U.S. Private*, pg. 1695
GIBBS WIRE & STEEL CO.—See Gibbs Wire & Steel Company, Inc.; *U.S. Private*, pg. 1695
GIULIANI METALLI S.A.S.—See CRONIMET Holding GmbH; *Int'l*, pg. 1855
GKN SINTER METALS LTDA—See GKN plc; *Int'l*, pg. 2985
GKW (OVERSEAS TRADING) LIMITED—See GKW Limited; *Int'l*, pg. 2986
GLASER-MILLER CO. INC.; *U.S. Private*, pg. 1706
GLOBAL METCORP LTD; *Int'l*, pg. 2999
GMH GROUP DO BRASIL—See Georgsmarienhutte Holding GmbH; *Int'l*, pg. 2940
GMH INDIA PVT. LTD.—See Georgsmarienhutte Holding GmbH; *Int'l*, pg. 2940
GMH RINGVERTRIEBS GMBH—See Georgsmarienhutte Holding GmbH; *Int'l*, pg. 2940
GOLIK STEEL COMPANY LIMITED—See Golik Holdings Limited; *Int'l*, pg. 3036
GONVARRI STEEL SERVICES—See Corporacion Gestamp SL; *Int'l*, pg. 1804
GOOD STEEL PARTNERS CO., LTD.; *Int'l*, pg. 3039
GRASS VALLEY AUSTRALIA PTY LTD—See Black Dragon Capital LLC; *U.S. Private*, pg. 571
GRASS VALLEY BELGIUM NV—See Black Dragon Capital LLC; *U.S. Private*, pg. 571
GRASS VALLEY CANADA, INC.—See Black Dragon Capital LLC; *U.S. Private*, pg. 571
GRASS VALLEY CHINA CO. LTD.—See Black Dragon Capital LLC; *U.S. Private*, pg. 571

GRASS VALLEY DO BRASIL COMERCIO E SERVICOS DE EQUIPAMENTOS DE TELECOMUNICACOES LTDA—See Black Dragon Capital LLC; *U.S. Private*, pg. 571
GRASS VALLEY INDIA PTE. LTD.—See Black Dragon Capital LLC; *U.S. Private*, pg. 571
GRASS VALLEY ITALIA S.R.L.—See Black Dragon Capital LLC; *U.S. Private*, pg. 571
GRASS VALLEY MALAYSIA SDN BHD—See Black Dragon Capital LLC; *U.S. Private*, pg. 571
GRASS VALLEY NEDERLAND B.V.—See Black Dragon Capital LLC; *U.S. Private*, pg. 571
GREAT WESTERN TECHNOLOGIES INC.—See Great Western Minerals Group Ltd.; *Int'l*, pg. 3066
GRODITZER VERTRIEBSGESELLSCHAFT MBH—See Georgsmarienhutte Holding GmbH; *Int'l*, pg. 2940
GUANGZHOU HANWA TRADING CO., LTD.—See Hanwa Co., Ltd.; *Int'l*, pg. 3262
GWP INDUSTRIES INC.; *U.S. Private*, pg. 1821
HAGERTY STEEL & ALUMINUM CO.—See Reliance Steel & Aluminum Co.; *U.S. Public*, pg. 1780
HAKUDO (THAILAND) CO., LTD.—See Hakudo Co., Ltd.; *Int'l*, pg. 3219
HALFEN AS—See CRH plc; *Int'l*, pg. 1844
HAMILTON METALS INC.; *U.S. Private*, pg. 1848
HANIL CAN CO LIMITED—See Ball Corporation; *U.S. Public*, pg. 267
HANNING & KAHL L.P.—See HANNING & KAHL GmbH & Co KG; *Int'l*, pg. 3257
HANWA AMERICAN CORP.—See Hanwa Co., Ltd.; *Int'l*, pg. 3262
HANWA AMERICAN CORP.—See Hanwa Co., Ltd.; *Int'l*, pg. 3262
HANWA (BEIJING) CO., LTD.—See Hanwa Co., Ltd.; *Int'l*, pg. 3262
HANWA CHILE LIMITADA—See Hanwa Co., Ltd.; *Int'l*, pg. 3262
HANWA CO., LTD.; *Int'l*, pg. 3261
HANWA CO., LTD.—See Hanwa Co., Ltd.; *Int'l*, pg. 3262
HANWA CO., LTD.—See Hanwa Co., Ltd.; *Int'l*, pg. 3262
HANWA CO., LTD.—See Hanwa Co., Ltd.; *Int'l*, pg. 3262
HANWA CO., LTD.—See Hanwa Co., Ltd.; *Int'l*, pg. 3262
HANWA DAISUN CO., LTD.—See Hanwa Co., Ltd.; *Int'l*, pg. 3262
HANWA (DALIAN) CO., LTD.—See Hanwa Co., Ltd.; *Int'l*, pg. 3262
HANWA EUROPE B.V.—See Hanwa Co., Ltd.; *Int'l*, pg. 3262
HANWA FELLOWS ENGINEERING (CHINA) CO., LTD.—See Hanwa Co., Ltd.; *Int'l*, pg. 3262
HANWA FELLOWS ENGINEERING (THAILAND) CO., LTD.—See Hanwa Co., Ltd.; *Int'l*, pg. 3262
HANWA INDIA PRIVATE LTD.—See Hanwa Co., Ltd.; *Int'l*, pg. 3262
HANWA (MALAYSIA) SDN. BHD.—See Hanwa Co., Ltd.; *Int'l*, pg. 3262
HANWA METALS CO., LTD.—See Hanwa Co., Ltd.; *Int'l*, pg. 3262
HANWA MEXICANA, S.A. DE C.V.—See Hanwa Co., Ltd.; *Int'l*, pg. 3262
HANWA MIDDLE EAST FZE—See Hanwa Co., Ltd.; *Int'l*, pg. 3262
HANWA (QINGDAO) CO., LTD.—See Hanwa Co., Ltd.; *Int'l*, pg. 3262
HANWA SMC STEEL SERVICE HA NOI CO.—See Hanwa Co., Ltd.; *Int'l*, pg. 3262
HANWA STEEL SERVICE (DONGGUAN) CO., LTD.—See Hanwa Co., Ltd.; *Int'l*, pg. 3262
HANWA STEEL SERVICE MEXICANA, S.A. DE C.V.—See Hanwa Co., Ltd.; *Int'l*, pg. 3263
HANWA TRADING (SHANGHAI) CO., LTD.—See Hanwa Co., Ltd.; *Int'l*, pg. 3263
HANWA VIETNAM CO., LTD.—See Hanwa Co., Ltd.; *Int'l*, pg. 3263
HARBOR GROUP INCORPORATED; *U.S. Private*, pg. 1859
HARBOR STEEL & SUPPLY CORPORATION—See Harbor Group Incorporated; *U.S. Private*, pg. 1859
HARDING COMPANY INC.—See ALP Industries, Inc.; *U.S. Private*, pg. 196
HAROLD A. O'NEIL CO., INC.; *U.S. Private*, pg. 1866
HARRIS STEEL CO.; *U.S. Private*, pg. 1870
HASCALL STEEL COMPANY-ECORSE PLANT—See Hascall Steel Company Inc.; *U.S. Private*, pg. 1878
HASCALL STEEL COMPANY INC.; *U.S. Private*, pg. 1878
HASKINS STEEL CO., INC.; *U.S. Private*, pg. 1878
HAYASHI METAL CORP.—See Alconix Corporation; *Int'l*, pg. 302
HAYNES INTERNATIONAL, INC.—See Acerinox, S.A.; *Int'l*, pg. 100
HBIS BEIJING INTERNATIONAL TRADE CO., LTD.—See HBIS Group Co., Ltd.; *Int'l*, pg. 3295
HBIS GROUP PURCHASING CORPORATION—See HBIS Group Co., Ltd.; *Int'l*, pg. 3296
HBIS GROUP SALES CORPORATION—See HBIS Group Co., Ltd.; *Int'l*, pg. 3296
H&D STEEL SERVICE, INC.; *U.S. Private*, pg. 1822
HELENS ROR AB—See Benteler International AG; *Int'l*, pg. 977

HELENS ROR A/S—See Benteler International AG; *Int'l*, pg. 977
HELLERMANNTYTON (MEXICO) S. DE R.L. DE C.V.—See Aptiv PLC; *Int'l*, pg. 525
HENG HUP HOLDINGS LTD.; *Int'l*, pg. 3345
HERAEUS S.P.A.—See Heraeus Holding GmbH; *Int'l*, pg. 3358
HERTI FRANCE—See Herti AD; *Int'l*, pg. 3365
HERTI GERMANY GMBH—See Herti AD; *Int'l*, pg. 3365
HERTI UK LTD.—See Herti AD; *Int'l*, pg. 3365
HESHAN GOLIK METAL MANUFACTURING CO., LIMITED—See Golik Holdings Limited; *Int'l*, pg. 3036
HESHAN HANG KEI STEEL WIRE MANUFACTURING CO., LIMITED—See Golik Holdings Limited; *Int'l*, pg. 3036
HIBBING TACONITE COMPANY—See United States Steel Corporation; *U.S. Public*, pg. 2236
HICKMAN, WILLIAMS & COMPANY; *U.S. Private*, pg. 1933
HICKMAN, WILLIAMS & COMPANY—See Hickman, Williams & Company; *U.S. Private*, pg. 1933
HIGH STEEL SERVICE CENTER LLC—See High Industries, Inc.; *U.S. Private*, pg. 1935
HINKLE METALS & SUPPLY CO. INC.; *U.S. Private*, pg. 1949
H.K. CASTINGS, INC.—See Hatch & Kirk, Inc.; *U.S. Private*, pg. 1879
HL THORNE & CO., LTD.; *Int'l*, pg. 3430
HOA PHAT TRADING CO., LTD.—See Hoa Phat Group Joint Stock Company; *Int'l*, pg. 3435
HODGSON CUSTOM ROLLING INC.; *Int'l*, pg. 3438
HONDA TRADING CANADA, INC.—See Honda Motor Co., Ltd.; *Int'l*, pg. 3462
HORIZON STEEL COMPANY; *U.S. Private*, pg. 1982
HORIZONTAL UNIP. LDA—See Horizal; *Int'l*, pg. 3479
HO WAH GENTING BERHAD; *Int'l*, pg. 3434
HOWCO METALS INC.; *U.S. Private*, pg. 1995
HUA ENG WIRE & CABLE CO., LTD. - KAO-NAN FACTORY—See Hua Eng Wire & Cable Co., Ltd.; *Int'l*, pg. 3509
HUAJIN INTERNATIONAL HOLDINGS LIMITED; *Int'l*, pg. 3512
HUDBAY MARKETING AND SALES INC.—See HudBay Minerals Inc.; *Int'l*, pg. 3521
HUDSON TOOL STEEL CORPORATION—See Ryerson Holding Corporation; *U.S. Public*, pg. 1829
HUGO NEU CORPORATION; *U.S. Private*, pg. 2004
HUNTER DOUGLAS METALS—See 3G Capital Partners L.P.; *U.S. Private*, pg. 13
HUNTINGTON STEEL & SUPPLY CO.; *U.S. Private*, pg. 2010
HUSTEEL USA, INC.—See HUSTEEL CO., Ltd.; *Int'l*, pg. 3540
HYNES INDUSTRIES INC.—See Crossplane Capital Management LP; *U.S. Private*, pg. 1107
HYSCO STEEL INDIA, LTD.—See Hyundai Motor Company; *Int'l*, pg. 3558
HYUNDAI BEIJING STEEL PROCESS CO., LTD. (CHINA)—See Hyundai Steel Company; *Int'l*, pg. 3560
HYUNDAI CORPORATION (SHANGHAI) CO., LTD.—See Hyundai Corporation; *Int'l*, pg. 3555
HYUNDAI STEEL AMERICA, INC.—See Hyundai Steel Company; *Int'l*, pg. 3560
HYUNDAI STEEL SLOVAKIA S.R.O.—See Hyundai Steel Company; *Int'l*, pg. 3560
HYUNDAI STEEL USA, INC.—See Hyundai Steel Company; *Int'l*, pg. 3561
ICD ALLOYS AND METALS, LLC—See ICD Group International Inc.; *U.S. Private*, pg. 2030
ICD METALS, LLC—See ICD Group International Inc.; *U.S. Private*, pg. 2030
IDEAL STEEL & BUILDERS' SUPPLIES, LLC—See The Ideal Group, Inc.; *U.S. Private*, pg. 4055
INDEPENDENT STEEL—See Esmark Incorporated; *U.S. Private*, pg. 1426
INDEPENDENT TUBULAR CORP.; *U.S. Private*, pg. 2061
INDUSTRIAL METAL SUPPLY COMPANY; *U.S. Private*, pg. 2067
INDUSTRIAL PIPING SPECIALISTS INC.; *U.S. Private*, pg. 2067
INDUSTRIAL SALES COMPANY INC.; *U.S. Private*, pg. 2068
INDUSTRIAL STEEL & WIRE COMPANY; *U.S. Private*, pg. 2068
INDUSTRIAL TUBE & STEEL CORPORATION; *U.S. Private*, pg. 2068
INFRA-METALS CO.—See Reliance Steel & Aluminum Co.; *U.S. Public*, pg. 1780
INFRA-METALS CO.—See Reliance Steel & Aluminum Co.; *U.S. Public*, pg. 1780
INOXCENTER CANARIAS, S.A.—See Acerinox, S.A.; *Int'l*, pg. 101
INOXIDABLES DE EUSKADI S.A.—See Acerinox, S.A.; *Int'l*, pg. 101
INTERNATIONAL WIRE CO.—See Atlas Holdings, LLC; *U.S. Public*, pg. 376
INTERPLEX TECHNOLOGY (H.K.) LIMITED—See Blackstone Inc.; *U.S. Public*, pg. 355
INTERSTATE STEEL CO. INC.—See Tang Industries Inc.; *U.S. Private*, pg. 3930

423510 — METAL SERVICE CENTE... CORPORATE AFFILIATIONS

N.A.I.C.S. Index

INTERTRADE LIMITED—See RTX Corporation; *U.S. Public*, pg. 1823
INTER-WIRE PRODUCTS INC.; *U.S. Private*, pg. 2107
INTSEL STEEL—See Triple-S Steel Holdings Inc.; *U.S. Private*, pg. 4237
IPCO PROCESS SYSTEM (SHANGHAI) LTD.—See FAM AB; *Int'l*, pg. 2611
JABO SUPPLY CORPORATION; *U.S. Private*, pg. 2173
JACK RUBIN & SONS INC.; *U.S. Private*, pg. 2174
JACKSON METAL SERVICES INC.; *U.S. Private*, pg. 2178
JADE STEEL GROUP, LTD.; *U.S. Private*, pg. 2181
JADE-STERLING STEEL CO. INC.; *U.S. Private*, pg. 2181
J.A. KOERNER & COMPANY; *U.S. Private*, pg. 2157
J.D. FIELDS & COMPANY INC.; *U.S. Private*, pg. 2161
J.D. RUSH COMPANY INC.; *U.S. Private*, pg. 2161
JEFFORDS STEEL & SPECIALTY CO.; *U.S. Private*, pg. 2198
JEMISON-DEMSEY METALS; *U.S. Private*, pg. 2199
JEMISON-DEMSEY METALS—See Jemison-Demsey Metals; *U.S. Private*, pg. 2199
JIANGMEN GOLIK METAL MANUFACTURING CO., LTD.—See Golik Holdings Limited; *Int'l*, pg. 3036
JIM'S SUPPLY CO. INC.; *U.S. Private*, pg. 2210
JIN HENG LI HARDWARE SDN BHD—See HG Metal Manufacturing Limited; *Int'l*, pg. 3375
JINXI VODAR ENGINEERING CO., LTD.—See China Oriental Group Company Limited; *Int'l*, pg. 1538
J.O. GALLOUP COMPANY—See The Kendall Group, Inc.; *U.S. Private*, pg. 4064
JOHN BOUCHARD & SONS COMPANY - FOUNDRY DIVISION—See John Bouchard & Sons Company; *U.S. Private*, pg. 2220
JOY PIPE USA LLC; *U.S. Private*, pg. 2238
KANTO D-BAR STEEL CORPORATION—See Godo Steel, Ltd.; *Int'l*, pg. 3020
KELLYCO METAL DETECTOR SUPERSTORE; *U.S. Private*, pg. 2277
KELLY PIPE CO., LLC—See Shapco, Inc.; *U.S. Private*, pg. 3625
KELLY PIPE CO LLC—See Shapco, Inc.; *U.S. Private*, pg. 3625
KEMPER AIP METALS LLC—See Gebr. Kemper GmbH & Co. KG; *Int'l*, pg. 2906
KEMPER ASIA PACIFIC TRADING LLP—See Gebr. Kemper GmbH & Co. KG; *Int'l*, pg. 2906
KEMPER TRADING SHANGHAI CO. LTD.—See Gebr. Kemper GmbH & Co. KG; *Int'l*, pg. 2906
KENILWORTH STEEL CO. INC.; *U.S. Private*, pg. 2284
KENNEDY WIRE ROPE & SLING CO.; *U.S. Private*, pg. 2285
KENWAL CANADA, INC.—See Kenwal Steel Corp.; *U.S. Private*, pg. 2289
KENWAL STEEL CORP.; *U.S. Private*, pg. 2289
KENWAL STEEL CORP.—See Kenwal Steel Corp.; *U.S. Private*, pg. 2289
KENWOOD PAINTED METALS, INC; *U.S. Private*, pg. 2289
KGS STEEL INC.; *U.S. Private*, pg. 2301
KINDLIMANN SA—See Benteler International AG; *Int'l*, pg. 977
KLEIN STEEL DIRECT ROCHESTER—See Klein Steel Service Inc.; *U.S. Private*, pg. 2319
KLEIN STEEL OF SYRACUSE—See Klein Steel Service Inc.; *U.S. Private*, pg. 2319
KLEIN STEEL OF WESTERN NEW YORK—See Klein Steel Service Inc.; *U.S. Private*, pg. 2319
KLEIN STEEL SERVICE INC.; *U.S. Private*, pg. 2319
KOCH'S CUT & SUPPLY STEEL CENTRE (PTY) LTD—See ARGENT INDUSTRIAL LIMITED; *Int'l*, pg. 560
KREHER STEEL CO. - DETROIT—See Duferco S.A.; *Int'l*, pg. 2223
KREHER STEEL COMPANY, LLC—See Duferco S.A.; *Int'l*, pg. 2223
KREHER WIRE PROCESSING, INC.—See Duferco S.A.; *Int'l*, pg. 2223
KURT ORBAN PARTNERS, LLC; *U.S. Private*, pg. 2358
LAIBE CORPORATION; *U.S. Private*, pg. 2373
LAKESIDE METALS INC.; *U.S. Private*, pg. 2378
LAPHAM-HICKEY STEEL CORP.; *U.S. Private*, pg. 2391
LATAS INDUSTRIA DE EMBALAGENS DE ALUMINIO DE BRASIL LTDA.—See Ball Corporation; *U.S. Public*, pg. 267
LATROBE SPECIALTY STEEL COMPANY DISTRIBUTION—See Carpenter Technology Corporation; *U.S. Public*, pg. 439
LEECO STEEL, LLC—See O'Neal Industries, Inc.; *U.S. Private*, pg. 2979
LEE STEEL CORPORATION; *U.S. Private*, pg. 2413
LIBERTY STEEL PRODUCTS INC.; *U.S. Private*, pg. 2447
LIEBOVICH/PDM STEEL & ALUMINUM COMPANY—See Reliance Steel & Aluminum Co.; *U.S. Public*, pg. 1781
LINDQUIST STEELS INCORPORATED; *U.S. Private*, pg. 2460
LIVINGSTON PIPE AND TUBE INC.; *U.S. Private*, pg. 2474
LOEFFEL STEEL PRODUCTS INC.; *U.S. Private*, pg. 2480
LOKS PLASMA SERVICES LIMITED—See A. M. Castle & Co.; *U.S. Public*, pg. 11
LONGHORN STEEL & FLAMECUTTING, INC.—See Joint Holdings/Basic Metal Industries, Inc.; *U.S. Private*, pg. 2230
LOTTERS & MIRUNA ARAMES LTD.—See Drahtwerk Friedr. Lotters GmbH & Co. KG; *Int'l*, pg. 2200
LOTTERS POLSKA SP. Z O.O.—See Drahtwerk Friedr. Lotters GmbH & Co. KG; *Int'l*, pg. 2200
LOUISIANA UTILITIES SUPPLY COMPANY—See Ferguson plc; *Int'l*, pg. 2638
LOVEMAN STEEL CORPORATION; *U.S. Private*, pg. 2503
LVI-DAHL OY—See Compagnie de Saint-Gobain SA; *Int'l*, pg. 1724
MAANSHAN IRON & STEEL (HK) LIMITED—See China Baowu Steel Group Corp., Ltd.; *Int'l*, pg. 1486
MAAS-HANSEN STEEL CORPORATION; *U.S. Private*, pg. 2530
MACDERMID GRAPHIC SOLUTIONS EUROPE SAS—See Element Solutions Inc.; *U.S. Public*, pg. 727
MACDERMID GRAPHIC SOLUTIONS LLC—See Element Solutions Inc.; *U.S. Public*, pg. 727
MACDERMID PERFORMANCE HONG KONG LTD.—See Element Solutions Inc.; *U.S. Public*, pg. 726
MAC GROUP INCORPORATED; *U.S. Private*, pg. 2531
MAGIC STEEL CORPORATION; *U.S. Private*, pg. 2546
MAGNECO/METREL UK LTD.—See Magneco/Metrel, Inc.; *U.S. Private*, pg. 2547
MAGNEQUENCH INTERNATIONAL, INC.—See Brookfield Corporation; *Int'l*, pg. 1181
MAJESTIC STEEL SERVICE, INC.; *U.S. Private*, pg. 2554
MALAYSIAN MEGA GALVANISER SDN. BHD.—See All-greentech International PLC; *Int'l*, pg. 338
MANDEL METALS INC.; *U.S. Private*, pg. 2562
MANZI METALS, INC.; *U.S. Private*, pg. 2567
MARATHON METALS LLC—See MNP Corporation; *U.S. Private*, pg. 2756
MARCO STEEL & ALUMINUM INC.—See Triple-S Steel Holdings Inc.; *U.S. Private*, pg. 4237
MARMON/KEYSTONE CORPORATION—See Berkshire Hathaway Inc.; *U.S. Public*, pg. 309
MARMON/KEYSTONE CORPORATION—See Berkshire Hathaway Inc.; *U.S. Public*, pg. 309
MARS STEEL CORPORATION; *U.S. Private*, pg. 2588
MARUCCI CLUBHOUSE, LLC—See Compass Diversified Holdings; *U.S. Public*, pg. 560
MARUCCI HITTERS HOUSE, LLC—See Compass Diversified Holdings; *U.S. Public*, pg. 560
MA STEEL INTERNATIONAL TRADE AND ECONOMIC CORPORATION—See China Baowu Steel Group Corp., Ltd.; *Int'l*, pg. 1486
MATERION ADVANCED MATERIALS GERMANY GMBH—See Materion Corporation; *U.S. Public*, pg. 1395
MATERION BRUSH INTERNATIONAL, INC.—See Materion Corporation; *U.S. Public*, pg. 1395
MATERION BRUSH INTERNATIONAL—See Materion Corporation; *U.S. Public*, pg. 1395
MATERION BRUSH INTERNATIONAL—See Materion Corporation; *U.S. Public*, pg. 1395
MATERION BRUSH SINGAPORE SHANGHAI—See Materion Corporation; *U.S. Public*, pg. 1395
MATERION IRELAND LTD.—See Materion Corporation; *U.S. Public*, pg. 1395
MATERION KOREA LTD.—See Materion Corporation; *U.S. Public*, pg. 1395
MATERION MICROELECTRONICS & SERVICES—See Materion Corporation; *U.S. Public*, pg. 1396
MATRIX REFRACTORIES DIVISION—See Allied Mineral Products, Inc.; *U.S. Private*, pg. 187
MATTHEWS BRONZE PTY. LTD.—See Matthews International Corporation; *U.S. Public*, pg. 1399
MAURICE PINCOFF COMPANY INC.; *U.S. Private*, pg. 2615
MAZEL & COMPANY INCORPORATED; *U.S. Private*, pg. 2623
MCNEILUS STEEL INC.; *U.S. Private*, pg. 2644
MEFRO WHEELS CHINA CO., LTD.—See Crestview Partners, L.P.; *U.S. Private*, pg. 1097
MEFRO WHEELS US SERVICES, INC.—See Crestview Partners, L.P.; *U.S. Private*, pg. 1098
MEGA MEX, L.P.; *U.S. Private*, pg. 2660
MERCURY AIRCRAFT, MEXICO S. DE R.L. DE C.V.—See Mercury Aircraft Inc.; *U.S. Private*, pg. 2670
MERFISH PIPE & SUPPLY, CO.—See Reliance Steel & Aluminum Co.; *U.S. Public*, pg. 1780
MERIT ENTERPRISES, INC.—See Brookfield Corporation; *Int'l*, pg. 1175
METALCENTER, INC.—See Reliance Steel & Aluminum Co.; *U.S. Public*, pg. 1780
METAL EXCHANGE CORPORATION; *U.S. Private*, pg. 2680
METALLOY INDUSTRIES INC.; *U.S. Private*, pg. 2681
METALLOY METALLE-LEGIERUNGEN GMBH—See CRONIMET Holding GmbH; *Int'l*, pg. 1855
METAL & RECYCLING COMPANY K.S.C.C.—See Agility; *Int'l*, pg. 210
METAL RESOURCE SOLUTIONS; *U.S. Private*, pg. 2680
METALS & ALLOYS INTERNATIONAL LTD.—See CRONIMET Holding GmbH; *Int'l*, pg. 1855
METALS USA, INC.—See Reliance Steel & Aluminum Co.; *U.S. Public*, pg. 1780
METALS USA PLATES AND SHAPES NORTHEAST, L.P.—See Reliance Steel & Aluminum Co.; *U.S. Public*, pg. 1781
METALS USA PLATES AND SHAPES SOUTHEAST, INC.—See Reliance Steel & Aluminum Co.; *U.S. Public*, pg. 1781
METROLINA STEEL INC.; *U.S. Private*, pg. 2687
METROPOLITAN ALLOYS CORPORATION—See Mac Group Incorporated; *U.S. Private*, pg. 2531
M. GLOSSER & SONS INC.; *U.S. Private*, pg. 2526
MID-AMERICA STEEL CORP.; *U.S. Private*, pg. 2707
MID CITY STEEL CORP.; *U.S. Private*, pg. 2705
MIDWEST METALS CORPORATION; *U.S. Private*, pg. 2722
MIDWEST PIPE & STEEL INC.; *U.S. Private*, pg. 2722
THE MILL STEEL CO., INC.; *U.S. Private*, pg. 4079
MINMETALS AUSTRALIA PTY. LTD.—See China Rare Earth Resources And Technology Co., Ltd.; *Int'l*, pg. 1546
MINMETALS GERMANY GMBH—See China Rare Earth Resources And Technology Co., Ltd.; *Int'l*, pg. 1546
MINMETALS, INC. (L.A.)—See China Rare Earth Resources And Technology Co., Ltd.; *Int'l*, pg. 1546
MINMETALS JAPAN CORPORATION—See China Rare Earth Resources And Technology Co., Ltd.; *Int'l*, pg. 1546
MINMETALS KOREA CO., LTD.—See China Rare Earth Resources And Technology Co., Ltd.; *Int'l*, pg. 1546
MINMETALS NANJING INTERNATIONAL TRADING CO., LTD.—See China Rare Earth Resources And Technology Co., Ltd.; *Int'l*, pg. 1546
MINMETALS NORTH EUROPE AB—See China Rare Earth Resources And Technology Co., Ltd.; *Int'l*, pg. 1546
MINMETALS R.S.A. (PTY) LTD.—See China Rare Earth Resources And Technology Co., Ltd.; *Int'l*, pg. 1546
MINMETALS SOUTH-EAST ASIA CORPORATION PTE. LTD.—See China Rare Earth Resources And Technology Co., Ltd.; *Int'l*, pg. 1546
MINMETALS SPAIN S.A.—See China Rare Earth Resources And Technology Co., Ltd.; *Int'l*, pg. 1546
MINMETALS (UK) LTD.—See China Rare Earth Resources And Technology Co., Ltd.; *Int'l*, pg. 1546
MINMETALS XIAMEN ENTERPRISES CO., LTD.—See China Rare Earth Resources And Technology Co., Ltd.; *Int'l*, pg. 1546
MINMETALS XINJIANG ALA-SHANKOU TRADING CO., LTD.—See China Rare Earth Resources And Technology Co., Ltd.; *Int'l*, pg. 1546
MINMETALS YANTAI CO., LTD.—See China Rare Earth Resources And Technology Co., Ltd.; *Int'l*, pg. 1546
MINMETALS ZHEJIANG INTERNATIONAL TRADING CO., LTD.—See China Rare Earth Resources And Technology Co., Ltd.; *Int'l*, pg. 1546
MISSOURI VALLEY STEEL CO.—See Owen Industries, Inc.; *U.S. Private*, pg. 3054
MODESTO STEEL CO INC.; *U.S. Private*, pg. 2763
MONARCH STEEL COMPANY—See American Consolidated Industries; *U.S. Private*, pg. 228
MONICO ALLOYS, INC.; *U.S. Private*, pg. 2770
MORSE DISTRIBUTION INC.; *U.S. Private*, pg. 2790
MORSE INDUSTRIES INC.; *U.S. Private*, pg. 2790
MOTOFIT LIMITED—See Advanex Inc.; *Int'l*, pg. 163
MRC GLOBAL (BELGIUM) NV—See MRC Global Inc.; *U.S. Public*, pg. 1480
MRC GLOBAL (GERMANY) GMBH—See MRC Global Inc.; *U.S. Public*, pg. 1480
MRC GLOBAL (ITALY) SRL—See MRC Global Inc.; *U.S. Public*, pg. 1481
MRC GLOBAL (NETHERLANDS) B.V.—See MRC Global Inc.; *U.S. Public*, pg. 1481
MRC GLOBAL (NEW ZEALAND) LIMITED—See MRC Global Inc.; *U.S. Public*, pg. 1481
MRC GLOBAL (SINGAPORE) PTE. LTD.—See MRC Global Inc.; *U.S. Public*, pg. 1481
M & S ALLOYS LTD.—See CRONIMET Holding GmbH; *Int'l*, pg. 1855
M.S.T. STEEL CORPORATION; *U.S. Private*, pg. 2529
MT WATERWORKS, LLC—See Dakota Supply Group Inc.; *U.S. Private*, pg. 1147
MUELLER METALS INC.; *U.S. Private*, pg. 2810
MUELLER STREAMLINE CO.—See Mueller Industries, Inc.; *U.S. Public*, pg. 1484
MULL INDUSTRIES INC.; *U.S. Private*, pg. 2811
MURPHY & NOLAN INC.; *U.S. Private*, pg. 2815
NAPCO STEEL INC.; *U.S. Private*, pg. 2834
NASHVILLE STEEL CORP.; *U.S. Private*, pg. 2836
NASLON FUJI FILTER (CHANGSHU) CO., LTD.—See Daido Steel Co., Ltd.; *Int'l*, pg. 1923
NASLON KOREA CO., LTD.—See Daido Steel Co., Ltd.; *Int'l*, pg. 1923
NATIONAL ELECTRONIC ALLOYS; *U.S. Private*, pg. 2853
NATIONAL MATERIAL LIMITED PARTNERSHIP—See Tang Industries Inc.; *U.S. Private*, pg. 3930
NATIONAL NAIL CORP.; *U.S. Private*, pg. 2859
NATIONAL PIPE HANGER CO. CORP; *U.S. Private*, pg. 2860
NATIONAL SPECIALTY ALLOYS, INC.—See Reliance Steel & Aluminum Co.; *U.S. Public*, pg. 1781

N.A.I.C.S. INDEX

423510 — METAL SERVICE CENTE...

NATIONAL SPECIALTY ALLOYS; *U.S. Private*, pg. 2863
NAYLER PETROSEALS LTD—See Tailwind Capital Group, LLC; *U.S. Private*, pg. 3924
N.B. HANDY COMPANY; *U.S. Private*, pg. 2827
NEW PROCESS STEEL LP; *U.S. Private*, pg. 2905
NEXGEN METALS, INC.; *U.S. Private*, pg. 2919
NICHEL LEGHE SPA—See CRONIMET Holding GmbH; *Int'l*, pg. 1855
NIKKO METALS HONG KONG LTD.—See ENEOS Holdings, Inc.; *Int'l*, pg. 2416
NIKKO METALS SHANGHAI CO., LTD.—See ENEOS Holdings, Inc.; *Int'l*, pg. 2416
N. MERFISH PLUMBING SUPPLY CO.; *U.S. Private*, pg. 2827
NOBELCLAD EUROPE GMBH & CO., KG—See DMC Global Inc.; *U.S. Public*, pg. 671
NOORD-NEDERLANDSE SCHROOTVERWERKING B.V.—See Benteler International AG; *Int'l*, pg. 977
NORFOLK IRON & METAL CO. INC.; *U.S. Private*, pg. 2937
NORRIS SALES ASSOCIATES INC.; *U.S. Private*, pg. 2939
NORTH AMERICAN STAINLESS MEXICO S.A. DE C.V.—See Acerinox, S.A.; *Int'l*, pg. 101
NORTH AMERICAN STEEL CANADA, INC.—See Acerinox, S.A.; *Int'l*, pg. 101
NORTHERN PLAINS STEEL CO.—See Owen Industries, Inc.; *U.S. Private*, pg. 3054
NORTHERN STATES METALS CORP.; *U.S. Private*, pg. 2954
NORTHERN STEEL CASTINGS INC.; *U.S. Private*, pg. 2954
NORTH SEA CABLES NORGE AS—See DNOW Inc.; *U.S. Public*, pg. 671
NORTH SHORE SUPPLY COMPANY INC.; *U.S. Private*, pg. 2947
NORTHSTAR STEEL & ALUMINUM; *U.S. Private*, pg. 2958
NORTHWEST STEEL & PIPE INC.; *U.S. Private*, pg. 2961
NST SAIGON COIL CENTER CO., LTD.—See Hanwa Co., Ltd.; *Int'l*, pg. 3263
OJSC PLANT OF PURE IRON—See CRONIMET Holding GmbH; *Int'l*, pg. 1855
OLD DOMINION SUPPLY, INC.—See Ferguson plc; *Int'l*, pg. 2638
OLIVER STEEL PLATE CO.—See A. M. Castle & Co.; *U.S. Public*, pg. 11
OLYMPIC FOUNDRY INC.; *U.S. Private*, pg. 3012
OLYMPIC METALS, INC.—See Reliance Steel & Aluminum Co.; *U.S. Public*, pg. 1781
OLYMPIC STEEL-CHAMBERSBURG DIVISION—See Olympic Steel Inc.; *U.S. Public*, pg. 1571
OLYMPIC STEEL-CHICAGO DIVISION—See Olympic Steel Inc.; *U.S. Public*, pg. 1571
OLYMPIC STEEL-CLEVELAND DIVISION—See Olympic Steel Inc.; *U.S. Public*, pg. 1571
OLYMPIC STEEL-CONNECTICUT DIVISION—See Olympic Steel Inc.; *U.S. Public*, pg. 1571
OLYMPIC STEEL-DETROIT—See Olympic Steel Inc.; *U.S. Public*, pg. 1571
OLYMPIC STEEL INC.; *U.S. Public*, pg. 1570
OLYMPIC STEEL IOWA, INC.—See Olympic Steel Inc.; *U.S. Public*, pg. 1570
OLYMPIC STEEL LAFAYETTE, INC.—See Olympic Steel Inc.; *U.S. Public*, pg. 1571
OLYMPIC STEEL-MINNEAPOLIS DIVISION—See Olympic Steel Inc.; *U.S. Public*, pg. 1571
OLYMPIC STEEL TRADING, INC.—See Olympic Steel Inc.; *U.S. Public*, pg. 1571
OMEGA STEEL CO.; *U.S. Private*, pg. 3015
OMNISOURCE, LLC—See Steel Dynamics, Inc.; *U.S. Public*, pg. 1942
O'NEAL FLAT ROLLED METALS, LLC - MONROE—See O'Neal Industries, Inc.; *U.S. Private*, pg. 2979
O'NEAL FLAT ROLLED METALS, LLC—See O'Neal Industries, Inc.; *U.S. Private*, pg. 2979
O'NEAL STEEL, INC.—See O'Neal Industries, Inc.; *U.S. Private*, pg. 2979
OOO MEFRO WHEELS RUSSIA—See Crestview Partners, L.P.; *U.S. Private*, pg. 1097
OREGON FERALLOY PARTNERS—See Evraz plc; *Int'l*, pg. 2574
OREGON FERALLOY PARTNERS—See Reliance Steel & Aluminum Co.; *U.S. Public*, pg. 1780
ORTIZ ENGINEERED PRODUCTS, INC.—See Insteel Industries, Inc.; *U.S. Public*, pg. 1134
OSCAR WINSKI CO. INC.; *U.S. Private*, pg. 3046
OVERSEAS DEVELOPMENT CORP.; *U.S. Private*, pg. 3053
OWEN INDUSTRIES, INC.; *U.S. Private*, pg. 3054
PACEMAKER STEEL AND PIPING CO.; *U.S. Private*, pg. 3064
PACESETTER STEEL SERVICE, INC.—See Flack Steel LLC; *U.S. Private*, pg. 1538
PACIFIC HIDE & FUR DEPOT; *U.S. Private*, pg. 3067
PACIFIC METAL CO—See Reliance Steel & Aluminum Co.; *U.S. Public*, pg. 1781
PACO STEELE & ENGINEERING CORP.; *U.S. Private*, pg. 3073
PALABORA ASIA PTE LIMITED—See General Nice Development Limited; *Int'l*, pg. 2919

PALABORA ASIA PTE LIMITED—See HBIS Group Co., Ltd.; *Int'l*, pg. 3296
PALABORA EUROPE LIMITED—See General Nice Development Limited; *Int'l*, pg. 2919
PALABORA EUROPE LIMITED—See HBIS Group Co., Ltd.; *Int'l*, pg. 3296
PARAGON PLUS INC.; *U.S. Private*, pg. 3091
PARAGON STEEL ENTERPRISES LLC; *U.S. Private*, pg. 3091
PARKER SCAFFOLDING CO LIMITED—See Enviri Corporation; *U.S. Public*, pg. 781
PAXTON & VIERLING STEEL COMPANY- A DIV OF OWEN INDUSTRIES INC—See Owen Industries, Inc.; *U.S. Private*, pg. 3054
PDM STEEL SERVICE CENTER-FRESNO—See Reliance Steel & Aluminum Co.; *U.S. Public*, pg. 1781
PDM STEEL SERVICE CENTER-SANTA CLARA—See Reliance Steel & Aluminum Co.; *U.S. Public*, pg. 1781
PDM STEEL SERVICE CENTERS, INC.—See Reliance Steel & Aluminum Co.; *U.S. Public*, pg. 1781
PDM STEEL SERVICE CENTER-SPANISH FORK—See Reliance Steel & Aluminum Co.; *U.S. Public*, pg. 1781
PDM STEEL SERVICE CENTER-SPARKS—See Reliance Steel & Aluminum Co.; *U.S. Public*, pg. 1781
PDM - WOODLAND—See Reliance Steel & Aluminum Co.; *U.S. Public*, pg. 1781
PECHTER INC.; *U.S. Private*, pg. 3126
PEERLESS STEEL COMPANY INC.; *U.S. Private*, pg. 3128
PENNSYLVANIA SLING CO. INC.—See ALP Industries, Inc.; *U.S. Private*, pg. 196
PENNSYLVANIA STEEL COMPANY, INC; *U.S. Private*, pg. 3137
PENNSYLVANIA STEEL COMPANY, LUCAS STEEL DIVISION—See Pennsylvania Steel Company, Inc; *U.S. Private*, pg. 3137
PENOLES METALS & CHEMICALS INC—See Grupo BAL; *Int'l*, pg. 3121
PGM GROUP SP. Z O.O.—See Elemental Holding S.A.; *Int'l*, pg. 2358
PGM OF TEXAS LLC—See Elemental Holding S.A.; *Int'l*, pg. 2358
PHOENIX CORPORATION—See Reliance Steel & Aluminum Co.; *U.S. Public*, pg. 1781
PHOENIX METALS COMPANY—See Reliance Steel & Aluminum Co.; *U.S. Public*, pg. 1781
PHOENIX METALS COMPANY—See Reliance Steel & Aluminum Co.; *U.S. Public*, pg. 1781
PIERCE ALUMINUM COMPANY INC.; *U.S. Private*, pg. 3178
PIONEER STEEL CORPORATION; *U.S. Private*, pg. 3188
PIPE DISTRIBUTORS INC.—See PDI Group Inc.; *U.S. Private*, pg. 3122
P. KAY METAL SUPPLY INC.; *U.S. Private*, pg. 3060
PLATINIUM M.M. SPOLKA Z OGRANICZONA ODPOWIEDZIALNOSCIA SP.K.—See Elemental Holding S.A.; *Int'l*, pg. 2358
PLUS TEN STAINLESS, INC.—See O'Neal Industries, Inc.; *U.S. Private*, pg. 2979
PM RECOVERY INCORPORATED; *U.S. Private*, pg. 3217
PORCELEN LIMITED CONNECTICUT LLC—See G&S Metal Products Co. Inc.; *U.S. Private*, pg. 1629
PORTER WARNER INDUSTRIES LLC; *U.S. Private*, pg. 3232
POSTLE ALUMINUM CO. LLC—See Strength Capital Partners, LLC; *U.S. Private*, pg. 3839
POTTINGER STEEL WORKS, INC.—See Alro Steel Corporation; *U.S. Private*, pg. 202
PRECISION FLAMECUTTING AND STEEL, INC.—See Reliance Steel & Aluminum Co.; *U.S. Public*, pg. 1781
PRECISION STEEL SERVICES INC.; *U.S. Private*, pg. 3246
PRECISION STEEL WAREHOUSE, INC.—See Berkshire Hathaway Inc.; *U.S. Public*, pg. 315
PRECISION STRIP INC.; *U.S. Private*, pg. 3246
PREMIER STEEL INC.; *U.S. Private*, pg. 3251
PRENSAS SCHULER S.A.—See ANDRITZ AG; *Int'l*, pg. 456
PRINCE & IZANT COMPANY; *U.S. Private*, pg. 3264
PROFESSIONAL METAL CORPORATION; *U.S. Private*, pg. 3275
PROGRESSIVE ALLOY STEELS UNLIMITED, LLC; *U.S. Private*, pg. 3278
PROGRESS RAIL CANADA CORPORATION—See Caterpillar, Inc.; *U.S. Public*, pg. 453
PRO METCO INC.; *U.S. Private*, pg. 3270
PROSOFT TECHNOLOGY (ASIA PACIFIC) SDN BHD—See Belden, Inc.; *U.S. Public*, pg. 294
PROSOFT TECHNOLOGY, INC.—See Belden, Inc.; *U.S. Public*, pg. 294
PROSOFT TECHNOLOGY SAS—See Belden, Inc.; *U.S. Public*, pg. 294
PSM FASTENER CORPORATION—See Bulten AB; *Int'l*, pg. 1215
PT BENTELER DISTRIBUTION INDONESIA—See Benteler International AG; *Int'l*, pg. 977
PT CILEGON FABRICATORS—See IHI Corporation; *Int'l*, pg. 3606
PT HALTRACO SARANA MULIA—See Huettenes-Albertus Chemische Werke GmbH; *Int'l*, pg. 3523

PT. HANWA INDONESIA—See Hanwa Co., Ltd.; *Int'l*, pg. 3263
PT HG METAL DISTRIBUTION INDONESIA—See HG Metal Manufacturing Limited; *Int'l*, pg. 3375
PT KONUTARA SEJATI—See China Hanking Holdings Limited; *Int'l*, pg. 1506
PT MRC GLOBAL INDONESIA—See MRC Global Inc.; *U.S. Public*, pg. 1481
QUALITY FLOAT WORKS, INC.; *U.S. Private*, pg. 3319
QUALITY STEELS CORPORATION—See Miller Consolidated Industries Inc.; *U.S. Private*, pg. 2733
RANDALL METALS CORPORATION; *U.S. Private*, pg. 3353
RASMUSSEN WIRE ROPE RIGGING CO—See RC Rasmussen Corporation; *U.S. Private*, pg. 3361
RAY TECH ACOT SINGAPORE PTE. LTD.—See Acma Ltd.; *Int'l*, pg. 107
RECAT GMBH—See Elemental Holding S.A.; *Int'l*, pg. 2358
REGAL STEEL CO.; *U.S. Private*, pg. 3385
RELIANCE METALCENTER ASIA PACIFIC PTE. LTD.—See Reliance Steel & Aluminum Co.; *U.S. Public*, pg. 1781
RELIANCE METALS (SHANGHAI) CO., LTD.—See Reliance Steel & Aluminum Co.; *U.S. Public*, pg. 1781
REMINGTON STEEL, INC.—See Westfield Steel Inc.; *U.S. Private*, pg. 4498
REXAM PENSION TRUSTEES LIMITED—See Ball Corporation; *U.S. Public*, pg. 268
THE RICHARDSON TRIDENT COMPANY, L.L.C.—See Reliance Steel & Aluminum Co.; *U.S. Public*, pg. 1781
RI HONG STAINLESS (SHANGHAI) CO., LTD.—See Hanwa Co., Ltd.; *Int'l*, pg. 3263
RI-KUAN METAL CORPORATION—See Casetek Holdings Limited; *Int'l*, pg. 1351
RILEY WELDING & FABRICATING LLC—See Stewart & Tate, Inc.; *U.S. Private*, pg. 3811
RIO GRANDE STEEL, LTD.; *U.S. Private*, pg. 3438
RJ TORCHING, INC.; *U.S. Private*, pg. 3449
ROBERT JAMES SALES INC.; *U.S. Private*, pg. 3458
ROGERS IRON & METAL CORP.—See Yaffe Iron & Metal Company Inc.; *U.S. Private*, pg. 4584
ROLLED ALLOYS, INC.; *U.S. Private*, pg. 3474
ROLLED ALLOYS LTD.—See Rolled Alloys, Inc.; *U.S. Private*, pg. 3474
ROLLED ALLOYS SINGAPORE, LTD.—See Rolled Alloys, Inc.; *U.S. Private*, pg. 3474
ROLLED ALLOYS—See Rolled Alloys, Inc.; *U.S. Private*, pg. 3474
ROLLED ALLOYS (SUZHOU) LTD.—See Rolled Alloys, Inc.; *U.S. Private*, pg. 3474
ROLLED STEEL PRODUCTS CORPORATION; *U.S. Private*, pg. 3474
ROUND 2 CORP., LLC—See Praesidian Capital Corp.; *U.S. Private*, pg. 3241
ROUSTER WIRE ROPE & RIGGING INC.—See Mazzella Lifting Technologies; *U.S. Private*, pg. 2623
R&S STEEL COMPANY INC.—See Triple-S Steel Holdings Inc.; *U.S. Private*, pg. 4237
RYERSON CANADA, INC.—See Ryerson Holding Corporation; *U.S. Public*, pg. 1829
SABEL INDUSTRIES INC.; *U.S. Private*, pg. 3520
SAGINAW PIPE COMPANY INC.; *U.S. Private*, pg. 3528
SAINT-GOBAIN HES GMBH—See Compagnie de Saint-Gobain SA; *Int'l*, pg. 1735
SAINT-GOBAIN PAM DEUTSCHLAND GMBH—See Compagnie de Saint-Gobain SA; *Int'l*, pg. 1735
SALZGITTER BAUELEMENTE GMBH—See FALK Building Systems BV; *Int'l*, pg. 2611
SANKO INTERNATIONAL INC.; *U.S. Private*, pg. 3546
SAUERESSIG BASKI ONCESI HAZIRLIK SISTEMIER SANAJI VE TRICARCT AMONIN SIRKETI—See Matthews International Corporation; *U.S. Public*, pg. 1401
SCHACH MATT HANDELS + VERTRIEBS GMBH—See CRONIMET Holding GmbH; *Int'l*, pg. 1855
SCHEU STEEL SUPPLY COMPANY—See SMC Companies; *U.S. Private*, pg. 3693
SCHNITZER PUERTO RICO, INC.—See Radius Recycling, Inc.; *U.S. Public*, pg. 1760
SCHULER AG—See ANDRITZ AG; *Int'l*, pg. 456
SCHULER CARTEC ENGINEERING GMBH & CO. KG—See ANDRITZ AG; *Int'l*, pg. 456
SCHULER SALES & SERVICE (SHANGHAI) CO., LTD.—See ANDRITZ AG; *Int'l*, pg. 456
SCHULER THAILAND CO. LTD.—See ANDRITZ AG; *Int'l*, pg. 456
SCION INC.; *U.S. Private*, pg. 3574
SCOT INDUSTRIES INC.; *U.S. Private*, pg. 3576
SCRAPENA S.A.—See Commercial Metals Company; *U.S. Public*, pg. 545
SEACOAST ELECTRIC COMPANY; *U.S. Private*, pg. 3584
SERVICE STEEL AEROSPACE CORPORATION—See Reliance Steel & Aluminum Co.; *U.S. Public*, pg. 1781
SESAMEE MEXICANA, S.A. DE C.V.—See The Eastern Company; *U.S. Public*, pg. 2069
SFC KOENIG GMBH—See IDEX Corp.; *U.S. Public*, pg. 1092
SHAPCO, INC.; *U.S. Private*, pg. 3625
SHENZHEN DYNA PRECAST CONCRETE PRODUCTS

423510 — METAL SERVICE CENTE...

CO., LIMITED—See Golik Holdings Limited; *Int'l*, pg. 3036
SHINSEI SEIKI CO., LTD—See Bunka Shutter Co., Ltd.; *Int'l*, pg. 1216
SIAM HANWA CO., LTD.—See Hanwa Co., Ltd.; *Int'l*, pg. 3263
SIEGAL STEEL COMPANY—See Steel Warehouse of Wisconsin, Inc.; *U.S. Private*, pg. 3796
SIMS BROTHERS INC.; *U.S. Private*, pg. 3669
SINO RICHFIELD PTE. LTD.—See Chu Kong Petroleum and Natural Gas Steel Pipe Holdings Limited; *Int'l*, pg. 1589
SIOUX CITY FOUNDRY CO.; *U.S. Private*, pg. 3671
SIPI METALS CORP.; *U.S. Private*, pg. 3671
SISKIN STEEL AND SUPPLY CO., INC.—See Reliance Steel & Aluminum Co.; *U.S. Public*, pg. 1781
SKIFFY S.A. (PTY) LTD.—See Essentra plc; *Int'l*, pg. 2512
SLAY STEEL, INC.; *U.S. Private*, pg. 3688
SLOPAK—See Ball Corporation; *U.S. Public*, pg. 268
SMG INDUSTRIES INC.; *U.S. Public*, pg. 1896
SMITH & DE SHIELDS INC.; *U.S. Private*, pg. 3693
SMITH PIPE & STEEL COMPANY—See Reliance Steel & Aluminum Co.; *U.S. Public*, pg. 1779
SOL'S PIPE & STEEL INC.; *U.S. Private*, pg. 3706
SOUDAN METALS COMPANY INC.; *U.S. Private*, pg. 3716
SOUTHERN ALUMINUM FINISHING CO. INC.; *U.S. Private*, pg. 3729
SOUTHERN STEEL SUPPLY, LLC—See Reliance Steel & Aluminum Co.; *U.S. Public*, pg. 1781
SOUTHERN TOOL STEEL, INC.—See Ryerson Holding Corporation; *U.S. Public*, pg. 1829
SPECIAL METALS INC.; *U.S. Private*, pg. 3748
SPECIAL METALS WIGGIN LTD.—See Berkshire Hathaway Inc.; *U.S. Public*, pg. 315
SPECIALTY METALS CORPORATION; *U.S. Private*, pg. 3750
SPECIALTY PIPE & TUBE CO. OF TEXAS INC.—See Ascent Industries Co.; *U.S. Public*, pg. 210
SPECIALTY PIPE & TUBE INC.—See Ascent Industries Co.; *U.S. Public*, pg. 210
SPECTRA METAL SALES INC.; *U.S. Private*, pg. 3751
S&P STEEL PRODUCTS INC.; *U.S. Private*, pg. 3513
STAMPTECH, INC.—See Amzak Capital Management, LLC; *U.S. Private*, pg. 270
STANDARD TUBE SALES CORPORATION; *U.S. Private*, pg. 3782
STARK METAL SALES, INC.—See Pennsylvania Steel Company, Inc; *U.S. Private*, pg. 3137
STAR SHINE GLOBAL TRADING SDN. BHD.—See BlueScope Steel Limited; *Int'l*, pg. 1074
STATE STEEL SUPPLY CO; *U.S. Private*, pg. 3793
STAUB METALS CORPORATION; *U.S. Private*, pg. 3794
STEEL BAR—See Reliance Steel & Aluminum Co; *U.S. Public*, pg. 1781
STEEL ENCOUNTERS INC.; *U.S. Private*, pg. 3796
STEELFAB INC. OF ALABAMA—See Steelfab Inc.; *U.S. Private*, pg. 3797
STEEL & PIPES INC.; *U.S. Private*, pg. 3795
STEEL & PIPE SUPPLY COMPANY INC.; *U.S. Private*, pg. 3795
STEEL SERVICES INCORPORATED; *U.S. Private*, pg. 3796
STEEL SUMMIT OHIO; *U.S. Private*, pg. 3796
STEEL WAREHOUSE OF WISCONSIN, INC.; *U.S. Private*, pg. 3796
STEPHENS PIPE & STEEL INC.; *U.S. Private*, pg. 3803
STEWARD STEEL INC.; *U.S. Private*, pg. 3811
STEWART STAINLESS SUPPLY INC.; *U.S. Private*, pg. 3811
ST. LOUIS PIPE & SUPPLY, INC.; *U.S. Private*, pg. 3772
STULZ-SICKLES STEEL CO.; *U.S. Private*, pg. 3844
SUDAMIN FRANCE S.A.S—See AMG Critical Materials N.V.; *Int'l*, pg. 426
SUDAMIN SPRL—See AMG Critical Materials N.V.; *Int'l*, pg. 426
SUNBELT MATERIAL HANDLING INC.; *U.S. Private*, pg. 3865
SUNBELT-TURRET STEEL, INC.—See Ryerson Holding Corporation; *U.S. Public*, pg. 1829
SUN STEEL CO.—See Esmark Incorporated; *U.S. Private*, pg. 1426
SUPERIOR GROUP, INC.; *U.S. Private*, pg. 3878
SUPERIOR METAL PRODUCTS CO.; *U.S. Private*, pg. 3879
SUPPLY DYNAMICS LLC—See Exiger LLC; *U.S. Private*, pg. 1449
SWEENEY STEEL SERVICE CORP; *U.S. Private*, pg. 3891
SWEETWATER STEEL CO., INC.; *U.S. Private*, pg. 3892
SYNTOM METAL RECYCLING SP. Z O.O.—See Elemental Holding S.A.; *Int'l*, pg. 2358
TACO METALS INC.; *U.S. Private*, pg. 3920
TAD INOX SERVICE BV—See ERG S.p.A.; *Int'l*, pg. 2491
TAD INOX SERVICE GMBH—See ERG S.p.A.; *Int'l*, pg. 2491
TADLOCK PIPE & EQUIPMENT INC.; *U.S. Private*, pg. 3921
TAIWAN HANWA KOGYO CO., LTD.—See Hanwa Co., Ltd.; *Int'l*, pg. 3263

TANAKA STEEL TRADING CO., LTD.—See Hanwa Co., Ltd.; *Int'l*, pg. 3263
TANG INDUSTRIES INC.; *U.S. Private*, pg. 3930
TCI PRECISION METALS, INC.; *U.S. Private*, pg. 3942
TCT STAINLESS STEEL INC—See ERG S.p.A.; *Int'l*, pg. 2491
TCT STAINLESS STEEL OF NASHVILLE INC—See ERG S.p.A.; *Int'l*, pg. 2491
TEXAS PIPE & SUPPLY COMPANY LTD.; *U.S. Private*, pg. 3976
TEX ISLE SUPPLY INC.; *U.S. Private*, pg. 3974
THAI BEVERAGE CAN LTD.—See Ball Corporation; *U.S. Public*, pg. 268
THREE D METALS INC.; *U.S. Private*, pg. 4163
TIANJIN ATLANTIC WELDING CONSUMABLES SALES CO., LTD—See Atlantic China Welding Consumables, Inc.; *Int'l*, pg. 674
TICO TITANIUM INC.; *U.S. Private*, pg. 4167
TIMET GERMANY, GMBH—See Berkshire Hathaway Inc.; *U.S. Public*, pg. 315
TIMKENSTEEL (SHANGHAI) CORPORATION LIMITED—See Metallus Inc.; *U.S. Public*, pg. 1427
TIMKENSTEEL UK LIMITED—See Metallus Inc.; *U.S. Public*, pg. 1427
TIOGA PIPE SUPPLY CO. INC.; *U.S. Private*, pg. 4175
TITAN STEEL CORP.; *U.S. Private*, pg. 4177
TOMA METAL, INC.—See Reliance Steel & Aluminum Co.; *U.S. Public*, pg. 1781
TOMA METALS, INC.—See Reliance Steel & Aluminum Co.; *U.S. Public*, pg. 1782
TOOL STEEL SERVICE, INC.; *U.S. Private*, pg. 4185
TORREY HILLS TECHNOLOGIES, LLC; *U.S. Private*, pg. 4190
TOTAL TOOL SUPPLY INC., CRANE & HOIST DIVISION—See Total Tool Supply Inc.; *U.S. Private*, pg. 4192
TOTAL TOOL SUPPLY INC.; *U.S. Private*, pg. 4192
TOTTEN TUBES, INC.; *U.S. Private*, pg. 4192
TOWN & COUNTRY INDUSTRIES—See Hendricks Holding Company, Inc.; *U.S. Private*, pg. 1915
TRIDENT STEEL CORP.; *U.S. Private*, pg. 4230
TRIPLE-S STEEL SUPPLY CO. INC.—See Triple-S Steel Holdings Inc.; *U.S. Private*, pg. 4237
TRI STAR METALS INC.; *U.S. Private*, pg. 4221
TRUSTED SUPPLY CHAIN PARTNERS; *U.S. Private*, pg. 4251
TSI HOLDING COMPANY; *U.S. Private*, pg. 4253
TTI LAGUNA PHILIPPINES INC.—See The Carlyle Group Inc.; *U.S. Public*, pg. 2055
TUBE SUPPLY, LLC—See Triple-S Steel Holdings Inc.; *U.S. Private*, pg. 4237
TUBULAR STEEL, INC.—See Reliance Steel & Aluminum Co.; *U.S. Public*, pg. 1782
TURRET STEEL INDUSTRIES, INC.—See Ryerson Holding Corporation; *U.S. Public*, pg. 1829
TW METALS—See O'Neal Industries, Inc.; *U.S. Private*, pg. 2979
ULBRICH ASIA METALS MALAYSIA SDN BHD—See Ulbrich Stainless Steel & Special Metals, Inc.; *U.S. Private*, pg. 4275
ULBRICH OF CALIFORNIA, INC.—See Ulbrich Stainless Steel & Special Metals, Inc.; *U.S. Private*, pg. 4276
ULBRICH OF ILLINOIS, INC.—See Ulbrich Stainless Steel & Special Metals, Inc.; *U.S. Private*, pg. 4276
ULBRICH PRECISION SPECIAL METALS (SUZHOU) CO., LTD.—See Ulbrich Stainless Steel & Special Metals, Inc.; *U.S. Private*, pg. 4275
ULBRICH SOLAR TECHNOLOGIES OREGON LLC—See Ulbrich Stainless Steel & Special Metals, Inc.; *U.S. Private*, pg. 4275
UNISTEEL, LLC—See Ellwood Group, Inc.; *U.S. Private*, pg. 1375
UNITED ALLOYS & METALS, INC—See CRONIMET Holding GmbH; *Int'l*, pg. 1855
UNITED PIPE & STEEL CORP.—See Reliance Steel & Aluminum Co.; *U.S. Public*, pg. 1780
UNITED STATES BRASS & COPPER CO.; *U.S. Private*, pg. 4298
UNITED STATES STEEL TUBULAR PRODUCTS—See United States Steel Corporation; *U.S. Public*, pg. 2237
UNITED STEEL SERVICE, INC.; *U.S. Private*, pg. 4300
UNITED STEEL SUPPLY, LLC—See Steel Dynamics, Inc.; *U.S. Public*, pg. 1942
VACUHEAT VERWALTUNGS GMBH—See AMG Critical Materials N.V.; *Int'l*, pg. 426
VALBRUNA AG—See Acciaierie Valbruna S.p.A.; *Int'l*, pg. 89
VALBRUNA CANADA LTD.—See Acciaierie Valbruna S.p.A.; *Int'l*, pg. 89
VALBRUNA GULF FZE—See Acciaierie Valbruna S.p.A.; *Int'l*, pg. 89
VALBRUNA MEXICO, S.A. DE C.V.—See Acciaierie Valbruna S.p.A.; *Int'l*, pg. 89
VALBRUNA NEDERLAND B.V.—See Acciaierie Valbruna S.p.A.; *Int'l*, pg. 89
VALBRUNA NORDIC AB—See Acciaierie Valbruna S.p.A.; *Int'l*, pg. 89
VALBRUNA NORDIC OY—See Acciaierie Valbruna S.p.A.; *Int'l*, pg. 89

VALBRUNA POLSKA SP. Z.O.O—See Acciaierie Valbruna S.p.A.; *Int'l*, pg. 89
VALBRUNA STAINLESS, INC.—See Acciaierie Valbruna S.p.A.; *Int'l*, pg. 89
VALBRUNA STAINLESS SDN. BHD—See Acciaierie Valbruna S.p.A.; *Int'l*, pg. 89
VALBRUNA STAINLESS—See Acciaierie Valbruna S.p.A.; *Int'l*, pg. 90
VALBRUNA STAINLESS—See Acciaierie Valbruna S.p.A.; *Int'l*, pg. 90
VALBRUNA UK LTD—See Acciaierie Valbruna S.p.A.; *Int'l*, pg. 90
VALEX KOREA CO., LTD.—See Reliance Steel & Aluminum Co.; *U.S. Public*, pg. 1782
VALIANT STEEL AND EQUIPMENT; *U.S. Private*, pg. 4332
VAN PELT CORPORATION; *U.S. Private*, pg. 4340
VAN PELT - SERVICE STEEL DIVISION—See Van Pelt Corporation; *U.S. Private*, pg. 4340
VAN SHUNG CHONG HONG LIMITED—See Hong Kong Shanghai Alliance Holdings Limited; *Int'l*, pg. 3467
VASS PIPE & STEEL CO. INC.; *U.S. Private*, pg. 4347
VDM METALS BENELUX B.V.—See Acerinox, S.A.; *Int'l*, pg. 101
VDM METALS GMBH—See Acerinox, S.A.; *Int'l*, pg. 101
VDM METALS (GUANGZHOU) TRADING CO., LTD.—See Acerinox, S.A.; *Int'l*, pg. 101
VDM METALS KOREA CO., LTD.—See Acerinox, S.A.; *Int'l*, pg. 101
VDM (SHANGHAI) HIGH PERFORMANCE METALS TRADING CO., LTD.—See Acerinox, S.A.; *Int'l*, pg. 101
VELLANO BROS., INC.; *U.S. Private*, pg. 4354
VICTORY STEEL PRODUCTS CORP.; *U.S. Private*, pg. 4379
VIKING MATERIALS, INC.—See Reliance Steel & Aluminum Co.; *U.S. Public*, pg. 1782
VIKING PROCESSING CORPORATION; *U.S. Private*, pg. 4382
V&S DELAWARE GALVANIZING LLC—See Hill & Smith PLC; *Int'l*, pg. 3392
V&S LEBANON GALVANIZING LLC—See Hill & Smith PLC; *Int'l*, pg. 3392
V&S TAUNTON GALVANIZING, LLC—See Hill & Smith PLC; *Int'l*, pg. 3392
WARREN STEEL PRODUCTS INC.; *U.S. Private*, pg. 4444
WATER WORKS SUPPLY COMPANY—See Core & Main, Inc.; *U.S. Public*, pg. 576
WAYLAND INC.—See ALP Industries, Inc.; *U.S. Private*, pg. 196
WEISNER STEEL PRODUCTS INC.; *U.S. Private*, pg. 4472
WESERWIND UK LTD.—See Georgsmarienhutte Holding GmbH; *Int'l*, pg. 2940
WEST COAST WIRE ROPE & RIGGING, INC.; *U.S. Private*, pg. 4484
WESTFIELD STEEL INC.; *U.S. Private*, pg. 4498
WHITE STAR STEEL—See Nashville Steel Corp.; *U.S. Private*, pg. 2836
WILIAN HOLDING CO., INC.; *U.S. Private*, pg. 4520
WILLIAMS METALS AND WELDING ALLOYS, INC.; *U.S. Private*, pg. 4526
WISCONSIN STEEL & TUBE CORPORATION; *U.S. Private*, pg. 4549
WORLD CLASS INDUSTRIES INC.; *U.S. Private*, pg. 4565
WRISCO INDUSTRIES INC.; *U.S. Private*, pg. 4574
WYLIE STEEL INC.—See Eagle National Steel Ltd; *U.S. Private*, pg. 1310
YARDE METALS INC.; *U.S. Private*, pg. 4586
ZINC EXCEL CO., LTD.—See Dowa Holdings Co., Ltd.; *Int'l*, pg. 2184

423520 — COAL AND OTHER MINERAL AND ORE MERCHANT WHOLESALERS

ACTIVE MINERALS INTERNATIONAL, LLC—See Golden Gate Capital Management II, LLC; *U.S. Private*, pg. 1730
AFARAK TRADING LTD.—See Afarak Group SE; *Int'l*, pg. 185
AL-GHANAEM INDUSTRIAL COMPANY—See Fouad Alghanim & Sons Group of Companies; *Int'l*, pg. 2753
ALLEY-CASSETTY BRICK NASHVILLE DIV.—See Alley-Cassetty Companies; *U.S. Private*, pg. 180
ALLEY-CASSETTY COMPANIES; *U.S. Private*, pg. 180
ALPHA COAL SALES COMPANY, LLC—See Alpha Natural Resources, Inc.; *U.S. Private*, pg. 199
ALTA FUELS, LLC—See World Kinect Corporation; *U.S. Public*, pg. 2380
AMCI INTERNATIONAL INC.—See KM Investment Corporation; *U.S. Private*, pg. 2321
AMERICAN METALS COAL INTRNATIONAL—See KM Investment Corporation; *U.S. Private*, pg. 2321
AMES GOLDSMITH UK LTD—See Ames Goldsmith Corp.; *U.S. Private*, pg. 261
ANMOL INDIA LIMITED; *Int'l*, pg. 473
APPALACHIA COAL SALES COMPANY, INC.—See Alpha Natural Resources, Inc.; *U.S. Private*, pg. 198
ARGUS ENERGY LLC.; *U.S. Private*, pg. 322
ASF GROUP LIMITED; *Int'l*, pg. 606
ASHAPURA INTERNATIONAL LIMITED—See Ashapura

Minechem Limited; *Int'l*, pg. 606
ASHCOR TECHNOLOGIES LTD.—See ATCO Ltd.; *Int'l*, pg. 666
ASIA GREEN ENERGY PUBLIC COMPANY LIMITED; *Int'l*, pg. 612
AUSOM ENTERPRISE LIMITED; *Int'l*, pg. 716
AVANI RESOURCES PTE LTD.; *Int'l*, pg. 734
BEL NICKEL RESOURCES LIMITED—See BEL Global Resources Holdings Limited; *Int'l*, pg. 963
BENGUETRADE, INC—See Benguet Corporation; *Int'l*, pg. 974
BIOXYTRAN, INC.; *U.S. Public*, pg. 339
CARBOEX, S.A.—See Enel S.p.A.; *Int'l*, pg. 2412
CASCADE COAL LIMITED—See Galilee Energy Limited; *Int'l*, pg. 2873
CCS SUPPLY CHAIN MANAGEMENT CO., LTD.; *Int'l*, pg. 1369
CDII MINERALS, INC.—See CD International Enterprises, Inc.; *U.S. Public*, pg. 461
CHINA BEST GROUP HOLDING LIMITED; *Int'l*, pg. 1486
CNT85 INC.; *Int'l*, pg. 1678
COAL ENERGY RESOURCES INC.; *U.S. Private*, pg. 953
COAL NETWORK, INC.; *U.S. Private*, pg. 953
COALSALES, LLC—See Peabody Energy Corporation; *U.S. Public*, pg. 1659
COALTRADE INTERNATIONAL, LLC—See Peabody Energy Corporation; *U.S. Public*, pg. 1659
COMAT CARAS SEVERIN SA; *Int'l*, pg. 1707
CONDOR S.A.—See Condor Gold Plc; *Int'l*, pg. 1766
CORONADO GLOBAL RESOURCES INC.; *Int'l*, pg. 1802
CORPORACION DEL COBRE (U.S.A.), INC.—See Corporacion Nacional del Cobre de Chile; *Int'l*, pg. 1805
CROWN COAL & COKE CO. INC.; *U.S. Private*, pg. 1110
DENSIMIX-E&B INC.—See American Securities LLC; *U.S. Private*, pg. 253
DOWA METALS & MINING (THAILAND) CO., LTD.—See Dowa Holdings Co., Ltd.; *Int'l*, pg. 2183
EASTERN COAL SUPPLIES LIMITED—See Galilee Energy Limited; *Int'l*, pg. 2873
ECCA HOLDINGS PTY LTD—See Groupe Bruxelles Lambert SA; *Int'l*, pg. 3100
ENERGY EARTH PUBLIC COMPANY LIMITED; *Int'l*, pg. 2422
EXXARO INTERNATIONAL COAL TRADING BV—See Exxaro Resources Ltd.; *Int'l*, pg. 2592
GROVE ENERGY INC.—See Chesapeake Utilities Corporation; *U.S. Public*, pg. 485
GTI ENERGY LTD; *Int'l*, pg. 3151
GUJARAT METALLIC COAL & COKE LIMITED; *Int'l*, pg. 3176
HARSCO METALS MIDDLE EAST FZE—See Enviri Corporation; *U.S. Public*, pg. 781
HECLA GREENS CREEK MINING COMPANY—See Hecla Mining Company; *U.S. Public*, pg. 1019
HENAN DAYOU ENERGY CO., LTD.; *Int'l*, pg. 3342
HICKMAN, WILLIAMS CANADA, INC.—See Hickman, Williams & Company; *U.S. Private*, pg. 1933
HM ROYAL INC.; *U.S. Private*, pg. 1954
HMS BERGBAU AFRICA (PTY.) LTD.—See HMS Bergbau AG; *Int'l*, pg. 3432
HMS BERGBAU AG; *Int'l*, pg. 3432
HMS BERGBAU SINGAPORE (PTE.) LTD.—See HMS Bergbau AG; *Int'l*, pg. 3432
HMS BERGBAU USA CORP.—See HMS Bergbau AG; *Int'l*, pg. 3432
HULLERAS DEL NORTE, S.A.; *Int'l*, pg. 3528
ILUKA RESOURCES INC.—See Iluka Resources Limited; *Int'l*, pg. 3616
ILUKA TRADING (SHANGHAI) CO., LTD.—See Iluka Resources Limited; *Int'l*, pg. 3616
INTEGRITY COAL SALES INC.; *U.S. Private*, pg. 2102
INTEGRITY INTERNATIONAL CORP.—See Integrity Coal Sales Inc.; *U.S. Private*, pg. 2102
JAMES RIVER COAL SALES INC.—See James River Coal Company; *U.S. Private*, pg. 2185
KANAWHA RIVER TERMINALS LLC—See SunCoke Energy, Inc.; *U.S. Public*, pg. 1964
KM INVESTMENT CORPORATION; *U.S. Private*, pg. 2321
LINTON FUEL OILS LIMITED—See World Kinect Corporation; *U.S. Public*, pg. 2380
LOGAN & KANAWHA COAL COMPANY, INC.—See International Industries, Inc.; *U.S. Private*, pg. 2117
MID-CONTINENT MINERALS CORPORATION; *U.S. Private*, pg. 2708
MID-VOL COAL SALES, INC.—See ArcelorMittal S.A.; *Int'l*, pg. 546
MINERAIS U.S. LLC—See Assore Limited; *Int'l*, pg. 649
MINERAL HECLA, S.A. DE C.V.—See Hecla Mining Company; *U.S. Public*, pg. 1019
MINMETALS, INC.—See China Rare Earth Resources And Technology Co., Ltd.; *Int'l*, pg. 1546
NAUGHTON ENERGY CORPORATION; *U.S. Private*, pg. 2868
NNRF, INC.; *U.S. Private*, pg. 2932
OASIS MIDSTREAM SERVICES LLC—See Chord Energy Corporation; *U.S. Public*, pg. 490
OXBOW CARBON & MINERALS LLC—See Oxbow Corporation; *U.S. Private*, pg. 3056
OXBOW COAL B.V.—See Oxbow Corporation; *U.S. Private*, pg. 3056
OXBOW COAL LTD.—See Oxbow Corporation; *U.S. Private*, pg. 3056
PALABORA US—See General Nice Development Limited; *Int'l*, pg. 2919
PALABORA US—See HBIS Group Co., Ltd.; *Int'l*, pg. 3296
PEABODY COALTRADE, LLC—See Peabody Energy Corporation; *U.S. Public*, pg. 1659
PHOENIX COAL COMPANY, INC.; *U.S. Public*, pg. 3172
POWER MOUNTAIN COAL COMPANY—See Alpha Natural Resources, Inc.; *U.S. Private*, pg. 199
PRASSAS METAL PRODUCTS, INC.—See The Mill Steel Co., Inc.; *U.S. Private*, pg. 4079
PRINCE INTERNATIONAL CORPORATION—See American Securities LLC; *U.S. Private*, pg. 253
PT. BHARINTO EKATAMA—See Banpu Public Company Limited; *Int'l*, pg. 852
PT. HMS BERGBAU INDONESIA—See HMS Bergbau AG; *Int'l*, pg. 3432
SCIENTIFIC ENERGY, INC.; *U.S. Public*, pg. 1848
SEAFORTH MINERAL & ORE CO., INC.; *U.S. Private*, pg. 3584
STRATEGIC MINERALS EUROPE LTD.—See Gunsynd plc; *Int'l*, pg. 3185
SUTTONS LIMITED—See Bord na Mona Plc; *Int'l*, pg. 1113
THERMO FUELS COMPANY, INC.—See The AES Corporation; *U.S. Public*, pg. 2032
UNIONVALE COAL CO. INC.; *U.S. Private*, pg. 4285
UPPER LAKES COAL COMPANY INC.; *U.S. Private*, pg. 4312
VINA AGE CO., LTD.—See Asia Green Energy Public Company Limited; *Int'l*, pg. 612
WAROQUIER COAL INC.; *U.S. Private*, pg. 4443
WORLD MINERALS INTERNATIONAL SALES SA—See Groupe Bruxelles Lambert SA; *Int'l*, pg. 3100

423610 — ELECTRICAL APPARATUS AND EQUIPMENT, WIRING SUPPLIES, AND RELATED EQUIPMENT MERCHANT WHOLESALERS

1-800 NY BULBS, LIMITED—See Tarsier Ltd.; *U.S. Public*, pg. 1982
4 STAR ELECTRONICS, INC.; *U.S. Private*, pg. 14
4WALL ENTERTAINMENT, INC. - ORANGE COUNTY—See 4Wall Entertainment, Inc.; *U.S. Private*, pg. 15
AA ELECTRIC INC.; *U.S. Private*, pg. 29
AA ELECTRIC SE INC.—See AA Electric Inc.; *U.S. Private*, pg. 29
ABB ASEA BROWN BOVERI LTD.—See ABB Ltd.; *Int'l*, pg. 50
ABB AUSTRALIA PTY LIMITED—See ABB Ltd.; *Int'l*, pg. 50
ABB E-MOBILITY B.V.—See ABB Ltd.; *Int'l*, pg. 50
ABB GROUP HOLDINGS PTY. LTD.—See ABB Ltd.; *Int'l*, pg. 51
ABB INC. - TURBOCHARGING—See ABB Ltd.; *Int'l*, pg. 51
ABB INSTALLATION PRODUCTS INC.—See ABB Ltd.; *Int'l*, pg. 52
ABB INVESTMENTS (PTY.) LTD.—See ABB Ltd.; *Int'l*, pg. 52
ABB MANAGEMENT SERVICES LTD.—See ABB Ltd.; *Int'l*, pg. 53
ABB PTE. LTD.—See ABB Ltd.; *Int'l*, pg. 53
ABB S.A.—See ABB Ltd.; *Int'l*, pg. 54
ABB SHANGHAI TRANSFORMER CO. LTD.—See ABB Ltd.; *Int'l*, pg. 49
ABB XIAMEN ELECTRICAL CONTROLGEAR CO. LTD.—See ABB Ltd.; *Int'l*, pg. 49
ABB XIAMEN SWITCHGEAR CO. LTD.—See ABB Ltd.; *Int'l*, pg. 55
ABLEREX ELECTRONICS (BEIJING) CO., LTD.—See Ablerex Electronics Co., Ltd.; *Int'l*, pg. 63
ABLEREX ELECTRONICS ITALY S.R.L.—See Ablerex Electronics Co., Ltd.; *Int'l*, pg. 63
ABLEREX ELECTRONICS (S) PTE. LTD.—See Ablerex Electronics Co., Ltd.; *Int'l*, pg. 63
ABLEREX ELECTRONICS (SUZHOU) CO., LTD.—See Ablerex Electronics Co., Ltd.; *Int'l*, pg. 63
ACBEL POLYTECH (MALAYSIA) SDN. BHD.—See AcBel Polytech Inc.; *Int'l*, pg. 78
ACCELINK DENMARK A/S—See Accelink Technologies Co., Ltd.; *Int'l*, pg. 80
ACE PILLAR (S) PTE LTD—See ACE PILLAR Co., Ltd; *Int'l*, pg. 94
ACE WIRE & CABLE CO. INC.; *U.S. Private*, pg. 57
ACO GROUP BERHAD; *Int'l*, pg. 107
ACTION ELECTRIC SALES CO. INC.; *U.S. Private*, pg. 67
ACTIVE ELECTRICAL SUPPLY COMPANY; *U.S. Private*, pg. 69
ADDTECH COMPONENTS AB—See Addtech AB; *Int'l*, pg. 131
ADDTECH TRANSMISSION AB—See Addtech AB; *Int'l*, pg. 131
ADIATOR AB—See Addtech AB; *Int'l*, pg. 131
ADI GLOBAL DISTRIBUTION AB—See Resideo Technologies, Inc.; *U.S. Public*, pg. 1789
ADI PUERTO RICO—See Honeywell International Inc.; *U.S. Public*, pg. 1049
ADI—See Honeywell International Inc.; *U.S. Public*, pg. 1049
ADTEC EUROPE LIMITED—See Adtec Plasma Technology Co., Ltd.; *Int'l*, pg. 154
AD TECHNOLOGY LTD.—See Adtec Plasma Technology Co., Ltd.; *Int'l*, pg. 154
ADTEC TECHNOLOGY, INC.—See Adtec Plasma Technology Co., Ltd.; *Int'l*, pg. 154
ADVANCED DATACOMM SOLUTIONS, INC.; *U.S. Private*, pg. 89
ADVANCED INDUSTRIAL DEVICES, INC.; *U.S. Private*, pg. 90
ADVANCED MOTION SYSTEMS INC.—See Applied Industrial Technologies, Inc.; *U.S. Public*, pg. 170
ADVANCED POWER SOLUTIONS; *U.S. Private*, pg. 92
ADVANCE ELECTRICAL SUPPLY CO.; *U.S. Private*, pg. 83
ADVAN GROUP CO., LTD.; *Int'l*, pg. 155
ADVANTAGE INDUSTRIAL AUTOMATION INC.—See Graybar Electric Company, Inc.; *U.S. Private*, pg. 1760
ADVANTECH JAPAN CO., LTD.—See Advantech Co., Ltd.; *Int'l*, pg. 164
A.E. PETSCHE SAS—See Arrow Electronics, Inc.; *U.S. Public*, pg. 194
AEROQUIP IBERICA S.L.—See Eaton Corporation plc; *Int'l*, pg. 2277
AEROTECH CHINA—See Aerotech Inc.; *U.S. Private*, pg. 119
AEROTECH KK—See Aerotech Inc.; *U.S. Private*, pg. 119
AEROTECH TAIWAN—See Aerotech Inc.; *U.S. Private*, pg. 119
AIKO CORPORATION; *Int'l*, pg. 232
AIM ELECTRONICS; *U.S. Private*, pg. 132
AIR-COM PNEUMATYKA AUTOMATYKA S.C.—See AIRTEC Pneumatic GmbH; *Int'l*, pg. 249
AIR HYDRO POWER INC.; *U.S. Private*, pg. 139
AIRMOVENT LIMITED—See AoFrio Limited; *Int'l*, pg. 487
AIRTEC FRANCE SARL—See AIRTEC Pneumatic GmbH; *Int'l*, pg. 249
AIRTEC PNEUMATIC C.C.—See AIRTEC Pneumatic GmbH; *Int'l*, pg. 249
AIRTEC PNEUMATICS INC—See AIRTEC Pneumatic GmbH; *Int'l*, pg. 249
AIRTEC PNEUMATICS UK LTD.—See AIRTEC Pneumatic GmbH; *Int'l*, pg. 249
AIRTEC PNEUMATIC SWEDEN AB—See AIRTEC Pneumatic GmbH; *Int'l*, pg. 249
A&J ELECTRIC CABLE CORP.; *U.S. Private*, pg. 20
ALAMEDA ELECTRICAL DISTRIBUTORS INC.; *U.S. Private*, pg. 149
ALARMAX DISTRIBUTORS INC.; *U.S. Private*, pg. 150
ALARM CENTER, INC.; *U.S. Private*, pg. 150
ALFA LAVAL TECHNOLOGIES AB—See Alfa Laval AB; *Int'l*, pg. 312
AL JABER LIGHTING LLC—See Al Jaber Group; *Int'l*, pg. 279
ALLIED ELECTRIC MOTOR SERVICE; *U.S. Private*, pg. 186
ALLIED MOTION DORDRECHT B.V.—See Allient Inc.; *U.S. Public*, pg. 80
ALLIED MOTION PORTUGAL—See Allient Inc.; *U.S. Public*, pg. 80
ALLIED MOTION STOCKHOLM—See Allient Inc.; *U.S. Public*, pg. 80
ALLIED WHOLESALE ELECTRICAL SUPPLY INCORPORATED; *U.S. Private*, pg. 191
ALL POWER PRODUCTS INC.—See Quanta Services, Inc.; *U.S. Public*, pg. 1750
ALL PRO SALES, INC. - HOUSTON—See All Pro Sales, Inc.; *U.S. Private*, pg. 171
ALL PRO SALES, INC.; *U.S. Private*, pg. 171
ALLSALE ELECTRIC INC.; *U.S. Private*, pg. 193
ALL-SPEC INDUSTRIES, INC.—See Distribution Solutions Group, Inc.; *U.S. Public*, pg. 668
ALLTOP ELECTRONICS (SUZHOU) LTD.—See Alltop Technology Co., Ltd.; *Int'l*, pg. 361
ALPHA ASSEMBLY SOLUTIONS KOREA LTD.—See Element Solutions Inc.; *U.S. Public*, pg. 726
ALPHA ELECTRIC SUPPLY CORPORATION; *U.S. Private*, pg. 197
ALPS ELECTRIC EUROPE GMBH—See Alps Alpine Co., Ltd.; *Int'l*, pg. 376
AL QURAISHI ELECTRIC SERVICES OF SAUDI ARABIA—See Ali Zaid Al-Quraishi & Brothers Co.; *Int'l*, pg. 323
AMBIENT WEATHER CO.; *U.S. Private*, pg. 217
AMERCABLE INCORPORATED; *U.S. Private*, pg. 219
AMERICAN BATTERY COMPANY—See East Penn Manufacturing Co., Inc.; *U.S. Private*, pg. 1317
AMERICAN ELECTRIC SUPPLY INC.; *U.S. Private*, pg. 231
AMERICAN FIRE TECHNOLOGIES, INC—See Littlejohn & Co., LLC; *U.S. Private*, pg. 2471
AMERICAN LIGHTING SUPPLY INC—See ForceField Energy Inc.; *U.S. Private*, pg. 1563
AMERICAN POWER SYSTEMS, LLC; *U.S. Private*, pg. 244
AMPHENOL BAR-TEC, LTD.—See Amphenol Corporation; *U.S. Public*, pg. 127

423610 — ELECTRICAL APPARATU...

AMPLI SA; *Int'l*, pg. 435
ANALOG DEVICES LTD.—See Analog Devices, Inc.; *U.S. Public*, pg. 135
ANCA MOTION TAIWAN CO., LTD—See ANCA Pty Ltd; *Int'l*, pg. 448
ANETA LIGHTING AS—See Byggma ASA; *Int'l*, pg. 1235
ANIXTER BULGARIA EOOD—See WESCO International, Inc.; *U.S. Public*, pg. 2350
ANIXTER CANADA, INC.—See WESCO International, Inc.; *U.S. Public*, pg. 2350
ANIXTER EGYPT LLC—See WESCO International, Inc.; *U.S. Public*, pg. 2350
ANIXTER ESPANA S.L.—See WESCO International, Inc.; *U.S. Public*, pg. 2350
ANIXTER INC.—See WESCO International, Inc.; *U.S. Public*, pg. 2350
ANIXTER JORVEX S.A.C.—See WESCO International, Inc.; *U.S. Public*, pg. 2350
ANIXTER LIMITED—See WESCO International, Inc.; *U.S. Public*, pg. 2350
ANIXTER LOGISTICA DO BRASIL LTDA—See WESCO International, Inc.; *U.S. Public*, pg. 2350
ANIXTER POWER SOLUTIONS CANADA INC.—See WESCO International, Inc.; *U.S. Public*, pg. 2350
ANIXTER SAUDI ARABIA LIMITED—See WESCO International, Inc.; *U.S. Public*, pg. 2350
ANIXTER SINGAPORE PTE. LTD.—See WESCO International, Inc.; *U.S. Public*, pg. 2350
ANIXTER SVERIGE AB—See WESCO International, Inc.; *U.S. Public*, pg. 2350
ANIXTER THAILAND INC.—See WESCO International, Inc.; *U.S. Public*, pg. 2350
ANIXTER (U.K.) LIMITED—See WESCO International, Inc.; *U.S. Public*, pg. 2350
ANRITSU LIMITED—See Anritsu Corporation; *Int'l*, pg. 475
ANY BREAKERS, INC.; *U.S. Private*, pg. 289
A.O. SMITH ELECTRICAL PRODUCTS GMBH—See Regal Rexnord Corporation; *U.S. Public*, pg. 1772
APEX INTEGRATED SECURITY SOLUTIONS, LLC—See GTCR LLC; *U.S. Private*, pg. 1801
APPLETON GROUP - CHERRYVILLE—See Emerson Electric Co.; *U.S. Public*, pg. 740
APPLIED INDUSTRIAL CONTROLS, INC.—See Frontenac Company LLC; *U.S. Private*, pg. 1614
APPLIED INDUSTRIAL TECHNOLOGIES - CA LLC—See Applied Industrial Technologies, Inc.; *U.S. Public*, pg. 170
APPLIED MACHINE & MOTION CONTROL, INC.—See Genuine Parts Company; *U.S. Public*, pg. 933
APS POWER SOLUTIONS LLC—See Emek Elektrik Endustrisi A.S.; *Int'l*, pg. 2377
ARB HOLDINGS LIMITED; *Int'l*, pg. 536
ARKANSAS ELECTRICAL OUTLET INC.; *U.S. Private*, pg. 325
ARMADA NANO TECHNOLOGIES GROUP INC.; *U.S. Private*, pg. 329
ARMET ALARM & ELECTRONICS INC.; *U.S. Private*, pg. 330
ARRIS GROUP, INC. - OPERATIONS—See CommScope Holding Company, Inc.; *U.S. Public*, pg. 547
ARRIS - HONG KONG—See CommScope Holding Company, Inc.; *U.S. Public*, pg. 548
ARTESANIAS BAJA, S. A. DE C.V.—See Hubbell Incorporated; *U.S. Public*, pg. 1066
ARTHUR J. HURLEY COMPANY, INC.; *U.S. Private*, pg. 341
ASEA BROWN BOVERI S.A. DE C.V.—See ABB Ltd.; *Int'l*, pg. 53
ASIA ELECTRONICS HK TECHNOLOGIES LIMITED—See Computime Group Limited; *Int'l*, pg. 1760
ASSOCIATED OF LOS ANGELES; *U.S. Private*, pg. 356
ASSOCIATED WHOLESALE ELECTRIC CO.—See Associated of Los Angeles; *U.S. Private*, pg. 356
ATLANTA ELECTRICAL DISTRIBUTORS, LLC—See WESCO International, Inc.; *U.S. Public*, pg. 2351
ATLAS AMERICAN CORPORATION; *U.S. Private*, pg. 375
ATR LIGHTING ENTERPRISES, INC.; *U.S. Private*, pg. 381
AUMA ACTUATORS (CHINA) CO., LTD.—See AUMA Riester GmbH & Co. KG; *Int'l*, pg. 704
AUMA ACTUATORS LTD.—See AUMA Riester GmbH & Co. KG; *Int'l*, pg. 704
AUMA ACTUATORS MIDDLE EAST WLL—See AUMA Riester GmbH & Co. KG; *Int'l*, pg. 705
AUMA ACTUATORS (SINGAPORE) PTE LTD—See AUMA Riester GmbH & Co. KG; *Int'l*, pg. 704
AUMA-ARMATURENANTRIEBE GES.M.B.H.—See AUMA Riester GmbH & Co. KG; *Int'l*, pg. 705
AUMA AUTOMACAO DO BRASIL LTDA.—See AUMA Riester GmbH & Co. KG; *Int'l*, pg. 705
AUMA BENELUX B.V.B.A.—See AUMA Riester GmbH & Co. KG; *Int'l*, pg. 704
AUMA BENELUX B.V.—See AUMA Riester GmbH & Co. KG; *Int'l*, pg. 704
AUMA ENDUSTRI KONTROL SISTEMLERI LIMITED SIRKETI—See AUMA Riester GmbH & Co. KG; *Int'l*, pg. 704
AUMA FINLAND OY—See AUMA Riester GmbH & Co. KG; *Int'l*, pg. 704
AUMA FRANCE S.A.R.L.—See AUMA Riester GmbH & Co. KG; *Int'l*, pg. 704
AUMA INDIA PRIVATE LIMITED—See AUMA Riester GmbH & Co. KG; *Int'l*, pg. 704
AUMA ITALIANA S.R.L.—See AUMA Riester GmbH & Co. KG; *Int'l*, pg. 704
AUMA JAPAN CO., LTD.—See AUMA Riester GmbH & Co. KG; *Int'l*, pg. 704
AUMA POLSKA SP. Z O.O.—See AUMA Riester GmbH & Co. KG; *Int'l*, pg. 704
AUMA (SCHWEIZ) AG—See AUMA Riester GmbH & Co. KG; *Int'l*, pg. 704
AUMA SERVOPOHONY SPOL. S.R.O.—See AUMA Riester GmbH & Co. KG; *Int'l*, pg. 704
AUMA SOUTH AFRICA (PTY) LTD.—See AUMA Riester GmbH & Co. KG; *Int'l*, pg. 705
AUMA TECHNOLOGY AUTOMATIONS LTD—See AUMA Riester GmbH & Co. KG; *Int'l*, pg. 704
AURA LIGHT APS—See FSN Capital Partners AS; *Int'l*, pg. 2799
AURA LIGHT A/S—See FSN Capital Partners AS; *Int'l*, pg. 2798
AURA LIGHT FRANCE SARL—See FSN Capital Partners AS; *Int'l*, pg. 2799
AURA LIGHT GMBH—See FSN Capital Partners AS; *Int'l*, pg. 2799
AURA LIGHT GREECE—See FSN Capital Partners AS; *Int'l*, pg. 2799
AURA LIGHT ITALY S.R.L.—See FSN Capital Partners AS; *Int'l*, pg. 2799
AURA LIGHT OY—See FSN Capital Partners AS; *Int'l*, pg. 2799
AURALIGHT POLSKA SP. Z O.O.—See FSN Capital Partners AS; *Int'l*, pg. 2799
AURA LIGHT PORTUGAL UNIPESSOAL, LDA—See FSN Capital Partners AS; *Int'l*, pg. 2799
AURA LIGHT SPAIN, S.L.U.—See FSN Capital Partners AS; *Int'l*, pg. 2799
AURA LIGHT TRADING (SHANGHAI) CO., LTD—See FSN Capital Partners AS; *Int'l*, pg. 2799
AURA LIGHT USA INC—See FSN Capital Partners AS; *Int'l*, pg. 2799
AURA LONG LIFE LAMPS LTD.—See FSN Capital Partners AS; *Int'l*, pg. 2799
AURORA JAPAN CORP.—See Aurora Corporation; *Int'l*, pg. 713
AUSTRALIAN AUTOMOTIVE ELECTRICAL WHOLESALE PTY LTD—See Bapcor Limited; *Int'l*, pg. 857
AUSTRIAMICROSYSTEMS ITALY S.R.L.—See ams AG; *Int'l*, pg. 440
AUTOMATIC CONTROL SYSTEMS INC.—See Financiere de L'Odet; *Int'l*, pg. 2665
AUTOMATIC ENTRANCES OF WISCONSIN, INC.—See Alpine Investors; *U.S. Private*, pg. 201
AUTOMATION ENGINEERING CO., INC.; *U.S. Private*, pg. 399
AUTONOMOUSTUFF LLC—See Hexagon AB; *Int'l*, pg. 3367
AVANTI PRODUCTS, LLC—See The Legacy Companies; *U.S. Private*, pg. 4069
AVNET ELECTRONICS MARKETING—See Avnet, Inc.; *U.S. Public*, pg. 250
AVON WESCO—See WESCO International, Inc.; *U.S. Public*, pg. 2351
AXE DISTRIBUTION SOLUTIONS TRINIDAD, LTD.—See WESCO International, Inc.; *U.S. Public*, pg. 2350
BABSCO SUPPLY, INC.; *U.S. Private*, pg. 422
BALDWIN SUPPLY COMPANY; *U.S. Private*, pg. 459
BANGKOK OA COMS CO., LTD.—See Bangkok Business Equipment Automation Co., Ltd.; *Int'l*, pg. 833
BARBIZON LIGHTING COMPANY; *U.S. Private*, pg. 472
BARRY SALES ENGINEERING INC.; *U.S. Private*, pg. 481
BASF RENEWABLE ENERGY GMBH—See BASF SE; *Int'l*, pg. 881
BASLER ELECTRIC COMPANY (SINGAPORE) PTE LTD.—See Basler Electric Company; *U.S. Private*, pg. 485
BASLER, INC.—See Basler AG; *Int'l*, pg. 887
BASS-UNITED FIRE & SECURITY SYSTEMS, INC.—See The Carlyle Group Inc.; *U.S. Public*, pg. 2053
BATES SALES COMPANY INC.; *U.S. Private*, pg. 486
BATTERY SALES; *U.S. Private*, pg. 488
BAXTERS PTY LTD—See Bapcor Limited; *Int'l*, pg. 857
BAYNES ELECTRIC SUPPLY CO. INC.—See Granite City Electric Supply Co., Inc.; *U.S. Private*, pg. 1755
BAY STAGE LIGHTING COMPANY, INC.; *U.S. Private*, pg. 494
BEACON ELECTRIC SUPPLY; *U.S. Private*, pg. 504
BEACON LIGHTING EUROPE GMBH—See Beacon Lighting Group Ltd; *Int'l*, pg. 932
BEARING SPECIALTY COMPANY INC.; *U.S. Private*, pg. 507
BECKMANN ELEKTRONIK GMBH—See Arlitech Electronic Corp.; *Int'l*, pg. 573
BEIJER ELECTRONICS INC.—See Ependion AB; *Int'l*, pg. 2459
BEIJING CHUBB FIRE SECURITY SYSTEMS CO., LIMITED—See Carrier Global Corporation; *U.S. Public*, pg. 440
BELDEN INTERNATIONAL INC. - HONG KONG OFFICE—See Belden, Inc.; *U.S. Public*, pg. 294
BELIMO ACTUATORS (INDIA) PVT LTD—See BELIMO Holding AG; *Int'l*, pg. 964
BELIMO ACTUATORS LTD.—See BELIMO Holding AG; *Int'l*, pg. 964
BELIMO ACTUATORS LTD.—See BELIMO Holding AG; *Int'l*, pg. 964
BELIMO ACTUATORS LTD.—See BELIMO Holding AG; *Int'l*, pg. 964
BELIMO ACTUATORS LTD.—See BELIMO Holding AG; *Int'l*, pg. 964
BELIMO ACTUATORS LTD.—See BELIMO Holding AG; *Int'l*, pg. 964
BELIMO ACTUATORS PTY. LTD.—See BELIMO Holding AG; *Int'l*, pg. 964
BELIMO ACTUATORS (SHANGHAI) TRADING LTD.—See BELIMO Holding AG; *Int'l*, pg. 964
BELIMO A/S—See BELIMO Holding AG; *Int'l*, pg. 964
BELIMO AUTOMATION AG—See BELIMO Holding AG; *Int'l*, pg. 964
BELIMO AUTOMATION FZE—See BELIMO Holding AG; *Int'l*, pg. 964
BELIMO AUTOMATION UK LTD.—See BELIMO Holding AG; *Int'l*, pg. 964
BELIMO BRASIL COMERCIO DE AUTOMACAO LTDA.—See BELIMO Holding AG; *Int'l*, pg. 965
BELIMO BULGARIA LTD.—See BELIMO Holding AG; *Int'l*, pg. 965
BELIMO CZ SPOL. S R.O.—See BELIMO Holding AG; *Int'l*, pg. 965
BELIMO IBERICA DE SERVOMOTORES S.A.—See BELIMO Holding AG; *Int'l*, pg. 965
BELIMO SERVOMOTORI S.R.L.—See BELIMO Holding AG; *Int'l*, pg. 965
BELIMO SILOWNIKI S.A.—See BELIMO Holding AG; *Int'l*, pg. 965
BELIMO S.R.L.—See BELIMO Holding AG; *Int'l*, pg. 965
BELL ELECTRICAL SUPPLY INC.; *U.S. Private*, pg. 518
BELL EQUIPMENT AUSTRALIA (PTY) LIMITED—See Bell Equipment Limited; *Int'l*, pg. 966
BELL EQUIPMENT (SEA) PTE LIMITED—See Bell Equipment Limited; *Int'l*, pg. 966
BELLEZZA CLUB JAPAN INC.—See Brother Industries, Ltd.; *Int'l*, pg. 1196
BEL MANUFACTURERA, S.A. DE C.V.—See Hubbell Incorporated; *U.S. Public*, pg. 1066
BEL POWER SOLUTIONS LIMITED—See Bel Fuse Inc.; *U.S. Public*, pg. 293
BELTING CO. OF CINCINNATI INC.; *U.S. Private*, pg. 521
BENFIELD ELECTRIC INTERNATIONAL LTD. INC.—See H.H. Benfield Electric Supply Company Inc.; *U.S. Private*, pg. 1826
BENFIELD ELECTRIC JAPAN CO. LTD.—See H.H. Benfield Electric Supply Company Inc.; *U.S. Private*, pg. 1826
BENFIELD LIGHTING, INC.—See H.H. Benfield Electric Supply Company Inc.; *U.S. Private*, pg. 1826
BENG HUI MARINE ELECTRICAL PTE LTD—See BH Global Corporation Limited; *Int'l*, pg. 1009
BERKEL (IRELAND) LIMITED—See Illinois Tool Works Inc.; *U.S. Public*, pg. 1101
BEVAN SECURITY SYSTEMS INC.—See Pye-Barker Fire & Safety, LLC; *U.S. Private*, pg. 3309
BEVI DANMARK A/S—See Addtech AB; *Int'l*, pg. 132
BEVI ELECTRIC SHANGHAI CO., LTD.—See Addtech AB; *Int'l*, pg. 132
BEYOND COMPONENTS OF MASS INC.; *U.S. Private*, pg. 548
BHATIA BROTHERS & PARTNERS L.L.C—See Bhatia Brothers Group; *Int'l*, pg. 1013
BJB CO., LTD.—See BJB GMBH & CO. KG; *Int'l*, pg. 1053
BJB ELECTRIC DONGGUAN LTD.—See BJB GMBH & CO. KG; *Int'l*, pg. 1053
BJB ELECTRIC L.P.—See BJB GMBH & CO. KG; *Int'l*, pg. 1053
BJB ELECTRIC TAIWAN CORPORATION—See BJB GMBH & CO. KG; *Int'l*, pg. 1053
BJB PROCESA S.A.—See BJB GMBH & CO. KG; *Int'l*, pg. 1053
BJB S.P.A.—See BJB GMBH & CO. KG; *Int'l*, pg. 1053
BJB (UK) LTD.—See BJB GMBH & CO. KG; *Int'l*, pg. 1053
BJ ELECTRIC SUPPLY, INC.; *U.S. Private*, pg. 568
B&K ELECTRIC WHOLESALE; *U.S. Private*, pg. 418
BLACK BOX NETWORK SERVICES—See Black Box Limited; *Int'l*, pg. 1057
BLACK ELECTRICAL SUPPLY; *U.S. Private*, pg. 571
BLAZER ELECTRIC SUPPLY COMPANY OF COLORADO SPRINGS—See Graybar Electric Company, Inc.; *U.S. Private*, pg. 1760
BLONDER TONGUE INTERNATIONAL INC.—See Blonder Tongue Laboratories, Inc.; *U.S. Public*, pg. 362
BONDIOLI I PAVESI UKRAINE L.L.C.—See Bondioli & Pavesi S.p.A.; *Int'l*, pg. 1106
BONDIOLI & PAVESI HYDRAULIC AND MECHANICAL COMPONENT (HANGZHOU) CO., LTD—See Bondioli & Pavesi S.p.A.; *Int'l*, pg. 1105

N.A.I.C.S. INDEX

423610 — ELECTRICAL APPARATU...

BONDIOLI & PAVESI INDIA PVT. LTD.—See Bondioli & Pavesi S.p.A.; *Int'l*, pg. 1105
BONDIOLI & PAVESI LTD.—See Bondioli & Pavesi S.p.A.; *Int'l*, pg. 1105
BONDIOLI & PAVESI SP.ZO.O.—See Bondioli & Pavesi S.p.A.; *Int'l*, pg. 1106
BORDER STATES ELECTRIC SUPPLY LLC—See Border States Industries, Inc.; *U.S. Private*, pg. 617
BORDER STATES INDUSTRIES, INC.; *U.S. Private*, pg. 617
BORDER STATES INDUSTRIES, INC.—See Border States Industries, Inc.; *U.S. Private*, pg. 617
BORDER STATES INDUSTRIES, INC. - UTILICOR DIVISION—See Border States Industries, Inc.; *U.S. Private*, pg. 617
BOURNS DE MEXICO, S. DE R.L. DE C.V. - AUTOMOTIVE DIVISION—See Bourns, Inc.; *U.S. Private*, pg. 624
BOURNS, INC. - CIRCUIT PROTECTION DIVISION—See Bourns, Inc.; *U.S. Private*, pg. 624
BP COMPONENTES HIDRAULICOS E MECANICOS LTDA.—See Bondioli & Pavesi S.p.A.; *Int'l*, pg. 1106
BPN TRANSMISSOES LTDA.—See Bondioli & Pavesi S.p.A.; *Int'l*, pg. 1106
BRANCHSERV SYSTEMS INTEGRATION LLC—See Custom Vault Corp; *U.S. Private*, pg. 1130
BREAKERS UNLIMITED—See Breakers Unlimited Inc.; *U.S. Private*, pg. 642
BREHOB CORPORATION; *U.S. Private*, pg. 644
BRILONER LEUCHTEN GMBH; *Int'l*, pg. 1164
BRODRENE A & O JOHANSEN A/S; *Int'l*, pg. 1173
BROKEN ARROW ELECTRIC SUPPLY INC.; *U.S. Private*, pg. 661
BROWNS ELECTRICAL SUPPLY CO.; *U.S. Private*, pg. 669
BROWNSTOWN ELECTRIC SUPPLY CO. INC.; *U.S. Private*, pg. 670
BRUCKNER SUPPLY CO., INC.—See WESCO International, Inc.; *U.S. Public*, pg. 2351
BRYANT ELECTRIC SUPPLY COMPANY INC.—See Nautic Partners, LLC; *U.S. Public*, pg. 2872
BRYANT ELECTRIC SUPPLY COMPANY INC.—See Nautic Partners, LLC; *U.S. Public*, pg. 2872
B&S ELECTRIC SUPPLY CO. INC.; *U.S. Private*, pg. 419
BUCKEYE POWER SALES COMPANY INC; *U.S. Private*, pg. 677
BUDGET LIGHTING INC.; *U.S. Private*, pg. 679
BULBMAN INC; *U.S. Private*, pg. 684
BULBTRONICS INC.; *U.S. Private*, pg. 684
BURRUS & MATTHEWS, INC.; *U.S. Private*, pg. 692
BUSH AUSTRALIA PTY LIMITED—See Harvard International Ltd.; *Int'l*, pg. 3280
BUSH SUPPLY COMPANY—See Border States Industries, Inc.; *U.S. Private*, pg. 618
BUSSMANN, S. DE R.L. DE C.V.—See Eaton Corporation plc; *Int'l*, pg. 2279
BUTLER'S ELECTRIC SUPPLY; *U.S. Private*, pg. 697
BUTLER SUPPLY INC.; *U.S. Private*, pg. 697
BYD EUROPE B.V.—See BYD Company Limited; *Int'l*, pg. 1234
BYD JAPAN CO., LTD.—See BYD Company Limited; *Int'l*, pg. 1234
CABLENA DO BRASIL LTDA - TELECOM PLANT—See Grupo Carso, S.A.B. de C.V.; *Int'l*, pg. 3123
CABLES PLUS LLC; *U.S. Private*, pg. 711
CAE INC.; *Int'l*, pg. 1248
CAIN ELECTRICAL SUPPLY CORP.; *U.S. Private*, pg. 714
CALVERT WIRE & CABLE CORPORATION; *U.S. Private*, pg. 724
CANARE CORPORATION OF TAIWAN—See Canare Electric Co., Ltd.; *Int'l*, pg. 1288
CANDELA CORPORATION; *U.S. Private*, pg. 733
CANGRO INDUSTRIES INC.—See Applied Industrial Technologies, Inc.; *U.S. Public*, pg. 171
CAPARO MIDDLE EAST FZ—See Caparo Group Ltd.; *Int'l*, pg. 1301
CAPE ELECTRICAL SUPPLY INC.—See Graybar Electric Company, Inc.; *U.S. Private*, pg. 1760
CAPITAL LIGHTING, INC.; *U.S. Private*, pg. 741
CAPITAL WHOLESALE ELECTRIC CO.; *U.S. Private*, pg. 742
CAPITOL BUSINESS EQUIPMENT, INC.—See Champion Industries, Inc.; *U.S. Public*, pg. 478
CARDELLO ELECTRIC SUPPLY COMPANY—See Element Partners, LLC; *U.S. Private*, pg. 1357
CAR & GENERAL (KENYA) LIMITED; *Int'l*, pg. 1319
CARLO GAVAZZI AUTOMATION SPA—See Carlo Gavazzi Holding AG; *Int'l*, pg. 1338
CARLO GAVAZZI LOGISTICS SPA—See Carlo Gavazzi Holding AG; *Int'l*, pg. 1339
CARLO GAVAZZI UNIPESSOAL LDA—See Carlo Gavazzi Holding AG; *Int'l*, pg. 1339
CAROL'S LIGHTING AND FAN SHOP; *U.S. Private*, pg. 767
CARRIER FIRE & SECURITY AUSTRALIA PTY LTD—See Carrier Global Corporation; *U.S. Public*, pg. 442
CARRIER FIRE & SECURITY B.V.—See Carrier Global Corporation; *U.S. Public*, pg. 442
CARRIER FIRE & SECURITY DANMARK A/S—See Carrier Global Corporation; *U.S. Public*, pg. 442
CARRIER FIRE & SECURITY DEUTSCHLAND GMBH—See Carrier Global Corporation; *U.S. Public*, pg. 442
CARRIER FIRE & SECURITY EMEA BV—See Carrier Global Corporation; *U.S. Public*, pg. 442
CARRIER FIRE & SECURITY ESPANA SL—See Carrier Global Corporation; *U.S. Public*, pg. 442
CARRIER FIRE & SECURITY FRANCE S.A.S.—See Carrier Global Corporation; *U.S. Public*, pg. 442
CARRIER FIRE & SECURITY IRELAND LIMITED—See Carrier Global Corporation; *U.S. Public*, pg. 442
CARRIER FIRE & SECURITY ITALIA S.R.L.—See Carrier Global Corporation; *U.S. Public*, pg. 442
CARRIER FIRE & SECURITY NORGE AS—See Carrier Global Corporation; *U.S. Public*, pg. 442
CARRIER FIRE & SECURITY POLSKA SP. Z O.O.—See Carrier Global Corporation; *U.S. Public*, pg. 442
CARRIER FIRE & SECURITY SOUTH AFRICA PTY LTD—See Carrier Global Corporation; *U.S. Public*, pg. 442
CARRIER FIRE & SECURITY SVERIGE AB—See Carrier Global Corporation; *U.S. Public*, pg. 442
CARRIER FIRE & SECURITY UK LIMITED—See Carrier Global Corporation; *U.S. Public*, pg. 442
CASCADE MICROTECH CHINA (SHANGHAI) CO., LTD.—See FormFactor, Inc.; *U.S. Public*, pg. 868
CASCADE MICROTECH GMBH—See FormFactor, Inc.; *U.S. Public*, pg. 868
CASCADE MICROTECH JAPAN, INC.—See FormFactor, Inc.; *U.S. Public*, pg. 868
CBT CO.—See Belting Co. of Cincinnati Inc.; *U.S. Private*, pg. 521
CCA-WESCO—See WESCO International, Inc.; *U.S. Public*, pg. 2352
C-D ELECTRIC, INC.—See B&M Industrial, Inc.; *U.S. Private*, pg. 419
CDR DE MEXICO S. DE R.L. DE C.V.—See Hubbell Incorporated; *U.S. Public*, pg. 1066
CENTRAL CAROLINA SECURITY—See The Philadelphia Contributionship; *U.S. Private*, pg. 4094
CENTRAL WHOLESALE ELECTRICAL DISTRIBUTORS INC.; *U.S. Private*, pg. 826
CEZ LOGISTIKA, S.R.O.—See CEZ, a.s.; *Int'l*, pg. 1426
CG SALES NETWORKS FRANCE S.A.—See Avantha Group; *Int'l*, pg. 736
CHAMPION WIRE & CABLE LLC; *U.S. Private*, pg. 847
CHANCELLOR, INC.; *U.S. Private*, pg. 847
CHAPPELL AGENCY, INC.; *U.S. Private*, pg. 850
CHARLES E. SINGLETON COMPANY INC; *U.S. Private*, pg. 852
CHELSEA LIGHTING NYC, LLC—See Kinzie Capital Partners LP; *U.S. Private*, pg. 2313
CHEYENNE INDUSTRIES, LLC; *U.S. Private*, pg. 876
CHINA INC.; *U.S. Private*, pg. 886
CHINA TELETECH LIMITED—See China Teletech Holding, Inc.; *Int'l*, pg. 1558
CHINT ELECTRICS EUROPE S.R.L—See Chint Group Corporation; *Int'l*, pg. 1571
CHINT ELETRICOS AMERICA DO SUL LTDA—See Chint Group Corporation; *Int'l*, pg. 1571
CHINT WEST ASIA & AFRICA FZE—See Chint Group Corporation; *Int'l*, pg. 1571
CHIYODA INTEGRE CO. (PENANG) SDN. BHD.—See Chiyoda Integre Co., Ltd.; *Int'l*, pg. 1575
CHLORIDE POWER ELECTRONICS INC.—See Vertiv Holdings Co; *U.S. Public*, pg. 2288
CHOO CHIANG HOLDINGS LTD.; *Int'l*, pg. 1582
CHORI IMAGING CORPORATION—See Chori Co., Ltd.; *Int'l*, pg. 1583
CHROMA NEW MATERIAL CORPORATION—See Chroma ATE Inc.; *Int'l*, pg. 1588
CHROMA SYSTEMS SOLUTIONS, INC.—See Chroma ATE Inc.; *Int'l*, pg. 1588
CINCON ELECTRONICS CO., LTD.; *Int'l*, pg. 1610
CITY ELECTRIC COMPANY INC.; *U.S. Private*, pg. 905
CITY ELECTRIC SUPPLY COMPANY; *U.S. Private*, pg. 905
CLAYTON ENGINEERING COMPANY; *U.S. Private*, pg. 918
CLEEVE TECHNOLOGY INCORPORATED; *Int'l*, pg. 1657
CLIFFORD POWER SYSTEMS INC.; *U.S. Private*, pg. 943
CLS ABERDEEN LIMITED—See CLS Holdings plc; *Int'l*, pg. 1664
CMEC JAPAN COMPANY LTD.—See China Machinery Engineering Corporation; *Int'l*, pg. 1516
CMG ELECTRIC MOTORS (UK) LTD.—See CMG Pty. Ltd.; *Int'l*, pg. 1670
COBRA WIRE & CABLE INC.—See Audax Group, Limited Partnership; *U.S. Private*, pg. 387
COILS UNLIMITED—See Standex International; *U.S. Public*, pg. 1930
COLLIGNON ENG SA - BRUXELLES DIVISION—See Eiffage S.A.; *Int'l*, pg. 2329
COLLIGNON LUXEMBOURG SARL—See Eiffage S.A.; *Int'l*, pg. 2329
THE COLONIAL ELECTRIC SUPPLY COMPANY; *U.S. Private*, pg. 4011
COLUMBIA-MBF, INC.—See Clayton, Dubilier & Rice, LLC; *U.S. Private*, pg. 919
COMINIX (PHILIPPINES), INC.—See Cominix Co., Ltd.; *Int'l*, pg. 1713
COMINIX VIETNAM CO., LTD—See Cominix Co., Ltd.; *Int'l*, pg. 1714
COMMERCIAL HEATING SUPPLY—See Torrington Supply Company, Incorporated; *U.S. Private*, pg. 4190
COMMERCIAL LIGHTING PRODUCTS LTD.; *Int'l*, pg. 1715
COMMUNICATION AND SYSTEM SOLUTION PUBLIC COMPANY LIMITED; *Int'l*, pg. 1720
COMMUNICATION CABLES, LLC—See WESCO International, Inc.; *U.S. Public*, pg. 2351
COMMUNICATIONS PRODUCTS & SERVICES; *U.S. Private*, pg. 988
COMMUNICATIONS SUPPLY CORPORATION—See WESCO International, Inc.; *U.S. Public*, pg. 2351
COMPANIA AGROINDUSTRIAL AGROCUEROS S.A.—See Spectrum Brands Holdings, Inc.; *U.S. Public*, pg. 1915
COMRENT INTERNATIONAL, LLC—See Ashtead Group Plc; *Int'l*, pg. 609
COMTRON SYSTEMS, INC.—See Pye-Barker Fire & Safety, LLC; *U.S. Private*, pg. 3309
CONDUCTIX-WAMPFLER LTDA—See CVC Capital Partners SICAV-FIS S.A.; *Int'l*, pg. 1887
CONDUCTIX-WAMPFLER S.DE RL DE C.V.—See CVC Capital Partners SICAV-FIS S.A.; *Int'l*, pg. 1887
CONDUMEX INC.—See Grupo Carso, S.A.B. de C.V.; *Int'l*, pg. 3123
CONEC CORPORATION—See Amphenol Corporation; *U.S. Public*, pg. 129
CONEC ELEKTRONISCHE BAUELEMENTE GMBH—See Amphenol Corporation; *U.S. Public*, pg. 129
CONEC POLSKA SP. Z O.O.—See Amphenol Corporation; *U.S. Public*, pg. 130
CONEC SHANGHAI INTERNATIONAL CO., LTD.—See Amphenol Corporation; *U.S. Public*, pg. 130
CONEC S.R.O.—See Amphenol Corporation; *U.S. Public*, pg. 130
CONSOLIDATED ELECTRICAL DISTRIBUTOR (PTY) LTD—See ARB HOLDINGS LIMITED; *Int'l*, pg. 536
CONSOLIDATED ELECTRICAL DISTRIBUTORS, INC.—See Blackfriars Corp.; *U.S. Private*, pg. 574
CONTINENTAL MARKETING; *U.S. Private*, pg. 1030
CONTROLLER SERVICE & SALES CO INC; *U.S. Private*, pg. 1034
COOPERATIVE ELECTRIC ENERGY UTILITY SUPPLY, INC.; *U.S. Private*, pg. 1042
COOPER BUSSMANN (U.K.) LIMITED—See Eaton Corporation plc; *Int'l*, pg. 2277
COOPER CONTROLS LIMITED—See Eaton Corporation plc; *Int'l*, pg. 2277
COOPER CONTROLS LTD. - NORTH AMERICA—See Eaton Corporation plc; *Int'l*, pg. 2277
COOPER CROUSE-HINDS PTE. LTD.—See Eaton Corporation plc; *Int'l*, pg. 2278
COOPER CROUSE-HINDS, S. DE R.L. DE C.V.—See Eaton Corporation plc; *Int'l*, pg. 2278
COOPER CSA SRL—See Eaton Corporation plc; *Int'l*, pg. 2277
COOPER ELECTRICAL AUSTRALIA PTY. LIMITED—See Eaton Corporation plc; *Int'l*, pg. 2277
COOPER ELECTRIC (SHANGHAI) CO. LTD.—See Eaton Corporation plc; *Int'l*, pg. 2278
COOPER INDUSTRIES HOLDINGS GMBH—See Eaton Corporation plc; *Int'l*, pg. 2277
COOPER INDUSTRIES RUSSIA LLC—See Eaton Corporation plc; *Int'l*, pg. 2277
COOPER KOREA LTD.—See Eaton Corporation plc; *Int'l*, pg. 2278
COOPER NOTIFICATION, INC.—See Eaton Corporation plc; *Int'l*, pg. 2278
COOPER POWER SYSTEMS DO BRASIL LTDA.—See Eaton Corporation plc; *Int'l*, pg. 2278
COOPER POWER SYSTEMS, LLC—See Eaton Corporation plc; *Int'l*, pg. 2278
COOPER SAFETY B.V.—See Eaton Corporation plc; *Int'l*, pg. 2279
COOPER SHANGHAI POWER CAPACITOR CO., LTD.—See Eaton Corporation plc; *Int'l*, pg. 2279
COOPER UNIVEL S.A.—See Eaton Corporation plc; *Int'l*, pg. 2279
COOPER WIRING DEVICES, INC.—See Eaton Corporation plc; *Int'l*, pg. 2278
COOPER XI'AN FUSEGEAR CO., LTD.—See Eaton Corporation plc; *Int'l*, pg. 2279
CORTELCO SYSTEMS PUERTO RICO, INC.—See Cortelco Systems Holding Corp.; *U.S. Private*, pg. 1060
COSLIGHT-NEWGEN LTD.—See Coslight Technology International Group Limited; *Int'l*, pg. 1810
COSLIGHT USA INC.—See Coslight Technology International Group Limited; *Int'l*, pg. 1810
COUTURE LAMPS, INC.—See China Baofeng (International) Ltd.; *Int'l*, pg. 1485
COVENTRY ELECTRICAL SUPPLIES LTD.—See City Electric Supply Company; *U.S. Private*, pg. 905
COVERCO S.R.L.—See Franklin Electric Co., Inc.; *U.S. Public*, pg. 878

423610 — ELECTRICAL APPARATU...

CP COMPANY—See OEP Capital Advisors, L.P.; *U.S. Private*, pg. 3000
CREATIVE STAGE LIGHTING CO.; *U.S. Private*, pg. 1090
CRESCENT ELECTRIC SUPPLY COMPANY; *U.S. Private*, pg. 1093
CRUM ELECTRIC SUPPLY CO., INC.; *U.S. Private*, pg. 1114
C.T.E. SYSTEMS, INC.—See Associated Time & Parking Controls, Inc.; *U.S. Private*, pg. 357
CTS CORPORATION U.K. LTD.—See CTS Corporation; *U.S. Public*, pg. 603
CTS INDIA PRIVATE LIMITED—See CTS Corporation; *U.S. Public*, pg. 603
CTS JAPAN, INC.—See CTS Corporation; *U.S. Public*, pg. 603
CTS OF CANADA CO.—See CTS Corporation; *U.S. Public*, pg. 603
CTS SINGAPORE PTE., LTD.—See CTS Corporation; *U.S. Public*, pg. 603
CTS (TIANJIN) ELECTRONICS COMPANY LTD.—See CTS Corporation; *U.S. Public*, pg. 603
CUMMINS POWER SYSTEMS—See Cummins Inc.; *U.S. Public*, pg. 606
CUMMINS SALES AND SERVICE (SINGAPORE) PTE. LTD.—See Cummins Inc.; *U.S. Public*, pg. 607
CURRENT SOLUTIONS, LLC—See River Associates Investments, LLC; *U.S. Private*, pg. 3443
CURTIS H STOUT INC.; *U.S. Private*, pg. 1126
CURTIS INDUSTRIES INC.—See Powers Holdings, Inc.; *U.S. Private*, pg. 3240
CVS SYSTEMS INC.; *U.S. Private*, pg. 1132
CYBERPOWER SYSTEMS B.V.—See CyberPower Systems, Inc.; *Int'l*, pg. 1893
CYBER POWER SYSTEMS FRANCE—See CyberPower Systems, Inc.; *Int'l*, pg. 1893
CYBERPOWER SYSTEMS K.K.—See CyberPower Systems, Inc.; *Int'l*, pg. 1894
DAHL-BECK ELECTRIC CO.; *U.S. Private*, pg. 1144
DAKOTA SUPPLY GROUP INC.; *U.S. Private*, pg. 1147
DASCAN INDUSTRIAL CONTROLS, INC.—See DASCAN Industrial Controls; *Int'l*, pg. 1973
DASH ENTERPRISES INC.; *U.S. Private*, pg. 1162
DATA SECURITY SOLUTIONS, LLC—See WSFS Financial Corporation; *U.S. Public*, pg. 2384
DAVE CARTER & ASSOCIATES, INC.; *U.S. Private*, pg. 1168
DAVIS WHOLESALE ELECTRIC INC.; *U.S. Private*, pg. 1174
DDK LTD.—See Fujikura Ltd.; *Int'l*, pg. 2827
DEALERS ELECTRICAL SUPPLY CO.; *U.S. Private*, pg. 1182
DECATUR INDUSTRIAL ELECTRIC; *U.S. Private*, pg. 1186
DE DIETRICH PROCESS SYSTEMS IRELAND LTD.—See De Dietrich Process Systems S.A.; *Int'l*, pg. 1995
DEEP SEA ELECTRONICS LIMITED—See Generac Holdings Inc.; *U.S. Public*, pg. 912
DELANDE SUPPLY CO. INC.; *U.S. Private*, pg. 1193
DELAWARE ELECTRO INDUSTRIES INC.; *U.S. Private*, pg. 1194
DELCO WIRE AND CABLE LIMITED—See Industrial Electric Wire & Cable Inc.; *U.S. Private*, pg. 2066
DELTA ELECTRONICS (ARGENTINA) S.R.L.—See Delta Electronics, Inc.; *Int'l*, pg. 2016
DELTA ELECTRONICS (COLOMBIA) S.A.S—See Delta Electronics, Inc.; *Int'l*, pg. 2016
DELTA ELECTRONICS (GERMANY) GMBH—See Delta Electronics, Inc.; *Int'l*, pg. 2016
DELTA ELECTRONICS (PERU) INC. S.R.L.—See Delta Electronics, Inc.; *Int'l*, pg. 2018
DELTA NETWORKS (SHANGHAI) LTD.—See Delta Electronics, Inc.; *Int'l*, pg. 2018
DELTATECH CONTROLS USA, LLC—See Sensata Technologies Holding plc; *U.S. Public*, pg. 1866
DEMESNE ELECTRICAL SALES UK LIMITED—See Demesne Electrical Sales Limited; *Int'l*, pg. 2025
DENKYO GROUP HOLDINGS CO., LTD.; *Int'l*, pg. 2028
DENNEY ELECTRIC SUPPLY; *U.S. Private*, pg. 1205
DENYO TRADING CO LTD—See Denyo Co., Ltd.; *Int'l*, pg. 2040
DESCO INC.; *U.S. Private*, pg. 1211
DESERT ELECTRIC SUPPLY; *U.S. Private*, pg. 1212
DESIGN/SYSTEMS GROUP, INC.—See GTCR LLC; *U.S. Private*, pg. 1802
DESIGN TRENDS, LLC—See Craftmade International, Inc.; *U.S. Private*, pg. 1082
DIALIGHT ASIA PTE. LTD.—See Dialight plc; *Int'l*, pg. 2104
DIALIGHT BTI A/S—See Dialight plc; *Int'l*, pg. 2104
DIALIGHT EUROPE LIMITED—See Dialight plc; *Int'l*, pg. 2104
DICKMAN SUPPLY INCORPORATED; *U.S. Private*, pg. 1227
DIESELEC THISTLE GENERATORS LIMITED—See DCC plc; *Int'l*, pg. 1990
DIVERSIFIED LIGHTING ASSOCIATES INC.; *U.S. Private*, pg. 1243
DIVERSIFIED SUPPLY INC.; *U.S. Private*, pg. 1243
DIXON MIDLAND LIGHTING CO.; *U.S. Private*, pg. 1246
DMG INCORPORATED; *U.S. Private*, pg. 1248

DN LIGHTING CO., LTD.—See Dai Nippon Toryo Co., Ltd.; *Int'l*, pg. 1916
DOLAN NORTHWEST LLC; *U.S. Private*, pg. 1254
DOMINION ELECTRIC SUPPLY COMPANY, INC.; *U.S. Private*, pg. 1256
DOMINION KINCAID GENERATION L.L.C.—See Dominion Energy, Inc.; *U.S. Public*, pg. 674
DON BLACKBURN & COMPANY; *U.S. Private*, pg. 1257
DONGBU LIGHTEC EUROPE LTD.—See GeumVit Corp.; *Int'l*, pg. 2954
DONGBU LIGHTEC JAPAN CO., LTD.—See GeumVit Corp.; *Int'l*, pg. 2954
DONGBU LIGHTEC USA INC—See GeumVit Corp.; *Int'l*, pg. 2954
DONGBU LIGHTEC (YANTAI) CO., LTD.—See GeumVit Corp.; *Int'l*, pg. 2954
DON KYATT SPARE PARTS (QLD) PTY LTD—See Bapcor Limited; *Int'l*, pg. 857
DORCY INTERNATIONAL H.K LTD—See Dorcy International Inc.; *U.S. Private*, pg. 1262
DORCY INTERNATIONAL INC.; *U.S. Private*, pg. 1262
DORCY PACIFIC PTY LTD—See Dorcy International Inc.; *U.S. Private*, pg. 1262
D.P. BROWN OF DETROIT INC.—See Genuine Parts Company; *U.S. Public*, pg. 933
DREISILKER ELECTRIC MOTORS INC.; *U.S. Private*, pg. 1276
DRIVHUSET AB—See Addtech AB; *Int'l*, pg. 132
DRON & DICKSON LTD.; *Int'l*, pg. 2205
DSI DISTRIBUTING, INC.; *U.S. Private*, pg. 1281
D SQUARE ENERGY LLC; *U.S. Private*, pg. 1136
D-TRUST GMBH—See Bundesdruckerei GmbH; *Int'l*, pg. 1215
DYNA-BRITE LIGHTING, INC.; *U.S. Private*, pg. 1297
EAO AUTOMOTIVE GMBH & CO. KG—See EAO AG; *Int'l*, pg. 2267
EAO CORPORATION—See EAO AG; *Int'l*, pg. 2267
EAO SCHWEIZ AG—See EAO AG; *Int'l*, pg. 2267
EAO SWITCH CORPORATION—See EAO AG; *Int'l*, pg. 2267
EATON AEROSPACE LLC—See Eaton Corporation plc; *Int'l*, pg. 2279
EATON CONTROLS, S. DE R.L. DE C.V.—See Eaton Corporation plc; *Int'l*, pg. 2279
EATON CONTROLS (UK) LIMITED—See Eaton Corporation plc; *Int'l*, pg. 2279
EATON ELECTRICAL MEXICO - GUADALAJARA SALES OFFICE—See Eaton Corporation plc; *Int'l*, pg. 2280
EATON ELECTRICAL MEXICO - MONTERREY SALES OFFICE—See Eaton Corporation plc; *Int'l*, pg. 2280
EATON ELECTRICAL SYSTEMS LIMITED—See Eaton Corporation plc; *Int'l*, pg. 2280
EATON ELECTRIC APS—See Eaton Corporation plc; *Int'l*, pg. 2281
EATON ELECTRIC LIMITED—See Eaton Corporation plc; *Int'l*, pg. 2281
EATON ELECTRIC SPRL—See Eaton Corporation plc; *Int'l*, pg. 2280
EATON ELEKTRIK TICARET LIMITED SIRKETI—See Eaton Corporation plc; *Int'l*, pg. 2280
EATON ENTERPRISES (HUNGARY) KFT.—See Eaton Corporation plc; *Int'l*, pg. 2280
EATON FZE—See Eaton Corporation plc; *Int'l*, pg. 2280
EATON GERMANY GMBH—See Eaton Corporation plc; *Int'l*, pg. 2281
EATON HOLDING SE & CO. KG—See Eaton Corporation plc; *Int'l*, pg. 2280
EATON HYDRAULICS LLC—See Eaton Corporation plc; *Int'l*, pg. 2280
EATON INDUSTRIAL SYSTEMS PRIVATE LIMITED—See Eaton Corporation plc; *Int'l*, pg. 2281
EATON INDUSTRIES (BELGIUM) BVBA—See Eaton Corporation plc; *Int'l*, pg. 2281
EATON INDUSTRIES GMBH—See Eaton Corporation plc; *Int'l*, pg. 2281
EATON INDUSTRIES II G.M.B.H.—See Eaton Corporation plc; *Int'l*, pg. 2281
EATON INDUSTRIES (JAPAN) LTD.—See Eaton Corporation plc; *Int'l*, pg. 2280
EATON INDUSTRIES PTY. LTD.—See Eaton Corporation plc; *Int'l*, pg. 2281
EATON INDUSTRIES, S. DE R.L. DE C.V.—See Eaton Corporation plc; *Int'l*, pg. 2280
EATON INDUSTRIES (SHANGHAI) CO., LTD.—See Eaton Corporation plc; *Int'l*, pg. 2281
EATON MANUFACTURING GMBH—See Eaton Corporation plc; *Int'l*, pg. 2281
EATON ONTARIO SALES—See Eaton Corporation plc; *Int'l*, pg. 2279
EATON PHOENIXTEC MMPL CO.,LTD.—See Eaton Corporation plc; *Int'l*, pg. 2281
EATON POWER QUALITY AB—See Eaton Corporation plc; *Int'l*, pg. 2281
EATON POWER QUALITY LIMITED—See Eaton Corporation plc; *Int'l*, pg. 2281
EATON POWER QUALITY S.A.—See Eaton Corporation plc; *Int'l*, pg. 2279

CORPORATE AFFILIATIONS

EATON POWER SOLUTIONS LTDA.—See Eaton Corporation plc; *Int'l*, pg. 2279
EATON POWER SOLUTIONS - MEXICO & CENTRAL AMERICA—See Eaton Corporation plc; *Int'l*, pg. 2280
EATON TECHNOLOGIES, S. DE R.L. DE C.V.—See Eaton Corporation plc; *Int'l*, pg. 2280
EB ELEKTRO AS—See Addtech AB; *Int'l*, pg. 132
EBULB, INC.; *U.S. Private*, pg. 1326
ECHO GROUP, INC.; *U.S. Private*, pg. 1327
ECHO SYSTEMS—See Echo Group, Inc.; *U.S. Private*, pg. 1327
ECKART LLC; *U.S. Private*, pg. 1327
ECK ENTERPRISES LLC; *U.S. Private*, pg. 1327
EDGES ELECTRICAL GROUP; *U.S. Private*, pg. 1334
E.D. SUPPLY CO. INC.; *U.S. Private*, pg. 1305
EDWARDS JAPAN LIMITED—See Atlas Copco AB; *Int'l*, pg. 682
E&E ACQUIRING LLC; *U.S. Private*, pg. 1301
EECOL ELECTRIC ULC—See WESCO International, Inc.; *U.S. Public*, pg. 2351
EIS, INC.—See Audax Group, Limited Partnership; *U.S. Private*, pg. 387
EIS, INC.—See Audax Group, Limited Partnership; *U.S. Private*, pg. 387
EIS, INC.—See Audax Group, Limited Partnership; *U.S. Private*, pg. 387
EIS, INC. - TEMPE—See Audax Group, Limited Partnership; *U.S. Private*, pg. 387
EITA ELECTRIC SDN. BHD.—See Eita Resources Berhad; *Int'l*, pg. 2336
EITA TECHNOLOGIES PTE. LTD.—See Eita Resources Berhad; *Int'l*, pg. 2336
ELCOR INC.—See Mueller Electric Company; *U.S. Private*, pg. 2810
ELECTRI-CABLE ASSEMBLIES, INC.—See Graham Holdings Company; *U.S. Public*, pg. 955
ELECTRICAL DISTRIBUTORS; *U.S. Private*, pg. 1353
ELECTRICAL ENGINEERING & EQUIPMENT COMPANY INC.; *U.S. Private*, pg. 1353
ELECTRICAL EQUIPMENT COMPANY; *U.S. Private*, pg. 1353
ELECTRICAL EQUIPMENT COMPANY—See Electrical Equipment Company; *U.S. Private*, pg. 1353
ELECTRICAL POWER PRODUCTS INC.; *U.S. Private*, pg. 1353
ELECTRICAL SALES INC.—See Winsupply, Inc.; *U.S. Private*, pg. 4545
ELECTRICAL SUPPLIES INC.; *U.S. Private*, pg. 1353
ELECTRICAL WHOLESALE SUPPLY CO. INC.; *U.S. Private*, pg. 1353
ELECTRICAL WHOLESALE SUPPLY CO. UTAH; *U.S. Private*, pg. 1353
ELECTRIC FIXTURE & SUPPLY COMPANY INC.; *U.S. Private*, pg. 1352
ELECTRIC MOTOR SALES & SUPPLY CO.; *U.S. Private*, pg. 1352
ELECTRIC MOTOR SERVICE INC.; *U.S. Private*, pg. 1352
ELECTRIC MOTOR SERVICE—See Tri-State Armature & Electric Works, Inc.; *U.S. Private*, pg. 4223
ELECTRIC SPECIALTIES COMPANY—See Per Mar Security Services; *U.S. Private*, pg. 3146
ELECTRIC SUPPLY CO.; *U.S. Private*, pg. 1352
ELECTRIC SUPPLY & EQUIPMENT CO. INC.; *U.S. Private*, pg. 1352
ELECTRIC SUPPLY, INC.; *U.S. Private*, pg. 1352
ELECTRIC SUPPLY, INC.; *U.S. Private*, pg. 1352
ELECTROHOLD SALES AD—See Eurohold Bulgaria AD; *Int'l*, pg. 2553
ELECTROLOCK INC.; *U.S. Private*, pg. 1354
ELECTROMANUFACTURAS, S. DE R.L. DE C.V.—See Eaton Corporation plc; *Int'l*, pg. 2278
ELECTRO-MATIC PRODUCTS, INC.—See Electro-Matic Ventures, Inc.; *U.S. Private*, pg. 1354
ELECTROREP-ENERGY PRODUCTS; *U.S. Private*, pg. 1356
ELECTROREP, INC.—See Forward Solutions; *U.S. Private*, pg. 1578
ELECTRO-WIRE INC.—See Audax Group, Limited Partnership; *U.S. Private*, pg. 387
ELEKTRA NORESTE S.A.—See Empresas Publicas de Medellin ESP; *Int'l*, pg. 2392
ELEKTRISOLA COMPANY LIMITED—See Elektrisola Dr. Gerd Schildbach GmbH & Co. KG; *Int'l*, pg. 2356
ELEKTRISOLA FRANCE SA—See Elektrisola Dr. Gerd Schildbach GmbH & Co. KG; *Int'l*, pg. 2356
ELEKTRISOLA INDIA PVT. LTD—See Elektrisola Dr. Gerd Schildbach GmbH & Co. KG; *Int'l*, pg. 2356
ELEKTRISOLA KOREA CO. LTD.—See Elektrisola Dr. Gerd Schildbach GmbH & Co. KG; *Int'l*, pg. 2356
ELEKTROIMPORTOREN AS; *Int'l*, pg. 2357
ELKOME GROUP OY—See Addtech AB; *Int'l*, pg. 133
ELLIOTT ELECTRIC SUPPLY; *U.S. Private*, pg. 1364
ELTROTREC S.A.C.; *Int'l*, pg. 2371
ELVEY SECURITY TECHNOLOGIES (PTY) LTD—See Hudaco Industries Limited; *Int'l*, pg. 3521
EMERSON NETWORK POWER ITALIA SRL—See Emerson Electric Co.; *U.S. Public*, pg. 742
EMERSON PROCESS MANAGEMENT ROSEMOUNT

N.A.I.C.S. INDEX

423610 — ELECTRICAL APPARATU...

INC—See Emerson Electric Co.; *U.S. Public*, pg. 747
EMS INDUSTRIAL INC.; *U.S. Private*, pg. 1388
ENDO LIGHTING ACCESSORIES INDIA PRIVATE LIMITED—See ENDO Lighting Corporation; *Int'l*, pg. 2404
ENDO LIGHTING SE ASIA PTE. LTD—See ENDO Lighting Corporation; *Int'l*, pg. 2404
ENDO LIGHTING VIETNAM CO. LTD.—See ENDO Lighting Corporation; *Int'l*, pg. 2404
ENDO TRADE (BEIJING) CO., LTD.—See ENDO Lighting Corporation; *Int'l*, pg. 2404
ENDO TRADE (BEIJING) SHANGHAI CO., LTD—See ENDO Lighting Corporation; *Int'l*, pg. 2404
ENDRESS+HAUSER CHILE LTD.—See Endress+Hauser (International) Holding AG; *Int'l*, pg. 2407
ENDRESS+HAUSER (HELLAS) S.A.—See Endress+Hauser (International) Holding AG; *Int'l*, pg. 2406
ENDRESS+HAUSER SA/NV—See Endress+Hauser (International) Holding AG; *Int'l*, pg. 2408
ENERGOCOM - VEGA DISTRIBUTION LLP—See Grieshaber Holding GmbH; *Int'l*, pg. 3083
ENERGY MANAGEMENT CONTROL CORPORATION—See Huron Capital Partners LLC; *U.S. Private*, pg. 2011
ENERGY MANAGEMENT CORPORATION; *U.S. Private*, pg. 1395
ENERGY PRODUCTS INC.; *U.S. Private*, pg. 1395
ENERSYS LLC—See EnerSys; *U.S. Public*, pg. 766
ENVIRONMENTAL STRESS SYSTEMS, INC.—See Chroma ATE Inc.; *Int'l*, pg. 1588
ENVIROTROLSC, LLC—See Comfort Systems USA, Inc.; *U.S. Public*, pg. 544
ENYE LTD. CORPORATION—See BELIMO Holding AG; *Int'l*, pg. 965
EPPENDORF S.R.L.—See Eppendorf AG; *Int'l*, pg. 2464
EPRIM, A.S.—See CEZ, a.s.; *Int'l*, pg. 1428
E. SAM JONES DISTRIBUTOR INCORPORATED; *U.S. Private*, pg. 1304
ESCO FINANCIAL AND TRANSMISSIONS LTD.—See Esco Financial & Engineering Company S.A/N.V.; *Int'l*, pg. 2501
ESCO TRANSMISJA MOCY SP. Z O.O.—See Esco Financial & Engineering Company S.A/N.V.; *Int'l*, pg. 2501
ESKANET S.A.—See WESCO International, Inc.; *U.S. Public*, pg. 2351
ESPEC TECHNO CORP.—See ESPEC Corp.; *Int'l*, pg. 2505
E-SWITCH, INC.—See Stein Industries, Inc.; *U.S. Private*, pg. 3797
ETC ENDURE ENERGY L.L.C.—See Energy Transfer LP; *U.S. Public*, pg. 763
ETC INTERSTATE PROCUREMENT COMPANY, LLC—See Energy Transfer LP; *U.S. Public*, pg. 763
ETIBALTUS UAB—See Andlinger & Company, Inc.; *U.S. Private*, pg. 279
ETI POLAM SP.Z.O.O.—See Andlinger & Company, Inc.; *U.S. Private*, pg. 278
ETI UKRAINE LTD.—See Andlinger & Company, Inc.; *U.S. Private*, pg. 278
ETS (PORTSMOUTH) LIMITED—See Addtech AB; *Int'l*, pg. 133
EUPEN CABLE USA INC.; *U.S. Private*, pg. 1433
EURO-COSLIGHT GMBH—See Coslight Technology International Group Limited; *Int'l*, pg. 1810
EUROLAITE OY—See Addtech AB; *Int'l*, pg. 133
EUROTEC SRL—See Illinois Tool Works Inc.; *U.S. Public*, pg. 1103
EVERFAST RECHARGEABLES LIMITED—See Eveready Industries India Ltd; *Int'l*, pg. 2563
EVERGREEN OAK ELECTRIC SUPPLY & SALES CO. INC.; *U.S. Private*, pg. 1439
EVERLIGHT AMERICAS, INC.—See Everlight Electronics Co., Ltd.; *Int'l*, pg. 2567
EVERLIGHT CANADA, INC.—See Everlight Electronics Co., Ltd.; *Int'l*, pg. 2567
EVN ENERGIEVERTRIEB GMBH & CO KG—See EVN AG; *Int'l*, pg. 2571
EVN NETZ GMBH—See EVN AG; *Int'l*, pg. 2571
EVOLUTION LIGHTING CANADA—See Boyne Capital Management, LLC; *U.S. Private*, pg. 628
EVPU CR S.R.O.—See EVPU a.s.; *Int'l*, pg. 2573
FAIRFIELD TRADING COMPANY LTD.—See Addtech AB; *Int'l*, pg. 133
FASTEMS AB—See Helvar Merca Oy AB; *Int'l*, pg. 3339
FASTEMS K.K.—See Helvar Merca Oy AB; *Int'l*, pg. 3339
FASTEMS LLC—See Helvar Merca Oy AB; *Int'l*, pg. 3339
FASTEMS S.R.L.—See Helvar Merca Oy AB; *Int'l*, pg. 3339
FASTEMS SYSTEMS GMBH—See Helvar Merca Oy AB; *Int'l*, pg. 3339
FDK ELECTRONICS GMBH—See Fujitsu Limited; *Int'l*, pg. 2832
THE F.D. LAWRENCE ELECTRIC COMPANY; *U.S. Private*, pg. 4027
FEDERAL BATTERIES QLD PTY LTD—See Bapcor Limited; *Int'l*, pg. 857
FEELUX LIGHTING, INC.—See FEELUX Co., Ltd.; *Int'l*, pg. 2632

FEI KOREA LTD.—See Thermo Fisher Scientific Inc.; *U.S. Public*, pg. 2147
FIDELITY ADT (PTY) LTD—See Fidelity Security Group (Pty) Ltd.; *Int'l*, pg. 2654
FILTER SENSING TECHNOLOGIES, INC.—See CTS Corporation; *U.S. Public*, pg. 603
FIRE ALARM CONTROL SYSTEMS, INC.—See The Carlyle Group Inc.; *U.S. Public*, pg. 2053
FIREANGEL SAFETY TECHNOLOGY LIMITED—See FireAngel Safety Technology Group Plc; *Int'l*, pg. 2678
FIRE SYSTEMS PROFESSIONALS, LLC—See The Riverside Company; *U.S. Private*, pg. 4108
FIVE STAR ELECTRIC MOTORS; *U.S. Private*, pg. 1537
FLECO INDUSTRIES, LLC—See CORE Industrial Partners, LLC; *U.S. Private*, pg. 1048
FLETCHER-REINHARDT COMPANY; *U.S. Private*, pg. 1543
FLOLO CORPORATION; *U.S. Private*, pg. 1546
FLOORING INDUSTRIES LTD.—See Mohawk Industries, Inc.; *U.S. Public*, pg. 1457
FLOW-TEKNIKK AS—See Addtech AB; *Int'l*, pg. 133
FOLEY GROUP, INC.—See Convergence Partners, Inc.; *U.S. Private*, pg. 1035
FOREST HILLS ELECTRICAL SUPPLY, INC.—See Turtle & Hughes, Inc.; *U.S. Private*, pg. 4262
FORIND AVIO ELETTRONICA S.P.A.; *Int'l*, pg. 2733
FORTIS BELIZE LIMITED—See Fortis Inc.; *Int'l*, pg. 2739
FORTUNE ELECTRIC CO., LTD.; *Int'l*, pg. 2743
FOSRICH CO., LTD.; *Int'l*, pg. 2748
FOX-ROWDEN-MCBRAYER INC.; *U.S. Private*, pg. 1585
FRANKLIN ELECTRIC (BOTSWANA) PTY LTD—See Franklin Electric Co., Inc.; *U.S. Public*, pg. 878
FRANKLIN ELECTRIC CANADA, INC.—See Franklin Electric Co., Inc.; *U.S. Public*, pg. 878
FRANKLIN ELECTRIC HOLDING B.V.—See Franklin Electric Co., Inc.; *U.S. Public*, pg. 878
FRANKLIN ELECTRIC INDIA PRIVATE LTD.—See Franklin Electric Co., Inc.; *U.S. Public*, pg. 878
FRANKLIN ELECTRIC (SOUTH AFRICA) PTY. LTD.—See Franklin Electric Co., Inc.; *U.S. Public*, pg. 878
FRANKLIN ELECTRIC SPOL S.R.O.—See Franklin Electric Co., Inc.; *U.S. Public*, pg. 878
FRANKLIN FUELING SISTEMAS DE COMBUSTIVEIS LTDA—See Franklin Electric Co., Inc.; *U.S. Public*, pg. 878
FRANKLIN FUELING SYSTEMS AUSTRALIA PTY. LTD.—See Franklin Electric Co., Inc.; *U.S. Public*, pg. 878
FRANKLIN FUELING SYSTEMS FRANCE SARL—See Franklin Electric Co., Inc.; *U.S. Public*, pg. 878
FRENCH GERLEMAN ELECTRIC CO., INC.; *U.S. Private*, pg. 1608
FROMM ELECTRIC SUPPLY CORPORATION; *U.S. Private*, pg. 1613
FROST ELECTRIC SUPPLY COMPANY INC.; *U.S. Private*, pg. 1616
FS CABLES LIMITED—See Diploma PLC; *Int'l*, pg. 2128
FSG FACILITY SOLUTIONS GROUP; *U.S. Private*, pg. 1618
FTT LLC—See Acroud AB; *Int'l*, pg. 109
FUJI ELECTRIC CORPORATION OF AMERICA—See Fuji Electric Co., Ltd.; *Int'l*, pg. 2811
FUJI ELECTRIC TECHNICA CO., LTD.—See Fuji Electric Co., Ltd.; *Int'l*, pg. 2812
FUJII TSUSHIN INC.—See Fujii Sangyo Corporation; *Int'l*, pg. 2826
FUJIKURA AMERICA INC.—See Fujikura Ltd.; *Int'l*, pg. 2827
FUJI N2TELLIGENCE GMBH—See Fuji Electric Co., Ltd.; *Int'l*, pg. 2812
FULL COMPASS SYSTEMS LTD. INC.; *U.S. Private*, pg. 1620
FURUNO KANSAI HAMBAI CO., LTD.—See Furuno Electric Co., Ltd.; *Int'l*, pg. 2848
FURUNO SYSTEMS CO ,LTD.—See Furuno Electric Co., Ltd.; *Int'l*, pg. 2848
FUTURE ELECTRONICS CORP.—See Future Electronics Inc.; *Int'l*, pg. 2854
GARO POLSKA SP. Z O.O.—See Garo AB; *Int'l*, pg. 2885
GASTON SECURITY INC.—See Apollo Global Management, Inc.; *U.S. Public*, pg. 146
G. E. CRANE N.Z. HOLDINGS LTD—See Fletcher Building Limited; *Int'l*, pg. 2700
GEFRAN BENELUX N.V.—See Gefran S.p.A.; *Int'l*, pg. 2912
GENERAC MOBILE PRODUCTS, LLC—See Generac Holdings Inc.; *U.S. Public*, pg. 912
GENERAL PHOTONICS CORPORATION—See Luna Innovations Incorporated; *U.S. Public*, pg. 1348
GEOPHYSICAL ELECTRICAL SUPPLY, INC.; *U.S. Private*, pg. 1681
GETRIEBEBAU NORD AG—See Getriebebau NORD GmbH & Co. KG; *Int'l*, pg. 2953
GETRIEBEBAU NORD GMBH—See Getriebebau NORD GmbH & Co. KG; *Int'l*, pg. 2953
GEWISS UK LTD—See Gewiss S.p.A.; *Int'l*, pg. 2955
G&G ELECTRIC & PLUMBING DISTRIBUTORS; *U.S. Private*, pg. 1628
GILSON ENGINEERING SALES, INC.; *U.S. Private*, pg. 1701

GK EQUITIES SDN. BHD.—See George Kent (Malaysia) Berhad; *Int'l*, pg. 2938
GLAMOX FAR EAST PTE LTD.—See Arendals Fossekompani ASA; *Int'l*, pg. 559
GLENBARD ELECTRIC SUPPLY INC.—See Revere Electric Supply Company; *U.S. Private*, pg. 3414
GOLDEN LIGHTING COMPANY; *U.S. Private*, pg. 1732
GP BATTERIES (AMERICAS) INC.—See Gold Peak Technology Group Limited; *Int'l*, pg. 3025
GP BATTERIES (U.K.) LIMITED—See Gold Peak Technology Group Limited; *Int'l*, pg. 3025
GP BATTERY MARKETING (KOREA) LIMITED—See Gold Peak Technology Group Limited; *Int'l*, pg. 3025
GP BATTERY MARKETING (SINGAPORE) PTE. LTD.—See Gold Peak Technology Group Limited; *Int'l*, pg. 3025
GRANITE CITY ELECTRIC SUPPLY CO., INC.; *U.S. Private*, pg. 1755
GRANITE ELECTRICAL SUPPLY, INC.—See Edges Electrical Group; *U.S. Private*, pg. 1334
GRAYBAR CANADA LIMITED—See Graybar Electric Company, Inc.; *U.S. Private*, pg. 1760
GRAYBAR ELECTRIC CANADA LIMITED—See Graybar Electric Company, Inc.; *U.S. Private*, pg. 1760
GRAYBAR ELECTRIC COMPANY, INC.; *U.S. Private*, pg. 1759
GRESCO UTILITY SUPPLY INC.; *U.S. Private*, pg. 1783
GRIFFITH ELECTRIC SUPPLY COMPANY; *U.S. Private*, pg. 1789
GRODNO SA; *Int'l*, pg. 3087
GROSS ELECTRIC INC.; *U.S. Private*, pg. 1792
GUH ELECTRICAL (BW) SDN. BHD.—See GUH Holdings Berhad; *Int'l*, pg. 3173
GULF DURA INDUSTRIES L.L.C—See Gulf General Investment Company PSC; *Int'l*, pg. 3180
HABIA BENELUX BV—See Beijer Alma AB; *Int'l*, pg. 942
HABIA CABLE CHINA LTD—See Beijer Alma AB; *Int'l*, pg. 942
HABIA CABLE LTD—See Beijer Alma AB; *Int'l*, pg. 942
HACIENDA LIGHTING, INCORPORATED; *U.S. Private*, pg. 1838
HADDON-MCCLELLAN ASSOCIATES INC.; *U.S. Private*, pg. 1839
HAGEMEYER NORTH AMERICA—See Nautic Partners, LLC; *U.S. Private*, pg. 2872
HAIMO INTERNATIONAL FZE—See Haimo Technologies Group Corp.; *Int'l*, pg. 3211
HALEX—See Berkshire Hathaway Inc.; *U.S. Public*, pg. 300
HAMAMATSU PHOTONICS NORDEN AB—See Hamamatsu Photonics K.K.; *Int'l*, pg. 3235
HANA TECHNOLOGY CO., LTD.—See Adtec Plasma Technology Co., Ltd.; *Int'l*, pg. 154
HANMO CORPORATION—See BELIMO Holding AG; *Int'l*, pg. 965
HANNAN SUPPLY COMPANY; *U.S. Private*, pg. 1855
HARISON TOSHIBA USA INC.—See Harison Toshiba Lighting Corp.; *Int'l*, pg. 3277
HARMON & SULLIVAN ASSOCIATES, INC.—See Cincon Electronics Co., Ltd.; *Int'l*, pg. 1610
HARRIS ELECTRIC SUPPLY CO., INC.—See Border States Industries, Inc.; *U.S. Private*, pg. 618
HARTFORD ELECTRIC SUPPLY CO.; *U.S. Private*, pg. 1873
HASTEN SYSTEMS—See AC Corporation; *U.S. Private*, pg. 45
HAZMASTERS INC.—See WESCO International, Inc.; *U.S. Public*, pg. 2351
HCB TECHNOLOGIES LIMITED—See Bapcor Limited; *Int'l*, pg. 857
HEDEMORA TURBO & DIESEL AB—See Engenco Limited; *Int'l*, pg. 2427
HEIDRIVE S.R.O.—See Allient Inc.; *U.S. Public*, pg. 80
HELUKABEL AB—See HELUKABEL GmbH; *Int'l*, pg. 3338
HELUKABEL AG—See HELUKABEL GmbH; *Int'l*, pg. 3338
HELUKABEL AUSTRIA GMBH—See HELUKABEL GmbH; *Int'l*, pg. 3338
HELUKABEL BELGIUM BVBA—See HELUKABEL GmbH; *Int'l*, pg. 3338
HELUKABEL B.V.—See HELUKABEL GmbH; *Int'l*, pg. 3338
HELUKABEL CANADA INC.—See HELUKABEL GmbH; *Int'l*, pg. 3338
HELUKABEL CZ S.R.O.—See HELUKABEL GmbH; *Int'l*, pg. 3338
HELUKABEL FRANCE SARL—See HELUKABEL GmbH; *Int'l*, pg. 3338
HELUKABEL INDIA PVT.LTD.—See HELUKABEL GmbH; *Int'l*, pg. 3338
HELUKABEL INT TRADING (SHANGHAI) CO., LTD.—See HELUKABEL GmbH; *Int'l*, pg. 3338
HELUKABEL ITALIA S.R.L.—See HELUKABEL GmbH; *Int'l*, pg. 3338
HELUKABEL KABLO SAN. VE TIC. LTD. STI.—See HELUKABEL GmbH; *Int'l*, pg. 3338
HELUKABEL KOREA CO., LTD.—See HELUKABEL GmbH; *Int'l*, pg. 3338
HELUKABEL MALAYSIA SDN BHD—See HELUKABEL GmbH; *Int'l*, pg. 3338

423610 — ELECTRICAL APPARATU...

HELUKABEL POLSKA SP.Z O.O.—See HELUKABEL GmbH; *Int'l*, pg. 3338
HELUKABEL RUSSIA—See HELUKABEL GmbH; *Int'l*, pg. 3338
HELUKABEL SINGAPORE PTE. LTD.—See HELUKABEL GmbH; *Int'l*, pg. 3338
HELUKABEL SOUTH AFRICA (PTY) LTD.—See HELUKABEL GmbH; *Int'l*, pg. 3338
HELUKABEL (THAILAND) CO. LTD.—See HELUKABEL GmbH; *Int'l*, pg. 3338
HELUKABEL (UK) LTD.—See HELUKABEL GmbH; *Int'l*, pg. 3338
HELUKABEL USA, INC.—See HELUKABEL GmbH; *Int'l*, pg. 3338
HELUSTA UAB—See HELUKABEL GmbH; *Int'l*, pg. 3338
HELVAR AB—See Helvar Merca Oy AB; *Int'l*, pg. 3339
HELVAR GMBH—See Helvar Merca Oy AB; *Int'l*, pg. 3339
HELVAR KFT.—See Helvar Merca Oy AB; *Int'l*, pg. 3339
HELVAR LIGHTING (SUZHOU) CO., LTD.—See Helvar Merca Oy AB; *Int'l*, pg. 3339
HELVAR LTD—See Helvar Merca Oy AB; *Int'l*, pg. 3339
HELVAR SRL—See Helvar Merca Oy AB; *Int'l*, pg. 3339
HENAN MACHINERY & ELECTRIC IMPORT & EXPORT CO., LTD.—See China Machinery Engineering Corporation; *Int'l*, pg. 1516
HERMOS GESELLSCHAFT FUR STEUER-, MESS- UND REGELTECHNIK MBH—See CEZ, a.s.; *Int'l*, pg. 1428
HERNING UNDERGROUND SUPPLY INC.—See WESCO International, Inc.; *U.S. Public*, pg. 2351
HEWTECH (BANGKOK) CO., LTD.—See Hirakawa Hewtech Corp.; *Int'l*, pg. 3403
HEWTECH HONG KONG LTD.—See Hirakawa Hewtech Corp.; *Int'l*, pg. 3403
HEWTECH SHANGHAI TRADING CO., LTD.—See Hirakawa Hewtech Corp.; *Int'l*, pg. 3403
HEXATRONIC NEW ZEALAND LTD.—See Hexatronic Group AB; *Int'l*, pg. 3371
H.H. BENFIELD ELECTRIC SUPPLY COMPANY INC.; *U.S. Private*, pg. 1826
HIBINO LIGHTING INC.—See Hibino Corporation; *Int'l*, pg. 3383
HILEC, LLC—See Delfingen Industry, S.A.; *Int'l*, pg. 2013
HI-LEX INDIA (P) LTD.—See Hi-Lex Corporation; *Int'l*, pg. 3380
HI-LINE UTILITY SUPPLY COMPANY—See WESCO International, Inc.; *U.S. Public*, pg. 2351
HILL COUNTRY ELECTRIC SUPPLY, L.P.—See WESCO International, Inc.; *U.S. Public*, pg. 2351
HIND ELECTRONIKA INDIA PRIVATE LIMITED—See HIOKI E.E. Corporation; *Int'l*, pg. 3401
HITACHI NICO TRANSMISSION CO., LTD.—See Hitachi, Ltd.; *Int'l*, pg. 3420
HITACHI POWER SYSTEMS AMERICA, LTD.—See Hitachi, Ltd.; *Int'l*, pg. 3414
HITACHI T&D SOLUTIONS, INC.—See Hitachi, Ltd.; *Int'l*, pg. 3422
THE HITE COMPANY; *U.S. Private*, pg. 4053
HITZINGER GMBH—See Dr. Aichhorn GmbH; *Int'l*, pg. 2190
THE H. LEFF ELECTRIC COMPANY; *U.S. Private*, pg. 4040
H.M. CRAGG CO.; *U.S. Private*, pg. 1835
HOBART FOSTER BELGIUM B.V.B.A.—See Illinois Tool Works Inc.; *U.S. Public*, pg. 1104
HOBART (JAPAN) K.K.—See Illinois Tool Works Inc.; *U.S. Public*, pg. 1103
HOBART KOREA CO. LTD.—See Illinois Tool Works Inc.; *U.S. Public*, pg. 1104
HOCHIKI AMERICA CORPORATION—See Hochiki Corporation; *Int'l*, pg. 3437
HOEI DENKI CO., LTD.—See Fuji Electric Co., Ltd.; *Int'l*, pg. 2812
HOI TUNG (SHENZHEN) CO., LTD.—See China Merchants Group Limited; *Int'l*, pg. 1521
HOKKAIDO FUJI ELECTRIC CO., LTD.—See Fuji Electric Co., Ltd.; *Int'l*, pg. 2812
HOKURIKU HITACHI CO., LTD.—See Hitachi, Ltd.; *Int'l*, pg. 3423
HOLDER ELECTRIC SUPPLY, INC.; *U.S. Private*, pg. 1962
HOLDING CO ADMIE (IPTO) SA; *Int'l*, pg. 3450
HOLT ELECTRIC INC.; *U.S. Private*, pg. 1968
HOMELAND SAFETY SYSTEMS INC.—See Alpine Investors; *U.S. Private*, pg. 201
HONEYWELL ELECTRONIC MATERIALS (THAILAND) CO., LTD.—See Honeywell International Inc.; *U.S. Public*, pg. 1051
HONEYWELL SECURITY & COMMUNICATIONS CANADA—See Honeywell International Inc.; *U.S. Public*, pg. 1050
HONGKONG ACE PILLAR CO., LTD—See ACE PILLAR Co., Ltd; *Int'l*, pg. 94
HONG KONG SHANGHAI ALLIANCE HOLDINGS LIMITED; *Int'l*, pg. 3467
HORIZON SOLUTIONS CORP.; *U.S. Private*, pg. 1982
HOUSTON ARMATURE WORKS INC.; *U.S. Private*, pg. 1993
HOUSTON WIRE & CABLE COMPANY—See Dot Family Holdings LLC; *U.S. Private*, pg. 1264
HST MATERIALS, INC.—See JBC Technologies, Inc.; *U.S. Private*, pg. 2193

HUBBELL CANADA, INC.—See Hubbell Incorporated; *U.S. Public*, pg. 1066
HUBBELL DISTRIBUTION, INC.—See Hubbell Incorporated; *U.S. Public*, pg. 1066
HUBBELL KOREA, LTD.—See Hubbell Incorporated; *U.S. Public*, pg. 1066
HUBBELL PICKERING LP—See Hubbell Incorporated; *U.S. Public*, pg. 1066
HUBBELL PRODUCTS MEXICO S. DE R.L. DE C.V.—See Hubbell Incorporated; *U.S. Public*, pg. 1067
HUBER+SUHNER AB—See Huber + Suhner AG; *Int'l*, pg. 3519
HUBER+SUHNER AMERICA LATINA LTDA—See Huber + Suhner AG; *Int'l*, pg. 3519
HUBER+SUHNER A/S—See Huber + Suhner AG; *Int'l*, pg. 3519
HUBER+SUHNER ELECTRONICS PRIVATE LIMITED—See Huber + Suhner AG; *Int'l*, pg. 3519
HUBER+SUHNER (MALAYSIA) SDN. BHD—See Huber + Suhner AG; *Int'l*, pg. 3519
HUGE DISTRIBUTION PROPRIETARY LIMITED—See Huge Group Limited; *Int'l*, pg. 3524
HUNT ELECTRIC SUPPLY COMPANY INC.; *U.S. Private*, pg. 2009
HUNZICKER BROTHERS INC.; *U.S. Private*, pg. 2011
HUPP ELECTRIC MOTORS INC.; *U.S. Private*, pg. 2011
HUTCHESON & COMPANY INC.; *U.S. Private*, pg. 2014
IBOCO; *Int'l*, pg. 3576
IDEAL INDUSTRIES INDIA PRIVATE LIMITED.—See IDEAL Industries Inc; *U.S. Private*, pg. 2036
IDEC AUSTRALIA PTY. LTD.—See IDEC Corporation; *Int'l*, pg. 3589
IDEC (BEIJING) CORPORATION—See IDEC Corporation; *Int'l*, pg. 3589
IDEC CANADA LTD.—See IDEC Corporation; *Int'l*, pg. 3589
IDEC CORPORATION—See IDEC Corporation; *Int'l*, pg. 3589
IDEC ENGINEERING SERVICE CORPORATION—See IDEC Corporation; *Int'l*, pg. 3590
IDEC IZUMI ASIA PTE. LTD.—See IDEC Corporation; *Int'l*, pg. 3590
IDEC IZUMI (H.K.) CO., LTD.—See IDEC Corporation; *Int'l*, pg. 3590
IDEC (SHANGHAI) CORPORATION—See IDEC Corporation; *Int'l*, pg. 3589
IDEC (SHENZHEN) CORPORATION—See IDEC Corporation; *Int'l*, pg. 3589
IDEC TAIWAN CORPORATION—See IDEC Corporation; *Int'l*, pg. 3590
IDLEWOOD ELECTRIC SUPPLY INC.; *U.S. Private*, pg. 2038
IEWC BRAZIL—See Industrial Electric Wire & Cable Inc.; *U.S. Private*, pg. 2066
IEWC GERMANY GMBH—See Industrial Electric Wire & Cable Inc.; *U.S. Private*, pg. 2066
IEWC MEXICO, S. DE R.L. DE C.V.—See Industrial Electric Wire & Cable Inc.; *U.S. Private*, pg. 2066
IEWC ONTARIO—See Industrial Electric Wire & Cable Inc.; *U.S. Private*, pg. 2066
IEWC SUZHOU—See Industrial Electric Wire & Cable Inc.; *U.S. Private*, pg. 2066
IEWC UK & IRELAND LTD.—See Industrial Electric Wire & Cable Inc.; *U.S. Private*, pg. 2066
I KNOW PARTS & WRECKING PTY LTD—See Bapcor Limited; *Int'l*, pg. 857
INCO SPOLKA Z O.O.—See Bundesdruckerei GmbH; *Int'l*, pg. 1216
INDEPENDENT ELECTRIC SUPPLY; *U.S. Private*, pg. 2059
INDUCTORS INC.; *U.S. Private*, pg. 2064
INDUSTRIAL AUTOMATION CONTROLS; *U.S. Private*, pg. 2064
INDUSTRIAL BATTERY & CHARGER, INC.; *U.S. Private*, pg. 2064
INDUSTRIAL ELECTRIC WIRE & CABLE INC.; *U.S. Private*, pg. 2066
INDUSTRIAL ELECTRIC WIRE & CABLE NORTHWEST—See Industrial Electric Wire & Cable Inc.; *U.S. Private*, pg. 2066
INLINE ELECTRIC SUPPLY CO., INC.; *U.S. Private*, pg. 2079
INLINE ELECTRIC SUPPLY CO., INC.—See Inline Electric Supply Co., Inc.; *U.S. Private*, pg. 2079
INLINE ELECTRIC SUPPLY CO., INC.—See Inline Electric Supply Co., Inc.; *U.S. Private*, pg. 2079
INTEGRATED TECHNICAL SYSTEMS, INC.; *U.S. Private*, pg. 2101
INTERACT HOLDINGS GROUP, INC.; *U.S. Public*, pg. 1140
INTERNATIONAL DEVELOPMENT, LLC; *U.S. Private*, pg. 2116
INTERNATIONAL ELECTRICAL SALES CORPORATION; *U.S. Private*, pg. 2116
INTERSTATE COMPANIES, INC.; *U.S. Private*, pg. 2124
INTERSTATE ELECTRICAL SUPPLY, INC.; *U.S. Private*, pg. 2124
IPAS AS—See Addtech AB; *Int'l*, pg. 133
ISOLENGE TERMO CONSTRUCOES LTDA—See Illinois Tool Works Inc.; *U.S. Public*, pg. 1108

ISOTEK S.R.L.—See Endress+Hauser (International) Holding AG; *Int'l*, pg. 2408
IS RAYFAST LIMITED—See Diploma PLC; *Int'l*, pg. 2128
ITT INDUSTRIES INC.—See ITT Inc.; *U.S. Public*, pg. 1178
ITW CP DISTRIBUTION CENTER HOLLAND BV—See Illinois Tool Works Inc.; *U.S. Public*, pg. 1105
IVIGIL UK LIMITED—See Ac&C International Co., Ltd.; *Int'l*, pg. 74
I WIRELESS; *U.S. Private*, pg. 2026
JAEGER POWAY AUTOMOTIVE SYSTEMS (SHENZHEN) LTD.—See AdCapital AG; *Int'l*, pg. 126
JAPAN TSS, INC.—See FTGroup Co Ltd; *Int'l*, pg. 2800
JAS OCEANIA PTY LTD—See Bapcor Limited; *Int'l*, pg. 857
J.D. MARTIN CO. INC.; *U.S. Private*, pg. 2161
JDW MANAGEMENT CO.; *U.S. Private*, pg. 2196
JESCO LIGHTING GROUP, LLC; *U.S. Private*, pg. 2203
JESCO WHOLESALE ELECTRICAL SUPPLIES INC.; *U.S. Private*, pg. 2203
JETTER TECHNOLOGIES PTE LTD.—See Bucher Industries AG; *Int'l*, pg. 1207
JEUMONT DRIVES SYSTEMS SAS—See Altawest Group; *Int'l*, pg. 388
JEUMONT ELECTRIC MIDDLE EAST—See Altawest Group; *Int'l*, pg. 388
J.H. LARSON ELECTRICAL COMPANY; *U.S. Private*, pg. 2166
J.H. LARSON ELECTRICAL COMPANY—See J.H. Larson Electrical Company; *U.S. Private*, pg. 2166
JME INCORPORATED; *U.S. Private*, pg. 2215
THE JOHN A. BECKER COMPANY; *U.S. Private*, pg. 4059
JOHNSON ELECTRIC SUPPLY CO.; *U.S. Private*, pg. 2227
JO-KELL INCORPORATED; *U.S. Private*, pg. 2217
JP RYAN ENTERPRISES INC.; *U.S. Private*, pg. 2239
JSB LIGHTING—See Hancock & Gore Ltd.; *Int'l*, pg. 3242
KABELMAT WICKELTECHNIK GMBH.—See HELUKABEL GmbH; *Int'l*, pg. 3339
KAMIC SECURITY AB—See Amplex AB; *Int'l*, pg. 434
KANSAS CITY ELECTRICAL SUPPLY CO.; *U.S. Private*, pg. 2260
KANTO HITACHI CO., LTD.—See Hitachi, Ltd.; *Int'l*, pg. 3423
KANTO SOGO SHIZAI CO., LTD.—See Fujii Sangyo Corporation; *Int'l*, pg. 2826
K/E ELECTRIC SUPPLY CORP.; *U.S. Private*, pg. 2252
KENDALL ELECTRIC INC.—See The Kendall Group, Inc.; *U.S. Private*, pg. 4064
KENDALL ELECTRIC—See The Kendall Group, Inc.; *U.S. Private*, pg. 4064
THE KENDALL GROUP, INC.; *U.S. Private*, pg. 4064
KENNEWICK INDUSTRIAL & ELECTRICAL SUPPLY INC.; *U.S. Private*, pg. 2286
KEY WEST LAMP COMPANY INC.; *U.S. Private*, pg. 2294
KILPATRICK SALES INC.; *U.S. Private*, pg. 2304
KIMBALL ELECTRONICS - MEXICO, S.A. DE C.V.—See Kimball Electronics, Inc.; *U.S. Public*, pg. 1228
KING WIRE INC.; *U.S. Private*, pg. 2310
KINSLEY GROUP, INC.; *U.S. Private*, pg. 2313
KIRBY RISK CORPORATION; *U.S. Private*, pg. 2314
KIT ZELLER, INC.—See Littlejohn & Co., LLC; *U.S. Private*, pg. 2471
KJC CORPORATION—See Career Technology (MFG.) Co., Ltd.; *Int'l*, pg. 1323
KJDE CORP.; *U.S. Private*, pg. 2317
K&M ELECTRIC SUPPLY INC.; *U.S. Private*, pg. 2250
KMM TELECOMMUNICATIONS; *U.S. Private*, pg. 2321
K&N ELECTRIC INC.; *U.S. Private*, pg. 2250
K&N ELECTRIC MOTORS INC.; *U.S. Private*, pg. 2250
KOURT SECURITY PARTNERS LLC; *U.S. Private*, pg. 2345
KOVALSKY-CARR ELECTRIC SUPPLY CO., INC.—See United Electric Supply Company, Inc.; *U.S. Private*, pg. 4291
KRIZ-DAVIS CO., INC.; *U.S. Private*, pg. 2352
KURZ ELECTRIC SOLUTIONS INC.; *U.S. Private*, pg. 2358
KYOKUYO ELECTRIC CO., LTD.—See Daeyang Electric Co., Ltd.; *Int'l*, pg. 1911
LAMPGALLERIAN I VAXJO AB—See BHG Group AB; *Int'l*, pg. 1015
LAPPIN ELECTRIC COMPANY—See Blackfriars Corp.; *U.S. Private*, pg. 574
LAREDO ALARM SYSTEMS INC.; *U.S. Private*, pg. 2392
LASER PHOTONICS CORPORATION; *U.S. Public*, pg. 1294
LAVANTURE PRODUCTS COMPANY INC.; *U.S. Private*, pg. 2400
LB ELECTRIC SUPPLY CO. INC.; *U.S. Private*, pg. 2403
LEA NETWORKS, LLC—See HF Company; *Int'l*, pg. 3374
LEBANON POWER & APPARATUS COMPANY, INC.—See Air Hydro Power Inc.; *U.S. Private*, pg. 139
LED SUPPLY CO.—See Applied UV, Inc.; *U.S. Public*, pg. 173
LEFF ELECTRIC - BEDFORD HEIGHTS—See The H. Leff Electric Company; *U.S. Private*, pg. 4040
LEFF ELECTRIC - ELYRIA—See The H. Leff Electric Company; *U.S. Private*, pg. 4040
LEFF ELECTRIC - MENTOR—See The H. Leff Electric Company; *U.S. Private*, pg. 4040
LEFF ELECTRIC - STRONGSVILLE—See The H. Leff Elec-

423610 — ELECTRICAL APPARATU...

tric Company; *U.S. Private*, pg. 4040
LEFF ELECTRIC - WARREN—See The H. Leff Electric Company; *U.S. Private*, pg. 4041
LEFF ELECTRIC - YOUNGSTOWN—See The H. Leff Electric Company; *U.S. Private*, pg. 4041
LEVITON MIDDLE EAST—See Leviton Manufacturing Company, Inc.; *U.S. Private*, pg. 2437
LEVITON NETWORK SOLUTIONS PVT. LTD.—See Leviton Manufacturing Company, Inc.; *U.S. Private*, pg. 2437
LEXEL BATTERY (JAPAN) CO., LTD.—See Coslight Technology International Group Limited; *Int'l*, pg. 1810
L & H SUPPLY CO. INC.—See Mainco Investments Inc.; *U.S. Private*, pg. 2552
LIBERTY AV SOLUTIONS—See WESCO International, Inc.; *U.S. Public*, pg. 2351
LIGHTHOUSE LIMITED—See Hadco Limited; *Int'l*, pg. 3205
LIGHTING & LAMP CORP.; *U.S. Private*, pg. 2453
LIGHTNING BUG LTD.; *U.S. Private*, pg. 2453
LIGON ELECTRIC SUPPLY COMPANY INC. OF NC—See Arthur's Enterprises, Inc.; *U.S. Private*, pg. 342
LINAIR TECHNOLOGIES (TAIWAN) CO., LTD—See Acesian Partners Limited; *Int'l*, pg. 102
LINCOLN BRICK AND STONE INC.; *U.S. Private*, pg. 2457
LINETEC SERVICES, LLC—See Southwest Gas Holdings, Inc.; *U.S. Public*, pg. 1913
LOAD CONTROLS SYSTEMS PTE LTD—See Affirma Capital Limited; *Int'l*, pg. 187
THE LOEB ELECTRIC COMPANY, INC.; *U.S. Private*, pg. 4071
LOS ANGELES RUBBER COMPANY; *U.S. Private*, pg. 2497
LOWE ELECTRIC SUPPLY COMPANY; *U.S. Private*, pg. 2504
LOYD'S ELECTRIC SUPPLY INC.; *U.S. Private*, pg. 2506
L&S ELECTRIC INC. - IRON MOUNTAIN—See L&S Electric Inc.; *U.S. Private*, pg. 2363
L&S ELECTRIC INC.; *U.S. Private*, pg. 2363
L&S ELECTRIC OF CANADA—See L&S Electric Inc.; *U.S. Private*, pg. 2363
LUMASENSE EQUIPMENT INDIA PVT. LTD. CO.—See Advanced Energy Industries, Inc.; *U.S. Public*, pg. 47
LUX CO., LTD.—See Helios Techno Holding Co., Ltd.; *Int'l*, pg. 3330
LUXDESIGN AS—See Amplex AB; *Int'l*, pg. 434
MACLEAN INTERNATIONAL GROUP LIMITED—See DNOW Inc.; *U.S. Private*, pg. 671
MADISON ELECTRIC COMPANY; *U.S. Private*, pg. 2542
MADISON ELECTRIC SERVICE—See Tri-State Armature & Electric Works, Inc.; *U.S. Private*, pg. 4223
MAG INSTRUMENT INC.; *U.S. Private*, pg. 2545
MAILIAO POWER CORP.—See Formosa Plastics Corporation; *Int'l*, pg. 2736
MAINTENANCE ENGINEERING; *U.S. Private*, pg. 2554
MAJOR SUPPLY INC.; *U.S. Private*, pg. 2555
MALTBY ELECTRIC SUPPLY COMPANY; *U.S. Private*, pg. 2558
MARAZZI DEUTSCHLAND G.M.B.H.—See Mohawk Industries, Inc.; *U.S. Public*, pg. 1457
MARAZZI DISTRIBUTION, INC.—See Mohawk Industries, Inc.; *U.S. Public*, pg. 1457
MARAZZI GROUP F.Z.E.—See Mohawk Industries, Inc.; *U.S. Public*, pg. 1457
MARAZZI GROUP TRADING (SHANGHAI) CO. LTD.—See Mohawk Industries, Inc.; *U.S. Public*, pg. 1457
MARCONE SUPPLY COMPANY; *U.S. Private*, pg. 2572
MARK C. POPE ASSOCIATES INC.; *U.S. Private*, pg. 2577
MARM LIGHTING LTD—See Dionic Industrial & Trading S.A; *Int'l*, pg. 2128
MARS ELECTRIC CO., INC.; *U.S. Private*, pg. 2588
MARUMBI TRANSMISSORA DE ENERGIA S.A.—See Companhia Paranaense de Energia; *Int'l*, pg. 1748
MATA DE SANTA GENEBRA TRANSMISSAO S.A.—See Companhia Paranaense de Energia; *Int'l*, pg. 1748
MAT'HYGIENE SAS—See Bunzl plc; *Int'l*, pg. 1219
MAURICE ELECTRICAL SUPPLY COMPANY; *U.S. Private*, pg. 2615
MAXETA AS—See Addtech AB; *Int'l*, pg. 134
MAXIM FIRE SYSTEMS LLC—See Highview Capital, LLC; *U.S. Private*, pg. 1942
MAYDENKI SDN. BHD.—See ACO Group Berhad; *Int'l*, pg. 107
MAYER ELECTRIC FINANCIAL CORPORATION—See Mayer Electric Supply Company Inc.; *U.S. Private*, pg. 2621
MAYER ELECTRIC SUPPLY COMPANY INC.; *U.S. Private*, pg. 2621
MAYER ELECTRIC SUPPLY COMPANY, INC.—See Mayer Electric Supply Company Inc.; *U.S. Private*, pg. 2621
MAYNARDS ELECTRIC SUPPLY, INC.; *U.S. Private*, pg. 2622
MCCOY FIRE & SAFETY, INC.—See Capital Alignment Partners, Inc.; *U.S. Private*, pg. 738
MCCOY FIRE & SAFETY, INC.—See Lynch Holdings, LLC; *U.S. Private*, pg. 2521
MCGEE CO.; *U.S. Private*, pg. 2634
MCNAUGHTON-MCKAY ELECTRIC COMPANY; *U.S. Private*, pg. 2643
MEASUREMENT TECHNOLOGY LIMITED—See Eaton Corporation plc; *Int'l*, pg. 2278
MEDIAMARKET S.P.A.CON SOCIO UNICO—See Ceconomy AG; *Int'l*, pg. 1385
MEDIA MARKT TV-HIFI-ELEKTRO GMBH FREIBURG—See Ceconomy AG; *Int'l*, pg. 1381
MEDLER ELECTRIC COMPANY INC.; *U.S. Private*, pg. 2657
MELETIO ELECTRICAL SUPPLY CO.; *U.S. Private*, pg. 2662
MERCEDES ELECTRIC SUPPLY, INC.; *U.S. Private*, pg. 2668
METROPOLITAN LIGHTING FIXTURE CO.—See Minka Lighting Inc.; *U.S. Private*, pg. 2742
METRO WIRE & CABLE CO; *U.S. Private*, pg. 2687
MG CHINA TRADING LTD.—See Mohawk Industries, Inc.; *U.S. Public*, pg. 1457
MGN & ASSOCIATES INC.; *U.S. Private*, pg. 2695
MICHIGAN CHANDELIER COMPANY, LLC—See Seneca Partners Inc.; *U.S. Private*, pg. 3606
MICHIGAN CHANDELIER COMPANY, LLC—See Uniprop, Inc.; *U.S. Private*, pg. 4286
MICHIGAN ELECTRIC SUPPLY CO.; *U.S. Private*, pg. 2700
MICRO CONTROL MANUFACTURING INC.—See Stack Electronics; *U.S. Private*, pg. 3774
MICROLEASE S.R.L.—See Platinum Equity, LLC; *U.S. Private*, pg. 3203
MICROSEC AB—See Amplex AB; *Int'l*, pg. 434
MID COAST ELECTRIC SUPPLY INC.; *U.S. Private*, pg. 2705
MID ISLAND ELECTRICAL SALES CORP.—See Turtle & Hughes, Inc.; *U.S. Private*, pg. 4262
MID STATE SUPPLY CO., LLC—See Crest Industries, LLC; *U.S. Private*, pg. 1096
MIDTOWN ELECTRIC SUPPLY CORP.; *U.S. Private*, pg. 2718
MIDWEST ALARM SERVICES INC.—See Per Mar Security Services; *U.S. Private*, pg. 3146
MIDWEST CONTROLS INC.; *U.S. Private*, pg. 2720
MID-WEST WHOLESALE LIGHTING CORP.; *U.S. Private*, pg. 2710
MIE HITACHI CO., LTD.—See Hitachi, Ltd.; *Int'l*, pg. 3423
MINARIK CORPORATION—See Littlejohn & Co., LLC; *U.S. Private*, pg. 2471
MINKA LIGHTING INC.; *U.S. Private*, pg. 2742
MK BATTERY ASIA PACIFIC PTY LIMITED—See East Penn Manufacturing Co., Inc.; *U.S. Private*, pg. 1317
MK BATTERY INTERNATIONAL LTD—See East Penn Manufacturing Co., Inc.; *U.S. Private*, pg. 1317
M&M LIGHTING LP; *U.S. Private*, pg. 2524
MONARCH ELECTRIC COMPANY INC.—See Blackfriars Corp.; *U.S. Private*, pg. 574
MORGAN FIRE & SAFETY INC—See Littlejohn & Co., LLC; *U.S. Private*, pg. 2472
MORSSMITT ASIA, LTD.—See Westinghouse Air Brake Technologies Corporation; *U.S. Public*, pg. 2358
MOTORI SOMMERSI RIAVVOLGIBILI S.R.L.—See Franklin Electric Co., Inc.; *U.S. Public*, pg. 878
MOTORS & DRIVES LLC—See Troy Industrial Solutions LLC; *U.S. Private*, pg. 4243
MOVOMECH PRONOMIC GMBH—See Amplex AB; *Int'l*, pg. 434
MSB GROUP, INC.—See Advanced Electronic Services, Inc.; *U.S. Private*, pg. 89
MTC TRANSFORMERS, INC.; *U.S. Private*, pg. 2809
MTL INSTRUMENTS BV—See Eaton Corporation plc; *Int'l*, pg. 2278
MTL INSTRUMENTS PVT. LIMITED—See Eaton Corporation plc; *Int'l*, pg. 2278
MURRAY FEISS IMPORT CORP; *U.S. Private*, pg. 2816
MWM ENERGY AUSTRALIA PTY LTD—See Caterpillar, Inc.; *U.S. Public*, pg. 452
NATIONAL ELECTRIC SUPPLY CO., INC.—See Crescent Electric Supply Company; *U.S. Private*, pg. 1093
NATIONAL GARDEN WHOLESALE; *U.S. Private*, pg. 2855
NATIONAL-STANDARD CO.—See The Heico Companies, L.L.C.; *U.S. Private*, pg. 4050
NATIONAL STANDARD—See The Heico Companies, L.L.C.; *U.S. Private*, pg. 4050
NATIONAL TRADING CO.—See Hayel Saeed Anam Group of Companies; *Int'l*, pg. 3291
NEDCO ELECTRICAL SUPPLY, INC.; *U.S. Private*, pg. 2879
NED LIQUIDATING INC.—See Graybar Electric Company, Inc.; *U.S. Private*, pg. 1760
NEEDHAM ELECTRIC SUPPLY - FITCHBURG—See WESCO International, Inc.; *U.S. Public*, pg. 2352
NEEDHAM ELECTRIC SUPPLY, LLC—See WESCO International, Inc.; *U.S. Public*, pg. 2351
NEHER ELECTRIC SUPPLY INC.; *U.S. Private*, pg. 2880
NELCO PRODUCTS INC.; *U.S. Private*, pg. 2882
NELSON ELECTRIC SUPPLY CO. INC.; *U.S. Private*, pg. 2883
NEWAVE ENERGY (JIANGMEN) LTD.—See ABB Ltd.; *Int'l*, pg. 54
NEWCO INC.; *U.S. Private*, pg. 2914
NEW ENERGY DISTRIBUTING, INC.—See Olympia Chimney Supply Holdings, LLC; *U.S. Private*, pg. 3012
NEWTECH SYSTEMS, INC.—See GTCR LLC; *U.S. Private*, pg. 1802
NIIGATA HITACHI CO., LTD.—See Hitachi, Ltd.; *Int'l*, pg. 3423
NIPPON ELEKTRISOLA LTD.—See Elektrisola Dr. Gerd Schildbach GmbH & Co. KG; *Int'l*, pg. 2356
NIPPON MIK CORP.—See Arlitech Electronic Corp.; *Int'l*, pg. 573
NIXON POWER SERVICES COMPANY—See Geneva Corporation; *U.S. Private*, pg. 1670
NOARK ELECTRIC (ROMANIA) S.R.O.—See Chint Group Corporation; *Int'l*, pg. 1571
NOARK ELECTRIC (SHANGHAI) CO., LTD.—See Chint Group Corporation; *Int'l*, pg. 1571
NOARK ELECTRIC (USA) INC.—See Chint Group Corporation; *Int'l*, pg. 1571
NOLAN POWER GROUP, LLC—See High Road Capital Partners, LLC; *U.S. Private*, pg. 1936
NORD DRIVESYSTEMS BRASIL LTDA.—See Getriebebau NORD GmbH & Co. KG; *Int'l*, pg. 2953
NORD DRIVESYSTEMS CO., LTD.—See Getriebebau NORD GmbH & Co. KG; *Int'l*, pg. 2953
NORD DRIVESYSTEMS GUC AKTARMA SISTEMLERI SAN. VE TIC. LTD. STI.—See Getriebebau NORD GmbH & Co. KG; *Int'l*, pg. 2953
NORD DRIVESYSTEMS PTP, LDA.—See Getriebebau NORD GmbH & Co. KG; *Int'l*, pg. 2953
NORD DRIVESYSTEMS PTY LTD—See Getriebebau NORD GmbH & Co. KG; *Int'l*, pg. 2953
NORD DRIVESYSTEMS PVT. LTD.—See Getriebebau NORD GmbH & Co. KG; *Int'l*, pg. 2953
NORD DRIVE SYSTEMS SA DE CV—See Getriebebau NORD GmbH & Co. KG; *Int'l*, pg. 2953
NORD DRIVSYSTEM AB—See Getriebebau NORD GmbH & Co. KG; *Int'l*, pg. 2953
NORD GEAR DANMARK A/S—See Getriebebau NORD GmbH & Co. KG; *Int'l*, pg. 2953
NORD GEAR NORGE A/S—See Getriebebau NORD GmbH & Co. KG; *Int'l*, pg. 2953
NORD GEAR OY—See Getriebebau NORD GmbH & Co. KG; *Int'l*, pg. 2953
NORD HAJTASTECHNIKA KFT.—See Getriebebau NORD GmbH & Co. KG; *Int'l*, pg. 2953
NORDIC ENERGY LINK AS—See Eesti Energia AS; *Int'l*, pg. 2318
NORD-MOTORIDUTTORI S.R.L.—See Getriebebau NORD GmbH & Co. KG; *Int'l*, pg. 2953
NORD MOTORREDUCTORES S.A.—See Getriebebau NORD GmbH & Co. KG; *Int'l*, pg. 2953
NORD NAPEDY SP. Z O.O.—See Getriebebau NORD GmbH & Co. KG; *Int'l*, pg. 2953
NORD POGONI D.O.O—See Getriebebau NORD GmbH & Co. KG; *Int'l*, pg. 2953
NORD-POHANECI TECHNIKA, S. R. O.—See Getriebebau NORD GmbH & Co. KG; *Int'l*, pg. 2953
NORD POHONY, S.R.O.—See Getriebebau NORD GmbH & Co. KG; *Int'l*, pg. 2953
NORD REDUCTEURS SARL—See Getriebebau NORD GmbH & Co. KG; *Int'l*, pg. 2953
NOREX AS—See Eaton Corporation plc; *Int'l*, pg. 2282
NORTH AMERICAN BREAKER CO., LLC—See The PNC Financial Services Group, Inc.; *U.S. Public*, pg. 2120
NORTHEAST POWER SYSTEMS, INC.—See American Superconductor Corporation; *U.S. Public*, pg. 110
NORTH ELECTRIC SUPPLY, INC.; *U.S. Private*, pg. 2945
NORTHERN VIDEO SYSTEMS, INC.—See WESCO International, Inc.; *U.S. Public*, pg. 2351
NORTHWEST ELECTRICAL SUPPLY CO. INC.; *U.S. Private*, pg. 2959
NOSTERS (PVT) LTD.—See BELIMO Holding AG; *Int'l*, pg. 965
NOTOCO INDUSTRIES LLC; *U.S. Private*, pg. 2965
THE NOVA GROUP; *U.S. Private*, pg. 4085
NOVA LIGHTING LTD—See Hadco Limited; *Int'l*, pg. 3205
NRG KENDALL, LLC—See NRG Energy, Inc.; *U.S. Public*, pg. 1550
NUANCE SYSTEMS, LLC—See Wynnchurch Capital, L.P.; *U.S. Private*, pg. 4577
NU-LITE ELECTRICAL WHOLESALERS, INC.—See Blackfriars Corp.; *U.S. Private*, pg. 575
OCEAN POWER TECHNOLOGIES, INC.; *U.S. Public*, pg. 1562
OCEAN TECHNICAL SYSTEMS LIMITED—See Eaton Corporation plc; *Int'l*, pg. 2282
OHM INTERNATIONAL CORPORATION; *U.S. Private*, pg. 3005
OMNI CABLE, LLC—See Dot Family Holdings LLC; *U.S. Private*, pg. 1264
OOO AUMAPRIVODSERVICE—See AUMA Riester GmbH & Co. KG; *Int'l*, pg. 705
OOO NORD PRIVODY—See Getriebebau NORD GmbH & Co. KG; *Int'l*, pg. 2953
OOO PRIWODY AUMA—See AUMA Riester GmbH & Co. KG; *Int'l*, pg. 705
OPTICAL SOLUTIONS AUSTRALIA (ACT) PTY. LIMITED—See Hexatronic Group AB; *Int'l*, pg. 3371
OPTICAL SOLUTIONS AUSTRALIA (QUEENSLAND) PTY LIMITED—See Hexatronic Group AB; *Int'l*, pg. 3371

423610 — ELECTRICAL APPARATU...   CORPORATE AFFILIATIONS

OPTICAL SOLUTIONS (SYDNEY CITY) PTY. LTD.—See Hexatronic Group AB; *Int'l*, pg. 3371
OPTICAL SOLUTIONS (VICTORIA) PTY. LTD.—See Hexatronic Group AB; *Int'l*, pg. 3371
OPTICAL SOLUTIONS (WA) PTY. LTD.—See Hexatronic Group AB; *Int'l*, pg. 3371
OPTICAL SWITCH CORPORATION; *U.S. Private*, pg. 3034
ORANGE POWER T & D EQUIPMENTS PVT. LTD.—See AT Capital Pte Limited; *Int'l*, pg. 664
O'ROURKE SALES COMPANY; *U.S. Private*, pg. 2980
ORYX TECHNOLOGY CORP.; *U.S. Public*, pg. 1619
OVERSEAS ENTERPRISES—See BELIMO Holding AG; *Int'l*, pg. 965
OWEN ELECTRIC SUPPLY INC.; *U.S. Private*, pg. 3054
PACER ELECTRONICS OF FLORIDA, INC.; *U.S. Private*, pg. 3064
PACIFIC PARTS & CONTROLS INC.; *U.S. Private*, pg. 3069
PACIFIC WESTERN AGENCIES, INC.; *U.S. Private*, pg. 3071
PACS INDUSTRIES INC.; *U.S. Private*, pg. 3073
PAIGE ELECTRIC COMPANY, LLP—See Audax Group, Limited Partnership; *U.S. Private*, pg. 390
PAK LIGHTING AUSTRALIA PTY LTD—See Guangdong PAK Corporation Co. Ltd.; *Int'l*, pg. 3158
PANSYSTEM S.R.L.—See Arrow Electronics, Inc.; *U.S. Public*, pg. 199
PARRISH-HARE ELECTRICAL SUPPLY CORPORATION; *U.S. Private*, pg. 3100
PASOTEC GMBH—See Allient Inc.; *U.S. Public*, pg. 80
PEEK PROMET D.O.O.—See Egeria Capital Management B.V.; *Int'l*, pg. 2323
PENLINK AB—See Addtech AB; *Int'l*, pg. 134
PERFORMANCE ELECTRICAL PRODUCTS,INC.—See Emek Elektrik Endustrisi A.S.; *Int'l*, pg. 2377
PERGO (EUROPE) AB—See Mohawk Industries, Inc.; *U.S. Public*, pg. 1458
PERTEN INSTRUMENTS ITALIA SRL—See Revvity, Inc.; *U.S. Public*, pg. 1795
PETERSON COMPANY INC.; *U.S. Private*, pg. 3160
PHUC LOC ENGINEERING & TRADING CO., LTD.—See CHINO Corporation; *Int'l*, pg. 1571
PHUC SON TECHNOLOGY CO., LTD.—See Adtec Plasma Technology Co., Ltd.; *Int'l*, pg. 154
PIONEER CRITICAL POWER INC.—See CleanSpark, Inc.; *U.S. Public*, pg. 511
PIONEER CUSTOM ELECTRICAL PRODUCTS CORP.—See Guggenheim Partners, LLC; *U.S. Private*, pg. 1812
PIONEER PUMP HOLDINGS PTY.—See Franklin Electric Co., Inc.; *U.S. Public*, pg. 878
PIONEER PUMP SOLUTIONS LTD.—See Franklin Electric Co., Inc.; *U.S. Public*, pg. 879
PIONEER SALES GROUP, INC.; *U.S. Private*, pg. 3188
PLATI ELETTROFORNITURE S.P.A.—See Accursia Capital GmbH; *Int'l*, pg. 94
PLEA SDN. BHD.—See FoundPac Group Berhad; *Int'l*, pg. 2754
PLP ARGENTINA SRL—See Preformed Line Products Company; *U.S. Public*, pg. 1714
PLP RUSSIA LTD.—See Preformed Line Products Company; *U.S. Public*, pg. 1714
POINT COMM, INC.—See RCM Technologies, Inc.; *U.S. Public*, pg. 1767
POWELL INDUSTRIES ASIA, PTE. LTD.—See Powell Industries, Inc.; *U.S. Public*, pg. 1705
POWER EQUIPMENT DIRECT INC.—See Ferguson plc; *Int'l*, pg. 2638
POWER-FLO TECHNOLOGIES INC.; *U.S. Private*, pg. 3239
POWER LLC; *U.S. Private*, pg. 3238
POWERMEC AB—See Addtech AB; *Int'l*, pg. 134
POWERMEC APS—See Addtech AB; *Int'l*, pg. 134
POWERMEC AS—See Addtech AB; *Int'l*, pg. 134
POWERNOR AS—See Addtech AB; *Int'l*, pg. 134
POWER PRODUCT SERVICES, INC.—See High Road Capital Partners, LLC; *U.S. Private*, pg. 1936
POWER PROTECTION, UNLIMITED—See Incline MGMT Corp.; *U.S. Private*, pg. 2054
POWER-SONIC CORPORATION; *U.S. Private*, pg. 3239
POWER-SONIC EUROPE LTD.—See Power-Sonic Corporation; *U.S. Private*, pg. 3239
POWER TECHNOLOGIES (PROPRIETARY) LIMITED—See Altron Limited; *Int'l*, pg. 399
POWER & TELEPHONE SUPPLY COMPANY; *U.S. Private*, pg. 3237
POWER UTILITY PRODUCTS COMPANY—See WJ Partners, LLC; *U.S. Private*, pg. 4551
PRECISION MULTIPLE CONTROLS INC; *U.S. Private*, pg. 3245
PREFORMED LINE PRODUCTS (FRANCE) SAS—See Preformed Line Products Company; *U.S. Public*, pg. 1714
PREMIER SILICA LLC—See Pioneer Natural Resources Company; *U.S. Public*, pg. 1693
PREMIUM FLOORS AUSTRALIA PTY LIMITED—See Mohawk Industries, Inc.; *U.S. Public*, pg. 1458
PRG EML PRODUCTIONS—See The Jordan Company, L.P.; *U.S. Private*, pg. 4061

PRG NOCTURNE—See The Jordan Company, L.P.; *U.S. Private*, pg. 4061
PRIMARY SUPPLY INC.; *U.S. Private*, pg. 3261
PRIME/HOME IMPRESSIONS, LLC—See Craftmade International, *U.S. Private*, pg. 1082
PRIORITY WIRE & CABLE INC.; *U.S. Private*, pg. 3267
PROCTER & GAMBLE DISTRIBUTION S.R.L.—See The Procter & Gamble Company; *U.S. Public*, pg. 2121
PROFESSIONAL ELECTRIC PRODUCTS COMPANY, INC.; *U.S. Private*, pg. 3275
PROGRESSIVE LIGHTING INC.; *U.S. Private*, pg. 3279
PROHEAT, INC.—See Gryphon Investors, LLC; *U.S. Private*, pg. 1799
PROJECT LIGHTING CO. INC.; *U.S. Private*, pg. 3280
PROTEGIS, LLC—See Align Capital Partners, LLC; *U.S. Private*, pg. 167
PT ANIXTER INDONESIA—See WESCO International, Inc.; *U.S. Public*, pg. 2351
PT.COMINIX INDONESIA—See Cominix Co., Ltd.; *Int'l*, pg. 1714
PT HELUKABEL INDONESIA—See HELUKABEL GmbH; *Int'l*, pg. 3339
PURKEY'S FLEET, ELECTRIC, INC.—See Windjammer Capital Investors, LLC; *U.S. Private*, pg. 4538
QUICK CONNECTORS, INC.—See Intervale Capital, LLC; *U.S. Private*, pg. 2127
QX LTD.—See Aecon Group Inc.; *Int'l*, pg. 172
RAMCO INNOVATIONS, INC.—See Sukup Manufacturing Co; *U.S. Private*, pg. 3850
RANTRONICS INTERNATIONAL LTD.; *U.S. Private*, pg. 3355
RATIONAL MOTION GMBH—See Dana Incorporated; *U.S. Public*, pg. 623
RAYBRO ELECTRIC SUPPLIES—See Blackfriars Corp.; *U.S. Private*, pg. 574
RAYMOND DE STEIGER INC.; *U.S. Private*, pg. 3359
RAYOVAC EUROPE LIMITED—See Spectrum Brands Holdings, Inc.; *U.S. Public*, pg. 1915
RECREATIONAL SPORTS & IMPORTS INC.; *U.S. Private*, pg. 3372
RED HAWK FIRE & SECURITY (NY) LLC—See GTCR LLC; *U.S. Private*, pg. 1802
REED CITY POWER LINE SUPPLY CO., INC.; *U.S. Private*, pg. 3382
REGAL BELOIT FZE—See Regal Rexnord Corporation; *U.S. Public*, pg. 1773
REGAL POWER TRANSMISSION SOLUTIONS—See Regal Rexnord Corporation; *U.S. Public*, pg. 1773
REGENCY ENTERPRISES INC.; *U.S. Private*, pg. 3386
RELECTRIC, INC; *U.S. Private*, pg. 3393
RELEVANT INDUSTRIAL LLC; *U.S. Private*, pg. 3393
RELIABLE FIRE EQUIPMENT CO.; *U.S. Private*, pg. 3394
RESIDEO TECHNOLOGIES, INC.; *U.S. Public*, pg. 1789
REVCO ELECTRICAL SUPPLY, INC.; *U.S. Private*, pg. 3413
REVERE ELECTRIC SUPPLY COMPANY; *U.S. Private*, pg. 3414
THE REYNOLDS COMPANY—See McNaughton-McKay Electric Company; *U.S. Private*, pg. 2643
RG ENGINEERING INC.; *U.S. Private*, pg. 3420
RICHARDS ELECTRIC MOTOR CO.; *U.S. Private*, pg. 3428
RICHARDS ELECTRIC SUPPLY CO., INC.; *U.S. Private*, pg. 3429
RICHARDSON RFPD JAPAN KK—See Arrow Electronics, Inc.; *U.S. Public*, pg. 200
RICHARDSON RFPD KOREA LTD.—See Arrow Electronics, Inc.; *U.S. Public*, pg. 200
RICHARDSON RFPD TAIWAN—See Arrow Electronics, Inc.; *U.S. Public*, pg. 200
RIFFLE & ASSOCIATES INC.; *U.S. Private*, pg. 3435
RITE PRODUCTS INCORPORATED—See BELIMO Holding AG; *Int'l*, pg. 965
ROBCO, INC.; *U.S. Private*, pg. 3457
ROBINSON ELECTRIC SUPPLY CO.; *U.S. Private*, pg. 3461
ROBOTEC SYSTEMS GMBH—See HELUKABEL GmbH; *Int'l*, pg. 3339
ROCKINGHAM ELECTRICAL SUPPLY COMPANY, INC.; *U.S. Private*, pg. 3466
RS2 TECHNOLOGIES, LLC—See ACRE, LLC; *U.S. Private*, pg. 65
RSI INC.; *U.S. Private*, pg. 3497
RUHLAND-KALLENBORN & CO. GMBH—See Hornbach Holding AG & Co. KGaA; *Int'l*, pg. 3482
RUMSEY ELECTRIC COMPANY; *U.S. Private*, pg. 3504
RURAL ELECTRIC SUPPLY COOPERATIVE INC.; *U.S. Private*, pg. 3504
RUTAB AS—See Addtech AB; *Int'l*, pg. 135
SAFEPAK CORPORATION—See Custom Vault Corp; *U.S. Private*, pg. 1130
SALUS CONTROLS GMBH—See Computime Group Limited; *Int'l*, pg. 1760
SALUS CONTROLS PLC—See Computime Group Limited; *Int'l*, pg. 1760
SARL CONEC FRANCE—See Amphenol Corporation; *U.S. Public*, pg. 132
SATCO PRODUCTS INC.; *U.S. Private*, pg. 3552

SATCO PRODUCTS INC.—See Satco Products Inc.; *U.S. Private*, pg. 3553
SCAN-AM MARINE SERVICES, INC.—See GenNx360 Capital Partners, L.P.; *U.S. Private*, pg. 1672
SCANDITRON SWEDEN STENCILS—See Amplex AB; *Int'l*, pg. 434
SCHAEDLER/YESCO DISTRIBUTION, INC.; *U.S. Private*, pg. 3563
SCHM SERVICE CO., LTD.—See Hitachi, Ltd.; *Int'l*, pg. 3424
SCHWING ELECTRICAL SUPPLY CORP.; *U.S. Private*, pg. 3573
S.C.NORD DRIVESYSTEMS S.R.L.—See Getriebebau NORD GmbH & Co. KG; *Int'l*, pg. 2953
SCOTT ELECTRIC COMPANY; *U.S. Private*, pg. 3576
S&D SERVICE & DISTRIBUTION GMBH—See McNaughton-McKay Electric Company; *U.S. Private*, pg. 2643
SEA WIRE & CABLE INC.; *U.S. Private*, pg. 3583
SECURITY & ACCESS SYSTEMS—See Financial Investments Corporation; *U.S. Private*, pg. 1507
SECURITY FIRST ALARM KING—See Kimberlite Corp.; *U.S. Private*, pg. 2305
SEFELEC GMBH—See Eaton Corporation plc; *Int'l*, pg. 2282
SELECTA PRODUCTS INC.; *U.S. Private*, pg. 3601
SEMI-GENERAL, INC.; *U.S. Private*, pg. 3603
SENCOMMUNICATIONS, INC.; *U.S. Private*, pg. 3605
SENTRY WATCH INC.—See Pye-Barker Fire & Safety, LLC; *U.S. Private*, pg. 3309
SEQUEL ELECTRICAL SUPPLY, LLC—See Border States Industries, Inc.; *U.S. Private*, pg. 618
SHANGHAI PHILLIPS INDUSTRIES VEHICLE COMPONENTS MANUFACTURING LTD.—See Phillips Industries; *U.S. Private*, pg. 3171
SHANOR ELECTRIC SUPPLY INC.; *U.S. Private*, pg. 3625
SHEALY ELECTRICAL WHOLESALERS, INC.—See Border States Industries, Inc.; *U.S. Private*, pg. 618
SHEPHERD ELECTRIC SUPPLY COMPANY—See Graybar Electric Company, Inc.; *U.S. Private*, pg. 1760
SHIJIA U.S.—See Henan Shijia Photons Technology Co., Ltd.; *Int'l*, pg. 3343
SHIKOKU HITACHI CO., LTD.—See Hitachi, Ltd.; *Int'l*, pg. 3424
SHINGLE & GIBB AUTOMATION LLC—See Graybar Electric Company, Inc.; *U.S. Private*, pg. 1760
SHOOK & FLETCHER INSULATION CO., INC. - ATLANTA DIVISION—See Shook & Fletcher Insulation Co., Inc.; *U.S. Private*, pg. 3639
SHOOK & FLETCHER INSULATION CO., INC. - BIRMINGHAM DIVISION—See Shook & Fletcher Insulation Co., Inc.; *U.S. Private*, pg. 3639
SHOOK & FLETCHER INSULATION CO., INC. - CHATTANOOGA DIVISION—See Shook & Fletcher Insulation Co., Inc.; *U.S. Private*, pg. 3639
SHOOK & FLETCHER INSULATION CO., INC. - DECATUR DIVISION—See Shook & Fletcher Insulation Co., Inc.; *U.S. Private*, pg. 3640
SHOOK & FLETCHER INSULATION CO., INC. - KNOXVILLE DIVISION—See Shook & Fletcher Insulation Co., Inc.; *U.S. Private*, pg. 3640
SHOOK & FLETCHER INSULATION CO., INC. - MOBILE DIVISION—See Shook & Fletcher Insulation Co., Inc.; *U.S. Private*, pg. 3640
SIGMA ELECTRIC MANUFACTURING CORPORATION—See Argand Partners, LP; *U.S. Private*, pg. 319
SIGNAL CAPITAL CORPORATION—See WESCO International, Inc.; *U.S. Public*, pg. 2351
SIGNATURE CONTROL SYSTEMS, LLC—See TIBA Parking LLC; *U.S. Private*, pg. 4166
SIMONSVOSS TECHNOLOGIES AB—See Allegion Public Limited Company; *Int'l*, pg. 335
SIMONSVOSS TECHNOLOGIES FZE—See Allegion Public Limited Company; *Int'l*, pg. 335
SIMONSVOSS TECHNOLOGIES LIMITED—See Allegion Public Limited Company; *Int'l*, pg. 335
SINGAPORE RESOURCES, INC.; *U.S. Private*, pg. 3669
SINIT, A.S.—See CEZ, a.s.; *Int'l*, pg. 1428
SLP UK LTD.—See Koller Enterprises, Inc.; *U.S. Private*, pg. 2341
SMC ELECTRIC SUPPLY—See Southern Materials Company; *U.S. Private*, pg. 3733
SOLAR FRONTIER K.K.—See Idemitsu Kosan Co., Ltd.; *Int'l*, pg. 3592
SOMMER GMBH—See Diploma PLC; *Int'l*, pg. 2129
SONCA PRODUCTS LIMITED—See Energizer Holdings, Inc.; *U.S. Public*, pg. 761
SOUTH ATLANTIC TRANSPORTATION CORPORATION; *U.S. Private*, pg. 3719
SOUTH DADE ELECTRICAL SUPPLY; *U.S. Private*, pg. 3722
SOUTHEASTERN ELECTRICAL DISTRIBUTORS INC.; *U.S. Private*, pg. 3727
SOUTHEASTERN POLE SALES, INC.; *U.S. Private*, pg. 3728
SOUTHERN CONTROLS, INC.; *U.S. Private*, pg. 3730

N.A.I.C.S. INDEX

423610 — ELECTRICAL APPARATU...

SOUTHLAND LIGHTING SALES, INC.; *U.S. Private*, pg. 3737
SPATRONIC GMBH—See Harvia Oyj; *Int'l*, pg. 3281
SPECIALTY LIGHTING INC.; *U.S. Private*, pg. 3750
SPECTRUM BRANDS HRVATSKA D.O.O.—See Spectrum Brands Holdings, Inc.; *U.S. Public*, pg. 1916
SPRINGFIELD ELECTRIC SUPPLY COMPANY; *U.S. Private*, pg. 3764
SRC ELECTRICAL LLC—See SRC Holdings Corporation; *U.S. Private*, pg. 3767
STANDARD ELECTRIC COMPANY; *U.S. Private*, pg. 3778
STANDARD ELECTRIC CO.—See Blackfriars Corp.; *U.S. Private*, pg. 574
STANDARD ELECTRIC CO.—See Blackfriars Corp.; *U.S. Private*, pg. 574
STANDARD ELECTRIC CO.—See Blackfriars Corp.; *U.S. Private*, pg. 574
STANDARD ELECTRIC CO.—See Blackfriars Corp.; *U.S. Private*, pg. 574
STANDARD ELECTRIC CO.—See Blackfriars Corp.; *U.S. Private*, pg. 574
STANDARD ELECTRIC CO.—See Blackfriars Corp.; *U.S. Private*, pg. 574
STANDARD ELECTRIC CO.—See Blackfriars Corp.; *U.S. Private*, pg. 575
STANDARD ELECTRIC CO.—See Blackfriars Corp.; *U.S. Private*, pg. 575
STANDARD ELECTRIC CO.—See Blackfriars Corp.; *U.S. Private*, pg. 575
STANDARD ELECTRIC CO.—See Blackfriars Corp.; *U.S. Private*, pg. 575
STANDARD ELECTRIC SUPPLY CO. INC.; *U.S. Private*, pg. 3778
STANDARD ELECTRIC SUPPLY CO.—See Blackfriars Corp.; *U.S. Private*, pg. 574
STANDARD ELECTRIC SUPPLY CO.—See Standard Electric Supply Co. Inc.; *U.S. Private*, pg. 3778
STANION WHOLESALE ELECTRIC CO. INC.; *U.S. Private*, pg. 3782
STAR ASSET SECURITY, LLC—See Wind Point Advisors LLC; *U.S. Private*, pg. 4535
STATE ELECTRIC SUPPLY COMPANY—See Arthur's Enterprises, Inc.; *U.S. Private*, pg. 342
STATE ELECTRIC SUPPLY COMPANY—See Arthur's Enterprises, Inc.; *U.S. Private*, pg. 342
STATE ELECTRIC SUPPLY CO.—See Arthur's Enterprises, Inc.; *U.S. Private*, pg. 342
STATE ELECTRIC SUPPLY CO.—See Arthur's Enterprises, Inc.; *U.S. Private*, pg. 342
STAUBO ELEKTRO MASKIN AS—See Addtech AB; *Int'l*, pg. 135
STEINER ELECTRIC COMPANY - CHICAGO—See Steiner Electric Company; *U.S. Private*, pg. 3798
STEINER ELECTRIC COMPANY; *U.S. Private*, pg. 3798
S-TEK INC.; *U.S. Private*, pg. 3514
STE OBCHODNI SLUZBY SPOL, S R.O.—See CEZ, a.s.; *Int'l*, pg. 1428
ST. LOUIS-METRO ELECTRICAL SUPPLY, INC.—See Graybar Electric Company, Inc.; *U.S. Private*, pg. 1760
ST. LOUIS METRO ELECTRIC SUPPLY; *U.S. Private*, pg. 3772
STOCK FAIRFIELD CORPORATION—See Blackstone Inc.; *U.S. Public*, pg. 360
STOKES ELECTRIC COMPANY; *U.S. Private*, pg. 3816
STONE EAGLE ELECTRICAL SUPPLY LIMITED PARTNERSHIP—See WESCO International, Inc.; *U.S. Public*, pg. 2351
STONEWAY ELECTRIC SUPPLY INC.—See Crescent Electric Supply Company; *U.S. Private*, pg. 1093
STUSSER ELECTRIC COMPANY—See Blackfriars Corp.; *U.S. Private*, pg. 574
SUMMIT ELECTRIC SUPPLY COMPANY; *U.S. Private*, pg. 3854
SUN SUPPLY INC.; *U.S. Private*, pg. 3864
SUPERIOR SIGNALS, INC.—See Group Thermote & Vanhalst; *Int'l*, pg. 3090
SURE POWER, INC.—See Eaton Corporation plc; *Int'l*, pg. 2282
SWIFT ELECTRICAL SUPPLY CO.; *U.S. Private*, pg. 3893
SWITCHES PLUS, INC.—See EAO AG; *Int'l*, pg. 2267
SYSTEM SENSOR CANADA—See Honeywell International Inc.; *U.S. Public*, pg. 1049
SYSTEM SENSOR EUROPE—See Honeywell International Inc.; *U.S. Public*, pg. 1049
TACOMA ELECTRIC SUPPLY INC.—See Winsupply, Inc.; *U.S. Private*, pg. 4545
TAEKYONG ELECTRONICS CORP.—See Arlitech Electronic Corp.; *Int'l*, pg. 573
TAIWAN HEWTECH CORP.—See Hirakawa Hewtech Corp.; *Int'l*, pg. 3403
TAW MACON SERVICE CTR—See Tampa Armature Works Inc.; *U.S. Private*, pg. 3928
T&B RETAIL CONSUMER PRODUCTS—See ABB Ltd.; *Int'l*, pg. 52
TCF, INC.—See Taylor Power Systems, Inc.; *U.S. Private*, pg. 3940
T C INTERNATIONAL TRADING CO., LTD—See CNlight Co., Ltd.; *Int'l*, pg. 1677
TDI POWER SYSTEMS - COMMERCIAL PRODUCTS DIVISION—See TDI Power Systems; *U.S. Private*, pg. 3944
TDI POWER SYSTEMS - DYNALOAD DIVISION—See TDI Power Systems; *U.S. Private*, pg. 3944
TECH LIGHTING L.L.C.—See AEA Investors LP; *U.S. Private*, pg. 114
TECHNIBUS, INC.—See IES Holdings, Inc.; *U.S. Public*, pg. 1094
TECHNOLOGIA MEXICANA S.A. DE C.V.—See CTS Corporation; *U.S. Public*, pg. 603
TECHNOLOGY RESEARCH CORPORATION—See Southwire Company, LLC; *U.S. Public*, pg. 3742
TECNODIESEL S.A.S.—See Aiphone Co., Ltd.; *Int'l*, pg. 235
TELEDYNE VARISYSTEMS, INC.—See Teledyne Technologies Incorporated; *U.S. Public*, pg. 1995
TEXAS LIGHTING SALES INCORPORATED; *U.S. Private*, pg. 3976
TEZAO S.R.O.—See Aiphone Co., Ltd.; *Int'l*, pg. 235
THEA & SCHOEN, INC.; *U.S. Private*, pg. 4140
THERMON HEAT TRACING SERVICES-I, INC.—See Thermon Group Holdings, Inc.; *U.S. Public*, pg. 2155
THERMON LATINOAMERICANA, S. DE R.L. DE C.V.—See Thermon Group Holdings, Inc.; *U.S. Public*, pg. 2155
THOMAS SUPPLY COMPANY INC.; *U.S. Private*, pg. 4158
THORN AUSTRALIA PTY LTD—See Credit Corp Group Limited; *Int'l*, pg. 1835
THORPE ELECTRIC SUPPLY INC.; *U.S. Private*, pg. 4163
TIANJIN-VEGA CO. LTD.—See Grieshaber Holding GmbH; *Int'l*, pg. 3083
TITAN ENERGY SYSTEMS INC.—See PIONEER POWER SOLUTIONS, INC.; *U.S. Public*, pg. 1693
TOLEDO MOLDING & DIE, LLC—See Grammer AG; *Int'l*, pg. 3053
TONER CABLE EQUIPMENT INC.; *U.S. Private*, pg. 4184
TOPAZ LIGHTING CORP; *U.S. Private*, pg. 4187
TORK PRODUCTS, INC.; *U.S. Private*, pg. 4189
TOTAL MACHINE SOLUTIONS, INC.—See Applied Industrial Technologies, Inc.; *U.S. Public*, pg. 171
TOTAL POWERGEN SOLUTIONS—See Audax Group, Limited Partnership; *U.S. Private*, pg. 390
TOTAL POWER LTD.—See Audax Group, Limited Partnership; *U.S. Private*, pg. 390
TPC HOLDINGS, LLC—See Audax Group, Limited Partnership; *U.S. Private*, pg. 390
TPC WIRE & CABLE CORP.—See Audax Group, Limited Partnership; *U.S. Private*, pg. 390
TRADE SOURCE INTERNATIONAL, INC.—See Craftmade International, Inc.; *U.S. Private*, pg. 1082
TRANSMISSION AUSTRALIA PTY., LTD.—See Regal Rexnord Corporation; *U.S. Public*, pg. 1773
T&R ELECTRIC SUPPLY COMPANY, INC.; *U.S. Private*, pg. 3910
TRIARC LTD; *U.S. Private*, pg. 4227
TRI CITY SUPPLY, INC.—See Freeman Spogli & Co. Incorporated; *U.S. Private*, pg. 1606
TRI-ED DISTRIBUTION INC.—See WESCO International, Inc.; *U.S. Public*, pg. 2351
TRI-ED PUERTO RICO LTD. INC.—See WESCO International, Inc.; *U.S. Public*, pg. 2351
TRINERGI AB—See Addtech AB; *Int'l*, pg. 135
TRIPLE H SPECIALTY CO. INC.; *U.S. Private*, pg. 4237
TRI-POWER MPT, INC.—See Genstar Capital, LLC; *U.S. Private*, pg. 1678
TRISEN ASIA CONTROL PTE. LIMITED—See China Automation Group Limited; *Int'l*, pg. 1484
TRI-STATE ARMATURE & ELECTRIC WORKS, INC.; *U.S. Private*, pg. 4223
TRI STATE SUPPLY COMPANY, INC.; *U.S. Private*, pg. 4221
TRI-STATE UTILITY PRODUCTS INC.—See American Water Works Company, Inc.; *U.S. Public*, pg. 112
T STATS SUPPLY INC.; *U.S. Private*, pg. 3909
TUFVASSON TESCH AB—See Addtech AB; *Int'l*, pg. 135
TULSAT CORP.—See ADDvantage Technologies Group, Inc.; *U.S. Public*, pg. 40
TURTLE & HUGHES, INC.; *U.S. Private*, pg. 4262
ULSTER ELECTRIC SUPPLY CO. INC.; *U.S. Private*, pg. 4277
UNICABLE INCORPORATED; *U.S. Private*, pg. 4281
UNIFIED POWER, LLC—See Incline MGMT Corp.; *U.S. Private*, pg. 2054
UNILIN NORTH AMERICA, LLC—See Mohawk Industries, Inc.; *U.S. Public*, pg. 1458
UNILIN NORWAY AS—See Mohawk Industries, Inc.; *U.S. Public*, pg. 1458
UNILIN POLAND SP.Z O.O.—See Mohawk Industries, Inc.; *U.S. Public*, pg. 1458
UNITED ELECTRIC SUPPLY COMPANY, INC.; *U.S. Private*, pg. 4291
UNITED LIGHTING AND SUPPLY CO.; *U.S. Private*, pg. 4293
UNITED UTILITY SUPPLY COOPERATIVE INC.; *U.S. Private*, pg. 4301
UPCHURCH ELECTRIC SUPPLY CO.; *U.S. Private*, pg. 4311
USA TECHNOLOGY SERVICES, LLC; *U.S. Private*, pg. 4321
U.S. ELECTRICAL SERVICES, INC.—See Blackfriars Corp.; *U.S. Private*, pg. 574
UTILITY TRAILER SALES COMPANY ARIZONA; *U.S. Private*, pg. 4326
VADTEK LLC.; *U.S. Private*, pg. 4329
VALIDUS DC SYSTEMS INC.—See ABB Ltd.; *Int'l*, pg. 52
VALLEN DISTRIBUTION INC.—See Nautic Partners, LLC; *U.S. Private*, pg. 2872
VALLEY ELECTRIC SUPPLY CORP.; *U.S. Private*, pg. 4333
VALLEY LIGHTING, LLC; *U.S. Private*, pg. 4334
VALLEY TRANSFORMER CO—See Trilantic Capital Management L.P.; *U.S. Private*, pg. 4231
VAN METER INC.; *U.S. Private*, pg. 4340
VEGA AUSTRALIA PTY LTD—See Grieshaber Holding GmbH; *Int'l*, pg. 3083
VEGA INDIA LEVEL & PRESSURE MEASUREMENT PVT. LTD.—See Grieshaber Holding GmbH; *Int'l*, pg. 3083
VEGA INSTRUMENTOS S.A.—See Grieshaber Holding GmbH; *Int'l*, pg. 3083
VEGA INSTRUMENTS CO., LTD.—See Grieshaber Holding GmbH; *Int'l*, pg. 3083
VEGA INSTRUMENTS LTD.—See Grieshaber Holding GmbH; *Int'l*, pg. 3083
VEGA INSTRUMENTS SA PTY LTD—See Grieshaber Holding GmbH; *Int'l*, pg. 3083
VEGA INSTRUMENTS (SEA) PTE LTD.—See Grieshaber Holding GmbH; *Int'l*, pg. 3083
VEGA ITALIA S.R.L.—See Grieshaber Holding GmbH; *Int'l*, pg. 3083
VEGA MIDDLE EAST LLC—See Grieshaber Holding GmbH; *Int'l*, pg. 3083
VEGA N.V/S.A.—See Grieshaber Holding GmbH; *Int'l*, pg. 3083
VEGAS ELECTRIC SUPPLY—See Blackfriars Corp.; *U.S. Private*, pg. 575
VEGA SEVIYE VE BASINC OLCUM CIHAZLARI TICARET LTD. STI.—See Grieshaber Holding GmbH; *Int'l*, pg. 3083
VEGA TECHNIQUE S.A.S.—See Grieshaber Holding GmbH; *Int'l*, pg. 3083
VIBRALIGN INC.—See ACOEM Group; *Int'l*, pg. 107
VIBRATION CONTROL LTD.—See Embelton Limited; *Int'l*, pg. 2375
VICKERS SYSTEMS LTD.—See Eaton Corporation plc; *Int'l*, pg. 2281
VIKING ACQUISITIONS, S. DE RL DE CV—See Spectrum Brands Holdings, Inc.; *U.S. Public*, pg. 1917
VILLA LIGHTING SUPPLY CO. INC.; *U.S. Private*, pg. 4383
VINCENT LIGHTING SYSTEMS CO.; *U.S. Private*, pg. 4385
VOLLAND ELECTRIC EQUIPMENT; *U.S. Private*, pg. 4410
VOSS ELECTRIC COMPANY; *U.S. Private*, pg. 4413
WABASH ELECTRIC SUPPLY INC.; *U.S. Private*, pg. 4423
WADA DENKI CO., LTD.—See Ablerex Electronics Co., Ltd.; *Int'l*, pg. 63
WALKER INDUSTRIAL PRODUCTS, INC.—See Graybar Electric Company, Inc.; *U.S. Private*, pg. 1760
WARREN ELECTRIC SUPPLY, INC.; *U.S. Private*, pg. 4443
WARSHAUER ELECTRIC SUPPLY COMPANY; *U.S. Private*, pg. 4445
WARSHAW, INC.—See Dunes Point Capital, LLC; *U.S. Private*, pg. 1289
WASSCO; *U.S. Private*, pg. 4450
WATTS INDUSTRIES BELGIUM BVBA—See Watts Water Technologies, Inc.; *U.S. Public*, pg. 2337
WEDCO INC.; *U.S. Private*, pg. 4468
WELD POWER SERVICE COMPANY, INC.; *U.S. Private*, pg. 4473
WELDY-LAMONT ASSOCIATES INC.; *U.S. Private*, pg. 4474
WELLS-KEOWN & ASSOCIATES INC.; *U.S. Private*, pg. 4476
WENDLER AB—See Addtech AB; *Int'l*, pg. 136
WERNER ELECTRIC SUPPLY COMPANY; *U.S. Private*, pg. 4482
WERNER ELECTRIC SUPPLY COMPANY—See Van Meter Inc.; *U.S. Private*, pg. 4340
WERNER ELECTRIC SUPPLY COMPANY—See Werner Electric Supply Company; *U.S. Private*, pg. 4482
WESCO ANIXTER USVI, LLC—See WESCO International, Inc.; *U.S. Public*, pg. 2352
WESCO DISTRIBUTION INC. - MIDLOTHIAN—See WESCO International, Inc.; *U.S. Public*, pg. 2352
WESCO DISTRIBUTION, INC.—See WESCO International, Inc.; *U.S. Public*, pg. 2352
WESCO EQUITY CORPORATION—See WESCO International, Inc.; *U.S. Public*, pg. 2352
WESCO INTEGRATED SUPPLY, INC.—See Nautic Partners, LLC; *U.S. Private*, pg. 2872
WESCO MANUFACTURED STRUCTURES-MERIDIAN—See WESCO International, Inc.; *U.S. Public*, pg. 2352
WESCO NEVADA, LTD.—See WESCO International, Inc.; *U.S. Public*, pg. 2352
WESTERN ELECTRICAL SALES INC.; *U.S. Private*, pg. 4492
WESTERN EXTRALITE COMPANY—See Border States Industries, Inc.; *U.S. Private*, pg. 618

423610 — ELECTRICAL APPARATU...

WESTERN SWITCHES & CONTROLS; *U.S. Private,* pg. 4497
WEST FIRE SYSTEMS, INC.—See The Carlyle Group Inc.; *U.S. Public,* pg. 2053
WEST-LITE SUPPLY CO., INC.—See Facility Solutions Group, Inc.; *U.S. Private,* pg. 1460
WEST VIRGINIA ELECTRIC SUPPLY CO; *U.S. Private,* pg. 4487
WHOLESALE ELECTRIC SUPPLY CO. INC.; *U.S. Private,* pg. 4514
WHOLESALE SUPPLY GROUP INC.; *U.S. Private,* pg. 4514
WIEDENBACH-BROWN CO. INC.—See Blackfriars Corp.; *U.S. Private,* pg. 575
WILEC—See ACTOM (Pty) Ltd.; *Int'l,* pg. 121
WILLE ELECTRIC SUPPLY CO.; *U.S. Private,* pg. 4521
WILLIAMS DISTRIBUTING - MOTORS & DRIVES—See Williams Distributing Inc.; *U.S. Private,* pg. 4525
WILLIAMS SUPPLY INC.; *U.S. Private,* pg. 4526
WINDY CITY WIRE CABLE & TECHNOLOGY PRODUCTS LLC—See Diploma PLC; *Int'l,* pg. 2129
WINPOWER INC.—See Winco Generators; *U.S. Private,* pg. 4533
WIRE SHOP INC.; *U.S. Private,* pg. 4546
W. L. GORE & ASSOCIATES (PACIFIC) PTE LTD.—See W.L. Gore & Associates, Inc.; *U.S. Private,* pg. 4421
WOLBERG ELECTRICAL SUPPLY CO. INC; *U.S. Private,* pg. 4553
WOLFF BROTHERS SUPPLY, INC.; *U.S. Private,* pg. 4554
WOMACK ELECTRIC SUPPLY CO., INC.—See Crescent Electric Supply Company; *U.S. Private,* pg. 1093
WOMACK ELECTRIC & SUPPLY CO.; *U.S. Private,* pg. 4555
WOODHEAD ASIA PTE. LTD.—See Koch Industries, Inc.; *U.S. Private,* pg. 2335
WORLDWIDE ELECTRIC CORP.—See AEA Investors LP; *U.S. Private,* pg. 116
WRIGHT LINE LLC—See Eaton Corporation plc; *Int'l,* pg. 2282
WSA SYSTEMS-BOCA INC.—See Huron Capital Partners LLC; *U.S. Private,* pg. 2012
YALE ELECTRIC SUPPLY CO.; *U.S. Private,* pg. 4585
YAMATAKE AUTOMATION PRODUCTS (SHANGHAI) CO., LTD.—See Azbil Corporation; *Int'l,* pg. 777
YANCEY POWER SYSTEMS, INC.—See Yancey Bros. Co.; *U.S. Private,* pg. 4585
YESCO ELECTRICAL SUPPLY, INC.; *U.S. Private,* pg. 4588
YOUNG & CHAMPAGNE COMPANY—See Young & Champagne Electrical Sales Inc.; *U.S. Private,* pg. 4592
YUASA BATTERY INC.; *U.S. Private,* pg. 4595
ZAO UPONOR RUS—See Georg Fischer AG; *Int'l,* pg. 2938
ZEBRA TECHNOLOGIES SPAIN, S.L.—See Zebra Technologies Corporation; *U.S. Public,* pg. 2402
ZEBRA TEKNOLOJILERI SISTEM COZUMLERI ANONIM SIRKETA—See Zebra Technologies Corporation; *U.S. Public,* pg. 2402
ZERO POINT; *U.S. Private,* pg. 4602

423620 — HOUSEHOLD APPLIANCES, ELECTRIC HOUSEWARES, AND CONSUMER ELECTRONICS MERCHANT WHOLESALERS

1ST IN VIDEO-MUSIC WORLD, INC.; *U.S. Private,* pg. 4
1ST SOURCE SERVALL INC.; *U.S. Private,* pg. 4
24 SHOPPING CO., LTD.—See C.P. All Public Company Limited; *Int'l,* pg. 1243
3Q CO., LTD.—See EDION Corporation; *Int'l,* pg. 2310
3Y POWER TECHNOLOGY (TAIWAN) INC.—See FSP Technology Inc.; *Int'l,* pg. 2800
AAAA WORLD IMPORT EXPORT; *U.S. Private,* pg. 30
AAC ACOUSTIC TECHNOLOGIES—See AAC Technologies Holdings Inc.; *Int'l,* pg. 31
AAC ACOUSTIC TECHNOLOGIES SWEDEN AB—See AAC Technologies Holdings Inc.; *Int'l,* pg. 31
AARON KITCHEN & BATH DESIGN GALLERY—See Aaron & Company Inc.; *U.S. Private,* pg. 32
ABATTOIR SA/NV; *Int'l,* pg. 48
ABSOCOLD CORPORATION; *U.S. Private,* pg. 44
ACTION S.A.; *Int'l,* pg. 119
ADB SERVICES S.A.—See Advanced Digital Broadcast Holdings SA; *Int'l,* pg. 158
ADEXI A/S—See Elof Hansson AB; *Int'l,* pg. 2368
ADITYA VISION LIMITED; *Int'l,* pg. 149
ADMEA SA; *Int'l,* pg. 151
ADVANCED DIGITAL BROADCAST HONG KONG LTD.—See Advanced Digital Broadcast Holdings SA; *Int'l,* pg. 158
ADVANCED DIGITAL BROADCAST INC.—See Advanced Digital Broadcast Holdings SA; *Int'l,* pg. 158
ADVANCED DIGITAL BROADCAST ITALIA S.R.L—See Advanced Digital Broadcast Holdings SA; *Int'l,* pg. 158
ADVANCED DIGITAL BROADCAST LTD.—See Advanced Digital Broadcast Holdings SA; *Int'l,* pg. 158
ADVANCED DIGITAL BROADCAST POLSKA SP. Z.O.O.—See Advanced Digital Broadcast Holdings SA; *Int'l,* pg. 158
ADVANCED DIGITAL BROADCAST S.A.—See Advanced Digital Broadcast Holdings SA; *Int'l,* pg. 158
ADYEN INC.—See Adyen N.V.; *Int'l,* pg. 169
ADYEN JAPAN K.K.—See Adyen N.V.; *Int'l,* pg. 169
AERUS ELECTROLUX CANADA—See Aerus LLC; *U.S. Private,* pg. 120
AFTRON ELECTRONICS—See Al-Futtaim Private Company LLC; *Int'l,* pg. 285
A-GAS AMERICAS, INC.—See A-Gas Limited; *Int'l,* pg. 19
A-GAS (AUSTRALIA) PTY LTD—See A-Gas Limited; *Int'l,* pg. 19
A-GAS (SEA) PTE LTD—See A-Gas Limited; *Int'l,* pg. 19
A-GAS (SHANGHAI) CHEMICAL CO. LTD—See A-Gas Limited; *Int'l,* pg. 19
A-GAS (SOUTH AFRICA) (PTY) LTD—See A-Gas Limited; *Int'l,* pg. 19
A-GAS (THAILAND) LTD—See A-Gas Limited; *Int'l,* pg. 19
AGRIMART CORP.—See Adeka Corporation; *Int'l,* pg. 142
AIPTEK INTERNATIONAL GMBH—See AIPTEK International Inc.; *Int'l,* pg. 235
AIRCRAFT CABIN SYSTEMS; *U.S. Private,* pg. 140
AIRTECH SYSTEM CO., LTD.—See AIRTECH JAPAN, LTD.; *Int'l,* pg. 249
AJ ADVANCE TECHNOLOGY PUBLIC COMPANY LIMITED; *Int'l,* pg. 255
ALBA BROADCASTING CORPORATION LIMITED—See Harvard International Ltd.; *Int'l,* pg. 3280
ALBA RADIO LIMITED—See Harvard International Ltd.; *Int'l,* pg. 3280
ALCO DIGITAL DEVICES LIMITED—See Alco Holdings Limited; *Int'l,* pg. 301
ALCO ELECTRONICS (SHENZHEN) LIMITED—See Alco Holdings Limited; *Int'l,* pg. 301
ALCO INTERNATIONAL LIMITED—See Alco Holdings Limited; *Int'l,* pg. 301
AL-FUTTAIM ACE COMPANY L.L.C—See Al-Futtaim Private Company LLC; *Int'l,* pg. 285
AL-FUTTAIM ELECTRONICS—See Al-Futtaim Private Company LLC; *Int'l,* pg. 285
AL-FUTTAIM PANATECH COMPANY LLC—See Al-Futtaim Private Company LLC; *Int'l,* pg. 285
ALI FOODSERVICE EQUIPMENT (SHANGHAI) CO., LTD.—See Ali Holding S.r.l; *Int'l,* pg. 320
ALLAN REHNSTROM AB—See Addtech AB; *Int'l,* pg. 131
ALLEGION INTERNATIONAL AG—See Allegion Public Limited Company; *Int'l,* pg. 335
ALL INC.; *U.S. Private,* pg. 171
ALLSTATE G.E.S. APPLIANCE, INC.; *U.S. Private,* pg. 193
ALMO CORPORATION—See DCC plc; *Int'l,* pg. 1989
ALPINE ELECTRONICS OF AMERICA, INC.—See Alps Alpine Co., Ltd.; *Int'l,* pg. 375
ALSO HUNGARY KFT.—See Droege Group AG; *Int'l,* pg. 2205
ALSO SLOVAKIA S.R.O.—See Droege Group AG; *Int'l,* pg. 2205
ALSO TECHNOLOGY SRL—See Droege Group AG; *Int'l,* pg. 2205
AMPLIFON AG—See Amplifon S.p.A.; *Int'l,* pg. 435
AMRE SUPPLY CANADA INC.—See Ferguson plc; *Int'l,* pg. 2637
ANNAX GMBH—See Westinghouse Air Brake Technologies Corporation; *U.S. Public,* pg. 2357
ANNAX POLSKA SP. Z.O.O.—See Westinghouse Air Brake Technologies Corporation; *U.S. Public,* pg. 2357
ANNAX SCHEIZ AG—See Westinghouse Air Brake Technologies Corporation; *U.S. Public,* pg. 2357
ANNAX (SUZHOU) RAIL SYSTEMS CO., LTD.—See Westinghouse Air Brake Technologies Corporation; *U.S. Public,* pg. 2357
A. O. SMITH INDIA WATER PRODUCTS PRIVATE LIMITED—See A. O. Smith Corporation; *U.S. Public,* pg. 11
AO WORLD PLC; *Int'l,* pg. 487
APPLE OPERATIONS INTERNATIONAL—See Apple Inc.; *U.S. Public,* pg. 169
APPLIANCE PARTS DEPOT INC.; *U.S. Private,* pg. 297
APPLICA CANADA CORPORATION—See Spectrum Brands Holdings, Inc.; *U.S. Public,* pg. 1916
APPLICA CONSUMER PRODUCTS, INC.—See Spectrum Brands Holdings, Inc.; *U.S. Public,* pg. 1916
A.P. WAGNER INC.; *U.S. Private,* pg. 27
ARC E-COMMERCE AB—See BHG Group AB; *Int'l,* pg. 1014
ARD DISTRIBUTORS INC.; *U.S. Private,* pg. 317
ARIZONA WHOLESALE SUPPLY COMPANY; *U.S. Private,* pg. 325
ARMOUR NORDIC AB—See AAMP of Florida, Inc.; *U.S. Private,* pg. 32
ARMOUR NORDIC AS—See AAMP of Florida, Inc.; *U.S. Private,* pg. 32
ARTEX TRADING COMPANY LTD.—See Hayel Saeed Anam Group of Companies; *Int'l,* pg. 3290
ASA ELECTRONICS LLC—See VOXX International Corporation; *U.S. Public,* pg. 2310
ASIA DRAGON INTERNATIONAL LIMITED—See Alco Holdings Limited; *Int'l,* pg. 301
THE AUDIO HOUSE, INC.—See National Amusements, Inc.; *U.S. Private,* pg. 2844
AUDIO-TECHNICA CENTRAL EUROPE LTD—See Audio-Technica Corporation; *Int'l,* pg. 701
AUDIO-TECHNICA NIEDERLASSUNG DEUTSCHLAND—See Audio-Technica Corporation; *Int'l,* pg. 701
AUDIO-TECHNICA SAS—See Audio-Technica Corporation; *Int'l,* pg. 701
AUDIO-TECHNICA TAIWAN CO., LTD.—See Audio-Technica Corporation; *Int'l,* pg. 701
AUDIOVOX ATLANTA CORP.—See VOXX International Corporation; *U.S. Public,* pg. 2310
AUDIOVOX MEXICO, S DE RR DE CV—See VOXX International Corporation; *U.S. Public,* pg. 2310
AUMAKE LIMITED; *Int'l,* pg. 705
AUTCO DISTRIBUTING INC.—See *U.S. Private,* pg. 396
AUTO SOUND COMPANY INCORPORATED; *U.S. Private,* pg. 397
AUTOTYPE HOLDINGS (USA), INC.—See Element Solutions Inc.; *U.S. Public,* pg. 725
AVI-SPL, INC. - CHICAGO—See Marlin Equity Partners, LLC; *U.S. Private,* pg. 2583
AVI-SPL, INC. - FORT LAUDERDALE—See Marlin Equity Partners, LLC; *U.S. Private,* pg. 2583
AVI-SPL, INC. - JACKSONVILLE—See Marlin Equity Partners, LLC; *U.S. Private,* pg. 2583
AVI-SPL, INC. - ORLANDO—See Marlin Equity Partners, LLC; *U.S. Private,* pg. 2583
AVI-SPL, INC. - TALLAHASSEE—See Marlin Equity Partners, LLC; *U.S. Private,* pg. 2583
AVI-SPL, INC. - WASHINGTON, D.C.—See Marlin Equity Partners, LLC; *U.S. Private,* pg. 2583
AVNET SILICA—See Avnet, Inc.; *U.S. Public,* pg. 250
AXON PUBLIC SAFETY UK LIMITED—See Axon Enterprise, Inc.; *U.S. Public,* pg. 256
BAGAREN OCH KOCKEN AB—See Egmont Fonden; *Int'l,* pg. 2325
BANG & OLUFSEN AG—See Bang & Olufsen a/s; *Int'l,* pg. 831
BANG & OLUFSEN AMERICA, INC.—See Bang & Olufsen a/s; *Int'l,* pg. 831
BANG & OLUFSEN A/S—See Bang & Olufsen a/s; *Int'l,* pg. 831
BANG & OLUFSEN N.V./S.A.—See Bang & Olufsen a/s; *Int'l,* pg. 831
BANG & OLUFSEN UNITED KINGDOM LTD.—See Bang & Olufsen a/s; *Int'l,* pg. 831
BECKMAN AUSTRALIA APS—See Danaher Corporation; *U.S. Public,* pg. 624
BELKIN TRADING (SHANGHAI) COMPANY LTD.—See Hon Hai Precision Industry Co., Ltd.; *Int'l,* pg. 3456
BENCHMARK ELECTRONICS MANUFACTURING SOLUTIONS (MOORPARK), INC.—See Benchmark Electronics, Inc.; *U.S. Public,* pg. 295
BEST BUY CANADA LTD.—See Best Buy Co., Inc.; *U.S. Public,* pg. 326
BESTBUY.COM, LLC—See Best Buy Co., Inc.; *U.S. Public,* pg. 326
BIG BAZAAR—See Future Corporate Resources Limited; *Int'l,* pg. 2853
BIMEKS BILGI ISLEM VE DIS TICARET A.S.; *Int'l,* pg. 1032
BLODGETT SUPPLY CO. INC.—See SPL Associates Inc.; *U.S. Private,* pg. 3759
BLUESTEM FARM & RANCH SUPPLY, INC.; *U.S. Private,* pg. 598
BM MIAMI INC.; *U.S. Private,* pg. 600
BRAUN NORTH AMERICA—See The Procter & Gamble Company; *U.S. Public,* pg. 2124
BREVILLE MEXICO, S.A. DE C.V.—See Breville Group Limited; *Int'l,* pg. 1150
BRIGHTHOUSE GROUP PLC; *Int'l,* pg. 1162
BRIMAG DIGITAL AGE LTD.; *Int'l,* pg. 1164
BROOKE DISTRIBUTORS INC.; *U.S. Private,* pg. 663
BROWN APPLIANCE PARTS COMPANY; *U.S. Private,* pg. 666
CABLEREADY CORPORATION; *U.S. Private,* pg. 711
CADAC EUROPE B.V.—See Dometic Group AB; *Int'l,* pg. 2160
CAMEC (NZ) LIMITED—See Fleetwood Limited; *Int'l,* pg. 2699
CAMPING GAZ (SCHWEIZ) AG—See Newell Brands Inc.; *U.S. Public,* pg. 1515
CANDY HOOVER AG—See Haier Smart Home Co., Ltd.; *Int'l,* pg. 3209
CANDY HOOVER AUSTRIA GMBH—See Haier Smart Home Co., Ltd.; *Int'l,* pg. 3209
CANDY HOOVER BELGIUM NV—See Haier Smart Home Co., Ltd.; *Int'l,* pg. 3209
CANDY HOOVER CR S.R.O.—See Haier Smart Home Co., Ltd.; *Int'l,* pg. 3209
CANDY HOOVER GMBH—See Haier Smart Home Co., Ltd.; *Int'l,* pg. 3210
CANDY HOOVER HUNGARY KFT.—See Haier Smart Home Co., Ltd.; *Int'l,* pg. 3210
CANDY HOOVER NEDERLAND B.V.—See Haier Smart Home Co., Ltd.; *Int'l,* pg. 3210
CANDY HOOVER POLSKA SP. Z O.O.—See Haier Smart Home Co., Ltd.; *Int'l,* pg. 3210
CANDY HOOVER ROMANIA S. R. L.—See Haier Smart

N.A.I.C.S. INDEX

423620 — HOUSEHOLD APPLIANCE...

Home Co., Ltd.; *Int'l*, pg. 3210
CAPITAL DISTRIBUTING, INC.; *U.S. Private*, pg. 739
CARAD SA; *Int'l*, pg. 1319
CARLO GAVAZZI AB—See Carlo Gavazzi Holding AG; *Int'l*, pg. 1338
CARLO GAVAZZI AUTOMATION SINGAPORE PTE LTD—See Carlo Gavazzi Holding AG; *Int'l*, pg. 1338
CARRIER ENTERPRISE CANADA LTD.—See Carrier Global Corporation; *U.S. Public*, pg. 440
CASHWELL APPLIANCE PARTS INC.; *U.S. Private*, pg. 783
CASTLE BRIDGE IMPACT MEDIA INC.; *Int'l*, pg. 1357
CEAVCO AUDIO-VISUAL COMPANY; *U.S. Private*, pg. 804
CECONOMY AG; *Int'l*, pg. 1373
CELLECOR GADGETS LIMITED; *Int'l*, pg. 1392
CELLO WORLD LIMITED; *Int'l*, pg. 1394
CENWOOD KITCHENS—See Central Woodwork, Inc.; *U.S. Private*, pg. 826
C.E. SUNDBERG COMPANY INC.; *U.S. Private*, pg. 706
CHEE CORP.; *Int'l*, pg. 1459
CHEF'S CATALOGUE, INC.—See JH Partners LLC; *U.S. Private*, pg. 2207
CIC MARKETING (PTY) LIMITED—See CIC Holdings Limited; *Int'l*, pg. 1602
CLARION CORPORATION OF AMERICA—See FORVIA SE; *Int'l*, pg. 2745
CLARION SALES CORPORATION—See FORVIA SE; *Int'l*, pg. 2745
CLARK & CLARK INC.; *U.S. Private*, pg. 912
CLAS OHLSON LTD.—See Clas Ohlson AB; *Int'l*, pg. 1651
CLASSIC COLLISION, INC.; *U.S. Private*, pg. 916
THE CLIMATIC CORPORATION; *U.S. Private*, pg. 4010
CLIMATIC HOME PRODUCTS—See The Climatic Corporation; *U.S. Private*, pg. 4010
C&L SUPPLY INC.; *U.S. Private*, pg. 703
COAST WHOLESALE APPLIANCES INC.; *Int'l*, pg. 1681
COMMERCIAL SOLUTIONS, INC.—See Paychex, Inc.; *U.S. Public*, pg. 1655
COMPANY SHOP LIMITED—See Biffa Group Limited; *Int'l*, pg. 1020
COMSERVE NETWORK NETHERLANDS B.V.—See FIC Global, INC; *Int'l*, pg. 2653
CONAN ELECTRIC MANUFACTURING LIMITED—See Allan International Holdings Limited; *Int'l*, pg. 332
CONSUMERS WAREHOUSE CENTER INC.—See Consumers Kitchens & Baths; *U.S. Private*, pg. 1026
COOLPAD TECHNOLOGIES INC.—See Coolpad Group Limited; *Int'l*, pg. 1789
COPA CORPORATION, INC.; *Int'l*, pg. 1792
COUPANG, INC.; *Int'l*, pg. 1819
CPS DISTRIBUTORS INC.; *U.S. Private*, pg. 1080
CREST RADIUS INC.; *Int'l*, pg. 1841
CRYSTAL PROMOTIONS INC.; *U.S. Private*, pg. 1115
C&S WASTE SERVICES INC.—See Peoria Disposal Company/Area Disposal Service, Inc.; *U.S. Private*, pg. 3143
CURTIS INTERNATIONAL LTD.; *Int'l*, pg. 1880
DACOSTA MANNINGS INC.—See Barbados Shipping & Trading Co. Ltd.; *Int'l*, pg. 858
DALBANI CORPORATION; *U.S. Private*, pg. 1148
DAS DISTRIBUTORS INC.; *U.S. Private*, pg. 1160
DASP GROUP LLC; *U.S. Private*, pg. 1162
DAWSON MMP LIMITED—See Ali Holding S.r.l.; *Int'l*, pg. 321
DAYTON APPLIANCE PARTS CO. INC.—See Berkshire Partners LLC; *U.S. Private*, pg. 535
DE'LONGHI AMERICA INC.—See De'Longhi S.p.A.; *Int'l*, pg. 1997
DE'LONGHI SWITZERLAND AG—See De'Longhi S.p.A.; *Int'l*, pg. 1997
DENSO TEN AMERICA LIMITED—See Denso Corporation; *Int'l*, pg. 2030
DHYAANI TILE & MARBLEZ LIMITED; *Int'l*, pg. 2101
DIAL ONE WOLFEDALE ELECTRIC LTD.; *Int'l*, pg. 2103
DIGITAL TECH INC.—See Coolpad Group Limited; *Int'l*, pg. 1789
DIONIC TRADING LTD—See Dionic Industrial & Trading S.A; *Int'l*, pg. 2128
DIRECTED ELECTRONICS CANADA, INC.—See Charlesbank Capital Partners, LLC; *U.S. Private*, pg. 855
D&L PARTS CO. INC.; *U.S. Private*, pg. 1138
D&M PROFESSIONAL—See Bain Capital, LP; *U.S. Private*, pg. 438
DOMETIC SCANDINAVIA AB—See Dometic Group AB; *Int'l*, pg. 2160
DON ERICKSON INC.; *U.S. Private*, pg. 1257
DONGGUAN YULONG TELECOMMUNICATION TECH CO., LTD.—See Coolpad Group Limited; *Int'l*, pg. 1789
DON'S APPLIANCES LLC—See Kodiak Building Partners LLC; *U.S. Private*, pg. 2336
DON WALTER KITCHEN DISTRIBUTORS; *U.S. Private*, pg. 1259
DOOLITTLE DISTRIBUTING INC.; *U.S. Private*, pg. 1261
DORO AB; *Int'l*, pg. 2179
DOSHISHA CO., LTD.; *Int'l*, pg. 2180
DRILLOT CORPORATION; *U.S. Private*, pg. 1277
DYNAMIC MARKETING, INC.; *U.S. Private*, pg. 1298
EAGLE ASSOCIATES INC.; *U.S. Private*, pg. 1308
EASTECH MICROACOUSTICS (HK) LIMITED—See Eastern Holding Limited; *Int'l*, pg. 2272
EAST SYNERGY LIMITED—See Eastern Asia Technology Ltd.; *Int'l*, pg. 2271
ECLIPSE MOBILE ELECTRONICS—See Denso Corporation; *Int'l*, pg. 2030
ECOST.COM, INC.—See Insight Enterprises, Inc.; *U.S. Public*, pg. 1130
ECS ELECTRICAL CABLE SUPPLY LTD.; *Int'l*, pg. 2301
EDION EAST CORPORATION—See EDION Corporation; *Int'l*, pg. 2310
EFTC OPERATING CORPORATION—See Benchmark Electronics, Inc.; *U.S. Public*, pg. 296
EISAGOGIKI EMPORIKI ELLADOS A.E.—See Audio Group Greece B.V.; *Int'l*, pg. 701
ELCO HOLLAND B.V.—See Elco Limited; *Int'l*, pg. 2345
ELECTORI CO., LTD.—See Hibino Corporation; *Int'l*, pg. 3383
ELECTRA AIR CONDITIONING INDUSTRIES 2006 LIMITED—See Elco Limited; *Int'l*, pg. 2345
ELECTRICAL DISTRIBUTING INC.; *U.S. Private*, pg. 1353
ELECTRICAL HOME-AIDS PTY LTD—See Godfreys Group Limited; *Int'l*, pg. 3019
ELECTRO BRAND, INC.; *U.S. Private*, pg. 1353
ELECTROLUX AG—See AB Electrolux; *Int'l*, pg. 39
ELECTROLUX APPLIANCES S.P.A.—See AB Electrolux; *Int'l*, pg. 39
ELECTROLUX ASSOCIATED COMPANY B.V.—See AB Electrolux; *Int'l*, pg. 39
ELECTROLUX A.S.—See AB Electrolux; *Int'l*, pg. 39
ELECTROLUX CANADA CORP.—See Bissell Homecare, Inc.; *U.S. Private*, pg. 566
ELECTROLUX COMERCIAL VENEZUELA C.A—See AB Electrolux; *Int'l*, pg. 39
ELECTROLUX DEL PARAGUAY S.A.—See AB Electrolux; *Int'l*, pg. 41
ELECTROLUX D.O.O.—See AB Electrolux; *Int'l*, pg. 41
ELECTROLUX ESTONIA LTD—See AB Electrolux; *Int'l*, pg. 39
ELECTROLUX HEMPRODUKTER AB—See AB Electrolux; *Int'l*, pg. 40
ELECTROLUX HOME APPLIANCES SDN BHD—See AB Electrolux; *Int'l*, pg. 40
ELECTROLUX HOME PRODUCTS AS—See AB Electrolux; *Int'l*, pg. 40
ELECTROLUX HOME PRODUCTS DENMARK A/S—See AB Electrolux; *Int'l*, pg. 40
ELECTROLUX HOME PRODUCTS NORWAY AS—See AB Electrolux; *Int'l*, pg. 40
ELECTROLUX IRELAND LTD—See AB Electrolux; *Int'l*, pg. 40
ELECTROLUX JAPAN LTD.—See AB Electrolux; *Int'l*, pg. 40
ELECTROLUX LJUBLJANA D.O.O.—See AB Electrolux; *Int'l*, pg. 40
ELECTROLUX PROFESSIONAL AS—See AB Electrolux; *Int'l*, pg. 40
ELECTRONICPARTNER GMBH—See ElectronicPartner Handel SE; *Int'l*, pg. 2354
ELECTRONICS MART INDIA LIMITED; *Int'l*, pg. 2354
ELECTRONIZET SA—See Ackermans & van Haaren NV; *Int'l*, pg. 105
ELEMENT LIGHTING DESIGN LIMITED—See e Lighting Group Holdings Limited; *Int'l*, pg. 2246
E LIGHTING GROUP HOLDINGS LIMITED; *Int'l*, pg. 2246
ELIS NEDERLAND B.V.—See Eurazeo SE; *Int'l*, pg. 2528
ELKO EHF.—See Festi hf; *Int'l*, pg. 2646
ELLIS MEARES & SON INC.; *U.S. Private*, pg. 1374
EMBRACO EUROPE S.R.L.—See Whirlpool Corporation; *U.S. Public*, pg. 2367
EMERSON CLIMATE TECHNOLOGIES RETAIL SOLUTIONS EUROPE S.R.L.—See Emerson Electric Co.; *U.S. Public*, pg. 743
ENDESA X WAY S.L.—See Enel S.p.A.; *Int'l*, pg. 2412
ENDRESS+HAUSER A/S—See Endress+Hauser (International) Holding AG; *Int'l*, pg. 2406
ENDRESS+HAUSER (PTY.) LTD.—See Endress+Hauser (International) Holding AG; *Int'l*, pg. 2406
ENDRESS Y HAUSER, S.A.—See Endress+Hauser (International) Holding AG; *Int'l*, pg. 2406
ENERGY EARTH LLC; *U.S. Private*, pg. 1395
ENERGY OGRE, LLC; *U.S. Private*, pg. 1395
ERPA DIS TICARET PAZ. VE SAN LTD STI—See Eroglu Holding AS; *Int'l*, pg. 2496
ERP POWER LLC—See Angeles Equity Partners, LLC; *U.S. Private*, pg. 282
E&S INTERNATIONAL ENTERPRISES INC.; *U.S. Private*, pg. 1301
ETS MOUSSIER; *Int'l*, pg. 2524
EVRIHOLDER PRODUCTS LLC—See Kainos Capital, LLC; *U.S. Private*, pg. 2255
EXI IAUSTO AB—See Aldes Aeraulique SAS; *Int'l*, pg. 304
FACTORY BUILDER STORES INC.; *U.S. Private*, pg. 1460
FACTORY DIRECT APPLIANCE INC.; *U.S. Private*, pg. 1460
FAVI ENTERTAINMENT; *U.S. Private*, pg. 1484
FEINIU E-COMMERCE HONG KONG LIMITED—See Alibaba Group Holding Limited; *Int'l*, pg. 326
F.G. EUROPE S.A.; *Int'l*, pg. 2596
FIAMMA PROPERTIES SDN BHD—See Fiamma Holdings Berhad; *Int'l*, pg. 2650
FIAMMA TRADING SDN. BHD.—See Fiamma Holdings Berhad; *Int'l*, pg. 2650
FIMACO SDN. BHD.—See Fiamma Holdings Berhad; *Int'l*, pg. 2650
FINE SOUNDS ASIA LIMITED—See Fine Sounds S.p.A.; *Int'l*, pg. 2673
FIRST COAST SUPPLY INC.; *U.S. Private*, pg. 1516
FISHER & PAYKEL CUSTOMER SERVICES PTY LIMITED—See Haier Smart Home Co., Ltd.; *Int'l*, pg. 3210
FISHER & PAYKEL (SINGAPORE) PTE LIMITED—See Haier Smart Home Co., Ltd.; *Int'l*, pg. 3210
FLURIDA GROUP, INC.; *U.S. Private*, pg. 1552
FOSTER ELECTRIC (THAILAND) CO., LTD.—See Foster Electric Co., Ltd.; *Int'l*, pg. 2749
FOURLIS TRADE AEBE—See FOURLIS HOLDINGS S.A.; *Int'l*, pg. 2755
FOXCONN SINGAPORE PTE. LTD.—See Hon Hai Precision Industry Co., Ltd.; *Int'l*, pg. 3457
THE FRETZ CORPORATION; *U.S. Private*, pg. 4031
FREUDENBERG HOME & CLEANING SOLUTIONS S.R.O.—See Freudenberg SE; *Int'l*, pg. 2786
FUJITSU COMPONENTS EUROPE B.V.—See Fujitsu Limited; *Int'l*, pg. 2834
FUJITSU GENERAL (AUSTRALIA) PTY. LIMITED; *Int'l*, pg. 2832
FUTURE SHOP LTD.—See Best Buy Co., Inc.; *U.S. Public*, pg. 326
GALANZ (NORTH AMERICA) INC.—See Guangdong Galanz Group Co., Ltd.; *Int'l*, pg. 3154
GIGLIO GROUP S.P.A.; *Int'l*, pg. 2972
GILLETTE (HONG KONG) LIMITED—See The Procter & Gamble Company; *U.S. Public*, pg. 2124
GLOBAL EXPRESS (HK) LIMITED—See Allan International Holdings Limited; *Int'l*, pg. 332
GODFREYS GROUP LIMITED; *Int'l*, pg. 3019
GOME TELECOM EQUIPMENT CO., LTD.; *Int'l*, pg. 3037
GORENJE BELUX S.A.R.L.—See Hisense Co., Ltd.; *Int'l*, pg. 3407
GORENJE KUCHEN GMBH—See Hisense Co., Ltd.; *Int'l*, pg. 3407
GP ACOUSTICS (HK) LIMITED—See Gold Peak Technology Group Limited; *Int'l*, pg. 3025
GRAZZIOTIN S.A.; *Int'l*, pg. 3063
GREE ELECTRIC (THAILAND) CO., LTD.—See Gree Electric Appliances, Inc. of Zhuhai; *Int'l*, pg. 3068
GRUNDIG AUSTRALIA PTY LIMITED—See Harvard International Ltd.; *Int'l*, pg. 3280
GRUPO COMERCIAL GOMO, S.A. DE C.V.; *Int'l*, pg. 3125
GSH CORPORATION LIMITED; *Int'l*, pg. 3144
HAMBURG BROTHERS; *U.S. Private*, pg. 1847
HAMILTON BEACH BRANDS CANADA, INC.—See Hamilton Beach Brands Holding Company; *U.S. Public*, pg. 981
HAMMOND ELECTRONICS LIMITED—See Hammond Manufacturing Co. Ltd.; *Int'l*, pg. 3238
HAMMOND MANUFACTURING COMPANY INC—See Hammond Manufacturing Co. Ltd.; *Int'l*, pg. 3238
HANSSEM CORPORATION—See Hanssem Co., Ltd.; *Int'l*, pg. 3261
HARVARD INTERNATIONAL (HONG KONG) LIMITED—See Harvard International Ltd.; *Int'l*, pg. 3280
HARVARD INTERNATIONAL LTD.; *Int'l*, pg. 3280
H&C ANIMAL HEALTH, LLC; *U.S. Private*, pg. 1822
HEALTHWISE; *U.S. Private*, pg. 1898
HELEN OF TROY TEXAS CORPORATION—See Helen of Troy Limited; *Int'l*, pg. 3328
HEMMY AB—See BHG Group AB; *Int'l*, pg. 1015
HISENSE USA CORPORATION—See Hisense Co., Ltd.; *Int'l*, pg. 3408
HISENSE VISUAL TECHNOLOGY CO., LTD.—See Hisense Co., Ltd.; *Int'l*, pg. 3408
HITACHI EUROPE S.A.—See Hitachi, Ltd.; *Int'l*, pg. 3417
HITACHI GLOBAL LIFE SOLUTIONS, INC.—See Hitachi, Ltd.; *Int'l*, pg. 3417
HITACHI HOME ELECTRONICS VIETNAM CO., LTD.—See Hitachi, Ltd.; *Int'l*, pg. 3419
HITACHI (HONG KONG) LTD.—See Hitachi, Ltd.; *Int'l*, pg. 3413
HITACHI SALES (MACAU) LTD.—See Hitachi, Ltd.; *Int'l*, pg. 3421
HITACHI SALES (M) SDN BHD—See Hitachi, Ltd.; *Int'l*, pg. 3414
HITACHI SALES (THAILAND), LTD.—See Hitachi, Ltd.; *Int'l*, pg. 3421
HK GLOBAL TRADING LTD.; *U.S. Private*, pg. 1953
HOBART GMBH—See Illinois Tool Works Inc.; *U.S. Public*, pg. 1104
HOCK SIN LEONG GROUP BERHAD; *Int'l*, pg. 3438
HONG KONG VICTORIA WELL INDUSTRIAL LIMITED—See Doshisha Co., Ltd.; *Int'l*, pg. 2180
HOSHIZAKI TOKYO K.K.—See Hoshizaki Corporation; *Int'l*, pg. 3484
HOWARD'S APPLIANCES, INC.; *U.S. Private*, pg. 1995
H&R AUTO RADIO SERVICE INCORPORATED; *U.S. Private*, pg. 1823

423620 — HOUSEHOLD APPLIANCE...

HUNTER VENTILADORES DE MEXICO S.A. DE C.V.—See Griffon Corporation; *U.S. Public*, pg. 969
HYUNDAI CORPORATION HOLDINGS CO., LTD.—See Hyundai Corporation; *Int'l*, pg. 3555
ICOM NEW ZEALAND—See ICOM INCORPORATED; *Int'l*, pg. 3583
IDELLE LABS, LTD.—See Helen of Troy Limited; *Int'l*, pg. 3329
IFIRE GROUP LTD.—See CTS Corporation; *U.S. Public*, pg. 603
IMPACT MERCHANDISING CORP.—See Vista West, Inc.; *U.S. Private*, pg. 4403
INDESIT COMPANY OSTERREICH GES. M.B.H—See Whirlpool Corporation; *U.S. Public*, pg. 2367
INNOWAVE MARKETING GROUP, LLC; *U.S. Private*, pg. 2084
INTEGRITY ELECTRONICS INC.; *U.S. Private*, pg. 2102
IP GANSOW GMBH—See Tennant Company; *U.S. Public*, pg. 2016
IROBOT AUSTRIA GMBH—See iRobot Corp.; *U.S. Public*, pg. 1171
ITEKNIK HOLDING CORPORATION; *U.S. Public*, pg. 1175
JAIR ELECTRONICS CORPORATION; *U.S. Private*, pg. 2182
JARDINIER CORP.; *U.S. Private*, pg. 2188
JEL MARKETING (VIETNAM) JOINT VENTURE CO., LTD.—See GSH Corporation Limited; *Int'l*, pg. 3144
JERDON STYLE LLC; *U.S. Private*, pg. 2201
JET.COM, INC.—See Walmart Inc.; *U.S. Public*, pg. 2325
J.H. FAGAN COMPANY; *U.S. Private*, pg. 2165
JITCO GROUP LIMITED; *U.S. Private*, pg. 2211
J & J MUNICIPAL SUPPLY, INC.—See Core & Main, Inc.; *U.S. Public*, pg. 576
KABCORP, INC.; *U.S. Private*, pg. 2253
KAJIHARA INDUSTRIAL CO., LTD.—See Denkyo Group Holdings Co.,Ltd.; *Int'l*, pg. 2028
KANGAS & ASSOCIATES, LLC; *U.S. Private*, pg. 2260
KARAN ELECTRIC MANUFACTURING LIMITED—See Allan International Holdings Limited; *Int'l*, pg. 332
KARINPIA CO., LTD.—See Doshisha Co., Ltd.; *Int'l*, pg. 2180
KELTECH, INC.—See Bradford-White Corporation; *U.S. Private*, pg. 632
KING OF FANS, INC.; *U.S. Private*, pg. 2309
KINGSTON SALES CORPORATION—See Paychex, Inc.; *U.S. Public*, pg. 1655
KITAMURA CO., LTD.—See Culture Convenience Club Co., Ltd.; *Int'l*, pg. 1877
LASONIC ELECTRONICS CORPORATION; *U.S. Private*, pg. 2395
L&D APPLIANCES CORPORATION; *U.S. Private*, pg. 2362
LES FABRICATIONS HAMMOND QUEBEC INC—See Hammond Manufacturing Co. Ltd.; *Int'l*, pg. 3238
LINWAVE TECHNOLOGY LIMITED—See Alaris Holdings Limited; *Int'l*, pg. 291
LIVERPOOL ENTERPRISES INC.; *U.S. Private*, pg. 2473
LUFTHANSA WORLDSHOP GMBH—See Deutsche Lufthansa AG; *Int'l*, pg. 2070
MACLEAN ELECTRICAL (AUSTRALIA) PTY LTD.—See DNOW Inc.; *U.S. Public*, pg. 671
MAGNADYNE CORPORATION; *U.S. Private*, pg. 2546
MARANTZ AMERICA INC.—See Bain Capital, LP; *U.S. Private*, pg. 438
MAR-CONE APPLIANCE PARTS CENTER INC.—See Mar-Cone Appliance Parts Co.; *U.S. Private*, pg. 2569
MAS, INC.; *U.S. Private*, pg. 2600
MAYTAG COMERCIAL, S. DE R.L. DE C.V.—See Whirlpool Corporation; *U.S. Public*, pg. 2367
M. BLOCK & SONS, INC.; *U.S. Private*, pg. 2526
MDM COMMERCIAL ENTERPRISES, INC.; *U.S. Private*, pg. 2646
MEDIA MARKT TV-HIFI-ELEKTRO GMBH FRANKFURT—See Ceconomy AG; *Int'l*, pg. 1381
MERCATOR BH D.O.O.—See Fortenova Group d.d.; *Int'l*, pg. 2738
METRO APPLIANCES & MORE; *U.S. Private*, pg. 2685
METRO APPLIANCES & MORE—See Metro Appliances & More; *U.S. Private*, pg. 2685
MILESTONE DISTRIBUTORS INC.; *U.S. Private*, pg. 2728
MITO CORPORATION; *U.S. Private*, pg. 2751
MKS INDUSTRIES INCORPORATED; *U.S. Private*, pg. 2753
MOLEX CONNECTIVITY GMBH—See Koch Industries, Inc.; *U.S. Private*, pg. 2334
MONTE CARLO CEILING FAN COMPANY—See AEA Investors LP; *U.S. Private*, pg. 114
MOORE FANS LTD—See Moore Fans LLC; *U.S. Private*, pg. 2780
MOUNTAIN WEST DISTRIBUTORS; *U.S. Private*, pg. 2800
MRC GLOBAL (FINLAND) OY—See MRC Global Inc.; *U.S. Public*, pg. 1480
MULTIMEDIA DEVICES LIMITED—See Alco Holdings Limited; *Int'l*, pg. 301
NATIONAL BRANDS, INC.; *U.S. Private*, pg. 2849
NAVARRE DISTRIBUTION SERVICES, INC.—See WYNIT, Inc.; *U.S. Private*, pg. 4576
NDA DISTRIBUTORS, LLC.—See Elbi S.P.A.; *Int'l*, pg. 2344
NELSON & SMALL INC.; *U.S. Private*, pg. 2883

NEWELL OPERATING COMPANY—See Newell Brands Inc.; *U.S. Public*, pg. 1514
NINGBO XINGPU FIVE STAR APPLIANCE CO., LTD—See Best Buy Co., Inc.; *U.S. Public*, pg. 326
NISHIHATSU CO., LTD.—See Denyo Co., Ltd.; *Int'l*, pg. 2040
NOW NETHERLANDS B.V.—See DNOW Inc.; *U.S. Public*, pg. 671
NUHC, INC.—See Arrow Electronics, Inc.; *U.S. Public*, pg. 199
OREGON SCIENTIFIC BRASIL LTDA—See IDT International Limited; *Int'l*, pg. 3597
OREGON SCIENTIFIC FRANCE S.A.R.L.—See IDT International Limited; *Int'l*, pg. 3597
OREGON SCIENTIFIC IBERICA, S.A.—See IDT International Limited; *Int'l*, pg. 3597
OREGON SCIENTIFIC, INC.—See IDT International Limited; *Int'l*, pg. 3597
OWLET, INC.; *U.S. Public*, pg. 1628
OY ELECTROLUX KOTITALOUSKONEET AB—See AB Electrolux; *Int'l*, pg. 41
PERTAMA HOLDINGS LIMITED—See Harvey Norman Holdings Ltd; *Int'l*, pg. 3281
PIFCO LTD.—See Spectrum Brands Holdings, Inc.; *U.S. Public*, pg. 1916
PIONEER ELECTRONICS SERVICE—See EQT AB; *Int'l*, pg. 2470
PIONEER ELECTRONICS TECHNOLOGY—See EQT AB; *Int'l*, pg. 2470
PIONEER ELECTRONICS (USA) INC.—See EQT AB; *Int'l*, pg. 2470
PIONEER NORTH AMERICA INC.—See EQT AB; *Int'l*, pg. 2470
PLUG-INS ELECTRONIX—See Al-Futtaim Private Company LLC; *Int'l*, pg. 285
POWR-FLITE—See Tacony Corporation; *U.S. Private*, pg. 3921
PRECISION TRADING CORP.; *U.S. Private*, pg. 3247
PROCTER & GAMBLE (MALAYSIA) SDN. BHD.—See The Procter & Gamble Company; *U.S. Public*, pg. 2121
PT. HITACHI MODERN SALES INDONESIA—See Hitachi, Ltd.; *Int'l*, pg. 3424
QVC ESERVICE LLC & CO. KG—See Qurate Retail, Inc.; *U.S. Public*, pg. 1758
QVC HANDEL S.A R.L. & CO. KG—See Qurate Retail, Inc.; *U.S. Public*, pg. 1758
RADIO DISTRIBUTING CO.; *U.S. Private*, pg. 3343
RAYOVAC ARGENTINA SRL—See Energizer Holdings, Inc.; *U.S. Public*, pg. 761
RAYOVAC CHILE SOCIEDAD COMERCIAL LTDA—See Energizer Holdings, Inc.; *U.S. Public*, pg. 761
RAYOVAC COSTA RICA, SA—See Energizer Holdings, Inc.; *U.S. Public*, pg. 761
RAYOVAC DOMINICAN REPUBLIC, SA—See Energizer Holdings, Inc.; *U.S. Public*, pg. 761
RAYOVAC EL SALVADOR SA DE CV—See Energizer Holdings, Inc.; *U.S. Public*, pg. 761
R&B WHOLESALE DISTRIBUTORS; *U.S. Private*, pg. 3331
REALFLEET CO., LTD.—See BALS CORPORATION; *Int'l*, pg. 811
RED PEACOCK INTERNATIONAL, INC.; *U.S. Private*, pg. 3375
REMINGTON CONSUMER PRODUCTS (IRELAND) LTD.—See Spectrum Brands Holdings, Inc.; *U.S. Public*, pg. 1916
REMINGTON CONSUMER PRODUCTS—See Spectrum Brands Holdings, Inc.; *U.S. Public*, pg. 1916
REMINGTON PRODUCTS NEW ZEALAND LTD.—See Spectrum Brands Holdings, Inc.; *U.S. Public*, pg. 1916
RESOURCE PARTNERS ENTERPRISES, LLC—See Suarez Corporation Industries; *U.S. Private*, pg. 3847
RETAIL PARTNERS COLRUYT GROUP NV—See Colruyt Group N.V.; *Int'l*, pg. 1705
RIEMAN & ARSZMAN CUSTOM DISTRIBUTORS; *U.S. Private*, pg. 3434
RIGGS DISTRIBUTING, INC.; *U.S. Private*, pg. 3435
RODNIC LLC—See Benchmark Electronics, Inc.; *U.S. Public*, pg. 296
RTO DISTRIBUTION INC—See goeasy Ltd.; *Int'l*, pg. 3021
SADCO, INC.; *U.S. Private*, pg. 3522
SAVITECH CORP.—See Diodes Incorporated; *U.S. Public*, pg. 667
SCHULER INC.—See ANDRITZ AG; *Int'l*, pg. 456
SELECTCOMFORT.COM CORPORATION—See Sleep Number Corporation; *U.S. Public*, pg. 1894
SHARKNINJA EUROPE LIMITED—See SharkNinja, Inc.; *U.S. Public*, pg. 1873
SHARP CORPORATION MEXICO S.A DE C.V.—See Hon Hai Precision Industry Co., Ltd.; *Int'l*, pg. 3458
SHARP CORPORATION MEXICO, S.A. DE C.V.—See Hon Hai Precision Industry Co., Ltd.; *Int'l*, pg. 3458
SHARP CORPORATION OF AUSTRALIA PTY. LTD.—See Hon Hai Precision Industry Co., Ltd.; *Int'l*, pg. 3458
SHARP CORPORATION OF NEW ZEALAND LTD.—See Hon Hai Precision Industry Co., Ltd.; *Int'l*, pg. 3458
SHARP ELECTRONICS BENELUX B.V.—See Hon Hai Precision Industry Co., Ltd.; *Int'l*, pg. 3458
SHARP ELECTRONICS CORP. - HUNTINGTON BEACH

CORPORATE AFFILIATIONS

OFFICE—See Hon Hai Precision Industry Co., Ltd.; *Int'l*, pg. 3458
SHARP ELECTRONICS (EUROPE) GMBH—See Hon Hai Precision Industry Co., Ltd.; *Int'l*, pg. 3458
SHARP ELECTRONICS (EUROPE) GMBH—See Hon Hai Precision Industry Co., Ltd.; *Int'l*, pg. 3458
SHARP ELECTRONICS FRANCE S.A.—See Hon Hai Precision Industry Co., Ltd.; *Int'l*, pg. 3458
SHARP ELECTRONICS INCORPORATED OF KOREA—See Hon Hai Precision Industry Co., Ltd.; *Int'l*, pg. 3458
SHARP ELECTRONICS (NORDIC) AB—See Hon Hai Precision Industry Co., Ltd.; *Int'l*, pg. 3458
SHARP ELECTRONICS OF CANADA LTD.—See Hon Hai Precision Industry Co., Ltd.; *Int'l*, pg. 3458
SHARP ELECTRONICS (SCHWEIZ) AG—See Hon Hai Precision Industry Co., Ltd.; *Int'l*, pg. 3458
SHARP HONG KONG LIMITED—See Hon Hai Precision Industry Co., Ltd.; *Int'l*, pg. 3458
SHARP MIDDLE EAST FREE ZONE ESTABLISHMENT—See Hon Hai Precision Industry Co., Ltd.; *Int'l*, pg. 3458
SHARP-ROXY SALES & SERVICE CO (M) SDN. BHD.—See Hon Hai Precision Industry Co., Ltd.; *Int'l*, pg. 3457
SHARP-ROXY SALES (SINGAPORE) PTE., LTD.—See Hon Hai Precision Industry Co., Ltd.; *Int'l*, pg. 3459
SHARP THAI CO., LTD.—See Hon Hai Precision Industry Co., Ltd.; *Int'l*, pg. 3459
SHARP TRADING CORPORATION—See Hon Hai Precision Industry Co., Ltd.; *Int'l*, pg. 3459
SHENZHEN MALIMALIBOX TRADING CORPORATION LIMITED—See Eastern Holding Limited; *Int'l*, pg. 2272
SIANO APPLIANCE DISTRIBUTORS; *U.S. Private*, pg. 3645
SIERRA SELECT DISTRIBUTORS; *U.S. Private*, pg. 3647
SIGNAL PERFECTION LTD.—See Marlin Equity Partners, LLC; *U.S. Private*, pg. 2583
SINO ELECTRONICS LIMITED—See Central Wealth Group Holdings Limited; *Int'l*, pg. 1410
SLI SYLVANIA S.A.—See Havell's India Ltd.; *Int'l*, pg. 3286
SMARTWARES—See H2 Equity Partners B.V.; *Int'l*, pg. 3199
SOKE-HUNGARIA KFT—See Newell Brands Inc.; *U.S. Public*, pg. 1515
SOUTHEASTERN APPLIANCES AND MORE, LLC—See The Climatic Corporation; *U.S. Private*, pg. 4010
SPECTRUM BRANDS AUSTRALIA PTY. LTD.—See Spectrum Brands Holdings, Inc.; *U.S. Public*, pg. 1916
SPECTRUM BRANDS DENMARK A/S—See Spectrum Brands Holdings, Inc.; *U.S. Public*, pg. 1916
SPECTRUM BRANDS EUROPE GMBH—See Spectrum Brands Holdings, Inc.; *U.S. Public*, pg. 1916
SPECTRUM BRANDS HHI MEXICO, S DE RL DE C.V.—See Spectrum Brands Holdings, Inc.; *U.S. Public*, pg. 1916
SPECTRUM BRANDS HHI (SHENZHEN) CO., LTD—See Spectrum Brands Holdings, Inc.; *U.S. Public*, pg. 1916
SPECTRUM BRANDS HHI (ZHONGSHAN) CO., LTD—See Spectrum Brands Holdings, Inc.; *U.S. Public*, pg. 1916
SPECTRUM BRANDS ITALIA S.R.L.—See Spectrum Brands Holdings, Inc.; *U.S. Public*, pg. 1916
SPECTRUM BRANDS NORWAY AS—See Spectrum Brands Holdings, Inc.; *U.S. Public*, pg. 1916
SPECTRUM BRANDS SINGAPORE PRIVATE LIMITED—See Spectrum Brands Holdings, Inc.; *U.S. Public*, pg. 1916
SPECTRUM BRANDS (UK) LIMITED—See Spectrum Brands Holdings, Inc.; *U.S. Public*, pg. 1916
SPOT COOLERS INC.; *U.S. Private*, pg. 3761
STANLEY SECURITY OY—See Stanley Black & Decker, Inc.; *U.S. Public*, pg. 1935
STELLAR MANAGEMENT GROUP, INC.; *U.S. Private*, pg. 3799
SUB-ZERO GROUP EAST LLC; *U.S. Private*, pg. 3847
SUES, YOUNG & BROWN INC.; *U.S. Private*, pg. 3849
SUNDAY CO., LTD.—See AEON Co., Ltd.; *Int'l*, pg. 178
SWEEGEN, INC.; *U.S. Public*, pg. 1968
TACONY CORPORATION; *U.S. Private*, pg. 3921
TAMPA BAY SYSTEMS SALES INC.; *U.S. Private*, pg. 3929
TAOBAO—See Alibaba Group Holding Limited; *Int'l*, pg. 326
TEAC AMERICA, INC.—See Evolution Capital Management LLC; *U.S. Private*, pg. 1443
TECH DATA HUNGARY KFT.—See TD Synnex Corp; *U.S. Public*, pg. 1986
TECH DATA MOBILE BELGIUM, BVBA—See TD Synnex Corp; *U.S. Public*, pg. 1986
TEPELNE HOSPODARSTVI MESTA USTI NAD LABEM S.R.O.—See CEZ, a.s.; *Int'l*, pg. 1428
TEPLO KLASTEREC S.R.O.—See CEZ, a.s.; *Int'l*, pg. 1429
THEBRANDHOUSE LTD—See Cim Financial Services Limited; *Int'l*, pg. 1607
THORN GROUP LIMITED—See ICM Limited; *Int'l*, pg. 3582
TIGER CORP. DIRECT, INC.—See Insight Enterprises, Inc.; *U.S. Public*, pg. 1130
TREVARROW INC.; *U.S. Private*, pg. 4219
TRIBLES INC.; *U.S. Private*, pg. 4227
TRI STATE DISTRIBUTORS INC.; *U.S. Private*, pg. 4221

N.A.I.C.S. INDEX

423690 — OTHER ELECTRONIC PA...

TROJAN ELECTRONIC SUPPLY CO., INC.; *U.S. Private,* pg. 4241
TROXELL COMMUNICATIONS, INC.—See AEA Investors LP; *U.S. Public,* pg. 116
TRUE FABRICATIONS; *U.S. Private,* pg. 4247
TUPPERWARE FRANCE S.A.—See Tupperware Brands Corporation; *U.S. Public,* pg. 2204
TV SPECIALISTS INC.; *U.S. Private,* pg. 4263
T&W SALES INC.; *U.S. Private,* pg. 3910
UAB ABC DATA LIETUVA—See Droege Group AG; *Int'l,* pg. 2205
UPSTATE ELECTRONIC WHOLESALERS; *U.S. Private,* pg. 4313
VERTICAL CUBED—See Fine Sounds S.p.A.; *Int'l,* pg. 2673
VICMARR AUDIO INC.; *U.S. Private,* pg. 4377
VIEWSONIC AUSTRALIA PTY. LTD.—See ViewSonic Corporation; *U.S. Private,* pg. 4381
VIEWSONIC CHINA LIMITED—See ViewSonic Corporation; *U.S. Private,* pg. 4381
VIEWSONIC HONG KONG LTD—See ViewSonic Corporation; *U.S. Private,* pg. 4381
VIEWSONIC SINGAPORE PTE LTD—See ViewSonic Corporation; *U.S. Private,* pg. 4381
VIEWSONIC TECHNOLOGY GMBH—See ViewSonic Corporation; *U.S. Private,* pg. 4381
VIKING RANGE, LLC; *U.S. Private,* pg. 4382
VISTA WEST, INC.; *U.S. Private,* pg. 4403
VOXX ACCESSORIES CORP.; *U.S. Private,* pg. 4414
VOXX ELECTRONICS CORPORATION—See VOXX International Corporation; *U.S. Public,* pg. 2311
VSM SEWING INC.—See Platinum Equity, LLC; *U.S. Private,* pg. 3208
WELTRONICS CORP.; *U.S. Private,* pg. 4480
WESTAR CONTRACT KITCHEN & BATH CORP.; *U.S. Private,* pg. 4488
WHIRLPOOL AUSTRIA GMBH—See Whirlpool Corporation; *U.S. Public,* pg. 2367
WHIRLPOOL BULGARIA LTD.—See Whirlpool Corporation; *U.S. Public,* pg. 2367
WHIRLPOOL CROATIA LTD.—See Whirlpool Corporation; *U.S. Public,* pg. 2367
WHIRLPOOL EESTI OU—See Whirlpool Corporation; *U.S. Public,* pg. 2367
WHIRLPOOL GERMANY GMBH—See Whirlpool Corporation; *U.S. Public,* pg. 2367
WHIRLPOOL LATVIA S.I.A.—See Whirlpool Corporation; *U.S. Public,* pg. 2368
WHIRLPOOL MAROC S. AR.L.—See Whirlpool Corporation; *U.S. Public,* pg. 2368
WHIRLPOOL MICROWAVE PRODUCTS DEVELOPMENT LIMITED—See Whirlpool Corporation; *U.S. Public,* pg. 2368
WHIRLPOOL NORDIC A/S—See Whirlpool Corporation; *U.S. Public,* pg. 2368
WHIRLPOOL R&D S.R.L.—See Whirlpool Corporation; *U.S. Public,* pg. 2368
WHIRLPOOL SOUTHEAST ASIA PTE. LTD.—See Whirlpool Corporation; *U.S. Public,* pg. 2367
WHOLESALE ELECTRONIC SUPPLY, INC.; *U.S. Private,* pg. 4514
WIRELESS XCESSORIES GROUP, INC.; *U.S. Public,* pg. 2376
THE W.L. MAY COMPANY; *U.S. Private,* pg. 4132
WUHAN GOME ELECTRICAL APPLIANCE COMPANY LIMITED—See Gome Retail Holdings Limited; *Int'l,* pg. 3037
WYNIT DISTRIBUTION, LLC—See WYNIT, Inc.; *U.S. Private,* pg. 4576
XPRICE INC.—See DCM Holdings Co., Ltd.; *Int'l,* pg. 1992
YAMAHA ELECTRONICS MARKETING CORPORATION—See Hojgaard Holding A/S; *Int'l,* pg. 3442
ZEON LIMITED—See Herald Holdings Limited; *Int'l,* pg. 3358

423690 — OTHER ELECTRONIC PARTS AND EQUIPMENT MERCHANT WHOLESALERS

3M COLOMBIA S.A.—See 3M Company; *U.S. Public,* pg. 5
3 STEP IT AS—See 3 Step It Group Oy; *Int'l,* pg. 6
3 STEP IT (HONG KONG) LIMITED—See 3 Step It Group Oy; *Int'l,* pg. 6
3 STEP IT, INC.—See 3 Step It Group Oy; *Int'l,* pg. 6
3 STEP IT MALAYSIA SDN. BHD.—See 3 Step It Group Oy; *Int'l,* pg. 6
3 STEP IT OU—See 3 Step It Group Oy; *Int'l,* pg. 6
3 STEP IT SINGAPORE PTE LTD.—See 3 Step It Group Oy; *Int'l,* pg. 6
3 STEP IT SWEDEN AB—See 3 Step It Group Oy; *Int'l,* pg. 6
3 STEP IT UAB—See 3 Step It Group Oy; *Int'l,* pg. 6
3 STEP IT (UK) LIMITED—See 3 Step It Group Oy; *Int'l,* pg. 6
49ER COMMUNICATIONS; *U.S. Private,* pg. 15
7C SOLARPARKEN NV—See 7C Solarparken AG; *Int'l,* pg. 15
911 HELP NOW, LLC—See Global Technologies, Ltd.; *U.S. Public,* pg. 945
A3 MULTIMEDIA S.L.U.—See Atresmedia Corporacion de Medios de Comunicacion, S.A.; *Int'l,* pg. 693
AAA SUNDRIES INC.; *U.S. Private,* pg. 30
AAEON TECHNOLOGY (EUROPE) B.V.—See ASUSTeK Computer Inc.; *Int'l,* pg. 663
AAEON TECHNOLOGY SINGAPORE PTE LTD—See ASUSTeK Computer Inc.; *Int'l,* pg. 663
ABB STOTZ-KONTAKT/STRIEBEL & JOHN VERTRIEBS-GMBH—See ABB Ltd.; *Int'l,* pg. 50
ABCO ENERGY, INC.; *U.S. Public,* pg. 24
ABC PHONES OF NORTH CAROLINA, INC.; *U.S. Private,* pg. 36
ABILIS SYSTEMS LLC—See ALi Corporation; *Int'l,* pg. 320
ABRACON LLC—See Genstar Capital, LLC; *U.S. Private,* pg. 1673
ACAL AUSTRALIA PTY. LTD.—See discoverIE Group plc; *Int'l,* pg. 2132
ACAL BFI BELGIUM NV/SA—See discoverIE Group plc; *Int'l,* pg. 2132
ACAL BFI DENMARK—See discoverIE Group plc; *Int'l,* pg. 2132
ACAL BFI FRANCE SAS—See discoverIE Group plc; *Int'l,* pg. 2132
ACAL BFI GERMANY GMBH—See discoverIE Group plc; *Int'l,* pg. 2132
ACAL BFI GERMANY GMBH—See discoverIE Group plc; *Int'l,* pg. 2132
ACAL BFI GERMANY GMBH—See discoverIE Group plc; *Int'l,* pg. 2132
ACAL BFI IBERIA SLU—See discoverIE Group plc; *Int'l,* pg. 2132
ACAL BFI ITALY S.R.L.—See discoverIE Group plc; *Int'l,* pg. 2132
ACAL BFI ITALY SR—See discoverIE Group plc; *Int'l,* pg. 2132
ACAL BFI NETHERLANDS BV—See discoverIE Group plc; *Int'l,* pg. 2132
ACAL BFI NETHERLANDS BV—See discoverIE Group plc; *Int'l,* pg. 2133
ACAL BFI NORDIC AB—See discoverIE Group plc; *Int'l,* pg. 2133
ACAL BFI NORDIC AB—See discoverIE Group plc; *Int'l,* pg. 2133
ACAL BFI UK LTD—See discoverIE Group plc; *Int'l,* pg. 2132
ACAL BFI UK LTD—See discoverIE Group plc; *Int'l,* pg. 2132
ACAL NEDERLAND BV—See discoverIE Group plc; *Int'l,* pg. 2133
ACCEL AB—See Littelfuse, Inc.; *U.S. Public,* pg. 1326
ACCELINK TECHNOLOGIES EUROPE GMBH—See Accelink Technologies Co., Ltd.; *Int'l,* pg. 80
ACCELONIX IBERICA S.L.—See Accelonix Limited; *Int'l,* pg. 81
ACCESS CATALOG COMPANY LLC—See Centric Group LLC; *U.S. Private,* pg. 830
ACCESS CONTROL TECHNOLOGIES, INC.—See Clearlake Capital Group, L.P.; *U.S. Private,* pg. 935
ACC GERMANY GMBH—See Guangzhou Wanbao Group Co., Ltd.; *Int'l,* pg. 3168
ACCRELIST MEDICAL AESTHETICS (BM) PTE. LTD.—See Accrelist Ltd.; *Int'l,* pg. 93
ACCRELIST MEDICAL AESTHETICS (LOT1) PTE. LTD.—See Accrelist Ltd.; *Int'l,* pg. 93
ACCRELIST MEDICAL AESTHETICS (PENANG) SDN. BHD.—See Accrelist Ltd.; *Int'l,* pg. 93
ACCRELIST MEDICAL AESTHETICS (SPC) PTE. LTD.—See Accrelist Ltd.; *Int'l,* pg. 93
ACCTON TECHNOLOGY CORP—See Accton Technology Corporation; *Int'l,* pg. 93
ACCURIS NETWORKS LIMITED—See ESW Capital, LLC; *U.S. Private,* pg. 1431
ACCURIS NETWORKS MALAYSIA SDN. BHD.—See ESW Capital, LLC; *U.S. Private,* pg. 1431
ACCU-TECH CORPORATION—See WESCO International, Inc.; *U.S. Public,* pg. 2350
ACE OFFICE SOLUTIONS INC.—See Hon Hai Precision Industry Co., Ltd.; *Int'l,* pg. 3458
ACM RESEARCH (SHANGHAI), INC.—See Acm Research, Inc.; *U.S. Public,* pg. 35
ACTIFY LLC—See Hainan Traffic Administration Holding Co., Ltd.; *Int'l,* pg. 3215
ACTION ASIA (SHENZHEN) CO., LTD.—See Action Electronics Co., Ltd.; *Int'l,* pg. 119
ACTIONS TECHNOLOGY (HK) COMPANY LIMITED—See Actions Semiconductor Co., Ltd.; *Int'l,* pg. 119
ACTION TECHNOLOGY (JIAN) CO., LTD.—See Action Electronics Co., Ltd.; *Int'l,* pg. 119
ACTIV8 DISTRIBUTION LTD.; *Int'l,* pg. 119
ADAMS GLOBAL COMMUNICATIONS, LLC—See ADDvantage Technologies Group, Inc.; *U.S. Public,* pg. 40
ADATA TECHNOLOGY MEXICO SDRL DE CV—See ADATA Technology Co., Ltd.; *Int'l,* pg. 126
ADDVANTAGE TECHNOLOGIES GROUP OF MISSOURI INC—See Leveling 8, Inc.; *U.S. Private,* pg. 2434
ADDVANTAGE TECHNOLOGIES GROUP OF TEXAS—See Leveling 8, Inc.; *U.S. Private,* pg. 2434
ADEMCO 1 GMBH—See Resideo Technologies, Inc.; *U.S. Public,* pg. 1789
ADEMCO 1 LIMITED—See Resideo Technologies, Inc.; *U.S. Public,* pg. 1789
ADEMCO AUSTRIA GMBH—See Resideo Technologies, Inc.; *U.S. Public,* pg. 1789
ADEMCO CZ S.R.O.—See Resideo Technologies, Inc.; *U.S. Public,* pg. 1789
ADEMCO OTOMASYON LIMITED SIRKETI—See Resideo Technologies, Inc.; *U.S. Public,* pg. 1789
ADEMCO (PTY) LTD.—See Resideo Technologies, Inc.; *U.S. Public,* pg. 1789
ADEMCO SUPPLY S.R.L.—See Resideo Technologies, Inc.; *U.S. Public,* pg. 1789
ADI AMERICAN DISTRIBUTORS LLC—See Promus Holdings, LLC; *U.S. Private,* pg. 3283
ADI AMERICAN DISTRIBUTORS LLC—See Stonebridge Partners, LLC; *U.S. Private,* pg. 3827
ADVANCED FIBER RESOURCES (HK) LTD.—See Advanced Fiber Resources (Zhuhai) Ltd; *Int'l,* pg. 159
ADVANCED MICRO DEVICES, S.A.—See Advanced Micro Devices, Inc.; *U.S. Public,* pg. 48
ADVANCED NETWORK PRODUCTS, INC.—See Wells Fargo & Company; *U.S. Public,* pg. 2344
ADVANIDE GMBH—See Development Bank of Japan, Inc.; *Int'l,* pg. 2087
ADVANIDE INC.—See Development Bank of Japan, Inc.; *Int'l,* pg. 2087
ADVANIDE PTE. LTD.—See Development Bank of Japan, Inc.; *Int'l,* pg. 2087
ADVANTECH CO. SINGAPORE PTE. LTD.—See Advantech Co., Ltd.; *Int'l,* pg. 164
ADVA OPTICAL NETWORKING AB—See ADTRAN Holdings, Inc.; *U.S. Public,* pg. 44
ADVA OPTICAL NETWORKING (INDIA) PRIVATE LTD.—See ADTRAN Holdings, Inc.; *U.S. Public,* pg. 44
ADVA OPTICAL NETWORKING LTD.—See ADTRAN Holdings, Inc.; *U.S. Public,* pg. 44
ADVA OPTICAL NETWORKING PTY LTD.—See ADTRAN Holdings, Inc.; *U.S. Public,* pg. 44
ADVA OPTICAL NETWORKING SERVICOS BRAZIL LTDA.—See ADTRAN Holdings, Inc.; *U.S. Public,* pg. 44
ADVA OPTICAL NETWORKING SE—See ADTRAN Holdings, Inc.; *U.S. Public,* pg. 44
ADVA OPTICAL NETWORKING SE—See ADTRAN Holdings, Inc.; *U.S. Public,* pg. 44
ADVA OPTICAL NETWORKING SE—See ADTRAN Holdings, Inc.; *U.S. Public,* pg. 44
ADVA OPTICAL NETWORKING SE—See ADTRAN Holdings, Inc.; *U.S. Public,* pg. 44
ADVA OPTICAL NETWORKING SE—See ADTRAN Holdings, Inc.; *U.S. Public,* pg. 44
ADVA OPTICAL NETWORKING SINGAPORE PTE. LTD.—See ADTRAN Holdings, Inc.; *U.S. Public,* pg. 44
ADVA OPTICAL NETWORKING TRADING (SHENZHEN) LTD.—See ADTRAN Holdings, Inc.; *U.S. Public,* pg. 44
ADVENT-AWI HOLDINGS INC.; *Int'l,* pg. 167
ADVENT MARKETING INC.—See Advent-AWI Holdings Inc.; *Int'l,* pg. 167
AEE SOLAR, INC.—See Sunrun Inc.; *U.S. Public,* pg. 1965
A.E. PETSCHE BELGIUM BVBA—See Arrow Electronics, Inc.; *U.S. Public,* pg. 194
A.E. PETSCHE CANADA, INC.—See Arrow Electronics, Inc.; *U.S. Public,* pg. 194
A.E. PETSCHE UK LIMITED—See Arrow Electronics, Inc.; *U.S. Public,* pg. 195
A-GAS ELECTRONIC MATERIALS LTD—See A-Gas Limited; *Int'l,* pg. 19
AGC ELECTRONICS SINGAPORE PTE. LTD.—See AGC Inc.; *Int'l,* pg. 201
AHI ELECTRONICS WAREHOUSE (HANG ZHOU) CO., LTD.—See Audix Corporation; *Int'l,* pg. 702
AHI ELECTRONICS WAREHOUSE (WU JIANG) CO., LTD.—See Audix Corporation; *Int'l,* pg. 702
AHM ENGINEERING COMPANY LIMITED—See CCT Fortis Holdings Limited; *Int'l,* pg. 1369
AICHI MAGFINE TECHNOLOGY (PINGHU) CO., LTD.—See Aichi Steel Corporation; *Int'l,* pg. 230
AIPHONE CORPORATION—See Aiphone Co., Ltd.; *Int'l,* pg. 235
AIPHONE PTE. LTD.—See Aiphone Co., Ltd.; *Int'l,* pg. 235
AIPHONE PTY LTD.—See Aiphone Co., Ltd.; *Int'l,* pg. 235
AIPHONE SHANGHAI CO., LTD.—See Aiphone Co., Ltd.; *Int'l,* pg. 235
AIPHONE UK LIMITED—See Aiphone Co., Ltd.; *Int'l,* pg. 235
AIRGAIN, INC.; *U.S. Public,* pg. 68
AITECH RUGGED COMPUTER SYSTEMS; *U.S. Private,* pg. 143
AKM SEMICONDUCTOR, INC.—See Asahi Kasei Corporation; *Int'l,* pg. 595
ALCORLINK CORP.; *Int'l,* pg. 303
ALEGRE PTY LTD—See Assurant, Inc.; *U.S. Public,* pg. 214
ALEXANDER SCHNEIDER LTD.; *Int'l,* pg. 307
ALGAR S.P.A—See Fuji Corporation; *Int'l,* pg. 2809
ALI ZAID AL-QURAISHI & BROTHERS CO.; *Int'l,* pg. 323
ALL ACCESS COMMUNICATION TECHNOLOGY (SHEN-

423690 — OTHER ELECTRONIC PA...

ZHEN) LIMITED—See China All Access (Holdings) Limited; *Int'l*, pg. 1482
ALL AMERICAN SEMICONDUCTOR, LLC; *U.S. Private*, pg. 170
ALLAN CRAWFORD ASSOCIATES LIMITED; *Int'l*, pg. 332
ALL CONTROL ENTERPRISES INC.; *U.S. Private*, pg. 170
ALLFAX SPECIALTIES INC.; *U.S. Private*, pg. 181
ALLIANCE WIRELESS TECHNOLOGIES, INC.—See Terex Corporation; *U.S. Public*, pg. 2019
ALLIED ENTERPRISES INC.; *U.S. Private*, pg. 186
ALLSTAR MAGNETICS INC.; *U.S. Private*, pg. 193
ALLTRONICS MANUFACTURING (SHENZHEN) LIMITED—See Alltronics Holdings Limited; *Int'l*, pg. 361
ALMO PROFESSIONAL A/V—See DCC plc; *Int'l*, pg. 1989
ALPHA METALS (TAIWAN) INC—See Element Solutions Inc.; *U.S. Public*, pg. 726
ALPHA NETHERLANDS B.V.—See Element Solutions Inc.; *U.S. Public*, pg. 726
ALPHA NETWORKS INC.—See Alpha Networks Inc.; *Int'l*, pg. 369
ALPHA ONE LIMITED—See Digilife Technologies Limited; *Int'l*, pg. 2119
ALPHA TECHNICAL AND SERVICES INC.—See Alpha Networks Inc.; *Int'l*, pg. 369
ALPHA TELECOM INC.; *U.S. Private*, pg. 200
ALPS ELECTRIC (THAILAND) CO., LTD.—See Alps Alpine Co., Ltd.; *Int'l*, pg. 375
ALPS ELECTRONICS TAIWAN CO., LTD.—See Alps Alpine Co., Ltd.; *Int'l*, pg. 375
ALPS (SHANGHAI) INTERNATIONAL TRADING CO., LTD.—See Alps Alpine Co., Ltd.; *Int'l*, pg. 375
ALSO MPS GMBH—See Droege Group AG; *Int'l*, pg. 2205
ALSO NORDIC HOLDING OY—See Droege Group AG; *Int'l*, pg. 2205
ALTERNERGY LIMITED; *Int'l*, pg. 392
ALTER S.R.L.—See MKS Instruments, Inc.; *U.S. Public*, pg. 1452
ALTEX ELECTRONICS, LTD.; *U.S. Private*, pg. 208
ALTURNA DIRECT N.V.—See Amphenol Corporation; *U.S. Public*, pg. 126
AMACOM HOLDING BV—See DCC plc; *Int'l*, pg. 1989
AMBER TECHNOLOGY (NZ) LIMITED—See Ambertech Limited; *Int'l*, pg. 414
AMD JAPAN LTD.—See Advanced Micro Devices, Inc.; *U.S. Public*, pg. 48
AMERC OY—See ANTA Sports Products Limited; *Int'l*, pg. 481
AMERICA ACTION INC.—See Action Electronics Co., Ltd.; *Int'l*, pg. 119
AMERICA II ELECTRONICS, INC.; *U.S. Private*, pg. 220
AMERICAN CABLING & COMMUNICATIONS INC.—See North American Video Corporation; *U.S. Private*, pg. 2941
AMERICAN CONEC CORPORATION—See Amphenol Corporation; *U.S. Public*, pg. 126
AMERICAN ELECTRONIC COMPONENTS INC.; *U.S. Private*, pg. 231
AMERICAN ELECTRONIC RESOURCE; *U.S. Private*, pg. 231
AMERICAN RADIO CORP.—See VOXX International Corporation; *U.S. Public*, pg. 2310
AMERICAN TELECOMMUNICATIONS INC.; *U.S. Private*, pg. 257
AMERICAN ZETTLER INCORPORATED—See Zettler Components, Inc.; *U.S. Private*, pg. 4603
AMETEK PANALARM PRODUCTS—See AMETEK, Inc.; *U.S. Public*, pg. 117
AMKOR TECHNOLOGY EUROSERVICES, S.A.R.L.—See Amkor Technology, Inc.; *U.S. Public*, pg. 124
AMKOR TECHNOLOGY JAPAN, K.K.—See Amkor Technology, Inc.; *U.S. Public*, pg. 124
AMKOR TECHNOLOGY SINGAPORE HOLDING PTE. LTD.—See Amkor Technology, Inc.; *U.S. Public*, pg. 124
AMMON & RIZOS COMPANY INC.; *U.S. Private*, pg. 264
AMPHENOL BENELUX B.V.—See Amphenol Corporation; *U.S. Public*, pg. 127
AMPHENOL (XIAMEN) HIGH SPEED CABLE CO., LTD.—See Amphenol Corporation; *U.S. Public*, pg. 126
AMS INTERNATIONAL AG—See ams AG; *Int'l*, pg. 440
AMS SEMICONDUCTORS INDIA PVT LTD—See ams AG; *Int'l*, pg. 440
AMTEL CELLULAR SDN. BHD.—See Amtel Holdings Berhad; *Int'l*, pg. 442
ANALOG DEVICES AS—See Analog Devices, Inc.; *U.S. Public*, pg. 134
ANALOG DEVICES INTERNATIONAL U.C.—See Analog Devices, Inc.; *U.S. Public*, pg. 134
ANALOG DEVICES NEDERLAND B.V.—See Analog Devices, Inc.; *U.S. Public*, pg. 135
ANALOG DEVICES S.A.S—See Analog Devices, Inc.; *U.S. Public*, pg. 135
ANALYSER SERVICES TRINIDAD LTD.—See Addtech AB; *Int'l*, pg. 131
ANAREN MICROWAVE (EUROPE), INC.—See TTM Technologies, Inc.; *U.S. Public*, pg. 2203
ANCESTRY.COM LLC—See Blackstone Inc.; *U.S. Public*, pg. 347

ANDERS + KERN (U.K.) LIMITED—See Aukett Swanke Group Plc; *Int'l*, pg. 704
ANDERSON INDUSTRIAL HONG KONG LIMITED—See Anderson Industrial Corporation; *Int'l*, pg. 450
ANDERSON POWER PRODUCTS, LTD.—See IDEAL Industries Inc; *U.S. Private*, pg. 2036
ANDRITZ HYDRO CORP.—See ANDRITZ AG; *Int'l*, pg. 453
ANDRITZ HYDRO GMBH - UKRAINE REPRESENTATIVE OFFICE—See ANDRITZ AG; *Int'l*, pg. 453
ANDRITZ HYDRO SA—See ANDRITZ AG; *Int'l*, pg. 453
ANIXTER BELGIUM B.V.B.A.—See WESCO International, Inc.; *U.S. Public*, pg. 2350
ANIXTER ILETISIM SISTEMLERI PAZARLAMA VE TICARET A.S.—See WESCO International, Inc.; *U.S. Public*, pg. 2350
ANRITSU COMPANY, S.A. DE C.V—See Anritsu Corporation; *Int'l*, pg. 475
ANRITSU COMPANY—See Anritsu Corporation; *Int'l*, pg. 475
AOFRIO LIMITED; *Int'l*, pg. 487
APATOR ELKOMTECH S.A.—See Apator S.A.; *Int'l*, pg. 501
APEM AB—See IDEC Corporation; *Int'l*, pg. 3589
APEM BENELUX NV/SA—See IDEC Corporation; *Int'l*, pg. 3589
APEM COMPONENTS LTD.—See IDEC Corporation; *Int'l*, pg. 3589
APEM GMBH—See IDEC Corporation; *Int'l*, pg. 3589
APEM ITALIA S.R.L.—See IDEC Corporation; *Int'l*, pg. 3589
APEX ELECTRONICS (SHEN ZHEN) CO., LTD.—See Apex International Co., Ltd.; *Int'l*, pg. 511
APEX-I INTERNATIONAL CO., LTD.—See Gallant Precision Machining Co., Ltd.; *Int'l*, pg. 2873
API SYSTEMS INTEGRATORS—See APi Group Corporation; *Int'l*, pg. 513
APOLLO DISPLAY TECHNOLOGIES CORP.; *U.S. Private*, pg. 294
APPLIANCES COMPONENTS COMPANIES SPAIN, S.A.—See Guangzhou Wanbao Group Co., Ltd.; *Int'l*, pg. 3168
APP SYSTEMS SERVICES (INDIA) PVT LTD—See APP Systems Services Pte. Ltd.; *Int'l*, pg. 519
AQ TRANSFORMER SOLUTIONS INC.—See AQ Group AB; *Int'l*, pg. 527
ARAKAWA CHEMICAL (TAIPEI), LTD.—See Arakawa Chemical Industries, Ltd.; *Int'l*, pg. 534
ARGUS TECHNOLOGIES, INC.—See EnerSys; *U.S. Public*, pg. 768
ARIES CANADA LTD.—See Aries Industries Inc.; *U.S. Private*, pg. 322
ARLITECH ELECTRONIC CORP.; *Int'l*, pg. 573
ARQUIMED S.A.—See HORIBA Ltd; *Int'l*, pg. 3475
ARRAYENT, INC.—See Prodea Systems, Inc.; *U.S. Private*, pg. 3272
ARRIS BELGIUM BVBA—See CommScope Holding Company, Inc.; *U.S. Public*, pg. 547
ARRIS DE MEXICO S.A. DE C.V.—See CommScope Holding Company, Inc.; *U.S. Public*, pg. 548
ARRIS GROUP DE MEXICO S.A. DE C.V.—See CommScope Holding Company, Inc.; *U.S. Public*, pg. 548
ARRIS GROUP INDIA PRIVATE LIMITED—See CommScope Holding Company, Inc.; *U.S. Public*, pg. 548
ARRIS GROUP JAPAN K.K.—See CommScope Holding Company, Inc.; *U.S. Public*, pg. 548
ARRIS GROUP KOREA, INC.—See CommScope Holding Company, Inc.; *U.S. Public*, pg. 548
ARRIS GROUP RUSSIA LLC—See CommScope Holding Company, Inc.; *U.S. Public*, pg. 548
ARRIS INTERNATIONAL IBERIA S.L.—See CommScope Holding Company, Inc.; *U.S. Public*, pg. 548
ARRIS SOLUTIONS SPAIN S.L.—See CommScope Holding Company, Inc.; *U.S. Public*, pg. 548
ARRIS TECHNOLOGY, INC.—See CommScope Holding Company, Inc.; *U.S. Public*, pg. 548
ARRIS TELECOMUNICACIONES CHILE LTDA.—See CommScope Holding Company, Inc.; *U.S. Public*, pg. 548
ARRIS TELECOMUNICACOES DO BRASIL LTDA—See CommScope Holding Company, Inc.; *U.S. Public*, pg. 548
ARROW ALTECH DISTRIBUTION (PTY) LTD.—See Arrow Electronics, Inc.; *U.S. Public*, pg. 195
ARROW ASIA PAC LTD.—See Arrow Electronics, Inc.; *U.S. Public*, pg. 195
ARROW BRASIL S.A.—See Arrow Electronics, Inc.; *U.S. Public*, pg. 195
ARROW (CHINA) ELECTRONICS TRADING CO. LTD.—See Arrow Electronics, Inc.; *U.S. Public*, pg. 195
ARROW COMPONENTS (M) SDN BHD—See Arrow Electronics, Inc.; *U.S. Public*, pg. 195
ARROW COMPONENTS (NZ)—See Arrow Electronics, Inc.; *U.S. Public*, pg. 195
ARROW COMPONENTS—See Arrow Electronics, Inc.; *U.S. Public*, pg. 195
ARROW COMPONENTS SWEDEN AB—See Arrow Electronics, Inc.; *U.S. Public*, pg. 195
ARROW DENMARK, APS—See Arrow Electronics, Inc.; *U.S. Public*, pg. 195
ARROW ECS AUSTRALIA PTY. LIMITED—See Arrow Electronics, Inc.; *U.S. Public*, pg. 195

CORPORATE AFFILIATIONS

ARROW ECS BRASIL DISTRIBUIDORA LTDA.—See Arrow Electronics, Inc.; *U.S. Public*, pg. 196
ARROW ECS CANADA LTD.—See Arrow Electronics, Inc.; *U.S. Public*, pg. 198
ARROW ECS LTD.—See Arrow Electronics, Inc.; *U.S. Public*, pg. 196
ARROW ECS (NI) LIMITED—See Arrow Electronics, Inc.; *U.S. Public*, pg. 195
ARROWECS PORTUGAL SOCIEDADE UNIPESSOAL LDA.—See Arrow Electronics, Inc.; *U.S. Public*, pg. 195
ARROW ECS S.R.O.—See Arrow Electronics, Inc.; *U.S. Public*, pg. 196
ARROW ELECTRONICE S.R.L.—See Arrow Electronics, Inc.; *U.S. Public*, pg. 196
ARROW ELECTRONICS ASIA (S) PTE LTD.—See Arrow Electronics, Inc.; *U.S. Public*, pg. 196
ARROW ELECTRONICS AUSTRALIA PTY LTD.—See Arrow Electronics, Inc.; *U.S. Public*, pg. 196
ARROW ELECTRONICS CANADA LTD.—See Arrow Electronics, Inc.; *U.S. Public*, pg. 196
ARROW ELECTRONICS CHINA LTD.—See Arrow Electronics, Inc.; *U.S. Public*, pg. 196
ARROW ELECTRONICS COMPONENTS—See Arrow Electronics, Inc.; *U.S. Public*, pg. 196
ARROW ELECTRONICS COMPONENTS—See Arrow Electronics, Inc.; *U.S. Public*, pg. 196
ARROW ELECTRONICS COMPONENTS—See Arrow Electronics, Inc.; *U.S. Public*, pg. 197
ARROW ELECTRONICS COMPONENTS—See Arrow Electronics, Inc.; *U.S. Public*, pg. 197
ARROW ELECTRONICS COMPONENTS—See Arrow Electronics, Inc.; *U.S. Public*, pg. 197
ARROW ELECTRONICS COMPONENTS—See Arrow Electronics, Inc.; *U.S. Public*, pg. 197
ARROW ELECTRONICS COMPONENTS—See Arrow Electronics, Inc.; *U.S. Public*, pg. 197
ARROW ELECTRONICS COMPONENTS—See Arrow Electronics, Inc.; *U.S. Public*, pg. 197
ARROW ELECTRONICS COMPONENTS—See Arrow Electronics, Inc.; *U.S. Public*, pg. 197
ARROW ELECTRONICS COMPONENTS—See Arrow Electronics, Inc.; *U.S. Public*, pg. 197
ARROW ELECTRONICS COMPONENTS—See Arrow Electronics, Inc.; *U.S. Public*, pg. 197
ARROW ELECTRONICS COMPONENTS—See Arrow Electronics, Inc.; *U.S. Public*, pg. 197
ARROW ELECTRONICS COMPONENTS—See Arrow Electronics, Inc.; *U.S. Public*, pg. 197
ARROW ELECTRONICS COMPONENTS—See Arrow Electronics, Inc.; *U.S. Public*, pg. 197
ARROW ELECTRONICS COMPONENTS—See Arrow Electronics, Inc.; *U.S. Public*, pg. 197
ARROW ELECTRONICS COMPONENTS—See Arrow Electronics, Inc.; *U.S. Public*, pg. 197
ARROW ELECTRONICS COMPONENTS—See Arrow Electronics, Inc.; *U.S. Public*, pg. 197
ARROW ELECTRONICS COMPONENTS—See Arrow Electronics, Inc.; *U.S. Public*, pg. 197
ARROW ELECTRONICS COMPONENTS—See Arrow Electronics, Inc.; *U.S. Public*, pg. 197
ARROW ELECTRONICS COMPONENTS—See Arrow Electronics, Inc.; *U.S. Public*, pg. 197
ARROW ELECTRONICS COMPONENTS—See Arrow Electronics, Inc.; *U.S. Public*, pg. 197
ARROW ELECTRONICS CZECH REPUBLIC S.R.O.—See Arrow Electronics, Inc.; *U.S. Public*, pg. 197
ARROW ELECTRONICS D.O.O.—See Arrow Electronics, Inc.; *U.S. Public*, pg. 197
ARROW ELECTRONICS EMEASA S.R.L.—See Arrow Electronics, Inc.; *U.S. Public*, pg. 197
ARROW ELECTRONICS ESTONIA OU—See Arrow Electronics, Inc.; *U.S. Public*, pg. 197
ARROW ELECTRONICS GK—See Arrow Electronics, Inc.; *U.S. Public*, pg. 197
ARROW ELECTRONICS, INC.; *U.S. Public*, pg. 194
ARROW ELECTRONICS, INC.—See Arrow Electronics, Inc.; *U.S. Public*, pg. 198
ARROW ELECTRONICS INDIA LTD.—See Arrow Electronics, Inc.; *U.S. Public*, pg. 197
ARROW ELECTRONICS INTERNATIONAL, INC.—See Arrow Electronics, Inc.; *U.S. Public*, pg. 197
ARROW ELECTRONICS ITALIA S.R.L—See Arrow Electronics, Inc.; *U.S. Public*, pg. 197
ARROW ELECTRONICS MEXICO, S. DE R.L. DE

N.A.I.C.S. INDEX

423690 — OTHER ELECTRONIC PA...

C.V.—See Arrow Electronics, Inc.; *U.S. Public*, pg. 197
ARROW ELECTRONICS POLAND SP.Z.O.O.—See Arrow Electronics, Inc.; *U.S. Public*, pg. 195
ARROW ELECTRONICS (SHANGHAI) CO. LTD.—See Arrow Electronics, Inc.; *U.S. Public*, pg. 196
ARROW ELECTRONICS (SHENZHEN) CO. LTD.—See Arrow Electronics, Inc.; *U.S. Public*, pg. 196
ARROW ELECTRONICS SLOVAKIA S.R.O—See Arrow Electronics, Inc.; *U.S. Public*, pg. 198
ARROW ELECTRONICS—See Arrow Electronics, Inc.; *U.S. Public*, pg. 196
ARROW ELECTRONICS (SWEDEN) KB—See Arrow Electronics, Inc.; *U.S. Public*, pg. 196
ARROW ELECTRONICS (THAILAND) LIMITED—See Arrow Electronics, Inc.; *U.S. Public*, pg. 196
ARROW ELECTRONICS (THAILAND) LIMITED—See Arrow Electronics, Inc.; *U.S. Public*, pg. 196
ARROW ELECTRONICS (UK) LTD.—See Arrow Electronics, Inc.; *U.S. Public*, pg. 196
ARROW ELECTRONICS UKRAINE, LLC—See Arrow Electronics, Inc.; *U.S. Public*, pg. 198
ARROW ELECTRONICS UKRAINE, LLC—See Arrow Electronics, Inc.; *U.S. Public*, pg. 198
ARROW ELEKTRONIK TICARET, A.S.—See Arrow Electronics, Inc.; *U.S. Public*, pg. 198
ARROW ENTERPRISE COMPUTING SOLUTIONS LTD.—See Arrow Electronics, Inc.; *U.S. Public*, pg. 198
ARROW FINLAND OY—See Arrow Electronics, Inc.; *U.S. Public*, pg. 198
ARROW IBERIA ELECTRONICA, S.L.U.—See Arrow Electronics, Inc.; *U.S. Public*, pg. 198
ARROW NORDIC COMPONENTS AB—See Arrow Electronics, Inc.; *U.S. Public*, pg. 198
ARROW NORWAY A/S—See Arrow Electronics, Inc.; *U.S. Public*, pg. 198
ARROW/RAPAC, LTD.—See Arrow Electronics, Inc.; *U.S. Public*, pg. 198
ARROW UEC JAPAN, KK—See Arrow Electronics, Inc.; *U.S. Public*, pg. 198
ARROW VALUE RECOVERY DENMARK APS—See Arrow Electronics, Inc.; *U.S. Public*, pg. 198
AR'S CO., LTD.—See CHINO Corporation; *Int'l*, pg. 1570
ARTIZA NETWORKS, INC. - RANCHO PALOS VERDES BRANCH—See Artiza Networks, Inc.; *Int'l*, pg. 585
ARTLINK TECHNOLOGY CO. LTD.—See Arrow Electronics, Inc.; *U.S. Public*, pg. 198
ASAHI KASEI MICRODEVICES EUROPE SAS—See Asahi Kasei Corporation; *Int'l*, pg. 595
ASAHI KASEI MICRODEVICES KOREA CORP.—See Asahi Kasei Corporation; *Int'l*, pg. 595
ASBIS CR D.O.O.—See ASBISc Enterprises Plc; *Int'l*, pg. 600
ASBIS IT SOLUTIONS HUNGARY KFT.—See ASBISc Enterprises Plc; *Int'l*, pg. 600
ASCC, INC.; *U.S. Private*, pg. 346
ASCO/NUMATICS GMBH—See Emerson Electric Co.; *U.S. Public*, pg. 740
AS ETAL GROUP—See Amplex AB; *Int'l*, pg. 434
ASM ASSEMBLY TECHNOLOGY CO. LIMITED—See ASM INTERNATIONAL N.V.; *Int'l*, pg. 626
ASM CHINA LTD—See ASM INTERNATIONAL N.V.; *Int'l*, pg. 626
ASML AUSTIN—See ASML Holding N.V.; *Int'l*, pg. 627
ASML (SHANGHAI) INTERNATIONAL TRADING CO., LTD.—See ASML Holding N.V.; *Int'l*, pg. 627
ASPENCORE, LLC—See Arrow Electronics, Inc.; *U.S. Public*, pg. 198
ASSOCIATED INDUSTRIES; *U.S. Private*, pg. 356
ASSOCIATED TELEPHONE DESIGN INC.; *U.S. Private*, pg. 357
ASTEELFLASH BEDFORD LIMITED—See ASE Technology Holding Co., Ltd.; *Int'l*, pg. 604
ASTEELFLASH BONN GMBH—See ASE Technology Holding Co., Ltd.; *Int'l*, pg. 604
ASTEELFLASH EBERBACH GMBH—See ASE Technology Holding Co., Ltd.; *Int'l*, pg. 604
ASTEELFLASH FREMONT—See ASE Technology Holding Co., Ltd.; *Int'l*, pg. 604
ASTEELFLASH HERSFELD GMBH—See ASE Technology Holding Co., Ltd.; *Int'l*, pg. 605
ASTEELFLASH PLZEN S.R.O.—See ASE Technology Holding Co., Ltd.; *Int'l*, pg. 605
ASTEELFLASH SUZHOU—See ASE Technology Holding Co., Ltd.; *Int'l*, pg. 605
ASTEELFLASH TIJUANA—See ASE Technology Holding Co., Ltd.; *Int'l*, pg. 605
ASTI ELECTRONICS CORPORATION—See ASTI Corporation; *Int'l*, pg. 654
ASTI RESEARCH & DEVELOPMENT VIETNAM CORPORATION—See ASTI Corporation; *Int'l*, pg. 654
ASTREX ELECTRONICS INC.—See Berkshire Hathaway Inc.; *U.S. Public*, pg. 316
ASTRO GS SHOP SDN. BHD.—See Astro Malaysia Holdings Bhd; *Int'l*, pg. 662
ASTRONERGY GMBH—See Chint Group Corporation; *Int'l*, pg. 1571
ASTRONERGY SOLAR COMPANY CO., LTD.—See Chint Group Corporation; *Int'l*, pg. 1571

ASTRONERGY SOLAR, INC.—See Chint Group Corporation; *Int'l*, pg. 1571
ASTRONERGY SOLAR KOREA CO., LTD.—See Chint Group Corporation; *Int'l*, pg. 1571
ASTRONERGY SOLAR THAILAND CO., LTD—See Chint Group Corporation; *Int'l*, pg. 1571
ASTRO TECHNOLOGIES LTD.—See Fuji Corporation; *Int'l*, pg. 2809
ATAL SPOL S.R.O.—See Actia Group SA; *Int'l*, pg. 118
ATECH PERIPHERALS, INC.—See Aten International Co., Ltd.; *Int'l*, pg. 668
ATEN CANADA TECHNOLOGIES INC.—See Aten International Co., Ltd.; *Int'l*, pg. 668
ATEN CHINA CO., LTD.—See Aten International Co., Ltd.; *Int'l*, pg. 668
ATEP - AMKOR TECHNOLOGY PORTUGAL, S.A.—See Amkor Technology, Inc.; *U.S. Public*, pg. 124
ATM ELECTRONIC CORPORATION (HK) LIMITED—See Arrow Electronics, Inc.; *U.S. Public*, pg. 195
ATM ELECTRONIC CORP.—See Arrow Electronics, Inc.; *U.S. Public*, pg. 195
ATM ELECTRONICS TECHNOLOGY (SHENZHEN) CO. LTD.—See Arrow Electronics, Inc.; *U.S. Public*, pg. 195
ATOPTECH, INC.—See Avatar Integrated Systems, Inc.; *U.S. Private*, pg. 404
ATREL VIDEOSYSTEMS; *U.S. Private*, pg. 382
ATS JAPAN CORP.—See RTX Corporation; *U.S. Public*, pg. 1822
ATS KOREA—See RTX Corporation; *U.S. Public*, pg. 1822
AT & S SKANDINAVIA AB—See AT&S Austria Technologie & Systemtechnik Aktiengesellschaft; *Int'l*, pg. 665
AUDIO FIDELITY COMMUNICATIONS CORP.; *U.S. Private*, pg. 391
AUDIOVOX AUDIO VISUAL DIVISION—See VOXX International Corporation; *U.S. Public*, pg. 2310
AUDIOVOX ELECTRONICS CORPORATION—See VOXX International Corporation; *U.S. Public*, pg. 2310
AU OPTRONICS CORPORATION AMERICA—See AUO Corporation; *Int'l*, pg. 706
AU OPTRONICS EUROPE B.V.—See AUO Corporation; *Int'l*, pg. 706
AURES TECHNOLOGIES LTD.—See Aures Technologies; *Int'l*, pg. 710
AURES TECHNOLOGIES; *Int'l*, pg. 710
AUSTRIAMICROSYSTEMS FRANCE S.A.R.L.—See ams AG; *Int'l*, pg. 440
AUSTRIAMICROSYSTEMS SPAIN S.L.—See ams AG; *Int'l*, pg. 440
AUTHENTEC K.K.—See Apple Inc.; *U.S. Public*, pg. 169
AUXEL FTG SHANGHAI CO., LTD.—See Amphenol Corporation; *U.S. Public*, pg. 126
AVAD LLC—See Kingswood Capital Management LLC; *U.S. Private*, pg. 2312
AV CONCEPT LIMITED—See AV Concept Holdings Ltd; *Int'l*, pg. 733
AVC TECHNOLOGY (INTERNATIONAL) LIMITED—See AV Concept Holdings Ltd; *Int'l*, pg. 733
AVENIR TELECOM S.A.; *Int'l*, pg. 738
AVENT USI—See Avnet, Inc.; *U.S. Public*, pg. 249
AVIAT NETWORKS (AUSTRALIA) PTY. LTD.—See Aviat Networks, Inc.; *U.S. Public*, pg. 245
AVMAX AVIONICS—See Avmax Group Inc.; *Int'l*, pg. 748
AVNET ASIA PTE LTD—See Ingredion Incorporated; *U.S. Public*, pg. 1123
AVNET COMPONENTS BRASIL PARTICIPACOES LTDA.—See Avnet, Inc.; *U.S. Public*, pg. 250
AVNET COMPONENTS ISRAEL LIMITED—See Avnet, Inc.; *U.S. Public*, pg. 250
AVNET DE PUERTO RICO, INC.—See Avnet, Inc.; *U.S. Public*, pg. 252
AVNET ELECTRONICS MARKETING (AUSTRALIA) PTY LTD—See Ingredion Incorporated; *U.S. Public*, pg. 1123
AVNET ELECTRONICS MARKETING—See Avnet, Inc.; *U.S. Public*, pg. 250
AVNET ELECTRONICS MARKETING—See Avnet, Inc.; *U.S. Public*, pg. 250
AVNET ELECTRONICS MARKETING—See Avnet, Inc.; *U.S. Public*, pg. 250
AVNET ELECTRONICS TURKEY ITHALAT IHRACAT SANAYI VE TICARET LIMITED SIRKETI—See Avnet, Inc.; *U.S. Public*, pg. 251
AVNET EMBEDDED INDUSTRIA E COMERCIO LTDA—See Avnet, Inc.; *U.S. Public*, pg. 251
AVNET EMG AG—See Avnet, Inc.; *U.S. Public*, pg. 250
AVNET EMG ITALY S.R.L.—See Avnet, Inc.; *U.S. Public*, pg. 250
AVNET EMG LTD.—See Avnet, Inc.; *U.S. Public*, pg. 250
AVNET EM SP. Z.O.O.—See Avnet, Inc.; *U.S. Public*, pg. 250
AVNET IBERIA S.A.—See Avnet, Inc.; *U.S. Public*, pg. 251
AVNET INTEGRATED RESOURCES REPARO DE ELETRONICOS LTDA.—See Avnet, Inc.; *U.S. Public*, pg. 251
AVNET INTERNATIONAL (CANADA) LTD.—See Avnet, Inc.; *U.S. Public*, pg. 251
AVNET JAPAN (ASIA) LIMITED—See Avnet, Inc.; *U.S. Public*, pg. 251
AVNET JAPAN (HK) LIMITED—See Avnet, Inc.; *U.S. Public*, pg. 251

AVNET JAPAN (MALAYSIA) SDN. BHD.—See Avnet, Inc.; *U.S. Public*, pg. 251
AVNET JAPAN (SINGAPORE) PTE LTD.—See Avnet, Inc.; *U.S. Public*, pg. 251
AVNET KABUSHIKI KAISHA—See Avnet, Inc.; *U.S. Public*, pg. 251
AVNET KOREA, INC.—See Ingredion Incorporated; *U.S. Public*, pg. 1123
AVNET LOGISTICS B.V.B.A.—See Avnet, Inc.; *U.S. Public*, pg. 251
AVNET MALAYSIA SDN BHD—See Avnet, Inc.; *U.S. Public*, pg. 251
AVNET NORTEC AS—See Avnet, Inc.; *U.S. Public*, pg. 252
AVNET NORTEC OY—See Avnet, Inc.; *U.S. Public*, pg. 252
AVNET (SHANGHAI) LIMITED—See Ingredion Incorporated; *U.S. Public*, pg. 1123
AVNET SILICA—See Avnet, Inc.; *U.S. Public*, pg. 251
AVNET SOLUTIONS PTE. LTD.—See Avnet, Inc.; *U.S. Public*, pg. 252
AVNET SP. Z.O.O.—See Avnet, Inc.; *U.S. Public*, pg. 252
AVNET S.R.L.—See Avnet, Inc.; *U.S. Public*, pg. 252
AVNET TECHNOLOGY ELECTRONICS MARKETING (TAIWAN) CO., LTD.—See Avnet, Inc.; *U.S. Public*, pg. 252
AVNET TECHNOLOGY SOLUTIONS (CHINA) LTD—See TD Synnex Corp; *U.S. Public*, pg. 1985
AVNET TECHNOLOGY SOLUTIONS (TIANJIN) LTD—See TD Synnex Corp; *U.S. Public*, pg. 1985
AVNET TECHNOLOGY (THAILAND) LTD.—See TD Synnex Corp; *U.S. Public*, pg. 1985
AVNET TIME—See Avnet, Inc.; *U.S. Public*, pg. 251
AVNET UNIDUX (HK) LIMITED—See Avnet, Inc.; *U.S. Public*, pg. 252
AVNET UNIDUX (MALAYSIA) SDN. BHD.—See Avnet, Inc.; *U.S. Public*, pg. 252
AVNET UNIDUX (THAILAND) COMPANY LIMITED—See Avnet, Inc.; *U.S. Public*, pg. 252
AVOCENT FREMONT CORP.—See Vertiv Holdings Co; *U.S. Public*, pg. 2288
AVOCENT JAPAN KK—See Emerson Electric Co.; *U.S. Public*, pg. 742
AVT INTERNATIONAL LIMITED—See Apex Ace Holding Limited; *Int'l*, pg. 509
AZTEC COMPONENTS, INC.; *U.S. Private*, pg. 415
AZTEC ENTERPRISES, INC.; *U.S. Private*, pg. 416
BAG ELECTRONICS GMBH—See ams AG; *Int'l*, pg. 438
BAKER & MCAULIFFE HOLDINGS PTY LTD—See Hancock & Gore Ltd.; *Int'l*, pg. 3242
BAN LEONG CHIN INTER CO., LTD.—See Ban Leong Technologies Limited; *Int'l*, pg. 814
BARCO VISUAL SOLUTIONS, INC.—See Barco N.V.; *Int'l*, pg. 864
BARCO VISUAL SOLUTIONS S.A. DE C.V.—See Barco N.V.; *Int'l*, pg. 864
BARNES DISTRIBUTION NORTH AMERICA—See MSC Industrial Direct Co.; *U.S. Public*, pg. 1483
BARRY SALES INC.; *U.S. Private*, pg. 481
BAYWA R.E. SOLARSYSTEME GMBH—See BayWa AG; *Int'l*, pg. 917
BCD SEMICONDUCTOR MANUFACTURING LIMITED—See Diodes Incorporated; *U.S. Public*, pg. 667
BEACON ELECTRONIC ASSOCIATES, INC.; *U.S. Private*, pg. 504
BEAMER & MORE GMBH—See Droege Group AG; *Int'l*, pg. 2205
BEARCOM INC.—See Bertram Capital Management, LLC; *U.S. Private*, pg. 540
BEARCOM WIRELESS—See Bertram Capital Management, LLC; *U.S. Private*, pg. 540
BECKER COMMUNICATIONS, INC.; *U.S. Private*, pg. 510
BEGHELLI ASIA PACIFIC LTD.—See Beghelli S.p.A.; *Int'l*, pg. 941
BEIJING ALL ACCESS NOTER COMMUNICATION TECHNOLOGY CO., LIMITED—See China All Access (Holdings) Limited; *Int'l*, pg. 1482
BEIJING DONGJIN SEMICHEM CO., LTD.—See Dongjin Semichem Co., Ltd.; *Int'l*, pg. 2168
BEIJING HORIBA METRON INSTRUMENTS CO., LTD.—See HORIBA Ltd; *Int'l*, pg. 3475
BEIJING VIASAT SCIENCE & TECHNOLOGY CO., LTD.—See ViaSat, Inc.; *U.S. Public*, pg. 2291
BELAM INC.; *U.S. Private*, pg. 516
BELDEN COMMERCIAL SERVICES B.V.—See Belden, Inc.; *U.S. Public*, pg. 293
BELDEN HIRSCHMANN NETWORKING SYSTEM TRADING (SHANGHAI) CO. LTD.—See Belden, Inc.; *U.S. Public*, pg. 293
BELDEN & HIRSCHMANN - SPAIN—See Belden, Inc.; *U.S. Public*, pg. 293
BELMONT TECHNOLOGY REMARKETING—See Belmont Trading Company; *U.S. Private*, pg. 521
BELMONT TRADING COMPANY; *U.S. Private*, pg. 521
BENQ EUROPE B.V.—See BenQ Corporation; *Int'l*, pg. 975
BENQ LATIN AMERICA CORP.—See BenQ Corporation; *Int'l*, pg. 975
BERTECH-KELEX, INC.; *U.S. Private*, pg. 539
BESI USA, INC.—See BE Semiconductor Industries N.V.; *Int'l*, pg. 931

423690 — OTHER ELECTRONIC PA...

BEST TAIWAN INC.—See Action Electronics Co., Ltd.; *Int'l*, pg. 119
BETA SQUARED LITHOGRAPHY, INC.; *U.S. Private*, pg. 545
BETA SQUARED LITHOGRAPHY SINGAPORE PTE LTD.—See Beta Squared Lithography, Inc.; *U.S. Private*, pg. 545
BHASKARI ELECTRICAL SYSTEMS PVT. LTD.—See Annapurna Bhaskari Group; *Int'l*, pg. 473
B.H.T. ELECTRONICS PURCHASING INC.; *U.S. Private*, pg. 420
BINATONE COMMUNICATIONS EUROPE—See Binatone Electronics International Ltd.; *Int'l*, pg. 1033
BINATONE GLOBAL ELECTRONICS (SHENZHEN) CO. LIMITED—See Binatone Electronics International Ltd.; *Int'l*, pg. 1033
BINATONE NORTH AMERICA INC.—See Binatone Electronics International Ltd.; *Int'l*, pg. 1033
BINATONE TELECOMMUNICATION PVT LIMITED—See Binatone Electronics International Ltd.; *Int'l*, pg. 1033
BISCO INDUSTRIES, INC.—See EACO Corporation; *U.S. Public*, pg. 701
BITCENTRALCOM INC.—See Bitcentral Inc.; *U.S. Private*, pg. 567
BITCENTRAL INC.; *U.S. Private*, pg. 566
BIZIT SYSTEMS (M) SDN. BHD.—See Aimflex Berhad; *Int'l*, pg. 233
BKW SMART ENERGY & MOBILITY AG—See BKW AG; *Int'l*, pg. 1054
BLACK BOX COMUNICACIONES, S.A.—See Black Box Limited; *Int'l*, pg. 1057
BLACK BOX DATACOM B.V.—See Black Box Limited; *Int'l*, pg. 1057
BLACK BOX GMBH—See Black Box Limited; *Int'l*, pg. 1057
BLACK BOX INTERNATIONAL B.V.—See Black Box Limited; *Int'l*, pg. 1057
BLACK BOX NETWORK SERVICES CORPORATION—See Black Box Limited; *Int'l*, pg. 1058
BLACK BOX NETWORK SERVICES INDIA PRIVATE LIMITED—See Black Box Limited; *Int'l*, pg. 1058
BLACK BOX NETWORK SERVICES NV—See Black Box Limited; *Int'l*, pg. 1058
BLACK STAR NETWORKS, INC.; *U.S. Private*, pg. 573
BLUE SKY NETWORK, LLC; *U.S. Private*, pg. 593
BLUFF CITY DISTRIBUTING CO., INC.; *U.S. Private*, pg. 599
BMH WOOD TECHNOLOGY AB—See BMH Technology Oy; *Int'l*, pg. 1076
BOAT AMERICA CORPORATION—See Berkshire Hathaway Inc.; *U.S. Public*, pg. 303
BOSE A/S - NORWAY REPRESENTATIVE OFFICE—See Bose Corporation; *U.S. Private*, pg. 619
BOSE GMBH - CONSUMER DIRECT DIVISION—See Bose Corporation; *U.S. Private*, pg. 620
BOSE LIMITED—See Bose Corporation; *U.S. Private*, pg. 620
BOURNS ELECTRONICS, LTD.—See Bourns, Inc.; *U.S. Private*, pg. 624
BOURNS TRADING (SHANGHAI) CO., LTD.—See Bourns, Inc.; *U.S. Private*, pg. 624
BRADLEY REPRESENTATIVES; *U.S. Private*, pg. 633
BRIGHT FUTURE INTERNATIONAL LIMITED—See Bang & Olufsen a/s; *Int'l*, pg. 831
BRIGHT LED EUROPE GMBH—See Bright Led Electronics Corp.; *Int'l*, pg. 1161
BRIGHTPOINT NZ LIMITED—See Hainan Traffic Administration Holding Co., Ltd.; *Int'l*, pg. 3215
BRIGHTSTAR 20:20 MOBILE—See Brightstar Capital Partners, L.P.; *U.S. Private*, pg. 653
BRINNO, INC.; *Int'l*, pg. 1164
THE BRIX GROUP INC.; *U.S. Private*, pg. 4000
BROADCASTSTORE.COM; *U.S. Private*, pg. 659
BROADCAST SUPPLY WORLDWIDE, INC.; *U.S. Private*, pg. 659
BROADFIELD DISTRIBUTING INC.; *U.S. Private*, pg. 659
THE BROKER FORUM INC.—See KKR & Co. Inc.; *U.S. Public*, pg. 1267
BRUCE TECHNOLOGIES EUROPE GMBH—See Amtech Systems, Inc.; *U.S. Public*, pg. 133
BTC ELECTRONIC COMPONENTS, INC.—See Audax Group, Limited Partnership; *U.S. Private*, pg. 388
BTC HOLDINGS INC.—See Blackfoot Telephone Cooperative, Inc.; *U.S. Private*, pg. 573
BTC INDUSTRIBATTERIER AB—See Addtech AB; *Int'l*, pg. 132
BUHL INDUSTRIES INC.; *U.S. Private*, pg. 681
BUKALAPAK.COM PT TBK; *Int'l*, pg. 1212
BULL WILL CO., LTD; *Int'l*, pg. 1214
BUREAU D'ELECTRONIQUE APPLIQUEE S.A.—See Halma plc; *Int'l*, pg. 3230
BURST COMMUNICATIONS INC.; *U.S. Private*, pg. 692
B.V. ARROW ELECTRONICS DLC—See Arrow Electronics, Inc.; *U.S. Public*, pg. 198
CABLEORGANIZER.COM, INC.; *U.S. Private*, pg. 711
CABLE PLUS INC.; *U.S. Private*, pg. 711
CADEX ELECTRONICS GMBH—See Cadex Electronics Inc.; *Int'l*, pg. 1248
CALDARO AB—See Addtech AB; *Int'l*, pg. 132

CALIFORNIA EASTERN LABORATORIES, INC.; *U.S. Private*, pg. 719
CANADIAN SOLAR PROJECTS K.K.—See Canadian Solar Inc.; *Int'l*, pg. 1286
CANON SEMICONDUCTOR ENGINEERING KOREA INC.—See Canon Inc.; *Int'l*, pg. 1296
CANON SEMICONDUCTOR EQUIPMENT TAIWAN, INC.—See Canon Inc.; *Int'l*, pg. 1296
CANPANGO, S.A.—See ScanSource, Inc.; *U.S. Public*, pg. 1843
CANVAS SYSTEMS B.V.—See Avnet, Inc.; *U.S. Public*, pg. 252
CANVAS SYSTEMS UK LIMITED—See Avnet, Inc.; *U.S. Public*, pg. 252
CAPI-LUX NETHERLANDS B.V.—See B&S Group S.A.; *Int'l*, pg. 784
CAPXON EUROPE GMBH—See Capxon International Electronic Co Ltd; *Int'l*, pg. 1318
CARDAX SALES & SERVICES SDN. BHD.—See AWC Berhad; *Int'l*, pg. 752
CARDINAL COMPONENTS INC.; *U.S. Private*, pg. 750
CAREER TECHNOLOGY (H.K.) LTD.—See Career Technology (MFG.) Co., Ltd.; *Int'l*, pg. 1323
CAREER TECHNOLOGY (S) PTE. LTD.—See Career Technology (MFG.) Co., Ltd.; *Int'l*, pg. 1323
CARLIT SINGAPORE PTE., LTD.—See Carlit Co., Ltd.; *Int'l*, pg. 1338
CARLO GAVAZZI AS—See Carlo Gavazzi Holding AG; *Int'l*, pg. 1338
CARLO GAVAZZI BV—See Carlo Gavazzi Holding AG; *Int'l*, pg. 1339
CARLO GAVAZZI HANDEL A/S—See Carlo Gavazzi Holding AG; *Int'l*, pg. 1339
CARLO GAVAZZI INDUSTRI KAUNAS UAB—See Carlo Gavazzi Holding AG; *Int'l*, pg. 1339
CARLO GAVAZZI LDA—See Carlo Gavazzi Holding AG; *Int'l*, pg. 1339
CARLO GAVAZZI SARL—See Carlo Gavazzi Holding AG; *Int'l*, pg. 1339
CARLO GAVAZZI SPA—See Carlo Gavazzi Holding AG; *Int'l*, pg. 1339
CARLO GAVAZZI UK LTD—See Carlo Gavazzi Holding AG; *Int'l*, pg. 1339
CARLTON-BATES COMPANY OF TENNESSEE INC.—See WESCO International, Inc.; *U.S. Public*, pg. 2351
CARLTON-BATES COMPANY - SAINT LOUIS—See WESCO International, Inc.; *U.S. Public*, pg. 2351
CARLTON-BATES COMPANY—See WESCO International, Inc.; *U.S. Public*, pg. 2351
CASA COMMUNICATIONS LIMITED—See Casa Systems, Inc.; *U.S. Private*, pg. 778
CASA COMMUNICATIONS TECHNOLOGY S.L.—See Casa Systems, Inc.; *U.S. Private*, pg. 778
CASA SYSTEMS, INC.; *U.S. Private*, pg. 778
CASCO SCHOELLER GMBH—See Amphenol Corporation; *U.S. Public*, pg. 129
CASIO COMPUTER (HONG KONG) LTD.—See Casio Computer Co., Ltd.; *Int'l*, pg. 1353
CASIO MALAYSIA, SDN. BHD.—See Casio Computer Co., Ltd.; *Int'l*, pg. 1353
CASIO TECHNO CO., LTD.—See Casio Computer Co., Ltd.; *Int'l*, pg. 1353
CATVISION LIMITED; *Int'l*, pg. 1361
C-COR ARGENTINA S.R.L.—See CommScope Holding Company, Inc.; *U.S. Public*, pg. 548
CCT TECH INTERNATIONAL LIMITED—See CCT Fortis Holdings Limited; *Int'l*, pg. 1369
CCT TELECOM (HK) LIMITED—See CCT Fortis Holdings Limited; *Int'l*, pg. 1370
CECOL, INC.—See Citizen Watch Co., Ltd.; *Int'l*, pg. 1623
C-E (DEUTSCHLAND) GMBH—See Citizen Watch Co., Ltd.; *Int'l*, pg. 1623
CE GLOBAL SOURCING GMBH—See HPI AG; *Int'l*, pg. 3500
CELLITE AB—See Addtech AB; *Int'l*, pg. 132
CENTAUR CORPORATION; *U.S. Private*, pg. 809
CENTROTHERM PHOTOVOLTAICS ITALIA S.R.L.—See centrotherm photovoltaics AG; *Int'l*, pg. 1415
CENTROTHERM PHOTOVOLTAICS USA INC.—See centrotherm photovoltaics AG; *Int'l*, pg. 1415
CEOTRONICS S.A.R.L.—See CeoTronics AG; *Int'l*, pg. 1420
CERTIFIED SUPPLY INC.—See Johnstone Supply Inc.; *U.S. Private*, pg. 2230
CE SCHWEIZ AG—See HPI AG; *Int'l*, pg. 3500
CE UK LTD—See HPI AG; *Int'l*, pg. 3500
CHANGCHUN HUF AUTOMOTIVE LOCK CO. LTD.—See Huf Hulsbeck & Furst GmbH & Co. KG; *Int'l*, pg. 3523
CHATTERBOX LIMITED—See CSE Global Ltd.; *Int'l*, pg. 1864
CHEMO ELECTRIC A/S—See Addtech AB; *Int'l*, pg. 132
CHEMTRONICS CHINA—See Chemtronics Co., Ltd.; *Int'l*, pg. 1464
CHEMTRONICS EUROPE S.R.O—See Chemtronics Co., Ltd.; *Int'l*, pg. 1464
CHEMTRONICS USA INC—See Chemtronics Co., Ltd.; *Int'l*, pg. 1464
CHENGDU DONGJIN SEMICHEM CO., LTD.—See Dongjin Semichem Co., Ltd.; *Int'l*, pg. 2168
CHEVALIER ITECH THAI LIMITED—See Chevalier International Holdings Limited; *Int'l*, pg. 1474
CHIEFTRON INTERNATIONAL INC.—See Av Tech Corporation; *Int'l*, pg. 733
CHINA SECURITY & SURVEILLANCE DISTRIBUTION (PRC), INC—See China Security & Surveillance Technology, Inc.; *Int'l*, pg. 1550
CHINATRONIC TECHNOLOGY LIMITED—See Avnet, Inc.; *U.S. Public*, pg. 252
CHINNEY ALLIANCE ENGINEERING LIMITED—See Chinney Alliance Group Limited; *Int'l*, pg. 1570
CHINT ENERGY SLU—See Chint Group Corporation; *Int'l*, pg. 1571
CHIP ONE STOP, INC.—See Arrow Electronics, Inc.; *U.S. Public*, pg. 198
CHIP-TECH, LTD.; *U.S. Private*, pg. 886
CHONGQING BOE OPTOELECTRONICS TECHNOLOGY CO., LTD.—See BOE Technology Group Co., Ltd.; *Int'l*, pg. 1099
CHUNG FU CO., LTD; *Int'l*, pg. 1597
CHUO ELECTRONICS CO., LTD.; *Int'l*, pg. 1598
CINCOM MIYANO TAIWAN CO., LTD.—See Citizen Watch Co., Ltd.; *Int'l*, pg. 1623
CIRCA TELECOM USA INC—See Equistone Partners Europe Limited; *Int'l*, pg. 2487
CIRCULAR CONNECTORS INC.; *U.S. Private*, pg. 900
CISCO SYSTEMS AUSTRALIA PTY LIMITED—See Cisco Systems, Inc.; *U.S. Public*, pg. 497
CISCO SYSTEMS AUSTRIA GMBH—See Cisco Systems, Inc.; *U.S. Public*, pg. 497
CISCO SYSTEMS G.K.—See Cisco Systems, Inc.; *U.S. Public*, pg. 498
CISCO SYSTEMS INTERNETWORKING (IRELAND) LIMITED—See Cisco Systems, Inc.; *U.S. Public*, pg. 498
CISCO TECHNOLOGIES (THAILAND) LIMITED—See Cisco Systems, Inc.; *U.S. Public*, pg. 499
CISCO TECHNOLOGY BELGUIM BVBA—See Cisco Systems, Inc.; *U.S. Public*, pg. 499
CISCO TECHNOLOGY DENMARK APS—See Cisco Systems, Inc.; *U.S. Public*, pg. 499
CISCO VIDEO TECHNOLOGIES ISRAEL LTD.—See Cisco Systems, Inc.; *U.S. Public*, pg. 499
CITIZEN SAKAE TRADING CO., LTD.—See Citizen Watch Co., Ltd.; *Int'l*, pg. 1624
CKD CORPORATION—See CKD Corporation; *Int'l*, pg. 1639
CLARION EUROPA GMBH—See FORVIA SE; *Int'l*, pg. 2745
CLARK-POWELL ASSOCIATES INC.; *U.S. Private*, pg. 914
CLARO S.A.—See America Movil, S.A.B. de C.V.; *Int'l*, pg. 421
CLASSIC COMPONENTS CORP.; *U.S. Private*, pg. 916
CLEAR BLUE TECHNOLOGIES INTERNATIONAL, INC.; *Int'l*, pg. 1656
CMK AMERICA CORPORATION—See CMK Corporation; *Int'l*, pg. 1670
CMS COMMUNICATIONS INC.; *U.S. Private*, pg. 951
CNBMIT CO., LTD—See China National Building Material Group Co., Ltd.; *Int'l*, pg. 1525
COBAR EUROPE B.V.—See BALVER ZINN Josef Jost GmbH & Co. KG; *Int'l*, pg. 812
COBHAM ELECTRONIC SYSTEMS, INC. - SAN JOSE—See Advent International Corporation; *U.S. Private*, pg. 99
COBHAM LONG ISLAND INC.—See Advent International Corporation; *U.S. Private*, pg. 99
COBHAM NEW JERSEY INC.—See Advent International Corporation; *U.S. Private*, pg. 99
COBHAM RAD EUROPE LIMITED—See Advent International Corporation; *U.S. Private*, pg. 99
COBRA ELECTRONICS EMEA—See Monomoy Capital Partners LLC; *U.S. Private*, pg. 2772
CODAN LTD. - NORTH AMERICA - LMR—See Codan Limited; *Int'l*, pg. 1688
CODAN RADIO COMMUNICATIONS ME JLT—See Codan Limited; *Int'l*, pg. 1688
CODAN (UK) LTD—See Codan Limited; *Int'l*, pg. 1688
CODAN (US) INC—See Codan Limited; *Int'l*, pg. 1688
COGELEC SA; *Int'l*, pg. 1694
COHERENT SWITZERLAND AG—See Coherent Corp.; *U.S. Public*, pg. 527
COLE WIRE & CABLE CO. INC.; *U.S. Private*, pg. 966
COMBAN TELECOM SYSTEMS AB—See Comba Telecom Systems Holdings Limited; *Int'l*, pg. 1708
COMBA TELECOM SYSTEMS (SINGAPORE) PTE. LTD.—See Comba Telecom Systems Holdings Limited; *Int'l*, pg. 1708
COMBINED PRECISION COMPONENTS LIMITED—See Avnet, Inc.; *U.S. Public*, pg. 252
COMET TECHNOLOGIES USA, INC.—See Comet Holding AG; *Int'l*, pg. 1710
COMMODITY COMPONENTS INTERNATIONAL; *U.S. Private*, pg. 985
COMM-TEC GMBH—See DCC plc; *Int'l*, pg. 1989
COMMUNICATIONS PRODUCTS INC.; *U.S. Private*, pg. 988
COMMUNICATIONS TELEVIDEO LTD; *U.S. Private*, pg. 989

N.A.I.C.S. INDEX

423690 — OTHER ELECTRONIC PA...

COMPANHIA HAMA PORTUGAL, LDA—See Hama GmbH & Co KG; *Int'l*, pg. 3234
COMPEQ TECHNOLOGY (HUIZHOU) CO., LTD.—See Compeq Manufacturing Co., Ltd.; *Int'l*, pg. 1753
COMPODIUM INTERNATIONAL AB; *Int'l*, pg. 1753
COMPONENTS CENTER INC.; *U.S. Private*, pg. 1002
COMPONENTS DISTRIBUTORS INC.; *U.S. Private*, pg. 1002
COMPRODUCTS INC.; *U.S. Private*, pg. 1003
COMPUDATA INC.; *U.S. Private*, pg. 1003
COMTRADE SAS—See DCC plc; *Int'l*, pg. 1989
CONDUCTIX-WAMPFLER AB—See CVC Capital Partners SICAV-FIS S.A.; *Int'l*, pg. 1886
CONDUCTIX-WAMPFLER SRL—See CVC Capital Partners SICAV-FIS S.A.; *Int'l*, pg. 1887
CONERGY ITALIA SPA—See Kawa Capital Management, Inc.; *U.S. Private*, pg. 2266
CONERGY SAS—See Kawa Capital Management, Inc.; *U.S. Private*, pg. 2266
CONNECTIVITY SOLUTIONS—See Bel Fuse Inc.; *U.S. Public*, pg. 293
CONTINENTAL TRADING FRANCE SAS—See Continental Aktiengesellschaft; *Int'l*, pg. 1783
CONVERGE NETHERLANDS BV.—See Arrow Electronics, Inc.; *U.S. Public*, pg. 199
CONVERGE—See Arrow Electronics, Inc.; *U.S. Public*, pg. 199
COOPER PRETRONICA LDA.—See Eaton Corporation plc; *Int'l*, pg. 2278
CORAD TECHNOLOGY LTD.—See HORIBA Ltd; *Int'l*, pg. 3475
CORINEX COMMUNICATIONS, A.S.—See Corinex Communications Corp.; *Int'l*, pg. 1801
CORNING OPTICAL COMMUNICATIONS - UK—See Corning Incorporated; *U.S. Public*, pg. 578
COSCO (BEIJING) MARINE ELECTRONIC EQUIPMENT LIMITED—See China COSCO Shipping Corporation Limited; *Int'l*, pg. 1492
COWAY (M) SDN. BHD.—See Coway Co., Ltd.; *Int'l*, pg. 1821
COWAY USA INC.—See Coway Co., Ltd.; *Int'l*, pg. 1821
CPG INTERNATIONAL GMBH—See CPG International S.p.A.; *Int'l*, pg. 1824
CPG INTERNATIONAL PTY LIMITED—See CPG International S.p.A.; *Int'l*, pg. 1824
CREDENCE SOUND & VISION LIMITED; *Int'l*, pg. 1834
CREE EUROPE GMBH—See Wolfspeed, Inc.; *U.S. Public*, pg. 2377
CREEMA LTD.; *Int'l*, pg. 1837
CREE SWEDEN AB—See Wolfspeed, Inc.; *U.S. Public*, pg. 2377
CROMPTON LIGHTING PTY LIMITED—See Bain Capital, LP; *U.S. Private*, pg. 439
CROSSCOM NATIONAL INC.; *U.S. Private*, pg. 1106
CS (AUSTRALIA) PTY LIMITED—See Illinois Tool Works Inc.; *U.S. Public*, pg. 1102
CSE-W ARTHUR FISHER LIMITED—See CSE Global Ltd.; *Int'l*, pg. 1863
CSL COMMUNICATION (SHENZHEN) CO LTD—See Digilife Technologies Limited; *Int'l*, pg. 2119
CUI-CANADA, INC.—See Orbital Infrastructure Group, Inc.; *U.S. Public*, pg. 1615
CUMATIX AB—See Addtech AB; *Int'l*, pg. 132
CUMBERLAND ELECTRONICS INC.; *U.S. Private*, pg. 1122
CUMMINS ALLISON PTY LTD—See Crane NXT, Co.; *U.S. Public*, pg. 591
CUSTOM POWER, LLC—See Elan Growth Partners, LLC; *U.S. Private*, pg. 1349
CVILUX (SINGAPORE) CORPORATION—See CviLux Corporation; *Int'l*, pg. 1889
CYLON CONTROLS (BEIJING) LTD—See ABB Ltd.; *Int'l*, pg. 56
CYLON CONTROLS LIMITED—See ABB Ltd.; *Int'l*, pg. 56
DACOMSA, S.A. DE C.V.—See Grupo Kuo, S.A.B. de C.V.; *Int'l*, pg. 3131
DAE-JIN SEMICONDUCTOR CO., LTD.; *Int'l*, pg. 1905
DAEWOO ELECTRONICS DEME FZE.—See Dongbu Group; *Int'l*, pg. 2165
DAEWOO ELECTRONICS MANUFACTURING POLAND SP. Z O.O.—See Dongbu Group; *Int'l*, pg. 2165
DAEWOO ELECTRONICS MIDDLE EAST FZE LTD.—See Dongbu Group; *Int'l*, pg. 2165
DAEWOO ELECTRONICS SALES UK LTD.—See Dongbu Group; *Int'l*, pg. 2165
DAEWOO ELECTRONICS S.A.—See Dongbu Group; *Int'l*, pg. 2165
DAHL INTERNATIONAL AB—See Compagnie de Saint-Gobain SA; *Int'l*, pg. 1732
DAIHEN ADVANCED COMPONENT, INC.—See Daihen Corporation; *Int'l*, pg. 1926
DAILEY & WELLS COMMUNICATIONS; *U.S. Private*, pg. 1145
DAISHINKU (HK) LTD—See Daishinku Corp.; *Int'l*, pg. 1942
DAITO ME HOLDINGS CO., LTD.; *Int'l*, pg. 1943
DAITRON (SHENZHEN) CO., LTD.—See Daitron Co., Ltd.; *Int'l*, pg. 1944

DAITRON (TAIWAN) CO., LTD.—See Daitron Co., Ltd.; *Int'l*, pg. 1944
DAITRON (THAILAND) CO., LTD.—See Daitron Co., Ltd.; *Int'l*, pg. 1944
DAIWA MUSEN DENKI CO., LTD.—See Denkyo Group Holdings Co.,Ltd.; *Int'l*, pg. 2028
DALIAN FUJI BINGSHAN CONTROL SYSTEMS CO., LTD.—See Fuji Electric Co., Ltd.; *Int'l*, pg. 2810
DALIS ELECTRONICS—See Components Center Inc.; *U.S. Private*, pg. 1002
DAMBALLA, INC.—See K1 Investment Management, LLC; *U.S. Private*, pg. 2252
DANFOSS AUTOMATIC CONTROLS MANAGEMENT (SHANGHAI) CO. LTD.—See Danfoss A/S; *Int'l*, pg. 1959
DANFOSS (NEW ZEALAND) LTD.—See Danfoss A/S; *Int'l*, pg. 1959
DATA MODUL ELECTRONICS TECHNOLOGY (SHANGHAI) CO. LTD.—See Arrow Electronics, Inc.; *U.S. Public*, pg. 199
DATA MODUL FRANCE S.A R.L—See Arrow Electronics, Inc.; *U.S. Public*, pg. 199
DATA MODUL FRANCE, S.A.R.L.—See Data Modul AG; *Int'l*, pg. 1976
DATA MODUL HONG KONG LTD.—See Arrow Electronics, Inc.; *U.S. Public*, pg. 199
DATA MODUL ITALIA S.R.L.—See Arrow Electronics, Inc.; *U.S. Public*, pg. 199
DATA MODUL WEIKERSHEIM GMBH—See Arrow Electronics, Inc.; *U.S. Public*, pg. 199
DATANET INFRASTRUCTURE GROUP (PTY) LIMITED—See Alviva Holdings Limited; *Int'l*, pg. 402
DATANG TELECOM TECHNOLOGY CO., LTD.; *Int'l*, pg. 1979
DATASONIC SMART SOLUTIONS SDN BHD—See Datasonic Group Berhad; *Int'l*, pg. 1979
DATASONIC TECHNOLOGIES SDN BHD—See Datasonic Group Berhad; *Int'l*, pg. 1979
DAYANG INTERNATIONAL (SINGAPORE) PTE LTD—See Daheng New Epoch Technology, Inc.; *Int'l*, pg. 1913
DAYANG INTERNATIONAL (THAILAND) CO., LTD—See Daheng New Epoch Technology, Inc.; *Int'l*, pg. 1913
DDS KOREA, INC.—See DDS; *Int'l*, pg. 1994
DEDC, INC.; *U.S. Private*, pg. 1188
DELLTRON CO. INC.; *U.S. Private*, pg. 1197
DELPHI AUTOMOTIVE SYSTEMS UK LIMITED—See Aptiv PLC; *Int'l*, pg. 524
DELTA ELECTRONICS (CHENZHOU) CO., LTD.—See Delta Electronics, Inc.; *Int'l*, pg. 2016
DELTA ELECTRONICS (ITALY) S.R.L.—See Delta Electronics, Inc.; *Int'l*, pg. 2017
DELTA ELECTRONICS (JAPAN) INC.—See Delta Electronics, Inc.; *Int'l*, pg. 2017
DELTA GREENTECH (CHINA) CO., LTD.—See Delta Electronics, Inc.; *Int'l*, pg. 2018
DELTA SOLUTIONS (FINLAND) OY—See Delta Electronics, Inc.; *Int'l*, pg. 2018
DENSO TEN SINGAPORE PRIVATE LIMITED—See Denso Corporation; *Int'l*, pg. 2030
DEPENDABLE COMPONENT SUPPLY CORP.; *U.S. Private*, pg. 1208
DETECT, INC. - INTERNATIONAL DIVISION—See DeTect, Inc.; *U.S. Private*, pg. 1216
DETECTOR TECHNOLOGY LIMITED—See Newell Brands Inc.; *U.S. Public*, pg. 1514
DETEWE COMMUNICATIONS GMBH—See Searchlight Capital Partners, L.P.; *U.S. Private*, pg. 3589
DEUTA AMERICA CORP.—See DEUTA-WERKE GmbH; *Int'l*, pg. 2049
DEXERIALS HONG KONG LIMITED—See Development Bank of Japan, Inc.; *Int'l*, pg. 2087
DEXERIALS KOREA CORPORATION—See Development Bank of Japan, Inc.; *Int'l*, pg. 2087
DEXERIALS SINGAPORE PTE. LTD.—See Development Bank of Japan, Inc.; *Int'l*, pg. 2087
DEXERIALS TAIWAN CORPORATION—See Development Bank of Japan, Inc.; *Int'l*, pg. 2087
DICK SMITH (WHOLESALE) PTY. LTD.—See Anchorage Capital Partners Pty. Limited; *Int'l*, pg. 448
DICOPEL, INC.—See Arrow Electronics, Inc.; *U.S. Public*, pg. 199
DIGI INTERNATIONAL LIMITED—See Digi International Inc.; *U.S. Public*, pg. 662
DIGI INTERNATIONAL SPAIN S.A.—See Digi International Inc.; *U.S. Public*, pg. 662
DIGI-KEY CORPORATION; *U.S. Private*, pg. 1229
DIGIMERGE TECHNOLOGIES INC.—See Teledyne Technologies Incorporated; *U.S. Public*, pg. 1993
DIGITALGLUE—See P2 Capital Partners, LLC; *U.S. Private*, pg. 3061
DIGITALGLUE—See Silver Lake Group, LLC; *U.S. Private*, pg. 3656
DINGDONG (CAYMAN) LTD.; *Int'l*, pg. 2127
DIODES FABTECH INC.—See Diodes Incorporated; *U.S. Public*, pg. 667
DIODES JAPAN K.K.—See Diodes Incorporated; *U.S. Public*, pg. 667

DIODES TAIWAN S.A.R.L—See Diodes Incorporated; *U.S. Public*, pg. 667
DISCOUNT TWO WAY RADIO CORPORATION; *U.S. Private*, pg. 1237
DISTECH CONTROLS ENERGY SERVICES INC.—See Acuity Brands, Inc.; *U.S. Public*, pg. 37
DISTECH CONTROLS PORTUGAL DOMEBUS—See Acuity Brands, Inc.; *U.S. Public*, pg. 37
DISTECH CONTROLS PTE LTD—See Acuity Brands, Inc.; *U.S. Public*, pg. 37
DISTECH CONTROLS SAS—See Acuity Brands, Inc.; *U.S. Public*, pg. 37
DIVERSIFIED ELECTRONICS INC.; *U.S. Private*, pg. 1242
DMC INTERNATIONAL IMAGING LTD.—See Airbus SE; *Int'l*, pg. 243
DMD PRODUCTS, LLC; *U.S. Private*, pg. 1248
DOMINANT OPTO TECHNOLOGIES JAPAN KK—See D & O Green Technologies Berhad; *Int'l*, pg. 1898
DOMINANT SEMICONDUCTORS KOREA INC.—See D & O Green Technologies Berhad; *Int'l*, pg. 1898
DONGBU DAEWOO ELECTRONICS JAPAN CO., LTD.—See Dongbu Group; *Int'l*, pg. 2165
DONGGUAN IM DIGITAL ELECTRONICS CO. LTD—See IM Co., Ltd.; *Int'l*, pg. 3617
DONGGUAN LIESHENG ELECTRONIC TECHNOLOGY CO., LTD.; *Int'l*, pg. 2167
DONGJIN SEMICHEM CO., LTD. - BALAN PLANT—See Dongjin Semichem Co., Ltd.; *Int'l*, pg. 2168
DONGJIN SEMICHEM CO., LTD. - INCHEON PLANT—See Dongjin Semichem Co., Ltd.; *Int'l*, pg. 2168
DONGJIN SEMICHEM CO., LTD. - SHIWHA PLANT—See Dongjin Semichem Co., Ltd.; *Int'l*, pg. 2168
DONGJIN SEMICHEM ORDOS CITY TECHNOLOGY CO., LTD.—See Dongjin Semichem Co., Ltd.; *Int'l*, pg. 2168
DONGJIN SEMICHEM TECHNOLOGY (QIDONG) CO., LTD.—See Dongjin Semichem Co., Ltd.; *Int'l*, pg. 2168
DONGJIN SEMICHEM (XI'AN) SEMICONDUCTOR MATERIALS CO., LTD.—See Dongjin Semichem Co., Ltd.; *Int'l*, pg. 2168
DOOSAN ELECTRO-MATERIALS SINGAPORE PTE CO., LTD.—See Doosan Corporation; *Int'l*, pg. 2173
DOT MOBILE SDN BHD—See Digilife Technologies Limited; *Int'l*, pg. 2119
DOVE ELECTRONIC COMPONENTS; *U.S. Private*, pg. 1268
DOVITECH A/S—See Addtech AB; *Int'l*, pg. 132
DRAGON GROUP INTERNATIONAL LIMITED—See ASTI Holdings Limited; *Int'l*, pg. 655
DRAYTEK CO.—See DrayTek Corporation; *Int'l*, pg. 2200
DRITTE TENVA PROPERTY GMBH NETTETAL—See Avnet, Inc.; *U.S. Public*, pg. 252
DSP GROUP (SHENZHEN) LIMITED—See Synaptics Incorporated; *U.S. Public*, pg. 1969
DUELCO A/S—See Addtech AB; *Int'l*, pg. 132
DYNALINK MODEMS LTD.—See Casa Systems, Inc.; *U.S. Private*, pg. 778
EAF FRANCE SA—See discoverIE Group plc; *Int'l*, pg. 2133
EAGLERISE E&E INC.—See Eaglerise Electric & Electronic (China) Co., Ltd.; *Int'l*, pg. 2266
EAGLERISE E&E (USA), INC.—See Eaglerise Electric & Electronic (China) Co., Ltd.; *Int'l*, pg. 2266
EARL & BROWN COMPANY; *U.S. Private*, pg. 1312
EASTELE TECHNOLOGY CHINA LIMITED—See Avnet, Inc.; *U.S. Public*, pg. 252
EASTERN DRAGON EXPRESS (H.K.) LTD.—See HPI AG; *Int'l*, pg. 3500
EASTERN STATES COMPONENTS, INC.; *U.S. Private*, pg. 1321
EBARA REFRIGERATION EQUIPMENT & SYSTEMS (CHINA) CO., LTD.—See Ebara Corporation; *Int'l*, pg. 2283
EBV ELECTROLINK (PTY) LTD—See Avnet, Inc.; *U.S. Public*, pg. 251
EBV ELEKTRONIK APS—See Avnet, Inc.; *U.S. Public*, pg. 252
EBV ELEKTRONIK D.O.O.—See Avnet, Inc.; *U.S. Public*, pg. 252
EBV ELEKTRONIK, DRUZBA ZA POSREDOVANJE D.O.O.—See Avnet, Inc.; *U.S. Public*, pg. 252
EBV ELEKTRONIK EOOD—See Avnet, Inc.; *U.S. Public*, pg. 252
EBV ELEKTRONIK FRANCE SAS—See Avnet, Inc.; *U.S. Public*, pg. 252
EBV ELEKTRONIK GMBH & CO. KG—See Avnet, Inc.; *U.S. Public*, pg. 251
EBV ELEKTRONIK GMBH & CO. KG—See Avnet, Inc.; *U.S. Public*, pg. 252
EBV-ELEKTRONIK GMBH—See Avnet, Inc.; *U.S. Public*, pg. 252
EBV ELEKTRONIK KFT—See Avnet, Inc.; *U.S. Public*, pg. 251
EBV ELEKTRONIK LTD.—See Avnet, Inc.; *U.S. Public*, pg. 251
EBV ELEKTRONIK M—See Avnet, Inc.; *U.S. Public*, pg. 251
EBV ELEKTRONIK SAS—See Avnet, Inc.; *U.S. Public*, pg. 252
EBV ELEKTRONIK SPAIN S.L.—See Avnet, Inc.; *U.S. Public*, pg. 252

EBV ELEKTRONIK SPOL. S.R.O.—See Avnet, Inc.; *U.S. Public*, pg. 251
EBV ELEKTRONIK SP. Z O.O.—See Avnet, Inc.; *U.S. Public*, pg. 252
EBV ELEKTRONIK S.R.L.—See Avnet, Inc.; *U.S. Public*, pg. 251
EBV ELEKTRONIK S.R.L.—See Avnet, Inc.; *U.S. Public*, pg. 252
EBV ELEKTRONIK S.R.O.—See Avnet, Inc.; *U.S. Public*, pg. 252
EBV ELEKTRONIK TICARET LTD.—See Avnet, Inc.; *U.S. Public*, pg. 251
EBV ELEKTRONIK TOV—See Avnet, Inc.; *U.S. Public*, pg. 252
EBV ELEKTRONIK, UNIPESSOAL LDA.—See Avnet, Inc.; *U.S. Public*, pg. 252
ECKELMANN AUTOMATION TECHNOLOGY (SHANGHAI) CO., LTD.—See Eckelmann AG; *Int'l*, pg. 2289
ECKELMANN INDUSTRIAL AUTOMATION TECHNOLOGIES (BEIJING) CO., LTD.—See Eckelmann AG; *Int'l*, pg. 2290
ECKELMANN S.R.O.—See Eckelmann AG; *Int'l*, pg. 2290
ECOBEE TECHNOLOGIES ULC—See Generac Holdings Inc.; *U.S. Public*, pg. 913
ECOMAL ELEKTRONSKE KOMPONENTE D.O.O.—See Vishay Intertechnology, Inc.; *U.S. Public*, pg. 2302
ECOMAL HUNGARY KFT.—See Vishay Intertechnology, Inc.; *U.S. Public*, pg. 2302
ECOMAL POLAND SP. Z O.O.—See Vishay Intertechnology, Inc.; *U.S. Public*, pg. 2302
E COMMUNICATIONS SYSTEMS INC.; *U.S. Private*, pg. 1300
ECONOCOM PRODUCTS AND SOLUTIONS SAS—See Econocom Group SA; *Int'l*, pg. 2297
ECS INC.; *U.S. Private*, pg. 1331
EDGE ELECTRONICS INC.; *U.S. Private*, pg. 1334
EDIMAX COMPUTER COMPANY—See Edimax Technology Co., Ltd.; *Int'l*, pg. 2310
EDIMAX TECHNOLOGY AUSTRALIA PTY. LTD.—See Edimax Technology Co., Ltd.; *Int'l*, pg. 2310
EDIMAX TECHNOLOGY (SE ASIA) PTE. LTD.—See Edimax Technology Co., Ltd.; *Int'l*, pg. 2310
E-DIRECT CORP—See Accton Technology Corporation; *Int'l*, pg. 94
EDISON OPTO (DONG GUAN) CO., LTD.—See Edison Opto Corp.; *Int'l*, pg. 2311
EDISON OPTO USA CORPORATION—See Edison Opto Corp.; *Int'l*, pg. 2311
EDOM TECHNOLOGY (SHANGHAI) LTD.—See EDOM Technology Co., Ltd.; *Int'l*, pg. 2313
E&E COMPONENTS (HK) LIMITED—See Everlight Electronics Co., Ltd.; *Int'l*, pg. 2567
EET EUROPARTS AB—See FSN Capital Partners AS; *Int'l*, pg. 2799
EET EUROPARTS A/S—See FSN Capital Partners AS; *Int'l*, pg. 2799
EET EUROPARTS AS—See FSN Capital Partners AS; *Int'l*, pg. 2799
EET EUROPARTS BV—See FSN Capital Partners AS; *Int'l*, pg. 2799
EET EUROPARTS B.V.—See FSN Capital Partners AS; *Int'l*, pg. 2799
EET EUROPARTS EGYPT—See FSN Capital Partners AS; *Int'l*, pg. 2799
EET EUROPARTS GMBH—See FSN Capital Partners AS; *Int'l*, pg. 2799
EET EUROPARTS GMBH—See FSN Capital Partners AS; *Int'l*, pg. 2799
EET EUROPARTS GMBH—See FSN Capital Partners AS; *Int'l*, pg. 2799
EET EUROPARTS LTD—See FSN Capital Partners AS; *Int'l*, pg. 2799
EET EUROPARTS OY—See FSN Capital Partners AS; *Int'l*, pg. 2799
EET EUROPARTS (PTY) LTD—See FSN Capital Partners AS; *Int'l*, pg. 2799
EET EUROPARTS S.A.—See FSN Capital Partners AS; *Int'l*, pg. 2799
EET EUROPARTS SP. Z O.O.—See FSN Capital Partners AS; *Int'l*, pg. 2799
EET EUROPARTS S.R.L.—See FSN Capital Partners AS; *Int'l*, pg. 2799
EET EUROPARTS S.R.O.—See FSN Capital Partners AS; *Int'l*, pg. 2799
EET FRANCE SAS—See FSN Capital Partners AS; *Int'l*, pg. 2799
EET PORTUGAL—See FSN Capital Partners AS; *Int'l*, pg. 2799
EFACEC MOZAMBIQUE, LDA.—See Efacec Capital, SGPS, S.A.; *Int'l*, pg. 2318
EFACEC PRAHA S.R.O.—See Efacec Capital, SGPS, S.A.; *Int'l*, pg. 2318
EFACEC SERVICOS CORPORATIVOS, SA—See Efacec Capital, SGPS, S.A.; *Int'l*, pg. 2318
EFACEC SISTEMAS ESPANA, S.L.—See Efacec Capital, SGPS, S.A.; *Int'l*, pg. 2318
EFACEC TUNIS—See Efacec Capital, SGPS, S.A.; *Int'l*, pg. 2318

EG (SHANGHAI) COMMERCIAL CO., LTD.—See Amplex AB; *Int'l*, pg. 434
EGUANA GMBH—See Eguana Technologies Inc.; *Int'l*, pg. 2326
E+HPS PTE. LTD.—See Ellipsiz Ltd.; *Int'l*, pg. 2366
EIC INTERNATIONAL CO., LTD—See Electronics Industry Public Company Limited; *Int'l*, pg. 2354
EIC SEMICONDUCTOR, INC.—See Electronics Industry Public Company Limited; *Int'l*, pg. 2354
E-INFOCHIPS PRIVATE LIMITED—See Arrow Electronics, Inc.; *U.S. Public*, pg. 200
EITA POWER SYSTEM SDN. BHD.—See Eita Resources Berhad; *Int'l*, pg. 2336
EKS ASIA LTD.—See Eks France; *Int'l*, pg. 2339
EKS INTERNATIONAL SWEDEN AB—See Eks France; *Int'l*, pg. 2339
EKS INTERNATIONAL (UK) LTD.—See Eks France; *Int'l*, pg. 2339
ELCOFLEX (SUZHOU) CO., LTD.—See Career Technology (MFG.) Co., Ltd.; *Int'l*, pg. 1323
ELCOM INC.; *U.S. Private*, pg. 1350
ELECTRICAL INSULATION SUPPLIERS DE MEXICO, S.A. DE C.V.—See Genuine Parts Company; *U.S. Public*, pg. 932
ELECTRIC CONNECTOR TECHNOLOGY CO., LTD. - CARLSBAD BRANCH—See Electric Connector Technology Co., Ltd.; *Int'l*, pg. 2348
ELECTRO MECHANICAL SYSTEMS LTD.; *Int'l*, pg. 2352
ELECTRONIC CUSTOM DISTRIBUTORS, INC.—See Resideo Technologies, Inc.; *U.S. Public*, pg. 1789
ELECTRONIC PAYMENT EXCHANGE, INC.—See North American Bancard, LLC; *U.S. Private*, pg. 2940
ELECTRONIC SUPPLY COMPANY—See H.I.G. Capital, LLC; *U.S. Private*, pg. 1827
ELECTRONIC SYSTEMS PROTECTION, INC.; *U.S. Private*, pg. 1356
ELECTRO-REPS INC.; *U.S. Private*, pg. 1354
ELECTRO SCIENTIFIC INDUSTRIES EUROPE LTD.—See MKS Instruments, Inc.; *U.S. Public*, pg. 1452
ELECTRO SONIC INC.; *Int'l*, pg. 2353
ELEMENT14 ASIA PTE. LTD.—See Avnet, Inc.; *U.S. Public*, pg. 253
ELEMENT14 CO., LTD.—See Avnet, Inc.; *U.S. Public*, pg. 253
ELEMENT14 HOLDING BV—See Avnet, Inc.; *U.S. Public*, pg. 253
ELEMENT14 INDIA PVT LIMITED—See Avnet, Inc.; *U.S. Public*, pg. 253
ELEMENT14 LIMITED—See Avnet, Inc.; *U.S. Public*, pg. 253
ELEMENT14 LIMITED—See Avnet, Inc.; *U.S. Public*, pg. 253
ELEMENT14 PTE LTD—See Avnet, Inc.; *U.S. Public*, pg. 253
ELEMENT14 PTE. LTD.—See Avnet, Inc.; *U.S. Public*, pg. 253
ELEMENT14 PTY LTD—See Avnet, Inc.; *U.S. Public*, pg. 253
ELEMENT14. S. DE R.L. DE C.V—See Avnet, Inc.; *U.S. Public*, pg. 253
ELEMENT14 SDN. BHD.—See Avnet, Inc.; *U.S. Public*, pg. 254
ELEMENT 14 SP. ZOO—See Avnet, Inc.; *U.S. Public*, pg. 253
ELES S.P.A.; *Int'l*, pg. 2359
E-LIFE MALL CORPORATION; *Int'l*, pg. 2248
ELKO C.E., S.A.—See Arrow Electronics, Inc.; *U.S. Public*, pg. 199
ELLIPSIZ COMMUNICATIONS TAIWAN LTD—See Ellipsiz Ltd.; *Int'l*, pg. 2366
ELLIPSIZ DSS PTE. LTD.—See Ellipsiz Ltd.; *Int'l*, pg. 2366
ELLIPSIZ INETEST (SHANGHAI) CO., LTD—See Ellipsiz Ltd.; *Int'l*, pg. 2366
ELLIPSIZ INETEST (SUZHOU) CO., LTD.—See Ellipsiz Ltd.; *Int'l*, pg. 2366
ELLIPSIZ (SHANGHAI) INTERNATIONAL LTD—See Ellipsiz Ltd.; *Int'l*, pg. 2366
ELMA ELECTRONIC FRANCE SASU—See Elma Electronic AG; *Int'l*, pg. 2367
ELMA ELECTRONIC ISRAEL LTD—See Elma Electronic AG; *Int'l*, pg. 2367
ELMOS KOREA LTD—See ELMOS Semiconductor AG; *Int'l*, pg. 2368
ELON AB; *Int'l*, pg. 2368
EL PASO COMMUNICATION SYSTEMS, INC.; *U.S. Private*, pg. 1349
ELTECH AUTOMATION A/S—See Addtech AB; *Int'l*, pg. 133
ELTEK ARGENTINA S.R.L.—See Delta Electronics, Inc.; *Int'l*, pg. 2017
ELTEK AUSTRALIA PTY LTD.—See Delta Electronics, Inc.; *Int'l*, pg. 2017
ELTEK EGYPT ASA—See Delta Electronics, Inc.; *Int'l*, pg. 2017
ELTEK INC.—See Delta Electronics, Inc.; *Int'l*, pg. 2017
ELTEK ITALIA S.R.L.—See Delta Electronics, Inc.; *Int'l*, pg. 2017
ELTEK PAKISTAN (PVT) LTD.—See Delta Electronics, Inc.; *Int'l*, pg. 2017

ELTEK PERU SRL—See Delta Electronics, Inc.; *Int'l*, pg. 2017
ELTEK POLSKA SP. Z O.O.—See Delta Electronics, Inc.; *Int'l*, pg. 2017
ELTEK POWER INC.—See Delta Electronics, Inc.; *Int'l*, pg. 2017
ELTEK POWER (MALAYSIA) SDN. BHD—See Delta Electronics, Inc.; *Int'l*, pg. 2017
ELTEK POWER OY—See Delta Electronics, Inc.; *Int'l*, pg. 2017
ELTEK POWER PTE. LTD.—See Delta Electronics, Inc.; *Int'l*, pg. 2017
ELTEK POWER SWEDEN AB—See Delta Electronics, Inc.; *Int'l*, pg. 2017
ELTEK SGS PVT. LTD.—See Delta Electronics, Inc.; *Int'l*, pg. 2017
EMCOMP INTERNATIONAL AB—See Addtech AB; *Int'l*, pg. 133
EMCOMP SCANDINAVIA AB—See Addtech AB; *Int'l*, pg. 133
EMERALD TECHNOLOGIES—See Crestview Partners, L.P.; *U.S. Private*, pg. 1098
EMERSON NETWORK POWER AB—See Emerson Electric Co.; *U.S. Public*, pg. 747
EMERSON NETWORK POWER - EMBEDDED COMPUTING GMBH—See Emerson Electric Co.; *U.S. Public*, pg. 745
EMERSON NETWORK POWER PAKISTAN (PRIVATE) LIMITED—See Emerson Electric Co.; *U.S. Public*, pg. 745
EMERSON PROCESS MANAGEMENT, VALVE AUTOMATION DIVISION—See Emerson Electric Co.; *U.S. Public*, pg. 748
EMMENDINGER MASCHINENBAU GMBH; *Int'l*, pg. 2384
EMP SOLUTIONS, INC.; *U.S. Public*, pg. 753
EMX ENTERPRISES LIMITED; *Int'l*, pg. 2395
ENDRICH BAUELEMENTE S.L.—See Endrich Bauelemente Vertriebs GmbH; *Int'l*, pg. 2409
ENDRICH GES.M.B.H—See Endrich Bauelemente Vertriebs GmbH; *Int'l*, pg. 2409
ENECSYS LLC—See Enecsys plc; *Int'l*, pg. 2411
ENECSYS TAIWAN LIMITED—See Enecsys plc; *Int'l*, pg. 2411
ENKER D.D.; *Int'l*, pg. 2440
ENSEO INC; *U.S. Private*, pg. 1402
ENTEGRIS KOREA LTD.—See Entegris, Inc.; *U.S. Public*, pg. 776
ENVIROLOGIC AB; *Int'l*, pg. 2454
EOS DEFENSE SYSTEMS PTE LIMITED—See Electro Optic Systems Holdings Limited; *Int'l*, pg. 2353
EOS OPTRONICS GMBH—See Electro Optic Systems Holdings Limited; *Int'l*, pg. 2353
EOS TECHNOLOGIES, INC.—See Electro Optic Systems Holdings Limited; *Int'l*, pg. 2353
EO TECHNICS INTERNATIONAL, INC.—See EO Technics Co., Ltd.; *Int'l*, pg. 2457
EQUIPMENT SALES CO.—See Fuji Corporation; *Int'l*, pg. 2809
ERC PARTS INC.; *U.S. Private*, pg. 1417
ERIC ELECTRONICS, INC.; *U.S. Private*, pg. 1419
ERNI ASIA HOLDING PTE LTD—See ERNI Electronics GmbH; *Int'l*, pg. 2494
ERNI CABLE SYSTEMS AG—See ERNI Electronics GmbH; *Int'l*, pg. 2494
ERNI ELECTRONICS AG—See ERNI Electronics GmbH; *Int'l*, pg. 2494
ERNI ELECTRONICS CHINA—See ERNI Electronics GmbH; *Int'l*, pg. 2494
ERNI ELECTRONICS LTD.—See ERNI Electronics GmbH; *Int'l*, pg. 2494
EROS ELECTRICALS LLC—See Aiphone Co., Ltd.; *Int'l*, pg. 235
ERYMA SOGETREL GROUP; *Int'l*, pg. 2500
ESHEL TECHNOLOGY GROUP, INC.—See Arrow Electronics, Inc.; *U.S. Public*, pg. 199
ESQUIRE RADIO & ELECTRONICS INC.; *U.S. Private*, pg. 1427
ESSCO COLLINS LIMITED—See L3Harris Technologies, Inc.; *U.S. Public*, pg. 1281
ESS ELECTRONICS TECHNOLOGY (SHENZHEN) CO., LTD.—See Imperium Partners Group, LLC; *U.S. Private*, pg. 2050
ESSEX X-RAY & MEDICAL EQUIPMENT LTD—See HEICO Corporation; *U.S. Public*, pg. 1020
ESS TECHNOLOGY INTERNATIONAL (KOREA) LTD.—See Imperium Partners Group, LLC; *U.S. Private*, pg. 2050
EST-SMT LLC—See ESPEC Corp.; *Int'l*, pg. 2505
ETAL GROUP (PVT.) LTD.—See Amplex AB; *Int'l*, pg. 434
ETAL (UK) LTD.—See Amplex AB; *Int'l*, pg. 434
ETEQ COMPONENTS INTERNATIONAL PTE LTD.—See Arrow Electronics, Inc.; *U.S. Public*, pg. 199
ETEQ COMPONENTS PTE LTD.—See Arrow Electronics, Inc.; *U.S. Public*, pg. 199
ETEQ COMPONENTS PTE LTD.—See Arrow Electronics, Inc.; *U.S. Public*, pg. 199
EUROFINS PRECISION TEM, LLC—See Eurofins Scientific S.E.; *Int'l*, pg. 2547

N.A.I.C.S. INDEX

423690 — OTHER ELECTRONIC PA...

EUROPTRONIC (HK) COMPANY LIMITED—See Europtronic Group Ltd.; *Int'l*, pg. 2557
EUROTEC LTD.—See Carel Industries S.p.A.; *Int'l*, pg. 1324
EUTECH INSTRUMENTS PTE LTD.—See Thermo Fisher Scientific Inc.; *U.S. Public*, pg. 2146
EVERLIGHT JAPAN CORPORATION—See Everlight Electronics Co., Ltd.; *Int'l*, pg. 2567
EVERLIGHT PTE. LTD.—See Everlight Chemical Industrial Co.; *Int'l*, pg. 2567
EVLITE ELECTRONICS CO., LTD.—See Everlight Electronics Co., Ltd.; *Int'l*, pg. 2567
EVS BROADCAST UK LTD.—See EVS Broadcast Equipment S.A.; *Int'l*, pg. 2574
EXCEL CELL ELECTRONIC (USA) CORP.—See Excel Cell Electronic Co., Ltd.; *Int'l*, pg. 2577
EXCEL TECH, INC.—See Arrow Electronics, Inc.; *U.S. Public*, pg. 195
EXECUTONE TELECOMMUNICATIONS, LLC; *U.S. Private*, pg. 1448
EXERTIS ARC TELECOM LIMITED—See DCC plc; *Int'l*, pg. 1990
EXTREME NETWORKS UK LIMITED—See Extreme Networks, Inc.; *U.S. Public*, pg. 813
EZVIZ EUROPE B.V.—See Hangzhou Hikvision Digital Technology Co., Ltd.; *Int'l*, pg. 3247
FAI ELECTRONICS—See Future Electronics Inc.; *Int'l*, pg. 2854
FAMINGO PTE LTD.—See Gold Peak Technology Group Limited; *Int'l*, pg. 3025
FAP PAFAL S.A.—See Apator S.A.; *Int'l*, pg. 501
FARADAY TECHNOLOGY CORPORATION; *Int'l*, pg. 2617
FARNELL AG—See Avnet, Inc.; *U.S. Public*, pg. 253
FARNELL (BELGIUM) NV—See Avnet, Inc.; *U.S. Public*, pg. 253
FARNELL COMPONENTS AB—See Avnet, Inc.; *U.S. Public*, pg. 253
FARNELL COMPONENTS (IRELAND) LIMITED—See Avnet, Inc.; *U.S. Public*, pg. 253
FARNELL COMPONENTS SL—See Avnet, Inc.; *U.S. Public*, pg. 253
FARNELL DANMARK AS—See Avnet, Inc.; *U.S. Public*, pg. 253
FARNELL (FRANCE) SAS—See Avnet, Inc.; *U.S. Public*, pg. 253
FARNELL GMBH—See Avnet, Inc.; *U.S. Public*, pg. 254
FARNELL ITALIA SRL—See Avnet, Inc.; *U.S. Public*, pg. 254
FARNELL (NETHERLANDS) BV—See Avnet, Inc.; *U.S. Public*, pg. 253
FAURECIA INDUSTRIES S.A.S.—See FORVIA SE; *Int'l*, pg. 2746
FB HELISERVICES LIMITED—See Advent International Corporation; *U.S. Private*, pg. 99
FDK AMERICA INC.—See Fujitsu Limited; *Int'l*, pg. 2832
FDK HONG KONG LTD.—See Fujitsu Limited; *Int'l*, pg. 2832
FDK KOREA LTD.—See Fujitsu Limited; *Int'l*, pg. 2832
FDK TAIWAN LTD.—See Fujitsu Limited; *Int'l*, pg. 2832
FENGHUA ADVANCED TECHNOLOGY (HK) LTD—See Guangdong Fenghua Advanced Technology (Holding) Co., Ltd.; *Int'l*, pg. 3154
FERROTEC AMC MALAYSIA SDN. BHD.—See Ferrotec Holdings Corporation; *Int'l*, pg. 2643
FIBERSYSTEM AB—See Addtech AB; *Int'l*, pg. 133
FIDELITONE, INC.; *U.S. Private*, pg. 1502
FINEMOST LIMITED—See Invesco Ltd.; *U.S. Public*, pg. 1161
FIREFLY COMPUTERS, LLC—See Rotunda Capital Partners LLC; *U.S. Private*, pg. 3488
FIRST SOLAR JAPAN GK—See First Solar, Inc.; *U.S. Public*, pg. 847
FLAME ENTERPRISES INCORPORATED; *U.S. Private*, pg. 1540
FLEX LIGHTING SOLUTIONS, INC.—See Flex Ltd.; *Int'l*, pg. 2702
FLEXMEDICAL SLOVAKIA S.R.O.—See Flex Ltd.; *Int'l*, pg. 2702
FLEXTRONICS AUSTRALIA PTY LTD—See Flex Ltd.; *Int'l*, pg. 2702
FLEXTRONICS AUTOMOTIVE USA, INC.—See Flex Ltd.; *Int'l*, pg. 2702
FLEXTRONICS ELECTRONICS (MAURITIUS) LIMITED—See Flex Ltd.; *Int'l*, pg. 2702
FLEXTRONICS INTERNATIONAL POLAND SP Z.O.O.—See Flex Ltd.; *Int'l*, pg. 2703
FLEXTRONICS SALES & MARKETING NORTH ASIA (L) LTD.—See Flex Ltd.; *Int'l*, pg. 2704
FLINT DISTRIBUTION LIMITED—See Avnet, Inc.; *U.S. Public*, pg. 253
FLUKE PRECISION MEASUREMENT LTD.—See Fortive Corporation; *U.S. Public*, pg. 870
FONEX SAS—See FONEX Data Systems Inc.; *Int'l*, pg. 2726
FORTUNE ELECTRIC CO., LTD. - NORTH AMERICAN DIVISION—See Fortune Electric Co., Ltd.; *Int'l*, pg. 2743
FORUM GUIDO MONZANI S.R.L.—See BPER BANCA S.p.A; *Int'l*, pg. 1132
FORWARD INDUSTRIES (SWITZERLAND) GMBH—See Forward Industries, Inc.; *U.S. Public*, pg. 874
FOSTER ELECTRIC CO., (HONG KONG) LTD.—See Foster Electric Co., Ltd.; *Int'l*, pg. 2749
FOSTER ELECTRIC (U.S.A.), INC.—See Foster Electric Co., Ltd.; *Int'l*, pg. 2749
FOSTER ELECTRONICS LIMITED—See Foster Electric Co., Ltd.; *Int'l*, pg. 2750
FOSTEX CO., LTD.—See Foster Electric Co., Ltd.; *Int'l*, pg. 2750
FREQUENCY TELECOM; *Int'l*, pg. 2773
FSP NORTH AMERICA, INC.—See FSP Technology Inc.; *Int'l*, pg. 2800
FUJI ELECTRIC (ASIA) CO., LTD.—See Fuji Electric Co., Ltd.; *Int'l*, pg. 2811
FUJI ELECTRIC ASIA PACIFIC PTE. LTD.—See Fuji Electric Co., Ltd.; *Int'l*, pg. 2811
FUJI ELECTRIC (CHINA) CO., LTD.—See Fuji Electric Co., Ltd.; *Int'l*, pg. 2811
FUJI ELECTRIC FA KOREA CO., LTD.—See Fuji Electric Co., Ltd.; *Int'l*, pg. 2811
FUJI ELECTRIC HONG KONG CO., LTD.—See Fuji Electric Co., Ltd.; *Int'l*, pg. 2811
FUJI ELECTRIC INDUSTRIES SINGAPORE PRIVATE LTD.—See Fuji Electric Co., Ltd.; *Int'l*, pg. 2811
FUJI ELECTRIC SALES MALAYSIA SDN. BHD.—See Fuji Electric Co., Ltd.; *Int'l*, pg. 2812
FUJI ELECTRIC SALES PHILIPPINES, INC.—See Fuji Electric Co., Ltd.; *Int'l*, pg. 2812
FUJI ELECTRIC (SHANGHAI) CO., LTD.—See Fuji Electric Co., Ltd.; *Int'l*, pg. 2811
FUJI ELECTRIC VIETNAM CO., LTD.—See Fuji Electric Co., Ltd.; *Int'l*, pg. 2812
FUJIFILM ELECTRONIC MATERIALS (HONG KONG) CO., LTD.—See FUJIFILM Holdings Corporation; *Int'l*, pg. 2824
FUJIFILM ELECTRONIC MATERIALS KOREA CO., LTD.—See FUJIFILM Holdings Corporation; *Int'l*, pg. 2824
FUJIFILM ELECTRONIC MATERIALS (SINGAPORE) PTE. LTD.—See FUJIFILM Holdings Corporation; *Int'l*, pg. 2824
FUJIFILM ELECTRONIC MATERIALS TAIWAN CO., LTD.—See FUJIFILM Holdings Corporation; *Int'l*, pg. 2824
FUJIKURA AMERICA, INC. - DDK CONNECTOR DIVISION—See Fujikura Ltd.; *Int'l*, pg. 2827
FUJIKURA AUTOMOTIVE AMERICA LLC.—See Fujikura Ltd.; *Int'l*, pg. 2827
FUJIKURA EUROPE LTD. - ELECTRONICS DIVISION—See Fujikura Ltd.; *Int'l*, pg. 2828
FUJIKURA HONG KONG LTD. - DDK CONNECTOR DIVISION—See Fujikura Ltd.; *Int'l*, pg. 2828
FUJITSU COMPONENTS AMERICA, INC.—See Fujitsu Limited; *Int'l*, pg. 2833
FUJITSU COMPONENTS ASIA PTE, LTD.—See FUJITSU COMPONENT LIMITED; *Int'l*, pg. 2832
FUJITSU COMPONENTS KOREA LIMITED—See FUJITSU COMPONENT LIMITED; *Int'l*, pg. 2832
FUJITSU DO BRASIL LTDA—See Fujitsu Limited; *Int'l*, pg. 2834
FUJITSU ELECTRONIC COMPONENTS (SHANGHAI) CO., LTD.—See FUJITSU COMPONENT LIMITED; *Int'l*, pg. 2832
FUJITSU PHILIPPINES, INC.—See Fujitsu Limited; *Int'l*, pg. 2835
FUJITSU SEMICONDUCTOR KOREA LIMITED—See Fujitsu Limited; *Int'l*, pg. 2835
FUJITSU TAIWAN LIMITED—See Fujitsu Limited; *Int'l*, pg. 2836
FUKOKU DENKO CO., LTD.—See DKK Co., Ltd.; *Int'l*, pg. 2139
FULL COMPASS SYSTEMS CONTRACTORS LLC—See Full Compass Systems Ltd. Inc.; *U.S. Private*, pg. 1620
FUNAI CORPORATION, INC.—See Funai Electric Co., Ltd.; *Int'l*, pg. 2844
FURUNO DANMARK A/S—See Furuno Electric Co., Ltd.; *Int'l*, pg. 2847
FUSION TRADE, INC.; *U.S. Private*, pg. 1626
FUTABA DENSHI CORP. (S) PTE. LTD.—See Futaba Corporation; *Int'l*, pg. 2850
FUTABA ELECTRONICS COMPONENTS KOREA CO., LTD.—See Futaba Corporation; *Int'l*, pg. 2850
FUTABA (HONG KONG) CORPORATION LTD.—See Futaba Corporation; *Int'l*, pg. 2850
FUTABA INTERNATIONAL TRADING (SHANGHAI) CO., LTD.—See Futaba Corporation; *Int'l*, pg. 2850
FUTURE ELECTRONICS AB—See Future Electronics Inc.; *Int'l*, pg. 2854
FUTURE ELECTRONICS A/S—See Future Electronics Inc.; *Int'l*, pg. 2854
FUTURE ELECTRONICS AUSTRIA GMBH—See Future Electronics Inc.; *Int'l*, pg. 2854
FUTURE ELECTRONICS CORP.—See Future Electronics Inc.; *Int'l*, pg. 2854
FUTURE ELECTRONICS CORP., CANADA—See Future Electronics Inc.; *Int'l*, pg. 2854
FUTURE ELECTRONICS CORP., CANADA—See Future Electronics Inc.; *Int'l*, pg. 2854
FUTURE ELECTRONICS CORP.—See Future Electronics Inc.; *Int'l*, pg. 2854
FUTURE ELECTRONICS CORP.—See Future Electronics Inc.; *Int'l*, pg. 2854
FUTURE ELECTRONICS CORP.—See Future Electronics Inc.; *Int'l*, pg. 2854
FUTURE ELECTRONICS CORP.—See Future Electronics Inc.; *Int'l*, pg. 2854
FUTURE ELECTRONICS CORP.—See Future Electronics Inc.; *Int'l*, pg. 2854
FUTURE ELECTRONICS CORP.—See Future Electronics Inc.; *Int'l*, pg. 2854
FUTURE ELECTRONICS CORP.—See Future Electronics Inc.; *Int'l*, pg. 2854
FUTURE ELECTRONICS CORP.—See Future Electronics Inc.; *Int'l*, pg. 2854
FUTURE ELECTRONICS CORP.—See Future Electronics Inc.; *Int'l*, pg. 2854
FUTURE ELECTRONICS CORP.—See Future Electronics Inc.; *Int'l*, pg. 2854
FUTURE ELECTRONICS CORP.—See Future Electronics Inc.; *Int'l*, pg. 2854
FUTURE ELECTRONICS CORP.—See Future Electronics Inc.; *Int'l*, pg. 2854
FUTURE ELECTRONICS CORP.—See Future Electronics Inc.; *Int'l*, pg. 2854
FUTURE ELECTRONICS CORP.—See Future Electronics Inc.; *Int'l*, pg. 2854
FUTURE ELECTRONICS DEUTSCHLAND GMBH—See Future Electronics Inc.; *Int'l*, pg. 2855
FUTURE ELECTRONICS INC. (DISTRIBUTION) PTE LTD.—See Future Electronics Inc.; *Int'l*, pg. 2855
FUTURE ELECTRONICS INC.; *Int'l*, pg. 2854
FUTURE ELECTRONICS INC.—See Future Electronics Inc.; *Int'l*, pg. 2855
FUTURE ELECTRONICS INC. (WAREHOUSE) PTE LTD—See Future Electronics Inc.; *Int'l*, pg. 2855
FUTURE ELECTRONICS KFT—See Future Electronics Inc.; *Int'l*, pg. 2855
FUTURE ELECTRONICS LTD.—See Future Electronics Inc.; *Int'l*, pg. 2855
FUTURE ELECTRONICS OU—See Future Electronics Inc.; *Int'l*, pg. 2856
FUTURE ELECTRONICS SAS—See Future Electronics Inc.; *Int'l*, pg. 2856
FUTURE ELECTRONICS (SHANGHAI) CO., LTD—See Future Electronics Inc.; *Int'l*, pg. 2854
GALAXY MARKETING; *U.S. Private*, pg. 1636
GALCO INDUSTRIAL ELECTRONICS, INC.—See Freeman Spogli & Co. Incorporated; *U.S. Private*, pg. 1606
GALTRONICS USA INC—See Baylin Technologies Inc.; *Int'l*, pg. 914
GARMIN BELUX N.V./S.A—See Garmin Ltd.; *Int'l*, pg. 2885
GARMIN DEUTSCHLAND GMBH—See Garmin Ltd.; *Int'l*, pg. 2885
GARMIN FRANCE SAS—See Garmin Ltd.; *Int'l*, pg. 2885
GARMIN INDIA PRIVATE LTD.—See Garmin Ltd.; *Int'l*, pg. 2885
GARMIN PORTUGAL - EQUIPAMENTOS DE COMUNICACOES E DE NAVEGACAO LTDA.—See Garmin Ltd.; *Int'l*, pg. 2885
GARMIN SUOMI OY—See Garmin Ltd.; *Int'l*, pg. 2885
GARMIN SWEDEN AB—See Garmin Ltd.; *Int'l*, pg. 2885
GARMIN SWEDEN TECHNOLOGIES AB—See Garmin Ltd.; *Int'l*, pg. 2885
GATELY COMMUNICATION COMPANY—See Sentinel Capital Partners, L.L.C.; *U.S. Private*, pg. 3609
GBH COMMUNICATIONS INC.; *U.S. Private*, pg. 1653
GBI SALES PTY., LTD.—See GBI Holdings Pty., Ltd.; *Int'l*, pg. 2893
GDC DIGITAL CINEMA NETWORK (BRASIL) LTD—See Huayi Brothers Media Corp.; *Int'l*, pg. 3515
GDC DIGITAL CINEMA NETWORK GG—See Huayi Brothers Media Corp.; *Int'l*, pg. 3515
GDC DIGITAL CINEMA NETWORK (MEXICO) S. DE R.L. DE C.V.—See Huayi Brothers Media Corp.; *Int'l*, pg. 3515
GDC DIGITAL CINEMA NETWORK (PERU), SAC—See Huayi Brothers Media Corp.; *Int'l*, pg. 3515
GDC DIGITAL CINEMA TECHNOLOGY EUROPE, SL—See Huayi Brothers Media Corp.; *Int'l*, pg. 3515
GDC TECHNOLOGY (BEIJING) LIMITED—See Huayi Brothers Media Corp.; *Int'l*, pg. 3516
GDC TECHNOLOGY INDIA PVT. LTD.—See Huayi Brothers Media Corp.; *Int'l*, pg. 3516
GDC TECHNOLOGY PTE LIMITED—See Huayi Brothers Media Corp.; *Int'l*, pg. 3516
GDC TECHNOLOGY (SHENZHEN) LIMITED—See Huayi Brothers Media Corp.; *Int'l*, pg. 3516
GDC TECHNOLOGY (USA) LLC—See Huayi Brothers Media Corp.; *Int'l*, pg. 3516
GEFRAN SUISSE SA—See Gefran S.p.A.; *Int'l*, pg. 2912
GE HUNGARY KFT.—See General Electric Company; *U.S. Public*, pg. 917
GENERAL DYNAMICS SATCOM TECHNOLOGIES ASIA PRIVATE LIMITED—See General Dynamics Corporation; *U.S. Public*, pg. 915
GENERAL INSTRUMENT LLC—See CommScope Holding Company, Inc.; *U.S. Public*, pg. 548
GENERAL SEMICONDUCTOR (CHINA) CO., LTD.—See Vishay Intertechnology, Inc.; *U.S. Public*, pg. 2302

GENES TECH GROUP HOLDINGS COMPANY LIMITED; *Int'l*, pg. 2921
GENUINE SOLUTIONS LIMITED; *Int'l*, pg. 2930
GEWISS CHILE LTDA—See Gewiss S.p.A.; *Int'l*, pg. 2955
GEWISS ELEKTRIK TESISAT MALZEMELERI TICARET LTD.—See Gewiss S.p.A.; *Int'l*, pg. 2955
GEWISS FRANCE SA—See Gewiss S.p.A.; *Int'l*, pg. 2955
GEWISS GULF FZE—See Gewiss S.p.A.; *Int'l*, pg. 2955
GEWISS IBERICA SA—See Gewiss S.p.A.; *Int'l*, pg. 2955
GEWISS PORTUGAL LDA—See Gewiss S.p.A.; *Int'l*, pg. 2955
GEWISS ROMANIA SRL—See Gewiss S.p.A.; *Int'l*, pg. 2955
GEWISS TRADING (SHANGHAI) CO., LTD.—See Gewiss S.p.A.; *Int'l*, pg. 2955
GIFTEE, INC.; *Int'l*, pg. 2970
GIGACOM AB—See Addtech AB; *Int'l*, pg. 133
GIGADEVICE SEMICONDUCTOR (BEIJING) INC - SANTA CLARA BRANCH—See GigaDevice Semiconductor (Beijing) Inc; *Int'l*, pg. 2971
GIGADEVICE SEMICONDUCTOR EUROPE LTD—See GigaDevice Semiconductor (Beijing) Inc; *Int'l*, pg. 2971
GILBARCO AUSTRALIA PTY LTD.—See Vontier Corporation; *U.S. Public*, pg. 2308
GITIESSE S.R.L.—See Eaton Corporation plc; *Int'l*, pg. 2281
GIZA TECHNOLOGIES INC.; *U.S. Private*, pg. 1703
GLENTEL INC.—See BCE Inc.; *Int'l*, pg. 927
GLOBAL ACCESS UNLIMITED INC.; *U.S. Private*, pg. 1711
GLOBAL CELLULAR INC.; *U.S. Private*, pg. 1712
GLOBAL-E ONLINE LTD.; *Int'l*, pg. 3003
GLOBAL OPTICS LIMITED—See Global-Tech Advanced Innovations Inc.; *Int'l*, pg. 3003
GLYN HUNGARY KFT.—See GLYN GmbH & Co. KG; *Int'l*, pg. 3011
GLYN LTD.—See GLYN GmbH & Co. KG; *Int'l*, pg. 3011
GLYN LTD.—See GLYN GmbH & Co. KG; *Int'l*, pg. 3011
GLYN POLAND—See GLYN GmbH & Co. KG; *Int'l*, pg. 3011
GLYN SCHWEDEN—See GLYN GmbH & Co. KG; *Int'l*, pg. 3011
GO TELECOM BV—See DCC plc; *Int'l*, pg. 1991
GP ACOUSTICS GMBH—See Gold Peak Technology Group Limited; *Int'l*, pg. 3025
GP ACOUSTICS INTERNATIONAL LIMITED—See Gold Peak Technology Group Limited; *Int'l*, pg. 3025
GP ACOUSTICS (MIDDLE EAST) DWC-LLC—See Gold Peak Technology Group Limited; *Int'l*, pg. 3025
GP ACOUSTICS (TAIWAN) LIMITED—See Gold Peak Technology Group Limited; *Int'l*, pg. 3025
GP BATTERY MARKETING (MALAYSIA) SDN. BHD.—See Gold Peak Technology Group Limited; *Int'l*, pg. 3025
GP ELECTRONICS (HONG KONG) LIMITED—See Gold Peak Technology Group Limited; *Int'l*, pg. 3025
GRASS VALLEY FRANCE S.A—See Black Dragon Capital LLC; *U.S. Private*, pg. 571
GRAYBOW COMMUNICATIONS GROUP, INC.; *U.S. Private*, pg. 1760
GRAYLOC PRODUCTS, L.L.C.—See Oceaneering International, Inc.; *U.S. Public*, pg. 1562
GRAYLOC PRODUCTS LTD.—See Oceaneering International, Inc.; *U.S. Public*, pg. 1562
GREEN PACKET (AUSTRALIA) PTY. LTD.—See Green Packet Berhad; *Int'l*, pg. 3072
GROTHUSEN GESMBH; *Int'l*, pg. 3088
GROUP SENSE LIMITED—See Century Sunshine Group Holdings Limited; *Int'l*, pg. 1419
GRUBER INDUSTRIES INC.; *U.S. Private*, pg. 1796
GRUPO ANTOLIN CAMBRAI S.A.S.—See Grupo Antolin-Irausa, S.A.; *Int'l*, pg. 3119
GRUPO ANTOLIN-DEUTSCHLAND, GMBH—See Grupo Antolin-Irausa, S.A.; *Int'l*, pg. 3119
GRUPO ANTOLIN-FRANCE, S.A.S.—See Grupo Antolin-Irausa, S.A.; *Int'l*, pg. 3119
GRUPO ANTOLIN-VALENCA COMPONENTES AUTOMOVEL SOC. UNIPESSOAL, LDA.—See Grupo Antolin-Irausa, S.A.; *Int'l*, pg. 3120
GSI GROUP PRECISION TECHNOLOGIES (SUZHOU) CO., LTD.—See Novanta Inc.; *U.S. Public*, pg. 1548
GS YUASA INTERNATIONAL LTD.—See GS Yuasa Corporation; *Int'l*, pg. 3143
GUANGDONG ALL ACCESS NOTER COMMUNICATION TECHNOLOGY CO., LIMITED—See China All Access (Holdings) Limited; *Int'l*, pg. 1482
GUANGZHOU CASA COMMUNICATION TECHNOLOGY LTD.—See Casa Systems, Inc.; *U.S. Private*, pg. 778
GUANGZHOU YI-LIANG TRADING CO., LTD.—See Everlight Electronics Co., Ltd.; *Int'l*, pg. 2567
GUDECO ELEKTRONIK HANDELS GMBH; *Int'l*, pg. 3171
GUGGISBERG KURZ AG—See BKW AG; *Int'l*, pg. 1055
GUOAN INTERNATIONAL LIMITED—See CITIC Group Corporation; *Int'l*, pg. 1620
HACH ULTRA JAPAN KK—See Danaher Corporation; *U.S. Public*, pg. 627
HAGIWARA AMERICA, INC.—See Hagiwara Electric Holdings Co., Ltd.; *Int'l*, pg. 3207
HAGIWARA ELECTRIC EUROPE GMBH—See Hagiwara Electric Holdings Co., Ltd.; *Int'l*, pg. 3207
HAGIWARA ELECTRIC KOREA CO., LTD.—See Hagiwara Electric Holdings Co., Ltd.; *Int'l*, pg. 3207
HAGIWARA ELECTRIC (SHANGHAI) CO., LTD.—See Hagiwara Electric Holdings Co., Ltd.; *Int'l*, pg. 3207
HAGIWARA ELECTRIC (THAILAND) CO., LTD.—See Hagiwara Electric Holdings Co., Ltd.; *Int'l*, pg. 3207
HALO ELECTRONICS INC.; *U.S. Private*, pg. 1845
HAMA B.V.—See Hama GmbH & Co KG; *Int'l*, pg. 3234
HAMA DISTRIBUTION ROMANIA SRL—See Hama GmbH & Co KG; *Int'l*, pg. 3234
HAMA EURL—See Hama GmbH & Co KG; *Int'l*, pg. 3234
HAMA KFT.—See Hama GmbH & Co KG; *Int'l*, pg. 3234
HAMAMATSU CORPORATION—See Hamamatsu Photonics K.K.; *Int'l*, pg. 3235
HAMAMATSU PHOTONICS DEUTSCHLAND GMBH—See Hamamatsu Photonics K.K.; *Int'l*, pg. 3235
HAMAMATSU PHOTONICS FRANCE S.A.R.L.—See Hamamatsu Photonics K.K.; *Int'l*, pg. 3235
HAMAMATSU PHOTONICS ITALIA S.R.L.—See Hamamatsu Photonics K.K.; *Int'l*, pg. 3235
HAMA NV—See Hama GmbH & Co KG; *Int'l*, pg. 3234
HAMA POLSKA SP. Z.O.O.—See Hama GmbH & Co KG; *Int'l*, pg. 3234
HAMA SLOVAKIA SPOL.S.R.O.—See Hama GmbH & Co KG; *Int'l*, pg. 3234
HAMA SPOL. S R.O.—See Hama GmbH & Co KG; *Int'l*, pg. 3234
HAMA TECHNICS AG—See Hama GmbH & Co KG; *Int'l*, pg. 3234
HAMA TECHNICS HANDELS GMBH—See Hama GmbH & Co KG; *Int'l*, pg. 3234
HAMA TECHNICS S.L.—See Hama GmbH & Co KG; *Int'l*, pg. 3234
HAMA (UK) LTD.—See Hama GmbH & Co KG; *Int'l*, pg. 3234
HAMEE INDIA PVT. LTD.—See Hamee Corp.; *Int'l*, pg. 3237
HAMEE KOREA CO., LTD.—See Hamee Corp.; *Int'l*, pg. 3237
HAMEE SHANGHAI TRADE CO., LTD.—See Hamee Corp.; *Int'l*, pg. 3237
HAMEE TAIWAN, CORP.—See Hamee Corp.; *Int'l*, pg. 3237
HAMEE US, CORP.—See Hamee Corp.; *Int'l*, pg. 3237
HAMMOND ELECTRONICS INC.; *U.S. Private*, pg. 1849
HANA MICROELECTRONICS, INC.—See Hana Microelectronics Public Company Limited; *Int'l*, pg. 3241
HANWHA SYSTEMS CO., LTD.; *Int'l*, pg. 3267
HARADA AUTOMOTIVE ANTENNA (PHILIPPINES), INC.—See HARADA INDUSTRY CO., LTD.; *Int'l*, pg. 3269
HARADA INDUSTRIES (EUROPE) LIMITED—See HARADA INDUSTRY CO., LTD.; *Int'l*, pg. 3269
HARADA INDUSTRY OF AMERICA, INC.—See HARADA INDUSTRY CO., LTD.; *Int'l*, pg. 3269
HARPER & TWO; *U.S. Private*, pg. 1867
HARRIS CORP. - ELECTRONIC SYSTEMS DIVISION - ELECTRONIC WARFARE SYSTEMS - CLIFTON—See L3Harris Technologies, Inc.; *U.S. Public*, pg. 1279
HARRY KRANTZ COMPANY; *U.S. Private*, pg. 1872
HARRY'S ELECTRONICS INC.; *U.S. Private*, pg. 1872
HDK AMERICA INC.—See Hokuriku Electric Industry Co., Ltd.; *Int'l*, pg. 3444
HDK CHINA LTD.—See Hokuriku Electric Industry Co., Ltd.; *Int'l*, pg. 3444
HEADSET SOLUTIONS AFRICA PROPRIETARY LIMITED—See AYO Technology Solutions Ltd.; *Int'l*, pg. 775
HEBEI NOTER COMMUNICATION TECHNOLOGY CO., LIMITED—See China All Access (Holdings) Limited; *Int'l*, pg. 1482
HEFEI BOE OPTOELECTRONICS TECHNOLOGY CO., LTD.—See BOE Technology Group Co., Ltd.; *Int'l*, pg. 1099
HEFEI DONGJIN SEMICHEM CO., LTD.—See Dongjin Semichem Co., Ltd.; *Int'l*, pg. 2168
HEILIND ELECTRONICS, INC.; *U.S. Private*, pg. 1904
HENGXIN SHAMBOLA CULTURE CO., LTD.; *Int'l*, pg. 3347
HERMAN ELECTRONICS, INC.; *U.S. Private*, pg. 1925
HEYDERHOFF GMBH—See Aiphone Co., Ltd.; *Int'l*, pg. 235
HF DANYKO AS—See Addtech AB; *Int'l*, pg. 133
H&F EUROPE LIMITED—See Hitachi Zosen Corporation; *Int'l*, pg. 3410
H&F SERVICES (THAILAND) CO., LTD.—See Hitachi Zosen Corporation; *Int'l*, pg. 3410
HIFI ORIENT THAI PLC—See Hon Hai Precision Industry Co., Ltd.; *Int'l*, pg. 3459
HIGH SEAS TECHNOLOGY, INC.—See Pipe Welders Inc.; *U.S. Private*, pg. 3189
HIGH TECH COMPUTER (H.K.) LIMITED—See HTC Corporation; *Int'l*, pg. 3508
HILCO INC.; *U.S. Private*, pg. 1943
HIMAX ANALOGIC, INC.—See Himax Technologies, Inc.; *Int'l*, pg. 3396
HIMAX DISPLAY (USA) INC.—See Himax Technologies, Inc.; *Int'l*, pg. 3396
HIMAX MEDIA SOLUTIONS, INC.—See Himax Technologies, Inc.; *Int'l*, pg. 3397
HINSTEC CO., LTD.—See HIOKI E.E. Corporation; *Int'l*, pg. 3401
HI-P ELECTRONICS PTE. LTD.—See Hi-P International Limited; *Int'l*, pg. 3381
HI-P (TIANJIN) TECHNOLOGY CO., LTD.—See Hi-P International Limited; *Int'l*, pg. 3381
HIS COMPANY, INC.—See Distribution Solutions Group, Inc.; *U.S. Public*, pg. 668
HITACHI ASIA (M) SDN BHD—See Hitachi, Ltd.; *Int'l*, pg. 3414
HITACHI AUSTRALIA PTY LTD—See Hitachi, Ltd.; *Int'l*, pg. 3414
HITACHI CANADA—See Hitachi, Ltd.; *Int'l*, pg. 3415
HITACHI DE VENEZUELA, C.A.—See Hitachi, Ltd.; *Int'l*, pg. 3422
HITACHI DIGITAL MEDIA GROUP - RUSSIA—See Hitachi, Ltd.; *Int'l*, pg. 3416
HITACHI DIGITAL PRODUCTS CHINA CO., LTD.—See Hitachi, Ltd.; *Int'l*, pg. 3416
HITACHI ELECTRONICS ENGINEERING AMERICA—See Hitachi, Ltd.; *Int'l*, pg. 3414
HITACHI HIGH-TECH AMERICA, INC.—See Hitachi, Ltd.; *Int'l*, pg. 3418
HITACHI HIGH-TECHNOLOGIES HONG KONG LTD.—See Hitachi, Ltd.; *Int'l*, pg. 3418
HITACHI HIGH-TECHNOLOGIES (THAILAND) LTD.—See Hitachi, Ltd.; *Int'l*, pg. 3418
HITACHI INDIA TRADING PVT, LTD.—See Hitachi, Ltd.; *Int'l*, pg. 3419
HITACHI INTERNATIONAL (HOLLAND) B.V.—See Hitachi, Ltd.; *Int'l*, pg. 3419
HITACHI MEXICO, S.A. DE C.V.—See Hitachi, Ltd.; *Int'l*, pg. 3420
HITACHI VIA MECHANICS (USA), INC.—See Hitachi, Ltd.; *Int'l*, pg. 3414
HITACHI ZOSEN FUKUI U.S.A., INC.—See Hitachi Zosen Corporation; *Int'l*, pg. 3411
HITECH & DEVELOPMENT WIRELESS SWEDEN HOLDING AB; *Int'l*, pg. 3425
HI-TECH HOME; *U.S. Private*, pg. 1932
HK ASIA HOLDINGS LTD.; *Int'l*, pg. 3428
HKC INTERNATIONAL (THAILAND) CO. LTD.—See HKC International Holdings Limited; *Int'l*, pg. 3428
H.K. WENTWORTH LIMITED—See Element Solutions Inc.; *U.S. Public*, pg. 726
H.K. WENTWORTH PTY LIMITED—See Element Solutions Inc.; *U.S. Public*, pg. 726
HMS INDUSTRIAL NETWORKS LTD—See HMS Networks AB; *Int'l*, pg. 3433
HMS INDUSTRIAL NETWORKS SAS—See HMS Networks AB; *Int'l*, pg. 3433
HMS NETWORKS AB; *Int'l*, pg. 3432
HOEI ELECTRONICS (S) PRIVATE LTD.—See Fuji Electric Co., Ltd.; *Int'l*, pg. 2812
HOEI HONG KONG CO., LTD.—See Fuji Electric Co., Ltd.; *Int'l*, pg. 2812
HOKURIKU HONG KONG CO., LTD.—See Hokuriku Electric Industry Co., Ltd.; *Int'l*, pg. 3445
HOKURIKU (SHANGHAI) INTERNATIONAL TRADING CO., LTD.—See Hokuriku Electric Industry Co., Ltd.; *Int'l*, pg. 3445
HOKURIKU U.S.A. LTD.—See Hokuriku Electric Industry Co., Ltd.; *Int'l*, pg. 3445
HOLDERS TECHNOLOGY GMBH—See Holders Technology plc; *Int'l*, pg. 3450
HOLDERS TECHNOLOGY UK LTD—See Holders Technology plc; *Int'l*, pg. 3450
HOLLYLAND CO., LTD.—See Hollyland Group Holdings Limited; *Int'l*, pg. 3452
HOLY STONE (EUROPE) LTD.—See Holy Stone Enterprise Co., Ltd.; *Int'l*, pg. 3454
HOLY STONE INTERNATIONAL TRADING (SHANGHAI) CO., LTD.—See Holy Stone Enterprise Co., Ltd.; *Int'l*, pg. 3454
HOMESTEAD SHOP (M) SDN BHD—See Digilife Technologies Limited; *Int'l*, pg. 2119
HONEYWELL SPOL. SR.O.—See Honeywell International Inc.; *U.S. Public*, pg. 1051
HONG KONG COMMUNICATIONS COMPANY LIMITED—See HKC International Holdings Limited; *Int'l*, pg. 3428
HONG KONG HOSIDEN LTD—See Hosiden Corporation; *Int'l*, pg. 3484
HONG KONG THREE-CIRCLE ELECTRONIC CO., LTD.—See Chaozhou Three-Circle Group Co., Ltd.; *Int'l*, pg. 1447
HOOSIER EQUIPMENT BROKERS, INC.; *U.S. Private*, pg. 1978
HORIBA ABX S.A.S.—See HORIBA Ltd; *Int'l*, pg. 3475
HORIBA ABX SAS—See HORIBA Ltd; *Int'l*, pg. 3476
HORIBA ABX S.A.S.—See HORIBA Ltd; *Int'l*, pg. 3476
HORIBA ABX SAS—See HORIBA Ltd; *Int'l*, pg. 3476
HORIBA (AUSTRIA) GMBH—See HORIBA Ltd; *Int'l*, pg. 3475
HORIBA FUELCON GMBH—See HORIBA Ltd; *Int'l*, pg. 3476
HORIBA INSTRUMENTS BRASIL, LTDA—See HORIBA Ltd; *Int'l*, pg. 3476
HORIBA JOBIN YVON GMBH—See HORIBA Ltd; *Int'l*, pg. 3476
HORIBA LTD - HORIBA CZECH OLOMOUC FACTORY—See HORIBA Ltd; *Int'l*, pg. 3476
HORIBA OOO—See HORIBA Ltd; *Int'l*, pg. 3476

N.A.I.C.S. INDEX

423690 — OTHER ELECTRONIC PA...

HORIBA TOCADERO GMBH—See HORIBA Ltd; *Int'l*, pg. 3477
HORIBA VIETNAM COMPANY LIMITED—See HORIBA Ltd; *Int'l*, pg. 3477
HOSIDEN EUROPE GMBH—See Hosiden Corporation; *Int'l*, pg. 3484
HOSIDEN (SHENZHEN) CO., LTD.—See Hosiden Corporation; *Int'l*, pg. 3484
HOTAN CORP.—See CMC Magnetics Corporation; *Int'l*, pg. 1669
HOUSTON 2-WAY RADIO, INC.—See Littlejohn & Co., LLC; *U.S. Private*, pg. 2472
HO WAH GENTING TRADING SDN. BHD.—See Ho Wah Genting Berhad; *Int'l*, pg. 3435
HOWTEH TECHNOLOGY CO., LTD.; *Int'l*, pg. 3494
HUAWEI DEL PER S.A.C.—See Huawei Investment & Holding Co., Ltd.; *Int'l*, pg. 3515
HUAWEI TECH. INVESTMENT CO., LTD—See Huawei Investment & Holding Co., Ltd.; *Int'l*, pg. 3515
HUAWEI TECH INVESTMENT TASHKENT MCHJ—See Huawei Investment & Holding Co., Ltd.; *Int'l*, pg. 3515
HUAWEI TECHNOLOGIES (BOLIVIA) S.R.L.—See Huawei Investment & Holding Co., Ltd.; *Int'l*, pg. 3515
HUAWEI TECHNOLOGIES CO. LTD—See Huawei Investment & Holding Co., Ltd.; *Int'l*, pg. 3515
HUAWEI TECHNOLOGIES DE MEXICO, S.A. DE C.V.—See Huawei Investment & Holding Co., Ltd.; *Int'l*, pg. 3515
HUAWEI TECHNOLOGIES DUESSELDORF GMBH—See Huawei Investment & Holding Co., Ltd.; *Int'l*, pg. 3515
HUAWEI TECHNOLOGIES PHILS., INC.—See Huawei Investment & Holding Co., Ltd.; *Int'l*, pg. 3515
HUAWEI TECHNOLOGIES SWEDEN AB—See Huawei Investment & Holding Co., Ltd.; *Int'l*, pg. 3515
HUAWEI TECHNOLOGIES TANZANIA CO., LTD—See Huawei Investment & Holding Co., Ltd.; *Int'l*, pg. 3515
HUAWEI TECHNOLOGIES- (U) CO., LTD—See Huawei Investment & Holding Co., Ltd.; *Int'l*, pg. 3515
HUAWEI TECHNOLOGIES (UK) CO LTD—See Huawei Investment & Holding Co., Ltd.; *Int'l*, pg. 3515
HUBER + SUHNER (AUSTRALIA) PTY. LTD.—See Huber + Suhner AG; *Int'l*, pg. 3519
HUBER + SUHNER FRANCE—See Huber + Suhner AG; *Int'l*, pg. 3519
HUBER + SUHNER GMBH—See Huber + Suhner AG; *Int'l*, pg. 3519
HUBER+SUHNER (THAILAND) CO., LTD—See Huber + Suhner AG; *Int'l*, pg. 3519
HUDACO INDUSTRIES PTY LTD.—See Hudaco Industries Limited; *Int'l*, pg. 3521
HUIZHOU SPEED WIRELESS TECHNOLOGY - SAN JOSE BRANCH—See Huizhou Speed Wireless Technology Co., Ltd.; *Int'l*, pg. 3527
HUTTON COMMUNICATIONS INC.—See Rupe Investment Corporation; *U.S. Private*, pg. 3504
HYDROSTATIC EXTRUSIONS LTD.—See Bruker Corporation; *U.S. Public*, pg. 406
HYPER ADVANCE SDN. BHD.—See Aiphone Co., Ltd.; *Int'l*, pg. 235
HYPERTEC LIMITED—See DCC plc; *Int'l*, pg. 1991
HYTERA COMUNICACOES DO BRASIL LTDA.—See Hytera Communications Corporation Limited; *Int'l*, pg. 3555
HYT TELECOMUNICATION (UK) CO., LTD.—See Hytera Communications Corporation Limited; *Int'l*, pg. 3554
HYVE SOLUTIONS CORPORATION—See TD Synnex Corp; *U.S. Public*, pg. 1984
I2S LINESCAN IMAGING INC.—See i2S SA; *Int'l*, pg. 3566
IAC BOET STOPSON SAS—See AEA Investors LP; *U.S. Private*, pg. 114
IAC SIM ENGINEERING—See AEA Investors LP; *U.S. Private*, pg. 114
IAC STOPSON ESPANOLOA, SA—See AEA Investors LP; *U.S. Private*, pg. 114
IBC SOLAR AG; *Int'l*, pg. 3569
IBIDEN CANADA INC.—See Ibiden Co., Ltd.; *Int'l*, pg. 3575
IBIDEN KOREA CO., LTD.—See Ibiden Co., Ltd.; *Int'l*, pg. 3575
IBIDEN TAIWAN CO., LTD.—See Ibiden Co., Ltd.; *Int'l*, pg. 3576
IBIDEN U.S.A. CORP.—See Ibiden Co., Ltd.; *Int'l*, pg. 3575
ICC FUNDING INC.; *U.S. Private*, pg. 2029
ICOM AMERICA, INC.—See ICOM INCORPORATED; *Int'l*, pg. 3583
IC PLUS CORP.; *Int'l*, pg. 3577
ICS INDUSTRIES PTY LTD—See EnerSys; *U.S. Public*, pg. 767
IDENTIV (JAPAN) KK—See Identiv, Inc.; *U.S. Public*, pg. 1089
IDENTIV GMBH—See Identiv, Inc.; *U.S. Public*, pg. 1089
IDT COMMUNICATION TECHNOLOGY LIMITED—See IDT International Limited; *Int'l*, pg. 3596
IDT DATA SYSTEM LIMITED—See IDT International Limited; *Int'l*, pg. 3596
IDT SONICVISION LIMITED—See IDT International Limited; *Int'l*, pg. 3596
IDT TECHNOLOGY LIMITED—See IDT International Limited; *Int'l*, pg. 3596

IKEGAMI ELECTRONICS ASIA PSIFIC PTE. LTD.—See Ikegami Tsushinki Co., Ltd.; *Int'l*, pg. 3610
IKEGAMI ELECTRONICS (U.S.A.), INC.—See Ikegami Tsushinki Co., Ltd.; *Int'l*, pg. 3610
IKT GRUPPEN AS—See Dustin Group AB; *Int'l*, pg. 2235
IMAGE SENSING SYSTEMS GERMANY, GMBH—See Autoscope Technologies Corporation; *U.S. Public*, pg. 238
IMAGINATION TECHNOLOGIES KK—See Canyon Bridge Capital Partners, Inc.; *Int'l*, pg. 1300
IMAGINE COMMUNICATIONS - MEXICO—See The Gores Group, LLC; *U.S. Private*, pg. 4035
IM (HK) CO., LTD.—See IM Co., Ltd.; *Int'l*, pg. 3617
IMMIXSOLUTIONS, INC.—See Arrow Electronics, Inc.; *U.S. Public*, pg. 200
IMMIXTECHNOLOGY, INC.—See Arrow Electronics, Inc.; *U.S. Public*, pg. 200
INDUSTRIAL COIL INC.—See Jay Industrial Repair, Inc.; *U.S. Private*, pg. 2192
INDUSTRIAL ELECTRONIC SUPPLY; *U.S. Private*, pg. 2066
INDUSTRIAL SCIENTIFIC AUSTRALIA PTY LTD—See Fortive Corporation; *U.S. Public*, pg. 871
INDUSTRIAL SCIENTIFIC CORPORATION PTE. LTD.—See Fortive Corporation; *U.S. Public*, pg. 871
INDUSTRIAL SCIENTIFIC FRANCE SAS—See Fortive Corporation; *U.S. Public*, pg. 871
INDUSTRIAL SCIENTIFIC FZCO—See Fortive Corporation; *U.S. Public*, pg. 871
INDUSTRIAL SCIENTIFIC INDIA PVT. LTD—See Fortive Corporation; *U.S. Public*, pg. 871
INDUSTRIAL SCIENTIFIC LTD—See Fortive Corporation; *U.S. Public*, pg. 871
INDUSTRIAL VIDEO & CONTROL CO.; *U.S. Private*, pg. 2069
INDUSTRIAL VIDEO CORPORATION; *U.S. Private*, pg. 2069
INETEST MALAYSIA SDN. BHD.—See Ellipsiz Ltd.; *Int'l*, pg. 2366
INFINERA ASIA LIMITED—See Infinera Corporation; *U.S. Public*, pg. 1117
INFINERA INDIA PVT. LTD—See Infinera Corporation; *U.S. Public*, pg. 1117
INFINERA LIMITED—See Infinera Corporation; *U.S. Public*, pg. 1117
INGRAM MICRO AB—See Hainan Traffic Administration Holding Co., Ltd.; *Int'l*, pg. 3215
INGRAM MICRO CONSUMER ELECTRONICS—See Hainan Traffic Administration Holding Co., Ltd.; *Int'l*, pg. 3214
INGRAM MICRO HOSTING B.V.—See Hainan Traffic Administration Holding Co., Ltd.; *Int'l*, pg. 3214
INGRAM MICRO INDIA SSC PRIVATE LIMITED—See Hainan Traffic Administration Holding Co., Ltd.; *Int'l*, pg. 3214
INGRAM MICRO ISTANBUL MERKEZ—See Hainan Traffic Administration Holding Co., Ltd.; *Int'l*, pg. 3214
INGRAM MICRO MEXICO LLC—See Hainan Traffic Administration Holding Co., Ltd.; *Int'l*, pg. 3215
INGRAM MICRO MOBILITY FINLAND OY—See Hainan Traffic Administration Holding Co., Ltd.; *Int'l*, pg. 3215
INGRAM MICRO MOBILITY PHILIPPINES, INC.—See Hainan Traffic Administration Holding Co., Ltd.; *Int'l*, pg. 3215
INGRAM MICRO S.A.C.—See Hainan Traffic Administration Holding Co., Ltd.; *Int'l*, pg. 3215
INGRAM MICRO SERVICES GMBH—See Hainan Traffic Administration Holding Co., Ltd.; *Int'l*, pg. 3215
INGRAM MICRO (SHANGHAI) COMMERCIAL FACTORING CO., LTD.—See Hainan Traffic Administration Holding Co., Ltd.; *Int'l*, pg. 3214
INGRAM MICRO SLOVAKIA, S. R. O—See Hainan Traffic Administration Holding Co., Ltd.; *Int'l*, pg. 3215
INGRAM MICRO SP. Z O.O.—See Hainan Traffic Administration Holding Co., Ltd.; *Int'l*, pg. 3215
INJURED GADGETS LLC; *U.S. Private*, pg. 2077
INNOVATIVE COMMUNICATION CONCEPTS, INC.; *U.S. Private*, pg. 2082
INNOVATIVE CONTROL SYSTEMS, INC.—See Dover Corporation; *U.S. Public*, pg. 681
INOUEKI (THAILAND) CO., LTD.—See Air Water Inc.; *Int'l*, pg. 240
INSULECTRO; *U.S. Private*, pg. 2094
INTEGRATED A/V SYSTEMS LLC—See AEA Investors LP; *U.S. Private*, pg. 116
INTEL SEMICONDUCTOR LIMITED—See Intel Corporation; *U.S. Public*, pg. 1139
INTEL TECHNOLOGY ASIA PTE. LTD.—See Intel Corporation; *U.S. Public*, pg. 1139
INTERACT INCORPORATED; *U.S. Private*, pg. 2108
INTER-COMMERCIAL BUSINESS SYSTEMS; *U.S. Private*, pg. 2107
INTERCOMP U.S.A., INC.; *U.S. Private*, pg. 2109
INTERCONNECTOR GMBH—See EnBW Energie Baden-Wurttemberg AG; *Int'l*, pg. 2399
INTERNATIONAL PROTECTION GROUP, INC.—See Allied Universal Manager LLC; *U.S. Private*, pg. 190
INTERNET SERVICES CORPORATION; *U.S. Private*, pg. 2122

INTERSTATE CONNECTING COMPONENTS—See Heilind Electronics, Inc.; *U.S. Private*, pg. 1904
I-PEX SINGAPORE PTE. LTD.—See I-PEX Inc.; *Int'l*, pg. 3564
IPRO TECHNOLOGY INC.—See EDOM Technology Co., Ltd.; *Int'l*, pg. 2313
IRIS TECHNOLOGY CORPORATION; *U.S. Private*, pg. 2138
IRUMOLD, S.L.U.—See Flex Ltd.; *Int'l*, pg. 2704
IVS INDUSTRIEVERTRETUNG SCHWEIGER GMBH—See Doro AB; *Int'l*, pg. 2179
JABIL CIRCUIT, SAS—See Jabil Inc.; *U.S. Public*, pg. 1181
JABIL GLOBAL SERVICES INDIA PRIVATE LIMITED—See Jabil Inc.; *U.S. Public*, pg. 1181
JAKAR ELECTRONICS, SPOL. S R.O.—See Arcline Investment Management LP; *U.S. Public*, pg. 314
JAPAN CARLIT (SHANGHAI) CO., LTD.—See Carlit Co., Ltd.; *Int'l*, pg. 1338
JDR MICRODEVICES INC.; *U.S. Public*, pg. 2196
JIT CORPORATION; *U.S. Private*, pg. 2211
JL AUDIO, INC.—See Garmin Ltd.; *Int'l*, pg. 2885
JOY! COMMUNICATIONS-FT. LAUDERDALE—See Joy! Communications; *U.S. Private*, pg. 2238
JRH ELECTRONICS L.L.C.; *U.S. Private*, pg. 2240
J&R INDUSTRIAL INC.—See ASE Technology Holding Co., Ltd.; *Int'l*, pg. 604
JSC VO MASHPRIBORINTORG—See ESPEC Corp.; *Int'l*, pg. 2505
JX NIPPON MINING & METALS SINGAPORE PTE. LTD.—See ENEOS Holdings, Inc.; *Int'l*, pg. 2416
JX NIPPON MINING & METALS USA, INC.—See ENEOS Holdings, Inc.; *Int'l*, pg. 2416
K-1 TECHNOLOGIES; *U.S. Private*, pg. 2250
KANOO POWER SOLUTIONS—See Ebrahim K. Kanoo Company B.S.C.; *Int'l*, pg. 2286
KAUPPAHUONE HARJU OY—See Einhell Germany AG; *Int'l*, pg. 2333
KDL COMMUNICATIONS CORPORATION—See Windstream Holdings, Inc.; *U.S. Public*, pg. 2373
KEF JAPAN, INC.—See Gold Peak Technology Group Limited; *Int'l*, pg. 3025
KEHOE COMPONENT SALES INC.; *U.S. Private*, pg. 2273
KEIMOS 1988 U.S. INC.—See AMETEK, Inc.; *U.S. Public*, pg. 120
KELTRON CONNECTORS—See Keltron Electronics Corp.; *U.S. Private*, pg. 2281
KEYMILE AG—See DZS Inc.; *U.S. Public*, pg. 701
KEYMILE KFT.—See DZS Inc.; *U.S. Public*, pg. 701
KEYMILE LLC—See DZS Inc.; *U.S. Public*, pg. 701
KEYMILE LTDA.—See DZS Inc.; *U.S. Public*, pg. 701
KEYMILE LTD.—See DZS Inc.; *U.S. Public*, pg. 701
KEYMILE SP. Z O.O.—See DZS Inc.; *U.S. Public*, pg. 701
KEYMILE SYSTEMS JLT—See DZS Inc.; *U.S. Public*, pg. 701
KEYMILE SYSTEMS PTY. LTD—See DZS Inc.; *U.S. Public*, pg. 701
KEYMILE TEKNOLOJI SISTEMLERI LTD. STI.—See DZS Inc.; *U.S. Public*, pg. 701
KGP TELECOMMUNICATIONS, INC.; *U.S. Private*, pg. 2301
KIMBALL ELECTRONICS INC.; *U.S. Private*, pg. 2305
KIMPEX. INC—See Daeyang Electric Co., Ltd.; *Int'l*, pg. 1911
KITTIWAKE DEVELOPMENTS LIMITED—See Parker Hannifin Corporation; *U.S. Public*, pg. 1641
KJELL & COMPANY—See FSN Capital Partners AS; *Int'l*, pg. 2799
KLEGG ELECTRONICS, INC.; *U.S. Public*, pg. 1269
KLEO HALBLEITERTECHNIK GMBH—See Carl-Zeiss-Stiftung; *Int'l*, pg. 1336
KNURR AG—See Vertiv Holdings Co; *U.S. Public*, pg. 2289
KNURR NORGE AS—See Vertiv Holdings Co; *U.S. Public*, pg. 2289
KNURR S.A.R.L.—See Vertiv Holdings Co; *U.S. Public*, pg. 2289
KOKUSAI SEMICONDUCTOR EQUIPMENT CORPORATION—See KKR & Co. Inc.; *U.S. Public*, pg. 1257
KOM AUTOMATION, INC.—See Graybar Electric Company, Inc.; *U.S. Private*, pg. 1760
KOREA SHINKO TRADING CO., LTD.—See Fujitsu Limited; *Int'l*, pg. 2838
KSM ELECTRONICS INC.; *U.S. Private*, pg. 2355
KYLE ENTERPRISES LLC; *U.S. Private*, pg. 2360
L-3 COMMUNICATIONS VALMARINE AS—See L3Harris Technologies, Inc.; *U.S. Public*, pg. 1283
L3 CTS AIRLINE ACADEMY (NZ) LIMITED—See L3Harris Technologies, Inc.; *U.S. Public*, pg. 1283
L-3 G.A. INTERNATIONAL, INC.—See L3Harris Technologies, Inc.; *U.S. Public*, pg. 1283
L3 TECHNOLOGIES CANADA INC.—See L3Harris Technologies, Inc.; *U.S. Public*, pg. 1284
LAMERS HIGH TECH SYSTEMS B.V.—See Aalberts N.V.; *Int'l*, pg. 35
LAM RESEARCH CO., LTD.—See Lam Research Corporation; *U.S. Public*, pg. 1289
LAM RESEARCH MALAYSIA SDN. BHD.—See Lam Research Corporation; *U.S. Public*, pg. 1290

423690 — OTHER ELECTRONIC PA...
CORPORATE AFFILIATIONS

LAM RESEARCH MANUFACTURING KOREA, LLC—See Lam Research Corporation; *U.S. Public*, pg. 1290
LBF ENTERPRISES; *U.S. Private*, pg. 2403
LEARNKEY INCORPORATED; *U.S. Private*, pg. 2408
LEE HARTMAN & SONS INC.; *U.S. Private*, pg. 2413
LERRO CORPORATION; *U.S. Private*, pg. 2431
LEWAN & ASSOCIATES, INC.—See Xerox Holdings Corporation; *U.S. Public*, pg. 2388
LEXCOM TELECOMMUNICATIONS; *U.S. Private*, pg. 2440
LEXTAR ELECTRONICS (SUZHOU) CO., LTD.—See Ennostar Inc.; *Int'l*, pg. 2444
LINEAR TECHNOLOGY CORPORATION LIMITED—See Analog Devices, Inc.; *U.S. Public*, pg. 135
LINEAR TECHNOLOGY GMBH—See Analog Devices, Inc.; *U.S. Public*, pg. 135
LINEAR TECHNOLOGY PTE. LTD.—See Analog Devices, Inc.; *U.S. Public*, pg. 135
LINEAR TECHNOLOGY (TAIWAN) CORPORATION—See Analog Devices, Inc.; *U.S. Public*, pg. 135
LINKSYS—See Hon Hai Precision Industry Co., Ltd.; *Int'l*, pg. 3456
LITTELFUSE FAR EAST, PTE. LTD.—See Littelfuse, Inc.; *U.S. Public*, pg. 1327
LITTELFUSE S. DE R.L. DE C.V.—See Littelfuse, Inc.; *U.S. Public*, pg. 1327
LO-Q VIRTUAL QUEUING INC.—See accesso Technology Group Plc; *Int'l*, pg. 89
L'ORANGE FUEL INJECTION (NINGBO) CO., LTD.—See Woodward, Inc.; *U.S. Public*, pg. 2377
L'ORANGE FUEL INJECTION TRADING (SUZHOU) CO., LTD.—See Woodward, Inc.; *U.S. Public*, pg. 2377
LOREX CORPORATION—See Teledyne Technologies Incorporated; *U.S. Public*, pg. 1993
LOREX TECHNOLOGY INC.—See Teledyne Technologies Incorporated; *U.S. Public*, pg. 1993
LSP COMMUNICATIONS PTY LIMITED—See Aware Super Pty Ltd; *Int'l*, pg. 752
LTG DISPLAY AB—See Amplex AB; *Int'l*, pg. 434
LUMENETIX, INC.—See Angeles Equity Partners, LLC; *U.S. Private*, pg. 282
LUMILEDS NETHERLANDS B.V.—See Apollo Global Management, Inc.; *U.S. Public*, pg. 153
LUSCOMBE ENGINEERING COMPONENTS CO. INC.; *U.S. Private*, pg. 2516
LYDROMMET AS—See DistIT AB; *Int'l*, pg. 2136
LYNN ASSOCIATES INC.; *U.S. Private*, pg. 2521
MACDONALD HUMFREY (AUTOMATION) SEA PTE. LTD.—See L3Harris Technologies, Inc.; *U.S. Public*, pg. 1284
MAGDEV LIMITED—See Bunting Magnetics Co.; *U.S. Private*, pg. 686
MANAGEMENT DATA SYSTEMS INTERNATIONAL; *U.S. Private*, pg. 2560
MANUFACTURING ASSEMBLY SOLUTIONS OF MONTERREY, INC.—See Nortech Systems Incorporated; *U.S. Public*, pg. 1536
MARSHALL INDUSTRIES, INC.; *U.S. Private*, pg. 2592
MARSH ELECTRONICS, INC.; *U.S. Private*, pg. 2591
MARTCO INC.; *U.S. Private*, pg. 2593
MARTEX CO., LTD.—See Holy Stone Enterprise Co., Ltd.; *Int'l*, pg. 3454
MARTIN BRUUSGAARD AS—See Addtech AB; *Int'l*, pg. 134
MARUBUN/ARROW (HK) LIMITED—See Arrow Electronics, Inc.; *U.S. Public*, pg. 199
MARUBUN/ARROW (M) SDN. BHD—See Arrow Electronics, Inc.; *U.S. Public*, pg. 199
MARUBUN/ARROW (SHANGHAI) CO.—See Arrow Electronics, Inc.; *U.S. Public*, pg. 199
MARUBUN/ARROW (S) PTE LTD.—See Arrow Electronics, Inc.; *U.S. Public*, pg. 199
MARUBUN/ARROW (THAILAND) CO., LTD.—See Arrow Electronics, Inc.; *U.S. Public*, pg. 199
MARUBUN/ARROW (THAILAND) CO.—See Arrow Electronics, Inc.; *U.S. Public*, pg. 199
MARVAC ELECTRONICS; *U.S. Private*, pg. 2597
MASTER ELECTRONICS—See Master International Corp.; *U.S. Private*, pg. 2607
MASTER INTERNATIONAL CORP.; *U.S. Private*, pg. 2607
MAXIM INTEGRATED PRODUCTS INDIA SALES PVT LTD.—See Analog Devices, Inc.; *U.S. Public*, pg. 135
MAXIM INTEGRATED PRODUCTS INTERNATIONAL SALES JAPAN GK—See Analog Devices, Inc.; *U.S. Public*, pg. 135
MAXIM JAPAN CO., LTD.—See Analog Devices, Inc.; *U.S. Public*, pg. 136
MAXLINEAR ASIA SINGAPORE PTE. LTD.—See MaxLinear, Inc.; *U.S. Public*, pg. 1403
MAXSON INDUSTRIES LIMITED—See Gold Peak Technology Group Limited; *Int'l*, pg. 3025
M.B.R. INDUSTRIES, INC.; *U.S. Private*, pg. 2528
MCDONALD INDUSTRIES, INC.—See World Micro, Inc.; *U.S. Private*, pg. 4566
MEDIUM GMBH—See Droege Group AG; *Int'l*, pg. 2205
MEL FOSTER CO. INC.; *U.S. Private*, pg. 2661
MELLON TECHNOLOGY PTE LTD—See Digilife Technologies Limited; *Int'l*, pg. 2119
MEMEC GROUP LIMITED—See Avnet, Inc.; *U.S. Public*, pg. 253

MENARA NETWORKS, INC.—See IPG Photonics Corporation; *U.S. Public*, pg. 1167
METRIC TEST EQUIPMENT, INC.; *U.S. Private*, pg. 2685
METROLINE INC.; *U.S. Private*, pg. 2687
METSO ENDRESS+HAUSER OY—See Endress+Hauser (International) Holding AG; *Int'l*, pg. 2408
MICHAEL ELECTRIC, INC.—See Black Box Limited; *Int'l*, pg. 1058
MICROCOM TECHNOLOGIES, INC.; *U.S. Private*, pg. 2703
MICRON SEMICONDUCTOR ASIA PTE. LTD.—See Micron Technology, Inc.; *U.S. Public*, pg. 1438
MICRON SEMICONDUCTOR (DEUTSCHLAND) GMBH—See Micron Technology, Inc.; *U.S. Public*, pg. 1437
MICRON TECHNOLOGY ASIA PACIFIC, INC.—See Micron Technology, Inc.; *U.S. Public*, pg. 1438
MICRON TECHNOLOGY, INC. - CRUCIAL DIVISION—See Micron Technology, Inc.; *U.S. Public*, pg. 1438
MICRORAM ELECTRONICS INC.; *U.S. Private*, pg. 2704
MICROSEMI IRELAND, LTD.—See Microchip Technology Incorporated; *U.S. Public*, pg. 1437
MICROTRONICA LTD.—See Arrow Electronics, Inc.; *U.S. Public*, pg. 199
MICROWAVE MEASUREMENT DIVISION—See Anritsu Corporation; *Int'l*, pg. 475
MID-STATE COMMUNICATIONS & ELECTRONICS, INC.; *U.S. Private*, pg. 2709
MID STATE DISTRIBUTING COMPANY; *U.S. Private*, pg. 2706
MIDWEST MEDIA GROUP INC.; *U.S. Private*, pg. 2722
MILANO BROTHERS INTERNATIONAL CORPORATION; *U.S. Private*, pg. 2726
MILLENNIUM CELL, INC.; *U.S. Public*, pg. 1446
MILTIMORE SALES, INC.; *U.S. Private*, pg. 2738
MIRA CHINA LTD.—See HORIBA Ltd; *Int'l*, pg. 3477
MITA-TEKNIK LLC—See Axcel Management A/S; *Int'l*, pg. 762
MITA-TEKNIK (NINGBO) CO. LTD.—See Axcel Management A/S; *Int'l*, pg. 762
MITA-TEKNIK TECHNOLOGY PRIVATE LTD.—See Axcel Management A/S; *Int'l*, pg. 762
MITEL PORTUGAL S.A.—See Searchlight Capital Partners, L.P.; *U.S. Private*, pg. 3589
MITSUBISHI WIRELESS COMMUNICATIONS, INC.—See Hyosung Heavy Industries Corp.; *Int'l*, pg. 3552
MMD SAS—See Groupe SFPI SA; *Int'l*, pg. 3111
MOBILE LADS CORP.; *U.S. Public*, pg. 1454
MOCON ITALIA S.R.L.—See AMETEK, Inc.; *U.S. Public*, pg. 120
MODERN ELECTRONICS COMPANY LTD.—See Al Faisaliah Group; *Int'l*, pg. 277
MODERN ENTERPRISE SOLUTIONS INC.; *U.S. Private*, pg. 2760
MODERN MASS MEDIA INC.; *U.S. Private*, pg. 2761
MODULI ELETTRONICI E COMPONENTI S.P.A.—See Arlitech Electronic Corp.; *Int'l*, pg. 573
MODUSLINK RECOVERY LLC—See Steel Connect, Inc.; *U.S. Public*, pg. 1941
MODUSLINK SECURITIES CORPORATION—See Steel Connect, Inc.; *U.S. Public*, pg. 1941
MORCOM INTERNATIONAL, INC.; *U.S. Private*, pg. 2782
MORE ELECTRONICS APS—See C C P Contact Probes Co., Ltd.; *Int'l*, pg. 1237
MOTOROLA SOLUTIONS AUSTRALIA PTE. LTD.—See Motorola Solutions, Inc.; *U.S. Public*, pg. 1478
MOTOROLA SOLUTIONS CANADA INC.—See Motorola Solutions, Inc.; *U.S. Public*, pg. 1478
MOTOROLA SOLUTIONS INDIA PVT. LTD.—See Motorola Solutions, Inc.; *U.S. Public*, pg. 1478
MOTOROLA SOLUTIONS ITALIA S.P.A.—See Motorola Solutions, Inc.; *U.S. Public*, pg. 1478
MOTOROLA TRADING CENTER PTE. LTD.—See Motorola Solutions, Inc.; *U.S. Public*, pg. 1478
MOUNTAIN TELECOMMUNICATIONS SALES INC.; *U.S. Private*, pg. 2800
MOUNTAIN WEST TELECOM INC.; *U.S. Private*, pg. 2800
MOUSER ELECTRONICS INC.—See Berkshire Hathaway Inc.; *U.S. Public*, pg. 316
MOUSER ELECTRONICS PTE. LTD.—See Berkshire Hathaway Inc.; *U.S. Public*, pg. 316
MPX INC.—See Windstream Holdings, Inc.; *U.S. Public*, pg. 2373
MSC INVESTOREN GMBH—See Avnet, Inc.; *U.S. Public*, pg. 253
MSC (MALTA) LIMITED—See Avnet, Inc.; *U.S. Public*, pg. 253
MSC TECHNOLOGIES SYSTEMS GMBH—See Avnet, Inc.; *U.S. Public*, pg. 253
M S C - VERTRIEBS - SK S. R. O.—See Avnet, Inc.; *U.S. Public*, pg. 253
M-TRON INDUSTRIES, INC.; *U.S. Public*, pg. 1351
MULTICARD AG—See Adon Production AG; *Int'l*, pg. 152
NAC GROUP INC.; *U.S. Private*, pg. 2829
NANJING JIN MEI GALLIUM CO., LTD.—See AXT, Inc.; *U.S. Public*, pg. 256
NAVE COMMUNICATIONS COMPANY—See ADDvantage Technologies Group, Inc.; *U.S. Public*, pg. 40

ND SATCOM DEFENCE GMBH—See Airbus SE; *Int'l*, pg. 245
ND SATCOM, INC.—See Airbus SE; *Int'l*, pg. 245
NEDCO ELECTRONICS INCORPORATED; *U.S. Private*, pg. 2879
NEP ELECTRONICS INC.; *U.S. Private*, pg. 2885
NETSOURCE TECHNOLOGY INC.; *U.S. Private*, pg. 2888
NETSTAR AUSTRALIA PTY LTD—See Altron Limited.; *Int'l*, pg. 399
NEWARK CORPORATION—See Avnet, Inc.; *U.S. Public*, pg. 254
NEWAX, INC.; *U.S. Private*, pg. 2913
NEW SENSOR CORPORATION; *U.S. Private*, pg. 2906
N.F. SMITH & ASSOCIATES, LP; *U.S. Private*, pg. 2828
NMC CAT—See Nebraska Machinery Company Inc.; *U.S. Private*, pg. 2878
NORTH AMERICAN VIDEO CORPORATION; *U.S. Private*, pg. 2941
NORTH ATLANTIC COMPONENTS, INC.; *U.S. Private*, pg. 2942
NORTH COAST TECHNICAL SALES, INC.—See Sole Source Capital LLC; *U.S. Private*, pg. 3708
NORTHEAST COMMUNICATIONS INC.; *U.S. Private*, pg. 2949
NORTHERN CATV SALES INC.; *U.S. Private*, pg. 2952
NOVELLUS SYSTEMS INTERNATIONAL TRADING (SHANGHAI) CO. LTD—See Lam Research Corporation; *U.S. Public*, pg. 1290
NOVELLUS SYSTEMS ITALY SRL—See Lam Research Corporation; *U.S. Public*, pg. 1290
NOW ELECTRONICS, INC.; *U.S. Private*, pg. 2968
NRC ELECTRONICS, INC.; *U.S. Private*, pg. 2969
NRS PRINTING SOLUTIONS AG—See Droege Group AG; *Int'l*, pg. 2205
NU HORIZONS ELECTRONICS PTY LTD.—See Arrow Electronics, Inc.; *U.S. Public*, pg. 199
NUJAY TECHNOLOGIES INC.—See ICAPE Holding S.A.; *Int'l*, pg. 3578
NYPRO DEUTSCHLAND GMBH—See Jabil Inc.; *U.S. Public*, pg. 1181
OASIS SALES CORP.; *U.S. Private*, pg. 2986
OCLARO JAPAN K.K.—See Lumentum Holdings Inc.; *U.S. Public*, pg. 1348
OMAC SALES LIMITED—See Hana Microelectronics Public Company Limited; *Int'l*, pg. 3241
OMNI CIRCUITS INTERNATIONAL LLC.; *U.S. Private*, pg. 3016
OMNIVISION TECHNOLOGIES (SHANGHAI) CO., LTD.—See CITIC Group Corporation; *Int'l*, pg. 1619
OMNIVISION TECHNOLOGIES (SHANGHAI) CO., LTD.—See CITIC Securities Co., Ltd.; *Int'l*, pg. 1622
OMNIVISION TECHNOLOGIES (SHANGHAI) CO., LTD.—See Hua Capital Management Co., Ltd.; *Int'l*, pg. 3509
ONEROOF ENERGY, INC.—See OneRoof Energy Group, Inc.; *U.S. Public*, pg. 1603
ON SEMICONDUCTOR FRANCE SAS—See ON Semiconductor Corporation; *U.S. Public*, pg. 1600
ONTILITY LLC—See N.F. Smith & Associates, LP; *U.S. Private*, pg. 2828
OOO ELTEK—See Delta Electronics, Inc.; *Int'l*, pg. 2017
OOO GEWISS RUSSIA—See Gewiss S.p.A.; *Int'l*, pg. 2955
OPTIMA EPS CORP—See Elma Electronic AG; *Int'l*, pg. 2367
OPTIMAL PLUS LTD.—See National Instruments Corporation; *U.S. Private*, pg. 2858
OPTUS INC.; *U.S. Private*, pg. 3036
ORBITAL GAS SYSTEMS LTD.—See Orbital Infrastructure Group, Inc.; *U.S. Public*, pg. 1615
ORBITAL GAS SYSTEMS, NORTH AMERICA, INC.—See Orbital Infrastructure Group, Inc.; *U.S. Public*, pg. 1615
ORBIT SYSTEMS, INC.; *U.S. Private*, pg. 3038
ORBOTECH INC.—See KLA Corporation; *U.S. Public*, pg. 1268
OREGON SCIENTIFIC AUSTRALIA PTY LIMITED—See IDT International Limited; *Int'l*, pg. 3596
OREGON SCIENTIFIC GLOBAL DISTRIBUTION LIMITED—See IDT International Limited; *Int'l*, pg. 3596
OREGON SCIENTIFIC ITALIA SPA—See IDT International Limited; *Int'l*, pg. 3597
OREGON SCIENTIFIC (U.K.) LIMITED—See IDT International Limited; *Int'l*, pg. 3596
ORMIC COMPONENTS LTD.—See Avnet, Inc.; *U.S. Public*, pg. 253
OSCILLOQUARTZ FINLAND OY—See ADTRAN Holdings, Inc.; *U.S. Public*, pg. 44
OTN SYSTEMS NV—See Belden, Inc.; *U.S. Public*, pg. 294
OUME ELECTRONICS CO., LTD.—See AOI Electronics Co., Ltd.; *Int'l*, pg. 488
OY FARNELL AB—See Avnet, Inc.; *U.S. Public*, pg. 254
PACE ELECTRONICS INC.; *U.S. Private*, pg. 3063
PACPARTS INC.; *U.S. Private*, pg. 3073
PALM PICTURES, LLC—See Palm Entertainment Properties LLC; *U.S. Private*, pg. 3079
PARK DISTRIBUTORS, INC.; *U.S. Private*, pg. 3096
PARKER HANNIFIN FRANCE SAS—See Parker Hannifin Corporation; *U.S. Public*, pg. 1646

N.A.I.C.S. INDEX

423690 — OTHER ELECTRONIC PA...

PARTMINER DIRECT—See PartMiner, Inc.; *U.S. Private,* pg. 3101
PARTMINER, INC.; *U.S. Private,* pg. 3101
PARTSEARCH TECHNOLOGIES; *U.S. Private,* pg. 3103
PARTS EXPRESS INTERNATIONAL; *U.S. Private,* pg. 3103
PASTERNACK ENTERPRISES, INC.—See Windjammer Capital Investors, LLC; *U.S. Private,* pg. 4538
PCG PARENT CORP.—See Arrow Electronics, Inc.; *U.S. Public,* pg. 199
PCG TRADING, LLC—See Arrow Electronics, Inc.; *U.S. Public,* pg. 199
PC MALL SERVICES, INC.—See Insight Enterprises, Inc.; *U.S. Public,* pg. 1130
PDSI B.V.—See Avnet, Inc.; *U.S. Public,* pg. 253
PEERLESS ELECTRONICS INC.; *U.S. Private,* pg. 3128
PEI-GENESIS INC.; *U.S. Private,* pg. 3130
PERSONAL COMMUNICATION CENTER; *U.S. Private,* pg. 3155
PESTINGER GMBH—See Droege Group AG; *Int'l,* pg. 2205
PETER PARTS ELECTRONICS INC.; *U.S. Private,* pg. 3159
PHASE 1 TECHNOLOGY CORP.; *U.S. Private,* pg. 3166
PHASECOM, INC.; *U.S. Private,* pg. 3166
PHILIPS LUMILEDS LIGHTING COMPANY SDN. BHD.—See Apollo Global Management, Inc.; *U.S. Public,* pg. 153
PHILLIPS COMMUNICATION & EQUIPMENT CO.; *U.S. Private,* pg. 3170
PHOENICS ELECTRONICS CORPORATION—See Avnet, Inc.; *U.S. Public,* pg. 253
PHOENIX TELECOM SOLUTIONS, INC.; *U.S. Private,* pg. 3174
PHONETEC LP; *U.S. Private,* pg. 3174
PHOTONICS MANAGEMENT CORP.—See Hamamatsu Photonics K.K.; *Int'l,* pg. 3235
PHOTOP TECHNOLOGIES, INC.—See Coherent Corp.; *U.S. Public,* pg. 529
PICO DIGITAL INC.—See H.I.G. Capital, LLC; *U.S. Private,* pg. 1828
PICTUREPHONE, INC.—See AMETEK, Inc.; *U.S. Public,* pg. 121
PIHER INTERNATIONAL CORPORATION—See Parker Hannifin Corporation; *U.S. Public,* pg. 1642
PIONEER INDUSTRIAL COMPONENTS (HONG KONG) CO., LTD.—See EQT AB; *Int'l,* pg. 2471
PIONEER MAGNETICS INC.—See Greenbriar Equity Group, L.P; *U.S. Private,* pg. 1776
PITTWAY 3 GMBH—See Resideo Technologies, Inc.; *U.S. Public,* pg. 1789
PITTWAY BVBA—See Resideo Technologies, Inc.; *U.S. Public,* pg. 1789
PITTWAY HOMES SYSTEMS, S.L.—See Resideo Technologies, Inc.; *U.S. Public,* pg. 1789
POLYCOM TECHNOLOGY (R&D) CENTER PRIVATE LIMITED—See HP Inc.; *U.S. Public,* pg. 1065
POLYCOM UNIFIED ILETISIM SANAYI VE TICARET LIMITED SIRKETI—See HP Inc.; *U.S. Public,* pg. 1065
PORTABLES UNLIMITED INC.; *U.S. Private,* pg. 3231
PORTER BURGESS COMPANY; *U.S. Private,* pg. 3231
POWELL ELECTRONICS EUROPE BV—See Powell Electronics Inc.; *U.S. Private,* pg. 3237
POWELL ELECTRONICS INC.; *U.S. Private,* pg. 3236
POWER SOLUTIONS; *U.S. Private,* pg. 3238
POWERSTRIDE BATTERY CO. INC.; *U.S. Private,* pg. 3240
POWER SUPPLY COMPONENTS INC.; *U.S. Private,* pg. 3239
POWER TECHNIC APS—See Addtech AB; *Int'l,* pg. 134
POWER & TELEPHONE SUPPLY COMPANY DO BRASIL—See Power & Telephone Supply Company; *U.S. Private,* pg. 3237
POWER & TELEPHONE SUPPLY S.A. DE C.V.—See Power & Telephone Supply Company; *U.S. Private,* pg. 3237
PRECISION INTERCONNECT CONVERSIONS CORP.; *U.S. Private,* pg. 3245
PREMIER COMPONENTS DISTRBUTION CORP.—See OptConnect, LLC; *U.S. Private,* pg. 3034
PREMIER FARNELL CANADA LIMITED—See Avnet, Inc.; *U.S. Public,* pg. 254
PREMIER FARNELL ELECTRONICS DE MEXICO SRL—See Avnet, Inc.; *U.S. Public,* pg. 254
PREMIER FARNELL (SCOTLAND) LIMITED—See Avnet, Inc.; *U.S. Public,* pg. 254
PREMIER FARNELL UK LTD—See Avnet, Inc.; *U.S. Public,* pg. 254
PREMTEK INTERNATIONAL INC.—See Hanmi Semiconductor Co., Ltd.; *Int'l,* pg. 3256
PRICE MASTER CORPORATION; *U.S. Private,* pg. 3258
PRIME CONTROLS, LP; *U.S. Private,* pg. 3261
PRIME E-TECH INTERNATIONAL PTE. LTD.—See Hanmi Semiconductor Co., Ltd.; *Int'l,* pg. 3256
PROCOM ANTENNAS AB—See Amphenol Corporation; *U.S. Public,* pg. 132
PROCOM FRANCE SARL—See Amphenol Corporation; *U.S. Public,* pg. 132
PROFESSIONAL PRODUCTS, INC.; *U.S. Private,* pg. 3276
PROJECTIONS UNLIMITED INC.; *U.S. Private,* pg. 3281
PRO-SAFE, INCORPORATED; *U.S. Private,* pg. 3271
PSP BRASIL—See ESPEC Corp.; *Int'l,* pg. 2505

PT. ANDRITZ HYDRO—See ANDRITZ AG; *Int'l,* pg. 453
PT CHEMTRONICS INDONESIA—See Chemtronics Co., Ltd.; *Int'l,* pg. 1464
PT. DONGJIN INDONESIA—See Dongjin Semichem Co., Ltd.; *Int'l,* pg. 2168
PT. EMERSON INDONESIA—See Emerson Electric Co.; *U.S. Public,* pg. 751
P.T. FOSTER ELECTRIC INDONESIA—See Foster Electric Co., Ltd.; *Int'l,* pg. 2750
PT GDC TECHNOLOGY INDONESIA—See Huayi Brothers Media Corp.; *Int'l,* pg. 3516
PTGI EUROPE, B.V.—See INNOVATE Corp.; *U.S. Public,* pg. 1126
PT HORIBA INDONESIA—See HORIBA Ltd; *Int'l,* pg. 3478
PT. KDS INDONESIA—See Daishinku Corp.; *Int'l,* pg. 1942
PT SELULAR GLOBAL NET—See Digilife Technologies Limited; *Int'l,* pg. 2119
PT TECH DATA ADVANCED SOLUTIONS INDONESIA—See TD Synnex Corp; *U.S. Public,* pg. 1986
PUMAS AUTOMATION & ROBOTICS PTE. LTD.—See Convum Ltd.; *Int'l,* pg. 1788
PYROBAN (SUZHOU) SAFETY SYSTEMS CO., LTD.—See Caterpillar, Inc.; *U.S. Public,* pg. 453
Q-FREE THAILAND CO LTD—See Guardian Capital Group Limited; *Int'l,* pg. 3170
QINGDAO GOERTEK TECHNOLOGY CO., LTD.—See GoerTek Inc.; *Int'l,* pg. 3021
QOMO HITEVISION, LLC.; *U.S. Private,* pg. 3313
QONIAC GMBH—See KLA Corporation; *U.S. Public,* pg. 1269
QONIAC JAPAN LTD.—See KLA Corporation; *U.S. Public,* pg. 1269
QONIAC KOREA LTD.—See KLA Corporation; *U.S. Public,* pg. 1269
QORVO BELGIUM NV—See Qorvo, Inc.; *U.S. Public,* pg. 1743
QORVO DENMARK APS—See Qorvo, Inc.; *U.S. Public,* pg. 1743
QORVO DEZHOU CO., LTD.—See Qorvo, Inc.; *U.S. Public,* pg. 1743
QORVO UTRECHT, B.V.—See Qorvo, Inc.; *U.S. Public,* pg. 1743
QUADREP INCORPORATED; *U.S. Private,* pg. 3316
QUALITY DISTRIBUTORS, LLC; *U.S. Private,* pg. 3318
QUEST TECHNOLOGY INTERNATIONAL, INC.; *U.S. Private,* pg. 3326
RADAR, INC.; *U.S. Private,* pg. 3342
RADIO PARTS COMPANY INC.; *U.S. Private,* pg. 3344
RAF FLUID POWER, INC.—See Electro-Matic Ventures, Inc.; *U.S. Private,* pg. 1354
RALPH'S OF LAFAYETTE INC.; *U.S. Private,* pg. 3350
RAMBUS CANADA INC.—See Rambus Inc.; *U.S. Public,* pg. 1762
RAMTECH ELECTRONICS LIMITED—See Halma plc; *Int'l,* pg. 3232
RAND TECHNOLOGY INC.; *U.S. Private,* pg. 3353
RAUSCH NETZWERKTECHNIK GMBH—See Avnet, Inc.; *U.S. Public,* pg. 254
RAVE LLC—See Bruker Corporation; *U.S. Public,* pg. 407
REALISE TECH-SERVICE CO., LTD.—See Action Electronics Co., Ltd.; *Int'l,* pg. 119
REAL TIME LOGIC, INC.—See Kratos Defense & Security Solutions, Inc.; *U.S. Public,* pg. 1276
RECELLULAR INCORPORATED; *U.S. Private,* pg. 3370
RECREATIONAL PRODUCTS DIV.—See Bell Industries, Inc.; *U.S. Public,* pg. 295
RECUPERATOR S.P.A.—See Carel Industries S.p.A.; *Int'l,* pg. 1324
RED EDUCATION PTY. LTD.—See Arrow Electronics, Inc.; *U.S. Public,* pg. 199
REDLINE COMMUNICATIONS ROMANIA LTD.—See Aviat Networks, Inc.; *U.S. Public,* pg. 246
REM ELECTRONICS SUPPLY CO. INC.; *U.S. Private,* pg. 3395
RENDELL SALES COMPANY LIMITED—See I-PEX Inc.; *Int'l,* pg. 3564
RESIDEO INTERNATIONAL (INDIA) PVT. LTD.—See Resideo Technologies, Inc.; *U.S. Public,* pg. 1789
RESIDEO KORLATOLT FELELOSSEGU TARSASAG—See Resideo Technologies, Inc.; *U.S. Public,* pg. 1789
RESIDEO LIFE CARE SOLUTIONS LLC—See Resideo Technologies, Inc.; *U.S. Public,* pg. 1789
RESIDEO SARL—See Resideo Technologies, Inc.; *U.S. Public,* pg. 1790
RESIDEO S.R.L.—See Resideo Technologies, Inc.; *U.S. Public,* pg. 1790
RESIDEO S.R.O.—See Resideo Technologies, Inc.; *U.S. Public,* pg. 1790
RIBBON COMMUNICATIONS FEDERAL INC.—See Ribbon Communications Inc.; *U.S. Public,* pg. 1797
RICHARDSON ELECTRONICS BENELUX B.V.—See Richardson Electronics, Ltd.; *U.S. Public,* pg. 1798
RICHARDSON ELECTRONICS DO BRASIL LTDA.—See Richardson Electronics, Ltd.; *U.S. Public,* pg. 1798
RICHARDSON ELECTRONICS IBERICA S.A.—See Richardson Electronics, Ltd.; *U.S. Public,* pg. 1798
RICHARDSON ELECTRONICS INDIA PRIVATE LIMITED—See Richardson Electronics, Ltd.; *U.S. Public,* pg. 1798
RICHARDSON ELECTRONICS LTD.-CENTRAL—See Richardson Electronics, Ltd.; *U.S. Public,* pg. 1798
RICHARDSON ELECTRONICS, LTD.; *U.S. Public,* pg. 1797
RICHARDSON ELECTRONICS S.R.L.—See Richardson Electronics, Ltd.; *U.S. Public,* pg. 1798
RICHARDSON RFPD AUSTRALIA PTY. LTD.—See Arrow Electronics, Inc.; *U.S. Public,* pg. 200
RICHARDSON RFPD CANADA, INC.—See Arrow Electronics, Inc.; *U.S. Public,* pg. 196
RICHARDSON RFPD FRANCE SAS—See Arrow Electronics, Inc.; *U.S. Public,* pg. 200
RICHARDSON RFPD GERMANY GMBH—See Arrow Electronics, Inc.; *U.S. Public,* pg. 200
RICHARDSON RFPD, INC.—See Arrow Electronics, Inc.; *U.S. Public,* pg. 200
RICHARDSON RFPD ISRAEL LTD.—See Arrow Electronics, Inc.; *U.S. Public,* pg. 200
RICHARDSON RFPD ITALY SRL—See Arrow Electronics, Inc.; *U.S. Public,* pg. 200
RICHARDSON RFPD NETHERLANDS BV—See Arrow Electronics, Inc.; *U.S. Public,* pg. 200
RICHARDSON RFPD SINGAPORE—See Arrow Electronics, Inc.; *U.S. Public,* pg. 200
RICHARDSON RFPD SPAIN SL—See Arrow Electronics, Inc.; *U.S. Public,* pg. 200
RICHARDSON RFPD SWEDEN AB—See Arrow Electronics, Inc.; *U.S. Public,* pg. 200
RICHARDSON RFPD (THAILAND) LIMITED—See Arrow Electronics, Inc.; *U.S. Public,* pg. 200
RICHARDSON RFPD UK LTD.—See Arrow Electronics, Inc.; *U.S. Public,* pg. 200
RICHMOND ELECTRICAL SUPPLY, LLC—See Graybar Electric Company, Inc.; *U.S. Private,* pg. 1760
R.J. THROCKMORTON SALES CO.; *U.S. Private,* pg. 3337
R&K TECH AB—See Addtech AB; *Int'l,* pg. 134
RMG NETWORKS LIMITED—See RMG Networks Holding Corporation; *U.S. Private,* pg. 3452
RNM DYNAMICS (PHILS) INC.—See Hanmi Semiconductor Co., Ltd.; *Int'l,* pg. 3256
ROADSTAR DEUTSCHLAND GMBH—See Harvard International Ltd.; *Int'l,* pg. 3280
ROADSTAR ITALIA SPA—See Harvard International Ltd.; *Int'l,* pg. 3280
ROADSTAR MANAGEMENT SA—See Harvard International Ltd.; *Int'l,* pg. 3280
ROBERT MCKEOWN CO. INC.; *U.S. Private,* pg. 3458
ROBTEC URUGUAY—See 3D Systems Corporation; *U.S. Public,* pg. 4
ROCHESTER ELECTRONICS INC.; *U.S. Private,* pg. 3463
ROCKWELL AUTOMATION GERMANY G.M.B.H. & CO. KG—See Rockwell Automation, Inc.; *U.S. Public,* pg. 1806
ROCKWEST TECHNOLOGY GROUP LLC—See Identiv, Inc.; *U.S. Public,* pg. 1089
ROGERS KOREA, INC.—See Rogers Corporation; *U.S. Public,* pg. 1808
ROGERS (SHANGHAI) INTERNATIONAL TRADING CO. LTD.—See Rogers Corporation; *U.S. Public,* pg. 1808
ROGERS TAIWAN, INC.—See Rogers Corporation; *U.S. Public,* pg. 1808
ROGERS TECHNOLOGIES SINGAPORE, INC.—See Rogers Corporation; *U.S. Public,* pg. 1808
ROSE ELECTRONICS DISTRIBUTING CO, INC.—See Tropical Battery Company Limited; *U.S. Public,* pg. 2198
R.O. WHITESELL & ASSOCIATES, INC.; *U.S. Private,* pg. 3339
RSG ELECTRONIC COMPONENTS GMBH—See discoverIE Group plc; *Int'l,* pg. 2133
RTI TECHNOLOGY CHINA LIMITED—See Avnet, Inc.; *U.S. Public,* pg. 254
SABRE SITE SOLUTIONS—See The Jordan Company, L.P.; *U.S. Private,* pg. 4061
SAF NORTH AMERICA LLC—See A/S SAF Tehnika; *Int'l,* pg. 28
SAGER ELECTRICAL SUPPLY CO—See Berkshire Hathaway Inc.; *U.S. Public,* pg. 316
SAHARA PRESENTATION SYSTEMS LIMITED—See Boxlight Corporation; *U.S. Public,* pg. 377
SAIA BURGESS CONTROLS ITALIA S.R.L.—See Honeywell International Inc.; *U.S. Public,* pg. 1052
SAIA BURGESS CONTROLS USA INC.—See Honeywell International Inc.; *U.S. Public,* pg. 1052
SALES GROUP INC.; *U.S. Private,* pg. 3532
SAMTEC ASIA PACIFIC PTE LTD.—See Samtec, Inc.; *U.S. Private,* pg. 3538
SAMTEC FRANCE—See Samtec, Inc.; *U.S. Private,* pg. 3538
SAMTEC HONG KONG LIMITED—See Samtec, Inc.; *U.S. Private,* pg. 3538
SAMTEC TAIWAN LIMITED—See Samtec, Inc.; *U.S. Private,* pg. 3538
SANYO SEMICONDUCTOR CORPORATION—See ON Semiconductor Corporation; *U.S. Public,* pg. 1601
SANYO SEMICONDUCTOR (H.K.) CO., LTD.—See ON Semiconductor Corporation; *U.S. Public,* pg. 1601

423690 — OTHER ELECTRONIC PA...   CORPORATE AFFILIATIONS

SATELCO AG—See Bogen Communications International Inc.; *U.S. Public*, pg. 367
SATEL-FEI, S.A.—See Frequency Electronics, Inc.; *U.S. Public*, pg. 885
SATELLITE ENGINEERING GROUP—See WESCO International, Inc.; *U.S. Public*, pg. 2352
SATSERVICE GESELLSCHAFT FUR KOMMUNIKATIONS-SYSTEME MBH—See Calian Group Ltd.; *Int'l*, pg. 1264
SCANDITRON DANMARK A/S—See Amplex AB; *Int'l*, pg. 434
SCANDITRON FINLAND OY—See Fuji Corporation; *Int'l*, pg. 2810
SCANDITRON FINLAND STENCILS—See Amplex AB; *Int'l*, pg. 434
SCANDITRON SP. Z.O.O.—See Amplex AB; *Int'l*, pg. 434
SCANDITRON SVERIGE AB—See Amplex AB; *Int'l*, pg. 434
SCANSOURCE SECURITY, INC.—See ScanSource, Inc.; *U.S. Public*, pg. 1843
SCHUSTER ELECTRONICS INC.—See TLC Electronics, Inc.; *U.S. Private*, pg. 4178
SCN UK GROUP LTD.—See Addtech AB; *Int'l*, pg. 135
SCOTT CABLE COMMUNICATIONS; *U.S. Private*, pg. 3576
SCREENBEAM INC.—See Ban Leong Technologies Limited; *Int'l*, pg. 814
SCREEN SERVICE DO BRASIL LTDA.—See DB Elettronica Telecomunicazioni SpA; *Int'l*, pg. 1986
SD GERMANY GMBH—See Spectral Dynamics, Inc.; *U.S. Private*, pg. 3751
SEACHANGE POLSKA SP ZOO—See SeaChange International, Inc.; *U.S. Public*, pg. 1851
SEAMCOM GMBH & CO. KG—See Droege Group AG; *Int'l*, pg. 2205
SEATRONICS, INC.—See Buckthorn Partners LLP; *Int'l*, pg. 1210
SEATRONICS, INC.—See OEP Capital Advisors, L.P.; *U.S. Private*, pg. 2997
SEATRONICS LTD.—See Buckthorn Partners LLP; *Int'l*, pg. 1210
SEATRONICS LTD.—See OEP Capital Advisors, L.P.; *U.S. Private*, pg. 2997
SE-CONSULTING GMBH—See Broadcom Inc.; *U.S. Public*, pg. 390
SECURITY EQUIPMENT SUPPLY INC.; *U.S. Private*, pg. 3595
SECURITY MERCHANTS AUSTRALIA PTY LTD.—See ASSA ABLOY AB; *Int'l*, pg. 640
SED INTERNATIONAL, INC.—See SED International Holdings, Inc.; *U.S. Private*, pg. 3597
SEMICONDUCTOR COMPONENTS INDUSTRIES, LLC—See ON Semiconductor Corporation; *U.S. Public*, pg. 1601
SENSATA TECHNOLOGIES CHINA CO., LTD.—See Sensata Technologies Holding plc; *U.S. Public*, pg. 1865
SENSIBLE MICRO CORPORATION; *U.S. Private*, pg. 3607
SENSITRON S.R.L.—See Halma plc; *Int'l*, pg. 3232
SENSOR CONTROL NORDIC AB—See Addtech AB; *Int'l*, pg. 135
SENTIENT ENERGY, INC.—See Koch Industries, Inc.; *U.S. Private*, pg. 2332
SEPTON ELECTRONIC AB—See DistIT AB; *Int'l*, pg. 2136
SESCO DATACOMM—See Arthur's Enterprises, Inc.; *U.S. Private*, pg. 342
SESCO EFACEC SDN. BHD.—See Efacec Capital, SGPS, S.A.; *Int'l*, pg. 2318
SHANGHAI ALL ACCESS NOTER COMMUNICATION TECHNOLOGY CO., LIMITED—See China All Access (Holdings) Limited; *Int'l*, pg. 1482
SHANGHAI DAISHINKU INTERNATIONAL TRADING CO., LTD—See Daishinku Corp.; *Int'l*, pg. 1942
SHANGHAI SHINKO TRADING LTD.—See Fujitsu Limited; *Int'l*, pg. 2838
SHANGHAI SIM-BCD SEMICONDUCTOR MANUFACTURING CO., LTD.—See Diodes Incorporated; *U.S. Public*, pg. 667
SHANGHAI VISHAY SEMICONDUCTORS LTD.—See Vishay Intertechnology, Inc.; *U.S. Public*, pg. 2302
SHANGHAI ZANUSSI ELETTROMECCANICA CO., LTD.—See Guangzhou Wanbao Group Co., Ltd.; *Int'l*, pg. 3168
SHANNON PRECISION INC.; *U.S. Private*, pg. 3625
SHARP BUSINESS SYSTEMS (INDIA) PRIVATE LIMITED—See Hon Hai Precision Industry Co., Ltd.; *Int'l*, pg. 3457
SHARP MICROELECTRONICS OF THE AMERICAS—See Hon Hai Precision Industry Co., Ltd.; *Int'l*, pg. 3458
SHARP NEC DISPLAY SOLUTIONS OF AMERICA, INC.—See Hon Hai Precision Industry Co., Ltd.; *Int'l*, pg. 3459
SHARP SINGAPORE ELECTRONICS CORPORATION PTE. LTD.—See Hon Hai Precision Industry Co., Ltd.; *Int'l*, pg. 3459
SHIBAURA TECHNOLOGY INTERNATIONAL CORP.; *U.S. Private*, pg. 3635
SHOKAI FAR EAST LTD.; *U.S. Private*, pg. 3639
SIA BK LATVIA—See Hangzhou Hikvision Digital Technology Co., Ltd.; *Int'l*, pg. 3248
SIGMATRON INTERNATIONAL, INC.; *U.S. Public*, pg. 1877

SILICON LABS EMBER, INC.—See Silicon Laboratories Inc.; *U.S. Public*, pg. 1880
SILICON QUEST INTERNATIONAL; *U.S. Private*, pg. 3652
SILICON VALLEY MICROELECTRONICS INC.; *U.S. Private*, pg. 3652
SILICONWARE USA, INC.—See ASE Technology Holding Co.; *Int'l*, pg. 605
SILTERRA SALES & MARKETING (L) LTD.—See Dagang NeXchange Berhad; *Int'l*, pg. 1912
SILTERRA USA INC.—See Dagang NeXchange Berhad; *Int'l*, pg. 1912
SIMCONA ELECTRONICS CORP; *U.S. Private*, pg. 3665
SIMPLY, INC.; *U.S. Public*, pg. 1882
SINGAPORE COMMUNICATIONS EQUIPMENT CO. PTE LTD.—See HKC International Holdings Limited; *Int'l*, pg. 3428
SINGAPORE HAGIWARA PTE. LTD.—See Hagiwara Electric Holdings Co., Ltd.; *Int'l*, pg. 3207
SKYLANE OPTICS SA—See Amphenol Corporation; *U.S. Public*, pg. 132
SKYWALKER COMMUNICATION INC.; *U.S. Private*, pg. 3686
SKYWORKS SOLUTIONS WORLDWIDE, INC.—See Skyworks Solutions, Inc.; *U.S. Public*, pg. 1893
SMART ROOFS SOLAR, INC.; *U.S. Private*, pg. 3691
SMC NETWORKS INC—See Accton Technology Corporation; *Int'l*, pg. 94
SMC NETWORKS SPAIN SL—See Accton Technology Corporation; *Int'l*, pg. 94
SOLID MARKETING INC.; *U.S. Private*, pg. 3709
SOLID OPTICS EU N.V.—See Amphenol Corporation; *U.S. Public*, pg. 132
SOLID OPTICS LLC—See Amphenol Corporation; *U.S. Public*, pg. 132
SOLID STATE INC.; *U.S. Private*, pg. 3709
SOLMATES B.V.—See Lam Research Corporation; *U.S. Public*, pg. 1290
SOUND SOLUTIONS INTERNATIONAL CO., LTD.—See Hon Hai Precision Industry Co., Ltd.; *Int'l*, pg. 3459
SOUTHERN ELECTRONICS SUPPLY; *U.S. Private*, pg. 3731
SOUTHERN STATES MARKETING INC.; *U.S. Private*, pg. 3735
SOUTHWEST ELECTRONIC ENERGY CORP.—See Ultralife Corporation; *U.S. Public*, pg. 2224
SPECTRAL DYNAMICS (UK) LTD.—See Spectral Dynamics, Inc.; *U.S. Private*, pg. 3751
SPECTRA RESEARCH CORPORATION—See HORIBA Ltd; *Int'l*, pg. 3478
SPECTRUM INTERNATIONAL CORPORATION; *U.S. Private*, pg. 3753
SPECTRUM SALES INC.; *U.S. Private*, pg. 3753
SPECTRUM TECHNOLOGIES, INC.; *U.S. Private*, pg. 3753
SPIE COMMUNICATIONS—See Clayton, Dubilier & Rice, LLC; *U.S. Private*, pg. 926
STALEY COMMUNICATION, INC.; *U.S. Private*, pg. 3776
STANDARD AUDIO AB—See Aiphone Co., Ltd.; *Int'l*, pg. 235
STANLEY BLACK & DECKER (HELLAS) EPE—See Stanley Black & Decker, Inc.; *U.S. Public*, pg. 1934
STANLEY HEALTHCARE SOLUTIONS FRANCE SARL—See Stanley Black & Decker, Inc.; *U.S. Public*, pg. 1935
STAR WERKS INC.; *U.S. Private*, pg. 3785
STAUB ELECTRONICS LTD.—See Resideo Technologies, Inc.; *U.S. Public*, pg. 1790
STEINEL (UK) LTD.—See ADCURAM Group AG; *Int'l*, pg. 128
STEPHEN IMPORTS INC.; *U.S. Private*, pg. 3802
STEREN ELECTRONICS INTERNATIONAL LLC; *U.S. Private*, pg. 3804
STEVEN ENGINEERING, INC.; *U.S. Private*, pg. 3808
STEVENS COMMUNICATIONS INC.; *U.S. Private*, pg. 3809
STIG WAHLSTROM AUTOMATIK AB—See Addtech AB; *Int'l*, pg. 135
STOKVIS TAPES ESTONIA OU—See Illinois Tool Works Inc.; *U.S. Public*, pg. 1110
STORTECH ELECTRONICS LTD.—See discoverIE Group plc; *Int'l*, pg. 2133
SUNBELT TELECOMMUNICATIONS INC.; *U.S. Private*, pg. 3865
SUN CHAIN TECHNOLOGY CORP.—See Arrow Electronics, Inc.; *U.S. Public*, pg. 200
SUNJET COMPONENTS CORP.—See EDOM Technology Co., Ltd.; *Int'l*, pg. 2313
SUNTRON CORPORATION—See Blum Capital Partners, L.P.; *U.S. Private*, pg. 599
SUNTRON CORPORATION—See HCI Equity Management, L.P.; *U.S. Private*, pg. 1889
SUPERIOR COMMUNICATIONS PRODUCTS; *U.S. Private*, pg. 3876
SURE PROMISE LIMITED—See Hanison Construction Holdings Limited; *Int'l*, pg. 3252
SURFACE MOUNT DISTRIBUTION; *U.S. Private*, pg. 3884
SURGE COMPONENTS, INC.; *U.S. Public*, pg. 1967
SUZO-HAPP GROUP AMERICAS (AR) S.R.L.—See ACON Investments, LLC; *U.S. Private*, pg. 63
SUZO-HAPP GROUP DO BRASIL LTDA—See ACON Investments, LLC; *U.S. Private*, pg. 63

SUZO-HAPP GROUP GMBH—See ACON Investments, LLC; *U.S. Private*, pg. 63
SUZO-HAPP GROUP (NL) BV—See ACON Investments, LLC; *U.S. Private*, pg. 63
SUZO-HAPP GROUP SP. ZO,O—See ACON Investments, LLC; *U.S. Private*, pg. 63
SUZO-HAPP GROUP (UK) LTD.—See ACON Investments, LLC; *U.S. Private*, pg. 63
SYMMETRY ELECTRONICS CORP.—See Berkshire Hathaway Inc.; *U.S. Public*, pg. 316
SYRINIX LIMITED—See Badger Meter, Inc.; *U.S. Public*, pg. 264
SYS-TECH, INC.—See Jack Henry & Associates, Inc.; *U.S. Public*, pg. 1183
SYSTEMS DEPOT; *U.S. Private*, pg. 3907
TABULA, INC.; *U.S. Private*, pg. 3920
TAI CORPORATION; *U.S. Private*, pg. 3923
TAITRON COMPONENTS INCORPORATED; *U.S. Public*, pg. 1979
TAIWAN HOSIDEN CO., LTD.,—See Hosiden Corporation; *Int'l*, pg. 3485
TAIWAN I-O DATA DEVICE, INC.—See I-O DATA DEVICE, INC.; *Int'l*, pg. 3563
TALLEY INC.; *U.S. Private*, pg. 3927
TAMPEREEN SAHKOPALVELU OY—See Addtech AB; *Int'l*, pg. 135
TARGUS INDIA PVT. LTD.—See Targus Group International, Inc.; *U.S. Private*, pg. 3934
TCA/HORIBA SISTEMAS DE TESTES AUTOMOTIVOS LTDA.—See HORIBA Ltd; *Int'l*, pg. 3478
TCM TRADING & SERVICE COMPANY LIMITED—See Astena Holdings Co., Ltd.; *Int'l*, pg. 653
TD MOBILE CORPORATION—See Denso Corporation; *Int'l*, pg. 2033
TD TECH DATA AB—See TD Synnex Corp; *U.S. Public*, pg. 1986
TECH DATA ADVANCED SOLUTIONS (ANZ) LIMITED—See TD Synnex Corp; *U.S. Public*, pg. 1986
TECH DATA ADVANCED SOLUTIONS (INDIA) PRIVATE LIMITED—See TD Synnex Corp; *U.S. Public*, pg. 1985
TECH DATA ADVANCED SOLUTIONS (MALAYSIA) SDN. BHD.—See TD Synnex Corp; *U.S. Public*, pg. 1985
TECH DATA ADVANCED SOLUTIONS (SINGAPORE) PTE. LTD.—See TD Synnex Corp; *U.S. Public*, pg. 1985
TECH DATA ADVANCED SOLUTIONS (THAILAND) LIMITED—See TD Synnex Corp; *U.S. Public*, pg. 1986
TECH DATA BRASIL, LTDA—See TD Synnex Corp; *U.S. Public*, pg. 1986
TECH DATA COLOMBIA S.A.S.—See TD Synnex Corp; *U.S. Public*, pg. 1986
TECH DATA COMPUTER SERVICE (MACAU) LIMITED—See TD Synnex Corp; *U.S. Public*, pg. 1986
TECH DATA DISTRIBUTION IRELAND—See TD Synnex Corp; *U.S. Public*, pg. 1985
TECH DATA MOBILE NETHERLANDS B.V.—See TD Synnex Corp; *U.S. Public*, pg. 1987
TECH DATA (SINGAPORE) PTE. LTD.—See TD Synnex Corp; *U.S. Public*, pg. 1986
TECHLINE INC.; *U.S. Private*, pg. 3952
TECHNIC INNOVATIVE SURFACE TECHNOLOGIES FACILITY—See Technic Incorporated; *U.S. Private*, pg. 3953
TEKTRONIX INTERNATIONAL SALES GMBH—See Fortive Corporation; *U.S. Public*, pg. 872
TELAMON CORPORATION; *U.S. Private*, pg. 3959
TELAMON INTERNATIONAL CORP.—See Telamon Corporation; *U.S. Private*, pg. 3959
TELCOBUY.COM LLC—See World Wide Technology Holding Co., LLC; *U.S. Private*, pg. 4568
TELECOM ENTERPRISES INC.; *U.S. Private*, pg. 3960
TELEDYNE DEFENSE ELECTRONICS, LLC—See Teledyne Technologies Incorporated; *U.S. Public*, pg. 1993
TELEDYNE E2V US, INC.—See Teledyne Technologies Incorporated; *U.S. Public*, pg. 1995
TELEDYNE LECROY, S.A.R.L—See Teledyne Technologies Incorporated; *U.S. Public*, pg. 1994
TELEDYNE RAD-ICON IMAGING CORP.—See Teledyne Technologies Incorporated; *U.S. Public*, pg. 1995
TELETRONIC SERVICES INC.; *U.S. Private*, pg. 3962
TELEVAS HOLDINGS SDN. BHD.—See FSBM Holdings Berhad; *Int'l*, pg. 2798
TELIT WIRELESS SOLUTIONS LTD.—See DBAY Advisors Limited; *Int'l*, pg. 1988
TELIT WIRELESS SOLUTIONS (PTY) LTD.—See DBAY Advisors Limited; *Int'l*, pg. 1988
TELMAR NETWORK TECHNOLOGY-COUNCIL BLUFFS—See Jabil Inc.; *U.S. Public*, pg. 1182
TELMAR NETWORK TECHNOLOGY INC.—See Jabil Inc.; *U.S. Public*, pg. 1182
TELMIL ELECTRONICS, INC.—See Avnet, Inc.; *U.S. Public*, pg. 254
TELNET CORP.—See Guest-Tek Interactive Entertainment Ltd.; *Int'l*, pg. 3172
TELPRO INC.; *U.S. Private*, pg. 3962
TEMPEST TELECOM SOLUTIONS, LLC; *U.S. Private*, pg. 3963
TERMINAL SUPPLY INC.; *U.S. Private*, pg. 3969
TERMOTEC DE CHIHUAHUA, S.A. DE C.V.—See Emerson

N.A.I.C.S. INDEX

423710 — HARDWARE MERCHANT W...

Electric Co.; *U.S. Public*, pg. 752
TESEQ INC.—See AMETEK, Inc.; *U.S. Public*, pg. 119
TESEQ K.K.—See AMETEK, Inc.; *U.S. Public*, pg. 119
TESSCO TECHNOLOGIES, INC.—See Lee Equity Partners LLC; *U.S. Private*, pg. 2412
TESSCO TECHNOLOGIES, INC.—See Twin Point Capital, LLC; *U.S. Private*, pg. 4265
TEST EQUIPMENT DISTRIBUTORS, LLC—See X-Ray Industries Inc.; *U.S. Private*, pg. 4579
TEXAS INSTRUMENTS BELGIUM SA—See Texas Instruments Incorporated; *U.S. Public*, pg. 2026
TEXAS INSTRUMENTS FRANCE SA—See Texas Instruments Incorporated; *U.S. Public*, pg. 2026
TEXAS INSTRUMENTS HONG KONG LTD.—See Texas Instruments Incorporated; *U.S. Public*, pg. 2026
TEXAS INSTRUMENTS ITALIA S.P.A.—See Texas Instruments Incorporated; *U.S. Public*, pg. 2026
TEXAS INSTRUMENTS JAPAN LTD.—See Texas Instruments Incorporated; *U.S. Public*, pg. 2026
TEXAS INSTRUMENTS LIMITED—See Texas Instruments Incorporated; *U.S. Public*, pg. 2026
TEXAS INSTRUMENTS SOUTHEAST ASIA PTE. LTD.—See Texas Instruments Incorporated; *U.S. Public*, pg. 2026
THERMO PROJECTS LIMITED—See Thermo Fisher Scientific Inc.; *U.S. Public*, pg. 2154
THIN FILM EQUIPMENT S.R.L.—See Plasma-Therm, LLC; *U.S. Private*, pg. 3198
TIANMA MICROELECTRONICS KOREA CO., LTD—See AVIC International Holdings Limited; *Int'l*, pg. 742
TIANMA MICROELECTRONICS (USA) INC.—See AVIC International Holdings Limited; *Int'l*, pg. 742
TJR PROCUREMENT, LLC; *U.S. Private*, pg. 4178
TK6, INC.; *U.S. Private*, pg. 4178
TME GMBH—See GlassBridge Enterprises, Inc.; *U.S. Public*, pg. 939
TODINO ENGINEERING SALES INC.; *U.S. Private*, pg. 4181
TOMOIKE INDUSTRIAL (H.K.) LIMITED—See CDW Holding Ltd.; *Int'l*, pg. 1372
TONAR INDUSTRIES INC.; *U.S. Private*, pg. 4184
TOTAL COMMUNICATIONS INC.; *U.S. Private*, pg. 4190
TOWNSEND COATES LTD.—See discoverIE Group plc; *Int'l*, pg. 2134
TOYO ADTEC CO., LTD.—See Denki Company Limited; *Int'l*, pg. 2027
TOYO KUNI ELECTRONICS CO. LTD.—See Audix Corporation; *Int'l*, pg. 702
TREMBLY ASSOCIATES INC.; *U.S. Private*, pg. 4217
TRIBECA TECHNOLOGY SOLUTIONS INC.; *U.S. Private*, pg. 4227
TRIDENT MICROSYSTEMS (JAPAN) GK—See Trident Microsystems, Inc.; *U.S. Private*, pg. 4230
TRIDENT MICROSYSTEMS (KOREA) LTD.—See Trident Microsystems, Inc.; *U.S. Private*, pg. 4230
TRI-ELECTRONICS INC.; *U.S. Private*, pg. 4222
TRITRONICS, INC.—See Bain Capital, LP; *U.S. Private*, pg. 444
TROIS ELECTRONICS (WUXI) CO., LTD.—See Di-Nikko Engineering Co., Ltd.; *Int'l*, pg. 2101
TROIS ENGINEERING PRETEC HONG KONG LTD.—See Di-Nikko Engineering Co., Ltd.; *Int'l*, pg. 2101
TROIS (THAILAND) CO., LTD.—See Di-Nikko Engineering Co., Ltd.; *Int'l*, pg. 2101
TRUEDYNE SENSORS AG—See Endress+Hauser (International) Holding AG; *Int'l*, pg. 2409
TTI, INC.—See Berkshire Hathaway Inc.; *U.S. Public*, pg. 316
TTM TECHNOLOGIES TORONTO, INC.—See TTM Technologies, Inc.; *U.S. Public*, pg. 2203
TURNKEY TECHNOLOGIES, INC.; *U.S. Private*, pg. 4261
TV EARS; *U.S. Private*, pg. 4263
TWO-WAY COMMUNICATIONS INC.; *U.S. Private*, pg. 4267
TYLER GRIFFIN CO., INC.—See G&G Technical Inc.; *U.S. Private*, pg. 1629
UAB FUTURE ELECTRONICS—See Future Electronics Inc.; *Int'l*, pg. 2856
UHS PTY LTD—See Carrier Global Corporation; *U.S. Public*, pg. 444
ULTRA SOURCE ELECTRONICS (SZ) CO, LTD—See Arrow Electronics, Inc.; *U.S. Public*, pg. 200
ULTRA SOURCE TECHNOLOGY CORP.—See Arrow Electronics, Inc.; *U.S. Public*, pg. 200
UNIDIX (MALAYSIA) SDN BHD—See Avnet, Inc.; *U.S. Public*, pg. 251
UNIDUX (SINGAPORE) PTE LTD—See Avnet, Inc.; *U.S. Public*, pg. 251
UNIDUX (THAILAND) CO., LTD.—See Avnet, Inc.; *U.S. Public*, pg. 251
UNIFIEDCOMMUNICATIONS.COM; *U.S. Private*, pg. 4283
UNION TECHNOLOGY CORP.—See Arcline Investment Management LP; *U.S. Private*, pg. 315
UNITRONEX CORPORATION; *U.S. Private*, pg. 4302
UNIVERSAL GLOBAL SCIENTIFIC INDUSTRIAL CO., LTD.—See ASE Technology Holding Co., Ltd.; *Int'l*, pg. 604
UNIVERSAL POWER GROUP, INC.; *U.S. Private*, pg. 4306

UNIVERSAL RELAY—See Park Distributors, Inc.; *U.S. Private*, pg. 3096
UNIVERSAL SPECTRUM CORPORATION—See Hamamatsu Photonics K.K.; *Int'l*, pg. 3235
UNIWIZ TRADE SALES, INC.—See Razer Inc.; *U.S. Private*, pg. 3359
UPT COMPONENT (S) PTE. LTD.—See Europtronic Group Ltd.; *Int'l*, pg. 2557
UPT CRYPSON COMPONENT (SHANGHAI) CO., LTD.—See Europtronic Group Ltd.; *Int'l*, pg. 2557
USI ELECTRIC, INC.—See Universal Security Instruments, Inc.; *U.S. Public*, pg. 2262
US MICRO PRODUCTS, INC.; *U.S. Private*, pg. 4319
VACTEK A/S—See Addtech AB; *Int'l*, pg. 135
VALUE-TRONICS INTERNATIONAL, INC.; *U.S. Private*, pg. 4338
VANCE BALDWIN, INC.—See Bain Capital, LP; *U.S. Private*, pg. 444
VCOM INTERNATIONAL MULTI-MEDIA CORPORATION; *U.S. Private*, pg. 4349
VENKEL LTD.; *U.S. Private*, pg. 4356
VERIZON TELEPRODUCTS—See Verizon Communications Inc.; *U.S. Public*, pg. 2286
VERTEX WIRELESS LLC; *U.S. Private*, pg. 4370
VETERANS TRADING CO., LLC.; *U.S. Private*, pg. 4374
VH FIBRE OPTICS PROPRIETARY LIMITED—See Alviva Holdings Limited; *Int'l*, pg. 402
VIA OPTRONICS, LTD.—See Ayala Corporation; *Int'l*, pg. 774
VIA OPTRONICS (SUZHOU) CO., LTD—See Ayala Corporation; *Int'l*, pg. 774
VIDEO GROUP DISTRIBUTORS; *U.S. Private*, pg. 4380
VIDEO KING GAMING & ENTERTAINMENT CANADA LIMITED—See Video King Gaming Systems, LLC; *U.S. Private*, pg. 4380
VIDEO KING GAMING SYSTEMS, LLC - BINGO KING DIVISION—See Video King Gaming Systems, LLC; *U.S. Private*, pg. 4380
VIDEO KING GAMING SYSTEMS, LLC - BINGO TECHNOLOGY & SUPPLY DIVISION—See Video King Gaming Systems, LLC; *U.S. Private*, pg. 4380
VIDEO SECURITY SPECIALISTS, INC.; *U.S. Private*, pg. 4380
VINGCARD ELSAFE JAPAN CORPORATION—See ASSA ABLOY AB; *Int'l*, pg. 641
VINGCARD ELSAFE PACIFIC CORPORATION—See ASSA ABLOY AB; *Int'l*, pg. 641
VIRGINIA ELECTRONIC COMPONENTS LLC; *U.S. Private*, pg. 4387
VIRTUAL CHIP EXCHANGE, INC.—See HPI AG; *Int'l*, pg. 3500
VIRTUAL MEDIA INTEGRATION, LLC—See Varex Imaging Corporation; *U.S. Public*, pg. 2275
VISHAY CHINA CO. LTD.—See Vishay Intertechnology, Inc.; *U.S. Public*, pg. 2302
VISHAY SEMICONDUCTOR ITALIANA S.P.A.—See Vishay Intertechnology, Inc.; *U.S. Public*, pg. 2303
VISUALIMITS, LLC—See NRT Technologies Inc.; *U.S. Private*, pg. 2970
VITEC BROADCAST SERVICES INC.—See The Carlyle Group Inc.; *U.S. Public*, pg. 2050
VOICE COMM, LLC—See Tygon Peak Capital; *U.S. Private*, pg. 4267
VOXX INTERNATIONAL CORPORATION; *U.S. Public*, pg. 2310
VTECH ADVANCED AMERICAN TELEPHONES; *U.S. Private*, pg. 4415
VT ZERO LIMITED—See Cybernaut International Holdings Company Limited; *Int'l*, pg. 1893
V.V. & SONS LLC—See Bhatia Brothers Group; *Int'l*, pg. 1014
VYRIAN, INC.; *U.S. Private*, pg. 4417
WALKER & ASSOCIATES, INC.; *U.S. Private*, pg. 4428
WALKER COMPONENT GROUP INC.; *U.S. Private*, pg. 4428
WARBA MECHANICAL EQUIPMENTS L.L.C.—See Arabi Holding Group Company K.S.C.C.; *Int'l*, pg. 533
WARD DAVIS ASSOCIATES INC.; *U.S. Private*, pg. 4441
WATTS COPY SYSTEMS INC.; *U.S. Private*, pg. 4456
WEIFANG GOERTEK ELECTRONICS CO., LTD.—See GoerTek Inc.; *Int'l*, pg. 3021
WEISLER & ASSOCIATES INC.; *U.S. Private*, pg. 4472
WESCO - ANIXTER ISRAEL LTD.—See WESCO International, Inc.; *U.S. Public*, pg. 2351
WE SELL CELLULAR, INC.; *U.S. Private*, pg. 4462
WES-GARDE COMPONENTS GROUP INC.; *U.S. Private*, pg. 4482
WESTAK, INC.; *U.S. Private*, pg. 4488
WESTAK INTERNATIONAL SALES INC.—See Westak, Inc.; *U.S. Private*, pg. 4488
WEST COAST ENGINEERING SERVICE—See Zaharoni Industries, Inc.; *U.S. Private*, pg. 4597
WESTCON GROUP EUROPEAN OPERATIONS LIMITED—See TD Synnex Corp; *U.S. Public*, pg. 1987
WESTERN SECURITY SYSTEMS, INC.—See Mountain Acquisition Company, LLC; *U.S. Private*, pg. 2798
WHOLESALE ELECTRIC SUPPLY HOUSTON LP; *U.S. Private*, pg. 4514

THE WHOLESALE HOUSE INC.; *U.S. Private*, pg. 4135
WHOLESALE INDUSTRIAL ELECTRONICS, INC.; *U.S. Private*, pg. 4514
WINCHESTER INTERCONNECT CORPORATION—See Aptiv PLC; *Int'l*, pg. 526
WIRELESS DEVICE SUPPLY CO., LTD.—See Advanced Info Service Plc; *Int'l*, pg. 160
WIRELESSUSA, INC.; *U.S. Private*, pg. 4547
WISE COMPONENTS INC.; *U.S. Private*, pg. 4549
W. L. GORE & ASSOCIATES TECHNOLOGIES (SHENZHEN) CO., LTD—See W.L. Gore & Associates, Inc.; *U.S. Private*, pg. 4421
WOLFSTRIKE DISTRIBUTORS LTD.—See FE Investments Limited; *Int'l*, pg. 2629
WOLFSTRIKE DISTRIBUTORS PTY LIMITED—See FE Investments Limited; *Int'l*, pg. 2629
WORLD MICRO, INC.; *U.S. Private*, pg. 4566
WORLD MOBILE CORPORATION—See GEO Holdings Corporation; *Int'l*, pg. 2932
WORLD PRODUCTS INC.; *U.S. Private*, pg. 4566
WORLDWIDE SUPPLY; *U.S. Private*, pg. 4570
WPCS INTERNATIONAL - SUISUN CITY, INC.; *U.S. Private*, pg. 4571
XEROX FINANCIAL SERVICES NORWAY AS—See Xerox Holdings Corporation; *U.S. Public*, pg. 2390
XEROX HELLAS AEE—See Xerox Holdings Corporation; *U.S. Public*, pg. 2390
XIAMEN ZETTLER ELECTRONICS CO., LTD.—See Zettler Components, Inc.; *U.S. Private*, pg. 4603
XIANGTAN IM DIGITAL ELECTRONICS CO. LTD—See IM Co., Ltd.; *Int'l*, pg. 3617
XILINX ESTONIA O.U.—See Advanced Micro Devices, Inc.; *U.S. Public*, pg. 49
XILINX SARL—See Advanced Micro Devices, Inc.; *U.S. Public*, pg. 49
XPLACE GMBH—See Ceconomy AG; *Int'l*, pg. 1388
XPLOSION INCORPORATED; *U.S. Private*, pg. 4582
YANGZHOU EDISON OPTO CORPORATION—See Edison Opto Corp.; *Int'l*, pg. 2311
YEL ELECTRONICS HONG KONG LIMITED—See Avnet, Inc.; *U.S. Public*, pg. 254
YEL ELECTRONICS PTE LTD—See Avnet, Inc.; *U.S. Public*, pg. 254
YI-LIANG INTERNATIONAL TRADE (SHANGHAI) LTD.—See Everlight Electronics Co., Ltd.; *Int'l*, pg. 2567
YULI ELECTRONIC CO., LTD.—See FSP Technology Inc.; *Int'l*, pg. 2800
ZACK ELECTRONICS, INC.; *U.S. Private*, pg. 4597
ZAHARONI INDUSTRIES, INC.; *U.S. Private*, pg. 4597
ZENON DIGITAL RADIO, S.L.—See Cellnex Telecom, S.A.; *Int'l*, pg. 1394
ZETTLER ELECTRONICS BELGIUM B.V.B.A. - S.P.R.L.—See Zettler Components, Inc.; *U.S. Private*, pg. 4603
ZETTLER ELECTRONICS GMBH—See Zettler Components, Inc.; *U.S. Private*, pg. 4603
ZETTLER ELECTRONICS (HK) LTD.—See Zettler Components, Inc.; *U.S. Private*, pg. 4603
ZETTLER ELECTRONICS POLAND SP.Z.O.O—See Zettler Components, Inc.; *U.S. Private*, pg. 4603
Z-MAR TECHNOLOGY INC.; *U.S. Private*, pg. 4596
ZYGO CORPORATION - WESTERN REGIONAL OFFICE—See AMETEK, Inc.; *U.S. Public*, pg. 119
ZYGO K.K.—See AMETEK, Inc.; *U.S. Public*, pg. 119
ZYGOLAMDA METROLOGY INSTRUMENT (SHANGHAI) CO., LTD.—See AMETEK, Inc.; *U.S. Public*, pg. 119
ZYGOLOT GMBH—See AMETEK, Inc.; *U.S. Public*, pg. 119
ZYGO TAIWAN CO., LTD.—See AMETEK, Inc.; *U.S. Public*, pg. 119

423710 — HARDWARE MERCHANT WHOLESALERS

A.A. CASEY CO.; *U.S. Private*, pg. 24
A & A JEWELRY TOOLS FINDINGS; *U.S. Private*, pg. 17
ABABA BOLT; *U.S. Private*, pg. 33
ACCURATE COMPONENT SALES, INC.—See MSC Industrial Direct Co., Inc.; *U.S. Public*, pg. 1483
ACE HARDWARE CORPORATION; *U.S. Private*, pg. 56
ACE TOOL REPAIR, INC.; *U.S. Private*, pg. 57
ACF COMPONENTS & FASTENERS; *U.S. Private*, pg. 58
ACME CONSTRUCTION SUPPLY CO. INC.; *U.S. Private*, pg. 60
ACME UNITED (ASIA PACIFIC) LTD.—See Acme United Corporation; *U.S. Public*, pg. 35
ACTION BOLT & TOOL COMPANY; *U.S. Private*, pg. 67
ACTIVE SCREW & FASTENER; *U.S. Private*, pg. 70
ADI—See Honeywell International Inc.; *U.S. Public*, pg. 1049
ADVANSA PTY. LTD.; *Int'l*, pg. 164
A&E MANUFACTURING COMPANY; *U.S. Private*, pg. 20
AERO-GLEN INTERNATIONAL, LLC—See HEICO Corporation; *U.S. Public*, pg. 1021
AEROSCOUT LLC—See Stanley Black & Decker, Inc.; *U.S. Public*, pg. 1931
AERO-SPACE SOUTHWEST INC.—See Bossard Holding AG; *Int'l*, pg. 1117

423710 — HARDWARE MERCHANT W...

AGIE CHARMILLES LTD.—See Georg Fischer AG; *Int'l*, pg. 2934
THE A.G. MAURO COMPANY—See American Securities LLC; *U.S. Private*, pg. 249
AHORN-GERATE & WERKZEUGE VERTRIEBS GMBH—See Simpson Manufacturing Company, Inc.; *U.S. Public*, pg. 1882
AKRON HARDWARE CONSULTANTS, INC.; *U.S. Private*, pg. 146
ALABAMA BOLT & SUPPLY, INC.—See Air Hydro Power Inc.; *U.S. Private*, pg. 139
ALASKA INDUSTRIAL HARDWARE INC.—See Bering Straits Native Corporation; *U.S. Private*, pg. 532
ALBERT BERNER DEUTSCHLAND GMBH—See Berner SE; *Int'l*, pg. 988
ALFRA RUSSLAND OVERTIME JSC—See Alfred Raith GmbH; *Int'l*, pg. 317
ALFRA UK, LTD.—See Alfred Raith GmbH; *Int'l*, pg. 317
ALFRA USA, LLC—See Alfred Raith GmbH; *Int'l*, pg. 317
ALLEGIS CORPORATION; *U.S. Private*, pg. 177
ALLIED FASTENER & TOOL INC.; *U.S. Private*, pg. 186
ALLMETAL SCREW PRODUCTS CORP.; *U.S. Private*, pg. 192
ALL STATE FASTENER CORPORATION; *U.S. Private*, pg. 172
ALLTRADE TOOL LLC; *U.S. Private*, pg. 194
AL-MUHAIDIB HARDWARE—See A.K. Al-Muhaidib & Sons Group of Companies; *Int'l*, pg. 24
AMADA MACHINE TOOLS EUROPE GMBH FRANCE—See Amada Holdings Co., Ltd.; *Int'l*, pg. 404
AMARILLO HARDWARE COMPANY; *U.S. Private*, pg. 216
AMERICAN FASTENERS INC.; *U.S. Private*, pg. 233
APACHE SUPPLY, INC.—See Ram Tool & Supply Co. Inc.; *U.S. Private*, pg. 3351
APPLIED INDUSTRIAL TECHNOLOGIES - TX LP—See Applied Industrial Technologies, Inc.; *U.S. Public*, pg. 170
ARCHER SCREW PRODUCTS INC.; *U.S. Private*, pg. 310
ARCHITECTURAL BUILDING SUPPLY CO.—See Platinum Equity, LLC; *U.S. Private*, pg. 3208
ASSA ABLOY EAST AFRICA LTD.—See ASSA ABLOY AB; *Int'l*, pg. 633
ASSEMBLY FASTENERS INC.; *U.S. Private*, pg. 353
ATLAS WATER SYSTEMS, INC.; *U.S. Private*, pg. 380
AUSTIN HARDWARE & SUPPLY INC.; *U.S. Private*, pg. 395
BARGAIN SUPPLY COMPANY; *U.S. Private*, pg. 474
BAY TOOL & SUPPLY INC.; *U.S. Private*, pg. 495
BECKNELL WHOLESALE I LP; *U.S. Private*, pg. 511
BENIDORM LOCKS S.L.—See Groupe SFPI SA; *Int'l*, pg. 3111
BERLANDS INC.; *U.S. Private*, pg. 535
BLACK AND DECKER, S.A. DE C.V.—See Stanley Black & Decker, Inc.; *U.S. Public*, pg. 1936
B&L BOLT, INC.—See Audax Group, Limited Partnership; *U.S. Private*, pg. 387
BLISH-MIZE CO.; *U.S. Private*, pg. 581
BLUEGRASS TOOL WAREHOUSE INC.; *U.S. Private*, pg. 596
BLUE RIDGE KNIVES, INC.; *U.S. Private*, pg. 592
BOEING DISTRIBUTION SERVICES II GMBH—See The Boeing Company; *U.S. Public*, pg. 2040
BOEING DISTRIBUTION SERVICES SP Z.O.O—See RTX Corporation; *U.S. Public*, pg. 1822
BONCO IRONMONGERY LIMITED—See E. Bon Holdings Ltd; *Int'l*, pg. 2249
BOSSARD AEROSPACE, INC.—See Bossard Holding AG; *Int'l*, pg. 1117
BOSSARD AEROSPACE SWITZERLAND AG—See Bossard Holding AG; *Int'l*, pg. 1117
BOSSARD NORWAY AS—See Bossard Holding AG; *Int'l*, pg. 1117
BOSSARD ONTARIO INC.—See Bossard Holding AG; *Int'l*, pg. 1117
BOSTWICK-BRAUN COMPANY; *U.S. Private*, pg. 622
BOSUN TOOLS INC.—See Bosun Co Ltd; *Int'l*, pg. 1118
BOYSEN AEROSPACE U.S., INC.—See Bossard Holding AG; *Int'l*, pg. 1117
BOYSEN GMBH—See Bossard Holding AG; *Int'l*, pg. 1117
BRABNER & HOLLON, INC.; *U.S. Private*, pg. 630
BRANAM FASTENING SYSTEMS INC.—See MSD Capital, L.P.; *U.S. Private*, pg. 2807
BUCKEYE FASTENERS INC.—See Fastener Industries Inc.; *U.S. Private*, pg. 1482
BUILDERS' HARDWARE & SUPPLY CO.; *U.S. Private*, pg. 682
BUILDING CHOICES LIMITED—See Fletcher Building Limited; *Int'l*, pg. 2699
BUILDING FASTENERS OF MINNESOTA INC.; *U.S. Private*, pg. 646
BUNTING DOOR & HARDWARE CO., INC.—See Platinum Equity, LLC; *U.S. Private*, pg. 3208
BURG-WAECHTER S.A.R.L—See Burg-Wachter KG; *Int'l*, pg. 1223
CALIFORNIA HARDWARE COMPANY—See Amarillo Hardware Company; *U.S. Private*, pg. 216
CAPITOL HARDWARE COMPANY, INC.; *U.S. Private*, pg. 744

CARLSON JPM STORE FIXTURES—See Stein Industries, Inc.; *U.S. Private*, pg. 3797
CAROLINA CHAIN & CABLE CO. INC.—See ALP Industries, Inc.; *U.S. Private*, pg. 196
CAROLINA DOOR CONTROLS, INC.; *U.S. Private*, pg. 767
CARREL SA—See Descours & Cabaud SA; *Int'l*, pg. 2044
CARSON'S NUT-BOLT & TOOL CO.; *U.S. Private*, pg. 774
CARTER-WATERS LLC—See The Sterling Group, L.P.; *U.S. Private*, pg. 4122
CASCADE WHOLESALE HARDWARE INC.—See Parr Lumber Company Inc.; *U.S. Private*, pg. 3099
CCOM GROUP, INC.—See Daikin Industries, Ltd.; *Int'l*, pg. 1935
CENTRAL INDIANA HARDWARE CO.; *U.S. Private*, pg. 821
CHARLES G. HARDY, INC.—See GMS Inc.; *U.S. Public*, pg. 948
CHARLES MCMURRAY COMPANY; *U.S. Private*, pg. 853
CHICAGO LUMBER COMPANY OF OMAHA; *U.S. Private*, pg. 878
CHRISTIAN WHOLESALE DISTRIBUTORS, INC.; *U.S. Private*, pg. 891
CIRCLE BOLT & NUT COMPANY INC.; *U.S. Private*, pg. 899
CLARK & BARLOW HARDWARE CO.—See Logan Square Aluminum Supply, Inc.; *U.S. Private*, pg. 2481
CLEMENT HARDWARE, INC.—See Zeskind's Hardware, Inc.; *U.S. Private*, pg. 4602
CLEVELAND HARDWARE & FORGING CO.; *U.S. Private*, pg. 941
CLEVELAND VICON CO. INC.; *U.S. Private*, pg. 941
CLEVER REINFORCEMENT IBERICA-MATERIAIS DE CONSTRUCAO, LDA.—See Simpson Manufacturing Company, Inc.; *U.S. Public*, pg. 1882
COLONIAL HARDWARE CORP.; *U.S. Private*, pg. 971
COLONY HARDWARE SUPPLY CO. INC.; *U.S. Private*, pg. 972
COMMERCIAL BARGAINS INC.; *U.S. Private*, pg. 983
COMPATICO, INC.; *U.S. Private*, pg. 999
COMPUAGE INFOCOM (S) PTE. LTD.—See Compuage Infocom Ltd.; *Int'l*, pg. 1754
CONNEXCENTER SA—See Stanley Black & Decker, Inc.; *U.S. Public*, pg. 1932
CONSTRUCTION TOOL SERVICE INC.; *U.S. Private*, pg. 1024
CONTRACT HARDWARE INC.; *U.S. Private*, pg. 1032
COPPER STATE BOLT & NUT CO. INC.; *U.S. Private*, pg. 1045
CORRECTION PRODUCTS CO.; *U.S. Private*, pg. 1058
COUNTY HOME IMPROVEMENT CENTER; *U.S. Private*, pg. 1068
COVENTRY GROUP LIMITED COVENTRY FASTENERS DIVISION—See Coventry Group Limited; *Int'l*, pg. 1821
C. P. JAKOBSENS EFTF. APS.—See Groupe SFPI SA; *Int'l*, pg. 3111
C.R. LAURENCE CO., INC.—See KPS Capital Partners, LP; *U.S. Private*, pg. 2348
CRL GLASS MACHINERY—See KPS Capital Partners, LP; *U.S. Private*, pg. 2348
DALLAS FASTENER, INC.—See Birmingham Fastener & Supply Inc.; *U.S. Private*, pg. 564
DAYTON SUPERIOR CANADA LTD.—See Dayton Superior Corporation; *U.S. Private*, pg. 1178
D.B. ROBERTS COMPANY—See Heilind Electronics, Inc.; *U.S. Private*, pg. 1904
THE DELANEY, CO.—See HCI Equity Management, L.P.; *U.S. Private*, pg. 1889
DESCOURS & CABAUD NORMANDIE—See Descours & Cabaud SA; *Int'l*, pg. 2044
DESCOURS & CABAUD PACA—See Descours & Cabaud SA; *Int'l*, pg. 2044
DESCOURS & CABAUD RHONE ALPES AUVERGNE—See Descours & Cabaud SA; *Int'l*, pg. 2044
DESOTO SALES INC.; *U.S. Private*, pg. 1215
DIAMOND BLADE WAREHOUSE INC.—See Granite Creek Capital Partners, LLC; *U.S. Private*, pg. 1755
DISTRIBUTION AMERICA, INC.; *U.S. Private*, pg. 1239
DIVERSIFIED FASTENING SYSTEMS; *U.S. Private*, pg. 1242
DIXIE CONSTRUCTION PRODUCTS INC.; *U.S. Private*, pg. 1245
DO IT BEST CORP.; *U.S. Private*, pg. 1249
DOM SICHERHEITSTECHNIK GMBH & CO. KG—See Groupe SFPI SA; *Int'l*, pg. 3111
DORMAKABA EAD GMBH—See dormakaba Holding AG; *Int'l*, pg. 2178
DORMAKABA ESPANA S.A.U.—See dormakaba Holding AG; *Int'l*, pg. 2178
DORMAKABA GULF FZE—See dormakaba Holding AG; *Int'l*, pg. 2179
DORMAKABA IRELAND LTD.—See dormakaba Holding AG; *Int'l*, pg. 2179
DORMAKABA PORTUGAL S.A.U.—See dormakaba Holding AG; *Int'l*, pg. 2179
DORMAKABA UK LIMITED - HITCHIN OFFICE—See dormakaba Holding AG; *Int'l*, pg. 2179
DRIVEKORE INC.; *U.S. Private*, pg. 1278

DUNCAN BOLT; *U.S. Private*, pg. 1287
DYNAMIC FASTENER SERVICE INC.; *U.S. Private*, pg. 1298
EASTERN WIN METALS & MACHINERY PTE LTD—See HupSteel Limited; *Int'l*, pg. 3538
THE E.B. BRADLEY CO., INC.; *U.S. Private*, pg. 4024
E. BON BUILDING MATERIALS COMPANY LIMITED—See E. Bon Holdings Ltd; *Int'l*, pg. 2250
E. BON HOLDINGS LTD; *Int'l*, pg. 2249
ELEKTROMETAL A.D.; *Int'l*, pg. 2357
EMERY-WATERHOUSE COMPANY—See Ace Hardware Corporation; *U.S. Private*, pg. 56
EMHART TEKNOLOGIES (INDIA) PRIVATE LIMITED—See Stanley Black & Decker, Inc.; *U.S. Public*, pg. 1934
EMKA BENELUX B.V.—See EMKA-Beschlagteile GmbH & Co. KG; *Int'l*, pg. 2383
EMKA BESCHLAGTEILE AG—See EMKA-Beschlagteile GmbH & Co. KG; *Int'l*, pg. 2383
EMKA BESCHLAGTEILE GES.M.B.H.—See EMKA-Beschlagteile GmbH & Co. KG; *Int'l*, pg. 2383
EMKA BESCHLAGTEILE SRL—See EMKA-Beschlagteile GmbH & Co. KG; *Int'l*, pg. 2383
EMKA HELLAS S.A.—See EMKA-Beschlagteile GmbH & Co. KG; *Int'l*, pg. 2383
EMKA INDIA PANEL ACCESSORIES PVT LTD—See EMKA-Beschlagteile GmbH & Co. KG; *Int'l*, pg. 2383
EMKA ITALIA S.R.L.—See EMKA-Beschlagteile GmbH & Co. KG; *Int'l*, pg. 2383
EMKA KILIT SISTEMLERI METAL SAN. VE TIC. LTD. STI.—See EMKA-Beschlagteile GmbH & Co. KG; *Int'l*, pg. 2383
EMKA MEXICO BESCHLAGTEILE S. DE R.L. DE C.V.—See EMKA-Beschlagteile GmbH & Co. KG; *Int'l*, pg. 2383
EMKA MIDDLE EAST LLC—See EMKA-Beschlagteile GmbH & Co. KG; *Int'l*, pg. 2383
EMKA OKOVI D.O.O.—See EMKA-Beschlagteile GmbH & Co. KG; *Int'l*, pg. 2383
EMKA POLSKA SP. Z. O. O.—See EMKA-Beschlagteile GmbH & Co. KG; *Int'l*, pg. 2383
EMKA SCANDINAVIA AB—See EMKA-Beschlagteile GmbH & Co. KG; *Int'l*, pg. 2383
ESTIC (THAILAND) CO., LTD.—See Estic Corporation; *Int'l*, pg. 2518
ETAC ALARME SERVICES SECURITY SA—See Stanley Black & Decker, Inc.; *U.S. Public*, pg. 1932
EXACTITUDE, INC.—See Platinum Equity, LLC; *U.S. Private*, pg. 3208
FABORY CENTRES BELGIUM N.V.—See W.W. Grainger, Inc.; *U.S. Public*, pg. 2319
FABORY FRANCE S.A.—See W.W. Grainger, Inc.; *U.S. Public*, pg. 2319
FABORY KOTOELEM KERESKEDELMI KFT—See W.W. Grainger, Inc.; *U.S. Public*, pg. 2319
FABORY NEDERLAND B.V.—See W.W. Grainger, Inc.; *U.S. Public*, pg. 2319
FABORY POLAND SP. Z.O.O.—See W.W. Grainger, Inc.; *U.S. Public*, pg. 2319
FABORY PORTUGAL LDA.—See W.W. Grainger, Inc.; *U.S. Public*, pg. 2319
FABORY SHANGHAI CO. LTD.—See W.W. Grainger, Inc.; *U.S. Public*, pg. 2319
FABORY SLOVAKIA SRO—See W.W. Grainger, Inc.; *U.S. Public*, pg. 2319
FABORY SRL—See W.W. Grainger, Inc.; *U.S. Public*, pg. 2319
FABORY UK LTD.—See W.W. Grainger, Inc.; *U.S. Public*, pg. 2319
FAIRWAY SUPPLY INC.; *U.S. Private*, pg. 1465
FASTCO (SHANGHAI) TRADING CO., LTD.—See Fastenal Company; *U.S. Public*, pg. 823
FASTEC INDUSTRIAL—See WESCO International, Inc.; *U.S. Public*, pg. 2351
FASTENAL SERVICES S. DE R.L. DE C.V.—See Fastenal Company; *U.S. Public*, pg. 824
FASTENAL SINGAPORE P.T.E. LTD.—See Fastenal Company; *U.S. Public*, pg. 824
FASTENERS INC.; *U.S. Private*, pg. 1482
FASTENER TOOL & SUPPLY INC.; *U.S. Private*, pg. 1482
FASTEQ LIMITED—See Platinum Equity, LLC; *U.S. Private*, pg. 3210
THE FAUCET-QUEENS, INC.—See Incline MGMT Corp.; *U.S. Private*, pg. 2054
FBS FIRST COAST INC.; *U.S. Private*, pg. 1485
FERRAMENTA 2000 SPA—See Descours & Cabaud SA; *Int'l*, pg. 2044
FISCHER ARGENTINA S.A.—See fischerwerke GmbH & Co. KG; *Int'l*, pg. 2692
FISCHER A/S—See fischerwerke GmbH & Co, KG; *Int'l*, pg. 2692
FISCHER AUSTRIA GMBH—See Dortmunder Gussasphalt GmbH & Co. KG; *Int'l*, pg. 2180
FISCHER BENELUX B.V.—See fischerwerke GmbH & Co. KG; *Int'l*, pg. 2692
FISCHER BRASIL INDUSTRIA E COMERCIO LTDA.—See fischerwerke GmbH & Co. KG; *Int'l*, pg. 2692
FISCHER COBEMABEL SNC—See fischerwerke GmbH & Co. KG; *Int'l*, pg. 2692

N.A.I.C.S. INDEX

423710 — HARDWARE MERCHANT W...

FISCHER FINLAND OY—See fischerwerke GmbH & Co. KG; *Int'l*, pg. 2692
FISCHER FIXINGS LLC—See fischerwerke GmbH & Co. KG; *Int'l*, pg. 2692
FISCHER FIXINGS UK LTD.—See fischerwerke GmbH & Co. KG; *Int'l*, pg. 2692
FISCHER FZE—See fischerwerke GmbH & Co. KG; *Int'l*, pg. 2692
FISCHER HELLAS EMPORIKI EPE—See fischerwerke GmbH & Co. KG; *Int'l*, pg. 2692
FISCHER HUNGARIA BT.—See fischerwerke GmbH & Co. KG; *Int'l*, pg. 2692
FISCHER IBERICA S.A.U.—See fischerwerke GmbH & Co. KG; *Int'l*, pg. 2692
FISCHER INNOVATIVE SOLUTIONS CO. LTD.—See fischerwerke GmbH & Co. KG; *Int'l*, pg. 2692
FISCHER INTERNATIONAL S.R.O.—See fischerwerke GmbH & Co. KG; *Int'l*, pg. 2692
FISCHER ITALIA S.R.L—See fischerwerke GmbH & Co. KG; *Int'l*, pg. 2692
FISCHER JAPAN K.K.—See fischerwerke GmbH & Co. KG; *Int'l*, pg. 2692
FISCHER KOREA CO., LTD—See fischerwerke GmbH & Co. KG; *Int'l*, pg. 2692
FISCHER METAL SANAYI VE TICARET LTD STI—See fischerwerke GmbH & Co. KG; *Int'l*, pg. 2692
FISCHER NORGE AS—See fischerwerke GmbH & Co. KG; *Int'l*, pg. 2692
FISCHERPOLSKA SP.Z O.O—See fischerwerke GmbH & Co. KG; *Int'l*, pg. 2692
FISCHER S. A. S.—See fischerwerke GmbH & Co. KG; *Int'l*, pg. 2692
FISCHER SISTEMAS DE FIJACION, S.A. DE C.V.—See fischerwerke GmbH & Co. KG; *Int'l*, pg. 2692
FISCHER S.K. S.R.O.—See fischerwerke GmbH & Co. KG; *Int'l*, pg. 2692
FISCHER SVERIGE AB—See fischerwerke GmbH & Co. KG; *Int'l*, pg. 2692
FISCHER SYSTEMS ASIA PTE. LTD.—See fischerwerke GmbH & Co. KG; *Int'l*, pg. 2692
FISCHER (TAICANG) FIXINGS CO. LTD.—See fischerwerke GmbH & Co. KG; *Int'l*, pg. 2692
FISCHERWERKE PORTUGAL, LDA.—See fischerwerke GmbH & Co. KG; *Int'l*, pg. 2692
FISKARS SPAIN S.L.—See Fiskars Oyj Abp; *Int'l*, pg. 2694
FLORIDA HARDWARE LLC; *U.S. Private*, pg. 1548
FM MATTSSON MORA GROUP NEDERLAND BV—See FM Mattsson Mora Group AB; *Int'l*, pg. 2717
FM MATTSSON MORA GROUP NORGE AS—See FM Mattsson Mora Group AB; *Int'l*, pg. 2717
FORT RECOVERY INDUSTRIES INC.; *U.S. Private*, pg. 1574
FRATTALONE'S HARDWARE; *U.S. Private*, pg. 1599
FREUD, INC.; *U.S. Private*, pg. 1610
GATES AUSTRALIA PTY. LTD.—See Blackstone Inc.; *U.S. Public*, pg. 353
GENERAL FASTENERS COMPANY INC.; *U.S. Private*, pg. 1665
GENERAL SECURITY, INC.; *U.S. Private*, pg. 1667
GERRARDS (COMERCIAL OFFSHORE DE MACAU) LTD—See Beijing Health (Holdings) Limited; *Int'l*, pg. 951
GIANT ACE SDN. BHD.—See Ace Hardware Corporation; *U.S. Private*, pg. 56
GRAINGER DOMINICANA SRL—See W.W. Grainger, Inc.; *U.S. Public*, pg. 2319
GRAINGER GUAM L.L.C.—See W.W. Grainger, Inc.; *U.S. Public*, pg. 2320
GRAINGER INDUSTRIAL MRO DE COSTA RICA, S.R.L.—See W.W. Grainger, Inc.; *U.S. Public*, pg. 2320
GRAINGER INTERNATIONAL HOLDINGS B.V.—See W.W. Grainger, Inc.; *U.S. Public*, pg. 2320
GRAINGER PERU S.R.L.—See W.W. Grainger, Inc.; *U.S. Public*, pg. 2320
GREAT LAKES CUSTOM TOOL MFG, INC.; *U.S. Private*, pg. 1764
GREAT NECK SAW MANUFACTURERS, INC.; *U.S. Private*, pg. 1766
HAFELE AMERICA CO. INC.; *U.S. Private*, pg. 1839
HANDY HARDWARE WHOLESALE INC.—See Littlejohn & Co., LLC; *U.S. Private*, pg. 2470
HARD PARTS DIRECT B.V.—See Dover Corporation; *U.S. Public*, pg. 681
HARDWARE CONSULTANTS—See Platinum Equity, LLC; *U.S. Private*, pg. 3208
HARDWARE DISTRIBUTION WAREHOUSES, INC.; *U.S. Private*, pg. 1863
HARDWARE HOLDINGS—See Littlejohn & Co., LLC; *U.S. Private*, pg. 2470
HARDWARE & LUMBER LIMITED—See GraceKennedy Limited; *Int'l*, pg. 3049
HARDWARE SUPPLIERS OF AMERICA; *U.S. Private*, pg. 1864
H. CILLEKENS & B.V.—See dormakaba Holding AG; *Int'l*, pg. 2179
HD SUPPLY REPAIR & REMODEL, LLC—See Clayton, Dubilier & Rice, LLC; *U.S. Private*, pg. 930
HDW-GREENWOOD DISTRIBUTION CENTER—See Hardware Distribution Warehouses, Inc.; *U.S. Private*, pg. 1863
HEADS & ALLTHREADS PRIVATE LIMITED—See Park-Ohio Holdings Corp.; *U.S. Public*, pg. 1639
HEARTLAND AMERICA, INC.; *U.S. Private*, pg. 1899
HERRAJES HETTICH, S.A. DE C.V.—See Hettich Holding GmbH & Co. oHG; *Int'l*, pg. 3365
HETTICH AUSTRALIA PTY LTD—See Hettich Holding GmbH & Co. oHG; *Int'l*, pg. 3365
HETTICH CANADA L.P.—See Hettich Holding GmbH & Co. oHG; *Int'l*, pg. 3365
HETTICH FRANCE SCS—See Hettich Holding GmbH & Co. oHG; *Int'l*, pg. 3365
HETTICH HARDWARE ACCESSORIES (SHANGHAI) CO. LTD—See Hettich Holding GmbH & Co. oHG; *Int'l*, pg. 3365
HETTICH IBERIA S.L. EN COM.—See Hettich Holding GmbH & Co. oHG; *Int'l*, pg. 3365
HETTICH ITALIA SRL—See Hettich Holding GmbH & Co. oHG; *Int'l*, pg. 3365
HETTICH JAPAN K.K.—See Hettich Holding GmbH & Co. oHG; *Int'l*, pg. 3365
HETTICH MIDDLE EAST JLT.—See Hettich Holding GmbH & Co. oHG; *Int'l*, pg. 3366
HETTICH POLSKA SP. Z O.O.—See Hettich Holding GmbH & Co. oHG; *Int'l*, pg. 3366
HETTICH SINGAPORE (S.E.A.) PTE LTD—See Hettich Holding GmbH & Co. oHG; *Int'l*, pg. 3366
HETTICH SKANDINAVISKA AB—See Hettich Holding GmbH & Co. oHG; *Int'l*, pg. 3366
HETTICH SR S.R.O.—See Hettich Holding GmbH & Co. oHG; *Int'l*, pg. 3366
HETTICH TR MOBILYA TEKNIK MALZEMELERI SAN. VE TIC. LTD. STI.—See Hettich Holding GmbH & Co. oHG; *Int'l*, pg. 3365
HETTICH (UK) LTD—See Hettich Holding GmbH & Co. oHG; *Int'l*, pg. 3365
HGH HARDWARE SUPPLY INC.; *U.S. Private*, pg. 1930
H&G SALES INC.; *U.S. Private*, pg. 1822
HI-ACE TRADING CO., LTD.—See Chun Yu Works & Co., Ltd.; *Int'l*, pg. 1596
HOBERG LUXEMBOURG AG—See Groupe SFPI SA; *Int'l*, pg. 3111
HOBERG N.V.—See Groupe SFPI SA; *Int'l*, pg. 3111
HODELL-NATCO INDUSTRIES INC.—See Nautic Partners, LLC; *U.S. Private*, pg. 2871
HOME & GARDEN SHOWPLACE—See ACON Investments, LLC; *U.S. Private*, pg. 63
HOME HARDWARE CENTER; *U.S. Private*, pg. 1971
HOOTEN'S, LLC.; *U.S. Private*, pg. 1978
HORIZON DISTRIBUTION, INC.; *U.S. Private*, pg. 1980
HOTBATH SRL—See FM Mattsson Mora Group AB; *Int'l*, pg. 2717
HOUSE-HASSON HARDWARE COMPANY-PERSINGER—See House-Hasson Hardware Company; *U.S. Private*, pg. 1992
HOUSE-HASSON HARDWARE COMPANY; *U.S. Private*, pg. 1992
HOWARD BERGER CO. LLC—See Littlejohn & Co., LLC; *U.S. Private*, pg. 2470
HUF DO BRASIL LTDA.—See Huf Hulsbeck & Furst GmbH & Co. KG; *Int'l*, pg. 3523
HUF JAPAN CO., LTD.—See Huf Hulsbeck & Furst GmbH & Co. KG; *Int'l*, pg. 3523
HUNTSVILLE FASTENER & SUPPLY INC.—See Birmingham Fastener & Supply Inc.; *U.S. Private*, pg. 564
HYPERION MATERIALS & TECHNOLOGIES GERMANY GMBH—See KKR & Co. Inc.; *U.S. Public*, pg. 1253
ILLINOIS INDUSTRIAL TOOL INC.; *U.S. Private*, pg. 2042
IMES DEXIS—See Descours & Cabaud SA; *Int'l*, pg. 2044
INDUSTRIAL CASTER & WHEEL CO.; *U.S. Private*, pg. 2065
INDUSTRIAL THREADED PRODUCTS; *U.S. Private*, pg. 2068
INTERCOASTAL, INC.—See HCI Equity Management, L.P.; *U.S. Private*, pg. 1889
INVENTORY SALES CO., INC.; *U.S. Private*, pg. 2131
ISC GMBH—See Einhell Germany AG; *Int'l*, pg. 2334
ISCO INC.—See ASKO Holding A.S.; *Int'l*, pg. 625
ISERO B.V.—See Grafton Group plc; *Int'l*, pg. 3051
ITW AUSTRALIA PTY. LTD.—See Illinois Tool Works Inc.; *U.S. Public*, pg. 1104
ITW BEFESTIGUNGSSYSTEME GMBH—See Illinois Tool Works Inc.; *U.S. Public*, pg. 1104
ITW NEXUS UK—See Illinois Tool Works Inc.; *U.S. Public*, pg. 1106
IWATA BOLT USA INC.; *U.S. Public*, pg. 2152
JACKSON BUILDING CENTRES LTD. - CLASSIC HARDWARE—See Grafton Group plc; *Int'l*, pg. 3051
JACKSON WHOLESALE HARDWARE; *U.S. Private*, pg. 2179
JAMES DOORCHECK, INC.—See Platinum Equity, LLC; *U.S. Private*, pg. 3208
JBL HAWAII, LTD.; *U.S. Private*, pg. 2193
JENSEN DISTRIBUTION SERVICES—See Ace Hardware Corporation; *U.S. Private*, pg. 56
JEVEKA B.V.—See Bossard Holding AG; *Int'l*, pg. 1117
J.G. EDELEN CO. INC.; *U.S. Private*, pg. 2165
JLM WHOLESALE INC.—See Dominus Capital, L.P.; *U.S. Private*, pg. 1257
JMD SECURITE SA—See Stanley Black & Decker, Inc.; *U.S. Public*, pg. 1933
JOHN F MAHANEY, CO.—See Kinderhook Industries, LLC; *U.S. Private*, pg. 2306
JOHNSON HARDWARE CO.; *U.S. Private*, pg. 2228
JOHN WAGNER ASSOCIATES, INC.; *U.S. Private*, pg. 2225
KABA JAYA SECURITY SDN. BHD.—See dormakaba Holding AG; *Int'l*, pg. 2179
KALTY & SALIOS SALES INC.; *U.S. Private*, pg. 2258
KANEBRIDGE CORPORATION; *U.S. Private*, pg. 2260
KASS INDUSTRIAL SUPPLY CORP.; *U.S. Private*, pg. 2264
KELLEY BROS; *U.S. Private*, pg. 2275
KENNETH CROSBY, LLC—See DXP Enterprises, Inc.; *U.S. Public*, pg. 697
KITCHEN CRAFT OF CANADA—See MasterBrand, Inc.; *U.S. Public*, pg. 1394
KOMAR SCREW CORP.; *U.S. Private*, pg. 2342
KVT-TEHNIKA PRITRJEVANJA, D.O.O.—See Bossard Holding AG; *Int'l*, pg. 1117
LA FORCE LLC—See DNS Capital, LLC; *U.S. Private*, pg. 1249
LAMAN BV—See Descours & Cabaud SA; *Int'l*, pg. 2044
LAWSON PRODUCTS, INC.—See Distribution Solutions Group, Inc.; *U.S. Public*, pg. 668
LAWSON PRODUCTS, INC.—See Distribution Solutions Group, Inc.; *U.S. Public*, pg. 668
LEGGETT & PLATT ADMINISTRADORA, S.A. DE C.V.—See Leggett & Platt, Incorporated; *U.S. Public*, pg. 1303
LEGGETT & PLATT ASIA LIMITED—See Leggett & Platt, Incorporated; *U.S. Public*, pg. 1303
LEGGETT & PLATT CANADA CO.—See Leggett & Platt, Incorporated; *U.S. Public*, pg. 1303
LEGGETT & PLATT COMPONENTS COMPANY, INC.—See Leggett & Platt, Incorporated; *U.S. Public*, pg. 1303
LEGGETT & PLATT DE MEXICO, S. DE R.L. DE C.V.—See Leggett & Platt, Incorporated; *U.S. Public*, pg. 1303
LEGGETT & PLATT (SHANGHAI) CO. LTD.—See Leggett & Platt, Incorporated; *U.S. Public*, pg. 1302
L.E. SMITH CO.; *U.S. Private*, pg. 2365
LIBERTY HARDWARE MANUFACTURING CORPORATION—See Masco Corporation; *U.S. Public*, pg. 1390
LOCKEY CORP.—See Ingersoll Rand Inc.; *U.S. Public*, pg. 1122
MACLEAN FASTENERS, LLC—See MacLean-Fogg Company; *U.S. Private*, pg. 2537
MALCO INTERNATIONAL—See Malco Products, Inc.; *U.S. Private*, pg. 2556
MARKET HARDWARE LIMITED—See Grafton Group plc; *Int'l*, pg. 3051
MASSFORD (HONG KONG) LIMITED—See E. Bon Holdings Ltd; *Int'l*, pg. 2250
MASTER LOCK EUROPE, S.A.S.—See Fortune Brands Innovations, Inc.; *U.S. Public*, pg. 873
MCGARD INC.; *U.S. Private*, pg. 2634
MCG METRIC COMPONENTS GMBH—See Metric & Multistandard Components Corporation; *U.S. Private*, pg. 2684
MELCO INDUSTRIAL SUPPLIES CO., LIMITED—See Cosmos Machinery Enterprises Limited; *Int'l*, pg. 1813
METABO CORPORATION; *U.S. Private*, pg. 2679
METALPLAST-CZESTOCHOWA SP. Z O.O.—See Groupe SFPI SA; *Int'l*, pg. 3111
MICRO PLASTICS INTERNATIONAL S.A. DE C.V. DE R.L.—See Essentra plc; *Int'l*, pg. 2511
MID-STATE BOLT & NUT CO., INC.; *U.S. Private*, pg. 2709
MID-STATES BOLT & SCREW CO.—See MPE Partners, LLC; *U.S. Private*, pg. 2803
MIDWEST FASTENER CORPORATION; *U.S. Private*, pg. 2721
MID-WEST WHOLESALE HARDWARE CO.—See High Road Capital Partners, LLC; *U.S. Private*, pg. 1936
M&M SALES INCORPORATED; *U.S. Private*, pg. 2525
MONKS & CRANE INDUSTRIAL GROUP LIMITED—See GIL Investments Ltd.; *Int'l*, pg. 2973
MONROE HARDWARE COMPANY; *U.S. Private*, pg. 2773
MORGAN & SAMPSON USA; *U.S. Private*, pg. 2783
MOTOR CITY FASTENER, LLC—See Kian Capital Partners, LLC; *U.S. Private*, pg. 2302
MOTOR CITY FASTENER, LLC—See Oakland Standard Co., LLC; *U.S. Private*, pg. 2985
MUDD-LYMAN SALES & SERVICES CORPORATION; *U.S. Private*, pg. 2810
MULLER CONSTRUCTION SUPPLY; *U.S. Private*, pg. 2811
NATIONAL-GENERAL SUPPLY, INC.; *U.S. Private*, pg. 2865
NATIONAL PRECISION—See EACO Corporation; *U.S. Public*, pg. 701
NAVIMRO CO., LTD.—See W.W. Grainger, Inc.; *U.S. Public*, pg. 2320
ND ELECTRONICS (KUNSHAN) CO., LTD.—See H.B. Fuller Company; *U.S. Public*, pg. 978
ND INDUSTRIES A.S.—See H.B. Fuller Company; *U.S. Public*, pg. 978

423710 — HARDWARE MERCHANT W...

NEU'S BUILDING CENTER, INC.; *U.S. Private*, pg. 2890
NHR, LLC; *U.S. Private*, pg. 2924
NORBAR TORQUE TOOLS PRIVATE LIMITED—See Snap-on Incorporated; *U.S. Public*, pg. 1898
NORBAR TORQUE TOOLS (SHANGHAI) LTD—See Snap-on Incorporated; *U.S. Public*, pg. 1898
NORBY DISTRIBUTING CO.; *U.S. Private*, pg. 2935
NORMBAU BESCHLAGE UND AUSSTATTUNGS GMBH—See Ingersoll Rand Inc.; *U.S. Public*, pg. 1122
OHIO POWER TOOL; *U.S. Private*, pg. 3005
OKEE INDUSTRIES INC.; *U.S. Private*, pg. 3007
OMAHA FASTENER, INC.—See Birmingham Fastener & Supply Inc., *U.S. Private*, pg. 564
OOO FISCHER BEFESTIGUNGSSYSTEME RUS—See fischerwerke GmbH & Co. KG; *Int'l*, pg. 2692
OPTIMAS OE SOLUTIONS GMBH—See AIP, LLC; *U.S. Private*, pg. 134
OPTIMAS OE SOLUTIONS LTD.—See AIP, LLC; *U.S. Private*, pg. 134
ORGILL, INC.; *U.S. Private*, pg. 3041
OUTWATER PLASTIC INDUSTRIES, INC.—See Foga System International AB; *Int'l*, pg. 2721
PACKAGING INCORPORATED—See TruArc Partners, L.P.; *U.S. Private*, pg. 4245
PARKER PGI—See HM International; *U.S. Private*, pg. 1954
PICARD SERRURES—See Groupe SFPI SA; *Int'l*, pg. 3111
PINNACLE DOOR & HARDWARE, INC.—See Platinum Equity, LLC; *U.S. Private*, pg. 3209
PORTEOUS FASTENER COMPANY INC.; *U.S. Private*, pg. 3231
POSNER INDUSTRIES INC.; *U.S. Private*, pg. 3234
PREFERRED FURNITURE COMPONENTS INC.; *U.S. Private*, pg. 3248
PRIME-LINE PRODUCTS COMPANY; *U.S. Private*, pg. 3262
PROCTOR ACE HARDWARE NEPTUNE BEACH—See Ace Hardware Corporation; *U.S. Private*, pg. 56
PRO FASTENING SYSTEMS INC.; *U.S. Private*, pg. 3269
PRO GROUP, INC.; *U.S. Private*, pg. 3269
PROSOUTH FASTENER—See Birmingham Fastener & Supply Inc.; *U.S. Private*, pg. 564
PSM CELADA FASTENERS S.R.L.—See Bulten AB; *Int'l*, pg. 1214
PSS WEST, INC.—See W.W. Grainger, Inc.; *U.S. Public*, pg. 2320
PT FEDSIN REKAYASA PRATAMA—See Federal International (2000) Ltd; *Int'l*, pg. 2630
QUALITY BOLT & SCREW CORP.; *U.S. Private*, pg. 3318
R3 METRO SOUTH TEC—See Bunzl plc; *Int'l*, pg. 1217
RAPISCAN SECURITY PRODUCTS (USA), INC.—See OSI Systems, Inc.; *U.S. Public*, pg. 1622
RCH DISTRIBUTORS INC.—See Riechman Crosby Hays Company, Inc.; *U.S. Private*, pg. 3434
REGITAR U.S.A., INC.; *U.S. Private*, pg. 3389
ROBERT SKEELS & CO.; *U.S. Private*, pg. 3459
ROCK ISLAND CORPORATION; *U.S. Private*, pg. 3465
ROYAL UNITED CORPORATION; *U.S. Private*, pg. 3494
SANDOVAL CRUZ COMPANY; *U.S. Private*, pg. 3544
SCHILLER HARDWARE INC.; *U.S. Private*, pg. 3565
SCHULL CONSTRUCTION CO.; *U.S. Private*, pg. 3570
SEWELL HARDWARE CO., INC.; *U.S. Private*, pg. 3620
SHANGHAI ESTIC CO., LTD.—See Estic Corporation; *Int'l*, pg. 2518
SHANGHAI TONGSHENG TRADING CO.,LTD.—See Chun Yu Works & Co., Ltd.; *Int'l*, pg. 1596
SHANGHAI UCHEE HARDWARE PRODUCTS CO., LTD—See Chun Yu Works & Co., Ltd.; *Int'l*, pg. 1596
SHANNON HARDWARE CO. LTD; *U.S. Private*, pg. 3625
SHEREX FASTENING SOLUTIONS, LLC—See Tinicum Enterprises, Inc.; *U.S. Private*, pg. 4174
SIMPSON STRONG-TIE ASIA LIMITED—See Simpson Manufacturing Company, Inc.; *U.S. Public*, pg. 1883
SIMPSON STRONG-TIE AUSTRALIA PTY LIMITED—See Simpson Manufacturing Company, Inc.; *U.S. Public*, pg. 1883
SIMPSON STRONG-TIE CANADA, LIMITED—See Simpson Manufacturing Company, Inc.; *U.S. Public*, pg. 1883
SIMPSON STRONG-TIE EUROPE EURL—See Simpson Manufacturing Company, Inc.; *U.S. Public*, pg. 1883
SIMPSON STRONG-TIE GMBH—See Simpson Manufacturing Company, Inc.; *U.S. Public*, pg. 1883
SIMPSON STRONG-TIE INTERNATIONAL, INC.—See Simpson Manufacturing Company, Inc.; *U.S. Public*, pg. 1883
SIMPSON STRONG-TIE (NEW ZEALAND) LIMITED—See Simpson Manufacturing Company, Inc.; *U.S. Public*, pg. 1883
SIMPSON STRONG-TIE SP.Z.O.O.—See Simpson Manufacturing Company, Inc.; *U.S. Public*, pg. 1883
SNAP-ON INCORPORATED; *U.S. Public*, pg. 1897
SOONER BOLT & SUPPLY INC.; *U.S. Private*, pg. 3715
SOUTHERN FASTENERS & SUPPLY, INC.—See Park-Ohio Holdings Corp.; *U.S. Public*, pg. 1640
S. PARKER HARDWARE MANUFACTURING CORP.; *U.S. Private*, pg. 3515
SPOKANE HARDWARE SUPPLY, INC.; *U.S. Private*, pg. 3759
S&S BUILDERS HARDWARE CO.; *U.S. Private*, pg. 3513
STANLEY BLACK & DECKER LIMITED—See Stanley Black & Decker, Inc.; *U.S. Public*, pg. 1934
STANLEY BLACK & DECKER UK LIMITED—See Stanley Black & Decker, Inc.; *U.S. Public*, pg. 1934
STANLEY FASTENING SYSTEMS POLAND SP. Z O.O.—See Stanley Black & Decker, Inc.; *U.S. Public*, pg. 1935
STANLEY GRUNDSTUECKSVERWALTUNGS GMBH—See Stanley Black & Decker, Inc.; *U.S. Public*, pg. 1935
STAR SALES & DISTRIBUTING; *U.S. Private*, pg. 3785
STAR STAINLESS SCREW CO.; *U.S. Private*, pg. 3785
STEEL ETC., LLP; *U.S. Private*, pg. 3796
SUNNEN S.R.O.—See Sunnen Products Company; *U.S. Private*, pg. 3868
SUPPLYCORE INC.; *U.S. Private*, pg. 3882
SUPPLY TECHNOLOGIES CR S.R.O.—See Park-Ohio Holdings Corp.; *U.S. Public*, pg. 1640
SUPPLY TECHNOLOGIES—See Park-Ohio Holdings Corp.; *U.S. Public*, pg. 1640
SURE - LOC HARDWARE, INC.—See ASSA ABLOY AB; *Int'l*, pg. 640
S.W. ANDERSON COMPANY, INC.; *U.S. Private*, pg. 3519
SWESAFE AB—See ASSA ABLOY AB; *Int'l*, pg. 640
SYNVENTIVE MOLDING SOLUTIONS BV—See Barnes Group Inc.; *U.S. Public*, pg. 277
SYNVENTIVE MOLDING SOLUTIONS LDA—See Barnes Group Inc.; *U.S. Public*, pg. 277
SYNVENTIVE MOLDING SOLUTIONS LIMITED—See Barnes Group Inc.; *U.S. Public*, pg. 278
SYNVENTIVE MOLDING SOLUTIONS SAS—See Barnes Group Inc.; *U.S. Public*, pg. 278
SYNVENTIVE MOLDING SOLUTIONS S.R.L.—See Barnes Group Inc.; *U.S. Public*, pg. 278
SYNVENTIVE MOLDING SOLUTIONS S.R.O.—See Barnes Group Inc.; *U.S. Public*, pg. 278
TACOMA SCREW PRODUCTS, INC.; *U.S. Private*, pg. 3921
TAYLOR COTTON & RIDLEY INC.; *U.S. Private*, pg. 3939
TECHNIKS, LLC—See Z Capital Group, LLC; *U.S. Private*, pg. 4595
TECHPRO TRADING LIMITED—See E. Bon Holdings Ltd; *Int'l*, pg. 2250
TELFORDS (PORTLAOISE) LIMITED—See Grafton Group plc; *Int'l*, pg. 3051
TEXAS TOOL DISTRIBUTORS INC.; *U.S. Private*, pg. 3977
TFI/EPI LLC; *U.S. Private*, pg. 3979
THRUWAY FASTENERS INC.; *U.S. Private*, pg. 4165
TIMBERLINE FASTENERS, INC.; *U.S. Private*, pg. 4172
TOMARCO CONTRACTOR SPECIALTIES; *U.S. Private*, pg. 4183
TORQUE CONTROL SPECIALISTS PTY LTD—See Snap-on Incorporated; *U.S. Public*, pg. 1899
TOWNSEND DOOR & HARDWARE—See MSCO Inc.; *U.S. Private*, pg. 2806
TRELOCK ASIA PACIFIC LIMITED—See Allegion Public Limited Company; *Int'l*, pg. 335
TRICO AUTOMOTIVE SYSTEMS CO., LTD—See Crowne Group LLC; *U.S. Private*, pg. 1112
TULLAMORE HARDWARE LIMITED—See Grafton Group plc; *Int'l*, pg. 3051
TWIN CITY HARDWARE COMPANY; *U.S. Private*, pg. 4265
UCEM SISTEMAS DE SEGURIDAD S.A.—See Groupe SFPI SA; *Int'l*, pg. 3111
UNITED HARDWARE DISTRIBUTING CO.; *U.S. Private*, pg. 4293
UNITED MANUFACTURERS SUPPLIES, INC.; *U.S. Private*, pg. 4294
VINEX VIETNAM CO., LTD.—See FUJISOFT INCORPORATED; *Int'l*, pg. 2830
WALCRO, INC.—See ShoreView Industries, LLC; *U.S. Private*, pg. 3642
WALLACE HARDWARE COMPANY, INC.; *U.S. Private*, pg. 4430
WESCO AIRCRAFT CANADA INC.—See Platinum Equity, LLC; *U.S. Private*, pg. 3210
WESCO AIRCRAFT HARDWARE CORP.—See Platinum Equity, LLC; *U.S. Private*, pg. 3210
WESTERN TOOL SUPPLY CORPORATION; *U.S. Private*, pg. 4497
WFS LTD.—See W.W. Grainger, Inc.; *U.S. Public*, pg. 2320
WFS (USA) LTD.—See W.W. Grainger, Inc.; *U.S. Public*, pg. 2320
WHARTON HARDWARE & SUPPLY; *U.S. Private*, pg. 4504
WHITE CAP CONSTRUCTION SUPPLY, INC.—See Clayton, Dubilier & Rice, LLC; *U.S. Private*, pg. 930
WHITE CAP, L.P.—See Clayton, Dubilier & Rice, LLC; *U.S. Private*, pg. 930
WINDSOR FACTORY SUPPLY INC.—See W.W. Grainger, Inc.; *U.S. Public*, pg. 2320
WINZER CORPORATION—See ShoreView Industries, LLC; *U.S. Private*, pg. 3642
WOODIE'S DIY LIMITED—See Grafton Group plc; *Int'l*, pg. 3051
YALE-CORBIN CANADA LIMITED—See ASSA ABLOY AB; *Int'l*, pg. 637
ZAO FISKARS BRANDS RUS—See Fiskars Oyj Abp; *Int'l*, pg. 2694

423720 — PLUMBING AND HEATING EQUIPMENT AND SUPPLIES (HYDRONICS) MERCHANT WHOLESALERS

AARON & COMPANY INC.; *U.S. Private*, pg. 32
ABB S.A./N.V.—See ABB Ltd.; *Int'l*, pg. 54
ABLE DISTRIBUTING CO. INC.—See Blackfriars Corp.; *U.S. Private*, pg. 575
ABM INTERNATIONAL LIMITED; *Int'l*, pg. 63
A-BOY PLUMBING & ELECTRICAL SUPPLY; *U.S. Private*, pg. 22
ACTION PLUMBING SUPPLY CO.; *U.S. Private*, pg. 67
ACTIVE PLUMBING SUPPLY CO; *U.S. Private*, pg. 70
ADEL WHOLESALERS, INC.; *U.S. Private*, pg. 77
AES DISTRIBUTED ENERGY, INC.—See The AES Corporation; *U.S. Public*, pg. 2030
AFFILIATED STEAM EQUIPMENT COMPANY; *U.S. Private*, pg. 122
AFFILIATED STEAM EQUIPMENT CO. - WISCONSIN—See Affiliated Steam Equipment Company; *U.S. Private*, pg. 122
AF SUPPLY CORP.; *U.S. Private*, pg. 121
AGROVOJVODINA EXPORT - IMPORT A.D.; *Int'l*, pg. 221
AHLSELL APS—See Ahlsell AB; *Int'l*, pg. 223
AIR PURCHASES INCORPORATED; *U.S. Private*, pg. 139
AKG DO BRASIL—See Autokuhler GmbH & Co. KG; *Int'l*, pg. 727
AKG FRANCE S.A.S—See Autokuhler GmbH & Co. KG; *Int'l*, pg. 727
AKG JAPAN LTD.—See Autokuhler GmbH & Co. KG; *Int'l*, pg. 727
AKG KOREA LTD.—See Autokuhler GmbH & Co. KG; *Int'l*, pg. 727
AKG NORTH AMERICAN OPERATIONS, INC.—See Autokuhler GmbH & Co. KG; *Int'l*, pg. 727
AKG TERMOTEKNIK SISTEMLER SAN. VE TIC. LTD.—See Autokuhler GmbH & Co. KG; *Int'l*, pg. 727
AKG UK LIMITED—See Autokuhler GmbH & Co. KG; *Int'l*, pg. 727
ALFA LAVAL AALBORG INC.—See Alfa Laval AB; *Int'l*, pg. 309
ALFA LAVAL NORDIC A/S—See Alfa Laval AB; *Int'l*, pg. 310
ALFA LAVAL SIA—See Alfa Laval AB; *Int'l*, pg. 311
ALFA LAVAL SPOL S.R.O.—See Alfa Laval AB; *Int'l*, pg. 311
ALLIANCE MANUFACTURERS REPRESENTATIVES INC.; *U.S. Private*, pg. 183
ALLIED SYSTEMS INC.; *U.S. Private*, pg. 188
ALL-TEX PIPE & SUPPLY, INC.; *U.S. Private*, pg. 174
ALTECNIC LTD.—See Caleffi S.p.A.; *Int'l*, pg. 1263
AMERICAN COPPER & BRASS, LLC—See Worth Investment Group, LLC; *U.S. Private*, pg. 4570
AMERICAN INTERNATIONAL SUPPLY INC.; *U.S. Private*, pg. 238
AMERICAN STANDARD CANADA, INC.—See Sun Capital Partners, Inc.; *U.S. Private*, pg. 3858
AMG IDEALCAST SOLAR CORPORATION—See AMG Critical Materials N.V.; *Int'l*, pg. 425
AMIAD FILTRATION SYSTEMS INDIA PVT LTD—See Amiad Water Systems Ltd.; *Int'l*, pg. 427
AMIAD USA INC.—See Amiad Water Systems Ltd.; *Int'l*, pg. 427
APEX SUPPLY COMPANY; *U.S. Private*, pg. 293
APPLIED THERMAL SYSTEMS—See Gryphon Investors, LLC; *U.S. Private*, pg. 1799
APR SUPPLY CO.; *U.S. Private*, pg. 300
ARDENTE SUPPLY CO. INC.; *U.S. Private*, pg. 317
ARIZONA PARTSMASTER INC.; *U.S. Private*, pg. 324
ASAP INDUSTRIAL SUPPLY, INC.—See Winsupply, Inc.; *U.S. Private*, pg. 4544
AS FEB—See Ahlsell AB; *Int'l*, pg. 223
ASTIVITA LIMITED; *Int'l*, pg. 655
ATLANTIC COASTAL SUPPLY, INC—See Winsupply, Inc.; *U.S. Private*, pg. 4545
ATLANTIC PLUMBING SUPPLY CORP.; *U.S. Private*, pg. 374
ATLAS COPCO COMPRESSOR AB—See Atlas Copco AB; *Int'l*, pg. 678
AUBURN SUPPLY CO. INC.; *U.S. Private*, pg. 385
AVF GULF JLT—See AVK Holding A/S; *Int'l*, pg. 746
AVK ARMADAN SP. Z O.O.—See AVK Holding A/S; *Int'l*, pg. 746
AVK BELGIUM NV—See AVK Holding A/S; *Int'l*, pg. 746
AVK FINLAND OY—See AVK Holding A/S; *Int'l*, pg. 746
AVK FLOW CONTROL A/S—See AVK Holding A/S; *Int'l*, pg. 746
AVK FRANCE S.A.S.—See AVK Holding A/S; *Int'l*, pg. 746
AVK INDUSTRIAL PTY LTD—See AVK Holding A/S; *Int'l*, pg. 747
AVK INDUSTRIAL VALVE SINGAPORE PTE. LTD.—See AVK Holding A/S; *Int'l*, pg. 747
AVK ITALIA S.R.L.—See AVK Holding A/S; *Int'l*, pg. 747
AVK NEDERLAND B.V.—See AVK Holding A/S; *Int'l*, pg. 747
AVK NORGE AS—See AVK Holding A/S; *Int'l*, pg. 747
AVK PHILIPPINES INC.—See AVK Holding A/S; *Int'l*, pg. 747
AVK SVERIGE AB—See AVK Holding A/S; *Int'l*, pg. 747
AVK UK LIMITED—See AVK Holding A/S; *Int'l*, pg. 747

N.A.I.C.S. INDEX

423720 — PLUMBING AND HEATIN...

AVK VALVES (BEIJING) CO LTD—See AVK Holding A/S; *Int'l*, pg. 747
AVK VALVES COMPANY HONG KONG LTD.—See AVK Holding A/S; *Int'l*, pg. 747
AVK VALVES KOREA CO., LTD.—See AVK Holding A/S; *Int'l*, pg. 747
AVK VALVES (SHANGHAI) CO. LTD.—See AVK Holding A/S; *Int'l*, pg. 747
AVK VALVES SOUTHERN AFRICA PTY. LTD.—See AVK Holding A/S; *Int'l*, pg. 747
AVK VALVULAS DO BRASIL LTDA.—See AVK Holding A/S; *Int'l*, pg. 747
AVK VALVULAS S.A.—See AVK Holding A/S; *Int'l*, pg. 747
AVK VIETNAM CO. LTD.—See AVK Holding A/S; *Int'l*, pg. 747
AVK VOD-KA A.S.—See AVK Holding A/S; *Int'l*, pg. 747
BABCOCK & WILCOX BEIJING CO., LTD.—See Babcock & Wilcox Enterprises, Inc.; *U.S. Public*, pg. 262
BABCOCK & WILCOX LOIBL GMBH—See Deutsche Invest Capital Partners GmbH; *Int'l*, pg. 2066
BABCOCK & WILCOX VOLUND AB—See AUCTUS Capital Partners AG; *Int'l*, pg. 700
BARTLE & GIBSON CO. LTD.; *Int'l*, pg. 870
BATAILLE MATERIAUX; *Int'l*, pg. 889
BATISTYL PRODUCTION; *Int'l*, pg. 889
BAXI AB—See BDR Thermea Group B.V.; *Int'l*, pg. 930
BAXI BELGIUM SA/NV—See BDR Thermea Group B.V.; *Int'l*, pg. 930
BAXI CALEFACCION, SLU—See BDR Thermea Group B.V.; *Int'l*, pg. 930
BAXI HEATING (SLOVAKIA) S.R.O—See BDR Thermea Group B.V.; *Int'l*, pg. 930
BAXI INNOTECH GMBH—See BDR Thermea Group B.V.; *Int'l*, pg. 930
BAXI ROMANIA SA—See BDR Thermea Group B.V.; *Int'l*, pg. 930
BAXI-SENERTEC UK LTD—See BDR Thermea Group B.V.; *Int'l*, pg. 930
BAXI SISTEMAS DE AQUECIMENTO UNIPESSOAL LDA—See BDR Thermea Group B.V.; *Int'l*, pg. 930
BAYSHORE SUPPLY & LIGHTS; *U.S. Private*, pg. 497
BDR THERMEA (CZECH REPUBLIC) S.R.O.—See BDR Thermea Group B.V.; *Int'l*, pg. 930
BDR THERMEA (TIANJIN) CO. LTD—See BDR Thermea Group B.V.; *Int'l*, pg. 930
BELLIARD MATERIAUX; *Int'l*, pg. 967
BELL PUMP SERVICE COMPANY; *U.S. Private*, pg. 519
BEST PLUMBING TILE & STONE INC.; *U.S. Private*, pg. 543
BEST PLUMBING TILE & STONE INC.—See Best Plumbing Tile & Stone Inc.; *U.S. Private*, pg. 543
BEST PLUMBING TILE & STONE INC.—See Best Plumbing Tile & Stone Inc.; *U.S. Private*, pg. 543
BIRWELCO USA INC.—See Boustead Singapore Limited; *Int'l*, pg. 1120
BLACKMAN PLUMBING SUPPLY CO. INC., MINEOLA BRANCH—See Blackman Plumbing Supply Co. Inc.; *U.S. Private*, pg. 576
BLACKMAN PLUMBING SUPPLY CO. INC.; *U.S. Private*, pg. 576
BLACKMAN PLUMBING SUPPLY CO. INC.—See Blackman Plumbing Supply Co. Inc.; *U.S. Private*, pg. 576
BLACKMAN PLUMBING SUPPLY CO. INC.—See Blackman Plumbing Supply Co. Inc.; *U.S. Private*, pg. 576
BLACKMAN PLUMBING SUPPLY CO. INC.—See Blackman Plumbing Supply Co. Inc.; *U.S. Private*, pg. 576
BLACKMAN PLUMBING SUPPLY CO. INC.—See Blackman Plumbing Supply Co. Inc.; *U.S. Private*, pg. 576
BLACKMAN PLUMBING SUPPLY CO. INC.—See Blackman Plumbing Supply Co. Inc.; *U.S. Private*, pg. 576
BLACKMAN PLUMBING SUPPLY CO. INC.—See Blackman Plumbing Supply Co. Inc.; *U.S. Private*, pg. 576
BLACKMAN PLUMBING SUPPLY CO. INC.—See Blackman Plumbing Supply Co. Inc.; *U.S. Private*, pg. 576
BLACKMAN PLUMBING SUPPLY CO. INC.—See Blackman Plumbing Supply Co. Inc.; *U.S. Private*, pg. 576
BLACKMAN PLUMBING SUPPLY CO. INC.—See Blackman Plumbing Supply Co. Inc.; *U.S. Private*, pg. 576
BLAKE EQUIPMENT COMPANY INC.; *U.S. Private*, pg. 578
BLAZE KING INDUSTRIES CANADA LTD.—See Decisive Dividend Corporation; *Int'l*, pg. 2001
BLAZE KING INDUSTRIES INC.—See Decisive Dividend Corporation; *Int'l*, pg. 2001
BLUEWATER AB; *Int'l*, pg. 1075
BOLAND TRANE SERVICES INC.; *U.S. Private*, pg. 610
BOND PLUMBING SUPPLY INCORPORATED; *U.S. Private*, pg. 613
BRIGGS INC.; *U.S. Private*, pg. 651
BRITA (USA), INC.—See The Clorox Company; *U.S. Public*, pg. 2062
BROOKS FORGINGS LTD.; *Int'l*, pg. 1194
BROSSETTE SAS—See Compagnie de Saint-Gobain SA; *Int'l*, pg. 1724
BRUCE SUPPLY CORP.—See Ferguson plc; *Int'l*, pg. 2637
BURKE ENGINEERING COMPANY; *U.S. Private*, pg. 688
BUTTNER ENERGIE- UND TROCKNUNGSTECHNIK GMBH—See G. Siempelkamp GmbH & Co. KG; *Int'l*, pg. 2864

CALEFFI ARMATUREN GMBH—See Caleffi S.p.A.; *Int'l*, pg. 1263
CALEFFI FRANCE CONSULTING—See Caleffi S.p.A.; *Int'l*, pg. 1263
CALEFFI INTERNATIONA N.V.—See Caleffi S.p.A.; *Int'l*, pg. 1263
CALEFFI LDA.—See Caleffi S.p.A.; *Int'l*, pg. 1263
CALEFFI NORTH AMERICA, INC.—See Caleffi S.p.A.; *Int'l*, pg. 1263
CALEFFI S.P.A.; *Int'l*, pg. 1263
CAL-STEAM, INC.—See Ferguson plc; *Int'l*, pg. 2637
CAPITOL DISTRICT SUPPLY CO. INC.—See Watsco, Inc.; *U.S. Public*, pg. 2336
CAPITOL GROUP INC.; *U.S. Private*, pg. 744
C BENNETT BUILDING SUPPLY INC.; *U.S. Private*, pg. 701
CB & K SUPPLY INC.; *U.S. Private*, pg. 796
CB SUPPLIES LTD.—See American Granby, Inc.; *U.S. Private*, pg. 235
CC DISTRIBUTORS INC; *U.S. Private*, pg. 799
CCI THERMAL TECHNOLOGIES TEXAS, INC.—See Thermon Group Holdings, Inc.; *U.S. Public*, pg. 2155
CENTRAL SUPPLY CO., INC.; *U.S. Private*, pg. 825
CENTRAL WHOLESALERS, INC.; *U.S. Private*, pg. 826
CEPEX FRANCE S.A.S.—See Fluidra SA; *Int'l*, pg. 2714
CEPEX GMBH—See Fluidra SA; *Int'l*, pg. 2714
CEPEX PORTUGAL, LDA—See Fluidra SA; *Int'l*, pg. 2714
CEPEX S.R.L.—See Fluidra SA; *Int'l*, pg. 2714
C&E SERVICES INC.; *U.S. Public*, pg. 702
CHAUX ET ENDUITS DE SAINT ASTIER; *Int'l*, pg. 1457
CHRIS-MORE INCORPORATED; *U.S. Private*, pg. 890
CICSA INDUSTRIALES DEL CALOR S.L.—See Arbonia AG; *Int'l*, pg. 538
CITY PLUMBING & ELECTRIC SUPPLY COMPANY; *U.S. Private*, pg. 906
CKA SALES L.L.C.; *U.S. Private*, pg. 909
CK TRADING CO., LTD.—See CK SAN-ETSU Co., Ltd.; *Int'l*, pg. 1639
CLAYTON SISTEMAS DE VAPOR, S. L.—See Clayton Industries Co.; *U.S. Private*, pg. 918
CLEAN ENERGY (THAILAND) CO., LTD.—See Clenergy (Xiamen) Technology Co., Ltd.; *Int'l*, pg. 1658
CLENERGY AMERICA INC—See Clenergy (Xiamen) Technology Co., Ltd.; *Int'l*, pg. 1658
CLENERGY EUROPE LIMITED—See Clenergy (Xiamen) Technology Co., Ltd.; *Int'l*, pg. 1658
CLENERGY PTY LTD—See Clenergy (Xiamen) Technology Co., Ltd.; *Int'l*, pg. 1658
CLEVELAND PLUMBING SUPPLY CO., INC.; *U.S. Private*, pg. 941
CMC SUPPLY INC.; *U.S. Private*, pg. 950
CMS INFRA TRADING SDN. BHD.—See Cahya Mata Sarawak Berhad; *Int'l*, pg. 1251
COLE INDUSTRIAL, INC.; *U.S. Private*, pg. 966
COLLINS PIPE & SUPPLY CO., INC.; *U.S. Private*, pg. 969
COMAP HELLAS S.A.—See Aalberts N.V.; *Int'l*, pg. 33
COMAP (UK) LIMITED—See Aalberts N.V.; *Int'l*, pg. 33
COMFORT PRODUCTS DISTRIBUTING LLC—See Watsco, Inc.; *U.S. Public*, pg. 2336
COMMERCIAL PIPE & SUPPLY CORP.; *U.S. Private*, pg. 984
COMPTOIR DES FERS ET METAUX SA (CFM)—See Ferguson plc; *Int'l*, pg. 2637
CONNOR CO. INC.; *U.S. Private*, pg. 1018
CONSOLIDATED SUPPLY CO.; *U.S. Private*, pg. 1022
CONSOLIDATED SUPPLY CO.—See Consolidated Supply Co.; *U.S. Private*, pg. 1022
CONSOLIDATED SUPPLY CO.—See Consolidated Supply Co.; *U.S. Private*, pg. 1022
CONSOLIDATED WATER (BAHAMAS) LIMITED—See Consolidated Water Co. Ltd.; *Int'l*, pg. 1771
CONSOLIDATED WATER (BELIZE) LIMITED—See Belize Water Services Limited; *Int'l*, pg. 965
CONTRACTORS PIPE & SUPPLY CORP.; *U.S. Private*, pg. 1032
COOLGIANTS AG; *Int'l*, pg. 1789
COONEY BROTHERS INC—See Vergani & Associates, LLC; *U.S. Private*, pg. 4359
CORR TECH, INC.; *U.S. Private*, pg. 1058
CRANE CANADA CO.—See Groupe Deschenes Inc.; *Int'l*, pg. 3101
CRAWFORD SUPPLY COMPANY; *U.S. Private*, pg. 1086
CRAWFORD SUPPLY—See Crawford Supply Company; *U.S. Private*, pg. 1086
CREATE CORPORATION; *Int'l*, pg. 1831
CREGGER COMPANY INC.; *U.S. Private*, pg. 1092
CRESCENT PLUMBING SUPPLY CO; *U.S. Private*, pg. 1094
CREST/GOOD MANUFACTURING CO.; *U.S. Private*, pg. 1096
CUENOD S.A.S.—See Ariston Holding N.V.; *Int'l*, pg. 567
CUNNINGHAM SUPPLY INCORPORATED; *U.S. Private*, pg. 1123
DAMPER TECHNOLOGY INDIA PVT. LTD.—See AVK Holding A/S; *Int'l*, pg. 747
DANCO INC.; *U.S. Private*, pg. 1153
DAVID GOODING INC.; *U.S. Private*, pg. 1170
D.D. PROMOTERM S.R.L.—See BDR Thermea Group B.V.; *Int'l*, pg. 930

DDR AMERICAS INC.—See BDR Thermea Group B.V.; *Int'l*, pg. 930
DEACON INDUSTRIAL SUPPLY COMPANY INC.—See The Macomb Group, Inc.; *U.S. Private*, pg. 4073
DE DIETRICH REMEHA GMBH—See BDR Thermea Group B.V.; *Int'l*, pg. 930
DE DIETRICH TECHNIKA GRZEWCZA SP. Z O.O—See BDR Thermea Group B.V.; *Int'l*, pg. 931
DE DIETRICH THERMIQUE IBERIA S.L.U—See BDR Thermea Group B.V.; *Int'l*, pg. 931
DE DIETRICH THERMIQUE, S.A.S.—See BDR Thermea Group B.V.; *Int'l*, pg. 931
DELTA FAUCET COMPANY—See Masco Corporation; *U.S. Public*, pg. 1391
DELWOOD SUPPLY COMPANY—See Progressive Plumbing Supply, Co.; *U.S. Private*, pg. 3279
DESCHENES & FILS LTEE—See Groupe Deschenes Inc.; *Int'l*, pg. 3102
D.H. ADAMS COMPANY, INC. - LEOMINSTER—See D.H. Adams Company, Inc.; *U.S. Private*, pg. 1142
D.H. ADAMS COMPANY, INC.; *U.S. Private*, pg. 1142
DI-SEP SYSTEMS INTERNATIONAL—See RLR, Inc.; *U.S. Private*, pg. 3451
DIVERSEY ACTING OFF-SHORE CAPITAL MANAGEMENT LIMITED LIABILITY COMPANY—See Sealed Air Corporation; *U.S. Public*, pg. 1852
DIVERSEY ESPANA PRODUCTION, S.L.—See Sealed Air Corporation; *U.S. Public*, pg. 1852
DIVERSEY FRANCE SERVICES S.A.S.—See Sealed Air Corporation; *U.S. Public*, pg. 1852
DIVERSEY GERMANY PRODUCTION OHG—See Sealed Air Corporation; *U.S. Public*, pg. 1852
DIVERSEY HELLAS SOCIETE ANONYME CLEANING AND TRADING SYSTEMS—See Sealed Air Corporation; *U.S. Public*, pg. 1852
DIVERSEY HUNGARY MANUFACTURE AND TRADE LIMITED LIABILITY COMPANY—See Sealed Air Corporation; *U.S. Public*, pg. 1852
DIVERSEY SVERIGE AB—See Sealed Air Corporation; *U.S. Public*, pg. 1853
DIVERSEY SWITZERLAND PRODUCTION GMBH—See Sealed Air Corporation; *U.S. Public*, pg. 1853
DOWAL PLUMBING SUPPLY CO INC—See F.W. Webb Company; *U.S. Private*, pg. 1457
DOWNEAST ENERGY—See NGL Energy Partners LP; *U.S. Public*, pg. 1527
DURR UNIVERSAL EUROPE LTD.—See Durr AG; *Int'l*, pg. 2231
DURR UNIVERSAL S. DE R.L. DE C.V.—See Durr AG; *Int'l*, pg. 2231
DURST CORPORATION; *U.S. Private*, pg. 1294
EAGLE EQUIPMENT COMPANY INC.—See Kenny Pipe & Supply, Inc.; *U.S. Private*, pg. 2286
EARTHCORE INDUSTRIES LLC.; *U.S. Private*, pg. 1314
EASTERN PENN SUPPLY COMPANY (EPSCO); *U.S. Private*, pg. 1320
ECO ENERGIETECHNIK GMBH—See UGI Corporation; *U.S. Public*, pg. 2222
EGING PHOTOVOLTAIC EUROPE GMBH—See EGing Photovoltaic Technology Co., Ltd.; *Int'l*, pg. 2324
EGING PHOTOVOLTAIC TECHNOLOGY CO., LTD.—See EGing Photovoltaic Technology Co., Ltd.; *Int'l*, pg. 2324
ELECTROLUX PROFESSIONAL BV—See AB Electrolux; *Int'l*, pg. 40
ELECTRO-OIL INTERNATIONAL A/S—See Ferguson plc; *Int'l*, pg. 2638
ELKHART PRODUCTS LIMITED—See Aalberts N.V.; *Int'l*, pg. 34
ELMCO SALES INC.—See Acorn Engineering Company, Inc.; *U.S. Private*, pg. 63
EMCO CORPORATION - BRITISH COLUMBIA—See Blackfriars Corp.; *U.S. Private*, pg. 575
EMCO CORPORATION—See Blackfriars Corp.; *U.S. Private*, pg. 575
EMERSON-SWAN INC.; *U.S. Private*, pg. 1382
ENERGIEWONEN B.V.—See E.ON SE; *Int'l*, pg. 2257
ENGINEERING & EQUIPMENT COMPANY INC.; *U.S. Private*, pg. 1398
EPSCO INTERNATIONAL INC.—See Burelle S.A.; *Int'l*, pg. 1222
ETNA SHARED SERVICES; *U.S. Private*, pg. 1432
EVERETT J. PRESCOTT INC.; *U.S. Private*, pg. 1438
EWING IRRIGATION PRODUCTS INC.; *U.S. Private*, pg. 1444
EXPRESS PIPE & SUPPLY CO. INC.; *U.S. Private*, pg. 1451
FAGER COMPANY; *U.S. Private*, pg. 1461
FAMOUS INDUSTRIES INC.—See Famous Enterprises Inc.; *U.S. Private*, pg. 1471
FARNSWORTH WHOLESALE COMPANY; *U.S. Private*, pg. 1480
FERGUSON ENTERPRISES INC; *U.S. Private*, pg. 1497
FERGUSON ENTERPRISES, INC.—See Ferguson plc; *Int'l*, pg. 2637
FERGUSON ENTERPRISES, INC.—See Ferguson plc; *Int'l*, pg. 2637
FERGUSON ENTERPRISES, INC.—See Ferguson plc; *Int'l*, pg. 2637

423720 — PLUMBING AND HEATIN...

FERGUSON ENTERPRISES, LLC—See Ferguson plc; *Int'l*, pg. 2637
FERGUSON ENTERPRISES—See Ferguson plc; *Int'l*, pg. 2637
FERGUSON SUPPLY CO.; *U.S. Private*, pg. 1497
FERGUSON WATERWORKS—See Ferguson plc; *Int'l*, pg. 2638
FERGUSON WATERWORKS—See Ferguson plc; *Int'l*, pg. 2638
FERGUSON WATERWORKS—See Ferguson plc; *Int'l*, pg. 2638
FILTRATION & CONTROL SYSTEMS PTE LTD.—See Amiad Water Systems Ltd.; *Int'l*, pg. 427
FIRST SUPPLY GROUP INC.—See First Supply LLC; *U.S. Private*, pg. 1529
FIRST SUPPLY LLC - EAU CLAIRE—See First Supply LLC; *U.S. Private*, pg. 1529
FIRST SUPPLY LLC; *U.S. Private*, pg. 1529
FIRST SUPPLY MILWAUKEE INC.—See First Supply LLC; *U.S. Private*, pg. 1529
FIRST SUPPLY—See First Supply LLC; *U.S. Private*, pg. 1529
FLAMCO AG—See Aalberts N.V.; *Int'l*, pg. 34
FLAMCO FLEXCON LTD.—See Aalberts N.V.; *Int'l*, pg. 34
FLAMCO LIMITED—See Aalberts N.V.; *Int'l*, pg. 34
FLOCOR INC.—See Groupe Deschenes Inc.; *Int'l*, pg. 3102
FLORIDA INDUSTRIAL PRODUCTS INC.; *U.S. Private*, pg. 1549
FLO SYSTEMS, INC.—See Bain Capital, LP; *U.S. Private*, pg. 432
FLOWATER, INC.—See Bluewater AB; *Int'l*, pg. 1075
FORRER SUPPLY COMPANY INC.; *U.S. Private*, pg. 1572
FOSHAN HEPWORTH PIPE COMPANY LTD.—See Bharti Enterprises Limited; *Int'l*, pg. 1012
FRANK I. ROUNDS COMPANY; *U.S. Private*, pg. 1594
FRONTIER WATER SYSTEMS, LLC—See Xylem Inc.; *U.S. Public*, pg. 2394
FUSION GROUP HOLDINGS PTY LIMITED—See AVK Holding A/S; *Int'l*, pg. 747
FUSION ROMANIA SRL—See AVK Holding A/S; *Int'l*, pg. 747
FUTURE MANAGEMENT INVESTMENTS B.V.—See Future Pipe Industries Group Ltd.; *Int'l*, pg. 2857
FUTURE PIPE INDUSTRIES B.V.—See Future Pipe Industries Group Ltd.; *Int'l*, pg. 2857
FUTURE PIPE INDUSTRIES, INC.—See Future Pipe Industries Group Ltd.; *Int'l*, pg. 2857
FUTURE PIPE INDUSTRIES LIMITED—See Future Pipe Industries Group Ltd.; *Int'l*, pg. 2857
FUTURE PIPE INDUSTRIES L.L.C.—See Future Pipe Industries Group Ltd.; *Int'l*, pg. 2857
FUTURE PIPE INDUSTRIES L.L.C.—See Future Pipe Industries Group Ltd.; *Int'l*, pg. 2857
FUTURE PIPE INDUSTRIES (PVT) LTD.—See Future Pipe Industries Group Ltd.; *Int'l*, pg. 2857
FUTURE PIPE INDUSTRIES Q.C.J.S.C—See Future Pipe Industries Group Ltd.; *Int'l*, pg. 2857
FUTURE PIPE INDUSTRIES S.A.E.—See Future Pipe Industries Group Ltd.; *Int'l*, pg. 2857
FUTURE PIPE INDUSTRIES S.A.L.—See Future Pipe Industries Group Ltd.; *Int'l*, pg. 2857
FUTURE PIPE LIMITED—See Future Pipe Industries Group Ltd.; *Int'l*, pg. 2857
FUTURE PIPE SARL—See Future Pipe Industries Group Ltd.; *Int'l*, pg. 2857
FWC—See Farnsworth Wholesale Company; *U.S. Private*, pg. 1480
F.W. WEBB COMPANY; *U.S. Private*, pg. 1457
F.W. WEBB COMPANY - VICTOR MANUFACTURING DIVISION—See F.W. Webb Company; *U.S. Private*, pg. 1457
GALVANO GROOTHANDEL BV—See Compagnie de Saint-Gobain SA; *Int'l*, pg. 1723
GATEWAY SUPPLY COMPANY INC.; *U.S. Private*, pg. 1651
GEBERIT AB—See Geberit AG; *Int'l*, pg. 2904
GEBERIT B.V.—See Geberit AG; *Int'l*, pg. 2904
GEBERIT MARKETING E DISTRIBUZIONE SA—See Geberit AG; *Int'l*, pg. 2904
GEBERIT NV—See Geberit AG; *Int'l*, pg. 2904
GEBERIT OY—See Geberit AG; *Int'l*, pg. 2905
GEBERIT PRODAJA D.O.O.—See Geberit AG; *Int'l*, pg. 2905
GEBERIT PRODUKTIONS AG—See Geberit AG; *Int'l*, pg. 2905
GEBERIT PTY LTD.—See Geberit AG; *Int'l*, pg. 2905
GEBERIT SHANGHAI INVESTMENT ADMINISTRATION CO., LTD.—See Geberit AG; *Int'l*, pg. 2905
GEBERIT SHANGHAI TRADING CO. LTD.—See Geberit AG; *Int'l*, pg. 2905
GEBERIT SOUTH EAST ASIA PTE. LTD.—See Geberit AG; *Int'l*, pg. 2905
GEBERIT SOUTHERN AFRICA (PTY.) LTD.—See Geberit AG; *Int'l*, pg. 2905
GEBERIT SP.Z.O.O.—See Geberit AG; *Int'l*, pg. 2905
GEBERIT TECHNIK AG—See Geberit AG; *Int'l*, pg. 2905
GEBERIT VERTRIEBS AG—See Geberit AG; *Int'l*, pg. 2905
GENERAL PLUMBING SUPPLY COMPANY INC.; *U.S. Private*, pg. 1666

GENERAL PLUMBING SUPPLY; *U.S. Private*, pg. 1666
GENSCO INC.; *U.S. Private*, pg. 1673
GEORGE FISCHER IPS PTY LTD—See Georg Fischer AG; *Int'l*, pg. 2937
GEORGE FISCHER SALES LTD—See Georg Fischer AG; *Int'l*, pg. 2937
GEORGE T. SANDERS COMPANY; *U.S. Private*, pg. 1683
GEORG FISCHER PIPING SYSTEMS LTD—See Georg Fischer AG; *Int'l*, pg. 2936
GEORG FISCHER PIPING SYSTEMS LTD—See Georg Fischer AG; *Int'l*, pg. 2936
GEORG FISCHER PIPING SYSTEMS PVT LTD—See Georg Fischer AG; *Int'l*, pg. 2936
GEORG FISCHER PIPING SYSTEMS (TRADING) LTD—See Georg Fischer AG; *Int'l*, pg. 2936
GEORG FISCHER ROHRLEITUNGSSYSTEME (SCHWEIZ) AG—See Georg Fischer AG; *Int'l*, pg. 2936
GEORG FISCHER SISTEMAS DE TUBULACOES LTDA—See Georg Fischer AG; *Int'l*, pg. 2937
GLASVERARBEITUNGSGESELLSCHAFT DEGGENDORF MBH—See Arbonia AG; *Int'l*, pg. 538
GOLDEN WEST PIPE & SUPPLY CO.; *U.S. Private*, pg. 1734
GOODIN COMPANY; *U.S. Private*, pg. 1739
GOVERNALE CO., INC.—See Burnham Holdings, Inc.; *U.S. Public*, pg. 412
GRAFTON GROUP PLC; *Int'l*, pg. 3050
GRAND HALL EUROPE B.V.—See Grand Hall Enterprise Company Ltd.; *Int'l*, pg. 3055
GRANITE GROUP WHOLESALE LLC; *U.S. Private*, pg. 1755
GRANITE GROUP WHOLESALE, LLC—See Granite Group Wholesale LLC; *U.S. Private*, pg. 1755
GRAY-HODGES CORPORATION; *U.S. Private*, pg. 1759
GREAT WESTERN SUPPLY, INC.; *U.S. Private*, pg. 1768
GREENBRIER PETROLEUM CORPORATION—See MRC Global Inc.; *U.S. Public*, pg. 1481
GREENLINE A/S—See Brodrene A & O Johansen A/S; *Int'l*, pg. 1173
GROUPE DESCHENES INC.; *Int'l*, pg. 3101
GROVE SUPPLY INC.; *U.S. Private*, pg. 1794
GWA GROUP LIMITED; *Int'l*, pg. 3190
GWA TRADING (SHANGHAI) CO., LTD.—See GWA Group Limited; *Int'l*, pg. 3190
H2O SUPPLY INC.—See Winsupply, Inc.; *U.S. Private*, pg. 4545
HAJOCA CORP. - COSTA MESA—See Blackfriars Corp.; *U.S. Private*, pg. 575
HAJOCA CORP. - HAWTHORNE—See Blackfriars Corp.; *U.S. Private*, pg. 575
HAJOCA CORP. - LOS ANGELES—See Blackfriars Corp.; *U.S. Private*, pg. 575
HAJOCA CORPORATION—See Blackfriars Corp.; *U.S. Private*, pg. 575
HAJOCA CORP. - STROUDSBURG—See Blackfriars Corp.; *U.S. Private*, pg. 575
HANSGROHE DEUTSCHLAND VERTRIEBS GMBH—See Masco Corporation; *U.S. Public*, pg. 1390
HARRY COOPER SUPPLY COMPANY; *U.S. Private*, pg. 1871
HARRY S. EKLOF JR. & ASSOCIATES INC.; *U.S. Private*, pg. 1872
HARTEREI VTN WITTEN GMBH—See E.ON SE; *Int'l*, pg. 2255
HEATLINK GROUP, INC.—See Mueller Industries, Inc.; *U.S. Public*, pg. 1484
HEATLINK GROUP USA, LLC—See Mueller Industries, Inc.; *U.S. Public*, pg. 1484
HEATMERCHANTS—See Ferguson plc; *Int'l*, pg. 2638
HENNESY MECHANICAL SALES, LLC—See DXP Enterprises, Inc.; *U.S. Public*, pg. 697
HENRY QUENTZEL PLUMBING SUPPLY CO., INC.; *U.S. Private*, pg. 1919
HERBERTS ROR AB—See Bravida Holding AB; *Int'l*, pg. 1142
HEROSE IBERICA SL—See HEROSE GMBH; *Int'l*, pg. 3364
HEROSE LIMITED—See HEROSE GMBH; *Int'l*, pg. 3364
HEROSE TRADING CO., LTD.—See HEROSE GMBH; *Int'l*, pg. 3364
HIDRIA HEATEC D.O.O.—See Hidria d.o.o.; *Int'l*, pg. 3384
HIRSCH PIPE & SUPPLY CO., INC.; *U.S. Private*, pg. 1951
HODGES SUPPLY COMPANY; *U.S. Private*, pg. 1959
HOMANS ASSOCIATES LLC—See Watsco, Inc.; *U.S. Public*, pg. 2336
HONOLD & LA PAGE, INC.; *U.S. Private*, pg. 1977
HORN GLASS ASIA PACIFIC SDN. BHD.—See Certina Holding AG; *Int'l*, pg. 1423
HORN GLASS TECHNOLOGY (BEIJING) CO., LTD—See Certina Holding AG; *Int'l*, pg. 1423
HOSE & FITTINGS ETC.; *U.S. Private*, pg. 1984
HUGHES MACHINERY COMPANY; *U.S. Private*, pg. 2003
HVAC SUPPLY—See Geary Pacific Corporation; *U.S. Private*, pg. 1655
HYDROLOGIC DISTRIBUTION COMPANY—See Winsupply, Inc.; *U.S. Private*, pg. 4545
I.D. BOOTH INC.; *U.S. Private*, pg. 2027
IDEAL SUPPLY CO.; *U.S. Private*, pg. 2036
IHRIE SUPPLY CO. INC.; *U.S. Private*, pg. 2040

CORPORATE AFFILIATIONS

INDEPENDENT PIPE PRODUCTS INC.—See Georg Fischer AG; *Int'l*, pg. 2936
INDEPENDENT PIPE & SUPPLY CORPORATION; *U.S. Private*, pg. 2060
INDUSTRIAL SALES COMPANY INC.; *U.S. Private*, pg. 2068
INDVA SVERIGE AB—See AVK Holding A/S; *Int'l*, pg. 748
INTERAPP DEUTSCHLAND GMBH—See AVK Holding A/S; *Int'l*, pg. 748
INTERAPP GES.M.B.H.—See AVK Holding A/S; *Int'l*, pg. 748
INTERAPP VALCOM S.A.—See AVK Holding A/S; *Int'l*, pg. 748
INTERCOUNTY SUPPLY INC.; *U.S. Private*, pg. 2110
IPEX USA LLC—See Aliaxis S.A./N.V.; *Int'l*, pg. 325
IRR SUPPLY CENTERS INC.; *U.S. Private*, pg. 2140
ISIFLO SAS—See Aalberts N.V.; *Int'l*, pg. 34
JACLO INDUSTRIES—See Durst Corporation; *U.S. Private*, pg. 1294
J.D. DADDARIO CO. INC.; *U.S. Private*, pg. 2160
J.H. LARSON ELECTRICAL COMPANY-HUDSON—See J.H. Larson Electrical Company; *U.S. Private*, pg. 2166
J. LORBER CO. INC.; *U.S. Private*, pg. 2156
JOHN M. HARTEL CO. INC.; *U.S. Private*, pg. 2223
JOMAR GROUP LTD.; *U.S. Private*, pg. 2230
JOPLIN SUPPLY COMPANY—See Harry Cooper Supply Company; *U.S. Private*, pg. 1871
JOTUL FRANCE S.A.—See OpenGate Capital Management, LLC; *U.S. Private*, pg. 3030
JOTUL LITHUANIA—See OpenGate Capital Management, LLC; *U.S. Private*, pg. 3030
KEELING COMPANY; *U.S. Private*, pg. 2272
KEIDEL SUPPLY COMPANY INC.—See Winsupply, Inc.; *U.S. Private*, pg. 4545
KELLER SUPPLY COMPANY INC.; *U.S. Private*, pg. 2275
KELLY'S PIPE & SUPPLY CO.—See Blackfriars Corp.; *U.S. Private*, pg. 575
KENNY PIPE & SUPPLY, INC.; *U.S. Private*, pg. 2286
KESSLER SALES & DISTRIBUTION LLC—See Mueller Industries, Inc.; *U.S. Public*, pg. 1484
KINECT SOLAR, LLC; *U.S. Private*, pg. 2307
KLIMAN SALES INC.; *U.S. Private*, pg. 2320
K.L. MCCOY & ASSOCIATES; *U.S. Private*, pg. 2252
KOHLER AUSTRALIA—See Kohler Company; *U.S. Private*, pg. 2339
LA CROSSE PLUMBING SUPPLY CO. INC.—See First Supply LLC; *U.S. Private*, pg. 1529
L.A. HAZARD & SONS INC.—See IRR Supply Centers Inc.; *U.S. Private*, pg. 2140
LAKES PIPE & SUPPLY CORP.; *U.S. Private*, pg. 2376
LANGE PLUMBING SUPPLY, INC.; *U.S. Private*, pg. 2389
LARSEN SUPPLY COMPANY INC.; *U.S. Private*, pg. 2393
LAWRENCE PLUMBING SUPPLY CO.—See Ferguson plc; *Int'l*, pg. 2638
L/B WATER SERVICE INC.; *U.S. Private*, pg. 2367
LEEPS SUPPLY CO. INC.; *U.S. Private*, pg. 2415
LEE SUPPLY CORP.; *U.S. Private*, pg. 2414
THE LEMNA CORPORATION; *U.S. Private*, pg. 4069
LEMNA INTERNATIONAL INC.—See The Lemna Corporation; *U.S. Private*, pg. 4069
LEMNA USA INC.—See The Lemna Corporation; *U.S. Private*, pg. 4069
LEWIS-SMITH CORPORATION; *U.S. Private*, pg. 2440
LIBB CO. INC.; *U.S. Private*, pg. 2442
LINCOLN PRODUCTS—See Ferguson plc; *Int'l*, pg. 2638
LINDY SPRINGS; *U.S. Private*, pg. 2460
LOCKE SUPPLY CO.; *U.S. Private*, pg. 2478
LONGLEY SUPPLY COMPANY, INC.; *U.S. Private*, pg. 2492
LUMMUS TECHNOLOGY HEAT TRANSFER B.V.—See McDermott International, Inc.; *U.S. Public*, pg. 1405
LUTE PLUMBING SUPPLY INC.; *U.S. Private*, pg. 2516
THE MACOMB GROUP, INC.; *U.S. Private*, pg. 4073
MANZARDO SPA—See Ferguson plc; *Int'l*, pg. 2638
MATCO-NORCA, LLC—See NIBCO Inc.; *U.S. Private*, pg. 2924
MAY SUPPLY COMPANY—See Winsupply, Inc.; *U.S. Private*, pg. 4545
MB FAMILY HOLDINGS, INC.—See Winsupply, Inc.; *U.S. Private*, pg. 4545
MCKENZIE SUPPLY COMPANY; *U.S. Private*, pg. 2638
M. COOPER WINSUPPLY—See Winsupply Inc.; *U.S. Private*, pg. 4544
MDM SUPPLY INCORPORATED; *U.S. Private*, pg. 2646
MEIBES RUS OOO—See Aalberts N.V.; *Int'l*, pg. 35
MERCURY PARTNERS 90 BI INC.; *U.S. Private*, pg. 2671
MHH FRANCE S.A.S—See BayWa AG; *Int'l*, pg. 918
MICHIGAN AIR PRODUCTS CO.; *U.S. Private*, pg. 2700
MID-CITY SUPPLY CO. INC.; *U.S. Private*, pg. 2707
MILFORD SUPPLY CO. INC.; *U.S. Private*, pg. 2729
MINVALCO, INC.—See Building Controls & Solutions; *U.S. Private*, pg. 682
M&L SUPPLY COMPANY INCORPORATED; *U.S. Private*, pg. 2524
MMA RENEWABLE VENTURES—See Fundamental Advisors LP; *U.S. Private*, pg. 1623
MODERN SUPPLY COMPANY INC.; *U.S. Private*, pg. 2762

N.A.I.C.S. INDEX

423720 — PLUMBING AND HEATIN...

MOEN INC.—See Fortune Brands Innovations, Inc.; *U.S. Public*, pg. 873
MOORE SUPPLY CO. INC.; *U.S. Private*, pg. 2780
MORALLY WHOLESALE, INC.; *U.S. Private*, pg. 2781
MOREHOUSE-HUBER, INC.—See Blue Sea Capital Management LLC; *U.S. Private*, pg. 592
MORROW CONTROL & SUPPLY CO; *U.S. Private*, pg. 2790
MOUNTAINLAND SUPPLY COMPANY; *U.S. Private*, pg. 2801
MOUNTAIN STATES PIPE & SUPPLY COMPANY; *U.S. Private*, pg. 2800
MOUNTAIN SUPPLY CO; *U.S. Private*, pg. 2800
MRC CANADA ULC—See MRC Global Inc.; *U.S. Public*, pg. 1481
MRC GLOBAL AUSTRALIA PTY LTD—See MRC Global Inc.; *U.S. Public*, pg. 1481
MRC GLOBAL (FRANCE) SAS—See MRC Global Inc.; *U.S. Public*, pg. 1481
MRC TRANSMARK B.V.—See MRC Global Inc.; *U.S. Public*, pg. 1481
MRC TRANSMARK GROUP B.V.—See MRC Global Inc.; *U.S. Public*, pg. 1481
MRC TRANSMARK ITALY SRL—See MRC Global Inc.; *U.S. Public*, pg. 1481
MRC TRANSMARK LIMITED—See MRC Global Inc.; *U.S. Public*, pg. 1481
MRC TRANSMARK NV—See MRC Global Inc.; *U.S. Public*, pg. 1481
MULTIJOINT SA—See Descours & Cabaud SA; *Int'l*, pg. 2044
NAPAC, INC.—See WJ Partners, LLC; *U.S. Private*, pg. 4551
NATIONAL ROAD UTILITY SUPPLY, INC.—See The C.I. Thornburg Co., Inc.; *U.S. Private*, pg. 4003
NATIONAL SAFETY ASSOCIATES; *U.S. Private*, pg. 2862
NEENAN COMPANY; *U.S. Private*, pg. 2880
NEMATIQ PTY. LTD.—See Clean TeQ Water Limited; *Int'l*, pg. 1654
NEWMAN ASSOCIATES, INC—See NEFCO Corp.; *U.S. Private*, pg. 2880
NEW YORK REPLACEMENT PARTS CORP.; *U.S. Private*, pg. 2912
N.H. YATES & CO., INC.; *U.S. Private*, pg. 2828
NICKLAS SUPPLY INC.; *U.S. Private*, pg. 2926
NOLAND COMPANY—See Winsupply Inc.; *U.S. Private*, pg. 4544
NORMAN SUPPLY COMPANY; *U.S. Private*, pg. 2938
NORTHEASTERN SUPPLY INC.; *U.S. Private*, pg. 2951
NORTH SOUTH SUPPLY INC.; *U.S. Private*, pg. 2947
NORTHWEST PIPE FITTINGS, INC.; *U.S. Private*, pg. 2961
NOVIA CORPORATION, INC.—See Hill & Smith PLC; *Int'l*, pg. 3392
NUTLEY HEATING & COOLING SUPPLY CO.; *U.S. Private*, pg. 2974
NU-WAY SUPPLY COMPANY INC.; *U.S. Private*, pg. 2972
OAG AG—See Frauenthal Holding AG; *Int'l*, pg. 2767
OATEY SUPPLY CHAIN SERVICES, INC.—See Oatey Company; *U.S. Private*, pg. 2986
OCEAN CONVERSION (BVI) LTD.—See Consolidated Water Co. Ltd.; *Int'l*, pg. 1771
OPW SLOVAKIA S.R.O.—See Dover Corporation; *U.S. Public*, pg. 682
ORBE VALVE INC.—See AVK Holding A/S; *Int'l*, pg. 748
ORBINOX BRASIL INDUSTRIA E COMERCIO LTDA.—See AVK Holding A/S; *Int'l*, pg. 748
ORBINOX COMERCIAL S.L.—See AVK Holding A/S; *Int'l*, pg. 748
ORBINOX S.A.—See AVK Holding A/S; *Int'l*, pg. 748
ORBINOX VALVES INTERNATIONAL SA—See AVK Holding A/S; *Int'l*, pg. 748
OSLIN NATION CO.—See HTS Engineering Ltd.; *Int'l*, pg. 3509
PACE SUPPLY CORP.; *U.S. Private*, pg. 3064
PACIFIC PLUMBING SUPPLY CO.; *U.S. Private*, pg. 3070
PAN WEST CORP.; *U.S. Private*, pg. 3084
PARAMOUNT SUPPLY CO. INC.; *U.S. Private*, pg. 3093
PAREX INDUSTRIES LIMITED—See Emerson Electric Co.; *U.S. Public*, pg. 751
PASCO SPECIALTY & MANUFACTURING INC.; *U.S. Private*, pg. 3104
PEABODY SUPPLY COMPANY INC.; *U.S. Private*, pg. 3122
PENCO CORPORATION; *U.S. Private*, pg. 3132
PENDLETON ASSOCIATES INC; *U.S. Private*, pg. 3132
PERRY SUPPLY COMPANY INCORPORATED; *U.S. Private*, pg. 3154
PHOCEENNE SAS—See Groupe BPCE; *Int'l*, pg. 3095
PIPELINE SUPPLY INCORPORATED; *U.S. Private*, pg. 3189
PIPING ALLOYS INC.; *U.S. Private*, pg. 3190
PIPING SYSTEM INDONESIA PT.—See BELIMO Holding AG; *Int'l*, pg. 965
PLIMPTON & HILLS CORPORATION; *U.S. Private*, pg. 3214
PLUMBERS SUPPLY CO. INC.; *U.S. Private*, pg. 3214
PLUMBERS SUPPLY COMPANY; *U.S. Private*, pg. 3215
THE PLUMBERY INC.—See Slakey Brothers Inc.; *U.S. Private*, pg. 3687

PLUMBING DISTRIBUTORS INC.; *U.S. Private*, pg. 3215
PLUMBING & INDUSTRIAL SUPPLY CO.; *U.S. Private*, pg. 3215
THE PLUMBING SOURCE, INC.—See Ferguson plc; *Int'l*, pg. 2638
PLUMBING SPECIALTIES & SUPPLIES, INC.—See Ferguson plc; *Int'l*, pg. 2638
PLUMBMASTER INC.—See Dunes Point Capital, LLC; *U.S. Private*, pg. 1289
PLUMB SUPPLY COMPANY, INC.—See Templeton Coal Company, Inc.; *U.S. Private*, pg. 3963
PORTER PIPE & SUPPLY COMPANY; *U.S. Private*, pg. 3232
PORTLAND GROUP INC. - NEWTON—See Portland Group Inc.; *U.S. Private*, pg. 3233
PORTLAND GROUP INC.; *U.S. Private*, pg. 3233
PORTLAND VALVE & FITTING COMPANY; *U.S. Private*, pg. 3233
PREMIER PUMP & SUPPLY, INC.; *U.S. Private*, pg. 3251
PROCTOR SALES INC.; *U.S. Private*, pg. 3272
PROGRESSIVE PLUMBING SUPPLY, CO.; *U.S. Private*, pg. 3279
PROLUX SOLUTIONS AG—See Arbonia AG; *Int'l*, pg. 538
PROSOURCE LLC—See Blue Sea Capital Management LLC; *U.S. Private*, pg. 592
PRO-SPEC INC.; *U.S. Private*, pg. 3271
PRO-TECH VALVE SALES, INC.—See Forum Energy Technologies, Inc.; *U.S. Public*, pg. 874
PT. CHUGAI RO INDONESIA—See Chugai Ro Co., Ltd.; *Int'l*, pg. 1594
PT CONSOLIDATED WATER BALI—See Consolidated Water Co. Ltd.; *Int'l*, pg. 1771
PTC SRL—See Emak S.p.A.; *Int'l*, pg. 2373
PT. DOWA THERMOTECH FURNACES—See Dowa Holdings Co., Ltd.; *Int'l*, pg. 2184
PT FUTURE PIPE INDUSTRIES—See Future Pipe Industries Group Ltd.; *Int'l*, pg. 2857
PUGET SOUND PIPE & SUPPLY CO; *U.S. Private*, pg. 3302
QUALITY CERAMICS (SALES) LIMITED—See Anchorage Capital Group, L.L.C.; *U.S. Private*, pg. 274
QUALITY CERAMICS (SALES) LIMITED—See CVC Capital Partners SICAV-FIS S.A.; *Int'l*, pg. 1888
RADIATORSONLINE.COM LTD.—See Brickability Group plc; *Int'l*, pg. 1151
RAL SUPPLY GROUP INC.; *U.S. Private*, pg. 3349
RAMPART PLUMBING & HEATING SUPPLY INC.; *U.S. Private*, pg. 3352
R.D. BITZER CO. INC.; *U.S. Private*, pg. 3335
READING FOUNDRY & SUPPLY CO.; *U.S. Private*, pg. 3366
REECE-HOPPER SALES, LLC - HOUSTON—See Reece-Hopper Sales, LLC; *U.S. Private*, pg. 3381
REEVES-WIEDEMAN COMPANY; *U.S. Private*, pg. 3384
REMEHA B.V.—See BDR Thermea Group B.V.; *Int'l*, pg. 931
REMEHA SRL—See BDR Thermea Group B.V.; *Int'l*, pg. 931
REPUBLIC PLUMBING SUPPLY COMPANY INC.; *U.S. Private*, pg. 3402
REX PIPE & SUPPLY CO.; *U.S. Private*, pg. 3417
R.F. MACDONALD CO.; *U.S. Private*, pg. 3336
RICHARDS PLUMBING & HEATING SUPPLIES; *U.S. Private*, pg. 3429
R.J. WALKER CO. INC.; *U.S. Private*, pg. 3337
ROBERTSON DEVELOPMENT INC.; *U.S. Private*, pg. 3460
ROBERTSON HEATING SUPPLY CO., INC.; *U.S. Private*, pg. 3460
ROBERTSON SUPPLY INC.; *U.S. Private*, pg. 3460
ROBINSON SUPPLY CO. INC.; *U.S. Private*, pg. 3462
ROSEN SUPPLY COMPANY INC.—See Winsupply, Inc.; *U.S. Private*, pg. 4545
RUNDLE-SPENCE MANUFACTURING CO; *U.S. Private*, pg. 3504
R.V. CLOUD CO.; *U.S. Private*, pg. 3340
RYAN HERCO PRODUCTS CORP.—See Clayton, Dubilier & Rice, LLC; *U.S. Private*, pg. 926
SANDERS PLUMBING SUPPLY INC.; *U.S. Private*, pg. 3543
SAN-ETSU METALS (SHANGHAI) CO., LTD.—See CK SAN-ETSU Co., Ltd.; *Int'l*, pg. 1639
SANI-TECH WEST, INC.—See 3i Group plc; *Int'l*, pg. 9
SANTA FE WINWATER; *U.S. Private*, pg. 3547
SCHAEFER PLUMBING SUPPLY CO.; *U.S. Private*, pg. 3563
SCHOLZEN PRODUCTS COMPANY INC.; *U.S. Private*, pg. 3568
SCHRAUWEN SANITAIR EN VERWARMING BVBA—See CRH plc; *Int'l*, pg. 1848
SCHULHOF COMPANY; *U.S. Private*, pg. 3570
SCHUMACHER & SEILER INC.; *U.S. Private*, pg. 3570
SCHWANK GESMBH—See Schwank Inc.; *U.S. Private*, pg. 3572
SECON SOLAR LTD.—See Grafton Group plc; *Int'l*, pg. 3051
SECURITY PLUMBING & HEATING SUPPLY CO.—See Winsupply Inc.; *U.S. Private*, pg. 4544
SELKIRK CORPORATION—See Canada Pension Plan Investment Board; *Int'l*, pg. 1282

SERVICE SUPPLY OF VICTORIA, INC.; *U.S. Private*, pg. 3616
SEYMOUR INDUSTRIES LTD.—See American Granby, Inc.; *U.S. Private*, pg. 235
SHETUCKET PLUMBING SUPPLY INC.—See Granite Group Wholesale LLC; *U.S. Private*, pg. 1755
SHIRES (IRELAND) LIMITED—See Anchorage Capital Group, L.L.C.; *U.S. Private*, pg. 274
SHIRES (IRELAND) LIMITED—See CVC Capital Partners SICAV-FIS S.A.; *Int'l*, pg. 1888
SIA AKG THERMOTECHNIK LATVIA—See Autokuhler GmbH & Co. KG; *Int'l*, pg. 727
SIA UPONOR LATVIA—See Georg Fischer AG; *Int'l*, pg. 2937
SID HARVEY INDUSTRIES, INC.; *U.S. Private*, pg. 3645
SIMONS SUPPLY CO. INC.; *U.S. Private*, pg. 3666
S.L.M. DISTRIBUTION—See Carrefour SA; *Int'l*, pg. 1346
SMARDAN-HATCHER COMPANY; *U.S. Private*, pg. 3690
SNOW AND JONES INC.; *U.S. Private*, pg. 3700
SOLCO PLUMBING SUPPLY INC.; *U.S. Private*, pg. 3708
SONNYS HOME CENTER INC.; *U.S. Private*, pg. 3714
SOUTHERN MATERIALS COMPANY; *U.S. Private*, pg. 3733
SOUTHERN PIPE & SUPPLY CO., INC.; *U.S. Private*, pg. 3734
SOUTHLAND PLUMBING SUPPLY INC.; *U.S. Private*, pg. 3737
SPECIFIED SYSTEMS INC.; *U.S. Private*, pg. 3751
SPECMA AB—See Aktieselskabet Schouw & Co.; *Int'l*, pg. 266
SPIG COOLING TOWERS INDIA PRIVATE LIMITED—See Babcock & Wilcox Enterprises, Inc.; *U.S. Public*, pg. 263
SPIG KOREA LTD.—See Babcock & Wilcox Enterprises, Inc.; *U.S. Public*, pg. 263
SPIG KUHLTURMTECHNOLOGIEN GMBH—See Babcock & Wilcox Enterprises, Inc.; *U.S. Public*, pg. 263
SPIG SOGUTMA SISTEMLERI TLC LDT—See Babcock & Wilcox Enterprises, Inc.; *U.S. Public*, pg. 263
SPIG S.P.A.—See Babcock & Wilcox Enterprises, Inc.; *U.S. Public*, pg. 263
SPIG TORRES DE RESFRIAMENTO LTDA.—See Babcock & Wilcox Enterprises, Inc.; *U.S. Public*, pg. 263
SPS COMPANIES INC.; *U.S. Private*, pg. 3765
STADLER-VIEGA—See Georg Fischer AG; *Int'l*, pg. 2938
STANDARD PLUMBING SUPPLY COMPANY, INC.; *U.S. Private*, pg. 3781
STEARNS PLUMBING INC—See Wiseway Supply Inc.; *U.S. Private*, pg. 4550
STEINHOUSE SUPPLY CO INC—See Southern Pipe & Supply Co., Inc.; *U.S. Private*, pg. 3734
STILLWELL HANSEN INC.; *U.S. Private*, pg. 3812
ST. LOUIS BOILER SUPPLY, INC.; *U.S. Private*, pg. 3770
STRITT & PRIEBE, INC.; *U.S. Private*, pg. 3840
SUNBELT MARKETING INC.—See Sunbelt Marketing Investment Corp.; *U.S. Private*, pg. 3865
SUNBELT MARKETING INVESTMENT CORP. - DEERFIELD BEACH—See Sunbelt Marketing Investment Corp.; *U.S. Private*, pg. 3865
SUNBELT MARKETING INVESTMENT CORP.; *U.S. Private*, pg. 3865
SUNPOWER MALAYSIA MANUFACTURING SDN. BHD.—See SunPower Corporation; *U.S. Public*, pg. 1965
SUNWAVE HOME COMFORT INC.—See Cricket Energy Holdings, Inc.; *Int'l*, pg. 1849
SUPERIOR PRODUCTS DISTRIBUTORS INC.; *U.S. Private*, pg. 3880
SUPPLY NEW ENGLAND INC.; *U.S. Private*, pg. 3882
SUZHOU ZHI SHENG INFORMATION TECHNOLOGY CO., LTD.—See Yum China Holdings, Inc.; *U.S. Public*, pg. 2399
SWEETWATER LLC; *U.S. Private*, pg. 3892
TAIWAN SAN-ETSU CO., LTD.—See CK SAN-ETSU Co., Ltd.; *Int'l*, pg. 1639
TEC UTILITIES SUPPLY INC.; *U.S. Private*, pg. 3951
TEMPLETON COAL COMPANY, INC.; *U.S. Private*, pg. 3963
THETFORD B.V.—See The Dyson-Kissner-Moran Corporation; *U.S. Private*, pg. 4024
THOMAS SOMERVILLE CO. INC.; *U.S. Private*, pg. 4158
THOMPSON DISTRIBUTION COMPANY, INC.; *U.S. Private*, pg. 4159
THOMPSON-DURKEE COMPANY INC.; *U.S. Private*, pg. 4162
THOMSON BROTHERS LIMITED—See Ferguson plc; *Int'l*, pg. 2638
THRIFTY SUPPLY CO.; *U.S. Private*, pg. 4165
TORRINGTON SUPPLY COMPANY, INCORPORATED; *U.S. Private*, pg. 4190
TRADELINK PLUMBING CENTRES—See Fletcher Building Limited; *Int'l*, pg. 2699
TRINITY WHOLESALE DISTRIBUTORS, INC.; *U.S. Private*, pg. 4236
TRUMBULL INDUSTRIES INC.; *U.S. Private*, pg. 4250
TURNER INDUSTRIES GROUP LLC PIPE FABRICATION DIV—See Turner Industries Group, L.L.C.; *U.S. Private*, pg. 4261

423720 — PLUMBING AND HEATIN...

TWI INTERNATIONAL, INC.—See Waxman Industries, Inc.; *U.S. Private,* pg. 4459
TWI INTERNATIONAL TAIWAN, INC.—See Waxman Industries, Inc.; *U.S. Private,* pg. 4459
UNITED PLUMBING SUPPLY CO.; *U.S. Private,* pg. 4295
UNIVERSAL ACOUSTIC & EMISSION TECHNOLOGIES PVT. LTD.—See Durr AG; *Int'l,* pg. 2231
UPONOR AB—See Georg Fischer AG; *Int'l,* pg. 2937
UPONOR A/S—See Georg Fischer AG; *Int'l,* pg. 2937
UPONOR (DEUTSCHLAND) GMBH—See Georg Fischer AG; *Int'l,* pg. 2937
UPONOR EESTI OU—See Georg Fischer AG; *Int'l,* pg. 2937
UPONOR GMBH—See Georg Fischer AG; *Int'l,* pg. 2937
UPONOR HISPANIA, S.A.—See Georg Fischer AG; *Int'l,* pg. 2937
UPONOR LIMITED—See Georg Fischer AG; *Int'l,* pg. 2938
UPONOR PORTUGAL - SISTEMAS PARA FLUIDOS LDA.—See Georg Fischer AG; *Int'l,* pg. 2938
UPONOR S.A.R.L.—See Georg Fischer AG; *Int'l,* pg. 2937
UPONOR SP. Z O.O.—See Georg Fischer AG; *Int'l,* pg. 2938
UPONOR S.R.O.—See Georg Fischer AG; *Int'l,* pg. 2938
UPONOR SUOMI OY—See Georg Fischer AG; *Int'l,* pg. 2938
UPONOR TEXNIKES LYSEIS GIA KTIRIA AE—See Georg Fischer AG; *Int'l,* pg. 2938
UPONOR VERTRIEBS GMBH—See Georg Fischer AG; *Int'l,* pg. 2937
US SUPPLY COMPANY INC.; *U.S. Private,* pg. 4320
UTILITY EQUIPMENT COMPANY; *U.S. Private,* pg. 4326.
VAGA TEHNIKA EESTI OU—See Brodrene A & O Johansen A/S; *Int'l,* pg. 1173
VAMAC INC.; *U.S. Private,* pg. 4338
VATECH 2000 APS—See AVK Holding A/S; *Int'l,* pg. 748
VENTURE PIPE & SUPPLY; *U.S. Private,* pg. 4358
VINA ASAHI CO., LTD.—See ASAHI EITO Co., Ltd.; *Int'l,* pg. 593
VIVA ENERGI A/S—See Bravida Holding AB; *Int'l,* pg. 1142
VJ STANLEY, INC.—See Stritt & Priebe, Inc.; *U.S. Private,* pg. 3840
VP SUPPLY CORP.; *U.S. Private,* pg. 4414
V&W SUPPLY COMPANY; *U.S. Private,* pg. 4327
W A BRAGG & CO INC.—See Plumbing Distributors Inc.; *U.S. Private,* pg. 3215
WALKER'S SUPPLY COMPANY INC.—See Wallace Hardware Company, Inc.; *U.S. Private,* pg. 4431
W.A. ROOSEVELT COMPANY; *U.S. Private,* pg. 4418
WASCO GROOTHANDELSGROEP CENTRAL VERWARMING BV—See Ferguson plc; *Int'l,* pg. 2638
WASCO HOLDING BV—See Gilde Equity Management (GEM) Benelux Partners B.V.; *Int'l,* pg. 2975
WASHBURN GARFIELD CORPORATION—See Collins Pipe & Supply Co., Inc.; *U.S. Private,* pg. 969
WASHINGTON ENERGY SERVICES COMPANY INC.—See Northwest Water Heater Inc.; *U.S. Private,* pg. 2962
WATERBOSS EUROPE, SRL—See A. O. Smith Corporation; *U.S. Public,* pg. 12
WATER PRODUCTS COMPANY OF ILLINOIS, INC.; *U.S. Private,* pg. 4451
WATERWORKS OPERATING COMPANY LLC—See RH; *U.S. Public,* pg. 1796
WATERWORKS SUPPLIES & SERVICES LIMITED—See Blackfriars Corp.; *U.S. Private,* pg. 575
WATKINS HIRE LIMITED—See Carrier Global Corporation; *U.S. Public,* pg. 444
WATLOW FRANCE S.A.R.L.—See Tinicum Enterprises, Inc.; *U.S. Private,* pg. 4174
WATLOW LIMITED—See Tinicum Enterprises, Inc.; *U.S. Private,* pg. 4174
WATLOW SINGAPORE PTE. LTD.—See Tinicum Enterprises, Inc.; *U.S. Private,* pg. 4175
WATLOW TAIWAN CORPORATION—See Tinicum Enterprises, Inc.; *U.S. Private,* pg. 4175
WATTS BENELUX—See Watts Water Technologies, Inc.; *U.S. Public,* pg. 2337
WATTS INDUSTRIES DEUTSCHLAND GMBH—See Watts Water Technologies, Inc.; *U.S. Public,* pg. 2337
WAVIN BELGIUM N.V.—See Bharti Enterprises Limited; *Int'l,* pg. 1012
WAVIN OVERSEAS B.V.—See Bharti Enterprises Limited; *Int'l,* pg. 1012
W.A.W. SPOL S.R.O.—See Compagnie de Saint-Gobain SA; *Int'l,* pg. 1737
WAXMAN CONSUMER PRODUCTS GROUP INC.—See Waxman Industries, Inc.; *U.S. Private,* pg. 4459
WEINSTEIN SUPPLY CORPORATION; *U.S. Private,* pg. 4472
WELLONS INC.; *U.S. Private,* pg. 4476
WEST COAST WINSUPPLY CO.—See Winsupply Inc.; *U.S. Private,* pg. 4544
WESTCO FLOW CONTROL LIMITED.—See Aalberts N.V.; *Int'l,* pg. 36
WESTERN NEVADA SUPPLY CO.; *U.S. Private,* pg. 4494
WESTERN STEEL & PLUMBING INC.—See Dakota Supply Group Inc.; *U.S. Private,* pg. 1147
WHOLESALE PLUMBING SUPPLY CO.; *U.S. Private,* pg. 4514
WILKINSON SUPPLY COMPANY; *U.S. Private,* pg. 4521

WILKINS WATER CONTROL PRODUCTS—See Zurn Elkay Water Solutions Corporation; *U.S. Public,* pg. 2414
WISEWAY SUPPLY INC.; *U.S. Private,* pg. 4550
WMS SALES INC.; *U.S. Private,* pg. 4552
WOLSELEY AUSTRIA AG—See Ferguson plc; *Int'l,* pg. 2638
WOLSELEY FRANCE SAS—See Ferguson plc; *Int'l,* pg. 2638
WOLSELEY INDUSTRIAL PRODUCTS GROUP INC—See Ferguson plc; *Int'l,* pg. 2638
WOLSELEY (SCHWEIZ) AG—See Ferguson plc; *Int'l,* pg. 2638
WOLSELEY UK LTD.—See Ferguson plc; *Int'l,* pg. 2638.
WOLVERINE BRASS, INC.—See Dunes Point Capital, LLC; *U.S. Private,* pg. 1289
WONDERFUEL, LLC—See Duraflame, Inc.; *U.S. Private,* pg. 1292
WOODHILL SUPPLY INC.—See The Macomb Group, Inc.; *U.S. Private,* pg. 4073
WOODWARD IDS SWITZERLAND AG—See Woodward, Inc.; *U.S. Public,* pg. 2378
WOOL WHOLESALE PLUMBING SUPPLY, INC.; *U.S. Private,* pg. 4561
WORLY PLUMBING SUPPLY INC.; *U.S. Private,* pg. 4570
YELLOW THUNDER CORPORATION; *U.S. Private,* pg. 4587
YORK CORRUGATING CO.; *U.S. Private,* pg. 4590
YOUR OTHER WAREHOUSE—See The Home Depot, Inc.; *U.S. Public,* pg. 2089
ZURN INDUSTRIES—See Zurn Elkay Water Solutions Corporation; *U.S. Public,* pg. 2414

423730 — WARM AIR HEATING AND AIR-CONDITIONING EQUIPMENT AND SUPPLIES MERCHANT WHOLESALERS

2J SUPPLY INC.; *U.S. Private,* pg. 7
AAF-LUFTTECHNIK GMBH—See Daikin Industries, Ltd.; *Int'l,* pg. 1932
ABAC CATALUNYA S.L.—See Atlas Copco AB; *Int'l,* pg. 677
ABR WHOLESALERS INC.; *U.S. Private,* pg. 39
ACCESS INTERNATIONAL PROJECTS (PVT) LTD.—See Daikin Industries, Ltd.; *Int'l,* pg. 1932
ACDOCTOR.COM INC.—See Watsco, Inc.; *U.S. Public,* pg. 2336
AC DOCTOR LLC—See Watsco, Inc.; *U.S. Public,* pg. 2336
ACES A/C SUPPLY INC.; *U.S. Private,* pg. 58
ACE SUPPLY CO. INC.; *U.S. Private,* pg. 57
ACI MECHANICAL & HVAC SALES; *U.S. Private,* pg. 59
ACME REFRIGERATION OF BATON ROUGE, LLC—See Watsco, Inc.; *U.S. Public,* pg. 2336
AC PRO; *U.S. Private,* pg. 45
AC SUPPLY COMPANY; *U.S. Private,* pg. 46
AC WORLD ELECTRONICS LTD.—See Daikin Industries, Ltd.; *Int'l,* pg. 1932
A. DIETRICH KALTE KLIMA LUFTUNG AG—See BKW AG; *Int'l,* pg. 1054
ADVANCED ENERGY MANAGEMENT LTD.; *Int'l,* pg. 158
ADVANCED FILTRATION CONCEPTS, INC.—See Komline-Sanderson Corporation; *U.S. Private,* pg. 2342
ADVANCED HORIZONS INC.; *U.S. Private,* pg. 90
AIR CONTROL PRODUCTS INC.; *U.S. Private,* pg. 138
AIR DISTRIBUTION ENTERPRISES, INC.; *U.S. Private,* pg. 138
AIRECO SUPPLY, INC.; *U.S. Private,* pg. 141
AIREFCO INC.—See Ferguson plc; *Int'l,* pg. 2637
AIR ENERGY, INC.; *U.S. Private,* pg. 138
AIR FILTER SUPPLY, INC.—See Audax Group, Limited Partnership; *U.S. Private,* pg. 389
AIR MANAGEMENT SUPPLY—See Century Air Conditioning Supply Inc.; *U.S. Private,* pg. 831
AIRMAN ASIA SDN. BHD.—See Hokuetsu Industries Co. Ltd.; *Int'l,* pg. 3444
AIRMAN-FUSHENG (SHANGHAI) ELECTROMECHANICAL CO., LTD—See Hokuetsu Industries Co., Ltd.; *Int'l,* pg. 3444
AIRMAN USA CORPORATION—See Hokuetsu Industries Co., Ltd.; *Int'l,* pg. 3444
AIR PURCHASES OF NEW HAMPSHIRE—See Ridgemont Partners Management LLC; *U.S. Private,* pg. 3433
AIRREPS HAWAII—See Heide & Cook Mechanical Contractors; *U.S. Private,* pg. 1904
AIR SYSTEMS DISTRIBUTORS LLC—See Watsco, Inc.; *U.S. Public,* pg. 2336
AIR TREATMENT CORP.; *U.S. Private,* pg. 140
AITKEN SPENCE ENGINEERING SOLUTIONS (PVT) LTD.—See Daikin Industries, Ltd.; *Int'l,* pg. 1932
ALFA LAVAL INC. - PRODUCT CENTER—See Alfa Laval AB; *Int'l,* pg. 309
AL-HASSAN G.I. SHAKER COMPANY; *Int'l,* pg. 286
ALLIED REFRIGERATION INC.; *U.S. Private,* pg. 187
ALLRED'S INC.; *U.S. Private,* pg. 193
ALL WORLD MACHINERY SUPPLY, INC.—See Daikin Industries, Ltd.; *Int'l,* pg. 1932
ALUP KOMPRESSOREN POLSKA SP. Z.O.O.—See Atlas Copco AB; *Int'l,* pg. 677
AO SVERIGE AB—See Brodrene A & O Johansen A/S; *Int'l,* pg. 1173

APCO, INC.—See Winsupply, Inc.; *U.S. Private,* pg. 4544
AQUA AIR PRODUCTS INC.; *U.S. Private,* pg. 302
ASAG AIR SYSTEM AG—See BKW AG; *Int'l,* pg. 1054
ASPEN REFRIGERANTS, INC.—See Hudson Technologies, Inc.; *U.S. Public,* pg. 1068
ASSOCIATED EQUIPMENT COMPANY OF DELAWARE; *U.S. Private,* pg. 355
ASTON AIR CONTROL PTE LTD—See Anderco Investment Pte Ltd; *Int'l,* pg. 450
ATLANTIC SERVICE & SUPPLY LLC—See Watsco, Inc.; *U.S. Public,* pg. 2336
ATLAS COPCO POLSKA SP. Z.O.O.—See Atlas Copco AB; *Int'l,* pg. 680
AUER STEEL & HEATING SUPPLY CO. INC.; *U.S. Private,* pg. 391
AUER STEEL & HEATING SUPPLY COMPANY, TWIN CITIES, INC.—See Auer Steel & Heating Supply Co. Inc.; *U.S. Private,* pg. 391
AWA AMERICAS LLC—See BITZER SE; *Int'l,* pg. 1051
BAKER DISTRIBUTING COMPANY LLC—See Watsco, Inc.; *U.S. Public,* pg. 2336
BARDON SUPPLIES LIMITED—See Groupe Deschenes Inc.; *Int'l,* pg. 3101
BARTOS INDUSTRIES LLC; *U.S. Private,* pg. 484
THE BEHLER-YOUNG CO., INC.; *U.S. Private,* pg. 3993
BEIJER REF (MAURITIUS) LTD.—See Beijer Ref AB; *Int'l,* pg. 944
BELIMO AUTOMATION NORGE A / S—See BELIMO Holding AG; *Int'l,* pg. 964
BELIMO SERVOMOTOREN BV—See BELIMO Holding AG; *Int'l,* pg. 965
BELIMO STELLANTRIEBE VERTRIEBS GMBH—See BELIMO Holding AG; *Int'l,* pg. 965
BENJAMIN OBDYKE, INC.; *U.S. Private,* pg. 526
BENOIST BROS. SUPPLY CO. INC.; *U.S. Private,* pg. 528
BENOIST BROTHERS SUPPLY CO—See Gryphon Investors, LLC; *U.S. Private,* pg. 1800
B.GRIMM AIR CONDITIONING LIMITED—See B. Grimm Group; *Int'l,* pg. 788
B. GRIMM CARRIER (THAILAND) LIMITED—See Carrier Global Corporation; *U.S. Public,* pg. 440
B.GRIMM TRADING CORPORATION LIMITED—See B. Grimm Group; *Int'l,* pg. 788
BILL LYNCH ASSOCIATES, LLC; *U.S. Private,* pg. 557
BITZER AUSTRIA GMBH—See BITZER SE; *Int'l,* pg. 1051
BITZER BENELUX BVBA—See BITZER SE; *Int'l,* pg. 1051
BITZER CANADA INC.—See BITZER SE; *Int'l,* pg. 1051
BITZER CIS LTD.—See BITZER SE; *Int'l,* pg. 1051
BITZER COMPRESSORES LTDA—See BITZER SE; *Int'l,* pg. 1051
BITZER COMPRESSORES S.A.—See BITZER SE; *Int'l,* pg. 1051
BITZER COMPRESSORS (BEIJING) LTD.—See BITZER SE; *Int'l,* pg. 1051
BITZER FRANCE S.A.R.L.—See BITZER SE; *Int'l,* pg. 1051
BITZER INDIA PRIVATE LIMITED—See BITZER SE; *Int'l,* pg. 1051
BITZER ITALIA S.R.L.—See BITZER SE; *Int'l,* pg. 1051
BITZER JAPAN K.K.—See BITZER SE; *Int'l,* pg. 1051
BITZER KOREA CO., LTD.—See BITZER SE; *Int'l,* pg. 1051
BITZER KUHLMASCHINENBAU (S.A.) (PROPRIETARY) LTD.—See BITZER SE; *Int'l,* pg. 1051
BITZER MEXICO, S. DE R.L. DE C.V.—See BITZER SE; *Int'l,* pg. 1051
BITZER (PORTUGAL) COMPRESSORES PARA FRIO, S.A.—See BITZER SE; *Int'l,* pg. 1051
BITZER REFRIGERATION ASIA LIMITED—See BITZER SE; *Int'l,* pg. 1051
BITZER REFRIGERATION ASIA PTE., LTD.—See BITZER SE; *Int'l,* pg. 1051
BITZER REFRIGERATION ASIA PTE. LTD.—See BITZER SE; *Int'l,* pg. 1051
BITZER REFRIGERATION ASIA PTE LTD—See BITZER SE; *Int'l,* pg. 1051
BITZER REFRIGERATION TECHNOLOGY (CHINA) CO. LTD.—See BITZER SE; *Int'l,* pg. 1051
BITZER SCROLL, INC.—See BITZER SE; *Int'l,* pg. 1052
BITZER (SOUTH EAST ASIA) SDN. BHD.—See BITZER SE; *Int'l,* pg. 1051
BITZER UK LIMITED—See BITZER SE; *Int'l,* pg. 1052
BKW AEK CONTRACTING AG—See BKW AG; *Int'l,* pg. 1054
BLEVINS INC.; *U.S. Private,* pg. 581
BLUE STAR INTERNATIONAL FZCO—See Blue Star Limited; *Int'l,* pg. 1070
BLUE STAR QATAR WLL—See Blue Star Limited; *Int'l,* pg. 1070
BOONE PLUMBING & HEATING SUPPLY INC.—See Groupe Deschenes Inc.; *Int'l,* pg. 3101
BRADFORD INDUSTRIAL SUPPLY; *U.S. Private,* pg. 631
BRAUER SUPPLY COMPANY; *U.S. Private,* pg. 640
BRINK-INNOSOURCE GMBH—See CENTROTEC SE; *Int'l,* pg. 1414
BROCK-MCVEY COMPANY—See A.Y. McDonald Manufacturing Co.; *U.S. Private,* pg. 29
BRUCE-ROGERS COMPANY—See Ferguson plc; *Int'l,* pg. 2637

N.A.I.C.S. INDEX

423730 — WARM AIR HEATING AN...

BRUNDAGE ASSOCIATES INCORPORATED; *U.S. Private*, pg. 672
BTN TURBOCHARGER SERVICE LIMITED—See Blackstone Inc.; *U.S. Public*, pg. 359
BUCKLEY ASSOCIATES INC.; *U.S. Private*, pg. 678
BUTCHER DISTRIBUTORS INC.; *U.S. Private*, pg. 696
CALIFORNIA HYDRONICS CORPORATION; *U.S. Private*, pg. 719
CALVERLEY SUPPLY CO. INC.; *U.S. Private*, pg. 724
CARRIER BRYANT MIDSOUTH—See Carrier Global Corporation; *U.S. Public*, pg. 440
CARRIER ENTERPRISE NORTHEAST, LLC—See Watsco, Inc.; *U.S. Public*, pg. 2336
CARRIER KUWAIT AIRCONDITIONING K.S.C.—See Carrier Global Corporation; *U.S. Public*, pg. 442
CARRIER (MALAYSIA) SDN. BHD.—See Carrier Global Corporation; *U.S. Public*, pg. 440
CARRIER OKLAHOMA—See Carrier Global Corporation; *U.S. Public*, pg. 442
CARRIER OY—See Carrier Global Corporation; *U.S. Public*, pg. 443
CARRIER (PUERTO RICO), INC.—See Watsco, Inc.; *U.S. Public*, pg. 2336
CARRIER PUERTO RICO—See Carrier Global Corporation; *U.S. Public*, pg. 442
CARRIER SINGAPORE (PTE.) LTD.—See Carrier Global Corporation; *U.S. Public*, pg. 442
CARRIER (THAILAND) LIMITED—See Carrier Global Corporation; *U.S. Public*, pg. 440
CARRIER VIETNAM AIR CONDITIONING COMPANY LIMITED—See Carrier Global Corporation; *U.S. Public*, pg. 443
CARROLL AIR SYSTEMS INC.—See Daikin Industries, Ltd.; *Int'l*, pg. 1936
CARR SUPPLY INC.; *U.S. Private*, pg. 771
CAYCE MILL SUPPLY COMPANY INC.; *U.S. Private*, pg. 795
CENTURY AIR CONDITIONING SUPPLY INC.; *U.S. Private*, pg. 831
CFM COMPANY; *U.S. Private*, pg. 843
CFM DISTRIBUTORS, INC.; *U.S. Private*, pg. 843
CFM EQUIPMENT DISTRIBUTORS INC.; *U.S. Private*, pg. 843
CGL CORPORATION; *U.S. Private*, pg. 844
CHARLES D. JONES & COMPANY INC.; *U.S. Private*, pg. 851
CHOFU SEISAKUSHO CO., LTD.; *Int'l*, pg. 1577
CIVIMECH (PVT) LTD—See Daikin Industries, Ltd.; *Int'l*, pg. 1932
CLIMA SVERIGE AB—See Beijer Ref AB; *Int'l*, pg. 944
CLIMATIC COMFORT PRODUCTS, LLC—See The Climatic Corporation; *U.S. Private*, pg. 4010
CLIMAT LOCATION SAS—See ANDREWS SYKES GROUP PLC; *Int'l*, pg. 452
COASTAL SUPPLY COMPANY INC.—See Beijer Ref AB; *Int'l*, pg. 944
COBURN SUPPLY COMPANY INC; *U.S. Private*, pg. 958
COMFORT AIR DISTRIBUTING INC.—See Ridgemont Partners Management LLC; *U.S. Private*, pg. 3433
COMFORT SERVICES INC.; *U.S. Private*, pg. 981
COMFORT SUPPLY, INC.; *U.S. Private*, pg. 981
COMFORT SUPPLY; *U.S. Private*, pg. 981
CONCEPCION INDUSTRIAL CORPORATION; *Int'l*, pg. 1764
CONFIDENCE TRADE LIMITED—See Daikin Industries, Ltd.; *Int'l*, pg. 1932
CONTRACTORS HEATING-COOLING SUPPLY, LLC; *U.S. Private*, pg. 1032
CONTROL HOLDINGS CORPORATION; *U.S. Private*, pg. 1034
COOLMARK BV—See Beijer Ref AB; *Int'l*, pg. 944
COOL OR COSY (QLD) PTY. LTD.—See AWN Holdings Limited; *Int'l*, pg. 753
COOLTECH ENGINEERING SERVICES (PVT) LTD.—See Daikin Industries, Ltd.; *Int'l*, pg. 1932
CORKEN STEEL PRODUCTS COMPANY; *U.S. Private*, pg. 1050
CRESCENT PARTS & EQUIPMENT COMPANY; *U.S. Private*, pg. 1094
CUSTOM WHOLESALE SUPPLY CO. INC.; *U.S. Private*, pg. 1130
DAIKIN AIR CONDITIONING ARGENTINA S.A.—See Daikin Industries, Ltd.; *Int'l*, pg. 1933
DAIKIN AIRCONDITIONING ARGENTINA—See Daikin Industries, Ltd.; *Int'l*, pg. 1933
DAIKIN AIRCONDITIONING CHILE S.A.—See Daikin Industries, Ltd.; *Int'l*, pg. 1933
DAIKIN AIRCONDITIONING COLOMBIA S.A.S—See Daikin Industries, Ltd.; *Int'l*, pg. 1933
DAIKIN AIR CONDITIONING EGYPT S.A.E.—See Daikin Industries, Ltd.; *Int'l*, pg. 1933
DAIKIN AIRCONDITIONING GREECE S. A.—See Daikin Industries, Ltd.; *Int'l*, pg. 1933
DAIKIN AIRCONDITIONING INDIA PRIVATE LIMITED—See Daikin Industries, Ltd.; *Int'l*, pg. 1933
DAIKIN AIRCONDITIONING KOREA CO., LTD.—See Daikin Industries, Ltd.; *Int'l*, pg. 1933
DAIKIN AIRCONDITIONING (MALAYSIA) SDN., BHD.—See Daikin Industries, Ltd.; *Int'l*, pg. 1933
DAIKIN AIRCONDITIONING MEXICO, S. DE R.L. DE C.V.—See Daikin Industries, Ltd.; *Int'l*, pg. 1933
DAIKIN AIRCONDITIONING PERU S.A.C.—See Daikin Industries, Ltd.; *Int'l*, pg. 1933
DAIKIN AIRCONDITIONING POLAND SP. Z O.O.—See Daikin Industries, Ltd.; *Int'l*, pg. 1933
DAIKIN AIRCONDITIONING PORTUGAL S.A.—See Daikin Industries, Ltd.; *Int'l*, pg. 1933
DAIKIN AIR CONDITIONING (VIETNAM) JOINT STOCK COMPANY—See Daikin Industries, Ltd.; *Int'l*, pg. 1932
DAIKIN APPLIED GERMANY GMBH—See Daikin Industries, Ltd.; *Int'l*, pg. 1933
DAIKIN APPLIED LATIN AMERICA, L.L.C—See Daikin Industries, Ltd.; *Int'l*, pg. 1933
DAIKIN APPLIED (MALAYSIA) SDN. BHD.—See Daikin Industries, Ltd.; *Int'l*, pg. 1933
DAIKIN ARKEMA REFRIGERANTS TRADING (SHANGHAI) CO., LTD.—See Daikin Industries, Ltd.; *Int'l*, pg. 1934
DAIKIN CHEMICAL SOUTHEAST ASIA CO., LTD.—See Daikin Industries, Ltd.; *Int'l*, pg. 1934
DAIKIN FUKUSHI SERVICE CO., LTD.—See Daikin Industries, Ltd.; *Int'l*, pg. 1934
DAIKIN HOLDINGS (USA), INC.—See Daikin Industries, Ltd.; *Int'l*, pg. 1934
DAIKIN HVAC SOLUTION TOHOKU CO., LTD.—See Daikin Industries, Ltd.; *Int'l*, pg. 1934
DAIKIN MALAYSIA SALES & SERVICE SDN. BHD.—See Daikin Industries, Ltd.; *Int'l*, pg. 1934
DAIKIN MCQUAY MIDDLE EAST FZE—See Daikin Industries, Ltd.; *Int'l*, pg. 1935
DAIKIN U.S. CORPORATION—See Daikin Industries, Ltd.; *Int'l*, pg. 1935
DAMUTH TRANE; *U.S. Private*, pg. 1151
DEALERS SUPPLY COMPANY INC.; *U.S. Private*, pg. 1182
DE LA RUE BV—See De La Rue plc; *Int'l*, pg. 1996
DELTA NEU BENELUX N.V.—See Groupe SFPI SA; *Int'l*, pg. 3111
DELTA NEU LIMITED—See Groupe SFPI SA; *Int'l*, pg. 3111
DELTA NEU MAROC S.A.—See Groupe SFPI SA; *Int'l*, pg. 3111
DELTA NEU NEDERLAND BV—See Groupe SFPI SA; *Int'l*, pg. 3111
DELTA NEU S.A.S.—See Groupe SFPI SA; *Int'l*, pg. 3111
DELTA T EQUIPMENT; *U.S. Private*, pg. 1202
DENSO ACE CORPORATION—See Denso Corporation; *Int'l*, pg. 2029
DENSO SALES BELGIUM N.V.—See Denso Corporation; *Int'l*, pg. 2031
DESCAIR INC.—See Groupe Deschenes Inc.; *Int'l*, pg. 3101
DESCHENES & FILS LTEE—See Groupe Deschenes Inc.; *Int'l*, pg. 3101
DESCHENES & FILS LTEE—See Groupe Deschenes Inc.; *Int'l*, pg. 3102
DESCO PLUMBING & HEATING SUPPLY INC.—See Groupe Deschenes Inc.; *Int'l*, pg. 3102
DESIGN AIR—See U.S. Venture, Inc.; *U.S. Private*, pg. 4272
DIAL INDUSTRIES INCORPORATED; *U.S. Private*, pg. 1222
DIAL MANUFACTURING INC.—See Dial Industries Incorporated; *U.S. Private*, pg. 1222
DINAIR EKONOMIFILTER AS—See Daikin Industries, Ltd.; *Int'l*, pg. 1936
DINAIR FILTON SIA—See Daikin Industries, Ltd.; *Int'l*, pg. 1936
DISTRIBUTOR CORPORATION OF NEW ENGLAND INC.; *U.S. Private*, pg. 1239
DMG CORPORATION; *U.S. Private*, pg. 1248
DONALDSON NEDERLAND B.V.—See Donaldson Company, Inc.; *U.S. Public*, pg. 675
DUKIN INDUSTRIES CO., LTD.—See Daikin Industries, Ltd.; *Int'l*, pg. 1935
DUNCAN SUPPLY CO. INC.; *U.S. Private*, pg. 1288
DUNPHEY & ASSOCIATES SUPPLY CO.—See Watsco, Inc.; *U.S. Public*, pg. 2336
DVL GROUP, INC.; *U.S. Private*, pg. 1295
DYNAC UK LTD.—See Dynac Sdn. Bhd.; *Int'l*, pg. 2238
EAST COAST METAL DISTRIBUTORS—See Watsco, Inc.; *U.S. Public*, pg. 2336
ECM (USA), INC.—See ECM Technologies SAS; *Int'l*, pg. 2292
ECONOMY REFRIGERATION HEATING VENTILATION SUPPLY CORP.; *U.S. Private*, pg. 1330
EDENKOOL PTE LTD—See Far East Group Limited; *Int'l*, pg. 2616
ED'S SUPPLY COMPANY INC.—See Gryphon Investors, LLC; *U.S. Private*, pg. 1798
ELECTRO MART LIMITED—See Daikin Industries, Ltd.; *Int'l*, pg. 1935
ELITE RADIO & ENGINEERING CO., LTD.—See Daikin Industries, Ltd.; *Int'l*, pg. 1935
EMERSON CLIMATE TECHNOLOGIES AUSTRALIA PTY. LTD.—See Emerson Electric Co.; *U.S. Public*, pg. 743
EMERSON CLIMATE TECHNOLOGIES, S.R.O.—See Emerson Electric Co.; *U.S. Public*, pg. 745
EMERSON ELECTRIC (TAIWAN) COMPANY LIMITED—See Emerson Electric Co.; *U.S. Public*, pg. 744
EMTROL-BUELL TECHNOLOGIES—See CECO Environmental Corp.; *U.S. Public*, pg. 463
ENDRESS+HAUSER B.V.—See Endress+Hauser (International) Holding AG; *Int'l*, pg. 2407
ENDRESS+HAUSER PORTUGAL, LDA—See Endress+Hauser (International) Holding AG; *Int'l*, pg. 2407
ENERGY TRANSFER SOLUTIONS INC—See DVL Group, Inc.; *U.S. Private*, pg. 1295
E.ON AVACON WARME GMBH—See E.ON SE; *Int'l*, pg. 2252
E.ON VARME SVERIGE AB—See E.ON SE; *Int'l*, pg. 2255
EPTING DISTRIBUTORS INC.; *U.S. Private*, pg. 1414
EQUINOXE KFT CG—See Beijer Ref AB; *Int'l*, pg. 944
EXCELSIOR MANUFACTURING & SUPPLY CORP.—See Carrier Global Corporation; *U.S. Public*, pg. 444
EXCELSIOR MANUFACTURING & SUPPLY CORP.—See Watsco, Inc.; *U.S. Public*, pg. 2336
FAMOUS DISTRIBUTION INC.—See Famous Enterprises Inc.; *U.S. Private*, pg. 1471
FAMOUS ENTERPRISES INC.; *U.S. Private*, pg. 1471
FAR EAST ENTERPRISES (PENANG) SD BHD—See Far East Group Limited; *Int'l*, pg. 2616
FAULKNER/HAYNES & ASSOCIATES, INC.; *U.S. Private*, pg. 1483
FERGUSON HEATING & COOLING—See Ferguson plc; *Int'l*, pg. 2637
FERGUSON LYON CONKLIN & COMPANY INC.—See Ferguson plc; *Int'l*, pg. 2638
FILTER & COATING TECHNOLOGY, INC.—See Genstar Capital, LLC; *U.S. Private*, pg. 1678
FILTROS BALDWIN DE MEXICO S.A. DE C.V.—See Parker Hannifin Corporation; *U.S. Public*, pg. 1641
FLEGLER INVESTMENT COMPANY; *U.S. Private*, pg. 1542
FLINT WARM AIR SUPPLY CO. (FWA); *U.S. Private*, pg. 1545
FRANCE AIR MANAGEMENT SA—See AIRVANCE GROUP; *Int'l*, pg. 250
FRESCO EME LIMITED—See Daikin Industries, Ltd.; *Int'l*, pg. 1935
FUJI ELECTRIC INDIA PVT. LTD.—See Fuji Electric Co., Ltd.; *Int'l*, pg. 2811
GBG INC. OF PENNSYLVANIA; *U.S. Private*, pg. 1653
GBS LTD.—See Gil-Bar Industries, Inc.; *U.S. Private*, pg. 1698
GEA POLACEL COOLING TOWERS, LLC—See GEA Group Aktiengesellschaft; *Int'l*, pg. 2901
GEARY PACIFIC CORPORATION; *U.S. Private*, pg. 1655
GEARY PACIFIC OF ARIZONA - FORT MOJAVE—See Geary Pacific Corporation; *U.S. Private*, pg. 1655
GEARY PACIFIC SUPPLY - SACRAMENTO—See Geary Pacific Corporation; *U.S. Private*, pg. 1655
GEBERIT PLUMBING TECHNOLOGY INDIA PVT. LTD.—See Geberit AG; *Int'l*, pg. 2905
GEMAIRE DISTRIBUTORS LLC—See Watsco, Inc.; *U.S. Public*, pg. 2336
GENERAL WHOLESALE DISTRIBUTORS; *U.S. Private*, pg. 1668
GEORGE T. HALL CO. INC.; *U.S. Private*, pg. 1683
GIL-BAR INDUSTRIES, INC.; *U.S. Private*, pg. 1698
GOALAND ENERGY CONSERVATION TECH USA LTD.—See Guangzhou Goaland Energy Conservation Tech Co., Ltd.; *Int'l*, pg. 3165
GOODMAN DISTRIBUTION—See Daikin Industries, Ltd.; *Int'l*, pg. 1935
GOODMAN DISTRIBUTION—See Daikin Industries, Ltd.; *Int'l*, pg. 1935
GOODMAN DISTRIBUTION—See Daikin Industries, Ltd.; *Int'l*, pg. 1935
GOODMAN DISTRIBUTION SOUTHEAST, INC.—See Daikin Industries, Ltd.; *Int'l*, pg. 1935
GRAHAM VACUUM AND HEAT TRANSFER TECHNOLOGY CO., LTD.—See Graham Corporation; *U.S. Public*, pg. 954
GREEN POINT ASIA PACIFIC PTE. LTD.—See BITZER SE; *Int'l*, pg. 1052
GREEN POINT KOREA CO. LTD.—See BITZER SE; *Int'l*, pg. 1052
GREEN POINT UK LIMITED—See BITZER SE; *Int'l*, pg. 1052
GREENPOINT US, LLC—See BITZER SE; *Int'l*, pg. 1052
GROUPE AIRWELL SA; *Int'l*, pg. 3091
GUANGZHOU NEWLY MECHANICAL & ELECTRICAL CO., LTD.—See Daikin Industries, Ltd.; *Int'l*, pg. 1935
GUANGZHOU SMART GRID INFORMATION TECHNOLOGY CO., LTD.—See Guangzhou Goaland Energy Conservation Tech Co., Ltd.; *Int'l*, pg. 3165
GUSTAVE A. LARSON COMPANY; *U.S. Private*, pg. 1819
G.W. BERKHEIMER CO. INC.; *U.S. Private*, pg. 1631
THE HABEGGER CORPORATION; *U.S. Private*, pg. 4041
HAROON ENGINEERING LTD.—See Daikin Industries, Ltd.; *Int'l*, pg. 1935
HARP INTERNATIONAL LIMITED; *Int'l*, pg. 3278
HARP MIDDLE EAST L.L.C—See Harp International Limited; *Int'l*, pg. 3278
HARP USA INC.—See Harp International Limited; *Int'l*, pg. 3278
THE HARRY ALTER COMPANY—See Carrier Global Cor-

423730 — WARM AIR HEATING AN...

poration; *U.S. Public*, pg. 444
THE HARRY ALTER COMPANY—See Watsco, Inc.; *U.S. Public*, pg. 2337
HAYNES MECHANICAL SYSTEMS; *U.S. Private*, pg. 1885
HEATING & COOLING SUPPLY LLC—See Watsco, Inc.; *U.S. Public*, pg. 2336
HEIDLER HOLDINGS, INC.—See Core & Main, Inc.; *U.S. Public*, pg. 576
HENG YI DA MACHINE (YINCHUAN) CO., LTD.—See Daikin Industries, Ltd.; *Int'l*, pg. 1935
HIDRIA BH D.O.O.—See Hidria d.o.o.; *Int'l*, pg. 3384
HIDRIA C.Z.—See Hidria d.o.o.; *Int'l*, pg. 3384
HIDRIA D.O.O.E.L.—See Hidria d.o.o.; *Int'l*, pg. 3384
HIDRIA PODGORICA D.O.O.—See Hidria d.o.o.; *Int'l*, pg. 3384
HIDRIA POLSKA SP. Z O.O.—See Hidria d.o.o.; *Int'l*, pg. 3384
HIMAL REFRIGERATION & ELECTRICAL INDUSTRIES PVT. LTD.—See Daikin Industries, Ltd.; *Int'l*, pg. 1935
HITACHI PLANT TECHNOLOGIES, LTD.—See Hitachi, Ltd.; *Int'l*, pg. 3420
HOBBS AND ASSOCIATES INC.—See Madison Dearborn Partners, LLC; *U.S. Private*, pg. 2541
HOFFMAN & HOFFMAN INC.; *U.S. Private*, pg. 1959
HOKUETSU INDUSTRIES EUROPE B.V.—See Hokuetsu Industries Co., Ltd.; *Int'l*, pg. 3444
HOTAI DEVELOPMENT CO., LTD.—See Daikin Industries, Ltd.; *Int'l*, pg. 1935
HOWARD INDUSTRIES; *U.S. Private*, pg. 1994
HOWDEN JAPAN LIMITED—See Chart Industries, Inc.; *U.S. Public*, pg. 482
HOWDEN TURBOMACHINERY S.R.L.—See Chart Industries, Inc.; *U.S. Public*, pg. 482
HOWDEN UK LIMITED—See Chart Industries, Inc.; *U.S. Public*, pg. 482
HOWDEN VENTILATOREN GMBH—See Chart Industries, Inc.; *U.S. Public*, pg. 482
HRP LIMITED—See Beijer Ref AB; *Int'l*, pg. 944
HUMAK ENGINEERING (PVT) LTD.—See Daikin Industries, Ltd.; *Int'l*, pg. 1935
THE HUNTON GROUP; *U.S. Private*, pg. 4055
HVAC DISTRIBUTORS, INC.; *U.S. Private*, pg. 2015
HVAC ENGINEERING LIMITED—See Daikin Industries, Ltd.; *Int'l*, pg. 1935
HVAC SALES AND SUPPLY CO. INC.; *U.S. Private*, pg. 2015
HYDRONIC & STEAM EQUIPMENT CO., INC.; *U.S. Private*, pg. 2018
ICE ENERGY INC.; *U.S. Private*, pg. 2030
IDAC (PRIVATE) LIMITED—See Daikin Industries, Ltd.; *Int'l*, pg. 1935
IKM HVAC PRODUCTION SP. Z.O.O.—See IKM Gruppen AS; *Int'l*, pg. 3611
INCE DISTRIBUTING INCORPORATED; *U.S. Private*, pg. 2053
INGERSOLL-RAND AB—See Ingersoll Rand Inc.; *U.S. Public*, pg. 1121
INGERSOLL-RAND GMBH—See Ingersoll Rand Inc.; *U.S. Public*, pg. 1121
INGERSOLL-RAND ITS JAPAN LTD.—See Ingersoll Rand Inc.; *U.S. Public*, pg. 1121
INGERSOLL-RAND S.A. DE C.V.—See Ingersoll Rand Inc.; *U.S. Public*, pg. 1121
INJAR, S.A.—See ACS, Actividades de Construccion y Servicios, S.A.; *Int'l*, pg. 114
INTERNATIONAL COMPRESSOR DISTRIBUTION N.V.—See Atlas Copco AB; *Int'l*, pg. 678
ISA INSTALLATIONS-,STEUERUNGS UND AUTOMATISIERUNGS GMBH—See Icahn Enterprises L.P.; *U.S. Public*, pg. 1084
JACKSON SUPPLY COMPANY; *U.S. Private*, pg. 2178
JAMES M. PLEASANTS COMPANY INC.; *U.S. Private*, pg. 2184
JAY N. NELSON INC.; *U.S. Private*, pg. 2192
J&B SUPPLY, INC.; *U.S. Private*, pg. 2154
JOHNSON SUPPLY & EQUIPMENT CORP.; *U.S. Private*, pg. 2229
JOHNSTONE SUPPLY INC.; *U.S. Private*, pg. 2230
JOHNSTONE SUPPLY, INC.—See Johnstone Supply Inc.; *U.S. Private*, pg. 2230
JORBAN-RISCOE ASSOCIATES INC.; *U.S. Private*, pg. 2234
J.S.S ENTERPRISES (PVT) LTD.—See Daikin Industries, Ltd.; *Int'l*, pg. 1935
KADE TRADING GMBH—See Standard Motor Products, Inc.; *U.S. Public*, pg. 1929
KAILING HYDRAULIC TECHNOLOGY (SHANGHAI) CO., LTD.—See Daikin Industries, Ltd.; *Int'l*, pg. 1935
KAN-THERM GMBH—See Aalberts N.V.; *Int'l*, pg. 34
KBC, INC.; *U.S. Private*, pg. 2268
K D HYDRAULICS, LTD.—See Daikin Industries, Ltd.; *Int'l*, pg. 1935
KEIHIN PANALFA LTD.—See Hitachi Astemo, Ltd.; *Int'l*, pg. 3409
KLIMAMIETEN AS GMBH—See ANDREWS SYKES GROUP PLC; *Int'l*, pg. 452
KOCH AIR LLC—See Koch Enterprises, Inc.; *U.S. Private*, pg. 2326

KOCH AIR—See Koch Enterprises, Inc.; *U.S. Private*, pg. 2326
KSW, INC.—See The Related Companies, L.P.; *U.S. Private*, pg. 4103
L&H AIRCO; *U.S. Private*, pg. 2362
LIEBERT CORPORATION—See Vertiv Holdings Co; *U.S. Public*, pg. 2289
LIN CHI HYDRAULICS CO., LTD.—See Daikin Industries, Ltd.; *Int'l*, pg. 1936
LODAM ELECTRONICS A/S—See BITZER SE; *Int'l*, pg. 1052
LOGIS-TECH, INC.; *U.S. Private*, pg. 2481
LOHMILLER & COMPANY; *U.S. Private*, pg. 2482
LONG BUILDING TECHNOLOGIES; *U.S. Private*, pg. 2490
LONGLEY SUPPLY COMPANY, INC.—See Longley Supply Company, Inc.; *U.S. Private*, pg. 2492
L.R. GORRELL COMPANY INC.; *U.S. Private*, pg. 2367
MARLEY ENGINEERED PRODUCTS—See SPX Technologies, Inc.; *U.S. Public*, pg. 1921
M&A SUPPLY COMPANY INC.; *U.S. Private*, pg. 2524
MAXITROL COMPANY - COLON DIVISION—See Maxitrol Company; *U.S. Private*, pg. 2619
MCCALLS INC.; *U.S. Private*, pg. 2626
MCN DISTRIBUTORS INC.; *U.S. Private*, pg. 2643
MECHANICAL EQUIPMENT CO. INC.—See Mingledorff's Inc.; *U.S. Private*, pg. 2742
MECHANICAL REPS INC.—See Mechanical Reps Inc.; *U.S. Private*, pg. 2649
MIA CORPORATION (PVT) LTD.—See Daikin Industries, Ltd.; *Int'l*, pg. 1936
MICONTROLS INC.—See The Stephens Group, LLC; *U.S. Private*, pg. 4121
MIDGLEY-HUBER INC.; *U.S. Private*, pg. 2714
MID-WAY SUPPLY INC.; *U.S. Private*, pg. 2709
MINGLEDORFF'S INC.; *U.S. Private*, pg. 2742
M.K. ELECTRONICS LIMITED—See Daikin Industries, Ltd.; *Int'l*, pg. 1936
MONROE EQUIPMENT, INC.; *U.S. Private*, pg. 2773
MUNCH'S SUPPLY LLC—See Ridgemont Partners Management LLC; *U.S. Private*, pg. 3433
NANDEE INTER-TRADE CO., LTD.—See Daikin Industries, Ltd.; *Int'l*, pg. 1936
NATIONAL EXCELSIOR COMPANY—See Carrier Global Corporation; *U.S. Public*, pg. 444
NATIONAL EXCELSIOR COMPANY—See Watsco, Inc.; *U.S. Public*, pg. 2336
NAUGHTON'S PLUMBING SALES CO., INC.; *U.S. Private*, pg. 2868
N B HANDY & CO INC.—See Industrial Opportunity Partners, LLC; *U.S. Private*, pg. 2067
NEREUS OY—See Georg Fischer AG; *Int'l*, pg. 2937
NEW JERSEY METER CO.—See Elaine, Inc.; *U.S. Private*, pg. 1349
NICHOLAS CONSOLIDATED INC.; *U.S. Private*, pg. 2925
NICOTRA GEBHARDT NV—See Regal Rexnord Corporation; *U.S. Public*, pg. 1773
NITRIANSKA TEPLARENSKA SPOLOCNOST, A.S.—See Arca Capital Slovakia, A.S.; *Int'l*, pg. 539
NORMAN S. WRIGHT & CO.; *U.S. Private*, pg. 2938
NORMAN WRIGHT MECHANICAL EQUIPMENT CORP.; *U.S. Private*, pg. 2938
N.V. DANFOSS S.A.—See Danfoss A/S; *Int'l*, pg. 1961
O'CONNOR COMPANY INC.; *U.S. Private*, pg. 2978
O'CONNOR COMPANY; *U.S. Private*, pg. 2978
OK KIZAI CO., LTD.—See Daikin Industries, Ltd.; *Int'l*, pg. 1936
ON SITE POWER CO., LTD.—See Idemitsu Kosan Co., Ltd.; *Int'l*, pg. 3592
OREGON SCIENTIFIC (DEUTSCHLAND) GMBH—See IDT International Limited; *Int'l*, pg. 3596
PARTS SERVICES INTERNATIONAL LLC—See Industrial Distribution Resources, LLC; *U.S. Private*, pg. 2065
PEIRCE-PHELPS, INC.; *U.S. Private*, pg. 3130
PENGUIN ENGINEERING LIMITED—See Daikin Industries, Ltd.; *Int'l*, pg. 1936
POLARPUMPEN AB—See BHG Group AB; *Int'l*, pg. 1014
PORT ENTERPRISES (GUAM) INC.—See Daikin Industries, Ltd.; *Int'l*, pg. 1936
POTTER DISTRIBUTING INCORPORATED; *U.S. Private*, pg. 3235
POWER FLUIDTRONICS & INDUSTRIES SDN. BHD.—See Daikin Industries, Ltd.; *Int'l*, pg. 1936
PREMIER ENGINEERING LTD.—See Daikin Industries, Ltd.; *Int'l*, pg. 1936
PREMIER SALES INC.; *U.S. Private*, pg. 3251
PRODFROID SA—See Ackermans & van Haaren NV; *Int'l*, pg. 105
PT. BITZER COMPRESSORS INDONESIA—See BITZER SE; *Int'l*, pg. 1052
PT. DAIKIN AIRCONDITIONING INDONESIA—See Daikin Industries, Ltd.; *Int'l*, pg. 1936
PT. DAIKIN APPLIED SOLUTIONS INDONESIA—See Daikin Industries, Ltd.; *Int'l*, pg. 1936
PT. ETERNA KARYA SEJAHTERA—See Daikin Industries, Ltd.; *Int'l*, pg. 1936
R.A. TOWNSEND COMPANY; *U.S. Private*, pg. 3334
REFRICENTER OF MIAMI INC.—See Refricentro Inc.; *U.S. Private*, pg. 3384

REFRICENTRO INC.; *U.S. Private*, pg. 3384
RELIANCE COMFORT LIMITED PARTNERSHIP—See CK Asset Holdings Limited; *Int'l*, pg. 1635
R.E. MICHEL COMPANY INC.; *U.S. Private*, pg. 3335
R.F. PECK CO., INC.—See Ardian SAS; *Int'l*, pg. 554
RILEY SALES INC.; *U.S. Private*, pg. 3437
RL DEPPMANN COMPANY; *U.S. Private*, pg. 3450
R.L. KISTLER INC.; *U.S. Private*, pg. 3338
ROBERT MADDEN INDUSTRIES; *U.S. Private*, pg. 3458
ROCHESTER SUPPLY CORPORATION—See First Supply LLC; *U.S. Private*, pg. 1529
RUSSELL SIGLER INC.; *U.S. Private*, pg. 3507
SAS DECTRON COMPANY—See Madison Industries Holdings LLC; *U.S. Private*, pg. 2543
SCAN ENGINEERING (PVT) LTD.—See Daikin Industries, Ltd.; *Int'l*, pg. 1936
SC GEA KLIMATECHNIK SRL—See GEA Group Aktiengesellschaft; *Int'l*, pg. 2903
SEM DAIKIN CO, LTD.—See Daikin Industries, Ltd.; *Int'l*, pg. 1936
S.G. TORRICE CO., INC.—See Ferguson plc; *Int'l*, pg. 2638
SHANGHAI HONGKAI HYDLAULICS EQUIPMENT CO., LTD.—See Daikin Industries, Ltd.; *Int'l*, pg. 1936
SHORE DISTRIBUTORS INC.; *U.S. Private*, pg. 3641
SIAM DAIKIN SALES CO., LTD.—See Daikin Industries, Ltd.; *Int'l*, pg. 1936
SIG AIR HANDLING HUNGARY KFT—See AIRVANCE GROUP; *Int'l*, pg. 250
SIG AIR HANDLING ROMANIA SRL—See AIRVANCE GROUP; *Int'l*, pg. 250
SLAKEY BROTHERS INC.; *U.S. Private*, pg. 3687
SMARTEDGE; *U.S. Private*, pg. 3692
SOLAR SUPPLY, INC.; *U.S. Private*, pg. 3707
SOLAR SUPPLY OF HOUSTON INC.—See Solar Supply, Inc.; *U.S. Private*, pg. 3707
SOLAR SUPPLY OF LAFAYETTE INC.—See Solar Supply, Inc.; *U.S. Private*, pg. 3707
SOLAR SUPPLY OF LAKE CHARLES INC.—See Solar Supply, Inc.; *U.S. Private*, pg. 3707
SOLAR SUPPLY OF LOUISIANA INC.—See Solar Supply, Inc.; *U.S. Private*, pg. 3707
SOUTH CENTRAL COMPANY INC.; *U.S. Private*, pg. 3720
SOUTHERN REFRIGERATION CORP.; *U.S. Private*, pg. 3735
SOUTH SIDE CONTROL SUPPLY CO.; *U.S. Private*, pg. 3724
SPECIALTY A/C PRODUCTS INC.; *U.S. Private*, pg. 3749
SPX TECHNOLOGIES (PTY) LTD.—See SPX Technologies, Inc.; *U.S. Public*, pg. 1921
S.R.S. BITZER S.A.R.L.—See BITZER SE; *Int'l*, pg. 1052
STANDARD AIR & LITE CORPORATION; *U.S. Private*, pg. 3777
STANDARD SUPPLY & DISTRIBUTING CO. INC.; *U.S. Private*, pg. 3781
STORER EQUIPMENT COMPANY LTD.; *U.S. Private*, pg. 3831
SUNBELT RENTALS CLIMATE CONTROL SERVICES—See Ashtead Group Plc; *Int'l*, pg. 609
SUNRUN INC.; *U.S. Public*, pg. 1965
SUPERIOR DISTRIBUTION OF INDIANAPOLIS; *U.S. Private*, pg. 3876
SUPERIOR DISTRIBUTORS OF CHICAGO—See Superior Distribution of Indianapolis; *U.S. Private*, pg. 3876
SUPERIOR EQUIPMENT SALES INC.; *U.S. Private*, pg. 3877
SUPERMARKET ENVIRONMENTAL SERVICES CO.; *U.S. Private*, pg. 3881
S.W. ANDERSON SALES CORP.—See Ferguson plc; *Int'l*, pg. 2638
TAICIN SY CO., LTD.—See Daikin Industries, Ltd.; *Int'l*, pg. 1936
TAIWAN DAIKIN ADVANCED CHEMICALS, INC.—See Daikin Industries, Ltd.; *Int'l*, pg. 1936
TAIWAN NICHINETU CO., LTD.—See Air Water Inc.; *Int'l*, pg. 1936
TARRANT SERVICE, INC.; *U.S. Private*, pg. 3934
TECHNO HVAC SYSTEM LTD.—See Daikin Industries, Ltd.; *Int'l*, pg. 1936
TEMPERATURE CONTROL SYSTEMS, INC.—See The Stephens Group, LLC; *U.S. Private*, pg. 4121
TEMPERATURE EQUIPMENT CORPORATION - MELROSE PARK—See Carrier Global Corporation; *U.S. Public*, pg. 444
TEMPERATURE EQUIPMENT CORPORATION - MELROSE PARK—See Watsco, Inc.; *U.S. Public*, pg. 2336
TEMPERATURE EQUIPMENT CORPORATION—See Carrier Global Corporation; *U.S. Public*, pg. 444
TEMPERATURE EQUIPMENT CORPORATION—See Watsco, Inc.; *U.S. Public*, pg. 2336
TEMPERATURE SYSTEMS, INC.; *U.S. Private*, pg. 3963
TERADYNE ROBOTS (GERMANY) GMBH—See Teradyne, Inc.; *U.S. Public*, pg. 2018
THERMAL EQUIPMENT SERVICE, INC.—See Comfort Systems USA, Inc.; *U.S. Public*, pg. 544
THERMAL MECHANICS, INC.; *U.S. Private*, pg. 4142
THERMO ENERGY SOLUTIONS, INC.—See Gibraltar Industries, Inc.; *U.S. Public*, pg. 936

N.A.I.C.S. INDEX
423740 — REFRIGERATION EQUIP...

THERMO KING CENTRAL CAROLINAS, LLC; *U.S. Private*, pg. 4142
THOMAS J. FINNEGAN COMPANY; *U.S. Private*, pg. 4156
THREE STATES SUPPLY COMPANY LLC—See Watsco, Inc.; *U.S. Public*, pg. 2337
TLA INC.; *U.S. Private*, pg. 4178
TOM BARROW COMPANY—See Ardian SAS; *Int'l*, pg. 554
TORO-AIRE INC.; *U.S. Private*, pg. 4189
TOSHIBA CARRIER UK LIMITED—See Carrier Global Corporation; *U.S. Public*, pg. 444
TOTAL MECHANICAL, INC.; *U.S. Private*, pg. 4191
TRADEWINDS DISTRIBUTING COMPANY, LLC—See Watsco, Inc.; *U.S. Public*, pg. 2337
TRANSCOM ELECTRONICS LIMITED—See Daikin Industries, Ltd.; *Int'l*, pg. 1936
TRIANGLE SALES INC.; *U.S. Private*, pg. 4226
TRISTATE HVAC EQUIPMENT LLP; *U.S. Private*, pg. 4238
TROPIC SUPPLY INC.; *U.S. Private*, pg. 4242
TUCO INDUSTRIAL PRODUCTS, INC.—See I Squared Capital Advisors (US) LLC; *U.S. Private*, pg. 2021
UNITED PRODUCTS DISTRIBUTORS INC.; *U.S. Private*, pg. 4296
US AIRCONDITIONING DISTRIBUTORS, INC.; *U.S. Private*, pg. 4317
VICTOR DISTRIBUTING COMPANY; *U.S. Private*, pg. 4377
VIRGINIA AIR DISTRIBUTORS INC.; *U.S. Private*, pg. 4387
VIVASA (PVT) LTD.—See Daikin Industries, Ltd.; *Int'l*, pg. 1937
VLADMIR, LTD.; *U.S. Private*, pg. 4407
WAECO SWEDEN WSE AB—See Dometic Group AB; *Int'l*, pg. 2161
WARD MECHANICAL EQUIPMENT INC.; *U.S. Private*, pg. 4441
WARMLYYOURS.COM INC.; *U.S. Private*, pg. 4442
WASHINGTON AIR REPS INC.; *U.S. Private*, pg. 4446
WATSCO, INC.; *U.S. Public*, pg. 2336
WEATHERTECH DISTRIBUTING CO. INC; *U.S. Private*, pg. 4463
WESSON, INC.; *U.S. Private*, pg. 4483
WESTCO CHINNEY LIMITED—See Chinney Alliance Group Limited; *Int'l*, pg. 1570
WHOLESALE HEATING & COOLING SUPPLY COMPANY; *U.S. Private*, pg. 4514
WICHITA SHEET METAL SUPPLY CO., INC.—See WSM Industries Inc.; *U.S. Private*, pg. 4574
WILLIAMSON-THERMOFLO—See SPX Technologies, Inc.; *U.S. Public*, pg. 1922
WOLF ENERGIESPARSYSTEME OOO—See CENTROTEC SE; *Int'l*, pg. 1415
WOLF ENERGIESYSTEMEN B.V.—See CENTROTEC SE; *Int'l*, pg. 1415
WOLF FRANCE S.A.S.—See CENTROTEC SE; *Int'l*, pg. 1415
WOLF HVAC SYSTEMS CO., LTD.—See CENTROTEC SE; *Int'l*, pg. 1415
WOLF ITALIA S.R.L.—See CENTROTEC SE; *Int'l*, pg. 1415
WSM INDUSTRIES INC.; *U.S. Private*, pg. 4574
YEOMANS DISTRIBUTING COMPANY; *U.S. Private*, pg. 4588

423740 — REFRIGERATION EQUIPMENT AND SUPPLIES MERCHANT WHOLESALERS

ABCO REFRIGERATION SUPPLY CORP.; *U.S. Private*, pg. 36
ACAL CONTROLS LTD.—See discoverIE Group plc; *Int'l*, pg. 2132
A-GAS INTERNATIONAL LTD.—See KKR & Co. Inc.; *U.S. Public*, pg. 1237
AIRCON TEKNIK A/S—See Beijer Ref AB; *Int'l*, pg. 944
AIR PRO HOLDINGS, INC.; *U.S. Private*, pg. 139
ALFACO POLSKA SP.Z.O.O.—See Carel Industries S.p.A.; *Int'l*, pg. 1324
AMERICAN REFRIGERATION SUPPLIES, INC.—See Kitchell Corporation; *U.S. Private*, pg. 2316
ASPEN REFRIGERANTS, INC.—See Hudson Technologies, Inc.; *U.S. Public*, pg. 1068
ASSOCIATED LEASE CORP.—See Associated Grocers of New England, Inc.; *U.S. Private*, pg. 356
AXFLOW SPA—See Axel Johnson Gruppen AB; *Int'l*, pg. 763
BARSCO INC.; *U.S. Private*, pg. 482
BASSETT INC.—See Omega Enterprises Inc.; *U.S. Private*, pg. 3015
BEIJER ECR IBERICA S.L.—See Beijer Ref AB; *Int'l*, pg. 943
BEIJER REF CZECH S.R.O.—See Beijer Ref AB; *Int'l*, pg. 944
BEIJER REF INDIA PVT. LTD.—See Beijer Ref AB; *Int'l*, pg. 944
BEIJER REF LATVIA SIA—See Beijer Ref AB; *Int'l*, pg. 944
BEIJER REF POLSKA SP.Z.O.O.—See Beijer Ref AB; *Int'l*, pg. 944
BERLING S.A.; *Int'l*, pg. 986
BJC SPECIALTIES CO., LTD.—See Berli Jucker Public Co. Ltd.; *Int'l*, pg. 985
BKF-KLIMA A/S—See Beijer Ref AB; *Int'l*, pg. 944
CARPIGIANI CENTRO SURAMERICA DO BRASIL LTDA—See Ali Holding S.r.l; *Int'l*, pg. 320
CARPIGIANI FRANCE S.A.—See Ali Holding S.r.l; *Int'l*, pg. 320
CARPIGIANI JAPAN CO., LTD.—See Ali Holding S.r.l; *Int'l*, pg. 321
CARPIGIANI SHANGHAI—See Ali Holding S.r.l; *Int'l*, pg. 320
CARPIGIANI UK LTD—See Ali Holding S.r.l; *Int'l*, pg. 321
CARRIER REFRIGERACION IBERICA SA—See Carrier Global Corporation; *U.S. Public*, pg. 441
CARRIER REFRIGERATION BENELUX B.V.—See Haier Smart Home Co., Ltd.; *Int'l*, pg. 3210
CARRIER REFRIGERATION DISTRIBUTION FRANCE SAS—See Carrier Global Corporation; *U.S. Public*, pg. 443
CARRIER REFRIGERATION OPERATIONS FRANCE SAS—See Carrier Global Corporation; *U.S. Public*, pg. 443
CARRIER REFRIGERATION SWEDEN AB—See Carrier Global Corporation; *U.S. Public*, pg. 443
CARRIER SAUDI SERVICE COMPANY—See Carrier Global Corporation; *U.S. Public*, pg. 443
CARRIER S.C.S.—See Carrier Global Corporation; *U.S. Public*, pg. 443
CARRIER TRANSICOLD EUROPE—See Carrier Global Corporation; *U.S. Public*, pg. 442
CFM SOGUTMA VE OTOMASYON A.S.—See Carel Industries S.p.A.; *Int'l*, pg. 1324
COFELY REFRIGERATION BV—See ENGIE SA; *Int'l*, pg. 2430
COFELY REFRIGERATION GMBH—See ENGIE SA; *Int'l*, pg. 2430
COFRISET S.A.S.—See Beijer Ref AB; *Int'l*, pg. 944
COLEMAN UK LIMITED—See Newell Brands Inc.; *U.S. Public*, pg. 1515
COMPLETE AIR SUPPLY PTY. LTD.—See Beijer Ref AB; *Int'l*, pg. 944
CONVOY SERVICING COMPANY INC.; *U.S. Private*, pg. 1036
COOLAIR KLIMASYSTEME GMBH—See Beijer Ref AB; *Int'l*, pg. 944
COOLSYS, INC.—See Ares Management Corporation; *U.S. Public*, pg. 189
DANFOSS (PTY) LTD.—See Danfoss A/S; *Int'l*, pg. 1959
DAWMEC LIMITED—See GEA Group Aktiengesellschaft; *Int'l*, pg. 2897
DEAN & WOOD LTD.—See Beijer Ref AB; *Int'l*, pg. 944
DELMO SA—See Beijer Ref AB; *Int'l*, pg. 944
DENNIS SUPPLY COMPANY; *U.S. Private*, pg. 1205
EASTERN REFRIGERATION SUPPLY CO.; *Int'l*, pg. 2273
EASYAIRCONDITIONING GROUP LIMITED—See Beijer Ref AB; *Int'l*, pg. 944
EBARA THERMAL SYSTEMS (THAILAND) CO., LTD.—See Ebara Corporation; *Int'l*, pg. 2283
ECR BELGIUM BVBA—See Beijer Ref AB; *Int'l*, pg. 944
ECR ITALY SPA—See Beijer Ref AB; *Int'l*, pg. 944
ECR NEDERLAND B.V.—See Beijer Ref AB; *Int'l*, pg. 944
ELECTROLUX CENTRAL AND EASTERN EUROPE GES. M.B.H. NFG. KG.—See AB Electrolux; *Int'l*, pg. 39
ENGIE SERVICES NEW ZEALAND LIMITED—See ENGIE SA; *Int'l*, pg. 2431
FAR EAST ENTERPRISES (JOHOR BAHRU) SDN BHD—See Far East Group Limited; *Int'l*, pg. 2616
FAR EAST ENTERPRISES (KUALA LUMPUR) SDN BHD—See Far East Group Limited; *Int'l*, pg. 2616
FAR EAST GROUP LIMITED; *Int'l*, pg. 2616
FAR EAST REFRIGERATION (KUCHING) SDN BHD—See Far East Group Limited; *Int'l*, pg. 2616
FAR EAST REFRIGERATION LIMITED—See Far East Group Limited; *Int'l*, pg. 2616
FOLLETT LLC—See The Middleby Corporation; *U.S. Public*, pg. 2113
GEA GRASSO SPOLKA Z O.O.—See GEA Group Aktiengesellschaft; *Int'l*, pg. 2902
GEA GRASSO S.R.O.—See GEA Group Aktiengesellschaft; *Int'l*, pg. 2902
GEA GRENCO AFRICA (PTY) LTD—See GEA Group Aktiengesellschaft; *Int'l*, pg. 2899
GEA REFRIGERATION COMPONENTS (AUSTRALIA) PTY. LTD.—See GEA Group Aktiengesellschaft; *Int'l*, pg. 2902
GEA REFRIGERATION COMPONENTS (NORDIC) A/S—See GEA Group Aktiengesellschaft; *Int'l*, pg. 2902
GEA REFRIGERATION COMPONENTS (UK) LTD.—See GEA Group Aktiengesellschaft; *Int'l*, pg. 2902
GFF SA—See Beijer Ref AB; *Int'l*, pg. 944
G & L BEIJER FORVALTNING AB—See Beijer Ref AB; *Int'l*, pg. 944
GLOBAL COOLING, INC.—See Liberty Broadband Corporation; *U.S. Public*, pg. 1310
GRAM COMMERCIAL A/S—See Hoshizaki Corporation; *Int'l*, pg. 3483
GRAM COMMERCIAL BV—See Hoshizaki Corporation; *Int'l*, pg. 3483
GRAM DEUTSCHLAND GMBH—See Hoshizaki Corporation; *Int'l*, pg. 3483
GRAM (UK) LTD.—See Hoshizaki Corporation; *Int'l*, pg. 3483
GREAVES AIRCONDITIONING (PVT.) LTD—See Cherat Packaging Limited; *Int'l*, pg. 1471
HAWS AVLIS DO BRASIL—See Haws Corporation; *U.S. Private*, pg. 1884
H.D. SHELDON & COMPANY INC.; *U.S. Private*, pg. 1825
HEATCRAFT GEELONG PTY LTD—See Lennox International Inc.; *U.S. Public*, pg. 1307
H. JESSEN JURGENSEN A/S—See Beijer Ref AB; *Int'l*, pg. 944
HOSHIZAKI SINGAPORE PTE LTD.—See Hoshizaki Corporation; *Int'l*, pg. 3484
HUTTO REFRIGERATION SALES & SERVICE, LLC.—See Freeman Spogli & Co. Incorporated; *U.S. Private*, pg. 1606
ICE MAKE REFRIGERATION LTD.; *Int'l*, pg. 3579
INDEPENDENT SUPPLY COMPANY INC.—See Blackfriars Corp.; *U.S. Private*, pg. 575
INGERSOLL-RAND SERVICES AND TRADING LIMITED LIABILITY COMPANY—See Ingersoll Rand Inc.; *U.S. Public*, pg. 1121
INSCO DISTRIBUTING, INC.; *U.S. Private*, pg. 2085
KATOM RESTAURANT SUPPLY INC; *U.S. Private*, pg. 2265
KULMAKOMPONENTIDE OU—See Beijer Ref AB; *Int'l*, pg. 944
KYLMA AB—See Beijer Ref AB; *Int'l*, pg. 944
LANE EQUIPMENT CO. INC.; *U.S. Private*, pg. 2388
LUCE SCHWAB & KASE INC.; *U.S. Private*, pg. 2510
METRACLARK SOUTH AFRICA PROPRIETY LTD.—See Beijer Ref AB; *Int'l*, pg. 944
METRACLARK TANZANIA (PTY.) LTD.—See Beijer Ref AB; *Int'l*, pg. 944
MHPT ENGINEERING SDN. BHD.—See Hitachi, Ltd.; *Int'l*, pg. 3423
MODERN ICE EQUIPMENT & SUPPLY CO.; *U.S. Private*, pg. 2761
MOTORS & ARMATURES, INC.; *U.S. Private*, pg. 2797
MULTIPLEX INTERNATIONAL SALES CORP.—See Multiplex Company Inc.; *U.S. Private*, pg. 2813
MVE BIOLOGICAL SOLUTIONS US, LLC—See Cryoport, Inc.; *U.S. Public*, pg. 600
NEWMAC MFG. INC.—See United States Stove Company; *U.S. Private*, pg. 4300
OY COMBI COOL AB—See Beijer Ref AB; *Int'l*, pg. 945
POCONO PRODUCE CO. INC.; *U.S. Private*, pg. 3219
PT. GEA GRASSO INDONESIA—See GEA Group Aktiengesellschaft; *Int'l*, pg. 2903
QUIMOBASICOS, S.A. DE C.V.—See Cydsa S.A.B. de C.V.; *Int'l*, pg. 1895
RC&E, LLC—See Southfield Capital Advisors, LLC; *U.S. Private*, pg. 3736
REFRIGERATION & ELECTRIC SUPPLY CO.; *U.S. Private*, pg. 3384
REFRIGERATION SUPPLIES DISTRIBUTORS; *U.S. Private*, pg. 3384
REFRIGERATION SUPPLIES DISTRIBUTORS—See Refrigeration Supplies Distributors; *U.S. Private*, pg. 3384
RK SLOVAKIA S.R.O.—See Beijer Ref AB; *Int'l*, pg. 945
ROGERS SUPPLY COMPANY INC.; *U.S. Private*, pg. 3472
RSP SYSTEMS PTE LTD—See Far East Group Limited; *Int'l*, pg. 2616
SAN ANTONIO THERMO KING, INC.—See Kirby Corporation; *U.S. Public*, pg. 1235
SANKI KEISO CO., LTD.—See CHINO Corporation; *Int'l*, pg. 1571
SCHLOSSER MOLLER KULDE AS—See Beijer Ref AB; *Int'l*, pg. 945
SCOTSMAN INDUSTRIES (S) PTE LTD.—See Ali Holding S.r.l; *Int'l*, pg. 321
SINCLAIR SLOVAKIA S.R.O.—See Beijer Ref AB; *Int'l*, pg. 945
SOUTHWEST TEXAS EQUIPMENT DISTRIBUTORS INC.; *U.S. Private*, pg. 3741
S.W.H. SUPPLY COMPANY; *U.S. Private*, pg. 3519
TAYLOR FREEZERS SALES CO., INC.; *U.S. Private*, pg. 3940
THERMAL SUPPLY INC.; *U.S. Private*, pg. 4142
THERMO KING CHRISTENSEN INC.; *U.S. Private*, pg. 4142
THERMO KING QUAD CITIES INC.; *U.S. Private*, pg. 4142
THERMO KING SALES & SERVICE, INC.; *U.S. Private*, pg. 4143
THRIVE LIFE, LLC; *U.S. Private*, pg. 4165
TOTALIGENT, INC.; *U.S. Public*, pg. 2165
TRANSPORT REFRIGERATION INC.; *U.S. Private*, pg. 4210
TT COIL LTD.—See Beijer Ref AB; *Int'l*, pg. 945
UAB BEIJER REF—See Beijer Ref AB; *Int'l*, pg. 945
UNIECHEMIE B.V.—See Beijer Ref AB; *Int'l*, pg. 945
UNITED REFRIGERATION, INC.; *U.S. Private*, pg. 4296
UNITED REFRIGERATION OF CANADA LTD.—See United Refrigeration, Inc.; *U.S. Private*, pg. 4296
UNIVERSAL INDUSTRIES CORPORATION (PTY) LIMITED—See TRG Management LP; *U.S. Private*, pg. 4220
WELLINGTON LATIN AMERICA SERVICES SA DE CV—See AoFrio Limited; *Int'l*, pg. 487
WERNER KUSTER AG—See Beijer Ref AB; *Int'l*, pg. 945
WESTBURNE SUPPLY, INC.; *U.S. Private*, pg. 4489

423740 — REFRIGERATION EQUIP...

WITTICHEN SUPPLY COMPANY—See Gryphon Investors, LLC; *U.S. Private*, pg. 1800
YOUNG SUPPLY CO.; *U.S. Private*, pg. 4593

423810 — CONSTRUCTION AND MINING (EXCEPT OIL WELL) MACHINERY AND EQUIPMENT MERCHANT WHOLESALERS

3D DOMINIQUE DECLERCQ DISTRIBUTION—See FAYAT SAS; *Int'l*, pg. 2624
ADIDAS SPOR MALZEMELERI SATIS VE PAZARLAMA A.S.—See adidas AG; *Int'l*, pg. 147
A.E. FINLEY & ASSOCIATES OF TENNESSEE, INC.; *U.S. Private*, pg. 25
AFTERMARKET PARTS INC—See Matt Management Inc.; *U.S. Private*, pg. 2613
AIS CONSTRUCTION EQUIPMENT CORP.; *U.S. Private*, pg. 142
AKTIO CORPORATION—See Aktio Holdings Corporation; *Int'l*, pg. 267
ALBAN TRACTOR COMPANY INC.—See Carter Machinery Company, Inc.; *U.S. Private*, pg. 776
ALLIED MACHINERY CORPORATION; *U.S. Private*, pg. 186
ALTORFER INC.; *U.S. Private*, pg. 210
ALTRAD AND B.V.B.A—See Altrad Investment Authority SAS; *Int'l*, pg. 397
ALTRAD BALLIAUW SP. Z O.O.—See Altrad Investment Authority SAS; *Int'l*, pg. 397
ALTRAD BAUMANN GMBH—See Altrad Investment Authority SAS; *Int'l*, pg. 397
ALTRAD BEAVER 84 LTD—See Altrad Investment Authority SAS; *Int'l*, pg. 397
ALTRAD BENELUX NV—See Altrad Investment Authority SAS; *Int'l*, pg. 397
ALTRAD BETONIERA SI ESAFODAJE ROMANIA S.R.L.—See Altrad Investment Authority SAS; *Int'l*, pg. 397
ALTRAD BRAGAGNOLO ITALIA SRL—See Altrad Investment Authority SAS; *Int'l*, pg. 397
ALTRAD CEDRIA—See Altrad Investment Authority SAS; *Int'l*, pg. 397
ALTRAD HOFMANINGER GMBH—See Altrad Investment Authority SAS; *Int'l*, pg. 397
ALTRAD - KONSKIE SPOLKA Z O.O.—See Altrad Investment Authority SAS; *Int'l*, pg. 397
ALTRAD MOSTOSTAL MONTAZ SP. Z O.O.—See Altrad Investment Authority SAS; *Int'l*, pg. 397
ALTRAD NSG LIMITED—See Altrad Investment Authority SAS; *Int'l*, pg. 397
ALTRAD PLETTAC IBERICA, S. L.—See Altrad Investment Authority SAS; *Int'l*, pg. 397
ALTRAD PLETTAC PRODUCTION GMBH—See Altrad Investment Authority SAS; *Int'l*, pg. 397
ALTRAD PLETTAC SARL—See Altrad Investment Authority SAS; *Int'l*, pg. 397
ALTRAD-POMORZE SPOLKA Z O.O.—See Altrad Investment Authority SAS; *Int'l*, pg. 398
ALTRAD-PRYMAT SP. Z O. O.—See Altrad Investment Authority SAS; *Int'l*, pg. 398
ALTRAD RODISOLA S.A.—See Altrad Investment Authority SAS; *Int'l*, pg. 397
ALTRAD SOFRAMAT ETEM S.A.—See Altrad Investment Authority SAS; *Int'l*, pg. 398
ALVIN EQUIPMENT COMPANY INC.; *U.S. Private*, pg. 214
AMECO CHILE S.A.—See Fluor Corporation; *U.S. Public*, pg. 857
AMERICAN STATE EQUIPMENT CO. INC.; *U.S. Private*, pg. 255
ANDERSON MACHINERY COMPANY; *U.S. Private*, pg. 277
ANDRITZ DELKOR (PTY) LTD.—See ANDRITZ AG; *Int'l*, pg. 454
ANTELOPE OIL TOOL & MANUFACTURING COMPANY—See Intervale Capital, LLC; *U.S. Private*, pg. 2127
ARGO AB—See Copperstone Resources AB; *Int'l*, pg. 1794
ARING EQUIPMENT COMPANY INC.; *U.S. Private*, pg. 323
ARNOLD MACHINERY CO - CONSTRUCTION & MINING DIVISION—See Arnold Machinery Company; *U.S. Private*, pg. 333
ARNOLD MACHINERY COMPANY; *U.S. Private*, pg. 333
ASAHI G&S SDN. BHD.—See ARE Holdings, Inc.; *Int'l*, pg. 557
ASAHI PRETEC CORPORATION—See ARE Holdings, Inc.; *Int'l*, pg. 557
ASAHI PRETEC KOREA CO., LTD.—See ARE Holdings, Inc.; *Int'l*, pg. 557
ASSET MANAGEMENT SERVICE S.R.L.—See I.M.A. Industria Macchine Automatiche S.p.A.; *Int'l*, pg. 3566
ASSOCIATED DRYWALL SUPPLIERS, INC.—See American Securities LLC; *U.S. Private*, pg. 248
ATLAS BOBCAT, INC.—See Atlas Lift Truck Rentals & Sales, Inc.; *U.S. Private*, pg. 379
ATLAS COPCO CMT SWEDEN AB—See Atlas Copco AB; *Int'l*, pg. 678

ATLAS COPCO DRC SPRL—See Atlas Copco AB; *Int'l*, pg. 678
ATLAS COPCO FORAGE ET CONSTRUCTION S.A.S.—See Atlas Copco AB; *Int'l*, pg. 678
ATLAS COPCO GHANA LTD—See Atlas Copco AB; *Int'l*, pg. 679
ATLAS COPCO IRAN AB—See Atlas Copco AB; *Int'l*, pg. 679
ATLAS COPCO KOMPRESSOREN UND DRUCKLUFTTECHNIK GMBH—See Atlas Copco AB; *Int'l*, pg. 679
ATLAS COPCO LIETUVA UAB—See Atlas Copco AB; *Int'l*, pg. 679
ATLAS COPCO (MALAYSIA) SDN. BHD.—See Atlas Copco AB; *Int'l*, pg. 677
ATLAS COPCO ROMANIA S.R.L.—See Atlas Copco AB; *Int'l*, pg. 680
ATLAS COPCO TANZANIA LTD—See Atlas Copco AB; *Int'l*, pg. 681
ATLAS COPCO UK HOLDINGS LTD—See Atlas Copco AB; *Int'l*, pg. 681
ATLAS COPCO VENEZUELA SA—See Atlas Copco AB; *Int'l*, pg. 681
ATLAS COPCO VIETNAM COMPANY LTD—See Atlas Copco AB; *Int'l*, pg. 681
ATS ASPHALTTECHNIK GMBH—See FAYAT SAS; *Int'l*, pg. 2624
BAKER HUGHES AUSTRALIA PTY LIMITED—See Baker Hughes Company; *U.S. Public*, pg. 264
BANE MACHINERY FORT WORTH, LP—See George P. Bane, Inc.; *U.S. Private*, pg. 1682
BANNER PLANT LIMITED—See Henry Boot PLC; *Int'l*, pg. 3354
BARBOT CM MAXILLY—See FAYAT SAS; *Int'l*, pg. 2624
BAUER-PILECO INC.—See BAUER Aktiengesellschaft; *Int'l*, pg. 892
BAYNE MINERAL SYSTEMS, INC.—See Crushing Equipment Solutions, LLC; *U.S. Private*, pg. 1114
BEARD EQUIPMENT CO. INC.; *U.S. Private*, pg. 506
BEAUREGARD EQUIPMENT INC.; *U.S. Private*, pg. 508
BELL EQUIPMENT (DEUTSCHLAND) GMBH—See Bell Equipment Limited; *Int'l*, pg. 966
BELL EQUIPMENT SALES SOUTH AFRICA LIMITED—See Bell Equipment Limited; *Int'l*, pg. 966
BELL EQUIPMENT UK LIMITED—See Bell Equipment Limited; *Int'l*, pg. 966
BELL EQUIPMENT (ZAMBIA) LIMITED—See Bell Equipment Limited; *Int'l*, pg. 966
BELL FRANCE SARL—See Bell Equipment Limited; *Int'l*, pg. 966
BERRY COMPANIES, INC.; *U.S. Private*, pg. 538
B & G EQUIPMENT, INC.; *U.S. Private*, pg. 417
BH BOTSWANA (PTY) LTD.; *Int'l*, pg. 1009
BIA BURKINA SARL—See BIA Overseas S.A.; *Int'l*, pg. 1017
BIA B.V./S.A—See BIA Overseas S.A.; *Int'l*, pg. 1017
BIA CAMEROON—See BIA Overseas S.A.; *Int'l*, pg. 1017
BIA COTE D'IVOIRE—See BIA Overseas S.A.; *Int'l*, pg. 1017
BIA GUINEE S.A.—See BIA Overseas S.A.; *Int'l*, pg. 1017
BIA N.V./S.A.—See BIA Overseas S.A.; *Int'l*, pg. 1017
BIA OVERSEAS S.A.; *Int'l*, pg. 1017
BIA POINTE NOIRE—See BIA Overseas S.A.; *Int'l*, pg. 1017
BIA ZAMBIA—See BIA Overseas S.A.; *Int'l*, pg. 1017
BIERSCHBACH EQUIPMENT & SUPPLY CO.; *U.S. Private*, pg. 551
BILL MILLER EQUIPMENT SALES; *U.S. Private*, pg. 557
BILT RITE SCAFFOLD CO; *U.S. Private*, pg. 559
BLANCHARD INVESTMENTS, INC.—See WRB Enterprises, Inc.; *U.S. Private*, pg. 4572
B-LIGHT CO., LTD.—See AB&Company Co., Ltd.; *Int'l*, pg. 47
BLIZZARD INDUSTRIAL SUPPLY—See Raleigh Mine & Industrial Supply, Inc.; *U.S. Private*, pg. 3349
BOBCAT BENSHEIM GMBH—See Doosan Corporation; *Int'l*, pg. 2172
BOBCAT ENTERPRISES INC.; *U.S. Private*, pg. 606
BOBCAT OF BOSTON, INC.; *U.S. Private*, pg. 606
BOBCAT OF CONNECTICUT INC.; *U.S. Private*, pg. 606
BOBCAT OF HOUSTON, INC.—See Berry Companies, Inc.; *U.S. Private*, pg. 538
BOBCAT OF THE ROCKIES, LLC—See Berry Companies, Inc.; *U.S. Private*, pg. 538
BOBCO INC.; *U.S. Private*, pg. 606
BOMAG (CHINA) CONSTRUCTION MACHINERY CO., LTD—See FAYAT SAS; *Int'l*, pg. 2624
BOMAG FRANCE S.A.S.—See FAYAT SAS; *Int'l*, pg. 2624
BOMAG (GREAT BRITAIN) LTD—See FAYAT SAS; *Int'l*, pg. 2624
BOMAG ITALIA SRL.—See FAYAT SAS; *Int'l*, pg. 2624
BOMAG MASCHINENHANDELSGESELLSCHAFT M.B.H.—See FAYAT SAS; *Int'l*, pg. 2624
BOMAG PAVING PRODUCTS INC—See FAYAT SAS; *Int'l*, pg. 2624
BOMAG SINGAPORE—See FAYAT SAS; *Int'l*, pg. 2624
BRADKEN HOLDINGS PTY LIMITED—See Hitachi, Ltd.; *Int'l*, pg. 3415
BRAKE SUPPLY CO.—See Koch Enterprises, Inc.; *U.S. Private*, pg. 2326
BRAMCO INC.; *U.S. Private*, pg. 635

CORPORATE AFFILIATIONS

BRANDEIS MACHINERY & SUPPLY COMPANY—See Bramco Inc.; *U.S. Private*, pg. 635
BRANDT TRACTOR LTD.—See Brandt Industries Ltd.; *Int'l*, pg. 1140
BRIGHT EQUIPMENT INC.; *U.S. Private*, pg. 651
BROOKS TRACTOR INCORPORATED—See Brooks Incorporated; *U.S. Private*, pg. 664
BUCYRUS MINING AUSTRALIA PTY. LTD.—See Caterpillar, Inc.; *U.S. Public*, pg. 449
BUILDING MAINTENANCE & SUPPLY; *U.S. Private*, pg. 683
BURCH MATERIALS CO., INC.—See PennSpring Capital, LLC; *U.S. Private*, pg. 3136
BURRIS EQUIPMENT CO—See Alta Equipment Group Inc.; *U.S. Public*, pg. 86
BUTLER MACHINERY COMPANY; *U.S. Private*, pg. 697
BYSTRONIC BENELUX B.V.—See Bystronic AG; *Int'l*, pg. 1236
CADECI INTERNATIONAL CORPORATION; *U.S. Private*, pg. 712
CAMERON ARGENTINA S.A.I.C.—See Schlumberger Limited; *U.S. Public*, pg. 1843
CAMERON NORGE AS—See Schlumberger Limited; *U.S. Public*, pg. 1843
CAPITOL MATERIALS, INCORPORATED—See GMS Inc.; *U.S. Public*, pg. 948
CAROLINA TRACTOR & EQUIPMENT CO.; *U.S. Private*, pg. 768
CARROLL DISTRIBUTING & CONSTRUCTION SUPPLY; *U.S. Private*, pg. 773
CATERPILLAR GLOBAL MINING EQUIPMENT LLC—See Caterpillar, Inc.; *U.S. Public*, pg. 450
CATERPILLAR SOUTHERN AFRICA (PTY) LTD.—See Caterpillar, Inc.; *U.S. Public*, pg. 452
CATERPILLAR TOHUKU LTD.—See Caterpillar, Inc.; *U.S. Public*, pg. 452
CATERPILLAR (U.K.) LIMITED—See Caterpillar, Inc.; *U.S. Public*, pg. 451
C&C HOLDING INC.; *U.S. Private*, pg. 702
CECIL I. WALKER MACHINERY CO.; *U.S. Private*, pg. 804
CHARLOTTE TRACTOR COMPANY—See BobCo Inc.; *U.S. Private*, pg. 606
CHEMFLOW PRODUCTS, LLC—See Relevant Industrial LLC; *U.S. Private*, pg. 3393
CHICAGO PNEUMATIC CONSTRUCTION EQUIPMENT AB—See Atlas Copco AB; *Int'l*, pg. 681
CHINA HEFENG RESCUE EQUIPMENT, INC.; *Int'l*, pg. 1507
CHRISTIANIA SPIGERVERK AS—See Simpson Manufacturing Company, Inc.; *U.S. Public*, pg. 1882
CHUO BUILD INDUSTRY CO., LTD.—See Asahi Kasei Corporation; *Int'l*, pg. 595
CHUWA BUSSAN CO., LTD.—See China Communications Construction Company Limited; *Int'l*, pg. 1490
CLARENCE L. BOYD COMPANY; *U.S. Private*, pg. 910
CLARK MACHINERY COMPANY; *U.S. Private*, pg. 913
CLEVELAND BROTHERS EQUIPMENT CO., INC.; *U.S. Private*, pg. 940
CLEVELAND BROTHERS EQUIPMENT—See Cleveland Brothers Equipment Co., Inc.; *U.S. Private*, pg. 940
CLM EQUIPMENT COMPANY, INC.; *U.S. Private*, pg. 945
CLOVERDALE EQUIPMENT CO. OF WEST MICHIGAN—See Cloverdale Equipment Co.; *U.S. Private*, pg. 948
C.L. PRESSER COMPANY; *U.S. Private*, pg. 708
CN WOOD CO. INC.; *U.S. Private*, pg. 952
COAST CRANE CO.-PASCO—See Apollo Global Management, Inc.; *U.S. Public*, pg. 153
THE COLUMBUS EQUIPMENT COMPANY INC.; *U.S. Private*, pg. 4011
COLUMBUS MCKINNON SINGAPORE PTE. LTD.—See Columbus McKinnon Corporation; *U.S. Public*, pg. 535
COMMERCIAL BUILDERS GROUP LLC—See GMS Inc.; *U.S. Public*, pg. 948
COMPACT EXCAVATOR SALES, LLC—See IHI Corporation; *Int'l*, pg. 3604
CONCRETE ACCESSORIES COMPANY, INC.; *U.S. Private*, pg. 1011
CONFLOW INC.—See Conflow Limited; *Int'l*, pg. 1768
CON FORMS ASIA SDN BHD—See Construction Forms, Inc.; *U.S. Private*, pg. 1023
CONNELL FINANCE COMPANY, INC.—See The Connell Company; *U.S. Private*, pg. 4014
CONNELL RICE & SUGAR DIV.—See The Connell Company; *U.S. Private*, pg. 4014
CONSTRUCTION EQUIPMENT COMPANY; *U.S. Private*, pg. 1023
CONSTRUCTION, SUPPLY & SERVICE PTY LTD—See Domino's Pizza Enterprises Ltd.; *Int'l*, pg. 2162
CONTRACTORS EQUIPMENT LP—See Brandt Industries Ltd.; *Int'l*, pg. 1140
CORYS BUILDING MATERIALS—See Green Coast Enterprises LLC; *Int'l*, pg. 3070
COTANA CONSTRUCTION JOINT STOCK COMPANY—See Cotana Group Joint Stock Company; *Int'l*, pg. 1815

N.A.I.C.S. INDEX

423810 — CONSTRUCTION AND MI...

COTANA INVESTMENT CONSULTANCY & TRADING JOINT STOCK COMPANY—See Cotana Group Joint Stock Company; *Int'l*, pg. 1815
CROSS COUNTRY INFRASTRUCTURE SERVICES, INC.—See Odyssey Investment Partners, LLC; *U.S. Private*, pg. 2995
CUMMINGS MCGOWAN & WEST INC.; *U.S. Private*, pg. 1123
DARRAGH CO; *U.S. Private*, pg. 1159
DEKPOL STEEL SP. Z O.O.—See Dekpol S.A.; *Int'l*, pg. 2006
DEL CORPORATION; *U.S. Private*, pg. 1192
DESERT ENERGY EQUIPMENT, INC.; *U.S. Private*, pg. 1212
DHC SUPPLIES INC.; *U.S. Private*, pg. 1221
DIAMOND EQUIPMENT INC.; *U.S. Private*, pg. 1223
DIESEL MACHINERY INC.; *U.S. Private*, pg. 1229
DIRECT SCAFFOLD SUPPLY, INC.—See Highlander Partners, LP; *U.S. Private*, pg. 1939
DITCH WITCH EQUIPMENT CO. INC.—See The Pape Group, Inc.; *U.S. Private*, pg. 4090
DITCH WITCH EQUIPMENT OF TENNESSE INC.; *U.S. Private*, pg. 1240
DITCH WITCH MINNESOTA INC.; *U.S. Private*, pg. 1240
DITCH WITCH OF HOUSTON—See Bluestem Equity, Ltd.; *U.S. Private*, pg. 598
DOOSAN BOBCAT CHILE S.A.—See Doosan Corporation; *Int'l*, pg. 2172
DOOSAN INFRACORE NORTH AMERICA LLC—See Doosan Corporation; *Int'l*, pg. 2173
DOVER BMCS ACQUISITION CORP.—See Dover Corporation; *U.S. Public*, pg. 679
DOWNER CLADDING SYSTEMS LTD.—See Eleco Plc; *Int'l*, pg. 2347
DOYLE EQUIPMENT COMPANY INC.; *U.S. Private*, pg. 1270
DRESSTA CO., LTD.—See Guangxi Liugong Machinery Co., Ltd.; *Int'l*, pg. 3163
EAGLE POWER & EQUIPMENT CORP.; *U.S. Private*, pg. 1310
EDWARD EHRBAR INC.; *U.S. Private*, pg. 1340
EGIL ENG & CO. AS—See Addtech AB; *Int'l*, pg. 133
EICKHOFF CORPORATION—See Eickhoff Maschinenfabrik GmbH; *Int'l*, pg. 2328
EKK, INC.—See Eagle Industry Co., Ltd.; *Int'l*, pg. 2265
ELB EQUIPMENT LIMITED - MINING & QUARRYING EQUIPMENT DIVISION—See ELB Group Limited; *Int'l*, pg. 2343
ELB EQUIPMENT LIMITED—See ELB Group Limited; *Int'l*, pg. 2343
ELLIOTT & FRANTZ INC.; *U.S. Private*, pg. 1364
THE EMPIRE CRANE COMPANY, LLC—See Bigge Crane & Rigging Company; *U.S. Private*, pg. 555
EMPIRE HYDRAULIC SERVICE—See Empire Southwest LLC; *U.S. Private*, pg. 1385
EMPIRE MACHINERY—See Empire Southwest LLC; *U.S. Private*, pg. 1385
EMPIRE SOUTHWEST LLC; *U.S. Private*, pg. 1385
ENGCON AUSTRIA GMBH—See Engcon AB; *Int'l*, pg. 2426
ENGCON FRANCE S.A.S—See Engcon AB; *Int'l*, pg. 2426
ENGCON GERMANY GMBH—See Engcon AB; *Int'l*, pg. 2426
ENGCON NORTH AMERICA INC.—See Engcon AB; *Int'l*, pg. 2426
ENGCON UNITED KINGDOM LTD.—See Engcon AB; *Int'l*, pg. 2426
ENSSOLUTIONS LTD.—See Enssolutions Group Inc.; *Int'l*, pg. 2448
EPIROC SWEDEN AB—See Epiroc AB; *Int'l*, pg. 2462
EQUIPEMENTS FDS INC.; *Int'l*, pg. 2485
EQUIPEMENTS & SERVICE MAURITANIE SARL—See BIA Overseas S.A.; *Int'l*, pg. 1017
EQUIPEMENTS & SERVICES BIA—See BIA Overseas S.A.; *Int'l*, pg. 1017
ERB EQUIPMENT CO. INC.; *U.S. Private*, pg. 1417
ERB EQUIPMENT—See Erb Equipment Co. Inc.; *U.S. Private*, pg. 1417
EUREKA PUMPS AS - TANANGER—See HitecVision AS; *Int'l*, pg. 3425
EV MARTIN CORPORATION; *U.S. Private*, pg. 1434
FABICK CAT; *U.S. Private*, pg. 1458
FABICK CAT - SPRINGFIELD—See Fabick CAT; *U.S. Private*, pg. 1458
FABICK CAT - WISCONSIN—See Fabick CAT; *U.S. Private*, pg. 1458
FAIRBANK EQUIPMENT, INC.—See Great Range Capital, LLC; *U.S. Private*, pg. 1767
FARIS MACHINERY COMPANY; *U.S. Private*, pg. 1474
FARNHAM & PFILE CONSTRUCTION, INC.; *U.S. Private*, pg. 1480
FARRELL EQUIPMENT & SUPPLY CO., INC.; *U.S. Private*, pg. 1481
FAYAT BOMAG POLSKA SP. Z O.O.—See FAYAT SAS; *Int'l*, pg. 2624
FAYAT BOMAG RUS LLC—See FAYAT SAS; *Int'l*, pg. 2625
FERRONORDIC AB; *Int'l*, pg. 2642
FERRONORDIC GMBH—See Ferronordic AB; *Int'l*, pg. 2642

FERRONORDIC KAZAKHSTAN LLP—See Ferronordic AB; *Int'l*, pg. 2642
FERRONORDIC MACHINES LLC—See Ferronordic AB; *Int'l*, pg. 2642
FHP VILEDA S.C.S.—See Freudenberg SE; *Int'l*, pg. 2785
FINKBINER EQUIPMENT CO. INC.—See American State Equipment Co. Inc.; *U.S. Private*, pg. 255
FINNING ARGENTINA S.A.—See Finning International Inc.; *Int'l*, pg. 2676
FINNING BOLIVIA S.A.—See Finning International Inc.; *Int'l*, pg. 2676
FINNING CANADA INC.—See Finning International Inc.; *Int'l*, pg. 2676
FINNING CHILE S.A.—See Finning International Inc.; *Int'l*, pg. 2676
FINNING SOLUCIONES MINERAS S.A.—See Finning International Inc.; *Int'l*, pg. 2676
FINNING (UK) LTD.—See Finning International Inc.; *Int'l*, pg. 2676
FINNING URUGUAY S.A.—See Finning International Inc.; *Int'l*, pg. 2676
FLINT EQUIPMENT CO. - ATLANTA—See Flint Equipment Holdings, Inc.; *U.S. Private*, pg. 1545
FLINT EQUIPMENT CO.—See Flint Equipment Holdings, Inc.; *U.S. Private*, pg. 1545
FLINT EQUIPMENT CO. - WEST COLUMBIA—See Flint Equipment Holdings, Inc.; *U.S. Private*, pg. 1545
FLSMIDTH MINERALS A/S—See FLSmidth & Co. A/S; *Int'l*, pg. 2710
FLSMIDTH MINERALS INC.—See FLSmidth & Co. A/S; *Int'l*, pg. 2712
FLSMIDTH MINERALS LTD.—See FLSmidth & Co. A/S; *Int'l*, pg. 2711
FLSMIDTH SHANGHAI LTD.—See FLSmidth & Co. A/S; *Int'l*, pg. 2711
FLUID END SALES, INC.; *U.S. Private*, pg. 1552
FOLEY EQUIPMENT COMPANY—See Dean Operations, Inc.; *U.S. Private*, pg. 1184
FOLEY INDUSTRIES, INC.; *U.S. Private*, pg. 1558
FONTANESI AND KANN COMPANY; *U.S. Private*, pg. 1560
FOREMOST INDUSTRIES LP—See Foremost Income Fund; *Int'l*, pg. 2731
FORM SERVICES INC.; *U.S. Private*, pg. 1569
FORM TECH CONCRETE FORMS INC.—See Clayton, Dubilier & Rice, LLC; *U.S. Private*, pg. 930
FRAMATEQ S.A.S.; *Int'l*, pg. 2759
FRANK'S SUPPLY COMPANY INC.; *U.S. Private*, pg. 1596
FREUDENBERG HOUSEHOLD PRODUCTS AS—See Freudenberg SE; *Int'l*, pg. 2786
FREUDENBERG HOUSEHOLD PRODUCTS INC.—See Freudenberg SE; *Int'l*, pg. 2787
FREUDENBERG HOUSEHOLD PRODUCTS LP—See Freudenberg SE; *Int'l*, pg. 2787
FREUDENBERG HOUSEHOLD PRODUCTS LP—See Freudenberg SE; *Int'l*, pg. 2787
FREUDENBERG HOUSEHOLD PRODUCTS LTD.—See Freudenberg SE; *Int'l*, pg. 2787
FREUDENBERG POTREBY PRO DOMACNOST, K.S.—See Freudenberg SE; *Int'l*, pg. 2787
FREUDENBERG PRODUCTOS DEL HOGAR, S.A. DE C.V.—See Freudenberg SE; *Int'l*, pg. 2787
FUJII SANGYO CORPORATION; *Int'l*, pg. 2826
FURUKAWA ROCK DRILL CO., LTD.—See Furukawa Co., Ltd.; *Int'l*, pg. 2847
GARDEN STATE ENGINE & EQUIPMENT CO.; *U.S. Private*, pg. 1643
GATEWAY BOBCAT, LLC—See Brightstar Capital Partners, L.P.; *U.S. Private*, pg. 653
GBO FASTENING SYSTEMS AB—See Simpson Manufacturing Company, Inc.; *U.S. Public*, pg. 1882
GBO FASTENING SYSTEMS AB—See Simpson Manufacturing Company, Inc.; *U.S. Public*, pg. 1882
GBO FASTENING SYSTEMS AB—See Simpson Manufacturing Company, Inc.; *U.S. Public*, pg. 1882
GBO FASTENING SYSTEMS AB—See Simpson Manufacturing Company, Inc.; *U.S. Public*, pg. 1882
GEA PROCESS MUHENDISLIK MAKINE INSAAT TAAHUT ITHALAT IHRACAT DANISMANLIK SANAYI VE TICARET LTD. STI.—See GEA Group Aktiengesellschaft; *Int'l*, pg. 2901
GENERAL EQUIPMENT & SUPPLIES INC.; *U.S. Private*, pg. 1664
GENERATION UK LIMITED—See Altrad Investment Authority SAS; *Int'l*, pg. 398
GEORGINO INDUSTRIAL SUPPLY; *U.S. Private*, pg. 1685
GILES & RANSOME, INC.; *U.S. Private*, pg. 1699
GLOBAL DRILLING SUPPLIERS INC.; *U.S. Private*, pg. 1713
GOLDEN EQUIPMENT COMPANY—See Power Equipment Company; *U.S. Private*, pg. 3238
GRADALL INDUSTRIES, INC.—See Alamo Group Inc.; *U.S. Public*, pg. 71
GREAT LAKES GYPSUM SUPPLY; *U.S. Private*, pg. 1764
GREENSBORO TRACTOR COMPANY—See BobCo Inc.; *U.S. Private*, pg. 607
GULF SPECIAL SERVICES, INC.; *U.S. Private*, pg. 1816
THE G.W. VAN KEPPEL CO. - KANSAS CITY

MISSOURI—See The G.W. Van Keppel Company; *U.S. Private*, pg. 4031
THE G.W. VAN KEPPEL COMPANY; *U.S. Private*, pg. 4031
HANES SUPPLY INC.; *U.S. Private*, pg. 1853
HARNISH GROUP INC.; *U.S. Private*, pg. 1866
HARSCO INFRASTRUCTURE—See Brand Industrial Services, Inc.; *U.S. Private*, pg. 636
HAUHINCO LP—See Hauhinco Maschinenfabrik G. Hausherr Jochums GmbH & Co. KG; *Int'l*, pg. 3285
H.B. FULLER CONSTRUCTION PRODUCTS INC.—See H.B. Fuller Company; *U.S. Public*, pg. 977
HEAVY EQUIPMENT SERVICES, INC.—See The Helm Group; *U.S. Private*, pg. 4051
HEAVY MACHINES, INC.; *U.S. Private*, pg. 1902
H&E EQUIPMENT SERVICES (CALIFORNIA), LLC—See H&E Equipment Services, Inc.; *U.S. Public*, pg. 976
H&E EQUIPMENT SERVICES LLC—See H&E Equipment Services, Inc.; *U.S. Public*, pg. 976
HENDERSON AUCTIONS—See JAH Enterprises, Inc.; *U.S. Private*, pg. 2182
HEXTAR INDUSTRIES BERHAD; *Int'l*, pg. 3373
HIGHWAY EQUIPMENT COMPANY; *U.S. Private*, pg. 1942
HIGHWAY EQUIPMENT & SUPPLY CO.; *U.S. Private*, pg. 1942
HITACHI CONSTRUCTION MACHINERY AFRICA PTY. LTD.—See Hitachi, Ltd.; *Int'l*, pg. 3415
HITACHI CONSTRUCTION MACHINERY AUSTRALIA PTY. LTD.—See Hitachi, Ltd.; *Int'l*, pg. 3416
HITACHI CONSTRUCTION MACHINERY EURASIA SALES LLC—See Hitachi, Ltd.; *Int'l*, pg. 3416
HITACHI CONSTRUCTION MACHINERY MIDDLE EAST CORPORATION FZE—See Hitachi, Ltd.; *Int'l*, pg. 3416
HITACHI CONSTRUCTION MACHINERY N.V.—See Hitachi, Ltd.; *Int'l*, pg. 3416
HITACHI CONSTRUCTION MACHINERY SOUTHERN AFRICA CO., LTD.—See Hitachi, Ltd.; *Int'l*, pg. 3416
HITACHI CONSTRUCTION MACHINERY (UK) LIMITED—See Hitachi, Ltd.; *Int'l*, pg. 3415
HI-WAY EQUIPMENT COMPANY INC.—See Midwesco Industries Inc.; *U.S. Private*, pg. 2719
H&L MESABI COMPANY; *U.S. Private*, pg. 1823
HOBI OUTDOOR POWER EQUIPMENT—See The Pape Group, Inc.; *U.S. Private*, pg. 4090
HOE LEONG MACHINERY (H.K.) LIMITED—See Hoe Leong Corporation Ltd.; *Int'l*, pg. 3439
HOLT OF CALIFORNIA INC.; *U.S. Private*, pg. 1968
HONNEN EQUIPMENT CO.—See 4 Rivers Equipment LLC; *U.S. Private*, pg. 14
H.O. PENN MACHINERY COMPANY INC.; *U.S. Private*, pg. 1835
HOWARD P. FAIRFIELD, LLC; *U.S. Private*, pg. 1995
H&R CONSTRUCTION PARTS & EQUIPMENT, INC.—See Kinderhook Industries, LLC; *U.S. Private*, pg. 2306
HUB CONSTRUCTION SPECIALTIES, INC.—See The Sterling Group, L.P.; *U.S. Private*, pg. 4122
HYUNDAI CONSTRUCTION EQUIPMENT SERVICE CO., LTD.—See Hyundai Heavy Industries Co., Ltd.; *Int'l*, pg. 3557
IDEAL CAPITAL BERHAD; *Int'l*, pg. 3588
IMPROVED CONSTRUCTION METHODS INC.; *U.S. Private*, pg. 2051
INDUSTRIAL LADDER & SUPPLY CO.; *U.S. Private*, pg. 2066
INFRASERV US, LLC—See Brightstar Capital Partners, L.P.; *U.S. Private*, pg. 653
INTERNATIONAL WATERJET PARTS, INC.; *U.S. Private*, pg. 2121
INTERSTATE EQUIPMENT COMPANY; *U.S. Private*, pg. 2124
IRON PEDDLERS, INC.; *U.S. Private*, pg. 2139
ISOJOEN KONEHALLI OY—See Grafton Group plc; *Int'l*, pg. 3051
JACK'S HEAVY EQUIPMENT INCORPORATED; *U.S. Private*, pg. 2175
JAH ENTERPRISES, INC.; *U.S. Private*, pg. 2182
JAMES W. BELL CO. INC.; *U.S. Private*, pg. 2185
JANELL INC.; *U.S. Private*, pg. 2186
J.A. RIGGS TRACTOR CO.; *U.S. Private*, pg. 2158
JASPER ENGINEERING & EQUIPMENT CO.; *U.S. Private*, pg. 2190
J&B MATERIALS, INC.—See GMS Inc.; *U.S. Public*, pg. 948
JCB CONSTRUCTION EQUIPMENT AUSTRALIA—See CFC Group Pty. Ltd.; *Int'l*, pg. 1429
J.C. SMITH; *U.S. Private*, pg. 2160
JESCO INC.; *U.S. Private*, pg. 2203
J.H. FLETCHER & CO.; *U.S. Private*, pg. 2165
JOE MONEY MACHINERY CO. INC.; *U.S. Private*, pg. 2218
JOHNSON MACHINERY CO.; *U.S. Private*, pg. 2228
JUMP DISTRIBUTORS (THAILAND) CO LTD—See Freudenberg SE; *Int'l*, pg. 2789
KANU EQUIPMENT CONGO LIMITED—See Apex Partners Proprietary Limited; *Int'l*, pg. 512
KANU EQUIPMENT CONGO LIMITED—See TRG Management LP; *U.S. Private*, pg. 4219
KANU EQUIPMENT COTE'IVOIRE LIMITED—See Apex Partners Proprietary Limited; *Int'l*, pg. 512
KANU EQUIPMENT COTE'IVOIRE LIMITED—See TRG Management LP; *U.S. Private*, pg. 4219

423810 — CONSTRUCTION AND MI...

KANU EQUIPMENT GHANA LIMITED—See Apex Partners Proprietary Limited; *Int'l*, pg. 512
KANU EQUIPMENT GHANA LIMITED—See TRG Management LP; *U.S. Private*, pg. 4219
KANU EQUIPMENT LIBERIA LTD.—See Apex Partners Proprietary Limited; *Int'l*, pg. 512
KANU EQUIPMENT LIBERIA LTD.—See TRG Management LP; *U.S. Private*, pg. 4219
KANU EQUIPMENT SIERRA LEONE—See Apex Partners Proprietary Limited; *Int'l*, pg. 512
KANU EQUIPMENT SIERRA LEONE—See TRG Management LP; *U.S. Private*, pg. 4220
KC BOBCAT INC.—See Berry Companies, Inc.; *U.S. Private*, pg. 538
KDR SUPPLY, INC.; *U.S. Private*, pg. 2270
KELBE BROS EQUIPMENT CO. INC.; *U.S. Private*, pg. 2274
KEMACH EQUIPMENT (PTY) LTD.—See BH Botswana (Pty) Ltd.; *Int'l*, pg. 1009
KEMPER EQUIPMENT INC.; *U.S. Private*, pg. 2282
KIEWIT CONSTRUCTION GROUP, INC.—See Peter Kiewit Sons', Inc.; *U.S. Private*, pg. 3158
KIMBALL EQUIPMENT COMPANY; *U.S. Private*, pg. 2305
KNIPFING ASPHALT SOLUTIONS, INC.—See C & L Services LLC; *U.S. Private*, pg. 701
LANO EQUIPMENT INC.; *U.S. Private*, pg. 2390
LASSE HOLST AS—See AF Gruppen ASA; *Int'l*, pg. 184
LEE BROTHERS BILSTON LIMITED—See Bunzl plc; *Int'l*, pg. 1218
LESLIE EQUIPMENT COMPANY; *U.S. Private*, pg. 2432
LINCOLN CONTRACTORS SUPPLY INC.; *U.S. Private*, pg. 2457
LIUGONG DRESSTA MACHINERY SP. Z O.O.—See Guangxi Liugong Machinery Co., Ltd.; *Int'l*, pg. 3163
LOGAN CORPORATION; *U.S. Private*, pg. 2480
LOUISIANA MACHINERY COMPANY INC.; *U.S. Private*, pg. 2499
LOW COUNTRY MACHINERY, INC.; *U.S. Private*, pg. 2504
LTZ CHEMNITZ GMBH—See BayWa AG; *Int'l*, pg. 918
LYLE MACHINERY CO.; *U.S. Private*, pg. 2520
LYONS EQUIPMENT COMPANY, INC.—See CJ Logging Equipment LLC; *U.S. Private*, pg. 908
MACALLISTER MACHINERY CO. INC.; *U.S. Private*, pg. 2531
MACHINE MAINTENANCE, INC.; *U.S. Private*, pg. 2535
MACQUEEN EQUIPMENT, LLC—See Rotunda Capital Partners LLC; *U.S. Private*, pg. 3488
M.A. DEATLEY CONSTRUCTION INC.; *U.S. Private*, pg. 2527
MANITOWOC CRANE CARE - FRANCE—See The Manitowoc Company, Inc.; *U.S. Public*, pg. 2111
MANITOWOC CRANE GROUP GERMANY GMBH—See The Manitowoc Company, Inc.; *U.S. Public*, pg. 2111
MANITOWOC CRANE GROUP (UK) LTD.—See The Manitowoc Company, Inc.; *U.S. Public*, pg. 2111
MANITOWOC DEBARKING TECHNOLOGY—See Heavy Machines, Inc.; *U.S. Private*, pg. 1902
MAP LIMITED—See Anderson Group Limited; *Int'l*, pg. 450
MAP RENTALS, INC.—See The Sterling Group, L.P.; *U.S. Private*, pg. 4123
MARTIN EQUIPMENT OF ILLINOIS; *U.S. Private*, pg. 2595
MASA CONCRETE PLANTS INDIA PVT. LTD.—See CGS Management AG; *Int'l*, pg. 1435
MASAHA HEAVY EQUIPMENT CO.—See Fouad Alghanim & Sons Group of Companies; *Int'l*, pg. 2753
MASA MIDDLE EAST FZCO—See CGS Management AG; *Int'l*, pg. 1435
MASA TIANJIN BUILDING MATERIAL MACHINERY CO., LTD.—See CGS Management AG; *Int'l*, pg. 1435
MASA-USA, LLC—See CGS Management AG; *Int'l*, pg. 1435
MBA AG—See CNH Industrial N.V.; *Int'l*, pg. 1674
MCCANN INDUSTRIES INC.; *U.S. Private*, pg. 2626
MCLEAN COMPANY; *U.S. Private*, pg. 2640
MCQUADE & BANNIGAN, INC.; *U.S. Private*, pg. 2644
MEADE TRACTOR - LOUISVILLE—See Meade Tractor; *U.S. Private*, pg. 2647
MECALAC IDF, S.A.S—See Groupe Mecalac S.A.; *Int'l*, pg. 3108
METALUBIA—See BIA Overseas S.A.; *Int'l*, pg. 1017
MICHIGAN TRACTOR & MACHINERY CO.; *U.S. Private*, pg. 2701
MID-CONTINENT SAFETY LLC—See DXP Enterprises, Inc.; *U.S. Public*, pg. 697
MILAN SUPPLY COMPANY—See Franklin Electric Co., Inc.; *U.S. Public*, pg. 878
MILLER-BRADFORD & RISBERG, INC.; *U.S. Private*, pg. 2736
MILTON CAT—See Southworth-Milton Inc.; *U.S. Private*, pg. 3743
MIRAMAR BOBCAT, INC.—See Brightstar Capital Partners, L.P.; *U.S. Private*, pg. 653
MODERN BUILDERS SUPPLY, INC.—See SiteOne Landscape Supply, Inc.; *U.S. Public*, pg. 1889
MODERN MACHINERY CO.—See Washington Corporations; *U.S. Private*, pg. 4446
MSA DE CHILE, EQUIPOS DE SEGURIDAD LTDA.—See MSA Safety Incorporated; *U.S. Public*, pg. 1482

MSA DEL PERU S.A.C.—See MSA Safety Incorporated; *U.S. Public*, pg. 1482
MSA EGYPT LLC—See MSA Safety Incorporated; *U.S. Public*, pg. 1481
MSA HONG KONG LTD.—See MSA Safety Incorporated; *U.S. Public*, pg. 1482
MSA INDIA LIMITED—See MSA Safety Incorporated; *U.S. Public*, pg. 1482
MSA MIDDLE EAST FZE—See MSA Safety Incorporated; *U.S. Public*, pg. 1482
MSA SAFETY ROMANIA S.R.L.—See MSA Safety Incorporated; *U.S. Public*, pg. 1482
MSA S.E. ASIA PTE. LTD.—See MSA Safety Incorporated; *U.S. Public*, pg. 1482
MSA SPAIN, S.L.—See MSA Safety Incorporated; *U.S. Public*, pg. 1482
MSA THAILAND LIMITED—See MSA Safety Incorporated; *U.S. Public*, pg. 1482
MTA DISTRIBUTORS, LLC—See Thompson Distribution, LLC; *U.S. Private*, pg. 4159
MULTI SERVICES DECOUPE S.A.—See Simpson Manufacturing Company, Inc.; *U.S. Public*, pg. 1882
MUNICIPAL SUPPLY INC.; *U.S. Private*, pg. 2814
MURPHY TRACTOR & EQUIPMENT CO., INC.; *U.S. Private*, pg. 2816
MUSTANG POWER SYSTEMS—See Mustang Tractor & Equipment Company; *U.S. Private*, pg. 2819
MUSTANG TRACTOR & EQUIPMENT COMPANY; *U.S. Private*, pg. 2819
NATIONAL CAPITAL INDUSTRIES; *U.S. Private*, pg. 2849
NATIONAL ENERGY HOLDING COMPANY INC.—See Raleigh Mine & Industrial Supply, Inc.; *U.S. Private*, pg. 3350
NEBRASKA MACHINERY COMPANY INC.; *U.S. Private*, pg. 2878
NEW HOLLAND CONSTRUCTION—See CNH Industrial N.V.; *Int'l*, pg. 1674
NEWMAN REGENCY GROUP, INC.—See H.I.G. Capital, LLC; *U.S. Private*, pg. 1834
NINGBO E&J BRUSHES CO LTD—See Freudenberg SE; *Int'l*, pg. 2790
NIXON-EGLI EQUIPMENT CO.; *U.S. Private*, pg. 2930
NORTHERN ENGINE & SUPPLY CO.; *U.S. Private*, pg. 2952
OCT EQUIPMENT LLC—See Associated Supply Company Inc.; *U.S. Private*, pg. 357
OHIO CAT—See Ohio Machinery Co.; *U.S. Private*, pg. 3004
OHIO VALLEY SUPPLY, INC.—See GMS Inc.; *U.S. Public*, pg. 948
OY ATLAS COPCO TOOLS AB—See Atlas Copco AB; *Int'l*, pg. 684
PALADIN BRANDS, LLC—See Stanley Black & Decker, Inc.; *U.S. Public*, pg. 1933
PAN CONTINENTAL RESOURCES, INC.; *U.S. Private*, pg. 3084
PAPE MACHINERY, INC.—See The Pape Group, Inc.; *U.S. Private*, pg. 4090
PAPE MACHINERY—See The Pape Group, Inc.; *U.S. Private*, pg. 4090
PAPE MACHINERY—See The Pape Group, Inc.; *U.S. Private*, pg. 4090
PATTEN INDUSTRIES, INC.; *U.S. Private*, pg. 3111
PENG KOON HEAVY MACHINERY PTE LTD—See Affirma Capital Limited; *Int'l*, pg. 187
PETE HONNEN EQUIPMENT CO. INC.; *U.S. Private*, pg. 3157
PETERSEN INC.—See Bain Capital, LP; *U.S. Private*, pg. 442
PETERSEN INC.—See Compass Advisers Group LLC; *U.S. Private*, pg. 998
PETERSEN INC.—See Pine Island Capital Partners LLC; *U.S. Private*, pg. 3182
PETERSON TRACTOR COMPANY; *U.S. Private*, pg. 3160
PHILLIPPI EQUIPMENT CO.; *U.S. Private*, pg. 3170
PIK WIRTGEN UKRAINE—See Deere & Company; *U.S. Public*, pg. 647
PIPECO SERVICES; *U.S. Private*, pg. 3189
PLASTERER EQUIPMENT CO. INC.; *U.S. Private*, pg. 3198
POTTER EQUIPMENT CO—See Machine Maintenance, Inc.; *U.S. Private*, pg. 2535
POWELL SALES INC.; *U.S. Private*, pg. 3237
POWER EQUIPMENT COMPANY INC; *U.S. Private*, pg. 3238
POWER MOTIVE CORPORATION; *U.S. Private*, pg. 3238
POWER RENTAL & SALES, LLC—See The Stephens Group, LLC; *U.S. Private*, pg. 4121
PRIMACH TECHNOLOGY PTE LTD—See D&G TECHNOLOGY HOLDING CO., LTD.; *Int'l*, pg. 1899
PROCESS MACHINERY INC.; *U.S. Private*, pg. 3272
PRODECO, A.S.—See CEZ, a.s.; *Int'l*, pg. 1428
PROFESSIONAL PAVEMENT PRODUCTS, INC.; *U.S. Private*, pg. 3275
PT ATLAS COPCO INDONESIA—See Atlas Copco AB; *Int'l*, pg. 684
PTC ERS SA DE CV—See FAYAT SAS; *Int'l*, pg. 2626
PTC PILING EQUIPMENT (FAR EAST) PTE LTD—See FAYAT SAS; *Int'l*, pg. 2626
PTC USA—See FAYAT SAS; *Int'l*, pg. 2626

PT MSA INDONESIA LTD—See MSA Safety Incorporated; *U.S. Public*, pg. 1482
P T NASARAL KEKAL MEDAL—See Bucher Industries AG; *Int'l*, pg. 1208
PUCKETT MACHINERY COMPANY INC.; *U.S. Private*, pg. 3301
PUERTO RICO WIRE PRODUCTS INC.; *U.S. Private*, pg. 3302
QUINN COMPANY INC.; *U.S. Private*, pg. 3328
QUINN CO.; *U.S. Private*, pg. 3328
QUINN USED PARTS INC—See Quinn Company Inc.; *U.S. Private*, pg. 3328
RANSOME ENGINE—See Giles & Ransome, Inc.; *U.S. Private*, pg. 1699
RASMUSSEN EQUIPMENT COMPANY; *U.S. Private*, pg. 3356
RASMUSSEN EQUIPMENT CO.—See RC Rasmussen Corporation; *U.S. Private*, pg. 3361
R.B. EVERETT & COMPANY; *U.S. Private*, pg. 3334
RC RASMUSSEN CORPORATION; *U.S. Private*, pg. 3361
RECO EQUIPMENT INC.; *U.S. Private*, pg. 3371
REGAL CORPORATION; *U.S. Private*, pg. 3385
REGATE TECHNOLOGY, INC.—See AWC Frac Valves Inc.; *U.S. Private*, pg. 410
REUSS-SEIFERT GMBH—See CRH plc; *Int'l*, pg. 1848
REUTER EQUIPMENT COMPANY; *U.S. Private*, pg. 3412
REX SPENCER EQUIPMENT COMPANY INC.—See VLP Holding Co. Inc.; *U.S. Private*, pg. 4408
RIGGS RENTAL SERVICES INC.—See J.A. Riggs Tractor Co.; *U.S. Private*, pg. 2158
RING POWER CORPORATION; *U.S. Private*, pg. 3438
RING POWER CORPORATION—See Ring Power Corporation; *U.S. Private*, pg. 3438
RINGPOWER CORP—See Ring Power Corporation; *U.S. Private*, pg. 3438
RISH EQUIPMENT COMPANY—See Davis Mining & Manufacturing Inc.; *U.S. Private*, pg. 1174
RITZ SAFETY, LLC; *U.S. Private*, pg. 3442
RM WILSON CO. INC.; *U.S. Private*, pg. 3451
ROAD BUILDERS MACHINERY & SUPPLY CO.; *U.S. Private*, pg. 3453
ROAD MACHINERY & SUPPLIES COMPANY; *U.S. Private*, pg. 3453
ROCK EQUIPMENT INC.—See J.W. Jones Company, LLC; *U.S. Private*, pg. 2172
ROLAND MACHINERY COMPANY INC.; *U.S. Private*, pg. 3474
ROSS EQUIPMENT INC.; *U.S. Private*, pg. 3485
ROTH GERUSTE AG—See Altrad Investment Authority SAS; *Int'l*, pg. 397
ROWAND MACHINERY COMPANY; *U.S. Private*, pg. 3490
RPM MACHINERY LLC; *U.S. Private*, pg. 3495
RUDD EQUIPMENT COMPANY INC.—See Ferronordic AB; *Int'l*, pg. 2642
SCH CORPORATION SDN BHD—See Hextar Industries Berhad; *Int'l*, pg. 3373
SCOTT EQUIPMENT COMPANY, LLC; *U.S. Private*, pg. 3576
SCOTT EQUIPMENT INCORPORATED; *U.S. Private*, pg. 3576
SCOTT-GALLAHER, INC.—See Highway Equipment Company; *U.S. Private*, pg. 1942
SEELY EQUIPMENT & SUPPLY CO., INC.—See Modern Group Ltd.; *U.S. Private*, pg. 2761
SELLERS EQUIPMENT INC.; *U.S. Private*, pg. 3602
SELLERS EQUIPMENT INC.—See Sellers Equipment Inc.; *U.S. Private*, pg. 3602
SHINWA MACHINERY CO., LTD.—See DAIHO CORPORATION; *Int'l*, pg. 1927
SHOOK & FLETCHER SUPPLY CO. OF ALABAMA, INC.—See Shook & Fletcher Insulation Co., Inc.; *U.S. Private*, pg. 3640
SIMPSON STRONG-TIE CHILE LIMITADA—See Simpson Manufacturing Company, Inc.; *U.S. Public*, pg. 1883
SIMPSON STRONG-TIE SOUTH AFRICA (PTY) LTD—See Simpson Manufacturing Company, Inc.; *U.S. Public*, pg. 1883
SINCLAIR WELL PRODUCTS INC.; *U.S. Private*, pg. 3669
SOCIEDADE ATLAS COPCO DE PORTUGAL LDA—See Atlas Copco AB; *Int'l*, pg. 684
SONSRAY MACHINERY, LLC—See Sonsray, Inc.; *U.S. Private*, pg. 3714
SOUTHEASTERN EQUIPMENT CO., INC.; *U.S. Private*, pg. 3727
SOUTHERN STAR LEASING, LLC—See Grupo Argos S.A.; *Int'l*, pg. 3121
SPOKANE MACHINERY COMPANY—See Capital Machine Technologies, Inc.; *U.S. Private*, pg. 741
S&P REINFORCEMENT NORDIC APS—See Simpson Manufacturing Company, Inc.; *U.S. Public*, pg. 1883
STAFFORD DEVELOPMENT COMPANY; *U.S. Private*, pg. 3775
STAHL CRANESYSTEMS SHANGHAI CO. LTD.—See Columbus McKinnon Corporation; *U.S. Public*, pg. 536
STAN HOUSTON EQUIPMENT CO.; *U.S. Private*, pg. 3777
STAR EQUIPMENT, LTD.; *U.S. Private*, pg. 3784
STATE EQUIPMENT INC.; *U.S. Private*, pg. 3791

N.A.I.C.S. INDEX 423820 — FARM AND GARDEN MAC...

STEVE'S EQUIPMENT SERVICE, INC.; *U.S. Private*, pg. 3808
STONE PRODUCTS INC.—See The Beaver Excavating Company, Inc.; *U.S. Private*, pg. 3992
STOWERS MACHINERY CORP; *U.S. Private*, pg. 3832
STRACON GYM S.A.—See Ashmore Group plc; *Int'l*, pg. 608
STRIBLING EQUIPMENT LLC—See GS&L Enterprises Incorporated; *U.S. Private*, pg. 1800
SUTTLE EQUIPMENT INC.; *U.S. Private*, pg. 3887
SWEENEY BROTHERS TRACTOR CO.; *U.S. Private*, pg. 3891
TDL EQUIPMENT LTD—See Ballyvesey Holdings Limited; *Int'l*, pg. 809
TEREX CONSTRUCTION AMERICAS—See Terex Corporation; *U.S. Public*, pg. 2019
TEREX CONSTRUCTION—See Terex Corporation; *U.S. Public*, pg. 2019
TEXAS TIMBERJACK, INC.—See TreeCon Resources, Inc.; *U.S. Private*, pg. 2187
THOMPSON MACHINERY COMMERCE CORPORATION; *U.S. Private*, pg. 4160
THOMPSON TRACTOR COMPANY; *U.S. Private*, pg. 4162
TIDEWATER EQUIPMENT COMPANY; *U.S. Private*, pg. 4168
TIFFIN PARTS LLC—See The Heico Companies, L.L.C.; *U.S. Private*, pg. 4051
TITAN MACHINERY D.O.O.—See Titan Machinery Inc.; *U.S. Public*, pg. 2160
TOHOKU HITACHI CO., LTD.—See Hitachi, Ltd.; *Int'l*, pg. 3424
TOMEC CORPORATION—See Aktio Holdings Corporation; *Int'l*, pg. 267
TOM LOFTUS INC.; *U.S. Private*, pg. 4182
TRACEY ROAD EQUIPMENT INC.; *U.S. Private*, pg. 4200
TRACTOR & EQUIPMENT COMPANY; *U.S. Private*, pg. 4201
TRACTOR & EQUIPMENT COMPANY—See Tractor & Equipment Company; *U.S. Private*, pg. 4201
TRAD HIRE & SALES LTD.—See Altrad Investment Authority SAS; *Int'l*, pg. 398
TRAMAC CORPORATION; *U.S. Private*, pg. 4204
TREKKER TRACTOR, LLC; *U.S. Private*, pg. 4217
TRENCH SHORING COMPANY; *U.S. Private*, pg. 4218
TRIAD MACHINERY INC.; *U.S. Private*, pg. 4225
TRI-BORO CONSTRUCTION SUPPLIES INC.—See Clayton, Dubilier & Rice, LLC; *U.S. Private*, pg. 930
TRICO EQUIPMENT SERVICES LLC; *U.S. Private*, pg. 4229
TRI-STATE TRUCK & EQUIPMENT, INC.; *U.S. Private*, pg. 4224
TWIN CITY TRACTOR & EQUIPMENT INC.; *U.S. Private*, pg. 4265
TYLER EQUIPMENT CORPORATION; *U.S. Private*, pg. 4267
UNDERCARRIAGE SPECIALISTS INC.—See Clarence L. Boyd Company; *U.S. Private*, pg. 911
UNITED BINTANG MACHINERY SDN. BHD.—See Ideal United Bintang Berhad; *Int'l*, pg. 3589
UNITED CENTRAL INDUSTRIAL SUPPLY COMPANY—See Clayton, Dubilier & Rice, LLC; *U.S. Private*, pg. 926
UNITED CONSTRUCTION & FORESTRY, LLC—See Fernandez Holdings, Inc.; *U.S. Private*, pg. 1497
US-HM STRAW CONSTRUCTION MATERIAL INT'L, INC.; *U.S. Private*, pg. 4320
U.S. MUNICIPAL SUPPLY, INC.; *U.S. Private*, pg. 4271
US-PS ENERGYSAVE CONSTRUCTION MATERIAL INT'L, INC.; *U.S. Private*, pg. 4320
VALLEY FARMS SUPPLY, INC.—See Franklin Electric Co., Inc.; *U.S. Public*, pg. 879
VALLEY SUPPLY & EQUIPMENT CO.; *U.S. Private*, pg. 4335
VERMEER EQUIPMENT OF TEXAS INC.; *U.S. Private*, pg. 4366
VERMEER GREAT PLAINS INC.; *U.S. Private*, pg. 4366
VERMEER GREAT PLAINS INC.—See Vermeer Great Plains Inc.; *U.S. Private*, pg. 4366
VERMEER GREAT PLAINS INC.—See Vermeer Great Plains Inc.; *U.S. Private*, pg. 4366
VERMEER MIDWEST, INC.; *U.S. Private*, pg. 4366
VERMEER SALES & SERVICE INC.—See Vermeer Southeast Sales & Service, Inc.; *U.S. Private*, pg. 4367
VERMEER SALES & SERVICE OF COLORADO, INC.; *U.S. Private*, pg. 4366
VERMEER SALES SOUTHWEST INC.; *U.S. Private*, pg. 4366
VERMEER SOUTHEAST SALES & SERVICE, INC.; *U.S. Private*, pg. 4367
THE VICTOR L. PHILLIPS COMPANY INC.—See VLP Holding Co. Inc.; *U.S. Private*, pg. 4408
VIMCO INC.; *U.S. Private*, pg. 4384
VINTAGE PARTS; *U.S. Private*, pg. 4386
VLP HOLDING CO. INC.; *U.S. Private*, pg. 4408
WAGNER EQUIPMENT CO.; *U.S. Private*, pg. 4426
WAGNER-SMITH EQUIPMENT CO.—See MDU Resources Group, Inc.; *U.S. Public*, pg. 1411
WESTROCK COMPANY, INC.; *U.S. Private*, pg. 4500
WEST SIDE TRACTOR SALES CO.; *U.S. Private*, pg. 4487
WHAYNE SUPPLY COMPANY; *U.S. Private*, pg. 4504
WHEELER MACHINERY CO.; *U.S. Private*, pg. 4505
WHITE OAK EQUIPMENT INC.—See McClung-Logan Equipment Company, Inc.; *U.S. Private*, pg. 2629
WHITE STAR MACHINERY & SUPPLY CO.—See Berry Companies, Inc.; *U.S. Private*, pg. 538
W.I. CLARK COMPANY; *U.S. Private*, pg. 4420
WILLIAMS EQUIPMENT & SUPPLY COMPANY—See The Sterling Group, L.P.; *U.S. Private*, pg. 4122
WILSON EQUIPMENT COMPANY INC.; *U.S. Private*, pg. 4530
WILSON-FINLEY COMPANY; *U.S. Private*, pg. 4531
WIRTGEN AMERICA INC.—See Deere & Company; *U.S. Public*, pg. 648
WIRTGEN ANKARA MAKINA SANAYI VE TICARET LTD. STI.—See Deere & Company; *U.S. Public*, pg. 648
WIRTGEN AUSTRALIA PTY LTD—See Deere & Company; *U.S. Public*, pg. 648
WIRTGEN BELGIUM B.V.B.A.—See Deere & Company; *U.S. Public*, pg. 648
WIRTGEN (CHINA) MACHINERY CO., LTD.—See Deere & Company; *U.S. Public*, pg. 647
WIRTGEN EESTI OU—See Deere & Company; *U.S. Public*, pg. 648
WIRTGEN FRANCE SAS—See Deere & Company; *U.S. Public*, pg. 648
WIRTGEN INDIA PVT. LTD.—See Deere & Company; *U.S. Public*, pg. 648
WIRTGEN MACCHINE SRL.—See Deere & Company; *U.S. Public*, pg. 648
WIRTGEN NORWAY AS—See Deere & Company; *U.S. Public*, pg. 648
WIRTGEN OSTERREICH GMBH—See Deere & Company; *U.S. Public*, pg. 648
WIRTGEN SINGAPORE PTE. LTD.—See Deere & Company; *U.S. Public*, pg. 648
WIRTGEN SOUTH AFRICA (PTY) LTD.—See Deere & Company; *U.S. Public*, pg. 648
WIRTGEN-SRBIJA D.O.O.—See Deere & Company; *U.S. Public*, pg. 648
WIRTGEN (THAILAND) CO. LTD.—See Deere & Company; *U.S. Public*, pg. 648
WIRTGEN ZWICKAU VERTRIEBS- UND SERVICE GMBH—See Deere & Company; *U.S. Public*, pg. 648
WITCH EQUIPMENT COMPANY, INC.; *U.S. Private*, pg. 4550
WORLDWIDE CONSTRUCTION EQUIPMENT INC.; *U.S. Private*, pg. 4569
WYOMING MACHINERY COMPANY; *U.S. Private*, pg. 4579
YELLOWHOUSE MACHINERY CO.; *U.S. Private*, pg. 4587
YUNGTAY-HITACHI CONSTRUCTION MACHINERY CO., LTD.—See Hitachi, Ltd.; *Int'l*, pg. 3416
ZAO VOLVO VOSTOK—See AB Volvo; *Int'l*, pg. 47
ZIEGLER INC. - ALTOONA—See Ziegler Inc.; *U.S. Private*, pg. 4604
ZIEGLER INC.; *U.S. Private*, pg. 4604

423820 — FARM AND GARDEN MACHINERY AND EQUIPMENT MERCHANT WHOLESALERS

ABEMEC B.V.—See BayWa AG; *Int'l*, pg. 915
ABILENE MACHINE INC.; *U.S. Private*, pg. 38
ADAIR FEED & GRAIN COMPANY; *U.S. Private*, pg. 73
ADRITEC EGYPT—See Adritec Group International, E.C.; *Int'l*, pg. 153
ADRITEC LEBANON—See Adritec Group International, E.C.; *Int'l*, pg. 153
ADRITEC ROMANIA S.L.R—See Adritec Group International, E.C.; *Int'l*, pg. 153
ADRITEC SOUTH AFRICA—See Adritec Group International, E.C.; *Int'l*, pg. 153
AEBI SCHMIDT INTERNATIONAL AG—See Aebi Schmidt Holding AG; *Int'l*, pg. 170
AFS FRANCHISE-SYSTEME GMBH—See BayWa AG; *Int'l*, pg. 915
AG-CHEM EUROPE FERTILIZER EQUIPMENT BV—See AGCO Corporation; *U.S. Public*, pg. 58
AGCO A/S—See AGCO Corporation; *U.S. Public*, pg. 58
AGCO CANADA LTD.—See AGCO Corporation; *U.S. Public*, pg. 58
AGCO (CHINA) INVESTMENT CO., LTD.—See AGCO Corporation; *U.S. Public*, pg. 58
AGCO FEUCHT GMBH—See AGCO Corporation; *U.S. Public*, pg. 58
AGCO FEUCHT GMBH—See AGCO Corporation; *U.S. Public*, pg. 58
AGCO GMBH—See AGCO Corporation; *U.S. Public*, pg. 58
AGCO LTD.—See AGCO Corporation; *U.S. Public*, pg. 58
AGCO POWER OY—See AGCO Corporation; *U.S. Public*, pg. 58
AGLAND CORP.; *Int'l*, pg. 211
AG-MEIER INDUSTRIES LLC; *U.S. Private*, pg. 125
AGPOINT AUSTRALIA—See Great Western Corporation Pty. Ltd.; *Int'l*, pg. 3066
AG POWER ENTERPRISE INC.; *U.S. Private*, pg. 125
AG-POWER INC.; *U.S. Private*, pg. 125
AGRAVIS RAIFFEISEN-MARKT GMBH—See AGRAVIS Raiffeisen AG; *Int'l*, pg. 215
AGRAVIS TECHNIK BVL GMBH—See AGRAVIS Raiffeisen AG; *Int'l*, pg. 215
AGRAVIS TECHNIK HEIDE-ALTMARK GMBH—See AGRAVIS Raiffeisen AG; *Int'l*, pg. 215
AGRAVIS TECHNIK LENNE-LIPPE GMBH—See AGRAVIS Raiffeisen AG; *Int'l*, pg. 215
AGRAVIS TECHNIK MUNSTERLAND-EMS GMBH—See AGRAVIS Raiffeisen AG; *Int'l*, pg. 215
AGRAVIS TECHNIK POLSKA SP. Z O.O.—See AGRAVIS Raiffeisen AG; *Int'l*, pg. 215
AGRAVIS TECHNIK RAIFFEISEN GMBH—See AGRAVIS Raiffeisen AG; *Int'l*, pg. 215
AGRAVIS TECHNIK SACHSEN-ANHALT/BRANDENBURG GMBH—See AGRAVIS Raiffeisen AG; *Int'l*, pg. 215
AGRAVIS TECHNIK SALTENBROCK GMBH—See AGRAVIS Raiffeisen AG; *Int'l*, pg. 215
AGRAVIS VERSICHERUNGSSERVICE GMBH & CO. KG—See AGRAVIS Raiffeisen AG; *Int'l*, pg. 215
AGRIEURO CORP.; *Int'l*, pg. 217
AGRIFOCUS LIMITADA—See Element Solutions Inc.; *U.S. Public*, pg. 725
AGRILIANCE, LLC—See CHS INC.; *U.S. Public*, pg. 491
AGRILIANCE, LLC—See Land O'Lakes, Inc.; *U.S. Private*, pg. 2383
AGRI-SUPPLY COMPANY INC.—See Direct Distributors Inc.; *U.S. Private*, pg. 1235
AGRIVISION GROUP, LLC; *U.S. Private*, pg. 130
AGROMEHANIKA AD; *Int'l*, pg. 220
AGROTEC A.S.—See Agrofert Holding, a.s.; *Int'l*, pg. 218
AGROTECHNIC MORAVIA A.S.—See Agrofert Holding, a.s.; *Int'l*, pg. 218
AGVANTAGE FS, INC.; *U.S. Private*, pg. 130
AG-WEST DISTRIBUTING COMPANY; *U.S. Private*, pg. 125
ALAMO GROUP (IA) INC.—See Alamo Group Inc.; *U.S. Public*, pg. 71
ALAMO GROUP (TX), INC.—See Alamo Group Inc.; *U.S. Public*, pg. 71
ALBANY TRACTOR CO. - LAWN & GARDEN DIVISION—See Flint Equipment Holdings, Inc.; *U.S. Private*, pg. 1545
ALBANY TRACTOR CO.—See Flint Equipment Holdings, Inc.; *U.S. Private*, pg. 1545
ALLEGHENY SURFACE TECHNOLOGY—See Allegheny Bradford Corporation; *U.S. Private*, pg. 175
ALMA TRACTOR & EQUIPMENT INC.; *U.S. Private*, pg. 195
AL SWIDERSKI IMPLEMENT INC.; *U.S. Private*, pg. 147
AMEROP PRODUCTS; *U.S. Private*, pg. 261
ANGLO-THAI CO. LTD.—See Hup Soon Global Corporation Limited; *Int'l*, pg. 3538
APPLE FARM SERVICE INC.; *U.S. Private*, pg. 296
AQUARIUS IRRIGATION SUPPLY INC.; *U.S. Private*, pg. 303
ARENDS BROS. INC.; *U.S. Private*, pg. 318
ARIZONA MACHINERY CO.; *U.S. Private*, pg. 324
ARNOLD'S OF WILLMAR INCORPORATED; *U.S. Private*, pg. 333
ATLANTIC TRACTOR—See McCombie Group, LLC; *U.S. Private*, pg. 2629
THE AYRES COMPANY—See Ayres-Delta Implement, Inc.; *U.S. Private*, pg. 415
AYRES-DELTA IMPLEMENT OF BELZONI, INC.—See Ayres-Delta Implement, Inc.; *U.S. Private*, pg. 414
BAKER IMPLEMENT CO. INC.; *U.S. Private*, pg. 456
BARIBEAU IMPLEMENT COMPANY; *U.S. Private*, pg. 474
BAYWA HANDELS-SYSTEME-SERVICE GMBH—See BayWa AG; *Int'l*, pg. 916
BAYWA R.E GMBH—See BayWa AG; *Int'l*, pg. 916
BAYWA-TANKSTELLEN-GMBH—See BayWa AG; *Int'l*, pg. 917
B.B. HOBBS, INC.; *U.S. Private*, pg. 420
BEARD IMPLEMENT CO.; *U.S. Private*, pg. 506
BEAVER VALLEY SUPPLY CO. INC.; *U.S. Private*, pg. 509
BELKORP AG, LLC—See Belkorp Industries, Inc.; *Int'l*, pg. 965
BEN BURGESS & COMPANY; *Int'l*, pg. 969
BENES SERVICE CO.; *U.S. Private*, pg. 525
BIRKEY'S FARM STORE INC.; *U.S. Private*, pg. 564
BISHOP & WACHHOLZ INC.—See Minnesota Ag Group Inc.; *U.S. Private*, pg. 2743
BLAIN SUPPLY, INC.; *U.S. Private*, pg. 577
BLANCHARD EQUIPMENT CO. INC.; *U.S. Private*, pg. 579
BLUFF EQUIPMENT, INC.; *U.S. Private*, pg. 599
BODENSTEINER IMPLEMENT COMPANY; *U.S. Private*, pg. 608
BONDIOLI & PAVESI INC.—See Bondioli & Pavesi S.p.A.; *Int'l*, pg. 1106
BOSTON LAWNMOWER COMPANY—See The Crandall-Hicks Company, Inc.; *U.S. Private*, pg. 4016
BRATNEY EQUIPMENT COMPANY INC—See K.B.C. Group Inc.; *U.S. Private*, pg. 2251
BRIGGS & STRATTON AUSTRALIA PTY. LIMITED—See Briggs & Stratton Corporation; *U.S. Private*, pg. 650
BRIGGS & STRATTON FRANCE S.A.R.L.—See Briggs & Stratton Corporation; *U.S. Private*, pg. 651

423820 — FARM AND GARDEN MAC...

BRIGGS & STRATTON GERMANY GMBH—See Briggs & Stratton Corporation; *U.S. Private*, pg. 651
BRIGGS & STRATTON NEW ZEALAND LIMITED—See Briggs & Stratton Corporation; *U.S. Private*, pg. 651
BRIGGS & STRATTON U.K. LIMITED—See Briggs & Stratton Corporation; *U.S. Private*, pg. 651
BROUWERS EQUIPMENT B.V.—See GEA Group Aktiengesellschaft; *Int'l*, pg. 2897
BRUNA BROS IMPLEMENT LLC; *U.S. Private*, pg. 672
BS BAUFACHHANDEL BRANDS & SCHNITZLER VERWALTUNGS-GMBH—See BayWa AG; *Int'l*, pg. 920
THE BUCKLIN TRACTOR & IMPLEMENT CO; *U.S. Private*, pg. 4002
BURNIPS EQUIPMENT COMPANY; *U.S. Private*, pg. 689
BYSTRONIC IBERICA S.A.—See Bystronic AG; *Int'l*, pg. 1236
CAL-COAST MACHINERY, INC.; *U.S. Private*, pg. 715
CALDWELL IMPLEMENT COMPANY; *U.S. Private*, pg. 716
CAMPBELL TRACTOR & IMPLEMENT CO.; *U.S. Private*, pg. 730
CAPAGRI SAS—See Exel Industries SA; *Int'l*, pg. 2582
CAPITAL TRACTOR INC.; *U.S. Private*, pg. 742
CAPSTONE COMMODITIES, LLC—See The Andersons Incorporated; *U.S. Public*, pg. 2034
CARGILL (MALAYSIA) SDN BHD—See Cargill, Inc.; *U.S. Private*, pg. 755
CARL F. STATZ & SONS INC.; *U.S. Private*, pg. 762
CARRICO IMPLEMENT CO. INC.; *U.S. Private*, pg. 772
CARRS BILLINGTON AGRICULTURE (SALES) LTD.—See Carr's Group PLC; *Int'l*, pg. 1343
CARSWELL DISTRIBUTING COMPANY; *U.S. Private*, pg. 775
CASTONGIAS INC.; *U.S. Private*, pg. 785
CAZENOVIA EQUIPMENT CO., INC.; *U.S. Private*, pg. 796
CENTRAL IRRIGATION SUPPLY INC.; *U.S. Private*, pg. 822
CENTRE BRETAGNE MOTOCULTURE; *Int'l*, pg. 1411
CENTURY EQUIPMENT INC.; *U.S. Private*, pg. 832
CENTURY EQUIPMENT INC.—See Century Equipment Inc.; *U.S. Private*, pg. 832
CEREA, A.S.—See Agrofert Holding, a.s.; *Int'l*, pg. 219
CERVUS EQUIPMENT CORPORATION—See Brandt Industries Ltd.; *Int'l*, pg. 1140
CHAMBERLAIN HOLDINGS LIMITED—See Deere & Company; *U.S. Public*, pg. 646
CHRISTY ENTERPRISES, INC.; *U.S. Private*, pg. 892
CIMBRIA BRATNEY CO.—See K.B.C. Group Inc.; *U.S. Private*, pg. 2251
CIMBRIA HEID ITALIA SRL—See AGCO Corporation; *U.S. Public*, pg. 58
CISCO EQUIPMENT - LUBBOCK—See Cisco Ford Equipment, Inc.; *U.S. Private*, pg. 900
CISCO EQUIPMENT - SAN ANGELO—See Cisco Ford Equipment, Inc.; *U.S. Private*, pg. 900
CLAAS NORDOSTBAYERN GMBH & CO. KG—See BayWa AG; *Int'l*, pg. 917
CLASS NORDOSTBAYERN GMBH & CO. KG—See BayWa AG; *Int'l*, pg. 917
CLASS SUDOSTBAYERN GMBH—See BayWa AG; *Int'l*, pg. 917
C-LINES FRANCE SAS—See AGCO Corporation; *U.S. Public*, pg. 58
CNH INTERNATIONAL S.A.—See CNH Industrial N.V.; *Int'l*, pg. 1674
CNH PORTUGAL-COMERCIO DE TRACTORES E MAQUINAS AGRICOLAS LTDA—See CNH Industrial N.V.; *Int'l*, pg. 1674
COAST PUMP & SUPPLY CO. INC.; *U.S. Private*, pg. 954
COMER INC.—See Comer Industries S.p.A.; *Int'l*, pg. 1710
COMER INDUSTRIES SARL—See Comer Industries S.p.A.; *Int'l*, pg. 1710
COMER INDUSTRIES U.K. LTD—See Comer Industries S.p.A.; *Int'l*, pg. 1710
COOK TRACTOR CO. INC.; *U.S. Private*, pg. 1038
CORSICA IMPLEMENT CO. INC.; *U.S. Private*, pg. 1060
CRAWFORD & CRAWFORD, INC.—See Adair Feed & Grain Company; *U.S. Private*, pg. 73
CREEL TRACTOR COMPANY; *U.S. Private*, pg. 1092
CROSS BROTHERS IMPLEMENT INC.; *U.S. Private*, pg. 1104
CROSS IMPLEMENT INC.; *U.S. Private*, pg. 1105
CRUSTBUSTER-SPEED KING, INC.; *U.S. Private*, pg. 1114
CUKUROVA ZIRAAT ENDUSTRI VE TIC. A.S.—See Cukurova Holding A.S.; *Int'l*, pg. 1876
DAEDONG USA INC.—See Daedong Corporation; *Int'l*, pg. 1906
DANDRIDGE EQUIPMENT INC.; *U.S. Private*, pg. 1153
DAVIS PIPE & SUPPLY, INC.—See Leonard Green & Partners, L.P.; *U.S. Private*, pg. 2429
DEBOFFE; *Int'l*, pg. 1998
DEERE & COMPANY; *U.S. Public*, pg. 646
DEERLAND FARM EQUIPMENT (1985) LTD.; *Int'l*, pg. 2003
DELTA IMPLEMENT COMPANY—See Ayres-Delta Implement, Inc.; *U.S. Private*, pg. 414
DELTA IMPLEMENT CO. OF ROLLING FORK—See Ayres-Delta Implement, Inc.; *U.S. Private*, pg. 414

DIARYGOLD ASIA LIMITED—See Dairygold Co-Operative Society Ltd; *Int'l*, pg. 1940
DIESEL & MOTOR ENGINEERING PLC; *Int'l*, pg. 2115
DIRECT DISTRIBUTORS INC.; *U.S. Private*, pg. 1235
DIXIE SALES COMPANY INC.; *U.S. Private*, pg. 1245
D & K IMPLEMENT LLC; *U.S. Private*, pg. 1136
DON MEDLIN CO.; *U.S. Private*, pg. 1258
DORMANKO DERTIG (PTY) LTD.—See AFGRI Limited; *Int'l*, pg. 188
DTL DONAU-TANKLAGERGESELLSCHAFT, MBH & CO. KG—See BayWa AG; *Int'l*, pg. 917
EAST COAST SPRINKLER SUPPLY; *U.S. Private*, pg. 1316
EAST WEST AGRO AB; *Int'l*, pg. 2270
EASY BIO PHILIPPINES, INC.—See Easy Holdings Co., Ltd.; *Int'l*, pg. 2275
EDNEY DISTRIBUTING COMPANY; *U.S. Private*, pg. 1338
EGERSUND TRADING AS—See Egersund Group AS; *Int'l*, pg. 2323
EG TRANSPORTATION SERVICES LLC—See Unrivaled Brands, Inc.; *U.S. Public*, pg. 2263
EIKMASKIN AS—See AGCO Corporation; *U.S. Public*, pg. 58
ELDER SALES & SERVICE INC.; *U.S. Private*, pg. 1351
ELDRIDGE SUPPLY COMPANY; *U.S. Private*, pg. 1351
EMAK DEUTSCHLAND GMBH—See Emak S.p.A.; *Int'l*, pg. 2373
EMAK U.K. LTD.—See Emak S.p.A.; *Int'l*, pg. 2373
ENGINEERING SERVICES & PRODUCTS COMPANY INC.; *U.S. Private*, pg. 1399
ENGINE WAREHOUSE INC.; *U.S. Private*, pg. 1397
ENLOW TRACTOR AUCTION, INC.; *U.S. Private*, pg. 1401
ERNEST DOE & SONS LIMITED; *Int'l*, pg. 2494
ERNIE WILLIAMS LTD; *U.S. Private*, pg. 1422
EUROGREEN CZ S.R.O.—See BayWa AG; *Int'l*, pg. 917
EVERGREEN IMPLEMENT CO.; *U.S. Private*, pg. 1439
EZ CLONE ENTERPRISES INC.—See GrowLife, Inc.; *U.S. Public*, pg. 972
FARMCHEM CORPORATION; *U.S. Private*, pg. 1475
FARM EQUIPMENT COMPANY; *U.S. Private*, pg. 1475
FARMER AUTOMATIC GMBH & CO. KG—See AGCO Corporation; *U.S. Public*, pg. 58
FARMER BOY AGRICULTURAL SYSTEMS INC.; *U.S. Private*, pg. 1475
FARMERS INC.; *U.S. Private*, pg. 1478
FARMERS SUPPLY SALES INC.; *U.S. Private*, pg. 1479
FEI, INC; *U.S. Private*, pg. 1493
FE (INDIA) LIMITED; *Int'l*, pg. 2629
FERTILIZER DEALER SUPPLY INC.; *U.S. Private*, pg. 1499
FERTILIZER EQUIPMENT INC.; *U.S. Private*, pg. 1499
FEUERSTRATER GMBH—See AGRAVIS Raiffeisen AG; *Int'l*, pg. 215
FINDLAY IMPLEMENT CO.; *U.S. Private*, pg. 1508
FISKARS GARDEN & OUTDOOR LIVING—See Fiskars Oyj Abp; *Int'l*, pg. 2693
FISKARS NORWAY AS—See Fiskars Oyj Abp; *Int'l*, pg. 2694
FOSS (BEIJING) SCIENCE, TECHNOLOGY & TRADING CO.—See Foss A/S; *Int'l*, pg. 2748
FOSS INDIA PVT. LTD.—See Foss A/S; *Int'l*, pg. 2748
FOXLAND HARVESTORE INC.; *U.S. Private*, pg. 1585
FREELIN-WADE—See Coilhose Pneumatics Inc.; *U.S. Private*, pg. 964
FRONTLINE AG LLC; *U.S. Private*, pg. 1616
FRUIT GROWERS SUPPLY CO. - FGS ONTARIO CARTON PLANT—See Fruit Growers Supply Co.; *U.S. Private*, pg. 1617
GEA WESTFALIASURGE ACIER SAS—See GEA Group Aktiengesellschaft; *Int'l*, pg. 2904
GEA WESTFALIASURGE UK LTD.—See GEA Group Aktiengesellschaft; *Int'l*, pg. 2904
GENERAL IMPLEMENT DISTRIBUTORS—See Arnold Machinery Company; *U.S. Private*, pg. 333
GIFORE AGRICULTURAL SCIENCE & TECHNOLOGY SERVICE CO., LTD.; *Int'l*, pg. 2970
GJ&L INC.; *U.S. Private*, pg. 1703
GKN WALTERSCHEID GETRIEBE GMBH—See GKN plc; *Int'l*, pg. 2985
G & M SALES OF EASTERN NC, INC.; *U.S. Private*, pg. 1628
GOLDEN STATE IRRIGATION SERVICES; *U.S. Private*, pg. 1733
GOLDEN WEST IRRIGATION & EQUIPMENT LLC; *U.S. Private*, pg. 1734
GOOSENECK IMPLEMENT COMPANY; *U.S. Private*, pg. 1741
GRASSLAND EQUIPMENT & IRRIGATION CORPORATION; *U.S. Private*, pg. 1758
GRASSLAND EQUIPMENT & IRRIGATION CORP.—See Grassland Equipment & Irrigation Corporation; *U.S. Private*, pg. 1758
GRASSLAND EQUIPMENT & IRRIGATION CORP.—See Grassland Equipment & Irrigation Corporation; *U.S. Private*, pg. 1758
GREAT WESTERN TILLAGE—See Great Western Corporation Pty. Ltd.; *Int'l*, pg. 3066
GREENHOUSE SOLUTIONS INC.; *U.S. Public*, pg. 964
GREENWAY-MALDEN EQUIPMENT CO.; *U.S. Private*, pg. 1781
GROSSENBURG IMPLEMENT, INC.; *U.S. Private*, pg. 1792

GROWGENERATION OKLAHOMA CORP.—See GrowGeneration Corp.; *U.S. Public*, pg. 972
GROW SOLUTIONS HOLDINGS, INC.; *U.S. Public*, pg. 972
GSI CUMBERLAND DE MEXICO, S. DE RL DE CV—See AGCO Corporation; *U.S. Public*, pg. 58
GUNDELACH GMBH—See AGRAVIS Raiffeisen AG; *Int'l*, pg. 215
HAMMOND TRACTOR COMPANY; *U.S. Private*, pg. 1850
HANSON'S AUTO & IMPLEMENT INC.; *U.S. Private*, pg. 1857
HARDI CROP PROTECTION SA LTD.—See Exel Industries SA; *Int'l*, pg. 2582
HARDI INC.—See Exel Industries SA; *Int'l*, pg. 2582
HARDI LTD—See Exel Industries SA; *Int'l*, pg. 2582
HAUG IMPLEMENT CO. INC; *U.S. Private*, pg. 1880
HEARTLAND EQUIPMENT, INC.; *U.S. Private*, pg. 1900
HENDERSON IMPLEMENT CO. INC.; *U.S. Private*, pg. 1914
HERDER IMPLEMENTOS E MAQUINAS AGRICOLAS LTDA.—See Alamo Group Inc.; *U.S. Public*, pg. 71
HERGOTT FARM EQUIPMENT LTD.; *Int'l*, pg. 3361
HIGH TECH IRRIGATION INC.; *U.S. Private*, pg. 1937
HILLSBORO EQUIPMENT INCORPORATED; *U.S. Private*, pg. 1947
HLH AGRI INTERNATIONAL PTE LTD—See Hong Lai Huat Group Limited; *Int'l*, pg. 3467
HOMIER & SONS INC.; *U.S. Private*, pg. 1976
HORIZON DISTRIBUTORS, INC.—See Pool Corporation; *U.S. Public*, pg. 1701
HORIZON EQUIPMENT; *U.S. Private*, pg. 1980
HORIZON—See Pool Corporation; *U.S. Public*, pg. 1701
HORNBACH BAUMARKT AG—See Hornbach Holding AG & Co. KGaA; *Int'l*, pg. 3481
H&R AGRI-POWER, INC.; *U.S. Private*, pg. 1823
HUNTER & COMPANY PLC; *Int'l*, pg. 3536
HUNTER EQUIPMENT INC—See Brandt Holdings Company; *U.S. Private*, pg. 638
HUNTER EQUIPMENT—See Brandt Holdings Company; *U.S. Private*, pg. 638
HURST FARM SUPPLY INC.; *U.S. Private*, pg. 2013
HUSQVARNA DEUTSCHLAND GMBH—See Husqvarna AB; *Int'l*, pg. 3539
HUTSON, INC. - JASPER—See Hutson, Inc.; *U.S. Private*, pg. 2014
HUTSONS AG EQUIPMENT INCORPORATED; *U.S. Private*, pg. 2014
IBA INC.; *U.S. Private*, pg. 2028
INDUSTRIAL MACHINE & TOOL COMPANY INC.; *U.S. Private*, pg. 2066
IRRIGATION SPECIALISTS INC.; *U.S. Private*, pg. 2141
IRRIGATION STATION LLP; *U.S. Private*, pg. 2141
JACOBI SALES INC.; *U.S. Private*, pg. 2179
JAMES RIVER EQUIPMENT, CO.—See Brandt Holdings Company; *U.S. Private*, pg. 638
JAYCOX IMPLEMENT INC.; *U.S. Private*, pg. 2192
JDAMC—See Deere & Company; *U.S. Public*, pg. 646
JENNER EQUIPMENT CO.; *U.S. Private*, pg. 2200
JENSEN & PILEGARD; *U.S. Private*, pg. 2200
JERRY PATE TURF & IRRIGATION INC; *U.S. Private*, pg. 2202
JOHN DAY COMPANY; *U.S. Private*, pg. 2221
JOHN DEERE CANADA ULC—See Deere & Company; *U.S. Public*, pg. 646
JOHN DEERE GMBH & CO. KG—See Deere & Company; *U.S. Public*, pg. 646
JOHN DEERE INDIA PRIVATE LIMITED—See Deere & Company; *U.S. Public*, pg. 646
JOHN DEERE POLSKA SP. ZO.O—See Deere & Company; *U.S. Public*, pg. 647
JOHN DEERE POLSKA SP. Z O.O.—See Deere & Company; *U.S. Public*, pg. 647
JOHN DEERE (PTY.) LTD.—See Deere & Company; *U.S. Public*, pg. 646
JOHN DEERE WALLDORF GMBH & CO. KG—See Deere & Company; *U.S. Public*, pg. 647
JONES TRACTOR & EQUIPMENT CO., INC.; *U.S. Private*, pg. 2234
KAKNES LANDSCAPE SUPPLY, INC.—See SiteOne Landscape Supply, Inc.; *U.S. Public*, pg. 1888
KANEQUIP, INC.; *U.S. Private*, pg. 2260
KAYE CORPORATION; *U.S. Private*, pg. 2266
KAYTON INTERNATIONAL, INC.; *U.S. Private*, pg. 2267
KELLANDS AGRICULTURAL LTD.—See Alamo Group Inc.; *U.S. Public*, pg. 70
KENNEY MACHINERY CORPORATION; *U.S. Private*, pg. 2286
KES SCIENCE & TECHNOLOGY, INC.—See Applied UV, Inc.; *U.S. Public*, pg. 173
KIBBLE EQUIPMENT INC.—See Brandt Holdings Company; *U.S. Private*, pg. 639
KIBBLE EQUIPMENT—See Brandt Holdings Company; *U.S. Private*, pg. 639
KILPATRICK COMPANY INC.; *U.S. Private*, pg. 2304
KILPATRICK TURF & INDUSTRIAL EQUIPMENT—See Kilpatrick Company Inc.; *U.S. Private*, pg. 2304
KLEINE EQUIPMENT; *U.S. Private*, pg. 2319
KOLETZKY IMPLEMENT, INC.; *U.S. Private*, pg. 2341

N.A.I.C.S. INDEX

423820 — FARM AND GARDEN MAC...

KUHN FARM MACHINERY LTD—See Bucher Industries AG; *Int'l*, pg. 1209
KUHN IBERICA SA—See Bucher Industries AG; *Int'l*, pg. 1209
KUHN ITALIA SRL.—See Bucher Industries AG; *Int'l*, pg. 1209
KUHN MASCHINEN-VERTRIEB GMBH—See Bucher Industries AG; *Int'l*, pg. 1209
KUHN MASZYNY ROLNICZE SP. Z.O.O—See Bucher Industries AG; *Int'l*, pg. 1209
KUHNS EQUIPMENT COMPANY; *U.S. Private*, pg. 2356
KUHN VOSTOK LLC—See Bucher Industries AG; *Int'l*, pg. 1209
KULKER S.A.S.—See Groupe ELYDAN; *Int'l*, pg. 3102
KUNAU IMPLEMENT CO. INC.; *U.S. Private*, pg. 2357
LAGERHAUS TECHNIK-CENTER GMBH & CO. KG—See BayWa AG; *Int'l*, pg. 918
LANDMARK EQUIPMENT; *U.S. Private*, pg. 2385
LANDTECHNIK STEIGRA GMBH—See AGRAVIS Raiffeisen AG; *Int'l*, pg. 215
LARSON IMPLEMENT INC.—See Minnesota Ag Group Inc.; *U.S. Private*, pg. 2743
LASSETER TRACTOR CO., INC.; *U.S. Private*, pg. 2395
LATTEC I/S—See Foss A/S; *Int'l*, pg. 2749
LAVI INDUSTRIES INC. - NEW YORK FACILITY—See Lavi Industries Inc.; *U.S. Private*, pg. 2400
LAWRENCE TRACTOR COMPANY INC.; *U.S. Private*, pg. 2402
LEBERGE & CURTIS, INC.—See Cazenovia Equipment Co., Inc.; *U.S. Private*, pg. 796
LEINBACH MACHINERY CO.; *U.S. Private*, pg. 2420
LELY AUSTRALIA PTY LTD—See AGCO Corporation; *U.S. Public*, pg. 59
LENZ INC.; *U.S. Private*, pg. 2422
LIECHTY FARM EQUIPMENT INC.; *U.S. Private*, pg. 2448
LINDSAY SULAMA VE ALTYAPI SANAYI VE TICARCT A.S.—See Lindsay Corporation; *U.S. Public*, pg. 1319
LIVINGSTON MACHINERY CO.; *U.S. Private*, pg. 2474
LONGHORN, INC.; *U.S. Private*, pg. 2492
LORENZ RUBARTH LANDTECHNIK GMBH—See AGRAVIS Raiffeisen AG; *Int'l*, pg. 215
LOWE TRACTOR & EQUIPMENT, INC.; *U.S. Private*, pg. 2504
M3 SAS—See Groupe Dubreuil SA; *Int'l*, pg. 3102
MARSHALL ASSOCIATES, INC.; *U.S. Private*, pg. 2592
MARUNAKA CO., LTD.—See AEON Co., Ltd.; *Int'l*, pg. 178
MATROT UK LTD—See Exel Industries SA; *Int'l*, pg. 2582
MAYFIELD EQUIPMENT CO.; *U.S. Private*, pg. 2621
MCLEAN IMPLEMENT INCORPORATED; *U.S. Private*, pg. 2641
MEADE TRACTOR; *U.S. Private*, pg. 2647
MENKE AGRAR GMBH—See AGRAVIS Raiffeisen AG; *Int'l*, pg. 215
MESSICK FARM EQUIPMENT INC.; *U.S. Private*, pg. 2679
MEYER EQUIPMENT, CO.; *U.S. Private*, pg. 2692
MIDLAND IMPLEMENT COMPANY, INC.; *U.S. Private*, pg. 2715
MILLER SELLNER IMPLEMENT INC.; *U.S. Private*, pg. 2735
MINNESOTA AG GROUP INC.; *U.S. Private*, pg. 2743
MODERN FARM EQUIPMENT CORP.; *U.S. Private*, pg. 2760
MOUNTAIN VIEW EQUIPMENT CO. INC.; *U.S. Private*, pg. 2800
MTD PRODUCTS, INC.—See Stanley Black & Decker, Inc.; *U.S. Public*, pg. 1933
MTI DISTRIBUTING COMPANY INC.—See The Toro Company; *U.S. Public*, pg. 2135
MV EQUIPMENT LLC; *U.S. Private*, pg. 2821
MV EQUIPMENT—See MV Equipment LLC; *U.S. Private*, pg. 2821
NASCO INTERNATIONAL, INC.—See Geneve Holdings Corp.; *U.S. Private*, pg. 1671
NAVOS FARM TECHNIC S.R.O.—See Agrofert Holding, a.s.; *Int'l*, pg. 219
NEESE, INC.—See 1847 Holdings LLC; *U.S. Public*, pg. 2
NEFF CO.; *U.S. Private*, pg. 2880
NEUHAUS & COMPANY INC.; *U.S. Private*, pg. 2890
NEW ENGLAND POTTERY, LLC—See Central Garden & Pet Company; *U.S. Public*, pg. 473
NEW-TEC OST VERTRIEBSGESELLSCHAFT FUR AGRARTECHNIK MBH—See AGRAVIS Raiffeisen AG; *Int'l*, pg. 215
NEW-TEC WEST VERTRIEBSGESELLSCHAFT FUR AGRARTECHNIK MBH—See AGRAVIS Raiffeisen AG; *Int'l*, pg. 215
THE NIEMEYER CORPORATION; *U.S. Private*, pg. 4084
NILSEN FEED & GRAIN COMPANY; *U.S. Private*, pg. 2927
NORTHLAND LAWN SPORT & EQUIPMENT; *U.S. Private*, pg. 2955
N&S TRACTOR CO. INC.; *U.S. Private*, pg. 2827
NUECES FARM CENTER INC.; *U.S. Private*, pg. 2972
OASE ASIA PACIFIC PTE LTD—See Argand Partners, LP; *U.S. Private*, pg. 319
OASE CHINA—See Argand Partners, LP; *U.S. Private*, pg. 319
OASE GMBH—See Argand Partners, LP; *U.S. Private*, pg. 319

OASE MIDDLE EAST FZE—See Argand Partners, LP; *U.S. Private*, pg. 319
OASE NORTH AMERICA, INC.—See Argand Partners, LP; *U.S. Private*, pg. 319
OASE TURKIYE—See Argand Partners, LP; *U.S. Private*, pg. 319
OASE (UK) LTD.—See Argand Partners, LP; *U.S. Private*, pg. 319
OHIO AG EQUIPMENT SALES CO., INC.—See Ohio Machinery Co.; *U.S. Private*, pg. 3004
OLIVER M. DEAN, INC.; *U.S. Private*, pg. 3011
OREGON TRAIL EQUIPMENT LLC; *U.S. Private*, pg. 3040
PALS, INC.; *U.S. Private*, pg. 3082
PARGA PARK- UND GARTENTECHNIK GESELLSCHAFT M.B.H—See BayWa AG; *Int'l*, pg. 918
PARRISH EQUIPMENT SUPPLY INC.; *U.S. Private*, pg. 3100
PARTMASTER (PTY) LTD.—See AFGRI Limited; *Int'l*, pg. 188
PATTLEN ENTERPRISES INC.; *U.S. Private*, pg. 3111
PETTIT MACHINERY INC.; *U.S. Private*, pg. 3163
PHELPS IMPLEMENT CORPORATION; *U.S. Private*, pg. 3167
PIONEER FARM EQUIPMENT CO.; *U.S. Private*, pg. 3187
P&K EQUIPMENT INC.; *U.S. Private*, pg. 3059
PLAINVIEW AGRI POWER INC.—See Minnesota Ag Group Inc.; *U.S. Private*, pg. 2743
PLANTERS EQUIPMENT CO.—See Ayres-Delta Implement, Inc.; *U.S. Private*, pg. 415
POLK COUNTY FARMERS CO-OP INC.; *U.S. Private*, pg. 3224
PREMIER FEED MILLS COMPANY LIMITED—See Flour Mills of Nigeria Plc.; *Int'l*, pg. 2709
PREMIER IRRIGATION ADRITEC INDIA—See Adritec Group International, E.C.; *Int'l*, pg. 153
PRENGER'S INC.; *U.S. Private*, pg. 3252
PRICE BROS EQUIPMENT CO; *U.S. Private*, pg. 3258
PROPHETSTOWN EQUIPMENT INC.; *U.S. Private*, pg. 3286
PROSPECT IMPLEMENT, INC.—See Ron's Equipment Co Inc.; *U.S. Private*, pg. 3477
QUALITY IMPLEMENT COMPANY; *U.S. Private*, pg. 3319
RAIFFEISEN-LAGERHAUS INVESTITIONSHOLDING GMBH—See BayWa AG; *Int'l*, pg. 918
RAIFFEISEN LIENEN-LENGERICH GMBH—See AGRAVIS Raiffeisen AG; *Int'l*, pg. 215
RAY LEE EQUIPMENT COMPANY—See Western Equipment LLC; *U.S. Private*, pg. 4493
RDO EQUIPMENT CO.—See R.D. Offutt Company; *U.S. Private*, pg. 3335
RDO VERMEER, LLC—See R.D. Offutt Company; *U.S. Private*, pg. 3335
REAMS SPRINKLER SUPPLY COMPANY; *U.S. Private*, pg. 3370
REVELS TRACTOR CO. INC.; *U.S. Private*, pg. 3413
RICHARDS TRACTORS & IMPLEMENTS; *U.S. Private*, pg. 3429
RIECHMANN BROS LLC; *U.S. Private*, pg. 3434
RIESTERER & SCHNELL INC.; *U.S. Private*, pg. 3434
RI-SOLUTION DATA GMBH—See BayWa AG; *Int'l*, pg. 918
RITCHIE IMPLEMENT INC.; *U.S. Private*, pg. 3441
R.M. WADE & CO.—See Arnold Machinery Company; *U.S. Private*, pg. 333
ROEDER IMPLEMENT INC.; *U.S. Private*, pg. 3470
RON'S EQUIPMENT CO INC.; *U.S. Private*, pg. 3477
R.P.M. TECH INC.—See Alamo Group Inc.; *U.S. Public*, pg. 71
RUETERS RED POWER; *U.S. Private*, pg. 3502
RWA UKRAJINA LLC—See BayWa AG; *Int'l*, pg. 918
RYAN LAWN & TREE INC.; *U.S. Private*, pg. 3510
SAATZUCHT GLEISDORF GESELLSCHAFT M.B.H—See BayWa AG; *Int'l*, pg. 919
S.A. CAMP COMPANIES; *U.S. Private*, pg. 3515
SALEM FARM SUPPLY INC.; *U.S. Private*, pg. 3531
SALYER LAND COMPANY; *U.S. Private*, pg. 3535
SCHENKELBERG IMPLEMENT COMPANY; *U.S. Private*, pg. 3564
SCHERRMAN'S IMPLEMENT & APPLIANCE; *U.S. Private*, pg. 3564
SCHLUETER CO.; *U.S. Private*, pg. 3565
SCHOLTEN'S EQUIPMENT INC.; *U.S. Private*, pg. 3567
SEABOARD PRODUCE DISTRIBUTORS; *U.S. Private*, pg. 3583
SEEDBURO EQUIPMENT CO.; *U.S. Private*, pg. 3597
SEMA EQUIPMENT, INC; *U.S. Private*, pg. 3603
SHEARER FARM INC.; *U.S. Private*, pg. 3629
SHERRILL, INC.—See Gridiron Capital, LLC; *U.S. Private*, pg. 1786
SHIVVERS INC.; *U.S. Private*, pg. 3638
SIGOURNEY TRACTOR & IMPLEMENT; *U.S. Private*, pg. 3651
SIMMONS IRRIGATION SUPPLY INC.; *U.S. Private*, pg. 3665
SIMPLY GREEN LAWN SPRINKLERS, INC.—See Ryan Lawn & Tree Inc.; *U.S. Private*, pg. 3510
SIMPSON NORTON CORPORATION—See Connor, Clark & Lunn Financial Group; *Int'l*, pg. 1769

SINCLAIR TRACTOR—See Sigourney Tractor & Implement; *U.S. Private*, pg. 3651
SIOUX AUTOMATION CENTER INC.; *U.S. Private*, pg. 3670
SITEONE LANDSCAPE SUPPLY, LLC—See SiteOne Landscape Supply, Inc.; *U.S. Public*, pg. 1889
SMITHCO, INC.; *U.S. Private*, pg. 3697
SMITH PIPE & SUPPLY INC.; *U.S. Private*, pg. 3695
SMITH TRACTOR CO. INC.; *U.S. Private*, pg. 3696
SMITH TURF & IRRIGATION CO.; *U.S. Private*, pg. 3696
SORUM TRACTOR CO., INC.—See AGCO Corporation; *U.S. Public*, pg. 58
SOUTHERN MARKETING AFFILIATES, INC.; *U.S. Private*, pg. 3733
SOUTHERN MARKETING AFFILIATES OF THE SOUTHWEST, INC.—See Southern Marketing Affiliates, Inc.; *U.S. Private*, pg. 3733
SOUTHWEST REGIONAL REPRESENTATIVES, INC.; *U.S. Private*, pg. 3740
SPAREX INC.—See AGCO Corporation; *U.S. Public*, pg. 59
SPAREX LIMITED APS—See AGCO Corporation; *U.S. Public*, pg. 59
SPAREX NEW ZEALAND LTD—See AGCO Corporation; *U.S. Public*, pg. 59
SPARTAN DISTRIBUTORS INC.; *U.S. Private*, pg. 3746
SRW PRODUCTS; *U.S. Private*, pg. 3768
STANDRIDGE EQUIPMENT CO., INC.; *U.S. Private*, pg. 3782
STOLLER INTERNATIONAL INC.; *U.S. Private*, pg. 3816
STONE PLUS, INC.—See SiteOne Landscape Supply, Inc.; *U.S. Public*, pg. 1889
STORR TRACTOR CO.; *U.S. Private*, pg. 3832
STRAUB INTERNATIONAL INC.—See KanEquip, Inc.; *U.S. Private*, pg. 2260
STRINGERS INTERNATIONAL INC.; *U.S. Private*, pg. 3840
SUNBELT OUTDOOR PRODUCTS INC.—See Deere & Company; *U.S. Public*, pg. 647
SUNSHINE EQUIPMENT CO., INC.; *U.S. Private*, pg. 3871
SWIDERSKI EQUIPMENT, INC.; *U.S. Private*, pg. 3893
SYDENSTRICKERS FARM & LAWN; *U.S. Private*, pg. 3898
TECHNIK CENTER ALPEN GMBH—See AGRAVIS Raiffeisen AG; *Int'l*, pg. 215
TECHNIKCENTER GRIMMA GMBH—See BayWa AG; *Int'l*, pg. 919
TECNO POULTRY EQUIPMENT S.P.A.—See AGCO Corporation; *U.S. Public*, pg. 59
TECVIS GMBH—See AGRAVIS Raiffeisen AG; *Int'l*, pg. 215
TEETER IRRIGATION INC.; *U.S. Private*, pg. 3958
TENNESSEE TRACTOR, LLC - JACKSON—See Charter Communications, Inc.; *U.S. Public*, pg. 483
T.N.T. EQUIPMENT INC.; *U.S. Private*, pg. 3912
TORO AUSTRALIA GROUP SALES PTY. LTD—See The Toro Company; *U.S. Public*, pg. 2135
TORO AUSTRALIA PTY. LTD.—See The Toro Company; *U.S. Public*, pg. 2135
TORO WORLDWIDE PARTS DISTRIBUTION CENTER—See The Toro Company; *U.S. Public*, pg. 2135
TRACTOR CENTRAL LLC; *U.S. Private*, pg. 4201
TRACTOR CENTRAL - MONDOVI—See Tractor Central LLC; *U.S. Private*, pg. 4201
TRI GREEN TRACTOR, LLC—See TTG Equipment, LLC; *U.S. Private*, pg. 4254
TRIPLE W. EQUIPMENT INC.—See Missoula Cartage Co. Inc.; *U.S. Private*, pg. 2748
TROXEL EQUIPMENT CO.—See TTG Equipment, LLC; *U.S. Private*, pg. 4254
TRUE NORTH EQUIPMENT CO.; *U.S. Private*, pg. 4248
TRU-POWER INC.; *U.S. Private*, pg. 4244
TURF PRODUCTS CORPORATION; *U.S. Private*, pg. 4259
UAB AGROTECHNIKOS CENTRAS—See AUGA group, AB; *Int'l*, pg. 703
THE URBAN FARMER STORE, INC.—See Leonard Green & Partners, L.P.; *U.S. Private*, pg. 2429
USC LLC; *U.S. Private*, pg. 4322
US DAIRY SYSTEMS INC.; *U.S. Private*, pg. 4318
US-FEIWO AGRICULTURAL INDUSTRY INTERNATIONAL, INC.; *U.S. Private*, pg. 4320
VALLEY IMPLEMENT & MOTOR CO.; *U.S. Private*, pg. 4334
VALLEY TRUCK & TRACTOR CO.; *U.S. Private*, pg. 4335
VALUE IMPLEMENT; *U.S. Private*, pg. 4337
VANDERLOOP EQUIPMENT, INC.; *U.S. Private*, pg. 4343
VAN WALL EQUIPMENT INC.; *U.S. Private*, pg. 4341
VERTICAL SUPPLY GROUP—See Gridiron Capital, LLC; *U.S. Private*, pg. 1786
VETTER EQUIPMENT COMPANY; *U.S. Private*, pg. 4374
VICTUS EMAK SP. Z.O.O.—See Emak S.p.A.; *Int'l*, pg. 2373
VUCOVICH INC.; *U.S. Private*, pg. 4415
WADE INC.; *U.S. Private*, pg. 4424
WADE INC.—See Wade Inc.; *U.S. Private*, pg. 4424
WALKER-SCHORK INTERNATIONAL INC.; *U.S. Private*, pg. 4429
WARD IMPLEMENT COMPANY; *U.S. Private*, pg. 4441
WARREN POWER & MACHINERY, INC.; *U.S. Private*, pg. 4444
WENGERS FARM MACHINERY INC.; *U.S. Private*, pg. 4481

423820 — FARM AND GARDEN MAC...

WESTERN DISTRICT AGRICENTRE PTY. LTD.—See AGCO Corporation; *U.S. Public*, pg. 60
WESTERN EQUIPMENT DISTRIBUTORS, INC.; *U.S. Private*, pg. 4493
WESTERN EQUIPMENT LLC; *U.S. Private*, pg. 4493
WESTFIELD INDUSTRIES—See Ag Growth International Inc.; *Int'l*, pg. 198
WEST PLAINS IMPLEMENT CO., INC.; *U.S. Private*, pg. 4486
WESTVET WHOLESALE PTY. LTD.—See Apiam Animal Health Limited; *Int'l*, pg. 515
WILFRED MACDONALD INC.; *U.S. Private*, pg. 4520
WILLIAM NOBBE & CO., INC.; *U.S. Private*, pg. 4524
WILLIAMSON COUNTY EQUIPMENT CO., INC.; *U.S. Private*, pg. 4527
WILLIAMS TRACTOR INC.; *U.S. Private*, pg. 4527
WINGENFELD ENERGIE GMBH—See BayWa AG; *Int'l*, pg. 919
WINSTON TRACTOR COMPANY—See BobCo Inc.; *U.S. Private*, pg. 607
W.P. LAW INC.; *U.S. Private*, pg. 4422
WW MANUFACTURING CO. INC.—See W W Capital Corporation; *U.S. Private*, pg. 4417
WYATT IRRIGATION CO.—See Winsupply Inc.; *U.S. Private*, pg. 4544
WYLIE IMPLEMENT & SPRAY CENTER-AMARILLO—See Wylie Manufacturing Company; *U.S. Private*, pg. 4576
WYLIE MANUFACTURING COMPANY; *U.S. Private*, pg. 4576
Z-BEST PRODUCTS; *U.S. Private*, pg. 4596
ZHANG JIA GANG MANITOWOC CRANE TRADING CO. LTD.—See The Manitowoc Company, Inc.; *U.S. Public*, pg. 2111

423830 — INDUSTRIAL MACHINERY AND EQUIPMENT MERCHANT WHOLESALERS

101059035 SASKATCHEWAN LTD.; *Int'l*, pg. 1
2M COMPANY INC.—See Franklin Electric Co., Inc.; *U.S. Public*, pg. 878
3D EUROPEAN HOLDINGS LTD.—See 3D Systems Corporation; *U.S. Public*, pg. 4
3M A/S—See 3M Company; *U.S. Public*, pg. 8
3M JAPAN PRODUCTS LIMITED—See 3M Company; *U.S. Public*, pg. 6
4 RIVERS EQUIPMENT LLC; *U.S. Private*, pg. 14
A.A. ANDERSON COMPANY INCORPORATED; *U.S. Private*, pg. 24
AARON EQUIPMENT COMPANY; *U.S. Private*, pg. 32
ABAC AIR COMPRESSORS S.A PTY LTD.—See Atlas Copco AB; *Int'l*, pg. 677
ABATIX CORP.; *U.S. Private*, pg. 34
ABB AUTOMATION E.C.—See ABB Ltd.; *Int'l*, pg. 50
ABB D.O.O. ZAGREB—See ABB Ltd.; *Int'l*, pg. 50
ABB ECUADOR S.A—See ABB Ltd.; *Int'l*, pg. 50
ABB ENGINEERING TRADING AND SERVICE LTD.—See ABB Ltd.; *Int'l*, pg. 50
ABB GLOBAL MARKETING FZ LLC—See ABB Ltd.; *Int'l*, pg. 51
ABB INDUSTRIES (L.L.C.)—See ABB Ltd.; *Int'l*, pg. 51
ABB INTERNATIONAL MARKETING LTD.—See ABB Ltd.; *Int'l*, pg. 50
ABB INTERNATIONAL MARKETING LTD.—See ABB Ltd.; *Int'l*, pg. 53
ABB LIMITED—See ABB Ltd.; *Int'l*, pg. 53
ABB LTDA.—See ABB Ltd.; *Int'l*, pg. 53
ABB LTD.—See ABB Ltd.; *Int'l*, pg. 53
ABB LTD.—See ABB Ltd.; *Int'l*, pg. 53
ABB LTD.—See ABB Ltd.; *Int'l*, pg. 53
ABB MAGHREB SERVICES S.A.—See ABB Ltd.; *Int'l*, pg. 53
ABB NEAR EAST TRADING LTD.—See ABB Ltd.; *Int'l*, pg. 53
ABB (PRIVATE) LTD.—See ABB Ltd.; *Int'l*, pg. 49
ABB S.A.—See ABB Ltd.; *Int'l*, pg. 53
ABB S.A.—See ABB Ltd.; *Int'l*, pg. 54
ABB SIA—See ABB Ltd.; *Int'l*, pg. 54
ABB TECHNOLOGIES S.A.—See ABB Ltd.; *Int'l*, pg. 55
ABB UAB—See ABB Ltd.; *Int'l*, pg. 55
ABB VIETNAM—See ABB Ltd.; *Int'l*, pg. 55
ABC ELECTRIC CORP.—See Bain Capital, LP; *U.S. Private*, pg. 432
ABCO SYSTEMS LLC; *U.S. Private*, pg. 36
ABCO WELDING & INDUSTRIAL SUPPLIES INC.; *U.S. Private*, pg. 36
ABDULLA FOUAD-TESTRADE DIVISION—See Abdulla Fouad Holding Co.; *Int'l*, pg. 59
ABDULLA NASS & PARTNERS CO. LTD.—See Abdulla Ahmed Nass Group WLL; *Int'l*, pg. 58
ABERDEEN DYNAMICS SUPPLY INC.; *U.S. Private*, pg. 38
AB LKI KALDMAN OY; *Int'l*, pg. 41
ABSOLUTE HAITIAN CORPORATION—See Haitian International Holdings Ltd.; *Int'l*, pg. 3217
ABSOLUTE MACHINE TOOL INC.; *U.S. Private*, pg. 44
ABUS LEVAGE FRANCE S.A.S.; *Int'l*, pg. 47
ACARLAR DIS TICARET VE MAKINA SANAYI A S—See Haulotte Group SA; *Int'l*, pg. 3285

ACCUDYNE INDUSTRIES ASIA PTE. LTD.—See BC Partners LLP; *Int'l*, pg. 922
ACCUDYNE INDUSTRIES ASIA PTE. LTD.—See The Carlyle Group Inc.; *U.S. Public*, pg. 2044
ACCU-LUBE MANUFACTURING GMBH—See Illinois Tool Works Inc.; *U.S. Public*, pg. 1101
ACCURATE AIR ENGINEERING INCORPORATED—See Atlas Copco AB; *Int'l*, pg. 680
ACE INDUSTRIES INC.; *U.S. Private*, pg. 57
ACE TANK & EQUIPMENT CO.; *U.S. Private*, pg. 57
ACI CONTROLS INC.; *U.S. Private*, pg. 59
ACIETA LLC—See Angeles Equity Partners, LLC; *U.S. Private*, pg. 282
ACME ELECTRIC MOTOR INC.; *U.S. Private*, pg. 60
ACTION LIFT, INC.; *U.S. Private*, pg. 67
ADDTECH ENERGY & EQUIPMENT AB—See Addtech AB; *Int'l*, pg. 131
A&D INSTRUMENTS (THAILAND) LIMITED—See A&D Co., Ltd.; *Int'l*, pg. 18
ADIXEN VACUUM TECHNOLOGY KOREA LTD.—See Dr. Ing. K. Busch GmbH; *Int'l*, pg. 2194
ADLINK TECHNOLOGY (CHINA) CO., LTD.—See ADLINK Technology, Inc.; *Int'l*, pg. 150
ADLINK TECHNOLOGY JAPAN CORPORATION—See ADLINK Technology, Inc.; *Int'l*, pg. 150
ADVANCED EQUIPMENT COMPANY; *U.S. Private*, pg. 89
ADVANCED FLUID SYSTEMS INC.; *U.S. Private*, pg. 89
ADVANCED MACHINERY COMPANIES; *U.S. Private*, pg. 91
ADVANCED PROCESS EQUIPMENT (THAILAND) CO., LTD.—See Advanced Holdings Ltd.; *Int'l*, pg. 159
ADVANCE RIKO, INC.—See CHINO Corporation; *Int'l*, pg. 1570
ADVANEX (HK) LTD.—See Advanex Inc.; *Int'l*, pg. 163
ADVENT ELECTRIC, INC.; *U.S. Private*, pg. 95
AEBI SCHMIDT ITALIA S.R.L.—See Aebi Schmidt Holding AG; *Int'l*, pg. 170
AEG POWER SOLUTIONS IBERICA SL—See 3W Power S.A.; *Int'l*, pg. 10
AEM MICROTRONICS (M) SDN. BHD.—See AEM Holdings Ltd.; *Int'l*, pg. 175
AEROCOM GMBH & CO.—See aerocom GmbH & Co.; *Int'l*, pg. 180
AEROCOM NEUMATICA S. L.—See aerocom GmbH & Co.; *Int'l*, pg. 180
AERO INDUSTRIAL TOOL CO., INC.; *U.S. Private*, pg. 118
AEROSTAR AEROSPACE MANUFACTURING, INC.—See Nautic Partners, LLC; *U.S. Private*, pg. 2868
AERRE S.R.L.—See Edizione S.r.l.; *Int'l*, pg. 2311
AFP INDUSTRIES, INC.; *U.S. Private*, pg. 124
AFT AUTOMATION AND CONVEYING SYSTEMS (SHANGHAI) CO. LTD.—See Certina Holding AG; *Int'l*, pg. 1423
AFT AUTOMATION LIMITED—See Certina Holding AG; *Int'l*, pg. 1423
AFT AUTOMATISIERUNGS- UND FORDERTECHNIK GMBH & CO. KG—See Certina Holding AG; *Int'l*, pg. 1423
AFT-FORDERANLAGEN BAUTZEN GMBH & CO. KG—See Certina Holding AG; *Int'l*, pg. 1423
AFT KOREA CO. LTD.—See Certina Holding AG; *Int'l*, pg. 1423
AGFA GRAPHICS ARGENTINA S.A.—See Agfa-Gevaert N.V.; *Int'l*, pg. 207
AGFA GRAPHICS AUSTRIA GMBH—See Agfa-Gevaert N.V.; *Int'l*, pg. 207
AGFA GRAPHICS GERMANY GMBH & CO. KG—See Agfa-Gevaert N.V.; *Int'l*, pg. 207
AGFA GRAPHICS LTD.—See Agfa-Gevaert N.V.; *Int'l*, pg. 207
AGFA GRAPHICS MIDDLE EAST FZCO—See Agfa-Gevaert N.V.; *Int'l*, pg. 207
AGFA GRAPHICS SWITZERLAND AG—See Agfa-Gevaert N.V.; *Int'l*, pg. 207
AGIE CHARMILLES CHINA (SHENZHEN) LTD—See Georg Fischer AG; *Int'l*, pg. 2934
AGIE CHARMILLES CHINA (TIANJIN) LTD—See Georg Fischer AG; *Int'l*, pg. 2934
AGIE CHARMILLES GMBH—See Georg Fischer AG; *Int'l*, pg. 2934
AGIE CHARMILLES LTD.—See Georg Fischer AG; *Int'l*, pg. 2934
AGIE CHARMILLES SA—See Georg Fischer AG; *Int'l*, pg. 2934
AGIE CHARMILLES SERVICES SA—See Georg Fischer AG; *Int'l*, pg. 2934
AGI INDUSTRIES, INC.; *U.S. Private*, pg. 127
AGL WELDING SUPPLY CO. INC.; *U.S. Private*, pg. 128
AGR ASIA LIMITED—See Clayton, Dubilier & Rice, LLC; *U.S. Private*, pg. 924
AGR EUROPE GMBH—See Clayton, Dubilier & Rice, LLC; *U.S. Private*, pg. 924
AGR EUROPE S.R.L.—See Clayton, Dubilier & Rice, LLC; *U.S. Private*, pg. 924
AIR COMPONENTS & ENGINEERING; *U.S. Private*, pg. 138
AIR COMPRESSOR ENGINEERING COMPANY; *U.S. Private*, pg. 138
AIR DRAULICS ENGINEERING CO.—See Applied Industrial Technologies, Inc.; *U.S. Public*, pg. 170

AIRDYNE INC.; *U.S. Private*, pg. 141
AIR FLOW—See Enerphase Industrial Solutions, Inc.; *U.S. Private*, pg. 1396
AIR & HYDRAULIC EQUIPMENT, INC.; *U.S. Private*, pg. 138
AIR-HYDRAULIC SYSTEMS INC.—See Applied Industrial Technologies, Inc.; *U.S. Public*, pg. 170
AIRO LAM LIMITED; *Int'l*, pg. 248
AIR POWER, INC.; *U.S. Private*, pg. 139
AIR POWER OF NEBRASKA, INC.—See Atlas Copco AB; *Int'l*, pg. 680
AIR SYSTEMS SALES INC.; *U.S. Private*, pg. 139
AIRTECH GROUP, INC.—See IDEX Corp; *U.S. Public*, pg. 1089
AIR TECHNOLOGIES, INC.—See Genstar Capital, LLC; *U.S. Private*, pg. 1678
AISAN CORPORATION OF AMERICA, INC.—See Aisan Industry Co., Ltd.; *Int'l*, pg. 250
AJ HOWARD INDUSTRIAL SUPPLIES LIMITED—See W.W. Grainger, Inc.; *U.S. Public*, pg. 2319
AJINOMOTO TRADING, INC.—See Ajinomoto Company, Inc.; *Int'l*, pg. 257
A.J. JERSEY INC.; *U.S. Private*, pg. 26
AKHURST MACHINERY INC.—See Akhurst Machinery Limited; *Int'l*, pg. 263
AKHURST MACHINERY LIMITED; *Int'l*, pg. 263
AKIYAMA CORPORATION AMERICA—See Akiyama International Company Ltd.; *Int'l*, pg. 263
ALASKA PUMP & SUPPLY, INC.—See DXP Enterprises, Inc.; *U.S. Public*, pg. 697
ALBANY INTERNATIONAL PTY. LTD.—See Albany International Corp.; *U.S. Public*, pg. 72
ALFA LAVAL AALBORG NIJMEGEN BV—See Alfa Laval AB; *Int'l*, pg. 308
ALFA LAVAL AEBE—See Alfa Laval AB; *Int'l*, pg. 308
ALFA LAVAL FLOW INC.—See Alfa Laval AB; *Int'l*, pg. 309
ALFA LAVAL INC. - KENOSHA—See Alfa Laval AB; *Int'l*, pg. 309
ALFA-LAVAL INC.—See Alfa Laval AB; *Int'l*, pg. 310
ALFA LAVAL S.A. DE C.V.—See Alfa Laval AB; *Int'l*, pg. 310
ALFA LAVAL S.A.—See Alfa Laval AB; *Int'l*, pg. 311
ALFONS HAAR INCORPORATED—See Alfons Haar Maschinenbau GmbH & Co. KG; *Int'l*, pg. 315
ALFONS HAAR SVENSKA AB—See Alfons Haar Maschinenbau GmbH & Co. KG; *Int'l*, pg. 315
ALFRED HERBERT (INDIA) LTD.; *Int'l*, pg. 316
ALLA PUBLIC COMPANY LIMITED; *Int'l*, pg. 332
ALLEGHENY HIGH LIFT INCORPORATED; *U.S. Private*, pg. 176
ALLEN CODING GMBH—See Illinois Tool Works Inc.; *U.S. Public*, pg. 1101
ALLIANCE COMPRESSORS INC.—See Ingersoll Rand Inc.; *U.S. Public*, pg. 1120
ALLIED FITTING LP; *U.S. Private*, pg. 186
ALL-LIFT OF GEORGIA INC.; *U.S. Private*, pg. 173
ALL PRINTING RESOURCES INC.; *U.S. Private*, pg. 171
ALLWEILER FINLAND OY AB—See KKR & Co. Inc.; *U.S. Public*, pg. 1242
ALL WORLD MACHINERY SUPPLY, INC.—See Daikin Industries, Ltd.; *Int'l*, pg. 1932
ALMAR ASSOCIATES INC.; *U.S. Private*, pg. 195
ALOI MATERIALS HANDLING INC; *U.S. Private*, pg. 195
A.L.P.A. EQUIPMENT; *Int'l*, pg. 25
ALPHA MATERIAL HANDLING CO., INC.; *U.S. Private*, pg. 198
ALPHA SOUTHWEST, INC.—See Pike Street Capital, LP; *U.S. Public*, pg. 3180
ALPINE AMERICAN—See Hosokawa Micron Corporation; *Int'l*, pg. 3486
ALPINE AUTOMATION LIMITED—See Illinois Tool Works Inc.; *U.S. Public*, pg. 1101
ALPINE SYSTEMS CORPORATION—See Illinois Tool Works Inc.; *U.S. Public*, pg. 1101
ALSTOM SERVICES SDN. BHD.—See Alstom S.A.; *Int'l*, pg. 380
ALTA EQUIPMENT HOLDINGS, INC.—See Alta Equipment Group Inc.; *U.S. Public*, pg. 86
ALTA LIFT TRUCK SERVICES, INC.—See Alta Equipment Group Inc.; *U.S. Public*, pg. 86
ALTECH ASIA PACIFIC VIETNAM CO., LTD.—See Altech Co., Ltd.; *Int'l*, pg. 388
ALTECH CO., LTD.; *Int'l*, pg. 388
AL-USOOL GENERAL TRADING COMPANY LTD.—See Eng. Shabah Al-Shammery & Partners Co.; *Int'l*, pg. 2426
AMADA AMERICA, INC.—See Amada Holdings Co., Ltd.; *Int'l*, pg. 404
AMADA BUTSURYU CO., LTD.—See Amada Holdings Co., Ltd.; *Int'l*, pg. 403
AMADA CO., LTD.—See Amada Holdings Co., Ltd.; *Int'l*, pg. 403
AMADA CUTTING TECHNOLOGIES, INC.—See Amada Holdings Co., Ltd.; *Int'l*, pg. 404
AMADA DE MEXICO, S. DE R.L. DE C.V.—See Amada Holdings Co., Ltd.; *Int'l*, pg. 404
AMADA GMBH—See Amada Holdings Co., Ltd.; *Int'l*, pg. 404

N.A.I.C.S. INDEX

423830 — INDUSTRIAL MACHINER...

AMADA HONG KONG CO., LTD.—See Amada Holdings Co., Ltd.; *Int'l*, pg. 404
AMADA INTERNATIONAL INDUSTRY & TRADING (SHANGHAI) CO., LTD.—See Amada Holdings Co., Ltd.; *Int'l*, pg. 404
AMADA INTERNATIONAL TRADING (SHENZHEN) CO., LTD—See Amada Holdings Co., Ltd.; *Int'l*, pg. 404
AMADA ITALIA S.R.L.—See Amada Holdings Co., Ltd.; *Int'l*, pg. 404
AMADA MACHINE TOOLS AMERICA, INC.—See Amada Holdings Co., Ltd.; *Int'l*, pg. 404
AMADA MACHINE TOOLS CO., LTD.—See Amada Holdings Co., Ltd.; *Int'l*, pg. 404
AMADA MACHINE TOOLS EUROPE GMBH—See Amada Holdings Co., Ltd.; *Int'l*, pg. 404
AMADA (MALAYSIA) SDN. BHD.—See Amada Holdings Co., Ltd.; *Int'l*, pg. 403
AMADA MAQUINARIA S.I.—See Amada Holdings Co., Ltd.; *Int'l*, pg. 404
AMADA S.A.—See Amada Holdings Co., Ltd.; *Int'l*, pg. 404
AMADA SINGAPORE (1989) PTE. LTD.—See Amada Holdings Co., Ltd.; *Int'l*, pg. 403
AMADA SWEDEN AB—See Amada Holdings Co., Ltd.; *Int'l*, pg. 404
AMADA TAIWAN, INC.—See Amada Holdings Co., Ltd.; *Int'l*, pg. 404
AMADA (THAILAND) CO., LTD.—See Amada Holdings Co., Ltd.; *Int'l*, pg. 403
AMADA TURKIYE MAKINA TEKNOLOJI SANAYI VE TICARET LTD.—See Amada Holdings Co., Ltd.; *Int'l*, pg. 404
AMADA UNITED KINGDOM LIMITED—See Amada Holdings Co., Ltd.; *Int'l*, pg. 404
AMADA VIETNAM CO., LTD.—See Amada Holdings Co., Ltd.; *Int'l*, pg. 403
AMANO TIME & ECOLOGY DE MEXICO S.A.DE C.V.—See Amano Corporation; *Int'l*, pg. 411
AMERICANA COMPANIES INC.; *U.S. Private*, pg. 258
AMERICAN CALIBRATION, INC.—See Concept Machine Tool Sales, LLC; *U.S. Private*, pg. 1008
AMERICAN CONTROLS INC.; *U.S. Private*, pg. 228
AMERICAN GRANBY, INC.; *U.S. Private*, pg. 235
AMERICAN INDUSTRIAL CORPORATION; *U.S. Private*, pg. 237
AMERICAN LAUBSCHER CORPORATION; *U.S. Private*, pg. 239
AMERICAN LIFT TRUCK SERVICES LLC; *U.S. Private*, pg. 239
AMERICAN-MARSH PUMPS; *U.S. Private*, pg. 258
AMERICAN METAL SUPPLY CO, INC.—See MacArthur Co.; *U.S. Private*, pg. 2534
AMERICAN ROBOTICS, INC.—See Ondas Holdings, Inc.; *U.S. Public*, pg. 1602
AMERICAN SALES COMPANY, INC.—See The Shurtleff & Andrews Corp.; *U.S. Private*, pg. 4117
AMERICAN SWISS PRODUCTS CO, INC.; *U.S. Private*, pg. 256
AMERICAN UNIC CORP.—See Spelna, Inc.; *U.S. Private*, pg. 3754
AMERICAN WELDING & GAS, INC.—See Advance Auto Parts, Inc.; *U.S. Public*, pg. 44
AMETEK ADVANCED INDUSTRIES, INC.—See AMETEK, Inc.; *U.S. Public*, pg. 117
AMS CORPORATION; *U.S. Private*, pg. 266
ANBO INC.—See ANDRITZ AG; *Int'l*, pg. 455
ANCO SP. Z O.O.—See E.ON SE; *Int'l*, pg. 2251
ANCRA NEW ZEALAND LIMITED—See The Heico Companies, L.L.C.; *U.S. Private*, pg. 4050
ANDERSEN & ASSOCIATES INC.; *U.S. Private*, pg. 275
ANDERSON AMERICA CORP.—See Anderson Industrial Corporation; *Int'l*, pg. 450
ANDERSON MACHINERY (SINGAPORE) PTE. LTD.—See Anderson Industrial Corporation; *Int'l*, pg. 450
ANDERSON SERVICES; *U.S. Private*, pg. 277
ANDRESS ENGINEERING ASSOCIATES INC.; *U.S. Private*, pg. 279
ANDRITZ AG - RUSSIA REPRESENTATIVE OFFICE—See ANDRITZ AG; *Int'l*, pg. 452
ANDRITZ AG—See ANDRITZ AG; *Int'l*, pg. 455
ANDRITZ AG—See ANDRITZ AG; *Int'l*, pg. 455
ANDRITZ AG - TAIWAN REPRESENTATIVE OFFICE—See ANDRITZ AG; *Int'l*, pg. 452
ANDRITZ ASSELIN-THIBEAU—See ANDRITZ AG; *Int'l*, pg. 454
ANDRITZ AUTOMATION LTD.—See ANDRITZ AG; *Int'l*, pg. 454
ANDRITZ BOISFER IGGESUND S.A.S.—See ANDRITZ AG; *Int'l*, pg. 454
ANDRITZ B.V.—See ANDRITZ AG; *Int'l*, pg. 455
ANDRITZ CHILE LTDA.—See ANDRITZ AG; *Int'l*, pg. 452
ANDRITZ (CHINA) LTD.—See ANDRITZ AG; *Int'l*, pg. 452
ANDRITZ CONSTRUCOES E MONTAGENS LTDA.—See ANDRITZ AG; *Int'l*, pg. 455
ANDRITZ DIES & ROLLS B.V.—See ANDRITZ AG; *Int'l*, pg. 452
ANDRITZ ENVIRONMENTAL ENGINEERING (SHANGHAI) CO., LTD.—See ANDRITZ AG; *Int'l*, pg. 455

ANDRITZ EUROSLOT FRANCE SAS—See ANDRITZ AG; *Int'l*, pg. 455
ANDRITZ FABRICS & ROLLS AG—See ANDRITZ AG; *Int'l*, pg. 455
ANDRITZ FABRICS & ROLLS INC.—See ANDRITZ AG; *Int'l*, pg. 455
ANDRITZ FABRICS & ROLLS S.A. DE C.V.—See ANDRITZ AG; *Int'l*, pg. 455
ANDRITZ FBB GMBH—See ANDRITZ AG; *Int'l*, pg. 455
ANDRITZ FEED & BIOFUEL A/S—See ANDRITZ AG; *Int'l*, pg. 452
ANDRITZ FEED & BIOFUEL B.V.—See ANDRITZ AG; *Int'l*, pg. 453
ANDRITZ FEED & BIOFUEL—See ANDRITZ AG; *Int'l*, pg. 452
ANDRITZ FZCO—See ANDRITZ AG; *Int'l*, pg. 455
ANDRITZ GOUDA B.V.—See ANDRITZ AG; *Int'l*, pg. 455
ANDRITZ HYDRO AG—See ANDRITZ AG; *Int'l*, pg. 455
ANDRITZ HYDRO BRASIL LTDA.—See ANDRITZ AG; *Int'l*, pg. 455
ANDRITZ HYDRO CANADA INC.—See ANDRITZ AG; *Int'l*, pg. 455
ANDRITZ HYDRO C.A.—See ANDRITZ AG; *Int'l*, pg. 453
ANDRITZ HYDRO DRC SARL—See ANDRITZ AG; *Int'l*, pg. 455
ANDRITZ HYDRO GMBH - VIETNAM REPRESENTATIVE OFFICE—See ANDRITZ AG; *Int'l*, pg. 455
ANDRITZ HYDRO HAMMERFEST (UK) LIMITED—See ANDRITZ AG; *Int'l*, pg. 455
ANDRITZ HYDRO LTDA.—See ANDRITZ AG; *Int'l*, pg. 453
ANDRITZ HYDRO LTDA.—See ANDRITZ AG; *Int'l*, pg. 455
ANDRITZ HYDRO LTD. STI.—See ANDRITZ AG; *Int'l*, pg. 453
ANDRITZ HYDRO LTEE/LTD.—See ANDRITZ AG; *Int'l*, pg. 453
ANDRITZ HYDRO NEPAL PVT. LTD.—See ANDRITZ AG; *Int'l*, pg. 453
ANDRITZ HYDRO OY—See ANDRITZ AG; *Int'l*, pg. 455
ANDRITZ HYDRO PRIVATE LIMITED—See ANDRITZ AG; *Int'l*, pg. 453
ANDRITZ HYDRO (PTY.) LTD.—See ANDRITZ AG; *Int'l*, pg. 455
ANDRITZ HYDRO S.A.—See ANDRITZ AG; *Int'l*, pg. 453
ANDRITZ HYDRO S.L.—See ANDRITZ AG; *Int'l*, pg. 453
ANDRITZ HYDRO S.R.O.—See ANDRITZ AG; *Int'l*, pg. 453
ANDRITZ HYDRO (SU), LDA.—See ANDRITZ AG; *Int'l*, pg. 455
ANDRITZ HYDRO, UNIPESSOAL LDA.—See ANDRITZ AG; *Int'l*, pg. 455
ANDRITZ LTD./LTEE.—See ANDRITZ AG; *Int'l*, pg. 454
ANDRITZ MEWA GMBH—See ANDRITZ AG; *Int'l*, pg. 455
ANDRITZ MEWA KFT.—See ANDRITZ AG; *Int'l*, pg. 455
ANDRITZ NOVIMPIANTI S.R.L.—See ANDRITZ AG; *Int'l*, pg. 455
ANDRITZ (NZ) LTD.—See ANDRITZ AG; *Int'l*, pg. 456
ANDRITZ O&M PRIVATE LIMITED—See ANDRITZ AG; *Int'l*, pg. 455
ANDRITZ PTY. LTD.—See ANDRITZ AG; *Int'l*, pg. 454
ANDRITZ RITZ IMMOBILIEN GMBH—See ANDRITZ AG; *Int'l*, pg. 455
ANDRITZ RITZ PTE. LTD.—See ANDRITZ AG; *Int'l*, pg. 455
ANDRITZ SDN. BHD.—See ANDRITZ AG; *Int'l*, pg. 455
ANDRITZ SELAS S.A.S.—See ANDRITZ AG; *Int'l*, pg. 454
ANDRITZ SEPARATION INDUSTRIA E COMERCIO DE EQUIPAMENTOS DE FILTRACAO LTDA.—See ANDRITZ AG; *Int'l*, pg. 452
ANDRITZ SEPARATION LTDA.—See ANDRITZ AG; *Int'l*, pg. 452
ANDRITZ SEPARATION—See ANDRITZ AG; *Int'l*, pg. 454
ANDRITZ (SHANGHAI) EQUIPMENT & ENGINEERING CO., LTD.—See ANDRITZ AG; *Int'l*, pg. 455
ANDRITZ SINGAPORE PTE. LTD.—See ANDRITZ AG; *Int'l*, pg. 455
ANDRITZ SLOVAKIA S.R.O.—See ANDRITZ AG; *Int'l*, pg. 455
ANDRITZ SOUTEC AG—See ANDRITZ AG; *Int'l*, pg. 455
ANDRITZ TECHNOLOGIES AB—See ANDRITZ AG; *Int'l*, pg. 455
ANDRITZ TECHNOLOGIES H.K. LTD.—See ANDRITZ AG; *Int'l*, pg. 455
ANDRITZ (THAILAND) LTD.—See ANDRITZ AG; *Int'l*, pg. 452
ANDRITZ THERMTEC B.V.—See ANDRITZ AG; *Int'l*, pg. 455
ANDRITZ URUGUAY S.A.—See ANDRITZ AG; *Int'l*, pg. 455
ANDRITZ - WOLFENSBERGER SPECIAL ALLOY FOUNDRY CO., LTD.—See ANDRITZ AG; *Int'l*, pg. 455
ANEST IWATA EUROPE S.R.L.—See ANEST IWATA Corporation; *Int'l*, pg. 458
ANEST IWATA FRANCE S.A.—See ANEST IWATA Corporation; *Int'l*, pg. 458
ANEST IWATA SHANGHAI COATING MACHINERY CO., LTD.—See ANEST IWATA Corporation; *Int'l*, pg. 458
ANEST IWATA (SHANGHAI) CORPORATION—See ANEST IWATA Corporation; *Int'l*, pg. 458
ANEST IWATA (U.K.) LTD.—See ANEST IWATA Corporation; *Int'l*, pg. 458

ANEST IWATA VIETNAM CO., LTD.—See ANEST IWATA Corporation; *Int'l*, pg. 458
ANRITSU AB—See Anritsu Corporation; *Int'l*, pg. 475
ANRITSU EMEA LTD—See Anritsu Corporation; *Int'l*, pg. 475
ANRITSU INFIVIS CO., LTD.—See Anritsu Corporation; *Int'l*, pg. 475
ANS DISTRIBUTING LLC—See MidOcean Partners, LLP; *U.S. Private*, pg. 2716
ANSTALT FUR STROMUNGSMASCHINEN GMBH—See ANDRITZ AG; *Int'l*, pg. 455
ANT SINAI VE TIC.URUNLERI PAZ. A.S—See Ag Anadolu Grubu Holding Anonim Sirketi; *Int'l*, pg. 197
APEX TOOL S.R.L.—See Bain Capital, LP; *U.S. Private*, pg. 430
APO HOLDINGS INC.; *U.S. Private*, pg. 294
APPLIED FLUID POWER INC.; *U.S. Private*, pg. 298
APPLIED HANDLING INC.; *U.S. Private*, pg. 298
APPLIED INDUSTRIAL TECHNOLOGIES - PA LLC—See Applied Industrial Technologies, Inc.; *U.S. Public*, pg. 170
APPLIED INDUSTRIAL TECHNOLOGIES PTY LTD.—See Applied Industrial Technologies, Inc.; *U.S. Public*, pg. 170
APP SYSTEMS SERVICES PTE. LTD.; *Int'l*, pg. 519
AQUATEC INC.; *U.S. Private*, pg. 303
ARBON EQUIPMENT PTY LIMITED—See Rite-Hite Holding Corporation; *U.S. Private*, pg. 3442
ARBOR MATERIAL HANDLING INC.; *U.S. Private*, pg. 308
ARBURG AG—See Arburg GmbH & Co.; *Int'l*, pg. 539
ARBURG A/S—See Arburg GmbH & Co.; *Int'l*, pg. 539
ARBURG BV—See Arburg GmbH & Co.; *Int'l*, pg. 539
ARBURG GESMBH—See Arburg GmbH & Co.; *Int'l*, pg. 539
ARBURG (HK) LTD.—See Arburg GmbH & Co.; *Int'l*, pg. 539
ARBURG HUNGARIA KFT.—See Arburg GmbH & Co.; *Int'l*, pg. 539
ARBURG, INC.—See Arburg GmbH & Co.; *Int'l*, pg. 539
ARBURG LTDA.—See Arburg GmbH & Co.; *Int'l*, pg. 539
ARBURG N.V.—See Arburg GmbH & Co.; *Int'l*, pg. 539
ARBURG POLSKA SP. Z O O.—See Arburg GmbH & Co.; *Int'l*, pg. 539
ARBURG, S.A. DE C.V.—See Arburg GmbH & Co.; *Int'l*, pg. 539
ARBURG SDN BHD—See Arburg GmbH & Co.; *Int'l*, pg. 539
ARBURG SPOL. S R. O.—See Arburg GmbH & Co.; *Int'l*, pg. 539
ARBURG (THAILAND) CO., LTD.—See Arburg GmbH & Co.; *Int'l*, pg. 539
ARCET EQUIPMENT COMPANY; *U.S. Private*, pg. 310
ARCHITECTURAL PANEL PRODUCTS, INC.; *U.S. Private*, pg. 311
ARDISEIS FZCO—See CGG; *Int'l*, pg. 1431
ARGO INTERNATIONAL CORPORATION—See Argo Turboserve Corporation; *U.S. Private*, pg. 320
ARNOLD MACHINERY COMPANY - MATERIAL HANDLING DIVISION—See Arnold Machinery Company; *U.S. Private*, pg. 333
ARO GMBH—See Ingersoll Rand Inc.; *U.S. Public*, pg. 1120
AROTECH CORPORATION—See Greenbriar Equity Group, L.P.; *U.S. Private*, pg. 1775
ARROYO PROCESS EQUIPMENT INC.; *U.S. Private*, pg. 337
ASAHI AV TRADING CO ,LTD—See Asahi Yukizai Corporation; *Int'l*, pg. 598
ASA SAFETY SUPPLY—See Trivest Partners, LP; *U.S. Private*, pg. 4240
ASBURY WILKINSON, INC.—See Great Mill Rock LLC; *U.S. Private*, pg. 1766
ASCO NUMATICS, S.A.—See Emerson Electric Co.; *U.S. Public*, pg. 740
ASEA BROWN BOVERI LTD.—See ABB Ltd.; *Int'l*, pg. 55
ASEA BROWN BOVERI (PTY) LTD—See ABB Ltd.; *Int'l*, pg. 55
ASEA BROWN BOVERI, S.A.—See ABB Ltd.; *Int'l*, pg. 55
ASEA BROWN BOVERI, S.A.—See ABB Ltd.; *Int'l*, pg. 55
ASEA BROWN BOVERI, S.A.—See ABB Ltd.; *Int'l*, pg. 55
ASM AMERICA INC.—See ASM INTERNATIONAL N.V.; *Int'l*, pg. 626
A/S PARTS LIMITED—See Ingersoll Rand Inc.; *U.S. Public*, pg. 1120
A/S PREBEN Z JENSEN—See Beijer Alma AB; *Int'l*, pg. 942
ASSOCIATED EQUIPMENT SALES CO.; *U.S. Private*, pg. 355
ASSOCIATED POWER, INC.; *U.S. Private*, pg. 357
ASSOCIATED SUPPLY COMPANY INC.; *U.S. Private*, pg. 357
ASSOCIATED WELDING SUPPLY INC.; *U.S. Private*, pg. 357
ATG-LUTHER & MAELZER ASIA LTD.—See Cohu, Inc.; *U.S. Public*, pg. 530
ATI GARRYSON—See ATI Inc.; *U.S. Public*, pg. 221
ATKA KUNSTSTOFFVERARBEITUNG GMBH; *Int'l*, pg. 670
ATLANTA FORKLIFTS, INC.; *U.S. Private*, pg. 370
ATLANTIC DETROIT DIESEL-ALLISON, LLC; *U.S. Private*, pg. 373
ATLANTIC LIFT TRUCK INC.; *U.S. Private*, pg. 373
ATLANTIC ZEISER (ASIA) SDN. BHD.—See Atlantic Zeiser GmbH & Co.; *Int'l*, pg. 676

3917

423830 — INDUSTRIAL MACHINER...

ATLANTIC ZEISER S.A.—See Atlantic Zeiser GmbH & Co.; *Int'l*, pg. 676
ATLANTIC ZEISER S.A.S.—See Atlantic Zeiser GmbH & Co.; *Int'l*, pg. 676
ATLAS COPCO AB; *Int'l*, pg. 676
ATLAS COPCO COMPRESSOR CANADA—See Atlas Copco AB; *Int'l*, pg. 681
ATLAS COPCO (CYPRUS) LTD—See Atlas Copco AB; *Int'l*, pg. 677
ATLAS COPCO EASTERN AFRICA LTD—See Atlas Copco AB; *Int'l*, pg. 678
ATLAS COPCO EQUIPMENT EGYPT S.A.E.—See Atlas Copco AB; *Int'l*, pg. 678
ATLAS COPCO HELLAS AE—See Atlas Copco AB; *Int'l*, pg. 679
ATLAS COPCO NEDERLAND B.V.—See Atlas Copco AB; *Int'l*, pg. 679
ATLAS COPCO SECOROC LLC—See Atlas Copco AB; *Int'l*, pg. 680
ATLAS COPCO TOOLS AB—See Atlas Copco AB; *Int'l*, pg. 681
ATLAS COPCO TOOLS & ASSEMBLY SYSTEMS LLC—See Atlas Copco AB; *Int'l*, pg. 681
ATLAS COPCO TOOLS A/S—See Atlas Copco AB; *Int'l*, pg. 677
ATLAS ELEVATORS GENERAL TRADING & CONTRACTING COMPANY; *Int'l*, pg. 685
ATLAS GLOBAL FZE—See Atlas Group of Companies; *Int'l*, pg. 685
ATLAS INTERNATIONAL LIFT TRUCKS—See Atlas Lift Truck Rentals & Sales, Inc.; *U.S. Private*, pg. 379
ATLAS LIFT TRUCK RENTALS & SALES, INC.; *U.S. Private*, pg. 379
ATLAS TOYOTA MATERIAL HANDLING INC—See Atlas Lift Truck Rentals & Sales, Inc.; *U.S. Private*, pg. 379
ATS INDUSTRIAL SUPPLY, S. DE R.L. DE C.V.—See MSC Industrial Direct Co., Inc.; *U.S. Public*, pg. 1483
ATTICA HYDRAULIC EXCHANGE, INC.—See Clearlake Capital Group, L.P.; *U.S. Private*, pg. 933
AUDIO INTERVISUAL DESIGN, INC.—See Advanced Systems Group, LLC; *U.S. Private*, pg. 92
AUROTECH CORPORATION—See Disco Corporation; *Int'l*, pg. 2131
AUSTIN PUMP & SUPPLY COMPANY INC; *U.S. Private*, pg. 396
AUSTRO ENGINEERING CAPE (PTY) LIMITED—See enX Group Limited; *Int'l*, pg. 2456
AUSTRO (PTY) LIMITED—See enX Group Limited; *Int'l*, pg. 2456
AUSTRO WOOD (PTY) LIMITED—See enX Group Limited; *Int'l*, pg. 2456
AUSTRO WOODWORKING MACHINES & TOOLS—See enX Group Limited; *Int'l*, pg. 2456
AUTOCAM DE BRASIL USINAGEM LTDA—See NN, Inc.; *U.S. Private*, pg. 1530
AUTOMATIK DO BRAZIL MAQUINAS PARA INDUSTRIA DO PLASTICO LTDA.—See Dover Corporation; *U.S. Public*, pg. 681
AUTOMATIK PLASTICS MACHINERY SDN. BHD.—See Dover Corporation; *U.S. Public*, pg. 681
AUTOMATIK PLASTICS MACHINERY (TAIWAN) LTD.—See Dover Corporation; *U.S. Public*, pg. 681
AUTOMATION, INC.—See Applied Industrial Technologies, Inc.; *U.S. Public*, pg. 171
AUTO SUPPLIERS LIMITED—See Freudenberg SE; *Int'l*, pg. 2782
AUTO TRUCK GROUP, LLC—See Holman Automotive Group, Inc.; *U.S. Private*, pg. 1967
AVANTEC, INC.; *U.S. Private*, pg. 404
AVANTEC ITALY S.R.L.—See AVANTEC Zerspantechnik GmbH; *Int'l*, pg. 735
AVANTEC USA, LLC—See AVANTEC Zerspantechnik GmbH; *Int'l*, pg. 735
AVENTICS AB—See Emerson Electric Co.; *U.S. Public*, pg. 742
AVENTICS AG—See Emerson Electric Co.; *U.S. Public*, pg. 742
AVENTICS AS—See Emerson Electric Co.; *U.S. Public*, pg. 742
AVENTICS B.V.—See Emerson Electric Co.; *U.S. Public*, pg. 742
AVENTICS GMBH—See Emerson Electric Co.; *U.S. Public*, pg. 742
AVENTICS HUNGARY KFT.—See Emerson Electric Co.; *U.S. Public*, pg. 742
AVENTICS INDIA PRIVATE LIMITED—See Emerson Electric Co.; *U.S. Public*, pg. 742
AVENTICS MEXICO, S. DE R.L. DE C.V.—See Emerson Electric Co.; *U.S. Public*, pg. 742
AVENTICS OY—See Emerson Electric Co.; *U.S. Public*, pg. 742
AVENTICS PNEUMATICS EQUIPMENT (CHANGZHOU) CO., LTD.—See Emerson Electric Co.; *U.S. Public*, pg. 742
AVENTICS PNEUMATICS TRADING (SHANGHAI) CO., LTD.—See Emerson Electric Co.; *U.S. Public*, pg. 742
AVENTICS S.A.S.—See Emerson Electric Co.; *U.S. Public*, pg. 742

AVENTICS, SPOL. S.R.O.—See Emerson Electric Co.; *U.S. Public*, pg. 742
AVENTICS SP. Z O.O.—See Emerson Electric Co.; *U.S. Public*, pg. 742
AVENTICS S.R.L.—See Emerson Electric Co.; *U.S. Public*, pg. 742
AVEST CO., LTD—See Dynavest Pte. Ltd.; *Int'l*, pg. 2242
AVIACION REGIONAL CANTABRA, A.I.E.—See Banco Santander, S.A.; *Int'l*, pg. 825
AVK AUSTRALIA PTY LTD—See AVK Holding A/S; *Int'l*, pg. 746
AVTPUMP APS—See AESSEAL Plc; *Int'l*, pg. 183
AVT RELIABILITY LTD.—See AESSEAL Plc; *Int'l*, pg. 182
AWC INC.; *U.S. Private*, pg. 410
AWISCO NY CORPORATION; *U.S. Private*, pg. 411
A.W. MILLER—See A.W. Miller Technical Sales Inc.; *U.S. Private*, pg. 28
A.W. MILLER TECHNICAL SALES INC.; *U.S. Private*, pg. 28
AXFLOW AB—See Axel Johnson Gruppen AB; *Int'l*, pg. 762
AXFLOW DC B.V.—See Axel Johnson Gruppen AB; *Int'l*, pg. 762
AXFLOW GESMBH—See Axel Johnson Gruppen AB; *Int'l*, pg. 762
AXFLOW KFT—See Axel Johnson Gruppen AB; *Int'l*, pg. 762
AXFLOW LIMITED—See Axel Johnson Gruppen AB; *Int'l*, pg. 762
AXFLOW LTD.—See Axel Johnson Gruppen AB; *Int'l*, pg. 763
AXFLOW LTD.—See Axel Johnson Gruppen AB; *Int'l*, pg. 763
AXFLOW N.V. / S.A.—See Axel Johnson Gruppen AB; *Int'l*, pg. 763
AXFLOW SP. Z O.O.—See Axel Johnson Gruppen AB; *Int'l*, pg. 763
AXFLOW SRL—See Axel Johnson Gruppen AB; *Int'l*, pg. 762
AXFLOW S.R.O., O.Z.P.Z.O.—See Axel Johnson Gruppen AB; *Int'l*, pg. 763
AXFLOW SYSTEMS B.V.—See Axel Johnson Gruppen AB; *Int'l*, pg. 763
AXLOAD AB—See Axel Johnson Gruppen AB; *Int'l*, pg. 763
AXYZ OHIO VALLEY REGION, INC.—See AXYZ Automation Group Inc.; *Int'l*, pg. 773
AYEN ELEKTRIK TICARET A.S.—See Ayen Enerji AS; *Int'l*, pg. 774
AZBIL ROYALCONTROLS CO., LTD.—See Azbil Corporation; *Int'l*, pg. 777
AZBIL TRADING CO., LTD.—See Azbil Corporation; *Int'l*, pg. 777
AZO, INC.—See AZO GmbH & Co. KG; *Int'l*, pg. 780
AZO INGREDIENTS AUTOMATION SYSTEM (TIANJIN) CO., LTD.—See AZO GmbH & Co. KG; *Int'l*, pg. 780
AZO LIQUIDS GMBH—See AZO GmbH & Co. KG; *Int'l*, pg. 780
AZO UK LTD.—See AZO GmbH & Co. KG; *Int'l*, pg. 780
AZTECH CONTROLS CORPORATION; *U.S. Private*, pg. 416
B2B INDUSTRIAL PACKAGING, LLC—See GenNx360 Capital Partners, L.P.; *U.S. Private*, pg. 1672
THE BAILEY COMPANY INC.; *U.S. Private*, pg. 3990
BAILEY INTERNATIONAL, LLC—See Pfingsten Partners, LLC; *U.S. Private*, pg. 3164
BAJAJ CONEAGLE LLC—See Bajaj Steel Industries Ltd.; *Int'l*, pg. 804
BAKER THERMAL SOLUTIONS LLC—See The Middleby Corporation; *U.S. Public*, pg. 2113
BALDWIN FRANCE S.A.R.L.—See Forsyth Capital Investors LLC; *U.S. Private*, pg. 1573
BALDWIN GRAPHIC EQUIPMENT PTY.—See Forsyth Capital Investors LLC; *U.S. Private*, pg. 1573
BALTEC CORPORATION—See BalTec Maschinenbau AG; *Int'l*, pg. 812
BALTEC (UK) LTD.—See BalTec Maschinenbau AG; *Int'l*, pg. 812
BANGKOK ENSHU MACHINERY CO., LTD.—See Enshu Limited; *Int'l*, pg. 2446
BANNER INDUSTRIES INC.; *U.S. Private*, pg. 469
BARKER AIR & HYDRAULICS INC.; *U.S. Private*, pg. 475
BARLOWORLD EQUIPMENT - SOUTHERN AFRICA—See Barloworld Ltd.; *Int'l*, pg. 866
BARLOWORLD FINANZAUTO—See Barloworld Ltd.; *Int'l*, pg. 866
BARLOWORLD MERA SA—See Barloworld Ltd.; *Int'l*, pg. 866
BARNEYS PUMPS INC.; *U.S. Private*, pg. 477
BARO COMPANIES—See Applied Industrial Technologies, Inc.; *U.S. Public*, pg. 171
BAROID DRILLING FLUIDS DIVISION—See Halliburton Company; *U.S. Public*, pg. 980
BARON INDUSTRIES, INC.—See Alta Equipment Group Inc.; *U.S. Public*, pg. 86
BAROUH EATON (CANADA) LTD.—See Ko-Rec-Type Corp.; *U.S. Private*, pg. 2325
BASIN ENGINE & PUMP, INC.—See Applied Industrial Technologies, Inc.; *U.S. Public*, pg. 171
BASIN SUPPLY FZCO—See J Fitzgibbons LLC; *U.S. Private*, pg. 2153

CORPORATE AFFILIATIONS

BASTIDE MANUTENTION; *Int'l*, pg. 888
BAUCH POWERTRAIN COMPONENTS CO., LTD.—See BAUCH Engineering GmbH & Co. KG; *Int'l*, pg. 891
BAUER KOMPRESSOREN BEIJING LTD.—See BAUER COMP Holding AG; *Int'l*, pg. 894
BAUER KOMPRESSOREN KOREA LIMITED—See BAUER COMP Holding AG; *Int'l*, pg. 894
BAUER KOMPRESSOREN RUSSIA LTD.—See BAUER COMP Holding AG; *Int'l*, pg. 894
BAUER KOMPRESSOREN SERVICE, S.L.U.—See BAUER COMP Holding AG; *Int'l*, pg. 894
BAUER KOMPRESSOREN TURKIYE—See BAUER COMP Holding AG; *Int'l*, pg. 894
BAUER KOMPRESSOREN UK LTD.—See BAUER COMP Holding AG; *Int'l*, pg. 894
BAYO; *Int'l*, pg. 914
BAYOU CITY PUMP COMPANY—See The Gorman-Rupp Company; *U.S. Public*, pg. 2085
BEARINGS & OIL SEALS SPECIALISTS INC.—See Applied Industrial Technologies, Inc.; *U.S. Public*, pg. 171
BEHLEN MFG. CO.; *U.S. Private*, pg. 515
BEHRINGER LTD.—See Behringer GmbH; *Int'l*, pg. 942
BEIJER INDUSTRI AB—See Beijer Alma AB; *Int'l*, pg. 942
BEIJING-FANUC MECHATRONICS CO., LTD.—See FANUC Corporation; *Int'l*, pg. 2614
BEJAC CORPORATION; *U.S. Private*, pg. 516
BEKA JAPAN CO., LTD.—See The Timken Company; *U.S. Public*, pg. 2132
BEKALUBE FRANCE S.A.S.—See The Timken Company; *U.S. Public*, pg. 2132
BEKALUBE IBERICA, S.L.U.—See The Timken Company; *U.S. Public*, pg. 2132
BEKA LUBE PRODUCTS INC.—See The Timken Company; *U.S. Public*, pg. 2132
BEKALUBE S.R.L.—See The Timken Company; *U.S. Public*, pg. 2132
BEKA LUBRICATION SYSTEMS (KUNSHAN) CO., LTD.—See The Timken Company; *U.S. Public*, pg. 2132
BEKAWORLD SINGAPORE PTE. LTD.—See The Timken Company; *U.S. Public*, pg. 2132
BELFAB, INC.—See Enpro Inc.; *U.S. Public*, pg. 774
BELL EQUIPMENT LIMITED; *Int'l*, pg. 965
BELL FORK LIFT INC.; *U.S. Private*, pg. 518
BELL-MARK CORPORATION; *U.S. Private*, pg. 519
BELLOFRAM INSTRUMENTS (INDIA) PVT. LTD.—See Desco Corporation; *U.S. Private*, pg. 1211
BEL POWER PRODUCTS INC.—See Bel Fuse Inc.; *U.S. Public*, pg. 293
BELT-WIDE INDUSTRIES, INC.—See Lummus Corporation; *U.S. Private*, pg. 2514
BEL VALVES LTD—See British Engines Ltd.; *Int'l*, pg. 1171
BEPCO DEUTSCHLAND GMBH—See Group Thermote & Vanhalst; *Int'l*, pg. 3089
BEPEX ASIA LIMITED—See Bepex International, LLC; *U.S. Private*, pg. 529
BERGMAN & BEVING AB; *Int'l*, pg. 980
BERKSHIRE-WESTWOOD GRAPHICS GROUP; *U.S. Private*, pg. 535
BERND GROUP INC.; *U.S. Private*, pg. 536
BERRY MATERIAL HANDLING, INC.—See Berry Companies, Inc.; *U.S. Private*, pg. 538
BERRY TRACTOR & EQUIPMENT CO—See Berry Companies, Inc.; *U.S. Private*, pg. 538
BERTELKAMP AUTOMATION INC.; *U.S. Private*, pg. 539
BERTHOLD FRANCE SAS—See BERTHOLD TECHNOLOGIES GmbH & Co. KG; *Int'l*, pg. 997
BERTHOLD ITALIA S.R.L.—See BERTHOLD TECHNOLOGIES GmbH & Co. KG; *Int'l*, pg. 997
BERTHOLD TECHNOLOGIES (BELGIUM) NV/SA—See BERTHOLD TECHNOLOGIES GmbH & Co. KG; *Int'l*, pg. 997
BERTHOLD TECHNOLOGIES GMBH—See BERTHOLD TECHNOLOGIES GmbH & Co. KG; *Int'l*, pg. 997
BERTHOLD TECHNOLOGIES (SCHWEIZ) GMBH—See BERTHOLD TECHNOLOGIES GmbH & Co. KG; *Int'l*, pg. 997
BERTHOLD TECHNOLOGIES (U.K.) LTD.—See BERTHOLD TECHNOLOGIES GmbH & Co. KG; *Int'l*, pg. 997
BERTHOLD TECHNOLOGIES U.S.A. LLC—See BERTHOLD TECHNOLOGIES GmbH & Co. KG; *Int'l*, pg. 997
BESI JAPAN CO. LTD.—See BE Semiconductor Industries N.V.; *Int'l*, pg. 931
BEUTTER PRAZISIONS-KOMPONENTEN GMBH & CO. KG; *Int'l*, pg. 1004
BGI USA, INC.; *U.S. Private*, pg. 548
B. GRIMM GROUP—See B. Grimm Group; *Int'l*, pg. 788
BIESSE CANADA INC.—See Biesse S.p.A.; *Int'l*, pg. 1020
BIESSE GROUP AUSTRALIA PTY LTD.—See Biesse S.p.A.; *Int'l*, pg. 1020
BIESSE GROUP DEUTSCHLAND GMBH—See Biesse S.p.A.; *Int'l*, pg. 1020
BIESSE GROUP FRANCE SARL—See Biesse S.p.A.; *Int'l*, pg. 1020
BIESSE GROUP UK LTD.—See Biesse S.p.A.; *Int'l*, pg. 1020

N.A.I.C.S. INDEX

423830 — INDUSTRIAL MACHINER...

BIESSERVICE SCANDINAVIA AB—See Biesse S.p.A.; *Int'l*, pg. 1020
BIG RED INC.; *U.S. Private*, pg. 553
BIONIME (PINGTAN) CO., LTD.—See Bionime Corporation; *Int'l*, pg. 1040
BIRKETT CUTMASTER LIMITED—See Carclo plc; *Int'l*, pg. 1321
BIS PRODUCTION PARTNER AB—See Bilfinger SE; *Int'l*, pg. 1025
BIT BROKERS INTERNATIONAL, LTD.; *U.S. Private*, pg. 566
BITS FROM BYTES, LTD.—See 3D Systems Corporation; *U.S. Public*, pg. 4
BLACK EQUIPMENT CO. INC.; *U.S. Private*, pg. 572
BLACK HAWK ENERGY SERVICES, INC.—See Steel Partners Holdings L.P.; *U.S. Public*, pg. 1943
BLACKHAWK INDUSTRIAL - OMAHA—See TruArc Partners, L.P.; *U.S. Private*, pg. 4244
BLACKHAWK INDUSTRIAL - PEORIA—See TruArc Partners, L.P.; *U.S. Private*, pg. 4244
BLACKHAWK INDUSTRIAL - SPRINGFIELD—See TruArc Partners, L.P.; *U.S. Private*, pg. 4244
BLACKTECH OTOMOTIV SANAYI VE TICARET A.S.—See Freudenberg SE; *Int'l*, pg. 2782
BLADES CO. INC.; *U.S. Private*, pg. 577
BLADES MACHINERY CO INC—See Blades Co. Inc.; *U.S. Private*, pg. 577
BLAGDON PUMP HOLDINGS LTD.—See IDEX Corp; *U.S. Public*, pg. 1089
BLAKE & PENDLETON INC.; *U.S. Private*, pg. 578
BLUELINE RENTAL—See The Pape Group, Inc.; *U.S. Private*, pg. 4090
BLUE OCEAN TECHNOLOGIES LLC—See Oceaneering International, Inc.; *U.S. Public*, pg. 1562
BLUESTAR INDUSTRIES, LLC; *U.S. Private*, pg. 598
BMC, SPOL. S.R.O.—See Agrofert Holding, a.s.; *Int'l*, pg. 219
BMH TECHNOLOGY AB—See BMH Technology Oy; *Int'l*, pg. 1076
BMH TECHNOLOGY OY—See BMH Technology Oy; *Int'l*, pg. 1076
BMH TECHNOLOGY SP. Z O.O.—See BMH Technology Oy; *Int'l*, pg. 1076
BNI COAL, LTD.—See ALLETE, Inc.; *U.S. Public*, pg. 79
BOBCAT EQUIPMENT LTD.—See Doosan Corporation; *Int'l*, pg. 2172
BOBCAT WEST—See The Pape Group, Inc.; *U.S. Private*, pg. 4090
BOBST (AFRICA & MIDDLE EAST) LTD.—See Bobst Group S.A.; *Int'l*, pg. 1095
BOBST BRASIL LTDA.—See Bobst Group S.A.; *Int'l*, pg. 1095
BOBST GROUP BENELUX N.V.—See Bobst Group S.A.; *Int'l*, pg. 1095
BOBST GROUP ITALIA S.P.A.—See Bobst Group S.A.; *Int'l*, pg. 1095
BOBST GROUP NORTH AMERICA, INC.—See Bobst Group S.A.; *Int'l*, pg. 1095
BOBST JAPAN LTD.—See Bobst Group S.A.; *Int'l*, pg. 1096
BOBST MALAYSIA SDN. BHD.—See Bobst Group S.A.; *Int'l*, pg. 1096
BOBST (SEA) PTE LTD—See Bobst Group S.A.; *Int'l*, pg. 1095
BOBST (TAIWAN) LTD.—See Bobst Group S.A.; *Int'l*, pg. 1095
BODITSE (PTY) LIMITED—See Alviva Holdings Limited; *Int'l*, pg. 401
BOGLE AND TIMMS LIMITED—See W.W. Grainger, Inc.; *U.S. Public*, pg. 2319
BOHL CRANE INC.; *U.S. Private*, pg. 609
BOHL EQUIPMENT CO.; *U.S. Private*, pg. 609
BOHNERT INTERNATIONAL, INC.—See Wolter Group LLC; *U.S. Private*, pg. 4554
BOLZONI AURAMO CANADA LTD—See Hyster-Yale Materials Handling, Inc.; *U.S. Public*, pg. 1080
BOLZONI LIMITED—See Hyster-Yale Materials Handling, Inc.; *U.S. Public*, pg. 1080
BOMAR PNEUMATICS, INC.—See Blue Sea Capital Management LLC; *U.S. Private*, pg. 592
BOMBAS GOULDS S.A.—See ITT Inc.; *U.S. Public*, pg. 1177
BOMBAS LEAO SA—See Franklin Electric Co., Inc.; *U.S. Public*, pg. 878
BON ACCORD CASPIAN—See Groupe BPCE; *Int'l*, pg. 3095
BOND FLUIDAIRE INC.—See Exotic Automation & Supply, Inc.; *U.S. Private*, pg. 1449
BOND FLUIDAIRE INC.—See Exotic Automation & Supply, Inc.; *U.S. Private*, pg. 1449
BONFIGLIOLI FRANCE SA—See Bonfiglioli Riduttori S.p.A.; *Int'l*, pg. 1106
BORETS-WEATHERFORD DO BRASIL LTDA.—See Tangent Fund Management LLC; *U.S. Private*, pg. 3930
BORNQUIST INC.; *U.S. Private*, pg. 619
BOURN & KOCH, INC.-REPLACEMENT PARTS DIVISION—See Berkshire Hathaway Inc.; *U.S. Public*, pg. 298

BOWE SYSTEC, CEE, S.A.—See BOWE SYSTEC AG; *Int'l*, pg. 1123
BOWMAN HOLLIS MANUFACTURING, INC.; *U.S. Private*, pg. 626
BRACKER GMBH INNOVATIVER MASCHINENBAU—See Blackstone Inc.; *U.S. Public*, pg. 360
BRADFORD SUPPLY COMPANY; *U.S. Private*, pg. 632
BRAMMER PLC—See Advent International Corporation; *U.S. Private*, pg. 98
BRANDT & HILL INC.; *U.S. Private*, pg. 638
BRANOM INSTRUMENT CO. INC.; *U.S. Private*, pg. 640
BRANSON MACHINERY LLC—See Dongkuk Steel Mill Co., Ltd.; *Int'l*, pg. 2169
BRAPENTA ELETRONICA LTDA.—See Illinois Tool Works Inc.; *U.S. Public*, pg. 1102
BRAUER MATERIAL HANDLING SYSTEMS, INC.; *U.S. Private*, pg. 640
B&R AUTOMACAO INDUSTRIAL LTDA.—See ABB Ltd.; *Int'l*, pg. 56
B+R AUTOMATIZACE, SPOL. S R.O.—See ABB Ltd.; *Int'l*, pg. 56
B&R AUTOMATYKA PRZEMYSLOWA SP. Z.O.O.—See ABB Ltd.; *Int'l*, pg. 56
B&R AUTOMAZIONE INDUSTRIALE S.R.L.—See ABB Ltd.; *Int'l*, pg. 56
BRAY SALES SOUTHERN CALIFORNIA INC.—See Bray International, Inc.; *U.S. Private*, pg. 642
BREEN INTERNATIONAL SDN BHD—See Breen International Pte. Ltd.; *Int'l*, pg. 1144
BR ENDUSTRIYEL OTOMASYON SANAYI VE TICARET LIMITED—See ABB Ltd.; *Int'l*, pg. 56
BRENNAN INDUSTRIES INC.; *U.S. Private*, pg. 645
BREVINI FLUID POWER BEIJING CO. LTD.—See Dana Incorporated; *U.S. Public*, pg. 621
BREVINI FLUID POWER DISTRIBUTION S.R.L.—See Dana Incorporated; *U.S. Public*, pg. 621
BREVINI FLUID POWER VENETO S.R.L.—See Dana Incorporated; *U.S. Public*, pg. 621
BRIGGS EQUIPMENT S.A. DE C.V.—See Sammons Enterprises, Inc.; *U.S. Private*, pg. 3537
BRI INC.; *U.S. Private*, pg. 647
B&R INDUSTRIAL AUTOMATION A/S—See ABB Ltd.; *Int'l*, pg. 56
B&R INDUSTRIAL AUTOMATION CO., LTD.—See ABB Ltd.; *Int'l*, pg. 56
B&R INDUSTRIAL AUTOMATION CO. LTD.—See ABB Ltd.; *Int'l*, pg. 56
B&R INDUSTRIAL AUTOMATION CORP.—See ABB Ltd.; *Int'l*, pg. 56
B&R INDUSTRIAL AUTOMATION INC.—See ABB Ltd.; *Int'l*, pg. 56
B&R INDUSTRIAL AUTOMATION LTD.—See ABB Ltd.; *Int'l*, pg. 56
B&R INDUSTRIAL AUTOMATION, OOO—See ABB Ltd.; *Int'l*, pg. 56
B&R INDUSTRIAL AUTOMATION PTE LTD—See ABB Ltd.; *Int'l*, pg. 56
B&R INDUSTRIAL AUTOMATION PVT. LTD.—See ABB Ltd.; *Int'l*, pg. 56
B&R INDUSTRIAL AUTOMATION—See ABB Ltd.; *Int'l*, pg. 56
B&R INDUSTRIAUTOMATION AB—See ABB Ltd.; *Int'l*, pg. 56
B&R INDUSTRIE-AUTOMATION AG—See ABB Ltd.; *Int'l*, pg. 56
B&R INDUSTRIE-ELEKTRONIK GMBH—See ABB Ltd.; *Int'l*, pg. 56
B&R INDUSTRIELE AUTOMATISIERUNG B.V.—See ABB Ltd.; *Int'l*, pg. 56
B&R INDUSTRIELLE AUTOMATISERING BV—See ABB Ltd.; *Int'l*, pg. 56
B&R K.K.—See ABB Ltd.; *Int'l*, pg. 56
B&R MOLL, INC.; *U.S. Private*, pg. 419
BROADWIND SERVICES, LLC—See Broadwind, Inc.; *U.S. Public*, pg. 392
BRODIE TOYOTA-LIFT; *U.S. Private*, pg. 661
BROEN SEI SRL—See Aalberts N.V.; *Int'l*, pg. 33
BROMI MASKIN AB; *Int'l*, pg. 1173
BROOKS ASSOCIATES INC.; *U.S. Private*, pg. 664
BROOKS EQUIPMENT COMPANY, LLC—See H.I.G. Capital, LLC; *U.S. Private*, pg. 1827
BROOKS INCORPORATED; *U.S. Private*, pg. 664
BROOKS INSTRUMENT GMBH—See Illinois Tool Works Inc.; *U.S. Public*, pg. 1102
BROOKS INSTRUMENT KFT—See Illinois Tool Works Inc.; *U.S. Public*, pg. 1102
BROTHER SEWING MACHINES EUROPE GMBH—See Brother Industries, Ltd.; *Int'l*, pg. 1196
BROTOMATIC S.L.; *Int'l*, pg. 1198
BUCHER HIDROLIK SISTEMLERI TIC. LTD.—See Bucher Industries AG; *Int'l*, pg. 1207
BUCHER HYDRAULICS LTD—See Bucher Industries AG; *Int'l*, pg. 1207
BUCHER HYDRAULICS PVT LTD—See Bucher Industries AG; *Int'l*, pg. 1207
BUCHER HYDRAULICS SAS—See Bucher Industries AG; *Int'l*, pg. 1207

BUCKEYE PUMPS INC.—See Genstar Capital, LLC; *U.S. Private*, pg. 1678
BULOVA TECHNOLOGIES MACHINERY LLC—See Bulova Technologies Group, Inc.; *U.S. Public*, pg. 685
BURCKHARDT COMPRESSION (US) INC.—See Burckhardt Compression Holding AG; *Int'l*, pg. 1220
BURKE HANDLING SYSTEMS, INC.; *U.S. Private*, pg. 688
BURNS CONTROLS COMPANY; *U.S. Private*, pg. 691
BUSCH COLOMBIA SAS—See Dr. Ing. K. Busch GmbH; *Int'l*, pg. 2192
BUSCH LLC - MORGAN HILL—See Dr. Ing. K. Busch GmbH; *Int'l*, pg. 2193
BUSCH LLC—See Dr. Ing. K. Busch GmbH; *Int'l*, pg. 2193
BUSCH PERU SRL—See Dr. Ing. K. Busch GmbH; *Int'l*, pg. 2193
BUSCH VACUUM FZE—See Dr. Ing. K. Busch GmbH; *Int'l*, pg. 2193
BYSTRONIC ASIA PTE. LTD.—See Bystronic AG; *Int'l*, pg. 1236
BYSTRONIC DEUTSCHLAND GMBH—See Bystronic AG; *Int'l*, pg. 1236
BYSTRONIC FRANCE SAS—See Bystronic AG; *Int'l*, pg. 1236
BYSTRONIC SCANDINAVIA AB—See Bystronic AG; *Int'l*, pg. 1236
CABI S.R.L.—See Biesse S.p.A.; *Int'l*, pg. 1020
CABOT INDIA LIMITED—See Cabot Corporation; *U.S. Public*, pg. 416
CALDERA, INC.—See Dover Corporation; *U.S. Public*, pg. 678
CALDER GMBH—See Flowserve Corporation; *U.S. Public*, pg. 855
CALIFORNIA TOOL & WELDING SUPPLIES; *U.S. Private*, pg. 721
CAL-LIFT, INC.; *U.S. Private*, pg. 715
CALOLYMPIC GLOVE & SAFETY CO., INC.; *U.S. Private*, pg. 723
CALTROL—See Caltrol, Inc.; *U.S. Private*, pg. 724
CAMERON FLOW CONTROL TECHNOLOGY (UK) LIMITED—See Schlumberger Limited; *U.S. Public*, pg. 1843
CAMOZZI AUTOMATION AB—See Camozzi Group; *Int'l*, pg. 1273
CAMOZZI AUTOMATION APS—See Camozzi Group; *Int'l*, pg. 1273
CAMOZZI AUTOMATION AS—See Camozzi Group; *Int'l*, pg. 1273
CAMOZZI AUTOMATION B.V.—See Camozzi Group; *Int'l*, pg. 1273
CAMOZZI AUTOMATION GMBH—See Camozzi Group; *Int'l*, pg. 1273
CAMOZZI AUTOMATION GMBH—See Camozzi Group; *Int'l*, pg. 1273
CAMOZZI AUTOMATION LTD.—See Camozzi Group; *Int'l*, pg. 1273
CAMOZZI AUTOMATION SARL—See Camozzi Group; *Int'l*, pg. 1273
CAMOZZI AUTOMATION SP. Z O.O.—See Camozzi Group; *Int'l*, pg. 1273
CAMOZZI IBERICA SL—See Camozzi Group; *Int'l*, pg. 1273
CAMOZZI OTOMASYON A.S.—See Camozzi Group; *Int'l*, pg. 1274
CAMOZZI S.R.O.—See Camozzi Group; *Int'l*, pg. 1274
CANON PRODUCTION PRINTING GERMANY GMBH & CO.KG—See Canon Inc.; *Int'l*, pg. 1296
THE CANTWELL MACHINERY COMPANY INC.; *U.S. Private*, pg. 4004
CAPP USA, INC.; *U.S. Private*, pg. 745
CARDINAL MACHINERY, INC.; *U.S. Private*, pg. 750
CARGOTEC (ARE) GULF WLL—See Cargotec Corporation; *Int'l*, pg. 1326
CARGOTEC AUSTRIA GMBH—See Cargotec Corporation; *Int'l*, pg. 1326
CARGOTEC BELGIUM NV—See Cargotec Corporation; *Int'l*, pg. 1326
CARGOTEC IBERIA SA—See Cargotec Corporation; *Int'l*, pg. 1327
CARGOTEC USA INC.—See Cargotec Corporation; *Int'l*, pg. 1326
CARL ERIC JOHNSON INC.; *U.S. Private*, pg. 762
CARLETON EQUIPMENT COMPANY; *U.S. Private*, pg. 763
CARL ZEISS SERVICES S.A.R.L.—See Carl-Zeiss-Stiftung; *Int'l*, pg. 1335
CAROLINA FLUID COMPONENTS, LLC; *U.S. Private*, pg. 768
CAROLINA HANDLING LLC; *U.S. Private*, pg. 768
CAROTEK INC.—See Ad Bel Ltd.; *U.S. Private*, pg. 71
CARRIER EUROPE SCA—See Carrier Vibrating Equipment, Inc.; *U.S. Private*, pg. 772
CARRIER VIBRATING EQUIPMENT (CANADA) LTD.—See Carrier Vibrating Equipment, Inc.; *U.S. Private*, pg. 772
CARRUTH-DOGGETT INC.—See Doggett Equipment Services, Ltd.; *U.S. Private*, pg. 1253
CARRYLIFT GROUP—See CorpAcq Holdings Limited; *Int'l*, pg. 1802
CARTER & VERPLANCK, INC.; *U.S. Private*, pg. 775
CASCADE CONTROLS NORTHWEST; *U.S. Private*, pg. 779

423830 — INDUSTRIAL MACHINER...

CASCADE MACHINERY & ELECTRIC; *U.S. Private*, pg. 781
CATALYST HANDLING SERVICE CO., LLC.; *U.S. Private*, pg. 786
CATCHING FLUIDPOWER INC.—See Littlejohn & Co., LLC; *U.S. Private*, pg. 2470
CATERAIR SERVICOS DE BORDO E HOTELARIA S.A.—See Deutsche Lufthansa AG; *Int'l*, pg. 2067
CATERPILLAR ENERGY SOLUTIONS ASIA PACIFIC PTE. LTD.—See Caterpillar, Inc.; *U.S. Public*, pg. 449
CATERPILLAR GLOBAL MINING SARL—See Caterpillar, Inc.; *U.S. Public*, pg. 450
CATERPILLAR (LANGFANG) MINING EQUIPMENT CO., LTD.—See Caterpillar, Inc.; *U.S. Public*, pg. 449
CATERPILLAR MEXICO S.A. DE C.V.—See Caterpillar, Inc.; *U.S. Public*, pg. 451
CATERPILLAR PROPULSION INTERNATIONAL TRADING (SHANGHAI) CO. LTD.—See Caterpillar, Inc.; *U.S. Public*, pg. 451
CATERPILLAR PROPULSION ISTANBUL MAKINA TICARET LIMITED SIRKETI—See Caterpillar, Inc.; *U.S. Public*, pg. 451
CATERPILLAR PROPULSION ITALY S.R.L.—See Caterpillar, Inc.; *U.S. Public*, pg. 451
CATERPILLAR PROPULSION PTE. LTD.—See Caterpillar, Inc.; *U.S. Public*, pg. 451
CATERPILLAR PROPULSION SINGAPORE PTE. LTD.—See Caterpillar, Inc.; *U.S. Public*, pg. 451
CATERPILLAR PROPULSION SPAIN, S.L.—See Caterpillar, Inc.; *U.S. Public*, pg. 452
CAT PUMPS INTERNATIONAL N.V.—See Diversified Dynamics Corporation; *U.S. Private*, pg. 1242
CAVOTEC REALTY NORWAY AS—See Cavotec SA; *Int'l*, pg. 1363
CB ENGINEERING LTD; *Int'l*, pg. 1364
CBI EUROPE B.V.—See Terex Corporation; *U.S. Public*, pg. 2018
CC-HEFTRUCKS BVBA—See Group Thermote & Vanhalst; *Int'l*, pg. 3089
C&C HYDRAULICS, INC.; *U.S. Private*, pg. 702
CDS MOVING EQUIPMENT INC.; *U.S. Private*, pg. 803
CEE KAY SUPPLY INC.; *U.S. Private*, pg. 805
CEFLA LADENBAU—See Cefla S.C.; *Int'l*, pg. 1389
CEMEX INNOVATION HOLDING LTD.—See CEMEX, S.A.B. de C.V.; *Int'l*, pg. 1399
CENDRILL SUPPLY PTY LIMITED—See Downer EDI Limited; *Int'l*, pg. 2185
CENTRAL POWER DISTRIBUTORS; *U.S. Private*, pg. 824
CENTRAL POWER SYSTEMS & SERVICES; *U.S. Private*, pg. 824
CENTRAL TUBE & BAR, INC.—See Olympic Steel Inc.; *U.S. Public*, pg. 1570
CENTRAL WELDING SUPPLY CO. INC.; *U.S. Private*, pg. 826
CENTRIFUGES UNLIMITED INC.—See GEA Group Aktiengesellschaft; *Int'l*, pg. 2898
CENTROMQTION—See Lone Star Funds; *U.S. Private*, pg. 2485
CENTURY TECHNOLOGY GROUP; *U.S. Private*, pg. 834
CERINNOV LIMITED—See Cerinnov Group SA; *Int'l*, pg. 1422
CERTEX DANMARK A/S—See Axel Johnson Gruppen AB; *Int'l*, pg. 763
CERTEX EESTI OU—See Axel Johnson Gruppen AB; *Int'l*, pg. 764
CERTEX FINLAND OY—See Axel Johnson Gruppen AB; *Int'l*, pg. 764
CERTEX LATVIJA SIA—See Axel Johnson Gruppen AB; *Int'l*, pg. 764
CERTEX LIETUVA UAB—See Axel Johnson Gruppen AB; *Int'l*, pg. 764
CERTEX LIFTING LTD—See Axel Johnson Gruppen AB; *Int'l*, pg. 764
CERTEX LIFTING & SERVICE GMBH—See Axel Johnson Gruppen AB; *Int'l*, pg. 764
CERTEX NORGE AS—See Axel Johnson Gruppen AB; *Int'l*, pg. 764
CERTEX SVENSKA AB—See Axel Johnson Gruppen AB; *Int'l*, pg. 764
CERTIFIED POWER INC.—See Brinkmere Capital Partners LLC; *U.S. Private*, pg. 655
CERTIFIED SLINGS, INC.; *U.S. Private*, pg. 842
CERVETTI RICAMBI SPA—See GB Ricambi S.p.A.; *Int'l*, pg. 2893
C.E. THURSTON & SONS DISTRIBUTING, LLC—See C.E. Thurston & Sons Incorporated; *U.S. Private*, pg. 706
CFE EQUIPMENT; *U.S. Private*, pg. 843
C.F.K. CNC-FERTIGUNGSTECHNIK KRIFTEL GMBH—See Gesco AG; *Int'l*, pg. 2945
CFS ASIA LTD.—See GEA Group Aktiengesellschaft; *Int'l*, pg. 2897
CFS CHILE COMERCIALIZADORA LIMITADA—See GEA Group Aktiengesellschaft; *Int'l*, pg. 2897
CGE CONTINENTAL GLASS ENGINEERING GMBH; *Int'l*, pg. 1430
CGR CORNELIO GHINASSI RICAMBI SPA—See GB Ricambi S.p.A.; *Int'l*, pg. 2893

CHAMPION MACHINE, LLC—See Dulany Industries Inc.; *U.S. Private*, pg. 1286
CHAMPION SCREW MACHINE ENGINEERING, INC.; *U.S. Private*, pg. 846
CHAMPIONS MACHINE TOOL SALES, INC.; *U.S. Private*, pg. 847
CHANGCHUN NOK-FREUDENBERG OILSEAL CO., LTD.—See Freudenberg SE; *Int'l*, pg. 2782
CHAR-GRILLER—See The Middleby Corporation; *U.S. Public*, pg. 2113
CHARMILLES MIKRON—See Georg Fischer AG; *Int'l*, pg. 2934
CHART AUSTRALIA PTY LTD.—See Chart Industries, Inc.; *U.S. Public*, pg. 481
CHART ENERGY AND CHEMICALS WUXI CO., LTD.—See Chart Industries, Inc.; *U.S. Public*, pg. 481
CHART FRANCE SAS—See Chart Industries, Inc.; *U.S. Public*, pg. 481
CHART ITALY S.R.L.—See Chart Industries, Inc.; *U.S. Public*, pg. 481
CHART JAPAN CO., LTD.—See Chart Industries, Inc.; *U.S. Public*, pg. 481
CHASM CONSULTING PTY. LTD.—See Enovis Corporation; *U.S. Public*, pg. 772
C&H DISTRIBUTORS, LLC—See Franz Haniel & Cie. GmbH; *Int'l*, pg. 2763
CHEETAH MEDICAL, INC.—See Baxter International Inc.; *U.S. Public*, pg. 281
CHEMITHON SURFACE FINISHING INC.—See Chemithon Enterprises, Inc.; *U.S. Private*, pg. 872
CHEN FULL INTERNATIONAL CO., LTD.; *Int'l*, pg. 1464
CHENGDU KDT MACHINERY CO., LTD—See Guangzhou KDT Machinery Co.,Ltd; *Int'l*, pg. 3166
CHERNOFF SALES INC.; *U.S. Private*, pg. 873
CHE SCIENTIFIC COMPANY (H.K.) LIMITED—See CHINO Corporation; *Int'l*, pg. 1570
CHEVALIER ITECH SERVICES LIMITED—See Chevalier International Holdings Limited; *Int'l*, pg. 1474
C.H. HOLDERBY CO.; *U.S. Private*, pg. 707
CHICAGO PRINTING COMPANY, INC.—See Johns-Byrne Co.; *U.S. Private*, pg. 2226
CHINA MACHINERY ENGINEERING ARGENTINA SA—See China Machinery Engineering Corporation; *Int'l*, pg. 1516
CHINA MACHINERY ENGINEERING CO., HUBEI LTD.—See China Machinery Engineering Corporation; *Int'l*, pg. 1516
CHINA MACHINERY & EQUIPMENT (HK) CO., LTD.—See China Machinery Engineering Corporation; *Int'l*, pg. 1516
CHINA MERCHANTS LOSCAM (ASIA PACIFIC) CO., LIMITED—See China Merchants Group Limited; *Int'l*, pg. 1521
CHINA NATIONAL UNITED EQUIPMENT GROUP CORP.—See China National Building Material Group Co., Ltd.; *Int'l*, pg. 1525
CHINO CORPORATION (THAILAND) LIMITED—See CHINO Corporation; *Int'l*, pg. 1570
CHINO WORKS AMERICA, INC.—See CHINO Corporation; *Int'l*, pg. 1570
CHOICE EQUIPOS Y SERVICIOS S.A.C—See Fluor Corporation; *U.S. Public*, pg. 857
CHOSUN WELDING JAPAN CO., LTD.—See CS HOLDINGS CO., LTD.; *Int'l*, pg. 1861
CHROMA ATE EUROPE B.V.—See Chroma ATE Inc.; *Int'l*, pg. 1587
CHROMA ATE INC.—See Chroma ATE Inc.; *Int'l*, pg. 1588
CHROMA ATE (SUZHOU) CO., LTD.—See Chroma ATE Inc.; *Int'l*, pg. 1587
CHROMA ELECTRONICS (SHANGHAI) CO., LTD.—See Chroma ATE Inc.; *Int'l*, pg. 1588
CHROMA ELECTRONICS (SHENZHEN) CO., LTD.—See Chroma ATE Inc.; *Int'l*, pg. 1588
CHROMA GERMANY GMBH—See Chroma ATE Inc.; *Int'l*, pg. 1587
CHROMA JAPAN CORP.—See Chroma ATE Inc.; *Int'l*, pg. 1588
CHROMA SYSTEMS SOLUTIONS, INC.—See Chroma ATE Inc.; *Int'l*, pg. 1588
C.H. SPENCER & COMPANY; *U.S. Private*, pg. 707
CIB CORPORATION; *U.S. Private*, pg. 896
CIMTAS BORULAMA SANAYI VE TICARET LTD. STI.—See Enka Insaat ve Sanayi A.S.; *Int'l*, pg. 2440
CIRCOR DOVIANUS HOLDINGS B.V.—See KKR & Co. Inc.; *U.S. Public*, pg. 1242
CIRRUS SERVICES LLC—See Beyond, Inc.; *U.S. Public*, pg. 327
CISCAR; *Int'l*, pg. 1618
CISCO AIR SYSTEMS, INC.—See DXP Enterprises, Inc.; *U.S. Public*, pg. 697
CISCO-EAGLE INCORPORATED—See Cisco-Eagle Inc.; *U.S. Private*, pg. 900
CISCO-EAGLE INC.; *U.S. Private*, pg. 900
CISCO-EAGLE INC.—See Cisco-Eagle Inc.; *U.S. Private*, pg. 900
CISCO FORD EQUIPMENT, INC.; *U.S. Private*, pg. 900
CISCO, INC.—See Morrison Industrial Equipment Company; *U.S. Private*, pg. 2789
THE C.I. THORNBURG CO., INC.; *U.S. Private*, pg. 4003

CITIC HEAVY INDUSTRIES CHILE SPA.—See CITIC Heavy Industries Co., Ltd.; *Int'l*, pg. 1621
CITIC-HEAVY INDUSTRIES CO., LTD.—See CITIC Heavy Industries Co., Ltd.; *Int'l*, pg. 1621
CITIC HEAVY INDUSTRIES SOUTH AFRICA PTY LTD.—See CITIC Heavy Industries Co., Ltd.; *Int'l*, pg. 1621
CITIC HIC AUSTRALIA PTY. LTD.—See CITIC Heavy Industries Co., Ltd.; *Int'l*, pg. 1621
CITIC SMCC PROCESS TECHNOLOGY PTY LTD.—See CITIC Heavy Industries Co., Ltd.; *Int'l*, pg. 1621
CITIZEN MACHINERY EUROPE GMBH—See Citizen Watch Co., Ltd.; *Int'l*, pg. 1624
CITIZEN SYSTEMS EUROPE GMBH—See Citizen Watch Co., Ltd.; *Int'l*, pg. 1624
CJSC DOOSAN INTERNATIONAL RUSSIA—See Doosan Corporation; *Int'l*, pg. 2172
C.K. INDUSTRIAL ENGINEERS LIMITED—See L3Harris Technologies, Inc.; *U.S. Public*, pg. 1281
CLAAS INDUSTRIETECHNIK GMBH—See Claas KGaA mbH; *Int'l*, pg. 1641
CLAAS RESEAU AGRICOLE S.A.S.—See Claas KGaA mbH; *Int'l*, pg. 1641
CLARKE POWER SERVICES, INC.; *U.S. Private*, pg. 914
CLEAN HARBORS SURFACE RENTALS PARTNERSHIP—See Clean Harbors, Inc.; *U.S. Public*, pg. 509
CLEANING TECHNOLOGIES GROUP, LLC—See Alpha Capital Partners, Ltd.; *U.S. Private*, pg. 197
CLEARY DEVELOPMENTS INC.; *U.S. Private*, pg. 939
CLEAVER-BROOKS SALES AND SERVICE, INC.—See Harbour Group Industries, Inc.; *U.S. Private*, pg. 1860
CLIPPARD EUROPE, S.A.—See Clippard Instrument Laboratory Inc.; *U.S. Private*, pg. 945
CLYDE BERGEMANN AFRICA (PTY) LTD—See Clyde Blowers Capital IM LLP; *Int'l*, pg. 1664
CLYDE BERGEMANN BEEKAY INDIA PRIVATE LIMITED—See Clyde Blowers Capital IM LLP; *Int'l*, pg. 1664
CLYDE BERGEMANN COLOMBIA S.A.S.—See Clyde Blowers Capital IM LLP; *Int'l*, pg. 1665
CLYDE BERGEMANN CONTROLS PVT. LTD—See Clyde Blowers Capital IM LLP; *Int'l*, pg. 1665
CLYDE BERGEMANN DO BRASIL LTDA.—See Clyde Blowers Capital IM LLP; *Int'l*, pg. 1665
CLYDE BERGEMANN ENERGY & ENVIRONMENTAL TECHNOLOGY (BEIJING) CO., LTD.—See Clyde Blowers Capital IM LLP; *Int'l*, pg. 1665
CLYDE BERGEMANN EP TECH S.R.L.—See Clyde Blowers Capital IM LLP; *Int'l*, pg. 1665
CLYDE BERGEMANN HUATONG MATERIALS HANDLING CO., LTD.—See Clyde Blowers Capital IM LLP; *Int'l*, pg. 1665
CLYDE BERGEMANN SCANDINAVIA OY—See Clyde Blowers Capital IM LLP; *Int'l*, pg. 1665
CLYDE BERGEMANN TERMOTEC GMBH—See Clyde Blowers Capital IM LLP; *Int'l*, pg. 1665
CLYDE BERGEMANN TR ENERJI SERVIS A. S.—See Clyde Blowers Capital IM LLP; *Int'l*, pg. 1665
CLYDE UNION DB LIMITED—See Lone Star Funds; *U.S. Private*, pg. 2485
CLYDE UNION MIDDLE EAST LLC.—See Lone Star Funds; *U.S. Private*, pg. 2485
CLYDE UNION PUMPS MIDDLE EAST FZE—See Lone Star Funds; *U.S. Private*, pg. 2485
C&M CONVEYOR INC—See CapitalWorks, LLC; *U.S. Private*, pg. 742
CNC SYSTEMS INC.; *U.S. Private*, pg. 952
COASTAL WELDING SUPPLY INC.; *U.S. Private*, pg. 957
COAST CRANE OF UTAH INC.—See Giuffre Bros Cranes, Inc.; *U.S. Private*, pg. 1703
COESIA HEALTH & BEAUTY INC.—See Coesia S.p.A.; *Int'l*, pg. 1689
COESIA INDIA PRIVATE LTD.—See Coesia S.p.A.; *Int'l*, pg. 1689
COGENT, INC.; *U.S. Private*, pg. 962
COGNEX POLAND Z.O.O—See Cognex Corporation; *U.S. Public*, pg. 523
COGNEX VIETNAM COMPANY LTD.—See Cognex Corporation; *U.S. Public*, pg. 523
COLEMAN INSTRUMENT COMPANY; *U.S. Private*, pg. 967
THE COLMAN GROUP INC.—See The Jordan Company, L.P.; *U.S. Private*, pg. 4060
COLTEC DO BRASIL PRODUCTOS INDUSTRIAIS LTDA.—See Enpro Inc.; *U.S. Public*, pg. 774
COLUMBIA SPECIALTY COMPANY, INC.; *U.S. Private*, pg. 977
COLUMBUS MCKINNON ASIA PACIFIC LTD.—See Columbus McKinnon Corporation; *U.S. Public*, pg. 535
COLUMBUS MCKINNON ASIA PACIFIC PTE. LTD.—See Columbus McKinnon Corporation; *U.S. Public*, pg. 535
COLUMBUS MCKINNON AUSTRIA GMBH—See Columbus McKinnon Corporation; *U.S. Public*, pg. 535
COLUMBUS MCKINNON CORPORATION LTD.—See Columbus McKinnon Corporation; *U.S. Public*, pg. 535
COLUMBUS MCKINNON (HANGZHOU) INDUSTRIES CO. LTD.—See Columbus McKinnon Corporation; *U.S. Public*, pg. 535

423830 — INDUSTRIAL MACHINER...

COLUMBUS MCKINNON IBERICA S.L.U.—See Columbus McKinnon Corporation; *U.S. Public*, pg. 536
COLUMBUS MCKINNON IRELAND, LTD.—See Columbus McKinnon Corporation; *U.S. Public*, pg. 536
COLUMBUS MCKINNON ITALIA S.R.L.—See Columbus McKinnon Corporation; *U.S. Public*, pg. 536
COLUMBUS MCKINNON RUSSIA LLC—See Columbus McKinnon Corporation; *U.S. Public*, pg. 536
COLUMBUS MCKINNON SWITZERLAND AG—See Columbus McKinnon Corporation; *U.S. Public*, pg. 536
CO.MA.DI.S. S.P.A.—See I.M.A. Industria Macchine Automatiche S.p.A.; *Int'l*, pg. 3565
COMAP NORDIC AB—See Aalberts N.V.; *Int'l*, pg. 33
COMERCIALIZADORA EMERSON NETWORK POWER CHILE LIMITADA—See Emerson Electric Co.; *U.S. Public*, pg. 744
COMINGERSOLL-COMERCIO E INDUSTRIA DE EQUIPAMENTOS S.A.—See Ingersoll Rand Inc.; *U.S. Public*, pg. 1118
COMINIX CO., LTD.; *Int'l*, pg. 1713
COMPAGNIE HOBART S.A.S.—See Illinois Tool Works Inc.; *U.S. Public*, pg. 1102
COMPAIR GMBH—See Ingersoll Rand Inc.; *U.S. Public*, pg. 1119
COMPLETE ENVIRONMENTAL PRODUCTS, INC.; *U.S. Private*, pg. 1000
COMPLETE SUPPLY, INC.—See Beacon Roofing Supply, Inc.; *U.S. Public*, pg. 285
COMPRESSED AIR SYSTEMS, INC.—See Atlas Copco AB; *Int'l*, pg. 681
COMPRESSED AIR TECHNOLOGIES, INC.—See Atlas Copco AB; *Int'l*, pg. 681
COMPRESSION SERVICES DE MEXICO, S.A. DE C.V.—See Enerflex Ltd.; *Int'l*, pg. 2418
COMPRESSOR PRODUCTS INTERNATIONAL COLOMBIA S.A.S.—See Enpro Inc.; *U.S. Public*, pg. 774
COMPTECH CORPORATION; *U.S. Private*, pg. 1003
CONCEPT MACHINE TOOL SALES, LLC; *U.S. Private*, pg. 1008
THE CONDIT COMPANY INC.—See Industrial Distribution Resources, LLC; *U.S. Private*, pg. 2065
CONSEW CONSOLIDATED SEWING MACHINE CORP.—See Consew; *U.S. Private*, pg. 1019
CONSEW; *U.S. Private*, pg. 1019
CONSOLIDATED DIESEL, INC.—See Cummins Inc.; *U.S. Public*, pg. 605
CONSTRUCTION EQUIPMENT PARTS INC.—See Ed Bell Investments Company Inc.; *U.S. Private*, pg. 1331
CONTAINER SYSTEMS INC.; *U.S. Private*, pg. 1027
CONTIGEA SA—See Itron, Inc.; *U.S. Public*, pg. 1175
CONTINENTAL ENGINES, INC.—See Palmer Johnson Enterprises, Inc.; *U.S. Private*, pg. 3081
CONTRAST EQUIPMENT, INC.—See Genstar Capital, LLC; *U.S. Private*, pg. 1678
CONTROL4 EMEA LTD—See Resideo Technologies, Inc.; *U.S. Public*, pg. 1790
CONTROLES INDUSTRIELS DE L'ENTANG—See Mistras Group, Inc.; *U.S. Public*, pg. 1451
CONTROLS FOR MOTION AUTOMATION INC.; *U.S. Private*, pg. 1035
CONTROL SOUTHERN INC.; *U.S. Private*, pg. 1034
CONTROL SUPPLY CORP.; *U.S. Private*, pg. 1034
CONVEYCO TECHNOLOGIES INC.; *U.S. Private*, pg. 1036
CONVEYOR HANDLING COMPANY, INC.; *U.S. Private*, pg. 1036
CONVEYORS & MATERIALS HANDLING INC.; *U.S. Private*, pg. 1036
CONVUM KOREA CO., LTD.—See Convum Ltd.; *Int'l*, pg. 1788
CONVUM (THAILAND) CO., LTD.—See Convum Ltd.; *Int'l*, pg. 1787
CONVUM USA, INC.—See Convum Ltd.; *Int'l*, pg. 1787
COOPER CROUSE-HINDS JAPAN KK—See Eaton Corporation plc; *Int'l*, pg. 2278
COOPER TOOLS SAS—See Bain Capital, LP; *U.S. Private*, pg. 430
COPERION K-TRON (SHANGHAI) CO. LTD.—See Hillenbrand, Inc.; *U.S. Public*, pg. 1036
CORNELIUS AUSTRALIA PTY. LTD.—See Berkshire Hathaway Inc.; *U.S. Public*, pg. 309
CORROSION FLUID PRODUCTS CORP.; *U.S. Private*, pg. 1059
CORROSION SPECIALTIES, LLC—See Ridgemont Partners Management LLC; *U.S. Private*, pg. 3432
CORTECH ENGINEERING, INC.—See DXP Enterprises, Inc.; *U.S. Public*, pg. 697
CORTECO CHINA CO. LTD.—See Freudenberg SE; *Int'l*, pg. 2782
COSALT BALLYCLARE LIMITED—See Cosalt plc; *Int'l*, pg. 1809
COSMOS MACHINERY ENTERPRISES LIMITED; *Int'l*, pg. 1813
COSMOS MACHINERY INTERNATIONAL LTD.—See Cosmos Machinery Enterprises Limited; *Int'l*, pg. 1813
COSTA LEAL EL VICTOR ELECTRONICA-PNEUMATICA, LDA.; *Int'l*, pg. 1814
COZZINI DO BRASIL LTDA—See The Middleby Corporation; *U.S. Public*, pg. 2113

CRAFT EQUIPMENT COMPANY; *U.S. Private*, pg. 1081
CRAIGCOR DISTRIBUTION CO (PTY) LTD—See ARB HOLDINGS LIMITED; *Int'l*, pg. 536
CRANE (ASIA PACIFIC) PTE. LTD.—See Crane NXT, Co.; *U.S. Public*, pg. 590
CRANE AUSTRALIA PTY. LTD.—See Crane NXT, Co.; *U.S. Public*, pg. 590
CRANE DISTRIBUTION PROPERTIES LIMITED—See Fletcher Building Limited; *Int'l*, pg. 2699
CRANE ENGINEERING SALES, LLC—See AEA Investors LP; *U.S. Private*, pg. 113
CRANE HOLDINGS (GERMANY) GMBH—See Crane NXT, Co.; *U.S. Public*, pg. 590
CRANE NUCLEAR, INC.—See Crane NXT, Co.; *U.S. Public*, pg. 589
CRANE PROCESS FLOW TECHNOLOGIES S.P.R.L.—See Crane NXT, Co.; *U.S. Public*, pg. 590
CRANE PROCESS FLOW TECHNOLOGIES S.R.L.—See Crane NXT, Co.; *U.S. Public*, pg. 591
CRANE RESISTOFLEX GMBH—See Crane NXT, Co.; *U.S. Public*, pg. 591
CRELLIN HANDLING EQUIPMENT INC; *U.S. Private*, pg. 1092
CRIGLER ENTERPRISES, INC.; *U.S. Private*, pg. 1100
CROMWELL CZECH REPUBLIC S.R.O.—See W.W. Grainger, Inc.; *U.S. Public*, pg. 2319
CROMWELL GROUP (INTERNATIONAL) LIMITED—See W.W. Grainger, Inc.; *U.S. Public*, pg. 2319
CROMWELL PTY LIMITED—See W.W. Grainger, Inc.; *U.S. Public*, pg. 2319
CROMWELL SP Z.O.O—See W.W. Grainger, Inc.; *U.S. Public*, pg. 2319
CROMWELL TOOLS LTD.—See W.W. Grainger, Inc.; *U.S. Public*, pg. 2319
CROMWELL TOOLS, PT—See W.W. Grainger, Inc.; *U.S. Public*, pg. 2319
CROMWELL TOOLS SDN. BHD.—See W.W. Grainger, Inc.; *U.S. Public*, pg. 2319
CROMWELL TOOLS (SHANGHAI) CO. LTD.—See W.W. Grainger, Inc.; *U.S. Public*, pg. 2319
CROMWELL TOOLS (THAILAND) CO. LTD.—See W.W. Grainger, Inc.; *U.S. Public*, pg. 2319
CROSS COMPANY; *U.S. Private*, pg. 1104
CROWN EQUIPMENT PTY LTD—See Crown Equipment Corporation; *U.S. Private*, pg. 1111
CROWN GABELSTAPLER GMBH & CO. KG—See Crown Equipment Corporation; *U.S. Private*, pg. 1111
CROWN LIFTERS LTD.; *Int'l*, pg. 1857
CROWN LIFT TRUCKS—See Crown Equipment Corporation; *U.S. Private*, pg. 1111
CRUSHING EQUIPMENT SOLUTIONS, LLC; *U.S. Private*, pg. 1104
CS MACROLITE—See CS CORPORATION; *Int'l*, pg. 1861
CULLUM & BROWN INC.; *U.S. Private*, pg. 1121
CUMMINS AMERICAS, INC.—See Cummins Inc.; *U.S. Public*, pg. 605
CUMMINS ATLANTIC LLC—See Cummins Inc.; *U.S. Public*, pg. 605
CUMMINS BRIDGEWAY COLUMBUS, LLC—See Cummins Inc.; *U.S. Public*, pg. 605
CUMMINS BRIDGEWAY GROVE CITY, LLC—See Cummins Inc.; *U.S. Public*, pg. 605
CUMMINS BRIDGEWAY TOLEDO, LLC—See Cummins Inc.; *U.S. Public*, pg. 605
CUMMINS CANADA LIMITED—See Cummins Inc.; *U.S. Public*, pg. 605
CUMMINS CENTRAL POWER—See Cummins Inc.; *U.S. Public*, pg. 605
CUMMINS CROSSPOINT—See Cummins Inc.; *U.S. Public*, pg. 605
CUMMINS DIESEL SALES CORPORATION—See Cummins Inc.; *U.S. Public*, pg. 605
CUMMINS FILTRATION GMBH—See Cummins Inc.; *U.S. Public*, pg. 606
CUMMINS GHANA LIMITED—See Cummins Inc.; *U.S. Public*, pg. 606
CUMMINS NORWAY AS—See Cummins Inc.; *U.S. Public*, pg. 606
CUMMINS NPOWER LLC—See Cummins Inc.; *U.S. Public*, pg. 606
CUMMINS POWER GENERATION (S) PTE. LTD.—See Cummins Inc.; *U.S. Public*, pg. 606
CUMMINS ROCKY MOUNTAIN LLC—See Cummins Inc.; *U.S. Public*, pg. 607
CUMMINS SALES AND SERVICE PHILIPPINES INC.—See Cummins Inc.; *U.S. Public*, pg. 607
CUMMINS SOUTHEASTERN POWER, INC.—See Cummins Inc.; *U.S. Public*, pg. 607
CUMMINS SOUTH INC.—See Cummins Inc.; *U.S. Public*, pg. 607
CUMMINS U.K. PENSION PLAN TRUSTEE LTD.—See Cummins Inc.; *U.S. Public*, pg. 607
CUMMINS-WAGNER CO., INC.; *U.S. Public*, pg. 1123
CUMMINS WEST AFRICA LIMITED—See Cummins Inc.; *U.S. Public*, pg. 607
CURLIN, INC.—See Southfield Capital Advisors, LLC; *U.S. Private*, pg. 3736
CUSTOM BILT METALS; *U.S. Private*, pg. 1128

CW ADVANCED TECHNOLOGIES PTE. LTD.—See CW Group Holdings Limited; *Int'l*, pg. 1890
CW GROUP PTE. LTD.—See CW Group Holdings Limited; *Int'l*, pg. 1890
C.W. ROD TOOL CO., INC.—See DXP Enterprises, Inc.; *U.S. Public*, pg. 697
D.A. CRISWELL SALES INC.—See VanZandt Controls, LLC; *U.S. Private*, pg. 4345
DAE RYUK INTERNATIONAL INC—See Daeryuk Can Co., Ltd.; *Int'l*, pg. 1908
DAH BANG PRINTING INK MANUFACTORY LIMITED—See Golik Holdings Limited; *Int'l*, pg. 3036
DAH CHONG HONG INDUSTRIAL MACHINERY CO., LTD.—See Honda Motor Co., Ltd.; *Int'l*, pg. 3460
DAIDO INDIA PVT. LTD.—See Daido Kogyo Co., Ltd.; *Int'l*, pg. 1920
DAIFUKU INTRALOGISTICS VIETNAM CO., LTD.—See Daifuku Co., Ltd.; *Int'l*, pg. 1925
DAIFUKU OCEANIA LIMITED—See Daifuku Co., Ltd.; *Int'l*, pg. 1925
DAIFUKU PLUSMORE CO., LTD.—See Daifuku Co., Ltd.; *Int'l*, pg. 1925
DAIHEN KOREA CO., LTD.—See Daihen Corporation; *Int'l*, pg. 1926
DAIICHI JITSUGYO (AMERICA), INC.—See Daiichi Jitsugyo Co. Ltd.; *Int'l*, pg. 1927
DAIICHI JITSUGYO ASIA PTE LTD—See Daiichi Jitsugyo Co. Ltd.; *Int'l*, pg. 1927
DAIICHI JITSUGYO CO. LTD.; *Int'l*, pg. 1927
DAIICHI JITSUGYO DO BRASIL COMERCIO DE MAQUINAS LTDA—See Daiichi Jitsugyo Co. Ltd.; *Int'l*, pg. 1927
DAIICHI JITSUGYO (GUANGZHOU), TRADING CO., LTD.—See Daiichi Jitsugyo Co. Ltd.; *Int'l*, pg. 1927
DAIICHI JITSUGYO (HONG KONG), LIMITED—See Daiichi Jitsugyo Co. Ltd.; *Int'l*, pg. 1927
DAIICHI JITSUGYO INDIA PVT. LTD.—See Daiichi Jitsugyo Co. Ltd.; *Int'l*, pg. 1927
DAI-ICHI JITSUGYO (MALAYSIA) SDN. BHD.—See Daiichi Jitsugyo Co. Ltd.; *Int'l*, pg. 1927
DAIICHI JITSUGYO PHILIPPINES, INC.—See Daiichi Jitsugyo Co. Ltd.; *Int'l*, pg. 1927
DAIICHI JITSUGYO PUERTO RICO, INC—See Daiichi Jitsugyo Co. Ltd.; *Int'l*, pg. 1927
DAIICHI JITSUGYO (VIETNAM) CO., LTD.—See Daiichi Jitsugyo Co. Ltd.; *Int'l*, pg. 1927
DAIKI AXIS INDIA PVT. LTD.—See Daiki Axis Co., Ltd.; *Int'l*, pg. 1932
DAIKI AXIS SINGAPORE PTE. LTD.—See Daiki Axis Co., Ltd.; *Int'l*, pg. 1932
DA INVENT CO., LTD.—See Daiki Axis Co., Ltd.; *Int'l*, pg. 1932
DAKE CORPORATION—See JSJ Corporation; *U.S. Private*, pg. 2241
DALE L PRENTICE CO.; *U.S. Private*, pg. 1148
DANA (DEUTSCHLAND) GRUNDSTUCKVERWALTUNGS GMBH—See Dana Incorporated; *U.S. Public*, pg. 622
DANAHER MOTION—See Danaher Corporation; *U.S. Public*, pg. 626
DANA SAC CANADA LIMITED—See Dana Incorporated; *U.S. Public*, pg. 622
DANA SAC GERMANY GMBH—See Dana Incorporated; *U.S. Public*, pg. 622
DANA SAC KOREA CO., LTD.—See Dana Incorporated; *U.S. Public*, pg. 622
DANA SAC NEW ZEALAND LIMITED—See Dana Incorporated; *U.S. Public*, pg. 622
DANA SAC S.E. ASIA PTE. LTD.—See Dana Incorporated; *U.S. Public*, pg. 622
DANA SAC TURKEY REDUKTOR SANAYI VE TICARET LIMITED SIRKETI—See Dana Incorporated; *U.S. Public*, pg. 622
DANA STRUCTURAL PRODUCTS, LLC—See Dana Incorporated; *U.S. Public*, pg. 623
DANFOSS INDUSTRIES, SA DE CV—See Danfoss A/S; *Int'l*, pg. 1960
DANFOSS POWER SOLUTIONS PTE. LTD.—See Danfoss A/S; *Int'l*, pg. 1960
DANIEL INDUSTRIES CANADA INC.—See Emerson Electric Co.; *U.S. Public*, pg. 746
DANIEL MEASUREMENT CONTROL—See Emerson Electric Co.; *U.S. Public*, pg. 746
DANMAR INDUSTRIES, INC.; *U.S. Private*, pg. 1157
DAS SERVICES, INC.—See Convum Ltd.; *Int'l*, pg. 1788
DATA PHYSICS (BHARAT/ INDIA) PVT. LTD.—See Battery Ventures, L.P.; *U.S. Private*, pg. 488
DATA PHYSICS (DEUTSCHLAND/ GERMANY) GMBH—See Battery Ventures, L.P.; *U.S. Private*, pg. 488
DATA PHYSICS (FRANCE) S.A.—See Battery Ventures, L.P.; *U.S. Private*, pg. 488
DATA PHYSICS (UK) LTD.—See Battery Ventures, L.P.; *U.S. Private*, pg. 488
DATARAN TENAGA (M) SDN. BHD.—See CITIC Group Corporation; *Int'l*, pg. 1620
DATA-STITCH INC.; *U.S. Private*, pg. 1164
DATRON AUSTRIA GMBH—See Datron AG; *Int'l*, pg. 1982
DAVIS H. ELLIOT COMPANY INC.; *U.S. Private*, pg. 1173

423830 — INDUSTRIAL MACHINER...

DAWSON & ASSOCIATES, INC.—See HS Holdings, LLC; *U.S. Private*, pg. 1998
DC KATSUYA CO., LTD.—See DIC Corporation; *Int'l*, pg. 2107
DD POWER HOLDINGS (PTY) LIMITED—See Hudaco Industries Limited; *Int'l*, pg. 3521
DECCO INC.—See Comfort Systems USA, Inc.; *U.S. Public*, pg. 543
DECO TOOL SUPPLY COMPANY—See MSC Industrial Direct Co., Inc.; *U.S. Public*, pg. 1483
DE DIETRICH DO BRASIL LTDA—See De Dietrich Process Systems S.A.; *Int'l*, pg. 1995
DE DIETRICH EQUIPOS QUIMICOS SL—See De Dietrich Process Systems S.A.; *Int'l*, pg. 1995
DEEP SOUTH EQUIPMENT COMPANY; *U.S. Private*, pg. 1189
DELACHAUX METAL INC.—See CVC Capital Partners SICAV-FIS S.A.; *Int'l*, pg. 1887
DELTA MATERIALS HANDLING INC.; *U.S. Private*, pg. 1201
DELTA PROCESS EQUIPMENT INC.—See DXP Enterprises, Inc.; *U.S. Public*, pg. 697
DENYO KOSAN CO., LTD.—See Denyo Co., Ltd.; *Int'l*, pg. 2040
DENYO UNITED MACHINERY PTE LTD.—See Denyo Co., Ltd.; *Int'l*, pg. 2040
DEREK LANE & CO LIMITED—See Flowtech Fluidpower plc; *Int'l*, pg. 2709
DESCOURS & CABAUD ILE-DE-F—See Descours & Cabaud SA; *Int'l*, pg. 2044
DESCOURS & CABAUD SAVOIE—See Descours & Cabaud SA; *Int'l*, pg. 2044
DESIGN MACHINING UNLIMITED INC.—See Appulse Corporation; *Int'l*, pg. 522
DESMET ROSEDOWNS LTD.—See Alfa Laval AB; *Int'l*, pg. 312
DET LOGISTICS (USA) CORPORATION—See Delta Electronics, Inc.; *Int'l*, pg. 2018
DEUTZ CORPORATION—See DEUTZ AG; *Int'l*, pg. 2086
DEUTZ CS S.R.O.—See DEUTZ AG; *Int'l*, pg. 2086
DEVILBISS RANSBURG DE MEXICO, S. DE R.L. DE C.V.—See Carlisle Companies Incorporated; *U.S. Public*, pg. 436
D&F DISTRIBUTORS INC.—See DXP Enterprises, Inc.; *U.S. Public*, pg. 697
D-FLOW TECHNOLOGY, AB—See Badger Meter, Inc.; *U.S. Public*, pg. 263
DHK SOLUTION CORPORATION—See Disco Corporation; *Int'l*, pg. 2131
DIBERT VALVE & FITTING CO. INC.; *U.S. Private*, pg. 1225
DID EUROPE S.R.L.—See Daido Kogyo Co., Ltd.; *Int'l*, pg. 1920
DIEFFENBACHER ASIA PACIFIC SDN. BHD.—See Dieffenbacher Holding GmbH & Co. KG; *Int'l*, pg. 2114
DIEFFENBACHER AUSTRALASIA PTY. LTD.—See Dieffenbacher Holding GmbH & Co. KG; *Int'l*, pg. 2114
DIEFFENBACHER CUSTOMER SUPPORT, LLC—See Dieffenbacher Holding GmbH & Co. KG; *Int'l*, pg. 2114
DIEFFENBACHER DO BRASIL CONSTRUCAO DE MAQUINAS E INSTALACOES LTDA.—See Dieffenbacher Holding GmbH & Co. KG; *Int'l*, pg. 2114
DIEFFENBACHER INDIA PVT. LTD.—See Dieffenbacher Holding GmbH & Co. KG; *Int'l*, pg. 2114
DIEFFENBACHER MACHINERY (CHANGZHOU) CO., LTD.—See Dieffenbacher Holding GmbH & Co. KG; *Int'l*, pg. 2114
DIEFFENBACHER MACHINERY SERVICES (BEIJING) CO., LTD.—See Dieffenbacher Holding GmbH & Co. KG; *Int'l*, pg. 2114
DIEFFENBACHER PANELBOARD OY—See Dieffenbacher Holding GmbH & Co. KG; *Int'l*, pg. 2114
DIEFFENBACHER USA, INC.—See Dieffenbacher Holding GmbH & Co. KG; *Int'l*, pg. 2114
DIEHL GAS METERING GMBH—See Diehl Stiftung & Co. KG; *Int'l*, pg. 2114
DIEHL METERING APS—See Diehl Stiftung & Co. KG; *Int'l*, pg. 2115
DIEHL METERING FZE—See Diehl Stiftung & Co. KG; *Int'l*, pg. 2115
DIEHL METERING GESMBH—See Diehl Stiftung & Co. KG; *Int'l*, pg. 2115
DIEHL METERING (JINAN) CO. LTD.—See Diehl Stiftung & Co. KG; *Int'l*, pg. 2115
DIEHL METERING LIMITED—See Diehl Stiftung & Co. KG; *Int'l*, pg. 2115
DIEHL METERING S.A.S.—See Diehl Stiftung & Co. KG; *Int'l*, pg. 2115
DIEHL METERING SP. Z O.O.—See Diehl Stiftung & Co. KG; *Int'l*, pg. 2115
DIEHL METERING S.R.L.—See Diehl Stiftung & Co. KG; *Int'l*, pg. 2115
DIEHL METERING SYSTEMS GMBH—See Diehl Stiftung & Co. KG; *Int'l*, pg. 2115
DIESEL INJECTION SERVICE CO., INC.; *U.S. Private*, pg. 1228
DIESEL MOTOR NORDIC AB—See DEUTZ AG; *Int'l*, pg. 2086

DIESEL MOTOR NORDIC A/S—See DEUTZ AG; *Int'l*, pg. 2086
DIESEL POWER EQUIPMENT COMPANY INCORPORATED; *U.S. Private*, pg. 1229
DIETZEL UNIVOLT DEUTSCHLAND GMBH—See Dietzel GmbH; *Int'l*, pg. 2117
DIJET INCORPORATED—See DIJET Industrial Co., Ltd; *Int'l*, pg. 2125
DILLON SUPPLY COMPANY—See Descours & Cabaud SA; *Int'l*, pg. 2044
DIRINGER S.A.—See Iep Invest SA; *Int'l*, pg. 3597
DISCO HI-TEC AMERICA, INC.—See Disco Corporation; *Int'l*, pg. 2132
DISCO HI-TEC CHINA CO., LTD.—See Disco Corporation; *Int'l*, pg. 2131
DISCO HI-TEC EUROPE GMBH—See Disco Corporation; *Int'l*, pg. 2132
DISCO HI-TEC FRANCE SARL—See Disco Corporation; *Int'l*, pg. 2132
DISCO HI-TEC KOREA CORPORATION—See Disco Corporation; *Int'l*, pg. 2132
DISCO HI-TEC PHILIPPINES, INC.—See Disco Corporation; *Int'l*, pg. 2132
DISCO HI-TEC (SINGAPORE) PTE. LTD.—See Disco Corporation; *Int'l*, pg. 2132
DISCO HI-TEC TAIWAN CO., LTD.—See Disco Corporation; *Int'l*, pg. 2132
DISCO HI-TEC UK LTD.—See Disco Corporation; *Int'l*, pg. 2132
DISENOS CONSTRUCCIONES Y FABRICACIONES HISPANOAMERICANAS, S.A.—See Applied Industrial Technologies, Inc.; *U.S. Public*, pg. 171
DISTEFANO TECHNOLOGY & MANUFACTURING—See Behlen Mfg. Co.; *U.S. Private*, pg. 515
DISTRIBUIDORA CUMMINS S.A. SUCURSAL BOLIVIA—See Cummins Inc.; *U.S. Public*, pg. 607
DISTRIBUTIONS JRV INC. - LIFTING DIVISION—See Distributions JRV Inc.; *Int'l*, pg. 2137
DITCH WITCH OF SOUTH TEXAS—See Bluestem Equity, LLC; *U.S. Private*, pg. 598
DITCH WITCH SALES INC.; *U.S. Private*, pg. 1240
DIVERSIFIED AIR SYSTEMS INC.; *U.S. Private*, pg. 1241
DIVERSIFIED DYNAMICS CORPORATION; *U.S. Private*, pg. 1242
DIXON GROUP CANADA LIMITED—See Dixon Valve & Coupling Company; *U.S. Private*, pg. 1246
DIXON VALVE & COUPLING COMPANY - DIXON QUICK COUPLING DIVISION—See Dixon Valve & Coupling Company; *U.S. Private*, pg. 1246
DJK GLOBAL MEXICO, S.A. DE C.V.—See Daiichi Jitsugyo Co. Ltd.; *Int'l*, pg. 1927
DJK (TAIWAN) CORP.—See Daiichi Jitsugyo Co. Ltd.; *Int'l*, pg. 1927
DKK-TOA ALICE CORPORATION—See DKK-TOA Corporation; *Int'l*, pg. 2139
DKK-TOA ANALYTICA CORPORATION—See DKK-TOA Corporation; *Int'l*, pg. 2139
DKK-TOA IWATE CORPORATION—See DKK-TOA Corporation; *Int'l*, pg. 2139
D.L. THURROTT INC.—See INSCO, Inc.; *U.S. Private*, pg. 2085
DME OF CANADA, LTD.—See Hillenbrand, Inc.; *U.S. Public*, pg. 1037
DMG MORI AUSTRIA GMBH—See DMG MORI Co., Ltd.; *Int'l*, pg. 2143
DMG MORI BIELEFELD GMBH—See DMG MORI Co., Ltd.; *Int'l*, pg. 2143
DMG MORI BRASIL—See DMG MORI Co., Ltd.; *Int'l*, pg. 2143
DMG MORI CZECH, S.R.O.—See DMG MORI Co., Ltd.; *Int'l*, pg. 2143
DMG MORI DENMARK APS—See DMG MORI Co., Ltd.; *Int'l*, pg. 2143
DMG MORI ELLISON TECHNOLOGIES—See Ellison Technologies Inc.; *U.S. Private*, pg. 1374
DMG MORI FRANCE - HAUTE-SAVOIE—See DMG MORI Co., Ltd.; *Int'l*, pg. 2144
DMG MORI FRANCE S.A.S.—See DMG MORI Co., Ltd.; *Int'l*, pg. 2143
DMG MORI FRANKFURT GMBH—See DMG MORI Co., Ltd.; *Int'l*, pg. 2143
DMG MORI GIOBAL MARKETING GMBH—See DMG MORI Co., Ltd.; *Int'l*, pg. 2144
DMG MORI HILDEN GMBH—See DMG MORI Co., Ltd.; *Int'l*, pg. 2143
DMG MORI HUNGARY KFT.—See DMG MORI Co., Ltd.; *Int'l*, pg. 2144
DMG MORI IBERICA S.L.U.—See DMG MORI Co., Ltd.; *Int'l*, pg. 2144
DMG MORI INDIA PVT. LTD.—See DMG MORI Co., Ltd.; *Int'l*, pg. 2144
DMG MORI ISTANBUL MAKINE TICARET VE SERVIS LIMITED SIRKETI—See DMG MORI Co., Ltd.; *Int'l*, pg. 2144
DMG MORI ITALIA S.R.L.—See DMG MORI Co., Ltd.; *Int'l*, pg. 2144
DMG MORI KOREA CO., LTD.—See DMG MORI Co., Ltd.; *Int'l*, pg. 2144

DMG MORI MIDDLE EAST FZE—See DMG MORI Co., Ltd.; *Int'l*, pg. 2144
DMG MORI MUNCHEN GMBH—See DMG MORI Co., Ltd.; *Int'l*, pg. 2143
DMG MORI NETHERLANDS B.V.—See DMG MORI Co., Ltd.; *Int'l*, pg. 2144
DMG MORI POLSKA SP. Z O.O.—See DMG MORI Co., Ltd.; *Int'l*, pg. 2144
DMG MORI SEIKI CANADA INC.—See DMG MORI Co., Ltd.; *Int'l*, pg. 2144
DMG MORI SINGAPORE PTE. LTD.—See DMG MORI Co., Ltd.; *Int'l*, pg. 2145
DMG MORI SOFTWARE SOLUTIONS GMBH—See DMG MORI Co., Ltd.; *Int'l*, pg. 2144
DMG MORI TAIWAN CO. LTD.—See DMG MORI Co., Ltd.; *Int'l*, pg. 2145
DMG MORI UK LIMITED—See DMG MORI Co., Ltd.; *Int'l*, pg. 2144
DMG MORI USED MACHINES GMBH—See DMG MORI Co., Ltd.; *Int'l*, pg. 2144
DMG VERTRIEBS UND SERVICE GMBH DECKEL MAHO GILDEMEISTER—See DMG MORI Co., Ltd.; *Int'l*, pg. 2143
DMW CORPORATION - HOUSTON BRANCH—See DMW Corporation; *Int'l*, pg. 2147
DMW CORPORATION INDIA PRIVATE LIMITED—See DMW Corporation; *Int'l*, pg. 2147
DNOW CANADA ULC—See DNOW Inc.; *U.S. Public*, pg. 671
DNOW DE MEXICO S DE RL DE CV—See DNOW Inc.; *U.S. Public*, pg. 671
DNP AMERICA, LLC—See Dai Nippon Printing Co., Ltd.; *Int'l*, pg. 1914
DNP ID SYSTEM CO., LTD.—See Dai Nippon Printing Co., Ltd.; *Int'l*, pg. 1914
DOGA CZ S.R.O.—See Doga; *Int'l*, pg. 2154
DOGA FZ—See Doga; *Int'l*, pg. 2154
DOGA INDUSTRIES—See Doga; *Int'l*, pg. 2154
DOGA; *Int'l*, pg. 2154
DOIG CORPORATION; *U.S. Private*, pg. 1254
DOMINION AIR & MACHINERY CO.; *U.S. Private*, pg. 1256
DOMINION CAROLINA SALES INC.; *U.S. Private*, pg. 1256
DOMINO HIGHVOLTAGE SUPPLY INC.—See Quanta Services, Inc.; *U.S. Public*, pg. 1751
DOMINO KOREA LIMITED—See Brother Industries, Ltd.; *Int'l*, pg. 1197
DOMINO NORTH AMERICA—See Brother Industries, Ltd.; *Int'l*, pg. 1197
DOMINO PRINTECH INDIA LLP—See Brother Industries, Ltd.; *Int'l*, pg. 1197
DOMINO PRINTING MEXICO SA DE CV—See Brother Industries, Ltd.; *Int'l*, pg. 1197
DOMINO PRINTING SOLUTIONS INC.—See Brother Industries, Ltd.; *Int'l*, pg. 1197
DONALDSON (CHINA) TRADING CO., LTD—See Donaldson Company, Inc.; *U.S. Public*, pg. 675
DONGGUAN HEITKAMP & THUMANN METAL PRODUCTS LTD.—See Heitkamp & Thumann KG; *Int'l*, pg. 3326
DOOSAN ELECTRO-MATERIALS AMERICA, LLC—See Doosan Corporation; *Int'l*, pg. 2173
DOOSAN HEAVY INDUSTRIES AMERICA LLC—See Doosan Corporation; *Int'l*, pg. 2173
DOOSAN HEAVY INDUSTRIES JAPAN CORP.—See Doosan Corporation; *Int'l*, pg. 2173
DOOSAN INTERNATIONAL AUSTRALIA PTY LTD—See Doosan Corporation; *Int'l*, pg. 2173
DOOSAN INTERNATIONAL UK LTD.—See Doosan Corporation; *Int'l*, pg. 2173
D.O.O. TEHNOALAT—See August Rueggeberg GmbH & Co. KG PFERD-Werkzeuge; *Int'l*, pg. 703
DOPPELMAYR AUSTRALIA PTY. LTD.—See Doppelmayr Group; *Int'l*, pg. 2174
DOPPELMAYR FINN OY—See Doppelmayr Group; *Int'l*, pg. 2174
DOPPELMAYR LIFTS (NZ) LTD.—See Doppelmayr Group; *Int'l*, pg. 2174
DOPPELMAYR SKIDALYFTUR HF.—See Doppelmayr Group; *Int'l*, pg. 2174
DORIAN DRAKE INTERNATIONAL, INC.; *U.S. Private*, pg. 1262
DOUBLE A TRAILER SALES INC.; *U.S. Private*, pg. 1265
DOUGHERTY EQUIPMENT CO. INC.; *U.S. Private*, pg. 1266
DOVE EQUIPMENT—See ICAFe, Inc.; *U.S. Private*, pg. 2029
DQW CHEMICAL ROMANIA S.R.L.—See Dow Inc.; *U.S. Public*, pg. 685
DRAEGER SAFETY CANADA LTD.—See Draegerwerk AG & Co. KGaA; *Int'l*, pg. 2197
DRAEGER SAFETY (THAILAND) LTD.—See Draegerwerk AG & Co. KGaA; *Int'l*, pg. 2197
DRILLERS SERVICE, LLC—See Franklin Electric Co., Inc.; *U.S. Public*, pg. 878
DRILLING & PRODUCTION RESOURCES, INC.—See Parker Hannifin Corporation; *U.S. Public*, pg. 1641
DRIL-QUIP (NIGERIA) LTD—See Dril-Quip, Inc.; *U.S. Public*, pg. 687

423830 — INDUSTRIAL MACHINER...

DR. LANGE NEDERLAND B.V.—See Danaher Corporation; *U.S. Public*, pg. 626
DRONCO FRANCE SARL—See Jason Industries, Inc.; *U.S. Private*, pg. 2189
DRONCO SCANDINAVIA AB—See Jason Industries, Inc.; *U.S. Private*, pg. 2189
D.R. SMITH CO., INC.—See H.I.G. Capital, LLC; *U.S. Private*, pg. 1833
DTS FLUID POWER LLC; *U.S. Private*, pg. 1282
DUHIG AND CO. INC.; *U.S. Private*, pg. 1285
DUKANE INTELLIGENT ASSEMBLY SOLUTIONS—See Dukane Corporation; *U.S. Private*, pg. 1285
DUNCAN INDUSTRIAL SOLUTIONS INC.—See TruArc Partners, L.P.; *U.S. Private*, pg. 4245
DUNLAP SALES, INC.; *U.S. Private*, pg. 1290
DUO-FAST DE ESPANA S.A.—See Illinois Tool Works Inc.; *U.S. Public*, pg. 1102
DUO-FAST KOREA CO. LTD.—See Illinois Tool Works Inc.; *U.S. Public*, pg. 1102
DURKIN EQUIPMENT CO. INC.—See Midwest Automation Inc.; *U.S. Private*, pg. 2720
DUROC MACHINE TOOL AS—See Duroc AB; *Int'l*, pg. 2229
DUROC MACHINE TOOL OU—See Duroc AB; *Int'l*, pg. 2229
DURR ECOCLEAN INC—See Durr AG; *Int'l*, pg. 2231
DURR JAPAN K.K.—See Durr AG; *Int'l*, pg. 2231
DURR SYSTEMS MAKINE MUHENDISLIK PROJE ITHALAT VE IHRACAT LTD—See Durr AG; *Int'l*, pg. 2231
DXP ENTERPRISES, INC.; *U.S. Public*, pg. 697
DYNACERT GMBH—See dynaCERT Inc.; *Int'l*, pg. 2239
DYNA-LIFT, INC.; *U.S. Private*, pg. 1297
DYNAMIC AUTOMATION; *U.S. Private*, pg. 1297
DYNAMIC TOOLING SERVICES (PRIVATE) LIMITED—See Chien Wei Precise Technology Co., Ltd.; *Int'l*, pg. 1477
DYNAPAC DO BRASIL IND. COM LTDA.—See FAYAT SAS; *Int'l*, pg. 2624
DYNAPATH SYSTEMS, INC.; *U.S. Private*, pg. 1299
EADS DISTRIBUTION, LLC—See Applied Industrial Technologies, Inc.; *U.S. Public*, pg. 171
EAST BAY CLARKLIFT INC.; *U.S. Private*, pg. 1315
EASTERN CONTROLS INC.; *U.S. Private*, pg. 1319
EASTERN INDUSTRIAL SUPPLIES INC.; *U.S. Private*, pg. 1320
EASTERN LIFT TRUCK CO. INC.; *U.S. Private*, pg. 1320
EASTERN STATES ASSOCIATES INC.; *U.S. Private*, pg. 1321
EATON ELECTRIC (SOUTH AFRICA) PTY LTD.—See Eaton Corporation plc; *Int'l*, pg. 2280
EATON INTERNATIONAL INDUSTRIES NIGERIA LIMITED—See Eaton Corporation plc; *Int'l*, pg. 2281
EBARA BOMBAS AMERICA DO SUL LTDA.—See Ebara Corporation; *Int'l*, pg. 2282
EBARA BOMBAS COLOMBIA S.A.S.—See Ebara Corporation; *Int'l*, pg. 2283
EBARA-BYRON JACKSON, LTD.—See Ebara Corporation; *Int'l*, pg. 2283
EBARA DENSAN (KUNSHAN) MFG. CO., LTD.—See Ebara Corporation; *Int'l*, pg. 2283
EBARA GREAT PUMPS CO., LTD.—See Ebara Corporation; *Int'l*, pg. 2283
EBARA POMPY POLSKA SP. Z O.O.—See Ebara Corporation; *Int'l*, pg. 2283
EBARA PRECISION MACHINERY TAIWAN INCORPORATED—See Ebara Corporation; *Int'l*, pg. 2283
EBARA PUMP INDUSTRIES P.J.S.—See Ebara Corporation; *Int'l*, pg. 2283
EBARA PUMPS MEXICO, S.A. DE C.V.—See Ebara Corporation; *Int'l*, pg. 2283
EBARA PUMPS PHILIPPINES, INC.—See Ebara Corporation; *Int'l*, pg. 2283
EBARA PUMPS RUS LIMITED LIABILITY COMPANY—See Ebara Corporation; *Int'l*, pg. 2282
EBARA PUMPS SAUDI ARABIA LLC—See Ebara Corporation; *Int'l*, pg. 2283
EBARA PUMPS SOUTH AFRICA (PTY) LTD.—See Ebara Corporation; *Int'l*, pg. 2283
ECONO PRODUCTS INC.; *U.S. Private*, pg. 1329
EC POWER SYSTEMS; *U.S. Private*, pg. 1326
EESCO DISTRIBUTION—See WESCO International, Inc.; *U.S. Public*, pg. 2351
EFACEC SINGAPORE PTE, LTD—See Efacec Capital, SGPS, S.A.; *Int'l*, pg. 2318
EFFER S.P.A.—See Cargotec Corporation; *Int'l*, pg. 1327
EGASCA, S.A.—See Citizen Watch Co., Ltd.; *Int'l*, pg. 1625
EGGELHOF INCORPORATED; *U.S. Private*, pg. 1344
EGYPTIAN PETROLEUM HH RIG MANUFACTURING S.A.E CO.—See Honghua Group Ltd; *Int'l*, pg. 3470
EISENMANN CORPORATION—See Eisenmann AG; *Int'l*, pg. 2336
EISENMANN DO BRASIL EQUIPAMENTOS INDUSTRIAIS LTDA—See Eisenmann AG; *Int'l*, pg. 2336
EISENMANN FRANCE SARL—See Eisenmann AG; *Int'l*, pg. 2336
EISENMANN INDIA PVT. LTD.—See Eisenmann AG; *Int'l*, pg. 2336
EISENMANN INGENIERIA S.A.—See Eisenmann AG; *Int'l*, pg. 2336
EISENMANN ITALIA S.R.L.—See Eisenmann AG; *Int'l*, pg. 2336
EISENMANN S.A. DE C.V.—See Eisenmann AG; *Int'l*, pg. 2336
EISENMANN SHANGHAI CO., LTD.—See Eisenmann AG; *Int'l*, pg. 2336
EISENMANN SURFACE FINISHING SYSTEMS INDIA PVT. LTD.—See Eisenmann AG; *Int'l*, pg. 2336
EISENMANN THERMAL SOLUTIONS GMBH & CO. KG—See Eisenmann AG; *Int'l*, pg. 2336
EISENMANN U.K. LTD.—See Eisenmann AG; *Int'l*, pg. 2336
ELECTRODES, INC.; *U.S. Private*, pg. 1354
ELECTROGEN INTERNATIONAL LTD.—See The Manitowoc Company, Inc.; *U.S. Public*, pg. 2111
ELECTRONICS FOR IMAGING, INC. - LEBANON—See Siris Capital Group, LLC; *U.S. Private*, pg. 3672
ELECTRONICS FOR IMAGING, INC. MASSACHUSETTS—See Siris Capital Group, LLC; *U.S. Private*, pg. 3672
ELECTRO SCIENTIFIC INDUSTRIES, INC.—See MKS Instruments, Inc.; *U.S. Public*, pg. 1452
ELECTRO SCIENTIFIC INDUSTRIES SINGAPORE PTE LTD.—See MKS Instruments, Inc.; *U.S. Public*, pg. 1452
ELEVADORES OTIS S/A—See Otis Worldwide Corporation; *U.S. Public*, pg. 1623
ELGI COMPRESSORES DO BRAZIL LTDA—See ELGI Equipments Limited; *Int'l*, pg. 2360
ELGI COMPRESSORS TRADING (SHANGHAI) CO., LTD—See ELGI Equipments Limited; *Int'l*, pg. 2360
ELLIOT ELECTRIC COMPANY INC.—See Davis H. Elliot Company Inc.; *U.S. Private*, pg. 1173
ELLIOTT EBARA SINGAPORE PTE. LTD.—See Ebara Corporation; *Int'l*, pg. 2284
ELLIOTT MATSUURA CANADA, INC.; *Int'l*, pg. 2366
ELLIPSIZ SECOND SOURCE INC—See Ellipsiz Ltd.; *Int'l*, pg. 2366
ELLISON TECHNOLOGIES INC.; *U.S. Private*, pg. 1374
ELLISON TECHNOLOGIES, INC.—See Ellison Technologies Inc.; *U.S. Private*, pg. 1374
ELLISON TECHNOLOGIES, INC.—See Ellison Technologies Inc.; *U.S. Private*, pg. 1374
ELMARCO S.R.O.—See BNP Paribas SA; *Int'l*, pg. 1089
ELTEX-ELEKTROSTATIK-GESELLSCHAFT MIT BESCHRANKTER HAFTUNG—See Illinois Tool Works Inc.; *U.S. Public*, pg. 1103
ELUMATEC ASIA PTE LTD.—See Cifin S.r.l.; *Int'l*, pg. 1606
ELUMATEC AUSTRALIA PTY. LTD.—See Cifin S.r.l.; *Int'l*, pg. 1606
ELUMATEC AUSTRIA GMBH—See Cifin S.r.l.; *Int'l*, pg. 1606
ELUMATEC BENELUX B.V.—See Cifin S.r.l.; *Int'l*, pg. 1606
ELUMATEC BULGARIA EOOD—See Cifin S.r.l.; *Int'l*, pg. 1606
ELUMATEC CHILE LIMITADA—See Cifin S.r.l.; *Int'l*, pg. 1606
ELUMATEC CZ S.R.O.—See Cifin S.r.l.; *Int'l*, pg. 1606
ELUMATEC DE AMERICA LATINA S.A.—See Cifin S.r.l.; *Int'l*, pg. 1606
ELUMATEC D.O.O.—See Cifin S.r.l.; *Int'l*, pg. 1606
ELUMATEC INDIA PRIVATE LIMITED—See Cifin S.r.l.; *Int'l*, pg. 1606
ELUMATEC ITALIA S.R.L.—See Cifin S.r.l.; *Int'l*, pg. 1606
ELUMATEC KOREA CO. LTD.—See Cifin S.r.l.; *Int'l*, pg. 1606
ELUMATEC LITHUANIA UAB—See Cifin S.r.l.; *Int'l*, pg. 1606
ELUMATEC MACHINERY SHANGHAI CO. LTD.—See Cifin S.r.l.; *Int'l*, pg. 1606
ELUMATEC MAKINE VE SERVIS SAN. VE TIC. LTD. STI.—See Cifin S.r.l.; *Int'l*, pg. 1606
ELUMATEC MALAYSIA SDN BHD—See Cifin S.r.l.; *Int'l*, pg. 1606
ELUMATEC MASCHINEN D.O.O.—See Cifin S.r.l.; *Int'l*, pg. 1606
ELUMATEC MASCHINEN SH.P.K.—See Cifin S.r.l.; *Int'l*, pg. 1606
ELUMATEC MIDDLE EAST LLC—See Cifin S.r.l.; *Int'l*, pg. 1606
ELUMATEC NORGE AS—See Cifin S.r.l.; *Int'l*, pg. 1606
ELUMATEC NORTH AMERICA INC.—See Cifin S.r.l.; *Int'l*, pg. 1606
ELUMATEC POLSKA SP. Z O.O.—See Cifin S.r.l.; *Int'l*, pg. 1606
ELUMATEC ROMANIA SRL..—See Cifin S.r.l.; *Int'l*, pg. 1606
ELUMATEC SHENZHEN CO. LTD.—See Cifin S.r.l.; *Int'l*, pg. 1606
ELUMATEC SKANDINAVIEN AB—See Cifin S.r.l.; *Int'l*, pg. 1606
ELUMATEC SLOVENSKO, S.R.O.—See Cifin S.r.l.; *Int'l*, pg. 1606
ELUMATEC SOUTH AFRICA (PTY) LTD.—See Cifin S.r.l.; *Int'l*, pg. 1606
ELUMATEC SOUTH AFRICA (PTY) LTD.—See Cifin S.r.l.; *Int'l*, pg. 1606
ELUMATEC SWISS AG—See Cifin S.r.l.; *Int'l*, pg. 1606
ELUMATEC UNITED KINGDOM LTD.—See Cifin S.r.l.; *Int'l*, pg. 1606
EMCO WHEATON CORP.—See Ingersoll Rand Inc.; *U.S. Public*, pg. 1118
EMCO WHEATON UK—See Ingersoll Rand Inc.; *U.S. Public*, pg. 1118
EMCO WHEATON USA, INC.—See Ingersoll Rand Inc.; *U.S. Public*, pg. 1118
E&M ELECTRIC & MACHINERY; *U.S. Private*, pg. 1301
EMERSON AUTOMATION SOLUTIONS FINAL CONTROL GERMANY GMBH—See Emerson Electric Co.; *U.S. Public*, pg. 743
EMERSON AUTOMATION SOLUTIONS FINAL CONTROL HUNGARY KFT.—See Emerson Electric Co.; *U.S. Public*, pg. 748
EMERSON AUTOMATION SOLUTIONS FINAL CONTROL NETHERLANDS B.V.—See Emerson Electric Co.; *U.S. Public*, pg. 745
EMERSON AUTOMATION SOLUTIONS FINAL CONTROL POLSKA SP. Z O.O.—See Emerson Electric Co.; *U.S. Public*, pg. 743
EMERSON AUTOMATION SOLUTIONS GMBH—See Emerson Electric Co.; *U.S. Public*, pg. 743
EMERSON CLIMATE TECHNOLOGIES (SOUTH AFRICA) (PTY) LTD.—See Emerson Electric Co.; *U.S. Public*, pg. 743
EMERSON PROCESS MANAGEMENT A/S—See Emerson Electric Co.; *U.S. Public*, pg. 746
EMERSON PROCESS MANAGEMENT DE COLOMBIA SAS—See Emerson Electric Co.; *U.S. Public*, pg. 749
EMERSON PROCESS MANAGEMENT OY—See Emerson Electric Co.; *U.S. Public*, pg. 747
EMERSON SAUDI ARABIA LLC—See Emerson Electric Co.; *U.S. Public*, pg. 745
EMERSON (TAIWAN) LIMITED—See Emerson Electric Co.; *U.S. Public*, pg. 743
EMHART GLASS OOO—See Bucher Industries AG; *Int'l*, pg. 1208
EMUGE-FRANKEN AB—See EMUGE-Werk Richard Glimpel GmbH & Co. KG; *Int'l*, pg. 2394
EMUGE-FRANKEN AB—See EMUGE-Werk Richard Glimpel GmbH & Co. KG; *Int'l*, pg. 2394
EMUGE-FRANKEN (BULGARIA) E.O.O.D.—See EMUGE-Werk Richard Glimpel GmbH & Co. KG; *Int'l*, pg. 2394
EMUGE-FRANKEN NASTROJE SPOL. S R.O—See EMUGE-Werk Richard Glimpel GmbH & Co. KG; *Int'l*, pg. 2394
EMUGE-FRANKEN SARL—See EMUGE-Werk Richard Glimpel GmbH & Co. KG; *Int'l*, pg. 2394
EMUGE-FRANKEN SERVISNI CENTRUM, S.R.O.—See EMUGE-Werk Richard Glimpel GmbH & Co. KG; *Int'l*, pg. 2394
EMUGE-FRANKEN, S.L.—See EMUGE-Werk Richard Glimpel GmbH & Co. KG; *Int'l*, pg. 2394
EMUGE-FRANKEN, S.R.L.—See EMUGE-Werk Richard Glimpel GmbH & Co. KG; *Int'l*, pg. 2394
EMUGE-FRANKEN TECHNIK—See EMUGE-Werk Richard Glimpel GmbH & Co. KG; *Int'l*, pg. 2394
EMUGE-FRANKEN TEHNIKA D.O.O.—See EMUGE-Werk Richard Glimpel GmbH & Co. KG; *Int'l*, pg. 2394
EMUGE-FRANKEN TOOLING SERVICE D.O.O.—See EMUGE-Werk Richard Glimpel GmbH & Co. KG; *Int'l*, pg. 2394
EMUGE-FRANKEN TOOLS ROMANIA SRL—See EMUGE-Werk Richard Glimpel GmbH & Co. KG; *Int'l*, pg. 2394
EMUGE-FRANKEN UK LIMITED—See EMUGE-Werk Richard Glimpel GmbH & Co. KG; *Int'l*, pg. 2394
EMUGE PRAZISIONSWERKZEUGE GMBH—See EMUGE-Werk Richard Glimpel GmbH & Co. KG; *Int'l*, pg. 2394
ENDRESS AND HAUSER ARABIA LLC—See Endress+Hauser (International) Holding AG; *Int'l*, pg. 2406
ENDRESS+HAUSER AB—See Endress+Hauser (International) Holding AG; *Int'l*, pg. 2406
ENDRESS+HAUSER ALGERIE SARL—See Endress+Hauser (International) Holding AG; *Int'l*, pg. 2406
ENDRESS+HAUSER ARGENTINA S.A.—See Endress+Hauser (International) Holding AG; *Int'l*, pg. 2406
ENDRESS+HAUSER AS—See Endress+Hauser (International) Holding AG; *Int'l*, pg. 2406
ENDRESS+HAUSER (BALTIC) UAB—See Endress+Hauser (International) Holding AG; *Int'l*, pg. 2406
ENDRESS+HAUSER (BRASIL) INSTRUMENTACAO E AUTOMACAO LTDA—See Endress+Hauser (International) Holding AG; *Int'l*, pg. 2406
ENDRESS+HAUSER CANADA LTD.—See Endress+Hauser (International) Holding AG; *Int'l*, pg. 2407
ENDRESS+HAUSER (CHINA) AUTOMATION INSTRUMENTATION CO. LTD.—See Endress+Hauser (International) Holding AG; *Int'l*, pg. 2406
ENDRESS+HAUSER CONDUCTA, INC.—See Endress+Hauser (International) Holding AG; *Int'l*, pg. 2407
ENDRESS+HAUSER CONTROLE E AUTOMACAO LTDA.—See Endress+Hauser (International) Holding AG; *Int'l*, pg. 2407
ENDRESS+HAUSER CZECH S.R.O.—See Endress+Hauser (International) Holding AG; *Int'l*, pg. 2407

423830 — INDUSTRIAL MACHINER...

ENDRESS+HAUSER ELEKTRONIK SAN.VE TIC. A.S.—See Endress+Hauser (International) Holding AG; *Int'l*, pg. 2407
ENDRESS+HAUSER FLOWTEC (CHINA) CO., LTD.—See Endress+Hauser (International) Holding AG; *Int'l*, pg. 2407
ENDRESS+HAUSER FLOWTEC (INDIA) PVT. LTD.—See Endress+Hauser (International) Holding AG; *Int'l*, pg. 2407
ENDRESS+HAUSER (INDIA) AUTOMATION INSTRUMENTATION PVT. LTD.—See Endress+Hauser (International) Holding AG; pg. 2406
ENDRESS+HAUSER (INDIA) PVT. LTD.—See Endress+Hauser (International) Holding AG; *Int'l*, pg. 2406
ENDRESS+HAUSER JAPAN CO.,LTD.—See Endress+Hauser (International) Holding AG; *Int'l*, pg. 2407
ENDRESS+HAUSER KOREA CO., LTD.—See Endress+Hauser (International) Holding AG; *Int'l*, pg. 2407
ENDRESS+HAUSER MAGYARORSZAG FOLYAMATMUSZEREZESI KFT.—See Endress+Hauser (International) Holding AG; *Int'l*, pg. 2407
ENDRESS+HAUSER MESSTECHNIK GMBH+CO. KG—See Endress+Hauser (International) Holding AG; *Int'l*, pg. 2407
ENDRESS + HAUSER MEXICO, S.A. DE C.V.—See Endress+Hauser (International) Holding AG; *Int'l*, pg. 2406
ENDRESS+HAUSER (M) SDN. BHD.—See Endress+Hauser (International) Holding AG; *Int'l*, pg. 2406
ENDRESS+HAUSER (QATAR) L.L.C.—See Endress+Hauser (International) Holding AG; *Int'l*, pg. 2406
ENDRESS+HAUSER ROMANIA SRL—See Endress+Hauser (International) Holding AG; *Int'l*, pg. 2407
ENDRESS+HAUSER SAS - CERNAY—See Endress+Hauser (International) Holding AG; *Int'l*, pg. 2408
ENDRESS+HAUSER SAS—See Endress+Hauser (International) Holding AG; *Int'l*, pg. 2408
ENDRESS+HAUSER (SCHWEIZ) AG—See Endress+Hauser (International) Holding AG; *Int'l*, pg. 2406
ENDRESS+HAUSER (SEA) PTE LTD.—See Endress+Hauser (International) Holding AG; *Int'l*, pg. 2406
ENDRESS+HAUSER SHANGHAI AUTOMATION EQUIPMENT CO. LTD.—See Endress+Hauser (International) Holding AG; *Int'l*, pg. 2408
ENDRESS+HAUSER (UAE) LLC—See Endress+Hauser (International) Holding AG; *Int'l*, pg. 2406
ENDRESS+HAUSER (USA) AUTOMATION INSTRUMENTATION INC.—See Endress+Hauser (International) Holding AG; *Int'l*, pg. 2407
ENDRESS+HAUSER VENEZUELA S.A.—See Endress+Hauser (International) Holding AG; *Int'l*, pg. 2408
ENDRESS+HAUSER WETZER GMBH + CO. KG—See Endress+Hauser (International) Holding AG; *Int'l*, pg. 2408
ENDRESS+HAUSER WETZER INDIA PVT. LTD.—See Endress+Hauser (International) Holding AG; *Int'l*, pg. 2408
ENDRESS+HAUSER YAMANASHI CO. LTD.—See Endress+Hauser (International) Holding AG; *Int'l*, pg. 2408
ENERGIA DE CASABLANCA SA; *Int'l*, pg. 2420
ENERGY EQUIPMENT & SUPPLY, INC.—See Ingersoll Rand Inc.; *U.S. Public*, pg. 1120
ENERGY SOLUTIONS INTERNATIONAL, INC.—See Emerson Electric Co.; *U.S. Public*, pg. 749
ENERGY SOLUTIONS INTERNATIONAL LTD.—See Emerson Electric Co.; *U.S. Public*, pg. 749
ENERGY SOLUTIONS INTERNATIONAL SAS—See Emerson Electric Co.; *U.S. Public*, pg. 749
ENERPAC BV—See Enerpac Tool Group Corp.; *U.S. Public*, pg. 765
ENERPAC LTD.—See Enerpac Tool Group Corp.; *U.S. Public*, pg. 765
ENERPAC—See Enerpac Tool Group Corp.; *U.S. Public*, pg. 765
ENERTECH ENERGIE UND TECHNIK GMBH—See E.ON SE; *Int'l*, pg. 2253
ENGINEERED PRODUCTS—See The Pape Group, Inc.; *U.S. Private*, pg. 4090
ENGMAN-TAYLOR COMPANY INC.—See MSC Industrial Direct Co., Inc.; *U.S. Public*, pg. 1483
ENPRO ASSOCIATES, LLC—See Enpro Inc.; *U.S. Public*, pg. 774
ENPRO, INC.; *U.S. Private*, pg. 1401
ENSHU GMBH—See Enshu Limited; *Int'l*, pg. 2446
ENSHU (QINGDAO) LIMITED—See Enshu Limited; *Int'l*, pg. 2446
ENSHU (THAILAND) LIMITED—See Enshu Limited; *Int'l*, pg. 2446
ENSHU USA CORPORATION—See Enshu Limited; *Int'l*, pg. 2446
ENSHU VIETNAM CO., LTD.—See Enshu Limited; *Int'l*, pg. 2446
ENVIRONMATE TECH CORP.—See ESPEC Corp.; *Int'l*, pg. 2505
ENVIRONMENTAL ANALYSIS CENTER CO., LTD.—See Daiki Axis Co., Ltd.; *Int'l*, pg. 1932
ENVIROSIGHT, LLC—See IDEX Corp; *U.S. Public*, pg. 1090
ENX GROUP LIMITED; *Int'l*, pg. 2456
ENZA AIR PROPRIETARY LIMITED—See Ingersoll Rand Inc.; *U.S. Public*, pg. 1118
E.O. HABHEGGER COMPANY INC.; *U.S. Private*, pg. 1306
EPIROC USA LLC—See Epiroc AB; *Int'l*, pg. 2462
EPRODUCTION SOLUTIONS, INC.—See Weatherford International plc; *U.S. Public*, pg. 2341
EQUIPAMENTOS CIENTIFICOS INSTRON LTD.—See Illinois Tool Works Inc.; *U.S. Public*, pg. 1108
EQUIPCO INC.; *U.S. Private*, pg. 1415
EQUIPMENT & CONTROLS, INC.; *U.S. Private*, pg. 1415
EQUIPMENT CO. W.L.L.—See Equipment Holding Company K.S.C.C.; *Int'l*, pg. 2485
EQUIPMENT INC.; *U.S. Private*, pg. 1415
EQUIPMENT & SYSTEMS FOR THE INDUSTRY; *U.S. Private*, pg. 1415
EQUIPMENT WORLD INC.; *Int'l*, pg. 2485
EQUIPT MANUFACTURING, INC.—See Hines Corporation; *U.S. Private*, pg. 1949
E.R.H.S.A.; *Int'l*, pg. 2260
ESAB ASIA/PACIFIC PTE. LTD.—See Enovis Corporation; *U.S. Public*, pg. 770
ESAB GROUP CANADA, INC.—See Enovis Corporation; *U.S. Public*, pg. 770
ESAB INDIA LTD.-KOLKATA—See Enovis Corporation; *U.S. Public*, pg. 770
ESAB SP.Z.O.O.—See Enovis Corporation; *U.S. Public*, pg. 771
ESAB VAMBERK A.S.—See Enovis Corporation; *U.S. Public*, pg. 771
ESAB VAMBERK, S.R.O.—See Enovis Corporation; *U.S. Public*, pg. 771
ESAB WELDING & CUTTING GMBH—See Enovis Corporation; *U.S. Public*, pg. 772
ESCO AANDRIJVINGEN B.V.—See Esco Financial & Engineering Company S.A/N.V.; *Int'l*, pg. 2501
ESHELMAN COMPANY INC.; *U.S. Private*, pg. 1425
ESI ACQUISITION CORPORATION—See Applied Industrial Technologies, Inc.; *U.S. Public*, pg. 171
ESI ELECTRONIC EQUIPMENT (SHANGHAI) CO., LTD.—See MKS Instruments, Inc.; *U.S. Public*, pg. 1452
ESPEC (CHINA) LIMITED—See ESPEC Corp.; *Int'l*, pg. 2505
ESPEC SOUTH EAST ASIA SDN. BHD.—See ESPEC Corp.; *Int'l*, pg. 2505
ESPERA-BELGIUM B.V.B.A.—See ESPERA-WERKE GMBH; *Int'l*, pg. 2506
ESPERA IBERICA S.A.—See ESPERA-WERKE GMBH; *Int'l*, pg. 2505
ESPERA-NEDERLAND B.V.—See ESPERA-WERKE GMBH; *Int'l*, pg. 2506
ESPERA S.A.R.L.—See ESPERA-WERKE GMBH; *Int'l*, pg. 2506
ESPERA SCHWEIZ GMBH—See ESPERA-WERKE GMBH; *Int'l*, pg. 2506
ESSENDANT CANADA, INC.—See Sycamore Partners Management, LP; *U.S. Private*, pg. 3896
ESSENTIAL ENERGY SERVICES LTD. - TRYTON RENTALS DIVISION—See Element Technical Services Inc.; *Int'l*, pg. 2358
EUREKA PUMP AS—See HitecVision AS; *Int'l*, pg. 3425
EUREKA PUMP AS—See HitecVision AS; *Int'l*, pg. 3425
EUREKA PUMPS AMERICAS, INC.—See HitecVision AS; *Int'l*, pg. 3425
EUREKA PUMPS AS - KRISTIANSUND—See HitecVision AS; *Int'l*, pg. 3425
EUREKA PUMPS AS—See HitecVision AS; *Int'l*, pg. 3425
EUREKA PUMPS AS - SORUMSAND—See HitecVision AS; *Int'l*, pg. 3425
EUREKA PUMPS KOREA—See HitecVision AS; *Int'l*, pg. 3425
EUROCOPTER CHINA CO LTD—See Airbus SE; *Int'l*, pg. 243
EUROELETTRO HAMMOND S.P.A—See Hammond Power Solutions Inc.; *Int'l*, pg. 3239
EUROMAC SISTEMAS DE CONFECCION, S.A.—See CF Italia srl; *Int'l*, pg. 1429
EURO RESSURS AS—See Bilfinger SE; *Int'l*, pg. 1028
EVATEC EUROPE GMBH—See Evatec AG; *Int'l*, pg. 2561
EVATEC ITALIA S.R.L—See Evatec AG; *Int'l*, pg. 2561
EVATEC (LIECHTENSTEIN) AG—See Evatec AG; *Int'l*, pg. 2560
EVATEC PROCESS SYSTEMS B.V.—See Evatec AG; *Int'l*, pg. 2561
EVI WEATHERFORD INC.—See Weatherford International plc; *U.S. Public*, pg. 2339
EXPORT OIL FIELD SUPPLY COMPANY INTERNATIONAL; *U.S. Private*, pg. 1450
EXTERRAN ARGENTINA S.R.L.—See Enerflex Ltd.; *Int'l*, pg. 2418
EXTERRAN BAHRAIN S.P.C.—See Enerflex Ltd.; *Int'l*, pg. 2418
EXTERRAN BOLIVIA LTDA.—See Enerflex Ltd.; *Int'l*, pg. 2418
EXTERRAN BRASIL LTDA—See Enerflex Ltd.; *Int'l*, pg. 2419
EXTERRAN EASTERN HEMISPHERE FZE—See Enerflex Ltd.; *Int'l*, pg. 2418
EXTERRAN ENERGY MALAYSIA SDN. BHD.—See Enerflex Ltd.; *Int'l*, pg. 2419
EXTERRAN ENERGY SOLUTIONS, L.P. - HOUSTON (BRITTMOORE) PLANT—See Enerflex Ltd.; *Int'l*, pg. 2419
EXTERRAN ENERGY SOLUTIONS, L.P. - HOUSTON (ROSSLYN) PLANT—See Enerflex Ltd.; *Int'l*, pg. 2419
EXTERRAN HOLDING COMPANY NL B.V.—See Enerflex Ltd.; *Int'l*, pg. 2419
EXTERRAN INTERNATIONAL SA—See Enerflex Ltd.; *Int'l*, pg. 2419
EXTERRAN OFFSHORE PTE. LTD.—See Enerflex Ltd.; *Int'l*, pg. 2419
EXTERRAN—See Enerflex Ltd.; *Int'l*, pg. 2418
EXTERRAN—See Enerflex Ltd.; *Int'l*, pg. 2418
EXTERRAN—See Enerflex Ltd.; *Int'l*, pg. 2418
EXTERRAN—See Enerflex Ltd.; *Int'l*, pg. 2419
EXTERRAN—See Enerflex Ltd.; *Int'l*, pg. 2419
EXTERRAN—See Enerflex Ltd.; *Int'l*, pg. 2419
EXTERRAN—See Enerflex Ltd.; *Int'l*, pg. 2419
EXTERRAN—See Enerflex Ltd.; *Int'l*, pg. 2419
EZ LOADER ADJUSTABLE SALES CORPORATION, INC.—See EZ Loader Boat Trailers, Inc.; *U.S. Private*, pg. 1454
FABRICO, INC.—See Enpro Inc.; *U.S. Public*, pg. 775
FACTORY CLEANING EQUIPMENT, INC.—See Incline MGMT Corp.; *U.S. Private*, pg. 2053
FAIRBORN CEMENT COMPANY LLC—See Eagle Materials Inc.; *U.S. Public*, pg. 702
FAIVELEY TRANSPORT TAMWORTH LTD—See Westinghouse Air Brake Technologies Corporation; *U.S. Public*, pg. 2358
FALCON EXECUTIVE AVIATION, INC.; *U.S. Private*, pg. 1466
THE FALKIRK MINING CO.—See NACCO Industries, Inc.; *U.S. Public*, pg. 1490
FALLSWAY EQUIPMENT CO., INC.; *U.S. Private*, pg. 1468
FANUC AMERICA CORPORATION—See FANUC Corporation; *Int'l*, pg. 2614
FANUC EUROPE CORPORATION, S.A.—See FANUC Corporation; *Int'l*, pg. 2614
FANUC FA BULGARIA LTD.—See FANUC Corporation; *Int'l*, pg. 2614
FANUC FA UK LIMITED—See FANUC Corporation; *Int'l*, pg. 2614
FANUC ROBOMACHINE EUROPE GMBH—See FANUC Corporation; *Int'l*, pg. 2614
FARM PUMP AND IRRIGATION CO.; *U.S. Private*, pg. 1475
FARWEST CORROSION CONTROL CO.; *U.S. Private*, pg. 1481
FASTCUT TOOL CORPORATION—See Talbot Holdings Inc.; *U.S. Private*, pg. 3925
FAST & FLUID MANAGEMENT AUSTRALIA—See IDEX Corp; *U.S. Public*, pg. 1090
FAST & FLUID MANAGEMENT EAST EUROPE SP. Z.O.O.—See IDEX Corp; *U.S. Public*, pg. 1090
FASVER SAS—See Illinois Tool Works Inc.; *U.S. Public*, pg. 1103
FAULHABER BENELUX B.V.—See Dr. Fritz Faulhaber GmbH & Co. KG; *Int'l*, pg. 2191
FAULHABER DRIVE SYSTEM TECHNOLOGY (TAICANG) CO., LTD.—See Dr. Fritz Faulhaber GmbH & Co. KG; *Int'l*, pg. 2191
FAULHABER FRANCE SAS—See Dr. Fritz Faulhaber GmbH & Co. KG; *Int'l*, pg. 2191
FAULHABER SINGAPORE PTE LTD—See Dr. Fritz Faulhaber GmbH & Co. KG; *Int'l*, pg. 2191
FAURE HERMAN METER, INC.—See BNP Paribas SA; *Int'l*, pg. 1083
FB INDUSTRIES INC.—See Atlas Energy Solutions Inc.; *U.S. Public*, pg. 224
FCX PERFORMANCE, INC.—See Applied Industrial Technologies, Inc.; *U.S. Public*, pg. 171
FEI AUSTRALIA PTY LTD.—See Thermo Fisher Scientific Inc.; *U.S. Public*, pg. 2147
FE JONES (BUILDERS) LIMITED—See Emerson Developments (Holdings) Limited; *Int'l*, pg. 2379
FE LLC CAMOZZI AUTOMATION—See Camozzi Group; *Int'l*, pg. 1274
FENNER DUNLOP WHYALLA PTD. LTD—See Compagnie Generale des Etablissements Michelin SCA; *Int'l*, pg. 1745
FENWICK IBERICA S.A.—See Fuji Corporation; *Int'l*, pg. 2809
FERGUSON ENTERPRISES, INC.—See Ferguson plc; *Int'l*, pg. 2637
FESTO - AUTOMACAO, UNIPESSOAL, LDA.—See Festo

N.A.I.C.S. INDEX

423830 — INDUSTRIAL MACHINER...

AG & Co. KG; *Int'l*, pg. 2646
FESTO AUTOMATION LTD.—See Festo AG & Co. KG; *Int'l*, pg. 2647
FESTO INC.—See Festo AG & Co. KG; *Int'l*, pg. 2647
FESTO ISRAEL LTD—See Festo AG & Co. KG; *Int'l*, pg. 2647
FESTO S.R.L.—See Festo AG & Co. KG; *Int'l*, pg. 2648
FESTO, S.R.O.—See Festo AG & Co. KG; *Int'l*, pg. 2648
FFG ASIA-PACIFIC LTD.—See Fair Friend Group; *Int'l*, pg. 2604
FFG EUROPE MACHINERY (BEIJING) CO., LTD.—See Fair Friend Group; *Int'l*, pg. 2604
FFG RUSSIA (RUSSIA) AUTOMATION SOLUTIONS—See Fair Friend Group; *Int'l*, pg. 2604
F&H FOOD EQUIPMENT CO; *U.S. Private*, pg. 1454
FHP HELLAS S.A.—See Freudenberg SE; *Int'l*, pg. 2785
FIBA TECHNOLOGIES INC.; *U.S. Private*, pg. 1501
FIBERSPAR AUSTRALIA PTY. LTD.—See NOV, Inc.; *U.S. Public*, pg. 1544
FIBERSPAR LINEPIPE CANADA LTD.—See NOV, Inc.; *U.S. Public*, pg. 1544
FIERO FLUID POWER INC.—See Hartfiel Automation; *U.S. Private*, pg. 1873
FILTERMECH PLANT SALES LIMITED—See CorpAcq Holdings Limited; *Int'l*, pg. 1802
FILTRA CONSULTANTS & ENGINEERS LTD.; *Int'l*, pg. 2663
FINNING (IRELAND) LIMITED—See Finning International Inc.; *Int'l*, pg. 2676
FISCHER PUMP & VALVE COMPANY—See Tencarva Machinery Company, LLC; *U.S. Private*, pg. 3965
FISHER & PAYKEL PRODUCTION MACHINERY LIMITED—See Haier Smart Home Co., Ltd.; *Int'l*, pg. 3210
FIT SERVICE S.P.A.—See Carrier Global Corporation; *U.S. Public*, pg. 443
FITTINGS, INC.—See Bridgestone Corporation; *Int'l*, pg. 1156
FIVE STAR EQUIPMENT INC.; *U.S. Private*, pg. 1538
FLAGLERCE HOLDINGS, LLC—See Alta Equipment Group Inc.; *U.S. Public*, pg. 86
FLEXCO PTE LTD—See Flexible Steel Lacing Company; *U.S. Private*, pg. 1544
FLEXLINK AUTOMATION SDN BHD—See Coesia S.p.A.; *Int'l*, pg. 1689
FLEXLINK AUTOMATION (SHANGHAI) CO. LTD.—See Coesia S.p.A.; *Int'l*, pg. 1689
FLEXLINK SYSTEMS B.V.—See Coesia S.p.A.; *Int'l*, pg. 1689
FLEXLINK SYSTEMS CANADA, INC.—See Coesia S.p.A.; *Int'l*, pg. 1689
FLEXLINK SYSTEMS ESPANA, SL—See Coesia S.p.A.; *Int'l*, pg. 1689
FLEXLINK SYSTEMS GMBH—See Coesia S.p.A.; *Int'l*, pg. 1689
FLEXLINK SYSTEMS, INC.—See Coesia S.p.A.; *Int'l*, pg. 1689
FLEXLINK SYSTEMS INDIA PVT. LTD.—See Coesia S.p.A.; *Int'l*, pg. 1689
FLEXLINK SYSTEMS KFT.—See Coesia S.p.A.; *Int'l*, pg. 1689
FLEXLINK SYSTEMS LTDA—See Coesia S.p.A.; *Int'l*, pg. 1689
FLEXLINK SYSTEMS LTD—See Coesia S.p.A.; *Int'l*, pg. 1689
FLEXLINK SYSTEMS N.V.—See Coesia S.p.A.; *Int'l*, pg. 1689
FLEXLINK SYSTEMS POLSKA SP. Z O.O.—See Coesia S.p.A.; *Int'l*, pg. 1689
FLEXLINK SYSTEMS PTE LTD—See Coesia S.p.A.; *Int'l*, pg. 1689
FLEXLINK SYSTEMS PTY LTD—See Coesia S.p.A.; *Int'l*, pg. 1689
FLEXLINK SYSTEMS SAS—See Coesia S.p.A.; *Int'l*, pg. 1689
FLEXLINK SYSTEMS—See Coesia S.p.A.; *Int'l*, pg. 1689
FLEXLINK SYSTEMS—See Coesia S.p.A.; *Int'l*, pg. 1689
FLEXLINK SYSTEMS—See Coesia S.p.A.; *Int'l*, pg. 1689
FLEXLINK SYSTEMS S.P.A.—See Coesia S.p.A.; *Int'l*, pg. 1689
FLEXLINK SYSTEMS S.R.O.—See Coesia S.p.A.; *Int'l*, pg. 1689
FLEXOPACK DENMARK APS—See FLEXOPACK S.A.; *Int'l*, pg. 2705
FLEXO PRODUCTS LIMITED; *Int'l*, pg. 2705
F&L INDUSTRIAL SOLUTIONS, INC.—See Genuine Parts Company; *U.S. Public*, pg. 933
FLINT POWER SYSTEMS—See Flint Equipment Holdings, Inc.; *U.S. Private*, pg. 1545
FLODYNE INC.; *U.S. Private*, pg. 1546
FLO-LINE HYDRAULICS PTE LTD.; *Int'l*, pg. 2707
FLOMAX PRODUCTS, INC.—See Shale-Inland Holdings LLC; *U.S. Private*, pg. 3623
FLORIDA LIFT SYSTEMS, INC.; *U.S. Private*, pg. 1549
FLOTEC CORPORATION; *U.S. Private*, pg. 1551
FLOVAL EQUIPMENT LTD.; *Int'l*, pg. 2709
FLOWSERVE AUSTRALIA PTY. LTD.—See Flowserve Corporation; *U.S. Public*, pg. 855

FLOWSERVE (AUSTRIA) GMBH—See Flowserve Corporation; *U.S. Public*, pg. 855
FLOWSERVE BELGIUM N.V.—See Flowserve Corporation; *U.S. Public*, pg. 855
FLOWSERVE B.V.—See Flowserve Corporation; *U.S. Public*, pg. 855
FLOWSERVE CANADA CORP.—See Flowserve Corporation; *U.S. Public*, pg. 855
FLOWSERVE CHILE S.A.—See Flowserve Corporation; *U.S. Public*, pg. 855
FLOWSERVE COLOMBIA, LTDA.—See Flowserve Corporation; *U.S. Public*, pg. 855
FLOWSERVE DORTMUND GMBH & CO. KG—See Flowserve Corporation; *U.S. Public*, pg. 856
FLOWSERVE ESSEN GMBH—See Flowserve Corporation; *U.S. Public*, pg. 856
FLOWSERVE FINLAND OY—See Flowserve Corporation; *U.S. Public*, pg. 855
FLOWSERVE FLOW CONTROL BENELUX BV—See Flowserve Corporation; *U.S. Public*, pg. 856
FLOWSERVE FLOW CONTROL GMBH—See Flowserve Corporation; *U.S. Public*, pg. 856
FLOWSERVE GB LIMITED—See Flowserve Corporation; *U.S. Public*, pg. 856
FLOWSERVE INDIA CONTROLS PVT. LTD.—See Flowserve Corporation; *U.S. Public*, pg. 856
FLOWSERVE INTERNATIONAL LIMITED—See Flowserve Corporation; *U.S. Public*, pg. 856
FLOWSERVE PMV USA INC.—See Flowserve Corporation; *U.S. Public*, pg. 856
FLOWSERVE POMPES S.A.S.—See Flowserve Corporation; *U.S. Public*, pg. 856
FLOWSERVE PTE. LTD.—See Flowserve Corporation; *U.S. Public*, pg. 856
FLOWSERVE S.A.S.—See Flowserve Corporation; *U.S. Public*, pg. 856
FLOWSERVE SIHI BULGARIA EOOD—See Flowserve Corporation; *U.S. Public*, pg. 856
FLOWSERVE SIHI HUNGARY KFT—See Flowserve Corporation; *U.S. Public*, pg. 856
FLOWSERVE SIHI (SCHWEIZ) GMBH—See Flowserve Corporation; *U.S. Public*, pg. 856
FLOWSERVE S.R.L.—See Flowserve Corporation; *U.S. Public*, pg. 856
FLOWSERVE WOODBRIDGE DIVISION—See Flowserve Corporation; *U.S. Public*, pg. 855
FLOW-TECH, INC.—See Cross Company; *U.S. Private*, pg. 1104
FLOW THRU SYSTEMS INC.—See Libra Industries, Incorporated; *U.S. Private*, pg. 2447
FLOWTREND INC.—See Audax Group, Limited Partnership; *U.S. Private*, pg. 388
FLSMIDTH ABON PTY. LTD.—See FLSmidth & Co. A/S; *Int'l*, pg. 2711
FLSMIDTH DORR-OLIVER EIMCO GMBH—See FLSmidth & Co. A/S; *Int'l*, pg. 2711
FLSMIDTH DORR-OLIVER EIMCO PTY LIMITED—See FLSmidth & Co. A/S; *Int'l*, pg. 2711
FLSMIDTH GMBH—See FLSmidth & Co. A/S; *Int'l*, pg. 2710
FLSMIDTH HAMBURG GMBH—See FLSmidth & Co. A/S; *Int'l*, pg. 2710
FLSMIDTH KREBS AUSTRALIA PTY. LTD.—See FLSmidth & Co. A/S; *Int'l*, pg. 2711
FLSMIDTH PFISTER LTDA.—See FLSmidth & Co. A/S; *Int'l*, pg. 2712
FLSMIDTH PRIVATE LIMITED—See FLSmidth & Co. A/S; *Int'l*, pg. 2711
FLSMIDTH PTY. LTD.—See FLSmidth & Co. A/S; *Int'l*, pg. 2711
FLSMIDTH PTY. LTD.—See FLSmidth & Co. A/S; *Int'l*, pg. 2711
FLSMIDTH ROYMEC (PTY.) LTD.—See FLSmidth & Co. A/S; *Int'l*, pg. 2711
FLSMIDTH RUS OOO—See FLSmidth & Co. A/S; *Int'l*, pg. 2710
FLSMIDTH S.A.C.—See FLSmidth & Co. A/S; *Int'l*, pg. 2711
FLSMIDTH S.A. DE C.V.—See FLSmidth & Co. A/S; *Int'l*, pg. 2711
FLSMIDTH SARL—See FLSmidth & Co. A/S; *Int'l*, pg. 2710
FLSMIDTH S.A.—See FLSmidth & Co. A/S; *Int'l*, pg. 2711
FLSMIDTH S.A.—See FLSmidth & Co. A/S; *Int'l*, pg. 2711
FLSMIDTH WIESBADEN GMBH—See FLSmidth & Co. A/S; *Int'l*, pg. 2711
FLUID MANAGEMENT COMPANY, LLC; *U.S. Private*, pg. 1552
FLUID MECHANICS, LLC—See Woodward, Inc.; *U.S. Public*, pg. 2378
FLUID POWER AUTOMATION LLC—See Airline Hydraulics Corporation; *U.S. Private*, pg. 141
FLUID POWER PRODUCTS INC.; *U.S. Private*, pg. 1552
FLUID POWER SALES, INC.—See Applied Industrial Technologies, Inc.; *U.S. Public*, pg. 171
FLUID PROCESS EQUIPMENT, INC.; *U.S. Private*, pg. 1552
FLUID SERVICE CORPORATION—See TruArc Partners, L.P.; *U.S. Private*, pg. 4245
FLUID SYSTEMS HAWAII INC.—See Consolidated Supply Co.; *U.S. Private*, pg. 1022

FMH MATERIAL HANDLING SOLUTIONS—See GNCO, Inc.; *U.S. Private*, pg. 1723
FMS MACHINE TOOL DISTRIBUTORS; *U.S. Private*, pg. 1555
FOLCOMER EQUIPMENT CORPORATION; *U.S. Private*, pg. 1557
FOLEY EQUIPMENT COMPANY—See Foley Industries, Inc.; *U.S. Private*, pg. 1558
FONDERIES NICOLAS SAS—See CVC Capital Partners SICAV-FIS S.A.; *Int'l*, pg. 1887
FORALITH EQUIPMENT AG.—See BAUER Aktiengesellschaft; *Int'l*, pg. 893
FORANKRA ESPANA SL—See Axel Johnson Gruppen AB; *Int'l*, pg. 764
FORCE AMERICA INC.; *U.S. Private*, pg. 1563
FORD-GELATT & ASSOCIATES, INC.; *U.S. Private*, pg. 1565
FORDIA GROUP INC.—See Epiroc AB; *Int'l*, pg. 2462
FORKLIFT OF CAPE GIRARDEAU—See Forklift of St. Louis Inc.; *U.S. Private*, pg. 1569
FORKLIFT OF ST. LOUIS INC.; *U.S. Private*, pg. 1569
FORKLIFTS OF CENTRAL MISSOURI—See Forklift of St. Louis Inc.; *U.S. Private*, pg. 1569
FORKLIFTS OF MINNESOTA, INC.; *U.S. Private*, pg. 1569
FORKLIFTS OF NORTH DAKOTA, INC.—See Forklifts of Minnesota, Inc.; *U.S. Private*, pg. 1569
FORKLIFTS OF QUINCY, INC.—See Forklift of St. Louis Inc.; *U.S. Private*, pg. 1569
FORKLIFT SYSTEMS INC.; *U.S. Private*, pg. 1569
FORNEY INDUSTRIES INC.; *U.S. Private*, pg. 1572
FORTUNE INTERNATIONAL, INC.; *U.S. Private*, pg. 1577
FORUM CANADA ULC—See Forum Energy Technologies, Inc.; *U.S. Public*, pg. 873
FORUM ENERGY ASIA PACIFIC PTE. LTD.—See Forum Energy Technologies, Inc.; *U.S. Public*, pg. 873
FPE LIMITED—See Diploma PLC; *Int'l*, pg. 2128
FRANK EDWARDS CO. INC.; *U.S. Private*, pg. 1594
FRANKLIN ELECTRIC COLOMBIA SAS—See Franklin Electric Co., Inc.; *U.S. Public*, pg. 878
FRED V. FOWLER COMPANY, INC.; *U.S. Private*, pg. 1601
FRES-CO SYSTEM USA INCORPORATED; *U.S. Private*, pg. 1609
FRESNO OXYGEN; *U.S. Private*, pg. 1610
FREUDENBERG AUSTRIA GMBH—See Freudenberg SE; *Int'l*, pg. 2785
FREUDENBERG PRODUCTOS DEL HOGAR LTDA.—See Freudenberg SE; *Int'l*, pg. 2787
FREUDENBERG SIMMERRINGE KFT.—See Freudenberg SE; *Int'l*, pg. 2788
FRHAM SAFETY PRODUCTS INC.; *U.S. Private*, pg. 1610
FRIMANN-BERNER AS—See Berner SE; *Int'l*, pg. 988
FRISTAM B.V.—See FRISTAM Pumpen F. Stamp GmbH & Co. KG; *Int'l*, pg. 2793
FRISTAM IBERICA S.L.—See FRISTAM Pumpen F. Stamp GmbH & Co. KG; *Int'l*, pg. 2793
FRISTAM POLSKA SP.Z.O.O—See FRISTAM Pumpen F. Stamp GmbH & Co. KG; *Int'l*, pg. 2793
FRISTAM PUMPEN, OOO—See FRISTAM Pumpen F. Stamp GmbH & Co. KG; *Int'l*, pg. 2793
FRISTAM PUMPER A/S—See FRISTAM Pumpen F. Stamp GmbH & Co. KG; *Int'l*, pg. 2793
FRISTAM PUMPS (I) PVT LTD—See FRISTAM Pumpen F. Stamp GmbH & Co. KG; *Int'l*, pg. 2793
FRISTAM PUMPS JAPAN CO., LTD.—See FRISTAM Pumpen F. Stamp GmbH & Co. KG; *Int'l*, pg. 2793
FRISTAM PUMPS LTD.—See FRISTAM Pumpen F. Stamp GmbH & Co. KG; *Int'l*, pg. 2793
FRISTAM PUMPS SOUTH EAST ASIA PTE. LTD—See FRISTAM Pumpen F. Stamp GmbH & Co. KG; *Int'l*, pg. 2793
FRISTAM PUMPS (TAICANG) CO., LTD.—See FRISTAM Pumpen F. Stamp GmbH & Co. KG; *Int'l*, pg. 2793
FRISTAM PUMPS (UK) LIMITED PARTNERSHIP—See FRISTAM Pumpen F. Stamp GmbH & Co. KG; *Int'l*, pg. 2793
FRITZ MASSONG GMBH; *Int'l*, pg. 2794
FTNON DELFT B.V.—See John Bean Technologies Corporation; *U.S. Public*, pg. 1191
FTNON USA INC.—See John Bean Technologies Corporation; *U.S. Public*, pg. 1191
FT SYSTEM S.R.L.—See Antares Vision SpA; *Int'l*, pg. 482
FUJI DIE TRADING (SHANGHAI) CO., LTD.—See Fuji Die Co., Ltd.; *Int'l*, pg. 2810
FUJI DO BRASIL MAQUINAS INDUSTRIAIS LTDA.—See Fuji Corporation; *Int'l*, pg. 2810
FUJILLOY INDIA PRIVATE LIMITED—See Fuji Die Co., Ltd.; *Int'l*, pg. 2810
FUJILLOY MALAYSIA SDN. BHD.—See Fuji Die Co., Ltd.; *Int'l*, pg. 2810
FUJITA SOLUTION PARTNERS CO., LTD.—See FUJITA ENGINEERING Co., Ltd.; *Int'l*, pg. 2831
FUJITEC ARGENTINA S.A.—See Fujitec Co., Ltd.; *Int'l*, pg. 2831
FUJITEC (MALAYSIA) SDN BHD—See Fujitec Co., Ltd.; *Int'l*, pg. 2831
FUREY FILTER & PUMP INC.—See Genstar Capital, LLC; *U.S. Private*, pg. 1678

423830 — INDUSTRIAL MACHINERY   CORPORATE AFFILIATIONS

FURUNO ESPANA SA—See Furuno Electric Co., Ltd.; *Int'l*, pg. 2847
FURUNO FINLAND OY—See Furuno Electric Co., Ltd.; *Int'l*, pg. 2848
FURUNO SVERIGE AB—See Furuno Electric Co., Ltd.; *Int'l*, pg. 2848
FUSION POLSKA SP. Z O.O.—See AVK Holding A/S; *Int'l*, pg. 747
G2METRIC LIMITED—See Searchlight Capital Partners, L.P.; *U.S. Private*, pg. 3588
GAFFNEY-KROESE SUPPLY CORP.; *U.S. Private*, pg. 1634
GAFFNEY-KROESE SUPPLY INDIA PRIVATE LIMITED—See Gaffney-Kroese Supply Corp.; *U.S. Private*, pg. 1634
GAFFNEY-KROESE SUPPLY PRIVATE LIMITED—See Gaffney-Kroese Supply Corp.; *U.S. Private*, pg. 1634
GAFFNEY-KROESE TRINIDAD LIMITED—See Gaffney-Kroese Supply Corp.; *U.S. Private*, pg. 1634
GAFFNEY-KROESE UK LTD—See Gaffney-Kroese Supply Corp.; *U.S. Private*, pg. 1634
GALAXY TECHNOLOGIES CORP.; *U.S. Private*, pg. 1636
GALLO EQUIPMENT CO.; *U.S. Private*, pg. 1639
GAMMON EQUIPMENT COMPANY INC.; *U.S. Private*, pg. 1641
GARDNER DENVER IBERICA, SL—See Ingersoll Rand Inc.; *U.S. Public*, pg. 1119
GARDNER INC.; *U.S. Private*, pg. 1643
GARLAND'S, INC.; *U.S. Private*, pg. 1644
GARLOCK DO BRASIL PRODUTOS INDUSTRIAIS LTDA.—See Enpro Inc.; *U.S. Public*, pg. 775
GARLOCK PIPELINE TECHNOLOGIES, INC.—See Enpro Inc.; *U.S. Public*, pg. 775
GARLOCK PIPELINE TECHNOLOGIES LIMITED—See Enpro Inc.; *U.S. Public*, pg. 775
GARLOCK SINGAPORE PTE. LTD.—See Enpro Inc.; *U.S. Public*, pg. 775
GAS ARABIAN SERVICES CO.; *Int'l*, pg. 2887
GAS CONDITIONING OF MEXICO, S. DE R.L. DE C.V.—See Enerflex Ltd.; *Int'l*, pg. 2419
GAS EQUIPMENT COMPANY, INC.; *U.S. Private*, pg. 1647
GCF, INC.; *U.S. Private*, pg. 1653
G.D AUTOMATIC PACKAGING—See Coesia S.p.A.; *Int'l*, pg. 1689
G.D AUTOMATISCHE VERPACKUNGSMASCHINEN GMBH—See Coesia S.p.A.; *Int'l*, pg. 1689
G.D CHINA AUTOMATIC MACHINERY LTD.—See Coesia S.p.A.; *Int'l*, pg. 1689
G.D. INDIA PVT. LTD.—See Coesia S.p.A.; *Int'l*, pg. 1690
GEA BARR ROSIN, INC.—See GEA Group Aktiengesellschaft; *Int'l*, pg. 2897
GEA BARR ROSIN LTD.—See GEA Group Aktiengesellschaft; *Int'l*, pg. 2897
GEA ENGENHARIA DE PROCESSOS E SISTEMA INDUSTRIAIS DO BRASIL LTDA—See GEA Group Aktiengesellschaft; *Int'l*, pg. 2898
GEA MECHANICAL EQUIPMENT US, INC.—See GEA Group Aktiengesellschaft; *Int'l*, pg. 2901
GEA MIDDLE EAST FZE—See GEA Group Aktiengesellschaft; *Int'l*, pg. 2900
GEA PROCESS ENGINEERING JAPAN LTD.—See GEA Group Aktiengesellschaft; *Int'l*, pg. 2901
GEA PROCESS ENGINEERING LTD.—See GEA Group Aktiengesellschaft; *Int'l*, pg. 2901
GEA PROCESS ENGINEERING OOO—See GEA Group Aktiengesellschaft; *Int'l*, pg. 2902
GEA PROCESS ENGINEERING OY—See GEA Group Aktiengesellschaft; *Int'l*, pg. 2902
GEA PROCESS ENGINEERING (PTY) LTD.—See GEA Group Aktiengesellschaft; *Int'l*, pg. 2901
GEA PROCESS ENGINEERING S.P.A.—See GEA Group Aktiengesellschaft; *Int'l*, pg. 2902
GEA TUCHENHAGEN US, LLC—See GEA Group Aktiengesellschaft; *Int'l*, pg. 2900
GEA WESTFALIA SEPARATOR DK A/S—See GEA Group Aktiengesellschaft; *Int'l*, pg. 2900
GEA WESTFALIA SEPARATOR IBERICA, S.A.—See GEA Group Aktiengesellschaft; *Int'l*, pg. 2900
GEA WESTFALIA SEPARATOR NEDERLAND B.V.—See GEA Group Aktiengesellschaft; *Int'l*, pg. 2900
GEA WESTFALIA SEPARATOR (S.E.A.) PTE. LTD.—See GEA Group Aktiengesellschaft; *Int'l*, pg. 2900
GEMA EUROPE S.R.L.—See Graco, Inc.; *U.S. Public*, pg. 953
GEMA (SHANGHAI) CO., LTD.—See Graco, Inc.; *U.S. Public*, pg. 953
GENERAC MEXICO ADMINISTRACION, S.A. DE C.V.—See Generac Holdings Inc.; *U.S. Public*, pg. 912
GENERAL COMMERCIAL & INDUSTRIAL SA; *Int'l*, pg. 2918
GENERAL COMMERCIAL NORTHERN GREECE S.A.—See GENERAL COMMERCIAL & INDUSTRIAL SA; *Int'l*, pg. 2918
GENERAL MACHINERY COMPANY INC.; *U.S. Private*, pg. 1665
GENERAL PARTS OF MINNESOTA INC.; *U.S. Private*, pg. 1666

GENERAL SULLIVAN CORP.—See General Sullivan Group Inc.; *U.S. Private*, pg. 1667
GENEVA CORPORATION; *U.S. Private*, pg. 1670
GENOYER GROUP, INC.—See Groupe BPCE; *Int'l*, pg. 3095
GENTEX FRANCE, SAS—See Gentex Corporation; *U.S. Public*, pg. 931
GE OIL & GAS ROTOFLOW—See General Electric Company; *U.S. Public*, pg. 919
GEORGE E. BOOTH CO., INC.; *U.S. Private*, pg. 1681
GEORGE FISCHER (M) SDN BHD—See Georg Fischer AG; *Int'l*, pg. 2937
GEORGE I. REITZ & SONS INC.; *U.S. Private*, pg. 1682
GEORGE KOCH SONS DE MEXICO S. DE R.L. DE C.V.—See Koch Enterprises, Inc.; *U.S. Private*, pg. 2326
GEORGE W. WARDEN COMPANY INCORPORATED; *U.S. Private*, pg. 1683
GEORG FISCHER A/S—See Georg Fischer AG; *Int'l*, pg. 2935
GEORG FISCHER CO LTD—See Georg Fischer AG; *Int'l*, pg. 2935
GEPBER HUNGARIA KFT—See Group Thermote & Vanhalst; *Int'l*, pg. 3089
G.E. RICHARDS GRAPHIC SUPPLIES CO. INC.; *U.S. Private*, pg. 1685
GERLINGER STEEL & SUPPLY COMPANY, CO.; *U.S. Private*, pg. 1686
GEROTECH INC.; *U.S. Private*, pg. 1687
GF AGIECHARMILLES—See Georg Fischer AG; *Int'l*, pg. 2934
GFC, LTD.; *Int'l*, pg. 2956
GF CONTROLS GMBH—See Barnes Group Inc.; *U.S. Public*, pg. 277
GICON PUMPS & EQUIPMENT, LLC; *U.S. Private*, pg. 1697
GICON PUMPS & EQUIPMENT, LTD.; *U.S. Private*, pg. 1697
GIESECKE & DEVRIENT SYSTEMS CANADA, INC.—See Giesecke & Devrient GmbH; *Int'l*, pg. 2969
GI INDUSTRIES, INC.; *U.S. Private*, pg. 1691
GIKEN EUROPE B.V.—See GIKEN Ltd.; *Int'l*, pg. 2972
GIKEN SEISAKUSHO ASIA PTE. LTD.—See GIKEN Ltd.; *Int'l*, pg. 2972
GIL-MAR MANUFACTURING CO.; *U.S. Private*, pg. 1698
GIUFFRE BROS CRANES, INC.; *U.S. Private*, pg. 1703
GKN SINTER METALS GMBH BAD BRUCKENAU—See GKN plc; *Int'l*, pg. 2985
GLAS-CRAFT, INC.—See Graco, Inc.; *U.S. Public*, pg. 953
GLAUBER EQUIPMENT CORP.; *U.S. Private*, pg. 1707
GLEASON CORPORATION; *U.S. Private*, pg. 1708
GLEASON MILANO—See Gleason Corporation; *U.S. Private*, pg. 1708
GLOBAL CONCEPTS ENTERPRISE; *U.S. Private*, pg. 1713
GLOBAL EDM SUPPLIES, INC.; *U.S. Private*, pg. 1713
GLOBAL EQUIPMENT COMPANY INC.—See Global Industrial Company; *U.S. Public*, pg. 942
GLOBAL ONE-PAK LIMITED—See Coral Products PLC; *Int'l*, pg. 1795
GLOBAL SOURCING GROUP, INC.; *U.S. Private*, pg. 1717
GLOBAL SOURCING INC.; *U.S. Private*, pg. 1717
GLORY GLOBAL SOLUTIONS GMBH—See GLORY Ltd.; *Int'l*, pg. 3010
GLORY MECHATRONICS LTD.—See GLORY Ltd.; *Int'l*, pg. 3010
GLORY NASCA LTD.—See GLORY Ltd.; *Int'l*, pg. 3009
GLORY TECHNO 24 CO., LTD.—See GLORY Ltd.; *Int'l*, pg. 3010
GL&V INDIA PVT. LTD.—See GL&V Pulp & Paper; *Int'l*, pg. 2986
GL&V SWEDEN AB - STOCKHOLM—See GL&V Pulp & Paper; *Int'l*, pg. 2986
GL&V SWEDEN AB - TAMPERE—See GL&V Pulp & Paper; *Int'l*, pg. 2986
GMES LLC—See Incline MGMT Corp.; *U.S. Private*, pg. 2053
GODREJ AMERICAS INC. USA.—See Godrej & Boyce Mfg. Co. Ltd.; *Int'l*, pg. 3020
GOETTFERT (CHINA) LIMITED—See GOTTFERT Werkstoff-Prufmaschinen GmbH; *Int'l*, pg. 3044
GOETTFERT - DATAPHYSICS INSTRUMENTS INDIA PVT. LTD.—See GOTTFERT Werkstoff-Prufmaschinen GmbH; *Int'l*, pg. 3044
GOETTFERT INC.—See GOTTFERT Werkstoff-Prufmaschinen GmbH; *Int'l*, pg. 3044
GOINDUSTRY-DOVEBID (AUSTRALIA) PTY. LTD.—See Liquidity Services, Inc.; *U.S. Public*, pg. 1320
GOINDUSTRY-DOVEBID (HONG KONG) LTD—See Liquidity Services, Inc.; *U.S. Public*, pg. 1320
GOINDUSTRY-DOVEBID (MALAYSIA) SDN. BHD.—See Liquidity Services, Inc.; *U.S. Public*, pg. 1321
GOINDUSTRY-DOVEBID MEXICO SA DE CV—See Liquidity Services, Inc.; *U.S. Public*, pg. 1321
GOINDUSTRY-DOVEBID PHILIPPINES, INC.—See Liquidity Services, Inc.; *U.S. Public*, pg. 1321
GOINDUSTRY-DOVEBID (SHANGHAI) CO., LTD.—See Liquidity Services, Inc.; *U.S. Public*, pg. 1321
GOINDUSTRY DOVEBID (S) PTE. LTD.—See Liquidity Services, Inc.; *U.S. Public*, pg. 1320

GOLDBELL EQUIPMENT SDN BHD—See Goldbell Corporation; *Int'l*, pg. 3027
GOODTECH ENVIRONMENT SORUMSAND AS—See Goodtech ASA; *Int'l*, pg. 3041
GORMAN-RUPP BELGIUM SA—See The Gorman-Rupp Company; *U.S. Public*, pg. 2085
THE GORMAN-RUPP INTERNATIONAL COMPANY—See The Gorman-Rupp Company; *U.S. Public*, pg. 2085
GORMAN-RUPP RENTAL SPRL—See The Gorman-Rupp Company; *U.S. Public*, pg. 2085
GOSIGER INC.; *U.S. Private*, pg. 1744
GOT-RACK.COM INC.; *U.S. Private*, pg. 1744
GOULDS PUMPS, INC. - HUNTINGTON—See ITT Inc.; *U.S. Public*, pg. 1177
GOULDS PUMPS (NY), INC.—See ITT Inc.; *U.S. Public*, pg. 1177
GPM INDUSTRIES, INC.; *U.S. Private*, pg. 1748
GRACO DISTRIBUTION BVBA—See Graco, Inc.; *U.S. Public*, pg. 953
GRACO FLUID EQUIPMENT (SUZHOU) CO., LTD.—See Graco, Inc.; *U.S. Public*, pg. 953
GRACO INDIA PRIVATE LIMITED—See Graco, Inc.; *U.S. Public*, pg. 953
GRAPHICS INTERNATIONAL INC.; *U.S. Private*, pg. 1758
GRAY LIFT INCORPORATED; *U.S. Private*, pg. 1759
GRAZIANO TORTONA S.R.L.—See DMG MORI Co., Ltd.; *Int'l*, pg. 2144
GRAZIANO TRANSMISSIONI UK LTD.—See Dana Incorporated; *U.S. Public*, pg. 623
GRC INC.; *U.S. Private*, pg. 1761
GREATOO (INDIA) PRIVATE CO., LTD.—See Greatoo Intelligent Equipment Inc.; *Int'l*, pg. 3067
GREINER EXTRUSION US, INC.—See Greiner Holding AG; *Int'l*, pg. 3079
GRENZEBACH AUTOMATION GMBH—See Grenzebach Maschinenbau GmbH; *Int'l*, pg. 3081
GRENZEBACH CORPORATION—See Grenzebach Maschinenbau GmbH; *Int'l*, pg. 3081
GRENZEBACH DO BRASIL—See Grenzebach Maschinenbau GmbH; *Int'l*, pg. 3082
GRENZEBACH MACHINERY (INDIA) PVT. LTD.—See Grenzebach Maschinenbau GmbH; *Int'l*, pg. 3082
GRENZEBACH MACHINERY (SHANGHAI) LTD.—See Grenzebach Maschinenbau GmbH; *Int'l*, pg. 3082
GRENZEBACH MACHINERY, TAIWAN LTD.—See Grenzebach Maschinenbau GmbH; *Int'l*, pg. 3082
GRENZEBACH MASHTECH, LLC—See Grenzebach Maschinenbau GmbH; *Int'l*, pg. 3082
GROBER INDUSTRIAL SERVICES SDN. BHD.—See Darco Water Technologies Limited; *Int'l*, pg. 1972
GROBET FILE COMPANY OF AMERICA, INC.—See Hammond, Kennedy, Whitney & Company, Inc.; *U.S. Private*, pg. 1850
GROUP HES LIMITED—See Flowtech Fluidpower plc; *Int'l*, pg. 2709
GROUP THERMOTE & VANHALST; *Int'l*, pg. 3089
GRUPPO RIELLO SISTEMI FRANCE—See Gruppo Riello Sistemi S.p.A.; *Int'l*, pg. 3141
GRUPPO RIELLO SISTEMI GERMANY GMBH—See Gruppo Riello Sistemi S.p.A.; *Int'l*, pg. 3141
GRUPPO RIELLO SISTEMI NORTH AMERICA—See Gruppo Riello Sistemi S.p.A.; *Int'l*, pg. 3141
GS GLOBAL RESOURCES, INC.; *U.S. Private*, pg. 1800
GT ENGINEERING & ASSOCIATES, LTD.—See Westinghouse Air Brake Technologies Corporation; *U.S. Public*, pg. 2358
GTP GREEN BELL INC.; *U.S. Private*, pg. 1807
GULF CONTROLS CO. - ACTION HYDRAULICS DIVISION—See Employee Owned Holdings, Inc.; *U.S. Private*, pg. 1386
GULF CONTROLS COMPANY, LLC—See Employee Owned Holdings, Inc.; *U.S. Private*, pg. 1386
GURIT (INDIA) PVT. LTD.—See Gurit Holding AG; *Int'l*, pg. 3187
GUSHER PUMPS (SHANGHAI) CO., LTD.—See Ruthman Pump & Engineering Inc.; *U.S. Private*, pg. 3508
GUTSCHE ENVIRONMENTAL TECHNOLOGY (YIXING) CO. LTD.—See Lydall, Inc.; *U.S. Public*, pg. 1349
GUYSON SA—See Guyson International Limited; *Int'l*, pg. 3189
GUYSON SDN BHD—See Guyson International Limited; *Int'l*, pg. 3189
G&W EQUIPMENT, INC.; *U.S. Private*, pg. 1629
HAAR AUSTRALIA PTY LTD—See Alfons Haar Maschinenbau GmbH & Co. KG; *Int'l*, pg. 315
HAAR PENINSULAR S.L.—See Alfons Haar Maschinenbau GmbH & Co. KG; *Int'l*, pg. 315
HAAR SALZBURG GMBH & CO. KG—See Alfons Haar Maschinenbau GmbH & Co. KG; *Int'l*, pg. 316
HAARSLEV INC.—See Altor Equity Partners AB; *Int'l*, pg. 394
HAARSLEV INDUSTRIES GMBH—See Altor Equity Partners AB; *Int'l*, pg. 395
HAARSLEV INDUSTRIES LTD.—See Altor Equity Partners AB; *Int'l*, pg. 395
HAARSLEV INDUSTRIES SDN BHD—See Altor Equity Partners AB; *Int'l*, pg. 395

423830 — INDUSTRIAL MACHINER...

HAARSLEV INDUSTRIES—See Altor Equity Partners AB; *Int'l*, pg. 394

HAARSLEV UK LTD.—See Altor Equity Partners AB; *Int'l*, pg. 395

HAAS FACTORY OUTLET LLC—See Morris Group, Inc.; *U.S. Private*, pg. 2787

HAAS FACTORY OUTLET—See Gerotech Inc.; *U.S. Private*, pg. 1687

HAAS FACTORY OUTLET—See Gerotech Inc.; *U.S. Private*, pg. 1687

HACH LANGE GMBH—See Danaher Corporation; *U.S. Public*, pg. 626

HACO-ATLANTIC, INC.—See Haco N.V.; *Int'l*, pg. 3205

HADEF FRANCE MANUTENTION ET LEVAGE INDUSTRIEL SARL—See HEINRICH DE FRIES GmbH; *Int'l*, pg. 3324

HAGEMEYER NORTH AMERICA—See Nautic Partners, LLC; *U.S. Private*, pg. 2872

HAGGARD & STOCKING ASSOCIATES INC.; *U.S. Private*, pg. 1840

HAITIAN HUAYUAN (JAPAN) MACHINERY CO., LTD—See Haitian International Holdings Ltd.; *Int'l*, pg. 3217

HAITIAN HUAYUAN MACHINERY (INDIA) PRIVATE LIMITED—See Haitian International Holdings Ltd.; *Int'l*, pg. 3217

HAITIAN HUAYUAN MIDDLE EAST MAKINA DIS TICARET LIMITED SIRKETI—See Haitian International Holdings Ltd.; *Int'l*, pg. 3217

HAITIAN HUAYUAN SOUTH AMERICA COMERCIO DE MAQUINAS LTDA.—See Haitian International Holdings Ltd.; *Int'l*, pg. 3217

HAITIAN IBERICA, S.L.—See Haitian International Holdings Ltd.; *Int'l*, pg. 3217

HAITIAN MIDDLE EAST FZC—See Haitian International Holdings Ltd.; *Int'l*, pg. 3217

HAITIAN RUSSIA LTD—See Haitian International Holdings Ltd.; *Int'l*, pg. 3217

HAKLIFT ABT OY—See Axel Johnson Gruppen AB; *Int'l*, pg. 764

HAKLIFT BALTIC OU—See Axel Johnson Gruppen AB; *Int'l*, pg. 764

HALDER SCHNEIDTECHNIK GMBH—See Erwin Halder KG; *Int'l*, pg. 2500

HALLIDIE MACHINE TOOL SALES, INC.; *U.S. Private*, pg. 1844

HALLITE SEALING SOLUTIONS INDIA PRIVATE LIMITED—See Compagnie Generale des Etablissements Michelin SCA; *Int'l*, pg. 1742

HAMAI CO., LTD. - ASHIKAGA FACTORY—See Hamai Co., Ltd.; *Int'l*, pg. 3235

HAMAI INDUSTRIES LIMITED; *Int'l*, pg. 3235

HAMILTON MESSTECHNIK GMBH—See Hamilton Co., Inc.; *U.S. Private*, pg. 1847

HAMMOND POWER SOLUTIONS INC.; *Int'l*, pg. 3238

HAMMOND POWER SOLUTIONS, INC.—See Hammond Power Solutions Inc.; *Int'l*, pg. 3239

HAMMOND POWER SOLUTIONS S.A. DE C.V.—See Hammond Power Solutions Inc.; *Int'l*, pg. 3239

HANDAN JISHAN REAL ESTATE DEVELOPMENT CO., LTD.—See China Jishan Holdings Limited; *Int'l*, pg. 1513

HANDI-RAMP; *U.S. Private*, pg. 1852

HANDLING SYSTEMS INC.; *U.S. Private*, pg. 1853

HANGZHOU FAIR FINE ELECTROMECHANICS CO., LTD.—See Fair Friend Group; *Int'l*, pg. 2604

HANGZHOU FUJIKURA RUBBER LTD.—See Fujikura Composites Inc.; *Int'l*, pg. 2826

HANGZHOU GLORY FRIEND MACHINERY TECHNOLOGY CO., LTD.—See Fair Friend Group; *Int'l*, pg. 2604

HANLA M&E CO., LTD.—See HANLA IMS CO., LTD.; *Int'l*, pg. 3256

HANNA INSTRUMENTS INC.; *U.S. Private*, pg. 1854

HANTOVER INC.; *U.S. Private*, pg. 1857

HARPAK-ULMA ENGINEERING—See Harpak-ULMA Packaging, LLC; *U.S. Private*, pg. 1867

HARRY HOLLAND & SON, INC.; *U.S. Private*, pg. 1871

HARTWELL ENVIRONMENTAL CORP.—See DXP Enterprises, Inc.; *U.S. Public*, pg. 697

HARTWIG INC.; *U.S. Private*, pg. 1874

HARVEY TOOL COMPANY, LLC—See Summit Partners, L.P.; *U.S. Private*, pg. 3855

THE HASELDEN COMPANY, INC.—See Komline-Sanderson Corporation; *U.S. Private*, pg. 2342

HASHIMOTO SOGYO HOLDINGS CO., LTD.; *Int'l*, pg. 3283

HASKEL FRANCE SAS—See BC Partners LLP; *Int'l*, pg. 922

HASKEL FRANCE SAS—See The Carlyle Group Inc.; *U.S. Public*, pg. 2044

HATCH & KIRK, INC.; *U.S. Private*, pg. 1879

HATFIELD & COMPANY INC.; *U.S. Private*, pg. 1879

HAULOTTE ARGENTINA S.A.—See Haulotte Group SA; *Int'l*, pg. 3285

HAULOTTE FRANCE SARL.—See Haulotte Group SA; *Int'l*, pg. 3285

HAVLIK INTERNATIONAL MACHINERY INC.—See Mill City Capital, L.P.; *U.S. Private*, pg. 2730

HA WAINWRIGHT (GROUP) LIMITED—See Diploma PLC; *Int'l*, pg. 2128

HAWTHORNE LIFT SYSTEMS—See HCI Equity Management, L.P.; *U.S. Private*, pg. 1889

HAWTHORNE MACHINERY COMPANY; *U.S. Private*, pg. 1884

HAYES PUMP, INC.; *U.S. Private*, pg. 1884

HC FORKLIFT AMERICA CORPORATION—See GreatStar Group Co., Ltd.; *Int'l*, pg. 3067

HCH BEARING GERMANY GMBH—See China Huanchi Bearing Group Co., Ltd.; *Int'l*, pg. 1509

HCH BEARING ITALY SRL—See China Huanchi Bearing Group Co., Ltd.; *Int'l*, pg. 1509

HCM SYSTEMS, INC.; *U.S. Private*, pg. 1890

HEARTLAND PUMP RENTAL & SALES, INC.—See Xylem Inc.; *U.S. Public*, pg. 2396

HEATSOURCE, INC.—See HS Holdings, LLC; *U.S. Private*, pg. 1998

HEAVY MACHINES, INC. - FINLEY LLC DIVISION—See Heavy Machines, Inc.; *U.S. Private*, pg. 1902

HEIDELBERG CANADA GRAPHIC EQUIPMENT LTD.—See Heidelberger Druckmaschinen AG; *Int'l*, pg. 3321

HEIDELBERGER CIS OOO—See Heidelberger Druckmaschinen AG; *Int'l*, pg. 3322

HEIDELBERGER DRUCKMASCHINEN AUSTRIA VERTRIEBS-GMBH—See Heidelberger Druckmaschinen AG; *Int'l*, pg. 3322

HEIDELBERGER DRUCKMASCHINEN OSTEUROPA VERTRIEBS-GMBH 4—See Heidelberger Druckmaschinen AG; *Int'l*, pg. 3322

HEIDELBERG GRAPHIC EQUIPMENT LTD.—See Heidelberger Druckmaschinen AG; *Int'l*, pg. 3321

HEIDELBERG HELLAS A.E.E.—See Heidelberger Druckmaschinen AG; *Int'l*, pg. 3321

HEIDELBERG HONG KONG—See EAC Invest AS; *Int'l*, pg. 2261

HEIDELBERG PRAHA SPOL S.R.O.—See Heidelberger Druckmaschinen AG; *Int'l*, pg. 3322

HEIDELBERG SLOVENSKO S.R.O.—See Heidelberger Druckmaschinen AG; *Int'l*, pg. 3322

HEIDELBERG USA, INC.—See Heidelberger Druckmaschinen AG; *Int'l*, pg. 3322

HELGELAND PLAST AS—See Egersund Group AS; *Int'l*, pg. 2323

HELGET SAFETY SUPPLY INC.; *U.S. Private*, pg. 1906

HENRY PRODUCTION INCORPORATED; *U.S. Private*, pg. 1919

H ENTERPRISES INTERNATIONAL INC.; *U.S. Private*, pg. 1822

HERAEUS ELECTRO-NITE AB—See Heraeus Holding GmbH; *Int'l*, pg. 3357

HERAEUS ELECTRO-NITE (AUST.) PTY. LTD.—See Heraeus Holding GmbH; *Int'l*, pg. 3357

HERAEUS ELECTRO-NITE CANADA LTD.—See Heraeus Holding GmbH; *Int'l*, pg. 3357

HERAEUS ELECTRO-NITE CHELYABINSK LLC—See Heraeus Holding GmbH; *Int'l*, pg. 3357

HERAEUS ELECTRO-NITE ESPANA, S.L.—See Heraeus Holding GmbH; *Int'l*, pg. 3357

HERAEUS ELECTRO-NITE FRANCE S.A.R.L.—See Heraeus Holding GmbH; *Int'l*, pg. 3357

HERAEUS ELECTRO-NITE INSTRUMENTOS LTDA.—See Heraeus Holding GmbH; *Int'l*, pg. 3357

HERAEUS ELECTRO-NITE ITALY S.R.L.—See Heraeus Holding GmbH; *Int'l*, pg. 3357

HERAEUS ELECTRO-NITE JAPAN LTD.—See Heraeus Holding GmbH; *Int'l*, pg. 3357

HERAEUS ELECTRO-NITE (U.K.) LTD.—See Heraeus Holding GmbH; *Int'l*, pg. 3357

HERCULES EUROPE BV—See Diploma PLC; *Int'l*, pg. 2128

HERCULES SEALING PRODUCTS INC.—See Diploma PLC; *Int'l*, pg. 2128

HERC-U-LIFT, INC.; *U.S. Private*, pg. 1921

HERRON VALVE, INC.—See Proconex Management Group Inc.; *U.S. Private*, pg. 3272

HERROZ SDN. BHD.—See HPMT Holding Berhad; *Int'l*, pg. 3501

HESSE INDUSTRIAL SALES INC.; *U.S. Private*, pg. 1928

HESSEL HOLDING CO. INC.; *U.S. Private*, pg. 1928

HESSLE FORK TRUCKS LTD—See CorpAcq Holdings Limited; *Int'l*, pg. 1802

HFO CHICAGO, LLC—See Morris Group, Inc.; *U.S. Private*, pg. 2787

HF SUPPLIERS (SCOTLAND) LIMITED—See W.W. Grainger, Inc.; *U.S. Public*, pg. 2320

H.G. MAKELIM COMPANY; *U.S. Private*, pg. 1826

HIAB CHILE S.A.—See Cargotec Corporation; *Int'l*, pg. 1326

HIAB IBERIA, S.L.—See Cargotec Corporation; *Int'l*, pg. 1328

HIAB ITALIA S.R.L.—See Cargotec Corporation; *Int'l*, pg. 1328

HIAB KK—See Cargotec Corporation; *Int'l*, pg. 1326

HIAB NORWAY AS—See Cargotec Corporation; *Int'l*, pg. 1328

HIAB SDN BHD—See Cargotec Corporation; *Int'l*, pg. 1328

HIBIYA TSUSHOU CO., LTD.—See Hibiya Engineering Ltd; *Int'l*, pg. 3383

HIBON INC.—See Ingersoll Rand Inc.; *U.S. Public*, pg. 1120

HIDRIA TEHNOLOSKI CENTER D. O. O.—See Hidria d.o.o.; *Int'l*, pg. 3384

HIDRIA USA INC.—See Hidria d.o.o.; *Int'l*, pg. 3384

HIELKEMA TESTEQUIPMENT B.V.—See ESPEC Corp.; *Int'l*, pg. 2505

HIGHCON SYSTEMS LTD.; *Int'l*, pg. 3387

HIGHLAND HYDRAULICS, INC.—See Headco Industries; *U.S. Private*, pg. 1891

HIKOKI POWER TOOLS ASIA CO., LTD.—See KKR & Co. Inc.; *U.S. Public*, pg. 1257

HIKOKI POWER TOOLS FRANCE S.A.S.—See KKR & Co. Inc.; *U.S. Public*, pg. 1257

HIKOKI POWER TOOLS IBERICA, S.A.—See KKR & Co. Inc.; *U.S. Public*, pg. 1257

HIKOKI POWER TOOLS INDIA PRIVATE LTD.—See KKR & Co. Inc.; *U.S. Public*, pg. 1257

HIKOKI POWER TOOLS ITALIA SPA—See KKR & Co. Inc.; *U.S. Public*, pg. 1257

HIKOKI POWER TOOLS NORWAY AS—See KKR & Co. Inc.; *U.S. Public*, pg. 1257

HIKOKI POWER TOOLS RUS L.L.C.—See KKR & Co. Inc.; *U.S. Public*, pg. 1257

HIKOKI POWER TOOLS SWEDEN AB—See KKR & Co. Inc.; *U.S. Public*, pg. 1257

HIKOKI POWER TOOLS (U.K.) LTD.—See KKR & Co. Inc.; *U.S. Public*, pg. 1257

HILO MAINTENANCE SYSTEMS, INC.; *U.S. Private*, pg. 1948

HILONG USA LLC.—See Hilong Holding Limited; *Int'l*, pg. 3393

HIMILE EUROPE, LLC—See Himile Mechanical Science & Technology Co., Ltd; *Int'l*, pg. 3397

HIMILE (THAILAND) CO., LTD.—See Himile Mechanical Science & Technology Co., Ltd; *Int'l*, pg. 3397

HIOKI (SHANGHAI) SALES & TRADING CO., LTD.—See HIOKI E.E. Corporation; *Int'l*, pg. 3401

HIRATA ENGINEERING, INC.—See Hirata Corporation; *Int'l*, pg. 3403

HIRATA FIELD ENGINEERING CO., LTD.—See Hirata Corporation; *Int'l*, pg. 3403

HIROSHIMA GAS LIVING CO., LTD.—See Hiroshima Gas Co., Ltd.; *Int'l*, pg. 3405

HIRSCH BUSINESS CONCEPTS, LLC—See Hirsch International Corp.; *U.S. Private*, pg. 1950

HIRSCH INTERNATIONAL CORP.; *U.S. Private*, pg. 1950

HISAKA (CHINA) CO., LTD.—See Hisaka Works, Ltd.; *Int'l*, pg. 3406

HISAKA KOREA CO., LTD.—See Hisaka Works, Ltd.; *Int'l*, pg. 3406

HISAKA WORKS (SINGAPORE) PTE LTD.—See Hisaka Works, Ltd.; *Int'l*, pg. 3406

HISAKA WORKS (THAILAND) CO., LTD.—See Hisaka Works, Ltd.; *Int'l*, pg. 3406

HITACHI BUILDING SYSTEMS CO., LTD.—See Hitachi, Ltd.; *Int'l*, pg. 3415

HITACHI (CHINA), LTD.—See Hitachi, Ltd.; *Int'l*, pg. 3413

HITACHI CONSTRUCTION MACHINERY MOZAMBIQUE LIMITED—See Hitachi, Ltd.; *Int'l*, pg. 3416

HITACHI ELEVATOR (CHINA) CO., LTD.—See Hitachi, Ltd.; *Int'l*, pg. 3416

HITACHI ENVIRONMENTAL TECHNOLOGY (YIXING) CO., LTD.—See Hitachi, Ltd.; *Int'l*, pg. 3417

HITACHI HIGH TECHNOLOGIES AMERICA, INC. - DALLAS—See Hitachi, Ltd.; *Int'l*, pg. 3418

HITACHI HIGH TECHNOLOGIES AMERICA, INC. - PLEASANTON—See Hitachi, Ltd.; *Int'l*, pg. 3418

HITACHI HIGH TECHNOLOGIES AMERICA, INC.—See Hitachi, Ltd.; *Int'l*, pg. 3418

HITACHI HIGH-TECHNOLOGIES CANADA INC.—See Hitachi, Ltd.; *Int'l*, pg. 3418

HITACHI INDUSTRIAL EQUIPMENT DRIVE & SOLUTIONS CO., LTD.—See Hitachi, Ltd.; *Int'l*, pg. 3419

HITACHI INDUSTRIAL EQUIPMENT (MALAYSIA) SDN. BHD.—See Hitachi, Ltd.; *Int'l*, pg. 3419

HITACHI KOREA LTD.—See Hitachi, Ltd.; *Int'l*, pg. 3420

HITACHI (SHANGHAI) TRADING CO.—See Hitachi, Ltd.; *Int'l*, pg. 3413

HITACHI ZOSEN HANDLING SYSTEM CO., LTD.—See Hitachi Zosen Corporation; *Int'l*, pg. 3411

HI-TECH SPRAY EQUIPMENT, S.A.—See Graco, Inc.; *U.S. Public*, pg. 953

HITEK LIMITED—See Diploma PLC; *Int'l*, pg. 2128

HKX INC.—See Diploma PLC; *Int'l*, pg. 2128

HM PLANT LTD.—See Hitachi, Ltd.; *Int'l*, pg. 3415

HOBART DO BRASIL LTDA.—See Illinois Tool Works Inc.; *U.S. Public*, pg. 1104

HOCKMAN-LEWIS LIMITED; *U.S. Private*, pg. 1959

HOERBIGER DE COLOMBIA LTDA.—See Hoerbiger Holding AG; *Int'l*, pg. 3440

HOERBIGER DEL ECUADOR, S.A.—See Hoerbiger Holding AG; *Int'l*, pg. 3440

HOERBIGER DRIVE TECHNOLOGY (CHANGZHOU) CO. LTD.—See Hoerbiger Holding AG; *Int'l*, pg. 3440

HOERBIGER INDIA PRIVATE LTD.—See Hoerbiger Holding AG; *Int'l*, pg. 3440

HOERBIGER (WUXI) AUTOMATION TECHNOLOGY CO., LTD.—See Hoerbiger Holding AG; *Int'l*, pg. 3440

HOHNER MAQUINARIA DE ARTES GRAFICAS S.L.—See Hohner Maschinenbau GmbH; *Int'l*, pg. 3442

HOHNER STITCHING PRODUCTS INC.—See Hohner Maschinenbau GmbH; *Int'l*, pg. 3442

HOHNER STITCHING TECHNOLOGY (NANJING) CO., LTD.—See Hohner Maschinenbau GmbH; *Int'l*, pg. 3442
HOHNER UK LTD.—See Hohner Maschinenbau GmbH; *Int'l*, pg. 3442
HOJ ENGINEERING & SALES CO., LLC; *U.S. Private*, pg. 1961
HOKE INC.; *U.S. Private*, pg. 1961
HOLLI-TEX SUPPLY CO.; *U.S. Private*, pg. 1965
HOLLYSYS (ASIA PACIFIC) PTE. LIMITED—See Hollysys Automation Technologies Ltd.; *Int'l*, pg. 3452
HOMA POMPEN B.V.—See HOMA Pumpenfabrik GmbH; *Int'l*, pg. 3454
HOME RIGHT—See Diversified Dynamics Corporation; *U.S. Private*, pg. 1242
HONGHUA INTERNATIONAL DE VENEZUELA, C.A.—See Honghua Group Ltd; *Int'l*, pg. 3471
HONGHUA INTERNATIONAL SUCURSAL COLOMBIA—See Honghua Group Ltd; *Int'l*, pg. 3470
HONGHUA INTERNATIONAL UKRAINE CO., LTD.—See Honghua Group Ltd; *Int'l*, pg. 3470
HONGHUA SUCURSAL BOLIVIA—See Honghua Group Ltd; *Int'l*, pg. 3471
HOP CHEONG TECHNOLOGY (INTERNATIONAL) LIMITED—See HNA International Investment Holdings Limited; *Int'l*, pg. 3433
HORMANN WARNSYSTEME GMBH—See Hormann Holding GmbH & Co. KG; *Int'l*, pg. 3480
HOSHIZAKI HOKKAIDO K.K.—See Hoshizaki Corporation; *Int'l*, pg. 3483
HOSHIZAKI HOKUSHINETSU K.K.—See Hoshizaki Corporation; *Int'l*, pg. 3483
HOSHIZAKI KANTO K.K.—See Hoshizaki Corporation; *Int'l*, pg. 3483
HOSHIZAKI KEIHAN K.K.—See Hoshizaki Corporation; *Int'l*, pg. 3483
HOSHIZAKI KITAKYU K.K.—See Hoshizaki Corporation; *Int'l*, pg. 3483
HOSHIZAKI NANKYU K.K.—See Hoshizaki Corporation; *Int'l*, pg. 3483
HOSHIZAKI OKINAWA CO LTD—See Hoshizaki Corporation; *Int'l*, pg. 3483
HOSHIZAKI SHIKOKU K.K.—See Hoshizaki Corporation; *Int'l*, pg. 3484
HOSHIZAKI TOKAI CO., LTD.—See Hoshizaki Corporation; *Int'l*, pg. 3484
HOSOKAWA ALPINE AMERICAN INC.—See Hosokawa Micron Corporation; *Int'l*, pg. 3485
HOSOKAWA ALPINE JAPAN CO., LTD.—See Hosokawa Micron Corporation; *Int'l*, pg. 3485
HOSOKAWA BEPEX GMBH—See Hosokawa Micron Corporation; *Int'l*, pg. 3485
HOSOKAWA DE MEXICO S.A. DE C.V.—See Hosokawa Micron Corporation; *Int'l*, pg. 3486
HOSOKAWA MICRON (KOREA) LTD—See Hosokawa Micron Corporation; *Int'l*, pg. 3486
HOSOKAWA MICRON (SHANGHAI) POWDER MACHINERY CO. LTD—See Hosokawa Micron Corporation; *Int'l*, pg. 3486
HOUSE OF TOOLS & ENGINEERING; *U.S. Private*, pg. 1992
HOWA (TIANJIN) MACHINERY CO., LTD.—See Howa Machinery, Ltd.; *Int'l*, pg. 3493
HOWDEN FRANCE—See Chart Industries, Inc.; *U.S. Public*, pg. 482
HOWDEN TURBOWERKE GMBH—See Chart Industries, Inc.; *U.S. Public*, pg. 482
HOWELL TRACTOR AND EQUIPMENT LLC—See Lanco International Inc.; *U.S. Private*, pg. 2382
HOWLAND PUMP & SUPPLY CO. INC.; *U.S. Private*, pg. 1996
HR MACHINERY INC.; *U.S. Private*, pg. 1998
HSD S.P.A.—See Biesse S.p.A.; *Int'l*, pg. 1020
HSD USA, INC.—See Biesse S.p.A.; *Int'l*, pg. 1020
HUBER SUPPLY CO. INC.; *U.S. Private*, pg. 2000
HUDACO INDUSTRIES LIMITED; *Int'l*, pg. 3521
HUDACO TRADING LTD—See Hudaco Industries Limited; *Int'l*, pg. 3521
HUDACO TRANSMISSION (PTY) LTD—See Hudaco Industries Limited; *Int'l*, pg. 3521
HUGG & HALL EQUIPMENT COMPANY; *U.S. Private*, pg. 2003
HUHTAMAKI, MOLDED FIBER TECHNOLOGY B.V.—See Huhtamaki Oyj; *Int'l*, pg. 3525
HULLER HILLE GMBH—See Fair Friend Group; *Int'l*, pg. 2604
HULL LIFT TRUCK INC.; *U.S. Private*, pg. 2005
HUNT ENGINE INCORPORATED; *U.S. Private*, pg. 2009
HUNTING ENERGY SERVICES INC.—See Hunting Plc; *Int'l*, pg. 3537
HUON FERS SOUDAGE; *Int'l*, pg. 3537
HURCO MANUFACTURING LTD.—See Hurco Companies, Inc.; *U.S. Public*, pg. 1076
HURST JAWS OF LIFE, INC—See IDEX Corp; *U.S. Public*, pg. 1090
HUSQVARNA FRANCE SAS—See Husqvarna AB; *Int'l*, pg. 3539
HUSSMANN (THAILAND) COMPANY LIMITED—See Ingersoll Rand Inc.; *U.S. Public*, pg. 1120

HUTCHISON HAYES SEPARATION INC.—See Alfa Laval AB; *Int'l*, pg. 309
HUTSON, INC.; *U.S. Private*, pg. 2014
HUYCK.WANGNER JAPAN LIMITED - ASAHI PLANT—See ANDRITZ AG; *Int'l*, pg. 455
HY-BON ENGINEERING COMPANY, INC.—See Turnbridge Capital, LLC; *U.S. Private*, pg. 4260
HYCO INDUSTRIAL SALES CORP.—See Hyundai Group; *Int'l*, pg. 3557
HYDAC ACCESSORIES GMBH—See Hydac International GmbH; *Int'l*, pg. 3544
HYDAC AG—See Hydac International GmbH; *Int'l*, pg. 3544
HYDAC BELARUS—See Hydac International GmbH; *Int'l*, pg. 3544
HYDAC B.V.—See Hydac International GmbH; *Int'l*, pg. 3544
HYDAC FLUIDTEKNIK AB—See Hydac International GmbH; *Int'l*, pg. 3545
HYDAC HIDRAULIKA ES SZURESTECHNIKA KFT.—See Hydac International GmbH; *Int'l*, pg. 3545
HYDAC LTD. STI.—See Hydac International GmbH; *Int'l*, pg. 3545
HYDAC OY—See Hydac International GmbH; *Int'l*, pg. 3545
HYDAC S.A.R.L.—See Hydac International GmbH; *Int'l*, pg. 3545
HYDAC S.P.A.—See Hydac International GmbH; *Int'l*, pg. 3545
HYDAC SP. Z O.O.—See Hydac International GmbH; *Int'l*, pg. 3545
HYDAC TECHNOLOGY CORPORATION, HYDRAULIC DIVISION—See Hydac Technology Corporation; *U.S. Private*, pg. 2016
HYDAC TECHNOLOGY LIMITED—See Hydac International GmbH; *Int'l*, pg. 3545
HYDAC TECHNOLOGY PTE. LTD.—See Hydac International GmbH; *Int'l*, pg. 3545
HYDAC TECHNOLOGY SDN. BHD.—See Hydac International GmbH; *Int'l*, pg. 3545
HYDAC TECHNOLOGY (SHANGHAI) LTD.—See Hydac International GmbH; *Int'l*, pg. 3545
HYDAC TECHNOLOGY SL—See Hydac International GmbH; *Int'l*, pg. 3545
HYDAC UKRAINE—See Hydac International GmbH; *Int'l*, pg. 3545
HYDRADYNE, LLC—See Applied Industrial Technologies, Inc.; *U.S. Public*, pg. 171
HYDRAFLOW EQUIPMENT CO.; *U.S. Private*, pg. 2017
HYDRA-GRENE A/S—See Aktieselskabet Schouw & Co.; *Int'l*, pg. 266
HYDRA GRENE HYDRAULICS EQUIPMENT ACCESSORY (TIANJIN) CO. LTD—See Aktieselskabet Schouw & Co.; *Int'l*, pg. 266
HYDRA GRENE INDIA PRIVATE LIMITED—See Aktieselskabet Schouw & Co.; *Int'l*, pg. 266
HYDRA-POWER SYSTEMS INC.; *U.S. Private*, pg. 2017
HYDRAQUIP DISTRIBUTION, INC.—See Employee Owned Holdings, Inc.; *U.S. Private*, pg. 1386
HYDRASPECMA COMPONENTS AB—See Aktieselskabet Schouw & Co.; *Int'l*, pg. 266
HYDRAULIC CONTROLS, INC.; *U.S. Private*, pg. 2017
HYDROAIR HUGHES, LLC—See Applied Industrial Technologies, Inc.; *U.S. Public*, pg. 171
HYDRO AIR LLC—See Applied Industrial Technologies, Inc.; *U.S. Public*, pg. 171
HYDROFLEX-HYDRAULICS BELGIUM NV—See Flowtech Fluidpower plc; *Int'l*, pg. 2709
HYDROFLEX-HYDRAULICS BV—See Flowtech Fluidpower plc; *Int'l*, pg. 2709
HYDROFLEX-HYDRAULICS ROTTERDAM BV—See Flowtech Fluidpower plc; *Int'l*, pg. 2709
HYDROKIT UK LTD—See Hydrokit; *Int'l*, pg. 3548
HYDROMAT INC.; *U.S. Private*, pg. 2018
HYDRO+ SA—See The Gorman-Rupp Company; *U.S. Public*, pg. 2085
HYDROTECH INC.—See Fluid System Components Inc.; *U.S. Private*, pg. 1552
HYSPECO INC.; *U.S. Private*, pg. 2020
HYSTER-YALE AUSTRALIA HOLDING PTY LTD.—See Hyster-Yale Materials Handling, Inc.; *U.S. Public*, pg. 1080
HYSTER-YALE DEUTSCHLAND GMBH—See Hyster-Yale Materials Handling, Inc.; *U.S. Public*, pg. 1080
HYSTER-YALE ITALIA SPA—See Hyster-Yale Materials Handling, Inc.; *U.S. Public*, pg. 1080
HY-TEK MATERIAL HANDLING, INC.—See Dunes Point Capital, LLC; *U.S. Private*, pg. 1288
HZF SERVICES (MALAYSIA) SDN. BHD.—See Hitachi Zosen Corporation; *Int'l*, pg. 3412
IAI AMERICA, INC.—See IAI Corporation; *Int'l*, pg. 3568
IAI INDUSTRIEROBOTER GMBH—See IAI Corporation; *Int'l*, pg. 3568
IAS—See Shaw Electric Inc.; *U.S. Private*, pg. 3628
IBC NORTH AMERICA INC.; *U.S. Private*, pg. 2028
IDAHO MATERIAL HANDLING INC.—See Hoj Engineering & Sales Co., LLC; *U.S. Private*, pg. 1961
IDEAL SUPPLY COMPANY LIMITED—See Groupe Deschenes Inc.; *Int'l*, pg. 3102
IDEX PUMP TECHNOLOGIES (IRELAND) LIMITED—See IDEX Corp; *U.S. Public*, pg. 1091

IDRA CHINA LTD—See Idra s.r.l.; *Int'l*, pg. 3596
IDRA PRESSEN GMBH—See Idra s.r.l.; *Int'l*, pg. 3596
ID TECHNOLOGY LLC - UPPER MIDWEST OFFICE—See Leonard Green & Partners, L.P.; *U.S. Private*, pg. 2427
II-VI BENELUX N.V.—See Coherent Corp.; *U.S. Public*, pg. 528
II-VI ITALIA S.R.L.—See Coherent Corp.; *U.S. Public*, pg. 528
II-VI SUISSE S.A.R.L.—See Coherent Corp.; *U.S. Public*, pg. 529
IKAR-IMPULSE LTD.—See Disco Corporation; *Int'l*, pg. 2132
IKEGAI (SHANGHAI) MACHINERY COMPANY—See Fair Friend Group; *Int'l*, pg. 2604
IKKA (HONG KONG) CO., LIMITED—See Abico Group; *Int'l*, pg. 61
IKM HVAC AS—See IKM Gruppen AS; *Int'l*, pg. 3611
IKM PRODUCTION TECHNOLOGY AS—See IKM Gruppen AS; *Int'l*, pg. 3611
IKM SOLIDTECH AS—See IKM Gruppen AS; *Int'l*, pg. 3611
IKM STAINLESS TECHNOLOGY AS—See IKM Gruppen AS; *Int'l*, pg. 3611
IKM SUBSEA AS—See IKM Gruppen AS; *Int'l*, pg. 3611
IKM SUBSEA BRASIL LTDA—See IKM Gruppen AS; *Int'l*, pg. 3611
IKM SUBSEA MALAYSIA SDN. BHD—See IKM Gruppen AS; *Int'l*, pg. 3611
IKM SUBSEA MIDDLE EAST FZE—See IKM Gruppen AS; *Int'l*, pg. 3611
IKM SUBSEA SINGAPORE PTE LTD—See IKM Gruppen AS; *Int'l*, pg. 3611
IKM TESTING MALAYSIA SDN. BHD—See IKM Gruppen AS; *Int'l*, pg. 3612
IKM TESTING MEXICO S DE RL DE CV—See IKM Gruppen AS; *Int'l*, pg. 3612
ILAPAK ISRAEL LTD.—See ILAPAK S.A.; *Int'l*, pg. 3613
ILFA FEINSTLEITERTECHNIK GMBH; *Int'l*, pg. 3614
ILLINOIS AUTO ELECTRIC CO. - MIDWEST ENGINE WAREHOUSE DIVISION—See Illinois Auto Electric Co.; *U.S. Private*, pg. 2042
ILLINOIS AUTO ELECTRIC CO.; *U.S. Private*, pg. 2042
ILMO PRODUCTS COMPANY; *U.S. Private*, pg. 2043
IMA ASIA PACIFIC PTE. LTD.—See ADCURAM Group AG; *Int'l*, pg. 128
IMA EST VERPACKUNGSSYSTEME HANDELSGESELLSCHAFT GM.BH.—See I.M.A. Industria Macchine Automatiche S.p.A.; *Int'l*, pg. 3565
IMA GERMANY GMBH—See I.M.A. Industria Macchine Automatiche S.p.A.; *Int'l*, pg. 3565
IMA UK LTD.—See I.M.A. Industria Macchine Automatiche S.p.A.; *Int'l*, pg. 3566
IMPACT AIR SYSTEMS LTD.—See Addtech AB; *Int'l*, pg. 134
IMPROVED MACHINERY INC.—See Ingersoll Rand Inc.; *U.S. Public*, pg. 1120
INDECK POWER EQUIPMENT COMPANY; *U.S. Private*, pg. 2054
INDOFF INC.—See Global Industrial Company; *U.S. Public*, pg. 942
INDUCTOTHERM GROUP CANADA LTD.—See Indel, Inc.; *U.S. Private*, pg. 2055
INDUQUIP, C.A.—See Nordson Corporation; *U.S. Public*, pg. 1533
INDUSTRIA DE TURBO PROPULSORES S.A. - AJALVIR PLANT—See Bain Capital, LP; *U.S. Private*, pg. 433
INDUSTRIA DE TURBO PROPULSORES S.A. - SEVILLE PLANT—See Bain Capital, LP; *U.S. Private*, pg. 433
INDUSTRIAL ASSETS CORP.; *U.S. Private*, pg. 2064
INDUSTRIAL BELTING & TRANSMISSION, INC.; *U.S. Private*, pg. 2064
INDUSTRIAL DIESEL INC.; *U.S. Private*, pg. 2065
INDUSTRIAL DISPOSAL SUPPLY COMPANY; *U.S. Private*, pg. 2065
INDUSTRIAL DISTRIBUTION RESOURCES, LLC; *U.S. Private*, pg. 2065
INDUSTRIAL EQUIPMENT CO. OF HOUSTON; *U.S. Private*, pg. 2066
INDUSTRIAL-IRRIGATION SERVICES; *U.S. Private*, pg. 2069
INDUSTRIAL MILL & MAINTENANCE SUPPLY INC.; *U.S. Private*, pg. 2067
INDUSTRIAL MOTOR POWER COPORATION; *U.S. Private*, pg. 2067
INDUSTRIAL SUPPLY COMPANY INC.; *U.S. Private*, pg. 2068
INDUSTRIAL SUPPLY SOLUTIONS, INC.; *U.S. Private*, pg. 2068
INDUSTRIAL SUPPLY SOLUTIONS, INC.—See Industrial Supply Solutions, Inc.; *U.S. Private*, pg. 2068
INDUSTRIAL WELDING SUPPLY INC.; *U.S. Private*, pg. 2069
INDUSTRIE PLASTIC ELSASSER GMBH—See Illinois Tool Works Inc.; *U.S. Public*, pg. 1108
INENCO GROUP PTY LTD.—See Genuine Parts Company; *U.S. Public*, pg. 933
INFASTECH (SHENZHEN) LIMITED—See Stanley Black & Decker, Inc.; *U.S. Public*, pg. 1932
INGERSOLL-RAND ARCHITECTURAL HARDWARE (AUS-

423830 — INDUSTRIAL MACHINER...

TRALIA) PTY LIMITED—See Ingersoll Rand Inc.; *U.S. Public,* pg. 1120
INGERSOLL-RAND CHARITABLE FOUNDATION—See Ingersoll Rand Inc.; *U.S. Public,* pg. 1121
INGERSOLL-RAND (HONG KONG) LIMITED—See Ingersoll Rand Inc.; *U.S. Public,* pg. 1120
INGERSOLL-RAND KOREA LIMITED—See Ingersoll Rand Inc.; *U.S. Public,* pg. 1121
INGERSOLL-RAND MACHINERY (SHANGHAI) COMPANY LIMITED—See Ingersoll Rand Inc.; *U.S. Public,* pg. 1121
INGERSOLL-RAND MALAYSIA CO. SDN. BHD.—See Ingersoll Rand Inc.; *U.S. Public,* pg. 1121
INGERSOLL-RAND NETHERLANDS B.V.—See Ingersoll Rand Inc.; *U.S. Public,* pg. 1121
INGRAM MICRO APS—See Hainan Traffic Administration Holding Co., Ltd.; *Int'l,* pg. 3214
INJECTION MOLDERS SUPPLY COMPANY; *U.S. Private,* pg. 2077
INLINE SERVICES, INC.; *U.S. Private,* pg. 2079
INMOBILIARIA CIT., S.A. DE C.V.—See Illinois Tool Works Inc.; *U.S. Public,* pg. 1108
INNSE-BERARDI GMBH—See Camozzi Group; *Int'l,* pg. 1274
INNSE-BERARDI INC.—See Camozzi Group; *Int'l,* pg. 1274
INOTEC COATINGS & HYDRAULICS, INC.—See Corrosion & Abrasion Solutions Ltd.; *Int'l,* pg. 1806
INSATECH A/S—See Addtech AB; *Int'l,* pg. 134
INSCO, INC.; *U.S. Private,* pg. 2085
INSERCO BRASIL SERVICOS INDUSTRIAIS LTDA.—See Dieffenbacher Holding GmbH & Co. KG; *Int'l,* pg. 2114
INSTRON DEUTSCHLAND GMBH—See Illinois Tool Works Inc.; *U.S. Public,* pg. 1108
INSTRON FRANCE S.A.S.—See Illinois Tool Works Inc.; *U.S. Public,* pg. 1108
INSTRON JAPAN CO. LTD.—See Illinois Tool Works Inc.; *U.S. Public,* pg. 1108
INSTRON KOREA LLC—See Illinois Tool Works Inc.; *U.S. Public,* pg. 1108
INSTRUMART; *U.S. Private,* pg. 2094
INSTRUMENT ASSOCIATES INC.; *U.S. Private,* pg. 2094
INTER-AMERICAN OIL WORKS INC.; *U.S. Private,* pg. 2107
INTERFACE SEALING SOLUTIONS, EUROPE SARL—See Lydall, Inc.; *U.S. Public,* pg. 1349
INTERMARKET CORP.; *U.S. Private,* pg. 2112
INTERMOUNTAIN VALVE & CONTROLS INC.—See Bray International, Inc.; *U.S. Private,* pg. 642
INTERNATIONAL TOOL MANUFACTURING; *U.S. Private,* pg. 2121
INVICTA VALVES LTD.—See AVK Holding A/S; *Int'l,* pg. 747
IOOO SIEMPELKAMP BEL—See G. Siempelkamp GmbH & Co. KG; *Int'l,* pg. 2864
IOS ACQUISITIONS, INC.—See L.B. Foster Company; *U.S. Public,* pg. 1278
IOS/PCI, LLC—See L.B. Foster Company; *U.S. Public,* pg. 1278
IPCO GERMANY GMBH—See FAM AB; *Int'l,* pg. 2611
IPCO PROCESS SYSTEMS B.V.—See FAM AB; *Int'l,* pg. 2611
IPCO RUS LTD—See FAM AB; *Int'l,* pg. 2611
IRONLINE COMPRESSION LIMITED PARTNERSHIP—See Staple Street Capital LLC; *U.S. Private,* pg. 3784
THE ISAACS COMPANY—See Fluid System Components Inc.; *U.S. Private,* pg. 1552
ISC ITALIA S.R.L.—See Einhell Germany AG; *Int'l,* pg. 2334
ISCO INDUSTRIES LLC; *U.S. Private,* pg. 2143
ISRA VISION JAPAN CORP LTD—See Atlas Copco AB; *Int'l,* pg. 683
ISRA VISION LASOR GMBH—See Atlas Copco AB; *Int'l,* pg. 682
ITALPARTS ITALIA S.R.L.—See Epiroc AB; *Int'l,* pg. 2463
ITEK AS—See Addtech AB; *Int'l,* pg. 133
ITRON AUSTRIA GMBH—See Itron, Inc.; *U.S. Public,* pg. 1176
ITRON CANADA, INC.—See Itron, Inc.; *U.S. Public,* pg. 1176
ITRON DISTRIBUCION S.A. DE C.V.—See Itron, Inc.; *U.S. Public,* pg. 1176
ITRON LLC—See Itron, Inc.; *U.S. Public,* pg. 1176
ITRON MEASUREMENTS & SYSTEMS (PROPRIETARY) LIMITED—See Itron, Inc.; *U.S. Public,* pg. 1176
ITRON METERING SYSTEMS SINGAPORE PTE LTD.—See Itron, Inc.; *U.S. Public,* pg. 1176
ITRON POLSKA SP. Z O.O.—See Itron, Inc.; *U.S. Public,* pg. 1176
ITRON SWEDEN AB—See Itron, Inc.; *U.S. Public,* pg. 1176
ITT BLAKERS PTY LTD—See ITT Inc.; *U.S. Public,* pg. 1177
ITT FLUID TECHNOLOGY INTERNATIONAL, INC.—See ITT Inc.; *U.S. Public,* pg. 1178
ITT INC.; *U.S. Public,* pg. 1177
ITT PURE-FLO (UK) LTD.—See ITT Inc.; *U.S. Public,* pg. 1178
ITW ARK-LES CORPORATION—See Illinois Tool Works Inc.; *U.S. Public,* pg. 1104
ITW AUTOMOTIVE COMPONENTS (LANGFANG) CO., LTD.—See Illinois Tool Works Inc.; *U.S. Public,* pg. 1104
ITW BAILLY COMTE S.A.S.—See Illinois Tool Works Inc.; *U.S. Public,* pg. 1104

ITW BEFESTIGUNGSSYSTEME ALPEN GMBH—See Illinois Tool Works Inc.; *U.S. Public,* pg. 1104
ITW CER—See Illinois Tool Works Inc.; *U.S. Public,* pg. 1104
ITW COLOMBIA S.A.S.—See Illinois Tool Works Inc.; *U.S. Public,* pg. 1105
ITW CONSTRUCTION PRODUCTS OU—See Illinois Tool Works Inc.; *U.S. Public,* pg. 1105
ITW DO BRASIL INDUSTRIAL E COMERCIAL LTDA.—See Illinois Tool Works Inc.; *U.S. Public,* pg. 1108
ITW EF&C FRANCE SAS—See Illinois Tool Works Inc.; *U.S. Public,* pg. 1105
ITW GRAPHICS (THAILAND) LTD.—See Illinois Tool Works Inc.; *U.S. Public,* pg. 1106
ITW GSE APS—See Illinois Tool Works Inc.; *U.S. Public,* pg. 1106
ITW IRELAND—See Illinois Tool Works Inc.; *U.S. Public,* pg. 1106
ITW (NINGBO) COMPONENTS & FASTENINGS SYSTEMS CO., LTD.—See Illinois Tool Works Inc.; *U.S. Public,* pg. 1104
ITW PERFORMANCE POLYMERS APS—See Illinois Tool Works Inc.; *U.S. Public,* pg. 1107
ITW RICHMOND TECHNOLOGY—See Illinois Tool Works Inc.; *U.S. Public,* pg. 1107
ITW RIVEX S.A.S.—See Illinois Tool Works Inc.; *U.S. Public,* pg. 1107
ITW WELDING PRODUCTS B.V.—See Illinois Tool Works Inc.; *U.S. Public,* pg. 1108
IVAN DOVERSPIKE CO.; *U.S. Private,* pg. 2150
IVES EQUIPMENT CORPORATION—See Frontenac Company LLC; *U.S. Private,* pg. 1614
IWI INC.; *U.S. Private,* pg. 2152
IZUMI SHOKO CO., LTD.—See Daido Kogyo Co., Ltd.; *Int'l,* pg. 1921
JACO ENVIRONMENTAL INC.; *U.S. Private,* pg. 2179
JAMES H. CROSS CO.; *U.S. Private,* pg. 2184
JAMES PRECISION ENGINEERING PTE LTD—See Chien Wei Precise Technology Co., Ltd.; *Int'l,* pg. 1477
JAMES RIVER EQUIPMENT INC.; *U.S. Private,* pg. 2185
JAPAN AJAX MAGNETHERMIC CO., LTD.—See Park-Ohio Holdings Corp.; *U.S. Public,* pg. 1639
JASPER ENGINES & TRANSMISSIONS, INC.—See Jasper Engine & Transmission Exchange Inc.; *U.S. Private,* pg. 2190
JATASCO, INC.—See The Eads Company; *U.S. Private,* pg. 4024
JAYBEE ENG. (HOLDINGS) PTY. LTD.—See ANDRITZ AG; *Int'l,* pg. 456
JAYCO INTERNATIONAL; *U.S. Private,* pg. 2192
JBM TECHNOLOGIES, INC.; *U.S. Private,* pg. 2194
JBT FOOD & DAIRY SYSTEMS SARL—See John Bean Technologies Corporation; *U.S. Public,* pg. 1192
JCI INDUSTRIES INC.; *U.S. Private,* pg. 2194
J. & D. GEARS LIMITED—See Westinghouse Air Brake Technologies Corporation; *U.S. Public,* pg. 2358
JEFFERDS CORPORATION; *U.S. Private,* pg. 2197
JENS S. TRANSMISJONER AS—See Axel Johnson Gruppen AB; *Int'l,* pg. 763
JERGENS INDIA PRIVATE, LTD.—See Jergens Inc.; *U.S. Private,* pg. 2201
JF CORP.—See MidOcean Partners, LLP; *U.S. Private,* pg. 2716
J.H. BENNETT & COMPANY INC.; *U.S. Private,* pg. 2165
J.H. WRIGHT & ASSOCIATES INC.; *U.S. Private,* pg. 2166
JINAN ZHENGTE AUTOMATION TECHNOLOGY CO., LTD.—See Endress+Hauser (International) Holding AG; *Int'l,* pg. 2408
JIS DISTRIBUTION LLC—See Jergens Inc.; *U.S. Private,* pg. 2201
JLG EMEA B.V.—See Oshkosh Corporation; *U.S. Public,* pg. 1620
JLG GROUND SUPPORT EUROPE BVBA—See Oshkosh Corporation; *U.S. Public,* pg. 1620
J.M. GRIMSTAD INC.; *U.S. Private,* pg. 2168
JML-SYSTEM AB—See Dustin Group AB; *Int'l,* pg. 2235
JM PROCESS SYSTEMS INC.; *U.S. Private,* pg. 2214
JOBE & COMPANY INC.; *U.S. Private,* pg. 2217
JOBS GMBH—See Fair Friend Group; *Int'l,* pg. 2604
JOBS INC.—See Fair Friend Group; *Int'l,* pg. 2604
JOBS PRC—See Fair Friend Group; *Int'l,* pg. 2604
JOBS SARL—See Fair Friend Group; *Int'l,* pg. 2604
JOHN BEAN TECHNOLOGIES HONG KONG LIMITED—See John Bean Technologies Corporation; *U.S. Public,* pg. 1191
JOHN BEAN TECHNOLOGIES HONG KONG LTD. - PHILIPPINES OFFICE—See John Bean Technologies Corporation; *U.S. Public,* pg. 1191
JOHN BEAN TECHNOLOGIES LTD.—See John Bean Technologies Corporation; *U.S. Public,* pg. 1191
JOHN BEAN TECHNOLOGIES MIDDLE EAST FZE—See John Bean Technologies Corporation; *U.S. Public,* pg. 1191
JOHN BEAN TECHNOLOGIES SA—See John Bean Technologies Corporation; *U.S. Public,* pg. 1192
JOHN BEAN TECHNOLOGIES SP. Z O.O.—See John Bean Technologies Corporation; *U.S. Public,* pg. 1192
JOHN BEAN TECHNOLOGIES (THAILAND) LTD.—See John Bean Technologies Corporation; *U.S. Public,* pg. 1191

JOHN DEERE AGRICULTURAL HOLDINGS, INC.—See Deere & Company; *U.S. Public,* pg. 647
JOHN DEERE FOREIGN SALES CORPORATION LIMITED—See Deere & Company; *U.S. Public,* pg. 646
JOHN DEERE LAWN AND GROUNDS CARE HOLDINGS, INC.—See Deere & Company; *U.S. Public,* pg. 646
JOHN H. CARTER COMPANY INCORPORATED; *U.S. Private,* pg. 2222
JOHN HENRY FOSTER COMPANY OF SAINT LOUIS INC.; *U.S. Private,* pg. 2222
JOHN M. ELLSWORTH CO., INC.; *U.S. Private,* pg. 2223
JOHNSON EQUIPMENT COMPANY INC.; *U.S. Private,* pg. 2227
JOHNSON & TOWERS, INC.; *U.S. Private,* pg. 2226
JOHNSTON INDUSTRIAL SUPPLY, INC.; *U.S. Private,* pg. 2230
JOHNSTON SUPPLY INC.; *U.S. Private,* pg. 2230
JOSEPH INDUSTRIES INC.—See Fastener Industries Inc.; *U.S. Private,* pg. 1482
JOT AUTOMATION BEIJING LTD.—See Head Invest Oy; *Int'l,* pg. 3301
JOT AUTOMATION INC.—See Head Invest Oy; *Int'l,* pg. 3301
JOT AUTOMATION ITALY S.R.L.—See Head Invest Oy; *Int'l,* pg. 3301
JOT AUTOMATION KFT.—See Head Invest Oy; *Int'l,* pg. 3301
JOT AUTOMATION VIETNAM LTD.—See Head Invest Oy; *Int'l,* pg. 3301
J&S ENGINEERING CORP.—See ESPEC Corp.; *Int'l,* pg. 2505
JTE MACHINE SYSTEMS, INC.—See Druid Capital Partners, LLC; *U.S. Private,* pg. 1279
JUFFALI TECHNICAL EQUIPMENT COMPANY—See E.A. Juffali & Brothers Company; *Int'l,* pg. 2251
JUMP INTERNATIONAL TRADING (SHANGHAI) CO LTD—See Freudenberg SE; *Int'l,* pg. 2789
JUST ADD PLASTICS INC.; *U.S. Private,* pg. 2245
J.W. HARRIS CO., INC.—See Lincoln Electric Holdings, Inc.; *U.S. Public,* pg. 1317
J & Y INTERNATIONAL COMPANY LIMITED—See Dream International Ltd; *Int'l,* pg. 2203
KAESER COMPRESSORS INC.; *U.S. Private,* pg. 2254
KALMAR PORT MACHINERY (SHENZHEN) CO., LTD—See Cargotec Corporation; *Int'l,* pg. 1327
KANSAS/OKLAHOMA MACHINE TOOLS, INC.; *U.S. Private,* pg. 2261
KAUKOMARKKINAT OY—See Aspo Oyj; *Int'l,* pg. 631
KAYNAK TEKNIGI SANAYI VE TICARET A.S.—See Lincoln Electric Holdings, Inc.; *U.S. Public,* pg. 1317
KBA DOCUSYS, INC.; *U.S. Private,* pg. 2268
KBC TOOLS INCORPORATED; *U.S. Private,* pg. 2268
K-D SUPPLY CORPORATION; *U.S. Private,* pg. 2250
KDT EUROPE SP Z O O—See Guangzhou KDT Machinery Co., Ltd; *Int'l,* pg. 3166
KECKLEY COMPANY; *U.S. Private,* pg. 2271
K.E. FISCHER L.L.C.—See Deutsche Beteiligungs AG; *Int'l,* pg. 2063
KENKO UTILITY SUPPLY INC.; *U.S. Private,* pg. 2284
KENNAMETAL AMSG GMBH—See Kennametal Inc.; *U.S. Public,* pg. 1222
KENNAMETAL ARGENTINA S.A.—See Kennametal Inc.; *U.S. Public,* pg. 1221
KENNAMETAL CHILE LTDA.—See Kennametal Inc.; *U.S. Public,* pg. 1221
KENNAMETAL DO BRASIL LTDA.—See Kennametal Inc.; *U.S. Public,* pg. 1223
KENNAMETAL ENERGY, MINING & CONSTRUCTION SOLUTIONS—See Kennametal Inc.; *U.S. Public,* pg. 1221
KENNAMETAL HUNGARIA KFT.—See Kennametal Inc.; *U.S. Public,* pg. 1222
KENNAMETAL ITALIA PRODUZIONE S.R.L.—See Kennametal Inc.; *U.S. Public,* pg. 1222
KENNEDY ENGINE CO., INC.; *U.S. Private,* pg. 2284
KENNEDY ENGINEERING & ASSOCIATES GROUP, LLC.—See Volkert, Inc.; *U.S. Private,* pg. 4410
KERN COUNTY TRACTOR PARTS, INC.—See Kinderhook Industries, LLC; *U.S. Private,* pg. 2306
KERR PUMP AND SUPPLY INC.; *U.S. Private,* pg. 2291
KEY EQUIPMENT & SUPPLY COMPANY; *U.S. Private,* pg. 2293
KFE (SHENZHEN) CO., LTD.—See Cosmos Machinery Enterprises Limited; *Int'l,* pg. 1813
KFE (SUZHOU) CO., LTD.—See Cosmos Machinery Enterprises Limited; *Int'l,* pg. 1813
KFE (THAILAND) CO., LTD.—See Cosmos Machinery Enterprises Limited; *Int'l,* pg. 1813
KHANSAHEB SYKES LLC—See ANDREWS SYKES GROUP PLC; *Int'l,* pg. 452
KINETICO BELGIUM HOLDINGS NV—See Axel Johnson Gruppen AB; *Int'l,* pg. 765
KINGJARL CORPORATION—See Endress+Hauser (International) Holding AG; *Int'l,* pg. 2408
KIRO GRIFOLS S.L.—See Grifols, S.A.; *Int'l,* pg. 3085

423830 — INDUSTRIAL MACHINER...

KITO CANADA INC.—See The Carlyle Group Inc.; *U.S. Public*, pg. 2055
KITO EUROPE GMBH—See The Carlyle Group Inc.; *U.S. Public*, pg. 2055
KMC AB—See Addtech AB; *Int'l*, pg. 131
KMH SYSTEMS, INC.; *U.S. Private*, pg. 2321
KMI SERVICES PTE LTD—See Fair Friend Group; *Int'l*, pg. 2604
KNAPPCO CORPORATION—See Dover Corporation; *U.S. Public*, pg. 681
KNOX OIL FIELD SUPPLY, INC.—See Applied Industrial Technologies, Inc.; *U.S. Public*, pg. 171
KOCH AUSTRALIA PTY. LTD.—See Koch Industries, Inc.; *U.S. Private*, pg. 2332
KOCH-GLITSCH CANADA, LP—See Koch Industries, Inc.; *U.S. Private*, pg. 2332
KOCH TECNOLOGIA QUIMICA LTDA.—See Koch Industries, Inc.; *U.S. Private*, pg. 2332
KOIS BROTHERS EQUIPMENT CO.; *U.S. Private*, pg. 2340
KOKI HOLDINGS AMERICA LTD. - CANADA—See KKR & Co. Inc.; *U.S. Public*, pg. 1257
KOKI HOLDINGS AMERICA LTD.—See KKR & Co. Inc.; *U.S. Public*, pg. 1257
KOMA PRECISION INC.; *U.S. Private*, pg. 2341
KONSTANCE PNEUMATICS—See Penn-Air & Hydraulics Corp.; *U.S. Private*, pg. 3135
KOUVO AUTOMATION OY—See Addtech AB; *Int'l*, pg. 134
KRAFT POWER CORP.; *U.S. Private*, pg. 2349
KREMLIN-REXSON SA—See Exel Industries SA; *Int'l*, pg. 2582
KRUGE-AIR, INC.—See H.I.G. Capital, LLC; *U.S. Private*, pg. 1831
KUHN GROUP SAS—See Bucher Industries AG; *Int'l*, pg. 1209
KYC MACHINE CO., LTD.—See Fair Friend Group; *Int'l*, pg. 2604
KYC MACHINE INDUSTRY CO. LTD. - NISHIWAKI PLANT—See Fair Friend Group; *Int'l*, pg. 2604
KYC MACHINE INDUSTRY CO. LTD.—See Fair Friend Group; *Int'l*, pg. 2604
KYC SORIMACHI CO., LTD.—See Fair Friend Group; *Int'l*, pg. 2604
KYOEI FUTABA ENGINEERING CO., LTD.—See Cosmos Machinery Enterprises Limited; *Int'l*, pg. 1813
LAETUS FRANCE SARL.—See Coesia S.p.A.; *Int'l*, pg. 1690
LAETUS IBERICA—See Coesia S.p.A.; *Int'l*, pg. 1690
LAETUS MEXICO S. DE R.L. DE C.V.—See Coesia S.p.A.; *Int'l*, pg. 1690
LAGLER AUSTRALIA—See Eugen Lagler GmbH; *Int'l*, pg. 2526
LAM VALVES INC.—See Eggelhof Incorporated; *U.S. Private*, pg. 1344
LASER DESIGN, INC.—See Nordson Corporation; *U.S. Public*, pg. 1532
LASTRA ATTREZZATURE S.R.L.—See Agfa-Gevaert N.V.; *Int'l*, pg. 209
LATHROP-TROTTER CO, INC.—See Koch Enterprises, Inc.; *U.S. Private*, pg. 2326
LAWSON PRODUCTS INC. (ONTARIO)—See Distribution Solutions Group, Inc.; *U.S. Public*, pg. 668
LAWSON PRODUCTS, INC.—See Distribution Solutions Group, Inc.; *U.S. Public*, pg. 668
LAWSON PRODUCTS, INC.—See Distribution Solutions Group, Inc.; *U.S. Public*, pg. 669
LECORP, INC.; *U.S. Private*, pg. 2410
THE LEE COMPANY SCANDINAVIA AB—See The Lee Company; *U.S. Private*, pg. 4069
LEE MATHEWS EQUIPMENT INC.; *U.S. Private*, pg. 2413
LEE PRODUCTS LTD.—See The Lee Company; *U.S. Private*, pg. 4068
LEIPURIN ESTONIA AS—See Aspo Oyj; *Int'l*, pg. 631
LENSER ASIA SDN. BHD.—See ANDRITZ AG; *Int'l*, pg. 456
LENSER FILTRATION GMBH—See ANDRITZ AG; *Int'l*, pg. 456
LESLIE EQUIPMENT COMPANY - MARIETTA—See Leslie Equipment Company; *U.S. Private*, pg. 2432
LESLIE EQUIPMENT COMPANY—See Leslie Equipment Company; *U.S. Private*, pg. 2432
LETCO MEDICAL, LLC—See Fagron NV; *Int'l*, pg. 2603
LEVEL5 TOOLS, LLC—See Worthington Industries, Inc.; *U.S. Public*, pg. 2382
L.F. GEORGE INC.; *U.S. Private*, pg. 2365
L&H TECHNOLOGIES INC.; *U.S. Private*, pg. 2362
LIBERTY METAL PRODUCTS CO.—See The Handy/Kenlin Group; *U.S. Private*, pg. 4043
LIBERTY SUPPLY INC.; *U.S. Private*, pg. 2447
LIDA SAS—See Air Products & Chemicals, Inc.; *U.S. Public*, pg. 66
LIFT ATLANTA INCORPORATED; *U.S. Private*, pg. 2452
LIFTECH EQUIPMENT COMPANIES, INC.—See Alta Equipment Group Inc.; *U.S. Public*, pg. 86
LIFT INC.; *U.S. Private*, pg. 2452
LIFT MATERIAL AUSTRALIA PTY LTD—See Dewhurst Group plc; *Int'l*, pg. 2091
LIFT SOLUTIONS, INC.; *U.S. Private*, pg. 2452
LIFT TRUCK SERVICE CENTER INC.; *U.S. Private*, pg. 2452

THE LILLY COMPANY INC.; *U.S. Private*, pg. 4070
THE LINCOLN ELECTRIC COMPANY (NEW ZEALAND) LIMITED—See Lincoln Electric Holdings, Inc.; *U.S. Public*, pg. 1318
THE LINCOLN ELECTRIC COMPANY OF CANADA LP—See Lincoln Electric Holdings, Inc.; *U.S. Public*, pg. 1318
THE LINCOLN ELECTRIC COMPANY OF SOUTH AFRICA (PTY) LTD.—See Lincoln Electric Holdings, Inc.; *U.S. Public*, pg. 1318
LINCOLN ELECTRIC ITALIA S.R.L.—See Lincoln Electric Holdings, Inc.; *U.S. Public*, pg. 1317
LINCOLN ELECTRIC SVERIGE—See Lincoln Electric Holdings, Inc.; *U.S. Public*, pg. 1318
LINXIS GROUP—See Hillenbrand, Inc.; *U.S. Public*, pg. 1037
LIPTEN COMPANY LLC; *U.S. Private*, pg. 2465
LIQUIP INTERNATIONAL PTY LIMITED—See Dover Corporation; *U.S. Public*, pg. 681
LISTA AUSTRIA GMBH—See GreatStar Group Co., Ltd.; *Int'l*, pg. 3068
LISTA ITALIA S.R.L.—See GreatStar Group Co., Ltd.; *Int'l*, pg. 3068
LISTA SISTEMAS DE ALMACENAJE, S.A.—See GreatStar Group Co., Ltd.; *Int'l*, pg. 3068
LISTA UK LTD.—See GreatStar Group Co., Ltd.; *Int'l*, pg. 3068
LITEPOINT JAPAN K.K.—See Teradyne, Inc.; *U.S. Public*, pg. 2018
LITEPOINT TECHNOLOGY (SHANGHAI) COMPANY, LTD.—See Teradyne, Inc.; *U.S. Public*, pg. 2018
LLC ANDRITZ HYDRO—See ANDRITZ AG; *Int'l*, pg. 456
LLC EXTERRAN VOSTOK—See Enerflex Ltd.; *Int'l*, pg. 2419
LLC GLASTON—See Glaston Oyj Abp; *Int'l*, pg. 2989
LM MASKIN AS—See HEINRICH DE FRIES GmbH; *Int'l*, pg. 3324
L&M WELDING SUPPLY, INC.—See CI Capital Partners LLC; *U.S. Private*, pg. 895
LOCKE EQUIPMENT SALES CO.; *U.S. Private*, pg. 2478
LOFA INDUSTRIES, LLC—See Harbour Group Industries, Inc.; *U.S. Private*, pg. 1860
LOGISTEC GULF COAST LLC—See Blue Wolf Capital Partners LLC; *U.S. Private*, pg. 594
LOMA SYSTEMS (CANADA) INC.—See Illinois Tool Works Inc.; *U.S. Public*, pg. 1109
LORENTZEN & WETTRE S.A.R.L.—See ABB Ltd.; *Int'l*, pg. 50
LOSCAM AUSTRALIA PTY LTD.—See China Merchants Group Limited; *Int'l*, pg. 1521
LOSCAM (MALAYSIA) SDN. BHD.—See China Merchants Group Limited; *Int'l*, pg. 1521
LOSCAM (NEW ZEALAND) LIMITED—See China Merchants Group Limited; *Int'l*, pg. 1521
LOSCAM PACKAGING EQUIPMENT LEASING (SHANGHAI) CO., LTD.—See China Merchants Group Limited; *Int'l*, pg. 1521
LOSCAM (PHILIPPINES), INC.—See China Merchants Group Limited; *Int'l*, pg. 1521
LOSCAM (SINGAPORE) PRIVATE LIMITED—See China Merchants Group Limited; *Int'l*, pg. 1521
LOSCAM (THAILAND) LIMITED—See China Merchants Group Limited; *Int'l*, pg. 1521
LOSCAM VIETNAM CO., LTD.—See China Merchants Group Limited; *Int'l*, pg. 1521
LOUISIANA CHEMICAL EQUIPMENT CO., LLC—See Woodvine Group, LLC; *U.S. Private*, pg. 4561
LSC ENVIRONMENTAL PRODUCTS, LLC—See Ancor Holdings, L.P.; *U.S. Private*, pg. 275
THE L.S. STARRETT COMPANY OF AUSTRALIA PTY LTD—See MiddleGround Management, LP; *U.S. Private*, pg. 2713
THE L.S. STARRETT COMPANY OF CANADA LIMITED—See MiddleGround Management, LP; *U.S. Private*, pg. 2713
THE L.S. STARRETT COMPANY OF MEXICO S. DE R.L. DE C.V.—See MiddleGround Management, LP; *U.S. Private*, pg. 2713
LUITHAGEN NV—See Agfa-Gevaert N.V.; *Int'l*, pg. 209
LUMITRON INC—See Fortive Corporation; *U.S. Public*, pg. 870
LUMMUS AUSTRALIA PTY. LTD.—See Lummus Corporation; *U.S. Private*, pg. 2514
LUMMUS DO BRASIL LTDA.—See Lummus Corporation; *U.S. Private*, pg. 2514
LUND-IORIO, INC.—See Forward Solutions; *U.S. Private*, pg. 1578
LYDALL INDUSTRIAL TEXTILE MANUFACTURING COMPANY (WUXI) LIMITED—See Lydall, Inc.; *U.S. Public*, pg. 1349
M2S MIDDLE EAST FZE—See BC Partners LLP; *Int'l*, pg. 922
M2S MIDDLE EAST FZE—See The Carlyle Group Inc.; *U.S. Public*, pg. 2044
MAAG AUTOMATIK, INC.—See Dover Corporation; *U.S. Public*, pg. 681
MAAG AUTOMATIK PLASTICS MACHINERY (SHANGHAI) CO., LTD.—See Dover Corporation; *U.S. Public*, pg. 681

MAAG AUTOMATIK SRL—See Dover Corporation; *U.S. Public*, pg. 681
MAAG PUMP SYSTEMS PTE. LTD.—See Dover Corporation; *U.S. Public*, pg. 682
MAAG PUMP SYSTEMS SAS—See Dover Corporation; *U.S. Public*, pg. 682
MACHINERY SALES CO.; *U.S. Private*, pg. 2536
MACHINERY SYSTEMS INC.; *U.S. Private*, pg. 2536
MACHINERY TOOLING & SUPPLY LLC—See Machinery Systems Inc.; *U.S. Private*, pg. 2536
MACHINE TOOL TECHNOLOGIES INC.; *U.S. Private*, pg. 2535
MACHINE & WELDING SUPPLY COMPANY; *U.S. Private*, pg. 2535
MACHINING TIME SAVERS INC.; *U.S. Private*, pg. 2536
MACK BORING & PARTS CO.; *U.S. Private*, pg. 2536
MACOMB PIPE & SUPPLY CO. INC.; *U.S. Private*, pg. 2538
MAG INDIA INDUSTRIAL AUTOMATION SYSTEMS PVT. LTD.—See MAG IAS Holdings, Inc.; *U.S. Private*, pg. 2545
MAGNESCALE AMERICAS INC.—See DMG MORI Co., Ltd.; *Int'l*, pg. 2145
MAGNESCALE EUROPE GMBH—See DMG MORI Co., Ltd.; *Int'l*, pg. 2145
MAGNETEK CANADA ULC—See Columbus McKinnon Corporation; *U.S. Public*, pg. 536
MAGNETO & DIESEL INJECTOR SERVICE, INC.—See Warren Equity Partners, LLC; *U.S. Private*, pg. 4443
MAGNETO POWER, LLC—See Power Distributors, LLC; *U.S. Private*, pg. 3238
MAGYAR OPTIKAI MUVEK VIZMERESTECHNIKAI ZARTKORUEN MUKODO RESZVENYTARSASAG—See Diehl Stiftung & Co. KG; *Int'l*, pg. 2115
MAHORASHA CO., LTD.—See Cosmos Machinery Enterprises Limited; *Int'l*, pg. 1813
MAHR CHINA LTD.—See Carl Mahr Holding GmbH; *Int'l*, pg. 1333
MAHR DO BRASIL LTDA.—See Carl Mahr Holding GmbH; *Int'l*, pg. 1333
MAHR JAPAN CO., LTD.—See Carl Mahr Holding GmbH; *Int'l*, pg. 1333
MAHR KOREA LTD.—See Carl Mahr Holding GmbH; *Int'l*, pg. 1333
MAHR METERING SYSTEMS CORPORATION—See Carl Mahr Holding GmbH; *Int'l*, pg. 1333
MAHR POLSKA S.P.O.O.—See Carl Mahr Holding GmbH; *Int'l*, pg. 1333
MAHR PRECISION METROLOGY SUZHOU LTD.—See Carl Mahr Holding GmbH; *Int'l*, pg. 1333
MAHR TRADING CO., LTD.—See Carl Mahr Holding GmbH; *Int'l*, pg. 1333
MAINE OXY-ACETYLENE SUPPLY CO.; *U.S. Private*, pg. 2552
MAIN LINE SUPPLY CO. INC.; *U.S. Private*, pg. 2551
MAINTAINCO INC.; *U.S. Private*, pg. 2554
MALIN INTEGRATED HANDLING SOLUTIONS & DESIGN; *U.S. Private*, pg. 2557
M. ALJANICH ASSOCIATES INC.; *U.S. Private*, pg. 2526
MALLORY SAFETY & SUPPLY LLC - SAN BERNARDINO—See Mallory Safety & Supply LLC; *U.S. Private*, pg. 2558
MALNOVE PACKAGING SYSTEMS INC.—See Malnove Incorporated; *U.S. Private*, pg. 2558
MALONEY METALCRAFT LTD.—See Avingtrans plc; *Int'l*, pg. 744
MARESCO INTERNATIONAL CORP.; *U.S. Private*, pg. 2573
MARINE & INDUSTRIAL SUPPLY COMPANY, INC.; *U.S. Private*, pg. 2574
MARPAN INC.; *U.S. Private*, pg. 2586
MARQMETRIX, INC.—See Thermo Fisher Scientific Inc.; *U.S. Public*, pg. 2149
MARSHALL W NELSON & ASSOCIATES, INC.—See Relevant Industrial LLC; *U.S. Private*, pg. 3393
MARSH BELLOFRAM EUROPE LTD—See Desco Corporation; *U.S. Private*, pg. 1211
MARTIN BULK HANDLING SOLUTIONS (PTY) LIMITED—See Martin Engineering; *U.S. Private*, pg. 2595
MARTIN ENGINEERING COMPANY INDIA PRIVATE LIMITED—See Martin Engineering; *U.S. Private*, pg. 2595
MARTIN ENGINEERING GMBH—See Martin Engineering; *U.S. Private*, pg. 2595
MARTIN ENGINEERING ITALY SRL—See Martin Engineering; *U.S. Private*, pg. 2595
MARTIN ENGINEERING LIMITED—See Martin Engineering; *U.S. Private*, pg. 2595
MARTIN ENGINEERING LTDA.—See Martin Engineering; *U.S. Private*, pg. 2595
MARTIN ENGINEERING PERU SRL—See Martin Engineering; *U.S. Private*, pg. 2595
MARTIN ENGINEERING SARL—See Martin Engineering; *U.S. Private*, pg. 2595
MARTIN ENGINEERING S. DE R.L. DE C.V.—See Martin Engineering; *U.S. Private*, pg. 2595

N.A.I.C.S. INDEX

423830 — INDUSTRIAL MACHINER...

MARUBENI CITIZEN-CINCOM INC.—See Citizen Watch Co., Ltd.; *Int'l*, pg. 1625
MARZOLI INTERNATIONAL, INC.—See Camozzi Group; *Int'l*, pg. 1274
MASCHINEN UND APPARATEBAU GOTZEN GMBH—See Gesco AG; *Int'l*, pg. 2945
MASON WEST INC.—See Gladstone Management Corporation; *U.S. Private*, pg. 1705
MASSEY-CHESSON, INC.—See Applied Industrial Technologies, Inc.; *U.S. Public*, pg. 171
MASTER MECHANIC MFG. CO.—See Brinkmere Capital Partners LLC; *U.S. Private*, pg. 655
MASTERPIECE MACHINE & MANUFACTURING COMPANY—See Sanmina Corporation; *U.S. Public*, pg. 1840
MASTER PUMPS & EQUIPMENT CORPORATION; *U.S. Private*, pg. 2607
MATCON LIMITED—See IDEX Corp; *U.S. Public*, pg. 1091
MATECO PODESTY RUCHOME SP Z OO—See Group Thermote & Vanhalst; *Int'l*, pg. 3089
MATERIAL HANDLING INC; *U.S. Private*, pg. 2609
MATERIAL HANDLING PRODUCTS CORP; *U.S. Private*, pg. 2609
MATERIAL HANDLING SERVICES, LLC; *U.S. Private*, pg. 2609
MATERIAL HANDLING SUPPLY, INC.; *U.S. Private*, pg. 2609
MATERIAL HANDLING TECHNOLOGIES; *U.S. Private*, pg. 2609
MATERIALS HANDLING EQUIPMENT CORP.; *U.S. Private*, pg. 2609
MATHAND, INC.; *U.S. Private*, pg. 2610
MATTHEWS KODIERSYSTEME GMBH—See Matthews International Corporation; *U.S. Public*, pg. 1400
MATTHEWS MARKING SYSTEMS SWEDEN AB—See Matthews International Corporation; *U.S. Public*, pg. 1400
MAURER SUPPLY INC.; *U.S. Private*, pg. 2615
MAX DAETWYLER CORP.—See Daetwyler Global Tec Holding AG; *Int'l*, pg. 1909
MAXON LIFT CORP.; *U.S. Private*, pg. 2619
MAXX MANUFACTURING LLC—See HTC Purenergy Inc.; *Int'l*, pg. 3508
MCCAIN BINDERY SYSTEMS, INC.—See Numerical Concepts, Inc.; *U.S. Private*, pg. 2973
MCCALL HANDLING CO.; *U.S. Private*, pg. 2626
MCCARTY EQUIPMENT CO., LTD.—See Clayton, Dubilier & Rice, LLC; *U.S. Private*, pg. 926
MCCON BUILDING & PETROLEUM SERVICES, INC.—See MidOcean Partners, LLP; *U.S. Private*, pg. 2716
MCDANIEL MACHINERY, INC.; *U.S. Private*, pg. 2631
MCDONALD EQUIPMENT COMPANY; *U.S. Private*, pg. 2632
MCDONOUGH ELEVATOR SALES & RENTALS INC—See McDonough Corporation; *U.S. Private*, pg. 2632
MCGEE COMPANY; *U.S. Private*, pg. 2634
MCKENNA ENGINEERING & EQUIPMENT CO., INC.—See Wynnchurch Capital, L.P.; *U.S. Private*, pg. 4577
MCKINLEY EQUIPMENT CORP.; *U.S. Private*, pg. 2638
MCKINNEY PETROLEUM EQUIPMENT, INC.—See Kian Capital Partners, LLC; *U.S. Private*, pg. 2302
MCKINNEY PETROLEUM EQUIPMENT, INC.—See RFE Investment Partners; *U.S. Private*, pg. 3419
MECALUX BELGIUM S.A.—See Acerolux SL; *Int'l*, pg. 101
MECALUX FRANCE S.A.R.L.—See Acerolux SL; *Int'l*, pg. 101
MECALUX GMBH—See Acerolux SL; *Int'l*, pg. 101
MECALUX MILANO, S.R.L.—See Acerolux SL; *Int'l*, pg. 102
MECALUX SERVIS, S.A.—See Acerolux SL; *Int'l*, pg. 102
MECALUX SP. Z O.O.—See Acerolux SL; *Int'l*, pg. 102
MECALUX (UK) LTD.—See Acerolux SL; *Int'l*, pg. 101
MECHPUMP SDN. BHD.—See Dancomech Holdings Berhad; *Int'l*, pg. 1959
MECO NORTH FLORIDA INC.—See Meco of Atlanta Incorporated; *U.S. Private*, pg. 2649
MECO OF ATLANTA INCORPORATED; *U.S. Private*, pg. 2649
MEDART INC.; *U.S. Private*, pg. 2650
MEDCO TOOL OF ST. LOUIS, INC.—See Sycamore Partners Management, LP; *U.S. Private*, pg. 3896
MEDICAL PACKAGING, INC.—See The Zabel Companies, LLC; *U.S. Private*, pg. 4140
MEDLEY MATERIAL HANDLING CO.; *U.S. Private*, pg. 2657
MEEDER EQUIPMENT COMPANY; *U.S. Private*, pg. 2659
MEE ENTERPRISES INC.; *U.S. Private*, pg. 2659
ME ELECMETAL COMERCIAL PERU S.A.C.—See Compania Electro Metalurgica S.A.; *Int'l*, pg. 1749
MEHRING AG—See Alfred Raith GmbH; *Int'l*, pg. 317
MELCO INDUSTRIAL SUPPLIES (SHANGHAI) CO., LTD—See Cosmos Machinery Enterprises Limited; *Int'l*, pg. 1813
MELETT NORTH AMERICA, INC—See Westinghouse Air Brake Technologies Corporation; *U.S. Public*, pg. 2358
MEMCO INC.; *U.S. Private*, pg. 2663
MENNENS AMSTERDAM BV—See Axel Johnson Gruppen AB; *Int'l*, pg. 764
MENNENS BELGIUM—See Axel Johnson Gruppen AB; *Int'l*, pg. 764

MENNENS DONGEN BV—See Axel Johnson Gruppen AB; *Int'l*, pg. 764
MENNENS GRONINGEN BV—See Axel Johnson Gruppen AB; *Int'l*, pg. 764
MENNENS HENGELO BV—See Axel Johnson Gruppen AB; *Int'l*, pg. 764
MENNENS SCHIEDAM BV—See Axel Johnson Gruppen AB; *Int'l*, pg. 764
MERIS D.O.O.—See Endress+Hauser (International) Holding AG; *Int'l*, pg. 2408
MERRIMAC INDUSTRIAL SALES INC.; *U.S. Private*, pg. 2676
MESA EQUIPMENT & SUPPLY COMPANY; *U.S. Private*, pg. 2677
METARIS CORP.—See Clearlake Capital Group, L.P.; *U.S. Private*, pg. 933
METARIS, INC.—See Clearlake Capital Group, L.P.; *U.S. Private*, pg. 933
METHODS MACHINE TOOLS INC.; *U.S. Private*, pg. 2684
METRIC INDUSTRIAL OY—See Addtech AB; *Int'l*, pg. 134
METTLER-TOLEDO GARVENS GMBH—See Mettler-Toledo International, Inc.; *U.S. Public*, pg. 1432
METTLER-TOLEDO - PRODUCT INSPECTION—See Mettler-Toledo International, Inc.; *U.S. Public*, pg. 1432
MGE EQUIPAMENTOS E SERVICOS FERROVIARIOS LTDA.—See Caterpillar, Inc.; *U.S. Public*, pg. 452
M.G. NEWELL CORPORATION; *U.S. Private*, pg. 2529
MHC SYSTEMS, LLC; *U.S. Private*, pg. 2695
MH EQUIPMENT COMPANY; *U.S. Private*, pg. 2695
MH EQUIPMENT—See MH Equipment Company; *U.S. Private*, pg. 2695
MH EQUIPMENT—See MH Equipment Company; *U.S. Private*, pg. 2695
MIAMI INDUSTRIAL TRUCKS INC.; *U.S. Private*, pg. 2696
MICHIGAN ARC PRODUCTS; *U.S. Private*, pg. 2700
MICROLEASE FRANCE—See Platinum Equity, LLC; *U.S. Private*, pg. 3203
MICRO OFFICE SYSTEMS, INC.—See Medsphere Systems Corp.; *U.S. Private*, pg. 2658
MICRO PRODUCTS COMPANY; *U.S. Private*, pg. 2702
MID COLUMBIA FORKLIFT, INC.; *U.S. Private*, pg. 2705
MIDCON INVESTORS INC.; *U.S. Private*, pg. 2710
MIDDLEBY WORLDWIDE MEXICO SA DE CV—See The Middleby Corporation; *U.S. Public*, pg. 2115
MIDDLE EAST WORLD FACTORIES EQUIPMENT L.L.C—See Gulf General Investment Company PSC; *Int'l*, pg. 3180
MIDLAND CHANDLERS LIMITED—See LKQ Corporation; *U.S. Public*, pg. 1335
MIDWAY INDUSTRIAL SUPPLY, INC.—See Genstar Capital, LLC; *U.S. Private*, pg. 1678
MIDWEST AUTOMATION INC.; *U.S. Private*, pg. 2720
MIDWEST MANUFACTURING RESOURCES, INC. - HAAS FACTORY OUTLET MIDWEST DIVISION—See Morris Group, Inc.; *U.S. Private*, pg. 2787
MIDWEST MANUFACTURING RESOURCES, INC.—See Morris Group, Inc.; *U.S. Private*, pg. 2787
MID-WEST MERCHANDISING CORP.—See Printers' Service, Inc.; *U.S. Private*, pg. 3265
MIDWEST METALS, INC.—See McCarthy Bush Corporation; *U.S. Private*, pg. 2626
MIDWEST SIGN & SCREEN PRINTING SUPPLY COMPANY, INC.; *U.S. Private*, pg. 2723
MIDWEST VALVE PARTS SUPPLY COMPANY, INC.—See Wynnchurch Capital, L.P.; *U.S. Private*, pg. 4577
MIE INDUSTRIAL SDN.BHD.—See CTCI Corporation; *Int'l*, pg. 1870
MIGHTY USA, INC.; *U.S. Private*, pg. 2724
MI-JACK CANADA, INC.—See Lanco International Inc.; *U.S. Private*, pg. 2382
MIKE JORDAN CO. INC.; *U.S. Private*, pg. 2725
MILLER PROCTOR NICKOLAS INC.; *U.S. Private*, pg. 2735
MILLER SUPPLY OF WEST VIRGINIA INCORPORATED; *U.S. Private*, pg. 2735
MILLTRONICS USA, INC.—See Hurco Companies, Inc.; *U.S. Public*, pg. 1076
MILTEC UV; *U.S. Private*, pg. 2738
MINNESOTA SUPPLY COMPANY; *U.S. Private*, pg. 2743
MINUTEMAN DISTRIBUTORS INC.; *U.S. Private*, pg. 2745
MISSISSIPPI WELDERS SUPPLY CO.; *U.S. Private*, pg. 2748
MITCHELL LEWIS & STAVER CO.; *U.S. Private*, pg. 2750
MITEK CANADA, INC.—See Berkshire Hathaway Inc.; *U.S. Public*, pg. 313
MJ ECOPOWER HYBRID SYSTEMS, INC.—See Lanco International Inc.; *U.S. Private*, pg. 2382
MJK AUTOMATION APS—See Xylem Inc.; *U.S. Public*, pg. 2394
M.L. BALL CO. INC.; *U.S. Private*, pg. 2529
M&L INDUSTRIES, INC.; *U.S. Private*, pg. 2524
M&M PUMP & SUPPLY CO. INC.; *U.S. Private*, pg. 2524
M&M SUPPLY CO.; *U.S. Private*, pg. 2525
MODERN EQUIPMENT SALES & RENTAL CO. - KING OF PRUSSIA—See Modern Group Ltd.; *U.S. Private*, pg. 2760
MODERN EQUIPMENT SALES & RENTAL CO.—See Modern Group Ltd.; *U.S. Private*, pg. 2760

MODERN EQUIPMENT SALES & RENTAL CO. - WILMINGTON—See Modern Group Ltd.; *U.S. Private*, pg. 2760
MODERN HANDLING EQUIPMENT COMPANY—See Modern Group Ltd.; *U.S. Private*, pg. 2760
MODERN HANDLING EQUIPMENT OF N.J., INC.—See Modern Group Ltd.; *U.S. Private*, pg. 2761
MODINE CIS ITALY SRL—See Modine Manufacturing Company; *U.S. Public*, pg. 1455
MODINE SODERKOPING AB—See Modine Manufacturing Company; *U.S. Public*, pg. 1455
MODUL SYSTEME ENGINEERING GMBH—See ANDRITZ AG; *Int'l*, pg. 456
MONARCH KNITTING MACHINERY CORP.; *U.S. Private*, pg. 2769
MONARCH, LLC; *U.S. Private*, pg. 2769
MONNEX INDUSTRIES INC.—See Monnex International Inc.; *U.S. Private*, pg. 2771
MONNEX INTERNATIONAL INC.; *U.S. Private*, pg. 2771
MONROE ENGINEERING, LLC—See AEA Investors LP; *U.S. Private*, pg. 114
MONUMENTAL SUPPLY CO. INC.; *U.S. Private*, pg. 2777
MOODY-PRICE INC.; *U.S. Private*, pg. 2778
MOORE SPECIAL TOOL AG—See PMT Group Inc; *U.S. Private*, pg. 3219
MORANDO S.R.L.—See Groupe Legris Industries; *Int'l*, pg. 3107
MORI SEIKI TRADING LTD.—See DMG MORI Co., Ltd.; *Int'l*, pg. 2145
MORRELL INCORPORATED; *U.S. Private*, pg. 2786
MORRIS GROUP, INC. - MORRIS GREAT LAKES DIVISION—See Morris Group, Inc.; *U.S. Private*, pg. 2787
MORRIS GROUP, INC. - MORRIS SOUTH DIVISION—See Morris Group, Inc.; *U.S. Private*, pg. 2787
MORRIS GROUP, INC.; *U.S. Private*, pg. 2787
MORRIS GROUP, INC. - VELOCITY PRODUCTS DIVISION—See Morris Group, Inc.; *U.S. Private*, pg. 2787
MORRIS MIDWEST, LLC—See Morris Group, Inc.; *U.S. Private*, pg. 2787
MORRIS MIDWEST, LLC—See Morris Group, Inc.; *U.S. Private*, pg. 2787
MORRISON INDUSTRIAL EQUIPMENT COMPANY; *U.S. Private*, pg. 2789
MORRISON INDUSTRIAL EQUIPMENT COMPANY—See Morrison Industrial Equipment Company; *U.S. Private*, pg. 2789
MORRIS SOUTH, LLC-HUNTSVILLE—See Morris Group, Inc.; *U.S. Private*, pg. 2787
MORRIS SOUTH, LLC—See Morris Group, Inc.; *U.S. Private*, pg. 2787
MOSIER FLUID POWER OF INDIANA; *U.S. Private*, pg. 2793
MOTION & CONTROL ENTERPRISES LLC—See Frontenac Company LLC; *U.S. Private*, pg. 1614
MOTORCAR PARTS OF AMERICA, INC.; *U.S. Public*, pg. 1477
MOUNTAIN AIR COMPRESSOR INC.—See Hitachi, Ltd.; *Int'l*, pg. 3417
MOUNTAIN PACIFIC MACHINERY; *U.S. Private*, pg. 2799
MOVETEC OY—See Addtech AB; *Int'l*, pg. 134
MPOWER, INC.; *U.S. Private*, pg. 2804
MP SYSTEMS, INC.—See Morris Group, Inc.; *U.S. Private*, pg. 2787
MRC ENERGY PIPING AS—See MRC Global Inc.; *U.S. Public*, pg. 1480
MRC FLANGEFITT LIMITED—See MRC Global Inc.; *U.S. Public*, pg. 1480
MRC GLOBAL (CANADA) ULC—See MRC Global Inc.; *U.S. Public*, pg. 1480
MRC GLOBAL (KOREA) LIMITED—See MRC Global Inc.; *U.S. Public*, pg. 1481
MRC GLOBAL (SWEDEN) AB—See MRC Global Inc.; *U.S. Public*, pg. 1481
MRC GLOBAL (THAILAND) COMPANY LIMITED—See MRC Global Inc.; *U.S. Public*, pg. 1481
MRC MSD ENGINEERING PTE. LTD.—See MRC Global Inc.; *U.S. Public*, pg. 1481
MRC SOLBERG & ANDERSEN AS—See MRC Global Inc.; *U.S. Public*, pg. 1481
MRC TEAMTRADE AS—See MRC Global Inc.; *U.S. Public*, pg. 1481
MRC TRANSMARK KAZAKHSTAN LLP—See MRC Global Inc.; *U.S. Public*, pg. 1481
MRC VALVE AUTOMATION CENTER—See MRC Global Inc.; *U.S. Public*, pg. 1481
MSC INDUSTRIAL DIRECT CO., INC.; *U.S. Public*, pg. 1483
MSI-PRO COMPANY—See Jewett-Cameron Trading Company Ltd.; *U.S. Public*, pg. 1190
M.S. JACOBS & ASSOCIATES; *U.S. Private*, pg. 2529
MTL INSTRUMENTS GMBH—See Eaton Corporation plc; *Int'l*, pg. 2278
MTL INSTRUMENTS PTY. LIMITED—See Eaton Corporation plc; *Int'l*, pg. 2278
MTL INSTRUMENTS SARL—See Eaton Corporation plc; *Int'l*, pg. 2278

423830 — INDUSTRIAL MACHINER...

MT SUPPLY, INC.—See TruArc Partners, L.P.; *U.S. Private*, pg. 4245
MUELLER GRAPHIC SUPPLY INC.; *U.S. Private*, pg. 2810
MULTITEST ELECTRONIC SYSTEMS (PHILIPPINES) CORPORATION—See Cohu, Inc.; *U.S. Public*, pg. 530
MULTITRODE PTY LTD—See Xylem Inc.; *U.S. Public*, pg. 2394
MUTUAL LIQUID GAS & EQUIPMENT CO., INC.; *U.S. Private*, pg. 2820
MWM (BEIJING) CO., LTD.—See Caterpillar, Inc.; *U.S. Public*, pg. 452
MYOTOKU CONVUM CHINA CO., LTD.—See Convum Ltd.; *Int'l*, pg. 1788
MYOTOKU TECHNOLOGIES INC.—See Convum Ltd.; *Int'l*, pg. 1788
NACCO INDUSTRIES, INC.; *U.S. Public*, pg. 1489
NACCO MATERIALS HANDLING FRANCE S.A.R.L.—See Hyster-Yale Materials Handling, Inc.; *U.S. Public*, pg. 1080
NAKAGAWA ENGINEERING CONSULTING (SHANGHAI) CO., LTD.—See Hisaka Works, Ltd.; *Int'l*, pg. 3406
NALCO FAB-TECH LLC—See Modern Group, Ltd.; *U.S. Private*, pg. 2761
NATIONAL-OILWELL PTE. LTD.—See NOV, Inc.; *U.S. Public*, pg. 1546
NATIONAL OILWELL VARCO ALMANSOORI SERVICES—See NOV, Inc.; *U.S. Public*, pg. 1546
NATIONAL OILWELL VARCO—See NOV, Inc.; *U.S. Public*, pg. 1546
NATIONAL PUMP COMPANY—See The Gorman-Rupp Company; *U.S. Public*, pg. 2085
NAUMANN/HOBBS MATERIAL HANDLING, INC.—See HCI Equity Management, L.P.; *U.S. Private*, pg. 1889
NAZDAR COMPANY - NAZDAR SOURCEONE DIVISION—See Thrall Enterprises, Inc.; *U.S. Private*, pg. 4163
NEAL H. KNAPP, LLC; *U.S. Private*, pg. 2877
NEFF ENGINEERING COMPANY, INC.; *U.S. Private*, pg. 2880
NELSON-JAMESON INC.; *U.S. Private*, pg. 2884
NETMERCURY, INC. - AUSTIN—See Wynnchurch Capital, L.P.; *U.S. Private*, pg. 4577
NETMERCURY, INC. - FREMONT—See Wynnchurch Capital, L.P.; *U.S. Private*, pg. 4577
NETMERCURY, INC.—See Wynnchurch Capital, L.P.; *U.S. Private*, pg. 4577
NETWORK INTERNATIONAL INC.—See Liquidity Services, Inc.; *U.S. Public*, pg. 1321
NETZSCH AUSTRALIA PTY LTD—See Erich Netzsch GmbH & Co. Holding KG; *Int'l*, pg. 2491
NETZSCH INDUSTRIA E COMERCIO DE EQUIPAMENTOS DE MOAGEM LTDA.—See Erich Netzsch GmbH & Co. Holding KG; *Int'l*, pg. 2492
NETZSCH JAPAN K.K.—See Erich Netzsch GmbH & Co. Holding KG; *Int'l*, pg. 2492
NETZSCH LOHNMAHLTECHNIK GMBH—See Erich Netzsch GmbH & Co. Holding KG; *Int'l*, pg. 2492
NETZSCH MAKINE SANAYI VE TICARET LTD. STI.—See Erich Netzsch GmbH & Co. Holding KG; *Int'l*, pg. 2492
NETZSCH MEXICO S.A. DE C.V.—See Erich Netzsch GmbH & Co. Holding KG; *Int'l*, pg. 2492
NETZSCH PERU SOCIEDAD ANONIMA CERRADO—See Erich Netzsch GmbH & Co. Holding KG; *Int'l*, pg. 2492
NETZSCH POMPEN NEDERLAND B.V.—See Erich Netzsch GmbH & Co. Holding KG; *Int'l*, pg. 2492
NETZSCH POMPE & SISTEMI ITALIA SRL—See Erich Netzsch GmbH & Co. Holding KG; *Int'l*, pg. 2492
NETZSCH PUMPEN & SYSTEME GMBH—See Erich Netzsch GmbH & Co. Holding KG; *Int'l*, pg. 2492
NETZSCH PUMPS BELLUX BVBA—See Erich Netzsch GmbH & Co. Holding KG; *Int'l*, pg. 2492
NETZSCH PUMPS RUS OOO—See Erich Netzsch GmbH & Co. Holding KG; *Int'l*, pg. 2492
NETZSCH PUMPS & SYSTEMS LTD.—See Erich Netzsch GmbH & Co. Holding KG; *Int'l*, pg. 2492
NETZSCH SCIENTIFIC INSTRUMENTS TRADING (SHANGHAI) LTD.—See Erich Netzsch GmbH & Co. Holding KG; *Int'l*, pg. 2492
NETZSCH SERVICE NORDESTE LTDA.—See Erich Netzsch GmbH & Co. Holding KG; *Int'l*, pg. 2492
NETZSCH SOUTHERN AFRICA (PTY) LTD.—See Erich Netzsch GmbH & Co. Holding KG; *Int'l*, pg. 2492
NETZSCH TECHNOLOGIES INDIA PVT. LTD. - SALCETTE FACTORY—See Erich Netzsch GmbH & Co. Holding KG; *Int'l*, pg. 2492
NETZSCH TULA ZAO—See Erich Netzsch GmbH & Co. Holding KG; *Int'l*, pg. 2492
NETZSCH VAKUMIX GMBH—See Erich Netzsch GmbH & Co. Holding KG; *Int'l*, pg. 2492
NEWORLD ELECTRONICS LTD.—See Chroma ATE Inc.; *Int'l*, pg. 1588
NEWPORT SPECTRA-PHYSICS LTD.—See MKS Instruments, Inc.; *U.S. Public*, pg. 1453
NEW TRONICS CO., LTD.—See Disco Corporation; *Int'l*, pg. 2132
NEXUS AUSTRALASIA PTY LTD—See EBOS Group Limited; *Int'l*, pg. 2285
NEXUS TECHNOLOGIES PTY LTD—See Resideo Technologies, Inc.; *U.S. Public*, pg. 1790
NIAGARA CONSERVATION CORPORATION; *U.S. Private*, pg. 2924
NIXON ENERGY SOLUTIONS—See Geneva Corporation; *U.S. Private*, pg. 1670
N.J. MALIN & ASSOCIATES, LP; *U.S. Private*, pg. 2828
NL SUPERVISION COMPANY A/S—See FLSmidth & Co. A/S; *Int'l*, pg. 2712
NMC MATERIAL HANDLING INC.—See Nebraska Machinery Company Inc.; *U.S. Private*, pg. 2878
NMHG DISTRIBUTION PTY. LIMITED—See Hyster-Yale Materials Handling, Inc.; *U.S. Public*, pg. 1080
NMHG OREGON, LLC—See Hyster-Yale Materials Handling, Inc.; *U.S. Public*, pg. 1080
NORCO, INC.; *U.S. Private*, pg. 2936
NORDEN GMBH—See Coesia S.p.A.; *Int'l*, pg. 1690
NORDEN MACHINERY AB—See Coesia S.p.A.; *Int'l*, pg. 1690
NORDSON DANMARK A/S—See Nordson Corporation; *U.S. Public*, pg. 1533
NORDSON DIMA B.V.—See Nordson Corporation; *U.S. Public*, pg. 1533
NORDSON INDIA PRIVATE LIMITED—See Nordson Corporation; *U.S. Public*, pg. 1534
NORDSON SA (PTY) LTD.—See Nordson Corporation; *U.S. Public*, pg. 1534
NORDSON SELECT GMBH—See Nordson Corporation; *U.S. Public*, pg. 1534
NORDSON (SHANGHAI) BUSINESS CONSULTING CO., LTD.—See Nordson Corporation; *U.S. Public*, pg. 1533
NORDSON XALOY EUROPE GMBH—See Nordson Corporation; *U.S. Public*, pg. 1534
NORLIFT OF OREGON, INC.; *U.S. Private*, pg. 2938
NORMAN EQUIPMENT COMPANY; *U.S. Private*, pg. 2938
NORTH AMERICAN EQUIPMENT UPFITTERS, INC.; *U.S. Private*, pg. 2940
NORTH AMERICAN HYDRAULICS INC.; *U.S. Private*, pg. 2940
NORTHEAST CONTROLS INC.; *U.S. Private*, pg. 2949
NORTHLAND INDUSTRIAL TRUCK CO. INC.—See Alta Equipment Group Inc.; *U.S. Public*, pg. 86
NORTH STAR IMAGING EUROPE SAS—See Illinois Tool Works Inc.; *U.S. Public*, pg. 1109
NORTHWEST HANDLING SYSTEMS, INC.; *U.S. Private*, pg. 2960
NORTHWEST PUMP & EQUIPMENT CO.—See H.I.G. Capital, LLC; *U.S. Private*, pg. 1833
NORTHWEST SUPPLY COMPANY INC.; *U.S. Private*, pg. 2961
NOUVELLE SOCIETE MAGIDEUTZ S.A.—See DEUTZ AG; *Int'l*, pg. 2086
NOVASPECT INC.; *U.S. Private*, pg. 2967
NUBCO PROPRIETARY LIMITED—See Coventry Group Limited; *Int'l*, pg. 1821
NUMATIC ENGINEERING INC.; *U.S. Private*, pg. 2973
O.A. NEWTON & SON CO; *U.S. Private*, pg. 2981
OCE-DEUTSCHLAND GMBH—See Canon Inc.; *Int'l*, pg. 1294
OE MEYER CO.; *U.S. Private*, pg. 2996
OERLIKON LEYBOLD VACUUM KOREA LTD.—See Atlas Copco AB; *Int'l*, pg. 684
OERLIKON SOLDADURA SA—See Lincoln Electric Holdings, Inc.; *U.S. Public*, pg. 1317
OERLIKON VACUUM ROMANIA KON TRADE SRL—See Atlas Copco AB; *Int'l*, pg. 684
OERLIKON VACUUM TURKEY TEKSER A.S.—See Atlas Copco AB; *Int'l*, pg. 684
OHA INSTRUMENTS INC.—See Wise El Santo Company Inc.; *U.S. Private*, pg. 4549
OHIO TOOL SYSTEMS, INC.; *U.S. Private*, pg. 3005
OHIO TRANSMISSION CORPORATION—See Genstar Capital, LLC; *U.S. Private*, pg. 1678
OIL-AIR PRODUCTS INC.; *U.S. Private*, pg. 3006
OIL & GAS EQUIPMENT CORP.; *U.S. Private*, pg. 3006
OILGEAR TOWLER S.R.L.—See Wynnchurch Capital, L.P.; *U.S. Private*, pg. 4578
OILMEN'S EQUIPMENT CORP.; *U.S. Private*, pg. 3006
O'KEEFE ELEVATOR COMPANY INC.—See Advent International Corporation; *U.S. Private*, pg. 106
O'KEEFE ELEVATOR COMPANY INC.—See Cinven Limited; *Int'l*, pg. 1614
OKI BEARING CANADA INC.—See Sycamore Partners Management, LP; *U.S. Private*, pg. 3896
OK MARINE AS—See Egersund Group AS; *Int'l*, pg. 2324
OKUTATU (MACAO COMMERCIAL OFFSHORE) LIMITED—See EVA Precision Industrial Holdings Limited; *Int'l*, pg. 2560
OLAER AS—See Parker Hannifin Corporation; *U.S. Public*, pg. 1643
OLAER AUSTRIA GMBH—See Parker Hannifin Corporation; *U.S. Public*, pg. 1643
OLAER USA, INC.—See Parker Hannifin Corporation; *U.S. Public*, pg. 1643
THE OLDHAM GROUP; *U.S. Private*, pg. 4088
OMNILIFT INC.; *U.S. Private*, pg. 3017
O-M SHANGHAI CO., LTD.—See Daiwabo Holdings Co., Ltd.; *Int'l*, pg. 1949
OMW CORPORATION; *U.S. Private*, pg. 3018
ONYX FOR ENGINEERING & INTEGRATED SOLUTIONS PLC—See Endress+Hauser (International) Holding AG; *Int'l*, pg. 2408
OOO AZO RUS—See AZO GmbH & Co. KG; *Int'l*, pg. 780
OOO CUMMINS—See Cummins Inc.; *U.S. Public*, pg. 609
OOO DIEFFENBACHER MOSCOW—See Dieffenbacher Holding GmbH & Co. KG; *Int'l*, pg. 2114
OOO EISENMANN—See Eisenmann AG; *Int'l*, pg. 2336
OOO EISENMANN TOGLIATTI—See Eisenmann AG; *Int'l*, pg. 2336
OOO ELUMATEC RUS—See Cifin S.r.l.; *Int'l*, pg. 1606
OOO EMUGE-FRANKEN—See EMUGE-Werk Richard Glimpel GmbH & Co. KG; *Int'l*, pg. 2408
OOO FLEXLINK SYSTEMS—See Coesia S.p.A.; *Int'l*, pg. 1689
OOO HAARSLEV INDUSTRIES—See Altor Equity Partners AB; *Int'l*, pg. 395
OOO HYDAC INTERNATIONAL—See Hydac International GmbH; *Int'l*, pg. 3545
OOO LEIPURIEN TUKKU—See Aspo Oyj; *Int'l*, pg. 631
OPECO INC.; *U.S. Private*, pg. 3028
OPW FLUID TRANSFER GROUP EUROPE B.V.—See Dover Corporation; *U.S. Public*, pg. 679
ORION SOUTH INC.; *U.S. Private*, pg. 3043
OSHKOSH DEFENSE, LLC—See Oshkosh Corporation; *U.S. Public*, pg. 1621
OTC DAIHEN INDIA PVT. LTD.—See Daihen Corporation; *Int'l*, pg. 1926
OTC INDUSTRIAL (SHANGHAI) CO., LTD.—See Daihen Corporation; *Int'l*, pg. 1926
OTC (TAIWAN) CO., LTD.—See Daihen Corporation; *Int'l*, pg. 1926
OTIS AB—See Otis Worldwide Corporation; *U.S. Public*, pg. 1623
OUJOT EESTI—See Head Invest Oy; *Int'l*, pg. 3301
OVERSEAS SERVICE CORPORATION-EXCHANGE DIV—See Overseas Service Corporation; *U.S. Private*, pg. 3053
OXARC INC.; *U.S. Private*, pg. 3056
OY ATLAS COPCO LOUHINTATEKNIIKKA AB—See Atlas Copco AB; *Int'l*, pg. 684
OYEX HANDELS GMBH—See AG Anadolu Grubu Holding A.S.; *Int'l*, pg. 197
PABCO FLUID POWER COMPANY; *U.S. Private*, pg. 3062
P/A BOHEMIA S.R.O.—See P/A Industries, Inc.; *U.S. Private*, pg. 3061
PACE MATERIAL HANDLING, INC.—See On-Point Group, LLC; *U.S. Private*, pg. 3019
PACIFIC INDUSTRIES INC.; *U.S. Private*, pg. 3067
PACIFIC INTEGRATED HANDLING INC.; *U.S. Private*, pg. 3067
PACIFIC LIQUID AND AIR SYSTEMS—See Solaray Corporation; *U.S. Private*, pg. 3707
PACIFIC MATERIAL HOLDING SOLUTIONS, INC.; *U.S. Private*, pg. 3068
PACIFIC POWER PRODUCTS COMPANY; *U.S. Private*, pg. 3070
PACIFIC SCIENTIFIC AVIATION SERVICES COMPANY—See Parker Hannifin Corporation; *U.S. Public*, pg. 1643
PAC INSTRUMENTS (THAILAND) COMPANY LIMITED—See Roper Technologies, Inc.; *U.S. Public*, pg. 1812
PADNOS LEITELT, INC.—See Louis Padnos Iron & Metal Company; *U.S. Private*, pg. 2498
PA INC.; *U.S. Private*, pg. 3062
PALM PETERBILT-GMC TRUCKS INC.; *U.S. Private*, pg. 3079
PAMARCO GLOBAL GRAPHICS (PGG)—See J.P. Kotts & Co.; *U.S. Private*, pg. 2170
PANAH JAYA SERVICES SDN. BHD.—See Annica Holdings Limited; *Int'l*, pg. 474
PANTROPIC POWER PRODUCTS INC.; *U.S. Private*, pg. 3087
PAPE D.W., INC.—See The Pape Group, Inc.; *U.S. Private*, pg. 4090
THE PAPE GROUP, INC.; *U.S. Private*, pg. 4090
PARADIGM FRANCE S.A.—See Emerson Electric Co.; *U.S. Public*, pg. 751
PARGREEN SALES ENGINEERING CORP.; *U.S. Private*, pg. 3094
PARKER HANNIFIN AKTIEBOLAG—See Parker Hannifin Corporation; *U.S. Public*, pg. 1644
PARKER HANNIFIN CORPORATION CHILE LTDA.—See Parker Hannifin Corporation; *U.S. Public*, pg. 1645
PARKER HANNIFIN CYLINDER DIVISION—See Parker Hannifin Corporation; *U.S. Public*, pg. 1647
PARKER HANNIFIN EMEA S.A.R.L.—See Parker Hannifin Corporation; *U.S. Public*, pg. 1645
PARKER HANNIFIN ENGINEERED POLYMER SYSTEMS DIVISION—See Parker Hannifin Corporation; *U.S. Public*, pg. 1643
PARKER HANNIFIN GMBH & CO. KG VERTRIEBS- UND SERVICEZENTRALE—See Parker Hannifin Corporation; *U.S. Public*, pg. 1647
PARKER HANNIFIN GMBH—See Parker Hannifin Corporation; *U.S. Public*, pg. 1647
PARKER HANNIFIN ITALY SRL—See Parker Hannifin Cor-

poration; *U.S. Public*, pg. 1648
PARKER HANNIFIN MANUFACTURING SRL—See Parker Hannifin Corporation; *U.S. Public*, pg. 1648
PARKER HANNIFIN MANUFACTURING (UK) LIMITED—See Parker Hannifin Corporation; *U.S. Public*, pg. 1648
PARKER HANNIFIN PARTNER B LLC—See Parker Hannifin Corporation; *U.S. Public*, pg. 1648
PARKER HANNIFIN PORTUGAL UNIPESSOAL LDA—See Parker Hannifin Corporation; *U.S. Public*, pg. 1648
PARKER HANNIFIN VERWALTUNGS-GMBH—See Parker Hannifin Corporation; *U.S. Public*, pg. 1649
PARKER MIDDLE EAST FZE—See Parker Hannifin Corporation; *U.S. Public*, pg. 1649
PARKSON CANADA CORPORATION—See Axel Johnson Gruppen AB; *Int'l*, pg. 765
PARTS TOWN LLC—See Berkshire Partners LLC; *U.S. Private*, pg. 535
PATTEN POWER SYSTEMS INC.—See Patten Industries, Inc.; *U.S. Private*, pg. 3111
PATTON'S, INC.—See ELGI Equipments Limited; *Int'l*, pg. 2360
PB HOIDALE CO. INC.; *U.S. Private*, pg. 3118
PCB PIEZOTRONICS LTD—See Amphenol Corporation; *U.S. Public*, pg. 131
PCB PIEZOTRONICS S.A.—See Amphenol Corporation; *U.S. Public*, pg. 131
PCB PIEZOTRONICS SRL—See Amphenol Corporation; *U.S. Public*, pg. 131
PCM USA INC.—See Gevelot S.A.; *Int'l*, pg. 2954
PCS FERGUSON CANADA INC.—See Dover Corporation; *U.S. Public*, pg. 682
PEARCE INDUSTRIES INC.; *U.S. Private*, pg. 3125
PEARSE-PEARSON COMPANY INC.; *U.S. Private*, pg. 3126
PEERLESS CHINA MANUFACTURING CO. LTD.—See CECO Environmental Corp.; *U.S. Public*, pg. 464
PEERLESS SUPPLY INC.; *U.S. Private*, pg. 3129
PENGATE HANDLING SYSTEMS OF NY—See Pengate Handling Systems Inc.; *U.S. Private*, pg. 3133
PENN-AIR & HYDRAULICS CORP.; *U.S. Private*, pg. 3135
PENSKE POWER SYSTEMS PTY LTD—See Penske Automotive Group, Inc.; *U.S. Public*, pg. 1665
PENTA DON OOO—See Illinois Tool Works Inc.; *U.S. Public*, pg. 1110
PERCEPTRON METROLOGY TECHNOLOGY (SHANGHAI) CO. LTD.—See Atlas Copco AB; *Int'l*, pg. 680
PERFECTION MACHINERY SALES, INC.; *U.S. Private*, pg. 3148
PERKINS POWER CORP.—See Southeast Diesel Corp.; *U.S. Private*, pg. 3725
PERRY PROCESS EQUIPMENT LTD.—See Perry Videx LLC; *U.S. Private*, pg. 3154
PERRY SUPPLY INC.—See Drummond Company, Inc.; *U.S. Private*, pg. 1280
PERRY VIDEX LLC; *U.S. Private*, pg. 3154
PERTEN INSTRUMENTS INC.—See Revvity, Inc.; *U.S. Public*, pg. 1795
PETER HENNINGSEN S.A.C.—See BERICAP GmbH & Co. KG; *Int'l*, pg. 981
PETROLEUM EQUIPMENT CO., INC.—See The Rosewood Corporation; *U.S. Private*, pg. 4112
PETROLEUM EQUIPMENT & SERVICE, INC.; *U.S. Private*, pg. 3162
PFEIFFER VACUUM AUSTRIA GMBH—See Dr. Ing. K. Busch GmbH; *Int'l*, pg. 2194
PFEIFFER VACUUM INC.—See Dr. Ing. K. Busch GmbH; *Int'l*, pg. 2194
PFEIFFER VACUUM INDIA LTD.—See Dr. Ing. K. Busch GmbH; *Int'l*, pg. 2194
PFEIFFER VACUUM ITALIA S.P.A.—See Dr. Ing. K. Busch GmbH; *Int'l*, pg. 2194
PFEIFFER VACUUM KOREA LTD.—See Dr. Ing. K. Busch GmbH; *Int'l*, pg. 2194
PFEIFFER VACUUM LTD.—See Dr. Ing. K. Busch GmbH; *Int'l*, pg. 2194
PFEIFFER VACUUM SCANDINAVIA AB—See Dr. Ing. K. Busch GmbH; *Int'l*, pg. 2194
PFEIFFER VACUUM (SCHWEIZ) AG—See Dr. Ing. K. Busch GmbH; *Int'l*, pg. 2194
PFEIFFER VACUUM (SHANGHAI) CO., LTD.—See Dr. Ing. K. Busch GmbH; *Int'l*, pg. 2194
PGI INTERNATIONAL, LTD.—See Parker Hannifin Corporation; *U.S. Public*, pg. 1643
PHILLIPS CORPORATION; *U.S. Private*, pg. 3170
PHOCEENNE ASIA PTE. LTD.—See Groupe BPCE; *Int'l*, pg. 3095
PHOCEENNE CHILI LTDA.—See Groupe BPCE; *Int'l*, pg. 3095
PHOCEENNE S.A.—See Groupe BPCE; *Int'l*, pg. 0005
PHOENIX WELDING SUPPLY, INC.; *U.S. Private*, pg. 3174
PICOTECH LTD.—See Disco Corporation; *Int'l*, pg. 2132
PIERCE PUMP—See Applied Industrial Technologies, Inc.; *U.S. Public*, pg. 171
PIE TNUFA LTD.—See Haulotte Group SA; *Int'l*, pg. 3285
PINNACLE MACHINE TOOLS, INC.; *U.S. Private*, pg. 3185
PINNACLE MACHINE TOOLS, INC.—See Pinnacle Machine Tools, Inc.; *U.S. Private*, pg. 3185

PINNACLE MICRO NAMIBIA (PTY) LIMITED—See Aliviva Holdings Limited; *Int'l*, pg. 402
PIPE SUPPORTS ASIA LTD—See Hill & Smith PLC; *Int'l*, pg. 3392
PITT AUTO ELECTRIC COMPANY; *U.S. Private*, pg. 3191
PLAGEMAN ASSOCIATES INC.; *U.S. Private*, pg. 3194
PLAYER & CORNISH LIMITED—See Enpro Inc.; *U.S. Public*, pg. 775
PLENTY ISLAND (THAI) CO., LTD.—See Aurotek Corporation; *Int'l*, pg. 714
PLURIFILTER D.O.O.—See Ingersoll Rand Inc.; *U.S. Public*, pg. 1122
PNEU-FORCE—See Penn-Air & Hydraulics Corp.; *U.S. Private*, pg. 3135
PNEUMEC KONTROLLS PRIVATE LIMITED—See Convum Ltd.; *Int'l*, pg. 1788
P&N HOMAG IMPORTACAO E COMERCIO LTDA.—See Cifin S.r.l.; *Int'l*, pg. 1606
PNUCOR LLC—See Voigt-Abernathy Company, Inc.; *U.S. Private*, pg. 4409
POMPES FRISTAM S.N.C.—See FRISTAM Pumpen F. Stamp GmbH & Co. KG; *Int'l*, pg. 2793
POSTROM MASKINER AS—See BOWE SYSTEC AG; *Int'l*, pg. 1123
POULAIN DISTRIBUTION—See Carrefour SA; *Int'l*, pg. 1346
POWELL CANADA INC.—See Powell Industries, Inc.; *U.S. Public*, pg. 1705
POWER DISTRIBUTORS, LLC; *U.S. Private*, pg. 3237
POWER DRIVES INC.; *U.S. Private*, pg. 3238
POWER EQUIPMENT CO. MEMPHIS; *U.S. Private*, pg. 3238
POWER SERVICE, INC.—See DNOW Inc.; *U.S. Public*, pg. 671
POWERS PROCESS CONTROLS—See Watts Water Technologies, Inc.; *U.S. Public*, pg. 2337
POWER SYSTEMS, LLC—See Applied Industrial Technologies, Inc.; *U.S. Public*, pg. 171
POWER TOWERS LIMITED—See Oshkosh Corporation; *U.S. Public*, pg. 1621
POWIN ENERGY CORPORATION; *U.S. Public*, pg. 1706
PPM TECHNOLOGIES, INC.—See Warburg Pincus LLC; *U.S. Private*, pg. 4438
PRECICULTURE SAS—See Exel Industries SA; *Int'l*, pg. 2582
PRECISE TECH ELECTRONICS LTD.—See ESPEC Corp.; *Int'l*, pg. 2505
PRECISION FITTING & GAUGE CO; *U.S. Private*, pg. 3245
PRECISION IBC INC; *U.S. Private*, pg. 3245
PREFERRED PUMP & EQUIPMENT LP; *U.S. Private*, pg. 3248
PREMIER MACHINERY INC.; *U.S. Private*, pg. 3250
PRESSENSYSTEME SCHULER-MEXICO, S.A. DE C.V.—See ANDRITZ AG; *Int'l*, pg. 456
PRESSMASTERS INC.; *U.S. Private*, pg. 3255
PRESS PARTS OUTLET GMBH—See Heidelberger Druckmaschinen AG; *Int'l*, pg. 3322
PRICE ENGINEERING COMPANY INC.; *U.S. Private*, pg. 3258
PRIMARY FLOW SIGNAL INC.; *U.S. Private*, pg. 3260
PRIMARY SOURCING CORPORATION—See Sanmina Corporation; *U.S. Public*, pg. 1840
PRIME AIR, LLC—See HEICO Corporation; *U.S. Public*, pg. 1020
PRIMET FLUID POWER COMPANY, INC.—See Frontenac Company LLC; *U.S. Private*, pg. 1614
PRINTERS' SERVICE, INC.; *U.S. Private*, pg. 3265
PRISCO EUROPE LTD.—See Printers' Service, Inc.; *U.S. Private*, pg. 3265
PRISCO/PACIFIC, INC.—See Printers' Service, Inc.; *U.S. Private*, pg. 3266
PROCESS AUTOMATION (EUROPE) LIMITED—See Asia Tele-Net & Technology Corporation Limited; *Int'l*, pg. 615
PROCESS AUTOMATION TAIWAN CO. LTD—See Asia Tele-Net & Technology Corporation Limited; *Int'l*, pg. 616
PROCESS CONTROL SYSTEMS INTERNATIONAL; *U.S. Private*, pg. 3271
PROCESS PUMPS & EQUIPMENT INC.—See John H. Carter Company Incorporated; *U.S. Private*, pg. 2222
PROCONEX INC.—See Proconex Management Group Inc.; *U.S. Private*, pg. 3272
PROCONEX MANAGEMENT GROUP INC.; *U.S. Private*, pg. 3272
PROCONNEX GMBH—See AWS Achslagerwerk Stassfurt GmbH; *Int'l*, pg. 753
PRODUCT HANDLING DESIGN INC.; *U.S. Private*, pg. 3273
PRODUCTIVITY INC.; *U.S. Private*, pg. 3274
PROEPTA, S.A. DE C.V—See Bunzl plc; *Int'l*, pg. 1219
PROFILE PACKAGING INC—See PPi Technologies Global, LLC; *U.S. Private*, pg. 3240
PROFRAC SERVICES LLC; *U.S. Private*, pg. 3277
PROGRESSIVE COMPONENTS INTERNATIONAL CORPORATION; *U.S. Private*, pg. 3278
PROGRESSIVE HYDRAULICS, INC.; *U.S. Private*, pg. 3279
PROLATAMEX, S.A. DE C.V.—See Crown Holdings, Inc.; *U.S. Public*, pg. 598

PROLIFT INDUSTRIAL EQUIPMENT CO., LLC; *U.S. Private*, pg. 3282
PROMOTER HYDRAULICS PTE. LTD.—See 9R Limited; *Int'l*, pg. 17
PRO-ROD INC.—See Dover Corporation; *U.S. Public*, pg. 682
PROVEL, S.R.L.—See 3D Systems Corporation; *U.S. Public*, pg. 4
PROVENTIA GMBH—See Head Invest Oy; *Int'l*, pg. 3301
PROXES TECHNOLOGY GMBH—See Capvis AG; *Int'l*, pg. 1318
PT ABB SAKTI INDUSTRI—See ABB Ltd.; *Int'l*, pg. 56
PT. ALTECH ASIA PACIFIC INDONESIA—See Altech Co., Ltd.; *Int'l*, pg. 388
PT ARBURG—See Arburg GmbH & Co.; *Int'l*, pg. 539
PT BROTHER INTERNATIONAL SALES INDONESIA—See Brother Industries, Ltd.; *Int'l*, pg. 1198
PT CKD TRADING INDONESIA—See CKD Corporation; *Int'l*, pg. 1593
PT. CLYDE BERGEMANN INDONESIA—See Clyde Blowers Capital IM LLP; *Int'l*, pg. 1665
PT. DJK INDONESIA—See Daiichi Jitsugyo Co. Ltd.; *Int'l*, pg. 1927
PT EMERSON SOLUTIONS INDONESIA—See Emerson Electric Co.; *U.S. Public*, pg. 750
PT. ENSHU INDONESIA—See Enshu Limited; *Int'l*, pg. 2446
PT. EXTERRAN INDONESIA—See Enerflex Ltd.; *Int'l*, pg. 2419
PT FLEXLINK SYSTEMS—See Coesia S.p.A.; *Int'l*, pg. 1689
PT FLSMIDTH INDONESIA—See FLSmidth & Co. A/S; *Int'l*, pg. 2710
PT FRISTINDO JAYA PUMP—See FRISTAM Pumpen F. Stamp GmbH & Co. KG; *Int'l*, pg. 2793
PT FUSION TECHNOLOGIES INDONESIA—See AVK Holding A/S; *Int'l*, pg. 747
P.T. HEIDELBERG INDONESIA—See Heidelberger Druckmaschinen AG; *Int'l*, pg. 3322
PT. HISAKA WORKS INDONESIA—See Hisaka Works, Ltd.; *Int'l*, pg. 3406
PT HTECH TOOLS INDONESIA—See Halcyon Technology Public Company Limited; *Int'l*, pg. 3227
PT. INA NUSANTARA ABADI—See ANEST IWATA Corporation; *Int'l*, pg. 458
P.T. LOSCAM INDONESIA—See China Merchants Group Limited; *Int'l*, pg. 1521
PT NETZSCH INDONESIA—See Erich Netzsch GmbH & Co. Holding KG; *Int'l*, pg. 2493
PTNW EQUITY, INC.—See Pike Street Capital, LP; *U.S. Private*, pg. 3179
PT. OTC DAIHEN INDONESIA—See Daihen Corporation; *Int'l*, pg. 1926
PT PARKER HANNIFIN INDONESIA—See Parker Hannifin Corporation; *U.S. Public*, pg. 1643
PT PHOCEENNE INDONESIE—See Groupe BPCE; *Int'l*, pg. 3095
PT. SUPERHELINDO JAYA—See Hyundai Group; *Int'l*, pg. 3557
PT TATINDO HEAVYEQUIPMENT—See Affirma Capital Limited; *Int'l*, pg. 187
PUFFER SWEIVEN; *U.S. Private*, pg. 3302
PUMPING SOLUTIONS, INC.—See DXP Enterprises, Inc.; *U.S. Public*, pg. 698
PUMPING SYSTEMS INC.; *U.S. Private*, pg. 3303
PUMPS PARTS & SERVICE INC.; *U.S. Private*, pg. 3304
PUMPTRON (PROPRIETARY) LIMITED—See The Gorman-Rupp Company; *U.S. Public*, pg. 2085
PUNCH GRAPHIX UK LTD.—See Iep Invest SA; *Int'l*, pg. 3597
PUNCH TECHNIX NV—See Iep Invest SA; *Int'l*, pg. 3597
PURVIS BEARING SERVICE LTD.; *U.S. Private*, pg. 3307
PYROTEK (ASIA) LTD.—See Pyrotek Incorporated; *U.S. Private*, pg. 3311
Q.E.D. ENVIRONMENTAL SYSTEMS LIMITED—See Graco, Inc.; *U.S. Public*, pg. 954
Q-FREE SVERIGE AB—See Guardian Capital Group Limited; *Int'l*, pg. 3170
Q-MATION INC.; *U.S. Private*, pg. 3312
QUALITY BUILDING CONTROLS, INC.—See Huron Capital Partners LLC; *U.S. Private*, pg. 2011
QUALITY HYDRAULICS & PNEUMATICS INC.; *U.S. Private*, pg. 3319
QUALITY PACKAGING, INC.; *U.S. Private*, pg. 3320
QUANTEL PRIVATE LTD.—See Chroma ATE Inc.; *Int'l*, pg. 1588
QUEST ENGINEERING, INC.; *U.S. Private*, pg. 3325
QUIMICA INDUSTRIAL MEDITERRANEO, S.L.—See Illinois Tool Works Inc.; *U.S. Public*, pg. 1110
QUZHOU JISHAN REAL ESTATE DEVELOPMENT CO., LTD.—See China Jishan Holdings Limited; *Int'l*, pg. 1513
R3 SAFETY—See Bunzl plc; *Int'l*, pg. 1217
RADIODETECTION CORP.—See SPX Technologies, Inc.; *U.S. Public*, pg. 1921
RADWELL INTERNATIONAL, INC.—See CVC Capital Partners SICAV-FIS S.A.; *Int'l*, pg. 1885
RALPH W. EARL CO., INC.; *U.S. Private*, pg. 3350
R.A. MUELLER, INC.—See DXP Enterprises, Inc.; *U.S. Public*, pg. 698
RANSBURG INDUSTRIAL FINISHING K.K.—See Carlisle

423830 — INDUSTRIAL MACHINER...

Companies Incorporated; *U.S. Public*, pg. 436
RAU SERTA HYDRAULIK GMBH—See Hydrokit; *Int'l*, pg. 3548
RAY LEWIS & CO.—See AEA Investors LP; *U.S. Private*, pg. 115
RAYMOND DISTRIBUTION-MEXICO, S.A. DE C.V.—See OEP Capital Advisors, L.P.; *U.S. Private*, pg. 2998
RAYMOND HANDLING CONCEPTS CORPORATION; *U.S. Private*, pg. 3359
RBI CORPORATION; *U.S. Private*, pg. 3360
R.B. INTERNATIONAL INC.; *U.S. Private*, pg. 3334
RECO, LLC—See WESCO International, Inc.; *U.S. Public*, pg. 2352
RED BALL OXYGEN CO. INC.; *U.S. Private*, pg. 3373
RED RIVER MACHINERY INC.; *U.S. Private*, pg. 3375
REED MANUFACTURING COMPANY—See J.F. Shea Co., Inc.; *U.S. Private*, pg. 2164
REIS SERVICE GMBH—See GLORY Ltd.; *Int'l*, pg. 3010
RELIABLE INDUSTRIES INC.; *U.S. Private*, pg. 3394
REM SALES, LLC—See Morris Group, Inc.; *U.S. Private*, pg. 2787
RENTZEL PUMP MANUFACTURING, LP; *U.S. Private*, pg. 3400
REPUBLIC CRANE & EQUIPMENT CO.; *U.S. Private*, pg. 3402
REPUBLIC INDUSTRIES; *U.S. Private*, pg. 3402
RESCAN INTERNATIONAL PTY. LIMITED—See Compagnie Generale des Etablissements Michelin SCA; *Int'l*, pg. 1745
RESSORTS SPEC, SAS—See Barnes Group Inc.; *U.S. Public*, pg. 277
REVCO INDUSTRIES, INC.—See Bunzl plc; *Int'l*, pg. 1219
REX SUPPLY COMPANY—See Production Tool Supply Company, LLC; *U.S. Private*, pg. 3273
R&F INDUSTRIES, INC.; *U.S. Private*, pg. 3332
RG INDUSTRIES, INC.; *U.S. Private*, pg. 3420
RHINE EQUIPMENT COMPANY; *U.S. Private*, pg. 3421
RHM FLUID POWER INC.; *U.S. Private*, pg. 3421
RICE CHRIST, INC.; *U.S. Private*, pg. 3425
RICHARDS SUPPLY COMPANY; *U.S. Private*, pg. 3429
RIEKES EQUIPMENT COMPANY; *U.S. Private*, pg. 3434
RIELLO MANDELLI MACHINE TOOLS UK LTD.—See Gruppo Riello Sistemi S.p.A.; *Int'l*, pg. 3141
RIELLO SISTEMI (SHANGHAI) TRADE CO., LTD—See Gruppo Riello Sistemi S.p.A.; *Int'l*, pg. 3141
RIMCO INC.; *U.S. Private*, pg. 3437
RIMOLDI OF AMERICA INC.—See CF Italia srl; *Int'l*, pg. 1429
RING LIFT—See Ring Power Corporation; *U.S. Private*, pg. 3438
RIO GRANDE DRYWALL SUPPLY CO LLC—See Eagle Materials Inc.; *U.S. Public*, pg. 702
RITE-HITE CORPORATION—See Rite-Hite Holding Corporation; *U.S. Private*, pg. 3442
RITE-HITE FROMMELT DIVISION—See Rite-Hite Holding Corporation; *U.S. Private*, pg. 3442
RITE-HITE HOLDING CORPORATION; *U.S. Private*, pg. 3441
RJMS CORPORATION; *U.S. Private*, pg. 3449
R J SAFETY SUPPLY CO, INC.—See Mallory Safety & Supply LLC; *U.S. Private*, pg. 2558
ROBERT DIETRICK CO. INC.; *U.S. Private*, pg. 3457
THE ROBERT E. MORRIS COMPANY—See Morris Group, Inc.; *U.S. Private*, pg. 2787
ROBERT REISER & COMPANY INC.; *U.S. Private*, pg. 3459
ROBIN HOOD SUPPLIES, INC.; *U.S. Private*, pg. 3460
ROBUSCHI BENELUX BV—See Ingersoll Rand Inc.; *U.S. Public*, pg. 1119
ROCKWELL AUTOMATION AB—See Rockwell Automation, Inc.; *U.S. Public*, pg. 1805
ROCKWELL AUTOMATION B.V.—See Rockwell Automation, Inc.; *U.S. Public*, pg. 1805
ROCKWELL AUTOMATION INDIA LTD.—See Rockwell Automation, Inc.; *U.S. Public*, pg. 1806
ROCKWELL AUTOMATION JAPAN CO., LTD.—See Rockwell Automation, Inc.; *U.S. Public*, pg. 1806
ROCKWELL AUTOMATION L.L.C.—See Rockwell Automation, Inc.; *U.S. Public*, pg. 1806
ROCKWELL AUTOMATION PUERTO RICO, INC.—See Rockwell Automation, Inc.; *U.S. Public*, pg. 1806
ROCKY MOUNTAIN INDUSTRIAL SUPPLY, INC—See Mallory Safety & Supply LLC; *U.S. Private*, pg. 2558
ROCKY MOUNTAIN OILFIELD WAREHOUSE; *U.S. Private*, pg. 3469
RODEM INC.; *U.S. Private*, pg. 3470
ROFIN-SINAR TECHNOLOGIES, INC.—See Coherent Corp.; *U.S. Public*, pg. 527
RONCO MACHINE AND RIGGING; *U.S. Private*, pg. 3478
RONDO B.V.—See DPG Media Group NV; *Int'l*, pg. 2189
ROSCO PETROAVANCE LIMITED—See Agostini's Limited; *Int'l*, pg. 213
ROSEMOUNT INC.—See Emerson Electric Co.; *U.S. Public*, pg. 747
ROSEMOUNT INC.—See Emerson Electric Co.; *U.S. Public*, pg. 747
RO SYSTEC GROUP SRL—See BOWE SYSTEC AG; *Int'l*, pg. 1123

ROTARY COMPRESSOR SYSTEMS, INC.—See EQT AB; *Int'l*, pg. 2478
ROTHENBERGER AUSTRALIA PTY. LTD.—See Dr. Helmut Rothenberger Holding GmbH; *Int'l*, pg. 2191
ROTHENBERGER BENELUX BVBA—See Dr. Helmut Rothenberger Holding GmbH; *Int'l*, pg. 2191
ROTHENBERGER DO BRASIL LTDA.—See Dr. Helmut Rothenberger Holding GmbH; *Int'l*, pg. 2192
ROTHENBERGER FRANCE S.A.—See Dr. Helmut Rothenberger Holding GmbH; *Int'l*, pg. 2191
ROTHENBERGER HELLAS S.A.—See Dr. Helmut Rothenberger Holding GmbH; *Int'l*, pg. 2191
ROTHENBERGER HUNGARY KFT.—See Dr. Helmut Rothenberger Holding GmbH; *Int'l*, pg. 2191
ROTHENBERGER ITALIANA S.R.L.—See Dr. Helmut Rothenberger Holding GmbH; *Int'l*, pg. 2191
ROTHENBERGER NEDERLAND BV—See Dr. Helmut Rothenberger Holding GmbH; *Int'l*, pg. 2191
ROTHENBERGER PIPE TOOL (SHANGHAI) CO., LTD.—See Dr. Helmut Rothenberger Holding GmbH; *Int'l*, pg. 2191
ROTHENBERGER POLSKA SP. Z.O.O.—See Dr. Helmut Rothenberger Holding GmbH; *Int'l*, pg. 2191
ROTHENBERGER S.A.—See Dr. Helmut Rothenberger Holding GmbH; *Int'l*, pg. 2191
ROTHENBERGER SCANDINAVIA A/S—See Dr. Helmut Rothenberger Holding GmbH; *Int'l*, pg. 2191
ROTHENBERGER SCHWEIZ AG—See Dr. Helmut Rothenberger Holding GmbH; *Int'l*, pg. 2191
ROTHENBERGER SWEDEN AB—See Dr. Helmut Rothenberger Holding GmbH; *Int'l*, pg. 2191
ROTHENBERGER UK LIMITED—See Dr. Helmut Rothenberger Holding GmbH; *Int'l*, pg. 2191
ROYAL SUPPLY CO.; *U.S. Private*, pg. 3493
ROY SMITH COMPANY INC.; *U.S. Private*, pg. 3491
RR CANADA INC.—See Fenix Outdoor International AG; *Int'l*, pg. 2634
RRR INDUSTRIAL SALES, INC.—See Reece-Hopper Sales, LLC; *U.S. Private*, pg. 3381
R.S. BRASWELL COMPANY INC.; *U.S. Private*, pg. 3339
RUHRPUMEN INDIA PRIVATE LIMITED—See Corporacion EG S.A.; *Int'l*, pg. 1803
RUMPKE HYDRAULICS & MACHINING—See Rumpke Consolidated Companies, Inc.; *U.S. Private*, pg. 3503
RUSSELL HALL CO.—See Bain Capital, LP; *U.S. Private*, pg. 441
SABRE ITALIA S.R.L.—See Sabre Corporation; *U.S. Public*, pg. 1833
SAENGVITH 2000 CO. LTD.—See Atlas Copco AB; *Int'l*, pg. 684
SAFE RACK, LLC; *U.S. Private*, pg. 3523
SAFETY SOLUTIONS, INC.—See W.W. Grainger, Inc.; *U.S. Public*, pg. 2320
SAFETY TODAY INC.—See Volk Enterprises, Inc.; *U.S. Private*, pg. 4410
SAMES KREMLIN SAS—See Exel Industries SA; *Int'l*, pg. 2582
SAMPLE BROTHERS, INC.—See SBI Incorporated; *U.S. Private*, pg. 3560
SAMS ADVANCE CLIMATIC TECHNOLOGIES—See ESPEC Corp.; *Int'l*, pg. 2505
SANKI TECHNOS CO., LTD.—See Hitachi, Ltd.; *Int'l*, pg. 3424
SANMINA-SCI DO BRAZIL LDTA.—See Sanmina Corporation; *U.S. Public*, pg. 1841
SANTA FE VAN LINES CO. LTD.—See EAC Invest AS; *Int'l*, pg. 2262
SARL GLOBAL SERVICE INDUSTRY—See Doga; *Int'l*, pg. 2154
SATAIR USA INC. - MIAMI—See Airbus SE; *Int'l*, pg. 244
SCALES AIR COMPRESSOR CORP; *U.S. Private*, pg. 3560
SCARABEE AVIATION GROUP B.V.—See Daifuku Co., Ltd.; *Int'l*, pg. 1926
SCB INTERNATIONAL HOLDINGS, LLC—See SER Capital Partners LLC; *U.S. Private*, pg. 3612
SCHOELLER INSTRUMENTS, S.R.O.—See ESPEC Corp.; *Int'l*, pg. 2505
SCHULER INDIA PRIVATE LIMITED—See ANDRITZ AG; *U.S. Public*, pg. 456
S.C. HYDAC SRL—See Hydac International GmbH; *Int'l*, pg. 3545
SCIENTIFIC SALES, INC.; *U.S. Private*, pg. 3574
SCOTSCO INC.; *U.S. Private*, pg. 3576
SCOTT INDUSTRIAL SYSTEMS INC.; *U.S. Private*, pg. 3577
SCR EUROPE SRL—See Merck & Co., Inc.; *U.S. Public*, pg. 1421
SEALS UNLIMITED HOLDING CO., INC.—See Applied Industrial Technologies, Inc.; *U.S. Public*, pg. 171
SEBASTIAN EQUIPMENT CO. INC.; *U.S. Private*, pg. 3593
SE EQUIPMENT, INC.—See Brandt Holdings Company; *U.S. Private*, pg. 639
SEIDEL DIESEL GROUP; *U.S. Private*, pg. 3599
SELWAY MACHINE TOOL CO. INC.; *U.S. Private*, pg. 3603
SENSORWISE, INC.—See Sanmina Corporation; *U.S. Public*, pg. 1841
SENSUS CANADA INC.—See Xylem Inc.; *U.S. Public*, pg. 2394

SENTINEL FLUID CONTROLS, LLC—See Applied Industrial Technologies, Inc.; *U.S. Public*, pg. 171
SERVATECHNIK AG—See Atlas Copco AB; *Int'l*, pg. 677
SERVCO OILFIELD SUPPLY CANADA LTD.—See Applied Industrial Technologies, Inc.; *U.S. Public*, pg. 171
SERVICE FILTRATION OF CANADA LIMITED.—See SERFILCO, Inc.; *U.S. Private*, pg. 3613
SERVICE INDUSTRIES LLC—See Thomas Engineering Inc.; *U.S. Private*, pg. 4155
SETPOINT INTEGRATED SOLUTIONS, INC.—See Middle-Ground Management, LP; *U.S. Private*, pg. 2712
S.G. MORRIS CO., LLC—See Applied Industrial Technologies, Inc.; *U.S. Public*, pg. 171
SGX SENSORTECH CHINA LIMITED—See Amphenol Corporation; *U.S. Public*, pg. 132
SGX SENSORTECH GMBH—See Amphenol Corporation; *U.S. Public*, pg. 132
SGX SENSORTECH SA—See Amphenol Corporation; *U.S. Public*, pg. 132
SHALTZ FLUID POWER INC.; *U.S. Private*, pg. 3623
SHANGHAI-FANUC ROBOMACHINE CO., LTD.—See FANUC Corporation; *Int'l*, pg. 2615
SHANGHAI FTNON FOOD PROCESSING EQUIPMENT CO., LTD.—See John Bean Technologies Corporation; *U.S. Public*, pg. 1192
SHANGHAI HYSTER FORKLIFT, LTD.—See Hyster-Yale Materials Handling, Inc.; *U.S. Public*, pg. 1080
SHANGHAI HYUNDAI ELEVATOR MANUFACTURING CO., LTD.—See Hyundai Group; *Int'l*, pg. 3557
SHANGHAI MOTION CONTROL TECHNOLOGY CO. LTD.—See Eastern Industrial Automation; *U.S. Private*, pg. 1320
SHANGHAI WOOD BASED PANEL MACHINERY CO., LTD.—See Dieffenbacher Holding GmbH & Co. KG; *Int'l*, pg. 2114
SHANGHAI YISHI TRADING CO., LTD.—See Daiichi Jitsugyo Co. Ltd.; *Int'l*, pg. 1927
SHANGHAI ZHONG JING IMPORT & EXPORT CORPORATION—See China Machinery Engineering Corporation; *Int'l*, pg. 1516
SHANNAHAN CRANE & HOIST INC.—See Rotunda Capital Partners LLC; *U.S. Private*, pg. 3487
SHAOXING JISHAN ZHIYE CO., LTD.—See China Jishan Holdings Limited; *Int'l*, pg. 1513
SHAPE, INC.—See H.I.G. Capital, LLC; *U.S. Private*, pg. 1834
SHERMAN INTERNATIONAL CORPORATION; *U.S. Private*, pg. 3634
SHEZHEN ATLANTIC WELDING CONSUMABLES CO., LTD—See Atlantic China Welding Consumables, Inc.; *Int'l*, pg. 674
SHIELDS HARPER & CO. INC.; *U.S. Private*, pg. 3636
SHINSEI JAPAN INDUSTRY CO LTD—See AnnAik Limited; *Int'l*, pg. 473
SHIVELY BROTHERS INC.; *U.S. Private*, pg. 3638
SHOALTER AUTOMATION (UK) LIMITED—See Hong Kong Technology Venture Company Limited; *Int'l*, pg. 3467
SHOPPAS MATERIAL HANDLING; *U.S. Private*, pg. 3640
SIA LEIPURIN—See Aspo Oyj; *Int'l*, pg. 631
SIDENER ENGINEERING COMPANY, INC.—See Exotic Automation & Supply, Inc.; *U.S. Private*, pg. 1449
SIEMPELKAMP BARCELONA—See G. Siempelkamp GmbH & Co. KG; *Int'l*, pg. 2864
SIEMPELKAMP CZ S. R. O.—See G. Siempelkamp GmbH & Co. KG; *Int'l*, pg. 2865
SIEMPELKAMP DO BRASIL LTDA.—See G. Siempelkamp GmbH & Co. KG; *Int'l*, pg. 2865
SIEMPELKAMP FRANCE SARL—See G. Siempelkamp GmbH & Co. KG; *Int'l*, pg. 2865
SIEMPELKAMP INDIA PVT. LTD.—See G. Siempelkamp GmbH & Co. KG; *Int'l*, pg. 2865
SIEMPELKAMP ISTANBUL—See G. Siempelkamp GmbH & Co. KG; *Int'l*, pg. 2865
SIEMPELKAMP L.P.—See G. Siempelkamp GmbH & Co. KG; *Int'l*, pg. 2865
SIEMPELKAMP MOSCOW OOO—See G. Siempelkamp GmbH & Co. KG; *Int'l*, pg. 2865
SIEMPELKAMP MSDG S.A.S.—See G. Siempelkamp GmbH & Co. KG; *Int'l*, pg. 2865
SIEMPELKAMP PTE. LTD.—See G. Siempelkamp GmbH & Co. KG; *Int'l*, pg. 2865
SIEMPELKAMP PTE. LTD.—See G. Siempelkamp GmbH & Co. KG; *Int'l*, pg. 2865
SIEMPELKAMP PTY. LTD.—See G. Siempelkamp GmbH & Co. KG; *Int'l*, pg. 2865
SIERRA CONCEPTS MANUFACTURING COMPANY INC.—See Ellison Technologies Inc.; *U.S. Private*, pg. 1374
SIEWERT EQUIPMENT CO. INC.—See Cummins-Wagner Co., Inc.; *U.S. Private*, pg. 1123
SIGMA CORPORATION; *U.S. Private*, pg. 3648
SIGNODE FRANCE S.A.S.—See Crown Holdings, Inc.; *U.S. Public*, pg. 599
SILGAN DISPENSING SYSTEMS ALKMAAR B.V.—See Silgan Holdings, Inc.; *U.S. Public*, pg. 1878
SILGAN DISPENSING SYSTEMS ALKMAAR B.V.—See Silgan Holdings, Inc.; *U.S. Public*, pg. 1878
SILGAN DISPENSING SYSTEMS ALKMAAR B.V.—See Sil-

N.A.I.C.S. INDEX   423830 — INDUSTRIAL MACHINER...

gan Holdings, Inc.; *U.S. Public*, pg. 1878
SILGAN DISPENSING SYSTEMS ALKMAAR B.V.—See Silgan Holdings, Inc.; *U.S. Public*, pg. 1879
SILGAN DISPENSING SYSTEMS LACROST S.A.S.—See Silgan Holdings, Inc.; *U.S. Public*, pg. 1879
SILGAN DISPENSING SYSTEMS LE TREPORT S.A.S.—See Silgan Holdings, Inc.; *U.S. Public*, pg. 1879
SILGAN DISPENSING SYSTEMS & PACKAGING DO BRASIL INDUSTRIA DE EMBALAGENS LTDA.—See Silgan Holdings, Inc.; *U.S. Public*, pg. 1878
SILGAN DISPENSING SYSTEMS THOMASTON CORPORATION—See Silgan Holdings, Inc.; *U.S. Public*, pg. 1879
SILICE DEL ISTMO, S.A. DE C.V.—See Crown Holdings, Inc.; *U.S. Public*, pg. 599
SILICON VALLEY SHELVING & EQUIPMENT; *U.S. Private*, pg. 3652
SILVER HOLDING CORP.—See Ingersoll Rand Inc.; *U.S. Public*, pg. 1122
SIMCO TECHNOLOGIES INC.—See B&D Industrial, Inc.; *U.S. Private*, pg. 418
SIMPLIMATIC ENGINEERING HOLDINGS LLC; *U.S. Private*, pg. 3667
SINDUS ANDRITZ LTDA.—See ANDRITZ AG; *Int'l*, pg. 456
SINO AMERICAN MACHINERY CORPORATION—See China Machinery Engineering Corporation; *Int'l*, pg. 1516
S.J. SMITH CO., INC.; *U.S. Private*, pg. 3517
S&K ACQUISITION CORP; *U.S. Private*, pg. 3513
SLATER CONTROLS, INC.; *U.S. Private*, pg. 3687
S-LINE, LLC—See The Heico Companies, L.L.C.; *U.S. Private*, pg. 4050
SLOAN EQUIPMENT SALES CO. INC.; *U.S. Private*, pg. 3689
SMITH INSTRUMENT—See The Kendall Group, Inc.; *U.S. Private*, pg. 4064
SMITH PUMP COMPANY INC.; *U.S. Private*, pg. 3695
SNA TOOLS BELGIUM BVBA—See Snap-on Incorporated; *U.S. Public*, pg. 1898
SNK AMERICA, INC.—See Fair Friend Group; *Int'l*, pg. 2605
SNK AMERICA, INC.—See Fair Friend Group; *Int'l*, pg. 2605
SNORKEL JAPAN CO., LTD.—See Xtreme Manufacturing, LLC; *U.S. Private*, pg. 4583
SNORKEL NEW ZEALAND LIMITED—See Xtreme Manufacturing, LLC; *U.S. Private*, pg. 4583
SO.F.TER. S.R.L.—See Celanese Corporation; *U.S. Public*, pg. 465
SO.F.TER. US, INC.—See Celanese Corporation; *U.S. Public*, pg. 465
SOGESSO - SOCIEDADE DE GESSOS DE SOURE, S.A.—See Camargo Correa S.A.; *Int'l*, pg. 1268
SOLO CUP COMPANY—See Dart Container Corporation; *U.S. Public*, pg. 1160
SOLUTIA THERMINOL CO., LTD.—See Eastman Chemical Company; *U.S. Public*, pg. 706
SOLUTIONS INDUSTRIELLES ULC—See Applied Industrial Technologies, Inc.; *U.S. Public*, pg. 171
SONNY'S ENTERPRISES INC.; *U.S. Private*, pg. 3714
SOONER LIFT INC.; *U.S. Private*, pg. 3715
SOUDRONIC, LTD.; *U.S. Private*, pg. 3716
SOUTHEASTERN MANUFACTURERS AGENTS, INC.; *U.S. Private*, pg. 3728
SOUTHERN CALIFORNIA MATERIAL HANDLING; *U.S. Private*, pg. 3729
SOUTHERN MATERIAL HANDLING CO.—See Hugg & Hall Equipment Company; *U.S. Private*, pg. 2003
SOUTHERN PETROLEUM EQUIPMENT COMPANY, INC.—See Kennedy Tank & Manufacturing Company, Inc.; *U.S. Private*, pg. 2285
SOUTHERN PUMP & TANK COMPANY—See Kian Capital Partners, LLC; *U.S. Private*, pg. 2302
SOUTHERN PUMP & TANK COMPANY—See RFE Investment Partners; *U.S. Private*, pg. 3419
SOUTHERN STATES TOYOTALIFT—See Florida Lift Systems, Inc.; *U.S. Private*, pg. 1549
SOUTHWEST HEATER & CONTROLS, INC.—See Gryphon Investors, LLC; *U.S. Private*, pg. 1799
SOUTHWEST MATERIAL HANDLING INC.; *U.S. Private*, pg. 3740
SOYER MAGYARORSZAG KFT.—See Heinz Soyer Bolzenschweisstechnik GmbH; *Int'l*, pg. 3325
SPARROWS OFFSHORE LLC—See Altrad Investment Authority SAS; *Int'l*, pg. 398
SPECIALIZED AUTOMATION SERVICES, LLC.; *U.S. Private*, pg. 3748
SPECIALTY TOOL, INC.; *U.S. Private*, pg. 3751
SPECMA HYDRAULIC - OEM DIVISION—See Aktieselskabet Schouw & Co.; *Int'l*, pg. 266
SPENCER FLUID POWER—See Applied Industrial Technologies, Inc.; *U.S. Public*, pg. 171
SPIRIT GLOBAL ENERGY SOLUTIONS, INC.—See Dover Corporation; *U.S. Public*, pg. 682
SPRAY EQUIPMENT & SERVICE CENTER, INC.; *U.S. Private*, pg. 3762
SPRAYING SYSTEMS CO.; *U.S. Private*, pg. 3762
SPRINT SAFETY, INC.—See Littlejohn & Co., LLC; *U.S. Private*, pg. 2472
SPX FLOW TECHNOLOGY GERMANY GMBH—See Lone Star Funds; *U.S. Private*, pg. 2486
SPX FLOW TECHNOLOGY LONDON LIMITED—See Lone Star Funds; *U.S. Private*, pg. 2487
SPX FLOW TECHNOLOGY—See Lone Star Funds; *U.S. Private*, pg. 2486
SPX (SHANGHAI) FLOW TECHNOLOGY CO., LTD.—See Lone Star Funds; *U.S. Private*, pg. 2486
S&S INDUSTRIAL MARKETING; *U.S. Private*, pg. 3514
SSMC LIMITED—See Platinum Equity, LLC; *U.S. Private*, pg. 3208
STAHL CRANESYSTEMS FZE—See Columbus McKinnon Corporation; *U.S. Public*, pg. 536
STAHL CRANESYSTEMS INC.—See Columbus McKinnon Corporation; *U.S. Public*, pg. 536
STAHL CRANESYSTEMS LTD.—See Columbus McKinnon Corporation; *U.S. Public*, pg. 536
STAHL CRANESYSTEMS S.A.S.—See Columbus McKinnon Corporation; *U.S. Public*, pg. 536
STAHL CRANESYSTEMS S.L.—See Columbus McKinnon Corporation; *U.S. Public*, pg. 536
STANDARD DUPLICATING MACHINES CORPORATION - STANDARD BUSINESS SYSTEMS DIVISION—See Standard Duplicating Machines Corporation; *U.S. Private*, pg. 3778
STANDARDWERK EUGEN REIS GMBH—See GLORY Ltd.; *Int'l*, pg. 3010
STANDEX INTERNATIONAL S.R.L.—See Standex International; *U.S. Public*, pg. 1931
STANLEY M. PROCTOR COMPANY, LLC—See Applied Industrial Technologies, Inc.; *U.S. Public*, pg. 171
STANLEY UK SALES LIMITED—See Stanley Black & Decker, Inc.; *U.S. Public*, pg. 1936
STAR INTERNATIONAL, INC.; *U.S. Private*, pg. 3784
STARRETT (ASIA) PTE. LTD.—See MiddleGround Management, LP; *U.S. Private*, pg. 2713
STARRETT GMBH—See MiddleGround Management, LP; *U.S. Private*, pg. 2713
STARRETT (NEW ZEALAND) LIMITED—See MiddleGround Management, LP; *U.S. Private*, pg. 2713
S.T.A. S.R.L.—See Aega ASA; *Int'l*, pg. 173
STATCO ENGINEERING & FABRICATORS INC.; *U.S. Private*, pg. 3790
STATECH SLOVAKIA S.R.O.—See Group Thermote & Vanhalst; *Int'l*, pg. 3089
STATECH S.R.O.—See Group Thermote & Vanhalst; *Int'l*, pg. 3090
STEFFEN MIDWEST INC.—See Americold Realty Trust, Inc.; *U.S. Public*, pg. 113
STEMCO LP—See Enpro Inc.; *U.S. Public*, pg. 775
STEMCO PRODUCTS, INC.—See Enpro Inc.; *U.S. Public*, pg. 775
STEMCO VEHICLE TECHNOLOGY (SHANGHAI) CO. LTD.—See Enpro Inc.; *U.S. Public*, pg. 775
STEPP EQUIPMENT COMPANY—See H.I.G. Capital, LLC; *U.S. Private*, pg. 1833
STERILSYSTEMS GMBH—See Dr. Honle AG; *Int'l*, pg. 2192
STERLING ACCESS CC—See Haulotte Group SA; *Int'l*, pg. 3285
STERLING FLUID SYSTEMS (CZECH REPUBLIC) S.R.O.—See Flowserve Corporation; *U.S. Public*, pg. 857
STERLING FLUID SYSTEMS (POLASKA) SP.Z.O.O.—See Flowserve Corporation; *U.S. Public*, pg. 857
STERLING FLUID SYSTEMS (ROMANIA) S.R.L.—See Flowserve Corporation; *U.S. Public*, pg. 857
STEWART & STEVENSON FDDA LLC—See Kirby Corporation; *U.S. Public*, pg. 1236
STI ELECTRONICS, INC.; *U.S. Private*, pg. 3812
STILES MACHINERY, INC.—See Durr AG; *Int'l*, pg. 2232
STRAPACK INC.; *U.S. Private*, pg. 3833
STRAPEX HOLDING GMBH—See Crown Holdings, Inc.; *U.S. Public*, pg. 600
STRATE WELDING SUPPLY CO. INC.; *U.S. Private*, pg. 3834
STROH DIE CASTING CO.; *U.S. Private*, pg. 3840
STROMQUIST & COMPANY INC.; *U.S. Private*, pg. 3840
STROTHMANN (SHANGHAI) CO. LTD.—See G. Siempelkamp GmbH & Co. KG; *Int'l*, pg. 2865
STS OPERATING INC.—See Clayton, Dubilier & Rice, LLC; *U.S. Private*, pg. 926
SULLAIR AUSTRALIA PTY LTD—See Hitachi, Ltd.; *Int'l*, pg. 3417
SUMITOMO NACCO MATERIALS HANDLING SALES CO., LTD.—See Hyster-Yale Materials Handling, Inc.; *U.S. Public*, pg. 1080
SUMMIT HANDLING SYSTEMS INC.; *U.S. Private*, pg. 3851
SUNBELT SUPPLY CO.—See Clearlake Capital Group, L.P.; *U.S. Private*, pg. 937
SUNNEN PRODUCTS LIMITED—See Sunnen Products Company; *U.S. Public*, pg. 3868
SUNNEN SAS—See Sunnen Products Company; *U.S. Private*, pg. 3868
SUN PACIFIC HOLDING CORP; *U.S. Public*, pg. 1963
SUPERIOR SEWING MACHINE & SUPPLY LLC; *U.S. Private*, pg. 3880
SVENSKA BLOUNT AB—See American Securities LLC; *U.S. Private*, pg. 247
SVENSKA BLOUNT AB—See P2 Capital Partners, LLC; *U.S. Private*, pg. 3062
SVP CANADA INC.—See Platinum Equity, LLC; *U.S. Private*, pg. 3207
SVP EUROPE SPA—See Platinum Equity, LLC; *U.S. Private*, pg. 3207
SWAGELOK BAKU—See Swagelok Company; *U.S. Private*, pg. 3889
SWAGELOK KAZAKHSTAN—See Swagelok Company; *U.S. Private*, pg. 3889
SWANSON-JAPAN LTD—See Swanson Systems, Inc.; *U.S. Private*, pg. 3891
SWIFT INDUSTRIAL POWER INC.; *U.S. Private*, pg. 3893
SWISS PRECISION INSTRUMENTS, INC.—See MSC Industrial Direct Co., Inc.; *U.S. Public*, pg. 1483
SWP N.Z. LIMITED—See Lincoln Electric Holdings, Inc.; *U.S. Public*, pg. 1318
SYDNOR HYDRO INC.; *U.S. Private*, pg. 3898
SYLPHID INC.—See Daiki Axis Co., Ltd.; *Int'l*, pg. 1932
SYSTEC SISTEM TEKNOLOJILERI A.S.—See BOWE SYSTEC AG; *Int'l*, pg. 1123
SYSTEM 3R EUROPE GMBH—See Georg Fischer AG; *Int'l*, pg. 2937
SYSTEM 3R ITALIA SRL—See Georg Fischer AG; *Int'l*, pg. 2935
SYSTEM 3R SHANGHAI CO LTD—See Georg Fischer AG; *Int'l*, pg. 2935
SYSTEM 3R USA INC.—See Georg Fischer AG; *Int'l*, pg. 2935
SYSTEM SCALE CORPORATION; *U.S. Private*, pg. 3907
SYSTEMS SPECIALTIES COMPANY; *U.S. Private*, pg. 3908
TAIYO TECHNO, LTD.—See Parker Hannifin Corporation; *U.S. Public*, pg. 1649
TAJIMA-HIRSCH INCORPORATED—See Hirsch International Corp.; *U.S. Private*, pg. 1951
TAMPA FORK LIFT INC.; *U.S. Private*, pg. 3929
TANASIO INDUSTRIAL GASES CYF—See Air Products & Chemicals, Inc.; *U.S. Public*, pg. 67
TATE ENGINEERING SYSTEMS INC.; *U.S. Private*, pg. 3936
TAYLOR AIR CENTER—See Atlas Copco AB; *Int'l*, pg. 684
TAYLOR'S INDUSTRIAL SERVICES, L.L.C.; *U.S. Private*, pg. 3941
TBI INDUSTRIES S.R.O.—See Enovis Corporation; *U.S. Public*, pg. 773
T.D. WILLIAMSON ASIA PACIFIC PTY LTD.—See T.D. Williamson, Inc.; *U.S. Public*, pg. 3911
TECHNETICS UK LIMITED—See Enpro Inc.; *U.S. Public*, pg. 775
TECHNICAL EQUIPMENT SALES COMPANY—See Morris Group, Inc.; *U.S. Private*, pg. 2787
TECHNOLINES S.R.L.—See EMC Limited; *Int'l*, pg. 2376
TECNOCONTROL CHILE LTDA.—See Grupo Empresarial San Jose, S.A.; *Int'l*, pg. 3128
TEECO PRODUCTS INC.; *U.S. Private*, pg. 3958
TEKNIKPRODUKTER NORDIC AB—See Addtech AB; *Int'l*, pg. 135
TEKNIK TRADING INC.—See Clover Systems Inc.; *U.S. Private*, pg. 947
TEMPLE ASSOCIATES INC.—See CenterOak Partners LLC; *U.S. Private*, pg. 816
TEM SYSTEMS, INC.; *U.S. Private*, pg. 3963
TENCARVA MACHINERY COMPANY, LLC - ALCOA—See Tencarva Machinery Company, LLC; *U.S. Private*, pg. 3965
TENCARVA MACHINERY COMPANY, LLC - BROOKHAVEN—See Tencarva Machinery Company, LLC; *U.S. Private*, pg. 3965
TENCARVA MACHINERY COMPANY, LLC - CHARLOTTE—See Tencarva Machinery Company, LLC; *U.S. Private*, pg. 3965
TENCARVA MACHINERY COMPANY, LLC - CHATTANOOGA—See Tencarva Machinery Company, LLC; *U.S. Private*, pg. 3965
TENCARVA MACHINERY COMPANY, LLC - CHESAPEAKE—See Tencarva Machinery Company, LLC; *U.S. Private*, pg. 3965
TENCARVA MACHINERY COMPANY, LLC - COLUMBIA—See Tencarva Machinery Company, LLC; *U.S. Private*, pg. 3965
TENCARVA MACHINERY COMPANY, LLC - GREENVILLE—See Tencarva Machinery Company, LLC; *U.S. Private*, pg. 3965
TENCARVA MACHINERY COMPANY, LLC - JACKSON—See Tencarva Machinery Company, LLC; *U.S. Private*, pg. 3965
TENCARVA MACHINERY COMPANY, LLC - JOHNSON CITY—See Tencarva Machinery Company, LLC; *U.S. Private*, pg. 3965
TENCARVA MACHINERY COMPANY, LLC - LITTLE ROCK—See Tencarva Machinery Company, LLC; *U.S. Private*, pg. 3965
TENCARVA MACHINERY COMPANY, LLC - MEMPHIS—See Tencarva Machinery Company, LLC; *U.S. Private*, pg. 3965
TENCARVA MACHINERY COMPANY, LLC -

423830 — INDUSTRIAL MACHINER...

NASHVILLE—See Tencarva Machinery Company, LLC; *U.S. Private*, pg. 3965
TENCARVA MACHINERY COMPANY, LLC - NORTH CHARLESTON—See Tencarva Machinery Company, LLC; *U.S. Private*, pg. 3965
TENCARVA MACHINERY COMPANY, LLC - RICHMOND—See Tencarva Machinery Company, LLC; *U.S. Private*, pg. 3965
TENCARVA MACHINERY COMPANY, LLC - SALEM—See Tencarva Machinery Company, LLC; *U.S. Private*, pg. 3965
TENCARVA MACHINERY COMPANY, LLC; *U.S. Private*, pg. 3965
TENCARVA MACHINERY COMPANY, LLC - WILMINGTON—See Tencarva Machinery Company, LLC; *U.S. Private*, pg. 3965
TEREX AERIAL WORK PLATFORMS—See Terex Corporation; *U.S. Public*, pg. 2019
TEREX BETIM EQUIPAMENTO LTDA—See Terex Corporation; *U.S. Public*, pg. 2019
TEREX CORPORATION; *U.S. Public*, pg. 2018
TERRAPIN UTILITY SERVICES, INC.—See American States Water Company; *U.S. Public*, pg. 110
TERRASOURCE GLOBAL CORPORATION—See Hillenbrand, Inc.; *U.S. Public*, pg. 1037
TERRE HILL CONCRETE PRODUCTS, INC. - TERRE HILL STORMWATER SYSTEMS DIVISION—See Terre Hill Concrete Products, Inc.; *U.S. Private*, pg. 3972
TEXAS INSTRUMENTS ESPANA, S.A.—See Texas Instruments Incorporated; *U.S. Public*, pg. 2026
TEXAS IRON WORKS INC.—See Dril-Quip, Inc.; *U.S. Public*, pg. 688
TEXAS PROCESS EQUIPMENT CO.; *U.S. Private*, pg. 3977
THERMAL DEVICES, INC.—See Gryphon Investors, LLC; *U.S. Private*, pg. 1799
THERMAL & MECHANICAL EQUIPMENT, LLC; *U.S. Private*, pg. 4142
THERMEX-THERMATRON SYSTEMS, LLC—See Druid Capital Partners, LLC; *U.S. Private*, pg. 1279
THERM-O-DISC, INC. - NORTHVILLE—See One Rock Capital Partners, LLC; *U.S. Private*, pg. 3023
THERMO ELECTRON LED S.A.S.—See Thermo Fisher Scientific Inc.; *U.S. Public*, pg. 2152
THOMPSON INTERNATIONAL INC.; *U.S. Private*, pg. 4160
THOMPSON & JOHNSON EQUIPMENT CO.; *U.S. Private*, pg. 4158
THURNE-MIDDLEBY LTD—See The Middleby Corporation; *U.S. Public*, pg. 2115
TIANJIN ACE PILLAR ENTERPRISE CO., LTD.—See ACE PILLAR Co., Ltd; *Int'l*, pg. 94
TIC-MS, LLC—See Transcat, Inc.; *U.S. Public*, pg. 2179
TIDELAND SIGNAL LIMITED—See Xylem Inc.; *U.S. Public*, pg. 2395
TIHERT - EAD—See Herti AD; *Int'l*, pg. 3365
TILTON EQUIPMENT COMPANY; *U.S. Private*, pg. 4171
TITAN MACHINERY BULGARIA AD—See Titan Machinery Inc.; *U.S. Public*, pg. 2160
TLS ENERGIMATNING AB—See Addtech AB; *Int'l*, pg. 135
TOOL CENTER, INC.—See Mattsco Supply Co.; *U.S. Private*, pg. 2614
TOOL FABRICATION CORPORATION—See TruArc Partners, L.P.; *U.S. Private*, pg. 4245
TOOL MART INC.; *U.S. Private*, pg. 4185
TOOL-SMITH COMPANY, INC.; *U.S. Private*, pg. 4185
TOOL SOURCE WAREHOUSE, INC.—See GMS Inc.; *U.S. Public*, pg. 948
TOP LINE PROCESS EQUIPMENT COMPANY—See Edgewater Services, LLC; *U.S. Private*, pg. 1335
TOTAL EQUIPMENT COMPANY; *U.S. Private*, pg. 4191
TOTAL SERVICE SUPPLY INC.; *U.S. Private*, pg. 4191
TOTAL TEMPERATURE INSTRUMENTATION, INC.; *U.S. Private*, pg. 4192
TOWLIFT INC.; *U.S. Private*, pg. 4196
TOYOTA LIFT OF SOUTH TEXAS—See Doggett Equipment Services, Ltd.; *U.S. Private*, pg. 1253
TPH (UK) LIMITED—See Dole plc; *Int'l*, pg. 2158
TRACTOR AND GRADER SUPPLIES (PTY) LTD—See Apex Partners Proprietary Limited; *Int'l*, pg. 512
TRACTOR AND GRADER SUPPLIES (PTY) LTD—See TRG Management LP; *U.S. Private*, pg. 4220
TRACTOR SUPPLY COMPANY; *U.S. Public*, pg. 2178
TRADE HOUSE HILONG-RUS CO. LTD.—See Hilong Holding Limited; *Int'l*, pg. 3393
TRADITIE N. V.—See HEINRICH DE FRIES GmbH; *Int'l*, pg. 3324
TRANSCOM TECHNIK, SPOL. S R.O.—See Endress+Hauser (International) Holding AG; *Int'l*, pg. 2409
TRANSWEIGH INDIA LTD.—See FLsmidth & Co. A/S; *Int'l*, pg. 2711
TRASFOTEX S.R.L.—See Freudenberg SE; *Int'l*, pg. 2790
TRATAMAQ CA—See Ingersoll Rand Inc.; *U.S. Public*, pg. 1122
TREATMENT EQUIPMENT COMPANY; *U.S. Private*, pg. 4216
TREZOS & ASSOCIATES S.A.—See Bischof + Klein GmbH & Co. KG; *Int'l*, pg. 1049

TRIAD TECHNOLOGIES; *U.S. Private*, pg. 4225
TRI-CONTROL AUTOMATION COMPANY LIMITED—See China Automation Group Limited; *Int'l*, pg. 1483
TRIDENT MACHINE TOOLS, LLC—See Morris Group, Inc.; *U.S. Private*, pg. 2787
TRIFACTOR LLC—See Air Transport Services Group, Inc.; *U.S. Private*, pg. 67
TRIFLO INTERNATIONAL, INC.; *U.S. Private*, pg. 4230
TRINITY MINING AND CONSTRUCTION EQUIPMENT, INC.—See Trinity Industries, Inc.; *U.S. Public*, pg. 2194
TRINOVA INC.—See Gold Eagle Company; *U.S. Private*, pg. 1728
TRIPLE-S AS—See Addtech AB; *Int'l*, pg. 131
TRIPLEX CHILE LTDA.—See Cargotec Corporation; *Int'l*, pg. 1329
TRISTATE MACHINERY, INC.; *U.S. Private*, pg. 4238
TRI-W GROUP, INC.—See OEP Capital Advisors, L.P.; *U.S. Private*, pg. 3000
TRYTON TOOL SERVICES LTD.—See Element Technical Services, Inc.; *Int'l*, pg. 2358
TTS GREECE LTD.—See Cargotec Corporation; *Int'l*, pg. 1329
TTS KOREA INC.—See Cargotec Corporation; *Int'l*, pg. 1329
TUBES INC.; *U.S. Private*, pg. 4256
TUBULAR TEXTILE MACHINERY, INC.; *U.S. Private*, pg. 4256
TUFFY MANUFACTURING INDUSTRIES, INC.—See Myers Industries, Inc.; *U.S. Public*, pg. 1488
TULSA RIG IRON INC.; *U.S. Private*, pg. 4258
TULSA TRENCHLESS INC—See Tulsa Rig Iron Inc.; *U.S. Private*, pg. 4258
TURBO DRIVE LTD.—See Cummins Inc.; *U.S. Public*, pg. 609
TVH BRASIL PECAS LTDA.—See Group Thermote & Vanhalst; *Int'l*, pg. 3090
TVH PARTS CO.—See Group Thermote & Vanhalst; *Int'l*, pg. 3090
TVH UK LTD.—See Group Thermote & Vanhalst; *Int'l*, pg. 3090
TWIN DISC SRL—See Twin Disc, Incorporated; *U.S. Public*, pg. 2207
TWIN STATE TRUCKS INC.; *U.S. Private*, pg. 4266
TWSCO; *U.S. Private*, pg. 4267
UNIFAITH MACHINE TOOLS COMPANY LIMITED—See Combine Will International Holdings Limited; *Int'l*, pg. 1709
UNIFILLER SYSTEMS UK LTD.—See Hillenbrand, Inc.; *U.S. Public*, pg. 1037
UNISON INTERNATIONAL CORP.—See Unison Pacific Corporation; *U.S. Private*, pg. 4286
UNITED ENGINES, LLC—See Kirby Corporation; *U.S. Public*, pg. 1235
UNITED EQUIPMENT PTY LTD—See Elphinstone Pty Ltd; *Int'l*, pg. 2369
UNITED FORKTRUCKS LTD—See CorpAcq Holdings Limited; *Int'l*, pg. 1802
UNITED SHOE MACHINERY CORP.; *U.S. Private*, pg. 4297
UNITED TECHNICAL & ALLIED SERVICES LIMITED—See Chellarams Plc; *Int'l*, pg. 1460
UNIVERSAL CHEMICAL AND SUPPLY; *U.S. Private*, pg. 4304
UNIVERSAL FORKLIFT SUPPLY LLC—See Ranger Lift Trucks; *U.S. Private*, pg. 3355
UNIVOLT CANADA LTD.—See Dietzel GmbH; *Int'l*, pg. 2117
UNIVOLT (HK) LIMITED—See Dietzel GmbH; *Int'l*, pg. 2117
UNIVOLT HUNGARIA KFT.—See Dietzel GmbH; *Int'l*, pg. 2117
UNIVOLT (UK) LTD.—See Dietzel GmbH; *Int'l*, pg. 2117
URSCHEL LATINOAMERICA S.R.L.—See Urschel Laboratories Incorporated; *U.S. Private*, pg. 4316
US EQUIPMENT CO. INC.; *U.S. Private*, pg. 4318
US GROUP INC.; *U.S. Private*, pg. 4318
US MATERIALS HANDLING CORP.; *U.S. Private*, pg. 4319
US TECH SERVICES INC.; *U.S. Private*, pg. 4320
US-TQ BEVERAGE PRODUCTS INT'L, INC.; *U.S. Private*, pg. 4320
UTILITY SALES & SERVICE, INC.; *U.S. Private*, pg. 4326
UTILITY SERVICE & SUPPLY INC.; *U.S. Private*, pg. 4326
UTILITY TRAILER SALES OF CENTRAL CALIFORNIA; *U.S. Private*, pg. 4327
VAAHTO PULP & PAPER MACHINERY DISTRIBUTION (SHANGHAI) CO. LTD.—See Lone Star Funds; *U.S. Private*, pg. 2487
VALIN CORPORATION—See Graybar Electric Company, Inc.; *U.S. Private*, pg. 1760
VALLEY DETROIT DIESEL ALLISON; *U.S. Private*, pg. 4333
VALMONT INDUSTRIES, INC.; *U.S. Public*, pg. 2273
VALMONT STRUCTURES PRIVATE LIMITED—See Valmont Industries, Inc.; *U.S. Public*, pg. 2274
VALVESOURCE LTD—See Azzalin Srl; *Int'l*, pg. 782
VANDERBURGH & CO., INC.; *U.S. Private*, pg. 4342
THE VAPORMATIC CO., LTD.—See Deere & Company; *U.S. Public*, pg. 647
VARISPEED (PTY) LTD—See Hudaco Industries Limited; *Int'l*, pg. 3521
VBS INC., MATERIAL HANDLING EQUIPMENT; *U.S. Private*, pg. 4348

VEECO ASIA PTE. LTD.—See Veeco Instruments Inc.; *U.S. Public*, pg. 2276
VEECO INSTRUMENTS (SHANGHAI) CO. LTD.—See Veeco Instruments Inc.; *U.S. Public*, pg. 2277
VEECO KOREA INC.—See Veeco Instruments Inc.; *U.S. Public*, pg. 2277
VEECO TAIWAN INC.—See Veeco Instruments Inc.; *U.S. Public*, pg. 2277
VERMEER GREAT PLAINS INC.—See Vermeer Great Plains Inc.; *U.S. Public*, pg. 4366
VERMEER MIDSOUTH INC; *U.S. Private*, pg. 4366
VERMEER-WISCONSIN INC.; *U.S. Private*, pg. 4367
VERNET BEHRINGER SA—See Behringer GmbH; *Int'l*, pg. 942
VESCO MATERIAL HANDLING EQUIPMENT; *U.S. Private*, pg. 4371
VEZERS PRECISION INDUSTRIAL CO.; *U.S. Private*, pg. 4374
VIAVI SOLUTIONS INC. - INDIANAPOLIS SALES OFFICE—See Viavi Solutions Inc.; *U.S. Public*, pg. 2295
VIBRA SCREW INC.; *U.S. Private*, pg. 4376
VIBRATECHNIQUES S.A.S.—See Atlas Copco AB; *Int'l*, pg. 684
VICTORY WHITE METAL COMPANY, INC.; *U.S. Private*, pg. 4379
VIKING EQUIPMENT CO. KNOXVILLE; *U.S. Private*, pg. 4382
VIN SERVICE S.R.L.—See Aalberts N.V.; *Int'l*, pg. 36
VINSON PROCESS CONTROLS CO. LP; *U.S. Private*, pg. 4386
VJK INC.—See National Amusements, Inc.; *U.S. Private*, pg. 2844
VOIGT-ABERNATHY COMPANY, INC.; *U.S. Private*, pg. 4409
VOLK DO BRASIL LTDA—See Bunzl plc; *Int'l*, pg. 1220
VOLK EUROPE LTD—See Volk Enterprises, Inc.; *U.S. Private*, pg. 4410
VOLVO POLAND SP. Z.O.O.—See AB Volvo; *Int'l*, pg. 46
VOSS EQUIPMENT INCORPORATED; *U.S. Private*, pg. 4413
VRV ASIA PACIFIC PRIVATE LIMITED—See Chart Industries, Inc.; *U.S. Public*, pg. 482
VRV S.R.L.—See Chart Industries, Inc.; *U.S. Public*, pg. 482
VSM AUSTRIA GMBH—See Platinum Equity, LLC; *U.S. Private*, pg. 3208
VSM BELGIE BVBA—See Platinum Equity, LLC; *U.S. Private*, pg. 3208
VSM GERMANY GMBH—See Platinum Equity, LLC; *U.S. Private*, pg. 3208
VSM NETHERLANDS BV—See Platinum Equity, LLC; *U.S. Private*, pg. 3208
VSM SWITZERLAND GMBH—See Platinum Equity, LLC; *U.S. Private*, pg. 3208
WAGNER-HOSOKAWA MICRON LTD—See Hosokawa Micron Corporation; *Int'l*, pg. 3486
THE WALLING CO., INC.—See The Walling Company, Inc.; *U.S. Private*, pg. 4133
THE WALLING COMPANY, INC.; *U.S. Private*, pg. 4133
WALTER PAYTON POWER EQUIPMENT—See The Manitowoc Company, Inc.; *U.S. Public*, pg. 2111
WALTON'S INC.; *U.S. Private*, pg. 4435
WANNER PUMPS LTD.—See Wanner Engineering Inc.; *U.S. Private*, pg. 4436
WAREHOUSE EQUIPMENT & SUPPLY CO.; *U.S. Private*, pg. 4441
WAREHOUSE SOLUTIONS INC.; *U.S. Private*, pg. 4442
WARKAUS WORKS OY—See ANDRITZ AG; *Int'l*, pg. 457
WARREN ALLOY VALVE FITTING LP; *U.S. Private*, pg. 4443
WARRIOR TRACTOR & EQUIPMENT COMPANY INC.; *U.S. Private*, pg. 4445
WASHINGTON LIFTRUCK INC.; *U.S. Private*, pg. 4447
WATSON HEGNER CORPORATION; *U.S. Private*, pg. 4455
WATTS EQUIPMENT CO., INC.; *U.S. Private*, pg. 4456
WATTS INDUSTRIES BULGARIA EAD—See Watts Water Technologies, Inc.; *U.S. Public*, pg. 2337
WATTS INDUSTRIES TUNISIA S.A.S.—See Watts Water Technologies, Inc.; *U.S. Public*, pg. 2337
WATTS INDUSTRIES U.K. LTD.—See Watts Water Technologies, Inc.; *U.S. Public*, pg. 2338
WATTS (NINGBO) INTERNATIONAL TRADING CO., LTD.—See Watts Water Technologies, Inc.; *U.S. Public*, pg. 2337
WAUKESHA-PEARCE INDUSTRIES—See Pearce Industries, Inc.; *U.S. Private*, pg. 3125
WB SUPPLY LLC—See J Fitzgibbons LLC; *U.S. Private*, pg. 2153
W.D. MATTHEWS MACHINERY CO.; *U.S. Private*, pg. 4419
WEAVER FLUID POWER, INC.—See RG Industries, Inc.; *U.S. Private*, pg. 3420
WEIKUANG MECH. ENG. (NANJING) CO., LTD.—See Chroma ATE Inc.; *Int'l*, pg. 1588
WELCH EQUIPMENT COMPANY INC.; *U.S. Private*, pg. 4473
WELDING ENGINEERING SUPPLY CO.; *U.S. Private*, pg. 4474
WELDSTAR COMPANY; *U.S. Private*, pg. 4474
WERRES CORPORATION; *U.S. Private*, pg. 4482

N.A.I.C.S. INDEX

423840 — INDUSTRIAL SUPPLIES...

WERTS WELDING & TANK SERVICE; *U.S. Private*, pg. 4482
WESCO GAS & WELDING SUPPLY INC.; *U.S. Private*, pg. 4482
WESTAIR GAS & EQUIPMENT LP.; *U.S. Private*, pg. 4488
WESTEC AUTOMATION LTD.—See Convum Ltd.; *Int'l*, pg. 1788
WESTERN BRANCH DIESEL INCORPORATED; *U.S. Private*, pg. 4491
WESTERN CAROLINA FORKLIFT INC.; *U.S. Private*, pg. 4491
WESTERN DIESEL SERVICES, INC.; *U.S. Private*, pg. 4492
WESTERN INTEGRATED TECHNOLOGIES, INC.; *U.S. Private*, pg. 4494
WESTERN PACIFIC CRANE & EQUIPMENT LLC—See Lanco International Inc.; *U.S. Private*, pg. 2382
WESTERN PAPERS—See International Paper Company; *U.S. Public*, pg. 1158
WESTERN STATES MACHINERY CORPORATION; *U.S. Private*, pg. 4497
WESTLAKE AUDIO INC.; *U.S. Private*, pg. 4498
WESTOVER CORPORATION; *U.S. Private*, pg. 4500
W.F.C. HOLDING S.P.A.—See EFORT Intelligent Equipment Co., Ltd.; *Int'l*, pg. 2321
WHEELER MATERIAL HANDLING; *U.S. Private*, pg. 4505
WHITNEY/PIRANHA/BERTSCH—See Mega Manufacturing Inc.; *U.S. Private*, pg. 2660
WHOLESALE PUMP & SUPPLY INC.; *U.S. Private*, pg. 4514
WHOLESALE TOOL CO., INC.; *U.S. Private*, pg. 4515
WIDECO US INC—See Grupo BAL; *Int'l*, pg. 3121
WIESE USA, INC.; *U.S. Private*, pg. 4517
THE WILSON COMPANY S. DE R.L. DE C.V.—See Wilson Tool International Inc.; *U.S. Private*, pg. 4531
WILSON COMPANY; *U.S. Private*, pg. 4530
WILSON IRON WORKS INC.; *U.S. Private*, pg. 4531
WILSON TOOL ARGENTINA, S.R.L.—See Wilson Tool International Inc.; *U.S. Private*, pg. 4531
WILSON TOOL INTERNATIONAL A/S—See Wilson Tool International Inc.; *U.S. Private*, pg. 4531
WINCHESTER EQUIPMENT CO.; *U.S. Private*, pg. 4533
W-INDUSTRIES - LOUISIANA LLC—See CSE Global Ltd.; *Int'l*, pg. 1864
WISCONSIN LIFT TRUCK CORP.; *U.S. Private*, pg. 4548
WISE FORKLIFT INC.; *U.S. Private*, pg. 4550
WISSENSCHAFTICH TECHNISCHE WERKSTAETTEN GMBH—See Xylem Inc.; *U.S. Public*, pg. 2395
WISTRA CERINNOV GMBH—See Cerinnov Group SA; *Int'l*, pg. 1422
WITCO SYSTEMS INC—See Wisconsin Lift Truck Corp.; *U.S. Private*, pg. 4548
W.M. SPRINKMAN CORP.; *U.S. Private*, pg. 4422
WOLTER GROUP LLC; *U.S. Private*, pg. 4554
WOMACK MACHINE SUPPLY CO.—See Platte River Ventures, LLC; *U.S. Private*, pg. 3211
WYLACO SUPPLY COMPANY, INC.; *U.S. Private*, pg. 4576
WYNRIGHT CORPORATION—See Daifuku Co., Ltd.; *Int'l*, pg. 1926
XALOY EXTRUSION LLC—See Nordson Corporation; *U.S. Public*, pg. 1534
XERIUM CHINA CO., LTD.—See ANDRITZ AG; *Int'l*, pg. 457
XOMOX CHIHUAHUA S.A. DE C.V.—See Crane NXT, Co.; *U.S. Public*, pg. 591
XOMOX FRANCE S.A.S.—See Crane NXT, Co.; *U.S. Public*, pg. 591
XYLEM ANALYTICS AUSTRALIA PTY LTD.—See Xylem Inc.; *U.S. Public*, pg. 2395
XYLEM ANALYTICS UK LTD—See Xylem Inc.; *U.S. Public*, pg. 2395
XYLEM DEWATERING SOLUTIONS, INC.—See Xylem Inc.; *U.S. Public*, pg. 2396
XYLEM EUROPE GMBH—See Xylem Inc.; *U.S. Public*, pg. 2395
XYLEM FLOW CONTROL LIMITED—See Xylem Inc.; *U.S. Public*, pg. 2395
XYLEM PCI MEMBRANES POLSKA S.P. Z.O.O.—See Xylem Inc.; *U.S. Public*, pg. 2397
XYLEM WATER SOLUTIONS GLOBAL SERVICES AB—See Xylem Inc.; *U.S. Public*, pg. 2397
XYLEM WATER SOLUTIONS LIETUVA, UAB—See Xylem Inc.; *U.S. Public*, pg. 2397
XYLEM WATER SOLUTIONS METZ SAS—See Xylem Inc.; *U.S. Public*, pg. 2397
XYLEM WATER SOLUTIONS MIDDLE EAST REGION FZCO—See Xylem Inc.; *U.S. Public*, pg. 2397
XYLEM WATER SOLUTIONS USA, INC.—See Xylem Inc.; *U.S. Public*, pg. 2397
XYLEM WATER SYSTEMS MEXICO S. DE R.L. DE C.V.—See Xylem Inc.; *U.S. Public*, pg. 2397
YALE ENGINEERING PRODUCTS (PTY.) LTD.—See Columbus McKinnon Corporation; *U.S. Public*, pg. 536
YALE INDUSTRIAL PRODUCTS ASIA CO. LTD.—See Columbus McKinnon Corporation; *U.S. Public*, pg. 536
YALE KENTUCKIANA INC.; *U.S. Private*, pg. 4585
YALE LIFTING SOLUTIONS (PTY.) LTD.—See Columbus McKinnon Corporation; *U.S. Public*, pg. 536
YANTAI LUDOWICI MINERAL PROCESSING EQUIPMENT LIMITED—See FLSmidth & Co. A/S; *Int'l*, pg. 2712
YASHIMA CO., LTD.—See CK SAN-ETSU Co., Ltd.; *Int'l*, pg. 1639
YASHYL DUNYA LLC—See Endress+Hauser (International) Holding AG; *Int'l*, pg. 2409
ZEPRO DANMARK A/S—See Cargotec Corporation; *Int'l*, pg. 1329
ZHEJIANG JISHAN HOLDINGS LTD.—See China Jishan Holdings Limited; *Int'l*, pg. 1513
ZI-ARGUS LTD.—See ATS Corporation; *Int'l*, pg. 695
ZIMMERMAN-MCDONALD MACHINERY, INC.; *U.S. Private*, pg. 4605
ZORN COMPRESSOR & EQUIPMENT CO.; *U.S. Private*, pg. 4609
ZORO TOOLS, INC.—See W.W. Grainger, Inc.; *U.S. Public*, pg. 4482
ZY-TECH DE VENEZUELA S.A.—See Forum Energy Technologies, Inc.; *U.S. Public*, pg. 874

423840 — INDUSTRIAL SUPPLIES MERCHANT WHOLESALERS

3D SYSTEMS, INC.—See 3D Systems Corporation; *U.S. Public*, pg. 4
3NINE USA INC.—See Grimaldi Industri AB; *Int'l*, pg. 3085
3P FRIGOGLASS ROMANIA SRL—See Frigoglass S.A.I.C.; *Int'l*, pg. 2792
AASEBY INDUSTRIAL MACHINING, LLC—See Gremada Industries Inc.; *U.S. Private*, pg. 1783
ABB LTD.—See ABB Ltd.; *Int'l*, pg. 53
ABBOTT RUBBER COMPANY, INC.; *U.S. Private*, pg. 35
ABB S.A.—See ABB Ltd.; *Int'l*, pg. 53
ABEL UNLIMITED INC.; *U.S. Private*, pg. 37
ABES TECHNOSEAL—See Hudaco Industries Limited; *Int'l*, pg. 3521
ABRASIVE-TOOL CORPORATION; *U.S. Private*, pg. 40
ABRO INDUSTRIES, INC.; *U.S. Private*, pg. 40
A&B VALVE & PIPING SYSTEMS, LLC; *U.S. Private*, pg. 19
ACADIANA BEARING CO—See Purvis Bearing Service Ltd.; *U.S. Private*, pg. 3307
ACCURATE COMPONENT SALES - CEDAR RAPIDS—See MSC Industrial Direct Co., Inc.; *U.S. Public*, pg. 1483
ACCURATE ENGINEERING INC.—See Austin Engineering Co. Ltd.; *Int'l*, pg. 718
ACE TOOL CO.—See Sycamore Partners Management, LP; *U.S. Private*, pg. 3896
ACHEM INDUSTRY AMERICA, INC.—See ACHEM Technology Corporation; *Int'l*, pg. 103
ACHILLES GROUP LIMITED—See Bridgepoint Group Plc; *Int'l*, pg. 1153
ACL AIRSHOP PTE LTD.—See Ranger Aerospace LLC; *U.S. Private*, pg. 3354
ACL AIRSHOP (SHANGHAI) LIMITED—See Ranger Aerospace LLC; *U.S. Private*, pg. 3354
ACTIVE SALES CO. INC.; *U.S. Private*, pg. 70
ACTUANT CHINA LTD.—See Enerpac Tool Group Corp.; *U.S. Public*, pg. 765
ADVANCED AUTOMATION INC.—See Doerfer Corporation; *U.S. Private*, pg. 1253
ADVANCED ENERGY INDUSTRIES—See Advanced Energy Industries, Inc.; *U.S. Public*, pg. 47
ADVANCED ENERGY XI'AN CO. LTD.—See Advanced Energy Industries, Inc.; *U.S. Public*, pg. 47
ADVANCED SEALING & SUPPLY COMPANY, INC.—See LKCM Headwater Investments; *U.S. Private*, pg. 2475
AES GLOBAL HOLDINGS PTE LTD.—See Advanced Energy Industries, Inc.; *U.S. Public*, pg. 47
AESSEAL ARGENTINA SA—See AESSEAL Plc; *Int'l*, pg. 182
AESSEAL AUSTRALIA PTY LTD—See AESSEAL Plc; *Int'l*, pg. 182
AESSEAL BENELUX BV—See AESSEAL Plc; *Int'l*, pg. 182
AESSEAL BRASIL LTDA—See AESSEAL Plc; *Int'l*, pg. 182
AESSEAL CANADA INC.—See AESSEAL Plc; *Int'l*, pg. 182
AESSEAL CARIBBEAN LIMITED—See AESSEAL Plc; *Int'l*, pg. 182
AESSEAL CHILE SA—See AESSEAL Plc; *Int'l*, pg. 182
AESSEAL CHINA LTD.—See AESSEAL Plc; *Int'l*, pg. 182
AESSEAL COLOMBIA S.A.—See AESSEAL Plc; *Int'l*, pg. 183
AESSEAL CZECH S.R.O.—See AESSEAL Plc; *Int'l*, pg. 182
AESSEAL DANMARK A/S—See AESSEAL Plc; *Int'l*, pg. 182
AESSEAL DEUTSCHLAND GMBH—See AESSEAL Plc; *Int'l*, pg. 182
AESSEAL FINLAND OY—See AESSEAL Plc; *Int'l*, pg. 182
AESSEAL FRANCE SAS—See AESSEAL Plc; *Int'l*, pg. 182
AESSEAL IBERICA S.L.—See AESSEAL Plc; *Int'l*, pg. 182
AESSEAL IRELAND LTD—See AESSEAL Plc; *Int'l*, pg. 183
AESSEAL ITALIA S.R.L.—See AESSEAL Plc; *Int'l*, pg. 182
AESSEAL MEXICO S. DE R.L. DE C.V.—See AESSEAL Plc; *Int'l*, pg. 182
AESSEAL MIDDLE EAST FZE—See AESSEAL Plc; *Int'l*, pg. 182
AESSEAL (M) SDN BHD—See AESSEAL Plc; *Int'l*, pg. 182
AESSEAL NORWAY AS—See AESSEAL Plc; *Int'l*, pg. 182
AESSEAL POLSKA SP. Z O.O.—See AESSEAL Plc; *Int'l*, pg. 182
AESSEAL SAUDI ARABIA CO. LTD.—See AESSEAL Plc; *Int'l*, pg. 182
AESSEAL SIZDIRMAZLIK SISTEMLERI TIC.LTD.STI.—See AESSEAL Plc; *Int'l*, pg. 182
AESSEAL (SWEDEN) AB—See AESSEAL Plc; *Int'l*, pg. 183
AESSEAL TAIWAN CO., LTD—See AESSEAL Plc; *Int'l*, pg. 182
AESSEAL UNIVEDA LDA—See AESSEAL Plc; *Int'l*, pg. 182
AFC INDUSTRIES, INC.—See Bertram Capital Management, LLC; *U.S. Private*, pg. 539
AGRAVIS TECHNIK CENTER GMBH—See AGRAVIS Raiffeisen AG; *Int'l*, pg. 215
AKWEL CHIPPENHAM UK LIMITED—See AKWEL; *Int'l*, pg. 268
AL AFRAH AL SHARQIYA GENERAL TRADING AND CONTRACTING COMPANY W.L.L.—See Caesars Group; *Int'l*, pg. 1249
ALFAGOMMA AMERICA INC.—See Alfagomma S.p.A.; *Int'l*, pg. 315
ALFAGOMMA DO BRASIL LTDA—See Alfagomma S.p.A.; *Int'l*, pg. 315
ALLEN & WEBB INDUSTRIAL SUPPLY; *U.S. Private*, pg. 178
ALLIED RUBBER & RIGGING SUPPLY—See AEA Investors LP; *U.S. Private*, pg. 115
ALL-LIFT SYSTEMS, INC.—See Dunes Point Capital, LLC; *U.S. Private*, pg. 1288
ALLOY & STAINLESS FASTENERS, INC.; *U.S. Private*, pg. 193
ALL-PRO FASTENERS INC.; *U.S. Private*, pg. 173
ALL SEALS, INC.—See Diploma PLC; *Int'l*, pg. 2128
ALL-STATE INDUSTRIES INC.—See Blue Sage Capital, L.P.; *U.S. Private*, pg. 592
ALL-TEX INC.; *U.S. Private*, pg. 174
AL MUHAIDIB TECHNICAL SUPPLIES COMPANY—See A.K. Al-Muhaidib & Sons Group of Companies; *Int'l*, pg. 24
ALPHA GRAPHIC INDIA LTD.; *Int'l*, pg. 368
ALRO METALS PLUS, KALAMAZOO—See Alro Steel Corporation; *U.S. Private*, pg. 202
ALRO STEEL CORPORATION - ALRO INDUSTRIAL SUPPLY DIVISION—See Alro Steel Corporation; *U.S. Private*, pg. 202
ALTERNATIVE HOSE, INC.; *U.S. Private*, pg. 207
ALTRA INDUSTRIAL MOTION INDIA PRIVATE LTD.—See Regal Rexnord Corporation; *U.S. Public*, pg. 1772
ALTRA INDUSTRIAL MOTION SOUTH AFRICA (PTY.) LTD.—See Regal Rexnord Corporation; *U.S. Public*, pg. 1772
AMAG BENELUX B. V.—See AMAG Austria Metall AG; *Int'l*, pg. 407
AMCOR FLEXIBLES ALZIRA S.L.U.—See Amcor plc; *Int'l*, pg. 417
AMCOR FLEXIBLES - ASHLAND INC—See Amcor plc; *Int'l*, pg. 417
AMCOR FLEXIBLES BARCELONA—See Amcor plc; *Int'l*, pg. 417
AMERICAN & EFIRD CANADA INCORPORATED—See The Kroger Co.; *U.S. Public*, pg. 2108
AMERICAN HAKKO PRODUCTS, INC.; *U.S. Private*, pg. 235
AMERICAN HOLT CORP.—See Arcline Investment Management LP; *U.S. Private*, pg. 313
AMERICAN INDUSTRIAL STEEL & SUPPLY, LLC—See Hendricks Holding Company, Inc.; *U.S. Private*, pg. 1915
AMERICAN RIGGING & SUPPLY—See The Carpenter Group; *U.S. Private*, pg. 4005
AMERICAN SEAL & PACKAGING, INC.—See Align Capital Partners, LLC; *U.S. Private*, pg. 167
AMI BEARINGS, INC.; *U.S. Private*, pg. 263
AMPLE WEALTH ENTERPRISE LTD.—See Eson Precision Ind. Co., Ltd.; *Int'l*, pg. 2504
AMTOON INCORPORATION—See China Merchants Group Limited; *Int'l*, pg. 1521
A&M WHOLESALE HARDWARE SUPPLY COMPANY; *U.S. Private*, pg. 20
ANAPAC—See Enerpac Tool Group Corp.; *U.S. Public*, pg. 765
ANCA JAPAN—See ANCA Pty Ltd; *Int'l*, pg. 447
ANCA MACHINE TOOL (SHANGHAI) CO. LTD—See ANCA Pty Ltd; *Int'l*, pg. 447
ANCA MACHINE TOOLS PRIVATE LTD—See ANCA Pty Ltd; *Int'l*, pg. 448
ANCA (THAILAND) LTD—See ANCA Pty Ltd; *Int'l*, pg. 447
ANCHOR CONSTRUCTION INDUSTRIAL PRODUCTS LTD; *Int'l*, pg. 448
ANCHOR RUBBER PRODUCTS, LLC—See Align Capital Partners, LLC; *U.S. Private*, pg. 167
ANCOFER STAHLHANDEL GMBH—See AG der Dillinger Huttenwerke; *Int'l*, pg. 197
ANEST IWATA-MEDEA INC—See ANEST IWATA Corporation; *Int'l*, pg. 458
ANICH INDUSTRIES, INC.—See DoALL Company; *U.S. Private*, pg. 1250
ANIS OPAKOWANIA SP. Z.O.O—See Groupe Guillin SA; *Int'l*, pg. 3103
AOC TECHNO CO., LTD.—See Asahi Yukizai Corporation; *Int'l*, pg. 598

423840 — INDUSTRIAL SUPPLIES...

APACHE INC.—See Genuine Parts Company; *U.S. Public*, pg. 933
APG L.P. - KNOXVILLE—See The CapStreet Group LLC; *U.S. Private*, pg. 4004
APG L.P.—See The CapStreet Group LLC; *U.S. Private*, pg. 4004
APPLIED INDUSTRIAL TECHNOLOGIES - DBB, INC.—See Applied Industrial Technologies, Inc.; *U.S. Public*, pg. 170
APPLIED INDUSTRIAL TECHNOLOGIES, INC. - LONDON—See Applied Industrial Technologies, Inc.; *U.S. Public*, pg. 170
APPLIED INDUSTRIAL TECHNOLOGIES, INC.; *U.S. Public*, pg. 170
APPLIED INDUSTRIAL TECHNOLOGIES - INDIANA LLC—See Applied Industrial Technologies, Inc.; *U.S. Public*, pg. 170
APPLIED INDUSTRIAL TECHNOLOGIES - MBC, INC.—See Applied Industrial Technologies, Inc.; *U.S. Public*, pg. 170
APPLIED MAINTENANCE SUPPLIES & SOLUTIONS—See Applied Industrial Technologies, Inc.; *U.S. Public*, pg. 170
APPLIED MEXICO, S.A. DE C.V.—See Applied Industrial Technologies, Inc.; *U.S. Public*, pg. 170
APPLIED POWER PRODUCTS INC.; *U.S. Private*, pg. 299
ARAMSCO, INC.—See American Securities LLC; *U.S. Private*, pg. 247
ARATRON AB—See Addtech AB; *Int'l*, pg. 131
ARATRON KURT WIIG AS—See Addtech AB; *Int'l*, pg. 132
ARBILL INDUSTRIES INC.; *U.S. Private*, pg. 308
ARCONIC FASTENING SYSTEMS & RINGS - TUCSON—See Howmet Aerospace Inc.; *U.S. Public*, pg. 1061
ARION GROUP CORP.; *U.S. Public*, pg. 192
ARKANSAS MILL SUPPLY COMPANY; *U.S. Private*, pg. 326
ARKANSAS PACKAGING PRODUCTS, INC.; *U.S. Private*, pg. 326
ARONSON-CAMPBELL INDUSTRIAL SUPPLY INC.; *U.S. Private*, pg. 334
ASADA U CO., LTD.—See Chori Co., Ltd.; *Int'l*, pg. 1583
ASAHI DIAMOND INDUSTRIAL AUSTRALIA PTY., LTD.—See Asahi Diamond Industrial Co. Ltd.; *Int'l*, pg. 592
ASEA BROWN BOVERI LTDA.—See ABB Ltd.; *Int'l*, pg. 55
AS GREINER PACKAGING—See Greiner Holding AG; *Int'l*, pg. 3078
ASIA AMERICA CORPORATION—See Argosy Capital Group, LLC; *U.S. Private*, pg. 321
ASSOCIATED SPRING RAYMOND—See OEP Capital Advisors, L.P.; *U.S. Private*, pg. 2998
ATLANTIC FASTENERS CO., INC.—See Applied Industrial Technologies, Inc.; *U.S. Public*, pg. 170
ATLAS SUPPLY, INC.—See Beacon Roofing Supply, Inc.; *U.S. Public*, pg. 285
AURORA BEARING CO—See The Timken Company; *U.S. Public*, pg. 2132
AUSTIN DISTRIBUTING & MANUFACTURING CORP.; *U.S. Private*, pg. 395
AUTOMOTIVE FASTENERS INC.; *U.S. Private*, pg. 400
AVANTOR FLUID HANDLING, LLC—See Avantor, Inc.; *U.S. Public*, pg. 241
A&W BEARINGS & SUPPLY CO.; *U.S. Private*, pg. 21
AZBIL BRAZIL LIMITED—See Azbil Corporation; *Int'l*, pg. 777
BADGER WELDING SUPPLIES INC.; *U.S. Private*, pg. 424
BAKER SPECIALTY & SUPPLY CO; *U.S. Private*, pg. 456
BAKKINN VORUHOTEL EHF.—See Festi hf; *Int'l*, pg. 2646
BALDWIN FILTERS (AUST) PTY LIMITED—See Parker Hannifin Corporation; *U.S. Public*, pg. 1640
BALDWIN FILTERS (PTY) LTD. SA—See Parker Hannifin Corporation; *U.S. Public*, pg. 1641
BALL TRADING FRANCE S.A.S.—See Ball Corporation; *U.S. Public*, pg. 266
BALL TRADING GERMANY GMBH—See Ball Corporation; *U.S. Public*, pg. 266
THE BALL TRADING NETHERLANDS B.V.—See Ball Corporation; *U.S. Public*, pg. 266
BALL TRADING POLAND SP. Z O.O.—See Ball Corporation; *U.S. Public*, pg. 266
BALL TRADING UK LTD.—See Ball Corporation; *U.S. Public*, pg. 266
BAODING NOBO RUBBER PRODUCTION CO., LTD.—See Great Wall Motor Company Limited; *Int'l*, pg. 3066
BARNES DISTRIBUTION—See MSC Industrial Direct Co., Inc.; *U.S. Public*, pg. 1483
BARNES INTERNATIONAL SRL—See Komline-Sanderson Corporation; *U.S. Private*, pg. 2342
BARREL ACCESSORIES & SUPPLY COMPANY, INC.; *U.S. Private*, pg. 479
BARTLETT BEARING COMPANY INC.; *U.S. Private*, pg. 483
BARTLETT BEARING COMPANY INC.—See Bartlett Bearing Company Inc.; *U.S. Private*, pg. 483
BAUGHMAN SEALS INC—See Baughman Group Ltd; *U.S. Private*, pg. 490
B&D TECHNOLOGIES—See B&D Industrial, Inc.; *U.S. Private*, pg. 418
BEARING DISTRIBUTORS AND DRIVES, INC.—See Applied Industrial Technologies, Inc.; *U.S. Public*, pg. 171
BEARING DISTRIBUTORS, INC.—See Applied Industrial Technologies, Inc.; *U.S. Public*, pg. 171
BEARING HEADQUARTERS CO.—See Headco Industries; *U.S. Private*, pg. 1891
BEARING SALES CORPORATION; *U.S. Private*, pg. 506
BEARING SERVICE COMPANY; *U.S. Private*, pg. 506
BEARING SERVICE INC.; *U.S. Private*, pg. 506
BEARING SERVICE & SUPPLY INC.; *U.S. Private*, pg. 506
BEARINGS LIMITED; *U.S. Private*, pg. 507
BEARINGS OF KENTUCKY—See Neill-LaVielle Supply Co.; *U.S. Private*, pg. 2882
BEARING SUPPLY CO. OF ODESSA; *U.S. Private*, pg. 507
B.E.E. INDUSTRIAL SUPPLY, INC.—See Mallory Safety & Supply LLC; *U.S. Private*, pg. 2558
BEEMER PRECISION, INC.; *U.S. Private*, pg. 514
BEIJER OY—See Beijer Alma AB; *Int'l*, pg. 942
BELIMO AIRCONTROLS (CAN), INC.—See BELIMO Holding AG; *Int'l*, pg. 964
BELIMO AUTOMATION HANDELSGESELLSCHAFT M.B.H.—See BELIMO Holding AG; *Int'l*, pg. 964
BELTING INDUSTRIES CO. INC.; *U.S. Private*, pg. 521
BELTSERVICE CORPORATION; *U.S. Private*, pg. 521
BENCHMARK INDUSTRIAL, INC.; *U.S. Private*, pg. 524
BENFIELD ELECTRIC AND ELEVATOR SUPPLY CORP.—See H.H. Benfield Electric Supply Company Inc.; *U.S. Private*, pg. 1826
BENGT LUNDIN AB—See Altor Equity Partners AB; *Int'l*, pg. 396
BENZLER ANTRIEBSTECHNIK G.M.B.H—See Elecon Engineering Company Ltd.; *Int'l*, pg. 2348
BENZLERS ITALIA S.R.L.—See Elecon Engineering Company Ltd.; *Int'l*, pg. 2348
BENZLERS SYSTEMS AB—See Elecon Engineering Company Ltd.; *Int'l*, pg. 2348
BENZLER TBA B.V.—See Elecon Engineering Company Ltd.; *Int'l*, pg. 2348
BENZLER TRANSMISSION A.S.—See Elecon Engineering Company Ltd.; *Int'l*, pg. 2348
BERLIN PACKAGING - FORT LEE—See Keystone Group, L.P.; *U.S. Private*, pg. 2296
BERLIN PACKAGING LLC—See Keystone Group, L.P.; *U.S. Private*, pg. 2296
BERLIN PACKAGING - PITTSBURGH—See Keystone Group, L.P.; *U.S. Private*, pg. 2297
BERLIN PACKAGING - RANCHO CUCAMONGA—See Keystone Group, L.P.; *U.S. Private*, pg. 2297
BERNABE COTE D'IVOIRE; *Int'l*, pg. 986
BESTTECHNICA EOOD—See Besttechnica TM - Radomir; *Int'l*, pg. 1000
B.G.E. SERVICE & SUPPLY LTD.; *Int'l*, pg. 789
BIG RED FASTENERS, INC.; *U.S. Private*, pg. 553
BIG V WHOLESALE CO. INC.—See Vaughan Furniture Company Inc.; *U.S. Private*, pg. 4348
BILLERUDKORSNAS MANAGED PACKAGING AB—See Billerud AB; *Int'l*, pg. 1030
BINKELMAN CORPORATION; *U.S. Private*, pg. 561
BIRMINGHAM FASTENER & SUPPLY INC.; *U.S. Private*, pg. 564
BISCHOF + KLEIN ASIA PTE. LTD.—See Bischof + Klein GmbH & Co. KG; *Int'l*, pg. 1048
BISCHOF + KLEIN FRANCE SAS—See Bischof + Klein GmbH & Co. KG; *Int'l*, pg. 1048
BISCHOF + KLEIN MIDDLE EAST CO.—See Bischof + Klein GmbH & Co. KG; *Int'l*, pg. 1048
BISCHOF + KLEIN (SHANGHAI) TRADING CO. LTD.—See Bischof + Klein GmbH & Co. KG; *Int'l*, pg. 1048
B+K BETEILIGUNGEN GMBH—See Bischof + Klein GmbH & Co. KG; *Int'l*, pg. 1048
B+K POLSKA GMBH SP.K.—See Bischof + Klein GmbH & Co. KG; *Int'l*, pg. 1048
BLACK & COMPANY; *U.S. Private*, pg. 569
BLAIR RUBBER COMPANY—See IKO Enterprises Ltd.; *Int'l*, pg. 3612
BLASTERPRODUKTER I KOPING AB—See Addtech AB; *Int'l*, pg. 132
BLUE POINT TOOL & SUPPLY CO, INC.—See FICODIS Inc.; *Int'l*, pg. 2653
BOB DEAN SUPPLY, INC.; *U.S. Private*, pg. 604
BOB DEAN SUPPLY INC.—See Bob Dean Supply, Inc.; *U.S. Private*, pg. 604
BOBST GROUP CENTRAL EUROPE SPOL. S R.O.—See Bobst Group S.A.; *Int'l*, pg. 1095
BOBST GROUP IBERICA, S.L.—See Bobst Group S.A.; *Int'l*, pg. 1095
BOBST GROUP LATINOAMERICA NORTE S.A. DE CV.—See Bobst Group S.A.; *Int'l*, pg. 1095
BOBST GROUP POLSKA SP. Z O.O.—See Bobst Group S.A.; *Int'l*, pg. 1096
BOBST GROUP SINGAPORE PTE LTD—See Bobst Group S.A.; *Int'l*, pg. 1096
BOBST GROUP THAILAND LTD—See Bobst Group S.A.; *Int'l*, pg. 1096
BOBST GROUP VOSTOK LLC—See Bobst Group S.A.; *Int'l*, pg. 1096
BOBST SCANDINAVIA APS—See Bobst Group S.A.; *Int'l*, pg. 1096
BOBST (SHANGHAI) LTD—See Bobst Group S.A.; *Int'l*, pg. 1095
BOBST UK & IRELAND LTD—See Bobst Group S.A.; *Int'l*, pg. 1096
BOEING DISTRIBUTION SERVICES, INC.- PARAMUS—See The Boeing Company; *U.S. Public*, pg. 2040
BOLTTECH MANNINGS, INC.—See Grey Mountain Partners, LLC; *U.S. Private*, pg. 1784
BOND FLUIDAIRE INC.—See Exotic Automation & Supply, Inc.; *U.S. Private*, pg. 1449
BONG RETAIL SOLUTIONS AB—See Bong AB; *Int'l*, pg. 1107
BOSSARD NORTH AMERICA, INC. - MILWAUKEE—See Bossard Holding AG; *Int'l*, pg. 1117
BOSSARD NORTH AMERICA, INC.—See Bossard Holding AG; *Int'l*, pg. 1117
THE BOULDER COMPANY—See Bertram Capital Management, LLC; *U.S. Private*, pg. 540
BOWMAN HOLLIS MANUFACTURING CO., INC. - LAGRANGE—See Bowman Hollis Manufacturing, Inc.; *U.S. Private*, pg. 626
BRANCE KRACHY COMPANY INC.; *U.S. Private*, pg. 635
BRANHAM CORP.—See LKCM Headwater Investments; *U.S. Private*, pg. 2475
BREEN INTERNATIONAL PTE. LTD.; *Int'l*, pg. 1144
BREVINI FINLAND OY—See Dana Incorporated; *U.S. Public*, pg. 621
BRIDGESTONE HOSEPOWER - ARIZONA—See Bridgestone Corporation; *Int'l*, pg. 1156
BRON TAPES LLC—See Rotunda Capital Partners LLC; *U.S. Private*, pg. 3488
BRONZE HEADQUARTERS, INC.—See Headco Industries; *U.S. Private*, pg. 1891
BTS SP. Z O.O.; *Int'l*, pg. 1206
BUCKEYE INDUSTRIAL SUPPLY CO.—See MSC Industrial Direct Co., Inc.; *U.S. Public*, pg. 1483
BUCKEYE RUBBER & PACKING CO.; *U.S. Private*, pg. 677
C4 INCORPORATED; *U.S. Private*, pg. 710
CALIFORNIA INDUSTRIAL RUBBER COMPANY; *U.S. Private*, pg. 719
CAL PACIFIC PRODUCTS INC.; *U.S. Private*, pg. 715
CAMERON VALVES & MEASUREMENT—See Schlumberger Limited; *U.S. Public*, pg. 1843
CAMOZZI AUTOMATION OU—See Camozzi Group; *Int'l*, pg. 1273
CAMOZZI BENELUX B.V.—See Camozzi Group; *Int'l*, pg. 1273
CAMOZZI DO BRASIL LTDA.—See Camozzi Group; *Int'l*, pg. 1274
CAMOZZI GMBH—See Camozzi Group; *Int'l*, pg. 1273
CAMOZZI GMBH—See Camozzi Group; *Int'l*, pg. 1273
CAMOZZI INDIA PRIVATE LIMITED—See Camozzi Group; *Int'l*, pg. 1273
CAMOZZI MALAYSIA SDN. BHD.—See Camozzi Group; *Int'l*, pg. 1273
CAMOZZI NEUMATICA S.A. DE C.V.—See Camozzi Group; *Int'l*, pg. 1274
CAMOZZI NEUMATICA S.A.—See Camozzi Group; *Int'l*, pg. 1274
CAMOZZI PNEUMATIC KAZAKHSTAN LLP—See Camozzi Group; *Int'l*, pg. 1274
CAMOZZI PNEUMATIC LLC—See Camozzi Group; *Int'l*, pg. 1274
CAMOZZI PNEUMATICS INC—See Camozzi Group; *Int'l*, pg. 1274
CAMOZZI PNEUMATICS LTD.—See Camozzi Group; *Int'l*, pg. 1274
CAMOZZI PNEUMATIQUE SARL—See Camozzi Group; *Int'l*, pg. 1274
CAMOZZI R.O.—See Camozzi Group; *Int'l*, pg. 1274
CAMOZZI VENEZUELA S.A.—See Camozzi Group; *Int'l*, pg. 1274
CARGILL ASIA PACIFIC HOLDINGS PTE LIMITED—See Cargill, Inc.; *U.S. Private*, pg. 755
CARGILL HONG KONG LTD.—See Cargill, Inc.; *U.S. Private*, pg. 756
CARLSON HOLDINGS, INC.; *U.S. Private*, pg. 765
CARPENTER BROTHERS INC.; *U.S. Private*, pg. 770
C.B. LYNN COMPANY—See Distribution Solutions Group, Inc.; *U.S. Public*, pg. 668
CEMEX HAITI S.A.—See CEMEX, S.A.B. de C.V.; *Int'l*, pg. 1398
CEMEX JAMAICA LIMITED—See CEMEX, S.A.B. de C.V.; *Int'l*, pg. 1398
CENTA NORDIC AB—See Zurn Elkay Water Solutions Corporation; *U.S. Public*, pg. 2413
CENTRAL-MCGOWAN INC.; *U.S. Private*, pg. 826
CENTURION CONTAINER LLC—See Greif Inc.; *U.S. Public*, pg. 966
CENTURION SAFETY PRODUCTS LIMITED; *Int'l*, pg. 1417
CENTURY FASTENERS CORP.; *U.S. Private*, pg. 832
CERADYNE, INC.—See 3M Company; *U.S. Public*, pg. 8
C.E. THURSTON & SONS INC. - EMPIRE INDUSTRIAL PRODUCTS—See C.E. Thurston & Sons Incorporated; *U.S. Private*, pg. 706

423840 — INDUSTRIAL SUPPLIES...

CHAIR CITY SUPPLY COMPANY, INC.; U.S. Private, pg. 845
CHAMPION CONTAINER CORPORATION; U.S. Private, pg. 846
CHEMITHON SURFACE FINISHING, INC.—See Chemithon Enterprises, Inc.; U.S. Private, pg. 872
CHERYONG ELECTRIC CO., LTD—See Cheryong Industrial Co Ltd; Int'l, pg. 1472
CHERYONG INDUSTRIAL CO LTD - DAEJEON FACTORY—See Cheryong Industrial Co Ltd; Int'l, pg. 1472
CHINA INTERNATIONAL MARINE CONTAINERS (HONG KONG) LIMITED—See China International Marine Containers (Group) Co., Ltd.; Int'l, pg. 1511
CHIORINO, INC.—See Chiorino S.p.A.; Int'l, pg. 1572
CHORI (CHINA) CO., LTD.—See Chori Co., Ltd.; Int'l, pg. 1583
CHORI COMERCIAL DE MEXICO S.A. DE C.V.—See Chori Co., Ltd.; Int'l, pg. 1583
CHORI GLEX CO., LTD.—See Chori Co., Ltd.; Int'l, pg. 1583
CHORI KOREA CO., LTD.—See Chori Co., Ltd.; Int'l, pg. 1583
CHORI TRADING INDIA PTE. LTD.—See Chori Co., Ltd.; Int'l, pg. 1583
CHORI VIETNAM CO., LTD.—See Chori Co., Ltd.; Int'l, pg. 1583
CHRISTY REFRACTORIES COMPANY LLC; U.S. Private, pg. 892
CHS-CONTAINER A/S—See CHS CONTAINER Handel GmbH; Int'l, pg. 1589
CHS CONTAINER BULGARIA LTD.—See CHS CONTAINER Handel GmbH; Int'l, pg. 1589
CHS CONTAINER HANDEL B.V.—See CHS CONTAINER Handel GmbH; Int'l, pg. 1589
CHS CONTAINER SERVIS LTD STI—See CHS CONTAINER Handel GmbH; Int'l, pg. 1589
CHS SUDCON GMBH—See CHS CONTAINER Handel GmbH; Int'l, pg. 1589
CINCINNATI CONTAINER COMPANY INCORPORATED; U.S. Private, pg. 897
CIRCOR ENERGY PRODUCTS (CANADA) ULC—See KKR & Co. Inc.; U.S. Public, pg. 1242
CITIZEN MACHINERY UNITED KINGDOM, LTD.—See Citizen Watch Co., Ltd.; Int'l, pg. 1624
CITY MAINTENANCE SUPPLY; U.S. Private, pg. 906
CLEAN ROOMS WEST, INC.—See Hodess Cleanroom Construction, LLC; U.S. Private, pg. 1959
C.L. SMITH COMPANY INC.; U.S. Private, pg. 708
COHN & GREGORY, INC.; U.S. Private, pg. 963
COLMAR BELTING CO., INC.—See Genuine Parts Company; U.S. Public, pg. 933
COMINIX MEXICO S.A. DE C.V.—See Cominix Co., Ltd.; Int'l, pg. 1714
COMMERCIAL FOODSERVICE REPAIR, INC.—See HCI Equity Management, L.P.; U.S. Private, pg. 1889
THE COMMERCIAL GROUP LIFTING PRODUCTS; U.S. Private, pg. 4011
COMPAGNIE GENERAL BEARING SERVICE, INC.; Int'l, pg. 1741
CONCOTE CORPORATION; U.S. Private, pg. 1011
CONDUCTIX-WAMPFLER PVT LTD—See CVC Capital Partners SICAV-FIS S.A.; Int'l, pg. 1887
CONNEY SAFETY PRODUCTS, LLC—See WESCO International, Inc.; U.S. Public, pg. 2351
CONSOLIDATED CHEMICAL CORPORATION; U.S. Private, pg. 1020
CONSUMERS INTERSTATE CORPORATION; U.S. Private, pg. 1026
CONTAINER RESOURCES INC.—See Kelso & Company, L.P.; U.S. Private, pg. 2278
CONTINENTAL WESTERN CORPORATION; U.S. Private, pg. 1031
CONTITECH KAUTSCHUK- UND KUNSTSTOFF-VERTRIEBSGESELLSCHAFT—See Continental Aktiengesellschaft; Int'l, pg. 1780
CONTITECH PRINTING BLANKET SHANGHAI LTD.—See Continental Aktiengesellschaft; Int'l, pg. 1780
CONTITECH PRINT SERVICE (S) PTE. LTD.—See Continental Aktiengesellschaft; Int'l, pg. 1780
CONVEYCO MANUFACTURING COMPANY; U.S. Private, pg. 1036
CONVEYORS & DRIVES, INC.; U.S. Private, pg. 1036
CONVIBER INC.; U.S. Private, pg. 1036
COOL CAPS INDUSTRIES LIMITED; Int'l, pg. 1788
COREX US LLC—See Ox Paper Tube & Core, Inc.; U.S. Private, pg. 3056
CORNERSTONE CONTROLS INC.; U.S. Private, pg. 1052
THE CORNWELL QUALITY TOOLS CO., INC.; U.S. Private, pg. 4015
CORPORATE EQUIPMENT COMPANY, LLC—See DXP Enterprises, Inc.; U.S. Public, pg. 697
CORROSION PRODUCTS & EQUIPMENT, INC. - ALBANY—See Corrosion Products & Equipment, Inc.; U.S. Private, pg. 1059
COSMETIC PACKAGING GROUP—See O. Berk Company L.L.C.; U.S. Private, pg. 2981
COVENTRY GROUP LIMITED; Int'l, pg. 1821

CPI SALES, INC.—See Central States Industrial Supply, Inc.; U.S. Private, pg. 825
CRASTI & COMPANY PTY. LTD.—See Close the Loop Limited; Int'l, pg. 1661
CROWN PACKAGING INTERNATIONAL INC.; U.S. Private, pg. 1111
CRP INDUSTRIES OF CALIFORNIA INC.—See CRP Industries Inc.; U.S. Private, pg. 1113
CURTISS-WRIGHT ANTRIEBSTECHNIK GMBH—See Curtiss-Wright Corporation; U.S. Public, pg. 611
CUSTOM BUILDING PRODUCTS; U.S. Private, pg. 1128
CUTTING TOOLS INC.; U.S. Private, pg. 1132
C.W. HAYDEN CO., INC.; U.S. Private, pg. 709
DAIDO METAL EUROPE LTD—See Daido Metal Corporation; Int'l, pg. 1921
DAIDO METAL GERMANY GMBH—See Daido Metal Corporation; Int'l, pg. 1921
DAIDO METAL RUSSIA LLC—See Daido Metal Corporation; Int'l, pg. 1921
DAIWA YOKI CO., LTD.—See Daiwa Can Company; Int'l, pg. 1944
DALTON BEARING SERVICE, INC.; U.S. Private, pg. 1150
DANA ITALIA, SPA—See Dana Incorporated; U.S. Public, pg. 622
DANFOSS (TIANJIN) LTD.—See Danfoss A/S; Int'l, pg. 1959
DARLING BOLT CO.; U.S. Private, pg. 1159
DAUGHTRIDGE SALES CO., INC.—See Frontenac Company LLC; U.S. Private, pg. 1614
DAVID C. GREENBAUM CO. INC.; U.S. Private, pg. 1169
DAY ASSOCIATES, INC.—See Thomas Scientific, LLC; U.S. Private, pg. 4157
DAYTON SUPPLY & TOOL CO.—See Genuine Parts Company; U.S. Public, pg. 933
D&C DISTRIBUTORS, LLC—See Advanced Container Technologies, Inc.; U.S. Public, pg. 46
DE DIETRICH PROCESS SYSTEMS S.A.-COURCOURONNES SITE—See De Dietrich Process Systems S.A.; Int'l, pg. 1995
DEERWOOD FASTENERS INTERNATIONAL—See Berkshire Hathaway Inc.; U.S. Public, pg. 310
DEKOMTE BENELUX BVBA—See DEKOMTE de Temple Kompensator-Technik GmbH; Int'l, pg. 2006
DEKOMTE BOHEMIA, S.R.O.—See DEKOMTE de Temple Kompensator-Technik GmbH; Int'l, pg. 2006
DEKOMTE DE TEMPLE IBERIA S.L.—See DEKOMTE de Temple Kompensator-Technik GmbH; Int'l, pg. 2006
DEKOMTE DE TEMPLE KOMPENSATOR-TECHNIK LLC—See DEKOMTE de Temple Kompensator-Technik GmbH; Int'l, pg. 2006
DEKOMTE DE TEMPLE KOMPENSATOR-TECHNIK OOO—See DEKOMTE de Temple Kompensator-Technik GmbH; Int'l, pg. 2006
DEKOMTE DE TEMPLE KOMPENSATOR-TECHNIK SAUDI ARABIA—See DEKOMTE de Temple Kompensator-Technik GmbH; Int'l, pg. 2006
DEKOMTE DE TEMPLE KOMPENSATOR-TECHNIK (S) PTE. LTD.—See DEKOMTE de Temple Kompensator-Technik GmbH; Int'l, pg. 2006
DEKOMTE DE TEMPLE KOMPENSATOR-TECHNIK (UK) LTD.—See DEKOMTE de Temple Kompensator-Technik GmbH; Int'l, pg. 2006
DEKOMTE DE TEMPLE LLC—See DEKOMTE de Temple Kompensator-Technik GmbH; Int'l, pg. 2006
DEKOMTE FRANCE SARL—See DEKOMTE de Temple Kompensator-Technik GmbH; Int'l, pg. 2006
DEKOMTE POLSKA SP. Z O.O.—See DEKOMTE de Temple Kompensator-Technik GmbH; Int'l, pg. 2006
DELO WELDING & INDUSTRIAL SUPPLY, INC.—See Jackson Welding Supply Co., Inc.; U.S. Private, pg. 2178
DEMA EUROPE LLC—See Dema Engineering Co.; U.S. Private, pg. 1203
DENCO SALES CO.; U.S. Private, pg. 1204
DENKA CHEMICALS GMBH—See Denki Company Limited; Int'l, pg. 2027
DENKA CHEMICALS HONG KONG LTD.—See Denki Company Limited; Int'l, pg. 2027
DENKA CHEMICALS SHANGHAI CO., LTD.—See Denki Company Limited; Int'l, pg. 2027
DERRY ENTERPRISES INC.; U.S. Private, pg. 1210
DESTACO UK LIMITED—See Dover Corporation; U.S. Public, pg. 678
DEVICE ENG CO., LTD.—See ESPEC Corp.; Int'l, pg. 2505
DGI SUPPLY—See DoALL Company; U.S. Private, pg. 1250
DIAMOND INNOVATIONS, INC. - PACIFIC HEADQUARTERS—See KKR & Co. Inc.; U.S. Public, pg. 1253
DIAMOND INNOVATIONS INTERNATIONAL, INC. - EUROPEAN HEADQUARTERS—See KKR & Co. Inc.; U.S. Public, pg. 1253
DIAMOND TRADING COMPANY—See Anglo American PLC; Int'l, pg. 462
DIC (GUANGZHOU) CO., LTD.—See DIC Corporation; Int'l, pg. 2107
DICHTOMATIK A.B.—See Freudenberg SE; Int'l, pg. 2783
DICHTOMATIK AMERICAS, LP—See Freudenberg SE; Int'l, pg. 2783
DICHTOMATIK B.V.—See Freudenberg SE; Int'l, pg. 2783

DICHTOMATIK CANADA, INC.—See Freudenberg SE; Int'l, pg. 2783
DICHTOMATIK (CHINA) CO., LTD.—See Freudenberg SE; Int'l, pg. 2783
DICHTOMATIK HANDELSGESELLSCHAFT MBH—See Freudenberg SE; Int'l, pg. 2783
DICHTOMATIK KFT.—See Freudenberg SE; Int'l, pg. 2783
DICHTOMATIK LTD.—See Freudenberg SE; Int'l, pg. 2783
DICHTOMATIK S.A.S. DI EXTERNA ITALIA S.R.L.—See Freudenberg SE; Int'l, pg. 2783
DICHTOMATIK S.A.S—See Freudenberg SE; Int'l, pg. 2783
DICHTOMATIK S.R.L.—See Freudenberg SE; Int'l, pg. 2783
DICHTOMATIK VERTRIEBSGESELLSCHAFT FUR TECHNISCHE DICHTUNGEN MBH—See Freudenberg SE; Int'l, pg. 2783
DIC INTERNATIONAL AUSTRALIA PTY. LTD.—See DIC Corporation; Int'l, pg. 2108
DIC INTERNATIONAL (THAILAND) CO., LTD.—See DIC Corporation; Int'l, pg. 2108
DIC MACHINERY & PRINTER'S SUPPLIES, INC.—See DIC Corporation; Int'l, pg. 2108
DIC (MALAYSIA) SDN. BHD.—See DIC Corporation; Int'l, pg. 2107
DIC (SHANGHAI) CO., LTD.—See DIC Corporation; Int'l, pg. 2107
DIC (TAIWAN) LTD.—See DIC Corporation; Int'l, pg. 2107
DIC TRADING (HK) LTD.—See DIC Corporation; Int'l, pg. 2108
DILLINGER ESPANA S.L.U.—See AG der Dillinger Huttenwerke; Int'l, pg. 197
DILLINGER HUTTE SERVICES B.V.—See AG der Dillinger Huttenwerke; Int'l, pg. 197
DILLINGER HUTTE VERTRIEB GMBH—See AG der Dillinger Huttenwerke; Int'l, pg. 197
DILLINGER INDIA STEEL SERVICE CENTER PRIVATE LTD.—See AG der Dillinger Huttenwerke; Int'l, pg. 197
DILLINGER NEDERLAND B.V.—See AG der Dillinger Huttenwerke; Int'l, pg. 197
DISCOUNT CLEANING PRODUCTS; U.S. Private, pg. 1237
DISTRIBUTIONS JRV INC.; Int'l, pg. 2137
DISTRIBUTION SOLUTIONS GROUP, INC.; U.S. Public, pg. 668
DIY GROUP, INC.; U.S. Private, pg. 1246
DJK EUROPE GMBH—See Daiichi Jitsugyo Co. Ltd.; Int'l, pg. 1927
DNOW AUSTRALIA PTY. LTD.—See DNOW Inc.; U.S. Public, pg. 671
DNOW L.P.—See DNOW Inc.; U.S. Public, pg. 671
DNP HOSO CO., LTD.—See Dai Nippon Printing Co., Ltd.; Int'l, pg. 1914
DOALL COMPANY; U.S. Private, pg. 1250
DOBY VERROLEC FZE—See Heitkamp & Thumann KG; Int'l, pg. 3326
DOMER GMBH & CO. KG STANZ- UND UMFORMTECHNOLOGIE—See Gesco AG; Int'l, pg. 2945
DOM-NEDERLAND—See Groupe SFPI SA; Int'l, pg. 3111
DOM POLSKA SP.Z.O.O.—See Groupe SFPI SA; Int'l, pg. 3111
DONALDSON FILTRATION OSTERREICH, GMBH—See Donaldson Company, Inc.; U.S. Public, pg. 675
DOPAK INC.—See KKR & Co. Inc.; U.S. Public, pg. 1242
DRAGO SUPPLY COMPANY INC.—See Genuine Parts Company; U.S. Public, pg. 933
DRIVES & CONVEYORS INC.; U.S. Private, pg. 1278
DSR INTERNATIONAL CORP—See DSR Corp.; Int'l, pg. 2210
DS SMITH PACKAGING CESKA REPUBLICA S.R.O.—See DS Smith Plc; Int'l, pg. 2208
DUCAPLAST S.A.S—See DS Smith Plc; Int'l, pg. 2209
DUNCAN CO.; U.S. Private, pg. 1287
DUNHAM RUBBER & BELTING CORP.—See Platte River Ventures, LLC; U.S. Private, pg. 3211
DUVAL CONTAINER COMPANY—See Kelso & Company, L.P.; U.S. Private, pg. 2278
DXB ACL AIRSHOP DWC LLC—See Ranger Aerospace LLC; U.S. Private, pg. 3354
DYNABRADE INTERNATIONAL SALES CORPORATION—See Dynabrade, Inc.; U.S. Private, pg. 1297
THE EADS COMPANY; U.S. Private, pg. 4024
EAGLEBURGMANN COLOMBIA, S.A.S.—See Freudenberg SE; Int'l, pg. 2783
EAGLEBURGMANN INDUSTRIES LP—See Freudenberg SE; Int'l, pg. 2784
EAGLEBURGMANN KE A/S—See Freudenberg SE; Int'l, pg. 2784
EAGLEBURGMANN KE, INC.—See Freudenberg SE; Int'l, pg. 2784
EAGLEBURGMANN POLAND SP. Z O.O.—See Freudenberg SE; Int'l, pg. 2784
EAGLEBURGMANN PRODUCTION CENTER S.A. DE C.V.—See Freudenberg SE; Int'l, pg. 2784
EAGLEBURGMANN SAUDI ARABIA CO. LTD.—See Freudenberg SE; Int'l, pg. 2784
EAGLE SALES COMPANY INCORPORATED; U.S. Private, pg. 1310

423840 — INDUSTRIAL SUPPLIES...

EARNEST MACHINE PRODUCTS CO.; *U.S. Private*, pg. 1314
EASTERN INDUSTRIAL AUTOMATION; *U.S. Private*, pg. 1319
EASTERN STATES MINE SUPPLY CO.—See Raleigh Mine & Industrial Supply, Inc.; *U.S. Private*, pg. 3349
EAST WEST INDUSTRIAL ENGINEERING CO. INC.; *U.S. Private*, pg. 1318
ECKART & FINARD, INC.—See Bertram Capital Management, LLC; *U.S. Private*, pg. 540
E.D. LUCE PACKAGING—See O. Berk Company L.L.C.; *U.S. Private*, pg. 2981
EDM SUPPLIES, INC.—See Global EDM Supplies, Inc.; *U.S. Private*, pg. 1713
EFC INTERNATIONAL INC.; *U.S. Private*, pg. 1343
EINHELL INTRATEK MUHENDISLIK VE DIS TICARET A.S.—See Einhell Germany AG; *Int'l*, pg. 2333
EISENMANN AG; *Int'l*, pg. 2336
EKK EAGLE INDUSTRY ASIA-PACIFIC PTE. LTD.—See Eagle Industry Co., Ltd.; *Int'l*, pg. 2265
ELECON MIDDLE EAST FZCO—See Elecon Engineering Company Ltd.; *Int'l*, pg. 2348
ELECON SINGAPORE PTE. LIMITED—See Elecon Engineering Company Ltd.; *Int'l*, pg. 2348
ELECON US TRANSMISSION LIMITED—See Elecon Engineering Company Ltd.; *Int'l*, pg. 2348
ELEMENT SIX S.A.—See Anglo American PLC; *Int'l*, pg. 462
ELEMENT SIX U.S. CORPORATION—See Anglo American PLC; *Int'l*, pg. 462
ELLEAIR BUSINESS SUPPORT CO., LTD.—See Daio Paper Corporation; *Int'l*, pg. 1940
ELRING GASKETS (PTY) LTD.—See ElringKlinger AG; *Int'l*, pg. 2369
ELRINGKLINGER LOGISTIC SERVICE GMBH—See ElringKlinger AG; *Int'l*, pg. 2370
ELRING PARTS LTD.—See ElringKlinger AG; *Int'l*, pg. 2369
ELTECO AS—See Addtech AB; *Int'l*, pg. 133
EMCO INC.; *U.S. Private*, pg. 1379
EMHART GLASS GMBH—See Bucher Industries AG; *Int'l*, pg. 1208
EMHART GLASS LTD.—See Bucher Industries AG; *Int'l*, pg. 1208
EMHART GLASS PTE. LTD.—See Bucher Industries AG; *Int'l*, pg. 1208
EMHART GLASS S.A.—See Bucher Industries AG; *Int'l*, pg. 1208
EMHART GLASS S.R.L.—See Bucher Industries AG; *Int'l*, pg. 1208
EMHART GLASS SWEDEN AB—See Bucher Industries AG; *Int'l*, pg. 1209
EMHART HARTTUNG A/S—See Stanley Black & Decker, Inc.; *U.S. Public*, pg. 1934
EMIRIAN S.A.I.C.F.I.R.—See Stanley Black & Decker, Inc.; *U.S. Public*, pg. 1932
EMPIRE AUTOMATION SYSTEMS INC; *U.S. Private*, pg. 1384
EMPIRE STAPLE CO.; *U.S. Private*, pg. 1385
ENCON SAFETY PRODUCTS—See Nautic Partners, LLC; *U.S. Private*, pg. 2872
ENDRESS+HAUSER INC. - NORTHEAST REGIONAL CENTER—See Endress+Hauser (International) Holding AG; *Int'l*, pg. 2407
ENERGOREMONT KOZLODUY EOOD—See Dietsmann N.V.; *Int'l*, pg. 2117
ENERGY & PROCESS CORP.—See Ferguson plc; *Int'l*, pg. 2637
ENERPAC S.P.A.—See Enerpac Tool Group Corp.; *U.S. Public*, pg. 765
ENGINEERED COMPONENTS CO; *U.S. Private*, pg. 1398
ENGINEERED SEAL PRODUCTS, INC.; *U.S. Private*, pg. 1398
ENG KONG CONTAINER SERVICES (JOHOR) SDN BHD—See Eng Kong Holdings Pte Ltd.; *Int'l*, pg. 2426
ENG KONG CONTAINER SERVICES (PENANG) SDN BHD.—See Eng Kong Holdings Pte Ltd.; *Int'l*, pg. 2426
EPPENDORF NORDIC APS—See Eppendorf AG; *Int'l*, pg. 2464
EPPERSON & COMPANY INC.—See Genuine Parts Company; *U.S. Public*, pg. 933
ERIE BEARINGS CO. INC.; *U.S. Private*, pg. 1420
ERIE TOOL & SUPPLY CO.—See Jergens Inc.; *U.S. Private*, pg. 2201
ERIKS NORTH AMERICA, INC.—See LKCM Headwater Investments; *U.S. Private*, pg. 2475
E & R INDUSTRIAL SALES, INC.—See Paradigm Capital Partners; *U.S. Private*, pg. 3089
E & R TOOLING AND SOLUTIONS DE MEXICO, S. DE R.L. DE C.V.—See W.W. Grainger, Inc.; *U.S. Public*, pg. 2319
ESD-CENTER AB.—See Addtech AB; *Int'l*, pg. 133
ESSENTRA MALAYSIA SDN. BHD.—See Essentra plc; *Int'l*, pg. 2511
ESSVE PRODUKTER AB—See Bergman & Beving AB; *Int'l*, pg. 980
EXPERITEC INC.; *U.S. Private*, pg. 1450
EXXONMOBIL CORPORATION—See Exxon Mobil Corporation; *U.S. Public*, pg. 815
FAMOUS SUPPLY CO—See Famous Enterprises Inc.; *U.S. Private*, pg. 1471

FASTENAL (SHANGHAI) INTERNATIONAL TRADING CO. LTD.—See Fastenal Company; *U.S. Public*, pg. 823
FASTENING SOLUTION INC; *U.S. Private*, pg. 1482
FASTER DO BRASIL LTDA.—See Helios Technologies, Inc.; *U.S. Public*, pg. 1023
FASTER GERMANY GMBH—See Helios Technologies, Inc.; *U.S. Public*, pg. 1023
FASTER HYDRAULICS PVT. LTD.—See Helios Technologies, Inc.; *U.S. Public*, pg. 1023
FASTER HYDRAULICS SHANGHAI CO. LTD.—See Helios Technologies, Inc.; *U.S. Public*, pg. 1023
FAST-SPEC, INC.—See Summit Industries, Inc.; *U.S. Private*, pg. 3854
F.B. WRIGHT CO.; *U.S. Private*, pg. 1455
FERGUSON GROUP AUSTRALIA PTY LTD—See First Reserve Management, L.P.; *U.S. Private*, pg. 1526
FERGUSON GROUP LTD—See First Reserve Management, L.P.; *U.S. Private*, pg. 1526
FERGUSON GROUP SINGAPORE PTE LTD—See First Reserve Management, L.P.; *U.S. Private*, pg. 1526
FERGUSON MIDDLE EAST FZE—See First Reserve Management, L.P.; *U.S. Private*, pg. 1526
FERGUSON NORGE AS—See First Reserve Management, L.P.; *U.S. Private*, pg. 1526
FESTO CORPORATION—See Festo AG & Co. KG; *Int'l*, pg. 2647
FIBERS, INC.—See Pioneer Industries, Inc.; *U.S. Private*, pg. 3187
FICODIS INC.; *Int'l*, pg. 2653
FIXTURE FINDERS (DE) LLC—See Hilco Trading, LLC; *U.S. Private*, pg. 1943
FLEXASEAL ENGINEERED SEALS AND SYSTEMS, LLC; *U.S. Private*, pg. 1543
FLEX-A-SEAL, INC.—See Flexaseal Engineered Seals and Systems, LLC; *U.S. Private*, pg. 1543
FLEXON INDUSTRIES INC.; *U.S. Private*, pg. 1544
FLORIDA BEARINGS—See Littlejohn & Co., LLC; *U.S. Private*, pg. 2471
FLORIDA GRAPHIC SERVICES, INC.—See Monomoy Capital Partners LLC; *U.S. Private*, pg. 2772
FLORIDA ROPE & SUPPLY, INC.—See ALP Industries, Inc.; *U.S. Private*, pg. 196
FLORIDA SEALING PRODUCTS—See Applied Industrial Technologies, Inc.; *U.S. Public*, pg. 171
FLORIDA SEAL & RUBBER, LLC—See Wyatt Seal Inc.; *U.S. Private*, pg. 4575
FLO-TEC, INC.; *U.S. Private*, pg. 1546
FLUID FLOW PRODUCTS INC.; *U.S. Private*, pg. 1552
FLUID SYSTEM COMPONENTS INC.; *U.S. Private*, pg. 1552
FLUID SYSTEMS ENGINEERING, INC.—See Frontenac Company LLC; *U.S. Private*, pg. 1614
FOCKE & CO. (UK) LTD.—See Focke & Co. (GmbH & Co.) Verpackungsmaschinen; *Int'l*, pg. 2718
FOCKE (HONG KONG) LTD.—See Focke & Co. (GmbH & Co.) Verpackungsmaschinen; *Int'l*, pg. 2718
FOCKE (SINGAPORE) PTE LTD—See Focke & Co. (GmbH & Co.) Verpackungsmaschinen; *Int'l*, pg. 2718
FONDERIE MORA GAVARDO SPA—See Camozzi Group; *Int'l*, pg. 1274
FONTANA AMERICA INC.—See Fontana Luigi S.p.A.; *Int'l*, pg. 2726
FOOK CHEONG HO INTERNATIONAL LIMITED—See China Over Grand Financial Leasing Group Co., Ltd.; *Int'l*, pg. 1501
FORGE INDUSTRIES, INC.; *U.S. Private*, pg. 1568
FORMICA SKANDINAVIEN AB—See HAL Trust N.V.; *Int'l*, pg. 3223
FORT WORTH BOLT & TOOL CO.; *U.S. Private*, pg. 1575
FOUNTAIN CAN CORPORATION—See Daiwa Can Company; *Int'l*, pg. 1944
FOX INTERNATIONAL LTD., INC.—See Video Display Corporation; *U.S. Public*, pg. 2296
FPT FT, MYERS, LLC—See Soave Enterprises, LLC; *U.S. Private*, pg. 3702
FRANK W. WINNE & SON, INC.; *U.S. Private*, pg. 1596
FREEMAN FEED SERVICE INC—See Fremar Farmers Cooperative Inc.; *U.S. Private*, pg. 1608
FREUDENBERG-NOK-COMPONENTES BRASIL LTDA.—See Freudenberg SE; *Int'l*, pg. 2789
FREUDENBERG OIL & GAS CANADA INC.—See Freudenberg SE; *Int'l*, pg. 2787
FREUDENBERG OIL & GAS PTE. LTD.—See Freudenberg SE; *Int'l*, pg. 2787
FREUDENBERG OIL & GAS TECHNOLOGIES AS—See Freudenberg SE; *Int'l*, pg. 2787
FREUDENBERG OIL & GAS TECHNOLOGIES LTD.—See Freudenberg SE; *Int'l*, pg. 2787
FREUDENBERG OIL & GAS TECHNOLOGIES SDN. BHD.—See Freudenberg SE; *Int'l*, pg. 2787
FREUDENBERG OIL & GAS UK LTD.—See Freudenberg SE; *Int'l*, pg. 2787
FREUDENBERG SIMRIT POLSKA SP. Z O.O.—See Freudenberg SE; *Int'l*, pg. 2788
FTL SEALS TECHNOLOGY LTD—See IDEX Corp.; *U.S. Public*, pg. 1090
FUJIFILM SERICOL POLSKA SP. Z O.O.—See FUJIFILM Holdings Corporation; *Int'l*, pg. 2823

CORPORATE AFFILIATIONS

FUJIKURA COMPOSITES EUROPE B.V.—See Fujikura Composites Inc.; *Int'l*, pg. 2826
FUJI SEAL IBERIA, S.L.U—See Fuji Seal International, Inc.; *Int'l*, pg. 2816
FUKOKU AMERICA, INC.—See Fukoku Co., Ltd.; *Int'l*, pg. 2838
FUKOKU (SHANGHAI) TRADING CO., LTD.—See Fukoku Co., Ltd.; *Int'l*, pg. 2838
FUKUOKA KOGYO CO., LTD.—See Hanwa Co., Ltd.; *Int'l*, pg. 3262
FULTON SUPPLY COMPANY INC.; *U.S. Private*, pg. 1622
FURNACE PARTS, LLC—See Advent International Corporation; *U.S. Private*, pg. 100
FUTURA AGRARHANDEL GMBH—See AGRAVIS Raiffeisen AG; *Int'l*, pg. 215
GAMUT SUPPLY LLC—See W.W. Grainger, Inc.; *U.S. Public*, pg. 2319
GARDNER MARSH GAS EQUIPMENT COMPANY, INC.; *U.S. Private*, pg. 1643
GARLAND C. NORRIS CO.—See S.P. Richards Company; *U.S. Private*, pg. 3518
GAS EQUIPMENT COMPANY INC.—See Gas Equipment Company, Inc.; *U.S. Private*, pg. 1647
GASSO PORTUGAL LDA—See Comercial Gasso SA; *Int'l*, pg. 1710
GDW CANADIAN DIVISION—See Graycliff Partners LP; *U.S. Private*, pg. 1760
GDW EUROPEAN DIVISION—See Graycliff Partners LP; *U.S. Private*, pg. 1760
GDW WESTERN DIVISION—See Graycliff Partners LP; *U.S. Private*, pg. 1760
GEA TUCHENHAGEN CANADA, INC.—See GEA Group Aktiengesellschaft; *Int'l*, pg. 2900
GENERAL RUBBER PLASTICS OF LOUISVILLE; *U.S. Private*, pg. 1667
GENERAL TOOL & SUPPLY CO. INC.—See Genuine Parts Company; *U.S. Public*, pg. 933
GENERAL WORK PRODUCTS, INC.—See Altamont Capital Partners; *U.S. Private*, pg. 204
GENESIS SYSTEMS, INC.—See Wynnchurch Capital, L.P.; *U.S. Private*, pg. 4577
GENESIS VII INC.; *U.S. Private*, pg. 1670
GERARD KLUYSKENS COMPANY INC.; *U.S. Private*, pg. 1686
GERMANISCHER LLOYD INDUSTRIAL SERVICES EGYPT LTD.—See DNV GL Group AS; *Int'l*, pg. 2149
GE STEAM POWER S & E AFRICA PROPRIETARY LIMITED—See General Electric Company; *U.S. Public*, pg. 918
GHX INDUSTRIAL, LLC—See Clayton, Dubilier & Rice, LLC; *U.S. Private*, pg. 926
GIMATIC AUTOMATION TECHNOLOGY (SHANGHAI) CO., LTD.—See Barnes Group Inc.; *U.S. Public*, pg. 277
GIMATIC BALKAN D.O.O. BEOGRAD - SAVSKI VENAC—See Barnes Group Inc.; *U.S. Public*, pg. 277
GIMATIC FRANCE S.A.R.L.—See Barnes Group Inc.; *U.S. Public*, pg. 277
GIMATIC JAPAN LIMITED—See Barnes Group Inc.; *U.S. Public*, pg. 277
GIMATIC KOREA LIMITED—See Barnes Group Inc.; *U.S. Public*, pg. 277
GIMATIC NORDIC A.B.—See Barnes Group Inc.; *U.S. Public*, pg. 277
GIMATIC OTOMASYON TICARET ANONIM SIRKETI—See Barnes Group Inc.; *U.S. Public*, pg. 277
GIMATIC POLSKA SP. Z O.O—See Barnes Group Inc.; *U.S. Public*, pg. 277
GIMATIC SISTEMI INDUSTRIJSKA AVTOMATIZACIJA, D.O.O.—See Barnes Group Inc.; *U.S. Public*, pg. 277
GIMATRADE S.R.L.—See Barnes Group Inc.; *U.S. Public*, pg. 277
GLEASON-HURTH MASCHINEN UND WERKZEUGE GMBH—See Gleason Corporation; *U.S. Private*, pg. 1708
GLEASON METROLOGY SYSTEMS CORPORATION—See Gleason Corporation; *U.S. Private*, pg. 1708
GLOBAL INDUSTRIAL COMPONENTS; *U.S. Private*, pg. 1714
GLOBAL INTERTRADE GROUP—See Hayel Saeed Anam Group of Companies; *Int'l*, pg. 3290
GOLD PEG INTERNATIONAL PTY. LTD.—See Hochland SE; *Int'l*, pg. 3437
GORE INDUSTRIAL PRODUCTS TRADE (SHANGHAI) CO., LTD—See W.L. Gore & Associates, Inc.; *U.S. Private*, pg. 4421
GRADE EIGHT CORP; *U.S. Private*, pg. 1750
GRAINGER CARIBE INC.—See W.W. Grainger, Inc.; *U.S. Public*, pg. 2319
GRAINGER CHINA LLC—See W.W. Grainger, Inc.; *U.S. Public*, pg. 2320
GRAINGER INDUSTRIAL SUPPLY INDIA PVT. LTD.—See W.W. Grainger, Inc.; *U.S. Public*, pg. 2320
GRAINGER PANAMA S.A.—See W.W. Grainger, Inc.; *U.S. Public*, pg. 2320
GRAPHIC PACKAGING INTERNATIONAL S.P.A.—See Graphic Packaging Holding Company; *U.S. Public*, pg. 959

N.A.I.C.S. INDEX

423840 — INDUSTRIAL SUPPLIES...

GREAT LAKES FILTERS—See Acme Mills Co. Inc.; *U.S. Private*, pg. 61
GREAT LAKES POWER PRODUCTS INC.; *U.S. Private*, pg. 1765
GREAT LAKES RUBBER & SUPPLY; *U.S. Private*, pg. 1765
GREENE RUBBER COMPANY; *U.S. Private*, pg. 1777
GREENE TOOL SYSTEMS, INC.—See The Jordan Company, L.P.; *U.S. Private*, pg. 4060
GREINER ASSISTEC, S. A. DE C. V.—See Greiner Holding AG; *Int'l*, pg. 3079
GREINER ASSISTEC S.R.L.—See Greiner Holding AG; *Int'l*, pg. 3079
GREINER ASSISTEC S.R.O.—See Greiner Holding AG; *Int'l*, pg. 3080
GREINER I JP PACKAGING D.O.O.—See Greiner Holding AG; *Int'l*, pg. 3079
GREINER PACKAGING AG—See Greiner Holding AG; *Int'l*, pg. 3080
GREINER PACKAGING B.V.—See Greiner Holding AG; *Int'l*, pg. 3079
GREINER PACKAGING CORP.—See Greiner Holding AG; *Int'l*, pg. 3079
GREINER PACKAGING DISTRIBUTION SARL—See Greiner Holding AG; *Int'l*, pg. 3079
GREINER PACKAGING D.O.O.—See Greiner Holding AG; *Int'l*, pg. 3079
GREINER PACKAGING GMBH—See Greiner Holding AG; *Int'l*, pg. 3079
GREINER PACKAGING KFT.—See Greiner Holding AG; *Int'l*, pg. 3079
GREINER PACKAGING SLUSOVICE S.R.O—See Greiner Holding AG; *Int'l*, pg. 3080
GREINER PACKAGING SP. Z O.O.—See Greiner Holding AG; *Int'l*, pg. 3079
GREINER PACKAGING S.R.L—See Greiner Holding AG; *Int'l*, pg. 3079
GREINER PACKAGING S.R.O.—See Greiner Holding AG; *Int'l*, pg. 3080
GREINER PACKAGING VERTRIEBS GMBH—See Greiner Holding AG; *Int'l*, pg. 3079
GROEBNER & ASSOCIATES INC.; *U.S. Private*, pg. 1791
GROUP KZ LLP—See DNOW Inc.; *U.S. Public*, pg. 671
GRUPO POCHTECA S.A.B. DE C.V.; *Int'l*, pg. 3133
G-TEKT EUROPE MANUFACTURING LTD.—See G-TEKT Corporation; *Int'l*, pg. 2863
GT SALES & MANUFACTURING INC.; *U.S. Private*, pg. 1801
GUALA CLOSURES NORTH AMERICA, INC.—See Guala Closures S.p.A.; *Int'l*, pg. 3152
GUARDIAN PACKAGING INDUSTRIES, LP—See Conner Industries, Inc.; *U.S. Private*, pg. 1017
GUDEL A.S.—See Gudel Group AG; *Int'l*, pg. 3171
GUDEL GMBH—See Gudel Group AG; *Int'l*, pg. 3171
GUDEL GMBH—See Gudel Group AG; *Int'l*, pg. 3171
GUDEL INC.—See Gudel Group AG; *Int'l*, pg. 3171
GUDEL INDIA PVT. LTD.—See Gudel Group AG; *Int'l*, pg. 3171
GUDEL INTERNATIONAL TRADING CO. LTD.—See Gudel Group AG; *Int'l*, pg. 3171
GUDEL LINEARTEC CO., LTD.—See Gudel Group AG; *Int'l*, pg. 3171
GUDEL LINEARTEC CO. LTD.—See Gudel Group AG; *Int'l*, pg. 3171
GUDEL LINEARTEC INC.—See Gudel Group AG; *Int'l*, pg. 3171
GUDEL LINEARTEC (U.K.) LTD.—See Gudel Group AG; *Int'l*, pg. 3171
GUDEL OTOMASYON LTD. STI.—See Gudel Group AG; *Int'l*, pg. 3171
GUDEL SAS—See Gudel Group AG; *Int'l*, pg. 3171
GUDEL SP. Z O.O.—See Gudel Group AG; *Int'l*, pg. 3171
GUDEL S.R.L.—See Gudel Group AG; *Int'l*, pg. 3171
GUDEL TSC S.A. DE C.V.—See Gudel Group AG; *Int'l*, pg. 3171
GULF COAST MARINE SUPPLY COMPANY INC.; *U.S. Private*, pg. 1815
GULF-GREAT LAKES PACKAGING CORPORATION; *U.S. Private*, pg. 1817
GULF SYSTEMS INC.; *U.S. Private*, pg. 1817
HABASIT ARGENTINA S.A.—See Habasit AG; *Int'l*, pg. 3202
HABASIT GESELLSCHAFT M.B.H.—See Habasit AG; *Int'l*, pg. 3202
HABASIT HISPANICA S.A.—See Habasit AG; *Int'l*, pg. 3202
HABASIT ITALIANA SPA—See Habasit AG; *Int'l*, pg. 3202
HABASIT KAYIS SAN VE TIC. LTD.—See Habasit AG; *Int'l*, pg. 3202
HABASIT NIPPON CO. LTD See Habasit AG; *Int'l*, pg. 3202
HABASIT ROSSI (TAIWAN) LIMITED—See Habasit AG; *Int'l*, pg. 3202
HABASIT (SHANGHAI) CO. LTD.—See Habasit AG; *Int'l*, pg. 3201
HABASIT UKRAINE LLC—See Habasit AG; *Int'l*, pg. 3202
HABERKORN D.O.O.—See Haberkorn Holding AG; *Int'l*, pg. 3202

HABERKORN EOOD—See Haberkorn Holding AG; *Int'l*, pg. 3202
HABERKORN SP. Z O.O.—See Haberkorn Holding AG; *Int'l*, pg. 3202
HABERKORN S.R.O.—See Haberkorn Holding AG; *Int'l*, pg. 3202
HAGEMEYER CANADA—See Nautic Partners, LLC; *U.S. Private*, pg. 2872
HAGEMEYER NORTH AMERICA—See Nautic Partners, LLC; *U.S. Private*, pg. 2872
HAGEMEYER NORTH AMERICA—See Nautic Partners, LLC; *U.S. Private*, pg. 2872
HAHN SYSTEMS, LLC—See Descours & Cabaud SA; *Int'l*, pg. 2044
HALIFAX RACK AND SCREW NORTH AMERICA—See Halifax Rack & Screw Cutting Co. Ltd.; *Int'l*, pg. 3229
HAMPTON RUBBER COMPANY INC.—See AEA Investors LP; *U.S. Private*, pg. 115
HANGZHOU DAHUI FOAM PUMP COMPANY LTD—See Daiwa Can Company; *Int'l*, pg. 1944
HANNO WERK GMBH & CO. KG; *Int'l*, pg. 3257
HANS-JURGEN KEIL ANLAGENBAU GMBH & CO. KG; *Int'l*, pg. 3259
HARDWARE SPECIALTY CO. INC.; *U.S. Private*, pg. 1863
HARGIS INDUSTRIES INC.—See Hillman Solutions Corp.; *U.S. Public*, pg. 1038
HARGRAVE POWER, INC.—See Quanta Services, Inc.; *U.S. Public*, pg. 1751
HARMONIC DRIVE ESPANA, S.L.U.—See Harmonic Drive Systems Inc.; *Int'l*, pg. 3277
HARMONIC DRIVE FRANCE SAS—See Harmonic Drive Systems Inc.; *Int'l*, pg. 3277
HARMONIC DRIVE SYSTEMS (SHANGHAI) CO., LTD.—See Harmonic Drive Systems Inc.; *Int'l*, pg. 3277
HARMONIC DRIVE UK LIMITED—See Harmonic Drive Systems Inc.; *Int'l*, pg. 3277
HART INDUSTRIES INC.; *U.S. Private*, pg. 1873
HAUN WELDING SUPPLY INC.; *U.S. Private*, pg. 1880
H.B. FULLER POLAND SP.Z.O.O.—See H.B. Fuller Company; *U.S. Public*, pg. 978
HEADCO INDUSTRIES; *U.S. Private*, pg. 1891
HEADWATER EQUIPMENT SALES LTD; *Int'l*, pg. 3301
HEARRON SALES, INC.—See Platinum Equity, LLC; *U.S. Private*, pg. 3209
H&E EQUIPMENT SERVICES (MIDWEST), INC.—See H&E Equipment Services, Inc.; *U.S. Public*, pg. 976
HEITKAMP & THUMANN (S) PTE LTD.—See Heitkamp & Thumann KG; *Int'l*, pg. 3326
HEPHAIST SEIKO (SHANGHAI) CO., LTD.—See Heheist Co., Ltd.; *Int'l*, pg. 3308
HERMES ABRASIVES (CANADA) LTD.—See Hermes Schleifmittel GmbH & Co. KG; *Int'l*, pg. 3363
HEYER CORP.; *U.S. Private*, pg. 1928
HILOS A&E DE HONDURAS, S.A.—See Platinum Equity, LLC; *U.S. Private*, pg. 3201
HILOS AMERICAN & EFIRD DE MEXICO, S.A. DE C.V.—See The Kroger Co.; *U.S. Public*, pg. 2108
HILTAP FITTINGS LTD.—See Dover Corporation; *U.S. Public*, pg. 681
HI-PACK GROUP FOR PACKAGING SOLUTION—See Hayel Saeed Anam Group of Companies; *Int'l*, pg. 3290
HISCO, INC.—See Distribution Solutions Group, Inc.; *U.S. Public*, pg. 668
HIS COMPANY, INC. - HISCOMEX DIVISION—See Distribution Solutions Group, Inc.; *U.S. Public*, pg. 668
HJULEX AB—See Addtech AB; *Int'l*, pg. 133
HKS ENTERPRISES INC.; *U.S. Private*, pg. 1953
HOFER POWERTAIN PRODUCTS UK LTD.—See ElringKlinger AG; *Int'l*, pg. 2370
HOFER POWERTRAIN PRODUCTS GMBH—See ElringKlinger AG; *Int'l*, pg. 2370
HOFFMEYER COMPANY INC.; *U.S. Private*, pg. 1960
HOI TUNG (SHANGHAI) LIMITED—See China Merchants Group Limited; *Int'l*, pg. 1521
HONEYWELL SAFETY PRODUCTS ITALIA SRL—See Honeywell International Inc.; *U.S. Public*, pg. 1049
HONKA JAPAN INC.—See Honkarakenne Oyj; *Int'l*, pg. 3471
HOOVER CONTAINER SOLUTIONS NORWAY AS—See First Reserve Management, L.P.; *U.S. Private*, pg. 1526
HOOVER CONTAINER SOLUTIONS PTY. LTD.—See First Reserve Management, L.P.; *U.S. Private*, pg. 1526
HOPE GROUP CORPORATION; *U.S. Private*, pg. 1979
HORN INTERNATIONAL PACKAGING—See Horn Packaging Corporation; *U.S. Private*, pg. 1983
HPS S.R.L.—See Hammond Power Solutions Inc.; *Int'l*, pg. 3239
HRS LOGISTICS, INC.—See Derry Enterprises Inc.; *U.S. Private*, pg. 1210
HTH HEATECH INC.; *Int'l*, pg. 3508
H&T MARSBERG GMBH & CO. KG.—See Heitkamp & Thumann KG; *Int'l*, pg. 3326
H&T WATERBURY INC.—See Heitkamp & Thumann KG; *Int'l*, pg. 3326
HUBBARD SUPPLY CO.; *U.S. Private*, pg. 2000
HUB SUPPLY COMPANY—See Genuine Parts Company; *U.S. Public*, pg. 933
HUHTAMAKI FOODSERVICE POLAND SP. Z.O.O.—See Huhtamaki Oyj; *Int'l*, pg. 3525
HYDAC A/S—See Hydac International GmbH; *Int'l*, pg. 3544
HYDRA FLOW WEST INC.—See Atlas Copco AB; *U.S. Public*, pg. 682
HYDR-O-SEAL, INC.; *U.S. Private*, pg. 2017
HYDRO SYSTEMS COMPANY—See Dover Corporation; *U.S. Public*, pg. 679
HYQUIP, LLC—See Applied Industrial Technologies, Inc.; *U.S. Public*, pg. 171
IBT CENTRAL DISTRIBUTION CENTER—See IBT, Inc.; *U.S. Private*, pg. 2029
IBT, INC.; *U.S. Private*, pg. 2029
ICAFE, INC.; *U.S. Private*, pg. 2029
ICP BUILDING SOLUTIONS GROUP—See Audax Group, Limited Partnership; *U.S. Private*, pg. 388
IDEAL ELECTRIC SUPPLY CORPORATION; *U.S. Private*, pg. 2036
ILJIN DIAMOND CO LTD; *Int'l*, pg. 3614
IMEX INTERNATIONAL INC.; *U.S. Private*, pg. 2047
IMPACT INDUSTRIAL SUPPLIES INC.; *U.S. Private*, pg. 2048
IMPERIAL SUPPLIES LLC—See W.W. Grainger, Inc.; *U.S. Public*, pg. 2320
INDEPENDENT CAN COMPANY — DISTRIBUTION DIV—See Independent Can Company; *U.S. Private*, pg. 2058
INDEPENDENT PLASTIC INC.; *U.S. Private*, pg. 2060
INDUSTRIAL CONTAINER & SUPPLY; *U.S. Private*, pg. 2065
INDUSTRIAL FINISHES & SYSTEMS INC.; *U.S. Private*, pg. 2066
INDUSTRIAL & MARINE EQUIPMENT CO., INC.—See AEA Investors LP; *U.S. Private*, pg. 115
INDUSTRIAL SPECIALTIES, LLC—See Aberdeen Dynamics Supply Inc.; *U.S. Private*, pg. 38
INDUSTRIAL WELDING SUPPLIES OF HATTIESBURG, INC.—See Tatum Development Corp.; *U.S. Private*, pg. 3936
INFASTECH (AUSTRALIA) PTY LIMITED—See Stanley Black & Decker, Inc.; *U.S. Public*, pg. 1934
INMARK, LLC - BIOMEDICAL PACKAGING DIVISION—See Kelso & Company, L.P.; *U.S. Private*, pg. 2278
INTEGRATED SCM CO., LTD.—See FM Global Logistics Holdings Berhad; *Int'l*, pg. 2717
INTERPLEX AUTOMATION, INC.—See Blackstone Inc.; *U.S. Public*, pg. 355
INTERPLEX ELECTRONIC HANGZHOU CO., LTD.—See Blackstone Inc.; *U.S. Public*, pg. 355
INTERPLEX ELECTRONICS MALAYSIA SDN. BHD.—See Blackstone Inc.; *U.S. Public*, pg. 355
INTERPLEX HUNGARY, KFT.—See Blackstone Inc.; *U.S. Public*, pg. 355
INTERSTATE PRODUCTS, INC.; *U.S. Private*, pg. 2125
INTER-UNION TECHNOHANDEL GESELLSCHAFT M.B.H.—See Deutsche Bahn AG; *Int'l*, pg. 2052
ISAF DRAHTWERK GMBH—See Lincoln Electric Holdings, Inc.; *U.S. Public*, pg. 1317
ISRAEL ANDLER & SON INC.; *U.S. Private*, pg. 2147
ITW PACKAGING (SHANGHAI) CO., LTD.—See Crown Holdings, Inc.; *U.S. Public*, pg. 599
ITW WELDING PRODUCTS LIMITED LIABILITY COMPANY—See Illinois Tool Works Inc.; *U.S. Public*, pg. 1108
ITW ZIP-PAK PACKAGING (SHANGHAI) LTD.—See Illinois Tool Works Inc.; *U.S. Public*, pg. 1108
JACKOVICH INDUSTRIAL & CONSTRUCTION SUPPLY, INC.—See Colville Capital LLC; *U.S. Private*, pg. 979
JACON AIRCRAFT SUPPLY CO. INC.; *U.S. Private*, pg. 2180
JAMAICA BEARINGS CO. INC.; *U.S. Private*, pg. 2182
JAN-MAR SALES LIMITED—See Bunzl plc; *Int'l*, pg. 1218
JARVIS SUPPLY CO., INC.—See TruArc Partners, L.P.; *U.S. Private*, pg. 4245
JASON INDUSTRIAL, INC.; *U.S. Private*, pg. 2189
JB ALLOY CORPORATION; *U.S. Private*, pg. 2193
J F GOOD COMPANY INC—See Famous Enterprises Inc.; *U.S. Private*, pg. 1472
J. HENRY HOLLAND CORPORATION—See Industrial Sales Company Inc.; *U.S. Private*, pg. 2068
J.H. WILLIAMS TOOL GROUP—See Snap-on Incorporated; *U.S. Public*, pg. 1897
JOHN H. FRISCHKORN, JR. INC.; *U.S. Private*, pg. 2222
JOHNSON PACKINGS & INDUSTRIAL PRODUCTS INC.—See Gallagher Fluid Seals Inc.; *U.S. Private*, pg. 1638
JOHNSTONE SUPPLY; *U.S. Private*, pg. 2230
JOHNSTON INDUSTRIAL SUPPLY INC.; *U.S. Private*, pg. 2230
JOHN WHILE SPRINGS (SHANGHAI) CO., LTD.—See Beijer Alma AB; *Int'l*, pg. 943
JONES ENTERPRISES INC.; *U.S. Private*, pg. 2233
JOSEF KIHLBERG AB—See Illinois Tool Works Inc.; *U.S. Public*, pg. 1108
JPW (TOOL) AG—See Tenex Capital Management, L.P.; *U.S. Private*, pg. 3966
J ROYAL CO. INC.-BARRINGTON—See Diploma PLC; *Int'l*, pg. 2128
J. ROYAL CO. INC.—See Diploma PLC; *Int'l*, pg. 2128

3941

423840 — INDUSTRIAL SUPPLIES...

J SUPPLY CO.; *U.S. Private*, pg. 2153
J.W. WINCO, INC.; *U.S. Private*, pg. 2172
KAMAN CORPORATION—See Arcline Investment Management LP; *U.S. Private*, pg. 314
KAMAN FLUID POWER, LLC—See Littlejohn & Co., LLC; *U.S. Private*, pg. 2471
KAMAN INDUSTRIAL TECHNOLOGIES CORPORATION—See Littlejohn & Co., LLC; *U.S. Private*, pg. 2470
KAMAN SPECIALTY BEARINGS & ENGINEERED PRODUCTS, GMBH—See Arcline Investment Management LP; *U.S. Private*, pg. 314
KAMEN INDUSTRIAL SUPPLIES INC.—See Kamen Industrial Technologies; *U.S. Private*, pg. 2258
KAMEN INDUSTRIAL TECHNOLOGIES; *U.S. Private*, pg. 2258
KAUFMAN CONTAINER CO.; *U.S. Private*, pg. 2265
KE-BURGMANN UK LTD.—See Freudenberg SE; *Int'l*, pg. 2789
KEEN COMPRESSED GAS COMPANY; *U.S. Private*, pg. 2272
KEEN COMPRESSED GAS—See Keen Compressed Gas Company; *U.S. Private*, pg. 2272
KELLY SUPPLY COMPANY; *U.S. Private*, pg. 2277
KENTEK OY—See Diploma PLC; *Int'l*, pg. 2128
KESTER COMPONENTS (M) SDN. BHD.—See Illinois Tool Works Inc.; *U.S. Public*, pg. 1108
K & H SALES, INC.—See DoALL Company; *U.S. Private*, pg. 1250
KINEX-EXIM, SPOL. S R.O.—See HTC holding a.s.; *Int'l*, pg. 3508
KNOTTS CO. INC.; *U.S. Private*, pg. 2323
KOLS CONTAINERS—See O. Berk Company L.L.C.; *U.S. Private*, pg. 2981
KRAYDEN, INC.—See Audax Group, Limited Partnership; *U.S. Private*, pg. 388
KS BEARINGS—See KS International Investment Corp.; *U.S. Private*, pg. 2354
KUNDINGER FLUID POWER, INC.; *U.S. Private*, pg. 2357
KUNSHAN KUANGRUI PACKAGE MATERIAL CO., LTD.—See Eson Precision Ind. Co., Ltd.; *Int'l*, pg. 2504
KURT MANUFACTURING CO. INC. - KURT ENGINEERED SYSTEMS DIVISION—See Kurt Manufacturing Co. Inc.; *U.S. Private*, pg. 2357
KURT MANUFACTURING CO. INC. - KURT SCREW MACHINING AND HYDRAULICS DIVISIONS—See Kurt Manufacturing Co. Inc.; *U.S. Private*, pg. 2358
KYANA PACKAGING & INDUSTRIAL SUPPLY, INC.; *U.S. Private*, pg. 2359
LAKESIDE SUPPLY CO. INC.; *U.S. Private*, pg. 2378
LAMIN-ART, INC.—See Arborite; *Int'l*, pg. 539
LCC FOCKE SERVICE ST.-PB—See Focke & Co. (GmbH & Co.) Verpackungsmaschinen; *Int'l*, pg. 2718
LEE SUPPLY COMPANY INC.—See Core & Main, Inc.; *U.S. Public*, pg. 576
LEPAGE'S CORPORATION; *U.S. Private*, pg. 2431
LIBERTY BELL WHOLESALE; *U.S. Private*, pg. 2443
LINCOLN STRUCTURAL SOLUTIONS LLC—See Owen Industries, Inc.; *U.S. Private*, pg. 3054
LINC SYSTEMS, INC.; *U.S. Private*, pg. 2456
LINEAR INDUSTRIES LTD.; *U.S. Private*, pg. 2460
LINPAC PACKAGING AS—See Strategic Value Partners, LLC; *U.S. Private*, pg. 3836
LM WIND POWER (SPAIN) SLU—See General Electric Company; *U.S. Public*, pg. 920
LOGAN & WHALEY CO.; *U.S. Private*, pg. 2480
LOGOPLASTE CANADA INC.—See The Carlyle Group Inc.; *U.S. Public*, pg. 2048
LOGOPLASTE CZECH, S.R.O.—See The Carlyle Group Inc.; *U.S. Public*, pg. 2048
LOGOPLASTE DO BRASIL LTDA—See The Carlyle Group Inc.; *U.S. Public*, pg. 2048
LOGOPLASTE ELST B.V.—See The Carlyle Group Inc.; *U.S. Public*, pg. 2048
LOGOPLASTE MEXICO S DE R.L. DE C.V—See The Carlyle Group Inc.; *U.S. Public*, pg. 2048
LOGOPLASTE (M) KUANTAN SDN BHD—See The Carlyle Group Inc.; *U.S. Public*, pg. 2048
LOGOPLASTE RUSSIA LLC—See The Carlyle Group Inc.; *U.S. Public*, pg. 2048
LOGOPLASTE UKRAINE LLC—See The Carlyle Group Inc.; *U.S. Public*, pg. 2048
LOGOPLASTE USA, INC.—See The Carlyle Group Inc.; *U.S. Public*, pg. 2048
LOWRY'S INC.—See Beacon Roofing Supply, Inc.; *U.S. Public*, pg. 286
LOWRY'S—See Beacon Roofing Supply, Inc.; *U.S. Public*, pg. 286
LTC, INC.—See PRL Inc.; *U.S. Private*, pg. 3269
LUNDGRENS NORGE AS—See Beijer Alma AB; *Int'l*, pg. 943
LWG ZURN AUSTRALIA PTY LTD.—See Zurn Elkay Water Solutions Corporation; *U.S. Public*, pg. 2413
LYNCO FLANGE & FITTING, INC.; *U.S. Private*, pg. 2521
MACAULAY CONTROLS CO—See H.I.G. Capital, LLC; *U.S. Private*, pg. 1834
MACPHERSON WESTERN TOOL & SUPPLY CO. INC. - TOOL & GAGE ASSOCIATES DIVISION—See Macpherson Western Tool & Supply Co. Inc.; *U.S. Private*, pg. 2538
MAGNEQUENCH (TIANJIN) CO., LTD.—See Brookfield Corporation; *Int'l*, pg. 1181
MAHAR TOOL SUPPLY COMPANY INC.; *U.S. Private*, pg. 2550
MALAYSIAHOSOKAWA MICRON MALAYSIA SDN. BHD.—See Hosokawa Micron Corporation; *Int'l*, pg. 3486
MARCO RUBBER & PLASTIC PRODUCTS, INC.—See Align Capital Partners, LLC; *U.S. Private*, pg. 167
MARIAN INC.; *U.S. Private*, pg. 2574
MARKET QUEST, INC.—See Bischof + Klein GmbH & Co. KG; *Int'l*, pg. 1048
MARSH INDUSTRIES, INC.—See Industrial Opportunity Partners, LLC; *U.S. Private*, pg. 2067
MARTIN FASTENING SOLUTIONS—See MSCO Inc.; *U.S. Private*, pg. 2806
MARTIN FLUID POWER COMPANY, INC.; *U.S. Private*, pg. 2595
MARTIN INDUSTRIAL SUPPLY—See MSCO Inc.; *U.S. Private*, pg. 2806
MARTIN SUPPLY COMPANY INC.; *U.S. Private*, pg. 2596
MASTER'S SUPPLY, INC.; *U.S. Private*, pg. 2608
MASTHEAD INDUSTRIES INC—See Bridgestone Corporation; *Int'l*, pg. 1160
MATERION BRUSH GMBH—See Materion Corporation; *U.S. Public*, pg. 1395
MATERION BRUSH (SINGAPORE) PTE LTD.—See Materion Corporation; *U.S. Public*, pg. 1395
MATERION CERAMICS INC—See Materion Corporation; *U.S. Public*, pg. 1395
MATRIX INTERNATIONAL LTD.; *U.S. Private*, pg. 2612
MAU-SHERWOOD SUPPLY CO; *U.S. Private*, pg. 2614
MAYR FRANCE S.A.—See Christian Mayr GmbH & Co. KG; *Int'l*, pg. 1586
MAYR ITALIA S.R.L.—See Christian Mayr GmbH & Co. KG; *Int'l*, pg. 1586
MAYR KOREA CO. LTD.—See Christian Mayr GmbH & Co. KG; *Int'l*, pg. 1586
MAYR KUPPLUNGEN AG—See Christian Mayr GmbH & Co. KG; *Int'l*, pg. 1586
MAYR POLSKA SP. Z O.O.—See Christian Mayr GmbH & Co. KG; *Int'l*, pg. 1586
MAYR POWER TRANSMISSION (ZHANGJIAGANG) CO., LTD.—See Christian Mayr GmbH & Co. KG; *Int'l*, pg. 1586
MAYR TRANSMISSION (S) PTE LTD.—See Christian Mayr GmbH & Co. KG; *Int'l*, pg. 1586
MB AUTOMAXI UK LTD—See Accent Equity Partners AB; *Int'l*, pg. 81
MCCLURE ASSOCIATES INC.; *U.S. Private*, pg. 2629
MCE DISTRIBUTING AND SUPPLY; *U.S. Private*, pg. 2633
MCGUIRE BEARING COMPANY, INC.; *U.S. Private*, pg. 2636
MCMASTER-CARR SUPPLY COMPANY; *U.S. Private*, pg. 2642
MCMASTERS-KOSS CO.; *U.S. Private*, pg. 2642
MECHANICAL SUPPLY—See Northern Machining & Repair, Inc.; *U.S. Private*, pg. 2953
MECHATRONICS INC.; *U.S. Private*, pg. 2649
MECO OF SAVANNAH INC.—See Meco of Atlanta Incorporated; *U.S. Private*, pg. 2649
MERWIN-STOLTZ CO., INC.—See DoALL Company; *U.S. Private*, pg. 1250
MESA INDUSTRIES INC.; *U.S. Private*, pg. 2677
METALCO SA—See Descours & Cabaud SA; *Int'l*, pg. 2044
METALTEK INTERNATIONAL - METALTEK ENERGY PRODUCTS DIVISION—See MetalTek International; *U.S. Private*, pg. 2682
METALTEK INTERNATIONAL - METALTEK ENERGY SOLUTIONS DIVISION—See MetalTek International; *U.S. Private*, pg. 2682
METRIC & MULTISTANDARD COMPONENTS CORPORATION; *U.S. Private*, pg. 2684
MICROLEASE LIMITED—See Platinum Equity, LLC; *U.S. Private*, pg. 3202
MID-ATLANTIC FASTENERS INC.—See Carlson Holdings, Inc.; *U.S. Private*, pg. 765
MID IOWA TOOLS INCORPORATED; *U.S. Private*, pg. 2706
MID-STATES SUPPLY COMPANY, INC.; *U.S. Private*, pg. 2709
MIDWAY INDUSTRIES INC.; *U.S. Private*, pg. 2719
MIDWESCO INDUSTRIES INC.; *U.S. Private*, pg. 2719
MIDWESTERN PIPE LINE PRODUCTS CO. INC.—See Midwesco Industries Inc.; *U.S. Private*, pg. 2719
MIDWEST INDUSTRIAL RUBBER INC.—See Advent International Corporation; *U.S. Private*, pg. 98
MILLER BEARINGS DIVISION - WESTMORELAND—See Genuine Parts Company; *U.S. Public*, pg. 933
MILL-ROSE CLEAN-FIT—See Mill-Rose Company; *U.S. Private*, pg. 2730
MILL SUPPLIES INC.; *U.S. Private*, pg. 2730
MINE SERVICE COMPANY INC.; *U.S. Private*, pg. 2741
MINE SUPPLY COMPANY INC.; *U.S. Private*, pg. 2741
MINNESOTA FLEXIBLE CORP.; *U.S. Private*, pg. 2743
MINOR RUBBER CO.—See Minor Rubber Co., Inc.; *U.S. Private*, pg. 2744
MIRACLE SUPPLY CO. INC.; *U.S. Private*, pg. 2745
MISSOURI POWER TRANSMISSION, INC.—See Genuine Parts Company; *U.S. Public*, pg. 933
MITTEN FLUIDPOWER INC.; *U.S. Private*, pg. 2751
MIXING SOLUTIONS LIMITED—See Lone Star Funds; *U.S. Private*, pg. 2485
MIYAKO KAGAKU CO., LTD.—See Chori Co., Ltd.; *Int'l*, pg. 1583
M. LUKAS COMPANY—See API Group Corporation; *Int'l*, pg. 514
MODCHEM LTD. AGENCIES—See Bischof + Klein GmbH & Co. KG; *Int'l*, pg. 1048
MODERN SUPPLY CO., INC.—See Modern Welding Company, Inc.; *U.S. Private*, pg. 2762
MOLINS TOBACCO MACHINERY LTD.—See Coesia S.p.A.; *Int'l*, pg. 1690
MOLYCORP CHEMICALS & OXIDES (EUROPE) LTD.—See Brookfield Corporation; *Int'l*, pg. 1181
MOMAR, INC. - SAFETYMAN DIVISION—See Momar, Inc.; *U.S. Private*, pg. 2768
MONT BLANC FRANCE SAS—See Accent Equity Partners AB; *Int'l*, pg. 81
MOTION & FLOW CONTROL PRODUCTS, INC.—See Colville Capital LLC; *U.S. Private*, pg. 979
MOTION INDUSTRIES (CANADA) INC.—See Genuine Parts Company; *U.S. Public*, pg. 933
MOTION INDUSTRIES, INC.—See Genuine Parts Company; *U.S. Public*, pg. 933
M-PAK, INC.; *U.S. Private*, pg. 2526
MR. BOX LTD—See WillScot Mobile Mini Holdings Corp.; *U.S. Public*, pg. 2372
MRC GLOBAL (US) INC.—See MRC Global Inc.; *U.S. Public*, pg. 1481
MSCO INC.; *U.S. Private*, pg. 2806
M SEALS AB—See Diploma PLC; *Int'l*, pg. 2129
MUELLER SALES CORP.—See Central States Industrial Supply, Inc.; *U.S. Private*, pg. 825
MUNNELL & SHERRILL INC.; *U.S. Private*, pg. 2814
MURDOCK COMPANIES INC.; *U.S. Private*, pg. 2814
NADELLA GMBH—See The Timken Company; *U.S. Public*, pg. 2133
NADELLA INC.—See The Timken Company; *U.S. Public*, pg. 2133
NALCO DISTRIBUTING, INC.; *U.S. Private*, pg. 2831
NAP GLADU - TORONTO—See Audax Group, Limited Partnership; *U.S. Private*, pg. 389
NASHVILLE RUBBER & GASKET COMPANY, INC.; *U.S. Private*, pg. 2836
NATIONAL HOSE & ACCESSORY, INC.—See AEA Investors LP; *U.S. Private*, pg. 115
NATIONAL PACKAGING SERVICES; *U.S. Private*, pg. 2860
NAZ-DAR COMPANY—See Thrall Enterprises, Inc.; *U.S. Private*, pg. 4163
NEFCO CORP.; *U.S. Private*, pg. 2880
NEILL-LAVIELLE SUPPLY CO.; *U.S. Private*, pg. 2882
NEILL SUPPLY CO., INC—See Core & Main, Inc.; *U.S. Public*, pg. 576
NEO PERFORMANCE MATERIALS INC.—See Brookfield Corporation; *Int'l*, pg. 1181
NEWCO (H.K.) LIMITED—See Honghua Group Ltd; *Int'l*, pg. 3471
NEWCO VALVES LP; *U.S. Private*, pg. 2914
NEW YORK BITUMINOUS PRODUCTS CORP.; *U.S. Private*, pg. 2908
N.H. BRAGG & SONS; *U.S. Private*, pg. 2828
NIHO (SINGAPORE) PTE LTD—See HG Metal Manufacturing Limited; *Int'l*, pg. 3375
NOMO AB—See Axel Johnson Gruppen AB; *Int'l*, pg. 763
NORD AANDRIJVINGEN BELGIE NV—See Getriebebau NORD GmbH & Co. KG; *Int'l*, pg. 2953
NORD AANDRIJVINGEN NEDERLAND B.V.—See Getriebebau NORD GmbH & Co. KG; *Int'l*, pg. 2953
NORFIELD INDUSTRIES; *U.S. Private*, pg. 2937
NORTHEAST AIR SOLUTIONS INC—See Daikin Industries, Ltd.; *Int'l*, pg. 1936
NORTHERN STATES SUPPLY INC—See Building Fasteners of Minnesota Inc.; *U.S. Private*, pg. 682
NORTH STATE SUPPLY CO., INC.—See Cadent Energy Partners, LLC; *U.S. Private*, pg. 713
NORTHWEST WIRE ROPE & SLING COMPANY—See ALP Industries, Inc.; *U.S. Private*, pg. 196
NOTT COMPANY; *U.S. Private*, pg. 2965
NOVA HYDRAULICS INC.—See Frontenac Company LLC; *U.S. Private*, pg. 1614
NOV OIL & GAS SERVICES SOUTH AFRICA—See NOV, Inc.; *U.S. Public*, pg. 1545
NPS WORLDWIDE--UK LIMITED—See National Packaging Services Corporation; *U.S. Private*, pg. 2860
NTC NUCLEACTION—See Groupe Gorge S.A.; *Int'l*, pg. 3103
OAK MOUNTAIN INDUSTRIES, INC.—See Osceola Capital Management, LLC; *U.S. Private*, pg. 3047
O. BERK COMPANY L.L.C.; *U.S. Private*, pg. 2981
O. BERK COMPANY OF NEW ENGLAND—See O. Berk Company L.L.C.; *U.S. Private*, pg. 2981

N.A.I.C.S. INDEX

423840 — INDUSTRIAL SUPPLIES...

OERLIKON SKANDINAVIEN AB—See Lincoln Electric Holdings, Inc.; *U.S. Public*, pg. 1318
O-I ESTONIA AS—See O-I Glass, Inc.; *U.S. Public*, pg. 1559
OIL SYSTEMS, INC.—See MetalTek International; *U.S. Private*, pg. 2682
O-I (SHANGHAI) GLASS CONTAINER CO., LTD.—See O-I Glass, Inc.; *U.S. Public*, pg. 1559
OLIVER H. VAN HORN CO., LLC; *U.S. Private*, pg. 3011
ONEX INC.; *U.S. Private*, pg. 3026
OOO GREINER PACKAGING—See Greiner Holding AG; *Int'l*, pg. 3079
OOO HABASIT LTD.—See Habasit AG; *Int'l*, pg. 3202
ORBINOX DEUTSHLAND GMBH—See AVK Holding A/S; *Int'l*, pg. 748
ORS NASCO, INC.—See Sycamore Partners Management, LP; *U.S. Private*, pg. 3897
THE OVERBY GROUP INC.—See Bischof + Klein GmbH & Co. KG; *Int'l*, pg. 1049
OXFORD BUILDERS SUPPLIES—See EllisDon Corporation; *Int'l*, pg. 2367
OY BENZLER AB—See Elecon Engineering Company Ltd.; *Int'l*, pg. 2348
PACIFIC MECHANICAL SUPPLY; *U.S. Private*, pg. 3068
PACIFIC RUBBER & PACKING, INC.; *U.S. Private*, pg. 3070
PACIFIC WESTERN CONTAINER CORP.—See Blower Dempsay Corporation; *U.S. Private*, pg. 584
PACKAGING CORPORATION OF ILLINOIS—See Packaging Corporation of America; *U.S. Public*, pg. 1633
PAN AMERICAN TOOL CORPORATION; *U.S. Private*, pg. 3084
PAPERWORKS INDUSTRIES, INC. - DALLAS PLANT—See Sun Capital Partners, Inc.; *U.S. Private*, pg. 3860
PAPERWORKS INDUSTRIES, INC. - MENDON PLANT—See Sun Capital Partners, Inc.; *U.S. Private*, pg. 3860
PAPERWORKS INDUSTRIES, INC. - WILKES-BARRE PLANT—See Sun Capital Partners, Inc.; *U.S. Private*, pg. 3860
PARAMOUNT CAN COMPANY INC.; *U.S. Private*, pg. 3092
PARKER HANNIFIN CHOMERICS (M) SDN. BHD.—See Parker Hannifin Corporation; *U.S. Public*, pg. 1644
PARKER HANNIFIN POLYFLEX—See Parker Hannifin Corporation; *U.S. Public*, pg. 1646
PARK-OHIO INDUSTRIES, INC.—See Park-Ohio Holdings Corp.; *U.S. Public*, pg. 1639
PARRISH ENTERPRISES, LTD.; *U.S. Private*, pg. 3100
PATTON INDUSTRIAL PRODUCTS; *U.S. Private*, pg. 3111
PAYSON BRONCO, INC.—See Payson Casters, Inc.; *U.S. Private*, pg. 3117
PCL (PTE) LTD—See Eng Kong Holdings Pte Ltd.; *Int'l*, pg. 2426
PEARLMAN CORPORATION—See Harbour Group Industries, Inc.; *U.S. Private*, pg. 1860
PENAGA DRESSER SDN. BHD.—See Deleum Berhad; *Int'l*, pg. 2012
PENINSULA COMPONENTS INC.; *U.S. Private*, pg. 3133
PENNSYLVANIA TOOL SALES & SERVICE; *U.S. Private*, pg. 3137
PENTAIR VALVES & CONTROLS DISTRIBUTION CZECH S.R.O.—See Emerson Electric Co.; *U.S. Public*, pg. 751
PENTAIR VALVES & CONTROLS (FRANCE) S.C.A—See Emerson Electric Co.; *U.S. Public*, pg. 751
PFERD, INC.—See August Rueggeberg GmbH & Co. KG PFERD-Werkzeuge; *Int'l*, pg. 703
PFI, LLC—See Dot Family Holdings LLC; *U.S. Private*, pg. 1264
PIONEER INDUSTRIAL CORPORATION; *U.S. Private*, pg. 3187
PIONEER SUPPLY COMPANY INC.; *U.S. Private*, pg. 3188
PIPESTONE EQUIPMENT LLC—See Pike Street Capital, LP; *U.S. Private*, pg. 3180
POLAR SERVICE CENTERS, INC.—See Questor Management Company, LLC; *U.S. Private*, pg. 3326
PORIN LAAKERI OY—See Axel Johnson Gruppen AB; *Int'l*, pg. 763
POROTECHNOLOGY, INC.—See Micromeritics Instrument Corporation, Inc.; *U.S. Private*, pg. 2704
POWER/MATION; *U.S. Private*, pg. 3239
POWER PACKER DO BRASIL LTDA.—See Enerpac Tool Group Corp.; *U.S. Public*, pg. 766
POWER PROCESS EQUIPMENT INC.; *U.S. Private*, pg. 3238
POWER & PUMPS INC.; *U.S. Private*, pg. 3237
POWER TOOLS & SUPPLY INC.; *U.S. Private*, pg. 3239
POWERTRACK INTERNATIONAL, LLC—See Tecum Capital Partners, LLC; *U.S. Private*, pg. 3957
PRC INDUSTRIAL SUPPLY, INC.—See AEA Investors LP; *U.S. Private*, pg. 115
PREBEN Z. JENSEN A/S—See Beijer Alma AB; *Int'l*, pg. 043
PRICE CONTAINER & PACKAGING CORPORATION—See Ares Management Corporation; *U.S. Public*, pg. 191
PRODUCTION COMPONENTS, INC.; *U.S. Private*, pg. 3273
PRODUCTION TOOL SUPPLY COMPANY, LLC; *U.S. Private*, pg. 3273
PRODUCTO/DIECO—See PMT Group Inc; *U.S. Private*, pg. 3219

PROPAC INTERNATIONAL AB—See Bong AB; *Int'l*, pg. 1107
PROTECTIVE INDUSTRIAL PRODUCTS, INC.—See Odyssey Investment Partners, LLC; *U.S. Public*, pg. 2995
PROVEEDORA DE SEGURIDAD INDUSTRIAL DEL GOLFO S.A. DE C.V.—See Nautic Partners, LLC; *U.S. Private*, pg. 2872
PSB TECHNOLOGIES PTE LTD—See Doerfer Corporation; *U.S. Private*, pg. 1253
PT BOBST GROUP INDONESIA—See Bobst Group S.A.; *Int'l*, pg. 1096
PT. BRIDGESTONE ENGINEERED PRODUCTS INDONESIA—See Bridgestone Corporation; *Int'l*, pg. 1160
P-T COUPLING COMPANY—See Parrish Enterprises, Ltd.; *U.S. Private*, pg. 3100
PT CROMWELL TOOLS—See W.W. Grainger, Inc.; *U.S. Public*, pg. 2320
PT MONOTARO INDONESIA—See W.W. Grainger, Inc.; *U.S. Public*, pg. 2320
PV ENGINEERING SA PTY LTD—See AVK Holding A/S; *Int'l*, pg. 748
PYROTEK ENGINEERING MATERIALS LTD.—See Pyrotek Incorporated; *U.S. Private*, pg. 3311
PYROTEK FZE—See Pyrotek Incorporated; *U.S. Private*, pg. 3311
PYROTEK INC.—See Pyrotek Incorporated; *U.S. Private*, pg. 3311
PYROTEK KOREA—See Pyrotek Incorporated; *U.S. Private*, pg. 3311
PYROTEK MEXICO, S. DE R. L. DE C. V.—See Pyrotek Incorporated; *U.S. Private*, pg. 3311
PYROTEK NETHERLANDS B.V.—See Pyrotek Incorporated; *U.S. Private*, pg. 3311
PYROTEK REFRAKTER SANAYI VE TICARET LTD. STI.—See Pyrotek Incorporated; *U.S. Private*, pg. 3311
PYROTEK SA—See Pyrotek Incorporated; *U.S. Private*, pg. 3311
PYROTEK THAILAND CO. LTD.—See Pyrotek Incorporated; *U.S. Private*, pg. 3311
PYROVEN C.A.—See Pyrotek Incorporated; *U.S. Private*, pg. 3311
QUALITY MILL SUPPLY CO. INC.; *U.S. Private*, pg. 3319
QUEST ENVIRONMENTAL & SAFETY PRODUCTS, INC.; *U.S. Private*, pg. 3325
R3 AWM—See Bunzl plc; *Int'l*, pg. 1217
R3, LLC—See Bunzl plc; *Int'l*, pg. 1217
RADICON TRANSMISSION UK LIMITED—See Elecon Engineering Company Ltd.; *Int'l*, pg. 2348
RAHWAY STEEL DRUM COMPANY, INC.—See Kelso & Company, L.P.; *U.S. Private*, pg. 2278
RAILTECH AUSTRALIA LTD.—See CVC Capital Partners SICAV-FIS S.A.; *Int'l*, pg. 1887
RAK INDUSTRIES INC.; *U.S. Private*, pg. 3349
RAM CONSOLIDATED INDUSTRIES, INC.; *U.S. Private*, pg. 3350
RAMSTROM TRANSMISSION AB—See Addtech AB; *Int'l*, pg. 135
RAM TOOL & SUPPLY CO. INC.; *U.S. Private*, pg. 3351
RA RODRIGUEZ INC.; *U.S. Private*, pg. 3340
RATERMANN MANUFACTURING, INC.; *U.S. Private*, pg. 3357
RAY MURRAY INC.; *U.S. Private*, pg. 3358
RBC AEROSTRUCTURES LLC—See RBC Bearings Incorporated; *U.S. Public*, pg. 1766
R&B COMPANY—See Core & Main, Inc.; *U.S. Public*, pg. 576
RBI BEARING CANADA - CALGARY—See R.B. International Inc.; *U.S. Private*, pg. 3334
RBI BEARING CANADA - TORONTO—See R.B. International Inc.; *U.S. Private*, pg. 3334
REECE SUPPLY COMPANY OF DALLAS; *U.S. Private*, pg. 3381
REECE SUPPLY COMPANY OF HOUSTON—See Reece Supply Company of Dallas; *U.S. Private*, pg. 3381
REECE SUPPLY COMPANY OF SAN ANTONIO—See Reece Supply Company of Dallas; *U.S. Private*, pg. 3381
REEFERTEC PTE LTD—See Eng Kong Holdings Pte Ltd.; *Int'l*, pg. 2426
REGAL INDUSTRIES LLC—See Salem Tools, Inc.; *U.S. Private*, pg. 3531
REIS ENVIRONMENTAL INC.—See Wise El Santo Company Inc.; *U.S. Private*, pg. 4549
RELIABLE BEARING CO. LTD.—See FICODIS Inc.; *Int'l*, pg. 2653
REMCO SUPPLY INC.; *U.S. Private*, pg. 3396
RENGO RIVERWOOD PACKAGING, LTD.—See Graphic Packaging Holding Company; *U.S. Public*, pg. 959
REPLENEX INC.; *U.S. Private*, pg. 3401
REXNORD INTERNATIONAL INC.—See Zurn Elkay Water Solutions Corporation; *U.S. Public*, pg. 2413
RIECHMAN CROSBY HAYS COMPANY, INC.; *U.S. Private*, pg. 3434
RIEGLER & CO. KG—See Brd. Klee A/S; *Int'l*, pg. 1143
RITCHIE ENGINEERING COMPANY; *U.S. Private*, pg. 3441
ROCKET SUPPLY—See Wulco Inc.; *U.S. Private*, pg. 4575
ROCKY MOUNTAIN SUPPLY INC.—See DXP Enterprises, Inc.; *U.S. Public*, pg. 698

RODNEY HUNT-FONTAINE LTD.—See Zurn Elkay Water Solutions Corporation; *U.S. Public*, pg. 2414
ROLLON B.V.—See The Timken Company; *U.S. Public*, pg. 2133
ROLLON GMBH—See The Timken Company; *U.S. Public*, pg. 2133
ROLLON INDIA PVT. LTD.—See The Timken Company; *U.S. Public*, pg. 2133
ROLLON LTD. UK LIMITED—See The Timken Company; *U.S. Public*, pg. 2133
ROLLON S.A.R.L.—See The Timken Company; *U.S. Public*, pg. 2133
ROTARY DIES, S.L.—See MPE Partners, LLC; *U.S. Private*, pg. 2803
ROTOMETRICS AUSTRALIA PTY. LTD.—See MPE Partners, LLC; *U.S. Private*, pg. 2803
ROTOMETRICS CANADA INC.—See MPE Partners, LLC; *U.S. Private*, pg. 2803
ROTOMETRICS CHINA LTD.—See MPE Partners, LLC; *U.S. Private*, pg. 2803
ROTOMETRICS INTERNATIONAL LTD—See MPE Partners, LLC; *U.S. Private*, pg. 2803
ROTOMETRICS ITALIA SRL—See MPE Partners, LLC; *U.S. Private*, pg. 2803
ROTOMETRICS ROTATIONSWERKZEUGE GMBH—See MPE Partners, LLC; *U.S. Private*, pg. 2803
ROTOMETRICS (SE ASIA) CO., LTD.—See MPE Partners, LLC; *U.S. Private*, pg. 2803
ROYAL BRASS INC.; *U.S. Private*, pg. 3491
ROYAL CRESCENT VALLEY, INC.—See Royal Gold, Inc.; *U.S. Public*, pg. 1815
ROYALWOLF TRADING NEW ZEALAND LIMITED—See United Rentals, Inc.; *U.S. Public*, pg. 2235
RR USA INC.; *U.S. Private*, pg. 3496
R.S. HUGHES CO., INC.; *U.S. Private*, pg. 3339
RUBBER & ACCESSORIES, INC.; *U.S. Private*, pg. 3499
RUBBER & SPECIALTIES INC.; *U.S. Private*, pg. 3499
RUSTON INDUSTRIAL SUPPLIES, INC.; *U.S. Private*, pg. 3507
RUTHERFORD EQUIPMENT INC.; *U.S. Private*, pg. 3507
R.V. EVANS COMPANY; *U.S. Private*, pg. 3340
R/W CONNECTION, INC.—See AEA Investors LP; *U.S. Private*, pg. 115
SAARLUX STAHL GMBH & CO. KG—See AG der Dillinger Huttenwerke; *Int'l*, pg. 197
SAFETY SERVICES INCORPORATED; *U.S. Private*, pg. 3525
SAFEWARE INC.; *U.S. Private*, pg. 3525
SALEM TOOLS, INC.; *U.S. Private*, pg. 3531
SALES SYSTEMS LIMITED; *U.S. Private*, pg. 3532
SAW SERVICE OF AMERICA INC.; *U.S. Private*, pg. 3557
SCHERMERHORN BROTHERS CO.; *U.S. Private*, pg. 3564
SD - KOMES, A.S.—See CEZ, a.s.; *Int'l*, pg. 1428
SEABOARD SALES CORP.—See Seaboard Corporation; *U.S. Public*, pg. 1851
SEAL DYNAMICS LLC—See HEICO Corporation; *U.S. Public*, pg. 1021
SEAL DYNAMICS LLC—See HEICO Corporation; *U.S. Public*, pg. 1021
SEMITORR GROUP, INC.—See Wynnchurch Capital, L.P.; *U.S. Private*, pg. 4577
SEMMELMEYER-CORBY COMPANY; *U.S. Private*, pg. 3605
SEPR KERAMIK GMBH & CO KG—See Compagnie de Saint-Gobain SA; *Int'l*, pg. 1728
SEWART SUPPLY INC.; *U.S. Private*, pg. 3619
S&F SUPPLIES INC.; *U.S. Private*, pg. 3513
SHANGHAI DAIWA CAN TRADING COMPANY—See Daiwa Can Company; *Int'l*, pg. 1944
SHENZHEN PYROTEK INC.—See Pyrotek Incorporated; *U.S. Private*, pg. 3311
SHIPPERS SUPPLY COMPANY INC.; *U.S. Private*, pg. 3637
SID TOOL CO., INC.—See MSC Industrial Direct Co., Inc.; *U.S. Public*, pg. 1483
SIGMA HANDELS GMBH—See Trimble, Inc.; *U.S. Public*, pg. 2191
SIGNODE ACME INC.—See Crown Holdings, Inc.; *U.S. Public*, pg. 599
SILGAN DISPENSING SYSTEMS NETHERLANDS B.V.—See Silgan Holdings, Inc.; *U.S. Public*, pg. 1879
SILGAN METAL PACKAGING GERMANY GMBH—See Silgan Holdings, Inc.; *U.S. Public*, pg. 1879
SILGAN WHITE CAP AMERICAS LLC—See Silgan Holdings, Inc.; *U.S. Public*, pg. 1879
SILGAN WHITE CAP ESPANA S.L.—See Silgan Holdings, Inc.; *U.S. Public*, pg. 1879
SKAMOL AMERICAS, INC.—See FSN Capital Partners AS; *Int'l*, pg. 2800
SKAMOL RUS LLC—See FSN Capital Partners AS; *Int'l*, pg. 2800
S.L. FUSCO INC.; *U.S. Private*, pg. 3518
SLS-TECHNACO S.R.O—See Descours & Cabaud SA; *Int'l*, pg. 2044
SMARTZ PTE LTD—See Eng Kong Holdings Pte Ltd.; *Int'l*, pg. 2426
SMITH FASTENER CO., INC.—See Kian Capital Partners, LLC; *U.S. Private*, pg. 2302

423840 — INDUSTRIAL SUPPLIES...

SMITH FASTENER CO., INC.—See Oakland Standard Co., LLC; *U.S. Private*, pg. 2985
SOBRA D.O.O.—See Bischof + Klein GmbH & Co. KG; *Int'l*, pg. 1049
SODENSHA CO., LTD.—See Hanwa Co., Ltd.; *Int'l*, pg. 3263
SONOCO CONTRACT SERVICES S. DE R.L. DE C.V.—See Sonoco Products Company; *U.S. Public*, pg. 1906
SOUND SEAL & PACKING CO.—See Flexaseal Engineered Seals and Systems, LLC; *U.S. Private*, pg. 1543
SOUTH COAST SUPPLY COMPANY; *U.S. Private*, pg. 3721
SOUTHERN CENTRIFUGAL, INC.—See MetalTek International; *U.S. Private*, pg. 2682
SOUTHERN FASTENING SYSTEMS, INC.; *U.S. Private*, pg. 3731
SOUTHERN INDUSTRIAL TECHNOLOGIES INC.—See Bearing Service Company; *U.S. Private*, pg. 506
SOUTHWEST VALVE & EQUIPMENT—See H.I.G. Capital, LLC; *U.S. Private*, pg. 1834
SOVAC GROSSHANDEL UND VERTRETUNGEN IN INDUSTRIEPRODUKTEN GMBH—See Compagnie de Saint-Gobain SA; *Int'l*, pg. 1726
SPARTAN TOOL SUPPLY COMPANY, INC.—See Foundation Investment Partners, LLC; *U.S. Private*, pg. 1580
SPECIALISED WELDING PRODUCTS PTY. LTD.—See Lincoln Electric Holdings, Inc.; *U.S. Public*, pg. 1318
SPECIALITES INDUSTRIELLES HARVEY ULC—See Applied Industrial Technologies, Inc.; *U.S. Public*, pg. 171
SPECIFICATION SEALS, INC.—See The Goldman Sachs Group, Inc.; *U.S. Public*, pg. 2080
SPECTRUM TECHNOLOGIES USA, INC.—See Paragon Energy Solutions, LLC; *U.S. Private*, pg. 3091
SPENCER PRODUCTS CO. INC.—See Tuttle Group Inc.; *U.S. Private*, pg. 4263
S&S SPECIALTY SYSTEMS, LLC—See C. G. Bretting Manufacturing Co., Inc.; *U.S. Private*, pg. 705
STAFAST PRODUCTS INC.; *U.S. Private*, pg. 3774
STANLEY SUPPLY & SERVICES, INC.—See Stanley Black & Decker, Inc.; *U.S. Public*, pg. 1936
STARMER PACKAGING PTY. LTD.—See Bischof + Klein GmbH & Co. KG; *Int'l*, pg. 1049
STEFAN TAGESSON—See Bischof + Klein GmbH & Co. KG; *Int'l*, pg. 1049
STELLAR INDUSTRIAL SUPPLY LLC; *U.S. Private*, pg. 3799
STERLING SEAL & SUPPLY, INC.—See Sterling Consolidated Corp.; *U.S. Public*, pg. 1946
STEWART-HUNT INC.—See AEA Investors LP; *U.S. Private*, pg. 115
STONCOR SOUTH CONE S.A.—See RPM International Inc.; *U.S. Public*, pg. 1819
STRATEGIC DISTRIBUTION SERVICES DE MEXICO, S.A. DE C.V.—See Independence Capital Partners, LLC; *U.S. Private*, pg. 2056
STRATEGIC DISTRIBUTION SERVICES DE MEXICO, S.A. DE C.V.—See Pouschine Cook Capital Management LLC; *U.S. Private*, pg. 3236
SUN CHEMICALS S.A.-PIGMENTS INTERNATIONAL—See DIC Corporation; *Int'l*, pg. 2111
SUPERIOR EAST, INC.—See Superior Products Distributors Inc.; *U.S. Private*, pg. 3880
SUPERIOR SUPPLY & STEEL; *U.S. Private*, pg. 3880
SUPPLY TECHNOLOGIES LLC—See Park-Ohio Holdings Corp.; *U.S. Public*, pg. 1640
SUPPLY TECHNOLOGIES—See Park-Ohio Holdings Corp.; *U.S. Public*, pg. 1640
SUR-SEAL, INC.; *U.S. Private*, pg. 3883
SWANSON-FLOSYSTEMS CO.; *U.S. Private*, pg. 3891
SWISS TOOL SYSTEMS AG—See RBC Bearings Incorporated; *U.S. Public*, pg. 1766
SYDEK HANG FUNG TRADING CO., LTD.—See Hang Fung International Industrial Co., Ltd.; *Int'l*, pg. 3244
T&A INDUSTRIAL LTD; *U.S. Private*, pg. 3909
TAIWAN CHORI MERCHANDISE COOPERATION LTD.—See Chori Co., Ltd.; *Int'l*, pg. 1583
TALLADEGA MACHINERY & SUPPLY CO., INC.; *U.S. Private*, pg. 3926
TDS AUTOMATION, INC.—See Doerfer Corporation; *U.S. Private*, pg. 1253
TEAM-PACK GMBH—See Arla Foods amba; *Int'l*, pg. 573
TEAM TECHNOLOGIES, INC.—See Clearlake Capital Group, L.P.; *U.S. Private*, pg. 937
TECH AIR OF NEW YORK, INC.—See CI Capital Partners LLC; *U.S. Private*, pg. 895
TECH-LONG INC.—See Guangzhou Tech-Long Packaging Machinery Co., Ltd.; *Int'l*, pg. 3168
TECHNICAL PARTS ESTABLISHMENT—See Bhatia Brothers Group; *Int'l*, pg. 1014
TECHNI-TOOL INC.—See Distribution Solutions Group, Inc.; *U.S. Public*, pg. 669
TECH SYN CORPORATION; *U.S. Private*, pg. 3952
TENGCO INC.; *U.S. Private*, pg. 3967
TEXAS RUBBER SUPPLY, INC.—See AEA Investors LP; *U.S. Private*, pg. 115
THB INC.; *U.S. Private*, pg. 3980
THOMAS PIPE & SUPPLY CO.—See Winsupply, Inc.; *U.S. Private*, pg. 4545

THOMPSON INDUSTRIAL SUPPLY INC.; *U.S. Private*, pg. 4160
THRALL ENTERPRISES, INC.; *U.S. Private*, pg. 4163
THUMANN & HEITKAMP HONG KONG LTD.—See Heitkamp & Thumann KG; *Int'l*, pg. 3326
TIEN LEE HONG CO., LTD.—See DIC Corporation; *Int'l*, pg. 2111
TIFCO INDUSTRIES INC.; *U.S. Private*, pg. 4169
TIMBERLINE PLASTICS, INC.; *U.S. Private*, pg. 4172
TIMKEN ESPANA, S.L.—See The Timken Company; *U.S. Public*, pg. 2133
TIMKEN (SHANGHAI) DISTRIBUTION AND SALES CO., LTD.—See The Timken Company; *U.S. Public*, pg. 2133
TITAN FASTENER PRODUCTS, INC.—See Nautic Partners, LLC; *U.S. Private*, pg. 2871
TKD GMBH—See Descours & Cabaud SA; *Int'l*, pg. 2044
TOOL & ABRASIVE SUPPLY, INC.—See DoALL Company; *U.S. Private*, pg. 1250
TOOL SERVICE CORPORATION—See TruArc Partners, L.P.; *U.S. Private*, pg. 4245
TOOL SUPPLY, INC.—See DXP Enterprises, Inc.; *U.S. Public*, pg. 698
TOTAL FILTRATION SERVICES, INC.—See Parker Hannifin Corporation; *U.S. Public*, pg. 1650
TOV GREINER PACKAGING—See Greiner Holding AG; *Int'l*, pg. 3080
TOWER FASTENERS CO., INC.—See MSC Industrial Direct Co., Inc.; *U.S. Public*, pg. 1483
TPC FZE—See Bhatia Brothers Group; *Int'l*, pg. 1014
THE TRACTORS & ENGINEERING CO.—See Chemical Industries Holding Company; *Int'l*, pg. 1462
TRANSMISSION & FLUID EQUIPMENT COMPANY; *U.S. Private*, pg. 4209
TRANSPLY INC.; *U.S. Private*, pg. 4210
TRAVERS TOOL COMPANY INC.; *U.S. Private*, pg. 4214
TRENTON S.P.A.—See FLY Srl; *Int'l*, pg. 2716
TRICO WELDING SUPPLIES, INC.—See BBHC, Inc.; *U.S. Public*, pg. 284
TRIMAN INDUSTRIES, INC.—See AE Industrial Partners, LP; *U.S. Private*, pg. 112
TRIQWORLD GMBH—See Altor Equity Partners AB; *Int'l*, pg. 396
TRIOWORLD LUNDIN AS—See Altor Equity Partners AB; *Int'l*, pg. 396
TRIOWORLD OMBREE D'ANJOU SAS—See Altor Equity Partners AB; *Int'l*, pg. 397
TRIOWORLD OY—See Altor Equity Partners AB; *Int'l*, pg. 397
TRIPLEX INC.; *U.S. Private*, pg. 4238
TROY INDUSTRIAL SOLUTIONS LLC; *U.S. Private*, pg. 4243
TRV INVESTMENTS LLC—See Citigroup Inc.; *U.S. Public*, pg. 504
TRYAD SERVICE CORPORATION—See J.D. Rush Company Inc.; *U.S. Public*, pg. 2161
TUBE CONTROL AB—See Addtech AB; *Int'l*, pg. 135
TUBEX PACKAGING MATERIALS CO. LTD.—See CAG Holding GmbH; *Int'l*, pg. 1251
TURNER INDUSTRIAL SUPPLY CO.; *U.S. Private*, pg. 4260
TURNER SUPPLY COMPANY; *U.S. Private*, pg. 4261
TUTTLE GROUP INC.; *U.S. Private*, pg. 4263
ULTRA SONIC SEAL INC.—See Sonics & Materials, Inc.; *U.S. Private*, pg. 3714
UNICO HABERKORN AG—See Haberkorn Holding AG; *Int'l*, pg. 3202
UNIDEX GROUP INC.; *U.S. Private*, pg. 4282
UNIQUE-INTASCO USA, INC.—See Taglich Private Equity LLC; *U.S. Private*, pg. 3922
UNITED PLUMBING & HEATING SUPPLY CO.; *U.S. Private*, pg. 4295
UNITED TOOL & FASTENER COMPANY; *U.S. Private*, pg. 4301
UNIVERSAL SEWING SUPPLY INC.; *U.S. Private*, pg. 4306
URSA INSULATION, S.A.—See Lone Star Global Acquisitions, LLC; *U.S. Private*, pg. 2489
USA FASTENER GROUP INC—See American Securities LLC; *U.S. Private*, pg. 250
US NITTO; *U.S. Private*, pg. 4319
VAG MIDDLE EAST DMCC—See Aurelius Equity Opportunities SE & Co. KGaA; *Int'l*, pg. 710
VAG VALVES INDIA (PRIVATE) LTD.—See Aurelius Equity Opportunities SE & Co. KGaA; *Int'l*, pg. 710
VAG VALVES USA INC.—See Zurn Elkay Water Solutions Corporation; *U.S. Public*, pg. 2414
VALLEY RUBBER & GASKET CO. INC.—See LKCM Headwater Investments; *U.S. Private*, pg. 2475
VANCE HOLDINGS INC.; *U.S. Private*, pg. 4342
VANN CORPORATION—See Bando Chemical Industries, Ltd.; *Int'l*, pg. 831
VAN SON HOLLAND INK CORPORATION OF AMERICA; *U.S. Private*, pg. 4341
VETERAN LOGISTICS, INC.; *U.S. Private*, pg. 4373
VG EMBALLAGE SAS—See Compagnie de Saint-Gobain SA; *Int'l*, pg. 1733
VICTORY FOAM, INC.; *U.S. Private*, pg. 4378
VICTORY PACKAGING, LP—See WestRock Company; *U.S. Public*, pg. 2362

VIRGINIA-CAROLINA BELTING, INC.—See AEA Investors LP; *U.S. Private*, pg. 115
VISTA PROPPANTS AND LOGISTICS INC.; *U.S. Private*, pg. 4403
VOORHIES SUPPLY COMPANY, LLC—See Genuine Parts Company; *U.S. Public*, pg. 933
VOTO MANUFACTURERS SALES CO. INC.; *U.S. Private*, pg. 4413
VYCMEX MEXICO, S.A. DE C.V.—See Applied Industrial Technologies, Inc.; *U.S. Public*, pg. 170
WABTEC (BEIJING) INVESTMENT CO. LTD.—See Westinghouse Air Brake Technologies Corporation; *U.S. Public*, pg. 2359
WABTEC BRASIL FABRICACAO E MANUTENCAO DE EQUIPAMENTOS LTDA—See Westinghouse Air Brake Technologies Corporation; *U.S. Public*, pg. 2359
WACO ASSOCIATES INC.; *U.S. Private*, pg. 4424
WALTER WOOD SUPPLY CO.; *U.S. Private*, pg. 4434
WEIMER BEARING & TRANSMISSION; *U.S. Private*, pg. 4471
WEINSTOCK BROTHERS CORP.; *U.S. Private*, pg. 4472
W.E JOHNSON EQUIPMENT COMPANY; *U.S. Private*, pg. 4420
WELSCO INC.; *U.S. Private*, pg. 4479
WEST AMERICAN RUBBER CO., LLC; *U.S. Private*, pg. 4483
WESTERN FLUID COMPONENTS, INC.—See Littlejohn & Co., LLC; *U.S. Private*, pg. 2471
WESTFALIA BRASIL COMPONENTES METALICOS LTDA.—See Heitkamp & Thumann KG; *Int'l*, pg. 3326
WESTFALIA, INC.—See Heitkamp & Thumann KG; *Int'l*, pg. 3327
WESTFALIA METAL COMPONENTS INDIA PVT. LTD.—See Heitkamp & Thumann KG; *Int'l*, pg. 3326
WESTFALIA METAL S.R.O.—See Heitkamp & Thumann KG; *Int'l*, pg. 3326
WESTFALIA SHANGHAI TRADING CO. LTD.—See Heitkamp & Thumann KG; *Int'l*, pg. 3327
WEST-HUB BUILDING CORP.—See Crown Packaging International Inc.; *U.S. Private*, pg. 1111
WESTLUND—See Blackfriars Corp.; *U.S. Private*, pg. 575
THE WILLAMETTE VALLEY COMPANY; *U.S. Private*, pg. 4136
THE WILLAMETTE VALLEY COMPANY - SOUTHERN DIVISION LOUISIANA—See The Willamette Valley Company; *U.S. Private*, pg. 4136
WILLGAIN ENTERPRISES, INC.—See Tomar Industries, Inc.; *U.S. Private*, pg. 4183
THE WILLIAMETTE VALLEY COMPANY - SOUTHERN DIVISION GEORGIA—See The Willamette Valley Company; *U.S. Private*, pg. 4136
WILLINGHAM WELDING SOLUTIONS, INC.—See Gas Innovations Inc.; *U.S. Private*, pg. 1647
WIND RIVER HOLDINGS, L.P.; *U.S. Private*, pg. 4536
WINMEGA TECHNOLOGY CORP.—See Acter Co., Ltd.; *Int'l*, pg. 117
THE WINSTON CO.; *U.S. Private*, pg. 4137
WISCONSIN CENTRIFUGAL, INC.—See MetalTek International; *U.S. Private*, pg. 2682
WISE EL SANTO COMPANY INC.; *U.S. Private*, pg. 4549
W. L. GORE & ASSOCIATES (SOUTH AFRICA) (PROPRIETARY) LTD.—See W.L. Gore & Associates, Inc.; *U.S. Private*, pg. 4421
WOLTCOM, INC. - EASTERN DIVISION—See Woltcom, Inc.; *U.S. Private*, pg. 4554
WORLD COOPERAGE COMPANY INC.—See Isco Holding Company Inc.; *U.S. Private*, pg. 2143
WORLD PAC PAPER, LLC; *U.S. Private*, pg. 4566
W. & O. SUPPLY, INC.—See MiddleGround Management, LP; *U.S. Private*, pg. 2712
W.P. & R.S. MARS COMPANY; *U.S. Private*, pg. 4422
WRIDGWAYS AUSTRALIA LIMITED—See EAC Invest AS; *Int'l*, pg. 2262
WRIGHT INDUSTRIES, INC.—See Doerfer Corporation; *U.S. Private*, pg. 1253
WULCO INC.; *U.S. Private*, pg. 4575
W.W. GRAINGER, INC.; *U.S. Public*, pg. 2319
WYATT SEAL INC.; *U.S. Private*, pg. 4575
YEAGER SUPPLY, INC.; *U.S. Private*, pg. 4587
ZEAL INTERNATIONAL CO., LTD.—See Eson Precision Ind. Co., Ltd.; *Int'l*, pg. 2504
ZEPF TECHNOLOGIES—See Barry-Wehmiller Companies, Inc.; *U.S. Private*, pg. 482
ZHENJIANG ZHONG CHUAN HITACHI ZOSEN MACHINERY CO., LTD—See Hitachi Zosen Corporation; *Int'l*, pg. 3412
ZHONGBAN TRADING (SHANGHAI) CO., LTD.—See Cominix Co., Ltd.; *Int'l*, pg. 1714
ZIEGLER BOLT & PARTS CO.; *U.S. Private*, pg. 4603
ZIEGLER TOOLS INC.—See MSCO Inc.; *U.S. Private*, pg. 2806
ZUCKERMAN-HONICKMAN INC.; *U.S. Private*, pg. 4609

423850 — SERVICE ESTABLISHMENT EQUIPMENT AND SUPPLIES MERCHANT WHOLESALERS

N.A.I.C.S. INDEX

423850 — SERVICE ESTABLISHME...

3WIRE GROUP INC.—See Berkshire Hathaway Inc.; *U.S. Public*, pg. 308
5 ALARM FIRE & SAFETY EQUIPMENT, LLC—See Rotunda Capital Partners LLC; *U.S. Private*, pg. 3488
A-1 CHEMICAL, INC.—See Inland Supply Co.; Inc.; *U.S. Private*, pg. 2079
ABLE PROFIT (HONG KONG) LIMITED—See Grand Peace Group Holdings Limited; *Int'l*, pg. 3056
ACCOMMODATION MOLLEN, INC.—See Bain Capital, LP; *U.S. Private*, pg. 440
ACE JANITORIAL SUPPLY CO., INC.—See Creative Technologies Corp.; *U.S. Private*, pg. 1090
ACE-TEX ENTERPRISES INC.—See Crown Capital Investments LLC; *U.S. Private*, pg. 1110
ADB INTERESTS, LLC; *U.S. Private*, pg. 76
AEGIS FIRE PROTECTION SYSTEMS, LLC.; *U.S. Private*, pg. 116
AERIAL COMPANY INC.—See Sally Beauty Holdings, Inc.; *U.S. Public*, pg. 1838
AGGORA LIMITED—See Bunzl plc; *Int'l*, pg. 1217
ALLEN ENTERPRISES, INC.; *U.S. Private*, pg. 178
ALLEN EQUIPMENT, INC.—See American Securities LLC; *U.S. Private*, pg. 247
ALLEN EQUIPMENT, INC.—See Cleaners Closet Inc.; *U.S. Private*, pg. 931
ALLSTON SUPPLY CO., INC.—See Bain Capital, LP; *U.S. Private*, pg. 440
ALPES ENTRETIEN DISTRIBUTION SAS—See Bunzl plc; *Int'l*, pg. 1217
ALVF, INC.—See EVI Industries, Inc.; *U.S. Public*, pg. 803
ART OF BUSINESS, INC.; *U.S. Private*, pg. 340
ASSOCIATED PAPER INC.; *U.S. Private*, pg. 356
ATLANTA FIXTURE & SALES COMPANY INC.—See Sysco Corporation; *U.S. Public*, pg. 1973
ATLANTIC AMERICAN FIRE EQUIPMENT COMPANY INC.; *U.S. Private*, pg. 371
AUTOMATIC PRODUCTS INTERNATIONAL LTD.—See Crane NXT, Co.; *U.S. Public*, pg. 591
BARING INDUSTRIES, INC.—See Duray/J.F. Duncan Industries, Inc.; *U.S. Private*, pg. 1293
BATESVILLE CANADA LTD.—See Hillenbrand, Inc.; *U.S. Public*, pg. 1035
B&B EQUIPMENT & SUPPLY COMPANY INC.—See Begley Company; *U.S. Private*, pg. 514
BEE SALES COMPANY; *U.S. Private*, pg. 513
BERGHOEF GMBH—See Mohawk Industries, Inc.; *U.S. Public*, pg. 1457
BERGHOEF-HOUT B.V.—See Mohawk Industries, Inc.; *U.S. Public*, pg. 1457
BERMIL INDUSTRIES CORP.; *U.S. Private*, pg. 535
BIZERBA CANADA INC.; *Int'l*, pg. 1053
BLANC SAS—See Bunzl plc; *Int'l*, pg. 1217
BLUE RIDGE RESCUE SUPPLIERS, INC.—See Platte River Ventures, LLC; *U.S. Private*, pg. 3211
BORTEK INDUSTRIES INC.; *U.S. Private*, pg. 619
BOSTON IRRIGATION SUPPLY CO; *U.S. Private*, pg. 621
BOURGOGNE HYGIENE ENTRETIEN SAS—See Bunzl plc; *Int'l*, pg. 1217
BRADY DISTRIBUTING COMPANY INC.; *U.S. Private*, pg. 633
BRELIAN, INC.; *U.S. Private*, pg. 644
BRIDGEPOINT SYSTEMS; *U.S. Private*, pg. 649
BUNZL CATERING SUPPLIES LIMITED—See Bunzl plc; *Int'l*, pg. 1217
BUNZL HIGIENE E LIMPEZA LTDA.—See Bunzl plc; *Int'l*, pg. 1217
BUNZL IRELAND LIMITED—See Bunzl plc; *Int'l*, pg. 1217
BUNZL MAGYARORSZAG KFT—See Bunzl plc; *Int'l*, pg. 1217
BUNZL VERPACKUNGEN GMBH—See Bunzl plc; *Int'l*, pg. 1218
BURMAX COMPANY INC.; *U.S. Private*, pg. 689
BUSINESS DEVELOPMENT SALES; *U.S. Private*, pg. 694
CALE AUSTRALIA PTY. LTD.—See Astorg Partners S.A.S.; *Int'l*, pg. 656
CALE PARKING IBERICA SL—See Astorg Partners S.A.S.; *Int'l*, pg. 656
CANTWELL-CLEARY CO., INC.; *U.S. Private*, pg. 736
CANWEST CRANE & EQUIPMENT LTD.—See Hyduke Energy Services Inc.; *Int'l*, pg. 3548
CAR KLEEN NEW ZEALAND LTD.; *Int'l*, pg. 1319
CASCO INDUSTRIES INC.; *U.S. Private*, pg. 781
CATEQUIP S.A.—See Berkshire Hathaway Inc.; *U.S. Public*, pg. 310
CENTRAL SANITARY SUPPLY COMPANY—See Kelso & Company, L.P.; *U.S. Private*, pg. 2279
CHAPMAN PROPERTIES; *U.S. Private*, pg. 850
CHESHER EQUIPMENT LTD.; *Int'l*, pg. 1472
CLARK SECURITY PRODUCTS, INC.—See WESCO International, Inc.; *U.S. Public*, pg. 2351
CLEAN CARE A/S—See Bunzl plc; *Int'l*, pg. 1218
CLEVELAND COIN MACHINE EXCHANGE, INC.; *U.S. Private*, pg. 940
COMMERCIAL LAUNDRY EQUIPMENT COMPANY, LLC—See EVI Industries, Inc.; *U.S. Public*, pg. 803
COMPTOIR DE BRETAGNE SAS—See Bunzl plc; *Int'l*, pg. 1218
CONSOLIDATED LAUNDRY EQUIPMENT, INC.—See EVI Industries, Inc.; *U.S. Public*, pg. 803
CONTEC INC.; *U.S. Private*, pg. 1027
CONTINENTAL CHEF SUPPLIES LIMITED—See Bunzl plc; *Int'l*, pg. 1218
COSGROVE ENTERPRISES INC.—See Bain Capital, LP; *U.S. Private*, pg. 440
CP RETAILINK CO., LTD.—See C.P. All Public Company Limited; *Int'l*, pg. 1243
CS LAUNDRY SYSTEM SDN. BHD.—See BCM Alliance Berhad; *Int'l*, pg. 928
CWPS ONLINE; *U.S. Private*, pg. 1132
DAYCON PRODUCTS COMPANY, INC.; *U.S. Private*, pg. 1177
DAYCON PRODUCTS COMPANY, INC.—See Daycon Products Company, Inc.; *U.S. Private*, pg. 1177
DAYCON—See Daycon Products Company, Inc.; *U.S. Private*, pg. 1177
DIRECT MACHINERY SALES CORP.—See Laundrylux Inc.; *U.S. Private*, pg. 2398
DISTRIMONDO AG—See Bunzl plc; *Int'l*, pg. 1218
DYNAMIC LAUNDRY SYSTEMS, INC.—See BDT Capital Partners, LLC; *U.S. Private*, pg. 502
EDMAR CLEANING CORP.; *U.S. Private*, pg. 1337
E.J. THOMAS COMPANY; *U.S. Private*, pg. 1306
ELECTROLUX PROFESSIONAL AB; *Int'l*, pg. 2353
ELECTROLUX PROFESSIONAL AG—See Electrolux Professional AB; *Int'l*, pg. 2353
ENVIRONMENTAL SERVICES SPECIALISTS; *U.S. Private*, pg. 1408
ENVOY SOLUTIONS LLC—See Kelso & Company, L.P.; *U.S. Private*, pg. 2279
ENVOY SOLUTIONS LLC—See Warburg Pincus LLC; *U.S. Private*, pg. 4436
FABRICLEAN SUPPLY, INC.; *U.S. Private*, pg. 1459
FAMECCANICA DATA S.P.A.—See Angelini ACRAF S.p.A.; *Int'l*, pg. 460
FAMECCANICA DATA S.P.A.—See The Procter & Gamble Company; *U.S. Public*, pg. 2120
FICHOT HYGIENE SAS—See Bunzl plc; *Int'l*, pg. 1218
FINLEY FIRE EQUIPMENT CO.; *U.S. Private*, pg. 1510
FIREGUARD, INC.; *U.S. Private*, pg. 1511
FIRETRADE ENGINEERING PCL; *Int'l*, pg. 2679
FISHMAN SUPPLY INC.; *U.S. Private*, pg. 1535
FLORIDA COMMERCIAL LAUNDRY SYSTEMS, INC.; *U.S. Private*, pg. 1547
FOCUS PACKAGING & SUPPLY CO.—See Bain Capital, LP; *U.S. Private*, pg. 440
FOMA NORGE AS—See Tennant Company; *U.S. Public*, pg. 2016
FOUR STAR SALON SERVICES INC.; *U.S. Private*, pg. 1582
FRANCE SECURITE SAS—See Bunzl plc; *Int'l*, pg. 1218
FRANZ JANITORIAL SERVICE & SUPPLY, INC.—See Bain Capital, LP; *U.S. Private*, pg. 440
FREUDENBERG HAZTARTASI CIKKEK KERESKEDELMI BT—See Freudenberg SE; *Int'l*, pg. 2786
GATHR OUTDOORS—See Centre Partners Management LLC; *U.S. Private*, pg. 828
GEKAY SALES & SERVICE CO. INC.; *U.S. Private*, pg. 1656
GILBARCO ACIS KFT.—See Vontier Corporation; *U.S. Public*, pg. 2308
GILBARCO ACIS SRL—See Vontier Corporation; *U.S. Public*, pg. 2308
GLENDALE PLUMBING & FIRE SUPPLY, INC.; *U.S. Private*, pg. 1710
GLORY USA, INC.—See GLORY Ltd.; *Int'l*, pg. 3010
GM EQUIPEMENT S.A.S.—See Bunzl plc; *Int'l*, pg. 1218
GORM, INC.—See Kelso & Company, L.P.; *U.S. Private*, pg. 2279
GORM, INC.—See Warburg Pincus LLC; *U.S. Private*, pg. 4437
GUYSON CN—See Guyson International Limited; *Int'l*, pg. 3189
HALL-MARK FIRE APPARATUS, INC.—See AIP, LLC; *U.S. Private*, pg. 135
HALL-MARK FIRE APPARATUS - TEXAS, LLC—See AIP, LLC; *U.S. Private*, pg. 135
HANGZHOU CHUHUAN SCIENCE & TECHNOLOGY COMPANY LIMITED; *Int'l*, pg. 3246
HENDRIX HOTEL & RESTAURANT EQUIPMENT & SUPPLIES LTD.—See Blue Point Capital Partners, LLC; *U.S. Private*, pg. 590
HENDRIX LONDON—See Blue Point Capital Partners, LLC; *U.S. Private*, pg. 590
HESCO INC.; *U.S. Private*, pg. 1927
HILL & FOSS, INC.—See Berkshire Partners LLC; *U.S. Private*, pg. 535
HILTON SUPPLY MANAGEMENT LLC—See Hilton Worldwide Holdings, Inc.; *U.S. Public*, pg. 1041
HOLCHEM LABORATORIES LIMITED—See Ecolab Inc.; *U.S. Public*, pg. 714
HP PRODUCTS CORPORATION; *U.S. Private*, pg. 1996
HUGHES ENTERPRISES INC.; *U.S. Private*, pg. 2003
IDN-ACME INC.—See IDN Inc.; *U.S. Private*, pg. 2038
IDN-H.HOFFMAN INC.; *U.S. Private*, pg. 2038
IDN INC.; *U.S. Private*, pg. 2038
IMPERIAL IRRIGATION SUPPLY, INC.; *U.S. Private*, pg. 2049
INDUSTRIAL PRODUCTS ENTERPISES LLC; *U.S. Private*, pg. 2068
INLAND SUPPLY CO., INC.; *U.S. Private*, pg. 2079
INTERCLEAN ASSISTANCE ICA S.A.—See Tennant Company; *U.S. Public*, pg. 2016
INTERSPIRO INC.; *U.S. Private*, pg. 2123
IPC EAGLE CORPORATION—See Tennant Company; *U.S. Public*, pg. 2016
IP CLEANING S.R.L.—See Tennant Company; *U.S. Public*, pg. 2016
ISTANBUL TICARET HIRDAVAT SANAYI A.S.—See Bunzl plc; *Int'l*, pg. 1218
ISTANBUL TICARET IS GUVENLIGI VE ENDUSTRIYEL SANAYI URUNLER A.S.—See Bunzl plc; *Int'l*, pg. 1218
JD BEAUTY CO., LLC—See ACON Investments, LLC; *U.S. Private*, pg. 62
JEMI INC.; *U.S. Private*, pg. 2199
JET TRADING CO., LTD.—See Ashimori Industry Co., Ltd.; *Int'l*, pg. 607
JOHNSTON NORTH AMERICA INC—See Bucher Industries AG; *Int'l*, pg. 1208
JON-DON, LLC—See Incline MGMT Corp.; *U.S. Private*, pg. 2053
JT PACKARD & ASSOCIATES, INC.—See ABB Ltd.; *Int'l*, pg. 52
KANNEGIESSER BENELUX B.V.—See Hebert Kannegiesser GmbH; *Int'l*, pg. 3306
KANNEGIESSER ESPANA, S.L.—See Hebert Kannegiesser GmbH; *Int'l*, pg. 3306
KANNEGIESSER ETECH, INC.—See Hebert Kannegiesser GmbH; *Int'l*, pg. 3306
KANNEGIESSER FRANCE S.A.—See Hebert Kannegiesser GmbH; *Int'l*, pg. 3306
KANNEGIESSER UK LTD.—See Hebert Kannegiesser GmbH; *Int'l*, pg. 3306
KATZSON BROS, INC.; *U.S. Private*, pg. 2265
KENWAY DISTRIBUTORS INC.; *U.S. Private*, pg. 2289
KOFFLER SALES, LLC; *U.S. Private*, pg. 2337
KULLANATMARKET ELEKTRONIK PAZARLAMA TICARET ANONIM SIRKETI—See Bunzl plc; *Int'l*, pg. 1218
LAGASSE, INC.—See Sycamore Partners Management, LP; *U.S. Private*, pg. 3897
LAUNDRY PRO OF FLORIDA, INC.—See EVI Industries, Inc.; *U.S. Public*, pg. 803
LAUN-DRY SUPPLY COMPANY INC.; *U.S. Private*, pg. 2398
L. FISHMAN & SON INC.; *U.S. Private*, pg. 2364
LIEBERMAN COMPANIES, INC.—See American Vending Sales, Inc.; *U.S. Private*, pg. 258
LIGNE T SAS—See Bunzl plc; *Int'l*, pg. 1218
L.N. CURTIS & SONS - NORTHWEST DIVISION—See L.N. Curtis & Sons; *U.S. Private*, pg. 2366
L.N. CURTIS & SONS; *U.S. Private*, pg. 2366
LOCKHART CATERING EQUIPMENT LIMITED—See Bunzl plc; *Int'l*, pg. 1219
MAINTENANCE SOLUTIONS INC.; *U.S. Private*, pg. 2554
MAINTENANCE SUPPLY COMPANY INC.; *U.S. Private*, pg. 2554
MAINTENANCE SUPPLY HEADQUARTERS, LP—See Lowe's Companies, Inc.; *U.S. Public*, pg. 1343
MARSHALL SUPPLY CO.; *U.S. Private*, pg. 2593
MARTIN-RAY LAUNDRY SYSTEMS, INC.—See EVI Industries, Inc.; *U.S. Public*, pg. 803
MATTHEWS INTERNATIONAL CORP. - CASKET DIVISION DISTRIBUTION CENTER—See Matthews International Corporation; *U.S. Public*, pg. 1400
MELTON COMPANY, INC.—See Matthews International Corporation; *U.S. Public*, pg. 1400
MERMAID MARITIME VIETNAM COMPANY LTD.—See Erria A/S; *Int'l*, pg. 2497
MIKARA CORPORATION; *U.S. Private*, pg. 2724
MILE HI FROZEN FOODS CO.; *U.S. Private*, pg. 2727
THE MINNESOTA CHEMICAL COMPANY; *U.S. Private*, pg. 4080
MULTILINE A/S—See Bunzl plc; *Int'l*, pg. 1219
NATIONAL SALON RESOURCES—See Mikara Corporation; *U.S. Private*, pg. 2724
NEILL CORPORATION; *U.S. Private*, pg. 2882
NEW JIGU TRADING CORP.; *U.S. Private*, pg. 2898
NEW MOTION LIMITED—See Bucher Industries AG; *Int'l*, pg. 1208
NORMSTAHL GMBH—See ASSA ABLOY AB; *Int'l*, pg. 640
NORTH AMERICA FIRE EQUIPMENT COMPANY; *U.S. Private*, pg. 2939
NOVA SALON SYSTEMS; *U.S. Private*, pg. 2966
N.S. FARRINGTON CO.; *U.S. Private*, pg. 2828
O'HANRAHAN CONSULTANTS, INC.—See Washworld, Inc.; *U.S. Private*, pg. 4450
OMNI FACILITY SERVICES—See Omni Facility Services, Inc.; *U.S. Private*, pg. 3016
PACIFIC SALON SYSTEMS INC.—See Sally Beauty Holdings, Inc.; *U.S. Public*, pg. 1839
P.B. GAST & SONS INCORPORATED; *U.S. Private*, pg. 3060
PEEL'S BEAUTY SUPPLY INC.; *U.S. Private*, pg. 3128
PHENIX SUPPLY COMPANY INC.; *U.S. Private*, pg. 3167

423850 — SERVICE ESTABLISHME...

PHILIP ROSENAU CO., INC.—See Bain Capital, LP; *U.S. Private*, pg. 440
PHILLIPS SUPPLY CO. INC.; *U.S. Private*, pg. 3171
PIONEER MANUFACTURING COMPANY; *U.S. Private*, pg. 3187
PREMIER BEAUTY SUPPLY INC.; *U.S. Private*, pg. 3249
PREMIUM INC.; *U.S. Private*, pg. 3251
PROCTER & GAMBLE SERVICES COMPANY N.V.—See The Procter & Gamble Company; *U.S. Public*, pg. 2122
PROCTER & GAMBLE SOUTH AMERICA HOLDING B.V.—See The Procter & Gamble Company; *U.S. Public*, pg. 2123
PRODIM SAS—See Carrefour SA; *Int'l*, pg. 1346
PWS INC.—See BDT Capital Partners, LLC; *U.S. Private*, pg. 502
QUEEN CITY FIRE EQUIPMENT, INC.—See TruArc Partners, L.P.; *U.S. Private*, pg. 4244
RAYO WHOLESALE INC.; *U.S. Private*, pg. 3359
RELIABLE OIL EQUIPMENT INC.; *U.S. Private*, pg. 3394
RESTOCKIT.COM; *U.S. Private*, pg. 3409
REWARD SUPPLY CO. PTY. LTD.—See Groupe BPCE; *Int'l*, pg. 3095
RIDE ENTERTAINMENT SYSTEMS, INC.; *U.S. Private*, pg. 3432
R.L. WILLIAMS COMPANY; *U.S. Private*, pg. 3338
ROOSTER ESSENTIALS APP SPV, LLC—See APPLife Digital Solutions, Inc.; *U.S. Public*, pg. 173
SAEBE COMPAGNIET APS—See Bunzl plc; *Int'l*, pg. 1219
SALLY BEAUTY HOLDINGS, INC.; *U.S. Public*, pg. 1838
SALON INNOVATIONS INC.; *U.S. Private*, pg. 3533
SERVICE DIRECTION INC.; *U.S. Private*, pg. 3615
SERVICIOS MULTIVENDING LTDA.—See Embotelladora Andina S.A.; *Int'l*, pg. 2375
SHAFFER DISTRIBUTING COMPANY; *U.S. Private*, pg. 3623
SHANGHAI COSAFETY TECHNOLOGY CO., LTD.—See Bunzl plc; *Int'l*, pg. 1219
SKIEN STORKJOKKEN AS—See Bunzl plc; *Int'l*, pg. 1219
SKYLINE EQUIPMENT, LLC—See EVI Industries, Inc.; *U.S. Public*, pg. 803
SML CANADA ACQUISITION CORP.—See Steven Madden, Ltd.; *U.S. Public*, pg. 1947
SOLSBURY HILL LLC; *U.S. Private*, pg. 3710
SOUTHEASTERN SALON SUPPLIERS, INC.; *U.S. Private*, pg. 3729
SOUTHERN BEAUTY ENTERPRISES—See Beauty Enterprises Inc.; *U.S. Private*, pg. 509
SOUTHERN LOCK & SUPPLY CO.; *U.S. Private*, pg. 3732
S&S BEAUTY SUPPLIES INCORPORATED; *U.S. Private*, pg. 3513
STADTRAUM SYSTEMS SP.Z O.O—See Astorg Partners S.A.S.; *Int'l*, pg. 657
STANDARD COMPANIES INC.; *U.S. Private*, pg. 3778
STEINER-ATLANTIC CORP—See EVI Industries, Inc.; *U.S. Public*, pg. 803
STRATEGIC EQUIPMENT & SUPPLY CORP.—See Warburg Pincus LLC; *U.S. Private*, pg. 4440
SUN SUN TRADING CO. INC.; *U.S. Private*, pg. 3864
SUPERIOR HOLDING CORP.; *U.S. Private*, pg. 3878
SUPPLY PRO INC.—See Bunzl plc; *Int'l*, pg. 1218
SUPPLYWORKS—See The Home Depot, Inc.; *U.S. Public*, pg. 2089
TENNANT EUROPE B.V.—See Tennant Company; *U.S. Public*, pg. 2016
TENNANT SALES AND SERVICE COMPANY—See Tennant Company; *U.S. Public*, pg. 2016
TEPE SANITARY SUPPLY, INC.—See Bain Capital, LP; *U.S. Private*, pg. 441
THORNE ELECTRIC COMPANY; *U.S. Private*, pg. 4162
TINGUE, BROWN & CO.; *U.S. Private*, pg. 4173
TRI-STATE TECHNICAL SERVICES, INC.—See EVI Industries, Inc.; *U.S. Public*, pg. 803
TWEEZERMAN INTERNATIONAL—See Henkel AG & Co. KGaA; *Int'l*, pg. 3354
UNITED FABRICARE SUPPLY INC.; *U.S. Private*, pg. 4291
VALUTEC AB—See Addtech AB; *Int'l*, pg. 135
VALUTEC OY—See Addtech AB; *Int'l*, pg. 135
VAN DYKE SUPPLY CO., INC.—See Gridiron Capital, LLC; *U.S. Private*, pg. 1786
VON SCHRADER COMPANY; *U.S. Private*, pg. 4412
WAGNER SUPPLY CO, INC.—See Bain Capital, LP; *U.S. Private*, pg. 441
WALLIS ENERGY CO. INC.—See Wallis Companies, Inc.; *U.S. Private*, pg. 4431
WALTER E. NELSON CO.; *U.S. Private*, pg. 4433
WASHING EQUIPMENT OF TEXAS; *U.S. Private*, pg. 4445
WASHING EQUIPMENT TECHNOLOGIES, INC.—See Simoniz USA, Inc.; *U.S. Private*, pg. 3666
WASHINGTON AUTOMATED, LLC—See EVI Industries, Inc.; *U.S. Public*, pg. 803
WASHWORLD, INC.; *U.S. Private*, pg. 4450
WASSERSTROM COMPANY; *U.S. Private*, pg. 4450
WEITA AG—See Bunzl plc; *Int'l*, pg. 1220
WESTERN STATE DESIGN INC.—See EVI Industries, Inc.; *U.S. Public*, pg. 803
WEST FLORIDA SUPPLY, CO.—See City Maintenance Supply; *U.S. Private*, pg. 906
WGS AG—See Bunzl plc; *Int'l*, pg. 1220

WHOLESALE COMMERCIAL LAUNDRY EQUIPMENT SE, LLC—See EVI Industries, Inc.; *U.S. Public*, pg. 803
WILDMAN BUSINESS GROUP INC.; *U.S. Private*, pg. 4519
WILLIAMSPORT BARBER AND BEAUTY CORP.—See The Stephan Company; *U.S. Public*, pg. 2132
W. L. GORE & ASSOCIATES DO BRASIL LTDA.—See W.L. Gore & Associates, Inc.; *U.S. Private*, pg. 4421
WORLDWIDE LAUNDRY, INC.—See EVI Industries, Inc.; *U.S. Public*, pg. 803
WYK SORBENTS, LLC; *U.S. Private*, pg. 4576
XYLEM ANALYTICS AUSTRALIA PTY LIMITED—See Xylem Inc.; *U.S. Public*, pg. 2395
YANKEE EQUIPMENT SYSTEMS, INC.—See EVI Industries, Inc.; *U.S. Public*, pg. 803

423860 — TRANSPORTATION EQUIPMENT AND SUPPLIES (EXCEPT MOTOR VEHICLE) MERCHANT WHOLESALERS

A2C AIR COST CONTROL SAS—See HEICO Corporation; *U.S. Public*, pg. 1019
A2Z SMART TECHNOLOGIES CORP.; *Int'l*, pg. 30
AAR AIRCRAFT TURBINE CENTER—See AAR Corp.; *U.S. Public*, pg. 13
AAR DEFENSE SYSTEMS & LOGISTICS—See AAR Corp.; *U.S. Public*, pg. 13
AAR LANDING GEAR LLC—See AAR Corp.; *U.S. Public*, pg. 13
AAR SUPPLY CHAIN, INC.—See AAR Corp.; *U.S. Public*, pg. 13
ADMIRAL MARINE CONTINENTAL SUPPLIES BV—See Admiral Marine Supplies Limited; *Int'l*, pg. 152
ADMIRAL MARINE SERVICES PVT LTD—See Admiral Marine Supplies Limited; *Int'l*, pg. 152
ADMIRAL MARINE SUPPLIES LIMITED; *Int'l*, pg. 151
ADMIRAL MARINE SUPPLIES LTD—See Admiral Marine Supplies Limited; *Int'l*, pg. 152
ADMIRAL MARINE SUPPLIES LTD—See Admiral Marine Supplies Limited; *Int'l*, pg. 152
ADMIRAL MARINE SUPPLIES PTE LTD—See Admiral Marine Supplies Limited; *Int'l*, pg. 152
AE MATERIALS GROUP, INC. - FLORIDA—See AE Industrial Partners, LP; *U.S. Private*, pg. 111
AERCAP HOLDINGS N.V.; *Int'l*, pg. 179
AEROKLAS MALAYSIA SDN. BHD.—See Eastern Polymer Group Public Company Limited; *Int'l*, pg. 2273
AEROSPACE DISTRIBUTORS INC.; *U.S. Private*, pg. 119
AEROSPACE DISTRIBUTORS PTE LTD—See Aerospace Distributors Inc.; *U.S. Private*, pg. 119
AEROSPACE PRODUCTS INTERNATIONAL, INC. - ASIA PACIFIC—See Resilience Capital Partners, LLC; *U.S. Private*, pg. 3405
AEROSPACE PRODUCTS INTERNATIONAL, INC. - CANADA—See Resilience Capital Partners, LLC; *U.S. Private*, pg. 3405
AEROSPACE PRODUCTS INTERNATIONAL, INC.—See Resilience Capital Partners, LLC; *U.S. Private*, pg. 3405
AEROTECH WORLD TRADE CORP.; *U.S. Private*, pg. 120
AEROTECH WORLD TRADE LTD.—See Aerotech World Trade Corp.; *U.S. Private*, pg. 120
AIDC USA LLC—See Aerospace Industrial Development Corporation; *Int'l*, pg. 181
AIRBUS MILITARY NORTH AMERICA—See Airbus SE; *Int'l*, pg. 244
AIR COST CONTROL GERMANY GMBH—See HEICO Corporation; *U.S. Public*, pg. 1019
AIRCRAFT INSTRUMENT & RADIO CO.; *U.S. Private*, pg. 140
AIRCRAFT SPRUCE & SPECIALTY CO.—See Irwin International, Inc.; *U.S. Private*, pg. 2142
AIRPARTS COMPANY INC.; *U.S. Private*, pg. 142
AIR POWER INC.—See Van Bortel Aircraft Inc.; *U.S. Private*, pg. 4339
AIRSPARES—See Airbus SE; *Int'l*, pg. 244
AIR TECHNOLOGY ENGINES, INC.; *U.S. Private*, pg. 140
A&K RAILROAD MATERIALS INC.; *U.S. Private*, pg. 20
ALEXANDER/RYAN MARINE & SAFETY CO.; *U.S. Private*, pg. 164
ALIGN AEROSPACE FRANCE SAS—See AVIC International Holdings Limited; *Int'l*, pg. 742
ALIGN AEROSPACE LLC—See AVIC International Holdings Limited; *Int'l*, pg. 742
ALLEGHENY RAIL PRODUCTS—See L.B. Foster Company; *U.S. Public*, pg. 1278
ALLIED INTERNATIONAL CORP.; *U.S. Private*, pg. 186
ALSTOM INVESTMENT COMPANY LIMITED—See Alstom S.A.; *Int'l*, pg. 379
ALSTOM KHADAMAT S.A.—See Alstom S.A.; *Int'l*, pg. 379
ALSTOM KOREA TRANSPORT LTD.—See Alstom S.A.; *Int'l*, pg. 379
ALSTOM SCHIENENFAHRZEUGE AG—See Alstom S.A.; *Int'l*, pg. 379
ALSTOM TRANSPORT AUSTRALIA PTY LIMITED—See Alstom S.A.; *Int'l*, pg. 379
ALSTOM TRANSPORT AZERBAIJAN LLC—See Alstom S.A.; *Int'l*, pg. 380

ALSTOM TRANSPORT CANADA INC.—See Alstom S.A.; *Int'l*, pg. 380
ALSTOM TRANSPORT HUNGARY ZRT.—See Alstom S.A.; *Int'l*, pg. 380
ALSTOM TRANSPORT INDIA LIMITED—See Alstom S.A.; *Int'l*, pg. 380
ALSTOM TRANSPORT NORWAY AS—See Alstom S.A.; *Int'l*, pg. 380
ALSTOM TRANSPORT (THAILAND) CO., LTD.—See Alstom S.A.; *Int'l*, pg. 379
ALSTOM TRANSPORT VIETNAM LTD.—See Alstom S.A.; *Int'l*, pg. 380
ALSTOM ULASIM ANONIM SIRKETI ANKARA SUBESI—See Alstom S.A.; *Int'l*, pg. 380
AMACPI CORP.; *U.S. Private*, pg. 215
AMERICAN GENERAL SUPPLIES, INC.; *U.S. Private*, pg. 235
AMSTED RAIL COMPANY, INC.—See AMSTED Industries Incorporated; *U.S. Private*, pg. 267
ANHUI GREAT WALL MILITARY INDUSTRY CO., LTD.; *Int'l*, pg. 467
APOLLO AEROSPACE COMPONENTS INDIA PRIVATE LIMITED—See Park-Ohio Holdings Corp.; *U.S. Public*, pg. 1638
APOLLO AEROSPACE COMPONENTS SP.Z.O.O.—See Park-Ohio Holdings Corp.; *U.S. Public*, pg. 1638
APPROACH SIGNS LIMITED—See Fletcher Building Limited; *Int'l*, pg. 2699
ASKARI ENTERPRISES PVT LTD—See Army Welfare Trust LLC; *Int'l*, pg. 575
A-SONIC AVIATION SOLUTIONS PTE LTD—See A-Sonic Aerospace Limited; *Int'l*, pg. 20
ATF AEROSPACE LLC—See ATF, Inc.; *U.S. Private*, pg. 367
ATLANTIC TRACK & TURNOUT CO.; *U.S. Private*, pg. 375
AUSTAL MUSCAT LLC—See Austal Limited; *Int'l*, pg. 716
AUSTAL USA LLC—See Austal Limited; *Int'l*, pg. 716
AUSTAL VIET NAM CO., LTD.—See Austal Limited; *Int'l*, pg. 716
AVANT AEROSPACE, LLC—See The Sterling Group, L.P.; *U.S. Private*, pg. 4123
AVIATECH CORPORATION; *U.S. Private*, pg. 406
AVIATION LABORATORIES, INC.; *U.S. Private*, pg. 406
AVIATION MINING SOLUTIONS, INC.; *U.S. Private*, pg. 406
AVIATION SPARES & SERVICES INTERNATIONAL CO.; *U.S. Private*, pg. 406
AVIC INTERNATIONAL OFFSHORE (XIAMEN) CO., LTD.—See China Merchants Group Limited; *Int'l*, pg. 1520
AVIC INTERNATIONAL SHIP DEVELOPMENT (CHINA) CO., LTD.—See China Merchants Group Limited; *Int'l*, pg. 1520
AVIO-DIEPEN B.V.—See Kirkhill Aircraft Parts Co.; *U.S. Private*, pg. 2314
AVIO-DIEPEN INC.—See Kirkhill Aircraft Parts Co.; *U.S. Private*, pg. 2314
AVMAX SPARES EAST AFRICA LIMITED—See Avmax Group Inc.; *Int'l*, pg. 748
BAI, INC.; *U.S. Private*, pg. 425
BAS PART SALES LLC; *U.S. Private*, pg. 484
BAY ASSOCIATES INC.; *U.S. Private*, pg. 492
BEIJING GEISMAR RAILWAYS EQUIPMENT TRADING CO., LTD.—See Geismar S.A.; *Int'l*, pg. 2912
BEIJING ORIENTAL JICHENG CO.,LTD; *Int'l*, pg. 954
BEIJING WABTEC HUAXIA TECHNOLOGY COMPANY LTD.—See Westinghouse Air Brake Technologies Corporation; *U.S. Public*, pg. 2357
BLUE SKY INDUSTRIES, INC.—See Audax Group, Limited Partnership; *U.S. Private*, pg. 388
BOEING DISTRIBUTION SERVICES SAS—See The Boeing Company; *U.S. Public*, pg. 2040
BOEING INTERNATIONAL CORP. - AUSTRALIA—See The Boeing Company; *U.S. Public*, pg. 2040
BOEING INTERNATIONAL CORP. - FRANCE—See The Boeing Company; *U.S. Public*, pg. 2040
BOEING UK LTD. - HOUNSLOW—See The Boeing Company; *U.S. Public*, pg. 2041
BOEING UNITED KINGDOM LIMITED—See The Boeing Company; *U.S. Public*, pg. 2040
BOMBARDIER CORP.—See Bombardier Inc.; *Int'l*, pg. 1104
BOMBARDIER TRANSPORTATION (SWITZERLAND) LTD.—See Alstom S.A.; *Int'l*, pg. 382
BOYLAN SALES INC.; *U.S. Private*, pg. 628
BRALCO METALS (AUSTRALIA) PTY LTD.—See Reliance Steel & Aluminum Co.; *U.S. Public*, pg. 1779
BRUNSWICK HUNGARY MANUFACTURING AND TRADING LIMITED LIABILITY COMPANY—See Brunswick Corporation; *U.S. Public*, pg. 407
BRUNSWICK MARINE IN EMEA, INC.—See Brunswick Corporation; *U.S. Public*, pg. 408
BYRNE, RICE & TURNER, INC.; *U.S. Private*, pg. 701
CARGO EQUIPMENT CORP.—See Prospect Hill Growth Partners, L.P.; *U.S. Private*, pg. 3288
CASCO LTD.; *Int'l*, pg. 1351
CASCO RUSSIA—See CASCO Ltd.; *Int'l*, pg. 1351
CASCO SINGAPORE—See CASCO Ltd.; *Int'l*, pg. 1351
C. C. MARINE DISTRIBUTORS INC.; *U.S. Private*, pg. 1240
CENTURION INVESTMENTS INC.; *U.S. Private*, pg. 831
CERTIFIED PARTS CORPORATION; *U.S. Private*, pg. 841

CFM INTERNATIONAL INC.—See General Electric Company; *U.S. Public*, pg. 918
CHAND, LLC—See Bollinger Shipyards, Inc.; *U.S. Private*, pg. 611
CHINA HOLDINGS GROUP, INC.; *U.S. Private*, pg. 886
CHORI MACHINERY CO., LTD.—See Chori Co., Ltd.; *Int'l*, pg. 1583
CLARKSONS BRASIL LTDA.—See Clarkson PLC; *Int'l*, pg. 1651
CLARKSONS DENMARK ADS—See Clarkson PLC; *Int'l*, pg. 1651
CLARKSONS ESG CORE PLUS AS—See Clarkson PLC; *Int'l*, pg. 1651
CLARKSONS SECURITIES CANADA INC.—See Clarkson PLC; *Int'l*, pg. 1651
CLARKSONS SECURITIES INC.—See Clarkson PLC; *Int'l*, pg. 1651
CNIM TRANSPORT EQUIPMENT CO., LTD—See CNIM Constructions Industrielles de la Mediterranee SA; *Int'l*, pg. 1677
COBRASMA S.A.; *Int'l*, pg. 1683
COMET INDUSTRIES INC.; *U.S. Private*, pg. 981
CONTRAIL AVIATION SUPPORT, LLC—See Air T, Inc.; *U.S. Public*, pg. 67
CORLAND, CO.; *U.S. Private*, pg. 1050
CUTTER HOLDING CO. - CUTTER AVIATION - DALLAS-ADDISON FACILITY—See Cutter Holding Co.; *U.S. Private*, pg. 1131
DALLAS AEROSPACE OPERATIONS—See RTX Corporation; *U.S. Public*, pg. 1823
DASSAULT AIRCRAFT SERVICES INDIA PVT. LTD.—See Groupe Industriel Marcel Dassault S.A.; *Int'l*, pg. 3105
DASSAULT FALCON BUSINESS SERVICES (BEIJING) CO., LTD.—See Groupe Industriel Marcel Dassault S.A.; *Int'l*, pg. 3105
DASSAULT FALCON JET CORP.—See Groupe Industriel Marcel Dassault S.A.; *Int'l*, pg. 3105
DASSAULT FALCON JET CORP.—See Groupe Industriel Marcel Dassault S.A.; *Int'l*, pg. 3105
DASSAULT FALCON JET DO BRASIL LTDA.—See Groupe Industriel Marcel Dassault S.A.; *Int'l*, pg. 3105
DASSAULT FALCON MIDDLE EAST—See Groupe Industriel Marcel Dassault S.A.; *Int'l*, pg. 3105
DASSAULT INTERNATIONAL DO BRASIL LTDA—See Groupe Industriel Marcel Dassault S.A.; *Int'l*, pg. 3105
DASSAULT PROCUREMENT SERVICES—See Groupe Industriel Marcel Dassault S.A.; *Int'l*, pg. 3105
DDC ELECTRONICS LTD.—See TransDigm Group Incorporated; *U.S. Public*, pg. 2182
DDC ELECTRONIQUE, S.A.R.L.—See TransDigm Group Incorporated; *U.S. Public*, pg. 2182
DDC ELEKTRONIK, GMBH—See TransDigm Group Incorporated; *U.S. Public*, pg. 2182
DESSER TIRE & RUBBER CO., LLC—See VSE Corporation; *U.S. Public*, pg. 2313
DEUTZ ASIA-PACIFIC (PTE) LTD.—See DEUTZ AG; *Int'l*, pg. 2086
DHAP LTD—See Leggett & Platt, Incorporated; *U.S. Public*, pg. 1301
DIESEL DISTRIBUTORS AUSTRALIA PTY LIMITED—See Bapcor Limited; *Int'l*, pg. 857
DMI SCANDINAVIA AS—See DMI UK Ltd.; *Int'l*, pg. 2145
DODSON AVIATION INCORPORATED—See Dodson International, Inc.; *U.S. Private*, pg. 1252
DODSON INTERNATIONAL, INC.; *U.S. Private*, pg. 1252
DODSON INTERNATIONAL PARTS INC.—See Dodson International, Inc.; *U.S. Private*, pg. 1252
DONOVAN MARINE INC.; *U.S. Private*, pg. 1261
DS HULL COMPANY INCORPORATED; *U.S. Private*, pg. 1281
DYNATECH INTERNATIONAL CORP.; *U.S. Private*, pg. 1300
DYNCORP AEROSPACE OPERATIONS LTD.—See Cerberus Capital Management, L.P.; *U.S. Private*, pg. 838
EADS CASA—See Airbus SE; *Int'l*, pg. 246
EADS NORWAY NUF—See Airbus SE; *Int'l*, pg. 246
EAGLE ENGINEERING AEROSPACE KOREA CO., LTD.—See Eagle Industry Co., Ltd.; *Int'l*, pg. 2265
EAGLE ENGINEERING AEROSPACE SINGAPORE PTE. LTD.—See Eagle Industry Co., Ltd.; *Int'l*, pg. 2265
EAGLE ENGINEERING AEROSPACE TAIWAN CO., LTD.—See Eagle Industry Co., Ltd.; *Int'l*, pg. 2265
EAST AIR CORPORATION; *U.S. Private*, pg. 1315
EAST COAST AVIATION LLC; *U.S. Private*, pg. 1316
EGYPTIAN TRANSPORTATION & LOGISTICS COMPANY—See Egyptian Transport & Commercial Services Company S.A.E.; *Int'l*, pg. 2327
EGYTRANS DEPOT SOLUTIONS COMPANY—See Egyptian Transport & Commercial Services Company S.A.E.; *Int'l*, pg. 2327
ELECON ENGINEERING COMPANY LTD.; *Int'l*, pg. 2348
ELECTRIC CAR DISTRIBUTORS INC.; *U.S. Private*, pg. 1352
ELECTRO ENTERPRISES, INC.—See Audax Group, Limited Partnership; *U.S. Private*, pg. 388
ELLIOTT TURBOMACHINERY S.A.—See Ebara Corporation; *Int'l*, pg. 2284
ELLWOOD NATIONAL CRANKSHAFT CO—See Ellwood Group, Inc.; *U.S. Private*, pg. 1375
EMBRAER AIRCRAFT HOLDING INC.—See Embraer S.A.; *Int'l*, pg. 2375
EMPHOR FZCO; *Int'l*, pg. 2386
ENBRIDGE ENERGY PARTNERS, L.P.—See Enbridge Inc.; *Int'l*, pg. 2397
ERS INDUSTRIES INC.; *U.S. Private*, pg. 1423
ESTERLINE SENSORS SERVICES AMERICAS, INC.—See TransDigm Group Incorporated; *U.S. Public*, pg. 2180
ETA GLOBAL, INC.—See Copley Equity Partners,LLC; *U.S. Private*, pg. 1045
EUROAVIONICS GMBH—See HENSOLDT AG; *Int'l*, pg. 3355
EUROCOPTER INDIA PVT LTD—See Airbus SE; *Int'l*, pg. 244
EUROCOPTER JAPAN RG CO. LTD.—See Airbus SE; *Int'l*, pg. 244
EXTEX ENGINEERED PRODUCTS, INC.—See Arcline Investment Management LP; *U.S. Private*, pg. 314
FEDERAL MARINE TRANSMISSIONS, INC.; *U.S. Private*, pg. 1489
FINCANTIERI MARINE SYSTEMS NORTH AMERICA INC.—See Fincantieri S.p.A.; *Int'l*, pg. 2671
FISHERIES SUPPLY COMPANY; *U.S. Private*, pg. 1535
FLIGHT DIRECTOR INC.; *U.S. Private*, pg. 1545
FRED. OLSEN FLY OG LUFTMATERIELL AS—See Fred. Olsen & Co.; *Int'l*, pg. 2768
FUNOTEC (DALIAN) CO., LTD.—See Furuno Electric Co., Ltd.; *Int'l*, pg. 2847
FURUNO (CYPRUS) LTD.—See Furuno Electric Co., Ltd.; *Int'l*, pg. 2847
FURUNO DEUTSCHLAND GMBH—See Furuno Electric Co., Ltd.; *Int'l*, pg. 2847
FURUNO ELECTRIC (MALAYSIA) SDN. BHD.—See Furuno Electric Co., Ltd.; *Int'l*, pg. 2847
FURUNO PANAMA, S.A.—See Furuno Electric Co., Ltd.; *Int'l*, pg. 2848
FURUNO POLSKA SP. Z O.O.—See Furuno Electric Co., Ltd.; *Int'l*, pg. 2848
FURUNO SINGAPORE PTE LTD—See Furuno Electric Co., Ltd.; *Int'l*, pg. 2848
FURUNO (UK) LTD.—See Furuno Electric Co., Ltd.; *Int'l*, pg. 2847
FURUNO USA, INC.—See Furuno Electric Co., Ltd.; *Int'l*, pg. 2847
GAS DRIVE GLOBAL LP—See Enerflex Ltd.; *Int'l*, pg. 2419
GA TELESIS LLC; *U.S. Private*, pg. 1632
GE AVIATION DISTRIBUTION JAPAN CO., LTD.—See General Electric Company; *U.S. Public*, pg. 918
GEISMAR DO BRASIL MATERIAL FERROVIARIO LTDA—See Geismar S.A.; *Int'l*, pg. 2912
GEISMAR SEA PTE LTD—See Geismar S.A.; *Int'l*, pg. 2912
GEISMAR (UK) LTD—See Geismar S.A.; *Int'l*, pg. 2912
GENERAL AVIATION TECHNOLOGIES, L.P.—See G.A.S. Capital, Inc.; *U.S. Private*, pg. 1630
GENERAL DYNAMICS EUROPEAN LAND SYSTEMS GERMANY GMBH—See General Dynamics Corporation; *U.S. Public*, pg. 914
GENERAL TRANSPORT EQUIPMENT PTY. LTD.—See CIMC Vehicle (Group) Co., Ltd.; *Int'l*, pg. 1608
GKN AEROSPACE DEUTSCHLAND GMBH—See GKN plc; *Int'l*, pg. 2984
GLOBAL PARTS, INC.—See VSE Corporation; *U.S. Public*, pg. 2313
GREINER AEROSPACE INC.—See Greiner Holding AG; *Int'l*, pg. 3079
GREINER AEROSPACE (SHANGHAI) CO., LTD.—See Greiner Holding AG; *Int'l*, pg. 3079
H. ALBERT GMBH; *Int'l*, pg. 3194
HEARTLAND COMMUNICATIONS GROUP—See Heartland Community Group Inc; *U.S. Private*, pg. 1899
HELI-MART INC.; *U.S. Private*, pg. 1906
H-E PARTS INTERNATIONAL LLC—See Hitachi, Ltd.; *Int'l*, pg. 3415
HERCULES WIRE ROPE & SLING CO., INC.; *U.S. Private*, pg. 1921
HERNDON PRODUCTS, INC.—See HCI Equity Management, L.P.; *U.S. Private*, pg. 1889
HEXCEL EUROPE LIMITED—See Hexcel Corporation; *U.S. Public*, pg. 1033
HEXCEL REINFORCEMENTS CORP.—See Hexcel Corporation; *U.S. Public*, pg. 1033
HOBIE CAT AUSTRALASIA PTY LTD—See Hobie Cat Company; *U.S. Private*, pg. 1958
HOI TUNG MARINE MACHINERY SUPPLIERS LIMITED—See China Merchants Group Limited; *Int'l*, pg. 1521
HOLLAND PUMP OF LOUISIANA, INC—See Arcus Infrastructure Partners LLP; *Int'l*, pg. 553
HONEYWELL AEROSPACE AVIONICS MALAYSIA SDN BHD.—See Honeywell International Inc.; *U.S. Public*, pg. 1047
HONEYWELL AEROSPACE DE MEXICO, S. DE R.L. DE C.V.—See Honeywell International Inc.; *U.S. Public*, pg. 1047
HONEYWELL CONTROL SYSTEMS LTD.—See Honeywell International Inc.; *U.S. Public*, pg. 1051
HONEYWELL EUROPE NV—See Honeywell International Inc.; *U.S. Public*, pg. 1051
HONEYWELL HOLDINGS PTY. LTD.—See Honeywell International Inc.; *U.S. Public*, pg. 1051
HONEYWELL TECHNOLOGIES SARL—See Honeywell International Inc.; *U.S. Public*, pg. 1051
HUNTER CANADA—See Hunter Engineering Company; *U.S. Private*, pg. 2009
HYUNDAI ONE ASIA PTE. LTD.—See Hyundai Corporation; *Int'l*, pg. 3555
IKM ALFA SOLUTION AS—See IKM Gruppen AS; *Int'l*, pg. 3611
IKM OPERATIONS AS—See IKM Gruppen AS; *Int'l*, pg. 3611
IKM SUBSEA MOTOR SOLUTIONS AS—See IKM Gruppen AS; *Int'l*, pg. 3611
IKM TECH TEAM SOLUTIONS AS—See IKM Gruppen AS; *Int'l*, pg. 3611
I.M.P. GROUP INTERNATIONAL INC. - PACIFIC AVIONICS & INSTRUMENTS DIVISION—See I.M.P. Group International Inc.; *Int'l*, pg. 3566
IMT DEFENCE CORP—See Mission Essential Personnel, LLC; *U.S. Private*, pg. 2747
IMTRA CORPORATION; *U.S. Private*, pg. 2051
INDUSTRY-RAILWAY SUPPLIERS, INC.; *U.S. Private*, pg. 2069
INTEGRATED PROCUREMENT TECHNOLOGIES, INC.; *U.S. Private*, pg. 2100
INTERFAST AG—See Bossard Holding AG; *Int'l*, pg. 1117
INTERMEC TECHNOLOGIES (S) PTE LTD—See Honeywell International Inc.; *U.S. Public*, pg. 1050
IRVINGQ FRANCE SAA—See TransDigm Group Incorporated; *U.S. Public*, pg. 2182
IRVIN-GQ LIMITED—See TransDigm Group Incorporated; *U.S. Public*, pg. 2182
ITT CONTROL TECHNOLOGIES EMEA GMBH—See ITT Inc.; *U.S. Public*, pg. 1178
JAMESTOWN DISTRIBUTORS; *U.S. Private*, pg. 2185
JB&A AVIATION INC.; *U.S. Private*, pg. 2193
J.B. DUNN COMPANY INC.; *U.S. Private*, pg. 2158
JERRY'S MARINE SERVICE FL, LLC—See Lewis Marine Supply Inc.; *U.S. Private*, pg. 2439
JET INTERNATIONAL CO., LLC; *U.S. Private*, pg. 2204
JH GLOBAL SERVICES, INC.; *U.S. Private*, pg. 2207
KIRKHILL AIRCRAFT PARTS CO.; *U.S. Private*, pg. 2314
K-MAX CORPORATION—See Arcline Investment Management LP; *U.S. Private*, pg. 314
KOVALCHICK SALVAGE CO.; *U.S. Private*, pg. 2345
KVT FASTENING GMBH—See Bossard Holding AG; *Int'l*, pg. 1117
KVT-FASTENING SPOL. S.R.O.—See Bossard Holding AG; *Int'l*, pg. 1117
KVT FASTENING SP Z O.O.—See Bossard Holding AG; *Int'l*, pg. 1117
KVT-FASTENING S.R.L.—See Bossard Holding AG; *Int'l*, pg. 1117
L3HARRIS MAS INC.—See L3Harris Technologies, Inc.; *U.S. Public*, pg. 1284
LAND 'N' SEA DISTRIBUTING, INC.—See Brunswick Corporation; *U.S. Public*, pg. 407
LANKHORST TASELAAR B.V.—See Brunswick Corporation; *U.S. Public*, pg. 408
LENCO MARINE SOLUTIONS, LLC—See Brunswick Corporation; *U.S. Public*, pg. 408
LEWIS MARINE SUPPLY INC.; *U.S. Private*, pg. 2439
LEWMAR INC.—See LCI Industries; *U.S. Public*, pg. 1295
L.G. PIKE CONSTRUCTION CO.; *U.S. Private*, pg. 2366
LIAONING POLY ARMOR VEHICLE CO., LTD.—See China Poly Group Corporation; *Int'l*, pg. 1541
LIFE FITNESS (ATLANTIC) B.V.—See KPS Capital Partners, LP; *U.S. Private*, pg. 2347
LIFE FITNESS ITALIA S.R.L.—See KPS Capital Partners, LP; *U.S. Private*, pg. 2347
LIFE SAFETY DISTRIBUTION AG—See Honeywell International Inc.; *U.S. Public*, pg. 1051
LONGWOOD INTERNATIONAL, INC.—See Westinghouse Air Brake Technologies Corporation; *U.S. Public*, pg. 2358
M7 AEROSPACE LP—See Elbit Systems Limited; *Int'l*, pg. 2344
MACHINIO CORP.—See Liquidity Services, Inc.; *U.S. Public*, pg. 1321
MACKAY COMMUNICATIONS, INC.; *U.S. Private*, pg. 2536
MADISON COMPONENTS LLC; *U.S. Private*, pg. 2540
MARYSVILLE MARINE DISTRIBUTORS; *U.S. Private*, pg. 2600
MATRIX AVIATION, INC.—See Greenwich AeroGroup, Inc.; *U.S. Private*, pg. 1781
MECABRIVE IND. SAS—See Figeac-Aero SA; *Int'l*, pg. 2660
MEGGITT AEROSPACE ASIA PACIFIC PTE LIMITED—See Parker Hannifin Corporation; *U.S. Public*, pg. 1641
MEGGITT AIRCRAFT BRAKING SYSTEMS CORPORATION—See Parker Hannifin Corporation; *U.S. Public*, pg. 1642
MERCHANTS JAPAN COMPANY LIMITED—See China Merchants Group Limited; *Int'l*, pg. 1521
MIDWEST RAILROAD TIE SALES; *U.S. Private*, pg. 2722
MILPA TICARI VE SINAI URUNLER PAZARLAMA SANAYI

423860 — TRANSPORTATION EQUI...

VE TICARET A.S.—See Adil Bey Holding A.S.; *Int'l*, pg. 148
M INTERNATIONAL INC.; *U.S. Private*, pg. 2523
MOBITEC AB—See Audax Group, Limited Partnership; *U.S. Private*, pg. 389
MODERN TRACK MACHINERY—See Geismar S.A.; *Int'l*, pg. 2912
MOOG AG—See Moog Inc.; *U.S. Public*, pg. 1469
MOOG CONTROL SYSTEMS (SHANGHAI) CO., LTD.—See Moog Inc.; *U.S. Public*, pg. 1470
MOOG DE ARGENTINA SRL—See Moog Inc.; *U.S. Public*, pg. 1470
MORS SMITT ASIA, LTD.—See Westinghouse Air Brake Technologies Corporation; *U.S. Public*, pg. 2358
MORS SMITT BV—See Westinghouse Air Brake Technologies Corporation; *U.S. Public*, pg. 2358
MORS SMITT FRANCE S.A.S.—See Westinghouse Air Brake Technologies Corporation; *U.S. Public*, pg. 2358
MORS SMITT TECHNOLOGIES, INC.—See Westinghouse Air Brake Technologies Corporation; *U.S. Public*, pg. 2358
MORS SMITT UK LTD.—See Westinghouse Air Brake Technologies Corporation; *U.S. Public*, pg. 2358
MOTORFLUG BADEN-BADEN GMBH—See Airbus SE; *Int'l*, pg. 244
MTQ ENGINE SYSTEMS (AUST) PTY LTD—See Bapcor Limited; *Int'l*, pg. 857
NATIONAL RAILWAY SUPPLY INC.; *U.S. Private*, pg. 2861
NORDISK ASIA PACIFIC LTD—See TransDigm Group Incorporated; *U.S. Public*, pg. 2183
NORTH SAILS DIRECT—See Windway Capital Corp.; *U.S. Private*, pg. 4539
NOVAR ED & S LIMITED—See Honeywell International Inc.; *U.S. Public*, pg. 1051
NRE POWER SYSTEMS, INC.—See National Railway Equipment Company; *U.S. Private*, pg. 2861
NRE WHEEL WORKS INC.—See National Railway Equipment Company; *U.S. Private*, pg. 2861
OMAHA AIRPLANE SUPPLY CO.; *U.S. Private*, pg. 3014
ONTIC ENGINEERING & MANUFACTURING, INC.—See CVC Capital Partners SICAV-FIS S.A.; *Int'l*, pg. 1884
PAXTON COMPANY; *U.S. Private*, pg. 3115
PCM TRANSPORT AND INDUSTRIAL SUPPLIES LIMITED—See B. Grimm Group; *Int'l*, pg. 788
PEREGRINE AVIATION SERVICES; *U.S. Private*, pg. 3147
PERUZZI BUICK GMC; *U.S. Private*, pg. 3156
PLAINS ALL AMERICAN PIPELINE, L.P.; *U.S. Public*, pg. 1696
POLY JILIN AMMUNITION MANUFACTURING CO., LTD.—See China Poly Group Corporation; *Int'l*, pg. 1541
PRIME AIR EUROPE LIMITED—See HEICO Corporation; *U.S. Public*, pg. 1020
PROFESSIONAL AVIATION ASSOCIATES, INC.—See Greenwich AeroGroup, Inc.; *U.S. Private*, pg. 1781
PT.FURUNO ELECTRIC INDONESIA—See Furuno Electric Co., Ltd.; *Int'l*, pg. 2848
QUALITY AIRCRAFT ACCESSORIES, INC.—See BOK Financial Corporation; *U.S. Public*, pg. 367
RADIUS AEROSPACE, INC.—See Arlington Capital Partners LLC; *U.S. Private*, pg. 328
RAIL LINE COMPONENTS, S.L.U.—See Construcciones y Auxiliar de Ferrocarriles S.A.; *Int'l*, pg. 1777
REGIONAL ONE, INC.—See Exchange Income Corporation; *Int'l*, pg. 2579
RETAIL IN MOTION LIMITED—See Deutsche Lufthansa AG; *Int'l*, pg. 2070
RICHARDS MARINE MARKETING, INC.—See West Coast Sales & Associates LLC; *U.S. Private*, pg. 4484
RICON CORP.—See Westinghouse Air Brake Technologies Corporation; *U.S. Public*, pg. 2359
RIORDAN MATERIALS CORPORATION—See DXP Enterprises, Inc.; *U.S. Public*, pg. 698
SAIC—See Leidos Holdings, Inc.; *U.S. Public*, pg. 1304
SATAIR CHINA—See Airbus SE; *Int'l*, pg. 244
SATAIR PTE. LTD.—See Airbus SE; *Int'l*, pg. 244
SATAIR UK—See Airbus SE; *Int'l*, pg. 244
SATAIR USA INC.—See Airbus SE; *Int'l*, pg. 244
SEA-DOG CORPORATION—See Patrick Industries, Inc.; *U.S. Public*, pg. 1653
SEATTLE AERO LLC; *U.S. Private*, pg. 3591
SEATTLE MARINE & FISHING SUPPLY CO.; *U.S. Private*, pg. 3592
SHANGHAI POLY TECHNOLOGIES CO., LTD.—See China Poly Group Corporation; *Int'l*, pg. 1541
SHOREMASTER INC.—See High Street Capital Management, Inc.; *U.S. Private*, pg. 1937
SHUTTLEWAGON, INC.—See Westinghouse Air Brake Technologies Corporation; *U.S. Public*, pg. 2359
SIGMA INSPECTION AS—See IKM Gruppen AS; *Int'l*, pg. 3612
S.M. OSGOOD COMPANY; *U.S. Private*, pg. 3518
SOURCE TWO SPARES INC.; *U.S. Private*, pg. 3718
SPAERO TRADE GMBH—See Airbus SE; *Int'l*, pg. 244
STS COMPONENT SOLUTIONS, LLC—See STS Aviation Group; *U.S. Private*, pg. 3842
SUN AVIATION, INC.; *U.S. Private*, pg. 3858
SUNSHINE AVIONICS LLC—See HEICO Corporation; *U.S. Public*, pg. 1020
TAYLOR MADE SYSTEMS—See LCI Industries; *U.S. Public*, pg. 1295
TELAIR INTERNATIONAL AB—See TransDigm Group Incorporated; *U.S. Public*, pg. 2183
TELAIR INTERNATIONAL SERVICES PTE. LTD.—See TransDigm Group Incorporated; *U.S. Public*, pg. 2183
TEM EQUIPMENT MANAGEMENT GMBH—See Stonepeak Partners L.P.; *U.S. Private*, pg. 3829
TIANJIN POLY SAGAWA TRADING CO., LTD.—See China Poly Group Corporation; *Int'l*, pg. 1541
TPG AERONAUTIK SDN. BHD.—See CB Industrial Product Holding Berhad; *Int'l*, pg. 1364
T.P.S. AVIATION INC.; *U.S. Private*, pg. 3912
TRACE WORLDWIDE CORP.; *U.S. Private*, pg. 4200
TRANSAERO INC.; *U.S. Private*, pg. 4206
TRAVELERS MARINE, LLC—See The Travelers Companies, Inc.; *U.S. Public*, pg. 2136
TRIMBLE ELECTRONIC PRODUCTS (SHANGHAI) CO., LTD.—See Trimble, Inc.; *U.S. Public*, pg. 2192
TRIMBLE NAVIGATION AUSTRALIA PTY. LIMITED—See Trimble, Inc.; *U.S. Public*, pg. 2192
TRIMBLE NAVIGATION IBERICA S.L.—See Trimble, Inc.; *U.S. Public*, pg. 2192
TRIMBLE NAVIGATION SINGAPORE PTE LIMITED—See Trimble, Inc.; *U.S. Public*, pg. 2192
TRIUMPH ACCESSORY SERVICES-GRAND PRAIRIE, INC.—See Triumph Group, Inc.; *U.S. Public*, pg. 2196
TRIUMPH CONTROLS FRANCE SAS—See Triumph Group, Inc.; *U.S. Public*, pg. 2197
TRIUMPH FABRICATIONS - ORANGEBURG, INC.—See Triumph Group, Inc.; *U.S. Public*, pg. 2197
TRIUMPH STRUCTURES - FARNBOROUGH, LTD.—See Triumph Group, Inc.; *U.S. Public*, pg. 2197
TTS SINGAPORE PTE. LTD.—See Cargotec Corporation; *Int'l*, pg. 1329
UNITED AEROSPACE CORP.—See YMC Aviation Inc.; *U.S. Private*, pg. 4589
UNIVERSAL TURBINE PARTS, LLC; *U.S. Private*, pg. 4307
VAN BORTEL AIRCRAFT INC.; *U.S. Private*, pg. 4339
VAS AERO SERVICES, LLC—See H.I.G. Capital, LLC; *U.S. Private*, pg. 1832
VOLATUS AEROSPACE CORP.—See Drone Delivery Canada Corp.; *Int'l*, pg. 2205
VOLVO PENTA CANADA LTD.—See AB Volvo; *Int'l*, pg. 42
VOLVO PENTA OF THE AMERICAS, INC.—See AB Volvo; *Int'l*, pg. 42
WESCO AIRCRAFT EUROPE, LTD.—See Platinum Equity, LLC; *U.S. Private*, pg. 3210
WESCO AIRCRAFT GERMANY GMBH—See Platinum Equity, LLC; *U.S. Private*, pg. 3210
WESCO AIRCRAFT ITALY SRL—See Platinum Equity, LLC; *U.S. Private*, pg. 3210
WESTERN AIRCRAFT, INC.—See Greenwich AeroGroup, Inc.; *U.S. Private*, pg. 1781
WHITE INDUSTRIES, INC.—See Bas Part Sales LLC; *U.S. Private*, pg. 484
WILLIAM F. HURST CO., INC.; *U.S. Private*, pg. 4523
WILLIAMS INTERNATIONAL COMPANY LLC—See The Williams Companies, Inc.; *U.S. Public*, pg. 2142
WINDSOR MARINE PTE. LTD.—See Financiere SYZ & CO SA; *Int'l*, pg. 2669
WOODWARD BULGARIA EOOD—See Woodward, Inc.; *U.S. Public*, pg. 2377
WUXI JINXIN GROUP COMPANY LIMITED—See Westinghouse Air Brake Technologies Corporation; *U.S. Public*, pg. 2360
YMC AVIATION INC.; *U.S. Private*, pg. 4589
YSD DOORS, S.A. DE C.V—See The Greenbrier Companies, Inc.; *U.S. Public*, pg. 2086
ZGA AIRCRAFT PARTS, INC.—See Zotti Group Aviation, Inc.; *U.S. Private*, pg. 4609
ZIRCON ENGINEERING PTE LTD—See Daeyang Electric Co., Ltd.; *Int'l*, pg. 1911

423910 — SPORTING AND RECREATIONAL GOODS AND SUPPLIES MERCHANT WHOLESALERS

2ND SWING; *U.S. Private*, pg. 7
360 INC.; *U.S. Private*, pg. 8
'47 BRAND, LLC; *U.S. Private*, pg. 1
ABOUTGOLF LTD.; *U.S. Private*, pg. 39
ACCELL NORTH AMERICA, INC.—See Regent, L.P.; *U.S. Private*, pg. 3387
ACUSPORT CORPORATION; *U.S. Private*, pg. 71
ADAMS GOLF, INC.—See Taylor Made Golf Company, Inc.; *U.S. Private*, pg. 3940
ADIDAS ARGENTINA S.A.—See adidas AG; *Int'l*, pg. 146
ADIDAS AUSTRALIA PTY. LIMITED—See adidas AG; *Int'l*, pg. 146
ADIDAS AUSTRIA GMBH—See adidas AG; *Int'l*, pg. 146
ADIDAS BALTICS SIA—See adidas AG; *Int'l*, pg. 146
ADIDAS BENELUX B.V.—See adidas AG; *Int'l*, pg. 146
ADIDAS BUDAPEST KFT.—See adidas AG; *Int'l*, pg. 146
ADIDAS BULGARIA EAD—See adidas AG; *Int'l*, pg. 146
ADIDAS CHILE LTDA.—See adidas AG; *Int'l*, pg. 146
ADIDAS COLOMBIA LTDA.—See adidas AG; *Int'l*, pg. 146
ADIDAS CROATIA D.O.O.—See adidas AG; *Int'l*, pg. 146
ADIDAS CR S.R.O.—See adidas AG; *Int'l*, pg. 146
ADIDAS (CYPRUS) LIMITED—See adidas AG; *Int'l*, pg. 146
ADIDAS DANMARK A/S—See adidas AG; *Int'l*, pg. 146
ADIDAS DE MEXICO S.A. DE C.V.—See adidas AG; *Int'l*, pg. 147
ADIDAS DO BRASIL LTDA.—See adidas AG; *Int'l*, pg. 147
ADIDAS EMERGING MARKET L.L.C.—See adidas AG; *Int'l*, pg. 146
ADIDAS EMERGING MARKETS FZE—See adidas AG; *Int'l*, pg. 146
ADIDAS ESPANA S.A.U.—See adidas AG; *Int'l*, pg. 147
ADIDAS FRANCE S.A.R.L.—See adidas AG; *Int'l*, pg. 147
ADIDAS HELLAS A.E.—See adidas AG; *Int'l*, pg. 147
ADIDAS HONG KONG LTD.—See adidas AG; *Int'l*, pg. 147
ADIDAS INDIA PRIVATE LTD.—See adidas AG; *Int'l*, pg. 147
ADIDAS INTERNATIONAL MARKETING B.V.—See adidas AG; *Int'l*, pg. 147
ADIDAS INTERNATIONAL TRADING B.V.—See adidas AG; *Int'l*, pg. 147
ADIDAS ISRAEL LTD.—See adidas AG; *Int'l*, pg. 147
ADIDAS JAPAN K.K.—See adidas AG; *Int'l*, pg. 147
ADIDAS LATIN AMERICA, S.A.—See adidas AG; *Int'l*, pg. 147
ADIDAS LEVANT LIMITED—See adidas AG; *Int'l*, pg. 147
ADIDAS (MALAYSIA) SDN. BHD.—See adidas AG; *Int'l*, pg. 146
ADIDAS NORGE A/S—See adidas AG; *Int'l*, pg. 147
ADIDAS NORTH AMERICA, INC.—See adidas AG; *Int'l*, pg. 147
ADIDAS POLAND SP. Z. O. O.—See adidas AG; *Int'l*, pg. 147
ADIDAS ROMANIA S.R.L.—See adidas AG; *Int'l*, pg. 147
ADIDAS SARRAGAN FRANCE S.A.R.L.—See adidas AG; *Int'l*, pg. 147
ADIDAS SERBIA D.O.O.—See adidas AG; *Int'l*, pg. 147
ADIDAS SINGAPORE PTE. LTD.—See adidas AG; *Int'l*, pg. 147
ADIDAS SLOVAKIA S.R.O.—See adidas AG; *Int'l*, pg. 147
ADIDAS SOURCING LIMITED—See adidas AG; *Int'l*, pg. 147
ADIDAS (SOUTH AFRICA) (PTY) LTD.—See adidas AG; *Int'l*, pg. 146
ADIDAS SPORT GMBH—See adidas AG; *Int'l*, pg. 147
ADIDAS SUOMI OY—See adidas AG; *Int'l*, pg. 147
ADIDAS (SUZHOU) CO. LTD.—See adidas AG; *Int'l*, pg. 146
ADIDAS SVERIGE AB—See adidas AG; *Int'l*, pg. 147
ADIDAS TEAM, INC.—See adidas AG; *Int'l*, pg. 146
ADIDAS (THAILAND) CO., LTD.—See adidas AG; *Int'l*, pg. 146
ADIDAS TRGOVINA D.O.O.—See adidas AG; *Int'l*, pg. 147
ADIDAS (UK) LTD.—See adidas AG; *Int'l*, pg. 146
AKVA GROUP CHILE S.A.—See Egersund Group AS; *Int'l*, pg. 2323
AKVA GROUP NORTH AMERICA INC.—See Egersund Group AS; *Int'l*, pg. 2323
AKVA GROUP SCOTLAND LTD.—See Egersund Group AS; *Int'l*, pg. 2323
ALL-SPORTS LLC—See Peak Global Holdings, LLC; *U.S. Private*, pg. 3123
AMER SPORTS ASIA SERVICES LIMITED—See ANTA Sports Products Limited; *Int'l*, pg. 479
AMER SPORTS AUSTRIA GMBH—See ANTA Sports Products Limited; *Int'l*, pg. 479
AMER SPORTS CANADA, INC.—See ANTA Sports Products Limited; *Int'l*, pg. 479
AMER SPORTS CHINA—See ANTA Sports Products Limited; *Int'l*, pg. 479
AMER SPORTS CZECH REPUBLIC S.R.O.—See ANTA Sports Products Limited; *Int'l*, pg. 480
AMER SPORTS DENMARK APS—See ANTA Sports Products Limited; *Int'l*, pg. 480
AMER SPORTS ESTONIA—See ANTA Sports Products Limited; *Int'l*, pg. 480
AMER SPORTS EUROPEAN CENTER AG—See ANTA Sports Products Limited; *Int'l*, pg. 480
AMER SPORTS EUROPE GMBH—See ANTA Sports Products Limited; *Int'l*, pg. 480
AMER SPORTS EUROPE SERVICES GMBH—See ANTA Sports Products Limited; *Int'l*, pg. 480
AMER SPORTS ITALIA S.P.A.—See ANTA Sports Products Limited; *Int'l*, pg. 480
AMER SPORTS MALAYSIA SDN BHD—See ANTA Sports Products Limited; *Int'l*, pg. 481
AMER SPORTS NORGE A/S—See ANTA Sports Products Limited; *Int'l*, pg. 480
AMER SPORTS POLAND SP. Z.O.O.—See ANTA Sports Products Limited; *Int'l*, pg. 480
AMER SPORTS RUSSIA—See ANTA Sports Products Limited; *Int'l*, pg. 480
AMER SPORTS SA—See ANTA Sports Products Limited; *Int'l*, pg. 480
AMER SPORTS SHANGHAI TRADING LTD.—See ANTA Sports Products Limited; *Int'l*, pg. 480
AMER SPORTS SLOVAKIA—See ANTA Sports Products Limited; *Int'l*, pg. 480
AMER SPORTS SOURCING LTD.—See ANTA Sports Products Limited; *Int'l*, pg. 480

N.A.I.C.S. INDEX

423910 — SPORTING AND RECREA...

AMER SPORTS UK & IRELAND LTD—See ANTA Sports Products Limited; *Int'l*, pg. 480
ANACONDA SPORTS, INC.; *U.S. Private*, pg. 271
ANGLING DIRECT PLC; *Int'l*, pg. 461
AQUA-GON INC.; *U.S. Private*, pg. 303
ARCANA POOL SYSTEMS GMBH—See BWT Aktiengesellschaft; *Int'l*, pg. 1233
ARGON TECHNOLOGIES, INC.—See Centre Partners Management LLC; *U.S. Private*, pg. 828
ARGOSY INTERNATIONAL INC.; *U.S. Private*, pg. 322
ARSENAL STRENGTH LLC; *U.S. Private*, pg. 339
ASIAN WORLD OF MARTIAL ARTS, INC.; *U.S. Private*, pg. 351
ASTRAL - BAZENOVE PRISLUSENSTVI, S.R.O.—See Fluidra SA; *Int'l*, pg. 2713
ASTRAL EXPORT, S.A.—See Fluidra SA; *Int'l*, pg. 2713
ASTRAL INDIA PRIVATE LTD—See Fluidra SA; *Int'l*, pg. 2713
ASTRAL ITALIA SPA—See Fluidra SA; *Int'l*, pg. 2713
ASTRAL MARAZUL—See Fluidra SA; *Int'l*, pg. 2713
ASTRAL NIGERIA LTD—See Fluidra SA; *Int'l*, pg. 2713
ASTRAL PISCINE S.A.S—See Fluidra SA; *Int'l*, pg. 2713
ASTRALPOOL CHILE LTD—See Fluidra SA; *Int'l*, pg. 2713
ASTRALPOOL CHINA—See Fluidra SA; *Int'l*, pg. 2713
ASTRALPOOL CYPRUS LTD—See Fluidra SA; *Int'l*, pg. 2714
ASTRAL POOL HELLAS SA—See Fluidra SA; *Int'l*, pg. 2713
ASTRAL POOL SWIMMING POOL EQUIPMENT (SHANGHAI) LTD., CO—See Fluidra SA; *Int'l*, pg. 2713
ASTRALPOOL SWITZERLAND S.A.—See Fluidra SA; *Int'l*, pg. 2714
ASTRALPOOL THAILAND CO., LTD—See Fluidra SA; *Int'l*, pg. 2714
ASTRAL SCANDINAVIA A/S—See Fluidra SA; *Int'l*, pg. 2713
ASTRAL SNG—See Fluidra SA; *Int'l*, pg. 2713
ASTRAL SWEDEN AB—See Fluidra SA; *Int'l*, pg. 2713
ASTRAL UK LTD—See Fluidra SA; *Int'l*, pg. 2714
ATHLETICS UNLIMITED, INC.—See Bain Capital, LP; *U.S. Private*, pg. 451
ATOMIC SKI USA INC.—See ANTA Sports Products Limited; *Int'l*, pg. 480
AUS HOLDCO PTY. LIMITED—See Brunswick Corporation; *U.S. Public*, pg. 407
AWR SPORTS LLC—See Peak Global Holdings, LLC; *U.S. Private*, pg. 3123
AZIMUT BENETTI SERVICES USA, INC.—See Azimut-Benetti S.p.A.; *Int'l*, pg. 780
BATTLE CREEK EQUIPMENT CO.; *U.S. Private*, pg. 489
BAUER HOCKEY, INC.—See Fairfax Financial Holdings Limited; *Int'l*, pg. 2605
BAY STATE POOL SUPPLIES INC.; *U.S. Private*, pg. 494
BD LIFT AB—See Amplex AB; *Int'l*, pg. 434
BESTWAY (EUROPE) S.R.L.—See Bestway Global Holding Inc.; *Int'l*, pg. 1001
BESTWAY (USA), INC.—See Bestway Global Holding Inc.; *Int'l*, pg. 1001
BG SPORTS EUROPE SARL—See Fenway Partners, LLC; *U.S. Private*, pg. 1495
BIG ROCK SPORTS, LLC—See Peak Global Holdings, LLC; *U.S. Private*, pg. 3123
BOLLINGER INDUSTRIES, INC.; *U.S. Public*, pg. 367
BRIDGESTONE CYCLE WEST JAPAN SALES CO., LTD.—See Bridgestone Corporation; *Int'l*, pg. 1158
BROWNING VIANA FABRICA DE ARMAS E ARTIGOS DE DESPORTO SA—See Herstal, S.A.; *Int'l*, pg. 3364
BUNZL DISTRIBUTIE SRL—See Bunzl plc; *Int'l*, pg. 1217
BWG HOLDINGS I CORP—See AEA Investors LP; *U.S. Private*, pg. 113
CALLAWAY GOLF CANADA LTD.—See Topgolf Callaway Brands Corp.; *U.S. Public*, pg. 2164
CENTURY LLC; *U.S. Private*, pg. 833
CERTIKIN PORTUGAL SA—See Fluidra SA; *Int'l*, pg. 2714
CERTIKIN SWIMMING POOL PRODUCTS INDIA PVT LTD.—See Fluidra SA; *Int'l*, pg. 2714
CHAMPION EUROPE S.R.L.—See Hanesbrands Inc.; *U.S. Public*, pg. 982
CHEMOFORM AUSTRIA GMBH—See Chemoform AG; *Int'l*, pg. 1463
CHEMOFORM CZ S.R.O.—See Chemoform AG; *Int'l*, pg. 1463
CHEMOFORM POLSKA SP. Z O.O.—See Chemoform AG; *Int'l*, pg. 1463
CHEMOFORM ROMANIA S.R.L.—See Chemoform AG; *Int'l*, pg. 1463
CHI HUA FITNESS CO., LTD.; *Int'l*, pg. 1475
CINDERELLA INC.; *U.S. Private*, pg. 898
CLASSIC PRODUCTS CORP.; *U.S. Private*, pg. 916
COLUMBIA SPORTSWEAR COMMERCIAL (SHANGHAI) CO., LTD.—See Columbia Sportswear Company; *U.S. Public*, pg. 535
COMBAT BRANDS, LLC; *U.S. Private*, pg. 980
COMBAT SPORTS—See Fairfax Financial Holdings Limited; *Int'l*, pg. 2605
COMBIWITH CORPORATION—See Combi Corporation; *Int'l*, pg. 1708
COMPLETE BOWLING SERVICE, INC.; *U.S. Private*, pg. 1000

CORTZ, INC.—See Leonard Green & Partners, L.P.; *U.S. Private*, pg. 2426
COSMOS TRAWL A/S—See Hampidjan hf; *Int'l*, pg. 3239
CREAS F&C CO., LTD.; *Int'l*, pg. 1831
CROSSLAKE SALES INC.; *U.S. Private*, pg. 1106
CSI SPORTS LLC—See Peak Global Holdings, LLC; *U.S. Private*, pg. 3123
CYCLEUROPE FINLAND OY—See Grimaldi Industri AB; *Int'l*, pg. 3086
CYCLEUROPE INDUSTRIES SAS—See Grimaldi Industri AB; *Int'l*, pg. 3085
CYCLEUROPE JAPAN CO., LTD.—See Grimaldi Industri AB; *Int'l*, pg. 3086
CYCLEUROPE NORGE AS—See Grimaldi Industri AB; *Int'l*, pg. 3086
CYCLEUROPE UK LTD—See Grimaldi Industri AB; *Int'l*, pg. 3085
CYCLEUROPE USA INC.—See Grimaldi Industri AB; *Int'l*, pg. 3085
CY-TECH GMBH—See Brunswick Corporation; *U.S. Public*, pg. 407
DAIWA CORPORATION—See Globeride, Inc.; *Int'l*, pg. 3007
DANCIN' DOGG GOLF; *U.S. Private*, pg. 1153
DAVE'S CLAREMORE RV INC.—See Lazydays Holdings, Inc.; *U.S. Public*, pg. 1294
DAVIDSON'S INC.; *U.S. Private*, pg. 1172
DAZADI INC.; *U.S. Private*, pg. 1178
DIAMOND NATION; *U.S. Private*, pg. 1223
DIVE N SURF; *U.S. Private*, pg. 1240
DYACO JAPAN CO., LTD.—See Dyaco International Inc.; *Int'l*, pg. 2238
EASTERN SKATEBOARD SUPPLY INC.; *U.S. Private*, pg. 1321
ELECTRA BICYCLE COMPANY, LLC—See Trek Bicycle Corporation; *U.S. Private*, pg. 4217
ELLETT BROTHERS, INC.; *U.S. Private*, pg. 1363
ELMEC ROMANIA SRL—See Folli Follie S.A.; *Int'l*, pg. 2721
EMOTION KAYAKS, INC.—See Lifetime Products Inc.; *U.S. Private*, pg. 2451
EMSCO INC.; *U.S. Private*, pg. 1388
ERGON MARINE & INDUSTRIAL SUPPLY, INC.—See Ergon, Inc.; *U.S. Private*, pg. 1418
ESPOMEGA S. DE R.L. DE C.V—See Bunzl plc; *Int'l*, pg. 1218
EXEL SPORTS SWEDEN AB—See Exel Composites Oyj; *Int'l*, pg. 2582
THE FINALS—See Swimwear Anywhere, Inc.; *U.S. Private*, pg. 3893
FITELL CORPORATION; *Int'l*, pg. 2695
FIVE TEN EUROPE NV/SA—See adidas AG; *Int'l*, pg. 146
FLAGHOUSE INC.; *U.S. Private*, pg. 1539
FLUIDRA MAGYARORSZAG KFT—See Fluidra SA; *Int'l*, pg. 2714
FLUIDRA POLSKA SP.Z O.O.—See Fluidra SA; *Int'l*, pg. 2714
FLUIDRA SOUTH AFRICA (PTY) LTD.—See Fluidra SA; *Int'l*, pg. 2714
FOLSOM CORPORATION; *U.S. Private*, pg. 1559
FORE-PAR GROUP INC.; *U.S. Private*, pg. 1565
FRASERS GROUP PLC; *Int'l*, pg. 2765
FRITZ BERGER GMBH; *Int'l*, pg. 2793
GAME 7 ATHLETICS S.R.L.—See Hanesbrands Inc.; *U.S. Public*, pg. 983
GARY YAMAMOTO CUSTOM BAITS; *U.S. Private*, pg. 1647
GENCO TRADE SRL—See FOURLIS HOLDINGS S.A.; *Int'l*, pg. 2755
GIANT BICYCLE CO. PTY. LTD.—See Giant Manufacturing Co., Ltd.; *Int'l*, pg. 2961
GIANT BIKES IBERICA S.A.—See Giant Manufacturing Co., Ltd.; *Int'l*, pg. 2961
GIANT DEUTSCHLAND GMBH—See Giant Manufacturing Co., Ltd.; *Int'l*, pg. 2961
GIANT EUROPE B.V.—See Giant Manufacturing Co., Ltd.; *Int'l*, pg. 2961
GIANT HOLLAND B.V.—See Giant Manufacturing Co., Ltd.; *Int'l*, pg. 2961
GIANT ITALIA S.R.L.—See Giant Manufacturing Co., Ltd.; *Int'l*, pg. 2961
GIANT POLSKA SP. Z.O.O.—See Giant Manufacturing Co., Ltd.; *Int'l*, pg. 2961
GIRO SPORT DESIGN—See Vista Outdoor Inc.; *U.S. Public*, pg. 2305
G. JOANNOU CYCLE CO. INC.; *U.S. Private*, pg. 1630
GOLF DIGEST ONLINE INC.; *Int'l*, pg. 3035
GROUPE GO SPORT SA—See Finatis SA; *Int'l*, pg. 2670
GRUPO SBF S.A.; *Int'l*, pg. 3135
GUNTHER'S ATHLETIC SERVICE, INC.—See Fenway Partners, LLC; *U.S. Private*, pg. 1495
HACHIK DISTRIBUTORS, INC.; *U.S. Private*, pg. 1838
HAMPIDJAN AUSTRALIA PTY LTD—See Hampidjan hf; *Int'l*, pg. 3239
HAMPIDJAN BALTIC UAB—See Hampidjan hf; *Int'l*, pg. 3239
HAMPIDJAN CANADA LTD.—See Hampidjan hf; *Int'l*, pg. 3239
HAMPIDJAN NEW ZEALAND LTD—See Hampidjan hf; *Int'l*, pg. 3239

HAMPIDJAN RUSSIA LTD.—See Hampidjan hf; *Int'l*, pg. 3239
HAMPIDJAN USA INC.—See Hampidjan hf; *Int'l*, pg. 3239
HANES ITALY SRL—See Hanesbrands Inc.; *U.S. Public*, pg. 983
HARRISON-HOGE INDUSTRIES, INC.; *U.S. Private*, pg. 1871
HAYWARD/IMG—See CCMP Capital Advisors, LP; *U.S. Private*, pg. 800
HAYWARD/IMG—See MSD Capital, L.P.; *U.S. Private*, pg. 2807
HEAD CANADA INC.—See Head B.V.; *Int'l*, pg. 3300
HEAD FRANCE S.A.S.—See Head B.V.; *Int'l*, pg. 3300
HEAD GERMANY GMBH—See Head B.V.; *Int'l*, pg. 3300
HEAD JAPAN CO., LTD.—See Head B.V.; *Int'l*, pg. 3300
HEAD SPAIN S.A.—See Head B.V.; *Int'l*, pg. 3300
HEAD SPORT GMBH—See Head B.V.; *Int'l*, pg. 3300
HEAD TECHNOLOGY GMBH—See Head B.V.; *Int'l*, pg. 3300
HEAD UK LTD—See Head B.V.; *Int'l*, pg. 3300
HECKLER & KOCH INC.—See BAE Systems plc; *Int'l*, pg. 798
HENRY'S TACKLE LLC—See Peak Global Holdings, LLC; *U.S. Private*, pg. 3123
HILL COUNTRY WHOLESALE INC.—See Peter Pan Bus Lines, Inc.; *U.S. Private*, pg. 3159
HLC, LLC—See MiddleGround Management, LP; *U.S. Private*, pg. 2712
HOBBY-POOL TECHNOLOGIES GMBH—See BWT Aktiengesellschaft; *Int'l*, pg. 1233
HTM USA HOLDINGS INC.—See Head B.V.; *Int'l*, pg. 3300
HYDROAIR INTERNATIONAL A/S—See AEA Investors LP; *U.S. Private*, pg. 113
HYLETE, INC.; *U.S. Private*, pg. 2019
IBD BIKES UK LIMITED—See Dorel Industries, Inc.; *Int'l*, pg. 2176
IMPERIAL INTERNATIONAL—See H. Betti Industries, Inc.; *U.S. Private*, pg. 1824
INARIA INTERNATIONAL INC.—See Fairfax Financial Holdings Limited; *Int'l*, pg. 2605
INDOOR CYCLING GROUP GMBH—See Brunswick Corporation; *U.S. Public*, pg. 408
INTERNATIONAL BRAND MANAGEMENT LIMITED—See Frasers Group plc; *Int'l*, pg. 2765
INTERNETFITNESS.COM, INC.; *U.S. Private*, pg. 2122
INTERSPORT ATHLETICS AE—See FOURLIS HOLDINGS S.A.; *Int'l*, pg. 2755
INTERSPORT ISI, D.O.O.—See Enterprise Investors Sp. z o.o.; *Int'l*, pg. 2452
INTER VALLEY POOL SUPPLY, INC.—See GHK Capital Partners LP; *U.S. Private*, pg. 1690
INTEX DEVELOPMENT COMPANY LTD.—See Intex Recreation Corp.; *U.S. Private*, pg. 2128
INTEX TRADING B. V.—See Intex Recreation Corp.; *U.S. Private*, pg. 2128
INTEX TRADING S.R.O.—See Intex Recreation Corp.; *U.S. Private*, pg. 2128
INTREPID SOUTHEAST INC.; *U.S. Private*, pg. 2129
JACK WOLFSKIN GMBH & CO. KGAA—See Topgolf Callaway Brands Corp.; *U.S. Public*, pg. 2164
JAPANA CO., LTD.—See Alpen Co., Ltd.; *Int'l*, pg. 366
J&B IMPORTERS INC.; *U.S. Private*, pg. 2153
J&B IMPORTERS PACIFIC INC.—See J&B Importers Inc.; *U.S. Private*, pg. 2153
JEANNEAU AMERICA INC.—See Beneteau S.A; *Int'l*, pg. 972
JERRY'S SPORTS CENTER, INC.; *U.S. Private*, pg. 2202
JET-LINE PRODUCTS INC.—See Pool Corporation; *U.S. Public*, pg. 1701
JET LINE PRODUCTS LONG ISLAND—See Pool Corporation; *U.S. Public*, pg. 1701
JET LINE PRODUCTS OF SOUTH JERSEY, LLC—See Pool Corporation; *U.S. Public*, pg. 1701
JET LINE PRODUCTS TEXAS, LLC—See Pool Corporation; *U.S. Public*, pg. 1701
JUNCKER BIKE PARTS B.V.—See Accell Group N.V.; *Int'l*, pg. 80
K2 SPORTS EUROPE GMBH—See Kohlberg & Company, LLC; *U.S. Private*, pg. 2338
KA-BAR KNIVES, INC.—See CUTCO Corporation; *U.S. Private*, pg. 1131
KAL KUSTOM ENTERPRISES; *U.S. Private*, pg. 2256
KEE ACTION SPORTS CANADA—See KEE Action Sports LLC; *U.S. Private*, pg. 2271
KEE ACTION SPORTS EUROPE—See KEE Action Sports LLC; *U.S. Private*, pg. 2271
KEE ACTION SPORTS LLC; *U.S. Private*, pg. 2271
KELTY, INC.—See Exxel Outdoors, Inc.; *U.S. Private*, pg. 1453
KENT INTERNATIONAL INC.; *U.S. Private*, pg. 2207
KIESLER POLICE SUPPLY INC.; *U.S. Private*, pg. 2304
KILDEMOES A/S—See Grimaldi Industri AB; *Int'l*, pg. 3086
KING PAR CORPORATION; *U.S. Private*, pg. 2309
KIOTI GOLF CO., LTD.—See Daedong Corporation; *Int'l*, pg. 1906
KITBAG LIMITED—See Kynetic LLC; *U.S. Private*, pg. 2360
KLAFS AG—See Kohler Company; *U.S. Private*, pg. 2339

423910 — SPORTING AND RECREA...

KLAFS AMERICAS—See Kohler Company; *U.S. Private*, pg. 2339
KLAFS GMBH—See Kohler Company; *U.S. Private*, pg. 2339
KLONE LAB, LLC—See Madison Parker Capital; *U.S. Private*, pg. 2544
KNIGHTS APPAREL, INC.—See Hanesbrands Inc.; *U.S. Public*, pg. 983
KNORR SYSTEMS INC.—See Court Square Capital Partners, L.P.; *U.S. Private*, pg. 1069
KOGA TRADING A.G.—See Accell Group N.V.; *Int'l*, pg. 81
KOMBI, LTD.; *U.S. Private*, pg. 2342
K. WAH ASPHALT LIMITED—See Galaxy Entertainment Group Limited; *Int'l*, pg. 2871
LAFUMA AMERICA, INC.—See Calida Holding AG; *Int'l*, pg. 1264
LAFUMA BV—See Calida Holding AG; *Int'l*, pg. 1264
LAWRENCE A. BROOKS INC.; *U.S. Private*, pg. 2401
LESLIE'S, INC.; *U.S. Public*, pg. 1308
LFS INC.—See Trident Seafoods Corporation; *U.S. Private*, pg. 4230
LIFE FITNESS BRASIL—See KPS Capital Partners, LP; *U.S. Private*, pg. 2347
LIFE FITNESS JAPAN, LTD.—See KPS Capital Partners, LP; *U.S. Private*, pg. 2347
LINCOLN EQUIPMENT, INC.; *U.S. Private*, pg. 2457
LITEHOUSE PRODUCTS INC.; *U.S. Private*, pg. 2467
LLC ADIDAS, LTD.—See adidas AG; *Int'l*, pg. 146
LOEKIE B.V.—See Accell Group N.V.; *Int'l*, pg. 81
LSH INDUSTRIAL SOLUTIONS PTE. LTD.—See Bunzl plc; *Int'l*, pg. 1218
LUCKY BUMS LLC; *U.S. Private*, pg. 2511
MAJESTIC PRODUCTS B.V.—See Bunzl plc; *Int'l*, pg. 1219
MAMMUT SPORTS GROUP GMBH—See Bystronic AG; *Int'l*, pg. 1236
MAMMUT SPORTS GROUP INC.—See Bystronic AG; *Int'l*, pg. 1236
MANEX & POWER MARINE LTD—See Cullinan Holdings Limited; *Int'l*, pg. 1877
MARES ASIA PACIFIC LTD.—See Head B.V.; *Int'l*, pg. 3300
MASTEN-WRIGHT, INC.; *U.S. Private*, pg. 2607
MAURICE SPORTING GOODS, INC.—See Peak Global Holdings, LLC; *U.S. Private*, pg. 3123
MAVERIK LACROSSE—See Fairfax Financial Holdings Limited; *Int'l*, pg. 2605
MAVIC, INC.—See ANTA Sports Products Limited; *Int'l*, pg. 480
MAX SOURCE HOLDING LTD—See Brookfield Corporation; *Int'l*, pg. 1181
MG GOLF INC.; *U.S. Private*, pg. 2694
MIDWAY U.S.A. INC.—See Midway Ford Truck Center Inc.; *U.S. Private*, pg. 2718
MITSUSHIBA INTERNATIONAL INC.; *U.S. Private*, pg. 2751
MONARCH POOL SYSTEMS EUROPE S.A.S.—See Amotiv Limited; *Int'l*, pg. 431
MOUNTAIN HARDWEAR, INC.—See Columbia Sportswear Company; *U.S. Public*, pg. 535
MOUNTAINS PLUS OUTDOOR GEAR; *U.S. Private*, pg. 2801
MOUNTED MEMORIES, INC.—See Kynetic LLC; *U.S. Private*, pg. 2360
MT SPORTS LLC—See Peak Global Holdings, LLC; *U.S. Private*, pg. 3123
NASHVILLE SPORTING GOODS, LLC—See Genesco Inc.; *U.S. Public*, pg. 930
NIKE EUROPEAN OPERATIONS NETHERLANDS B.V.—See NIKE, Inc.; *U.S. Public*, pg. 1529
NIKITA EHF—See ANTA Sports Products Limited; *Int'l*, pg. 480
NORTH COUNTRY MARKETING LTD.; *U.S. Private*, pg. 2944
NORTHERN WHOLESALE SUPPLY, LLC—See Sun Capital Partners, Inc.; *U.S. Private*, pg. 3860
NORTH SAILS GROUP, LLC—See Windway Capital Corp.; *U.S. Private*, pg. 4539
NUCCI BROS INC.; *U.S. Private*, pg. 2972
OFB REISEN GMBH—See Global Business Travel Group, Inc.; *U.S. Public*, pg. 941
OGIO INTERNATIONAL, INC.—See Topgolf Callaway Brands Corp.; *U.S. Public*, pg. 2164
OLD TIME SPORTS, INC.—See '47 Brand, LLC; *U.S. Private*, pg. 1
OURAY SPORTSWEAR, LLC; *U.S. Private*, pg. 3050
OUTDOOR SPECIALTY PRODUCTS, INC.; *U.S. Public*, pg. 1624
PACIFIC CYCLE INC.—See Dorel Industries, Inc.; *Int'l*, pg. 2176
PACIFIC SPORTS EXCHANGE, INC.; *U.S. Public*, pg. 1632
PANACEA PRODUCTS CORPORATION; *U.S. Private*, pg. 3084
PERFORMANCE PLUS CARTS—See Morgan Stanley; *U.S. Public*, pg. 1474
POOL CORPORATION; *U.S. Public*, pg. 1701
POOLDAWG.COM, INC.; *U.S. Private*, pg. 3228
POOL SUPPLIER, S.L.—See Fluidra SA; *Int'l*, pg. 2714
POOL WATER PRODUCTS INC.; *U.S. Private*, pg. 3228

P & R CANVAS, LLC.—See Pipe Welders Inc.; *U.S. Private*, pg. 3189
PROFESSIONAL FITNESS CONCEPTS, INC.; *U.S. Private*, pg. 3275
PROPHET CORP.; *U.S. Private*, pg. 3286
PRO-TEC INDUSTRIES—See V. F. Corporation; *U.S. Public*, pg. 2269
P.T. ADIDAS INDONESIA LTD.—See adidas AG; *Int'l*, pg. 146
PT VIKING SEATECH INDONESIA—See Enerpac Tool Group Corp.; *U.S. Public*, pg. 766
PYRAMYD AIR LTD.—See Gen Cap America, Inc.; *U.S. Private*, pg. 1660
QUALITY POOL SUPPLY CO.; *U.S. Private*, pg. 3320
QUEENSWAY GOLF INTERNATIONAL LIMITED—See China Fortune Investments (Holding) Limited; *Int'l*, pg. 1503
RAND INTERNATIONAL LEISURE PRODUCTS; *U.S. Private*, pg. 3353
RAWLINGS CANADA INC.—See Major League Baseball; *U.S. Private*, pg. 2555
RAWLINGS CANADA INC.—See The Seidler Company, LLC; *U.S. Private*, pg. 4116
RECREATIONAL PRODUCTS DIV.—See Bell Industries, Inc.; *U.S. Public*, pg. 295
REEBOK-CCM HOCKEY AS—See adidas AG; *Int'l*, pg. 147
REEBOK-CCM HOCKEY OY—See Leonard Green & Partners, L.P.; *U.S. Private*, pg. 2425
REEBOK DE MEXICO, S.A. DE C.V.—See Leonard Green & Partners, L.P.; *U.S. Private*, pg. 2425
REEBOK INDIA COMPANY—See Leonard Green & Partners, L.P.; *U.S. Private*, pg. 2424
REEBOK IRELAND LIMITED—See adidas AG; *Int'l*, pg. 146
REEBOK JOFA AB—See Leonard Green & Partners, L.P.; *U.S. Private*, pg. 2424
REEBOK JOFA AS—See Leonard Green & Partners, L.P.; *U.S. Private*, pg. 2424
REGENT SPORTS CORPORATION; *U.S. Private*, pg. 3387
RFC, INC.—See Leonard Green & Partners, L.P.; *U.S. Private*, pg. 2424
RIDDELL, INC.—See Fenway Partners, LLC; *U.S. Private*, pg. 1495
ROLLER DERBY SKATE CORP.; *U.S. Private*, pg. 3474
R&R POOL & PATIO INC.; *U.S. Private*, pg. 3333
RSR GROUP TEXAS INC—See RSR Group Inc.; *U.S. Private*, pg. 3497
RUSSELL EUROPE LIMITED—See Berkshire Hathaway Inc.; *U.S. Public*, pg. 305
SALOMON CANADA SPORTS LTD—See ANTA Sports Products Limited; *Int'l*, pg. 480
SC ADIDAS UKRAINE—See adidas AG; *Int'l*, pg. 146
SCHOOLMASTERS—See School-Tech, Inc.; *U.S. Private*, pg. 3568
SCHOOL-TECH, INC.; *U.S. Private*, pg. 3568
SCHWIMMBAD-SAUNA-AUSSTATTUNGS-GROSSHANDELS GESMBH—See Fluidra SA; *Int'l*, pg. 2714
SCP BENELUX SA—See Pool Corporation; *U.S. Public*, pg. 1701
SCP DISTRIBUTORS LLC—See Pool Corporation; *U.S. Public*, pg. 1702
SCP FRANCE SAS—See Pool Corporation; *U.S. Public*, pg. 1702
SCP POOL DISTRIBUTORS SPAIN S.L.—See Pool Corporation; *U.S. Public*, pg. 1702
SEABOARD INDUSTRIES; *U.S. Private*, pg. 3583
SEA EAGLE BOATS, INC.—See Harrison-Hoge Industries, Inc.; *U.S. Private*, pg. 1871
SECURE LINE S.R.L.—See Bunzl plc; *Int'l*, pg. 1219
SECURE SERVICE S.R.L.—See Bunzl plc; *Int'l*, pg. 1219
SEEMANN SUB GMBH & CO KG—See Johnson Outdoors Inc.; *U.S. Public*, pg. 1201
SERVICE SUPPLY LIMITED, INC.; *U.S. Private*, pg. 3616
SHAN POOLS, INC.; *U.S. Private*, pg. 3625
SHOCO INC.; *U.S. Private*, pg. 3639
SIDELINE, INC.—See Jones Plastic & Engineering Company, LLC; *U.S. Private*, pg. 2234
SIERRA DESIGNS, INC.—See Exxel Outdoors, Inc.; *U.S. Private*, pg. 1453
SIMMS FISHING PRODUCTS CORP.—See Vista Outdoor Inc.; *U.S. Public*, pg. 2305
SKI CHALET INC.; *U.S. Private*, pg. 3681
SLUMBERJACK INC.—See Exxel Outdoors, Inc.; *U.S. Private*, pg. 1453
SMART PARTS INC.; *U.S. Private*, pg. 3691
SOG INTERNATIONAL, INC.; *U.S. Private*, pg. 3706
SOUTHEAST MARINE SALES AND SERVICES, INC.—See Correct Craft, Inc.; *U.S. Private*, pg. 1058
SPA PARTS PLUS; *U.S. Private*, pg. 3743
SPORTS LICENSED DIVISION OF THE ADIDAS GROUP, LLC—See adidas AG; *Int'l*, pg. 146
SPORTSMAN SUPPLY INC.; *U.S. Private*, pg. 3761
SPORTS UNLIMITED, INC.; *U.S. Private*, pg. 3761
S/R INDUSTRIES INC.; *U.S. Private*, pg. 3519
SSF SCHWIMMBAD GMBH—See Kohler Company; *U.S. Private*, pg. 2339
SSI INTERNATIONAL (HK) LTD.—See Head B.V.; *Int'l*, pg. 3300

CORPORATE AFFILIATIONS

STAR STRUCK/PROTEAM, INC.—See Kynetic LLC; *U.S. Private*, pg. 2360
SUPERIOR POOL PRODUCTS, INC.—See Pool Corporation; *U.S. Public*, pg. 1702
SWIX SPORT JAPAN K.K.—See Ferd AS; *Int'l*, pg. 2636
SWIX SPORT USA INC.—See Ferd AS; *Int'l*, pg. 2636
TAYLOR MADE GOLF LIMITED—See Taylor Made Golf Company, Inc.; *U.S. Private*, pg. 3940
TAYLOR MADE KOREA LTD.—See adidas AG; *Int'l*, pg. 146
TAYLOR MADE PRODUCTS—See LCI Industries; *U.S. Public*, pg. 1295
TEE OFF, LLC—See adidas AG; *Int'l*, pg. 146
THANE DIRECT UK LTD.—See H.I.G. Capital, LLC; *U.S. Private*, pg. 1832
TORAU SPORT AG—See Goldwin, Inc.; *Int'l*, pg. 3035
TOTAL SAFETY SUPPLY BELGIUM BVBA—See Bunzl plc; *Int'l*, pg. 1219
THE TRAVEL HAMMOCK INC.; *U.S. Private*, pg. 4128
TRB SYSTEMS INTERNATIONAL, INC.; *U.S. Public*, pg. 2186
TRI YEOVIL UK LIMITED—See Frasers Group plc; *Int'l*, pg. 2765
TUNTURI NEW FITNESS B.V.—See Accell Group N.V.; *Int'l*, pg. 81
UNIFIED MARINE INC.; *U.S. Private*, pg. 4282
UNIFIED MARINE, INC.; *U.S. Private*, pg. 4283
UNIVERSAL ATHLETIC SERVICE, INC.; *U.S. Private*, pg. 4303
USA SUMMIT DISTRIBUTION, LLC.; *U.S. Private*, pg. 4321
VARIFLEX INC.—See Transom Capital Group, LLC; *U.S. Private*, pg. 4209
VARTEX AB—See Accell Group N.V.; *Int'l*, pg. 81
VELO & OXYGEN OY—See Grimaldi Industri AB; *Int'l*, pg. 3086
V.F. GRACE INC.; *U.S. Private*, pg. 4328
VICSA SAFETY PERU S.A.C.—See Bunzl plc; *Int'l*, pg. 1219
VICSA STEELPRO COLOMBIA S.A.S—See Bunzl plc; *Int'l*, pg. 1219
VIKING SEATECH LTD.—See Buckthorn Partners LLP; *Int'l*, pg. 1210
VIKING SEATECH LTD.—See OEP Capital Advisors, L.P.; *U.S. Private*, pg. 2997
VOLKL SPORTS GMBH & CO. KG—See Kohlberg & Company, LLC; *U.S. Private*, pg. 2338
WEST END DIVING & SALVAGE, INC.; *U.S. Private*, pg. 4485
WILD SALES, LLC.; *U.S. Private*, pg. 4518
WINORA STAIGER GMBH—See Accell Group N.V.; *Int'l*, pg. 80
WOLVERINE SPORTS—See School-Tech, Inc.; *U.S. Private*, pg. 3568
WORLDMART SERVICES LTD.—See Brookfield Corporation; *Int'l*, pg. 1181
WORLDWIDE GOLF ENTERPRISES, INC.; *U.S. Private*, pg. 4569
W.W. ADCOCK INC.; *U.S. Private*, pg. 4423
YAKGEAR, INC.—See T-H Marine Supplies Inc.; *U.S. Private*, pg. 3910
ZODIAC GROUP AUSTRALIA PTY. LTD.—See The Carlyle Group Inc.; *U.S. Public*, pg. 2057
ZODIAC ITALIA SRL—See The Carlyle Group Inc.; *U.S. Public*, pg. 2057
ZODIAC POOL DEUTSCHLAND GMBH - MOMBRIS—See The Carlyle Group Inc.; *U.S. Public*, pg. 2057
ZODIAC POOL IBERICA S.L.U.—See The Carlyle Group Inc.; *U.S. Public*, pg. 2057
ZODIAC POOL SYSTEMS CANADA, INC.—See The Carlyle Group Inc.; *U.S. Public*, pg. 2057

423920 — TOY AND HOBBY GOODS AND SUPPLIES MERCHANT WHOLESALERS

4KIDZ INC.; *U.S. Private*, pg. 15
ABOUT TIME INC.; *U.S. Private*, pg. 39
ADAMAS VENTURES, INC.; *Int'l*, pg. 124
ADC DOLLS INC.—See Gefinor S.A.; *Int'l*, pg. 2911
AERIAL BOUQUETS; *U.S. Private*, pg. 117
AGETEC INC.; *U.S. Private*, pg. 127
AG INDUSTRIES, INC.—See AG Ajikawa Corporation; *Int'l*, pg. 196
AJUNGILAK AS—See Bystronic AG; *Int'l*, pg. 1236
A LARGE EVIL CORPORATION LTD.—See Funko Inc.; *U.S. Public*, pg. 893
AL QURAISHI LEISURE SERVICES—See Ali Zaid Al-Quraishi & Brothers Co.; *Int'l*, pg. 323
AMAIN.COM, INC.; *U.S. Private*, pg. 215
AMERICAN FITNESS WHOLESALERS LLC—See Gotham Cigars, LLC; *U.S. Private*, pg. 1745
AMERICAN GIRL PLACE INC.—See Mattel, Inc.; *U.S. Public*, pg. 1398
AMERICAN PROMOTIONAL EVENTS, INC.—See Anderson Companies, Inc.; *U.S. Private*, pg. 276
ASIA PIONEER ENTERTAINMENT LIMITED—See Asia Pioneer Entertainment Holdings Limited; *Int'l*, pg. 614
THE BABY EINSTEIN COMPANY, LLC—See The Walt Disney Company; *U.S. Public*, pg. 2139
BALL, BOUNCE & SPORT, INC.; *U.S. Private*, pg. 460

N.A.I.C.S. INDEX

423930 — RECYCLABLE MATERIAL...

BANDAI ESPANA S.A.—See BANDAI NAMCO Holdings Inc.; *Int'l*, pg. 828
BANDAI (GUANGZHOU) CO., LTD.—See BANDAI NAMCO Holdings Inc.; *Int'l*, pg. 828
BANDAI (H.K.) CO., LTD.—See BANDAI NAMCO Holdings Inc.; *Int'l*, pg. 828
BANDAI KOREA CO., LTD.—See BANDAI NAMCO Holdings Inc.; *Int'l*, pg. 828
BANDAI NAMCO GAMES FRANCE S.A.S.—See BANDAI NAMCO Holdings Inc.; *Int'l*, pg. 829
BANDAI NAMCO TOYS & COLLECTIBLES AMERICA INC.—See BANDAI NAMCO Holdings Inc.; *Int'l*, pg. 828
BANDAI POLSKA SP. Z O.O.—See BANDAI NAMCO Holdings Inc.; *Int'l*, pg. 828
BANDAI S.A.—See BANDAI NAMCO Holdings Inc.; *Int'l*, pg. 828
BANDAI U.K. LTD.—See BANDAI NAMCO Holdings Inc.; *Int'l*, pg. 828
BATTAT INC.; *U.S. Private*, pg. 487
BIG TREE GROUP INC.; *Int'l*, pg. 1022
B.J. ALAN COMPANY; *U.S. Private*, pg. 420
BUILD-A-BEAR WORKSHOP DENMARK APS—See Build-A-Bear Workshop, Inc.; *U.S. Public*, pg. 409
CAPCOM ENTERTAINMENT, INC.—See Capcom Co., Ltd.; *Int'l*, pg. 1302
CARRERA REVELL OF AMERICAS, INC.; *U.S. Private*, pg. 771
CARTA MUNDI, INC.—See Cartamundi N.V.; *Int'l*, pg. 1348
CARTAMUNDI IRELAND LTD.—See Hasbro, Inc.; *U.S. Public*, pg. 988
CENTRIC HOLDINGS S.A.; *Int'l*, pg. 1413
CHELSEA TEDDY BEAR COMPANY—See EBSCO Industries, Inc.; *U.S. Private*, pg. 1324
COMBI (SHANGHAI) CO., LTD.—See Combi Corporation; *Int'l*, pg. 1708
COMBI (TAIWAN) CO., LTD.—See Combi Corporation; *Int'l*, pg. 1708
CRANIUM, INC.—See Hasbro, Inc.; *U.S. Public*, pg. 987
CREATIVE SALES & MARKETING ASSOCIATES; *U.S. Private*, pg. 1090
CRICUT, INC.—See North Cove Partners; *U.S. Private*, pg. 2944
DAPAT INC.; *U.S. Private*, pg. 1158
DISCOVERY TOYS, LLC—See Eos International, Inc.; *U.S. Private*, pg. 1411
DREAMGEAR, LLC; *U.S. Private*, pg. 1275
DREAM VINA CO., LTD.—See Dream International Ltd; *Int'l*, pg. 2202
ELECTRONICS BOUTIQUE AUSTRALIA PTY. LTD.—See GameStop Corp.; *U.S. Public*, pg. 895
ELECTRONICS BOUTIQUE CANADA INC.—See GameStop Corp.; *U.S. Public*, pg. 895
EMERY DISTRIBUTORS INC.; *U.S. Private*, pg. 1382
ENDLESS GAMES INC.—See Goliath International Holding BV; *Int'l*, pg. 3036
ENTERTAINMENT EARTH, INC.; *U.S. Private*, pg. 1404
FISHER-PRICE, INC.—See Mattel, Inc.; *U.S. Public*, pg. 1398
FUNKO INC.; *U.S. Public*, pg. 892
GAME SOURCE, INC.; *U.S. Private*, pg. 1640
GAMESTOP DEUTSCHLAND GMBH—See GameStop Corp.; *U.S. Public*, pg. 895
GAMESTOP NORWAY AS—See GameStop Corp.; *U.S. Public*, pg. 896
GAMESTOP SCHWEIZ GMBH—See GameStop Corp.; *U.S. Public*, pg. 896
GAMESTOP SWEDEN AB—See GameStop Corp.; *U.S. Public*, pg. 896
GAMES WORKSHOP DEUTSCHLAND GMBH—See Games Workshop Group PLC; *Int'l*, pg. 2877
GAMES WORKSHOP OZ PTY LIMITED—See Games Workshop Group PLC; *Int'l*, pg. 2877
GAMES WORKSHOP-SQUARE ONE—See Games Workshop Group PLC; *Int'l*, pg. 2877
GIFTCRAFT INC.—See Giftcraft Ltd.; *Int'l*, pg. 2970
GIOCHI PREZIOSI S.P.A.; *Int'l*, pg. 2977
GRAUPNER / SJ GMBH; *Int'l*, pg. 3061
HAPPINET MARKETING CORPORATION—See Happinet Corporation; *Int'l*, pg. 3269
HASBRO AUSTRALIA PTY LTD—See Hasbro, Inc.; *U.S. Public*, pg. 987
HASBRO B.V.—See Hasbro, Inc.; *U.S. Public*, pg. 987
HASBRO DEUTSCHLAND GMBH—See Hasbro, Inc.; *U.S. Public*, pg. 988
HASBRO HELLAS INDUSTRIAL & COMMERCIAL COMPANY S.A.—See Hasbro, Inc.; *U.S. Public*, pg. 988
HASBRO HONG KONG LIMITED—See Hasbro, Inc.; *U.S. Public*, pg. 988
HASBRO MANAGERIAL SERVICES LLC—See Hasbro, Inc.; *U.S. Public*, pg. 988
HASBRO S.A.—See Hasbro, Inc.; *U.S. Public*, pg. 988
HASBRO TOYS & GAMES HOLDINGS, S.L.—See Hasbro, Inc.; *U.S. Public*, pg. 988
HOBBICO, INC.; *U.S. Private*, pg. 1958
HOBBYTYME DISTRIBUTORS; *U.S. Private*, pg. 1958
HORIZON HOBBY DISTRIBUTORS; *U.S. Private*, pg. 1981
IDT ELECTRONIC PRODUCTS LIMITED—See IDT International Limited; *Int'l*, pg. 3596

INGRAM ENTERPRISES INC.; *U.S. Private*, pg. 2076
INNEX, INC.; *U.S. Private*, pg. 2080
INNOVATIVE USA, INC.; *U.S. Private*, pg. 2083
INTERNATIONAL PLAYTHINGS, LLC—See Epoch Co. Ltd.; *Int'l*, pg. 2463
JAKKS SALES CORPORATION—See JAKKS Pacific, Inc.; *U.S. Public*, pg. 1186
KELLY TOYS HOLDINGS, LLC—See Berkshire Hathaway Inc.; *U.S. Public*, pg. 298
KELLYTOY USA INC.; *U.S. Private*, pg. 2277
KIDS PREFERRED INC.; *U.S. Private*, pg. 2303
KLSLV D.O.O—See I. KLOUKINAS - I. LAPPAS CONSTRUCTION & COMMERCE S.A.; *Int'l*, pg. 3565
LAI GA TOYS CO. LIMITED—See Amuse Group Holding Ltd.; *Int'l*, pg. 442
LANCASTER BINGO CO. INC.; *U.S. Private*, pg. 2381
LOUNGEFLY, LLC—See Funko Inc.; *U.S. Public*, pg. 893
MAISTO INTERNATIONAL, INC.; *U.S. Private*, pg. 2554
MANHATTAN GROUP LLC—See Crown Crafts, Inc.; *U.S. Public*, pg. 596
MARKLIN, INC.—See Gebr. Marklin & Cie. GmbH; *Int'l*, pg. 2909
MARKLIN-VERTRIEBS AG—See Gebr. Marklin & Cie. GmbH; *Int'l*, pg. 2909
MCKENZIE SPORTS PRODUCTS LLC—See Gridiron Capital, LLC; *U.S. Private*, pg. 1786
MEGA BRANDS AUSTRALIA PTY. LTD.—See Mattel, Inc.; *U.S. Public*, pg. 1398
MEGA BRANDS EUROPE NV—See Mattel, Inc.; *U.S. Public*, pg. 1398
MEGA BRANDS ITALY SPA—See Mattel, Inc.; *U.S. Public*, pg. 1398
MEGA BRANDS LATINOAMERICA SA DE CV—See Mattel, Inc.; *U.S. Public*, pg. 1398
MGA ENTERTAINMENT, INC.; *U.S. Private*, pg. 2694
MICROMANIA GROUP SAS—See GameStop Corp.; *U.S. Public*, pg. 896
MIDASPLAYER AB—See Microsoft Corporation; *U.S. Public*, pg. 1439
MING WIN ELECTRONICS LIMITED—See IDT International Limited; *Int'l*, pg. 3596
MOTORSPORT MARKETING, INC.—See Peterson Manufacturing Company Inc.; *U.S. Private*, pg. 3160
NYKO TECHNOLOGIES INC.; *U.S. Private*, pg. 2976
ORIENTAL TRADING COMPANY, INC.—See Berkshire Hathaway Inc.; *U.S. Public*, pg. 313
PARADISE GALLERIES, INC.; *U.S. Private*, pg. 3090
PERKINS GROUP SERVICES—See Cathay Investments Limited; *Int'l*, pg. 1360
PET QWERKS, INC.—See Platinum Equity, LLC; *U.S. Private*, pg. 3202
P'KOLINO LLC; *U.S. Private*, pg. 3059
PLAYAGS MEXICO, S. DE R.L. DE C.V.—See PlayAGS, Inc.; *U.S. Public*, pg. 1697
PLAYMOBIL AUSTRIA GMBH—See Geobra Brandstatter GmbH & Co. KG; *Int'l*, pg. 2932
PLAYMOBIL CANADA INC.—See Geobra Brandstatter GmbH & Co. KG; *Int'l*, pg. 2932
PLAYMOBIL FRANCE SARL—See Geobra Brandstatter GmbH & Co. KG; *Int'l*, pg. 2932
PLAYMOBIL HELLAS S.A.—See Geobra Brandstatter GmbH & Co. KG; *Int'l*, pg. 2932
PLAYMOBIL IBERICA S.A.U.—See Geobra Brandstatter GmbH & Co. KG; *Int'l*, pg. 2932
PLAYMOBIL MERCHANDISING MEXICANA, S.A. DE C.V.—See Geobra Brandstatter GmbH & Co. KG; *Int'l*, pg. 2932
PLAYMOBIL SWISS GMBH—See Geobra Brandstatter GmbH & Co. KG; *Int'l*, pg. 2932
PLAYMOBIL UK LTD.—See Geobra Brandstatter GmbH & Co. KG; *Int'l*, pg. 2932
PLAYMONSTER LLC—See Audax Group, Limited Partnership; *U.S. Private*, pg. 390
PLAY VISIONS, INC.; *U.S. Private*, pg. 3212
PRESSMAN TOY CORPORATION; *U.S. Private*, pg. 3255
PRESTIGE TOY CORP.; *U.S. Private*, pg. 3256
QIANHAI MERCANTILE EXCHANGE CO., LTD.—See Hong Kong Exchanges & Clearing Limited; *Int'l*, pg. 3466
S.A. HASBRO N.V.—See Hasbro, Inc.; *U.S. Public*, pg. 988
SBAR'S, INC.; *U.S. Private*, pg. 3559
SENTIMENTS INC.—See Prospect Hill Growth Partners, L.P.; *U.S. Private*, pg. 3288
SMALL WORLD TOYS—See Rivenrock Capital LLC; *U.S. Private*, pg. 3443
SMILEMAKERS FOR CHILDREN CO.—See Berkshire Hathaway Inc.; *U.S. Public*, pg. 313
SMILEMAKERS, INC.—See Berkshire Hathaway Inc.; *U.S. Public*, pg. 313
SOUTHERN HOBBY SUPPLY INC.; *U.S. Private*, pg. 3732
TEN THOUSAND VILLAGES; *U.S. Private*, pg. 3964
TOTSY MANUFACTURING COMPANY, INC.; *U.S. Private*, pg. 4192
TY INC.; *U.S. Private*, pg. 4267
UNEEDA DOLL COMPANY, LTD.; *U.S. Private*, pg. 4281
VALLEY WHOLESALE COMPANY INC.; *U.S. Private*, pg. 4336
WHOW GAMES GMBH—See Azerion Group N.V.; *Int'l*, pg. 778

WINDY CITY NOVELTIES, INC.; *U.S. Private*, pg. 4540
WM. K. WALTHERS, INC.; *U.S. Private*, pg. 4552
WMS INTERNATIONAL (MACAU) LIMITED—See Light & Wonder, Inc.; *U.S. Public*, pg. 1315
WRT WORLD ENTERPRISES INC.; *U.S. Private*, pg. 4574
XTC PRODUCTS, INC.; *U.S. Private*, pg. 4583

423930 — RECYCLABLE MATERIAL MERCHANT WHOLESALERS

AADLEN BROTHERS AUTO WRECKING; *U.S. Private*, pg. 31
ABLE WASTE MANAGEMENT LTD.—See Hills Waste Solutions Limited; *Int'l*, pg. 3393
ACE BATTERY SALES, INC.; *U.S. Private*, pg. 56
ACME REFINING SCRAP IRON & METAL COMPANY; *U.S. Private*, pg. 61
ACT-B RECYCLING CO., LTD.—See Dowa Holdings Co., Ltd.; *Int'l*, pg. 2182
ADVANCED ENVIRONMENTAL RECYCLING TECHNOLOGIES, INC.—See CRH plc; *Int'l*, pg. 1845
AEVITAS SPECIALTY SERVICES CORP.—See Aevitas, Inc.; *Int'l*, pg. 183
AGC FABRITECH CO., LTD.—See AGC Inc.; *Int'l*, pg. 202
AGMET METALS INC; *U.S. Private*, pg. 128
ALBERT BROS., INC.; *U.S. Private*, pg. 152
ALCO IRON & METAL CO.; *U.S. Private*, pg. 154
ALIPLAST FRANCE RECYCLAGE S.A.S.—See Hera S.p.A.; *Int'l*, pg. 3356
A&L IRON AND METAL COMPANY; *U.S. Private*, pg. 20
ALLAN COMPANY; *U.S. Private*, pg. 174
ALLEGHENY RAW MATERIALS, LLC—See AMG Resources Corp.; *U.S. Private*, pg. 262
ALLEN COUNTY RECYCLERS INC.; *U.S. Private*, pg. 178
ALLIED ALLOYS LP—See Stainless Steel Midwest LLC; *U.S. Private*, pg. 3776
ALLIED METAL, LLC; *U.S. Private*, pg. 186
ALLY WASTE SERVICES, LLC; *U.S. Private*, pg. 194
ALTER TRADING CORPORATION; *U.S. Private*, pg. 206
AMERICAN IRON & STEEL COMPANY; *U.S. Private*, pg. 238
AMERICAN METALS COMPANY, INC.; *U.S. Private*, pg. 241
AMG RESOURCES PACIFIC CORP—See AMG Resources Corp.; *U.S. Private*, pg. 262
AMITA HOLDINGS CO., LTD.; *Int'l*, pg. 428
ANHEUSER-BUSCH RECYCLING CORPORATION—See Anheuser-Busch InBev SA/NV; *Int'l*, pg. 465
ARYAVAN ENTERPRISE LIMITED; *Int'l*, pg. 588
A. SHEFTEL AND SONS, INC.; *U.S. Private*, pg. 23
A&S METALS - MODESTO—See SGS Enterprises Inc.; *U.S. Private*, pg. 3622
A&S OF CASTROVILLE INC—See SGS Enterprises Inc.; *U.S. Private*, pg. 3622
THE ASSOCIATION OF PLASTIC RECYCLERS; *U.S. Private*, pg. 3989
ATLAS METAL & IRON CORPORATION; *U.S. Private*, pg. 379
ATM RECYCLING, INC.; *U.S. Private*, pg. 381
AUTO SHRED RECYCLING, LLC—See European Metal Recycling Limited; *Int'l*, pg. 2557
BAKER IRON & METAL CO. INC.—See Cohen Brothers, Inc.; *U.S. Private*, pg. 962
BALL PIPE & SUPPLY INC.—See Yaffe Iron & Metal Company Inc.; *U.S. Private*, pg. 4584
BALLYVESEY RECYCLING SOLUTIONS LTD—See Ballyvesey Holdings Limited; *Int'l*, pg. 809
BATLINER PAPER STOCK COMPANY, INC.—See Pioneer Industries, Inc.; *U.S. Private*, pg. 3187
B CLINKSTON & SONS INC.—See Louis Padnos Iron & Metal Company; *U.S. Private*, pg. 2498
BEACON RECYCLING INC.—See Beacon Redevelopment Industrial Corp.; *U.S. Public*, pg. 285
BEHR IRON & STEEL, INC.—See Alter Trading Corporation; *U.S. Private*, pg. 207
BENFIELD SANITATION SERVICES, INC.—See Republic Services, Inc.; *U.S. Public*, pg. 1786
BERG MILL SUPPLY COMPANY INC.; *U.S. Private*, pg. 530
BERMCO ALUMINUM; *U.S. Private*, pg. 535
BESTWAY RECYCLING COMPANY INC.; *U.S. Private*, pg. 544
BLAZE RECYCLING & METALS LLC—See Newell Recycling Southeast, LLC; *U.S. Private*, pg. 2914
BORG COMPRESSED STEELE; *U.S. Private*, pg. 618
BOWERS FIBERS INC.; *U.S. Private*, pg. 625
BROOKFIELD AUTO WRECKERS INC.; *U.S. Private*, pg. 663
BROWNWOOD IRON & METAL CO—See M. Lipsitz & Co., Ltd.; *U.S. Private*, pg. 2527
BRYAN IRON & METAL, LTD.—See M. Lipsitz & Co., Ltd.; *U.S. Private*, pg. 2527
BUYMYTRONICS.COM; *U.S. Private*, pg. 699
CABLO METALL-RECYCLING UND HANDEL GMBH—See Aurubis AG; *Int'l*, pg. 715
CALBAG METALS CO.; *U.S. Private*, pg. 716
CALBAG METALS CO. - TACOMA—See Calbag Metals Co.; *U.S. Private*, pg. 716

3951

423930 — RECYCLABLE MATERIAL...

CAL MICRO RECYCLING—See Tide Rock Holdings, LLC; *U.S. Private*, pg. 4167
CAMDEN IRON & METAL INC.; *U.S. Private*, pg. 728
CANUSA CORPORATION; *U.S. Private*, pg. 736
C & D SCRAP METAL RECYCLERS CO, INC.—See Merchants Metals Recycling II CD, LLC; *U.S. Private*, pg. 2670
CEDARWOOD-YOUNG COMPANY, INC.—See Allan Company; *U.S. Private*, pg. 174
CELLMARK PERU S.A.C.—See CellMark AB; *Int'l*, pg. 1393
CELLMARK RECYCLING BENELUX BV—See CellMark AB; *Int'l*, pg. 1393
CELLMARK THAILAND CO LTD—See CellMark AB; *Int'l*, pg. 1393
CHIMIREC AVRASYA ENDUSTRIYEL ATIK SAN. VE TIC. LTD.—See Chimirec; *Int'l*, pg. 1479
CHIMIREC POLSKA SP. Z O.O.—See Chimirec; *Int'l*, pg. 1480
CHIMIREC; *Int'l*, pg. 1479
CITY CARTON INC.; *U.S. Private*, pg. 905
CITY FIBERS INC.; *U.S. Private*, pg. 905
CLEAN HARBORS CANADA INC.—See Clean Harbors, Inc.; *U.S. Public*, pg. 509
CMC RECYCLING—See Commercial Metals Company; *U.S. Public*, pg. 545
COEXPAN BRASIL EMBALAGENS LTDA—See Coexpan S.A.; *Int'l*, pg. 1690
COEXPAN DEUTSCHLAND GMBH—See Coexpan S.A.; *Int'l*, pg. 1690
COEXPAN FRANCE SA—See Coexpan S.A.; *Int'l*, pg. 1690
COEXPAN MEXICO, S.A DE C.V.—See Coexpan S.A.; *Int'l*, pg. 1690
COHEN BROTHERS, INC.; *U.S. Private*, pg. 962
COMPLETE RESOURCES COMPANY—See Complete General Construction Co. Inc.; *U.S. Private*, pg. 1000
CONSOLIDATED SCRAP RESOURCES; *U.S. Private*, pg. 1022
CONTINENTAL PAPER GRADING CO. INC.; *U.S. Private*, pg. 1030
CORNEC SAS; *Int'l*, pg. 1801
COVANTA BABYLON, INC.—See EQT AB; *Int'l*, pg. 2473
COVANTA BRISTOL, INC.—See EQT AB; *Int'l*, pg. 2473
COVANTA DELAWARE VALLEY LLC—See EQT AB; *Int'l*, pg. 2473
COVANTA HUDSON VALLEY RENEWABLE ENERGY LLC—See EQT AB; *Int'l*, pg. 2473
COVANTA ONONDAGA LIMITED PARTNERSHIP—See EQT AB; *Int'l*, pg. 2474
COVANTA PITTSFIELD, LLC—See EQT AB; *Int'l*, pg. 2474
COVANTA UNION, LLC—See EQT AB; *Int'l*, pg. 2474
COVANTA WARREN ENERGY RESOURCE CO., LLC—See EQT AB; *Int'l*, pg. 2474
CUSTOM ALLOY SCRAP SALES, INC.; *U.S. Private*, pg. 1128
THE DAVID J. JOSEPH COMPANY—See Nucor Corporation; *U.S. Public*, pg. 1554
DC MATERIALS, INC.—See Vulcan Materials Company; *U.S. Public*, pg. 2314
DELTA GROUP PTY LTD - CONCRETE RECYCLING DIVISION—See Delta Group Pty Ltd; *Int'l*, pg. 2018
DELTA GROUP PTY LTD - METAL RECYCLING DIVISION—See Delta Group Pty Ltd; *Int'l*, pg. 2018
DERICHEBOURG UMWELT GMBH—See Derichebourg S.A.; *Int'l*, pg. 2042
DOMINION NICKEL ALLOYS LTD.; *Int'l*, pg. 2161
DONALD WARD LIMITED; *Int'l*, pg. 2163
DOWA ENVIRONMENTAL MANAGEMENT CO., LTD.—See Dowa Holdings Co., Ltd.; *Int'l*, pg. 2183
DOWA METALS & MINING AMERICA, INC.—See Dowa Holdings Co., Ltd.; *Int'l*, pg. 2183
DS SMITH RECYCLING UK LIMITED—See DS Smith Plc; *Int'l*, pg. 2209
DYNAMIC RECYCLING; *U.S. Private*, pg. 1298
ECO-SYSTEM RECYCLING CO., LTD.—See Dowa Holdings Co., Ltd.; *Int'l*, pg. 2184
EKO-KOM, A.S.; *Int'l*, pg. 2339
ELG UTICA ALLOYS (HARTFORD), INC.—See ELG Utica Alloys, Inc.; *U.S. Private*, pg. 1359
EMPIRE SERVICES, INC.—See Greenwave Technology Solutions, Inc.; *U.S. Public*, pg. 965
EMR LTD—See European Metal Recycling Limited; *Int'l*, pg. 2556
ENVI-PAK A.S.; *Int'l*, pg. 2453
ETABLISSEMENTS EMILE LLAU; *Int'l*, pg. 2519
EUROPEAN METAL RECYCLING BV—See European Metal Recycling Limited; *Int'l*, pg. 2556
EUROPEAN METAL RECYCLING GMBH—See European Metal Recycling Limited; *Int'l*, pg. 2556
EUROPEAN METAL RECYCLING GMBH—See European Metal Recycling Limited; *Int'l*, pg. 2556
F.A.P'S INC.—See Stellex Capital Management LP; *U.S. Private*, pg. 3800
FARNELL ELECTRONIC COMPONENTS LIMITED—See Avnet, Inc.; *U.S. Public*, pg. 253
FAR WEST FIBERS INC.; *U.S. Private*, pg. 1473
FERROUS PROCESSING & TRADING CO.—See Soave Enterprises, LLC; *U.S. Private*, pg. 3702
FREEDOM METALS INC.; *U.S. Private*, pg. 1603

FRITZ ENTERPRISES INC.; *U.S. Private*, pg. 1613
FU'AN QINGMEI ENERGY MATERIALS CO., LTD.—See GEM Co., Ltd.; *Int'l*, pg. 2914
FULUHASHI EPO CORPORATION; *Int'l*, pg. 2844
GALLOO N.V.; *Int'l*, pg. 2875
GARDEN STREET IRON & METAL; *U.S. Private*, pg. 1643
GAUTAM EXIM LIMITED; *Int'l*, pg. 2891
GDB INTERNATIONAL, INC.; *U.S. Private*, pg. 1654
GEM (CHENZHOU) SOLID WASTE TREATMENT CO., LTD.—See GEM Co., Ltd.; *Int'l*, pg. 2914
GEM ECOPRO NEW ENERGY MATERIALS CO., LTD.—See GEM Co., Ltd.; *Int'l*, pg. 2914
GEM SUPPLY CHAIN MANAGEMENT (SHANGHAI) CO., LTD.—See GEM Co., Ltd.; *Int'l*, pg. 2914
GEM (TIANJIN) URBAN MINERALS RECYCLING INDUSTRY DEVELOPMENT CO., LTD.—See GEM Co., Ltd.; *Int'l*, pg. 2914
GEM (WUHAN) NEW ENERGY VEHICLE SERVICE CO., LTD.—See GEM Co., Ltd.; *Int'l*, pg. 2914
GEM (WUHAN) URBAN MINERALS RECYCLING INDUSTRY PARK DEVELOPMENT CO., LTD.—See GEM Co., Ltd.; *Int'l*, pg. 2914
GENERAL METALS OF TACOMA, INC.—See Radius Recycling, Inc.; *U.S. Public*, pg. 1760
GLENCORE CANADA CORPORATION—See Glencore plc; *Int'l*, pg. 2990
GLOBAL IMPEX, INC.; *U.S. Private*, pg. 1714
GLOBAL RECYCLING INC.; *U.S. Private*, pg. 1717
GOLDEN INDUSTRIES INC.; *U.S. Private*, pg. 1732
GREENLAND (AMERICA) INC.; *U.S. Private*, pg. 1778
GREENLEAF AUTO RECYCLERS, LLC—See LKQ Corporation; *U.S. Public*, pg. 1334
GREEN PARTS INTERNATIONAL, INC.; *U.S. Private*, pg. 1773
GREENSTAR LLC—See Waste Management, Inc.; *U.S. Public*, pg. 2333
GREIF PLASTICS ITALY PACKAGING SERVICE—See Greif Inc.; *U.S. Public*, pg. 968
GUANGZHOU ASIA STEEL CO., LTD.—See China Metal Recycling (Holdings) Limited; *Int'l*, pg. 1524
GUANWEI RECYCLING CORP.; *Int'l*, pg. 3169
HENAN MUTONG ENVIRONMENTAL INDUSTRY CO., LTD.—See GEM Co., Ltd.; *Int'l*, pg. 2914
HERBOLD MECKESHEIM GMBH—See Hillenbrand, Inc.; *U.S. Public*, pg. 1036
HERITAGE ENVIRONMENTAL SERVICES, LLC—See EQT AB; *Int'l*, pg. 2482
HERMAN STRAUSS INC.; *U.S. Private*, pg. 1925
HERSHMAN CAPITAL CORP.; *U.S. Private*, pg. 1927
HI-GREEN CARBON LIMITED; *Int'l*, pg. 3380
HOLLANDER INTERNATIONAL SYSTEMS LIMITED—See Vista Equity Partners, LLC; *U.S. Private*, pg. 4400
HUBEI ERZHONG RENEWABLE RESOURCES MARKET DEVELOPMENT CO., LTD.—See GEM Co., Ltd.; *Int'l*, pg. 2914
HUGO NEU-PROLER CO.—See Hugo Neu Corporation; *U.S. Private*, pg. 2004
HUMAN N, INC; *Int'l*, pg. 3529
HUNAN GEM YINGHONG RESOURCE RECYCLING CO., LTD.—See GEM Co., Ltd.; *Int'l*, pg. 2914
HURON VALLEY STEEL CORP.; *U.S. Private*, pg. 2012
HYMAN BRICKLE & SON, INC.; *U.S. Private*, pg. 2019
I.H. SCHLEZINGER, INC.—See Cohen Brothers, Inc.; *U.S. Private*, pg. 962
IMS RECYCLING SERVICE INC.; *U.S. Private*, pg. 2051
INNER MONGOLIA XINCHUANG RESOURCE RECYCLING CO., LTD.—See GEM Co., Ltd.; *Int'l*, pg. 2914
INTERNATIONAL METALS EKCO LTD.; *U.S. Private*, pg. 2188
ISCO METALS & SUPPLY, LLC—See European Metal Recycling Limited; *Int'l*, pg. 2557
ISMECA EUROPE SEMICONDUCTOR SA—See Cohu, Inc.; *U.S. Public*, pg. 529
ISMECA SEMICONDUCTOR (SUZHOU) CO. LTD.—See Cohu, Inc.; *U.S. Public*, pg. 529
ITALMACERI S.R.L.—See DS Smith Plc; *Int'l*, pg. 2209
JARVIS METALS RECYCLING INC.; *U.S. Private*, pg. 2188
JIANGXI GEM RESOURCE RECYCLING CO., LTD.—See GEM Co., Ltd.; *Int'l*, pg. 2914
JIANGXI GEM SCRAPPED CAR RECYCLING CO., LTD.—See GEM Co., Ltd.; *Int'l*, pg. 2914
JINGMEN DEWEI GEM TUNGSTEN RESOURCE RECYCLING CO., LTD.—See GEM Co., Ltd.; *Int'l*, pg. 2914
JINGMEN GEM CO., LTD.—See GEM Co., Ltd.; *Int'l*, pg. 2914
JINGMEN LVYUAN ENVIRONMENTAL PROTECTION INDUSTRY DEVELOPMENT CO., LTD.—See GEM Co., Ltd.; *Int'l*, pg. 2914
JOSEPH BEHR & SONS INC.; *U.S. Private*, pg. 2236
KEYWELL LLC; *U.S. Private*, pg. 2300
LINN PAPER STOCK COMPANY; *U.S. Private*, pg. 2462
LKQ ALL MODELS CORP.—See LKQ Corporation; *U.S. Public*, pg. 1335
LOEB INDUSTRIES INC.; *U.S. Private*, pg. 2479
LOUIS COHEN & SONS, INC.—See Medico Industries, Inc.; *U.S. Private*, pg. 2656
LOUIS PADNOS IRON & METAL COMPANY; *U.S. Private*, pg. 2498

CORPORATE AFFILIATIONS

LOUIS PADNOS IRON & METAL COMPANY - WYOMING RECYCLING DIVISION—See Louis Padnos Iron & Metal Company; *U.S. Private*, pg. 2498
MANITOBA CORPORATION; *U.S. Private*, pg. 2564
M.A. NORDEN COMPANY INC.; *U.S. Private*, pg. 2527
MARKET STREET RECYCLING LLC—See M. Lipsitz & Co., Ltd.; *U.S. Private*, pg. 2527
MARTEX FIBER SOUTHERN CORPORATION—See Leigh Fibers, Inc.; *U.S. Private*, pg. 2419
MASTER FIBERS INCORPORATED; *U.S. Private*, pg. 2607
M. BURSTEIN CO. INC.—See BMH Corp.; *U.S. Private*, pg. 600
MEGA METALS, INC.—See Audax Group, Limited Partnership; *U.S. Private*, pg. 390
MERVIS INDUSTRIES INC.; *U.S. Private*, pg. 2677
METALICO AKRON, INC.—See Metalico Inc.; *U.S. Private*, pg. 2681
METALICO ANNACO—See Metalico Inc.; *U.S. Private*, pg. 2681
METALICO NIAGARA, INC.—See Metalico Inc.; *U.S. Private*, pg. 2681
METALICO YOUNGSTOWN, INC.—See Metalico Inc.; *U.S. Private*, pg. 2681
METAL MANAGEMENT CONNECTICUT, INC.—See Sims Limited; *U.S. Public*, pg. 1883
METAL MANAGEMENT MIDWEST, INC.—See Sims Limited; *U.S. Public*, pg. 1883
METAL MANAGEMENT OHIO, INC.—See Sims Limited; *U.S. Public*, pg. 1883
METALS RECYCLING, L.L.C.—See Radius Recycling, Inc.; *U.S. Public*, pg. 1760
METAL TRADING CORPORATION; *U.S. Private*, pg. 2680
METRO METALS NORTHWEST INC.; *U.S. Private*, pg. 2686
MILLER COMPRESSING CO., INC.; *U.S. Private*, pg. 2733
MISSOURI METAL RECYCLING INC.—See Yaffe Iron & Metal Company Inc.; *U.S. Private*, pg. 4584
M. LIPSITZ & CO., LTD.; *U.S. Private*, pg. 2527
MODERN AMERICAN RECYCLING SERVICES, INC.; *U.S. Private*, pg. 2759
MORMIL CORP.—See Radius Recycling, Inc.; *U.S. Public*, pg. 1760
MOSKOWITZ BROS INC.—See Cohen Brothers, Inc.; *U.S. Private*, pg. 962
NATIONAL FIBER SUPPLY LLC; *U.S. Private*, pg. 2853
NATIONAL STEEL COMPRESSING—See M. Lipsitz & Co., Ltd.; *U.S. Private*, pg. 2527
NEWCO METALS INC.; *U.S. Private*, pg. 2914
NEWELL RECYCLING SOUTHEAST, LLC; *U.S. Private*, pg. 2914
NILES IRON & METAL CO. INC.; *U.S. Private*, pg. 2927
NIPPON PGM EUROPE S.R.O.—See Dowa Holdings Co., Ltd.; *Int'l*, pg. 2184
NORTHSTAR PULP AND PAPER CO.—See Casella Waste Systems, Inc.; *U.S. Public*, pg. 446
NORTHWEST WOOLEN MILLS—See Hyman Brickle & Son, Inc.; *U.S. Private*, pg. 2019
NOVUS WOOD GROUP, LP; *U.S. Private*, pg. 2968
OK IRON & METAL CO—See M. Lipsitz & Co., Ltd.; *U.S. Private*, pg. 2527
OMNISOURCE CORPORATION—See Steel Dynamics, Inc.; *U.S. Public*, pg. 1942
PACIFIC OROVILLE POWER, INC.—See EQT AB; *Int'l*, pg. 2474
PADNOS-SUMMIT—See Louis Padnos Iron & Metal Company; *U.S. Private*, pg. 2499
PERF GO-GREEN HOLDINGS, INC.; *U.S. Public*, pg. 1674
PICK-N-PULL AUTO DISMANTLERS—See Radius Recycling, Inc.; *U.S. Public*, pg. 1760
PICK-N-PULL AUTO & TRUCK DISMANTLERS—See Radius Recycling, Inc.; *U.S. Public*, pg. 1760
PIELET BROS TRADING INC.; *U.S. Private*, pg. 3178
PIONEER INDUSTRIES, INC.; *U.S. Private*, pg. 3187
PLASTIC REVOLUTIONS, INC.; *U.S. Private*, pg. 3199
PNG RECYCLING LIMITED—See Sims Limited; *U.S. Public*, pg. 1884
POLLOCK CORPORATION; *U.S. Private*, pg. 3225
PONCA IRON & METAL INC.—See Yaffe Iron & Metal Company Inc.; *U.S. Private*, pg. 4584
PRIME PLASTIC PRODUCTS, INC.; *U.S. Private*, pg. 3262
PROLERIZED NEW ENGLAND COMPANY LLC—See Radius Recycling, Inc.; *U.S. Public*, pg. 1760
PSC METALS - GARN, LLC—See Icahn Enterprises L.P.; *U.S. Public*, pg. 1085
PSC METALS INC.—See Icahn Enterprises L.P.; *U.S. Public*, pg. 1084
PSC METALS INC.—See Icahn Enterprises L.P.; *U.S. Public*, pg. 1085
PSC METALS—See Icahn Enterprises L.P.; *U.S. Public*, pg. 1084
PSC METALS—See Icahn Enterprises L.P.; *U.S. Public*, pg. 1084
RECOGIDA DE ACEITES Y GRASAS MARESME, S.L.U.—See Cie Automotive S.A.; *Int'l*, pg. 1605
RE COMMUNITY HOLDINGS II, INC.; *U.S. Private*, pg. 3364
RECYCLE AMERICA CO., L.L.C.—See Waste Management, Inc.; *U.S. Public*, pg. 2331

N.A.I.C.S. INDEX

423940 — JEWELRY, WATCH, PRE...

RECYCLE METAL & COMMODITIES PRIVATE LTD—See European Metal Recycling Limited; *Int'l*, pg. 2556
RECYCLE MIDLAND—See M. Lipsitz & Co., Ltd.; *U.S. Private*, pg. 2527
RECYCLING SERVICES, INC.—See Waste Management, Inc.; *U.S. Public*, pg. 2331
RECYCLING SERVICES INTERNATIONAL—See IMS Recycling Service Inc.; *U.S. Private*, pg. 2051
REVIVAL EXPANSION SA—See Galloo n.v.; *Int'l*, pg. 2875
RIVERSIDE SCRAP IRON & METAL CORPORATION; *U.S. Private*, pg. 3446
ROYAL PAPER STOCK COMPANY INC.; *U.S. Private*, pg. 3493
R.S. DAVIS RECYCLING, INC.; *U.S. Private*, pg. 3339
SADOFF & RUDOY INDUSTRIES, LLP; *U.S. Private*, pg. 3523
SALINA IRON & METAL CO.—See Allmetal Recycling, LLC; *U.S. Private*, pg. 192
SCHNITZER FRESNO, INC.—See Radius Recycling, Inc.; *U.S. Public*, pg. 1760
SCHNITZER NORTHEAST-CONCORD—See Radius Recycling, Inc.; *U.S. Public*, pg. 1760
SCHNITZER SOUTHEAST - ATLANTA—See Radius Recycling, Inc.; *U.S. Public*, pg. 1760
SCHNITZER SOUTHEAST - MACON—See Radius Recycling, Inc.; *U.S. Public*, pg. 1760
SCHNITZER STEEL BILLINGS—See Radius Recycling, Inc.; *U.S. Public*, pg. 1760
SCHNITZER STEEL HAWAII CORP.—See Radius Recycling, Inc.; *U.S. Public*, pg. 1760
SCHNITZER STEEL INDUSTRIES, INC.-WOODINVILLE—See Radius Recycling, Inc.; *U.S. Public*, pg. 1760
S.D. RICHMAN SONS, INC.; *U.S. Private*, pg. 3517
SDR PLASTICS, INC.; *U.S. Private*, pg. 3581
SEATTLE IRON & METALS CORP.; *U.S. Private*, pg. 3592
THE SEFA GROUP INC.—See Heidelberg Materials AG; *Int'l*, pg. 3314
SERVICE ALUMINUM CORP.; *U.S. Private*, pg. 3614
SGS ENTERPRISES INC.; *U.S. Private*, pg. 3622
SHANXI HONGYANG HAIOU WEEE RECOVERY & TREATMENT CO., LTD.—See GEM Co., Ltd.; *Int'l*, pg. 2914
SHAPIRO SALES COMPANY; *U.S. Private*, pg. 3625
SHINE BROS CORP.; *U.S. Private*, pg. 3637
SIA REFONDA—See BLRT Grupp AS; *Int'l*, pg. 1066
SIMON METALS LLC—See Graham Capital Group, LLC; *U.S. Private*, pg. 1751
SIMS E-RECYCLING (NZ) LIMITED—See Sims Limited; *U.S. Public*, pg. 1884
SIMS INDUSTRIAL PTY LIMITED—See Sims Limited; *U.S. Public*, pg. 1884
SIMSMETAL INDUSTRIES LIMITED—See Sims Limited; *U.S. Public*, pg. 1884
SIMS METAL MANAGEMENT - JERSEY CITY—See Sims Limited; *U.S. Public*, pg. 1884
SIMS M+R GMBH—See Sims Limited; *U.S. Public*, pg. 1884
SIMS RECYCLING SOLUTIONS AB—See Sims Limited; *U.S. Public*, pg. 1884
SIMS RECYCLING SOLUTIONS PTE LIMITED—See Sims Limited; *U.S. Public*, pg. 1884
SMH SUDDEUTSCHE METALLHANDELSGESELLSCHAFT MIT BESCHRANKTER HAFTUNG—See Diehl Stiftung & Co. KG; *Int'l*, pg. 2115
SOS METALS, INC.—See Berkshire Hathaway Inc.; *U.S. Public*, pg. 314
SOUTHERN RECYCLING INC.—See Houchens Industries, Inc.; *U.S. Private*, pg. 1990
SOUTHERN RECYCLING SALES, LLC—See European Metal Recycling Limited; *Int'l*, pg. 2557
SOUTHERN SCRAP RECYCLING MORGAN CITY, LLC—See European Metal Recycling Limited; *Int'l*, pg. 2557
SPC CORPORATION-PHILADELPHIA—See Camden Iron & Metal Inc.; *U.S. Private*, pg. 728
SPURLOCK SCRAP INC.; *U.S. Private*, pg. 3765
SSI INTERNATIONAL, INC.—See Radius Recycling, Inc.; *U.S. Public*, pg. 1760
STEELBRO INTERNATIONAL CO. INC.; *U.S. Private*, pg. 3796
SUN VALLEY FILM WASH, INC.—See PyroPure, Inc.; *U.S. Private*, pg. 3310
SYNCOT PLASTICS, INC.—See Vinmar International Limited; *U.S. Private*, pg. 4385
TECH-R2; *U.S. Private*, pg. 3952
TENENBAUM RECYCLING GROUP, LLC—See Alter Trading Corporation; *U.S. Private*, pg. 207
TENNESSEE VALLEY RECYCLING LLC; *U.S. Private*, pg. 3968
TERRELL IRON & METAL INC.—See M. Lipsitz & Co., Ltd.; *U.S. Private*, pg. 2527
THALHEIMER BROTHERS, INC.—See Audax Group, Limited Partnership; *U.S. Private*, pg. 390
THERMO FLUIDS INC.; *U.S. Private*, pg. 4142
TIANJIN BRANCH OF WUHAN GEM URBAN MINERAL EQUIPMENT CO., LTD.—See GEM Co., Ltd.; *Int'l*, pg. 2914
TOP METAL BUYERS INC.; *U.S. Private*, pg. 4186
TRADEMARK METALS RECYCLING LLC—See Nucor Corporation; *U.S. Public*, pg. 1554
TRANZACT CORPORATION—See Metalico Inc.; *U.S. Private*, pg. 2681
TRISHYIRAYA RECYCLING INDIA PRIVATE LTD.—See Sims Limited; *U.S. Public*, pg. 1884
TSR RECYCLING GMBH & CO. KG—See Alfa Acciai SpA; *Int'l*, pg. 307
TSR RECYCLING GMBH & CO. KG—See CRONIMET Holding GmbH; *Int'l*, pg. 1855
TYLER IRON & METAL COMPANY—See M. Lipsitz & Co., Ltd.; *U.S. Private*, pg. 2527
UNITED-SOUTHERN WASTE MATERIAL CO; *U.S. Private*, pg. 4302
UPSTATE SHREDDING, LLC; *U.S. Private*, pg. 4313
USHER ENTERPRISES, INC.—See The Pritzker Group - Chicago, LLC; *U.S. Private*, pg. 4100
VERSATILE METALS INC.; *U.S. Private*, pg. 4369
VIRIDOR (MARTOCK) LIMITED—See KKR & Co. Inc.; *U.S. Public*, pg. 1266
WASTE RECYCLING INC.; *U.S. Private*, pg. 4450
WECO TRADING INC.; *U.S. Private*, pg. 4468
WEEDHIRE INTERNATIONAL, INC.; *U.S. Private*, pg. 4469
WESSCO, LLC—See Nucor Corporation; *U.S. Public*, pg. 1554
WEYERHAEUSER COMPANY; *U.S. Public*, pg. 2365
WUHAN CITY CIRCLE (XIANTAO) URBAN MINERAL RESOURCES MARKET CO., LTD.—See GEM Co., Ltd.; *Int'l*, pg. 2914
WUHAN HANNENGTONG NEW ENERGY VEHICLE SERVICE CO., LTD.—See GEM Co., Ltd.; *Int'l*, pg. 2914
WUHAN SANYONG GEM AUTO PARTS REMANUFACTURING CO., LTD.—See GEM Co., Ltd.; *Int'l*, pg. 2914
YAFFE IRON & METAL COMPANY INC.; *U.S. Private*, pg. 4584
YANGZHOU NINGDA PRECIOUS METAL CO., LTD.—See GEM Co., Ltd.; *Int'l*, pg. 2914
YARD WORKS, LLC—See SiteOne Landscape Supply, Inc.; *U.S. Public*, pg. 1889
YUYAO XINGYOU METAL MATERIALS CO., LTD.—See GEM Co., Ltd.; *Int'l*, pg. 2914

423940 — JEWELRY, WATCH, PRECIOUS STONE, AND PRECIOUS METAL MERCHANT WHOLESALERS

ACCORD WATCH & JEWELLERY (INTERNATIONAL) LIMITED—See Asia Commercial Holdings Limited; *Int'l*, pg. 611
A CLASSIC TIME WATCH COMPANY INC.; *U.S. Private*, pg. 18
ALKA DIAMOND INDUSTRIES LIMITED; *Int'l*, pg. 329
AMANAYA VENTURES LIMITED; *Int'l*, pg. 410
A-MARK PRECIOUS METALS, INC.; *U.S. Public*, pg. 10
AMBROSE CHINA LIMITED—See Dickson Concepts (International) Limited; *Int'l*, pg. 2112
AMERICAN EXCHANGE GROUP; *U.S. Private*, pg. 232
AMERICAN HARTFORD GOLD GROUP LLC; *U.S. Private*, pg. 235
AMIKAM & PARAS DIAMOND CORPORATION; *U.S. Private*, pg. 263
ANSHUNI COMMERCIALS LIMITED; *Int'l*, pg. 479
ANTOLINI LUIGI & C. S.P.A.; *Int'l*, pg. 484
ARCADIA JEWELLERY LIMITED—See Affluent Partners Holdings Limited; *Int'l*, pg. 188
ARCOS HONG KONG LTD.—See ALROSA Co. Ltd.; *Int'l*, pg. 377
ASCH/GROSSBARDT, INC.; *U.S. Private*, pg. 348
ASIA BROADBAND, INC.; *U.S. Public*, pg. 213
ASIA COMMERCIAL HOLDINGS LIMITED; *Int'l*, pg. 611
ASIA TIME CORPORATION; *Int'l*, pg. 616
BAUER-WALSER AG; *Int'l*, pg. 894
BAUME & MERCIER, INC.—See Compagnie Financiere Richemont S.A.; *Int'l*, pg. 1741
BELAIR TIME CORP.—See Selco LLC; *U.S. Private*, pg. 3600
BEL-ORO INTERNATIONAL, INC.—See Berkshire Hathaway Inc.; *U.S. Public*, pg. 316
BENNETT BROTHERS, INC.; *U.S. Private*, pg. 527
BERTOLUCCI SA—See Dickson Concepts (International) Limited; *Int'l*, pg. 2112
BLUE DIAMONDS JEWELLERY WORLDWIDE PLC—See Hayleys PLC; *Int'l*, pg. 3291
BLUE NILE, INC.—See Bain Capital, LP; *U.S. Private*, pg. 436
BMC CAPITAL, INC.; *U.S. Private*, pg. 600
BORDERLESS HOLDINGS, INC.; *U.S. Private*, pg. 618
BREITLING CHINA LIMITED—See CVC Capital Partners SICAV-FIS S.A.; *Int'l*, pg. 1883
BREITLING FRANCE S.A.R.L.—See CVC Capital Partners SICAV-FIS S.A.; *Int'l*, pg. 1883
BREITLING ITALIA SRL—See CVC Capital Partners SICAV-FIS S.A.; *Int'l*, pg. 1883
BREITLING JAPAN LTD—See CVC Capital Partners SICAV-FIS S.A.; *Int'l*, pg. 1883
BREITLING USA INC.—See CVC Capital Partners SICAV-FIS S.A.; *Int'l*, pg. 1883
BUCHERER AG; *Int'l*, pg. 1209
BUY GOLD AND SILVER CORP.—See A-Mark Precious Metals, Inc.; *U.S. Public*, pg. 10
BUYSELL TECHNOLOGIES CO., LTD.; *Int'l*, pg. 1230
CALIFORNIA NUMISMATIC INVESTMENTS INC.; *U.S. Private*, pg. 720
CANNAGISTICS, INC.; *U.S. Public*, pg. 430
CARL SCHAEFER GOLD- UND SILBERSCHEIDEANSTALT GMBH—See Blue Cap AG; *Int'l*, pg. 1067
CAROLE INC.; *U.S. Private*, pg. 767
CASIO BRASIL COMERCIO DE PRODUTOS ELETRONICOS LTDA.—See Casio Computer Co., Ltd.; *Int'l*, pg. 1353
CENTRAL DYNAMIC INTERNATIONAL LIMITED—See Fulum Group Holdings Limited; *Int'l*, pg. 2844
C. HAFNER GMBH + CO. KG; *Int'l*, pg. 1240
CHARLESTON GOLD & DIAMOND EXCHANGE, INC.—See Envela Corporation; *U.S. Public*, pg. 780
CHASE-DURER LTD.; *U.S. Private*, pg. 860
CHATHAM CREATED GEMS INC.; *U.S. Private*, pg. 868
CHOPARD (ASIA) PTE LTD—See Chopard & Cie S.A.; *Int'l*, pg. 1582
CHOPARD (GREAT BRITAIN) LTD—See Chopard & Cie S.A.; *Int'l*, pg. 1582
CHOPARD HONG KONG LTD—See Chopard & Cie S.A.; *Int'l*, pg. 1582
CHOPARD IBERICA S,L—See Chopard & Cie S.A.; *Int'l*, pg. 1582
CHOPARD ITALIA S.R.L—See Chopard & Cie S.A.; *Int'l*, pg. 1582
CHOPARD JAPAN LTD—See Chopard & Cie S.A.; *Int'l*, pg. 1582
CHOPARD MALAYSIA SDN BHD—See Chopard & Cie S.A.; *Int'l*, pg. 1582
CHOPARD MARKETING SERVICES, INC—See Chopard & Cie S.A.; *Int'l*, pg. 1582
CHOPARD TRADING (SHANGHAI) CO. LTD—See Chopard & Cie S.A.; *Int'l*, pg. 1582
CHOPARD UHRENHANDELS GMBH—See Chopard & Cie S.A.; *Int'l*, pg. 1582
CHOPARD USA LTD.—See Chopard & Cie S.A.; *Int'l*, pg. 1582
CHRIST JUWELIERE UND UHRMACHER SEIT 1863 GMBH—See 3i Group plc; *Int'l*, pg. 8
CHRONOSWISS ASIA PTE LTD—See Cortina Holdings Limited; *Int'l*, pg. 1808
CITIZEN WATCH CO. OF AMERICA, INC.—See Citizen Watch Co., Ltd.; *Int'l*, pg. 1624
CLOVER CORPORATION; *U.S. Private*, pg. 947
C. MAHENDRA EXPORTS LTD.; *Int'l*, pg. 1240
CNK INTERNATIONAL CO., LTD.; *Int'l*, pg. 1677
COBB HONG KONG—See W.R. Cobb Company; *U.S. Private*, pg. 4422
COINEX INC.; *U.S. Private*, pg. 965
COININVEST GMBH—See StoneX Group Inc.; *U.S. Public*, pg. 1951
THE COLIBRI GROUP, INC.—See CITIC Group Corporation; *Int'l*, pg. 1619
THE COLIBRI GROUP, INC.—See Founders Equity, Inc.; *U.S. Private*, pg. 1581
CONCORD WATCH COMPANY, S.A.—See Movado Group, Inc.; *U.S. Public*, pg. 1479
CONDUITY CAPITAL PLC; *Int'l*, pg. 1766
CONTINENTAL JEWELLERY (UK) LTD.—See Continental Holdings Limited; *Int'l*, pg. 1784
CORTINA HOLDINGS LIMITED; *Int'l*, pg. 1808
CORTINA WATCH CO., LTD.—See Cortina Holdings Limited; *Int'l*, pg. 1808
CORTINA WATCH HK LIMITED—See Cortina Holdings Limited; *Int'l*, pg. 1808
CORTINA WATCH PTE LTD.—See Cortina Holdings Limited; *Int'l*, pg. 1808
CORTINA WATCH SDN BHD—See Cortina Holdings Limited; *Int'l*, pg. 1808
CORTINA WATCH (THAILAND) CO., LTD.—See Cortina Holdings Limited; *Int'l*, pg. 1808
CORUM USA LLC—See Corum Watches S.A.R.L.; *Int'l*, pg. 1808
COSTAR INTERNATIONAL ENTERPRISES, INC.; *U.S. Private*, pg. 1063
C SMALL GROUP LIMITED—See China Silver Group Limited; *Int'l*, pg. 1551
DAMIANI INTERNATIONAL B.V.—See Damiani S.p.A.; *Int'l*, pg. 1957
DAMIANI JAPAN K.K.—See Damiani S.p.A.; *Int'l*, pg. 1957
DANIEL K INC.; *U.S. Private*, pg. 1156
DARSHAN ORNA LIMITED; *Int'l*, pg. 1973
DCK CONCESSIONS LTD.; *Int'l*, pg. 1991
DELACOUR ASIA PACIFIC PTE. LTD.—See Eurosports Global Limited; *Int'l*, pg. 2558
DE RIGO FRANCE SAS—See De Rigo S.p.A.; *Int'l*, pg. 1996
DE RIGO HELLAS S.A.—See De Rigo S.p.A.; *Int'l*, pg. 1996
DE RIGO JAPAN CO., LTD.—See De Rigo S.p.A.; *Int'l*, pg. 1997
DERIGO OY—See De Rigo S.p.A.; *Int'l*, pg. 1997
DE RIGO PORTUGAL, LDA.—See De Rigo S.p.A.; *Int'l*, pg. 1997
DE RIGO VISION AUSTRALIA PTY LTD—See De Rigo S.p.A.; *Int'l*, pg. 1997

423940 — JEWELRY, WATCH, PRE...

DE RIGO VISION ESPANA SA—See De Rigo S.p.A.; *Int'l*, pg. 1997
DE RIGO VISION MIDDLE EAST FZCO—See De Rigo S.p.A.; *Int'l*, pg. 1997
DE RIGO VISION TRADING CO., LTD.—See De Rigo S.p.A.; *Int'l*, pg. 1997
DIAMOND SA; *Int'l*, pg. 2105
DICKSON CONCEPTS (RETAIL) LIMITED—See Dickson Concepts (International) Limited; *Int'l*, pg. 2112
DICKSON (SHANGHAI) COMPANY LIMITED—See Dickson Concepts (International) Limited; *Int'l*, pg. 2112
THE DICKSON TRADING (TAIWAN) CO., LTD.—See Dickson Concepts (International) Limited; *Int'l*, pg. 2112
DKSH LUXURY AND LIFESTYLE EUROPE GMBH—See Diethelm Keller Holding Limited; *Int'l*, pg. 2116
DOMINION DIAMOND (INDIA) PRIVATE LIMITED—See Burgundy Diamond Mines Limited; *Int'l*, pg. 1224
DONALD BRUCE & CO.; *U.S. Private*, pg. 1259
EASTERN GOLD JADE CO., LTD.; *Int'l*, pg. 2272
EBEL WATCHES S.A.—See Movado Group, Inc.; *U.S. Public*, pg. 1479
EBOHR LUXURIES INTERNATIONAL CO., LIMITED—See Citychamp Watch & Jewellery Group Limited; *Int'l*, pg. 1629
EBULLION, INC.; *Int'l*, pg. 2287
EHINGER-SCHWARZ GMBH & CO. KG; *Int'l*, pg. 2328
EIGHTY JEWELLERS LIMITED; *Int'l*, pg. 2331
EMERCHANDISE GROUP LLC; *U.S. Private*, pg. 1380
EMPIRE DIAMOND CORPORATION; *U.S. Private*, pg. 1384
ENVELA CORPORATION; *U.S. Public*, pg. 779
ERNEST BOREL (GUANGZHOU) CO., LTD.—See Citychamp Watch & Jewellery Group Limited; *Int'l*, pg. 1629
ETHOS LIMITED; *Int'l*, pg. 2523
ETSY, INC.; *U.S. Public*, pg. 797
EUGENE BIRO CORP.; *U.S. Private*, pg. 1433
EUROPEAN PRECIOUS METAL TRADING GMBH—See StoneX Group Inc.; *U.S. Public*, pg. 1951
EWJ MACAU COMPANY LIMITED—See Emperor Watch & Jewellery Limited; *Int'l*, pg. 2386
EXQUISITE TIMEPIECES, INC.; *U.S. Private*, pg. 1452
FABERGE (UK) LIMITED—See Gemfields Group Limited; *Int'l*, pg. 2916
FAIRCHILD INTERNATIONAL—See Envela Corporation; *U.S. Public*, pg. 780
• FARBEST INDUSTRIES LTD.—See Citizen Watch Co., Ltd.; *Int'l*, pg. 1625
FESTARIA HOLDINGS CO., LTD.; *Int'l*, pg. 2646
FITZ DESIGN; *U.S. Private*, pg. 1536
FOLLI FOLLIE HONG KONG LTD.—See Folli Follie S.A.; *Int'l*, pg. 2721
FOLLI FOLLIE KOREA LTD.—See Folli Follie S.A.; *Int'l*, pg. 2721
FOLLI FOLLIE MALAYSIA LTD.—See Folli Follie S.A.; *Int'l*, pg. 2721
FOLLI FOLLIE POLAND SP. Z O.O.—See Folli Follie S.A.; *Int'l*, pg. 2721
FOLLI FOLLIE SINGAPORE LTD.—See Folli Follie S.A.; *Int'l*, pg. 2721
FOLLI FOLLIE SPAIN S.A.—See Folli Follie S.A.; *Int'l*, pg. 2721
FOLLI FOLLIE TAIWAN LTD.—See Folli Follie S.A.; *Int'l*, pg. 2721
FOLLI FOLLIE THAILAND LTD.—See Folli Follie S.A.; *Int'l*, pg. 2721
FOSSIL (AUSTRALIA) PTY LTD.—See Fossil Group, Inc.; *U.S. Public*, pg. 874
FOSSIL (EAST) LIMITED—See Fossil Group, Inc.; *U.S. Public*, pg. 874
FOSSIL EUROPE B.V.—See Fossil Group, Inc.; *U.S. Public*, pg. 874
FOSSIL EUROPE GMBH—See Fossil Group, Inc.; *U.S. Public*, pg. 875
FOSSIL FRANCE SA—See Fossil Group, Inc.; *U.S. Public*, pg. 875
FOSSIL PARTNERS, L.P.—See Fossil Group, Inc.; *U.S. Public*, pg. 875
FOSSIL TIME MALAYSIA SDN. BHD.—See Fossil Group, Inc.; *U.S. Public*, pg. 874
FOSSIL U.K. HOLDINGS LTD.—See Fossil Group, Inc.; *U.S. Public*, pg. 875
FOSSIL UK LTD.—See Fossil Group, Inc.; *U.S. Public*, pg. 875
THE FRANKLIN MINT, LLC—See Sequential Brands Group, Inc.; *U.S. Public*, pg. 1868
FREEMAN PRODUCTS—See Trophy Holdings Inc.; *U.S. Private*, pg. 4242
FULUHASHI CORPORATION (VIETNAM) LTD.—See Fuluhashi EPO Corporation; *Int'l*, pg. 2844
FURA SERVICES DMCC—See Fura Gems Inc.; *Int'l*, pg. 2846
GEM DIAMONDS MARKETING SERVICES BVBA—See Gem Diamonds Limited; *Int'l*, pg. 2914
GEMPORIA PARTNERSHIP LIMITED; *Int'l*, pg. 2916
GENENDER INTERNATIONAL INC.; *U.S. Private*, pg. 1660
GEPCO, LTD.; *U.S. Private*, pg. 1685
GOLD BY GOLD S.A.; *Int'l*, pg. 3023
GOLDLINE INC.—See A-Mark Precious Metals, Inc.; *U.S. Public*, pg. 10

GRAFF DIAMONDS HONG KONG LIMITED—See Graff Diamonds International Ltd.; *Int'l*, pg. 3050
HARRY BOCK COMPANY INC.; *U.S. Private*, pg. 1871
HELLENIC DISTRIBUTIONS S.A.—See Folli Follie S.A.; *Int'l*, pg. 2721
HENGDELI HOLDINGS LIMITED; *Int'l*, pg. 3346
HERAEUS PRECIOUS METALS MANAGEMENT INC.—See Heraeus Holding GmbH; *Int'l*, pg. 3357
HERMES INTERNATIONAL SCA; *Int'l*, pg. 3362
HERMES OF PARIS, INC.—See Hermes International SCA; *Int'l*, pg. 3363
HESS FINE ARTS, INC.; *U.S. Private*, pg. 1927
HIGH DESERT MINERAL RESOURCES, INC.—See Royal Gold, Inc.; *U.S. Public*, pg. 1815
H.STERN BUENOS AIRES—See H. Stern Com & Ind., S.A.; *Int'l*, pg. 3195
H.STERN ISRAEL—See H. Stern Com & Ind., S.A.; *Int'l*, pg. 3195
H.STERN LIMA—See H. Stern Com & Ind., S.A.; *Int'l*, pg. 3195
HYUNDAI HOME SHOPPING NETWORK CORPORATION—See Hyundai Department Store Co., Ltd.; *Int'l*, pg. 3556
IBB AMSTERDAM BV; *Int'l*, pg. 3569
IMAGE WATCHES, INC.; *U.S. Private*, pg. 2045
INDIAN JEWELERS SUPPLY CO.; *U.S. Private*, pg. 2061
INTERNATIONAL PRECIOUS METALS INCORPORATED; *U.S. Private*, pg. 2119
JAMES & SONS LTD.; *U.S. Private*, pg. 2183
JC TRADING INC.; *U.S. Private*, pg. 2194
JERRS PLUS INC.; *U.S. Private*, pg. 2202
JK FINDINGS USA—See JK Jewelry Inc.; *U.S. Private*, pg. 2211
JK JEWELRY INC.; *U.S. Private*, pg. 2211
JOHN HARDY USA, INC.; *U.S. Private*, pg. 2222
J&T COINS, LLC; *U.S. Private*, pg. 2155
JUVENIA (HONG KONG) COMPANY LIMITED—See Asia Commercial Holdings Limited; *Int'l*, pg. 611
JUVENIA MONTRES S.A.—See Asia Commercial Holdings Limited; *Int'l*, pg. 611
K&R INDUSTRIES INC.; *U.S. Private*, pg. 2250
KWIAT INC.; *U.S. Private*, pg. 2359
LAZARE KAPLAN INTERNATIONAL, INC.; *U.S. Private*, pg. 2402
LE PETIT-FILS DE L.U. CHOPARD FRANCE SAS—See Chopard & Cie S.A.; *Int'l*, pg. 1582
LEVY MARKETING & AWARDS; *U.S. Private*, pg. 2437
LIBERTY INVESTMENT EXCHANGE; *U.S. Private*, pg. 2444
LINKS OF LONDON, INC.—See Folli Follie S.A.; *Int'l*, pg. 2721
LINKS OF LONDON (INTERNATIONAL) LTD.—See Folli Follie S.A.; *Int'l*, pg. 2721
LION LAM DIAMOND CORP.; *U.S. Private*, pg. 2464
LONDON COIN GALLERIES INCORPORATED; *U.S. Private*, pg. 2483
LOU MADDALONI JEWELERS INC.; *U.S. Private*, pg. 2498
LUGANO DIAMONDS & JEWELRY, INC.—See Compass Diversified Holdings; *U.S. Public*, pg. 560
MAGICIAN INDUSTRIAL COMPANY LIMITED—See China Automobile New Retail (Holdings) Limited; *Int'l*, pg. 1484
MAN SANG JEWELLERY COMPANY LIMITED—See Affluent Partners Holdings Limited; *Int'l*, pg. 188
MARKET VECTORS REDEEMABLE GOLD TRUST—See Van Eck Associates Corp.; *U.S. Private*, pg. 4340
MGDL DISTRIBUTION PTY LTD—See Movado Group, Inc.; *U.S. Public*, pg. 1479
MGI LUXURY ASIA PACIFIC LTD.—See Movado Group, Inc.; *U.S. Public*, pg. 1479
MGI LUXURY GROUP G.M.B.H.—See Movado Group, Inc.; *U.S. Public*, pg. 1479
MINMETALS TONGLING GEM STONE CO., LTD.—See China Rare Earth Resources And Technology Co., Ltd.; *Int'l*, pg. 1546
MODERN COIN WHOLESALE INC.; *U.S. Private*, pg. 2760
MORE CONCEPT LIMITED—See China Automobile New Retail (Holdings) Limited; *Int'l*, pg. 1484
MOVADO GROUP DEUTSCHLAND G.M.B.H.—See Movado Group, Inc.; *U.S. Public*, pg. 1479
MOVADO GROUP OF CANADA, INC.—See Movado Group, Inc.; *U.S. Public*, pg. 1480
MOVADO WATCH COMPANY, S.A.—See Movado Group, Inc.; *U.S. Public*, pg. 1479
M.Z. BERGER & CO., INC.; *U.S. Private*, pg. 2529
NIXON EUROPE S.A.R.L.—See Trilantic Capital Management L.P.; *U.S. Private*, pg. 4231
NIXON, INC.—See Trilantic Capital Management L.P.; *U.S. Private*, pg. 4231
O.C. TANNER MANUFACTURING, INC.—See O.C. Tanner Company Inc.; *U.S. Private*, pg. 2981
O.C. TANNER RECOGNITION COMPANY, INC.—See O.C. Tanner Company Inc.; *U.S. Private*, pg. 2981
OKURA HOLDINGS CORPORATION—See GEO Holdings Corporation; *Int'l*, pg. 2932
OREGON SCIENTIFIC ENTERPRISE (SHANGHAI) LIMITED—See IDT International Limited; *Int'l*, pg. 3597
OTC INTERNATIONAL, LTD.; *U.S. Private*, pg. 3049

PACIFIC TIME CO., LTD.—See Cortina Holdings Limited; *Int'l*, pg. 1808
PACIFIC TIME PTE LTD.—See Cortina Holdings Limited; *Int'l*, pg. 1808
PANDAAMERICA CORP.; *U.S. Private*, pg. 3085
PATTERSON GARNET CORP.—See Peckham Industries, Inc.; *U.S. Private*, pg. 3127
PERSONALIZATIONMALL.COM, LLC—See 1-800-FLOWERS.COM, Inc.; *U.S. Public*, pg. 1
PLATINUM GUILD INTERNATIONAL (USA) JEWELRY, INC.; *U.S. Private*, pg. 3210
PROVIDENT METALS CORP.—See A-Mark Precious Metals, Inc.; *U.S. Public*, pg. 10
PYROFUSE—See Sigmund Cohn Corp.; *U.S. Private*, pg. 3649
RDI DIAMONDS, INC.; *U.S. Private*, pg. 3364
THE REALREAL, INC.; *U.S. Public*, pg. 2125
RICHEMONT AUSTRALIA PTY LIMITED—See Compagnie Financiere Richemont S.A.; *Int'l*, pg. 1741
RICHEMONT INTERNATIONAL SA—See Compagnie Financiere Richemont S.A.; *Int'l*, pg. 1741
RIO GRANDE INC.—See Berkshire Hathaway Inc.; *U.S. Public*, pg. 316
RLG DO BRASIL VAREJO LTDA.—See Compagnie Financiere Richemont S.A.; *Int'l*, pg. 1741
ROSYBLUE HONG KONG LTD.—See Rosy Blue Inc.; *U.S. Private*, pg. 3486
ROSY BLUE INC.; *U.S. Private*, pg. 3486
ROSY BLUE (INDIA) PVT. LTD.—See Rosy Blue Inc.; *U.S. Private*, pg. 3486
ROSY BLUE JEWELRY INC.—See Rosy Blue Inc.; *U.S. Private*, pg. 3486
ROSY BLUE LTD—See Rosy Blue Inc.; *U.S. Private*, pg. 3486
ROSY BLUE NV—See Rosy Blue Inc.; *U.S. Private*, pg. 3486
ROSYBLUE TRADING LLC—See Rosy Blue Inc.; *U.S. Private*, pg. 3486
ROSY BLUE TRADING (PTY) LTD—See Rosy Blue Inc.; *U.S. Private*, pg. 3486
SARASOTA RARE COIN GALLERY, INC.; *U.S. Private*, pg. 3549
SELCO LLC; *U.S. Private*, pg. 3600
SILO PHARMA INC.; *U.S. Public*, pg. 1880
SILVER TOWNE LP; *U.S. Private*, pg. 3662
SKAGEN DESIGNS, LTD.—See Fossil Group, Inc.; *U.S. Public*, pg. 875
SO ACCURATE GROUP INC.; *U.S. Private*, pg. 3701
SOCIETE CARTIER SAS—See Compagnie Financiere Richemont S.A.; *Int'l*, pg. 1741
SPECTRUM NUMISMATICS INTERNATIONAL, INC.—See Spectrum Group International, Inc.; *U.S. Public*, pg. 1917
STEVE PADIS JEWELRY PLUS ENTERPRISES; *U.S. Private*, pg. 3808
SUNCITI MANUFACTURERS LTD.—See Citizen Watch Co., Ltd.; *Int'l*, pg. 1625
SUNSHINE MINTING INC.; *U.S. Private*, pg. 3872
SWISSAM PRODUCTS LIMITED—See Movado Group, Inc.; *U.S. Public*, pg. 1480
SWISS LION AG—See Bucherer AG; *Int'l*, pg. 1209
SWISS TECHNOLOGY PRODUCTION SA—See Fossil Group, Inc.; *U.S. Public*, pg. 875
TACORI ENTERPRISES; *U.S. Private*, pg. 3921
TCJC INC.—See Charisma Brands, LLC; *U.S. Private*, pg. 850
TIME CITY (HONG KONG) LIMITED—See Asia Commercial Holdings Limited; *Int'l*, pg. 611
TOP WIN INTERNATIONAL TRADING LIMITED—See Citychamp Watch & Jewellery Group Limited; *Int'l*, pg. 1629
TOUCAN LLC; *U.S. Private*, pg. 4192
TROPHY HOLDINGS INC.; *U.S. Private*, pg. 4242
VISTATECH ENTERPRISES LTD.; *U.S. Private*, pg. 4403
VLC DISTRIBUTION COMPANY; *U.S. Private*, pg. 4408
WAKMANN WATCH (INTERNATIONAL) COMPANY LIMITED—See Asia Commercial Holdings Limited; *Int'l*, pg. 611
WATSONS PERSONAL CARE STORES SDN. BHD.—See CK Hutchison Holdings Limited; *Int'l*, pg. 1638
WORLDWIDE DIAMOND CO.; *U.S. Public*, pg. 4569
WORTHINGTON JEWELERS; *U.S. Private*, pg. 4570
ZEON FAR EAST LIMITED—See Herald Holdings Limited; *Int'l*, pg. 3358

423990 — OTHER MISCELLANEOUS DURABLE GOODS MERCHANT WHOLESALERS

2-K PURCHASING CENTRE INC; *Int'l*, pg. 3
AA IMPORTING; *U.S. Private*, pg. 29
ABLOY SECURITY INC.—See ASSA ABLOY AB; *Int'l*, pg. 636
AC COIN & SLOT SERVICE COMPANY; *U.S. Private*, pg. 45
ACCUREC LLC; *U.S. Private*, pg. 55
ADISH INTERNATIONAL CORPORATION—See Adish Co., Ltd.; *Int'l*, pg. 149
AFI EUROPE N.V—See Africa Israel Investments Ltd.; *Int'l*, pg. 190

423990 — OTHER MISCELLANEOUS...

AGOSTINI'S LIMITED; *Int'l*, pg. 213
AKWEL GEBZE TURKEY OTOMOTIVE SANAYI LIMITED SIRKETI—See AKWEL; *Int'l*, pg. 268
ALASKA PACIFIC TRADING COMPANY; *U.S. Private*, pg. 151
ALEXANDER/RYAN MARINE AND SAFETY LLC—See Court Square Capital Partners, L.P.; *U.S. Private*, pg. 1068
ALL-AMERICAN FIRE EQUIPMENT, INC.; *U.S. Private*, pg. 173
ALLAND ET ROBERT; *Int'l*, pg. 333
ALLEGRO CORPORATION; *U.S. Private*, pg. 178
ALL SAFE INDUSTRIES, INC.; *U.S. Private*, pg. 172
ALMY D.O.O.; *Int'l*, pg. 364
ALPI INTERNATIONAL, LTD; *U.S. Private*, pg. 200
ALSAEED TRADING COMPANY LTD.—See Hayel Saeed Anam Group of Companies; *Int'l*, pg. 3290
AMERICAN PROMOTIONAL EVENTS, INC.—See Anderson Companies, Inc.; *U.S. Private*, pg. 276
AMERICAN RETAIL ALLIANCE CORP.—See Leone Asset Management, Inc.; *U.S. Public*, pg. 1308
AMERISAFE INC.—See Dunes Point Capital, LLC; *U.S. Private*, pg. 1289
AMINCO INTERNATIONAL (USA) INC.; *U.S. Private*, pg. 263
AMPEX JAPAN LTD.—See Ampex Corporation; *U.S. Private*, pg. 266
ANCERO, LLC; *U.S. Private*, pg. 272
ANDERSON MERCHANDISERS, L.P.—See Anderson Companies, Inc.; *U.S. Private*, pg. 276
ANNA INTERNATIONAL LIMITED—See BWT Aktiengesellschaft; *Int'l*, pg. 1232
APG SECURITY LLC—See Allied Universal Manager LLC; *U.S. Private*, pg. 190
ARMADA HOLDINGS PTY LTD—See BlackWall Limited; *Int'l*, pg. 1062
AROSELLOS, S.A. DE C.V.—See Parker Hannifin Corporation; *U.S. Public*, pg. 1640
A ROSENTHAL (CAPE) (PTY) LTD.—See Agra Limited; *Int'l*, pg. 213
A ROSENTHAL (PTY) LTD.—See Agra Limited; *Int'l*, pg. 213
ARTISAN CONSUMER GOODS, INC.; *U.S. Public*, pg. 208
ASSA ABLOY SALES & MARKETING GROUP, INC.—See ASSA ABLOY AB; *Int'l*, pg. 637
ATLANTIC ZEISER SRL—See Atlantic Zeiser GmbH & Co.; *Int'l*, pg. 676
AVC CORP.; *U.S. Private*, pg. 404
AVKARE, INC.—See Amneal Pharmaceuticals, Inc.; *U.S. Public*, pg. 125
AVNERA CORPORATION—See Skyworks Solutions, Inc.; *U.S. Public*, pg. 1893
BALFOUR TIMBER COMPANY INC.; *U.S. Private*, pg. 459
BANDAI NAMCO AMUSEMENT EUROPE LTD.—See BANDAI NAMCO Holdings Inc.; *Int'l*, pg. 829
BARBER MONUMENTS LTD.—See Family Memorials Inc.; *Int'l*, pg. 2612
BASE-LINE, INC.; *U.S. Private*, pg. 484
BAUMER BETRIEBSHYGIENE VERTRIEBSGESELLSCHAFT MBH—See Bunzl plc; *Int'l*, pg. 1217
BAUPRO GMBH—See Etex SA/NV; *Int'l*, pg. 2521
BAY AREA BARRICADE SERVICE, INC.—See Trilantic Capital Management L.P.; *U.S. Private*, pg. 4231
BENELLI U.S.A. CORPORATION—See Fabbrica d'Armi Pietro Beretta S.p.A.; *Int'l*, pg. 2598
BENSUSSEN-DEUTSCH & ASSOCIATES INC.; *U.S. Private*, pg. 528
BENTRE AQUAPRODUCT IMPORT & EXPORT JOINT STOCK COMPANY; *Int'l*, pg. 977
BILLERUD SCANDINAVIA—See Billerud AB; *Int'l*, pg. 1030
B&J MUSIC LIMITED—See TPG Capital, L.P.; *U.S. Public*, pg. 2173
BLADE HQ, LLC; *U.S. Private*, pg. 577
BOGATI URNS COMPANY; *U.S. Private*, pg. 609
BOSSARD AUSTRALIA PTY LTD—See Bossard Holding AG; *Int'l*, pg. 1117
BOUNDLESS NETWORK; *U.S. Private*, pg. 623
BOWEN & POMEROY PTY. LTD.; *Int'l*, pg. 1124
BRADY IDENTIFICACION S.L.U.—See Brady Corporation; *U.S. Public*, pg. 378
BRAND ADDITION LIMITED—See Elysian Capital LLP; *Int'l*, pg. 2372
BRIGHTSTAR CORPORATION; *U.S. Private*, pg. 653
BUFFET GROUP CHINA—See Fondations Capital SA; *Int'l*, pg. 2725
BUFFET GROUP DISTRIBUTION GERMANY GMBH—See Fondations Capital SA; *Int'l*, pg. 2725
BUFFET GROUP JAPAN—See Fondations Capital SA; *Int'l*, pg. 2725
BUFFET GROUP USA, INC.—See Fondations Capital SA; *Int'l*, pg. 2725
BUILDING MATERIALS FINANCE, INC.—See Installed Building Products, Inc.; *U.S. Public*, pg. 1132
BUNZL AUSTRALASIA LTD—See Bunzl plc; *Int'l*, pg. 1217
BUNZL DE MEXICO S.A. DE C.V—See Bunzl plc; *Int'l*, pg. 1218
BUNZL DISTRIBUTION DANMARK A/S—See Bunzl plc; *Int'l*, pg. 1217

BUNZL DISTRIBUTION SPAIN, S.A.U.—See Bunzl plc; *Int'l*, pg. 1217
CALIFORNIA SAFETY & SUPPLY CO.—See Mallory Safety & Supply LLC; *U.S. Private*, pg. 2558
CAMFOUR, INC.—See Peter Pan Bus Lines, Inc.; *U.S. Private*, pg. 3159
CAMPBELL POOLS INC.; *Int'l*, pg. 1274
CAMSING GLOBAL, LLC; *U.S. Private*, pg. 732
CANAL WOOD LLC; *U.S. Private*, pg. 733
CANAL WOOD LLC—See Canal Wood LLC; *U.S. Private*, pg. 733
CANAL WOOD LLC—See Canal Wood LLC; *U.S. Private*, pg. 733
CAPCOM CO., LTD. - UENO FACILITY—See Capcom Co., Ltd.; *Int'l*, pg. 1302
CARTA MUNDI HUNGARY KFT.—See Cartamundi N.V.; *Int'l*, pg. 1347
CASCADIA VEHICLE TENTS, LLC—See Centre Partners Management LLC; *U.S. Private*, pg. 828
CASCIO MUSIC COMPANY INC.—See Geneva Supply, Inc.; *U.S. Private*, pg. 1670
CECISA - COMERCIO INTERNACIONAL S.A.—See Camargo Correa S.A.; *Int'l*, pg. 1267
CEG INTERACTIVE ENTERTAINMENT GMBH—See Capcom Co., Ltd.; *Int'l*, pg. 1302
CENTRAL SOUTH DISTRIBUTION, INC.; *U.S. Private*, pg. 824
CERAMTEC COMMERCIALE ITALIANA—See BC Partners LLP; *Int'l*, pg. 923
CERAMTEC FRANCE—See BC Partners LLP; *Int'l*, pg. 923
CERAMTEC MEDICAL PRODUCTS DIVISION CHINA—See BC Partners LLP; *Int'l*, pg. 923
CHAGRIN SAFETY SUPPLY, INC.—See Innovest Global, Inc.; *U.S. Public*, pg. 1127
CHUBU SUISAN CO., LTD.; *Int'l*, pg. 1594
CITIZEN (CHINA) PRECISION MACHINERY CO., LTD. - SHANGHAI BRANCH—See Citizen Watch Co., Ltd.; *Int'l*, pg. 1624
CJ JAPAN CORP.—See CJ Corporation; *Int'l*, pg. 1632
CKD CORPORATION—See CKD Corporation; *Int'l*, pg. 1639
CLOUD B, INC.—See Vinco Ventures, Inc.; *U.S. Public*, pg. 2298
CNJ DISTRIBUTING CORPORATION; *U.S. Private*, pg. 952
COHERENT (BEIJING) COMMERCIAL COMPANY LTD.—See Coherent Corp.; *U.S. Public*, pg. 526
COMBI ASIA LIMITED—See Combi Corporation; *Int'l*, pg. 1708
COMBI USA, INC.—See Combi Corporation; *Int'l*, pg. 1708
COMPLETE SALES & SERVICE; *U.S. Private*, pg. 1001
CONTROLLED PRODUCTS SYSTEMS GROUP, INC. - LOS ANGELES—See The Duchossois Group, Inc.; *U.S. Private*, pg. 4023
CONTROLLED PRODUCTS SYSTEMS GROUP, INC.—See The Duchossois Group, Inc.; *U.S. Private*, pg. 4023
COUSINEAU FOREST PRODUCTS, INC.—See Cousineau Inc.; *U.S. Private*, pg. 1071
CPIF VENTURE, INC.—See Colgate-Palmolive Company; *U.S. Public*, pg. 531
CRIST GROUP INC.—See Bain Capital, LP; *U.S. Private*, pg. 432
DALLAS-FORT WORTH ROOFING SUPPLY, LLC—See Beacon Roofing Supply, Inc.; *U.S. Public*, pg. 286
DAUGERON & FILS SAS—See Bunzl plc; *Int'l*, pg. 1218
THE DAVITT & HANSER MUSIC CO.—See Hanser Holdings International; *U.S. Private*, pg. 1856
DEI HOLDINGS, INC. - SOUND UNITED DIVISION—See Charlesbank Capital Partners, LLC; *U.S. Private*, pg. 855
DELTA DOOR & HARDWARE, LLC—See Platinum Equity, LLC; *U.S. Private*, pg. 3208
DELTA PLUS BENELUX N.V.—See Delta Plus Group; *Int'l*, pg. 2019
DELTA PLUS INDIA PVT. LTD.—See Delta Plus Group; *Int'l*, pg. 2019
DELTA PLUS (U.K.) LTD—See Delta Plus Group; *Int'l*, pg. 2019
DELTA PLUS UKRAINA SARL—See Delta Plus Group; *Int'l*, pg. 2019
DENON ELECTRONICS USA LLC—See Bain Capital, LP; *U.S. Private*, pg. 438
DENVER SIGN SUPPLY CO., INC.; *U.S. Private*, pg. 1208
DEP DISTRIBUTION EXCLUSIVE LTEE; *Int'l*, pg. 2040
DESIGN INTEGRATED TECHNOLOGY, INC.—See SPARC Holding Company; *U.S. Private*, pg. 3745
DIAMOND VISION SYSTEMS DIVISION—See Hyosung Heavy Industries Corp.; *Int'l*, pg. 3552
DIVAL SAFETY EQUIPMENT INC.; *U.S. Private*, pg. 1240
DOOR TO DOOR ORGANICS—See Dori Media Group Ltd.; *Int'l*, pg. 2176
DORI MEDIA AMERICA INC.—See Dori Media Group Ltd.; *Int'l*, pg. 2176
THE DOUGLAS STEAM SAW MILL & TIMBER COMPANY LIMITED—See Haldane Fisher Ltd.; *Int'l*, pg. 3227
DOWA GALLIUM WAX SALES CO., LTD.—See Dowa Holdings Co., Ltd.; *Int'l*, pg. 2183
DUALITE SALES & SERVICE, INC.; *U.S. Private*, pg. 1282
DUFRY BABASEL MULHOUSE LTD.—See Avolta AG; *Int'l*, pg. 749
DUNI A/S—See Duni AB; *Int'l*, pg. 2226

DUNI BENELUX B.V.—See Duni AB; *Int'l*, pg. 2226
DUNI BENELUX B.V.—See Duni AB; *Int'l*, pg. 2226
DUNI SALES POLAND SP. Z O.O.—See Duni AB; *Int'l*, pg. 2227
DUNI VERWALTUNGS GMBH—See Duni AB; *Int'l*, pg. 2226
DUNI ZAO—See Duni AB; *Int'l*, pg. 2227
DURAFLAME, INC.; *U.S. Private*, pg. 1292
E1 ENTERTAINMENT U.S. LP; *U.S. Private*, pg. 1307
EAGLE ONE GOLF PRODUCTS—See U.S. Eagle Corporation; *U.S. Private*, pg. 4270
EASTECH ELECTRONICS (HK) LIMITED—See Eastern Asia Technology Ltd.; *Int'l*, pg. 2271
EASTERN ASIA TECHNOLOGY (HK) LIMITED—See Eastern Asia Technology Ltd.; *Int'l*, pg. 2271
EGGER ROMANIA SRL—See Fritz Egger GmbH & Co.; *Int'l*, pg. 2793
ELAUT GERMANY GMBH—See Elaut International N.V.; *Int'l*, pg. 2343
ELAUT SPAIN SL—See Elaut International N.V.; *Int'l*, pg. 2343
ELAUT USA, INC.—See Elaut International N.V.; *Int'l*, pg. 2343
EMD MUSIC S.A.; *Int'l*, pg. 2376
E&M INTERNATIONAL, INC.—See Chenega Corporation; *U.S. Private*, pg. 872
ENERSYS A/S—See EnerSys; *U.S. Public*, pg. 766
ENERSYS AS—See EnerSys; *U.S. Public*, pg. 766
ENVIVA PELLETS NORTHAMPTON, LLC—See Enviva Inc.; *U.S. Public*, pg. 782
E.S.I. WORLDWIDE, INC.—See E&S International Enterprises Inc.; *U.S. Private*, pg. 1301
ESLINGAR S.A.—See Delta Plus Group; *Int'l*, pg. 2020
EUCATEX OF NORTH AMERICA, INC.—See Eucatex S.A. Industria e Comercio; *Int'l*, pg. 2525
EXTOL COMMERCIAL LIMITED; *Int'l*, pg. 2592
FANTAS EYES INC.; *U.S. Private*, pg. 1472
FEDERAL RESOURCES SUPPLY COMPANY—See KLH Capital L.P.; *U.S. Private*, pg. 2319
FGI OPERATING COMPANY, LLC—See Cerberus Capital Management, L.P.; *U.S. Private*, pg. 838
FHP DI R. FREUDENBERG S.A.S.—See Freudenberg SE; *Int'l*, pg. 2785
FIRE EATER HUNGARIA KFT.—See Fire Eater A/S; *Int'l*, pg. 2678
FIRE EATER NORGE AS—See Fire Eater A/S; *Int'l*, pg. 2678
FIRE EATER SPOL. S.R.O.—See Fire Eater A/S; *Int'l*, pg. 2678
FIRSTSTREET FOR BOOMERS AND BEYOND, INC.—See Peloton Equity LLC; *U.S. Private*, pg. 3131
FISKARS BRANDS ITALY S.R.L.—See Fiskars Oyj Abp; *Int'l*, pg. 2693
FISKARS BRANDS PTY. LTD.—See Fiskars Oyj Abp; *Int'l*, pg. 2693
FISKARS SWEDEN AB—See Fiskars Oyj Abp; *Int'l*, pg. 2694
FITTERS (S) PTE LTD.—See FITTERS Diversified Berhad; *Int'l*, pg. 2695
FOCUSRITE NOVATION DEUTSCHLAND—See Focusrite plc; *Int'l*, pg. 2720
FOUNDATION BUILDING MATERIALS, LLC—See American Securities LLC; *U.S. Private*, pg. 248
FROMM INTERNATIONAL, INC.—See Firelight Capital Partners LLC; *U.S. Private*, pg. 1512
FUJI ENTERTAINMENT AMERICA, INC—See Fuji Media Holdings, Inc.; *Int'l*, pg. 2814
FULGHUM FIBRES CHILE S.A.—See Rentech, Inc.; *U.S. Private*, pg. 3400
GAMA 29 SAS—See Bunzl plc; *Int'l*, pg. 1218
GAMES WORKSHOP SL—See Games Workshop Group PLC; *Int'l*, pg. 2877
GAP (ITALY) SRL.—See The Gap, Inc.; *U.S. Public*, pg. 2074
GAUSELMANN GROSSHANDEL GMBH—See Gauselmann AG; *Int'l*, pg. 2890
GEBRUDER GAUSELMANN GMBH—See Gauselmann AG; *Int'l*, pg. 2890
GEORGIA FIRE-RESCUE SUPPLY—See Ilustrato Pictures International Inc.; *Int'l*, pg. 3616
GERALD METALS S.A.—See Gerald Metals Inc.; *U.S. Private*, pg. 1686
GOBLIN FRANCE SARL—See Goblin India Ltd.; *Int'l*, pg. 3018
GOLD SEAL AVON POLYMERS PRIVATE LIMITED—See AKWEL; *Int'l*, pg. 268
GOOD SPORTSMAN MARKETING, LLC; *U.S. Private*, pg. 1738
GPS SERVICES, INC.—See The Gap, Inc.; *U.S. Public*, pg. 2074
GRAPHLINE INC.—See Base-Line, Inc.; *U.S. Private*, pg. 484
GREEN CROW CORPORATION; *U.S. Private*, pg. 1772
GREENWOOD PRODUCTS, INC.—See StoneCalibre, LLC; *U.S. Private*, pg. 3827
GROSS & JANES CO.—See Koppers Holdings Inc.; *U.S. Public*, pg. 1271
GS INTER, INC.; *U.S. Private*, pg. 1800
GUANGZHOU HOSHINO GAKKI TRADING CO., LTD.—See Hoshino Gakki Co., Ltd.; *Int'l*, pg. 3483
GUILFORD AUTOMOCION IBERICA, S.L.—See Lear Cor-

423990 — OTHER MISCELLANEOUS...

poration; *U.S. Public*, pg. 1297
GUILFORD DEUTSCHLAND GMBH—See Lear Corporation; *U.S. Public*, pg. 1297
GUITAR SALON INTERNATIONAL; *U.S. Private*, pg. 1814
GULF & BASCO—See Kodiak Building Partners LLC; *U.S. Private*, pg. 2336
GUTHY-RENKER CORP. - SANTA MONICA OFFICE—See Guthy-Renker Corporation; *U.S. Private*, pg. 1820
HAROLD T. ILLING CO. INC; *U.S. Private*, pg. 1867
HARRIS FIRE PROTECTION CO INC.—See Knox Lane LP; *U.S. Private*, pg. 2324
HAYLEX B.V.—See Hayleys PLC; *Int'l*, pg. 3292
HEARTLAND TANNING INC.; *U.S. Private*, pg. 1900
HENSON SALES GROUP LTD.—See Cinpak, Inc.; *U.S. Private*, pg. 898
HIBINO ASIA PACIFIC LIMITED—See Hibino Corporation; *Int'l*, pg. 3383
HOLDAL S.A.L.; *Int'l*, pg. 3449
HOLIDAY ENTERTAINMENT CO., LTD.; *Int'l*, pg. 3450
HYDE'S DISTRIBUTION; *Int'l*, pg. 3546
HYMNARIO - EAW (HK) LIMITED—See Tymphany Corp.; *U.S. Private*, pg. 4268
IAC ACOUSTICS ITALIANA SPA—See AEA Investors LP; *U.S. Private*, pg. 114
IAO PARTNERS—See D.R. Horton, Inc.; *U.S. Public*, pg. 620
IHI INC.—See IHI Corporation; *Int'l*, pg. 3604
ILIM TIMBER EUROPE GMBH—See Ilim Timber Inadstri OOO; *Int'l*, pg. 3614
IMPULSE NOVELTIES INC.; *U.S. Private*, pg. 2051
INDUSTRIAL ACOUSTICS COMPANY GMBH—See AEA Investors LP; *U.S. Private*, pg. 114
INDUSTRIAL ENERGY INC.—See Russell Lands Inc.; *U.S. Private*, pg. 3506
INFANTINO, LLC—See Aterian Investment Management, L.P.; *U.S. Private*, pg. 367
INGRAM CUSTOMER SYSTEMS INC.—See Ingram Industries, Inc.; *U.S. Private*, pg. 2076
INLAND WATER WORKS SUPPLY CO.—See Core & Main, Inc.; *U.S. Public*, pg. 576
INTERNATIONAL WHOLESALE SUPPLY, INC.; *U.S. Private*, pg. 2122
INTERNATIONNAL BULLION & METAL BROKERS—See IBB Amsterdam BV; *Int'l*, pg. 3569
INTERSCHOLASTIC TRADING COMPANY LLC; *U.S. Private*, pg. 2123
INTUMEX S.R.O.—See Etex SA/NV; *Int'l*, pg. 2522
IOWA FIRE EQUIPMENT COMPANY—See Pye-Barker Fire & Safety, LLC; *U.S. Private*, pg. 3309
JACOBS TRADING, LLC; *U.S. Private*, pg. 2180
J. LEUTENEGGER PTY LTD.—See E.C. Birch Proprietary Limited; *Int'l*, pg. 2251
JOURNEY HEALTH & LIFESTYLE—See Peloton Equity LLC; *U.S. Private*, pg. 3131
KASPIEN HOLDINGS INC.—See Kaspien Holdings Inc.; *U.S. Public*, pg. 1214
KENNEDY CULVERT & SUPPLY COMPANY—See Ferguson plc; *Int'l*, pg. 2638
KENT BUSINESS SYSTEMS CORP.; *U.S. Private*, pg. 2287
KIRK & MATZ LTD.; *U.S. Private*, pg. 2314
KOORSEN PROTECTION SERVICES; *U.S. Private*, pg. 2343
KRACIE HOME PRODUCTS SALES LTD.—See Hoyu Co., Ltd.; *Int'l*, pg. 3499
KRAUS USA - DISTRIBUTION CENTER—See Hilco Trading, LLC; *U.S. Private*, pg. 1944
KSG DISTRIBUTING, INC.; *U.S. Private*, pg. 2354
LAMINATE TECHNOLOGIES OF TENNESSEE—See Laminate Technologies Inc.; *U.S. Private*, pg. 2380
LANDS' END JAPAN, K.K.—See Lands' End, Inc.; *U.S. Public*, pg. 1292
THE LANTIS EYEWEAR CORPORATION; *U.S. Private*, pg. 4067
LANVIN JAPAN K.K.—See Fosun International Limited; *Int'l*, pg. 2751
LASGO CHRYSALIS—See Bertelsmann SE & Co. KGaA; *Int'l*, pg. 990
LATIN PERCUSSION INC.; *U.S. Private*, pg. 2397
LEON KOROL COMPANY; *U.S. Private*, pg. 2423
LEVIN PROFESSIONAL SERVICES; *U.S. Private*, pg. 2435
L & G FOREST PRODUCTS LTD.—See Grafton Group plc; *Int'l*, pg. 3051
LIBERTY GLOVE & SAFETY, INC.; *U.S. Private*, pg. 2444
LIBRARY VIDEO COMPANY; *U.S. Private*, pg. 2447
LIFETIME BRANDS, INC. - BUILT DIVISION—See Lifetime Brands, Inc.; *U.S. Public*, pg. 1313
L.N. CURTIS & SONS - INTERMOUNTAIN DIVISION—See L.N. Curtis & Sons; *U.S. Private*, pg. 2366
L.N. CURTIS & SONS - PACIFIC SOUTH DIVISION—See L.N. Curtis & Sons; *U.S. Private*, pg. 2367
L.N. CURTIS & SONS - SOUTHWEST DIVISION—See L.N. Curtis & Sons; *U.S. Private*, pg. 2367
LONE STAR CONTAINER SALES CORP.—See Lone Star Corrugated Container, Corporation; *U.S. Private*, pg. 2484
LONGULF TRRADING (UK) LTD.—See Hayel Saeed Anam Group of Companies; *Int'l*, pg. 3290
LOSBERGER U.S., LLC—See Gilde Buy Out Partners B.V.; *Int'l*, pg. 2975
L&R DISTRIBUTORS, INC.—See Platinum Equity, LLC; *U.S. Private*, pg. 3205
LUGGAGE AMERICA INCORPORATED; *U.S. Private*, pg. 2512
LYNN ROBERTS INTERNATIONAL; *U.S. Private*, pg. 2522
MALLORY SAFETY & SUPPLY LLC; *U.S. Private*, pg. 2557
MARINE ACCESSORIES CORPORATION—See Patrick Industries, Inc.; *U.S. Public*, pg. 1261
MARMIC FIRE & SAFETY CO., INC.—See KKR & Co. Inc.; *U.S. Public*, pg. 1261
MASTER MAGNETICS INC.—See Factor 89 Partners, LLC; *U.S. Private*, pg. 1460
MATERIAL CONTROL SYSTEMS INC.; *U.S. Private*, pg. 2609
MATROX EUROPE LTD—See Zebra Technologies Corporation; *U.S. Public*, pg. 2401
MDI WORLDWIDE UK LTD—See MDI Worldwide; *U.S. Private*, pg. 2646
MECOM LTD.; *U.S. Private*, pg. 2650
MEI QUERETARO S. DE R.L. DE CV—See Crane NXT, Co.; *U.S. Public*, pg. 591
MERCHSOURCE, LLC—See AEA Investors LP; *U.S. Private*, pg. 116
MIDSTATES CONTAINER COMPANY—See Cleveland Steel Container Corporation; *U.S. Private*, pg. 941
MILLENNIUM MARKETING CONSULTANTS, INC.; *U.S. Private*, pg. 2732
MILLS TALBOT COMPANY—See Flynn & Reynolds Agency Inc.; *U.S. Private*, pg. 1553
MISTCO, INC.—See Rhode Island Novelty, Inc.; *U.S. Private*, pg. 3422
MOBILE EDGE, LLC; *U.S. Private*, pg. 2757
MOBILE FOREST PRODUCTS INC; *U.S. Private*, pg. 2757
MTD PRODUCTS BENELUX B.V.—See Stanley Black & Decker, Inc.; *U.S. Public*, pg. 1933
MULTI-MEDIA DISTRIBUTION CORP.; *U.S. Private*, pg. 2812
MUNICIPAL EMERGENCY SERVICES, INC.—See Platte River Ventures, LLC; *U.S. Private*, pg. 3211
NEWELL RUBBERMAID DISTRIBUTION LLC—See Newell Brands Inc.; *U.S. Public*, pg. 1514
NEWPORT TIMBER LLC—See Interstate Resources, Inc.; *U.S. Private*, pg. 2125
NICOLAS ENTRETIEN SAS—See Bunzl plc; *Int'l*, pg. 1219
NOSTALGIA FAMILY BRANDS, INC.; *U.S. Private*, pg. 2965
OLD NAVY (APPAREL), LLC—See The Gap, Inc.; *U.S. Public*, pg. 2074
OMNI CONNECTION INTERNATIONAL, INC.—See Cerberus Capital Management, L.P.; *U.S. Private*, pg. 838
OMNISPHERE CORP.; *U.S. Private*, pg. 3017
OPO, INC.—See Bausch Health Companies Inc.; *Int'l*, pg. 897
ORGANIZE.COM, INC.; *U.S. Private*, pg. 3041
ORR CORPORATION; *U.S. Private*, pg. 3044
ORRU SAS—See Bunzl plc; *Int'l*, pg. 1219
OTTERBOX PRODUCTS LLC; *U.S. Private*, pg. 3050
PAN OCEANIC EYEWEAR LTD.; *U.S. Private*, pg. 3084
PARAMOUNT HOME ENTERTAINMENT (AUSTRALASIA) PTY, LIMITED—See National Amusements, Inc.; *U.S. Private*, pg. 2843
PARAMOUNT HOME ENTERTAINMENT (DENMARK) I/S—See National Amusements, Inc.; *U.S. Private*, pg. 2843
PARAMOUNT HOME ENTERTAINMENT INTERNATIONAL LIMITED—See National Amusements, Inc.; *U.S. Private*, pg. 2843
PELICAN PRODUCTS AUSTRALIA PTY LTD—See Platinum Equity, LLC; *U.S. Private*, pg. 3207
PELICAN PRODUCTS K.K.—See Platinum Equity, LLC; *U.S. Private*, pg. 3207
PELICAN PRODUCTS KOREA LTD—See Platinum Equity, LLC; *U.S. Private*, pg. 3207
PELICAN PRODUCTS SINGAPORE PTE LTD—See Platinum Equity, LLC; *U.S. Private*, pg. 3207
PELICAN PRODUCTS ULC—See Platinum Equity, LLC; *U.S. Private*, pg. 3207
PELI PRODUCTS, S.L.U.—See Platinum Equity, LLC; *U.S. Private*, pg. 3207
POLARIS CHEMICALS SPRL—See Bunzl plc; *Int'l*, pg. 1219
POLDER PRODUCTS, LLC—See Topspin Partners, L.P.; *U.S. Private*, pg. 4188
POTLATCH MINNESOTA TIMBERLANDS, LLC—See PotlatchDeltic Corporation; *U.S. Public*, pg. 1704
PRAJIN 1 STOP DISTRIBUTORS; *U.S. Private*, pg. 3243
PRECISION LASER SERVICES, INC.; *U.S. Private*, pg. 3245
PREMIER PRODUCT SALES, INC.; *U.S. Private*, pg. 3250
PRO TOUR MEMORABILIA; *U.S. Private*, pg. 3270
PSR COMPANY INC.; *U.S. Private*, pg. 3298
PUTUMAYO WORLD MUSIC INC.; *U.S. Private*, pg. 3308
REGAL LAGER, INC.; *U.S. Private*, pg. 3385
REVISION MILITARY LTD.—See ASGARD Partners & Co., LLC; *U.S. Private*, pg. 349
REVISION MILITARY LTD.—See Merit Capital Partners; *U.S. Private*, pg. 2674
RHODE ISLAND NOVELTY, INC.; *U.S. Private*, pg. 3422
R.H. VERDUYN GRANITE CO. LTD.—See Family Memorials Inc.; *Int'l*, pg. 2612
RIGHTSSCALE, INC.—See Faith, Inc.; *Int'l*, pg. 2609
ROTHENBERGER BULGARIA GMBH—See Dr. Helmut Rothenberger Holding GmbH; *Int'l*, pg. 2191
ROTHENBERGER NARADI A STROJE, S.R.O.—See Dr. Helmut Rothenberger Holding GmbH; *Int'l*, pg. 2191
ROTHENBERGER-TOOLS SA (PTY) LTD.—See Dr. Helmut Rothenberger Holding GmbH; *Int'l*, pg. 2192
ROTHENBERGER WERKZEUG UND MASCHINEN GMBH—See Dr. Helmut Rothenberger Holding GmbH; *Int'l*, pg. 2191
ROYAL PET SUPPLIES INC.—See Quarry Capital Management LLC; *U.S. Private*, pg. 3324
RSR GROUP INC.; *U.S. Private*, pg. 3497
RSR WHOLESALE GUNS INC.—See RSR Group Inc.; *U.S. Private*, pg. 3497
RSR WHOLESALE GUNS WEST INC.—See RSR Group Inc.; *U.S. Private*, pg. 3497
RSR WHOLESALE SOUTH INC.—See RSR Group Inc.; *U.S. Private*, pg. 3497
RWP TRANSFER INC.; *U.S. Private*, pg. 3509
SAFETY SOURCE, INC.—See Ritz Safety, LLC; *U.S. Private*, pg. 3442
SAFETY & SUPPLY COMPANY—See Mallory Safety & Supply LLC; *U.S. Private*, pg. 2558
SAINT-GOBAIN BUILDING DISTRIBUTION (IRELAND) LTD.—See Compagnie de Saint-Gobain SA; *Int'l*, pg. 1729
SAMAKIL, S.A.—See Iberpapel Gestion SA; *Int'l*, pg. 3574
SAMPCO OF TEXAS, INC.—See Sampco Inc.; *U.S. Private*, pg. 3537
SANDERSON SAFETY SUPPLY CO. INC.; *U.S. Private*, pg. 3543
SANDUSCO, INC.; *U.S. Private*, pg. 3545
SANDUSKY DISTRIBUTING COMPANY, INC.—See Sandusco, Inc.; *U.S. Private*, pg. 3545
SCHNEIDER AUTOMATEN GMBH & CO. KG—See Gauselmann AG; *Int'l*, pg. 2890
SCHUYLER WOOD PELLET, LLC—See Rentech, Inc.; *U.S. Private*, pg. 3400
SEALASKA CORPORATION; *U.S. Private*, pg. 3584
SIERRA FOREST PRODUCTS, INC.; *U.S. Private*, pg. 3647
SIEVERS EQUIPMENT CO.; *U.S. Private*, pg. 3648
SINO-FOREST (SUZHOU) TRADING CO., LTD.—See Emerald Plantation Holdings Limited; *Int'l*, pg. 2378
SINO-WOOD PARTNERS LIMITED—See Emerald Plantation Holdings Limited; *Int'l*, pg. 2378
SKARDA EQUIPMENT COMPANY, INC.—See Certified Power Solutions; *U.S. Private*, pg. 842
SKYDDA I SVERIGE AB—See Bergman & Beving AB; *Int'l*, pg. 980
SODISCOL SAS—See Bunzl plc; *Int'l*, pg. 1219
SOPECAL HYGIENE SAS—See Bunzl plc; *Int'l*, pg. 1219
SOURCE ONE DISTRIBUTORS, INC.; *U.S. Private*, pg. 3718
SOUTHGATE TIMBER CO. INC.; *U.S. Private*, pg. 3736
SPARTAN SURFACES, INC.—See Floor & Decor Holdings, Inc.; *U.S. Public*, pg. 853
SPB SWEDEN AB—See Spectrum Brands Holdings, Inc.; *U.S. Public*, pg. 1916
SPECMA HYDRAULIC - SYSTEM DIVISION—See Aktieselskabet Schouw & Co.; *Int'l*, pg. 266
SPECTRUM BRANDS BULGARIA EOOD—See Spectrum Brands Holdings, Inc.; *U.S. Public*, pg. 1916
SPECTRUM BRANDS COLOMBIA S.A.—See Spectrum Brands Holdings, Inc.; *U.S. Public*, pg. 1916
SPECTRUM BRANDS HRVATSKA D.O.O.—See Spectrum Brands Holdings, Inc.; *U.S. Public*, pg. 1916
SPECTRUM BRANDS NORWAY AS—See Spectrum Brands Holdings, Inc.; *U.S. Public*, pg. 1916
SPECTRUM BRANDS ROMANIA S.R.L.—See Spectrum Brands Holdings, Inc.; *U.S. Public*, pg. 1916
SPECTRUM BRANDS SPAIN S.L.—See Spectrum Brands Holdings, Inc.; *U.S. Public*, pg. 1916
SPECTRUM BRANDS TRGOVINA, D.O.O.—See Spectrum Brands Holdings, Inc.; *U.S. Public*, pg. 1916
SQUIRE BOONE CAVERNS INCORPORATED; *U.S. Private*, pg. 3766
STACI CORP.—See Centre Lane Partners, LLC; *U.S. Private*, pg. 827
STEED TIMBER CO. INC.; *U.S. Private*, pg. 3795
STOW (UK) LIMITED—See Blackstone Inc.; *U.S. Public*, pg. 348
SUNBELT PACKAGING, LLC.—See Kelso & Company, L.P.; *U.S. Private*, pg. 2279
SUNBELT PACKAGING, LLC—See Warburg Pincus LLC; *U.S. Private*, pg. 4436
SUPER GENERAL TRADING CO. LLC—See Bhatia Brothers Group; *Int'l*, pg. 1014
SWEENEY HARDWOODS, INC.—See R.E. Sweeney Company Inc.; *U.S. Private*, pg. 3335
TARGUS GROUP INTERNATIONAL, INC.; *U.S. Private*, pg. 3933
TECHNICAL EQUIPMENT CO., INC.—See JCI Industries Inc.; *U.S. Private*, pg. 2194

N.A.I.C.S. INDEX

424110 — PRINTING AND WRITIN...

TERRA TIMBERS PTY LTD—See Brickworks Limited; *Int'l*, pg. 1152
THERMOS K.K.—See Thermos L.L.C.; *U.S. Private*, pg. 4143
THERMOS (SINGAPORE) PTE LTD—See Thermos L.L.C.; *U.S. Private*, pg. 4143
TIMBERLAND EUROPE B.V.—See V. F. Corporation; *U.S. Public*, pg. 2268
TOOL FRANCE S.A.R.L.—See Tenex Capital Management, L.P.; *U.S. Private*, pg. 3966
TOP HITS INC.; *U.S. Private*, pg. 4186
TOPICS ENTERTAINMENT INC.; *U.S. Private*, pg. 4187
TOTAL PLASTICS, INC.- LIFE SCIENCES—See Prophet Equity L.P.; *U.S. Private*, pg. 3286
TRADEX INTERNATIONAL, INC.; *U.S. Private*, pg. 4202
TRAVELPRO PRODUCTS, INC.—See MidOcean Partners, LLP; *U.S. Private*, pg. 2717
TRICORBRAUN INC.—See Ares Management Corporation; *U.S. Public*, pg. 191
TRILLIUM CORPORATION; *U.S. Private*, pg. 4231
T.R. MILLER CO., INC.—See Stran & Company, Inc.; *U.S. Public*, pg. 1953
TRUGLO, INC.—See Good Sportsman Marketing, LLC; *U.S. Private*, pg. 1738
TRUNKI INC.—See Heroes Technology Ltd.; *Int'l*, pg. 3364
TUPPERWARE ESPANA, S.A.—See Tupperware Brands Corporation; *U.S. Public*, pg. 2204
TUPPERWARE NORDIC A/S—See Tupperware Brands Corporation; *U.S. Public*, pg. 2204
TUPPERWARE OSTERREICH G.M.B.H.—See Tupperware Brands Corporation; *U.S. Public*, pg. 2204
TUPPERWARE POLSKA SP.Z O.O.—See Tupperware Brands Corporation; *U.S. Public*, pg. 2204
TUPPERWARE ROMANIA S.R.L.—See Tupperware Brands Corporation; *U.S. Public*, pg. 2204
TUPPERWARE SOUTHERN AFRICA (PROPRIETARY) LIMITED—See Tupperware Brands Corporation; *U.S. Public*, pg. 2204
UFP FOLKSTON, LLC—See UFP Industries, Inc.; *U.S. Public*, pg. 2219
UNIVERSAL FOREST PRODUCTS FOUNDATION—See UFP Industries, Inc.; *U.S. Public*, pg. 2221
VALORA MANAGEMENT AG—See Fomento Economico Mexicano, S.A.B. de C.V.; *Int'l*, pg. 2724
VENTURI, INC.; *U.S. Private*, pg. 4358
VIDEOTAPE PRODUCTS INC.; *U.S. Private*, pg. 4380
VP DISTRIBUTORS, LLC—See Virtus Investment Partners, Inc.; *U.S. Public*, pg. 2301
WALL TIMBER PRODUCTS INC.; *U.S. Private*, pg. 4430
WALSH - BLYTH & TURTON WHOLESALE—See Bunzl plc; *Int'l*, pg. 1217
WALSH TIMBER COMPANY LLC; *U.S. Private*, pg. 4433
WARD TIMBER LTD; *U.S. Private*, pg. 4441
WAREHOUSE GOODS LLC—See Greenlane Holdings, Inc.; *U.S. Public*, pg. 965
WAX WORKS INC.; *U.S. Private*, pg. 4459
WEST CHESTER HOLDINGS, INC.; *U.S. Private*, pg. 4484
WESTERN SAFETY PRODUCTS, INC.—See Bunzl plc; *Int'l*, pg. 1218
W. JOE SHAW INCORPORATED; *U.S. Private*, pg. 4418
WORLD ENTERPRISES; *U.S. Private*, pg. 4565
XINHUI CIMC WOOD CO., LTD.—See China International Marine Containers (Group) Co., Ltd.; *Int'l*, pg. 1512
YELLOWSTONE PLASTICS, INC.; *U.S. Private*, pg. 4588
YORTER INTERNATIONAL LIMITED—See Franklin Electronic Publishers, Inc.; *U.S. Private*, pg. 1597

424110 — PRINTING AND WRITING PAPER MERCHANT WHOLESALERS

AARON GROUP OF COMPANIES; *U.S. Private*, pg. 32
ALL FLORIDA PAPER; *U.S. Private*, pg. 170
ANCHOR PAPER COMPANY; *U.S. Private*, pg. 273
ARGOTEC DEUTSCHLAND GMBH—See Mativ Holdings, Inc.; *U.S. Public*, pg. 1396
ATHENS PAPER CO. - DISTRIBUTION—See Athens Paper Company, Inc.; *U.S. Private*, pg. 368
ATHENS PAPER COMPANY, INC.; *U.S. Private*, pg. 367
ATHENS PAPER CO.—See Athens Paper Company, Inc.; *U.S. Private*, pg. 367
ATHENS PAPER CO.—See Athens Paper Company, Inc.; *U.S. Private*, pg. 367
BILLERUD TRADING (SHANGHAI) CO. LTD—See Billerud AB; *Int'l*, pg. 1030
BOSWORTH PAPERS INC.; *U.S. Private*, pg. 622
BROWN PAPER COMPANY INC.; *U.S. Private*, pg. 668
BRW PAPER CO., INC.—See Gould Paper Corporation; *U.S. Private*, pg. 1745
BURGO BENELUX SA—See Burgo Group S.p.A.; *Int'l*, pg. 1223
BURGO DISTRIBUZIONE SRL—See Burgo Group S.p.A.; *Int'l*, pg. 1223
BURGO NORTH AMERICA INC—See Burgo Group S.p.A.; *Int'l*, pg. 1224
BURGO POLASKA SP Z O O—See Burgo Group S.p.A.; *Int'l*, pg. 1224
BURGO UK LTD—See Burgo Group S.p.A.; *Int'l*, pg. 1224

B.W. WILSON PAPER COMPANY INCORPORATED; *U.S. Private*, pg. 421
CARPENTER PAPER COMPANY; *U.S. Private*, pg. 770
CASE PAPER CO., INC.—See Case Paper Company Inc.; *U.S. Private*, pg. 782
CASE PAPER COMPANY INC.; *U.S. Private*, pg. 782
CASE PAPER CO. OF ILLINOIS, INC.—See Case Paper Company Inc.; *U.S. Private*, pg. 782
CELLMARK INC.—See CellMark AB; *Int'l*, pg. 1394
CELLMARK M.E. LLC—See CellMark AB; *Int'l*, pg. 1393
CELLMARK PAPER CANADA INC—See CellMark AB; *Int'l*, pg. 1393
CELLMARK PAPER SA DE CV—See CellMark AB; *Int'l*, pg. 1393
CELLMARK PAPIER SAS—See CellMark AB; *Int'l*, pg. 1393
CELLMARK PULP AND PAPER INC—See CellMark AB; *Int'l*, pg. 1393
CELLMARK SA—See CellMark AB; *Int'l*, pg. 1393
CENTRAL MICHIGAN PAPER COMPANY; *U.S. Private*, pg. 822
CENTRAL NATIONAL ESPANOLA S.A.—See Central National Gottesman Inc.; *U.S. Private*, pg. 823
CENTRAL NATIONAL GOTTESMAN INC.; *U.S. Private*, pg. 823
CHAROEN AKSORN HOLDING GROUP CO. LTD.; *Int'l*, pg. 1451
CLAMPITT PAPER COMPANY; *U.S. Private*, pg. 910
CLIFFORD PAPER INC.; *U.S. Private*, pg. 943
COPAIMEX, S.A.—See Iberpapel Gestion SA; *Int'l*, pg. 3574
CORONET PAPER PRODUCTS ENTERPRISES OF FLORIDA LLC.; *U.S. Private*, pg. 1053
DAI NIPPON PRINTING CO., LTD.; *Int'l*, pg. 1914
DENNIS PAPER COMPANY; *U.S. Private*, pg. 1205
DIE CUTS WITH A VIEW; *U.S. Private*, pg. 1228
DIGITEX CANADA INC.—See Xerox Holdings Corporation; *U.S. Public*, pg. 2386
DISTRIBUIDORA PAPELERA, S.A.—See Iberpapel Gestion SA; *Int'l*, pg. 3574
DNP (AMERICA), INC.—See Dai Nippon Printing Co., Ltd.; *Int'l*, pg. 1914
DNP CORPORATION USA—See Dai Nippon Printing Co., Ltd.; *Int'l*, pg. 1914
E. AARON ENTERPRISES INC.—See Aaron Group of Companies; *U.S. Private*, pg. 32
EUROPAPIER ADRIA D.O.O—See Heinzel Holding GmbH; *Int'l*, pg. 3325
EUROPAPIER ALPE D.O.O.—See Heinzel Holding GmbH; *Int'l*, pg. 3325
EUROPAPIER BOHEMIA SPOL. S R.O.—See Heinzel Holding GmbH; *Int'l*, pg. 3325
EUROPAPIER BUDAPEST KFT.—See Heinzel Holding GmbH; *Int'l*, pg. 3325
EUROPAPIER BULGARIA EOOD—See Heinzel Holding GmbH; *Int'l*, pg. 3325
EUROPAPIER CIS OOO—See Heinzel Holding GmbH; *Int'l*, pg. 3325
EUROPAPIER DUNAV D.O.O.—See Heinzel Holding GmbH; *Int'l*, pg. 3325
EUROPAPIER HERCEGTISAK D.O.O.—See Heinzel Holding GmbH; *Int'l*, pg. 3325
EUROPAPIER-IMPAP SP. Z O.O.—See Heinzel Holding GmbH; *Int'l*, pg. 3325
EUROPAPIER ROMANIA SRL—See Heinzel Holding GmbH; *Int'l*, pg. 3325
EUROPAPIER SLOVENSKO, S.R.O.—See Heinzel Holding GmbH; *Int'l*, pg. 3325
FEDRIGONI SPA; *Int'l*, pg. 2631
FIELD PAPER CO. INC.; *U.S. Private*, pg. 1504
FRANK AMBROSE INC.; *U.S. Private*, pg. 1593
FUJIFILM GLOBAL GRAPHIC SYSTEMS CO., LTD.—See FUJIFILM Holdings Corporation; *Int'l*, pg. 2824
FUJI XEROX ASIA PACIFIC PTE. LTD.—See FUJIFILM Holdings Corporation; *Int'l*, pg. 2825
FUJI XEROX MANUFACTURING CO., LTD.—See FUJIFILM Holdings Corporation; *Int'l*, pg. 2825
FUJI XEROX SERVICE CREATIVE CO., LTD.—See FUJIFILM Holdings Corporation; *Int'l*, pg. 2825
FUJI XEROX SERVICE LINK CO., LTD.—See FUJIFILM Holdings Corporation; *Int'l*, pg. 2825
GOULD INTERNATIONAL PACKAGING—See Gould Paper Corporation; *U.S. Private*, pg. 1745
GOULD PAPER NORTH AMERICA—See Gould Paper Corporation; *U.S. Private*, pg. 1745
GRAPHIC COMMUNICATIONS HOLDINGS; *U.S. Private*, pg. 1757
GUANGDONG RENGO PACKAGING COMPANY LIMITED—See Hung Hing Printing Group Limited; *Int'l*, pg. 3535
HANKUK PAPER USA, INC.—See Haesung Industrial Co., Ltd.; *Int'l*, pg. 3205
HANSOL PNS CO., LTD.—See Hansol Group; *Int'l*, pg. 3260
HEIDELBERG SPAIN S.L.U.—See Heidelberger Druckmaschinen AG; *Int'l*, pg. 3322
HEINZEL GRAPHIC PAPER ITALIA S.R.L.—See Heinzel Holding GmbH; *Int'l*, pg. 3325
HEINZEL GRAPHIC PAPER POLSKA SP. Z.O.O.—See Heinzel Holding GmbH; *Int'l*, pg. 3325

HEINZEL IMPORT-EXPORT, INC.—See Heinzel Holding GmbH; *Int'l*, pg. 3326
HOKUETSU PAPER SALES CO., LTD.—See Hokuetsu Corporation; *Int'l*, pg. 3444
HOLMEN GMBH—See Holmen AB; *Int'l*, pg. 3452
HORIZON PAPER CO., INC.; *U.S. Private*, pg. 1982
IBERBARNA PAPEL, S.A.—See Iberpapel Gestion SA; *Int'l*, pg. 3574
INTERNATIONAL PAPER COMPANY—See International Paper Company; *U.S. Public*, pg. 1156
INTERNATIONAL PAPER-HUNGARY KEREKEDELMI KFT.—See International Paper Company; *U.S. Public*, pg. 1157
INTERNATIONAL PAPER S.A.—See International Paper Company; *U.S. Public*, pg. 1157
J.C. PAPER—See Central National Gottesman Inc.; *U.S. Private*, pg. 823
KELLY SPICERS INC.—See Central National Gottesman Inc.; *U.S. Private*, pg. 823
LAAKIRCHEN PAPIER AG—See Heinzel Holding GmbH; *Int'l*, pg. 3325
THE LABEL SMITH LLC—See Heartwood Partners, LLC; *U.S. Private*, pg. 1901
LECTA BENELUX SA—See CVC Capital Partners SICAV-FIS S.A.; *Int'l*, pg. 1888
LECTA DEUTSCHLAND GMBH—See CVC Capital Partners SICAV-FIS S.A.; *Int'l*, pg. 1887
LECTA HQ SA—See CVC Capital Partners SICAV-FIS S.A.; *Int'l*, pg. 1887
LECTA MAROC SARL—See CVC Capital Partners SICAV-FIS S.A.; *Int'l*, pg. 1888
LECTA MEXICO S. DE R.L. DE C.V.—See CVC Capital Partners SICAV-FIS S.A.; *Int'l*, pg. 1888
LECTA NORTH AMERICA INC—See CVC Capital Partners SICAV-FIS S.A.; *Int'l*, pg. 1888
LECTA PAPER UK LTD—See CVC Capital Partners SICAV-FIS S.A.; *Int'l*, pg. 1888
LEWIS PAPER INTERNATIONAL INC.—See Central National Gottesman Inc.; *U.S. Private*, pg. 823
LIBERTY PAPER PRODUCTS LLC—See Elm Creek Partners; *U.S. Private*, pg. 1375
LINDENMEYR MUNROE—See Central National Gottesman Inc.; *U.S. Private*, pg. 823
MAC PAPERS, INC.—See Monomoy Capital Partners LLC; *U.S. Private*, pg. 2772
MAC PAPERS, INC.—See Monomoy Capital Partners LLC; *U.S. Private*, pg. 2772
MAGNUM PRINT SOLUTIONS, INC.; *U.S. Private*, pg. 2549
MANIPULACION Y RECUPERACION MAREPA, S.A.—See Fomento de Construcciones y Contratas, S.A.; *Int'l*, pg. 2723
MIDLAND PAPER COMPANY; *U.S. Private*, pg. 2715
MIDLAND PAPER CO.—See Midland Paper Company; *U.S. Private*, pg. 2715
MIDLAND PAPER CO.—See Midland Paper Company; *U.S. Private*, pg. 2715
MIDLAND PAPER CO.—See Midland Paper Company; *U.S. Private*, pg. 2715
MIDLAND PAPER—See Midland Paper Company; *U.S. Private*, pg. 2715
MILLCRAFT PAPER - CINCINNATI SALES & DISTRIBUTION CENTER—See The Millcraft Paper Company Inc.; *U.S. Private*, pg. 4079
THE MILLCRAFT PAPER COMPANY INC.; *U.S. Private*, pg. 4079
MONO MACHINES LLC.; *U.S. Private*, pg. 2771
THE MOSAICA GROUP LLC; *U.S. Private*, pg. 4081
MURNANE PAPER COMPANY; *U.S. Private*, pg. 2815
NEWELL PAPER CO. OF GULFPORT—See Jackson Paper Company; *U.S. Private*, pg. 2178
NEWELL PAPER CO. OF HATTIESBURG—See Jackson Paper Company; *U.S. Private*, pg. 2178
NEWELL PAPER CO. OF MERIDIAN—See Jackson Paper Company; *U.S. Private*, pg. 2178
NORD PAPIER SA—See CVC Capital Partners SICAV-FIS S.A.; *Int'l*, pg. 1888
OFFICE DEPOT BUSINESS SOLUTIONS DIVISION—See The ODP Corporation; *U.S. Public*, pg. 2117
OLMSTED-KIRK COMPANY OF HOUSTON, INC.—See Olmsted-Kirk Paper Company; *U.S. Private*, pg. 3011
OLMSTED-KIRK PAPER COMPANY; *U.S. Private*, pg. 3011
OREN INTERNATIONAL INC.; *U.S. Private*, pg. 3040
PAN AMERICAN PAPERS, INC.; *U.S. Private*, pg. 3084
PAPERPLUS—See Clayton, Dubilier & Rice, LLC; *U.S. Private*, pg. 929
PAPERPLUS—See Clayton, Dubilier & Rice, LLC; *U.S. Private*, pg. 929
PAPER TIGERS INC.; *U.S. Private*, pg. 3088
PAPERWORKS INC.—See Diversified Chemical Technologies Inc.; *U.S. Private*, pg. 1241
PAPYRUS AS—See Altor Equity Partners AB; *Int'l*, pg. 395
PAPYRUS A/S—See Altor Equity Partners AB; *Int'l*, pg. 395
PAPYRUS FINLAND OY—See Altor Equity Partners AB; *Int'l*, pg. 395
PAPYRUS GROEP NEDERLAND B.V.—See Altor Equity Partners AB; *Int'l*, pg. 395
PAPYRUS HUNGARIA ZRT—See Altor Equity Partners AB; *Int'l*, pg. 395

424110 — PRINTING AND WRITIN...

PAPYRUS NORGE AS—See Altor Equity Partners AB; pg. 395
PAPYRUS SCHWEIZ AG—See Altor Equity Partners AB; Int'l, pg. 395
PAPYRUS SIA—See Altor Equity Partners AB; Int'l, pg. 395
PAPYRUS SP. Z O.O.—See Altor Equity Partners AB; Int'l, pg. 395
PAPYRUS SVERIGE AB—See Altor Equity Partners AB; Int'l, pg. 395
PATERSON CARD & PAPER CO.; U.S. Private, pg. 3105
PEN BOUTIQUE LIMITED; U.S. Private, pg. 3132
PEREZ TRADING CO. INC.; U.S. Private, pg. 3147
PREMIER & COMPANIES INC; U.S. Private, pg. 3249
PRINTING MANAGEMENT ASSOCIATES; U.S. Private, pg. 3266
PRIORITY PAPERS, INC.—See Aaron Group of Companies; U.S. Private, pg. 32
PT. CELLMARK INTERINDO TRADE—See CellMark AB; Int'l, pg. 1394
REDD PAPER COMPANY; U.S. Private, pg. 3377
RELYCO SALES, INC.; U.S. Private, pg. 3395
REMARK PAPER COMPANY INC.; U.S. Private, pg. 3396
RICHARD BAUER & CO. INC.; U.S. Private, pg. 3427
ROOSEVELT PAPER COMPANY—See Roosevelt Paper Company; U.S. Private, pg. 3480
SABIN ROBBINS PAPER CO.; U.S. Private, pg. 3520
SIGNS.COM, INC.; U.S. Private, pg. 3651
SOUTHERN SECURITIES LTD.; U.S. Private, pg. 3735
SPICERS CANADA ULC—See Central National Gottesman Inc.; U.S. Private, pg. 823
STEEN MACEK PAPER CO. INC.; U.S. Private, pg. 3797
STERLING PAPER COMPANY; U.S. Private, pg. 3806
STRICKLAND COMPANIES, INC.; U.S. Private, pg. 3839
TORRASPAPEL PORTUGAL LDA—See CVC Capital Partners SICAV-FIS S.A.; Int'l, pg. 1888
UAB PAPYRUS LIETUVA—See Altor Equity Partners AB; Int'l, pg. 395
VERITIV - DENVER—See Clayton, Dubilier & Rice, LLC; U.S. Private, pg. 929
VERITIV EXPRESS—See Clayton, Dubilier & Rice, LLC; U.S. Private, pg. 929
VERITIV - INDIANAPOLIS—See Clayton, Dubilier & Rice, LLC; U.S. Private, pg. 929
VERITIV—See Clayton, Dubilier & Rice, LLC; U.S. Private, pg. 929
VERITIV—See Clayton, Dubilier & Rice, LLC; U.S. Private, pg. 929
VERITIV—See Clayton, Dubilier & Rice, LLC; U.S. Private, pg. 929
VERITIV—See Clayton, Dubilier & Rice, LLC; U.S. Private, pg. 929
VERITIV—See Clayton, Dubilier & Rice, LLC; U.S. Private, pg. 929
VERITIV—See Clayton, Dubilier & Rice, LLC; U.S. Private, pg. 929
VERITIV—See Clayton, Dubilier & Rice, LLC; U.S. Private, pg. 929
VERITIV—See Clayton, Dubilier & Rice, LLC; U.S. Private, pg. 929
VERITIV—See Clayton, Dubilier & Rice, LLC; U.S. Private, pg. 929
VERITIV—See Clayton, Dubilier & Rice, LLC; U.S. Private, pg. 929
VERITIV—See Clayton, Dubilier & Rice, LLC; U.S. Private, pg. 929
VERITIV—See Clayton, Dubilier & Rice, LLC; U.S. Private, pg. 929
VERITIV—See Clayton, Dubilier & Rice, LLC; U.S. Private, pg. 929
WADE PAPER CORPORATION; U.S. Private, pg. 4424
WILFRIED HEINZEL AG—See Heinzel Holding GmbH; Int'l, pg. 3325
ZAO INTERNATIONAL PAPER—See International Paper Company; U.S. Public, pg. 1158
ZICUIMEX FRANCE, S.A.R.L.—See Iberpapel Gestion SA; Int'l, pg. 3574
ZICUPAP, S.A.—See Iberpapel Gestion SA; Int'l, pg. 3574

424120 — STATIONERY AND OFFICE SUPPLIES MERCHANT WHOLESALERS

3M PORTUGAL, LDA—See 3M Company; U.S. Public, pg. 7
3M UK HOLDINGS LIMITED—See 3M Company; U.S. Public, pg. 7
ABBA MARKETING SDN. BHD.—See Asia File Corporation Bhd.; Int'l, pg. 612
ACCO ASIA LIMITED—See ACCO Brands Corporation; U.S. Public, pg. 32
ACCO BRANDS AUSTRALIA HOLDING PTY LTD.—See ACCO Brands Corporation; U.S. Public, pg. 32
ACCO BRANDS PORTUGUESA LDA—See ACCO Brands Corporation; U.S. Public, pg. 32
ACS BUSINESS SUPPLIES LIMITED; Int'l, pg. 109
ACTION ENVELOPE & PRINTING CO., INC.; U.S. Private, pg. 67
ADVEO ITALIA S. R. L.—See ADVEQ Group International, S.A.; Int'l, pg. 167
ALLIED ENVELOPE CO. INC.; U.S. Private, pg. 186
AMERICAN MINORITY BUSINESS FORMS, INC.; U.S. Private, pg. 241
AMERICAN SOLUTIONS FOR BUSINESS; U.S. Private, pg. 254
ANCHOR INTERNATIONAL BV—See IG Design Group Plc; Int'l, pg. 3600
APEX OFFICE PRODUCTS, INC.; U.S. Private, pg. 293
APTAR (THAILAND) LTD.—See AptarGroup, Inc.; U.S. Public, pg. 174
ARAM INCORPORATED; U.S. Private, pg. 307
ARCTIC OFFICE MACHINE INC.; U.S. Private, pg. 315
ARTHUR BROWN & BRO., INC.; U.S. Private, pg. 341
ASKUL CORPORATION; Int'l, pg. 625
A.T. CROSS (FRANCE) S.A.—See Transom Capital Group, LLC; U.S. Private, pg. 4209
A.T. CROSS LIMITED—See Transom Capital Group, LLC; U.S. Private, pg. 4209
A.T. CROSS LIMITED—See Transom Capital Group, LLC; U.S. Private, pg. 4209
AVERY DENNISON SCANDINAVIA AB—See Avery Dennison Corporation; U.S. Public, pg. 244
AVERY TICO S.R.L.—See CCL Industries Inc.; Int'l, pg. 1367
AVERY ZWECKFORM GMBH—See Avery Dennison Corporation; U.S. Public, pg. 244
A.W. FABER-CASTELL AUSTRIA GMBH—See Faber-Castell AG; Int'l, pg. 2599
A.W. FABER-CASTELL COLOMBIA LTDA.—See Faber-Castell AG; Int'l, pg. 2599
A.W. FABER-CASTELL (S) PTE. LTD.—See Faber-Castell AG; Int'l, pg. 2598
BAJAN GROUP, INC.—See Velocity Print Solutions; U.S. Private, pg. 4354
BALL OFFICE PRODUCTS; U.S. Private, pg. 460
BANNER BUSINESS SERVICES LIMITED—See Endless LLP; Int'l, pg. 2403
BANNER MANAGEMENT COMPANY INC.—See A&S, Inc.; U.S. Private, pg. 21
BANPRESTO SALES CO., LTD.—See BANDAI NAMCO Holdings Inc.; Int'l, pg. 829
BASSOTECH INC.; U.S. Private, pg. 486
BAY AREA INDUSTRIAL SERVICES INC.; U.S. Private, pg. 491
BJC INDUSTRIAL AND TRADING CO., LTD.—See Berli Jucker Public Co. Ltd.; Int'l, pg. 985
B.L.L. HOLDINGS LTD; Int'l, pg. 790
BONG DANMARK A/S—See Bong AB; Int'l, pg. 1106
BONG DENMARK A/S—See Bong AB; Int'l, pg. 1106
BONG ENVELO SRL—See Bong AB; Int'l, pg. 1106
BONG LATVIJA SIA—See Bong AB; Int'l, pg. 1107
BONG PACKAGING S.R.L.—See Bong AB; Int'l, pg. 1107
BONG SCHWEIZ AG—See Bong AB; Int'l, pg. 1107
THE BRADLEY MARKETING GROUP; U.S. Private, pg. 3999
BRAND ADVANTAGE GROUP—See Deluxe Corporation; U.S. Public, pg. 652
BRYDENS RETAIL INC.—See ANSA McAL Limited; Int'l, pg. 476
BRYDENS XPRESS (OFFICE SUPPLIES) INC.—See ANSA McAL Limited; Int'l, pg. 476
BULLDOG OFFICE PRODUCTS INC.; U.S. Private, pg. 685
BUYONLINENOW.COM; U.S. Private, pg. 699
CANON ELECTRONICS BUSINESS SYSTEMS INC.—See Canon Inc.; Int'l, pg. 1293
CANON IRELAND BUSINESS EQUIPMENT LTD.—See Canon Inc.; Int'l, pg. 1293
CAPITAL OFFICE PRODUCTS; U.S. Private, pg. 741
CARDINAL OFFICE360—See Office Three Sixty, Inc.; U.S. Private, pg. 3002
CAROLINA IMAGING & COMPUTER PRODUCTS, INC.; U.S. Private, pg. 768
CARTRIDGE SAVE LIMITED; Int'l, pg. 1348
CHARLES LEONARD INC.; U.S. Private, pg. 852
CHECKPOINT SYSTEMS HONG KONG LIMITED—See CCL Industries Inc.; Int'l, pg. 1368
COLAMCO INC.; U.S. Private, pg. 965
COL PUBLIC COMPANY LIMITED; Int'l, pg. 1697
CONNECTICUT BUSINESS SYSTEMS, LLC—See Xerox Holdings Corporation; U.S. Public, pg. 2387
COOLEY GROUP, INC.; U.S. Private, pg. 1039
COPIERSUPPLYSTORE; U.S. Private, pg. 1045
COPY SOLUTIONS, INC.; U.S. Private, pg. 1045
COROPLAST SPOLKA Z O.O.—See Coroplast Fritz Muller GmbH und Co. KG; Int'l, pg. 1802
COROPLAST TAPE CORPORATION—See Coroplast Fritz Muller GmbH und Co. KG; Int'l, pg. 1802
COROPLAST TUNISIE SARL—See Coroplast Fritz Muller GmbH und Co. KG; Int'l, pg. 1802
CRITES & RIDDELL BASICS; Int'l, pg. 1850
CURRENT MEDIA GROUP, LLC—See Regent, L.P.; U.S. Private, pg. 3387
CURTIS 1000, INC.—See Taylor Corporation; U.S. Private, pg. 3938
DALIAN DYNIC OFFICE PRODUCTS CO., LTD.—See Dynic Corporation; Int'l, pg. 2242
DATABAZAAR INDIA PVT. LTD.—See E-Max Group, Inc.; U.S. Private, pg. 1302
DATA IMAGING & ASSOCIATES; U.S. Private, pg. 1163
DDI CUSTOMER SERVICE, INC.; U.S. Private, pg. 1181
DEANNES OFFICE & COMPUTER SUPPLIES; U.S. Private, pg. 1185
DEB SVERIGE AB—See S.C. Johnson & Son, Inc.; U.S. Private, pg. 3515
DELUXE SMALL BUSINESS SERVICES—See Deluxe Corporation; U.S. Public, pg. 652
DELUXE STRATEGIC SOURCING, INC.—See Deluxe Corporation; U.S. Public, pg. 652
DEMCO, INC.—See Wall Family Enterprise, Inc.; U.S. Private, pg. 4430
DESIGNER GREETINGS INC.; U.S. Private, pg. 1214
DEUBLIN ITALIANA—See Hoerbiger Holding AG; Int'l, pg. 3439
DIGITAL STORAGE INCORPORATED—See Dexxon Groupe SA; Int'l, pg. 2093
DON GRESSWELL LTD.—See Wall Family Enterprise, Inc.; U.S. Private, pg. 4430
DRAWING BOARD—See Taylor Corporation; U.S. Private, pg. 3938
EATONFORM INC.; U.S. Private, pg. 1323
ECONOFFICE PRODUCTS & SUPPLIES, INC.; U.S. Private, pg. 1329
EDDING INTERNATIONAL GMBH—See Edding AG; Int'l, pg. 2304
ELOF HANSSON AB-SUC.—See Elof Hansson AB; Int'l, pg. 2368
ELOF HANSSON (AUSTRALIA) PTY LTD—See Elof Hansson AB; Int'l, pg. 2368
ELOF HANSSON FIBER LLC—See Elof Hansson AB; Int'l, pg. 2368
ELOF HANSSON (INDIA) PVT LTD—See Elof Hansson AB; Int'l, pg. 2368
ELOF HANSSON INTERNATIONAL AB—See Elof Hansson AB; Int'l, pg. 2368
ELOF HANSSON K.K.—See Elof Hansson AB; Int'l, pg. 2368
ELOF HANSSON LTDA—See Elof Hansson AB; Int'l, pg. 2368
ELOF HANSSON PULP AND PAPER LTD—See Elof Hansson AB; Int'l, pg. 2368
ELOF HANSSON PULP & PAPER SINGAPORE PTE LTD—See Elof Hansson AB; Int'l, pg. 2368
E-MAX GROUP, INC.; U.S. Private, pg. 1302
ERASER DUST, INC.; U.S. Private, pg. 1417
ESSELTE DANMARK APS—See ACCO Brands Corporation; U.S. Public, pg. 32
ESSELTE S.P.A—See ACCO Brands Corporation; U.S. Public, pg. 33
ESSENDANT HONG KONG LIMITED—See Sycamore Partners Management, LP; U.S. Private, pg. 3897
ESSENDANT INC.—See Sycamore Partners Management, LP; U.S. Private, pg. 3896
ESSENTRA (INDIA) PRIVATE LIMITED—See Essentra plc; Int'l, pg. 2511
ESSENTRA PACKAGING INC.—See Essentra plc; Int'l, pg. 2511
ESSENTRA PACKAGING PTE. LIMITED—See Essentra plc; Int'l, pg. 2511
EUROPEAN OFFICE SYSTEMS B.V.—See ECO Supplies Europe AB; Int'l, pg. 2292
EUROPEAN OFFICE SYSTEMS GMBH—See ECO Supplies Europe AB; Int'l, pg. 2292
EUROPEAN OFFICE SYSTEMS S.A.R.L—See ECO Supplies Europe AB; Int'l, pg. 2292
EVO BUSINESS SUPPLIES LIMITED—See Endless LLP; Int'l, pg. 2403
EXPRESSIONS UNLIMITED, INC.—See Designer Greetings Inc.; U.S. Private, pg. 1214
FARO INTERNATIONAL, INC.—See AuBEX Corporation; Int'l, pg. 698
FARRATECH, INC.; U.S. Private, pg. 1480
FELLOWES BENELUX B.V.—See Fellowes, Inc.; U.S. Private, pg. 1494
FELLOWES HI-Q MALAYSIA SDN BHD.—See Fellowes, Inc.; U.S. Private, pg. 1494
FELLOWES HI-Q SINGAPORE PTE LTD.—See Fellowes, Inc.; U.S. Private, pg. 1494
FELLOWES JAPAN K.K.—See Fellowes, Inc.; U.S. Private, pg. 1494
FELLOWES RU LTD—See Fellowes, Inc.; U.S. Private, pg. 1494
FELLOWES UNITED KINGDOM LTD.—See Fellowes, Inc.; U.S. Private, pg. 1494
F&H SUPPLY CO. INC.; U.S. Private, pg. 1455
FIDUCIAL OFFICE SOLUTIONS SA; Int'l, pg. 2655
FINDEL EDUCATION LIMITED—See Endless LLP; Int'l, pg. 2403
FORMOST GRAPHIC COMMUNICATIONS, INC.; U.S. Private, pg. 1571
FORMS & SUPPLY, INC.; U.S. Private, pg. 1571
FREVVO INC.—See LoneTree Capital LLC; U.S. Private, pg. 2490
FUJIFILM BUSINESS INNOVATION CORPORATION—See FUJIFILM Holdings Corporation; Int'l, pg. 2825

N.A.I.C.S. INDEX

424130 — INDUSTRIAL AND PERS...

FUTURE ACE E-COMMERCE SDN. BHD.—See CWG Holdings Berhad; *Int'l*, pg. 1890
G.A. BLANCO & SONS INC.; *U.S. Private*, pg. 1630
GARVEY'S OFFICE PRODUCTS; *U.S. Private*, pg. 1646
GASCOGNE SPAIN SL—See Gascogne SA; *Int'l*, pg. 2888
GBS CORP.; *U.S. Private*, pg. 1653
GENERAL BINDING LLC—See ACCO Brands Corporation; *U.S. Public*, pg. 33
GIVE SOMETHING BACK LLC; *U.S. Private*, pg. 1703
GORILLA STATIONERS LLC; *U.S. Private*, pg. 1744
GRAPHIC LABEL, INC.—See Sole Source Capital LLC; *U.S. Private*, pg. 3708
GROSSMARK MARKETING GROUP; *U.S. Private*, pg. 1792
HALLMARK CARDS, INC. - ENFIELD—See Hallmark Cards, Inc.; *U.S. Private*, pg. 1844
HALLMARK PUERTO RICO INC.—See Hallmark Cards, Inc.; *U.S. Private*, pg. 1844
HAMCO MANUFACTURING & DISTRIBUTING LLC—See Griffin Holdings, LLC; *U.S. Private*, pg. 1788
HAMELIN B.V.—See Groupe Hamelin S.A.; *Int'l*, pg. 3104
HAMELIN B.V.—See Groupe Hamelin S.A.; *Int'l*, pg. 3104
HAMELIN, LDA.—See Groupe Hamelin S.A.; *Int'l*, pg. 3104
HAMELIN POLSKA SP. Z O.O.—See Groupe Hamelin S.A.; *Int'l*, pg. 3104
HAMELIN S.A.—See Groupe Hamelin S.A.; *Int'l*, pg. 3104
HAMELIN S.A.S.—See Groupe Hamelin S.A.; *Int'l*, pg. 3104
HAMELIN S.P.A.—See Groupe Hamelin S.A.; *Int'l*, pg. 3104
HIGHSMITH, LLC—See Wall Family Enterprise, Inc.; *U.S. Private*, pg. 4430
HITI DIGITAL EUROPE S.R.L—See HiTi Digital Inc.; *Int'l*, pg. 3426
HITI DIGITAL, INC.—See HiTi Digital Inc.; *Int'l*, pg. 3426
HITI DIGITAL SINGAPORE PTE LTD—See HiTi Digital Inc.; *Int'l*, pg. 3426
HITI DIGITAL (SUZHOU), INC.—See HiTi Digital Inc.; *Int'l*, pg. 3426
HOUSEFREEDOM CO., LTD.; *Int'l*, pg. 3491
HUMMELS OFFICE EQUIPMENT CO.; *U.S. Private*, pg. 2007
HUNG YEN BOOK PUBLISHING & EDUCATIONAL EQUIPMENT JSC; *Int'l*, pg. 3535
HYGRADE BUSINESS GROUP—See Hygrade Business Group Inc.; *U.S. Private*, pg. 2018
IBUYOFFICESUPPLY.COM; *U.S. Private*, pg. 2029
IG DESIGN GROUP AMERICAS, INC.—See IG Design Group Plc; *Int'l*, pg. 3600
IMAGEQUEST, INC.—See Xerox Holdings Corporation; *U.S. Public*, pg. 2387
IMPACT NETWORKING, LLC.; *U.S. Private*, pg. 2048
INDIANA RECORDS MANAGERS, INC.; *U.S. Private*, pg. 2062
INGRAM MICRO ARGENTINA, S.A.—See Hainan Traffic Administration Holding Co., Ltd.; *Int'l*, pg. 3214
INLAND BUSINESS MACHINES, INC.—See Xerox Holdings Corporation; *U.S. Public*, pg. 2387
INNOV8 SOLUTIONS USA LLC; *U.S. Private*, pg. 2081
INNOVATIVE OFFICE SOLUTIONS LLC; *U.S. Private*, pg. 2083
INTEGRATED MEDIA MANAGEMENT, INC.—See Ocean-Sound Partners, LP; *U.S. Private*, pg. 2990
INTERNATIONAL GREETINGS (UK) LIMITED—See IG Design Group Plc; *Int'l*, pg. 3600
INVITATION CONSULTANTS, INC.; *U.S. Private*, pg. 2133
IP CANADIAN PACKAGING OPERATIONS INC.—See International Paper Company; *U.S. Public*, pg. 1155
KALOS, INC.—See Fusion Health Technologies Corporation; *U.S. Private*, pg. 1625
KRAMER & LEONARD INC.; *U.S. Private*, pg. 2349
LEGAMASTER GMBH—See Edding AG; *Int'l*, pg. 2304
LEITZ ACCO BRANDS GMBH & CO. KG—See ACCO Brands Corporation; *U.S. Public*, pg. 33
LEVENGER COMPANY; *U.S. Private*, pg. 2434
LLC FABER-CASTELL ANADOLU—See Faber-Castell AG; *Int'l*, pg. 2599
LONESOURCE, INC.; *U.S. Private*, pg. 2489
MAKING MEMORIES WHOLESALE INC.—See Advent International Corporation; *U.S. Private*, pg. 103
MARUDAS GRAPHICS, INC.; *U.S. Private*, pg. 2597
MASCO ASIA (SHENZHEN) CO. LTD.—See Masco Corporation; *U.S. Public*, pg. 1390
MBF EMBALAGENS LTDA.—See AptarGroup, Inc.; *U.S. Public*, pg. 174
METO INTERNATIONAL GMBH—See CCL Industries Inc.; *Int'l*, pg. 1368
MIDLAND GIS SOLUTIONS, LLC—See Peak Rock Capital LLC; *U.S. Private*, pg. 3124
MIDWEST SINGLE SOURCE INC.; *U.S. Private*, pg. 2723
MILLER-COOPER PRINTING INK COMPANY LLC—See Grand Rapids Printing Ink Company; *U.S. Private*, pg. 1753
MINTON-JONES CO. INC.; *U.S. Private*, pg. 2745
MONARCH INDUSTRIES, INC.—See Avery Dennison Corporation; *U.S. Public*, pg. 244
MY1STOP LLC; *U.S. Private*, pg. 2823
NCR INTERNATIONAL OF PUERTO RICO—See NCR Voyix Corporation; *U.S. Public*, pg. 1503
NEWELL AUSTRALIA PTY. LIMITED—See Newell Brands Inc.; *U.S. Public*, pg. 1514

NEW ENGLAND OFFICE SUPPLY INC.; *U.S. Private*, pg. 2894
NEW TECHNOLOGY INVESTMENTS, INC.—See RMS Omega Technologies Group, Inc.; *U.S. Private*, pg. 3452
NEXTIRAONE—See Black Box Limited; *Int'l*, pg. 1058
NOBILIS INC.; *U.S. Private*, pg. 2932
NOVATECH INC. - HATTIESBURG—See Perpetual Capital, LLC; *U.S. Private*, pg. 3153
NXP LIMITED—See Platinum Equity, LLC; *U.S. Private*, pg. 3210
OCE-FRANCE S.A.—See Canon Inc.; *Int'l*, pg. 1294
OFFICE DEPOT BUSINESS SOLUTIONS DIVISION-NEW JERSEY—See The ODP Corporation; *U.S. Public*, pg. 2117
OFFICEMART OFFICE PROFESSIONAL SOLUTIONS SA—See AVE S.A.; *Int'l*, pg. 737
OFFICEMATE INTERNATIONAL CORPORATION; *U.S. Private*, pg. 3002
OFFICE SOLUTIONS BUSINESS PRODUCTS SERVICES; *U.S. Private*, pg. 3002
OFFICETEAM GROUP LIMITED—See Heritage Group Ltd.; *Int'l*, pg. 3361
OLYMPIA SALES, INC.; *U.S. Private*, pg. 3012
ON-TARGET SUPPLIES & LOGISTICS; *U.S. Private*, pg. 3019
OOO SEAQUIST CLOSURES—See AptarGroup, Inc.; *U.S. Public*, pg. 174
OPTIMUM SYSTEM PRODUCTS INC.; *U.S. Private*, pg. 3035
PA DISTRIBUTION LLC; *U.S. Private*, pg. 3062
PENCILS.COM—See California Cedar Products Company; *U.S. Private*, pg. 718
THE PENN COMPANIES - IMPRINTSUSA—See The Penn Companies; *U.S. Private*, pg. 4092
PF CONCEPT UK OPERATIONS LTD—See Charlesbank Capital Partners, LP; *U.S. Private*, pg. 856
PREMIER PRINT & SERVICES GROUP INCORPORATED; *U.S. Private*, pg. 3250
PREMIER STATIONERY LIMITED—See Asia File Corporation Bhd.; *Int'l*, pg. 612
RAPIDFORMS, INC.—See Deluxe Corporation; *U.S. Public*, pg. 652
REIGN PRINT SOLUTIONS, INC.—See RBO PrintLogistix, Inc.; *U.S. Private*, pg. 3360
RIBBONS EXPRESS, INC.; *U.S. Private*, pg. 3425
R. K. DIXON COMPANY—See Xerox Holdings Corporation; *U.S. Public*, pg. 2388
SAFEGUARD BUSINESS SYSTEMS LIMITED—See Deluxe Corporation; *U.S. Public*, pg. 652
SCAPA (SHANGHAI) INTERNATIONAL TRADING COMPANY LTD—See Mativ Holdings, Inc.; *U.S. Public*, pg. 1397
SCHOOL SPECIALTY CANADA, LTD.—See School Specialty, Inc.; *U.S. Public*, pg. 1848
SCHOOL SPECIALTY, INC.; *U.S. Public*, pg. 1848
SCHURMAN FINE PAPERS & PAPYRUS FRANCHISE CORPORATION; *U.S. Private*, pg. 3571
SCHUSTER COMPANY; *U.S. Private*, pg. 3571
SERENDIB INVESTMENTS PTE LIMITED—See Fijian Holdings Limited; *Int'l*, pg. 2662
THE SHAMROCK COMPANIES INC.; *U.S. Private*, pg. 4117
SIN CHUAN MARKETING SDN. BHD.—See Asia File Corporation Bhd.; *Int'l*, pg. 612
SMITH OFFICE & COMPUTER SUPPLY; *U.S. Private*, pg. 3695
SPICERS ADMINISTRACION Y SERVICIOS, S.L.—See ADVEO Group International, S.A.; *Int'l*, pg. 167
SPICERS BELGIUM NV—See ADVEO Group International, S.A.; *Int'l*, pg. 167
SPICERS DEUTSCHLAND GMBH—See ADVEO Group International, S.A.; *Int'l*, pg. 167
SPIRAL BINDING LLC—See Hilltop Private Capital, LLC; *U.S. Private*, pg. 1947
SPIRAL BINDING LLC—See KCB Management LLC; *U.S. Private*, pg. 2269
S. P. RICHARDS CO. CANADA INC.—See Genuine Parts Company; *U.S. Public*, pg. 933
S.P. RICHARDS COMPANY; *U.S. Private*, pg. 3518
STAPLES CONTRACT & COMMERCIAL, INC.—See Sycamore Partners Management, LP; *U.S. Private*, pg. 3897
STAPLES THE OFFICE SUPERSTORE, LLC.—See Sycamore Partners Management, LP; *U.S. Private*, pg. 3897
S&T OFFICE PRODUCTS, INC.; *U.S. Private*, pg. 3514
SUGARLAND SHOPPING CENTRE PTY LIMITED—See AMP Limited; *Int'l*, pg. 433
THE SUPPLY ROOM COMPANIES INC.; *U.S. Private*, pg. 4125
TAG SYSTEMS SMART SOLUTIONS S.L.U.—See Austriacard Holdings AG; *Int'l*, pg. 724
TEAMTEK WHOLESALE; *U.S. Private*, pg. 3951
TODAY'S BUSINESS PRODUCTS; *U.S. Private*, pg. 4180
TRI COASTAL DESIGN GROUP INC; *U.S. Private*, pg. 4220
TRIPLETT OFFICE ESSENTIALS; *U.S. Private*, pg. 4238
TROWBRIDGE ENTERPRISES; *U.S. Private*, pg. 4243
UNITED STATIONERS SUPPLY CO.—See Sycamore Partners Management, LP; *U.S. Private*, pg. 3896
UNITED STATIONERS TECHNOLOGY SERVICES LLC—See Sycamore Partners Management, LP; *U.S. Private*, pg. 3897
UNITED SUPPLY; *U.S. Private*, pg. 4300
URBAN OFFICE PRODUCTS, INC.; *U.S. Private*, pg. 4314
VALOIS (IRELAND) LIMITED—See AptarGroup, Inc.; *U.S. Public*, pg. 175
VANGUARD DIRECT INC.; *U.S. Private*, pg. 4343
VICTORIAN GREETINGS—See Victorian Paper Company; *U.S. Private*, pg. 4378
VICTORIAN PAPER COMPANY; *U.S. Private*, pg. 4378
VICTORIAN PAPERS—See Victorian Paper Company; *U.S. Private*, pg. 4378
VICTORIAN TRADING CO.—See Victorian Paper Company; *U.S. Private*, pg. 4378
VOLK CORPORATION; *U.S. Private*, pg. 4410
WARDENS OFFICE INC.; *U.S. Private*, pg. 4441
THE WEEKS-LERMAN GROUP LLC; *U.S. Private*, pg. 4134
WEST COAST PAPER COMPANY; *U.S. Private*, pg. 4484
WILLIAMS OF SWANSEA LIMITED—See Cathay Investments Limited; *Int'l*, pg. 1360
WINBROOK INC.; *U.S. Private*, pg. 4533
WORLDTECH COMPUTERS INC.; *U.S. Private*, pg. 4569
WPC POLA SP. Z O.O.—See W.P. Carey Inc.; *U.S. Public*, pg. 2316
XEROX AG—See Xerox Holdings Corporation; *U.S. Public*, pg. 2389
XEROX AUSTRIA GMBH—See Xerox Holdings Corporation; *U.S. Public*, pg. 2389
XEROX CANADA INC.—See Xerox Holdings Corporation; *U.S. Public*, pg. 2390
XEROX (EUROPE) LTD.—See Xerox Holdings Corporation; *U.S. Public*, pg. 2388
XEROX (IRELAND) LIMITED—See Xerox Holdings Corporation; *U.S. Public*, pg. 2388
XEROX LIMITED—See Xerox Holdings Corporation; *U.S. Public*, pg. 2389
XEROX PROPERTY SERVICES LIMITED—See Xerox Holdings Corporation; *U.S. Public*, pg. 2390
XSE GROUP INC.; *U.S. Private*, pg. 4582

424130 — INDUSTRIAL AND PERSONAL SERVICE PAPER MERCHANT WHOLESALERS

ACCO BRANDS ITALIA S.R.L.—See ACCO Brands Corporation; *U.S. Public*, pg. 32
ACME PAPER & SUPPLY CO. INC.; *U.S. Private*, pg. 61
ACTION BAG COMPANY; *U.S. Private*, pg. 67
AHLSTROM-MUNKSJO JAPAN INC.—See Ahlstrom Capital Oy; *Int'l*, pg. 224
AHLSTROM-MUNKSJO JAPAN INC.—See Bain Capital, LP; *U.S. Private*, pg. 429
AHLSTROM-MUNKSJO MONTERREY, S. DE R.L. DE C.V.—See Ahlstrom Capital Oy; *Int'l*, pg. 224
AHLSTROM-MUNKSJO MONTERREY, S. DE R.L. DE C.V.—See Bain Capital, LP; *U.S. Private*, pg. 429
AHLSTROM SALES HELSINKI OY—See Ahlstrom Capital Oy; *Int'l*, pg. 224
AHLSTROM SALES HELSINKI OY—See Bain Capital, LP; *U.S. Private*, pg. 429
ALL AMERICAN CONTAINERS OF GEORGIA, LLC—See Clayton, Dubilier & Rice, LLC; *U.S. Private*, pg. 928
ALL AMERICAN CONTAINERS OF PUERTO RICO, LLC—See Clayton, Dubilier & Rice, LLC; *U.S. Private*, pg. 928
ALL AMERICAN CONTAINERS OF SOUTHERN CALIFORNIA INC.—See Clayton, Dubilier & Rice, LLC; *U.S. Private*, pg. 928
ALL AMERICAN CONTAINERS OF TAMPA, LLC—See Clayton, Dubilier & Rice, LLC; *U.S. Private*, pg. 928
ALL AMERICAN CONTAINERS OF TEXAS INC.—See Clayton, Dubilier & Rice, LLC; *U.S. Private*, pg. 928
ALL AMERICAN CONTAINERS OF THE MIDWEST INC.—See Clayton, Dubilier & Rice, LLC; *U.S. Private*, pg. 928
ALL AMERICAN CONTAINERS OF THE NORTHEAST, LLC—See Clayton, Dubilier & Rice, LLC; *U.S. Private*, pg. 928
ALL AMERICAN CONTAINERS OF THE PACIFIC COAST INC.—See Clayton, Dubilier & Rice, LLC; *U.S. Private*, pg. 928
AMCOR TOBACCO PACKAGING NOVGOROD—See Amcor plc; *Int'l*, pg. 417
AMERICA CHUNG NAM LLC; *U.S. Private*, pg. 220
AMERICA CHUNG NAM TRANSPORTATION LLC—See America Chung Nam LLC; *U.S. Private*, pg. 220
AMERICAN PAPER TOWEL CO. LLC; *U.S. Private*, pg. 243
AMERICAN PAPER & TWINE COMPANY; *U.S. Private*, pg. 243
APACHE GROUP OF MINNESOTA, INC.—See Bain Capital, LP; *U.S. Private*, pg. 440
ARCO INDUSTRIAL SALES INC.; *U.S. Private*, pg. 315
ARCTIC PAPER BALTIC STATES SIA—See Arctic Paper S.A.; *Int'l*, pg. 551
ARCTIC PAPER BENELUX S.A.—See Arctic Paper S.A.; *Int'l*, pg. 551

ARCTIC PAPER DANMARK A/S—See Arctic Paper S.A.; *Int'l,* pg. 551
ARCTIC PAPER DEUTSCHLAND GMBH—See Arctic Paper S.A.; *Int'l,* pg. 551
ARCTIC PAPER ESPANA SL—See Arctic Paper S.A.; *Int'l,* pg. 551
ARCTIC PAPER FRANCE SAS—See Arctic Paper S.A.; *Int'l,* pg. 551
ARCTIC PAPER ITALIA SRL—See Arctic Paper S.A.; *Int'l,* pg. 551
ARCTIC PAPER NORGE AS—See Arctic Paper S.A.; *Int'l,* pg. 551
ARCTIC PAPER PAPIERHANDELS GMBH—See Arctic Paper S.A.; *Int'l,* pg. 551
ARCTIC PAPER POLSKA SP. Z O.O.—See Arctic Paper S.A.; *Int'l,* pg. 552
ARCTIC PAPER SCHWEIZ AG—See Arctic Paper S.A.; *Int'l,* pg. 552
ARCTIC PAPER SVERIGE AB—See Arctic Paper S.A.; *Int'l,* pg. 552
ARCTIC PAPER UK LIMITED—See Arctic Paper S.A.; *Int'l,* pg. 552
ARDAGH GLASS HOLMEGAARD A/S—See Ardagh Group S.A.; *Int'l,* pg. 553
ARDAGH GLASS ITALY S.R.L.—See Ardagh Group S.A.; *Int'l,* pg. 553
ARDAGH GLASS LIMMARED AB—See Ardagh Group S.A.; *Int'l,* pg. 553
ARDAGH GLASS SALES LIMITED—See Ardagh Group S.A.; *Int'l,* pg. 553
ARDAGH METAL BEVERAGE EUROPE GMBH—See Ardagh Group S.A.; *Int'l,* pg. 553
ASSOCIATED SALES & BAG COMPANY INCORPORATED; *U.S. Private,* pg. 357
AUGUST PACKAGING INC.; *U.S. Private,* pg. 392
AVERY DENNISON GULF FZCO—See Avery Dennison Corporation; *U.S. Public,* pg. 244
AVERY DENNISON (NEDERLAND) B.V.—See Avery Dennison Corporation; *U.S. Public,* pg. 243
BACON & GRAHAM, INC.—See Wellspring Capital Management LLC; *U.S. Private,* pg. 4477
B.A.G. CORP.; *U.S. Private,* pg. 420
BAOLONG INTERNATIONAL CO., LTD.; *Int'l,* pg. 856
BARNES PAPER COMPANY INCORPORATED; *U.S. Private,* pg. 477
BEMIS PACKAGING DEUTSCHLAND GMBH—See Amcor plc; *Int'l,* pg. 418
BERNARD KLEIN INC.; *U.S. Private,* pg. 536
BGR INC.; *U.S. Private,* pg. 549
B & G WHOLESALE DISTRIBUTING, INC.; *U.S. Private,* pg. 417
BILLERUD GULF—See Billerud AB; *Int'l,* pg. 1030
BILTMORE TRADING CORPORATION—See HCI Equity Management, L.P.; *U.S. Private,* pg. 1889
BLOWER DEMPSAY CORPORATION; *U.S. Private,* pg. 584
THE BOELTER COMPANIES INC.; *U.S. Private,* pg. 3995
THE BOELTER COMPANIES INC.—See The Boelter Companies Inc.; *U.S. Private,* pg. 3995
BOXES ETC. II, LLC—See Monomoy Capital Partners LLC; *U.S. Private,* pg. 2772
THE BOXMAKER INC.—See The Boxmaker Inc.; *U.S. Private,* pg. 3998
THE BOXMAKER INC.—See The Boxmaker Inc.; *U.S. Private,* pg. 3998
BRAME SPECIALTY COMPANY INC.; *U.S. Private,* pg. 635
BRANDT BOX & PAPER CO INC; *U.S. Private,* pg. 638
BROWN PACKAGING; *U.S. Private,* pg. 668
BUNZL & BIACH GES.M.B.H—See Heinzel Holding GmbH; *Int'l,* pg. 3325
BUNZL CS S.R.O.—See Bunzl plc; *Int'l,* pg. 1217
BUNZL DISTRIBUTION OKLAHOMA, INC.—See Bunzl plc; *Int'l,* pg. 1217
BUNZL DISTRIBUTION USA, LLC—See Bunzl plc; *Int'l,* pg. 1217
BUNZL MINNEAPOLIS, LLC—See Bunzl plc; *Int'l,* pg. 1217
BUNZL USA HOLDINGS LLC—See Bunzl plc; *Int'l,* pg. 1217
BUNZL USA, LLC—See Bunzl plc; *Int'l,* pg. 1217
BURKE SUPPLY COMPANY INC.; *U.S. Private,* pg. 688
CALIFORNIA SUPPLY, INC.; *U.S. Private,* pg. 720
CALIFORNIA SUPPLY, INC. - UNION CITY—See California Supply, Inc.; *U.S. Private,* pg. 720
CALPINE CONTAINERS INC.—See Rainier Partners LP; *U.S. Private,* pg. 3348
THE CANNON GROUP INC.; *U.S. Private,* pg. 4004
CAREO KFT—See Apollo Global Management, Inc.; *U.S. Public,* pg. 159
CAREO LIMITED—See Apollo Global Management, Inc.; *U.S. Public,* pg. 159
CAREO SP. Z O.O.—See Apollo Global Management, Inc.; *U.S. Public,* pg. 159
CAREO S.R.O.—See Apollo Global Management, Inc.; *U.S. Public,* pg. 159
CARTER PAPER & PACKAGING, INC.; *U.S. Private,* pg. 776
CARTHAGO SRL—See CVC Capital Partners SICAV-FIS S.A.; *Int'l,* pg. 1888
CENTRAL BAG COMPANY; *U.S. Private,* pg. 819

CENTRAL PAPER COMPANY INC.; *U.S. Private,* pg. 824
CENTRAL PAPER PRODUCTS CO., INC.—See Bain Capital, LP; *U.S. Private,* pg. 440
CENTURY SUNSHINE PAPER (USA) INC.—See China Sunshine Paper Holdings Company Limited; *Int'l,* pg. 1556
CHELSEA INTERNATIONAL CO., LTD.—See GEO Holdings Corporation; *Int'l,* pg. 2932
CHRIS CAM CORPORATION; *U.S. Private,* pg. 889
CHUDY PACKAGING CO. INC.; *U.S. Private,* pg. 893
CHUN YIK (MACAO COMMERCIAL OFFSHORE) LIMITED—See Hop Fung Group Holdings Ltd; *Int'l,* pg. 3473
CICS DISTRIBUTORS PTE. LTD.—See Central Global Berhad; *Int'l,* pg. 1407
CITY PAPER COMPANY; *U.S. Private,* pg. 906
CMPC EUROPE LIMITED—See Empresas CMPC S.A.; *Int'l,* pg. 2389
CMPC USA, INC.—See Empresas CMPC S.A.; *Int'l,* pg. 2390
COFFEE DISTRIBUTING CORP.; *U.S. Private,* pg. 961
COLE PAPERS INC.; *U.S. Private,* pg. 966
COLLINS GMBH & CO. KG.—See Eroglu Holding AS; *Int'l,* pg. 2496
COLUMBUS PAPER COMPANY, INC.—See Bain Capital, LP; *U.S. Private,* pg. 440
COMMONWEALTH PACKAGING COMPANY, PACKAGING SERVICE—See Commonwealth Packaging Company; *U.S. Private,* pg. 987
COMMONWEALTH PACKAGING COMPANY; *U.S. Private,* pg. 987
COMMUNICATIONS PAPERS—See Gould Paper Corporation; *U.S. Private,* pg. 1745
CONSOLIDATED PAPER CO.—See Paper Enterprises, Inc.; *U.S. Private,* pg. 3088
CONVERMAT CORPORATION; *U.S. Private,* pg. 1035
COPAMEX NORTH AMERICA—See Corporativo Copamex, S.A. de C.V.; *Int'l,* pg. 1806
CORNELL PAPER & BOX INC.; *U.S. Private,* pg. 1051
CRESTCHIC PLC; *Int'l,* pg. 1841
CRK, LLC—See Welch Packaging Group, Inc.; *U.S. Private,* pg. 4473
CROWN PACKAGING CORP.; *U.S. Private,* pg. 1111
C&S PAPER (HUBEI) CO., LTD.—See C&S Paper Co., Ltd.; *Int'l,* pg. 1239
C&S PAPER (SICHUAN) CO., LTD.—See C&S Paper Co., Ltd.; *Int'l,* pg. 1239
C&S PAPER YUNFU CO., LTD.—See C&S Paper Co., Ltd.; *Int'l,* pg. 1239
CUSCAPI SINGAPORE PTE. LTD.—See Cuscapi Berhad; *Int'l,* pg. 1880
CUSCAPI (THAIL) CO. LTD.—See Cuscapi Berhad; *Int'l,* pg. 1880
CUSTOM PACKAGING INC.—See Custom Packaging Inc.; *U.S. Private,* pg. 1129
DACOTAH PAPER CO.; *U.S. Private,* pg. 1144
DADE PAPER & BAG, LLC - ATLANTA FACILITY—See Bain Capital, LP; *U.S. Private,* pg. 440
DADE PAPER & BAG, LLC - GREENSBORO FACILITY—See Bain Capital, LP; *U.S. Private,* pg. 440
DADE PAPER & BAG, LLC - GULF STATES FACILITY—See Bain Capital, LP; *U.S. Private,* pg. 440
DADE PAPER & BAG, LLC - JACKSONVILLE FACILITY—See Bain Capital, LP; *U.S. Private,* pg. 440
DADE PAPER & BAG, LLC - MID-ATLANTIC FACILITY—See Bain Capital, LP; *U.S. Private,* pg. 440
DADE PAPER & BAG, LLC - ORLANDO FACILITY—See Bain Capital, LP; *U.S. Private,* pg. 440
DADE PAPER & BAG, LLC - PUERTO RICO FACILITY—See Bain Capital, LP; *U.S. Private,* pg. 440
DADE PAPER & BAG, LLC—See Bain Capital, LP; *U.S. Private,* pg. 440
DADE PAPER & BAG, LLC - TRI-STATE FACILITY—See Bain Capital, LP; *U.S. Private,* pg. 440
DADE PAPER CRUISE LINE—See Bain Capital, LP; *U.S. Private,* pg. 440
DAMSKY PAPER COMPANY; *U.S. Private,* pg. 1151
DATACARD SOUTH PACIFIC PTY. LTD.—See DataCard Corporation; *U.S. Private,* pg. 1165
D. BENEDETTO INC.; *U.S. Private,* pg. 1139
DELTA PACKAGING & SUPPLY, LLC—See Kelso & Company, L.P.; *U.S. Private,* pg. 2279
DELTA PACKAGING & SUPPLY, LLC—See Warburg Pincus LLC; *U.S. Private,* pg. 4436
DEL-THO INDUSTRIES INC.; *U.S. Private,* pg. 1193
DIXIE PAPER COMPANY; *U.S. Private,* pg. 1245
D-K TRADING CORP.; *U.S. Private,* pg. 1139
DNP TRADING CO., LTD.—See Dai Nippon Printing Co., Ltd.; *Int'l,* pg. 1915
DUNSIRN PARTNERS LLC; *U.S. Private,* pg. 1290
DUROPACK D.O.O.—See DS Smith Plc; *Int'l,* pg. 2209
DUROPACK STARPACK KFT.—See DS Smith Plc; *Int'l,* pg. 2209
D&S ANASTOPOULOS SA; *Int'l,* pg. 1899
DS SMITH PACKAGING DEUTSCHLAND STIFTUNG & CO. KG—See DS Smith Plc; *Int'l,* pg. 2208
DYNEA (GUANGDONG) CO., LTD.—See AICA Kogyo Company, Limited; *Int'l,* pg. 229

EBP SUPPLY SOLUTIONS; *U.S. Private,* pg. 1324
E. CALLSEN & CO. A.S.—See BERICAP GmbH & Co. KG; *Int'l,* pg. 981
ELLIOTT TAPE INC.; *U.S. Private,* pg. 1373
ELOF HANSSON INC.—See Elof Hansson AB; *Int'l,* pg. 2368
ELOF HANSSON PAPER & BOARD, INC.—See Elof Hansson AB; *Int'l,* pg. 2368
EMPIRE PAPER COMPANY; *U.S. Private,* pg. 1385
EMPRESA DISTRIBUIDORA DE PAPELES Y CARTONES SPA—See Empresas CMPC S.A.; *Int'l,* pg. 2389
ERNEST PAPER PRODUCTS, INC.; *U.S. Private,* pg. 1421
ESSITY AKTIEBOLAG; *Int'l,* pg. 2516
EUGENE ALLARD PRODUITS D'EMBALLAGE & D'ENTRETIEN INC—See Bain Capital, LP; *U.S. Private,* pg. 440
EUROPAPIER INTERNATIONAL AG—See Heinzel Holding GmbH; *Int'l,* pg. 3325
EXCELLENT PACKAGING & SUPPLY; *U.S. Private,* pg. 1446
FEDON AMERICA, INC—See EssilorLuxottica SA; *Int'l,* pg. 2515
FIDELITY PAPER & SUPPLY CORP.; *U.S. Private,* pg. 1503
FIRST QUALITY PRODUCTS, INC.—See First Quality Enterprises, Inc.; *U.S. Private,* pg. 1524
FLAT ENTERPRISES INC.; *U.S. Private,* pg. 1541
FLEXSOL PACKAGING CORP.—See Alpha Industries, Inc.; *U.S. Private,* pg. 197
FORMAN EQUIPMENT, INC.—See Forman Inc.; *U.S. Private,* pg. 1569
FORMAN INC.; *U.S. Private,* pg. 1569
FORSAC MEXICO S.A. DE C.V.—See Empresas CMPC S.A.; *Int'l,* pg. 2390
FORTON ENTERPRISES LIMITED—See Essity Aktiebolag; *Int'l,* pg. 2517
FOX VALLEY CONTAINERS, INC.—See Kelso & Company, L.P.; *U.S. Private,* pg. 2278
FPC DISTRIBUTION, INC.—See Kelso & Company, L.P.; *U.S. Private,* pg. 2279
FPC DISTRIBUTION, INC.—See Warburg Pincus LLC; *U.S. Private,* pg. 4437
FPCO INTERNATIONAL PACKAGE CO., LTD.—See FP Corporation; *Int'l,* pg. 2756
FPCO ISHIDA CO., LTD.—See FP Corporation; *Int'l,* pg. 2756
FPCO UEDA CO.—See FP Corporation; *Int'l,* pg. 2756
FRONTIER PACKAGING, INC.—See Gen Cap America, Inc.; *U.S. Private,* pg. 1659
GASCOGNE ITALIA SRL—See Gascogne SA; *Int'l,* pg. 2887
GASCOGNE USA INC—See Gascogne SA; *Int'l,* pg. 2888
GEORGIA-PACIFIC LLC—See Koch Industries, Inc.; *U.S. Private,* pg. 2327
THE GIBSON GROUP INC.; *U.S. Private,* pg. 4033
GK PACKAGING INC.; *U.S. Private,* pg. 1703
GLATFELTER FRANCE SARL—See Glatfelter Corporation; *U.S. Public,* pg. 939
GLATFELTER STEINFURT GMBH—See Glatfelter Corporation; *U.S. Public,* pg. 939
GOLDMAN PAPER COMPANY, INC.—See Bain Capital, LP; *U.S. Private,* pg. 440
GOTAPACK INTERNATIONAL AB—See Addtech AB; *Int'l,* pg. 133
GOULD MIDWEST, INC.—See Stephen Gould Corporation; *U.S. Private,* pg. 3802
GOULD PAPER COMPANY OF MARYLAND LLC—See Gould Paper Corporation; *U.S. Private,* pg. 1745
GOULD PAPER CORP. - MID ATLANTIC—See Gould Paper Corporation; *U.S. Private,* pg. 1745
GOULD PAPER OF FLORIDA, INC.—See Stephen Gould Corporation; *U.S. Private,* pg. 3802
GOULD PAPER OF FLORIDA, INC.—See Stephen Gould Corporation; *U.S. Private,* pg. 3802
GPA, SPECIALTY SUBSTRATE SOLUTIONS; *U.S. Private,* pg. 1747
GRAPHIC PACKAGING INTERNATIONAL CANADA, ULC—See Graphic Packaging Holding Company; *U.S. Public,* pg. 958
GRAPHIC PACKAGING INTERNATIONAL GATESHEAD LIMITED—See Graphic Packaging Holding Company; *U.S. Public,* pg. 958
GRAPHIC PRODUCTS CORPORATION; *U.S. Private,* pg. 1757
GREAT SOUTHWEST PAPER CO., INC.—See Bain Capital, LP; *U.S. Private,* pg. 441
GREIF FLEXIBLES FRANCE SARL—See Greif Inc.; *U.S. Public,* pg. 967
GUILLIN DEUTSCHLAND GMBH—See Groupe Guillin SA; *Int'l,* pg. 3103
GUILLIN ITALIA SPA—See Groupe Guillin SA; *Int'l,* pg. 3104
GUILLIN POLSKA NIEPRUSZEWO SP. Z O.O.—See Groupe Guillin SA; *Int'l,* pg. 3104
GUILLIN PORTUGAL, UNIPESSOAL, LDA—See Groupe Guillin SA; *Int'l,* pg. 3104
HARDER CORP.; *U.S. Private,* pg. 1862
HARSCO METALS GROUP LIMITED—See Enviri Corporation; *U.S. Public,* pg. 780
HATHAWAY INC.; *U.S. Private,* pg. 1880
HEBBERD KULOW ENTERPRISES; *U.S. Private,* pg. 1902

N.A.I.C.S. INDEX

424130 — INDUSTRIAL AND PERS...

HERITAGE PAPER COMPANY, INC.; *U.S. Private*, pg. 1924
HERITAGE PAPER CO.—See Pioneer Packing Inc.; *U.S. Private*, pg. 3187
HIGHLAND-EXCHANGE SERVICE COOPERATIVE INC.; *U.S. Private*, pg. 1939
HOGLA-KIMBERLY LTD.—See Kimberly-Clark Corporation; *U.S. Public*, pg. 1229
HOLMEN ITALIA SRL—See Holmen AB; *Int'l*, pg. 3452
HOLMEN NEDERLAND B.V.—See Holmen AB; *Int'l*, pg. 3452
HOLMEN PAPER AG—See Holmen AB; *Int'l*, pg. 3453
HOLMEN PAPER IBERICA SL—See Holmen AB; *Int'l*, pg. 3453
HOLMEN PAPER LTD.—See Holmen AB; *Int'l*, pg. 3453
HOLMEN PAPIERS—See Holmen AB; *Int'l*, pg. 3453
HOLMEN S.A.S.—See Holmen AB; *Int'l*, pg. 3453
HPE INC.—See The Gibson Group Inc.; *U.S. Private*, pg. 4033
H. R. SPINNER CORPORATION; *U.S. Private*, pg. 1825
H.T. BERRY CO. INC.—See Kelso & Company, L.P.; *U.S. Private*, pg. 2279
H.T. BERRY CO. INC.—See Warburg Pincus LLC; *U.S. Private*, pg. 4436
HUFF PAPER COMPANY INC.; *U.S. Private*, pg. 2002
HUHTAMAKI HONG KONG LIMITED TAIWAN BRANCH OFFICE—See Huhtamaki Oyj; *Int'l*, pg. 3525
HUHTAMAKI HUNGARY KFT—See Huhtamaki Oyj; *Int'l*, pg. 3525
HUHTAMAKI (LISBURN) LTD—See Huhtamaki Oyj; *Int'l*, pg. 3525
HUHTAMAKI TAILORED PACKAGING PTY. LTD.—See Huhtamaki Oyj; *Int'l*, pg. 3526
HUHTAMAKI TURKEY GIDA SERVISI AMBALAJI A.S.—See Huhtamaki Oyj; *Int'l*, pg. 3526
IFP CANADA CORPORATION—See The Kraft Group LLC; *U.S. Private*, pg. 4065
IFP CORPORATE SERVICES SDN. BHD.—See The Kraft Group LLC; *U.S. Private*, pg. 4065
IGGESUND PAPERBOARD EUROPE B.V.—See Holmen AB; *Int'l*, pg. 3453
IGGESUND PAPERBOARD INC.—See Holmen AB; *Int'l*, pg. 3453
IGGESUND PAPER & BOARD SERVICE B.V.—See Holmen AB; *Int'l*, pg. 3453
IMPERIAL DADE, LLC—See Bain Capital, LP; *U.S. Private*, pg. 440
INDEPENDENT PAPERBOARD MARKETING INC.; *U.S. Private*, pg. 2060
INTEGRATED PACKAGING CORP.; *U.S. Private*, pg. 2100
INTERNATIONAL FOREST PRODUCTS CORPORATION—See The Kraft Group LLC; *U.S. Private*, pg. 4065
INTERNATIONAL FOREST PRODUCTS (H.K.) LTD.—See The Kraft Group LLC; *U.S. Private*, pg. 4065
INTERNATIONAL FOREST PRODUCTS (SHANGHAI)—See The Kraft Group LLC; *U.S. Private*, pg. 4065
INTERNATIONAL FOREST PRODUCTS SVENSKA KB—See The Kraft Group LLC; *U.S. Private*, pg. 4066
INTERNATIONAL FOREST PRODUCTS (UK)—See The Kraft Group LLC; *U.S. Private*, pg. 4066
INTERNATIONAL PAPER MADRID MILL, S.L.—See International Paper Company; *U.S. Public*, pg. 1157
THE I SUPPLY COMPANY; *U.S. Private*, pg. 4055
ITALIAN AMERICAN CORP.—See Central National Gottesman Inc.; *U.S. Private*, pg. 823
JACKSON PAPER COMPANY; *U.S. Private*, pg. 2178
JIANGMEN ZHONGSHUN PAPER INDUSTRY CO., LTD.—See C&S Paper Co., Ltd.; *Int'l*, pg. 1239
JM INDUSTRIES INC.; *U.S. Private*, pg. 2214
JOE PIPER INC.; *U.S. Private*, pg. 2218
JOSHEN PAPER & PACKAGING CO. INC.—See Bunzl plc; *Int'l*, pg. 1218
JS AG PACKAGING, INC.—See Rainier Partners LP; *U.S. Private*, pg. 3348
KALAYAAN LAND CORPORATION—See Kimberly-Clark Corporation; *U.S. Public*, pg. 1229
KAPSTONE ASIA LIMITED—See WestRock Company; *U.S. Public*, pg. 2361
KINGSBURY PACKAGING (LIMAVADY) LTD.—See Bunzl plc; *Int'l*, pg. 1218
LAMB & ASSOCIATES INC.; *U.S. Private*, pg. 2379
L&B PAPER INC.; *U.S. Private*, pg. 2362
LIBERTY DISTRIBUTORS INC.; *U.S. Private*, pg. 2443
LIGHTNING PACKAGING SUPPLIES LIMITED—See Bunzl plc; *Int'l*, pg. 1218
LINDENMEYR BOOK PUBLISHING PAPERS—See Central National Gottesman Inc.; *U.S. Private*, pg. 823
LINDENMEYR CENTRAL—See Central National Gottesman Inc.; *U.S. Private*, pg. 823
LONDON BIO PACKAGING LIMITED—See Bunzl plc; *Int'l*, pg. 1219
LOVAN INDUSTRIES, INC.—See Bain Capital, LP; *U.S. Private*, pg. 441
LUCART IBERICA S.L.U.—See Cartiera Lucchese S.p.A.; *Int'l*, pg. 1348
MANSFIELD PAPER CO. INC.; *U.S. Private*, pg. 2566

MATERA PAPER COMPANY, INC.—See Ferguson plc; *Int'l*, pg. 2638
MAT-PAC INC.—See HCI Equity Management, L.P.; *U.S. Private*, pg. 1889
MATTHIAS PAPER CORPORATION; *U.S. Private*, pg. 2614
MAUI CHEMICAL & PAPER PRODUCTS, INC.; *U.S. Private*, pg. 2614
MAXCO SUPPLY INC., BOX DIVISION—See Maxco Supply Inc.; *U.S. Private*, pg. 2617
MAXCO SUPPLY INC.; *U.S. Private*, pg. 2617
MAXFLOW MEMBRAN FILTRATION GMBH—See EnviTec Biogas AG; *Int'l*, pg. 2455
MAYFIELD PAPER CO. INC.; *U.S. Private*, pg. 2621
MCLAUGHLIN PAPER CO. INC.; *U.S. Private*, pg. 2640
MCNEELY PLASTIC PRODUCTS INC.—See Alpha Industries, Inc.; *U.S. Private*, pg. 197
THE M. CONLEY COMPANY; *U.S. Private*, pg. 4073
MED PACKAGING SARL—See International Paper Company; *U.S. Public*, pg. 1157
MICHELSEN PACKAGING CO. INC.; *U.S. Private*, pg. 2700
MID-CONTINENT PAPER & DISTRIBUTING COMPANY, INC.—See Bain Capital, LP; *U.S. Private*, pg. 440
MIDLAND PAPER CO.—See Midland Paper Company; *U.S. Private*, pg. 2715
MIDWEST PACKAGING SOLUTIONS; *U.S. Private*, pg. 2722
MILLER PAPER COMPANY—See GVH Management; *U.S. Private*, pg. 1820
MI TECHNOLOGIES, INC.; *U.S. Private*, pg. 2695
MORESCO DISTRIBUTING CO.—See Bain Capital, LP; *U.S. Private*, pg. 441
MORRISETTE PAPER COMPANY INC.; *U.S. Private*, pg. 2788
MORRISON DISTRIBUTION & MARKETING; *U.S. Private*, pg. 2789
MOUNTAIN AREA COUNCIL—See Dairy Farmers of America, Inc.; *U.S. Private*, pg. 1146
MT PACKAGING INC.; *U.S. Private*, pg. 2808
MULTI-WALL PACKAGING—See Illinois Tool Works Inc.; *U.S. Public*, pg. 1109
NAKA'S, INC.; *U.S. Private*, pg. 2831
NEMEF B.V.—See ASSA ABLOY AB; *Int'l*, pg. 640
NETWORK SERVICES COMPANY; *U.S. Private*, pg. 2889
NICHOLS PAPER & SUPPLY CO. INC.—See Bain Capital, LP; *U.S. Private*, pg. 441
NORTHERN SALES COMPANY OF ALASKA, INC.; *U.S. Private*, pg. 2954
NORTHWEST ARKANSAS PAPER CO., INC.; *U.S. Private*, pg. 2958
OAKLAND PACKAGING SUPPLY; *U.S. Private*, pg. 2984
ONE SOURCE INDUSTRIES, LLC—See Westminster Capital Inc.; *U.S. Private*, pg. 4499
PACIFIC PACKAGING PRODUCTS, INC.; *U.S. Private*, pg. 3069
PACKAGING 2 BUY LIMITED—See Bunzl plc; *Int'l*, pg. 1219
PACKAGING TAPE INC.; *U.S. Private*, pg. 3072
PAK WEST PAPER & PACKAGING LLC—See Blower Dempsay Corporation; *U.S. Private*, pg. 584
PAPER & CHEMICAL SUPPLY CO.; *U.S. Private*, pg. 3087
PAPERCLIP INC.; *U.S. Public*, pg. 1636
PAPER CUTTERS INC.; *U.S. Private*, pg. 3088
PAPER ENTERPRISES, INC.; *U.S. Private*, pg. 3088
PAPER PRODUCTS CO. INC.; *U.S. Private*, pg. 3088
PAPER SOURCE, INC.—See Elliott Management Corporation; *U.S. Private*, pg. 1373
PAPETERIES DE GASCOGNE GMBH—See Gascogne SA; *Int'l*, pg. 2888
PARKER HANNIFIN S.R.O., PACKING DIVISION—See Parker Hannifin Corporation; *U.S. Public*, pg. 1649
PENINSULAR PAPER COMPANY, INC.—See Bain Capital, LP; *U.S. Private*, pg. 440
PERLEN FRANCE SARL—See CPH Chemie + Papier Holding AG; *Int'l*, pg. 1824
PERRIN BERNARD SUPOWITZ, LLC—See Kelso & Company, L.P.; *U.S. Private*, pg. 2278
PFS SALES COMPANY—See Kelso & Company, L.P.; *U.S. Private*, pg. 2279
PFS SALES COMPANY—See Warburg Pincus LLC; *U.S. Private*, pg. 4437
PIONEER NORTHERN INC.—See Pioneer Packing Inc.; *U.S. Private*, pg. 3188
PIONEER PACKING INC.; *U.S. Private*, pg. 3187
POLLOCK INVESTMENTS INC.; *U.S. Private*, pg. 3225
POLYEDRA SPA—See CVC Capital Partners SICAV-FIS S.A.; *Int'l*, pg. 1887
PORTABRANDS LIMITED—See Bunzl plc; *Int'l*, pg. 1219
PREMIAFLEX PLASTICS LTD.—See Advanced Chemical Industries Limited; *Int'l*, pg. 158
PRIDE PRODUCTS CORP; *U.S. Private*, pg. 3259
PT CUSCAPI INDONESIA—See Cuscapi Berhad; *Int'l*, pg. 1880
QUPACO INC.; *U.S. Private*, pg. 3331
RELIABLE CONTAINER CORPORATION—See Koch Industries, Inc.; *U.S. Private*, pg. 2329
RENARD PAPER COMPANY, INC.—See HP Products Corporation; *U.S. Private*, pg. 1996
RENO DE MEDICI ALMAZAN—See Apollo Global Management, Inc.; *U.S. Public*, pg. 159

RETAILERS SUPPLY CO INC.—See American Securities LLC; *U.S. Private*, pg. 247
RIVERSIDE PAPER COMPANY INC.; *U.S. Private*, pg. 3445
RIVER VALLEY PAPER CO.; *U.S. Private*, pg. 3444
R.J. SCHINNER CO. INC.; *U.S. Private*, pg. 3337
ROHRER CORP. - BUFORD PLANT—See Wellspring Capital Management LLC; *U.S. Public*, pg. 4477
ROOSEVELT PAPER COMPANY—See Roosevelt Paper Company; *U.S. Private*, pg. 3480
ROYAL PAPER CORPORATION; *U.S. Private*, pg. 3493
ROYAL PAPERS INC.; *U.S. Private*, pg. 3493
RPC TEDECO-GIZEH GMBH—See Berry Global Group, Inc; *U.S. Public*, pg. 325
RUDD CONTAINER CORPORATION; *U.S. Private*, pg. 3500
RX SYSTEMS INC.; *U.S. Private*, pg. 3509
SARANTIS BULGARIA LTD—See Gr. Sarantis S.A.; *Int'l*, pg. 3047
SCHILLING PAPER COMPANY INC.; *U.S. Private*, pg. 3565
SCHWARZ PAPER COMPANY; *U.S. Private*, pg. 3572
SEAMAN PAPER ASIA CO LTD—See Seaman Paper Company of Massachusetts Inc.; *U.S. Private*, pg. 3585
SEAPORT INTERNATIONAL INC.; *U.S. Private*, pg. 3586
S. FREEDMAN & SONS, INC.; *U.S. Private*, pg. 3515
SHAMROCK SCIENTIFIC SPECIALTY SYSTEMS, INC.; *U.S. Private*, pg. 3624
SHIP-PAC CORP.—See Central National Gottesman Inc.; *U.S. Private*, pg. 823
SHIP-PAC INC.; *U.S. Private*, pg. 3637
SILVANIA RESOURCES INC.; *U.S. Private*, pg. 3653
SIMPLICITY PATTERNS INTERNATIONAL LTD. INC.—See Conso International Corporation; *U.S. Private*, pg. 1020
SISTEMAS Y TECHNICAS DE SEGURIDAD, S.A.—See ASSA ABLOY AB; *Int'l*, pg. 640
SOUTHEASTERN PAPER GROUP, INC.; *U.S. Private*, pg. 3728
SOUTHWEST PAPER COMPANY INC.; *U.S. Private*, pg. 3740
THE STEPHEN GOULD CORPORATION—See Stephen Gould Corporation; *U.S. Private*, pg. 3802
STEPHEN GOULD CORP—See Stephen Gould Corporation; *U.S. Private*, pg. 3802
STEPHEN GOULD, INC./LA—See Stephen Gould Corporation; *U.S. Private*, pg. 3802
STEPHEN GOULD OF CAROLINA, INC./CHARLOTTE DIV.—See Stephen Gould Corporation; *U.S. Private*, pg. 3802
STEPHEN GOULD OF CAROLINA, INC.—See Stephen Gould Corporation; *U.S. Private*, pg. 3802
STEPHEN GOULD OF CONNECTICUT CORP.—See Stephen Gould Corporation; *U.S. Private*, pg. 3802
STEPHEN GOULD OF ILLINOIS, INC.—See Stephen Gould Corporation; *U.S. Private*, pg. 3802
STEPHEN GOULD OF INDIANA, INC.—See Stephen Gould Corporation; *U.S. Private*, pg. 3802
STEPHEN GOULD OF MARYLAND, INC.—See Stephen Gould Corporation; *U.S. Private*, pg. 3802
STEPHEN GOULD OF MICHIGAN, INC.—See Stephen Gould Corporation; *U.S. Private*, pg. 3802
STEPHEN GOULD OF NEW ENGLAND, INC.—See Stephen Gould Corporation; *U.S. Private*, pg. 3802
STEPHEN GOULD OF OHIO, CORP.—See Stephen Gould Corporation; *U.S. Private*, pg. 3802
STEPHEN GOULD OF OHIO, CORP.—See Stephen Gould Corporation; *U.S. Private*, pg. 3802
STEPHEN GOULD OF TENNESSEE, INC.—See Stephen Gould Corporation; *U.S. Private*, pg. 3802
STEPHEN GOULD OF TEXAS, INC.—See Stephen Gould Corporation; *U.S. Private*, pg. 3802
STRAUSS PAPER CO., INC.—See Bain Capital, LP; *U.S. Private*, pg. 440
SUN HING PAPER COMPANY, LIMITED—See Hung Hing Printing Group Limited; *Int'l*, pg. 3535
S. WALTER PACKAGING CORP.—See LMP Management Group, Inc.; *U.S. Private*, pg. 2476
SWISH WHITE RIVER LTD.; *U.S. Private*, pg. 3894
TAIHEI SANGYO CO., LTD.—See Dynic Corporation; *Int'l*, pg. 2243
TALGE DESCARTAVEIS DO BRASIL LTDA.—See Bunzl plc; *Int'l*, pg. 1219
TAPE PRODUCTS COMPANY INC.; *U.S. Private*, pg. 3932
TARHEEL PAPER & SUPPLY CO.; *U.S. Private*, pg. 3934
TCL PONSA MANUFACTURING LIMITED (TPM)—See CEMEX, S.A.B. de C.V.; *Int'l*, pg. 1400
TECNOPACKING, S.L.U.—See Bunzl plc; *Int'l*, pg. 1219
TEXTAPE, INC.; *U.S. Private*, pg. 3978
THERMOFLEX AG—See Groupe Guillin SA; *Int'l*, pg. 3104
TIFFIN PAPER COMPANY; *U.S. Private*, pg. 4169
TILIBRA PRODUTOS DE PAPELARIA LTDA—See ACCO Brands Corporation; *U.S. Public*, pg. 33
TOMAR INDUSTRIES, INC.; *U.S. Private*, pg. 4183
TRADCORP S.A.—See BERICAP GmbH & Co. KG; *Int'l*, pg. 981
TRANSIT SA—See Burelle S.A.; *Int'l*, pg. 1223
TREBOR INC.; *U.S. Private*, pg. 4216
TRI-STAR PACKAGING SUPPLIES LIMITED—See Bunzl plc; *Int'l*, pg. 1219
TWO-TWO-FREE LIMITED—See Huasheng International

424130 — INDUSTRIAL AND PERS...

Holding Limited; *Int'l*, pg. 3514
ULINE, INC.; *U.S. Private*, pg. 4276
UNGER COMPANY; *U.S. Private*, pg. 4281
UNITED STATIONERS HONG KONG LIMITED—See Sycamore Partners Management, LP; *U.S. Private*, pg. 3897
VALLEY PACKAGING INC.; *U.S. Private*, pg. 4334
VARIA-PACK NV—See Bunzl plc; *Int'l*, pg. 1219
VENTURES ASSOCIATES, INC.—See Naka's, Inc.; *U.S. Private*, pg. 2831
VERITIV OPERATING COMPANY - NEW BERLIN—See Clayton, Dubilier & Rice, LLC; *U.S. Private*, pg. 929
VERITIV—See Clayton, Dubilier & Rice, LLC; *U.S. Private*, pg. 929
VERITIV—See Clayton, Dubilier & Rice, LLC; *U.S. Private*, pg. 929
VERITIV—See Clayton, Dubilier & Rice, LLC; *U.S. Private*, pg. 929
VICTORY PACKAGING; *U.S. Private*, pg. 4379
VISTAPAK INDUSTRIES INC.; *U.S. Private*, pg. 4403
VOLM BAG COMPANY, INC.; *U.S. Private*, pg. 4411
WEBER PAPER CO.; *U.S. Private*, pg. 4465
WEIR CANADA INC.—See Axel Johnson Gruppen AB; *Int'l*, pg. 765
WESTERN PAPER DISTRIBUTORS, INC.—See Bain Capital, LP; *U.S. Private*, pg. 441
WESTROCK ASIA, K.K.—See WestRock Company; *U.S. Public*, pg. 2362
WESTROCK MWV HONG KONG LIMITED—See WestRock Company; *U.S. Public*, pg. 2362
WG SERVICES, INC.—See Datatec Limited; *Int'l*, pg. 1981
WOODWORKS UNLIMITED; *U.S. Private*, pg. 4561
WORLDPACK TRADING B.V.—See Bunzl plc; *Int'l*, pg. 1220
YPV DISTRIBUTION, INC.—See Kelso & Company, L.P.; *U.S. Private*, pg. 2279
YPV DISTRIBUTION, INC.—See Warburg Pincus LLC; *U.S. Private*, pg. 4437
ZHEJIANG ZHONG SHUN PAPER INDUSTRY CO., LTD.—See C&S Paper Co., Ltd.; *Int'l*, pg. 1239

424210 — DRUGS AND DRUGGISTS&APOS; SUNDRIES MERCHANT WHOLESALERS

111, INC.; *Int'l*, pg. 2
1PM INDUSTRIES, INC.; *U.S. Public*, pg. 2
AA ASIA LIMITED—See Walgreens Boots Alliance, Inc.; *U.S. Public*, pg. 2321
ABBOTT AUSTRALASIA PTY. LTD.—See Abbott Laboratories; *U.S. Public*, pg. 14
ABBOTT HEALTHCARE B.V.—See Abbott Laboratories; *U.S. Public*, pg. 14
ABBOTT INFORMATICS SPAIN, S.A.—See Abbott Laboratories; *U.S. Public*, pg. 15
ABBOTT IRELAND LIMITED—See Abbott Laboratories; *U.S. Public*, pg. 15
ABBOTT LABORATORIES DE MEXICO S.A. DE C.V.—See Abbott Laboratories; *U.S. Public*, pg. 16
ABBOTT LABORATORIES FINANCE B.V.—See Abbott Laboratories; *U.S. Public*, pg. 15
ABBOTT MEDICAL DANMARK AS—See Abbott Laboratories; *U.S. Public*, pg. 17
ABBOTT MEDICAL ESTONIA OU—See Abbott Laboratories; *U.S. Public*, pg. 17
ABBOTT MEDICAL GMBH—See Abbott Laboratories; *U.S. Public*, pg. 17
ABBOTT MEDICAL (PORTUGAL) DISTRIBUICAO DE PRODUTOS MEDICOS LDA—See Abbott Laboratories; *U.S. Public*, pg. 16
ABBOTT MEDICAL (SCHWEIZ) AG—See Abbott Laboratories; *U.S. Public*, pg. 16
ABBOTT MEDICAL SWEDEN AB—See Abbott Laboratories; *U.S. Public*, pg. 17
ABBOTT PRODUTOS OTICOS LTDA.—See Abbott Laboratories; *U.S. Public*, pg. 17
ABBVIE BIOFARMACEVTSKA DRUZBA D.O.O.—See AbbVie Inc.; *U.S. Public*, pg. 21
ABBVIE BIOPHARMACEUTICALS LTD.—See AbbVie Inc.; *U.S. Public*, pg. 21
ABBVIE PROMOCAO, L.DA—See AbbVie Inc.; *U.S. Public*, pg. 22
ABIO MARKETING SDN. BHD.—See Apex Healthcare Berhad; *Int'l*, pg. 511
A & B PROCESS SYSTEMS CORP.—See John Bean Technologies Corporation; *U.S. Public*, pg. 1191
ACARIAHEALTH, INC.—See Centene Corporation; *U.S. Public*, pg. 468
ACARIAHEALTH PHARMACY #11, INC.—See Centene Corporation; *U.S. Public*, pg. 467
ACARIAHEALTH PHARMACY #13, INC.—See Centene Corporation; *U.S. Public*, pg. 467
ACETO (SHANGHAI) LTD.—See Aceto Corporation; *U.S. Private*, pg. 58
ACINO SUPPLY AG—See Avista Capital Partners, L.P.; *U.S. Private*, pg. 408
ACRO PHARMACEUTICAL SERVICES LLC—See Premier, Inc.; *U.S. Public*, pg. 1715
ACTELION PHARMACEUTICALS HELLAS SA—See Johnson & Johnson; *U.S. Public*, pg. 1193

ACTELION PHARMACEUTICALS KOREA LTD.—See Johnson & Johnson; *U.S. Public*, pg. 1194
ACTELION PHARMACEUTICALS MEXICO S.A. DE C.V.—See Johnson & Johnson; *U.S. Public*, pg. 1194
ACTIVE MOTIF-EUROPE—See Active Motif, Inc.; *U.S. Private*, pg. 70
ADAPT PHARMA INC.—See Emergent BioSolutions Inc.; *U.S. Public*, pg. 739
AESYNT HOLDINGS, INC.—See Omnicell, Inc.; *U.S. Public*, pg. 1572
AESYNT, INC.—See Omnicell, Inc.; *U.S. Public*, pg. 1572
AFICOM; *Int'l*, pg. 189
AGILE PHARMA (MALTA) LIMITED—See Aurobindo Pharma Ltd.; *Int'l*, pg. 712
AII CLUBMAN—See American International Industries Company; *U.S. Private*, pg. 238
AIM CANADA INC—See Aim International, Inc.; *U.S. Private*, pg. 132
AIM U.S.A. INC.—See Aim International, Inc.; *U.S. Private*, pg. 132
AIRCRAFT MAINTENANCE SUPPORT SERVICES LIMITED—See John Bean Technologies Corporation; *U.S. Public*, pg. 1191
ALAMO PHARMA SERVICES, INC.—See JLL Partners, LLC; *U.S. Private*, pg. 2212
ALAMO PHARMA SERVICES, INC.—See Water Street Healthcare Partners, LLC; *U.S. Private*, pg. 4452
ALBIREO AB—See Albireo Pharma, Inc.; *U.S. Public*, pg. 74
ALCURA FRANCE—See Walgreens Boots Alliance, Inc.; *U.S. Public*, pg. 2321
ALCURA HEALTH ESPANA, S.A.—See Walgreens Boots Alliance, Inc.; *U.S. Public*, pg. 2321
ALEXION ILAC TICARET LIMITED SIRKETI—See AstraZeneca PLC; *Int'l*, pg. 659
ALEXION PHARMA INTERNATIONAL TRADING—See AstraZeneca PLC; *Int'l*, pg. 659
ALEXION PHARMA MIDDLE EAST FZ-LLC—See AstraZeneca PLC; *Int'l*, pg. 659
ALEXION SERVICES LATIN AMERICA, INC.—See AstraZeneca PLC; *Int'l*, pg. 659
ALFRESA HEALTHCARE CORPORATION—See Alfresa Holdings Corporation; *Int'l*, pg. 317
ALFRESA MEDICAL SERVICE CORPORATION—See Alfresa Holdings Corporation; *Int'l*, pg. 317
ALFRESA NIKKEN SANGYO CORPORATION—See Alfresa Holdings Corporation; *Int'l*, pg. 317
AL GLOBAL CORPORATION—See Youngevity International Corp.; *U.S. Public*, pg. 2399
ALGOL CHEMICALS AB—See Algol Oy; *Int'l*, pg. 318
ALGOL CHEMICALS APS—See Algol Oy; *Int'l*, pg. 318
ALGOL CHEMICALS AS—See Algol Oy; *Int'l*, pg. 318
ALGOL CHEMICALS OU—See Algol Oy; *Int'l*, pg. 318
ALKALOID DOO (PODGORICA)—See Alkaloid A.D. Skopje; *Int'l*, pg. 330
ALKALOID DOO (SARAJEVO)—See Alkaloid A.D. Skopje; *Int'l*, pg. 330
ALKALOID D.O.O.—See Alkaloid A.D. Skopje; *Int'l*, pg. 330
ALKALOID DOO (ZAGREB)—See Alkaloid A.D. Skopje; *Int'l*, pg. 330
ALKALOID E.D.O.O—See Alkaloid A.D. Skopje; *Int'l*, pg. 330
ALKALOID-FARM D.O.O.—See Alkaloid A.D. Skopje; *Int'l*, pg. 330
ALKALOID KONS DOOEL—See Alkaloid A.D. Skopje; *Int'l*, pg. 330
ALKALOIDPHARMA SA—See Alkaloid A.D. Skopje; *Int'l*, pg. 330
ALKALOID SH.P.K. (TIRANA)—See Alkaloid A.D. Skopje; *Int'l*, pg. 330
ALKALOID USA LLC—See Alkaloid A.D. Skopje; *Int'l*, pg. 330
ALK&KOS SH.P.K.—See Alkaloid A.D. Skopje; *Int'l*, pg. 330
ALK & KOS SHPK—See Alkaloid A.D. Skopje; *Int'l*, pg. 330
ALK-SCHERAX ARZNEIMITTEL GMBH—See Bayer Aktiengesellschaft; *Int'l*, pg. 904
ALLERGAN APS—See AbbVie Inc.; *U.S. Public*, pg. 22
ALLERGAN CZ, S.R.O.—See AbbVie Inc.; *U.S. Public*, pg. 22
ALLERGAN DEVELOPMENT VENTURES I UK—See AbbVie Inc.; *U.S. Public*, pg. 22
ALLERGAN D.O.O. BEOGRAD—See AbbVie Inc.; *U.S. Public*, pg. 22
ALLERGAN HUNGARY KFT.—See AbbVie Inc.; *U.S. Public*, pg. 22
ALLERGAN INC.—See AbbVie Inc.; *U.S. Public*, pg. 23
ALLERGAN MIDDLE EAST LIMITED—See AbbVie Inc.; *U.S. Public*, pg. 22
ALLERGAN PRODUCTOS FARMACEUTICOS LTDA.—See AbbVie Inc.; *U.S. Public*, pg. 22
ALLERGAN SAUDI ARABIA LLC—See AbbVie Inc.; *U.S. Public*, pg. 22
ALLERGAN SCIENTIFIC OFFICE—See AbbVie Inc.; *U.S. Public*, pg. 22
ALLERGAN SINGAPORE PTE. LTD.—See AbbVie Inc.; *U.S. Public*, pg. 22
ALLERGAN SINGAPORE PTE. LTD.—See AbbVie Inc.; *U.S. Public*, pg. 22
ALLERGAN SK S.R.O.—See AbbVie Inc.; *U.S. Public*, pg. 22

ALLERGAN SP. Z.O.O.—See AbbVie Inc.; *U.S. Public*, pg. 22
ALLERGAN SRL—See AbbVie Inc.; *U.S. Public*, pg. 22
ALLERGAN UKRAINE, LLC—See AbbVie Inc.; *U.S. Public*, pg. 22
ALLIANCE BOOTS SOURCING (HONG KONG) LIMITED—See Walgreens Boots Alliance, Inc.; *U.S. Public*, pg. 2321
ALLIANCE HEALTHCARE DEUTSCHLAND AG—See Walgreens Boots Alliance, Inc.; *U.S. Public*, pg. 2322
ALLIANCE HEALTHCARE ESPANA S.A.—See Walgreens Boots Alliance, Inc.; *U.S. Public*, pg. 2322
ALLIANCE HEALTHCARE GROUP FRANCE—See Walgreens Boots Alliance, Inc.; *U.S. Public*, pg. 2322
ALLIANCE HEALTHCARE GROUP FRANCE—See Walgreens Boots Alliance, Inc.; *U.S. Public*, pg. 2322
ALLIANCE HEALTHCARE ITALIA SPA—See Walgreens Boots Alliance, Inc.; *U.S. Public*, pg. 2322
ALLIANCE HEALTHCARE LTD.—See Walgreens Boots Alliance, Inc.; *U.S. Public*, pg. 2321
ALLIANCE HEALTHCARE NORGE A.S.—See Walgreens Boots Alliance, Inc.; *U.S. Public*, pg. 2322
ALLIANCE HEALTHCARE, S.R.O.—See Walgreens Boots Alliance, Inc.; *U.S. Public*, pg. 2322
ALLIANCE PHARMA PLC; *Int'l*, pg. 340
ALLIED HERBALS LIMITED; *Int'l*, pg. 357
ALLOGA FRANCE—See Walgreens Boots Alliance, Inc.; *U.S. Public*, pg. 2322
ALLWELLNESS HOLDINGS GROUP LIMITED; *Int'l*, pg. 361
ALMAC PHARMACEUTICAL SERVICES PTE. LTD.—See Almac Sciences Group Ltd.; *Int'l*, pg. 362
ALMUS FRANCE—See Walgreens Boots Alliance, Inc.; *U.S. Public*, pg. 2322
ALNYLAM AUSTRIA GMBH—See Alnylam Pharmaceuticals, Inc.; *U.S. Public*, pg. 82
ALNYLAM BRASIL FARMACEUTICA LTDA.—See Alnylam Pharmaceuticals, Inc.; *U.S. Public*, pg. 82
ALNYLAM GERMANY GMBH—See Alnylam Pharmaceuticals, Inc.; *U.S. Public*, pg. 82
ALOETTE COSMETICS, INC.; *U.S. Private*, pg. 195
ALPHEGA APOTHEKENPARTNER GMBH—See Walgreens Boots Alliance, Inc.; *U.S. Public*, pg. 2322
ALPHEGA—See Walgreens Boots Alliance, Inc.; *U.S. Public*, pg. 2322
ALPIC BIOTECH LTD.—See Delta Plus Group; *Int'l*, pg. 2019
ALTERNA HOLDINGS CORP.—See Henkel AG & Co. KGaA; *Int'l*, pg. 3353
ALTO PHARMACEUTICALS, INC.; *U.S. Private*, pg. 210
AMARIN PHARMA, INC.—See AMARIN CORPORATION PLC; *Int'l*, pg. 412
A MARTINS & FERNANDES S.A—See Guerbet SA; *Int'l*, pg. 3172
A. MARTINS & FERNANDES—See Guerbet SA; *Int'l*, pg. 3172
AMBIENT HEALTHCARE, INC.—See Harvest Partners L.P.; *U.S. Private*, pg. 1876
AMBIENTIS RADIOPROTECAO LTDA—See Eckert & Ziegler Strahlen- und Medizintechnik AG; *Int'l*, pg. 2290
AMCON DISTRIBUTING COMPANY, INC.—See AMCON Distributing Company; *U.S. Public*, pg. 92
AMERICA GREAT HEALTH; *U.S. Public*, pg. 95
AMERICAN CUTTING EDGE, INC.—See CB Manufacturing & Sales Co., Inc.; *U.S. Private*, pg. 796
AMERICAN INTERNATIONAL INDUSTRIES COMPANY; *U.S. Private*, pg. 238
AMERICAN VETERINARY PHARMACEUTICALS—See CSR Company Inc.; *U.S. Private*, pg. 1117
AMERISOURCEBERGEN DRUG CORPORATION—See Cencora, Inc.; *U.S. Public*, pg. 466
AMERISOURCEBERGEN SERVICES CORPORATION—See Cencora, Inc.; *U.S. Public*, pg. 466
AMERISOURCEBERGEN—See Cencora, Inc.; *U.S. Public*, pg. 466
AMERISOURCEBERGEN—See Cencora, Inc.; *U.S. Public*, pg. 466
AMERISOURCEBERGEN—See Cencora, Inc.; *U.S. Public*, pg. 466
AMERISOURCEBERGEN—See Cencora, Inc.; *U.S. Public*, pg. 466
AMERISOURCEBERGEN—See Cencora, Inc.; *U.S. Public*, pg. 466
AMERISOURCEBERGEN—See Cencora, Inc.; *U.S. Public*, pg. 466
AMERISOURCEBERGEN—See Cencora, Inc.; *U.S. Public*, pg. 466
AMERISOURCEBERGEN—See Cencora, Inc.; *U.S. Public*, pg. 466
AMERISOURCEBERGEN—See Cencora, Inc.; *U.S. Public*, pg. 466
AMERISOURCEBERGEN—See Cencora, Inc.; *U.S. Public*, pg. 466
AMERISOURCEBERGEN—See Cencora, Inc.; *U.S. Public*, pg. 466

N.A.I.C.S. INDEX

424210 — DRUGS AND DRUGGISTS...

AMERISOURCEBERGEN—See Cencora, Inc.; *U.S. Public*, pg. 466
AMERISOURCEBERGEN SPECIALTY GROUP—See Cencora, Inc.; *U.S. Public*, pg. 466
AMGEN AB—See Amgen Inc.; *U.S. Public*, pg. 122
AMGEN AUSTRALIA PTY LTD.—See Amgen Inc.; *U.S. Public*, pg. 122
AMGEN BELGIUM S.A. N.V.—See Amgen Inc.; *U.S. Public*, pg. 122
AMGEN-BIO-FARMACEUTICA, LDA.—See Amgen Inc.; *U.S. Public*, pg. 123
AMGEN B.V.—See Amgen Inc.; *U.S. Public*, pg. 122
AMGEN CANADA INC.—See Amgen Inc.; *U.S. Public*, pg. 122
AMGEN EUROPE B.V.—See Amgen Inc.; *U.S. Public*, pg. 122
AMGEN (EUROPE) GMBH—See Amgen Inc.; *U.S. Public*, pg. 122
AMGEN GMBH—See Amgen Inc.; *U.S. Public*, pg. 122
AMGEN GMBH—See Amgen Inc.; *U.S. Public*, pg. 123
AMGEN LIMITED—See Amgen Inc.; *U.S. Public*, pg. 123
AMGEN S.A.—See Amgen Inc.; *U.S. Public*, pg. 123
AMGEN S.A.—See Amgen Inc.; *U.S. Public*, pg. 123
AMGEN S.P.A.—See Amgen Inc.; *U.S. Public*, pg. 123
AMI CO., LTD.—See Astena Holdings Co., Ltd.; *Int'l*, pg. 653
AMICUS THERAPEUTICS K.K.—See Amicus Therapeutics, Inc.; *U.S. Public*, pg. 124
AMIL ASSISTENCIA MEDICA INTERNACIONAL S.A.—See UnitedHealth Group Incorporated; *U.S. Public*, pg. 2239
AMINO CHEMICALS LIMITED—See ABA Chemicals Corporation; *Int'l*, pg. 47
AMOREPACIFIC AUSTRALIA PTY. LTD.—See Amorepacific Corp.; *Int'l*, pg. 430
AMOREPACIFIC JAPAN CO., LTD.—See Amorepacific Corp.; *Int'l*, pg. 430
AMOREPACIFIC SINGAPORE PTE CO LTD.—See Amorepacific Corp.; *Int'l*, pg. 430
AMPLYX PHARMACEUTICALS INC.—See Pfizer Inc.; *U.S. Public*, pg. 1679
AMWAY BELGIUM CO—See Alticor Inc.; *U.S. Private*, pg. 208
AMWAY DENMARK APS—See Alticor Inc.; *U.S. Private*, pg. 209
AMWAY DOMINICAN REPUBLIC, LLC—See Alticor Inc.; *U.S. Private*, pg. 209
AMWAY ROMANIA MARKETING S.R.L.—See Alticor Inc.; *U.S. Private*, pg. 209
ANABOLIC LABORATORIES INC.; *U.S. Private*, pg. 271
ANCHOR PHARMACY & MEDICAL SUPPLIES; *U.S. Private*, pg. 273
ANDLAND OVERSEAS S.A.—See Abbott Laboratories; *U.S. Public*, pg. 19
ANGELINI FARMACEUTICA LDA.—See Angelini ACRAF S.p.A.; *Int'l*, pg. 460
ANGELINI FARMACEUTICA S.A.—See Angelini ACRAF S.p.A.; *Int'l*, pg. 460
ANGELINI ILAC SAN. VE TIC. A.S.—See Angelini ACRAF S.p.A.; *Int'l*, pg. 460
ANGELINI PHARMA BULGARIA EOOD—See Angelini ACRAF S.p.A.; *Int'l*, pg. 460
ANGELINI PHARMACEUTICALS (PVT) LTD—See Angelini ACRAF S.p.A.; *Int'l*, pg. 460
ANGELINI PHARMACEUTICALS ROMANIA S.R.L.—See Angelini ACRAF S.p.A.; *Int'l*, pg. 460
ANGELINI PHARMA HELLAS S.A.—See Angelini ACRAF S.p.A.; *Int'l*, pg. 460
ANGELINI PHARMA MAGYARORSZAG KFT.—See Angelini ACRAF S.p.A.; *Int'l*, pg. 460
ANGELINI PHARMA OSTERREICH GMBH—See Angelini ACRAF S.p.A.; *Int'l*, pg. 460
ANGELINI PHARMA RUS LLC—See Angelini ACRAF S.p.A.; *Int'l*, pg. 460
ANGELINI PHARMA SLOVENSKA REPUBLIKA S. R. O.—See Angelini ACRAF S.p.A.; *Int'l*, pg. 460
ANZAG ROSTOCK GMBH & CO. KG—See Walgreens Boots Alliance, Inc.; *U.S. Public*, pg. 2321
APEX PHARMACY CORPORATE SDN. BHD.—See Apex Healthcare Berhad; *Int'l*, pg. 511
APEX PHARMACY MARKETING SDN. BHD.—See Apex Healthcare Berhad; *Int'l*, pg. 511
APEX PHARMA MARKETING PTE. LTD.—See Apex Healthcare Berhad; *Int'l*, pg. 511
APODANNORDIC PHARMAPACKAGING A/S—See Fagron NV; *Int'l*, pg. 2603
APOTEX ILAC SAN.TIC.LTD.STI.—See SK Capital Partners, LP; *U.S. Private*, pg. 3678
APOTEX NETHERLANDS BV—See SK Capital Partners, LP; *U.S. Private*, pg. 3678
APOTEX NICARAGUA, S.A.—See SK Capital Partners, LP; *U.S. Private*, pg. 3679
APOTEX PANAMA, S.A.—See SK Capital Partners, LP; *U.S. Private*, pg. 3679
APOTEX POLSKA SP. Z.O.O.—See Aurobindo Pharma Ltd.; *Int'l*, pg. 712
APOTEX PTY LTD.—See SK Capital Partners, LP; *U.S. Private*, pg. 3679
APTAR BALLINASLOE LIMITED—See AptarGroup, Inc.; *U.S. Public*, pg. 174

APTAR CKYNE S.R.O.—See AptarGroup, Inc.; *U.S. Public*, pg. 174
APTAR FRANCE S.A.S.—See AptarGroup, Inc.; *U.S. Public*, pg. 174
APTAR FREYUNG GMBH—See AptarGroup, Inc.; *U.S. Public*, pg. 174
APTAR ITALIA S.P.A.—See AptarGroup, Inc.; *U.S. Public*, pg. 174
APTAR MEZZOVICO S.A.—See AptarGroup, Inc.; *U.S. Public*, pg. 174
APTAR RADOLFZELL GMBH—See AptarGroup, Inc.; *U.S. Public*, pg. 174
APTAR TORELLO, S.A.—See AptarGroup, Inc.; *U.S. Public*, pg. 174
APTAR VILLINGEN GMBH—See AptarGroup, Inc.; *U.S. Public*, pg. 174
ARATA VIETNAM COMPANY LIMITED—See Arata Corporation; *Int'l*, pg. 536
ARDELL INTERNATIONAL, INC.—See American International Industries Company; *U.S. Private*, pg. 238
AR-EX LTD.; *U.S. Private*, pg. 306
ARICH ENTERPRISE CO., LTD.; *Int'l*, pg. 564
ARRAIL G ROUP LIMITED; *Int'l*, pg. 578
ARROWEDGE LTD.; *Int'l*, pg. 580
ASD HEALTHCARE—See Cencora, Inc.; *U.S. Public*, pg. 466
ASD SPECIALTY HEALTHCARE, INC.—See Cencora, Inc.; *U.S. Public*, pg. 466
ASENCE PHARMA PVT. LTD.—See Ambalal Sarabhai Enterprises Ltd.; *Int'l*, pg. 413
ASHFIELD HEALTHCARE IRELAND LIMITED—See Clayton, Dubilier & Rice, LLC; *U.S. Private*, pg. 927
ASIAN LIFE CO., LTD.—See Asian Phytoceuticals Public Company Limited; *Int'l*, pg. 619
ASPEN GLOBAL INCORPORATED—See Aspen Pharmacare Holdings Limited; *Int'l*, pg. 629
ASPEN MEDICAL PRODUCTS MALAYSIA SDN. BHD.—See Aspen Pharmacare Holdings Limited; *Int'l*, pg. 629
ASPEN PHARMACARE CANADA INC.—See Aspen Pharmacare Holdings Limited; *Int'l*, pg. 629
ASSOCIATED PHARMACIES INC.; *U.S. Private*, pg. 356
ASTELLAS PHARMA AUSTRALIA PTY LTD—See Astellas Pharma Inc.; *Int'l*, pg. 652
ASTELLAS PHARMA B.V.—See Astellas Pharma Inc.; *Int'l*, pg. 652
ASTELLAS PHARMA CANADA, INC.—See Astellas Pharma Inc.; *Int'l*, pg. 653
ASTELLAS PHARMA D.O.O.—See CEZ, a.s.; *Int'l*, pg. 1426
ASTELLAS PHARMA GMBH—See Astellas Pharma Inc.; *Int'l*, pg. 652
ASTELLAS PHARMA GMBH—See Astellas Pharma Inc.; *Int'l*, pg. 652
ASTELLAS PHARMA INDIA PRIVATE LIMITED—See Astellas Pharma Inc.; *Int'l*, pg. 652
ASTELLAS PHARMA INTERNATIONAL B.V.—See Astellas Pharma Inc.; *Int'l*, pg. 652
ASTELLAS PHARMA KOREA, INC.—See Astellas Pharma Inc.; *Int'l*, pg. 652
ASTELLAS PHARMA MALAYSIA SDN. BHD.—See Astellas Pharma Inc.; *Int'l*, pg. 652
ASTELLAS PHARMA SINGAPORE PTE. LTD.—See Astellas Pharma Inc.; *Int'l*, pg. 652
ASTELLAS PHARMA SP.Z.O.O.—See Astellas Pharma Inc.; *Int'l*, pg. 652
ASTELLAS PHARMA TECH CO., LTD—See Astellas Pharma Inc.; *Int'l*, pg. 652
ASTELLAS PHARMA (THAILAND) CO., LTD.—See Astellas Pharma Inc.; *Int'l*, pg. 652
ASTRAZENECA B.V.—See AstraZeneca PLC; *Int'l*, pg. 659
ASTRAZENECA ICELAND—See AstraZeneca PLC; *Int'l*, pg. 660
ASTRAZENECA ILAC SANAYI VE TICARET LIMITED—See AstraZeneca PLC; *Int'l*, pg. 661
ASTRAZENECA (ISRAEL) LTD.—See AstraZeneca PLC; *Int'l*, pg. 659
ASTRAZENECA KOREA (SOUTH)—See AstraZeneca PLC; *Int'l*, pg. 660
ASTRAZENECA LIMITED—See AstraZeneca PLC; *Int'l*, pg. 660
ASTRAZENECA LUXEMBOURG S.A.R.L.—See AstraZeneca PLC; *Int'l*, pg. 660
ASTRAZENECA - PRODUTOS FARMACEUTICOS, LDA.—See AstraZeneca PLC; *Int'l*, pg. 659
ASTRAZENECA SOUTH AFRICA—See AstraZeneca PLC; *Int'l*, pg. 661
ATARA BIOTHERAPEUTICS SWITZERLAND GMBH—See Atara Biotherapeutics, Inc.; *U.S. Public*, pg. 220
ATLANTIC HEALTH PARTNERS, LLC—See Roper Technologies, Inc.; *U.S. Public*, pg. 1810
ATLAS OPERATIONS, INC.; *U.S. Public*, pg. 379
AUROBINDO PHARMA (MALTA) LIMITED—See Aurobindo Pharma Ltd.; *Int'l*, pg. 712
AUROMEDICS PHARMA LLC—See Aurobindo Pharma Ltd.; *Int'l*, pg. 712
AUROPHARMA INC.—See Aurobindo Pharma Ltd.; *Int'l*, pg. 712

AURORA DEUTSCHLAND GMBH—See Aurora Cannabis Inc.; *Int'l*, pg. 713
AUSTROPLANT ARZNEIMITTEL GMBH—See Dr. Willmar Schwabe GmbH & Co. KG; *Int'l*, pg. 2195
AVENIR WELLNESS SOLUTIONS OF CALIFORNIA, LLC—See Avenir Wellness Solutions, Inc.; *U.S. Public*, pg. 242
AVESTHAGEN, INC.—See Avesthagen Limited; *Int'l*, pg. 740
AVESTHAGEN PTE. LTD.—See Avesthagen Limited; *Int'l*, pg. 740
AVESTHAGEN PVT. LTD.—See Avesthagen Limited; *Int'l*, pg. 740
AVETHAGEN M-E FZ-LLC—See Avesthagen Limited; *Int'l*, pg. 740
AVEX PHARMACEUTICALS PTE. LTD.—See Apex Healthcare Berhad; *Int'l*, pg. 511
AVITUM S.R.L—See B. Braun Melsungen AG; *Int'l*, pg. 786
BACTOLAC PHARMACEUTICAL, INC.; *U.S. Private*, pg. 423
BANKS INTEGRATION GROUP, INC.—See The Graham Group, Inc.; *U.S. Private*, pg. 4036
BARENTZ APS—See Cinven Limited; *Int'l*, pg. 1611
BARENTZ D.O.O.—See Cinven Limited; *Int'l*, pg. 1611
BARENTZ HUNGARY KFT.—See Cinven Limited; *Int'l*, pg. 1611
BARENTZ IRELAND LIMITED—See Cinven Limited; *Int'l*, pg. 1611
BARENTZ N.V.—See Cinven Limited; *Int'l*, pg. 1611
BARENTZ SPOL. S.R.O.—See Cinven Limited; *Int'l*, pg. 1611
BARENTZ UA LLC—See Cinven Limited; *Int'l*, pg. 1611
BASILEA PHARMACEUTICA DEUTSCHLAND GMBH—See Basilea Pharmaceutica Ltd.; *Int'l*, pg. 887
BASILEA PHARMACEUTICA S.R.L.—See Basilea Pharmaceutica Ltd.; *Int'l*, pg. 887
BAUSCH & LOMB—See Bausch Health Companies Inc.; *Int'l*, pg. 896
BAXTER ARGENTINA S.A.—See Baxter International Inc.; *U.S. Public*, pg. 280
BAXTER DEUTSCHLAND GMBH—See Baxter International Inc.; *U.S. Public*, pg. 280
BAXTER MEDICO FAMACEUTICA, LDA.—See Baxter International Inc.; *U.S. Public*, pg. 281
BAYER CO. (MALAYSIA) SDN. BHD.—See Bayer Aktiengesellschaft; *Int'l*, pg. 902
BAYER CONSUMER CARE AG—See Bayer Aktiengesellschaft; *Int'l*, pg. 902
BAYER D.O.O.—See Bayer Aktiengesellschaft; *Int'l*, pg. 906
BAYER EAST AFRICA LTD.—See Bayer Aktiengesellschaft; *Int'l*, pg. 904
BAYER HEALTHCARE CONSUMER CARE—See Bayer Aktiengesellschaft; *Int'l*, pg. 904
BAYER HUNGARIA KFT.—See Bayer Aktiengesellschaft; *Int'l*, pg. 905
BAYER LIMITED—See Bayer Aktiengesellschaft; *Int'l*, pg. 905
BAYER (MALAYSIA) SDN. BHD.—See Bayer Aktiengesellschaft; *Int'l*, pg. 901
BAYER PUERTO RICO, INC.—See Bayer Aktiengesellschaft; *Int'l*, pg. 902
BAYER S.A.—See Bayer Aktiengesellschaft; *Int'l*, pg. 906
BAYER S.A.—See Bayer Aktiengesellschaft; *Int'l*, pg. 906
BAYER (SOUTH EAST ASIA) PTE LTD.—See Bayer Aktiengesellschaft; *Int'l*, pg. 902
BAYER, SPOL. S.R.O.—See Bayer Aktiengesellschaft; *Int'l*, pg. 906
BAYER UK LIMITED—See Bayer Aktiengesellschaft; *Int'l*, pg. 906
BAYER VIETNAM LTD.—See Bayer Aktiengesellschaft; *Int'l*, pg. 906
BAZI, INC.—See Charlie's Holdings, Inc.; *U.S. Public*, pg. 480
B. BRAUN MEDICAL A/S—See B. Braun Melsungen AG; *Int'l*, pg. 786
B. BRAUN MEDICAL EOOD—See B. Braun Melsungen AG; *Int'l*, pg. 786
B. BRAUN MEDICAL INTERNATIONAL S.L.—See B. Braun Melsungen AG; *Int'l*, pg. 786
B. BRAUN MEDICAL N.V./ S.A.—See B. Braun Melsungen AG; *Int'l*, pg. 786
B. BRAUN PHARMACEUTICALS S.A.—See B. Braun Melsungen AG; *Int'l*, pg. 787
B. BRAUN (SHANDONG) PHARMACEUTICAL MANUFACTURING CO., LTD—See B. Braun Melsungen AG; *Int'l*, pg. 786
BBYE CORPORATION; *Int'l*, pg. 921
BEAUTY ENTERPRISES INC.; *U.S. Private*, pg. 509
BEAUTYGE DENMARK A/S—See MacAndrews & Forbes Incorporated; *U.S. Private*, pg. 2533
BECTON DICKINSON LTD.—See Becton, Dickinson & Company; *U.S. Public*, pg. 289
BEE-ALIVE INC.; *U.S. Private*, pg. 513
BEIJING HANMI PHARMACEUTICAL CO., LTD.—See Hanmi Pharmaceutical Co., Ltd.; *Int'l*, pg. 3256
BEIJING TONG REN TANG (AUCKLAND) COMPANY LIMITED—See Beijing Tong Ren Tang Chinese Medicine Company Limited; *Int'l*, pg. 958

424210 — DRUGS AND DRUGGISTS...

BEIJING TONG REN TANG CANADA CO. LTD.—See Beijing Tong Ren Tang Chinese Medicine Company Limited; *Int'l*, pg. 958
BEIJING TONG REN TANG GULF FZ-LLC—See Beijing Tong Ren Tang Chinese Medicine Company Limited; *Int'l*, pg. 958
BEIJING TONGRENTANG GULF MEDICAL CLINIC LLC—See Beijing Tong Ren Tang Chinese Medicine Company Limited; *Int'l*, pg. 959
BEIJING TONG REN TANG POLAND SP.ZO.O.—See Beijing Tong Ren Tang Chinese Medicine Company Limited; *Int'l*, pg. 958
BEIJING TONG REN TANG SCIENCE ARTS (SINGAPORE) CO. PTE. LTD.—See Beijing Tong Ren Tang Chinese Medicine Company Limited; *Int'l*, pg. 959
BELLCO DRUG CORP.—See Cencora, Inc.; *U.S. Public*, pg. 467
BELLCO HEALTH CORP.—See Cencora, Inc.; *U.S. Public*, pg. 467
BENCHMARK BRANDS INC.; *U.S. Private*, pg. 523
BENEFIT HOLDING, INC.—See IQVIA Holdings Inc.; *U.S. Public*, pg. 1168
BENEV COMPANY, INC.—See ExoCoBio Inc.; *Int'l*, pg. 2586
BERACA INGREDIENTES NATURAIS S.A.—See Clariant AG; *Int'l*, pg. 1645
BERJAYA PHARMACY DISTRIBUTION SDN BHD—See Berjaya Corporation Berhad; *Int'l*, pg. 984
BERLIMED - ESPECIALIDADES FARMACEUTICAS LDA.—See Bayer Aktiengesellschaft; *Int'l*, pg. 907
BESSE MEDICAL SUPPLY—See Cencora, Inc.; *U.S. Public*, pg. 466
BETTER CHOICE COMPANY, INC.; *U.S. Public*, pg. 326
BGP PRODUCTS APS—See Viatris Inc.; *U.S. Public*, pg. 2293
BGP PRODUCTS OPERATIONS GMBH—See Viatris Inc.; *U.S. Public*, pg. 2293
BIMEDA, INC.; *U.S. Private*, pg. 560
BIOALGAE S.A.—See Abbott Laboratories; *U.S. Public*, pg. 19
BIOCODEX AB—See Biocodex SA; *Int'l*, pg. 1036
BIOCODEX OY—See Biocodex SA; *Int'l*, pg. 1036
BIOCODEX SIA—See Biocodex SA; *Int'l*, pg. 1036
BIOCODEX UAB—See Biocodex SA; *Int'l*, pg. 1036
BIOCOMPATIBLES INC.—See Boston Scientific Corporation; *U.S. Public*, pg. 373
BIOCSL (NZ) LTD—See CSL Limited; *Int'l*, pg. 1867
BIODTECH, INC.; *U.S. Private*, pg. 561
BIOGEN (ARGENTINA) SRL—See Biogen Inc.; *U.S. Public*, pg. 336
BIOGEN AUSTRALIA PTY LTD—See Biogen Inc.; *U.S. Public*, pg. 336
BIOGEN SWEDEN AB—See Biogen Inc.; *U.S. Public*, pg. 337
BIOGEN U.S. CORPORATION—See Biogen Inc.; *U.S. Public*, pg. 337
BIOLOGICAL SPECIALTY COMPANY LLC—See BioIVT, LLC; *U.S. Private*, pg. 562
BIO-RAD FRANCE—See Bio-Rad Laboratories, Inc.; *U.S. Public*, pg. 332
BIO-RAD HUNGARY TRADING LTD.—See Bio-Rad Laboratories, Inc.; *U.S. Public*, pg. 332
BIO-RAD LABORATORIES E.P.E.—See Bio-Rad Laboratories, Inc.; *U.S. Public*, pg. 333
BIO-RAD LABORATORIES ISRAEL (1996) LTD.—See Bio-Rad Laboratories, Inc.; *U.S. Public*, pg. 333
BIO-RAD LABORATORIES S.A.—See Bio-Rad Laboratories, Inc.; *U.S. Public*, pg. 333
BIO-RAD LABORATORIOS BRASIL LTDA.—See Bio-Rad Laboratories, Inc.; *U.S. Public*, pg. 333
BIOSAUDE - PRODUTOS FARMACEUTICOS, LDA.—See Alfa-Wassermann S.p.A.; *Int'l*, pg. 314
BIOSCRIP MEDICAL SUPPLY SERVICES, LLC—See Option Care Health, Inc.; *U.S. Public*, pg. 1609
BIOTEST FRANCE SARL—See Biotest AG; *Int'l*, pg. 1043
BIOTEST K.K.—See Biotest AG; *Int'l*, pg. 1043
BIOTEST MEDICAL, S.L.U.—See Biotest AG; *Int'l*, pg. 1043
BIOTEST (SCHWEIZ) AG—See Biotest AG; *Int'l*, pg. 1043
BIOTEST (UK) LTD.—See Biotest AG; *Int'l*, pg. 1043
BIPSO GMBH—See Bracco S.p.A.; *Int'l*, pg. 1134
BLACKMORES (MALAYSIA) SDN BHD—See Blackmores Limited; *Int'l*, pg. 1061
BLACKMORES (NEW ZEALAND) LIMITED—See Blackmores Limited; *Int'l*, pg. 1061
BLACKMORES (SINGAPORE) PTE LIMITED—See Blackmores Limited; *Int'l*, pg. 1061
BLACKMORES (TAIWAN) LIMITED—See Blackmores Limited; *Int'l*, pg. 1061
BLACKMORES (THAILAND) LIMITED—See Blackmores Limited; *Int'l*, pg. 1061
BLAIREX LABORATORIES, INC.; *U.S. Public*, pg. 578
BLINC INC.; *U.S. Private*, pg. 581
BLUE SKY BIOTECH, INC.—See LakePharma, Inc.; *U.S. Private*, pg. 2376
BOEHRINGER INGELHEIM BH D.O.O—See C.H. Boehringer Sohn AG & Co. KG; *Int'l*, pg. 1241
BOEHRINGER INGELHEIM (CANADA) LTD.—See C.H. Boehringer Sohn AG & Co. KG; *Int'l*, pg. 1240
BOEHRINGER INGELHEIM C.A.—See C.H. Boehringer Sohn AG & Co. KG; *Int'l*, pg. 1241
BOEHRINGER INGELHEIM DEL ECUADOR CIA. LTDA.—See C.H. Boehringer Sohn AG & Co. KG; *Int'l*, pg. 1242
BOEHRINGER INGELHEIM FINLAND KY—See C.H. Boehringer Sohn AG & Co. KG; *Int'l*, pg. 1241
BOEHRINGER INGELHEIM INTERNATIONAL TRADING (SHANGHAI) CO. LTD.—See C.H. Boehringer Sohn AG & Co. KG; *Int'l*, pg. 1242
BOEHRINGER INGELHEIM ISRAEL LTD—See C.H. Boehringer Sohn AG & Co. KG; *Int'l*, pg. 1242
BOEHRINGER INGELHEIM LTDA.—See C.H. Boehringer Sohn AG & Co. KG; *Int'l*, pg. 1242
BOEHRINGER INGELHEIM NORWAY KS—See C.H. Boehringer Sohn AG & Co. KG; *Int'l*, pg. 1241
BOEHRINGER INGELHEIM (N.Z.) LIMITED—See C.H. Boehringer Sohn AG & Co. KG; *Int'l*, pg. 1241
BOEHRINGER INGELHEIM PHARMA GES MBH—See C.H. Boehringer Sohn AG & Co. KG; *Int'l*, pg. 1242
BOEHRINGER INGELHEIM SERBIA D.O.O.—See C.H. Boehringer Sohn AG & Co. KG; *Int'l*, pg. 1242
BOEHRINGER INGELHEIM ZAGREB D.O.O.—See C.H. Boehringer Sohn AG & Co. KG; *Int'l*, pg. 1242
BOIRON RO SRL—See Boiron Group; *Int'l*, pg. 1101
BONAMOUR, INC.; *U.S. Private*, pg. 613
BOOTS APOTEK AS—See Walgreens Boots Alliance, Inc.; *U.S. Public*, pg. 2323
BOOTS RETAIL USA INC.—See Walgreens Boots Alliance, Inc.; *U.S. Public*, pg. 2322
BORGHESE, INC.; *U.S. Public*, pg. 618
BOTS INC.; *U.S. Public*, pg. 375
BRACCO FAR EAST LTD.—See Bracco S.p.A.; *Int'l*, pg. 1134
BRACCO OSTERREICH GMBH—See Bracco S.p.A.; *Int'l*, pg. 1134
BRACCO SUISSE S.A.—See Bracco S.p.A.; *Int'l*, pg. 1134
BRACCO UK LTD.—See Bracco S.p.A.; *Int'l*, pg. 1134
BRAZIL PHARMA S.A.; *Int'l*, pg. 1142
BRIGHT GREEN CORPORATION; *U.S. Public*, pg. 382
BRISTOL-MYERS DE VENEZUELA, S.A.—See Bristol-Myers Squibb Company; *U.S. Public*, pg. 384
BRISTOL-MYERS K.K.—See Bristol-Myers Squibb Company; *U.S. Public*, pg. 384
BRISTOL-MYERS SQUIBB AG—See Bristol-Myers Squibb Company; *U.S. Public*, pg. 385
BRISTOL-MYERS SQUIBB B.V.—See Bristol-Myers Squibb Company; *U.S. Public*, pg. 385
BRISTOL-MYERS SQUIBB CANADA CO.—See Bristol-Myers Squibb Company; *U.S. Public*, pg. 385
BRISTOL-MYERS SQUIBB DE GUATEMALA, S.A.—See Bristol-Myers Squibb Company; *U.S. Public*, pg. 385
BRISTOL-MYERS SQUIBB FARMACEUTICA LTDA—See Bristol-Myers Squibb Company; *U.S. Public*, pg. 385
BRISTOL-MYERS SQUIBB MARKETING SERVICES S.R.L.—See Bristol-Myers Squibb Company; *U.S. Public*, pg. 385
BRISTOL-MYERS SQUIBB PUERTO RICO, INC. - HUMACAO PLANT—See Bristol-Myers Squibb Company; *U.S. Public*, pg. 385
BRISTOL-MYERS SQUIBB, S.A.U.—See Bristol-Myers Squibb Company; *U.S. Public*, pg. 385
B&S FRAGRANCES & COSMETICS INC.; *U.S. Private*, pg. 419
BSK CORPORATION—See Ilshin Spinning Co., Ltd.; *Int'l*, pg. 3616
BUKA INVESTMENTS LIMITED; *Int'l*, pg. 1212
BUNZL HEALTHCARE GMBH—See Bunzl plc; *Int'l*, pg. 1217
BURLINGTON DRUG COMPANY, INC.—See J.M. Smith Corporation; *U.S. Private*, pg. 2169
CAMPHOR TECHNOLOGIES, INC.; *U.S. Private*, pg. 731
CANADABIS CAPITAL, INC.; *Int'l*, pg. 1282
CANCER GENETICS ITALIA, S.R.L.—See Vyant Bio, Inc.; *U.S. Public*, pg. 2315
CANTOURAGE GROUP SE; *Int'l*, pg. 1299
CARDINAL HEALTH 107, LLC—See Cardinal Health, Inc.; *U.S. Public*, pg. 433
CARDINAL HEALTH, INC. - GREENSBORO—See Cardinal Health, Inc.; *U.S. Public*, pg. 434
CARDINAL HEALTH, INC. - ZANESVILLE—See Cardinal Health, Inc.; *U.S. Public*, pg. 434
CARDINAL HEALTH P.R. 120, INC.—See Cardinal Health, Inc.; *U.S. Public*, pg. 433
CAREDX INTERNATIONAL AB—See CareDx, Inc.; *U.S. Public*, pg. 435
CAREDX PTY LTD.—See CareDx, Inc.; *U.S. Public*, pg. 435
CAREMARK RX, LLC—See CVS Health Corporation; *U.S. Public*, pg. 615
CAREPOINT PARTNERS; *U.S. Private*, pg. 754
CATALENT CTS (EDINBURGH) LIMITED—See Catalent, Inc.; *U.S. Public*, pg. 448
CATALENT CTS (SINGAPORE) PVT LTD—See Catalent, Inc.; *U.S. Public*, pg. 448
CATALENT MICRON TECHNOLOGIES LIMITED—See Catalent, Inc.; *U.S. Public*, pg. 448
CATALENT ONTARIO LIMITED—See Catalent, Inc.; *U.S. Public*, pg. 448
CATALENT URUGUAY S.A.—See Catalent, Inc.; *U.S. Public*, pg. 448
CAWACHI LIMITED; *Int'l*, pg. 1363
CBBEAUTY LTD—See MacAndrews & Forbes Incorporated; *U.S. Private*, pg. 2533
CCM MARKETING SDN BHD—See Batu Kawan Berhad; *Int'l*, pg. 890
CELGENE DISTRIBUTION BV—See Bristol-Myers Squibb Company; *U.S. Public*, pg. 386
CELGENE LIMITED—See Bristol-Myers Squibb Company; *U.S. Public*, pg. 386
CELGENE PHARMACEUTICAL (SHANGHAI) COMPANY LIMITED—See Bristol-Myers Squibb Company; *U.S. Public*, pg. 386
CENCORA, INC.; *U.S. Public*, pg. 466
CENDUIT GMBH—See IQVIA Holdings Inc.; *U.S. Public*, pg. 1168
CENDUIT JAPAN GK—See IQVIA Holdings Inc.; *U.S. Public*, pg. 1168
CENDUIT LLC—See Thermo Fisher Scientific Inc.; *U.S. Public*, pg. 2145
CENTRAFARM B.V.—See Bain Capital, LP; *U.S. Private*, pg. 443
CENTRAFARM B.V.—See Cinven Limited; *Int'l*, pg. 1613
CENTRE AUDITIU SANT BOI SL—See Amplifon S.p.A.; *Int'l*, pg. 435
CENTRIC GROUP LLC; *U.S. Private*, pg. 829
CERRINI CONFISERIE GMBH—See EMERAM Capital Partners GmbH; *Int'l*, pg. 2378
CESAR CASTILLO, INC.; *U.S. Private*, pg. 842
CHAPIN MEDICAL COMPANY INC.; *U.S. Private*, pg. 849
CHARLES BOWMAN & CO. INC.; *U.S. Private*, pg. 851
CHARLES RIVER ENDOTOXIN AND MICROBIAL DETECTION SINGAPORE PTE. LTD.—See Charles River Laboratories International, Inc.; *U.S. Public*, pg. 479
CHAROEN POKPHAND (TAIWAN) CO., LTD.—See Charoen Pokphand Foods Public Company Limited; *Int'l*, pg. 1452
CHECKPOINT DISTRIBUTION B.V.—See B&S Group S.A.; *Int'l*, pg. 784
CHECKPOINT TRADING B.V.—See B&S Group S.A.; *Int'l*, pg. 784
CHEMGEN CORP.—See Elanco Animal Health Incorporated; *U.S. Public*, pg. 722
CHEM-IMPEX INTERNATIONAL, INC.; *U.S. Private*, pg. 870
CHENGDU AIXIN ZHONGHONG BIOLOGICAL TECHNOLOGY CO., LTD.—See AiXin Life International, Inc.; *Int'l*, pg. 254
CHIESI BULGARIA LTD.—See Chiesi Farmaceutici SpA; *Int'l*, pg. 1478
CHIESI CZ S.R.O.—See Chiesi Farmaceutici SpA; *Int'l*, pg. 1478
CHIESI HELLAS S.A.—See Chiesi Farmaceutici SpA; *Int'l*, pg. 1477
CHIESI ILAC TICARET A.S.—See Chiesi Farmaceutici SpA; *Int'l*, pg. 1477
CHIESI MEXICO, SA DE CV—See Chiesi Farmaceutici SpA; *Int'l*, pg. 1477
CHIESI PHARMACEUTICALS BV—See Chiesi Farmaceutici SpA; *Int'l*, pg. 1478
CHIESI PHARMACEUTICAL (SHANGHAI) CO., LTD—See Chiesi Farmaceutici SpA; *Int'l*, pg. 1477
CHIESI PHARMACEUTICALS LLC—See Chiesi Farmaceutici SpA; *Int'l*, pg. 1478
CHIESI POLAND SP. Z O.O.—See Chiesi Farmaceutici SpA; *Int'l*, pg. 1478
CHIESI SLOVAKIA S.R.O.—See Chiesi Farmaceutici SpA; *Int'l*, pg. 1478
CHIESI SLOVENIJA, D.O.O—See Chiesi Farmaceutici SpA; *Int'l*, pg. 1478
CHINA NATIONAL MEDICINES CORPORATION LTD.—See China National Pharmaceutical Group Corporation; *Int'l*, pg. 1533
CHRISTINA LAKE CANNABIS CORP.; *Int'l*, pg. 1587
CHUNGHWA YUMING HEALTHCARE CO., LTD.—See China Chemical & Pharmaceutical Co., Ltd.; *Int'l*, pg. 1488
CILAG PHARMACEUTICALS GMBH—See Johnson & Johnson; *U.S. Public*, pg. 1194
CILAG PRODUCTS GMBH—See Johnson & Johnson; *U.S. Public*, pg. 1194
CIPLA AUSTRALIA PTY LIMITED—See Cipla Ltd.; *Int'l*, pg. 1617
CIPLA MALAYSIA SDN. BHD.—See Cipla Ltd.; *Int'l*, pg. 1617
CIPLA MAROC SA—See Cipla Ltd.; *Int'l*, pg. 1616
CIPLA MEDPRO DISTRIBUTION CENTRE (PTY) LIMITED—See Cipla Ltd.; *Int'l*, pg. 1617
CIRCA LLC—See Walgreens Boots Alliance, Inc.; *U.S. Public*, pg. 2322
CITRA LABS, LLC—See Zimmer Biomet Holdings, Inc.; *U.S. Public*, pg. 2406
CLARINS BV—See Clarins S.A.; *Int'l*, pg. 1648
CLARINS USA INC.—See Clarins S.A.; *Int'l*, pg. 1649
CLICKS DIRECT MEDICINES (PROPRIETARY) LIMITED—See Clicks Group Limited; *Int'l*, pg. 1658

N.A.I.C.S. INDEX
424210 — DRUGS AND DRUGGISTS...

CLINECT PTY LTD—See EBOS Group Limited; *Int'l*, pg. 2285
CLINTARA, LLC—See Genstar Capital, LLC; *U.S. Private*, pg. 1675
CLIVE CHRISTIAN PERFUME LIMITED—See Clive Christian Limited; *Int'l*, pg. 1660
COGSTATE LIMITED; *Int'l*, pg. 1695
COLGATE-PALMOLIVE COMERCIAL LTDA.—See Colgate-Palmolive Company; *U.S. Public*, pg. 532
COLLECTION CENTER, INC.—See StarTek, Inc.; *U.S. Private*, pg. 3788
COLOMER FRANCE SAS—See MacAndrews & Forbes Incorporated; *U.S. Private*, pg. 2534
COLOR ME BEAUTIFUL, INC.; *U.S. Private*, pg. 973
COLPHARMA, S.R.L.—See FAES Farma, S.A.; *Int'l*, pg. 2601
COMMUNITY SPECIALTY PHARMACY, LLC—See Scienture Holdings, Inc.; *U.S. Private*, pg. 1849
COMPUMEDICS USA, INC.—See Compumedics Limited; *Int'l*, pg. 1757
CONMED DENMARK APS—See CONMED Corporation; *U.S. Public*, pg. 567
CONTINENTAL VITAMIN CO., INC.; *U.S. Private*, pg. 1031
CONTRACT PHARMACY SERVICES; *U.S. Private*, pg. 1032
COOPERVISION IBERIA SL—See The Cooper Companies, Inc.; *U.S. Public*, pg. 2066
COOPERVISION IBERIA SL—See The Cooper Companies, Inc.; *U.S. Public*, pg. 2066
CORDEN PHARMA SWITZERLAND LLC—See Astorg Partners S.A.S.; *Int'l*, pg. 656
CORPORATIVO FRAGUA, S.A.B. DE C.V.; *Int'l*, pg. 1806
COSMECCA SUZHOU CO., LTD.—See Cosmecca Korea Co.,Ltd.; *Int'l*, pg. 1811
COSMETICA NACIONAL S.A.—See Godrej & Boyce Mfg. Co. Ltd.; *Int'l*, pg. 3020
COSMETIC SOLUTIONS, LLC—See Lee Equity Partners LLC; *U.S. Private*, pg. 2412
COSMETIQUE, INC.; *U.S. Private*, pg. 1062
COSMOFARM LTD.—See COSMOS HEALTH INC.; *U.S. Public*, pg. 585
COSMO RESEARCH & DEVELOPMENT S.R.L.—See Cosmo Pharmaceuticals N.V.; *Int'l*, pg. 1813
COSMO S.P.A.,—See Cosmo Pharmaceuticals N.V.; *Int'l*, pg. 1813
COSWAY (CHINA) CO. LTD—See Berjaya Corporation Berhad; *Int'l*, pg. 984
COSWAY CO INC.; *U.S. Private*, pg. 1063
COSWAY (M) SDN BHD—See Berjaya Corporation Berhad; *Int'l*, pg. 984
COUNTRY CONDOS LTD; *Int'l*, pg. 1818
COVIS PHARMACEUTICALS INC.; *U.S. Private*, pg. 1073
CRESCITA THERAPEUTICS, INC.; *Int'l*, pg. 1840
CRODA PERUANA S.A.C—See Croda International plc; *Int'l*, pg. 1852
CRODA POLAND SP. Z O.O.—See Croda International plc; *Int'l*, pg. 1852
CRODA TRADING (SHANGHAI) CO., LTD.—See Croda International plc; *Int'l*, pg. 1852
CROMA PHARMACEUTICALS INC.—See Bausch Health Companies Inc.; *Int'l*, pg. 897
CROMA PHARMA SL—See Bausch Health Companies Inc.; *Int'l*, pg. 897
CRUCELL UK LTD.—See Johnson & Johnson; *U.S. Public*, pg. 1194
CRUCELL VACCINES INC.—See Johnson & Johnson; *U.S. Public*, pg. 1195
CSC PHARMACEUTICALS S.A.—See Angelini ACRAF S.p.A.; *Int'l*, pg. 460
CS HEALTH STORE SDN BHD—See Apex Healthcare Berhad; *Int'l*, pg. 511
CSL BEHRING AB—See CSL Limited; *Int'l*, pg. 1865
CSL BEHRING B.V.—See CSL Limited; *Int'l*, pg. 1865
CSL BEHRING GMBH—See CSL Limited; *Int'l*, pg. 1865
CSL BEHRING K.K.—See CSL Limited; *Int'l*, pg. 1865
CSL BEHRING MEPE—See CSL Limited; *Int'l*, pg. 1865
CSL BEHRING S.A.—See CSL Limited; *Int'l*, pg. 1865
CSR COMPANY INC.; *U.S. Private*, pg. 1117
CURIUM NETHERLANDS HOLDING B.V. - CZECH BRANCH—See Curium SAS; *Int'l*, pg. 1878
CURIUM SWEDEN AB—See Curium SAS; *Int'l*, pg. 1878
CURRAX PHARMACEUTICALS LLC; *U.S. Private*, pg. 1125
CVS PHARMACY, INC.—See CVS Health Corporation; *U.S. Public*, pg. 615
CYSTIC FIBROSIS FOUNDATION PHARMACY, LLC—See Walgreens Boots Alliance, Inc.; *U.S. Public*, pg. 2323
DAIICHI SANKYO AUSTRIA GMBH—See Daiichi Sankyo Co., Ltd.; *Int'l*, pg. 1929
DAIICHI SANKYO BELGIUM NV/SA—See Daiichi Sankyo Co., Ltd.; *Int'l*, pg. 1929
DAIICHI SANKYO ESPANA, S.A.—See Daiichi Sankyo Co., Ltd.; *Int'l*, pg. 1930
DAIICHI SANKYO FRANCE S.A.S.—See Daiichi Sankyo Co., Ltd.; *Int'l*, pg. 1930
DAIICHI SANKYO HONG KONG LIMITED—See Daiichi Sankyo Co., Ltd.; *Int'l*, pg. 1930
DAIICHI SANKYO ITALIA S.P.A.—See Daiichi Sankyo Co., Ltd.; *Int'l*, pg. 1930
DAIICHI SANKYO KOREA CO., LTD.—See Daiichi Sankyo Co., Ltd.; *Int'l*, pg. 1930
DAIICHI SANKYO NEDERLAND B.V.—See Daiichi Sankyo Co., Ltd.; *Int'l*, pg. 1930
DAIICHI SANKYO PHARMACEUTICAL (BEIJING) CO., LTD.—See Daiichi Sankyo Co., Ltd.; *Int'l*, pg. 1930
DAIICHI SANKYO PHARMACEUTICAL (SHANGHAI) CO., LTD.—See Daiichi Sankyo Co., Ltd.; *Int'l*, pg. 1930
DAIICHI SANKYO PORTUGAL, LDA.—See Daiichi Sankyo Co., Ltd.; *Int'l*, pg. 1930
DAIICHI SANKYO (SCHWEIZ) AG—See Daiichi Sankyo Co., Ltd.; *Int'l*, pg. 1929
DAIICHI SANKYO TAIWAN LTD.—See Daiichi Sankyo Co., Ltd.; *Int'l*, pg. 1930
DAIICHI SANKYO UK LIMITED—See Daiichi Sankyo Co., Ltd.; *Int'l*, pg. 1930
DAKO DEUTSCHLAND GMBH—See Agilent Technologies, Inc.; *U.S. Public*, pg. 61
DAKO FRANCE S.A.S.—See Agilent Technologies, Inc.; *U.S. Public*, pg. 61
DAKO JAPAN INC.—See Agilent Technologies, Inc.; *U.S. Public*, pg. 61
DAKOTA DRUG, INC.; *U.S. Public*, pg. 1147
DAKO UK LTD—See Agilent Technologies, Inc.; *U.S. Public*, pg. 61
DAXEN, INC.—See DXN Holdings Bhd.; *Int'l*, pg. 2237
DAY LEWIS PLC.; *Int'l*, pg. 1985
DCC HEALTHCARE—See DCC plc; *Int'l*, pg. 1990
DCC VITAL LIMITED—See DCC plc; *Int'l*, pg. 1990
DCS PHARMA AG—See IMCD N.V.; *Int'l*, pg. 3621
DEB AUSTRALIA PTY LIMITED—See S.C. Johnson & Son, Inc.; *U.S. Private*, pg. 3515
DEB CANADA—See S.C. Johnson & Son, Inc.; *U.S. Private*, pg. 3515
DEB FRANCE SAS—See S.C. Johnson & Son, Inc.; *U.S. Private*, pg. 3515
DEB GROUP LIMITED—See S.C. Johnson & Son, Inc.; *U.S. Private*, pg. 3515
DEB GROUP MALAYSIA SDN BHD—See S.C. Johnson & Son, Inc.; *U.S. Private*, pg. 3515
DEB IBERIA S.L.—See S.C. Johnson & Son, Inc.; *U.S. Private*, pg. 3515
DEB NEW ZEALAND—See S.C. Johnson & Son, Inc.; *U.S. Private*, pg. 3515
DEB SINGAPORE PTE. LTD.—See S.C. Johnson & Son, Inc.; *U.S. Private*, pg. 3515
DEB-STOKO EUROPE GMBH—See S.C. Johnson & Son, Inc.; *U.S. Private*, pg. 3516
DEB-STOKO EUROPE GMBH—See S.C. Johnson & Son, Inc.; *U.S. Private*, pg. 3516
DEB SWARFEGA A/S—See S.C. Johnson & Son, Inc.; *U.S. Private*, pg. 3515
DEB SWARFEGA NORGE AS—See S.C. Johnson & Son, Inc.; *U.S. Private*, pg. 3515
DEB USA, INC.—See S.C. Johnson & Son, Inc.; *U.S. Private*, pg. 3516
DECAHEDRON LTD.—See COSMOS HEALTH INC.; *U.S. Public*, pg. 585
DE COLLEGIALE BEREIDING BV—See Fagron NV; *Int'l*, pg. 2603
DELFI MARKETING SDN. BHD.—See Delfi Limited; *Int'l*, pg. 2012
DENTSU MEDICAL COMMUNICATIONS, INC.—See Dentsu Group Inc.; *Int'l*, pg. 2038
DERMA GLISTEN, INC.; *U.S. Private*, pg. 1209
DERMAVANT SCIENCES LTD.—See Organon & Co.; *U.S. Public*, pg. 1616
DESERT PET, LLC—See Cardinal Health, Inc.; *U.S. Public*, pg. 434
DEUTSCHE HOMOOPATHIE-UNION DHU ARZNEIMITTEL GMBH & CO. KG—See Dr. Willmar Schwabe GmbH & Co. KG; *Int'l*, pg. 2195
DHANI HEALTHCARE LIMITED—See Dhani Services Ltd.; *Int'l*, pg. 2098
DHRUV WELLNESS LIMITED; *Int'l*, pg. 2100
DHU IBERICA, S.A.—See Dr. Willmar Schwabe GmbH & Co. KG; *Int'l*, pg. 2195
DIAGNOSTICS & DESIGNS INC.; *U.S. Private*, pg. 1222
DIAM AUSTRALIA PTY. LTD.—See Ardian SAS; *Int'l*, pg. 555
DIAM DEUTSCHLAND GMBH—See Ardian SAS; *Int'l*, pg. 555
DIAM JAPAN K.K.—See Ardian SAS; *Int'l*, pg. 555
DIAM TUNISIA SARL—See Ardian SAS; *Int'l*, pg. 555
DIAM TURKIYE—See Ardian SAS; *Int'l*, pg. 555
DIAM UK LTD—See Ardian SAS; *Int'l*, pg. 555
DICKINSON BRANDS, INC.; *U.S. Private*, pg. 1227
DIMED S.A. DISTRIBUIDORA DE MEDICAMENTOS; *Int'l*, pg. 2125
DIPLOMAT GEORGIA, LLC—See Diplomat Holdings Ltd.; *Int'l*, pg. 2129
DIPLOMAT NEW ZEALAND LIMITED—See Diplomat Holdings Ltd.; *Int'l*, pg. 2129
DIRECT HEALTHCARE LTD; *Int'l*, pg. 2129
DIRECT PHARMACY SERVICE, INC.; *U.S. Private*, pg. 1235
DISHMAN NETHERLANDS B.V.—See Dishman Carbogen Amcis Limited; *Int'l*, pg. 2135
DISHMAN PHARMACEUTICALS & CHEMICALS (SHANGHAI) CO. LTD.—See Dishman Carbogen Amcis Limited; *Int'l*, pg. 2135
DISHMAN PHARMA SOLUTIONS AG.—See Dishman Carbogen Amcis Limited; *Int'l*, pg. 2135
DISTRIBUCIONES UQUIFA S.A.S.—See Abbott Laboratories; *U.S. Public*, pg. 19
DIXIE HEALTH, INC.; *U.S. Private*, pg. 1245
DKSH INDIA PVT. LTD.—See Diethelm Keller Holding Limited; *Int'l*, pg. 2116
DKSH PHARMACEUTICAL (SHANGHAI) LTD.—See Diethelm Keller Holding Limited; *Int'l*, pg. 2116
DKSH TECHNOLOGY SDN. BHD.—See Diethelm Keller Holding Limited; *Int'l*, pg. 2117
DOCMED TECHNOLOGY PTE. LTD.—See Hyphens Pharma International Limited; *Int'l*, pg. 3553
DOHMEN INVESTMENT GROUP, LLC—See Dohmen Co.; *U.S. Private*, pg. 1254
DONALD WARDLE & SON LTD—See Co-operative Group Limited; *Int'l*, pg. 1679
DONG-A AMERICA CORP—See Dong-A Socio Holdings Co., Ltd.; *Int'l*, pg. 2164
DOSEAID PTY LTD—See EBOS Group Limited; *Int'l*, pg. 2285
DR. FALK PHARMA BENELUX B.V.—See Dr. Falk Pharma GmbH; *Int'l*, pg. 2191
DR. FALK PHARMA ESPANA S.L.—See Dr. Falk Pharma GmbH; *Int'l*, pg. 2191
DR. FALK PHARMA GMBH; *Int'l*, pg. 2190
DR. FALK PHARMA LLC—See Dr. Falk Pharma GmbH; *Int'l*, pg. 2191
DR FALK PHARMA UK LTD—See Dr. Falk Pharma GmbH; *Int'l*, pg. 2190
DR. GERHARD MANN CHEM.-PHARM. FABRIK GESELLSCHAFT MIT BESCHRANKTER HAFTUNG—See Bausch Health Companies Inc.; *Int'l*, pg. 897
DROGARIA MAIS ECONOMICA S.A.—See Brazil Pharma S.A.; *Int'l*, pg. 1143
DROGUERIA DE LA VILLA INC.—See FMC Inc.; *U.S. Private*, pg. 1554
DR. REDDY'S LABORATORIES (AUSTRALIA) PTY. LIMITED—See Dr. Reddy's Laboratories Limited; *Int'l*, pg. 2195
DR. REDDY'S LABORATORIES (EU) LIMITED—See Dr. Reddy's Laboratories Limited; *Int'l*, pg. 2195
DR. REDDY'S LABORATORIES, INC.—See Dr. Reddy's Laboratories Limited; *Int'l*, pg. 2195
DR. REDDY'S LABORATORIES LLC—See Dr. Reddy's Laboratories Limited; *Int'l*, pg. 2195
DR. REDDY'S LABORATORIES LOUISIANA LLC—See Dr. Reddy's Laboratories Limited; *Int'l*, pg. 2195
DR. REDDY'S LABORATORIES (PROPRIETARY) LIMITED—See Dr. Reddy's Laboratories Limited; *Int'l*, pg. 2195
DR. REDDY'S LABORATORIES ROMANIA SRL—See Dr. Reddy's Laboratories Limited; *Int'l*, pg. 2195
DR. REDDY'S NEW ZEALAND LTD.—See Dr. Reddy's Laboratories Limited; *Int'l*, pg. 2195
DUCHEMBIO CO., LTD.; *Int'l*, pg. 2223
DUDLEY PRODUCTS INC.; *U.S. Private*, pg. 1284
DWF OF OMAHA—See Denver Wholesale Florists Company; *U.S. Private*, pg. 1208
EARTH SUPPLIED PRODUCTS LLC; *U.S. Private*, pg. 1314
EARUM PHARMACEUTICALS LIMITED; *Int'l*, pg. 2269
EAST-WEST DISTRIBUTING CO.—See Walgreens Boots Alliance, Inc.; *U.S. Public*, pg. 2323
EBN SINA MEDICAL W.L.L.—See Aamal Company Q.S.C.; *Int'l*, pg. 36
ECKERT & ZIEGLER CHEMOTRADE GMBH—See Eckert & Ziegler Strahlen- und Medizintechnik AG; *Int'l*, pg. 2290
ECMOHO LIMITED; *Int'l*, pg. 2292
ECO ANIMAL HEALTH LIMITED—See ECO Animal Health Group plc; *Int'l*, pg. 2292
ECOGEN EUROPE LTD.—See Redhawk Holdings Corp.; *U.S. Public*, pg. 1770
ECOSWAY KOREA, INC.—See Berjaya Corporation Berhad; *Int'l*, pg. 984
ECZACIBASI-BAXTER HOSPITAL SUPPLY CO.—See Eczacibasi Holding A.S.; *Int'l*, pg. 2301
ECZACIBASI GIRISIM CO.—See Eczacibasi Holding A.S.; *Int'l*, pg. 2301
ECZACIBASI HIJYEN URUNLERI SANAYI VE TICARET A.S.—See Eczacibasi Holding A.S.; *Int'l*, pg. 2301
ECZACIBASI OCCUPATIONAL HEALTH AND SAFETY SERVICES—See Eczacibasi Holding A.S.; *Int'l*, pg. 2301
E.D. CRANE & ASSOCIATES; *U.S. Private*, pg. 1305
EDEN COMPANY, INC.; *U.S. Private*, pg. 1333
EHP ECZACIBASI HEALTH CARE PRODUCTS JOINT STOCK CO.—See Eczacibasi Holding A.S.; *Int'l*, pg. 2301
EIG GLOBAL (CHINA) CO. LTD.—See Esthetics International Group Berhad; *Int'l*, pg. 2518
EIG GLOBAL (HK) LTD.—See Esthetics International Group Berhad; *Int'l*, pg. 2518
EIG GLOBAL PTE LTD—See Esthetics International Group Berhad; *Int'l*, pg. 2518

424210 — DRUGS AND DRUGGISTS...   CORPORATE AFFILIATIONS

EIG PHARMA ASIA SDN. BHD.—See Esthetics International Group Berhad; *Int'l*, pg. 2518
EISAI AB—See Eisai Co., Ltd.; *Int'l*, pg. 2335
EISAI DISTRIBUTION CO., LTD.—See Eisai Co., Ltd.; *Int'l*, pg. 2335
EISAI FARMACEUTICA S.A.—See Eisai Co., Ltd.; *Int'l*, pg. 2335
EISAI FARMACEUTICA, UNIPESSOAL LDA.—See Eisai Co., Ltd.; *Int'l*, pg. 2335
EISAI GESMBH—See Eisai Co., Ltd.; *Int'l*, pg. 2335
EISAI GMBH—See Eisai Co., Ltd.; *Int'l*, pg. 2335
EISAI KOREA, INC.—See Eisai Co., Ltd.; *Int'l*, pg. 2335
EISAI (MALAYSIA) SDN. BHD.—See Eisai Co., Ltd.; *Int'l*, pg. 2334
EISAI PHARMA AG—See Eisai Co., Ltd.; *Int'l*, pg. 2335
EISAI S.A.S.—See Eisai Co., Ltd.; *Int'l*, pg. 2335
EISAI (SINGAPORE) PTE. LTD.—See Eisai Co., Ltd.; *Int'l*, pg. 2334
EISAI S.R.L.—See Eisai Co., Ltd.; *Int'l*, pg. 2335
ELANCO GESELLSCHAFT M.B.H.—See Elanco Animal Health Incorporated; *U.S. Public*, pg. 723
ELANCO PRODUCTS LIMITED—See Elanco Animal Health Incorporated; *U.S. Public*, pg. 723
ELASTEC S.R.L—See Merck & Co., Inc.; *U.S. Public*, pg. 1416
ELECTRA-BOX DIAGNOSTICA APS—See Addtech AB; *Int'l*, pg. 133
ELI LILLY AND COMPANY (IRELAND) LTD.—See Eli Lilly & Company; *U.S. Public*, pg. 733
ELI LILLY BENELUX, S.A.—See Eli Lilly & Company; *U.S. Public*, pg. 732
ELI LILLY DANMARK A/S—See Eli Lilly & Company; *U.S. Public*, pg. 732
ELI LILLY FARMACEVTSKA DRUZBA, D.O.O.—See Eli Lilly & Company; *U.S. Public*, pg. 733
ELI LILLY GMBH—See Eli Lilly & Company; *U.S. Public*, pg. 733
ELI LILLY HRVATSKA D.O.O.—See Eli Lilly & Company; *U.S. Public*, pg. 732
ELI LILLY INTERAMERICA INC., Y COMPANIA LIMITADA—See Eli Lilly & Company; *U.S. Public*, pg. 732
ELI LILLY ISRAEL LTD.—See Eli Lilly & Company; *U.S. Public*, pg. 732
ELI LILLY (SINGAPORE) PTE. LTD.—See Eli Lilly & Company; *U.S. Public*, pg. 732
ELI LILLY TRADING (SHANGHAI) COMPANY LIMITED—See Eli Lilly & Company; *U.S. Public*, pg. 733
ELITECH GROUP SAS—See Bruker Corporation; *U.S. Public*, pg. 406
ELIZABETH ARDEN (NEW ZEALAND) LIMITED—See MacAndrews & Forbes Incorporated; *U.S. Private*, pg. 2533
EMAMI LTD; *Int'l*, pg. 2374
EMEDASIA SDN. BHD.—See Hong Seng Consolidated Berhad; *Int'l*, pg. 3469
EMERGENT BIOSOLUTIONS CANADA INC.—See Emergent BioSolutions Inc.; *U.S. Public*, pg. 739
EMERGENT COUNTERMEASURES INTERNATIONAL LTD.—See Emergent BioSolutions Inc.; *U.S. Public*, pg. 740
EMPOWERED PRODUCTS, INC.; *U.S. Private*, pg. 1387
EMPOWERED PRODUCTS NEVADA, INC.—See Empowered Products, Inc.; *U.S. Private*, pg. 1387
ENCLARA HEALTH, LLC—See Consonance Capital Partners LLC; *U.S. Private*, pg. 1023
ENERGIZER GROUP HOLLAND B.V.—See Edgewell Personal Care Company; *U.S. Public*, pg. 718
ENZYMOTEC USA, INC.—See International Flavors & Fragrances Inc.; *U.S. Public*, pg. 1151
EPIC ETAILERS, LLC; *U.S. Private*, pg. 1412
EPITHERAPEUTICS APS—See Gilead Sciences, Inc.; *U.S. Public*, pg. 936
ESCALON MEDICAL IMAGING—See Escalon Medical Corp.; *U.S. Public*, pg. 793
ESI CANADA—See The Cigna Group; *U.S. Public*, pg. 2061
ESSERE BENESSERE SPA; *Int'l*, pg. 2512
ESSEX MEDIPHARMA (ZHUHAI) COMPANY LIMITED—See Essex Bio-Technology Limited; *Int'l*, pg. 2512
ESTEE LAUDER COORDINATION CENTER BVBA—See The Estee Lauder Companies Inc.; *U.S. Public*, pg. 2073
ESTHETICS CONCEPT SDN.BHD.—See Esthetics International Group Berhad; *Int'l*, pg. 2518
ETREA SA—See CSL Limited; *Int'l*, pg. 1866
EURODIFARM S.R.L.—See Deutsche Post AG; *Int'l*, pg. 2080
EUROFRAGANCE, LLC—See Eurofragance SLU; *Int'l*, pg. 2552
EURO RX ARZNEIMITTEL GMBH—See Arzneiwerk AG VIDA; *Int'l*, pg. 589
EUSA PHARMA (US) LLC—See Essex Woodlands Management, Inc.; *U.S. Private*, pg. 1428
EU YAN SANG (HONG KONG) LIMITED—See Eu Yan Sang International Ltd.; *Int'l*, pg. 2525
EVOTEC (UK) LTD.—See Evotec SE; *Int'l*, pg. 2573
EWI CORPORATION—See Bristol-Myers Squibb Company; *U.S. Public*, pg. 386

EXCELLERX, INC.—See Consonance Capital Partners LLC; *U.S. Private*, pg. 1023
EXELAN PHARMACEUTICALS, INC.—See Cipla Ltd.; *Int'l*, pg. 1617
EXTRAWELL PHARMACEUTICAL (HK) LIMITED—See Extrawell Pharmaceutical Holdings Ltd.; *Int'l*, pg. 2592
EYEGATE PHARMA S.A.S.—See Kiora Pharmaceuticals, Inc.; *U.S. Public*, pg. 1235
EYS KANGHONG HERBAL PTE LTD—See Eu Yan Sang International Ltd.; *Int'l*, pg. 2525
FADAPHARMA DEL ECUADOR S.A.—See Abbott Laboratories; *U.S. Public*, pg. 19
FAGRON CARE SP. Z.O.O.—See Fagron NV; *Int'l*, pg. 2603
FAIRN & SWANSON INC.; *U.S. Private*, pg. 1464
FAIRY FOREST CO., LTD.—See Fantasista Co., Ltd.; *Int'l*, pg. 2613
FAREVA HOLDING SA—See Fareva SA; *Int'l*, pg. 2618
FAREVA ITUPEVA—See Fareva SA; *Int'l*, pg. 2618
FAREVA LOUVEIRA—See Fareva SA; *Int'l*, pg. 2618
FAREVA RICHMOND INC.—See Fareva SA; *Int'l*, pg. 2618
FARMACEUTICA MONT BLANC, S.L.—See Abbott Laboratories; *U.S. Public*, pg. 19
FARMACEUTICA REMEDIA S.A.; *Int'l*, pg. 2619
FARMACIAS AHUMADA S.A.—See Walgreens Boots Alliance, Inc.; *U.S. Public*, pg. 2322
FARMACOLOGIA EM AQUICULTURA VETERINARIA LTDA.—See Abbott Laboratories; *U.S. Public*, pg. 19
FARMACOL S.A.; *Int'l*, pg. 2619
FARMACOSMO S.P.A.; *Int'l*, pg. 2619
FARMINDUSTRIA S.A.—See Abbott Laboratories; *U.S. Public*, pg. 19
FDC VITAMINS, INC.—See B. Riley Financial, Inc.; *U.S. Public*, pg. 261
FDC VITAMINS, INC.—See Irradiant Partners, LP; *U.S. Private*, pg. 2141
FEMTOBIOMED INC.; *Int'l*, pg. 2633
FFF ENTERPRISES INC.; *U.S. Private*, pg. 1500
F.G.J CO., LTD.—See H2O Retailing Corp.; *Int'l*, pg. 3200
F.H.G. CORPORATION—See H.I.G. Capital, LLC; *U.S. Private*, pg. 1829
FIRMENICH BJORGE BIOMARIN AS—See Firmenich International SA; *Int'l*, pg. 2680
FIRMENICH CO LTD—See Firmenich International SA; *Int'l*, pg. 2680
FIRMENICH DENMARK APS—See Firmenich International SA; *Int'l*, pg. 2680
FIRMENICH FZ-LLC—See Firmenich International SA; *Int'l*, pg. 2680
FIRMENICH GMBH—See Firmenich International SA; *Int'l*, pg. 2680
FIRMENICH GRASSE SAS—See Firmenich International SA; *Int'l*, pg. 2680
FIRMENICH LLC—See Firmenich International SA; *Int'l*, pg. 2680
FIRMENICH LLC—See Firmenich International SA; *Int'l*, pg. 2680
FIRMENICH VIETNAM LLC—See Firmenich International SA; *Int'l*, pg. 2680
FIRMENICH WELLINGBOROUGH (UK) LTD—See Firmenich International SA; *Int'l*, pg. 2680
FIRST CHINA PHARMACEUTICAL GROUP, INC.; *Int'l*, pg. 2682
FISIOPHARMA S.R.L.—See BIOTON S.A.; *Int'l*, pg. 1043
FIT-BIOCEUTICALS LIMITED—See Blackmores Limited; *Int'l*, pg. 1061
FIVE STAR FRAGRANCE COMPANY, INC.—See Perfumania Holdings, Inc.; *U.S. Private*, pg. 3150
FLAMEL TECHNOLOGIES INC.—See AVADEL PHARMACEUTICALS PLC; *Int'l*, pg. 734
FLORIEN FITOATIVOS LTDA—See Fagron NV; *Int'l*, pg. 2603
FLORI ROBERTS—See Color Me Beautiful, Inc.; *U.S. Private*, pg. 973
FLUIDX LTD—See Azenta, Inc.; *U.S. Public*, pg. 258
FMC INC.; *U.S. Private*, pg. 1554
FOLEYS INC.; *U.S. Private*, pg. 1558
FOODSCIENCE CORPORATION—See Wind Point Advisors LLC; *U.S. Private*, pg. 4534
FOREVERLIVING.COM LLC—See Forever Living Products International, Inc.; *U.S. Private*, pg. 1567
FRAGRANCES EXCLUSIVE INC.—See Chanel S.A.; *Int'l*, pg. 1441
FRAGRANCEX.COM; *U.S. Private*, pg. 1586
FRAMESI USA, INC.—See Framesi S.p.A.; *Int'l*, pg. 2759
FRENCH TRANSIT LTD.—See Juggernaut Management, LLC; *U.S. Private*, pg. 2242
FRESENIUS KABI CANADA LTD.—See Fresenius SE & Co. KGaA; *Int'l*, pg. 2777
FRESH INC.; *U.S. Private*, pg. 1609
FREUND-CHINEWAY PHARMACEUTICAL TECHNOLOGY CENTER CO., LTD.—See Freund Corporation; *Int'l*, pg. 2791
FRUIT OF THE EARTH INC.; *U.S. Private*, pg. 1617
FULLER SUPPLY CO. INC.; *U.S. Private*, pg. 1621
FV PHARMA INTERNATIONAL CORP.; *Int'l*, pg. 2859
GABA B.V.—See Colgate-Palmolive Company; *U.S. Public*, pg. 532

GALDERMA BRASIL LTDA.—See Abu Dhabi Investment Authority; *Int'l*, pg. 71
GALDERMA BRASIL LTDA.—See EQT Corporation; *U.S. Public*, pg. 785
GALDERMA INTERNATIONAL SAS—See Abu Dhabi Investment Authority; *Int'l*, pg. 71
GALDERMA INTERNATIONAL SAS—See EQT Corporation; *U.S. Public*, pg. 785
GALEN LIMITED—See Almac Sciences Group Ltd.; *Int'l*, pg. 363
GAMA HEALTHCARE AUSTRALIA PTY LTD.—See Hancock & Gore Ltd.; *Int'l*, pg. 3242
GAMBRO INDUSTRIES SAS—See Baxter International Inc.; *U.S. Public*, pg. 282
GEDEON RICHTER AUSTRALIA PTY. LTD.—See Gedeon Richter Plc.; *Int'l*, pg. 2909
GEDEON RICHTER AUSTRIA GMBH—See Gedeon Richter Plc.; *Int'l*, pg. 2909
GEDEON RICHTER BOLIVIA SRL—See Gedeon Richter Plc.; *Int'l*, pg. 2909
GEDEON RICHTER CHILE SPA—See Gedeon Richter Plc.; *Int'l*, pg. 2909
GEDEON RICHTER CROATIA D.O.O.—See Gedeon Richter Plc.; *Int'l*, pg. 2910
GEDEONRICHTER ECUADOR S.A.—See Gedeon Richter Plc.; *Int'l*, pg. 2910
GEDEON RICHTER MARKETING POLSKA SP. Z O.O.—See Gedeon Richter Plc.; *Int'l*, pg. 2910
GEDEON RICHTER PERU S.A.C.—See Gedeon Richter Plc.; *Int'l*, pg. 2910
GEDEON RICHTER SLOVAKIA S.R.O.—See Gedeon Richter Plc.; *Int'l*, pg. 2910
GE HEALTHCARE JAPAN CORPORATION—See GE HealthCare Technologies Inc.; *U.S. Public*, pg. 909
GEMCHEM, INC.—See American Vanguard Corporation; *U.S. Public*, pg. 112
GEMS SERVICES S.A.—See Eli Lilly & Company; *U.S. Public*, pg. 733
GENERAL PERFUME & COSMETICS DISTRIBUTORS INC.; *U.S. Private*, pg. 1666
GENFIT CORPORATION—See Genfit S.A.; *Int'l*, pg. 2923
GENNBIO, INC.; *Int'l*, pg. 2925
GETINGE TREASURY AB—See Getinge AB; *Int'l*, pg. 2950
GEUMSAN GINSENG HERB DEVELOPMENT AGENCY; *Int'l*, pg. 2954
GILEAD SCIENCES ISRAEL LIMITED—See Gilead Sciences, Inc.; *U.S. Public*, pg. 937
GILEAD SCIENCES LTD.—See Gilead Sciences, Inc.; *U.S. Public*, pg. 937
GILEAD SCIENCES SWITZERLAND SARL—See Gilead Sciences, Inc.; *U.S. Public*, pg. 937
GILLETTE AESOP LTD.—See The Procter & Gamble Company; *U.S. Public*, pg. 2124
GIVAUDAN AUSTRIA GMBH—See Givaudan S.A.; *Int'l*, pg. 2980
GIVAUDAN CHILE LTDA—See Givaudan S.A.; *Int'l*, pg. 2980
GIVAUDAN COLOMBIA SA—See Givaudan S.A.; *Int'l*, pg. 2980
GIVAUDAN CR, S.R.O.—See Givaudan S.A.; *Int'l*, pg. 2980
GIVAUDAN DEUTSCHLAND GMBH—See Givaudan S.A.; *Int'l*, pg. 2980
GIVAUDAN FRANCE AROMES SAS—See Givaudan S.A.; *Int'l*, pg. 2980
GIVAUDAN PERU SAC—See Givaudan S.A.; *Int'l*, pg. 2981
GIVAUDAN SCANDINAVIA A/S—See Givaudan S.A.; *Int'l*, pg. 2981
GLAXOSMITHKLINE EXPORT LIMITED GHANA—See GSK plc; *Int'l*, pg. 3147
GLAXOSMITHKLINE LIMITED—See GSK plc; *Int'l*, pg. 3149
GLAXOSMITHKLINE PUERTO RICO—See GSK plc; *Int'l*, pg. 3148
GLAXOSMITHKLINE TRADING SERVICES LIMITED—See GSK plc; *Int'l*, pg. 3149
GLENMARK PHARMACEUTICALS COLOMBIA LTDA.—See Glenmark Pharmaceuticals Limited; *Int'l*, pg. 2992
GLENMARK PHARMACEUTICALS SK SRO—See Glenmark Pharmaceuticals Limited; *Int'l*, pg. 2992
GLENMARK PHARMACEUTICALS SP Z.O.O.—See Glenmark Pharmaceuticals Limited; *Int'l*, pg. 2992
GLENMARK PHARMACEUTICALS S.R.L.—See Glenmark Pharmaceuticals Limited; *Int'l*, pg. 2992
GLENMARK PHARMACEUTICALS S.R.O.—See Glenmark Pharmaceuticals Limited; *Int'l*, pg. 2992
GLOBAL COSMETICS, INC.; *Int'l*, pg. 2994
GLOBAL SCIENCE AND TECHNOLOGY LTD.—See Avantor, Inc.; *U.S. Public*, pg. 241
GLOBUS MEDICAL SWEDEN AB—See Globus Medical, Inc.; *U.S. Public*, pg. 947
GLOMED PHARMACEUTICAL COMPANY LIMITED—See Abbott Laboratories; *U.S. Public*, pg. 20
GLORYFEEL GMBH—See Bayer Aktiengesellschaft; *Int'l*, pg. 908
GNC HONG KONG LIMITED—See Ares Management Corporation; *U.S. Public*, pg. 189
GODECKE GMBH—See Pfizer Inc.; *U.S. Public*, pg. 1680
GODREJ CONSUMER PRODUCTS (UK) LTD—See

N.A.I.C.S. INDEX

424210 — DRUGS AND DRUGGISTS...

Jordan/Zalaznick Advisers, Inc.; *U.S. Private*, pg. 2235
GODREJ NIGERIA LTD.—See Godrej & Boyce Mfg. Co. Ltd.; *Int'l*, pg. 3021
GOLDEN NEO LIFE DIAMITE INTERNATIONAL; *U.S. Private*, pg. 1732
GOLDENWELL BIOTECH, INC.; *U.S. Public*, pg. 951
GOOD LIFE CHEMIST—See Aamal Company Q.S.C.; *Int'l*, pg. 36
GOOD NEIGHBOR PHARMACY—See Cencora, Inc.; *U.S. Public*, pg. 467
GOPHARMA S.R.L.—See IMCD N.V.; *Int'l*, pg. 3621
GOSHEN HEALTH SYSTEM; *U.S. Private*, pg. 1744
G-PHARMA AG—See CSL Limited; *Int'l*, pg. 1866
GRAND BRILLIANCE GROUP HOLDINGS LTD.; *Int'l*, pg. 3054
GRAND MILLS COMPANY PJSC—See Agthia Group PJSC; *Int'l*, pg. 222
GREEN BITS, INC.—See Courier Plus, Inc.; *U.S. Private*, pg. 1068
GRIFOLS NORDIC AB—See Grifols, S.A.; *Int'l*, pg. 3084
GRUPO CASA SABA S.A.B. DE C.V.—See Grupo Xtra S.A. de C.V.; *Int'l*, pg. 3139
GSK AZERBAIJAN—See GSK plc; *Int'l*, pg. 3145
GSK BELARUS—See GSK plc; *Int'l*, pg. 3145
GSK COMMERCIAL SP. Z O.O.—See GSK plc; *Int'l*, pg. 3145
GSK CONSUMER HEALTHCARE—See GSK plc; *Int'l*, pg. 3145
GSK CYPRUS—See GSK plc; *Int'l*, pg. 3145
GSK MALTA—See GSK plc; *Int'l*, pg. 3145
GSK SERVICES SP. Z O.O.—See GSK plc; *Int'l*, pg. 3145
GUANGXI LIUZHOU PHARMACEUTICAL CO., LTD.; *Int'l*, pg. 3163
GUARDIAN SURVIVAL GEAR, INC.; *U.S. Private*, pg. 1810
GUERBET ARGENTINA LIMITED - ARGENTINA BRANCH OFFICE—See Guerbet SA; *Int'l*, pg. 3172
GUERBET ARGENTINA LIMITED—See Guerbet SA; *Int'l*, pg. 3172
GUERBET FRANCE, SA—See Guerbet SA; *Int'l*, pg. 3172
GUERBET ILAC TIBBI A.S.—See Guerbet SA; *Int'l*, pg. 3172
GUERBET JAPAN KK—See Guerbet SA; *Int'l*, pg. 3172
GUERBET LABORATORIES LTD.—See Guerbet SA; *Int'l*, pg. 3172
GYNOPHARM DE VENEZUELA, C.A.—See Abbott Laboratories; *U.S. Public*, pg. 20
GYNOPHARM S.A.—See Abbott Laboratories; *U.S. Public*, pg. 20
HABA HONG KONG LIMITED—See HABA LABORATORIES, INC.; *Int'l*, pg. 3201
HAIRHOUSE WAREHOUSE ONLINE PTY. LTD.; *Int'l*, pg. 3217
HAMELN PHAMA PLUS GMBH—See Hameln Group GmbH; *Int'l*, pg. 3237
HAMELN PHARMACEUTICALS LTD.—See Hameln Group GmbH; *Int'l*, pg. 3237
HANALL BIOPHARMA CO., LTD. - BUSINESS DEVELOPMENT DIVISION—See HanAll BioPharma Co., Ltd.; *Int'l*, pg. 3241
HANALL BIOPHARMA CO., LTD. - INTERNATIONAL EXPORTS DIVISION—See HanAll BioPharma Co., Ltd.; *Int'l*, pg. 3241
HANCOCKS PHARMACY & SURGICAL; *U.S. Private*, pg. 1852
HANFANG TRADING COMPANY LIMITED—See Hua Han Health Industry Holdings Limited; *Int'l*, pg. 3509
HANKOOK COSMETICS CO., LTD.—See Hankook Cosmetics Manufacturing Co., Ltd.; *Int'l*, pg. 3253
HARBIN PHARMACEUTICAL GROUP SANJING PHARMACEUTICAL CO., LTD; *Int'l*, pg. 3271
HARIMA-KYOWA CO., LTD.; *Int'l*, pg. 3276
THE HARVARD DRUG GROUP, LLC—See Cardinal Health, Inc.; *U.S. Public*, pg. 434
HAWAII MEGA-COR., INC.—See Patterson Companies, Inc.; *U.S. Public*, pg. 1653
HAYAT PHARMACEUTICAL INDUSTRIES; *Int'l*, pg. 3290
H&B STORES LTD.—See Dabur India Ltd; *Int'l*, pg. 1903
H.C. PHARMACY CENTRAL, INC.—See University of Pittsburgh Medical Center; *U.S. Private*, pg. 4309
H.D. SMITH WHOLESALE DRUG CO. INC.; *U.S. Private*, pg. 1825
H.D. SMITH WHOLESALE DRUG CO. INC.—See H.D. Smith Wholesale Drug Co. Inc.; *U.S. Private*, pg. 1825
HEALTHCARE-TECH CORPORATION—See Air Water Inc.; *U.S. Public*, pg. 240
HEALTHWAY SHOPPING NETWORK, INC.; *U.S. Private*, pg. 1898
HEARTLAND HOMECARE SERVICES, INC.; *U.S. Private*, pg. 1900
HEEL BELGIUM NV—See Delton AG; *Int'l*, pg. 2021
HEEL BIOLOGISCHE GENEESMIDDELEN B.V.—See Delton AG; *Int'l*, pg. 2021
HEEL POLSKA SP. Z O.O.—See Delton AG; *Int'l*, pg. 2021
HEMP NATURALS, INC.; *U.S. Public*, pg. 1025
HENGAN PHARMACARE COMPANY LIMITED—See Hengan International Group Co. Ltd.; *Int'l*, pg. 3345
HENRY SCHEIN ANIMAL HEALTH—See Clayton, Dubilier & Rice, LLC; *U.S. Private*, pg. 921

HENRY SCHEIN ANIMAL HEALTH—See TPG Capital, L.P.; *U.S. Public*, pg. 2170
HENRY SCHEIN MEDICAL—See Henry Schein, Inc.; *U.S. Public*, pg. 1025
HERBA CHEMOSAN APOTHEKER-AG—See McKesson Corporation; *U.S. Public*, pg. 1408
HERBALIFE INTERNATIONAL OF AMERICA, INC.—See Herbalife Nutrition Ltd.; *Int'l*, pg. 3359
HERBALIFE NUTRITION LTD.; *Int'l*, pg. 3359
HERITAGE BRANDS LIMITED; *Int'l*, pg. 3361
HEYLTEX CORPORATION—See HEYL Chemisch-pharmazeutische Fabrik GmbH und Co. KG; *Int'l*, pg. 3374
THE HIMALAYA DRUG COMPANY FZCO—See Himalaya Drug Company; *Int'l*, pg. 3396
THE HIMALAYA DRUG COMPANY L.L.C.—See Himalaya Drug Company; *Int'l*, pg. 3396
THE HIMALAYA DRUG COMPANY PTE LTD—See Himalaya Drug Company; *Int'l*, pg. 3396
THE HIMALAYA DRUG COMPANY (PTY) LTD—See Himalaya Drug Company; *Int'l*, pg. 3396
HISAMITSU AMERICA, INC.—See Hisamitsu Pharmaceutical Co., Inc.; *Int'l*, pg. 3406
HOBI KOZMETIK IMALAT SANAYI VE—See Dabur India Ltd; *Int'l*, pg. 1903
HOCKS.COM, INC.—See HealthWarehouse.com, Inc.; *U.S. Public*, pg. 1017
HOLISTA BIOTECH SDN BHD—See Holista CollTech Limited; *Int'l*, pg. 3450
HOLLAND & BARRETT RETAIL LIMITED—See KKR & Co. Inc.; *U.S. Public*, pg. 1264
HORIZON PHARMA AG—See Amgen Inc.; *U.S. Public*, pg. 123
HORIZON PHARMA GMBH—See Amgen Inc.; *U.S. Public*, pg. 123
HORIZON PHARMA, INC.—See Amgen Inc.; *U.S. Public*, pg. 123
HORIZON PHARMA USA, INC.—See Amgen Inc.; *U.S. Public*, pg. 123
HOVID INC.—See Hovid Berhad; *Int'l*, pg. 3492
HOVID LIMITED—See Hovid Berhad; *Int'l*, pg. 3492
HOVID MARKETING SDN. BHD.—See Hovid Berhad; *Int'l*, pg. 3492
HRA PHARMA DEUTSCHLAND, GMBH—See Astorg Partners S.A.S.; *Int'l*, pg. 656
HRA PHARMA DEUTSCHLAND, GMBH—See The Goldman Sachs Group, Inc.; *U.S. Public*, pg. 2077
HRA PHARMA IBERIA S.L.—See Astorg Partners S.A.S.; *Int'l*, pg. 656
HRA PHARMA IBERIA S.L.—See The Goldman Sachs Group, Inc.; *U.S. Public*, pg. 2077
HRA PHARMA ITALIA S.R.L.—See Astorg Partners S.A.S.; *Int'l*, pg. 656
HRA PHARMA ITALIA S.R.L.—See The Goldman Sachs Group, Inc.; *U.S. Public*, pg. 2077
HRA PHARMA UK & IRELAND LTD—See Astorg Partners S.A.S.; *Int'l*, pg. 656
HRA PHARMA UK & IRELAND LTD—See The Goldman Sachs Group, Inc.; *U.S. Public*, pg. 2077
HUMAX PHARMACEUTICAL S.A.—See Bausch Health Companies Inc.; *Int'l*, pg. 897
HYGEN PHARMACEUTICALS, INC.; *U.S. Private*, pg. 2018
HYPHENS PHARMA PTE. LTD.—See Hyphens Pharma International Limited; *Int'l*, pg. 3553
HZNP USA LLC—See Amgen Inc.; *U.S. Public*, pg. 123
IBNSINA PHARMA CO.; *Int'l*, pg. 3576
IDEV TECHNOLOGIES B.V.—See Abbott Laboratories; *U.S. Public*, pg. 20
IDEXX PHARMACEUTICALS, INC.—See IDEXX Laboratories, Inc.; *U.S. Public*, pg. 1093
IMCD MALAYSIA SDN BHD—See IMCD N.V.; *Int'l*, pg. 3622
IMMUNO-VET SERVICES (PTY) LTD SOUTH AFRICA—See Eli Lilly & Company; *U.S. Public*, pg. 733
IMONEY TOOLS LLC; *U.S. Private*, pg. 2048
IMPERIAL DISTRIBUTORS, INC.; *U.S. Private*, pg. 2049
INCYTE BIOSCIENCES AUSTRIA GMBH—See Incyte Corporation; *U.S. Public*, pg. 1115
INCYTE BIOSCIENCES FRANCE—See Incyte Corporation; *U.S. Public*, pg. 1115
INCYTE BIOSCIENCES GERMANY GMBH—See Incyte Corporation; *U.S. Public*, pg. 1115
INCYTE BIOSCIENCES IBERIA S.L.—See Incyte Corporation; *U.S. Public*, pg. 1115
INCYTE BIOSCIENCES INTERNATIONAL S.A R.L.—See Incyte Corporation; *U.S. Public*, pg. 1115
INCYTE BIOSCIENCES ITALY S.R.L.—See Incyte Corporation; *U.S. Public*, pg. 1115
INCYTE BIOSCIENCES JAPAN G.K.—See Incyte Corporation; *U.S. Public*, pg. 1115
INCYTE BIOSCIENCES TECHNICAL OPERATIONS S.A R.L.—See Incyte Corporation; *U.S. Public*, pg. 1115
INCYTE BIOSCIENCES UK LTD—See Incyte Corporation; *U.S. Public*, pg. 1115
INNISFREE COSMETICS INDIA PRIVATE LIMITED—See Amorepacific Corp.; *Int'l*, pg. 430
INNOPHOS NUTRITION, INC.—See One Rock Capital Partners, LLC; *U.S. Private*, pg. 3022

INSMED GERMANY GMBH—See Insmed Incorporated; *U.S. Public*, pg. 1131
INSMED NETHERLANDS B.V.—See Insmed Incorporated; *U.S. Public*, pg. 1131
INSTANT DIAGNOSTIC SYSTEMS, INC.—See Cardinal Health, Inc.; *U.S. Public*, pg. 434
INTELLIGENT FINGERPRINTING LIMITED—See Intelligent Bio Solutions, Inc.; *U.S. Public*, pg. 1140
INTENDIS MANUFACTURING S.P.A.—See Bayer Aktiengesellschaft; *Int'l*, pg. 908
INTER AMERICAN COSMETICS INC.; *U.S. Private*, pg. 2106
INTERCHEM CORPORATION; *U.S. Private*, pg. 2109
INTERNATIONAL FINAF 2000 S.A.—See Angelini ACRAF S.p.A.; *Int'l*, pg. 460
INTERNATIONAL INDEMNITY LTD.—See Merck & Co., Inc.; *U.S. Public*, pg. 1416
INTERVET DEUTSCHLAND GMBH—See Merck & Co., Inc.; *U.S. Public*, pg. 1416
INTERVET HELLAS A.E.—See Merck & Co., Inc.; *U.S. Public*, pg. 1416
INTERVET (IRELAND) LIMITED—See Merck & Co., Inc.; *U.S. Public*, pg. 1416
INTERVET LLC—See Merck & Co., Inc.; *U.S. Public*, pg. 1417
INTERVET (PROPRIETARY) LIMITED—See Merck & Co., Inc.; *U.S. Public*, pg. 1416
INTERVET S.A.S—See Merck & Co., Inc.; *U.S. Public*, pg. 1417
INTERVET, S.R.O.—See Merck & Co., Inc.; *U.S. Public*, pg. 1417
IOOO ALGOL CHEMICALS—See Algol Oy; *Int'l*, pg. 318
IQVIA RDS EASTERN HOLDINGS GMBH—See IQVIA Holdings Inc.; *U.S. Public*, pg. 1170
IQVIA RDS UK HOLDINGS LIMITED—See IQVIA Holdings Inc.; *U.S. Public*, pg. 1170
ISATORI, INC.—See FitLife Brands, Inc.; *U.S. Public*, pg. 852
JA COSMETICS CORP.—See TPG Capital, L.P.; *U.S. Public*, pg. 2174
JANSSEN-CILAG AG—See Johnson & Johnson; *U.S. Public*, pg. 1197
JANSSEN-CILAG AS—See Johnson & Johnson; *U.S. Public*, pg. 1197
JANSSEN-CILAG GMBH—See Johnson & Johnson; *U.S. Public*, pg. 1197
JANSSEN-CILAG PHARMACEUTICAL S.A.C.I.—See Johnson & Johnson; *U.S. Public*, pg. 1197
JANSSEN-CILAG PHARMA GMBH—See Johnson & Johnson; *U.S. Public*, pg. 1197
JANSSEN-CILAG S.A.—See Johnson & Johnson; *U.S. Public*, pg. 1197
JANSSEN INC.—See Johnson & Johnson; *U.S. Public*, pg. 1196
JANSSEN SCIENCES IRELAND UC—See Johnson & Johnson; *U.S. Public*, pg. 1197
JARROW FORMULAS, INC.—See New Mountain Capital, LLC; *U.S. Private*, pg. 2903
JAT PHARMACY, LLC—See Midwest Veterinary Supply, Inc.; *U.S. Private*, pg. 2723
JBT FOOD AND DAIRY SYSTEMS B.V.—See John Bean Technologies Corporation; *U.S. Public*, pg. 1191
JBT FOOD & DAIRY SYSTEMS INC.—See John Bean Technologies Corporation; *U.S. Public*, pg. 1191
JEFFERS, INC.; *U.S. Public*, pg. 2197
JEFFERSPET.COM—See Jeffers, Inc.; *U.S. Private*, pg. 2197
JINNY BEAUTY SUPPLY CO. INC.; *U.S. Private*, pg. 2210
JOEY NEW YORK, INC.; *U.S. Public*, pg. 1190
JOHN PAUL MITCHELL SYSTEMS; *U.S. Private*, pg. 2223
JOHNSON & JOHNSON CONSUMER FRANCE SAS—See Kenvue Inc.; *U.S. Public*, pg. 1223
JOHNSON & JOHNSON CONSUMER NV/SA—See Kenvue Inc.; *U.S. Public*, pg. 1223
JOHNSON & JOHNSON INDUSTRIAL LTDA.—See Kenvue Inc.; *U.S. Public*, pg. 1224
JOHNSON & JOHNSON INTERNATIONAL S.A.—See Johnson & Johnson; *U.S. Public*, pg. 1198
JOHNSON & JOHNSON K.K.—See Johnson & Johnson; *U.S. Public*, pg. 1198
JOHNSON & JOHNSON LTD.—See Johnson & Johnson; *U.S. Public*, pg. 1198
JOHNSON & JOHNSON MEDICAL S.A.—See Johnson & Johnson; *U.S. Public*, pg. 1199
JOHNSON & JOHNSON MEDICAL (SHANGHAI) LTD.—See Johnson & Johnson; *U.S. Public*, pg. 1198
JOHNSON & JOHNSON MEDICAL S.P.A.—See Johnson & Johnson; *U.S. Public*, pg. 1199
JOHNSON & JOHNSON (NEW ZEALAND) LIMITED—See Johnson & Johnson; *U.S. Public*, pg. 1198
JOHNSON & JOHNSON PRODUCTS INC.—See Johnson & Johnson; *U.S. Public*, pg. 1199
JOHNSON & JOHNSON S.A.—See Johnson & Johnson; *U.S. Public*, pg. 1199
JOHNSON & JOHNSON; *U.S. Public*, pg. 1193
JOM PHARMACEUTICAL SERVICES, INC.—See Johnson & Johnson; *U.S. Public*, pg. 1196
JPG PHARMA NV—See Fagron NV; *Int'l*, pg. 2603

JSC ASTELLAS PHARMA—See Astellas Pharma Inc.; *Int'l*, pg. 653
KABAFUSION HOLDINGS, LLC—See The Pritzker Group - Chicago, LLC; *U.S. Private*, pg. 4099
KALAHARI MEDICAL DISTRIBUTORS (PROPRIETARY) LIMITED—See Clicks Group Limited; *Int'l*, pg. 1658
KEYSOURCE MEDICAL, INC.; *U.S. Private*, pg. 2295
KIMIA SUCHI MARKETING SDN BHD—See Berjaya Corporation Berhad; *Int'l*, pg. 984
KIM INTERNATIONAL CORPORATION—See Greenlane Holdings, Inc.; *U.S. Public*, pg. 965
KINDS RESOURCE SDN. BHD.—See Hai-O Enterprise Berhad; *Int'l*, pg. 3209
KING DRUG COMPANY OF FLORENCE INC.—See Lyndale Enterprises Inc.; *U.S. Private*, pg. 2521
KINRAY, INC.—See Cardinal Health, Inc.; *U.S. Public*, pg. 434
KONZERN US HOLDING CORPORATION—See CHINA MEDICINE CORPORATION; *Int'l*, pg. 1518
KOWA PHARMACEUTICALS CO., LTD.—See Alfresa Holdings Corporation; *Int'l*, pg. 317
KRAMER LABORATORIES, INC.—See Avista Capital Partners, L.P.; *U.S. Private*, pg. 408
KURON CORPORATION LIMITED—See Do Day Dream PCL; *Int'l*, pg. 2152
LABORATOIRE GLAXOSMITHKLINE—See GSK plc; *Int'l*, pg. 3149
LABORATOIRES MERCK SHARP & DOHME-CHIBRET SNC—See Merck & Co., Inc.; *U.S. Public*, pg. 1417
LABORATORIES 3M SANTE SAS—See 3M Company; *U.S. Public*, pg. 6
LABORATORIOS HEEL ESPANA, S.A.U.—See Delton AG; *Int'l*, pg. 2021
LACOMED, SPOL. S R.O.—See CEZ, a.s.; *Int'l*, pg. 1429
LADY BURD EXCLUSIVE PRIVATE LABEL COSMETICS; *U.S. Private*, pg. 2372
LAKE REGION MEDICAL SDN. BHD.—See Integer Holdings Corporation; *U.S. Public*, pg. 1135
LANELABS USA INC.; *U.S. Private*, pg. 2388
LASSO MARKETING, INC.—See IQVIA Holdings Inc.; *U.S. Public*, pg. 1169
LEECHES U.S.A. LTD.—See Accurate Chemical & Scientific Corporation; *U.S. Private*, pg. 55
LEE-SILSBY COMPOUNDING PHARMACY—See Osceola Capital Management, LLC; *U.S. Private*, pg. 3047
LIFECELL EMEA LIMITED—See AbbVie Inc.; *U.S. Public*, pg. 24
LIFECELL EMEA LIMITED—See AbbVie Inc.; *U.S. Public*, pg. 24
LILLY NEDERLAND FINANCE B.V.—See Eli Lilly & Company; *U.S. Public*, pg. 733
LLC BOEHRINGER INGELHEIM—See C.H. Boehringer Sohn AG & Co. KG; *Int'l*, pg. 1242
LOHMANN ANIMAL HEALTH BETEILIGUNGS GMBH—See Eli Lilly & Company; *U.S. Public*, pg. 733
LOHMANN ANIMAL HEALTH INTERNATIONAL, INC.—See Eli Lilly & Company; *U.S. Public*, pg. 733
LOLLIPOP CORPORATION; *U.S. Private*, pg. 2483
LUCAS MEYER COSMETICS CANADA INC.—See Clariant AG; *Int'l*, pg. 1648
LUCKWEL PHARMACEUTICALS INC.; *U.S. Private*, pg. 2511
LUMENIS (FRANCE) SARL—See Boston Scientific Corporation; *U.S. Public*, pg. 375
LYNDALE ENTERPRISES INC.; *U.S. Private*, pg. 2521
MADISON PHARMACEUTICALS INC.—See Cipla Ltd.; *Int'l*, pg. 1617
MAESA HOME—See F&B Group; *Int'l*, pg. 2595
MALECON PHARMACY, INC.—See Omni Health, Inc.; *U.S. Private*, pg. 3016
MALLINCKRODT BELGIUM BVBA—See Curium SAS; *Int'l*, pg. 1879
MARIANNA IMPORTS INC.; *U.S. Private*, pg. 2574
MARY KAY COSMETICS DE ESPANA, S.A.—See Mary Kay Holding Corporation; *U.S. Private*, pg. 2599
MARY KAY COSMETICS LTD.—See Mary Kay Holding Corporation; *U.S. Private*, pg. 2599
MARY KAY COSMETICS POLAND SP. Z. O.O.—See Mary Kay Holding Corporation; *U.S. Private*, pg. 2599
MARY KAY COSMETICS PTY. LTD.—See Mary Kay Holding Corporation; *U.S. Private*, pg. 2599
MARY KAY COSMETICS (TAIWAN) INC.—See Mary Kay Holding Corporation; *U.S. Private*, pg. 2599
MARY KAY COSMETICS (U.K.) LTD.—See Mary Kay Holding Corporation; *U.S. Private*, pg. 2599
MARY KAY PHILIPPINES, INC.—See Mary Kay Holding Corporation; *U.S. Private*, pg. 2599
MASON DISTRIBUTORS, INC.; *U.S. Private*, pg. 2602
MASON VITAMINS, INC.—See Mason Distributors, Inc.; *U.S. Private*, pg. 2602
MCKESSON CORPORATION; *U.S. Public*, pg. 1407
MCKESSON EUROPE AG—See McKesson Corporation; *U.S. Public*, pg. 1408
MCKESSON MEDICAL-SURGICAL INC.—See McKesson Corporation; *U.S. Public*, pg. 1408
MCKESSON PHARMACEUTICAL—See McKesson Corporation; *U.S. Public*, pg. 1408
MCKESSON SPECIALTY HEALTH—See McKesson Corporation; *U.S. Public*, pg. 1408

MCNEIL HEALTHCARE (UK) LIMITED—See Kenvue Inc.; *U.S. Public*, pg. 1224
MEAD JOHNSON JAMAICA LTD.—See Bristol-Myers Squibb Company; *U.S. Public*, pg. 386
MECHANICAL SERVANTS, LLC—See Lil' Drug Store Products, Inc.; *U.S. Private*, pg. 2455
MEDA A/S—See Viatris Inc.; *U.S. Public*, pg. 2293
MEDAG AB—See Viatris Inc.; *U.S. Public*, pg. 2294
MEDA PHARMACEUTICALS LTD—See Viatris Inc.; *U.S. Public*, pg. 2294
MEDA PHARMA SIA—See Viatris Inc.; *U.S. Public*, pg. 2293
MEDA PHARMA SOUTH AFRICA (PTY) LIMITED—See Viatris Inc.; *U.S. Public*, pg. 2293
MEDEX SA—See Guerbet SA; *Int'l*, pg. 3172
MEDICAL MART SUPPLIES LIMITED—See Medline Industries, LP; *U.S. Private*, pg. 2657
MEDICIS AESTHETICS CANADA, LTD.—See Bausch Health Companies Inc.; *Int'l*, pg. 898
MEDICONSTANT PHARMACY (AMPANG) SDN. BHD.—See Bioalpha Holdings Berhad; *Int'l*, pg. 1036
MEDICONSTANT PHARMACY (KLANG) SDN. BHD.—See Bioalpha Holdings Berhad; *Int'l*, pg. 1036
MEDIMARK SCIENTIFIC LIMITED—See Byotrol Limited; *Int'l*, pg. 1235
MEDIMPEX JAMAICA LTD—See Gedeon Richter Plc.; *Int'l*, pg. 2910
MEDIMPEX WEST INDIES LTD—See Gedeon Richter Plc.; *Int'l*, pg. 2910
MEDINOVA AG—See Diethelm Keller Holding Limited; *Int'l*, pg. 2117
MEDIPLUS (ECONOMIC ZONE) N.V.—See Gedeon Richter Plc.; *Int'l*, pg. 2910
MEDIQ PHARMA SERVICES—See Advent International Corporation; *U.S. Private*, pg. 104
MEDISOURCE IRELAND LIMITED—See DCC plc; *Int'l*, pg. 1991
MEDISUITE, LLC—See ADDvise Group AB; *Int'l*, pg. 136
MEDIWEST NORWAY AS—See Bayer Aktiengesellschaft; *Int'l*, pg. 908
MEDKLINN INTERNATIONAL SDN. BHD.—See Esthetics International Group Berhad; *Int'l*, pg. 2518
MEDSHOP SINGAPORE PTE. LTD.—See Bunzl plc; *Int'l*, pg. 1219
MEGAPHARM GMBH PHARMAZEUTISCHE ERZEUGNISSE—See Walgreens Boots Alliance, Inc.; *U.S. Public*, pg. 2322
MEISHO CO., LTD.—See Alfresa Holdings Corporation; *Int'l*, pg. 317
MERCHANDISE, INC.; *U.S. Private*, pg. 2669
MERCK & CO., INC.; *U.S. Public*, pg. 1415
MERCK & CO. INC.—See Merck & Co., Inc.; *U.S. Public*, pg. 1418
MERCK SHARP & DOHME ANIMAL HEALTH, S.L.—See Merck & Co., Inc.; *U.S. Public*, pg. 1419
MERCK SHARP & DOHME BV—See Merck & Co., Inc.; *U.S. Public*, pg. 1420
MERCK SHARP & DOHME DE VENEZUELA SRL—See Merck & Co., Inc.; *U.S. Public*, pg. 1420
MERCK SHARP & DOHME (I.A.) CORP.—See Merck & Co., Inc.; *U.S. Public*, pg. 1419
MERCK SHARP & DOHME (I.A.) CORP.—See Merck & Co., Inc.; *U.S. Public*, pg. 1419
MERCK SHARP & DOHME (I.A.) CORP.—See Merck & Co., Inc.; *U.S. Public*, pg. 1419
MERCK SHARP & DOHME (I.A.) CORP.—See Merck & Co., Inc.; *U.S. Public*, pg. 1419
MERCK SHARP & DOHME (I.A.) CORP.—See Merck & Co., Inc.; *U.S. Public*, pg. 1419
MERCK SHARP & DOHME ILACLARI LIMITED SIRKETI—See Merck & Co., Inc.; *U.S. Public*, pg. 1420
MERCK SHARP & DOHME IRELAND (HUMAN HEALTH) LTD—See Merck & Co., Inc.; *U.S. Public*, pg. 1420
MERCK SHARP & DOHME (NEW ZEALAND) LIMITED—See Merck & Co., Inc.; *U.S. Public*, pg. 1419
MERCK SHARP & DOHME PERU SRL—See Merck & Co., Inc.; *U.S. Public*, pg. 1420
MERCK SHARP & DOHME (SWEDEN) AB—See Merck & Co., Inc.; *U.S. Public*, pg. 1419
MERIT PHARMACEUTICALS; *U.S. Private*, pg. 2674
METAGENICS INCORPORATED—See Alticor Inc.; *U.S. Private*, pg. 209
MIAMI-LUKEN INC.; *U.S. Private*, pg. 2697
MIDDLEPORT FAMILY HEALTH CENTER; *U.S. Private*, pg. 2713
MIDWEST VETERINARY SUPPLY, INC.; *U.S. Private*, pg. 2723
MILEX PUERTO RICO—See The Cooper Companies, Inc.; *U.S. Public*, pg. 2066
MILLER DRUG; *U.S. Private*, pg. 2733
MINTOLOGY LIMITED—See Edgewell Personal Care Company; *U.S. Public*, pg. 718
MIRAECELLBIO CO., LTD.—See BYON Co., Ltd.; *Int'l*, pg. 1235
MIX 1 LIFE INC.; *U.S. Public*, pg. 1452
MOL-IMAGE MOLECULAR IMAGING CO.—See Eczacibasi Holding A.S.; *Int'l*, pg. 2301
MORINDA INC.—See NewAge, Inc.; *U.S. Public*, pg. 1513

MORRIS & DICKSON CO., LLC - RETAIL AND HOSPITAL DIVISION—See Morris & Dickson Co., LLC; *U.S. Private*, pg. 2786
MORRIS & DICKSON CO., LLC; *U.S. Private*, pg. 2786
MOUNTAIN VIEW MARKETING INC.; *U.S. Private*, pg. 2800
MOVACO, S.A.—See Grifols, S.A.; *Int'l*, pg. 3084
MSB PERFUME HOLDING DIFFUSION GMBH—See BI-Invest Advisors S.A.; *Int'l*, pg. 1017
MSB PERFUME HOLDINGS LTD.—See BI-Invest Advisors S.A.; *Int'l*, pg. 1017
MSD ANIMAL HEALTH A/S—See Merck & Co., Inc.; *U.S. Public*, pg. 1417
MSD ANIMAL HEALTH BVBA—See Merck & Co., Inc.; *U.S. Public*, pg. 1417
MSD ANIMAL HEALTH FZ-LLC—See Merck & Co., Inc.; *U.S. Public*, pg. 1417
MSD ANIMAL HEALTH (SHANGHAI) TRADING CO., LTD.—See Merck & Co., Inc.; *U.S. Public*, pg. 1417
MSD ANIMAL HEALTH VIETNAM CO. LTD.—See Merck & Co., Inc.; *U.S. Public*, pg. 1418
MSD FINLAND OY—See Merck & Co., Inc.; *U.S. Public*, pg. 1418
MSD GREECE—See Merck & Co., Inc.; *U.S. Public*, pg. 1418
MSD IT GLOBAL INNOVATION CENTER S.R.O.—See Merck & Co., Inc.; *U.S. Public*, pg. 1418
MSD KOREA LTD.—See Merck & Co., Inc.; *U.S. Public*, pg. 1418
MSD (NORGE) A/S—See Merck & Co., Inc.; *U.S. Public*, pg. 1417
MSD PANAMA—See Merck & Co., Inc.; *U.S. Public*, pg. 1418
MSD PHARMACEUTICALS LLC—See Merck & Co., Inc.; *U.S. Public*, pg. 1418
MSD PHILIPPINES—See Merck & Co., Inc.; *U.S. Public*, pg. 1418
MSD POLSKA SP. Z O.O.—See Merck & Co., Inc.; *U.S. Public*, pg. 1418
MSD (THAILAND) LTD.—See Merck & Co., Inc.; *U.S. Public*, pg. 1417
MSD VACCINS—See Merck & Co., Inc.; *U.S. Public*, pg. 1418
MYLAN B.V.—See Viatris Inc.; *U.S. Public*, pg. 2293
MYLAN DURA GMBH—See Viatris Inc.; *U.S. Public*, pg. 2294
MYLAN IRE HEALTHCARE LIMITED—See Viatris Inc.; *U.S. Public*, pg. 2293
MYLAN LABORATORIES SAS—See Viatris Inc.; *U.S. Public*, pg. 2294
MYLAN MEDICAL SAS—See Viatris Inc.; *U.S. Public*, pg. 2294
MYLAN PHARMA GROUP LTD.—See Viatris Inc.; *U.S. Public*, pg. 2294
NABSYS, INC.—See Hitachi, Ltd.; *Int'l*, pg. 3418
NATCO AL RAZI COMPANY—See Hayel Saeed Anam Group of Companies; *Int'l*, pg. 3290
NATURALIFE ECO VITE LABS; *U.S. Private*, pg. 2867
NATURAL SUPPLEMENT ASSOCIATION INC.; *U.S. Private*, pg. 2867
NATURE'S ONE, LLC—See Bobbie Baby, Inc.; *U.S. Private*, pg. 606
NATURE'S WAY PRODUCTS, INC.—See Dr. Willmar Schwabe GmbH & Co. KG; *Int'l*, pg. 2195
NATURWAREN ITALIA S.R.L.—See Dr. Theiss Naturwaren GmbH; *Int'l*, pg. 2195
NEOGEN AUSTRALASIA PTY LIMITED—See Neogen Corporation; *U.S. Public*, pg. 1505
NEOGEN CANADA—See Neogen Corporation; *U.S. Public*, pg. 1505
NEOGEN FOOD & ANIMAL SECURITY (INDIA) PVT, LTD.—See Neogen Corporation; *U.S. Public*, pg. 1505
NEUTRA CORP.; *U.S. Public*, pg. 1510
NEVINAR COSMETICS LTD.—See Clarins S.A.; *Int'l*, pg. 1649
NEWPORT SALES INC.; *U.S. Private*, pg. 2916
NEW YORK FRAGRANCE INC.; *U.S. Private*, pg. 2909
NEXT GREEN WAVE HOLDINGS, INC.—See Planet 13 Holdings, Inc.; *U.S. Public*, pg. 1697
NICOLAS VILLALBA WHOLESALERS; *U.S. Private*, pg. 2926
NORSK MEDISINALDEPOT AS—See McKesson Corporation; *U.S. Public*, pg. 1408
NORTH CAROLINA MUTUAL WHOLESALE DRUG COMPANY; *U.S. Private*, pg. 2943
NUDE BY NATURE PTY LIMITED—See Crescent Capital Partners Ltd.; *Int'l*, pg. 1839
NUMARK LABORATORIES, INC.; *U.S. Private*, pg. 2973
NU SKIN ENTERPRISES, INC.; *U.S. Public*, pg. 1551
NU SKIN ENTERPRISES (THAILAND) LIMITED—See Nu Skin Enterprises, Inc.; *U.S. Public*, pg. 1552
NU SKIN ENTERPRISES VIETNAM, LLC—See Nu Skin Enterprises, Inc.; *U.S. Public*, pg. 1552
NU SKIN, INC.—See Nu Skin Enterprises, Inc.; *U.S. Public*, pg. 1552
NUTRICHEM DIAT + PHARMA GMBH—See B. Braun Melsungen AG; *Int'l*, pg. 787
NUTRIMETICS FRANCE SAS—See Tupperware Brands

N.A.I.C.S. INDEX

424210 — DRUGS AND DRUGGISTS...

Corporation; *U.S. Public*, pg. 2204
NUTRI USA, INC.—See Option Care Health, Inc.; *U.S. Public*, pg. 1610
NV ASTRAZENECA SA—See AstraZeneca PLC; *Int'l*, pg. 661
NXGEN BRANDS LLC; *U.S. Public*, pg. 1558
OCULUS INNOVATIVE SCIENCES NETHERLANDS B.V.—See Sonoma Pharmaceuticals, Inc.; *U.S. Public*, pg. 1909
OKTAL PHARMA D.O.O.—See Walgreens Boots Alliance, Inc.; *U.S. Public*, pg. 2322
OLERUP GMBH—See CareDx, Inc.; *U.S. Public*, pg. 435
OLERUP SSP AB—See CareDx, Inc.; *U.S. Public*, pg. 435
OMNICARE PHARMACIES OF PENNSYLVANIA WEST, LLC—See CVS Health Corporation; *U.S. Public*, pg. 616
OMP INC.; *U.S. Private*, pg. 3017
ONCOLOGY THERAPEUTIC NETWORK—See Cardinal Health, Inc.; *U.S. Public*, pg. 434
ONEONCOLOGY, INC.—See TPG Capital, L.P.; *U.S. Public*, pg. 2175
OOO ALKALOID RUS—See Alkaloid A.D. Skopje; *Int'l*, pg. 330
OPTINOSE AS—See OptiNose, Inc.; *U.S. Public*, pg. 1609
OPTUMRX HOME DELIVERY OF OHIO, LLC—See UnitedHealth Group Incorporated; *U.S. Public*, pg. 2247
ORENDA INTERNATIONAL, LLC; *U.S. Private*, pg. 3040
ORGANOGENESIS SWITZERLAND GMBH—See Organogenesis Holdings Inc.; *U.S. Public*, pg. 1615
ORIGINAL ADDITIONS (BEAUTY PRODUCTS) LTD.—See Yellow Wood Partners LLC; *U.S. Private*, pg. 4587
OTC DIRECT LTD.—See Walgreens Boots Alliance, Inc.; *U.S. Public*, pg. 2322
OUTPUT PHARMA SERVICES GMBH—See Esperite N.V.; *Int'l*, pg. 2506
OXYFRESH WORLDWIDE, INC.—See Young Living Essential Oils, LC; *U.S. Private*, pg. 4593
PACHEM DISTRIBUTION INC.—See BRENNTAG SE; pg. 1149
PARAFLUID GMBH—See FUCHS SE; *Int'l*, pg. 2804
PARAMOUNT BEAUTY DISTRIBUTING ASSOCIATES INC.; *U.S. Private*, pg. 3092
PATHEON INC.—See Thermo Fisher Scientific Inc.; *U.S. Public*, pg. 2151
PAYLESS DRUG STORES INC.; *U.S. Private*, pg. 3117
PEKING TONGRENTANG (M) SDN. BHD—See Beijing Tong Ren Tang Chinese Medicine Company Limited; *Int'l*, pg. 959
PERFUME HOLDING ASIA PTE LTD—See BI-Invest Advisors S.A.; *Int'l*, pg. 1017
PERFUME HOLDING CORP.—See BI-Invest Advisors S.A.; *Int'l*, pg. 1017
PERFUME HOLDING LLC—See BI-Invest Advisors S.A.; *Int'l*, pg. 1017
PERFUME HOLDING SAS—See BI-Invest Advisors S.A.; *Int'l*, pg. 1017
PERLEN CONVERTING L.L.C.—See CPH Chemie + Papier Holding AG; *Int'l*, pg. 1824
PEVONIA INTERNATIONAL WEST—See Pevonia International, LLC; *U.S. Private*, pg. 3164
PFIZER GULF FZ-LLC—See Pfizer Inc.; *U.S. Public*, pg. 1681
PFIZER PHARMA PFE GMBH—See Pfizer Inc.; *U.S. Public*, pg. 1682
PFIZER PTE. LTD.—See Pfizer Inc.; *U.S. Public*, pg. 1682
PHARMA BELGIUM FLANDRIA—See McKesson Corporation; *U.S. Public*, pg. 1408
PHARMA BELGIUM SA—See McKesson Corporation; *U.S. Public*, pg. 1408
PHARMACY BUSINESS ASSOCIATION; *U.S. Private*, pg. 3165
PHARMACY RETAILING NZ LIMITED—See EBOS Group Limited; *Int'l*, pg. 2285
PHARMAFOODS PTY LTD—See Blackmores Limited; *Int'l*, pg. 1061
PHARMA INTERNATIONAL S.A.—See Abbott Laboratories; *U.S. Public*, pg. 20
PHARM-ALLERGAN GMBH—See AbbVie Inc.; *U.S. Public*, pg. 24
PHARMALOGIC HOLDINGS CORP.—See Webster Equity Partners, LLC; *U.S. Private*, pg. 4467
PHARMAPORTS LLC—See Chunghwa Chemical Synthesis & Biotech Co., Ltd.; *Int'l*, pg. 1598
PHARM ASSESS, INC.—See BlackRock, Inc.; *U.S. Public*, pg. 347
PHARMAVET MAROC S.A.—See Merck & Co., Inc.; *U.S. Public*, pg. 1420
PHARM PLUS ACQUISITION, INC.—See Cencora, Inc.; *U.S. Public*, pg. 467
PHAT PANDA LLC; *U.S. Private*, pg. 3166
PIERIS AUSTRALIA PTY LIMITED—See Pieris Pharmaceuticals, Inc.; *U.S. Public*, pg. 1690
PIERIS PHARMACEUTICALS GMBH—See Pieris Pharmaceuticals, Inc.; *U.S. Public*, pg. 1690
PINNACLE LIFE SCIENCE PRIVATE LIMITED—See Aarti Drugs Ltd.; *Int'l*, pg. 38
PK INTERNATIONAL INC.; *U.S. Private*, pg. 3193
PLASMACARE, INC.—See Grifols, S.A.; *Int'l*, pg. 3084
PLAYGIRL INDUSTRIES, INC.; *U.S. Private*, pg. 3212
PLF INTERNATIONAL LIMITED—See John Bean Technologies Corporation; *U.S. Public*, pg. 1192
PORTOLA ITALIA S.R.L.—See AstraZeneca PLC; *Int'l*, pg. 659
PORTOLA OSTERREICH GMBH—See AstraZeneca PLC; *Int'l*, pg. 659
PORTOLA PHARMACEUTICALS ESPANA S.L.—See AstraZeneca PLC; *Int'l*, pg. 659
PORTOLA PHARMA UK LTD.—See AstraZeneca PLC; *Int'l*, pg. 659
PORTOLA SCHWEIZ GMBH—See AstraZeneca PLC; *Int'l*, pg. 659
PRESCRIPTIVES INC.—See The Estee Lauder Companies Inc.; *U.S. Public*, pg. 2073
PRESTIUM PHARMA, INC.—See Viatris Inc.; *U.S. Public*, pg. 2294
PRIME CARE PHARMACY SERVICES, INC.—See Precision LTC Pharmacy; *U.S. Private*, pg. 3245
PRIME WELLNESS OF CONNECTICUT, LLC—See Acreage Holdings, Inc.; *U.S. Public*, pg. 36
PRIME WELLNESS OF PENNSYLVANIA, LLC—See Acreage Holdings, Inc.; *U.S. Public*, pg. 36
PRIMUS PHARMACEUTICALS, INC.; *U.S. Private*, pg. 3263
PRIVATE LABEL NUTRACEUTICALS, LLC.; *U.S. Private*, pg. 3268
PROCOS S.P.A.—See CBC Co., Ltd.; *Int'l*, pg. 1365
PROCTER & GAMBLE DISTRIBUTING (PHILIPPINES) INC.—See The Procter & Gamble Company; *U.S. Public*, pg. 2121
PROCTER & GAMBLE SERVICSE EESTI OU—See The Procter & Gamble Company; *U.S. Public*, pg. 2123
PRODUCTOS COSMETICOS, S.L.U.—See The Procter & Gamble Company; *U.S. Public*, pg. 2123
PRODUCTOS FARMACEUTICOS HEEL CHILE LTDA.—See Delton AG; *Int'l*, pg. 2021
PROMEDEV, LLC; *U.S. Private*, pg. 3282
PROMETIC BIOSCIENCES (USA), INC.—See Thomvest Ventures LLC; *U.S. Private*, pg. 4162
PRONDIL S.A.—See Merck & Co., Inc.; *U.S. Public*, pg. 1421
PROVET QLD PTY LTD.—See Clayton, Dubilier & Rice, LLC; *U.S. Private*, pg. 922
PROVET QLD PTY LTD.—See TPG Capital, L.P.; *U.S. Public*, pg. 2170
PRZEDSIEBIORSTWO FARMACEUTYCZNE JELFA SA—See Bausch Health Companies Inc.; *Int'l*, pg. 898
PT ARMOXINDO FARMA—See Bausch Health Companies Inc.; *Int'l*, pg. 897
PT BARENTZ—See Cinven Limited; *Int'l*, pg. 1611
PT FIRMENICH AROMATICS INDONESIA—See Firmenich International SA; *Int'l*, pg. 2681
PT. HISAMITSU PHARMA INDONESIA—See Hisamitsu Pharmaceutical Co., Inc.; *Int'l*, pg. 3406
PT INTRASARI RAYA—See Godrej & Boyce Mfg. Co. Ltd.; *Int'l*, pg. 3021
PURDUE PRODUCTS L.P.—See Purdue Pharma LP; *U.S. Private*, pg. 3305
PURE RATIOS INC.—See 4Front Ventures Corp.; *U.S. Public*, pg. 9
PUSH, INC.; *U.S. Private*, pg. 3307
QK HEALTHCARE, INC.—See Quality King Distributors Inc.; *U.S. Private*, pg. 3319
Q-MED INTERNATIONAL TRADING (SHANGHAI) LTD—See Abu Dhabi Investment Authority; *Int'l*, pg. 71
Q-MED INTERNATIONAL TRADING (SHANGHAI) LTD—See EQT Corporation; *U.S. Public*, pg. 785
Q-MED S.A.R.L.—See Abu Dhabi Investment Authority; *Int'l*, pg. 72
Q-MED S.A.R.L.—See EQT Corporation; *U.S. Public*, pg. 785
Q-MED SPAIN S.L.—See Abu Dhabi Investment Authority; *Int'l*, pg. 72
Q-MED SPAIN S.L.—See EQT Corporation; *U.S. Public*, pg. 785
QUALITY KING DISTRIBUTORS INC.; *U.S. Private*, pg. 3319
QUALITY KING FRAGRANCE, INC.—See Perfumania Holdings, Inc.; *U.S. Private*, pg. 3150
QUASFAR M&F S.A.—See Eurofins Scientific S.E.; *Int'l*, pg. 2551
QUIDEL IRELAND LIMITED—See QuidelOrtho Corporation; *U.S. Public*, pg. 1757
QUINTILES ENTERPRISE MANAGEMENT (SHANGHAI) CO. LTD.—See IQVIA Holdings Inc.; *U.S. Public*, pg. 1170
QUINTILES HONG KONG LIMITED—See IQVIA Holdings Inc.; *U.S. Public*, pg. 1170
RAPID DIAGNOSTICS, INC.—See Bausch Health Companies Inc.; *Int'l*, pg. 898
RAY'S FOOD PLACE; *U.S. Private*, pg. 3359
REDDY HOLDING GMBH—See Dr. Reddy's Laboratories Limited; *Int'l*, pg. 2195
REDDY PHARMA IBERIA SA—See Dr. Reddy's Laboratories Limited; *Int'l*, pg. 2195
RED HALL PHARMACY LIMITED—See Bestway (Holdings) Limited; *Int'l*, pg. 1001
REGA FARMA-PROMOCAO DE PRODUTOS FARMACEUTICOS, S.A—See Angelini ACRAF S.p.A.; *Int'l*, pg. 460
REGENERON IRELAND—See Regeneron Pharmaceuticals, Inc.; *U.S. Public*, pg. 1775
RENAPHARMA-VIFOR AB—See CSL Limited; *Int'l*, pg. 1866
RESMED CZ S.R.O.—See ResMed Inc.; *U.S. Public*, pg. 1790
RESMED SLEEP SOLUTIONS LIMITED—See ResMed Inc.; *U.S. Public*, pg. 1791
RESPIRATORY DISTRIBUTORS INC.; *U.S. Private*, pg. 3407
REVIVA LABS, INC.—See SenDayCo, LLC; *U.S. Private*, pg. 3605
REVLON (PUERTO RICO), INC.—See MacAndrews & Forbes Incorporated; *U.S. Private*, pg. 2533
REXALL SUNDOWN, INC.—See KKR & Co. Inc.; *U.S. Public*, pg. 1264
RITA-ANN DISTRIBUTORS—See Sun Capital Partners, Inc.; *U.S. Private*, pg. 3860
RITA CORPORATION; *U.S. Private*, pg. 3441
R.I.T.A INTERNATIONAL INC.—See RITA Corporation; *U.S. Private*, pg. 3441
ROSS ORGANIC SPECIALTY SALES, INC.—See EQT AB; *Int'l*, pg. 2469
ROYAL SUPPLY CO; *U.S. Private*, pg. 3493
RUSK, INC.—See American Securities LLC; *U.S. Private*, pg. 248
RYUYAKU CO., LTD.—See Alfresa Holdings Corporation; *Int'l*, pg. 317
SABINSA CORPORATION; *U.S. Private*, pg. 3521
SALIX PHARMACEUTICALS, INC.—See Bausch Health Companies Inc.; *Int'l*, pg. 898
SANDSRX, LLC; *U.S. Private*, pg. 3545
SANGAM LABORATORIES LTD—See Camlin Fine Sciences Ltd.; *Int'l*, pg. 1273
SANNOVA CO., LTD.—See Eisai Co., Ltd.; *Int'l*, pg. 2335
SANTANA S.A. DROGARIA FARMACIAS—See Brazil Pharma S.A.; *Int'l*, pg. 1143
SARANTICS CZECH REPUBLIC SRO—See Gr. Sarantis S.A.; *Int'l*, pg. 3047
SARANTIS SERBIA LTD—See Gr. Sarantis S.A.; *Int'l*, pg. 3047
SAS AND COMPANY LIMITED—See MacAndrews & Forbes Incorporated; *U.S. Private*, pg. 2533
SAVEWAY COMPOUNDING PHARMACY, LLC—See Myonex, LLC; *U.S. Private*, pg. 2825
SCA PHARMACEUTICALS, LLC—See Excellere Capital Management LLC; *U.S. Private*, pg. 1446
SCA PHARMACEUTICALS, LLC—See The Vistria Group, LP; *U.S. Private*, pg. 4132
S.C. CROMA ROMANIA SRL—See Bausch Health Companies Inc.; *Int'l*, pg. 898
SCHULKE FRANCE SARL—See EQT AB; *Int'l*, pg. 2479
SCHULKE POLSKA SP.Z O.O.—See EQT AB; *Int'l*, pg. 2479
SCHWABE CZECH REPUBLIC S.R.O.—See Dr. Willmar Schwabe GmbH & Co. KG; *Int'l*, pg. 2195
SCHWABE HUNGARY KFT—See Dr. Willmar Schwabe GmbH & Co. KG; *Int'l*, pg. 2195
SCHWABE NORTH AMERICA, INC.—See Dr. Willmar Schwabe GmbH & Co. KG; *Int'l*, pg. 2195
SCHWABE PHARMA AG—See Dr. Willmar Schwabe GmbH & Co. KG; *Int'l*, pg. 2195
SCHWABE PHARMA ASIA PACIFIC PTE. LTD.—See Dr. Willmar Schwabe GmbH & Co. KG; *Int'l*, pg. 2196
SCHWABE PHARMA (UK) LTD.—See Dr. Willmar Schwabe GmbH & Co. KG; *Int'l*, pg. 2195
SCHWABE SLOVAKIA S.R.O.—See Dr. Willmar Schwabe GmbH & Co. KG; *Int'l*, pg. 2196
S.C. JOHNSON AND SON KENYA LIMITED—See Johnson & Johnson; *U.S. Public*, pg. 1200
SCS BOEHRINGER INGELHEIM COMM. V.—See C.H. Boehringer Sohn AG & Co. KG; *Int'l*, pg. 1243
SEBASTIAN EUROPE GMBH—See The Procter & Gamble Company; *U.S. Public*, pg. 2123
SEPTODONT INC.; *U.S. Private*, pg. 3611
SEQIRUS—See CSL Limited; *Int'l*, pg. 1866
SEREX—See Walgreens Boots Alliance, Inc.; *U.S. Public*, pg. 2322
THE SERVICE COMPANY LIMITED—See Godfreys Group Limited; *Int'l*, pg. 3020
SESSIONS SPECIALTY COMPANY; *U.S. Private*, pg. 3617
SEXY HAIR CONCEPTS, LLC—See Henkel AG & Co. KGaA; *Int'l*, pg. 3353
SHAKLEE CORPORATION—See Activated Holdings LLC; *U.S. Private*, pg. 68
SHAKLEE CORPORATION—See Ripplewood Holdings LLC; *U.S. Private*, pg. 3439
SHAKLEE U.S.—See Activated Holdings LLC; *U.S. Private*, pg. 69
SHAKLEE U.S.—See Ripplewood Holdings LLC; *U.S. Private*, pg. 3440
SHAVEKIT LIMITED—See Edgewell Personal Care Company; *U.S. Public*, pg. 718
SHIKOKU ALFRESA CORPORATION—See Alfresa Holdings Corporation; *Int'l*, pg. 317
SHIN ENTERPRISES INC.; *U.S. Private*, pg. 3637
SIA GLAXOSMITHKLINE LATVIA—See GSK plc; *Int'l*, pg. 3149
SIA THE HIMALAYA DRUG COMPANY—See Himalaya

424210 — DRUGS AND DRUGGISTS...

Drug Company; *Int'l*, pg. 3396
SIBMEDICA SRL—See Farmaceutica REMEDIA S.A.; *Int'l*, pg. 2619
SICHUAN SUNHEAL PHARMACEUTICAL CO., LTD.—See Chengdu Easton Biopharmaceuticals Co., Ltd.; *Int'l*, pg. 1467
SIERRA HOME MEDICAL PRODUCTS, INC.—See UnitedHealth Group Incorporated; *U.S. Public*, pg. 2250
SIGNET EXCIPIENTS PRIVATE LTD.—See IMCD N.V.; *Int'l*, pg. 3622
SINCLAIR PHARMA FRANCE—See Huadong Medicine Co., Ltd.; *Int'l*, pg. 3511
SINCLAIR PHARMA GMBH—See Huadong Medicine Co., Ltd.; *Int'l*, pg. 3511
SINOPHARM MEDICINE HOLDING CO., LTD.—See China National Pharmaceutical Group Corporation; *Int'l*, pg. 1534
SK3 GROUP, INC.; *U.S. Private*, pg. 3680
SKILLS IN HEALTHCARE GMBH DEUTSCHLAND—See Walgreens Boots Alliance, Inc.; *U.S. Public*, pg. 2323
SKINOURISHMENT, LLC—See Clarus Corporation; *U.S. Public*, pg. 508
SKYPHARM, S.A.—See COSMOS HEALTH INC.; *U.S. Public*, pg. 585
SMITH DRUG COMPANY—See J.M. Smith Corporation; *U.S. Private*, pg. 2169
SMITH MEDICAL PARTNERS, LLC—See H.D. Smith Wholesale Drug Co. Inc.; *U.S. Private*, pg. 1825
SOMACEUTICALS, INC.—See GlobeStar Therapeutics Corporation; *U.S. Public*, pg. 946
SOMERSET PHARMACEUTICALS INC.—See Viatris Inc.; *U.S. Public*, pg. 2294
SOMODY INC.—See Sun Capital Partners, Inc.; *U.S. Private*, pg. 3861
SONDERBORG VAERKTOJSFABRIK A/S—See Flex Ltd.; *Int'l*, pg. 2704
SOURCEONE GLOBAL PARTNERS LLC; *U.S. Private*, pg. 3718
SOUTH YARRA PHARMA PTY. LTD.—See Apiam Animal Health Limited; *Int'l*, pg. 515
SPALY BIOQUIMICA, S.A.—See Eli Lilly & Company; *U.S. Public*, pg. 732
SRL, INC. - AKITA SALES DIVISION—See H.U. Group Holdings, Inc.; *Int'l*, pg. 3197
SRL, INC. - AOMORI SALES DIVISION—See H.U. Group Holdings, Inc.; *Int'l*, pg. 3197
SRL, INC. - ASAHIKAWA SALES DIVISION—See H.U. Group Holdings, Inc.; *Int'l*, pg. 3197
SRL, INC. - ATSUGI SALES DIVISION I—See H.U. Group Holdings, Inc.; *Int'l*, pg. 3197
SRL, INC. - CHIBA II SALES DIVISION—See H.U. Group Holdings, Inc.; *Int'l*, pg. 3197
SRL, INC. - CHIBA I SALES DIVISION—See H.U. Group Holdings, Inc.; *Int'l*, pg. 3197
SRL, INC. - FUKUI SALES DIVISION—See H.U. Group Holdings, Inc.; *Int'l*, pg. 3197
SRL, INC. - FUKUOKA NISHI SALES DIVISION—See H.U. Group Holdings, Inc.; *Int'l*, pg. 3197
SRL, INC. - FUKUSHIMA CHUO SALES DIVISION—See H.U. Group Holdings, Inc.; *Int'l*, pg. 3197
SRL, INC. - GIFU SALES DIVISION—See H.U. Group Holdings, Inc.; *Int'l*, pg. 3197
SRL, INC. - GUNMA SALES DIVISION II—See H.U. Group Holdings, Inc.; *Int'l*, pg. 3197
SRL, INC. - HACHIOJI SALES DIVISION I—See H.U. Group Holdings, Inc.; *Int'l*, pg. 3197
SRL, INC. - HAKODATE SALES DIVISION—See H.U. Group Holdings, Inc.; *Int'l*, pg. 3197
SRL, INC. - HAMAMATSU SALES DIVISION—See H.U. Group Holdings, Inc.; *Int'l*, pg. 3197
SRL, INC. - HIMEJI SALES DIVISION—See H.U. Group Holdings, Inc.; *Int'l*, pg. 3197
SRL, INC. - HIROSHIMA SALES DIVISION—See H.U. Group Holdings, Inc.; *Int'l*, pg. 3197
SRL, INC. - IBARAKI SALES DIVISION II—See H.U. Group Holdings, Inc.; *Int'l*, pg. 3197
SRL, INC. - KAGOSHIMA SALES DIVISION—See H.U. Group Holdings, Inc.; *Int'l*, pg. 3197
SRL, INC. - KANAZAWA SALES DIVISION—See H.U. Group Holdings, Inc.; *Int'l*, pg. 3197
SRL, INC. - KENKO SALES DIVISION I—See H.U. Group Holdings, Inc.; *Int'l*, pg. 3197
SRL, INC. - KENKO SALES DIVISION—See H.U. Group Holdings, Inc.; *Int'l*, pg. 3197
SRL, INC. - KITA KANTO SALES DIVISION II—See H.U. Group Holdings, Inc.; *Int'l*, pg. 3197
SRL, INC. - KITAKYUSHU SALES DIVISION—See H.U. Group Holdings, Inc.; *Int'l*, pg. 3197
SRL, INC. - KOCHI SALES DIVISION—See H.U. Group Holdings, Inc.; *Int'l*, pg. 3198
SRL, INC. - KOFU SALES DIVISION II—See H.U. Group Holdings, Inc.; *Int'l*, pg. 3198
SRL, INC. - KUMAMOTO SALES DIVISION—See H.U. Group Holdings, Inc.; *Int'l*, pg. 3198
SRL, INC. - KURUME SALES DIVISION VII—See H.U. Group Holdings, Inc.; *Int'l*, pg. 3198
SRL, INC. - KYOTO SALES DIVISION—See H.U. Group Holdings, Inc.; *Int'l*, pg. 3198

SRL, INC. - MATSUYAMA SALES DIVISION—See H.U. Group Holdings, Inc.; *Int'l*, pg. 3198
SRL, INC. - MIE SALES DIVISION—See H.U. Group Holdings, Inc.; *Int'l*, pg. 3198
SRL, INC. - MIYAZAKI SALES DIVISION—See H.U. Group Holdings, Inc.; *Int'l*, pg. 3198
SRL, INC. - MORIOKA SALES DIVISION—See H.U. Group Holdings, Inc.; *Int'l*, pg. 3198
SRL, INC. - NAGANO SALES DIVISION II—See H.U. Group Holdings, Inc.; *Int'l*, pg. 3198
SRL, INC. - NAGASAKI SALES DIVISION—See H.U. Group Holdings, Inc.; *Int'l*, pg. 3198
SRL, INC. - NAGOYA I SALES DIVISION—See H.U. Group Holdings, Inc.; *Int'l*, pg. 3198
SRL, INC. - NARA SALES DIVISION—See H.U. Group Holdings, Inc.; *Int'l*, pg. 3198
SRL, INC. - NIIGATA SALES DIVISION II—See H.U. Group Holdings, Inc.; *Int'l*, pg. 3198
SRL, INC. - NOTO SALES DIVISION—See H.U. Group Holdings, Inc.; *Int'l*, pg. 3198
SRL, INC. - OITA SALES DIVISION—See H.U. Group Holdings, Inc.; *Int'l*, pg. 3198
SRL, INC. - OKAYAMA SALES DIVISION—See H.U. Group Holdings, Inc.; *Int'l*, pg. 3198
SRL, INC. - OKAZAKI SALES DIVISION—See H.U. Group Holdings, Inc.; *Int'l*, pg. 3198
SRL, INC. - OKINAWA SALES DIVISION VII—See H.U. Group Holdings, Inc.; *Int'l*, pg. 3198
SRL, INC. - OSAKA CHUO SALES DIVISION—See H.U. Group Holdings, Inc.; *Int'l*, pg. 3198
SRL, INC. - OSAKA KITA SALES DIVISION—See H.U. Group Holdings, Inc.; *Int'l*, pg. 3198
SRL, INC. - OSAKA MINAMI SALES DIVISION—See H.U. Group Holdings, Inc.; *Int'l*, pg. 3198
SRL, INC. - SAGA SALES DIVISION—See H.U. Group Holdings, Inc.; *Int'l*, pg. 3198
SRL, INC. - SAITAMA SALES DIVISION—See H.U. Group Holdings, Inc.; *Int'l*, pg. 3198
SRL, INC. - SAPPORO SALES DIVISION—See H.U. Group Holdings, Inc.; *Int'l*, pg. 3198
SRL, INC. - SASEBO SALES DIVISION—See H.U. Group Holdings, Inc.; *Int'l*, pg. 3198
SRL, INC. - SENDAI SALES DIVISION—See H.U. Group Holdings, Inc.; *Int'l*, pg. 3198
SRL, INC. - SHIGA SALES DIVISION—See H.U. Group Holdings, Inc.; *Int'l*, pg. 3198
SRL, INC. - SHIZUOKA SALES DIVISION—See H.U. Group Holdings, Inc.; *Int'l*, pg. 3198
SRL, INC. - TAKAMATSU SALES DIVISION—See H.U. Group Holdings, Inc.; *Int'l*, pg. 3198
SRL, INC. - TOKUSHIMA SALES DIVISION—See H.U. Group Holdings, Inc.; *Int'l*, pg. 3198
SRL, INC. - TOKYO III SALES DIVISION—See H.U. Group Holdings, Inc.; *Int'l*, pg. 3198
SRL, INC. - TOKYO II SALES DIVISION—See H.U. Group Holdings, Inc.; *Int'l*, pg. 3198
SRL, INC. - TOKYO I SALES DIVISION—See H.U. Group Holdings, Inc.; *Int'l*, pg. 3198
SRL, INC. - TOKYO IV SALES DIVISION—See H.U. Group Holdings, Inc.; *Int'l*, pg. 3198
SRL, INC. - TOKYO V SALES DIVISION—See H.U. Group Holdings, Inc.; *Int'l*, pg. 3198
SRL, INC. - TOYAMA SALES DIVISION VII—See H.U. Group Holdings, Inc.; *Int'l*, pg. 3198
SRL, INC. - TSUKUBA SALES DIVISION II—See H.U. Group Holdings, Inc.; *Int'l*, pg. 3198
SRL, INC. - UEDA SALES DIVISION II—See H.U. Group Holdings, Inc.; *Int'l*, pg. 3198
SRL, INC. - UTSUNOMIYA SALES DIVISION II—See H.U. Group Holdings, Inc.; *Int'l*, pg. 3199
SRL, INC. - WAKAYAMA SALES DIVISION—See H.U. Group Holdings, Inc.; *Int'l*, pg. 3199
SRL, INC. - YAMAGATA SALES DIVISION—See H.U. Group Holdings, Inc.; *Int'l*, pg. 3199
SRL, INC. - YOKOHAMA II SALES DIVISION—See H.U. Group Holdings, Inc.; *Int'l*, pg. 3199
SRL, INC. - YOKOHAMA I SALES DIVISION—See H.U. Group Holdings, Inc.; *Int'l*, pg. 3199
SRL, INC. - YOKOSUKA SALES DIVISION I—See H.U. Group Holdings, Inc.; *Int'l*, pg. 3199
SSP CO. LTD.—See C.H. Boehringer Sohn AG & Co. KG; *Int'l*, pg. 1243
STALLERGENES, INC.—See B-FLEXION Group Holdings SA; *Int'l*, pg. 785
STARTEK HEALTH SERVICES, INC.—See StarTek, Inc.; *U.S. Private*, pg. 3788
STATKING CONSULTING, INC.—See Genesis Biotechnology Group, LLC; *U.S. Private*, pg. 1669
STD PHARMACEUTICAL PRODUCTS LIMITED—See Merit Medical Systems, Inc.; *U.S. Public*, pg. 1425
STEADYMED THERAPEUTICS, INC.—See United Therapeutics Corporation; *U.S. Public*, pg. 2238
SUMMIT THERAPEUTICS INC.; *U.S. Public*, pg. 1961
SUPERMARKET DISTRIBUTORS OF AMERICA; *U.S. Private*, pg. 3881
SUPERNAIL—See American International Industries Company; *U.S. Private*, pg. 238

CORPORATE AFFILIATIONS

SUPPLEMENT HUNT, INC.—See Aytu BioPharma, Inc.; *U.S. Public*, pg. 257
SUPRE INC.; *U.S. Private*, pg. 3882
SURGICAL SITE SOLUTIONS, INC.—See Becton, Dickinson & Company; *U.S. Public*, pg. 292
SURPLUS DIABETIC, INC.—See ADDvise Group AB; *Int'l*, pg. 136
SYNERGY CHC CORP.; *U.S. Public*, pg. 1970
TALBOOM B.V.—See Clarins S.A.; *Int'l*, pg. 1649
TESARO BIO SPAIN, S.L.U.—See GSK plc; *Int'l*, pg. 3149
TFB, INC—See H.U. Group Holdings, Inc.; *Int'l*, pg. 3196
THAMES VALLEY APOTHECARY, LLC—See Acreage Holdings, Inc.; *U.S. Public*, pg. 36
THRIFTY DRUG STORES, INC.; *U.S. Private*, pg. 4164
TM S.R.L.—See Apollo Global Management, Inc.; *U.S. Public*, pg. 162
TNH SPECIALTY PHARMACY II; *U.S. Private*, pg. 4180
TOBIRA THERAPEUTICS, INC.—See AbbVie Inc.; *U.S. Public*, pg. 23
TOLMAR PHARMACEUTICALS, INC.—See TOLMAR, Inc.; *U.S. Private*, pg. 4182
TOP RX INC.; *U.S. Private*, pg. 4186
TOV ALGOL CHEMICALS—See Algol Oy; *Int'l*, pg. 318
TOV MARY KAY (UKRAINE) LTD—See Mary Kay Holding Corporation; *U.S. Private*, pg. 2599
TOWNLEY INC.; *U.S. Private*, pg. 4198
TRIGLORY (H.K.) LIMITED—See Heng Tai Consumables Group Limited; *Int'l*, pg. 3345
TRI-K INDUSTRIES, INC.—See Galaxy Surfactants Limited; *Int'l*, pg. 2872
TRI-K INDUSTRIES - PROTEINS DIV—See Galaxy Surfactants Limited; *Int'l*, pg. 2872
TRISTRATA INC.; *U.S. Private*, pg. 4238
TRUE COLORS STUDIO; *U.S. Private*, pg. 4247
TULIP DRUG DISPENSARY CO., LTD.—See FALCO Holdings Co., Ltd.; *Int'l*, pg. 2610
TWINCARE GROUP—See TRG Management LP; *U.S. Private*, pg. 4220
UAB ABBOTT MEDICAL LITHUANIA—See Abbott Laboratories; *U.S. Public*, pg. 21
UAB KRUZAS NORDIC COSMETICS DISTRIBUTION—See Berner Oy; *Int'l*, pg. 988
UCYCLYD PHARMA, INC.—See Bausch Health Companies Inc.; *Int'l*, pg. 898
UNILFARMA-UNIAO INTERNACIONAL DE LABORATORIOS FARMACEUTICOS, LDA.—See C.H. Boehringer Sohn AG & Co. KG; *Int'l*, pg. 1242
UNIONE FARMACEUTICA DISTRIBUZIONE SA—See CSL Limited; *Int'l*, pg. 1866
UNIPEX BENELUX NV—See Groupe Unipex SAS; *Int'l*, pg. 3112
UNIPEX SOLUTIONS FRANCE S.A.S.—See Groupe Unipex SAS; *Int'l*, pg. 3112
UNITED DRUG WHOLESALE LIMITED—See McKesson Corporation; *U.S. Public*, pg. 1409
UNITED PHARMACEUTICAL DISTRIBUTORS (PROPRIETARY) LIMITED—See Clicks Group Limited; *Int'l*, pg. 1658
UNIVERSAL PHARMACEUTICAL MEDICAL SUPPLY CO, INC.—See Z Capital Group, LLC; *U.S. Private*, pg. 4595
US BIOSERVICES CORPORATION—See Cencora, Inc.; *U.S. Public*, pg. 467
UTERON PHARMA SPRL—See AbbVie Inc.; *U.S. Public*, pg. 23
VALEANT LLC—See Bausch Health Companies Inc.; *Int'l*, pg. 898
VALUE DRUG COMPANY; *U.S. Private*, pg. 4337
VAYA PHARMA, INC.—See International Flavors & Fragrances Inc.; *U.S. Public*, pg. 1154
VERTEX PHARMACEUTICALS (AUSTRALIA) PTY. LTD.—See Vertex Pharmaceuticals Incorporated; *U.S. Public*, pg. 2287
VERTEX PHARMACEUTICALS GMBH—See Vertex Pharmaceuticals Incorporated; *U.S. Public*, pg. 2287
VERTEX PHARMACEUTICALS (ITALY) S.R.L.—See Vertex Pharmaceuticals Incorporated; *U.S. Public*, pg. 2287
VERTEX PHARMACEUTICALS (NETHERLANDS) B.V.—See Vertex Pharmaceuticals Incorporated; *U.S. Public*, pg. 2287
VERTEX PHARMACEUTICALS (SPAIN), S.L.—See Vertex Pharmaceuticals Incorporated; *U.S. Public*, pg. 2287
VERTICAL PHARMACEUTICALS, LLC—See RVL Pharmaceuticals plc; *U.S. Public*, pg. 1827
VETERINARY & POULTRY SUPPLY; *U.S. Private*, pg. 4374
VICTOR MEDICAL CO.; *U.S. Private*, pg. 4377
VIFOR PHARMA NEDERLAND B.V.—See CSL Limited; *Int'l*, pg. 1867
VIIVHIV HEALTHCARE UNIPESSOAL LDA—See GSK plc; *Int'l*, pg. 3150
VITACOST.COM, INC.—See The Kroger Co.; *U.S. Public*, pg. 2109
VITAMEDICA, INC.—See Upexi, Inc.; *U.S. Public*, pg. 2264
VITAMIN FACTORY—See Integrated Biopharma, Inc.; *U.S. Public*, pg. 1136
VITASCO GMBH—See Walgreens Boots Alliance, Inc.; *U.S. Public*, pg. 2324
VRX PHARMACY, LLC—See Centene Corporation; *U.S. Public*, pg. 470

N.A.I.C.S. INDEX

VSM BELGIUM BVBA—See Dr. Willmar Schwabe GmbH & Co. KG; *Int'l*, pg. 2196
VSM GENEESMIDDELEN BV—See Dr. Willmar Schwabe GmbH & Co. KG; *Int'l*, pg. 2196
VWR INTERNATIONAL BVBA—See Avantor, Inc.; *U.S. Public*, pg. 242
VWR INTERNATIONAL GMBH—See Avantor, Inc.; *U.S. Public*, pg. 241
VWR INTERNATIONAL S.A.S.—See Avantor, Inc.; *U.S. Public*, pg. 242
WALGREENS OF NORTH CAROLINA, INC.—See Walgreens Boots Alliance, Inc.; *U.S. Public*, pg. 2324
WARNER CHILCOTT NEDERLAND B.V—See AbbVie Inc.; *U.S. Public*, pg. 24
WARNER CHILCOTT PHARMACEUTICALS S.A.R.L.—See AbbVie Inc.; *U.S. Public*, pg. 24
WATER-JEL TECHNOLOGIES, LLC—See Water Street Healthcare Partners, LLC; *U.S. Private*, pg. 4452
WEBER & JUDD PHARMACY; *U.S. Private*, pg. 4465
WELLDYNERX, LLC—See The Carlyle Group Inc.; *U.S. Public*, pg. 2057
WELL-MED GLOBAL LLC—See Vivakor, Inc.; *U.S. Public*, pg. 2307
THE WEST COMPANY ITALIA S.R.L.—See West Pharmaceutical Services, Inc.; *U.S. Public*, pg. 934
WESTERN PHARMACEUTICALS S.A.—See Abbott Laboratories; *U.S. Public*, pg. 21
WHAWON PHARM CO., LTD.—See IMCD N.V.; *Int'l*, pg. 3623
WHITESBURG ARH HOSPITAL; *U.S. Private*, pg. 4512
WILLIAMS MEDICAL SUPPLIES LIMITED—See DCC plc; *Int'l*, pg. 1991
WILSEY BENNETT REAL ESTATE DIVISION—See Wilsey Bennett Company; *U.S. Private*, pg. 4529
WINCONCEPT AG—See CSL Limited; *Int'l*, pg. 1867
WORLDBRANDS EUROPE B.V.—See B&S Group S.A.; *Int'l*, pg. 784
W. SPITZNER ARZNEIMITTELFABRIK GMBH—See Dr. Willmar Schwabe GmbH & Co. KG; *Int'l*, pg. 2196
XEPA-SOUL PATTINSON (S) PTE. LTD.—See Apex Healthcare Berhad; *Int'l*, pg. 511
XIZANG RUNHE PHARMACEUTICAL CO., LTD.—See Chengdu Easton Biopharmaceuticals Co., Ltd.; *Int'l*, pg. 1467
ZAO MARY KAY—See Mary Kay Holding Corporation; *U.S. Private*, pg. 2599

424310 — PIECE GOODS, NOTIONS, AND OTHER DRY GOODS MERCHANT WHOLESALERS

A&E BANGLADESH LTD.—See Platinum Equity, LLC; *U.S. Private*, pg. 3201
A.E. NATHAN COMPANY INC.; *U.S. Private*, pg. 25
AGC ASIA PACIFIC (INDIA) PVT. LTD.—See AGC Inc.; *Int'l*, pg. 203
AGC AUTOMOTIVE (CHINA) CO., LTD.—See AGC Inc.; *Int'l*, pg. 203
ALPARGATAS FRANCE S.A.R.L.—See Cambuhy Investimentos Ltda.; *Int'l*, pg. 1270
ALPARGATAS ITALY S.R.L.—See Cambuhy Investimentos Ltda.; *Int'l*, pg. 1270
ALPARGATAS PORTUGAL LIMITED—See Cambuhy Investimentos Ltda.; *Int'l*, pg. 1270
ALPARGATAS SPAIN S.L.U.—See Cambuhy Investimentos Ltda.; *Int'l*, pg. 1270
ALPARGATAS UK LTD—See Cambuhy Investimentos Ltda.; *Int'l*, pg. 1270
ALPARGATAS USA INC.—See Cambuhy Investimentos Ltda.; *Int'l*, pg. 1270
AMERICAN DAWN INC.; *U.S. Private*, pg. 230
ANUKARAN COMMERCIAL ENTERPRISES LIMITED; *Int'l*, pg. 485
ANZEA TEXTILES, INC.—See C F Stinson, Inc.; *U.S. Private*, pg. 701
ARCHITEX INTERNATIONAL; *U.S. Private*, pg. 311
ARIHANT MULTI COMMERCIAL LIMITED; *Int'l*, pg. 564
ASAHI KASEI TRADING CO., LTD.—See Asahi Kasei Corporation; *Int'l*, pg. 596
ATHARV ENTERPRISES LIMITED; *Int'l*, pg. 669
AUTHENTIC HOLDINGS, INC.; *U.S. Public*, pg. 228
AZEARTH CORPORATION; *Int'l*, pg. 778
BARROW INDUSTRIES INCORPORATED; *U.S. Private*, pg. 481
BAUM TEXTILE MILLS INC.; *U.S. Private*, pg. 490
BDK HOLDINGS, INC.; *U.S. Private*, pg. 500
BEAULIEU INTERNATIONAL GROUP NV BERRY YARNS PLANT—See Beaulieu International Group NV; *Int'l*, pg. 934
BEAULIEU INTERNATIONAL GROUP NV WEIHAI PLANT—See Beaulieu International Group NV; *Int'l*, pg. 934
BEAULIEU INTERNATIONAL GROUP NV WIELSBEKE PLANT—See Beaulieu International Group NV; *Int'l*, pg. 934
BEAULIEU TECHNICAL TEXTILES NV—See Beaulieu International Group NV; *Int'l*, pg. 934

BITEKS IPLIK A.S.—See Bilici Yatirim Sanayi ve Ticaret A.S.; *Int'l*, pg. 1030
BOB BARKER COMPANY, INC.; *U.S. Private*, pg. 603
BORGO 21 SA—See Giorgio Armani S.p.A.; *Int'l*, pg. 2978
BREWER SEWING SUPPLIES CO; *U.S. Private*, pg. 647
BRUNSCHWIG & FILS, INC.—See Kravet, Inc.; *U.S. Private*, pg. 2350
CALLISTA INDUSTRIES LTD.; *Int'l*, pg. 1265
CAMIRA FABRICS GMBH—See Camira Fabrics Ltd.; *Int'l*, pg. 1273
CAMIRA GROUP, INC—See Camira Fabrics Ltd.; *Int'l*, pg. 1273
CARIBBEAN ROOF TILE COMPANY LIMITED—See ANSA McAL Limited; *Int'l*, pg. 477
CARNEGIE FABRICS, LLC—See Calera Capital Management, Inc.; *U.S. Private*, pg. 717
CAROLACE INDUSTRIES INC.—See Carolace Embroidery Co., Inc.; *U.S. Private*, pg. 767
CAROLYN FABRICS INC.; *U.S. Private*, pg. 769
CARR TEXTILE CORPORATION; *U.S. Private*, pg. 771
CATHAY COMPOSITES LTD—See Cathay Investments Limited; *Int'l*, pg. 1360
CCL LABEL A/S—See CCL Industries Inc.; *Int'l*, pg. 1368
CCL LABEL S.R.L.—See CCL Industries Inc.; *Int'l*, pg. 1368
C F STINSON, INC.; *U.S. Private*, pg. 701
CGPC AMERICA CORPORATION—See China General Plastics Corporation; *Int'l*, pg. 1504
CHAMBERS FABRICS INC.; *U.S. Private*, pg. 846
CHARLES SAMELSON, INC.; *U.S. Private*, pg. 853
CHEM-DRY UK LIMITED—See Chem-Dry Franchising Limited; *Int'l*, pg. 1460
CHORI AMERICA, INC.—See Chori Co., Ltd.; *Int'l*, pg. 1583
CHORI (DALIAN) COMMERCIAL IMPORT EXPORT CO., LTD.—See Chori Co., Ltd.; *Int'l*, pg. 1583
CMI ENTERPRISES INC.; *U.S. Private*, pg. 951
COAST PAD & TRIM CORP.; *U.S. Private*, pg. 954
COATS CRAFTS UK—See Coats Group plc; *Int'l*, pg. 1682
COLEFAX & FOWLER GMBH—See Colefax Group PLC; *Int'l*, pg. 1697
COLEMAN KOREA CO., LTD.—See Newell Brands Inc.; *U.S. Public*, pg. 1513
COMFORT CARE—See Lew Jan Textile Corp.; *U.S. Private*, pg. 2437
CONTINENTAL WORSTEDS INC.; *U.S. Private*, pg. 1031
CORAGGIO DESIGN, INC.; *U.S. Private*, pg. 1046
CORPORATE IMAGING CONCEPTS, INC—See W.R. Berkley Corporation; *U.S. Public*, pg. 2317
COSMOPOLITAN TRADING CORP.; *U.S. Private*, pg. 1062
COWTAN & TOUT, INC.—See Colefax Group PLC; *Int'l*, pg. 1697
CRESTMONT FABRICS, LTD.; *U.S. Private*, pg. 1097
CROWN COMMERCIAL FRANCE SAS—See Crown Holdings, Inc.; *U.S. Public*, pg. 597
CROWN COMMERCIAL POLSKA SP. Z.O.O.—See Crown Holdings, Inc.; *U.S. Public*, pg. 598
DELTA APPAREL, INC.; *U.S. Public*, pg. 652
DELTA INDUSTRIAL RESOURCES LIMITED; *Int'l*, pg. 2019
DESIGNTEX GROUP INC.—See Steelcase Inc.; *U.S. Public*, pg. 1944
DIAGRAPH CORPORATION SDN. BHD—See Illinois Tool Works Inc.; *U.S. Public*, pg. 1102
DIAGRAPH MEXICO, S.A. DE C.V.—See Illinois Tool Works Inc.; *U.S. Public*, pg. 1102
DICKSON EXPRESS COMPANY LIMITED—See Dickson Concepts (International) Limited; *Int'l*, pg. 2112
DIVINUS FABRICS LIMITED; *Int'l*, pg. 2137
DL HOLDINGS GROUP LIMITED; *Int'l*, pg. 2140
DOLCE & GABBANA DO BRASIL COMERICO, IMPORTACAO E PARTICIPACOES LTDA.—See Dolce & Gabbana S.R.L.; *Int'l*, pg. 2157
DOLCE & GABBANA HONG KONG LTD—See Dolce & Gabbana S.R.L.; *Int'l*, pg. 2157
DOLCE & GABBANA JAPAN K.K.—See Dolce & Gabbana S.R.L.; *Int'l*, pg. 2157
DOLCE & GABBANA SHANGHAI CO., LTD.—See Dolce & Gabbana S.R.L.; *Int'l*, pg. 2157
DOLCE & GABBANA S.R.L. - INCISA IN VAL D'ARNO FACILITY—See Dolce & Gabbana S.R.L.; *Int'l*, pg. 2157
DOLCE & GABBANA S.R.L. - LONATE POZZOLO FACILITY—See Dolce & Gabbana S.R.L.; *Int'l*, pg. 2157
DRAPERYCRAFTERS INC.—See Frank Kasmir & Associates Inc.; *U.S. Private*, pg. 1595
DUAL AUTOMOTIVE TECHNOLOGIES (SHANGHAI) CO., LTD.—See DUAL Co. Ltd; *Int'l*, pg. 2217
DURALEE MULTIFABRICS, INC.; *U.S. Private*, pg. 1292
DYNIC INTERNATIONAL TRADING (SHANGHAI) CO., LTD.—See Dynic Corporation; *Int'l*, pg. 2242
EAGLE BUTTON CO., INC.; *U.S. Private*, pg. 1308
EASTERN SILK MILLS INC.; *U.S. Private*, pg. 1321
E.E. SCHENCK COMPANY; *U.S. Private*, pg. 1305
EMDAY; *U.S. Private*, pg. 1379
EMHART GLASS INTERNATIONAL SA—See Bucher Industries AG; *Int'l*, pg. 1208
EMHART GLASS JAPAN CO LTD.—See Bucher Industries AG; *Int'l*, pg. 1208
ESPRIT ITALY DISTRIBUTION S.R.L.—See Esprit Holdings Limited; *Int'l*, pg. 2507
FALK INDUSTRIES INC.; *U.S. Private*, pg. 1467

FIBERTEX ELEPHANT ESPANA, S.L.—See Aktieselskabet Schouw & Co.; *Int'l*, pg. 265
FLASTER CORP.; *U.S. Private*, pg. 1540
FLEX-PAC, INC.; *U.S. Private*, pg. 1543
FOLIA INC.—See P. Kaufmann, Inc.; *U.S. Private*, pg. 3060
FOLKTUNE LIMITED—See Fountain Set (Holdings) Limited; *Int'l*, pg. 2754
FOUNTAIN SET LIMITED—See Fountain Set (Holdings) Limited; *Int'l*, pg. 2754
FRANCONIA INTERNATIONAL INC.; *U.S. Private*, pg. 1593
FRANK KASMIR & ASSOCIATES INC.; *U.S. Private*, pg. 1594
FREUDENBERG NONWOVENS LP—See Freudenberg SE; *Int'l*, pg. 2787
FREUDENBERG NONWOVENS ROMANIA S.R.L.—See Freudenberg SE; *Int'l*, pg. 2787
FREUDENBERG PERFORMANCE MATERIALS LP—See Freudenberg SE; *Int'l*, pg. 2787
FREUDENBERG TEXTILE TECHNOLOGIES, S.A.—See Freudenberg SE; *Int'l*, pg. 2788
F. SCHUMACHER & CO.; *U.S. Private*, pg. 1455
GBL INDUSTRIES LIMITED; *Int'l*, pg. 2893
GENERAL FABRICS COMPANY; *U.S. Private*, pg. 1665
GETZNER TEXTIL HANDEL GMBH—See Getzner Textil AG; *Int'l*, pg. 2954
GETZNER TEXTIL WEBEREI GMBH—See Getzner Textil AG; *Int'l*, pg. 2954
GHUSHINE FINTRRADE OCEAN LIMITED; *Int'l*, pg. 2960
GLEAM FABMAT LIMITED; *Int'l*, pg. 2990
THE GLEN RAVEN TECHNICAL FABRICS LLC—See Glen Raven, Inc.; *U.S. Private*, pg. 1709
GRANDMA TRADING & AGENCIES LIMITED; *Int'l*, pg. 3058
GROSS-KOBRICK CORP.; *U.S. Private*, pg. 1792
GROZ-BECKERT ASIA PRIVATE LIMITED—See Groz-Beckert KG; *Int'l*, pg. 3113
GROZ-BECKERT CARDING BELGIUM NV—See Groz-Beckert KG; *Int'l*, pg. 3113
GROZ-BECKERT DE MEXICO S.A. DE C.V.—See Groz-Beckert KG; *Int'l*, pg. 3113
GROZ-BECKERT JAPAN K.K.—See Groz-Beckert KG; *Int'l*, pg. 3113
GROZ-BECKERT KOREA CO., LTD.—See Groz-Beckert KG; *Int'l*, pg. 3113
GROZ-BECKERT SALES & SERVICES VIETNAM CO., LTD.—See Groz-Beckert KG; *Int'l*, pg. 3113
GROZ-BECKERT (SHANGHAI) TRADING CO., LTD.—See Groz-Beckert KG; *Int'l*, pg. 3113
GROZ-BECKERT SINGAPORE PTE. LTD.—See Groz-Beckert KG; *Int'l*, pg. 3113
GROZ-BECKERT TAIWAN LTD.—See Groz-Beckert KG; *Int'l*, pg. 3113
GROZ-BECKERT TRADING (SHENZHEN) CO., LTD.—See Groz-Beckert KG; *Int'l*, pg. 3113
GROZ-BECKERT TURKEY TEKSTIL MAKINE PARCALARI TICARET LIMITED SIRKETI—See Groz-Beckert KG; *Int'l*, pg. 3113
GSI ABROS CO., LTD.—See GSI Creos Corporation; *Int'l*, pg. 3144
GSI CREOS FIBER & TEXTILE PINGHU CO., LTD.—See GSI Creos Corporation; *Int'l*, pg. 3144
GSI CREOS (THAILAND) CO., LTD.—See GSI Creos Corporation; *Int'l*, pg. 3144
GSI (SHENZHEN) LIMITED—See GSI Creos Corporation; *Int'l*, pg. 3144
GTM (EUROPE) LIMITED—See Gul Ahmed Textile Mills Ltd.; *Int'l*, pg. 3178
GUM TREE FABRICS INC.; *U.S. Private*, pg. 1818
HAHA GENERATION CORP.; *U.S. Private*, pg. 3207
HANES DYE & FINISHING—See Leggett & Platt, Incorporated; *U.S. Public*, pg. 1302
HANES INDUSTRIES—See Leggett & Platt, Incorporated; *U.S. Public*, pg. 1302
HANSEL TEXTIL INTERLINING GMBH—See Freudenberg SE; *Int'l*, pg. 2789
HELLY-HANSEN (UK) LTD.—See Canadian Tire Corporation Limited; *Int'l*, pg. 1286
HEMMERS-ITEX TEXTIL IMPORT EXPORT GMBH—See BENCIS Capital Partners B.V.; *Int'l*, pg. 970
HIGH FASHION GARMENTS, INC.—See High Fashion International Limited; *Int'l*, pg. 3385
HILOS A&E DE MEXICO SA DE CV—See Platinum Equity, LLC; *U.S. Private*, pg. 3201
HILOS A&E DOMINICANA LTD—See Platinum Equity, LLC; *U.S. Private*, pg. 3201
HONG KONG SEIBU ENTERPRISE COMPANY LIMITED—See Dickson Concepts (International) Limited; *Int'l*, pg. 2112
HORIZON GROUP USA INC.; *U.S. Private*, pg. 1981
HORNWOOD INC.—See Hornwood Inc.; *U.S. Private*, pg. 1984
HUAFON FOREIGN TRADE CO., LTD.—See Huafon Chemical Co., Ltd.; *Int'l*, pg. 3511
HUESKER ASIA PACIFIC PTE. LTD.—See HUESKER Synthetic GmbH; *Int'l*, pg. 3522
HUESKER INC.—See HUESKER Synthetic GmbH; *Int'l*, pg. 3522

424310 — PIECE GOODS, NOTION...

HUESKER LTDA.—See HUESKER Synthetic GmbH; *Int'l*, pg. 3522
HUESKER LTD.—See HUESKER Synthetic GmbH; *Int'l*, pg. 3522
HUESKER OOO—See HUESKER Synthetic GmbH; *Int'l*, pg. 3522
HUESKER S.A—See HUESKER Synthetic GmbH; *Int'l*, pg. 3522
HUESKER SAS—See HUESKER Synthetic GmbH; *Int'l*, pg. 3522
HUESKER S.R.L.—See HUESKER Synthetic GmbH; *Int'l*, pg. 3522
HUESKER SYNTHETIC B.V.—See HUESKER Synthetic GmbH; *Int'l*, pg. 3522
IDENTCO IDENTIFICATION CORP.; *U.S. Private*, pg. 2037
IITTALA GMBH—See Fiskars Oyj Abp; *Int'l*, pg. 2695
IMPRESSIONS IN PRINT, INC.; *U.S. Private*, pg. 2050
INTEGRA APPARELS AND TEXTILES PVT LTD—See Ashok Piramal Group; *Int'l*, pg. 608
INTEGRITY TEXTILES INC.; *U.S. Private*, pg. 2104
IPROMOTEU, INC.—See Champlain Capital Management LLC; *U.S. Private*, pg. 847
JEFFCO FIBRES, INC.; *U.S. Private*, pg. 2197
JEFFREY FABRICS INC.; *U.S. Private*, pg. 2198
JIANGYIN DUAL TECH CO., LTD—See DUAL Co. Ltd; *Int'l*, pg. 2217
JOE-ANNE COMPANY INTERNATIONAL; *U.S. Private*, pg. 2219
JOHN K. BURCH COMPANY INCORPORATED; *U.S. Private*, pg. 2222
J. ROBERT SCOTT INC.; *U.S. Private*, pg. 2157
JUSHI FRANCE SAS—See China National Building Material Group Co., Ltd.; *Int'l*, pg. 1526
JUSHI GROUP (HK) SINOSIA COMPOSITE MATERIALS CO., LTD.—See China Jushi Co., Ltd.; *Int'l*, pg. 1513
JUSHI USA FIBERGLASS CO LTD—See China National Building Material Group Co., Ltd.; *Int'l*, pg. 1526
KADANT NORDIC AB—See Kadant Inc.; *U.S. Public*, pg. 1212
KADANT PAAL GMBH—See Kadant Inc.; *U.S. Public*, pg. 1212
KENNETH MEYER CO INC—See Dessin/Fournir, Inc.; *U.S. Private*, pg. 1215
KRAVET FABRICS INC.; *U.S. Private*, pg. 2350
LAINIERE DE PICARDIE, INC.—See Chargeurs SA; *Int'l*, pg. 1449
LEIGH FIBERS, INC., WAREHOUSE & DISTRIBUTION—See Leigh Fibers, Inc.; *U.S. Private*, pg. 2419
LEVCOR INTERNATIONAL INC.; *U.S. Private*, pg. 2433
LEWIS & SHERON TEXTILE COMPANY; *U.S. Private*, pg. 2437
LEW JAN TEXTILE CORP.; *U.S. Private*, pg. 2437
LOOMCRAFT TEXTILE & SUPPLY CO.; *U.S. Private*, pg. 2494
LSSM SALES, INC.—See Revolution Capital Group, LLC; *U.S. Private*, pg. 3416
MADEIRA USA LTD.; *U.S. Private*, pg. 2539
MALIBU TEXTILES INC.; *U.S. Private*, pg. 2557
MANDHANA INDUSTRIES LTD (EXPORT DIVISION) UNIT I—See GB Global Limited; *Int'l*, pg. 2892
MARY'S GROUP, LTD.—See Rachel Allan, LLC; *U.S. Private*, pg. 3342
MCC INDUSTRY COMPANY LIMITED—See Chori Co., Ltd.; *Int'l*, pg. 1583
MIAMI CORP.; *U.S. Private*, pg. 2696
MICROFIBRES EUROPE N.V.—See Acasa Group BVBA; *Int'l*, pg. 78
MIDWEST TRADING GROUP, INC.—See Dawn Patrol Partners, LLC; *U.S. Private*, pg. 1175
M&J TRIMMING COMPANY INC.; *U.S. Private*, pg. 2524
MOMENTUM TEXTILES INC.; *U.S. Private*, pg. 2768
MON CHERI BRIDALS INC.; *U.S. Private*, pg. 2768
MOUNT VERNON MILLS, INC., RIEGEL TEXTILE DIV. (ALTO)—See R.B. Pamplin Corporation; *U.S. Private*, pg. 3334
MOUNT VERNON MILLS, INC., RIEGEL TEXTILE DIV.—See R.B. Pamplin Corporation; *U.S. Private*, pg. 3334
MOUNT VERNON MILLS, INC.—See R.B. Pamplin Corporation; *U.S. Private*, pg. 3334
M&S FAB INC.; *U.S. Private*, pg. 2525
MURRAY A. GOLDENBERG TEXTILES; *U.S. Private*, pg. 2816
MUSTO LIMITED—See Canadian Tire Corporation Limited; *Int'l*, pg. 1286
NASSIMI CORPORATION; *U.S. Private*, pg. 2837
NILORN DENMARK - FORSALJNING—See Duroc AB; *Int'l*, pg. 2229
NORTH AMERICAN TRADING, LLC.; *U.S. Private*, pg. 2941
ORBIT EXPORTS LTD.; *U.S. Private*, pg. 3038
PEACHTREE FABRICS INC.; *U.S. Private*, pg. 3123
PINDLER & PINDLER INC.; *U.S. Private*, pg. 3182
P. KAUFMANN INC.; *U.S. Private*, pg. 3060
POLLACK; *U.S. Private*, pg. 3224
PONTETORTO S.P.A.—See Daidoh Limited; *Int'l*, pg. 1924
PO SUN PIECE GOODS COMPANY LIMITED—See Carnival Group International Holdings Limited; *Int'l*, pg. 1342
PRESSMAN-GUTMAN CO. INC.; *U.S. Private*, pg. 3255
PRESTIGE PET PRODUCTS, INC.—See For The Earth Corp.; *U.S. Public*, pg. 864
PT GROZ-BECKERT INDONESIA—See Groz-Beckert KG; *Int'l*, pg. 3113
PT. GSI CREOS INDONESIA—See GSI Creos Corporation; *Int'l*, pg. 3145
PYROTEK ENGINEERING MATERIALS (PTY) LTD.—See Pyrotek Incorporated; *U.S. Private*, pg. 3311
RAYTEX FABRICS INC.; *U.S. Private*, pg. 3359
RIVIERA TRADING INC.; *U.S. Private*, pg. 3448
ROBERT KAUFMAN CO. INC.; *U.S. Private*, pg. 3458
ROSEBRAND WIPERS INC.; *U.S. Private*, pg. 3482
ROSHAN TRADING INC.; *U.S. Private*, pg. 3484
RUBENSTEIN & ZIFF, INC.; *U.S. Private*, pg. 3499
SALONQUEST, LLC—See American Securities LLC; *U.S. Private*, pg. 248
SAM M. BUTLER INC.; *U.S. Private*, pg. 3535
SCHOELLER ASIA CO., LTD.—See FORMOSA TAFFETA CO., LTD.; *Int'l*, pg. 2736
SHANGHAI FUJIX TRADING CO., LTD.—See FUJIX Ltd.; *Int'l*, pg. 2838
SHASON INC.; *U.S. Private*, pg. 3627
SHENZHEN FAUN TEXTILES LIMITED—See Fountain Set (Holdings) Limited; *Int'l*, pg. 2754
SHILLCRAFT, INC.; *U.S. Private*, pg. 3636
SPRINGFIELD LLC—See Milliken & Company; *U.S. Private*, pg. 2737
STEIN FIBERS LTD.; *U.S. Private*, pg. 3797
SUZHOU IL JEONG CO., LTD—See Il Jeong Industrial Co., Ltd; *Int'l*, pg. 3613
SYKEL ENTERPRISES INC.; *U.S. Private*, pg. 3898
SYMPHONY FABRICS CORP.; *U.S. Private*, pg. 3899
TAJIMA GOSEN CO., LTD.—See GSI Creos Corporation; *Int'l*, pg. 3145
TEXTILE IMPORT INC.; *U.S. Private*, pg. 3978
TEXTILES FROM EUROPE INC.; *U.S. Private*, pg. 3978
THAI ASAHI KASEI SPANDEX CO., LTD.—See Asahi Kasei Corporation; *Int'l*, pg. 597
TINGUE, BROWN & CO.—See Tingue, Brown & Co; *U.S. Private*, pg. 4173
TOMMY HILFIGER MARKETING LIMITED—See Dickson Concepts (International) Limited; *Int'l*, pg. 2112
TOP VALUE FABRICS INC.; *U.S. Private*, pg. 4186
TRADE SUPPLIES, LLC—See Sole Source Capital LLC; *U.S. Private*, pg. 3708
TRIMSOL BRAZIL, LTDA.—See DUAL Co. Ltd; *Int'l*, pg. 2217
TRIMSOL CZECH REPUBLIC S.R.O.—See DUAL Co. Ltd; *Int'l*, pg. 2217
TRIMSOL ROMANIA SRL—See DUAL Co. Ltd; *Int'l*, pg. 2217
TRIVANTAGE, LLC—See Glen Raven, Inc.; *U.S. Private*, pg. 1709
UNITED NOTIONS INC.; *U.S. Private*, pg. 4295
VALIANT PRODUCTS CORP.; *U.S. Private*, pg. 4331
VARIETY DISTRIBUTORS INC.; *U.S. Private*, pg. 4347
VILENE CREATE CO., LTD.—See Freudenberg SE; *Int'l*, pg. 2791
VK NORTH AMERICA LLC—See Kadant Inc.; *U.S. Public*, pg. 1212
WAVERLY FABRICS—See Iconix Acquisition LLC; *U.S. Private*, pg. 2033
WESTEX INC.—See Milliken & Company; *U.S. Private*, pg. 2737
W. GAMBY & CO.; *U.S. Private*, pg. 4418
WOLFORD (SCHWEIZ) AG—See Fosun International Limited; *Int'l*, pg. 2752
WOODEN SHIPS OF HOBOKEN; *U.S. Private*, pg. 4557
YANTAI DUAL CAR INTERIOR CO., LTD.—See DUAL Co. Ltd; *Int'l*, pg. 2217
ZABIN INDUSTRIES INC.; *U.S. Private*, pg. 4596

424340 — FOOTWEAR MERCHANT WHOLESALERS

361 EUROPE B.V.—See 361 Degrees International Limited; *Int'l*, pg. 7
361 USA, INC—See 361 Degrees International Limited; *Int'l*, pg. 7
ACHILLES HONG KONG CO., LTD.—See Achilles Corporation; *Int'l*, pg. 103
ACI INTERNATIONAL; *U.S. Private*, pg. 59
ACORN PRODUCTS CO. INC.; *U.S. Private*, pg. 63
ADIDAS TREFOIL TRADING (U.K.) LIMITED—See adidas AG; *Int'l*, pg. 147
AEROGROUP INTERNATIONAL LLC—See Palladin Consumer Retail Partners, LLC; *U.S. Private*, pg. 3077
ALLBIRDS, INC.; *U.S. Public*, pg. 78
ALSINCO SA; *Int'l*, pg. 379
ALTO ENTERPRISES, INC.; *U.S. Private*, pg. 210
AMERICAN SPORTING GOODS CORPORATION—See Caleres, Inc.; *U.S. Public*, pg. 422
ART STONE THEATRICAL CORP.; *U.S. Private*, pg. 340
ASICS AMERICA CORPORATION—See ASICS Corporation; *Int'l*, pg. 620
ATSCO FOOTWEAR GROUP; *U.S. Private*, pg. 382
AUSTRALIAN FOOTWEAR PTY LTD—See Fusion Retail Brands, Pty. Ltd.; *Int'l*, pg. 2849
BAOF INTERNATIONAL LIMITED—See Golden Solar New Energy Technology Holdings Limited; *Int'l*, pg. 3032
BAY RAG CORPORATION; *U.S. Private*, pg. 494
BBC INTERNATIONAL LLC; *U.S. Private*, pg. 498
BETTS GROUP PTY. LTD.; *Int'l*, pg. 1004
BIRKENSTOCK USA, LP; *U.S. Private*, pg. 564
BOKSIT A.D.; *Int'l*, pg. 1102
BOSNA TRGOVINA A.D.; *Int'l*, pg. 1116
BRAND COLLECTIVE PTY. LTD.—See Anchorage Capital Partners Pty. Limited; *Int'l*, pg. 448
BRANDS EUROPEAN SHOE TRADE; *Int'l*, pg. 1140
BRIGHT STAR FOOTWEAR, INC.—See Iconix Acquisition LLC; *U.S. Private*, pg. 2032
CAPARROS CORPORATION; *U.S. Private*, pg. 737
CCC S.A.; *Int'l*, pg. 1366
CCC SHOES & BAGS SP. Z O.O.—See CCC S.A.; *Int'l*, pg. 1366
CELS ENTERPRISES, INC.; *U.S. Private*, pg. 808
CHARLES DAVID OF CALIFORNIA; *U.S. Private*, pg. 852
C&J CLARK CANADA, LTD.—See C&J Clark Limited; *Int'l*, pg. 1238
CLARKS COMPANIES NORTH AMERICA—See C&J Clark Limited; *Int'l*, pg. 1239
CLASSIQUE FOOTWEAR INC.; *U.S. Private*, pg. 917
COBIAN CORP.; *U.S. Private*, pg. 957
COLE HAAN, INC.—See Apax Partners LLP; *Int'l*, pg. 503
COLE HAAN JAPAN, INC.—See Apax Partners LLP; *Int'l*, pg. 503
COMFORT ONE SHOES L-1 CORPORATION; *U.S. Private*, pg. 981
CONFEZIONI MODA ITALIA S.R.L.—See PVH Corp.; *U.S. Public*, pg. 1739
CONNORS, DAMESHEK, FONG & MANCUSO, INC.; *U.S. Private*, pg. 1018
CONSOLIDATED SHOE COMPANY INC.; *U.S. Private*, pg. 1022
CONVERSE INC.—See NIKE, Inc.; *U.S. Public*, pg. 1528
CROCS ONLINE, INC.—See Crocs, Inc.; *U.S. Public*, pg. 595
CROCS RETAIL, INC.—See Crocs, Inc.; *U.S. Public*, pg. 595
DANSKO INC.; *U.S. Private*, pg. 1157
DECKERS EUROPE LTD.—See Deckers Outdoor Corporation; *U.S. Public*, pg. 645
DECKERS OUTDOOR INTERNATIONAL LIMITED—See Deckers Outdoor Corporation; *U.S. Public*, pg. 645
DECKERS RETAIL, LLC—See Deckers Outdoor Corporation; *U.S. Public*, pg. 645
DEER STAGS CONCEPTS, INC.; *U.S. Private*, pg. 1190
DEXTER SHOE COMPANY—See Berkshire Hathaway Inc.; *U.S. Public*, pg. 299
DIADORA AMERICA, INC.—See Diadora Invicta; *Int'l*, pg. 2101
DIANA FERRARI (AUSTRALIA) PTY LTD—See Fusion Retail Brands, Pty. Ltd.; *Int'l*, pg. 2849
DIVA ACQUISITION CORP.—See Steven Madden, Ltd.; *U.S. Public*, pg. 1947
DOLCE VITA HOLDINGS, INC.—See Steven Madden, Ltd.; *U.S. Public*, pg. 1947
DONGGUAN LEEWAY FOOTWEAR COMPANY LIMITED—See Caleres, Inc.; *U.S. Public*, pg. 422
DSW SHOE WAREHOUSE, INC.—See Schottenstein Stores Corporation; *U.S. Private*, pg. 3569
DYNASTY FOOTWEAR LTD; *U.S. Private*, pg. 1300
EASTLAND SHOE CORPORATION; *U.S. Private*, pg. 1322
ECCO BALTIC SIA—See Ecco Sko A/S; *Int'l*, pg. 2288
ECCO SHOE PRODUCTION PTE. LTD.—See Ecco Sko A/S; *Int'l*, pg. 2288
ECCO SHOES CANADA, INC.—See Ecco Sko A/S; *Int'l*, pg. 2288
ECCO SHOES (NZ) LIMITED—See Ecco Sko A/S; *Int'l*, pg. 2288
ECCO SHOES PACIFIC PTY. LTD.—See Ecco Sko A/S; *Int'l*, pg. 2288
ECCO USA INC.—See Ecco Sko A/S; *Int'l*, pg. 2288
ELAN-POLO INC.; *U.S. Private*, pg. 1350
ES ORIGINALS INC.; *U.S. Private*, pg. 1424
FILA USA, INC.—See FILA Holdings Corporation; *Int'l*, pg. 2662
FLORSHEIM, INC.—See Weyco Group, Inc.; *U.S. Public*, pg. 2365
FLORSHEIM SHOES EUROPE S.R.L.—See Weyco Group, Inc.; *U.S. Public*, pg. 2365
FOOT LOCKER ARTIGOS DESPORTIVOS E DE TEMPOS LIVRES, LDA.—See Foot Locker, Inc.; *U.S. Public*, pg. 863
FOOT LOCKER AUSTRIA GMBH—See Foot Locker, Inc.; *U.S. Public*, pg. 863
FOOT LOCKER DENMARK B.V.—See Foot Locker, Inc.; *U.S. Public*, pg. 863
FOOT LOCKER FRANCE S.A.S.—See Foot Locker, Inc.; *U.S. Public*, pg. 863
FOOT LOCKER SPAIN S.L.—See Foot Locker, Inc.; *U.S. Public*, pg. 863
FOOT LOCKER SWITZERLAND LLC—See Foot Locker, Inc.; *U.S. Public*, pg. 863

N.A.I.C.S. INDEX

424350 — CLOTHING AND CLOTHI...

FOOTWEAR UNLIMITED INC.; *U.S. Private*, pg. 1562
FORTUNE FOOTWEAR INC.; *U.S. Private*, pg. 1577
FREEDOM SPORTSLINE LIMITED—See Foot Locker, Inc.; *U.S. Public*, pg. 863
THE FRYE COMPANY—See Jimlar Corporation; *U.S. Private*, pg. 2210
GEARCOR, INC.—See Incline MGMT Corp.; *U.S. Private*, pg. 2053
GENTLEFIT TRADING LIMITED—See Daphne International Holdings Limited; *Int'l*, pg. 1970
GFOOT CO., LTD.; *Int'l*, pg. 2957
GRAVIS FOOTWEAR INC.—See Burton Snowboard Company; *U.S. Private*, pg. 693
GROUPE ROYER—See Apax Partners LLP; *Int'l*, pg. 504
HANA SPORTS INC.; *U.S. Private*, pg. 1852
HARBOR FOOTWEAR GROUP, LTD.; *U.S. Private*, pg. 1859
HERMES SELLIER SAS—See Hermes International SCA; *Int'l*, pg. 3363
HI-TEC ESPANA S.A.—See Hi-Tec Sports PLC; *Int'l*, pg. 3381
HITECH SPORTS PTY LTD—See Hi-Tec Sports PLC; *Int'l*, pg. 3381
HI-TEC NEDERLAND BV—See Hi-Tec Sports PLC; *Int'l*, pg. 3381
HI-TEC SPORTS CANADA LTD.—See Hi-Tec Sports PLC; *Int'l*, pg. 3381
HI-TEC SPORTS INTERNATIONAL HOLDINGS B.V.—See Apex Global Brands Inc.; *U.S. Private*, pg. 292
HI-TEC SPORTS USA, INC.—See Hi-Tec Sports PLC; *Int'l*, pg. 3381
HITIT AYAKKABI SAAT MUCEVHERAT TURIZM INSAAT PETROL SAN. VE TIC. LTD.STI.—See Hitit Holding A.S.; *Int'l*, pg. 3426
ICONIX INTERNATIONAL INC.—See Iconix Acquisition LLC; *U.S. Private*, pg. 2032
INTERNATIONAL SEAWAY TRADING CORPORATION; *U.S. Private*, pg. 2120
INTER-PACIFIC CORPORATION; *U.S. Private*, pg. 2107
JACK SCHWARTZ SHOES, INC.; *U.S. Private*, pg. 2174
JIMLAR CORPORATION; *U.S. Private*, pg. 2210
JP ORIGINAL CORP.; *U.S. Private*, pg. 2239
JUST FABULOUS, INC.; *U.S. Private*, pg. 2245
KARL VOEGELE AG—See CCC S.A.; *Int'l*, pg. 1366
LAI WAH FOOTWEAR TRADING LIMITED—See Hillhouse Investment Management Limited; *Int'l*, pg. 3393
LASANTE CO., LTD.—See EM Systems Co., Ltd.; *Int'l*, pg. 2372
MADDEN INTERNATIONAL LTD.—See Steven Madden, Ltd.; *U.S. Public*, pg. 1947
MANCHESTER UNITED MERCHANDISING LIMITED—See NIKE, Inc.; *U.S. Public*, pg. 1528
MERCURY INTERNATIONAL TRADING CORP.; *U.S. Private*, pg. 2670
ME TOO MARK TUCKER INC.; *U.S. Private*, pg. 2646
MICHIGAN INDUSTRIAL SHOE CO.—See Saf-Gard Safety Shoe Co.; *U.S. Private*, pg. 3523
MILLIE'S COMPANY LIMITED—See Hillhouse Investment Management Limited; *Int'l*, pg. 3393
MIRABELL FOOTWEAR LIMITED—See Hillhouse Investment Management Limited; *Int'l*, pg. 3393
NEW YORK TRANSIT INC.; *U.S. Private*, pg. 2912
NIKE 360 HOLDING B.V.—See NIKE, Inc.; *U.S. Public*, pg. 1529
NIKE AUSTRALIA PTY. LTD.—See NIKE, Inc.; *U.S. Public*, pg. 1529
NIKE DE MEXICO S DE R.L. DE C.V.—See NIKE, Inc.; *U.S. Public*, pg. 1529
NIKE DEUTSCHLAND GMBH—See NIKE, Inc.; *U.S. Public*, pg. 1529
NIKE GROUP HOLDING B.V.—See NIKE, Inc.; *U.S. Public*, pg. 1529
NIKE INDIA PRIVATE LIMITED—See NIKE, Inc.; *U.S. Public*, pg. 1529
NIKE ISRAEL LTD.—See NIKE, Inc.; *U.S. Public*, pg. 1529
NIKE JAPAN CORP.—See NIKE, Inc.; *U.S. Public*, pg. 1529
NIKE SPORTS KOREA CO., LTD.—See NIKE, Inc.; *U.S. Public*, pg. 1529
NINA FOOTWEAR CORP.; *U.S. Private*, pg. 2928
NJD SPECIALTY RETAIL, INC.; *U.S. Private*, pg. 2930
NUMBER 1 SHOES LIMITED—See Bapcor Limited; *Int'l*, pg. 857
NUNN-BUSH SHOE COMPANY—See Weyco Group, Inc.; *U.S. Public*, pg. 2365
PALMS CROSSING TOWN CENTER, LLC—See Washington Prime Group Inc.; *U.S. Private*, pg. 4448
RBK THAILAND, INC.—See Leonard Green & Partners, L.P.; *U.S. Private*, pg. 2424
RENFRO BV—See The Renco Group Inc.; *U.S. Private*, pg. 4104
RENFRO CANADA INC.—See The Renco Group Inc.; *U.S. Private*, pg. 4104
RENFRO JAPAN—See The Renco Group Inc.; *U.S. Private*, pg. 4104
RENFRO MEXICO, S.A. DE C.V.—See The Renco Group Inc.; *U.S. Private*, pg. 4104
R HANNAH & CO LIMITED—See Bapcor Limited; *Int'l*, pg. 857

RICHLEE SHOE COMPANY—See Alto Enterprises, Inc.; *U.S. Private*, pg. 210
ROCKY BRANDS CANADA, INC.—See Rocky Brands, Inc.; *U.S. Public*, pg. 1807
ROCKY CANADA, INC.—See Rocky Brands, Inc.; *U.S. Public*, pg. 1807
SAFETY SHOE DISTRIBUTORS; *U.S. Private*, pg. 3525
SCHC, INC.—See Shoe Carnival, Inc.; *U.S. Public*, pg. 1875
SCHUH LIMITED—See Genesco Inc.; *U.S. Public*, pg. 930
SCLC, INC.—See Shoe Carnival, Inc.; *U.S. Public*, pg. 1875
SENSES MARKETING INTERNATIONAL LIMITED—See Hillhouse Investment Management Limited; *Int'l*, pg. 3393
SHOE CARNIVAL VENTURES, LLC—See Shoe Carnival, Inc.; *U.S. Public*, pg. 1875
SHOEFAYRE LIMITED—See Co-operative Group Limited; *Int'l*, pg. 1679
SHOE SHOW, INC.; *U.S. Private*, pg. 3639
SHOES & SOX PTY LTD—See Anchorage Capital Partners Pty. Limited; *Int'l*, pg. 448
SHOE SUPERSTORE PTY LTD.—See Accent Group Limited; *Int'l*, pg. 81
SIDNEY RICH ASSOCIATES INC.—See Caleres, Inc.; *U.S. Public*, pg. 422
SKECHERS GUANGZHOU CO., LTD.—See Skechers U.S.A., Inc.; *U.S. Public*, pg. 1891
SKECHERS RETAIL INDIA PRIVATE LIMITED—See Skechers U.S.A., Inc.; *U.S. Public*, pg. 1891
SKECHERS U.S.A., INC.; *U.S. Public*, pg. 1891
SOREL CORPORATION—See Columbia Sportswear Company; *U.S. Public*, pg. 535
SPERRY TOP-SIDER, INC.—See Wolverine World Wide, Inc.; *U.S. Public*, pg. 2377
STACCATO FOOTWEAR COMPANY LIMITED—See Hillhouse Investment Management Limited; *Int'l*, pg. 3393
STACY ADAMS SHOE COMPANY—See Weyco Group, Inc.; *U.S. Public*, pg. 2365
STONE AGE EQUIPMENT, INC.—See adidas AG; *Int'l*, pg. 146
STRIDE RITE CHILDREN'S GROUP, INC.—See Wolverine World Wide, Inc.; *U.S. Public*, pg. 2377
STUART WEITZMAN, LLC—See Tapestry, Inc.; *U.S. Public*, pg. 1981
SUBTYPE PTY. LTD.—See Accent Group Limited; *Int'l*, pg. 81
TAIWAN TOPLINE, INC.—See Topline Imports, Inc.; *U.S. Private*, pg. 4187
TEXON MANAGEMENT LTD—See Coats Group plc; *Int'l*, pg. 1682
TIMBERLAND ESPANA, S.A.—See V. F. Corporation; *U.S. Public*, pg. 2268
TOPLINE FOOTWEAR CHINA, LTD.—See Topline Imports, Inc.; *U.S. Private*, pg. 4187
TOPLINE IMPORTS, INC.; *U.S. Private*, pg. 4187
TRENDY IMPORTS S.A. DE C.V.—See Steven Madden, Ltd.; *U.S. Public*, pg. 1947
TRETORN SWEDEN AB—See Leonard Green & Partners, L.P.; *U.S. Private*, pg. 2425
TRIMFOOT CO., LLC; *U.S. Private*, pg. 4232
UNISA AMERICA INC.—See Unisa Holdings Incorporated; *U.S. Private*, pg. 4286
UNISA EUROPA HOLDINGS INC.—See Unisa Holdings Incorporated; *U.S. Private*, pg. 4286
VANS, INC.—See V. F. Corporation; *U.S. Public*, pg. 2269
VILLA, INC.; *U.S. Private*, pg. 4383
VIONIC GROUP LLC—See Caleres, Inc.; *U.S. Public*, pg. 422
WEAR WELL FOOTWEAR LIMITED—See Hevea B.V.; *Int'l*, pg. 3367
WEYCO GROUP, INC.; *U.S. Public*, pg. 2365
WOLFF SHOE COMPANY INC.; *U.S. Private*, pg. 4554
WOLVERINE EUROPE LIMITED—See Wolverine World Wide, Inc.; *U.S. Public*, pg. 2377
WOLVERINE OUTDOORS, INC.—See Wolverine World Wide, Inc.; *U.S. Public*, pg. 2377

424350 — CLOTHING AND CLOTHING ACCESSORIES MERCHANT WHOLESALERS

1092072 ONTARIO INC; *Int'l*, pg. 1
525 MADE IN AMERICA INC.; *U.S. Private*, pg. 16
80STEES.COM INC.; *U.S. Private*, pg. 17
AARDVARK SWIM & SPORT, INC.; *U.S. Private*, pg. 32
ABERCROMBIE & FITCH EUROPE SA—See Abercrombie & Fitch Co.; *U.S. Public*, pg. 25
ABERCROMBIE & FITCH TRADING CO.—See Abercrombie & Fitch Co.; *U.S. Public*, pg. 25
ACCESSORY EXCHANGE L.L.C.—See Bag Bazaar Ltd.; *U.S. Private*, pg. 425
ACCESSORY NETWORK GROUP INC.; *U.S. Private*, pg. 53
ACQUI POLO SAS—See Ralph Lauren Corporation; *U.S. Public*, pg. 1761
ADASTRIA ASIA CO., LTD.—See Adastria Co., Ltd.; *Int'l*, pg. 126
ADASTRIA GENERAL SUPPORT CO., LTD.—See Adastria Co., Ltd.; *Int'l*, pg. 126

ADASTRIA KOREA CO., LTD.—See Adastria Co., Ltd.; *Int'l*, pg. 126
ADASTRIA TAIWAN CO., LTD.—See Adastria Co., Ltd.; *Int'l*, pg. 126
ADORN FASHIONS INC.; *U.S. Private*, pg. 82
ADRIANNA PAPELL, LLC; *U.S. Private*, pg. 82
A.D. SUTTON & SONS; *U.S. Private*, pg. 25
AEFFE FRANCE S.A.R.L.—See Aeffe SpA; *Int'l*, pg. 173
AEFFE SPA; *Int'l*, pg. 173
AEFFE USA INC—See Aeffe SpA; *Int'l*, pg. 173
AFRIKA4U; *Int'l*, pg. 192
AGE GROUP LTD.; *U.S. Private*, pg. 126
AGENT PROVOCATEUR LIMITED—See Four Marketing Ltd.; *Int'l*, pg. 2755
A&H SPORTSWEAR CO. INC; *U.S. Private*, pg. 20
AIDAN INDUSTRIES, INC.; *U.S. Private*, pg. 131
AIMEE LYNN ACCESSORIES INC.; *U.S. Private*, pg. 133
ALEX APPAREL GROUP, INC.—See Independence Capital Partners, LLC; *U.S. Public*, pg. 2057
ALKO DISTRIBUTORS, INC.; *U.S. Private*, pg. 169
ALL FASHIONS IMPORTS INC.; *U.S. Private*, pg. 170
ALMAR SALES CO. INC.; *U.S. Private*, pg. 195
ALPHA GARMENT INC.; *U.S. Private*, pg. 197
ALPHA SHIRT—See Bain Capital, LP; *U.S. Public*, pg. 437
AMEREX FASHION GROUP—See Amerex Group, Inc.; *U.S. Private*, pg. 219
AMEREX GROUP, INC.; *U.S. Private*, pg. 219
AMERICANA COMPANY INC.; *U.S. Private*, pg. 258
AMERICAN T-SHIRT CO—See Watumull Brothers Ltd. Inc.; *U.S. Private*, pg. 4456
AMICA APPAREL CORP—See Maran Inc.; *U.S. Private*, pg. 2569
AMMO VAREJO LTDA—See Coteminas Companhia de Tecidos Norte de Minas; *Int'l*, pg. 1817
AMPA 2P SAS—See Dorel Industries, Inc.; *Int'l*, pg. 2176
AMPA DEVELOPPEMENT SAS—See Dorel Industries, Inc.; *Int'l*, pg. 2176
ANDREW SPORTS CLUB INC.; *U.S. Private*, pg. 279
ANDREW & SUZANNE CO. INC.—See G-III Apparel Group, Ltd.; *U.S. Public*, pg. 893
ANSELL NORWAY AS—See Ansell Limited; *Int'l*, pg. 478
ANTINEA S.R.L.—See Giorgio Armani S.p.A.; *Int'l*, pg. 2978
ANVIL KNITWEAR, INC.—See Gildan Activewear Inc.; *Int'l*, pg. 2973
AOYAMA CAPITAL CO., LTD.—See AOYAMA TRADING Co. Ltd.; *Int'l*, pg. 498
APRICA KOREA CO., LTD.—See Newell Brands Inc.; *U.S. Public*, pg. 1513
AQUARIUS LTD. INC.; *U.S. Private*, pg. 303
ARITZIA, INC.; *Int'l*, pg. 567
ASCENA GLOBAL SOURCING HONG KONG LIMITED—See Mahwah Bergen Retail Group, Inc.; *U.S. Private*, pg. 2550
ASIAN EUROPEAN FOOTWEAR; *Int'l*, pg. 617
ATLANTIC HOSIERY, INC.; *U.S. Private*, pg. 373
AUBURN HOSIERY MILLS, INC.—See GMM Capital LLC; *U.S. Private*, pg. 1722
AUGUST SILK INC.—See High Fashion International Limited; *Int'l*, pg. 3385
AVOCA HANDWEAVERS LIMITED—See Aramark; *U.S. Public*, pg. 177
AVOCA HANDWEAVERS SHOPS LIMITED—See Aramark; *U.S. Public*, pg. 177
AZZEDINE ALAIA S.A.S.; *Int'l*, pg. 783
BAG BAZAAR LTD.; *U.S. Private*, pg. 425
BARVIC; *Int'l*, pg. 870
BASICNET S.P.A.; *Int'l*, pg. 886
B.B. DAKOTA INC.—See Steven Madden, Ltd.; *U.S. Public*, pg. 1947
BEACH PATROL INC.; *U.S. Private*, pg. 503
BEBE & CO. SAS—See Dorel Industries, Inc.; *Int'l*, pg. 2176
BEN ELIAS INDUSTRIES CORP; *U.S. Private*, pg. 522
BEN SHERMAN USA—See Oxford Industries, Inc.; *U.S. Public*, pg. 1629
BENTEX KIDDIE CORPORATION; *U.S. Private*, pg. 528
BERKSHIRE FASHIONS INC.; *U.S. Private*, pg. 533
BETMAR HATS, INC.—See Bollman Hat Co.; *U.S. Private*, pg. 611
BIJOUX INTERNATIONAL INC.; *U.S. Private*, pg. 556
BILLABONG INTERNATIONAL LIMITED—See Leonard Green & Partners, L.P.; *U.S. Private*, pg. 2424
BILLY REID, INC.; *U.S. Private*, pg. 559
BJ ACQUISITION LLC—See Steven Madden, Ltd.; *U.S. Public*, pg. 1947
BJORN BORG FINLAND OY—See Bjorn Borg AB; *Int'l*, pg. 1054
BJORN BORG UK LIMITED—See Bjorn Borg AB; *Int'l*, pg. 1054
BLUE CANOE BODYWEAR; *U.S. Private*, pg. 585
BOARDRIDERS, INC.—See Leonard Green & Partners, L.P.; *U.S. Private*, pg. 2424
BODY ONE S.A.; *Int'l*, pg. 1097
BONNIE INTERNATIONAL—See Golden Touch Imports, Inc.; *U.S. Private*, pg. 1734
BONOBOS, INC.—See WHP Global; *U.S. Private*, pg. 4515
THE BOPPY COMPANY, LLC—See BI-Invest Advisors S.A.; *Int'l*, pg. 1017

N.A.I.C.S. Index

424350 — CLOTHING AND CLOTHI... CORPORATE AFFILIATIONS

BOSHIWA INTERNATIONAL HOLDING LIMITED; *Int'l*, pg. 1116
BOSS MANUFACTURING COMPANY—See Boss Holdings, Inc.; *U.S. Public*, pg. 371
BOXERCRAFT INCORPORATED; *U.S. Private*, pg. 626
BRAND CONCEPTS LIMITED; *Int'l*, pg. 1139
BRETMOR HEADWEAR, INC.; *U.S. Private*, pg. 646
BRIGGS NEW YORK CORP.—See Sun Capital Partners, Inc.; *U.S. Private*, pg. 3859
BRODER BROS., CO.—See Bain Capital, LP; *U.S. Private*, pg. 437
BRONER GLOVE COMPANY INC.; *U.S. Private*, pg. 662
BRUNELLO CUCINELLI KUWAIT FOR READYMADE & NOVELTY CLOTHES RETAIL WLL—See Brunello Cucinelli S.p.A.; *Int'l*, pg. 1200
BRUNELLO CUCINELLI MIDDLE EAST LLC—See Brunello Cucinelli S.p.A.; *Int'l*, pg. 1200
BTX GROUP A/S—See Sun Capital Partners, Inc.; *U.S. Private*, pg. 3861
BUENO OF CALIFORNIA INC.; *U.S. Private*, pg. 680
BUSY BODY FITNESS IN MOTION; *U.S. Private*, pg. 696
BY DESIGN LLC; *U.S. Private*, pg. 700
CALVIN KLEIN, INC.—See PVH Corp.; *U.S. Public*, pg. 1739
CAPELLI EUROPE GMBH—See GMA Accessories/Capelli of New York; *U.S. Private*, pg. 1721
CAPELLI OF NEW YORK INC.—See GMA Accessories/Capelli of New York; *U.S. Private*, pg. 1721
CEJON ACCESSORIES, INC.—See Steven Madden, Ltd.; *U.S. Public*, pg. 1947
CELEBRITY INTERNATIONAL INC.; *U.S. Private*, pg. 806
CENTURY 21 PROMOTIONS, INC.; *U.S. Private*, pg. 831
CG INTIMATES INC.—See iFabric Corp.; *Int'l*, pg. 3598
CGS INDUSTRIES, INC.; *U.S. Private*, pg. 844
CHARGEURS WOOL (SOUTH AFRICA) (PTY) LTD—See Chargeurs SA; *Int'l*, pg. 1449
CHARLE CO., LTD.; *Int'l*, pg. 1450
CHATEAU INTERNATIONAL INC.; *U.S. Private*, pg. 860
CHERRY STIX LTD.; *U.S. Private*, pg. 874
CHIORI APPAREL INC.—See Maran Inc.; *U.S. Private*, pg. 2569
CHLOE SAS—See Compagnie Financiere Richemont S.A.; *Int'l*, pg. 1741
CHORI (DALIAN) TRADING CO., LTD.—See Chori Co., Ltd.; *Int'l*, pg. 1583
CHORUS GIRL INC.; *U.S. Private*, pg. 889
CLAIRE'S ACCESSORIES UK LTD.—See Apollo Global Management, Inc.; *U.S. Public*, pg. 148
CLAIRE'S AUSTRIA GMBH—See Apollo Global Management, Inc.; *U.S. Public*, pg. 148
CLAIRE'S CANADA CORP.—See Apollo Global Management, Inc.; *U.S. Public*, pg. 148
CLAIRE'S FRANCE S.A.S.—See Apollo Global Management, Inc.; *U.S. Public*, pg. 148
CLAIRE'S NIPPON CO., LTD.—See Apollo Global Management, Inc.; *U.S. Public*, pg. 148
CLAIRE'S SWITZERLAND GMBH—See Apollo Global Management, Inc.; *U.S. Public*, pg. 149
CLUETT AMERICAN INVESTMENT CORP.; *U.S. Private*, pg. 949
CLUETT INTERNATIONAL GROUP—See Cluett American Investment Corp.; *U.S. Private*, pg. 949
COLISEUM—See Andrew Sports Club Inc.; *U.S. Private*, pg. 280
COLLEGE CONCEPTS LLC—See Robinson Manufacturing Company Inc.; *U.S. Private*, pg. 3462
COLONIAL INDUSTRIAL PRODUCTS; *U.S. Private*, pg. 971
COLUMBIA SPORTSWEAR CANADA LP—See Columbia Sportswear Company; *U.S. Public*, pg. 535
COLUMBIA SPORTSWEAR COMPANY; *U.S. Public*, pg. 534
COLUMBIA SPORTSWEAR DENMARK APS—See Columbia Sportswear Company; *U.S. Public*, pg. 535
COLUMBIA SPORTSWEAR FINLAND OY—See Columbia Sportswear Company; *U.S. Public*, pg. 535
COLUMBIA SPORTSWEAR FRANCE S.A.S.—See Columbia Sportswear Company; *U.S. Public*, pg. 535
COLUMBIA SPORTSWEAR GMBH—See Columbia Sportswear Company; *U.S. Public*, pg. 535
COLUMBIA SPORTSWEAR INTERNATIONAL SARL—See Columbia Sportswear Company; *U.S. Public*, pg. 535
COLUMBIA SPORTSWEAR KOREA—See Columbia Sportswear Company; *U.S. Public*, pg. 535
COLUMBIA SPORTSWEAR USA CORPORATION—See Columbia Sportswear Company; *U.S. Public*, pg. 535
COME ON STRONG INC.; *U.S. Private*, pg. 981
CRAZY DOG TSHIRTS; *U.S. Private*, pg. 1086
CROSSLAND ASSOCIATES INC.; *U.S. Private*, pg. 1106
CROSS PLUS INC.; *Int'l*, pg. 1856
CRYSTAL KOBE LTD. INC.; *U.S. Private*, pg. 1115
CULLEN & WHIM INC.; *U.S. Private*, pg. 1121
DANARA INTERNATIONAL, LTD.; *U.S. Private*, pg. 1152
DANSKIN—See Iconix Acquisition LLC; *U.S. Private*, pg. 2032
DAVID MEISTER—See Sun Capital Partners, Inc.; *U.S. Private*, pg. 3859
DAWSON CASHMERE LLC—See Dawson International PLC; *Int'l*, pg. 1984
DBH WORLDWIDE, LLC; *U.S. Private*, pg. 1179
DB PLUS INC.—See Jerrs Plus Inc.; *U.S. Private*, pg. 2202
DELUX S.R.O.—See Descours & Cabaud SA; *Int'l*, pg. 2044
DEMOCRACY CLOTHING—See Sun Capital Partners, Inc.; *U.S. Private*, pg. 3859
DETSKY MIR GROUP; *Int'l*, pg. 2048
DIJION CO., LTD—See Chori Co., Ltd.; *Int'l*, pg. 1583
DIONIC INDUSTRIAL & TRADING S.A; *Int'l*, pg. 2127
DK FOOT & CASUAL, INC.; *U.S. Private*, pg. 1247
DNE GROUP LTD.; *U.S. Private*, pg. 1249
DOLCE & GABBANA USA, INC.—See Dolce & Gabbana S.R.L.; *Int'l*, pg. 2157
DON MART CLOTHES INC.—See Charles Navasky & Company; *U.S. Private*, pg. 853
THE DONNA KARAN COMPANY LLC—See G-III Apparel Group, Ltd.; *U.S. Public*, pg. 894
DOREL CONSULTING (SHANGHAI) CO., LTD.—See Dorel Industries, Inc.; *Int'l*, pg. 2176
DORFMAN-PACIFIC COMPANY; *U.S. Private*, pg. 1262
DPJ CLOTHING LTD.—See Bombay Rayon Fashions Limited; *Int'l*, pg. 1104
DREAMWEAR, INC.; *U.S. Private*, pg. 1275
DREWEX S.A.; *Int'l*, pg. 2204
DUTCH BRAND MANAGEMENT BV—See Bjorn Borg AB; *Int'l*, pg. 1054
DUTEXDOR; *Int'l*, pg. 2235
DYNASTY FASHIONS, INC.; *U.S. Private*, pg. 1300
EAST JEAN LIMITED—See Giordano International Limited; *Int'l*, pg. 2977
EASYKNIT GLOBAL COMPANY LIMITED—See Easyknit International Holdings Ltd.; *Int'l*, pg. 2276
THE ECHO DESIGN GROUP, INC.; *U.S. Private*, pg. 4025
EDDIE BAUER, INC.—See Leonard Green & Partners, L.P.; *U.S. Private*, pg. 2424
EDEREL SPORT INC.; *U.S. Private*, pg. 1333
EDOB ABWICKLUNGS AG—See Regent, L.P.; *U.S. Private*, pg. 3387
EISENBERG INTERNATIONAL CORPORATION; *U.S. Private*, pg. 1347
ELBERTON MANUFACTURING COMPANY INCORPORATED; *U.S. Private*, pg. 1350
ELLIOTT LUCCA—See Indonesian Imports, Inc.; *U.S. Private*, pg. 2064
E.M. LAWRENCE LTD.; *U.S. Private*, pg. 1306
ESCADA AMERICA LLC—See Regent, L.P.; *U.S. Private*, pg. 3387
ESCADA BENELUX BV—See Regent, L.P.; *U.S. Private*, pg. 3387
ESCADA HONG KONG LTD.—See Regent, L.P.; *U.S. Private*, pg. 3387
ESCADA MONTE CARLO S.A.M.—See Regent, L.P.; *U.S. Private*, pg. 3387
ESCADA PORTUGAL UNIPESSOAL LIMITADA—See Regent, L.P.; *U.S. Private*, pg. 3387
ESCADA SWITZERLAND LTD.—See Regent, L.P.; *U.S. Private*, pg. 3387
ESCADA TEXTILIEN-VERTRIEBSGES.M.B.H.—See Regent, L.P.; *U.S. Private*, pg. 3387
ESPORTIA INTERNATIONAL INC.; *U.S. Private*, pg. 1427
ESPRIT HOLDINGS LIMITED; *Int'l*, pg. 2506
ESPRIT SWITZERLAND DISTRIBUTION AG—See Esprit Holdings Limited; *Int'l*, pg. 2507
E.S. SUTTON INC.; *U.S. Private*, pg. 1307
EX OFFICIO, LLC—See Newell Brands Inc.; *U.S. Public*, pg. 1514
EXTRA SPORTS WEAR INC.; *U.S. Private*, pg. 1452
FANNIN INDUSTRIES INCORPORATED; *U.S. Private*, pg. 1472
FASHION DYNAMICS SINGAPORE PTE LTD.—See FJ Benjamin Holdings Ltd.; *Int'l*, pg. 2697
FASHIONOLOGY GROUP LLC—See Hilco Trading, LLC; *U.S. Private*, pg. 1943
FASHIONOLOGY GROUP LLC—See Tengram Capital Partners, Limited Partnership; *U.S. Private*, pg. 3967
FLEET STREET LTD.; *U.S. Private*, pg. 1542
FNG GROUP NV; *Int'l*, pg. 2718
FORIA INTERNATIONAL INC.; *U.S. Private*, pg. 1569
FORMOUS CORP.; *Int'l*, pg. 2736
FOWNES BROTHERS & CO., INC.; *U.S. Private*, pg. 1583
FOX HEAD CANADA, INC.—See Vista Outdoor Inc.; *U.S. Public*, pg. 2305
FOX HEAD EUROPE, SL—See Vista Outdoor Inc.; *U.S. Public*, pg. 2305
FOX RACING U.S.A. INC.—See Vista Outdoor Inc.; *U.S. Public*, pg. 2305
FREE PEOPLE—See Urban Outfitters, Inc.; *U.S. Public*, pg. 2265
FRESH PRODUCE SPORTSWEAR INC.; *U.S. Private*, pg. 1610
FU DA INTERNATIONAL LTD; *U.S. Private*, pg. 1619
FUTAI USA INC.; *U.S. Private*, pg. 1626
GATOR OF FLORIDA INCORPORATED; *U.S. Private*, pg. 1651
GAZAL CORPORATION LIMITED—See PVH Corp.; *U.S. Public*, pg. 1739
GB GMBH—See Goodbaby International Holdings Limited; *Int'l*, pg. 3039
GERBER CHILDRENSWEAR LLC - GREENVILLE OPERATIONS CENTER—See Gerber Childrenswear LLC; *U.S. Private*, pg. 1686
GERBER CHILDRENSWEAR LLC; *U.S. Private*, pg. 1686
GERRY WEBER INTERNATIONAL AG; *Int'l*, pg. 2944
GGUMBI CO,. LTD.; *Int'l*, pg. 2958
GIGLIO.COM S.P.A.; *Int'l*, pg. 2972
GILDAN ACTIVEWEAR DISTRIBUTION INC.—See Gildan Activewear Inc.; *Int'l*, pg. 2973
GILDAN ACTIVEWEAR (EDEN) INC.—See Gildan Activewear Inc.; *Int'l*, pg. 2973
GINZA YAMAGATAYA CO., LTD.; *Int'l*, pg. 2977
GIORDANO LIMITED—See Giordano International Limited; *Int'l*, pg. 2977
GIORDANO ORIGINALS (SINGAPORE) PRIVATE LTD—See Giordano International Limited; *Int'l*, pg. 2978
GIORGIO ARMANI CORPORATION—See Giorgio Armani S.p.A.; *Int'l*, pg. 2978
GIORGIO ARMANI DISTRIBUZIONE SRL—See Giorgio Armani S.p.A.; *Int'l*, pg. 2978
GIORGIO ARMANI RETAIL SRL—See Giorgio Armani S.p.A.; *Int'l*, pg. 2978
GLOBAL CLOTHING NETWORK INC.; *U.S. Private*, pg. 1712
GLOBAL STYLE CO., LTD.; *Int'l*, pg. 3001
GLOSS MIND APPAREL (HONG KONG) LIMITED—See Giordano International Limited; *Int'l*, pg. 2978
GLOVES INTERNATIONAL INC.; *U.S. Private*, pg. 1720
GMA ACCESSORIES/CAPELLI OF NEW YORK; *U.S. Private*, pg. 1721
GNO INTERNATIONAL LLC; *U.S. Private*, pg. 1723
GOLDLION DISTRIBUTION (M) SDN. BHD.—See Goldlion Holdings Limited; *Int'l*, pg. 3033
GOLDLION ENTERPRISE (SINGAPORE) PTE LIMITED—See Goldlion Holdings Limited; *Int'l*, pg. 3033
GOLDSTONE HOSIERY CO. INC.; *U.S. Private*, pg. 1735
GREINER'S INC.; *U.S. Private*, pg. 1783
GROUPE DYNAMITE INC.; *Int'l*, pg. 3102
GROUP E LTD. INC.; *U.S. Private*, pg. 1793
GSI CREOS BRASIL LTDA—See GSI Creos Corporation; *Int'l*, pg. 3144
GTM SPORTSWEAR; *U.S. Private*, pg. 1807
GUANGZHOU CABBEEN CLOTHING CO., LTD.—See Cabbeen Fashion Limited; *Int'l*, pg. 1245
G.U. CO., LTD.—See Fast Retailing Co., Ltd.; *Int'l*, pg. 2621
GUNZE DISTRIBUTION CO., LTD.—See Gunze Limited; *Int'l*, pg. 3185
GUNZE INTERNATIONAL HONG KONG LIMITED—See Gunze Limited; *Int'l*, pg. 3185
H2O SHOPPING CENTER DEVELOPMENT CO. LTD.—See H2O Retailing Corp.; *Int'l*, pg. 3200
HAAS OUTDOORS INC.; *U.S. Private*, pg. 1837
HADDAD APPAREL GROUP, LTD.; *U.S. Private*, pg. 1838
HADDAD ORGANIZATION LTD.; *U.S. Private*, pg. 1839
HAGGAR CANADA CO.—See Perseus LLC; *U.S. Private*, pg. 3155
HAMCO, INC.—See Crown Crafts, Inc.; *U.S. Public*, pg. 596
HAMPSHIRE BRANDS—See Hampshire Group Limited; *U.S. Private*, pg. 1851
HAMPSHIRE DESIGNERS, INC. NY—See Hampshire Group Limited; *U.S. Private*, pg. 1851
HAMPSHIRE DESIGNERS, INC. SC—See Hampshire Group Limited; *U.S. Private*, pg. 1851
HAMPTON SPORTSWEAR (PTY) LIMITED—See AVI Limited; *Int'l*, pg. 740
HANESBRANDS DIRECT, LLC—See Hanesbrands Inc.; *U.S. Public*, pg. 983
HANESBRANDS PHILIPPINES INC.—See Hanesbrands Inc.; *U.S. Public*, pg. 983
HANESBRANDS ROH ASIA LTD.—See Hanesbrands Inc.; *U.S. Public*, pg. 983
HARRY J. RASHTI & CO. INC.; *U.S. Private*, pg. 1872
HARTSTRINGS LLC—See Parigi Group Ltd; *U.S. Private*, pg. 3094
H&C HEADWEAR-CHICAGO—See H&C Headwear Inc.; *U.S. Private*, pg. 1822
H&C HEADWEAR-DALLAS—See H&C Headwear Inc.; *U.S. Private*, pg. 1822
H&C HEADWEAR INC.; *U.S. Private*, pg. 1822
HELLY HANSEN BENELUX B.V.—See Canadian Tire Corporation Limited; *Int'l*, pg. 1286
HELLY-HANSEN DEUTSCHLAND GMBH—See Canadian Tire Corporation Limited; *Int'l*, pg. 1286
HELLY HANSEN SCHWEIZ AG—See Canadian Tire Corporation Limited; *Int'l*, pg. 1286
HEMAS MANUFACTURING (PTE) LTD—See Hemas Holdings PLC; *Int'l*, pg. 3340
HIGH FASHION KNIT COMPANY LIMITED—See High Fashion International Limited; *Int'l*, pg. 3385
HIMARAYA CO., LTD.; *Int'l*, pg. 3396
HI-ROLLERS SPORTSWEAR LTD.—See E.S. Sutton Inc.; *U.S. Private*, pg. 1307
HIT UNION COMPANY LTD.; *Int'l*, pg. 3408
H&M HENNES & MAURITZ FAR EAST LTD—See H&M Hennes & Mauritz AB; *Int'l*, pg. 3192
H&M HENNES & MAURITZ (HK) LTD—See H&M Hennes & Mauritz AB; *Int'l*, pg. 3192
H&M HENNES & MAURITZ SP.Z.O.O.—See H&M Hennes & Mauritz AB; *Int'l*, pg. 3192

N.A.I.C.S. INDEX 424350 — CLOTHING AND CLOTHI...

N.A.I.C.S. Index

H&M HENNES & MAURITZ S.R.L.—See H&M Hennes & Mauritz AB; *Int'l*, pg. 3192
HOT TUNA AUSTRALIA PTY LTD.—See Concha plc; *Int'l*, pg. 1764
IDEA NUOVA INC.; *U.S. Private*, pg. 2035
IDEELI INC.—See Groupon Inc.; *U.S. Public*, pg. 972
IKE BEHAR APPAREL & DESIGN LTD.; *U.S. Private*, pg. 2041
IMAGE FIRST PROFESSIONAL AP; *U.S. Private*, pg. 2044
INDUSTRIAS OXFORD DE MERIDA S.A. DE CV—See Oxford Industries, Inc.; *U.S. Public*, pg. 1629
INTERNATIONAL INTIMATES, INC.; *U.S. Private*, pg. 2118
INTIMO INC.; *U.S. Private*, pg. 2128
INTRADECO APPAREL, INC.—See Intradeco, Inc.; *U.S. Private*, pg. 2129
INTRADECO, INC.; *U.S. Private*, pg. 2129
ISACO INTERNATIONAL INC.; *U.S. Private*, pg. 2142
IT USA INC.; *U.S. Private*, pg. 2148
IVORY INTERNATIONAL, INC.; *U.S. Private*, pg. 2151
JACKSON CORPORATION; *U.S. Private*, pg. 2176
JACQUES MORET, INC.; *U.S. Private*, pg. 2180
JADE EASTERN TRADING INC.; *U.S. Private*, pg. 2181
JANTZEN INC.—See Perry Ellis International, Inc.; *U.S. Private*, pg. 3154
JAYLYN SALES INC.; *U.S. Private*, pg. 2192
J. BREED CLOTHING INC.; *U.S. Private*, pg. 2155
JONES APPAREL GROUP CANADA, LP—See Premier Brands Group Holdings LLC; *U.S. Private*, pg. 3249
JONES INTERNATIONAL LIMITED—See Premier Brands Group Holdings LLC; *U.S. Private*, pg. 3249
JONES & MITCHELL SPORTSWEAR—See Boxercraft Incorporated; *U.S. Private*, pg. 626
JONES NEW YORK OUTERWEAR—See Amerex Group, Inc.; *U.S. Private*, pg. 219
JOY MARK INC.; *U.S. Private*, pg. 2238
JUNIOR GALLERY LTD.; *U.S. Private*, pg. 2244
J.W.E. INC.; *U.S. Private*, pg. 2172
KAKTUS SPORTSWEAR INC.; *U.S. Private*, pg. 2256
KAPPA FRANCE S.A.S.—See BasicNet S.p.A.; *Int'l*, pg. 886
KARMALOOP LLC—See Shiekh LLC; *U.S. Private*, pg. 3635
KATE SPADE JAPAN CO., LTD.—See Tapestry, Inc.; *U.S. Public*, pg. 1981
KATE SPADE LLC—See Tapestry, Inc.; *U.S. Public*, pg. 1981
KAYSER-ROTH CORPORATION—See Golden Lady S.p.A.; *Int'l*, pg. 3030
KELLWOOD COMPANY—See Sun Capital Partners, Inc.; *U.S. Private*, pg. 3859
KELLWOOD COMPANY - WESTERN REGION—See Sun Capital Partners, Inc.; *U.S. Private*, pg. 3859
KENNETH COLE PRODUCTIONS, INC.—See KCP Holdco, Inc.; *U.S. Private*, pg. 2270
KENNETH GORDON/IAG, INC.—See Individualized Apparel Group; *U.S. Private*, pg. 2064
KENVIN INCORPORATED; *U.S. Private*, pg. 2289
KEVIN'S WHOLESALE LLC; *U.S. Private*, pg. 2292
KIZAN INTERNATIONAL INC.; *U.S. Private*, pg. 2317
KNICK KNACK, INC.; *U.S. Private*, pg. 2322
KNITWORK PRODUCTIONS CORP.; *U.S. Private*, pg. 2322
KNITWORKS DESIGN ZONE, INC.; *U.S. Private*, pg. 2322
KNL INCORPORATED; *U.S. Private*, pg. 2322
KNOT STANDARD, LLC—See Billy Reid, Inc.; *U.S. Private*, pg. 559
KOMAN SPORTSWEAR MANUFACTURING CORP.; *U.S. Private*, pg. 2341
KOMODIDAD DISTRIBUTORS INC.; *U.S. Private*, pg. 2342
LANSINOH LABORATORIES INC.; *U.S. Private*, pg. 2390
LANVIN INC.—See Fosun International Limited; *Int'l*, pg. 2751
LA REDOUTE CATALOG BENELUX—See Galeries Lafayette SA; *Int'l*, pg. 2872
LA REDOUTE SUISSE SA—See Galeries Lafayette SA; *Int'l*, pg. 2872
LA REGALE LLC; *U.S. Private*, pg. 2369
LARRY L. ROTHCHILD'S—See S. Rothschild & Co., Inc.; *U.S. Private*, pg. 3515
L.A.T APPAREL, LLC; *U.S. Private*, pg. 2364
LEADING LADY COMPANIES; *U.S. Private*, pg. 2406
LEONARD A. FEINBERG INCORPORATED; *U.S. Private*, pg. 2423
LEVI STRAUSS & CO.—See Levi Strauss & Co.; *U.S. Public*, pg. 1308
LEVI STRAUSS & CO.—See Levi Strauss & Co.; *U.S. Public*, pg. 1308
LEVI STRAUSS & CO.—See Levi Strauss & Co.; *U.S. Public*, pg. 1308
LIFE SPORT LTD.—See adidas AG; *Int'l*, pg. 146
LILLA P LLC; *U.S. Private*, pg. 2455
L&L MANUFACTURING CO.; *U.S. Private*, pg. 2363
LMC RIGHT START, INC.—See giggle, Inc.; *U.S. Private*, pg. 1697
LOLLYTOGS, LTD.; *U.S. Private*, pg. 2483
LOLLYTOGS—See Lollytogs, Ltd.; *U.S. Private*, pg. 2483
LOUISE PARIS LTD.; *U.S. Private*, pg. 2499
LOUIS FERAUD INC.—See Feraud Sarl; *Int'l*, pg. 2635
LOU LEVY & SONS FASHIONS INC.; *U.S. Private*, pg. 2498
L.S.C., LLC—See Komar Company; *U.S. Private*, pg. 2341
LULU'S; *U.S. Private*, pg. 2513
MAD ENGINE, LLC—See Platinum Equity, LLC; *U.S. Private*, pg. 3205
MADISON MAIDEN; *U.S. Private*, pg. 2544
MAMIYE SALES, INC.; *U.S. Private*, pg. 2559
MARAN INC.; *U.S. Private*, pg. 2569
MARCRAFT APPAREL GROUP; *U.S. Private*, pg. 2572
MARINA, INC.—See Jump Design Group; *U.S. Private*, pg. 2243
MARKER VOLKL (INTERNATIONAL) SALES GMBH—See Kohlberg & Company, LLC; *U.S. Private*, pg. 2338
MARMOT MOUNTAIN EUROPE GMBH—See Newell Brands Inc.; *U.S. Public*, pg. 1514
MATCHPOINT; *U.S. Private*, pg. 2609
MAYER/BERKSHIRE CORPORATION; *U.S. Private*, pg. 2621
THE MCCALL PATTERN COMPANY, INC.—See IG Design Group Plc; *Int'l*, pg. 3600
MCCALL PATTERN COMPANY LIMITED—See IG Design Group Plc; *Int'l*, pg. 3600
MCCUBBIN HOSIERY, LLC—See Guardian Capital Partners, LLC; *U.S. Private*, pg. 1810
MEDIUSA, LP.; *U.S. Private*, pg. 2657
MERCHANDIZE LIQUIDATORS, LLC; *U.S. Private*, pg. 2669
M&F WESTERN PRODUCTS INC.; *U.S. Private*, pg. 2524
M HIDARY & COMPANY INC.; *U.S. Private*, pg. 2523
MICHAEL GERALD LTD. INC.; *U.S. Private*, pg. 2697
MICHAEL STARS, INC.; *U.S. Private*, pg. 2698
MIDWEST APPAREL GROUP INC.; *U.S. Private*, pg. 2719
MIKEN SALES INC.; *U.S. Private*, pg. 2726
MISS SPORTSWEAR INC.; *U.S. Private*, pg. 2746
MIZRAHI ENTERPRISES INC.; *U.S. Private*, pg. 2752
MJC ACQUISITION, LLC—See Webster Equity Partners, LLC; *U.S. Private*, pg. 4467
MMARTAN TEXTIL LTDA.—See Coteminas Companhia de Tecidos Norte de Minas; *Int'l*, pg. 1817
M & M DIRECT LIMITED—See Bestseller A/S; *Int'l*, pg. 1000
MOBILE EIGHT APPAREL CORP—See Mobile Eight Holding Ltd.; *U.S. Private*, pg. 2757
MORNING LAVENDER LLC; *U.S. Private*, pg. 2785
MOSAIC BRANDS LTD—See Alceon Group Pty Ltd.; *Int'l*, pg. 300
MOTENG INTERNATIONAL INCORPORATED; *U.S. Private*, pg. 2795
THE MOUNTAIN CORPORATION—See Gladstone Management Corporation; *U.S. Private*, pg. 1705
MS BUBBLES INC.; *U.S. Private*, pg. 2806
MY MICHELLE—See Sun Capital Partners, Inc.; *U.S. Private*, pg. 3859
NATIONAL WHOLESALE COMPANY INC.; *U.S. Private*, pg. 2864
NEWPORT APPAREL CORPORATION; *U.S. Private*, pg. 2916
NEW WORLD IMPORTS INC.; *U.S. Private*, pg. 2908
NINE WEST GROUP, INC.—See Premier Brands Group Holdings LLC; *U.S. Private*, pg. 3249
NINE WEST JEANSWEAR GROUP, INC.—See Premier Brands Group Holdings LLC; *U.S. Private*, pg. 3249
NORM THOMPSON OUTFITTERS INC.—See Bluestem Brands, Inc.; *U.S. Private*, pg. 598
THE NORTHWEST COMPANY; *U.S. Private*, pg. 4084
O&K INC.; *U.S. Private*, pg. 2977
OMNIBUS PRESS—See Music Sales Corporation; *U.S. Private*, pg. 2818
ONE 3 TWO, INC.; *U.S. Private*, pg. 3020
ORBIT BABY, INC.—See Compass Diversified Holdings; *U.S. Public*, pg. 560
OTOMIX, INC.; *U.S. Private*, pg. 3049
OTTO INTERNATIONAL INC.; *U.S. Private*, pg. 3050
OUTRAGEOUS INC.; *U.S. Private*, pg. 3051
OXFORD PRODUCTS (INTERNATIONAL) LIMITED—See Oxford Industries, Inc.; *U.S. Public*, pg. 1629
PACIFIC TRAIL INC.—See Columbia Sportswear Company; *U.S. Public*, pg. 535
PACO SPORT LTD. INC.; *U.S. Private*, pg. 3073
PAIGE DENIM—See TSG Consumer Partners LLC; *U.S. Private*, pg. 4253
PARIGI GROUP LTD; *U.S. Private*, pg. 3094
PARIGI INTERNATIONAL INC.; *U.S. Private*, pg. 3094
PERRY ELLIS EUROPE LIMITED—See Perry Ellis International, Inc.; *U.S. Private*, pg. 3154
PKA KLOCKER GMBH—See Bunzl plc; *Int'l*, pg. 1219
PLAYTEX PRODUCTS, LLC—See Edgewell Personal Care Company; *U.S. Public*, pg. 718
PLUGG—See Andrew Sports Club Inc.; *U.S. Private*, pg. 280
PRANA LIVING, LLC—See Columbia Sportswear Company; *U.S. Public*, pg. 535
PREGER & WERTENTEIL, INC.; *U.S. Private*, pg. 3248
PRIVATE LABEL BY G INC.; *U.S. Private*, pg. 3268
PROMGIRL, LLC; *U.S. Private*, pg. 3283
PSFK LLC; *U.S. Private*, pg. 3297
PUBLIC CLOTHING COMPANY INC.; *U.S. Private*, pg. 3298
PURPLEREAL.COM, CORP.; *U.S. Private*, pg. 3307
PVH FINLAND OY—See PVH Corp.; *U.S. Public*, pg. 1739
PVH SUPERBA/INSIGNIA NECKWEAR, INC.—See PVH Corp.; *U.S. Public*, pg. 1739
PVH WHOLESALE CORP.—See PVH Corp.; *U.S. Public*, pg. 1739
QST INDUSTRIES (SHANGHAI) CO., LTD.—See QST Industries, Inc.; *U.S. Private*, pg. 3314
QUINN APPAREL INC.; *U.S. Private*, pg. 3328
QUIZZ SPORTSWEAR INC.; *U.S. Private*, pg. 3329
RAFAELLA APPAREL GROUP, INC.—See Perry Ellis International, Inc.; *U.S. Private*, pg. 3154
RAINBOW WEST APPAREL, INC.—See Platinum Equity, LLC; *U.S. Private*, pg. 3203
RALPH LAUREN FRANCE S.A.S.—See Ralph Lauren Corporation; *U.S. Public*, pg. 1761
THE RALPH LAUREN WOMENSWEAR COMPANY, L.P.—See Ralph Lauren Corporation; *U.S. Public*, pg. 1762
RAM GRAPHICS, INC.; *U.S. Private*, pg. 3351
RANDA NECKWEAR CORP.—See Randa Corp.; *U.S. Private*, pg. 3353
REBORN PRODUCTS CO., INC.—See Kinderhook Industries, LLC; *U.S. Private*, pg. 2307
REDCATS ITALY S.R.L.—See Galeries Lafayette SA; *Int'l*, pg. 2872
REGENT INTERNATIONAL; *U.S. Private*, pg. 3387
RENOWN INX INCORPORATED—See Atsugi Co., Ltd.; *Int'l*, pg. 696
RETAIL 161 LIMITED—See Hallenstein Glasson Holdings Limited; *Int'l*, pg. 3230
RE-UNION DIVISION—See Seattle Pacific Industries, Inc.; *U.S. Private*, pg. 3592
R.G. RILEY & SONS INC.; *U.S. Private*, pg. 3336
RICHARD CANTRELL; *U.S. Private*, pg. 3428
RIPT APPAREL, LLC; *U.S. Private*, pg. 3440
R&N KNITTED; *U.S. Private*, pg. 3332
ROOCHI TRADERS (NY) INC.; *U.S. Private*, pg. 3478
ROUNDY APPAREL; *U.S. Private*, pg. 3489
ROYCE APPAREL INC.; *U.S. Private*, pg. 3494
ROYTEX, INC.; *U.S. Private*, pg. 3494
R. SISKIND & CO. INC.; *U.S. Private*, pg. 3334
SAG HARBOR—See Sun Capital Partners, Inc.; *U.S. Private*, pg. 3859
THE SAK—See Indonesian Imports, Inc.; *U.S. Private*, pg. 2064
SAMARA BROTHERS LLC; *U.S. Private*, pg. 3536
SAN MAR CORPORATION; *U.S. Private*, pg. 3542
SARAMAX APPAREL GROUP INC.; *U.S. Private*, pg. 3549
SASHA HANDBAGS INC.; *U.S. Private*, pg. 3552
SA VIGNOBLES DE LAROSE—See Allianz SE; *Int'l*, pg. 355
SCALA EVENINGWEAR, INC.; *U.S. Private*, pg. 3560
SCHIESSER INTERNATIONAL NEDERLAND BV—See GMM Capital LLC; *U.S. Private*, pg. 1722
SCOPE IMPORTS INC.; *U.S. Private*, pg. 3575
SEAMLESS TEXTILES, LLC—See Hanesbrands Inc.; *U.S. Public*, pg. 983
SEATTLE PACIFIC INDUSTRIES, INC.; *U.S. Private*, pg. 3592
SEATTLE PACIFIC INDUSTRIES, INC., UNIONBAY DIVISION—See Seattle Pacific Industries, Inc.; *U.S. Private*, pg. 3592
SEIGO CO., LTD.—See AOYAMA TRADING Co. Ltd.; *Int'l*, pg. 499
SHAW CREATIONS, INC.; *U.S. Private*, pg. 3627
SHEKNOWS LLC—See Great Hill Partners, L.P.; *U.S. Private*, pg. 1763
SHOPFORBAGS INC.; *U.S. Private*, pg. 3640
SIA SANGAR TRADING—See AS Sangar; *Int'l*, pg. 591
SIMINT S.P.A.—See Giorgio Armani S.p.A.; *Int'l*, pg. 2978
SKIVA INTERNATIONAL INC.; *U.S. Private*, pg. 3682
SKY HIGH UNLIMITED INC.; *U.S. Private*, pg. 3684
S.L. GILBERT COMPANY INC.; *U.S. Private*, pg. 3518
SMITH & EDWARDS COMPANY; *U.S. Private*, pg. 3693
SONETTE, INC.; *U.S. Private*, pg. 3712
SOUTH MOON SALES, INC.—See Ames Watson Holding LLC; *U.S. Private*, pg. 262
SPEX CLOTHING COMPANY INC.; *U.S. Private*, pg. 3756
SPORTIF USA INC.; *U.S. Private*, pg. 3760
STAR OF INDIA FASHIONS, INC.; *U.S. Private*, pg. 3785
STARWEAR INC.; *U.S. Private*, pg. 3788
STATON WHOLESALE INC.; *U.S. Private*, pg. 3793
STAUFFER GLOVE & SAFETY; *U.S. Private*, pg. 3794
ST. EVE INTERNATIONAL, INC.—See Komar Company; *U.S. Private*, pg. 2341
STEVE SELVIN ASSOCIATE INC; *U.S. Private*, pg. 3808
SUMMIT RIDGE CORPORATION; *U.S. Private*, pg. 3857
SUNDANCE CATALOG CO., LTD.—See Brentwood Associates; *U.S. Private*, pg. 646
SUPERIOR UNIFORM GROUP, INC. - MARTIN'S UNIFORMS DIVISION—See Superior Group Of Companies, Inc.; *U.S. Public*, pg. 1966
TANZARA INTERNATIONAL INC.; *U.S. Private*, pg. 3932
TAWIL ASSOCIATES INC.; *U.S. Private*, pg. 3937
TCX, LLC—See Delta Apparel, Inc.; *U.S. Public*, pg. 652
TEAMLINE, LTD.—See Bain Capital, LP; *U.S. Private*, pg. 451
TEXCOTE TECHNOLOGY (INTERNATIONAL) LIMITED—See Fullsun International Holdings Group Co., Limited; *Int'l*, pg. 2843
TIPSY ELVES LLC; *U.S. Private*, pg. 4176
TORRID INC.; *U.S. Private*, pg. 4190

424350 — CLOTHING AND CLOTHI...

TOTES ISOTONER CANADA LTD.—See Freeman Spogli & Co. Incorporated; *U.S. Private*, pg. 1606
TOTES ISOTONER (UK) LIMITED—See Freeman Spogli & Co. Incorporated; *U.S. Private*, pg. 1606
TO THE GAME, LLC—See Delta Apparel, Inc.; *U.S. Public*, pg. 652
TSC APPAREL, LLC—See Clayton, Dubilier & Rice, LLC; *U.S. Private*, pg. 926
TSHIRTBORDELLO.COM; *U.S. Private*, pg. 4253
TURBO HOLDINGS INC.; *U.S. Private*, pg. 4259
TUXEDO JUNCTION INC.; *U.S. Private*, pg. 4263
UNIFIRST CORPORATION; *U.S. Public*, pg. 2226
U-RIGHT GARMENTS LIMITED—See Fullsun International Holdings Group Co., Limited; *Int'l*, pg. 2843
USF COLLECTIONS INC.; *U.S. Private*, pg. 4323
VAN DALE INDUSTRIES INC.; *U.S. Private*, pg. 4339
VANETTI INC.; *U.S. Private*, pg. 4343
VAULT SPORTSWEAR, INC.; *U.S. Private*, pg. 4348
VBQ ACQUISITION B.V.—See G-III Apparel Group, Ltd.; *U.S. Public*, pg. 894
VENUS SWIMWEAR, INC.—See Golden Gate Capital Management II, LLC; *U.S. Private*, pg. 1731
VF ASIA LTD.—See V. F. Corporation; *U.S. Public*, pg. 2269
VF CZECH S.R.O.—See V. F. Corporation; *U.S. Public*, pg. 2269
VF EUROPE B.V.B.A.—See V. F. Corporation; *U.S. Public*, pg. 2269
VF SPORTSWEAR, INC.—See V. F. Corporation; *U.S. Public*, pg. 2269
VINCE, LLC—See Sun Capital Partners, Inc.; *U.S. Private*, pg. 3860
VIRGINIA T'S INC.; *U.S. Private*, pg. 4388
WATUMULL BROTHERS LTD. INC.; *U.S. Private*, pg. 4456
WEAR FIRST SPORTSWEAR INC.; *U.S. Private*, pg. 4462
WHITE + WARREN; *U.S. Private*, pg. 4508
WHITEWATER OUTDOORS INCORPORATED; *U.S. Private*, pg. 4512
WILK SHIRT CORP.; *U.S. Private*, pg. 4520
WILLIAM B. COLEMAN CO., INC.; *U.S. Private*, pg. 4522
WOLFORD AMERICA, INC.—See Fosun International Limited; *Int'l*, pg. 2752
XOXO—See Sun Capital Partners, Inc.; *U.S. Private*, pg. 3860
YICK FUNG FUR LTD.; *U.S. Private*, pg. 4589
YOOX ASIA LIMITED—See Compagnie Financiere Richemont S.A.; *Int'l*, pg. 1741
ZANELLA LTD.; *U.S. Private*, pg. 4597
Z. CAVARICCI INC.; *U.S. Private*, pg. 4596
ZORREL INTERNATIONAL, INC.; *U.S. Private*, pg. 4609

424410 — GENERAL LINE GROCERY MERCHANT WHOLESALERS

ACE ENDICO CORP.; *U.S. Private*, pg. 56
ACTION FOOD SALES INC.; *U.S. Private*, pg. 67
ADAMS WHOLESALE COMPANY; *U.S. Private*, pg. 75
ADVANCE SALES & MARKETING INC.; *U.S. Private*, pg. 87
ADVANTAGE SALES & MARKETING, LLC - SCHAUMBURG—See Leonard Green & Partners, L.P.; *U.S. Private*, pg. 2423
ADVANTAGE SALES & MARKETING LLC—See Leonard Green & Partners, L.P.; *U.S. Private*, pg. 2423
AFFILIATED FOODS, INC.; *U.S. Private*, pg. 121
AGRI-WEST INTERNATIONAL INC.; *U.S. Private*, pg. 129
ALI BIN ALI & PARTNERS—See Ali Bin Ali Establishment; *Int'l*, pg. 320
ALSTONS MARKETING COMPANY LIMITED—See ANSA McAL Limited; *Int'l*, pg. 477
AMCON DISTRIBUTING COMPANY; *U.S. Public*, pg. 92
AMERICAN ACE INTERNATIONAL CO.; *U.S. Private*, pg. 221
AMERICAN FOOD DISTRIBUTORS; *U.S. Private*, pg. 234
ARCOR A.G.—See Arcor Sociedad Anonima, Industrial y Comercial; *Int'l*, pg. 550
ARGIS-GALAC SEA; *Int'l*, pg. 561
ARM NATIONAL FOOD INC.; *U.S. Private*, pg. 329
ASSOCIATED FOOD STORES, INC.; *U.S. Private*, pg. 355
ASSOCIATED GROCERS, INC.; *U.S. Private*, pg. 356
ASSOCIATED GROCERS OF FLORIDA, INC.—See United Natural Foods, Inc.; *U.S. Public*, pg. 2231
ASSOCIATED GROCERS OF NEW ENGLAND, INC.; *U.S. Private*, pg. 355
ASSOCIATED GROCERS OF THE SOUTH, INC.; *U.S. Private*, pg. 356
ASSOCIATED WHOLESALE GROCERS, INC.; *U.S. Private*, pg. 357
ASTRA SUPERMARKET AND COMMERCIAL DIVISION—See Arab Supply & Trading Co.; *Int'l*, pg. 532
ATKINSON-CRAWFORD SALES CO.; *U.S. Private*, pg. 369
ATLANTIC FISH & DISTRIBUTING CO.; *U.S. Private*, pg. 373
AUSTRALIAN UNITED GROCERS PTY LTD—See Australian United Retailers Limited; *Int'l*, pg. 722
AXFOOD NARLIVS AB—See Axel Johnson Gruppen AB; *Int'l*, pg. 764
BAAZEEM TRADING COMPANY; *Int'l*, pg. 792

BALLESTER HERMANOS INC.; *U.S. Private*, pg. 461
BANGKOK MARKET INC.; *U.S. Private*, pg. 465
BANNER WHOLESALE GROCERS, INC.; *U.S. Private*, pg. 469
BASIC SALES & MARKETING; *U.S. Private*, pg. 485
B&B BEST-BUY FOODS INC.; *U.S. Private*, pg. 417
B&D SALES & MARKETING, INC.; *U.S. Private*, pg. 418
BEN E. KEITH COMPANY; *U.S. Private*, pg. 522
BENGARD MARKETING, INC.—See GrubMarket, Inc.; *U.S. Private*, pg. 1797
BETHEL-ECKERT ENTERPRISES INC.; *U.S. Private*, pg. 545
B. GREEN & CO.; *U.S. Private*, pg. 419
BIOPARK, S.R.O.—See CPI Property Group, S.A.; *Int'l*, pg. 1825
BI-RITE SERVICE FOOD CO.; *U.S. Private*, pg. 550
BLACKBURN-RUSSELL CO. INC.; *U.S. Private*, pg. 573
BLACK GOLD POTATO SALES INC.; *U.S. Private*, pg. 572
B&M EUROPEAN VALUE RETAIL S.A.; *Int'l*, pg. 784
BOGOPA ENTERPRISES INC.; *U.S. Private*, pg. 609
BOZZUTO'S INC.; *U.S. Private*, pg. 629
BRAKE BROS LTD. - ASHFORD HEAD OFFICE—See Sysco Corporation; *U.S. Public*, pg. 1973
BROTHERS TRADING CO. INC.; *U.S. Private*, pg. 665
BROWN FOODSERVICE, INC.; *U.S. Private*, pg. 667
BUTLER WHOLESALE PRODUCTS, INC.; *U.S. Private*, pg. 697
C. A. CURTZE COMPANY INC.; *U.S. Private*, pg. 704
CANTON FOOD COMPANY; *U.S. Private*, pg. 735
CARAMAGNO FOODS COMPANY; *U.S. Private*, pg. 748
CARO FOODS, INC.—See Performance Food Group Company; *U.S. Public*, pg. 1674
CARQUEST OF BUTTE—See Advance Auto Parts, Inc.; *U.S. Public*, pg. 45
CARROLL COUNTY FOODS, INC.—See Performance Food Group Company; *U.S. Public*, pg. 1674
CASH & CARRY GROCER INC.; *U.S. Private*, pg. 782
CASTELL HOWELL FOODS LTD.; *Int'l*, pg. 1356
CASTUS A/S—See FMCG Business Partner AB; *Int'l*, pg. 2717
CB DISTRIBUTORS, INC.; *U.S. Private*, pg. 796
CD HARTNETT COMPANY; *U.S. Private*, pg. 801
C&D TRADING INC.; *U.S. Private*, pg. 702
CENTRAL GROCERS CO-OP; *U.S. Private*, pg. 821
CERTIFIED WHOLESALERS INC.—See Associated Grocers of New England, Inc.; *U.S. Private*, pg. 356
C&G FOOD BROKERAGE INC.; *U.S. Private*, pg. 703
CHEVALIER INTERNATIONAL (USA), INC.—See Chevalier International Holdings Limited; *Int'l*, pg. 1473
CHEX FINER FOODS; *U.S. Private*, pg. 876
CHOICE FOODSERVICES, INC.; *U.S. Private*, pg. 888
CITY WIDE GOURMET FOODS INC.; *U.S. Private*, pg. 907
CJ FOODS, INC.—See CJ Corporation; *Int'l*, pg. 1631
COASTAL PACIFIC FOOD DISTRIBUTORS, INC.; *U.S. Private*, pg. 956
COHEN FOODS, INC.; *U.S. Private*, pg. 962
COLON BROTHERS INC.; *U.S. Private*, pg. 970
COMMERCE SUPERVALU WEST REGION—See United Natural Foods, Inc.; *U.S. Public*, pg. 2231
CONCO FOOD SERVICE—See Performance Food Group Company; *U.S. Public*, pg. 1675
CONDAL DISTRIBUTORS INC.; *U.S. Private*, pg. 1011
CORE-MARK HOLDING CO. INC.; *U.S. Public*, pg. 576
CORR-WILLIAMS COMPANY; *U.S. Private*, pg. 1058
CORTLAND PRODUCE COMPANY INC.; *U.S. Private*, pg. 1061
COSTA FARMS, LLC; *U.S. Private*, pg. 1062
CPG SALES & MARKETING INC.; *U.S. Private*, pg. 1080
C&S WHOLESALE GROCERS, INC.; *U.S. Private*, pg. 704
CW BROWER INC.; *U.S. Private*, pg. 1132
CYBA-STEVENS MANAGEMENT GROUP; *Int'l*, pg. 1891
DAGAB AB—See Axel Johnson Gruppen AB; *Int'l*, pg. 764
DAN VALLEY FOODS INC.; *U.S. Private*, pg. 1152
DEARBORN WHOLESALE GROCERS LP; *U.S. Private*, pg. 1185
DIAGEO BRANDS BV—See Diageo plc; *Int'l*, pg. 2102
DIAZ WHOLESALE & MANUFACTURING CO., INC.; *U.S. Private*, pg. 1225
DI GIORGIO CORPORATION—See Rose Partners LP; *U.S. Private*, pg. 3481
DISTAL INC.—See Gordon Food Service Inc.; *U.S. Private*, pg. 1743
DOLCE EUROPA—See International Gourmet Foods Inc.; *U.S. Private*, pg. 2117
DPI SPECIALTY FOODS, INC.—See KeHE Distributors, LLC; *U.S. Private*, pg. 2273
DPI WEST—See KeHE Distributors, LLC; *U.S. Private*, pg. 2273
DYNACO INC.; *U.S. Private*, pg. 1297
EBY-BROWN, COMPANY, LLC—See Performance Food Group Company; *U.S. Public*, pg. 1674
EBY-BROWN CO.—See Performance Food Group Company; *U.S. Public*, pg. 1674
EBY-BROWN MID-ATLANTIC—See Performance Food Group Company; *U.S. Public*, pg. 1674
ECHO INTERNATIONAL CO.; *U.S. Private*, pg. 1327
ECONOMY CASH & CARRY INC.; *U.S. Private*, pg. 1330
EDEN & TYE INC.; *U.S. Private*, pg. 1333

EHRLICH FOOD COMPANY INC.; *U.S. Private*, pg. 1346
ELLA'S KITCHEN (BRANDS) LIMITED—See The Hain Celestial Group, Inc.; *U.S. Public*, pg. 2086
ELLENBEE-LEGGETT COMPANY INC.; *U.S. Private*, pg. 1363
EL SOL FOODS LLC—See Cacique, Inc.; *U.S. Private*, pg. 712
EMPIRE FOOD BROKERS INC.; *U.S. Private*, pg. 1384
ENERGY BEVERAGE MANAGEMENT LLC—See Gulf Distributing Holdings LLC; *U.S. Private*, pg. 1816
EOM ACQUISITION CORP.—See AMCON Distributing Company; *U.S. Public*, pg. 93
EUROPEAN IMPORTS, LTD.—See Sysco Corporation; *U.S. Public*, pg. 1973
EURPAC SERVICE INCORPORATED; *U.S. Private*, pg. 1434
EVERS HEILIG, INC.; *U.S. Private*, pg. 1440
EVERS HEILIG, INC. - WAUKESHA—See Evers Heilig, Inc.; *U.S. Private*, pg. 1440
F&A FOOD SALES CO. INC.; *U.S. Private*, pg. 1454
FARMERS BOY LIMITED—See Clayton, Dubilier & Rice, LLC; *U.S. Private*, pg. 930
THE FEDERATED GROUP, INC.; *U.S. Private*, pg. 4028
FEROLIE CORPORATION; *U.S. Private*, pg. 1497
FIDELITY EXPRESS MONEY ORDER COMPANY—See GSC Enterprises, Inc.; *U.S. Private*, pg. 1800
FIVE-O MARKETING SERVICES INC.; *U.S. Private*, pg. 1538
FIVE STAR CUSTOM FOODS, LTD.—See Cargill, Inc.; *U.S. Private*, pg. 759
FOOD MARKETING GROUP INC.—See Brothers Trading Co. Inc.; *U.S. Private*, pg. 665
FOOD MARKETING SERVICES, INC.; *U.S. Private*, pg. 1561
FOOD MARKETING SERVICES—See Louis F. Leeper Company; *U.S. Private*, pg. 2498
FOOD SERVICES OF AMERICA, INC.—See US Foods Holding Corp.; *U.S. Public*, pg. 2266
FOOD WAREHOUSE CORPORATION; *U.S. Private*, pg. 1561
FRANZELLA PRODUCE INC.; *U.S. Private*, pg. 1598
FRENCH & BEAN—See Associated Grocers of New England, Inc.; *U.S. Private*, pg. 356
FRESHTEX PRODUCE LLC—See GrubMarket, Inc.; *U.S. Private*, pg. 1797
G&C MARKETING CO.; *U.S. Private*, pg. 1628
GDS FOODS INCORPORATED—See Kelso & Company, L.P.; *U.S. Private*, pg. 2278
GE FOODLAND, INC.; *U.S. Private*, pg. 1654
GENERAL TRADING CO., INC.; *U.S. Private*, pg. 1667
GEORGE O. PASQUEL CO.; *U.S. Private*, pg. 1682
GFS ONTARIO—See Gordon Food Service Inc.; *U.S. Private*, pg. 1743
GINSBERG'S INSTITUTIONAL FOODS, INC.; *U.S. Private*, pg. 1702
GLOVER FOODS, INC.; *U.S. Private*, pg. 1720
GOLDEN STATE FOODS-PHOENIX DIVISION—See Golden State Foods Corp.; *U.S. Private*, pg. 1733
GOLDEN STATE FOODS-ROCHESTER DIVISION—See Golden State Foods Corp.; *U.S. Private*, pg. 1733
GOLICK MARTINS INC.; *U.S. Private*, pg. 1736
GONZALEZ & TAPANES FOODS INC.—See GraceKennedy Limited; *Int'l*, pg. 3049
GORDON FOOD SERVICE INC.—See Gordon Food Service Inc.; *U.S. Private*, pg. 1743
GORDON FOOD SERVICE—See Gordon Food Service Inc.; *U.S. Private*, pg. 1743
GOYA FOODS, INC.; *U.S. Private*, pg. 1747
GOYA FOODS OF CALIFORNIA—See Goya Foods, Inc.; *U.S. Private*, pg. 1747
GOYA FOODS OF FLORIDA—See Goya Foods, Inc.; *U.S. Private*, pg. 1747
GOYA FOODS OF ILLINOIS—See Goya Foods, Inc.; *U.S. Private*, pg. 1747
GOYA FOODS OF LONG ISLAND—See Goya Foods, Inc.; *U.S. Private*, pg. 1747
GOYA FOODS OF SOUTH JERSEY—See Goya Foods, Inc.; *U.S. Private*, pg. 1747
GOYA FOODS OF TEXAS—See Goya Foods, Inc.; *U.S. Private*, pg. 1747
GRAVELEIJS PRODUKTER AB—See FMCG Business Partner AB; *Int'l*, pg. 2717
GREAT NORTHERN PRODUCTS, LTD.; *U.S. Private*, pg. 1766
GROCERS SUPPLY INTERNATIONAL, INC.—See C&S Wholesale Grocers, Inc.; *U.S. Private*, pg. 704
GROCERY MARKETING INC.; *U.S. Private*, pg. 1791
GROCERY SUPPLY COMPANY-SAN ANTONIO—See GSC Enterprises, Inc.; *U.S. Private*, pg. 1800
GROCERY SUPPLY COMPANY—See GSC Enterprises, Inc.; *U.S. Private*, pg. 1800
GROCERY SUPPLY COMPANY-SOUTHEAST—See GSC Enterprises, Inc.; *U.S. Private*, pg. 1800
HAFSA CORPORATION; *U.S. Private*, pg. 1839
HANKYU KITCHEN YELL, INC—See H2O Retailing Corp.; *Int'l*, pg. 3200
HARBOR WHOLESALE GROCERY INC.—See Harbor Foods Group Inc.; *U.S. Private*, pg. 1859

N.A.I.C.S. INDEX

424410 — GENERAL LINE GROCER...

HARVEY ALPERT & CO. INC.; *U.S. Private*, pg. 1877
HEART OF ENGLAND CO-OPERATIVE SOCIETY LIMITED; *Int'l*, pg. 3304
HEDDINGER BROKERAGE INC.; *U.S. Private*, pg. 1903
HERMANOS LOPEZ INC.; *U.S. Private*, pg. 1925
HERMANOS SANTIAGO CASH & CARRY; *U.S. Private*, pg. 1925
H&H DISTRIBUTING COMPANY, INC.; *U.S. Private*, pg. 1822
H.J. HEINZ GMBH—See 3G Capital Inc.; *U.S. Private*, pg. 10
H.J. HEINZ GMBH—See Berkshire Hathaway Inc.; *U.S. Public*, pg. 317
HOLIDAY WHOLESALE INC.; *U.S. Private*, pg. 1963
HOLLYWOOD SUPER MARKET INC.; *U.S. Private*, pg. 1966
HORIZON FOODS COMPANY; *U.S. Private*, pg. 1980
HORMEL FOODS AUSTRALIA PTY LTD.—See Hormel Foods Corporation; *U.S. Public*, pg. 1054
THE H.T. HACKNEY COMPANY; *U.S. Public*, pg. 4041
THE H.T. HACKNEY CO.—See The H.T. Hackney Company; *U.S. Private*, pg. 4041
THE H.T. HACKNEY CO.—See The H.T. Hackney Company; *U.S. Private*, pg. 4041
THE H.T. HACKNEY CO.—See The H.T. Hackney Company; *U.S. Private*, pg. 4041
HUNG SAN FOODS, INC.—See GrubMarket, Inc.; *U.S. Private*, pg. 1797
THE IJ COMPANY—See Performance Food Group Company; *U.S. Public*, pg. 1676
IMPORT WAREHOUSE INC.; *U.S. Private*, pg. 2050
INNOVATIVE CONCEPT GROUP; *U.S. Private*, pg. 2082
INNOVATIVE FOOD HOLDINGS, INC.; *U.S. Public*, pg. 1126
INTERFRESH INC.; *U.S. Private*, pg. 2110
INTERNATIONAL GOURMET FOODS INC.; *U.S. Private*, pg. 2117
INTERSTATE CATERERS; *U.S. Private*, pg. 2124
IRA HIGDON GROCERY, INC.; *U.S. Private*, pg. 2137
JACMAR COMPANIES, INC.; *U.S. Private*, pg. 2179
JANCO FOODS, INC.; *U.S. Private*, pg. 2186
JBJ SALES & ASSOCIATES INC.; *U.S. Private*, pg. 2193
JENNY CORPORATION OF OHIO; *U.S. Private*, pg. 2200
JETRO CASH & CARRY ENTERPRISES, LLC; *U.S. Private*, pg. 2204
J.F. MONTALVO CASH & CARRY INC.; *U.S. Private*, pg. 2164
JIM L. SHETAKIS DISTRIBUTING CO. INC.; *U.S. Private*, pg. 2209
JOHNSON O'HARE CO. INC.; *U.S. Private*, pg. 2228
KALOTI ENTERPRISES INC.; *U.S. Private*, pg. 2258
KELLEY FOODS OF ALABAMA, INC.—See Ben E. Keith Company; *U.S. Private*, pg. 522
KELLOGG ASIA PACIFIC PTE. LTD—See Kellanova; *U.S. Public*, pg. 1217
KELLOGG ASIA SDN. BHD.—See Kellanova; *U.S. Public*, pg. 1217
KELLOGG CARIBBEAN SERVICES COMPANY, INC.—See Kellanova; *U.S. Public*, pg. 1217
KERR PACIFIC CORP.; *U.S. Private*, pg. 2291
KEYCO DISTRIBUTORS, INC.; *U.S. Private*, pg. 2294
KEY FOOD STORES CO-OPERATIVE, INC.; *U.S. Private*, pg. 2293
KH INTERNATIONAL, INC.—See Gellert Global Group; *U.S. Private*, pg. 1656
KLASS INGREDIENTS INC.; *U.S. Private*, pg. 2317
KRAFT FOODS DEVELOPING MARKETS—See Mondelez International, Inc.; *U.S. Public*, pg. 1461
KRASDALE FOODS INC.; *U.S. Private*, pg. 2349
LABATT FOOD SERVICE; *U.S. Private*, pg. 2370
LA CENA FINE FOODS LTD.—See Diaz Wholesale & Manufacturing Co., Inc.; *U.S. Private*, pg. 1225
LAMM FOOD SERVICE, LLC—See Alvarez & Marsal, Inc.; *U.S. Private*, pg. 213
LAMM FOOD SERVICE, LLC—See Highview Capital, LLC; *U.S. Private*, pg. 1942
LARROC LTD.; *U.S. Private*, pg. 2392
LATINA NIAGARA IMPORTING CO.; *U.S. Private*, pg. 2397
LAUREL GROCERY COMPANY LLC; *U.S. Private*, pg. 2398
LAYN EUROPE SRL—See Guilin Layn Natural Ingredients Corp.; *Int'l*, pg. 3173
LAYN USA, INC.—See Guilin Layn Natural Ingredients Corp.; *Int'l*, pg. 3173
LEDYARD COMPANY; *U.S. Private*, pg. 2411
LEE BROS FOODSERVICE INC.; *U.S. Private*, pg. 2411
LGS SPECIALTY SALES LTD.; *U.S. Private*, pg. 2441
LITTLE BROWNIE PROPERTIES INC.; *U.S. Private*, pg. 2468
LONG WHOLESALE, INC.; *U.S. Private*, pg. 2492
LOSURDO FOODS, INC.; *U.S. Private*, pg. 2497
LOUIS F. LEEPER COMPANY; *U.S. Private*, pg. 2498
LUZO FOODSERVICE CORPORATION; *U.S. Private*, pg. 2518
MAJOR CASH & CARRY INC.—See Ko-Amex General Wholesale Inc.; *U.S. Private*, pg. 2325
MALGOR & CO. INC.; *U.S. Private*, pg. 2557
MARKET DAY CORPORATION; *U.S. Private*, pg. 2579

MARKET GROCERY COMPANY, INC.; *U.S. Private*, pg. 2579
MARKETING MANAGEMENT, INC.; *U.S. Private*, pg. 2580
MARQUEZ BROTHERS INTERNATIONAL, INC.; *U.S. Private*, pg. 2587
MARR S.P.A.—See Cremonini S.p.A.; *Int'l*, pg. 1838
MARTIN BROTHERS DISTRIBUTING COMPANY, INC.; *U.S. Private*, pg. 2594
MARTIN L WEINER & ASSOCIATES; *U.S. Private*, pg. 2595
MCLANE COMPANY, INC.—See Berkshire Hathaway Inc.; *U.S. Public*, pg. 312
MDI MANAGEMENT INC.—See Alex Lee, Inc.; *U.S. Private*, pg. 163
MENIGO FOODSERVICE AB—See Sysco Corporation; *U.S. Public*, pg. 1973
MENU MAKER FOODS INC.; *U.S. Private*, pg. 2667
MERCADO LATINO INC.; *U.S. Private*, pg. 2668
THE MERCHANTS COMPANY INC.—See Tatum Development Corp.; *U.S. Private*, pg. 3936
MERCHANTS DISTRIBUTORS, INC.—See Alex Lee, Inc.; *U.S. Private*, pg. 163
MERCHANTS FOODSERVICE—See Tatum Development Corp.; *U.S. Private*, pg. 3936
MERCHANTS FOODSERVICE—See Tatum Development Corp.; *U.S. Private*, pg. 3936
METCASH EXPORT SERVICES PTY. LTD.—See eCargo Holdings Limited; *Int'l*, pg. 2287
METROPOLITAN FOODS INC.; *U.S. Private*, pg. 2688
METROPOLITAN FOODS, INC.; *U.S. Private*, pg. 2688
METROPOLITAN FOODS—See Metropolitan Foods, Inc.; *U.S. Private*, pg. 2688
MITCHELL GROCERY CORP.; *U.S. Private*, pg. 2750
MON CHONG LOONG TRADING CORP.; *U.S. Private*, pg. 2768
MONDELEZ AUSTRALIA PTY. LTD.—See Mondelez International, Inc.; *U.S. Public*, pg. 1462
MONDELEZ BELGIUM BVBA—See Mondelez International, Inc.; *U.S. Public*, pg. 1462
MONDELEZ BULGARIA AD—See Mondelez International, Inc.; *U.S. Public*, pg. 1463
MONDELEZ CHINA CO., LTD.—See Mondelez International, Inc.; *U.S. Public*, pg. 1462
MONDELEZ DANMARK APS—See Mondelez International, Inc.; *U.S. Public*, pg. 1463
MONDELEZ HUNGARIA KFT—See Mondelez International, Inc.; *U.S. Public*, pg. 1463
MONDELEZ ITALIA S.R.L.—See Mondelez International, Inc.; *U.S. Public*, pg. 1463
MONDELEZ MALAYSIA SALES SDN. BHD.—See Mondelez International, Inc.; *U.S. Public*, pg. 1462
MONDELEZ NEDERLAND SERVICES B.V.—See Mondelez International, Inc.; *U.S. Public*, pg. 1463
MONDELEZ NORGE AS—See Mondelez International, Inc.; *U.S. Public*, pg. 1463
MONDELEZ PORTUGAL, UNIPESSOAL, LDA.—See Mondelez International, Inc.; *U.S. Public*, pg. 1463
MONDELEZ SINGAPORE PTE. LTD.—See Mondelez International, Inc.; *U.S. Public*, pg. 1462
MONDELEZ SVERIGE AB—See Mondelez International, Inc.; *U.S. Public*, pg. 1463
MONDELEZ WORLD TRAVEL RETAIL GMBH—See Mondelez International, Inc.; *U.S. Public*, pg. 1462
M&S FOOD SERVICE LTD.—See Gordon Food Service Inc.; *U.S. Private*, pg. 1743
NADER WHOLESALE GROCERS INC.; *U.S. Private*, pg. 2830
NADIA INC.; *U.S. Private*, pg. 2830
NASSER COMPANY INC.; *U.S. Private*, pg. 2837
NATURAL RETAIL GROUP, INC.—See United Natural Foods, Inc.; *U.S. Public*, pg. 2231
NEW YUNG WAH TRADING LLC; *U.S. Private*, pg. 2913
NOON IMPORT-EXPORT SALES, INC.; *U.S. Private*, pg. 2935
NORSK BUTIKKDRIFT AS—See Coop Norge SA; *Int'l*, pg. 1789
NORTH CENTER FOODSERVICE CORP.—See Performance Food Group Company; *U.S. Public*, pg. 1675
NORTHEAST CONCEPTS INC.—See Metz Enterprises Inc.; *U.S. Private*, pg. 2691
NU CAL FOODS INC.; *U.S. Private*, pg. 2971
NYW TRADING LLC—See New Yung Wah Trading LLC; *U.S. Private*, pg. 2913
OVERSEAS SERVICE CORPORATION; *U.S. Private*, pg. 3053
PACIFIC FOOD IMPORTERS INC.; *U.S. Private*, pg. 3067
PACIFIC GROSERVICE, INC.; *U.S. Private*, pg. 3067
PACIFIC VALLEY FOODS INC.; *U.S. Private*, pg. 3071
PARIS BROTHERS INC.; *U.S. Private*, pg. 3094
PARIS GOURMET OF NEW YORK INC.; *U.S. Private*, pg. 3095
PARKNSHOP (HK) LIMITED—See CK Hutchison Holdings Limited; *Int'l*, pg. 1638
THE PASTENE COMPANIES, LTD.; *U.S. Private*, pg. 4091
PENNSYLVANIA MACARONI COMPANY; *U.S. Private*, pg. 3137
PERFORMANCE FOOD GROUP AFI—See Performance Food Group Company; *U.S. Public*, pg. 1675
PERFORMANCE FOOD GROUP, INC. - BROADLINE DIVISION—See Performance Food Group Company; *U.S. Public*, pg. 1675
PERFORMANCE FOOD GROUP, INC.—See Performance Food Group Company; *U.S. Public*, pg. 1675
PERFORMANCE FOOD GROUP LITTLE ROCK—See Performance Food Group Company; *U.S. Public*, pg. 1675
PERFORMANCE FOOD GROUP OF TEXAS, LP—See Performance Food Group Company; *U.S. Public*, pg. 1675
PERFORMANCE FOOD GROUP—See Performance Food Group Company; *U.S. Public*, pg. 1675
PERFORMANCE FOOD GROUP VICTORIA—See Performance Food Group Company; *U.S. Public*, pg. 1675
PFG FLORIDA, LLC—See Performance Food Group Company; *U.S. Public*, pg. 1675
PFG-LESTER BROADLINE INC.—See Performance Food Group Company; *U.S. Public*, pg. 1675
PFG-MIDDENDORF—See Performance Food Group Company; *U.S. Public*, pg. 1675
PFG MILTONS—See Performance Food Group Company; *U.S. Public*, pg. 1675
PIGGLY WIGGLY ALABAMA DISTRIBUTING CO.; *U.S. Private*, pg. 3179
PLAZA PROVISION COMPANY; *U.S. Private*, pg. 3213
PLUMGOOD FOOD, LLC; *U.S. Private*, pg. 3215
PRICE KING WHOLESALE INC.; *U.S. Private*, pg. 3258
PROACTIVE SALES & MARKETING INC.—See Alliance Foods Inc.; *U.S. Private*, pg. 182
PRO-FAC COOPERATIVE, INC.; *U.S. Private*, pg. 3270
PROVISIONS LEGRAND INC.—See TraFon Group; *U.S. Private*, pg. 4203
PURITY WHOLESALE GROCERS, INC.; *U.S. Private*, pg. 3306
REINHART FOODSERVICE, LLC—See Performance Food Group Company; *U.S. Public*, pg. 1675
RESTAURANT DEPOT, LLC—See Jetro Cash & Carry Enterprises, LLC; *U.S. Private*, pg. 2204
RHEE BROS. INC.; *U.S. Private*, pg. 3421
RITCHIE GROCER COMPANY; *U.S. Private*, pg. 3441
ROBESONIA LOGISTICS LLC—See C&S Wholesale Grocers, Inc.; *U.S. Private*, pg. 704
RODON FOODS INC.; *U.S. Private*, pg. 3470
ROMA FOOD ENTERPRISES INC.—See Performance Food Group Company; *U.S. Public*, pg. 1676
ROSE TRUCKING CORP—See Rose Partners LP; *U.S. Private*, pg. 3481
RUBICON RESOURCES, LLC—See High Liner Foods Incorporated; *Int'l*, pg. 3385
SALADINO'S INC.; *U.S. Private*, pg. 3530
SALES MAX INC.; *U.S. Private*, pg. 3532
SAVAL FOODS CORPORATION; *U.S. Private*, pg. 3555
SDSP INC.; *U.S. Private*, pg. 3582
SHAMROCK FOODS - ARIZONA FOODS DIVISION—See Shamrock Foods Company; *U.S. Private*, pg. 3624
SHAMROCK FOODS - COLORADO FOODS DIVISION—See Shamrock Foods Company; *U.S. Private*, pg. 3624
SHOPRITE BEVERAGES, INC.—See Wakefern Food Corporation; *U.S. Private*, pg. 4427
SINCO INC.; *U.S. Private*, pg. 3669
SKH MANAGEMENT CO. INC.; *U.S. Private*, pg. 3681
SPECTRUM FOOD SERVICE, INC.; *U.S. Private*, pg. 3752
SUN LEE INC.; *U.S. Private*, pg. 3863
SUPERVALU, INC. - ANNISTON DISTRIBUTION CENTER—See United Natural Foods, Inc.; *U.S. Public*, pg. 2232
SUPERVALU, INC. - BILLINGS DISTRIBUTION CENTER—See United Natural Foods, Inc.; *U.S. Public*, pg. 2232
SUPERVALU, INC. - CHAMPAIGN DISTRIBUTION CENTER—See United Natural Foods, Inc.; *U.S. Public*, pg. 2232
SUPERVALU, INC. - EASTERN REGION—See United Natural Foods, Inc.; *U.S. Public*, pg. 2232
SUPERVALU, INC., FARGO DISTRIBUTION DIVISION—See United Natural Foods, Inc.; *U.S. Public*, pg. 2232
SUPERVALU, INC. - GREEN BAY DISTRIBUTION CENTER—See United Natural Foods, Inc.; *U.S. Public*, pg. 2232
SUPERVALU, INC., HARRISBURG DIVISION—See United Natural Foods, Inc.; *U.S. Public*, pg. 2232
SUPERVALU, INC., LEWIS GROCER DIVISION—See United Natural Foods, Inc.; *U.S. Public*, pg. 2232
SUPERVALU, INC. - MIDWEST REGION—See United Natural Foods, Inc.; *U.S. Public*, pg. 2232
SUPERVALU, INC., MILTON DIVISION—See United Natural Foods, Inc.; *U.S. Public*, pg. 2232
SUPERVALU, INC., MINNEAPOLIS DIVISION—See United Natural Foods, Inc.; *U.S. Public*, pg. 2232
SUPERVALU, INC., OHIO VALLEY DIVISION—See United Natural Foods, Inc.; *U.S. Public*, pg. 2232
SUPERVALU, INC., SPOKANE DIVISION—See United Natural Foods, Inc.; *U.S. Public*, pg. 2232
SUPERVALU, INC. - ST. LOUIS DISTRIBUTION CENTER—See United Natural Foods, Inc.; *U.S. Public*, pg. 2232
SUPERVALU, INC., TACOMA DIVISION—See United Natural Foods, Inc.; *U.S. Public*, pg. 2232

424410 — GENERAL LINE GROCER...

THE SYGMA NETWORK, INC.—See Sysco Corporation; *U.S. Public*, pg. 1977
SYSCO ASIAN FOODS, INC.—See Sysco Corporation; *U.S. Public*, pg. 1975
SYSCO BOSTON LLC—See Sysco Corporation; *U.S. Public*, pg. 1975
SYSCO CENTRAL ALABAMA, INC.—See Sysco Corporation; *U.S. Public*, pg. 1975
SYSCO CENTRAL ILLINOIS, INC.—See Sysco Corporation; *U.S. Public*, pg. 1975
SYSCO LOS ANGELES, INC.—See Sysco Corporation; *U.S. Public*, pg. 1976
SYSCO SAN DIEGO, INC.—See Sysco Corporation; *U.S. Public*, pg. 1977
SYSCO SEATTLE, INC.—See Sysco Corporation; *U.S. Public*, pg. 1977
TAPIA BROS. CO.; *U.S. Private*, pg. 3932
T-C DISTRIBUTION COMPANY; *U.S. Private*, pg. 3910
TEXAS EGG PRODUCTS, LLC—See Cal-Maine Foods, Inc.; *U.S. Public*, pg. 421
TEXAS JASMINE; *U.S. Private*, pg. 3976
TILLAMOOK CHEESE INC.—See Tillamook County Creamery Association; *U.S. Private*, pg. 4171
TOPCO ASSOCIATES LLC—See Topco Holdings Inc.; *U.S. Private*, pg. 4187
TOPCO HOLDINGS INC.; *U.S. Private*, pg. 4187
TOTAL FOODS CORPORATION; *U.S. Private*, pg. 4191
TOWN & COUNTRY FOODS, INC.—See Pine State Trading Co.; *U.S. Private*, pg. 3183
TRANSFER MARKETING INC.; *U.S. Private*, pg. 4207
TRICO USA, LLC.; *U.S. Private*, pg. 4229
TRIPIFOODS INC.; *U.S. Private*, pg. 4236
TRIUNFO IMPORT & EXPORT FOOD—See Seabra Group; *U.S. Private*, pg. 3583
TRI-VENTURE MARKETING LLC—See Leonard Green & Partners, L.P.; *U.S. Private*, pg. 2423
TUTS INTERNATIONAL EXPORT & IMPORT COMPANY—See Littlejohn & Co., LLC; *U.S. Private*, pg. 2472
UNION SUPPLY GROUP, INC.—See Aramark; *U.S. Public*, pg. 178
UNITED NATURAL FOODS, INC.—See United Natural Foods, Inc.; *U.S. Public*, pg. 2233
UNITED NATURAL FOODS WEST, INC.—See United Natural Foods, Inc.; *U.S. Public*, pg. 2233
URM STORES, INC.; *U.S. Private*, pg. 4316
USFI, INC.; *U.S. Private*, pg. 4323
UWAJIMAYA INC.; *U.S. Private*, pg. 4327
VALLET FOOD SERVICE INC.; *U.S. Private*, pg. 4332
VEG-LAND INC.—See Veg-Land Sales Inc.; *U.S. Private*, pg. 4353
VEG-LAND SALES INC.; *U.S. Private*, pg. 4353
VENDORS SUPPLY COMPANY INC.; *U.S. Private*, pg. 4356
VICTORY FOOD SERVICE DISTRIBUTORS; *U.S. Private*, pg. 4378
WAKEFERN FOOD CORPORATION; *U.S. Private*, pg. 4427
WAUKESHA WHOLESALE FOODS, INC.—See US Foods Holding Corp.; *U.S. Public*, pg. 2266
WEBCO GENERAL PARTNERSHIP; *U.S. Private*, pg. 4464
WESTERN FAMILY FOODS INC.—See Western Family Holding Co., Inc.; *U.S. Private*, pg. 4493
WESTERN FAMILY HOLDING CO., INC.; *U.S. Private*, pg. 4493
WEST SIDE FOODS INC.; *U.S. Private*, pg. 4487
WG WHITE & COMPANY; *U.S. Private*, pg. 4503
WHARTON COUNTY FOODS, LLC—See Cal-Maine Foods, Inc.; *U.S. Public*, pg. 421
WHITE ROSE FOODS—See Rose Partners LP; *U.S. Private*, pg. 3481
WILLIAM GEORGE PRODUCE CO., INC.; *U.S. Private*, pg. 4523
WILLIAMS FOODS INC.; *U.S. Private*, pg. 4525
WINKLER INCORPORATED; *U.S. Private*, pg. 4542
W.L. HALSEY GROCERY COMPANY, INC.; *U.S. Private*, pg. 4421
W.L. PETREY WHOLESALE COMPANY, INC.; *U.S. Private*, pg. 4421
WOODLAND PARTNERS LLC; *U.S. Private*, pg. 4559
WORLD BRANDS INC.—See Topco Holdings Inc.; *U.S. Private*, pg. 4187
WORLD SHIP SUPPLY TEXAS INCORPORATED; *U.S. Private*, pg. 4567
Y. HATA & CO. LTD.; *U.S. Private*, pg. 4584
YU BROTHERS, INC.; *U.S. Private*, pg. 4595
ZRII, LLC—See Zilis, LLC; *U.S. Private*, pg. 4604

424420 — PACKAGED FROZEN FOOD MERCHANT WHOLESALERS

ACC DISTRIBUTORS, INC.; *U.S. Private*, pg. 47
ADDISON FOODS INC.; *U.S. Private*, pg. 77
AEON NEXT CO., LTD.—See AEON Co., Ltd.; *Int'l*, pg. 177
AJC INTERNATIONAL, INC.; *U.S. Private*, pg. 143
AL-BERRI UNITED FOOD CO. LTD.—See Al-Osais International Holding Company; *U.S. Private*, pg. 287
ALLIED FOODS LIMITED—See DCC plc; *Int'l*, pg. 1989
ALPAGEL GAP; *Int'l*, pg. 366
AMERICAN INSTITUTIONAL FOODS—See AJC International, Inc.; *U.S. Private*, pg. 144
ANAAM INTERNATIONAL HOLDING COMPANY GROUP; *Int'l*, pg. 444
ANDERSON & FRYER EXPORTS INC.—See Twin Rivers Group Inc.; *U.S. Private*, pg. 4265
ANNIE'S ENTERPRISES, INC.—See General Mills, Inc.; *U.S. Public*, pg. 921
ANNIE'S HOMEGROWN, INC.—See General Mills, Inc.; *U.S. Public*, pg. 921
ARCHER-DANIELS-MIDLAND COMPANY; *U.S. Public*, pg. 180
ARDO A/S—See Ardo N.V.; *Int'l*, pg. 557
ARDOFOODS IRELAND LTD.—See Ardo N.V.; *Int'l*, pg. 557
ARDO GMBH—See Ardo N.V.; *Int'l*, pg. 557
ARDO MOCHOV S.R.O.—See Ardo N.V.; *Int'l*, pg. 556
ARDO SP.Z.O.O.—See Ardo N.V.; *Int'l*, pg. 557
ARDO UK LTD.—See Ardo N.V.; *Int'l*, pg. 557
ATLANTIC FIELD PLUME DE VEAU INC.; *U.S. Private*, pg. 373
BAKALARS SAUSAGE COMPANY, INC.; *U.S. Private*, pg. 454
BAMA FROZEN DOUGH LLC—See Bama Companies Inc.; *U.S. Private*, pg. 463
BASCOGEL; *Int'l*, pg. 871
BEAVER STREET FISHERIES, INC.; *U.S. Private*, pg. 509
BELLBOY CORPORATION; *U.S. Private*, pg. 519
BEMIS PIATRA NEAMT—See Amcor plc; *Int'l*, pg. 418
BEN E. KEITH FOODS OF OKLAHOMA—See Ben E. Keith Company; *U.S. Private*, pg. 522
BENJAMIN FOODS, LLC.; *U.S. Private*, pg. 526
BEST EXPRESS FOODS, INC.; *U.S. Private*, pg. 542
BIG QUILL RESOURCES INC.—See Compass Minerals International, Inc.; *U.S. Public*, pg. 560
BMMI B.S.C.; *Int'l*, pg. 1076
BONDUELLE POLSKA S.A.—See Bonduelle SAS; *Int'l*, pg. 1106
BOSTON AGREX INC.; *U.S. Private*, pg. 621
BOURBON FOODS USA CORPORATION—See Bourbon Corporation; *Int'l*, pg. 1120
BRAKE BROS FOODSERVICE LIMITED—See Sysco Corporation; *U.S. Public*, pg. 1973
BURRIS LOGISTICS; *U.S. Private*, pg. 691
BUZZ PRODUCTS, INC.; *U.S. Private*, pg. 699
CALNAC CO., LTD.—See Calbee, Inc.; *Int'l*, pg. 1261
CANYON BAKEHOUSE, LLC—See Flowers Foods, Inc.; *U.S. Public*, pg. 854
CARIBBEAN INTERNATIONAL FOODS CORPORATION—See TraFon Group; *U.S. Private*, pg. 4203
CENTRAL COLD STORAGE CORPORATION—See The VPS Companies Inc.; *U.S. Private*, pg. 4132
CENTRALIZED LEASING CORPORATION—See Golden State Foods Corp.; *U.S. Private*, pg. 1733
CENTROPROM A.D.; *Int'l*, pg. 1414
CHEF IN A BOX LIMITED—See Around Noon Foods Limited; *Int'l*, pg. 577
CHEFS PARTNER PTY LTD.—See Australian Agricultural Company Limited; *Int'l*, pg. 720
CHERRY CENTRAL COOPERATIVE, INC.; *U.S. Private*, pg. 874
CHINA RESOURCES NG FUNG LIMITED—See China Resources (Holdings) Co., Ltd.; *Int'l*, pg. 1548
CHIPITA BULGARIA S.A.—See Chipita S.A.; *Int'l*, pg. 1573
CHIPITA CZ S.R.O—See Chipita S.A.; *Int'l*, pg. 1573
CHIPITA GERMANY GMBH—See Chipita S.A.; *Int'l*, pg. 1573
CHIPITA GIDA URETIM A.S.—See Chipita S.A.; *Int'l*, pg. 1573
CHIPITA HUNGARY KFT.—See Chipita S.A.; *Int'l*, pg. 1573
CHIPITA INDIA PVT LTD.—See Chipita S.A.; *Int'l*, pg. 1573
CHIPITA POLAND S.P. Z.O.O.—See Chipita S.A.; *Int'l*, pg. 1573
CHIPITA ROMANIA S,R,L.—See Chipita S.A.; *Int'l*, pg. 1573
CHIPITA SAINT-PETERSBURG LLC—See Chipita S.A.; *Int'l*, pg. 1573
CHIPITA SLOVAKIA S.R.O.—See Chipita S.A.; *Int'l*, pg. 1573
CHIPITA UKRAINE TRADE LLC—See Chipita S.A.; *Int'l*, pg. 1573
CHIPITA YU A.D.—See Chipita S.A.; *Int'l*, pg. 1573
CITY GLATT, INC.; *U.S. Private*, pg. 906
C.K.H. FOOD TRADING PTE. LTD.—See Hanoi Beer Trading JSC; *Int'l*, pg. 3258
CLEAN SEAS SEAFOOD LTD.; *Int'l*, pg. 1654
COLORADO BOXED BEEF CO. - ATLANTA FACILITY—See Palladium Equity Partners, LLC; *U.S. Private*, pg. 3078
COLORADO BOXED BEEF CO. - CBBC INTERNATIONAL DIVISION—See Palladium Equity Partners, LLC; *U.S. Private*, pg. 3078
COLORADO FOOD PRODUCTS INC.; *U.S. Private*, pg. 974
COLRUYT GROUP N.V.; *Int'l*, pg. 1705
COMERCIALIZADORA NOVAVERDE S.A.—See Embotelladora Andina S.A.; *Int'l*, pg. 2375
COMMERCIAL ENTERPRISES LIMITED; *U.S. Private*, pg. 983
COOL LINK (HOLDINGS) LIMITED; *Int'l*, pg. 1789
COOL LINK & MARKETING PTE. LTD.—See Cool Link (Holdings) Limited; *Int'l*, pg. 1789
CORPORACION DISTRIBUIDORA DE ALIMENTOS S.A.—See Grupo Nutresa S.A.; *Int'l*, pg. 3133
COUNTRY RIBBON INC. - COUNTRY RIBBON FEED DIVISION—See Co-op Atlantic; *Int'l*, pg. 1679
COUNTRY RIBBON INC.—See Co-op Atlantic; *Int'l*, pg. 1679
CP WHOLESALE INDIA PRIVATE LIMITED—See C.P. All Public Company Limited; *Int'l*, pg. 1243
CRS ONE SOURCE; *U.S. Private*, pg. 1113
CSM AUSTRIA GMBH—See Rhone Group, LLC; *U.S. Private*, pg. 3423
CSM NORDIC A/S—See Rhone Group, LLC; *U.S. Private*, pg. 3423
DANIELS CHILLED FOODS LTD.—See The Hain Celestial Group, Inc.; *U.S. Public*, pg. 2086
DANIELS GROUP LIMITED—See The Hain Celestial Group, Inc.; *U.S. Public*, pg. 2086
DANISH CROWN K-PACK AB—See Danish Crown AmbA; *Int'l*, pg. 1964
DANISH CROWN UK LIMITED—See Danish Crown AmbA; *Int'l*, pg. 1964
DDC ENTERPRISE LIMITED; *Int'l*, pg. 1993
DELIVEROO PLC; *Int'l*, pg. 2013
DI CARLO DISTRIBUTORS INC.; *U.S. Private*, pg. 1222
DILGARD FROZEN FOODS INC.; *U.S. Private*, pg. 1231
DOERLE FOOD SERVICES, LLC—See Sysco Corporation; *U.S. Public*, pg. 1973
DOMINO'S PIZZA, INC.; *U.S. Public*, pg. 674
DPC DASH LTD.; *Int'l*, pg. 2187
EARP DISTRIBUTION CENTER; *U.S. Private*, pg. 1314
EC GROCER PTE. LTD.—See Cab Cakaran Corporation Berhad; *Int'l*, pg. 1245
ECOMIAM SA; *Int'l*, pg. 2296
ECONOMY FOODS, INC.—See Sysco Corporation; *U.S. Public*, pg. 1973
E.G. FORREST COMPANY INC.; *U.S. Private*, pg. 1305
ELBTAL TIEFKUHLKOST VERTRIEBS GMBH—See FRoSTA AG; *Int'l*, pg. 2797
ELGEKA S.A.; *Int'l*, pg. 2359
EMPRESA AGRICOLA SAN JUAN SA; *Int'l*, pg. 2388
ENCORE FRUIT MARKETING INC.; *U.S. Private*, pg. 1391
ENVASES DEL PACIFICO S.A.; *Int'l*, pg. 2453
ENZACOR PTY LIMITED—See BayWa AG; *Int'l*, pg. 919
FARM STAND FOODS; *U.S. Private*, pg. 1475
FLEMISH CO., LTD.—See euglena Co., Ltd.; *Int'l*, pg. 2526
FOOD INNOVATIONS, INC.—See Innovative Food Holdings, Inc.; *U.S. Public*, pg. 1126
FOOD JUNCTION MANAGEMENT PTE LTD—See BreadTalk Group Pte Ltd.; *Int'l*, pg. 1143
FOOD SERVICE SYSTEMS INC.—See The VPS Companies Inc.; *U.S. Private*, pg. 4132
FORM BIO CO., LTD.; *Int'l*, pg. 2733
FOUNTAIN FROZEN LTD.; *Int'l*, pg. 2754
FOX RIVER FOODS INC.—See Performance Food Group Company; *U.S. Public*, pg. 1674
FOX RIVER FOODS TRANSPORT INC.—See F.R.F. Systems Inc.; *U.S. Private*, pg. 1457
F. P. NATURAL INGREDIENTS S.A.S—See ARIAKE JAPAN Co., Ltd.; *Int'l*, pg. 564
FRANCE DISTRIBUTION SAS—See ARYZTA AG; *Int'l*, pg. 588
FREEZER QUEEN FOODS, INC.—See Home Market Foods Incorporated; *U.S. Private*, pg. 1971
FRESCA SAS—See ARYZTA AG; *Int'l*, pg. 588
FROSTA CR S.R.O.—See FRoSTA AG; *Int'l*, pg. 2797
FROSTA FRANCE S.A.R.L.—See FRoSTA AG; *Int'l*, pg. 2797
FROSTA HUNGARY KFT.—See FRoSTA AG; *Int'l*, pg. 2797
FROSTA ITALIA S.R.L.—See FRoSTA AG; *Int'l*, pg. 2797
FROSTA SP. Z O.O.—See FRoSTA AG; *Int'l*, pg. 2797
FROSTA TIEFKUHLKOST GMBH—See FRoSTA AG; *Int'l*, pg. 2797
FROSTA TIEFKUHLKOST GMBH U. L.—See FRoSTA AG; *Int'l*, pg. 2797
FROSTY ACRES BRANDS, INC.; *U.S. Private*, pg. 1617
FUDDRUCKERS OF ANNAPOLIS, LLC—See Luby's, Inc.; *U.S. Public*, pg. 1345
FUNNYBONES FOODSERVICE LIMITED—See GraceKennedy Limited; *Int'l*, pg. 3048
F.W. BRYCE, INC.; *U.S. Private*, pg. 1457
GAB EMPACADORA INC.; *U.S. Private*, pg. 1632
GENERAL MILLS BAKERY & FOODSERVICE PTY LTD—See General Mills, Inc.; *U.S. Public*, pg. 922
GENERAL MILLS CANADA CORP.—See General Mills, Inc.; *U.S. Public*, pg. 922
GENERAL MILLS DIRECT MARKETING, INC.—See General Mills, Inc.; *U.S. Public*, pg. 921
GFPT PUBLIC COMPANY LIMITED; *Int'l*, pg. 2957
GIMBERT SURGELES SARL; *Int'l*, pg. 2976
GLACIER SALES INC.; *U.S. Private*, pg. 1704
GLAZIER FOODS COMPANY; *U.S. Private*, pg. 1708
THE GLOBAL GREEN COMPANY LIMITED - HYDERABAD UNIT—See Avantha Group; *Int'l*, pg. 736
GLOBAL GREEN INTERNATIONAL NV—See Avantha Group; *Int'l*, pg. 736
GLOBAL GREEN USA LTD.—See Avantha Group; *Int'l*, pg. 736

N.A.I.C.S. INDEX

424430 — DAIRY PRODUCT (EXCE...

GOLDEN BOY PORTALES, LLC—See Post Holdings, Inc.; *U.S. Public*, pg. 1703
GOLDEN NUT COMPANY (USA) INC.—See Post Holdings, Inc.; *U.S. Public*, pg. 1703
THE GREAT FISH COMPANY—See Palladium Equity Partners, LLC; *U.S. Private*, pg. 3078
GREENCORE FROZEN FOODS LTD—See Greencore Group plc; *Int'l*, pg. 3074
THE GROCERY PEOPLE LTD.—See Federated Co-operatives Limited; *Int'l*, pg. 2631
GRUPO EMPRESARIAL PALACIOS ALIMENTACION SA—See The Carlyle Group Inc.; *U.S. Public*, pg. 2047
GRUPO HERDEZ, S.A.B. DE C.V.; *Int'l*, pg. 3130
GULF FOOD INDUSTRIES COMPANY—See Adeptio LLC; *Int'l*, pg. 143
GUNN'S HOMEMADE CAKES & PASTRY LTD.; *Int'l*, pg. 3184
HADCO LIMITED; *Int'l*, pg. 3205
HAITAI, INC.; *U.S. Private*, pg. 1841
HAMAMA MEIR TRADING (1996) LTD.; *Int'l*, pg. 3235
HAN FENG, INC.—See HF Foods Group Inc.; *U.S. Public*, pg. 1033
HANWA CANADA CORP.—See Hanwa Co., Ltd.; *Int'l*, pg. 3262
HANWA CO., (HONG KONG) LTD.—See Hanwa Co., Ltd.; *Int'l*, pg. 3262
HANWA EUROPE B.V.—See Hanwa Co., Ltd.; *Int'l*, pg. 3262
HARBOR SEAFOOD, INC.; *U.S. Private*, pg. 1859
HARBOUR MARINE PRODUCTS INC.; *Int'l*, pg. 3272
HEARTLAND FOOD PRODUCTS, LLC—See BOK Financial Corporation; *U.S. Public*, pg. 367
HELLER DISTRIBUTING CO. INC.; *U.S. Private*, pg. 1906
HERSHEY FOODS INTERNATIONAL TRADE (SHANGHAI) CO. LTD.—See The Hershey Co.; *U.S. Public*, pg. 2088
HIESTAND AUSTRIA GMBH—See ARYZTA AG; *Int'l*, pg. 589
HILCONA FRESH EXPRESS—See Coop-Gruppe Genossenschaft; *Int'l*, pg. 1790
HILTON FOODS LIMITED SP. Z.O.O.—See Hilton Food Group plc; *Int'l*, pg. 3395
HISSHO SUSHI; *U.S. Private*, pg. 1951
HMA AGRO INDUSTRIES LIMITED; *Int'l*, pg. 3431
HOCK SENG FOOD (M) SDN BHD—See Hosen Group Ltd; *Int'l*, pg. 3482
HOME MARKET FOODS INCORPORATED; *U.S. Private*, pg. 1971
HONEY BUN (1982) LTD.; *Int'l*, pg. 3465
HORIZON MEAT & SEAFOOD DISTRIBUTORS INC.; *U.S. Private*, pg. 1981
HORIZON MEAT & SEAFOOD OF GEORGIA INC.—See Horizon Meat & Seafood Distributors Inc.; *U.S. Private*, pg. 1981
HUEGLI HOLDING AG—See Coop-Gruppe Genossenschaft; *Int'l*, pg. 1789
IK HOLDINGS CO., LTD.; *Int'l*, pg. 3609
INN FOODS INC.—See The VPS Companies Inc.; *U.S. Private*, pg. 4132
INTERMARK FOODS, INC.; *U.S. Private*, pg. 2112
ISFI - INTERNATIONAL SPICE & FOOD IMPORT SA—See Gilde Equity Management (GEM) Benelux Partners B.V.; *Int'l*, pg. 2975
ISLAND OASIS FROZEN COCKTAIL CO.; *U.S. Private*, pg. 2145
J.A. WOLL HANDELS GMBH—See B&M European Value Retail S.A.; *Int'l*, pg. 784
JENNIE-O TURKEY STORE SALES, LLC—See Hormel Foods Corporation; *U.S. Public*, pg. 1054
J. HELLMAN FROZEN, INC.—See J. Hellman Produce, Inc.; *U.S. Private*, pg. 2156
J&J SNACK FOODS CORP./MIA—See J&J Snack Foods Corporation; *U.S. Public*, pg. 1180
JL MORISON (MALAYA) SDN BHD—See Berjaya Corporation Berhad; *Int'l*, pg. 984
JONAS BROWNE AND HUBBARD (GRENADA) LIMITED—See Goddard Enterprises Limited; *Int'l*, pg. 3019
KAY PACKING COMPANY INC.; *U.S. Private*, pg. 2266
KELLMAN, S. DE R.L. DE C.V.—See Kellanova; *U.S. Public*, pg. 1218
KELLOGG COMPANY OF IRELAND LIMITED—See Kellanova; *U.S. Public*, pg. 1218
KELLOGG EUROPE TRADING LIMITED—See Kellanova; *U.S. Public*, pg. 1218
KELLOGG FOODS (SHANGHAI) CO. LTD—See Kellanova; *U.S. Public*, pg. 1218
KELLOGG MANUFACTURING GMBH & CO. KG—See Kellanova; *U.S. Public*, pg. 1217
KELLOGG MARKETING AND SALES COMPANY (UK) LIMITED—See Kellanova; *U.S. Public*, pg. 1218
KELLOGG (QINGDAO) FOOD CO., LTD.—See Kellanova; *U.S. Public*, pg. 1217
KELLOGG SERVICIOS, S.C.—See Kellanova; *U.S. Public*, pg. 1218
KINGS HAWAIIAN BAKERY WEST, INC.—See King's Hawaiian Holding Company, Inc.; *U.S. Private*, pg. 2310
KOCH FOODS, INC.; *U.S. Private*, pg. 2326
KOCH POULTRY—See Koch Foods, Inc.; *U.S. Private*, pg. 2326

LA FOODS; *U.S. Private*, pg. 2368
LAMB WESTON SALES, INC.—See Lamb Weston Holdings, Inc.; *U.S. Public*, pg. 1291
LEBANON VALLEY COLD STORAGE, LP—See Bonduelle SAS; *Int'l*, pg. 1106
LIANYUNGANG AJINOMOTO RUYI FOODS CO., LTD.—See Ajinomoto Company, Inc.; *Int'l*, pg. 257
LIANYUNGANG AJINOMOTO RUYI FOODS CO., LTD.—See Grand Industrial Holding Co., Ltd.; *Int'l*, pg. 3055
LONE STAR CONSOLIDATED FOODS; *U.S. Private*, pg. 2484
L&T MEAT CO.; *U.S. Private*, pg. 2363
LUIGI UGOLOTTI S.R.L.—See ALFA, S.A.B. de C.V.; *Int'l*, pg. 314
MAINES PAPER & FOOD SERVICE, INC.; *U.S. Private*, pg. 2553
MAKRO (CAMBODIA) COMPANY LIMITED—See C.P. All Public Company Limited; *Int'l*, pg. 1244
MAMA'S CREATIONS, INC.; *U.S. Public*, pg. 1356
THE MARTIN-BROWER COMPANY, LLC—See Reyes Holdings, LLC; *U.S. Public*, pg. 3418
MATTINGLY FOODS INC.—See Creation Gardens, Inc.; *U.S. Private*, pg. 1087
MCCORMICK FRANCE, S.A.S.—See McCormick & Company, Incorporated; *U.S. Public*, pg. 1404
MCLANE FOODSERVICE, INC.—See Berkshire Hathaway Inc.; *U.S. Public*, pg. 312
MERCHANTS EXPORT INC.; *U.S. Private*, pg. 2670
M&M MEAT SHOPS LTD.—See Searchlight Capital Partners, L.P.; *U.S. Private*, pg. 3588
MOM BRANDS SSALES, LLC—See Post Holdings, Inc.; *U.S. Public*, pg. 1703
MONIN ASIA KL SDN BHD—See Groupe Monin SAS; *Int'l*, pg. 3109
MONIN SHANGHAI—See Groupe Monin SAS; *Int'l*, pg. 3109
MOONLIGHT PACKING CORPORATION; *U.S. Private*, pg. 2779
MURRY'S, INC.; *U.S. Private*, pg. 2816
NASS CORPORATION BSC (C) - NASS FOODS DIVISION—See Abdulla Ahmed Nass Group WLL; *Int'l*, pg. 58
NATIONAL CUSTOM PACKING INC.—See The VPS Companies Inc.; *U.S. Private*, pg. 4132
NHONG SHIM KELLOGG CO. LTD.—See Kellanova; *U.S. Public*, pg. 1218
NIPPON GOURMET TRADING COMPANY LIMITED—See Future Bright Holdings Limited; *Int'l*, pg. 2852
NORTHWESTERN SELECTA, INC.—See Northwestern Meat, Inc.; *U.S. Private*, pg. 2962
ODYSSEY ENTERPRISES, INC.; *U.S. Private*, pg. 2993
ORE-CAL CORPORATION; *U.S. Private*, pg. 3039
ORIGIN TOSHU CO., LTD—See AEON Co., Ltd.; *Int'l*, pg. 178
ORLEANS INTERNATIONAL, INC.; *U.S. Private*, pg. 3044
PACIFIC AGRI-PRODUCTS INC.; *U.S. Private*, pg. 3065
PACIFIC MARKETING GROUP INC.—See Dulcich, Inc.; *U.S. Private*, pg. 1286
PALISADES RANCH, INC.—See Sysco Corporation; *U.S. Public*, pg. 1975
PALLAS FOODS FARM FRESH UNLIMITED COMPANY—See Sysco Corporation; *U.S. Public*, pg. 1975
PALLAS FOODS UNLIMITED COMPANY—See Sysco Corporation; *U.S. Public*, pg. 1975
PASTENE INC.—See The Pastene Companies, Ltd.; *U.S. Private*, pg. 4091
PATE-DAWSON COMPANY; *U.S. Private*, pg. 3105
PERFORMANCE FOODSERVICE-SOMERSET, LLC—See Performance Food Group Company; *U.S. Public*, pg. 1675
PERINI COMERCIAL DE ALIMENTOS LTDA.—See Cencosud S.A.; *Int'l*, pg. 1401
PFG-POWELL—See Performance Food Group Company; *U.S. Public*, pg. 1675
PLAZA WAREHOUSING & REALTY CORPORATION—See Plaza Provision Company; *U.S. Private*, pg. 3213
POK BROTHERS SDN. BHD.—See Envictus International Holdings Limited; *Int'l*, pg. 2453
PON FOOD CORP—See Alvarez & Marsal, Inc.; *U.S. Private*, pg. 213
PON FOOD CORP—See Highview Capital, LLC; *U.S. Private*, pg. 1942
PREFCO DISTRIBUTION, LLC—See Palladium Equity Partners, LLC; *U.S. Private*, pg. 3078
PRIMO PIATTO, INC.—See Post Holdings, Inc.; *U.S. Public*, pg. 1704
PRODUCTOS Y DISTRIBUIDORA AZTECA, S.A. DE C.V.—See Gruma, S.A.B. de C.V.; *Int'l*, pg. 3114
PT ALAM SUBUR TIRTA KENCANA—See IMCD N.V.; *Int'l*, pg. 3622
PURAC CHINA—See Corbion N.V.; *Int'l*, pg. 1795
PURAC INDIA PRIVATE LIMITED—See Corbion N.V.; *Int'l*, pg. 1795
PURAC KOREA—See Corbion N.V.; *Int'l*, pg. 1795
PURAC MEXICO S DE RL DE CV—See Corbion N.V.; *Int'l*, pg. 1795
PUSZTA KONZERV KFT.—See Avantha Group; *Int'l*, pg. 736

QUAKER VALLEY FOODS INC.; *U.S. Private*, pg. 3317
QUALITY BAKERY PRODUCTS, LLC—See Charlesbank Capital Partners, LLC; *U.S. Private*, pg. 855
QUALITY FROZEN FOODS, INC.; *U.S. Private*, pg. 3319
REAL GOOD FOOD COMPANY, INC.; *U.S. Public*, pg. 1768
RE-CICLAR S.A.—See Embotelladora Andina S.A.; *Int'l*, pg. 2375
REDDY RAW, INC.; *U.S. Private*, pg. 3378
RHEINTAL TIEFKUHLKOST ZWEIGNIEDERLASSUNG DER FROSTA AG—See FRoSTA AG; *Int'l*, pg. 2797
R & H HALL TRADING LIMITED—See ARYZTA AG; *Int'l*, pg. 589
RICH PRODUCTS CORPORATION—See Rich Holdings, Inc.; *U.S. Private*, pg. 3426
RIVER VALLEY FOODS INC.; *U.S. Private*, pg. 3444
SCHOOL LUNCH PRODUCTS, INC.—See Alvarez & Marsal, Inc.; *U.S. Private*, pg. 213
SCHOOL LUNCH PRODUCTS, INC.—See Highview Capital, LLC; *U.S. Private*, pg. 1942
SCHWAN'S FOOD SERVICE, INC.—See The Schwan Food Company; *U.S. Private*, pg. 4115
SFS DISTRIBUTION SERVICES INC.—See Sales Force Won Ltd.; *U.S. Private*, pg. 3532
SIGMA ALIMENTOS NORESTE, S.A. DE C.V—See ALFA, S.A.B. de C.V.; *Int'l*, pg. 314
SIGMA FOODS INC.—See ALFA, S.A.B. de C.V.; *Int'l*, pg. 314
SIGNATURE FOODS, INC.; *U.S. Private*, pg. 3650
SMITH FOOD SALES, INC.—See Smith Frozen Foods, Inc.; *U.S. Private*, pg. 3695
SOUTHEAST FROZEN FOODS COMPANY LP; *U.S. Private*, pg. 3725
STAP INC.; *U.S. Private*, pg. 3783
SUISAN CO. LTD; *U.S. Private*, pg. 3850
SYSCO GULF COAST, INC.—See Sysco Corporation; *U.S. Public*, pg. 1976
SYSCO NASHVILLE, LLC—See Sysco Corporation; *U.S. Public*, pg. 1976
SYSCO NORTH DAKOTA, INC.—See Sysco Corporation; *U.S. Public*, pg. 1977
SYSCO VICTORIA, INC.—See Sysco Corporation; *U.S. Public*, pg. 1977
SYSCO WESTERN MINNESOTA, INC.—See Sysco Corporation; *U.S. Public*, pg. 1977
SYY NETHERLANDS C.V.—See Sysco Corporation; *U.S. Public*, pg. 1975
TAIWAN ARIAKE FOODS CO., LTD.—See ARIAKE JAPAN Co., Ltd.; *Int'l*, pg. 564
THREE J'S DISTRIBUTING, INC.; *U.S. Public*, pg. 4164
TMI TRADING CORP.—See CJ Corporation; *Int'l*, pg. 1631
TRADAVO INC; *U.S. Private*, pg. 4201
TRANS-GLOBAL PRODUCTS INC.; *U.S. Private*, pg. 4206
TRAVIS MEATS INC.; *U.S. Private*, pg. 4214
TWIN RIVERS GROUP INC.; *U.S. Private*, pg. 4265
TYSON FOODS, INC.; *U.S. Public*, pg. 2209
UNITED SEAFOOD IMPORTS INC.; *U.S. Private*, pg. 4297
UPPER LAKES FOODS INC.; *U.S. Private*, pg. 4312
VALLEY ISLE PRODUCE, INC.; *U.S. Private*, pg. 4334
VALLEY PACKING SERVICE INC.—See The VPS Companies Inc.; *U.S. Private*, pg. 4132
VAUGHAN FOODS, INC.—See Reser's Fine Foods Inc.; *U.S. Private*, pg. 3404
VIP SALES COMPANY, INC.; *U.S. Private*, pg. 4387
V. J. CATALANO INC.; *U.S. Private*, pg. 4328
THE VPS COMPANIES INC.; *U.S. Private*, pg. 4132
WALTKOCH LTD.; *U.S. Private*, pg. 4434
WHITE CASTLE DISTRIBUTING, INC.—See White Castle System, Inc.; *U.S. Private*, pg. 4508
WILD PLANET FOODS, INC.; *U.S. Private*, pg. 4518
WILLIAM FOOD COMPANY LIMITED—See Hong Kong Food Investment Holdings Limited; *Int'l*, pg. 3466
THE WORNICK COMPANY—See Veritas Capital Fund Management, LLC; *U.S. Private*, pg. 4365

424430 — DAIRY PRODUCT (EXCEPT DRIED OR CANNED) MERCHANT WHOLESALERS

ABS PECPLAN LTDA.—See Genus Plc; *Int'l*, pg. 2930
ALLIED DAIRY PRODUCTS INC.; *U.S. Private*, pg. 185
ALMARAI COMPANY LTD.; *Int'l*, pg. 363
THE AMBRIOLA COMPANY, INC.—See Gennaro Auricchio S.p.A.; *Int'l*, pg. 2924
ARABIAN FOOD & DAIRY FACTORIES—See HAK Algahtani Group of Companies; *Int'l*, pg. 3219
ARLA FOODS AS—See Arla Foods amba; *Int'l*, pg. 572
ARLA FOODS HELLAS S.A.—See Arla Foods amba; *Int'l*, pg. 572
ARLA FOODS INC.—See Arla Foods amba; *Int'l*, pg. 572
ARLA FOODS S.A.R.L.—See Arla Foods amba; *Int'l*, pg. 573
ARLA FOODS S.A.—See Arla Foods amba; *Int'l*, pg. 573
ARLA FOODS—See Arla Foods amba; *Int'l*, pg. 573
ARLA FOODS S.R.L.—See Arla Foods amba; *Int'l*, pg. 573
AURIC PACIFIC (M) SDN BHD—See Diethelm Keller Holding Limited; *Int'l*, pg. 2116
AVH DAIRY TRADE B.V.—See Emmi AG; *Int'l*, pg. 2384
AXELROD FOODS, INC.—See Catamount Dairy Holdings L.P.; *U.S. Private*, pg. 787

424430 — DAIRY PRODUCT (EXCE...

BADGER MURPHY FOODSERVICES; *U.S. Private*, pg. 424
BALFORD FARMS—See Milk Industry Management Corp.; *U.S. Private*, pg. 2729
BAUMANN KASE AG—See Emmi AG; *Int'l*, pg. 2384
BAYERNLAND EG; *Int'l*, pg. 913
BELFONTE DAIRY DISTRIBUTION INC.; *U.S. Private*, pg. 517
BETTINEHOEVE B.V.—See Emmi AG; *Int'l*, pg. 2384
BIO MILK LTD.; *Int'l*, pg. 1035
BLOSSOM FARM PRODUCTS CO.; *U.S. Private*, pg. 584
BLUE BELL CREAMERIES—See Blue Bell Creameries, L.P.; *U.S. Private*, pg. 585
BONIFAZ KOHLER GMBH—See Hochland SE; *Int'l*, pg. 3437
BUCKHEAD MEAT COMPANY—See Sysco Corporation; *U.S. Public*, pg. 1973
BUCKHEAD MEAT MIDWEST, INC.—See Sysco Corporation; *U.S. Public*, pg. 1973
BUCKHEAD MEAT OF DALLAS, INC.—See Sysco Corporation; *U.S. Public*, pg. 1973
BUCKHEAD MEAT OF DENVER, INC.—See Sysco Corporation; *U.S. Public*, pg. 1973
BUCKHEAD MEAT OF SAN ANTONIO, LP—See Sysco Corporation; *U.S. Public*, pg. 1973
BUCKHEAD MEAT & SEAFOOD OF HOUSTON, INC.—See Sysco Corporation; *U.S. Public*, pg. 1973
BURT LEWIS INTERNATIONAL CORP; *U.S. Private*, pg. 692
BUTLER FOODS OF PENSACOLA INC.; *U.S. Private*, pg. 697
CABOT CREAMERY CO-OPERATIVE INC.—See Agri-Mark, Inc.; *U.S. Private*, pg. 129
CAPITOL CHILLED FOODS (AUSTRALIA) PTY. LIMITED—See Bega Cheese Ltd.; *Int'l*, pg. 940
CARL COLTERYAHN DAIRY INC.; *U.S. Private*, pg. 762
CEDAR FARMS COMPANY, INC.; *U.S. Private*, pg. 804
CEFETRA DAIRY B.V.—See BayWa AG; *Int'l*, pg. 917
C.F. BURGER CREAMERY COMPANY; *U.S. Private*, pg. 707
CHOBANI AUSTRALIA PTY LTD—See Chobani, LLC; *U.S. Private*, pg. 887
CHOBANI, LLC; *U.S. Private*, pg. 887
CHURNY COMPANY INC.—See 3G Capital Inc.; *U.S. Private*, pg. 10
CHURNY COMPANY INC.—See Berkshire Hathaway Inc.; *U.S. Public*, pg. 317
CIAO BELLA GELATO COMPANY—See Encore Associates Inc.; *U.S. Private*, pg. 1390
CIAO BELLA GELATO COMPANY—See Sherbrooke Capital LLC; *U.S. Private*, pg. 3633
CLOVER LAKE COUNTY INC.—See Clover Stornetta Farms Inc.; *U.S. Private*, pg. 947
COBLENTZ DISTRIBUTING INC.; *U.S. Private*, pg. 958
CODIFRAIS S.A.S.—See Colruyt Group N.V.; *Int'l*, pg. 1705
COLONY BRANDS, INC.; *U.S. Private*, pg. 972
COOP NORGE INDUSTRI AS—See Coop Norge SA; *Int'l*, pg. 1789
COUNTRY FRESH, INC.—See Dean Foods Company; *U.S. Private*, pg. 1183
CREAM-O-LAND DAIRY INC.; *U.S. Private*, pg. 1087
CREMES UNLIMITED INC.; *U.S. Private*, pg. 1092
CRYSTAL FARMS REFRIGERATED DISTRIBUTION COMPANY—See Post Holdings, Inc.; *U.S. Public*, pg. 1703
DAIRYAMERICA, INC.; *U.S. Private*, pg. 1146
DAIRY FRESH FARMS INC.; *U.S. Private*, pg. 1146
DAIRY FRESH FOODS, INC.; *U.S. Private*, pg. 1146
DAN DAIRIES (UK) LIMITED—See Dairygold Co-Operative Society Ltd; *Int'l*, pg. 1940
DANONE PRODUITS FRAIS FRANCE—See Danone; *Int'l*, pg. 1968
DARI-FARMS ICE CREAM CO., INC.—See Diversis Capital, LLC; *U.S. Private*, pg. 1244
DEAN'S ICE CREAM—See Dean Foods Company; *U.S. Private*, pg. 1184
DERLE FARMS INC.; *U.S. Private*, pg. 1209
DESAILLY SA; *Int'l*, pg. 2043
EHRMANN AG; *Int'l*, pg. 2328
EVERYTHING FRESH LTD.; *Int'l*, pg. 2570
FAGE ITALIA S.R.L.—See Fage Dairy Industry S.A.; *Int'l*, pg. 2601
FAMILY DAIRIES USA; *U.S. Private*, pg. 1469
FESTIVAL ICE CREAM CORP.; *U.S. Private*, pg. 1499
FLORAS DISTRIBUTORS INC.; *U.S. Private*, pg. 1546
FONTERRA BRANDS LANKA (PRIVATE) LIMITED—See Fonterra Co-Operative Group Ltd.; *Int'l*, pg. 2726
FONTERRA BRANDS (NEW ZEALAND) LIMITED—See Fonterra Co-Operative Group Ltd; *Int'l*, pg. 2726
FONTERRA (JAPAN) LTD.—See Fonterra Co-Operative Group Ltd.; *Int'l*, pg. 2726
FONTERRA (USA) INC.—See Fonterra Co-Operative Group Ltd.; *Int'l*, pg. 2726
FOURTH GROUP INC.—See Byrne Dairy Inc.; *U.S. Private*, pg. 701
FROSTY TREATS INC.; *U.S. Private*, pg. 1617
FROZEN GOURMET INC.; *U.S. Private*, pg. 1617
GARELICK FARMS, LLC—See Dean Foods Company; *U.S. Private*, pg. 1184

GENERALE BISCUIT GLICO FRANCE S.A.—See Ezaki Glico Co., Ltd.; *Int'l*, pg. 2593
GENERAL MILLS—See General Mills, Inc.; *U.S. Public*, pg. 922
GOAT MILK POWDER B.V.—See Emmi AG; *Int'l*, pg. 2384
GREAT LAKES ICE CREAM INC.; *U.S. Private*, pg. 1764
GREEN GRASS FOODS, INC.—See MidOcean Partners, LLP; *U.S. Private*, pg. 2717
GREEN GRASS FOODS, INC.—See The Kroger Co.; *U.S. Public*, pg. 2108
HAPPY VALLEY NUTRITION LIMITED; *Int'l*, pg. 3269
HEILONGJIANG FEIHE DAIRY CO., LIMITED—See Feihe International, Inc.; *Int'l*, pg. 2632
HELUVA GOOD, LLC—See Catamount Dairy Holdings L.P.; *U.S. Private*, pg. 787
HILL COUNTRY DAIRIES INC.; *U.S. Private*, pg. 1945
HOCHLAND ESPANOLA S. A.—See Hochland SE; *Int'l*, pg. 3437
INSTANTWHIP-AKRON, INC.—See Instantwhip Foods, Inc.; *U.S. Private*, pg. 2092
INSTANTWHIP-BALTIMORE, INC.—See Instantwhip Foods, Inc.; *U.S. Private*, pg. 2092
INSTANTWHIP-BUFFALO, INC.—See Instantwhip Foods, Inc.; *U.S. Private*, pg. 2092
INSTANTWHIP-CHICAGO, INC.—See Instantwhip Foods, Inc.; *U.S. Private*, pg. 2092
INSTANTWHIP-CONNECTICUT, INC.—See Instantwhip Foods, Inc.; *U.S. Private*, pg. 2092
INSTANTWHIP-EASTERN NEW YORK, INC.—See Instantwhip Foods, Inc.; *U.S. Private*, pg. 2092
INSTANTWHIP-INDIANAPOLIS, INC.—See Instantwhip Foods, Inc.; *U.S. Private*, pg. 2092
INSTANTWHIP OF PENNSYLVANIA, INC.—See Instantwhip Foods, Inc.; *U.S. Private*, pg. 2092
INSTANTWHIP-ROCHESTER, INC.—See Instantwhip Foods, Inc.; *U.S. Private*, pg. 2092
JOE & ROSS INC.—See Guggenheim Partners, LLC; *U.S. Private*, pg. 1812
KASEREI STUDER AG—See Emmi AG; *Int'l*, pg. 2385
KBO ENTERPRISES INC.; *U.S. Private*, pg. 2268
KICKAPOO VALLEY CHEESE CORP.; *U.S. Private*, pg. 2302
KRAFT FOOD INGREDIENTS CORP.—See 3G Capital Inc.; *U.S. Private*, pg. 10
KRAFT FOOD INGREDIENTS CORP.—See Berkshire Hathaway Inc.; *U.S. Public*, pg. 318
KRINOS FOODS INC.; *U.S. Private*, pg. 2351
LACTALIS-ALBA S.R.L.—See Groupe Lactalis SA; *Int'l*, pg. 3106
LACTALIS INTERNATIONAL SNC—See Groupe Lactalis SA; *Int'l*, pg. 3106
LACTALIS SINGAPORE PTE. LTD.—See Bega Cheese Ltd.; *Int'l*, pg. 940
LACTALIS-UKRAINE, CJSC—See Groupe Lactalis SA; *Int'l*, pg. 3106
LAKES AREA COOPERATIVE; *U.S. Private*, pg. 2376
LLET NOSTRA ALIMENTARIA S.L.—See Emmi AG; *Int'l*, pg. 2385
LUVEL DAIRY PRODUCTS, INC.; *U.S. Private*, pg. 2518
MARINA ICE CREAM CO., INC.; *U.S. Private*, pg. 2574
MARMUM DAIRY FARM LLC—See Emirates Advanced Investments Group LLC; *Int'l*, pg. 2381
MARYLAND & VIRGINIA MILK PRODUCERS COOP ASSOCIATION INC; *U.S. Private*, pg. 2600
MASTERS GALLERY FOODS, INC.; *U.S. Private*, pg. 2608
MEDOSWEET FARMS INC.; *U.S. Private*, pg. 2658
MEHADRIN DAIRY CORP.; *U.S. Private*, pg. 2660
MMM SALES, INC.; *U.S. Private*, pg. 2755
MODERN FOODS LLC; *U.S. Private*, pg. 2760
MURFREESBORO PURE MILK COMPANY; *U.S. Private*, pg. 2815
NEOGEN GUATEMALA S.A.—See Neogen Corporation; *U.S. Public*, pg. 1505
NEWPORT MEAT NORTHERN CALIFORNIA, INC.—See Sysco Corporation; *U.S. Public*, pg. 1974
NEWPORT MEAT OF NEVADA, INC.—See Sysco Corporation; *U.S. Public*, pg. 1974
NEWPORT MEAT PACIFIC NORTHWEST, INC.—See Sysco Corporation; *U.S. Public*, pg. 1974
NEWPORT MEAT SOUTHERN CALIFORNIA, INC.—See Sysco Corporation; *U.S. Public*, pg. 1974
NU SKIN SLOVAKIA S.R.O.—See Nu Skin Enterprises, Inc.; *U.S. Public*, pg. 1552
PINT SIZE CORPORATION; *U.S. Private*, pg. 3186
PRODUCERS DAIRY FOODS, INC.; *U.S. Private*, pg. 3272
QUEENSBORO FARM PRODUCTS INC.; *U.S. Private*, pg. 3325
QUICK CHEK CORPORATION—See Murphy USA Inc.; *U.S. Public*, pg. 1487
RAY ALDERMAN & SONS INC.; *U.S. Private*, pg. 3358
ROCKVIEW DAIRIES INC.; *U.S. Private*, pg. 3467
SAMPSON VENTURES, LLC—See Dean Foods Company; *U.S. Private*, pg. 1184
SCHNEIDER VALLEY FARMS DAIRY—See Schneider's Dairy Holdings; *U.S. Private*, pg. 3567
SELECT MILK PRODUCERS INC.; *U.S. Private*, pg. 3600
SHULLSBURG CREAMERY INC.; *U.S. Private*, pg. 3644

SOUTHERN BELLE DAIRY CO. INC.; *U.S. Private*, pg. 3729
SOUTHERN ICE CREAM, CORP.—See Guggenheim Partners, LLC; *U.S. Private*, pg. 1812
SUNNY FLORIDA DAIRY INC.; *U.S. Private*, pg. 3868
SUNNY MORNING FOODS INC.; *U.S. Private*, pg. 3868
SUNRISE AG COOPERATIVE; *U.S. Private*, pg. 3869
SUNSHINE DAIRY FOODS INC.; *U.S. Private*, pg. 3871
SUNSHINE DAIRY INC.—See Sunshine Dairy Foods Inc.; *U.S. Private*, pg. 3871
SURE WINNER FOODS INC.; *U.S. Private*, pg. 3883
SUSU LEMBU ASLI (JOHORE) SDN. BHD.—See Asahi Group Holdings Ltd.; *Int'l*, pg. 593
SUSU LEMBU ASLI MARKETING SDN. BHD.—See Asahi Group Holdings Ltd.; *Int'l*, pg. 593
SWENSEN'S OF SINGAPORE PTE. LTD.—See ABR Holdings, Ltd.; *Int'l*, pg. 67
SWISS COLONY DATA CENTER INC.; *U.S. Private*, pg. 3894
SWISS VALLEY FARMS CO.—See Prairie Farms Dairy, Inc.; *U.S. Private*, pg. 3242
TASTY PURE FOOD CO. INC.; *U.S. Private*, pg. 3935
T.C. JACOBY & COMPANY, INC.; *U.S. Private*, pg. 3911
TOMALES BAY FOODS INC.—See Emmi AG; *Int'l*, pg. 2385
UNIPRO FOODSERVICE INC.; *U.S. Private*, pg. 4285
UNITED SALES PARTNERS LLC—See Dubai Investments PJSC; *Int'l*, pg. 2219
V. SUAREZ & COMPANY, INC.; *U.S. Private*, pg. 4328
WADDINGTON-RICHMAN, INC.; *U.S. Private*, pg. 4424
WALLABY YOGURT COMPANY, LLC—See Danone; *Int'l*, pg. 1967
WERHANE ENTERPRISES LTD.; *U.S. Private*, pg. 4481
WILLIAMS INLAND DISTRIBUTORS LLC; *U.S. Private*, pg. 4526
WISCONSIN CHEESE GROUP INC.; *U.S. Private*, pg. 4548
YOPLAIT FRANCE SAS—See General Mills, Inc.; *U.S. Public*, pg. 923
YOPLAIT IRELAND LIMITED—See General Mills, Inc.; *U.S. Public*, pg. 923
YOPLAIT SVERIGE AB—See General Mills, Inc.; *U.S. Public*, pg. 923
YOPLAIT UK LTD.—See General Mills, Inc.; *U.S. Public*, pg. 923
ZOPITAR LIMITED—See Donegal Investment Group Plc; *Int'l*, pg. 2163

424440 — POULTRY AND POULTRY PRODUCT MERCHANT WHOLESALERS

ACME FARMS, INC.; *U.S. Private*, pg. 60
ALLEN HARIM FOODS LLC—See Harim Holdings Co., Ltd.; *Int'l*, pg. 3275
AMERICAN EGG PRODUCTS, INC.—See Cal-Maine Foods, Inc.; *U.S. Public*, pg. 421
BRANKO A.S.; *Int'l*, pg. 1140
CAL-MAINE FOODS—See Cal-Maine Foods, Inc.; *U.S. Public*, pg. 421
CARGILL MEAT SOLUTIONS CORP.—See Cargill, Inc.; *U.S. Private*, pg. 758
CARGILL VALUE ADDED MEATS—See Cargill, Inc.; *U.S. Private*, pg. 758
CAROLINA EGG COMPANIES, INC.—See Braswell Milling Company; *U.S. Private*, pg. 640
CHARLES RIVER SPAFAS—See Charles River Laboratories International, Inc.; *U.S. Public*, pg. 480
C&O FOOD SERVICES INC.; *U.S. Private*, pg. 703
COUGLE COMMISSION COMPANY, INC.; *U.S. Private*, pg. 1065
COUNTRY EGGS INC.; *U.S. Private*, pg. 1066
COUNTRY SQUIRE FARM PRODUCTS; *U.S. Private*, pg. 1067
CROWN FOODS LLC; *U.S. Private*, pg. 1111
DAYBREAK FOODS INC.; *U.S. Private*, pg. 1176
DAYBREAK SUPERIOR MARKETING (PTY) LTD.—See AFGRI Limited; *Int'l*, pg. 188
DM SHIVTEX, INC.; *U.S. Private*, pg. 1248
EASTERN POULTRY DISTRIBUTORS INC.; *U.S. Private*, pg. 1320
EAST OLYMPIC POULTRY INC.; *U.S. Private*, pg. 1317
EGGRICULTURE FOODS LTD.; *Int'l*, pg. 2324
FRANZ FOODS INC.; *U.S. Private*, pg. 1598
GRUPO MELO S.A.; *Int'l*, pg. 3132
HALLMARK POULTRY PROCESSORS LTD.; *Int'l*, pg. 3230
HILLANDALE FARMS OF PA INC.; *U.S. Private*, pg. 1946
HYZA A.S.—See Agrofert Holding, a.s.; *Int'l*, pg. 219
IMLERS POULTRY; *U.S. Private*, pg. 2047
JL FOODS CO., INC.; *U.S. Private*, pg. 2211
JOYCE FARMS, INC.; *U.S. Private*, pg. 2238
KEITH SMITH COMPANY, INC.; *U.S. Private*, pg. 2274
KENDO TRADING PTE. LTD.—See Emerging Glory Sdn Bhd; *Int'l*, pg. 2379
KESSLERS INCORPORATED; *U.S. Private*, pg. 2291
KOCH FOODS LLC—See Koch Foods, Inc.; *U.S. Private*, pg. 2326
L&S FOOD SALES CORP.; *U.S. Private*, pg. 2363
LUBERSKI INC.; *U.S. Private*, pg. 2510
MARTIN PREFERRED FOODS LP; *U.S. Private*, pg. 2595

N.A.I.C.S. INDEX

424460 — FISH AND SEAFOOD ME...

MENNELLA'S POULTRY CO. INC.; *U.S. Private*, pg. 2666
M-G INC.; *U.S. Private*, pg. 2526
MIDWEST FOOD & POULTRY INC.; *U.S. Private*, pg. 2721
MOARK PRODUCTIONS INC.; *U.S. Private*, pg. 2756
NORBEST, INC.; *U.S. Private*, pg. 2935
NULAID FOODS INC.; *U.S. Private*, pg. 2973
POLIN POULTRY COMPANY INC.; *U.S. Private*, pg. 3224
POULTRY PRODUCTS COMPANY INC.; *U.S. Private*, pg. 3236
PRESTIGE FARMS INC.; *U.S. Private*, pg. 3256
QUALITY DISTRIBUTING UNION CITY—See Quality Distributing Company; *U.S. Private*, pg. 3318
RACE STREET FOODS INC.; *U.S. Private*, pg. 3341
RANDALL FOODS, INC.—See Highview Capital, LLC; *U.S. Private*, pg. 1942
REMBRANDT ENTERPRISES, INC.; *U.S. Private*, pg. 3396
R.W. SAUDER INC.; *U.S. Private*, pg. 3340
R.W. ZANT COMPANY; *U.S. Private*, pg. 3340
SAFA GOURMET FOOD PTE LTD—See Emerging Glory Sdn Bhd; *Int'l*, pg. 2379
SONSTEGARD FOODS COMPANY; *U.S. Private*, pg. 3714
SOUTH TEXAS APPLICATORS, INC.—See Cal-Maine Foods, Inc.; *U.S. Public*, pg. 421
STROMBERG'S UNLIMITED, INC.—See Grey Mountain Partners, LLC; *U.S. Private*, pg. 1784
SUTHERLAND'S FOODSERVICE, INC.; *U.S. Private*, pg. 3886
VISTA FOOD EXCHANGE, INC.; *U.S. Private*, pg. 4402
WAYNE-SANDERSON FARMS; *U.S. Private*, pg. 4460

424450 — CONFECTIONERY MERCHANT WHOLESALERS

AARHUSKARLSHAMN DO BRASIL DESENVOLVIMENTO DE NEGOSIOS LTDA.—See AAK AB; *Int'l*, pg. 32
ABDALLAH INCORPORATED; *U.S. Private*, pg. 37
ADEKA FOODS SALES CORPORATION—See Adeka Corporation; *Int'l*, pg. 141
AG SUPERMARKETS INC.—See Associated Grocers of New England, Inc.; *U.S. Private*, pg. 356
A.H. HERMEL CANDY & TOBACCO CO. INC.; *U.S. Private*, pg. 26
AL BAZZINI COMPANY INCORPORATION; *U.S. Private*, pg. 147
ALBERT USTER IMPORTS, INC.—See Vestar Capital Partners, LLC; *U.S. Private*, pg. 4372
ALFOREX SEEDS LLC—See Corteva, Inc.; *U.S. Public*, pg. 580
ALMOND ROCA INTERNATIONAL—See Brown & Haley; *U.S. Private*, pg. 666
AMERICAN NOVELTY INC; *U.S. Private*, pg. 242
AMES INTERNATIONAL INC.—See Puyallup Tribe of Indians; *U.S. Private*, pg. 3308
THE ANCHOR CIGAR & CANDY COMPANY INC.—See Tri County Wholesale Distributors Inc.; *U.S. Private*, pg. 4220
AP ATLANTIC DISTRIBUTION, INC.; *U.S. Private*, pg. 290
B.A. SWEETIE CANDY COMPANY; *U.S. Private*, pg. 420
BIG TREE ORGANIC FARMS, INC.—See Once Again Nut Butter Collective Inc.; *U.S. Private*, pg. 3019
BLOOMER CANDY CO.; *U.S. Private*, pg. 584
CADBURY TRADING HONG KONG LTD.—See Mondelez International, Inc.; *U.S. Public*, pg. 1461
CALBEE (HANGZHOU) FOODS CO., LTD.—See Calbee, Inc.; *Int'l*, pg. 1261
CALBEE POTATO, INC.—See Calbee, Inc.; *Int'l*, pg. 1261
CALBEE TANAWAT CO., LTD.—See Calbee, Inc.; *Int'l*, pg. 1261
CANDYKING DANMARK A/S—See Cloetta AB; *Int'l*, pg. 1660
CANDYKING FINLAND OY—See Cloetta AB; *Int'l*, pg. 1660
CANDYKING NORGE AS—See Cloetta AB; *Int'l*, pg. 1660
CANDYKING POLAND SP. Z O.O.—See Cloetta AB; *Int'l*, pg. 1661
CANDYKING SWEDEN AB—See Cloetta AB; *Int'l*, pg. 1661
CANDYKING UK LTD.—See Cloetta AB; *Int'l*, pg. 1661
CANDYMIX IRELAND LTD.—See Cloetta AB; *Int'l*, pg. 1661
CANDYRIFIC LLC; *U.S. Private*, pg. 734
CAPOL GMBH—See Freudenberg SE; *Int'l*, pg. 2782
CAPOL LLC—See Freudenberg SE; *Int'l*, pg. 2782
CAPOL (U.K.) LIMITED—See Freudenberg SE; *Int'l*, pg. 2782
CHARMS LLC—See Tootsie Roll Industries, Inc.; *U.S. Public*, pg. 2163
CLARK GUM COMPANY—See Slate Capital Group LLC; *U.S. Private*, pg. 3687
CLARK'S UK LIMITED—See The Hain Celestial Group, Inc.; *U.S. Public*, pg. 2086
CONSOLIDATED PRODUCTS SYSTEMS; *U.S. Private*, pg. 1021
CONTINENTAL CONCESSION SUPPLIES, INC.; *U.S. Private*, pg. 1028
CORDIALSA USA, INC.—See Grupo Nutresa S.A.; *Int'l*, pg. 3133
CREATIVE SNACKS CO., LLC—See KIND LLC; *U.S. Private*, pg. 2306
CULINARY DESTINATIONS LIMITED; *Int'l*, pg. 1876

DANONE NEDERLAND B.V. - FOODSERVICE—See Danone; *Int'l*, pg. 1968
DAVIDSON'S OF DUNDEE; *U.S. Private*, pg. 1172
DAYTON NUT SPECIALTIES INC.; *U.S. Private*, pg. 1177
DEB WHOLESALE, INC.; *U.S. Private*, pg. 1186
DERIGO SALES INC.; *U.S. Private*, pg. 1209
DR. TORRENTS, S.L.—See Tootsie Roll Industries, Inc.; *U.S. Public*, pg. 2163
EBY-BROWN CO.—See Performance Food Group Company; *U.S. Public*, pg. 1674
EZAKI GLICO USA CORPORATION—See Ezaki Glico Co., Ltd.; *Int'l*, pg. 2593
FERRERO U.S.A., INC.—See Ferrero International S.A.; *Int'l*, pg. 2640
FIGI'S BUSINESS SERVICES, INC.—See Mason Companies, Inc.; *U.S. Private*, pg. 2602
FIGI'S, INC.—See Mason Companies, Inc.; *U.S. Private*, pg. 2602
FIRST SOURCE, LLC - TENNESSEE—See Slate Capital Group LLC; *U.S. Private*, pg. 3687
FIVE STAR DISTRIBUTORS INC.—See Performance Food Group Company; *U.S. Public*, pg. 1674
THE FOREIGN CANDY COMPANY, INC.; *U.S. Private*, pg. 4029
FRITZ COMPANY; *U.S. Private*, pg. 1612
FUJI SUNNY FOODS CO., LTD.—See Fuji Oil Holdings Inc.; *Int'l*, pg. 2815
G&A SNACK DISTRIBUTING INC.—See Grande Foods California Corporation; *U.S. Private*, pg. 1753
GLICO CANADA CORPORATION—See Ezaki Glico Co., Ltd.; *Int'l*, pg. 2593
GLOBAL DINING, INC. - MYOGADANI FACTORY—See Global Dining, Inc.; *Int'l*, pg. 2994
HAI-O RAYA BHD.—See Hai-O Enterprise Berhad; *Int'l*, pg. 3209
HALFON CANDY COMPANY, INC.—See Harbor Foods Group Inc.; *U.S. Private*, pg. 1859
HARIBO DUNHILLS (PONTEFRACT) PLC—See HARIBO GmbH & Co. KG; *Int'l*, pg. 3275
HARIBO ESPANA S.A.U—See HARIBO GmbH & Co. KG; *Int'l*, pg. 3275
HARIBO ESPANA S.A.U—See HARIBO GmbH & Co. KG; *Int'l*, pg. 3275
HARIBO HUNGARIA KFT.—See HARIBO GmbH & Co. KG; *Int'l*, pg. 3275
HARIBO IRELAND LTD.—See HARIBO GmbH & Co. KG; *Int'l*, pg. 3275
HARIBO ITALIA S.P.A.—See HARIBO GmbH & Co. KG; *Int'l*, pg. 3275
HARIBO KONFETY OOO—See HARIBO GmbH & Co. KG; *Int'l*, pg. 3275
HARIBO LAKRIDS A/S—See HARIBO GmbH & Co. KG; *Int'l*, pg. 3275
HARIBO LAKRIDS OY AB—See HARIBO GmbH & Co. KG; *Int'l*, pg. 3275
HARIBO LAKRIS AS—See HARIBO GmbH & Co. KG; *Int'l*, pg. 3275
HARIBO LAKRITS AB—See HARIBO GmbH & Co. KG; *Int'l*, pg. 3275
HARIBO LAKRITZEN HANS RIEGEL BETRIEBSGES.M.B.H.—See HARIBO GmbH & Co. KG; *Int'l*, pg. 3275
HARIBO NEDERLAND B.V.—See HARIBO GmbH & Co. KG; *Int'l*, pg. 3275
HARIBO RICQLES-ZAN S.A.—See HARIBO GmbH & Co. KG; *Int'l*, pg. 3275
HARIBO SEKERLEME SAN. VE TIC. LTD. STI.—See HARIBO GmbH & Co. KG; *Int'l*, pg. 3275
HERSHEY JAPAN CO., LTD.—See The Hershey Co.; *U.S. Public*, pg. 2089
HUSSEL GESCHENKSTUDIO GMBH—See EMERAM Capital Partners GmbH; *Int'l*, pg. 2378
HYDE & HYDE INC.; *U.S. Private*, pg. 2016
HZPC AMERICA LATINA S.A.—See HZPC Holland B.V.; *Int'l*, pg. 3561
HZPC DEUTSCHLAND GMBH—See HZPC Holland B.V.; *Int'l*, pg. 3561
HZPC KANTAPERUNA OY—See HZPC Holland B.V.; *Int'l*, pg. 3561
HZPC POLSKA SP. Z.O.O—See HZPC Holland B.V.; *Int'l*, pg. 3561
HZPC PORTUGAL LDA—See HZPC Holland B.V.; *Int'l*, pg. 3561
HZPC SVERIGE AB—See HZPC Holland B.V.; *Int'l*, pg. 3561
HZPC UK LTD—See HZPC Holland B.V.; *Int'l*, pg. 3561
JOHN B. SANFILIPPO & SON, INC.—See John B. Sanfilippo & Son, Inc.; *U.S. Public*, pg. 1190
JONES VENDING & OCS DISTRIBUTING INC.; *U.S. Private*, pg. 2234
KAHLER-SENDERS GROUP INC.; *U.S. Private*, pg. 2254
KAUMY S.R.O.—See Fomento Economico Mexicano, S.A.B. de C.V.; *Int'l*, pg. 2724
KEEFE GROUP, INC.—See Centric Group LLC; *U.S. Private*, pg. 830
KEEFE SUPPLY COMPANY—See Centric Group LLC; *U.S. Private*, pg. 830
KILWIN'S CHOCOLATES FRANCHISE, INC.—See Levine Leichtman Capital Partners, LLC; *U.S. Private*, pg. 2436

K & W POPCORN INC.—See Preferred Popcorn LLC; *U.S. Private*, pg. 3248
LAFRONTERIZA LLC—See Grupo Bimbo, S.A.B. de C.V.; *Int'l*, pg. 3122
LIBERTO SPECIALTY COMPANY INC.; *U.S. Private*, pg. 2442
LINDT & SPRUNGLI (ASIA PACIFIC) LTD.—See Chocoladefabriken Lindt & Sprungli AG; *Int'l*, pg. 1576
LINDT & SPRUNGLI (AUSTRALIA) PTY. LTD.—See Chocoladefabriken Lindt & Sprungli AG; *Int'l*, pg. 1576
LINDT & SPRUNGLI (CANADA), INC.—See Chocoladefabriken Lindt & Sprungli AG; *Int'l*, pg. 1576
LINDT & SPRUNGLI (ESPANA) SA—See Chocoladefabriken Lindt & Sprungli AG; *Int'l*, pg. 1576
LINDT & SPRUNGLI (POLAND) SP. Z OO—See Chocoladefabriken Lindt & Sprungli AG; *Int'l*, pg. 1576
LINDT & SPRUNGLI (UK) LTD.—See Chocoladefabriken Lindt & Sprungli AG; *Int'l*, pg. 1576
MARS VIETNAM—See Mars, Incorporated; *U.S. Private*, pg. 2590
MONDELEZ JAPAN LTD—See Mondelez International, Inc.; *U.S. Public*, pg. 1464
MURRAYS CHEESE LLC—See The Kroger Co.; *U.S. Public*, pg. 2108
NASSAU CANDY DISTRIBUTORS INC.; *U.S. Private*, pg. 2837
NATURAL WORLD S.R.L.—See BRENNTAG SE; *Int'l*, pg. 1149
PEANUT PROCESSORS INC.; *U.S. Private*, pg. 3125
PERFORMANCE FOOD GROUP, INC. - PHOENIX SPECIALTY DISTRIBUTION CENTER—See Performance Food Group Company; *U.S. Public*, pg. 1675
PEZ CANDY, INC.; *U.S. Private*, pg. 3164
POTATO KAITSUKA CO. LTD.—See Calbee, Inc.; *Int'l*, pg. 1261
PT GLICO INDONESIA—See Ezaki Glico Co., Ltd.; *Int'l*, pg. 2593
R.L. ALBERT & SON, INC.; *U.S. Private*, pg. 3338
ROBERT ROBERTS LIMITED—See DCC plc; *Int'l*, pg. 1991
R.W. GARCIA CO., INC.—See Utz Brands, Inc.; *U.S. Public*, pg. 2267
RYT-WAY INDUSTRIES, LLC—See Charlesbank Capital Partners, LLC; *U.S. Private*, pg. 855
SANTA CLARA NUT COMPANY INC.; *U.S. Private*, pg. 3547
SHOWTIME CONCESSION SUPPLY INC.; *U.S. Private*, pg. 3643
SIGNATURE BRANDS, LLC—See Marvin Traub Associates, Inc.; *U.S. Private*, pg. 2598
SOLO FOODS, LLC—See Benford Capital Partners, LLC; *U.S. Private*, pg. 526
STUDIO SOCIO INC.—See Calbee, Inc.; *Int'l*, pg. 1262
SULTANA DISTRIBUTION SERVICES INC.; *U.S. Private*, pg. 3852
SUPERIOR NUT AND CANDY CO.; *U.S. Private*, pg. 3879
THAI CORP INTERNATIONAL (VIETNAM) CO. LTD.—See Berli Jucker Public Co. Ltd.; *Int'l*, pg. 985
THAI GLICO CO., LTD.—See Ezaki Glico Co., Ltd.; *Int'l*, pg. 2593
TIGER DISTRIBUTORS INC.; *U.S. Private*, pg. 4169
TRI INTERNATIONAL, INC.—See Tootsie Roll Industries, Inc.; *U.S. Public*, pg. 2163
TRUCO ENTERPRISES, LP—See Utz Brands, Inc.; *U.S. Public*, pg. 2268
VALORA SCHWEIZ AG—See Fomento Economico Mexicano, S.A.B. de C.V.; *Int'l*, pg. 2724
VALORA TRADE NORWAY AS—See Fomento Economico Mexicano, S.A.B. de C.V.; *Int'l*, pg. 2724
VALORA TRADE SWEDEN AB—See Fomento Economico Mexicano, S.A.B. de C.V.; *Int'l*, pg. 2724
VEND MART INC.; *U.S. Private*, pg. 4356
WAGERS INC.; *U.S. Private*, pg. 4425
WALTZFANCY CO., LTD.—See Fuji Oil Holdings Inc.; *Int'l*, pg. 2816
WARNER CANDY COMPANY; *U.S. Private*, pg. 4442
THE WARRELL CORP.—See Nassau Candy Distributors Inc.; *U.S. Private*, pg. 2837
WEAVER NUT COMPANY INC.; *U.S. Private*, pg. 4463
WEAVER POPCORN COMPANY, INC.; *U.S. Private*, pg. 4463
WRIGLEY BULGARIA EOOD—See Mars, Incorporated; *U.S. Private*, pg. 2591
THE WRIGLEY COMPANY (H.K.) LIMITED—See Mars, Incorporated; *U.S. Private*, pg. 2590
YONGO CO., LTD—See Adeka Corporation; *Int'l*, pg. 142
YORKSHIRE FOOD SALES CORP.; *U.S. Private*, pg. 4591

424460 — FISH AND SEAFOOD MERCHANT WHOLESALERS

ACME SMOKED FISH CORPORATION; *U.S. Private*, pg. 61
ADELPHIA SEAFOOD INC.; *U.S. Private*, pg. 77
ADMIRALTY ISLAND FISHERIES INC.; *U.S. Private*, pg. 81
AFFISH B.V.—See Camellia Plc; *Int'l*, pg. 1270
AKVA GROUP DENMARK A/S—See Egersund Group AS; *Int'l*, pg. 2323

424460 — FISH AND SEAFOOD ME...

ALPHA PRIME FOODS LIMITED—See Hang Sang (Siu Po) International Holding Company Limited; *Int'l*, pg. 3245
A.M. BRIGGS, INC.—See Sysco Corporation; *U.S. Public*, pg. 1973
ANDREAS SIMONSEN GMBH FROZEN FISH DIVISION—See Andreas Simonsen GmbH; *Int'l*, pg. 451
ANDREAS SIMONSEN GMBH; *Int'l*, pg. 451
AP HOLDINGS CO., LTD; *Int'l*, pg. 499
AQUABEST SEAFOOD, LLC.; *U.S. Private*, pg. 303
A. RAPTIS & SONS PTY. LTD.; *Int'l*, pg. 21
ARIAKE JAPAN CO LTD - KYUSHU PLANT—See ARIAKE JAPAN Co., Ltd.; *Int'l*, pg. 563
ASIAN ALLIANCE INTERNATIONAL CO., LTD.—See Asian Sea Corporation Public Company Limited; *Int'l*, pg. 619
ASIAN GROUP SCS EUROPE GMBH—See Asian Sea Corporation Public Company Limited; *Int'l*, pg. 619
ASIAN GROUP SERVICES CO., LTD.—See Asian Sea Corporation Public Company Limited; *Int'l*, pg. 619
ASPEN DISTRIBUTION SERVICES, INC.; *U.S. Private*, pg. 351
ATLANTA ORIENTAL FOOD WHOLESALE CO.; *U.S. Private*, pg. 371
BAMA SEA PRODUCTS INC.; *U.S. Private*, pg. 463
BARRAMUNDI GROUP LTD.; *Int'l*, pg. 867
BELLA COOLA FISHERIES LTD.; *Int'l*, pg. 966
BELL BENELUX N.V.—See Coop-Gruppe Genossenschaft; *Int'l*, pg. 1789
BHJ UK SEAFOODS LTD.—See Lauridsen Group Inc.; *U.S. Private*, pg. 2400
BIOMAR HELLENIC SA—See Aktieselskabet Schouw & Co.; *Int'l*, pg. 265
BIOMAR LTD.—See Aktieselskabet Schouw & Co.; *Int'l*, pg. 265
BLUEFIN SEAFOOD CORP; *U.S. Private*, pg. 596
BLUE HARVEST FOODS, LLC - HYGRADE DIVISION—See COFRA Holding AG; *Int'l*, pg. 1694
BLUE HARVEST FOODS, LLC—See COFRA Holding AG; *Int'l*, pg. 1694
BLUE STAR FOODS CORP.; *U.S. Public*, pg. 365
BLUNDELL SEAFOODS LTD.; *Int'l*, pg. 1075
CAB MARINE RESOURCES SDN. BHD.—See Cab Cakaran Corporation Berhad; *Int'l*, pg. 1245
CALEB HALEY & CO. INC.; *U.S. Private*, pg. 716
CANADIAN FISH EXPORTERS, INC.; *U.S. Private*, pg. 732
CAPE QUALITY SEAFOOD LTD.; *U.S. Private*, pg. 738
CAPTAIN MARDEN'S SEAFOODS, INC.; *U.S. Private*, pg. 746
CASPIAN STAR CAVIAR INC.; *U.S. Private*, pg. 783
CATALANO SEAFOOD LIMITED; *Int'l*, pg. 1358
CENTURY PACIFIC FOOD, INC. - GENERAL SANTOS CITY PLANT—See Century Pacific Food, Inc.; *Int'l*, pg. 1419
CENTURY PACIFIC FOOD, INC. - ZAMBOANGA PLANT—See Century Pacific Food, Inc.; *Int'l*, pg. 1419
CERTI-FRESH FOODS, INC.; *U.S. Private*, pg. 841
CHANG INTERNATIONAL INC.; *U.S. Private*, pg. 848
CHESAPEAKE BAY SEAFOOD HOUSE ASSOCIATES, LLC; *U.S. Private*, pg. 874
CHIA TAI YONGJI ENTERPRISE CO., LTD.—See Charoen Pokphand Foods Public Company Limited; *Int'l*, pg. 1452
CHIBA CHUO GYORUI CO., LTD.—See Chuo Gyorui Co., Ltd.; *Int'l*, pg. 1598
CHOICE CANNING CO., INC.; *U.S. Private*, pg. 888
CHUO FOODS CO., LTD.—See Chuo Gyorui Co., Ltd.; *Int'l*, pg. 1598
CHUO GYORUI CO., LTD.; *Int'l*, pg. 1598
CHUO KOAGE CO., LTD.—See Chuo Gyorui Co., Ltd.; *Int'l*, pg. 1598
CIE IMPORT PRODUITS ALIMENTAIRES; *Int'l*, pg. 1605
CITY SEA FOODS, INC.; *U.S. Private*, pg. 906
CJ SEAFOOD CORPORATION—See CJ Corporation; *Int'l*, pg. 1631
CMB SEAFOODS PTY. LTD.—See East 33 Limited; *Int'l*, pg. 2269
CNFC OVERSEAS FISHERY CO., LTD.; *Int'l*, pg. 1673
CONSERVES ET SALAISONS VANELLI; *Int'l*, pg. 1770
COX'S WHOLESALE SEAFOOD INC.; *U.S. Private*, pg. 1079
CROCKER & WINSOR SEAFOODS INC.; *U.S. Private*, pg. 1102
CROMARIS ITALY S.R.L.—See Adris Grupa d.d.; *Int'l*, pg. 153
DAN LACHS GMBH; *Int'l*, pg. 1957
DELCA DISTRIBUTORS INC.—See BMT Commodity Corporation; *U.S. Private*, pg. 601
DEL MAR SEAFOODS INC.; *U.S. Private*, pg. 1192
DHOFAR FISHERIES & FOOD INDUSTRIES COMPANY S.A.O.G.; *Int'l*, pg. 2099
DIXON FISHERIES INC.; *U.S. Private*, pg. 1246
DONGWON F&B CO., LTD - GANGJIN FACTORY—See Dongwon Enterprise Co., Ltd.; *Int'l*, pg. 2170
DONGWON F&B CO., LTD JEONGEUP FACTORY—See Dongwon Enterprise Co., Ltd.; *Int'l*, pg. 2170
DONGWON F&B CO., LTD.—See Dongwon Enterprise Co., Ltd.; *Int'l*, pg. 2170
DONGWON F&B CO., LTD SUWON FACTORY—See Dongwon Enterprise Co., Ltd.; *Int'l*, pg. 2170
DONGWON F&B (SHANGHAI) CO., LTD.—See Dongwon Enterprise Co., Ltd.; *Int'l*, pg. 2170
DONGWON JAPAN CO., LTD.—See Dongwon Enterprise Co., Ltd.; *Int'l*, pg. 2170
DRAGOY GROSSIST AS—See Austevoll Seafood ASA; *Int'l*, pg. 717
EAST 33 LIMITED; *Int'l*, pg. 2269
EAST COAST SEAFOOD INC.—See American Holdco Inc.; *U.S. Private*, pg. 236
EIWA INTERNATIONAL INC.; *U.S. Private*, pg. 1348
EKONE OYSTER CO.—See Taylor United Inc.; *U.S. Private*, pg. 3940
FARMERS SEAFOOD CO. INC.; *U.S. Private*, pg. 1479
FCF CO., LTD; *Int'l*, pg. 2627
FINE FOODS LIMITED; *Int'l*, pg. 2673
FINNMARK HAVFISKE AS—See Austevoll Seafood ASA; *Int'l*, pg. 717
FISCHMARKT HAMBURG-ALTONA GESELLSCHAFT MIT BESCHRANKTER HAFTUNG—See Hamburger Hafen und Logistik AG; *Int'l*, pg. 3236
F. J. O'HARA & SONS INC.; *U.S. Private*, pg. 1455
FORO-MAREE S.A.; *Int'l*, pg. 2737
F.P.N.I. BELGIUM N.V.—See ARIAKE JAPAN Co., Ltd.; *Int'l*, pg. 564
FRATELLO TRADE D.O.O.—See Fratello Trade JSC Banja Luka; *Int'l*, pg. 2767
FRESH ISLAND FISH CO. INC.; *U.S. Private*, pg. 1609
GEMINI SEA FOOD PLC; *Int'l*, pg. 2916
GENERAL OYSTER, INC.; *Int'l*, pg. 2919
GLENN SALES COMPANY INC.; *U.S. Private*, pg. 1711
THE GREAT AMERICAN SMOKED FISH CO.; *U.S. Private*, pg. 4038
GREAT WALL SEAFOOD LA, LLC—See HF Foods Group Inc.; *U.S. Public*, pg. 1033
HAMMERFEST INDUSTRIFISKE AS—See Austevoll Seafood ASA; *Int'l*, pg. 717
HANWA FOODS CO., LTD.—See Hanwa Co., Ltd.; *Int'l*, pg. 3262
HANWA THAILAND CO., LTD.—See Hanwa Co., Ltd.; *Int'l*, pg. 3262
HEFEI CHIA TAI CO., LTD.—See Charoen Pokphand Foods Public Company Limited; *Int'l*, pg. 1452
HI-SEAS OF DULAC INC.; *U.S. Private*, pg. 1932
H&N FOODS INTERNATIONAL, INC.; *U.S. Private*, pg. 1823
H & T SEAFOOD, INC.; *U.S. Private*, pg. 1822
HUNAN XIANGYUN BIOTECHNOLOGY CO., LTD.—See Dahu Aquaculture Company Limited; *Int'l*, pg. 1913
IBIDEN BUSSAN CO., LTD.—See Ibiden Co., Ltd.; *Int'l*, pg. 3575
ICELAND SEAFOOD ICELAND; *Int'l*, pg. 3579
IDAHO TROUT PROCESSORS COMPANY; *U.S. Private*, pg. 2035
INDEPENDENCE FISH COMPANY; *U.S. Private*, pg. 2058
INLAND SEAFOOD—See Inland Seafood; *U.S. Private*, pg. 2079
INTERNATIONAL MARINE PRODUCTS INC.—See Eiwa International Inc.; *U.S. Private*, pg. 1348
INTERSEA FISHERIES LTD.; *U.S. Private*, pg. 2123
IPSWICH SHELLFISH CO. INC.; *U.S. Private*, pg. 2137
ISLAMORADA FISH COMPANY LLC; *U.S. Private*, pg. 2144
ISLAND SEAFOOD INC.—See Dulcich, Inc.; *U.S. Private*, pg. 1286
JBS PACKING COMPANY INC.; *U.S. Private*, pg. 2194
JIANGSU HUAI YIN CHIA TAI CO., LTD.—See Charoen Pokphand Foods Public Company Limited; *Int'l*, pg. 1453
JOHNNY'S SEAFOOD COMPANY—See Dulcich, Inc.; *U.S. Private*, pg. 1286
JOHN OVENSTONE LTD—See African Equity Empowerment Investmts Limited; *Int'l*, pg. 191
KASHIWA UOICHIBA CO., LTD.—See Chuo Gyorui Co., Ltd.; *Int'l*, pg. 1598
KOHYO HOLLAND B.V.—See AEON Co., Ltd.; *Int'l*, pg. 178
KONAFISH COMPANY INC.—See Tropic Fish & Vegetable Center Inc.; *U.S. Private*, pg. 4242
KONTALI ANALYSE AS—See Arendals Fossekompani ASA; *Int'l*, pg. 559
LAKS- & VILDTCENTRALEN AS—See Austevoll Seafood ASA; *Int'l*, pg. 717
LEROY ALFHEIM AS—See Austevoll Seafood ASA; *Int'l*, pg. 717
LEROY AURORA AS—See Austevoll Seafood ASA; *Int'l*, pg. 717
LEROY BULANDET AS—See Austevoll Seafood ASA; *Int'l*, pg. 717
LEROY DELICO AS—See Austevoll Seafood ASA; *Int'l*, pg. 717
LEROY FINLAND OY—See Austevoll Seafood ASA; *Int'l*, pg. 717
LEROY FOSSEN AS—See Austevoll Seafood ASA; *Int'l*, pg. 717
LEROY MIDT AS—See Austevoll Seafood ASA; *Int'l*, pg. 717
LEROY NORGE AS—See Austevoll Seafood ASA; *Int'l*, pg. 717
LEROY NORWAY SEAFOODS AS—See Austevoll Seafood ASA; *Int'l*, pg. 717
LEROY PORTUGAL LDA.—See Austevoll Seafood ASA; *Int'l*, pg. 717
LEROY PROCESSING SPAIN SL—See Austevoll Seafood ASA; *Int'l*, pg. 717
LEROY SEAFOOD AB—See Austevoll Seafood ASA; *Int'l*, pg. 717
LEROY SEAFOOD AS—See Austevoll Seafood ASA; *Int'l*, pg. 717
LEROY SEAFOOD AS—See Austevoll Seafood ASA; *Int'l*, pg. 717
LEROY SEAFOOD HOLDING B.V.—See Austevoll Seafood ASA; *Int'l*, pg. 717
LEROY SEAFOOD ITALY S.R.L.—See Austevoll Seafood ASA; *Int'l*, pg. 718
LEROY SEAFOOD NETHERLANDS B.V.—See Austevoll Seafood ASA; *Int'l*, pg. 718
LEROY SEAFOOD UK LTD.—See Austevoll Seafood ASA; *Int'l*, pg. 718
LEROY SEAFOOD USA INC.—See Austevoll Seafood ASA; *Int'l*, pg. 718
LEROY SJOMATGRUPPEN AS—See Austevoll Seafood ASA; *Int'l*, pg. 718
LEROY SMOGEN SEAFOOD AB—See Austevoll Seafood ASA; *Int'l*, pg. 717
LEROY SVERIGE AB—See Austevoll Seafood ASA; *Int'l*, pg. 717
LEROY TRONDHEIM AS—See Austevoll Seafood ASA; *Int'l*, pg. 717
LEROY TURKEY SU URUNLERI SAN. VE TIC A.S—See Austevoll Seafood ASA; *Int'l*, pg. 717
LEROY VEST AS—See Austevoll Seafood ASA; *Int'l*, pg. 717
LES PECHERIES NORREF QUEBEC INC.—See Colabor Group Inc.; *Int'l*, pg. 1697
LEVITTOWN FISH MARKET INC.; *U.S. Private*, pg. 2437
L.M. SANDLER & SONS; *U.S. Private*, pg. 2366
LOBSTER TRAP CO. INC.; *U.S. Private*, pg. 2477
LOMBARDI'S SEAFOOD INC.; *U.S. Private*, pg. 2483
LOUISIANA FINE FOOD COMPANIES, INC.; *U.S. Private*, pg. 2499
LUND'S FISHERIES, INC.; *U.S. Private*, pg. 2515
MARDER TRAWLING, INC.; *U.S. Private*, pg. 2573
MARUHON HONMA SUISAN CO., LTD.—See Hanwa Co., Ltd.; *Int'l*, pg. 3263
MAYPORT C&C FISHERIES INC.; *U.S. Private*, pg. 2622
MELBU FRYSELAGER AS—See Austevoll Seafood ASA; *Int'l*, pg. 717
M.F. FOLEY COMPANY; *U.S. Private*, pg. 2528
MILKY WAY INTERNATIONAL TRADING; *U.S. Private*, pg. 2729
M&J SEAFOOD HOLDINGS LIMITED—See Sysco Corporation; *U.S. Public*, pg. 1974
M&J SEAFOOD LIMITED—See Sysco Corporation; *U.S. Public*, pg. 1973
MOREY'S SEAFOOD INTERNATIONAL LLC; *U.S. Private*, pg. 2782
M. SLAVIN & SONS LTD.; *U.S. Private*, pg. 2527
NAM PEI HONG SUM YUNG DRUGS COMPANY LIMITED—See China Healthwise Holdings Limited; *Int'l*, pg. 1507
NAUTICAL MARINE INC.; *U.S. Private*, pg. 2872
NETUNO USA INC.; *U.S. Private*, pg. 2888
NEWPORT INTERNATIONAL OF TIERRA VERDE, INC.; *U.S. Private*, pg. 2916
NORDLAND HAVFISKE AS—See Austevoll Seafood ASA; *Int'l*, pg. 717
NORSK OPPDRETTSERVICE AS—See Austevoll Seafood ASA; *Int'l*, pg. 718
NORSK OPPDRETTSSERVICE AS—See Austevoll Seafood ASA; *Int'l*, pg. 717
NORTHERN WIND INC.; *U.S. Private*, pg. 2955
NORTH PACIFIC CORPORATION; *U.S. Private*, pg. 2946
OCEANA SPV (PTY) LTD.—See Brimstone Investment Corporation Ltd.; *Int'l*, pg. 1164
OCEAN HARVEST WHOLESALE INC.; *U.S. Private*, pg. 2989
OCEAN STAGE INC.—See Chuo Gyorui Co., Ltd.; *Int'l*, pg. 1598
OCEAN TECHNOLOGY INC.; *U.S. Private*, pg. 2990
OFI MARKESA INTERNATIONAL—See Red Chamber Co.; *U.S. Private*, pg. 3373
OMNI SHRIMP, INC.; *U.S. Public*, pg. 1572
ORION SEAFOOD INTERNATIONAL, INC.; *U.S. Private*, pg. 3043
PACIFIC AMERICAN FISH CO., INC.; *U.S. Private*, pg. 3065
PACIFIC CHOICE SEAFOOD COMPANY—See Dulcich, Inc.; *U.S. Private*, pg. 1286
PACIFIC FRESH SEAFOOD—See Dulcich, Inc.; *U.S. Private*, pg. 1286
PACIFIC GIANT, INC.—See Han Sung Enterprise Co., Ltd.; *Int'l*, pg. 3240
PACIFIC PRIDE SEAFOOD INC.; *U.S. Private*, pg. 3070
PAUL PIAZZA & SON INC.; *U.S. Private*, pg. 3113
PELAGIA AS—See Austevoll Seafood ASA; *Int'l*, pg. 718
PHOENIX TRADING CORP.—See 3G Capital Partners L.P.; *U.S. Private*, pg. 13
PROSPECT ENTERPRISES INC.; *U.S. Private*, pg. 3287
PSI GUYANA INC.—See Seaboard Corporation; *U.S. Public*, pg. 1850
QINGDAO CHIA TAI AGRICULTURAL DEVELOPMENT

N.A.I.C.S. INDEX

424470 — MEAT AND MEAT PRODU...

CO., LTD.—See Charoen Pokphand Foods Public Company Limited; *Int'l*, pg. 1453
RED CHAMBER CO.; *U.S. Private*, pg. 3373
RIVERENCE HOLDINGS LLC; *U.S. Private*, pg. 3444
ROBERT WHOLEY & CO.; *U.S. Private*, pg. 3459
RUSSIA BALTIC PORK INVEST ASA—See Charoen Pokphand Foods Public Company Limited; *Int'l*, pg. 1453
SANDANGER AS—See Apetit Plc; *Int'l*, pg. 509
SANTA MONICA SEAFOOD CO.; *U.S. Private*, pg. 3547
SAS EUROSALMO—See Austevoll Seafood ASA; *Int'l*, pg. 717
SAS LEROY SEAFOOD FRANCE—See Austevoll Seafood ASA; *Int'l*, pg. 717
SAU-SEA FOODS, INC.; *U.S. Private*, pg. 3554
SEACREST SEAFOODS INC.—See Coastal Corporation Limited; *Int'l*, pg. 1681
SEAFOOD SALES INC.; *U.S. Private*, pg. 3584
SEAFOOD SUPPLY CO. INC; *U.S. Private*, pg. 3584
SEAFOOD TIP.—See Arendals Fossekompani ASA; *Int'l*, pg. 559
SEA LEVEL SEAFOODS, LLC—See Dulcich, Inc.; *U.S. Private*, pg. 1286
SEAPORT PRODUCTS CORP.; *U.S. Private*, pg. 3586
SEATTLE FISH COMPANY; *U.S. Private*, pg. 3592
SEATTLE SHRIMP & SEAFOOD COMPANY, INC.—See Hanwa Co., Ltd.; *Int'l*, pg. 3263
SEAWATER SEAFOOD COMPANY; *U.S. Private*, pg. 3592
SHENYANG CHIA TAI LIVESTOCK CO., LTD.—See Charoen Pokphand Foods Public Company Limited; *Int'l*, pg. 1453
SHIJIAZHUANG CHIA TAI CO., LTD.—See Charoen Pokphand Foods Public Company Limited; *Int'l*, pg. 1453
SHORE TRADING COMPANY; *U.S. Private*, pg. 3641
SINGLETON SEAFOOD—See Red Chamber Co.; *U.S. Private*, pg. 3373
SLADE GORTON & CO. INC.; *U.S. Private*, pg. 3687
SOUTHERN CONNECTION SEAFOOD, INC.; *U.S. Private*, pg. 3730
SOUTHWIND FOODS LLC—See Prospect Enterprises Inc.; *U.S. Private*, pg. 3287
SPENCE & CO., LTD.—See Alliance Select Foods International, Inc.; *Int'l*, pg. 341
STAR FISHERIES INC.; *U.S. Private*, pg. 3784
STEVE CONNOLLY SEAFOODS CO; *U.S. Private*, pg. 3808
STOCKHOLMS FISKAUKTION AB—See Sysco Corporation; *U.S. Public*, pg. 1975
TAMPA BAY FISHERIES, INC.—See Red Chamber Co.; *U.S. Private*, pg. 3373
TASTY SEAFOOD CO. INC.; *U.S. Private*, pg. 3935
TAYLOR SHELLFISH FARMS—See Taylor United Inc.; *U.S. Private*, pg. 3940
TOKYO KITAUO CO., LTD.—See Chuo Gyorui Co., Ltd.; *Int'l*, pg. 1598
TORRY HARRYS INC.; *U.S. Private*, pg. 4190
TRI-MARINE FISH COMPANY—See Tri-Star Marine International, Inc.; *U.S. Private*, pg. 4223
TRISOME FOODS, INC.; *U.S. Private*, pg. 4238
TROPICAL AQUACULTURE PRODUCTS, INC.—See GeneSeas Aquacultura Ltda.; *Int'l*, pg. 2921
TROPIC FISH & VEGETABLE CENTER INC.; *U.S. Private*, pg. 4242
TRUE NORTH SALMON CO. LTD.—See Cooke, Inc.; *Int'l*, pg. 1788
TRUE WORLD FOODS CHICAGO LLC—See Family Federation for World Peace & Unification; *U.S. Private*, pg. 1469
TRUE WORLD FOODS, INC. OF HAWAII—See Family Federation for World Peace & Unification; *U.S. Private*, pg. 1469
TRUE WORLD FOODS MIAMI LLC—See Family Federation for World Peace & Unification; *U.S. Private*, pg. 1469
TRUE WORLD FOODS NEW YORK LLC—See Family Federation for World Peace & Unification; *U.S. Private*, pg. 1469
TRUE WORLD FOODS SAN FRANCISCO LLC—See Family Federation for World Peace & Unification; *U.S. Private*, pg. 1469
TRUE WORLD FOODS SEATTLE LLC—See Family Federation for World Peace & Unification; *U.S. Private*, pg. 1469
WANCHESE FISH COMPANY, INC.—See Daniels Enterprises Inc.; *U.S. Private*, pg. 1156
WESTBANK CORPORATION INC.—See Daybrook Holdings Inc.; *U.S. Private*, pg. 1177
WORLDWIDE FOOD PRODUCTS INC.; *U.S. Private*, pg. 4569
WUHAN CHIA TAI CO., LTD.—See Charoen Pokphand Foods Public Company Limited; *Int'l*, pg. 1453
WYLAX INTERNATIONAL B.V.—See Camellia Plc; *Int'l*, pg. 1271
YOUNG'S SEAFOOD LIMITED—See CapVest Limited; *Int'l*, pg. 1318

424470 — MEAT AND MEAT PRODUCT MERCHANT WHOLESALERS

733907 ONTARIO LTD; *Int'l*, pg. 14
ABRAHAM GMBH—See Coop-Gruppe Genossenschaft; *Int'l*, pg. 1789
A.C. KISSLING, INC.; *U.S. Private*, pg. 24
ADAX S.A.S.—See Lauridsen Group Inc.; *U.S. Private*, pg. 2399
ALLIANCE GROUP (NZ) LTD—See Alliance Group Limited; *Int'l*, pg. 339
AMARO FOOD ENTERPRISES INC.; *U.S. Private*, pg. 216
AMERICAN FOODS GROUP, LLC—See Rosens Diversified, Inc.; *U.S. Private*, pg. 3484
AMERISTAR MEATS, INC.—See US Foods Holding Corp.; *U.S. Public*, pg. 2266
ANDERSON BONELESS BEEF, INC.—See FoodMaven Corporation; *U.S. Private*, pg. 1562
ANHUI FURUN MEAT PROCESSING CO., LTD—See China Yurun Food Group Limited; *Int'l*, pg. 1566
APPETITO PROVISION CO., INC.—See Premio Foods, Inc.; *U.S. Private*, pg. 3251
AS. CA. S.P.A.—See Cremonini S.p.A.; *Int'l*, pg. 1838
ASMO CORPORATION; *Int'l*, pg. 628
BALDINI ADRIATICA PESCA S.R.L.—See Cremonini S.p.A.; *Int'l*, pg. 1838
BAPI HOANG ANH GIA LAI JOINT STOCK COMPANY—See Hoang Anh Gia Lai Joint Stock Company; *Int'l*, pg. 3436
BELWOOD FOODS LIMITED—See Argent Group Europe Limited; *Int'l*, pg. 560
BEOGRAD PROMET A.D.; *Int'l*, pg. 978
BERGHORST FOODS SERVICES INC.; *U.S. Private*, pg. 531
BERNARD & SONS INC.; *U.S. Private*, pg. 535
BEST CUT LIMITED; *Int'l*, pg. 999
BHJ BALTIC UAB—See Lauridsen Group Inc.; *U.S. Private*, pg. 2399
BHJ FARUTEX SP. ZO.O.—See Lauridsen Group Inc.; *U.S. Private*, pg. 2399
BHJ FINLAND OY AB—See Lauridsen Group Inc.; *U.S. Private*, pg. 2399
BHJ KALINO FOOD AB—See Lauridsen Group Inc.; *U.S. Private*, pg. 2399
BHJ ROMANIA SRL—See Lauridsen Group Inc.; *U.S. Private*, pg. 2399
BHJ USA, INC.—See Lauridsen Group Inc.; *U.S. Private*, pg. 2400
BIRCHWOOD FOODS—See Kenosha Beef International Ltd. Inc.; *U.S. Private*, pg. 2287
BLUE RIBBON MEATS INC.; *U.S. Private*, pg. 591
BOAR'S HEAD PROVISIONS CO., INC.—See Frank Brunckhorst Co., LLC; *U.S. Private*, pg. 1593
BRF BRASIL FOODS PTE LTD—See BRF S.A.; *Int'l*, pg. 1151
THE BRUSS COMPANY—See Tyson Foods, Inc.; *U.S. Public*, pg. 2210
BUCKHEAD BEEF COMPANY—See Sysco Corporation; *U.S. Public*, pg. 1973
BUCKHEAD BEEF NORTHEAST—See Sysco Corporation; *U.S. Public*, pg. 1973
BURKE CORPORATION—See Hormel Foods Corporation; *U.S. Public*, pg. 1053
BUTLER REFRIGERATED MEATS, INC.—See Giant Eagle, Inc.; *U.S. Private*, pg. 1694
BUTTS FOODS INC.—See Palladium Equity Partners, LLC; *U.S. Private*, pg. 3078
CALVADA SALES COMPANY INC.; *U.S. Private*, pg. 724
CAMPOFRIO PORTUGAL, S.A.—See ALFA, S.A.B. de C.V.; *Int'l*, pg. 314
CARGILL FOODS FRANCE SAS—See Cargill, Inc.; *U.S. Private*, pg. 756
CARGILL MEAT SOLUTIONS—See Cargill, Inc.; *U.S. Private*, pg. 758
CARGILL MEAT SOLUTIONS—See Cargill, Inc.; *U.S. Private*, pg. 758
CATELLI BROS INC.; *U.S. Private*, pg. 788
CENTURY INTERNATIONAL TRADING INC.—See Orleans International, Inc.; *U.S. Private*, pg. 3044
CENTURY PACIFIC FOOD, INC. - CANNED MEAT PLANT—See Century Pacific Food, Inc.; *Int'l*, pg. 1418
CHER-MAKE SAUSAGE COMPANY—See Lakeside Foods, Inc.; *U.S. Private*, pg. 2377
COLORADO BOXED BEEF CO.—See Palladium Equity Partners, LLC; *U.S. Private*, pg. 3078
CORDINA CHICKEN FARMS PTY. LTD.; *Int'l*, pg. 1796
CPF DENMARK A/S—See Charoen Pokphand Foods Public Company Limited; *Int'l*, pg. 1452
CPF EUROPE S.A.—See Charoen Pokphand Foods Public Company Limited; *Int'l*, pg. 1452
CPF JAPAN CO., LTD.—See Charoen Pokphand Foods Public Company Limited; *Int'l*, pg. 1452
CP FOODS (UK) LIMITED—See Charoen Pokphand Foods Public Company Limited; *Int'l*, pg. 1452
CPF TOKYO CO., LTD.—See Charoen Pokphand Foods Public Company Limited; *Int'l*, pg. 1452
CRANSWICK CONVENIENCE FOODS—See Cranswick Plc; *Int'l*, pg. 1828
CRANSWICK COUNTRY FOODS (NORFOLK) LIMITED—See Cranswick Plc; *Int'l*, pg. 1828
CRETA FARM S.A.—See Creta Farm S.A.; *Int'l*, pg. 1842

CRITCHFIELD MEATS INC.; *U.S. Private*, pg. 1101
CUSTOM CORNED BEEF, INC.—See New Water Capital, L.P.; *U.S. Private*, pg. 2907
CUSTOM MADE MEALS LLC—See Stellex Capital Management LP; *U.S. Private*, pg. 3800
DALSON FOODS INC.; *U.S. Private*, pg. 1150
DANISH CROWN BEEF COMPANY A/S—See Danish Crown AmbA; *Int'l*, pg. 1964
DANISH CROWN - BEEF DIVISION S.A.—See Danish Crown AmbA; *Int'l*, pg. 1964
DANISH CROWN ESPANA S.A.—See Danish Crown AmbA; *Int'l*, pg. 1964
DANISH CROWN GMBH—See Danish Crown AmbA; *Int'l*, pg. 1964
DANISH CROWN SCHLACHTZENTRUM NORDFRIESLAND GMBH—See Danish Crown AmbA; *Int'l*, pg. 1964
DANISH CROWN SP.Z O.O.—See Danish Crown AmbA; *Int'l*, pg. 1964
DANISH CROWN USA INC—See Danish Crown AmbA; *Int'l*, pg. 1964
DAN'S PRIZE, INC.—See Hormel Foods Corporation; *U.S. Public*, pg. 1054
DAT-SCHAUB CASINGS (AUSTRALIA) PTY LTD—See Danish Crown AmbA; *Int'l*, pg. 1964
DAT-SCHAUB POLSKA SP. Z O.O.—See Danish Crown AmbA; *Int'l*, pg. 1964
DC TRADING CO., LTD—See Danish Crown AmbA; *Int'l*, pg. 1964
DEEN MEAT CO.; *U.S. Private*, pg. 1189
DELI-BOY INC.; *U.S. Private*, pg. 1196
DEL MONTE CAPITAL MEAT CO. INC.; *U.S. Private*, pg. 1192
DELTA FLEISCH HANDELS GMBH; *Int'l*, pg. 2018
DIAMOND CRYSTAL BREMEN, LLC—See Peak Rock Capital LLC; *U.S. Private*, pg. 3124
DIF ORGANVEREDLUNG GERHARD KUPERS GMBH & CO. KG—See Danish Crown AmbA; *Int'l*, pg. 1964
DILLON PROVISION COMPANY INC.; *U.S. Private*, pg. 1231
DUFOUR S.A.; *Int'l*, pg. 2223
DUNBIA GROUP; *Int'l*, pg. 2225
DUTCH PRIME FOODS INC.; *U.S. Private*, pg. 1294
EASTSIDE FOODS INC.; *U.S. Private*, pg. 1322
ECHO VALLEY MEATS, INC.; *U.S. Private*, pg. 1327
ECONOMY LOCKER STORAGE CO. INC.; *U.S. Private*, pg. 1330
EDDY PACKING CO., INC.—See Insight Equity Holdings LLC; *U.S. Private*, pg. 2086
ED MINIAT, INC.; *U.S. Private*, pg. 1331
EMPIRE PACKING COMPANY, L.P.; *U.S. Private*, pg. 1385
ENERGROUP HOLDINGS CORPORATION; *Int'l*, pg. 2422
ERO MEAT COMPANY; *U.S. Private*, pg. 1423
ESS-FOOD A/S—See Danish Crown AmbA; *Int'l*, pg. 1964
ESS-FOOD BRAZIL SERVICOS DE CONSULTORIA LTDA—See Danish Crown AmbA; *Int'l*, pg. 1964
ESS-FOOD (SHANGHAI) TRADING CO. LTD—See Danish Crown AmbA; *Int'l*, pg. 1964
EVANS MEATS, INCORPORATED; *U.S. Private*, pg. 1435
FAIRFAX MEADOW EUROPE LIMITED—See Argent Group Europe Limited; *Int'l*, pg. 560
FANCY FOODS INC.; *U.S. Private*, pg. 1472
FIRSTCLASS FOODS-TROJAN, INC.—See US Foods Holding Corp.; *U.S. Public*, pg. 2266
FLEURY MICHON SA; *Int'l*, pg. 2701
FOODCO HOLDING CO PJSC; *Int'l*, pg. 2727
FOODPACK B.V.—See Clayton, Dubilier & Rice, LLC; *U.S. Private*, pg. 926
FOYLE FOOD GROUP LTD.; *Int'l*, pg. 2756
FRANK BRUNCKHORST CO., LLC; *U.S. Private*, pg. 1593
FREEDMAN FOOD SERVICE OF DALLAS, INC.—See Sysco Corporation; *U.S. Public*, pg. 1973
FREEDMAN FOOD SERVICE OF SAN ANTONIO, LP—See Sysco Corporation; *U.S. Public*, pg. 1973
FRIGO ST. JOHANN AG—See Coop-Gruppe Genossenschaft; *Int'l*, pg. 1789
FRIMO S.A.M.—See Cremonini S.p.A.; *Int'l*, pg. 1838
FRUTAROM PRODUCTION GMBH—See International Flavors & Fragrances Inc.; *U.S. Public*, pg. 1152
FRUTAROM SAVORY SOLUTIONS GERMANY GMBH—See International Flavors & Fragrances Inc.; *U.S. Public*, pg. 1152
GERBER AGRI INTERNATIONAL, LLC; *U.S. Private*, pg. 1686
GODSHALL QUALITY MEATS INC.; *U.S. Private*, pg. 1724
GOLDEN STATE FOODS-CITY OF INDUSTRY DIVISION—See Golden State Foods Corp.; *U.S. Private*, pg. 1733
GOLDEN STATE FOODS-HAWAII DIVISION—See Golden State Foods Corp.; *U.S. Private*, pg. 1733
GOLDEN STATE FOODS-NORTHWEST DIVISION—See Golden State Foods Corp.; *U.S. Private*, pg. 1733
GOODNIGHT BROTHERS PRODUCE CO., INC.; *U.S. Private*, pg. 1740
GRADUS AD-STARA ZAGORA; *Int'l*, pg. 3050
GRUPO ALIMENTARIO ARGAL SA; *Int'l*, pg. 3119
GUARDAMIGLIO S.R.L.—See Cremonini S.p.A.; *Int'l*, pg. 1838
HARVEST FOOD COMPANY—See Sand Dollar Holdings

3983

424470 — MEAT AND MEAT PRODU...

Incorporated; *U.S. Private*, pg. 3542
HEARTLAND MEAT CO. INC.; *U.S. Private*, pg. 1900
HKFOODS PLC; *Int'l*, pg. 3428
HORIZON SALES, INC.; *U.S. Private*, pg. 1982
HORMEL FOODS CORP. - DELI DIVISION—See Hormel Foods Corporation; *U.S. Public*, pg. 1054
HORMEL FOODS CORPORATE SERVICES, LLC—See Hormel Foods Corporation; *U.S. Public*, pg. 1054
INDOGUNA (CAMBODIA) COMPANY LIMITED—See C.P. All Public Company Limited; *Int'l*, pg. 1244
INDOGUNA DUBAI L.L.C.—See C.P. All Public Company Limited; *Int'l*, pg. 1244
J&B WHOLESALE DISTRIBUTING, INC.—See J&B Group, Inc.; *U.S. Private*, pg. 2153
JD SWEID FOODS LTD.—See Hallmark Poultry Processors Ltd.; *Int'l*, pg. 3230
JETRO CASH & CARRY—See Jetro Cash & Carry Enterprises, LLC; *U.S. Private*, pg. 2204
JETRO CASH & CARRY—See Jetro Cash & Carry Enterprises, LLC; *U.S. Private*, pg. 2204
JETRO CASH & CARRY—See Jetro Cash & Carry Enterprises, LLC; *U.S. Private*, pg. 2204
JINAN WANRUN MEAT PROCESSING CO., LTD.—See China Yurun Food Group Limited; *Int'l*, pg. 1566
JOHN MILLS DISTRIBUTING CO. INC; *U.S. Private*, pg. 2223
JOHN R. MORREALE INCORPORATED; *U.S. Private*, pg. 2224
JOHN VOLPI & CO., INC.; *U.S. Private*, pg. 2225
JONES DAIRY FARM; *U.S. Private*, pg. 2232
JULIAN FREIRICH CO. INC.; *U.S. Private*, pg. 2243
KALLE AUSTRIA GMBH—See Clayton, Dubilier & Rice, LLC; *U.S. Private*, pg. 926
KALLE CHILE S.A.—See Clayton, Dubilier & Rice, LLC; *U.S. Private*, pg. 926
KALLE CZ, S.R.O.—See Clayton, Dubilier & Rice, LLC; *U.S. Private*, pg. 926
KALLE NALO POLSKA SP. Z O.O.—See Clayton, Dubilier & Rice, LLC; *U.S. Private*, pg. 926
KALLE NORDIC APS—See Clayton, Dubilier & Rice, LLC; *U.S. Private*, pg. 926
KALLE USA INC.—See Clayton, Dubilier & Rice, LLC; *U.S. Private*, pg. 926
KANSAS CITY SAUSAGE COMPANY; *U.S. Private*, pg. 2260
KAY FOODS INC.—See Kay Packing Company Inc.; *U.S. Private*, pg. 2266
KEN WEAVER MEATS INC.; *U.S. Private*, pg. 2282
KERN FOOD DISTRIBUTING INC.; *U.S. Private*, pg. 2290
K. HEEPS INC.; *U.S. Private*, pg. 2251
KIOLBASSA; *U.S. Private*, pg. 2313
KISSIN FRESH MEATS INC.; *U.S. Private*, pg. 2315
KLS UGGLARPS—See Danish Crown AmbA; *Int'l*, pg. 1965
LAND NEW ZEALAND LIMITED—See AFFCO Holdings Limited; *Int'l*, pg. 186
LARRY KLINE WHOLESALE MEATS, INC.; *U.S. Private*, pg. 2393
LEVONIAN BROTHERS INC.; *U.S. Private*, pg. 2437
L&H PACKING COMPANY; *U.S. Private*, pg. 2362
LINCOLN PROVISION, INC.; *U.S. Private*, pg. 2458
LOMBARDI BROTHERS MEAT PACKERS, INC.; *U.S. Private*, pg. 2483
LUCKY DUCK INTERNATIONAL FOOD B.V.—See Bangkok Ranch Public Company Limited; *Int'l*, pg. 835
MAISON DE SAVOIE SAS—See Coop-Gruppe Genossenschaft; *Int'l*, pg. 1790
MALCOLM MEATS COMPANY—See Sysco Corporation; *U.S. Public*, pg. 1974
MARCUS FOOD COMPANY, INC.; *U.S. Private*, pg. 2572
MARR FOODSERVICE IBERICA S.A.—See Cremonini S.p.A.; *Int'l*, pg. 1838
MARX COMPANIES, LLC; *U.S. Private*, pg. 2598
MCFARLING FOODS, INC.; *U.S. Private*, pg. 2634
MCKENZIE COUNTRY CLASSICS—See Kayem Foods, Inc.; *U.S. Private*, pg. 2266
MEAL MART INCORPORATED; *U.S. Private*, pg. 2647
THE MEAT MARKET INC.; *U.S. Private*, pg. 4077
METRO FOODS, INC.—See United Natural Foods, Inc.; *U.S. Public*, pg. 2232
MIAMI BEEF COMPANY INC.—See Trivest Partners, LP; *U.S. Private*, pg. 4240
MIDWEST PERISHABLES INC.; *U.S. Private*, pg. 2722
MIDWEST PRIDE INC.—See J&B Group, Inc.; *U.S. Private*, pg. 2153
MONOGRAM FOOD SOLUTIONS, LLC; *U.S. Private*, pg. 2771
MONTERREY PROVISION COMPANY, INC.—See KeHE Distributors, LLC; *U.S. Private*, pg. 2273
M&V PROVISIONS CO. INC.; *U.S. Private*, pg. 2525
NANJING YURUN FOOD CO., LTD.—See China Yurun Food Group Limited; *Int'l*, pg. 1566
NATIONAL DELI, LLC—See River Associates Investments, LLC; *U.S. Private*, pg. 3443
NEW CATERING S.R.L.—See Cremonini S.p.A.; *Int'l*, pg. 1838
NEW ZEALAND LAMB COOPERATIVE, INC.; *U.S. Private*, pg. 2913

NO NAME STEAKS LLC—See J&B Group, Inc.; *U.S. Private*, pg. 2153
NORTH AMERICAN PROVISIONER INC.—See North American Bison Cooperative; *U.S. Private*, pg. 2940
NORTHWESTERN MEAT, INC.; *U.S. Private*, pg. 2962
ORITZ CORPORATION; *U.S. Private*, pg. 3043
ORRELL'S FOOD SERVICE, INC.—See Ben E. Keith Company; *U.S. Private*, pg. 522
OSKUTEX GMBH—See Clayton, Dubilier & Rice, LLC; *U.S. Private*, pg. 926
OY DAT - SCHAUB FINLAND AB—See Danish Crown AmbA; *Int'l*, pg. 1964
PACKERS PROVISION CO. OF PUERTO RICO INC.—See TraFon Group; *U.S. Private*, pg. 4203
PERISHABLE DISTRIBUTORS OF IA—See Hy-Vee, Inc.; *U.S. Private*, pg. 2016
PILOT TRADING COMPANY INC.; *U.S. Private*, pg. 3181
PLAINVILLE FARMS, LLC—See The Hain Celestial Group, Inc.; *U.S. Public*, pg. 2087
PLUMROSE CARACAS C.A.—See EAC Invest AS; *Int'l*, pg. 2262
PLUSFOOD HUNGARY TRADE AND SERVICE LLC—See BRF S.A.; *Int'l*, pg. 1150
POLSEMANNEN AB—See Danish Crown AmbA; *Int'l*, pg. 1965
PORKY PRODUCTS INC.; *U.S. Private*, pg. 3229
PRAIMIT, S. A. DE C. V.—See ALFA, S.A.B. de C.V.; *Int'l*, pg. 313
PRESTON MEATS INC; *U.S. Private*, pg. 3256
PRITZLAFF WHOLESALE MEATS INC.; *U.S. Private*, pg. 3268
PURCELL INTERNATIONAL INC.; *U.S. Private*, pg. 3304
QUALITY FOOD COMPANY, INC.; *U.S. Private*, pg. 3319
QUIRCH FOODS, LLC—See Palladium Equity Partners, LLC; *U.S. Private*, pg. 3078
RANDOLPH PACKING CO.; *U.S. Private*, pg. 3354
RASTELLI BROTHERS INC.; *U.S. Private*, pg. 3357
RAYS WHOLESALE MEAT, INC.; *U.S. Private*, pg. 3359
READFIELD MEATS INC.—See Dominion Equity LLC; *U.S. Private*, pg. 1256
REALBEEF S.R.L.—See Cremonini S.p.A.; *Int'l*, pg. 1838
REAL MEAT COMPANY LTD.—See Amatheon Agri Holding N.V.; *Int'l*, pg. 413
RMH FOODS LLC—See Sandridge Food Corporation; *U.S. Private*, pg. 3544
R&R PROVISION COMPANY; *U.S. Private*, pg. 3383
SADIA URUGUAY S.A.—See BRF S.A.; *Int'l*, pg. 1151
SAMPCO INC.; *U.S. Private*, pg. 3537
SANCHEZ ALCARAZ S.L.U.—See Coop-Gruppe Genossenschaft; *Int'l*, pg. 1790
SAND DOLLAR HOLDINGS INCORPORATED; *U.S. Private*, pg. 3542
SANGER AUSTRALIA PTY LTD—See Bindaree Beef Pty. Limited; *Int'l*, pg. 1033
SCANFOODS LIMITED—See Cafe de Coral Holdings Limited; *Int'l*, pg. 1250
SCAN-HIDE A.M.B.A.—See Danish Crown AmbA; *Int'l*, pg. 1965
SEABOARD CORPORATION; *U.S. Public*, pg. 1850
SEAPORT MEAT COMPANY—See Pacific Ventures Group, Inc.; *U.S. Public*, pg. 1632
SHERWOOD FOOD DISTRIBUTORS- CLEVELAND DIV—See Sand Dollar Holdings Incorporated; *U.S. Private*, pg. 3542
SHERWOOD FOOD DISTRIBUTORS, LLC—See Sand Dollar Holdings Incorporated; *U.S. Private*, pg. 3542
SHOALS PROVISION INC.; *U.S. Private*, pg. 3639
SIAM FOOD SERVICES LIMITED—See C.P. All Public Company Limited; *Int'l*, pg. 1244
SMITH PACKING CO. INC.; *U.S. Private*, pg. 3695
SOUTHERN FOODS, INC. - HOME DIVISION—See Southern Foods, Inc.; *U.S. Private*, pg. 3732
SOUTHERN FOODS, INC.; *U.S. Private*, pg. 3731
S.S. LOGAN PACKING COMPANY; *U.S. Private*, pg. 3518
STAR FOOD PRODUCTS, INC.; *U.S. Private*, pg. 3784
STOCK .YARDS MEAT PACKING COMPANY—See US Foods Holding Corp.; *U.S. Public*, pg. 2266
STOCK YARDS PACKING CO., INC.—See US Foods Holding Corp.; *U.S. Public*, pg. 2266
SUGARDALE FOOD SERVICE—See Fresh Mark, Inc.; *U.S. Private*, pg. 1610
SUN BELT FOOD COMPANY, INC.; *U.S. Private*, pg. 3858
SUNRISE DAIRY—See Hy-Vee, Inc.; *U.S. Private*, pg. 2016
SUPERIOR FOODS COMPANY INC.; *U.S. Private*, pg. 3878
SUZHOU FURUN MEAT PROCESSING CO., LTD.—See China Yurun Food Group Limited; *Int'l*, pg. 1566
SYSCO NEWPORT MEAT COMPANY—See Sysco Corporation; *U.S. Public*, pg. 1977
TENNESSEE VALLEY HAM CO., INC.; *U.S. Private*, pg. 3968
THOMAS BROTHERS FOODS, LLC.; *U.S. Private*, pg. 4154
THOMAS BROTHERS HAM CO. INC.; *U.S. Private*, pg. 4155
TILLAMOOK COUNTRY SMOKER INC.—See Insignia Capital Group, L.P.; *U.S. Private*, pg. 2091
T&K SPOLKA Z.O.O.—See Darling Ingredients Inc.; *U.S. Public*, pg. 634

TONY'S FINE FOODS INC.—See United Natural Foods, Inc.; *U.S. Public*, pg. 2233
TRI-CITY MEATS INCORPORATED; *U.S. Private*, pg. 4221
TRI-MEATS INC.; *U.S. Private*, pg. 4222
TROYER FOODS, INC.; *U.S. Private*, pg. 4243
TULIP FOOD COMPANY AB—See Danish Crown AmbA; *Int'l*, pg. 1965
TULIP FOOD COMPANY FRANCE S.A.—See Danish Crown AmbA; *Int'l*, pg. 1965
TULIP FOOD COMPANY GMBH—See Danish Crown AmbA; *Int'l*, pg. 1965
TULIP FOOD COMPANY ITALIANA S.R.L.—See Danish Crown AmbA; *Int'l*, pg. 1965
TULIP FOOD COMPANY JAPAN CO. LTD—See Danish Crown AmbA; *Int'l*, pg. 1965
TULIP FOOD COMPANY—See Danish Crown AmbA; *Int'l*, pg. 1965
UNISTAR FOODS, INC.; *U.S. Private*, pg. 4287
UNIVERSAL MEATS (UK) LIMITED—See Tyson Foods, Inc.; *U.S. Public*, pg. 2210
UW PROVISION COMPANY, INC.; *U.S. Private*, pg. 4327
VALS DISTRIBUTING COMPANY; *U.S. Private*, pg. 4337
VIENNA SAUSAGE MFG. CO.; *U.S. Private*, pg. 4381
WALLACE & COOK FOOD SALES, INC.; *U.S. Private*, pg. 4430
WELLSHIRE FARMS, INC.—See Land O'Frost, Inc.; *U.S. Private*, pg. 2383
WEST COAST PRIME MEATS LLC; *U.S. Private*, pg. 4484
ZHONGXIANG PANLONG MEAT PROCESSING CO., LTD.—See China Yurun Food Group Limited; *Int'l*, pg. 1566
ZIMBO CZECHIA S.R.O.—See Coop-Gruppe Genossenschaft; *Int'l*, pg. 1790
ZIMBO FLEISCH- UND WURSTWAREN GMBH & CO. KG—See Coop-Gruppe Genossenschaft; *Int'l*, pg. 1790

424480 — FRESH FRUIT AND VEGETABLE MERCHANT WHOLESALERS

AARTSENFRUIT ASIA LTD.—See Aartsenfruit Holding B.V.; *Int'l*, pg. 38
AB BANAN-KOMPANIET—See Dole plc; *Int'l*, pg. 2157
ACE PRODUCE LTD.—See Dole plc; *Int'l*, pg. 2157
ADANI AGRI FRESH LTD—See Adani Enterprises Limited; *Int'l*, pg. 124
AGRIFRESH COMPANY LIMITED—See Agripure Holdings Company Limited; *Int'l*, pg. 218
AGRINURTURE, INC.; *Int'l*, pg. 217
AGROFRESH POLSKA SP. Z O.O.—See Paine Schwartz Partners, LLC; *U.S. Private*, pg. 3075
AGROFRESH SPAIN, S.L.—See Paine Schwartz Partners, LLC; *U.S. Private*, pg. 3075
ALBA FRUCT SA; *Int'l*, pg. 292
ALICHAMPI ALICANTE S.L.—See Dole plc; *Int'l*, pg. 2157
ALIMENTOS MARAVILLA S.A.; *Int'l*, pg. 328
ALSUM FARMS & PRODUCT, INC.; *U.S. Private*, pg. 203
ALTAFRESH LLC; *U.S. Private*, pg. 204
ANACO & GREEVE INTERNATIONAL B.V.—See Dole plc; *Int'l*, pg. 2158
ARMSTRONG PRODUCE LTD.—See Sysco Corporation; *U.S. Public*, pg. 1974
ARNOTTS (FRUIT) LIMITED—See Sysco Corporation; *U.S. Public*, pg. 1973
AROHERBS SPAIN S.L.—See Dole plc; *Int'l*, pg. 2157
ASF HOLLAND B.V.—See Dole plc; *Int'l*, pg. 2157
BAHAMAS FOOD SERVICES, LTD.—See Sysco Corporation; *U.S. Public*, pg. 1973
BAKKAVOR EUROPEAN MARKETING BV—See Bakkavor Group plc; *Int'l*, pg. 805
BAKKAVOR USA INC—See Bakkavor Group plc; *Int'l*, pg. 805
BALDOR SPECIALTY FOODS INC.; *U.S. Private*, pg. 458
BANDWAGON BROKERAGE LLC—See Cross Rapids Capital LP; *U.S. Private*, pg. 1105
BASIC AMERICAN FOODS, INC. - MOSES LAKE PROCESSING PLANT—See Basic American Foods, Inc.; *U.S. Private*, pg. 485
BAYWA GLOBAL PRODUCE GMBH—See BayWa AG; *Int'l*, pg. 916
BAYWA OBST GMBH & CO. KG—See BayWa AG; *Int'l*, pg. 916
B. CATALANI, INC.; *U.S. Private*, pg. 419
BELLA FRESH, LLC; *U.S. Private*, pg. 519
BERRYNE CO., LTD.—See Chudenko Corporation; *Int'l*, pg. 1594
BIKUREY HASADE HOLDINGS LTD; *Int'l*, pg. 1023
BLAND FARMS; *U.S. Private*, pg. 579
BOS BROTHERS FRUIT AND VEGETABLES BV—See Clayton, Dubilier & Rice, LLC; *U.S. Private*, pg. 930
BOSTON ORGANICS LLC—See GrubMarket, Inc.; *U.S. Private*, pg. 1797
BOTSFORD & GOODFELLOW, INC.; *U.S. Private*, pg. 623
BRDR. LEMBCKE A/S—See Dole plc; *Int'l*, pg. 2158
BUD ANTLE, INC.—See Dole plc; *Int'l*, pg. 2157
CAITO FOODS SERVICE INC.; *U.S. Private*, pg. 714
CARIBE FOOD CORPORATION; *U.S. Private*, pg. 761
CARREFOUR GLOBAL SOURCING ASIA LIMITED—See

N.A.I.C.S. INDEX

424480 — FRESH FRUIT AND VEG...

Carrefour SA; *Int'l*, pg. 1344
CARTIER SAADA; *Int'l*, pg. 1348
CARUSO PRODUCE, INC.; *U.S. Private*, pg. 777
CASTELLINI COMPANY, INC.; *U.S. Private*, pg. 784
C&D FRUIT & VEGETABLE CO., INC.; *U.S. Private*, pg. 702
CHAMPI CANARIAS S.L.—See Dole plc; *Int'l*, pg. 2157
CHAPMAN FRUIT CO INC.; *U.S. Private*, pg. 849
CHEF'S CHOICE PRODUCE CO.—See Sole Source Capital LLC; *U.S. Private*, pg. 3708
CHIQUITA BRANDS LLC - BETHLEHEM—See Banco Safra S.A.; *Int'l*, pg. 824
CHIQUITA BRANDS LLC - FORT LAUDERDALE—See Banco Safra S.A.; *Int'l*, pg. 824
CHIQUITA BRANDS LLC - WILMINGTON—See Banco Safra S.A.; *Int'l*, pg. 824
CHIQUITA FRESH NORTH AMERICA LLC—See Banco Safra S.A.; *Int'l*, pg. 824
CITRUS PLUS, INC.; *U.S. Private*, pg. 904
CITRUS PRODUCTS INC.; *U.S. Private*, pg. 904
CJB LEASING CO.; *U.S. Private*, pg. 909
CLARK, INC.; *U.S. Private*, pg. 914
CLUB CHEF LLC—See Taylor Fresh Foods Inc.; *U.S. Private*, pg. 3940
C.M. HOLTZINGER FRUIT CO. INC.; *U.S. Private*, pg. 708
COASTAL SUNBELT PRODUCE, LLC—See Continental Grain Company; *U.S. Private*, pg. 1029
COAST CITRUS DISTRIBUTORS INC.; *U.S. Private*, pg. 954
COAST PRODUCE COMPANY INC.; *U.S. Private*, pg. 954
COLLINS BROTHERS CORPORATION; *U.S. Private*, pg. 969
COMBS PRODUCE CO., L.P.—See Lipman & Lipman, Inc.; *U.S. Private*, pg. 2465
COMMUNITY SUFFOLK INC.; *U.S. Private*, pg. 997
COREY BROTHERS INC.; *U.S. Private*, pg. 1050
COSTAEXCHANGE LTD—See Costa Group of Companies; *Int'l*, pg. 1814
COSTA FRUIT & PRODUCE INC.; *U.S. Private*, pg. 1062
COUNTRY FRESH, LLC—See Dean Foods Company; *U.S. Private*, pg. 1183
CREATION GARDENS, INC.; *U.S. Private*, pg. 1087
CREATIVE FOOD GROUP LIMITED—See Bakkavor Group plc; *Int'l*, pg. 806
CROSSET COMPANY LLC—See Castellini Company, Inc.; *U.S. Private*, pg. 784
CUSTOM PRODUCE, INC.—See GrubMarket, Inc.; *U.S. Private*, pg. 1797
C.Y. FOOD TRADING (HK) COMPANY LIMITED—See China Wantian Holdings Limited; *Int'l*, pg. 1562
DANDREA PRODUCE, INC.; *U.S. Private*, pg. 1153
DAVID OPPENHEIMER & COMPANY I, LLC—See David Oppenheimer & Company; *Int'l*, pg. 1983
DAVID OPPENHEIMER & COMPANY; *Int'l*, pg. 1983
DEARDORFF-JACKSON COMPANY; *U.S. Private*, pg. 1185
DEL FRAILE FRUTAS Y VERDURAS S.L.—See Dole plc; *Int'l*, pg. 2157
DEL GAUDIO; *Int'l*, pg. 2010
DELICA FOODS HOLDINGS CO., LTD.; *Int'l*, pg. 2013
DEL MONTE B.V.—See Fresh Del Monte Produce Inc.; *U.S. Public*, pg. 885
DELTA PRODUCE MARKETING INC.; *U.S. Private*, pg. 1201
DESTINY ORGANICS, LLC; *U.S. Private*, pg. 1216
DIETZ & KOLODENKO CO.; *U.S. Private*, pg. 1229
DIMARE FRESH, INC.; *U.S. Private*, pg. 1232
DIMARE FRESH—See DiMare Fresh, Inc.; *U.S. Private*, pg. 1232
DIXIELAND PRODUCE INC.; *U.S. Private*, pg. 1245
DOLE EXOTICS B.V.—See Dole plc; *Int'l*, pg. 2157
DOLE FRESH FRUIT COMPANY—See Dole plc; *Int'l*, pg. 2157
DOLE FRESH FRUIT EUROPE OHG—See Dole plc; *Int'l*, pg. 2157
DOLE HELLAS LTD.—See Dole plc; *Int'l*, pg. 2157
DOLE NORDIC A/S—See Dole plc; *Int'l*, pg. 2157
DOLE SOUTH AFRICA (PTY), LTD.—See Dole plc; *Int'l*, pg. 2157
DOLE TROPICAL PRODUCTS LATIN AMERICA, LTD.—See Dole plc; *Int'l*, pg. 2158
DOMINION CITRUS LIMITED—See Dominion Holding Corporation; *Int'l*, pg. 2161
DOMINION CITRUS WHOLESALE—See Dominion Holding Corporation; *Int'l*, pg. 2161
DONEGAL POTATOES LIMITED—See Donegal Investment Group Plc; *Int'l*, pg. 2163
DRISCOLL'S OF FLORIDA, INC.—See Driscoll's, Inc; *U.S. Private*, pg. 1278
DYNASTY FARMS, INC.—See Pacific International Marketing, Inc.; *U.S. Private*, pg. 3068
EARTH BROTHERS, LTD.—See Performance Food Group Company; *U.S. Public*, pg. 1675
EASTERDAY FARMS PRODUCE CO.; *U.S. Private*, pg. 1319
EASTPACK LIMITED; *Int'l*, pg. 2274
ECO FARMS SALES INC.; *U.S. Private*, pg. 1328
ELMASU A.S.—See Goltas Cimento A.S.; *Int'l*, pg. 3037

ENZAFRUIT MARKETING LIMITED—See BayWa AG; *Int'l*, pg. 919
ENZAFRUIT NEW ZEALAND (CONTINENT) NV—See BayWa AG; *Int'l*, pg. 919
EUROGROUP DEUTSCHLAND GMBH—See Coop-Gruppe Genossenschaft; *Int'l*, pg. 1790
EVERFRESH AB—See Dole plc; *Int'l*, pg. 2158
EVERGRAIN GERMANY GMBH & CO. KG—See BayWa AG; *Int'l*, pg. 917
EXETER PRODUCE & STORAGE CO. LIMITED; *Int'l*, pg. 2584
FAMILY TREE PRODUCE; *U.S. Private*, pg. 1471
FDL CHINA—See Highlander Partners, LP.; *U.S. Private*, pg. 1939
FEDERAL FRUIT & PRODUCE CO., INC.; *U.S. Private*, pg. 1488
FIELDFRESH FOODS PVT. LTD.—See Bharti Enterprises Limited; *Int'l*, pg. 1013
FINER FOODS INC.; *U.S. Private*, pg. 1509
FOODPRO; *U.S. Private*, pg. 1562
FOUR SEASONS HARVEST LTD.—See Dole plc; *Int'l*, pg. 2158
FRANK DONIO, INC.; *U.S. Private*, pg. 1594
FRANKORT & KONING B.V.—See Dole plc; *Int'l*, pg. 2158
FRANKORT & KONING POLSKA SP. Z O.O.—See Dole plc; *Int'l*, pg. 2158
FRESCA GROUP LIMITED; *Int'l*, pg. 2774
FRESH DIRECT LIMITED—See Sysco Corporation; *U.S. Public*, pg. 1973
FRESHEDGE, LLC—See Wind Point Advisors LLC; *U.S. Private*, pg. 4534
FRESH EXPRESS FOODS CORPORATION, INC.; *U.S. Private*, pg. 1609
FRESH EXPRESS INC. - CHICAGO—See Banco Safra S.A.; *Int'l*, pg. 824
FRESH EXPRESS INC. - GRAND PRAIRIE—See Banco Safra S.A.; *Int'l*, pg. 824
FRESH EXPRESS INCORPORATED—See Banco Safra S.A.; *Int'l*, pg. 824
FRESH IDEAS INC.—See Costa Fruit & Produce Inc.; *U.S. Private*, pg. 1062
FRESHMAX NEW ZEALAND LTD.—See BayWa AG; *Int'l*, pg. 918
FRESHPACK PRODUCE, INC.—See Creation Gardens, Inc.; *U.S. Private*, pg. 1087
FRESHPOINT ARIZONA, INC.—See Sysco Corporation; *U.S. Public*, pg. 1974
FRESHPOINT ATLANTA, INC.—See Sysco Corporation; *U.S. Public*, pg. 1974
FRESHPOINT CENTRAL FLORIDA, INC.—See Sysco Corporation; *U.S. Public*, pg. 1974
FRESHPOINT DALLAS, INC.—See Sysco Corporation; *U.S. Public*, pg. 1974
FRESHPOINT, INC.—See Sysco Corporation; *U.S. Public*, pg. 1974
FRESHPOINT NASHVILLE, INC.—See Sysco Corporation; *U.S. Public*, pg. 1974
FRESHPOINT SOUTH FLORIDA, INC.—See Sysco Corporation; *U.S. Public*, pg. 1974
FRESHPOINT SOUTH TEXAS, LP—See Sysco Corporation; *U.S. Public*, pg. 1974
FRESHPOINT VANCOUVER, LTD.—See Sysco Corporation; *U.S. Public*, pg. 1974
FRESH QUEST INC; *U.S. Private*, pg. 1610
FRESHTROP FRUITS LTD. - PLANT - II—See Green AgRevolution Pvt Ltd.; *Int'l*, pg. 3069
FRESHTROP FRUITS LTD.—See Green AgRevolution Pvt Ltd.; *Int'l*, pg. 3069
FRESHWAY FOODS, INC.—See US Foods Holding Corp.; *U.S. Public*, pg. 2266
FRESKA PRODUCE INTERNATIONAL, LLC; *U.S. Private*, pg. 1610
FRESNO PRODUCE—See Alvarez & Marsal, Inc.; *U.S. Private*, pg. 213
FRESNO PRODUCE, INC.—See Highview Capital, LLC; *U.S. Private*, pg. 1942
FRUITPARTNER B.V.—See Dole plc; *Int'l*, pg. 2158
FRUTAFRUTA, INC.; *Int'l*, pg. 2797
FRUTAS FAUSTINO S.L.—See Dole plc; *Int'l*, pg. 2158
FRUTAS IRU S.A.—See Dole plc; *Int'l*, pg. 2158
FUERST DAY LAWSON INDIA PRIVATE LIMITED; *Int'l*, pg. 2804
FUERST DAY LAWSON LTD.—See Highlander Partners, LP.; *U.S. Private*, pg. 1939
FUJIAN HONGHUI FRUIT & VEGETABLE CO. LTD.—See Great-Sun Foods Co.,LTD.; *Int'l*, pg. 3066
GAMBLES ONTARIO PRODUCE INC.—See Dole plc; *Int'l*, pg. 2158
GARDEN-FRESH FOODS INC.; *U.S. Private*, pg. 1643
THE GARDEN WHOLESALE, INC.; *U.S. Private*, pg. 4032
GARGIULO, INC.; *U.S. Private*, pg. 1644
GASTRO PRIMO LIMITED—See Bakkavor Group plc; *Int'l*, pg. 806
GASTRO STAR AG—See Coop-Gruppe Genossenschaft; *Int'l*, pg. 1790
GENERAL PRODUCE CO. LTD.; *U.S. Private*, pg. 1666
GET FRESH PRODUCE LLC—See Wind Point Advisors LLC; *U.S. Private*, pg. 4534

GIORGIO FOODS INC; *U.S. Private*, pg. 1702
GLOBAL ORGANIC SPECIALTY SOURCE, INC.; *U.S. Private*, pg. 1716
GLOBAL PACIFIC PRODUCE, INC.; *U.S. Private*, pg. 1716
GOLBON—See Oppenheimer Companies, Inc.; *U.S. Private*, pg. 3033
GOLDEN CROWN DEPOT; *U.S. Private*, pg. 1730
GOLDEN HARVEST (MACAO COMMERCIAL OFFSHORE) LIMITED—See Heng Tai Consumables Group Limited; *Int'l*, pg. 3345
GOLDEN SECTOR AGRO-DEVELOPMENT LIMITED—See Heng Tai Consumables Group Limited; *Int'l*, pg. 3345
GOURMET VEG-PAQ, INC.; *U.S. Private*, pg. 1746
GRANT COUNTY FOODS INC.—See Castellini Company, Inc.; *U.S. Private*, pg. 784
GREENBERG FRUIT COMPANY—See Wind Point Advisors LLC; *U.S. Private*, pg. 4534
GROWERS DIRECT; *U.S. Private*, pg. 1795
GROWER SERVICES, LLC.; *U.S. Private*, pg. 1795
GROWER'S ORGANIC LLC.; *U.S. Private*, pg. 1795
GUANGZHOU ZHENGTONG LOGISTICS CO. LTD.—See Great-Sun Foods Co.,LTD.; *Int'l*, pg. 3066
GUILLIN NEDERLAND B.V.—See Groupe Guillin SA; *Int'l*, pg. 3104
HAPCO FARMS INC.; *U.S. Private*, pg. 1857
HILO PRODUCTS INC.; *U.S. Private*, pg. 1948
HIT KIT GLOBAL SOLUTIONS LIMITED; *Int'l*, pg. 3408
HOLLAR & GREENE PRODUCE CO. INC.; *U.S. Private*, pg. 1964
HORTICASH PLANTES; *Int'l*, pg. 3482
HORTIM SK, S.R.O.—See Dole plc; *Int'l*, pg. 2158
THE HORTON FRUIT COMPANY, INC.; *U.S. Private*, pg. 4054
IBERFRANCE POLAND—See Iberfrance; *Int'l*, pg. 3574
IBERFRANCE; *Int'l*, pg. 3574
ICA BANKEN AB—See ICA Gruppen AB; *Int'l*, pg. 3577
IDAHO POTATO PACKERS CORPORATION—See Nonpareil Corporation; *U.S. Private*, pg. 2934
ILLE ROUSSILLON; *Int'l*, pg. 3615
INTERNATIONAL PRODUCE LTD.—See Bunge Limited; *U.S. Public*, pg. 412
IPM PERTH LIMITED—See Donegal Investment Group Plc; *Int'l*, pg. 2163
ISACSSON FRUKT & GRONT AB—See Sysco Corporation; *U.S. Public*, pg. 1973
JACK BROWN PRODUCE, INC.; *U.S. Private*, pg. 2173
JAC. VANDENBERG, INC.; *U.S. Private*, pg. 2173
JBJ DISTRIBUTING INC.—See Veg-Land Sales Inc.; *U.S. Private*, pg. 4353
J. HELLMAN PRODUCE, INC.; *U.S. Private*, pg. 2156
JOHN H. BURROWS INC.; *U.S. Private*, pg. 2222
KEYSTONE FRUIT MARKETING INC.—See Arable Capital Partners LLC; *U.S. Private*, pg. 307
LAKESIDE FOODS, INC. - BELGIUM PLANT—See Lakeside Foods, Inc.; *U.S. Private*, pg. 2377
LAKESIDE FOODS, INC. - NEW RICHMOND PLANT—See Lakeside Foods, Inc.; *U.S. Private*, pg. 2377
LAKESIDE FOODS, INC. - PLAINVIEW PLANT—See Lakeside Foods, Inc.; *U.S. Private*, pg. 2377
LANCASTER FOODS, INC.—See Continental Grain Company; *U.S. Private*, pg. 1029
LIANYUNGANG FUSHI FOOD CO., LTD.—See Grand Industrial Holding Co., Ltd.; *Int'l*, pg. 3055
LIANYUNGANG LIFE RUYI FOODS CO., LTD—See Grand Industrial Holding Co., Ltd.; *Int'l*, pg. 3055
LIBERTY FRUIT COMPANY, INC.—See Russ Davis Wholesale; *U.S. Private*, pg. 3506
LJ DISTRIBUTORS INC.; *U.S. Private*, pg. 2474
L&M COMPANIES, INC.; *U.S. Private*, pg. 2363
LOFFREDO FRESH PRODUCE CO., INC.; *U.S. Private*, pg. 2480
LONDON FRUIT, INC.—See GrubMarket, Inc.; *U.S. Private*, pg. 1797
LOS ANGELES WHOLESALE PRODUCE MARKET; *U.S. Private*, pg. 2497
MAINE POTATO GROWERS, INC.; *U.S. Private*, pg. 2552
MENDEZ INTERNATIONAL TROPICAL FOODS, INC.—See GrubMarket, Inc.; *U.S. Private*, pg. 1797
MEREX FOOD CORP.—See Baldor Specialty Foods Inc.; *U.S. Private*, pg. 458
MESCHINO BANANA COMPANY—See Dominion Holding Corporation; *Int'l*, pg. 2161
MISSION PRODUCE EUROPE B.V.—See Mission Produce, Inc.; *U.S. Public*, pg. 1450
MISSION PRODUCE, INC.; *U.S. Public*, pg. 1450
MIXON FRUIT FARMS, INC.; *U.S. Private*, pg. 2752
M. LEVIN & COMPANY, INC.—See M. Levin & Company Holdings, Inc.; *U.S. Private*, pg. 2527
MOUNT DORA FARMS DE HONDURAS SRL—See Seaboard Corporation; *U.S. Public*, pg. 1850
MOUNT DORA FARMS, INC—See Seaboard Corporation; *U.S. Public*, pg. 1850
MUIR ENTERPRISES INC; *U.S. Private*, pg. 2811
NATIONAL FRUIT PRODUCT COMPANY, INC. - BRAND RETAIL DIVISION—See National Fruit Product Company, Inc.; *U.S. Private*, pg. 2855
NATIONAL FRUIT PRODUCT COMPANY, INC. - FOOD SERVICES DIVISION—See National Fruit Product Com-

424480 — FRESH FRUIT AND VEG...

pany, Inc.; *U.S. Private*, pg. 2855
NATIONAL FRUIT PRODUCT COMPANY, INC. - PRIVATE LABEL RETAIL DIVISION—See National Fruit Product Company, Inc.; *U.S. Private*, pg. 2855
NATURERIPE FARMS LLC; *U.S. Private*, pg. 2867
NEDALPAC B.V.—See Dole plc; *Int'l*, pg. 2158
NEW LIMECO, LLC; *U.S. Private*, pg. 2898
NOR-CAL PRODUCE, INC.—See United Natural Foods, Inc.; *U.S. Public*, pg. 2231
NORDIC FRUIT HOLDING AB—See Dole plc; *Int'l*, pg. 2158
NORTHAMPTON GROWERS PRODUCE SALES, INC.; *U.S. Private*, pg. 2948
NORTH BAY PRODUCE, INC.; *U.S. Private*, pg. 2942
NORTON FOLGATE MARKETING LTD—See Argent Group Europe Limited; *Int'l*, pg. 560
NOWASTE LOGISTICS AB—See Dole plc; *Int'l*, pg. 2158
NS BRANDS LTD—See Blue Road Management, L.P.; *U.S. Private*, pg. 592
OPPENHEIMER COMPANIES, INC.; *U.S. Private*, pg. 3033
OPPY ARGENTINA—See David Oppenheimer & Company; *Int'l*, pg. 1983
OPPY CHILE—See David Oppenheimer & Company; *Int'l*, pg. 1983
OPPY COSTA RICA—See David Oppenheimer & Company; *Int'l*, pg. 1983
OPPY PERU—See David Oppenheimer & Company; *Int'l*, pg. 1983
ORANGE WORLD INC.; *U.S. Private*, pg. 3038
ORCHARD WORLD LTD—See Argent Group Europe Limited; *Int'l*, pg. 560
ORGANICALLY GROWN CO.; *U.S. Private*, pg. 3041
THE ORIGINAL KEVIN GUIDRY PRODUCE MARKET, INC.; *U.S. Private*, pg. 4089
PARAGON FOOD SERVICE; *U.S. Private*, pg. 3091
PAUL KEMPOWSKI GMBH & CO. KG—See Dole plc; *Int'l*, pg. 2157
PEIRONE PRODUCE COMPANY—See URM Stores, Inc.; *U.S. Private*, pg. 4316
PETER CONDAKES COMPANY INC.; *U.S. Private*, pg. 3158
PEVIANI S.P.A.—See Dole plc; *Int'l*, pg. 2158
PIAZZA PRODUCE INC.—See Wind Point Advisors LLC; *U.S. Private*, pg. 4534
POUPART LTD—See Argent Group Europe Limited; *Int'l*, pg. 560
PREPWORLD LTD—See Argent Group Europe Limited; *Int'l*, pg. 560
PRIMAFRUIT LTD—See Fresca Group Limited; *Int'l*, pg. 2774
PROCACCI BROTHERS SALES CORPORATION—See Procacci Holdings LLC; *U.S. Private*, pg. 3271
PRODUCE EXCHANGE CO INC.; *U.S. Private*, pg. 3272
THE PRODUCE EXCHANGE INCORPORATED; *U.S. Private*, pg. 4100
THE PRODUCE EXCHANGE, INC.—See Lipman & Lipman, Inc.; *U.S. Private*, pg. 2465
PROFESSIONAL PRODUCE; *U.S. Private*, pg. 3276
PROGRESSIVE PRODUCE LLC—See Arable Capital Partners LLC; *U.S. Private*, pg. 307
REGAL MARKETING, INC.; *U.S. Private*, pg. 3385
RIO FRESH, INC.; *U.S. Private*, pg. 3438
ROOTS OF OXFORD LIMITED—See Sysco Corporation; *U.S. Public*, pg. 1975
RUSS DAVIS WHOLESALE; *U.S. Private*, pg. 3506
SANWA GROWERS INC.; *U.S. Private*, pg. 3548
SCHMIEDING ENTERPRISES INC.; *U.S. Private*, pg. 3566
SCHWARZ VIVA AG—See Coop-Gruppe Genossenschaft; *Int'l*, pg. 1790
SEALD SWEET LLC—See CVC Capital Partners SICAV-FIS S.A.; *Int'l*, pg. 1886
SEASON PRODUCE CO. INC.—See S&H Packing & Sales Co. Inc.; *U.S. Private*, pg. 3513
SHANGHAI HONGHUI FOOD CO., LTD.—See Great-Sun Foods Co.,LTD.; *Int'l*, pg. 3066
SIRNA & SONS, INC.—See Wind Point Advisors LLC; *U.S. Private*, pg. 4534
SIX L'S PACKING COMPANY, INC.—See Lipman & Lipman, Inc.; *U.S. Private*, pg. 2465
SPOLEM TYCHY SP. Z O.O.—See Emperia Holding S.A; *Int'l*, pg. 2386
SPRING VALLEY PRODUCE, INC.—See GrubMarket, Inc.; *U.S. Private*, pg. 1797
SUNFRESH PRODUCE, INC.; *U.S. Private*, pg. 3867
SUNKIST GROWERS, INC.; *U.S. Private*, pg. 3867
SUNNY FARMS, INC.; *U.S. Private*, pg. 3868
SUNSHINE RAISIN CORPORATION; *U.S. Private*, pg. 3872
SUPERVALU INTERNATIONAL—See United Natural Foods, Inc.; *U.S. Public*, pg. 2232
SYSCO PRODUCE MARKETING & MERCHANDISING SERVICES—See Sysco Corporation; *U.S. Public*, pg. 1977
TAYLOR FARMS; *U.S. Private*, pg. 3939
T&G GLOBAL LIMITED—See BayWa AG; *Int'l*, pg. 919
TOM LANGE COMPANY, INC.; *U.S. Private*, pg. 4182
TOTAL PRODUCE HOLDINGS B.V.—See Dole plc; *Int'l*, pg. 2158
TOTAL PRODUCE IRELAND LIMITED—See Dole plc; *Int'l*, pg. 2158

TOTAL PRODUCE NORDIC A/S—See Dole plc; *Int'l*, pg. 2158
TRIPLE B CORP; *U.S. Private*, pg. 4236
UMINA BROS INC.; *U.S. Private*, pg. 4278
UNITRADE HOLLAND B.V.—See Dole plc; *Int'l*, pg. 2158
UNIVEG DEUTSCHLAND GMBH—See CVC Capital Partners SICAV-FIS S.A.; *Int'l*, pg. 1886
UNIVEG FRUIT & VEGETABLES B.V.—See CVC Capital Partners SICAV-FIS S.A.; *Int'l*, pg. 1886
V.B. HOOK & CO., INC.; *U.S. Private*, pg. 4328
VEGIWORKS, INC.; *U.S. Private*, pg. 4354
VITALBERRY BV—See Argent Group Europe Limited; *Int'l*, pg. 560
WASHINGTON PRODUCE—See Caruso Produce, Inc.; *U.S. Private*, pg. 777
WELL-PICT INC.; *U.S. Private*, pg. 4474
WEST COAST TOMATO LLC—See McClure Properties Ltd.; *U.S. Private*, pg. 2629
WESTERN MIXERS INC.; *U.S. Private*, pg. 4494
WEYAND FOOD DISTRIBUTORS, INC.; *U.S. Private*, pg. 4503
WEYAND & SON INC.; *U.S. Private*, pg. 4502
WHOLESALE PRODUCE SUPPLY, LLC—See Cross Rapids Capital LP; *U.S. Private*, pg. 1105
WM. BOLTHOUSE FARMS, INC.—See Butterfly Equity LP; *U.S. Private*, pg. 698
WM MORRISON PRODUCE LIMITED—See Clayton, Dubilier & Rice, LLC; *U.S. Private*, pg. 930
WONDERFUL CITRUS PACKING LLC—See The Wonderful Company LLC; *U.S. Private*, pg. 4138
WORLD VARIETY PRODUCE, INC.; *U.S. Private*, pg. 4567
W.R. VERNON PRODUCE CO., INC.; *U.S. Private*, pg. 4422
YANTAI HONGHUI FOOD CO., LTD.—See Great-Sun Foods Co.,LTD.; *Int'l*, pg. 3066

424490 — OTHER GROCERY AND RELATED PRODUCTS MERCHANT WHOLESALERS

AARHUSKARLSHAMN CANADA LTD.—See AAK AB; *Int'l*, pg. 32
AARHUSKARLSHAMN LATIN AMERICA S.A.—See AAK AB; *Int'l*, pg. 32
AARHUSKARLSHAMN MEXICO, S.A. DE C.V.—See AAK AB; *Int'l*, pg. 32
ABASTECEDORA DE ALIMENTOS DE MEXICO, S.A. DE C.V.—See Grupo LALA S.A. de C.V.; *Int'l*, pg. 3131
ABC BAKERY SUPPLIES & EQUIPMENT, INC.; *U.S. Private*, pg. 35
ABC NA KOLACH SP. Z O.O.—See Eurocash S.A.; *Int'l*, pg. 2533
ABDULLAH AL OTHAIM MARKET CO.—See Abdullah Al-Othaim Markets Company; *Int'l*, pg. 59
ACI EDIBLE OILS LTD.—See Advanced Chemical Industries, Limited; *Int'l*, pg. 158
ACME FOOD SALES, INC.; *U.S. Private*, pg. 61
ACONCAGUA DISTRIBUCIONES SRL—See Sealed Air Corporation; *U.S. Public*, pg. 1852
ADAMS EXTRACT & SPICE LLC; *U.S. Private*, pg. 74
ADANI WILMAR LTD.; *Int'l*, pg. 125
ADDITIVE SOLUTIONS PTY LTD—See Cinven Limited; *Int'l*, pg. 1611
AEON PET CO., LTD.—See AEON Co., Ltd.; *Int'l*, pg. 177
AGRANA TRADING EOOD—See AGRANA Beteiligungs-AG; *Int'l*, pg. 214
AGT FOODS AUSTRALIA PTY LTD—See AGT Food and Ingredients Inc.; *Int'l*, pg. 221
A.H. HOFFMAN, INC.—See Good Earth, Inc.; *U.S. Private*, pg. 1738
AIXIN LIFE INTERNATIONAL, INC.; *Int'l*, pg. 254
AJINOMOTO GAMBROOKE, INC.—See Ajinomoto Company, Inc.; *Int'l*, pg. 256
AJINOMOTO COMPANY, INC.; *Int'l*, pg. 256
AJINOMOTO DE MEXICO, S. DE R.L. DE C.V.—See Ajinomoto Company, Inc.; *Int'l*, pg. 257
AJINOMOTO HEALTHY SUPPLY CO., INC.—See Ajinomoto Company, Inc.; *Int'l*, pg. 256
AJWA GROUP FOR FOOD INDUSTRIES HOLDING LTD. CO.; *Int'l*, pg. 258
AKYUREK TUKETIM URUNLERI PAZARLAMA DAGITIM VE TICARET AS; *Int'l*, pg. 268
ALAKARI WINES LTD—See Altia Oyj; *Int'l*, pg. 392
ALAMO CARIBE BAKERY DISTRIBUTORS; *U.S. Private*, pg. 149
ALBERT'S NEW ENGLAND—See United Natural Foods, Inc.; *U.S. Public*, pg. 2231
ALBERT'S ORGANICS—See United Natural Foods, Inc.; *U.S. Public*, pg. 2231
ALBERT'S ORGANICS TWIN CITIES—See United Natural Foods, Inc.; *U.S. Public*, pg. 2231
AL EID FOOD CO; *Int'l*, pg. 276
AL GHURAIR FOODS LLC—See Al Ghurair Investment LLC; *Int'l*, pg. 278
AL GHURAIR RESOURCES LLC—See Al Ghurair Investment LLC; *Int'l*, pg. 278
ALOIS DALLMAYR GASTRO-SERVICE GMBH & CO KG—See Alois Dallmayr KG; *Int'l*, pg. 365
ALPHA BAKING COMPANY, INC.; *U.S. Private*, pg. 196

ALTRI SALES, S.A.—See Altri, SGPS, S.A.; *Int'l*, pg. 398
AL WAHA FOR SOFT DRINKS, JUICES, MINERAL WATER, PLASTICS, & PLASTIC CAPS PRODUCTION LLC—See Coca-Cola Icecek A.S.; *Int'l*, pg. 1686
AMCON DISTRIBUTING COMPANY-CROSSVILLE—See AMCON Distributing Company; *U.S. Public*, pg. 92
AMENDOAS-HERDADE DA PALHETA I. LTD.; *Int'l*, pg. 420
AMERICAN AGCO INC.; *U.S. Private*, pg. 221
AMERICAN FOOD DISTRIBUTORS, LLC; *U.S. Private*, pg. 234
AMERICAN INSTANTS, INC.; *U.S. Private*, pg. 237
AMIRA NATURE FOODS LTD.; *Int'l*, pg. 428
AMPOL FOOD PROCESSING LTD.; *Int'l*, pg. 436
ANCRONA AB—See FMCG Business Partner AB; *Int'l*, pg. 2717
ANDALUSI BEVERAGES S.L.; *Int'l*, pg. 449
ANF SPECIALTIES INC.—See Texas Farm Products Company; *U.S. Private*, pg. 3975
ANHEUSER BUSCH INBEV ITALIA SPA—See Anheuser-Busch InBev SA/NV; *Int'l*, pg. 465
ANTONIO SOFO & SON IMPORTING CO. INC.; *U.S. Private*, pg. 288
ARAB SUPPLY & TRADING CO. - FOOD SUPPLY DIVISION—See Arab Supply & Trading Co.; *Int'l*, pg. 532
ARAMARK DENMARK APS—See Aramark; *U.S. Public*, pg. 177
ARCOR TRADING (SHANGHAI) CO. LTD.—See Arcor Sociedad Anonima, Industrial y Comercial; *Int'l*, pg. 550
ARCTIC FALLS SPRING WATER, INC.; *U.S. Private*, pg. 315
ARIHANT TOURNESOL LTD.; *Int'l*, pg. 565
ARLA FOODS ARTIS LTD—See Arla Foods amba; *Int'l*, pg. 572
ARLA FOODS DEUTSCHLAND GMBH—See Arla Foods amba; *Int'l*, pg. 572
ARROWHEAD MOUNTAIN SPRING WATER COMPANY—See Metropoulos & Co.; *U.S. Private*, pg. 2690
ARROWHEAD MOUNTAIN SPRING WATER COMPANY—See Metropoulos & Co.; *U.S. Private*, pg. 2690
ARROWHEAD MOUNTAIN SPRING WATER COMPANY—See Metropoulos & Co.; *U.S. Private*, pg. 2690
ARROWHEAD MOUNTAIN SPRING WATER COMPANY—See One Rock Capital Partners, LLC; *U.S. Private*, pg. 3021
ARROWHEAD MOUNTAIN SPRING WATER COMPANY—See One Rock Capital Partners, LLC; *U.S. Private*, pg. 3021
ARROWHEAD MOUNTAIN SPRING WATER COMPANY—See One Rock Capital Partners, LLC; *U.S. Private*, pg. 3021
ARROWHEAD WATER—See Metropoulos & Co.; *U.S. Private*, pg. 2690
ARROWHEAD WATER—See Metropoulos & Co.; *U.S. Private*, pg. 2690
ARROWHEAD WATER—See One Rock Capital Partners, LLC; *U.S. Private*, pg. 3021
ARROWHEAD WATER—See One Rock Capital Partners, LLC; *U.S. Private*, pg. 3021
ARTISAN SPECIALTY FOODS, INC.—See Innovative Food Holdings, Inc.; *U.S. Public*, pg. 1126
ASAOKA SPICE K.K.—See House Foods Group Inc.; *Int'l*, pg. 3490
ASIA GROCERY DISTRIBUTION LIMITED; *Int'l*, pg. 612
ASMUSSEN GMBH—See Compagnie des Levures Lesaffre SA; *Int'l*, pg. 1738
ASSOCIATED BUYERS, LLC—See Rainforest Distribution Corp; *U.S. Private*, pg. 3348
ASTRAL EXTRACTS, LTD.; *U.S. Private*, pg. 361
ATALANTA CORPORATION—See Gellert Global Group; *U.S. Private*, pg. 1656
ATAR URGUU JSC; *Int'l*, pg. 666
ATLANTIC FS S.A.S.—See Grupo Nutresa S.A.; *Int'l*, pg. 3133
ATLANTIC MULTIPOWER GMBH & CO. OHG—See ATLANTIC GRUPA d.d.; *Int'l*, pg. 674
ATLANTIC MULTIPOWER SRL—See ATLANTIC GRUPA d.d.; *Int'l*, pg. 674
ATLANTIC MULTIPOWER UK LTD—See ATLANTIC GRUPA d.d.; *Int'l*, pg. 674
ATLANTIC TRADE D.O.O., LJUBLJANA—See ATLANTIC GRUPA d.d.; *Int'l*, pg. 675
ATLAPAC TRADING COMPANY, INC.; *U.S. Private*, pg. 375
ATTARD & CO. FOODSTUFFS LTD.—See Attard & Co. Ltd.; *Int'l*, pg. 696
AUTOMATIC ROLLS OF BALTIMORE, INC.—See H&S Bakery Inc.; *U.S. Private*, pg. 1823
AUTOMATIC ROLLS OF NEW ENGLAND, INC.—See H&S Bakery Inc.; *U.S. Private*, pg. 1823
AUTOMATIC ROLLS OF NEW JERSEY, INC.—See H&S Bakery Inc.; *U.S. Private*, pg. 1823
AUTOMATIC ROLLS OF NORTH CAROLINA, LLC—See H&S Bakery Inc.; *U.S. Private*, pg. 1823
A.V. OLSSON TRADING CO. INC.; *U.S. Private*, pg. 28
AZERBAIJAN COCA-COLA BOTTLERS LIMITED LIABIL-

N.A.I.C.S. INDEX

424490 — OTHER GROCERY AND R...

ITY COMPANY—See Coca-Cola Icecek A.S.; *Int'l*, pg. 1686
BADIA SPICES, INC.; *U.S. Private*, pg. 424
BAIN ANDALUCIA, S.L.U.—See Borges Agricultural & Industrial Nuts S.A.; *Int'l*, pg. 1114
BAIN EXTREMADURA, S.L.U.—See Borges Agricultural & Industrial Nuts S.A.; *Int'l*, pg. 1114
BAIN-MAS COLOM S.L.U.—See Borges Agricultural & Industrial Nuts S.A.; *Int'l*, pg. 1114
BAKE RITE ROLLS, INC.—See H&S Bakery Inc.; *U.S. Private*, pg. 1823
BAKERS OF PARIS INC.; *U.S. Private*, pg. 457
BAKERY BARN, INC.; *U.S. Private*, pg. 457
BANTAM BAGELS, LLC—See Lancaster Colony Corporation; *U.S. Public*, pg. 1291
BARENTZ ASIA PACIFIC PTE. LTD.—See Cinven Limited; *Int'l*, pg. 1611
BARENTZ GIDA VE KIMYA TIC. LTD. STI.—See Cinven Limited; *Int'l*, pg. 1611
BARENTZ-SANDER AG—See Cinven Limited; *Int'l*, pg. 1611
BARENTZ SARL—See Cinven Limited; *Int'l*, pg. 1611
BARILLA AUSTRALIA PTY LTD—See Barilla Holding S.p.A.; *Int'l*, pg. 865
BARILLA AUSTRIA GMBH—See Barilla Holding S.p.A.; *Int'l*, pg. 865
BARILLA CANADA INC.—See Barilla Holding S.p.A.; *Int'l*, pg. 865
BARILLA DANMARK A/S—See Barilla Holding S.p.A.; *Int'l*, pg. 865
BARILLA DO BRASIL LTDA—See Barilla Holding S.p.A.; *Int'l*, pg. 865
BARILLA ESPANA S.L.—See Barilla Holding S.p.A.; *Int'l*, pg. 865
BARILLA JAPAN K.K.—See Barilla Holding S.p.A.; *Int'l*, pg. 865
BARILLA NETHERLANDS B.V.—See Barilla Holding S.p.A.; *Int'l*, pg. 865
BARILLA NORGE AS—See Barilla Holding S.p.A.; *Int'l*, pg. 865
BARILLA POLAND SP. Z.O.O.—See Barilla Holding S.p.A.; *Int'l*, pg. 865
BARILLA SINGAPORE PTE LTD—See Barilla Holding S.p.A.; *Int'l*, pg. 865
BARILLA SWITZERLAND A.G.—See Barilla Holding S.p.A.; *Int'l*, pg. 865
BARRIOS DISTRIBUTING; *U.S. Private*, pg. 480
BASTE; *Int'l*, pg. 888
BATORY FOODS INC.; *U.S. Private*, pg. 487
BAYWA R.E. SOLAR SYSTEMS CORPORATION—See BayWa AG; *Int'l*, pg. 916
BAYWA R.E. SOLAR SYSTEMS INC.—See BayWa AG; *Int'l*, pg. 916
BAYWA R.E. SOLAR SYSTEMS SP. Z O. O.—See BayWa AG; *Int'l*, pg. 917
BAYWA R.E. SOLAR SYSTEMS S.R.O.—See BayWa AG; *Int'l*, pg. 917
BEAR CREEK ORCHARDS, INC.—See 1-800-FLOWERS.COM, Inc.; *U.S. Public*, pg. 1
BECAFISA S.A. DE C.V.—See ED&F Man Holdings Limited; *Int'l*, pg. 2302
BELLEVUE CASH & CARRY LTD.—See Bestway (Holdings) Limited; *Int'l*, pg. 1000
BELLEVUE DISTRIBUTION SA—See Carrefour SA; *Int'l*, pg. 1343
BELL FLAVORS & FRAGRANCES DUFT UND AROMA GMBH—See Bell Flavors & Fragrances, Inc.; *U.S. Private*, pg. 518
BELL FLAVORS & FRAGRANCES DUFT UND AROMA GMBH—See Bell Flavors & Fragrances, Inc.; *U.S. Private*, pg. 518
BENEFICIOS VOLCAFE S.A.—See ED&F Man Holdings Limited; *Int'l*, pg. 2302
BERNICK COMPANIES; *U.S. Private*, pg. 537
BERNICKS PEPSICOLA INC.—See Bernick Companies; *U.S. Private*, pg. 537
BESTCAN FOOD TECHNOLOGICAL INDUSTRIAL SDN BHD—See Far East Organization Pte. Ltd.; *Int'l*, pg. 2616
BEST-IN OY—See Atria Plc; *Int'l*, pg. 694
BEVERAGE CORPORATION INTERNATIONAL, INC.—See National Beverage Corp.; *U.S. Public*, pg. 1494
BEVERAGE MARKETING USA INC.; *U.S. Private*, pg. 547
BEVERAGE WORKS NY INC.; *U.S. Private*, pg. 547
BFP WHOLESALE LTD.; *Int'l*, pg. 1006
BIG GEYSER INC.; *U.S. Private*, pg. 553
BIG LEAGUE FOODS, INC.—See Verus International, Inc.; *U.S. Public*, pg. 2290
B&K MANUFACTURING—See Byrnes & Kiefer Company; *U.S. Private*, pg. 701
B.K. MILLER CO., INC.; *U.S. Private*, pg. 420
BLACKMORES CHINA CO. LIMITED—See Blackmores Limited; *Int'l*, pg. 1061
BLACKMORES INDIA PRIVATE LIMITED—See Blackmores Limited; *Int'l*, pg. 1061
BLACKMORES KOREA LIMITED—See Blackmores Limited; *Int'l*, pg. 1061
BLACKMORES VIETNAM CO. LIMITED—See Blackmores Limited; *Int'l*, pg. 1061

BLENHEIM BOTTLERS INC.—See The Schafer Company Inc.; *U.S. Private*, pg. 4114
BLUE DIAMOND GROWERS - GLOBAL INGREDIENTS DIVISION—See Blue Diamond Growers; *U.S. Private*, pg. 588
BLUE DIAMOND VENTURES, INC.; *U.S. Public*, pg. 364
BLUEGRASS COCA COLA BOTTLING COMPANY—See The Coca-Cola Company; *U.S. Public*, pg. 2064
BLUE RIBBON FARM DAIRY INC.; *U.S. Private*, pg. 591
BLUETRITON BRANDS, INC.—See Metropoulos & Co.; *U.S. Private*, pg. 2690
BLUETRITON BRANDS, INC.—See One Rock Capital Partners, LLC; *U.S. Private*, pg. 3021
B.M. LAWRENCE & CO.; *U.S. Private*, pg. 421
BODY WISE INTERNATIONAL INC.; *U.S. Private*, pg. 608
BOLOGNUE HOLDINGS INC.; *U.S. Private*, pg. 611
BORAN MESRUBAT SANAYI VE TICARET A.S.—See Derluks Yatirim Holding A.S; *Int'l*, pg. 2042
BORA TIAL CO., LTD.; *Int'l*, pg. 1112
BORGES OF CALIFORNIA, INC.—See Borges Agricultural & Industrial Nuts S.A.; *Int'l*, pg. 1114
BOWEN JUICES INTERNATIONAL; *U.S. Private*, pg. 625
BRAGG LIVE FOOD PRODUCTS, LLC—See Swander Pace Capital, LLC; *U.S. Private*, pg. 3889
BRAKES FOODSERVICE NI LIMITED—See Sysco Corporation; *U.S. Public*, pg. 1973
BRAVA HOME, INC.—See The Middleby Corporation; *U.S. Public*, pg. 2113
BREMER AUTHENTIC INGREDIENTS—See Spectral Enterprises, Inc.; *U.S. Private*, pg. 3751
BREZELKONIG AG—See Fomento Economico Mexicano, S.A.B. de C.V.; *Int'l*, pg. 2724
BRITVIC NORTH AMERICA LLC—See Britvic plc; *Int'l*, pg. 1171
BROWNIE SPECIAL PRODUCTS CO. INC.—See Chattanooga Bakery Inc.; *U.S. Private*, pg. 868
BUHLER (CANADA) INC.—See Buhler AG; *Int'l*, pg. 1211
BUHLER LTD—See Buhler AG; *Int'l*, pg. 1212
BUHLER P.J.S.C—See Buhler AG; *Int'l*, pg. 1212
BUHLER SA—See Buhler AG; *Int'l*, pg. 1212
BUHLER SORTEX INC.—See Buhler AG; *Int'l*, pg. 1212
BYRNES & KIEFER COMPANY; *U.S. Private*, pg. 701
CAF-CAF INC.—See Compass Group PLC; *Int'l*, pg. 1750
CAFE CAPRIS S.A.—See ED&F Man Holdings Limited; *Int'l*, pg. 2302
CALDIC NEW ZEALAND LTD.—See Caldic B.V.; *Int'l*, pg. 1262
CALEDONIAN PRODUCE—See Bakkavor Group plc; *Int'l*, pg. 806
CALIFORNIA FAST FOODS SERVICES INC.; *U.S. Private*, pg. 719
CALPIS U.S.A. INC.—See Asahi Group Holdings Ltd.; *Int'l*, pg. 593
CAMERICAN INTERNATIONAL, INC.—See Gellert Global Group; *U.S. Private*, pg. 1656
CAMPBELL FOODSERVICE COMPANY—See Campbell Soup Company; *U.S. Public*, pg. 426
CAMPBELL SALES COMPANY—See Campbell Soup Company; *U.S. Public*, pg. 427
CAMPBELL SOUP FINLAND OY—See Campbell Soup Company; *U.S. Public*, pg. 427
CANNIBBLE FOODTECH LTD.; *Int'l*, pg. 1292
CANTEEN OF CANADA LIMITED—See Compass Group PLC; *Int'l*, pg. 1750
CARCAFE S.A—See ED&F Man Holdings Limited; *Int'l*, pg. 2302
CASH-WA DISTRIBUTING COMPANY; *U.S. Private*, pg. 782
CASH-WA FOOD SERVICE—See Cash-Wa Distributing Company; *U.S. Private*, pg. 783
CASING ASSOCIATES LLC—See Wolfson Casing Corp.; *U.S. Private*, pg. 4554
CEDAR'S MEDITERRANEAN FOODS, INC.; *U.S. Private*, pg. 805
CENTRAL COCA-COLA BOTTLING COMPANY, INC.; *U.S. Private*, pg. 819
CENTRAL RETAIL CORPORATION (CRC) CO. LIMITED—See Central Group Company Limited; *Int'l*, pg. 1407
CENTURY FOOD COMPANY LIMITED—See Century Global Commodities Corporation; *Int'l*, pg. 1418
CENTURY PACIFIC FOOD, INC. - COCONUT PRODUCTS PLANT—See Century Pacific Food, Inc.; *Int'l*, pg. 1419
CENTURY PACIFIC FOOD, INC. - DAIRY & MIXES PLANT—See Century Pacific Food, Inc.; *Int'l*, pg. 1419
CHALLENGE DAIRY PRODUCTS INC.; *U.S. Private*, pg. 845
CHAMPION RAISIN INTERNATIONAL—See Sunshine Raisin Corporation; *U.S. Private*, pg. 3872
CHAROEN POKPHAND FOODS CANADA INC.—See Charoen Pokphand Foods Public Company Limited; *Int'l*, pg. 1452
CHAVES BAKERY II, INC.; *U.S. Private*, pg. 868
CHEF MIDDLE EAST LTD—See The Chefs' Warehouse, Inc.; *U.S. Public*, pg. 2058
THE CHEFS' WAREHOUSE, INC.; *U.S. Public*, pg. 2058
THE CHEFS' WAREHOUSE WEST COAST LLC—See The Chefs' Warehouse, Inc.; *U.S. Public*, pg. 2059

CHENEY BROTHERS, INC., *U.S. Private*, pg. 872
CHESBAY DISTRIBUTING, LLC—See Reyes Holdings, LLC; *U.S. Private*, pg. 3418
CHIBA VEGOIL TANK TERMINAL CO., LTD.—See Fuji Oil Holdings Inc.; *Int'l*, pg. 2815
CHICAGO FOOD CORPORATION; *U.S. Private*, pg. 877
CHIMAB S.P.A.—See BRENNTAG SE; *Int'l*, pg. 1149
CHINA DILI GROUP MANAGEMENT LIMITED—See China Dili Group; *Int'l*, pg. 1498
CHINA MIST BRANDS, INC.—See Farmer Brothers Co.; *U.S. Public*, pg. 821
CHLORELLA SUPPLY CO., LTD—See Daesang Corporation; *Int'l*, pg. 1909
CHL SHIPPING B.V.—See ED&F Man Holdings Limited; *Int'l*, pg. 2302
CHS INDUSTRIES LTD.—See CHS INC.; *U.S. Public*, pg. 491
CHUAN SENG LEONG PTE. LTD.; *Int'l*, pg. 1589
CLARION S.A. AGROINDUSTRIAL; *Int'l*, pg. 1649
CLICK WHOLESALE DISTRIBUTING, INC.—See Craig Stein Beverage; *U.S. Private*, pg. 1083
CLOFINE DAIRY & FOOD PRODUCTS INC.; *U.S. Private*, pg. 945
CLOFINE FOOD PRODUCTS INTERNATIONAL INC.—See Clofine Dairy & Food Products Inc.; *U.S. Private*, pg. 945
CLUB RESTAURATION—See Danone; *Int'l*, pg. 1965
C.M. GOETTSCHE COMPANY, INC.—See Strohmeyer & Arpe Company; *U.S. Private*, pg. 3840
COCA-COLA AMATIL (PNG) LTD—See COCA-COLA EUROPACIFIC PARTNERS PLC; *Int'l*, pg. 1684
COCA-COLA BOTTLING CO. CONSOLIDATED - JACKSON, TN—See Coca-Cola Consolidated, Inc.; *U.S. Public*, pg. 2063
COCA COLA DE CHILE, S.A.—See The Coca-Cola Company; *U.S. Public*, pg. 2063
COCA-COLA EUROPACIFIC PARTNERS AUSTRALIA PTY. LIMITED—See COCA-COLA EUROPACIFIC PARTNERS PLC; *Int'l*, pg. 1684
COCA-COLA EUROPACIFIC PARTNERS BELGIUM SRL/B.V.—See COCA-COLA EUROPACIFIC PARTNERS PLC; *Int'l*, pg. 1684
COCA-COLA EUROPACIFIC PARTNERS FRANCE S.A.S.—See COCA-COLA EUROPACIFIC PARTNERS PLC; *Int'l*, pg. 1684
COCA-COLA EUROPACIFIC PARTNERS NORGE AS—See COCA-COLA EUROPACIFIC PARTNERS PLC; *Int'l*, pg. 1685
COCA-COLA EUROPACIFIC PARTNERS PAPUA NEW GUINEA LIMITED—See COCA-COLA EUROPACIFIC PARTNERS PLC; *Int'l*, pg. 1685
COCA-COLA GMBH—See The Coca-Cola Company; *U.S. Public*, pg. 2063
COCA-COLA GREAT BRITAIN—See The Coca-Cola Company; *U.S. Public*, pg. 2063
COCA-COLA HBC KOSOVO L.L.C.—See Coca-Cola HBC AG; *Int'l*, pg. 1686
COCA-COLA INTERAMERICAN CORPORATION—See The Coca-Cola Company; *U.S. Public*, pg. 2064
COCA-COLA LATIN AMERICA—See The Coca-Cola Company; *U.S. Public*, pg. 2064
COCA-COLA SATIS VE DAGITIM A.S.—See Coca-Cola Icecek A.S.; *Int'l*, pg. 1686
COCA-COLA SERVICIOS DE VENEZUELA, C.A.—See The Coca-Cola Company; *U.S. Public*, pg. 2065
COCA-COLA SOUTHERN AFRICA (PTY) LTD.—See The Coca-Cola Company; *U.S. Public*, pg. 2065
COFFEE AMERICA (USA) CORPORATION; *U.S. Private*, pg. 961
COFFEE PARTNERS LP—See Horizon Holdings LLC; *U.S. Private*, pg. 1981
COFI-COM TRADING PTY LIMITED—See ED&F Man Holdings Limited; *Int'l*, pg. 2302
COLABOR GROUP INC.; *Int'l*, pg. 1697
COLABOR LP—See Colabor Group Inc.; *Int'l*, pg. 1697
COLAVITA, USA, LLC; *U.S. Private*, pg. 965
COLRUYT RETAIL FRANCE SAS—See Colruyt Group N.V.; *Int'l*, pg. 1705
COMFORT FOODS, INC.—See Coffee Holding Company, Inc.; *U.S. Public*, pg. 522
COMMERCIALE SUCRIERE S.A.—See ED&F Man Holdings Limited; *Int'l*, pg. 2302
COMPANIA INTERNACIONAL DE PRODUCTOS UNIVERSALES ALIMENTICIOS LTDA—See Compagnie des Levures Lesaffre SA; *Int'l*, pg. 1738
CONAXESS TRADE AUSTRIA GMBH—See Aurelius Equity Opportunities SE & Co. KGaA; *Int'l*, pg. 708
CONAXESS TRADE SWEDEN AB—See Aurelius Equity Opportunities SE & Co. KGaA; *Int'l*, pg. 708
CONAXESS TRADE SWITZERLAND AG—See Aurelius Equity Opportunities SE & Co. KGaA; *Int'l*, pg. 708
CONO ITALIANO, INC.; *U.S. Private*, pg. 1018
CONSOLIDATED BEVERAGE CO.—See Coca-Cola Consolidated, Inc.; *U.S. Public*, pg. 2063
CONSOLIDATED DISTRIBUTION CORP LLC—See Bay Grove Capital LLC; *U.S. Private*, pg. 492
CONSUMER BRANDS LIMITED—See GraceKennedy Limited; *Int'l*, pg. 3048

424490 — OTHER GROCERY AND R...

CONSUMERS CHOICE COFFEE, INC.; *U.S. Private*, pg. 1026
CONTINENTAL BEVERAGES (PTY) LTD—See PepsiCo, Inc.; *U.S. Public*, pg. 1672
THE CONVENIENT WHOLESALERS OF AMERICA, INC.; *U.S. Private*, pg. 4014
COOKIES & MORE, INC.—See Sysco Corporation; *U.S. Public*, pg. 1974
COOP SCHWEIZ - INTERDISCOUNT DIVISION—See Coop-Gruppe Genossenschaft; *Int'l*, pg. 1790
CORE-MARK DISTRIBUTORS, INC.—See Core-Mark Holding Co. Inc.; *U.S. Public*, pg. 576
CORWIN BEVERAGE COMPANY; *U.S. Private*, pg. 1061
COSTA RICAN GOLD COFFEE CO.; *U.S. Private*, pg. 1062
COUNTRY HOME BAKERS, INC.—See J&J Snack Foods Corporation; *U.S. Public*, pg. 1179
CP AXTRA PUBLIC COMPANY LIMITED—See C.P. All Public Company Limited; *Int'l*, pg. 1243
CPF TRADING CO., LTD.—See Charoen Pokphand Foods Public Company Limited; *Int'l*, pg. 1452
CREATIVE FOODS—See David Wood Baking Limited; *Int'l*, pg. 1984
CROSSGAR PALLAS LTD—See Sysco Corporation; *U.S. Public*, pg. 1973
CROWN CO., LTD.—See Adeka Corporation; *Int'l*, pg. 142
CROWN FOOD ESPANA, S.A.U.—See Crown Holdings, Inc.; *U.S. Public*, pg. 599
CROWN PACKAGING EUROPEAN DIVISION GMBH—See Crown Holdings, Inc.; *U.S. Public*, pg. 599
CROWN PRINCE, INC.; *U.S. Private*, pg. 1112
CRUMBLEY PAPER CO. INC.; *U.S. Private*, pg. 1114
CSM IBERIA SA—See Rhone Group, LLC; *U.S. Private*, pg. 3423
CSM POLSKA SP. Z O.O.—See Rhone Group, LLC; *U.S. Private*, pg. 3423
CTC FOOD INTERNATIONAL; *U.S. Private*, pg. 1118
CURLEYS QUALITY FOODS LIMITED—See Sysco Corporation; *U.S. Public*, pg. 1973
DAESANG EUROPE B.V.—See Daesang Corporation; *Int'l*, pg. 1909
DAESANG (H.K.) LIMITED—See Daesang Corporation; *Int'l*, pg. 1909
DAESANG JAPAN INC.—See Daesang Corporation; *Int'l*, pg. 1909
DAHL SVERIGE—See Compagnie de Saint-Gobain SA; *Int'l*, pg. 1733
DAIEI TRADING CO. INC.; *U.S. Private*, pg. 1145
DAIOHS HONG KONG LIMITED—See Daiohs Corporation; *Int'l*, pg. 1940
DAIOHS KOREA CO. LTD.—See Daiohs Corporation; *Int'l*, pg. 1940
DAIOHS SINGAPORE PTE. LTD.—See Daiohs Corporation; *Int'l*, pg. 1940
DAIRYGOLD DEUTSCHLAND HANDLESGESELLSCHAFT MBH—See Dairygold Co-Operative Society Ltd; *Int'l*, pg. 1940
DAIRYGOLD FOOD INGREDIENTS (FRANCE) SAS—See Dairygold Co-Operative Society Ltd; *Int'l*, pg. 1940
DAIRYLAND PRODUCE, LLC—See The Chefs' Warehouse, Inc.; *U.S. Public*, pg. 2059
DAIRYLAND USA CORPORATION—See The Chefs' Warehouse, Inc.; *U.S. Public*, pg. 2059
THE DAKMAN VIETNAM COMPANY LIMITED—See ED&F Man Holdings Limited; *Int'l*, pg. 2303
DANDY LIONS LIMITED—See International Flavors & Fragrances Inc.; *U.S. Public*, pg. 1151
DANISCO ITALIA S.P.A.—See International Flavors & Fragrances Inc.; *U.S. Public*, pg. 1151
DARLEY BUTLER & CO. LTD.—See E.B. Creasy & Company PLC; *Int'l*, pg. 2251
DARLING INGREDIENTS INTERNATIONAL RENDERING AND SPECIALTIES B.V.—See Darling Ingredients Inc.; *U.S. Public*, pg. 634
DARMEX CASINGS SP.ZO.O—See Icahn Enterprises L.P.; *U.S. Public*, pg. 1084
DAT-SCHAUB AB—See Danish Crown AmbA; *Int'l*, pg. 1964
DAVIDSTEA (USA) INC.—See DAVIDsTEA Inc.; *Int'l*, pg. 1984
DAVIGEL BELIGUM S.A.—See Sysco Corporation; *U.S. Public*, pg. 1973
DAYS BEVERAGE INC.; *U.S. Private*, pg. 1177
DEBOLES NUTRITIONAL FOODS, INC.—See The Hain Celestial Group, Inc.; *U.S. Public*, pg. 2086
DE CECCO DEUTSCHLAND GMBH—See Fratelli De Cecco Di Filippo Fara San Martino S.p.A.; *Int'l*, pg. 2767
DE CECCO FRANCE SARL—See Fratelli De Cecco Di Filippo Fara San Martino S.p.A.; *Int'l*, pg. 2767
DE CECCO U.K. LTD—See Fratelli De Cecco Di Filippo Fara San Martino S.p.A.; *Int'l*, pg. 2767
DIMARK LTD; *Int'l*, pg. 2125
DIRECT EATS, INC.; *U.S. Private*, pg. 1235
DISCOUNT COFFEE.COM, INC.; *U.S. Private*, pg. 1237
DISPENSER BEVERAGES INC.; *U.S. Private*, pg. 1238
DISTRIVAL SA—See Carrefour SA; *Int'l*, pg. 1345
DKSH SHANGHAI LTD.—See Diethelm Keller Holding Limited; *Int'l*, pg. 2117
DOCTORS' PREFERRED, INC.—See Eagle Publishing Inc.; *U.S. Private*, pg. 1310

DOEHLER AUSTRALIA PTY LTD—See Dohler GmbH; *Int'l*, pg. 2156
DOEHLER BUKOVINA LLC—See Dohler GmbH; *Int'l*, pg. 2156
DOEHLER NATURAL FOOD & BEVERAGE INGREDIENTS (BANGKOK) CO., LTD.—See Dohler GmbH; *Int'l*, pg. 2156
DOEHLER NZ LTD.—See Dohler GmbH; *Int'l*, pg. 2156
DOHLER AUSTRIA GMBH—See Dohler GmbH; *Int'l*, pg. 2156
DOHLER EAST AFRICA LTD.—See Dohler GmbH; *Int'l*, pg. 2156
DOHLER EISLEBEN GMBH—See Dohler GmbH; *Int'l*, pg. 2156
DOHLER GMBH—See Dohler GmbH; *Int'l*, pg. 2156
DOSU MAYA MAYACILIK AS—See Compagnie des Levures Lesaffre SA; *Int'l*, pg. 1738
DP DISTRIBUTION LLC—See Bain Capital, LP; *U.S. Private*, pg. 440
DPI MID ATLANTIC—See KeHE Distributors, LLC; *U.S. Private*, pg. 2273
DPI MIDWEST—See KeHE Distributors, LLC; *U.S. Private*, pg. 2273
DPI NORTHWEST—See KeHE Distributors, LLC; *U.S. Private*, pg. 2273
DPI ROCKY MOUNTAIN—See KeHE Distributors, LLC; *U.S. Private*, pg. 2273
DREW'S LLC—See Frontenac Company LLC; *U.S. Private*, pg. 1614
DRL GROUP LTD.—See American Food Distributors; *U.S. Private*, pg. 234
DR. PEPPER BOTTLING CO. ELK CITY; *U.S. Private*, pg. 1271
DSR TAIKO BERHAD; *Int'l*, pg. 2210
DUFRITAL SPA—See Avolta AG; *Int'l*, pg. 749
DURANGO COCA-COLA BOTTLING CO.; *U.S. Private*, pg. 1292
DUTCH GOLD HONEY INC.; *U.S. Private*, pg. 1294
DW RICHARDS SONS INC.; *U.S. Private*, pg. 1295
DXN INTERNATIONAL (HONG KONG) LIMITED—See DXN Holdings Bhd.; *Int'l*, pg. 2237
DXN INTERNATIONAL PAKISTAN (PRIVATE) LIMITED—See DXN Holdings Bhd.; *Int'l*, pg. 2237
DXN INTERNATIONAL PERU S.A.C.—See DXN Holdings Bhd.; *Int'l*, pg. 2237
DXN MARKETING SDN. BHD.—See DXN Holdings Bhd.; *Int'l*, pg. 2237
EAGLE'S MARK INC.; *U.S. Private*, pg. 1311
EARTH FARE INC.; *U.S. Private*, pg. 1314
EASTMAN SPECIALTIES CORPORATION—See Eastman Chemical Company; *U.S. Public*, pg. 705
EAST WEST TEA COMPANY, LLC; *U.S. Private*, pg. 1319
ECHO TRADING CO., LTD.; *Int'l*, pg. 2289
ECKES-GRANINI IBERICA S.A.U.—See Eckes AG; *Int'l*, pg. 2291
EDEN FOODS INC.; *U.S. Private*, pg. 1333
EDEN SPRINGS ESPANA S.A.U—See Primo Water Corporation; *U.S. Public*, pg. 1718
EDEN SPRINGS INTERNATIONAL S.A.—See Primo Water Corporation; *U.S. Public*, pg. 1718
EDEN SPRINGS SCANDINAVIA AB—See Primo Water Corporation; *U.S. Public*, pg. 1718
EDEN SPRINGS SP. Z O.O.—See Primo Water Corporation; *U.S. Public*, pg. 1718
E D & F MAN ASIA PTE LIMITED—See ED&F Man Holdings Limited; *Int'l*, pg. 2302
E D & F MAN ASIA PTE LIMITED & SVG INTERMOL—See ED&F Man Holdings Limited; *Int'l*, pg. 2302
E D & F MAN BRASIL S.A.—See ED&F Man Holdings Limited; *Int'l*, pg. 2302
E D & F MAN CAPITAL MARKETS INC.—See ED&F Man Holdings Limited; *Int'l*, pg. 2302
E D & F MAN COMERCIO S.A. DE C.V.—See ED&F Man Holdings Limited; *Int'l*, pg. 2302
E D & F MAN COMMODITIES INDIA PVT LIMITED—See ED&F Man Holdings Limited; *Int'l*, pg. 2302
E D & F MAN COMMODITIES SP Z OO—See ED&F Man Holdings Limited; *Int'l*, pg. 2302
E D & F MAN DEUTSCHLAND GMBH—See ED&F Man Holdings Limited; *Int'l*, pg. 2302
E D & F MAN ESPANA, S.A.—See ED&F Man Holdings Limited; *Int'l*, pg. 2302
ED & F MAN GULF DMCC—See ED&F Man Holdings Limited; *Int'l*, pg. 2302
ED&F MAN HOLDINGS LIMITED; *Int'l*, pg. 2302
E D & F MAN KOREA LIMITED—See ED&F Man Holdings Limited; *Int'l*, pg. 2302
E D & F MAN LIQUID PRODUCTS BELGIUM N.V.—See ED&F Man Holdings Limited; *Int'l*, pg. 2302
ED&F MAN LIQUID PRODUCTS CZECH REPUBLIC S.R.O.—See ED&F Man Holdings Limited; *Int'l*, pg. 2303
E D & F MAN LIQUID PRODUCTS EUROPE BV—See ED&F Man Holdings Limited; *Int'l*, pg. 2302
E D & F MAN LIQUID PRODUCTS INC—See ED&F Man Holdings Limited; *Int'l*, pg. 2302
E D & F MAN LIQUID PRODUCTS IRELAND LIMITED—See ED&F Man Holdings Limited; *Int'l*, pg. 2302
E D & F MAN LIQUID PRODUCTS ITALIA S.R.L.—See

ED&F Man Holdings Limited; *Int'l*, pg. 2302
ED&F MAN LIQUID PRODUCTS UK—See ED&F Man Holdings Limited; *Int'l*, pg. 2303
E D & F MAN MALAYSIA SDN. BHD.—See ED&F Man Holdings Limited; *Int'l*, pg. 2302
E D & F MAN MOZAMBIQUE LTDA—See ED&F Man Holdings Limited; *Int'l*, pg. 2302
E D & F MAN NICARAGUA LIMITED—See ED&F Man Holdings Limited; *Int'l*, pg. 2302
E D & F MAN PERU S.A.C.—See ED&F Man Holdings Limited; *Int'l*, pg. 2302
E D & F MAN PHILIPPINES INC.—See ED&F Man Holdings Limited; *Int'l*, pg. 2302
E D & F MAN PORTUGAL, LDA—See ED&F Man Holdings Limited; *Int'l*, pg. 2302
E D & F MAN (SHANGHAI) CO., LIMITED—See ED&F Man Holdings Limited; *Int'l*, pg. 2302
E D & F MAN SUCRE SARL—See ED&F Man Holdings Limited; *Int'l*, pg. 2302
E D & F MAN SUGAR BULGARIA—See ED&F Man Holdings Limited; *Int'l*, pg. 2302
E D & F MAN SUGAR INC—See ED&F Man Holdings Limited; *Int'l*, pg. 2302
E D & F MAN TRGOVINA D.O.O.—See ED&F Man Holdings Limited; *Int'l*, pg. 2302
E D & F MAN URUGUAY SA—See ED&F Man Holdings Limited; *Int'l*, pg. 2302
EDGEWOOD VILLAGE MARKET INC.; *U.S. Private*, pg. 1336
EDWARD APFFEL CO; *U.S. Private*, pg. 1340
EKO FAGEL FISK O MITTEMELLAN AB—See Sysco Corporation; *U.S. Public*, pg. 1973
ELLIS COFFEE COMPANY; *U.S. Private*, pg. 1374
EMPRESAS DE NARINO LTDA.—See ED&F Man Holdings Limited; *Int'l*, pg. 2303
EMPRESAS DE NARIO LTDA.—See ED&F Man Holdings Limited; *Int'l*, pg. 2303
ENCO PRODUCTS LIMITED—See GraceKennedy Limited; *Int'l*, pg. 3048
ENCORE BEVERAGE, LLC—See Cork Distributors, LLC; *U.S. Private*, pg. 1050
ENTEMANN'S BAKERY OUTLET—See Grupo Bimbo, S.A.B. de C.V.; *Int'l*, pg. 3122
ENTEMANN'S/OROWEAT—See Grupo Bimbo, S.A.B. de C.V.; *Int'l*, pg. 3122
EPTA AMERICA LLC—See Mondelez International, Inc.; *U.S. Public*, pg. 1461
ERNTESEGEN NATURKOST GMBH—See Coop-Gruppe Genossenschaft; *Int'l*, pg. 1789
THE ESSENTIAL BAKING COMPANY; *U.S. Private*, pg. 4027
ESSEX GRAIN PRODUCTS, INC.; *U.S. Private*, pg. 1428
ETILER GIDA VE TICARI YATIRIMLAR SAN VE TIC A.S.; *Int'l*, pg. 2523
EURO CENTER TRADE S.R.O.—See AMBRA S.A.; *Int'l*, pg. 415
EUROGERM ANDINA—See Eurogerm SA; *Int'l*, pg. 2552
EUROGERM MAROC—See Eurogerm SA; *Int'l*, pg. 2552
EUROGERM MEXICO SA DE CV—See Eurogerm SA; *Int'l*, pg. 2552
EUROGERM SENEGAL—See Eurogerm SA; *Int'l*, pg. 2552
EURPAC SERVICE CO; *U.S. Private*, pg. 1434
EVERNUTRITION, INC.—See Trident Brands Incorporated; *U.S. Public*, pg. 2189
EXCEED WORLD, INC.; *Int'l*, pg. 2577
FALA GMBH—See Compagnie des Levures Lesaffre SA; *Int'l*, pg. 1738
FALCON COFFEES LIMITED—See Westrock Coffee Company; *U.S. Public*, pg. 2361
FARNER-BOCKEN CO.—See Core-Mark Holding Co. Inc.; *U.S. Public*, pg. 576
FASTEST, LLC—See Monster Beverage Corporation; *U.S. Public*, pg. 1465
FERRARELLE USA—See Ferrarelle S.p.A.; *Int'l*, pg. 2639
FINAGRA GROUP LIMITED—See Stone Point Capital LLC; *U.S. Private*, pg. 3821
FIRE & FLAVOR GRILLING CO; *U.S. Private*, pg. 1511
FIRST CALL TRADING CORPORATION; *U.S. Private*, pg. 1515
FIRST WORLD IMPORTS, INC.; *U.S. Private*, pg. 1531
FITZGERALD BROTHERS BEVERAGES; *U.S. Private*, pg. 1536
FLAVOR BURST CO. LLP—See The Middleby Corporation; *U.S. Public*, pg. 2113
FLORIDA BULK SALES INC.; *U.S. Private*, pg. 1547
FOCUS FOODSERVICE, LLC—See Sysco Corporation; *U.S. Public*, pg. 1973
FOOD TRAC LTD.—See Charoen Pokphand Foods Public Company Limited; *Int'l*, pg. 1452
FOYLE BIO-ENERGY—See Foyle Food Group Ltd.; *Int'l*, pg. 2756
FOYLE INGREDIENTS—See Foyle Food Group Ltd.; *Int'l*, pg. 2756
FREEDMAN FOOD SERVICE, INC.—See Sysco Corporation; *U.S. Public*, pg. 1973
FREEDMAN FOOD SERVICE OF DENVER, INC.—See Sysco Corporation; *U.S. Public*, pg. 1973

N.A.I.C.S. INDEX
424490 — OTHER GROCERY AND R...

FRESHFAYRE LIMITED—See Sysco Corporation; *U.S. Public*, pg. 1973

FRESH MADE, INC.—See Lifeway Foods, Inc.; *U.S. Public*, pg. 1313

FRESHPOINT CENTRAL CALIFORNIA, INC.—See Sysco Corporation; *U.S. Public*, pg. 1974

FRESHPOINT CONNECTICUT, LLC—See Sysco Corporation; *U.S. Public*, pg. 1974

FRESHPOINT DENVER, INC.—See Sysco Corporation; *U.S. Public*, pg. 1974

FRESHPOINT OKLAHOMA CITY, LLC—See Sysco Corporation; *U.S. Public*, pg. 1974

FRESHPOINT PUERTO RICO, LLC—See Sysco Corporation; *U.S. Public*, pg. 1974

FRESHPOINT SOUTHERN CALIFORNIA, INC.—See Sysco Corporation; *U.S. Public*, pg. 1974

FRESHPOINT TOMATO, LLC—See Sysco Corporation; *U.S. Public*, pg. 1974

FRISCHEPARADIES KG—See Dr. August Oetker KG; *Int'l*, pg. 2190

FRUITSMART, INC.—See Universal Corporation; *U.S. Public*, pg. 2254

FRUTAROM CHILE S.A.—See International Flavors & Fragrances Inc.; *U.S. Public*, pg. 1151

FUJIYA FOOD SERVICE CO., LTD.—See Fujiya Co., Ltd.; *Int'l*, pg. 2838

FULTON PROVISION COMPANY—See Sysco Corporation; *U.S. Public*, pg. 1974

FUSEAU; *Int'l*, pg. 2849

GAMESA USA, INC.—See PepsiCo, Inc.; *U.S. Public*, pg. 1670

GARDNER DISTRIBUTING CO.; *U.S. Private*, pg. 1643

GARRAWAYS LTD—See Primo Water Corporation; *U.S. Public*, pg. 1718

GBI ARGENTINA—See Compagnie des Levures Lesaffre SA; *Int'l*, pg. 1738

GENERAL MILLS SINGAPORE PTE. LTD.—See General Mills, Inc.; *U.S. Public*, pg. 921

GEORGE DELALLO COMPANY, INC.; *U.S. Private*, pg. 1681

GEOVITA FUNTIONAL INGREDIENTS S.R.L.—See Ebro Foods S.A.; *Int'l*, pg. 2286

GERS DISTRIBUTION; *Int'l*, pg. 2945

GIFT HOLDINGS INC.; *Int'l*, pg. 2970

GIVAUDAN IBERICA SA—See Givaudan S.A.; *Int'l*, pg. 2980

GIVAUDAN POLSKA SP. Z.O.O.—See Givaudan S.A.; *Int'l*, pg. 2981

GLANBIA INGREDIENTS, INC—See Glanbia Co-Operative Society Limited; *Int'l*, pg. 2988

GLANBIA NUTRITIONALS DEUTSCHLAND GMBH—See Glanbia Co-Operative Society Limited; *Int'l*, pg. 2988

GLANBIA NUTRITIONALS (NA), INC.—See Glanbia Co-Operative Society Limited; *Int'l*, pg. 2988

GLANBIA NUTRITIONALS SINGAPORE PTE LIMITED—See Glanbia Co-Operative Society Limited; *Int'l*, pg. 2988

GLANBIA NUTRITIONALS (SUZHOU) COMPANY LIMITED—See Glanbia Co-Operative Society Limited; *Int'l*, pg. 2988

GLANBIA NUTRITIONALS (UK) LIMITED—See Glanbia Co-Operative Society Limited; *Int'l*, pg. 2988

GLOBAL BAKERIES, LLC—See Surge Private Equity LLC; *U.S. Private*, pg. 3884

GLOBAL PET FOODS DISTRIBUTION LTD.—See Franchise Bancorp Inc.; *Int'l*, pg. 2760

GOBLIN INDIA LTD.; *Int'l*, pg. 3018

GOGLANIAN BAKERIES INC.; *U.S. Private*, pg. 1726

GOLDBERG AND SOLOVY FOODS, INC.—See Sysco Corporation; *U.S. Public*, pg. 1974

GOLDEN ORGANICS—See Innovative Food Holdings, Inc.; *U.S. Public*, pg. 1127

GOLDEN RESOURCES DEVELOPMENT INTERNATIONAL LIMITED; *Int'l*, pg. 3031

GOLDEN RESOURCES RICE TRADING LIMITED—See Golden Resources Development International Limited; *Int'l*, pg. 3031

GOLDEN SECTOR LIMITED—See Heng Tai Consumables Group Limited; *Int'l*, pg. 3345

GOLLUECKE & ROTHFOS GMBH—See ED&F Man Holdings Limited; *Int'l*, pg. 2303

GOODMANS MATZOH PRODUCTS INC—See Joyce Food Products Inc.; *U.S. Private*, pg. 2239

GORDON FOOD SERVICE - FLORIDA—See Gordon Food Service Inc.; *U.S. Private*, pg. 1743

GOUGEON FOURNITURES S.A.S.; *Int'l*, pg. 3044

GOURMONDO FOOD GMBH—See Delticom AG; *Int'l*, pg. 2021

GOYA FOODS INC.—See Goya Foods, Inc.; *U.S. Private*, pg. 1747

GRACE FOODS INTERNATIONAL LTD.—See GraceKennedy Limited; *Int'l*, pg. 3048

GRACE FOODS UK LIMITED—See GraceKennedy Limited; *Int'l*, pg. 3048

GRACEKENNEDY (BELIZE) LTD.—See GraceKennedy Limited; *Int'l*, pg. 3049

GRAND CENTRAL BAKERY; *U.S. Private*, pg. 1752

GRANUM INC.; *U.S. Private*, pg. 1757

GRAY & COMPANY; *U.S. Private*, pg. 1759

GREATVIEW BEIJING TRADING CO., LTD.—See Greatview Aseptic Packaging Company Limited; *Int'l*, pg. 3068

GREENFIELD BEVERAGE COMPANY INC—See Zink Distributing Inc; *U.S. Private*, pg. 4605

GREEN POLKADOT BOX INC.; *U.S. Public*, pg. 964

GREEN SPOT, INC.; *U.S. Private*, pg. 1774

GRUPO CORVI, S.A.B. DE C.V.; *Int'l*, pg. 3125

GRUPO LACTALIS IBERIA S.A.—See Groupe Lactalis SA; *Int'l*, pg. 3106

GUEST SUPPLY ASIA, LIMITED—See Sysco Corporation; *U.S. Public*, pg. 1976

GURMETUM S.R.O.—See AMBRA S.A.; *Int'l*, pg. 415

HADDON HOUSE FOODS PRODUCTS, INC.—See United Natural Foods, Inc.; *U.S. Public*, pg. 2231

HAELSSEN & LYON NORTH AMERICA CORPORATION—See Halssen & Lyon GmbH; *Int'l*, pg. 3233

HALE BROTHERS SUMMIT, LLC—See Performance Food Group Company; *U.S. Public*, pg. 1674

HAND ARNOLD TRINIDAD LIMITED—See Agostini's Limited; *Int'l*, pg. 213

HANGZHOU DANBI FOOD CO., LTD.—See Christine International Holdings Limited; *Int'l*, pg. 1587

HANNAN TANK TERMINAL CO., LTD.—See Fuji Oil Holdings Inc.; *Int'l*, pg. 2815

HA NOI - KINH BAC AGRICULTURE AND FOOD JOINT STOCK COMPANY; *Int'l*, pg. 3201

HARBOE SVERIGE AB—See Harboes Bryggeri A/S; *Int'l*, pg. 3271

HARCO DISTRIBUTORS INC.; *U.S. Private*, pg. 1861

HARLAN BAKERIES LLC; *U.S. Private*, pg. 1864

HARRIS FREEMAN & CO. LP; *U.S. Private*, pg. 1869

HARVEST CHOICE AUSTRALIA PTY. LTD.—See Lamb Weston Holdings, Inc.; *U.S. Public*, pg. 1291

HAWAII COFFEE COMPANY—See Paradise Beverages, Inc.; *U.S. Private*, pg. 3090

HAYLEYS CONSUMER PRODUCTS LTD.—See Hayleys PLC; *Int'l*, pg. 3292

HEBERT CANDIES; *U.S. Private*, pg. 1902

HENG YUI (MACAO) COMMERCIAL OFFSHORE LIMITED—See Heng Tai Consumables Group Limited; *Int'l*, pg. 3345

HERBAFOOD INGREDIENTS GMBH—See Herbstreith & Fox KG Pektin-Fabriken; *Int'l*, pg. 3360

HERBALIFE INTERNATIONAL OF AMERICA, INC. - TORRANCE—See Herbalife Nutrition Ltd.; *U.S. Public*, pg. 3360

HERBSTREITH & FOX INC.—See Herbstreith & Fox KG Pektin-Fabriken; *Int'l*, pg. 3360

HERBSTREITH & FOX KFT.—See Herbstreith & Fox KG Pektin-Fabriken; *Int'l*, pg. 3360

HILL'S PET NUTRITION, INC.—See Colgate-Palmolive Company; *U.S. Public*, pg. 533

HILL'S PET NUTRITION SALES, INC.—See Colgate-Palmolive Company; *U.S. Public*, pg. 533

H.J. HEINZ COMPANY (IRELAND) LIMITED—See 3G Capital Inc.; *U.S. Private*, pg. 10

H.J. HEINZ COMPANY (IRELAND) LIMITED—See Berkshire Hathaway Inc.; *U.S. Public*, pg. 317

HOCHLAND DEUTSCHLAND GMBH—See Hochland SE; *Int'l*, pg. 3437

HOCHLAND NATEC GMBH—See Hochland SE; *Int'l*, pg. 3437

HOCK SENG FOOD PTE LTD—See Hosen Group Ltd; *Int'l*, pg. 3482

HONOR FOODS, INC.—See Burris Logistics; *U.S. Private*, pg. 692

HOPS EXTRACT CORPORATION OF AMERICA—See S.S. Steiner Inc.; *U.S. Private*, pg. 3518

HOPSTEINER TRADING (ZHUHAI) CO., LTD.—See S.S. Steiner Inc.; *U.S. Private*, pg. 3518

HORIZON FOOD GROUP, INC.; *U.S. Private*, pg. 1980

HORIZON HOLDINGS LLC; *U.S. Private*, pg. 1981

HOSEN GROUP LTD; *Int'l*, pg. 3482

HOUSE OF JANE, INC.—See Visitalk Capital Corporation; *U.S. Private*, pg. 4392

HOUSE OF SPICES INDIA INC.; *U.S. Private*, pg. 1991

HSUS GINSENG ENTERPRISES, INC.; *U.S. Private*, pg. 1999

HUDSON BAKING COMPANY LLC—See Arbor Investment Group; *U.S. Private*, pg. 308

HUMM KOMBUCHA, LLC—See SYSTM Brands, LLC; *U.S. Private*, pg. 3908

HUTCHINSON (ANTIGUA) LIMITED—See Goddard Enterprises Limited; *Int'l*, pg. 3019

HWA TAI DISTRIBUTION SDN. BHD.—See Hwa Tai Industries Berhad; *Int'l*, pg. 3541

HYDR8 WATER—See Eneco Refresh Limited; *Int'l*, pg. 2411

IDAHO BEVERAGES INC.; *U.S. Private*, pg. 2034

IFF FRAGRANCE GMBH—See International Flavors & Fragrances Inc.; *U.S. Public*, pg. 1152

IFF LATIN AMERICAN HOLDINGS (ESPANA), S.L.—See International Flavors & Fragrances Inc.; *U.S. Public*, pg. 1152

IFRESH INC.; *U.S. Public*, pg. 1095

ILHWA AMERICAN CORPORATION—See Family Federation for World Peace & Unification; *U.S. Private*, pg. 1469

ILLYCAFFE FRANCE SAS—See illycaffe S.p.A.; *Int'l*, pg. 3615

ILLYCAFFE KOREA CO. LTD.—See illycaffe S.p.A.; *Int'l*, pg. 3615

ILLYCAFFE SHANGHAI CO. LTD.—See illycaffe S.p.A.; *Int'l*, pg. 3615

ILLYCAFFE' SUD AMERICA COM. IMP. EXP. LTD.—See illycaffe S.p.A.; *Int'l*, pg. 3615

ILLY ESPRESSO CANADA—See illycaffe S.p.A.; *Int'l*, pg. 3615

IMCD ASIA PTE. LTD.—See IMCD N.V.; *Int'l*, pg. 3621

IMCD INDIA—See IMCD N.V.; *Int'l*, pg. 3622

IMCD NEW ZEALAND LTD.—See IMCD N.V.; *Int'l*, pg. 3622

IMCD SWITZERLAND AG—See IMCD N.V.; *Int'l*, pg. 3622

IMCD TICARET PAZARLAMA VE DANISMANLIK LIMITED SIRKETI—See IMCD N.V.; *Int'l*, pg. 3622

INALCA ANGOLA L.T.D.A.—See Cremonini S.p.A.; *Int'l*, pg. 1838

INALCA KINSHASA S.P.R.L.—See Cremonini S.p.A.; *Int'l*, pg. 1838

INDIANA SUGARS, INC.; *U.S. Private*, pg. 2063

INGREDIENTS SOLUTIONS INC.; *U.S. Private*, pg. 2077

INKO SPORTS AG—See B. Braun Melsungen AG; *Int'l*, pg. 787

INTERBRAU GMBH—See Ameropa AG; *Int'l*, pg. 424

INTER-COUNTY BAKERS, INC.; *U.S. Private*, pg. 2107

INTERNATIONAL FLAVORS & FRAGRANCES (ASIA PACIFIC) PTE. LTD.—See International Flavors & Fragrances Inc.; *U.S. Public*, pg. 1152

INTERNATIONAL FLAVORS & FRAGRANCES (CHINA) LTD.—See International Flavors & Fragrances Inc.; *U.S. Public*, pg. 1152

INTERNATIONAL FLAVORS & FRAGRANCES (HANGZHOU) CO., LTD.—See International Flavors & Fragrances Inc.; *U.S. Public*, pg. 1152

INTERNATIONAL FLAVORS & FRAGRANCES I.F.F. (FRANCE) S.A.R.L.—See International Flavors & Fragrances Inc.; *U.S. Public*, pg. 1153

INTERNATIONAL FLAVORS & FRAGRANCES I.F.F. (ISRAEL) LTD.—See International Flavors & Fragrances Inc.; *U.S. Public*, pg. 1153

INTERNATIONAL FLAVORS & FRAGRANCES (KOREA), INC.—See International Flavors & Fragrances Inc.; *U.S. Public*, pg. 1152

INTERNATIONAL FLAVORS & FRAGRANCES (MEXICO), S. DE R.L. DE C.V.—See International Flavors & Fragrances Inc.; *U.S. Public*, pg. 1152

INTERNATIONAL FLAVORS & FRAGRANCES (POLAND) SP.Z.O.O.—See International Flavors & Fragrances Inc.; *U.S. Public*, pg. 1153

INTERNATIONAL FLAVORS & FRAGRANCES (THAILAND) LTD.—See International Flavors & Fragrances Inc.; *U.S. Public*, pg. 1153

INTERNATIONAL FLAVOURS & FRAGRANCES (AUSTRALIA) PTY. LTD.—See International Flavors & Fragrances Inc.; *U.S. Public*, pg. 1153

INTERRA INTERNATIONAL MEXICO, S. DE R.L. DE C.V.—See Seaboard Corporation; *U.S. Public*, pg. 1850

INTERSTATE POTATO PACKERS CORP.—See Oppenheimer Companies, Inc.; *U.S. Private*, pg. 3033

INVENTIVE FOOD TECHNOLOGY (ZQ) LTD.—See International Flavors & Fragrances Inc.; *U.S. Public*, pg. 1153

ISLAND NATURAL, INC.—See Nassau Candy Distributors Inc.; *U.S. Private*, pg. 2837

JAMAICA FLOUR MILLS LIMITED—See Archer-Daniels-Midland Company; *U.S. Public*, pg. 185

JAPELL CO., LTD.—See Arata Corporation; *Int'l*, pg. 536

J. KING'S FOOD SERVICE PROFESSIONALS INC.—See Sysco Corporation; *U.S. Public*, pg. 1974

JOFFREY'S COFFEE & TEA CO.; *U.S. Private*, pg. 2219

JOHN PATON, INC.; *U.S. Private*, pg. 2223

JOHNSON BROTHERS BAKERY SUPPLY; *U.S. Private*, pg. 2227

JOHN V. HEINEMAN COMPANY—See Paragon Food Service; *U.S. Private*, pg. 3091

JSC BVT EXIM—See Dohler GmbH; *Int'l*, pg. 2156

J. SOSNICK & SON INC.; *U.S. Private*, pg. 2157

KAFFEKNAPPEN AB—See Convini Sverige AB; *Int'l*, pg. 1787

KAIKU KMO S.L.—See Emmi AG; *Int'l*, pg. 2384

KAROM DRINKS S.R.L.—See AMBRA S.A.; *Int'l*, pg. 415

KEHE DISTRIBUTORS, LLC; *U.S. Private*, pg. 2273

KELLOGG SALES COMPANY—See Kellanova; *U.S. Public*, pg. 1218

KELSEN, INC.—See Ferrero International S.A.; *Int'l*, pg. 2641

KELSEN SOUTH AFRICA (PTY) LTD.—See Ferrero International S.A.; *Int'l*, pg. 2641

KENT FROZEN FOODS—See Sysco Corporation; *U.S. Public*, pg. 1974

KI GROUP S.P.A—See Bioera S.p.A.; *Int'l*, pg. 1037

KILOMBERO SUGAR DISTRIBUTORS LIMITED—See ED&F Man Holdings Limited; *Int'l*, pg. 2303

KING NUTS & RAAPHORST B.V.—See ACOMO N.V.; *Int'l*, pg. 108

KLEIN BROS. - SNACK & PACKAGED NUT DIVISON—See Klein Bros. Holdings, Ltd.; *U.S. Private*, pg. 2318

KLUMAN & BALTER LIMITED—See BRENNTAG SE; *Int'l*, pg. 1149

424490 — OTHER GROCERY AND R...

KO-AMEX GENERAL WHOLESALE INC.; *U.S. Private*, pg. 2325
KOREA THUMB VET CO., LTD.—See Harim Holdings Co., Ltd.; *Int'l*, pg. 3276
KRAFT HEINZ COMPANY - ADDISON—See 3G Capital Inc.; *U.S. Private*, pg. 10
KRAFT HEINZ COMPANY - ADDISON—See Berkshire Hathaway Inc.; *U.S. Public*, pg. 318
KUNA MEAT CO, INC.; *U.S. Private*, pg. 2357
KYAGALANYI COFFEE LIMITED—See ED&F Man Holdings Limited; *Int'l*, pg. 2303
LA BODEGA INC.; *U.S. Private*, pg. 2368
LACTALIS DEUTSCHLAND GMBH—See Groupe Lactalis SA; *Int'l*, pg. 3106
LACTALIS EUROPE DU NORD S.A.—See Groupe Lactalis SA; *Int'l*, pg. 3106
LACTALIS HONGRIE, S.R.O.—See Groupe Lactalis SA; *Int'l*, pg. 3106
LACTALIS LUXEMBOURG SENC—See Groupe Lactalis SA; *Int'l*, pg. 3106
LACTALIS POLSKA. SP. Z O.O.—See Groupe Lactalis SA; *Int'l*, pg. 3106
LACTALIS PORTUGAL, LDA—See Groupe Lactalis SA; *Int'l*, pg. 3106
LACTALIS UNITED KINGDOM LTD—See Groupe Lactalis SA; *Int'l*, pg. 3106
LA FANTANA SRL—See Axel Johnson Gruppen AB; *Int'l*, pg. 765
LANCER INTERNATIONAL SALES, INC.—See Hoshizaki Corporation; *Int'l*, pg. 3484
LA PREFERIDA, INC.; *U.S. Private*, pg. 2369
LARUE DISTRIBUTING COMPANY; *U.S. Private*, pg. 2394
LATICINIOS CAROLINA LTDA—See General Mills, Inc.; *U.S. Public*, pg. 922
LATIMER GROUP LIMITED—See Post Holdings, Inc.; *U.S. Public*, pg. 1703
LENTZ MILLING COMPANY—See Platinum Equity, LLC; *U.S. Private*, pg. 3205
LESAFFRE BULGARIA EOOD—See Compagnie des Levures Lesaffre SA; *Int'l*, pg. 1739
LESAFFRE CESKO, A.S.—See Compagnie des Levures Lesaffre SA; *Int'l*, pg. 1739
LESAFFRE CHILE S.A.—See Compagnie des Levures Lesaffre SA; *Int'l*, pg. 1739
LESAFFRE (FAR EAST) LTD.—See Compagnie des Levures Lesaffre SA; *Int'l*, pg. 1739
LESAFFRE INGREDIENTS SERVICES POLSKA SP. Z O.O.—See Compagnie des Levures Lesaffre SA; *Int'l*, pg. 1738
LESAFFRE INGREDIENTS SERVICES SA—See Compagnie des Levures Lesaffre SA; *Int'l*, pg. 1738
LESAFFRE MAROC—See Compagnie des Levures Lesaffre SA; *Int'l*, pg. 1739
LESAFFRE NORDIC AB—See Compagnie des Levures Lesaffre SA; *Int'l*, pg. 1739
LESAFFRE RS D.O.O.—See Compagnie des Levures Lesaffre SA; *Int'l*, pg. 1739
LESAFFRE SLOVENSKO, A.S.—See Compagnie des Levures Lesaffre SA; *Int'l*, pg. 1739
LESAFFRE UKRAINE LLC—See Compagnie des Levures Lesaffre SA; *Int'l*, pg. 1739
LESAFFRE URUGUAY S.A.—See Compagnie des Levures Lesaffre SA; *Int'l*, pg. 1739
LESAFFRE YEAST CORP.—See Compagnie des Levures Lesaffre SA; *Int'l*, pg. 1739
LEVADURAS Y AVIOS AZTECA, S.A. DE C.V.—See Compagnie des Levures Lesaffre SA; *Int'l*, pg. 1739
LEWIS VINCENNES, INC.—See Lewis Brothers Bakeries, Inc.; *U.S. Private*, pg. 2438
LIBERTY RICHTER—See World Finer Foods, Inc.; *U.S. Private*, pg. 4565
LIFE ON EARTH, INC.; *U.S. Public*, pg. 1312
LIFEVANTAGE CANADA LTD.—See LifeVantage Corporation; *U.S. Public*, pg. 1313
LIFEVANTAGE HONG KONG LIMITED—See LifeVantage Corporation; *U.S. Public*, pg. 1313
LIFEVANTAGE THAILAND COMPANY LIMITED—See LifeVantage Corporation; *U.S. Public*, pg. 1313
THE LIFEWAY KEFIR SHOP—See Lifeway Foods, Inc.; *U.S. Public*, pg. 1313
LIGHTBODY EUROPE SARL—See DBAY Advisors Limited; *Int'l*, pg. 1987
LION COFFEE COMPANY—See Paradise Beverages, Inc.; *U.S. Private*, pg. 3090
LIPARI FOODS OPERATING COMPANY, LLC—See Littlejohn & Co., LLC; *U.S. Private*, pg. 2472
LISY CORPORATION; *U.S. Private*, pg. 2467
LLC E D & F MAN—See ED&F Man Holdings Limited; *Int'l*, pg. 2303
LOMAR DISTRIBUTING—See Hy-Vee, Inc.; *U.S. Private*, pg. 2016
THE LONG COMPANY; *U.S. Private*, pg. 4072
LUCKS FOOD DECORATING COMPANY; *U.S. Private*, pg. 2511
MAGNETIC SPRINGS WATER COMPANY; *U.S. Private*, pg. 2547
MAISON SOLUTIONS INC.; *U.S. Public*, pg. 1355
MANASSEN FOODS AUSTRALIA PTY. LTD.—See Bright Food (Group) Co., Ltd.; *Int'l*, pg. 1161
MARCELLINO MARTINS & E JOHNSTON EXPORTADORES LTDA—See ED&F Man Holdings Limited; *Int'l*, pg. 2303
MARQUEZ BROTHERS NEVADA, INC.—See Marquez Brothers International, Inc.; *U.S. Private*, pg. 2587
MARQUEZ BROTHERS SOUTHWEST, INC.—See Marquez Brothers International, Inc.; *U.S. Private*, pg. 2587
MARTIN-BROWER OF CANADA CO.—See Reyes Holdings, LLC; *U.S. Private*, pg. 3418
MATINA GMBH—See Hubert Burda Media Holding Kommanditgesellschaft; *Int'l*, pg. 3520
MBC S.A.—See TPG Capital, L.P.; *U.S. Public*, pg. 2174
MCCORMICK SOUTH AFRICA PTY LIMITED—See McCormick & Company, Incorporated; *U.S. Public*, pg. 1404
MCLURES HONEY & MAPLE PRODUCTS—See Dutch Gold Honey Inc.; *U.S. Private*, pg. 1294
MEADOW FEEDS EASTERN CAPE (PTY) LIMITED—See Astral Foods Limited; *Int'l*, pg. 658
MERISON (AUSTRALIA) PTY. LTD.—See Bread Financial Holdings, Inc.; *U.S. Public*, pg. 381
MERISON RETAIL B.V.—See Bread Financial Holdings Inc.; *U.S. Public*, pg. 381
MERISON RETAIL (HK) LTD.—See Bread Financial Holdings Inc.; *U.S. Public*, pg. 381
METROPLEX HARRIMAN CORP.—See Metroplex Holdings Inc.; *U.S. Private*, pg. 2687
METROPLEX LONG ISLAND CORPORATION—See Metroplex Holdings Inc.; *U.S. Private*, pg. 2687
MIDWEST AGRI-COMMODITIES—See American Crystal Sugar Company; *U.S. Private*, pg. 98
MIDWEST AGRI-COMMODITIES—See Michigan Sugar Company; *U.S. Private*, pg. 2701
MIDWEST AGRI-COMMODITIES—See Minn-Dak Farmers Cooperative; *U.S. Private*, pg. 2742
MIDWEST AGRI-COMMODITIES—See Southern Minnesota Beet Sugar Cooperative; *U.S. Private*, pg. 3733
MILUPA COMMERCIAL S.A.—See Danone; *Int'l*, pg. 1966
MILUPA S.A.—See Danone; *Int'l*, pg. 1967
MODENA TRADING PTY LTD—See Autosports Group Limited; *Int'l*, pg. 732
MOLINOS DE HONDURAS S.A.—See ED&F Man Holdings Limited; *Int'l*, pg. 2303
MOMA FOODS LIMITED—See A.G. Barr plc; *Int'l*, pg. 24
MONDELEZ DEUTSCHLAND BISCUITS PRODUCTION GMBH—See Mondelez International, Inc.; *U.S. Public*, pg. 1462
MONDELEZ ESPANA POSTRES PRODUCTION, S.A.U.—See Mondelez International, Inc.; *U.S. Public*, pg. 1463
MONDELEZ INTERNATIONAL MANAGEMENT CENTER-EAST HANOVER—See Mondelez International, Inc.; *U.S. Public*, pg. 1464
MONDELEZ NEW ZEALAND—See Mondelez International, Inc.; *U.S. Public*, pg. 1464
MONSTER ENERGY COMPANY—See Monster Beverage Corporation; *U.S. Public*, pg. 1465
MONSTER ENERGY US LLC—See Monster Beverage Corporation; *U.S. Public*, pg. 1465
MSHALE COMMODITIES LIMITED (SUGAR)—See ED&F Man Holdings Limited; *Int'l*, pg. 2303
M. SIMON ZOOK CO. INC.; *U.S. Private*, pg. 2527
MYWEBGROCER INC.—See Mi9 Retail, Inc.; *U.S. Private*, pg. 2696
NABC, INC.—See NewAge, Inc.; *U.S. Public*, pg. 1513
NANTZE SPRINGS INC.; *U.S. Private*, pg. 2834
NAPOLI FOODS, INC.; *U.S. Private*, pg. 2835
NA SALES COMPANY INC.; *U.S. Private*, pg. 2829
NATCHEZ COCA-COLA BOTTLING CO.—See The Coca-Cola Company; *U.S. Public*, pg. 2065
NATFOOD IBERICA S.L.—See Bioera S.p.A.; *Int'l*, pg. 1037
NATIONAL FOOD GROUP; *U.S. Private*, pg. 2854
NATIONAL PRODUCTS MARKETING COMPANY—See Hayel Saeed Anam Group of Companies; *Int'l*, pg. 3291
NATION PIZZA AND FOODS, LLC; *U.S. Private*, pg. 2839
NATURE'S BEST, INC.—See KeHE Distributors, LLC; *U.S. Private*, pg. 2273
NEDCOFFEE BV—See Amtrada Holding B.V.; *Int'l*, pg. 442
NESTLE WATERS NORTH AMERICA INC. - BREA—See Metropoulos & Co.; *U.S. Private*, pg. 2690
NESTLE WATERS NORTH AMERICA INC. - BREA—See One Rock Capital Partners, LLC; *U.S. Private*, pg. 3021
NESTLE WATERS NORTH AMERICA INC. - BREINIGSVILLE—See Metropoulos & Co.; *U.S. Private*, pg. 2690
NESTLE WATERS NORTH AMERICA INC. - BREINIGSVILLE—See One Rock Capital Partners, LLC; *U.S. Private*, pg. 3021
NESTLE WATERS NORTH AMERICA INC. - DRACUT—See Metropoulos & Co.; *U.S. Private*, pg. 2690
NESTLE WATERS NORTH AMERICA INC. - DRACUT—See One Rock Capital Partners, LLC; *U.S. Private*, pg. 3021
NESTLE WATERS NORTH AMERICA INC. - GREENWICH—See Metropoulos & Co.; *U.S. Private*, pg. 2690
NESTLE WATERS NORTH AMERICA INC. - GREENWICH—See One Rock Capital Partners, LLC; *U.S. Private*, pg. 3021
NESTLE WATERS NORTH AMERICA INC. - RAYNHAM—See Metropoulos & Co.; *U.S. Private*, pg. 2690
NESTLE WATERS NORTH AMERICA INC. - RAYNHAM—See One Rock Capital Partners, LLC; *U.S. Private*, pg. 3021
NESTLE WATERS NORTH AMERICA INC. - THOUSAND PALMS—See Metropoulos & Co.; *U.S. Private*, pg. 2690
NESTLE WATERS NORTH AMERICA INC. - THOUSAND PALMS—See One Rock Capital Partners, LLC; *U.S. Private*, pg. 3021
NESTLE WATERS NORTH AMERICA INC. - WOODRIDGE—See Metropoulos & Co.; *U.S. Private*, pg. 2690
NESTLE WATERS NORTH AMERICA INC. - WOODRIDGE—See One Rock Capital Partners, LLC; *U.S. Private*, pg. 3021
NESTLE WATERS NORTH AMERICA INC. - ZEPHYRHILLS—See Metropoulos & Co.; *U.S. Private*, pg. 2690
NESTLE WATERS NORTH AMERICA INC. - ZEPHYRHILLS—See One Rock Capital Partners, LLC; *U.S. Private*, pg. 3021
NET SAVINGS LINK, INC.; *U.S. Private*, pg. 2886
NEVERFAIL SPRINGWATER CO (QLD) PTY LIMITED—See COCA-COLA EUROPACIFIC PARTNERS PLC; *Int'l*, pg. 1684
NEVERFAIL SPRINGWATER LIMITED—See COCA-COLA EUROPACIFIC PARTNERS PLC; *Int'l*, pg. 1684
NEW GENERATION CONSUMER GROUP, INC.; *U.S. Public*, pg. 1511
NEW KONDO TRADING COMPANY LIMITED—See Four Seas Mercantile Holdings Limited; *Int'l*, pg. 2755
NEW ORLEANS PIZZA CANADA INC—See Chairman's Brands Corporation; *Int'l*, pg. 1437
NISHIGEN COMPANY—See DAIKOKUTENBUSSAN CO., LTD.; *Int'l*, pg. 1937
NOON HOUR FOOD PRODUCTS, INC.; *U.S. Private*, pg. 2934
NOVEL INGREDIENT SERVICES, LLC—See One Rock Capital Partners, LLC; *U.S. Private*, pg. 3022
NUMIL GIDA URUNLERI SANAYI VE TICARET A.S.—See Danone; *Int'l*, pg. 1966
NUMIL HELLAS S.A.—See Danone; *Int'l*, pg. 1966
NUMIL HUNGARY TAPSZERKERESKEDELNI KFT.—See Danone; *Int'l*, pg. 1966
NUTREX, INC.—See Cyanotech Corporation; *U.S. Public*, pg. 617
NUTRICIA A/S—See Danone; *Int'l*, pg. 1966
NUTRICIA A.S.—See Danone; *Int'l*, pg. 1967
NUTRICIA AUSTRALIA PTY. LTD.—See Danone; *Int'l*, pg. 1966
NUTRICIA BELGIE N.V.—See Danone; *Int'l*, pg. 1966
NUTRICIA FRANCE S.A.—See Danone; *Int'l*, pg. 1966
NUTRICIA MEDICAL OY—See Danone; *Int'l*, pg. 1966
NUTRICIA NAHRUNGSMITTEL GMBH & CO. KG—See Danone; *Int'l*, pg. 1966
NUTRICIA NEDERLAND B.V.—See Danone; *Int'l*, pg. 1966
NUTRICIA (NEW ZEALAND) LTD.—See Danone; *Int'l*, pg. 1966
NUTRICIA NORDICA AB—See Danone; *Int'l*, pg. 1967
NUTRICIA NORGE AS—See Danone; *Int'l*, pg. 1967
NUTRICIA POLSKA SP. Z O.O.—See Danone; *Int'l*, pg. 1967
NUTRICIA PORTUGAL L.D.A.—See Danone; *Int'l*, pg. 1967
NUTRICIA S.R.L.—See Danone; *Int'l*, pg. 1967
NUTRICIA S.R.O.—See Danone; *Int'l*, pg. 1967
NUTRITIONAL PRODUCTS INTERNATIONAL INC.; *U.S. Private*, pg. 2974
NUZEE, INC.; *U.S. Public*, pg. 1557
NYWP ENTERPRISE LLC—See New Yung Wah Trading LLC; *U.S. Private*, pg. 2913
THE ODOM CORPORATION; *U.S. Private*, pg. 4088
OMNIABIOS S.R.L.—See Compagnie des Levures Lesaffre SA; *Int'l*, pg. 1739
ONETA COMPANY; *U.S. Private*, pg. 3026
OOO TECHNOLOGY POLIMERY—See Dohler GmbH; *Int'l*, pg. 2156
ORANGE PEEL ENTERPRISES, INC.; *U.S. Private*, pg. 3037
ORCHID ISLAND JUICE COMPANY; *U.S. Private*, pg. 3039
ORGANIZACION SAHUAYO, S.A.—See Grupo Corvi, S.A.B. de C.V.; *Int'l*, pg. 3125
ORIGINAL CRISPY PIZZA CRUST OF BOSTON CO. INC.; *U.S. Private*, pg. 3042
OROWEAT—See Grupo Bimbo, S.A.B. de C.V.; *Int'l*, pg. 3122
OY CONAXESS TRADE FINLAND AB—See Aurelius Equity Opportunities SE & Co. KGaA; *Int'l*, pg. 709
OZARKA WATER—See Metropoulos & Co.; *U.S. Private*, pg. 2690
OZARKA WATER—See One Rock Capital Partners, LLC; *U.S. Private*, pg. 3021
PAGO CROATIA D.O.O.—See Eckes AG; *Int'l*, pg. 2291
PAL-DO COMPANY INC.; *U.S. Private*, pg. 3076
PALOMAR MOUNTAIN PREMIUM SPRING WATER; *U.S. Private*, pg. 3082
P-AMERICAS, LLC—See PepsiCo, Inc.; *U.S. Public*, pg. 1669

N.A.I.C.S. INDEX

424490 — OTHER GROCERY AND R...

PANADIS, S.A. DE C.V.—See Compagnie des Levures Lesaffre SA; *Int'l*, pg. 1739
PANAMEX PACIFIC, INC; *U.S. Private*, pg. 3085
PANOS BRANDS LLC—See Hammond, Kennedy, Whitney & Company, Inc.; *U.S. Private*, pg. 1850
PARTNER IN PET FOOD SK S.R.O—See Cinven Limited; *Int'l*, pg. 1613
PASKERT DISTRIBUTING COMPANY; *U.S. Private*, pg. 3104
PEARLWATER MINERALQUELLEN AG—See Coop-Gruppe Genossenschaft; *Int'l*, pg. 1790
PEPE'S INC.; *U.S. Private*, pg. 3143
PEPSICO AMACOCO BEBIDAS DO BRASIL LTDA.—See PepsiCo, Inc.; *U.S. Public*, pg. 1669
PEPSICO FRANCE SNC—See PepsiCo, Inc.; *U.S. Public*, pg. 1671
PEPSI-COLA BOTTLING COMPANY OF ESTERVILLE INC.—See Pohlad Companies; *U.S. Private*, pg. 3220
PEPSI-COLA BOTTLING COMPANY OF FT. LAUDERDALE-PALM BEACH, LLC—See PepsiCo, Inc.; *U.S. Public*, pg. 1669
PEPSI-COLA BOTTLING CO OF ROXBORO, NC, INC.—See PepsiCo, Inc.; *U.S. Public*, pg. 1670
PEPSI-COLA COMPANY NEW HAVEN; *U.S. Private*, pg. 3145
PEPSI-COLA MANUFACTURING (IRELAND) UNLIMITED COMPANY—See PepsiCo, Inc.; *U.S. Public*, pg. 1669
PEPSI-COLA OF CORVALLIS, INC.—See PepsiCo, Inc.; *U.S. Public*, pg. 1669
PEPSI COLA OGDENSBURG BOTTLERS; *U.S. Private*, pg. 3145
PERFORMANCE FOOD GROUP, INC. - CUSTOMIZED DISTRIBUTION—See Performance Food Group Company; *U.S. Public*, pg. 1675
PETERS IMPORTS, INC.—See KeHE Distributors, LLC; *U.S. Private*, pg. 2273
PFG-THOMS PROESTLER COMPANY—See Performance Food Group Company; *U.S. Public*, pg. 1675
PHARMORE INGREDIENTS INC.; *U.S. Private*, pg. 3166
PINE STATE TRADING CO.; *U.S. Private*, pg. 3183
PIZZA KING INC.; *U.S. Private*, pg. 3193
PIZZA WHOLESALE LEXINGTON INC.; *U.S. Private*, pg. 3193
PJSC NADEZHDA—See Compagnie des Levures Lesaffre SA; *Int'l*, pg. 1739
PLUSPHARMA, INC.; *U.S. Private*, pg. 3215
POLAND SPRING BOTTLING—See Metropoulos & Co.; *U.S. Private*, pg. 2690
POLAND SPRING BOTTLING—See One Rock Capital Partners, LLC; *U.S. Private*, pg. 3021
POLAND SPRING CORPORATION—See Metropoulos & Co.; *U.S. Private*, pg. 2690
POLAND SPRING CORPORATION—See Metropoulos & Co.; *U.S. Private*, pg. 2690
POLAND SPRING CORPORATION—See One Rock Capital Partners, LLC; *U.S. Private*, pg. 3021
POLAND SPRING CORPORATION—See One Rock Capital Partners, LLC; *U.S. Private*, pg. 3021
POLYFORM PRODUCTS COMPANY, INC.—See CNL Strategic Capital Management LLC; *U.S. Private*, pg. 952
PONCE CARIBBEAN DISTRIBUTORS—See Able Sales Company, Inc.; *U.S. Private*, pg. 39
POST CONSUMER BRANDS, LLC—See Post Holdings, Inc.; *U.S. Public*, pg. 1704
POUYOUKAS FOODS (PROPRIETARY) LIMITED—See Famous Brands Limited; *Int'l*, pg. 2612
POWELL & MAHONEY LLC—See Fevertree Drinks plc; *Int'l*, pg. 2649
PRICKETTS DISTRIBUTING INC.; *U.S. Private*, pg. 3259
PRINCE OF PEACE ENTERPRISES; *U.S. Private*, pg. 3264
PRO A PRO DISTRIBUTION—See Colruyt Group N.V.; *Int'l*, pg. 1705
PROCESADORA DEL SUR S.A.—See ED&F Man Holdings Limited; *Int'l*, pg. 2303
P.S. INTERNATIONAL INC; *U.S. Private*, pg. 3061
P.T. ANEKA TUNA INDONESIA—See Hagoromo Foods Corporation; *Int'l*, pg. 3207
PT COCA-COLA DISTRIBUTION INDONESIA—See COCA-COLA EUROPACIFIC PARTNERS PLC; *Int'l*, pg. 1684
PT. E D & F MAN INDONESIA—See ED&F Man Holdings Limited; *Int'l*, pg. 2303
PT IMCD INDONESIA—See IMCD N.V.; *Int'l*, pg. 3622
P.T. VAN REES INDONESIA—See ACOMO N.V.; *Int'l*, pg. 108
PT VOLKOPI INDONESIA—See ED&F Man Holdings Limited; *Int'l*, pg. 2303
QUAKER OATS EUROPE, INC.—See PepsiCo, Inc.; *U.S. Public*, pg. 1671
QUAKER TRADING LIMITED—See PepsiCo, Inc.; *U.S. Public*, pg. 1671
QUALITY CUSTOM DISTRIBUTION - SUFFOLK—See Golden State Foods Corp.; *U.S. Private*, pg. 1733
QUALITY NATURALLY FOODS; *U.S. Private*, pg. 3320
QUENCHY CRUSTA SALES PTY LTD—See COCA-COLA EUROPACIFIC PARTNERS PLC; *Int'l*, pg. 1684
QUINCY PEPSI-COLA BOTTLING CO.; *U.S. Private*, pg. 3328

RAINFOREST DISTRIBUTION CORP; *U.S. Private*, pg. 3348
RAVENSWOOD INGREDIENTS PTY. LTD.—See BRENNTAG SE; *Int'l*, pg. 1149
REFRESHMENT PRODUCT SERVICES, INC.—See The Coca-Cola Company; *U.S. Public*, pg. 2065
REFRESHMENT SERVICES INC.; *U.S. Private*, pg. 3384
REFRESH WATERS PTY LTD.—See Eneco Refresh Limited; *Int'l*, pg. 2411
REFRESH WATERS QUEENSLAND PTY LTD.—See Eneco Refresh Limited; *Int'l*, pg. 2411
RESTAURANT CONCEPTS LLC—See Yum! Brands, Inc.; *U.S. Public*, pg. 2400
R. HIRT JR. CO.; *U.S. Private*, pg. 3333
THE RICE COMPANY OF FIJI LIMITED—See Flour Mills of Fiji Limited; *Int'l*, pg. 2708
RIVER KWAI INTERNATIONAL FOOD INDUSTRY COMPANY LIMITED—See Agripure Holdings Company Limited; *Int'l*, pg. 218
ROBERT ORR-SYSCO FOOD SERVICES, LLC—See Sysco Corporation; *U.S. Public*, pg. 1975
ROCKMAN COMPANY (U.S.A.), INC.; *U.S. Private*, pg. 3467
ROMAN MEAL COMPANY; *U.S. Private*, pg. 3476
RON-SON FOODS INC.; *U.S. Private*, pg. 3477
ROSE PARTNERS LP; *U.S. Private*, pg. 3481
ROTHSTEIN CORP.; *U.S. Private*, pg. 3487
ROUNDY'S SUPERMARKETS INC.—See The Kroger Co.; *U.S. Public*, pg. 2109
ROXY TRADING INC.; *U.S. Private*, pg. 3490
ROYAL COFFEE INC.; *U.S. Private*, pg. 3491
ROYBALT INGREDIENTS S.A. DE C.V—See BayWa AG; *Int'l*, pg. 919
ROYCO INTERNATIONAL INC.; *U.S. Private*, pg. 3494
RYAN TRADING CORP.; *U.S. Private*, pg. 3510
SAF DJAZAIR, SPA—See Compagnie des Levures Lesaffre SA; *Int'l*, pg. 1739
SAF DO BRASIL LTDA—See Compagnie des Levures Lesaffre SA; *Int'l*, pg. 1739
SAF IVOIRE SARL—See Compagnie des Levures Lesaffre SA; *Int'l*, pg. 1739
SALES FORCE WON LTD.; *U.S. Private*, pg. 3532
SAN FRANCISCO SALT COMPANY—See Wells Fargo & Company; *U.S. Public*, pg. 2344
SASKCAN HORIZON TRADING INC.—See AGT Food and Ingredients Inc.; *Int'l*, pg. 221
SAVONA FOODS, INC.; *U.S. Private*, pg. 3557
SCHWEBEL BAKING CO. OF PENNSYLVANIA INC.—See Schwebel Baking Co. Inc.; *U.S. Private*, pg. 3572
SCOBEE FOODS INCORPORATED; *U.S. Private*, pg. 3575
S. & D. COFFEE, INC.—See Westrock Coffee Company; *U.S. Public*, pg. 2361
SEABOARD ENERGIAS RENOVABLES Y ALIMENTOS S.R.L.—See Seaboard Corporation; *U.S. Public*, pg. 1851
SEMIFREDDI'S, INC.; *U.S. Private*, pg. 3604
SEMOULERIE DE BELLEVUE—See Danone; *Int'l*, pg. 1968
SENSIENT FLAVORS & FRAGRANCES SAS—See Sensient Technologies Corporation; *U.S. Public*, pg. 1867
SEOUL SHIK POOM INC.; *U.S. Private*, pg. 3611
SFERA S.P.A.—See Cremonini S.p.A.; *Int'l*, pg. 1838
SHAMROCK FOODS - NEW MEXICO FOODS DIVISION—See Shamrock Foods Company; *U.S. Private*, pg. 3624
SHANGHAI CHRISTINE FOODSTUFF CO., LTD.—See Christine International Holdings Limited; *Int'l*, pg. 1587
SIMBA QUIX SWAZILAND (PTY) LIMITED—See PepsiCo, Inc.; *U.S. Public*, pg. 1672
SIMON H. STEINER, HOPFEN, GMBH—See S.S. Steiner Inc.; *U.S. Private*, pg. 3518
SIMS TRADING COMPANY LTD.—See CITIC Group Corporation; *Int'l*, pg. 1621
SIOUX HONEY ASSOCIATION; *U.S. Private*, pg. 3671
SKOR WHOLESALE MARKETPLACE—See Colabor Group Inc.; *Int'l*, pg. 1697
SOBEYS INC.—See Empire Company Limited; *Int'l*, pg. 2387
SOBEYS QUEBEC DIVISION—See Empire Company Limited; *Int'l*, pg. 2387
SOLID GOLD PET, LLC—See Health and Happiness (H&H) International Holdings Limited; *Int'l*, pg. 3303
SOLUCIOUS S.A.—See Colruyt Group N.V.; *Int'l*, pg. 1705
SONAC ALMERE BV—See Darling Ingredients Inc.; *U.S. Public*, pg. 634
SONAC AUSTRALIA PTY, LTD—See Darling Ingredients Inc.; *U.S. Public*, pg. 634
SOUFFLET BIOTECHNOLOGIES SAS—See Etablissements J. Soufflet; *Int'l*, pg. 2519
SOUPMAN, INC.; *U.S. Public*, pg. 1910
SOUSSANA S.A.—See Danish Crown AmbA; *Int'l*, pg. 1964
SOUTHWEST BEVERAGE CO. INC.—See Mockler Beverage Co. LP; *U.S. Private*, pg. 2759
STAR FINE FOODS-BORGES USA—See Aceites Borges Pont, S.A.; *Int'l*, pg. 95
STAR MARKETING LTD.—See Health and Plant Protein Group Limited; *Int'l*, pg. 3303
STEINER HOPS LIMITED—See S.S. Steiner Inc.; *U.S. Private*, pg. 3518

STEMSATION USA, INC.; *U.S. Public*, pg. 1945
STERLING CORPORATION; *U.S. Private*, pg. 3805
STOKERS TENDEREX FARMS INC.; *U.S. Private*, pg. 3816
STROHMEYER & ARPE COMPANY; *U.S. Private*, pg. 3840
STROM PRODUCTS LTD.; *U.S. Private*, pg. 3840
SUKARI INVESTMENT COMPANY LIMITED—See Alteo Limited; *Int'l*, pg. 391
SUMMIT FOOD SERVICE DISTRIBUTORS, INC.—See Flanagan Foodservice, Inc.; *Int'l*, pg. 2698
SUN FAVORITE CO., LTD.—See Cheng Loong Corp.; *Int'l*, pg. 1466
SUNLAND VOLONTE AGENCY SDN. BHD.—See EA Holdings Berhad; *Int'l*, pg. 2261
SUN-MAID GROWERS OF CALIFORNIA; *U.S. Private*, pg. 3864
SURLY BREWING CO.; *U.S. Private*, pg. 3885
SUTTON CORPORATION; *U.S. Private*, pg. 3887
SWEET CORN PRODUCTS COMPANY LIMITED—See Agripure Holdings Company Limited; *Int'l*, pg. 218
SWISS CHALET FINE FOODS INC.; *U.S. Private*, pg. 3894
THE SYGMA NETWORK OF PENNSYLVANIA—See Sysco Corporation; *U.S. Public*, pg. 1977
SYNERGY AROMAS LTDA—See Carbery Group; *Int'l*, pg. 1320
SYNERGY (CORBY) LTD—See Carbery Group; *Int'l*, pg. 1320
SYNERGY FLAVORS (NY) COMPANY, LLC—See Carbery Group; *Int'l*, pg. 1320
SYNERGY FLAVORS (OH), LLC—See Carbery Group; *Int'l*, pg. 1320
SYNERGY FLAVOURS (THAILAND) LTD—See Carbery Group; *Int'l*, pg. 1320
SYNERGY (HIGH WYCOMBE) LTD—See Carbery Group; *Int'l*, pg. 1320
SYNERGY IRELAND—See Carbery Group; *Int'l*, pg. 1320
SYSCO ALBANY, LLC—See Sysco Corporation; *U.S. Public*, pg. 1975
SYSCO ARIZONA, INC.—See Sysco Corporation; *U.S. Public*, pg. 1975
SYSCO ARKANSAS—See Sysco Corporation; *U.S. Public*, pg. 1975
SYSCO ATLANTA, LLC—See Sysco Corporation; *U.S. Public*, pg. 1975
SYSCO AUSTIN, INC.—See Sysco Corporation; *U.S. Public*, pg. 1975
SYSCO BALTIMORE, LLC—See Sysco Corporation; *U.S. Public*, pg. 1975
SYSCO BARABOO, LLC—See Sysco Corporation; *U.S. Public*, pg. 1975
SYSCO CALGARY—See Sysco Corporation; *U.S. Public*, pg. 1975
SYSCO CANADA, INC.—See Sysco Corporation; *U.S. Public*, pg. 1975
SYSCO CENTRAL CALIFORNIA, INC.—See Sysco Corporation; *U.S. Public*, pg. 1975
SYSCO CENTRAL FLORIDA, INC.—See Sysco Corporation; *U.S. Public*, pg. 1975
SYSCO CENTRAL ONTARIO, INC.—See Sysco Corporation; *U.S. Public*, pg. 1975
SYSCO CENTRAL PENNSYLVANIA, LLC—See Sysco Corporation; *U.S. Public*, pg. 1975
SYSCO CENTRAL TEXAS, INC.—See Sysco Corporation; *U.S. Public*, pg. 1975
SYSCO CHARLOTTE, LLC—See Sysco Corporation; *U.S. Public*, pg. 1975
SYSCO CINCINNATI, LLC—See Sysco Corporation; *U.S. Public*, pg. 1975
SYSCO CLEVELAND, INC.—See Sysco Corporation; *U.S. Public*, pg. 1975
SYSCO COLUMBIA, LLC—See Sysco Corporation; *U.S. Public*, pg. 1975
SYSCO CONNECTICUT, LLC—See Sysco Corporation; *U.S. Public*, pg. 1975
SYSCO DALLAS, INC.—See Sysco Corporation; *U.S. Public*, pg. 1976
SYSCO DENVER, INC.—See Sysco Corporation; *U.S. Public*, pg. 1976
SYSCO DETROIT, LLC—See Sysco Corporation; *U.S. Public*, pg. 1976
SYSCO EASTERN MARYLAND, LLC—See Sysco Corporation; *U.S. Public*, pg. 1976
SYSCO EASTERN WISCONSIN, LLC—See Sysco Corporation; *U.S. Public*, pg. 1976
SYSCO GRAND RAPIDS, LLC—See Sysco Corporation; *U.S. Public*, pg. 1976
SYSCO GUEST SUPPLY, LLC - HAWAII DISTRIBUTION CENTER—See Sysco Corporation; *U.S. Public*, pg. 1976
SYSCO HAMPTON ROADS, INC.—See Sysco Corporation; *U.S. Public*, pg. 1976
SYSCO HAWAII, INC.—See Sysco Corporation; *U.S. Public*, pg. 1976
SYSCO HOUSTON, INC.—See Sysco Corporation; *U.S. Public*, pg. 1976
SYSCO IDAHO, INC.—See Sysco Corporation; *U.S. Public*, pg. 1976
SYSCO INDIANAPOLIS, LLC—See Sysco Corporation; *U.S. Public*, pg. 1976

424490 — OTHER GROCERY AND R...

SYSCO INTERMOUNTAIN, INC.—See Sysco Corporation; *U.S. Public*, pg. 1976
SYSCO IOWA, INC.—See Sysco Corporation; *U.S. Public*, pg. 1976
SYSCO JACKSONVILLE, INC.—See Sysco Corporation; *U.S. Public*, pg. 1976
SYSCO KANSAS CITY, INC.—See Sysco Corporation; *U.S. Public*, pg. 1976
SYSCO KELOWNA, LTD.—See Sysco Corporation; *U.S. Public*, pg. 1976
SYSCO LAS VEGAS, INC.—See Sysco Corporation; *U.S. Public*, pg. 1976
SYSCO LINCOLN TRANSPORTATION COMPANY, INC.—See Sysco Corporation; *U.S. Public*, pg. 1976
SYSCO LOUISVILLE, INC.—See Sysco Corporation; *U.S. Public*, pg. 1976
SYSCO MEMPHIS, LLC—See Sysco Corporation; *U.S. Public*, pg. 1976
SYSCO METRO NEW YORK, LLC—See Sysco Corporation; *U.S. Public*, pg. 1976
SYSCO MINNESOTA, INC.—See Sysco Corporation; *U.S. Public*, pg. 1976
SYSCO MONTANA, INC.—See Sysco Corporation; *U.S. Public*, pg. 1976
SYSCO NEW MEXICO, LLC—See Sysco Corporation; *U.S. Public*, pg. 1976
SYSCO NEW ORLEANS, LLC—See Sysco Corporation; *U.S. Public*, pg. 1976
SYSCO NORTHERN NEW ENGLAND, INC.—See Sysco Corporation; *U.S. Public*, pg. 1977
SYSCO OKLAHOMA—See Sysco Corporation; *U.S. Public*, pg. 1977
SYSCO PHILADELPHIA, LLC—See Sysco Corporation; *U.S. Public*, pg. 1977
SYSCO PITTSBURGH, LLC—See Sysco Corporation; *U.S. Public*, pg. 1977
SYSCO PORTLAND, INC.—See Sysco Corporation; *U.S. Public*, pg. 1977
SYSCO QUEBEC—See Sysco Corporation; *U.S. Public*, pg. 1975
SYSCO RALEIGH, LLC—See Sysco Corporation; *U.S. Public*, pg. 1977
SYSCO SACRAMENTO, INC.—See Sysco Corporation; *U.S. Public*, pg. 1977
SYSCO SOUTHEAST FLORIDA, LLC—See Sysco Corporation; *U.S. Public*, pg. 1977
SYSCO SOUTH FLORIDA, INC.—See Sysco Corporation; *U.S. Public*, pg. 1977
SYSCO SPOKANE, INC.—See Sysco Corporation; *U.S. Public*, pg. 1977
SYSCO ST. LOUIS, LLC—See Sysco Corporation; *U.S. Public*, pg. 1977
SYSCO SYRACUSE, LLC—See Sysco Corporation; *U.S. Public*, pg. 1977
SYSCO TORONTO—See Sysco Corporation; *U.S. Public*, pg. 1975
SYSCO VANCOUVER—See Sysco Corporation; *U.S. Public*, pg. 1975
SYSCO VENTURA, INC.—See Sysco Corporation; *U.S. Public*, pg. 1977
SYSCO VIRGINIA, LLC—See Sysco Corporation; *U.S. Public*, pg. 1977
TAIWAN DAIOHS CO., LTD.—See Daiohs Corporation; *Int'l*, pg. 1940
TAMA TRADING COMPANY; *U.S. Private*, pg. 3927
TAURA NATURAL INGREDIENTS (NORTH AMERICA) INC.—See International Flavors & Fragrances Inc; *U.S. Public*, pg. 1154
TAURA NATURAL INGREDIENTS NV—See International Flavors & Fragrances Inc.; *U.S. Public*, pg. 1154
TAYLOR HOPKINSON CORPORATION—See Brunel International N.V.; *Int'l*, pg. 1200
TAYLOR HOPKINSON LIMITED—See Brunel International N.V.; *Int'l*, pg. 1200
TAYLOR WINCH (COFFEE) LIMITED—See ED&F Man Holdings Limited; *Int'l*, pg. 2303
TAYLOR WINCH (TANZANIA) LIMITED—See ED&F Man Holdings Limited; *Int'l*, pg. 2303
TCHO VENTURES, INC.—See Ezaki Glico Co., Ltd.; *Int'l*, pg. 2593
TDC PETS, LLC—See Summit Partners, L.P.; *U.S. Private*, pg. 3855
TEE PEE OLIVES, INC./ ITALICA IMPORTS; *U.S. Private*, pg. 3957
TEXAS FARM PRODUCTS COMPANY; *U.S. Private*, pg. 3975
THAI MARBLE CORP., LTD.—See Golden Lime Public Company Limited; *Int'l*, pg. 3030
THERAVALUES CORPORATION—See Handok Inc.; *Int'l*, pg. 3243
TIANJIN DEFENG FOODS CO., LTD.—See Daesang Corporation; *Int'l*, pg. 1909
TIANJIN HEJIA XINGTAI CATERING MANAGEMENT COMPANY LIMITED—See Hop Hing Group Holdings Limited; *Int'l*, pg. 3473
TIZER LIMITED—See A.G. Barr plc; *Int'l*, pg. 24
TLD ACQUISITION CO. LLC; *U.S. Private*, pg. 4178
TOP LABEL INTERNATIONAL LIMITED—See Continental Holdings Limited; *Int'l*, pg. 1784
TORN & GLASSER INC.; *U.S. Private*, pg. 4189
TORTILLERIA ATOTONILCO INC.; *U.S. Private*, pg. 4190
TOSHOKU AMERICA, INC.—See Cargill, Inc.; *U.S. Private*, pg. 760
TOVANO B.V.—See ACOMO N.V.; *Int'l*, pg. 108
TRI-STATE BAKING CO.—See Affiliated Foods, Inc.; *U.S. Private*, pg. 122
TROPICAL NUT & FRUIT CO; *U.S. Private*, pg. 4242
TURANO BAKING COMPANY; *U.S. Private*, pg. 4258
TYLER MOUNTAIN WATER COMPANY; *U.S. Private*, pg. 4268
UNCLE WALLY'S LLC; *U.S. Private*, pg. 4279
UNFI CANADA, INC.—See United Natural Foods, Inc.; *U.S. Public*, pg. 2233
UNITED NATURAL FOODS, INC.; *U.S. Public*, pg. 2231
UNITED NATURAL FOODS, INC.—See United Natural Foods, Inc.; *U.S. Public*, pg. 2233
UNITED NATURAL FOODS, INC.—See United Natural Foods, Inc.; *U.S. Public*, pg. 2233
UNITED NATURAL FOODS, INC.—See United Natural Foods, Inc.; *U.S. Public*, pg. 2233
UNITED NATURAL FOODS, INC.—See United Natural Foods, Inc.; *U.S. Public*, pg. 2233
UNITED NATURAL TRADING, LLC—See United Natural Foods, Inc.; *U.S. Public*, pg. 2233
UNITED PULSE TRADING INC.—See AGT Food and Ingredients Inc.; *Int'l*, pg. 221
UNITRUST INDUSTRIAL CORP.; *U.S. Private*, pg. 4302
UNIVERSAL HEMP, LLC—See Acreage Holdings, Inc.; *U.S. Public*, pg. 36
US FOODS, INC.—See US Foods Holding Corp.; *U.S. Public*, pg. 2266
VALLEY BAKERS COOP ASSOCIATION; *U.S. Private*, pg. 4332
VALLEY FOOD SERVICES, LLC; *U.S. Private*, pg. 4333
VAN REES LLC—See ACOMO N.V.; *Int'l*, pg. 108
VAN REES NORTH AMERICA INC—See ACOMO N.V.; *Int'l*, pg. 108
VAN REES UK LTD.—See ACOMO N.V.; *Int'l*, pg. 108
VARUN BEVERAGES MOROCCO S.A.—See Affirma Capital Limited; *Int'l*, pg. 188
VARUN BEVERAGES (NEPAL) PRIVATE LIMITED—See Affirma Capital Limited; *Int'l*, pg. 188
VINO-KLUB.CZ, S. R. O.—See AMBRA S.A.; *Int'l*, pg. 415
VITA BARENTZ CO. LTD.—See Cinven Limited; *Int'l*, pg. 1611
VITA PI S.A.—See Atlantic Super Market S.A.; *Int'l*, pg. 675
VITA SPECIALTY FOODS—See SVB Food & Beverage Co.; *U.S. Private*, pg. 3888
VOLCAFE IBERIA S.A.—See ED&F Man Holdings Limited; *Int'l*, pg. 2303
VOLCAFE LIMITED—See ED&F Man Holdings Limited; *Int'l*, pg. 2303
VOLCAFE LTDA—See ED&F Man Holdings Limited; *Int'l*, pg. 2303
VOLCAFE SPECIALTY COFFEE CORP.—See ED&F Man Holdings Limited; *Int'l*, pg. 2303
VOLCAFE USA LLC—See ED&F Man Holdings Limited; *Int'l*, pg. 2303
WAELTI-SCHOENFELD S.A—See ED&F Man Holdings Limited; *Int'l*, pg. 2303
WALDEN FARMS CANADA—See Hammond, Kennedy, Whitney & Company, Inc.; *U.S. Private*, pg. 1850
WANDERPORT CORPORATION; *U.S. Private*, pg. 2325
WATER COOLERS (SCOTLAND) LIMITED—See Primo Water Corporation; *U.S. Public*, pg. 1718
WATSON SYSCO FOOD SERVICES, INC.—See Sysco Corporation; *U.S. Public*, pg. 1977
WEINSTEIN BEVERAGE CO. INC.; *U.S. Private*, pg. 4472
WELLTEK CORPORATION; *U.S. Private*, pg. 4472
WESTBRAE NATURAL FOODS, INC.—See The Hain Celestial Group, Inc.; *U.S. Public*, pg. 2087
WESTBRAE NATURAL, INC.—See The Hain Celestial Group, Inc.; *U.S. Public*, pg. 2087
WESTERN WYOMING BEVERAGES INC.; *U.S. Private*, pg. 4498
WESTIN FOODS, INC.; *U.S. Private*, pg. 4498
WET PLANET BEVERAGE CO.; *U.S. Private*, pg. 4502
WHITE ROCK PRODUCTS CORP.; *U.S. Private*, pg. 4509
WHOLE HARVEST FOODS, LLC—See Bunge Limited; *U.S. Public*, pg. 412
WIBERG CORPORATION OF CALIFORNIA—See International Flavors & Fragrances Inc.; *U.S. Public*, pg. 1154
WILD HARVEST LIMITED—See Sysco Corporation; *U.S. Public*, pg. 1973
WIMM-BILL-DANN JSC—See PepsiCo, Inc.; *U.S. Public*, pg. 1672
WINDSTONE FARMS, LLC—See Algood Food Company; *U.S. Private*, pg. 166
WINEYASAN, INC.—See GMO Internet Group, Inc.; *Int'l*, pg. 3014
W. NEWELL & CO., LLC—See United Natural Foods, Inc.; *U.S. Public*, pg. 2232
WOLFSON CASING CORP.; *U.S. Private*, pg. 4554
WORLD FINER FOODS, INC.; *U.S. Private*, pg. 4565
WORLDWIDE PRODUCE, INC.—See La Preferida, Inc.; *U.S. Private*, pg. 2369
WP BEVERAGES, LLC; *U.S. Private*, pg. 4571
YBBSTALER FRUIT POLSKA SP. Z O.O—See AGRANA Beteiligungs-AG; *Int'l*, pg. 214
YBBSTALER FRUIT POLSKA SP. Z O.O.—See BayWa AG; *Int'l*, pg. 919
YEO HIAP SENG (GUANGZHOU) FOOD & BEVERAGES LTD—See Far East Organization Pte. Ltd.; *Int'l*, pg. 2617
YEO HIAP SENG (MALAYSIA) BERHAD—See Far East Organization Pte. Ltd.; *Int'l*, pg. 2617
YEO HIAP SENG (SARAWAK) SDN BHD—See Far East Organization Pte. Ltd.; *Int'l*, pg. 2617
YHS HONG KONG (2000) PTE LIMITED—See Far East Organization Pte. Ltd.; *Int'l*, pg. 2617
YHS TRADING (USA) INC.—See Far East Organization Pte. Ltd.; *Int'l*, pg. 2617
YICHANG CHIA TAI CO., LTD.—See Charoen Pokphand Foods Public Company Limited; *Int'l*, pg. 1453
YILDIZ GRANINI MEYVE SUYU SANAYI VE TICARET A.S.—See Eckes AG; *Int'l*, pg. 2291
YOGEN FRUZ CANADA, INC.—See ABR Holdings, Ltd.; *Int'l*, pg. 67
YONEKAWA SUISAN CORPORATION—See Daisyo Corporation; *Int'l*, pg. 1943
ZANONTIAN & SONS INC.; *U.S. Private*, pg. 4598
ZATEC HOP COMPANY—See S.S. Steiner Inc.; *U.S. Private*, pg. 3518
ZB IMPORTING, INC.—See Peak Rock Capital LLC; *U.S. Private*, pg. 3124
ZHENA'S GYPSY TEA; *U.S. Private*, pg. 4603
ZIJA INTERNATIONAL, INC.—See Isagenix International, LLC; *U.S. Private*, pg. 2143
ZOUP! SPECIALTY PRODUCTS, LLC; *U.S. Private*, pg. 4609
ZURVITA HOLDINGS, INC.; *U.S. Public*, pg. 2414
ZYMES LESAFFRE S.A.—See Compagnie des Levures Lesaffre SA; *Int'l*, pg. 1739

424510 — GRAIN AND FIELD BEAN MERCHANT WHOLESALERS

21ST CENTURY COOPERATIVE CO.; *U.S. Private*, pg. 5
ADM AGRI-INDUSTRIES COMPANY—See Archer-Daniels-Midland Company; *U.S. Public*, pg. 184
ADM-COLLINGWOOD GRAIN—See Archer-Daniels-Midland Company; *U.S. Public*, pg. 181
ADM EDIBLE BEAN SPECIALTIES, INC.—See Archer-Daniels-Midland Company; *U.S. Public*, pg. 181
ADM GRAIN CO. - MENDOTA—See Archer-Daniels-Midland Company; *U.S. Public*, pg. 181
ADM GRAIN COMPANY—See Archer-Daniels-Midland Company; *U.S. Public*, pg. 181
ADM GRAIN COMPANY—See Archer-Daniels-Midland Company; *U.S. Public*, pg. 182
ADM GRAIN CO—See Archer-Daniels-Midland Company; *U.S. Public*, pg. 181
ADM GRAIN RIVER SYSTEM, INC.—See Archer-Daniels-Midland Company; *U.S. Public*, pg. 182
ADM GRAIN RIVER SYSTEM, INC.—See Archer-Daniels-Midland Company; *U.S. Public*, pg. 182
ADM MILLING CO.—See Archer-Daniels-Midland Company; *U.S. Public*, pg. 182
AGCO INC.; *U.S. Private*, pg. 126
AGCO OF SPEARMAN INC.; *U.S. Private*, pg. 126
AG ENVIRONMENTAL PRODUCTS, LLC—See Ag Processing Inc.; *U.S. Private*, pg. 125
AG FIRST FARMERS COOPERATIVE; *U.S. Private*, pg. 124
AG LAND CO-OP INC.; *U.S. Private*, pg. 124
AGMARK INTERMODAL SYSTEMS, INC.; *U.S. Private*, pg. 128
AG PARTNERS COOPERATIVE INC.; *U.S. Private*, pg. 124
AG PARTNERS L.L.C.—See Albert City Elevator, a Cooperative; *U.S. Private*, pg. 152
AG PLUS INC.; *U.S. Private*, pg. 124
AG PROCESSING INC.; *U.S. Private*, pg. 125
AGRIFARM INDUSTRIES LLC; *U.S. Private*, pg. 129
AGRI NORTHWEST—See Ag Reserves Inc; *U.S. Private*, pg. 125
AGRI PRODUCERS INC.; *U.S. Private*, pg. 129
AGRI SERVICES BRUNSWICK LLC; *U.S. Private*, pg. 129
AGROSALGA, S.L.; *Int'l*, pg. 220
AG VALLEY COOPERATIVE NON-STOCK; *U.S. Private*, pg. 125
AKRON SERVICES INC.; *U.S. Private*, pg. 146
ALABAMA FARMERS COOPERATIVE, INC.; *U.S. Private*, pg. 148
ALBERT CITY ELEVATOR, A COOPERATIVE; *U.S. Private*, pg. 152
ALL-AMERICAN CO-OP; *U.S. Private*, pg. 173
ALLIANCE GRAIN COMPANY INC.; *U.S. Private*, pg. 182
ALL POINTS COOPERATIVE; *U.S. Private*, pg. 171
ANCONA GRAIN INC.; *U.S. Private*, pg. 274
ANDALE FARMERS COOPERATIVE CO.; *U.S. Private*, pg. 275
THE ANDERSONS, INC. - AUBURN GRAIN—See The Andersons Incorporated; *U.S. Public*, pg. 2035
ANTHONY FARMERS COOP ELEVATOR CO.; *U.S. Private*, pg. 287
ARCHER DANIELS MIDLAND CO. (ADM)—See Archer-

Daniels-Midland Company; *U.S. Public*, pg. 184
ARCHER DANIELS MIDLAND CO.—See Archer-Daniels-Midland Company; *U.S. Public*, pg. 183
ARCHER DANIELS MIDLAND CO.—See Archer-Daniels-Midland Company; *U.S. Public*, pg. 183
ARCHER DANIELS MIDLAND CO.—See Archer-Daniels-Midland Company; *U.S. Public*, pg. 183
ARCHER DANIELS MIDLAND CO.—See Archer-Daniels-Midland Company; *U.S. Public*, pg. 183
ARCHER DANIELS MIDLAND CO.—See Archer-Daniels-Midland Company; *U.S. Public*, pg. 183
ARCHER DANIELS MIDLAND CO.—See Archer-Daniels-Midland Company; *U.S. Public*, pg. 184
ARCHER DANIELS MIDLAND CO.—See Archer-Daniels-Midland Company; *U.S. Public*, pg. 184
ARIZONA GRAINS INC.; *U.S. Private*, pg. 324
ARIZONA GRAIN VALLEY SEED—See Arizona Grains Inc.; *U.S. Private*, pg. 324
ARTHUR COMPANIES INC.; *U.S. Private*, pg. 341
ASPINWALL COOPERATIVE CO.; *U.S. Private*, pg. 352
ASSUMPTION COOPERATIVE GRAIN COMPANY; *U.S. Private*, pg. 359
ATTEBURY GRAIN, LLC; *U.S. Private*, pg. 383
AURORA COOPERATIVE; *U.S. Private*, pg. 394
AUST & HACHMANN E.K.; *Int'l*, pg. 716
BACIL PHARMA LIMITED; *Int'l*, pg. 795
BALTIC LOGISTIC HOLDING B.V.—See BayWa AG; *Int'l*, pg. 915
BARKLEY SEED INC.; *U.S. Private*, pg. 475
BARTLETT & COMPANY; *U.S. Private*, pg. 483
BATTLE CREEK FARMERS COOP; *U.S. Private*, pg. 489
BEACHNER GRAIN INC.; *U.S. Private*, pg. 503
BEATTIE FARMERS UNION COOPERATIVE ASSOCIATION; *U.S. Private*, pg. 507
BEE AGRICULTURAL COMPANY INC.; *U.S. Private*, pg. 512
BERTHOLD FARMERS ELEVATOR CO.; *U.S. Private*, pg. 539
BLACKWELL CO-OP; *U.S. Private*, pg. 577
BLANCHARD VALLEY FARMERS CO-OP; *U.S. Private*, pg. 579
BROOKLYN ELEVATOR INC.; *U.S. Private*, pg. 663
BRUBAKER GRAIN & CHEMICAL INC.; *U.S. Private*, pg. 670
BRUNING GRAIN & FEED CO. INC.; *U.S. Private*, pg. 672
BUNGE AGRIBUSINESS AUSTRALIA PTY. LTD.—See Bunge Limited; *U.S. Public*, pg. 411
BUNGE AGRIBUSINESS SINGAPORE PTE. LTD.—See Bunge Limited; *U.S. Public*, pg. 411
BUNGE AGRITRADE S.A.—See Bunge Limited; *U.S. Public*, pg. 411
BUNGE COLOMBIA S.A.S.—See Bunge Limited; *U.S. Public*, pg. 411
BUNGE COMERCIALIZADORA DE ENERGIA LTDA.—See Bunge Limited; *U.S. Public*, pg. 411
BUNGE CORPORATION—See Bunge Limited; *U.S. Public*, pg. 411
BUNGE DEUTSCHLAND G.M.B.H.—See Bunge Limited; *U.S. Public*, pg. 411
BUNGE ETGO L.P.—See Bunge Limited; *U.S. Public*, pg. 411
BUNGE FINANCE B.V.—See Bunge Limited; *U.S. Public*, pg. 411
BUNGE GLOBAL MARKETS, INC.—See Bunge Limited; *U.S. Public*, pg. 411
BUNGE HOLDINGS FRANCE S.A.S.—See Bunge Limited; *U.S. Public*, pg. 411
BUNGE IBERICA PORTUGAL, S.A.—See Bunge Limited; *U.S. Public*, pg. 411
BUNGE INVESTMENT IBERICA S.L.U.—See Bunge Limited; *U.S. Public*, pg. 411
BUNGE ITALIA S.P.A.—See Bunge Limited; *U.S. Public*, pg. 411
BUNGE MILLING, INC.—See Bunge Limited; *U.S. Public*, pg. 411
BUNGE - MORRISTOWN GRAIN COMPANY—See Bunge Limited; *U.S. Public*, pg. 411
BUNGE NORTH AMERICA, INC.—See Bunge Limited; *U.S. Public*, pg. 411
BUNGE S.A.—See Bunge Limited; *U.S. Public*, pg. 411
BUNGE (THAILAND) LTD.—See Bunge Limited; *U.S. Public*, pg. 411
CAIRO COOPERATIVE EQUITY EXCHANGE; *U.S. Private*, pg. 714
CARGILL AGHORIZONS—See Cargill, Inc.; *U.S. Private*, pg. 755
CARGILL AG HORIZONS—See Cargill, Inc.; *U.S. Private*, pg. 755
CARGILL AG HORIZONS—See Cargill, Inc.; *U.S. Private*, pg. 757
CARGILL AG HORIZONS—See Cargill, Inc.; *U.S. Private*, pg. 757
CARGILL ANIMAL NUTRITION—See Cargill, Inc.; *U.S. Private*, pg. 755
CARGILL ANIMAL NUTRITION—See Cargill, Inc.; *U.S. Private*, pg. 755
CARGILL ANIMAL NUTRITION—See Cargill, Inc.; *U.S. Private*, pg. 755

CARGILL, INC.; *U.S. Private*, pg. 754
CARGILL INC.—See Cargill, Inc.; *U.S. Private*, pg. 756
CARGILL INC.—See Cargill, Inc.; *U.S. Private*, pg. 756
CARGILL INC.—See Cargill, Inc.; *U.S. Private*, pg. 756
CARGILL INC.—See Cargill, Inc.; *U.S. Private*, pg. 756
CARGILL INC.—See Cargill, Inc.; *U.S. Private*, pg. 756
CARGILL INC.—See Cargill, Inc.; *U.S. Private*, pg. 756
CARGILL INC.—See Cargill, Inc.; *U.S. Private*, pg. 757
CARGILL INC.—See Cargill, Inc.; *U.S. Private*, pg. 757
CARGILL INC.—See Cargill, Inc.; *U.S. Private*, pg. 757
CARGILL INC.—See Cargill, Inc.; *U.S. Private*, pg. 757
CARGILL INC.—See Cargill, Inc.; *U.S. Private*, pg. 757
CARGILL INC.—See Cargill, Inc.; *U.S. Private*, pg. 757
CARGILL INC.—See Cargill, Inc.; *U.S. Private*, pg. 757
CARGILL LIMITED—See Cargill, Inc.; *U.S. Private*, pg. 757
CARGILL LIMITED—See Cargill, Inc.; *U.S. Private*, pg. 757
CARGILL LIMITED—See Cargill, Inc.; *U.S. Private*, pg. 757
CARGILL LIMITED—See Cargill, Inc.; *U.S. Private*, pg. 758
CARGILL—See Cargill, Inc.; *U.S. Private*, pg. 754
CEFETRA B.V.—See BayWa AG; *Int'l*, pg. 917
CEFETRA FEED SERVICE B.V.—See BayWa AG; *Int'l*, pg. 917
CENTRAL MONTANA COOPERATIVE—See CHS INC.; *U.S. Public*, pg. 492
CENTRAL OHIO FARMERS COOPERATIVE; *U.S. Private*, pg. 824
CENTRAL STATES ENTERPRISES, INC.; *U.S. Private*, pg. 825
CENTRAL WASHINGTON GRAIN GROWERS, INC.; *U.S. Private*, pg. 826
CEREAL BYPRODUCTS COMPANY INC.; *U.S. Private*, pg. 840
CEREALCOM SA; *Int'l*, pg. 1421
CERESCO MARKETING INC.—See Ceresco; *Int'l*, pg. 1422
CERES COMMODITIES, LLC—See The Redwood Group, LLC; *U.S. Private*, pg. 4103
CERES SOLUTIONS - TERRE HAUTE—See Ceres Solutions, LLP; *U.S. Private*, pg. 841
CERESTAR SAS—See Cargill, Inc.; *U.S. Private*, pg. 756
C&F FOODS INC.; *U.S. Private*, pg. 703
CHAFFEE LYNCHBURG FARMERS ELEVATOR—See Maple River Grain & Agronomy, LLC.; *U.S. Private*, pg. 2568
CHEBANSE CROP SERVICE INC.; *U.S. Private*, pg. 868
CHS DE PARAGUAY SRL—See CHS INC.; *U.S. Public*, pg. 491
CHS DO BRASIL LTDA.—See CHS INC.; *U.S. Public*, pg. 492
CHS ELBURN—See CHS INC.; *U.S. Public*, pg. 491
CHS-ELKTON—See CHS INC.; *U.S. Public*, pg. 492
CHS-HOLDREGE, INC.—See CHS INC.; *U.S. Public*, pg. 492
CHS NINGBO PROTEIN FOODS LTD.—See CHS INC.; *U.S. Public*, pg. 491
CHS-OKLEE—See CHS INC.; *U.S. Public*, pg. 492
CHS-OSTRANDER FARMER COOP ELEVATOR—See CHS INC.; *U.S. Public*, pg. 492
CHS SOUTH SIOUX CITY, INC.—See CHS INC.; *U.S. Public*, pg. 491
CHS URUGUAY SRL—See CHS INC.; *U.S. Public*, pg. 492
CLD PACIFIC GRAIN LLC—See Cargill, Inc.; *U.S. Private*, pg. 754
COGDILL FARM SUPPLY INC.; *U.S. Private*, pg. 962
COLLINGWOOD GRAIN INC.—See Archer-Daniels-Midland Company; *U.S. Public*, pg. 181
COLORADO COMMODITY TRADERS; *U.S. Private*, pg. 973
COMCEREAL SA BACAU; *Int'l*, pg. 1709
COMCEREAL SA BOTOSANI; *Int'l*, pg. 1709
COMCEREAL SA BUCURESTI; *Int'l*, pg. 1709
COMCEREAL SA SLOBOZIA; *Int'l*, pg. 1709
COMCEREAL SA TULCEA; *Int'l*, pg. 1709
THE CONNELL COMPANY; *U.S. Private*, pg. 4014
CONNELL EQUIPMENT LEASING—See The Connell Company; *U.S. Private*, pg. 4014
CONNELL GRAIN GROWERS INC.; *U.S. Private*, pg. 1017
CONNELL REALTY & DEVELOPMENT CO.—See The Connell Company; *U.S. Private*, pg. 4014
CO-OP COUNTRY FARMERS ELEVATOR; *U.S. Private*, pg. 953
COOPERATIVE ELEVATOR ASSOCIATION; *U.S. Private*, pg. 1042
CO-OPERATIVE ELEVATOR CO. INC.; *U.S. Private*, pg. 953
CO-OPERATIVE FEED DEALERS, INC.; *U.S. Private*, pg. 953
COOPERATIVE PRODUCERS, INC.; *U.S. Private*, pg. 1042
COOPERATIVE SUPPLY INC.; *U.S. Private*, pg. 1043
CORNERSTONE AG, LLC—See CHS INC.; *U.S. Public*, pg. 492
CORPORATION AIC-INVEST LLP; *Int'l*, pg. 1806
COUNTRY PARTNERS COOPERATIVE; *U.S. Private*, pg. 1067
COUNTRY PRIDE CO-OPERATIVE; *U.S. Private*, pg. 1067
CPI COOPERATIVE; *U.S. Private*, pg. 1080

CROPLAND CO-OP, INC.; *U.S. Private*, pg. 1103
CROSBY-NOONAN CO-OP ELEVATOR COMPANY; *U.S. Private*, pg. 1104
CROSSROADS COOPERATIVE ASSOCIATION; *U.S. Private*, pg. 1108
CRYSTAL VALLEY COOPERATIVE; *U.S. Private*, pg. 1116
CUSTER CITY FARMERS COOP EXCHANGE; *U.S. Private*, pg. 1127
DAKOTA PLAINS AGRICULTURAL CENTER LLC; *U.S. Private*, pg. 1147
DALHART CONSUMERS FUEL ASSOCIATION INC.; *U.S. Private*, pg. 1149
DANVILLE COOPERATIVE ASSOCIATION INC.; *U.S. Private*, pg. 1158
DAVENPORT UNION WAREHOUSE COMPANY; *U.S. Private*, pg. 1169
DAVIS COMMODITIES LIMITED; *Int'l*, pg. 1984
DECATUR COOPERATIVE ASSOCIATION; *U.S. Private*, pg. 1186
DELMAR COMMODITIES LTD. - GLADSTONE ELEVATOR FACILITY—See Ceres Global Ag Corp.; *U.S. Public*, pg. 475
DELMAR COMMODITIES LTD. - WESTROC ELEVATOR FACILITY—See Ceres Global Ag Corp.; *U.S. Public*, pg. 475
DELPHOS COOPERATIVE ASSOCIATION; *U.S. Private*, pg. 1199
DEMETER-CHEMUNG/ HARVARD DIVISION—See Demeter LP; *U.S. Private*, pg. 1203
DEMETER LP; *U.S. Private*, pg. 1203
DESHLER FARMERS ELEVATOR CO.; *U.S. Private*, pg. 1213
DODGE CITY COOPERATIVE EXCHANGE INC.; *U.S. Private*, pg. 1252
DRESSLER TRUCK SERVICE INC.; *U.S. Private*, pg. 1276
DUFFE GRAIN INC.; *U.S. Private*, pg. 1284
DUMAS CO-OP; *U.S. Private*, pg. 1286
EAST CENTRAL IOWA COOP; *U.S. Private*, pg. 1315
EASTERN FARMERS COOPERATIVE; *U.S. Private*, pg. 1319
EDON FARMERS COOPERATIVE ASSOCIATION; *U.S. Private*, pg. 1338
ELKHART GRAIN COMPANY; *U.S. Private*, pg. 1363
ELLSWORTH COOP; *U.S. Private*, pg. 1374
EVANS GRAIN & ELEVATOR CO. INC.; *U.S. Private*, pg. 1435
EVERGREEN FS INC.; *U.S. Private*, pg. 1439
EXPORT PACKERS COMPANY LIMITED; *Int'l*, pg. 2590
FARM CHEMICALS INC.; *U.S. Private*, pg. 1474
FARM CITY ELEVATOR INC.; *U.S. Private*, pg. 1474
FARMERS COOP ASSOCIATION; *U.S. Private*, pg. 1476
FARMERS CO-OP ELEVATOR CO. HUDSONVILLE; *U.S. Private*, pg. 1476
FARMERS COOP ELEVATOR OTTOSEN; *U.S. Private*, pg. 1476
FARMERS COOPERATIVE ASSOCIATION INC.; *U.S. Private*, pg. 1477
FARMERS COOPERATIVE ASSOCIATION; *U.S. Private*, pg. 1476
FARMERS COOPERATIVE ASSOCIATION; *U.S. Private*, pg. 1476
FARMERS COOPERATIVE ASSOCIATION; *U.S. Private*, pg. 1477
FARMERS COOPERATIVE CO. INC.; *U.S. Private*, pg. 1477
FARMERS COOPERATIVE COMPANY; *U.S. Private*, pg. 1477
FARMERS COOPERATIVE COMPANY; *U.S. Private*, pg. 1477
FARMERS COOPERATIVE CO.; *U.S. Private*, pg. 1477
FARMERS COOPERATIVE ELEVATOR COMPANY; *U.S. Private*, pg. 1477
FARMERS COOPERATIVE ELEVATOR COMPANY; *U.S. Private*, pg. 1477
FARMERS COOPERATIVE ELEVATOR CO.; *U.S. Private*, pg. 1477
FARMERS COOPERATIVE ELEVATOR CO.; *U.S. Private*, pg. 1477
FARMERS COOPERATIVE ELEVATOR CO.; *U.S. Private*, pg. 1477
FARMERS COOPERATIVE ELEVATOR OF SISSETON & NEW EFFINGTON; *U.S. Private*, pg. 1477
FARMERS COOPERATIVE EQUITY CO.; *U.S. Private*, pg. 1477
FARMERS COOPERATIVE GRAIN ASSOCIATION; *U.S. Private*, pg. 1477
FARMERS COOPERATIVE SOCIETY; *U.S. Private*, pg. 1477
FARMERS COOPERATIVE; *U.S. Private*, pg. 1476
FARMERS COOPERATIVE—See Farmers Cooperative; *U.S. Private*, pg. 1476
THE FARMERS COOP GRAIN ASSOCIATION; *U.S. Private*, pg. 4027
FARMERS COOP INC; *U.S. Private*, pg. 1476
FARMERS COOP MILL & ELEVATOR ASSOCIATION; *U.S. Private*, pg. 1476
FARMERS CO-OP OF HANSKA INC.; *U.S. Private*, pg. 1476

424510 — GRAIN AND FIELD BEA...

FARMERS ELEVATOR COMPANY OF MANTENO; *U.S. Private*, pg. 1478
FARMERS ELEVATOR COMPANY; *U.S. Private*, pg. 1478
FARMERS ELEVATOR CO-OP; *U.S. Private*, pg. 1477
FARMERS ELEVATOR CO.—See CHS INC.; *U.S. Public*, pg. 492
FARMERS ELEVATOR GRAIN & SUPPLY; *U.S. Private*, pg. 1478
FARMERS ELEVATOR OF LAKEFIELD; *U.S. Private*, pg. 1478
FARMERS FEED & GRAIN COMPANY; *U.S. Private*, pg. 1478
FARMERS GRAIN & COAL CO, INC.; *U.S. Private*, pg. 1478
FARMERS GRAIN COMPANY; *U.S. Private*, pg. 1478
FARMERS GRAIN OF LATHAM INC.; *U.S. Private*, pg. 1478
FARMERS MILL & ELEVATOR CO.; *U.S. Private*, pg. 1478
FARMERS UNION COOPERATIVE ASSOCIATION; *U.S. Private*, pg. 1479
FARMERS UNION COOPERATIVE; *U.S. Private*, pg. 1479
FARMERS UNION COOP; *U.S. Private*, pg. 1479
FARM SERVICE COOPERATIVE INC.; *U.S. Private*, pg. 1475
FARMWAY CO-OP INC.; *U.S. Private*, pg. 1480
FARMWAY; *U.S. Private*, pg. 1480
FEED INGREDIENT TRADING CORP.; *U.S. Private*, pg. 1492
FERTIMPORT S.A.—See Bunge Limited; *U.S. Public*, pg. 411
FESSENDEN CO-OP ASSOCIATION INC.; *U.S. Private*, pg. 1499
FINLEY FARMERS GRAIN & ELEVATOR COMPANY; *U.S. Private*, pg. 1510
FIVE STAR COOPERATIVE; *U.S. Private*, pg. 1537
F.J. KROB & CO., INC.; *U.S. Private*, pg. 1456
FLEMING FEED & GRAIN INC.; *U.S. Private*, pg. 1542
FOWLER ELEVATOR INC.; *U.S. Private*, pg. 1583
FREDERICKSBURG FARMERS COOP; *U.S. Private*, pg. 1602
FREMAR FARMERS COOPERATIVE INC.; *U.S. Private*, pg. 1608
FRENCHMAN VALLEY COOP.—See Frenchman Valley Farmers Coop. Inc.; *U.S. Private*, pg. 1609
FRENCHMAN VALLEY FARMERS COOP. INC.; *U.S. Private*, pg. 1609
FRONTIER AG, INC.; *U.S. Private*, pg. 1614
FRONTIER COOPERATIVE COMPANY, INC.; *U.S. Private*, pg. 1615
THE GARDEN CITY CO-OP INC - DIGHTON—See The Garden City Co-Op Inc.; *U.S. Private*, pg. 4032
THE GARDEN CITY CO-OP INC.; *U.S. Private*, pg. 4032
GATEWAY FS, INC.; *U.S. Private*, pg. 1650
GERALD GRAIN CENTER INC.; *U.S. Private*, pg. 1685
GIBBS CALIFORNIA WILD RICE; *U.S. Private*, pg. 1695
GLACIAL PLAINS COOPERATIVE; *U.S. Private*, pg. 1704
GLOBAL SWEETENERS TRADE DEVELOPMENT (DALIAN) CO., LTD.—See Global Sweeteners Holdings Limited; *Int'l*, pg. 3001
GOLD-EAGLE COOPERATIVE INC.; *U.S. Private*, pg. 1728
GOLD STAR FS INC.; *U.S. Private*, pg. 1728
GRAINCORP LIMITED; *Int'l*, pg. 3051
GRAINLAND COOPERATIVE - AMHERST—See Grainland Cooperative; *U.S. Private*, pg. 1752
GRAINLAND COOPERATIVE; *U.S. Private*, pg. 1752
GRANIT NEGOCE SA—See Axereal Union de Cooperatives Agricoles; *Int'l*, pg. 767
GREAT BEND COOPERATIVE ASSOCIATION; *U.S. Private*, pg. 1762
GREENWAY CO-OP SERVICE COMPANY; *U.S. Private*, pg. 1781
GRELTON ELEVATOR INC.; *U.S. Private*, pg. 1783
GRV GIBBS, INC.; *U.S. Private*, pg. 1797
GULF PACIFIC INC.; *U.S. Private*, pg. 1816
HALSTAD ELEVATOR COMPANY; *U.S. Private*, pg. 1846
HANENKRATT GRAIN CO., INC.; *U.S. Private*, pg. 1853
HARDIE'S FRUIT & VEGETABLE CO., LP—See The Chefs' Warehouse, Inc.; *U.S. Public*, pg. 2059
HARVEST LAND COOPERATIVE; *U.S. Private*, pg. 1875
HEARTLAND COOPERATIVE; *U.S. Private*, pg. 1899
HERITAGE COOPERATIVE INC.; *U.S. Private*, pg. 1922
HILLSDALE CO-OPERATIVE ELEVATOR CO.; *U.S. Private*, pg. 1947
HI-PLAINS COOPERATIVE ASSOCIATION; *U.S. Private*, pg. 1932
HOFFMAN & REED INC.; *U.S. Private*, pg. 1959
HONEYVILLE GRAIN INC.; *U.S. Private*, pg. 1976
HOPKINSVILLE ELEVATOR COMPANY, INC.; *U.S. Private*, pg. 1979
HOWARD FARMERS COOP ASSOCIATION; *U.S. Private*, pg. 1994
HUNTER GRAIN COMPANY; *U.S. Private*, pg. 2010
HUSKER COOP; *U.S. Private*, pg. 2013
INTERSTATE COMMODITIES INC.; *U.S. Private*, pg. 2124
IRSIK & DOLL FEED SERVICES INC.; *U.S. Private*, pg. 2141
IRVINGTON ELEVATOR COMPANY; *U.S. Private*, pg. 2142
JENNINGS-GOMER EQUITY INC.; *U.S. Private*, pg. 2200

JEWELL GRAIN COMPANY; *U.S. Private*, pg. 2205
JOHNSTON ENTERPRISES INC.; *U.S. Private*, pg. 2229
KALAMA EXPORTS LLC; *U.S. Private*, pg. 2256
THE KANZA CO-OPERATIVE EXCHANGE, INC.; *U.S. Private*, pg. 4064
KELLER GRAIN & FEED INC.; *U.S. Private*, pg. 2275
KELLEY BEAN CO., INC.; *U.S. Private*, pg. 2275
KENNEDY RICE DRYERS LLC; *U.S. Private*, pg. 2285
KEY COOPERATIVE; *U.S. Private*, pg. 2293
KOKOMO GRAIN CO., INC.; *U.S. Private*, pg. 2340
KOKOMO GRAIN CO., INC. - WINAMAC—See Kokomo Grain Co., Inc.; *U.S. Private*, pg. 2340
LACKAWANNA PRODUCTS CORP.; *U.S. Private*, pg. 2371
LAKE PRESTON COOPERATIVE ASSOCIATION; *U.S. Private*, pg. 2375
LEROY COOPERATIVE ASSOCIATION INC.; *U.S. Private*, pg. 2431
LEWIS COMMODITIES, INC.; *U.S. Private*, pg. 2438
L.H. HAYWARD & CO., LLC; *U.S. Private*, pg. 2366
LITTLEJOHN GRAIN INC.; *U.S. Private*, pg. 2472
LOWE'S PELLETS & GRAIN, INC.; *U.S. Private*, pg. 2505
LUCKEY FARMERS INC.; *U.S. Private*, pg. 2511
LUDLOW CO-OPERATIVE ELEVATOR COMPANY INC.; *U.S. Private*, pg. 2512
MADISON FARMERS ELEVATOR CO.; *U.S. Private*, pg. 2543
MAPLE RIVER GRAIN & AGRONOMY, LLC; *U.S. Private*, pg. 2568
MARQUIS GRAIN, INC.; *U.S. Private*, pg. 2587
MARTINSBURG FARMERS ELEVATORS CO; *U.S. Private*, pg. 2597
MAX YIELD COOPERATIVE; *U.S. Private*, pg. 2617
MAYFIELD GRAIN COMPANY INC.; *U.S. Private*, pg. 2621
MAYPORT FARMERS CO-OP; *U.S. Private*, pg. 2622
MCGEARY ORGANICS, INC.; *U.S. Private*, pg. 2634
MEADOWLAND FARMERS CO-OP INC.; *U.S. Private*, pg. 2647
MECHANICSBURG FARMERS GRAIN CO.; *U.S. Private*, pg. 2649
MERCER LANDMARK INC.; *U.S. Private*, pg. 2669
MID COLUMBIA PRODUCERS, INC.; *U.S. Private*, pg. 2706
MID COLUMBIA PRODUCERS, INC. - WASCO SEED PLANT—See Mid Columbia Producers, Inc.; *U.S. Private*, pg. 2706
MID-IOWA COOPERATIVE INC.; *U.S. Private*, pg. 2708
MID-KANSAS CO-OP ASSOCIATION; *U.S. Private*, pg. 2708
MIDLAND MARKETING COOP, INC.; *U.S. Private*, pg. 2715
MIDWAY COOP INC.; *U.S. Private*, pg. 2718
MIDWEST COOPERATIVES; *U.S. Private*, pg. 2720
MIDWEST FARMERS COOPERATIVE—See Frontier Cooperative Company, Inc.; *U.S. Private*, pg. 1615
MID-WOOD INC.; *U.S. Private*, pg. 2710
MINN-KOTA AG PRODUCTS, INC.; *U.S. Private*, pg. 2743
M&M SERVICE CO. INC.; *U.S. Private*, pg. 2525
MONSANTO CO. - LINCOLN—See Bayer Aktiengesellschaft; *Int'l*, pg. 908
MORROW COUNTY GRAIN GROWERS; *U.S. Private*, pg. 2790
MOUNTAIN VIEW CO-OP; *U.S. Private*, pg. 2800
MOUNT HAMILL ELEVATOR; *U.S. Private*, pg. 2798
MULVANE COOPERATIVE UNION INC.; *U.S. Private*, pg. 2813
NAGEL FARM SERVICE INC.; *U.S. Private*, pg. 2830
NASSAU FARMERS ELEVATOR CO.; *U.S. Private*, pg. 2837
NEMAHA COUNTY COOPERATIVE ASSOCIATION; *U.S. Private*, pg. 2884
NEW LONDON FARMERS COOPERATIVE; *U.S. Private*, pg. 2898
NEW VISION CO-OP; *U.S. Private*, pg. 2907
NICHOLS AGRISERVICE, LLC.; *U.S. Private*, pg. 2925
N.K. HURST CO., INC.; *U.S. Private*, pg. 2828
NORTH AMERICAN GRAIN INVESTMENTS, INC.—See Cargill, Inc.; *U.S. Private*, pg. 759
NORTH CENTRAL FARMERS ELEVATOR, INC.; *U.S. Private*, pg. 2943
NORTH CENTRAL GRAIN COOPERATIVE, INC.; *U.S. Private*, pg. 2943
NORTH CENTRAL KANSAS COOP; *U.S. Private*, pg. 2944
NORTHERN FEED & BEAN OF LUCERN; *U.S. Private*, pg. 2953
NORTHERN PARTNERS COOPERATIVE; *U.S. Private*, pg. 2954
NORTH IOWA COOPERATIVE; *U.S. Private*, pg. 2945
NORTHSTAR GENETICS LTD.—See Rob-See-Co; *U.S. Private*, pg. 3456
NORTHWEST GRAIN GROWERS, INC.; *U.S. Private*, pg. 2960
NORTHWEST GRAIN—See CHS INC.; *U.S. Public*, pg. 492
NORTHWOOD EQUITY ELEVATOR CO.; *U.S. Private*, pg. 2963
OBERBECK GRAIN CO.; *U.S. Private*, pg. 2986
ODESSA TRADING COMPANY INC.—See Ritzville Warehouse Co. Inc.; *U.S. Private*, pg. 3442
OFFERLE COOPERATIVE GRAIN & SUPPLY COMPANY; *U.S. Private*, pg. 3001

OKAW FARMERS COOPERATIVE, INC.; *U.S. Private*, pg. 3006
OLD DOMINION GRAIN CORPORATION—See The Mennel Milling Company; *U.S. Public*, pg. 4077
OOO SAVINSKAJA NIVA—See Ekosem-Agrar GmbH; *Int'l*, pg. 2339
ORANGE GROVE CO-OPERATIVE; *U.S. Private*, pg. 3037
PACIFIC GRAIN & FOODS; *U.S. Private*, pg. 3067
PACIFIC NORTHWEST FARMERS COOPERATIVE-GENESEE—See Pacific Northwest Farmers Cooperative; *U.S. Private*, pg. 3069
PACIFIC NORTHWEST FARMERS COOPERATIVE; *U.S. Private*, pg. 3069
PENDLETON GRAIN GROWERS INC.; *U.S. Private*, pg. 3132
PENNSYLVANIA AGRICULTURAL COMMODITIES MARKETING ASSOCIATION—See Perdue Farms Incorporated; *U.S. Private*, pg. 3147
PENNY NEWMAN GRAIN COMPANY; *U.S. Private*, pg. 3137
PERRYTON EQUITY; *U.S. Private*, pg. 3154
PETTISVILLE GRAIN CO.; *U.S. Private*, pg. 3163
PIONEER HI-BRED INTERNATIONAL—See Corteva, Inc.; *U.S. Public*, pg. 583
PIONEER HI-BRED INTERNATIONAL—See Corteva, Inc.; *U.S. Public*, pg. 583
PLAINS EQUITY EXCHANGE & COOPERATIVE UNION; *U.S. Private*, pg. 3195
PLAZA MAKOTI EQUITY ELEVATOR; *U.S. Private*, pg. 3212
PRAIRIE AG COOPERATIVE; *U.S. Private*, pg. 3242
PRAIRIE GRAIN PARTNERS LLC; *U.S. Private*, pg. 3242
PRAIRIE LAKES COOP; *U.S. Private*, pg. 3242
PRAIRIE LAND COOPERATIVE; *U.S. Private*, pg. 3242
PREMIER COS.; *U.S. Private*, pg. 3250
PRINSBURG FARMERS CO-OP; *U.S. Private*, pg. 3265
PRINZ GRAIN & FEED INC.; *U.S. Private*, pg. 3266
PRO COOPERATIVE INC.; *U.S. Private*, pg. 3269
PRODUCERS AG MARKETING ASSOCIATION; *U.S. Private*, pg. 3272
PRODUCERS GRAIN CO. INC.; *U.S. Private*, pg. 3273
RABIDEAU GRAIN & LUMBER, INC.; *U.S. Private*, pg. 3341
RANGELAND COOPERATIVES INC.; *U.S. Private*, pg. 3354
RAY-CARROLL COUNTY GRAIN GROWERS, INC.; *U.S. Private*, pg. 3359
RED RIVER GRAIN COMPANY; *U.S. Private*, pg. 3375
REED BROTHERS INC.—See Reed Grain & Bean Company, Inc.; *U.S. Private*, pg. 3382
REED GRAIN & BEAN COMPANY, INC.; *U.S. Private*, pg. 3382
RIADA TRADING COMPANY INCORPORATED; *U.S. Private*, pg. 3424
THE RICE COMPANY; *U.S. Private*, pg. 4106
RIGHT COOPERATIVE ASSOCIATION; *U.S. Private*, pg. 3435
RITZVILLE WAREHOUSE CO. INC.; *U.S. Private*, pg. 3442
RIVEKA BVBA—See BayWa AG; *Int'l*, pg. 919
RIVER REGION COOPERATIVE; *U.S. Private*, pg. 3444
RIVER VALLEY COOPERATIVE; *U.S. Private*, pg. 3444
ROBINSON & BELEW INC.; *U.S. Private*, pg. 3461
ROCK RIVER LUMBER & GRAIN CO; *U.S. Private*, pg. 3465
ROGGEN FARMERS ELEVATOR ASSOCIATION INC.; *U.S. Private*, pg. 3472
ROTHSAY FARMERS CO-OP; *U.S. Private*, pg. 3487
RPA CO-OP; *U.S. Private*, pg. 3495
RUDY INC.; *U.S. Private*, pg. 3502
RUGBY FARMERS UNION ELEVATOR COMPANY; *U.S. Private*, pg. 3502
SALEM GRAIN COMPANY INC.; *U.S. Private*, pg. 3531
SAND SEED SERVICE INCORPORATED; *U.S. Private*, pg. 3542
SCOTT COOPERATIVE ASSOCIATION; *U.S. Private*, pg. 3576
SCOTT EQUITY EXCHANGE CO.; *U.S. Private*, pg. 3576
THE SCOULAR CO. - MINNEAPOLIS CORPORATE OFFICE—See The Scoular Company; *U.S. Private*, pg. 4115
THE SCOULAR COMPANY; *U.S. Private*, pg. 4115
THE SCOULAR CO. - OVERLAND PARK CORPORATE OFFICE—See The Scoular Company; *U.S. Private*, pg. 4115
SCRANTON EQUITY EXCHANGE INC.; *U.S. Private*, pg. 3579
SEED TECHNOLOGY LIMITED—See BeyondSpring Inc.; *U.S. Public*, pg. 327
SERVICIOS ARGKEL, S.C.—See Kellanova; *U.S. Public*, pg. 1218
SHIPMAN ELEVATOR COMPANY; *U.S. Private*, pg. 3637
SINCLAIR ELEVATOR INC.; *U.S. Private*, pg. 3669
SKE MIDWESTERN INC.; *U.S. Private*, pg. 3681
SOONER COOPERATIVE INC.; *U.S. Private*, pg. 3715
SOUFFLET AGRICULTE LIMITED—See Etablissements J. Soufflet; *Int'l*, pg. 2519
SOUFFLET NEGOCE S.A.—See Etablissements J. Soufflet; *Int'l*, pg. 2519

N.A.I.C.S. INDEX

424590 — OTHER FARM PRODUCT ...

SOURIS RIVER COOPERATIVE; *U.S. Private*, pg. 3719
SOUTH CENTRAL CO-OP; *U.S. Private*, pg. 3720
SOUTH CENTRAL COOP; *U.S. Private*, pg. 3721
SOUTH CENTRAL GRAIN COOPERATIVE; *U.S. Private*, pg. 3721
SOUTH CENTRAL SERVICE COMPANY; *U.S. Private*, pg. 3721
SOUTH DAKOTA WHEAT GROWERS ASSOCIATION; *U.S. Private*, pg. 3722
SOUTH DAKOTA WHEAT GROWERS—See South Dakota Wheat Growers Association; *U.S. Private*, pg. 3722
SOUTHEAST FARMERS ELEVATORS COOP; *U.S. Private*, pg. 3725
SOUTHERN FS, INC.; *U.S. Private*, pg. 3732
SPARTA COOPERATIVE SERVICES; *U.S. Private*, pg. 3746
SPERRY UNION STORE, INC.; *U.S. Private*, pg. 3756
STANDISH MILLING COMPANY; *U.S. Private*, pg. 3782
STARKE COUNTY FARM BUREAU COOPERATIVE ASSOCIATION; *U.S. Private*, pg. 3787
STEWART GRAIN CO. INC.; *U.S. Private*, pg. 3811
STOCKLAND GRAIN COMPANY INC.; *U.S. Private*, pg. 3815
STRATTON EQUITY CO-OPERATIVE COMPANY INC.; *U.S. Private*, pg. 3837
SUBLETTE COOPERATIVE INC.; *U.S. Private*, pg. 3847
SUNRAY CO-OP, INC.; *U.S. Private*, pg. 3869
SUNRISE COOPERATIVE, INC.; *U.S. Private*, pg. 3869
SUNWEST FOODS INC.; *U.S. Private*, pg. 3874
SYNGENTA SEEDS N.V.—See China National Chemical Corporation; *Int'l*, pg. 1530
SYNGENTA SOUTH AFRICA (PTY) LIMITED—See China National Chemical Corporation; *Int'l*, pg. 1530
TALOMA FARMERS GRAIN COMPANY; *U.S. Private*, pg. 3927
TAMA-BENTON COOPERATIVE CO.; *U.S. Private*, pg. 3928
TERMINAL BAHIA BLANCA S.A.—See Bunge Limited; *U.S. Public*, pg. 412
TEXHOMA WHEAT GROWERS INC.; *U.S. Private*, pg. 3978
THOMPSONS LIMITED—See The Andersons Incorporated; *U.S. Public*, pg. 2034
TOP AG COOPERATIVE—See Top Egg; *U.S. Private*, pg. 4186
TOP EGG; *U.S. Private*, pg. 4186
TOPFLIGHT GRAIN COOPERATIVE INC.; *U.S. Private*, pg. 4187
TOWN & COUNTRY CO-OP INC.; *U.S. Private*, pg. 4196
TRAINOR GRAIN & SUPPLY CO.; *U.S. Private*, pg. 4204
TREMONT COOPERATIVE GRAIN CO; *U.S. Private*, pg. 4217
TRI CENTRAL CO-OP; *U.S. Private*, pg. 4220
TRINIDAD/BENHAM CORP.—See Trinidad/Benham Holding Co; *U.S. Private*, pg. 4233
TRIOAK FOODS, INC.; *U.S. Private*, pg. 4236
TWO RIVERS CONSUMERS COOP ASSOCIATION; *U.S. Private*, pg. 4266
UNITED AGRICULTURAL COOPERATIVE INC.; *U.S. Private*, pg. 4287
UNITED AG SERVICE INC.; *U.S. Private*, pg. 4287
UNITED COOPERATIVE; *U.S. Private*, pg. 4290
UNITED FARMERS COOPERATIVE; *U.S. Private*, pg. 4292
UNITED FARMERS COOPERATIVE; *U.S. Private*, pg. 4292
UNITED FEED COOP INC.; *U.S. Private*, pg. 4292
UNITED HARVEST LLC.; *U.S. Private*, pg. 4293
UNITED PLAINS AG—See CHS INC.; *U.S. Public*, pg. 493
UNITED WESTERN COOP; *U.S. Private*, pg. 4301
URSA FARMERS COOPERATIVE CO.; *U.S. Private*, pg. 4316
VALLEY CO-OP INC.; *U.S. Private*, pg. 4333
VIA FIELD; *U.S. Private*, pg. 4375
WALLOWA COUNTY GRAIN GROWERS; *U.S. Private*, pg. 4431
WATERTOWN COOPERATIVE ELEVATOR ASSOCIATION; *U.S. Private*, pg. 4454
WATSEKA INTERSTATE, LLC; *U.S. Private*, pg. 4455
WEST CENTRAL AGRICULTURAL SERVICE INC.; *U.S. Private*, pg. 4483
WEST CENTRAL FS, INC.; *U.S. Private*, pg. 4483
WESTERN CONSOLIDATED COOPERATIVES INC.; *U.S. Private*, pg. 4492
WESTERN IOWA COOPERATIVE; *U.S. Private*, pg. 4494
WEST SIDE GRAIN SALES CORP.—See West Side Unlimited Corporation; *U.S. Private*, pg. 4487
WHEATON-DUMONT COOP ELEVATOR INC.; *U.S. Private*, pg. 4505
WHEELER BROS. GRAIN CO.—See Wheeler Brothers Grain Co.; *U.S. Private*, pg. 4505
WHITE CLOUD GRAIN COMPANY INC.; *U.S. Private*, pg. 4508
WILSON FERTILIZER & GRAIN INC.; *U.S. Private*, pg. 4530
Z.T. KRUSZWICA S.A.—See Bunge Limited; *U.S. Public*, pg. 412

424520 — LIVESTOCK MERCHANT WHOLESALERS

101 LIVESTOCK MARKET INC.; *U.S. Private*, pg. 2
BALES CONTINENTAL COMMISSION COMPANY; *U.S. Private*, pg. 459
BIG RIVER RESOURCES WEST BURLINGTON, LLC; *U.S. Private*, pg. 554
BILLINGSLEY RANCH OUTFITTERS; *U.S. Private*, pg. 559
CARGILL MEAT SOLUTIONS—See Cargill, Inc.; *U.S. Private*, pg. 758
CARROLL COUNTY LIVESTOCK SALES BARN, INC.; *U.S. Private*, pg. 773
CENTRAL LIVESTOCK ASSOCIATION, INC.—See Cooperative Resources International Inc.; *U.S. Private*, pg. 1043
CHAROEN POKPHAND (INDIA) PRIVATE LIMITED—See Charoen Pokphand Foods Public Company Limited; *Int'l*, pg. 1452
COFCO LIMITED; *Int'l*, pg. 1691
DOMINIQUE'S LIVESTOCK MARKET; *U.S. Private*, pg. 1256
EMPIRE LIVESTOCK MARKETING LLC—See Dairy Farmers of America, Inc.; *U.S. Private*, pg. 1146
EQUITY COOP LIVESTOCK SALES ASSOCIATION; *U.S. Private*, pg. 1416
FARNAM COMPANIES, INC.—See Central Garden & Pet Company; *U.S. Public*, pg. 473
HARRISON & HETHERINGTON LIMITED—See H&H Group plc; *Int'l*, pg. 3191
JOHN SWAN LIMITED—See H&H Group plc; *Int'l*, pg. 3191
KEENELAND ASSOCIATION INC.; *U.S. Private*, pg. 2272
LEWISTON SALES INC.; *U.S. Private*, pg. 2440
LYNCH LIVESTOCK INC.; *U.S. Private*, pg. 2521
MILLER LIVESTOCK MARKETS INC.; *U.S. Private*, pg. 2734
MOUNT OLIVE LIVESTOCK MARKET; *U.S. Private*, pg. 2798
PGG WRIGHTSON LIMITED—See Agria Corporation; *Int'l*, pg. 216
PRODUCERS LIVESTOCK MARKETING ASSOCIATION; *U.S. Private*, pg. 3273
ROBERT WINNER SONS INC.; *U.S. Private*, pg. 3459
S&J VILLARI LIVESTOCK; *U.S. Private*, pg. 3513
SOUTH PACIFIC MEATS LIMITED—See AFFCO Holdings Limited; *Int'l*, pg. 186
UNITED PRODUCERS, INC.; *U.S. Private*, pg. 4296
WESTMINSTER LIVESTOCK AUCTION LLC; *U.S. Private*, pg. 4499
WINTER LIVESTOCK INC.; *U.S. Private*, pg. 4545

424590 — OTHER FARM PRODUCT RAW MATERIAL MERCHANT WHOLESALERS

ADM AGRO IBERICA S.L.U.—See Archer-Daniels-Midland Company; *U.S. Public*, pg. 181
ADM AGRO INDUSTRIES LATUR & VIZAG PRIVATE LIMITED—See Archer-Daniels-Midland Company; *U.S. Public*, pg. 181
ADM ASIA-PACIFIC TRADING PTE. LTD.—See Archer-Daniels-Midland Company; *U.S. Public*, pg. 181
ADM GERMANY GMBH—See Archer-Daniels-Midland Company; *U.S. Public*, pg. 181
ADM HUNGARY AGRO TRADING LLC—See Archer-Daniels-Midland Company; *U.S. Public*, pg. 182
ADM JAPAN LTD.—See Archer-Daniels-Midland Company; *U.S. Public*, pg. 182
ADM MAINZ GMBH—See Archer-Daniels-Midland Company; *U.S. Public*, pg. 182
ADM MALBORK S.A.—See Archer-Daniels-Midland Company; *U.S. Public*, pg. 182
ADM PARAGUAY SRL—See Archer-Daniels-Midland Company; *U.S. Public*, pg. 182
ADM PURA LIMITED—See Archer-Daniels-Midland Company; *U.S. Public*, pg. 182
ADM ROTHENSEE GMBH & CO. KG—See Archer-Daniels-Midland Company; *U.S. Public*, pg. 182
ADM (SHANGHAI) MANAGEMENT CO., LTD.—See Archer-Daniels-Midland Company; *U.S. Public*, pg. 181
AGFINITY, INC.; *U.S. Private*, pg. 127
AGROVOJVODINA KOMERCSERVIS AD; *Int'l*, pg. 221
ALLIANCE ONE INTERNATIONAL TABAK B.V.—See Pyxus International, Inc.; *U.S. Public*, pg. 1740
ALL POINTS COOPERATIVE—See All Points Cooperative; *U.S. Private*, pg. 171
ALZCHEM SHANGHAI CO., LTD.—See AlzChem Group AG; *Int'l*, pg. 402
AMOREPACIFIC GLOBAL OPERATIONS LIMITED—See Amorepacific Corp.; *Int'l*, pg. 430
AMPAS MAJU SDN BHD—See IJM Corporation Berhad; *Int'l*, pg. 3608
ARASCO FEED MILL CO.—See Arabian Agricultural Services Co.; *Int'l*, pg. 533
BANGKOK PRODUCE MERCHANDISING PLC—See Charoen Pokphand Foods Public Company Limited; *Int'l*, pg. 1451
BAYER CROPSCIENCE DEUTSCHLAND GMBH—See Bayer Aktiengesellschaft; *Int'l*, pg. 903
BIRDSONG CORPORATION; *U.S. Private*, pg. 564

BIRMINGHAM HIDE & TALLOW COMPANY INC.; *U.S. Private*, pg. 564
CALCOT, LTD.; *U.S. Private*, pg. 716
CANADA'S ISLAND GARDENS, INC.—See Pyxus International, Inc.; *U.S. Public*, pg. 1740
CAREMOLI DEUTSCHLAND GMBH—See Caremoli SpA; *Int'l*, pg. 1324
CAREMOLI INDIA, PVT. LTD.—See Caremoli SpA; *Int'l*, pg. 1324
CARGILL COTTON—See Cargill, Inc.; *U.S. Private*, pg. 756
CAROLINA INNOVATIVE FOOD INGREDIENTS, INC.—See Universal Corporation; *U.S. Public*, pg. 2254
CHICKASHA OF GEORGIA, LLC; *U.S. Private*, pg. 880
THE CLINT WILLIAMS COMPANY—See Texoma Peanut Company; *U.S. Private*, pg. 3978
COCOA MARKETING COMPANY (GHANA) LIMITED—See Ghana Cocoa Board; *Int'l*, pg. 2958
COFCO ARGENTINA S.A.—See COFCO Limited; *Int'l*, pg. 1691
COFFEE DAY GLOBAL LTD. - EXPORTS DIVISION—See Affirma Capital Limited; *Int'l*, pg. 187
CONQUIMICA S.A.—See BRENNTAG SE; *Int'l*, pg. 1149
CONSOLIDATED COTTON CO. INC.; *U.S. Private*, pg. 1020
CONTINAF B.V.—See Amtrada Holding B.V.; *Int'l*, pg. 442
COUNTRY VET WHOLESALING PTY. LTD.—See Apiam Animal Health Limited; *Int'l*, pg. 515
CRODA COLOMBIA—See Croda International plc; *Int'l*, pg. 1851
CROWN POINT LTD.—See Unaka Company Inc.; *U.S. Private*, pg. 4279
DAARNHOUWER & CO.—See Amtrada Holding B.V.; *Int'l*, pg. 442
DELI, INC.; *U.S. Private*, pg. 1196
DHANYA AGROINDUSTRIAL PVT. LTD.,—See Ecom Agroindustrial Corporation Ltd.; *Int'l*, pg. 2296
DIXIE BRANDS, INC.; *U.S. Private*, pg. 1244
DOSTER WAREHOUSE INC.; *U.S. Private*, pg. 1264
DUNAVANT ENTERPRISES, INC.; *U.S. Private*, pg. 1287
DUNAVANT ENTERPRISES—See Dunavant Enterprises, Inc.; *U.S. Private*, pg. 1287
EAGLE DAIRY DIRECT LLC—See Dairy Farmers of America, Inc.; *U.S. Private*, pg. 1146
EASTERLIN PECAN CO. INC.; *U.S. Private*, pg. 1319
ECOM ATLANTIC, INC; *U.S. Private*, pg. 1329
ELCO DIRECT LIMITED—See Bremworth Limited; *Int'l*, pg. 1145
FARMERS INVESTMENT COMPANY, INC.—See Bale of Kentucky, Inc.; *U.S. Private*, pg. 459
FARMSECURE HOLDINGS (PTY) LTD.; *Int'l*, pg. 2620
FASIG-TIPTON CO. INC.; *U.S. Private*, pg. 1481
FASIG-TIPTON KENTUCKY, INC.—See Fasig-Tipton Co. Inc.; *U.S. Private*, pg. 1481
FERONIA INCORPORATED SERVICES LIMITED—See Feronia Inc.; *Int'l*, pg. 2639
FIRST SEED FARMS INC.; *U.S. Private*, pg. 1527
GHANA COCOA BOARD - COCOA HEALTH AND EXTENSION DIVISION—See Ghana Cocoa Board; *Int'l*, pg. 2958
GHANA COCOA MARKETING COMPANY (UK) LTD—See Ghana Cocoa Board; *Int'l*, pg. 2958
GLASS HOUSE BRANDS INC.; *U.S. Public*, pg. 939
GOLDEN PEANUT & TREE NUTS S.A.—See Archer-Daniels-Midland Company; *U.S. Public*, pg. 185
GOLDLEAF PHARM, INC.—See Pyxus International, Inc.; *U.S. Public*, pg. 1740
GPOD OF IDAHO; *U.S. Private*, pg. 1748
GREAT LAKE CANNABIS CO.—See Biome Grow, Inc.; *Int'l*, pg. 1039
GROENEWOLD FUR & WOOL, CO.; *U.S. Private*, pg. 1791
HAIL & COTTON INC.—See Luckett Tobaccos Inc.; *U.S. Private*, pg. 2511
HAIL & COTTON—See Luckett Tobaccos Inc.; *U.S. Private*, pg. 2511
IJM EDIBLE OILS SDN BHD—See IJM Corporation Berhad; *Int'l*, pg. 3608
IMAKO A.D.; *Int'l*, pg. 3619
INNOVATIVE AG SERVICES CO.; *U.S. Private*, pg. 2081
JESS SMITH & SONS COTTON; *U.S. Private*, pg. 2203
KULIM MEWAH SDN BHD—See IJM Corporation Berhad; *Int'l*, pg. 3609
LANCASTER LEAF TOBACCO CO. OF PENNSYLVANIA—See Universal Corporation; *U.S. Public*, pg. 2254
LUCKETT TOBACCOS INC.; *U.S. Private*, pg. 2511
MONSANTO THAILAND LTD.—See Bayer Aktiengesellschaft; *Int'l*, pg. 909
NATIONAL CHICKS SWAZILAND (PTY) LIMITED—See Astral Foods Limited; *Int'l*, pg. 658
NUGL, INC.; *U.S. Public*, pg. 1555
NUNHEMS B.V.—See Bayer Aktiengesellschaft; *Int'l*, pg. 903
NUNHEMS CHILE S.A.—See Bayer Aktiengesellschaft; *Int'l*, pg. 903
NUNHEMS ITALY S.R.L.—See Bayer Aktiengesellschaft; *Int'l*, pg. 903
NUNHEMS POLAND SP. Z O.O.—See Bayer Aktiengesellschaft; *Int'l*, pg. 903

424590 — OTHER FARM PRODUCT ...

NUNHEMS SPAIN, S.A.—See Bayer Aktiengesellschaft; *Int'l*, pg. 903
NUNHEMS TOHUMCULUK LIMITED SIRKETI—See Bayer Aktiengesellschaft; *Int'l*, pg. 903
NUNHEMS USA, INC.—See Bayer Aktiengesellschaft; *Int'l*, pg. 903
OHSMAN & SONS COMPANY INC.; *U.S. Private*, pg. 3006
OLIVA TOBACCO COMPANY; *U.S. Private*, pg. 3010
OU AVENA NORDIC GRAIN—See Apetit Plc; *Int'l*, pg. 509
OVERSEAS COMMODEX CORP.—See Ferd AS; *Int'l*, pg. 2636
PALMS & COMPANY INC.; *U.S. Private*, pg. 3082
PESNELL-COTTON; *U.S. Private*, pg. 3156
PIONEER HI-BRED INTERNATIONAL—See Corteva, Inc.; *U.S. Public*, pg. 583
PIONEER HI-BRED INTERNATIONAL—See Corteva, Inc.; *U.S. Public*, pg. 583
PIONEER HI-BRED INTERNATIONAL—See Corteva, Inc.; *U.S. Public*, pg. 583
PIONEER HI-BRED INTERNATIONAL—See Corteva, Inc.; *U.S. Public*, pg. 583
PIONEER HI-BRED INTERNATIONAL—See Corteva, Inc.; *U.S. Public*, pg. 583
PIONEER HI-BRED INTERNATIONAL—See Corteva, Inc.; *U.S. Public*, pg. 583
PIONEER HI-BRED INTERNATIONAL—See Corteva, Inc.; *U.S. Public*, pg. 583
POLYNT COMPOSITES CANADA INC.—See Reichhold, Inc.; *U.S. Private*, pg. 3390
PT HINDOLI—See Cargill, Inc.; *U.S. Private*, pg. 759
RAINIER SEED INC.; *U.S. Private*, pg. 3348
RENFROE PECAN CO. INC.; *U.S. Private*, pg. 3398
SARL LEMEE—See EDP - Energias de Portugal, S.A.; *Int'l*, pg. 2315
SCOTMIN NUTRITION LIMITED—See Carr's Group PLC; *Int'l*, pg. 1343
SEED CO INTERNATIONAL LIMITED—See Cottco Holdings Limited; *Int'l*, pg. 1817
SEED CO LIMITED—See Cottco Holdings Limited; *Int'l*, pg. 1817
SIJAS PLANTATIONS SDN BHD—See IJM Corporation Berhad; *Int'l*, pg. 3609
SOUFFLET ALIMENTAIRE S.A.—See Etablissements J. Soufflet; *Int'l*, pg. 2519
SOUTHERN PEANUT CO. INC.; *U.S. Private*, pg. 3734
SOUTHWESTERN IRRIGATED COTTON GROWERS ASSOCIATION INC.; *U.S. Private*, pg. 3741
S.S. STEINER INC.; *U.S. Private*, pg. 3518
STAPLE COTTON COOPERATIVE ASSOCIATION/ITTA BENA—See Staple Cotton Cooperative Association; *U.S. Private*, pg. 3783
STAPLE COTTON COOPERATIVE ASSOCIATION; *U.S. Private*, pg. 3783
STOLLER TURKEY ORGANIK TARIM SANAYI TICARET A.S.—See Corteva, Inc.; *U.S. Public*, pg. 583
SUNFED PRODUCE LLC—See GrubMarket, Inc.; *U.S. Private*, pg. 1797
TASMAN INDUSTRIES INC.; *U.S. Private*, pg. 3935
TEXOMA PEANUT COMPANY; *U.S. Private*, pg. 3978
TIMAC AGRO AVRASYA ZIRAAT SAN.VE TIC. A.S.—See Compagnie Financiere et de Participations Roullier SA; *Int'l*, pg. 1740
TIMAC AGRO LATVIA SIA—See Compagnie Financiere et de Participations Roullier SA; *Int'l*, pg. 1740
TIMAC AGRO LT, UAB—See Compagnie Financiere et de Participations Roullier SA; *Int'l*, pg. 1740
TIMAC AGRO NEDERLAND B.V.—See Compagnie Financiere et de Participations Roullier SA; *Int'l*, pg. 1740
TIMAC AGRO SLOVAKIA, S.R.O.—See Compagnie Financiere et de Participations Roullier SA; *Int'l*, pg. 1740
TOO AVENA ASTANA—See Apetit Plc; *Int'l*, pg. 509
TOPBRANDS EUROPE B.V.—See B&S Group S.A.; *Int'l*, pg. 784
TRACOMEX B.V.—See BayWa AG; *Int'l*, pg. 919
UAB AGROSS—See AUGA group, AB; *Int'l*, pg. 703
UNITED COOPERATIVE; *U.S. Private*, pg. 4290
UNITED FEATHER & DOWN INC.; *U.S. Private*, pg. 4292
UNITED SUGARS CORP.—See American Crystal Sugar Company; *U.S. Public*, pg. 98
UNITED SUGARS CORP.—See Minn-Dak Farmers Cooperative; *U.S. Private*, pg. 2742
UNITED SUGARS CORP.—See United States Sugar Corporation; *U.S. Private*, pg. 4300
UNIVERSAL LEAF TOBACCO COMPANY, INC.—See Universal Corporation; *U.S. Public*, pg. 2254
URL AGRAR GMBH—See BayWa AG; *Int'l*, pg. 919
WEST PLAINS LLC; *U.S. Private*, pg. 4486
WILLIAM HOUDE LTD.—See Compagnie Financiere et de Participations Roullier SA; *Int'l*, pg. 1740
ZAO AVENA ST.PETERSBURG—See Apetit Plc; *Int'l*, pg. 509
ZUARI AGRI SCIENCES LIMITED—See Adventz Group; *Int'l*, pg. 167

424610 — PLASTICS MATERIALS AND BASIC FORMS AND SHAPES MERCHANT WHOLESALERS

3M EMEA, GMBH—See 3M Company; *U.S. Public*, pg. 5
AB SVENSKA WAVIN—See Bharti Enterprises Limited; *Int'l*, pg. 1012
A&C PLASTIC PRODUCTS INC.; *U.S. Private*, pg. 19
ACRILEX INC.; *U.S. Private*, pg. 65
ADS EUROPE B.V.—See Advanced Drainage Systems, Inc.; *U.S. Public*, pg. 46
ADTECH SYSTEMS INC.; *U.S. Private*, pg. 83
ADVANCED PLASTICS INCORPORATED; *U.S. Private*, pg. 92
AETNA PLASTICS CORP.—See Bain Capital, LP; *U.S. Private*, pg. 432
AGC GREEN-TECH CO., LTD.—See AGC Inc.; *Int'l*, pg. 202
AGRISTAR, INC.; *U.S. Public*, pg. 63
AGROFERT HUNGARIA KFT.—See Agrofert Holding, a.s.; *Int'l*, pg. 218
ALPINE SALES INC.; *U.S. Private*, pg. 202
ALPLA AVELLANEDA S.A.—See Alpla-Werke Alwin Lehner GmbH & Co. KG; *Int'l*, pg. 374
ALPLA BELGIUM N.V.—See Alpla-Werke Alwin Lehner GmbH & Co. KG; *Int'l*, pg. 374
ALPLA BH D.O.O. CITLUK—See Alpla-Werke Alwin Lehner GmbH & Co. KG; *Int'l*, pg. 374
ALPLA CARIBE INC.—See Alpla-Werke Alwin Lehner GmbH & Co. KG; *Int'l*, pg. 374
ALPLA COLOMBIA LTDA.—See Alpla-Werke Alwin Lehner GmbH & Co. KG; *Int'l*, pg. 374
ALPLA DE VENEZUELA S.A.—See Alpla-Werke Alwin Lehner GmbH & Co. KG; *Int'l*, pg. 374
ALPLA D.O.O—See Alpla-Werke Alwin Lehner GmbH & Co. KG; *Int'l*, pg. 374
ALPLA FRANCE SAS—See Alpla-Werke Alwin Lehner GmbH & Co. KG; *Int'l*, pg. 374
ALPLA (GUANGZHOU) PLASTIC CO., LTD.—See Alpla-Werke Alwin Lehner GmbH & Co. KG; *Int'l*, pg. 373
ALPLA (HEFEI) PLASTIC CO., LTD—See Alpla-Werke Alwin Lehner GmbH & Co. KG; *Int'l*, pg. 374
ALPLA HONDURAS SA—See Alpla-Werke Alwin Lehner GmbH & Co. KG; *Int'l*, pg. 374
ALPLA IBERICA S.A.—See Alpla-Werke Alwin Lehner GmbH & Co. KG; *Int'l*, pg. 374
ALPLA INDIA PRIVATE LTD.—See Alpla-Werke Alwin Lehner GmbH & Co. KG; *Int'l*, pg. 374
ALPLA ITALIA S.R.L—See Alpla-Werke Alwin Lehner GmbH & Co. KG; *Int'l*, pg. 374
ALPLA (JIANGSU) PLASTIC CO., LTD.—See Alpla-Werke Alwin Lehner GmbH & Co. KG; *Int'l*, pg. 374
ALPLA LLC—See Alpla-Werke Alwin Lehner GmbH & Co. KG; *Int'l*, pg. 374
ALPLA MEXICO S.A. DE C.V.—See Alpla-Werke Alwin Lehner GmbH & Co. KG; *Int'l*, pg. 374
ALPLA MUANYAG CSOMAGOLOIPARI KFT—See Alpla-Werke Alwin Lehner GmbH & Co. KG; *Int'l*, pg. 374
ALPLA NDM SP.Z.O.O—See Alpla-Werke Alwin Lehner GmbH & Co. KG; *Int'l*, pg. 374
ALPLA NEDERLAND B.V.—See Alpla-Werke Alwin Lehner GmbH & Co. KG; *Int'l*, pg. 374
ALPLA OPAKOWANIA Z TWORZYW SZTUCZNYCH SPOLKA Z.O.O.—See Alpla-Werke Alwin Lehner GmbH & Co. KG; *Int'l*, pg. 374
ALPLA PACKAGING LTD.—See Alpla-Werke Alwin Lehner GmbH & Co. KG; *Int'l*, pg. 374
ALPLA PACKAGING (VIETNAM) CO., LTD.—See Alpla-Werke Alwin Lehner GmbH & Co. KG; *Int'l*, pg. 374
ALPLA PLASTIK SANAYI VE TICARET LTD.—See Alpla-Werke Alwin Lehner GmbH & Co. KG; *Int'l*, pg. 374
ALPLA (SHANGHAI) PLASTIC CO., LTD—See Alpla-Werke Alwin Lehner GmbH & Co. KG; *Int'l*, pg. 374
ALPLA SPOL. S.R.O.—See Alpla-Werke Alwin Lehner GmbH & Co. KG; *Int'l*, pg. 374
ALPLA TASHKENT LRS—See Alpla-Werke Alwin Lehner GmbH & Co. KG; *Int'l*, pg. 374
ALPLA (TIANJIN) PLASTIC CO., LTD.—See Alpla-Werke Alwin Lehner GmbH & Co. KG; *Int'l*, pg. 374
ALPLA UK LIMITED—See Alpla-Werke Alwin Lehner GmbH & Co. KG; *Int'l*, pg. 374
ALPLA WAIDHOFEN GMBH—See Alpla-Werke Alwin Lehner GmbH & Co. KG; *Int'l*, pg. 374
ALPLA WERKE LEHNER GMBH & CO KG—See Alpla-Werke Alwin Lehner GmbH & Co. KG; *Int'l*, pg. 374
AMERICAN TRADING INTERNATIONAL; *U.S. Private*, pg. 257
AMERILUX INTERNATIONAL, LLC.; *U.S. Private*, pg. 260
AMERPLAST AB—See Chiltern Capital LLP; *Int'l*, pg. 1479
APG POLYTECH, LLC; *U.S. Private*, pg. 293
ASAHI ASIA PACIFIC PTE. LTD.—See Asahi Yukizai Corporation; *Int'l*, pg. 598
ASAHI KASEI PLASTICS (HONG KONG) CO., LTD.—See Asahi Kasei Corporation; *Int'l*, pg. 596
ASAHIKASEI PLASTICS (SHANGHAI) CO., LTD.—See Asahi Kasei Corporation; *Int'l*, pg. 596
ASAHI KASEI PLASTICS SINGAPORE PTE. LTD.—See Asahi Kasei Corporation; *Int'l*, pg. 596
ASIA CHEMICAL CORPORATION INC.; *U.S. Private*, pg. 351
ATLAN PLASTICS INC.; *U.S. Private*, pg. 370
AVY PRECISION METAL COMPONENTS (SUZHOU) CO., LTD—See AVY Precision Technology, Inc.; *Int'l*, pg. 751

CORPORATE AFFILIATIONS

AYER SALES INC.; *U.S. Private*, pg. 414
BAMBERGER POLYMERS, INC.; *U.S. Private*, pg. 463
BAMBERGER POLYMERS INTERNATIONAL CORP.—See Bamberger Polymers, Inc.; *U.S. Private*, pg. 463
BANDLOCK CORPORATION INC.—See Quanex Building Products Corp.; *U.S. Public*, pg. 1749
BASF POLYURETHANES SOUTH AFRICA (PTY.) LTD.—See BASF SE; *Int'l*, pg. 881
BAYER TPU (SHENZHEN) CO. LTD.—See Bayer Aktiengesellschaft; *Int'l*, pg. 906
BELCO PACKAGING SYSTEMS INC.; *U.S. Private*, pg. 517
BIKINI.COM—See Always Summer LLC; *U.S. Private*, pg. 214
BILLERUD TENOVA BIOPLASTICS AB—See Billerud AB; *Int'l*, pg. 1030
BIO-FLEX SOLUTIONS, L.L.C.—See Repligen Corporation; *U.S. Public*, pg. 1784
BLADE-TECH INDUSTRIES, INC.; *U.S. Private*, pg. 577
BOARDMAN INDUSTRIES INC.; *U.S. Private*, pg. 602
BOBST MANCHESTER LTD—See Bobst Group S.A.; *Int'l*, pg. 1096
BRASALPLA AMAZONIA INDUSTRIA DE EMBALAGENS LTDA.—See Alpla-Werke Alwin Lehner GmbH & Co. KG; *Int'l*, pg. 374
BRASALPLA BRASIL INDUSTRIA DE EMBALAGENS LTDA.—See Alpla-Werke Alwin Lehner GmbH & Co. KG; *Int'l*, pg. 374
BRASALPLA PERNAMBUCO INDUSTRIA DE EMBALAGENS LTDA.—See Alpla-Werke Alwin Lehner GmbH & Co. KG; *Int'l*, pg. 374
B. SCHOENBERG & CO. INC.; *U.S. Private*, pg. 419
CAL THERMOPLASTICS, INC.; *U.S. Private*, pg. 715
CARCLO TECHNICAL PLASTICS SHANGHAI CO. LIMITED—See Carclo plc; *Int'l*, pg. 1321
CASCADE ENGINEERING, INC.; *U.S. Private*, pg. 779
CHASE PLASTIC SERVICES, INC.; *U.S. Private*, pg. 860
CHEMIPLASTICA PLS.MEL.TIC.VE SAN. A.S.—See Chemiplastica S.p.A.; *Int'l*, pg. 1462
CHEMIPLASTICA SA DE CV—See Chemiplastica S.p.A.; *Int'l*, pg. 1462
CHEMIPLASTICA S.A.—See Chemiplastica S.p.A.; *Int'l*, pg. 1462
CHIYODA INTEGRE SLOVAKIA, S.R.O.—See Chiyoda Integre Co., Ltd.; *Int'l*, pg. 1575
CHOU-KOU MATERIALS CO., LTD.—See Eternal Materials Co., Ltd.; *Int'l*, pg. 2520
CIRRUS INTERNATIONAL FZC—See Flame Tree Group Holdings Ltd.; *Int'l*, pg. 2698
CO-EX CORP.—See Bayer Aktiengesellschaft; *Int'l*, pg. 902
COKO WERK PLASTIK IMALAT SANAYI LIMITED—See Coko-Werk GmbH & Co. KG; *Int'l*, pg. 1696
COKO-WERK POLSKA SP. Z O.O.—See Coko-Werk GmbH & Co. KG; *Int'l*, pg. 1696
COMPOSITES ONE LLC—See Avient Corporation; *U.S. Public*, pg. 247
COMPOSITES ONE; *U.S. Private*, pg. 1002
CONSOLIDATED PLASTICS CO. INC.; *U.S. Private*, pg. 1021
CONSOLIDATED PLASTICS CORP.; *U.S. Private*, pg. 1021
COPE PLASTICS INCORPORATED; *U.S. Private*, pg. 1044
CPS CHINA CO., LTD—See CPS GmbH; *Int'l*, pg. 1826
CURBELL PLASTICS, INC.—See Curbell, Inc.; *U.S. Private*, pg. 1124
DELTA INDUSTRIES—See Zuckerman-Honickman Inc.; *U.S. Private*, pg. 4609
DESON JAPAN CO., LTD.—See Huisheng International Holdings Limited; *Int'l*, pg. 3527
DIC SOUTH ASIA PRIVATE LIMITED—See DIC Corporation; *Int'l*, pg. 2108
DR. SHRINK, INC.; *U.S. Private*, pg. 1271
DUNMORE EUROPE GMBH—See Steel Partners Holdings L.P.; *U.S. Public*, pg. 1942
EMP OF FRANKLIN INC.—See Elgin Molded Plastics Inc.; *U.S. Private*, pg. 1359
ENSINGER ASIA HOLDING PTE LTD—See Ensinger GmbH; *Int'l*, pg. 2447
ENSINGER (CHINA) CO., LTD.—See Ensinger GmbH; *Int'l*, pg. 2447
ENSINGER DANMARK A/S—See Ensinger GmbH; *Int'l*, pg. 2447
ENSINGER FRANCE S.A.R.L.—See Ensinger GmbH; *Int'l*, pg. 2447
ENSINGER INDIA ENGINEERING PLASTICS PRIVATE LTD.—See Ensinger GmbH; *Int'l*, pg. 2447
ENSINGER INDUSTRIA DE PLASTICOS TECNICOS LTDA.—See Ensinger GmbH; *Int'l*, pg. 2447
ENSINGER ITALIA S.R.L.—See Ensinger GmbH; *Int'l*, pg. 2447
ENSINGER JAPAN CO., LTD.—See Ensinger GmbH; *Int'l*, pg. 2447
ENSINGER LIMITED—See Ensinger GmbH; *Int'l*, pg. 2447
ENSINGER MALAYSIA—See Ensinger GmbH; *Int'l*, pg. 2447
ENSINGER S.A.—See Ensinger GmbH; *Int'l*, pg. 2448
ENSINGER SINTIMID GMBH—See Ensinger GmbH; *Int'l*, pg. 2448
ENSINGER S.R.O.—See Ensinger GmbH; *Int'l*, pg. 2448

N.A.I.C.S. INDEX
424610 — PLASTICS MATERIALS ...

ENSINGER SWEDEN AB—See Ensinger GmbH; *Int'l*, pg. 2448
ER&GE (UK) LIMITED—See ER&GE GmbH; *Int'l*, pg. 2488
ESSENTRA COMPONENTS B.V.—See Essentra plc; *Int'l*, pg. 2511
ESSENTRA COMPONENTS GMBH—See Essentra plc; *Int'l*, pg. 2511
E.V. ROBERTS & ASSOCIATES, INC.—See Carl Marks & Co., Inc.; *U.S. Private*, pg. 763
EXOTIC AUTOMATION & SUPPLY, INC.; *U.S. Private*, pg. 1449
FARCO PLASTICS SUPPLY INC.; *U.S. Private*, pg. 1473
FATRA, A.S.—See Agrofert Holding, a.s.; *Int'l*, pg. 219
FERTAGRA DEUTSCHLAND GMBH—See Agrofert Holding, a.s.; *Int'l*, pg. 219
FIBER GLASS HAWAII INC.; *U.S. Private*, pg. 1501
FLAMBEAU, INC. - ARTBIN DIVISION—See Nordic Group of Companies, Ltd.; *U.S. Private*, pg. 2937
FORBO SIEGLING FRANCE S.A.S.—See Forbo Holding Ltd.; *Int'l*, pg. 2730
FORTEQ CZECH S.R.O.—See forteq Group; *Int'l*, pg. 2738
FORTEQ SUZHOU LTD.—See forteq Group; *Int'l*, pg. 2738
FP TRADING CO., LTD.—See FP Corporation; *Int'l*, pg. 2756
GARWARE POLYESTER LTD. - CHIKALTHANA WORKS—See Garware Hi-Tech Films Limited; *Int'l*, pg. 2886
GARWARE POLYESTER LTD. - NASIK WORKS—See Garware Hi-Tech Films Limited; *Int'l*, pg. 2886
GARWARE POLYESTER LTD. - WALUJ WORKS—See Garware Hi-Tech Films Limited; *Int'l*, pg. 2886
GEPE-BIWEX AB—See Gepe Holding AG; *Int'l*, pg. 2942
GERRESHEIMER PLASTIC PACKAGING S.A.S.—See Gerresheimer AG; *Int'l*, pg. 2944
GLOBAL CHEM INTERNATIONAL INC.; *U.S. Private*, pg. 1712
GLOBAL CONNECTIONS PUBLIC COMPANY LIMITED; *Int'l*, pg. 2994
GOLDEN EAGLE EXTRUSIONS INC.; *U.S. Private*, pg. 1730
GRAPHIC LAMINATING, INC.; *U.S. Private*, pg. 1757
GRUPA AZOTY COMPOUNDING SP. Z O.O.—See Grupa Azoty S.A.; *Int'l*, pg. 3115
GSC TECHNOLOGIES INC.—See KL Outdoor LLC; *U.S. Private*, pg. 2317
HASCO AMERICA INC.—See Berndorf AG; *Int'l*, pg. 987
HEPWORTH PME QATAR WLL—See Hepworth PME LLC; *Int'l*, pg. 3356
HEPWORTH WLL—See Hepworth PME LLC; *Int'l*, pg. 3356
HIRSCH POROZELL GMBH—See Hirsch Servo AG; *Int'l*, pg. 3405
HIRSCH POROZELL SP. Z O.O.—See Hirsch Servo AG; *Int'l*, pg. 3406
HIRSCH POROZELL S.R.L.—See Hirsch Servo AG; *Int'l*, pg. 3406
HOP INDUSTRIES CORPORATION; *U.S. Private*, pg. 1979
HUDACO INDUSTRIES LIMITED - ASTORE KEYMAK—See Hudaco Industries Limited; *Int'l*, pg. 3521
IBEROALPLA PORTUGAL LDA—See Alpla-Werke Alwin Lehner GmbH & Co. KG; *Int'l*, pg. 374
ICC INDUSTRIES B.V.—See ICC Industries, Inc.; *U.S. Private*, pg. 2030
ICD AMERICA, LLC.—See ICD Group International Inc.; *U.S. Private*, pg. 2030
IMPEX GLOBAL, LLC—See LSCG Management, Inc.; *U.S. Private*, pg. 2508
INEOS NEWTON AYCLIFFE LIMITED—See One Rock Capital Partners, LLC; *U.S. Private*, pg. 3023
JACOBSON VAN DEN BERG (HONG KONG) LIMITED—See Chinney Alliance Group Limited; *Int'l*, pg. 1570
JAPAN FINE COATINGS CO., LTD.—See Bayer Aktiengesellschaft; *Int'l*, pg. 907
KILOP USA, INC.; *U.S. Private*, pg. 2304
KM INTERNATIONAL CORPORATION; *U.S. Private*, pg. 2321
LAIRD PLASTICS, INC.—See Blackfriars Corp.; *U.S. Private*, pg. 575
LINPAC PACKAGING AUSTRALIA PTY LTD—See Strategic Value Partners, LLC; *U.S. Private*, pg. 3836
LINPAC PACKAGING BV—See Strategic Value Partners, LLC; *U.S. Private*, pg. 3836
LINPAC PACKAGING (CHANGZHOU) CO., LTD.—See Strategic Value Partners, LLC; *U.S. Private*, pg. 3836
LINPAC PACKAGING HUNGARIA KFT—See Strategic Value Partners, LLC; *U.S. Private*, pg. 3836
LINPAC PACKAGING INFIA ITALY S.R.L.—See Strategic Value Partners, LLC; *U.S. Private*, pg. 3836
LINPAC PACKAGING PRAVIA, S.A.—See Strategic Value Partners, LLC; *U.S. Private*, pg. 3836
LINPAC PACKAGING ROMANIA S.R.L.—See Strategic Value Partners, LLC; *U.S. Private*, pg. 3836
LINPAC PACKAGING SCANDINAVIA—See Strategic Value Partners, LLC; *U.S. Private*, pg. 3836
LINPAC PACKAGING SPOL. S.R.O.—See Strategic Value Partners, LLC; *U.S. Private*, pg. 3836
LINPAC PACKAGING SRO—See Strategic Value Partners, LLC; *U.S. Private*, pg. 3836
LINPAC PACKAGING VERONA SRL—See Strategic Value Partners, LLC; *U.S. Private*, pg. 3836
LUBECKER KUNSTSTOFFWERK GMBH—See Alpla-Werke Alwin Lehner GmbH & Co. KG; *Int'l*, pg. 374
MARCO POLO INTERNATIONAL, INC.; *U.S. Private*, pg. 2572
MEDICAL INDUSTRIAL PLASTICS; *U.S. Private*, pg. 2655
MEYER PLASTICS INC.; *U.S. Private*, pg. 2692
MFP PLASTICS LIMITED—See Grafton Group plc; *Int'l*, pg. 3051
M. HOLLAND COMPANY; *U.S. Private*, pg. 2526
MIDLAND PLASTICS INC.; *U.S. Private*, pg. 2715
MINNESOTA RUBBER & PLASTICS ASIA PACIFIC PTE. LTD.—See KKR & Co. Inc.; *U.S. Public*, pg. 1263
MODERN PLASTICS INC.—See Blackfriars Corp.; *U.S. Private*, pg. 575
MOSS PIECES PLASTIQUES S.A.R.L.—See Essentra plc; *Int'l*, pg. 2511
MULTI-PLASTICS, INC.; *U.S. Private*, pg. 2812
NEPTUNE HOLDING LIMITED—See CCT Fortis Holdings Limited; *Int'l*, pg. 1370
NEXEO PLASTICS, LLC—See One Rock Capital Partners, LLC; *U.S. Private*, pg. 3022
NORDFOLIEN POLSKA SP. Z O.O.—See Berry Global Group, Inc; *U.S. Public*, pg. 322
NUPIK FRANCE EURL—See FLO S.p.A.; *Int'l*, pg. 2707
NYTEF PLASTICS LTD.; *U.S. Private*, pg. 2977
OOO AMERPLAST—See Chiltern Capital LLP; *Int'l*, pg. 1479
OOO WAVIN RUS—See Bharti Enterprises Limited; *Int'l*, pg. 1012
OSTERMAN & CO. INC.; *U.S. Private*, pg. 3048
OVARPACK - EMBALAGENS S.A.—See Strategic Value Partners, LLC; *U.S. Private*, pg. 3836
OY KOKKO-FIBER AB—See IMCD N.V.; *Int'l*, pg. 3622
PACKAGING FILM SALES, INC.—See Bunzl plc; *Int'l*, pg. 1217
PATRICK PRODUCTS, INC.—See Clearlake Capital Group, L.P.; *U.S. Private*, pg. 937
PET-POWER DEUTSCHLAND GMBH—See Berry Global Group, Inc; *U.S. Public*, pg. 322
PET POWER HANDELS GMBH—See Berry Global Group, Inc; *U.S. Public*, pg. 322
PIEDMONT PLASTICS, INC.; *U.S. Private*, pg. 3178
PLASTIAPE SP. Z O.O.—See Berry Global Group, Inc; *U.S. Public*, pg. 322
PLASTIPAK MAROC—See Plastipak Holdings, Inc.; *U.S. Private*, pg. 3199
PLASTIPRINT INC.; *U.S. Private*, pg. 3200
POLYMERSHAPES LLC—See Blackfriars Corp.; *U.S. Private*, pg. 575
POLYNT COMPOSITES FRANCE S.A.—See Reichhold, Inc.; *U.S. Private*, pg. 3390
POLYNT COMPOSITES GERMANY GMBH—See Reichhold, Inc.; *U.S. Private*, pg. 3390
POLYNT COMPOSITES MALAYSIA SDN. BHD.—See Reichhold, Inc.; *U.S. Private*, pg. 3390
POLYNT COMPOSITES POLAND SP. Z O.O.—See Reichhold, Inc.; *U.S. Private*, pg. 3390
POLYNT COMPOSITES SPAIN, S.L.—See Reichhold, Inc.; *U.S. Private*, pg. 3390
POLYNT COMPOSITES UK LTD—See Reichhold, Inc.; *U.S. Private*, pg. 3390
POLYONE DE MEXICO DISTRIBUTION, S. DE R.L. DE C.V.—See Avient Corporation; *U.S. Public*, pg. 248
POLYPLASTICS MARKETING (INDIA) PVT LTD—See Daicel Corporation; *Int'l*, pg. 1920
POLYPLASTICS SHANGHAI LTD.—See Daicel Corporation; *Int'l*, pg. 1920
PRIMEPAK COMPANY; *U.S. Private*, pg. 3263
PROFESSIONAL PLASTICS CO. LTD.—See Professional Plastics, Inc.; *U.S. Private*, pg. 3276
PROFESSIONAL PLASTICS, INC.; *U.S. Private*, pg. 3276
PROFESSIONAL PLASTICS PTE LTD.—See Professional Plastics, Inc.; *U.S. Private*, pg. 3276
PROFEX S.A.S.—See OpenGate Capital Management, LLC; *U.S. Private*, pg. 3031
PROFIALIS POLSKA SP.Z.O.O.—See OpenGate Capital Management, LLC; *U.S. Private*, pg. 3031
PROFINE BELUX BVBA—See Arcapita Group Holdings Limited; *Int'l*, pg. 542
PROFINE NEDERLAND B.V.—See Arcapita Group Holdings Limited; *Int'l*, pg. 543
PROFINE POLSKA SP. Z O.O.—See Arcapita Group Holdings Limited; *Int'l*, pg. 543
PROFINE SCHWEIZ AG—See Arcapita Group Holdings Limited; *Int'l*, pg. 543
PRT RADOMSKO SP. Z O.O.—See Alpla-Werke Alwin Lehner GmbH & Co. KG; *Int'l*, pg. 374
PWS DANMARK A/S—See Berry Global Group, Inc; *U.S. Public*, pg. 322
PWS FINLAND OY—See Berry Global Group, Inc; *U.S. Public*, pg. 322
PWS NORGE AS—See Berry Global Group, Inc; *U.S. Public*, pg. 322
RD PLASTICS COMPANY, INC.; *U.S. Private*, pg. 3362
REGAL-PIEDMONT PLASTICS, LLC—See Piedmont Plastics, Inc.; *U.S. Private*, pg. 3178
REGAL-PIEDMONT PLASTICS, LLC—See Regal Plastic Supply Co.; *U.S. Private*, pg. 3385
REGAL PLASTIC SUPPLY COMPANY, INC.; *U.S. Private*, pg. 3385
REGAL SUPPLY COMPANY INC.; *U.S. Private*, pg. 3385
REICHHOLD CZ S.R.O.—See Reichhold, Inc.; *U.S. Private*, pg. 3391
REICHHOLD GMBH—See Reichhold, Inc.; *U.S. Private*, pg. 3391
REICHHOLD OY AB—See Reichhold, Inc.; *U.S. Private*, pg. 3391
REICHHOLD POLYMERS (TIANJIN) LTD.—See Reichhold, Inc.; *U.S. Private*, pg. 3391
REICHHOLD SAS—See Reichhold, Inc.; *U.S. Private*, pg. 3391
REICHHOLD TRADING (BEIJING) LTD.—See Reichhold, Inc.; *U.S. Private*, pg. 3391
RESIN FORMULATORS—See Carl Marks & Co., Inc.; *U.S. Private*, pg. 763
RESINTECH INC.; *U.S. Private*, pg. 3406
RESIN TECHNOLOGY LLC; *U.S. Private*, pg. 3405
ROCHEUX INTERNATIONAL INC.; *U.S. Private*, pg. 3464
ROCHEUX INTERNATIONAL—See Rocheux International Inc.; *U.S. Private*, pg. 3464
ROSSI COMERCIAL IMP. EXP. LTDA.—See ICC Industries, Inc.; *U.S. Private*, pg. 2030
ROTOTRON CORPORATION; *U.S. Private*, pg. 3487
RPC BEBO PLASTIK GMBH—See Berry Global Group, Inc; *U.S. Public*, pg. 324
RPC BRAMLAGE - LAINATE—See Berry Global Group, Inc; *U.S. Public*, pg. 324
RPC PROMENS AS—See Berry Global Group, Inc; *U.S. Public*, pg. 325
RPC PROMENS BJAEVERSKOV A/S—See Berry Global Group, Inc; *U.S. Public*, pg. 325
RPC PROMENS GROUP AS—See Berry Global Group, Inc; *U.S. Public*, pg. 325
RPC SUPERFOS BALKAN D.O.O.—See Berry Global Group, Inc; *U.S. Public*, pg. 325
RPC SUPERFOS ITALY S.R.L.—See Berry Global Group, Inc; *U.S. Public*, pg. 325
RPC SUPERFOS LA GENETE SAS—See Berry Global Group, Inc; *U.S. Public*, pg. 325
RPC SUPERFOS PAMPLONA SA—See Berry Global Group, Inc; *U.S. Public*, pg. 325
RPC SUPERFOS POLAND SP. Z O.O.—See Berry Global Group, Inc; *U.S. Public*, pg. 325
RPC SUPERFOS PORI OY—See Berry Global Group, Inc; *U.S. Public*, pg. 325
SAEPLAST NORWAY AS—See Berry Global Group, Inc; *U.S. Public*, pg. 325
SAMBRAILO PACKAGING INC.; *U.S. Private*, pg. 3536
S.C. ALPLA PLASTIC S.R.L.—See Alpla-Werke Alwin Lehner GmbH & Co. KG; *Int'l*, pg. 374
SHANNON INDUSTRIAL CORPORATION; *U.S. Private*, pg. 3625
SPA GALION ALGERIE—See Berry Global Group, Inc; *U.S. Public*, pg. 325
SPRAYCOM COMERCIO DE PECAS PARA AGRICOLTURA S.A.—See Emak S.p.A.; *Int'l*, pg. 2373
STRETCH ASSOCIATES, INC.; *U.S. Private*, pg. 3839
SUNCLEAR SRL—See Arkema S.A.; *Int'l*, pg. 571
TAGHLEEF INDUSTRIES GMBH—See Al Ghurair Group; *Int'l*, pg. 277
TAGHLEEF INDUSTRIES S.A.E.—See Al Ghurair Group; *Int'l*, pg. 277
TAGHLEEF INDUSTRIES S.L.U.—See Al Ghurair Group; *Int'l*, pg. 278
TECHNI-COAT INTERNATIONAL N.V.—See Akzo Nobel N.V.; *Int'l*, pg. 275
TELKO LTD.—See Aspo Oyj; *Int'l*, pg. 631
TOHKOHJUSHI CO., LTD.—See Fujikura Kasei Co., Ltd.; *Int'l*, pg. 2827
TRANSILWRAP COMPANY, INC.—See Nicolet Capital Partners, LLC; *U.S. Private*, pg. 2926
TRIAD PLASTICS INC.; *U.S. Private*, pg. 4225
TRI-STAR PLASTICS CORPORATION; *U.S. Private*, pg. 4223
TUPPERWARE AUSTRALIA PTY. LTD.—See Tupperware Brands Corporation; *U.S. Public*, pg. 2204
TUPPERWARE DEUTSCHLAND GMBH—See Tupperware Brands Corporation; *U.S. Public*, pg. 2204
TUPPERWARE D.O.O.—See Tupperware Brands Corporation; *U.S. Public*, pg. 2205
TUPPERWARE PRODUCTS, INC. WILMINGTON—See Tupperware Brands Corporation; *U.S. Public*, pg. 2204
TUPPERWARE (SUISSE) SA—See Tupperware Brands Corporation; *U.S. Public*, pg. 2204
UAB WAVIN BALTIC—See Bharti Enterprises Limited; *Int'l*, pg. 1012
VALUE VINYLS INC.; *U.S. Private*, pg. 4337
VINMAR INTERNATIONAL LIMITED; *U.S. Private*, pg. 4385
VINNOLIT SCHKOPAU GMBH—See Westlake Corporation; *U.S. Public*, pg. 2360
VSC PLASTICS COMPANY LIMITED—See Hong Kong Shanghai Alliance Holdings Limited; *Int'l*, pg. 3467
WAVIN GMBH—See Bharti Enterprises Limited; *Int'l*, pg. 1012

424610 — PLASTICS MATERIALS ...

WAVIN ITALIA S.P.A.—See Bharti Enterprises Limited; *Int'l*, pg. 1012
WAVIN UKRAIN O.O.O.T.O.V.—See Bharti Enterprises Limited; *Int'l*, pg. 1013
WEB-DON INC.; *U.S. Private*, pg. 4464
WIKO-USA INC.—See Berry Global Group, Inc; *U.S. Public*, pg. 324
WILFERT CHEMICAL NORDIC A/S—See Aspo Oyj; *Int'l*, pg. 631
YF INTERNATIONAL; *U.S. Private*, pg. 4589
ZAMIL ALPLA PLASTIC - MIDDLE EAST, LIMITED—See Alpla-Werke Alwin Lehner GmbH & Co. KG; *Int'l*, pg. 374
ZAO BAYER—See Bayer Aktiengesellschaft; *Int'l*, pg. 910
ZELLER PLASTIK SHANGHAI LIMITED—See Berry Global Group, Inc; *U.S. Public*, pg. 326
ZHENJIANG CHIMEI CHEMICAL CO., LTD.—See Chi Mei Group; *Int'l*, pg. 1475

424690 — OTHER CHEMICAL AND ALLIED PRODUCTS MERCHANT WHOLESALERS

1283465 ONTARIO INC.—See Swisher Hygiene Inc.; *U.S. Private*, pg. 3894
3M A/S—See 3M Company; *U.S. Public*, pg. 5
3M CANADA COMPANY—See 3M Company; *U.S. Public*, pg. 5
3M CHILE S.A.—See 3M Company; *U.S. Public*, pg. 5
3M DOMINICANA S.A.—See 3M Company; *U.S. Public*, pg. 5
3M ECUADOR C.A.—See 3M Company; *U.S. Public*, pg. 5
3M GUATEMALA, S.A.—See 3M Company; *U.S. Public*, pg. 6
3M HONG KONG LIMITED—See 3M Company; *U.S. Public*, pg. 6
3M INDIA LTD.—See 3M Company; *U.S. Public*, pg. 6
3M INTERAMERICA, INC.—See 3M Company; *U.S. Public*, pg. 6
3M INTERAMERICA, INC.—See 3M Company; *U.S. Public*, pg. 6
3M INTERAMERICA, INC. (TRINIDAD & TOBAGO DIV.)—See 3M Company; *U.S. Public*, pg. 6
3M KENYA LTD.—See 3M Company; *U.S. Public*, pg. 6
3M KOREA LTD.—See 3M Company; *U.S. Public*, pg. 6
3M MANUFACTURING VENEZUELA S.A.—See 3M Company; *U.S. Public*, pg. 6
3M NEDERLAND B.V.—See 3M Company; *U.S. Public*, pg. 6
3M NEW ZEALAND LTD.—See 3M Company; *U.S. Public*, pg. 6
3M NORGE A/S—See 3M Company; *U.S. Public*, pg. 6
3M OESTERREICH GES MBH—See 3M Company; *U.S. Public*, pg. 6
3M PANAMA S.A.—See 3M Company; *U.S. Public*, pg. 6
3M PERU S.A.—See 3M Company; *U.S. Public*, pg. 6
3M PHILIPPINES—See 3M Company; *U.S. Public*, pg. 6
3M PRECISION GRINDING GMBH—See 3M Company; *U.S. Public*, pg. 7
3M PUERTO RICO, INC.—See 3M Company; *U.S. Public*, pg. 7
3M RUSSIA—See 3M Company; *U.S. Public*, pg. 7
3M SANAYI VE TICARET AŞ—See 3M Company; *U.S. Public*, pg. 7
3M SINGAPORE PTE. LTD.—See 3M Company; *U.S. Public*, pg. 7
3M SOUTH AFRICA (PTY.) LTD.—See 3M Company; *U.S. Public*, pg. 7
3M (SUISSE) SA—See 3M Company; *U.S. Public*, pg. 5
3M TAIWAN LIMITED—See 3M Company; *U.S. Public*, pg. 7
3M UNITED KINGDOM, PLC—See 3M Company; *U.S. Public*, pg. 7
3M URUGUAY SA—See 3M Company; *U.S. Public*, pg. 7
5N PLUS ASIA LIMITED—See 5N Plus Inc.; *Int'l*, pg. 13
5N PLUS BELGIUM SA—See 5N Plus Inc.; *Int'l*, pg. 13
5N PLUS LUBECK GMBH—See 5N Plus Inc.; *Int'l*, pg. 13
5N PLUS UK LIMITED—See 5N Plus Inc.; *Int'l*, pg. 13
5N PLUS WISCONSIN INC—See 5N Plus Inc.; *Int'l*, pg. 13
5N PV GMBH—See 5N Plus Inc.; *Int'l*, pg. 13
THE 707 COMPANY—See Safeguard Chemical Corporation; *U.S. Private*, pg. 3524
7324215 CANADA INC.—See Swisher Hygiene Inc.; *U.S. Private*, pg. 3894
AAKASH CHEMICALS & DYESTUFFS, INC.—See CenterOak Partners LLC; *U.S. Private*, pg. 816
ACCENTUATE LIMITED; *Int'l*, pg. 82
ACCESS BUSINESS GROUP—See Alticor Inc.; *U.S. Private*, pg. 208
ACCOLADE FRANCE SAS—See Apollo Global Management, Inc.; *U.S. Public*, pg. 165
ACCURATE CHEMICAL & SCIENTIFIC CORPORATION; *U.S. Private*, pg. 55
ACETO B.V.—See Aceto Corporation; *U.S. Private*, pg. 58
ACETO CORPORATION; *U.S. Private*, pg. 58
ACETO FINECHEM GMBH—See Aceto Corporation; *U.S. Private*, pg. 58
ACETO FRANCE S.A.S.—See Aceto Corporation; *U.S. Private*, pg. 58

ACETO PHARMA GMBH—See Aceto Corporation; *U.S. Private*, pg. 58
ACETO PTE LTD.—See Aceto Corporation; *U.S. Private*, pg. 58
ACI CHEMICALS LTD.—See Advanced Chemical Industries Limited; *Int'l*, pg. 158
ACIDS CO., LTD.—See Dowa Holdings Co., Ltd.; *Int'l*, pg. 2183
ACME-HARDESTY CO.—See Jacob Stern & Sons, Inc.; *U.S. Private*, pg. 2179
ADAPCO, LLC—See EQT AB; *Int'l*, pg. 2469
ADEKA (ASIA) PTE. LTD.—See Adeka Corporation; *Int'l*, pg. 141
ADEKA CHEMICAL SUPPLY CORPORATION—See Adeka Corporation; *Int'l*, pg. 141
ADEKA (CHINA) CO., LTD.—See Adeka Corporation; *Int'l*, pg. 141
ADEKA CLEAN AID CORPORATION—See Adeka Corporation; *Int'l*, pg. 141
ADEKA USA CORP.—See Adeka Corporation; *Int'l*, pg. 142
ADHESIVES RESEARCH PTE LTD.—See Adhesive Research, Inc.; *U.S. Private*, pg. 79
ADVANCED POLYMER TECHNOLOGY CORPORATION; *U.S. Private*, pg. 92
AGC CHEMICALS ASIA PACIFIC PTE. LTD.—See AGC Inc.; *Int'l*, pg. 201
AGC CHEMICALS EUROPE, LTD.—See AGC Inc.; *Int'l*, pg. 202
AGC CHEMICALS TRADING (SHANGHAI) CO., LTD.—See AGC Inc.; *Int'l*, pg. 201
AGCO AUSTRALIA LTD.—See AGCO Corporation; *U.S. Public*, pg. 58
AGCO DANMARK A/S—See AGCO Corporation; *U.S. Public*, pg. 58
AGCO IBERIA SA—See AGCO Corporation; *U.S. Public*, pg. 58
AGCO SPZOO—See AGCO Corporation; *U.S. Public*, pg. 59
A.G. LAYNE INC.; *U.S. Private*, pg. 25
AGRI PHIL CORPORATION—See Calata Corporation; *Int'l*, pg. 1261
AGROCHEM PULAWY SP. Z O.O.—See Grupa Azoty S.A.; *Int'l*, pg. 3116
AGROFERT CHINA CO LTD—See Agrofert Holding, a.s.; *Int'l*, pg. 218
AGROKRAJINA A.D.; *Int'l*, pg. 220
AGRONAMIC (PTY) LTD—See Element Solutions Inc.; *U.S. Public*, pg. 725
AGROPODNIK DOMAZLICE A. S.—See Agrofert Holding, a.s.; *Int'l*, pg. 218
AG SCIENTIFIC, INC.—See Research Products International Corporation; *U.S. Private*, pg. 3404
AIR LIQUIDE WELDING CENTRAL EUROPE S.R.O.—See Lincoln Electric Holdings, Inc.; *U.S. Public*, pg. 1316
AIR LIQUIDE WELDING LUXEMBOURG S.A.—See Lincoln Electric Holdings, Inc.; *U.S. Public*, pg. 1316
AIR LIQUIDE WELDING MIDDLE EAST FZE—See Lincoln Electric Holdings, Inc.; *U.S. Public*, pg. 1316
AIR LIQUIDE WELDING (THAILAND) LTD—See Lincoln Electric Holdings, Inc.; *U.S. Public*, pg. 1316
AIR PRODUCTS & CHEMICALS, INC.; *U.S. Public*, pg. 64
AIR PRODUCTS GAS O.O.O.—See Air Products & Chemicals, Inc.; *U.S. Public*, pg. 65
AIR PRODUCTS GAZ SANAYI VI TICARET LIMITED—See Air Products & Chemicals, Inc.; *U.S. Public*, pg. 65
AIR PRODUCTS IRELAND LIMITED—See Air Products & Chemicals, Inc.; *U.S. Public*, pg. 65
AIR PRODUCTS MALAYSIA SDN BHD—See Air Products & Chemicals, Inc.; *U.S. Public*, pg. 65
AIR PRODUCTS PERFORMANCE MATERIALS GMBH—See Air Products & Chemicals, Inc.; *U.S. Public*, pg. 65
AIR PRODUCTS S.A.—See Air Products & Chemicals, Inc.; *U.S. Public*, pg. 65
AIR PRODUCTS SAS—See Air Products & Chemicals, Inc.; *U.S. Public*, pg. 65
AIR PRODUCTS SCHLUCHTERN GMBH—See Air Products & Chemicals, Inc.; *U.S. Public*, pg. 65
AIR PRODUCTS SLOVAKIA S.R.O.—See Air Products & Chemicals, Inc.; *U.S. Public*, pg. 66
AIR PRODUCTS SPOL S.R.O.—See Air Products & Chemicals, Inc.; *U.S. Public*, pg. 66
AIRWELD INC.; *U.S. Private*, pg. 142
AKASHI SDN. BHD.—See BRENNTAG SE; *Int'l*, pg. 1146
AKEMI BRASIL INDUSTRIA E COMERCIO LTDA.—See AKEMI chemisch technische Spezialfabrik GmbH; *Int'l*, pg. 262
AKEMI TECHNOLOGY INDIA PRIVATE LIMITED—See AKEMI chemisch technische Spezialfabrik GmbH; *Int'l*, pg. 262
AKISHIMA CHEMICAL INDUSTRIES CO., LTD—See Open-Gate Capital Management, LLC; *U.S. Private*, pg. 3030
AKROCHEM CORPORATION; *U.S. Private*, pg. 146
AKROS TRADING CO., LTD.—See Denki Company Limited; *Int'l*, pg. 2027
AKZO NOBEL ASIA CO., LTD.—See Akzo Nobel N.V.; *Int'l*, pg. 268
AKZO NOBEL CELLULOSIC SPECIALTIES INC.—See Akzo Nobel N.V.; *Int'l*, pg. 269

AKZO NOBEL SURFACE CHEMISTRY AB—See Akzo Nobel N.V.; *Int'l*, pg. 273
ALCOTRADE INC.; *U.S. Private*, pg. 154
ALENT ENTHONE CHEMISTRY (SHANGHAI) CO. LTD.—See Element Solutions Inc.; *U.S. Public*, pg. 726
ALENT HONG KONG LTD—See Element Solutions Inc.; *U.S. Public*, pg. 726
ALENT ITALIA SRL—See Element Solutions Inc.; *U.S. Public*, pg. 726
ALEXANDER CHEMICAL CORPORATION; *U.S. Private*, pg. 163
ALIANCYS FRANCE SAS—See CVC Capital Partners SICAV-FIS S.A.; *Int'l*, pg. 1886
ALIANCYS ITALIA S.R.L.—See CVC Capital Partners SICAV-FIS S.A.; *Int'l*, pg. 1886
ALKYL AMINES CHEMICALS LIMITED; *Int'l*, pg. 331
ALLCHEM INDUSTRIES GROUP; *U.S. Private*, pg. 175
ALLCHEM INDUSTRIES INDUSTRIAL CHEMICALS GROUP—See AllChem Industries Group; *U.S. Private*, pg. 175
ALLCHEM INDUSTRIES PERFORMANCE PRODUCTS—See AllChem Industries Group; *U.S. Private*, pg. 175
ALLCHEM INDUSTRIES PETROLEUM CHEMICALS GROUP—See AllChem Industries Group; *U.S. Private*, pg. 175
ALLCOAT TECHNOLOGY, INC.; *U.S. Private*, pg. 175
ALLIANCE CHIMIE ALGERIE SPA—See BRENNTAG SE; *Int'l*, pg. 1146
ALLIANCE TUNISIE S.A.R.L.—See BRENNTAG SE; *Int'l*, pg. 1146
ALLIED ENERGY CORP.; *U.S. Public*, pg. 80
ALPAC MARKETING SERVICES INC.; *U.S. Private*, pg. 196
ALPHA DYNO NOBEL; *U.S. Private*, pg. 197
ALPHAMIN S.A.—See BRENNTAG SE; *Int'l*, pg. 1146
AMBITO DAS S.A.—See Corteva, Inc.; *U.S. Public*, pg. 581
AMBRATEC GMBH—See Berner SE; *Int'l*, pg. 988
AMERCHOL CORPORATION—See Dow Inc.; *U.S. Public*, pg. 686
AMERICAN GAS PRODUCTS, LLC.—See Air Water Inc.; *U.S. Public*, pg. 239
AMERICAN OSMENT; *U.S. Private*, pg. 242
AMERICO CHEMICAL PRODUCTS, INC.—See Harbour Group Industries, Inc.; *U.S. Private*, pg. 1860
AMPCO MARKETING, L.L.C.—See Chevron Corporation; *U.S. Public*, pg. 487
AMPCO MARKETING, L.L.C.—See ConocoPhillips; *U.S. Public*, pg. 568
AMVAC CHEMICAL UK LTD.—See American Vanguard Corporation; *U.S. Public*, pg. 111
AMVAC MEXICO S. DE R.L. DE C.V.—See American Vanguard Corporation; *U.S. Public*, pg. 111
AMWAY CORPORATION—See Alticor Inc.; *U.S. Private*, pg. 208
ANQORE B.V.—See CVC Capital Partners SICAV-FIS S.A.; *Int'l*, pg. 1886
ANSA COATINGS JAMAICA LIMITED—See ANSA McAL Limited; *Int'l*, pg. 477
AOC (UK) LTD.—See The Alpha Corporation of Tennessee; *U.S. Private*, pg. 3984
APPLE FLAVOR & FRAGRANCE USA CORP.—See Apple Flavor & Fragrance Group Co., Ltd.; *Int'l*, pg. 520
APTECH GROUP, INC.; *U.S. Private*, pg. 302
AQUA-SERV ENGINEERS INC.—See Harpure Enterprises Inc.; *U.S. Private*, pg. 1868
ARABIAN CHEMICAL COMPANY (LATEX) LTD.—See Dow Inc.; *U.S. Public*, pg. 683
ARABIAN CHEMICAL COMPANY (LATEX) LTD.—See E.A. Juffali & Brothers Company; *Int'l*, pg. 2250
ARABIAN CHEMICAL COMPANY (POLYSTYRENE) LIMITED—See Dow Inc.; *U.S. Public*, pg. 683
ARABIAN CHEMICAL COMPANY (POLYSTYRENE) LIMITED—See E.A. Juffali & Brothers Company; *Int'l*, pg. 2251
ARCHROMA U.S., INC.—See SK Capital Partners, LP; *U.S. Private*, pg. 3679
ARCHWAY SALES, LLC—See One Rock Capital Partners, LLC; *U.S. Private*, pg. 3022
ARC PRODUCTS, INC.—See Lincoln Electric Holdings, Inc.; *U.S. Public*, pg. 1317
ARKEMA B.V.—See Arkema S.A.; *Int'l*, pg. 568
ARKEMA COATEX BRASIL INDUSTRIA E COMERCIO LTDA.—See Arkema S.A.; *Int'l*, pg. 569
ARKEMA COATINGS RESINS, S.A.U.—See Arkema S.A.; *Int'l*, pg. 569
ARKEMA CO. LTD—See Arkema S.A.; *Int'l*, pg. 569
ARKEMA DEUTSCHLAND GMBH—See Arkema S.A.; *Int'l*, pg. 569
ARKEMA K.K.—See Arkema S.A.; *Int'l*, pg. 569
ARKEMA LTD—See Arkema S.A.; *Int'l*, pg. 569
ARKEMA MEXICO S.A DE C.V—See Arkema S.A.; *Int'l*, pg. 569
ARKEMA NORTH EUROPE B.V.—See Arkema S.A.; *Int'l*, pg. 569
ARKEMA PTY. LTD.—See Arkema S.A.; *Int'l*, pg. 569
ARKEMA QUIMICA S.A—See Arkema S.A.; *Int'l*, pg. 569

N.A.I.C.S. INDEX

424690 — OTHER CHEMICAL AND ...

ARKEMA SHANGHAI DISTRIBUTION CO. LTD—See Arkema S.A.; *Int'l*, pg. 569
ARKEMA SP Z.O.O—See Arkema S.A.; *Int'l*, pg. 570
ARLA FOODS INGREDIENTS, INC.—See Arla Foods amba; *Int'l*, pg. 572
ARLA FOODS INGREDIENTS K.K.—See Arla Foods amba; *Int'l*, pg. 572
ARLA FOODS INGREDIENTS KOREA CO., LTD.—See Arla Foods amba; *Int'l*, pg. 572
ARLA FOODS INGREDIENTS S.A. DE C.V.—See Arla Foods amba; *Int'l*, pg. 572
AROMA S.A.—See International Flavors & Fragrances Inc.; *U.S. Public*, pg. 1151
ASAHI KASEI AMERICA, INC.—See Asahi Kasei Corporation; *Int'l*, pg. 595
ASAHI KASEI CHEMICALS KOREA CO., LTD.—See Asahi Kasei Corporation; *Int'l*, pg. 595
ASAHI ORGANIC CHEMICALS TRADING (SHANGHAI) CO., LTD.—See Asahi Yukizai Corporation; *Int'l*, pg. 598
ASAHI PHOTOPRODUCTS (UK) LTD.—See Asahi Kasei Corporation; *Int'l*, pg. 596
ASAHI YUKI HANBAI NISHI-NIHON K.K.—See Asahi Yukizai Corporation; *Int'l*, pg. 598
ASCENT AVIATION GROUP, INC.—See World Kinect Corporation; *U.S. Public*, pg. 2380
ASHLAND CZ S.R.O.—See Ashland Inc.; *U.S. Public*, pg. 211
ASHLAND INDUSTRIES EUROPE GMBH—See Ashland Inc.; *U.S. Public*, pg. 211
ASHLAND RHONE HOLDINGS B.V.—See Ashland Inc.; *U.S. Public*, pg. 212
ASHLAND SPECIALTIES BELGIUM BVBA—See Ashland Inc.; *U.S. Public*, pg. 212
ASHLAND SPECIALTIES HISPANIA S.L.—See Ashland Inc.; *U.S. Public*, pg. 212
ASHLAND SPECIALTIES SVERIGE AB—See Ashland Inc.; *U.S. Public*, pg. 212
ASHLAND SPECIALTIES UK LIMITED—See Ashland Inc.; *U.S. Public*, pg. 212
ASK CHEMICALS BENELUX B.V.—See Rhone Group, LLC; *U.S. Private*, pg. 3423
ASPOKEM INTERNATIONAL B.V.—See Aspo Oyj; *Int'l*, pg. 631
ATRO PROVITA GMBH—See Gelita AG; *Int'l*, pg. 2913
AUDAX-KECK GMBH; *Int'l*, pg. 700
AUSTIN CHEMICAL COMPANY INC.; *U.S. Private*, pg. 395
AVENUE INDUSTRIAL SUPPLY CO. LTD.—See Franz Haniel & Cie. GmbH; *Int'l*, pg. 2763
AVIENT JAPAN K.K.—See Avient Corporation; *U.S. Public*, pg. 247
AVIENT LUXEMBOURG S.A R.L.—See Avient Corporation; *U.S. Public*, pg. 247
AVK SEALING TECHNOLOGY (KUNSHAN) CO. LTD.—See AVK Holding A/S; *Int'l*, pg. 747
AV POUND & CO LTD—See Hobart Enterprises Ltd; *Int'l*, pg. 3436
AWAX S.P.A.; *Int'l*, pg. 752
AXCHEM SOLUTIONS INC.; *U.S. Private*, pg. 412
AXYS; *U.S. Private*, pg. 414
AZELIS AMERICAS—See EQT AB; *Int'l*, pg. 2469
AZELIS AUSTRALIA PTY. LIMITED—See EQT AB; *Int'l*, pg. 2469
AZELIS BULGARIA EAD—See EQT AB; *Int'l*, pg. 2469
AZELIS CANADA, INC.—See EQT AB; *Int'l*, pg. 2469
AZELIS CZECH REPUBLIC, S.R.O.—See EQT AB; *Int'l*, pg. 2469
AZELIS DEUTSCHLAND GMBH—See EQT AB; *Int'l*, pg. 2469
AZELIS DEUTSCHLAND KOSMETIK GMBH—See EQT AB; *Int'l*, pg. 2469
AZELIS ESPANA, S.A.—See EQT AB; *Int'l*, pg. 2469
AZELIS INDIA PRIVATE LIMITED—See EQT AB; *Int'l*, pg. 2469
AZELIS RUSSIA—See EQT AB; *Int'l*, pg. 2469
AZELIS S.A.—See EQT AB; *Int'l*, pg. 2469
AZELIS SERBIA—See EQT AB; *Int'l*, pg. 2469
AZELIS UK LIFE SCIENCES LTD—See EQT AB; *Int'l*, pg. 2469
BAC BV—See Thermo Fisher Scientific Inc.; *U.S. Public*, pg. 2145
BAKER PETROLITE LIMITED—See Baker Hughes Company; *U.S. Public*, pg. 265
BAMBERGER POLYMERS (CANADA), INC.—See Bamberger Polymers, Inc.; *U.S. Private*, pg. 463
BANNER CHEMICALS-BLUECAT-ADBLUE SOLUTIONS—See Banner Chemicals Limited; *Int'l*, pg. 851
BANNER CHEMICALS-OIL FIELD APPLICATIONS—See Banner Chemicals Limited; *Int'l*, pg. 851
BANNER CHEMICALS-SPECIALTY CHEMICALS—See Banner Chemicals Limited; *Int'l*, pg. 851
BANNER MEDICAL INC.—See MiddleGround Management, LP; *U.S. Private*, pg. 2711
BARRINGTON CHEMICAL CORP; *U.S. Private*, pg. 480
BARTON SOLVENTS INC.; *U.S. Private*, pg. 483
BASF AB—See BASF SE; *Int'l*, pg. 871
BASF AFRIQUE DE L'OUEST S.A.R.L—See BASF SE; *Int'l*, pg. 872

BASF AMERICAS CORPORATION—See BASF SE; *Int'l*, pg. 872
BASF A/S—See BASF SE; *Int'l*, pg. 871
BASF AS—See BASF SE; *Int'l*, pg. 872
BASF AUSTRALIA LTD.—See BASF SE; *Int'l*, pg. 877
BASF BELGIUM S.A./N.V.—See BASF SE; *Int'l*, pg. 872
BASF BOLIVIA S.R.L.—See BASF SE; *Int'l*, pg. 872
BASF CATALYSTS LLC—See BASF SE; *Int'l*, pg. 875
BASF CHILE S.A.—See BASF SE; *Int'l*, pg. 872
BASF COLOR SOLUTIONS FRANCE S.A.S.—See BASF SE; *Int'l*, pg. 874
BASF CONSTRUCTION CHEMICALS (CHINA) CO. LTD.—See BASF SE; *Int'l*, pg. 874
BASF CONSTRUCTION CHEMICALS SOUTH AFRICA (PTY) LTD.—See BASF SE; *Int'l*, pg. 881
BASF CORP. - CHARLOTTE (STEELE CREEK) TECHNICAL CENTER—See BASF SE; *Int'l*, pg. 876
BASF CORP. - NEWPORT PLANT—See BASF SE; *Int'l*, pg. 876
BASF CORP. - SUPERABSORBENTS NORTH AMERICA—See BASF SE; *Int'l*, pg. 876
BASF CORP. - TUCSON - MINING CHEMICALS—See BASF SE; *Int'l*, pg. 876
BASF DE COSTA RICA S.A.—See BASF SE; *Int'l*, pg. 882
BASF DE EL SALVADOR, S.A. DE C.V.—See BASF SE; *Int'l*, pg. 882
BASF DOMINICANA S.A.—See BASF SE; *Int'l*, pg. 877
BASF ECUATORIANA S.A.—See BASF SE; *Int'l*, pg. 878
BASF HUNGARIA KFT.—See BASF SE; *Int'l*, pg. 879
BASF INTERTRADE CORPORATION—See BASF SE; *Int'l*, pg. 876
BASF IRAN AG—See BASF SE; *Int'l*, pg. 879
BASF ITALIA S.P.A.—See BASF SE; *Int'l*, pg. 879
BASF KANOO GULF FZE—See BASF SE; *Int'l*, pg. 879
BASF LTD.—See BASF SE; *Int'l*, pg. 880
BASF MAROC S.A.—See BASF SE; *Int'l*, pg. 880
BASF METASHEEN—See BASF SE; *Int'l*, pg. 880
BASF NEW ZEALAND LTD.—See BASF SE; *Int'l*, pg. 877
BASF OY—See BASF SE; *Int'l*, pg. 880
BASF PANAMA S.A.—See BASF SE; *Int'l*, pg. 880
BASF PARAGUAYA S.A.—See BASF SE; *Int'l*, pg. 880
BASF PHILIPPINES, INC.—See BASF SE; *Int'l*, pg. 880
BASF PLC—See BASF SE; *Int'l*, pg. 882
BASF POLYURETHANES—See BASF SE; *Int'l*, pg. 872
BASF PORTUGUESA, LDA.—See BASF SE; *Int'l*, pg. 881
BASF QUIMICA COLOMBIANA S.A.—See BASF SE; *Int'l*, pg. 881
BASF SAUDI ARABIA LIMITED COMPANY—See BASF SE; *Int'l*, pg. 881
BASF (SCHWEIZ) AG - BASEL SITE—See BASF SE; *Int'l*, pg. 871
BASF SE - LAENDERBEREICH VERTRIEB EUROPE—See BASF SE; *Int'l*, pg. 881
BASF SINGAPORE PTE. LTD.—See BASF SE; *Int'l*, pg. 878
BASF SLOVENIJA D.O.O.—See BASF SE; *Int'l*, pg. 881
BASF SLOVENSKO S.R.O.—See BASF SE; *Int'l*, pg. 881
BASF SOUTH AFRICA (PTY.) LTD.—See BASF SE; *Int'l*, pg. 881
BASF S.P.A.—See BASF SE; *Int'l*, pg. 881
BASF SPOL. S.R.O.—See BASF SE; *Int'l*, pg. 882
BASF SRBIJA D.O.O.—See BASF SE; *Int'l*, pg. 881
BASF S.R.L.—See BASF SE; *Int'l*, pg. 881
BASF TUERK KIMYA SANAYI VE TICARET LTD. STI.—See BASF SE; *Int'l*, pg. 881
BASF TUERK KIMYA SANAYI VE TICARET LTD. STI.—See BASF SE; *Int'l*, pg. 881
BASF TUNISIE S.A.—See BASF SE; *Int'l*, pg. 881
BASF UAB - LATVIA—See BASF SE; *Int'l*, pg. 882
BASF UK LIMITED—See BASF SE; *Int'l*, pg. 882
BASF US VERWALTUNG GMBH—See BASF SE; *Int'l*, pg. 882
BASF WATERTECHNOLOGIES GMBH & CO. KG—See BASF SE; *Int'l*, pg. 882
BASF YAPI KIMYASALLARI SAN A/S—See BASF SE; *Int'l*, pg. 875
BAVARIA CARBON SPECIALITIES GMBH—See Graphite India Ltd; *Int'l*, pg. 3061
BAYER AUSTRIA GMBH.—See Bayer Aktiengesellschaft; *Int'l*, pg. 902
BAYER B.V.—See Bayer Aktiengesellschaft; *Int'l*, pg. 902
BAYER CROPSCIENCE, INC.—See Bayer Aktiengesellschaft; *Int'l*, pg. 903
BAYER-HANDELSGESELLSCHAFT MIT BESCHRANKTER HAFTUNG—See Bayer Aktiengesellschaft; *Int'l*, pg. 906
BAYER HELLAS AG—See Bayer Aktiengesellschaft; *Int'l*, pg. 905
BDI DISTRIBUTION WEST INC.—See Apollo Global Management, Inc.; *U.S. Public*, pg. 165
BEHN MEYER CHEMICALS (PHILIPPINES) INC.—See Behn Meyer (D) Holding AG & Co.; *Int'l*, pg. 941
BEHN MEYER CHEMICALS (QINGDAO) CO., LTD—See Behn Meyer (D) Holding AG & Co.; *Int'l*, pg. 941
BEHN MEYER CHEMICALS TAIWAN CO., LTD—See Behn Meyer (D) Holding AG & Co.; *Int'l*, pg. 941
BEHN MEYER CHEMICALS (T) CO., LTD—See Behn Meyer (D) Holding AG & Co.; *Int'l*, pg. 941
BEHN MEYER GROUP MALAYSIA—See Behn Meyer (D) Holding AG & Co.; *Int'l*, pg. 941

BEHN MEYER GROUP SINGAPORE—See Behn Meyer (D) Holding AG & Co.; *Int'l*, pg. 941
BEHN MEYER GROUP VIETNAM—See Behn Meyer (D) Holding AG & Co.; *Int'l*, pg. 941
BEHR PROCESS CORPORATION—See Masco Corporation; *U.S. Public*, pg. 1389
BELCO TECHNOLOGIES CORPORATION—See DuPont de Nemours, Inc.; *U.S. Public*, pg. 692
BENETECH INVESTMENTS CORP; *U.S. Private*, pg. 525
BENTECH S.A. (PTY) LTD.—See Benetech Investments Corp; *U.S. Private*, pg. 525
BEN WEITSMAN & SON INC.; *U.S. Private*, pg. 523
BERRYMAN PRODUCTS, INC.; *U.S. Private*, pg. 538
BG AGRO JSC; *Int'l*, pg. 1006
BIDDLE SAWYER CORPORATION; *U.S. Private*, pg. 551
BIEFFE MEDITAL NEDERLAND N.V.—See Baxter International Inc.; *U.S. Public*, pg. 281
B.I.G. MARKETING SDN. BHD.—See B.I.G. Industries Berhad; *Int'l*, pg. 790
BIO-CHEM TECHNOLOGY (HK) LIMITED—See Global Biochem Technology Group Company Limited; *Int'l*, pg. 2993
BIOFUEL ENERGY SYSTEMS, LLC—See Rentech, Inc.; *U.S. Private*, pg. 3400
BIO-RAD FRANCE HOLDING—See Bio-Rad Laboratories, Inc.; *U.S. Public*, pg. 332
BIOSUN BIOCHEMICALS, INC.—See BRAIN Biotech AG; *Int'l*, pg. 1137
BIOTAGE—See Biotage AB; *Int'l*, pg. 1042
BISLEY & COMPANY PTY. LTD.; *Int'l*, pg. 1049
BLUE CUBE BELGIUM BVBA—See Olin Corporation; *U.S. Public*, pg. 1570
BLUE CUBE CHEMICALS FZE—See Olin Corporation; *U.S. Public*, pg. 1570
BMP PHARMA TRADING AG; *Int'l*, pg. 1076
BONNA TERRA B.V.—See HZPC Holland B.V.; *Int'l*, pg. 3561
BOROUGE AUSTRALIA PTY LTD—See Abu Dhabi National Oil Company; *Int'l*, pg. 73
BOROUGE HONG KONG LTD—See Abu Dhabi National Oil Company; *Int'l*, pg. 73
BOROUGE LTD.—See Abu Dhabi National Oil Company; *Int'l*, pg. 73
BOROUGE PTE. LTD.—See Abu Dhabi National Oil Company; *Int'l*, pg. 73
BOROUGE PVT LTD.—See Abu Dhabi National Oil Company; *Int'l*, pg. 73
BOROUGE SALES AND MARKETING CO. LTD—See Abu Dhabi National Oil Company; *Int'l*, pg. 73
BOSTIK CANADA LTD.—See Arkema S.A.; *Int'l*, pg. 570
BOZZETO KIMYA SA. VE TIC. A.S.—See Aimia Inc.; *Int'l*, pg. 233
BOZZETTO INC.—See Aimia Inc.; *Int'l*, pg. 234
BOZZETTO POLSKA SP. Z O.O.—See Aimia Inc.; *Int'l*, pg. 234
BP CHEMICALS LTD.—See BP plc; *Int'l*, pg. 1128
BRADY INDUSTRIES INC.—See Kelso & Company, L.P.; *U.S. Private*, pg. 2279
BRADY INDUSTRIES INC.—See Warburg Pincus LLC; *U.S. Private*, pg. 4436
BRENNTAG AMSTERDAM B.V.—See BRENNTAG SE; *Int'l*, pg. 1146
BRENNTAG AUSTRIA GMBH—See BRENNTAG SE; *Int'l*, pg. 1146
BRENNTAG BANGLADESH LTD.—See BRENNTAG SE; *Int'l*, pg. 1146
BRENNTAG BETEILIGUNGS GMBH—See BRENNTAG SE; *Int'l*, pg. 1146
BRENNTAG CEE GMBH—See BRENNTAG SE; *Int'l*, pg. 1146
BRENNTAG CHEMICAL DISTRIBUTION (IRELAND) LTD.—See BRENNTAG SE; *Int'l*, pg. 1146
BRENNTAG CHEMICALS DISTRIBUTION (IRELAND) LIMITED—See BRENNTAG SE; *Int'l*, pg. 1146
BRENNTAG CHEMICALS MALAYSIA SDN. BHD.—See BRENNTAG SE; *Int'l*, pg. 1146
BRENNTAG CHEMICALS NIGERIA LIMITED—See BRENNTAG SE; *Int'l*, pg. 1146
BRENNTAG CHILE COMERCIAL E INDUSTRIAL LTDA.—See BRENNTAG SE; *Int'l*, pg. 1146
BRENNTAG COLOURS LTD.—See BRENNTAG SE; *Int'l*, pg. 1146
BRENNTAG COOPERATIEF U.A.—See BRENNTAG SE; *Int'l*, pg. 1147
BRENNTAG CR S.R.O.—See BRENNTAG SE; *Int'l*, pg. 1146
BRENNTAG D.O.O.—See BRENNTAG SE; *Int'l*, pg. 1148
BRENNTAG DUTCH C.V.—See BRENNTAG SE; *Int'l*, pg. 1147
BRENNTAG EL SALVADOR S.A. DE C.V.—See BRENNTAG SE; *Int'l*, pg. 1147
BRENNTAG EUROPEAN SERVICES GMBH & CO. KG—See BRENNTAG SE; *Int'l*, pg. 1147
BRENNTAG EXPORT SARL—See BRENNTAG SE; *Int'l*, pg. 1147
BRENNTAG GMBH—See BRENNTAG SE; *Int'l*, pg. 1147
BRENNTAG GMBH—See BRENNTAG SE; *Int'l*, pg. 1147
BRENNTAG GMBH—See BRENNTAG SE; *Int'l*, pg. 1147

424690 — OTHER CHEMICAL AND ...

BRENNTAG HOLDING GMBH—See BRENNTAG SE; *Int'l*, pg. 1147
BRENNTAG HONG KONG LIMITED—See BRENNTAG SE; *Int'l*, pg. 1147
BRENNTAG HRVATSKA D.O.O.—See BRENNTAG SE; *Int'l*, pg. 1146
BRENNTAG HUNGARIA KFT.—See BRENNTAG SE; *Int'l*, pg. 1147
BRENNTAG INDIA PRIVATE LTD.—See BRENNTAG SE; *Int'l*, pg. 1147
BRENNTAG INGREDIENTS INC.—See BRENNTAG SE; *Int'l*, pg. 1147
BRENNTAG INGREDIENTS (THAILAND) PUBLIC COMPANY LTD.—See BRENNTAG SE; *Int'l*, pg. 1147
BRENNTAG INTERNATIONAL CHEMICALS GMBH—See BRENNTAG SE; *Int'l*, pg. 1146
BRENNTAG KIMYA TICARET LIMITED SIRKETI—See BRENNTAG SE; *Int'l*, pg. 1147
BRENNTAG KOREA CO., LTD.—See BRENNTAG SE; *Int'l*, pg. 1147
BRENNTAG LANKA (PRIVATE) LIMITED—See BRENNTAG SE; *Int'l*, pg. 1147
BRENNTAG LJUBLJANA D.O.O.—See BRENNTAG SE; *Int'l*, pg. 1147
BRENNTAG LUBRICANTS, LLC—See BRENNTAG SE; *Int'l*, pg. 1147
BRENNTAG MAGHREB SAS—See BRENNTAG SE; *Int'l*, pg. 1147
BRENNTAG MALAYSIA SDN. BHD.—See BRENNTAG SE; *Int'l*, pg. 1147
BRENNTAG MAROC S.A.R.L.—See BRENNTAG SE; *Int'l*, pg. 1147
BRENNTAG NEDERLAND B.V.—See BRENNTAG SE; *Int'l*, pg. 1147
BRENNTAG NEW ZEALAND LIMITED—See BRENNTAG SE; *Int'l*, pg. 1147
BRENNTAG NORDIC AB—See BRENNTAG SE; *Int'l*, pg. 1147
BRENNTAG NORDIC AS—See BRENNTAG SE; *Int'l*, pg. 1146
BRENNTAG NORDIC A/S—See BRENNTAG SE; *Int'l*, pg. 1147
BRENNTAG NORDIC OY—See BRENNTAG SE; *Int'l*, pg. 1146
BRENNTAG NORTH AMERICA, INC.—See BRENNTAG SE; *Int'l*, pg. 1148
BRENNTAG N.V.—See BRENNTAG SE; *Int'l*, pg. 1147
BRENNTAG PACIFIC, INC. - FAIRBANKS—See BRENNTAG SE; *Int'l*, pg. 1148
BRENNTAG PACIFIC, INC.—See BRENNTAG SE; *Int'l*, pg. 1148
BRENNTAG PACIFIC, INC. - SOUTH GATE—See BRENNTAG SE; *Int'l*, pg. 1148
BRENNTAG PANAMA S.A.—See BRENNTAG SE; *Int'l*, pg. 1148
BRENNTAG PHILIPPINES INC.—See BRENNTAG SE; *Int'l*, pg. 1148
BRENNTAG POLSKA SP. Z O.O.—See BRENNTAG SE; *Int'l*, pg. 1146
BRENNTAG PORTUGAL LDA.—See BRENNTAG SE; *Int'l*, pg. 1148
BRENNTAG PORTUGAL-PRODUTOS QUIMICOS LDA.—See BRENNTAG SE; *Int'l*, pg. 1146
BRENNTAG PTE. LTD.—See BRENNTAG SE; *Int'l*, pg. 1148
BRENNTAG PTY. LTD.—See BRENNTAG SE; *Int'l*, pg. 1148
BRENNTAG PUERTO RICO, INC.—See BRENNTAG SE; *Int'l*, pg. 1148
BRENNTAG QUIMICA BRASIL LTDA.—See BRENNTAG SE; *Int'l*, pg. 1148
BRENNTAG QUIMICA S.A.—See BRENNTAG SE; *Int'l*, pg. 1146
BRENNTAG S.A.—See BRENNTAG SE; *Int'l*, pg. 1148
BRENNTAG SCHWEIZERHALL AG—See BRENNTAG SE; *Int'l*, pg. 1148
BRENNTAG (SHANGHAI) CHEMICAL TRADING CO., LIMITED—See BRENNTAG SE; *Int'l*, pg. 1146
BRENNTAG (SHANGHAI) ENTERPRISE MANAGEMENT CO., LTD.—See BRENNTAG SE; *Int'l*, pg. 1146
BRENNTAG SINGAPORE PTE. LTD.—See BRENNTAG SE; *Int'l*, pg. 1148
BRENNTAG SLOVAKIA S.R.O.—See BRENNTAG SE; *Int'l*, pg. 1146
BRENNTAG SOUTHWEST, INC. - BORGER—See BRENNTAG SE; *Int'l*, pg. 1148
BRENNTAG SOUTHWEST, INC. - LANCASTER—See BRENNTAG SE; *Int'l*, pg. 1148
BRENNTAG S.P.A.—See BRENNTAG SE; *Int'l*, pg. 1146
BRENNTAG SPECIALTIES—See BRENNTAG SE; *Int'l*, pg. 1148
BRENNTAG S.R.L.—See BRENNTAG SE; *Int'l*, pg. 1148
BRENNTAG (TAIWAN) CO. LTD.—See BRENNTAG SE; *Int'l*, pg. 1146
BRENNTAG (THAILAND) CO. LTD.—See BRENNTAG SE; *Int'l*, pg. 1146
BRENNTAG UK AND IRELAND LIMITED—See BRENNTAG SE; *Int'l*, pg. 1148
BRENNTAG (UK) LTD.—See BRENNTAG SE; *Int'l*, pg. 1146

BRENNTAG VASTGOED B.V.—See BRENNTAG SE; *Int'l*, pg. 1148
BRENNTAG VIETNAM COMPANY LIMITED—See BRENNTAG SE; *Int'l*, pg. 1148
BRI-CHEM SUPPLY LTD.—See Bri-Chem Corp.; *Int'l*, pg. 1151
BRINADD INTERNATIONAL COMPANY INC.—See United Salt Corporation; *U.S. Private*, pg. 4297
BRITE-TECH CORPORATION SDN. BERHAD—See Brite-Tech Berhad; *Int'l*, pg. 1165
BROWN CHEMICAL CO., INC.; *U.S. Private*, pg. 667
BTC EUROPE GMBH—See BASF SE; *Int'l*, pg. 882
BUCKLEY INDUSTRIES INC.; *U.S. Private*, pg. 678
BUCKMAN LABORATORIES PTY. LTD.—See Bulab Holdings, Inc.; *U.S. Private*, pg. 683
BUCKMAN'S INC.; *U.S. Private*, pg. 678
BUFA COMPOSITES BALTIC OU—See BUFA GmbH & Co. KG; *Int'l*, pg. 1211
BUFA COMPOSITES GMBH & CO. KG—See BUFA GmbH & Co. KG; *Int'l*, pg. 1211
BUILDING CHEMICAL SUPPLIES LIMITED—See New Mountain Capital, LLC; *U.S. Private*, pg. 2899
BURLINGTON CHEMICAL COMPANY INC.; *U.S. Private*, pg. 689
BYOTROL INC.—See Byotrol Limited; *Int'l*, pg. 1235
BYOTROL TECHNOLOGY LIMITED—See Byotrol Limited; *Int'l*, pg. 1235
CABOT AEROGEL GMBH—See Cabot Corporation; *U.S. Public*, pg. 416
CABOT BRASIL INDUSTRIA E COMERCIO LTDA.—See Cabot Corporation; *U.S. Public*, pg. 416
CABOT B.V.—See Cabot Corporation; *U.S. Public*, pg. 416
CABOT COLOMBIANA S.A.—See Cabot Corporation; *U.S. Public*, pg. 416
CABOT INTERNATIONAL GMBH—See Cabot Corporation; *U.S. Public*, pg. 417
CABOT PERFORMANCE MATERIALS NETHERLANDS B.V.—See Cabot Corporation; *U.S. Public*, pg. 417
CABOT PLASTICS HONG KONG LIMITED—See Cabot Corporation; *U.S. Public*, pg. 417
CABOT SWITZERLAND GMBH—See Cabot Corporation; *U.S. Public*, pg. 417
CAL-CHLOR CORPORATION; *U.S. Private*, pg. 715
CALIFORNIA AMMONIA CO.; *U.S. Private*, pg. 717
CALLAHAN CHEMICAL COMPANY; *U.S. Private*, pg. 722
CALLI GHANA LTD—See Element Solutions Inc.; *U.S. Public*, pg. 725
CALVATIS B.V.—See Calvatis GmbH; *Int'l*, pg. 1266
CALVATIS GMBH—See Calvatis GmbH; *Int'l*, pg. 1266
CALVATIS HIJYEN SAN. VE DS TIC. LTD. STI.—See Calvatis GmbH; *Int'l*, pg. 1266
CALVATIS SRL—See Calvatis GmbH; *Int'l*, pg. 1266
CALVATIS UAB—See Calvatis GmbH; *Int'l*, pg. 1266
CANADIAN AMERICAN STANDARD HEMP INC.—See Real Brands, Inc.; *U.S. Public*, pg. 1768
CANDLE SCIENCE INC.; *U.S. Private*, pg. 733
CAPITOL BUILDING SUPPLY, INC.—See GMS Inc.; *U.S. Public*, pg. 947
CAPRICORN CHEMICALS LTD.—See Hobart Enterprises Ltd; *Int'l*, pg. 3437
CARBOLINE (DALIAN) PAINT COMPANY LTD.—See RPM International Inc.; *U.S. Public*, pg. 1816
CARBOLINE (INDIA) PRIVATE LIMITED—See RPM International Inc.; *U.S. Public*, pg. 1816
CARGILL INC.—See Cargill, Inc.; *U.S. Private*, pg. 756
CARST & WALKER AUSTRALIA (PTY) LTD—See Hobart Enterprises Ltd; *Int'l*, pg. 3436
CARST & WALKER (EA) LIMITED—See Hobart Enterprises Ltd; *Int'l*, pg. 3436
CARTEMANI S.R.L.—See Hagleitner Hygiene International GmbH; *Int'l*, pg. 3207
THE CARY COMPANY; *U.S. Private*, pg. 4005
CASCADE COLUMBIA DISTRIBUTION COMPANY; *U.S. Private*, pg. 778
CASCO ADHESIVES (ASIA) PTE LTD—See Akzo Nobel N.V.; *Int'l*, pg. 273
CASCO ADHEZIVI D.O.O.—See Akzo Nobel N.V.; *Int'l*, pg. 273
CASCO BYGLIM A/S—See Akzo Nobel N.V.; *Int'l*, pg. 273
CA SPECIALITIES LLC—See Charkit Chemical Company, LLC; *U.S. Private*, pg. 851
CEDARCHEM, LLC—See Platinum Equity, LLC; *U.S. Private*, pg. 3204
CELLMARK ASIA PTE LTD—See CellMark AB; *Int'l*, pg. 1393
CELLMARK HELLAS SA—See CellMark AB; *Int'l*, pg. 1393
CELLMARK IBERICA SL—See CellMark AB; *Int'l*, pg. 1393
CELLMARK INDIA PRIVATE LIMITED—See CellMark AB; *Int'l*, pg. 1393
CELLMARK ITALY S.R.L.—See CellMark AB; *Int'l*, pg. 1393
CELLMARK KIMYA TIC AS—See CellMark AB; *Int'l*, pg. 1393
CELLMARK LTD—See CellMark AB; *Int'l*, pg. 1393
CELLMARK SHANGHAI CO LTD—See CellMark AB; *Int'l*, pg. 1393
CELLMARK TAIWAN CO LTD—See CellMark AB; *Int'l*, pg. 1393
CELLMARK UK LTD—See CellMark AB; *Int'l*, pg. 1393

CENTERCHEM, INC.—See LeBaronBrown Industries LLC; *U.S. Private*, pg. 2409
CENTRE WEST FOUNDRY SUPPLIES SDN. BHD.—See Huettenes-Albertus Chemische Werke GmbH; *Int'l*, pg. 3522
CENTRO TECNICO INDURA LIMITADA—See Air Products & Chemicals, Inc.; *U.S. Public*, pg. 66
CHACODAS S.A.—See Corteva, Inc.; *U.S. Public*, pg. 581
CHANG CHUN JAPAN CO., LTD.—See ChangChun Group; *Int'l*, pg. 1442
CHASE ELASTOMER CORPORATION—See HEXPOL AB; *Int'l*, pg. 3372
CHD CHEMICALS LTD.; *Int'l*, pg. 1458
CHEM32 LLC—See Ecovyst Inc.; *U.S. Public*, pg. 717
CHEMARCO, INC.—See JNS-SmithChem, LLC; *U.S. Private*, pg. 2217
CHEMAX INTERNATIONAL CORPORATION—See China Petrochemical Development Corp.; *Int'l*, pg. 1540
CHEMBOND CHEMICALS LTD - CONSTRUCTION CHEMICAL DIVISION—See Chembond Chemicals Ltd; *Int'l*, pg. 1461
CHEMBOND CHEMICALS LTD - MANUFACTURING PLANT—See Chembond Chemicals Ltd; *Int'l*, pg. 1461
CHEMBOND CHEMICALS LTD - MANUFACTURING PLANT—See Chembond Chemicals Ltd; *Int'l*, pg. 1461
CHEMETALL CANADA LIMITED—See BASF SE; *Int'l*, pg. 873
CHEMETALL FINLAND OY—See BASF SE; *Int'l*, pg. 873
CHEMEX CORPORATION; *U.S. Private*, pg. 871
CHEMFIT (PTY) LIMITED—See AECI Limited; *Int'l*, pg. 171
THE CHEMICAL COMPANY; *U.S. Private*, pg. 4007
CHEMICAL INTERCHANGE CO.; *U.S. Private*, pg. 871
CHEMICAL SOLVENTS INC.; *U.S. Private*, pg. 871
CHEMICAL SPECIALISTS & DEVELOPMENT, INC.—See One Rock Capital Partners, LLC; *U.S. Private*, pg. 3022
CHEMINOVA AGRO DE ARGENTINA S.A.—See FMC Corporation; *U.S. Public*, pg. 861
CHEMINOVA AGRO DE COLOMBIA SA—See FMC Corporation; *U.S. Public*, pg. 861
CHEMINOVA AGRO FRANCE S.A.S.—See FMC Corporation; *U.S. Public*, pg. 861
CHEMINOVA AGRO ITALIA S.R.L.—See FMC Corporation; *U.S. Public*, pg. 861
CHEMINOVA AGRO, S.A.—See FMC Corporation; *U.S. Public*, pg. 861
CHEMINOVA AUSTRIA GMBH—See FMC Corporation; *U.S. Public*, pg. 861
CHEMINOVA BULGARIA EOOD—See FMC Corporation; *U.S. Public*, pg. 861
CHEMINOVA POLSKA SP. Z O.O.—See FMC Corporation; *U.S. Public*, pg. 861
CHEMINOVA TAIWAN LTD—See FMC Corporation; *U.S. Public*, pg. 861
CHEMISPHERE CORPORATION; *U.S. Private*, pg. 871
CHEMLEASE JAPAN K.K.—See Freudenberg SE; *Int'l*, pg. 2782
CHEMLUBE INTERNATIONAL, INC.—See Glencore plc; *Int'l*, pg. 2990
CHEMO INDIA—See EQT AB; *Int'l*, pg. 2469
THE CHEMOURS CANADA COMPANY—See The Chemours Company; *U.S. Public*, pg. 2059
THE CHEMOURS CHEMICAL (SHANGHAI) COMPANY LIMITED—See The Chemours Company; *U.S. Public*, pg. 2059
THE CHEMOURS CHINA HOLDING CO., LTD.—See The Chemours Company; *U.S. Public*, pg. 2059
THE CHEMOURS COMPANY SINGAPORE PTE. LTD.—See The Chemours Company; *U.S. Public*, pg. 2059
CHEMOURS DEUTSCHLAND GMBH—See The Chemours Company; *U.S. Public*, pg. 2059
THE CHEMOURS INDIA PRIVATE LIMITED—See The Chemours Company; *U.S. Public*, pg. 2059
CHEMOURS INTERNATIONAL OPERATIONS SARL—See The Chemours Company; *U.S. Public*, pg. 2059
CHEMOURS KABUSHIKI KAISHA—See The Chemours Company; *U.S. Public*, pg. 2059
CHEMOURS KOREA INC.—See The Chemours Company; *U.S. Public*, pg. 2059
THE CHEMOURS MALAYSIA SDN. BHD.—See The Chemours Company; *U.S. Public*, pg. 2059
CHEMOURS NETHERLANDS BV—See The Chemours Company; *U.S. Public*, pg. 2059
THE CHEMOURS (TAIWAN) COMPANY LIMITED—See The Chemours Company; *U.S. Public*, pg. 2059
THE CHEMOURS (THAILAND) COMPANY LIMITED—See The Chemours Company; *U.S. Public*, pg. 2059
CHEMOX POUND LIMITED—See Hobart Enterprises Ltd; *Int'l*, pg. 3436
CHEMPOINT.COM-EMEA B.V.—See Apollo Global Management, Inc.; *U.S. Public*, pg. 165
CHEM QUIP INC.; *U.S. Private*, pg. 870
CHEMSERVE SYSTEMS (PTY) LIMITED—See AECI Limited; *Int'l*, pg. 171
CHEMSOLV INC.; *U.S. Private*, pg. 872
CHEMTRADE PHOSPHOROUS SPECIALTIES LLC—See Balmoral Funds LLC; *U.S. Private*, pg. 462

N.A.I.C.S. INDEX
424690 — OTHER CHEMICAL AND ...

CHEM-TREND AUSTRALIA PTY LTD—See Freudenberg SE; *Int'l*, pg. 2782
CHEM-TREND CHEMICALS CO. PVT. LTD.—See Freudenberg SE; *Int'l*, pg. 2782
CHEM-TREND COMERCIAL, S.A. DE C.V.—See Freudenberg SE; *Int'l*, pg. 2782
CHEM-TREND FRANCE S.A.S.U.—See Freudenberg SE; *Int'l*, pg. 2782
CHEM-TREND INDUSTRIA E COMERCIO DE PRODUTOS QUIMICOS LTDA.—See Freudenberg SE; *Int'l*, pg. 2782
CHEM-TREND ITALY DEL DR. GIAN FRANCO COLORI S.A.S.—See Freudenberg SE; *Int'l*, pg. 2782
CHEM-TREND KOREA LTD.—See Freudenberg SE; *Int'l*, pg. 2782
CHEM-TREND POLSKA SP. Z O.O.—See Freudenberg SE; *Int'l*, pg. 2782
CHEM-TREND (SHANGHAI) TRADING CO. LTD.—See Freudenberg SE; *Int'l*, pg. 2782
CHEM-TREND SINGAPORE PTE. LTD.—See Freudenberg SE; *Int'l*, pg. 2782
CHEM-TREND TRADING (THAILAND) CO. LTD.—See Freudenberg SE; *Int'l*, pg. 2782
CHEM-TREND VIETNAM COMPANY LIMITED—See Freudenberg SE; *Int'l*, pg. 2782
CHEROKEE CHEMICAL CO. INC.; *U.S. Private*, pg. 873
CHESHAM SPECIALTY INGREDIENTS LTD.—See EQT AB; *Int'l*, pg. 2469
CHINA NUCLEAR ENERGY INDUSTRY CORPORATION—See China National Nuclear Corporation; *Int'l*, pg. 1532
CHINA RESOURCES CHEMICALS HOLDINGS LTD.—See China Resources (Holdings) Co., Ltd.; *Int'l*, pg. 1548
CHONGQING CHEMETALL CHEMICALS CO., LTD.—See Albemarle Corporation; *U.S. Public*, pg. 73
CHOWGULE CONSTRUCTION TECHNOLOGIES PVT. LTD.—See Chowgule & Company Pvt. Ltd.; *Int'l*, pg. 1585
CHUGOKU MARINE PAINTS (GUANGDONG) LTD—See Chugoku Marine Paints, Ltd.; *Int'l*, pg. 1595
CHUGOKU MARINE PAINTS (TAIWAN) LTD—See Chugoku Marine Paints, Ltd.; *Int'l*, pg. 1595
CHUNMO INTERNATIONAL CO., LTD.—See Changzhou Tronly New Electronic Materials Co., Ltd.; *Int'l*, pg. 1446
CIMADJUVANTES - COMERCIALIZACAO E PRODUCAO DE ADJUVANTES PARA CIMENTO LDA—See Camargo Correa S.A.; *Int'l*, pg. 1267
CISCO TRADING COMPANY—See Al-Kout Industrial Projects Company K.S.C.C.; *Int'l*, pg. 286
CJ CHINA LTD.—See CJ Corporation; *Int'l*, pg. 1632
C & L AQUA PROFESSIONALS, INC.—See Hawkins, Inc.; *U.S. Public*, pg. 989
CLARIANT CONSULTING AG—See Clariant AG; *Int'l*, pg. 1646
CLARIANT DISTRIBUTION UK LIMITED—See Clariant AG; *Int'l*, pg. 1648
CLARIANT MASTERBATCHES (DEUTSCHLAND) GMBH—See Clariant AG; *Int'l*, pg. 1647
CLARIANT MASTERBATCHES (MALAYSIA) SDN BHD—See Clariant AG; *Int'l*, pg. 1645
CLARIANT MASTERBATCHES (SHANGHAI) LTD—See Clariant AG; *Int'l*, pg. 1645
CLARIANT OIL SERVICES SCANDINAVIA AS—See Clariant AG; *Int'l*, pg. 1646
CLARIANT SERVICES UK LTD—See Clariant AG; *Int'l*, pg. 1648
CLARKSON (DEUTSCHLAND) GMBH—See Clarkson PLC; *Int'l*, pg. 1650
CLASSIC SOLUTIONS, INC.—See Bain Capital, LP; *U.S. Private*, pg. 440
COASTAL CHEMICAL CO., LLC—See BRENNTAG SE; *Int'l*, pg. 1148
COATEX NETHERLANDS BV—See Arkema S.A.; *Int'l*, pg. 571
COCHIN MINERALS AND RUTILE LIMITED; *Int'l*, pg. 1686
COFCO (JAPAN) CO., LTD.—See COFCO Limited; *Int'l*, pg. 1691
COLE CHEMICAL & DISTRIBUTING, INC.; *U.S. Private*, pg. 966
COLGATE-PALMOLIVE CO., INSTITUTIONAL PRODUCTS DIV.—See Colgate-Palmolive Company; *U.S. Public*, pg. 532
COLONIAL CHEMICAL SOLUTIONS, INC.—See Colonial Group, Inc.; *U.S. Private*, pg. 971
CONNELL BROS. CO. LTD.—See Wilbur-Ellis Company; *U.S. Private*, pg. 4517
CONSTRUCTION CHEMICALS DIVISION IN BASF A/S—See BASF SE; *Int'l*, pg. 883
CONSTRUCTION SEALANTS SUPPLY; *U.S. Private*, pg. 1024
CONTINENTAL RESEARCH CORPORATION—See C&I Holdings Inc.; *U.S. Private*, pg. 703
COOLANTS PLUS, INC.; *U.S. Private*, pg. 1039
COSMETIC RHEOLOGIES LTD.—See BASF SE; *Int'l*, pg. 883
COSMOS INDUSTRIES LIMITED—See Corporate Merchant Bankers Limited; *Int'l*, pg. 1805
COVESTRO JAPAN LTD.—See Bayer Aktiengesellschaft; *Int'l*, pg. 907

CP FILMS VERTRIEBS GMBH—See Eastman Chemical Company; *U.S. Public*, pg. 704
CPM INDUSTRIES INC.; *U.S. Private*, pg. 1080
THE C. REISS COAL COMPANY—See Koch Industries, Inc.; *U.S. Private*, pg. 2333
CREST CHEMICALS (PTY) LIMITED—See AECI Limited; *Int'l*, pg. 171
CREST CHEMICALS (PTY) LIMITED—See BRENNTAG SE; *Int'l*, pg. 1149
CRODA ARGENTINA SA—See Croda International plc; *Int'l*, pg. 1851
CRODA CANADA LTD.—See Croda International plc; *Int'l*, pg. 1851
CRODA CHEMICALS INTERNATIONAL (MOSCOW) LTD—See Croda International plc; *Int'l*, pg. 1851
CRODA HOLDINGS FRANCE SAS—See Croda International plc; *Int'l*, pg. 1852
CRODA MEXICO, S.A. DE C.V.—See Croda International plc; *Int'l*, pg. 1852
CRODA MIDDLE EAST—See Croda International plc; *Int'l*, pg. 1852
CRODA (THAILAND) CO., LTD—See Croda International plc; *Int'l*, pg. 1851
CROPSTER AGRO LIMITED; *Int'l*, pg. 1855
CROUCH SUPPLY COMPANY, INC.; *U.S. Private*, pg. 1108
CS CABOT SPOL, S.R.O.—See Cabot Corporation; *U.S. Public*, pg. 416
CSM BIOCHEM TRADING SHANGHAI CO., LTD.—See Rhone Group, LLC; *U.S. Private*, pg. 3423
CSPC DERMAY EUROPE GMBH—See CSPC Pharmaceutical Group Limited; *Int'l*, pg. 1867
CUSTOM BLENDS, INC.—See Crest Group Inc.; *U.S. Private*, pg. 1095
CUSTOM CHEMICAL SERVICES INC.—See LeBaron-Brown Industries LLC; *U.S. Private*, pg. 2409
CVB ALBERT CARL GMBH & CO. KG—See BRENNTAG SE; *Int'l*, pg. 1149
CVH CHEMIE-VERTRIEB GMBH & CO.HANNOVER KG—See BRENNTAG SE; *Int'l*, pg. 1149
CVH CHEMIE-VERTRIEB VERWALTUNGSGESELLSCHAFT MBH—See BRENNTAG SE; *Int'l*, pg. 1149
CVM CHEMIE-VERTRIEB MAGDEBURG GMBH & CO. KG—See BRENNTAG SE; *Int'l*, pg. 1149
CVP CHEMIE-VERTRIEB BERLIN GMBH—See BRENNTAG SE; *Int'l*, pg. 1149
CYCLO INDUSTRIES, INC.—See Highlander Partners, LP.; *U.S. Private*, pg. 1939
DADCO (SUISSE) S.A.—See Dadco Alumina & Chemicals Ltd.; *Int'l*, pg. 1904
DAHM GASLOG GMBH—See Hoyer GmbH; *Int'l*, pg. 3498
DAICEL CHEMTECH, INC.—See Daicel Corporation; *Int'l*, pg. 1918
DAICEL EUROPE GMBH—See Daicel Corporation; *Int'l*, pg. 1918
DAICEL TRADING (SHANGHAI) LTD.—See Daicel Corporation; *Int'l*, pg. 1919
DAICEL (U.S.A.) INC.—See Daicel Corporation; *Int'l*, pg. 1918
DAIICHI YAKUHIN KOGYO CO., LTD.—See Carlit Co., Ltd.; *Int'l*, pg. 1338
DAIKIN CHEMICAL INTERNATIONAL TRADING (SHANGHAI) CO., LTD—See Daikin Industries, Ltd.; *Int'l*, pg. 1934
DAIKIN REFRIGERANTS EUROPE GMBH—See Daikin Industries, Ltd.; *Int'l*, pg. 1935
DANISCO POLAND SP. Z.O.O—See International Flavors & Fragrances Inc.; *U.S. Public*, pg. 1151
DAP CANADA CORP.—See RPM International Inc.; *U.S. Public*, pg. 1817
DAR-TECH INC.; *U.S. Private*, pg. 1158
DAUBERT CHEMICAL COMPANY, INC.—See Daubert Industries, Inc.; *U.S. Private*, pg. 1167
DAUBERT INDUSTRIES, INC.; *U.S. Private*, pg. 1167
DAVIS WHOLESALE SUPPLY INC.; *U.S. Private*, pg. 1174
DCI-BRAZIL—See Firmenich International SA; *Int'l*, pg. 2681
DEBRO CHEMICALS LTD; *Int'l*, pg. 1998
DELIAN TRADING (HK) CO., LTD.—See Guangdong Delian Group Co., Ltd.; *Int'l*, pg. 3153
DENKA CORPORATION—See Denki Company Limited; *Int'l*, pg. 2027
DEWOLF CHEMICAL INC.; *U.S. Private*, pg. 1219
DIALOG INTERNATIONAL (L) LTD.—See Dialog Group Berhad; *Int'l*, pg. 2104
DIC INTERNATIONAL (USA), LLC—See DIC Corporation; *Int'l*, pg. 2108
DIGIB ASIA PACIFIC PTE. LTD.—See BRENNTAG SE; *Int'l*, pg. 1149
DIPOL BALTIJA SIA—See BRENNTAG SE; *Int'l*, pg. 1149
DISTRUPOL B.V.—See One Rock Capital Partners, LLC; *U.S. Private*, pg. 3022
DISTRUPOL IRELAND LIMITED—See One Rock Capital Partners, LLC; *U.S. Private*, pg. 3022
DISTRUPOL LIMITED—See One Rock Capital Partners, LLC; *U.S. Private*, pg. 3022
DISTRUPOL NORDIC AB—See One Rock Capital Partners, LLC; *U.S. Private*, pg. 3022
DIVERSEY BRASIL INDUSTRIA QUIMICA LTDA.—See Sealed Air Corporation; *U.S. Public*, pg. 1852

DIVERSEY DANMARK APS—See Sealed Air Corporation; *U.S. Public*, pg. 1852
DIVERSEY DE ARGENTINA S.A.—See Platinum Equity, LLC; *U.S. Private*, pg. 3204
DIVERSEY EASTERN & CENTRAL AFRICA LIMITED—See Platinum Equity, LLC; *U.S. Private*, pg. 3204
DIVERSEY HYGIENE (TAIWAN) LTD.—See Platinum Equity, LLC; *U.S. Private*, pg. 3204
DIVERSEY HYGIENE (THAILAND) CO., LTD.—See Sealed Air Corporation; *U.S. Public*, pg. 1852
DIVERSEY JAMAICA LIMITED—See Sealed Air Corporation; *U.S. Public*, pg. 1852
DIVERSEY KIMYA SANAYI VE TICARET A.S.—See Sealed Air Corporation; *U.S. Public*, pg. 1852
DIVERSEY KOREA CO., LTD.—See Platinum Equity, LLC; *U.S. Private*, pg. 3204
DIVERSEY (MALAYSIA) SDN. BHD.—See Sealed Air Corporation; *U.S. Public*, pg. 1852
DIVERSEY PHILIPPINES, INC.—See Sealed Air Corporation; *U.S. Public*, pg. 1853
DIVERSEY PORTUGAL - SISTEMAS DE HIGIENE E LIMPEZA, UNIPESSOAL, LDA—See Sealed Air Corporation; *U.S. Public*, pg. 1853
DIVERSEY (PRIVATE) LIMITED—See Sealed Air Corporation; *U.S. Public*, pg. 1852
DIVERSEY SINGAPORE PTY. LTD.—See Sealed Air Corporation; *U.S. Public*, pg. 1853
DIVERSEY SLOVAKIA, S.R.O.—See Sealed Air Corporation; *U.S. Public*, pg. 1853
DIVERSEY SOUTH AFRICA (PTY.) LTD.—See Sealed Air Corporation; *U.S. Public*, pg. 1853
DIVERSEY SUOMI OY—See Sealed Air Corporation; *U.S. Public*, pg. 1853
DIXIE DYE & CHEMICAL INC.—See Exact Color Systems, LLC; *U.S. Private*, pg. 1445
DIXONS OF WESTERHOPE—See Air Products & Chemicals, Inc.; *U.S. Public*, pg. 66
DKK AMERICA MATERIALS, INC.—See Daiichi Kigenso Kagaku Kogyo Co., Ltd.; *Int'l*, pg. 1928
DKK (SHANGHAI) MATERIALS TRADING CO., LTD.—See Daiichi Kigenso Kagaku Kogyo Co., Ltd.; *Int'l*, pg. 1928
DKK THAI MATERIALS TRADING CO., LTD.—See Daiichi Kigenso Kagaku Kogyo Co., Ltd.; *Int'l*, pg. 1928
DKS (SHANGHAI) INTERNATIONAL TRADING CO., LTD.—See DKS Co. Ltd.; *Int'l*, pg. 2139
D.M. FIGLEY CO. INC.; *U.S. Private*, pg. 1142
DMK DRILLING FLUIDS LTD.; *Int'l*, pg. 2146
DNIPROAZOT JSC; *Int'l*, pg. 2148
DNT CORPORATION; *U.S. Private*, pg. 1249
DOEHLER GEORGIA, LTD—See Dohler GmbH; *Int'l*, pg. 2156
DOEHLER INDIA PVT. LTD.—See Dohler GmbH; *Int'l*, pg. 2155
DOEHLER ITALIA S.R.L.—See Dohler GmbH; *Int'l*, pg. 2155
DOEHLER KAZAKHSTAN LLP—See Dohler GmbH; *Int'l*, pg. 2155
DOEHLER MEXICO S.A. DE C.V.—See Dohler GmbH; *Int'l*, pg. 2155
DOEHLER NATURAL FOOD & BEVERAGE INGREDIENTS (JINSHAN) CO. LTD.—See Dohler GmbH; *Int'l*, pg. 2155
DOEHLER NF & BI—See Dohler GmbH; *Int'l*, pg. 2155
DOEHLER NORTH AMERICA—See Dohler GmbH; *Int'l*, pg. 2155
DOEHLER TASHKENT—See Dohler GmbH; *Int'l*, pg. 2155
DOEHLER UKRAINE LTD—See Dohler GmbH; *Int'l*, pg. 2155
DOE & INGALLS, INC.; *U.S. Private*, pg. 1252
DOE & INGALLS MANAGEMENT, LLC—See Thermo Fisher Scientific Inc.; *U.S. Public*, pg. 2146
DOHENY ENTERPRISES INC.; *U.S. Private*, pg. 1253
DOHLER AMERICA LATINA LTDA.—See Dohler GmbH; *Int'l*, pg. 2155
DOHLER COLOMBIA S.A.S—See Dohler GmbH; *Int'l*, pg. 2155
DOHLER CZ S.R.O.—See Dohler GmbH; *Int'l*, pg. 2155
DOHLER DINTER UKRAINE SKALA LTD.—See Dohler GmbH; *Int'l*, pg. 2155
DOHLER EGYPT FOR THE PRODUCTION OF NATURAL FOOD & BEVERAGE INGREDIENTS S.A.E.—See Dohler GmbH; *Int'l*, pg. 2155
DOHLER ESPANA NATURAL BEVERAGE INGREDIENTS S.L.—See Dohler GmbH; *Int'l*, pg. 2155
DOHLER FOOD & BEVERAGE INGREDIENTS RIZHAO CO. LTD.—See Dohler GmbH; *Int'l*, pg. 2155
DOHLER FOOD & BEVERAGE INGREDIENTS SHANGHAI CO. LTD.—See Dohler GmbH; *Int'l*, pg. 2155
DOHLER FRANCE S.A.R.L.—See Dohler GmbH; *Int'l*, pg. 2155
DOHLER GIDA SAN. VE TIC. LTD. STI.—See Dohler GmbH; *Int'l*, pg. 2155
DOHLER HOLLAND B.V.—See Dohler GmbH; *Int'l*, pg. 2155
DOHLER HUNGARIA KFT.—See Dohler GmbH; *Int'l*, pg. 2155
DOHLER IRANIAN LIMITED—See Dohler GmbH; *Int'l*, pg. 2156
DOHLER JAPAN K.K.—See Dohler GmbH; *Int'l*, pg. 2156
DOHLER MARMARA—See Dohler GmbH; *Int'l*, pg. 2156

DOHLER MIDDLE EAST LTD.—See Dohler GmbH; *Int'l*, pg. 2156
DOHLER NEUENKIRCHEN GMBH—See Dohler GmbH; *Int'l*, pg. 2156
DOHLER NEUSS GMBH—See Dohler GmbH; *Int'l*, pg. 2156
DOHLER POLSKA SP. Z O.O.—See Dohler GmbH; *Int'l*, pg. 2156
DOHLER ROGGEL B.V.—See Dohler GmbH; *Int'l*, pg. 2156
DOHLER ROMANIA S.R.L.—See Dohler GmbH; *Int'l*, pg. 2156
DOHLER SCANDINAVIA A/S—See Dohler GmbH; *Int'l*, pg. 2156
DOHLER SCHWEIZ AG—See Dohler GmbH; *Int'l*, pg. 2156
DOHLER SOFIA EOOD—See Dohler GmbH; *Int'l*, pg. 2156
DOHLER SOUTH AFRICA (PTY) LTD.—See Dohler GmbH; *Int'l*, pg. 2156
DOHLER (UK) LIMITED—See Dohler GmbH; *Int'l*, pg. 2155
DOHLER WEST AFRICA—See Dohler GmbH; *Int'l*, pg. 2156
DORSETT & JACKSON INC.; *U.S. Private*, pg. 1263
DOWAKSA ILERI KOMPOZIT MALZEMELER SAN. LTD. STI.—See Aksa Akrilik Kimya Sanayii A.S.; *Int'l*, pg. 264
DOW BRASIL INDUSTRIA E COMERCIO DE PRODUTOS QUIMICOS LTDA.—See Dow Inc.; *U.S. Public*, pg. 683
DOW CHEMICAL CANADA ULC—See Dow Inc.; *U.S. Public*, pg. 683
THE DOW CHEMICAL COMPANY - NORWICH—See Dow Inc.; *U.S. Public*, pg. 686
DOW CHEMICAL INTER-AMERICAN LIMITED—See Dow Inc.; *U.S. Public*, pg. 684
DOW CHEMICAL JAPAN LIMITED—See Dow Inc.; *U.S. Public*, pg. 684
DOW CHEMICAL PACIFIC LIMITED—See Dow Inc.; *U.S. Public*, pg. 684
DOW CHEMICAL (ZHANGJIAGANG) CO., LTD.—See Dow Inc.; *U.S. Public*, pg. 683
DOWD & GUILD, INC.; *U.S. Private*, pg. 1268
DOW QUIMICA CHILENA S.A.—See Dow Inc.; *U.S. Public*, pg. 685
DOW QUIMICA DE COLOMBIA S.A.—See Dow Inc.; *U.S. Public*, pg. 685
DOW VENEZUELA, C.A.—See Corteva, Inc.; *U.S. Public*, pg. 582
DPC INDUSTRIES INC.—See DX Holding Company Inc.; *U.S. Private*, pg. 1296
DR. D.A. DELIS AG—See BASF SE; *Int'l*, pg. 883
DRT AMERICA, INC.—See Firmenich International SA; *Int'l*, pg. 2681
DRT SPECIALTY CHEMICALS (WUXI) CO., LTD.—See Firmenich International SA; *Int'l*, pg. 2681
DUPONT ASTURIAS, S.L.—See Corteva, Inc.; *U.S. Public*, pg. 583
DU PONT FAR EAST, INC.—See Corteva, Inc.; *U.S. Public*, pg. 582
DUSKIN CO., LTD.; *Int'l*, pg. 2234
D.W. DICKEY & SONS INC.; *U.S. Private*, pg. 1143
DX DISTRIBUTORS INC.—See DX Holding Company Inc.; *U.S. Private*, pg. 1296
DXI INDUSTRIES INC.—See DX Holding Company Inc.; *U.S. Private*, pg. 1296
DX SERVICE COMPANY INC.—See DX Holding Company Inc.; *U.S. Private*, pg. 1296
DYNEA (NANJING) CO., LTD.—See AICA Kogyo Company, Limited; *Int'l*, pg. 229
DYNEA (SHANGHAI) CO., LTD.—See AICA Kogyo Company, Limited; *Int'l*, pg. 229
EASI INDUSTRIAL SUPPLIES LIMITED—See ANSA McAL Limited; *Int'l*, pg. 477
EASTMAN CHEMICAL ADVANCED MATERIALS B.V.—See Eastman Chemical Company; *U.S. Public*, pg. 704
EASTMAN CHEMICAL ASIA PACIFIC PTE. LTD.—See Eastman Chemical Company; *U.S. Public*, pg. 704
EASTMAN CHEMICAL CANADA, INC.—See Eastman Chemical Company; *U.S. Public*, pg. 704
EASTMAN CHEMICAL (CHINA) CO., LTD.—See Eastman Chemical Company; *U.S. Public*, pg. 704
EASTMAN CHEMICAL DO BRASIL LTDA.—See Eastman Chemical Company; *U.S. Public*, pg. 705
EASTMAN CHEMICAL ITALIA S.R.L.—See Eastman Chemical Company; *U.S. Public*, pg. 704
EASTMAN CHEMICAL JAPAN LIMITED—See Eastman Chemical Company; *U.S. Public*, pg. 705
EASTMAN CHEMICAL KOREA LTD.—See Eastman Chemical Company; *U.S. Public*, pg. 705
EASTMAN CHEMICAL (NANJING) CO., LTD.—See Eastman Chemical Company; *U.S. Public*, pg. 704
EASTMAN CHEMICAL WORKINGTON LIMITED—See Eastman Chemical Company; *U.S. Public*, pg. 705
EASTMAN COMPANY UK LIMITED—See Eastman Chemical Company; *U.S. Public*, pg. 705
EASTMAN FRANCE S.A.R.L.—See Eastman Chemical Company; *U.S. Public*, pg. 705
EASTMAN SERVICIOS CORPORATIVOS, S.A. DE C.V.—See Eastman Chemical Company; *U.S. Public*, pg. 705
EASTMAN (SHANGHAI) CHEMICAL COMMERCIAL CO., LTD.—See Eastman Chemical Company; *U.S. Public*, pg. 704
EASTMAN SPECIALTIES AS—See Eastman Chemical Company; *U.S. Public*, pg. 705
ECOLAB HYGIENE KFT.—See Ecolab Inc.; *U.S. Public*, pg. 713
ECOLAB KOREA LTD.—See Ecolab Inc.; *U.S. Public*, pg. 713
ECOLAB PRODUCTION BELGIUM BVBA—See Ecolab Inc.; *U.S. Public*, pg. 714
ECOLAB SAS—See Ecolab Inc.; *U.S. Public*, pg. 714
ECOLAB SNC—See Ecolab Inc.; *U.S. Public*, pg. 714
ECOLAB (TRINIDAD & TOBAGO)UNLIMITED—See Ecolab Inc.; *U.S. Public*, pg. 713
ECO SERVICES OPERATIONS CORP.—See Ecovyst Inc.; *U.S. Public*, pg. 717
ECOSYNTHETIX LTD.—See EcoSynthetix, Inc.; *Int'l*, pg. 2300
ECOTECH ENTERPRISES INC.—See Hawkins, Inc.; *U.S. Public*, pg. 989
ECOVYST INC.; *U.S. Public*, pg. 717
ECUPHAR VETERINARIA SL—See Animalcare Group plc; *Int'l*, pg. 471
E.D. OATES PTY. LTD.—See Freudenberg SE; *Int'l*, pg. 2783
ED SIMAL & ASSOCIATES INC.; *U.S. Private*, pg. 1332
EDWARDS SALES CORPORATION; *U.S. Private*, pg. 1342
E.I. DUPONT CANADA - THETFORD INC.—See DuPont de Nemours, Inc.; *U.S. Public*, pg. 693
EKO EXPORT S.A.; *Int'l*, pg. 2338
ELECO PRODUITS S.A.S.—See Dr. Honle AG; *Int'l*, pg. 2192
ELLSWORTH CORPORATION; *U.S. Private*, pg. 1375
ELTON CORPORATION D.O.O.—See ELTON INTERNATIONAL TRADING COMPANY S.A.; *Int'l*, pg. 2371
ELTON CORPORATION LTD—See ELTON INTERNATIONAL TRADING COMPANY S.A.; *Int'l*, pg. 2371
ELTON CORPORATION S.A.—See ELTON INTERNATIONAL TRADING COMPANY S.A.; *Int'l*, pg. 2371
ELTON INTERNATIONAL TRADING COMPANY S.A.; *Int'l*, pg. 2371
EMCO CHEMICAL DISTRIBUTORS INC.; *U.S. Private*, pg. 1379
ENARTIS ARGENTINA S.A.—See Esseco Group SRL; *Int'l*, pg. 2509
ENARTIS CENTRAL EUROPE S.R.O.—See Esseco Group SRL; *Int'l*, pg. 2509
ENARTIS CHILE LTDA—See Esseco Group SRL; *Int'l*, pg. 2509
ENARTIS PACIFIC PTY LTD—See Esseco Group SRL; *Int'l*, pg. 2509
ENARTIS SEPSA S.A.U.—See Esseco Group SRL; *Int'l*, pg. 2509
ENERGY & ENVIRONMENTAL SERVICE, INC.—See Enerlabs, Inc.; *U.S. Private*, pg. 1396
ENERSUL TECHNOLOGIES—See Berkshire Hathaway Inc.; *U.S. Public*, pg. 311
ENGELHARD ARGANDA S.L.—See BASF SE; *Int'l*, pg. 883
ENGELHARD ENERGY CORPORATION—See BASF SE; *Int'l*, pg. 875
ENGRO VOPAK TERMINAL LTD—See Engro Corporation Limited; *Int'l*, pg. 2435
ENRA KIMIA SDN. BHD.—See ENRA Group Berhad; *Int'l*, pg. 2445
ENTHONE GALVANOPLASTI SANAYI TICARET A.S.—See Element Solutions Inc.; *U.S. Public*, pg. 726
ENTHONE IBERICA S.A.—See Element Solutions Inc.; *U.S. Public*, pg. 726
ENTHONE SAS—See Element Solutions Inc.; *U.S. Public*, pg. 726
ENTHONE SDN BHD—See Element Solutions Inc.; *U.S. Public*, pg. 726
ENTHONE S.R.O.—See Element Solutions Inc.; *U.S. Public*, pg. 726
EPI (EUROPE) LIMITED—See EPI Environmental Technologies Inc.; *Int'l*, pg. 2460
EPIREZ CONSTRUCTION PRODUCTS PTY LIMITED—See Illinois Tool Works Inc.; *U.S. Public*, pg. 1107
EPOCH TECHNOLOGY CO., LTD.—See Air Water Inc.; *Int'l*, pg. 240
EPS INTERNATIONAL CO., LTD.—See EPS Holdings, Inc.; *Int'l*, pg. 2465
ESPRIX TECHNOLOGIES, LP; *U.S. Private*, pg. 1427
ESSENTRIX COMPONENTS JAPAN INC.—See Essentra plc; *Int'l*, pg. 2511
ESSENTRA COMPONENTS (PTY) LTD.—See Essentra plc; *Int'l*, pg. 2511
ESSENTRA COMPONENTS SAS—See Essentra plc; *Int'l*, pg. 2511
ESSENTRA FILTER PRODUCTS S.A.—See Essentra plc; *Int'l*, pg. 2511
ESSENTRA PACKAGING SRL—See Essentra plc; *Int'l*, pg. 2511
ESSENTRA PTE. LTD.—See Essentra plc; *Int'l*, pg. 2511
E.T. HORN COMPANY INC.; *U.S. Private*, pg. 1307
EUROCHEM COMERCIO DE PRODUTOS QUIMICOS LTDA—See EuroChem Mineral Chemical Company, OJSC; *Int'l*, pg. 2534
EURO CHEMO-PHARMA SDN BHD; *Int'l*, pg. 2531
EUROCHEM SERVICE POLSKA SP. Z O.O.—See BRENNTAG SE; *Int'l*, pg. 1149
EUROCHEM TRADING GMBH—See EuroChem Mineral Chemical Company, OJSC; *Int'l*, pg. 2533
EUROCHEM TRADING USA CORP.—See EuroChem Mineral Chemical Company, OJSC; *Int'l*, pg. 2534
EUROQUARZ GMBH; *Int'l*, pg. 2558
EURORESINS INTERNATIONAL GMBH—See Cathay Investments Limited; *Int'l*, pg. 1360
EURORESINS SCANDINAVIA OY—See Cathay Investments Limited; *Int'l*, pg. 1360
EURORESINS UK LTD.—See Cathay Investments Limited; *Int'l*, pg. 1360
EVERGREEN GARDEN CARE FRANCE SAS—See Exponent Private Equity LLP; *Int'l*, pg. 2590
EVERGREEN LABS, INC.; *U.S. Private*, pg. 1439
EVERINTEC GMBH—See Esseco Group SRL; *Int'l*, pg. 2509
EXACT COLOR SYSTEMS, LLC; *U.S. Private*, pg. 1444
EXPANCEL INC.—See Akzo Nobel N.V.; *Int'l*, pg. 274
EXTREME ADHESIVES, LLC—See H.B. Fuller Company; *U.S. Public*, pg. 977
EXXONMOBIL CHEMICAL LIMITED—See Exxon Mobil Corporation; *U.S. Public*, pg. 814
EXXONMOBIL CORPORATION—See Exxon Mobil Corporation; *U.S. Public*, pg. 815
FALLEK CHEMICAL S.A.—See ICC Industries, Inc.; *U.S. Private*, pg. 2029
FANCHEM, LTD.—See PVS Chemicals, Inc.; *U.S. Private*, pg. 3308
FAURECIA INNENRAUM SYSTEME GMBH—See FORVIA SE; *Int'l*, pg. 2746
FAURECIA INTERIEUR INDUSTRIE—See FORVIA SE; *Int'l*, pg. 2746
FERRO METAL & CHEMICAL CORPORATION LTD.—See Phibro Animal Health Corporation; *U.S. Public*, pg. 1685
FERRO SPECIALTY MATERIALS, LLC—See American Securities LLC; *U.S. Private*, pg. 251
FHP VILEDA S.A.—See Freudenberg SE; *Int'l*, pg. 2785
FINGER LAKES CHEMICALS INC.; *U.S. Private*, pg. 1509
FIRMENICH INTERNATIONAL FINE FRAGRANCE CENTER—See Firmenich International SA; *Int'l*, pg. 2680
FISCHER CHEMIC LIMITED; *Int'l*, pg. 2692
FLAVINE NORTH AMERICA, INC.; *U.S. Private*, pg. 1541
FLEXSYS VERKAUF GMBH—See Eastman Chemical Company; *U.S. Public*, pg. 706
FLLC TELKO—See Aspo Oyj; *Int'l*, pg. 631
FLORACHEM CORPORATION—See SK Capital Partners, LP; *U.S. Private*, pg. 3679
FLUORITA DE MEXICO, S.A. DE C.V.—See Grupo Empresarial Kaluz S.A. de C.V.; *Int'l*, pg. 3127
FMC-AGRO HUNGARY KFT.—See FMC Corporation; *U.S. Public*, pg. 862
FMC BIOPOLYMER AS—See DuPont de Nemours, Inc.; *U.S. Public*, pg. 693
FMC CORP. - BANGLADESH OFFICE—See FMC Corporation; *U.S. Public*, pg. 862
FMC CORP. - POLAND OFFICE—See FMC Corporation; *U.S. Public*, pg. 862
FMC SPECIALTY CHEMICALS RESEARCH & TECHNOLOGY CENTER—See FMC Corporation; *U.S. Public*, pg. 862
FORBO SIEGLING IBERICA S.A.—See Forbo Holding Ltd.; *Int'l*, pg. 2730
FORBO SIEGLING SVENSKA AB—See Forbo Holding Ltd.; *Int'l*, pg. 2730
FORMICA VERTRIEBS GMBH—See HAL Trust N.V.; *Int'l*, pg. 3223
FORT BEND SERVICES INC.; *U.S. Private*, pg. 1574
FOUR SEASONS SALES & SERVICE, INC.—See Houchens Industries, Inc.; *U.S. Private*, pg. 1990
FPC CORPORATION; *U.S. Private*, pg. 1586
FRANCIS DRILLING FLUIDS LTD.; *U.S. Private*, pg. 1587
FREUDENBERG NH CO. LTD.—See Freudenberg SE; *Int'l*, pg. 2787
FREUDENBERG PTY. LTD.—See Freudenberg SE; *Int'l*, pg. 2787
FREUDENBERG SIMRIT A/S—See Freudenberg SE; *Int'l*, pg. 2788
FREUDENBERG SIMRIT B.V.—See Freudenberg SE; *Int'l*, pg. 2788
FREUDENBERG SIMRIT KUFSTEIN GES.M.B.H. & CO. KG—See Freudenberg SE; *Int'l*, pg. 2788
FRI RESINS HOLDING CO.—See Arsenal Capital Management LP; *U.S. Private*, pg. 339
FRUTAROM BELGIUM N.V.—See International Flavors & Fragrances Inc.; *U.S. Public*, pg. 1151
FRUTAROM FRANCE S.A.R.L.—See International Flavors & Fragrances Inc.; *U.S. Public*, pg. 1151
FRUTAROM GERMANY GMBH—See International Flavors & Fragrances Inc.; *U.S. Public*, pg. 1151
FRUTAROM RUSSIA LTD.—See International Flavors & Fragrances Inc.; *U.S. Public*, pg. 1152
FRUTAROM SOUTH AFRICA (PROPRIETARY) LIMITED—See International Flavors & Fragrances Inc.; *U.S. Public*, pg. 1152
FRUTAROM (UK) LTD.—See International Flavors & Fra-

N.A.I.C.S. INDEX

424690 — OTHER CHEMICAL AND ...

grances Inc.; *U.S. Public*, pg. 1151
FUFENG (SINGAPORE) PTE. LTD—See Fufeng Group Limited; *Int'l*, pg. 2804
FUJIFILM ESPANA, S.A.—See FUJIFILM Holdings Corporation; *Int'l*, pg. 2821
FUJIFILM (THAILAND) LTD.—See FUJIFILM Holdings Corporation; *Int'l*, pg. 2821
FUJI HUNT IBERICA S.L.—See FUJIFILM Holdings Corporation; *Int'l*, pg. 2821
FUJI HUNT NORDIC AB—See FUJIFILM Holdings Corporation; *Int'l*, pg. 2821
FUJI SEAL EUROPE S.A.S.—See Fuji Seal International, Inc.; *Int'l*, pg. 2816
FUNFZEHNTE BASF ERWERBSGESELLSCHAFT MBH—See BASF SE; *Int'l*, pg. 883
FUTUREFUEL CHEMICAL COMPANY—See FutureFuel Corp.; *U.S. Public*, pg. 893
GAGE DO BRASIL LTDA.—See Gage Corporation; *U.S. Private*, pg. 1634
GAGE GLOBAL SERVICES—See Gage Corporation; *U.S. Private*, pg. 1634
GAGE PRODUCTS COMPANY DE MEXICO, S. DE R.L. DE C.V.—See Gage Corporation; *U.S. Private*, pg. 1634
GALACTIC BIOQUIMICOS LTDA.—See Finasucre S.A.; *Int'l*, pg. 2670
GALLADE CHEMICAL INC.; *U.S. Private*, pg. 1638
GANTRADE CORPORATION; *U.S. Private*, pg. 1641
GANTRADE EUROPE, LTD.—See Gantrade Corporation; *U.S. Private*, pg. 1641
GARDOSERV (PVT) LIMITED—See Cambria Africa Plc; *Int'l*, pg. 1269
GASES & ARC SUPPLY, INC.—See CI Capital Partners LLC; *U.S. Private*, pg. 895
GAS INNOVATIONS INC.; *U.S. Private*, pg. 1647
GATEWAY CHEMICALS, LTD.—See Iron Path Capital, L.P.; *U.S. Private*, pg. 2139
GCA CHEMICAL CORPORATION; *U.S. Private*, pg. 1653
GELITA AG - SUPPLY PLANT—See Gelita AG; *Int'l*, pg. 2913
GELITA AUSTRALIA PTY. LTD.—See Gelita AG; *Int'l*, pg. 2913
GELITA CANGNAN GELATINE CO. LTD.—See Gelita AG; *Int'l*, pg. 2913
GELITA DO BRASIL LTDA.—See Gelita AG; *Int'l*, pg. 2913
GELITA FRANCE SARL—See Gelita AG; *Int'l*, pg. 2913
GELITA (LIAOYUAN) GELATINE CO. LTD.—See Gelita AG; *Int'l*, pg. 2913
GELITA MEXICO S. DE R.L. DE C.V.—See Gelita AG; *Int'l*, pg. 2913
GELITA NEDERLAND B.V.—See Gelita AG; *Int'l*, pg. 2913
GELITA NZ. LTD.—See Gelita AG; *Int'l*, pg. 2913
GELITA SHANGHAI CONSULTING CO. LTD.—See Gelita AG; *Int'l*, pg. 2913
GELITA (SHANGHAI) ENTERPRISE MANAGEMENT CO., LTD—See Gelita AG; *Int'l*, pg. 2913
GELITA SOUTH AFRICA PTY. LTD.—See Gelita AG; *Int'l*, pg. 2913
GELITA SWEDEN AB—See Gelita AG; *Int'l*, pg. 2913
GELITA UK LTD.—See Gelita AG; *Int'l*, pg. 2913
GELITA USA INC.—See Gelita AG; *Int'l*, pg. 2913
GEMA MEXICO POWDER FINISHING, S. DE R.L. DE C.V.—See Graco, Inc.; *U.S. Public*, pg. 953
GEMBU CO., LTD.—See DKS Co. Ltd.; *Int'l*, pg. 2140
GENERAL AIR SERVICE & SUPPLY CO.; *U.S. Private*, pg. 1660
GENOVIQUE SPECIALTIES WUHAN YOUJI CHEMICAL CO., LTD.—See Eastman Chemical Company; *U.S. Public*, pg. 705
GEOCHEM INTERNATIONAL CORP.; *U.S. Private*, pg. 1680
GEO DRILLING FLUIDS INC.; *U.S. Private*, pg. 1680
GEORGE C. BRANDT INC.; *U.S. Private*, pg. 1681
GEORGE S. COYNE CHEMICAL CO. INC.; *U.S. Private*, pg. 1683
GEORGE UHE COMPANY, INC.; *U.S. Private*, pg. 1683
GEORGIA-PACIFIC RESINS, INC.—See Koch Industries, Inc.; *U.S. Private*, pg. 2329
GHW EUROCHEMICALS S.R.O.—See GHW International; *Int'l*, pg. 2960
GHW USA LLC—See GHW International; *Int'l*, pg. 2960
GHW (VIETNAM) CHEMICALS LIMITED COMPANY—See GHW International; *Int'l*, pg. 2960
GIFT INFINITE PUBLIC COMPANY LIMITED; *Int'l*, pg. 2970
GILBERT & JONES CO., INC.—See Gemspring Capital Management, LLC; *U.S. Private*, pg. 1659
GILLCO PRODUCTS, INC.—See EQT AB; *Int'l*, pg. 2469
G.J. CHEMICAL CO. INC.; *U.S. Private*, pg. 1630
GLOBAL BEAUTY IMAGE, INC.; *U.S. Private*, pg. 1712
GMZ, INC.—See EQT AB; *Int'l*, pg. 2469
GOLDEN EAGLE EXPLORATION LLC USA—See Aleator Energy Inc.; *Int'l*, pg. 305
GOLDEN HIGHWAY MEXICO, S. DE R.L. DE C.V.—See GHW International; *Int'l*, pg. 2960
GPM-HENKEL LTD.—See Henkel AG & Co. KGaA; *Int'l*, pg. 3348
GRACE ARGENTINA S.A.—See Standard Industries Holdings Inc.; *U.S. Private*, pg. 3779

GRACE BRASIL LTDA.—See Standard Industries Holdings Inc.; *U.S. Private*, pg. 3779
GRACO SUPPLY COMPANY—See Carl Marks & Co., Inc.; *U.S. Private*, pg. 762
GRAND PACIFIC PETROCHEMICAL CORPORATION; *Int'l*, pg. 3055
GRANEL SA—See Firmenich International SA; *Int'l*, pg. 2681
GRAPHITE INTERNATIONAL B.V.—See Graphite India Ltd; *Int'l*, pg. 3061
GRAYSTAR LLC; *U.S. Private*, pg. 1761
GREEN CHINA HOLDINGS LIMITED; *Int'l*, pg. 3070
GREENVILLE COLORANTS LLC—See ChromaScape, LLC; *U.S. Private*, pg. 892
GRUPA AZOTY ZAKLADY AZOTOWE CHORZOW S.A.—See Grupa Azoty S.A.; *Int'l*, pg. 3116
GRUPO MATERIAS PRIMAS S. DE R. L. DE C. V.—See Covia Holdings Corporation; *U.S. Private*, pg. 1072
GSI EXIM AMERICA INC.—See GSI Creos Corporation; *Int'l*, pg. 3144
GUANGDONG TIANHE AGRICULTURAL MEANS OF PRODUCTION CO., LTD.; *Int'l*, pg. 3161
GUANGXI ARAKAWA CHEMICAL INDUSTRIES, LTD.—See Arakawa Chemical Industries, Ltd.; *Int'l*, pg. 534
GUANGZHOU FAN YA JIA RONG TRADING CO., LTD.—See BRENNTAG SE; *Int'l*, pg. 1149
GUANGZHOU GHW TRADING CO., LTD.—See GHW International; *Int'l*, pg. 2960
GUERBET N.V.—See Guerbet SA; *Int'l*, pg. 3172
GUIZHOU CHANFERT ENTERPRISE CO., LTD.—See Guizhou Chanhen Chemical Corporation; *Int'l*, pg. 3174
HAAS FINECHEM (SHANGHAI) CO. LTD.—See Platinum Equity, LLC; *U.S. Private*, pg. 3210
HAAS GROUP INTERNATIONAL GMBH—See Platinum Equity, LLC; *U.S. Private*, pg. 3210
HAAS GROUP INTERNATIONAL INC.—See Platinum Equity, LLC; *U.S. Private*, pg. 3210
HAAS GROUP INTERNATIONAL SCM IRELAND LIMITED—See Platinum Equity, LLC; *U.S. Private*, pg. 3210
HAAS GROUP INTERNATIONAL SCM LIMITED—See Platinum Equity, LLC; *U.S. Private*, pg. 3210
HAAS TCM GROUP OF THE UK LIMITED—See Platinum Equity, LLC; *U.S. Private*, pg. 3210
HAAS TCM ITALIA SRL—See Platinum Equity, LLC; *U.S. Private*, pg. 3210
HAAS TCM OF ISRAEL INC.—See Platinum Equity, LLC; *U.S. Private*, pg. 3210
HAAS TCM SINGAPORE PTE. LTD.—See Platinum Equity, LLC; *U.S. Private*, pg. 3210
HA FOUNDRY CORE (CHANGCHUN) CO., LTD.—See Huettenes-Albertus Chemische Werke GmbH; *Int'l*, pg. 3523
HA FOUNDRY MATERIAL (SHANGHAI) CO., LTD.—See Huettenes-Albertus Chemische Werke GmbH; *Int'l*, pg. 3522
HAGLEITNER HYGIENE BOSNE I HERCEGOVINE D.O.O.—See Hagleitner Hygiene International GmbH; *Int'l*, pg. 3207
HAGLEITNER HYGIENE BULGARIA EOOD—See Hagleitner Hygiene International GmbH; *Int'l*, pg. 3207
HAGLEITNER HYGIENE CESKO S.R.O.—See Hagleitner Hygiene International GmbH; *Int'l*, pg. 3207
HAGLEITNER HYGIENE DEUTSCHLAND GMBH—See Hagleitner Hygiene International GmbH; *Int'l*, pg. 3207
HAGLEITNER HYGIENE D.O.O.—See Hagleitner Hygiene International GmbH; *Int'l*, pg. 3207
HAGLEITNER HYGIENE HRVATSKA D.O.O.—See Hagleitner Hygiene International GmbH; *Int'l*, pg. 3207
HAGLEITNER HYGIENE ITALIA S.R.L.—See Hagleitner Hygiene International GmbH; *Int'l*, pg. 3207
HAGLEITNER HYGIENE MAGYARORSZAG KFT.—See Hagleitner Hygiene International GmbH; *Int'l*, pg. 3207
HAGLEITNER HYGIENE ROMANIA S.R.L.—See Hagleitner Hygiene International GmbH; *Int'l*, pg. 3207
HAGLEITNER HYGIENE SLOVENSKO S.R.O.—See Hagleitner Hygiene International GmbH; *Int'l*, pg. 3207
HAGLEITNER HYGIENE SRBIJA D.O.O.—See Hagleitner Hygiene International GmbH; *Int'l*, pg. 3207
HAGLEITNER ITALIA S.R.L.—See Hagleitner Hygiene International GmbH; *Int'l*, pg. 3207
HAGLEITNER NWO DEUTSCHLAND GMBH—See Hagleitner Hygiene International GmbH; *Int'l*, pg. 3207
HAIKE TRADING HONGKONG LIMITED—See HaiKe Chemical Group Ltd; *Int'l*, pg. 3211
HA ITALIA S.P.A.—See Huettenes-Albertus Chemische Werke GmbH; *Int'l*, pg. 3523
HALL TECHNOLOGIES INC.; *U.S. Private*, pg. 1843
HARRIS & FORD, LLC; *U.S. Private*, pg. 1869
HARRISONS PENINSULAR SDN. BHD.—See Harrisons Holdings (Malaysia) Berhad; *Int'l*, pg. 3279
HARRISONS SABAH SDN. BHD.—See Harrisons Holdings (Malaysia) Berhad; *Int'l*, pg. 3279
HARRISONS TRAVEL SDN. BHD.—See Harrisons Holdings (Malaysia) Berhad; *Int'l*, pg. 3279
HARVEY SALT COMPANY INC; *U.S. Private*, pg. 1878
HARWICK STANDARD DISTRIBUTION CORPORATION; *U.S. Private*, pg. 1878

HASA, INC.—See GHK Capital Partners LP; *U.S. Private*, pg. 1690
HASE PETROLEUM WAX CO. INC.; *U.S. Private*, pg. 1878
HAVAY INDUSTRY INC.—See GHW International; *Int'l*, pg. 2960
HAVILAND CONSUMER PRODUCTS, INC.—See Haviland Enterprises Inc.; *U.S. Private*, pg. 1880
HAVILAND PRODUCTS COMPANY—See Haviland Enterprises Inc.; *U.S. Private*, pg. 1880
HAWKINS, INC.; *U.S. Public*, pg. 989
HAWKINS TERMINAL I—See Hawkins, Inc.; *U.S. Public*, pg. 989
HAYNIE INCORPORATED; *U.S. Private*, pg. 1885
H.B. FULLER ADHESIVES NETHERLANDS B.V.—See H.B. Fuller Company; *U.S. Public*, pg. 977
H.B. FULLER ADHESIVES ROMANIA SRL—See H.B. Fuller Company; *U.S. Public*, pg. 977
H.B. FULLER ESPANA, S.A.—See H.B. Fuller Company; *U.S. Public*, pg. 978
H.B. FULLER HUNGARY KFT.—See H.B. Fuller Company; *U.S. Public*, pg. 978
H.B. FULLER (NEW ZEALAND) LIMITED—See H.B. Fuller Company; *U.S. Public*, pg. 977
H&C HEADWEAR-NEW YORK—See H&C Headwear Inc.; *U.S. Private*, pg. 1822
H.C.I. CHEMICALS NEDERLAND B.V.—See BRENNTAG SE; *Int'l*, pg. 1149
HEAVY MATERIALS LLC—See Vulcan Materials Company; *U.S. Public*, pg. 2314
HELM AGRO US, INC.—See HELM AG; *Int'l*, pg. 3337
HELM AG; *Int'l*, pg. 3337
HELM ANDINA LTDA.—See HELM AG; *Int'l*, pg. 3337
HELM ARGENTINA S.R.L.—See HELM AG; *Int'l*, pg. 3337
HELM AUSTRIA GES.M.B.H.—See HELM AG; *Int'l*, pg. 3337
HELM CHEMICALS B.V.—See HELM AG; *Int'l*, pg. 3337
HELM CHINA LTD.—See HELM AG; *Int'l*, pg. 3337
HELM D3 SAS—See HELM AG; *Int'l*, pg. 3337
HELM DE MEXICO, S.A.—See HELM AG; *Int'l*, pg. 3337
HELM DUNGEMITTEL GMBH—See HELM AG; *Int'l*, pg. 3337
HELM ENGRAIS FRANCE S.A.R.L.—See HELM AG; *Int'l*, pg. 3337
HELM FERTILIZER GREAT BRITAIN LTD.—See HELM AG; *Int'l*, pg. 3337
HELM FRANCE S.A.R.L.—See HELM AG; *Int'l*, pg. 3337
HELM GREAT BRITAIN LTD.—See HELM AG; *Int'l*, pg. 3337
HELM HONG KONG LTD.—See HELM AG; *Int'l*, pg. 3337
HELM IBERICA, S.A.—See HELM AG; *Int'l*, pg. 3337
HELM JAPAN LTD.—See HELM AG; *Int'l*, pg. 3337
HELM KIMYA LTD. SIRKETI—See HELM AG; *Int'l*, pg. 3337
HELM KOREA LTD.—See HELM AG; *Int'l*, pg. 3337
HELM POLSKA SP. Z O.O—See HELM AG; *Int'l*, pg. 3338
HELM PORTUGAL, LDA.—See HELM AG; *Int'l*, pg. 3338
HELM SKANDINAVIEN A/S—See HELM AG; *Int'l*, pg. 3338
HELM U.S. CORPORATION—See HELM AG; *Int'l*, pg. 3337
HEMPEL-HAI HONG COATINGS (KUNSHAN) CO., LTD—See China Merchants Group Limited; *Int'l*, pg. 1521
HENKEL AUSTRALIA PTY. LTD.—See Henkel AG & Co. KGaA; *Int'l*, pg. 3349
HENKEL BALTI OU—See Henkel AG & Co. KGaA; *Int'l*, pg. 3350
HENKEL COLOMBIANA S.A.—See Henkel AG & Co. KGaA; *Int'l*, pg. 3350
HENKEL HAKUSUI CORPORATION—See Henkel AG & Co. KGaA; *Int'l*, pg. 3349
HENKEL LTDA.—See Henkel AG & Co. KGaA; *Int'l*, pg. 3351
HENKEL (MALAYSIA) SDN. BHD.—See Henkel AG & Co. KGaA; *Int'l*, pg. 3349
HENKEL NORGE AB—See Henkel AG & Co. KGaA; *Int'l*, pg. 3352
HERAEUS S.A.—See Heraeus Holding GmbH; *Int'l*, pg. 3358
HERCULES ARGENTINA S.A.—See Ashland Inc.; *U.S. Public*, pg. 212
HERCULES CHILE LIMITADA—See Ashland Inc.; *U.S. Public*, pg. 212
HERCULES HYDROCARBON HOLDINGS, INC.—See Ashland Inc.; *U.S. Public*, pg. 212
HERCULES PORTUGUESA, LDA.—See Ashland Inc.; *U.S. Public*, pg. 212
HICKMAN, WILLIAMS & COMPANY—See Hickman, Williams & Company; *U.S. Private*, pg. 1933
HILL BROTHERS CHEMICAL COMPANY INC. - SALT LAKE CITY—See Hill Brothers Chemical Company Inc.; *U.S. Private*, pg. 1944
HILL BROTHERS CHEMICAL COMPANY INC.; *U.S. Private*, pg. 1944
HILLTOP ENERGY INC.—See D.W. Dickey & Sons Inc.; *U.S. Private*, pg. 1143
HILLYARD, INC.; *U.S. Private*, pg. 1947
HILLYARD-ROVIC—See Hillyard, Inc.; *U.S. Private*, pg. 1947
HODOGAYA CHEMICAL KOREA CO., LTD.—See Hodogaya Chemical Co., Ltd.; *Int'l*, pg. 3438
HODOGAYA CHEMICAL (U.S.A.), INC.—See Hodogaya Chemical Co., Ltd.; *Int'l*, pg. 3438
HODOGAYA (SHANGHAI) TRADING CO., LTD.—See

424690 — OTHER CHEMICAL AND ...

Hodogaya Chemical Co., Ltd.; *Int'l*, pg. 3438
HOKKO SANGYO CO., LTD.—See HOKKO CHEMICAL INDUSTRY CO., LTD.; *Int'l*, pg. 3443
HOLANDA VENEZUELA C.A.—See BRENNTAG SE; *Int'l*, pg. 1149
HOLSTON GASES INC.; *U.S. Private*, pg. 1968
HONG YU MATERIALS CO., LTD.—See Headway Advanced Materials Inc.; *Int'l*, pg. 3302
HO TUNG CHEMICAL CORP.; *Int'l*, pg. 3434
HOUGHTON ASIA PACIFIC CO., LTD.—See Quaker Chemical Corporation; *U.S. Public*, pg. 1746
HOUGHTON CANADA INC.—See Quaker Chemical Corporation; *U.S. Public*, pg. 1746
HOUGHTON CHEMICAL CORPORATION; *U.S. Private*, pg. 1990
HOUGHTON CHEMICAL—See Houghton Chemical Corporation; *U.S. Private*, pg. 1990
HOUGHTON CZ S.R.O.—See Quaker Chemical Corporation; *U.S. Public*, pg. 1746
HOUGHTON DENMARK A/S—See Quaker Chemical Corporation; *U.S. Public*, pg. 1746
HOUGHTON JAPAN CO., LTD.—See Quaker Chemical Corporation; *U.S. Public*, pg. 1746
HOUGHTON KIMYA SAN A.S.—See Quaker Chemical Corporation; *U.S. Public*, pg. 1746
HOUGHTON MEXICO S.A. DE C.V.—See Quaker Chemical Corporation; *U.S. Public*, pg. 1746
HOUGHTON OIL (MALAYSIA) SDN. BHD.—See Quaker Chemical Corporation; *U.S. Public*, pg. 1746
HOUGHTON POLSKA SP. Z O.O.—See Quaker Chemical Corporation; *U.S. Public*, pg. 1746
HOUGHTON (SHANGHAI) SPECIALTY INDUSTRIAL FLUIDS CO. LTD.—See Hinduja Group Ltd.; *Int'l*, pg. 3399
HOUGHTON SVERIGE AB—See Quaker Chemical Corporation; *U.S. Public*, pg. 1746
HOUGHTON TAIWAN CO. LTD.—See Quaker Chemical Corporation; *U.S. Public*, pg. 1746
HOUGHTON UKRAINE LTD.—See Quaker Chemical Corporation; *U.S. Public*, pg. 1746
HOYER AUSTRIA GES. M.B.H.—See Hoyer GmbH; *Int'l*, pg. 3498
HOYER GLOBAL BRAZIL LTDA—See Hoyer GmbH; *Int'l*, pg. 3499
HOYER GLOBAL INC.—See Hoyer GmbH; *Int'l*, pg. 3499
HPI INT. TRADING & CHEMICAL GMBH—See HPI AG; *Int'l*, pg. 3500
HUBBARD-HALL, INC.; *U.S. Private*, pg. 2000
HUETTENES-ALBERTUS AUSTRALIA PTY. LTD.—See Huettenes-Albertus Chemische Werke GmbH; *Int'l*, pg. 3523
HUETTENES-ALBERTUS CHINA (HONGKONG) CO., LIMITED—See Huettenes-Albertus Chemische Werke GmbH; *Int'l*, pg. 3523
HUNAN PETROCHEMICAL SUPPLY & MARKETING CORPORATION—See China National Chemical Corporation; *Int'l*, pg. 1528
HUNTSMAN (KOREA) LIMITED—See Huntsman Corporation; *U.S. Public*, pg. 1073
HUNTSMAN P&A UERDINGEN GMBH—See Huntsman Corporation; *U.S. Public*, pg. 1073
HUNTSMAN P&A WASSERCHEMIE GMBH—See Huntsman Corporation; *U.S. Public*, pg. 1073
HUNTSMAN PETROCHEMICAL LLC—See Huntsman Corporation; *U.S. Public*, pg. 1074
HUNTSMAN PIGMENTS HONG KONG LIMITED—See Huntsman Corporation; *U.S. Public*, pg. 1074
HUNTSMAN PIGMENTS & TRADING PTY. LTD.—See Huntsman Corporation; *U.S. Public*, pg. 1074
HUTTENES-ALBERTUS POLSKA SP. Z.O.O.—See Huettenes-Albertus Chemische Werke GmbH; *Int'l*, pg. 3523
HUTTENES-ALBERTUS (UK) LTD.—See Huettenes-Albertus Chemische Werke GmbH; *Int'l*, pg. 3523
HYDRITE CHEMICAL COMPANY; *U.S. Private*, pg. 2017
IBIDEN CHEMICALS CO., LTD.—See Ibiden Co., Ltd.; *Int'l*, pg. 3575
ICC CHEMICAL CORPORATION—See ICC Industries, Inc.; *U.S. Private*, pg. 2029
ICC CHEMICALS S.R.L.—See ICC Industries, Inc.; *U.S. Private*, pg. 2030
ICC CHEMICALS UK LTD.—See ICC Industries, Inc.; *U.S. Private*, pg. 2030
ICC-CHEMOL KFT.—See ICC Industries, Inc.; *U.S. Private*, pg. 2030
ICC HANDELS AG—See ICC Industries, Inc.; *U.S. Private*, pg. 2030
ICC (HONG KONG) LTD.—See ICC Industries, Inc.; *U.S. Private*, pg. 2029
ICC INDUSTRIES B.V.—See ICC Industries, Inc.; *U.S. Private*, pg. 2030
ICC INDUSTRIES, INC.; *U.S. Private*, pg. 2029
ICD GROUP INTERNATIONAL INC.; *U.S. Private*, pg. 2030
IDEAL CHEMICAL & SUPPLY COMPANY; *U.S. Private*, pg. 2035
IDEMITSU CHEMICALS (HONG KONG) CO., LTD.—See Idemitsu Kosan Co., Ltd.; *Int'l*, pg. 3590
IGM RESINS USA INC—See Astorg Partners S.A.S.; *Int'l*, pg. 656

IHT HEALTH PRODUCTS, INC.—See Integrated Biopharma, Inc.; *U.S. Public*, pg. 1136
IMCD AUSTRALIA LIMITED—See IMCD N.V.; *Int'l*, pg. 3621
IMCD BALTICS UAB—See IMCD N.V.; *Int'l*, pg. 3621
IMCD BENELUX B.V.—See IMCD N.V.; *Int'l*, pg. 3621
IMCD BENELUX N.V.—See IMCD N.V.; *Int'l*, pg. 3621
IMCD BRASIL COMERCIO E INDUSTRIA DE PRODUTOS QUIMICOS LTDA—See IMCD N.V.; *Int'l*, pg. 3621
IMCD CANADA LIMITED—See IMCD N.V.; *Int'l*, pg. 3621
IMCD CZECH REPUBLIC A.S.—See IMCD N.V.; *Int'l*, pg. 3621
IMCD DANMARK A/S—See IMCD N.V.; *Int'l*, pg. 3621
IMCD DEUTSCHLAND GMBH & CO. KG—See IMCD N.V.; *Int'l*, pg. 3621
IMCD EGYPT LLC—See IMCD N.V.; *Int'l*, pg. 3621
IMCD ESPANA ESPECIALIDADES QUIMICAS, S.A.—See IMCD N.V.; *Int'l*, pg. 3621
IMCD FINLAND OY—See IMCD N.V.; *Int'l*, pg. 3622
IMCD FRANCE S.A.S.—See IMCD N.V.; *Int'l*, pg. 3622
IMCD ITALIA S.P.A.—See IMCD N.V.; *Int'l*, pg. 3622
IMCD KENYA LTD.—See IMCD N.V.; *Int'l*, pg. 3622
IMCD MAROC S.A.R.L.—See IMCD N.V.; *Int'l*, pg. 3621
IMCD MEXICO S.A. DE C.V.—See IMCD N.V.; *Int'l*, pg. 3622
IMCD MIDDLE EAST ZFCO—See IMCD N.V.; *Int'l*, pg. 3622
IMCD NORWAY AS—See IMCD N.V.; *Int'l*, pg. 3622
IMCD PHILIPPINES CORPORATION—See IMCD N.V.; *Int'l*, pg. 3622
IMCD PLASTICS (SHANGHAI) CO., LTD.—See IMCD N.V.; *Int'l*, pg. 3622
IMCD PORTUGAL PRODUTOS QUIMICOS, LDA.—See IMCD N.V.; *Int'l*, pg. 3621
IMCD RUS LLC—See IMCD N.V.; *Int'l*, pg. 3622
IMCD SINGAPORE PTE. LTD.—See IMCD N.V.; *Int'l*, pg. 3622
IMCD SOUTH AFRICA (PTY) LTD.—See IMCD N.V.; *Int'l*, pg. 3622
IMCD SOUTH EAST EUROPE GMBH—See IMCD N.V.; *Int'l*, pg. 3622
IMCD SWEDEN AB—See IMCD N.V.; *Int'l*, pg. 3622
IMCD (THAILAND) CO., LTD.—See IMCD N.V.; *Int'l*, pg. 3621
IMCD TUNISIA S.A.R.L.—See IMCD N.V.; *Int'l*, pg. 3622
IMCD UK LTD.—See IMCD N.V.; *Int'l*, pg. 3622
IMCD UKRAINE LLC—See IMCD N.V.; *Int'l*, pg. 3622
IMCD US—See IMCD N.V.; *Int'l*, pg. 3622
IMCD VIETNAM COMPANY LTD.—See IMCD N.V.; *Int'l*, pg. 3622
IMPACT! CHEMICAL TECHNOLOGIES, INC.—See Hastings Equity Partners, LLC; *U.S. Private*, pg. 1879
IMTT-BAYONNE—See Riverstone Holdings LLC; *U.S. Private*, pg. 3447
IMTT-GEISMAR—See Riverstone Holdings LLC; *U.S. Private*, pg. 3447
IMTT-GRETNA—See BWC Terminals LLC; *U.S. Private*, pg. 700
INDEPENDENT CHEMICAL CORP.; *U.S. Private*, pg. 2058
INDIANA OXYGEN COMPANY INCORPORATED; *U.S. Private*, pg. 2062
INDURA ECUADOR S.A.—See Air Products & Chemicals, Inc.; *U.S. Public*, pg. 66
INDURA PERU S.A.—See Air Products & Chemicals, Inc.; *U.S. Public*, pg. 66
INDURA URUGUAY S.A.—See Air Products & Chemicals, Inc.; *U.S. Public*, pg. 66
INDUSTRIAL AGRICOLA FORTALEZA IMPORTACAO E EXPORTACAO LTDA—See AGCO Corporation; *U.S. Public*, pg. 59
INDUSTRIAL CHEMICALS CORP.; *U.S. Private*, pg. 2065
INDUSTRIAL CHEMICALS INC.; *U.S. Private*, pg. 2065
INDUSTRIAL CHEMICALS INC—See Industrial Chemicals Inc.; *U.S. Private*, pg. 2065
INDUSTRIAL GAS DISTRIBUTORS—See Advance Auto Parts, Inc.; *U.S. Public*, pg. 45
INDUSTRIAL MECANICA AGRICOLA S. A.—See IMASA S.A.; *Int'l*, pg. 3620
INEOS CHLOR AMERICAS INC.—See One Rock Capital Partners, LLC; *U.S. Private*, pg. 3023
INEOS CHLOR ATLANTIK GMBH—See One Rock Capital Partners, LLC; *U.S. Private*, pg. 3022
INEOS CHLOR QUIMICA, SA—See One Rock Capital Partners, LLC; *U.S. Private*, pg. 3023
INEOS CHLOR SALES INTERNATIONAL LIMITED—See One Rock Capital Partners, LLC; *U.S. Private*, pg. 3023
INEOS ENTERPRISES FRANCE SAS—See One Rock Capital Partners, LLC; *U.S. Private*, pg. 3023
INEOS ITALIA SRL—See One Rock Capital Partners, LLC; *U.S. Private*, pg. 3023
INGEVITY GEORGIA, LLC—See Ingevity Corporation; *U.S. Public*, pg. 1122
INOTEC TAIWAN CO., LTD.—See Air Water Inc.; *Int'l*, pg. 240
INOUEKI (MALAYSIA) SDN. BHD.—See Air Water Inc.; *Int'l*, pg. 240
INOUEKI PHILIPPINES, INC.—See Air Water Inc.; *Int'l*, pg. 240
INQUIDE ITALIA SRL—See Fluidra SA; *Int'l*, pg. 2714
INTERCONNECT PRODUCTS DIVISION—See Methode Electronics, Inc.; *U.S. Public*, pg. 1428

INTERLATES LTD.—See BASF SE; *Int'l*, pg. 884
INTERNATIONAL CHEMICALS ENGINEERING PTY. LTD.—See ENRA Group Berhad; *Int'l*, pg. 2445
INTEROCEANIC CORPORATION; *U.S. Private*, pg. 2122
INTERSTATE CHEMICAL CO., INC.; *U.S. Private*, pg. 2124
INTERSTATE CHEMICAL—See Interstate Chemical Co., Inc.; *U.S. Private*, pg. 2124
INTREPID POTASH-MOAB, LLC—See Intrepid Potash, Inc.; *U.S. Public*, pg. 1159
INVERSIONES QUIMICAS S.A.—See BRENNTAG SE; *Int'l*, pg. 1149
ISOCHEM BETEILIGUNGS GMBH—See Aurelius Equity Opportunities SE & Co. KGaA; *Int'l*, pg. 708
ISP ASIA PACIFIC PTE. LTD.—See Ashland Inc.; *U.S. Public*, pg. 212
ISP DO BRASIL LTDA.—See Ashland Inc.; *U.S. Public*, pg. 213
ISP FRANCE MARKETING SARL—See Ashland Inc.; *U.S. Public*, pg. 213
ISP GLOBAL TECHNOLOGIES DEUTSCHLAND GMBH—See Ashland Inc.; *U.S. Public*, pg. 213
ISP JAPAN LTD.—See Ashland Inc.; *U.S. Public*, pg. 213
ISP (KOREA) LIMITED—See Ashland Inc.; *U.S. Public*, pg. 212
ISP TURKEY—See Ashland Inc.; *U.S. Public*, pg. 213
ITW PERFORMANCE POLYMERS & FLUIDS JAPAN CO. LTD.—See Illinois Tool Works Inc.; *U.S. Public*, pg. 1107
ITW PERFORMANCE POLYMERS & FLUIDS OOO—See Illinois Tool Works Inc.; *U.S. Public*, pg. 1107
ITW PERFORMANCE POLYMERS & FLUIDS PTE. LTD.—See Illinois Tool Works Inc.; *U.S. Public*, pg. 1107
ITW POLYMEX, S. DE R.L. DE C.V.—See Illinois Tool Works Inc.; *U.S. Public*, pg. 1107
ITW TEMB (QUFU) AUTOMOTIVE COOLING SYSTEMS CO. LTD.—See Illinois Tool Works Inc.; *U.S. Public*, pg. 1108
IVANHOE INDUSTRIES, INC.; *U.S. Private*, pg. 2150
JACKSON WELDING SUPPLY CO., INC.; *U.S. Private*, pg. 2178
JACOBSON (SHENZHEN) TRADING COMPANY LIMITED—See Chinney Alliance Group Limited; *Int'l*, pg. 1570
JAPEX,CO., LTD.—See Carlit Co., Ltd.; *Int'l*, pg. 1338
JCI JONES CHEMICALS, INC.; *U.S. Private*, pg. 2194
JEEN INTERNATIONAL CORP.—See H.I.G. Capital, LLC; *U.S. Private*, pg. 1832
JELMAR COMPANY; *U.S. Private*, pg. 2199
J.F. SHELTON CO., INC.—See Kelso & Company, L.P.; *U.S. Private*, pg. 2278
JLM INDUSTRIES, INC.; *U.S. Private*, pg. 2213
JOHNSONS WAX ESPANOLA, S.A.—See S.C. Johnson & Son, Inc.; *U.S. Private*, pg. 3516
JORDAN BROMINE COMPANY LIMITED—See Albemarle Corporation; *U.S. Public*, pg. 73
JRS INTERNATIONAL, LLC.—See ICD Group International Inc.; *U.S. Private*, pg. 2030
J. TECH SALES, L.L.C.; *U.S. Private*, pg. 2157
JUFFALI CHEMICAL COMPANY—See E.A. Juffali & Brothers Company; *Int'l*, pg. 2250
KAIMANN B.V.—See Compagnie de Saint-Gobain SA; *Int'l*, pg. 1723
KAIMANN FRANCE SAS—See Compagnie de Saint-Gobain SA; *Int'l*, pg. 1723
KAIMANN IBERIA S.L.—See Compagnie de Saint-Gobain SA; *Int'l*, pg. 1723
KAIMANN ITALIA S.R.L—See Compagnie de Saint-Gobain SA; *Int'l*, pg. 1723
KAIMANN UK LTD—See Compagnie de Saint-Gobain SA; *Int'l*, pg. 1723
KANTO CORPORATION; *U.S. Private*, pg. 2261
KATSURA SANGYO CO., LTD.—See Hodogaya Chemical Co., Ltd.; *Int'l*, pg. 3439
KEIHIN KASEHIN CENTER CO., LTD.—See ENEOS Holdings, Inc.; *Int'l*, pg. 2416
KEYSTONE ANILINE CORP.—See Milliken & Company; *U.S. Private*, pg. 2737
KISSNER GROUP HOLDINGS LP—See Stone Canyon Industries, LLC; *U.S. Private*, pg. 3817
KLUBER LUBRICATION AG (SCHWEIZ)—See Freudenberg SE; *Int'l*, pg. 2785
KLUBER LUBRICATION A.S.—See Freudenberg SE; *Int'l*, pg. 2785
KLUBER LUBRICATION AUSTRALIA PTY. LTD.—See Freudenberg SE; *Int'l*, pg. 2785
KLUBER LUBRICATION CHINA LTD.—See Freudenberg SE; *Int'l*, pg. 2785
KLUBER LUBRICATION FRANCE S.A.S.—See Freudenberg SE; *Int'l*, pg. 2785
KLUBER LUBRICATION GREAT BRITAIN LTD.—See Freudenberg SE; *Int'l*, pg. 2785
KLUBER LUBRICATION (PTY.) LTD.—See Freudenberg SE; *Int'l*, pg. 2785
KNIGHT EQUIPMENT PTY., LTD.—See IDEX Corp; *U.S. Public*, pg. 1091
KNIGHT U.K. LTD.—See IDEX Corp; *U.S. Public*, pg. 1091
KOCH CHEMICAL TECHNOLOGY GROUP INDIA PVT. LTD. - KOCH-GLITSCH MUMBAI DIVISION—See Koch Industries, Inc.; *U.S. Private*, pg. 2331

424690 — OTHER CHEMICAL AND ...

KOPPERS PERFORMANCE CHEMICALS AUSTRALIA PTY LTD—See Koppers Holdings Inc.; *U.S. Public*, pg. 1272
KOPPERS UK LIMITED—See Koppers Holdings Inc.; *U.S. Public*, pg. 1272
KRAFT CHEMICAL COMPANY; *U.S. Private*, pg. 2348
K.R. ANDERSON CO. INC.; *U.S. Private*, pg. 2252
KRONOS LIMITED—See Contran Corporation; *U.S. Private*, pg. 1033
KYNOL EUROPA IMPORT-EXPORT GMBH—See Gun Ei Chemical Industry Co., Ltd.; *Int'l*, pg. 3183
LAFFANS PETROCHEMICALS LIMITED—See Huntsman Corporation; *U.S. Public*, pg. 1074
LA JOHNSON FRANCAISE S.A.—See S.C. Johnson & Son, Inc.; *U.S. Private*, pg. 3516
LEBERMUTH COMPANY; *U.S. Private*, pg. 2409
LES INGREDIENTS ALIMENTAIRES BSA INC.—See International Flavors & Fragrances Inc.; *U.S. Public*, pg. 1153
LES PRODUITS CHIMIQUES ERPAC INC.—See Ecolab Inc.; *U.S. Public*, pg. 714
LHS (UK) LIMITED—See Ecolab Inc.; *U.S. Public*, pg. 714
LIDOCHEM, INC.; *U.S. Private*, pg. 2448
LIMITED LIABILITY COMPANY HUNTSMAN (UKRAINE)—See Huntsman Corporation; *U.S. Public*, pg. 1075
LIQUID TECHNOLOGY CORPORATION—See CI Capital Partners LLC; *U.S. Private*, pg. 895
LLC TELKO—See Aspo Oyj; *Int'l*, pg. 631
L.M. SCOFIELD COMPANY—See L.M. Scofield Company; *U.S. Private*, pg. 2366
LORD CHEMICAL PRODUCTS (MALAYSIA) SDN. BHD.—See Parker Hannifin Corporation; *U.S. Public*, pg. 1641
LORD CORPORATION PRODUCTS AND ENGINEERING, LTD.—See Parker Hannifin Corporation; *U.S. Public*, pg. 1641
LORD INTERNATIONAL TRADING (SHANGHAI) CO., LTD.—See Parker Hannifin Corporation; *U.S. Public*, pg. 1641
LUBRIZOL ADVANCED MATERIALS ASIA PACIFIC LIMITED—See Berkshire Hathaway Inc.; *U.S. Public*, pg. 319
LUBRIZOL ADVANCED MATERIALS EUROPE BVBA—See Berkshire Hathaway Inc.; *U.S. Public*, pg. 319
LUBRIZOL AUSTRALIA—See Berkshire Hathaway Inc.; *U.S. Public*, pg. 319
LUBRIZOL CANADA LTD.—See Berkshire Hathaway Inc.; *U.S. Public*, pg. 319
LUBRIZOL DEUTSCHLAND GMBH—See Berkshire Hathaway Inc.; *U.S. Public*, pg. 319
LUBRIZOL ESPANOLA, S.A.—See Berkshire Hathaway Inc.; *U.S. Public*, pg. 319
LUBRIZOL FRANCE SAS—See Berkshire Hathaway Inc.; *U.S. Public*, pg. 319
LUBRIZOL GMBH—See Berkshire Hathaway Inc.; *U.S. Public*, pg. 319
LUBRIZOL ITALIANA, S.P.A.—See Berkshire Hathaway Inc.; *U.S. Public*, pg. 319
LUBRIZOL JAPAN LIMITED—See Berkshire Hathaway Inc.; *U.S. Public*, pg. 319
LUBRIZOL LIMITED—See Berkshire Hathaway Inc.; *U.S. Public*, pg. 319
LUBRIZOL SOUTHEAST ASIA (PTE.) LTD.—See Berkshire Hathaway Inc.; *U.S. Public*, pg. 319
MACDERMID BENELUX B.V.—See Element Solutions Inc.; *U.S. Public*, pg. 727
MACDERMID CHEMICALS, INC.—See Element Solutions Inc.; *U.S. Public*, pg. 727
MACDERMID ESPANOLA S.A.—See Element Solutions Inc.; *U.S. Public*, pg. 727
MACDERMID FRANCE, S.A.—See Element Solutions Inc.; *U.S. Public*, pg. 727
MACDERMID GMBH—See Element Solutions Inc.; *U.S. Public*, pg. 727
MACDERMID HONG KONG LTD.—See Element Solutions Inc.; *U.S. Public*, pg. 727
MACDERMID ITALIANA SRL—See Element Solutions Inc.; *U.S. Public*, pg. 727
MACDERMID KOREA LTD.—See Element Solutions Inc.; *U.S. Public*, pg. 727
MACDERMID LTD—See Element Solutions Inc.; *U.S. Public*, pg. 727
MACDERMID MEXICO SA DE CV—See Element Solutions Inc.; *U.S. Public*, pg. 727
MACDERMID SINGAPORE PTE. LTD.—See Element Solutions Inc.; *U.S. Public*, pg. 727
MACDERMID TAIWAN LTD.—See Element Solutions Inc.; *U.S. Public*, pg. 727
MAGNABLEND, INC.—See Apollo Global Management, Inc.; *U.S. Public*, pg. 165
MANSI GLOBIZ INC.; *U.S. Private*, pg. 2566
MARCOR DEVELOPMENT CORP.—See KODA Enterprises Group, LLC; *U.S. Private*, pg. 2336
MARYLAND CHEMICAL COMPANY, INC.; *U.S. Private*, pg. 2600
MASNOVA QUIMICA S.A. DE C.V.—See AntarChile S.A.; *Int'l*, pg. 481
MASON CHEMICAL COMPANY—See Pilot Chemical Company; *U.S. Private*, pg. 3181
MASTERANK INC.; *U.S. Private*, pg. 2608
MASTER CHEMICAL EUROPE LTD.—See Master Chemical Corporation; *U.S. Private*, pg. 2607
MASTER CHEMICAL (SHANGHAI) CO., LTD.—See Master Chemical Corporation; *U.S. Private*, pg. 2607
MASTER CHEMICAL SIAM CO., LTD.—See Master Chemical Corporation; *U.S. Private*, pg. 2607
MASTER CHEMICAL (TIANJIN) CO., LTD.—See Master Chemical Corporation; *U.S. Private*, pg. 2607
MASTER CHEMICAL VIETNAM CO., LTD.—See Master Chemical Corporation; *U.S. Private*, pg. 2607
MASTER FLUID SOLUTIONS (INDIA) PRIVATE LIMITED—See Master Chemical Corporation; *U.S. Private*, pg. 2607
MATSCHEL OF FLAGLER INC.; *U.S. Private*, pg. 2612
MAYS CAPTREE—See Mays Chemical Company; *U.S. Private*, pg. 2623
MAYS CHEMICAL COMPANY; *U.S. Private*, pg. 2623
MAYS CHEMICAL COMPANY—See Mays Chemical Company; *U.S. Private*, pg. 2623
MAYZO, INC.; *U.S. Private*, pg. 2623
MCGILL AIRSEAL LLC—See The McGill Corporation; *U.S. Private*, pg. 4076
MELTEX ASIA PACIFIC CO., LTD.—See Astena Holdings Co., Ltd.; *Int'l*, pg. 653
MELTEX (HK) LTD.—See Astena Holdings Co., Ltd.; *Int'l*, pg. 653
MELTEX KOREA CO., LTD.—See Astena Holdings Co., Ltd.; *Int'l*, pg. 653
MELTEX TAIWAN INC.—See Astena Holdings Co., Ltd.; *Int'l*, pg. 653
MELTEX (TIANJIN) LTD.—See Astena Holdings Co., Ltd.; *Int'l*, pg. 653
MERISANT COMPANY—See MacAndrews & Forbes Incorporated; *U.S. Private*, pg. 2532
MESSER GAS PUERTO RICO, INC.—See CVC Capital Partners SICAV-FIS S.A.; *Int'l*, pg. 1885
METAUSEL SAS—See BRENNTAG SE; *Int'l*, pg. 1149
MEXICAN SILICATES S.A. DE C.V.—See Gruppo Minerali Maffei S.p.A.; *Int'l*, pg. 3140
MEXICHEM AMERICA, INC.—See Grupo Empresarial Kaluz S.A. de C.V.; *Int'l*, pg. 3127
MEXICHEM COMPUESTOS, S.A. DE C.V.—See Grupo Empresarial Kaluz S.A. de C.V.; *Int'l*, pg. 3127
MEXICHEM DERIVADOS COLOMBIA, S.A.—See Grupo Empresarial Kaluz S.A. de C.V.; *Int'l*, pg. 3127
MEXICHEM EL SALVADOR, S.A.—See Grupo Empresarial Kaluz S.A. de C.V.; *Int'l*, pg. 3127
MEXICHEM FLUOR JAPAN LTD.—See Grupo Empresarial Kaluz S.A. de C.V.; *Int'l*, pg. 3127
MEXICHEM FLUOR TAIWAN LIMITED—See Grupo Empresarial Kaluz S.A. de C.V.; *Int'l*, pg. 3127
MEXICHEM GUATEMALA, S.A.—See Grupo Empresarial Kaluz S.A. de C.V.; *Int'l*, pg. 3127
MEXICHEM HONDURAS, S.A.—See Grupo Empresarial Kaluz S.A. de C.V.; *Int'l*, pg. 3127
MEXICHEM NICARAGUA, S.A.—See Grupo Empresarial Kaluz S.A. de C.V.; *Int'l*, pg. 3127
MEXICHEM QUIMIR—See Grupo Empresarial Kaluz S.A. de C.V.; *Int'l*, pg. 3128
MEXICHEM SALINERA DEL SUR, S.A. DE C.V.—See Grupo Empresarial Kaluz S.A. de C.V.; *Int'l*, pg. 3128
MEXICHEM UK LTD—See Grupo Empresarial Kaluz S.A. de C.V.; *Int'l*, pg. 3128
MFG CHEMICAL, LLC—See Platte River Ventures, LLC; *U.S. Private*, pg. 3211
MFM DELAWARE INC.; *U.S. Private*, pg. 2693
MICHELMAN CHEMICALS PVT. LTD.—See Michelman Inc.; *U.S. Private*, pg. 2699
MICHELMAN SARL—See Michelman Inc.; *U.S. Private*, pg. 2699
MIDER-HELM METHANOL VERTRIEBS GMBH—See HELM AG; *Int'l*, pg. 3338
MILLCHEM ZAMBIA LIMITED—See Cambria Africa Plc; *Int'l*, pg. 1269
MINERAL RESEARCH & DEVELOPMENT—See Huntsman Corporation; *U.S. Public*, pg. 1073
MINERAL RESOURCES DE GUATEMALA S.A.—See Gruppo Minerali Maffei S.p.A.; *Int'l*, pg. 3140
MONSON COMPANIES INC.—See EQT AB; *Int'l*, pg. 2469
MOSS PLASTIC PRODUCTS TRADING (NINGBO) CO., LTD.—See OpenGate Capital Management, LLC; *U.S. Private*, pg. 3030
M/S. AMARAVATI INTERNATIONAL—See BASF SE; pg. 884
MSA SOURCING BV—See Cambria Africa Plc; *Int'l*, pg. 1269
MULTI-CHEM GROUP, LLC—See Halliburton Company; *U.S. Public*, pg. 980
MULTISOL GROUP LIMITED—See BRENNTAG SE; *Int'l*, pg. 1149
MULTISOL LIMITED—See BRENNTAG SE; *Int'l*, pg. 1149
MYANMAR BEHN MEYER CO. LTD.—See Behn Meyer (D) Holding AG & Co.; *Int'l*, pg. 941
NALCO COMPANY - SUGAR LAND—See Ecolab Inc.; *U.S. Public*, pg. 715
NALCO ENERGY SERVICES MIDDLE EAST HOLDINGS, INC.—See Ecolab Inc.; *U.S. Public*, pg. 715
NALCO INDUSTRIAL SERVICES (NANJING) CO., LTD.—See Ecolab Inc.; *U.S. Public*, pg. 715
NALCO PHILIPPINES INC.—See Ecolab Inc.; *U.S. Public*, pg. 716
NANTONG ARAKAWA CHEMICAL INDUSTRIES, LTD.—See Arakawa Chemical Industries, Ltd.; *Int'l*, pg. 535
NARDI AROMAS LTDA.—See International Flavors & Fragrances Inc.; *U.S. Public*, pg. 1154
NATIONAL SCIENTIFIC COMPANY LTD.—See Dabbagh Group Holding Company Ltd.; *Int'l*, pg. 1902
NATIONAL SILICATES PARTNERSHIP—See Ecovyst Inc.; *U.S. Public*, pg. 717
NCH AG—See NCH Corporation; *U.S. Private*, pg. 2875
NCH GMBH—See NCH Corporation; *U.S. Private*, pg. 2875
NCH IRELAND LTD.—See NCH Corporation; *U.S. Private*, pg. 2876
NCH (UK) LTD.—See NCH Corporation; *U.S. Private*, pg. 2875
NEDAMCO NORTH AMERICA CORPORATION—See Elcat Inc.; *U.S. Private*, pg. 1350
NETMRO INC.—See Platinum Equity, LLC; *U.S. Private*, pg. 3210
NEW LIFE CHEMICAL & EQUIPMENT, INC.—See Makai Capital Partners LLC; *U.S. Private*, pg. 2556
NEXEO PLASCHEM (SHANGHAI) CO., LTD.—See Apollo Global Management, Inc.; *U.S. Public*, pg. 165
NEXEO SOLUTIONS GERMANY GMBH—See Apollo Global Management, Inc.; *U.S. Public*, pg. 165
NEXEO SOLUTIONS ITALY SRL—See Apollo Global Management, Inc.; *U.S. Public*, pg. 165
NEXEO SOLUTIONS, LLC—See One Rock Capital Partners, LLC; *U.S. Private*, pg. 3022
NEXEO SOLUTIONS MEXICO S. DE R.L. DE C.V.—See Apollo Global Management, Inc.; *U.S. Public*, pg. 165
NEXEO SOLUTIONS PLASTICS UK LIMITED—See Apollo Global Management, Inc.; *U.S. Public*, pg. 165
NEXEO SOLUTIONS POLAND SP. Z O.O.—See Apollo Global Management, Inc.; *U.S. Public*, pg. 165
NEXEO SOLUTIONS RUS LLC—See Apollo Global Management, Inc.; *U.S. Public*, pg. 165
NEXEO SOLUTIONS SPAIN SLU—See Apollo Global Management, Inc.; *U.S. Public*, pg. 165
NEXEO SOLUTIONS SWEDEN AB—See Apollo Global Management, Inc.; *U.S. Public*, pg. 165
NIASA MEXICO, S. A. DE C. V.—See Grupo Lamosa S.A. de C.V.; *Int'l*, pg. 3132
NIKKA CO., LTD.—See Bell-Park Co., Ltd.; *Int'l*, pg. 966
NIPPON MACDERMID CO., LTD.—See Element Solutions Inc.; *U.S. Public*, pg. 728
NITEO PRODUCTS, LLC—See Highlander Partners, LP.; *U.S. Private*, pg. 1939
NITTA DUPONT INCORPORATED—See DuPont de Nemours, Inc.; *U.S. Public*, pg. 694
N. JONAS & COMPANY, INC.; *U.S. Private*, pg. 2827
NORCAL RESPIRATORY INC.—See Quipt Home Medical Corp.; *U.S. Public*, pg. 1757
NORCHEM, INC.—See Grupo Villar Mir, S.A.U.; *Int'l*, pg. 3138
NORFALCO INC.—See Glencore plc; *Int'l*, pg. 2991
NORFALCO SALES INC.—See Glencore plc; *Int'l*, pg. 2991
NORSECHEM MARKETING SDN. BHD.—See Hexza Corporation Berhad; *Int'l*, pg. 3373
NORSK JOHNSON'S WAX A/S—See S.C. Johnson & Son, Inc.; *U.S. Private*, pg. 3516
NORTH AMERICAN HOGANAS, INC.—See Hoganas AB; *Int'l*, pg. 3441
NOTTINGHAM COMPANY INC.—See Performance Process, Inc.; *U.S. Private*, pg. 3149
NOURYON FUNCTIONAL CHEMICALS AB—See GIC Pte. Ltd.; *Int'l*, pg. 2968
NOURYON FUNCTIONAL CHEMICALS AB—See The Carlyle Group Inc.; *U.S. Public*, pg. 2051
NOVA CHIMICA, S.R.L.—See Illinois Tool Works Inc.; *U.S. Public*, pg. 1109
NOVEL TECHNOLOGY LABORATORIES—See A.L. Wilson Chemical Co.; *U.S. Private*, pg. 27
NU-CALGON WHOLESALER INC.; *U.S. Private*, pg. 2971
NYPRO HUNGARY MUANYAGTECHNIKA KFT—See Jabil Inc.; *U.S. Public*, pg. 1181
THE OC LUGO CO., INC.—See Madison Industries Holdings LLC; *U.S. Private*, pg. 2543
ODORSTAR TECHNOLOGY, LLC—See OneWater Marine Inc.; *U.S. Public*, pg. 1604
OHTAKE-MEISHIN CHEMICAL CO., LTD.—See Chugoku Marine Paints, Ltd.; *Int'l*, pg. 1595
OIL-DRI CORPORATION OF AMERICA - INDUSTRIAL & AUTOMOTIVE DIVISION—See Oil-Dri Corporation of America; *U.S. Public*, pg. 1566
OIL-DRI S.A.—See Oil-Dri Corporation of America; *U.S. Public*, pg. 1566
OKAZAKI HA CHEMICALS CO. LTD.—See Huettenes-Albertus Chemische Werke GmbH; *Int'l*, pg. 3523
OOO BASF STROITELNYE SISTEMY—See BASF SE; *Int'l*, pg. 884
OOO BRENNTAG—See BRENNTAG SE; *Int'l*, pg. 1149

424690 — OTHER CHEMICAL AND ...

OOO CHEMINOVA—See FMC Corporation; *U.S. Public*, pg. 861
OOO SURTEC—See Freudenberg SE; *Int'l*, pg. 2790
OPTA GROUP LLC—See Speyside Equity LLC; *U.S. Private*, pg. 3756
ORION CHEMICAL TECHNOLOGIES; *U.S. Private*, pg. 3042
ORION ENGINEERED CARBONS TRADING (SHANGHAI) CO., LTD.—See Rhone Group, LLC; *U.S. Private*, pg. 3424
OXY VINYLS EXPORT SALES, LLC—See Occidental Petroleum Corporation; *U.S. Public*, pg. 1562
PACIFIC COAST CHEMICALS CO.; *U.S. Private*, pg. 3066
PANACOL-KOREA CO., LTD.—See Dr. Honle AG; *Int'l*, pg. 2192
PARTICLE SCIENCES INC.—See Agno Pharma; *U.S. Private*, pg. 128
PATHEON GMBH—See Thermo Fisher Scientific Inc.; *U.S. Public*, pg. 2151
PAVCO DE VENEZUELA, S.A.—See Grupo Empresarial Kaluz S.A. de C.V.; *Int'l*, pg. 3128
PB ANIMAL HEALTH DE MEXICO S. DE R.L. DE C.V.—See Phibro Animal Health Corporation; *U.S. Public*, pg. 1685
PCI PROMATEC—See Performance Contracting Group; *U.S. Private*, pg. 3148
PEACH STATE LAB, LLC—See Arsenal Capital Management LP; *U.S. Private*, pg. 339
PELICAN CHEMICAL TRADERS LTD.—See BRENNTAG SE; *Int'l*, pg. 1149
PERFORMANCE PROCESS, INC.; *U.S. Private*, pg. 3149
PERO ENGINEERING & SALES COMPANY, INC.; *U.S. Private*, pg. 3152
PERSTORP UK LTD.—See Ingevity Corporation; *U.S. Public*, pg. 1122
PHARMA WALDHOF GMBH—See Aceto Corporation; *U.S. Private*, pg. 58
PHIBRO ANIMAL HEALTH DE ARGENTINA SRL—See Phibro Animal Health Corporation; *U.S. Public*, pg. 1685
PHIBRO ANIMAL HEALTH LTD.—See Phibro Animal Health Corporation; *U.S. Public*, pg. 1685
PHIBRO ANIMAL HEALTH LTD.—See Phibro Animal Health Corporation; *U.S. Public*, pg. 1685
PHIBRO ANIMAL HEALTH (PROPRIETARY) LIMITED—See Phibro Animal Health Corporation; *U.S. Public*, pg. 1685
PHIBRO ANIMAL PTY LIMITED—See Phibro Animal Health Corporation; *U.S. Public*, pg. 1685
PHOENIX AROMAS & ESSENTIAL OILS, INC.—See SK Capital Partners, LP; *U.S. Private*, pg. 3679
PLANATOL GMBH—See Blue Cap AG; *Int'l*, pg. 1067
PLANATOL SYSTEM GMBH—See Blue Cap AG; *Int'l*, pg. 1067
THE PLAZA GROUP INC.; *U.S. Private*, pg. 4096
PLEXBOND QUIMICA S/A—See H.B. Fuller Company; *U.S. Public*, pg. 978
POLYVENTIVE LLC; *U.S. Private*, pg. 3226
POTTERS BALLOTINI LTD.—See Ecovyst Inc.; *U.S. Public*, pg. 717
PQ HOLDINGS AUSTRALIA PTY LIMITED—See Ecovyst Inc.; *U.S. Public*, pg. 717
PQ INTERNATIONAL COOPERATIE U.A.—See Ecovyst Inc.; *U.S. Public*, pg. 717
PQ SILICAS HOLDINGS SOUTH AFRICA PTY LTD.—See Ecovyst Inc.; *U.S. Public*, pg. 717
PQ SILICAS SOUTH AFRICA PTY LTD.—See Ecovyst Inc.; *U.S. Public*, pg. 717
PQ SILICAS UK LIMITED—See Ecovyst Inc.; *U.S. Public*, pg. 717
PRESTONE PRODUCTS CORP.—See Centerbridge Partners, L.P.; *U.S. Private*, pg. 815
PRIDE SOLVENTS & CHEMICAL COMPANY; *U.S. Private*, pg. 3260
PRIDE SOLVENTS & CHEMICAL CO. OF NEW JERSEY, INC.—See Pride Solvents & Chemical Company; *U.S. Private*, pg. 3260
PRINCE MINERALS, GMBH—See American Securities LLC; *U.S. Private*, pg. 253
PRINCE MINERALS, S.A.—See American Securities LLC; *U.S. Private*, pg. 253
PRISCO GRAPHICS OF CANADA, INC.—See Printers' Service, Inc.; *U.S. Private*, pg. 3266
PROBLEM SOLVING COMPANY LLC—See PROSOCO, Inc.; *U.S. Private*, pg. 3287
PROCTER & GAMBLE TECHNICAL CENTRES LIMITED—See The Procter & Gamble Company; *U.S. Public*, pg. 2123
PRODUCTO DIEMAKERS SUPPLIES LTD.—See PMT Group Inc; *U.S. Private*, pg. 3219
PROJEKTENTWICKLUNGS-GMBH FRIESENHEIMER INSEL—See BASF SE; *Int'l*, pg. 884
PROSIM KIMYA SANAYI VE TICARET LTD. STI.—See Bischof + Klein GmbH & Co. KG; *Int'l*, pg. 1048
PT. 3M INDONESIA—See 3M Company; *U.S. Public*, pg. 8
P.T. AIK MOH CHEMICALS INDONESIA—See BRENNTAG SE; *Int'l*, pg. 1149
PT ALL COSMOS INDONESIA—See All Cosmos Bio-Tech Holding Corporation; *Int'l*, pg. 332
P.T. BOZZETTO INDONESIA—See Aimia Inc.; *Int'l*, pg. 234

PT BRENNTAG INDONESIA—See BRENNTAG SE; *Int'l*, pg. 1149
P.T. CHAMPION KURNIA DJAJA TECHNOLOGIES—See Ecolab Inc.; *U.S. Public*, pg. 716
PT DIVERSEY INDONESIA—See Sealed Air Corporation; *U.S. Public*, pg. 1854
PT. DOEHLER INDONESIA—See Dohler GmbH; *Int'l*, pg. 2156
P.T. ECOLAB INTERNATIONAL INDONESIA—See Ecolab Inc.; *U.S. Public*, pg. 716
PTFE COMPOUNDS GERMANY GMBH—See Freudenberg SE; *Int'l*, pg. 2790
P.T. HUTCHINS CO., LTD.—See EQT AB; *Int'l*, pg. 2469
P.T. NALCO INDONESIA—See Ecolab Inc.; *U.S. Public*, pg. 716
PT. PRIMA SENTRA MEGAH—See Giti Tire Pte. Ltd.; *Int'l*, pg. 2979
P.T. STARIS CHEMICALS—See BRENNTAG SE; *Int'l*, pg. 1149
PURAC ASIA PACIFIC PTE. LTD.—See Corbion N.V.; *U.S. Public*, pg. 1795
PURAC DEUTSCHLAND GMBH—See Corbion N.V.; *Int'l*, pg. 1795
PURITY CYLINDER GASES INC.; *U.S. Private*, pg. 3306
PUR-O-ZONE, INC.; *U.S. Private*, pg. 3304
PVS CHEMICALS, INC.; *U.S. Private*, pg. 3308
PVS CHEMICALS SOLUTIONS INC. - COPLEY—See PVS Chemicals, Inc.; *U.S. Private*, pg. 3308
PVS-NOLWOOD CHEMICALS, INC.—See PVS Chemicals, Inc.; *U.S. Private*, pg. 3308
QUAKER CHEMICAL (AUSTRALASIA) PTY. LTD.—See Quaker Chemical Corporation; *U.S. Public*, pg. 1746
QUAKER CHEMICAL (CHINA) CO., LTD.—See Quaker Chemical Corporation; *U.S. Public*, pg. 1746
QUAKER CHEMICAL LIMITED—See Quaker Chemical Corporation; *U.S. Public*, pg. 1746
QUAKER CHEMICAL, S.A.—See Quaker Chemical Corporation; *U.S. Public*, pg. 1746
QUAKER CHEMICAL S.A.—See Quaker Chemical Corporation; *U.S. Public*, pg. 1746
QUAKER CHEMICAL, S.A.—See Quaker Chemical Corporation; *U.S. Public*, pg. 1746
QUAKER CITY CHEMICALS INC.; *U.S. Public*, pg. 3316
QUALITEK (SHANGHAI) TRADING CO., LTD.—See Qualitek International Inc.; *U.S. Private*, pg. 3317
QUIMICA EMPRESARIAL DE MEXICO, SA DE CV—See Cydsa S.A.B. de C.V.; *Int'l*, pg. 1895
QUIMICOS HOLANDA COSTA RICA S.A.—See BRENNTAG SE; *Int'l*, pg. 1149
QUIMIPRODUCTOS, S. DE R.L. DE C.V.—See Ecolab Inc.; *U.S. Public*, pg. 716
RANK MATERIALS SDN. BERHAD—See Brite-Tech Berhad; *Int'l*, pg. 1165
RAW MATERIALS CORPORATION; *U.S. Private*, pg. 3358
R.D. TAYLOR & COMPANY LIMITED—See Platinum Equity, LLC; *U.S. Private*, pg. 3210
R.E. CARROLL INC.; *U.S. Private*, pg. 3335
RECLAMATION TECHNOLOGIES, INC.—See BC Partners LLP; *Int'l*, pg. 923
RECLAMATION TECHNOLOGIES, INC.—See EQT AB; *Int'l*, pg. 2482
RECLAMATION TECHNOLOGIES USA, LLC—See BC Partners LLP; *Int'l*, pg. 923
RECLAMATION TECHNOLOGIES USA, LLC—See EQT AB; *Int'l*, pg. 2482
RECTORSEAL LLC—See CSW Industrials, Inc.; *U.S. Public*, pg. 601
REDBROOK BLENTECH LIMITED—See International Flavors & Fragrances Inc.; *U.S. Public*, pg. 1154
RED DEVIL, INC.; *U.S. Private*, pg. 3374
REDI-MIX CONCRETE, LP—See Vulcan Materials Company; *U.S. Public*, pg. 2314
REEM READY MIX LLC—See Alpha Dhabi Holding PJSC; *Int'l*, pg. 368
REG GRAYS HARBOR, LLC—See Chevron Corporation; *U.S. Public*, pg. 488
REMET CORPORATION—See BP plc; *Int'l*, pg. 1131
RENTECH NITROGEN FINANCE CORPORATION—See Rentech, Inc.; *U.S. Private*, pg. 3400
RESEARCH SOLUTIONS GROUP, INC.; *U.S. Private*, pg. 3404
RESOURCE ONE, INC.; *U.S. Private*, pg. 3407
RIBELIN SALES INC.—See EQT AB; *Int'l*, pg. 2469
R.N. EATON & COMPANY INC.; *U.S. Private*, pg. 3339
ROBOPROJEKT SP. Z.O.O—See Air Products & Chemicals, Inc.; *U.S. Public*, pg. 67
ROCKWOOD LITHIUM INDIA PVT. LTD.—See Albemarle Corporation; *U.S. Public*, pg. 73
ROCKWOOD LITHIUM KOREA LLC—See Albemarle Corporation; *U.S. Public*, pg. 73
ROCKWOOD LITHIUM SHANGHAI CO., LTD.—See Albemarle Corporation; *U.S. Public*, pg. 73
ROCKWOOD LITHIUM TAIWAN CO., LTD.—See Albemarle Corporation; *U.S. Public*, pg. 73
ROHM AND HAAS ELECTRONIC MATERIALS ASIA PACIFIC CO., LTD.—See DuPont de Nemours, Inc.; *U.S. Public*, pg. 694
ROHM AND HAAS ELECTRONIC MATERIALS CMP

INC.—See DuPont de Nemours, Inc.; *U.S. Public*, pg. 694
ROHM AND HAAS ELECTRONIC MATERIALS KOREA, LTD.—See DuPont de Nemours, Inc.; *U.S. Public*, pg. 694
ROHM AND HAAS FINLAND OY—See Dow Inc.; *U.S. Public*, pg. 686
ROHM AND HAAS INTERNATIONAL TRADING (SHANGHAI) CO., LTD.—See Dow Inc.; *U.S. Public*, pg. 686
ROHM & HAAS ELECTRONIC MATERIALS SINGAPORE PTE. LTD.—See DuPont de Nemours, Inc.; *U.S. Public*, pg. 694
ROMANA CHIMICI S.P.A—See BRENNTAG SE; *Int'l*, pg. 1149
ROWELL CHEMICAL CORPORATION; *U.S. Private*, pg. 3490
RUBBER NANO PRODUCTS EUROPE SRL—See Esseco Group SRL; *Int'l*, pg. 2509
RUGER CHEMICAL COMPANY, INC.—See H.I.G. Capital, LLC; *U.S. Private*, pg. 1832
RWM TECHNOLOGIES LLC—See Piedmont Chemical Industries, Inc.; *U.S. Private*, pg. 3148
S.A. HELM BENELUX N.V.—See HELM AG; *Int'l*, pg. 3338
SAI AUTOMOTIVE FRADLEY LTD.—See FORVIA SE; *Int'l*, pg. 2747
SAINT-GOBAIN GRADEVINSKI PROIZVODI HRVATSKA D.O.O.—See Compagnie de Saint-Gobain SA; *Int'l*, pg. 1728
SAINT-GOBAIN K.K.—See Compagnie de Saint-Gobain SA; *Int'l*, pg. 1731
SAL CHEMICAL CO. INC.; *U.S. Private*, pg. 3530
SALES DEL ISTMO, S.A. DE C.V.—See Cydsa S.A.B. de C.V.; *Int'l*, pg. 1895
SALES DE MAGNESIO LTDA—See Albemarle Corporation; *U.S. Public*, pg. 73
SAMUEL BANNER & CO.—See Banner Chemicals Limited; *Int'l*, pg. 851
SAPA PRODOTTI PLASTICI SAGL—See Baxter International Inc.; *U.S. Public*, pg. 284
SCANACON AB—See Alder Fund I AB; *Int'l*, pg. 304
SCANACON ASIA LTD.—See Alder Fund I AB; *Int'l*, pg. 304
SCANACON (SHANGHAI) ENVIRONMENTAL TECHNOLOGIES., LTD.—See Alder Fund I AB; *Int'l*, pg. 304
SCHIBLEY SOLVENTS & CHEMICAL CO.; *U.S. Private*, pg. 3564
SCHRAMM COATINGS GMBH—See Akzo Nobel N.V.; *Int'l*, pg. 275
SCHRAMM SSCP (HANOI) CO LTD.—See Akzo Nobel N.V.; *Int'l*, pg. 275
SCHRAMM SSCP (THAILAND) CO., LTD.—See Akzo Nobel N.V.; *Int'l*, pg. 275
SCI JACQUOT—See Apollo Global Management, Inc.; *U.S. Public*, pg. 165
S.C. JOHNSON AG—See S.C. Johnson & Son, Inc.; *U.S. Private*, pg. 3517
S.C. JOHNSON SCANDINAVIA AB—See S.C. Johnson & Son, Inc.; *U.S. Private*, pg. 3517
S.C. JOHNSON & SON PTY. LTD.—See S.C. Johnson & Son, Inc.; *U.S. Private*, pg. 3516
S.C. JOHNSON WAX BENELUX N.V./S.A.—See S.C. Johnson & Son, Inc.; *U.S. Private*, pg. 3517
SCOTT-GROSS COMPANY, INC.; *U.S. Private*, pg. 3577
SEELER INDUSTRIES INC.; *U.S. Private*, pg. 3598
SENEX EXPLOSIVES INC.; *U.S. Private*, pg. 3606
SERVICIOS BENETECH C.A.—See Benetech Investments Corp; *U.S. Private*, pg. 525
THE SEYDEL COMPANIES; *U.S. Private*, pg. 4117
SEYDEL INTERNATIONAL, INC.—See The Seydel Companies; *U.S. Private*, pg. 4117
SEYDEL-WOOLLEY & COMPANY—See The Seydel Companies; *U.S. Private*, pg. 4117
SHAMROCK CHICAGO CORP.; *U.S. Private*, pg. 3624
SHANGHAI ANYIJIE CHEMICAL LOGISTIC CO., LTD.—See BRENNTAG SE; *Int'l*, pg. 1149
SHANGHAI DIC PRESSURE-SENSITIVE ADHESIVE MATERIALS CO., LTD.—See DIC Corporation; *Int'l*, pg. 2109
SHANGHAI HA INTERNATIONAL TRADING CO. LTD.—See Huettenes-Albertus Chemische Werke GmbH; *Int'l*, pg. 3523
SHANGHAI JIA RONG TRADING CO., LTD.—See BRENNTAG SE; *Int'l*, pg. 1149
SHANGHAI LONG FENG FOOD ADDITIVES CO., LTD.—See DIC Corporation; *Int'l*, pg. 2109
SHANGHAI SAIFU CHEMICAL DEVELOPMENT CO., LTD.—See BRENNTAG SE; *Int'l*, pg. 1149
SHANGHAI YI RONG INTERNATIONAL TRADING CO., LTD.—See BRENNTAG SE; *Int'l*, pg. 1149
SHELL PAKISTAN LIMITED—See Asyad Holding Group; *Int'l*, pg. 664
SHENZHEN TONGDA CHEMICAL CORPORATION—See China National Chemical Corporation; *Int'l*, pg. 1527
SHERWIN-WILLIAMS DENMARK A/S—See The Sherwin-Williams Company; *U.S. Public*, pg. 2128
SHINMYUNG HA LTD.—See Huettenes-Albertus Chemische Werke GmbH; *Int'l*, pg. 3523
SHRIEVE CHEMICAL COMPANY LLC—See Gemspring Capital Management, LLC; *U.S. Private*, pg. 1659

SHRIEVE CHEMICAL (SHANGHAI) LTD.—See Gemspring Capital Management, LLC; *U.S. Private*, pg. 1659
SHRIEVE PRODUCTS INTERNATIONAL LIMITED—See Gemspring Capital Management, LLC; *U.S. Private*, pg. 1659
SHRIEVE QUIMICA DO BRASIL LTDA.—See Gemspring Capital Management, LLC; *U.S. Private*, pg. 1659
S I A BRENNTAG LATVIA—See BRENNTAG SE; *Int'l*, pg. 1149
SIA CABOT LATVIA—See Cabot Corporation; *U.S. Public*, pg. 417
SIA ELME MESSER L—See BLRT Grupp AS; *Int'l*, pg. 1066
SIEGLING DANMARK A/S—See Forbo Holding Ltd.; *Int'l*, pg. 2730
SIEGLING ITALIA S.P.A.—See Forbo Holding Ltd.; *Int'l*, pg. 2730
SIERRA CHEMICAL CO; *U.S. Private*, pg. 3646
SILMAR RESINS—See Interplastic Corporation; *U.S. Private*, pg. 2123
SIMITRI SPECIALTY CHEMICALS (PTY) LIMITED—See AECI Limited; *Int'l*, pg. 172
SIMRIT DISTRIBUTION ET CIE—See Freudenberg SE; *Int'l*, pg. 2790
SINO BRIGHT INTERNATIONAL TRADING LIMITED—See EcoGreen International Group Limited; *Int'l*, pg. 2295
SINOPEC CHEMICAL SALES COMPANY—See China Petrochemical Corporation; *Int'l*, pg. 1539
SINOPEC SALES COMPANY, LTD.—See China Petrochemical Corporation; *Int'l*, pg. 1539
SIROFLEX LTD.—See Arkema S.A.; *Int'l*, pg. 571
SLACK CHEMICAL CO. INC.; *U.S. Private*, pg. 3687
SLAFTER OIL CO—See Western Cooperative Company; *U.S. Private*, pg. 4492
SMALLEY & COMPANY INC; *U.S. Private*, pg. 3690
SOCIEDAD ESPANOLA DE CARBUROS METALICOS S.A.—See Air Products & Chemicals, Inc.; *U.S. Public*, pg. 67
SOCIETE COMMERCIALE TARDY ET CIE. S.A.R.L.—See BRENNTAG SE; *Int'l*, pg. 1149
SODIUM SOLUTIONS INC.—See Bri-Chem Corp.; *Int'l*, pg. 1151
SOLUTIA BRASIL LTDA.—See Eastman Chemical Company; *U.S. Public*, pg. 706
SOLUTIA HONG KONG LIMITED—See Eastman Chemical Company; *U.S. Public*, pg. 705
SOLUTIA ITALIA S.R.L.—See Eastman Chemical Company; *U.S. Public*, pg. 706
SOLUTIA JAPAN LIMITED—See Eastman Chemical Company; *U.S. Public*, pg. 706
SOLUTIA SINGAPORE PTE. LTD.—See Eastman Chemical Company; *U.S. Public*, pg. 706
SOLUTIA SOLAR GMBH—See Eastman Chemical Company; *U.S. Public*, pg. 706
SOLUTIA TLAXCALA S.A. DE C.V.—See Eastman Chemical Company; *U.S. Public*, pg. 706
SOLUTIA UK INVESTMENTS LTD.—See Eastman Chemical Company; *U.S. Public*, pg. 706
SOLVCHEM, INC.; *U.S. Private*, pg. 3711
SONAROME PRIVATE LIMITED—See International Flavors & Fragrances Inc.; *U.S. Public*, pg. 1154
SOVEREIGN CHEMICALS COMPANY—See Henkel AG & Co. KGaA; *Int'l*, pg. 3353
SPECIALTY POLYMER COATINGS USA, INC.—See RPM International Inc.; *U.S. Public*, pg. 1820
SPECIALTY PRODUCTS CZECH REPUBLIC S.R.O.—See Celanese Corporation; *U.S. Public*, pg. 465
STANLEY HOME PRODUCTS—See Victory Park Capital Advisors, LLC; *U.S. Private*, pg. 4379
STARTEX CHEMICAL, LLC—See Apollo Global Management, Inc.; *U.S. Public*, pg. 165
STATE CHEMICAL SALES COMPANY INTERNATIONAL INC.—See State Industrial Products Corporation; *U.S. Private*, pg. 3792
STATE CLEANING SOLUTIONS—See State Industrial Products Corporation; *U.S. Private*, pg. 3792
STAUBER NEW YORK, INC.—See Hawkins, Inc.; *U.S. Public*, pg. 989
STAUBER PERFORMANCE INGREDIENTS, INC.—See Hawkins, Inc.; *U.S. Public*, pg. 989
STEMACO USA, INC.; *U.S. Private*, pg. 3801
STERIFX, INC.—See Synergy Technologies, Inc.; *U.S. Private*, pg. 3904
STEWART SUPERABSORBENTS, LLC—See KKR & Co. Inc.; *U.S. Public*, pg. 1243
ST IBERICA LDA.—See Freudenberg SE; *Int'l*, pg. 2790
STORMTECH LLC—See Advanced Drainage Systems, Inc.; *U.S. Public*, pg. 46
STO-ZAP SP. Z O.O.—See Grupa Azoty S.A.; *Int'l*, pg. 3116
STP & DIN CHEMICALS SP. Z O.O.—See Air Products & Chemicals, Inc.; *U.S. Public*, pg. 67
SULPHURIC ACID TRADING CO.; *U.S. Private*, pg. 3852
SUMITOMO 3M LIMITED—See 3M Company; *U.S. Public*, pg. 8
SUNTEK AUSTRALIA PTY. LTD.—See Eastman Chemical Company; *U.S. Public*, pg. 706
SUN TRADING CO., LTD.—See Asahi Kasei Corporation; *Int'l*, pg. 597
SUOMEN UNIPOL OY—See Algol Oy; *Int'l*, pg. 318

SUPERIOR MATERIALS, INC.; *U.S. Private*, pg. 3879
SUPERIOR OIL CO., INC.; *U.S. Private*, pg. 3879
SUPERIOR SUPPLY CO., INC.—See Kelso & Company, L.P.; *U.S. Private*, pg. 2279
SUPERIOR SUPPLY CO., INC.—See Warburg Pincus LLC; *U.S. Private*, pg. 4437
SUPREME RESOURCES, INC.; *U.S. Private*, pg. 3883
SURTEC ADRIA D.O.O.—See Freudenberg SE; *Int'l*, pg. 2790
SURTEC BENELUX B.V.—See Freudenberg SE; *Int'l*, pg. 2790
SURTEC CACAK D.O.O.—See Freudenberg SE; *Int'l*, pg. 2790
SURTEC CHEMICALS INDIA PVT. LTD.—See Freudenberg SE; *Int'l*, pg. 2790
SURTEC CR S.R.O.—See Freudenberg SE; *Int'l*, pg. 2790
SURTEC DEUTSCHLAND GMBH—See Freudenberg SE; *Int'l*, pg. 2790
SURTEC DO BRASIL LTDA.—See Freudenberg SE; *Int'l*, pg. 2790
SURTEC D.O.O.—See Freudenberg SE; *Int'l*, pg. 2790
SURTEC FRANCE S.A.S.—See Freudenberg SE; *Int'l*, pg. 2790
SURTEC KOREA CO., LTD.—See Freudenberg SE; *Int'l*, pg. 2790
SURTEC METAL SURFACE TREATMENT TECHNOLOGY CO. LTD.—See Freudenberg SE; *Int'l*, pg. 2790
SURTEC MMC JAPAN KK—See Freudenberg SE; *Int'l*, pg. 2790
SURTEC POLSKA SP. Z O.O.—See Freudenberg SE; *Int'l*, pg. 2790
SURTEC PRODUKTE UND SYSTEME FUR DIE OBERFLACHENBEHANDLUNG GESMBH—See Freudenberg SE; *Int'l*, pg. 2790
SURTEC ROMANIA S.R.L.—See Freudenberg SE; *Int'l*, pg. 2790
SURTEC SCANDINAVIA APS—See Freudenberg SE; *Int'l*, pg. 2790
SURTEC SK S.R.O.—See Freudenberg SE; *Int'l*, pg. 2790
SURTEC SOUTH AFRICA PTY. LTD.—See Freudenberg SE; *Int'l*, pg. 2790
SURTEC VIET NAM CO., LTD.—See Freudenberg SE; *Int'l*, pg. 2790
SWISHER HYGIENE USA OPERATIONS, INC.—See Swisher Hygiene Inc.; *U.S. Private*, pg. 3894
SWISHER MAIDS, INC.—See Swisher Hygiene Inc.; *U.S. Private*, pg. 3894
SYNGENTA AGRO GMBH—See China National Chemical Corporation; *Int'l*, pg. 1529
SYNGENTA AGRO SERVICES AG—See China National Chemical Corporation; *Int'l*, pg. 1529
SYNGENTA CROP PROTECTION A/S—See China National Chemical Corporation; *Int'l*, pg. 1530
SYNGENTA CROP PROTECTION - FINLAND OFFICE—See China National Chemical Corporation; *Int'l*, pg. 1530
SYNGENTA IRELAND LIMITED—See China National Chemical Corporation; *Int'l*, pg. 1530
SYNGENTA POLSKA SP. Z O.O—See China National Chemical Corporation; *Int'l*, pg. 1529
SYNGENTA POLSKA SP. Z O.O—See China National Chemical Corporation; *Int'l*, pg. 1529
SYNGENTA UK LIMITED—See China National Chemical Corporation; *Int'l*, pg. 1530
TAMINCO DO BRASIL COMERCIO E INDUSTRIA DE AMINAS LTDA.—See Eastman Chemical Company; *U.S. Public*, pg. 706
TAMINCO FINLAND OY—See Eastman Chemical Company; *U.S. Public*, pg. 706
TANNER INDUSTRIES INC.; *U.S. Private*, pg. 3931
TANNIN CORPORATION; *U.S. Private*, pg. 3932
TARTARIC CHEMICALS CORPORATION; *U.S. Private*, pg. 3934
TECHNIC ASIA-PACIFIC PTE LTD.—See Technic Incorporated; *U.S. Private*, pg. 3953
TECHNIC TAIWAN CO., LTD.—See Technic Incorporated; *U.S. Private*, pg. 3953
TECH SPRAY, L.P.—See Illinois Tool Works Inc.; *U.S. Public*, pg. 1111
TELKO DENMARK A/S—See Aspo Oyj; *Int'l*, pg. 631
TELKO ESTONIA OU—See Aspo Oyj; *Int'l*, pg. 631
TELKO LATVIA SIA—See Aspo Oyj; *Int'l*, pg. 631
TELKO LIETUVA UAB—See Aspo Oyj; *Int'l*, pg. 631
TELKO OY—See Aspo Oyj; *Int'l*, pg. 631
TELKO SHANGHAI LTD.—See Aspo Oyj; *Int'l*, pg. 631
TEXAS ALLIED CHEMICALS INC.—See Texas Allied Holdings Inc.; *U.S. Private*, pg. 3974
THERMO FISHER SCIENTIFIC BALTICS UAB—See Thermo Fisher Scientific Inc.; *U.S. Public*, pg. 2154
THERMO FISHER SCIENTIFIC CHEMICALS INC.—See Thermo Fisher Scientific Inc.; *U.S. Public*, pg. 2153
TIANJIN TAI RONG CHEMICAL TRADING CO., LTD.—See BRENNTAG SE; *Int'l*, pg. 1150
TIANJIN ZHONG RONG CHEMICAL STORAGE CO., LTD.—See BRENNTAG SE; *Int'l*, pg. 1150
TIDY CAR INTERNATIONAL, INC.—See Ziebart International Corporation; *U.S. Private*, pg. 4603

TILLEY CHEMICAL CO., INC.—See SK Capital Partners, LP; *U.S. Private*, pg. 3680
TIOXIDE AMERICAS LLC—See Huntsman Corporation; *U.S. Public*, pg. 1075
TLC INGREDIENTS, INC.—See Gemspring Capital Management, LLC; *U.S. Private*, pg. 1659
TOHCHO CO., LIMITED—See Chori Co., Ltd.; *Int'l*, pg. 1583
TOLL COMPANY; *U.S. Private*, pg. 4182
TONSAN ADHESIVE U.S., INC.—See H.B. Fuller Company; *U.S. Public*, pg. 978
TRADEWINDS CHEMICALS CORPORATION—See BASF SE; *Int'l*, pg. 876
TRAMMO AG—See Trammo, Inc.; *U.S. Private*, pg. 4204
TRAMMO INDIA PVT. LIMITED—See Trammo, Inc.; *U.S. Private*, pg. 4204
TRAMMO PTE LTD.—See Trammo, Inc.; *U.S. Private*, pg. 4204
TRANSAMMONIA AG—See Trammo, Inc.; *U.S. Private*, pg. 4205
TRANSAMMONIA DIS TICARET LIMITED COMPANY—See Trammo, Inc.; *U.S. Private*, pg. 4205
TRANSAMMONIA INTERNACIONAL REPRESENTACOES LTDA.—See Trammo, Inc.; *U.S. Private*, pg. 4205
TRANSCHEM, INC.; *U.S. Private*, pg. 4207
TRANS EAST TRADING (KOREA) LTD.—See Trammo, Inc.; *U.S. Private*, pg. 4205
TREMCO ILLBRUCK CO., LTD.—See RPM International Inc.; *U.S. Public*, pg. 1820
TRIAD SERVICE SOLUTIONS, INC—See Tide Rock Holdings, LLC; *U.S. Private*, pg. 4168
TRICHROMATIC MEXICO S.DE.R.L.—See SK Capital Partners, LP; *U.S. Private*, pg. 3680
TRICHROMATIC MISR—See SK Capital Partners, LP; *U.S. Private*, pg. 3680
TRICHROMATIC WEST INC.—See SK Capital Partners, LP; *U.S. Private*, pg. 3680
TRIDE RUS OOO—See BRENNTAG SE; *Int'l*, pg. 1150
TROY CHEMICAL COMPANY B.V.—See Troy Corporation; *U.S. Private*, pg. 4243
TROY CHEMICAL COMPANY SP. Z O.O.—See Troy Corporation; *U.S. Private*, pg. 4243
TROY CHEMIE GMBH—See Troy Corporation; *U.S. Private*, pg. 4243
TROY FRANCE S.A.R.L.—See Troy Corporation; *U.S. Private*, pg. 4243
TRYCHEM FZCO—See BRENNTAG SE; *Int'l*, pg. 1150
TUMPEER CHEMICAL CO. INC.; *U.S. Private*, pg. 4258
UAB BRENNTAG LIETUVA—See BRENNTAG SE; *Int'l*, pg. 1150
UAB ELME MESSER LIT—See BLRT Grupp AS; *Int'l*, pg. 1066
UBAJAY DAS S.A.—See Corteva, Inc.; *U.S. Public*, pg. 582
UKRHIMFORMACIA LIMITED COMPANY—See GHW International; *Int'l*, pg. 2960
ULTRA-CHEM INC.; *U.S. Private*, pg. 4277
UNGERER FRAGRANCE & FLAVOUR (SHANGHAI) CO. LTD.—See Givaudan S.A.; *Int'l*, pg. 2982
UNITED ERIE—See Interstate Chemical Co., Inc.; *U.S. Private*, pg. 2124
UNITED MINERAL AND CHEMICAL CORPORATION—See ICD Group International Inc.; *U.S. Public*, pg. 2030
UNITED STATES WELDING, INC.; *U.S. Private*, pg. 4300
UNIVAR AB—See Apollo Global Management, Inc.; *U.S. Public*, pg. 165
UNIVAR AG—See Apollo Global Management, Inc.; *U.S. Public*, pg. 165
UNIVAR BELGIUM NV—See Apollo Global Management, Inc.; *U.S. Public*, pg. 165
UNIVAR BENELUX—See Apollo Global Management, Inc.; *U.S. Public*, pg. 165
UNIVAR BRASIL LTDA.—See Apollo Global Management, Inc.; *U.S. Public*, pg. 165
UNIVAR BV—See Apollo Global Management, Inc.; *U.S. Public*, pg. 165
UNIVAR CANADA LTD.—See Apollo Global Management, Inc.; *U.S. Public*, pg. 165
UNIVAR CZECH SRO—See Apollo Global Management, Inc.; *U.S. Public*, pg. 165
UNIVAR EGYPT LLC—See Apollo Global Management, Inc.; *U.S. Public*, pg. 165
UNIVAR FRANCE SNC—See Apollo Global Management, Inc.; *U.S. Public*, pg. 166
UNIVAR FRANCE—See Apollo Global Management, Inc.; *U.S. Public*, pg. 165
UNIVAR GMBH—See Apollo Global Management, Inc.; *U.S. Public*, pg. 165
UNIVAR HUNGARY SALES LIMITED LIABILITY CO—See Apollo Global Management, Inc.; *U.S. Public*, pg. 166
UNIVAR IBERIA S.A.—See Apollo Global Management, Inc.; *U.S. Public*, pg. 165
UNIVAR IRELAND—See Apollo Global Management, Inc.; *U.S. Public*, pg. 166
UNIVAR LIMITED—See Apollo Global Management, Inc.; *U.S. Public*, pg. 166
UNIVAR MIDDLE EAST-AFRICA FZE—See Apollo Global Management, Inc.; *U.S. Public*, pg. 166
UNIVAR NORDIC—See Apollo Global Management, Inc.; *U.S. Public*, pg. 166

424690 — OTHER CHEMICAL AND ...

UNIVAR POLAND SP.ZO.O—See Apollo Global Management, Inc.; *U.S. Public*, pg. 166
UNIVAR SINGAPORE PTE LTD—See Apollo Global Management, Inc.; *U.S. Public*, pg. 166
UNIVAR SOLUTIONS CHINA LTD.—See Apollo Global Management, Inc.; *U.S. Public*, pg. 166
UNIVAR SOLUTIONS HELLAS EPE—See Apollo Global Management, Inc.; *U.S. Public*, pg. 166
UNIVAR SOLUTIONS KIMYA SANAYI VE DIS TICARET LIMITED—See Apollo Global Management, Inc.; *U.S. Public*, pg. 166
UNIVAR SOLUTIONS LLC—See Apollo Global Management, Inc.; *U.S. Public*, pg. 166
UNIVAR SOLUTIONS PORTUGAL SA—See Apollo Global Management, Inc.; *U.S. Public*, pg. 166
UNIVAR SOLUTIONS SAS—See Apollo Global Management, Inc.; *U.S. Public*, pg. 166
UNIVAR SOLUTIONS SINGAPORE PTE LTD—See Apollo Global Management, Inc.; *U.S. Public*, pg. 166
UNIVAR SOLUTIONS SPAIN SA—See Apollo Global Management, Inc.; *U.S. Public*, pg. 166
UNIVAR SOLUTIONS UK LTD.—See Apollo Global Management, Inc.; *U.S. Public*, pg. 166
UNIVAR SOLUTIONS USA INC.—See Apollo Global Management, Inc.; *U.S. Public*, pg. 166
UNIVAR SOUTH-EAST EUROPE S.R.L.—See Apollo Global Management, Inc.; *U.S. Public*, pg. 166
UNIVAR S.P.A.—See Apollo Global Management, Inc.; *U.S. Public*, pg. 166
UNIVAR SPECIALTY CONSUMABLES LIMITED—See Apollo Global Management, Inc.; *U.S. Public*, pg. 166
UNIVAR UK LIMITED—See Apollo Global Management, Inc.; *U.S. Public*, pg. 166
UNIVAR ZWIJNDRECHT N.V.—See Apollo Global Management, Inc.; *U.S. Public*, pg. 166
UYEMURA INTERNATIONAL CORPORATION—See C.Uyemura & Co., Ltd.; *Int'l*, pg. 1244
UYEMURA INTERNATIONAL (SINGAPORE) PTE., LTD.—See C.Uyemura & Co., Ltd.; *Int'l*, pg. 1244
UYEMURA KOREA CO., LTD.—See C.Uyemura & Co., Ltd.; *Int'l*, pg. 1244
UYEMURA (SHANGHAI) CO., LTD.—See C.Uyemura & Co., Ltd.; *Int'l*, pg. 1244
VALERO ENERGY (IRELAND) LIMITED—See Valero Energy Corporation; *U.S. Public*, pg. 2272
VALERO ENERGY LTD—See Valero Energy Corporation; *U.S. Public*, pg. 2272
VALERO MARKETING IRELAND LIMITED—See Valero Energy Corporation; *U.S. Public*, pg. 2272
VALLEY SOLVENT COMPANY, INC.—See Apollo Global Management, Inc.; *U.S. Public*, pg. 166
VAN EYCK CHEMIE NV—See Apollo Global Management, Inc.; *U.S. Public*, pg. 166
VAN HORN METZ & CO. INC.; *U.S. Private*, pg. 4340
VELOX CMS S.R.O—See IMCD N.V.; *Int'l*, pg. 3622
VELOX COMPOSITES GMBH I.G.—See IMCD N.V.; *Int'l*, pg. 3622
VELOX DIS TIC.LTD.STI.—See IMCD N.V.; *Int'l*, pg. 3622
VELOX FRANCE S.A.S.—See IMCD N.V.; *Int'l*, pg. 3622
VELOX ITALIA S.R.L.—See IMCD N.V.; *Int'l*, pg. 3622
VELOX OY—See IMCD N.V.; *Int'l*, pg. 3622
VELOX POLAND SP.Z O.O.—See IMCD N.V.; *Int'l*, pg. 3622
VELOX SPECIALITIES AB—See IMCD N.V.; *Int'l*, pg. 3622
VELOX SPECIALITIES AB—See IMCD N.V.; *Int'l*, pg. 3622
VELOX TRADING S.L.U.—See IMCD N.V.; *Int'l*, pg. 3623
VELOX U.K. LTD—See IMCD N.V.; *Int'l*, pg. 3623
VENRO PETROLEUM CORPORATION; *U.S. Private*, pg. 4356
VIJALL, INC.—See Innospec Inc.; *U.S. Public*, pg. 1125
VITUSA PRODUCTS INC.; *U.S. Private*, pg. 4406
VIVION INC.—See Operio Group, LLC; *U.S. Private*, pg. 3032
VOLCLAY JAPAN CO., LTD.—See Minerals Technologies, Inc.; *U.S. Public*, pg. 1449
VWR INTERNATIONAL B.V.—See Avantor, Inc.; *U.S. Public*, pg. 241
VWR INTERNATIONAL GMBH—See Avantor, Inc.; *U.S. Public*, pg. 242
VWR INTERNATIONAL LTD—See Avantor, Inc.; *U.S. Public*, pg. 242
VWR INTERNATIONAL OY—See Avantor, Inc.; *U.S. Public*, pg. 242
VWR INTERNATIONAL S.R.O.—See Avantor, Inc.; *U.S. Public*, pg. 242
WALSH & ASSOCIATES, INC.; *U.S. Private*, pg. 4432
WATER SCIENCE TECHNOLOGIES, LLC—See Bain Capital, LP; *U.S. Private*, pg. 441
WATER SOLUTIONS UNLIMITED, INC.—See Hawkins, Inc.; *U.S. Public*, pg. 989
WEGO CHEMICAL & MINERAL CORPORATION; *U.S. Private*, pg. 4469
WEIHUA (RUDONG) TRADE CO., LTD.—See China Petrochemical Development Corp.; *Int'l*, pg. 1540
WEILER WELDING COMPANY INC.; *U.S. Private*, pg. 4471
WEIQIANG INTERNATIONAL TRADE (SHANGHAI) CO., LTD.—See China Petrochemical Development Corp.; *Int'l*, pg. 1540
WELLSTAR ENTERPRISES (HONG KONG) COMPANY LIMITED—See BRENNTAG SE; *Int'l*, pg. 1150
WEYERHAEUSER JAPAN LTD.—See Weyerhaeuser Company; *U.S. Public*, pg. 2365
WHISTLER MEDICAL MARIJUANA CORPORATION—See Aurora Cannabis Inc.; *Int'l*, pg. 713
WHITAKER OIL COMPANY; *U.S. Private*, pg. 4507
WILFERT CHEMICAL SWEDEN AB—See Aspo Oyj; *Int'l*, pg. 631
W. R. GRACE ARGENTINA S.A.—See Standard Industries Holdings Inc.; *U.S. Private*, pg. 3780
W. R. GRACE CAPITAL CORPORATION—See Standard Industries Holdings Inc.; *U.S. Private*, pg. 3780
YICHANG TINCI MATERIALS TECHNOLOGY CO., LTD.—See Guangzhou Tinci Materials Technology Company Limited; *Int'l*, pg. 3168
YINGCHENG SHINDOO IMPORT & EXPORT TRADING CO., LTD.—See Chengdu Wintrue Holding Co., Ltd.; *Int'l*, pg. 1469
Y.S. ASHKENAZI AGENCIES LTD.—See BRENNTAG SE; *Int'l*, pg. 1150
ZAO ASHLAND MSP—See Ashland Inc.; *U.S. Public*, pg. 213
ZCC EUROPE GMBH—See Hunan Nonferrous Metals Corporation Ltd.; *Int'l*, pg. 3533
ZEOCHEM PTE. LTD.—See CPH Chemie + Papier Holding AG; *Int'l*, pg. 1824
ZEUS QUIMICA S.A.U.—See Diethelm Keller Holding Limited; *Int'l*, pg. 2117
ZHEJIANG OMEX ENVIRONMENTAL ENGINEERING CO., LTD.—See DuPont de Nemours, Inc.; *U.S. Public*, pg. 694
ZHONG YUNG (INTERNATIONAL) CHEMICAL CO., LIMITED—See BRENNTAG SE; *Int'l*, pg. 1150
ZHUZHOU CEMENTED CARBIDE GROUP HONGKONG CO. LTD.—See Hunan Nonferrous Metals Corporation Ltd.; *Int'l*, pg. 3533
ZHUZHOU CEMENTED CARBIDE WORKS USA INC.—See Hunan Nonferrous Metals Corporation Ltd.; *Int'l*, pg. 3533
ZOS. B.V.—See HZPC Holland B.V.; *Int'l*, pg. 3561

424710 — PETROLEUM BULK STATIONS AND TERMINALS

4 VILLY INC.; *U.S. Private*, pg. 14
ABU DHABI PETROLEUM PORTS OPERATING COMPANY—See Abu Dhabi National Oil Company; *Int'l*, pg. 73
ACORN PETROLEUM; *U.S. Private*, pg. 63
ACREE OIL COMPANY; *U.S. Private*, pg. 65
ADA BELTRAMI COOP; *U.S. Private*, pg. 72
ADA RESOURCES, INC.—See Adams Resources & Energy, Inc.; *U.S. Public*, pg. 38
ADNOC DISTRIBUTION—See Abu Dhabi National Oil Company; *Int'l*, pg. 72
A.H. SCHADE INC.; *U.S. Private*, pg. 26
ALEXA ENERGY LTD.; *U.S. Private*, pg. 163
ALLSUP PETROLEUM INC.—See Allsup Enterprises Inc.; *U.S. Private*, pg. 194
AMPOL BENDIGO PTY LTD—See Ampol Limited; *Int'l*, pg. 436
ANADARKO OIL & GAS COMPANY—See Occidental Petroleum Corporation; *U.S. Public*, pg. 1561
ANCOM-CHEMQUEST TERMINALS SDN. BHD.—See Ancom Logistics Berhad; *Int'l*, pg. 449
ANDATEE CHINA MARINE FUEL SERVICES CORPORATION; *Int'l*, pg. 449
ANDERSON-GILYARD; *U.S. Private*, pg. 278
ANDREWS OIL COMPANY; *U.S. Private*, pg. 280
ARGUINDEGUI OIL COMPANY; *U.S. Private*, pg. 322
ATCO INCORPORATED; *U.S. Private*, pg. 365
AYERS OIL CO. INC.; *U.S. Private*, pg. 414
BAKER ENERGY INC.; *U.S. Private*, pg. 456
BALE OF KENTUCKY, INC.; *U.S. Private*, pg. 459
BALL TIRE & GAS INC.; *U.S. Private*, pg. 460
BANGLADESH AUTOCARS LIMITED; *Int'l*, pg. 835
BASSETT-HYLAND ENERGY COMPANY; *U.S. Private*, pg. 486
BATTLEGROUND OIL SPECIALTY TERMINAL COMPANY LLC—See Kinder Morgan, Inc.; *U.S. Public*, pg. 1232
BAUMAN OIL DISTRIBUTORS INC.; *U.S. Private*, pg. 490
BAYSIDE FUEL OIL DEPOT CORPORATION; *U.S. Private*, pg. 497
BECK OIL, INC.; *U.S. Private*, pg. 510
BECK SUPPLIERS, INC.; *U.S. Private*, pg. 510
BELCHER OIL CO. INC.; *U.S. Private*, pg. 517
BENNETTS OIL CO.; *U.S. Private*, pg. 528
BEST OIL COMPANY; *U.S. Private*, pg. 543
BEST-WADE PETROLEUM INC.—See Litco Petroleum Inc.; *U.S. Private*, pg. 2467
BIG CHIEF DISTRIBUTING CO. INC.; *U.S. Private*, pg. 552
BILL TERPENING INC.; *U.S. Private*, pg. 558
BI-PETRO, INC.; *U.S. Private*, pg. 550
BKEP OPERATING, L.L.C.—See Ergon, Inc.; *U.S. Private*, pg. 1418
BKEP SERVICES LLC—See Ergon, Inc.; *U.S. Private*, pg. 1418
BLACKWATER GEORGIA, LLC—See ArcLight Capital Holdings, LLC; *U.S. Private*, pg. 312
BLACKWATER MIDSTREAM CORP.—See ArcLight Capital Holdings, LLC; *U.S. Private*, pg. 312
BLAKE OIL COMPANY—See Conserv FS Inc.; *U.S. Private*, pg. 1019
BLANCHARDVILLE COOP OIL ASSOCIATION; *U.S. Private*, pg. 579
BLIGHT OIL COMPANY; *U.S. Private*, pg. 581
BLUE CIRCLE ENGINEERING LIMITED—See HELLENIQ ENERGY Holdings S.A; *Int'l*, pg. 3334
B&M OIL COMPANY, INC.—See BRENNTAG SE; *Int'l*, pg. 1146
BOBBY TAYLOR OIL COMPANY, INC.—See Parker Holding Company, Inc.; *U.S. Private*, pg. 3097
BOOTHEEL PETROLEUM COMPANY; *U.S. Private*, pg. 617
BOUNTYLAND PETROLEUM INC.; *U.S. Private*, pg. 624
BOWEN PETROLEUM INC.; *U.S. Private*, pg. 625
BP OIL COMPANY—See BP plc; *Int'l*, pg. 1127
BP PRODUCTS NORTH AMERICA INC.—See BP plc; *Int'l*, pg. 1127
BRABHAM OIL CO. INC.; *U.S. Private*, pg. 630
BRAD LANIER OIL CO. INC.; *U.S. Private*, pg. 631
BRIGHTOIL PETROLEUM HOLDINGS LIMITED; *Int'l*, pg. 1163
BROWNFIELD OIL COMPANY, INC.—See MFA Oil Company; *U.S. Private*, pg. 2693
BROWN OIL CO.; *U.S. Private*, pg. 668
BRUMFIELD OIL COMPANY INC.; *U.S. Private*, pg. 672
BUCHANAN OIL CORPORATION; *U.S. Private*, pg. 676
BUCKLEY OIL COMPANY INC.; *U.S. Private*, pg. 678
BUSCH DISTRIBUTORS INC.; *U.S. Private*, pg. 693
BUTLER PETROLEUM CORPORATION; *U.S. Private*, pg. 697
CALTEX PETROLEUM (VICTORIA) PTY LTD—See Ampol Limited; *Int'l*, pg. 436
CAMPBELL OIL & GAS COMPANY; *U.S. Private*, pg. 730
CAM PETROLI S.R.L.—See Camfin S.p.A.; *Int'l*, pg. 1272
CAM PETROLI S.R.L.—See Eni S.p.A.; *Int'l*, pg. 2436
CAMPO OIL COMPANY INC.; *U.S. Private*, pg. 731
CAPITAL CITY OIL INC.; *U.S. Private*, pg. 739
CAPITAL OIL INC.; *U.S. Private*, pg. 741
CARDWELL DISTRIBUTING, INC.—See AIP, LLC; *U.S. Private*, pg. 136
CAREY JOHNSON OIL COMPANY; *U.S. Private*, pg. 754
CARTERENERGY CORPORATION—See World Kinect Corporation; *U.S. Public*, pg. 2381
CARY OIL COMPANY, INC.—See COC Properties, Inc.; *U.S. Private*, pg. 958
C&B WAREHOUSE DISTRIBUTING; *U.S. Private*, pg. 702
CC DILLON CO.; *U.S. Private*, pg. 799
CEDAR MARINE TERMINALS, L.P.—See Vertex Energy, Inc.; *U.S. Public*, pg. 2287
CENDANA SUTERA SDN. BHD.—See Dialog Group Berhad; *Int'l*, pg. 2104
CENTRAL ARKANSAS PETROLEUM INC.; *U.S. Private*, pg. 818
CENTRAL LAKES COOPERATIVE; *U.S. Private*, pg. 822
CENTRAL NEW YORK OIL & GAS COMPANY, LLC—See Crestwood Equity Partners LP; *U.S. Public*, pg. 594
CENTRAL OIL & SUPPLY CORPORATION; *U.S. Private*, pg. 824
CENTURY PETROLEUM LTD.; *U.S. Private*, pg. 834
CERTAS ENERGY FRANCE SAS—See DCC plc; *Int'l*, pg. 1989
CERTAS ENERGY NORWAY AS—See DCC plc; *Int'l*, pg. 1989
CERTAS ENERGY—See DCC plc; *Int'l*, pg. 1989
CHAMBERLAIN OIL CO. INC.; *U.S. Private*, pg. 845
CHANDLER ENTERPRISES INC.; *U.S. Private*, pg. 848
CHAPMAN INC.; *U.S. Private*, pg. 849
CHERRY ENERGY; *U.S. Private*, pg. 874
CHILDERS OIL CO.; *U.S. Private*, pg. 882
CHRISTENSEN INC.; *U.S. Private*, pg. 890
CITY SERVICE, INC.; *U.S. Private*, pg. 907
C.K. SMITH & COMPANY INC.; *U.S. Private*, pg. 708
CLARKSVILLE OIL & GAS COMPANY INC.; *U.S. Private*, pg. 915
CLAY OIL CORP.; *U.S. Private*, pg. 918
CO-ALLIANCE LLP; *U.S. Private*, pg. 953
COLEMAN OIL COMPANY; *U.S. Private*, pg. 967
COLONIAL GROUP, INC.; *U.S. Private*, pg. 971
COLONIAL OIL INDUSTRIES, INC.—See Colonial Group, Inc.; *U.S. Private*, pg. 971
COLVIN OIL COMPANY INC.—See Andretti Petroleum, LLC; *U.S. Private*, pg. 279
COMBS OIL CO. INC.; *U.S. Private*, pg. 981
CONDON OIL COMPANY, INC.; *U.S. Private*, pg. 1012
CONNELL OIL INCORPORATED; *U.S. Private*, pg. 1017
CONOCOPHILLIPS RUSSIA INC.—See ConocoPhillips; *U.S. Public*, pg. 568
CONOCOPHILLIPS (U.K.) MARKETING & TRADING LIMITED—See ConocoPhillips; *U.S. Public*, pg. 568
COONEN INC.; *U.S. Private*, pg. 1040
COOPERATIVE GAS & OIL CO; *U.S. Private*, pg. 1042
COTTONWOOD CO-OP OIL COMPANY; *U.S. Private*, pg. 1064
COUGAR OIL INC.; *U.S. Private*, pg. 1064

N.A.I.C.S. INDEX 424710 — PETROLEUM BULK STAT...

N.A.I.C.S. Index

COYNE OIL CORPORATION; *U.S. Private*, pg. 1079
CRAWFORD OIL CO. INC.; *U.S. Private*, pg. 1086
CREST DISTRIBUTING INC.; *U.S. Private*, pg. 1095
CROSS PETROLEUM; *U.S. Private*, pg. 1105
CRUDUP OIL COMPANY INC.; *U.S. Private*, pg. 1113
CUMMINGS OIL CO. INC.; *U.S. Private*, pg. 1123
CUMMINGS OIL INC.; *U.S. Private*, pg. 1123
DAITO GAS PARTNER CORPORATION—See Daito Trust Construction Co., Ltd.; *Int'l*, pg. 1943
DAKOTA BULK TERMINAL LLC—See Kinder Morgan, Inc.; *U.S. Public*, pg. 1232
DAL CHEM, INC.—See AIP, LLC; *U.S. Private*, pg. 136
DALTON PETROLEUM INC.; *U.S. Private*, pg. 1150
DATS24 N.V.—See Colruyt Group N.V.; *Int'l*, pg. 1705
DAVID I. PETERSON INC.; *U.S. Private*, pg. 1170
DAWSON OIL CO., INC.; *U.S. Private*, pg. 1176
DCC ENERGI DANMARK A/S—See DCC plc; *Int'l*, pg. 1989
DERSCH ENERGIES INCORPORATED; *U.S. Private*, pg. 1210
DE SOTO FUELS INC.; *U.S. Private*, pg. 1181
DEVIN OIL CO. INC.; *U.S. Private*, pg. 1218
DF SHUMPERT OIL CO.; *U.S. Private*, pg. 1220
DHT MANAGEMENT AS—See DHT Holdings, Inc.; *Int'l*, pg. 2100
DHT MANAGEMENT S.A.M.—See DHT Holdings, Inc.; *Int'l*, pg. 2100
DHT SHIP MANAGEMENT (SINGAPORE) PTE. LTD.—See DHT Holdings, Inc.; *Int'l*, pg. 2100
DOMESTIC FUELS & LUBES—See Domestic Industries Inc.; *U.S. Private*, pg. 1255
DON SMALL & SONS OIL DISTRIBUTING CO. INC.; *U.S. Private*, pg. 1259
DOOLEY'S PETROLEUM INCORPORATED; *U.S. Private*, pg. 1261
DOR ALON ENERGY IN ISRAEL (1988) LTD; *Int'l*, pg. 2175
DOUGLASS DISTRIBUTING COMPANY INC.; *U.S. Private*, pg. 1267
DOWNEY OIL CO. INC.; *U.S. Private*, pg. 1269
DRAEGER OIL CO. INC.; *U.S. Private*, pg. 1271
DRAGON CROWN GROUP HOLDINGS LIMITED; *Int'l*, pg. 2199
DREW OIL COMPANY, INC.; *U.S. Private*, pg. 1276
DUGAN OIL CO. INC.; *U.S. Private*, pg. 1285
DUNKERQUE LNG SAS—See AXA S.A.; *Int'l*, pg. 757
DUNKERQUE LNG SAS—See Electricite de France S.A.; *Int'l*, pg. 2350
DUNLAP OIL COMPANY INC.; *U.S. Private*, pg. 1290
DURAN OIL CO; *U.S. Private*, pg. 1292
DUTCHESS TERMINALS INC.; *U.S. Private*, pg. 1294
EDEN OIL CO. INC.; *U.S. Private*, pg. 1333
ED STAUB & SONS—See Ed Staub & Sons Petroleum Inc.; *U.S. Private*, pg. 1332
EDWARD H. WOLF & SONS INC.; *U.S. Private*, pg. 1340
EDWARD H. WOLF & SONS INC.—See Edward H. Wolf & Sons Inc.; *U.S. Private*, pg. 1341
EDWARD'S OIL CO. INC.; *U.S. Private*, pg. 1341
ELENGY S.A.—See ENGIE SA; *Int'l*, pg. 2428
ELLIOTT BULK SERVICES, LLC—See Elliott Oil Co. Inc.; *U.S. Private*, pg. 1373
ELMER SMITH OIL COMPANY; *U.S. Private*, pg. 1376
EMERSON OIL CO. INC.; *U.S. Private*, pg. 1382
ENERGY TRANSFER OPERATING, L.P.—See Energy Transfer LP; *U.S. Public*, pg. 763
ENGIE GAS & LNG HOLDINGS LLC—See ENGIE SA; *Int'l*, pg. 2428
ENTERPRISE OIL CO.—See AIP, LLC; *U.S. Private*, pg. 136
E&V ENERGY CORPORATION; *U.S. Private*, pg. 1301
EZZIES WHOLESALE INC.; *U.S. Private*, pg. 1454
FARMERS UNION OIL MOHALL/SHERWOOD; *U.S. Private*, pg. 1479
FARMERS UNION OIL OF SOUTHERN VALLEY; *U.S. Private*, pg. 1479
FARMLAND CO-OP, INC.; *U.S. Private*, pg. 1480
FAUJI OIL TERMINAL & DISTRIBUTION COMPANY LIMITED—See Fauji Foundation; *Int'l*, pg. 2623
FAUSER OIL COMPANY INCORPORATED; *U.S. Private*, pg. 1484
FERGUSON BROS INC.; *U.S. Private*, pg. 1496
FERRELLGAS, INC. - ROOSEVELT PROPANE TERMINAL—See Ferrellgas Partners, L.P.; *U.S. Public*, pg. 829
FICKLER OIL COMPANY INC.; *U.S. Private*, pg. 1502
FIKES WHOLESALE INC.—See Casey's General Stores, Inc.; *U.S. Public*, pg. 446
FIRST ENERGY CORPORATION—See Parker Holding Company, Inc.; *U.S. Private*, pg. 3097
FLETCHER OIL CO. INC.—See Floco Unlimited Inc.; *U.S. Private*, pg. 1546
FLINT HILLS RESOURCES, LP—See Koch Industries, Inc.; *U.S. Private*, pg. 2327
FLOCO UNLIMITED INC.; *U.S. Private*, pg. 1546
FLORIDIAN NATURAL GAS STORAGE COMPANY, LLC—See Targa Resources Corp.; *U.S. Public*, pg. 1981
F. RAY MOORE OIL CO. INC.; *U.S. Private*, pg. 1455
FREEBORN COUNTY CO-OP OIL CO.; *U.S. Private*, pg. 1602
FREEMAN OIL COMPANY INC.; *U.S. Private*, pg. 1605
FRIDAY OIL CO. INC.; *U.S. Private*, pg. 1610
FROST OIL CO; *U.S. Private*, pg. 1616
FUELFIX PTY LTD—See Archer Capital Pty. Ltd.; *Int'l*, pg. 547
FUEL SOUTH INC.—See Jones Company, Inc.; *U.S. Private*, pg. 2232
GALAXIE CORPORATION; *U.S. Private*, pg. 1636
GALPGESTE, LDA.—See Galp Energia SGPS, S.A.; *Int'l*, pg. 2875
GARROW OIL CORP.; *U.S. Private*, pg. 1646
G&B OIL COMPANY INC.; *U.S. Private*, pg. 1628
GENE HARRIS PETROLEUM INC.; *U.S. Private*, pg. 1660
GENESIS ENERGY, L.P.; *U.S. Public*, pg. 930
GEORGE E. WARREN CORPORATION; *U.S. Private*, pg. 1681
GISH OIL CO.; *U.S. Private*, pg. 1702
GLADIEUX TRADING AND MARKETING CO. LP; *U.S. Private*, pg. 1704
G&M OIL CO. INC.; *U.S. Private*, pg. 1629
GM PETROLEUM DISTRIBUTORS INC.; *U.S. Private*, pg. 1721
GOOD OIL CO. INC.; *U.S. Private*, pg. 1738
GRACE ENERGY CORP.; *U.S. Private*, pg. 1748
GRAVES OIL COMPANY; *U.S. Private*, pg. 1759
GREAT LAKES PETROLEUM CO.; *U.S. Private*, pg. 1765
GREEN BAY TERMINAL CORPORATION—See CHS INC.; *U.S. Public*, pg. 492
GREEN BAY TERMINAL CORPORATION—See Marathon Petroleum Corporation; *U.S. Public*, pg. 1364
GREEN & CHAPMAN, INC.; *U.S. Private*, pg. 1771
GRESHAM PETROLEUM CO.; *U.S. Private*, pg. 1783
GULF OIL, LP—See ArcLight Capital Holdings, LLC; *U.S. Private*, pg. 312
GUTTMAN ENERGY, INC.—See Guttman Holdings, Inc.; *U.S. Private*, pg. 1820
HAGER OIL COMPANY INC.—See AIP, LLC; *U.S. Private*, pg. 136
HAMPEL OIL DISTRIBUTORS INC.; *U.S. Private*, pg. 1851
HANS ENERGY COMPANY LIMITED; *Int'l*, pg. 3259
HANSEN OIL CO.; *U.S. Private*, pg. 1856
HARPEL OIL COMPANY INC.; *U.S. Private*, pg. 1867
HAWKSTONE ASSOCIATES, INC.; *U.S. Private*, pg. 1883
HAYTER OIL COMPANY, INC.; *U.S. Private*, pg. 1885
H.C. LEWIS OIL COMPANY INC.; *U.S. Private*, pg. 1825
HENRY OIL COMPANY INC.; *U.S. Private*, pg. 1919
HESS CORP. - PORT READING REFINERY & TERMINAL—See Hess Corporation; *U.S. Public*, pg. 1030
HESTYA ENERGY BV—See Riverstone Holdings LLC; *U.S. Private*, pg. 3447
HICKS OIL-HICKS GAS, INC.; *U.S. Private*, pg. 1934
HIGHLAND CORPORATION; *U.S. Private*, pg. 1938
HISWAY PARTNERS, INC.; *U.S. Private*, pg. 1952
H.J. WALKER OIL CO. INC.; *U.S. Private*, pg. 1834
H&M WHOLESALE INC.; *U.S. Private*, pg. 1823
HOC INDUSTRIES INC.; *U.S. Private*, pg. 1958
HOKURIKU GAS CO., LTD.; *Int'l*, pg. 3445
HOME OIL & GAS COMPANY INC.; *U.S. Private*, pg. 1972
HOME SERVICE OIL CO. INC. - REYNO DIVISION—See Home Service Oil Co. Inc.; *U.S. Private*, pg. 1972
HONE OIL COMPANY INC.; *U.S. Private*, pg. 1976
HOPSON OIL CO. INC.; *U.S. Private*, pg. 1980
HOYER BULGARIA EOOD—See Hoyer GmbH; *Int'l*, pg. 3498
H&S OIL COMPANY INC.; *U.S. Private*, pg. 1824
HUNTER OIL CO. INC.; *U.S. Private*, pg. 2010
INLAND FUEL TERMINALS, INC.—See Santa Energy Corporation; *U.S. Private*, pg. 3547
INTERNATIONAL-MATEX TANK TERMINALS, INC.—See Riverstone Holdings LLC; *U.S. Private*, pg. 3447
INTER TERMINALS SWEDEN AB—See Brookfield Infrastructure Partners L.P.; *Int'l*, pg. 1193
ISAACS ENTERPRISES INC.; *U.S. Private*, pg. 2142
JACK BECKER DISTRIBUTORS, INC.; *U.S. Private*, pg. 2173
JACK GRIGGS INC.; *U.S. Private*, pg. 2174
JACKSON COUNTY OIL CO. INC.; *U.S. Private*, pg. 2176
JACKSON OIL COMPANY, INC.; *U.S. Private*, pg. 2178
JACOBUS ENERGY, INC.; *U.S. Private*, pg. 2180
JAMES P. HILL DISTRIBUTORS; *U.S. Private*, pg. 2184
JANKOVICH COMPANY; *U.S. Private*, pg. 2187
JBC INC.; *U.S. Private*, pg. 2193
J.B. CLARK OIL COMPANY INC.; *U.S. Private*, pg. 2158
J.B. DEWAR INC.; *U.S. Private*, pg. 2158
J.D. STREETT & CO., INC.; *U.S. Private*, pg. 2161
JEFFERSON CITY OIL CO. INC.; *U.S. Private*, pg. 2197
JERNIGAN OIL CO. INC.; *U.S. Private*, pg. 2201
JERRY LAWLEY INCORPORATED; *U.S. Private*, pg. 2202
JET GAS CORPORATION; *U.S. Private*, pg. 2204
JET TANKSTELLEN AUSTRIA GMBH—See Phillips 66 Company; *U.S. Public*, pg. 1688
J&H OIL COMPANY INC.; *U.S. Private*, pg. 2154
JIM HINTON OIL COMPANY INC.; *U.S. Private*, pg. 2209
JM OIL COMPANY INC.; *U.S. Private*, pg. 2214
JOHN G. WEATHERFORD INC.; *U.S. Private*, pg. 2221
JOHN L. BOND INC.—See Calfee Company of Dalton, Inc.; *U.S. Private*, pg. 717
JOHNSON OIL COMPANY GAYLORD; *U.S. Private*, pg. 2228
JOHN T. DAVIS OIL CO. INC.; *U.S. Private*, pg. 2225
JONES OIL CO. INC.; *U.S. Private*, pg. 2233
JONES PETROLEUM COMPANY, INC.; *U.S. Private*, pg. 2233
K.D. TIMMONS INC.; *U.S. Private*, pg. 2251
KEENAN ENERGY COMPANY INCORPORATED; *U.S. Private*, pg. 2272
KEHM OIL COMPANY; *U.S. Private*, pg. 2273
KENTUCKY OIL & REFINING COMPANY; *U.S. Private*, pg. 2288
KENTUCKY PETROLEUM SUPPLY, INC.; *U.S. Private*, pg. 2288
KEYSTOPS LLC; *U.S. Private*, pg. 2300
K&F DISTRIBUTORS INC.; *U.S. Private*, pg. 2249
KIDD JONES HENDERSON COUNTY; *U.S. Private*, pg. 2302
KINDER MORGAN SOUTHEAST TERMINALS LLC - KNOXVILLE—See Kinder Morgan, Inc.; *U.S. Public*, pg. 1233
KINDER MORGAN SOUTHEAST TERMINALS LLC - ROANOKE—See Kinder Morgan, Inc.; *U.S. Public*, pg. 1233
KMJ CONVENIENCE COMPANY; *U.S. Private*, pg. 2321
KNAPP OIL CO. INC.; *U.S. Private*, pg. 2321
KNIGHT ENTERPRISES INC.; *U.S. Private*, pg. 2322
KOLKHORST PETROLEUM COMPANY; *U.S. Private*, pg. 2341
KUYKENDALL & POWELL OIL CO.; *U.S. Private*, pg. 2359
LAFAIVE OIL CO.; *U.S. Private*, pg. 2372
LAKE REGION CO-OP OIL ASSOCIATION; *U.S. Private*, pg. 2375
LAMBERT OIL COMPANY INC.; *U.S. Private*, pg. 2380
LAMPTON-LOVE, INC.—See Ergon, Inc.; *U.S. Private*, pg. 1418
LANDES OIL INC.; *U.S. Private*, pg. 2385
LANMAN OIL COMPANY, INC.; *U.S. Private*, pg. 2390
LAUGHLIN OIL COMPANY; *U.S. Private*, pg. 2397
LAWRENCE OIL CO. INC.; *U.S. Private*, pg. 2401
LEMMEN OIL COMPANY—See Sun Capital Partners, Inc.; *U.S. Private*, pg. 3860
LENAWEE FUELS INC.; *U.S. Private*, pg. 2421
LEWIS PETROLEUM PRODUCTS CO.; *U.S. Private*, pg. 2439
LIBERTY OIL CO. INC.; *U.S. Private*, pg. 2446
LIGON OIL CO. INC.; *U.S. Private*, pg. 2455
LINK PETROLEUM INC.—See Gibson Energy Inc.; *Int'l*, pg. 2963
LIQUILUX GAS CORP.; *U.S. Private*, pg. 2466
THE LITTLE OIL COMPANY, INC.; *U.S. Private*, pg. 4071
LODI GAS STORAGE, LLC—See Brookfield Infrastructure Partners L.P.; *Int'l*, pg. 1190
LOTT OIL COMPANY, INC.; *U.S. Private*, pg. 2497
LOWRY OIL COMPANY INCORPORATED; *U.S. Private*, pg. 2506
LUBECON SYSTEMS, INC.—See BP plc; *Int'l*, pg. 1127
LUTHER P. MILLER, INC.; *U.S. Private*, pg. 2517
LYBARGER OIL INC.; *U.S. Private*, pg. 2519
LYDEN OIL COMPANY-LANSING DIVISION—See Lyden Oil Company; *U.S. Private*, pg. 2519
LYDEN OIL COMPANY-YOUNGSTOWN DIVISION—See Lyden Oil Company; *U.S. Private*, pg. 2519
MAGELLAN MIDSTREAM PARTNERS, L.P.—See ONEOK, Inc.; *U.S. Public*, pg. 1603
MAGELLAN PROCESSING, L.P.—See ONEOK, Inc.; *U.S. Public*, pg. 1603
MAGNESS OIL COMPANY INC.; *U.S. Private*, pg. 2547
MAJOR PETROLEUM INDUSTRIES INC.; *U.S. Private*, pg. 2555
MALLARD OIL COMPANY INC.; *U.S. Private*, pg. 2557
MARATHON FLINT OIL COMPANY; *U.S. Private*, pg. 2570
MARINE OIL CO. INC.; *U.S. Private*, pg. 2575
MAX ARNOLD & SONS, INC.; *U.S. Private*, pg. 2617
MAXEY ENERGY CO.; *U.S. Private*, pg. 2617
MCCORMIX CORP.; *U.S. Private*, pg. 2630
MCCRAW OIL CO. INC.; *U.S. Private*, pg. 2631
THE MCPHERSON COMPANIES, INC.—See MidMark Capital; *U.S. Private*, pg. 2716
MEL DAWSON INC.—See Chevron Corporation; *U.S. Public*, pg. 487
MELZER'S FUEL SERVICE INC.—See BP plc; *Int'l*, pg. 1127
MERRITT OIL CO. INC.; *U.S. Private*, pg. 2676
MFA OIL COMPANY; *U.S. Private*, pg. 2693
MIDDLETON OIL CO. INC.; *U.S. Private*, pg. 2714
MID-STATE PETROLEUM INC.; *U.S. Private*, pg. 2709
MIDWAY PETROLEUM CO. INC.; *U.S. Private*, pg. 2719
MIXSON OIL CO. INC.; *U.S. Private*, pg. 2752
MOLO OIL COMPANY INC.; *U.S. Private*, pg. 2767
MOORE OIL INC.; *U.S. Private*, pg. 2780
MORGAN OIL COMPANY INCORPORATED; *U.S. Private*, pg. 2784
MORGAN OIL COMPANY, INC.; *U.S. Private*, pg. 2784
MURPHY USA INC.; *U.S. Public*, pg. 1487
NANJING DRAGON CROWN LIQUID CHEMICAL TERMINAL COMPANY LIMITED—See Dragon Crown Group Holdings Limited; *Int'l*, pg. 2199
NASH OIL COMPANY INC.; *U.S. Private*, pg. 2836
NATIONAL FUEL GAS SUPPLY CORPORATION—See National Fuel Gas Company; *U.S. Public*, pg. 1494

424710 — PETROLEUM BULK STAT...

NATIONAL PETROLEUM INC.; *U.S. Private*, pg. 2860
NELSON DISTRIBUTING INC.; *U.S. Private*, pg. 2883
NEWELL FUEL SERVICE INC.; *U.S. Private*, pg. 2914
NEWTON OIL COMPANY, INC.; *U.S. Private*, pg. 2918
NEY OIL COMPANY; *U.S. Private*, pg. 2922
NIC HOLDING CORPORATION; *U.S. Private*, pg. 2925
NINGBO NINGXIANG LIQUID CHEMICALS TERMINAL CO., LTD.—See Dragon Crown Group Holdings Limited; *Int'l*, pg. 2199
NITTANY OIL COMPANY INC.; *U.S. Private*, pg. 2929
NORTHERN STAR COOPERATIVE; *U.S. Private*, pg. 2954
NORTH SHORE OIL COMPANY INC.; *U.S. Private*, pg. 2947
NORTHWEST ENTERPRISES INC.; *U.S. Private*, pg. 2960
NORTHWEST OIL COMPANY INC; *U.S. Private*, pg. 2961
OCCIDENTAL CHEMICAL DE MEXICO, S.A. DE C.V.—See Occidental Petroleum Corporation; *U.S. Public*, pg. 1561
OCCIDENTAL PERMIAN LTD.—See Occidental Petroleum Corporation; *U.S. Public*, pg. 1561
OCI INC.; *U.S. Private*, pg. 2992
O.D. SNIDER & SON INCORPARATED; *U.S. Private*, pg. 2981
OLIN OIL CO. INC.; *U.S. Private*, pg. 3010
OLIVER OIL COMPANY INC.; *U.S. Private*, pg. 3011
OMEGA PARTNERS JOLIET LLC—See Omega Partners III LLC; *U.S. Private*, pg. 3015
ONCUE MARKETING LLC; *U.S. Private*, pg. 3020
O'ROURKE DIST. CO., INC.; *U.S. Private*, pg. 2980
OWL SERVICES, INC.; *U.S. Private*, pg. 3055
PALMER OIL CO. INCORPORATED; *U.S. Private*, pg. 3081
PARADIGM SERVICES LLC; *U.S. Private*, pg. 3089
PARISH OIL CO. INC.; *U.S. Private*, pg. 3095
PARKER OIL COMPANY, INC.—See AIP, LLC; *U.S. Private*, pg. 136
PARSONS OIL COMPANY INC—See Kent Distributors Inc.; *U.S. Private*, pg. 2287
PAUL FISHER OIL COMPANY INC.; *U.S. Private*, pg. 3112
PEACOCK OIL CO. OF BAXLEY INC.; *U.S. Private*, pg. 3123
PEARL CITY ELEVATOR INC.; *U.S. Private*, pg. 3125
PEERLESS DISTRIBUTING CO.; *U.S. Private*, pg. 3128
PELICAN OIL INC.; *U.S. Private*, pg. 3130
PENINSULA OIL & PROPANE COMPANY; *U.S. Private*, pg. 3133
PERIMETER TERMINAL, LLC; *U.S. Private*, pg. 3150
PETROLEUM FUEL & TERMINAL COMPANY—See Apex Oil Company, Inc.; *U.S. Private*, pg. 293
PETROLEUM PRODUCTS CORP.; *U.S. Private*, pg. 3162
PETROLEUM PRODUCTS INC.; *U.S. Private*, pg. 3162
PETROLEUM SALES INC.; *U.S. Private*, pg. 3162
PETROLIANCE LLC - CHICAGO—See PetroLiance LLC; *U.S. Private*, pg. 3162
PETROLIANCE LLC; *U.S. Private*, pg. 3162
PETROPAC LTDA—See CAP S.A.; *Int'l*, pg. 1301
PHILLIPS 66 BANTRY BAY TERMINAL LIMITED—See Phillips 66 Company; *U.S. Public*, pg. 1688
PHILLIPS 66 CANADA LTD.—See Phillips 66 Company; *U.S. Public*, pg. 1688
PHILLIPS 66 COMPANY—See Phillips 66 Company; *U.S. Public*, pg. 1688
PHILLIPS 66 GMBH—See Phillips 66 Company; *U.S. Public*, pg. 1688
POLK OIL COMPANY INC.; *U.S. Private*, pg. 3224
PROGRESSIVE ENERGY INC.; *U.S. Private*, pg. 3279
PRO PETROLEUM, INC.—See BP plc; *Int'l*, pg. 1127
PURE PETROLEUM CORP.—See Cosco Capital, Inc.; *Int'l*, pg. 1809
PURVIS BROTHERS INC.; *U.S. Private*, pg. 3307
QSTAR FORSALJNING AB—See DCC plc; *Int'l*, pg. 1991
QUALITY OIL CO. INC.; *U.S. Private*, pg. 3320
QUALITY PETROLEUM CORP.; *U.S. Private*, pg. 3320
QUALITY PETROLEUM OF ALABAMA, INC.—See Quality Petroleum Corp.; *U.S. Private*, pg. 3320
QUALITY PETROLEUM—See Quality Petroleum Inc.; *U.S. Private*, pg. 3320
QUALITY STATE OIL CO. INC.; *U.S. Private*, pg. 3321
QUARLES PETROLEUM INCORPORATED; *U.S. Private*, pg. 3324
QUEEN CITY TERMINALS LLC—See Kinder Morgan, Inc.; *U.S. Public*, pg. 1234
QUICK FLASH OIL CO.—See Pugh Oil Company; *U.S. Private*, pg. 3303
RADCLIFF-ECONOMY MARINE SERVICES; *U.S. Private*, pg. 3342
RADIANT GROUP LLC; *U.S. Private*, pg. 3343
RAMOS OIL CO. INC.; *U.S. Private*, pg. 3351
REBEL OIL COMPANY, INC.; *U.S. Private*, pg. 3370
REDDING OIL CO. INC.; *U.S. Private*, pg. 3378
RED SPRINGS FUEL OIL COMPANY; *U.S. Private*, pg. 3376
REED OIL COMPANY; *U.S. Private*, pg. 3382
RELIANCE PETROLEUM COMPANY INC.—See Donnini Enterprises Inc.; *U.S. Private*, pg. 1261
RENN TRANSPORTATION, INC.; *U.S. Private*, pg. 3398
RESTRUCTURE INC.; *U.S. Private*, pg. 3410
RETIF OIL & FUEL, LLC; *U.S. Private*, pg. 3412
REYNOLDS OIL COMPANY INC.; *U.S. Private*, pg. 3418
RHODES INC.; *U.S. Private*, pg. 3422

R.H. SMITH DISTRIBUTING CO.; *U.S. Private*, pg. 3336
RICHARD OIL AND FUEL LLC—See AIP, LLC; *U.S. Private*, pg. 136
RICKER OIL COMPANY INC.—See Giant Eagle, Inc.; *U.S. Private*, pg. 1694
RICK KOCH OIL CO.; *U.S. Private*, pg. 3431
RIISER OIL COMPANY INC.; *U.S. Private*, pg. 3436
RISSER OIL CORP.; *U.S. Private*, pg. 3441
R.M. PARKS INCORPORATED; *U.S. Private*, pg. 3339
ROBERT FAWCETT & SON CO. INC.; *U.S. Private*, pg. 3457
ROBERTS-GIBSON INC.; *U.S. Private*, pg. 3460
ROBERT W. BAKER NURSERY INC.—See The Robert Baker Companies; *U.S. Private*, pg. 4111
ROCKY MOUNTAIN SUPPLY INC.; *U.S. Private*, pg. 3469
ROGER MERTENS DISTRIBUTORS; *U.S. Private*, pg. 3471
ROGERS PETROLEUM INC.; *U.S. Private*, pg. 3472
ROGERS PETROLEUM SERVICES INCORPORATED; *U.S. Private*, pg. 3472
RON'S OIL COMPANY; *U.S. Private*, pg. 3477
ROYCE GROFF OIL COMPANY; *U.S. Private*, pg. 3494
SAMPSON-BLADEN OIL CO. INC.; *U.S. Private*, pg. 3538
SANDERS OIL COMPANY INC.; *U.S. Private*, pg. 3543
SANGAREE OIL COMPANY INC.; *U.S. Private*, pg. 3546
SANTA ENERGY CORPORATION; *U.S. Private*, pg. 3547
S.B. COLLINS INC.; *U.S. Private*, pg. 3515
SC AMGAZ S.A.—See ENGIE SA; *Int'l*, pg. 2434
SCOTT PETROLEUM CORPORATION; *U.S. Private*, pg. 3577
SEAPORT SOUND TERMINAL LLC—See Targa Resources Corp.; *U.S. Public*, pg. 1981
SHASTA-SISKIYOU TRANSPORT; *U.S. Private*, pg. 3627
SHIRTCLIFF OIL CO.; *U.S. Private*, pg. 3637
SHORE TERMINALS LLC—See Sunoco LP; *U.S. Public*, pg. 1965
SMITH OIL CORPORATION; *U.S. Private*, pg. 3695
SMITH PETROLEUM INC.; *U.S. Private*, pg. 3695
SMITH ROGERS OIL CO. INC.; *U.S. Private*, pg. 3695
SMITH & WHITFIELD OILS INC.; *U.S. Private*, pg. 3694
SOUTHEASTERN ENERGY CORP.; *U.S. Private*, pg. 3727
SOUTHEASTERN OIL CO. INC.; *U.S. Private*, pg. 3728
SOUTHEASTERN PETROLEUM CO., INC.; *U.S. Private*, pg. 3728
SOUTHERN COUNTIES OIL CO.; *U.S. Private*, pg. 3730
SPEEDWAY PREPAID CARD LLC—See Marathon Petroleum Corporation; *U.S. Public*, pg. 1364
SPRAGUE OPERATING RESOURCES LLC—See Brookfield Corporation; *Int'l*, pg. 1182
S&S PETROLEUM INC.; *U.S. Private*, pg. 3514
STAPLES OIL CO. INC.; *U.S. Private*, pg. 3784
STEUBEN GAS STORAGE COMPANY—See Crestwood Equity Partners LP; *U.S. Public*, pg. 594
STOCKTON OIL COMPANY; *U.S. Private*, pg. 3815
STOHLMAN AND ROGERS INC.; *U.S. Private*, pg. 3816
STORY DISTRIBUTING CO.; *U.S. Private*, pg. 3832
STUBBS OIL COMPANY INC.; *U.S. Private*, pg. 3843
SUN WEST OIL COMPANY LLC; *U.S. Private*, pg. 3864
SUPERIOR FUELS, INC.; *U.S. Private*, pg. 3878
SUPERIOR PETROLEUM COMPANY; *U.S. Private*, pg. 3879
SWALLOW CO.; *U.S. Private*, pg. 3889
SWATI ENTERPRISES INC.; *U.S. Private*, pg. 3891
SWEETWATER VALLEY OIL CO.; *U.S. Private*, pg. 3892
SWETZ OIL CO. INC.; *U.S. Private*, pg. 3893
TANNER HOME & ENERGY; *U.S. Private*, pg. 3931
TARR LLC; *U.S. Private*, pg. 3934
TAYLOR OIL CO. OF WASHINGTON NC; *U.S. Private*, pg. 3940
TAYLOR OIL INC.; *U.S. Private*, pg. 3940
T&C WHOLESALE LLC—See Sunoco LP; *U.S. Public*, pg. 1965
TEAM SCHIERL COMPANIES; *U.S. Private*, pg. 3950
TERMINALS NEW ZEALAND LTD.—See Ampol Limited; *Int'l*, pg. 437
TESEI PETROLEUM INC.; *U.S. Private*, pg. 3973
TEXADIAN ENERGY CANADA LIMITED—See Par Pacific Holdings, Inc.; *U.S. Public*, pg. 1636
TEXPAR ENERGY INC.; *U.S. Private*, pg. 3978
THREE L INC.; *U.S. Private*, pg. 4164
TIGER ENTERPRISES INC.; *U.S. Private*, pg. 4169
TIRE AND OIL INC.; *U.S. Private*, pg. 4176
TNT PETROLEUM INC.; *U.S. Private*, pg. 4180
TOLEDO TERMINALING COMPANY LLC—See PBF Energy Inc.; *U.S. Public*, pg. 1657
TOM JONES INC.; *U.S. Private*, pg. 4182
TOMMY BROOKS OIL COMPANY; *U.S. Private*, pg. 4184
TOM YATES PETROLEUM CO. INC.; *U.S. Private*, pg. 4183
TOZAI OIL TERMINAL CO., LTD.—See Cosmo Energy Holdings Co., Ltd.; *Int'l*, pg. 1812
TOZAI OIL TERMINAL CO., LTD.—See ENEOS Holdings, Inc.; *Int'l*, pg. 2417
TREJO OIL CO. INC.; *U.S. Private*, pg. 4217
TRICOR REFINING, LLC—See Ergon, Inc.; *U.S. Private*, pg. 1418
TRICOR REFINING, LLC—See San Joaquin Refining Co.; *U.S. Private*, pg. 3541
TRILLIUM TRANSPORTATION FUELS, LLC—See Love's Travel Stops & Country Stores, Inc.; *U.S. Private*, pg. 2501
TRI-STATE OIL COMPANY, INC.; *U.S. Private*, pg. 4224
TRI-STATE PETROLEUM CORPORATION; *U.S. Private*, pg. 4224
TRI-STATE PETROLEUM INC.; *U.S. Private*, pg. 4224
TUGWELL OIL CO. INC.; *U.S. Private*, pg. 4257
UEBELHOR DEVELOPMENT INC.; *U.S. Private*, pg. 4274
UNITED OIL CORP; *U.S. Private*, pg. 4295
U.S. OIL—See U.S. Venture, Inc.; *U.S. Private*, pg. 4272
U.S. VENTURE, INC.; *U.S. Private*, pg. 4272
VALOR LLC; *U.S. Private*, pg. 4336
VANCOUVER OIL COMPANY INC.—See Jubitz Corporation; *U.S. Private*, pg. 2242
WAGNER OIL CO. INC.; *U.S. Private*, pg. 4426
WATTS PETROLEUM CORPORATION; *U.S. Private*, pg. 4456
WENGER OIL INC.; *U.S. Private*, pg. 4481
WESSELS OIL CO., INC.; *U.S. Private*, pg. 4483
WEST ARK OIL COMPANY—See Chapman Inc.; *U.S. Private*, pg. 849
WESTERN FLEET SERVICES, INC.—See Mansfield Energy Corp.; *U.S. Private*, pg. 2566
WESTERN PETROLEUM CO., INC.; *U.S. Private*, pg. 4495
WESTERN STATES PETROLEUM INC.; *U.S. Private*, pg. 4497
WHATLEY OIL & AUTO PARTS COMPANY INC.; *U.S. Private*, pg. 4504
W.H. BRESHEARS, INC.; *U.S. Private*, pg. 4420
W.H. EMMART & SON INC.; *U.S. Private*, pg. 4420
WHOLESALE PETROLEUM INC.; *U.S. Private*, pg. 4514
WILBURN OIL CO., INC.; *U.S. Private*, pg. 4518
WILD GOOSE STORAGE, LLC—See Brookfield Infrastructure Partners L.P.; *Int'l*, pg. 1190
WILLARD OIL COMPANY INC.; *U.S. Private*, pg. 4521
WINNSBORO PETROLEUM CO. INC.; *U.S. Private*, pg. 4543
WISE OIL & FUEL INCORPORATED; *U.S. Private*, pg. 4550
WOOD PETROLEUM CO., INC.; *U.S. Private*, pg. 4557
WORLD POINT TERMINALS, LP—See World Point Terminals, Inc.; *U.S. Private*, pg. 4566
WRIGHT VALLEY OIL INC.; *U.S. Private*, pg. 4573
YAKIMA COOPERATIVE ASSOCIATION; *U.S. Private*, pg. 4584
YODER OIL COMPANY INC.; *U.S. Private*, pg. 4589
ZENITH ENERGY LOGISTICS PARTNERS LP—See Warburg Pincus LLC; *U.S. Private*, pg. 4440
ZENITH ENERGY, L.P.—See Warburg Pincus LLC; *U.S. Private*, pg. 4440
ZURBUCHEN OIL, INC.—See Edward H. Wolf & Sons Inc.; *U.S. Private*, pg. 1341

424720 — PETROLEUM AND PETROLEUM PRODUCTS MERCHANT WHOLESALERS (EXCEPT BULK STATIONS AND TERMINALS)

284 FUEL SUPPLY, LLC—See Iowa 80 Group, Inc.; *U.S. Private*, pg. 2134
ABASTECEDORA DE COMBUSTIBLES S.A.—See AntarChile S.A.; *Int'l*, pg. 481
ABERCROMBIE OIL COMPANY INCORPORATED; *U.S. Private*, pg. 37
ABU DHABI NATIONAL OIL COMPANY FOR DISTRIBUTION—See Abu Dhabi National Oil Company; *Int'l*, pg. 73
ACCURATE LUBRICANTS & METALWORKING FLUIDS, INC.; *U.S. Private*, pg. 55
ACS PLYN, S.R.O.—See Arca Capital Slovakia, A.S.; *Int'l*, pg. 539
A.C.&T. CO. INC.; *U.S. Private*, pg. 25
ADANI BUNKERING PRIVATE LIMITED—See Adani Enterprises Limited; *Int'l*, pg. 124
ADVANCE PETROLEUM DISTRIBUTING CO.; *U.S. Private*, pg. 84
ADVANCE PETROLEUM, INC.—See World Kinect Corporation; *U.S. Public*, pg. 2380
ADVANCE PETROLEUM SERVICES LTD.—See Dabbagh Group Holding Company Ltd.; *Int'l*, pg. 1902
AE ADVANCED FUELS, INC.—See Aemetis, Inc.; *U.S. Public*, pg. 52
AFTON CHEMICAL ADDITIVES CORPORATION—See Newmarket Corporation; *U.S. Public*, pg. 1516
AFTON CHEMICAL DE MEXICO S.A. DE C.V.—See Newmarket Corporation; *U.S. Public*, pg. 1516
AIR BP AMERICAS—See BP plc; *Int'l*, pg. 1125
AIR BP ARGENTINA S.A.—See BP plc; *Int'l*, pg. 1125
AIR BP BRASIL S.A.—See BP plc; *Int'l*, pg. 1125
AIR BP CANADA LIMITED—See BP plc; *Int'l*, pg. 1125
AIR BP CHINA—See BP plc; *Int'l*, pg. 1125
AIR BP EASTERN MEDITERRANIAN LTD—See BP plc; *Int'l*, pg. 1125
AIR BP FINLAND OY—See BP plc; *Int'l*, pg. 1125
AIR BP ITALIA S.P.A.—See BP plc; *Int'l*, pg. 1125
AIR BP LIMITED—See BP plc; *Int'l*, pg. 1125
AIR BP MOSCOW—See BP plc; *Int'l*, pg. 1125
AIR BP NORWAY AS—See BP plc; *Int'l*, pg. 1126
AIR BP PUERTO RICO—See BP plc; *Int'l*, pg. 1125

N.A.I.C.S. INDEX 424720 — PETROLEUM AND PETRO...

N.A.I.C.S. Index

AIR BP SALES ROMANIA SRL—See BP plc; *Int'l*, pg. 1125
AIR BP SWEDEN AB—See BP plc; *Int'l*, pg. 1125
AIR BP SWITZERLAND—See BP plc; *Int'l*, pg. 1126
AKTOBE METALWARE PLANT JSC; *Int'l*, pg. 267
ALEXANDER OIL COMPANY; *U.S. Private*, pg. 164
ALLEN OIL COMPANY OF SYLACAUGA; *U.S. Private*, pg. 179
ALLIANCE ENERGY SERVICES, LLC; *U.S. Private*, pg. 182
ALLIANCE EXPRESS—See Delos Capital, LLC; *U.S. Private*, pg. 1198
ALLIED PROPANE SERVICE INC.; *U.S. Private*, pg. 187
ALLIED UTILITY PRODUCTS, INC.—See WESCO International, Inc.; *U.S. Public*, pg. 2351
AL MAHA PETROLEUM PRODUCTS MARKETING COMPANY S.A.O.G.; *Int'l*, pg. 281
ALOHA PETROLEUM, LTD.—See Sunoco LP; *U.S. Public*, pg. 1964
ALPARK PETROLEUM, INC.; *U.S. Private*, pg. 196
AMAR OIL CO. INC.; *U.S. Private*, pg. 216
AMERICAN LUBRICANTS INC—See Battenfeld Management Inc.; *U.S. Private*, pg. 488
ANAN INTERNATIONAL LIMITED; *Int'l*, pg. 446
ANDERSON GAS & PROPANE INC.; *U.S. Private*, pg. 277
ANDRETTI PETROLEUM, LLC; *U.S. Private*, pg. 279
ANTARGAZ NEDERLAND B.V.—See UGI Corporation; *U.S. Public*, pg. 2222
AO NNK-AMURNEFTEPRODUCT—See Alliance Oil Company Ltd.; *Int'l*, pg. 340
APACHE CRUDE OIL MARKETING, INC.—See APA Corporation; *U.S. Public*, pg. 143
APCO SERVICE STATIONS PTY. LTD.; *Int'l*, pg. 508
APOLLO OIL LLC; *U.S. Private*, pg. 295
APPLEGREEN PLC; *Int'l*, pg. 520
ARIZONA FUEL DISTRIBUTORS LLC; *U.S. Private*, pg. 324
ARNOLD AUTOMOTIVE AND OIL CO.; *U.S. Private*, pg. 333
ARNOLD OIL CO. INC.; *U.S. Private*, pg. 333
AROGAS INC.; *U.S. Private*, pg. 334
AR SANDRI INC.; *U.S. Private*, pg. 306
ARTAG HOLDINGS, INC.—See Quarles Petroleum Incorporated; *U.S. Private*, pg. 3324
ASHBRIDGE OIL CO. INC.; *U.S. Private*, pg. 349
ASHLAND DANMARK APS—See Ashland Inc.; *U.S. Public*, pg. 211
ASSOCIATED PETROLEUM PRODUCTS INC.; *U.S. Private*, pg. 356
ATLANTIC DETROIT DIESEL-ALLISON - POWER SYSTEMS—See Atlantic Detroit Diesel-Allison, LLC; *U.S. Private*, pg. 373
ATLAS ASIA PACIFIC INCORPORATED; *U.S. Private*, pg. 375
ATLAS OIL COMPANY—See Simon Holdings LLC; *U.S. Private*, pg. 3666
AUSTRALASIAN LUBRICANTS MANUFACTURING COMPANY PTY LTD—See Ampol Limited; *Int'l*, pg. 436
AUTORE OIL & PROPANE COMPANY; *U.S. Private*, pg. 401
AVALON PETROLEUM COMPANY; *U.S. Private*, pg. 403
AVCENTER INC.; *U.S. Private*, pg. 404
AVFUEL CORPORATION; *U.S. Private*, pg. 406
BARKMAN OIL CO. INC.; *U.S. Private*, pg. 475
BARRICK ENTERPRISES INC.—See USPP-Tri Lakes, LLC; *U.S. Private*, pg. 4323
BARRIER MOTOR FUELS INC.; *U.S. Private*, pg. 480
BARROWS COAL CO. INC.; *U.S. Private*, pg. 481
BATTENFELD GREASE (CANADA) LTD.—See Battenfeld Management Inc.; *U.S. Private*, pg. 488
BAY AREA OIL SUPPLY INC.; *U.S. Private*, pg. 492
BAY OIL COMPANY INC.; *U.S. Private*, pg. 494
B-B-F OIL COMPANY INC.; *U.S. Private*, pg. 419
BECO PETROLEUM PRODUCTS PLC.; *Int'l*, pg. 938
BEDFORD VALLEY PETROLEUM CORP; *U.S. Private*, pg. 512
BE FUELCARDS LTD.—See Edenred S.A.; *Int'l*, pg. 2307
BELASCO PETROLEUM CO. INC.; *U.S. Private*, pg. 516
BELL FUELS INC.; *U.S. Private*, pg. 518
BELLMAN OIL CO. INC.; *U.S. Private*, pg. 520
BENNETT EUBANKS OIL COMPANY; *U.S. Private*, pg. 527
BERGEN ENERGI FRANCE SARL—See World Kinect Corporation; *U.S. Public*, pg. 2380
BERGEN ENERGI NEDERLAND BV—See World Kinect Corporation; *U.S. Public*, pg. 2380
BERGEN ENERGI PORTEFOLJE AS—See World Kinect Corporation; *U.S. Public*, pg. 2380
BEST-WADE—See Litco Petroleum Inc.; *U.S. Private*, pg. 2467
BIGLER, LP; *U.S. Private*, pg. 555
BIG RIVER OIL COMPANY INC.; *U.S. Private*, pg. 554
BILL L. DOVER INC.; *U.S. Private*, pg. 557
BIOURJA TRADING, LLC; *U.S. Private*, pg. 563
BI-STATE PROPANE INC.—See UGI Corporation; *U.S. Public*, pg. 2221
BLODGETT OIL COMPANY, INC.; *U.S. Private*, pg. 583
BLUE RIDGE ENERGIES, INC.—See Blue Ridge Electric Membership Corporation; *U.S. Private*, pg. 591
BLUE SUN BIODIESEL; *U.S. Private*, pg. 593
BLYTHEWOOD OIL CO. INC.; *U.S. Private*, pg. 600
BOOTH WALTZ ENTERPRISES, INC.; *U.S. Private*, pg. 617
BOSSELMAN ENERGY INC.; *U.S. Private*, pg. 620
BOUCHER AND JONES FUELS; *Int'l*, pg. 1119
BOYETT PETROLEUM; *U.S. Private*, pg. 628
BP ALGERIA—See BP plc; *Int'l*, pg. 1126
BP ASIA PACIFIC (MALAYSIA)—See BP plc; *Int'l*, pg. 1128
BP AUSTRALIA PTY. LTD.—See BP plc; *Int'l*, pg. 1128
BP AUSTRIA AKTIENGESELLSCHAFT—See BP plc; *Int'l*, pg. 1128
BP DANMARK A/S—See BP plc; *Int'l*, pg. 1128
BP ENERGY DO BRAZIL LTDA—See BP plc; *Int'l*, pg. 1130
BP ENERGY MARKETING B.V.—See BP plc; *Int'l*, pg. 1129
BP EUROPA SE ODDZIAL W POLSCE—See BP plc; *Int'l*, pg. 1128
BP EUROPA SE—See BP plc; *Int'l*, pg. 1131
BP EUROPA SE ZWEIGNIEDERLASSUNG BP AUSTRIA AG—See BP plc; *Int'l*, pg. 1128
BP FUELS & LUBRICANTS—See BP plc; *Int'l*, pg. 1130
BP GLOBAL INVESTMENT SALALAH & CO LLC—See BP plc; *Int'l*, pg. 1129
BP HONG KONG LIMITED—See BP plc; *Int'l*, pg. 1129
BP HUNGARY LTD—See BP plc; *Int'l*, pg. 1129
BP JAPAN KK—See BP plc; *Int'l*, pg. 1129
BP KOREA LTD.—See BP plc; *Int'l*, pg. 1130
BP KOREA MARKETING LTD—See BP plc; *Int'l*, pg. 1130
BP KUWAIT LIMITED—See BP plc; *Int'l*, pg. 1129
BP LUBRICANTS A/S—See BP plc; *Int'l*, pg. 1128
BP MAGYARORSZAG KFT—See BP plc; *Int'l*, pg. 1129
BP MALAWI LIMITED—See BP plc; *Int'l*, pg. 1129
BP MARINE LIMITED—See BP plc; *Int'l*, pg. 1129
BP MARINE—See BP plc; *Int'l*, pg. 1129
BP MARKETING EGYPT LTD—See BP plc; *Int'l*, pg. 1128
BP MOZAMBIQUE LIMITED—See BP plc; *Int'l*, pg. 1129
BP NEDERLAND B.V.—See BP plc; *Int'l*, pg. 1129
BP OIL ESPANA S.A.—See BP plc; *Int'l*, pg. 1128
BP OIL HELLENIC SA—See BP plc; *Int'l*, pg. 1129
BP OIL NEW ZEALAND LIMITED—See BP plc; *Int'l*, pg. 1129
BP OIL SUPPLY COMPANY INC.—See BP plc; *Int'l*, pg. 1128
BP OIL SUPPLY COMPANY INC.—See BP plc; *Int'l*, pg. 1128
BP PETROCHINA JIANGMEN FUELS CO. LTD.—See BP plc; *Int'l*, pg. 1129
BP PETROCHINA JIANGMEN FUELS CO. LTD.—See China National Petroleum Corporation; *Int'l*, pg. 1533
BP POLSKA SP. Z O.O.—See BP plc; *Int'l*, pg. 1129
BP PRODUCTS NORTH AMERICA INC.—See BP plc; *Int'l*, pg. 1127
BP PRODUCTS NORTH AMERICA INC.—See BP plc; *Int'l*, pg. 1127
BP PRODUCTS NORTH AMERICA INC.—See BP plc; *Int'l*, pg. 1127
BP SCHMIERSTOFFE GMBH NFG. OHG—See BP plc; *Int'l*, pg. 1128
BP SHANGHAI TRADING CO. LTD.—See BP plc; *Int'l*, pg. 1129
BP SINGAPORE PTE. LIMITED—See BP plc; *Int'l*, pg. 1129
BP SOUTHERN AFRICA (PTY). LTD.—See BP plc; *Int'l*, pg. 1130
BP SOUTH-WEST PACIFIC LIMITED—See BP plc; *Int'l*, pg. 1129
BP SWAZILAND (PTY) LIMITED—See BP plc; *Int'l*, pg. 1129
BP SWITZERLAND—See BP plc; *Int'l*, pg. 1130
BP TANZANIA LIMITED—See BP plc; *Int'l*, pg. 1130
BRADFORD OIL COMPANY, INC.; *U.S. Private*, pg. 631
BRENCO MARKETING CORP; *U.S. Private*, pg. 645
BREWER-HENDLEY OIL CO; *U.S. Private*, pg. 647
BROADUS OIL CORP. OF ILLINOIS; *U.S. Private*, pg. 659
BRUCETON PETROLEUM CO. INC.—See Bruceton Farm Service, Inc.; *U.S. Private*, pg. 671
BUMGARNER OIL CO. INC.; *U.S. Private*, pg. 685
BURKE OIL CO., INC.; *U.S. Private*, pg. 688
BUTAGAZ SAS—See DCC plc; *Int'l*, pg. 1989
CALPAM MINERALOL GMBH—See Financiere de L'Odet; *Int'l*, pg. 2667
CALTEX PETROLEUM SERVICES PTY LTD—See Ampol Limited; *Int'l*, pg. 436
CAMBECK PETROLEUM CORP.; *U.S. Private*, pg. 725
CAMPBELL & SONS OIL COMPANY, INC.; *U.S. Private*, pg. 730
CAMPORA WHOLESALE PROPANE—See Campora Inc.; *U.S. Private*, pg. 731
CANYON STATE OIL COMPANY INC.—See Southern Counties Oil Co.; *U.S. Private*, pg. 3730
CAROLINA OIL CO. OF CONCORD; *U.S. Private*, pg. 768
CARROLL INDEPENDENT FUEL COMPANY; *U.S. Private*, pg. 773
CARSON OIL COMPANY; *U.S. Private*, pg. 774
CASE 'N DRUM OIL LP; *Int'l*, pg. 1351
CASEY CO.; *U.S. Private*, pg. 782
CASTROL AUSTRALIA PTY. LTD.—See BP plc; *Int'l*, pg. 1130
CASTROL AUSTRIA GMBH—See BP plc; *Int'l*, pg. 1130
CASTROL BRASIL LIMITADA—See BP plc; *Int'l*, pg. 1130
CASTROL CHILE SA—See BP plc; *Int'l*, pg. 1130
CASTROL COLOMBIA LIMITADA—See BP plc; *Int'l*, pg. 1130
CASTROL FRANCE SA—See BP plc; *Int'l*, pg. 1130
CASTROL HELLAS S.A.—See BP plc; *Int'l*, pg. 1130
CASTROL HUNGARY LTD—See BP plc; *Int'l*, pg. 1130
CASTROL INDUSTRIA—See BP plc; *Int'l*, pg. 1130
CASTROL INDUSTRIE SCHWITZERLAND—See BP plc; *Int'l*, pg. 1130
CASTROL IRELAND LTD.—See BP plc; *Int'l*, pg. 1130
CASTROL K.K.—See BP plc; *Int'l*, pg. 1130
CASTROL (MALAYSIA) SDN. BHD.—See BP plc; *Int'l*, pg. 1130
CASTROL NEDERLAND B.V.—See BP plc; *Int'l*, pg. 1130
CASTROL NZ LTD.—See BP plc; *Int'l*, pg. 1130
CASTROL PHILIPPINES, INC.—See BP plc; *Int'l*, pg. 1130
CASTROL SINGAPORE PTE. LTD.—See BP plc; *Int'l*, pg. 1130
CASTROL SLOVENSKO, S.R.O.—See BP plc; *Int'l*, pg. 1131
CENEX ZIP TRIP—See CHS INC.; *U.S. Public*, pg. 492
CENTER INDEPENDENT OIL COMPANY; *U.S. Private*, pg. 811
CENTREX EUROPE ENERGY & GAS AG—See Gazprombank JSC; *Int'l*, pg. 2892
CHAMBLISS LIMITED; *U.S. Private*, pg. 846
CHAMPION OIL COMPANY INC.—See Star Group, L.P.; *U.S. Public*, pg. 1937
CHAMPLAIN OIL CO. INC.; *U.S. Private*, pg. 847
CHAPP & BUSHEY OIL COMPANY; *U.S. Private*, pg. 850
CHARLES R. EVANS OIL CO. INC.; *U.S. Private*, pg. 853
CHARLOTTESVILLE OIL CO. INC.; *U.S. Private*, pg. 858
CHARM CO., LTD.—See ASKUL Corporation; *Int'l*, pg. 625
CHEMCHINA (SINGAPORE) PTE. LTD—See China National Chemical Corporation; *Int'l*, pg. 1526
CHEMCOLOR-BETA D.D.—See BP plc; *Int'l*, pg. 1131
CHESAPEAKE ENERGY MARKETING, LLC—See Expand Energy Corporation; *U.S. Public*, pg. 808
CICA SA—See Financiere de L'Odet; *Int'l*, pg. 2667
CIRCLE LUBRICANTS INC.—See AIP, LLC; *U.S. Private*, pg. 136
CITATION CRUDE MARKETING, INC.—See Citation Oil & Gas Corp.; *U.S. Private*, pg. 901
C&K PETROLEUM PRODUCTS; *U.S. Private*, pg. 703
CLEVELAND CAPITAL HOLDINGS, INC.; *U.S. Private*, pg. 940
CLINE ENERGY INC.; *U.S. Private*, pg. 943
C.N. BROWN COMPANY INC.; *U.S. Private*, pg. 708
CNOOC ENERGY TECHNOLOGY & SERVICES LTD.—See China National Offshore Oil Corp.; *Int'l*, pg. 1532
COEN OIL COMPANY; *U.S. Private*, pg. 960
COLES ENERGY INC.; *U.S. Private*, pg. 967
COLES PETROLEUM PRODUCTS INC.; *U.S. Private*, pg. 967
COLONIAL CARIBBEAN, INC.—See Colonial Group, Inc.; *U.S. Private*, pg. 971
COLORADO PETROLEUM PRODUCTS CO.; *U.S. Private*, pg. 974
COLVILLE INC.; *U.S. Private*, pg. 979
COMBINED OIL CO.—See U.S. Venture, Inc.; *U.S. Private*, pg. 4272
COMERCIO DE COMBUSTIVEIS E LUBRIFICANTES S.A.—See BP plc; *Int'l*, pg. 1131
COMMA OIL & CHEMICALS LIMITED—See Cosan S.A.; *Int'l*, pg. 1809
COMMUNITY CO-OPS OF LAKE PARK; *U.S. Private*, pg. 991
COMO LUBE & SUPPLIES, INC.; *U.S. Private*, pg. 998
COMO OIL COMPANY OF FLORIDA—See Palmdale Oil Company, Inc.; *U.S. Private*, pg. 3080
COMO OIL & PROPANE—See Interstate Energy LLC; *U.S. Private*, pg. 2124
COMPANIA DE PETROLEOS DE CHILE COPEC S.A.—See AntarChile S.A.; *Int'l*, pg. 481
COMPANIA OPERADORA DE GAS DEL AMAZONAS, S.A.C.—See Enagas, S.A.; *Int'l*, pg. 2396
CONCEPT PETROLEUM, INC.—See Morgan Stanley; *U.S. Public*, pg. 1471
CONCERN GALNAFTOGAS PJSC; *Int'l*, pg. 1764
CONCORD OIL COMPANY INC.—See Energy North Incorporated; *U.S. Private*, pg. 1395
CONCORD OIL OF NEWPORT INC.—See Energy North Incorporated; *U.S. Private*, pg. 1395
CONOCO SPECIALTY PRODUCTS LTD.—See Berkshire Hathaway Inc.; *U.S. Public*, pg. 308
CONOIL PLC.; *Int'l*, pg. 1769
CONSOLIDATED FUEL OIL COMPANY; *U.S. Private*, pg. 1020
CONSOLIDATED MIDWEST, INC.; *U.S. Private*, pg. 1021
CONSUMERS' CO-OPERATIVE REFINERIES LIMITED—See Federated Co-operatives Limited; *Int'l*, pg. 2630
COPELAND OIL & GAS CO. OF MBL; *U.S. Private*, pg. 1044
CORNWALL RESOURCES, INC.; *U.S. Public*, pg. 579
COSBY OIL COMPANY, INC.; *U.S. Private*, pg. 1061
COSMO BUSINESS ASSOCIATES CO., LTD.—See Cosmo Energy Holdings Co., Ltd.; *Int'l*, pg. 1811
COSMO ENERGY SOLUTIONS CO., LTD.—See Cosmo

424720 — PETROLEUM AND PETRO...

Energy Holdings Co., Ltd.; *Int'l*, pg. 1811
COSMO OIL PROPERTY SERVICE CO., LTD.—See Cosmo Energy Holdings Co., Ltd.; *Int'l*, pg. 1812
COUNTRYMARK COOPERATIVE, INC.; *U.S. Private*, pg. 1067
COVICH & WILLIAMS CO. INC.; *U.S. Private*, pg. 1072
COX OIL COMPANY; *U.S. Private*, pg. 1078
CRADDOCK OIL CO. INC.; *U.S. Private*, pg. 1081
C&R DISTRIBUTING INC.—See Nevada Trio Inc.; *U.S. Private*, pg. 2891
C. RENNER PETROLEUM; *U.S. Private*, pg. 705
CRESTWOOD CRUDE SERVICES LLC—See Crestwood Equity Partners LP; *U.S. Public*, pg. 594
CROSSAMERICA PARTNERS LP; *U.S. Public*, pg. 596
CROSS OIL COMPANY INC.; *U.S. Private*, pg. 1105
CROSSROAD FUEL SERVICE INC.; *U.S. Private*, pg. 1107
CRYSTAL FLASH ENERGY—See Heritage Group; *U.S. Private*, pg. 1923
C&S INC.; *U.S. Private*, pg. 703
CUNNINGHAM BUTANE GAS COMPANY; *U.S. Private*, pg. 1123
CURTIS OIL CO. INC.; *U.S. Private*, pg. 1126
DAIMARU ENAWIN CO., LTD.; *Int'l*, pg. 1938
DALOL OIL SHARE COMPANY; *Int'l*, pg. 1955
DAL-TEX CONSULTING, LLC—See Energy Transfer LP; *U.S. Public*, pg. 762
DANDY OIL CO. INC.; *U.S. Private*, pg. 1153
DANIELSON OIL COMPANY OF OKLAHOMA; *U.S. Private*, pg. 1156
DASSELS PETROLEUM INC.—See EDPO, LLC; *U.S. Private*, pg. 1338
D.A. STUART S.A—See Hinduja Group Ltd.; *Int'l*, pg. 3398
DAVIS COMPANY INC.; *U.S. Private*, pg. 1173
DAVISON OIL COMPANY INC.; *U.S. Private*, pg. 1175
DCC ENERGY LIMITED—See DCC plc; *Int'l*, pg. 1989
DCC PROPANE LLC—See DCC plc; *Int'l*, pg. 1990
DC OIL CO INC.—See The Kent Companies; *U.S. Private*, pg. 4065
D&D OIL CO. INC.; *U.S. Private*, pg. 1137
DEAD RIVER PETROLEUM CO.—See Dead River Company; *U.S. Private*, pg. 1182
DEAD RIVER TRANSPORT—See Dead River Company; *U.S. Private*, pg. 1182
DEARYBURY OIL & GAS INC.; *U.S. Private*, pg. 1185
DELEK MARKETING-BIG SANDY, LLC—See Delek Group Ltd.; *Int'l*, pg. 2011
DELEK PETROLEUM LTD.—See Delek Group Ltd.; *Int'l*, pg. 2011
DELTA WESTERN INC.—See Saltchuk Resources Inc.; *U.S. Private*, pg. 3534
DENNIS K. BURKE INC.; *U.S. Private*, pg. 1205
DENNISON LUBRICANTS; *U.S. Private*, pg. 1205
DENSON OIL COMPANY, INC.; *U.S. Private*, pg. 1206
DEUTSCHE CALPAM GMBH—See Financiere de L'Odet; *Int'l*, pg. 2667
DEUTSCHE CASTROL VERTRIEBSGESELLSCHAFT MBH—See BP plc; *Int'l*, pg. 1131
DIAMOND PROPANE, INC.—See Ferrellgas Partners, L.P.; *U.S. Public*, pg. 829
DIERMEIER ENERGIE GMBH—See BayWa AG; *Int'l*, pg. 917
DIESEL 24 LIMITED—See Edenred S.A.; *Int'l*, pg. 2307
DIFCO, INC.—See LTL Holdings, Inc.; *U.S. Private*, pg. 2509
DILMAR OIL COMPANY INC. - ATLANTA PLANT—See Dilmar Oil Company Inc.; *U.S. Private*, pg. 1232
DILMAR OIL COMPANY INC. - CHARLESTON PLANT—See Dilmar Oil Company Inc.; *U.S. Private*, pg. 1232
DILMAR OIL COMPANY INC. - CHARLOTTE PLANT—See Dilmar Oil Company Inc.; *U.S. Private*, pg. 1232
DILMAR OIL COMPANY INC. - COLUMBIA PLANT—See Dilmar Oil Company Inc.; *U.S. Private*, pg. 1232
DILMAR OIL COMPANY INC. - HENDERSON PLANT—See Dilmar Oil Company Inc.; *U.S. Private*, pg. 1232
DILMAR OIL COMPANY INC. - LATTA PLANT—See Dilmar Oil Company Inc.; *U.S. Private*, pg. 1232
DILMAR OIL COMPANY INC. - WILMINGTON PLANT—See Dilmar Oil Company Inc.; *U.S. Private*, pg. 1232
DIRECT FUELS LLC—See Sunoco LP; *U.S. Public*, pg. 1965
DITMAS OIL ASSOCIATES INC.—See Gaseteria Oil Corp.; *U.S. Private*, pg. 1648
DIXIE OIL COMPANY; *U.S. Private*, pg. 1245
DMF INC.; *U.S. Private*, pg. 1248
DOOLEY OIL INC.; *U.S. Private*, pg. 1261
DOOLITTLE OIL CO. INC.; *U.S. Private*, pg. 1261
DUNCAN OIL COMPANY; *U.S. Private*, pg. 1287
DUNNE MANNING INC.; *U.S. Private*, pg. 1290
DUTCH OIL COMPANY INC.; *U.S. Private*, pg. 1294
DYNEFF ESPAGNE SL—See AnAn International Limited; *Int'l*, pg. 446
DYNEFF SAS.—See AnAn International Limited; *Int'l*, pg. 446
DYNO OIL CO. INC.; *U.S. Private*, pg. 1300
E1 CORPORATION; *Int'l*, pg. 2260
EARHART PETROLEUM INC.; *U.S. Private*, pg. 1306
EASTERN MARKETING CORPORATION—See Energy Corporation of America; *U.S. Private*, pg. 1394

EASTERN OIL COMPANY; *U.S. Private*, pg. 1320
EASTERN SIERRA PROPANE—See Ferrellgas Partners, L.P.; *U.S. Public*, pg. 829
ECHOLS OIL COMPANY; *U.S. Private*, pg. 1327
EDENRED CORPORATE PAYMENT SAS—See Edenred S.A.; *Int'l*, pg. 2307
EDPO, LLC; *U.S. Private*, pg. 1338
ED STAUB & SONS PETROLEUM INC.; *U.S. Private*, pg. 1332
EKO ABEE—See HELLENiQ ENERGY Holdings S.A.; *Int'l*, pg. 3334
EKO BULGARIA EAD—See HELLENiQ ENERGY Holdings S.A.; *Int'l*, pg. 3334
EKO GEORGIA LTD—See HELLENiQ ENERGY Holdings S.A.; *Int'l*, pg. 3334
EKO YU AD—See HELLENiQ ENERGY Holdings S.A.; *Int'l*, pg. 3334
ELINOIL S.A.; *Int'l*, pg. 2361
EL.P.ET BALKANIKI S.A.—See HELLENiQ ENERGY Holdings S.A.; *Int'l*, pg. 3334
ELTM, L.P.—See Enbridge Inc.; *Int'l*, pg. 2397
E.M. GRAY & SON INC.; *U.S. Private*, pg. 1306
EMIRATES NATIONAL OIL COMPANY SINGAPORE PTE LTD—See Emirates National Oil Company Limited; *Int'l*, pg. 2381
EMPIRE GAS COMPANY INC.; *U.S. Private*, pg. 1385
EMPIRE OIL CO.—See Marathon Petroleum Corporation; *U.S. Public*, pg. 1363
EMPRESAS COPEC S.A.—See AntarChile S.A.; *Int'l*, pg. 481
ENCHI CORPORATION—See Marathon Petroleum Corporation; *U.S. Public*, pg. 1364
ENEOS FRONTIER COMPANY, LIMITED—See ENEOS Holdings, Inc.; *Int'l*, pg. 2417
ENEOS GLOBE CORPORATION—See ENEOS Holdings, Inc.; *Int'l*, pg. 2415
ENEOS WING CORPORATION—See ENEOS Holdings, Inc.; *Int'l*, pg. 2415
ENERGIE DIRECT MINERALOLHANDELSGESMBH—See DCC plc; *Int'l*, pg. 1990
ENERGY ALLIANCE TECHNOLOGY CORP.; *U.S. Private*, pg. 1393
ENERGY INTERNATIONAL FOR PETROLEUM PROJECTS KCSC—See Fouad Alghanim & Sons Group of Companies; *Int'l*, pg. 2753
ENESSANCE HOLDINGS CO., LTD.—See Idemitsu Kosan Co., Ltd.; *Int'l*, pg. 3590
ENI SUISSE S.A.—See Eni S.p.A.; *Int'l*, pg. 2437
ENI TRADING & SHIPPING INC—See Eni S.p.A.; *Int'l*, pg. 2438
ENKOR D.O.O.—See BP plc; *Int'l*, pg. 1131
E.ON BIOFOR SVERIGE AB—See E.ON SE; *Int'l*, pg. 2255
EPIC AVIATION, LLC—See BlackRock, Inc.; *U.S. Public*, pg. 346
EPIC AVIATION, LLC—See Blackstone Inc.; *U.S. Public*, pg. 358
EPIC AVIATION, LLC—See Cascade Investment LLC; *U.S. Private*, pg. 780
ERGON EUROPE MEA, INC.—See Ergon, Inc.; *U.S. Private*, pg. 1418
ERGON OIL PURCHASING, INC.—See Ergon, Inc.; *U.S. Private*, pg. 1418
ERGON-ST. JAMES, INC.—See Ergon, Inc.; *U.S. Private*, pg. 1418
ERIE PETROLEUM—See Reid Petroleum Corp.; *U.S. Private*, pg. 3391
ESSO NORGE AS—See Exxon Mobil Corporation; *U.S. Public*, pg. 814
E.S. THE THIRD INC.; *U.S. Private*, pg. 1307
EXEC AIR MONTANA, INC.—See Leading Edge Aviation, Inc.; *U.S. Private*, pg. 2406
EXXONMOBIL AUSTRALIA PTY LTD—See Exxon Mobil Corporation; *U.S. Public*, pg. 814
EXXONMOBIL EGYPT (S.A.E.)—See Exxon Mobil Corporation; *U.S. Public*, pg. 815
EXXONMOBIL FUELS & MARKETING—See Exxon Mobil Corporation; *U.S. Public*, pg. 815
EXXONMOBIL HONG KONG LIMITED—See Exxon Mobil Corporation; *U.S. Public*, pg. 815
EXXONMOBIL LUBRICANTS & PETROLEUM SPECIALTIES—See Exxon Mobil Corporation; *U.S. Public*, pg. 815
EYELLO CZ K.S.—See EnBW Energie Baden-Wurttemberg AG; *Int'l*, pg. 2401
EZ FUEL & TANK SOLUTIONS; *U.S. Private*, pg. 1454
F8 ENTERPRISES (HOLDINGS) GROUP LIMITED; *Int'l*, pg. 2598
FAL ENERGY CO., LTD.—See FAL Group of Companies; *Int'l*, pg. 2610
FANNON PETROLEUM SERVICES INC.; *U.S. Private*, pg. 1472
FARMERS MERCHANTS COOP OIL CO.; *U.S. Private*, pg. 1478
FARMERS UNION OIL BISMARCK/MANDAN; *U.S. Private*, pg. 1479
FARMERS UNION OIL COMPANY OF KENMARE; *U.S. Private*, pg. 1479
FARMERS UNION OIL MOORHEAD; *U.S. Private*, pg. 1479

CORPORATE AFFILIATIONS

FEECE OIL COMPANY; *U.S. Private*, pg. 1492
FLAMINGO OIL COMPANY; *U.S. Private*, pg. 1540
FLEET CARD FUELS INC.; *U.S. Private*, pg. 1541
FLEETCOR CZECH REPUBLIC SRO—See Corpay, Inc.; *U.S. Public*, pg. 579
FLEETCOR FUEL CARDS (EUROPE) LIMITED—See Corpay, Inc.; *U.S. Public*, pg. 580
FLEETCOR POLAND SPOEKA Z OGRANICZONA ODPOWIEDZIALNOSCIA—See Corpay, Inc.; *U.S. Public*, pg. 580
FLEETCOR SLOVAKIA S.R.O.—See Corpay, Inc.; *U.S. Public*, pg. 580
FLEETWING CORPORATION; *U.S. Private*, pg. 1542
FLORIDA KEYS FOOD STORES, INC.—See John R. McKenzie Jobber, Inc.; *U.S. Private*, pg. 2223
FLOYD ENERGY INC.; *U.S. Private*, pg. 1552
FLP HOLDINGS INC.; *U.S. Private*, pg. 1552
FLYERS ENERGY, LLC; *U.S. Private*, pg. 1553
FORMOSA OIL (ASIA PACIFIC) CORPORATION—See Formosa Petrochemical Corporation; *Int'l*, pg. 2735
FOSTER BLUE WATER OIL, LLC; *U.S. Private*, pg. 1578
FOSTER FUELS INC.; *U.S. Private*, pg. 1578
FRANGER GAS CO. INC.; *U.S. Private*, pg. 1593
FRED GARRISON OIL COMPANY; *U.S. Private*, pg. 1601
FREE ENTERPRISES INC.; *U.S. Private*, pg. 1602
FROESEL OIL COMPANY INC.—See Cross Oil Company Inc.; *U.S. Private*, pg. 1105
FRONK OIL CO. INC.; *U.S. Private*, pg. 1613
FTI CONSULTING DENMARK APS—See FTI Consulting, Inc.; *U.S. Public*, pg. 890
FUCHS LUBRICANTS (THAILAND) CO., LTD.—See FUCHS SE; *Int'l*, pg. 2803
FUCHS MAK DOOEL—See FUCHS SE; *Int'l*, pg. 2802
FUCHS PETROLUBE (MALAYSIA) SDN. BHD.—See FUCHS SE; *Int'l*, pg. 2803
THE FUELCARD COMPANY UK LTD.—See Corpay, Inc.; *U.S. Public*, pg. 580
FUEL CONTROLS INC.; *U.S. Private*, pg. 1619
FUEL MANAGEMENT SYSTEM—See Van Manen Petroleum Group; *U.S. Private*, pg. 4340
FUEL MANAGERS INC.; *U.S. Private*, pg. 1619
FUELS & SUPPLIES INC.; *U.S. Private*, pg. 1619
GALLAHAN OIL COMPANY INC.; *U.S. Private*, pg. 1639
GALP ACORES - DISTRIB. E COMERCIALIZACAO DE COMBUSTIVEIS E LUBRIFICANTES, S.A.—See Galp Energia SGPS, S.A.; *Int'l*, pg. 2875
GALP COMERCIALIZACAO PORTUGAL, LDA.—See Galp Energia SGPS, S.A.; *Int'l*, pg. 2875
GALP DISTRIBUICION OIL ESPANA, S.A.U.—See Galp Energia SGPS, S.A.; *Int'l*, pg. 2875
GALP ENERGIA ESPANA SAU—See Galp Energia SGPS, S.A.; *Int'l*, pg. 2875
GARY V. BURROWS INC.; *U.S. Private*, pg. 1646
GASBOTTLING N.V.—See UGI Corporation; *U.S. Public*, pg. 2222
GASINSULAR - COMBUSTIVEIS DO ATLANTICO, S.A.—See Galp Energia SGPS, S.A.; *Int'l*, pg. 2875
GAS LAND PETROLEUM INC.; *U.S. Private*, pg. 1647
GATEONE, INC.; *U.S. Private*, pg. 1649
GAUBERT OIL COMPANY INCORPORATED; *U.S. Private*, pg. 1651
GEER TANK TRUCKS INC.—See One Cypress Energy LLC; *U.S. Private*, pg. 3020
GENERAL PETROLEUM INCORPORATED; *U.S. Private*, pg. 1666
GENOL GESELLSCHAFT M.B.H. & CO. KG—See BayWa AG; *Int'l*, pg. 919
GEORGE C. STAFFORD & SONS INC.; *U.S. Private*, pg. 1681
GEORGE H. BLOUCH FUEL SERVICE; *U.S. Private*, pg. 1682
GEORGE W. LOWRY INC.; *U.S. Private*, pg. 1683
GERALDTON FUEL COMPANY PTY LTD—See Ampol Limited; *Int'l*, pg. 436
G. H. BERLIN-WINDWARD—See Booth Waltz Enterprises, Inc.; *U.S. Private*, pg. 617
GIANT OIL INC.; *U.S. Private*, pg. 1695
GIBB GROUP LTD.—See Clarkson PLC; *Int'l*, pg. 1651
GIB OIL (UK) LIMITED—See World Kinect Corporation; *U.S. Public*, pg. 2380
GIBSON ENERGY MARKETING, LLC—See Gibson Energy Inc.; *Int'l*, pg. 2963
GIBSON OIL CO.; *U.S. Private*, pg. 1696
GIER OIL CO. INC.; *U.S. Private*, pg. 1697
GINGA PETROLEUM (SINGAPORE) PTE LTD—See BGC Group, Inc.; *U.S. Public*, pg. 329
GLABARCO LEADER GROUP INC.—See Danaher Corporation; *U.S. Public*, pg. 627
GLASSMERE FUEL SERVICE INC.; *U.S. Private*, pg. 1707
GLENN DISTRIBUTOR INC.; *U.S. Private*, pg. 1710
GLOBAL PETROLEUM ALBANIA SH.A.—See HELLENiQ ENERGY Holdings S.A.; *Int'l*, pg. 3334
GLOBAL PROCESSING COMPANIES RUS, LIMITED LIABILITY COMPANY—See Corpay, Inc.; *U.S. Public*, pg. 580
GLOCKNER CHEVROLET CO., INC.; *U.S. Private*, pg. 1720
GLOCKNER OIL COMPANY INC.—See Glockner Chevrolet Co. Inc.; *U.S. Private*, pg. 1720

424720 — PETROLEUM AND PETRO...

N.A.I.C.S. INDEX

GOETZ ENERGY CORPORATION; *U.S. Private*, pg. 1726
GOIL PLC; *Int'l*, pg. 3022
GOLDEN GATE PETROLEUM CO.; *U.S. Private*, pg. 1732
GOLDENWEST LUBRICANTS, INC.; *U.S. Private*, pg. 1734
GPM PETROLEUM LP—See Haymaker Acquisition Corp.; *U.S. Private*, pg. 1885
GRAHAM C- STORES COMPANY; *U.S. Private*, pg. 1751
GRAHAM ENTERPRISE INC.; *U.S. Private*, pg. 1751
GRAND POWER (2019) CO., LTD.—See Asia Green Energy Public Company Limited; *Int'l*, pg. 612
GREAT GAS PETROLEUM (IRELAND) LIMITED—See DCC plc; *Int'l*, pg. 1991
GREENEVILLE OIL & PETROLEUM INC.; *U.S. Private*, pg. 1777
GROENEVELD LUBRICATION SOLUTIONS INC.—See The Timken Company; *U.S. Public*, pg. 2132
GROENEVELD LUBRICATION SOLUTIONS INC.—See The Timken Company; *U.S. Public*, pg. 2132
GROENEVELD LUBRICATION SOLUTIONS LIMITED—See The Timken Company; *U.S. Public*, pg. 2132
GROENEVELD LUBRICATION SOLUTIONS LTD.—See The Timken Company; *U.S. Public*, pg. 2132
GROENEVELD LUBRICATION SOLUTIONS PTY LTD.—See The Timken Company; *U.S. Public*, pg. 2132
GROENEVELD LUBRICATION SOLUTIONS S.R.L.—See The Timken Company; *U.S. Public*, pg. 2132
GROENEVELD POLSKA SP Z.O.O.—See The Timken Company; *U.S. Public*, pg. 2132
GRUNES GMBH—See EnBW Energie Baden-Wurttemberg AG; *Int'l*, pg. 2401
G&S SERVICES COMPANY; *U.S. Private*, pg. 1629
GULF LUBRICANTS UK LTD—See Hinduja Group Ltd.; *Int'l*, pg. 3398
GULF OIL INTERNATIONAL LTD.—See Hinduja Group Ltd.; *Int'l*, pg. 3398
GULF OIL NEDERLAND B.V.—See Hinduja Group Ltd.; *Int'l*, pg. 3399
GULF RAK OIL LLC—See Hinduja Group Ltd.; *Int'l*, pg. 3399
GULL NEW ZEALAND LTD.—See Ampol Limited; *Int'l*, pg. 436
HACKNEY PETROLEUM, INC.—See The H.T. Hackney Company; *U.S. Private*, pg. 4041
HALCO INDUSTRIES, LLC; *U.S. Private*, pg. 1841
HALRON LUBRICANTS INC.; *U.S. Private*, pg. 1846
H. A. MAPES, INC.—See Nouria Energy Corp.; *U.S. Private*, pg. 2965
HARMS OIL COMPANY; *U.S. Private*, pg. 1866
HARNOIS GROUPE PETROLIER INC.; *Int'l*, pg. 3278
HARPER INDUSTRIES INC.; *U.S. Private*, pg. 1867
HARPER OIL PRODUCTS INC.; *U.S. Private*, pg. 1867
HARRIS OIL COMPANY INC.—See Heartland, Inc.; *U.S. Private*, pg. 1901
HARRISON OIL & TIRE CO.; *U.S. Private*, pg. 1870
HARTFORD-WOOD RIVER TERMINAL LLC—See Piasa Motor Fuels LLC; *U.S. Private*, pg. 3175
HARTLAND FUEL PRODUCTS, LLC; *U.S. Private*, pg. 1874
HARTLEY COMPANY; *U.S. Private*, pg. 1874
HASCO OIL COMPANY, INC.; *U.S. Private*, pg. 1878
HAWAII PETROLEUM INC.; *U.S. Private*, pg. 1881
HAYES CITY CORPORATION; *U.S. Private*, pg. 1884
HEETCO INC.; *U.S. Private*, pg. 1903
HELLO FIOUL SA—See Financiere de L'Odet; *Int'l*, pg. 2667
HERITAGE PETROLEUM; *U.S. Private*, pg. 1924
HEUNGGU OIL CO., LTD.; *Int'l*, pg. 3366
HFOTCO LLC—See Energy Transfer LP; *U.S. Public*, pg. 764
HIGHLAND-EXCHANGE PETROLEUM SUPPLY CO. INC.—See Highland-Exchange Service Cooperative Inc.; *U.S. Private*, pg. 1939
HIGHTOWERS PETROLEUM COMPANY; *U.S. Private*, pg. 1941
HI-LINE COOPERATIVE INC.; *U.S. Private*, pg. 1931
THE HILLER GROUP INC.—See World Kinect Corporation; *U.S. Public*, pg. 2381
HILL PETROLEUM INC.; *U.S. Private*, pg. 1945
HILL PETROLEUM, INC.; *U.S. Private*, pg. 1945
HILL TOP OIL COMPANY INC.—See Nittany Oil Company Inc.; *U.S. Private*, pg. 2930
HITACHI HIGH-TECH NEXUS CORPORATION—See Hitachi, Ltd.; *Int'l*, pg. 3418
H.N. FUNKHOUSER & COMPANY INC.; *U.S. Private*, pg. 1835
HOCMON TRADE JOINT STOCK COMPANY; *Int'l*, pg. 3438
HOLLINGSWORTH OIL CO. INC.; *U.S. Private*, pg. 1965
HOLLINGSWORTH OIL CO.—See Hollingsworth Oil Co. Inc.; *U.S. Private*, pg. 1965
HOLLON OIL COMPANY; *U.S. Private*, pg. 1966
HOLTZMAN OIL CORP.; *U.S. Private*, pg. 1969
HOMAX OIL SALES INC.; *U.S. Private*, pg. 1970
HOME SERVICE OIL CO. INC. - DONIPHAN DIVISION—See Home Service Oil Co. Inc.; *U.S. Private*, pg. 1972
HOME SERVICE OIL CO. INC. - POPLAR BLUFF DIVISION—See Home Service Oil Co. Inc.; *U.S. Private*, pg. 1972

HOP ENERGY LLC—See Delos Capital, LLC; *U.S. Private*, pg. 1198
HORIZON RESOURCES; *U.S. Private*, pg. 1982
HOUGHTON EUROPE BV—See Hinduja Group Ltd.; *Int'l*, pg. 3399
HOUGHTON KIMYA SANAYI AS—See Hinduja Group Ltd.; *Int'l*, pg. 3399
HOUGHTON MEXICO S.A. DE C.V.—See Hinduja Group Ltd.; *Int'l*, pg. 3399
HOUGHTON ROMANIA S.R.L.—See Quaker Chemical Corporation; *U.S. Public*, pg. 1746
H&R CHEMPHARM GMBH—See H&R KGaA; *Int'l*, pg. 3193
H.R. LEWIS PETROLEUM CO.; *U.S. Private*, pg. 1835
H&R SOUTH AFRICA GMBH—See H&R KGaA; *Int'l*, pg. 3193
H&R SOUTH AFRICA (PTY) LIMITED—See H&R KGaA; *Int'l*, pg. 3193
H&R SOUTH AFRICA SALES (PTY) LIMITED—See H&R KGaA; *Int'l*, pg. 3193
H&R WAX MALAYSIA SDN. BHD.—See H&R KGaA; *Int'l*, pg. 3193
HUFFMAN OIL CO., INC.; *U.S. Private*, pg. 2003
HUNAN HESHUN PETROLEUM CO., LTD.; *Int'l*, pg. 3532
HUNG-GU OIL CO., LTD.; *Int'l*, pg. 3535
HUNTLEY OIL & GAS COMPANY; *U.S. Private*, pg. 2010
H.W. DRUMMOND INC.; *U.S. Private*, pg. 1836
HWRT OIL COMPANY, LLC.—See Piasa Motor Fuels LLC; *U.S. Private*, pg. 3175
HY-PER LUBE CORP.—See Bar's Products, Inc.; *U.S. Private*, pg. 471
IBIDEN INDUSTRIES CO., LTD.—See Ibiden Co., Ltd.; *Int'l*, pg. 3575
ICAN ENERGY CO.; *U.S. Private*, pg. 2029
IDEMITSU CHEMICALS EUROPE PLC—See Idemitsu Kosan Co., Ltd.; *Int'l*, pg. 3590
IDEMITSU INTERNATIONAL (ASIA) PTE. LTD.—See Idemitsu Kosan Co., Ltd.; *Int'l*, pg. 3591
IDEMITSU LUBE EUROPE GMBH—See Idemitsu Kosan Co., Ltd.; *Int'l*, pg. 3591
IDEMITSU LUBE INDIA PVT LTD.—See Idemitsu Kosan Co., Ltd.; *Int'l*, pg. 3591
IDEMITSU LUBE MIDDLE EAST & AFRICA FZE—See Idemitsu Kosan Co., Ltd.; *Int'l*, pg. 3591
ILS NORDIC AB—See Aspo Oyj; *Int'l*, pg. 631
IMPERIAL OIL COMPANY INC.—See Supertest Oil Company Inc.; *U.S. Private*, pg. 3881
IMPERIAL OIL LIMITED—See Exxon Mobil Corporation; *U.S. Public*, pg. 816
IMPERIAL OIL LIMITED—See Exxon Mobil Corporation; *U.S. Public*, pg. 816
IMPERIAL OIL LIMITED—See Exxon Mobil Corporation; *U.S. Public*, pg. 816
IMPERIAL OIL LIMITED—See Exxon Mobil Corporation; *U.S. Public*, pg. 816
IMTT-ILLINOIS—See Riverstone Holdings LLC; *U.S. Private*, pg. 3447
IMTT-RICHMOND-CA—See Riverstone Holdings LLC; *U.S. Private*, pg. 3447
IMTT-VIRGINIA—See Riverstone Holdings LLC; *U.S. Private*, pg. 3447
INCORR ENERGY GROUP LLC—See ARB Midstream, LLC; *U.S. Private*, pg. 308
THE INDEPENDENT OIL CORPORATION—See Molo Oil Company Inc.; *U.S. Private*, pg. 2767
INERGY GAS MARKETING, LLC—See Crestwood Equity Partners LP; *U.S. Public*, pg. 594
INTER ISLAND PETROLEUM, INC.—See Par Pacific Holdings, Inc.; *U.S. Public*, pg. 1636
INTERLUBE USA INC.—See The Timken Company; *U.S. Public*, pg. 2132
INTERSTATE FUEL SYSTEMS, INC.; *U.S. Private*, pg. 2124
INTERSTATE OIL COMPANY; *U.S. Private*, pg. 2125
INVENCO I2 LLC—See Vontier Corporation; *U.S. Public*, pg. 2309
ISGETT DISTRIBUTORS INC.; *U.S. Private*, pg. 2143
JACK A. ALLEN INC.; *U.S. Private*, pg. 2173
JACK RICH INCORPORATED; *U.S. Private*, pg. 2174
JACKSON OIL & SOLVENTS INC.; *U.S. Private*, pg. 2178
JACOBUS PETROLEUM PRODUCTS, LLC—See Jacobus Energy, Inc.; *U.S. Private*, pg. 2180
J.A.M. DISTRIBUTING COMPANY—See BRENNTAG SE; *Int'l*, pg. 1149
JAPAN GAS ENERGY CORPORATION—See ENEOS Holdings, Inc.; *Int'l*, pg. 2417
J. ARON & COMPANY (SINGAPORE) PTE.—See The Goldman Sachs Group, Inc.; *U.S. Public*, pg. 2082
JASPER OIL COMPANY; *U.S. Private*, pg. 2190
JAT OIL & SUPPLY INC.; *U.S. Private*, pg. 2191
J. CINCO, INC.; *U.S. Private*, pg. 2155
J.D. STREETT & CO., INC. - ST. LOUIS PARK PLANT—See J.D. Streett & Co., Inc.; *U.S. Private*, pg. 2161
J.D. STREETT & CO., INC. - ST. LOUIS RIVER PLANT—See J.D. Streett & Co., Inc.; *U.S. Private*, pg. 2161
JEFFRIES BROTHERS, INC.; *U.S. Private*, pg. 2198
JENKINS OIL COMPANY; *U.S. Private*, pg. 2199
THE JERRY BROWN CO, INC.; *U.S. Private*, pg. 4059

JET ENERGY TRADING GMBH—See Phillips 66 Company; *U.S. Public*, pg. 1688
JET TANKSTELLEN DEUTSCHLAND GMBH—See Phillips 66 Company; *U.S. Public*, pg. 1688
J.H. WILLIAMS OIL COMPANY INC.; *U.S. Private*, pg. 2166
J.J. GOUGE & SON OIL CO. INC.; *U.S. Private*, pg. 2167
J.J. POWELL INC.; *U.S. Private*, pg. 2167
JOHN C. BERRY & SONS INC.; *U.S. Private*, pg. 2220
JOHN R. MCKENZIE JOBBER, INC.; *U.S. Private*, pg. 2223
JOHNSON OIL CO. OF HALLOCK; *U.S. Private*, pg. 2228
JOHN T. HOWE INC.; *U.S. Private*, pg. 2225
JOHN W. STONE OIL DISTRIBUTORS LLC; *U.S. Private*, pg. 2225
JOMO RETAIL SERVICE CO., LTD.—See ENEOS Holdings, Inc.; *Int'l*, pg. 2417
JOVO ARCO ENERGY CO., LTD—See BP plc; *Int'l*, pg. 1131
J-QUEST CO., LTD.—See ENEOS Holdings, Inc.; *Int'l*, pg. 2417
JUGOPETROL AD—See HELLENIQ ENERGY Holdings S.A.; *Int'l*, pg. 3334
JV FUCHS MAST YLA UKRAINA—See FUCHS SE; *Int'l*, pg. 2804
JX NIPPON OIL & ENERGY USA INC.—See ENEOS Holdings, Inc.; *Int'l*, pg. 2417
KECK INC.; *U.S. Private*, pg. 2271
KELCO LIMITED; *U.S. Private*, pg. 2274
KENDRICK OIL CO. INC.; *U.S. Private*, pg. 2283
KES AIRPORT EQUIPMENT FUELLING B.V.—See Air France-KLM S.A.; *Int'l*, pg. 237
KIMBER PETROLEUM CORP.; *U.S. Private*, pg. 2305
KIMBRO OIL COMPANY INC.; *U.S. Private*, pg. 2305
KINECT ENERGY DENMARK A/S—See World Kinect Corporation; *U.S. Public*, pg. 2380
KINECT ENERGY GERMANY GMBH—See World Kinect Corporation; *U.S. Public*, pg. 2380
KINECT ENERGY GREEN SERVICES AS—See World Kinect Corporation; *U.S. Public*, pg. 2380
K.K. SHINYO SEKIYU—See Idemitsu Kosan Co., Ltd.; *Int'l*, pg. 3591
KLM OLIEMAATSCHAPPIJ B.V.—See Air France-KLM S.A.; *Int'l*, pg. 237
KLUBER LUBRICACION MEXICANA S.A. DE C.V.—See Freudenberg SE; *Int'l*, pg. 2785
KLUBER LUBRICATION CHILE LTDA.—See Freudenberg SE; *Int'l*, pg. 2785
KLUBER LUBRICATION CZ, S.R.O.—See Freudenberg SE; *Int'l*, pg. 2785
KLUBER LUBRICATION INDIA PVT. LTD.—See Freudenberg SE; *Int'l*, pg. 2785
KLUBER LUBRICATION (MALAYSIA) SDN. BHD.—See Freudenberg SE; *Int'l*, pg. 2785
KLUBER LUBRICATION NORDIC A/S—See Freudenberg SE; *Int'l*, pg. 2786
KLUBER LUBRICATION OOO—See Freudenberg SE; *Int'l*, pg. 2786
KLUBER LUBRICATION POLSKA SP. Z O.O.—See Freudenberg SE; *Int'l*, pg. 2786
KLUBER LUBRICATION (SHANGHAI) CO., LTD.—See Freudenberg SE; *Int'l*, pg. 2785
KOZAKURA SHOKAI CO.,LTD.—See Chori Co., Ltd.; *Int'l*, pg. 1583
KUNO OIL COMPANY INC.; *U.S. Private*, pg. 2357
KW FUELS INC.; *U.S. Private*, pg. 2359
LAIPPLE OIL INC.; *U.S. Private*, pg. 2373
LAND & SEA PETROLEUM, INC.—See RKA Petroleum Companies, LLC; *U.S. Private*, pg. 3450
LANK OIL CO. INC.; *U.S. Private*, pg. 2390
LARD OIL CO. INC.; *U.S. Private*, pg. 2391
LARD OIL COMPANY OF ACADIANA—See Lard Oil Co. Inc.; *U.S. Private*, pg. 2391
LARD OIL COMPANY—See Lard Oil Co. Inc.; *U.S. Private*, pg. 2391
LAY BROTHERS INC.; *U.S. Private*, pg. 2402
LEAKE OIL CO. INC.; *U.S. Private*, pg. 2407
LEFFERTS OIL TERMINAL INC.; *U.S. Private*, pg. 2415
LEHIGH FUELS—See Reading Anthracite Company; *U.S. Private*, pg. 3366
LEONARD E. BELCHER, INC.—See Petroleum Marketing Group Inc.; *U.S. Private*, pg. 3162
LEPIERS' INC.; *U.S. Private*, pg. 2431
L. G. JORDAN OIL CO., INC.; *U.S. Private*, pg. 2364
LICHTI BROTHERS COMPANY; *U.S. Private*, pg. 2448
LICKING VALLEY OIL CO. INC.; *U.S. Private*, pg. 2448
LINK ENERGY PTY LTD—See Ampol Limited; *Int'l*, pg. 436
LLC ALLIANCE OIL COMPANY MC—See Alliance Oil Company Ltd.; *Int'l*, pg. 340
LOCAL OIL DISTRIBUTING INC.; *U.S. Private*, pg. 2477
LONE STAR COMPANY INC.; *U.S. Private*, pg. 2484
LOTOS CZECHOWICE S.A.—See Grupa LOTOS S.A.; *Int'l*, pg. 3117
LOTOS INFRASTRUKTURA S.A.—See Grupa LOTOS S.A.; *Int'l*, pg. 3117
LOTOS PALIWA SP. Z O.O.—See Grupa LOTOS S.A.; *Int'l*, pg. 3117
LOTOS TANK SP. Z O.O.—See Grupa LOTOS S.A.; *Int'l*, pg. 3117
LOTOS TERMINALE S.A.—See Grupa LOTOS S.A.; *Int'l*, pg. 3117

424720 — PETROLEUM AND PETRO...

LPG 4 U LIMITED—See UGI Corporation; *U.S. Public*, pg. 2222
LP GAS B.V.—See DCC plc; *Int'l*, pg. 1990
LTL HOLDINGS, INC.; *U.S. Private*, pg. 2509
LUBE-TECH & PARTNERS, LLC—See Lubrication Technologies, Inc.; *U.S. Private*, pg. 2510
THE LUBRICANT COMPANY LIMITED—See World Kinect Corporation; *U.S. Public*, pg. 2381
LUBRICATION TECHNOLOGIES, INC.; *U.S. Private*, pg. 2510
LUBRICORP, LLC; *U.S. Private*, pg. 2510
LYDEN OIL COMPANY; *U.S. Private*, pg. 2519
LYKINS COMPANIES, INC.; *U.S. Private*, pg. 2519
LYKINS OIL COMPANY—See Lykins Companies, Inc.; *U.S. Private*, pg. 2520
LYKINS TRANSPORTATION—See Lykins Companies, Inc.; *U.S. Private*, pg. 2520
MAASSEN OIL COMPANY INC.—See Palmdale Oil Company, Inc.; *U.S. Private*, pg. 3080
MACRO OIL COMPANY INC.; *U.S. Private*, pg. 2538
MAHER OIL COMPANY INC.; *U.S. Private*, pg. 2550
MAJESTIC OIL CO. INC.; *U.S. Private*, pg. 2554
MANSFIELD OIL COMPANY OF GAINSVILLE, INC.—See Mansfield Energy Corp.; *U.S. Private*, pg. 2566
MARINE PETROBULK LTD.—See Washington Corporations; *U.S. Private*, pg. 4446
MARTIN COUNTY PETROLEUM & PROPANE; *U.S. Private*, pg. 2594
MARTIN EAGLE OIL COMPANY, INC.; *U.S. Private*, pg. 2594
MARTIN ENERGY SERVICES LLC—See Martin Resource Management Corporation; *U.S. Private*, pg. 2596
MARTIN PRODUCT SALES LLC—See Martin Resource Management Corporation; *U.S. Private*, pg. 2596
MARTIN RESOURCE MANAGEMENT CORPORATION; *U.S. Private*, pg. 2595
MARTIN RESOURCES, INC.—See Martin Resource Management Corporation; *U.S. Private*, pg. 2596
MASCO PETROLEUM, INC—See Bristol Bay Native Corporation; *U.S. Private*, pg. 656
MATERIAL SERVICES COMPANY, INC.—See American Airlines Group Inc.; *U.S. Public*, pg. 96
MATERIALS HANDLING SOLUTIONS LLC—See Energy Transfer LP; *U.S. Public*, pg. 764
MATSON DISTRIBUTING, INC.; *U.S. Private*, pg. 2612
MAUGER & COMPANY, INC.; *U.S. Private*, pg. 2614
MAXUM ENERGY LOGISTICS PARTNERS, LP; *U.S. Private*, pg. 2619
MAXUM PETROLEUM, INC.—See Berkshire Hathaway Inc.; *U.S. Public*, pg. 313
M.B. JONES OIL COMPANY INC.; *U.S. Private*, pg. 2528
MCCALL OIL & CHEMICAL CORP.; *U.S. Private*, pg. 2626
MCCORMICK MARKETING INC.; *U.S. Private*, pg. 2630
MCKENZIE OIL CO. INC.; *U.S. Private*, pg. 2638
MCLEOD OIL COMPANY INC.; *U.S. Private*, pg. 2641
MCNEECE BROTHERS OIL CO. INC.; *U.S. Private*, pg. 2643
MENARD OIL CO. INC.; *U.S. Private*, pg. 2665
MERCFUEL, INC.—See Mercury Air Group Inc.; *U.S. Private*, pg. 2670
MERCURY FUEL SERVICE INC.; *U.S. Private*, pg. 2670
MERCURY REFUELING, INC.—See Mercury Air Group Inc.; *U.S. Private*, pg. 2670
MERLE BOES INC.; *U.S. Private*, pg. 2675
METALWORKING LUBRICANTS COMPANY, INC.; *U.S. Private*, pg. 2682
MEYER OIL CO.; *U.S. Private*, pg. 2692
MG OIL INC.; *U.S. Private*, pg. 2694
MICHIGAN PETROLEUM TECHNOLOGIES, INC.—See AIP, LLC; *U.S. Private*, pg. 136
MIDCENTRAL ENERGY SERVICES, LLC; *U.S. Private*, pg. 2710
MID PAC CS, LLC—See Par Pacific Holdings, Inc.; *U.S. Public*, pg. 1636
MID SOUTH SALES, INC.; *U.S. Private*, pg. 2706
MID-STATE ENERGY INCORPORATED; *U.S. Private*, pg. 2709
MIDWAY OIL CORP.; *U.S. Private*, pg. 2719
MIDWEST BOTTLE GAS COMPANY—See Consolidated Midwest, Inc.; *U.S. Private*, pg. 1021
MIKE ROCHE INC.; *U.S. Private*, pg. 2725
MIRABITO FUEL GROUP; *U.S. Private*, pg. 2745
MIXON-NOLLNER OIL CO.; *U.S. Private*, pg. 2752
M&L PETROLEUM INC.; *U.S. Private*, pg. 2524
MOBIL OIL AUSTRALIA PTY LTD—See Exxon Mobil Corporation; *U.S. Public*, pg. 817
MOBIL OIL DEL PERU S A R L—See Exxon Mobil Corporation; *U.S. Public*, pg. 817
MOBIL OIL NEW ZEALAND LTD.—See Exxon Mobil Corporation; *U.S. Public*, pg. 817
MOBIL OIL TURK AS—See Exxon Mobil Corporation; *U.S. Public*, pg. 817
MODERN OIL COMPANY INC.; *U.S. Private*, pg. 2762
MOHR OIL COMPANY; *U.S. Private*, pg. 2765
MONUMENT OIL COMPANY; *U.S. Private*, pg. 2777
MOORE OIL CO., INC. - MONTGOMERY—See Moore Oil Co., Inc.; *U.S. Private*, pg. 2780
MOORE OIL CO., INC.; *U.S. Private*, pg. 2780

MORGAN DISTRIBUTING COMPANY INC.; *U.S. Private*, pg. 2783
MORRIS OIL OF MISSISSIPPI; *U.S. Private*, pg. 2788
MOTOR OILS INC.—See Abercrombie Oil Company Incorporated; *U.S. Private*, pg. 38
MOUNTAIN COUNTRY, LLC—See CHS INC.; *U.S. Public*, pg. 492
MSC DISTRIBUTING INC.; *U.S. Private*, pg. 2806
MURPHY OIL USA, INC.—See Murphy USA Inc.; *U.S. Public*, pg. 1487
MUTUAL OIL CO. INC.—See Truman Arnold Companies; *U.S. Private*, pg. 4250
N1 EHF.—See Festi hf; *Int'l*, pg. 2646
NAKAGAWA OIL CO., LTD—See Idemitsu Kosan Co., Ltd.; *Int'l*, pg. 3592
NAPA VALLEY PETROLEUM INC.; *U.S. Private*, pg. 2834
NATURLICHENERGIE SWISS NES GMBH—See EnBW Energie Baden-Wurttemberg AG; *Int'l*, pg. 2399
NEBRASKA-IOWA SUPPLY COMPANY; *U.S. Private*, pg. 2879
NEVADA TRIO INC.; *U.S. Private*, pg. 2891
NEW CENTURY TRANSPORTATION LLC—See Energy Transfer LP; *U.S. Public*, pg. 764
NEW DIXIE OIL CORPORATION; *U.S. Private*, pg. 2893
NGO PROPANE COOPERATIVE—See The Energy Cooperative, Inc.; *U.S. Private*, pg. 4026
NISBET OIL COMPANY; *U.S. Private*, pg. 2928
NOCO ENERGY CORP.; *U.S. Private*, pg. 2933
NOONAN BROTHERS PETROLEUM PRODUCTS; *U.S. Private*, pg. 2935
NORDIC LUBRICANTS AB—See BP plc; *Int'l*, pg. 1131
NORDIC LUBRICANTS A/S—See BP plc; *Int'l*, pg. 1131
NORD-WEST OELLEITUNG GMBH—See BP plc; *Int'l*, pg. 1131
NORMALAB FRANCE SAS—See HORIBA Ltd; *Int'l*, pg. 3477
NORTHERN OILFIELD SERVICES, INC.—See Saltchuk Resources Inc.; *U.S. Private*, pg. 3534
NORTHGATE PETROLEUM COMPANY; *U.S. Private*, pg. 2955
NORTH STAR PETROLEUM—See Saltchuk Resources Inc.; *U.S. Private*, pg. 3534
NUCKLES OIL COMPANY INC.; *U.S. Private*, pg. 2972
NWB NORD- UND WESTDEUTSCHE BUNKER GMBH—See Hoyer GmbH; *Int'l*, pg. 3499
NYNAS ARGENTINA SA—See Bitumina Industries Ltd.; *Int'l*, pg. 1050
NYNAS A/S—See Bitumina Industries Ltd.; *Int'l*, pg. 1050
NYNAS (AUSTRALIA) PTY LTD—See Bitumina Industries Ltd.; *Int'l*, pg. 1050
NYNAS BELGIUM AB—See Bitumina Industries Ltd.; *Int'l*, pg. 1050
NYNAS CANADA INC—See Bitumina Industries Ltd.; *Int'l*, pg. 1051
NYNAS MEXICO SA—See Bitumina Industries Ltd.; *Int'l*, pg. 1051
NYNAS NAPHTHENICS LTD—See Bitumina Industries Ltd.; *Int'l*, pg. 1051
NYNAS OY—See Bitumina Industries Ltd.; *Int'l*, pg. 1051
NYNAS PETROLEO SA—See Bitumina Industries Ltd.; *Int'l*, pg. 1051
NYNAS PTE, LTD—See Bitumina Industries Ltd.; *Int'l*, pg. 1051
NYNAS SA—See Bitumina Industries Ltd.; *Int'l*, pg. 1051
NYNAS SERVICIOS SA—See Bitumina Industries Ltd.; *Int'l*, pg. 1051
NYNAS (SOUTH AFRICA) (PTY) LTD—See Bitumina Industries Ltd.; *Int'l*, pg. 1050
NYNAS SP. Z O.O.—See Bitumina Industries Ltd.; *Int'l*, pg. 1051
NYNAS SRL—See Bitumina Industries Ltd.; *Int'l*, pg. 1051
NYNAS TECHNOL HANDELS GMBH—See Bitumina Industries Ltd.; *Int'l*, pg. 1051
NYNAS USA, INC—See Bitumina Industries Ltd.; *Int'l*, pg. 1051
NYNAS VERWALTUNGS GMBH—See Bitumina Industries Ltd.; *Int'l*, pg. 1051
OCEAN PETROLEUM CO. INC.; *U.S. Private*, pg. 2989
OCHS OIL COMPANY; *U.S. Private*, pg. 2992
O'CONNELL OIL ASSOCIATES INC.; *U.S. Private*, pg. 2977
OFFEN PETROLEUM, LLC—See Court Square Capital Partners, L.P.; *U.S. Private*, pg. 1069
OIL PATCH FUEL & SUPPLY INC.; *U.S. Private*, pg. 3006
OIL TRADING POLAND SP. Z O.O.—See Hinduja Group Ltd.; *Int'l*, pg. 3399
OLCO PETROLEUM GROUP INC.—See Morgan Stanley; *U.S. Public*, pg. 1475
OLIUDREIFING EHF.—See Festi hf; *Int'l*, pg. 2646
OLIUVERZLUN ISLANDS HF.—See Hagar hf.; *Int'l*, pg. 3206
OLSON OIL CO. INC.; *U.S. Private*, pg. 3011
OLSON OIL CO. INC.; *U.S. Private*, pg. 3011
OLYMPIA FUEL INC.; *U.S. Private*, pg. 3012
ONE CYPRESS ENERGY LLC; *U.S. Private*, pg. 3020
ORANGE LINE OIL COMPANY, INC.—See AIP, LLC; *U.S. Private*, pg. 136
ORCHARD ENERGY LIMITED—See World Kinect Corporation; *U.S. Public*, pg. 2381

ORTEGO OIL & SUPPLY CO. INC.; *U.S. Private*, pg. 3045
ORTON MOTORS INC.; *U.S. Private*, pg. 3045
OSAKA INTERNATIONAL REFINING COMPANY, LIMITED—See ENEOS Holdings, Inc.; *Int'l*, pg. 2418
OSAN PETROLEUM COMPANY INC.; *U.S. Private*, pg. 3046
OTORIO LTD.—See ANDRITZ AG; *Int'l*, pg. 456
OXBOW CARBON BATON ROUGE—See Oxbow Corporation; *U.S. Private*, pg. 3056
OXBOW CARBON & MINERALS INTERNATIONAL GMBH—See Oxbow Corporation; *U.S. Private*, pg. 3056
OXBOW COAL B.V.—See Oxbow Corporation; *U.S. Private*, pg. 3056
PACE FUELCARE LIMITED—See DCC plc; *Int'l*, pg. 1991
PALMDALE OIL COMPANY, INC.; *U.S. Private*, pg. 3080
PANEF, INC.; *U.S. Private*, pg. 3080
PAPCO, INC.—See World Kinect Corporation; *U.S. Public*, pg. 2381
PARACO GAS CORPORATION; *U.S. Private*, pg. 3089
PARACO SOUTH LLC—See Paraco Gas Corporation; *U.S. Private*, pg. 3089
PARENT PETROLEUM INC.; *U.S. Private*, pg. 3094
PAR HAWAII, INC.—See Par Pacific Holdings, Inc.; *U.S. Public*, pg. 1636
PARSLEY ENERGY MANAGEMENT, LLC—See Pioneer Natural Resources Company; *U.S. Public*, pg. 1693
PATTEN ENERGY ENTERPRISES, INC.—See Patten Energy Solutions Group, Inc.; *U.S. Private*, pg. 1653
PATTERSON OIL COMPANY; *U.S. Private*, pg. 3111
PAUL OIL COMPANY INC.; *U.S. Private*, pg. 3113
PAULSON OIL COMPANY INC.—See Berkshire Hathaway Inc.; *U.S. Public*, pg. 313
P&B PETROLEUM CO. INC.; *U.S. Private*, pg. 3058
PCO TRADING LTD—See Harbour Energy plc; *Int'l*, pg. 3271
PENINSULA PETROLEUM AS—See Gibunco Group Limited; *Int'l*, pg. 2963
PENINSULA PETROLEUM (BROKERS) LTD—See Gibunco Group Limited; *Int'l*, pg. 2963
PENINSULA PETROLEUM DMCC—See Gibunco Group Limited; *Int'l*, pg. 2963
PENINSULA PETROLEUM EPE—See Gibunco Group Limited; *Int'l*, pg. 2963
PENINSULA PETROLEUM FAR EAST PTE LTD—See Gibunco Group Limited; *Int'l*, pg. 2963
PENINSULA PETROLEUM INC.—See Gibunco Group Limited; *Int'l*, pg. 2963
PENINSULA PETROLEUM (MONACO) S.A.R.L—See Gibunco Group Limited; *Int'l*, pg. 2963
PENINSULA PETROLEUM PANAMA INC—See Gibunco Group Limited; *Int'l*, pg. 2963
PENINSULA PETROLEUM SA—See Gibunco Group Limited; *Int'l*, pg. 2963
PENINSULA PETROLEUM SL—See Gibunco Group Limited; *Int'l*, pg. 2963
PENINSULA PETROLEUM SOUTH AMERICA SA—See Gibunco Group Limited; *Int'l*, pg. 2963
PESTER MARKETING COMPANY—See Phillips 66 Company; *U.S. Public*, pg. 1688
PETR-ALL CORPORATION; *U.S. Private*, pg. 3161
PETRO AIR, CORP.—See World Kinect Corporation; *U.S. Public*, pg. 2381
PETRO-CANADA EUROPE LUBRICANTS LIMITED—See HF Sinclair Corporation; *U.S. Public*, pg. 1034
PETROCARD SYSTEMS INC. - FUEL DIVISION—See Bristol Bay Native Corporation; *U.S. Private*, pg. 656
PETROCARD SYSTEMS INC. - FUEL & LUBRICANT DIVISION—See Bristol Bay Native Corporation; *U.S. Private*, pg. 656
PETROCARD SYSTEMS INC. - LUBRICANT DIVISION—See Bristol Bay Native Corporation; *U.S. Private*, pg. 656
PETROCHOICE LLC; *U.S. Private*, pg. 3162
PETROGAL CABO VERDE, LDA.—See Galp Energia SGPS, S.A.; *Int'l*, pg. 2875
PETROGULF WLL—See Bhatia Brothers Group; *Int'l*, pg. 1014
PETROLEUM MARKETING GROUP INC.; *U.S. Private*, pg. 3162
PETROLEUM TRADERS CORPORATION; *U.S. Private*, pg. 3162
PETROLEUM WHOLESALE, LP; *U.S. Private*, pg. 3162
PETROLEUM WORLD, INC.—See Cleveland Capital Holdings, Inc.; *U.S. Private*, pg. 940
PETROLIANCE LLC - CLEVELAND—See PetroLiance LLC; *U.S. Private*, pg. 3162
PETRO-LINK, INC.; *U.S. Private*, pg. 3162
PETRO-LOCK INC.; *U.S. Private*, pg. 3162
PETRO MARINE SERVICES; *U.S. Private*, pg. 3161
PETROMARK INC.; *U.S. Private*, pg. 3162
PETRO PROGRESS PTE LTD—See Fuji Oil Company, Ltd.; *Int'l*, pg. 2815
PETRO SERVICE INC.; *U.S. Private*, pg. 3161
PETROSOUTH INC.; *U.S. Private*, pg. 3163
PHILLIPS 66 INTERNATIONAL TRADING PTE. LTD.—See Phillips 66 Company; *U.S. Public*, pg. 1688
PHILLIPS 66 LIMITED—See Phillips 66 Company; *U.S. Public*, pg. 1688

N.A.I.C.S. INDEX

424720 — PETROLEUM AND PETRO...

PHILLIPS 66 POLYPROPYLENE CANADA INC.—See Phillips 66 Company; *U.S. Public*, pg. 1688
PHILLIPS GAS COMPANY—See Phillips 66 Company; *U.S. Public*, pg. 1688
PHILLIPS UTILITY GAS CORPORATION—See Phillips 66 Company; *U.S. Public*, pg. 1688
PHOENIX OIL, INC.—See Adams Resources & Energy, Inc.; *U.S. Public*, pg. 38
PIASA MOTOR FUELS LLC; *U.S. Private*, pg. 3175
PICO PETROLEUM PRODUCTS LTD.—See Meritum Energy Holdings, LP; *U.S. Private*, pg. 2675
PIGOTT OIL COMPANY INC.; *U.S. Private*, pg. 3179
PIONEER PIPE LINE COMPANY—See Phillips 66 Company; *U.S. Public*, pg. 1688
PIPELINE OIL SALES INC.; *U.S. Private*, pg. 3189
PIPELINE PETROLEUM, INC.; *U.S. Private*, pg. 3189
PITMON OIL & GAS CO.; *U.S. Private*, pg. 3191
PIT STOP GAS INC.; *U.S. Private*, pg. 3190
PLAINS MARKETING, LP—See Plains All American Pipeline, L.P.; *U.S. Public*, pg. 1696
PLANTERS WAREHOUSE & LOAN CO.; *U.S. Private*, pg. 3198
PMI LUBRICANTS, INC.; *U.S. Private*, pg. 3218
POLIMERI EUROPA GMBH—See Eni S.p.A.; *Int'l*, pg. 2438
POLSINELLO FUELS INC.; *U.S. Private*, pg. 3225
POMA AUTOMATED FUELING INC.; *U.S. Private*, pg. 3226
PORT CONSOLIDATED INC.; *U.S. Private*, pg. 3230
PPC LUBRICANTS, INC.—See AIP, LLC; *U.S. Private*, pg. 136
PRAIRIE FARMERS ASSOCIATION, INC.; *U.S. Private*, pg. 3242
PREMIER OIL HOLDINGS LTD—See Harbour Energy plc; *Int'l*, pg. 2308
PRESTO FOOD STORES, INC.; *U.S. Private*, pg. 3256
PROPST BROTHERS DISTRIBUTORS; *U.S. Private*, pg. 3286
PT CASTROL INDONESIA—See BP plc; *Int'l*, pg. 1131
PT. JWC INDONESIA ENERGI—See C&G SYSTEMS INC.; *Int'l*, pg. 1238
PUGH OIL COMPANY INC.; *U.S. Private*, pg. 3303
QUALITY PETROLEUM INC.; *U.S. Private*, pg. 3320
QUANTUM ENERGY, INC.; *U.S. Public*, pg. 1754
RACEWAY PETROLEUM INC.; *U.S. Private*, pg. 3341
RAVENNA OIL CO.—See Croton Holding Company; *U.S. Private*, pg. 1108
RAY-CARROLL FUELS, L.L.C.—See Ray-Carroll County Grain Growers, Inc.; *U.S. Private*, pg. 3359
RED AND YELLOW CO., LTD—See Idemitsu Kosan Co., Ltd.; *Int'l*, pg. 3592
RED GIANT OIL COMPANY—See HF Sinclair Corporation; *U.S. Public*, pg. 1034
RED HORSE OIL COMPANY INCORPORATED; *U.S. Private*, pg. 3375
REDWOOD COMPANY; *U.S. Private*, pg. 3381
REG ALBERT LEA, LLC—See Chevron Corporation; *U.S. Public*, pg. 487
REGAL OIL INC.; *U.S. Private*, pg. 3385
REG ATLANTA, LLC—See Chevron Corporation; *U.S. Public*, pg. 487
REG DANVILLE, LLC—See Chevron Corporation; *U.S. Public*, pg. 487
REG GEISMAR, LLC—See Chevron Corporation; *U.S. Public*, pg. 487
REG MARKETING & LOGISTICS GROUP, LLC—See Chevron Corporation; *U.S. Public*, pg. 488
REG MASON CITY, LLC—See Chevron Corporation; *U.S. Public*, pg. 488
REG NEW BOSTON, LLC—See Chevron Corporation; *U.S. Public*, pg. 488
REG NEWTON, LLC—See Chevron Corporation; *U.S. Public*, pg. 488
REG RALSTON, LLC—See Chevron Corporation; *U.S. Public*, pg. 488
RELIABLE PROPANE, INC.—See Ferrellgas Partners, L.P.; *U.S. Public*, pg. 829
RESTRUCTURE PETRO MARKETING SERVICES—See Restructure Inc.; *U.S. Private*, pg. 3410
REX OIL COMPANY INC.; *U.S. Private*, pg. 3417
REX OIL COMPANY—See PetroChoice LLC; *U.S. Private*, pg. 3162
R.H. FOSTER ENERGY LLC; *U.S. Private*, pg. 3336
RHODES OIL COMPANY INC.; *U.S. Private*, pg. 3422
THE RIGHT FUELCARD COMPANY LIMITED—See Edenred S.A.; *Int'l*, pg. 2308
RILEY NATURAL GAS—See Chevron Corporation; *U.S. Public*, pg. 487
RINEHART OIL, INC.; *U.S. Private*, pg. 3437
RITE WAY OIL & GAS CO., INC.; *U.S. Private*, pg. 3441
RIVER CITY PETROLEUM, INC.; *U.S. Private*, pg. 3443
R.K. ALLEN OIL CO., INC.; *U.S. Private*, pg. 3338
RKA PETROLEUM COMPANIES, LLC; *U.S. Private*, pg. 3450
RK DISTRIBUTING INC.; *U.S. Private*, pg. 3450
R.L. VALLEE INC.; *U.S. Private*, pg. 3338
ROBERT V. JENSEN INC.; *U.S. Private*, pg. 3459
ROBERT W. AGEE OIL CO. INC.; *U.S. Private*, pg. 3459
ROLLETTE OIL CO. INC.; *U.S. Private*, pg. 3474

ROSCO PROCOM LIMITED—See Agostini's Limited; *Int'l*, pg. 213
ROYAL PETROLEUM CORPORATION; *U.S. Private*, pg. 3493
RUSHCO, INC.—See Rush Enterprises, Inc.; *U.S. Public*, pg. 1827
RUSHER OIL CO, INC.—See Sampson-Bladen Oil Co. Inc.; *U.S. Private*, pg. 3538
RYDER ENERGY DISTRIBUTION CORPORATION—See Ryder System, Inc.; *U.S. Public*, pg. 1828
SAHARA PETROLEUM SERVICES COMPANY S.A.E.—See National Energy Services Reunited Corp.; *U.S. Public*, pg. 1494
SANDFORD OIL COMPANY, INC.; *U.S. Private*, pg. 3543
SANDFORD OIL SOUTH TEXAS—See Sandford Oil Company, Inc.; *U.S. Private*, pg. 3543
SANTANNA NATURAL GAS CORP.; *U.S. Private*, pg. 3548
SANTMYER OIL CO. INC.; *U.S. Private*, pg. 3548
SANTMYER OIL CO. OF ASHLAND INC.—See Santmyer Oil Co. Inc.; *U.S. Private*, pg. 3548
SAPP BROS PETROLEUM, INC.; *U.S. Private*, pg. 3548
SCHAFER OIL COMPANY; *U.S. Private*, pg. 3563
SCHMITT SALES INC.; *U.S. Private*, pg. 3566
SEA-3 OF FLORIDA INC.—See Trammo, Inc.; *U.S. Private*, pg. 4204
SEACOR ENERGY CANADA LIMITED—See AIP, LLC; *U.S. Private*, pg. 136
SEARS PETROLEUM & TRANSPORT CORP.; *U.S. Private*, pg. 3591
SEC ENERGY PRODUCTS & SERVICES, L.P.—See Energy Transfer LP; *U.S. Public*, pg. 763
SELLERS PETROLEUM; *U.S. Private*, pg. 3602
SENECA HAWK HOLDING COMPANY INCORPORATED; *U.S. Private*, pg. 3606
SENTER PETROLEUM, INC.—See Par Pacific Holdings, Inc.; *U.S. Public*, pg. 1636
SERCOMGAS GAS SOLUTIONS, S.L.—See Enagas, S.A.; *Int'l*, pg. 2396
SERVICE ENERGY LLC; *U.S. Private*, pg. 3615
SERVICE OIL COMPANY—See J&H Oil Company Inc.; *U.S. Private*, pg. 2154
SHELLHORN & HILL INC.; *U.S. Private*, pg. 3631
SHELL JAPAN TRADING LTD.—See Idemitsu Kosan Co., Ltd.; *Int'l*, pg. 3592
SHERMAN V. ALLEN INC.; *U.S. Private*, pg. 3634
SHOWA SHELL BUSINESS & IT SOLUTIONS LIMITED—See Idemitsu Kosan Co., Ltd.; *Int'l*, pg. 3592
SIBLEY OIL COMPANY INC.; *U.S. Private*, pg. 3645
SIEGEL OIL COMPANY; *U.S. Private*, pg. 3646
SIEVEKING INC.; *U.S. Private*, pg. 3648
SILCO OIL COMPANY; *U.S. Private*, pg. 3652
SILVAS OIL CO. INC.; *U.S. Private*, pg. 3653
SIMMONS ENERGY SOLUTIONS, INC.—See Simmons Foods, Inc.; *U.S. Private*, pg. 3665
SIMONS PETROLEUM INC.—See Berkshire Hathaway Inc.; *U.S. Public*, pg. 313
SINGAPORE PETROLEUM CO. (HK) LTD.—See China National Petroleum Corporation; *Int'l*, pg. 1533
SINOPEC FUEL OIL SALES CO., LTD—See China Petrochemical Corporation; *Int'l*, pg. 1540
SINOPEC FUEL OIL (SINGAPORE) PTE. LTD.—See China Petrochemical Corporation; *Int'l*, pg. 1540
SINOPEC (HONG KONG) LIMITED—See China Petrochemical Corporation; *Int'l*, pg. 1539
SKS, INC.; *U.S. Private*, pg. 3683
SKYTANKING S. R. L.—See Eni S.p.A.; *Int'l*, pg. 2437
SMARTPETRO INC.—See Vontier Corporation; *U.S. Public*, pg. 2309
SMITH BROTHERS OIL COMPANY, INC.—See Quality Petroleum Corp.; *U.S. Private*, pg. 3320
SMITTY'S SUPPLY—See Smitty's Supply Inc.; *U.S. Private*, pg. 3698
SMO MOTOR FUELS, INC.—See The Wills Group, Inc.; *U.S. Private*, pg. 4136
SOCO GROUP INC.; *U.S. Private*, pg. 3704
SOMERS OIL SERVICE, INC.—See Taylor Energy, LLC; *U.S. Private*, pg. 3939
SOPOR - SOCIEDADE DISTRIBUIDORA DE COMBUSTIVEIS, S.A.—See Galp Energía SGPS, S.A.; *Int'l*, pg. 2876
SOUTH COAST OILS PTY LTD—See Ampol Limited; *Int'l*, pg. 436
SOUTHERN GAS & FUELS INC.; *U.S. Private*, pg. 3732
SOUTHERN MARYLAND OIL, INC.—See The Wills Group, Inc.; *U.S. Private*, pg. 4136
SPACE AGE FUEL INC.; *U.S. Private*, pg. 3743
SPEAKS OIL CO. INC.; *U.S. Private*, pg. 3747
SPENCER COMPANIES INC.; *U.S. Private*, pg. 3754
SPENCER DISTRIBUTING LP; *U.S. Private*, pg. 3755
SPORTS ANALYTICS LLC—See FTI Consulting, Inc.; *U.S. Public*, pg. 891
STALLINGS BROTHERS INC.; *U.S. Private*, pg. 3776
STATE GAS & OIL, LLC; *U.S. Private*, pg. 3792
STATOIL FUEL & RETAIL ASA—See FUCHS SE; *Int'l*, pg. 2804
STERN OIL COMPANY INC.; *U.S. Private*, pg. 3807
STEWART P. WILSON INC.; *U.S. Private*, pg. 3811
STOCKMAN OIL COMPANY; *U.S. Private*, pg. 3815

STONESTREET & STONESTREET; *U.S. Private*, pg. 3830
ST. ROMAIN OIL CO. INC.; *U.S. Private*, pg. 3773
STUARTS' PETROLEUM INC.; *U.S. Private*, pg. 3843
STURDY OIL COMPANY; *U.S. Private*, pg. 3844
SUBURBAN PROPANE, L.P.—See Suburban Propane Partners, L.P.; *U.S. Public*, pg. 1959
SULLIVAN PETROLEUM COMPANY LLC; *U.S. Private*, pg. 3851
SUNCOAST OIL CO. OF FLORIDA INC.; *U.S. Private*, pg. 3866
SUN COAST RESOURCES INC.—See AIP, LLC; *U.S. Private*, pg. 136
SUN COMPANY, INC.—See Energy Transfer LP; *U.S. Public*, pg. 764
SUNOCO LP; *U.S. Public*, pg. 1964
SUN PACIFIC ENERGY; *U.S. Private*, pg. 3863
SUPERIOR DESHLER INC.; *U.S. Private*, pg. 3876
SUPERIOR LUBRICANTS COMPANY; *U.S. Private*, pg. 3878
SUSSER PETROLEUM COMPANY LLC—See Sunoco LP; *U.S. Public*, pg. 1965
SUSSER PETROLEUM OPERATING COMPANY LLC—See Sunoco LP; *U.S. Public*, pg. 1965
SUTTONS OIL LIMITED—See Bord na Mona Plc; *Int'l*, pg. 1113
SWEA ENERGI AB—See DCC plc; *Int'l*, pg. 1991
SYNERGY PETROLEUM LLC; *U.S. Private*, pg. 3904
TAC ENERGY—See Truman Arnold Companies; *U.S. Private*, pg. 4250
TAIWAN NISSEKI CO., LTD.—See ENEOS Holdings, Inc.; *Int'l*, pg. 2417
TALENS MARINE & FUEL INC.; *U.S. Private*, pg. 3926
T/A TERMINALS, INC.—See Trammo, Inc.; *U.S. Private*, pg. 4204
TAT PETROLEUM (HK) PTE LIMITED—See BRENNTAG SE; *Int'l*, pg. 1150
TAT PETROLEUM PTE. LTD.—See BRENNTAG SE; *Int'l*, pg. 1150
TAT PETROLEUM (VIETNAM) CO., LTD.—See BRENNTAG SE; *Int'l*, pg. 1150
TAUBER OIL COMPANY; *U.S. Private*, pg. 3936
TAYLOR OIL CO., INC.; *U.S. Private*, pg. 3940
TELKO NORWAY AS—See Aspo Oyj; *Int'l*, pg. 631
TETC, LLC—See Energy Transfer LP; *U.S. Public*, pg. 764
TEXAS ENTERPRISES INC.; *U.S. Private*, pg. 3975
TEXON LP; *U.S. Private*, pg. 3978
TEXOR PETROLEUM COMPANY—See World Kinect Corporation; *U.S. Public*, pg. 2381
T.F. KURK INC.; *U.S. Private*, pg. 3912
THERMOGAS GAS- UND GERATEVERTRIEBS-GMBH—See EnBW Energie Baden-Wurttemberg AG; *Int'l*, pg. 2400
THIRD COST TERMINALS; *U.S. Private*, pg. 4145
THOMAS PETROLEUM, INC.; *U.S. Private*, pg. 4157
TITAN PROPANE LLC—See UGI Corporation; *U.S. Public*, pg. 2222
TOKYO SHELL PACK K.K.—See Idemitsu Kosan Co., Ltd.; *Int'l*, pg. 3592
TOM LOPES DISTRIBUTING INC.; *U.S. Private*, pg. 4183
TORO PETROLEUM CORP.; *U.S. Private*, pg. 4189
TOYO ENERGY CO., LTD.—See Hanwa Co., Ltd.; *Int'l*, pg. 3263
TRAJEN INC.; *U.S. Private*, pg. 4204
TRAMMOCHEM A.G.—See Trammo, Inc.; *U.S. Private*, pg. 4204
TRAMMOCHEM—See Trammo, Inc.; *U.S. Private*, pg. 4204
TRAMMO GAS DOMESTIC—See Trammo, Inc.; *U.S. Private*, pg. 4204
TRAMMO GAS INTERNATIONAL, INC.—See Trammo, Inc.; *U.S. Private*, pg. 4204
TRAMMO, INC.; *U.S. Private*, pg. 4204
TRAMMO MAGHREB S.A.R.L.—See Trammo, Inc.; *U.S. Private*, pg. 4204
TRAMMO PETROLEUM, INC.—See Trammo, Inc.; *U.S. Private*, pg. 4204
TRANSGLOBAL GAS & OIL COMPANY; *U.S. Private*, pg. 4208
TRANSMONTAIGNE MARKETING CANADA INC.—See Morgan Stanley; *U.S. Public*, pg. 1475
TRANSMONTAIGNE PRODUCT SERVICES, LLC—See Berkshire Hathaway Inc.; *U.S. Public*, pg. 313
TRI-CON INC.; *U.S. Private*, pg. 4221
TRI-COUNTY-PETROLEUM; *U.S. Private*, pg. 4222
TRI-GAS & OIL CO. INC.; *U.S. Private*, pg. 4222
TRIPLE S PETROLEUM COMPANY INC.; *U.S. Private*, pg. 4237
TRI STAR ENERGY, LLC; *U.S. Private*, pg. 4220
TRUEBLOOD OIL CO. INC.; *U.S. Private*, pg. 4248
TRUMAN ARNOLD COMPANIES; *U.S. Private*, pg. 4250
TUCKER OIL COMPANY INC.; *U.S. Private*, pg. 4256
TURNER GAS COMPANY INC.; *U.S. Private*, pg. 4260
TURPAK ELEKTROMANYETIK YAKIT IKMAL SISTEMLERI TICARET A.S.—See Vontier Corporation; *U.S. Public*, pg. 2309
TYREE OIL INC.; *U.S. Private*, pg. 4269
UAB FORTUM EKOSILUMA—See Fortum Oyj; *Int'l*, pg. 2742

424720 — PETROLEUM AND PETRO...

UAB LOTOS BALTIJA—See Grupa LOTOS S.A.; *Int'l*, pg. 3117
ULTRA POWER CORP.; *U.S. Private*, pg. 4277
UNIOIL PETROLEUM PHILIPPINES, INC.—See AT Capital Pte Limited; *Int'l*, pg. 664
UNIVERSAL BIOFUELS PRIVATE LIMITED—See Aemetis, Inc.; *U.S. Public*, pg. 52
UNO S.A. DE C.V.—See Grupo Terra S.A. de C.V.; *Int'l*, pg. 3137
UPI ENERGY LP—See Growmark, Inc.; *U.S. Private*, pg. 1795
URBIETA OIL CO.; *U.S. Private*, pg. 4315
USOURCE LLC—See Unitil Corporation; *U.S. Public*, pg. 2253
VAALCO GABON S.A.—See VAALCO Energy, Inc.; *U.S. Public*, pg. 2270
VALERO PERU S.A.C.—See Valero Energy Corporation; *U.S. Public*, pg. 2272
VALLEY WIDE COOPERATIVE INC.; *U.S. Private*, pg. 4336
VANGUARD PETROLEUM CORPORATION; *U.S. Private*, pg. 4344
VAN MANEN PETROLEUM GROUP; *U.S. Private*, pg. 4340
VAN UNEN / MIERSMA PROPANE, INC.—See EDPO, LLC; *U.S. Private*, pg. 1338
VAROUH OIL, INC.; *U.S. Private*, pg. 4347
VESCO OIL CORPORATION; *U.S. Private*, pg. 4371
VINING OIL & GAS LLC; *U.S. Private*, pg. 4385
VNG INNOVATION GMBH—See EnBW Energie Baden-Wurttemberg AG; *Int'l*, pg. 2400
VP TRANSPORTATION CO. INC.—See Texas Allied Holdings Inc.; *U.S. Private*, pg. 3974
WAGUESPACK OIL CO. INC.; *U.S. Private*, pg. 4426
WALLACE OIL COMPANY INC; *U.S. Private*, pg. 4431
WALTHALL OIL COMPANY; *U.S. Private*, pg. 4434
WARE OIL & SUPPLY COMPANY INC.; *U.S. Private*, pg. 4441
WARING OIL COMPANY, LLC; *U.S. Private*, pg. 4442
WARREN OIL COMPANY INC.; *U.S. Private*, pg. 4444
WASTE MANAGEMENT & PROCESSORS, INC—See Reading Anthracite Company; *U.S. Private*, pg. 3366
WD-40 COMPANY (AUSTRALIA) PTY. LTD.—See WD-40 Company; *U.S. Public*, pg. 2338
WD-40 COMPANY LTD.—See WD-40 Company; *U.S. Public*, pg. 2339
WD-40 PRODUCTS (CANADA) LTD.—See WD-40 Company; *U.S. Public*, pg. 2339
WEBBER OIL COMPANY; *U.S. Private*, pg. 4464
WENATCHEE PETROLEUM CO; *U.S. Private*, pg. 4480
WESTBIT AB—See BP plc; *Int'l*, pg. 1128
WESTERN ENERGY PTY. LTD.—See AGL Energy Limited; *Int'l*, pg. 211
WESTERN MARKETING INC.—See AIP, LLC; *U.S. Private*, pg. 136
WESTERN PETROLEUM COMPANY—See World Kinect Corporation; *U.S. Public*, pg. 2381
WEST OIL COMPANY INCORPORATED; *U.S. Private*, pg. 4486
WEST OIL COMPANY INC.—See First Reserve Management, L.P.; *U.S. Private*, pg. 1527
WHITE ARROW SERVICE STATIONS; *U.S. Private*, pg. 4508
WHITE GROUP PUBLIC COMPANY LIMITED—See Berli Jucker Public Co. Ltd.; *Int'l*, pg. 985
WHITE-TUCKER COMPANY; *U.S. Private*, pg. 4510
WICKLAND OIL CO., INC.—See Wickland Oil Corporation; *U.S. Private*, pg. 4515
WICKLAND OIL CORPORATION; *U.S. Private*, pg. 4515
WILLIAMS LUBRICANTS INC.—See Williams Oil Company Inc.; *U.S. Private*, pg. 4526
WILLIAMS OIL COMPANY INC.; *U.S. Private*, pg. 4526
WILLIS OIL CO. INC.; *U.S. Private*, pg. 4528
WILLOUGHBY INC.; *U.S. Private*, pg. 4528
WILSON OIL, INC.; *U.S. Private*, pg. 4531
WINDWARD PETROLEUM—See Booth Waltz Enterprises, Inc.; *U.S. Private*, pg. 617
WISURA GMBH—See FUCHS SE; *Int'l*, pg. 2804
WMPI PTY., LLC—See Reading Anthracite Company; *U.S. Private*, pg. 3366
WOODFIN HEATING INC.; *U.S. Private*, pg. 4558
WORLD FUEL SERVICES, INC.—See World Kinect Corporation; *U.S. Public*, pg. 2381
WORLD OIL GROUP, INC.; *U.S. Public*, pg. 2381
WYANDOTTE TRIBAL PETROLEUM, INC.—See Wyandotte Tribal Corporation; *U.S. Private*, pg. 4575
YACHT FUEL SERVICES LIMITED—See World Kinect Corporation; *U.S. Public*, pg. 2381
YORKSTON OIL CO.—See Christensen Inc.; *U.S. Private*, pg. 890

424810 — BEER AND ALE MERCHANT WHOLESALERS

7G DISTRIBUTING, LLC; *U.S. Private*, pg. 17
AB BEVERAGE CO., INC.; *U.S. Private*, pg. 33
ADAMS BEVERAGES, INC.; *U.S. Private*, pg. 73
ADAMS BEVERAGES OF NORTH CAROLINA, LLC—See Adams Beverages, Inc.; *U.S. Private*, pg. 73
AJAX DISTRIBUTING CO. INC.; *U.S. Private*, pg. 143
A.L. GEORGE INC.; *U.S. Private*, pg. 26
ALLAN S. GOODMAN INCORPORATED; *U.S. Private*, pg. 174
ALLSTATE BEVERAGE COMPANY LLC—See Gulf Distributing Holdings LLC; *U.S. Private*, pg. 1816
ALTIA EESTI AS—See Altia Oyj; *Int'l*, pg. 392
AMERICAN EAGLE DISTRIBUTING CO.; *U.S. Private*, pg. 231
AMOSKEAG BEVERAGES INC.; *U.S. Private*, pg. 264
ANDREWS DISTRIBUTING COMPANY, LLC; *U.S. Private*, pg. 280
ANDREWS DISTRIBUTING COMPANY OF NORTH TEXAS, LLC—See Andrews Distributing Company, LLC; *U.S. Private*, pg. 280
ANHEUSER-BUSCH INTERNATIONAL, INC.—See Anheuser-Busch InBev SA/NV; *Int'l*, pg. 465
ANHEUSER-BUSCH SALES OF HAWAII—See Anheuser-Busch InBev SA/NV; *Int'l*, pg. 465
ANHEUSER-BUSCH SALES OF LIMA—See Anheuser-Busch InBev SA/NV; *Int'l*, pg. 465
ANHEUSER-BUSCH SALES POMONA—See Anheuser-Busch InBev SA/NV; *Int'l*, pg. 465
ASAHI BEER TAIWAN CO., LTD.—See Asahi Group Holdings Ltd.; *Int'l*, pg. 593
ASAHI BEER U.S.A., INC.—See Asahi Group Holdings Ltd.; *Int'l*, pg. 593
ASAHI BEVERAGES (NZ) LTD.—See Asahi Group Holdings Ltd.; *Int'l*, pg. 593
ASAHI UK LTD.—See Asahi Group Holdings Ltd.; *Int'l*, pg. 593
ATLANTA BEVERAGE CO.; *U.S. Private*, pg. 370
AUGUST A. BUSCH & COMPANY OF MASSACHUSETTS, INC.—See Anheuser-Busch InBev SA/NV; *Int'l*, pg. 465
BACARDI BOTTLING CORPORATION—See Bacardi Limited; *Int'l*, pg. 794
BACCHUS IMPORTERS, LTD.—See Breakthru Beverage Group, LLC; *U.S. Private*, pg. 643
BAKER DISTRIBUTING CORP.; *U.S. Private*, pg. 456
BAY AREA DISTRIBUTING COMPANY; *U.S. Private*, pg. 491
BEAUCHAMP DISTRIBUTING COMPANY; *U.S. Private*, pg. 508
BEER CAPITOL DISTRIBUTING, LAKE COUNTRY, LLC; *U.S. Private*, pg. 514
BELOIT BEVERAGE CO. INC.; *U.S. Private*, pg. 521
BERTANI DOMAINS S.R.L.—See Angelini ACRAF S.p.A.; *Int'l*, pg. 460
BEST BRANDS BEVERAGE INC—See The United Group; *U.S. Private*, pg. 4129
BEST BUYS INTERNATIONAL AS—See Altia Oyj; *Int'l*, pg. 392
BETTER BRANDS SOUTH GEORGIA LLP—See J & L Ventures LLC; *U.S. Private*, pg. 2152
BEVCO AB—See Altia Oyj; *Int'l*, pg. 392
BEVERAGE MARKETING CORPORATION; *U.S. Private*, pg. 547
B.E. WRIGHT, INC.—See Wright Wisner Distributing Corp.; *U.S. Private*, pg. 4573
B FERNANDEZ & HNOS INC.; *U.S. Private*, pg. 417
BIBENDUM AB—See Altia Oyj; *Int'l*, pg. 392
BIRMINGHAM BEVERAGE COMPANY INC.—See Adams Beverages, Inc.; *U.S. Private*, pg. 73
BLUE RIDGE BEVERAGE COMPANY INCORPORATED; *U.S. Private*, pg. 591
BLUFF CITY BEER COMPANY; *U.S. Private*, pg. 599
BOB HALL INC.; *U.S. Private*, pg. 604
BOTTLE GREEN LIMITED—See DCC plc; *Int'l*, pg. 1989
BRASSERIE DE TAHITI SA; *Int'l*, pg. 1140
BREAKTHRU BEVERAGE ILLINOIS—See Breakthru Beverage Group, LLC; *U.S. Private*, pg. 643
BREAKTHRU BEVERAGE MINNESOTA—See Breakthru Beverage Group, LLC; *U.S. Private*, pg. 643
BREAKTHRU BEVERAGE NEVADA—See Breakthru Beverage Group, LLC; *U.S. Private*, pg. 643
BREAKTHRU BEVERAGE WISCONSIN—See Breakthru Beverage Group, LLC; *U.S. Private*, pg. 643
BREWERS RETAIL INC.; *Int'l*, pg. 1150
BRISSET BEER INTERNATIONAL, INC.; *Int'l*, pg. 1164
BROOKLYN BREWERY CORPORATION; *U.S. Private*, pg. 663
BROWN DISTRIBUTING COMPANY, INCORPORATED; *U.S. Private*, pg. 667
BROWN DISTRIBUTING COMPANY; *U.S. Private*, pg. 667
BROWN-FORMAN BEVERAGES AUSTRALIA PTY LTD.—See Brown-Forman Corporation; *U.S. Public*, pg. 403
BROWN-FORMAN BEVERAGES EUROPE, LTD.—See Brown-Forman Corporation; *U.S. Public*, pg. 403
BROWN-FORMAN BEVERAGES NORTH ASIA, LLC—See Brown-Forman Corporation; *U.S. Public*, pg. 403
BUQUET DISTRIBUTING COMPANY, INC.; *U.S. Private*, pg. 686
BURKHARDT DISTRIBUTING COMPANY—See Mitchell Companies; *U.S. Private*, pg. 2750
CA IMMO BIP LIEGENSCHAFTSVERWALTUNG GMBH—See Starwood Capital Group Global I, LLC; *U.S. Private*, pg. 3789
CARLSBERG UK LTD—See Carlsberg A/S; *Int'l*, pg. 1340
CARSON DISTRIBUTING COMPANY; *U.S. Private*, pg. 774
CARTER DISTRIBUTING COMPANY INC; *U.S. Private*, pg. 775
CENTRAL DISTRIBUTING CO.; *U.S. Private*, pg. 820
CHAMBAL BREWERIES & DISTILLERIES LIMITED; *Int'l*, pg. 1439
CHAMBERLAIN WHOLESALE GROCERY CO.; *U.S. Private*, pg. 846
CHARLES SELIGMAN DISTRIBUTING CO.; *U.S. Private*, pg. 853
CHEROKEE DISTRIBUTING COMPANY, INC.; *U.S. Private*, pg. 873
CHICAGO BEVERAGE SYSTEMS, LLC—See Reyes Holdings, LLC; *U.S. Private*, pg. 3418
C.H. WRIGHT, INC.—See Wright Wisner Distributing Corp.; *U.S. Private*, pg. 4573
CITY BEVERAGE COMPANY, INC.; *U.S. Private*, pg. 905
CLARK BEVERAGE GROUP, INC.—See C.C. Clark, Inc.; *U.S. Private*, pg. 706
CLARK DISTRIBUTING COMPANY, INC. - PADUCAH—See C.C. Clark, Inc.; *U.S. Private*, pg. 706
CLARK DISTRIBUTING COMPANY, INC.—See C.C. Clark, Inc.; *U.S. Private*, pg. 706
CLARKE DISTRIBUTORS INC.; *U.S. Private*, pg. 914
C&L DISTRIBUTING; *U.S. Private*, pg. 703
COHO DISTRIBUTING LLC; *U.S. Private*, pg. 964
COLEMAN DISTRIBUTING COMPANY; *U.S. Private*, pg. 967
COLUMBIA DISTRIBUTING INC.; *U.S. Private*, pg. 976
THE COLUMBUS DISTRIBUTING COMPANY INC.; *U.S. Private*, pg. 4011
CONE DISTRIBUTING INC.; *U.S. Private*, pg. 1012
CONSTELLATION BRANDS EUROPE TRADING S.A R.L.—See Constellation Brands, Inc.; *U.S. Public*, pg. 570
COORS DISTRIBUTING COMPANY—See Molson Coors Beverage Company; *U.S. Public*, pg. 1459
CORNISH ORCHARDS LTD.—See Asahi Group Holdings Ltd.; *Int'l*, pg. 593
COUNTY DISTRIBUTING COMPANY; *U.S. Private*, pg. 1068
CRAWFORD SALES COMPANY; *U.S. Private*, pg. 1086
CRESCENT CROWN DISTRIBUTING LLC; *U.S. Private*, pg. 1093
CRESCENT CROWN DISTRIBUTING LLC—See Crescent Crown Distributing LLC; *U.S. Private*, pg. 1093
CREST BEVERAGE, LLC—See Reyes Holdings, LLC; *U.S. Private*, pg. 3418
CROWN DISTRIBUTING INC.; *U.S. Private*, pg. 1110
CROWN IMPORTS LLC—See Constellation Brands, Inc.; *U.S. Public*, pg. 571
DAHLHEIMER DISTRIBUTING COMPANY, INC.; *U.S. Private*, pg. 1144
DANIEL L. JACOB & CO. INC.; *U.S. Private*, pg. 1156
DAYTON HEIDELBERG DISTRIBUTING CO INC.; *U.S. Private*, pg. 1177
DCI MIAMI, INC.—See ANSA McAL Limited; *Int'l*, pg. 477
DEL PAPA DISTRIBUTING CO.; *U.S. Private*, pg. 1193
DELTA DJAKARTA TBK; *Int'l*, pg. 2016
DELTA WHOLESALE LIQUORS, INC.—See Berkshire Hathaway Inc.; *U.S. Public*, pg. 304
DEMERARA DISTILLERS EUROPE BV—See Demerara Distillers Ltd.; *Int'l*, pg. 2025
DEMERARA DISTILLERS (USA) INC.—See Demerara Distillers Ltd.; *Int'l*, pg. 2025
DET DISTRIBUTING COMPANY INC.; *U.S. Private*, pg. 1216
DIAGEO GREAT BRITAIN LIMITED—See Diageo plc; *Int'l*, pg. 2102
DIAGEO NORTH AMERICA INC.—See Diageo plc; *Int'l*, pg. 2102
DON-LEE DISTRIBUTORS INC.; *U.S. Private*, pg. 1259
DUNDEE BREWING CO.—See Florida Ice and Farm Co. S.A.; *Int'l*, pg. 2707
DURDACH BROS. INC.; *U.S. Private*, pg. 1293
DUVEL MOORTGAT FRANCE SARL—See Fibemi NV; *Int'l*, pg. 2651
DUVEL MOORTGAT SHANGHAI LTD—See Fibemi NV; *Int'l*, pg. 2651
DUVEL MOORTGAT UK LTD.—See Fibemi NV; *Int'l*, pg. 2651
DUVEL MOORTGAT USA, LTD.—See Fibemi NV; *Int'l*, pg. 2652
EAGLE DISTRIBUTING CO. INC.; *U.S. Private*, pg. 1309
EAGLE DISTRIBUTING OF SHREVEPORT; *U.S. Private*, pg. 1309
EAGLE ROCK DISTRIBUTING COMPANY; *U.S. Private*, pg. 1310
EAGLE ROCK NORTH DISTRIBUTING COMPANY—See Eagle Rock Distributing Company; *U.S. Private*, pg. 1310
ESKYE SOLUTIONS, INC.; *U.S. Private*, pg. 1426
EVERGLADES BEVERAGE CORP.—See Sunburst Hospitality Corporation; *U.S. Private*, pg. 3865
FABIANO BROS INC.; *U.S. Private*, pg. 1458
FAIRWAYS BEVERAGE CORP.—See Sunburst Hospitality Corporation; *U.S. Private*, pg. 3865
FARRELL DISTRIBUTING CORP.; *U.S. Private*, pg. 1480

N.A.I.C.S. INDEX

424820 — WINE AND DISTILLED ...

FAUST DISTRIBUTING CO., INC.; *U.S. Private*, pg. 1484
FECHTEL BEVERAGE & SALES INC.; *U.S. Private*, pg. 1486
FERAL BREWING COMPANY PTY LTD—See COCA-COLA EUROPACIFIC PARTNERS PLC; *Int'l*, pg. 1684
FLORIDA DISTRIBUTING CO. LLC—See Reyes Holdings, LLC; *U.S. Private*, pg. 3418
FREDERICK P. WINNER, LTD.; *U.S. Private*, pg. 1602
FUN BEVERAGE INC.; *U.S. Private*, pg. 1622
GATE CITY BEVERAGE DISTRIBUTORS—See Reyes Holdings, LLC; *U.S. Private*, pg. 3418
GENERAL WHOLESALE COMPANY—See General Wholesale Company, Inc.; *U.S. Private*, pg. 1668
GIGLIO DISTRIBUTING COMPANY, INC.; *U.S. Private*, pg. 1698
GLAZER'S BEER AND BEVERAGE, LLC—See Glazer's Family of Companies; *U.S. Private*, pg. 1707
GOLD COAST BEVERAGE DISTRIBUTORS INC.; *U.S. Private*, pg. 1727
GOLD COAST EAGLE DISTRIBUTING L.P.; *U.S. Private*, pg. 1727
GOLDEN BEVERAGE COMPANY LLC; *U.S. Private*, pg. 1730
GOLDEN EAGLE DISTRIBUTING CO.; *U.S. Private*, pg. 1730
GOLDEN EAGLE DISTRIBUTING—See Golden Eagle Distributing Co.; *U.S. Private*, pg. 1730
GOLDEN EAGLE DISTRIBUTORS, INC.; *U.S. Private*, pg. 1730
GOLDRING GULF DISTRIBUTING COMPANY, LLC—See Gulf Distributing Holdings LLC; *U.S. Private*, pg. 1816
GREAT BAY DISTRIBUTORS INC.; *U.S. Private*, pg. 1762
GREAT LAKES BEVERAGE; *U.S. Private*, pg. 1764
GREENE BEVERAGE CO. INC.; *U.S. Private*, pg. 1776
GREY EAGLE DISTRIBUTORS INC.; *U.S. Private*, pg. 1784
GRIFFIN BEVERAGE CO.; *U.S. Private*, pg. 1787
GULF DISTRIBUTING COMPANY OF MOBILE LLC—See Gulf Distributing Holdings LLC; *U.S. Private*, pg. 1816
HANOI BEER ALCOHOL & BEVERAGE JOINT STOCK CORPORATION; *Int'l*, pg. 3258
HARALAMBOS DISTRIBUTING CO.; *U.S. Private*, pg. 1857
HARBOR DISTRIBUTING LLC—See Reyes Holdings, LLC; *U.S. Private*, pg. 3418
HARTFORD DISTRIBUTORS INC.; *U.S. Private*, pg. 1873
HEART OF AMERICA BEVERAGE COMPANY; *U.S. Private*, pg. 1898
HENRY J. LEE DISTRIBUTORS INC.—See Reyes Holdings, LLC; *U.S. Private*, pg. 3418
HENSLEY & CO.; *U.S. Private*, pg. 1920
HIGH GRADE BEVERAGE; *U.S. Private*, pg. 1935
HILL DISTRIBUTING COMPANY; *U.S. Private*, pg. 1945
HOFFMAN BEVERAGE CO., INC.—See Old Dominion Tobacco Company Inc.; *U.S. Private*, pg. 3008
HORIZON BEVERAGE CO.; *U.S. Private*, pg. 1980
HORIZON WINE & SPIRITS - NASHVILLE, INC.—See Berkshire Hathaway Inc.; *U.S. Public*, pg. 307
HORNELL BREWING CO., INC.—See Ferolito, Vultaggio & Sons; *U.S. Private*, pg. 1498
HOUSTON DISTRIBUTING COMPANY; *U.S. Private*, pg. 1993
HURON DISTRIBUTORS INC.; *U.S. Private*, pg. 2012
H. W. HERRELL DISTRIBUTING COMPANY; *U.S. Private*, pg. 1825
IDEAL DISTRIBUTING CO. INC.; *U.S. Private*, pg. 2036
I.H. CAFFEY DISTRIBUTING CO.; *U.S. Private*, pg. 2027
IHS DISTRIBUTING CO. INC.; *U.S. Private*, pg. 2040
INTERNATIONAL BEVERAGES INC.—See Brooklyn Brewery Corporation; *U.S. Private*, pg. 663
IOWA BEER & BEVERAGE COMPANY—See Iowa Beverage Systems Inc.; *U.S. Private*, pg. 2134
IOWA BEER & BEVERAGE LLC; *U.S. Private*, pg. 2134
JIM CAREY DISTRIBUTING COMPANY; *U.S. Private*, pg. 2208
J.J. TAYLOR COMPANIES INC.; *U.S. Private*, pg. 2167
J.J. TAYLOR DISTRIBUTING COMPANY OF MINNESOTA, INC.—See J.J. Taylor Companies Inc.; *U.S. Private*, pg. 2167
J.J. TAYLOR DISTRIBUTING OF FLORIDA, INC.—See J.J. Taylor Companies Inc.; *U.S. Private*, pg. 2167
J.J. TAYLOR DISTRIBUTING OF FLORIDA, INC.—See J.J. Taylor Companies Inc.; *U.S. Private*, pg. 2167
J & L VENTURES LLC; *U.S. Private*, pg. 2152
J&M DISTRIBUTING COMPANY, INC.; *U.S. Private*, pg. 2154
JOHN LENORE & COMPANY, INC.; *U.S. Private*, pg. 2222
JORDANO'S, INC.; *U.S. Private*, pg. 2235
KARBACH BREWING CO. LLC—See Anheuser-Busch InBev SA/NV; *Int'l*, pg. 465
KENT BEVERAGE COMPANY; *U.S. Private*, pg. 2287
KENTUCKY EAGLE BEER INC.; *U.S. Private*, pg. 2288
KOERNER DISTRIBUTOR INC.; *U.S. Private*, pg. 2336
KRAMER BEVERAGE CO. INC.; *U.S. Private*, pg. 2349
KRISTEN DISTRIBUTING CO.; *U.S. Private*, pg. 2352
KW ASSOCIATES LLC; *U.S. Private*, pg. 2359
LABATT BREWERIES ATLANTIC REGION—See Anheuser-Busch InBev SA/NV; *Int'l*, pg. 466

LABATT USA LLC—See Florida Ice and Farm Co. S.A.; *Int'l*, pg. 2708
LA GRANGE GROCERY CO.; *U.S. Private*, pg. 2368
LEE BEVERAGE CO. INC.; *U.S. Private*, pg. 2411
LEON FARMER AND COMPANY INC.; *U.S. Private*, pg. 2422
LE VECKE CORP.; *U.S. Private*, pg. 2405
THE LEWIS BEAR COMPANY; *U.S. Private*, pg. 4069
L & F DISTRIBUTORS LTD.; *U.S. Private*, pg. 2361
L & F DISTRIBUTORS—See L & F Distributors Ltd.; *U.S. Private*, pg. 2361
LIQUID INVESTMENTS, INC.; *U.S. Private*, pg. 2466
L. KNIFE & SON INC.; *U.S. Private*, pg. 2364
LOCHER BROS INC.; *U.S. Private*, pg. 2478
LOGRET IMPORT & EXPORT CO. INC.—See John Lenore & Company, Inc.; *U.S. Private*, pg. 2223
LUDWIG DISTRIBUTING CO., INC.; *U.S. Private*, pg. 2512
LUXURY BRANDS (PRIVATE) LIMITED—See Carson Cumberbatch PLC; *Int'l*, pg. 1347
MANHATTAN BEER DISTRIBUTORS LLC; *U.S. Private*, pg. 2563
THE MAPLE CITY ICE COMPANY; *U.S. Private*, pg. 4074
MARINE VIEW BEVERAGE, INC.—See CoHo Distributing LLC; *U.S. Private*, pg. 964
MARINE VIEW BEVERAGE, INC. - SUMNER—See CoHo Distributing LLC; *U.S. Private*, pg. 964
MARINE VIEW BEVERAGE, INC. - TUMWATER—See CoHo Distributing LLC; *U.S. Private*, pg. 964
MARIS DISTRIBUTING CO. INC.; *U.S. Private*, pg. 2576
MARKSTEIN BEVERAGE CO. UNION CITY; *U.S. Private*, pg. 2582
MARSALA BEVERAGE LLC; *U.S. Private*, pg. 2591
MCDONALD WHOLESALE CO.; *U.S. Private*, pg. 2632
METROPOLITAN WHOLESALE & RETAIL BEER; *U.S. Private*, pg. 2690
MICRO MAN DISTRIBUTORS, INC.; *U.S. Private*, pg. 2702
MILLER OF DENTON LTD.; *U.S. Private*, pg. 2735
MISSISSIPPI DISTRIBUTORS; *U.S. Private*, pg. 2748
MISSOURI EAGLE LLC; *U.S. Private*, pg. 2749
MITCHELL BEVERAGE, LLC—See Mitchell Companies; *U.S. Private*, pg. 2750
MITCHELL DISTRIBUTING COMPANY, INC.—See Mitchell Companies; *U.S. Private*, pg. 2750
MK DISTRIBUTORS INC.; *U.S. Private*, pg. 2753
MOLSON CANADA 2005—See Molson Coors Beverage Company; *U.S. Public*, pg. 1459
MONARCH BEVERAGE CO. INC.; *U.S. Private*, pg. 2768
MULLER INC.; *U.S. Private*, pg. 2811
NATIONAL WINE & SPIRITS, INC.; *U.S. Private*, pg. 2865
NECTAR IMPORTS LIMITED—See Asahi Group Holdings Ltd.; *Int'l*, pg. 594
NEVADA BEVERAGE CO.; *U.S. Private*, pg. 2891
NEW WEST DISTRIBUTING, INC.; *U.S. Private*, pg. 2908
N.H. SCHEPPERS DISTRIBUTING CO; *U.S. Private*, pg. 2828
NORTH COAST MERCANTILE CO.; *U.S. Private*, pg. 2944
NORTHEAST SALES DISTRIBUTING INC.; *U.S. Private*, pg. 2951
NORTH FLORIDA SALES; *U.S. Private*, pg. 2945
NORTH KANSAS CITY BEVERAGE CO.; *U.S. Private*, pg. 2945
NORTHWEST BEVERAGES INC.—See Johnson Brothers Liquor Company; *U.S. Private*, pg. 2227
ORANGE & BLUE DISTRIBUTING CO. INC.; *U.S. Private*, pg. 3036
ORRISON DISTRIBUTING LTD.; *U.S. Private*, pg. 3045
OWASCO BEVERAGE INC.; *U.S. Private*, pg. 3054
OY WENNERCO AB—See Altia Oyj; *Int'l*, pg. 392
PACIFIC BEVERAGE CO. INC.—See Jordano's, Inc.; *U.S. Private*, pg. 2236
PARADISE BEVERAGES, INC.; *U.S. Private*, pg. 3090
PAW PAW WINE DISTRIBUTORS COMPANY; *U.S. Private*, pg. 3115
PEPIN DISTRIBUTING COMPANY; *U.S. Private*, pg. 3144
PHILIPSON & SODERBERG AB—See Altia Oyj; *Int'l*, pg. 392
PHOENIX BEVERAGES, INC.; *U.S. Private*, pg. 3172
PINE STATE BEVERAGE CO.—See Pine State Trading Co.; *U.S. Private*, pg. 3183
PLATTSBURGH DISTRIBUTING CO, INC.—See Try-It Distributing Co. Inc.; *U.S. Private*, pg. 4251
PREMIER BEVERAGE COMPANY, LLC—See Breakthru Beverage Group, LLC; *U.S. Private*, pg. 643
PREMIER DISTRIBUTING COMPANY—See Hensley & Co.; *U.S. Private*, pg. 1920
PREMIUM BEERS OKLAHOMA LLC; *U.S. Private*, pg. 3251
PREMIUM BEVERAGES LIMITED—See Coopers Brewery Limited; *Int'l*, pg. 1792
PREMIUM BRANDS OF NORTHWEST ARKANSAS, INC.—See Franklin L. Haney Company; *U.S. Private*, pg. 1597
PREMIUM DISTRIBUTORS OF MARYLAND, LLC—See Reyes Holdings, LLC; *U.S. Private*, pg. 3418
PREMIUM DISTRIBUTORS OF VIRGINIA, LLC—See Reyes Holdings, LLC; *U.S. Private*, pg. 3418
QINGDAO TSINGTAO BEER & ASAHI BEVERAGE CO., LTD.—See Asahi Group Holdings Ltd.; *Int'l*, pg. 594

QUALITY BEVERAGE LP; *U.S. Private*, pg. 3317
QUALITY BEVERAGE—See Quality Beverage LP; *U.S. Private*, pg. 3318
RAHR CORPORATION; *U.S. Private*, pg. 3346
RELIABLE CHURCHILL, LLP—See Breakthru Beverage Group, LLC; *U.S. Private*, pg. 643
REYES BEVERAGE GROUP—See Reyes Holdings, LLC; *U.S. Private*, pg. 3417
R.H. BARRINGER DISTRIBUTING CO. INC.; *U.S. Private*, pg. 3336
R&K DISTRIBUTORS INC.; *U.S. Private*, pg. 3332
RMC DISTRIBUTING LLC; *U.S. Private*, pg. 3451
ROCKPORT HOLDING COMPANY INC.; *U.S. Private*, pg. 3467
RONCHETTI DISTRIBUTING CO.; *U.S. Private*, pg. 3478
R.S. LIPMAN BREWING COMPANY, LLC; *U.S. Private*, pg. 3339
S.A. VINA SANTA RITA—See Cristalerias de Chile S.A.; *Int'l*, pg. 1850
SCHILLING DISTRIBUTING CO. INC.; *U.S. Private*, pg. 3565
SCHOTT DISTRIBUTING CO. INC.; *U.S. Private*, pg. 3568
SENECA BEVERAGE CORPORATION; *U.S. Private*, pg. 3606
SHANGHAI ASEED CO., LTD.—See Aseed Holdings Co., Ltd.; *Int'l*, pg. 605
SIA MOBIL PLUS ADV—See Altia Oyj; *Int'l*, pg. 392
SILVER EAGLE DISTRIBUTORS LP; *U.S. Private*, pg. 3653
SILVER EAGLE DISTRIBUTORS LTD.; *U.S. Private*, pg. 3653
SILVER FOAM DISTRIBUTING CO.; *U.S. Private*, pg. 3653
SKOKIE VALLEY BEVERAGE COMPANY; *U.S. Private*, pg. 3683
SOUTHEAST BEVERAGE COMPANY; *U.S. Private*, pg. 3725
SOUTHERN BEVERAGE CO. INC.; *U.S. Private*, pg. 3729
SOUTHERN DISTRIBUTING CO. INC.; *U.S. Private*, pg. 3731
SOUTHERN EAGLE DISTRIBUTING, INC.; *U.S. Private*, pg. 3731
SOUTHERN EAGLE DISTRIBUTING, LLC; *U.S. Private*, pg. 3731
SPIRIT & SANZONE DISTRIBUTING CO.; *U.S. Private*, pg. 3758
SQUARE DRANKEN NEDERLAND B.V.—See B&S Group S.A.; *Int'l*, pg. 784
SR PERROTT INC.; *U.S. Private*, pg. 3767
STANDARD SALES CO. INC.; *U.S. Private*, pg. 3781
STAR INDUSTRIES INC.; *U.S. Private*, pg. 3784
STEIN DISTRIBUTING INC.—See C. Stein, Inc.; *U.S. Private*, pg. 705
STOKES DISTRIBUTING CO. INC.; *U.S. Private*, pg. 3816
STRAUB DISTRIBUTING CO. LTD; *U.S. Private*, pg. 3837
SUNCOAST BEVERAGE SALES, LLLP; *U.S. Private*, pg. 3865
SUN TZU CORP.; *U.S. Public*, pg. 1963
SUPERIOR DISTRIBUTING CO., INC.; *U.S. Private*, pg. 3876
SUPREME BEVERAGE CO. INC.; *U.S. Private*, pg. 3882
TENUTE RUFFINO S.R.L.—See Constellation Brands, Inc.; *U.S. Public*, pg. 571
T.F. LOUDERBACK, INC.—See Reyes Holdings, LLC; *U.S. Private*, pg. 3418
TOPA EQUITIES LTD, INC.; *U.S. Private*, pg. 4186
TOTAL BEVERAGE SOLUTION; *U.S. Private*, pg. 4190
TOWN & COUNTRY DISTRIBUTORS; *U.S. Private*, pg. 4196
TRIANGLE DISTRIBUTING COMPANY; *U.S. Private*, pg. 4226
TRI CITY DISTRIBUTORS LP; *U.S. Private*, pg. 4220
UNISTAN INC.; *U.S. Private*, pg. 4286
UNITED STATES BEVERAGE LLC; *U.S. Private*, pg. 4298
VENTURE SOUTH DISTRIBUTORS; *U.S. Private*, pg. 4358
WARREN DISTRIBUTING CO.; *U.S. Private*, pg. 4443
WESTERN BEVERAGE COMPANY; *U.S. Private*, pg. 4491
WESTERN BEVERAGE INC; *U.S. Private*, pg. 4491
WINDY CITY DISTRIBUTION; *U.S. Private*, pg. 4540
WINKEL DISTRIBUTING COMPANY; *U.S. Private*, pg. 4542
WISCONSIN DISTRIBUTORS L.P.; *U.S. Private*, pg. 4548
W&L SALES CO., INC.; *U.S. Private*, pg. 4417
WORLD BRANDS SERVICES LTD.—See GraceKennedy Limited; *Int'l*, pg. 3049
WRIGHT DISTRIBUTING CO., INC.; *U.S. Private*, pg. 4573
WRIGHT WISNER DISTRIBUTING CORP.; *U.S. Private*, pg. 4573
WTN SERVICES LLC—See 1-800-FLOWERS.COM, Inc.; *U.S. Public*, pg. 1
ZINK DISTRIBUTING INC; *U.S. Private*, pg. 4605

424820 — WINE AND DISTILLED ALCOHOLIC BEVERAGE MERCHANT WHOLESALERS

AB - INBEV FRANCE S.A.S.—See Anheuser-Busch InBev SA/NV; *Int'l*, pg. 464
ACADEMY DU VIN CO., LTD.—See Digital Garage, Inc.; *Int'l*, pg. 2121

424820 — WINE AND DISTILLED ...

ACCOLADE WINES JAPAN K.K.—See The Carlyle Group Inc.; *U.S. Public*, pg. 2044
ACCOLADE WINES SOUTH AFRICA (PTY) LTD.—See The Carlyle Group Inc.; *U.S. Public*, pg. 2044
ADAMBA IMPORTS INTERNATIONAL; *U.S. Private*, pg. 73
ADMIRAL WINE & LIQUOR CO.; *U.S. Private*, pg. 81
AHD ASSOCIATES INC.; *U.S. Private*, pg. 130
ALASKA DISTRIBUTORS CO.; *U.S. Private*, pg. 150
ALEXANDER BARON VON ESSEN WEINHANDELS GMBH—See Hawesko Holding AG; *Int'l*, pg. 3288
ALLIANCE BEVERAGE DISTRIBUTING COMPANY, LLC—See Breakthru Beverage Group, LLC; *U.S. Private*, pg. 643
ALLIED BEVERAGE GROUP L.L.C.; *U.S. Private*, pg. 185
ALTIA NORWAY SERVICES AS—See Altia Oyj; *Int'l*, pg. 392
ALTIA SWEDEN AB—See Altia Oyj; *Int'l*, pg. 392
AMORIM CORK AMERICA, INC.—See CORTICEIRA AMORIM, S.G.P.S., S.A.; *Int'l*, pg. 1807
ANGOSTURA LIMITED—See Angostura Holdings Limited; *Int'l*, pg. 463
ANGROPROMET PREHRANA A.D.; *Int'l*, pg. 463
ANKER AMSTERDAM SPIRITS B.V.—See B&S Group S.A.; *Int'l*, pg. 784
ARCUS AS—See Arcus ASA; *Int'l*, pg. 552
ARCUS FINLAND OY—See Arcus ASA; *Int'l*, pg. 552
ARCUS WINE BRANDS AS—See Arcus ASA; *Int'l*, pg. 552
ARTHUR G. LOMBARD & SONS INC.; *U.S. Private*, pg. 341
BACARDI GLOBAL BRANDS INC.—See Bacardi Limited; *Int'l*, pg. 794
BACARDI-MARTINI FINLAND—See Bacardi Limited; *Int'l*, pg. 794
BACARDI USA, INC.—See Bacardi Limited; *Int'l*, pg. 794
BACKYARD VINEYARDS CORP.—See Diamond Estates Wines & Spirits, Inc.; *Int'l*, pg. 2105
BADGER LIQUOR CO. INC.; *U.S. Private*, pg. 424
BANFI PRODUCT CORP.; *U.S. Private*, pg. 465
BANFI VINTNERS—See Banfi Product Corp.; *U.S. Private*, pg. 465
BANKS (BARBADOS) BREWERIES LIMITED—See Anheuser-Busch InBev SA/NV; *Int'l*, pg. 464
BARRY & FITZWILLIAM LTD.; *Int'l*, pg. 870
BB TRADE A.D.; *Int'l*, pg. 920
BEIJING BEER ASAHI CO., LTD.—See Asahi Group Holdings Ltd.; *Int'l*, pg. 593
BELLBOY BAR SUPPLY—See Bellboy Corporation; *U.S. Private*, pg. 520
THE BEN ARNOLD-SUNBELT BEVERAGE COMPANY OF SOUTH CAROLINA, L.P.—See Breakthru Beverage Group, LLC; *U.S. Private*, pg. 643
BEST CELLARS, INC.—See The Great Atlantic & Pacific Tea Company, Inc.; *U.S. Private*, pg. 4038
BEVERAGE DISTRIBUTORS COMPANY, LLC—See Breakthru Beverage Group, LLC; *U.S. Private*, pg. 643
BIBENDUM AS—See Altia Oyj; *Int'l*, pg. 392
BIBENDUM WINE LIMITED; *Int'l*, pg. 1018
BJT INC.; *U.S. Private*, pg. 568
BOISE SALES CO; *U.S. Private*, pg. 609
BOON RAWD BREWERY CO, LTD—See Asahi Group Holdings Ltd.; *Int'l*, pg. 593
BORDEAUX INDEX (HONG KONG) LTD.—See Bordeaux Index Ltd.; *Int'l*, pg. 1113
BORDEAUX INDEX LTD.; *Int'l*, pg. 1113
BORDEAUX INDEX (SINGAPORE) LTD.—See Bordeaux Index Ltd.; *Int'l*, pg. 1113
BORDEAUX INDEX US INC.—See Bordeaux Index Ltd.; *Int'l*, pg. 1113
BRESCOME BARTON INC.—See Quaker Equities Ltd., Inc.; *U.S. Private*, pg. 3316
BROWN-FORMAN AUSTRALIA PTY. LTD.—See Brown-Forman Corporation; *U.S. Public*, pg. 403
BROWN-FORMAN CORP., LOUISVILLE DISTILLERY—See Brown-Forman Corporation; *U.S. Public*, pg. 403
BROWN-FORMAN DEUTSCHLAND GMBH—See Brown-Forman Corporation; *U.S. Public*, pg. 403
BROWN-FORMAN LJUBLJANA MARKETING, D.O.O—See Brown-Forman Corporation; *U.S. Public*, pg. 403
BROWN-FORMAN WORLDWIDE (SHANGHAI) CO., LTD.—See Brown-Forman Corporation; *U.S. Public*, pg. 403
BRUSSELS CO., LTD.—See Amuse Inc.; *Int'l*, pg. 442
BRYANT DISTRIBUTING COMPANY; *U.S. Private*, pg. 673
BRYDEN STOKES LIMITED—See ANSA McAL Limited; *Int'l*, pg. 477
B&S HTG B.V.—See B&S Group S.A.; *Int'l*, pg. 784
B & S INTERNATIONAL HOLDINGS LTD.; *Int'l*, pg. 783
BUCHER VASLIN S.R.L.—See Bucher Industries AG; *Int'l*, pg. 1208
BUNDABERG DISTILLING COMPANY PTY. LIMITED—See Diageo plc; *Int'l*, pg. 2101
CAMPARI AMERICA LLC—See Alicros S.p.A.; *Int'l*, pg. 327
CAPITOL BEVERAGE SALES L.P.; *U.S. Private*, pg. 743
CARLSBERG CANADA INC.—See Carlsberg A/S; *Int'l*, pg. 1339
CARLSBERG HUNGARY SALES LIMITED LIABILITY COMPANY—See Carlsberg A/S; *Int'l*, pg. 1340
CARLSBERG INDIA PVT LTD—See Carlsberg A/S; *Int'l*, pg. 1340

CARLSBERG KAZAKHSTAN LTD.—See Carlsberg A/S; *Int'l*, pg. 1340
CARLSBERG MARKETING SDN BHD—See Carlsberg A/S; *Int'l*, pg. 1339
CARL TESDORPF GMBH—See Hawesko Holding AG; *Int'l*, pg. 3288
C&C GROUP PLC; *Int'l*, pg. 1238
C & C INTERNATIONAL LTD—See C&C Group Plc; *Int'l*, pg. 1238
CENLA BEVERAGE COMPANY, LLC—See Glazer's Family of Companies; *U.S. Private*, pg. 1707
CENTRAL DISTRIBUTORS, INC.—See Moon Distributors, Inc.; *U.S. Private*, pg. 2778
CHATEAUX ET DOMAINES WEINHANDELSGESELLSCHAFT MBH—See Hawesko Holding AG; *Int'l*, pg. 3288
CHATHAM IMPORTS INC—See Quaker Equities Ltd., Inc.; *U.S. Private*, pg. 3316
CHEVAL QUANCARD; *Int'l*, pg. 1473
CHINA TIANFEIHONG WINE, INC.; *Int'l*, pg. 1559
CHINA TOURISM GROUP DUTY FREE CORPORATION LIMITED; *Int'l*, pg. 1560
CLASSIC WINE IMPORTS, INC.—See Martignetti Companies; *U.S. Private*, pg. 2594
COFCO WINES & SPIRITS CO. LTD.—See COFCO Limited; *Int'l*, pg. 1692
COMMONWEALTH WINE & SPIRITS LLC; *U.S. Private*, pg. 987
COMPAGNIA DEI CARAIBI S.P.A.; *Int'l*, pg. 1721
COMPAGNIE CHAMPENOISE PH-CHPIPER HEIDSIECK SAS; *Int'l*, pg. 1722
COMPLI, INC.—See Vista Equity Partners, LLC; *U.S. Private*, pg. 4395
CONNECTICUT DISTRIBUTORS, INC.—See Breakthru Beverage Group, LLC; *U.S. Private*, pg. 643
CONNECT LOGISTICS SERVICES INC; *Int'l*, pg. 1769
CONSOLIDATED DISTILLED PRODUCTS—See National Wine & Spirits, Inc.; *U.S. Private*, pg. 2865
CORK DISTRIBUTORS, LLC; *U.S. Private*, pg. 1050
CORNEY & BARROW LIMITED—See Drake & Morgan Limited; *Int'l*, pg. 2200
CREAGER MERCANTILE; *U.S. Private*, pg. 1087
CRILLON IMPORTERS LTD.; *U.S. Private*, pg. 1100
CROWN WINE CELLARS LTD—See Crown Worldwide Holdings Ltd.; *Int'l*, pg. 1858
CTDD BEER IMPORTS LTD.—See Carlsberg A/S; *Int'l*, pg. 1339
CWD CHAMPAGNER- UND WEIN-DISTRIBUTIONSGESELLSCHAFT MBH & CO. KG—See Hawesko Holding AG; *Int'l*, pg. 3288
DALI BEER (GROUP) LIMITED COMPANY—See Carlsberg A/S; *Int'l*, pg. 1340
DECLAN DISTILLERS, LLC—See Constellation Brands, Inc.; *U.S. Public*, pg. 571
DELEGAT LIMITED—See Delegat's Group Limited; *Int'l*, pg. 2011
DEUTSCHWEIN CLASSICS GMBH & CO. KG—See Hawesko Holding AG; *Int'l*, pg. 3288
DIAGEO COLOMBIA S.A.—See Diageo plc; *Int'l*, pg. 2102
DIAGEO JAPAN K.K.—See Diageo plc; *Int'l*, pg. 2102
DIAGEO NORTH AMERICA, INC.—See Diageo plc; *Int'l*, pg. 2102
DIAGEO NORTH AMERICA INC.—See Diageo plc; *Int'l*, pg. 2102
DIAGEO NORTH AMERICA—See Diageo plc; *Int'l*, pg. 2102
DIAGEO SCOTLAND LIMITED—See Diageo plc; *Int'l*, pg. 2102
DIE STONSDORFEREI W. KOERNER GMBH & CO. KG—See Berentzen-Gruppe AG; *Int'l*, pg. 978
DIRECT WINES LIMITED; *Int'l*, pg. 2130
DISTILLERIE STOCK USA LTD.—See CVC Capital Partners SICAV-FIS S.A.; *Int'l*, pg. 1888
DREYFUS ASHBY INC.; *U.S. Private*, pg. 1277
DRINKS HUB ASIA PTE LTD—See Atlan Holdings Berhad; *Int'l*, pg. 674
D'VINE WINE, INC.—See Handcrafted Wines, LLC; *U.S. Private*, pg. 1852
EDWARD DILLON & CO. LTD.; *Int'l*, pg. 2316
EFES PAZARLAMA VE DAGITIM TICARET A.S.—See Anadolu Efes Biracilik ve Malt Sanayii A.S.; *Int'l*, pg. 445
EMPERIAL AMERICAS; *U.S. Private*, pg. 1384
EMPIRE DISTRIBUTORS, INC. - AUGUSTA—See Berkshire Hathaway Inc.; *U.S. Public*, pg. 312
EMPIRE DISTRIBUTORS INC-CHARLOTTE—See Berkshire Hathaway Inc.; *U.S. Public*, pg. 312
EMPIRE DISTRIBUTORS, INC. - SAVANNAH—See Berkshire Hathaway Inc.; *U.S. Public*, pg. 312
EMPIRE DISTRIBUTORS, INC.—See Berkshire Hathaway Inc.; *U.S. Public*, pg. 312
EMPIRE DISTRIBUTORS, INC. - TIFTON—See Berkshire Hathaway Inc.; *U.S. Public*, pg. 312
EMPIRE DISTRIBUTORS OF NORTH CAROLINA INC. - RALEIGH—See Berkshire Hathaway Inc.; *U.S. Public*, pg. 312
EMPIRE DISTRIBUTORS OF NORTH CAROLINA, INC. - WILMINGTON—See Berkshire Hathaway Inc.; *U.S. Public*, pg. 312
EMPIRE DISTRIBUTORS OF TENNESSEE, INC.—See Berkshire Hathaway Inc.; *U.S. Public*, pg. 304

EMPIRE MERCHANTS, LLC - BROOKLYN—See Breakthru Beverage Group, LLC; *U.S. Private*, pg. 643
EMPIRE MERCHANTS, LLC—See Breakthru Beverage Group, LLC; *U.S. Private*, pg. 643
EMPIRE MERCHANTS NORTH, LLC—See Breakthru Beverage Group, LLC; *U.S. Private*, pg. 643
ENCORE BRANDS, INC.; *U.S. Private*, pg. 1391
ENDEAVOUR GROUP LIMITED; *Int'l*, pg. 2402
ENERGY BEVERAGES LLC—See Monster Beverage Corporation; *U.S. Public*, pg. 1465
ENOTRIA GROUP LIMITED—See BlueGem Capital Partners LLP; *Int'l*, pg. 1071
EURO DISTRIBUTORS SDN BHD—See Carlsberg A/S; *Int'l*, pg. 1340
EUROPEAN FINE WINES LTD.; *Int'l*, pg. 2556
FARR VINTNERS LTD; *Int'l*, pg. 2620
FARR VINTNERS LTD—See Farr Vintners Ltd; *Int'l*, pg. 2620
FEDERAL DISTRIBUTORS, INC.; *U.S. Private*, pg. 1487
FEDERAL WINE & LIQUOR COMPANY INC.—See Fedway Associates Inc.; *U.S. Private*, pg. 1492
FEDWAY ASSOCIATES INC.; *U.S. Private*, pg. 1492
FINLANDIA VODKA WORLDWIDE LTD.—See Coca-Cola HBC AG; *Int'l*, pg. 1686
FORTH WINES LTD; *Int'l*, pg. 2738
FOX SALES; *U.S. Private*, pg. 1584
FRANK LIQUOR COMPANY INCORPORATED; *U.S. Private*, pg. 1595
FREDERICK WILDMAN & SONS LTD.—See Cantine Riunite & CIV S.C.Agr.; *Int'l*, pg. 1299
FRED NACKARD WHOLESALE LIQUOR CO.; *U.S. Private*, pg. 1601
FREE HOUSE WINE & SPIRITS LTD.—See Icon Fine Wine & Spirits Ltd.; *Int'l*, pg. 3583
FREIXENET U.S.A.—See Dr. August Oetker KG; *Int'l*, pg. 2190
FUNKIN LIMITED—See A.G. Barr plc; *Int'l*, pg. 23
FUNKY BUDDHA BREWERY LLC—See Constellation Brands, Inc.; *U.S. Public*, pg. 571
GALAXY WINE COMPANY LLC—See Wilson Daniels Wholesale LLC; *U.S. Private*, pg. 4530
GALLO WINE SALES OF NJ INC.; *U.S. Private*, pg. 1640
GALYPSO INTERNATIONAL; *U.S. Private*, pg. 1640
GATEWAY DISTRIBUTORS INC.—See Fedway Associates Inc.; *U.S. Private*, pg. 1492
GENERAL WHOLESALE COMPANY, INC.; *U.S. Private*, pg. 1668
GEORGIA CROWN DISTRIBUTING CO.; *U.S. Private*, pg. 1684
GHG COLOMBO PVT. LTD.—See Gulf Hotels Group B.S.C.; *Int'l*, pg. 3180
GILBEY'S OF IRELAND, LTD.—See C&C Group Plc; *Int'l*, pg. 1238
GLAZER'S DISTRIBUTORS OF ARKANSAS, INC.—See Glazer's Family of Companies; *U.S. Private*, pg. 1707
GLAZER'S DISTRIBUTORS OF INDIANA, LLC—See Glazer's Family of Companies; *U.S. Private*, pg. 1707
GLAZER'S DISTRIBUTORS OF IOWA, INC. - CEDAR RAPIDS—See Glazer's Family of Companies; *U.S. Private*, pg. 1707
GLAZER'S DISTRIBUTORS OF IOWA, INC.—See Glazer's Family of Companies; *U.S. Private*, pg. 1707
GLAZER'S DISTRIBUTORS OF MISSOURI, INC.—See Glazer's Family of Companies; *U.S. Private*, pg. 1707
GLAZER'S DISTRIBUTORS OF MISSOURI, INC. - SPRINGFIELD—See Glazer's Family of Companies; *U.S. Private*, pg. 1707
GLAZER'S DISTRIBUTORS OF TEXAS, INC. - DALLAS—See Glazer's Family of Companies; *U.S. Private*, pg. 1707
GLAZER'S DISTRIBUTORS OF TEXAS, INC. - PRESTIGE SALES DIVISION—See Glazer's Family of Companies; *U.S. Private*, pg. 1707
GLAZER'S DISTRIBUTORS OF TEXAS, INC. - SAN ANTONIO—See Glazer's Family of Companies; *U.S. Private*, pg. 1707
GLAZER'S DISTRIBUTORS OF TEXAS, INC.—See Glazer's Family of Companies; *U.S. Private*, pg. 1707
GLOBAL BEER GEORGIA, LLC—See Bank of Georgia Group PLC; *Int'l*, pg. 843
GLOBAL KEY INVESTMENT LIMITED; *Int'l*, pg. 2998
GOLDEN GUINEA BREWERIES PLC; *Int'l*, pg. 3029
GOYA FOODS OF FLORIDA—See Goya Foods, Inc.; *U.S. Private*, pg. 1747
GRAND VIN LTD.; *U.S. Private*, pg. 1753
GRANTHAM DISTRIBUTING COMPANY, INC.; *U.S. Private*, pg. 1757
GRAPE BEGINNINGS, INC.—See The Winebow Group, LLC; *U.S. Private*, pg. 4137
GRAPE EXPECTATIONS INC.; *U.S. Private*, pg. 1757
GREAT LAKES WINE & SPIRITS, LLC; *U.S. Private*, pg. 1765
GREENFIELD WINE COMPANY; *U.S. Private*, pg. 1778
GREEN PLAINS MADISON LLC—See Green Plains Inc.; *U.S. Public*, pg. 963
GREEN PLAINS MOUNT VERNON LLC—See Green Plains Inc.; *U.S. Public*, pg. 963

N.A.I.C.S. INDEX

424820 — WINE AND DISTILLED ...

GREEN PLAINS TRADE GROUP LLC—See Green Plains Inc.; *U.S. Public*, pg. 963
GREEN PLAINS YORK LLC—See Green Plains Inc.; *U.S. Public*, pg. 964
HAAS BROTHERS, LTD.; *U.S. Private*, pg. 1837
HAI LUEN TRADING CO., LTD.—See China Merchants Group Limited; *Int'l*, pg. 1521
HALEWOOD INTERNATIONAL LTD.; *Int'l*, pg. 3228
HANDCRAFTED WINES, LLC; *U.S. Private*, pg. 1852
HANSEATISCHES WEIN- UND SEKT-KONTOR HAWESKO GMBH & CO. KG—See Hawesko Holding AG; *Int'l*, pg. 3288
HARRISONS MARKETING & SERVICES SDN BHD—See Harrisons Holdings (Malaysia) Berhad; *Int'l*, pg. 3279
HEAVEN HILL DISTILLERIES, INC.; *U.S. Private*, pg. 1902
HENKELL & CO. SEKTKELLEREI KG—See Dr. August Oetker KG; *Int'l*, pg. 2190
THE HENRY WINE GROUP—See The Winebow Group, LLC; *U.S. Private*, pg. 4137
HILL INCORPORATED; *Int'l*, pg. 3392
HORIZON WINE & SPIRITS, INC.—See Berkshire Hathaway Inc.; *U.S. Public*, pg. 312
HOUSE OF BANFI—See Banfi Product Corp.; *U.S. Private*, pg. 465
ICONIC BRANDS, INC.; *U.S. Public*, pg. 1086
IFB AGRO INDUSTRIES LIMITED; *Int'l*, pg. 3598
INDEPENDENT LIQUOR (NZ) LTD.—See Asahi Group Holdings Ltd.; *Int'l*, pg. 593
INDIANA WHOLESALE WINE & LIQUOR CO.—See Johnson Brothers Liquor Company; *U.S. Private*, pg. 2227
INSTIL DRINKS LIMITED—See C&C Group Plc; *Int'l*, pg. 1238
IWL INTERNATIONALE WEIN LOGISTIK GMBH—See Hawesko Holding AG; *Int'l*, pg. 3288
JACK POUST & COMPANY, INC.; *U.S. Private*, pg. 2174
JERSEY NATIONAL CAPTIAL—See Fedway Associates Inc.; *U.S. Private*, pg. 1492
JOHNSON BROTHERS CAROLINA DISTRIBUTING—See Johnson Brothers Liquor Company; *U.S. Private*, pg. 2227
JOHNSON BROTHERS LIQUOR COMPANY OF RHODE ISLAND—See Johnson Brothers Liquor Company; *U.S. Private*, pg. 2227
JOHNSON BROTHERS LIQUOR COMPANY; *U.S. Private*, pg. 2227
JOYLAB, INC.—See BEENOS Inc.; *Int'l*, pg. 939
JWSIEG WINES; *U.S. Private*, pg. 2247
KENDALL-JACKSON—See Jackson Family Wines, Inc.; *U.S. Private*, pg. 2176
KING BEVERAGE INC.; *U.S. Private*, pg. 2309
KIRKWOOD DIAMOND CANADA—See Diamond Estates Wines & Spirits, Inc.; *Int'l*, pg. 2105
K&L BEVERAGE COMPANY, LLC—See Young's Holdings, Inc.; *U.S. Private*, pg. 4593
K & L DISTRIBUTORS, INC.; *U.S. Private*, pg. 2249
KOBRAND CORPORATION; *U.S. Private*, pg. 2326
LAIRD & COMPANY, INC.; *U.S. Private*, pg. 2373
LAIRD WINE & SPIRITS OF PA CO.—See Laird & Company, Inc.; *U.S. Private*, pg. 2373
LATITUDE BEVERAGE COMPANY; *U.S. Private*, pg. 2397
LAURENT-PERRIER UK LTD.—See Champagne Laurent-Perrier; *Int'l*, pg. 1440
LE MONDE DES GRANDS BORDEAUX CHATEAU CLASSIC S.A.R.L.—See Hawesko Holding AG; *Int'l*, pg. 3288
LEONARD KREUSCH, INC.; *U.S. Private*, pg. 2430
LQR HOUSE INC.; *U.S. Public*, pg. 1343
LTD PARK MV—See Bank of Georgia Group PLC; *Int'l*, pg. 843
LUXCO CLEVELAND DIVISION - BOTTLING & BLENDING FACILITY—See MGP Ingredients, Inc.; *U.S. Public*, pg. 1436
MAINE SPIRITS—See Pine State Trading Co.; *U.S. Private*, pg. 3183
MAIN & VINE LLC—See The Kroger Co.; *U.S. Public*, pg. 2108
MAISON JOHANES BOUBEE SAS—See Carrefour SA; *Int'l*, pg. 1345
MAJESTIC WINE & SPIRITS USA, INC.—See Allied Beverage Group L.L.C.; *U.S. Private*, pg. 185
MAJOR BRANDS, INC.; *U.S. Private*, pg. 2555
MARTIGNETTI COMPANIES OF NH—See Martignetti Companies; *U.S. Private*, pg. 2594
MARTIGNETTI COMPANIES; *U.S. Private*, pg. 2594
MARTIGNETTI COMPANIES - UNITED LIQUORS DIVISION—See Martignetti Companies; *U.S. Private*, pg. 2594
MATTHEW CLARK BIBENDUM LIMITED—See C&C Group Plc; *Int'l*, pg. 1238
MBC UNITED WHOLESALE LLC—See Unistan Inc.; *U.S. Private*, pg. 4287
MENDEZ & CO. INC.; *U.S. Private*, pg. 2666
MERITUS PRIME DISTRIBUTIONS INC.—See Cosco Capital, Inc.; *Int'l*, pg. 1809
MESA BEVERAGE CO., INC.—See Liquid Investments, Inc.; *U.S. Private*, pg. 2466
MHW LTD.; *U.S. Private*, pg. 2695
MICHAEL SKURNIK WINES, INC.; *U.S. Private*, pg. 2698

MIRANDA WINES PTY. LTD.—See Australian Vintage Ltd.; *Int'l*, pg. 723
M. & J. GLEESON INVESTMENTS LTD.—See C&C Group Plc; *Int'l*, pg. 1238
M&M BEVERAGES LLC; *U.S. Private*, pg. 2524
MONSIEUR HENRI WINE COMPANY—See Sazerac Company, Inc.; *U.S. Private*, pg. 3559
MONSIEUR TOUTON SELECTION LTD.—See Touton Holdings Ltd; *U.S. Private*, pg. 4193
MONTCALM WINE IMPORTERS LTD.—See Assicurazioni Generali S.p.A.; *Int'l*, pg. 647
MONTESQUIEU; *U.S. Private*, pg. 2776
MONTOSCO INC.—See Cosco Capital, Inc.; *Int'l*, pg. 1809
MOON DISTRIBUTORS, INC.; *U.S. Private*, pg. 2778
M.S. WALKER, INC. - MSW RHODE ISLAND FACILITY—See M.S. Walker, Inc.; *U.S. Private*, pg. 2529
MUTUAL WHOLESALE LIQUOR INC.; *U.S. Private*, pg. 2820
NATIONAL DISTRIBUTING COMPANY, INC.—See Republic National Distributing Company; *U.S. Private*, pg. 3402
NEGOCIANTS USA INC.—See The Winebow Group, LLC; *U.S. Private*, pg. 4137
NELSON'S GREEN BRIER DISTILLERY, LLC—See Constellation Brands, Inc.; *U.S. Public*, pg. 571
N.K.S. DISTRIBUTORS, INC.; *U.S. Private*, pg. 2828
NORTHEAST DRINKS GROUP LLC; *U.S. Private*, pg. 2950
NWS MICHIGAN INC.; *U.S. Private*, pg. 2975
OLD PEORIA COMPANY INC.—See Cosco Capital, Inc.; *U.S. Private*, pg. 3009
OPICI WINE COMPANY OF CONNECTICUT—See Opici Wine Group Inc.; *U.S. Private*, pg. 3032
OPICI WINE COMPANY OF NJ - AMERICAN BD—See Opici Wine Group Inc.; *U.S. Private*, pg. 3032
OPICI WINE GROUP INC.; *U.S. Private*, pg. 3032
OPICI WINES—See Opici Wine Group Inc.; *U.S. Private*, pg. 3032
OYSTER BAY WINES AUSTRALIA PTY LIMITED—See Delegat's Group Limited; *Int'l*, pg. 2011
PACIFIC WINE DISTRIBUTORS—See Epic Wine & Spirits; *U.S. Private*, pg. 1413
PALM BAY INTERNATIONAL, INC.; *U.S. Private*, pg. 3079
PARTIDA TEQUILA, LLC; *U.S. Private*, pg. 3101
PHILLIPS DISTRIBUTING CORP; *U.S. Private*, pg. 3170
PREMIER BEVERAGE INC.—See Glazer's Family of Companies; *U.S. Private*, pg. 1707
PREMIER WINE & SPIRITS INC.—See Cosco Capital, Inc.; *Int'l*, pg. 1809
PRESTIGE WINES DISTRIBUTORS, LLC—See Breakthru Beverage Group, LLC; *U.S. Private*, pg. 643
PRIPPS RINGNES AB—See Carlsberg A/S; *Int'l*, pg. 1340
PROVIN LTD—See Grand Vin Ltd.; *U.S. Private*, pg. 1753
PROXIMO SPIRITS, INC.; *U.S. Private*, pg. 3295
PRP WINE INTERNATIONAL INC.; *U.S. Private*, pg. 3295
PURPLE FEET WINES, LLC—See The Winebow Group, LLC; *U.S. Private*, pg. 4137
QUAKER EQUITIES LTD., INC.; *U.S. Private*, pg. 3316
QUALITY WINE COMPANY INC.—See Old Peoria Company Inc.; *U.S. Private*, pg. 3009
QUALITY WINE & SPIRITS, INC.—See The Winebow Group, LLC; *U.S. Private*, pg. 4137
REBEL WINE CO. LLC—See Trinchero Family Estates; *U.S. Private*, pg. 4232
REGAL & ROYAL WINE CO.—See Jackson Family Wines, Inc.; *U.S. Private*, pg. 2176
REPUBLIC NATIONAL DISTRIBUTING COMPANY; *U.S. Private*, pg. 3402
REPUBLIC NATIONAL DISTRIBUTING COMPANY—See Republic National Distributing Company; *U.S. Private*, pg. 3402
REPUBLIC NATIONAL DISTRIBUTING COMPANY—See Republic National Distributing Company; *U.S. Private*, pg. 3402
REPUBLIC NATIONAL DISTRIBUTING COMPANY—See Republic National Distributing Company; *U.S. Private*, pg. 3402
REPUBLIC NATIONAL DISTRIBUTING COMPANY—See Republic National Distributing Company; *U.S. Private*, pg. 3402
REPUBLIC NATIONAL DISTRIBUTING COMPANY—See Republic National Distributing Company; *U.S. Private*, pg. 3402
REPUBLIC NATIONAL DISTRIBUTING COMPANY - WASHINGTON—See Republic National Distributing Company; *U.S. Private*, pg. 3402
ROUST INC.—See CJSC Russian Standard Corporation; *Int'l*, pg. 1634
R&R MARKETING, LLC—See Breakthru Beverage Group, LLC; *U.S. Private*, pg. 643
RUDISILL ENTERPRISES, INC.; *U.S. Private*, pg. 3502
RUMS OF PUERTO RICO—See Puerto Rico Industrial Development Company; *U.S. Private*, pg. 3302
SARATOGA EAGLE SALES & SERVICES—See Try-It Distributing Co. Inc.; *U.S. Private*, pg. 4251
SAUD AUJAN & BROS. CO.—See Aujan Industries Co., L.L.C.; *Int'l*, pg. 704
SAVANNAH DISTRIBUTING CO. INC.; *U.S. Private*, pg. 3555
SEYCHELLES BREWERIES LIMITED—See Diageo plc; *Int'l*, pg. 2103

SHAW ROSS INTERNATIONAL IMPORTERS; *U.S. Private*, pg. 3628
SHINDONG WINE CO., LTD.—See Ilshin Spinning Co., Ltd.; *Int'l*, pg. 3616
SIGNATURE BEAUTY B.V.—See B&S Group S.A.; *Int'l*, pg. 784
SKYLAND DISTRIBUTING CO., INC.—See Northeast Sales Distributing Inc.; *U.S. Private*, pg. 2951
SOCIETA AGRICOLA TENIMENTI ANGELINI S.R.L.—See Angelini ACRAF S.p.A.; *Int'l*, pg. 460
SOUTHERN GLAZER'S WINE & SPIRITS, LLC—See Glazer's Family of Companies; *U.S. Private*, pg. 1707
SOUTHERN GLAZER'S WINE & SPIRITS OF HAWAII—See Glazer's Family of Companies; *U.S. Private*, pg. 1707
SOUTHERN GLAZER'S WINE & SPIRITS OF ILLINOIS-DIRECT WAREHOUSE SALES—See Glazer's Family of Companies; *U.S. Private*, pg. 1708
SOUTHERN GLAZER'S WINE & SPIRITS OF ILLINOIS—See Glazer's Family of Companies; *U.S. Private*, pg. 1708
SOUTHERN GLAZER'S WINE & SPIRITS OF NEW YORK—See Glazer's Family of Companies; *U.S. Private*, pg. 1708
SOUTHERN GLAZER'S WINE & SPIRITS OF NEW YORK - SYRACUSE—See Glazer's Family of Companies; *U.S. Private*, pg. 1708
SOUTHERN GLAZER'S WINE & SPIRITS OF PENNSYLVANIA—See Glazer's Family of Companies; *U.S. Private*, pg. 1708
SPIRIT INTERNATIONAL INC.; *U.S. Private*, pg. 3758
SPIRITS TIME INTERNATIONAL, INC.; *U.S. Public*, pg. 1919
THE STACOLE COMPANY, INC.—See The Winebow Group, LLC; *U.S. Private*, pg. 4137
STANDARD BEVERAGE CORPORATION; *U.S. Private*, pg. 3778
STANDARD DISTRIBUTING CO. INC.; *U.S. Private*, pg. 3778
STANTON SOUTH LLC—See Constellation Brands, Inc.; *U.S. Public*, pg. 571
STEELE WINES, INC.—See Shannon Ridge, Inc.; *U.S. Private*, pg. 3625
STIRRINGS LLC—See Diageo plc; *Int'l*, pg. 2103
STOLLER WHOLESALE WINE & SPIRITS; *U.S. Private*, pg. 3816
STROM AS—See Altia Oyj; *Int'l*, pg. 392
SURINAME ALCHOLIC BEVERAGES N.V.—See Angostura Holdings Limited; *Int'l*, pg. 463
TABLE & VINE, INC.—See Big Y Foods, Inc.; *U.S. Private*, pg. 555
TAKAMASAMUNE CO LTD—See Coca-Cola Bottlers Japan Holdings Inc.; *Int'l*, pg. 1684
TELIANI TRADING UKRAINE LTD.—See Bank of Georgia Group PLC; *Int'l*, pg. 843
THE TERLATO WINE GROUP; *U.S. Private*, pg. 4126
TERLATO WINES—See The Terlato Wine Group; *U.S. Private*, pg. 4126
TOBAGO MARKETING COMPANY LIMITED—See ANSA McAL Limited; *Int'l*, pg. 477
TOUTON HOLDINGS LTD; *U.S. Private*, pg. 4193
TRI COUNTY WHOLESALE DISTRIBUTORS INC.; *U.S. Private*, pg. 4220
TRINIDAD DISTILLERS LIMITED—See Angostura Holdings Limited; *Int'l*, pg. 463
TRYON DISTRIBUTING CO. LLC; *U.S. Private*, pg. 4252
T/WEE LIMITED—See ANSA McAL Limited; *Int'l*, pg. 477
TWIN LIQUORS; *U.S. Private*, pg. 4265
UNITED DISTRIBUTORS, INC.—See Unistan Inc.; *U.S. Private*, pg. 4286
THE UNITED GROUP; *U.S. Private*, pg. 4129
VERONI BRANDS CORP.; *U.S. Public*, pg. 2286
VERWALTUNGSGESELLSCHAFT HANSEATISCHES WEIN- UND SEKT-KONTOR HAWESKO M.B.H.—See Hawesko Holding AG; *Int'l*, pg. 3288
VICTOR L. ROBILIO COMPANY, INC.—See Glazer's Family of Companies; *U.S. Private*, pg. 1707
VIGNOBLEXPORT S.A.S.—See Deutsche Post AG; *Int'l*, pg. 2083
VINCOMPASS CORP.; *U.S. Private*, pg. 4385
VINEYARD BRANDS INC.; *U.S. Private*, pg. 4385
VINGRUPPEN I NORDEN AB—See Arcus ASA; *Int'l*, pg. 552
VINIFERA IMPORTS LTD.; *U.S. Private*, pg. 4385
VINORDIA AS—See Arcus ASA; *Int'l*, pg. 552
VINTAGE WINE SDN. BHD.—See Hai-O Enterprise Berhad; *Int'l*, pg. 3209
VINTAGE WINES, LLC—See The Winebow Group, LLC; *U.S. Private*, pg. 4137
VINTNER SELECT, INC.—See Michael Skurnik Wines, Inc.; *U.S. Private*, pg. 2698
VIRGIN WINES LTD.—See Direct Wines Limited; *Int'l*, pg. 2130
WASHINGTON WHOLESALE LIQUOR COMPANY, LLC—See Breakthru Beverage Group, LLC; *U.S. Private*, pg. 643
WEINLAND ARIANE ABAYAN GMBH & CO. KG—See Hawesko Holding AG; *Int'l*, pg. 3289
WEIN WOLF IMPORT GMBH & CO. VERTRIEBS KG—See Hawesko Holding AG; *Int'l*, pg. 3289

424820 — WINE AND DISTILLED ...

WEIN WOLF IMPORT GMBH & CO. VERTRIEBS KG—See Hawesko Holding AG; *Int'l*, pg. 3289
WFM BEVERAGE CORP.—See Amazon.com, Inc.; *U.S. Public*, pg. 91
WILSON DANIELS WHOLESALE LLC; *U.S. Private*, pg. 4530
WINC, INC.; *U.S. Public*, pg. 2372
WINEBOW, INC.—See The Winebow Group, LLC; *U.S. Private*, pg. 4137
WINECOMMUNE LLC; *U.S. Private*, pg. 4540
WINE&WINE CULTURE CO., LTD.—See Credit Saison Co., Ltd.; *Int'l*, pg. 1836
W.J. DEUTSCH & SONS LTD.; *U.S. Private*, pg. 4421
YOUNG'S MARKET COMPANY, LLC—See Young's Holdings, Inc.; *U.S. Private*, pg. 4593
YOUNG'S MARKET COMPANY OF ARIZONA, LLC—See Young's Holdings, Inc.; *U.S. Private*, pg. 4593
YOUNG'S MARKET COMPANY OF OREGON, LLC—See Young's Holdings, Inc.; *U.S. Private*, pg. 4593
YOUNG'S MARKET COMPANY OF WASHINGTON, LLC—See Young's Holdings, Inc.; *U.S. Private*, pg. 4593
YOUNG'S MARKET - HAWAII—See Young's Holdings, Inc.; *U.S. Private*, pg. 4593

424910 — FARM SUPPLIES MERCHANT WHOLESALERS

ABELL CORPORATION; *U.S. Private*, pg. 37
ACE OHLSSON PTY LIMITED—See Elders Limited; *Int'l*, pg. 2346
ACETO AGRICULTURAL CHEMICALS CORP.—See Aceto Corporation; *U.S. Private*, pg. 58
ACHP LEVICE A.S.—See Agrofert Holding, a.s.; *Int'l*, pg. 218
ACI LOGISTICS LIMITED—See Advanced Chemical Industries Limited; *Int'l*, pg. 158
THE ADAMS GROUP INC.; *U.S. Private*, pg. 3981
ADAMS WHOLESALE SUPPLY, INC.—See SiteOne Landscape Supply, Inc.; *U.S. Public*, pg. 1888
ADJUVANTS UNLIMITED, LLC—See KFM Enterprises, LLC; *U.S. Private*, pg. 2300
ADM ALLIANCE NUTRITION—See Archer-Daniels-Midland Company; *U.S. Public*, pg. 181
ADM ANIMAL NUTRITION (CAMBODIA) CO., LTD.—See Archer-Daniels-Midland Company; *U.S. Public*, pg. 181
ADM BENSON-QUINN COMPANY—See Archer-Daniels-Midland Company; *U.S. Public*, pg. 181
ADM GRAIN CO.—See Archer-Daniels-Midland Company; *U.S. Public*, pg. 181
ADMIS SINGAPORE PTE. LIMITED—See Archer-Daniels-Midland Company; *U.S. Public*, pg. 183
ADM MYANMAR COMPANY LIMITED—See Archer-Daniels-Midland Company; *U.S. Public*, pg. 182
ADM STF PTE. LTD.—See Archer-Daniels-Midland Company; *U.S. Public*, pg. 182
ADM STF SWITZERLAND SARL—See Archer-Daniels-Midland Company; *U.S. Public*, pg. 182
ADM VIETNAM CO., LTD.—See Archer-Daniels-Midland Company; *U.S. Public*, pg. 183
AGBEST LLC; *U.S. Private*, pg. 126
AG DISTRIBUTORS, INC.—See Tennessee Farmers Cooperative; *U.S. Private*, pg. 3967
AG/GRO FERTILIZER COMPANY; *U.S. Private*, pg. 125
AGLAND CO-OP; *U.S. Private*, pg. 128
AG-LAND FS, INC.; *U.S. Private*, pg. 125
AG PARTNERS CO-OP; *U.S. Private*, pg. 124
AGRA LIMITED; *Int'l*, pg. 213
AGRAR CARGO SPEDITION GMBH—See AGRAVIS Raiffeisen AG; *Int'l*, pg. 215
AGRARPRODUKTENHANDEL GMBH—See BayWa AG; *Int'l*, pg. 915
AGRAVIS KORNHAUS OSTWESTFALEN GMBH—See AGRAVIS Raiffeisen AG; *Int'l*, pg. 214
AGRAVIS MISCHFUTTER OLDENBURG/OSTFRIESLAND GMBH—See AGRAVIS Raiffeisen AG; *Int'l*, pg. 214
AGRAVIS MISCHFUTTER WESTFALEN GMBH—See AGRAVIS Raiffeisen AG; *Int'l*, pg. 214
AGRELIANT GENETICS LLC - LEBANON—See Groupe Limagrain Holding SA; *Int'l*, pg. 3108
AGRICOM LIMITED—See DLF Seeds A/S; *Int'l*, pg. 2141
AGRICULTURAL COMMODITIES INC.; *U.S. Private*, pg. 129
AGRICULTURAL SERVICE INC.; *U.S. Private*, pg. 129
AGRI-KING INC.; *U.S. Private*, pg. 129
AGRI NEGOCE S.A.—See Ameropa AG; *Int'l*, pg. 423
AGRO DISTRIBUTION, LLC—See CHS INC.; *U.S. Public*, pg. 491
AGROSAAT D.O.O—See BayWa AG; *Int'l*, pg. 915
AGTECH GLOBAL INTERNATIONAL, INC.; *U.S. Public*, pg. 63
AGVENTURES, LLC.; *U.S. Private*, pg. 130
AG VIEW FS, INC.; *U.S. Private*, pg. 125
AL GHURAIR FOODS - ANIMAL NUTRITION LLC—See Al Ghurair Investment LLC; *Int'l*, pg. 278
A.L. GILBERT COMPANY; *U.S. Private*, pg. 26
ALLERTON SUPPLY CO.; *U.S. Private*, pg. 180
ALLIED SEED LLC; *U.S. Private*, pg. 187
ALL PRO HORTICULTURE, INC.—See SiteOne Landscape Supply, Inc.; *U.S. Public*, pg. 1888
AMERICAN SEEDS, LLC—See Bayer Aktiengesellschaft; *Int'l*, pg. 908
AMERIGROW RECYCLING - DELRAY, LIMITED PARTNERSHIP; *U.S. Private*, pg. 259
AMEROPA AG; *Int'l*, pg. 423
AMEROPA ASIA PTE LTD—See Ameropa AG; *Int'l*, pg. 423
AMEROPA AUSTRALIA PTY LTD—See Ameropa AG; *Int'l*, pg. 423
AMEROPA (BEIJING) TRADING CO. LTD.—See Ameropa AG; *Int'l*, pg. 423
AMEROPA CHILE - SAS—See Ameropa AG; *Int'l*, pg. 423
AMEROPA COMMODITIES (PTY) LTD.—See Ameropa AG; *Int'l*, pg. 423
AMEROPA CONOSUR SRL.—See Ameropa AG; *Int'l*, pg. 423
AMEROPA DO BRASIL COMERCIAL AGRICOLA LTDA.—See Ameropa AG; *Int'l*, pg. 423
AMEROPA DUNGEMITTEL GMBH—See Ameropa AG; *Int'l*, pg. 423
AMEROPA EGYPT—See Ameropa AG; *Int'l*, pg. 424
AMEROPA FRANCE S.A.R.L—See Ameropa AG; *Int'l*, pg. 424
AMEROPA GESELLSCHAFT M.B.H.—See Ameropa AG; *Int'l*, pg. 424
AMEROPA IBERIA S.L.—See Ameropa AG; *Int'l*, pg. 424
AMEROPA INDIA PVT LTD—See Ameropa AG; *Int'l*, pg. 424
AMEROPA ITALIA SRL—See Ameropa AG; *Int'l*, pg. 424
AMEROPA LJUBLJANA D.O.O.—See Ameropa AG; *Int'l*, pg. 424
AMEROPA MIDDLE EAST - DMCC—See Ameropa AG; *Int'l*, pg. 424
AMEROPA POLSKA SP Z O.O.—See Ameropa AG; *Int'l*, pg. 424
AMEROPA ROMANIA SERVICES S.R.L.—See Ameropa AG; *Int'l*, pg. 424
AMEROPA TURKEY—See Ameropa AG; *Int'l*, pg. 424
AMEROPA UK LTD.—See Ameropa AG; *Int'l*, pg. 424
AMEROPA VIETNAM—See Ameropa AG; *Int'l*, pg. 424
AMEROPA ZITNI TERMINAL D.O.O.—See Ameropa AG; *Int'l*, pg. 424
AMIR MARKETING & INVESTMENTS IN AGRICULTURE LTD.; *Int'l*, pg. 428
ANCOM BIOSCIENCE SDN. BHD.—See Ancom Nylex Berhad; *Int'l*, pg. 449
ANDERSON HAY & GRAIN CO. INC.; *U.S. Private*, pg. 277
THE ANDERSONS LAWN FERTILIZER DIVISION, INC.—See The Andersons Incorporated; *U.S. Public*, pg. 2035
ANDFJORD SALMON AS; *Int'l*, pg. 450
AN GRIANAN GRAIN COMPANY LIMITED—See Donegal Investment Group Plc; *Int'l*, pg. 2163
ANHUI HUILONG AGRICULTURAL MEANS OF PRODUCTION CO., LTD.; *Int'l*, pg. 468
ANPARIO INC.—See Anpario plc; *Int'l*, pg. 474
ANPARIO MALAYSIA SDN. BHD.—See Anpario plc; *Int'l*, pg. 475
ANPARIO PTY. LTD.—See Anpario plc; *Int'l*, pg. 475
ANPARIO SAUDE E NUTRICAO ANIMAL LTDA.—See Anpario plc; *Int'l*, pg. 475
ANPARIO (SHANGHAI) BIOTECH CO., LTD.—See Anpario plc; *Int'l*, pg. 474
ANPARIO (THAILAND) LTD.—See Anpario plc; *Int'l*, pg. 474
APC NUTRITION, INC.—See Lauridsen Group Inc.; *U.S. Private*, pg. 2399
APC NUTRITION, LTD.—See Lauridsen Group Inc.; *U.S. Private*, pg. 2399
APC POLSKA SP. Z O.O.—See Lauridsen Group Inc.; *U.S. Private*, pg. 2399
ARCHER DANIELS MIDLAND CO.—See Archer-Daniels-Midland Company; *U.S. Public*, pg. 183
ARCHER DANIELS MIDLAND KOREA LLC—See Archer-Daniels-Midland Company; *U.S. Public*, pg. 184
ARCHONIC, LLC—See Marchex, Inc.; *U.S. Public*, pg. 1364
ARETT SALES CORPORATION; *U.S. Private*, pg. 318
ARVESTA BV; *Int'l*, pg. 587
ASTA AGRICULTURAL CO. LTD.—See Arab Supply & Trading Co.; *Int'l*, pg. 532
ASTRACHEM UKRAINE LTD.—See ASTRA INDUSTRIAL GROUP COMPANY; *Int'l*, pg. 657
ASTRA INDUSTRIAL COMPLEX CO. LTD.—See ASTRA INDUSTRIAL GROUP COMPANY; *Int'l*, pg. 657
ATHENS SEED COMPANY; *U.S. Private*, pg. 368
ATKINSON GRAIN & FERTILIZER INC.; *U.S. Private*, pg. 369
AUSWEST SEEDS PTY LIMITED—See Agria Corporation; *Int'l*, pg. 216
BANGKOK PRODUCE MERCHANDISING PUBLIC COMPANY LIMITED—See Charoen Pokphand Foods Public Company Limited; *Int'l*, pg. 1451
BARENBRUG RESEARCH USA—See Barenbrug Holding B.V.; *Int'l*, pg. 864
BARENBRUG USA—See Barenbrug Holding B.V.; *Int'l*, pg. 864
BASF AGRICULTURAL SOLUTIONS BELGIUM N.V.—See BASF SE; *Int'l*, pg. 872
BAYER CROPSCIENCE S.R.L.—See Bayer Aktiengesellschaft; *Int'l*, pg. 903
BAYERISCHE FUTTERSAATBAU GMBH—See BayWa AG; *Int'l*, pg. 917
BAYER KOREA LTD.—See Bayer Aktiengesellschaft; *Int'l*, pg. 905
BAYER LTD.—See Bayer Aktiengesellschaft; *Int'l*, pg. 905
BAY-HOUSTON TOWING CO; *U.S. Private*, pg. 495
BAY LAKES COOPERATIVE; *U.S. Private*, pg. 494
BAYWA BULGARIA EOOD—See BayWa AG; *Int'l*, pg. 916
BAYWA CR SPOL. S.R.O.—See BayWa AG; *Int'l*, pg. 916
BAYWA CS GMBH—See BayWa AG; *Int'l*, pg. 916
BEHN MEYER AGRICARE, PT.—See Behn Meyer (D) Holding AG & Co.; *Int'l*, pg. 941
BEJO SEEDS INC.—See Bejo Zaden B.V.; *Int'l*, pg. 962
BEN TAYLOR INC.; *U.S. Private*, pg. 523
B&G JAPAN CO., LTD.—See Cofco Biotechnology Co., Ltd.; *Int'l*, pg. 1691
B&G JAPAN CO., LTD.—See Finasucre S.A.; *Int'l*, pg. 2670
BHJ CANADA MEAT PRODUCTS INC.—See Lauridsen Group Inc.; *U.S. Private*, pg. 2399
BIG HORN COOPERATIVE MARKETING ASSOCIATION; *U.S. Private*, pg. 553
BINGHAM COOPERATIVE INC.; *U.S. Private*, pg. 560
BIOMAR IBERIA S.A.—See Aktieselskabet Schouw & Co.; *Int'l*, pg. 265
BIOMAR OOO—See Aktieselskabet Schouw & Co.; *Int'l*, pg. 265
BIOMAR SRL—See Aktieselskabet Schouw & Co.; *Int'l*, pg. 265
BLEYHL FARM SERVICE INC.; *U.S. Private*, pg. 581
BOLIVAR FARMERS EXCHANGE; *U.S. Private*, pg. 610
BONEY'S FARM STORE, INC.; *U.S. Private*, pg. 614
BOORT GRAIN COOPERATIVE LTD—See CHS INC.; *U.S. Public*, pg. 491
BORDER STATES COOPERATIVES—See CHS INC.; *U.S. Public*, pg. 491
BORDER VALLEY TRADING LTD; *U.S. Private*, pg. 618
BOR S.R.O.—See BayWa AG; *Int'l*, pg. 915
BOULDINCORP; *U.S. Private*, pg. 623
BOURDEAUS BROS OF MIDDLEBURY; *U.S. Private*, pg. 624
BRODERNA BERNER HANDELS AB—See Berner Oy; *Int'l*, pg. 988
BTR FARMERS CO-OP; *U.S. Private*, pg. 675
BUTTE COUNTY RICE GROWERS ASSOCIATION; *U.S. Private*, pg. 698
BUTTONWILLOW WAREHOUSE CO., INC.—See Tech Agricultural, Inc.; *U.S. Private*, pg. 3951
BWI COMPANIES INC.; *U.S. Private*, pg. 700
CACHE RIVER VALLEY SEED, LLC; *U.S. Private*, pg. 712
CALATA CORPORATION; *Int'l*, pg. 1261
CALAWAY TRADING, INC.—See Pacific Ag, LLC; *U.S. Private*, pg. 3065
CALIFORNIA STYLE PALMS, INC.; *U.S. Public*, pg. 423
CALLAHAN'S GENERAL STORE; *U.S. Private*, pg. 722
C-A-L RANCH STORES; *U.S. Private*, pg. 704
CARCAFE LTDA C.I.—See ED&F Man Holdings Limited; *Int'l*, pg. 2302
CARDINAL CHEMICALS INC.; *U.S. Private*, pg. 750
CARGILL AG HORIZONS—See Cargill, Inc.; *U.S. Private*, pg. 755
CARGILL AUSTRIA HANDELSGESELLSCHAFT M.B.H.—See Cargill, Inc.; *U.S. Private*, pg. 755
CARGILL DE MEXICO, S.A. DE C.V.—See Cargill, Inc.; *U.S. Private*, pg. 759
CARGILL INC.—See Cargill, Inc.; *U.S. Private*, pg. 757
CARGILL INC.—See Cargill, Inc.; *U.S. Private*, pg. 757
CARGILL INC.—See Cargill, Inc.; *U.S. Private*, pg. 757
CARGILL INC.—See Cargill, Inc.; *U.S. Private*, pg. 757
CARLIN SALES CORPORATION; *U.S. Private*, pg. 764
CAROLINA EASTERN AIKEN INC.—See Carolina Eastern Inc.; *U.S. Private*, pg. 767
CAROLINA EASTERN INC.; *U.S. Private*, pg. 767
CAROLINA EASTERN-MOLONY INC.—See Carolina Eastern Inc.; *U.S. Private*, pg. 767
CAROLINA EASTERN-VAIL INC.; *U.S. Private*, pg. 768
CARRS PROPERTIES LIMITED—See Carr's Group PLC; *Int'l*, pg. 1343
CAUDILL SEED & WAREHOUSE CO.; *U.S. Private*, pg. 794
CEDAR COUNTRY COOPERATIVE; *U.S. Private*, pg. 804
CEDAR COUNTY COOPERATIVE; *U.S. Private*, pg. 804
CEFETRA GROUP B.V.—See BayWa AG; *Int'l*, pg. 917
CEFETRA IBERICA S.L.U.—See BayWa AG; *Int'l*, pg. 917
CEFETRA LIMITED—See BayWa AG; *Int'l*, pg. 917
CEFETRA POLSKA SP. Z O.O.—See BayWa AG; *Int'l*, pg. 917
CEFETRA S.P.A.—See BayWa AG; *Int'l*, pg. 917
CENTRAL COOP; *U.S. Private*, pg. 820
CENTRAL ILLIANA AG INC.; *U.S. Private*, pg. 821
CENTRAL VALLEY AG COOPERATIVE; *U.S. Private*, pg. 825
CENTRAL WISCONSIN COOPERATIVE; *U.S. Private*, pg. 826
CENTRA SOTA COOPERATIVE; *U.S. Private*, pg. 818
CENTRO AGRICOLO FRIULANO S.R.L.—See BayWa AG; *Int'l*, pg. 917
CERES SOLUTIONS, LLP; *U.S. Private*, pg. 840
CF INDUSTRIES SALES, LLC—See CF Industries Holdings, Inc.; *U.S. Public*, pg. 477

N.A.I.C.S. INDEX

424910 — FARM SUPPLIES MERCH...

CHAMPION SEED COMPANY; *U.S. Private*, pg. 847
CHANDLER CO-OP; *U.S. Private*, pg. 848
CHANNEL BIO, LLC—See Bayer Aktiengesellschaft; *Int'l*, pg. 908
THE CHAS. C. HART SEED CO.; *U.S. Private*, pg. 4007
CHEMINOVA INDIA LIMITED—See FMC Corporation; *U.S. Public*, pg. 861
CHS AGRITRADE BULGARIA LTD.—See CHS INC.; *U.S. Public*, pg. 491
CHS AGRITRADE D.O.O—See CHS INC.; *U.S. Public*, pg. 491
CHS AGRITRADE HUNGARY LTD.—See CHS INC.; *U.S. Public*, pg. 491
CHS AGROMARKET, LLC—See CHS INC.; *U.S. Public*, pg. 491
CHS CANADA LP—See CHS INC.; *U.S. Public*, pg. 491
CHS ENERGY CANADA, INC.—See CHS INC.; *U.S. Public*, pg. 491
CHS HALLOCK, LLC—See CHS INC.; *U.S. Public*, pg. 491
CHSINC IBERICA SL—See CHS INC.; *U.S. Public*, pg. 492
CHS INDUSTRIES LTD—See CHS INC.; *U.S. Public*, pg. 491
CHS ITALY S.R.L.—See CHS INC.; *U.S. Public*, pg. 491
CHS KOREA, LLC—See CHS INC.; *U.S. Public*, pg. 491
CHS-M&M, INC.—See CHS INC.; *U.S. Public*, pg. 492
CHS-M&M, INC. - WIGGINS—See CHS INC.; *U.S. Public*, pg. 492
CHS NORTHWEST—See CHS INC.; *U.S. Public*, pg. 491
CHS-ROCHESTER—See CHS INC.; *U.S. Public*, pg. 492
CHS SERBIA D.O.O. NOVI SAD—See CHS INC.; *U.S. Public*, pg. 491
CHS (SHANGHAI) TRADING CO., LTD—See CHS INC.; *U.S. Public*, pg. 491
CHS-SHIPMAN, INC.—See CHS INC.; *U.S. Public*, pg. 492
CHS-SUB WHATCOM, INC—See CHS INC.; *U.S. Public*, pg. 492
CHS (TAIWAN) COMMODITY TRADING CO. LTD—See CHS INC.; *U.S. Public*, pg. 491
CHS TARIM VE GIDA SANAYII LIMITED SIRKETI—See CHS INC.; *U.S. Public*, pg. 491
CHS UKRAINE, LLC—See CHS INC.; *U.S. Public*, pg. 492
CHS-WINGER—See CHS INC.; *U.S. Public*, pg. 492
CITIZENS LLC; *U.S. Private*, pg. 903
CJ EUROPE GMBH—See CJ Corporation; *Int'l*, pg. 1632
CLEARWELL QUARRIES LIMITED—See Breedon Group plc; *Int'l*, pg. 1144
COASTAL AGROBUSINESS INC. - COLERAIN PLANT—See Coastal AgroBusiness Inc.; *U.S. Private*, pg. 955
COASTAL AGROBUSINESS INC. - DILLON PLANT—See Coastal AgroBusiness Inc.; *U.S. Private*, pg. 955
COASTAL AGROBUSINESS INC. - HAMILTON PLANT—See Coastal AgroBusiness Inc.; *U.S. Private*, pg. 955
COASTAL AGROBUSINESS INC. - HENDERSON PLANT—See Coastal AgroBusiness Inc.; *U.S. Private*, pg. 955
COASTAL AGROBUSINESS INC. - HENDERSONVILLE PLANT—See Coastal AgroBusiness Inc.; *U.S. Private*, pg. 955
COASTAL AGROBUSINESS INC. - KINSTON PLANT—See Coastal AgroBusiness Inc.; *U.S. Private*, pg. 955
COASTAL AGROBUSINESS INC. - MURFREESBORO PLANT—See Coastal AgroBusiness Inc.; *U.S. Private*, pg. 955
COASTAL AGROBUSINESS INC. - PANTEGO PLANT—See Coastal AgroBusiness Inc.; *U.S. Private*, pg. 955
COASTAL CAGES LTD.—See Hampidjan hf; *Int'l*, pg. 3239
COMMODITY MARKETING COMPANY; *U.S. Private*, pg. 985
COMMODITY SPECIALISTS COMPANY INC.; *U.S. Private*, pg. 985
CONSUMERS COOP RICHLAND COUNTY; *U.S. Private*, pg. 1026
CONSUMERS SUPPLY DISTRIBUTING, LLC—See CHS INC.; *U.S. Public*, pg. 492
CO-OP ATLANTIC; *Int'l*, pg. 1679
CO-OP SERVICE CENTER INC.; *U.S. Private*, pg. 953
COPAG-CIA CAPITAL DE ARMAZENS GERAIS S.A.—See ED&F Man Holdings Limited; *Int'l*, pg. 2302
COUNTRY PRIDE SERVICES CO-OPERATIVE; *U.S. Private*, pg. 1067
COUNTRYSIDE COOPERATIVE, INC.; *U.S. Private*, pg. 1067
CROOKHAM COMPANY INC.; *U.S. Private*, pg. 1103
CROSMAN SEED CORPORATION; *U.S. Private*, pg. 1104
CROSSROADS AG LLC; *U.S. Private*, pg. 1108
CULPEPER FARMERS COOPERATIVE INC; *U.S. Private*, pg. 1121
CUNNINGHAM FARMS INC.; *U.S. Private*, pg. 1123
C-W VALLEY CO-OP; *U.S. Private*, pg. 704
DAKOTA AGRONOMY PARTNERS, LLC—See CHS INC.; *U.S. Public*, pg. 492
DAKOTA PLAINS COOPERATIVE-LISBON—See Dakota Plains Cooperative; *U.S. Private*, pg. 1147
DAKOTA PLAINS COOPERATIVE; *U.S. Private*, pg. 1147
DALGETY AGRA POLSKA SP. Z.O.O.—See ARYZTA AG; *Int'l*, pg. 588
DAN'S FEED & SEED INC.; *U.S. Private*, pg. 1152
DANUFERT HANDELSGESELLSCHAFT MBH—See BayWa AG; *Int'l*, pg. 917
DASER AGRO S.A.—See Corteva, Inc.; *U.S. Public*, pg. 581
D&B SUPPLY COMPANY INC.; *U.S. Private*, pg. 1136
D&D TEXAS OUTFITTERS INC.; *U.S. Private*, pg. 1137
THE DE LONG CO. INC.; *U.S. Private*, pg. 4019
THE DE LONG COMPANY, INC.—See The De Long Co. Inc.; *U.S. Private*, pg. 4019
DELTA GROWERS ASSOCIATION; *U.S. Private*, pg. 1200
DELUXE FEEDS INC.; *U.S. Private*, pg. 1202
DENVER WHOLESALE FLORISTS OF ALBUQUERQUE—See Denver Wholesale Florists Company; *U.S. Private*, pg. 1208
DONOVAN FARMERS ELEVATOR COOP; *U.S. Private*, pg. 1261
DOOR COUNTY COOPERATIVE INC.; *U.S. Private*, pg. 1261
DORMAN BROTHERS, LLC—See J.R. Simplot Company; *U.S. Private*, pg. 2170
DOW AGROSCIENCES SOUTHERN AFRICA (PROPRIETARY) LIMITED—See Corteva, Inc.; *U.S. Public*, pg. 582
DRAGON CLAW USA INC.; *U.S. Private*, pg. 1271
DUPONT AGRICULTURAL PRODUCTS—See Corteva, Inc.; *U.S. Public*, pg. 582
EDDS SUPPLIES INC.; *U.S. Private*, pg. 1332
ED&F MAN CAPITAL MARKETS HONG KONG LIMITED—See ED&F Man Holdings Limited; *Int'l*, pg. 2303
ED&F MAN CAPITAL MARKETS MENA LIMITED—See ED&F Man Holdings Limited; *Int'l*, pg. 2303
ED&F MAN COMMODITIES EGYPT LIMITED—See ED&F Man Holdings Limited; *Int'l*, pg. 2303
ED&F MAN MOCAMBIQUE LIMITADA—See ED&F Man Holdings Limited; *Int'l*, pg. 2303
ED&F MAN TERMINALS IRELAND LIMITED—See ED&F Man Holdings Limited; *Int'l*, pg. 2303
ED&F MAN VENEZUELA S.A.—See ED&F Man Holdings Limited; *Int'l*, pg. 2303
EFFINGHAM EQUITY INC.; *U.S. Private*, pg. 1343
ELDON C. STUTSMAN INC.; *U.S. Private*, pg. 1351
EL TORO EXPORT; *U.S. Private*, pg. 1349
EQUOVIS GMBH—See AGRAVIS Raiffeisen AG; *Int'l*, pg. 215
ETX INC.—See El Toro Export; *U.S. Private*, pg. 1349
EUROGREEN GMBH—See BayWa AG; *Int'l*, pg. 917
EVANS LANDSCAPING INC.; *U.S. Private*, pg. 1435
EVERGREEN GARDEN CENTER, LLC—See GrowLife, Inc.; *U.S. Public*, pg. 972
FAITHWAY FEED CO. INC.; *U.S. Private*, pg. 1466
FARM COUNTRY CO-OP; *U.S. Private*, pg. 1474
FARMERS COOPERATIVE ASSOCIATION; *U.S. Private*, pg. 1476
FARMERS COOPERATIVE CO.; *U.S. Private*, pg. 1477
FARMERS COOPERATIVE INC.; *U.S. Private*, pg. 1477
FARMERS COOPERATIVE; *U.S. Private*, pg. 1476
FARMERS CO-OP SUPPLY & SHIPPING ASSOCIATION; *U.S. Private*, pg. 1476
FARMERS INDUSTRIES LIMITED—See GEA Group Aktiengesellschaft; *Int'l*, pg. 2897
FARMERS PRODUCE EXCHANGE; *U.S. Private*, pg. 1478
FARMERS SUPPLY ASSOCIATION; *U.S. Private*, pg. 1479
FARMERS UNION OIL COMPANY; *U.S. Private*, pg. 1479
FARMERS UNION OIL CO.; *U.S. Private*, pg. 1479
FARMERS WAREHOUSE—See A.L. Gilbert Company; *U.S. Private*, pg. 27
FARM SERVICE COMPANY; *U.S. Private*, pg. 1475
FARM SERVICE INCORPORATED; *U.S. Private*, pg. 1475
FAUJI FERTILIZER COMPANY LIMITED - PLANT I (GOTH MACHHI)—See Fauji Foundation; *Int'l*, pg. 2623
FEDERATION SAHANALA VANILLE—See Archer-Daniels-Midland Company; *U.S. Public*, pg. 185
FEED PRODUCTS SOUTH INC.; *U.S. Private*, pg. 1492
FIFIELD LAND CO.; *U.S. Private*, pg. 1505
FINN ALL SEASONS—See Finn Corporation; *U.S. Private*, pg. 1510
F.M. BROWN'S SONS INC.; *U.S. Private*, pg. 1456
FMC QUIMICA DO BRASIL LTDA—See FMC Corporation; *U.S. Public*, pg. 862
FMC (SUZHOU) CROP CARE CO., LTD—See FMC Corporation; *U.S. Public*, pg. 861
FORAGE GENETICS INTERNATIONAL, LLC—See Land O'Lakes, Inc.; *U.S. Private*, pg. 2383
FORFARMERS BEELITZ GMBH—See ForFarmers Group B.V; *Int'l*, pg. 2732
FORFARMERS BELGIUM B.V.B.A—See ForFarmers Group B.V; *Int'l*, pg. 2732
FORFARMERS BM GMBH—See ForFarmers Group B.V; *Int'l*, pg. 2732
FORFARMERS DML B.V.—See ForFarmers Group B.V; *Int'l*, pg. 2732
FORFARMERS HAMBURG GMBH & CO. KG—See ForFarmers Group B.V; *Int'l*, pg. 2732
FORFARMERS HENDRIX B.V.—See ForFarmers Group B.V; *Int'l*, pg. 2732
FORFARMERS LANGFORDEN GMBH—See ForFarmers Group B.V; *Int'l*, pg. 2732
FORFARMERS THESING MISCHFUTTER GMBH & CO. KG—See ForFarmers Group B.V; *Int'l*, pg. 2732
FORFARMERS UK LTD.—See ForFarmers Group B.V; *Int'l*, pg. 2732
FORNAZOR INTERNATIONAL INC.; *U.S. Private*, pg. 1572
FORSHAW INC.; *U.S. Private*, pg. 1573
FOSTERS INC.; *U.S. Private*, pg. 1579
FRICK SERVICES INC.; *U.S. Private*, pg. 1610
FRONTIER FS COOPERATIVE; *U.S. Private*, pg. 1615
FRONTIER FS COOPERATIVE—See Frontier FS Cooperative; *U.S. Private*, pg. 1615
FROY ASA—See The Goldman Sachs Group, Inc.; *U.S. Public*, pg. 2081
FULL CIRCLE AG; *U.S. Private*, pg. 1620
GAGE'S FERTILIZER & GRAIN, INC.; *U.S. Private*, pg. 1634
GARDENER'S SUPPLY COMPANY; *U.S. Private*, pg. 1643
GARDEN-WISE DISTRIBUTORS INC.; *U.S. Private*, pg. 1643
GARICK, LLC—See Hendricks Holding Company, Inc.; *U.S. Private*, pg. 1915
GIBSON FARMERS COOPERATIVE—See Tennessee Farmers Cooperative; *U.S. Private*, pg. 3967
GIGANTE SALMON AS; *Int'l*, pg. 2972
GIG GEFLUGELINTEGRATION GMBH—See AGRAVIS Raiffeisen AG; *Int'l*, pg. 215
GIMFLOW SDN. BHD.—See Greenyield Berhad; *Int'l*, pg. 3078
GIRASOLES DEL PLATA S.A.—See Adecoagro S.A.; *Int'l*, pg. 141
GOLD COIN (ZHANGZHOU) CO., LTD.—See Aboitiz Equity Ventures, Inc.; *Int'l*, pg. 66
GOLDEN FURROW FERTILIZER - BLOOMFIELD—See Golden Furrow Fertilizer Inc.; *U.S. Private*, pg. 1730
GOWAN COMPANY LLC; *U.S. Private*, pg. 1746
GRAINES VOLTZ SA; *Int'l*, pg. 3052
GRAINLAND COOPERATIVE; *U.S. Private*, pg. 1752
GRANGETTO FARM & GARDEN SUPPLY CO.; *U.S. Private*, pg. 1754
GREEN-IT TURF PRODUCTS INC.—See Central Garden & Pet Company; *U.S. Public*, pg. 473
GREENPOINT AG, LLC—See Tennessee Farmers Cooperative; *U.S. Private*, pg. 3967
GREENPOINT AG, LLC—See WinField United, LLC; *U.S. Private*, pg. 4541
GREEN PRAIRIE INTERNATIONAL INC.; *Int'l*, pg. 3072
GREEN RESOURCE, LLC.; *U.S. Private*, pg. 1774
GREENSMITH—See Arett Sales Corporation; *U.S. Private*, pg. 318
GREEN SOL INC.—See Frit Incorporated; *U.S. Private*, pg. 1612
GREEN SOURCE, LLC—See Bunzl plc; *Int'l*, pg. 1218
GREGER TOPSOIL—See Haines & Kibblehouse Inc.; *U.S. Private*, pg. 1841
GRIFFIN GREENHOUSE & NURSERY SUPPLIES, INC. - CONNECTICUT—See Griffin Greenhouse & Nursery Supplies, Inc.; *U.S. Private*, pg. 1787
GRIFFIN GREENHOUSE & NURSERY SUPPLIES, INC. - MAINE—See Griffin Greenhouse & Nursery Supplies, Inc.; *U.S. Private*, pg. 1787
GRIFFIN GREENHOUSE & NURSERY SUPPLIES, INC. - NEW JERSEY—See Griffin Greenhouse & Nursery Supplies, Inc.; *U.S. Private*, pg. 1787
GRIFFIN GREENHOUSE & NURSERY SUPPLIES, INC. - VIRGINIA—See Griffin Greenhouse & Nursery Supplies, Inc.; *U.S. Private*, pg. 1788
GROSOUTH INC.; *U.S. Private*, pg. 1792
GROWMARK FS, LLC—See Growmark, Inc.; *U.S. Private*, pg. 1795
GSI GROUP, LLC—See AGCO Corporation; *U.S. Public*, pg. 58
GUJARAT AMBUJA EXPORTS LTD.; *Int'l*, pg. 3175
GUYOMARC'H - VCN COMPANY LIMITED—See Archer-Daniels-Midland Company; *U.S. Public*, pg. 185
HAIFA NORTH AMERICA INCORPORATED—See TransResources, Inc.; *U.S. Private*, pg. 4206
HANSON BATH AND PORTLAND STONE LIMITED—See Heidelberg Materials AG; *Int'l*, pg. 3311
HAP SENG FERTILIZERS SDN. BHD.—See Hap Seng Consolidated Berhad; *Int'l*, pg. 3268
HARBACH GILLAN & NIXON INC.; *U.S. Private*, pg. 1857
HARMONY COUNTRY COOPERATIVE; *U.S. Private*, pg. 1866
HARVEST LAND CO-OP INC.; *U.S. Private*, pg. 1875
HARVEST POWER INC.; *U.S. Private*, pg. 1877
HARVEY FERTILIZER & GAS CO.; *U.S. Private*, pg. 1877
HAWAII GROWER PRODUCTS, INC.—See J.R. Simplot Company; *U.S. Private*, pg. 2170
HEARTLAND AG INC.; *U.S. Private*, pg. 1899
HEARTLAND COOPERATIVE SERVICES; *U.S. Private*, pg. 1899
HEDEGAARD A/S—See Danish Agro AmbA; *Int'l*, pg. 1963
HELM FERTILIZER CORP—See HELM AG; *Int'l*, pg. 3337
HELM FERTILIZER HELENA TERMINAL INC.—See HELM AG; *Int'l*, pg. 3337

424910 — FARM SUPPLIES MERCH...

HELM FERTILIZER TERMINAL INC.—See HELM AG; *Int'l*, pg. 3337
HENRY FARMERS COOPERATIVE INC.; *U.S. Private*, pg. 1918
HERITAGE FS INC.; *U.S. Private*, pg. 1923
HL HAMBURGER LEISTUNGSFUTTER GMBH—See AGRAVIS Raiffeisen AG; *Int'l*, pg. 215
HODOGAYA CHEMICAL EUROPE GMBH—See Hodogaya Chemical Co., Ltd.; *Int'l*, pg. 3438
HULL COOPERATIVE ASSOCIATION INC.; *U.S. Private*, pg. 2005
HUMMERT INTERNATIONAL INC.; *U.S. Private*, pg. 2007
HUNAN HONG YING BIOTECH CO., LTD.—See Guangdong VTR Bio-Tech Co., Ltd.; *Int'l*, pg. 3161
ILLINI FS INC.; *U.S. Private*, pg. 2042
IMASPRO RESOURCES SDN. BHD.—See IMASPRO Corporation Berhad; *Int'l*, pg. 3620
INTEGRITY FEEDS; *U.S. Private*, pg. 2102
INTERMOUNTAIN FARMERS ASSOCIATION - DRAPER FEED MILL—See Intermountain Farmers Association; *U.S. Private*, pg. 2113
INTERMOUNTAIN FARMERS ASSOCIATION - NORTH REGION FEED MILL—See Intermountain Farmers Association; *U.S. Private*, pg. 2113
INTERMOUNTAIN FARMERS ASSOCIATION; *U.S. Private*, pg. 2113
INTERMOUNTAIN FARMERS ASSOCIATION - SOUTH REGION FEED MILL—See Intermountain Farmers Association; *U.S. Private*, pg. 2113
INTERNATIONAL CHEMICAL COMPANY; *U.S. Private*, pg. 2115
INTERSAATZUCHT GMBH—See BayWa AG; *Int'l*, pg. 918
IOWA LIMESTONE COMPANY; *U.S. Private*, pg. 2135
JACOB STERN & SONS, INC. - TEXAS DIVISION—See Jacob Stern & Sons, Inc.; *U.S. Private*, pg. 2179
JAMES MARITIME HOLDINGS, INC.; *U.S. Public*, pg. 1187
J.B. PEARL SALES & SERVICE INC.; *U.S. Private*, pg. 2158
THE J.C. ROBINSON SEED COMPANY; *U.S. Private*, pg. 4058
J.D. HEISKELL & CO.; *U.S. Private*, pg. 2161
JIM HICKS & COMPANY INC.; *U.S. Private*, pg. 2209
JIMMY SANDERS, INC.—See Apollo Global Management, Inc.; *U.S. Public*, pg. 153
JIRDON AGRI CHEMICALS, INC.—See Western Cooperative Company; *U.S. Private*, pg. 4492
J.M. MCCONKEY & CO. INC.; *U.S. Private*, pg. 2169
JOHNSON CITY CHEMICAL CO. INC.; *U.S. Private*, pg. 2227
JONATHAN GREEN & SONS; *U.S. Private*, pg. 2231
JUMBUCK AUSTRALIA PTY. LTD.—See Aumake Limited; *Int'l*, pg. 705
JUNG SEED GENETICS—See Bayer Aktiengesellschaft; *Int'l*, pg. 908
KANESHO SOIL TREATMENT SPRL/BVBA—See Agro-Kanesho Co., Ltd.; *Int'l*, pg. 218
KEITHLY-WILLIAMS SEEDS INC.; *U.S. Private*, pg. 2274
KINNEY BONDED WAREHOUSE INC.; *U.S. Private*, pg. 2313
KNIGHT SEED COMPANY INC.; *U.S. Private*, pg. 2322
KOHYO AMERICA, INC.—See AEON Co., Ltd.; *Int'l*, pg. 178
KOVA FERTILIZER INC. - OHIO DIVISION—See Kova Fertilizer Inc.; *U.S. Private*, pg. 2345
KOVA FERTILIZER INC.; *U.S. Private*, pg. 2345
KUGLER COMPANY; *U.S. Private*, pg. 2356
LABUDDE GROUP, INC.; *U.S. Private*, pg. 2371
LA HACIENDA LIMITED—See Griffon Corporation; *U.S. Public*, pg. 969
L.A. HEARNE COMPANY; *U.S. Private*, pg. 2364
LAKELAND COOPERATIVE; *U.S. Private*, pg. 2376
LAKE MILLS FEED & GRAIN INC.—See Vita Plus Corporation; *U.S. Private*, pg. 4405
LAKE VILLAGE SEED & TIRE CO.; *U.S. Private*, pg. 2376
LANDHANDEL KNAUP GMBH—See BayWa AG; *Int'l*, pg. 918
LAND VIEW FERTILIZER INC.; *U.S. Private*, pg. 2384
LANGE-STEGMANN CO., INC.; *U.S. Private*, pg. 2389
LARSEN COOPERATIVE CO.—See CHS INC.; *U.S. Public*, pg. 492
LAUGHERY VALLEY AG CO-OP, INC.; *U.S. Private*, pg. 2397
LAWN AND GOLF SUPPLY CO., INC.; *U.S. Private*, pg. 2401
LEAFIELD FEEDS LTD.—See ForFarmers Group B.V.; *Int'l*, pg. 2732
LEFFINGWELL AG SALES CO. INC.; *U.S. Private*, pg. 2415
LEWIS-CLARK TERMINAL, INC.—See CHS INC.; *U.S. Public*, pg. 492
LHD LANDHANDEL DREBKAU IMPORT - UND EXPORT GMBH—See BayWa AG; *Int'l*, pg. 918
LIMAGRAIN ITALIA SPA—See Groupe Limagrain Holding SA; *Int'l*, pg. 3107
LIVENGOOD FEEDS INC.; *U.S. Private*, pg. 2473
L&L NURSERY SUPPLY, INC.; *U.S. Private*, pg. 2363
L&L PLANT SOIL DIVISION—See L&L Nursery Supply, Inc.; *U.S. Private*, pg. 2363
L&M FERTILIZER INC.; *U.S. Private*, pg. 2363

LYNGSO GARDEN MATERIALS, INC.; *U.S. Private*, pg. 2521
MAGNUM FEEDYARD, LLC.; *U.S. Private*, pg. 2549
MAGNUSON SOD/HAAG SERVICES; *U.S. Private*, pg. 2549
MATERIAL CHANGE LIMITED—See Heathpatch Ltd.; *Int'l*, pg. 3305
MAVIGA EAST AFRICA LIMITED—See ED&F Man Holdings Limited; *Int'l*, pg. 2303
MAVIGA GHANA LIMITED—See ED&F Man Holdings Limited; *Int'l*, pg. 2303
MEDITERRANEAN SEEDS LTD.—See Bayer Aktiengesellschaft; *Int'l*, pg. 908
MEHERRIN AGRICULTURE & CHEMICAL CO.; *U.S. Private*, pg. 2660
MFA ENTERPRISES, INC.—See MFA Incorporated; *U.S. Private*, pg. 2693
MG PRODUKT KFT—See Ameropa AG; *Int'l*, pg. 424
MICHLIG AGRICENTER INC.; *U.S. Private*, pg. 2701
MID-CENTRAL PRODUCTS LLC—See United Animal Health, Inc.; *U.S. Private*, pg. 4287
MIDSOUTH FARMERS CO-OP; *U.S. Private*, pg. 2717
MID VALLEY AGRICULTURAL SERVICES, INC.; *U.S. Private*, pg. 2706
MID-WEST FERTILIZER INC.; *U.S. Private*, pg. 2709
MILLER-BOWIE SUPPLY CO.; *U.S. Private*, pg. 2736
MINERA DEL ALTIPLANO SA—See FMC Corporation; *U.S. Public*, pg. 862
MISR PIONEER SEEDS COMPANY S.A.E.—See Corteva, Inc.; *U.S. Public*, pg. 582
MIXON SEED CO., INC.; *U.S. Private*, pg. 2752
MONSANTO CO. - ANKENY—See Bayer Aktiengesellschaft; *Int'l*, pg. 908
MONSANTO CO. - ASHTON—See Bayer Aktiengesellschaft; *Int'l*, pg. 908
MONSANTO CO. - BEAMAN—See Bayer Aktiengesellschaft; *Int'l*, pg. 908
MONSANTO CO. - BLOOMINGTON—See Bayer Aktiengesellschaft; *Int'l*, pg. 908
MONSANTO CO. - FARMER CITY—See Bayer Aktiengesellschaft; *Int'l*, pg. 908
MONSANTO CO. - GRINNELL—See Bayer Aktiengesellschaft; *Int'l*, pg. 908
MONSANTO CO. - STROMSBURG—See Bayer Aktiengesellschaft; *Int'l*, pg. 909
MONSANTO CO. - WASHINGTON DC—See Bayer Aktiengesellschaft; *Int'l*, pg. 909
MONSANTO CO. - WEST FARGO—See Bayer Aktiengesellschaft; *Int'l*, pg. 909
MONSANTO GIDA VE TARIM TICARET LIMITED SIRKETI—See Bayer Aktiengesellschaft; *Int'l*, pg. 909
MONSANTO HUNGARIA KFT.—See Bayer Aktiengesellschaft; *Int'l*, pg. 909
MONSANTO POLSKA SP. Z O.O.—See Bayer Aktiengesellschaft; *Int'l*, pg. 909
MONSANTO UKRAINE LLC—See Bayer Aktiengesellschaft; *Int'l*, pg. 909
MONTE VISTA CO-OP ASSOCIATION, INC.; *U.S. Private*, pg. 2775
MOSAIC POTASH CARLSBAD INC—See The Mosaic Company; *U.S. Public*, pg. 2116
MOYER & SON INC.; *U.S. Private*, pg. 2802
M TAIRHAIZ RAKTAIROZAISI EIS SZOLGAILTATOI KORLAITOLT FELELOSSEIGU TAIRSASAIG—See CHS INC.; *U.S. Public*, pg. 492
MUMMES INC.; *U.S. Private*, pg. 2813
MYANMAR GOLD COIN INTERNATIONAL CO., LTD.—See Gold Coin Holdings Sdn Bhd; *Int'l*, pg. 3024
NEBRASKA HARVEST CENTER INC.—See Claas KGaA mbH; *Int'l*, pg. 1640
NELSON MILL & AGRI-CENTER; *U.S. Private*, pg. 2883
NEW HORIZON F S INC.; *U.S. Private*, pg. 2897
NEWSOM SEED INC.—See SiteOne Landscape Supply, Inc.; *U.S. Public*, pg. 1889
NEXT GENERATION, INC.—See Kova Fertilizer Inc.; *U.S. Private*, pg. 2345
NEXUS AG (PTY) LTD—See Element Solutions Inc.; *U.S. Public*, pg. 728
NH3 SERVICE COMPANY; *U.S. Private*, pg. 2924
NICHINO EUROPE CO., LTD.—See Adeka Corporation; *Int'l*, pg. 142
NORDER SUPPLY, INC (NSI); *U.S. Private*, pg. 2936
NORTH CENTRAL CO-OP INC.; *U.S. Private*, pg. 2943
NORTHEAST TEXAS FARMERS CO-OP; *U.S. Private*, pg. 2951
NORTHERN RESOURCES COOPERATIVE; *U.S. Private*, pg. 2954
NORTHWEST FARM FOOD COOPERATIVE, INC.—See The Scoular Company; *U.S. Private*, pg. 4115
NORTHWEST WHOLESALE INC.; *U.S. Private*, pg. 2962
NUNHEMS DO BRASIL COMERCIO DE SEMENTES LTDA.—See Bayer Aktiengesellschaft; *Int'l*, pg. 903
NUNHEMS MAROC SARL—See BASF SE; *Int'l*, pg. 884
NUNHEMS MEXICO S.A. DE C.V.—See Bayer Aktiengesellschaft; *Int'l*, pg. 903
NUNHEMS NETHERLANDS B.V.—See Bayer Aktiengesellschaft; *Int'l*, pg. 903
OHIO MULCH SUPPLY INC.; *U.S. Private*, pg. 3005

OLDHAM CHEMICALS COMPANY INC.; *U.S. Private*, pg. 3010
ORSCHELN FARM & HOME LLC—See Orscheln Group; *U.S. Private*, pg. 3045
ORSCHELN INDUSTRIES PLATING DIVISION—See Orscheln Group; *U.S. Private*, pg. 3045
OTTAWA COOPERATIVE ASSOCIATION; *U.S. Private*, pg. 3049
THE PAGE SEED CO.; *U.S. Private*, pg. 4090
PALITAL GMBH & CO. KG.—See Bewital GmbH & Co. KG; *Int'l*, pg. 1004
PARIS FARMERS UNION; *U.S. Private*, pg. 3095
PASTURE GENETICS PTY LTD—See S&W Seed Co.; *U.S. Public*, pg. 1832
PAVO PFERDENAHRUNG GMBH—See ForFarmers Group B.V.; *Int'l*, pg. 2732
PAWNEE COUNTY COOPERATIVE ASSOCIATION; *U.S. Private*, pg. 3115
PENN STATE SEED CO. INC.; *U.S. Private*, pg. 3135
PETER SCHOENFELD S.A.—See ED&F Man Holdings Limited; *Int'l*, pg. 2303
PGG HSC FEED COMPANY, LLC—See CHS INC.; *U.S. Public*, pg. 492
PHI SEEDS PRIVATE LIMITED—See Corteva, Inc.; *U.S. Public*, pg. 582
PIONEER ARGENTINA, S.R.L.—See Corteva, Inc.; *U.S. Public*, pg. 582
PIONEER HI-BRED AUSTRALIA, PTY LTD.—See Corteva, Inc.; *U.S. Public*, pg. 582
PIONEER HI-BRED CANADA COMPANY—See Corteva, Inc.; *U.S. Public*, pg. 582
PIONEER HI-BRED INTERNATIONAL, INC.—See Corteva, Inc.; *U.S. Public*, pg. 582
PIONEER HI-BRED INTERNATIONAL—See Corteva, Inc.; *U.S. Public*, pg. 583
PIONEER HI-BRED INTERNATIONAL—See Corteva, Inc.; *U.S. Public*, pg. 583
PIONEER HI-BRED INTERNATIONAL—See Corteva, Inc.; *U.S. Public*, pg. 583
PIONEER HI-BRED INTERNATIONAL—See Corteva, Inc.; *U.S. Public*, pg. 583
PIONEER HI-BRED INTERNATIONAL—See Corteva, Inc.; *U.S. Public*, pg. 583
PIONEER HI-BRED INTERNATIONAL—See Corteva, Inc.; *U.S. Public*, pg. 583
PIONEER HI-BRED INTERNATIONAL—See Corteva, Inc.; *U.S. Public*, pg. 583
PIONEER HI-BRED INTERNATIONAL—See Corteva, Inc.; *U.S. Public*, pg. 583
PIONEER HI-BRED INTERNATIONAL—See Corteva, Inc.; *U.S. Public*, pg. 583
PIONEER HI-BRED INTERNATIONAL—See Corteva, Inc.; *U.S. Public*, pg. 583
PIONEER HI-BRED INTERNATIONAL—See Corteva, Inc.; *U.S. Public*, pg. 583
PIONEER HI-BRED ITALIA SRL—See Corteva, Inc.; *U.S. Public*, pg. 583
PIONEER HI-BRED PRODUCTION COMPANY—See Corteva, Inc.; *U.S. Public*, pg. 583
PIONEER HI-BRED SERVICES GMBH—See Corteva, Inc.; *U.S. Public*, pg. 583
PIONEER HI-BRED (THAILAND) CO. LIMITED—See Corteva, Inc.; *U.S. Public*, pg. 582
PIONEER SEMENCES S.A.S—See Corteva, Inc.; *U.S. Public*, pg. 583
PIONEER TOHUMCULUK A.S.—See Corteva, Inc.; *U.S. Public*, pg. 583
PLANTATION PRODUCTS INC; *U.S. Private*, pg. 3197
PLANTERS COOPERATIVE ASSOCIATION; *U.S. Private*, pg. 3197
PLANTERS GRAIN COOP ODEM TEXAS; *U.S. Private*, pg. 3197
PLANT IMPACT PLC - MORRISVILLE BRANCH—See Croda International plc; *Int'l*, pg. 1852
POINSETT FERTILIZER INC.; *U.S. Private*, pg. 3221
POOLE CHEMICAL CO. INC.; *U.S. Private*, pg. 3228
PORT CITY NITROGEN INC.—See Carolina Eastern Inc.; *U.S. Private*, pg. 768
POSEY COUNTY FARM BUREAU COOP ASSOCIATION; *U.S. Private*, pg. 3233
PRIMAGRA, A.S.—See Agrofert Holding, a.s.; *Int'l*, pg. 219
PRO-AG FARMERS COOPERATIVE; *U.S. Private*, pg. 3270
PRODUCER AG, LLC—See CHS INC.; *U.S. Public*, pg. 492
PRODUCERS CO-OP ASSOCIATION, INC.; *U.S. Private*, pg. 3272
PRODUCERS HYBRIDS; *U.S. Private*, pg. 3273
PT. ANPARIO BIOTECH INDONESIA—See Anpario plc; *Int'l*, pg. 475
PT BINA GUNA KIMIA—See FMC Corporation; *U.S. Public*, pg. 862
PT GOLD COIN INDONESIA—See Gold Coin Holdings Sdn Bhd; *Int'l*, pg. 3024
PUREFUN! INC.; *U.S. Private*, pg. 3306

N.A.I.C.S. INDEX

424920 — BOOK, PERIODICAL, A...

PUTNALS PREMIUM PINESTRAW INC.; *U.S. Private*, pg. 3307
QC SUPPLY LLC—See Charlesbank Capital Partners, LLC; *U.S. Private*, pg. 856
QUALI-PRO; *U.S. Private*, pg. 3317
QUALI TRADE INC.; *U.S. Private*, pg. 3317
QUALITY LIQUID FEEDS INC.; *U.S. Private*, pg. 3319
RAIFFEISEN AGRO D.O.O—See BayWa AG; *Int'l*, pg. 918
RAIFFEISEN AGRO MAGYARORSZAG KFT.—See BayWa AG; *Int'l*, pg. 918
RAIFFEISEN-LAGERHAUS GMBH—See BayWa AG; *Int'l*, pg. 918
RAIFFEISEN TRGOVINA D.O.O.—See BayWa AG; *Int'l*, pg. 918
RANCH & HOME SUPPLY LLC; *U.S. Private*, pg. 3352
RAVEN APPLIED TECHNOLOGIES, LLC—See CNH Industrial N.V.; *Int'l*, pg. 1676
RCP TECHNOLOGIES SDN. BHD.—See Greenyield Berhad; *Int'l*, pg. 3078
RED RIVER SPECIALTIES INC.; *U.S. Private*, pg. 3375
RED RIVER VAN ECK B.V.—See ACOMO N.V.; *Int'l*, pg. 108
REIFF GRAIN & FEED INC.; *U.S. Private*, pg. 3391
REINDERS INCORPORATED; *U.S. Private*, pg. 3392
RENERCO GEM 2 GMBH—See BayWa AG; *Int'l*, pg. 918
RENK SEED COMPANY; *U.S. Private*, pg. 3398
REUDINK B.V.—See ForFarmers Group B.V.; *Int'l*, pg. 2732
RICH FARMS INC.; *U.S. Private*, pg. 3426
RICKETTS FARM SERVICE, INC.; *U.S. Private*, pg. 3431
RIVER COUNTRY COOPERATIVE; *U.S. Private*, pg. 3443
RIVER COUNTRY CO-OP; *U.S. Private*, pg. 3443
ROCKINGHAM COOPERATIVE FARM BUREAU; *U.S. Private*, pg. 3466
ROCKY MOUNTAIN AGRONOMICS INC.; *U.S. Private*, pg. 3468
ROHM AND HAAS MEXICO, S. DE R.L. DE C.V.—See Dow Inc.; *U.S. Public*, pg. 686
ROHM AND HAAS SHANGHAI CHEMICAL INDUSTRY CO., LTD.—See DuPont de Nemours, Inc.; *U.S. Public*, pg. 694
ROSENS, INC.—See Rosens Diversified, Inc.; *U.S. Private*, pg. 3484
RWA INTERNATIONAL HOLDING GMBH—See BayWa AG; *Int'l*, pg. 919
RWA RAIFFEISEN AGRO D.O.O—See BayWa AG; *Int'l*, pg. 918
SABINA FARMERS EXCHANGE INC.; *U.S. Private*, pg. 3520
SAFEGUARD CHEMICAL CORPORATION; *U.S. Private*, pg. 3524
SAN LUIS OBISPO COUNTY FARM SUPPLY; *U.S. Private*, pg. 3541
SANTA MARIA SEEDS INC.; *U.S. Private*, pg. 3547
SAPEC AGRO MACAU LTD.—See Bridgepoint Group Plc; *Int'l*, pg. 1155
SAPEC AGRO S.A.—See Bridgepoint Group Plc; *Int'l*, pg. 1155
SAPEC AGRO, S.A.U.—See Bridgepoint Group Plc; *Int'l*, pg. 1155
SECURITY SEED & CHEMICAL LLC; *U.S. Private*, pg. 3596
SEED RESEARCH OF OREGON; *U.S. Private*, pg. 3597
SEEDWAY, LLC—See Growmark, Inc.; *U.S. Private*, pg. 1795
SEMENTI DOM DOTTO S.P.A.—See Assicurazioni Generali S.p.A.; *Int'l*, pg. 647
SEMINIS VEGETABLE SEEDS, INC.—See Bayer Aktiengesellschaft; *Int'l*, pg. 909
SEMPOL SPOL. S R.O—See BayWa AG; *Int'l*, pg. 919
SERVCO FS CO-OPERATIVE; *U.S. Private*, pg. 3614
SETNA NUTRICION SA—See Archer-Daniels-Midland Company; *U.S. Public*, pg. 185
SHANGHAI GUANGZHAO PLANT FAST GROWING TECHNOLOGY CO., LTD—See Guangzhao Industrial Forest Biotechnology Group Limited; *Int'l*, pg. 3164
SIEMER ENTERPRISES INC.; *U.S. Private*, pg. 3646
SIERRA PACIFIC TURF SUPPLY; *U.S. Private*, pg. 3647
SILVEREDGE COOPERATIVE; *U.S. Private*, pg. 3663
SKAGIT FARMERS SUPPLY; *U.S. Private*, pg. 3681
SMITH FEED SERVICE INC.—See Vita Plus Corporation; *U.S. Private*, pg. 4405
SOUTH DAKOTA SOYBEAN PROCESSORS LLC; *U.S. Public*, pg. 1911
SOUTHEAST COOPERATIVE SERVICE CO.; *U.S. Private*, pg. 3725
SOUTHEASTERN FARMERS COOPERATIVE; *U.S. Private*, pg. 3727
SOUTHERN AGRICULTURAL INSECTICIDES, INC.; *U.S. Private*, pg. 3729
SOUTHERN AGRICULTURAL INSECTICIDES—See Southern Agricultural Insecticides, Inc.; *U.S. Private*, pg. 3729
SOUTHERN AGRICULTURAL INSECTICIDES—See Southern Agricultural Insecticides, Inc.; *U.S. Private*, pg. 3729
THE SOUTHERN MULCH COMPANY, LLC; *U.S. Private*, pg. 4119
SRC CORP.; *U.S. Private*, pg. 3767
STANISLAUS FARM SUPPLY COMPANY; *U.S. Private*, pg. 3782
STATELINE COOPERATIVE INC.; *U.S. Private*, pg. 3793
ST. CLAIR SERVICE CO.; *U.S. Private*, pg. 3771
STEPHEN PASTURE SEEDS PTY LIMITED—See Agria Corporation; *Int'l*, pg. 216
STEPHENSON MARKETING COOPERATIVE, INC.; *U.S. Private*, pg. 3803
STIMULAN B.V.—See ForFarmers Group B.V.; *Int'l*, pg. 2733
STINE SEED COMPANY; *U.S. Private*, pg. 3813
STOCKMEN'S SUPPLY, INC.—See Animart Inc.; *U.S. Private*, pg. 283
STONINGTON FERTILIZER INC.; *U.S. Private*, pg. 3830
SUN BULB COMPANY, INC.; *U.S. Private*, pg. 3858
SUNBURST SEED COMPANY; *U.S. Private*, pg. 3865
SUN GRO HORTICULTURE DISTRIBUTION, INC.—See IKO Enterprises Ltd.; *Int'l*, pg. 3612
SUN GRO HORTICULTURE, INC.—See IKO Enterprises Ltd.; *Int'l*, pg. 3612
SUNRISE FS—See Growmark, Inc.; *U.S. Private*, pg. 1795
SUNTURF INC.; *U.S. Private*, pg. 3874
SUPERIOR AG RESOURCES CO-OP, INC.; *U.S. Private*, pg. 3875
SUPERIOR AG RESOURCES CO-OP—See Superior Ag Resources Co-op, Inc.; *U.S. Private*, pg. 3875
SUPERIOR AG RESOURCES CO-OP—See Superior Ag Resources Co-op, Inc.; *U.S. Private*, pg. 3875
SUPERIOR AG RESOURCES CO-OP—See Superior Ag Resources Co-op, Inc.; *U.S. Private*, pg. 3875
SUR GRO PLANT FOOD CO., INC.; *U.S. Private*, pg. 3883
SVALOEF WEIBULL AB—See BASF SE; *Int'l*, pg. 871
SWAN NET GUNDRY LTD.—See Hampidjan hf; *Int'l*, pg. 3239
SYLVITE SALES (USA); *U.S. Private*, pg. 3898
SYNGENTA AGRO D.O.O.—See China National Chemical Corporation; *Int'l*, pg. 1529
SYNGENTA ASIA PACIFIC PTE. LTD.—See China National Chemical Corporation; *Int'l*, pg. 1529
SYNGENTA BANGLADESH LIMITED—See China National Chemical Corporation; *Int'l*, pg. 1529
SYNGENTA CANADA INC.—See China National Chemical Corporation; *Int'l*, pg. 1529
SYNGENTA CROP PROTECTION MONTHEY SA—See China National Chemical Corporation; *Int'l*, pg. 1530
SYNGENTA CROP PROTECTION SDN BHD—See China National Chemical Corporation; *Int'l*, pg. 1530
SYNGENTA CZECH S.R.O.—See China National Chemical Corporation; *Int'l*, pg. 1530
SYNGENTA JAPAN CO., LTD.—See China National Chemical Corporation; *Int'l*, pg. 1530
SYNGENTA LAN—See China National Chemical Corporation; *Int'l*, pg. 1530
SYNGENTA POLSKA SP. Z O.O.—See China National Chemical Corporation; *Int'l*, pg. 1530
SYNGENTA S.A.—See China National Chemical Corporation; *Int'l*, pg. 1530
SYNGENTA SEEDS CO. LTD.—See China National Chemical Corporation; *Int'l*, pg. 1530
SYNGENTA SEEDS, LLC—See China National Chemical Corporation; *Int'l*, pg. 1530
SYNGENTA SLOVAKIA S.R.O.—See China National Chemical Corporation; *Int'l*, pg. 1530
SYNGENTA TAIWAN LTD—See China National Chemical Corporation; *Int'l*, pg. 1530
TAJBA, A.S.—See Agrofert Holding, a.s.; *Int'l*, pg. 219
TECH AGRICULTURAL, INC.; *U.S. Private*, pg. 3951
TERRAL SEED, INC.—See Corteva, Inc.; *U.S. Public*, pg. 583
T H AGRI-CHEMICALS, INC.; *U.S. Private*, pg. 3909
TIPTON FARMERS COOPERATIVE—See Tennessee Farmers Cooperative; *U.S. Private*, pg. 3967
TIPTON FARMERS COOPERATIVE—See WinField United, LLC; *U.S. Private*, pg. 4541
TRACTOR SUPPLY CO. OF TEXAS, LP—See Tractor Supply Company; *U.S. Public*, pg. 2178
TRAYLOR CHEMICAL & SUPPLY CO.; *U.S. Private*, pg. 4215
TRIANGLE CHEMICAL CO. INC.; *U.S. Private*, pg. 4226
TRI-STATE GARDEN SUPPLY INC.; *U.S. Private*, pg. 4224
TURF CARE SUPPLY CORP—See Platinum Equity, LLC; *U.S. Private*, pg. 3209
TURF & GARDEN, INC.—See Pool Corporation; *U.S. Public*, pg. 1701
TWO RIVERS COOPERATIVE; *U.S. Private*, pg. 4266
UNITED COOPERATIVE—See United Cooperative; *U.S. Private*, pg. 4290
UNITED FEED COMPANY—See Hayel Saeed Anam Group of Companies; *Int'l*, pg. 3291
UNITED SUPPLIERS, INC.—See Land O'Lakes, Inc.; *U.S. Private*, pg. 2383
URWILER OIL & FERTILIZER INC.; *U.S. Private*, pg. 4316
VALLEY FARMERS COOPERATIVE; *U.S. Private*, pg. 4333
VAN DIEST SUPPLY COMPANY—See Van Diest Family, LLC; *U.S. Private*, pg. 4339
VAN ZYVERDEN INC.; *U.S. Private*, pg. 4341
VETS PLUS, INC.; *U.S. Private*, pg. 4374
V-G SUPPLY COMPANY INC.; *U.S. Private*, pg. 4328
VOLUNTARY PURCHASING GROUPS, INC.; *U.S. Private*, pg. 4411
WABASH VALLEY SERVICE CO.; *U.S. Private*, pg. 4424
WACONIA FARM SUPPLY; *U.S. Private*, pg. 4424
WAGNER'S LLC; *U.S. Private*, pg. 4426
WAGNER'S LLC—See Wagner's LLC; *U.S. Private*, pg. 4426
WELLENS & CO., INC.; *U.S. Private*, pg. 4475
WEST CENTRAL DISTRIBUTION, LLC—See CHS INC.; *U.S. Public*, pg. 493
WESTERN COOPERATIVE COMPANY; *U.S. Private*, pg. 4492
WESTERN ORGANICS INC.—See GRO-WELL Brands Inc.; *U.S. Private*, pg. 1791
WESTERN RESERVE FARM COOPERATIVE; *U.S. Private*, pg. 4496
WESTERN SEEDS—See Evans Grain & Elevator Co. Inc.; *U.S. Private*, pg. 1435
WHEYFEED LTD.—See ForFarmers Group B.V.; *Int'l*, pg. 2733
WHITE RIVER COOPERATIVE INC.—See Premier Cos.; *U.S. Private*, pg. 3250
WILBUR-ELLIS COMPANY; *U.S. Private*, pg. 4517
WILBUR-ELLIS COMPANY—See Wilbur-Ellis Company; *U.S. Private*, pg. 4517
WILLIAM P. HEARNE INC.; *U.S. Private*, pg. 4524
WILSON INDUSTRIAL SALES CO.; *U.S. Private*, pg. 4531
WINNESHIEK COOPERATIVE ASSOCIATION; *U.S. Private*, pg. 4542
WORLD PET FOODS INC.—See Sunshine Mills Inc.; *U.S. Private*, pg. 3872
YODER & SONS INC.; *U.S. Private*, pg. 4589
YUNNAN VOLCAFE COMPANY LIMITED—See ED&F Man Holdings Limited; *Int'l*, pg. 2303
ZAMZOWS INC.; *U.S. Private*, pg. 4597
ZZN POLABI, A.S.—See Agrofert Holding, a.s.; *Int'l*, pg. 219

424920 — BOOK, PERIODICAL, AND NEWSPAPER MERCHANT WHOLESALERS

ADAMS BOOK CO. INC.; *U.S. Private*, pg. 73
ADVANCED EDUCATIONAL PRODUCTS, INC.; *U.S. Private*, pg. 89
ALDIPRESS B.V.—See DPG Media Group NV; *Int'l*, pg. 2188
ALIBRIS, INC.—See Keystone Group, L.P.; *U.S. Private*, pg. 2296
AMBASSADOR BOOK SERVICE, INC.; *U.S. Private*, pg. 217
AMERICAN INTERNATIONAL DISTRIBUTION CORPORATION—See Investors Corporation of Vermont; *U.S. Private*, pg. 2132
AMERICAN NEWS COMPANY, LLC; *U.S. Private*, pg. 242
AMERICAN WHOLESALE BOOK COMPANY INC.—See Books-A-Million, Inc.; *U.S. Private*, pg. 616
AMS PRESS INC.; *U.S. Private*, pg. 267
ARNAV CORPORATION LIMITED; *Int'l*, pg. 576
AUDIBLE LIMITED—See Amazon.com, Inc.; *U.S. Public*, pg. 90
BAKERS INC.; *U.S. Private*, pg. 457
BAKER & TAYLOR, LLC—See Follett Corporation; *U.S. Private*, pg. 1559
BEIJING MEDIA CORPORATION LIMITED; *Int'l*, pg. 954
BERNAN PRESS—See The Rowman & Littlefield Publishing Group, Inc.; *U.S. Private*, pg. 4112
BERTRAM GROUP LTD.—See Aurelius Equity Opportunities SE & Co. KGaA; *Int'l*, pg. 707
BETTER WORLD BOOKS; *U.S. Private*, pg. 547
BLACKWELL'S NORTH AMERICA INC.—See Elliott Management Corporation; *U.S. Private*, pg. 1365
BOOKAZINE COMPANY, INC.; *U.S. Private*, pg. 615
BOOK NETWORK INTERNATIONAL LIMITED—See Ingram Industries, Inc.; *U.S. Private*, pg. 2076
THE BOOKSOURCE INC.—See GL Group, Inc.; *U.S. Private*, pg. 1704
BOOKTOPIA PTY. LTD.; *Int'l*, pg. 1110
BOSTON HOMES—See Gannett Co., Inc.; *U.S. Public*, pg. 902
BRITISH AMERICAN TOBACCO (HONG KONG) LTD.—See British American Tobacco plc; *Int'l*, pg. 1166
BRODART CO.; *U.S. Private*, pg. 661
BUCH- UND PRESSE-GROSSVERTRIEB HAMBURG GMBH & CO. KG—See Axel Springer SE; *Int'l*, pg. 766
THE CAXTON PRINTERS LTD.; *U.S. Private*, pg. 4006
CBA INDUSTRIES INC.; *U.S. Private*, pg. 796
CELLMARK AB (SHANGHAI)—See CellMark AB; *Int'l*, pg. 1394
COMAG FORWARD—See Advance Publications, Inc.; *U.S. Private*, pg. 85
COMAG FORWARD—See The Hearst Corporation; *U.S. Private*, pg. 4047
COMAG SPECIALIST—See Advance Publications, Inc.; *U.S. Private*, pg. 85
COMAG SPECIALIST—See The Hearst Corporation; *U.S. Private*, pg. 4047
CONDE NAST, INC. - DETROIT—See Advance Publications, Inc.; *U.S. Private*, pg. 86
CONDE NAST & NATIONAL MAGAZINE DISTRIBUTORS LIMITED—See Advance Publications, Inc.; *U.S. Private*, pg. 85
CONDE NAST & NATIONAL MAGAZINE DISTRIBUTORS

424920 — BOOK, PERIODICAL, A...

LIMITED—See The Hearst Corporation; *U.S. Private*, pg. 4047
CONSORTIUM BOOK SALES & DISTRIBUTION, LLC—See Perseus Books, LLC; *U.S. Private*, pg. 3155
CONTEMPORARY SIGNED BOOKS, INC.; *U.S. Private*, pg. 1027
COWLEY DISTRIBUTING INC.; *U.S. Private*, pg. 1074
CURTIS CIRCULATION COMPANY; *U.S. Private*, pg. 1126
DAEDALUS BOOKS, INC.; *U.S. Private*, pg. 1144
DAKOTA NEWS INC.; *U.S. Private*, pg. 1147
DAWSON FRANCE SAS—See Aurelius Equity Opportunities SE & Co. KGaA; *Int'l*, pg. 708
DELTAMEDIA SA/NV—See bpost NV/SA; *Int'l*, pg. 1133
DESERET BOOK CO.—See Deseret Management Corporation; *U.S. Private*, pg. 1212
DIAMOND COMIC DISTRIBUTORS, INC.; *U.S. Private*, pg. 1223
DIREC CO., LTD.—See Dai Nippon Printing Co., Ltd.; *Int'l*, pg. 1915
DIRSON ENTERPRISES, INC.; *U.S. Private*, pg. 1236
DISTRIBUIDORA ALFA, S.A.—See Grupo Televisa, S.A.B.; *Int'l*, pg. 3136
DISTRIBUIDORAS UNIDAS, S.A.—See Grupo Televisa, S.A.B.; *Int'l*, pg. 3136
EBSCO CANADA LTD.—See EBSCO Industries, Inc.; *U.S. Private*, pg. 1324
EBSCO INDUSTRIES, INC. - SUBSCRIPTION SERVICES DIVISION—See EBSCO Industries, Inc.; *U.S. Private*, pg. 1325
EBSCO INDUSTRIES WESTWOOD—See EBSCO Industries, Inc.; *U.S. Private*, pg. 1325
EBSCO INFORMATION SERVICES—See EBSCO Industries, Inc.; *U.S. Private*, pg. 1325
EBSCO INTERNATIONAL INC.—See EBSCO Industries, Inc.; *U.S. Private*, pg. 1325
EDUCATIONAL DEVELOPMENT CORPORATION - HOME BUSINESS DIVISION—See Educational Develop; *U.S. Public*, pg. 720
EDUCATIONAL DEVELOPMENT CORPORATION; *U.S. Public*, pg. 719
EDUCATION UMBRELLA LTD.—See Aurelius Equity Opportunities SE & Co. KGaA; *Int'l*, pg. 708
ENIRO GULA SIDORNA FORSALJNING AB—See Eniro Group AB; *Int'l*, pg. 2439
ERASMUS ANTIQUARIAAT EN BOEKHANDEL B.V.—See Aurelius Equity Opportunities SE & Co. KGaA; *Int'l*, pg. 708
FALL RIVER NEWS CO. INC.; *U.S. Private*, pg. 1467
FAMILY BOOK CO., LTD.—See GEO Holdings Corporation; *Int'l*, pg. 2932
FOLLETT SCHOOL SOLUTIONS, INC.—See Francisco Partners Management, LP; *U.S. Private*, pg. 1589
GOPHER NEWS COMPANY; *U.S. Private*, pg. 1741
GREAT MIDWEST NEWS LLC.; *U.S. Private*, pg. 1765
GRUPO DISTRIBUIDORAS INTERMEX, S.A. DE C.V.—See Grupo Televisa, S.A.B.; *Int'l*, pg. 3136
GULL GMBH—See 7Days Group GmbH & Co. KG; *Int'l*, pg. 15
HAMILTON SYSTEM DISTRIBUTORS; *U.S. Private*, pg. 1848
HARLEQUIN RETAIL INC.—See News Corporation; *U.S. Public*, pg. 1519
HARRISBURG NEWS COMPANY INC.-HARRISBURG, PA—See Harrisburg News Company Inc.; *U.S. Private*, pg. 1870
HARRISBURG NEWS COMPANY INC.; *U.S. Private*, pg. 1870
HARVARD BUSINESS REVIEW—See Harvard Business School Publishing Corporation; *U.S. Private*, pg. 1875
HA TINH BOOK & EDUCATIONAL EQUIPMENT JOINT STOCK COMPANY; *Int'l*, pg. 3201
H.B. FENN AND COMPANY LTD.; *Int'l*, pg. 3195
HEARST BRAND DEVELOPMENT—See The Hearst Corporation; *U.S. Private*, pg. 4044
HEARTLAND COMMUNITY GROUP INC; *U.S. Private*, pg. 1899
HERFF JONES, INC. - YEARBOOK MARKETING—See Bain Capital, LP; *U.S. Private*, pg. 452
HERTZBERG-NEW METHOD INC.; *U.S. Private*, pg. 1927
HIGHLIGHTS FOR CHILDREN INTERNATIONAL, INC.—See Highlights for Children, Inc.; *U.S. Private*, pg. 1940
HOBONICHI CO., LTD.; *Int'l*, pg. 3437
HOLYOKE NEWS CO. INC.; *U.S. Private*, pg. 1969
HOUGHTON MIFFLIN HARCOURT PUBLISHING CO. - LEWISVILLE—See Veritas Capital Fund Management, LLC; *U.S. Private*, pg. 4363
HOUTSCHILD INTERNATIONALE BOEKHANDEL BV—See Aurelius Equity Opportunities SE & Co. KGaA; *Int'l*, pg. 708
H.P. KOPPLEMANN INC.; *U.S. Private*, pg. 1835
HUDSON NEWS COMPANY—See Avolta AG; *Int'l*, pg. 749
IMAGINE NATION BOOKS, LTD.; *U.S. Private*, pg. 2045
INGRAM BOOK GROUP INC.—See Ingram Industries, Inc.; *U.S. Private*, pg. 2076
INGRAM DISTRIBUTION GROUP INC.—See Ingram Industries, Inc.; *U.S. Private*, pg. 2077

INGRAM PERIODICALS INC.—See Ingram Industries, Inc.; *U.S. Private*, pg. 2076
THE INTERNET LANGUAGE COMPANY; *U.S. Private*, pg. 4057
JOHN MENZIES PLC—See Agility; *Int'l*, pg. 210
JW ENTERPRISES LTD.; *U.S. Private*, pg. 2246
KABLE DISTRIBUTION SERVICES, INC.—See AMREP Corporation; *U.S. Public*, pg. 133
KABLE MEDIA SERVICES, INC.—See AMREP Corporation; *U.S. Public*, pg. 133
KABLE NEWS CO., INC.—See AMREP Corporation; *U.S. Public*, pg. 133
KABLE NEWS COMPANY—See AMREP Corporation; *U.S. Public*, pg. 133
LECTORUM PUBLICATIONS, INC.; *U.S. Private*, pg. 2410
LEGATO PUBLISHERS GROUP—See Perseus Books, LLC; *U.S. Private*, pg. 3155
LEOMINSTER NEWS INC; *U.S. Private*, pg. 2422
MAPLE LOGISTICS SOLUTIONS—See The Maple-Vail Book Manufacturing Group; *U.S. Private*, pg. 4074
MARKET SELF CHILE SPA—See Bertelsmann SE & Co. KGaA; *Int'l*, pg. 993
MARUZEN BOOKMATES CO., LTD.—See Dai Nippon Printing Co., Ltd.; *Int'l*, pg. 1915
MARUZEN INTERNATIONAL CO., LTD.—See Dai Nippon Printing Co., Ltd.; *Int'l*, pg. 1915
MBS TEXTBOOK EXCHANGE, LLC—See Barnes & Noble Education, Inc.; *U.S. Public*, pg. 276
METRO NEWSPAPER ADVERTISING SERVICES, INC.—See Gemini Communications; *U.S. Private*, pg. 1657
METRO NEWSPAPER ADVERTISING SERVICES, INC.—See Gemini Communications; *U.S. Private*, pg. 1657
MID-STATES DISTRIBUTORS; *U.S. Private*, pg. 2709
NAPLES ILLUSTRATED—See Hour Media Group, LLC; *U.S. Private*, pg. 1991
NEW ENGLAND MOBILE BOOK FAIR; *U.S. Private*, pg. 2894
NEWSBANK, INC.; *U.S. Private*, pg. 2917
NEWS CORP INVESTMENTS UK & IRELAND—See News Corporation; *U.S. Public*, pg. 1520
NEWSWAYS DISTRIBUTORS; *U.S. Private*, pg. 2918
NORTHWEST NEWS CO., INC.; *U.S. Private*, pg. 2961
OZARK NEWS DISTRIBUTION INC.; *U.S. Private*, pg. 3058
PARTNERS BOOK DISTRIBUTING; *U.S. Private*, pg. 3101
PARTNERS BOOK DISTRIBUTING-WEST—See Partners Book Distributing; *U.S. Private*, pg. 3101
PBD, INC.; *U.S. Private*, pg. 3118
PENGUIN BOOKS, S.A.—See Bertelsmann SE & Co. KGaA; *Int'l*, pg. 991
PENGUIN BOOKS SOUTH AFRICA—See Bertelsmann SE & Co. KGaA; *Int'l*, pg. 991
PENGUIN RANDOM HOUSE GRUPO EDITORIAL, S.A. DE C.V.—See Bertelsmann SE & Co. KGaA; *Int'l*, pg. 993
PENGUIN RANDOM HOUSE GRUPO EDITORIAL, S.A.—See Bertelsmann SE & Co. KGaA; *Int'l*, pg. 993
PENGUIN RANDOM HOUSE GRUPO EDITORIAL S.A.S.—See Bertelsmann SE & Co. KGaA; *Int'l*, pg. 993
PERIODICAL MANAGEMENT GROUP INTERNATIONAL LTD.; *U.S. Private*, pg. 3150
PERSEUS DISTRIBUTION, INC.—See Perseus Books, LLC; *U.S. Private*, pg. 3155
PUBLISHERS GROUP WEST—See Perseus Books, LLC; *U.S. Private*, pg. 3155
READABOO, INC.; *U.S. Private*, pg. 3366
READER'S DIGEST ASSOCIATION FAR EAST LTD.—See RDA Holding Co.; *U.S. Private*, pg. 3363
RIZZOLI INTERNATIONAL PUBLICATIONS, INC.—See Fininvest S.p.A.; *Int'l*, pg. 2675
SCHOLASTIC INC. NATIONAL DISTRIBUTION CENTER—See Scholastic Corporation; *U.S. Public*, pg. 1847
SENEFELDER MISSET B.V.—See CirclePrinters Holding BV; *Int'l*, pg. 1618
SPEEDIMPEX USA INC.; *U.S. Private*, pg. 3753
SPRING ARBOR DISTRIBUTORS INC.—See Ingram Industries, Inc.; *U.S. Private*, pg. 2076
SUN OFFICE SERVICE, INC.—See Aramark; *U.S. Public*, pg. 178
TENNESSEE BOOK COMPANY LLC—See Ingram Industries, Inc.; *U.S. Private*, pg. 2076
THOMPSON SCHOOL BOOK DEPOSITORY; *U.S. Private*, pg. 4160
TRC, INC.—See Dai Nippon Printing Co., Ltd.; *Int'l*, pg. 1916
THE TUSCALOOSA NEWS—See Gannett Co., Inc.; *U.S. Public*, pg. 906
UBIWAY NV-SA—See bpost NV/SA; *Int'l*, pg. 1133
WELTBILD RETAIL GMBH & CO. KG—See Droege Group AG; *Int'l*, pg. 2205
WILEY-VCH GMBH—See John Wiley & Sons, Inc.; *U.S. Public*, pg. 1193
WORLD PUBLICATIONS INC.; *U.S. Private*, pg. 4567
ZANER-BLOSER, INC.—See Highlights for Children, Inc.; *U.S. Private*, pg. 1940

424930 — FLOWER, NURSERY STOCK, AND FLORISTS&APOS; SUPPLIES MERCHANT WHOLESALERS

ABC NURSERY INC; *U.S. Private*, pg. 36
AGREX LIMITED—See ENL Limited; *Int'l*, pg. 2441
ALEX R. MASSON INC.; *U.S. Private*, pg. 163
ALLEGRE PUERICULTURE S.A.S.—See Newell Brands Inc.; *U.S. Public*, pg. 1513
ALLSTATE FLORAL & CRAFT, INC.; *U.S. Private*, pg. 193
ALTMAN SPECIALTY PLANTS, INC.; *U.S. Private*, pg. 210
AMERICAN FARMS LLC; *U.S. Private*, pg. 233
AMERICAN FLORIST SUPPLY INC.; *U.S. Private*, pg. 234
AMPLEX INC.; *U.S. Private*, pg. 266
ANTHURIUM AND ORCHIDS LIMITED—See ENL Limited; *Int'l*, pg. 2441
ARIS HORTICULTURAL SERVICES—See Aris Horticulture, Inc.; *U.S. Private*, pg. 323
ARTGREEN CO., LTD.; *Int'l*, pg. 583
ASIAN FLORA LIMITED; *Int'l*, pg. 617
ASIAN POTTERY HOME & GARDEN SDN. BHD.—See CSH Alliance Berhad; *Int'l*, pg. 1865
ASPEN VALLEY LANDSCAPE SUPPLY, INC.—See SiteOne Landscape Supply, Inc.; *U.S. Public*, pg. 1889
ATLANTIC IRRIGATION OF CANADA INC.—See SiteOne Landscape Supply, Inc.; *U.S. Public*, pg. 1888
AUC SERVICE INC.—See Aucnet Inc.; *Int'l*, pg. 700
BAILEY NURSERIES INC.; *U.S. Private*, pg. 425
BAISCH & SKINNER INC.; *U.S. Private*, pg. 454
BAYER CROPSCIENCE LTDA.—See Bayer Aktiengesellschaft; *Int'l*, pg. 903
BEAUTY KADAN CO., LTD.; *Int'l*, pg. 935
BELL NURSERY HOLDINGS, LLC—See Central Garden & Pet Company; *U.S. Public*, pg. 473
BERKELEY FLORIST SUPPLY CO, INC.; *U.S. Private*, pg. 532
BILL DORAN COMPANY; *U.S. Private*, pg. 557
BISSETT NURSERY CORP.—See SiteOne Landscape Supply, Inc.; *U.S. Public*, pg. 1889
BREHOB NURSERY INC.—See DCA Outdoor, Inc.; *U.S. Private*, pg. 1179
CCC ASSOCIATES INC.; *U.S. Private*, pg. 799
C&C FLORAL INC.; *U.S. Private*, pg. 702
CICCOLELLA SPA; *Int'l*, pg. 1602
CLEVELAND PLANT AND FLOWER COMPANY; *U.S. Private*, pg. 941
CONROY'S INC.—See 1-800-FLOWERS.COM, Inc.; *U.S. Public*, pg. 1
CONTINENTAL FLORAL GREENS; *U.S. Private*, pg. 1029
COREY NURSERY CO. INC.; *U.S. Private*, pg. 1050
COUNTRY FLORAL SUPPLY INC; *U.S. Private*, pg. 1067
CROWN GARDENEX CO., LTD.—See Beauty Kadan Co., Ltd.; *Int'l*, pg. 935
DELAWARE VALLEY WHOLESALE FLORIST INC.; *U.S. Private*, pg. 1196
DELTA FLORAL DISTRIBUTORS INC.; *U.S. Private*, pg. 1200
DENVER WHOLESALE FLORISTS COMPANY; *U.S. Private*, pg. 1208
DWF OF BOISE—See Denver Wholesale Florists Company; *U.S. Private*, pg. 1208
DWF OF DALLAS—See Denver Wholesale Florists Company; *U.S. Private*, pg. 1208
DWF OF FLINT INC.—See Denver Wholesale Florists Company; *U.S. Private*, pg. 1208
DWF OF MILWAUKEE, INC.—See Denver Wholesale Florists Company; *U.S. Private*, pg. 1208
DWF OF NORTH KANSAS CITY—See Denver Wholesale Florists Company; *U.S. Private*, pg. 1208
DWF OF SAINT LOUIS, INC.—See Denver Wholesale Florists Company; *U.S. Private*, pg. 1208
DWF OF SALT LAKE, INC.—See Denver Wholesale Florists Company; *U.S. Private*, pg. 1208
DWF OF TOLEDO—See Denver Wholesale Florists Company; *U.S. Private*, pg. 1208
DWF SEATAC—See Denver Wholesale Florists Company; *U.S. Private*, pg. 1208
EAST HAVEN LANDSCAPE PRODUCTS—See SiteOne Landscape Supply, Inc.; *U.S. Public*, pg. 1889
ENL AGRI LIMITED—See ENL Limited; *Int'l*, pg. 2441
EQUIFLOR CORPORATION; *U.S. Private*, pg. 1415
EXOTIFLORS LIMITED—See ENL Limited; *Int'l*, pg. 2441
FARMERS WEST; *U.S. Private*, pg. 1480
FARMGIRL FLOWERS INC.; *U.S. Private*, pg. 1480
FERNLEA NURSERY INC.—See Fernlea Flowers Ltd.; *Int'l*, pg. 2639
FINEOUT ENTERPRISES INC.; *U.S. Private*, pg. 1509
FLORAL SUPPLY SYNDICATE; *U.S. Private*, pg. 1546
FLORIST DISTRIBUTING, INC.—See Hy-Vee, Inc.; *U.S. Private*, pg. 2016
FLORISTS SUPPLY LTD.; *Int'l*, pg. 2708
FOREMOSTCO INC.; *U.S. Private*, pg. 1566
FROM YOU FLOWERS LLC—See Tenth Avenue Holdings LLC; *U.S. Private*, pg. 3968
GILBERT H. WILD & SON, LLC; *U.S. Private*, pg. 1699
GREEN LEAF PLANTS—See Aris Horticulture, Inc.; *U.S. Private*, pg. 323

N.A.I.C.S. INDEX

424940 — TOBACCO PRODUCT AND...

GREENLEAF WHOLESALE FLORIST INC.; *U.S. Private*, pg. 1778
GRIFFIN GREENHOUSE & NURSERY SUPPLIES, INC.; *U.S. Private*, pg. 1787
HALEX BIOTECHNOLOGIES SDN. BHD.—See Hextar Global Berhad; *Int'l*, pg. 3373
HIAWATHA, INC.; *U.S. Private*, pg. 1932
HIBIYA-KADAN FLORAL CO., LTD.; *Int'l*, pg. 3383
HOUSE OF WESLEY, INC.; *U.S. Private*, pg. 1992
JACKSON & PERKINS COMPANY—See Evergreen SC, LLC; *U.S. Private*, pg. 1440
JACOBSON FLORAL SUPPLY INC.; *U.S. Private*, pg. 2180
J.W. PERRY INC.; *U.S. Private*, pg. 2172
KENNICOTT BROS CO. INC.; *U.S. Private*, pg. 2286
KILANG BIHUN BERSATU (EAST MALAYSIA) SDN BHD—See EKA Noodles Berhad; *Int'l*, pg. 2337
KRAEMER'S NURSERY INC.; *U.S. Private*, pg. 2348
KRUEGER FLORAL-N-GIFTS; *U.S. Private*, pg. 2353
LAND & COATES, INC.; *U.S. Private*, pg. 2382
LANDMARK NURSERIES INC.; *U.S. Private*, pg. 2385
LIBERTY HEALTH SCIENCES INC.—See Ayr Wellness Inc.; *Int'l*, pg. 775
LOMA VISTA NURSERY, INC.—See SiteOne Landscape Supply, Inc.; *U.S. Public*, pg. 1889
MAYESH WHOLESALE FLORIST, INC.; *U.S. Private*, pg. 2621
MEANS NURSERY INC.; *U.S. Private*, pg. 2647
MEDFORD NURSERY, INC.—See The Robert Baker Companies; *U.S. Private*, pg. 4111
MELLANO & COMPANY; *U.S. Private*, pg. 2662
MISSRY ASSOCIATES INC.; *U.S. Private*, pg. 2749
NORDLIE INC.; *U.S. Private*, pg. 2937
NORTHERN NURSERIES, INC.—See The Robert Baker Companies; *U.S. Private*, pg. 4111
NORTHLAND FARMS, LLC; *U.S. Private*, pg. 2955
NUNHEMS (BEIJING) SEED CO., LTD.—See BASF SE; *Int'l*, pg. 884
OASIS FLORALIFE CENTRAL EUROPE GMBH—See Smithers-Oasis Company; *U.S. Private*, pg. 3697
OASIS FLORALIFE COLOMBIA LTDA.—See Smithers-Oasis Company; *U.S. Private*, pg. 3697
ODAKYU LANDFLORA CO., LTD.—See Hibiya-Kadan Floral Co., Ltd.; *Int'l*, pg. 3383
OSCAR G CARLSTEDT CO. INC.; *U.S. Private*, pg. 3046
PACIFIC COAST EVERGREEN INC; *U.S. Private*, pg. 3066
PENNOCK COMPANY; *U.S. Private*, pg. 3136
PETE ROSE, INC.—See SiteOne Landscape Supply, Inc.; *U.S. Public*, pg. 1889
PIKES PEAK OF TEXAS INC.; *U.S. Private*, pg. 3180
PLANT MARKETING LLC; *U.S. Private*, pg. 3197
PREMIUM FLOWERS CORP.; *U.S. Private*, pg. 3251
PROVIDE COMMERCE, INC.—See Tenth Avenue Holdings LLC; *U.S. Private*, pg. 3968
REEVES FLORAL PRODUCTS, INC.; *U.S. Private*, pg. 3384
REINHOLD CORP.; *U.S. Private*, pg. 3392
RIVER VALLEY HORTICULTURAL PRODUCTS, INC.—See SiteOne Landscape Supply, Inc.; *U.S. Public*, pg. 1889
THE ROBERT BAKER COMPANIES; *U.S. Private*, pg. 4111
ROBERT BAKER, INC.—See The Robert Baker Companies; *U.S. Private*, pg. 4111
THE SAN FRANCISCO MUSIC BOX COMPANY—See Kier Group Holdings, LLC; *U.S. Private*, pg. 2304
SILVASEED CO.—See DroneSeed Co.; *U.S. Private*, pg. 1279
SMITHERS-OASIS ADRIA D.O.O.—See Smithers-Oasis Company; *U.S. Private*, pg. 3697
SMITHERS-OASIS AUSTRALIA PTY LTD—See Smithers-Oasis Company; *U.S. Private*, pg. 3697
SMITHERS-OASIS BELGIUM N.V.—See Smithers-Oasis Company; *U.S. Private*, pg. 3697
SMITHERS-OASIS DE MEXICO S.A. DE C.V.—See Smithers-Oasis Company; *U.S. Private*, pg. 3697
SMITHERS-OASIS FRANCE SARL—See Smithers-Oasis Company; *U.S. Private*, pg. 3697
SMITHERS-OASIS GERMANY GMBH—See Smithers-Oasis Company; *U.S. Private*, pg. 3697
SMITHERS-OASIS IBERICA, S.L.—See Smithers-Oasis Company; *U.S. Private*, pg. 3697
SMITHERS-OASIS INDIA PVT. LTD.—See Smithers-Oasis Company; *U.S. Private*, pg. 3697
SMITHERS-OASIS JAPAN CO., LTD.—See Smithers-Oasis Company; *U.S. Private*, pg. 3697
SMITHERS-OASIS KOREA CO., LTD.—See Smithers-Oasis Company; *U.S. Private*, pg. 3697
SMITHERS-OASIS MALAYSIA SDN BHD—See Smithers-Oasis Company; *U.S. Private*, pg. 3697
SMITHERS-OASIS U.K. LTD.—See Smithers-Oasis Company; *U.S. Private*, pg. 3697
SOUTHERN FLORAL CO.; *U.S. Private*, pg. 3731
SPEEDLING, INCORPORATED See Speedling Incorporated; *U.S. Private*, pg. 3753
STUPPY INCORPORATED; *U.S. Private*, pg. 3844
SUNSHINE BOUQUET COMPANY INC.; *U.S. Private*, pg. 3871
SUPER GARDEN CENTERS, INC.; *U.S. Private*, pg. 3874
SYNGENTA SEEDS A/S—See China National Chemical Corporation; *Int'l*, pg. 1530
TETERS FLORAL PRODUCTS, INC.; *U.S. Private*, pg. 3973
URBANSTEMS INC.; *U.S. Private*, pg. 4315
VAN'S INC.; *U.S. Private*, pg. 4341
VAN'S OF MICHIGAN, INC.—See Van's Inc.; *U.S. Private*, pg. 4341
VILLAGE NURSERIES WHOLESALE LLC—See TreeSap Farms, LLC; *U.S. Private*, pg. 4217
V&P NURSERIES INC.; *U.S. Private*, pg. 4327
WATANABE FLORAL, INC.; *U.S. Private*, pg. 4451
WINFIELD NURSERY, INC.—See The Robert Baker Companies; *U.S. Private*, pg. 4111
WORLD CLASS FLOWERS; *U.S. Private*, pg. 4565
ZIEGER & SONS INC.; *U.S. Private*, pg. 4603

424940 — TOBACCO PRODUCT AND ELECTRONIC CIGARETTE MERCHANT WHOLESALERS

ACADIA WHOLESALE & TOBACCO COMPANY, INC.; *U.S. Private*, pg. 47
A.E. WEASE INC.; *U.S. Private*, pg. 25
ALLIANCE ONE INTERNATIONAL A.G.—See Pyxus International, Inc.; *U.S. Public*, pg. 1740
ALLIANCE ONE INTERNATIONAL SERVICES LIMITED—See Pyxus International, Inc.; *U.S. Public*, pg. 1740
ALLIANCE ONE INTERNATIONAL SINGAPORE PTE LTD.—See Pyxus International, Inc.; *U.S. Public*, pg. 1740
ALLIANCE ONE MACEDONIA AD—See Pyxus International, Inc.; *U.S. Public*, pg. 1740
ALLIANCE ONE MYANMAR CO., LTD.—See Pyxus International, Inc.; *U.S. Public*, pg. 1740
ALLIANCE ONE SERVICES (THAILAND) LIMITED—See Pyxus International, Inc.; *U.S. Public*, pg. 1740
ALLIANCE ONE TOBACCO ARGENTINA S.A.—See Pyxus International, Inc.; *U.S. Public*, pg. 1740
ALLIANCE ONE TOBACCO GUATEMALA, S.A.—See Pyxus International, Inc.; *U.S. Public*, pg. 1740
ALLIANCE ONE TOBACCO (KENYA) LIMITED—See Pyxus International, Inc.; *U.S. Public*, pg. 1740
ALLIANCE ONE TOBACCO TANZANIA LTD.—See Pyxus International, Inc.; *U.S. Public*, pg. 1740
ALLIANCE ONE TOBACCO (UGANDA) LIMITED—See Pyxus International, Inc.; *U.S. Public*, pg. 1740
ALLIANCE ONE ZAMBIA LTD.—See Pyxus International, Inc.; *U.S. Public*, pg. 1740
A MONTEVERDI INC.; *U.S. Private*, pg. 18
AMSTER KIRTZ CO.; *U.S. Private*, pg. 268
AMY LYNN, INC.; *U.S. Private*, pg. 270
ANDALUSIA DISTRIBUTING COMPANY INC.; *U.S. Private*, pg. 275
BARBER & SONS INVESTMENT CO. INC.; *U.S. Private*, pg. 472
BATON ROUGE TOBACCO CO. INC.; *U.S. Private*, pg. 487
BELLBOY CIGARS—See Bellboy Corporation; *U.S. Private*, pg. 520
BELL TRADING INCORPORATED; *U.S. Private*, pg. 519
B&G WHOLESALE DISTRIBUTING INC.; *U.S. Private*, pg. 418
BRITISH AMERICAN TOBACCO (CAMBODIA) LIMITED—See British American Tobacco plc; *Int'l*, pg. 1166
BRITISH AMERICAN TOBACCO COLOMBIA S.A.S.—See British American Tobacco plc; *Int'l*, pg. 1166
BRITISH AMERICAN TOBACCO (CZECH REPUBLIC), S.R.O.—See British American Tobacco plc; *Int'l*, pg. 1166
BRITISH AMERICAN TOBACCO (GLP) LTD.—See British American Tobacco plc; *Int'l*, pg. 1166
BRITISH AMERICAN TOBACCO INTERNATIONAL LTD.—See British American Tobacco plc; *Int'l*, pg. 1166
BRITISH AMERICAN TOBACCO POLSKA TRADING SP. Z.O.O.—See British American Tobacco plc; *Int'l*, pg. 1167
BRITISH AMERICAN TOBACCO SWEDEN AB—See British American Tobacco plc; *Int'l*, pg. 1167
BRITISH AMERICAN TOBACCO UK LTD.—See British American Tobacco plc; *Int'l*, pg. 1167
BURKLUND DISTRIBUTORS INC.—See AMCON Distributing Company; *U.S. Public*, pg. 92
CAMPBELL WHOLESALE COMPANY, INC.; *U.S. Private*, pg. 731
C&B DISTRIBUTORS INC.; *U.S. Private*, pg. 702
CDF COLOMBIA S.A.—See CDF International Cooperatief U.A.; *Int'l*, pg. 1370
CDF DOMITIA SA—See CDF International Cooperatief U.A.; *Int'l*, pg. 1370
CENTURY DISTRIBUTORS, INC.; *U.S. Private*, pg. 832
CHAMBERS & OWEN, INC.; *U.S. Private*, pg. 846
CHARLIE'S TOBACCO OUTLET; *U.S. Private*, pg. 857
CHINA TOBACCO INTERNATIONAL (HK) COMPANY LIMITED; *Int'l*, pg. 1559
CITY WHOLESALE INC.—See Imperial Trading Co., Inc.; *U.S. Private*, pg. 2049
CLICK DISTRIBUTING CO INC.—See Fritz Company; *U.S. Private*, pg. 1612
COCHRAN BROS COMPANY INCORPORATED; *U.S. Private*, pg. 959
COD CO. INC.; *U.S. Private*, pg. 959
CONTINENTAL TOBACCO S.A.—See Universal Corporation; *U.S. Public*, pg. 2254
CORE-MARK INTERNATIONAL—See Core-Mark Holding Co. Inc.; *U.S. Public*, pg. 576
DAHL'S FOOD MART INC.; *U.S. Private*, pg. 1144
DELI-HTL TABAK MAATSCHAPPIJ B. V.—See Universal Corporation; *U.S. Public*, pg. 2254
DEUTSCH-HOLANDISCHE TABAKGESELLSCHAFT MBH—See Universal Corporation; *U.S. Public*, pg. 2254
DEUTSCH-HOLLANDISCHE TABAKGESELLSCHAFT MBH—See Universal Corporation; *U.S. Public*, pg. 2254
DOUGLAS COMPANIES INC.; *U.S. Private*, pg. 1266
DOUGLAS TOBACCO PRODUCTS CO.—See Douglas Companies Inc.; *U.S. Private*, pg. 1266
DUPNITSA-TABAC AD; *Int'l*, pg. 2227
EBY-BROWN CO.—See Performance Food Group Company; *U.S. Public*, pg. 1674
EBY-BROWN CO.—See Performance Food Group Company; *U.S. Public*, pg. 1674
EBY BROWN OHIO—See Performance Food Group Company; *U.S. Public*, pg. 1674
GADORA TOBACCO P.S.C.—See Pyxus International, Inc.; *U.S. Public*, pg. 1740
GARBER BROS INC.; *U.S. Private*, pg. 1642
GEM STATE DISTRIBUTORS INCORPORATED; *U.S. Private*, pg. 1657
GILLA INC.; *U.S. Public*, pg. 938
GOLDEN TOBACCO LIMITED; *Int'l*, pg. 3032
HARKEMA SERVICES, INC.—See Universal Corporation; *U.S. Public*, pg. 2254
HAROLD LEVINSON ASSOCIATES; *U.S. Private*, pg. 1867
HARRY FOURTUNIS INC.; *U.S. Private*, pg. 1871
HAWAIIAN ISLES ENTERPRISES, INC.; *U.S. Private*, pg. 1882
HILL CITY WHOLESALE CO. INC.; *U.S. Private*, pg. 1945
THE H.T. HACKNEY CO.—See The H.T. Hackney Company; *U.S. Private*, pg. 4041
INDIA IMPORTS INC.; *U.S. Private*, pg. 2061
INDOCO INTERNATIONAL B.V.—See Universal Corporation; *U.S. Public*, pg. 2254
J.E. CARSTEN COMPANY; *U.S. Private*, pg. 2161
J. F. JOHNSON, INC.; *U.S. Private*, pg. 2156
J.L. GADDY ENTERPRISES INC.; *U.S. Private*, pg. 2167
KAISER WHOLESALE, INC.; *U.S. Private*, pg. 2256
KLAFTERS INC.; *U.S. Private*, pg. 2317
LANCASTER LEAF TOBACCO COMPANY OF PENNSYLVANIA, INC.—See Universal Corporation; *U.S. Public*, pg. 2254
LAYMAN CANDY COMPANY, INC.; *U.S. Private*, pg. 2402
LIMITED LIABILITY COMPANY PHILIP MORRIS SALES & DISTRIBUTION—See Philip Morris International Inc.; *U.S. Public*, pg. 1685
MACKOUL DISTRIBUTORS INC.; *U.S. Private*, pg. 2537
MACON CIGAR & TOBACCO CO.; *U.S. Private*, pg. 2538
MANCHESTER WHOLESALE DISTRIBUTORS, INC.; *U.S. Private*, pg. 2562
MARY JANE'S CBD DISPENSARY, INC.; *U.S. Private*, pg. 2598
MCCARTY-HULL INC.; *U.S. Private*, pg. 2628
MCDOWELL SUPPLY COMPANY; *U.S. Private*, pg. 2633
MERRILL DISTRIBUTING INC.; *U.S. Private*, pg. 2676
MID-AMERICA WHOLESALE INCORPORATED; *U.S. Private*, pg. 2707
MIKE'S CIGARS DISTRIBUTORS, INC.; *U.S. Private*, pg. 2726
MILLER DISTRIBUTING INC.; *U.S. Private*, pg. 2733
MONTANO CIGARETTE CANDY & TOBACCO COMPANY INC.; *U.S. Private*, pg. 2775
MOZAMBIQUE LEAF TOBACCO, LIMITADA—See Universal Corporation; *U.S. Public*, pg. 2254
MTC DISTRIBUTING; *U.S. Private*, pg. 2808
MYERS-COX CO; *U.S. Private*, pg. 2824
NATIONAL SMOKELESS TOBACCO COMPANY LTD.—See Altria Group, Inc.; *U.S. Public*, pg. 89
NAT SHERMAN INC.; *U.S. Private*, pg. 2837
NEWARK TOBACCO & CANDY CO. INC.; *U.S. Private*, pg. 2913
NH CIGARS, LLC—See MGM Resorts International; *U.S. Public*, pg. 1435
NORTHERN BRANDS INTERNATIONAL, INC.—See British American Tobacco plc; *Int'l*, pg. 1168
NORTHWEST TOBACCO & CANDY CO.; *U.S. Private*, pg. 2962
OLD DOMINION TOBACCO COMPANY INC. - CAROLINA DIVISION—See Old Dominion Tobacco Company Inc.; *U.S. Private*, pg. 3008
OLD DOMINION TOBACCO COMPANY INC.; *U.S. Private*, pg. 3008
PAPASTRATOS CIGARETTES MANUFACTURING COMPANY S.A.—See Philip Morris International Inc.; *U.S. Public*, pg. 1685
PENNINGTONS INC.; *U.S. Private*, pg. 3136
PHILIP MORRIS APS—See Philip Morris International Inc.; *U.S. Public*, pg. 1685
PHILIP MORRIS ITALIA S.R.L.—See Philip Morris Interna-

424940 — TOBACCO PRODUCT AND...

tional Inc.; *U.S. Public*, pg. 1686
PHILIP MORRIS MANUFACTURING & TECHNOLOGY BOLOGNA S.P.A.—See Philip Morris International Inc.; *U.S. Public*, pg. 1686
PHILIP MORRIS POLSKA DISTRIBUTION SP. Z O.O.—See Philip Morris International Inc.; *U.S. Public*, pg. 1686
PHILIP MORRIS ROMANIA S.R.L.—See Philip Morris International Inc.; *U.S. Public*, pg. 1686
PHILIP MORRIS TRADING S.R.L.—See Philip Morris International Inc.; *U.S. Public*, pg. 1687
PHILIP MORRIS TRADING (THAILAND) COMPANY LIMITED—See Philip Morris International Inc.; *U.S. Public*, pg. 1687
PLAINFIELD TOBACCO & CANDY INC.; *U.S. Private*, pg. 3194
PROCESADORA UNITAB, S.A.—See Universal Corporation; *U.S. Public*, pg. 2254
PROFIGEN DO BRAZIL LDTA—See Altria Group, Inc.; *U.S. Public*, pg. 89
P.T. INDONESIA TRI SEMBILAM—See Pyxus International, Inc.; *U.S. Public*, pg. 1741
PUERTO RICO SUPPLIES CO. INC.—See Puerto Rico Supply Group; *U.S. Private*, pg. 3302
REIDSVILLE GROCERY CO. INC.; *U.S. Private*, pg. 3391
REPUBLIC TOBACCO LP; *U.S. Private*, pg. 3402
RGR CANADA INC.—See High Tide, Inc.; *Int'l*, pg. 3386
RICHMOND MASTER DISTRIBUTORS INC.—See AMCON Distributing Company; *U.S. Public*, pg. 93
R.L. LIPTON WHOLESALERS INC.—See Tri County Wholesale Distributors Inc.; *U.S. Private*, pg. 4220
R&M WHOLESALE CO. INC.; *U.S. Private*, pg. 3332
ROBERTS CIGAR & TOBACCO COMPANY; *U.S. Private*, pg. 3459
S. ABRAHAM & SONS, INC.; *U.S. Private*, pg. 3514
SHAFFER ENTERPRISES INC.; *U.S. Private*, pg. 3623
SJH DISTRIBUTING INC.; *U.S. Private*, pg. 3678
SLEDD CO.; *U.S. Private*, pg. 3688
SM NORGE A/S—See Philip Morris International Inc.; *U.S. Public*, pg. 1687
SOUTHCO DISTRIBUTING COMPANY; *U.S. Private*, pg. 3724
STEPHENSON WHOLESALE COMPANY INC.; *U.S. Private*, pg. 3803
SWD CORPORATION; *U.S. Private*, pg. 3891
SWEDISH MATCH DISTRIBUTION AB—See Philip Morris International Inc.; *U.S. Public*, pg. 1687
SWEDISH MATCH NORTH AMERICA INC.—See Philip Morris International Inc.; *U.S. Public*, pg. 1687
SWEDISH MATCH NORTH EUROPE AB—See Philip Morris International Inc.; *U.S. Public*, pg. 1687
TOM FITTS TOBACCO CO INC.; *U.S. Private*, pg. 4182
TREPCO IMPORTS & DISTRIBUTION LTD.; *U.S. Private*, pg. 4218
UAB PHILIP MORRIS LIETUVA—See Philip Morris International Inc.; *U.S. Public*, pg. 1687
UNIVERSAL LEAF (ASIA) PTE LTD.—See Universal Corporation; *U.S. Public*, pg. 2254
UNIVERSAL LEAF GERMANY GMBH—See Universal Corporation; *U.S. Public*, pg. 2254
UNIVERSAL LEAF NICARAGUA, S.A.—See Universal Corporation; *U.S. Public*, pg. 2254
UNIVERSAL LEAF NORTH AMERICA U. S., INC.—See Universal Corporation; *U.S. Public*, pg. 2254
UNIVERSAL LEAF PHILIPPINES INC.—See Universal Corporation; *U.S. Public*, pg. 2254
UNIVERSAL LEAF TABACOS S. A.—See Universal Corporation; *U.S. Public*, pg. 2254
UNIVERSAL LEAF TOBACCO HUNGARY PRIVATE LIMITED COMPANY—See Universal Corporation; *U.S. Public*, pg. 2254
U.S. SMOKELESS TOBACCO MANUFACTURING COMPANY LLC—See Altria Group, Inc.; *U.S. Public*, pg. 89
VAPE BRANDS INTERNATIONAL INC.—See Gilla Inc.; *U.S. Public*, pg. 938
VAPOR HUB INTERNATIONAL INC.; *U.S. Public*, pg. 2275
VAPOR SHARK, LLC—See Turning Point Brands, Inc.; *U.S. Public*, pg. 2205
ZAMBIA LEAF TOBACCO CO., LTD.—See Universal Corporation; *U.S. Public*, pg. 2254
ZIMBABWE LEAF TOBACCO COMPANY (PRIVATE) LIMITED—See Universal Corporation; *U.S. Public*, pg. 2254

424950 — PAINT, VARNISH, AND SUPPLIES MERCHANT WHOLESALERS

ABOFFS INC.; *U.S. Private*, pg. 39
AKZO NOBEL BALTICS AS—See Akzo Nobel N.V.; *Int'l*, pg. 268
AKZO NOBEL BALTICS SIA—See Akzo Nobel N.V.; *Int'l*, pg. 268
AKZO NOBEL CAR REFINISHES AB—See Akzo Nobel N.V.; *Int'l*, pg. 269
AKZO NOBEL CAR REFINISHES AG—See Akzo Nobel N.V.; *Int'l*, pg. 269
AKZO NOBEL COATINGS AS—See Akzo Nobel N.V.; *Int'l*, pg. 269
AKZO NOBEL COATINGS GMBH—See Akzo Nobel N.V.; *Int'l*, pg. 269
AKZO NOBEL COATINGS SP. Z O.O.—See Akzo Nobel N.V.; *Int'l*, pg. 269
AKZO NOBEL COATINGS SRL—See Akzo Nobel N.V.; *Int'l*, pg. 269
AKZO NOBEL DECORATIVE INTERNATIONAL—See Akzo Nobel N.V.; *Int'l*, pg. 269
AKZO NOBEL DISTRIBUTION OUEST S.A.S.—See Akzo Nobel N.V.; *Int'l*, pg. 271
AKZO NOBEL INDUSTRIAL COATINGS LTD—See Akzo Nobel N.V.; *Int'l*, pg. 271
AKZONOBEL PAINTS SP. Z O.O.—See Akzo Nobel N.V.; *Int'l*, pg. 270
AKZO NOBEL PAINTS VIETNAM LTD—See Akzo Nobel N.V.; *Int'l*, pg. 270
AKZONOBEL SA—See Akzo Nobel N.V.; *Int'l*, pg. 270
AKZO NOBEL WOOD COATINGS LTD—See Akzo Nobel N.V.; *Int'l*, pg. 273
ALERMAC INVERSIONES, S.A. DE C.V.—See PPG Industries, Inc.; *U.S. Public*, pg. 1707
ALPINE PRODUCTS INC.; *U.S. Private*, pg. 201
AMPACET SOUTH AMERICA S.R.L.—See Ampacet Corporation; *U.S. Private*, pg. 264
ANCHOR PAINT CO. OF DENVER INC.—See Anchor Paint Manufacturing Co. Inc.; *U.S. Private*, pg. 273
ANCHOR PAINT CO. OF OKLAHOMA CITY INC.—See Anchor Paint Manufacturing Co. Inc.; *U.S. Private*, pg. 273
ANEST IWATA AUSTRALIA PTY LTD—See ANEST IWATA Corporation; *Int'l*, pg. 458
ANEST IWATA SOUTH AFRICA PTY. LTD.—See ANEST IWATA Corporation; *Int'l*, pg. 458
AS CREATION (UK) LIMITED—See A.S. Creation Tapeten AG; *Int'l*, pg. 28
ASTEK WALLCOVERING, INC.; *U.S. Private*, pg. 360
AUDAX (UK)—See AUDAX-Keck GmbH; *Int'l*, pg. 700
AUTOMOTIVE COLOR & SUPPLY, LLC—See WILsquare Capital LLC; *U.S. Private*, pg. 4532
AUTOMOTIVE REFINISH TECHNOLOGIES LLC—See BASF SE; *Int'l*, pg. 875
AUTO REFINISH DISTRIBUTORS HOLDING CORP.; *U.S. Private*, pg. 397
AUTO REFINISH DISTRIBUTORS—See Auto Refinish Distributors Holding Corp.; *U.S. Private*, pg. 397
AZALEA COLOR COMPANY; *U.S. Private*, pg. 415
BASF COATINGS SERVICES AB—See BASF SE; *Int'l*, pg. 873
BASF COATINGS SERVICES ITALY SRL—See BASF SE; *Int'l*, pg. 879
BASF COATINGS SERVICES S.A.—See BASF SE; *Int'l*, pg. 873
BASF COATINGS SERVICES S.R.L.—See BASF SE; *Int'l*, pg. 873
BERGER PAINTS (HONG KONG) LTD.—See Asian Paints Limited; *Int'l*, pg. 618
BERGER PAINTS SINGAPORE PTE LTD; *Int'l*, pg. 980
BREWSTER WALLCOVERING INTERNATIONAL TRADE (SHANGHAI) LTD.—See Brewster Wallpaper Corp.; *U.S. Private*, pg. 647
CAPPELLE PIGNENES N.V.; *Int'l*, pg. 1315
CHROMAFLO TECHNOLOGIES FINLAND OY—See American Securities LLC; *U.S. Private*, pg. 251
CHUGOKU MARINE PAINTS (HELLAS) S.A.—See Chugoku Marine Paints, Ltd.; *Int'l*, pg. 1595
CHUGOKU MARINE PAINTS (HONGKONG) LTD—See Chugoku Marine Paints, Ltd.; *Int'l*, pg. 1595
CHUGOKU PAINTS BV—See Chugoku Marine Paints, Ltd.; *Int'l*, pg. 1595
CHUGOKU PAINTS (UK) LIMITED—See Chugoku Marine Paints, Ltd.; *Int'l*, pg. 1595
CLEVELAND PIGMENT & COLOR INC.—See Lancer Dispersions Inc.; *U.S. Private*, pg. 2382
CMP COATINGS INC—See Chugoku Marine Paints, Ltd.; *Int'l*, pg. 1595
COLORSUD SA—See Bystronic AG; *Int'l*, pg. 1236
COLOURS INC.; *U.S. Private*, pg. 975
COMMENDA ADRIA D.O.O.—See Akzo Nobel N.V.; *Int'l*, pg. 273
DAI NIPPON TORYO HANBAI CO., LTD.—See Dai Nippon Toryo Co., Ltd.; *Int'l*, pg. 1916
DEARCO DISTRIBUTING INC.—See Eponk Group Ltd.; *U.S. Private*, pg. 1414
DEJMARK GROUP S.R.O.; *Int'l*, pg. 2005
DEJMARK PARTNERS SRL—See Dejmark Group s.r.o.; *Int'l*, pg. 2005
DEJMARK SPOL. S R.O.—See Dejmark Group s.r.o.; *Int'l*, pg. 2005
DIC EUROPE - UK—See DIC Corporation; *Int'l*, pg. 2107
DISTRIBUIDORA KORMA, S.A. DE C.V.—See PPG Industries, Inc.; *U.S. Public*, pg. 1707
D.L. COUCH WALLCOVERING, INC.; *U.S. Private*, pg. 1142
DUCO SPECIALITY COATINGS (PTY) LIMITED—See AECI Limited; *Int'l*, pg. 171
DULUX—See Akzo Nobel N.V.; *Int'l*, pg. 274
DULUX PAINTS IRELAND LTD—See Akzo Nobel N.V.; *Int'l*, pg. 270
DURON, INC.—See The Sherwin-Williams Company; *U.S. Public*, pg. 2127
E. BEFFA S.A.—See Akzo Nobel N.V.; *Int'l*, pg. 274
ECI ENVIROCOATINGS (CANADA) INC.—See ECL Enviro-Clean Ventures Ltd.; *Int'l*, pg. 2291
ENDEKA CERAMICS S.A.—See American Securities LLC; *U.S. Private*, pg. 251
ENGLISH COLOR & SUPPLY LLC; *U.S. Private*, pg. 1400
EPKO INDUSTRIES INC.; *U.S. Private*, pg. 1413
EPONK GROUP LTD.; *U.S. Private*, pg. 1414
EST A.S.—See Asseco Poland S.A.; *Int'l*, pg. 641
EYKON WALL SOURCES INC.; *U.S. Private*, pg. 1454
FERRO CORPORATION (AUSTRALIA) PTY. LTD.—See American Securities LLC; *U.S. Private*, pg. 251
FERRO COULEURS FRANCE SA—See American Securities LLC; *U.S. Private*, pg. 251
FERRO ELECTRONIC MATERIALS INC.—See American Securities LLC; *U.S. Private*, pg. 251
FERRO ENAMEL DO BRASIL INDUSTRIA E COMERCIO LTDA.—See American Securities LLC; *U.S. Private*, pg. 252
FERRO FAR EAST LTD.—See American Securities LLC; *U.S. Private*, pg. 252
FERRO GMBH—See American Securities LLC; *U.S. Private*, pg. 252
FERRO HOLDING GMBH—See American Securities LLC; *U.S. Private*, pg. 252
FERRO (HOLLAND) B.V.—See American Securities LLC; *U.S. Private*, pg. 251
FERRO JAPAN K.K.—See American Securities LLC; *U.S. Private*, pg. 252
FERRO PERFORMANCE PIGMENTS SPAIN S.L.—See American Securities LLC; *U.S. Private*, pg. 252
FERRO (SUZHOU) PERFORMANCE MATERIALS CO., LTD.—See American Securities LLC; *U.S. Private*, pg. 251
FERRO (THAILAND) CO. LTD.—See American Securities LLC; *U.S. Private*, pg. 251
FINISHMASTER, INC.—See LKQ Corporation; *U.S. Public*, pg. 1336
FLUID MANAGEMENT CANADA, INC.—See IDEX Corp; *U.S. Public*, pg. 1090
FORMAN BUILDING SYSTEMS LIMITED—See Fletcher Building Limited; *Int'l*, pg. 2700
GLADWIN PAINT COMPANY AUSTIN, LTD.—See LKQ Corporation; *U.S. Public*, pg. 1336
GRATEX INDUSTRIES LIMITED; *Int'l*, pg. 3061
HAMILTON EQUIPMENT, INC.; *U.S. Private*, pg. 1847
HIGHLAND INTERNATIONAL, INC.—See Henkel AG & Co. KGaA; *Int'l*, pg. 3354
HIRSHFIELD'S INC.; *U.S. Private*, pg. 1951
HOLLAND COLOURS CANADA INC—See Holland Colours NV; *Int'l*, pg. 3451
HOLLAND COLOURS MEXICANA SA DE CV—See Holland Colours NV; *Int'l*, pg. 3451
HOLLAND COLOURS UK LTD—See Holland Colours NV; *Int'l*, pg. 3451
ICI SWIRE PAINTS (SHANGHAI) LTD.—See Akzo Nobel N.V.; *Int'l*, pg. 274
INTERBAY COATINGS INC.—See Odyssey Investment Partners, LLC; *U.S. Private*, pg. 2995
INTERNATIONAL PAINT (AKZO NOBEL CHILE) LTDA—See Akzo Nobel N.V.; *Int'l*, pg. 270
INTERNATIONAL PAINT (NEDERLAND) B.V.—See Akzo Nobel N.V.; *Int'l*, pg. 274
INTERNATIONAL PAINTS (CANADA) LTD—See Akzo Nobel N.V.; *Int'l*, pg. 271
INVERCOLOR BOLOGNA SRL—See The Sherwin-Williams Company; *U.S. Public*, pg. 2128
INVERCOLOR TOSCANA SRL—See The Sherwin-Williams Company; *U.S. Public*, pg. 2128
INVER INDUSTRIAL COATINGS SRL—See The Sherwin-Williams Company; *U.S. Public*, pg. 2128
ISVA VERNICI SRL—See The Sherwin-Williams Company; *U.S. Public*, pg. 2128
IVC INDUSTRIAL COATINGS INC.—See PPG Industries, Inc.; *U.S. Public*, pg. 1707
JANOVIC-PLAZA INC.—See Berkshire Hathaway Inc.; *U.S. Public*, pg. 300
JORDAN PEINTURE SA—See Akzo Nobel N.V.; *Int'l*, pg. 269
KEY WALLCOVERING INC.—See Mobile Paint Manufacturing Company of Delaware Inc.; *U.S. Private*, pg. 2757
KLUMPP COATINGS DO BRASIL LTD.—See The Sherwin-Williams Company; *U.S. Public*, pg. 2128
KOROSEAL WALL COVERINGS WEST—See RJF International Corporation; *U.S. Private*, pg. 3449
LIANYUNGANG DIC COLOR CO., LTD.—See DIC Corporation; *Int'l*, pg. 2107
MAGNUSON - HAGOPIAN ENTERPRISES, INC.—See LKQ Corporation; *U.S. Public*, pg. 1336
MARPEX CHEMICALS LTD.—See Cathay Investments Limited; *Int'l*, pg. 1360
MCF INVESTISSEMENT SA—See A.S. Creation Tapeten AG; *Int'l*, pg. 28
THE MERIT DISTRIBUTION GROUP, LLC—See Centre Lane Partners, LLC; *U.S. Private*, pg. 827
MOBILE PAINT CARRIBEAN—See Mobile Paint Manufac-

424990 — OTHER MISCELLANEOUS...

turing Company of Delaware Inc.; *U.S. Private*, pg. 2757
MOBILE PAINT MANUFACTURING COMPANY OF PUERTO RICO INC.—See Mobile Paint Manufacturing Company of Delaware Inc.; *U.S. Private*, pg. 2757
MORGAN DISTRIBUTION; *U.S. Private*, pg. 2783
NATIONAL COATINGS & SUPPLIES, INC.; *U.S. Private*, pg. 2850
NORDSON SCHWEIZ AG—See Nordson Corporation; *U.S. Public*, pg. 1533
NUBIOLA COLOMBIA PIGMENTOS S.A.S.—See American Securities LLC; *U.S. Private*, pg. 252
OLD MASTER PRODUCTS INC.; *U.S. Private*, pg. 3009
OLE MOE AS—See Einhell Germany AG; *Int'l*, pg. 2334
PAINTERS SUPPLY & EQUIPMENT CO.—See Odyssey Investment Partners, LLC; *U.S. Private*, pg. 2995
PENN COLOR INTERNATIONAL BV—See Penn Color Inc.; *U.S. Private*, pg. 3133
PINTURAS CORAL DE BOLIVIA LTDA—See Akzo Nobel N.V.; *Int'l*, pg. 274
PLASTIQUE ROYAL INC.—See LKQ Corporation; *U.S. Public*, pg. 1336
PPG ARCHITECTURAL COATINGS CANADA, INC.—See PPG Industries, Inc.; *U.S. Public*, pg. 1708
PPG COATINGS DANMARK AS—See PPG Industries, Inc.; *U.S. Public*, pg. 1708
PPG COATINGS DEUTSCHLAND GMBH—See PPG Industries, Inc.; *U.S. Public*, pg. 1708
PPG COATINGS NEDERLAND BV—See PPG Industries, Inc.; *U.S. Public*, pg. 1708
PPG COATINGS SOUTH AFRICA (PTY) LTD.—See PPG Industries, Inc.; *U.S. Public*, pg. 1708
PPG DEUTSCHLAND SALES SERVICES GMBH—See PPG Industries, Inc.; *U.S. Public*, pg. 1708
PPG HELLAS S.A.—See PPG Industries, Inc.; *U.S. Public*, pg. 1708
PPG INDUSTRIES BELGIUM S.A./N.V.—See PPG Industries, Inc.; *U.S. Public*, pg. 1709
PPG INDUSTRIES COLOMBIA LTDA.—See PPG Industries, Inc.; *U.S. Public*, pg. 1709
PPG INDUSTRIES LIPETSK LLC—See PPG Industries, Inc.; *U.S. Public*, pg. 1709
PPG KANSAI AUTOMOTIVE FINISHES CANADA, LP—See PPG Industries, Inc.; *U.S. Public*, pg. 1709
PPG PAINTS TRADING (SHANGHAI) CO., LTD.—See PPG Industries, Inc.; *U.S. Public*, pg. 1709
PPG RETAIL FRANCE SAS—See PPG Industries, Inc.; *U.S. Public*, pg. 1709
PROCOATINGS B.V.—See PPG Industries, Inc.; *U.S. Public*, pg. 1710
PROVINCIAL WALLCOVERINGS LTD.—See Brewster Wallpaper Corp.; *U.S. Private*, pg. 647
PT. ANEST IWATA INDONESIA—See ANEST IWATA Corporation; *Int'l*, pg. 458
P.T. FRIEDRICH KLUMPP WOODCOATINGS—See The Sherwin-Williams Company; *U.S. Public*, pg. 2128
PT HOLLAND COLOURS ASIA—See Holland Colours NV; *Int'l*, pg. 3451
RICCIARDI BROTHERS INC.; *U.S. Private*, pg. 3425
SADOLIN FARVELAND A/S—See Akzo Nobel N.V.; *Int'l*, pg. 274
SADVEL SA—See Akzo Nobel N.V.; *Int'l*, pg. 275
SAINT-GOBAIN ADFORS DEUTSCHLAND GMBH—See Compagnie de Saint-Gobain SA; *Int'l*, pg. 1729
SCHRAMM COATINGS IBERICA SA—See Akzo Nobel N.V.; *Int'l*, pg. 275
SEABROOK WALLCOVERINGS, INC.; *U.S. Private*, pg. 3583
SHERWIN-WILLIAMS CZECH SPOL. S.R.O—See The Sherwin-Williams Company; *U.S. Public*, pg. 2128
SHERWIN-WILLIAMS JERSEY LIMITED—See The Sherwin-Williams Company; *U.S. Public*, pg. 2128
SHERWIN-WILLIAMS PAINT STORES GROUP—See The Sherwin-Williams Company; *U.S. Public*, pg. 2128
SIGMAKALON NIGERIA LIMITED—See PPG Industries, Inc.; *U.S. Public*, pg. 1710
SIKKENS VERKOOP B.V.—See Akzo Nobel N.V.; *Int'l*, pg. 275
SILBERLINE BRASIL LIMITADA—See Silberline Manufacturing Co., Inc.; *U.S. Private*, pg. 3652
SILBERLINE PIGMENTOS, SRL DE CV—See Silberline Manufacturing Co., Inc.; *U.S. Private*, pg. 3652
SILBERLINE SPECIALTY EFFECT PIGMENTS INDIA PRIVATE LIMITED—See Silberline Manufacturing Co., Inc.; *U.S. Private*, pg. 3652
SOPAL—See Eiffage S.A.; *Int'l*, pg. 2331
SOUTHERN COLOR NORTH AMERICA INC.; *U.S. Private*, pg. 3730
SUNDAY PAINT CO., LTD.—See Dai Nippon Toryo Co., Ltd.; *Int'l*, pg. 1916
SURFACE MATERIAL SALES INC.; *U.S. Private*, pg. 3883
SWISS LACK THELER PERREN AG—See Bystronic AG; *Int'l*, pg. 1236
TAPE INDUSTRIAL SALES INC.—See Genstar Capital, LLC; *U.S. Private*, pg. 1678
THIBAUT, INC.—See The Riverside Company; *U.S. Private*, pg. 4110
THYBONY WALLCOVERINGS INC.; *U.S. Private*, pg. 4166

TIKKURILA AB—See PPG Industries, Inc.; *U.S. Public*, pg. 1710
TIKKURILA (CHINA) PAINTS CO., LTD.—See PPG Industries, Inc.; *U.S. Public*, pg. 1710
TIKKURILA COATINGS SP. Z.O.O.—See PPG Industries, Inc.; *U.S. Public*, pg. 1710
TIKKURILA D.O.O.E.L—See PPG Industries, Inc.; *U.S. Public*, pg. 1711
TOO TIKKURILA—See PPG Industries, Inc.; *U.S. Public*, pg. 1710
TRIGA COLOR, A.S.—See PPG Industries, Inc.; *U.S. Public*, pg. 1710
TRUVALUE MANUFACTURING CO.—See ACON Investments, LLC; *U.S. Private*, pg. 63
UAB SHERWIN-WILLIAMS LIETUVA—See The Sherwin-Williams Company; *U.S. Public*, pg. 2130
UAB TIKKURILA—See PPG Industries, Inc.; *U.S. Public*, pg. 1711
VALSPAR ARIES COATINGS, S. DE R.L. DE C.V.—See The Sherwin-Williams Company; *U.S. Public*, pg. 2129
THE VALSPAR (ASIA) CORPORATION LIMITED—See The Sherwin-Williams Company; *U.S. Public*, pg. 2129
VALSPAR AUTOMOTIVE AUSTRALIA PTY LIMITED—See The Sherwin-Williams Company; *U.S. Public*, pg. 2129
THE VALSPAR CORPORATION LIMITADA—See The Sherwin-Williams Company; *U.S. Public*, pg. 2129
VALSPAR D.O.O BEOGRAD—See The Sherwin-Williams Company; *U.S. Public*, pg. 2130
VALSPAR D.O.O—See The Sherwin-Williams Company; *U.S. Public*, pg. 2129
VALSPAR INDUSTRIES (IRELAND) LTD.—See The Sherwin-Williams Company; *U.S. Public*, pg. 2129
VANESCH VERF GROEP B.V.—See LKQ Corporation; *U.S. Public*, pg. 1337
VAROSSIEAU SURINAME NV—See PPG Industries, Inc.; *U.S. Public*, pg. 1711
VETRICERAMICI DE MEXICO, S. DE R.L. DE C.V.—See American Securities LLC; *U.S. Private*, pg. 252
WILLIAM F. MEYER COMPANY; *U.S. Private*, pg. 4523
WOLF-GORDON INC.—See Charger Investment Partners LP; *U.S. Private*, pg. 850
THE WOOSTER BRUSH COMPANY - RENO—See The Wooster Brush Company; *U.S. Private*, pg. 4139
ZAO SHERWIN-WILLIAMS—See The Sherwin-Williams Company; *U.S. Public*, pg. 2130

424990 — OTHER MISCELLANEOUS NONDURABLE GOODS MERCHANT WHOLESALERS

1888 MILLS, LLC - DISTRIBUTION FACILITY—See 1888 Mills, LLC; *U.S. Private*, pg. 3
26 CALIFORNIA BAZAR INC.; *U.S. Private*, pg. 6
ACCENT ANNEX ENTERPRISES INC.; *U.S. Private*, pg. 50
ACME TRADING CORPORATION; *U.S. Private*, pg. 61
ADERANS (SHANGHAI) CO., LTD.—See Aderans Co., Ltd.; *Int'l*, pg. 143
ADERANS THAI., LTD. (BURIRAM FACTORY)—See Aderans Co., Ltd.; *Int'l*, pg. 143
ADERANS THAI. LTD.—See Aderans Co., Ltd.; *Int'l*, pg. 143
ADVANCE BAG & PACKAGING CO.; *U.S. Private*, pg. 83
AFRICA PREPAID SERVICES (MOZAMBIQUE) LIMITADA—See Blue Label Telecoms Limited; *Int'l*, pg. 1068
A.I. FRIEDMAN LP; *U.S. Private*, pg. 26
AI TOPPER & CO; *Int'l*, pg. 227
AJWA EDIBLE OIL COMPANY LIMITED—See Ajwa Group for Food Industries Holding Ltd. Co.; *Int'l*, pg. 258
AKSA EGYPT ACRYLIC FIBER INDUSTRY SAE—See Aksa Akrilik Kimya Sanayii A.S.; *Int'l*, pg. 264
ALLCHEM INDUSTRIES PERFORMANCE PRODUCTS—See AllChem Industries Group; *U.S. Private*, pg. 175
ALLEGRO LIMITED—See Dole plc; *Int'l*, pg. 2158
ALLIED FELT GROUP—See Central Shippee, Inc.; *U.S. Private*, pg. 824
ALLSTAR PRODUCTS GROUP LLC; *U.S. Private*, pg. 193
ALVARO P. ESCANDON, INC.; *U.S. Private*, pg. 214
AMBRA SP. Z O.O.—See Emperia Holding S.A; *Int'l*, pg. 2385
AMERICAN HOUSE; *U.S. Private*, pg. 236
ANIMAL SUPPLY COMPANY LLC—See Summit Partners, L.P.; *U.S. Private*, pg. 3855
ANIMAL SUPPLY CO. WEST—See Summit Partners, L.P.; *U.S. Private*, pg. 3855
ANIMED DIRECT LIMITED—See CVS Group Plc; *Int'l*, pg. 1890
ANISA INTERNATIONAL, INC.; *U.S. Private*, pg. 283
AN LUXURY IMPORTS GP, LLC—See AutoNation, Inc.; *U.S. Public*, pg. 231
APET INC.; *U.S. Private*, pg. 291
APOLLO HAIR SYSTEMS INC; *U.S. Private*, pg. 294
ARATA CORPORATION; *Int'l*, pg. 536
ARLA FOODS B.V.—See Arla Foods amba; *Int'l*, pg. 572
ART SUPPLY ENTERPRISES INC.; *U.S. Private*, pg. 340
ASG MARKETING SDN. BHD.—See Ajiya Berhad; *Int'l*, pg. 258

ASHEBORO PAPER & PACKAGING, INC.; *U.S. Private*, pg. 349
ASSOCIATED PACKAGING INC.; *U.S. Private*, pg. 356
AS TALLINN DUTY FREE—See AS Infortar; *Int'l*, pg. 590
ATICO INTERNATIONAL USA, INC.; *U.S. Public*, pg. 369
A-T TRADE INC.; *U.S. Private*, pg. 22
AURELIUS COMMERCIAL BETEILIGUNGS GMBH—See Aurelius Equity Opportunities SE & Co. KGaA; *Int'l*, pg. 707
AZAD INTERNATIONAL INC.; *U.S. Private*, pg. 415
BARKER ADVERTISING SPECIALTY COMPANY; *U.S. Private*, pg. 475
BBVA SERVICIOS, S.A.—See Banco Bilbao Vizcaya Argentaria, S.A.; *Int'l*, pg. 817
BECKER MARKETING SERVICES INC.; *U.S. Private*, pg. 511
BEN S. LOEB, INC.; *U.S. Private*, pg. 523
BERGER COMPANY; *U.S. Private*, pg. 530
BESTHIDES GMBH—See Darling Ingredients Inc.; *U.S. Public*, pg. 633
BIMECO GARNHANDEL GMBH & CO. KG; *Int'l*, pg. 1032
BINNY MILLS LIMITED; *Int'l*, pg. 1034
BI-STATE PACKAGING INCORPORATED—See Group O Inc.; *U.S. Private*, pg. 1794
BLC COSMETICS PTY LTD—See Hancock & Gore Ltd.; *U.S. Public*, pg. 3242
BLUEWATER TRADING INC.; *U.S. Private*, pg. 599
BMT COMMODITY CORPORATION; *U.S. Private*, pg. 601
BONNIE PLANTS, LLC—See The Scotts Miracle-Gro Company; *U.S. Public*, pg. 2126
BORRACHAS E EQUIPAMENTOS ELGI LTDA—See Elgi Rubber Company Limited; *Int'l*, pg. 2360
BOTANY BAY IMPORTS & EXPORTS PTY LTD—See EBOS Group Limited; *Int'l*, pg. 2285
THE BOYDS COLLECTION, LTD.—See Enesco, LLC; *U.S. Private*, pg. 1397
THE BRADFORD GROUP; *U.S. Private*, pg. 3999
BRAWER BROS INC.; *U.S. Private*, pg. 641
BRIDGESTONE SINGAPORE PTE. LTD.—See Bridgestone Corporation; *Int'l*, pg. 1159
BROTEX (VIETNAM) CO., LTD—See Bros Eastern Co., Ltd.; *Int'l*, pg. 1195
THE BRUNA CORPORATION—See Genstar Capital, LLC; *U.S. Private*, pg. 1679
BSP MARKETING INC.; *U.S. Private*, pg. 675
BUYATAB ONLINE INC.—See Corpay, Inc.; *U.S. Public*, pg. 579
C2F, INC.; *U.S. Private*, pg. 709
CANDELA SALES COMPANY INC.; *U.S. Private*, pg. 733
CANDLE LAMP COMPANY, LLC—See Compass Diversified Holdings; *U.S. Public*, pg. 559
CANDYM ENTERPRISES LTD.; *Int'l*, pg. 1289
CAPE CRAFTSMEN, INC.—See Evergreen Enterprises, Inc.; *U.S. Private*, pg. 1439
CARGILL NORDIC A/S—See Cargill, Inc.; *U.S. Private*, pg. 758
CARLEN ENTERPRISES INC.; *U.S. Private*, pg. 763
CARL FISCHER MUSIC DISTRIBUTORS, INC.—See Carl Fischer, LLC; *U.S. Private*, pg. 762
CARROLL COMPANIES INC.; *U.S. Private*, pg. 773
CASTOR & POLLUX PET WORKS; *U.S. Private*, pg. 785
CASTRO MODEL LTD.; *Int'l*, pg. 1358
CBK LTD.—See MVP Group International, Inc.; *U.S. Private*, pg. 2821
CDI - SOCIETE COTONNIERE DE DISTRIBUTION S.A.—See StoneX Group Inc.; *U.S. Public*, pg. 1951
CE COMPETITIVE EDGE LLC; *U.S. Private*, pg. 803
CENNOX INC.; *U.S. Private*, pg. 809
CENTRAL SHIPPEE, INC.; *U.S. Private*, pg. 824
CHARLES SADEK IMPORT COMPANY INC.; *U.S. Private*, pg. 853
CHERRYBROOK PREMIUM PET SUPPLIES; *U.S. Private*, pg. 874
CHINA TONE LIMITED—See Dickson Concepts (International) Limited; *Int'l*, pg. 2112
CHINNEY ALLIANCE GROUP LIMITED; *Int'l*, pg. 1570
CHUCK LATHAM ASSOCIATES, INC.; *U.S. Private*, pg. 893
CINPAK, INC.; *U.S. Private*, pg. 898
CLASSIC SOFT TRIM INC.; *U.S. Private*, pg. 916
CLOSE OUT STORE; *U.S. Private*, pg. 946
C. MORELLO, PTY. LTD.—See Matthews International Corporation; *U.S. Public*, pg. 1399
COAST PACKAGING COMPANY; *U.S. Private*, pg. 954
COFCO FOOD MARKETING SERVICES, CO., LTD.—See COFCO Limited; *Int'l*, pg. 1692
COHN WHOLESALE FRUIT & GROCERY; *U.S. Private*, pg. 963
COLEMAN GUANGZHOU OUTDOOR LEISURE PRODUCTS COMPANY LTD.—See Newell Brands Inc.; *U.S. Public*, pg. 1515
COLUMBUS FOODS COMPANY; *U.S. Private*, pg. 979
COMM EXPRESS SERVICES SA (PROPRIETARY) LIMITED—See Blue Label Telecoms Limited; *Int'l*, pg. 1068
COMPPIL SA; *Int'l*, pg. 1754
CONCORD PAPER CORP.; *U.S. Private*, pg. 1010
CONTINENTAL TYRE AND RUBBER SINGAPORE PTE.

424990 — OTHER MISCELLANEOUS...   CORPORATE AFFILIATIONS

LTD.—See Continental Aktiengesellschaft; *Int'l*, pg. 1781
CONTITECH JAPAN CO. LTD.—See Continental Aktiengesellschaft; *Int'l*, pg. 1780
CORPORATE MARKETING, INC.—See Artcraft Promotional Concepts; *U.S. Private*, pg. 340
COSTCO DE MEXICO, S.A. DE C.V.—See Costco Wholesale Corporation; *U.S. Public*, pg. 587
COUSIN CORPORATION OF AMERICA; *U.S. Private*, pg. 1071
CRAVEN POTTERY INC.; *U.S. Private*, pg. 1086
CREATIONS DE PARIS CAMAFLEX VERTRIEBS GMBH—See Aderans Co., Ltd.; *Int'l*, pg. 143
CREATIVE SALES GROUP, INC.; *U.S. Private*, pg. 1090
C&S PACKAGING GROUP INC.; *U.S. Private*, pg. 704
CTH GMBH—See Darling Ingredients Inc.; *U.S. Public*, pg. 633
CTH PORTO - INDUSTRIA ALIMENTAR UNIPESSOAL LDA—See Darling Ingredients Inc.; *U.S. Public*, pg. 633
CUSTOM DECOR, INC.; *U.S. Private*, pg. 1128
CUSTOM PROTEIN CORPORATION; *U.S. Private*, pg. 1129
DAIRYGOLD TRADING LIMITED—See Dairygold Co-Operative Society Ltd; *Int'l*, pg. 1940
DARLING AWS LLC—See Darling Ingredients Inc.; *U.S. Public*, pg. 633
DARLING INTERNATIONAL NETHERLANDS B.V.—See Darling Ingredients Inc.; *U.S. Public*, pg. 634
DAVID C. POOLE COMPANY INC.; *U.S. Private*, pg. 1169
DECHRA VETERINARY PRODUCTS AB—See EQT AB; *Int'l*, pg. 2474
DECHRA VETERINARY PRODUCTS AS—See EQT AB; *Int'l*, pg. 2474
DECHRA VETERINARY PRODUCTS BV—See EQT AB; *Int'l*, pg. 2474
DECHRA VETERINARY PRODUCTS LIMITED—See EQT AB; *Int'l*, pg. 2474
DECHRA VETERINARY PRODUCTS LLC—See EQT AB; *Int'l*, pg. 2474
DECHRA VETERINARY PRODUCTS OY—See EQT AB; *Int'l*, pg. 2474
DECHRA VETERINARY PRODUCTS SAS—See EQT AB; *Int'l*, pg. 2474
DECHRA VETERINARY PRODUCTS SLU—See EQT AB; *Int'l*, pg. 2474
DECORATIVE CRAFTS, INC.; *U.S. Private*, pg. 1188
DECORA UKRAINA TOB—See Decora S.A.; *Int'l*, pg. 2001
DELKO S.A.; *Int'l*, pg. 2013
DIABLO VALLEY PACKAGING INC.—See Keystone Group, L.P.; *U.S. Private*, pg. 2297
DINOVITE INC.—See The Carlyle Group Inc.; *U.S. Public*, pg. 2049
DIRECT VAPOR LLC—See Turning Point Brands, Inc.; *U.S. Public*, pg. 2205
DOLPHIN INTERNATIONAL INC.; *U.S. Private*, pg. 1255
DOWNEAST CONCEPTS INC.; *U.S. Private*, pg. 1269
DP+COMPANY; *U.S. Private*, pg. 1270
D. VAN NOOIJEN B.V.—See Aderans Co., Ltd.; *Int'l*, pg. 143
D. VAN NOOIJEN B.V.—See Aderans Co., Ltd.; *Int'l*, pg. 143
EAGLE OTTAWA U.K. LTD.—See Lear Corporation; *U.S. Public*, pg. 1296
EARTHWISE BAG COMPANY, INC.—See Bunzl plc; *Int'l*, pg. 1217
EASTCOMPEACE (SINGAPORE) CO., LTD.—See Eastcompeace Technology Co., Ltd.; *Int'l*, pg. 2271
E&B GIFTWARE LLC—See Cortec Group Management Services, LLC; *U.S. Private*, pg. 1060
ECONOMIC PACKAGING CORPORATION; *U.S. Private*, pg. 1330
ECOSON B.V.—See Darling Ingredients Inc.; *U.S. Public*, pg. 634
EDGAR KLEINE KAPUNKT GMBH—See EssilorLuxottica SA; *Int'l*, pg. 2515
EFC (I) LIMITED; *Int'l*, pg. 2319
ELFA TRADING COMPANY INC.; *U.S. Private*, pg. 1359
ELGI RUBBER COMPANY BV—See Elgi Rubber Company Limited; *Int'l*, pg. 2360
ELGI RUBBER COMPANY LLC—See Elgi Rubber Company Limited; *Int'l*, pg. 2360
EMERSON PROCESS MANAGEMENT, S.L.—See Emerson Electric Co.; *U.S. Public*, pg. 747
EMICO MARKETING SDN. BHD.—See Emico Holdings Berhad; *Int'l*, pg. 2380
E. MISHAN & SONS, INC.; *U.S. Private*, pg. 1304
ENESCO FRANCE S.A.S.—See Enesco, LLC; *U.S. Private*, pg. 1397
ENESCO (HONG KONG) LTD.—See Enesco, LLC; *U.S. Private*, pg. 1397
ENMAR TRADING LTD—See Enka Insaat ve Sanayi A.S.; *Int'l*, pg. 2440
ENTERPRISE INTERNATIONAL LIMITED; *Int'l*, pg. 2451
ERS DIGITAL, INC.—See ARC DOCUMENT SOLUTIONS, INC.; *U.S. Public*, pg. 179
ETNA PRODUCTS CO. INC.; *U.S. Private*, pg. 1432
EUCATEX TINTAS E VERNIZES LTDA.—See Eucatex S.A. Industria e Comercio; *Int'l*, pg. 2525
EUROPAPIER - SRBIJA D.O.O.—See Heinzel Holding GmbH; *Int'l*, pg. 3325

FHP VILEDA SP. Z.O.O.—See Freudenberg SE; *Int'l*, pg. 2785
FIBER & YARN PRODUCTS INC.; *U.S. Private*, pg. 1501
FILA POLSKA SP. Z O.O.—See F.I.L.A. - Fabbrica Italiana Lapis ed Affini S.p.A.; *Int'l*, pg. 2597
FILZFELT INC.—See MillerKnoll, Inc.; *U.S. Public*, pg. 1447
FIRSTAR TRADE SERVICES CORPORATION—See U.S. Bancorp; *U.S. Public*, pg. 2212
FIRST MANUFACTURING COMPANY; *U.S. Private*, pg. 1521
FIRST NATIONAL TRADING CO. INC.; *U.S. Private*, pg. 1524
FITCO BV—See Aksa Akrilik Kimya Sanayii A.S.; *Int'l*, pg. 264
FITZ & FLOYD, INC.—See Lifetime Brands, Inc.; *U.S. Public*, pg. 1313
FLEX-PAC; *U.S. Private*, pg. 1543
FLOWER FACTORY INC.; *U.S. Private*, pg. 1551
FOTHERGILL CRENETTE LTD—See Groupe Porcher Industries; *Int'l*, pg. 3109
FREUDENBERG HOUSEHOLD PRODUCTS LP—See Freudenberg SE; *Int'l*, pg. 2787
GALLERY RARE LTD.—See Aucnet Inc.; *Int'l*, pg. 700
GATES GMBH—See Blackstone Inc.; *U.S. Public*, pg. 354
GELMART INDUSTRIES INC.; *U.S. Private*, pg. 1657
GENERAL BRANDS S.A.R.L.—See Holdal s.a.l.; *Int'l*, pg. 3449
GENERAL PET SUPPLY, INC.—See Central Garden & Pet Company; *U.S. Public*, pg. 473
GEORGE B. WOODCOCK & CO.; *U.S. Private*, pg. 1681
THE GERSON COMPANY INC.; *U.S. Private*, pg. 4033
GIVAUDAN UK LIMITED - STAINES—See Givaudan S.A.; *Int'l*, pg. 2980
GLOBAL CERAMIC MATERIALS LTD—See Darling Ingredients Inc.; *U.S. Public*, pg. 634
GOLDEN STATE FOODS CORP.; *U.S. Private*, pg. 1733
GOLDNER ASSOCIATES, INC.; *U.S. Private*, pg. 1735
GRANITE PACKAGING SUPPLY ONE CO.; *U.S. Private*, pg. 1756
GREENSPRING COMPANY—See American Public Media Group; *U.S. Private*, pg. 244
GREENWICH WORKSHOP INC.; *U.S. Private*, pg. 1781
GRIFFIN INDUSTRIES LLC—See Darling Ingredients Inc.; *U.S. Public*, pg. 634
GROUP III INTERNATIONAL, LTD.; *U.S. Private*, pg. 1793
GULF COAST PET SUPPLIES, INC.; *U.S. Private*, pg. 1815
GUMMER WHOLESALE INC.; *U.S. Private*, pg. 1818
GUNZE INTERNATIONAL USA INC.—See Gunze Limited; *Int'l*, pg. 3185
HALPERN IMPORT COMPANY INC.; *U.S. Private*, pg. 1846
HARBIN CHANGFANGYUAN HI-TECH ENVIRONMENT-FRIENDLY INDUSTRIAL CO., LTD—See CHINA GREEN MATERIAL TECHNOLOGIES, INC.; *Int'l*, pg. 1505
HARTA DISTRIBUTION NETWORK SDN. BHD.—See HPI Resources Berhad; *Int'l*, pg. 3500
HCW DISTRIBUTING CORP.—See HAUPPAUGE DIGITAL, INC.; *U.S. Public*, pg. 988
HEINZEL DEUTSCHLAND GMBH—See Heinzel Holding GmbH; *Int'l*, pg. 3325
HEINZEL SALES FRANCE S.A.S.—See Heinzel Holding GmbH; *Int'l*, pg. 3326
HEINZEL SALES ITALY S.R.L.—See Heinzel Holding GmbH; *Int'l*, pg. 3326
HEPAC B.V.—See Darling Ingredients Inc.; *U.S. Public*, pg. 634
HILDEBRANDT NETHERLANDS B.V.—See August Hildebrandt GmbH; *Int'l*, pg. 703
HILDEBRANDT USA, INC.—See August Hildebrandt GmbH; *Int'l*, pg. 703
HILL'S PET NUTRITION B.V.—See Colgate-Palmolive Company; *U.S. Public*, pg. 532
HILL'S PET NUTRITION CANADA INC.—See Colgate-Palmolive Company; *U.S. Public*, pg. 533
HILL'S PET NUTRITION DE MEXICO, S.A. DE C.V.—See Colgate-Palmolive Company; *U.S. Public*, pg. 533
HILL'S PET NUTRITION DENMARK APS—See Colgate-Palmolive Company; *U.S. Public*, pg. 533
HILL'S PET NUTRITION ESPANA, S.L.—See Colgate-Palmolive Company; *U.S. Public*, pg. 533
HILL'S PET NUTRITION GMBH—See Colgate-Palmolive Company; *U.S. Public*, pg. 533
HILL'S PET NUTRITION ITALIA, S.R.L.—See Colgate-Palmolive Company; *U.S. Public*, pg. 533
HILL'S PET NUTRITION (NZ) LIMITED—See Colgate-Palmolive Company; *U.S. Public*, pg. 532
HILL'S PET NUTRITION PTY. LTD.—See Colgate-Palmolive Company; *U.S. Public*, pg. 533
HILL'S PET NUTRITION SOUTH AFRICA PROPRIETARY LIMITED—See Colgate-Palmolive Company; *U.S. Public*, pg. 533
HILL'S PET NUTRITION SWITZERLAND GMBH—See Colgate-Palmolive Company; *U.S. Public*, pg. 533
HIND COMMERCE LIMITED; *Int'l*, pg. 3397
HKN, INC.; *U.S. Private*, pg. 1953
HOUR LOOP, INC.; *U.S. Public*, pg. 1056
H.P COTTON TEXTILE MILLS LTD.; *Int'l*, pg. 3196

HR-SERVICE NEDERLAND B.V.—See Darling Ingredients Inc.; *U.S. Public*, pg. 634
THE HUNTE CORPORATION; *U.S. Private*, pg. 4054
HYOSUNG (AMERICA), INC.—See Hyosung Corporation; *Int'l*, pg. 3550
HYOSUNG USA, INC. - LOS ANGELES OFFICE—See Hyosung Corporation; *Int'l*, pg. 3551
IBB DUBLIN LTD—See IBB Amsterdam BV; *Int'l*, pg. 3569
IBB PARIS SARL—See IBB Amsterdam BV; *Int'l*, pg. 3569
IDAHO PACKAGE COMPANY—See Kelso & Company, L.P.; *U.S. Private*, pg. 2279
IDAHO PACKAGE COMPANY—See Warburg Pincus LLC; *U.S. Private*, pg. 4437
IDEXX OPERATIONS, INC.—See IDEXX Laboratories, Inc.; *U.S. Public*, pg. 1093
IMAGING SUPPLIES & EQUIPMENT; *U.S. Private*, pg. 2046
IMPERIAL COMMODITIES CORP.; *U.S. Private*, pg. 2049
INNOVATION GRAPHICS; *U.S. Private*, pg. 2081
INTERNATIONAL PURCHASE SYSTEMS, INC.; *U.S. Private*, pg. 2119
JACK RICHESON & CO., INC.—See MPE Partners, LLC; *U.S. Private*, pg. 2803
JACOB STERN & SONS, INC.; *U.S. Private*, pg. 2179
JAPELL (HONG KONG) CO., LIMITED—See Arata Corporation; *Int'l*, pg. 536
J. CARROLL & ASSOCIATES, INC.—See Louis F. Leeper Company; *U.S. Private*, pg. 2498
JEEVES GMBH—See Battery Ventures, L.P.; *U.S. Private*, pg. 489
J.L. BUCHANAN INC.; *U.S. Private*, pg. 2167
JOHNSON BROS RUBBER CO.; *U.S. Private*, pg. 2226
JUPITER RESEARCH, LLC—See TILT Holdings Inc.; *U.S. Public*, pg. 2159
KANZLER GMBH—See Darling Ingredients Inc.; *U.S. Public*, pg. 634
KAPPA MAP GROUP, LLC; *U.S. Private*, pg. 2262
KATHERINE'S COLLECTION INC.; *U.S. Private*, pg. 2264
KEITH DOYLE & ASSOCIATES INC.; *U.S. Private*, pg. 2274
THE KENNEDY GROUP LIMITED—See W.W. Grainger, Inc.; *U.S. Public*, pg. 2320
KEYSTON BROS. INC.; *U.S. Private*, pg. 2295
KILLER BEE INC.—See Global Seafood Technologies; *U.S. Private*, pg. 1717
KINSOLE PTY LTD—See Hancock & Gore Ltd.; *Int'l*, pg. 3242
KOPLA AMERICA INC.—See BGFecomaterials CO., LTD.; *Int'l*, pg. 1007
KUDZU FABRICS INCORPORATED; *U.S. Private*, pg. 2356
KURT S. ADLER, INC.; *U.S. Private*, pg. 2358
KYOSAN SERVICE CORPORATION—See Denso Corporation; *Int'l*, pg. 2032
LAD'S PET SUPPLIES—See Summit Partners, L.P.; *U.S. Private*, pg. 3855
LAKIN TIRE WEST INC.—See The Carlyle Group Inc.; *U.S. Public*, pg. 2048
LA-LA IMPORTS INC.; *U.S. Private*, pg. 2370
LB INTERNATIONAL, INC.; *U.S. Private*, pg. 2403
LION BRAND YARN COMPANY; *U.S. Private*, pg. 2463
LLADRO USA INC.—See Weil Ceramics & Glass Inc.; *U.S. Private*, pg. 4471
LLC EUROPAPIER—See Heinzel Holding GmbH; *Int'l*, pg. 3325
LONE STAR PET SUPPLY, INC.—See Summit Partners, L.P.; *U.S. Private*, pg. 3855
LOWEN CORPORATION; *U.S. Private*, pg. 2505
LUCKY DOLLAR STORES INC.; *U.S. Private*, pg. 2511
MADERAS Y SINTETICOS DEL PERU S.A.C.—See GrupoNueva S.A.; *Int'l*, pg. 3139
M.A. INC.—See Midwest Real Estate Development; *U.S. Private*, pg. 2723
MAPA SPONTEX CE S.R.O.—See Newell Brands Inc.; *U.S. Public*, pg. 1514
MAPA SPONTEX POLSKA SP. Z.O.O.—See Newell Brands Inc.; *U.S. Public*, pg. 1514
MAPA SPONTEX UK LIMITED—See Newell Brands Inc.; *U.S. Public*, pg. 1514
MARKER DALBELLO VOLKL AUSTRIA GMBH—See Kohlberg & Company, LLC; *U.S. Private*, pg. 2338
MARKS INC.—See Mark's Card Shops Inc.; *U.S. Private*, pg. 2578
MASISA MANUFACTURA S.A. DE C.V.—See AntarChile S.A.; *Int'l*, pg. 481
MASISA PLC S.A.—See GrupoNueva S.A.; *Int'l*, pg. 3139
MASTERPET AUSTRALIA PTY LTD—See EBOS Group Limited; *Int'l*, pg. 2285
MAURCEXCO INTERNATIONAL—See Maurice Electrical Supply Company; *U.S. Private*, pg. 2615
MCKENZIE BUYING COMPANY—See Western Family Holding Co., Inc.; *U.S. Private*, pg. 4493
MEISNER GALLERY, INC.; *U.S. Private*, pg. 2661
THE MERCO GROUP INC.; *U.S. Private*, pg. 4078
MIDDLE EAST TRADING CO.—See Hayel Saeed Anam Group of Companies; *Int'l*, pg. 3290
MILLERS FORGE INC.; *U.S. Private*, pg. 2736
MIRTH INCORPORATED; *U.S. Private*, pg. 2746
MONFAIR MODEN VERTRIEBS GMBH—See Aderans Co., Ltd.; *Int'l*, pg. 143

N.A.I.C.S. INDEX

425120 — WHOLESALE TRADE AGE...

MR. CHRISTMAS INC.; *U.S. Private*, pg. 2804
NATHAN WEINER & ASSOCIATES INC.—See Sterling Supply Co. Inc.; *U.S. Private*, pg. 3807
NATIONAL PACKAGING SPECIALISTS, INC.; *U.S. Private*, pg. 2860
NATIONAL TECHNICAL SYSTEMS, INC. - SANTA CLARITA—See Aurora Capital Group, LLC; *U.S. Private*, pg. 393
NATUR COMPAGNIE GMBH—See Coop-Gruppe Genossenschaft; *Int'l*, pg. 1790
NATURES INNOVATION, INC.; *U.S. Private*, pg. 2867
NIKAIA, INC.; *U.S. Private*, pg. 2927
NILE MATCH COMPANY—See Chemical Industries Holding Company; *Int'l*, pg. 1462
NOKK EHF.—See BEWi ASA; *Int'l*, pg. 1004
NORSTAR INC.; *U.S. Private*, pg. 2939
OMNI PACKAGING CORPORATION—See Wellspring Capital Management LLC; *U.S. Private*, pg. 4478
OSTER GMBH—See Newell Brands Inc.; *U.S. Public*, pg. 1514
OUTRAGEOUS VENTURES, INC.; *U.S. Private*, pg. 3051
PAC WORLDWIDE CORPORATION; *U.S. Private*, pg. 3063
PARAMOUNT HOME ENTERTAINMENT (NORWAY) ANS—See National Amusements, Inc.; *U.S. Private*, pg. 2843
PARIS PRESENTS, INC.—See Yellow Wood Partners LLC; *U.S. Private*, pg. 4587
PARTYLITE GIFTS, INC.—See The Carlyle Group Inc.; *U.S. Public*, pg. 2052
PET FOOD WHOLESALE INC.; *U.S. Private*, pg. 3156
PEYTON'S-SOUTHEASTERN, INC.—See The Kroger Co.; *U.S. Public*, pg. 2109
PIEDMONT NATIONAL CORPORATION; *U.S. Private*, pg. 3177
PINCOTT INTERNATIONAL PTY LIMITED—See Elgi Rubber Company Limited; *Int'l*, pg. 2360
PORCHER DO BRASIL TECIDOS DE VIDROS LTDA.—See Groupe Porcher Industries; *Int'l*, pg. 3110
PRODUCT CLUB, INC.—See Burmax Company Inc.; *U.S. Private*, pg. 689
PRODUCTOS COLEMAN S.A.—See Newell Brands Inc.; *U.S. Public*, pg. 1515
PROFESSIONAL PACKAGING SYSTEMS INC.; *U.S. Private*, pg. 3275
PROFORMA ALBRECHT & COMPANY; *U.S. Private*, pg. 3277
PURE FISHING (GUANGZHOU) TRADING CO., LTD.—See Sycamore Partners Management, LP; *U.S. Private*, pg. 3896
PURE FISHING (THAILAND) CO., LTD.—See Sycamore Partners Management, LP; *U.S. Private*, pg. 3896
QUICKIE DE MEXICO, S. DE R.L. DE C.V.—See Newell Brands Inc.; *U.S. Public*, pg. 1514
QUIXOTE ENTERPRISE INC.; *U.S. Private*, pg. 3329
RAZ IMPORTS INC.; *U.S. Private*, pg. 3359
RECOGNITION SYSTEMS INC.; *U.S. Private*, pg. 3371
REDEMPTION PLUS, LLC.; *U.S. Private*, pg. 3378
RENDAC BVBA—See Darling Ingredients Inc.; *U.S. Public*, pg. 634
RENDAC ICKER GMBH & CO. KG—See Darling Ingredients Inc.; *U.S. Public*, pg. 634
RENE' OF PARIS—See Aderans Co., Ltd.; *Int'l*, pg. 144
ROCKY MOUNTAIN MEDICAL, LLC—See Coloplast A/S; *Int'l*, pg. 1704
ROMAN, INC.; *U.S. Private*, pg. 3476
ROUSSELOT ANGOULEME SAS—See Darling Ingredients Inc.; *U.S. Public*, pg. 634
ROUSSELOT ARGENTINA SA—See Darling Ingredients Inc.; *U.S. Public*, pg. 634
ROUSSELOT BVBA—See Darling Ingredients Inc.; *U.S. Public*, pg. 634
ROUSSELOT (DA'AN) GELATIN CO. LTD—See Darling Ingredients Inc.; *U.S. Public*, pg. 634
ROUSSELOT GELATIN SL—See Darling Ingredients Inc.; *U.S. Public*, pg. 634
ROUSSELOT (GUANGDONG) GELATIN CO. LTD—See Darling Ingredients Inc.; *U.S. Public*, pg. 634
ROUSSELOT ISLE SUR LA SORGUE SAS—See Darling Ingredients Inc.; *U.S. Public*, pg. 634
ROUSSELOT JAPAN KK—See Darling Ingredients Inc.; *U.S. Public*, pg. 634
ROUSSELOT (M) SDN.BHD—See Darling Ingredients Inc.; *U.S. Public*, pg. 634
ROUSSELOT (WHENZOU) GELATIN CO. LTD—See Darling Ingredients Inc.; *U.S. Public*, pg. 634
ROUSSELOT (ZHEJIANG) GELATIN CO. LTD—See Darling Ingredients Inc.; *U.S. Public*, pg. 634
SA&E INTERNATIONAL BAG & ACCESSORIES LLC; *U.S. Private*, pg. 3519
SALCO LEATHER; *U.S. Private*, pg. 3531
SANDERS MARKETING GROUP INC.; *U.S. Private*, pg. 3543
SANS FIBERS INCORPORATED—See AECI Limited; *Int'l*, pg. 171
SARANTIS HUNGARY KFT.—See Gr. Sarantis S.A.; *Int'l*, pg. 3047
THE SARUT GROUP; *U.S. Private*, pg. 4114
SCHROEDER & TREMAYNE INC.—See SBI Incorporated; *U.S. Private*, pg. 3560
SCOTT PET PRODUCTS INC.; *U.S. Private*, pg. 3577
THE SCOTTS COMPANY—See The Scotts Miracle-Gro Company; *U.S. Public*, pg. 2127
SELECTO PRODUCTS CO. INC.; *U.S. Private*, pg. 3601
SEVEN D WHOLESALE L.L.P.—See The DeGol Organization; *U.S. Private*, pg. 4019
SHERWIN-WILLIAMS PAINT STORES GROUP—See The Sherwin-Williams Company; *U.S. Public*, pg. 2128
SHIMS BARGAIN INC.; *U.S. Private*, pg. 3636
SHORR PACKAGING CORP.; *U.S. Private*, pg. 3642
SHRINK PACKAGING SYSTEMS CORP.; *U.S. Private*, pg. 3644
SIGMA SUPPLY INC.; *U.S. Private*, pg. 3649
THE SINGER GROUP; *U.S. Private*, pg. 4118
SINTEX NYLON AND COTTON PRODUCTS (PTE) LIMITED—See Chuang's Consortium International Limited; *Int'l*, pg. 1590
SNYDER PAPER CORPORATION; *U.S. Private*, pg. 3701
SONAC EINDHOVEN B.V.—See Darling Ingredients Inc.; *U.S. Public*, pg. 634
SONAC GENT BVBA—See Darling Ingredients Inc.; *U.S. Public*, pg. 634
SONAC HARLINGEN B.V.—See Darling Ingredients Inc.; *U.S. Public*, pg. 634
SONAC KIEL GMBH—See Darling Ingredients Inc.; *U.S. Public*, pg. 634
SPICERS FRANCE SAS—See ADVEO Group International, S.A.; *Int'l*, pg. 167
SP IMAGES LLC; *U.S. Private*, pg. 3743
S&S WORLDWIDE INC.; *U.S. Private*, pg. 3514
STARCO IMPEX INC.; *U.S. Private*, pg. 3786
STAR SALES CO., INC.; *U.S. Private*, pg. 3785
STERLING SUPPLY CO. INC.; *U.S. Private*, pg. 3807
SUBURBAN IMPORTS OF TROY, INC.—See Suburban Motors Company, LLC; *U.S. Private*, pg. 3848
SUMMA TRADING COMPANY INC.; *U.S. Private*, pg. 3853
SUN DRAGON IMPORT, INC.; *U.S. Private*, pg. 3863
SUN PET, LTD.—See Central Garden & Pet Company; *U.S. Public*, pg. 473
SUPERIOR FELT & FILTRATION LLC; *U.S. Private*, pg. 3878
TASK SOURCE INC.; *U.S. Private*, pg. 3935
TCL HUNT LIMITED—See BERICAP GmbH & Co. KG; *Int'l*, pg. 981
TECHNICAL MARKETING ASSOCIATES; *U.S. Private*, pg. 3954
TEJAS PB DISTRIBUTING, INC.—See Utz Brands, Inc.; *U.S. Public*, pg. 2268
TEKRA - EAST COAST DIVISION—See Audax Group, Limited Partnership; *U.S. Private*, pg. 387
THE THYMES, LLC; *U.S. Private*, pg. 4127
TITMAN TIP TOOLS GMBH—See Checkit plc; *Int'l*, pg. 1459
TOP NORDIC FINLAND OY—See Atea ASA; *Int'l*, pg. 667
TOPPERS LLC—See Camsing Global, LLC; *U.S. Private*, pg. 732
TRANS-MATE, INC.—See Highlander Partners, LP.; *U.S. Private*, pg. 1940
TRAVERS & COMPANY INC.; *U.S. Private*, pg. 4214
TRESSALLURE/GENERAL WIG—See Aderans Co., Ltd.; *Int'l*, pg. 144
TRIMS UNLIMITED; *U.S. Private*, pg. 4232
TRIPPIES INC.; *U.S. Private*, pg. 4238
TRISTAR PRODUCTS INC.; *U.S. Private*, pg. 4238
TRUCO ENTERPRISES INC.; *U.S. Private*, pg. 4247
UNIPAL GENERAL TRADING COMPANY PSC—See Arab Palestinian Investment Company; *Int'l*, pg. 531
UNITED NATIONAL CLOSEOUT STORES, INC.; *U.S. Private*, pg. 4294
UNITED PACKAGING SUPPLY CO.—See Kelso & Company, L.P.; *U.S. Private*, pg. 2279
UNITED PACKAGING SUPPLY CO.—See Warburg Pincus LLC; *U.S. Private*, pg. 4437
VADA BVBA—See Darling Ingredients Inc.; *U.S. Public*, pg. 634
VALORA TRADE DENMARK A/S—See Fomento Economico Mexicano, S.A.B. de C.V.; *Int'l*, pg. 2724
VAPOR BEAST LLC—See Turning Point Brands, Inc.; *U.S. Public*, pg. 2205
VEGETABLE GROWERS SUPPLY CO. INC.; *U.S. Private*, pg. 4354
VERONICA FOODS COMPANY; *U.S. Private*, pg. 4368
VINDA PAPER (BEIJING) LIMITED—See Essity Aktiebolag; *Int'l*, pg. 2517
VOLUME DISTRIBUTORS INC.; *U.S. Private*, pg. 4411
WANG-ZHENG CORPORATION SDN. BHD.—See Hengan International Group Co. Ltd.; *Int'l*, pg. 3346
WARNER BROS. WORLDWIDE CONSUMER PRODUCTS—See Warner Bros. Discovery, Inc.; *U.S. Public*, pg. 2329
WAVIN NEDERLAND B.V.—See Bharti Enterprises Limited; *Int'l*, pg. 1012
WAVIN NOVOTECH S.A.S.—See Bharti Enterprises Limited; *Int'l*, pg. 1013
WEIL CERAMICS & GLASS INC.; *U.S. Private*, pg. 4471
WEST PHARMACEUTICAL SERVICES VENEZUELA C.A.—See West Pharmaceutical Services, Inc.; *U.S. Public*, pg. 2353
WESTPORT CORPORATION; *U.S. Private*, pg. 4500
WESTROCK GMBH—See WestRock Company; *U.S. Public*, pg. 2362
WESTROCK PACKAGING SOLUTIONS KOREA, INC.—See WestRock Company; *U.S. Public*, pg. 2362
WESTSTAR DISTRIBUTING LTD.; *U.S. Private*, pg. 4501
WILHEIT PACKAGING LLC; *U.S. Private*, pg. 4520
W.N. VAN ALSTINE & SONS INC.; *U.S. Private*, pg. 4422
W. OLIVER TRIPP COMPANY, INC.; *U.S. Private*, pg. 4418
WORLDWIDE DISTRIBUTORS; *U.S. Private*, pg. 4569
WYLAND STUDIOS INC.—See Wyland Worldwide, LLC; *U.S. Private*, pg. 4576
YASUTOMO & CO.; *U.S. Private*, pg. 4586
YUSEI NISHI-KYUSHU SEIKA CO.,LTD.—See Crest Investments Co., Ltd.; *Int'l*, pg. 1840
ZIPPO GMBH—See Zippo Manufacturing Company, Inc.; *U.S. Private*, pg. 4606
ZIPPO U.K. LTD.—See Zippo Manufacturing Company, Inc.; *U.S. Private*, pg. 4606
ZONK GROUP INCORPORATED; *U.S. Private*, pg. 4608

425120 — WHOLESALE TRADE AGENTS AND BROKERS

3M COSTA RICA, S.A.—See 3M Company; *U.S. Public*, pg. 5
3M THAILAND LIMITED—See 3M Company; *U.S. Public*, pg. 7
3 PAGEN VERSAND UND HANDELSGESELLSCHAFT MBH—See Damartex SA; *Int'l*, pg. 1955
A. BILLITZ S.R.L.—See Coeclerici S.p.A.; *Int'l*, pg. 1688
AB KAROSSERITILLBEHOR—See Axel Johnson Gruppen AB; *Int'l*, pg. 763
ACHESON COLLOIDEN—See Henkel AG & Co. KGaA; *Int'l*, pg. 3353
ACHESON FRANCE S.A.—See Henkel AG & Co. KGaA; *Int'l*, pg. 3353
ACHESON ITALIANA S.R.L.—See Henkel AG & Co. KGaA; *Int'l*, pg. 3353
ACOMO N.V.; *Int'l*, pg. 108
ACOSTA FOODSERVICE—See Acosta, Inc.; *U.S. Private*, pg. 64
ACOSTA, INC.; *U.S. Private*, pg. 64
ACOSTA MILITARY SALES, LLC—See Acosta, Inc.; *U.S. Private*, pg. 64
ACOSTA SALES & MARKETING CO. - BOSTON/MARLBOROUGH OFFICE—See Acosta, Inc.; *U.S. Private*, pg. 64
ACOSTA SALES & MARKETING COMPANY—See Acosta, Inc.; *U.S. Private*, pg. 64
ACOSTA SALES & MARKETING CO. - PLEASANTON OFFICE—See Acosta, Inc.; *U.S. Private*, pg. 64
ACTIVITYREZ, LLC; *U.S. Private*, pg. 70
A.D.E. OF ARK-LA-TEX, INC.—See OPENLANE, Inc.; *U.S. Public*, pg. 1606
ADESA BIRMINGHAM, LLC—See OPENLANE, Inc.; *U.S. Public*, pg. 1606
ADESA DES MOINES, LLC—See OPENLANE, Inc.; *U.S. Public*, pg. 1606
ADESA LANSING, LLC—See OPENLANE, Inc.; *U.S. Public*, pg. 1606
ADESA LEXINGTON, LLC—See OPENLANE, Inc.; *U.S. Public*, pg. 1606
ADESA MEXICO, LLC—See OPENLANE, Inc.; *U.S. Public*, pg. 1606
ADESA MINNESOTA, LLC—See OPENLANE, Inc.; *U.S. Public*, pg. 1606
ADESA NEW YORK, LLC—See OPENLANE, Inc.; *U.S. Public*, pg. 1606
ADESA OHIO, LLC—See OPENLANE, Inc.; *U.S. Public*, pg. 1606
ADESA PENNSYLVANIA, LLC—See OPENLANE, Inc.; *U.S. Public*, pg. 1606
ADESA QUEBEC CORPORATION—See OPENLANE, Inc.; *U.S. Public*, pg. 1607
ADESA REMARKETING SERVICES INC.—See OPENLANE, Inc.; *U.S. Public*, pg. 1607
ADESA SAN DIEGO, LLC—See OPENLANE, Inc.; *U.S. Public*, pg. 1607
ADESA WISCONSIN, LLC—See OPENLANE, Inc.; *U.S. Public*, pg. 1607
A&D TECHNOLOGY TRADING (SHANGHAI) CO., LTD.—See A&D Co., Ltd.; *Int'l*, pg. 19
ADVERTUS D.O.O.—See Avtotehna, d.d.; *Int'l*, pg. 751
AEM TRADING S.R.L.—See A2A S.p.A.; *Int'l*, pg. 29
AERTICKET AG; *Int'l*, pg. 182
AGIE CHARMILLES JAPAN LTD.—See Georg Fischer AG; *Int'l*, pg. 2934
AGRIMONY COMMODITIES LTD; *Int'l*, pg. 217
AJC FOOD—See AJC International, Inc.; *U.S. Private*, pg. 143
AKG THERMAL SYSTEMS, INC.—See Autokuhler GmbH & Co. KG; *Int'l*, pg. 727
AL FAISALIAH GROUP; *Int'l*, pg. 277
ALIBABA.COM HONG KONG LIMITED—See Alibaba Group

425120 — WHOLESALE TRADE AGE...

Holding Limited; *Int'l*, pg. 326
ALIBABA.COM LIMITED—See Alibaba Group Holding Limited; *Int'l*, pg. 326
AL KHALILI UNITED ENTERPRISES LLC; *Int'l*, pg. 280
ALL MARINE SPARES INTERNATIONAL, LLC; *U.S. Private*, pg. 171
AMAZON.COM.CA, INC.—See Amazon.com, Inc.; *U.S. Public*, pg. 90
AMAZON.CO.UK LTD.—See Amazon.com, Inc.; *U.S. Public*, pg. 90
AMAZON JAPAN K.K.—See Amazon.com, Inc.; *U.S. Public*, pg. 90
AMG MEDIA NETWORKS LIMITED—See Adani Enterprises Limited; *Int'l*, pg. 124
AMSC CO., LTD.; *Int'l*, pg. 441
AMSONS APPARELS LTD; *Int'l*, pg. 441
ANSA MCAL TRADING LIMITED—See ANSA McAL Limited; *Int'l*, pg. 476
ANSA MCAL (U.S.) INC.—See ANSA McAL Limited; *Int'l*, pg. 476
ANSWEAR.COM SA; *Int'l*, pg. 479
ARCELOR INTERNATIONAL EXPORT S.A.—See ArcelorMittal S.A.; *Int'l*, pg. 543
ARENA.PL SA; *Int'l*, pg. 558
ARGENTEA SRL—See GPI S.p.A.; *Int'l*, pg. 3046
A.S. BRYDEN & SONS (BARBADOS) LTD.—See ANSA McAL Limited; *Int'l*, pg. 476
ASTRO MACHINE CORP.—See AstroNova, Inc.; *U.S. Public*, pg. 218
AT ADRIA D.O.O.—See Avtotehna, d.d.; *Int'l*, pg. 751
ATLANTIC UTILITY TRAILER SALES, INC.; *U.S. Private*, pg. 375
ATRIK D.O.O.—See Avtotehna, d.d.; *Int'l*, pg. 751
AT&T ENTERPRISE CANADA CO.—See AT&T Inc.; *U.S. Public*, pg. 219
AUCHAN E-COMMERCE FRANCE S.A.S—See Auchan Holding S.A.; *Int'l*, pg. 699
AUCHAN E-COMMERCE POLSKA SP. Z O.O.—See Auchan Holding S.A.; *Int'l*, pg. 699
AUREL BGC—See BGC Group, Inc.; *U.S. Public*, pg. 328
AUTO DEALERS EXCHANGE OF CONCORD, LLC—See OPENLANE, Inc.; *U.S. Public*, pg. 1607
AUTO DEALERS EXCHANGE OF MEMPHIS, LLC—See OPENLANE, Inc.; *U.S. Public*, pg. 1607
AVENTURA GROUP AB; *Int'l*, pg. 739
AVIATION FUEL INTERNATIONAL, INC.—See FUELSTREAM, INC.; *U.S. Public*, pg. 891
AVTERA D.O.O.—See Avtotehna, d.d.; *Int'l*, pg. 751
AVTOTEHNA OPREMA D.O.O.—See Avtotehna, d.d.; *Int'l*, pg. 751
BAKUER AMERICAN CO.—See Bakuer S.p.A.; *Int'l*, pg. 806
BALLI GROUP PLC; *Int'l*, pg. 809
BANDO TRADING CO., LTD.—See Bando Chemical Industries, Ltd.; *Int'l*, pg. 830
BASF DIGITAL FARMING GMBH—See BASF SE; *Int'l*, pg. 877
B+B VAKMEDIANET B.V.—See B+B Vakmedianet Groep B.V.; *Int'l*, pg. 784
BE-BUSINESS EXCHANGES S.A.—See Eurobank Ergasias Services and Holdings S.A.; *Int'l*, pg. 2532
BECK CONSULTING—See TA Associates, Inc.; *U.S. Private*, pg. 3914
BEECHMONT TOYOTA—See Beechmont Automotive Group; *U.S. Private*, pg. 513
BEHR PROCESS CANADA LTD.—See Masco Corporation; *U.S. Public*, pg. 1390
BEIJING YANLONG IMPORT & EXPORT CO., LTD.—See Beijing Jingcheng Machinery Electric Holding Co., Ltd.; *Int'l*, pg. 953
BGC CAPITAL MARKETS (HONG KONG) LTD.—See BGC Group, Inc.; *U.S. Public*, pg. 328
BGC CAPITAL MARKETS (JAPAN), LLC—See BGC Group, Inc.; *U.S. Public*, pg. 328
BGC CAPITAL MARKETS (SWITZERLAND) LLC—See BGC Group, Inc.; *U.S. Public*, pg. 328
BGC PARTNERS (AUSTRALIA) PTY. LTD.—See BGC Group, Inc.; *U.S. Public*, pg. 328
BGC SECURITIES (HONG KONG) LLC—See BGC Group, Inc.; *U.S. Public*, pg. 328
BGC SHOKEN KAISHA LIMITED—See BGC Group, Inc.; *U.S. Public*, pg. 328
BIROTEHNA D.O.O.—See Avtotehna, d.d.; *Int'l*, pg. 751
BISHOP BROTHERS AUTO AUCTION—See Cox Enterprises, Inc.; *U.S. Private*, pg. 1077
BIZBUYSELL.COM—See CoStar Group, Inc.; *U.S. Public*, pg. 586
BLACK & DECKER ARGENTINA S.A.—See Stanley Black & Decker, Inc.; *U.S. Public*, pg. 1936
BLACK & DECKER (IRELAND)—See Stanley Black & Decker, Inc.; *U.S. Public*, pg. 1936
BMK & ZANATPRODUKT A.D.; *Int'l*, pg. 1076
BRAUNS ONLINE MEDIA INC.; *U.S. Private*, pg. 641
BRAVE BISON GROUP PLC; *Int'l*, pg. 1141
BRISCOE TIMBER LIMITED—See EAC Invest AS; *Int'l*, pg. 2261
BUREAU VERITAS INTERNATIONAL TRADE AUSTRALIA PTY. LTD.—See Bureau Veritas S.A.; *Int'l*, pg. 1221

BUYERZONE.COM LLC—See Purch Group, Inc.; *U.S. Private*, pg. 3305
CABLE/CISCO—See The Carpenter Group; *U.S. Private*, pg. 4005
CAPITOL PIPE SUPPORTS—See Canerector Inc.; *Int'l*, pg. 1290
CARISAM-SAMUEL MEISEL (MD), INC.—See MOTCO, Inc.; *U.S. Private*, pg. 2795
CARREFOUR IMPORT SAS—See Carrefour SA; *Int'l*, pg. 1344
CARRIER NORTHEAST—See Carrier Global Corporation; *U.S. Public*, pg. 442
CASTROL (SWITZERLAND) AG—See BP plc; *Int'l*, pg. 1130
CATALOGS.COM; *U.S. Private*, pg. 786
CATERPILLAR LATIN AMERICA COMMERCIAL DIVISION—See Caterpillar, Inc.; *U.S. Public*, pg. 451
CATZ INTERNATIONAL B.V.—See ACOMO N.V.; *Int'l*, pg. 108
CELESTIAL COMMODITIES LIMITED—See CASH Financial Services Group Limited; *Int'l*, pg. 1352
CELLMARK BELGIUM NV—See CellMark AB; *Int'l*, pg. 1393
CELLMARK CHEMICALS LTD.—See CellMark AB; *Int'l*, pg. 1393
CELLMARK CHEMICALS SINGAPORE PTE LTD.—See CellMark AB; *Int'l*, pg. 1393
CELLMARK ESPANA SA—See CellMark AB; *Int'l*, pg. 1393
CELLMARK JAPAN—See CellMark AB; *Int'l*, pg. 1393
CELLMARK USA, LLC—See CellMark AB; *Int'l*, pg. 1393
CENTRAL GLASS TRADING (SHANGHAI) CO., LTD.—See Central Glass Co., Ltd.; *Int'l*, pg. 1406
CENTRAL PLAINS STEEL CO.—See Reliance Steel & Aluminum Co.; *U.S. Public*, pg. 1781
CENTRO FINANZIAMENTI S.P.A.—See Gruppo MutuiOnline S.p.A; *Int'l*, pg. 3140
CENTRO SERVIZI ASSET MANGEMENT S.R.L.—See Gruppo MutuiOnline S.p.A; *Int'l*, pg. 3141
CHELLARAMS PLC; *Int'l*, pg. 1460
CHENGDU TIANQI MACHINERY, METALS & MINERALS IMPORT & EXPORT CO., LTD.—See Chengdu Tianqi Industry (Group) Co., Ltd.; *Int'l*, pg. 1469
CHEVRON FRANCE SA—See Chevron Corporation; *U.S. Public*, pg. 486
CHINA NATIONAL PHARMACEUTICAL FOREIGN TRADE CORPORATION—See China National Pharmaceutical Group Corporation; *Int'l*, pg. 1533
CHINA STEEL GLOBAL TRADING CORPORATION—See China Steel Corporation; *Int'l*, pg. 1555
CHINA TING GARMENT MFG (GROUP) LIMITED—See China Ting Group Holdings Limited; *Int'l*, pg. 1559
CIELO S.A.; *Int'l*, pg. 1605
CITCO CURACAO—See Coeclerici S.p.A.; *Int'l*, pg. 1688
COECLERICI COAL & FUELS S.P.A. - RUSSIA BRANCH—See Coeclerici S.p.A.; *Int'l*, pg. 1688
COECLERICI COAL & FUELS SPA—See Coeclerici S.p.A.; *Int'l*, pg. 1688
COLES ONLINE PTY LTD—See Coles Group Limited; *Int'l*, pg. 1698
COLORADO AUTO AUCTION—See Cox Enterprises, Inc.; *U.S. Private*, pg. 1076
COLUMBUS FAIR AUTO AUCTION, INC.—See Huron Capital Partners LLC; *U.S. Private*, pg. 2012
COMMERCIAL VEHICLE AUCTIONS LTD—See Ballyvesey Holdings Limited; *Int'l*, pg. 809
COMPLETE RECYCLING SOLUTIONS LLC—See TerraCycle Inc.; *U.S. Private*, pg. 3971
COMPRESSED AIR PRODUCTS, INC.—See Atlas Copco AB; *Int'l*, pg. 681
CONTROL EQUIPMENT COMPANY—See The Eads Company; *U.S. Private*, pg. 4024
CONVENIENT PAYMENTS, LLC—See The Beekman Group, LLC; *U.S. Private*, pg. 3992
COOK (CHINA) MEDICAL TRADING CO., LTD.—See Cook Group Incorporated; *U.S. Private*, pg. 1037
COPART OF ARIZONA, INC.—See Copart, Inc.; *U.S. Public*, pg. 574
COPART OF TENNESSEE, INC.—See Copart, Inc.; *U.S. Public*, pg. 574
COSMO OIL MARKETING CO., LTD.—See Cosmo Energy Holdings Co., Ltd.; *Int'l*, pg. 1812
COSMO OIL OF U.S.A., INC.—See Cosmo Energy Holdings Co., Ltd.; *Int'l*, pg. 1812
COUNTRY HEDGING, INC.—See CHS INC.; *U.S. Public*, pg. 492
CUMMINS POWER SYSTEMS INC.—See Cummins Inc.; *U.S. Public*, pg. 606
CYBERCOM INTERNATIONAL CORP.—See Clayton, Dubilier & Rice, LLC; *U.S. Private*, pg. 927
CYBERCOM INTERNATIONAL CORP.—See Stone Point Capital LLC; *U.S. Private*, pg. 3826
CYMOT (PTY) LTD.; *Int'l*, pg. 1896
DAI NIPPON SHOJI CO., LTD.—See Dai Nippon Printing Co., Ltd.; *Int'l*, pg. 1915
DANGOTE GROUP LIMITED; *Int'l*, pg. 1962
DARWIN INTERNATIONAL TRADING (SHANGHAI) CO. LTD.—See Hexagon Holdings Berhad; *Int'l*, pg. 3370
DAYMON WORLDWIDE TRADING INC.—See Bain Capital, LP; *U.S. Private*, pg. 439

CORPORATE AFFILIATIONS

DEEP IMAGING TECHNOLOGIES, INC.; *U.S. Private*, pg. 1189
DEEP LIQUIDITY, INC.; *U.S. Private*, pg. 1189
DEKKER VACUUM TECHNOLOGIES, INC.—See Atlas Copco AB; *Int'l*, pg. 681
DESENIO GROUP AB; *Int'l*, pg. 2044
DETAL KONCEPT SP. Z O.O.—See Emperia Holding S.A; *Int'l*, pg. 2385
DINOS CECILE CO., LTD.—See Fuji Media Holdings, Inc.; *Int'l*, pg. 2813
DISKOMAT AB—See Gosta Torssell Holding AB; *Int'l*, pg. 3043
DISNEY SHOPPING, INC.—See The Walt Disney Company; *U.S. Public*, pg. 2138
DIVERSEY AUSTRIA TRADING GMBH—See Platinum Equity, LLC; *U.S. Private*, pg. 3204
DIVERSEY TRADING (SHANGHAI) CO., LTD.—See Platinum Equity, LLC; *U.S. Private*, pg. 3204
DKSH AUSTRALIA PTY. LTD.—See Diethelm Keller Holding Limited; *Int'l*, pg. 2116
DKSH JAPAN K.K.—See Diethelm Keller Holding Limited; *Int'l*, pg. 2116
DKSH KOREA LTD.—See Diethelm Keller Holding Limited; *Int'l*, pg. 2116
DKSH MALAYSIA SDN. BHD.—See Diethelm Keller Holding Limited; *Int'l*, pg. 2116
DKSH NETHERLANDS B.V.—See Diethelm Keller Holding Limited; *Int'l*, pg. 2116
DKSH (SHANGHAI) CO., LTD.—See Warburg Pincus LLC; *U.S. Private*, pg. 4437
DKSH SWITZERLAND LTD.—See Diethelm Keller Holding Limited; *Int'l*, pg. 2116
DKSH TAIWAN LTD.—See Diethelm Keller Holding Limited; *Int'l*, pg. 2116
DKSH (THAILAND) LIMITED—See Diethelm Keller Holding Limited; *Int'l*, pg. 2116
DOMAINMARKET.COM LLC; *U.S. Private*, pg. 1255
DORMAN TRADING COMPANY, INC.—See Miami International Holdings, Inc.; *U.S. Private*, pg. 2697
DRYTAC CORPORATION; *U.S. Private*, pg. 1281
EAC CHEMICALS SINGAPORE PTE. LTD.—See EAC Invest AS; *Int'l*, pg. 2261
EAC CONSUMER PRODUCTS LTD. APS—See EAC Invest AS; *Int'l*, pg. 2261
EAC (PHILIPPINES) INC.—See EAC Invest AS; *Int'l*, pg. 2261
E.A. GIBSON SHIPBROKERS LIMITED; *Int'l*, pg. 2250
EAI-EMBRAER AVIATION INTERNATIONAL—See Embraer S.A.; *Int'l*, pg. 2375
EASTERN HOME SHOPPING & LEISURE CO., LTD.—See Eastern Media International Corporation; *Int'l*, pg. 2273
EBAY CANADA LIMITED—See eBay Inc.; *U.S. Public*, pg. 709
EBS SERVICE CO LIMITED—See CME Group, Inc.; *U.S. Public*, pg. 1281
ED&F MAN LIQUID PRODUCTS NEDERLAND B.V.—See ED&F Man Holdings Limited; *Int'l*, pg. 2303
EDF TRADING LIMITED—See Electricite de France S.A.; *Int'l*, pg. 2350
EDF TRADING NORTH AMERICA, LLC—See Electricite de France S.A.; *Int'l*, pg. 2350
ELBI OF AMERICA INC—See Elbi S.P.A.; *Int'l*, pg. 2344
ELCOM INTERNATIONAL, INC.; *U.S. Private*, pg. 1350
EMERSON CLIMATE TECHNOLOGIES SARL—See Emerson Electric Co.; *U.S. Public*, pg. 744
EMERSON CLIMATE TECHNOLOGIES (SUZHOU) RESEARCH & DEVELOPMENT CO., LTD.—See Emerson Electric Co.; *U.S. Public*, pg. 744
EMERSON PROCESS MANAGEMENT AB—See Emerson Electric Co.; *U.S. Public*, pg. 746
EMPACADORA ECUATORIANO DANESA (ECUADASA) S.A.—See EAC Invest AS; *Int'l*, pg. 2261
ENDEAVOR BUSINESS MEDIA LLC; *U.S. Private*, pg. 1391
ENG. SHABAH AL-SHAMMERY & PARTNERS CO.; *Int'l*, pg. 2426
E.ON TRADING NORDIC AB—See E.ON SE; *Int'l*, pg. 2255
EQUINOR ASIA PACIFIC PTE. LTD.—See Equinor ASA; *Int'l*, pg. 2484
EQUINOR MARKETING & TRADING (US) INC.—See Equinor ASA; *Int'l*, pg. 2485
ESANG NETWORKS CO., LTD.; *Int'l*, pg. 2501
EUROSERVIZI PER I NOTAI S.R.L.—See Gruppo MutuiOnline S.p.A; *Int'l*, pg. 3141
EVED, LLC; *U.S. Private*, pg. 1436
EXIMO AGRO-MARKETING AG; *Int'l*, pg. 2585
EXPERLOGIX INC.—See Featheringill Capital, LLC; *U.S. Private*, pg. 1486
EXXONMOBIL OIL CORPORATION—See Exxon Mobil Corporation; *U.S. Public*, pg. 815
EZONEONLINE.IN—See Future Corporate Resources Limited; *Int'l*, pg. 2853
FACILITY CONCEPTS INC.; *U.S. Private*, pg. 1459
FAL GROUP OF COMPANIES; *Int'l*, pg. 2610
FEDERAL AUTOCAT RECYCLING, LLC—See Metalico Inc.; *U.S. Private*, pg. 2681
FEDERATED HEALTHCARE SUPPLY, INC.—See Federated Healthcare Supply Holdings, Inc.; *U.S. Private*, pg. 1491

N.A.I.C.S. INDEX

425120 — WHOLESALE TRADE AGE...

FERRELL NORTH AMERICA—See Ferrellgas Partners, L.P.; *U.S. Public*, pg. 829
FLINT HILLS RESOURCES CANADA, LP—See Koch Industries, Inc.; *U.S. Private*, pg. 2327
FLORISTS' TRANSWORLD DELIVERY, INC.—See Tenth Avenue Holdings LLC; *U.S. Private*, pg. 3968
FOOD EMPIRE HOLDINGS LIMITED; *Int'l*, pg. 2727
FOOSUNG HDS CO., LTD.—See Foosung Co., Ltd.; *Int'l*, pg. 2728
FORENSIC EXPERTS S.R.L.—See Gruppo MutuiOnline S.p.A; *Int'l*, pg. 3141
FOREST S.P.A.—See Campostano Group S.p.A.; *Int'l*, pg. 1275
FORTE FURNITURE LTD.—See Fabryki Mebli Forte S.A.; *Int'l*, pg. 2600
FORTE IBERIA—See Fabryki Mebli Forte S.A.; *Int'l*, pg. 2600
FORTE MOBILIER SARL—See Fabryki Mebli Forte S.A.; *Int'l*, pg. 2600
FORTE SK GMBH—See Fabryki Mebli Forte S.A.; *Int'l*, pg. 2600
FORTH'S FOODS, INC.; *U.S. Private*, pg. 1575
FP GROUP LIMITED—See Howden Group Holdings Limited; *Int'l*, pg. 3493
FRANCHISE DEVELOPMENT, L.P.; *U.S. Private*, pg. 1587
FRENCKEN GROUP LIMITED; *Int'l*, pg. 2772
FRU-CON MEXICO S.A. DE C.V.—See Bilfinger SE; *Int'l*, pg. 1026
FSP TECHNOLOGY KOREA CO., LTD.—See FSP Technology Inc.; *Int'l*, pg. 2800
FUBON MULTIMEDIA TECHNOLOGY CO., LTD.—See Fubon Financial Holding Co. Ltd.; *Int'l*, pg. 2802
FUJITA SHOJI CO., LTD.—See Daiwa House Industry Co., Ltd.; *Int'l*, pg. 1946
FUJIX INTERNATIONAL (HONG KONG) LTD.—See FUJIX Ltd.; *Int'l*, pg. 2838
GAVILON, LLC—See NGL Energy Partners LP; *U.S. Public*, pg. 1527
GDF SUEZ TRADING SAS—See ENGIE SA; *Int'l*, pg. 2429
GENERAL AVIATION SERVICES, L.L.C.—See G.A.S. Capital, Inc.; *U.S. Private*, pg. 1630
GEOFFREY HUGHES (EXPORT) PTY LIMITED—See Grove International Pty Limited; *Int'l*, pg. 3112
GETTER GROUP LTD.; *Int'l*, pg. 2953
GFE-MIR GMBH—See GFE-MIR Holdings AG; *Int'l*, pg. 2956
GIBSON (ASIA) LTD—See E.A. Gibson Shipbrokers Limited; *Int'l*, pg. 2250
GIBSON BROKERS PTE. LTD.—See E.A. Gibson Shipbrokers Limited; *Int'l*, pg. 2250
GIE ETEX PLASTICS GESTION—See Aliaxis S.A./N.V.; *Int'l*, pg. 324
GLENCORE GRAIN B.V.—See Glencore plc; *Int'l*, pg. 2990
GLENCORE GRAIN PTY. LTD.—See Glencore plc; *Int'l*, pg. 2990
GLOBAL E-TRADING SERVICES LIMITED—See Computer & Technologies Holdings Limited; *Int'l*, pg. 1758
GLOBAL MARKET GROUP LIMITED; *Int'l*, pg. 2999
GLOBAL SOURCES LTD.—See Blackstone Inc.; *U.S. Public*, pg. 360
GMO MAKESHOP CO. LTD.—See GMO Internet Group, Inc.; *Int'l*, pg. 3014
GMO SYSTEM CONSULTING, INC.—See GMO Internet Group, Inc.; *Int'l*, pg. 3014
GOLDENWAY, INC.; *Int'l*, pg. 3033
GOLDEO INC.; *U.S. Private*, pg. 1735
GOLDMAN SACHS CANADA INC.—See The Goldman Sachs Group, Inc.; *U.S. Public*, pg. 2076
GRACEKENNEDY LIMITED; *Int'l*, pg. 3048
GRAND INDUSTRIAL HOLDING CO., LTD.; *Int'l*, pg. 3055
GRAND RAPIDS AUTO AUCTION—See Huron Capital Partners LLC; *U.S. Private*, pg. 2012
GREENHAM—See Bunzl plc; *Int'l*, pg. 1217
GRIFFIN TRAVEL (HK) LTD.—See EAC Invest AS; *Int'l*, pg. 2261
GROVE INTERNATIONAL PTY LIMITED; *Int'l*, pg. 3112
GS GLOBAL CORP.—See GS Holdings Corp.; *Int'l*, pg. 3142
GSI TRADING HONG KONG LIMITED—See GSI Creos Corporation; *Int'l*, pg. 3144
GUNNEBO LTD.—See Gunnebo AB; *Int'l*, pg. 3184
GUNSAN EXPORTADORA E IMPORTADORA LTDA.—See GSI Creos Corporation; *Int'l*, pg. 3144
GUNVOR DEUTSCHLAND GMBH—See Gunvor Group Ltd.; *Int'l*, pg. 3185
GUNVOR SA—See Gunvor Group Ltd.; *Int'l*, pg. 3185
HANWHA INTERNATIONAL LLC—See Hanwha Group; *Int'l*, pg. 3265
HANWHA JAPAN CO., LTD.—See Hanwha Group; *Int'l*, pg. 3265
HARTREE PARTNERS, LP—See Brookfield Corporation; *Int'l*, pg. 1182
HAUTELOOK, INC.—See Nordstrom, Inc.; *U.S. Public*, pg. 1535
HC TRADING B.V.—See Heidelberg Materials AG; *Int'l*, pg. 3310
HENRY BATH B.V.—See CMST Development Co., Ltd.; *Int'l*, pg. 1672

HENRY BATH LLC—See CMST Development Co., Ltd.; *Int'l*, pg. 1672
HENRY BATH SINGAPORE PTE. LTD.—See CMST Development Co., Ltd.; *Int'l*, pg. 1672
HENRY BATH & SON LIMITED—See CMST Development Co., Ltd.; *Int'l*, pg. 1672
HEROES TECHNOLOGY LTD.; *Int'l*, pg. 3364
HIP-PETROHEMIJA A.D.; *Int'l*, pg. 3402
HIT FRISCHE GMBH & CO. KG—See Dohle Handelsgruppe Holding GmbH & Co. KG; *Int'l*, pg. 2155
HM SCIENCE INC.—See China National Pharmaceutical Group Corporation; *Int'l*, pg. 1534
HM SCIENCE INC.—See Hoyu Co., Ltd.; *Int'l*, pg. 3499
HONASA CONSUMER LIMITED; *Int'l*, pg. 3459
HONDA TRADING CORP.—See Honda Motor Co., Ltd.; *Int'l*, pg. 3462
HONEYWELL INTERNATIONAL, INC. - PUERTO RICO OFFICE—See Honeywell International Inc.; *U.S. Public*, pg. 1051
HOOD INDUSTRIES—See The Carpenter Group; *U.S. Private*, pg. 4005
HOUSTON AUTO AUCTION, INC.—See E Automotive Inc.; *Int'l*, pg. 2245
HSE24—See IAC Inc.; *U.S. Public*, pg. 1082
HSN CATALOG SERVICES, INC.—See Qurate Retail, Inc.; *U.S. Public*, pg. 1758
HUNTER PLASTICS LTD.—See Aliaxis S.A./N.V.; *Int'l*, pg. 324
HYUNDAI CORPORATION; *Int'l*, pg. 3555
ICAP SHIPPING DERIVATIVES LIMITED—See CME Group; *U.S. Public*, pg. 517
IDAHO MATERIAL HANDLING INC.—See Hoj Engineering & Sales Co., LLC; *U.S. Private*, pg. 1961
IGC INDUSTRIES LIMITED; *Int'l*, pg. 3602
IMARKETKOREA, INC.; *Int'l*, pg. 3620
IMC SUPPLY COMPANY—See Stellar Industrial Supply LLC; *U.S. Private*, pg. 3799
IMPACT INTERACTIVE, LLC—See AmWINS Group, Inc.; *U.S. Private*, pg. 269
INDUSTRIAL SUPPLY EXPORT CORPORATION; *U.S. Private*, pg. 2068
INGRAM MICRO CFS GERMANY GMBH—See Hainan Traffic Administration Holding Co., Ltd.; *Int'l*, pg. 3214
INTCOMEX, INC.; *U.S. Private*, pg. 2097
INTERMETRO INDUSTRIES CORPORATION—See Emerson Electric Co.; *U.S. Public*, pg. 750
ISTRA AVTO D.O.O.—See Avtotehna, d.d.; *Int'l*, pg. 751
JEANNIE'S KIDS CLUB—See Kids Stuff, Inc.; *U.S. Private*, pg. 2303
JIHSUN FUTURES CO., LTD.—See Fubon Financial Holding Co. Ltd.; *Int'l*, pg. 2802
JOHNSON THERMAL SYSTEMS INC.—See Mission Critical Group; *U.S. Private*, pg. 2747
JX METALS TRADING CO., LTD.—See ENEOS Holdings, Inc.; *Int'l*, pg. 2416
JX NIPPON OIL & ENERGY ASIA PTE. LTD.—See ENEOS Holdings, Inc.; *Int'l*, pg. 2417
KIRKPATRICK BROKERAGE CO.—See Acosta, Inc.; *U.S. Private*, pg. 64
KIRKSTONE LTD.—See Mahwah Bergen Retail Group, Inc.; *U.S. Private*, pg. 2550
KOCH SUPPLY & TRADING COMPANY LTD.—See Koch Industries, Inc.; *U.S. Private*, pg. 2333
KOCH SUPPLY & TRADING, LP—See Koch Industries, Inc.; *U.S. Private*, pg. 2333
KODAK NORGE A/S—See Eastman Kodak Company; *U.S. Public*, pg. 707
KODAK (SINGAPORE) PTE. LIMITED—See Eastman Kodak Company; *U.S. Public*, pg. 707
KODAK (TAIWAN) LIMITED—See Eastman Kodak Company; *U.S. Public*, pg. 707
KODAK (THAILAND) LIMITED—See Eastman Kodak Company; *U.S. Public*, pg. 707
KWONG LEE SHUN TRADING CO., LTD.—See Global-Tech Advanced Innovations Inc.; *Int'l*, pg. 3003
LAM RESEARCH SINGAPORE PTE. LTD.—See Lam Research Corporation; *U.S. Public*, pg. 1290
LANCASTER COLONY COMMERCIAL PRODUCTS, INC.—See Lancaster Colony Corporation; *U.S. Public*, pg. 1291
LAPHAM-HICKEY STEEL CORP.—See Lapham-Hickey Steel Corp.; *U.S. Private*, pg. 2391
LEGACYXCHANGE, INC.; *U.S. Private*, pg. 2417
LESLIE EQUIPMENT COMPANY—See Leslie Equipment Company; *U.S. Private*, pg. 2432
LESLIE EQUIPMENT COMPANY—See Leslie Equipment Company; *U.S. Private*, pg. 2432
LIBERTY HOUSE LIMITED—See GFG Alliance Limited; *Int'l*, pg. 2956
LIEBERT CORPORATION—See Vertiv Holdings Co; *U.S. Public*, pg. 2289
LOCAL CORPORATION; *U.S. Public*, pg. 1337
LORIC IMPORT & EXPORT CORP., LTD.—See CRRC Corporation Limited; *Int'l*, pg. 1858
MANHEIM CALIFORNIA—See Cox Enterprises, Inc.; *U.S. Private*, pg. 1076
MANHEIM HAWAII—See Cox Enterprises, Inc.; *U.S. Private*, pg. 1077

MANHEIM ITALIA S.R.L.—See Cox Enterprises, Inc.; *U.S. Private*, pg. 1077
MANHEIM LOUISVILLE AUTO AUCTION—See Cox Enterprises, Inc.; *U.S. Private*, pg. 1077
MANHEIM NORTHSTAR MINNESOTA—See Cox Enterprises, Inc.; *U.S. Private*, pg. 1077
MANHEIM'S GREATER PENSACOLA AUCTION—See Cox Enterprises, Inc.; *U.S. Private*, pg. 1077
MANHEIM'S OSHAWA DEALERS EXCHANGE—See Cox Enterprises, Inc.; *U.S. Private*, pg. 1077
MANHEIM TORONTO—See Cox Enterprises, Inc.; *U.S. Private*, pg. 1077
MANITOU EQUIPMENT CORP.; *U.S. Private*, pg. 2564
MAPCOM SYSTEMS, LLC—See Battery Ventures, L.P.; *U.S. Private*, pg. 489
MASADAR ENERGY COMPANY FOR GENERAL TRADING W.L.L.—See First Investment Company K.S.C.C.; *Int'l*, pg. 2685
MDF COMMERCE, INC.—See KKR & Co. Inc.; *U.S. Public*, pg. 1267
MEDIABRAINS, INC.; *U.S. Private*, pg. 2653
MEDIA-SATURN-E-BUSINESS GMBH—See Ceconomy AG; *Int'l*, pg. 1385
MERCANTILE OY AB—See Helvar Merca Oy AB; *Int'l*, pg. 3339
MERCHANDISE PARTNERS, LLC; *U.S. Private*, pg. 2669
MFG.COM, INC.; *U.S. Private*, pg. 2693
M.M.C., INC.; *U.S. Private*, pg. 2529
MONDIAL INTERNATIONAL CORPORATION; *U.S. Private*, pg. 2769
MOREVISIBILITY.COM, INC.; *U.S. Private*, pg. 2782
MOTCO, INC.; *U.S. Private*, pg. 2795
MSA JAPAN LTD.—See MSA Safety Incorporated; *U.S. Public*, pg. 1482
MULTI-PLASTICS EUROPE LTD.—See Multi-Plastics, Inc.; *U.S. Private*, pg. 2812
MULTI-PLASTICS, INC.—See Multi-Plastics, Inc.; *U.S. Private*, pg. 2812
MULTI-PLASTICS, INC.—See Multi-Plastics, Inc.; *U.S. Private*, pg. 2812
MULTI-PLASTICS, INC.—See Multi-Plastics, Inc.; *U.S. Private*, pg. 2812
MURPHY OIL TRADING COMPANY (EASTERN)—See Murphy USA Inc.; *U.S. Public*, pg. 1487
NEW ENGLAND CONTROLS, INC.—See Enerpac Tool Group Corp.; *U.S. Public*, pg. 766
NEWMAN & ULLMAN, INC.; *U.S. Private*, pg. 2915
NIAGARASTEEL—See Canerector Inc.; *Int'l*, pg. 1290
NIHON CABOT MICROELECTRONICS K.K.—See Entegris, Inc.; *U.S. Public*, pg. 776
NOVAX AB—See Axel Johnson Gruppen AB; *Int'l*, pg. 765
NUKEM GMBH—See Cameco Corporation; *Int'l*, pg. 1270
NUKEM, INC.—See Cameco Corporation; *Int'l*, pg. 1270
OBIHAI TECHNOLOGY INC.—See HP Inc.; *U.S. Public*, pg. 1064
OMEGA PLASTICS—See Alpha Industries, Inc.; *U.S. Private*, pg. 197
OMNI GLOBAL SOURCING SOLUTIONS INC.—See Bain Capital, LP; *U.S. Private*, pg. 439
OSIBODU & ASSOCIATES EXPORTING USA, LLC; *U.S. Private*, pg. 3047
OXYDE BELGIUM BVBA—See Oxyde Chemicals, Inc.; *U.S. Private*, pg. 3057
OXYDE CHEMICALS, INC.; *U.S. Private*, pg. 3057
OY VALORA TRADE FINLAND AB—See Fomento Economico Mexicano, S.A.B. de C.V.; *Int'l*, pg. 2724
PACIFIC WORLD TRADE INC.—See Cummins Inc.; *U.S. Public*, pg. 609
PAN PACIFIC COPPER SHANGHAI CO., LTD.—See ENEOS Holdings, Inc.; *Int'l*, pg. 2416
PARKER HANNIFIN CORP., AIRCRAFT WHEEL & BRAKE DIVISION—See Parker Hannifin Corporation; *U.S. Public*, pg. 1648
PEAKLOGIX, INC.—See Alta Equipment Group Inc.; *U.S. Public*, pg. 86
PERRY MACHINERY CZECH REPUBLIC S.R.O.—See Perry Videx LLC; *U.S. Private*, pg. 3154
PERRY MACHINERY POLAND LTD.—See Perry Videx LLC; *U.S. Private*, pg. 3154
PERSONAL CREATIONS INC.—See Claranova SA; *Int'l*, pg. 1642
PIPEDO HD—See Advantage Partners LLP; *Int'l*, pg. 164
PLUMROSE LATINOAMERICANA C.A.—See EAC Invest AS; *Int'l*, pg. 2262
PRESCIENT APPLIED INTELLIGENCE, INC.—See Repositrak Inc; *U.S. Public*, pg. 1785
PRESTIGIO PLAZA LTD.—See ASBISc Enterprises Plc; *Int'l*, pg. 600
PT BUKA PENGADAAN INDONESIA—See Bukalapak.com PT Tbk; *Int'l*, pg. 1213
QUINSERVIZI S.P.A.—See Gruppo MutuiOnline S.p.A; *Int'l*, pg. 3141
QUINTANA ASSOCIATES, INC.—See Thomas Scientific, LLC; *U.S. Private*, pg. 4157
QVC DELAWARE, INC.—See Qurate Retail, Inc.; *U.S. Public*, pg. 1758
RBO PRINTLOGISTIX, INC.; *U.S. Private*, pg. 3360

425120 — WHOLESALE TRADE AGE...

RED ROVER LTD.—See Kajeet, Inc.; *U.S. Private*, pg. 2256
REPARCO TRADING B.V.—See H2 Equity Partners B.V.; *Int'l*, pg. 3199
REPARCO UK LTD.—See H2 Equity Partners B.V.; *Int'l*, pg. 3199
REPLY! INC.; *U.S. Private*, pg. 3401
REPRO-MS 03 D.O.O.—See Avtotehna, d.d.; *Int'l*, pg. 751
REVERE GAS, INC.—See Quarles Petroleum Incorporated; *U.S. Private*, pg. 3324
RUE DU COMMERCE SAS—See Carrefour SA; *Int'l*, pg. 1346
RUST-OLEUM SALES CO., INC.—See RPM International Inc.; *U.S. Public*, pg. 1817
SAFECHARGE INTERNATIONAL GROUP LIMITED—See Nuvei Technologies; *U.S. Private*, pg. 2975
SAN DIEGO AUTO AUCTION INC.—See Cox Enterprises, Inc.; *U.S. Private*, pg. 1077
SANFORD AUTO DEALERS EXCHANGE, INC.—See OPENLANE, Inc.; *U.S. Public*, pg. 1607
SANGHAI FUJIX TRADING CO., LTD.—See FUJIX Ltd.; *Int'l*, pg. 2838
SANTA FE INTERNATIONAL PROJECTS LIMITED—See EAC Invest AS; *Int'l*, pg. 2262
SANTA FE RELOCATION SERVICES SINGAPORE PVT. LTD.—See EAC Invest AS; *Int'l*, pg. 2262
SANTA FE TRANSPORT INTERNATIONAL LIMITED—See EAC Invest AS; *Int'l*, pg. 2262
SCHAEFER REFRIGERATION INC.—See Total Comfort Solutions LLC; *U.S. Private*, pg. 4190
SDB TRADE INTERNATIONAL, LP; *U.S. Private*, pg. 3581
SERVICE MOTOR COMPANY; *U.S. Private*, pg. 3615
SHOPPING.COM INC.—See eBay Inc.; *U.S. Public*, pg. 709
SIDERMAR DI NAVIGAZIONE S.P.A.—See Coeclerici S.p.A.; *Int'l*, pg. 1689
SINNERSCHRADER DEUTSCHLAND GMBH—See Accenture plc; *Int'l*, pg. 88
SINO SANTA FE INTERNATIONAL SERVICES CORPORATION—See EAC Invest AS; *Int'l*, pg. 2262
SIPP INDUSTRIES, INC.; *U.S. Private*, pg. 1888
SJ CREATIONS, INC.—See Platinum Equity, LLC; *U.S. Private*, pg. 3205
SONOCO RECYCLING, INC.—See Sonoco Products Company; *U.S. Public*, pg. 1908
THE SOUTHERN CO., INC.—See The Rosewood Corporation; *U.S. Private*, pg. 4112
SOUTHLAND VENEERS LTD.—See EAC Invest AS; *Int'l*, pg. 2262
SPX PROCESS EQUIPMENT—See SPX Technologies, Inc.; *U.S. Public*, pg. 1921
STATESVILLE AUTO AUCTION—See Cox Enterprises, Inc.; *U.S. Private*, pg. 1077
STEEL PARK INTERNATIONAL PTE. LTD.—See BRC Asia Limited; *Int'l*, pg. 1143
STEEL PARK RESOURCES PTE. LTD.—See BRC Asia Limited; *Int'l*, pg. 1143
STOCK USA EXECUTION SERVICES INC; *U.S. Private*, pg. 3814
SUDAMIN HOLDING SPRL—See AMG Critical Materials N.V.; *Int'l*, pg. 426
SUNBILT LTD.—See Goddard Enterprises Limited; *Int'l*, pg. 3019
SUNRISE BROKERS (HONG KONG) LTD.—See BGC Group, Inc.; *U.S. Public*, pg. 330
SUNRISE BROKERS LLP—See BGC Group, Inc.; *U.S. Public*, pg. 330
THE SYGMA NETWORK, INC.—See Sysco Corporation; *U.S. Public*, pg. 1977
SYSCO WESTERN MINNESOTA—See Sysco Corporation; *U.S. Public*, pg. 1977
TAPPS B.V.—See GlobalData Plc; *Int'l*, pg. 3003
TECHTARGET, INC.; *U.S. Public*, pg. 1988
TELEDYNE ISRAEL COMPOSITE LTD.—See ATI Inc.; *U.S. Public*, pg. 222
TELEDYNE ITALY—See ATI Inc.; *U.S. Public*, pg. 222
TICKETCITY INC.; *U.S. Private*, pg. 4167
TOK TAIWAN CO., LTD.—See ChangChun Group; *Int'l*, pg. 1442
TRAXYS COMETALS USA LLC—See The Carlyle Group Inc.; *U.S. Public*, pg. 2056
TRUCKCENTER.COM, LLC—See Liquidity Services, Inc.; *U.S. Public*, pg. 1321
TRUCKERSB2B, INC.—See Celadon Group; *U.S. Public*, pg. 464
TSUTAYA ONLINE CO., LTD.—See Culture Convenience Club Co., Ltd.; *Int'l*, pg. 1877
TUCKER GMBH—See Stanley Black & Decker, Inc.; *U.S. Public*, pg. 1935
UNISON MARKETPLACE, INC.—See The Carlyle Group Inc.; *U.S. Public*, pg. 2056
UNISYS AUSTRALIA PROPRIETY LTD—See Unisys Corporation; *U.S. Public*, pg. 2228
UNIVERSAL HARDWARE & PLASTIC FACTORY LIMITED—See Aliaxis S.A./N.V.; *Int'l*, pg. 325
VARO ENERGY MARKETING AG—See AtlasInvest; *Int'l*, pg. 686
VELA TRADING SYSTEMS LLC—See Marlin Equity Partners, LLC; *U.S. Private*, pg. 2584

VERMEER NORTHEAST—See All Roads Company; *U.S. Private*, pg. 172
VINILIT S.A.—See Aliaxis S.A./N.V.; *Int'l*, pg. 325
VINILIT S.A.—See Etex SA/NV; *Int'l*, pg. 2523
WALMART.COM—See Walmart Inc.; *U.S. Public*, pg. 2325
WALTER DRAKE INC.—See The Carlyle Group Inc.; *U.S. Public*, pg. 2052
WATLOW JAPAN LTD.—See Tinicum Enterprises, Inc.; *U.S. Private*, pg. 4174
WEIR CANADA, INC.—See Axel Johnson Gruppen AB; *Int'l*, pg. 765
WESCO INTERNATIONAL, INC.; *U.S. Public*, pg. 2350
WHITEHALL PRODUCTS, INC.; *U.S. Private*, pg. 4511
WHOLESALE SUPPLY INC.—See Freeman Spogli & Co. Incorporated; *U.S. Private*, pg. 1606
WILSON IRON WORKS INC.—See Wilson Iron Works Inc.; *U.S. Private*, pg. 4531
WOODWARD COMPRESSOR SALES INC—See Atlas Copco AB; *Int'l*, pg. 680
WTWH MEDIA, LLC; *U.S. Private*, pg. 4574
X.COMMERCE, INC.—See Adobe Inc.; *U.S. Public*, pg. 43
XEROX DEL PERU, S.A.—See Xerox Holdings Corporation; *U.S. Public*, pg. 2391
YOUR AUCTION, INC.—See Huron Capital Partners LLC; *U.S. Private*, pg. 2012

441110 — NEW CAR DEALERS

1000 ISLAND RV CENTRE; *Int'l*, pg. 1
101013121 SASKATCHEWAN LTD; *Int'l*, pg. 1
101 VERMONT AUTO GROUP, INC.; *U.S. Private*, pg. 2
1028918 ONTARIO INC; *Int'l*, pg. 1
1035312 ONTARIO LIMITED; *Int'l*, pg. 1
1042735 ONTARIO INC; *Int'l*, pg. 1
1053038 ONTARIO LIMITED—See AutoCanada Inc.; *Int'l*, pg. 726
1101489 ONTARIO LTD; *Int'l*, pg. 2
1133571 ALBERTA LTD; *Int'l*, pg. 2
1336 NEWFOUNDLAND INC; *Int'l*, pg. 2
1166709 ONTARIO INC; *Int'l*, pg. 2
1170880 ONTARIO LIMITED; *Int'l*, pg. 2
128 AUTO GROUP; *U.S. Private*, pg. 2
128 FORD, INC.; *U.S. Private*, pg. 3
147766 CANADA INC; *Int'l*, pg. 2
1512804 ONTARIO INC; *Int'l*, pg. 2
166606 CANADA INC; *Int'l*, pg. 2
#1 COCHRAN, INC.; *U.S. Private*, pg. 1
330542 BC LTD; *Int'l*, pg. 6
3463192 CANADA INC.; *Int'l*, pg. 6
3617581 CANADA INC; *Int'l*, pg. 7
3770818 CANADA INC; *Int'l*, pg. 7
401-DIXIE NISSAN; *Int'l*, pg. 11
4236009 MANITOBA LTD—See AutoCanada Inc.; *Int'l*, pg. 726
440 FORD LINCOLN LAVAL—See Ford Motor Company; *U.S. Public*, pg. 865
502386 ALBERTA LTD; *Int'l*, pg. 12
561870 ONTARIO LTD; *Int'l*, pg. 13
591226 SASKATCHEWAN LTD; *Int'l*, pg. 13
595242 BC LTD; *Int'l*, pg. 13
598755 B.C. LTD; *Int'l*, pg. 13
669069 ALBERTA LTD; *Int'l*, pg. 14
845453 ONTARIO LTD; *Int'l*, pg. 15
866229 ONTARIO INC.; *Int'l*, pg. 15
89419 BC LTD; *Int'l*, pg. 15
9039-7571 QUEBEC INC; *Int'l*, pg. 16
9119-6832 QUEBEC INC; *Int'l*, pg. 16
942599 ONTARIO LIMITED; *Int'l*, pg. 16
970207 ONTARIO LIMITED; *Int'l*, pg. 16
979094 ALBERTA LTD; *Int'l*, pg. 16
982874 ONTARIO LTD; *Int'l*, pg. 16
988883 ONTARIO INC; *Int'l*, pg. 16
A-1 TOYOTA; *U.S. Private*, pg. 21
ABAJIAN MOTOR SALES; *U.S. Private*, pg. 34
ABBOTSFORD CHRYSLER DODGE JEEP RAM LTD.; *Int'l*, pg. 57
ABEL CHEVROLET PONTIAC BUICK; *U.S. Private*, pg. 37
ABERDEEN CHRYSLER CENTER INC.; *U.S. Private*, pg. 38
ABERS GARAGE INC.; *U.S. Private*, pg. 38
ABLE MOTORS CO., LTD.—See AAPICO Hitech plc; *Int'l*, pg. 37
ABODEINAUTO GMBH—See Baloise Holding AG; *Int'l*, pg. 810
ABRAHAM CHEVROLET-MIAMI, INC.—See AutoNation, Inc.; *U.S. Public*, pg. 232
ABRAHAM CHEVROLET-MIAMI, INC.—See AutoNation, Inc.; *U.S. Public*, pg. 232
ACADIANA DODGE, INC.; *U.S. Private*, pg. 47
ACER FIDUCIARY, INC.—See AutoNation, Inc.; *U.S. Public*, pg. 231
ACME NISSAN; *U.S. Private*, pg. 61
ACTION CHEVROLET BUICK GMC INC.; *Int'l*, pg. 119
ACTON FORD, INC.; *U.S. Private*, pg. 70
ACURA OF AUGUSTA; *U.S. Private*, pg. 71
ACURA OF OCEAN; *U.S. Private*, pg. 71
ACURA OF SEATTLE AT SOUTHCENTER—See Michael

CORPORATE AFFILIATIONS

O'Brien Enterprises, Inc.; *U.S. Private*, pg. 2698
ACURA OF WAPPINGERS FALLS; *U.S. Private*, pg. 71
ACURA SHERWAY—See Chesswood Group Limited; *Int'l*, pg. 1472
ADA FORD LINCOLN MOTORS; *U.S. Private*, pg. 72
ADAMS AUTOMOTIVE INC.; *U.S. Private*, pg. 73
ADAMS BUICK-GMC TRUCK, INC.; *U.S. Private*, pg. 74
ADAMS JEEP OF MARYLAND; *U.S. Private*, pg. 74
ADAMSON FORD INC.; *U.S. Private*, pg. 76
ADAMS TOYOTA LEES SUMMIT; *U.S. Private*, pg. 75
ADAMS TOYOTA; *U.S. Private*, pg. 75
ADELPHI ENTERPRISES L.P.; *U.S. Private*, pg. 77
ADMIRAL NISSAN INC.; *U.S. Private*, pg. 81
ADTRANS GROUP LTD—See Eagers Automotive Limited; *Int'l*, pg. 2263
ADVANCE CAR TECHNOLOGY COMPANY LIMITED—See Aucnet Inc.; *Int'l*, pg. 699
ADVANTAGE BMW MIDTOWN—See Group 1 Automotive, Inc.; *U.S. Public*, pg. 970
ADVANTAGECARS.COM, INC.—See Group 1 Automotive, Inc.; *U.S. Public*, pg. 970
ADZAM INC.; *U.S. Private*, pg. 111
AFFORDABLE CARS & FINANCE; *U.S. Private*, pg. 123
AGINCOURT AUTOHAUS INC.; *Int'l*, pg. 210
AHG 1 PTY LTD—See Eagers Automotive Limited; *Int'l*, pg. 2263
AIRDRIE CHRYSLER DODGE JEEP; *Int'l*, pg. 247
AIRPORT MARINA FORD—See Noarus Auto Group; *U.S. Private*, pg. 2932
AITKEN CHEVROLET BUICK GMC; *Int'l*, pg. 254
AJACCIO AUTOMOBILES; *Int'l*, pg. 255
A.K. DURNIN CHRYSLER JEEP INC; *U.S. Private*, pg. 26
ALAMO TOYOTA INC.; *U.S. Private*, pg. 149
ALAN BYER AUTO SALES INC.; *U.S. Private*, pg. 149
ALAN JAY AUTOMOTIVE NETWORK; *U.S. Private*, pg. 150
ALAN JAY CHRYSLER JEEP, INC.—See Alan Jay Automotive Management, Inc.; *U.S. Private*, pg. 149
ALAN JAY FORD LINCOLN MERCURY, INC.—See Alan Jay Automotive Management, Inc.; *U.S. Private*, pg. 150
ALAN WEBB AUTOMOTIVE GROUP; *U.S. Private*, pg. 150
ALASKA SALES & SERVICE, INC.; *U.S. Private*, pg. 151
ALBANY FORD INC.; *U.S. Private*, pg. 151
ALBERIC COLON AUTO SALES INC.; *U.S. Private*, pg. 152
ALBERT MOTORS INC.; *U.S. Private*, pg. 153
ALDERMAN'S CHEVROLET, INC.; *U.S. Private*, pg. 159
ALESAYI TRADING CORPORATION; *Int'l*, pg. 306
ALEXANDER AUTOMOTIVE; *U.S. Private*, pg. 163
ALEXANDER BUICK GMC CADILLAC; *U.S. Private*, pg. 163
ALEXANDER CHEVROLET—See Alexander Automotive; *U.S. Private*, pg. 163
ALEXANDER FORD CO. INC.—See Alexander Automotive; *U.S. Private*, pg. 163
ALEXANDER FORD LINCOLN-MERCURY, INC.—See Alexander Automotive Group; *U.S. Private*, pg. 163
ALEXANDRIA TOYOTA; *U.S. Private*, pg. 164
ALEX MONTGOMERY MT. WASHINGTON; *U.S. Private*, pg. 163
ALFANO MOTORCARS, INC.; *U.S. Private*, pg. 164
ALFORD MOTORS INC.; *U.S. Private*, pg. 165
ALFRED MATTHEWS, INC.; *U.S. Private*, pg. 165
ALFREDO'S FOREIGN CARS INC.; *U.S. Private*, pg. 166
ALFRED STEIN INC.; *U.S. Private*, pg. 166
AL-FUTTAIM TRADING ENTERPRISES COMPANY L.L.C—See Al-Futtaim Private Company LLC; *Int'l*, pg. 285
ALHAMBRA CHRYSLER JEEP DODGE; *U.S. Private*, pg. 166
ALHAMBRA NISSAN; *U.S. Private*, pg. 166
AL HENDRICKSON TOYOTA; *U.S. Private*, pg. 147
A&L HOLDING COMPANY INC.; *U.S. Private*, pg. 20
ALL AMERICAN FORD, INC.—See All American Auto Sales Group; *U.S. Private*, pg. 169
ALL AMERICAN FORD OF KINGSTON, LLC—See All American Auto Sales Group; *U.S. Private*, pg. 169
ALL AMERICAN SUBARU—See All American Auto Sales Group; *U.S. Private*, pg. 169
ALLAN VIGIL'S FORD; *U.S. Private*, pg. 170
ALLEGIANCE FIRE & RESCUE—See Allegiance Trucks, LLC; *U.S. Private*, pg. 176
ALLEN CHRISTIAN BUICK OLDSMOBILE PONTIAC GMC, INC.; *U.S. Private*, pg. 178
ALLEN GWYNN CHEVROLET; *U.S. Private*, pg. 179
ALLEN SAMUEL CHRYSLER DODGE JEEP; *U.S. Private*, pg. 179
ALLEN SAMUELS AUTO GROUP; *U.S. Private*, pg. 179
ALLEN SAMUELS CHEVROLET OF CORPUS CHRISTI, INC.—See AutoNation, Inc.; *U.S. Public*, pg. 232
ALLEN SAMUELS CHEVROLET OF WACO, INC.—See AutoNation, Inc.; *U.S. Public*, pg. 232
ALLEN SAMUELS CHEVROLET—See Allen Samuels Auto Group; *U.S. Private*, pg. 179
ALLEN TILLERY CHEVROLET, INC.; *U.S. Private*, pg. 180
ALLEN TURNER HYUNDAI INC.; *U.S. Private*, pg. 180
ALLISON BAVARIAN—See AutoNation, Inc.; *U.S. Public*, pg. 232
ALLISON BAVARIAN—See AutoNation, Inc.; *U.S. Public*, pg. 232

N.A.I.C.S. INDEX

441110 — NEW CAR DEALERS

ALLISON CHEVROLET INC.; *U.S. Private*, pg. 192
ALL R.V. SERVICE & REPAIR; *U.S. Private*, pg. 171
ALL STAR AUTOMOTIVE GROUP; *U.S. Private*, pg. 172
ALL-STAR CHEVROLET GEO, INC.; *U.S. Private*, pg. 173
ALL STAR DODGE CHRYSLER JEEP; *U.S. Private*, pg. 172
ALL STAR DODGE; *U.S. Private*, pg. 172
ALL STAR FORD LLC; *U.S. Private*, pg. 172
ALL STAR NISSAN—See All Star Automotive Group; *U.S. Private*, pg. 172
ALL-STATE FORD TRUCK SALES—See Hesco Parts Corporation; *U.S. Private*, pg. 1927
ALOHA AUTO GROUP, LTD.; *U.S. Private*, pg. 195
AL PACKER FORD - EAST—See Al Packer, Inc.; *U.S. Private*, pg. 147
ALPINE BUICK, PONTIAC, GMC; *U.S. Private*, pg. 200
AL SERRA AUTO PLAZA; *U.S. Private*, pg. 147
AL SERRA CHEVROLET; *U.S. Private*, pg. 147
ALTON E. BLAKLEY COMPANY INC.; *U.S. Private*, pg. 210
ALTRUI BROTHERS TRUCK SALES, INC.; *U.S. Private*, pg. 210
AMATO COLLISION CENTER, INC.; *U.S. Private*, pg. 216
AMDAHL MOTORS; *U.S. Private*, pg. 218
AMERICAN SERVICE CENTER ASSOCIATES LLC; *U.S. Private*, pg. 253
AMERICAN WAY MOTORS, INC.—See AutoNation, Inc.; *U.S. Public*, pg. 232
A M FORD SALES LTD; *Int'l*, pg. 18
AMIGO CHEVROLET; *U.S. Private*, pg. 263
AMITE CITY FORD INC.; *U.S. Private*, pg. 263
AMPLITUDE AUTOMOBILES; *Int'l*, pg. 436
ANCHOR SUBARU; *U.S. Private*, pg. 273
ANCIRA ENTERPRISES INC.; *U.S. Private*, pg. 274
AN COLLISION CENTER FTL SOUTH, INC.—See AutoNation, Inc.; *U.S. Public*, pg. 231
AN COLLISION CENTER OF LAS VEGAS, INC.—See AutoNation, Inc.; *U.S. Public*, pg. 231
AN COLLISION CENTER OF NORTH HOUSTON, INC.—See AutoNation, Inc.; *U.S. Public*, pg. 231
AN COLLISION CENTER OF TEMPE, INC.—See AutoNation, Inc.; *U.S. Public*, pg. 231
ANCONA ENTERPRISES INC; *U.S. Private*, pg. 274
AN CORPUS CHRISTI T. IMPORTS, LP—See AutoNation, Inc.; *U.S. Public*, pg. 231
AN COUNTY LINE FORD, INC.—See AutoNation, Inc.; *U.S. Public*, pg. 231
ANDERSEN & MARTINI HOLDING A/S; *Int'l*, pg. 450
ANDERSON AUTOMOTIVE GROUP INC.; *U.S. Private*, pg. 276
ANDERSON AUTOMOTIVE GROUP; *U.S. Private*, pg. 276
ANDERSON CHRYSLER JEEP INC.; *U.S. Private*, pg. 276
ANDERSON FORD MAZDA LLC; *U.S. Private*, pg. 276
ANDERSON MOTORS; *U.S. Private*, pg. 277
ANDERSON WEBER TOYOTA-LINCOLN-MERCURY; *U.S. Private*, pg. 277
ANDREW TOYOTA; *U.S. Private*, pg. 280
ANDY MOHR FORD; *U.S. Private*, pg. 281
ANDY MOHR NISSAN, INC.; *U.S. Private*, pg. 281
ANDY MOHR TRUCK CENTER; *U.S. Private*, pg. 281
ANDYS CAR AND TRUCK CENTER, INC.—See Glockner Chevrolet Co. Inc.; *U.S. Private*, pg. 1720
ANDY SHAW FORD; *U.S. Private*, pg. 281
AN FORT MYERS IMPORTS, LLC—See AutoNation, Inc.; *U.S. Public*, pg. 231
AN FREMONT LUXURY IMPORTS, INC.—See AutoNation, Inc.; *U.S. Public*, pg. 231
AN H. IMPORTS OF ATLANTA, LLC—See AutoNation, Inc.; *U.S. Public*, pg. 231
ANHUI YONGDA BAOYI AUTOMOBILE SALES AND SERVICES CO., LTD.—See China Yongda Automobiles Services Holdings Limited; *Int'l*, pg. 1564
AN IMPORTS OF FT. LAUDERDALE, INC.—See AutoNation, Inc.; *U.S. Public*, pg. 231
AN IMPORTS OF SPOKANE, INC.—See AutoNation, Inc.; *U.S. Public*, pg. 231
AN IMPORTS OF STEVENS CREEK, INC.—See AutoNation, Inc.; *U.S. Public*, pg. 231
AN IMPORTS ON WESTON ROAD, INC.—See AutoNation, Inc.; *U.S. Public*, pg. 231
AN LUXURY IMPORTS, LTD.—See AutoNation, Inc.; *U.S. Public*, pg. 231
AN LUXURY IMPORTS OF COCONUT CREEK, INC.—See AutoNation, Inc.; *U.S. Public*, pg. 231
AN LUXURY IMPORTS OF MARIETTA, LLC—See AutoNation, Inc.; *U.S. Public*, pg. 231
AN LUXURY IMPORTS OF PALM BEACH, INC.—See AutoNation, Inc.; *U.S. Public*, pg. 231
AN LUXURY IMPORTS OF PEMBROKE PINES—See AutoNation, Inc.; *U.S. Public*, pg. 231
AN LUXURY IMPORTS OF PHOENIX, INC.—See AutoNation, Inc.; *U.S. Public*, pg. 231
AN LUXURY IMPORTS OF SARASOTA, INC.—See AutoNation, Inc.; *U.S. Public*, pg. 231
AN LUXURY IMPORTS OF SPOKANE, INC.—See AutoNation, Inc.; *U.S. Public*, pg. 231
AN LUXURY IMPORTS OF TUCSON, INC.—See AutoNation, Inc.; *U.S. Public*, pg. 231
AN/MNI ACQUISITION CORP.—See AutoNation, Inc.; *U.S. Public*, pg. 232
AN MOTORS OF BROOKSVILLE, INC.—See AutoNation, Inc.; *U.S. Public*, pg. 231
AN MOTORS OF DALLAS, INC.—See AutoNation, Inc.; *U.S. Public*, pg. 231
AN MOTORS OF MEMPHIS, INC.—See AutoNation, Inc.; *U.S. Public*, pg. 231
AN MOTORS OF PEMBROKE, LLC—See AutoNation, Inc.; *U.S. Public*, pg. 231
AN MOTORS OF SCOTTSDALE, LLC—See AutoNation, Inc.; *U.S. Public*, pg. 231
AN MOTORS ON FEDERAL HIGHWAY, LLC—See AutoNation, Inc.; *U.S. Public*, pg. 231
AN MOTORS ON SOUTH PADRE, LP—See AutoNation, Inc.; *U.S. Public*, pg. 231
AN NORTH PHOENIX COLLISION, INC.—See AutoNation, Inc.; *U.S. Public*, pg. 231
AN/PF ACQUISITION CORP.—See AutoNation, Inc.; *U.S. Public*, pg. 232
AN SAN JOSE LUXURY IMPORTS, INC.—See AutoNation, Inc.; *U.S. Public*, pg. 231
AN SUBARU MOTORS, INC.—See AutoNation, Inc.; *U.S. Public*, pg. 231
AN SUBARU MOTORS, INC.—See AutoNation, Inc.; *U.S. Public*, pg. 232
ANTELOPE VALLEY FORD; *U.S. Private*, pg. 287
ANTHONY CHEVROLET CADILLAC; *U.S. Private*, pg. 287
ANTHONY PONTIAC GMC BUICK, INC.; *U.S. Private*, pg. 288
AN T. IMPORTS OF ATLANTA, LLC—See AutoNation, Inc.; *U.S. Public*, pg. 232
ANTWERPEN MOTOR CARS LTD.; *U.S. Private*, pg. 289
APPLE CHEVROLET INCORPORATED; *U.S. Private*, pg. 296
APPLE FORD INC.; *U.S. Private*, pg. 296
APPLE FORD; *U.S. Private*, pg. 296
APPLE TREE HONDA; *U.S. Private*, pg. 297
APPLEWAY CHEVROLET, INC.—See AutoNation, Inc.; *U.S. Public*, pg. 231
ARAPAHOE MOTORS, INC.; *U.S. Private*, pg. 307
ARCADIA CHEVROLET BUICK PONTIAC INC.; *U.S. Private*, pg. 309
ARCENEAUX FORD INC.; *U.S. Private*, pg. 310
ARCHER RV; *U.S. Private*, pg. 310
ARDMORE NISSAN; *U.S. Private*, pg. 317
ARISTOCRAT VOLKSWAGEN INC.; *U.S. Private*, pg. 323
ARMEN CADILLAC; *U.S. Private*, pg. 330
ARMSTRONG BUICK VOLKSWAGEN; *U.S. Private*, pg. 331
ARNGAR, INC.—See Sonic Automotive, Inc.; *U.S. Public*, pg. 1902
ARNIE BAUER, INC.; *U.S. Private*, pg. 332
ARNOLD-BAKER CHEVROLET; *U.S. Private*, pg. 333
ARNOLD CLARK AUTOMOBILES LIMITED; *Int'l*, pg. 576
ARR INVESTMENTS, LLC; *U.S. Private*, pg. 334
ARROW CARS INTERNATIONAL, INC.; *Int'l*, pg. 579
ARROW FORD INC.; *U.S. Private*, pg. 335
ART GAMBLIN MOTORS; *U.S. Private*, pg. 339
ART HILL INC.; *U.S. Private*, pg. 339
ARTMAR INC.; *U.S. Private*, pg. 343
ART MORAN PONTIAC-GMC TRUCK-MITSUBISHI INC.; *U.S. Private*, pg. 340
ARUNDEL FORD; *U.S. Private*, pg. 344
ARVAL TRADING SAS—See BNP Paribas SA; *Int'l*, pg. 1080
ASBURY ATLANTA AU L.L.C.—See Asbury Automotive Group, Inc.; *U.S. Public*, pg. 209
ASBURY ATLANTA HON LLC—See Asbury Automotive Group, Inc.; *U.S. Public*, pg. 209
ASBURY ATLANTA LEX LLC—See Asbury Automotive Group, Inc.; *U.S. Public*, pg. 209
ASBURY ATLANTA NIS LLC—See Asbury Automotive Group, Inc.; *U.S. Public*, pg. 210
ASBURY ATLANTA TOY 2 L.L.C.—See Asbury Automotive Group, Inc.; *U.S. Public*, pg. 209
ASBURY ATLANTA TOY LLC—See Asbury Automotive Group, Inc.; *U.S. Public*, pg. 210
ASBURY AUTOMOTIVE GROUP, INC.; *U.S. Public*, pg. 209
ASBURY AUTOMOTIVE JACKSONVILLE, L.P.—See Asbury Automotive Group, Inc.; *U.S. Public*, pg. 209
ASBURY FT. WORTH FORD, L.L.C.—See Asbury Automotive Group, Inc.; *U.S. Public*, pg. 209
ASBURY JAX FORD, LLC—See Asbury Automotive Group, Inc.; *U.S. Public*, pg. 209
ASHEVILLE CHEVROLET INC.; *U.S. Private*, pg. 349
AS INSIGNIA—See Bilia AB; *Int'l*, pg. 1029
ASTORG FORD LINCOLN-MERCURY OF PARKERSBURG, INC.; *U.S. Public*, pg. 361
ASTORG MOTOR CO.; *U.S. Private*, pg. 361
ASTRO INC.; *U.S. Private*, pg. 362
ASTRO LINCOLN, MERCURY, INC.; *U.S. Private*, pg. 362
ATAMIAN VOLKSWAGEN & HONDA, INC.; *U.S. Private*, pg. 364
AT AUTOMOBILES; *Int'l*, pg. 664
A & T CHEVROLET, INCORPORATED; *U.S. Private*, pg. 18
ATLANTIC AUTOMALL; *U.S. Private*, pg. 371
ATLANTIC AUTOMOTIVE CORP.; *U.S. Private*, pg. 371
ATLANTIC GREAT DANE INC.; *U.S. Private*, pg. 373
ATLANTIC TOYOTA; *U.S. Private*, pg. 375
ATTERBERY TRUCK SALES, INC.; *U.S. Private*, pg. 383
ATTRELL AUTO HOLDINGS LIMITED; *Int'l*, pg. 697
ATWOOD CHEVROLET INC.; *U.S. Private*, pg. 384
ATZENHOFFER CHEVROLET COMPANY; *U.S. Private*, pg. 384
AUBURN MOTOR SALES; *U.S. Private*, pg. 385
AUCKLAND AUTO COLLECTION LIMITED—See Eagers Automotive Limited; *Int'l*, pg. 2263
AUCLERT SAS; *Int'l*, pg. 699
AUDERA; *Int'l*, pg. 701
AUDETTE CADILLAC, INC.; *U.S. Private*, pg. 390
AUDI FARMINGTON HILLS—See Lithia Motors, Inc.; *U.S. Public*, pg. 1321
AUDI OF BERNARDSVILLE; *U.S. Private*, pg. 390
AUDI PEMBROKE PINES; *U.S. Private*, pg. 390
AUDI ZENTRUM AACHEN JACOBS AUTO GMBH—See Penske Automotive Group, Inc.; *U.S. Public*, pg. 1664
AUFFENBERG IMPORTS INC.; *U.S. Private*, pg. 391
AUFFENBERG OF CARBONDALE—See Chris Auffenberg Ford Inc.; *U.S. Private*, pg. 889
AUGES SALES & SERVICE; *U.S. Private*, pg. 392
AUGUSTA DODGE INC.; *U.S. Private*, pg. 392
AUT 6 PTY LTD—See Eagers Automotive Limited; *Int'l*, pg. 2263
AUTOBAHN MOTORCAR GROUP; *U.S. Private*, pg. 398
AUTO CLEARING CHRYSLER DODGE JEEP RAM; *Int'l*, pg. 724
AUTO COMPANY VIII, INC.—See AutoNation, Inc.; *U.S. Public*, pg. 232
AUTO COMPANY VII, INC.—See AutoNation, Inc.; *U.S. Public*, pg. 232
AUTO COMPANY VI, INC.—See AutoNation, Inc.; *U.S. Public*, pg. 232
AUTO COMPANY XIII, INC.—See AutoNation, Inc.; *U.S. Public*, pg. 232
AUTO COMPANY XII, INC.—See AutoNation, Inc.; *U.S. Public*, pg. 232
AUTO COMPANY XI, INC.—See AutoNation, Inc.; *U.S. Public*, pg. 232
AUTO COMPANY XIV, INC.—See AutoNation, Inc.; *U.S. Public*, pg. 232
AUTO COMPANY XIX, INC.—See AutoNation, Inc.; *U.S. Public*, pg. 232
AUTO COMPANY XVII, INC.—See AutoNation, Inc.; *U.S. Public*, pg. 232
AUTO COMPANY XXIII, INC.—See AutoNation, Inc.; *U.S. Public*, pg. 232
AUTO COMPANY XXII, INC.—See AutoNation, Inc.; *U.S. Public*, pg. 232
AUTO COMPANY XXI, INC.—See AutoNation, Inc.; *U.S. Public*, pg. 232
AUTO COMPANY XXVII, INC.—See AutoNation, Inc.; *U.S. Public*, pg. 232
AUTO COMPANY XXV, INC.—See AutoNation, Inc.; *U.S. Public*, pg. 232
AUTO DEALERSHIP III, LLC—See AutoNation, Inc.; *U.S. Public*, pg. 232
AUTO DEALERSHIP IV, LLC—See AutoNation, Inc.; *U.S. Public*, pg. 232
AUTO DEALERSHIP VI, LLC—See AutoNation, Inc.; *U.S. Public*, pg. 232
AUTO DEALERSHIP V, LLC—See AutoNation, Inc.; *U.S. Public*, pg. 232
AUTODESCUENTO, S.L.—See Banco Santander, S.A.; *Int'l*, pg. 825
AUTO EQUIPMENT INC.; *U.S. Private*, pg. 397
AUTO EXECUTIVES; *U.S. Private*, pg. 397
AUTOHAUS24 GMBH—See Banco Santander, S.A.; *Int'l*, pg. 825
AUTOHAUS BMW; *U.S. Private*, pg. 398
AUTOHAUS HANSA NORD GMBH—See Ernst Dello GmbH & Co. KG; *Int'l*, pg. 2494
AUTOHAUS HOLDINGS, INC.—See AutoNation, Inc.; *U.S. Public*, pg. 233
AUTOHAUS KRETTER GMBH; *Int'l*, pg. 726
AUTOHAUS LANCASTER, INC.; *U.S. Private*, pg. 398
AUTOHAUS NIX GMBH—See Penske Automotive Group, Inc.; *U.S. Public*, pg. 1664
AUTOHAUS ON EDENS INC.; *U.S. Private*, pg. 398
AUTOHAUS WIDMANN + WINTERHOLLER GMBH - FARCHANT—See Autohaus Widmann + Winterholler GmbH; *Int'l*, pg. 727
AUTOHAUS WIDMANN + WINTERHOLLER GMBH; *Int'l*, pg. 727
AUTO ITALIA EAD—See Eurohold Bulgaria AD; *Int'l*, pg. 2553
AUTO ITALIA LIMITED—See Auto Italia Holdings Limited; *Int'l*, pg. 724
AUTO MALL 46, INC.; *U.S. Private*, pg. 397
AUTOMAX CHRYSLER DODGE JEEP RAM; *U.S. Private*, pg. 400
AUTO MISSION LTD.—See AutoNation, Inc.; *U.S. Public*, pg. 232
AUTO MISSION LTD.—See AutoNation, Inc.; *U.S. Public*, pg. 232
AUTOMOBILE PROVENCE INNOVATION; *Int'l*, pg. 730
AUTOMOBILES MAUGER FORD; *Int'l*, pg. 730

441110 — NEW CAR DEALERS — CORPORATE AFFILIATIONS

AUTOMOBILES OF STATESVILLE, INC.; *U.S. Private*, pg. 400
AUTOMOBILES ORTHEZIENNES; *Int'l*, pg. 730
AUTOMOTIVE CAPITAL SERVICES, INC.—See Onity Group Inc.; *U.S. Public*, pg. 1604
AUTOMOTIVE HOLDINGS GROUP LIMITED—See Eagers Automotive Limited; *Int'l*, pg. 2263
AUTOMOTIVE MANAGEMENT GROUP, INC.; *U.S. Private*, pg. 400
AUTOMOTIVE SERVICE NETWORK, INC.; *U.S. Private*, pg. 401
AUTO MOTORS OF ENGLEWOOD, LLC—See AutoNation, Inc.; *U.S. Public*, pg. 232
AUTOMOVILISIMO Y TURISMO SA; *Int'l*, pg. 731
AUTONATION CHEVROLET CADILLAC CORPUS CHRISTI—See AutoNation, Inc.; *U.S. Public*, pg. 232
AUTONATION CHEVROLET FORT LAUDERDALE—See AutoNation, Inc.; *U.S. Public*, pg. 233
AUTONATION CHEVROLET SPOKANE VALLEY—See AutoNation, Inc.; *U.S. Public*, pg. 233
AUTONATION FORD AMHERST—See AutoNation, Inc.; *U.S. Public*, pg. 232
AUTONATION FORD FRISCO—See AutoNation, Inc.; *U.S. Public*, pg. 232
AUTONATION FORD MEMPHIS—See AutoNation, Inc.; *U.S. Public*, pg. 232
AUTONATION FORD PANAMA CITY—See AutoNation, Inc.; *U.S. Public*, pg. 232
AUTONATION FORD SOUTH FORT WORTH—See AutoNation, Inc.; *U.S. Public*, pg. 232
AUTONATION FORD TUSTIN—See AutoNation, Inc.; *U.S. Public*, pg. 232
AUTONATION FORD WOLFCASE—See AutoNation, Inc.; *U.S. Public*, pg. 233
AUTONATION FORT WORTH MOTORS, LTD.—See AutoNation, Inc.; *U.S. Public*, pg. 233
AUTONATION IMPORTS OF KATY, L.P.—See AutoNation, Inc.; *U.S. Public*, pg. 233
AUTONATION IMPORTS OF WINTER PARK, INC.—See AutoNation, Inc.; *U.S. Public*, pg. 233
AUTONATION IMPORTS OF WINTER PARK, INC.—See AutoNation, Inc.; *U.S. Public*, pg. 233
AUTONATION, INC.; *U.S. Public*, pg. 230
AUTONATION NISSAN ORANGE PARK—See AutoNation, Inc.; *U.S. Public*, pg. 233
AUTONATION TOYOTA CERRITOS—See AutoNation, Inc.; *U.S. Public*, pg. 233
AUTONATION TOYOTA CORPUS CHRISTI—See AutoNation, Inc.; *U.S. Public*, pg. 233
AUTONATION V. IMPORTS OF DELRAY BEACH, LLC—See AutoNation, Inc.; *U.S. Public*, pg. 233
AUTO NEJMA MAROC SA; *Int'l*, pg. 725
AUTORAMA INC.; *U.S. Private*, pg. 401
AUTO RELAIS SAGLIO; *Int'l*, pg. 725
AUTO SENATEUR INC; *Int'l*, pg. 725
AUTO'S ETC. LTD.; *U.S. Private*, pg. 397
AUTOSOURCE MOTORS LLC; *U.S. Private*, pg. 401
AUTOSPORTS GROUP LIMITED; *Int'l*, pg. 732
AUTOSPORT USA, INC.—See RumbleON, Inc.; *U.S. Public*, pg. 1826
AUTOS VEGA INC.; *U.S. Private*, pg. 401
AUTOVALLEY, SAS—See BNP Paribas SA; *Int'l*, pg. 1080
AUTOVANTI BRIANZA S.R.L.—See Penske Automotive Group, Inc.; *U.S. Public*, pg. 1664
AUTOVANTI MONZA S.R.L.—See Penske Automotive Group, Inc.; *U.S. Public*, pg. 1664
AUTOVEICOLI ERZELLI S.P.A.; *Int'l*, pg. 732
AUTO WEST GROUP; *Int'l*, pg. 725
AUTOWORLD KIA; *U.S. Private*, pg. 401
AUTOZENTRUM WEST KOLN GMBH—See General Motors Company; *U.S. Public*, pg. 926
AVALON FORD SALES LTD.; *Int'l*, pg. 734
AVENUE NISSAN SALES LTD.; *Int'l*, pg. 739
AVIS CAR SALES UTD, LLC—See Avis Budget Group, Inc.; *U.S. Public*, pg. 248
AVIS FORD INC.; *U.S. Private*, pg. 407
AVTO AKTIV SLO D.O.O.—See AutoWallis Public Limited Company; *Int'l*, pg. 732
AVTO UNION AD—See Eurohold Bulgaria AD; *Int'l*, pg. 2552
AW GOLDEN INC.; *U.S. Private*, pg. 410
A. W. TROUTMAN CO.; *U.S. Private*, pg. 23
AXTELL-TAYLOR GM, LLC; *U.S. Private*, pg. 414
AYERS CHEVROLET & OLDSMOBILE, INC.; *U.S. Private*, pg. 414
BABBITT FORD LINCOLN-MERCURY LLC; *U.S. Private*, pg. 421
BACHMAN AUTO GROUP; *U.S. Private*, pg. 422
BACHMAN-BERNARD AUTO MALLS; *U.S. Private*, pg. 423
BACHRODT MOTORS INC.; *U.S. Private*, pg. 423
BADANAI MOTORS LTD; *Int'l*, pg. 795
BADGER CHEVROLET BUICK, INC.—See Badger Truck and Automotive Group, Inc.; *U.S. Private*, pg. 424
BAIERL CHEVROLET, INC.—See Lithia Motors, Inc.; *U.S. Public*, pg. 1321
BAIERL TOYOTA—See Lithia Motors, Inc.; *U.S. Public*, pg. 1321

BAILEY GIBSON BUICK, PONTIAC & GMC, INC.; *U.S. Private*, pg. 425
BALE CHEVROLET; *U.S. Private*, pg. 459
BALES MOTOR COMPANY; *U.S. Private*, pg. 459
BALISE MOTOR SALES CO.; *U.S. Private*, pg. 459
BALLARD TRUCK CENTER OF WORCESTER; *U.S. Private*, pg. 460
BALL VOLVO & G M C TRUCKS; *U.S. Private*, pg. 460
BANCROFT MOTORS LTD; *Int'l*, pg. 828
BANNER FORD; *U.S. Private*, pg. 469
BARABOO MOTORS INC.; *U.S. Private*, pg. 471
BARBER AUTO SALES INC.; *U.S. Private*, pg. 472
BARBER BROTHERS MOTOR COMPANY; *U.S. Private*, pg. 472
BARBER FORD INC.; *U.S. Private*, pg. 472
BARBERINO BROTHERS, INC.; *U.S. Private*, pg. 472
BARLOW CHEVROLET; *U.S. Private*, pg. 476
BARNES-BAKER MOTORS INC.; *U.S. Private*, pg. 477
BARNETT CHRYSLER JEEP KIA; *U.S. Private*, pg. 477
BARON BROS, INC.; *U.S. Private*, pg. 478
BARONS AUTOMOTIVE LIMITED—See Group 1 Automotive, Inc.; *U.S. Public*, pg. 970
BARONS AUTOSTAR LIMITED—See Group 1 Automotive, Inc.; *U.S. Public*, pg. 970
BARRETT CHEVROLET, INC.; *U.S. Private*, pg. 479
BARRIE CHRYSLER DODGE JEEP RAM LTD.; *Int'l*, pg. 870
BARRY CULLEN CHEVROLET CADILLAC LTD; *Int'l*, pg. 870
BARRY PONTIAC-BUICK INC.; *U.S. Private*, pg. 481
BARRY'S CHEVROLET-BUICK, INC.; *U.S. Private*, pg. 481
BARSTOW MOTORS INC.; *U.S. Private*, pg. 482
BASKIN TRUCK & TRACTOR, INC.; *U.S. Private*, pg. 485
BASTY PERE ET FILS; *Int'l*, pg. 888
BATES NISSAN INC.; *U.S. Private*, pg. 486
BAUDRY AUTOMOBILES; *Int'l*, pg. 891
BAULOISE AUTOMOBILES S.A.; *Int'l*, pg. 894
BAUMANN CHRYSLER-JEEP-DODGE; *U.S. Private*, pg. 490
BAXTER AUTO GROUP; *U.S. Private*, pg. 491
BAY CHEVROLET, INC.; *U.S. Private*, pg. 492
BAY CHEVROLET; *U.S. Private*, pg. 492
BAYER MOTOR CO. INC.; *U.S. Private*, pg. 496
BAY KING CHRYSLER DODGE JEEP; *Int'l*, pg. 901
BAY RIDGE AUTOMOTIVE GROUP; *U.S. Private*, pg. 494
BAY RIDGE SUBARU; *U.S. Private*, pg. 494
BAY RIDGE VOLVO-AMERICAN INC.; *U.S. Private*, pg. 494
BAYSHORE FORD TRUCK SALES INC.; *U.S. Private*, pg. 496
BAYSIDE CHRYSLER JEEP DODGE INC.; *U.S. Private*, pg. 497
BAYVIEW CHRYSLER DODGE LTD.; *Int'l*, pg. 915
BAYWAY LINCOLN-MERCURY INC.; *U.S. Private*, pg. 497
B&B SAAB; *U.S. Private*, pg. 418
BEACH AUTOMOTIVE GROUP; *U.S. Private*, pg. 503
BEACH FORD, INC.; *U.S. Private*, pg. 503
BEACH FORD; *U.S. Private*, pg. 503
BEACH FORD SUFFOLK; *U.S. Private*, pg. 503
BEACON MOTORS, INC.—See AutoNation, Inc.; *U.S. Public*, pg. 233
BEADLES COULSDON LIMITED—See Group 1 Automotive, Inc.; *U.S. Public*, pg. 970
BEADLES DARTFORD LIMITED—See Group 1 Automotive, Inc.; *U.S. Public*, pg. 970
BEADLES MAIDSTONE LIMITED—See Group 1 Automotive, Inc.; *U.S. Public*, pg. 970
BEADLES MEDWAY LIMITED—See Group 1 Automotive, Inc.; *U.S. Public*, pg. 970
BEADLES SIDCUP LIMITED—See Group 1 Automotive, Inc.; *U.S. Public*, pg. 971
BEAMAN AUTOMOTIVE GROUP; *U.S. Private*, pg. 506
BEAN CHEVROLET BUICK GMC LTD.—See General Motors Company; *U.S. Public*, pg. 923
BEASLEY-WILSON, INCORPORATED; *U.S. Private*, pg. 507
BEATTIE DODGE CHRYSLER LTD.; *Int'l*, pg. 933
BEATY CHEVROLET COMPANY; *U.S. Private*, pg. 507
BEAUMONT AUTOMOBILES; *Int'l*, pg. 934
BEAUMONT MOTOR CO.—See Southeast Texas Classic Automotive; *U.S. Private*, pg. 3726
BEAU TOWNSEND FORD INC.; *U.S. Private*, pg. 507
BEAU TOWNSEND FORD LINCOLN, INC.; *U.S. Private*, pg. 507
BEAU TOWNSEND NISSAN, INC.; *U.S. Private*, pg. 508
BEAVERTON TOYOTA COMPANY INC.; *U.S. Private*, pg. 509
BECK CHEVROLET CO. INC.; *U.S. Private*, pg. 510
BECKER BUICK INC.; *U.S. Private*, pg. 510
BECKER MOTORS INC.; *U.S. Private*, pg. 511
BECKLEY AUTOMALL, INC.; *U.S. Private*, pg. 511
BECK & MASTEN AUTOMOTIVE GROUP, INC.—See Group 1 Automotive, Inc.; *U.S. Public*, pg. 971
BEDFORD NISSAN INC.; *U.S. Private*, pg. 512
BEECHMONT AUTOMOTIVE GROUP; *U.S. Private*, pg. 513
BEECHMONT FORD INC.; *U.S. Private*, pg. 513
BEECHMONT ISUZU—See Beechmont Automotive Group; *U.S. Private*, pg. 513

BEERENS O.C. NV—See General Motors Company; *U.S. Public*, pg. 927
BEIJING BAOZEN BAIWANG AUTOMOBILE SALES AND SERVICES CO., LTD.—See China Yongda Automobiles Services Holdings Limited; *Int'l*, pg. 1564
BEIJING BASHI MEDIA CO., LTD.; *Int'l*, pg. 946
BEIJING HUIBAOHANG AUTO SALES & SERVICES CO., LTD.—See China MeiDong Auto Holdings Limited; *Int'l*, pg. 1519
BELK FORD INC.; *U.S. Private*, pg. 518
BELLAMY STRICKLAND CHEVROLET GMC AND PONTIAC INC.; *U.S. Private*, pg. 519
BELLAVIA CHEVROLET BUICK; *U.S. Private*, pg. 519
BELL & BELL BUICK PONTIAC GMC ISUZU TRUCKS, INC.; *U.S. Private*, pg. 518
BELL DODGE, L.L.C.—See AutoNation, Inc.; *U.S. Public*, pg. 233
BELLEVUE AUTOMOTIVE, INC.—See AutoNation, Inc.; *U.S. Public*, pg. 233
BELLEVUE COLLISION, INC.—See AutoNation, Inc.; *U.S. Public*, pg. 233
BELLEVUE COLLISION, INC.—See AutoNation, Inc.; *U.S. Public*, pg. 233
BELL FORD INC.—See The Berge Group; *U.S. Private*, pg. 3993
BELL MOTORS, LLC—See AutoNation, Inc.; *U.S. Public*, pg. 233
BELTWAY BUICK INC.; *U.S. Private*, pg. 521
BELTWAY INTERNATIONAL TRUCKS, INC.; *U.S. Private*, pg. 521
BEMIDJI CHRYSLER CENTER, LLC.; *U.S. Private*, pg. 522
BEND-CDJR, LLC—See Lithia Motors, Inc.; *U.S. Public*, pg. 1321
BENGAL MOTOR COMPANY, LTD.—See AutoNation, Inc.; *U.S. Public*, pg. 233
BENGAL MOTOR COMPANY, LTD.—See AutoNation, Inc.; *U.S. Public*, pg. 233
BENNETT AUTOMOTIVE GROUP; *U.S. Private*, pg. 527
BENNETT BUICK GMC; *U.S. Private*, pg. 527
BENNETT CHEVROLET OLDSMOBILE CADILLAC LTD; *Int'l*, pg. 974
BENNETT DUNLOP FORD; *Int'l*, pg. 974
BENOY MOTOR SALES, INC.; *U.S. Private*, pg. 528
BENSON AUTOMOTIVE COMPANY; *U.S. Private*, pg. 528
BENSON CHRYSLER PLYMOUTH INC.; *U.S. Private*, pg. 528
BENSON LINCOLN MERCURY CORPORATION; *U.S. Private*, pg. 528
BENSON LINCOLN MERCURY INC.; *U.S. Private*, pg. 528
BENSON MOTORS CORPORATION; *U.S. Private*, pg. 528
BENTLEY TRUCK SERVICES, INC.; *U.S. Private*, pg. 528
BENZEL-BUSCH MOTOR CAR CORP.; *U.S. Private*, pg. 529
THE BERGE GROUP; *U.S. Private*, pg. 3993
BERGER CHEVROLET, INC.; *U.S. Private*, pg. 530
BERGER FAMILY DEALERSHIP; *U.S. Private*, pg. 530
BERGER MOTOR SALES INCORPORATED—See Young Automotive Group, Inc.; *U.S. Private*, pg. 4592
BERGEY'S CHEVROLET—See Bergeys Inc.; *U.S. Private*, pg. 531
BERGEYS INC.; *U.S. Private*, pg. 531
BERGLUND OAK RIDGE TOYOTA; *U.S. Private*, pg. 531
BERGSTROM CADILLAC OF MADISON—See Bergstrom Corp.; *U.S. Private*, pg. 531
BERGSTROM CORP.; *U.S. Private*, pg. 531
BERLIN CITY FORD, INC.—See Booth Creek Management Corporation; *U.S. Private*, pg. 617
BERLIN CITY'S CHEVROLET BUICK, INC.—See Booth Creek Management Corporation; *U.S. Private*, pg. 617
BERMAZ MOTOR SDN BHD—See Berjaya Corporation Berhad; *Int'l*, pg. 984
BERNARDI AUTOMALL TRUST; *U.S. Private*, pg. 536
BERNARDI HONDA; *U.S. Private*, pg. 536
BERNARDI'S HONDA; *U.S. Private*, pg. 536
BERTHOD MOTORS INC.; *U.S. Private*, pg. 539
BERT SMITH AUTOMOTIVE; *U.S. Private*, pg. 539
BERT SMITH OLDSMOBILE, INC.; *U.S. Private*, pg. 539
BERT WOLFE AUTOMOTIVE GROUP; *U.S. Private*, pg. 539
BERT WOLFE FORD; *U.S. Private*, pg. 539
BESHORE & KOLLER INC.; *U.S. Private*, pg. 541
BESSEY MOTOR SALES, INC.; *U.S. Private*, pg. 542
BEST CHEVROLET INC.; *U.S. Private*, pg. 542
BESTODECK LTD.; *Int'l*, pg. 1000
BETHESDA INVESTMENT HOLDING CO., INC.; *U.S. Private*, pg. 546
BETHESDA LUXURY IMPORTS, LLC—See AutoNation, Inc.; *U.S. Public*, pg. 233
BETTEN AUTO CENTER, INC.; *U.S. Private*, pg. 546
BETTENHAUSEN AUTOMOTIVE; *U.S. Private*, pg. 546
BETTEN IMPORTS; *U.S. Private*, pg. 546
BETULA CARS S.L.—See General Motors Company; *U.S. Public*, pg. 927
BEUCKMAN FORD INC.; *U.S. Private*, pg. 547
BEYER BROS. CORP.; *U.S. Private*, pg. 548
BEZEMA BUICK CORPORATION; *U.S. Private*, pg. 548
BHVT MOTORS INC.; *U.S. Private*, pg. 549
BIANCHI HONDA; *U.S. Private*, pg. 550

N.A.I.C.S. INDEX

441110 — NEW CAR DEALERS

BIENER AUTO GROUP, INC.; *U.S. Private*, pg. 551
BIG 2 TOYOTA; *U.S. Private*, pg. 552
BIG DEE AUTO SALES INC.; *U.S. Private*, pg. 553
BIGGER MITSUBISHI; *U.S. Private*, pg. 555
BIGGS PONTIAC; *U.S. Private*, pg. 555
BIG ISLAND TOYOTA INC—See David S. De Luz Sr Enterprises; *U.S. Private*, pg. 1171
BIG M FORD LINCOLN LTD.; *Int'l*, pg. 1021
BIG M ON DIXIE, LLC.; *U.S. Private*, pg. 553
BIG RED SPORTS IMPORTS, INC.; *U.S. Private*, pg. 554
BIG ROCK 2005 PTY LTD—See Eagers Automotive Limited; *Int'l*, pg. 2263
BIG ROCK PTY LTD—See Eagers Automotive Limited; *Int'l*, pg. 2263
BILCIRKELN MALMO AB—See General Motors Company; *U.S. Public*, pg. 926
BILIA EMOND LUXEMBOURG SA—See Bilia AB; *Int'l*, pg. 1029
BILIA GROUP GOTEBORG AB—See Bilia AB; *Int'l*, pg. 1029
BILL ALEXANDER FORD LINCOLN MERCURY, INC.; *U.S. Private*, pg. 556
BILL AYARES CHEVROLET, LLC—See AutoNation, Inc.; *U.S. Public*, pg. 233
BILL BARTH FORD, INC.; *U.S. Private*, pg. 556
BILL BLACK CHEVROLET CADILLAC INC.; *U.S. Private*, pg. 556
BILL BRITT MAZDA; *U.S. Private*, pg. 556
BILL BROWN FORD INC.—See Penske Automotive Group, Inc.; *U.S. Public*, pg. 1664
BILL BUCK CHEVROLET INC.; *U.S. Private*, pg. 556
BILL BUTLER CHRYSLER DODGE PLYMOUTH JEEP, INC.; *U.S. Private*, pg. 556
BILLCO MOTORS INC.; *U.S. Private*, pg. 559
BILL CURRIE FORD INC.; *U.S. Private*, pg. 556
BILL DELORD AUTOCENTER INC.; *U.S. Private*, pg. 556
BILL DODGE AUTO GROUP; *U.S. Private*, pg. 556
BILL GATTON ACURA MAZDA SATURN; *U.S. Private*, pg. 557
BILL GRAY VOLVO; *U.S. Private*, pg. 557
BILL HEARD ENTERPRISES, INC.; *U.S. Private*, pg. 557
BILL HESSER ENTERPRISES INC.; *U.S. Private*, pg. 557
BILL HOOD FORD INC.; *U.S. Private*, pg. 557
BILL HOUSTON FORD LTD.; *Int'l*, pg. 1030
BILL HOWICH CHRYSLER LTD.; *Int'l*, pg. 1030
BILLION HONDA OF IOWA CITY—See Billion Motors, Inc.; *U.S. Private*, pg. 559
BILLION MOTORS - CHRYSLER DODGE JEEP FIAT—See Billion Motors, Inc.; *U.S. Private*, pg. 559
BILLION MOTORS - GMC BUICK KIA—See Billion Motors, Inc.; *U.S. Private*, pg. 559
BILLION SOUTHTOWN, INC.—See Billion Motors, Inc.; *U.S. Private*, pg. 559
BILL JACOBS MOTORSPORT INC.; *U.S. Private*, pg. 557
BILL JARRETT FORD, INC.; *U.S. Private*, pg. 557
BILL LEWIS MOTORS INC.; *U.S. Private*, pg. 557
BILL LUKE CHRYSLER JEEP & DODGE, INC.; *U.S. Private*, pg. 557
BILL MACINTYRE CHEVROLET BUICK; *U.S. Private*, pg. 557
BILL MARSH AUTO MALL; *U.S. Private*, pg. 557
BILL MCCURLEY CHEVROLET; *U.S. Private*, pg. 557
BILL PAGE HONDA; *U.S. Private*, pg. 558
BILL PAGE IMPORTS INC.; *U.S. Private*, pg. 558
BILL PEARCE MOTORS INC.; *U.S. Private*, pg. 558
BILL PENNEY TOYOTA; *U.S. Private*, pg. 558
BILL RAPP SUPERSTORE; *U.S. Private*, pg. 558
BILL RAY NISSAN, INC.; *U.S. Private*, pg. 558
BILL ROBERTSON & SONS INCORPORATED; *U.S. Private*, pg. 558
BILL SEIDLE AUTOMOTIVE GROUP; *U.S. Private*, pg. 558
BILL SELIG FORD, INC.; *U.S. Private*, pg. 558
BILL SHULTZ CHEVROLET, INC.; *U.S. Private*, pg. 558
BILL SNETHKAMP INC.; *U.S. Private*, pg. 558
BILL SNETHKAMP LANSING DODGE—See Bill Snethkamp Inc.; *U.S. Private*, pg. 558
BILL SPURLOCK DODGE INC.; *U.S. Private*, pg. 558
BILL STASEK CHEVROLET; *U.S. Private*, pg. 558
BILL UTTER FORD; *U.S. Private*, pg. 558
BILL WALSH AUTOMOTIVE GROUP; *U.S. Private*, pg. 558
BILL WALSH FORD LINCOLN MERCURY KIA—See Bill Walsh Automotive Group; *U.S. Private*, pg. 558
BILL WHITE VOLKSWAGEN AUDI INC.; *U.S. Private*, pg. 558
BILL WRIGHT TOYOTA; *U.S. Private*, pg. 558
BILLY BENDER CHEVROLET INC.; *U.S. Private*, pg. 559
BILLY HOWELL FORD-LINCOLN; *U.S. Private*, pg. 559
BISMARCK HONDA NISSAN HYUNDAI; *U.S. Private*, pg. 566
BLADE CHEVROLET; *U.S. Private*, pg. 577
BLUEBERRY FORD MERCURY INC.; *U.S. Private*, pg. 596
BLUE MOUNTAIN CHRYSLER; *Int'l*, pg. 1069
BLUE STAR FORD LINCOLN SALES LTD; *Int'l*, pg. 1069
BMW HUNGARY KFT.—See Bayerische Motoren Werke Aktiengesellschaft; *Int'l*, pg. 911
BMW NORTHWEST INC.; *U.S. Private*, pg. 601
BMW OF AUSTIN; *U.S. Private*, pg. 601
BMW OF BAYSIDE; *U.S. Private*, pg. 601
BMW OF DARIEN; *U.S. Private*, pg. 601

BMW OF EL PASO—See Group 1 Automotive, Inc.; *U.S. Public*, pg. 970
BMW OF ESCONDIDO; *U.S. Private*, pg. 601
BMW OF MACON; *U.S. Private*, pg. 601
BMW OF MANHATTAN INC.—See Bayerische Motoren Werke Aktiengesellschaft; *Int'l*, pg. 912
BMW OF SILVER SPRING—See Atlantic Automotive Corp.; *U.S. Private*, pg. 371
BMW TORONTO; *Int'l*, pg. 1078
BOARDWALK VOLKSWAGEN; *U.S. Private*, pg. 602
BOB ALLEN-CHRYSLER PLYMOUTH DODGE; *U.S. Private*, pg. 603
BOB ALLEN FORD; *U.S. Private*, pg. 603
BOB ALLEN MOTOR MALL; *U.S. Private*, pg. 603
BOB BAKER AUTO GROUP; *U.S. Private*, pg. 603
BOB BARBOUR, INC.; *U.S. Private*, pg. 603
BOBB AUTOMOTIVE INC.; *U.S. Private*, pg. 606
BOB BOAST VOLKSWAGEN; *U.S. Private*, pg. 603
BOB-BOYD FORD MAZDA DODGE INC.—See Bob-Boyd Lincoln of Columbus; *U.S. Private*, pg. 606
BOB-BOYD LINCOLN OF COLUMBUS; *U.S. Private*, pg. 606
BOB BRADY DODGE INC.; *U.S. Private*, pg. 603
BOB BROCKLAND BUICK GMC; *U.S. Private*, pg. 603
BOB BROWN CHEVROLET, INC.; *U.S. Private*, pg. 603
BOBBY FORD INC.—See Sonic Automotive, Inc.; *U.S. Public*, pg. 1902
BOBBY LAYMAN CADILLAC GMC, INC.; *U.S. Private*, pg. 606
BOBBY MURRAY TOYOTA; *U.S. Private*, pg. 606
BOBBY RAHAL AUTO GROUP; *U.S. Private*, pg. 606
BOBBY RAHAL HONDA; *U.S. Private*, pg. 606
BOB CALDWELL CHRYSLER JEEP DODGE RAM; *U.S. Private*, pg. 604
BOB DAVIDSON FORD LINCOLN; *U.S. Private*, pg. 604
BOB DUNN HYUNDAI SUBARU; *U.S. Private*, pg. 604
BOB FISHER CHEVROLET, INC.; *U.S. Private*, pg. 604
BOB GRIMM CHEVROLET INC.; *U.S. Private*, pg. 604
BOB HEMBREE MOTOR COMPANY INC.; *U.S. Private*, pg. 604
BOB HOOK CHEVROLET; *U.S. Private*, pg. 604
BOB HOWARD CHEVROLET, INC.—See Group 1 Automotive, Inc.; *U.S. Public*, pg. 971
BOB HOWARD DODGE, INC.—See Group 1 Automotive, Inc.; *U.S. Public*, pg. 971
BOB HOWARD DOWNTOWN DODGE INC.; *U.S. Private*, pg. 604
BOB HOWARD MOTORS, INC.—See Group 1 Automotive, Inc.; *U.S. Public*, pg. 971
BOB HOWARD NISSAN, INC.—See Group 1 Automotive, Inc.; *U.S. Public*, pg. 971
BOB KING AUTO MALL; *U.S. Private*, pg. 604
BOB KING, INC.; *U.S. Private*, pg. 604
BOB MASSIE TOYOTA; *U.S. Private*, pg. 604
BOB MAXEY FORD, INC.; *U.S. Private*, pg. 604
BOB MOORE CADILLAC INC.; *U.S. Private*, pg. 604
BOB MOORE DODGE, LLC.; *U.S. Private*, pg. 604
BOB NEILL INC.; *U.S. Private*, pg. 604
BOB NOVICK AUTO MALL; *U.S. Private*, pg. 604
BOB RICHARDS, INC.; *U.S. Private*, pg. 605
BOB RIDINGS FORD INC.; *U.S. Private*, pg. 605
BOB ROHRMAN MOTORS INCORPORATED; *U.S. Private*, pg. 605
BOB ROSS BUICK, INC.; *U.S. Private*, pg. 605
BOB SAKS BUICK—See Farmington Hills Holding Company; *U.S. Private*, pg. 1480
BOB SIGHT FORD INC.; *U.S. Private*, pg. 605
BOB STALL CHEVROLET; *U.S. Private*, pg. 605
BOB SWOPE FORD, INC.; *U.S. Private*, pg. 605
BOB TAYLOR CHEVROLET INC.; *U.S. Private*, pg. 605
BOB TOMES FORD, INC.; *U.S. Private*, pg. 605
BOB UTTER FORD; *U.S. Private*, pg. 605
BOB WONDRIES FORD; *U.S. Private*, pg. 605
BOB ZIMMERMAN FORD INC.; *U.S. Private*, pg. 605
BOCKER CHEVROLET BUICK GMC CADILLAC; *U.S. Private*, pg. 606
BODWELL CHRYSLER-JEEP-DODGE; *U.S. Private*, pg. 608
BOERNER TRUCK CENTER; *U.S. Private*, pg. 609
BOHN BROTHERS TOYOTA; *U.S. Private*, pg. 609
THE BOHN ZONE; *U.S. Private*, pg. 3995
BOLLES MOTORS, INC.; *U.S. Private*, pg. 610
BOLTON FORD INC.; *U.S. Private*, pg. 611
BOMMARITO AUTOMOTIVE GROUP; *U.S. Private*, pg. 612
BOMMARITO CHEVROLET MAZDA INC.; *U.S. Private*, pg. 612
BONANDER PONTIAC INC.; *U.S. Private*, pg. 613
BONDYS FORD INC.; *U.S. Private*, pg. 613
BONES TOYOTA, INC.; *U.S. Private*, pg. 614
BONIFACE-HIERS INSURANCE AGENCY, INC.; *U.S. Private*, pg. 614
BONNER CHEVROLET CO. INC.; *U.S. Private*, pg. 614
BONNEVILLE & SON INC.; *U.S. Private*, pg. 614
BOONE FORD LINCOLN MERCURY, INC.; *U.S. Private*, pg. 616
BOOSE CHEVROLET CO., INC.; *U.S. Private*, pg. 616
BOOTH & LADUKE MOTORS, INC.; *U.S. Private*, pg. 616
BORCHERDING BUICK GMC; *U.S. Private*, pg. 617

THE BORDER COURT INC.—See The Schafer Company Inc.; *U.S. Private*, pg. 4114
BORDER INTERNATIONAL; *U.S. Private*, pg. 617
BORDER INTERNATIONAL TRUCKS; *U.S. Private*, pg. 617
BORGMAN FORD MAZDA; *U.S. Private*, pg. 618
BORMAN MOTOR COMPANY; *U.S. Private*, pg. 619
BORTON VOLVO, INC.; *U.S. Private*, pg. 619
BOSAK MOTORS OF HIGHLAND INC.; *U.S. Private*, pg. 619
BOSCH MOTORS; *U.S. Private*, pg. 619
BOUCHER CHEVROLET, INC.; *U.S. Private*, pg. 623
BOULDER CHEVROLET BUICK, INC.; *U.S. Private*, pg. 623
BOULEVARD AUTO SALES INC.; *U.S. Private*, pg. 623
BOURNIVAL INC.; *U.S. Private*, pg. 624
BOVA FRANCE; *Int'l*, pg. 1123
BOWDEN FORD LINCOLN MERCURY, INC.; *U.S. Private*, pg. 625
BOWEN SCARFF FORD SALES, INC.; *U.S. Private*, pg. 625
BOWKER BLACKBURN LTD.; *Int'l*, pg. 1124
BOYD AUTOMOTIVE; *U.S. Private*, pg. 627
BOYD CHEVROLET INC.; *U.S. Private*, pg. 627
BOYD COUNTY FORD; *U.S. Private*, pg. 627
BOYLAND HONDA; *U.S. Private*, pg. 628
BOYLE BUICK GMC; *U.S. Private*, pg. 628
BOYLES MOTOR SALES INCORPORATED; *U.S. Private*, pg. 628
BOZARD FORD CO.; *U.S. Private*, pg. 629
BOZEMAN FORD; *U.S. Private*, pg. 629
BRAD DEERY MOTORS, INC.; *U.S. Private*, pg. 630
BRADFORD FAIRWAY SALES & LEASING INC.; *U.S. Private*, pg. 631
BRADLEY CHEVROLET, INC.; *U.S. Private*, pg. 632
BRADLEY INVESTMENTS, INC.; *U.S. Private*, pg. 633
BRADSHAW AUTOMOTIVE GROUP, INC.; *U.S. Private*, pg. 633
BRAEGER CHEVROLET INC.—See Braeger Company of Wisconsin Inc.; *U.S. Private*, pg. 633
BRAEGER COMPANY OF WISCONSIN INC.; *U.S. Private*, pg. 633
BRAMAN CADILLAC INC.—See Braman Motors, Inc.; *U.S. Private*, pg. 635
BRAMAN IMPORTS, INC.; *U.S. Private*, pg. 635
BRAMAN MOTORS, INC.; *U.S. Private*, pg. 635
BRANDON HONDA—See Morgan Auto Group, LLC; *U.S. Private*, pg. 2783
BRANHAVEN CHRYSLER JEEP DODGE RAM; *U.S. Private*, pg. 639
BRASSO NISSAN; *Int'l*, pg. 1140
BRAVO CHEVROLET CADILLAC; *U.S. Private*, pg. 641
BREAKAWAY HONDA; *U.S. Private*, pg. 642
BREDEMANN CHEVROLET INC.; *U.S. Private*, pg. 644
BRENHAM CHRYSLER JEEP DODGE; *U.S. Private*, pg. 645
BRENTRIDGE FORD SALES; *Int'l*, pg. 1150
BRIAN BEMIS AUTO WORLD, INC.—See Brian Bemis Automotive Group, Ltd.; *U.S. Private*, pg. 647
BRIAN BEMIS, INC.—See Brian Bemis Automotive Group, Ltd.; *U.S. Private*, pg. 647
BRIARWOOD FORD, INC.; *U.S. Private*, pg. 648
BRICKNER CHRYSLER CENTER—See Brickner Motors, Inc.; *U.S. Private*, pg. 648
BRICKNER MOTORS, INC.; *U.S. Private*, pg. 648
BRICKNERS OF ANTIGO—See Brickner Motors, Inc.; *U.S. Private*, pg. 648
BRICKNER—See Brickner Motors, Inc.; *U.S. Private*, pg. 648
BRIEN MOTORS INC.; *U.S. Private*, pg. 650
BRIGHTON FORD-MERCURY INC.; *U.S. Private*, pg. 652
BRIGHTON MAZDA; *U.S. Private*, pg. 652
BRINSON AUTO GROUP; *U.S. Private*, pg. 655
BRISTOL HONDA—See Honda Motor Co., Ltd.; *Int'l*, pg. 3462
BRITISH MOTOR CAR DISTRIBUTORS LTD.; *U.S. Private*, pg. 657
BROADWAY AUTOMOTIVE-GREEN BAY, INC.—See Broadway Enterprises, Inc.; *U.S. Private*, pg. 660
BROCK FORD SALES; *Int'l*, pg. 1172
BRODIE BUICK MITSUBISHI KIA; *U.S. Private*, pg. 661
BRONCO MOTORS INC.; *U.S. Private*, pg. 662
BRONDES FORD TOLEDO; *U.S. Private*, pg. 662
BRONX HONDA; *U.S. Private*, pg. 662
BROOKDALE MOTOR SALES INC—See Luther Holding Company; *U.S. Private*, pg. 2517
BROOKLYN FORD; *U.S. Private*, pg. 663
BROOKS BIDDLE AUTOMOTIVE; *U.S. Private*, pg. 664
BROOME OLDSMOBILE CADILLAC INC.; *U.S. Private*, pg. 665
BROUGHTONS OF CHELTENHAM LTD—See Berjaya Corporation Berhad; *Int'l*, pg. 983
BROWN AUTOMOTIVE GROUP, INC.; *U.S. Private*, pg. 666
BROWN BROS. CADILLAC, INC.; *U.S. Private*, pg. 666
BROWN BROS FORD LINCOLN SALES & SERVICE; *Int'l*, pg. 1198
BROWN & BROWN CHEVROLET, INC.—See AutoNation, Inc.; *U.S. Public*, pg. 233
BROWN & BROWN CHEVROLET - SUPERSTITION

441110 — NEW CAR DEALERS

SPRINGS, LLC—See AutoNation, Inc.; *U.S. Public,* pg. 233
BROWN & BROWN NISSAN, INC.—See AutoNation, Inc.; *U.S. Public,* pg. 233
BROWN & BROWN NISSAN, INC.—See AutoNation, Inc.; *U.S. Public,* pg. 233
BROWN & BROWN NISSAN MESA, LLC—See AutoNation, Inc.; *U.S. Public,* pg. 233
BROWN & BROWN NISSAN MESA, LLC—See AutoNation, Inc.; *U.S. Public,* pg. 233
BROWN CHEVROLET CO. INC.; *U.S. Private,* pg. 667
BROWN IMPORTS INC.; *U.S. Private,* pg. 667
BROWNING MAZDA—See Dick Browning, Inc.; *U.S. Private,* pg. 1225
BROWN MOTORS, INC.; *U.S. Private,* pg. 668
BROWN MOTORS INC.; *U.S. Private,* pg. 668
BROWN PONTIAC AUTOMOTIVE GROUP LP; *U.S. Private,* pg. 668
BROWN'S AUTOMOTIVE GROUP LTD—See Safford Automotive Group; *U.S. Private,* pg. 3525
BROWNS' CHEVROLET; *Int'l,* pg. 1199
BROWN'S FAIRFAX NISSAN; *U.S. Private,* pg. 669
BROWN'S HONDA CITY—See Safford Automotive Group; *U.S. Private,* pg. 3525
BROWNS JEEP EAGLE CHRYSLER PLYMOUTH; *U.S. Private,* pg. 669
BROWN'S RICHMOND VOLKSWAGEN—See Safford Automotive Group; *U.S. Private,* pg. 3525
BROWNS SALES & LEASING INC.; *U.S. Private,* pg. 670
BROWN'S TOYOTA—See Safford Automotive Group; *U.S. Private,* pg. 3525
BROWN & WOOD, INC.; *U.S. Private,* pg. 666
BRUCE CAVENAUGH'S AUTOMART; *U.S. Private,* pg. 670
BRUCE LOWRIE CHEVROLET INC.; *U.S. Private,* pg. 671
BRUNER AUTO GROUP—See Bruner Motors, Inc.; *U.S. Private,* pg. 672
BRUNER MOTORS, INC.; *U.S. Private,* pg. 672
BRUNSWICK AUTO MART, INC.; *U.S. Private,* pg. 672
BRYAN CHEVROLET INC.; *U.S. Private,* pg. 673
BRYAN EASLER TOYOTA; *U.S. Private,* pg. 673
BRYAN HONDA-FAYETTEVILLE; *U.S. Private,* pg. 673
BRYAN IMPORTS INC.; *U.S. Private,* pg. 673
BS AUTO PRAHA SRO—See General Motors Company; *U.S. Public,* pg. 926
BUBBA OUSTALET INC.; *U.S. Private,* pg. 676
BUCKEYE FORD INC.; *U.S. Private,* pg. 677
BUCKEYE NISSAN INC.; *U.S. Private,* pg. 677
BUD BROWN VOLKSWAGEN; *U.S. Private,* pg. 678
BUD CLARY CHEVROLET CADILLAC INC.; *U.S. Private,* pg. 679
BUD CLARY TOYOTA OF YAKIMA; *U.S. Private,* pg. 679
BUD DAVIS CADILLAC, INC.; *U.S. Private,* pg. 679
BUDD BAER; *U.S. Private,* pg. 679
BUDDS' BMW; *Int'l,* pg. 1210
BUD KOUTS CHEVROLET COMPANY; *U.S. Private,* pg. 679
BUD SHELL FORD INC.; *U.S. Private,* pg. 679
BUENA PARK LUXURY IMPORTS, INC.—See AutoNation, Inc.; *U.S. Public,* pg. 233
BUERKLE AUTOMOTIVE GROUP; *U.S. Private,* pg. 680
BUERKLE HONDA—See Buerkle Automotive Group; *U.S. Private,* pg. 680
BUERKLE HYUNDAI—See Buerkle Automotive Group; *U.S. Private,* pg. 680
BUFFALO TRUCK CENTER; *U.S. Private,* pg. 681
BUFF WHELAN CHEVROLET & GEO, INC.; *U.S. Private,* pg. 680
BUHLER FORD, INC.; *U.S. Private,* pg. 681
BUICK GMC OF BEAVERTON—See Lithia Motors, Inc.; *U.S. Public,* pg. 1321
BULL MOTORS, LLC—See AutoNation, Inc.; *U.S. Public,* pg. 233
BURDICK TOYOTA; *U.S. Private,* pg. 686
BURGER CHRYSLER-JEEP; *U.S. Private,* pg. 686
BURIEN TOYOTA; *U.S. Private,* pg. 687
BURKE BROTHERS INC.; *U.S. Private,* pg. 688
BURLINGTON MOTORS INC.; *U.S. Private,* pg. 689
BURNS BUICK-GMC-HYUNDAI-HONDA; *U.S. Private,* pg. 691
BURNS FORD INC.; *U.S. Private,* pg. 691
BURTIS MOTOR COMPANY, INC.; *U.S. Private,* pg. 692
BURTNESS CHEVROLET, INC.; *U.S. Private,* pg. 692
BURTNESS CHEVROLET OF WHITEWATER—See Burtness Chevrolet, Inc.; *U.S. Private,* pg. 693
BUSH AUTO PLACE INC.; *U.S. Private,* pg. 693
BUSH INC.; *U.S. Private,* pg. 694
BUSSEYS AND SABBERTON BROS. LTD.; *Int'l,* pg. 1229
BUSS FORD LLC; *U.S. Private,* pg. 696
BUSS FORD SALES; *U.S. Private,* pg. 696
BUTCH OUSTALET CHEVROLET CADILLAC; *U.S. Private,* pg. 696
BUTCH OUSTALET FORD LINCOLN; *U.S. Private,* pg. 696
BUTLER AUTOMOTIVE GROUP INC.; *U.S. Private,* pg. 697
BUTTON MOTORS, INC.; *U.S. Private,* pg. 698
BYERLY FORD-NISSAN INC.; *U.S. Private,* pg. 700
BYTEK AUTOMOBILES INC.; *Int'l,* pg. 1237
CABRAL WESTERN MOTORS, INC.; *U.S. Private,* pg. 711

CADILLAC EUROPE GMBH—See General Motors Company; *U.S. Public,* pg. 923
CADILLAC OF ARLINGTON—See Group 1 Automotive, Inc.; *U.S. Public,* pg. 971
CADILLAC OF GREENWICH, INC.—See General Motors Company; *U.S. Public,* pg. 923
CADILLAC OF PORTLAND LLOYD CENTER, LLC—See Lithia Motors, Inc.; *U.S. Public,* pg. 1321
CAFFYNS PLC; *Int'l,* pg. 1250
CAINS INCORPORATED; *U.S. Private,* pg. 714
CAIN TOYOTA; *U.S. Private,* pg. 714
CALDWELL IMPORTS INC.; *U.S. Private,* pg. 716
CALESA MOTORS INC.; *U.S. Private,* pg. 717
CALKINS GMC; *U.S. Private,* pg. 721
CALSTAR MOTORS INC—See Parkley Holding Inc.; *U.S. Private,* pg. 3098
CAMBRIA AUTOMOBILES PLC; *Int'l,* pg. 1269
CAMBRIAN FORD SALES INC; *Int'l,* pg. 1269
CAMBRIDGE PLYMOUTH CHRYSLER LTD; *Int'l,* pg. 1269
CAM CLARK FORD; *Int'l,* pg. 1266
CAMCO ACURA; *Int'l,* pg. 1270
CAMELBACK FORD; *U.S. Private,* pg. 728
CAMINO REAL CHEVROLET; *U.S. Private,* pg. 729
CAMP AUTOMOTIVE, INC.—See Lithia Motors, Inc.; *U.S. Public,* pg. 1321
CAMPBELL CHRYSLER JEEP DODGE RAM; *U.S. Private,* pg. 730
CAMPBELL FORD; *Int'l,* pg. 1274
CAMPBELL NELSON VOLKSWAGEN; *U.S. Private,* pg. 730
CAN-BOW MOTORS LTD.; *Int'l,* pg. 1276
CANDY FORD, INC.; *U.S. Private,* pg. 734
CANNON AUTOMOTIVE GROUP, INC.; *U.S. Private,* pg. 734
CANSO FORD SALES; *Int'l,* pg. 1298
CANTIN CHEVROLET, INC.; *U.S. Private,* pg. 735
CANTON MOTOR SALES, INC.; *U.S. Private,* pg. 735
CANYON CREEK TOYOTA INC.; *Int'l,* pg. 1300
CAPITAL AUTOMOBILE COMPANY; *U.S. Private,* pg. 738
CAPITAL BUICK GMC; *U.S. Private,* pg. 739
CAPITAL CHEVROLET, INC.—See Capital Ford Inc.; *U.S. Private,* pg. 740
CAPITAL FORD INC.; *U.S. Private,* pg. 740
CAPITAL FORD LINCOLN WINNIPEG; *Int'l,* pg. 1311
CAPITAL MOTOR SALES INC.; *U.S. Private,* pg. 741
CAPITOL AUTO GROUP; *U.S. Private,* pg. 742
CAPITOL SUBURU—See Capitol Auto Group, Inc.; *U.S. Private,* pg. 743
CAPITOL VOLKSWAGEN, INC.; *U.S. Private,* pg. 745
CAPPO MANAGEMENT II, INC.—See Victory Automotive Group, Inc.; *U.S. Private,* pg. 4378
CAPPO MANAGEMENT, INC.—See Victory Automotive Group, Inc.; *U.S. Private,* pg. 4378
CAPPO MANAGEMENT VII, INC.—See Victory Automotive Group, Inc.; *U.S. Private,* pg. 4378
CAPPO MANAGEMENT VI, INC.—See Victory Automotive Group, Inc.; *U.S. Private,* pg. 4378
CAPPO MANAGEMENT XVII, INC.—See Victory Automotive Group, Inc.; *U.S. Private,* pg. 4378
CAPPO MANAGEMENT XXIII, INC.—See Victory Automotive Group, Inc.; *U.S. Private,* pg. 4378
CARASSO MOTORS LTD.; *Int'l,* pg. 1319
CARBIZ AUTOS; *U.S. Private,* pg. 748
CARBONE AUTO GROUP; *U.S. Private,* pg. 748
CAR CITY CHRYSLER; *U.S. Private,* pg. 747
CARDENAS MOTORS, INC.; *U.S. Private,* pg. 749
CARDIFF CAR CITY PTY LIMITED; *Int'l,* pg. 1321
CARDINAL CHEVROLET CADILLAC; *U.S. Private,* pg. 750
CARDINALE AUTOMOTIVE GROUP; *U.S. Private,* pg. 751
CARGIANT LTD.; *Int'l,* pg. 1325
CARIBBEAN AUTO MART INC.; *U.S. Private,* pg. 760
CARIBOO CHEVROLET BUICK GMC; *Int'l,* pg. 1330
CARL BLACK AUTOMOTIVE GROUP, LLC; *U.S. Private,* pg. 762
CARL BLACK CHEVROLET CO., INC.; *U.S. Private,* pg. 762
CARL BLACK OF ORLANDO, LLC—See Carl Black Automotive Group, LLC; *U.S. Private,* pg. 762
CARL GREGORY CHRYSLER; *U.S. Private,* pg. 762
CARL HOGAN AUTOMOTIVE, INC.; *U.S. Private,* pg. 762
CARLIN AUCTION SERVICES (NSW) PTY. LTD.—See Eagers Automotive Limited; *Int'l,* pg. 2264
CARLIN AUCTION SERVICES (QLD) PTY. LTD.—See Eagers Automotive Limited; *Int'l,* pg. 2264
CARLING MOTORS CO. LIMITED; *Int'l,* pg. 1338
CARLINS AUTOMOTIVE AUCTIONEERS (WA) PTY. LTD.—See Eagers Automotive Limited; *Int'l,* pg. 2264
CARLISLE MOTORS, LLC—See AutoNation, Inc.; *U.S. Public,* pg. 233
CARLSEN VOLVO; *U.S. Private,* pg. 764
CARLYLE MOTOR PRODUCTS LTD; *Int'l,* pg. 1341
CARMACK CAR CAPITOL INC.; *U.S. Private,* pg. 766
CARMAX, INC.; *U.S. Public,* pg. 437
CARMENITA FORD TRUCK SALES INC.; *U.S. Private,* pg. 766
CAROFFER, LLC—See CarGurus, Inc.; *U.S. Public,* pg. 435
CAROLINA COACH & MARINE; *U.S. Private,* pg. 767

CORPORATE AFFILIATIONS

CAROUSEL MOTOR GROUP—See Pohlad Companies; *U.S. Private,* pg. 3220
CARR AUTO GROUP; *U.S. Private,* pg. 771
CARR CHEVROLET, INC.; *U.S. Private,* pg. 771
CARR ENTERPRISES INC.; *U.S. Private,* pg. 771
CARRIAGE CORPORATION; *U.S. Private,* pg. 771
CARRIKER FORD INC.; *U.S. Private,* pg. 772
CARROLL SOUTH SHORE MOTORS INC.; *Int'l,* pg. 1346
CARSDIRECT.COM, INC.—See KKR & Co. Inc.; *U.S. Public,* pg. 1253
CARSOME SDN. BHD.; *Int'l,* pg. 1347
CARSON CITY TOYOTA; *U.S. Private,* pg. 774
CARSON DODGE CHRYSLER, INC.; *U.S. Private,* pg. 774
CARSON TOYOTA—See Fletcher Jones Management Group, Inc.; *U.S. Private,* pg. 1542
CAR STORE INC.; *U.S. Private,* pg. 747
CARSTORY, LLC—See Vroom, Inc.; *U.S. Public,* pg. 2312
CARTER CHEVROLET CO.; *U.S. Private,* pg. 775
CARTER CHEVROLET, INC.; *U.S. Private,* pg. 775
CARTER DODGE CHRYSLER LTD; *Int'l,* pg. 1348
CARTER MOTOR CARS LTD; *Int'l,* pg. 1348
CARTER MOTORS INC.; *U.S. Private,* pg. 776
CARTER OF MANCHESTER; *U.S. Private,* pg. 776
CARTRADE TECH LTD.; *Int'l,* pg. 1348
CARWELL, LLC—See AutoNation, Inc.; *U.S. Public,* pg. 233
CARWELL, LLC—See AutoNation, Inc.; *U.S. Public,* pg. 234
CASA AUTO GROUP; *U.S. Private,* pg. 777
CASA AUTOMOTIVE GROUP; *U.S. Private,* pg. 777
CASA CHRYSLER JEEP MITSUBISHI; *U.S. Private,* pg. 778
CASA FORD INC.; *U.S. Private,* pg. 778
CASCADE AUTO GROUP, LTD.; *U.S. Private,* pg. 778
CASEY AUTO GROUP, INC.; *U.S. Private,* pg. 782
CASTLE BUICK PONTIAC GMC INC.; *U.S. Private,* pg. 784
CASTLE CHEVROLET, INC.; *U.S. Private,* pg. 784
CASTLE HONDA; *U.S. Private,* pg. 785
CAVALCADE FORD LINCOLN SALES; *Int'l,* pg. 1361
CAVALIER FORD INC.; *U.S. Private,* pg. 794
CAVE CITY CHEVROLET/BUICK; *U.S. Private,* pg. 795
CAVENDER AUTO GROUP; *U.S. Private,* pg. 795
CAVENDER BROTHERS MANAGEMENT, LTD.; *U.S. Private,* pg. 795
CAVENDER BUICK COMPANY INC.; *U.S. Private,* pg. 795
CAVENDER CADILLAC; *U.S. Private,* pg. 795
CAWOOD AUTO COMPANY; *U.S. Private,* pg. 795
C & C FORD SALES, INCORPORATED; *U.S. Private,* pg. 701
CCS GROUP INC.; *U.S. Private,* pg. 801
CEDARBRAE VOLKSWAGEN LTD; *Int'l,* pg. 1388
CELEBRITY AUTO GROUP; *U.S. Private,* pg. 806
CELEBRITY FORD OF TOMS RIVER—See Celebrity Motor Car Company; *U.S. Private,* pg. 806
CELEBRITY MOTOR CAR COMPANY; *U.S. Private,* pg. 806
CELIK MOTOR TICARET A.S.—See AG Anadolu Grubu Holding A.S.; *Int'l,* pg. 197
CENTAUR IMPORT MOTORS (1977) LTD.; *Int'l,* pg. 1402
CENTENNIAL AUTOMOTIVE, LLC—See AutoNation, Inc.; *U.S. Public,* pg. 234
CENTER SUBARU—See GMST, LLC; *U.S. Private,* pg. 1723
CENTRAL BUICK GMC OF NORWOOD; *U.S. Private,* pg. 819
CENTRAL CADILLAC; *U.S. Private,* pg. 819
CENTRAL CHEVROLET COMPANY INC.; *U.S. Private,* pg. 819
CENTRAL CHRYSLER JEEP DODGE; *U.S. Private,* pg. 819
CENTRAL MAINE MOTORS AUTO GROUP; *U.S. Private,* pg. 822
CENTRAL STATES BUS SALES INC.; *U.S. Private,* pg. 825
CENTRE STATE INTERNATIONAL TRUCKS; *U.S. Private,* pg. 829
CENTRE VEHICULES INDUSTRIELS; *Int'l,* pg. 1411
CENTURY III CHEVY; *U.S. Private,* pg. 833
CERRITOS BODY WORKS, INC.—See AutoNation, Inc.; *U.S. Public,* pg. 234
CERRITOS DODGE CHRYSLER JEEP—See Dick Browning, Inc.; *U.S. Private,* pg. 1225
CERRITOS FORD, INC.—See The Conant Auto Retail Group; *U.S. Private,* pg. 4013
CERRITOS INFINITI; *U.S. Private,* pg. 841
CERRITOS NISSAN; *U.S. Private,* pg. 841
C.F. SCHWARTZ MOTOR COMPANY, INC.; *U.S. Private,* pg. 707
CHAMPION CHEVROLET INC.; *U.S. Private,* pg. 846
CHAMPION CHEVROLET, LLC—See AutoNation, Inc.; *U.S. Public,* pg. 234
CHAMPION FORD, INC.—See AutoNation, Inc.; *U.S. Public,* pg. 234
CHAMPION PORSCHE; *U.S. Private,* pg. 846
CHAMPLAIN MOTORS LTD.; *Int'l,* pg. 1440
CHANDLER COLLISION, INC.—See AutoNation, Inc.; *U.S. Public,* pg. 234
CHANDLERS GARAGE (BRIGHTON) LIMITED—See Group 1 Automotive, Inc.; *U.S. Public,* pg. 971
CHANDLERS GARAGE WORTHING LIMITED—See Group 1 Automotive, Inc.; *U.S. Public,* pg. 971

N.A.I.C.S. INDEX

441110 — NEW CAR DEALERS

CHANGSHA MEIDONG LEXUS AUTO SALES & SERVICES CO., LTD.—See China MeiDong Auto Holdings Limited; *Int'l*, pg. 1519
CHANGZHI BAOZEN LUFU AUTOMOBILE SALES AND SERVICES CO., LTD.—See China Yongda Automobiles Services Holdings Limited; *Int'l*, pg. 1564
CHAPMAN BMW ON CAMELBACK; *U.S. Private*, pg. 849
CHAPMAN CHRYSLER JEEP; *U.S. Private*, pg. 849
CHAPMAN DODGE CHRYSLER JEEP RAM; *U.S. Private*, pg. 849
CHAPMAN FORD—See Chapman Automotive Group LLC; *U.S. Private*, pg. 849
CHARAPP FORD NORTH; *U.S. Private*, pg. 850
CHARLES DAHER'S COMMONWEALTH MOTORS; *U.S. Private*, pg. 851
CHARLES GABUS FORD, INC.; *U.S. Private*, pg. 852
CHARLESGLEN LTD.; *Int'l*, pg. 1450
CHARLES RIVER SAAB—See Village Automotive Group; *U.S. Private*, pg. 4383
CHARLIE HILLARD, INC.—See AutoNation, Inc.; *U.S. Public*, pg. 234
CHARLIE HILLARD, INC.—See AutoNation, Inc.; *U.S. Public*, pg. 234
CHARLIE'S DODGE, INC.; *U.S. Private*, pg. 857
CHARLIE'S MOTOR MALL INC.; *U.S. Private*, pg. 857
CHARLIE THOMAS CHEVROLET, LTD.—See AutoNation, Inc.; *U.S. Public*, pg. 234
CHARLIE THOMAS COURTESY FORD, LTD.—See AutoNation, Inc.; *U.S. Public*, pg. 234
CHARLIE THOMAS FORD, LTD.—See AutoNation, Inc.; *U.S. Public*, pg. 234
CHARLIE THOMAS FORD, LTD.—See AutoNation, Inc.; *U.S. Public*, pg. 234
CHARRIER SA; *Int'l*, pg. 1454
CHARTRAND FORD; *Int'l*, pg. 1456
CHARTRES POIDS LOURDS (LECHEVALIER-DOURS) S.A.; *Int'l*, pg. 1456
CHASSAY AUTOMOBILES SAS; *Int'l*, pg. 1457
CHATHAM MOTOR SALES, INC.; *U.S. Private*, pg. 868
CHECKERED FLAG MOTOR CAR CO.; *U.S. Private*, pg. 869
CHENGDE MEIBAOHANG AUTO SALES & SERVICES CO., LTD.—See China MeiDong Auto Holdings Limited; *Int'l*, pg. 1519
CHERNER AUTOMOTIVE GROUP; *U.S. Private*, pg. 873
CHERRY CAPITAL CADILLAC SUBARU, LLC.; *U.S. Private*, pg. 874
CHERRY HILL IMPORTS CORP—See HSF Enterprises Inc.; *U.S. Private*, pg. 1999
CHESROWN CHEVROLET, LLC—See AutoNation, Inc.; *U.S. Public*, pg. 234
CHESROWN COLLISION CENTER, INC.—See AutoNation, Inc.; *U.S. Public*, pg. 234
CHEVALIER AUTOMOBILES INC.—See Chevalier International Holdings Limited; *Int'l*, pg. 1473
CHEVROLET 21, INC.; *U.S. Private*, pg. 876
CHEVROLET-BUICK OF QUINCY; *U.S. Private*, pg. 876
CHEVROLET CENTER INC.; *U.S. Private*, pg. 876
CHEVROLET FINLAND OY—See General Motors Company; *U.S. Public*, pg. 927
CHEVROLET OF BOAZ, INC.—See Alexander Automotive; *U.S. Private*, pg. 163
CHEVROLET OF MONTEBELLO; *U.S. Private*, pg. 876
CHEVROLET OF NOVATO, INC.—See General Motors Company; *U.S. Public*, pg. 923
CHEVROLET OF WOOSTER; *U.S. Private*, pg. 876
CHEVROLET OTOMOTIV TICARET LIMITED SIRKETI—See General Motors Company; *U.S. Public*, pg. 923
CHEVROLET SALES INDIA PRIVATE LTD.—See General Motors Company; *U.S. Public*, pg. 923
CHEVROLET SVERIGE AB—See General Motors Company; *U.S. Public*, pg. 926
CHEVROLET WORLD, INC.—See AutoNation, Inc.; *U.S. Public*, pg. 234
CHEVROLET WORLD, INC.—See AutoNation, Inc.; *U.S. Public*, pg. 234
CHEVY CHASE CARS; *U.S. Private*, pg. 876
CHICO NISSAN, INC.; *U.S. Private*, pg. 880
CHILDRE NISSAN, INC.; *U.S. Private*, pg. 883
CHINA RUNDONG AUTO GROUP LIMITED—See Greenland Holdings Corporation Limited; *Int'l*, pg. 3075
CHINA YONGDA AUTOMOBILES SERVICES HOLDINGS LIMITED; *Int'l*, pg. 1564
CHINA ZHENGTONG AUTO SERVICES HOLDINGS LIMITED; *Int'l*, pg. 1566
CHIPMAN & TAYLOR CHEVROLET; *U.S. Private*, pg. 886
CHOPARD AUTOMOBILES SAS; *Int'l*, pg. 1582
CHRIS AUFFENBERG FORD INC.; *U.S. Private*, pg. 889
CHRIS LEITH CHEVROLET, INC.; *U.S. Private*, pg. 889
CHRIS NIKEL'S AUTOHAUS INC.; *U.S. Private*, pg. 889
CHRIS POSEY, INC.; *U.S. Private*, pg. 890
CHRISTOPHER'S DODGE WORLD; *U.S. Private*, pg. 892
CHRYSLER JEEP 24; *U.S. Private*, pg. 893
CHRYSLER JEEP-GLEN BURNIE—See Tate Automotive Group; *U.S. Private*, pg. 3935
CHUCK ANDERSON FORD INC.; *U.S. Private*, pg. 893
CHUCK CLANCY FORD OF MARIETTA, LLC—See AutoNation, Inc.; *U.S. Public*, pg. 234
CHUCK CLANCY FORD OF MARIETTA, LLC—See AutoNation, Inc.; *U.S. Public*, pg. 234
CHUCK FAIRBANKS CHEVROLET, INC.; *U.S. Private*, pg. 893
CHUCK HUTTON CHEVROLET COMPANY; *U.S. Private*, pg. 893
CHUCK PATTERSON AUTO WORLD; *U.S. Private*, pg. 893
CHUCK STEVENS AUTOMOTIVE, INC.; *U.S. Private*, pg. 893
CHUCK VAN HORN DODGE, INC.; *U.S. Private*, pg. 893
CIRCLE AUTO GROUP; *U.S. Private*, pg. 899
CIRCLE IMPORTS; *U.S. Private*, pg. 900
CIRCLE INFINITI; *U.S. Private*, pg. 900
CITRUS MOTORS ONTARIO, INC.; *U.S. Private*, pg. 904
CITY BUICK CHEVROLET CADILLAC GMC; *Int'l*, pg. 1626
CITY CADILLAC BUICK GMC; *U.S. Private*, pg. 905
CITY FORD, LLC; *U.S. Private*, pg. 905
CITY FORD SALES LTD.; *Int'l*, pg. 1626
CITY ISUZU; *U.S. Private*, pg. 906
CITY MOTOR COMPANY; *U.S. Private*, pg. 906
CITY MOTORS (1981) PTY LTD—See Eagers Automotive Limited; *Int'l*, pg. 2263
CITYSIDE SUBARU, INC.; *U.S. Private*, pg. 907
CIVIC AUTOMOTIVE GROUP INC.; *U.S. Private*, pg. 908
CIVIC MOTORS HONDA; *Int'l*, pg. 1630
CLAIN AUTOMOTIVE TEAM; *U.S. Private*, pg. 910
CLAMART AUTOMOBILES; *Int'l*, pg. 1641
CLARK KNAPP MOTOR COMPANY, LLC.; *U.S. Private*, pg. 913
CLASON PONTIAC BUICK-GMC INC.; *U.S. Private*, pg. 915
CLASSIC CADILLAC GMC; *U.S. Private*, pg. 916
CLASSIC CHEVROLET; *U.S. Private*, pg. 916
CLASSIC CHEVROLET, INC.; *U.S. Private*, pg. 916
CLASSIC INTERNATIONAL, INC.; *U.S. Private*, pg. 916
CLASSIC-TYLER MOTORS INC.—See Southeast Texas Classic Automotive; *U.S. Private*, pg. 3726
CLAUDE NOLAN CADILLAC INC.; *U.S. Private*, pg. 917
CLAY NISSAN; *U.S. Private*, pg. 918
CLEAR LAKE INFINITI, LP—See John Eagle A Management, LLC; *U.S. Private*, pg. 2221
CLEO BAY USED CARS; *U.S. Private*, pg. 940
CLIFT BUICK GMC; *U.S. Private*, pg. 943
CLINT NEWELL MOTORS INC.; *U.S. Private*, pg. 944
CLINTON FAMILY FORD LINCOLN MERCURY OF ROCK HILL, INC.; *U.S. Private*, pg. 944
CLINTON FORD LINCOLN; *U.S. Private*, pg. 944
CLM ASSOCIATES LLC; *U.S. Private*, pg. 945
CLUSIAU SALES & RENTAL, INC.; *U.S. Private*, pg. 949
CLYDE REVORD MOTORS; *U.S. Private*, pg. 949
CMP - CLASSIC AUTOMOTIVE LTD; *Int'l*, pg. 1671
COAD CHEVROLET-CADILLAC, INC.—See Ancap Management Inc.; *U.S. Private*, pg. 272
COAD CHEVROLET, INC.—See Ancap Management Inc.; *U.S. Private*, pg. 272
COASTAL CADILLAC, INC.—See AutoNation, Inc.; *U.S. Public*, pg. 234
COASTAL FORD SALES LTD; *Int'l*, pg. 1681
COAST AUTO CENTER INC.; *U.S. Private*, pg. 954
COAST BMW NISSAN; *U.S. Private*, pg. 954
COAST COUNTIES TRUCK & EQUIPMENT CO.; *U.S. Private*, pg. 954
COCCIA LINCOLN-MERCURY INCORPORATED; *U.S. Private*, pg. 959
CODY CHEVROLET, INC.; *U.S. Private*, pg. 960
COFFMAN INTERNATIONAL INC.; *U.S. Private*, pg. 961
COFFMAN TRUCK SALES, INC.; *U.S. Private*, pg. 961
COGGIN AUTOMOTIVE CORP.—See Asbury Automotive Group, Inc.; *U.S. Public*, pg. 209
COGGIN FORD—See Asbury Automotive Group, Inc.; *U.S. Public*, pg. 209
COGSWELL MOTORS INC.; *U.S. Private*, pg. 962
COLE CHEVROLET-GEO INC.; *U.S. Private*, pg. 966
COLEMAN AUTO GROUP; *U.S. Private*, pg. 967
COLE VALLEY CADILLAC—See Cole Valley Motor Company, Ltd.; *U.S. Private*, pg. 966
COLE VALLEY MOTOR COMPANY, LTD.; *U.S. Private*, pg. 966
COLISEUM LEXUS OF OAKLAND; *U.S. Private*, pg. 967
THE COLLECTION, INC.; *U.S. Private*, pg. 4011
COLLEGE FORD LINCOLN LTD.; *Int'l*, pg. 1699
COLLEGE PARK MOTOR PRODUCTS LTD; *Int'l*, pg. 1699
COLLIERS OF BIRMINGHAM LIMITED—See Lithia Motors, Inc.; *U.S. Public*, pg. 1323
COLLINS AUTO GROUP, LLC; *U.S. Private*, pg. 969
COLONIAL CHEVROLET OF ACTON—See Colonial Automotive Group, Inc.; *U.S. Private*, pg. 970
COLONIAL HYUNDAI OF DOWNINGTOWN; *U.S. Private*, pg. 971
COLONIAL IMPORTS CORP.; *U.S. Private*, pg. 971
COLONIAL MOTOR MART; *U.S. Private*, pg. 971
COLONIAL NISSAN, INC.; *U.S. Private*, pg. 971
COLONIAL SUBARU, INC.; *U.S. Private*, pg. 972
COLONIAL TOYOTA; *U.S. Private*, pg. 972
COLONIAL VOLKSWAGEN; *U.S. Private*, pg. 972
COLONIAL WEST CHEVROLET OF FITCHBURG—See Colonial Automotive Group, Inc.; *U.S. Private*, pg. 970
COLONY FORD LINCOLN SALES; *Int'l*, pg. 1702
COLORADO RIVER FORD LINCOLN-MERCURY; *U.S. Private*, pg. 974
COLUMBIA CHRYSLER DODGE JEEP LTD.—See Go Auto; *Int'l*, pg. 3017
COLUMBIA NISSAN INC.—See Dick Smith Automotive Group; *U.S. Private*, pg. 1226
COLUMBUS MOTOR CAR COMPANY, INC.—See Germain Motor Company; *U.S. Private*, pg. 1686
COLUMBUS NISSAN INC.; *U.S. Private*, pg. 979
COLUSSY CHEVROLET INC.; *U.S. Private*, pg. 979
COMMONWEALTH DODGE; *U.S. Private*, pg. 986
COMMUNITY MOTOR CO. INC.; *U.S. Private*, pg. 996
COMOX VALLEY DODGE CHRYSLER JEEP RAM LTD.; *Int'l*, pg. 1721
COMPETITION CHEVROLET LTD.; *Int'l*, pg. 1753
COMPETITION TOYOTA LTD.; *Int'l*, pg. 1753
THE CONANT AUTO RETAIL GROUP; *U.S. Private*, pg. 4013
CONCORDE AUTOMOBILE LTD—See General Motors Company; *U.S. Public*, pg. 923
CONCOURS MOTORS INC.; *U.S. Private*, pg. 1011
CONDON LEASING CO. INC.; *U.S. Private*, pg. 1012
CONE AUTOMOBILES; *Int'l*, pg. 1767
CONLEY BUICK GMC SUBARU; *U.S. Private*, pg. 1014
CONLEY SUBARU; *U.S. Private*, pg. 1014
CONNELL CHEVROLET; *U.S. Private*, pg. 1017
CONNELL NISSAN; *U.S. Private*, pg. 1017
CONTEMPORARY CARS, INC.—See AutoNation, Inc.; *U.S. Public*, pg. 234
CONTEMPORARY MOTOR CARS, INC.; *U.S. Private*, pg. 1027
CONTI CAUSEWAY FORD INC.; *U.S. Private*, pg. 1028
CONTINENTAL CARS, INC.; *U.S. Private*, pg. 1028
CONTINENTAL MOTOR CO. INC.; *U.S. Private*, pg. 1030
CONWAY HEATON, INC.; *U.S. Private*, pg. 1036
COOK GM SUPERSTORE; *U.S. Private*, pg. 1037
COOK JEEP CHRYSLER, INC.; *U.S. Private*, pg. 1038
COOKSVILLE DODGE CHRYSLER INC.; *Int'l*, pg. 1788
COOK-WHITEHEAD FORD, INC.—See AutoNation, Inc.; *U.S. Public*, pg. 234
COON RAPIDS CHRYSLER, INC.; *U.S. Private*, pg. 1040
COOS BAY TOYOTA INC.—See Teton Auto Group; *U.S. Private*, pg. 3973
COPELAND CHEVROLET; *U.S. Private*, pg. 1044
COQUITLAM CHRYSLER DODGE JEEP LTD.; *Int'l*, pg. 1794
CORAL SPRINGS AUTOMALL; *U.S. Private*, pg. 1046
CORNHUSKER AUTO CENTER INC.; *U.S. Private*, pg. 1053
CORNING FORD, INC.; *U.S. Private*, pg. 1053
CORPORACION PROAUTO S.A.—See General Motors Company; *U.S. Public*, pg. 923
CORPUS CHRISTI ANUSA, LLC—See AutoNation, Inc.; *U.S. Public*, pg. 234
CORTESE DODGE INC.; *U.S. Private*, pg. 1060
CORTESE FORD INC.; *U.S. Private*, pg. 1060
CORWIN CHRYSLER DODGE JEEP; *U.S. Private*, pg. 1061
CORWIN FORD; *U.S. Private*, pg. 1061
CORWIN HONDA; *U.S. Private*, pg. 1061
CORY FAIRBANKS MAZDA INC.; *U.S. Private*, pg. 1061
COSTA MESA CARS, INC.—See AutoNation, Inc.; *U.S. Public*, pg. 234
COULTER CADILLAC INCORPORATED; *U.S. Private*, pg. 1065
COULTER MOTOR COMPANY LLC; *U.S. Private*, pg. 1065
COUNTRY CHEVROLET, INC.; *U.S. Private*, pg. 1066
COUNTRY CHEVROLET, INC.; *U.S. Private*, pg. 1066
COUNTRY CLUB AUTO GROUP; *U.S. Private*, pg. 1066
COUNTRY FORD TRUCKS INC.; *U.S. Private*, pg. 1067
COURTESY ACURA—See Don Jacobs Automotive Inc.; *U.S. Private*, pg. 1258
COURTESY AUTOMOTIVE CENTER; *U.S. Private*, pg. 1070
COURTESY BUICK GMC, INC.; *U.S. Private*, pg. 1070
COURTESY CHEV OLDS LTD.; *Int'l*, pg. 1819
COURTESY CHEVROLET CENTER; *U.S. Private*, pg. 1070
COURTESY CHEVROLET INC.—See AutoNation, Inc.; *U.S. Public*, pg. 234
COURTESY FORD INC.; *U.S. Private*, pg. 1070
COURTESY FORD LINCOLN SALES; *Int'l*, pg. 1819
COURTESY LINCOLN MERCURY INC.; *U.S. Private*, pg. 1070
COURTESY MITSUBISHI; *U.S. Private*, pg. 1070
COURTESY QUALITY BRANDON—See Asbury Automotive Group, Inc.; *U.S. Public*, pg. 209
COURTESY SPORTS INC.; *U.S. Private*, pg. 1070
COURY MOSS INC.; *U.S. Private*, pg. 1071
COVERT BUICK INC.; *U.S. Private*, pg. 1072
COVINGTON PIKE MOTORS, INC.—See AutoNation, Inc.; *U.S. Public*, pg. 234
COWBOY CHEVROLET BUICK PONTIAC GMC CADILLAC; *U.S. Private*, pg. 1073
COWBOY TOYOTA; *U.S. Private*, pg. 1073
COX AUTOMOTIVE LLC; *U.S. Private*, pg. 1074
COX CHEVROLET INC.; *U.S. Private*, pg. 1074
CRABTREE BUICK GMC, INC.; *U.S. Private*, pg. 1081

N.A.I.C.S. Index
441110 — NEW CAR DEALERS CORPORATE AFFILIATIONS

CRAIG & LANDRETH LEASING, INC.; *U.S. Private*, pg. 1082
CRAIG SCOTT REALITY INC.; *U.S. Private*, pg. 1083
CRAMER TOYOTA OF VENICE; *U.S. Private*, pg. 1085
CRANDALL FORD; *U.S. Private*, pg. 1085
CRAWFORD TRUCKS & EQUIPMENT, INC.; *U.S. Private*, pg. 1086
CREATIVE BUS SALES INC.; *U.S. Private*, pg. 1088
CREST AUTO GROUP; *U.S. Private*, pg. 1095
CREST CADILLAC INC.; *U.S. Private*, pg. 1095
CREST CADILLAC OF BIRMINGHAM, INC.; *U.S. Private*, pg. 1095
CREST CHEVROLET; *U.S. Private*, pg. 1095
CREST FORD, INC.; *U.S. Private*, pg. 1095
CREST LINCOLN MERCURY, INC.; *U.S. Private*, pg. 1096
CRESTMONT CADILLAC CORPORATION; *U.S. Private*, pg. 1097
CRESTVIEW CADILLAC CORPORATION; *U.S. Private*, pg. 1097
CRIPPEN AUTO MALL; *U.S. Private*, pg. 1101
CRIPPMANN; *U.S. Private*, pg. 1101
CRISWELL ACURA; *U.S. Private*, pg. 1101
CRISWELL PERFORMANCE CARS LLC.; *U.S. Private*, pg. 1101
CRIVELLI FORD INC.; *U.S. Private*, pg. 1102
C.R. LOUGHEAD; *U.S. Private*, pg. 708
CRONIC CHRYSLER JEEP DODGE RAM; *U.S. Private*, pg. 1103
CROPPER MOTORS; *Int'l*, pg. 1855
CROSBY VOLKSWAGEN INC; *Int'l*, pg. 1855
CROSS CREEK SUBARU, INC.; *U.S. Private*, pg. 1104
CROSS MOTORS CORP.; *U.S. Private*, pg. 1105
CROSSROADS FORD INC.; *U.S. Private*, pg. 1108
CROSSROADS FORD, INC.—See Crossroads Automotive Group; *U.S. Private*, pg. 1108
CROSSROADS FORD LTD; *U.S. Private*, pg. 1108
CROSSROADS NISSAN OF HICKORY, INC.—See Crossroads Automotive Group; *U.S. Private*, pg. 1108
CROTON AUTO PARK; *U.S. Private*, pg. 1108
CROUSE FORD SALES INC.; *U.S. Private*, pg. 1109
CROWE FORD SALES CO—See Morse Operations Inc.; *U.S. Private*, pg. 2790
CROWN AUTO DEALERSHIPS, INC.; *U.S. Private*, pg. 1110
CROWN AUTO GROUP—See Asbury Automotive Group, Inc.; *U.S. Public*, pg. 209
CROWN AUTOMOBILE COMPANY INC.; *U.S. Private*, pg. 1110
CROWN BUICK GMC; *U.S. Private*, pg. 1110
CROWN CHRYSLER JEEP, KIA, & EUROCARS - MERCEDES BENZ; *U.S. Private*, pg. 1110
CROWN DODGE OF FAYETTEVILLE; *U.S. Private*, pg. 1111
CROWN DODGE; *U.S. Private*, pg. 1110
CROWN FORD INC.; *U.S. Private*, pg. 1111
CROWN FORD LINCOLN MERCURY, INC.; *U.S. Private*, pg. 1111
CROWN MOTORS II LLC—See Crown Motors Ltd.; *U.S. Private*, pg. 1111
CROWN MOTORS LTD.; *U.S. Private*, pg. 1111
CROWN MOTORS OF CLEARWATER, INC.—See Crown Auto Dealerships, Inc.; *U.S. Private*, pg. 1110
CROWN MOTORS OF REDDING; *U.S. Private*, pg. 1111
CRYSTAL MOTOR CAR CO. INC.; *U.S. Private*, pg. 1115
C.S.A. CENTRO SERVIZI AUTOCARRI S.R.L.; *Int'l*, pg. 1244
CS AUTO, LTD.; *U.S. Private*, pg. 1116
C. SPECK MOTORS; *U.S. Private*, pg. 705
CT INTERCONTINENTAL, LTD.—See AutoNation, Inc.; *U.S. Public*, pg. 233
CT MOTORS, INC.—See AutoNation, Inc.; *U.S. Public*, pg. 233
CUETER CHRYSLER JEEP DODGE; *U.S. Private*, pg. 1120
CULBERSON STOWERS, INC.; *U.S. Private*, pg. 1120
CULVER CITY MOTOR CARS, INC.; *U.S. Private*, pg. 1122
CUMBERLAND CHRYSLER CENTER; *U.S. Private*, pg. 1122
CUNNINGHAM MOTORS, INC.; *U.S. Private*, pg. 1123
CURRY ACURA—See Curry Corporation; *U.S. Private*, pg. 1125
CURRY AUTOMOTIVE, LLC.; *U.S. Private*, pg. 1125
CURRY CORPORATION; *U.S. Private*, pg. 1125
CURRY HONDA—See Curry Corporation; *U.S. Private*, pg. 1125
CURRY HONDA—See Curry Corporation; *U.S. Private*, pg. 1126
CURRY HONDA—See Lithia Motors, Inc.; *U.S. Public*, pg. 1321
CURTIS C. GUNN, INC.; *U.S. Private*, pg. 1126
CURT WARNER CHEVROLET INC.; *U.S. Private*, pg. 1126
CUSH ENTERPRISES INC.; *U.S. Private*, pg. 1127
CUSTOMER 1 ONE INC.; *U.S. Private*, pg. 1130
CUTRUBUS MOTORS INC.; *U.S. Private*, pg. 1131
CUTSHAW CHEVROLET, INC.; *U.S. Private*, pg. 1131
CUTTER BUICK GMC—See Cutter of Maui, Inc.; *U.S. Private*, pg. 1131
CUTTER DODGE CHRYSLER JEEP OF PEARL CITY INC.; *U.S. Private*, pg. 1131
CUTTER MAZDA WAIPAHU—See Cutter of Maui, Inc.; *U.S. Private*, pg. 1131
CUTTER MITSUBISHI - AIEA—See Cutter of Maui, Inc.; *U.S. Private*, pg. 1131
CYCLE COUNTRY, INC.; *U.S. Private*, pg. 1134
DAHL FORD-LA CROSSE INC.; *U.S. Private*, pg. 1144
DALE DOWNIE NISSAN; *Int'l*, pg. 1950
DALE KIRK AUTOMOTIVE; *U.S. Private*, pg. 1148
DALE WILLEY PONTIAC-CADILLAC; *U.S. Private*, pg. 1149
D ALEX MACDONALD FORD LINCOLN; *Int'l*, pg. 1898
DALIAN AUTO ITALIA CAR TRADING CO., LTD.—See Auto Italia Holdings Limited; *Int'l*, pg. 725
DALLAS-H, INC.—See Lithia Motors, Inc.; *U.S. Public*, pg. 1322
DALLAS-T, INC.—See Lithia Motors, Inc.; *U.S. Public*, pg. 1322
DALMAR MOTORS LTD.; *Int'l*, pg. 1954
DAMASCUS MOTOR COMPANY INC.; *U.S. Private*, pg. 1151
DAMES CHEVROLET INC.; *U.S. Private*, pg. 1151
DAMS FORD LINCOLN SALES LTD.; *Int'l*, pg. 1957
DAN CUMMINS CHEVROLET-BUICK-PONTIAC, INC.; *U.S. Private*, pg. 1151
DAN DEERY MOTOR CO. OF WATERLOO, INC.; *U.S. Private*, pg. 1151
DAN DEERY TOYOTA; *U.S. Private*, pg. 1151
DANE GOUGE'S ASTORIA FORD; *U.S. Private*, pg. 1153
DAN HEMM AUTO GROUP; *U.S. Private*, pg. 1151
DANIEL J QUIRK INC.; *U.S. Private*, pg. 1154
DANIELS BMW; *U.S. Private*, pg. 1156
DANIELS CADILLAC, INC.; *U.S. Private*, pg. 1156
DANIELS MOTORS INC.; *U.S. Private*, pg. 1156
DANIEL'S OF ALBION, INC.; *U.S. Private*, pg. 1156
DAN KANE CHEVROLET CADILLAC; *Int'l*, pg. 1957
DANNY BECK CHEVROLET, INC.; *U.S. Private*, pg. 1157
DANNY ZECK FORD LINCOLN MERCURY; *U.S. Private*, pg. 1157
DAN PERKINS SUBARU—See Dan Perkins Auto Group; *U.S. Private*, pg. 1151
DAN PORTER MOTORS INC.; *U.S. Private*, pg. 1151
DAN TOBIN BUICK GMC, INC.; *U.S. Private*, pg. 1151
DAN VADEN CHEVROLET CADILLAC; *U.S. Private*, pg. 1152
DANVERS MOTOR COMPANY, INC.; *U.S. Private*, pg. 1158
DAN WOLF MOTORS OF NAPERVILLE, INC.—See Dan Wolf Incorporated; *U.S. Private*, pg. 1152
DAN WOLF'S CHEVROLET OF NAPERVILLE, INC.—See Dan Wolf Incorporated; *U.S. Private*, pg. 1152
DARBY BUICK-GMC INC.; *U.S. Private*, pg. 1158
DARCARS AUTOMOTIVE GROUP; *U.S. Private*, pg. 1158
DARCARS FORD—See DARCARS Automotive Group; *U.S. Private*, pg. 1158
DARCARS TOYOTA SCION; *U.S. Private*, pg. 1158
DAR CARS TOYOTA; *U.S. Private*, pg. 1158
D'ARCY BUICK GMC, INC.; *U.S. Private*, pg. 1138
D'ARCY HYUNDAI; *U.S. Private*, pg. 1138
DARLING'S INC.; *U.S. Private*, pg. 1159
DARRELL WALTRIP HONDA-VOLVO; *U.S. Private*, pg. 1159
DARU CAR AD—See Eurohold Bulgaria AD; *Int'l*, pg. 2553
DAVE DENNIS CHRYSLER JEEP DODGE; *U.S. Private*, pg. 1168
DAVE HAMILTON CHEVROLET-OLDS-JEEP INC.; *U.S. Private*, pg. 1168
DAVE KNAPP FORD LINCOLN INC.; *U.S. Private*, pg. 1168
DAVE KRING CHEVROLET CADILLAC; *U.S. Private*, pg. 1168
DAVE SINCLAIR FORD INC.; *U.S. Private*, pg. 1168
DAVE SINCLAIR LINCOLN MERCURY ST. PETERS INC.; *U.S. Private*, pg. 1168
DAVE SYVERSON INC.; *U.S. Private*, pg. 1168
DAVE SYVERSON TRUCK CENTER, INC.—See Dave Syverson Inc.; *U.S. Private*, pg. 1168
DAVE WHITE CHEVROLET, INC.; *U.S. Private*, pg. 1168
DAVID A. CAMPBELL CORPORATION; *U.S. Private*, pg. 1169
DAVID BRUCE AUTO CENTER INC.; *U.S. Private*, pg. 1169
DAVID CHEVROLET CORVETTE BUICK GMC LTD.; *Int'l*, pg. 1983
DAVID HOBBS HONDA; *U.S. Private*, pg. 1170
DAVID MCDAVID ACURA OF AUSTIN—See David McDavid Automotive Group; *U.S. Private*, pg. 1170
DAVID MCDAVID AUTOMOTIVE GROUP; *U.S. Private*, pg. 1170
DAVID MCDAVID HONDA—See David McDavid Automotive Group; *U.S. Private*, pg. 1170
DAVID MCDAVID NISSAN—See David McDavid Automotive Group; *U.S. Private*, pg. 1171
DAVID MCDAVID PLANO LINCOLN—See David McDavid Automotive Group; *U.S. Private*, pg. 1171
DAVID MCDERMOTT CHEVROLET—See McDermott Auto Group; *U.S. Private*, pg. 2631
DAVID MCDERMOTT OF NEW HAVEN—See McDermott Auto Group; *U.S. Private*, pg. 2631
DAVID MORRIS FINE CARS LTD.; *Int'l*, pg. 1983
DAVID R. MCGEORGE CAR CO. INC.; *U.S. Private*, pg. 1171
DAVID S. DE LUZ SR ENTERPRISES; *U.S. Private*, pg. 1171
DAVIDSON CHEVROLET INC.; *U.S. Private*, pg. 1171
DAVIDSON CHEVROLET; *U.S. Private*, pg. 1171
DAVID WILSON AUTOMOTIVE GROUP; *U.S. Private*, pg. 1171
DAVIS AUTOMOTIVE GROUP; *U.S. Private*, pg. 1173
DAVIS HYUNDAI; *U.S. Private*, pg. 1173
DAVIS MOORE AUTO GROUP, INC.; *U.S. Private*, pg. 1174
DAVIS-MOORE AUTOMOTIVE, INC.; *U.S. Private*, pg. 1174
DAVIS-MOORE CHEVROLET, INC.—See Davis-Moore Automotive, Inc.; *U.S. Private*, pg. 1175
DAX-AUTO SA; *Int'l*, pg. 1984
DAY FORD; *U.S. Private*, pg. 1176
DAY'S MOTOR GROUP; *Int'l*, pg. 1985
DAYTONA BR-GD, INC.; *U.S. Private*, pg. 1178
DAYTONA DODGE CHRYSLER JEEP RAM; *U.S. Private*, pg. 1178
DAYTON ANDREWS FIVE STAR CHRYSLER PLYMOUTH JEEP, INC.; *U.S. Private*, pg. 1177
DCH DELAWARE LLC—See Lithia Motors, Inc.; *U.S. Public*, pg. 1322
DCH FORD OF THOUSAND OAKS—See Lithia Motors, Inc.; *U.S. Public*, pg. 1322
DCH HONDA OF NANUET—See Lithia Motors, Inc.; *U.S. Public*, pg. 1322
DCH INVESTMENTS INC.—See Lithia Motors, Inc.; *U.S. Public*, pg. 1322
D&C HONDA CO. INC.; *U.S. Private*, pg. 1137
DCH PARAMUS HONDA—See Lithia Motors, Inc.; *U.S. Public*, pg. 1322
D. DAHLE MAZDA OF MURRAY; *U.S. Private*, pg. 1139
DDH INVESTMENTS OF SOUTH TEXAS; *U.S. Private*, pg. 1181
DEACON JONES AUTO GROUP; *U.S. Private*, pg. 1181
DEALER PRODUCT SERVICES, INC.—See Affinitiv, Inc.; *U.S. Private*, pg. 122
DEALERRATER; *U.S. Private*, pg. 1182
DEALERSCIENCE, LLC—See TrueCar, Inc.; *U.S. Public*, pg. 2199
DEAN ARBOUR CHEVROLET CADILLAC; *U.S. Private*, pg. 1183
DEAN COOLEY GM; *Int'l*, pg. 1998
DEAN SELLERS FORD INC.; *U.S. Private*, pg. 1184
DEARBORN MOTORS; *Int'l*, pg. 1998
DECATUR TRUCK & TRACTOR INC.; *U.S. Private*, pg. 1186
DECIDEBLOOM LTD.; *Int'l*, pg. 2000
DE CORMIER MOTOR SALES, INC.; *U.S. Private*, pg. 1181
DEDHAM NISSAN, INC.; *U.S. Private*, pg. 1188
DEEL VOLVO; *U.S. Private*, pg. 1189
DEERY BROTHERS CHEVROLET, INC.; *U.S. Private*, pg. 1190
DELACY FORD INC.; *U.S. Private*, pg. 1193
DELAWARE MOTOR SALES INC.; *U.S. Private*, pg. 1194
DE LILLO CHEVROLET; *U.S. Private*, pg. 1181
DELLA PONTIAC; *U.S. Private*, pg. 1197
DELLEN AUTOMOTIVE INC.; *U.S. Private*, pg. 1197
DEL MONTELL MOTORS LIMITED; *U.S. Private*, pg. 1192
DELRAY MOTORS; *U.S. Private*, pg. 1199
DELTA AUTO SALES SERVICE, INC.; *U.S. Private*, pg. 1199
DELTA MOTORS—See Delta Holding; *Int'l*, pg. 2018
DELUCA TOYOTA SCION; *U.S. Private*, pg. 1202
DEMAAGD GMC-NISSAN, INC.—See Demaagd Enterprises, LLC; *U.S. Private*, pg. 1203
DEMONTROND AUTO COUNTRY, INC.; *U.S. Private*, pg. 1204
DEMONTROND AUTOMOTIVE GROUP; *U.S. Private*, pg. 1204
DEMPEWOLF FORD LINCOLN; *U.S. Private*, pg. 1204
DENCHELS INCORPORATED; *U.S. Private*, pg. 1204
DENHAM FORD SALES LTD.; *Int'l*, pg. 2026
DENICAR S.R.L.—See General Motors Company; *U.S. Public*, pg. 926
DENNIS DILLON AUTO PARK TRUCK CENTER; *U.S. Private*, pg. 1205
DENNISON CORPORATION; *U.S. Private*, pg. 1205
DENNY ANDREWS FORD SALES INC.; *Int'l*, pg. 2028
DENNY MENHOLT FRONTIER CHEVROLET; *U.S. Private*, pg. 1205
DENOOYER CHEVROLET INC.; *U.S. Private*, pg. 1205
DEPAULA CHEVROLET - HUMMER; *U.S. Private*, pg. 1208
DESERT BUICK-GMC TRUCKS, L.L.C.—See AutoNation, Inc.; *U.S. Public*, pg. 234
DESERT EUROPEAN MOTORCARS, LTD.; *U.S. Private*, pg. 1212
DESERT GMC, L.L.C.—See AutoNation, Inc.; *U.S. Public*, pg. 234
DESERT SUN MOTORS; *U.S. Private*, pg. 1213
DESOTO AUTOMOTIVE ENTERPRISES INC; *U.S. Private*, pg. 1215
DESTINATION AUTO VENTURES INC; *Int'l*, pg. 2046
DESTINATION MAZDA VANCOUVER; *Int'l*, pg. 2046
DETER MOTOR CO.; *U.S. Private*, pg. 1216
DEUTSCH MOTORS INC.; *Int'l*, pg. 2049
DEVAN LOWE INC.; *U.S. Private*, pg. 1217

N.A.I.C.S. INDEX
441110 — NEW CAR DEALERS

DEVEREAUX MOTOR SALES INCORPORATED; *U.S. Private*, pg. 1218
DEVOE AUTOMOTIVE GROUP; *U.S. Private*, pg. 1218
DEWEY FORD INC.; *U.S. Private*, pg. 1219
DEWILDT CAR SALES LIMITED; *Int'l*, pg. 2091
DIABLO SUBARU; *U.S. Private*, pg. 1222
DIAMOND HONDA OF GLENDALE; *U.S. Private*, pg. 1223
DIAMOND VALLEY HONDA GROUP, LLC.; *U.S. Private*, pg. 1224
DIANE SAUER CHEVROLET, INC.; *U.S. Private*, pg. 1224
DICK BRANTMEIER FORD INC.—See Van Horn Automotive Group, Inc.; *U.S. Private*, pg. 4340
DICK CAMPAGNI'S CAPITAL FORD; *U.S. Private*, pg. 1225
DICK DEAN ECONOMY CARS INC.; *U.S. Private*, pg. 1225
DICK DEVOE BUICK CADILLAC—See DeVoe Automotive Group; *U.S. Private*, pg. 1219
DICK DYER & ASSOCIATES, INC.; *U.S. Private*, pg. 1225
DICK DYER TOYOTA; *U.S. Private*, pg. 1226
DICK EDWARDS FORD LINCOLN MERCURY; *U.S. Private*, pg. 1226
DICK GENTHE CHEVROLET; *U.S. Private*, pg. 1226
DICK GREENFIELD DODGE INC.; *U.S. Private*, pg. 1226
DICK HUVAERE'S RICHMOND CHRYSLER DODGE INC.; *U.S. Private*, pg. 1226
DICK MASHETER FORD, INC.; *U.S. Private*, pg. 1226
DICK MYERS CHRYSLER DODGE JEEP; *U.S. Private*, pg. 1226
DICK NORRIS BUICK PONTIAC GMC; *U.S. Private*, pg. 1226
DICK POE CHRYSLER-PLYMOUTH INC.; *U.S. Private*, pg. 1226
DICK POE MOTORS LP.; *U.S. Private*, pg. 1226
DICK SCOTT DODGE INC.—See Dick Scott Motor Mall Inc.; *U.S. Private*, pg. 1226
DICK SCOTT MOTOR MALL INC.; *U.S. Private*, pg. 1226
DICK'S COUNTRY CHRYSLER JEEP DODGE; *U.S. Private*, pg. 1226
DICK SMITH AUTOMOTIVE GROUP; *U.S. Private*, pg. 1226
DICK SMITH AUTO SALES INC.—See Dick Smith Automotive Group; *U.S. Private*, pg. 1226
DICK SMITH FORD—See Dick Smith Automotive Group; *U.S. Private*, pg. 1226
DICK SMITH INFINITI INC.—See Dick Smith Automotive Group; *U.S. Private*, pg. 1226
DICK SMITH NISSAN INC.—See Dick Smith Automotive Group; *U.S. Private*, pg. 1226
DICK SMITH NISSAN OF LEXINGTON—See Dick Smith Automotive Group; *U.S. Private*, pg. 1226
DIEHL FORD INC.; *U.S. Private*, pg. 1226
DIEPHOLZ CHEVROLET CADILLAC INC.; *U.S. Private*, pg. 1228
DIFFUSION AUTOMOBILE CLERMONTAISE; *Int'l*, pg. 2118
DILAWRI GROUP OF COMPANIES; *Int'l*, pg. 2125
DIMMITT AUTOMOTIVE GROUP; *U.S. Private*, pg. 1233
DINGWALL FORD SALES; *Int'l*, pg. 2127
DION INTERNATIONAL TRUCKS LLC; *U.S. Private*, pg. 1234
DIRECT AUTOMOTIVE GROUP, LLC.; *U.S. Private*, pg. 1234
DISBROWE CHEVROLET BUICK GMC CADILLAC; *Int'l*, pg. 2131
DISCOUNT VEHICLES AUSTRALIA PTY LTD—See carsales.com Limited; *Int'l*, pg. 1347
DISCOVERY FORD BURLINGTON LTD.; *Int'l*, pg. 2134
DISCOVERY HONDA; *Int'l*, pg. 2134
DISO MADRID S.L.R.—See General Motors Company; *U.S. Public*, pg. 927
DIXIE BUICK GMC TRUCK INC.; *U.S. Private*, pg. 1244
DIXIE MOTORS, INC.; *U.S. Private*, pg. 1245
DIXON, R B HOLDINGS LTD.; *Int'l*, pg. 2138
D.K FORD SALES; *Int'l*, pg. 1901
D/L MOTOR COMPANY—See AutoNation, Inc.; *U.S. Public*, pg. 234
D/L MOTOR COMPANY—See AutoNation, Inc.; *U.S. Public*, pg. 234
DLSA AUTOMOBILES; *Int'l*, pg. 2141
DMC ENTERPRISES INC.; *U.S. Private*, pg. 1248
DOAN BUICK; *U.S. Private*, pg. 1250
DOAN CHEVROLET LLC; *U.S. Private*, pg. 1250
DOAN DODGE CHRYSLER JEEP RAM FIAT—See West Herr Automotive Group, Inc.; *U.S. Private*, pg. 4485
DOBBS FORD, INC.—See AutoNation, Inc.; *U.S. Public*, pg. 234
DOBBS FORD OF MEMPHIS, INC.—See AutoNation, Inc.; *U.S. Public*, pg. 234
DOBBS MOBILE BAY, INC.—See AutoNation, Inc.; *U.S. Public*, pg. 234
DOBBS MOBILE BAY, INC.—See AutoNation, Inc.; *U.S. Public*, pg. 234
DOBBS MOTORS OF ARIZONA, INC.—See AutoNation, Inc.; *U.S. Public*, pg. 234
DOBBS MOTORS OF ARIZONA, INC.—See AutoNation, Inc.; *U.S. Public*, pg. 234
DOBRINSKI OF KINGFISHER, INC.; *U.S. Private*, pg. 1250
DODGE CHRYSLER JEEP OF WINTER HAVEN, INC.; *U.S. Private*, pg. 1252
DODGE CITY AUTO—See AutoCanada Inc.; *Int'l*, pg. 726

DODGE OF BELLEVUE, INC.—See AutoNation, Inc.; *U.S. Public*, pg. 234
DODGE OF BURNSVILLE, INC.; *U.S. Private*, pg. 1252
DOHERTY FORD; *U.S. Private*, pg. 1253
DOMINION MOTORS; *Int'l*, pg. 2161
DON BESSETTE MOTORS, INC.; *U.S. Private*, pg. 1257
DON BEYER MOTORS INC.; *U.S. Private*, pg. 1257
DON BROWN AUTOMOTIVE GROUP; *U.S. Private*, pg. 1257
DON CHALMERS FORD INC.; *U.S. Private*, pg. 1257
DON DAVIS BAY CITY—See Don Davis Dealerships, Inc.; *U.S. Private*, pg. 1257
DON DAVIS DEALERSHIPS, INC.; *U.S. Private*, pg. 1257
DON DAVIS FORD, INC.—See Don Davis Auto Group, Inc.; *U.S. Private*, pg. 1257
DON DAVIS MOTOR CO., INC.—See Don Davis Dealerships, Inc.; *U.S. Private*, pg. 1257
DONGGUAN DONGBU TOYOTA AUTO SALES & SERVICES CO., LTD.—See China MeiDong Auto Holdings Limited; *Int'l*, pg. 1519
DONGGUAN DONGMEI TOYOTA AUTO SALES & SERVICES CO., LTD.—See China MeiDong Auto Holdings Limited; *Int'l*, pg. 1519
DONGGUAN GUANFENG AUTO CO., LTD.—See China MeiDong Auto Holdings Limited; *Int'l*, pg. 1519
DON HALL GM SUPERCENTER; *U.S. Private*, pg. 1257
DON HATTAN CHEVROLET, INC.; *U.S. Private*, pg. 1257
DON HEATH'S AUTO HAUS, INC.; *U.S. Private*, pg. 1257
DON HILL AUTOMOTIVE ASSOCIATES INC.; *U.S. Private*, pg. 1257
DON HILL PONTIAC JEEP INC.—See Don Hill Automotive Associates Inc.; *U.S. Private*, pg. 1257
DON HINDS FORD INC.; *U.S. Private*, pg. 1258
DON JACOBS AUTOMOTIVE INC.; *U.S. Private*, pg. 1258
DON JACOBS IMPORTS, INC.; *U.S. Private*, pg. 1258
DON JACOBS TOYOTA; *U.S. Private*, pg. 1258
DON JOHNSON MOTORS INC.; *U.S. Private*, pg. 1258
DON JOHNSON MOTORS INC.; *U.S. Private*, pg. 1258
DON JOSEPH INCORPRATED; *U.S. Private*, pg. 1258
DON K CHEVROLET INC.; *U.S. Private*, pg. 1258
DONLEY FORD LINCOLN INC.; *U.S. Private*, pg. 1260
DONMAR CAR SALES LTD.; *Int'l*, pg. 2172
DON MASSEY CADILLAC LONE TREE—See Sonic Automotive, Inc.; *U.S. Public*, pg. 1902
DON MCCUE CHEVROLET & GEO INC.; *U.S. Private*, pg. 1258
DON MCCUE CHEVROLET; *U.S. Private*, pg. 1258
DON MCGILL TOYOTA OF HOUSTON; *U.S. Private*, pg. 1258
DON MEALEY CHEVROLET, INC.—See AutoNation, Inc.; *U.S. Public*, pg. 234
DON MEALEY CHEVROLET, INC.—See AutoNation, Inc.; *U.S. Public*, pg. 234
DON MEALEY IMPORTS, INC.—See AutoNation, Inc.; *U.S. Public*, pg. 234
DON MEALEY MAZDA; *U.S. Private*, pg. 1258
DON MILLER SUBARU EAST; *U.S. Private*, pg. 1258
DON MOORE NISSAN; *U.S. Private*, pg. 1258
DONOHOO CHEVROLET, LLC; *U.S. Private*, pg. 1261
DON REID FORD, INC.; *U.S. Private*, pg. 1258
DON RINGLER CHEVROLET CO. INC.; *U.S. Private*, pg. 1258
DON'S BROOKLYN CHEVROLET, INC.; *U.S. Private*, pg. 1259
DON SEELYE FORD INC.; *U.S. Private*, pg. 1259
DON THORNTON CADILLAC SAAB, INC.; *U.S. Private*, pg. 1259
DON VALLEY VOLKSWAGEN LTD.; *Int'l*, pg. 2162
DONWAY FORD SALES LTD.; *Int'l*, pg. 2172
DON WESSEL HONDA; *U.S. Private*, pg. 1259
DON WHEATON CHEVROLET BUICK GMC LTD.; *Int'l*, pg. 2162
DON WILLIAMSON NISSAN; *U.S. Private*, pg. 1259
DOONAN TRUCK & EQUIPMENT OF WICHITA, INC.; *U.S. Private*, pg. 1261
DORAL BUICK, PONTIAC, GMC; *U.S. Private*, pg. 1262
DOSSETT PONTIAC CADILLAC GMC; *U.S. Private*, pg. 1264
DOTHAN CHRYSLER DODGE JEEP RAM; *U.S. Private*, pg. 1265
DOUG HENRY BUICK GMC, INC.; *U.S. Private*, pg. 1266
DOUG HENRY CHEVROLET INC.; *U.S. Private*, pg. 1266
DOUGLAS MOTORS CORPORATION; *U.S. Private*, pg. 1267
DOUGLAS MOTORS INC.; *U.S. Private*, pg. 1267
DOUG MARSHALL CHEVROLET CORVETTE CADILLAC; *Int'l*, pg. 2181
DOVELL & WILLIAMS, INC.; *U.S. Private*, pg. 1268
DOW LEWIS MOTORS, INC.; *U.S. Private*, pg. 1268
DOW MOTORS (OTTAWA) LIMITED; *Int'l*, pg. 2182
DOWNEAST TOYOTA BMW INC.; *U.S. Private*, pg. 1269
DOWNEY FORD SALES; *Int'l*, pg. 2186
DOWNSVIEW CHRYSLER PLYMOUTH (1964) LTD.; *Int'l*, pg. 2187

DOWNTOWN AUTO CENTER; *U.S. Private*, pg. 1269
DOWNTOWN FORD SALES INC.; *U.S. Private*, pg. 1269
DOWNTOWN L.A. MOTORS, LP.; *U.S. Private*, pg. 1269
DOWNTOWN LA NISSAN MOTORS; *U.S. Private*, pg. 1269
DOWNTOWN PONTIAC BUICK (1983) LIMITED; *Int'l*, pg. 2187
DOYLE CHEVROLET-SUBARU; *U.S. Private*, pg. 1270
D-PATRICK INC.; *U.S. Private*, pg. 1139
DRACO, INC.; *U.S. Private*, pg. 1271
DRAPER CHEVROLET COMPANY; *U.S. Private*, pg. 1272
DRAYTON VALLEY FORD SALES LTD.; *Int'l*, pg. 2201
DREYER & REINBOLD INC.; *U.S. Private*, pg. 1277
DRIVE AUTO, INC.—See Sinclair, Inc.; *U.S. Public*, pg. 1885
DRIVE KAWASAKI BRISTOL—See DRIVE Motor Retail Limited; *Int'l*, pg. 2204
DRIVE MOTOR RETAIL LIMITED; *Int'l*, pg. 2204
DRIVERSIDE, INC.—See Advance Auto Parts, Inc.; *U.S. Public*, pg. 44
DRIVE VAUXHALL BURY ST. EDMUNDS—See DRIVE Motor Retail Limited; *Int'l*, pg. 2204
DROUBAY AUTOMOTIVE GROUP INCORPORATED; *U.S. Private*, pg. 1279
DRUM HILL FORD, INC.; *U.S. Private*, pg. 1279
DSU PETERBILT & GMC TRUCK, INC.; *U.S. Private*, pg. 1282
DUBLIN BUICK GMC; *U.S. Private*, pg. 1283
DUBREUIL AUTOMOBILES; *Int'l*, pg. 2222
DUEA MOTOR COMPANY INC.; *U.S. Private*, pg. 1284
DUFF AUTO SALES, INC—See Sutherlin Automotive Group, LLC; *U.S. Private*, pg. 3887
DUKE AUTOMOTIVE CORP.; *U.S. Private*, pg. 1285
DULLES MOTORCARS; *U.S. Private*, pg. 1286
DULUTH CHRYSLER JEEP DODGE & RAM; *U.S. Private*, pg. 1286
DUMAS AUTOMOBILES; *Int'l*, pg. 2224
DUNNING MOTOR SALES, INC.; *U.S. Private*, pg. 1290
DUPAGE DODGE CHRYSLER JEEP, INC.; *U.S. Private*, pg. 1291
DUPLESSIS BUICK GMC TRUCK, INC.; *U.S. Private*, pg. 1291
DURAND SA; *Int'l*, pg. 2228
DUROCHER AUTO SALES INC.; *U.S. Private*, pg. 1294
DUSTY RHODES FORD SALES INCORPORATED; *U.S. Private*, pg. 1294
DUTCH CHEVROLET BUICK; *U.S. Private*, pg. 1294
DUTCH MILLER CHEVROLET INC.; *U.S. Private*, pg. 1294
DUTCH MILLER KIA; *U.S. Private*, pg. 1294
DUTRO FORD LINCOLN MERCURY INC.; *U.S. Private*, pg. 1295
DUVAL ACURA—See Scott-McRae Automotive Group Inc.; *U.S. Private*, pg. 3578
DWAIN TAYLOR CHEVROLET-BUICK-GMC; *U.S. Private*, pg. 1295
DWAYNE LANES CHRYSLER DODGE JEEP RAM; *U.S. Private*, pg. 1295
DWWA INC.; *U.S. Private*, pg. 1296
EAGERS NOMINEES PTY LTD—See Eagers Automotive Limited; *Int'l*, pg. 2264
EAGLE BUICK GMC, INC.; *U.S. Private*, pg. 1308
EAGLE NORTH HOLDINGS INC; *Int'l*, pg. 2266
EAGLE RIVER CHRYSLER LTD.; *Int'l*, pg. 2266
EARL TINDOL FORD INC.; *U.S. Private*, pg. 1313
EARNHARDT CHRYSLER-JEEP—See Earnhardt's Auto Centers; *U.S. Private*, pg. 1314
EARNHARDT DODGE—See Earnhardt's Auto Centers; *U.S. Private*, pg. 1314
EARNHARDT FORD—See Earnhardt's Auto Centers; *U.S. Private*, pg. 1314
EARNHARDT HONDA—See Earnhardt's Auto Centers; *U.S. Private*, pg. 1314
EARNHARDT TOYOTA SCION; *U.S. Private*, pg. 1314
EAST BAY BMW; *U.S. Private*, pg. 1315
EAST BAY FORD TRUCK SALES, INC.; *U.S. Private*, pg. 1315
EAST COUNTY PREOWNED SUPERSTORE; *U.S. Private*, pg. 1316
EAST-COURT FORD LINCOLN SALES; *Int'l*, pg. 2271
EASTERN MOTORS LLC—See Al Fahim Group; *Int'l*, pg. 277
EASTEX DODGE OF BEAUMONT INC.—See Southeast Texas Classic Automotive; *U.S. Private*, pg. 3726
EASTGATE CHRYSLER JEEP, INC.; *U.S. Private*, pg. 1321
EAST HILLS CHEVROLET GEO; *U.S. Private*, pg. 1316
EASTSIDE DODGE CHRYSLER JEEP LTD.; *Int'l*, pg. 2275
EAST TENNESSEE NISSAN MORRISTOWN; *U.S. Private*, pg. 1318
EASTWAY PLYMOUTH CHRYSLER LTD; *Int'l*, pg. 2275
E AUTOMOTIVE INC.; *Int'l*, pg. 2245
EBB AUTO CO. INC.; *U.S. Private*, pg. 1323
EBLOCK, INC.—See E Automotive Inc.; *Int'l*, pg. 2245
ECHOPARK AL, LLC—See Sonic Automotive, Inc.; *U.S. Public*, pg. 1902
ECHOPARK AUTOMOTIVE, INC.—See Sonic Automotive, Inc.; *U.S. Public*, pg. 1902
ECHOPARK GA, LLC—See Sonic Automotive, Inc.; *U.S. Public*, pg. 1902
ECKENROD FORD LINCOLN MERCURY OF CULLMAN, INC.; *U.S. Private*, pg. 1327

441110 — NEW CAR DEALERS

CORPORATE AFFILIATIONS

ECONOMY WHEELS LTD; *Int'l*, pg. 2298
ED BOZARTH CHEVROLET AND BUICK, INC.; *U.S. Private*, pg. 1331
ED BOZARTH CHEVROLET COMPANY, INC.; *U.S. Private*, pg. 1331
EDDIE GILSTRAP MOTORS INCORPORATED; *U.S. Private*, pg. 1332
EDDIES TRUCK SALES INCORPORATED; *U.S. Private*, pg. 1332
EDDY'S TOYOTA OF WICHITA INC.; *U.S. Private*, pg. 1332
EDEN AUTOMOTIVE INVESTMENTS LIMITED; *Int'l*, pg. 2306
EDEN BRACKNELL—See Eden Automotive Investments Limited; *Int'l*, pg. 2306
EDEN (GM) LIMITED—See General Motors Company; *U.S. Public*, pg. 928
EDENTON MOTORS INC.; *U.S. Private*, pg. 1333
EDGREN MOTOR COMPANY, INC.—See AutoNation, Inc.; *U.S. Public*, pg. 234
EDGREN MOTOR COMPANY, INC.—See AutoNation, Inc.; *U.S. Public*, pg. 234
ED HICKS IMPORTS, LTD.; *U.S. Private*, pg. 1331
ED KENLEY FORD, INC.; *U.S. Private*, pg. 1331
ED KIRBY ADVENTURE; *U.S. Private*, pg. 1331
ED LEARN FORD LINCOLN LTD.; *Int'l*, pg. 2302
EDMARK GMC PONTIAC BUICK, INC.; *U.S. Private*, pg. 1337
ED MARTIN ACURA; *U.S. Private*, pg. 1331
ED MARTIN CHEVY CADILLAC; *U.S. Private*, pg. 1331
ED MULLINAX FORD, LLC—See AutoNation, Inc.; *U.S. Public*, pg. 234
ED SCHMIDT PONTIAC - GMC TRUCK, INC.; *U.S. Private*, pg. 1331
ED SCHULTS CHEVROLET CADILLAC; *U.S. Private*, pg. 1331
ED SHULTS CHEVROLET, INC.—See Shults Management Group, Inc.; *U.S. Private*, pg. 3644
ED SHULTS OF WARREN, INC.; *U.S. Private*, pg. 1332
ED VOYLES DEALERSHIPS; *U.S. Private*, pg. 1332
EDWARDS CHEVROLET - 280, INC.; *U.S. Private*, pg. 1342
EDWARDS CHEVROLET CO., INC.; *U.S. Private*, pg. 1342
EDWARDS GARAGE LTD.; *Int'l*, pg. 2317
ED WITTMEIER FORD INC.; *U.S. Private*, pg. 1332
EFIRD CHRYSLER JEEP DODGE; *U.S. Private*, pg. 1343
E.F. MOORE INC.; *U.S. Private*, pg. 1305
EGOLF MOTORS, INC.; *U.S. Private*, pg. 1344
ELDER AUTO, INC.—See Elder Automotive Group; *U.S. Private*, pg. 1350
ELDER FORD OF TAMPA, LLC—See Elder Automotive Group; *U.S. Private*, pg. 1350
EL DORADO MOTORS INC.; *U.S. Private*, pg. 1349
ELHART DODGE NISSAN HYUNDAI—See Elhart Management Corp.; *U.S. Private*, pg. 1359
ELHART MANAGEMENT CORP.; *U.S. Private*, pg. 1359
ELHART PONTIAC-GMC-TRUCK INC.—See Elhart Management Corp.; *U.S. Private*, pg. 1359
ELITE BMW; *Int'l*, pg. 2362
ELIZADE NIGERIA LIMITED; *Int'l*, pg. 2363
ELKINS FORD LAND; *U.S. Private*, pg. 1363
ELK RIVER FORD MERCURY, INC.; *U.S. Private*, pg. 1362
ELLIO LLC; *U.S. Private*, pg. 1364
ELLIOTT CHEVROLET, INC.; *U.S. Private*, pg. 1364
ELLIOTT/WILSON CAPITOL TRUCKS LLC; *U.S. Private*, pg. 1373
ELM CHEVROLET COMPANY, INC.; *U.S. Private*, pg. 1375
ELM FORD-MERCURY INC.; *U.S. Private*, pg. 1375
ELM GROVE DODGE CHRYSLER JEEP INC.; *U.S. Private*, pg. 1375
ELMHURST AUTO GROUP; *U.S. Private*, pg. 1376
ELMHURST BMW—See Elmhurst Auto Group; *U.S. Private*, pg. 1376
ELMHURST TOYOTA—See Elmhurst Auto Group; *U.S. Private*, pg. 1376
EL MOR CHEVROLET; *U.S. Private*, pg. 1349
ELMORE TOYOYA; *U.S. Private*, pg. 1377
EMD INTERNATIONAL HOLDINGS, INC.—See Caterpillar, Inc.; *U.S. Public*, pg. 452
EMERLING CHEVROLET INC.; *U.S. Private*, pg. 1381
EMERLING FORD, INC.; *U.S. Private*, pg. 1381
EMG MOTOR GROUP LTD—See EMG Holdings Ltd; *Int'l*, pg. 2380
EMICH SUBARU WEST, LLC—See AutoNation, Inc.; *U.S. Public*, pg. 234
EMICH SUBARU WEST, LLC—See AutoNation, Inc.; *U.S. Public*, pg. 235
EMIRATES MOTOR CO.—See Al Fahim Group; *Int'l*, pg. 277
EMPIRE FORD LINCOLN; *U.S. Private*, pg. 1385
EMPIRE HYUNDAI, INC.; *U.S. Private*, pg. 1385
EMPIRE NISSAN INC.—See Romero Motors Corporation; *U.S. Private*, pg. 3476
EMPIRE TRUCK SALES INC—See GS&L Enterprises Incorporated; *U.S. Private*, pg. 1800
ENCORE MOTORCARS OF SARASOTA, INC.; *U.S. Private*, pg. 1391
ENGLAND MOTOR CO. INC.; *U.S. Private*, pg. 1399
ENSIGN CHRYSLER DODGE JEEP; *Int'l*, pg. 2446
ENS TOYOTA; *Int'l*, pg. 2445
ENTRUST, INC.; *U.S. Private*, pg. 1406

EPINAL AUTO; *Int'l*, pg. 2460
ERHARD BMW OF BLOOMFIELD HILLS; *U.S. Private*, pg. 1419
ERICH HENKEL AUTOMOTIVE GROUP; *U.S. Private*, pg. 1419
ERICKSEN NISSAN; *Int'l*, pg. 2493
ERICKSON GMC; *U.S. Private*, pg. 1419
ERIKSEN CHEVROLET-BUICK; *U.S. Private*, pg. 1421
ERIN DODGE CHRYSLER LTD.; *Int'l*, pg. 2493
ERINMOTORWAY INVESTMENTS LIMITED; *Int'l*, pg. 2493
ERIN PARK AUTOMOTIVE PARTNERSHIP; *Int'l*, pg. 2493
ERNEST MCCARTY FORD, INC.; *U.S. Private*, pg. 1421
ERNIE PALMER, INC.; *U.S. Private*, pg. 1422
ERNIE VON SCHLEDORN LTD., INC.; *U.S. Private*, pg. 1422
ERNST AUTO CENTER INCORPORATED; *U.S. Private*, pg. 1423
ERNST DELLO GMBH & CO. KG; *Int'l*, pg. 2494
ERNST VON SCHLEDORN INC.; *U.S. Private*, pg. 1423
ESPLANADE LIMITED; *Int'l*, pg. 2506
ESTABROOK FORD LINCOLN MERCURY INC.; *U.S. Private*, pg. 1428
ESTERO BAY CHEVROLET, INC—See Group 1 Automotive, Inc.; *U.S. Public*, pg. 971
ETABLISSEMENTS EMILE GEORGET; *Int'l*, pg. 2519
ET INTERNATIONAL LTD; *U.S. Private*, pg. 1431
ETTLESON CADILLAC-BUICK-GMC, INC.; *U.S. Private*, pg. 1432
EUROMOTORS INC.; *U.S. Private*, pg. 1433
EUROPEAN AUTO SERVICE LTD.; *U.S. Private*, pg. 1434
EUROPEAN MOTORCARS; *U.S. Private*, pg. 1434
EURO PERFORMANCE CARS, INC.; *U.S. Private*, pg. 1433
EVANSTON SUBARU IN SKOKIE; *U.S. Private*, pg. 1435
EVERETT BUICK PONTIAC GMC; *U.S. Private*, pg. 1438
EVERETT CHEVROLET, INC.; *U.S. Private*, pg. 1438
EVERGREEN FORD; *U.S. Private*, pg. 1439
EWALD AUTOMOTIVE GROUP, LLC; *U.S. Private*, pg. 1444
EWALD CHEVROLET BUICK, LLC—See Ewald Automotive Group, LLC; *U.S. Private*, pg. 1444
EWALD CHRYSLER, LLC—See Ewald Automotive Group, LLC; *U.S. Private*, pg. 1444
EWALD'S HARTFORD FORD-LINCOLN-MERCURY, LLC—See Ewald Automotive Group, LLC; *U.S. Private*, pg. 1444
EWALD'S VENUS FORD, LLC; *U.S. Private*, pg. 1444
EXECUTIVE DODGE, INC.; *U.S. Private*, pg. 1447
EXECUTIVE JEEP NISSAN; *U.S. Private*, pg. 1447
EXPRESSWAY DODGE INC.; *U.S. Private*, pg. 1452
EXPRESSWAY MOTORS LTD; *Int'l*, pg. 2590
EYNON PONTIAC BUICK INC.; *U.S. Private*, pg. 1454
FAA CONCORD H, INC.—See Sonic Automotive, Inc.; *U.S. Public*, pg. 1902
FAA POWAY H, INC.—See Sonic Automotive, Inc.; *U.S. Public*, pg. 1902
FAA SERRAMONTE H, INC.—See Sonic Automotive, Inc.; *U.S. Public*, pg. 1902
FAIREY CHEVROLET CADILLAC; *U.S. Private*, pg. 1462
FAIRFAX IMPORTS, INC.; *U.S. Private*, pg. 1463
FAIRFIELD AUTO GROUP INC.; *U.S. Private*, pg. 1463
FAIRLANE FORD SALES INC.; *U.S. Private*, pg. 1464
FAIRVIEW COVE AUTO LTD.; *Int'l*, pg. 2609
FAIRWAY FORD HENDERSON, INC.; *U.S. Private*, pg. 1465
FAIRWAY FORD, INC.; *U.S. Private*, pg. 1465
FAIRWAY FORD OF AUGUSTA, INC.; *U.S. Private*, pg. 1465
FAIRWAY FORD SALES LTD.; *Int'l*, pg. 2609
FAIRWAY MOTORS INC.; *U.S. Private*, pg. 1465
FALCONET PTY LTD—See Eagers Automotive Limited; *Int'l*, pg. 2263
FALMOUTH TOYOTA, INC.; *U.S. Private*, pg. 1468
FALVEY'S MOTORS, INC.; *U.S. Private*, pg. 1468
FAMILY CHEVROLET CADILLAC; *U.S. Private*, pg. 1469
FAMILY CHRYSLER DODGE JEEP RAM; *U.S. Private*, pg. 1469
FAMILY FORD INC.; *U.S. Private*, pg. 1470
FAMILY FORD LINCOLN; *U.S. Private*, pg. 1470
FAMILY FORD OF EINFIELD; *U.S. Private*, pg. 1470
FAMILY, INC.; *Int'l*, pg. 2612
FAMILY MOTORS GROUP; *U.S. Private*, pg. 1471
FARMINGTON HILLS AUTOMOTIVE, LLC—See Suburban Motors Company, LLC; *U.S. Private*, pg. 3848
FARMINGTON HILLS HOLDING COMPANY; *U.S. Private*, pg. 1480
FARRISH OF FAIRFAX INC.; *U.S. Private*, pg. 1481
FASTRACK COMPLETE CAR CARE; *U.S. Private*, pg. 1482
FATHERS AND SONS INC.; *U.S. Private*, pg. 1483
FAULKNER BUICK, GMC TRUCK INC.; *U.S. Private*, pg. 1483
FAULKNER CADILLAC INC.; *U.S. Private*, pg. 1483
FAULKNER CHEVROLET INC.; *U.S. Private*, pg. 1483
FAULKNER CIOCCA FORD OF SOUDERTON; *U.S. Private*, pg. 1483
FAULKNER FORD MERCURY INC.; *U.S. Private*, pg. 1483
FAULKNER HARRISBURG INC.; *U.S. Private*, pg. 1483

FAWCETTS GARAGE (NEWBURY) LIMITED; *Int'l*, pg. 2623
F.C. KERBECK & SONS; *U.S. Private*, pg. 1456
FEDER'S SUBARU; *U.S. Private*, pg. 1487
FELDMANN IMPORTS MERCEDES-BENZ; *U.S. Private*, pg. 1493
FELIX CHEVROLET-CADILLAC; *U.S. Private*, pg. 1493
FERGUSON PONTIAC-GMC INC.; *U.S. Private*, pg. 1497
FERMAN CHEVROLET—See Ferman Automotive Management Services, Inc.; *U.S. Private*, pg. 1497
FERMAN MOTOR CAR CO., INC.—See Ferman Automotive Management Services, Inc.; *U.S. Private*, pg. 1497
FERRARI NORTH EUROPE LIMITED—See Ferrari N.V.; *Int'l*, pg. 2639
FESLER AUTO MALL; *U.S. Private*, pg. 1499
FIDELITY MOTORS LTD.—See Goddard Enterprises Limited; *Int'l*, pg. 3018
FIELDS BMW OF DAYTONA; *U.S. Private*, pg. 1504
FIELDS BMW; *U.S. Private*, pg. 1504
FIELDS IMPORTS INC.—See M.E. Fields Inc.; *U.S. Private*, pg. 2528
FIELDS JEEP, INC.—See M.E. Fields Inc.; *U.S. Private*, pg. 2528
FIELDS OF LAKE COUNTY INC.—See M.E. Fields Inc.; *U.S. Private*, pg. 2528
FIESTA FORD LINCOLN MERCURY; *U.S. Private*, pg. 1505
FIFTH AVENUE AUTO HAUS LTD.; *Int'l*, pg. 2660
FIKE CHEVROLET COMPANY; *U.S. Private*, pg. 1505
FIKES CHEVROLET BUICK INCORPORATED; *U.S. Private*, pg. 1505
FILIAGGI HOLDING COMPANY INC.; *U.S. Private*, pg. 1505
FINCHEY CORPORATION OF CA; *U.S. Private*, pg. 1508
FINDLAY AUTOMOTIVE INC.; *U.S. Private*, pg. 1508
FINDLAY LINCOLN; *U.S. Private*, pg. 1508
FINDLAY TOYOTA GROUP; *U.S. Private*, pg. 1508
FINDLAY VOLKSWAGEN; *U.S. Private*, pg. 1508
FIORE BUICK GMC; *U.S. Private*, pg. 1511
FIORE MOTORS INC.; *U.S. Private*, pg. 1511
FIRKINS CHRYSLER JEEP DODGE RAM; *U.S. Private*, pg. 1512
FIRST STATE CHEVROLET, INC.; *U.S. Private*, pg. 1529
FIRST TEAM FORD, LTD—See AutoNation, Inc.; *U.S. Public*, pg. 235
FIRST TEAM FORD, LTD.—See AutoNation, Inc.; *U.S. Public*, pg. 235
FIRST TEAM FORD OF MANATEE, LTD.—See AutoNation, Inc.; *U.S. Public*, pg. 235
FIRST TEAM HONDA—See Tallahassee Automotive, LLC; *U.S. Private*, pg. 3926
FIRST TEAM NISSAN OF CHRISTIANBURG—See Tallahassee Automotive, LLC; *U.S. Private*, pg. 3927
FIRST TEAM TOYOTA—See Tallahassee Automotive, LLC; *U.S. Private*, pg. 3927
FISCHER CHEVROLET & NISSAN; *U.S. Private*, pg. 1532
FISHER CHEVROLET INC.; *U.S. Private*, pg. 1534
FISKER INC.—See Fisker Inc.; *U.S. Public*, pg. 851
FIT KIT, INC.—See AutoNation, Inc.; *U.S. Public*, pg. 235
FIT KIT, INC.—See AutoNation, Inc.; *U.S. Public*, pg. 235
FITZGERALD AUTO MALLS; *U.S. Private*, pg. 1536
FITZPATRICK AUTO CENTER INC.; *U.S. Private*, pg. 1536
FITZPATRICK'S GMC TRUCKS, INC.; *U.S. Private*, pg. 1537
FIVE STAR DODGE INC.; *U.S. Private*, pg. 1537
FIVE STAR FORD; *U.S. Private*, pg. 1538
FIVE STAR INTERNATIONAL LLC; *U.S. Private*, pg. 1538
FIVE STAR MOTORS; *U.S. Private*, pg. 1538
FIVE STAR OF COLORADO INC.; *U.S. Private*, pg. 1538
FLAGSHIP AUTO CENTER; *U.S. Private*, pg. 1539
FLEET EQUIPMENT LLC.—See Stonepeak Partners L.P.; *U.S. Private*, pg. 3829
FLEMINGTON AUDI PORSCHE VOLKSWAGEN; *U.S. Private*, pg. 1542
FLETCH'S INC.; *U.S. Private*, pg. 1542
FLORENCE & WHITE FORD DEALERSHIP; *U.S. Private*, pg. 1546
FLOW AUTOMOTIVE CENTER OF WINSTON-SALEM, LLC; *U.S. Private*, pg. 1551
FLOW BMW; *U.S. Private*, pg. 1551
FLOW BUICK GMC OF WINSTON-SALEM; *U.S. Private*, pg. 1551
FLOW MOTORS, INC.; *U.S. Private*, pg. 1551
F. MCCLURE & SONS LTD.; *Int'l*, pg. 2595
FMI TRUCK SALES & SERVICE; *U.S. Private*, pg. 1554
FOLGER SUBARU OF CHARLOTTE; *U.S. Private*, pg. 1559
FOLSOM BUICK GMC; *U.S. Private*, pg. 1559
FOLSOM CHEVROLET; *U.S. Private*, pg. 1559
FOLSOM LAKE FORD; *U.S. Private*, pg. 1559
FOMO WORLDWIDE, INC.; *U.S. Public*, pg. 863
FORBES MOTORS INCORPORATED; *Int'l*, pg. 2729
FORD ALBERIC AUTO SALES; *U.S. Private*, pg. 1564
FORD AUTO BODY, INC.; *U.S. Private*, pg. 1564
FORD DEUTSCHLAND HOLDING GMBH—See Ford Motor Company; *U.S. Public*, pg. 865
FORD GROVES; *U.S. Private*, pg. 1564
FORDHAM AUTO SALES INC.; *U.S. Private*, pg. 1565

N.A.I.C.S. INDEX

441110 — NEW CAR DEALERS

FORD LINCOLN OF BELLEVUE—See AutoNation, Inc.; *U.S. Public*, pg. 235
FORD LINCOLN OF FRANKLIN—See Alexander Automotive Group; *U.S. Private*, pg. 163
FORD MOTOR CO. - LINCOLN DIVISION—See Ford Motor Company; *U.S. Public*, pg. 865
FORD MOTOR COMPANY OF NEW ZEALAND LTD.—See Ford Motor Company; *U.S. Public*, pg. 865
FORD OF KIRKLAND, INC.—See AutoNation, Inc.; *U.S. Public*, pg. 235
FORD OF MONTEBELLO, INC.; *U.S. Private*, pg. 1564
FORD OF OCALA INC.; *U.S. Private*, pg. 1564
FORD OF TULSA LLC; *U.S. Private*, pg. 1565
FORD TOWN OF ALBANY INC.; *U.S. Private*, pg. 1565
FOREST FORD, INC.; *U.S. Private*, pg. 1567
FOREST LAKE CHRYSLER DODGE JEEP & RAM; *U.S. Private*, pg. 1567
FORMO MOTORS; *Int'l*, pg. 2734
FORMULA FORD; *Int'l*, pg. 2736
FORMULA HONDA; *Int'l*, pg. 2737
FORRESTER LINCOLN-MERCURY INC.; *U.S. Private*, pg. 1572
FORT CITY CHRYSLER SALES LTD.; *Int'l*, pg. 2737
FORT MILL FORD, INC.—See Sonic Automotive, Inc.; *U.S. Public*, pg. 1902
FORT ROHR MOTORS INC.; *U.S. Private*, pg. 1575
FORTUNA MOTORS, INC.; *U.S. Private*, pg. 1577
FORZA MOTORS KOREA CORPORATION—See Hyosung Corporation; *Int'l*, pg. 3550
FOSHAN MEIXIN LEXUS AUTO SALES & SERVICES CO., LTD.—See China MeiDong Auto Holdings Limited; *Int'l*, pg. 1519
FOSS MOTORS, INC.; *U.S. Private*, pg. 1578
FOSTER CHEVROLET-CADILLAC, INC.; *U.S. Private*, pg. 1578
FOUNDATION AUTOMOTIVE CORP; *U.S. Private*, pg. 1579
FOURLANE FORD SALES LTD.; *Int'l*, pg. 2755
FOUR SEASONS ELECTRICAL SERVICES; *U.S. Private*, pg. 1582
FOUR SEASONS FORD; *U.S. Private*, pg. 1582
FOWLER BUICK-GMC INC.; *U.S. Private*, pg. 1583
FOWLER HYUNDAI LTD.; *Int'l*, pg. 2756
FOX AUTOMOTIVE GROUP—See AutoNation, Inc.; *U.S. Public*, pg. 235
FOX BUICK GMC—See DP Fox Ventures, LLC; *U.S. Private*, pg. 1270
FOX CHEVROLET, LLC—See AutoNation, Inc.; *U.S. Public*, pg. 235
FOX CHRYSLER DODGE JEEP; *U.S. Private*, pg. 1584
FOX FORD—See DP Fox Ventures, LLC; *U.S. Private*, pg. 1270
FOX HYUNDAI—See DP Fox Ventures, LLC; *U.S. Private*, pg. 1270
FOX MOTORS, LLC—See AutoNation, Inc.; *U.S. Public*, pg. 235
FOX TOYOTA SCION, INC.; *U.S. Private*, pg. 1585
FOX VALLEY TRUCK SERVICE INC.; *U.S. Private*, pg. 1585
FRANCIS SCOTT KEY AUDI; *U.S. Private*, pg. 1587
FRANKEL CADILLAC INC.; *U.S. Private*, pg. 1596
FRANK FLETCHER AUTO GROUP, LLC—See Frank Fletcher Companies, Ltd.; *U.S. Private*, pg. 1594
FRANK FLETCHER HONDA BENTONVILLE—See Frank Fletcher Companies, Ltd.; *U.S. Private*, pg. 1594
FRANK FLETCHER KIA BENTONVILLE—See Frank Fletcher Companies, Ltd.; *U.S. Private*, pg. 1594
FRANK FLETCHER NISSAN—See Frank Fletcher Companies, Ltd.; *U.S. Private*, pg. 1594
FRANK HYUNDAI—See Fornaca Inc.; *U.S. Private*, pg. 1572
FRANKLIN FORD; *U.S. Private*, pg. 1597
FRANKLIN PONTIAC BUICK GMC; *U.S. Private*, pg. 1597
FRANK MOTORS, INC.—See Fornaca Inc.; *U.S. Private*, pg. 1572
FRANK SHIREY CADILLAC INC.; *U.S. Private*, pg. 1595
FRANK SHIREY CADILLAC, INC.; *U.S. Private*, pg. 1595
FRANK SHOOP, INC.; *U.S. Private*, pg. 1595
FRANK W. DIVER INC.; *U.S. Private*, pg. 1595
FRASCONA BUICK, INC.; *U.S. Private*, pg. 1599
FRASER FORD SALES LTD.; *Int'l*, pg. 2765
FRED BEANS CHEVROLET, INCORPORATED; *U.S. Private*, pg. 1600
FRED BEANS FORD OF BOYERTOWN; *U.S. Private*, pg. 1600
FRED BEANS LINCOLN MERCURY; *U.S. Private*, pg. 1600
FRED BORMAN ENTERPRISES, INC.; *U.S. Private*, pg. 1600
FRED CARL'S NEW SALEM SAAB; *U.S. Private*, pg. 1600
FREDE, NORMAN CHEVROLET; *U.S. Private*, pg. 1601
FREDERICK CHEVROLET INC.; *U.S. Private*, pg. 1601
FREDERICK MOTOR CO.; *U.S. Private*, pg. 1602
FREDERICK SUPERMARKET OF CARS; *U.S. Private*, pg. 1602
FRED FORD MARTIN INC.; *U.S. Private*, pg. 1601
FRED FREDERICKS CHRYSLER; *U.S. Private*, pg. 1601
FRED HAAS COUNTRY, L.P.—See Haas & Haas, LLC; *U.S. Private*, pg. 1837

FRED HAAS MOTORS, LTD.—See Haas & Haas, LLC; *U.S. Private*, pg. 1837
FRED HAAS NISSAN, L.P.—See Haas & Haas, LLC; *U.S. Private*, pg. 1837
FRED JONES ENTERPRISES, INC.; *U.S. Private*, pg. 1601
FRED LAVERY COMPANY—See US Auto Group Limited; *U.S. Private*, pg. 4317
FRED MARTIN NISSAN LLC.; *U.S. Private*, pg. 1601
FRED MARTIN SUPERSTORE; *U.S. Private*, pg. 1601
FRED MUELLER AUTOMOTIVE, INC.; *U.S. Private*, pg. 1601
FREEDOM CHEVROLET - SAN ANTONIO—See Group 1 Automotive, Inc.; *U.S. Public*, pg. 971
FREEDOM FORD SALES LTD; *Int'l*, pg. 2769
FREEDOM LEXINGTON; *U.S. Private*, pg. 1603
FREEHOLD CHRYSLER JEEP; *U.S. Private*, pg. 1604
FREEHOLD FORD INC.; *U.S. Private*, pg. 1604
FREEHOLD PONTIAC BUICK GMC; *U.S. Private*, pg. 1604
FREEHOLD SUBARU-DODGE; *U.S. Private*, pg. 1604
FREEHOLD TOYOTA; *U.S. Private*, pg. 1604
FREELAND MOORE, INC.; *U.S. Private*, pg. 1605
FREEMAN AUTOMOTIVE COMPANY LLC; *U.S. Private*, pg. 1605
FREEWAY FORD TRUCK SALES, INC.; *U.S. Private*, pg. 1607
FREEWAY MOTORS INC.; *U.S. Private*, pg. 1607
FREIGHTLINER OF AUSTIN; *U.S. Private*, pg. 1607
FREIGHTLINER OF DES MOINES; *U.S. Private*, pg. 1608
FREIGHTLINER OF HARTFORD, INC.; *U.S. Private*, pg. 1608
FREIGHTLINER OF KELOWNA LTD.—See Velocity Vehicle Group; *U.S. Private*, pg. 4355
FREIGHTLINER OF NEW HAMPSHIRE - LEBANON—See Freightliner of New Hampshire; *U.S. Private*, pg. 1608
FREMONT AUTO CENTER INC.; *U.S. Private*, pg. 1608
FREMONT MOTOR COMPANY; *U.S. Private*, pg. 1608
FRENCHIES CHEVROLET; *U.S. Private*, pg. 1609
FRESNO TRUCK CENTER; *U.S. Private*, pg. 1610
FRIENDLY CHEVROLET CO. INC.; *U.S. Private*, pg. 1611
FRIENDLY CHEVROLET, INC.; *U.S. Private*, pg. 1611
FRIENDLY CHRYSLER JEEP; *U.S. Private*, pg. 1611
FRIENDLY FORD, INC.; *U.S. Private*, pg. 1611
FRIENDLY FORD; *U.S. Private*, pg. 1611
FRIENDSHIP AUTOMOTIVE INC.; *U.S. Private*, pg. 1612
FRONTIER CHRYSLER LTD; *Int'l*, pg. 2795
FRONTIER DODGE—See Autoplex Automotive LP; *U.S. Private*, pg. 401
FRONTIER FORD; *U.S. Private*, pg. 1615
FT. LAUDERDALE NISSAN, INC.—See AutoNation, Inc.; *U.S. Public*, pg. 235
FT. MYERS TOYOTA INC.; *U.S. Private*, pg. 1618
FUCCILLO AUTOMOTIVE GROUP INC.; *U.S. Private*, pg. 1619
FUCCILLO CHEVROLET PONTIAC BUICK; *U.S. Private*, pg. 1619
FUCCILLO CHRYSLER OF NELLISTON, INC.; *U.S. Private*, pg. 1619
FUJIAN YONGDA AUTOMOBILE SALES AND SERVICES CO., LTD.—See China Yongda Automobiles Services Holdings Limited; *Int'l*, pg. 1564
FULLER FORD, INC.; *U.S. Private*, pg. 1621
FUN TOWN RV LP; *U.S. Private*, pg. 1622
FURY MOTORS INC.; *U.S. Private*, pg. 1625
FUSZ, LOUIS NISSAN- MAZDA, INC.; *U.S. Private*, pg. 1626
FUTURE FORD OF CONCORD, LLC.; *U.S. Private*, pg. 1627
FUTURE SHERIDAN FORD SALES INC.; *U.S. Private*, pg. 1627
FUZHOU YONGDA AUTOMOBILE SALES AND SERVICES CO., LTD.—See China Yongda Automobiles Services Holdings Limited; *Int'l*, pg. 1564
FVTS ACQUISITION CO., INC.; *U.S. Private*, pg. 1628
FXC CHRYSLER PLYMOUTH INC.; *U.S. Private*, pg. 1628
GABRIELLI TRUCK SALES LTD.; *U.S. Private*, pg. 1632
GAC AUTO GROUP, INC.; *U.S. Private*, pg. 1632
GA CDJR MOTORS, LLC—See AutoNation, Inc.; *U.S. Public*, pg. 235
GA COLUMBUS IMPORTS, LLC—See AutoNation, Inc.; *U.S. Public*, pg. 235
GAFFNEY BUICK-GMC, INC.; *U.S. Private*, pg. 1634
GAGE CHEVROLET INC.; *U.S. Private*, pg. 1634
GAGE CHRYSLER-PLYMOUTH-DODGE INC.; *U.S. Private*, pg. 1634
GA H IMPORTS, LLC—See AutoNation, Inc.; *U.S. Public*, pg. 235
GA HY IMPORTS, LLC—See AutoNation, Inc.; *U.S. Public*, pg. 235
GAILLAC AUTO; *Int'l*, pg. 2869
GALAXY TOYOTA; *U.S. Private*, pg. 1636
GALEANA CHRYSLER DODGE JEEP—See Galeana Automotive Group; *U.S. Private*, pg. 1636
GALESBURG NISSAN; *U.S. Private*, pg. 1637
GALE TOYOTA; *U.S. Private*, pg. 1636
GALLERY AUTOMOTIVE GROUP, LLC; *U.S. Private*, pg. 1639
GALLES CHEVROLET COMPANY; *U.S. Private*, pg. 1639
GALLES CHEVROLET; *U.S. Private*, pg. 1639

GALLINGER FORD LINCOLN; *Int'l*, pg. 2874
GALLO MOTOR CENTER CORP.; *U.S. Private*, pg. 1640
GALLOWAY FAMILY OF DEALERSHIPS; *U.S. Private*, pg. 1640
GALPIN FORD INCORPORATED; *U.S. Private*, pg. 1640
GALPIN MOTORS, INC.; *U.S. Private*, pg. 1640
GALT CHRYSLER DODGE LTD.; *Int'l*, pg. 2876
GANANOQUE MOTORS LTD; *Int'l*, pg. 2880
GANLEY CHRYSLER JEEP DODGE RAM, INC.; *U.S. Private*, pg. 1641
GANLEY EAST INC.; *U.S. Private*, pg. 1641
GARAGE AUBREE; *Int'l*, pg. 2883
GARAGE AUTO DE L OUEST; *Int'l*, pg. 2883
GARAGE HEINZLE; *Int'l*, pg. 2883
GARAGE ISLA VERDE, INC.; *U.S. Private*, pg. 1642
GARAGE MARCEL VILLENEUVE INC.; *Int'l*, pg. 2883
GARAGE VURPILLOT; *Int'l*, pg. 2883
GARBER BUICK GMC; *U.S. Private*, pg. 1642
GARBER CHEVROLET INC.—See Garber Management Group Inc.; *U.S. Private*, pg. 1642
GARBER MANAGEMENT GROUP INC.; *U.S. Private*, pg. 1642
GARBER NISSAN INC.—See Garber Management Group Inc.; *U.S. Private*, pg. 1642
GARCIA IMPORTS INC.; *U.S. Private*, pg. 1642
GARDANNE AUTOMOBILES; *Int'l*, pg. 2884
GARFF ENTERPRISES, INC.; *U.S. Private*, pg. 1644
GARLYN O. SHELTON INC.; *U.S. Private*, pg. 1645
GARVEY VOLKSWAGEN INC.; *U.S. Private*, pg. 1646
GARY MATHEWS MOTORS INC.; *U.S. Private*, pg. 1646
GARY YEOMANS FORD INC.; *U.S. Private*, pg. 1647
GASTON GRAWEY; *Int'l*, pg. 2888
GATE CITY LINCOLN MERCURY; *U.S. Private*, pg. 1649
GATEWAY BUICK GMC; *U.S. Private*, pg. 1650
GATEWAY LINCOLN-MERCURY INCORPORATED; *U.S. Private*, pg. 1650
GATEWAY MANAGEMENT SERVICES LTD; *U.S. Private*, pg. 1650
GATOR CHRYSLER INC.; *U.S. Private*, pg. 1651
GATOR FORD TRUCK SALES INC.; *U.S. Private*, pg. 1651
GAULT CHEVROLET CO. INC.; *U.S. Private*, pg. 1652
G.B. IMPORT SALES & SERVICE, LLC—See AutoNation, Inc.; *U.S. Public*, pg. 235
GDS AUTOMOBILES; *Int'l*, pg. 2896
GEBHARDT AUTOMOTIVE INC.; *U.S. Private*, pg. 1655
GEMINI AUTO INC.; *Int'l*, pg. 2916
GEMY PONTIVY; *Int'l*, pg. 2916
GENDRON FORD; *Int'l*, pg. 2917
GENE EVANS FORD, LLC—See AutoNation, Inc.; *U.S. Public*, pg. 235
GENE EVANS FORD, LLC—See AutoNation, Inc.; *U.S. Public*, pg. 235
GENE HUGGINS IMPORTS INC.—See Pearson-Huggins Companies Inc.; *U.S. Private*, pg. 3126
GENE LATTA FORD INC.; *U.S. Private*, pg. 1660
GENE LATTA FORD, INC.; *U.S. Private*, pg. 1660
GENERAL MOTORS AUTOMOBILES PHILIPPINES, INC.—See General Motors Company; *U.S. Public*, pg. 924
GENERAL MOTORS JAPAN LIMITED—See General Motors Company; *U.S. Public*, pg. 925
GENERAL MOTORS TRKIYE LIMITED SIRKETI—See General Motors Company; *U.S. Public*, pg. 925
GENERAL TRUCK SALES & SERVICE; *U.S. Private*, pg. 1667
GENE STEVENS HONDA; *U.S. Private*, pg. 1660
GENGRAS MOTOR CARS, INC.; *U.S. Private*, pg. 1671
GENOA MOTORS INC.; *U.S. Private*, pg. 1673
GENSINGER MOTORS INC.; *U.S. Private*, pg. 1673
GENT STORE BY BILIA VERSTRAETEN BVBA—See Bilia AB; *Int'l*, pg. 1029
GEO. BYERS SONS HOLDING INC.; *U.S. Private*, pg. 1680
GEO. GROWNEY MOTORS, INC.; *U.S. Private*, pg. 1680
GEORGE BALLENTINE FORD INC.; *U.S. Private*, pg. 1681
GEORGE CHEVROLET A CALIFORNIA CORPORATION; *U.S. Private*, pg. 1681
GEORGE COLEMAN MOTOR CO., INC.; *U.S. Private*, pg. 1681
GEORGE GEE AUTOMOTIVE; *U.S. Private*, pg. 1682
GEORGE HARTE NISSAN INC.; *U.S. Private*, pg. 1682
GEORGE M. YOCUM, INCORPORATED; *U.S. Private*, pg. 1682
GEORGE NAHAS OLDSMOBILE INC.; *U.S. Private*, pg. 1682
GEORGE SUTHERLIN NISSAN, LLC—See AutoNation, Inc.; *U.S. Public*, pg. 235
GEORGE VETESNIK MOTORS INC.; *U.S. Private*, pg. 1683
GEORGE WEBER CHEVROLET COMPANY; *U.S. Private*, pg. 1683
GEORGIA AUTOMOTIVE GROUP, INC.—See General Motors Company; *U.S. Public*, pg. 925
GEORGIAN CHEVROLET BUICK GMC; *Int'l*, pg. 2939
GERALDINE NOMINEES PTY LTD—See Eagers Automotive Limited; *Int'l*, pg. 2263
GERALD JONES VOLKSWAGEN INC.; *U.S. Private*, pg. 1685
GERALD NISSAN OF NORTH AURORA; *U.S. Private*, pg. 1686

441110 — NEW CAR DEALERS

GERMAIN FORD OF COLUMBUS, LLC—See Germain Motor Company; *U.S. Private*, pg. 1687
GERMAIN LEXUS OF DUBLIN—See Germain Motor Company; *U.S. Private*, pg. 1687
GERMAIN LEXUS OF EASTON—See Germain Motor Company; *U.S. Private*, pg. 1687
GERMAIN MOTOR COMPANY; *U.S. Private*, pg. 1686
GERMAIN NISSAN OF NEW ALBANY, INC.—See Germain Motor Company; *U.S. Private*, pg. 1687
GERMAIN OF NAPLES, INC.—See Germain Motor Company; *U.S. Private*, pg. 1687
GERMAIN ON TAMIAMI, LLC—See Germain Motor Company; *U.S. Private*, pg. 1687
GERMAN AUTO IMPORT NETWORK - VANCOUVER ISLAND; *Int'l*, pg. 2942
GERRISH HONDA; *U.S. Private*, pg. 1687
GERRY WOOD AUTOMOTIVE, LLC; *U.S. Private*, pg. 1687
GERVAIS LINCOLN MERCURY INC.; *U.S. Private*, pg. 1688
GETTEL AUTOMOTIVE MANAGEMENT GROUP; *U.S. Private*, pg. 1689
GETTEL ENTERPRISE INC.; *U.S. Private*, pg. 1689
GETTEL FORD-MERCURY INC.; *U.S. Private*, pg. 1689
GEWEKE CO.; *U.S. Private*, pg. 1689
GEZON MOTORS, INC.; *U.S. Private*, pg. 1689
G&G INCORPORATED; *U.S. Private*, pg. 1628
GHABBOUR CONTINENTAL TRADING CO. S.A.E.—See Ghabbour Auto S.A.E.; *Int'l*, pg. 2958
GHENT CHEVROLET CADILLAC; *U.S. Private*, pg. 1690
GHENT MOTOR CO.; *U.S. Private*, pg. 1690
GIAI JACQUIS SAS; *Int'l*, pg. 2961
GIANT AUTOMOTIVE GROUP; *U.S. Private*, pg. 1694
GIANT AUTOS (1997) PTY LTD—See Eagers Automotive Limited; *Int'l*, pg. 2263
GIANT CHEVROLET COMPANY; *U.S. Private*, pg. 1694
GIBBS INTERNATIONAL TRUCK CENTERS INCORPORATED; *U.S. Private*, pg. 1695
GILBERT CHEVROLET INC.; *U.S. Private*, pg. 1698
GILBOY FORD MERCURY INC.; *U.S. Private*, pg. 1699
GILDNER AUTO GROUP; *U.S. Private*, pg. 1699
GILLAND CHEVROLET-PONTIAC-GMC INC.; *U.S. Private*, pg. 1700
GILL AUTOMOTIVE GROUP, INC.; *U.S. Private*, pg. 1700
GILLELAND CHEVROLET INC.; *U.S. Private*, pg. 1700
GILLIE HYDE AUTO GROUP; *U.S. Private*, pg. 1700
GILLISS & GILLISS INC.; *U.S. Private*, pg. 1700
GILLMAN CHRYSLER JEEP DODGE RAM—See Gillman Companies; *U.S. Private*, pg. 1700
GILLMAN COMPANIES; *U.S. Private*, pg. 1700
GILLMAN IMPORTS NORTH INC.—See Gillman Companies; *U.S. Private*, pg. 1700
GILLMAN NORTH INC.—See Gillman Companies; *U.S. Private*, pg. 1700
GILROY CHEVROLET CADILLAC INC.; *U.S. Private*, pg. 1701
GILROY HONDA, INC.; *U.S. Private*, pg. 1701
GINN CHEVROLET; *U.S. Private*, pg. 1702
GIRARD FORD; *U.S. Private*, pg. 1702
GIUFFRE; *U.S. Private*, pg. 1703
GIUFFRE VOLVO INC.; *U.S. Private*, pg. 1703
GJOVIK CHEVROLET BUICK PONTIAC GMC, INC.; *U.S. Private*, pg. 1703
GJOVIK FORD-MERCURY, INC.; *U.S. Private*, pg. 1703
GLASSFORD MOTORS LIMITED; *Int'l*, pg. 2989
GLASSMAN AUTOMOTIVE GROUP; *U.S. Private*, pg. 1706
GLASSMAN OLDSMOBILE INC.; *U.S. Private*, pg. 1707
GLENDALE DODGE CHRYSLER JEEP; *U.S. Private*, pg. 1710
GLENDALE INFINITI—See Sage Holding Company; *U.S. Private*, pg. 3526
GLENDALE NISSAN/INFINITI, INC.—See Sage Holding Company; *U.S. Private*, pg. 3526
GLENN E. THOMAS CHRYSLER DODGE JEEP; *U.S. Private*, pg. 1710
GLENN JONES AUTO CENTER; *U.S. Private*, pg. 1710
GLENN NISSAN INC.; *U.S. Private*, pg. 1710
GLENN POLK AUTOPLEX; *U.S. Private*, pg. 1710
GLENWAY MOTOR CAR CO., INC.; *U.S. Private*, pg. 1711
GLENWOOD SPRINGS FORD, INC.; *U.S. Private*, pg. 1711
G.L. SAYRE INCORPORATED; *U.S. Private*, pg. 1631
GM AUTOMOTIVE UK—See General Motors Company; *U.S. Public*, pg. 928
GMC BERGEYS INC.—See Bergeys Inc.; *U.S. Private*, pg. 531
GM DAEWOO UK LIMITED—See General Motors Company; *U.S. Public*, pg. 924
GMST, LLC; *U.S. Private*, pg. 1723
GO AUTO; *Int'l*, pg. 3017
GO CARS AND TRUCKS—See AutoNation, Inc.; *U.S. Public*, pg. 235
GOLD MOTORS, INC.; *U.S. Private*, pg. 1728
GOLDSTEIN ENTERPRISES INC.; *U.S. Private*, pg. 1735
GOLF MILL FORD; *U.S. Private*, pg. 1736
GOLLING PONTIAC GMC TRUCK INC.; *U.S. Private*, pg. 1736
GO MOTOR RETAILING LIMITED—See General Motors Company; *U.S. Public*, pg. 928
GOODMAN TRUCK & TRACTOR COMPANY, INC.; *U.S. Private*, pg. 1739

GOOD WHEELS AUTOMOTIVE GROUP LLC; *U.S. Private*, pg. 1738
GOODWIN'S CHEVROLET COMPANY; *U.S. Private*, pg. 1741
GORDIE BOUCHER FORD OF KENOSHA, INC.—See The Boucher Group, Inc.; *U.S. Private*, pg. 3998
GORDIE BOUCHER FORD OF MENOMONEE FALLS, INC.—See The Boucher Group, Inc.; *U.S. Private*, pg. 3998
GORDON CHEVROLET CO.; *U.S. Private*, pg. 1742
GORDON CHEVROLET-GEO; *U.S. Private*, pg. 1742
GORD SCOTT NISSAN; *Int'l*, pg. 3042
GORGES MOTOR COMPANY INC.; *U.S. Private*, pg. 1743
GORNO FORD; *U.S. Private*, pg. 1744
GOSS DODGE, INC.; *U.S. Private*, pg. 1744
GOSS DODGE INC.; *U.S. Private*, pg. 1744
GOSSETT MOTOR CARS INC.; *U.S. Private*, pg. 1744
GOULD CHEVROLET; *U.S. Private*, pg. 1745
GOVERNMENT BOULEVARD MOTORS, INC.—See AutoNation, Inc.; *U.S. Public*, pg. 235
GPI LA-H, LLC—See Group 1 Automotive, Inc.; *U.S. Public*, pg. 971
GPI NM-J, INC.—See Group 1 Automotive, Inc.; *U.S. Public*, pg. 971
GPI NM-LRII, INC.—See Group 1 Automotive, Inc.; *U.S. Public*, pg. 971
GPI TX-AII, INC.—See Group 1 Automotive, Inc.; *U.S. Public*, pg. 971
GPI TX-DMIV, INC.—See Group 1 Automotive, Inc.; *U.S. Public*, pg. 971
GPI TX-HIII, INC.—See Group 1 Automotive, Inc.; *U.S. Public*, pg. 971
GRABIAK CHEVROLET, INC.; *U.S. Private*, pg. 1748
GRAFF CHEVROLET COMPANY; *U.S. Private*, pg. 1750
GRAFF MOTOR SALES INC.; *U.S. Private*, pg. 1750
GRAFF TRUCK CENTERS INC.; *U.S. Private*, pg. 1750
GRAFT SALES AND SERVICE INC.; *U.S. Private*, pg. 1751
GRAHAM AUTOMALL; *U.S. Private*, pg. 1751
GRAHAM AUTOMOTIVE LLC—See Graham Holdings Company; *U.S. Public*, pg. 954
GRAINGER HONDA; *U.S. Private*, pg. 1751
GRAND AUTOS 2005 PTY LTD—See Eagers Automotive Limited; *Int'l*, pg. 2263
GRAND BUICK GMC KIA; *U.S. Private*, pg. 1752
GRAND BUICK, INC.; *U.S. Private*, pg. 1752
GRAND MOTORS PRESTIGE PTY LTD.; *Int'l*, pg. 3055
GRAND PRIX PERFORMANCE OF HICKSVILLE; *U.S. Private*, pg. 1753
GRANITE RUN BUICK GMC, INC.; *U.S. Private*, pg. 1756
GRANSPORT AUTO EOOD—See Eurohold Bulgaria AD; *Int'l*, pg. 2553
GRANVILLE TOYOTA; *Int'l*, pg. 3060
GRAPEVINE DODGE CHRYSLER JEEP; *U.S. Private*, pg. 1757
GRAVA OF MEDFORD, INC.; *U.S. Private*, pg. 1758
GRAY, BILL AUTOMOTIVE ENTERPRISES INC.; *U.S. Private*, pg. 1759
GRAY-DANIELS AUTO FAMILY—See Asbury Automotive Group, Inc.; *U.S. Public*, pg. 209
GRAY-DANIELS FORD; *U.S. Private*, pg. 1759
GRAYSON HYUNDAI-SUBARU; *U.S. Private*, pg. 1761
GREAT PLAINS FORD SALES; *Int'l*, pg. 3065
GREENBRIER CHRYSLER-JEEP—See Southern Hospitality Auto Group of Virginia; *U.S. Private*, pg. 3732
GREEN CHEVROLET-BUICK-GMC, INC.; *U.S. Private*, pg. 1772
GREEN CHEVROLET, INC.; *U.S. Private*, pg. 1772
GREEN FAMILY STORES, INC.; *U.S. Private*, pg. 1772
GREEN FORD INC.; *U.S. Private*, pg. 1773
GREEN FORD SALES INC.; *U.S. Private*, pg. 1773
GREEN GIFFORD MOTOR CORP.; *U.S. Private*, pg. 1773
GREENHOUS GROUP INC.; *Int'l*, pg. 3075
GREEN'S SUZUKI; *U.S. Private*, pg. 1774
GREEN TOYOTA OF LEXINGTON INC.; *U.S. Private*, pg. 1774
GREENTREE MOTORS DANBURY INC.; *U.S. Private*, pg. 1780
GREENWAY FORD, INC.; *U.S. Private*, pg. 1781
GREENWICH AUTOMOTIVE ENTERPRISES; *U.S. Private*, pg. 1781
GREENWICH HONDA; *U.S. Private*, pg. 1781
GREG BUICK PONTIAC CADILLAC; *U.S. Private*, pg. 1782
GREGG SMITH FORD LINCOLN MERCURY INC.; *U.S. Private*, pg. 1782
GREG LEBLANC INC.; *U.S. Private*, pg. 1782
GREGORIS NISSAN; *U.S. Private*, pg. 1783
GREG WEEKS INC.; *U.S. Private*, pg. 1782
GREINER PONTIAC-BUICK, INC.; *U.S. Private*, pg. 1783
GREINER SCHMIDT MOTOR COMPANY; *U.S. Private*, pg. 1783
GRIFFIN CHRYSLER DODGE JEEP; *U.S. Private*, pg. 1787
GRIFFIN FORD INC.; *U.S. Private*, pg. 1787
GRIFFIN FORD-LINCOLN-MERCURY INC.; *U.S. Private*, pg. 1787
GRIFFIN'S HUB CHRYSLER JEEP DODGE; *U.S. Private*, pg. 1788
GRIFFITH MOTOR COMPANY; *U.S. Private*, pg. 1789
GRIFFITH MOTORS INC.; *U.S. Private*, pg. 1789

GRIFFITHS FORD; *Int'l*, pg. 3083
GRINER PONTIAC CADILLAC NISSEN; *U.S. Private*, pg. 1790
GROGAN'S TOWNE CHRYSLER DODGE LLC—See Grogans Towne Chrysler Dodge Inc.; *U.S. Private*, pg. 1791
GROPPETTI AUTOMOTIVE; *U.S. Private*, pg. 1792
GROSSINGER CITY AUTOPLEX, INC.; *U.S. Private*, pg. 1792
GROSSINGER'S NORTH AUTOCORP, INC.; *U.S. Private*, pg. 1792
GROSSMAN CHEVROLET; *U.S. Private*, pg. 1792
GROSS MOTORS AUTOMOTIVE GROUP; *U.S. Private*, pg. 1792
GROUP 1 AUTOMOTIVE, INC.; *U.S. Public*, pg. 970
GROVERT MOTOR CO.; *U.S. Private*, pg. 1795
GRUBBS INFINITI, LTD.; *U.S. Private*, pg. 1796
GSL GM CITY; *Int'l*, pg. 3150
G.STONE MOTORS, INC.; *U.S. Private*, pg. 1631
GUAN CHAO HOLDINGS LIMITED; *Int'l*, pg. 3152
GUANGZHOU MEIBAOHANG AUTO SALES & SERVICES CO., LTD.—See China MeiDong Auto Holdings Limited; *Int'l*, pg. 1519
GUARAGUAO TRUCK SALES INC.; *U.S. Private*, pg. 1808
GUELPH NISSAN; *Int'l*, pg. 3172
GUELPH VOLKSWAGEN; *Int'l*, pg. 3172
GUESS FORD, INC.—See Guess Motors, Inc.; *U.S. Private*, pg. 1810
GUILDFORD MOTORS INC; *Int'l*, pg. 3173
GULF COAST TRUCK & EQUIPMENT CO., INC.; *U.S. Private*, pg. 1815
GULF INTERNATIONAL TRUCKS; *U.S. Private*, pg. 1816
GULF MANAGEMENT,INC.—See AutoNation, Inc.; *U.S. Public*, pg. 235
GUNN PONTIAC GMC, INC.—See Curtis C. Gunn, Inc.; *U.S. Private*, pg. 1126
GUNTHER MOTOR COMPANY; *U.S. Private*, pg. 1818
GUNTHER VOLKSWAGON OF COCONUT CREEK; *U.S. Private*, pg. 1818
GURLEY MOTOR COMPANY; *U.S. Private*, pg. 1819
GURNEE DODGE CHRYSLER JEEP, INC.; *U.S. Private*, pg. 1819
GURNEE HYUNDAI MOTORS; *U.S. Private*, pg. 1819
GUS MACHADO FORD, INC.—See Gus Machado Enterprises, Inc.; *U.S. Private*, pg. 1819
GUSTAFSON'S KIA; *Int'l*, pg. 3188
GUSWEILER GM CENTER; *U.S. Private*, pg. 1819
GUY SALMON HONDA LIMITED—See Penske Automotive Group, Inc.; *U.S. Public*, pg. 1666
GUY SALMON JAGUAR STOCKPORT—See Penske Automotive Group, Inc.; *U.S. Public*, pg. 1666
GUY SALMON LIMITED—See Penske Automotive Group, Inc.; *U.S. Public*, pg. 1666
GWINNETT PLACE HONDA—See The Hendrick Companies, LLC; *U.S. Private*, pg. 4051
HAAS, JEFF MAZDA; *U.S. Private*, pg. 1837
HADDAD DODGE; *U.S. Private*, pg. 1838
HADWIN WHITE PONTIAC - BUICK - GMC TRUCK; *U.S. Private*, pg. 1839
HAJI HUSEIN ALIREZA & CO. LTD.; *Int'l*, pg. 3219
HALDEMAN LINCOLN MERCURY, INC.; *U.S. Private*, pg. 1842
HALEY OF FARMVILLE, INC.; *U.S. Private*, pg. 1842
HALFWAY MOTORS 1989 LTD; *Int'l*, pg. 3229
HALIFAX CHRYSLER DODGE; *Int'l*, pg. 3229
HALLADAY MOTORS INC.; *U.S. Private*, pg. 1843
HALL AUTOMOTIVE; *U.S. Private*, pg. 1843
HALL AUTO WORLD INC.; *U.S. Private*, pg. 1843
HALL IMPORTS—See Hall Automotive; *U.S. Private*, pg. 1843
HALL MANAGEMENT COMPANY; *U.S. Private*, pg. 1843
HALLMARK FORD SALES LIMITED; *Int'l*, pg. 3230
HALLMARK JEEP INC.; *U.S. Private*, pg. 1845
HALLMARK VOLKSWAGEN MITSUBISHI; *U.S. Private*, pg. 1845
HALL NISSAN VIRGINIA BEACH; *U.S. Private*, pg. 1843
HAL MCBRIDE CAR SALES INCORPORATED; *U.S. Private*, pg. 1841
HALREC INC.; *U.S. Private*, pg. 1846
HAMBY CHEVROLET-BUICK-GMC TRUCK; *U.S. Private*, pg. 1847
HAMER TOYOTA INC.; *U.S. Private*, pg. 1847
HAMILTON IMPORTS; *U.S. Private*, pg. 1848
HAMMONASSET FORD-LINCOLN-MERCURY INC.; *U.S. Private*, pg. 1849
HAMPTON CHEVROLET MAZDA; *U.S. Private*, pg. 1851
HAMPTON TOYOTA; *U.S. Private*, pg. 1851
HANDAN BAOHE AUTOMOBILE SALES AND SERVICE CO., LTD.—See China Yongda Automobiles Services Holdings Limited; *Int'l*, pg. 1564
HANDY BUICK-GMC-CADILLAC INC.; *U.S. Private*, pg. 1853
HANFORD CHRYSLER-DODGE-JEEP, INC.; *U.S. Private*, pg. 1853
HANIGAN CHEVROLET; *U.S. Private*, pg. 1853
HANKOOK MOTORS INC.; *U.S. Private*, pg. 1854
HANLEES HILLTOP TOYOTA; *U.S. Private*, pg. 1854
HANNAH MOTOR COMPANY INCORPORATED; *U.S. Private*, pg. 1855

N.A.I.C.S. INDEX

441110 — NEW CAR DEALERS

HANNER CHEVROLET PONTIAC; *U.S. Private*, pg. 1855
HANSEL HONDA; *U.S. Private*, pg. 1856
HANSEN CHEVROLET CO.; *U.S. Private*, pg. 1856
HAP SENG STAR SDN. BHD.—See Hap Seng Consolidated Berhad; *Int'l*, pg. 3268
HARADEN MOTORCAR CORP.; *U.S. Private*, pg. 1857
HARBOR MOTORS; *U.S. Private*, pg. 1859
HARBOURVIEW AUTOHAUS LTD.; *Int'l*, pg. 3272
HARCHELROAD MOTORS INC.; *U.S. Private*, pg. 1861
HARDIN BUICK PONTIAC GMC; *U.S. Private*, pg. 1863
HARDIN HONDA; *U.S. Private*, pg. 1863
HARDY CHEVROLET, INC.; *U.S. Private*, pg. 1864
HARKNESS AUTO GROUP, INC.—See Pete Harkness Auto Group, Inc.; *U.S. Private*, pg. 3157
HAROLD MATTHEWS NISSAN INC.; *U.S. Private*, pg. 1867
HAROLD ZEIGLER AUTO GROUP, INC.; *U.S. Private*, pg. 1867
HAROLD ZEIGLER FORD LINCOLN MERCURY-ELKHART—See Harold Zeigler Lincoln-Mercury; *U.S. Private*, pg. 1867
HAROLD ZEIGLER LINCOLN-MERCURY; *U.S. Private*, pg. 1867
HARPER CHEVROLET-BUICK-GMC; *U.S. Private*, pg. 1867
HARRELD CHEVROLET CO.; *U.S. Private*, pg. 1868
HARRIS FORD, INC.; *U.S. Private*, pg. 1869
HARRIS MAZDA; *Int'l*, pg. 3278
HARRIS OLDSMOBILE, INCORPORATED; *U.S. Private*, pg. 1870
HARRISON FORD, INC.; *U.S. Private*, pg. 1870
HARR MOTOR COMPANY; *U.S. Private*, pg. 1868
HARRY FAIRBAIRN LIMITED—See Arnold Clark Automobiles Limited; *Int'l*, pg. 576
HARRY ROBINSON BUICK GMC; *U.S. Private*, pg. 1872
HARRY'S ON THE HILL; *U.S. Private*, pg. 1872
HARTE INFINITI INC.; *U.S. Private*, pg. 1873
HARTE NISSAN, INC.; *U.S. Private*, pg. 1873
HARTFORD TOYOTA SUPERSTORE; *U.S. Private*, pg. 1873
HARTWELL PLC; *Int'l*, pg. 3280
HARVEY CADILLAC COMPANY; *U.S. Private*, pg. 1877
HARVEY CADILLAC; *U.S. Private*, pg. 1877
HARVEY CHEVROLET CORPORATION; *U.S. Private*, pg. 1877
HARVEY GM, LLC—See Group 1 Automotive, Inc.; *U.S. Public*, pg. 971
HARVEY M. HARPER CO.; *U.S. Private*, pg. 1878
HASSEL MOTORS INC.—See Group 1 Automotive, Inc.; *U.S. Public*, pg. 971
HATCHER CHEVROLET BUICK PONTIAC OLDS GMC INC.; *U.S. Private*, pg. 1879
HATHEWAY (TRACADIE) LTEE; *Int'l*, pg. 3284
HAUTE-NORMANDIE VEHICULES INDUSTRIELS; *Int'l*, pg. 3285
HAVILL-SPOERL FORD LINCOLN, INC.; *U.S. Private*, pg. 1881
HAVILL-SPOERL MOTOR SALES, LTD.; *U.S. Private*, pg. 1881
HAWK AUTO GROUP; *U.S. Private*, pg. 1882
HAWKINS CHEVROLET INC.; *U.S. Private*, pg. 1883
HAWKINSON NISSAN, LLC.; *U.S. Private*, pg. 1883
HAWTHORNE AUTOMOBILE SALES CO.; *U.S. Private*, pg. 1884
HAYDOCY PONTIAC-GMC TRUCK INC.; *U.S. Private*, pg. 1884
HAYES CHRYSLER PLYMOUTH, INC.; *U.S. Private*, pg. 1884
HAYES FORD - LINCOLN MERCURY; *U.S. Private*, pg. 1884
HAYWOOD B. HYMAN JR. INC.; *U.S. Private*, pg. 1886
HBL, LLC—See Penske Automotive Group, Inc.; *U.S. Public*, pg. 1665
H & C MOTORS, INC.; *U.S. Private*, pg. 1822
HEADQUARTER TOYOTA; *U.S. Private*, pg. 1891
HEALEY BROTHERS AUTOMOTIVE; *U.S. Private*, pg. 1891
HEARTLAND FORD SALES, INC.; *Int'l*, pg. 3304
HEFFNER MOTORS LIMITED; *Int'l*, pg. 3308
HEIDEBREICHT, INC.; *U.S. Private*, pg. 1904
HEINRICH CHEVROLET; *U.S. Private*, pg. 1905
HEINTZ AUTOMOTIVE; *U.S. Private*, pg. 1905
HEISER AUTOMOTIVE GROUP INC.; *U.S. Private*, pg. 1905
HEISER TOYOTA, INC.; *U.S. Private*, pg. 1905
HELENA MOTORS, LLC; *U.S. Private*, pg. 1906
HELFMAN DODGE CHRYSLER JEEP FIAT; *U.S. Private*, pg. 1906
HELFMAN ENTERPRISES INC.; *U.S. Private*, pg. 1906
HELLER AUTO GROUP; *U.S. Private*, pg. 1906
HELLER MOTORS, INC.; *U.S. Private*, pg. 1907
HELSTON GARAGES GROUP; *Int'l*, pg. 3338
HEMPSTEAD FORD LINCOLN; *U.S. Private*, pg. 1913
HENDRICK BMW—See The Hendrick Companies, LLC; *U.S. Private*, pg. 4051
HENDRICK CHEVROLET CADILLAC; *U.S. Private*, pg. 1914
HENDRICK CHRYSLER JEEP; *U.S. Private*, pg. 1914
HENDRICK CORPORATION, LLC—See The Hendrick Companies, LLC; *U.S. Private*, pg. 4051
HENDRICK MOTORS OF CHARLOTTE—See The Hendrick Companies, LLC; *U.S. Private*, pg. 4051
HENDY GROUP LTD.; *Int'l*, pg. 3345
HENGYANG MEIBAOHANG AUTO SALES & SERVICES CO., LTD.—See China MeiDong Auto Holdings Limited; *Int'l*, pg. 1519
HENINGER TOYOTA; *Int'l*, pg. 3348
HENKEL CHRYSLER JEEP INC.; *U.S. Private*, pg. 1916
HENNESSY CADILLAC, INC.; *U.S. Private*, pg. 1916
HENNESSY LEXUS OF ATLANTA; *U.S. Private*, pg. 1916
HENNESSY'S RIVER VIEW FORD; *U.S. Private*, pg. 1916
HENRY DAY FORD, INC.; *U.S. Private*, pg. 1918
HENRY MOTORS INCORPORADO; *U.S. Private*, pg. 1919
HENSON FORD INC.—See Henson Motor Company Inc.; *U.S. Private*, pg. 1920
HENSON MOTOR COMPANY INC.; *U.S. Private*, pg. 1920
HERB CHAMBERS HONDA OF SEEKONK—See Herb Chambers of Somerville, Inc.; *U.S. Private*, pg. 1920
HERB CHAMBERS OF NATICK, INC.—See Herb Chambers of Somerville, Inc.; *U.S. Private*, pg. 1920
HERB CHAMBERS OF SOMERVILLE, INC.; *U.S. Private*, pg. 1920
HERB EASLEY MOTORS INC.; *U.S. Private*, pg. 1920
HERB GORDON MERCEDES-BENZ—See Atlantic Automotive Corp.; *U.S. Private*, pg. 371
HERB HALLMAN CHEVROLET INC.; *U.S. Private*, pg. 1920
HERB JONES CHEVROLET, INC.; *U.S. Private*, pg. 1920
HERITAGE AUTO MALL OF BEL AIR INC.—See Atlantic Automotive Corp.; *U.S. Private*, pg. 371
HERITAGE AUTOMOTIVE GROUP INC.; *U.S. Private*, pg. 1922
HERITAGE CADILLAC, INC.; *U.S. Private*, pg. 1922
HERITAGE CHEVROLET INC.; *U.S. Private*, pg. 1922
HERITAGE CHEVROLET, INC.—See Atlantic Automotive Corp.; *U.S. Private*, pg. 371
HERITAGE CHRYSLER DODGE JEEP RAM—See Atlantic Automotive Corp.; *U.S. Private*, pg. 371
HERITAGE FORD INC.; *U.S. Private*, pg. 1923
HERITAGE IMPORTS INC.—See Atlantic Automotive Corp.; *U.S. Private*, pg. 371
HERITAGE OF GAINESVILLE INC.—See RNMC Inc.; *U.S. Private*, pg. 3453
HERMAN COOK VOLKSWAGEN; *U.S. Private*, pg. 1925
HERRING FORD, INC.; *U.S. Private*, pg. 1926
HERSRUD CO. INC.; *U.S. Private*, pg. 1927
HERTRICH NISSAN JEEP EAGLE; *U.S. Private*, pg. 1927
HERZOG-MEIER INC.; *U.S. Private*, pg. 1927
HERZOG MEIER VOLKSWAGEN; *U.S. Private*, pg. 1927
HESSER OLDSMOBILE PONTIAC INC.; *U.S. Private*, pg. 1928
HESSER TOYOTA INC.—See Bill Hesser Enterprises Inc.; *U.S. Private*, pg. 557
HEYUAN GUANFENGHANG AUTO CO., LTD.—See China MeiDong Auto Holdings Limited; *Int'l*, pg. 1519
HGREG.COM; *U.S. Private*, pg. 1930
HGREG NISSAN BUENA PARK—See HGreg.com; *U.S. Private*, pg. 1931
H & H CHEVROLET OLDSMOBILE PONTIAC & CADILLAC; *U.S. Private*, pg. 1822
H&H CONTINENTAL MOTORS INC.; *U.S. Private*, pg. 1822
HIBBING CHRYSLER CENTER, LLC; *U.S. Private*, pg. 1932
HI-COUNTRY CHEVROLET INC.; *U.S. Private*, pg. 1931
HIDY MOTORS, INC.; *U.S. Private*, pg. 1934
HIGGINS CHEVROLET INC.; *U.S. Private*, pg. 1935
HIGHBURY FORD SALES LIMITED; *Int'l*, pg. 3386
HIGH COUNTRY CHEVROLET LTD.; *Int'l*, pg. 3385
HIGHLAND CHEVROLET BUICK GMC CADILLAC; *Int'l*, pg. 3387
HIGHLAND KACKELL PTY LTD—See Eagers Automotive Limited; *Int'l*, pg. 2263
HIGH RIVER FORD; *Int'l*, pg. 3386
HIGHT CHEVROLET BUICK GMC; *U.S. Private*, pg. 1941
HIGHWAY MOTORS INC.; *U.S. Private*, pg. 1942
HILBISH FORD; *U.S. Private*, pg. 1943
HILDEBRAND MOTORS LTD.; *Int'l*, pg. 3391
HILEY AUTO DEALERSHIPS, INC.; *U.S. Private*, pg. 1944
HILL CADILLAC; *U.S. Private*, pg. 1945
HILL COUNTRY ENTERPRISES; *U.S. Private*, pg. 1945
HILLCREST VOLKSWAGEN (1979) LTD; *Int'l*, pg. 3392
HILLER COMPANY INCORPORATED; *U.S. Private*, pg. 1946
HILL INTERNATIONAL TRUCKS LLC; *U.S. Private*, pg. 1945
HILL NISSAN, INC.; *U.S. Private*, pg. 1945
HILLTOP BUICK GMC INC.; *U.S. Private*, pg. 1947
HILLVIEW MOTORS; *U.S. Private*, pg. 1947
HILLYER'S MID CITY FORD INC.; *U.S. Private*, pg. 1947
HINCKLEYS INCORPORATED; *U.S. Private*, pg. 1948
HINES PARK LINCOLN MERCURY; *U.S. Private*, pg. 1949
HIRA AUTOMOBILES LIMITED; *Int'l*, pg. 3402
HIRNING PONTIAC BUICK INC.; *U.S. Private*, pg. 1950
HISSONG GROUP INC.; *U.S. Private*, pg. 1951
HIXSON AUTOPLEX OF ALEXANDRIA; *U.S. Private*, pg. 1953
HIXSON FORD MONROE; *U.S. Private*, pg. 1953
H & J CHEVROLET INC.—See Gill Automotive Group, Inc.; *U.S. Private*, pg. 1700
H & L CHEVROLET, INC.; *U.S. Private*, pg. 1822
H&L GARAGES LIMITED; *Int'l*, pg. 3191
H&N CHEVROLET BUICK CO. INC.; *U.S. Private*, pg. 1823
HOAK MOTORS INC.; *U.S. Private*, pg. 1957
HOFFMAN CHRYSLER PLYMOUTH JEEP; *U.S. Private*, pg. 1960
HOFFMAN FORD SALES INC.; *U.S. Private*, pg. 1960
HOFLANDT AUTOMOBILE; *Int'l*, pg. 3440
HOGAN CHEVROLET BUICK GMC LIMITED; *Int'l*, pg. 3441
HOGLUND BUS CO. INC.; *U.S. Private*, pg. 1961
HOLDEN NEW ZEALAND LIMITED—See General Motors Company; *U.S. Public*, pg. 926
HOLDIMAN MOTOR, INC.; *U.S. Private*, pg. 1962
HOLIDAY AUTO & TRUCK INC.; *U.S. Private*, pg. 1962
HOLIDAY CHEVROLET, LLC; *U.S. Private*, pg. 1962
HOLIDAY FORD SALES (1980) LIMITED; *Int'l*, pg. 3450
HOLLER DRIVER'S MART; *U.S. Private*, pg. 1964
HOLLINGSWORTH RICHARDS MAZDA; *U.S. Private*, pg. 1965
HOLLYWOOD CHRYSLER PLYMOUTH INC.; *U.S. Private*, pg. 1966
HOLLYWOOD IMPORTS LIMITED, INC.—See AutoNation, Inc.; *U.S. Public*, pg. 235
HOLLYWOOD KIA, INC.—See Morgan Auto Group, LLC; *U.S. Private*, pg. 2783
HOLMAN CADILLAC—See Holman Automotive Group, Inc.; *U.S. Private*, pg. 1967
HOLM AUTOMOTIVE CENTER; *U.S. Private*, pg. 1966
HOLMES TUTTLE FORD, INC.—See Tuttle-Click Automotive Group; *U.S. Private*, pg. 4263
HOLT MOTOR INC.; *U.S. Private*, pg. 1968
HOLT MOTORS, INC.; *U.S. Private*, pg. 1968
HOLZHAUER AUTO & TRUCK SALES, INC.; *U.S. Private*, pg. 1969
HOLZ MOTORS, INC.; *U.S. Private*, pg. 1969
HOMAN AUTO SALES, INC.; *U.S. Private*, pg. 1969
HOMER SKELTON FORD, INC.; *U.S. Private*, pg. 1973
HOMETOWN AUTO RETAILERS, INC.; *U.S. Private*, pg. 1975
HONDA AUTOMOBILES OF BARTLESVILLE; *U.S. Private*, pg. 1976
HONDA CARS MAKATI, INC.—See Ayala Corporation; *Int'l*, pg. 773
HONDA CARS OF CORONA; *U.S. Private*, pg. 1976
HONDA CARS OF ROCK HILL; *U.S. Private*, pg. 1976
HONDA CARS SAITAMA KITA CO., LTD.—See Hitachi Astemo, Ltd.; *Int'l*, pg. 3409
HONDA EAST—See Beechmont Automotive Group; *U.S. Private*, pg. 513
HONDA GABRIEL; *Int'l*, pg. 3459
HONDA ILE PERROT; *Int'l*, pg. 3459
HONDA MALIWAN COMPANY LIMITED—See Autocorp Holding Public Company Limited; *Int'l*, pg. 726
HONDA MOTORS INC.; *U.S. Private*, pg. 1976
HONDA OF AMES—See Lithia Motors, Inc.; *U.S. Public*, pg. 1322
HONDA OF ITHACA; *U.S. Private*, pg. 1976
HONDA OF SALEM; *U.S. Private*, pg. 1976
HONDA OF STATEN ISLAND; *U.S. Private*, pg. 1976
HONDA OF TIFFANY SPRINGS—See A&L Holding Company Inc.; *U.S. Private*, pg. 20
HONOLULU FORD, INC.—See Lithia Motors, Inc.; *U.S. Public*, pg. 1322
HOOD NORTHLAKE; *U.S. Private*, pg. 1977
HOOVER CHRYSLER JEEP INC.; *U.S. Private*, pg. 1978
HOOVER DODGE JEEP CHRYSLER, INC.; *U.S. Private*, pg. 1978
HOPKINS FORD, INC.; *U.S. Private*, pg. 1979
HOPKINS PONTIAC-GMC TRUCKS; *U.S. Private*, pg. 1979
HORACE G. ILDERTON INC.; *U.S. Private*, pg. 1980
HORIZON AUTOMOTIVE, INC.—See AutoNation, Inc.; *U.S. Public*, pg. 235
HORNE AUTO CENTER INC.; *U.S. Private*, pg. 1983
HORNE FORD INC.; *U.S. Private*, pg. 1983
HORNER PONTIAC BUICK INC.; *U.S. Private*, pg. 1983
HORST-ZIMMERMAN INC.; *U.S. Private*, pg. 1984
HOSELTON CHEVROLET INCORPORATED; *U.S. Private*, pg. 1985
HOSS VALUE CARS & TRUCKS INC.; *U.S. Private*, pg. 1988
HOUSE OF IMPORTS INC.; *U.S. Private*, pg. 1991
HOUSTON AUTO M. IMPORTS GREENWAY, LTD.—See AutoNation, Inc.; *U.S. Public*, pg. 235
HOUSTON AUTO M. IMPORTS GREENWAY, LTD.—See AutoNation, Inc.; *U.S. Public*, pg. 235
HOUSTON AUTO M. IMPORTS NORTH, LTD.—See AutoNation, Inc.; *U.S. Public*, pg. 235
HOVE BUICK-NISSAN; *U.S. Private*, pg. 1994
HOWARD BENTLEY BUICK GMC, INC.; *U.S. Private*, pg. 1994
HOYTE DODGE LTD.; *U.S. Private*, pg. 1996
H.R. OWEN PLC—See Berjaya Corporation Berhad; *Int'l*, pg. 983
HT AUTOMOTIVE, LLC—See Penske Automotive Group, Inc.; *U.S. Public*, pg. 1665

N.A.I.C.S. Index
441110 — NEW CAR DEALERS
CORPORATE AFFILIATIONS

HT&T COMPANY—See C. Brewer & Co. Ltd.; *U.S. Private*, pg. 705
HUBBARD CHEVROLET; *U.S. Private*, pg. 2000
HUBBARDS; *U.S. Private*, pg. 2000
HUB BUICK INC; *U.S. Private*, pg. 1999
HUB CITY FORD INC.; *U.S. Private*, pg. 2000
HUB CITY FORD, INC.; *U.S. Private*, pg. 2000
HUBERS INC.; *U.S. Private*, pg. 2001
HUBERT VESTER CHEVROLET; *U.S. Private*, pg. 2001
HUBLER CHEVROLET INC.; *U.S. Private*, pg. 2001
HUDIBURG CHEVROLET BUICK GMC; *U.S. Private*, pg. 2001
HUDSON AUTO SOURCE; *U.S. Private*, pg. 2001
HUDSON PONTIAC BUICK GMC TRUCK INC.; *U.S. Private*, pg. 2002
HUFFINES CHEVROLET LEWISVILLE—See Huffines Auto Group; *U.S. Private*, pg. 2003
HUFFINES CHRYSLER JEEP KIA DENTON—See Huffines Auto Group; *U.S. Private*, pg. 2003
HUFFINES CHRYSLER PLYMOUTH, INC.—See Huffines Auto Group; *U.S. Private*, pg. 2003
HUFFINES DODGE PLANO, L.P.—See Huffines Auto Group; *U.S. Private*, pg. 2003
HUFFINES HYUNDAI MCKINNEY, LP—See Huffines Auto Group; *U.S. Private*, pg. 2003
HUF KOREA LIMITED—See Huf Hulsbeck & Furst GmbH & Co. KG; *Int'l*, pg. 3523
HUGHES MOTORS INC.; *U.S. Private*, pg. 2003
HUNT CLUB FORD LINCOLN SALES LIMITED; *Int'l*, pg. 3536
HUNT CLUB NISSAN LTD.—See AutoCanada Inc.; *Int'l*, pg. 726
HUNTER CHEVROLET COMPANY INC.; *U.S. Private*, pg. 2009
HUNTINGTON FORD INC.; *U.S. Private*, pg. 2010
HURAY AUTOMOBILES SAS—See Groupe Dubreuil SA; *Int'l*, pg. 3102
HURLEY CHRYSLER PLYMOUTH; *U.S. Private*, pg. 2011
HURON MOTOR PRODUCTS LTD.; *Int'l*, pg. 3538
HUSKY INTERNATIONAL TRUCKS INC.; *U.S. Private*, pg. 2014
HUTCHENS CHEVROLET; *U.S. Private*, pg. 2014
HUTCHINS EUGENE NISSAN, INC.—See Lithia Motors, Inc.; *U.S. Public*, pg. 1323
HUTCHINS IMPORTED MOTORS, INC.—See Lithia Motors, Inc.; *U.S. Public*, pg. 1323
HUZHOU YONGDA AOCHENG AUTOMOBILE SALES AND SERVICES CO., LTD.—See China Yongda Automobiles Services Holdings Limited; *Int'l*, pg. 1564
HUZHOU YONGDA AUTOMOBILE SALES AND SERVICES CO., LTD.—See China Yongda Automobiles Services Holdings Limited; *Int'l*, pg. 1564
HUZHOU YONGDA LUBAO AUTOMOBILE SALES AND SERVICES CO., LTD.—See China Yongda Automobiles Services Holdings Limited; *Int'l*, pg. 1564
HVA IMPORTS, LLC—See AutoNation, Inc.; *U.S. Public*, pg. 235
HVM IMPORTS, LLC—See AutoNation, Inc.; *U.S. Public*, pg. 235
HVPH MOTOR CORPORATION—See Penske Automotive Group, Inc.; *U.S. Public*, pg. 1665
HVS MOTORS, LLC—See AutoNation, Inc.; *U.S. Public*, pg. 235
H.W. HUNTER INC.; *U.S. Private*, pg. 1836
H.W. MCKEVITT CO. INC.—See US Auto Group Limited; *U.S. Private*, pg. 4317
HW MCKEVITT CO. INC.—See US Auto Group Limited; *U.S. Private*, pg. 4317
HYATT AUTOMOTIVE LLC; *U.S. Private*, pg. 2016
HYLTON CHELTENHAM—See Hylton Group Ltd.; *Int'l*, pg. 3549
HYLTON GROUP LTD.; *Int'l*, pg. 3549
HYLTON OF WORCESTER—See Hylton Group Ltd.; *Int'l*, pg. 3549
HYUNDAI HELLAS S.A.—See AUTOHELLAS S.A.; *Int'l*, pg. 727
HYUNDAI MOTOR ESPANA, S.L.U.—See Hyundai Motor Company; *Int'l*, pg. 3559
HYUNDAI MOTOR EUROPE GMBH—See Hyundai Motor Company; *Int'l*, pg. 3559
HYUNDAI MOTOR POLAND SP. Z.O.O—See Hyundai Motor Company; *Int'l*, pg. 3559
HYUNDAI OF WESLEY CHAPEL, LLC.; *U.S. Private*, pg. 2020
HYUNDAI WEST-ISLAND; *Int'l*, pg. 3561
I.A. HEDIN BIL AB; *Int'l*, pg. 3565
ICAR; *Int'l*, pg. 3578
I.G. BURTON & CO. INC.; *U.S. Private*, pg. 2027
IMLAY CITY FORD; *U.S. Private*, pg. 2047
IMPERIAL INVESTMENT COMPANY INC.; *U.S. Private*, pg. 2049
IMPORTED CARS OF MARYLAND; *U.S. Private*, pg. 2050
IMPORT MOTORS INC.; *U.S. Private*, pg. 2050
INCIPE, LLC—See Hawk Auto Group; *U.S. Private*, pg. 1882
INDICAR OF DAYTONA INC.; *U.S. Private*, pg. 2063
INDY ROHR MOTORS INC.; *U.S. Private*, pg. 2069
INFINITE VELOCITY AUTOMOTIVE, INC.—See General Motors Company; *U.S. Public*, pg. 926
INFINITI NORTH SHORE; *U.S. Private*, pg. 2071
INFINITI OF ARDMORE, INC.; *U.S. Private*, pg. 2071
INFINITI OF BLOOMINGTON INC.—See Luther Holding Company; *U.S. Private*, pg. 2517
INFINITI OF COCONUT CREEK INC.; *U.S. Private*, pg. 2071
INFINITI OF HONOLULU; *U.S. Private*, pg. 2071
INFINITI OF MELBOURNE—See Kelly Automotive Group; *U.S. Private*, pg. 2276
INFINITI OF MEMPHIS, INC.—See Gossett Motor Cars Inc.; *U.S. Private*, pg. 1744
INFINITI OF NORWOOD; *U.S. Private*, pg. 2071
INFINITI ON CAMELBACK; *U.S. Private*, pg. 2071
INFINITI SOUTH BAY—See AutoNation, Inc.; *U.S. Public*, pg. 235
INFINITI TUSTIN—See AutoNation, Inc.; *U.S. Public*, pg. 235
ING COMMUNICATIONS CORP—See Aucnet Inc.; *Int'l*, pg. 700
INICIAL AUTOHAZ KFT.—See AutoWallis Public Limited Company; *Int'l*, pg. 732
INLAND CHEVROLET; *U.S. Private*, pg. 2078
INSKIP AUTO MALL—See Penske Automotive Group, Inc.; *U.S. Public*, pg. 1665
INTERNATIONAL CARS LTD.; *U.S. Private*, pg. 2115
INTERNATIONAL MOTOR CARS; *U.S. Private*, pg. 2119
INTERNATIONAL TRADE AGENCIES AND MARKETING CO. S.A.E.—See Ghabbour Auto S.A.E.; *Int'l*, pg. 2958
INTERNATIONAL TRUCKS OF HOUSTON; *U.S. Private*, pg. 2121
INTERSTATE MOTOR TRUCKS INC.; *U.S. Private*, pg. 2125
IRVINE IMPORTS, INC.—See AutoNation, Inc.; *U.S. Public*, pg. 235
ISLAND LINCOLN-MERCURY, INC.; *U.S. Private*, pg. 2145
I-STATE TRUCK CENTER—See Interstate Companies, Inc.; *U.S. Private*, pg. 2124
ISUZU AUTOMOTIVE DEALERSHIP, INC.—See Ayala Corporation; *Int'l*, pg. 773
IVAN GANDRUD CHEVROLET, INC.; *U.S. Private*, pg. 2150
IVAN LEONARD CHEVROLET, INC.; *U.S. Private*, pg. 2150
IVECO ARAC SANAYI VE TICARET A.S.—See CNH Industrial N.V.; *Int'l*, pg. 1675
IVECO AUSTRIA GMBH—See CNH Industrial N.V.; *Int'l*, pg. 1675
IVECO BAYERN GMBH—See CNH Industrial N.V.; *Int'l*, pg. 1675
IVECO DANMARK A/S—See CNH Industrial N.V.; *Int'l*, pg. 1675
IVECO ESPANA S.L.—See CNH Industrial N.V.; *Int'l*, pg. 1675
IVECO FINLAND OY—See CNH Industrial N.V.; *Int'l*, pg. 1675
IVECO L.V.I. S.A.S.—See CNH Industrial N.V.; *Int'l*, pg. 1675
IVECO NORD NUTZFAHRZEUGE GMBH—See CNH Industrial N.V.; *Int'l*, pg. 1675
IVECO NORD-OST NUTZFAHRZEUGE GMBH—See CNH Industrial N.V.; *Int'l*, pg. 1675
IVECO NORD SAS—See CNH Industrial N.V.; *Int'l*, pg. 1675
IVECO NORGE A.S.—See CNH Industrial N.V.; *Int'l*, pg. 1675
IVECO OTOMOTIV TICARET A.S.—See CNH Industrial N.V.; *Int'l*, pg. 1675
IVECO POLAND SP. Z O.O.—See CNH Industrial N.V.; *Int'l*, pg. 1675
IVECO PROVENCE S.A.S.—See CNH Industrial N.V.; *Int'l*, pg. 1675
IVECO SUD-WEST NUTZFAHRZEUGE GMBH—See CNH Industrial N.V.; *Int'l*, pg. 1675
IVECO SWEDEN A.B.—See CNH Industrial N.V.; *Int'l*, pg. 1676
IVECO TRUCK CENTRUM S.R.O.—See CNH Industrial N.V.; *Int'l*, pg. 1676
IVECO TRUCK SERVICES S.R.L.—See CNH Industrial N.V.; *Int'l*, pg. 1676
IVECO UKRAINE LLC—See CNH Industrial N.V.; *Int'l*, pg. 1676
IVECO WEST NUTZFAHRZEUGE GMBH—See CNH Industrial N.V.; *Int'l*, pg. 1676
JACK BOWKER FORD LEASING COMPANY; *U.S. Private*, pg. 2173
JACK BURFORD CHEVROLET-OLDSMOBILE-GEO, INC.; *U.S. Private*, pg. 2173
JACK CARUSO REGENCY DODGE INC.; *U.S. Private*, pg. 2173
JACK DEMMER FORD, INC.; *U.S. Private*, pg. 2173
JACK EVANS CHEVROLET CADILLAC; *U.S. Private*, pg. 2173
JACK GARRETT FORD, INC.; *U.S. Private*, pg. 2173
JACK GIAMBALVO MOTOR CO., INC.; *U.S. Private*, pg. 2173
JACK GOSCH FORD, INC.; *U.S. Private*, pg. 2173
JACK KAIN FORD, INC.; *U.S. Private*, pg. 2174
JACK KEY MOTOR COMPANY INC.; *U.S. Private*, pg. 2174
JACK KISSEE FORD AGENCY, INC.; *U.S. Private*, pg. 2174
JACK MADDEN FORD SALES INC.; *U.S. Private*, pg. 2174
JACK MAXTON CHEVROLET INCORPORATED; *U.S. Private*, pg. 2174
JACK SCHMITT FORD INC.; *U.S. Private*, pg. 2174
JACKSON AUTO GROUP; *U.S. Private*, pg. 2175
JACK WINEGARDNER CHEVROLET, INC.; *U.S. Private*, pg. 2175
JACK WOLF CADILLAC GMC; *U.S. Private*, pg. 2175
JACKY JONES FORD LINCOLN; *U.S. Private*, pg. 2179
JACOBS AUTO LAURENSBERG GMBH—See Penske Automotive Group, Inc.; *U.S. Public*, pg. 1665
JACOBS HOLDING GMBH—See Penske Automotive Group, Inc.; *U.S. Public*, pg. 1665
JAFFARIAN AUTOMOTIVE GROUP; *U.S. Private*, pg. 2181
JAGUAR ELMHURST—See Elmhurst Auto Group; *U.S. Private*, pg. 1376
JAGUAR LAND ROVER MINNEAPOLIS—See Luther Holding Company; *U.S. Private*, pg. 2517
JAGUAR LAND ROVER NORTH AMERICA, LLC—See Lithia Motors, Inc.; *U.S. Public*, pg. 1323
JAGUAR-LAND ROVER OF TACOMA—See Michael O'Brien Enterprises, Inc.; *U.S. Private*, pg. 2698
JAGUAR OF TAMPA—See Elder Automotive Group; *U.S. Private*, pg. 1350
JAKE SWEENEY CHRYSLER JEEP DODGE, INC.—See Jake Sweeney Automotive Inc.; *U.S. Private*, pg. 2182
JAMES MATTHEWS INC.; *U.S. Private*, pg. 2184
JANETTO HOLDINGS PTY LTD—See Eagers Automotive Limited; *Int'l*, pg. 2263
JANNELL MOTORS, INC.; *U.S. Private*, pg. 2187
JARDINE MOTORS GROUP UK LIMITED—See Lithia Motors, Inc.; *U.S. Public*, pg. 1323
JAY AUTOMOTIVE GROUP INC.—See Group 1 Automotive, Inc.; *U.S. Public*, pg. 971
JAY PONTIAC INC.; *U.S. Private*, pg. 2192
JAY WOLFE ACURA; *U.S. Private*, pg. 2192
JAY WOLFE TOYOTA OF WEST COUNTY; *U.S. Private*, pg. 2192
J.C. BILLION INC.; *U.S. Private*, pg. 2159
J. C. LEWIS FORD, LLC.; *U.S. Private*, pg. 2155
JCMC, INC.; *U.S. Private*, pg. 2195
JEEP CHRYSLER DODGE OF ONTARIO; *U.S. Private*, pg. 2196
JEFF BELZER'S CHEVROLET DODGE KIA; *U.S. Private*, pg. 2196
JEFF D'AMBROSIO AUTO GROUP; *U.S. Private*, pg. 2196
JEFFERSON CHEVROLET CO.; *U.S. Private*, pg. 2197
JEFF HUNTER MOTORS, INC.; *U.S. Private*, pg. 2196
JEFF LUNGREN CHEVROLET, INC.; *U.S. Private*, pg. 2196
JEFFREY AUTOMOTIVE GROUP; *U.S. Private*, pg. 2198
JEFFREY BUICK-NISSAN—See Jeffrey Automotive Group; *U.S. Private*, pg. 2198
JEFF SCHMITT AUTO GROUP; *U.S. Private*, pg. 2197
JEFF WYLER ALEXANDRIA, INC.—See Jeff Wyler Automotive Family, Inc.; *U.S. Private*, pg. 2197
JEFF WYLER EASTGATE, INC.—See Jeff Wyler Automotive Family, Inc.; *U.S. Private*, pg. 2197
JEFF WYLER FAIRFIELD, INC.—See Jeff Wyler Automotive Family, Inc.; *U.S. Private*, pg. 2197
JEFF WYLER FLORENCE, INC.—See Jeff Wyler Automotive Family, Inc.; *U.S. Private*, pg. 2197
JEFF WYLER FRANKFORT, INC.—See Jeff Wyler Automotive Family, Inc.; *U.S. Private*, pg. 2197
JEFF WYLER FT. THOMAS, INC.—See Jeff Wyler Automotive Family, Inc.; *U.S. Private*, pg. 2197
JEFF WYLER LOUISVILLE II, INC.—See Jeff Wyler Automotive Family, Inc.; *U.S. Private*, pg. 2197
JEFF WYLER SPRINGFIELD, INC.—See Jeff Wyler Automotive Family, Inc.; *U.S. Private*, pg. 2197
JENKINS DIESEL POWER, INC.; *U.S. Private*, pg. 2199
JENKINS FORD/MERCURY INC.; *U.S. Private*, pg. 2199
JENKINS HYUNDAI; *U.S. Private*, pg. 2199
JENKINS & WYNNE FORD INC.; *U.S. Private*, pg. 2199
JENNINGS ANDERSON FORD SALES; *U.S. Private*, pg. 2200
JENNINGS CHEVROLET, INC.; *U.S. Private*, pg. 2200
JENNINGS VALUE CENTER; *U.S. Private*, pg. 2200
JENNINGS VOLKSWAGEN INC.; *U.S. Private*, pg. 2200
JENSEN FORD INC.; *U.S. Private*, pg. 2200
JERRY BIGGERS CHEVROLET - ISUZU INC.; *U.S. Private*, pg. 2202
JERRY FERGUSON BUICK-GMC TRUCK LLC; *U.S. Private*, pg. 2202
JERRY HAAG MOTORS INC.; *U.S. Private*, pg. 2202
JERRY HAMM CHEVROLET INC.; *U.S. Private*, pg. 2202
JERRY HEFLIN COURTESY CHEVROLET; *U.S. Private*, pg. 2202
JERRY SEINER CHEVROLET, INC.; *U.S. Private*, pg. 2202
JERRY SEINER SALT LAKE—See Jerry Seiner Chevrolet, Inc.; *U.S. Private*, pg. 2202
JERRY'S FORD SALES INC.; *U.S. Private*, pg. 2202
JERRY SMITH CHEVROLET; *U.S. Private*, pg. 2202
JERRY ULM DODGE, INC.; *U.S. Private*, pg. 2202
JESSUP AUTO PLAZA; *U.S. Private*, pg. 2203
J.G. O'NEILL INC.; *U.S. Private*, pg. 2165
J.H. BENNETT INC.; *U.S. Private*, pg. 2165
JHS CORPORATION—See Montgomery Chevrolet; *U.S. Private*, pg. 2776
JIANGXI YONGDA RONGJIAN AUTOMOBILE SALES AND SERVICES CO., LTD.—See China Yongda Automobiles Services Holdings Limited; *Int'l*, pg. 1564

N.A.I.C.S. INDEX 441110 — NEW CAR DEALERS

N.A.I.C.S. Index

JIANGYIN BAOZEN AUTOMOBILE SALES AND SERVICES CO., LTD.—See China Yongda Automobiles Services Holdings Limited; *Int'l*, pg. 1564
JIAXING YONGDA TONGCHENG AUTO SALES AND SERVICE CO., LTD.—See China Yongda Automobiles Services Holdings Limited; *Int'l*, pg. 1564
JIAXING ZHIBAO AUTOMOBILE SALES AND SERVICE CO., LTD.—See China Yongda Automobiles Services Holdings Limited; *Int'l*, pg. 1564
JIM BAIER FORD LINCOLN MERCURY DODGE CHRYSLER JEEP; *U.S. Private*, pg. 2208
JIM BALL PONTIAC-BUICK-GMC, INC.; *U.S. Private*, pg. 2208
JIM BARNARD CHEVROLET, INC.; *U.S. Private*, pg. 2208
JIM BROWN CHEVROLET INC.; *U.S. Private*, pg. 2208
JIM BROWNE CHEVROLET, INC.—See General Motors Company; *U.S. Public*, pg. 926
JIM BURKE AUTOMOTIVE INC.; *U.S. Private*, pg. 2208
JIM BUTLER AUTO GROUP, LLC; *U.S. Private*, pg. 2208
JIM CAUSLEY, INC.; *U.S. Private*, pg. 2208
JIM CLICK FORD, LINCOLN-MERCURY, INC.—See Jim Click, Inc.; *U.S. Private*, pg. 2208
JIM CLICK, INC.; *U.S. Private*, pg. 2208
JIM COGDILL COMPANY—See Lithia Motors, Inc.; *U.S. Public*, pg. 1323
JIM COLEMAN CADILLAC INC.—See Bethesda Investment Holding Co., Inc.; *U.S. Private*, pg. 546
JIM COLEMAN TOYOTA, INC.—See Bethesda Investment Holding Co., Inc.; *U.S. Private*, pg. 546
JIM CRIVELLI CHEVROLET, INC.; *U.S. Private*, pg. 2208
JIM CURLEY DEALERSHIP; *U.S. Private*, pg. 2208
JIM DOYLE FORD; *U.S. Private*, pg. 2208
JIM ELLIS ATLANTA INC.; *U.S. Private*, pg. 2208
JIM FOREMAN PONTIAC INC.; *U.S. Private*, pg. 2208
JIM FUOCO MOTOR CO.; *U.S. Private*, pg. 2209
JIM GLOVER CHEVROLET ISUZU; *U.S. Private*, pg. 2209
JIM HERRICK MOTORS INC.; *U.S. Private*, pg. 2209
JIM HUDSON AUTOMOTIVE GROUP; *U.S. Private*, pg. 2209
JIM KERAS CHEVROLET MEMPHIS; *U.S. Private*, pg. 2209
JIM KERAS SUBARU; *U.S. Private*, pg. 2209
JIM MARSH AMERICAN CORP.; *U.S. Private*, pg. 2209
JIM MCKAY CHEVROLET INC.; *U.S. Private*, pg. 2209
JIMMIE VICKERS; *U.S. Private*, pg. 2210
JIM MURPHY BUICK GMC, INC.; *U.S. Private*, pg. 2209
JIMMY JONES TOYOTA OF ORANGEBURG; *U.S. Private*, pg. 2210
JIM QUINLAN CHEVROLET CO.—See AutoNation, Inc.; *U.S. Public*, pg. 235
JIM RAYSIK INC.; *U.S. Private*, pg. 2209
JIM RIEHL'S FRIENDLY BUICK HONDA HUMMER; *U.S. Private*, pg. 2209
JIM ROBINSON INC.; *U.S. Private*, pg. 2209
JIM RYAN CHEVROLET INC.; *U.S. Private*, pg. 2209
JIM SCHMIDT CHEVROLET-OLDSMOBILE, INC.; *U.S. Private*, pg. 2209
JIM SKINNER FORD; *U.S. Private*, pg. 2209
JIM SKINNER HONDA; *U.S. Private*, pg. 2209
JIM TAYLOR CHEVROLET, LLC.; *U.S. Private*, pg. 2210
JIM TIDWELL FORD, INC.—See Group 1 Automotive, Inc.; *U.S. Public*, pg. 971
JIM TRENARY CHEVROLET INC.; *U.S. Private*, pg. 2210
JIM VREELAND FORD; *U.S. Private*, pg. 2210
JIM WINTER BUICK-GMC TRUCK-NISSAN INC.; *U.S. Private*, pg. 2210
JIUJIANG DONGBU TOYOTA AUTO SALES & SERVICES CO., LTD.—See China MeiDong Auto Holdings Limited; *Int'l*, pg. 1519
J-K CHEVROLET, INC.; *U.S. Private*, pg. 2155
JM&A GROUP—See JM Family Enterprises Inc.; *U.S. Private*, pg. 2214
J & M CHEVROLET, INC.; *U.S. Private*, pg. 2152
JMK AUTO SALES INC.; *U.S. Private*, pg. 2216
JM LEXUS—See JM Family Enterprises Inc.; *U.S. Private*, pg. 2214
JN CHEVROLET; *U.S. Private*, pg. 2216
JOE BASIL CHEVROLET, INC.; *U.S. Private*, pg. 2218
JOE COOPER FORD INC.; *U.S. Private*, pg. 2218
JOE FISHER; *U.S. Private*, pg. 2218
JOE HALL FORD LINCOLN MERCURY NISSAN; *U.S. Private*, pg. 2218
JOE KIDD AUTOMOTIVE; *U.S. Private*, pg. 2218
JOE LUNGHAMER CHEVROLET, INC.; *U.S. Private*, pg. 2218
JOE MACHENS CAPITAL CITY FORD LINCOLN; *U.S. Private*, pg. 2218
JOE MACHENS FORD INC.; *U.S. Private*, pg. 2218
JOE MACPHERSON FORD—See AutoNation, Inc.; *U.S. Public*, pg. 235
JOE MACPHERSON FORD—See AutoNation, Inc.; *U.S. Public*, pg. 236
JOE MACPHERSON INFINITI—See AutoNation, Inc.; *U.S. Public*, pg. 236
JOE MYERS FORD; *U.S. Private*, pg. 2218
JOE RIZZA FORD, INC.; *U.S. Private*, pg. 2219
JOE SELF CHEVROLET INC.; *U.S. Private*, pg. 2219
JOE VAN HORN CHEVROLET, INC.; *U.S. Private*, pg. 2219
JOHN DEERY MOTOR CO.; *U.S. Private*, pg. 2221
JOHN DONOGHUE AUTOMOTIVE, INC.; *U.S. Private*, pg. 2221
JOHN EAGLE ACURA—See John Eagle A Management, LLC; *U.S. Private*, pg. 2221
JOHN EAGLE HONDA OF HOUSTON—See John Eagle A Management, LLC; *U.S. Private*, pg. 2221
JOHN EAGLE SPORT CITY MOTORS, LLP—See John Eagle A Management, LLC; *U.S. Private*, pg. 2221
JOHN HINDERER HONDA; *U.S. Private*, pg. 2222
JOHN HINE AUTO & TRUCK CENTER; *U.S. Private*, pg. 2222
JOHN HUBLER NISSAN-SUZUKI INC.; *U.S. Private*, pg. 2222
JOHN KENNEDY FORD LINCOLN MERCURY—See Kennedy Automotive Group Inc.; *U.S. Private*, pg. 2284
JOHN KENNEDY FORD OF PHOENIXVILLE—See Kennedy Automotive Group Inc.; *U.S. Private*, pg. 2284
JOHN KOHL AUTO CENTER INC.; *U.S. Private*, pg. 2222
JOHN L. SULLIVAN INVESTMENTS INC.—See John Sullivan Automotive Group; *U.S. Private*, pg. 2225
JOHN M. LANCE FORD, LLC—See AutoNation, Inc.; *U.S. Public*, pg. 236
JOHN NORTH FORD; *U.S. Private*, pg. 2223
JOHN N. SAUDER AUTO COMPANY; *U.S. Private*, pg. 2223
JOHNNY LONDOFF CHEVROLET, INC.; *U.S. Private*, pg. 2226
JOHN & PHIL'S TOYOTA-SUBARU INC.; *U.S. Private*, pg. 2219
JOHNSON AUTO PLAZA, INC.; *U.S. Private*, pg. 2226
JOHNSON DODGE CHRYSLER JEEP, INC.; *U.S. Private*, pg. 2227
JOHNSON HYUNDAI OF CARY INC.; *U.S. Private*, pg. 2228
JOHNSON MOTOR SALES INC.; *U.S. Private*, pg. 2228
JOHNSON SEWELL FORD LINCOLN MERCURY; *U.S. Private*, pg. 2229
JOHNSONS OF CHICKASHA INC.; *U.S. Private*, pg. 2229
JOHNSON TRUCK CENTER LLC—See Johnson & Towers, Inc.; *U.S. Private*, pg. 2226
JOHN SULLIVAN AUTOMOTIVE GROUP; *U.S. Private*, pg. 2224
JOHN VANCE MOTORS INC.; *U.S. Private*, pg. 2225
JOHN WIESNER INC.; *U.S. Private*, pg. 2225
JONES CHEVROLET INCORPORATED; *U.S. Private*, pg. 2232
JONES DEALERSHIPS; *U.S. Private*, pg. 2233
JONES FORD, INC.; *U.S. Private*, pg. 2233
JONES JUNCTION AUTO GROUP; *U.S. Private*, pg. 2233
JONES MOTOR CO. INC.; *U.S. Private*, pg. 2233
JON HALL CHEVROLET, INC.; *U.S. Private*, pg. 2231
JON HALL HONDA; *U.S. Private*, pg. 2231
JON MURDOCK, INC.; *U.S. Private*, pg. 2231
THE JORDAN AUTOMOTIVE GROUP; *U.S. Private*, pg. 4059
JORDAN FORD INC.; *U.S. Private*, pg. 2235
JORDAN MOTORS, INC.; *U.S. Private*, pg. 2235
JOSEPH AUTO GROUP; *U.S. Private*, pg. 2236
JOSEPH VOLKSWAGEN OF CINCINNATI—See Joseph Auto Group; *U.S. Private*, pg. 2236
J.O. WILLIAMS MOTORS, INC.; *U.S. Private*, pg. 2169
JOYCE MOTORS CORP.; *U.S. Private*, pg. 2239
J. PAWLEY MOTORS, INC.; *U.S. Private*, pg. 2156
JP CHEVROLET INC.; *U.S. Private*, pg. 2239
J&P HOLDINGS, LLC; *U.S. Private*, pg. 2155
JP MOTORS, INC.; *U.S. Private*, pg. 2239
J.P. THIBODEAUX INC.; *U.S. Private*, pg. 2170
JRJ INVESTMENTS, INC.—See AutoNation, Inc.; *U.S. Public*, pg. 235
J-R MOTORS COMPANY NORTH—See AutoNation, Inc.; *U.S. Public*, pg. 235
JUFFALI AUTOMOTIVE COMPANY—See E.A. Juffali & Brothers Company; *Int'l*, pg. 2250
JUNGE FORD INC.; *U.S. Private*, pg. 2244
JUNGE LINCOLN MERCURY INC.; *U.S. Private*, pg. 2244
JUPITER CHEVROLET, LP.; *U.S. Private*, pg. 2245
JUSTBETTERCARS.COM INC.; *U.S. Private*, pg. 2246
KAHLIG ENTERPRISES INC.; *U.S. Private*, pg. 2254
KAHLO CHRYSLER JEEP DODGE RAM; *U.S. Private*, pg. 2254
KAHLO JEEP CHRYSLER DODGE; *U.S. Private*, pg. 2254
KANSAS CITY FREIGHTLINER SALES INC.—See Penske Automotive Group, Inc.; *U.S. Public*, pg. 1664
KAREN RADLEY ACURA VOLKSWAGEN; *U.S. Private*, pg. 2262
KARL FLAMMER FORD, INC.; *U.S. Private*, pg. 2262
KARL KNAUZ MOTORS INC.; *U.S. Private*, pg. 2262
KARMART CHRYSLER DODGE VOLKSWAGEN MITSUBISHI; *U.S. Private*, pg. 2263
KATY-H, INC.—See Lithia Motors, Inc.; *U.S. Public*, pg. 1323
KAYSER CHRYSLER CENTER, INC.—See Kayser Automotive Group, LLC; *U.S. Private*, pg. 2267
KAYSER CHRYSLER CENTER OF WATERTOWN, INC.—See Kayser Automotive Group, LLC; *U.S. Private*, pg. 2267
KAYSER CHRYSLER CENTER STOUGHTON—See Kayser Automotive Group, LLC; *U.S. Private*, pg. 2267
KAYSER FORD, INC.—See Kayser Automotive Group, LLC; *U.S. Private*, pg. 2267
KEARNY MESA INFINITI; *U.S. Private*, pg. 2271
KEELER MOTOR CAR COMPANY, INC.; *U.S. Private*, pg. 2272
KEENE CHRYSLER, INC.; *U.S. Private*, pg. 2272
KEENE DODGE CO. INC.; *U.S. Private*, pg. 2272
KEESEE MOTOR CO.; *U.S. Private*, pg. 2273
KEETER MOTORS INC.; *U.S. Private*, pg. 2273
KEFFER HYUNDAI; *U.S. Private*, pg. 2273
KEFFER OF LITTLE RIVER, LLC—See Beach Automotive Group; *U.S. Private*, pg. 503
KEIM CHEVROLET INC.; *U.S. Private*, pg. 2273
KEITH HAWTHORNE FORD; *U.S. Private*, pg. 2274
KELLER BROS MOTOR CO.; *U.S. Private*, pg. 2274
KELLEY AUTOMOTIVE GROUP; *U.S. Private*, pg. 2275
KELLEY CHEVROLET INC.; *U.S. Private*, pg. 2275
KELLY AUTOMOTIVE GROUP; *U.S. Private*, pg. 2276
KELLY BMW; *U.S. Private*, pg. 2276
KELLY IMPORTS INC.; *U.S. Private*, pg. 2276
KELLY MANAGEMENT CORPORATION; *U.S. Private*, pg. 2276
KELLY NISSAN INC.; *U.S. Private*, pg. 2276
KELLY SUBARU & MITSUBISHI; *U.S. Private*, pg. 2277
KEMPTON CHEVROLET BUICK LTD; *U.S. Private*, pg. 2282
KENDALL H LLC—See Kendall Automotive Group Inc.; *U.S. Private*, pg. 2283
KENDALL IMPORTS LLC; *U.S. Private*, pg. 2283
KENDALL L LLC—See Kendall Automotive Group Inc.; *U.S. Private*, pg. 2283
KEN FOWLER MOTORS INC.; *U.S. Private*, pg. 2282
KEN GARFF NISSAN OF SALT LAKE—See Garff Enterprises, Inc.; *U.S. Private*, pg. 1644
KEN GARFF ST. GEORGE FORD LINCOLN—See Garff Enterprises, Inc.; *U.S. Private*, pg. 1644
KEN GRODY FORD; *U.S. Private*, pg. 2282
KENNEDY AUTOMOTIVE GROUP INC.; *U.S. Private*, pg. 2284
KEN NELSON AUTO PLAZA INC.; *U.S. Private*, pg. 2282
KENNESAW MOTOR SALES, INC.; *U.S. Private*, pg. 2286
KENNY KENT CHEVROLET CO. INC.; *U.S. Private*, pg. 2286
KENNY ROSS BUICK-GMC, INC.; *U.S. Private*, pg. 2286
KENNY THOMAS ENTERPRISES INC.; *U.S. Private*, pg. 2286
KENT CHEVROLET, CADILLAC, INC.; *U.S. Private*, pg. 2287
KENT-MICHAEL ENTERPRISES INC.; *U.S. Private*, pg. 2288
KENT RYLEE CHEVROLET-OLDSMOBILE, INC.; *U.S. Private*, pg. 2288
KENTUCKY AUTOMOTIVE CENTER OF GRAYSON; *U.S. Private*, pg. 2288
KEN WILSON FORD INC.; *U.S. Private*, pg. 2282
KENWOOD DEALER GROUP, INC.; *U.S. Private*, pg. 2289
KENWOOD LINCOLN MERCURY INC.; *U.S. Private*, pg. 2289
KENWORTH OF CENTRAL FLORIDA; *U.S. Private*, pg. 2289
KENWORTH OF INDIANAPOLIS INC.; *U.S. Private*, pg. 2289
KERBECK CADILLAC PONTIAC CHEVROLET, INC.; *U.S. Private*, pg. 2290
KERRY FORD INC.; *U.S. Private*, pg. 2291
KERRY TOYOTA TOWNE; *U.S. Private*, pg. 2291
KERRY VOLKSWAGEN; *U.S. Private*, pg. 2291
KEVIN WHITAKER CHEVROLET INC.; *U.S. Private*, pg. 2292
KEY AUTO CENTER—See Key Auto Group; *U.S. Private*, pg. 2292
KEY BUICK COMPANY; *U.S. Private*, pg. 2292
KEY CADILLAC, INC.; *U.S. Private*, pg. 2292
KEYES LEXUS—See Keyes Motors, Inc.; *U.S. Private*, pg. 2294
KEYES MOTORS, INC.; *U.S. Private*, pg. 2294
KEYES TOYOTA—See Keyes Motors, Inc.; *U.S. Private*, pg. 2294
KEYS AUTO CENTER—See Warren Henry Automobiles Inc.; *U.S. Private*, pg. 4444
KEYSER BROTHERS CADILLAC INC.; *U.S. Private*, pg. 2295
KEYSER & MILLER FORD INC.; *U.S. Private*, pg. 2295
KEYSTONE CHEVROLET INC.; *U.S. Private*, pg. 2295
KEYSTONE DODGE, INC.; *U.S. Private*, pg. 2296
KEYSTONE FORD; *U.S. Private*, pg. 2296
KIA OF SANTA FE; *U.S. Private*, pg. 2301
THE KIA STORE; *U.S. Private*, pg. 4065
KIM HANSEN CHEVROLET-OLDS; *U.S. Private*, pg. 2305
KING AUTO CENTER, INC.; *U.S. Private*, pg. 2308
KING BUICK GMC; *U.S. Private*, pg. 2309
KING COTTON MOTOR COMPANY OF COVINGTON; *U.S. Private*, pg. 2309
KING MOTOR CO. INC.; *U.S. Private*, pg. 2309
KING MOTOR COMPANY; *U.S. Private*, pg. 2309
KING O'ROURKE CADILLAC; *U.S. Private*, pg. 2309
KINGS CHRYSLER JEEP DODGE; *U.S. Private*, pg. 2311
KING'S COLONIAL FORD; *U.S. Private*, pg. 2310

441110 — NEW CAR DEALERS

KING'S CROWN FORD, INC.—See AutoNation, Inc.; *U.S. Public*, pg. 236
KING'S CROWN FORD, INC.—See AutoNation, Inc.; *U.S. Public*, pg. 236
KINGS FORD INC.; *U.S. Private*, pg. 2311
KINGS NISSAN INC.; *U.S. Private*, pg. 2311
KINGS TOYOTA—See Kenwood Dealer Group, Inc.; *U.S. Private*, pg. 2289
KINNEY MOTORS; *U.S. Private*, pg. 2313
KINSEL MOTORS INC.; *U.S. Private*, pg. 2313
KIRK BROTHERS FORD-LINCOLN, LLC; *U.S. Private*, pg. 2314
KIRKLAND MOTORS—See AutoNation, Inc.; *U.S. Public*, pg. 236
KIRKSVILLE MOTOR COMPANY; *U.S. Private*, pg. 2315
KISSELBACK FORD; *U.S. Private*, pg. 2315
KITAHARA PONTIAC-BUICK-GMC, INC.; *U.S. Private*, pg. 2316
K & J CHEVROLET, INC.; *U.S. Private*, pg. 2249
KLABEN CHRYSLER JEEP DODGE RAM; *U.S. Private*, pg. 2317
KLICK-LEWIS INC.; *U.S. Private*, pg. 2319
KLINE VOLVO INC.; *U.S. Private*, pg. 2320
K. NEAL INTERNATIONAL TRUCKS, INC.; *U.S. Private*, pg. 2251
KNOEPFLER CHEVROLET CO.; *U.S. Private*, pg. 2323
KNOPF MOTORS INC.; *U.S. Private*, pg. 2323
KNOXVILLE-CJD, LLC—See Lithia Motors, Inc.; *U.S. Public*, pg. 1323
KNUDTSEN CHEVROLET COMPANY; *U.S. Private*, pg. 2325
KOCOUREK AUTOMOTIVE GROUP; *U.S. Private*, pg. 2335
KOCOUREK CHEVROLET, INC.; *U.S. Private*, pg. 2335
KOCOUREK WAUSAU IMPORTS—See Kocourek Automotive Group; *U.S. Private*, pg. 2335
KOEPPEL MAZDA; *U.S. Private*, pg. 2336
KOERNER FORD OF SYRACUSE, INC.; *U.S. Private*, pg. 2336
KOETTING FORD, INC.; *U.S. Private*, pg. 2336
KOHLS-WEELBORG FORD; *U.S. Private*, pg. 2340
KOLOSSO AUTO SALES INC.; *U.S. Private*, pg. 2341
KOOL CHEVROLET, OLDSMOBILE, CADILLAC, INC.; *U.S. Private*, pg. 2343
KOONS FORD INC.; *U.S. Private*, pg. 2343
KOONS LINCOLN MERCURY, INC.; *U.S. Private*, pg. 2343
KOONS OF MANASSAS INC.; *U.S. Private*, pg. 2343
KOONS OF TYSONS CORNER CHEVY CHRYSLER—See Asbury Automotive Group, Inc.; *U.S. Public*, pg. 209
KOONS SILVER SPRING FORD LINCOLN; *U.S. Private*, pg. 2343
KOONS WESTMINSTER TOYOTA; *U.S. Private*, pg. 2343
KORUM MOTORS INC.; *U.S. Private*, pg. 2344
KOSSMAN'S, INC.; *U.S. Private*, pg. 2345
KP MOTORS LLC—See Asbury Automotive Group, Inc.; *U.S. Public*, pg. 209
KPM-UK TAXIS PLC—See Bowmark Capital LLP; *Int'l*, pg. 1124
KRAFT MOTORCAR COMPANY OF TALLAHASSEE, INC.; *U.S. Private*, pg. 2348
KRENZEN CADILLAC-PONTIAC INC.; *U.S. Private*, pg. 2351
KRIEGER AUTO GROUP; *U.S. Private*, pg. 2351
KRIEGER FORD INC.; *U.S. Private*, pg. 2351
KRIEGER MOTOR COMPANY INC.; *U.S. Private*, pg. 2351
KRISTAL CADILLAC, CHEVROLET, & GEO IMPORTS; *U.S. Private*, pg. 2352
KRUMLAND CO, LLC; *U.S. Private*, pg. 2353
KRUSE-WARTHAN DUBUQUE AUTO PLAZA; *U.S. Private*, pg. 2353
KUDICK CHEVROLET-BUICK, INC.; *U.S. Private*, pg. 2356
KUHIO MOTORS INC.; *U.S. Private*, pg. 2356
KUHN HONDA; *U.S. Private*, pg. 2356
KUNDERT MOTORS INC.; *U.S. Private*, pg. 2357
KUNES CHEVROLET; *U.S. Private*, pg. 2357
KUNES' COUNTRY FORD-LINCOLN-MERCURY, INC.; *U.S. Private*, pg. 2357
KUNI AUTO CENTER—See Holman Automotive Group, Inc.; *U.S. Private*, pg. 1967
KUNI DENVER MOTORS, LLC—See Holman Automotive Group, Inc.; *U.S. Private*, pg. 1967
KUNI GERMAN MOTORS, LLC—See Holman Automotive Group, Inc.; *U.S. Private*, pg. 1967
KUNI HONDA; *U.S. Private*, pg. 2357
KUNI HUBACHER MOTORS, LLC—See Holman Automotive Group, Inc.; *U.S. Private*, pg. 1967
KUNSHAN BAOZEN AUTOMOBILE SALES AND SERVICES CO., LTD.—See China Yongda Automobiles Services Holdings Limited; *Int'l*, pg. 1564
KUPPER CHEVROLET, INC.; *U.S. Private*, pg. 2357
KURTIS CHEVROLET, INC.; *U.S. Private*, pg. 2358
KW 1 ACQUISITION CO. LLC; *U.S. Private*, pg. 2359
KYNER'S AUTO SALES, INC.; *U.S. Private*, pg. 2360
LABADIE AUTO INC.; *U.S. Private*, pg. 2370
LACIMA INC.; *U.S. Private*, pg. 2371
LA CROSSE TRUCK CENTER INC.; *U.S. Private*, pg. 2368
LADD HANFORD AUTO GROUP; *U.S. Private*, pg. 2372
LAFAYETTE MOTOR SALES INC.; *U.S. Private*, pg. 2372

LAFFERTY CHEVROLET, INC.; *U.S. Private*, pg. 2372
LAFONTAINE AUTOMOTIVE GROUP, LLC; *U.S. Private*, pg. 2373
LAFONTAINE IMPORT MOTORS INC.; *U.S. Private*, pg. 2373
LAGER'S, INC.; *U.S. Private*, pg. 2373
LAIRD NOLLER AUTOMOTIVE INC.; *U.S. Private*, pg. 2374
LAIRD NOLLER FORD INCORPORATED; *U.S. Private*, pg. 2374
LAKE COUNTY DODGE INC.; *U.S. Private*, pg. 2375
LAKE FOREST SPORTSCARS LTD.; *U.S. Private*, pg. 2375
LAKE KEOWEE CHRYSLER DODGE JEEP RAM; *U.S. Private*, pg. 2375
LAKE MANAWA NISSAN INC.; *U.S. Private*, pg. 2375
LAKESHORE UTILITY TRAILER INC.; *U.S. Private*, pg. 2377
LAKESIDE CHEVROLET BUICK GMC LTD.—See General Motors Company; *U.S. Public*, pg. 926
LAKESIDE IMPORTS INC.; *U.S. Private*, pg. 2378
LAKESIDE INTERNATIONAL TRUCKS INC.; *U.S. Private*, pg. 2378
LAKEWOOD CHEVROLET—See AutoCanada Inc.; *Int'l*, pg. 726
LAKEWOOD FORD; *U.S. Private*, pg. 2379
LANCASTER AUTO GROUP; *U.S. Private*, pg. 2381
LANCASTER CARS LIMITED—See Lithia Motors, Inc.; *U.S. Public*, pg. 1323
LANCASTER MOTOR COMPANY LIMITED—See Lithia Motors, Inc.; *U.S. Public*, pg. 1323
LANCASTER SPECIALIST CARS LIMITED—See Lithia Motors, Inc.; *U.S. Public*, pg. 1323
LANCASTER SPORTS CARS LIMITED—See Lithia Motors, Inc.; *U.S. Public*, pg. 1323
LANCASTER TOYOTA INC.; *U.S. Private*, pg. 2381
LANDERS AUTO GROUP INC.; *U.S. Private*, pg. 2385
LANDERS AUTO GROUP, LLC—See Penske Automotive Group, Inc.; *U.S. Public*, pg. 1665
LANDERS-McLARTY BENTONVILLE LLC; *U.S. Private*, pg. 2385
LANDROVER ORLANDO; *U.S. Private*, pg. 2386
LAND ROVER SAN JOSE; *U.S. Private*, pg. 2384
LANGAN AUTOMOTIVE GROUP; *U.S. Private*, pg. 2388
LANGLEY MOTOR CO., INC.; *U.S. Private*, pg. 2389
LANNAN CHEVROLET INC.; *U.S. Private*, pg. 2390
LANPHERE ENTERPRISES INC.; *U.S. Private*, pg. 2390
LANZHOU MEIDONG LEXUS AUTO SALES & SERVICES CO., LTD.—See China MeiDong Auto Holdings Limited; *Int'l*, pg. 1519
LAPINE TRUCK SALES & EQUIPMENT CO. INC.; *U.S. Private*, pg. 2391
LAPLANTE CADILLAC CHEVROLET BUICK GMC LTD.—See General Motors Company; *U.S. Public*, pg. 926
LA ROCHE CHEVROLET-OLDSMOBILE-CADILLAC, INC.; *U.S. Private*, pg. 2369
LARRY FANNIN CHEVROLET-PONTIAC-BUICK; *U.S. Private*, pg. 2392
LARRY H. MILLER FORD MESA—See Larry H. Miller Group of Companies; *U.S. Private*, pg. 2392
LARRY H. MILLER GROUP DEALERSHIPS—See Larry H. Miller Group of Companies; *U.S. Private*, pg. 2392
LARRY H. MILLER HONDA—See Larry H. Miller Group of Companies; *U.S. Private*, pg. 2393
LARRY H. MILLER VOLKSWAGEN LAKEWOOD—See Larry H. Miller Group of Companies; *U.S. Private*, pg. 2393
LARRY MILLER SUNDANCE DODGE; *U.S. Private*, pg. 2393
LARRY REID'S BLOOMINGTON CHRYSLER JEEP DODGE RAM; *U.S. Private*, pg. 2393
LATHAM FORD-F, LLC—See Lithia Motors, Inc.; *U.S. Public*, pg. 1323
LATHAM MOTORS INC.; *U.S. Private*, pg. 2396
LAUREL FORD LINCOLN-MERCURY; *U.S. Private*, pg. 2398
LAUREL IMPORTS INC.—See Laurel Motors Holding Company; *U.S. Private*, pg. 2399
LAUREL MOTORS HOLDING COMPANY; *U.S. Private*, pg. 2399
LAUREL VALLEY MOTORS INC.—See Laurel Motors Holding Company; *U.S. Private*, pg. 2399
LAWLEY AUTOMOTIVE GROUP; *U.S. Private*, pg. 2401
LAWLEY MOTORS LLC; *U.S. Private*, pg. 2401
LAWRENCE HALL CHEVROLET INC.; *U.S. Private*, pg. 2401
LAWRENCE HALL CHEVROLET OLDSMOBILE BUICK INC.; *U.S. Private*, pg. 2401
LAWRENCEVILLE FORD LINCOLN MERCURY; *U.S. Private*, pg. 2402
LAYTON HILLS DODGE INC.; *U.S. Private*, pg. 2402
LBMP, LLC—See Lithia Motors, Inc.; *U.S. Public*, pg. 1323
LDLC, LLC—See Lithia Motors, Inc.; *U.S. Public*, pg. 1323
LEAGUE CITY-H, INC.—See Lithia Motors, Inc.; *U.S. Public*, pg. 1323
LE BRUN TOYOTA—See West Herr Automotive Group, Inc.; *U.S. Private*, pg. 4485
LEE A. FOLGER INC.; *U.S. Private*, pg. 2411

LEE AUTOMOTIVE GROUP INC.; *U.S. Private*, pg. 2411
LEE EDWARDS INC.; *U.S. Private*, pg. 2411
LEE HYUNDAI INC.; *U.S. Private*, pg. 2413
LEE KINSTLE CHEVROLET-OLDSMOBILE INC.; *U.S. Private*, pg. 2413
LEE PONTIAC-GMC, INC.—See Lee Automotive Group Inc.; *U.S. Private*, pg. 2411
LEESBURG MOTORS, LLC—See AutoNation, Inc.; *U.S. Public*, pg. 236
LEE'S SUMMIT HONDA INC.; *U.S. Private*, pg. 2414
LEGACY INFINITI; *U.S. Private*, pg. 2416
LEGACY NISSAN; *U.S. Private*, pg. 2416
LEHMAN DEALERSHIP ENTERPRISES, INC.—See Lithia Motors, Inc.; *U.S. Public*, pg. 1323
LEIF JOHNSON FORD INC.; *U.S. Private*, pg. 2419
LEITH HONDA ABERDEEN; *U.S. Private*, pg. 2420
LEITH INC.—See Holman Automotive Group, Inc.; *U.S. Private*, pg. 1967
LE JEUNE INVESTMENT INC.; *U.S. Private*, pg. 2405
LEJEUNE MOTOR COMPANY INC.; *U.S. Private*, pg. 2420
LEMAY AUTO GROUP; *U.S. Private*, pg. 2421
LEN STOLER INC.; *U.S. Private*, pg. 2421
LESON CHEVROLET COMPANY, INC.; *U.S. Private*, pg. 2432
LES PINKHAM LINCOLN MERCURY, INC.; *U.S. Private*, pg. 2431
LES STANFORD CHEVROLET INC.; *U.S. Private*, pg. 2432
LES STUMPF FORD; *U.S. Private*, pg. 2432
LESTER RAINES MAZDA—See Raines Imports, Inc.; *U.S. Private*, pg. 3347
LESTER RAINES MITSUBISHI—See Raines Imports, Inc.; *U.S. Private*, pg. 3347
LETA ENTERPRISES INC.; *U.S. Private*, pg. 2433
LEVIS CHEVROLET-CADILLAC; *U.S. Private*, pg. 2436
LEWIS CHEVROLET COMPANY—See Lewis One Plaza Center Corporation; *U.S. Private*, pg. 2439
LEWIS FORD—See Lewis Management Inc.; *U.S. Private*, pg. 2439
LEWIS MANAGEMENT INC.; *U.S. Private*, pg. 2439
LEWIS TOYOTA INC.; *U.S. Private*, pg. 2439
LEWISVILLE IMPORTS, LTD.—See AutoNation, Inc.; *U.S. Public*, pg. 236
LEXUS MANILA, INC.—See GT Capital Holdings, Inc.; *Int'l*, pg. 3151
LEXUS OF BELLEVUE—See Michael O'Brien Enterprises, Inc.; *U.S. Private*, pg. 2698
LEXUS OF CERRITOS LIMITED PARTNERSHIP—See AutoNation, Inc.; *U.S. Public*, pg. 236
LEXUS OF MAPLEWOOD—See North American Automotive Services, Inc.; *U.S. Private*, pg. 2940
LEXUS OF NORTH MIAMI; *U.S. Private*, pg. 2440
LEXUS OF SACRAMENTO—See RPM Management Inc.; *U.S. Private*, pg. 3495
LEXUS OF TACOMA—See Michael O'Brien Enterprises, Inc.; *U.S. Private*, pg. 2698
LEXUS OF THOUSAND OAKS; *U.S. Private*, pg. 2441
LEXUS OF TOLEDO; *U.S. Private*, pg. 2441
LEXUS OF VALENCIA; *U.S. Private*, pg. 2441
LFKF, LLC—See Lithia Motors, Inc.; *U.S. Public*, pg. 1323
LGPAC, INC.—See Lithia Motors, Inc.; *U.S. Public*, pg. 1323
LIA AUTO GROUP; *U.S. Private*, pg. 2442
LIA HONDA OF ALBANY—See Lia Auto Group; *U.S. Private*, pg. 2442
LIA HONDA WILLIAMSVILLE—See Lia Auto Group; *U.S. Private*, pg. 2442
LIA NISSAN LTD.—See Lia Auto Group; *U.S. Private*, pg. 2442
LIA TOYOTA OF COLONIE—See Lia Auto Group; *U.S. Private*, pg. 2442
LIBERTY AUTOMOTIVE LTD.; *U.S. Private*, pg. 2443
LIBERTY BUICK INC.; *U.S. Private*, pg. 2443
LIBERTY FORD LINCOLN MERCURY—See Jim Herrick Motors Inc.; *U.S. Private*, pg. 2209
LIBERTY IMPORTS INC.; *U.S. Private*, pg. 2444
LIBERTYVILLE BUICK, PONTIAC, GMC, INC.; *U.S. Private*, pg. 2447
LIBERTYVILLE LINCOLN SALES INC.; *U.S. Private*, pg. 2447
LIMA AUTO MALL INC.; *U.S. Private*, pg. 2456
LINDQUIST FORD INC.; *U.S. Private*, pg. 2460
LINDSAY CADILLAC COMPANY; *U.S. Private*, pg. 2460
LINDSAY CHEVROLET LLC; *U.S. Private*, pg. 2460
LINDSAY FORD, LLC; *U.S. Private*, pg. 2460
LINFEN BAOZEN AUTOMOBILE SALES AND SERVICES CO., LTD.—See China Yongda Automobiles Services Holdings Limited; *Int'l*, pg. 1564
LINHAI BAOZEN AUTOMOBILE SALES AND SERVICES CO., LTD.—See China Yongda Automobiles Services Holdings Limited; *Int'l*, pg. 1564
LINUS CADILLAC BUICK GMC; *U.S. Private*, pg. 2463
LINYI YUBAQHANG AUTOMOBILE SALES AND SERVICE COMPANY LIMITED—See China Yongda Automobiles Services Holdings Limited; *Int'l*, pg. 1564
LISHUI JIACHENG AUTOMOBILE SALES CO., LTD.—See China Yongda Automobiles Services Holdings Limited; *Int'l*, pg. 1564
LITHIA ACDM, INC.—See Lithia Motors, Inc.; *U.S. Public*, pg. 1323

N.A.I.C.S. INDEX 441110 — NEW CAR DEALERS

LITHIA BNM, INC.—See Lithia Motors, Inc.; *U.S. Public*, pg. 1323
LITHIA BRYAN TEXAS, INC.—See Lithia Motors, Inc.; *U.S. Public*, pg. 1323
LITHIA CDH, INC.—See Lithia Motors, Inc.; *U.S. Public*, pg. 1323
LITHIA CHRYSLER JEEP DODGE OF BILLINGS—See Lithia Motors, Inc.; *U.S. Public*, pg. 1324
LITHIA CJDO, INC.—See Lithia Motors, Inc.; *U.S. Public*, pg. 1323
LITHIA CJDSA, INC.—See Lithia Motors, Inc.; *U.S. Public*, pg. 1323
LITHIA CJDSF, INC.—See Lithia Motors, Inc.; *U.S. Public*, pg. 1323
LITHIA DE, INC.—See Lithia Motors, Inc.; *U.S. Public*, pg. 1324
LITHIA DMID, INC.—See Lithia Motors, Inc.; *U.S. Public*, pg. 1324
LITHIA DM, INC.—See Lithia Motors, Inc.; *U.S. Public*, pg. 1324
LITHIA DODGE OF TRI-CITIES, INC.—See Lithia Motors, Inc.; *U.S. Public*, pg. 1324
LITHIA FMF, INC.—See Lithia Motors, Inc.; *U.S. Public*, pg. 1324
LITHIA FORD LINCOLN OF FRESNO; *U.S. Private*, pg. 2467
LITHIA FORD OF BOISE, INC.—See Lithia Motors, Inc.; *U.S. Public*, pg. 1324
LITHIA HGF—See Lithia Motors, Inc.; *U.S. Public*, pg. 1324
LITHIA HMID, INC.—See Lithia Motors, Inc.; *U.S. Public*, pg. 1324
LITHIA KLAMATH, INC.—See Lithia Motors, Inc.; *U.S. Public*, pg. 1324
LITHIA MBDM, INC.—See Lithia Motors, Inc.; *U.S. Public*, pg. 1324
LITHIA MEDFORD HON, INC.—See Lithia Motors, Inc.; *U.S. Public*, pg. 1324
LITHIA MTLM, LLC—See Lithia Motors, Inc.; *U.S. Public*, pg. 1324
LITHIA NA, INC.—See Lithia Motors, Inc.; *U.S. Public*, pg. 1324
LITHIA ND ACQUISITION CORP. #3—See Lithia Motors, Inc.; *U.S. Public*, pg. 1324
LITHIA NF, INC.—See Lithia Motors, Inc.; *U.S. Public*, pg. 1324
LITHIA NISSAN OF AMES—See Lithia Motors, Inc.; *U.S. Public*, pg. 1324
LITHIA NSA, INC.—See Lithia Motors, Inc.; *U.S. Public*, pg. 1324
LITHIA OF ABILENE, INC.—See Lithia Motors, Inc.; *U.S. Public*, pg. 1325
LITHIA OF BELLINGHAM, LLC—See Lithia Motors, Inc.; *U.S. Public*, pg. 1325
LITHIA OF CORPUS CHRISTI, INC.—See Lithia Motors, Inc.; *U.S. Public*, pg. 1325
LITHIA OF DES MOINES, INC.—See Lithia Motors, Inc.; *U.S. Public*, pg. 1325
LITHIA OF EUGENE, LLC—See Lithia Motors, Inc.; *U.S. Public*, pg. 1325
LITHIA OF EUREKA, INC.—See Lithia Motors, Inc.; *U.S. Public*, pg. 1325
LITHIA OF GREAT FALLS, INC.—See Lithia Motors, Inc.; *U.S. Public*, pg. 1325
LITHIA OF HONOLULUBGMCC, LLC—See Lithia Motors, Inc.; *U.S. Public*, pg. 1325
LITHIA OF HONOLULUV, LLC—See Lithia Motors, Inc.; *U.S. Public*, pg. 1325
LITHIA OF KILLEEN, LLC—See Lithia Motors, Inc.; *U.S. Public*, pg. 1325
LITHIA OF MAUI-H, LLC—See Lithia Motors, Inc.; *U.S. Public*, pg. 1325
LITHIA OF MISSOULA, INC.—See Lithia Motors, Inc.; *U.S. Public*, pg. 1325
LITHIA OF ROSEBURG, INC.—See Lithia Motors, Inc.; *U.S. Public*, pg. 1325
LITHIA OF SANTA ROSA, INC.—See Lithia Motors, Inc.; *U.S. Public*, pg. 1325
LITHIA OF SEATTLE, INC.—See Lithia Motors, Inc.; *U.S. Public*, pg. 1325
LITHIA OF SOUTH CENTRAL AK, INC.—See Lithia Motors, Inc.; *U.S. Public*, pg. 1325
LITHIA OF SPOKANE, INC.—See Lithia Motors, Inc.; *U.S. Public*, pg. 1325
LITHIA OF STOCKTON-V, INC.—See Lithia Motors, Inc.; *U.S. Public*, pg. 1325
LITHIA OF TF, INC.—See Lithia Motors, Inc.; *U.S. Public*, pg. 1325
LITHIA OF WALNUT CREEK, INC.—See Lithia Motors, Inc.; *U.S. Public*, pg. 1325
LITHIA RENO-CJ, LLC—See Lithia Motors, Inc.; *U.S. Public*, pg. 1324
LITHIA RENO SUB-HYUN, INC.—See Lithia Motors, Inc.; *U.S. Public*, pg. 1324
LITHIA RENO-VW, LLC—See Lithia Motors, Inc.; *U.S. Public*, pg. 1324
LITHIA ROSE-FT, INC.—See Lithia Motors, Inc.; *U.S. Public*, pg. 1324

LITHIA SALMIR, INC.—See Lithia Motors, Inc.; *U.S. Public*, pg. 1324
LITHIA SEA P, INC.—See Lithia Motors, Inc.; *U.S. Public*, pg. 1325
LITHIA SEASIDE, INC.—See Lithia Motors, Inc.; *U.S. Public*, pg. 1325
LITHIA SOC, INC.—See Lithia Motors, Inc.; *U.S. Public*, pg. 1324
LITHIA SUBARU HYUNDAI GMC BUICK—See Lithia Motors, Inc.; *U.S. Public*, pg. 1325
LITHIA SUBARU OF FRESNO; *U.S. Private*, pg. 2467
LITHIA TA, INC.—See Lithia Motors, Inc.; *U.S. Public*, pg. 1325
LITHIA TR, INC.—See Lithia Motors, Inc.; *U.S. Public*, pg. 1325
LITHIA VF, INC.—See Lithia Motors, Inc.; *U.S. Public*, pg. 1325
LITTLETON CHEVROLET BUICK OLDS PONTIAC; *U.S. Private*, pg. 2472
LIUYANG MEIBAOHANG AUTO SALES & SERVICES CO., LTD.—See China MeiDong Auto Holdings Limited; *Int'l*, pg. 1519
LIVERMORE AUTO GROUP; *U.S. Private*, pg. 2473
LLL SALES CO LLC—See Lithia Motors, Inc.; *U.S. Public*, pg. 1323
LMBB, LLC—See Lithia Motors, Inc.; *U.S. Public*, pg. 1323
LMBP, LLC—See Lithia Motors, Inc.; *U.S. Public*, pg. 1323
LMK AUTO GROUP LTD.; *U.S. Private*, pg. 2476
LOCKHART CADILLAC INC.; *U.S. Private*, pg. 2478
LOCKHART CADILLAC SOUTH—See Lockhart Cadillac Inc.; *U.S. Private*, pg. 2478
LODI MOTORS INC.; *U.S. Private*, pg. 2479
LOEBER MOTORS, INC.; *U.S. Private*, pg. 2480
LOKEY KIA—See Lokey Motor Company; *U.S. Private*, pg. 2482
LOKEY NISSAN, INC.—See Lokey Motor Company; *U.S. Private*, pg. 2482
LOKEY SUBARU OF PORT RICHEY—See Lokey Motor Company; *U.S. Private*, pg. 2482
LOKEY VOLKSWAGEN—See Lokey Motor Company; *U.S. Private*, pg. 2482
LONG-LEWIS INCORPORATED; *U.S. Private*, pg. 2492
LONG-MCARTHUR INC.; *U.S. Private*, pg. 2492
LONG MOTORS INC.; *U.S. Private*, pg. 2491
LONGYAN MEIDONG LEXUS AUTO SALES & SERVICES CO., LTD.—See China MeiDong Auto Holdings Limited; *Int'l*, pg. 1519
LOREN AUTO GROUP; *U.S. Private*, pg. 2495
LOREN BERG CHEVROLET; *U.S. Private*, pg. 2495
LOS GATOS ACURA; *U.S. Private*, pg. 2497
LOU BACHRODT CHEVROLET INC.; *U.S. Private*, pg. 2498
LOU FUSZ AUTOMOTIVE NETWORK; *U.S. Private*, pg. 2498
LOU FUSZ MOTOR COMPANY—See Lou Fusz Automotive Network; *U.S. Private*, pg. 2498
LOU LARICHE CHEVROLET INC.—See LaFontaine Automotive Group, LLC; *U.S. Private*, pg. 2373
LOVE BUICK GMC, INC.; *U.S. Private*, pg. 2501
LOVE CHEVROLET COMPANY; *U.S. Private*, pg. 2501
LOWER GREAT LAKES KENWORTH INC; *U.S. Private*, pg. 2506
L.P. EVANS MOTORS, INC.—See AutoNation, Inc.; *U.S. Public*, pg. 236
L.P. EVANS MOTORS, INC.—See AutoNation, Inc.; *U.S. Public*, pg. 236
L.P. EVANS MOTORS WPB, INC.—See AutoNation, Inc.; *U.S. Public*, pg. 236
L.P. EVANS MOTORS WPB, INC.—See AutoNation, Inc.; *U.S. Public*, pg. 236
L&S TRUCK CENTER OF APPLETON; *U.S. Private*, pg. 2363
LUBBOCK MOTORS-T, INC.—See Group 1 Automotive, Inc.; *U.S. Public*, pg. 971
LUM'S AUTO CENTER INC.; *U.S. Private*, pg. 2513
LUNDE AUTO CENTER; *U.S. Private*, pg. 2515
LUND & FRANGIE MOTORS INC.; *U.S. Private*, pg. 2515
LUPIENT AUTOMOTIVE GROUP, INC.; *U.S. Private*, pg. 2515
LUPIENT CHEVROLET INC.; *U.S. Private*, pg. 2515
LUTHER BROOKDALE TOYOTA; *U.S. Private*, pg. 2516
LUTHER HOLDING COMPANY; *U.S. Private*, pg. 2516
LUTHERS RUDY WHITE BEAR MOTORS—See Luther Holding Company; *U.S. Private*, pg. 2517
LUXURY ORLANDO IMPORTS, INC.—See AutoNation, Inc.; *U.S. Public*, pg. 236
LUXURY WOODLANDS IMPORTS, INC.—See AutoNation, Inc.; *U.S. Public*, pg. 236
LYNCHBURG HYUNDAI MITSUBISHI INC; *U.S. Private*, pg. 2521
LYNCH FORD MOUNT VERNON INC.; *U.S. Private*, pg. 2520
LYNN LAYTON FORD; *U.S. Private*, pg. 2522
MAC HAIK CHEVEROLET; *U.S. Private*, pg. 2531
MACKENZIE MOTOR CO.; *U.S. Private*, pg. 2537
MACK GRUBBS MOTORS INC—See Walt Massey Automotive, Inc.; *U.S. Private*, pg. 4433
MADDEN LINCOLN MERCURY INC; *U.S. Private*, pg. 2539

MADERA AUTO CENTER; *U.S. Private*, pg. 2539
MAGIC ACQUISITION CORP.—See AutoNation, Inc.; *U.S. Public*, pg. 236
MAGIC ACQUISITION CORP.—See AutoNation, Inc.; *U.S. Public*, pg. 236
MAGNUSSEN'S AUBURN IMPORTS; *U.S. Private*, pg. 2549
MAGNUSSEN'S AUBURN TOYOTA; *U.S. Private*, pg. 2549
MAGUIRE AUTOMOTIVE GROUP; *U.S. Private*, pg. 2549
MAGUIRE AUTOMOTIVE, LLC; *U.S. Private*, pg. 2549
MAGUIRE CHEVROLET-CADILLAC—See Maguire Automotive, LLC; *U.S. Private*, pg. 2549
MAGUIRE IMPORTS—See Maguire Automotive, LLC; *U.S. Private*, pg. 2549
MAGUIRE'S FORD OF HERSHEY, PA. INC.; *U.S. Private*, pg. 2550
MAHER CHEVROLET INC.; *U.S. Private*, pg. 2550
MAITA ENTERPRISES INC.; *U.S. Private*, pg. 2554
MAITA'S NISSAN OF SACRAMENTO; *U.S. Private*, pg. 2554
MAITLAND LUXURY IMPORTS, INC.—See AutoNation, Inc.; *U.S. Public*, pg. 236
MAJESTIC MOTORS INC.; *U.S. Private*, pg. 2554
MALL CHEVROLET; *U.S. Private*, pg. 2557
MALL CHRYSLER-SUZUKI; *U.S. Private*, pg. 2557
MALOUF BUICK-GMC; *U.S. Private*, pg. 2558
MANCARI CHRYSLER JEEP INC.; *U.S. Private*, pg. 2562
MANCARI'S CHRYSLER JEEP INC.; *U.S. Private*, pg. 2562
MANCHESTER HONDA; *U.S. Private*, pg. 2562
MANCHESTER SUBARU; *U.S. Private*, pg. 2562
MANHATTAN AUTOMOBILE COMPANY—See Ford Motor Company; *U.S. Public*, pg. 866
MANHATTAN MOTORCARS, INC.; *U.S. Private*, pg. 2563
MANKATO FORD ACQUISITION CORP.; *U.S. Private*, pg. 2564
MANKATO MOTOR CO.; *U.S. Private*, pg. 2564
MANLY GMC BUICK HYUNDAI MITSUBISHI; *U.S. Private*, pg. 2564
MANN CHRYSLER-PLYMOUTH-DODGE-JEEP; *U.S. Private*, pg. 2564
MANSFIELD MOTOR GROUP; *U.S. Private*, pg. 2566
MANTECA FORD MERCURY, INC.; *U.S. Private*, pg. 2567
MAPLE HILL AUTO GROUP; *U.S. Private*, pg. 2568
MAPLE SHADE MOTOR CORP.; *U.S. Private*, pg. 2568
MARANELLO SALES LIMITED—See Penske Automotive Group, Inc.; *U.S. Public*, pg. 1665
MARCHANT CHEVROLET, INC.; *U.S. Private*, pg. 2571
MARC MILLER BUICK GMC, INC.; *U.S. Private*, pg. 2571
MARC MOTORS INC.; *U.S. Private*, pg. 2571
MARC MOTORS NISSAN—See Marc Motors Inc.; *U.S. Private*, pg. 2571
MARINE CHEVROLET COMPANY, INC.; *U.S. Private*, pg. 2575
MARIN LUXURY CARS, LLC.; *U.S. Private*, pg. 2574
MARINO CHRYSLER JEEP DODGE; *U.S. Private*, pg. 2576
MARION TOYOTA; *U.S. Private*, pg. 2576
MARK CHEVROLET INC.; *U.S. Private*, pg. 2577
MARK CHRISTOPHER AUTO CENTER; *U.S. Private*, pg. 2577
MARKLEY MOTORS INC.; *U.S. Private*, pg. 2582
MARK MITSUBISHI SCOTTSDALE; *U.S. Private*, pg. 2578
MARK MITSUBISHI; *U.S. Private*, pg. 2578
MARK MOTORS INC.; *U.S. Private*, pg. 2578
MARKQUART INC.; *U.S. Private*, pg. 2582
MARKS TRANSPORT, INC.—See AutoNation, Inc.; *U.S. Public*, pg. 236
MARK THOMAS MOTORS INC.; *U.S. Private*, pg. 2578
MARMIE MOTORS INC.; *U.S. Private*, pg. 2586
MAROONE AUTO PLAZA—See AutoNation, Inc.; *U.S. Public*, pg. 236
MAROONE DODGE, LLC—See AutoNation, Inc.; *U.S. Public*, pg. 236
MARQUARDT BUICK, INC.; *U.S. Private*, pg. 2586
MARSHAL MIZE FORD, INC.; *U.S. Private*, pg. 2592
MARSTALLER MOTORS, INC.; *U.S. Private*, pg. 2593
MARTENS CARS OF WASHINGTON, INC.; *U.S. Private*, pg. 2594
MARTENS VOLVO; *U.S. Private*, pg. 2594
MARTIN CADILLAC COMPANY, INC.; *U.S. Private*, pg. 2594
MARTIN CAR FINANCING INC.; *U.S. Private*, pg. 2594
MARTIN CHEVROLET-BUICK; *U.S. Private*, pg. 2594
MARTIN CHEVROLET SALES, INC.; *U.S. Private*, pg. 2594
MARTIN NEWARK DEALERSHIP, INC.; *U.S. Private*, pg. 2595
MARTY FELDMAN CHEVROLET, INC.; *U.S. Private*, pg. 2597
MARTY FRANICH FORD LINCOLN MERCURY INC; *U.S. Private*, pg. 2597
MARTY SUSSMAN MOTORS INC—See Marty Sussman Organization; *U.S. Private*, pg. 2597
MARTY SUSSMAN ORGANIZATION; *U.S. Private*, pg. 2597
MARVIN K. BROWN AUTO CENTER, INC.; *U.S. Private*, pg. 2598
MASON CITY FORD; *U.S. Private*, pg. 2601
MASSEY CADILLAC, INC.—See Sonic Automotive, Inc.; *U.S. Public*, pg. 1902

441110 — NEW CAR DEALERS

MASSEY MOTORS INC.; *U.S. Private*, pg. 2606
MASSEY; *U.S. Private*, pg. 2606
MASTER FLEET, LLC; *U.S. Private*, pg. 2607
MASTRIA BUICK-PONTIAC-GMC TRUCK; *U.S. Private*, pg. 2608
MATAGA OF STOCKTON; *U.S. Private*, pg. 2608
MATHEW'S DODGE CHRYSLER JEEP, INC.; *U.S. Private*, pg. 2611
MATHEWS FORD SANDUSKY, INC.; *U.S. Private*, pg. 2611
MATHEWS KENNEDY FORD LINCOLN-MERCURY INC.; *U.S. Private*, pg. 2611
MATHEW ZAHERI CORPORATION; *U.S. Private*, pg. 2610
MATT BLATT INC.; *U.S. Private*, pg. 2612
MATT CASTRUCCI, LLC; *U.S. Private*, pg. 2613
MATTHEWS AUTO GROUP; *U.S. Private*, pg. 2613
MATTHEWS HARGREAVES CHEVROLET; *U.S. Private*, pg. 2613
MATT SLAP SUBARU; *U.S. Private*, pg. 2613
MAUDLIN INTERNATIONAL TRUCKS, INC.; *U.S. Private*, pg. 2614
MAVERICK MOTORS, LLC; *U.S. Private*, pg. 2616
MAX MADSEN IMPORTS INC.; *U.S. Private*, pg. 2617
MAXTON MOTORS INC.; *U.S. Private*, pg. 2619
MAXWELL FORD, INC.—See Group 1 Automotive, Inc.; *U.S. Public*, pg. 971
MAXWELL-NII, INC.—See Group 1 Automotive, Inc.; *U.S. Public*, pg. 971
MAYPOLE CHEVROLET INC.; *U.S. Private*, pg. 2622
MAYSE AUTOMOTIVE GROUP; *U.S. Private*, pg. 2623
MAZDA KNOXVILLE; *U.S. Private*, pg. 2623
MAZDA OF MESQUITE; *U.S. Private*, pg. 2623
MAZDA OF WEST RIDGE—See West Herr Automotive Group, Inc.; *U.S. Private*, pg. 4485
MCCAFFERTY FORD SALES INC.; *U.S. Private*, pg. 2626
MCCALL-F, INC.—See Group 1 Automotive, Inc.; *U.S. Public*, pg. 971
MCCALL-TII, INC.—See Group 1 Automotive, Inc.; *U.S. Public*, pg. 971
MCCARTHY HYUNDAI; *U.S. Private*, pg. 2627
MCCLOSKEY MOTORS INC.; *U.S. Private*, pg. 2628
MCCLUSKEY CHEVROLET INC.; *U.S. Private*, pg. 2629
MCCOMBS WEST FORD; *U.S. Private*, pg. 2629
MCCONNELL AUTOMOTIVE; *U.S. Private*, pg. 2629
MCCORD BROS INC.; *U.S. Private*, pg. 2629
MCCOY FREIGHTLINER—See Penske Automotive Group, Inc.; *U.S. Public*, pg. 1665
MCCOY MOTORS INC.; *U.S. Private*, pg. 2630
MC CURRY-DECK MOTORS, INC.; *U.S. Private*, pg. 2625
MCDANIEL MOTOR CO.; *U.S. Private*, pg. 2631
MCDAVID HONDA—See David McDavid Automotive Group; *U.S. Private*, pg. 1171
MCDERMOTT AUTO GROUP; *U.S. Private*, pg. 2631
MCDONALD AUTOMOTIVE GROUP; *U.S. Private*, pg. 2632
MCDONALD FORD INC.; *U.S. Private*, pg. 2632
MCDONALD PONTIAC-CADILLAC-GMC-OLDS INC.; *U.S. Private*, pg. 2632
MCELENEY MOTORS INC.; *U.S. Private*, pg. 2633
MCELWAIN CHEVROLET & OLDSMOBILE; *U.S. Private*, pg. 2633
MCENEARNEY QUALITY, INC.—See ANSA McAL Limited; *Int'l*, pg. 476
MCFADDEN FORD, INC.—See Shults Management Group, Inc.; *U.S. Private*, pg. 3644
MCGRATH AUTOMOTIVE GROUP INC.; *U.S. Private*, pg. 2635
MCGRATH AUTOMOTIVE, INC.; *U.S. Private*, pg. 2635
MCGRATH CITY HYUNDAI—See McGrath Automotive, Inc.; *U.S. Private*, pg. 2635
MCGRATH HONDA—See McGrath Automotive, Inc.; *U.S. Private*, pg. 2635
MCGRATH LEXUS OF WESTMONT—See McGrath Automotive, Inc.; *U.S. Private*, pg. 2635
MCGRATH NISSAN; *U.S. Private*, pg. 2635
MCGUIRE CADILLAC; *U.S. Private*, pg. 2636
MCINERNEY INC.; *U.S. Private*, pg. 2637
MCINERNEY'S WOODHAVEN CHRYSLER JEEP; *U.S. Private*, pg. 2637
MCKAY'S CHRYSLER JEEP DODGE; *U.S. Private*, pg. 2637
MCKEE AUTO CENTER INC.; *U.S. Private*, pg. 2637
MCKENNA MOTOR COMPANY INC.; *U.S. Private*, pg. 2638
MCKENNA MOTORS INC.; *U.S. Private*, pg. 2638
MCKENNEY CHEVROLET; *U.S. Private*, pg. 2638
MCKIE FORD INC.; *U.S. Private*, pg. 2638
MCKIE FORD LINCOLN MERCURY; *U.S. Private*, pg. 2638
MCKINSEY MOTOR FORD; *U.S. Private*, pg. 2639
MCLAUGHLIN MOTORS; *U.S. Private*, pg. 2640
MCL MOTOR CARS (1992) INC.—See Dilawri Group of Companies; *Int'l*, pg. 2125
MCMAHON FORD, LLC.; *U.S. Private*, pg. 2642
MCMAHON FORD; *U.S. Private*, pg. 2642
MCM AUTOS PTY LTD—See Eagers Automotive Limited; *Int'l*, pg. 2263
MCMULLAN EQUIPMENT COMPANY, INC.; *U.S. Private*, pg. 2642
MCNABB CHEVROLET, OLDS, CADILLAC; *U.S. Private*, pg. 2643

MEADE GROUP INC.; *U.S. Private*, pg. 2647
MEADE LEXUS OF LAKESIDE—See Meade Group Inc.; *U.S. Private*, pg. 2647
MEADOR CHRYSLER JEEP; *U.S. Private*, pg. 2647
MEADOWLANDS NISSAN; *U.S. Private*, pg. 2647
MEDINA MANAGEMENT COMPANY, LLC; *U.S. Private*, pg. 2657
MEDVED AUTOPLEX; *U.S. Private*, pg. 2659
MEEHAN AUTOMOBILES INC.; *U.S. Private*, pg. 2659
M.E. FIELDS INC.; *U.S. Private*, pg. 2528
MELBORNE CITY AUTOS (2012) PTY LTD—See Eagers Automotive Limited; *Int'l*, pg. 2263
MEL HAMBELTON FORD INC.; *U.S. Private*, pg. 2661
MELLOY BROTHERS ENTERPRISES; *U.S. Private*, pg. 2662
MEL RAPTON HONDA; *U.S. Private*, pg. 2661
MELTON SALES, INC.; *U.S. Private*, pg. 2663
MELVILLE AUTOS PTY LTD—See Eagers Automotive Limited; *Int'l*, pg. 2263
MEMORIAL HIGHWAY CHEVROLET, INC.—See General Motors Company; *U.S. Public*, pg. 926
MENTOR MITSUBISHI; *U.S. Private*, pg. 2667
MERCED CHEVROLET, INC.—See General Motors Company; *U.S. Public*, pg. 926
MERCEDES-BENZ LYON SAS—See Chopard Automobiles SAS; *Int'l*, pg. 1582
MERCEDES-BENZ OF BROOKLYN; *U.S. Private*, pg. 2668
MERCEDES-BENZ OF CALDWELL; *U.S. Private*, pg. 2668
MERCEDES-BENZ OF CORAL GABLES; *U.S. Private*, pg. 2668
MERCEDES BENZ OF HAGERSTOWN; *U.S. Private*, pg. 2668
MERCEDES-BENZ OF NANUET; *U.S. Private*, pg. 2668
MERCEDES-BENZ OF NAPLES; *U.S. Private*, pg. 2668
MERCEDES-BENZ OF NORTHWEST ARKANSAS—See Superior Auto Group; *U.S. Private*, pg. 3876
MERCEDES BENZ OF NOVI; *U.S. Private*, pg. 2668
MERCEDES-BENZ OF PORTSMOUTH—See Kaplan Auto Group; *U.S. Private*, pg. 2261
MERCEDES-BENZ OF SARASOTA—See AutoNation, Inc.; *U.S. Public*, pg. 236
MERCEDES-BENZ OF SEATTLE; *U.S. Private*, pg. 2668
MERCEDES-BENZ OF SOUTH BAY—See AutoNation, Inc.; *U.S. Public*, pg. 236
MERCEDES-BENZ OF SPOKANE; *U.S. Private*, pg. 2669
MERCEDES-BENZ OF TRAVERSE CITY—See DP Fox Ventures, LLC; *U.S. Private*, pg. 1270
MERCEDES-BENZ RUSSIA SAO—See Avtodom OAO; *Int'l*, pg. 751
MERCEDES PORSCHE AUDI OF MELBOURNE; *U.S. Private*, pg. 2668
MERIT CHEVROLET COMPANY; *U.S. Private*, pg. 2674
MERLE STONE CHEVROLET CADILLAC; *U.S. Private*, pg. 2675
MEROLLIS CHEVROLET SALES & SERVICE INC.; *U.S. Private*, pg. 2675
MERRIMACK STREET GARAGE INC.; *U.S. Private*, pg. 2676
METRO FORD, INC.; *U.S. Private*, pg. 2685
METRO FORD-LINCOLN-MERCURY; *U.S. Private*, pg. 2685
METRO FORD SALES, INC.; *U.S. Private*, pg. 2685
METRO IMPORTS, INC.; *U.S. Private*, pg. 2685
METRO INFINITI, INC.—See HGreg.com; *U.S. Private*, pg. 1931
METRO MOTOR GROUP; *U.S. Private*, pg. 2686
MEYER BROTHERS AUTOMOTIVE CO.; *U.S. Private*, pg. 2692
MHC FORD—See Murphy-Hoffman Company; *U.S. Private*, pg. 2816
MHC KENWORTH CO. INC.—See Murphy-Hoffman Company; *U.S. Private*, pg. 2816
MIAMI AUTOMOTIVE RETAIL, INC.; *U.S. Private*, pg. 2696
MICHAEL CADILLAC INC.; *U.S. Private*, pg. 2697
MICHAEL HOHL MOTOR COMPANY; *U.S. Private*, pg. 2698
MICHAEL STEADS HILLTOP FORD KIA; *U.S. Private*, pg. 2698
MICHIGAN KENWORTH, INC.; *U.S. Private*, pg. 2701
MIDDLEKAUFF AUTOMOTIVE INC.; *U.S. Private*, pg. 2713
MIDDLETON FORD, INC.; *U.S. Private*, pg. 2714
MIDDLETOWN FORD SALES INC.; *U.S. Private*, pg. 2714
MIDDLETOWN FORD; *U.S. Private*, pg. 2714
MIDLANDS TRUCK & VAN LTD—See Ballyvesey Holdings Limited; *Int'l*, pg. 809
MIDPAC AUTO CENTER, INC.; *U.S. Private*, pg. 2717
MIDTOWN TOYOTA; *U.S. Private*, pg. 2718
MIDWAY CHEVROLET COMPANY; *U.S. Private*, pg. 2718
MIDWAY DODGE INC.; *U.S. Private*, pg. 2718
MIDWEST SUPERSTORE; *U.S. Private*, pg. 2723
MIKE ANDERSON CHEVROLET BUICK GMC TRUCK, INC.; *U.S. Private*, pg. 2724
MIKE BARNEY NISSAN; *U.S. Private*, pg. 2724
MIKE BURKART FORD MERCURY INC.; *U.S. Private*, pg. 2725
MIKE CASTRUCCI CHEVROLET SALES, INC.—See Mike Castrucci, LLC.; *U.S. Private*, pg. 2725
MIKE ERDMAN MOTORS INC.; *U.S. Private*, pg. 2725

CORPORATE AFFILIATIONS

MIKE FINNIN MOTORS INC.; *U.S. Private*, pg. 2725
MIKE HALL CHEVROLET, INC.—See AutoNation, Inc.; *U.S. Public*, pg. 236
MIKE MURPHY FORD INC.; *U.S. Private*, pg. 2725
MIKE PATTON AUTO; *U.S. Private*, pg. 2725
MIKE PERRY MOTOR CO.; *U.S. Private*, pg. 2725
MIKE PIAZZA HONDA; *U.S. Private*, pg. 2725
MIKE PILE BMW; *U.S. Private*, pg. 2725
MIKE REICHENBACH FORD LINCOLN MERCURY; *U.S. Private*, pg. 2725
MIKE SAVOIE CHEVROLET INC.; *U.S. Private*, pg. 2725
MIKE SHAD FORD, INC.—See AutoNation, Inc.; *U.S. Public*, pg. 236
MIKE SHAW BUICK GMC; *U.S. Private*, pg. 2725
MIKE SHAW SUBARU, INC.—See Asbury Automotive Group, Inc.; *U.S. Public*, pg. 209
MIKE SMITH AUTOPLEX DODGE, INC.—See Group 1 Automotive, Inc.; *U.S. Public*, pg. 971
MIKE SMITH TOYOTA MITSUBISHI KIA; *U.S. Private*, pg. 2725
MIKE STEVEN AUTO GROUP INC.; *U.S. Private*, pg. 2725
MILEA TRUCK SALES CORP.; *U.S. Private*, pg. 2727
MILES CHEVROLET INC.; *U.S. Private*, pg. 2727
MILLENNIUM TOYOTA; *U.S. Private*, pg. 2732
MILLER AUTO CLUB—See Miller Enterprises; *U.S. Private*, pg. 2734
MILLER AUTO GROUP; *U.S. Private*, pg. 2733
MILLER AUTOMOBILE CORPORATION; *U.S. Private*, pg. 2733
MILLER AUTO SALES INC.; *U.S. Private*, pg. 2733
MILLER BUICK-PONTIAC-GMC CO.; *U.S. Private*, pg. 2733
MILLER-DM, INC.—See Group 1 Automotive, Inc.; *U.S. Public*, pg. 971
MILLER - EDWARDS BUICK GMC; *U.S. Private*, pg. 2732
MILLER ENTERPRISES; *U.S. Private*, pg. 2734
MILLER FORD SALES INC.; *U.S. Private*, pg. 2734
MILLER MOTOR CAR CORP.; *U.S. Private*, pg. 2735
MILLER MOTORCARS INC.; *U.S. Private*, pg. 2735
MILLER PERSONNEL INC.—See Miller Resources International, Inc.; *U.S. Private*, pg. 2735
MILLER PONTIAC-BUICK-GMC INC.—See Miller Enterprises; *U.S. Private*, pg. 2734
MILLER'S CHRYSLER-PLYMOUTH JEEP; *U.S. Private*, pg. 2734
MILLS AUTO ENTERPRISES, INC.—See Mills Fleet Farm, Inc.; *U.S. Private*, pg. 2737
MILLS CHEVROLET CO., INC.; *U.S. Private*, pg. 2737
MILLS FORD OF WILLMAR; *U.S. Private*, pg. 2737
MILLS MOTOR, INC.—See Mills Fleet Farm, Inc.; *U.S. Private*, pg. 2737
MILNE RUSS FORD INC.; *U.S. Private*, pg. 2738
MILO GORDON CHRYSLER ISUZU MITSUBISHI; *U.S. Private*, pg. 2738
MILO PETERSON FORD; *U.S. Private*, pg. 2738
MILTON RUBEN CHEVROLET; *U.S. Private*, pg. 2738
MILTON RUBEN LEASING COMPANY—See Milton Ruben Chevrolet; *U.S. Private*, pg. 2738
MILTON RUBEN MOTORS, INC.—See Milton Ruben Chevrolet; *U.S. Private*, pg. 2738
MINI CENTER OF SAN ANTONIO; *U.S. Private*, pg. 2742
MINOT AUTOMOTIVE CENTER; *U.S. Private*, pg. 2744
MIRAK CHEVROLET-HYUNDAI, INC.; *U.S. Private*, pg. 2746
MISSION HILLS-H, INC.—See Lithia Motors, Inc.; *U.S. Public*, pg. 1325
MISTLIN HONDA INC.; *U.S. Private*, pg. 2750
MITCH CRAWFORD'S HOLIDAY MOTORS CO.; *U.S. Private*, pg. 2750
MITCHELL AUTOMOTIVE, INC.; *U.S. Private*, pg. 2750
MITCHELL MOTORS INC.; *U.S. Private*, pg. 2751
MITCHELL PONTIAC INC.; *U.S. Private*, pg. 2751
M&J MOTORS INC.; *U.S. Private*, pg. 2524
M & M DODGE HYUNDAI, INC; *U.S. Private*, pg. 2523
MOBERLY MOTOR; *U.S. Private*, pg. 2756
MODERN AUTOMOTIVE PERFORMANCE; *U.S. Private*, pg. 2759
MODERN CLASSIC MOTORS INC.—See Group 1 Automotive, Inc.; *U.S. Public*, pg. 972
MODERN NISSAN OF CONCORD, INC.; *U.S. Private*, pg. 2761
MODERN TOYOTA OF BOONE INC.; *U.S. Private*, pg. 2762
MODERN TOYOTA; *U.S. Private*, pg. 2762
MODESTO MOTOR CARS INC.; *U.S. Private*, pg. 2763
MOEHN ART CHEVROLET CO.; *U.S. Private*, pg. 2764
MOFFITTS INCORPORATED; *U.S. Private*, pg. 2765
MOFFITT VOLKSWAGON -MAZDA; *U.S. Private*, pg. 2765
MOHEGAN LAKE MOTORS; *U.S. Private*, pg. 2765
MOJAVE AUTO GROUP; *U.S. Private*, pg. 2765
MOJAVE MOTORS LTD.; *U.S. Private*, pg. 2765
MOLLE TOYOTA INCORPORATED; *U.S. Private*, pg. 2767
MOLLE VOLKSWAGON AUDI; *U.S. Private*, pg. 2767
MOLYE CHEVROLET OLDSMOBILE SALES; *U.S. Private*, pg. 2767
MOMENTUM AUTO GROUP; *U.S. Private*, pg. 2768
MONARCH LEASING INC.; *U.S. Private*, pg. 2769
MONEY ATUOMOTIVE CENTER INC.; *U.S. Private*, pg. 2770

441110 — NEW CAR DEALERS

MONROEVILLE CHRYSLER JEEP; *U.S. Private*, pg. 2774
MONROEVILLE DODGE; *U.S. Private*, pg. 2774
MONTALBANO INC.; *U.S. Private*, pg. 2774
MONTANO MOTORS, INC.; *U.S. Private*, pg. 2775
MONTE SHELTON JAGUAR; *U.S. Private*, pg. 2775
MONTESI MOTORS, INC.; *U.S. Private*, pg. 2776
MONTGOMERY CHEVROLET; *U.S. Private*, pg. 2776
MONTROSE FORD LINCOLN; *U.S. Private*, pg. 2777
MOOERS MOTOR CAR COMPANY INC.; *U.S. Private*, pg. 2778
MOORE CADILLAC HUMMER OF DULLES, LLC.; *U.S. Private*, pg. 2779
MOORE CHRYSLER, INC.; *U.S. Private*, pg. 2779
MORAN AUTOMOTIVE GROUP, INC.—See General Motors Company; *U.S. Public*, pg. 926
MORAN CHEVROLET INC.; *U.S. Private*, pg. 2781
MOREHART CHEVROLET CO; *U.S. Private*, pg. 2782
MOREIN MOTOR COMPANY INC.; *U.S. Private*, pg. 2782
MORGAN GMC-BUICK; *U.S. Private*, pg. 2783
MORGAN-McCLURE CHEVY BUICK CADILLAC, INC.; *U.S. Private*, pg. 2784
MORITZ KIA F.T. WORTH; *U.S. Private*, pg. 2785
MORONG BRUNSWICK—See WSMC Inc.; *U.S. Private*, pg. 4574
MORRIE'S BUFFALO FORD—See Morrie's Imports, Inc.; *U.S. Private*, pg. 2786
MORRIE'S CADILLAC—See Morrie's Imports, Inc.; *U.S. Private*, pg. 2786
MORRIS MOORE CHEVROLET-BUICK, INC.; *U.S. Private*, pg. 2788
MORRISON CHEVROLET INC.; *U.S. Private*, pg. 2789
MORRISON & SYLVESTER INC.; *U.S. Private*, pg. 2789
MORRIS PONTIAC GMC INC.; *U.S. Private*, pg. 2788
MORROW MOTOR SALES INC.; *U.S. Private*, pg. 2790
MORROW MOTORS INC.; *U.S. Private*, pg. 2790
MORSE CHEVROLET INC.; *U.S. Private*, pg. 2790
MORSE OPERATIONS INC.; *U.S. Private*, pg. 2790
MOSS BROS. CHRYSLER JEEP DODGE RAM; *U.S. Private*, pg. 2794
MOSS BROS. TOYOTA, INC.; *U.S. Private*, pg. 2794
MOSS MOTORS; *U.S. Private*, pg. 2794
MOSSY NISSAN INC.; *U.S. Private*, pg. 2795
MOSSY TOYOTA INC.; *U.S. Private*, pg. 2795
MOTOCROSS TOYOTA; *U.S. Private*, pg. 2796
MOTORCARS ACQUISITION IV, LLC—See Penske Automotive Group, Inc.; *U.S. Public*, pg. 1665
MOTORCARS ACQUISITION, LLC—See Penske Automotive Group, Inc.; *U.S. Public*, pg. 1665
MOTORCARS INTERNATIONAL INC.; *U.S. Private*, pg. 2797
MOTOR MART AUTO SALES; *U.S. Private*, pg. 2797
MOTOR REPRIS AUTOMOCIO S.L.—See General Motors Company; *U.S. Public*, pg. 927
MOTOR WERKS PARTNERS LP; *U.S. Private*, pg. 2797
MOUNTAIN VIEW FORD LINCOLN; *U.S. Private*, pg. 2800
MOUNT CLEMENS KIA; *U.S. Private*, pg. 2798
MR. WHEELS, INC—See AutoNation, Inc.; *U.S. Public*, pg. 236
MTC KENWORTH INC.; *U.S. Private*, pg. 2809
M.T.K. AUTO WEST LTD.—See Auto West Group; *Int'l*, pg. 725
MULLANE MOTORS; *U.S. Private*, pg. 2811
MULLEN MOTORS INC.; *U.S. Private*, pg. 2811
MULLINAX EAST, LLC—See AutoNation, Inc.; *U.S. Public*, pg. 236
MULLINAX FORD NORTH CANTON, INC.—See AutoNation, Inc.; *U.S. Public*, pg. 236
MULLINAX FORD SOUTH, INC.—See AutoNation, Inc.; *U.S. Public*, pg. 236
MULLINAX LINCOLN-MERCURY, INC.—See AutoNation, Inc.; *U.S. Public*, pg. 236
MULTI CHEVROLET INC.; *U.S. Private*, pg. 2812
MUNDAY MAZDA—See Group 1 Automotive, Inc.; *U.S. Public*, pg. 972
MUSSELMAN'S DODGE INC.; *U.S. Private*, pg. 2818
MUSSER MOTORS INC.; *U.S. Private*, pg. 2818
MUSSON-PATOUT AUTOMOTIVE GROUP INC.; *U.S. Private*, pg. 2819
MUTZ MOTORS L.P.; *U.S. Private*, pg. 2820
MUZI MOTORS INC.; *U.S. Private*, pg. 2820
MV MARKETING INC.; *U.S. Private*, pg. 2821
MVP NISSAN OF EXTON; *U.S. Private*, pg. 2822
MY AUTOGROUP; *U.S. Private*, pg. 2823
MY CHEVROLET—See MY Autogroup; *U.S. Private*, pg. 2823
MY NISSAN - KIA; *U.S. Private*, pg. 2823
NABER CHRYSLER DODGE JEEP RAM; *U.S. Private*, pg. 2829
NACARATO TRUCKS, INC.—See SF Holding Corp.; *U.S. Private*, pg. 3621
NANJING AUTO ITALIA CAR TRADING CO., LTD.—See Auto Italia Holdings Limited; *Int'l*, pg. 725
NANTONG BAOZEN AUTOMOBILE SALES AND SERVICES CO., LTD.—See China Yongda Automobiles Services Holdings Limited; *Int'l*, pg. 1564
NAPA CHRYSLER JEEP DODGE RAM VOLVO KIA—See Hanlees Hilltop Toyota; *U.S. Private*, pg. 1854
NAPERVILLE IMPORTS, INC.—See AutoNation, Inc.; *U.S. Public*, pg. 236
NAPLES DODGE INC.; *U.S. Private*, pg. 2834
NAPLES NISSAN; *U.S. Private*, pg. 2834
NAPLETON AUTO WERKS; *U.S. Private*, pg. 2834
NAPLETON BUICK GMC; *U.S. Private*, pg. 2834
NAPLETON NISSAN; *U.S. Private*, pg. 2834
NAPLETON RIVER OAKS CHRYSLER JEEP DODGE; *U.S. Private*, pg. 2834
NAPLETON SCHAUMBURG MOTORS, INC.—See North American Automotive Services, Inc.; *U.S. Private*, pg. 2940
NASH CHEVROLET CO., INC.; *U.S. Private*, pg. 2835
NATE WADE SUBARU; *U.S. Private*, pg. 2838
NATIONAL CITY VOLKSWAGEN; *U.S. Private*, pg. 2850
NATIONWIDE LIFT TRUCKS INC.; *U.S. Private*, pg. 2866
NATIONWIDE MOTOR SALES CORP; *U.S. Private*, pg. 2866
NAVARRE CHEVROLET INC.; *U.S. Private*, pg. 2872
NEBRASKA TRUCK CENTER, INC.; *U.S. Private*, pg. 2879
NEESSEN CHEVROLET INC.; *U.S. Private*, pg. 2880
NEIL HUFFMAN NISSAN INC.; *U.S. Private*, pg. 2882
NEIL HUFFMAN VOLKSWAGEN MAZDA SUBURU—See Neil Huffman Nissan Inc.; *U.S. Private*, pg. 2882
NELS GUNDERSON CHEVROLET, INC.; *U.S. Private*, pg. 2882
NELSON HALL CHEVROLET, INC.; *U.S. Private*, pg. 2883
NELSON NISSAN; *U.S. Private*, pg. 2883
NEMER CHRYSLER PLYMOUTH DODGE; *U.S. Private*, pg. 2884
NEMET MOTORS; *U.S. Private*, pg. 2884
NEMITH MOTOR CORP.; *U.S. Private*, pg. 2884
NERESON AUTOMOTIVE INC.; *U.S. Private*, pg. 2885
NESMITH CHEVROLET BUICK PONTIAC GMC; *U.S. Private*, pg. 2886
NEUVILLE CHRYSLER-DODGE-JEEP LLC.; *U.S. Private*, pg. 2891
NEW AGE INVESTMENTS INC.; *U.S. Private*, pg. 2892
NEW ALBANY MOTOR CO. INC.; *U.S. Private*, pg. 2892
NEWARK TOYOTA WORLD; *U.S. Private*, pg. 2913
NEW BRIGHTON FORD, INC.; *U.S. Private*, pg. 2892
NEWBY BUICK-OLDSMBILE-PONTIAC-GMC; *U.S. Private*, pg. 2914
NEW CARS INC.; *U.S. Private*, pg. 2893
NEWCASTLE COMMERCIAL VEHICLES PTY LTD—See Eagers Automotive Limited; *Int'l*, pg. 2263
NEW COUNTRY LEXUS OF WESTPORT; *U.S. Private*, pg. 2893
NEW ERA SALES CO., LTD.—See AAPICO Hitech plc; *Int'l*, pg. 37
NEW HOLLAND MOTOR COMPANY, INC.; *U.S. Private*, pg. 2897
NEW MOTORS INC.; *U.S. Private*, pg. 2899
NEW PORT AUTO CENTER, INC.; *U.S. Private*, pg. 2905
NEWPORT AUTO CENTER INC.; *U.S. Private*, pg. 2916
NEWPORT BEACH CARS, LLC—See AutoNation, Inc.; *U.S. Public*, pg. 236
NEW PORT RICHEY-H, LLC—See Lithia Motors, Inc.; *U.S. Public*, pg. 1325
NEW PORT RICHEY-V, LLC—See Lithia Motors, Inc.; *U.S. Public*, pg. 1325
NEW ROCHELLE TOYOTA; *U.S. Private*, pg. 2906
NEW SOUTH FORD, INC.; *U.S. Private*, pg. 2906
NEW WORLD CAR NISSAN, INC.; *U.S. Private*, pg. 2908
NEXT GREEN CAR LTD.—See Good Energy Group PLC; *Int'l*, pg. 3038
NICHOLS FORD, LTD.—See AutoNation, Inc.; *U.S. Public*, pg. 236
NICK ALEXANDER IMPORTS, INC—See Car Pros Automotive Group, Inc.; *U.S. Private*, pg. 747
NICK CHEVROLET & PONTIAC; *U.S. Private*, pg. 2925
NICK CORSELLO CHEVROLET INC.; *U.S. Private*, pg. 2925
NICK MAYER LINCOLN-MERCURY, INC.; *U.S. Private*, pg. 2925
NICK NICHOLAS FORD, INC.; *U.S. Private*, pg. 2925
THE NIELLO COMPANY; *U.S. Private*, pg. 4084
NIELLO VOLVO OF SACRAMENTO; *U.S. Private*, pg. 2927
NILES SALES & SERVICE, INC.—See Warren Henry Automobiles Inc.; *U.S. Private*, pg. 4444
NIMNICHT CHEVROLET COMPANY; *U.S. Private*, pg. 2928
NISSAN BONDESEN-HARDY INC.; *U.S. Private*, pg. 2928
NISSAN KIA WORLD; *U.S. Private*, pg. 2928
NISSAN LYNNES CITY INC.; *U.S. Private*, pg. 2928
NISSAN OF BAKERSFIELD; *U.S. Private*, pg. 2928
NISSAN OF BERGENFIELD INC.; *U.S. Private*, pg. 2928
NISSAN OF BOURNE; *U.S. Private*, pg. 2929
NISSAN OF BRANDON, INC.—See AutoNation, Inc.; *U.S. Public*, pg. 236
NISSAN OF COOL SPRINGS LLC; *U.S. Private*, pg. 2929
NISSAN OF HAWTHORNE; *U.S. Private*, pg. 2929
NISSAN OF HUNTINGTON; *U.S. Private*, pg. 2929
NISSAN OF MANHATTAN; *U.S. Private*, pg. 2929
NISSAN OF MELBOURNE; *U.S. Private*, pg. 2929
NISSAN OF NORWICH; *U.S. Private*, pg. 2929
NISSAN OF RENO; *U.S. Private*, pg. 2929
NISSAN OF ROANOKE RAPIDS; *U.S. Private*, pg. 2929
NISSAN SOUTH; *U.S. Private*, pg. 2929
NOARUS AUTO GROUP; *U.S. Private*, pg. 2932
NOBLE FORD; *U.S. Private*, pg. 2932
NORFOLK TRUCK CENTER INCORPORATED; *U.S. Private*, pg. 2937
NORM REEVES HONDA SUPERSTORE—See The Conant Auto Retail Group; *U.S. Private*, pg. 4013
NORRIS ACURA WEST; *U.S. Private*, pg. 2939
NORRIS AUTOMOTIVE GROUP; *U.S. Private*, pg. 2939
NORTH AMERICAN AUTOMOTIVE SERVICES, INC.; *U.S. Private*, pg. 2940
NORTH BAY CADILLAC CO. INC.; *U.S. Private*, pg. 2942
NORTH BAY FORD LINCOLN MERCURY; *U.S. Private*, pg. 2942
NORTH BROS. FORD; *U.S. Private*, pg. 2942
NORTH CITY (1981) PTY LTD—See Eagers Automotive Limited; *Int'l*, pg. 2263
NORTH COUNTY FORD INC.; *U.S. Private*, pg. 2944
NORTHCUTT CHEVROLET-BUICK CO.; *U.S. Private*, pg. 2949
NORTH END MAZDA OF LUNENBURG—See Colonial Automotive Group, Inc.; *U.S. Private*, pg. 970
NORTH END SUBARU OF LUNENBURG—See Colonial Automotive Group, Inc.; *U.S. Private*, pg. 970
NORTHERN AUTOMOTIVE, INC.; *U.S. Private*, pg. 2952
NORTHERN COMMERCIALS (MIRFIELD) LTD—See Clipper Logistics Group Ltd.; *Int'l*, pg. 1660
NORTHERN MOTOR COMPANY; *U.S. Private*, pg. 2953
NORTH FLORIDA MOTOR COMPANY; *U.S. Private*, pg. 2945
NORTHGATE FORD LINCOLN MERCURY—See Kenwood Dealer Group, Inc.; *U.S. Private*, pg. 2289
NORTH PALM HYUNDAI, LLC.; *U.S. Private*, pg. 2946
NORTH PARK LINCOLN MERCURY INC.; *U.S. Private*, pg. 2946
NORTHPOINT CHEVROLET, LLC—See AutoNation, Inc.; *U.S. Public*, pg. 236
NORTHPOINT FORD, INC.—See AutoNation, Inc.; *U.S. Public*, pg. 236
NORTH SHORE INFINITI INC.; *U.S. Private*, pg. 2946
NORTH SIDE FORD; *U.S. Private*, pg. 2947
NORTHSIDE NISSAN (1986) PTY. LTD.—See Eagers Automotive Limited; *Int'l*, pg. 2264
NORTH STAR AUTOMOTIVE GROUP; *U.S. Private*, pg. 2947
NORTH STAR CHEVROLET, INC.—See North Star Automotive Group; *U.S. Private*, pg. 2947
NORTH STAR PONTIAC, GMC, OLDSMOBILE, INC.—See North Star Automotive Group; *U.S. Private*, pg. 2947
NORTHTOWN AUTOMOTIVE CO., INC.; *U.S. Private*, pg. 2958
NORTHTOWN FORD MERCURY; *U.S. Private*, pg. 2958
NORTHWAY MOTORCAR CORPORATION—See Langan Automotive Group; *U.S. Private*, pg. 2388
NORTHWEST FINANCIAL GROUP, INC.—See AutoNation, Inc.; *U.S. Public*, pg. 236
NTAN, LLC—See Booth Creek Management Corporation; *U.S. Private*, pg. 617
NUFORD FORD PTY LTD—See Eagers Automotive Limited; *Int'l*, pg. 2263
NUSS TRUCK GROUP; *U.S. Private*, pg. 2974
NUTMEG INTERNATIONAL TRUCKS INC.; *U.S. Private*, pg. 2974
NYHUS CHEVROLET & BUICK INC.; *U.S. Private*, pg. 2976
NY LUXURY MOTORS OF MT. KISCO, INC.—See AutoNation, Inc.; *U.S. Public*, pg. 236
NY MT. KISCO LUXURY IMPORTS, INC.—See AutoNation, Inc.; *U.S. Public*, pg. 236
OAK LAWN TOYOTA; *U.S. Private*, pg. 2983
O'BRIEN AUTO PARK; *U.S. Private*, pg. 2977
OBRIEN IMPORTS, INC.; *U.S. Private*, pg. 2987
OCALA FREIGHTLINER, INC.—See Florida Truck Group; *U.S. Private*, pg. 1550
OCEAN CADILLAC INC.; *U.S. Private*, pg. 2989
OCEAN HONDA—See Victory Automotive Group, Inc.; *U.S. Private*, pg. 4378
OCEAN MAZDA; *U.S. Private*, pg. 2989
OCEAN MOTORS, INC.; *U.S. Private*, pg. 2989
OCEAN WAY MOTORS INC.; *U.S. Private*, pg. 2990
O'CONNOR GMC INC.; *U.S. Private*, pg. 2978
O.C. WELCH FORD LINCOLN INC.; *U.S. Private*, pg. 2981
O'DANIEL MOTORSALES INC.; *U.S. Private*, pg. 2978
OFFICINE BRENNERO S.P.A.—See CNH Industrial N.V.; *Int'l*, pg. 1675
O'GARA COACH COMPANY LLC; *U.S. Private*, pg. 2978
O'HARA CHRYSLER DODGE JEEP RAM; *U.S. Private*, pg. 2978
OK CHEVROLET, INC; *U.S. Private*, pg. 3006
OKOBOJI GM; *U.S. Private*, pg. 3008
OLATHE FORD SALES INC.; *U.S. Private*, pg. 3008
OLD FORGE SPRING HOUSE; *U.S. Private*, pg. 3009
OLIVER C. JOSEPH; *U.S. Private*, pg. 3010
OMAHA TRUCK CENTER INC.; *U.S. Private*, pg. 0014
O'MEARA FORD CENTER INC.; *U.S. Private*, pg. 2979
OMNIBUS BB TRANSPORTES, S. A.—See General Motors Company; *U.S. Public*, pg. 926
O'NEIL BUICK - GMC INC.; *U.S. Private*, pg. 2979
O'NEILL AUTOMOTIVE INC.; *U.S. Private*, pg. 2980
O'NEILLS CHEVROLET & BUICK; *U.S. Private*, pg. 2980

441110 — NEW CAR DEALERS

ONTARIO DODGE, INC.—See AutoNation, Inc.; *U.S. Public*, pg. 236
ONTARIO NISSAN INC.—See New Age Investments Inc.; *U.S. Private*, pg. 2892
OPEN ROAD BMW, INC.—See Open Road Auto Group; *U.S. Private*, pg. 3029
OPEN ROAD OF BRIDGEWATER, LLC—See Open Road Auto Group; *U.S. Private*, pg. 3029
ORANGE MOTOR COMPANY INC.; *U.S. Private*, pg. 3037
ORCHARD CHRYSLER DODGE JEEP; *U.S. Private*, pg. 3039
O'RIELLY CHEVROLET, INC.—See O'Rielly Motor Company; *U.S. Private*, pg. 2980
ORIENT MOTORS WLL—See Al Zayani Investments WLL; *Int'l*, pg. 283
ORLANDO DODGE; *U.S. Private*, pg. 3043
ORLANDO FREIGHTLINER INC.—See Florida Truck Group; *U.S. Private*, pg. 1551
ORLOR INC.; *U.S. Private*, pg. 3044
ORRIN B HAYES INC.; *U.S. Private*, pg. 3044
ORR INC.; *U.S. Private*, pg. 3044
ORR TOYOTA; *U.S. Private*, pg. 3044
OSBURN BUICK PONTIAC GMC TRUCK; *U.S. Private*, pg. 3046
O'STEEN VOLVO; *U.S. Private*, pg. 2980
OURISMAN AUTOMOTIVE GROUP; *U.S. Private*, pg. 3050
OURISMAN CHEVROLET COMPANY, INC.—See Ourisman Automotive Group; *U.S. Private*, pg. 3050
OURISMAN CHRYSLER DODGE JEEP RAM OF CLARKSVILLE—See Ourisman Automotive Group; *U.S. Private*, pg. 3050
OURISMAN DODGE, INC.—See Ourisman Automotive Group; *U.S. Private*, pg. 3050
OURISMAN MITSUBISHI—See Ourisman Automotive Group; *U.S. Private*, pg. 3050
OUTTEN CHEVROLET INC.; *U.S. Private*, pg. 3052
OVERSEAS MILITARY SALES CORPORATION; *U.S. Private*, pg. 3053
OVERTURF MOTOR CO. INC.; *U.S. Private*, pg. 3054
OWATONNA FORD CHRYSLER; *U.S. Private*, pg. 3054
OXENDALE CHRYSLER DODGE JEEP; *U.S. Private*, pg. 3056
OXMOOR FORD LINCOLN MERCURY, INC.; *U.S. Private*, pg. 3057
OXMOOR TOYOTA; *U.S. Private*, pg. 3057
PACIFIC NISSAN INC.; *U.S. Private*, pg. 3069
PACIFICO ENTERPRISES, INC.; *U.S. Private*, pg. 3072
PACIFICO FORD, INC.; *U.S. Private*, pg. 3072
PADDOCK CHEVROLET INC.; *U.S. Private*, pg. 3073
PAG DALY CITY LLC; *U.S. Private*, pg. 3074
PAGE TOYOTA, INC.; *U.S. Private*, pg. 3074
PAG GREENWICH M1, LLC—See Penske Automotive Group, Inc.; *U.S. Public*, pg. 1665
PAG MADISON L1, LLC—See Penske Automotive Group, Inc.; *U.S. Public*, pg. 1665
PAG MADISON T1, LLC—See Penske Automotive Group, Inc.; *U.S. Public*, pg. 1665
PAG ORLANDO PARTNERSHIP, LTD.—See Penske Automotive Group, Inc.; *U.S. Public*, pg. 1665
PAG WEST, LLC—See Penske Automotive Group, Inc.; *U.S. Public*, pg. 1665
PAINTER'S SUN COUNTRY MITSUBISHI; *U.S. Private*, pg. 3076
PALM AUTOMOTIVE GROUP; *U.S. Private*, pg. 3079
PALM BEACH IMPORTS INC.; *U.S. Private*, pg. 3079
PALM BEACH IMPORTS, INC.; *U.S. Private*, pg. 3079
PALM BEACH TOYOTA—See Penske Automotive Group, Inc.; *U.S. Public*, pg. 1665
PALM CHEVROLET OF GAINESVILLE; *U.S. Private*, pg. 3079
PALM CHRYSLER JEEP DODGE RAM; *U.S. Private*, pg. 3079
PALMEN AUTOMOTIVE GROUP INC.; *U.S. Private*, pg. 3080
PALMEN KIA; *U.S. Private*, pg. 3080
PALMER AUTO GROUP; *U.S. Private*, pg. 3080
PALMETTO CAR & TRUCK GROUP; *U.S. Private*, pg. 3081
PALMETTO CHEVROLET CO., INC.; *U.S. Private*, pg. 3081
PAMBY MOTORS INCORPORATED; *U.S. Private*, pg. 3083
PAPAS DODGE INC.; *U.S. Private*, pg. 3087
PAPE CHEVROLET INC.; *U.S. Private*, pg. 3087
PARADISE CHEVROLET; *U.S. Private*, pg. 3090
PARAGON ACURA; *U.S. Private*, pg. 3090
PARAGON MOTORS OF WOODSIDE, INC.; *U.S. Private*, pg. 3091
PARAMUS AUTO MALL CHEVROLET-HUMMER; *U.S. Private*, pg. 3093
PAR ENTERPRISES, INC.; *U.S. Private*, pg. 3089
PARETTI IMPORTS INC.; *U.S. Private*, pg. 3094
PARETTI MAZDA; *U.S. Private*, pg. 3094
PARIS CHEVROLET BUICK GMC; *U.S. Private*, pg. 3095
PARK AVENUE MOTORS CORP; *U.S. Private*, pg. 3095
PARK CHRYSLER JEEP; *U.S. Private*, pg. 3095
PARK CITY FORD; *U.S. Private*, pg. 3096
PARKER AUTO GROUP; *U.S. Private*, pg. 3097
PARKER CHEVROLET OLDS PONTIAC GEO INC.; *U.S. Private*, pg. 3097
PARK HONDA; *U.S. Private*, pg. 3096

PARKLEY HOLDING INC.; *U.S. Private*, pg. 3098
PARK PLACE MOTORCARS, LTD.; *U.S. Private*, pg. 3096
PARK PLACE VOLVO; *U.S. Private*, pg. 3096
PARKS AUTOMOTIVE INC.; *U.S. Private*, pg. 3098
PARKWAY BUICK GMC; *U.S. Private*, pg. 3098
PARKWAY FORD SALES 1996 LTD.—See Ford Motor Company; *U.S. Public*, pg. 865
PARKWAY MOTORCARS; *U.S. Private*, pg. 3099
PARKWAY MOTORS OF LEONIA INC.; *U.S. Private*, pg. 3099
PARSONS CHEVROLET-BUICK INC.; *U.S. Private*, pg. 3100
PATCHETT'S MOTORS INCORPORATED; *U.S. Private*, pg. 3105
PAT CLEMONS INC.; *U.S. Private*, pg. 3104
PATDAN LLC; *U.S. Private*, pg. 3105
PAT MCGRATH DODGE COUNTRY; *U.S. Private*, pg. 3105
PAT MILLIKEN FORD; *U.S. Private*, pg. 3105
PAT PECK NISSAN GULFPORT; *U.S. Private*, pg. 3105
PAT PECK NISSAN; *U.S. Private*, pg. 3105
PATRICK MOTORS INC.; *U.S. Private*, pg. 3110
PATRICK PONTIAC INC.; *U.S. Private*, pg. 3110
PATRIOT CHEVROLET GEO INC.; *U.S. Private*, pg. 3110
PATRIOT PONTIAC GMC BUICK LTD PARTNERSHIP; *U.S. Private*, pg. 3110
PATSY LOU BUICK GMC INC.; *U.S. Private*, pg. 3111
PATTERSON OLDSMOBILE-GMC-TOYOTA—See Foundation Automotive Corp; *U.S. Private*, pg. 1579
PATTY PECK HONDA; *U.S. Private*, pg. 3112
PAUL BROWN MOTORS, INC.; *U.S. Private*, pg. 3112
PAUL CERAME FORD; *U.S. Private*, pg. 3112
PAUL CONTE CADILLAC, INC.; *U.S. Private*, pg. 3112
PAUL HEURING MOTORS INC.; *U.S. Private*, pg. 3113
PAUL MILLER AUTO GROUP; *U.S. Private*, pg. 3113
PAUL SHERRY CHRYSLER-DODGE-JEEP INC.; *U.S. Private*, pg. 3113
PAUL THIGPEN CHEVROLET BUICK GMC; *U.S. Private*, pg. 3113
PAUL WALSH NISSAN, INC.; *U.S. Private*, pg. 3113
PAYNE-PIKE DEVELOPMENT CO.; *U.S. Private*, pg. 3117
PEAKE BMW; *U.S. Private*, pg. 3124
PEARSON BUICK GMC; *U.S. Private*, pg. 3126
PEARSON FORD; *U.S. Private*, pg. 3126
PEARSON-HUGGINS COMPANIES INC.; *U.S. Private*, pg. 3126
PEDERSEN TOYOTA-VOLVO INC.; *U.S. Private*, pg. 3127
PEGUES-HURST MOTOR COMPANY; *U.S. Private*, pg. 3130
PEMBROKE MOTORS, INC.—See AutoNation, Inc.; *U.S. Public*, pg. 236
PENCE BRIGGS INC.; *U.S. Private*, pg. 3132
PENNSYLVANIA TRUCK CENTERS, INC.; *U.S. Private*, pg. 3137
PENNYRILE FORD; *U.S. Private*, pg. 3138
PENSKE AUTOMOTIVE EUROPE GMBH—See Penske Automotive Group, Inc.; *U.S. Public*, pg. 1665
PENSKE AUTOMOTIVE GROUP, INC. - ARIZONA—See Penske Automotive Group, Inc.; *U.S. Public*, pg. 1665
PENSKE AUTOMOTIVE GROUP, INC. - SOUTHERN CALIFORNIA—See Penske Automotive Group, Inc.; *U.S. Public*, pg. 1665
PENSKE BUICK-GMC TRUCKS, INC.; *U.S. Private*, pg. 3138
PENSKE COMMERCIAL VEHICLES INVESTMENTS NZ PTY LTD.—See Penske Automotive Group, Inc.; *U.S. Public*, pg. 1665
PENSKE HONDA OF INDIANAPOLIS—See Penske Automotive Group, Inc.; *U.S. Public*, pg. 1665
PENSKE SPORTWAGEN HAMBURG GMBH—See Penske Automotive Group, Inc.; *U.S. Public*, pg. 1665
PENSKE SPORTWAGENZENTRUM GMBH—See Penske Automotive Group, Inc.; *U.S. Public*, pg. 1665
PEORIA TOYOTA SCION; *U.S. Private*, pg. 3143
PEPE MOTORS CORP.; *U.S. Private*, pg. 3143
PEPPERS AUTOMOTIVE GROUP, INC.; *U.S. Private*, pg. 3145
PERFORMANCE CHEVROLET LLC; *U.S. Private*, pg. 3148
PERFORMANCE PETROPLEX INC.; *U.S. Private*, pg. 3149
PERFORMANCE SUPERSTORE; *U.S. Private*, pg. 3150
PERFORMANCE TOYOTA; *U.S. Private*, pg. 3150
PERRY AUTO MALL; *U.S. Private*, pg. 3153
PERRY BUICK CO.; *U.S. Private*, pg. 3153
PERRY CHRYSLER DODGE JEEP RAM; *U.S. Private*, pg. 3153
PERRY FORD; *U.S. Private*, pg. 3154
PERRY LINCOLN MERCURY MAZDA; *U.S. Private*, pg. 3154
PERUZZI PONTIAC GMC TRUCK, INC.; *U.S. Private*, pg. 3156
PETE BAUR BUICK GMC INC.; *U.S. Private*, pg. 3157
PETE HARKNESS CHEVROLET BUICK, INC.—See Pete Harkness Auto Group, Inc.; *U.S. Private*, pg. 3157
PETE HARKNESS CHEVROLET—See Pete Harkness Auto Group, Inc.; *U.S. Private*, pg. 3157
PETE MANKINS AUTO; *U.S. Private*, pg. 3157
PETE MOORE CHEVROLET, INC.; *U.S. Private*, pg. 3157
PETERBILT NORTHERN ILLINOIS—See JX Enterprises Inc.; *U.S. Private*, pg. 2247

CORPORATE AFFILIATIONS

PETERBILT SPRINGFIELD INC.—See The Larson Group; *U.S. Private*, pg. 4067
PETER MUELLER, INC.; *U.S. Private*, pg. 3158
PETERS AUTO SALES INC.; *U.S. Private*, pg. 3159
PETERSBURG MOTOR COMPANY INC.; *U.S. Private*, pg. 3159
PETERSON GMC-KENWORTH INC.; *U.S. Private*, pg. 3160
PETERSON MOTOR COMPANY; *U.S. Private*, pg. 3160
PETERSON STAMPEDE DODGE CHRYSLER JEEP; *U.S. Private*, pg. 3160
PETERSON TOYOTA; *U.S. Private*, pg. 3160
PETE'S CAR SMART KIA; *U.S. Private*, pg. 3157
PETRO AUTOMOTIVE GROUP, INC.; *U.S. Private*, pg. 3161
PETTIJOHN AUTO CENTER INC.; *U.S. Private*, pg. 3163
PEYTON CRAMER AUTOMOTIVE—See AutoNation, Inc.; *U.S. Public*, pg. 237
PEYTON CRAMER FORD—See AutoNation, Inc.; *U.S. Public*, pg. 237
PEYTON CRAMER INFINITI—See AutoNation, Inc.; *U.S. Public*, pg. 237
PFEIFFER LINCOLN-MERCURY INC.; *U.S. Private*, pg. 3164
P & G CHEVROLET, INC.; *U.S. Private*, pg. 3058
PHELIA, LLC—See Hawk Auto Group; *U.S. Private*, pg. 1882
PHIL HUGHES AUTO SALES INC.; *U.S. Private*, pg. 3168
PHILLIPS BUICK PONTIAC GMC; *U.S. Private*, pg. 3170
PHILLIPS CHRYSLER JEEP DODGE RAM; *U.S. Private*, pg. 3170
PHIL LONG DENVER VALUCAR, LLC.; *U.S. Private*, pg. 3168
PHIL LONG LLC; *U.S. Private*, pg. 3168
PHIL MEADOR TOYOTA, INC.; *U.S. Private*, pg. 3168
PHILPOTT MOTORS, LTD.—See Sonic Automotive, Inc.; *U.S. Public*, pg. 1902
PHIL SMITH AUTOMOTIVE GROUP; *U.S. Private*, pg. 3168
PHIL WRIGHT AUTOPLEX CO.; *U.S. Private*, pg. 3168
PHOENIX-T, INC.—See Lithia Motors, Inc.; *U.S. Public*, pg. 1326
THE PHONE SHOPPE; *U.S. Private*, pg. 4095
PIAZZA ACURA OF ARDMORE; *U.S. Private*, pg. 3175
PIAZZA HONDA OF PHILADELPHIA; *U.S. Private*, pg. 3175
PICKARD CHRYSLER DODGE JEEP; *U.S. Private*, pg. 3176
PIEDMONT AUTOMOTIVE OF ANDERSON; *U.S. Private*, pg. 3176
PIEDMONT LIMOUSINE; *U.S. Private*, pg. 3177
PIEDMONT PETERBILT, LLC—See The Larson Group, Inc.; *U.S. Private*, pg. 4067
PIEHLER PONTIAC CORP.; *U.S. Private*, pg. 3178
PIERCE, LLC—See AutoNation, Inc.; *U.S. Public*, pg. 237
PIERSON AUTOMOTIVE INC.; *U.S. Private*, pg. 3179
PIERSON FORD LINCOLN MERCURY INC.; *U.S. Private*, pg. 3179
PIKES PEAK IMPORTS LTD.; *U.S. Private*, pg. 3180
PILES CHEVROLET-OLDS-PONTIAC-BUICK, INC.; *U.S. Private*, pg. 3180
PINE BELT ENTERPRISES; *U.S. Private*, pg. 3182
PINE BELT NISSAN OF TOMS RIVER; *U.S. Private*, pg. 3182
PINKERTON CHEVROLET-GEO, INC.; *U.S. Private*, pg. 3184
PINNACLE NISSAN; *U.S. Private*, pg. 3185
PIONEER CENTRES INC.; *U.S. Private*, pg. 3186
PIONEER GARAGE, INC.; *U.S. Private*, pg. 3187
PISCHKE MOTORS, INC.; *U.S. Private*, pg. 3190
PITTS TOYOTA INC.; *U.S. Private*, pg. 3191
PLACE MOTOR INC.; *U.S. Private*, pg. 3194
PLAINS CHEVROLET, LTD.—See AutoNation, Inc.; *U.S. Public*, pg. 237
PLANET CHRYSLER JEEP; *U.S. Private*, pg. 3195
PLANET HONDA—See Lithia Motors, Inc.; *U.S. Public*, pg. 1326
PLANET HYUNDAI SAHARA; *U.S. Private*, pg. 3196
PLANET SUBARU CAR DEALER; *U.S. Private*, pg. 3196
PLANET TOYOTA-SCION; *U.S. Private*, pg. 3196
PLATTNER AUTOMOTIVE GROUP, INC.; *U.S. Private*, pg. 3212
PLAZA LINCOLN MERCURY INC.; *U.S. Private*, pg. 3212
PLAZA MOTORS COMPANY; *U.S. Private*, pg. 3213
PLAZA MOTORS OF BROOKLYN; *U.S. Private*, pg. 3213
PLEASANTVILLE FORD INC.; *U.S. Private*, pg. 3213
POHANKA AUTO IMPORTS INC.—See Pohanka Auto North Inc.; *U.S. Private*, pg. 3220
POHANKA AUTO NORTH INC.; *U.S. Private*, pg. 3220
POHANKA HONDA; *U.S. Private*, pg. 3220
POHANKA OF SALISBURY—See Pohanka Auto North Inc.; *U.S. Private*, pg. 3220
POHANKA PROPERTIES INC.—See Pohanka Auto North Inc.; *U.S. Private*, pg. 3220
POHANKA TOYOTA SERVICE DEPARTMENT; *U.S. Private*, pg. 3220
POLLARD FRIENDLY FORD; *U.S. Private*, pg. 3225
POMOCO NISSAN; *U.S. Private*, pg. 3226
POMPANO NISSAN; *U.S. Private*, pg. 3227
POPULAR FORD SALES INC.; *U.S. Private*, pg. 3229

441110 — NEW CAR DEALERS

PORRECO NISSAN; U.S. Private, pg. 3229
PORT CITY IMPORTS, INC.—See AutoNation, Inc.; U.S. Public, pg. 237
PORTER CHEVROLET HYUNDAI; U.S. Private, pg. 3231
PORTER NISSAN INFINITI; U.S. Private, pg. 3231
PORT JEFF CHRYSLER PLYMOUTH JEEP EAGLE INC.; U.S. Private, pg. 3230
PORTSMOUTH CHEVROLET, INC.—See Key Auto Group; U.S. Private, pg. 2292
POTAMKIN MANHATTAN CORP; U.S. Private, pg. 3235
POTAMKIN NEW YORK L.P.; U.S. Private, pg. 3235
POTTSTOWN AUTO SALES INC; U.S. Private, pg. 3235
POWELL'S TRUCK & EQUIPMENT INC.—See K. Neal International Trucks, Inc.; U.S. Private, pg. 2251
POWELL-WATSON MOTORS INC.; U.S. Private, pg. 3237
POWER AUTO GROUP; U.S. Private, pg. 3237
POWER FORD; U.S. Private, pg. 3238
POWERS-SWAIN CHEVROLET INC.; U.S. Private, pg. 3240
PRECISION CHRYSLER JEEP DODGE RAM; U.S. Private, pg. 3244
PRECISION MOTOR CARS INC.; U.S. Private, pg. 3245
PRECISION MOTORCARS, INC.—See Asbury Automotive Group, Inc.; U.S. Public, pg. 210
PREMIER DODGE-CHRYSLER-JEEP—See Wilson County Automotive Dealer Group; U.S. Private, pg. 4530
PREMIERE CHEVROLET, INC.; U.S. Private, pg. 3251
PREMIERE TRUCK CENTERS, INC.; U.S. Private, pg. 3251
PREMIER GMC LTD.; U.S. Private, pg. 3250
PREMIUM TRUCK & TRAILER INC.—See Velocity Vehicle Group; U.S. Private, pg. 4355
PRESCOTT BROTHERS, INC.; U.S. Private, pg. 3254
PRESTIGE CHRYSLER DODGE INC.; U.S. Private, pg. 3255
PRESTIGE MOTORWORKS INC.; U.S. Private, pg. 3256
PRESTIGE OF BERGEN INC.; U.S. Private, pg. 3256
PRESTIGE PONTIAC BUICK GMC; U.S. Private, pg. 3256
PRESTIGE VOLKSWAGEN; U.S. Private, pg. 3256
PRESTON CHEVROLET CADILLAC KIA INC.; U.S. Private, pg. 3256
PRESTON FORD INC.; U.S. Private, pg. 3256
PRICE CARS LLC; U.S. Private, pg. 3258
PRICE CHEVROLET CO.—See Malloy Automotive of Winchester LLC; U.S. Private, pg. 2558
PRICE FORD LINCOLN; U.S. Private, pg. 3258
PRICE LEBLANC; U.S. Private, pg. 3258
PRIDE HYUNDAI OF SEEKONK; U.S. Private, pg. 3259
PRIME AUTO RESOURCES, INC.—See AutoNation, Inc.; U.S. Public, pg. 237
PRIME MOTOR GROUP—See GPB Capital Holdings, LLC; U.S. Private, pg. 1748
PRINCE AUTOMOTIVE GROUP INC.; U.S. Private, pg. 3264
PRINCETON BMW; U.S. Private, pg. 3264
PRINCETON CHEVROLET, INC.—See General Motors Company; U.S. Public, pg. 928
PRINCETON CHEVROLET, INC.—See General Motors Company; U.S. Public, pg. 928
PRINCETON LAND ROVER; U.S. Private, pg. 3264
PRITCHARD AUTO CO; U.S. Private, pg. 3267
PRO CHRYSLER JEEP INC.; U.S. Private, pg. 3269
PROSTROLLO ALL-AMERICAN AUTO MALL; U.S. Private, pg. 3289
PROSTROLLO MOTOR SALES, INC.; U.S. Private, pg. 3289
PROTHRO CHEVROLET BUICK GMC; U.S. Private, pg. 3290
PROTON CARS AUSTRALIA PTY LIMITED—See DRB-HICOM Berhad; Int'l, pg. 2202
PROTON CARS (UK) LTD—See DRB-HICOM Berhad; Int'l, pg. 2202
PROTON EDAR SDN. BHD.—See DRB-HICOM Berhad; Int'l, pg. 2202
PROTON SINGAPORE PTE LTD—See DRB-HICOM Berhad; Int'l, pg. 2202
PROTON TANJUNG MALIM SDN. BHD.—See DRB-HICOM Berhad; Int'l, pg. 2202
PT INDOMOBIL MULTI TRADA—See Gallant Venture Ltd.; Int'l, pg. 2874
PT INDOMOBIL PRIMA NIAGA—See Gallant Venture Ltd.; Int'l, pg. 2874
PT PROTON EDAR INDONESIA—See DRB-HICOM Berhad; Int'l, pg. 2202
PT WAHANA INDO TRADA—See Gallant Venture Ltd.; Int'l, pg. 2874
PUGMIRE AUTOMOTIVE GROUP; U.S. Private, pg. 3303
PUKLICH CHEVROLET, INC.; U.S. Private, pg. 3303
PUNDMANN MOTOR CO. INC.; U.S. Private, pg. 3304
PURCHASE FORD LINCOLN, INC.; U.S. Private, pg. 3305
PURITAN CHRYSLER-PLYMOUTH INC.; U.S. Private, pg. 3306
PURVIS FORD, INC.; U.S. Private, pg. 3307
PUTNAM CHEVROLET INC.—See Morse Operations Inc.; U.S. Private, pg. 2790
PUTNAM LEXUS; U.S. Private, pg. 3307
P&W FOREIGN CAR SERVICE INC.; U.S. Private, pg. 3059
PYE AUTOMOBILE SALES OF CHATTANOOGA; U.S. Private, pg. 3308

QINGYUAN MEIDONG LEXUS AUTO SALES & SERVICES CO., LTD.—See China MeiDong Auto Holdings Limited; Int'l, pg. 1519
QUALITY JEEP-CHRYSLER, INC.; U.S. Private, pg. 3319
QUALITY MOTOR CARS STOCKTON; U.S. Private, pg. 3320
QUALITY NISSAN, LTD.—See AutoNation, Inc.; U.S. Public, pg. 237
QUALITY PONTIAC GMC BUICK; U.S. Private, pg. 3320
QUANZHOU MEIDONG TOYOTA AUTO SALES & SERVICES CO., LTD.—See China MeiDong Auto Holdings Limited; Int'l, pg. 1519
QUEBEDEAUX BUICK GMC; U.S. Private, pg. 3325
QUEEN CITY MOTORS CO.; U.S. Private, pg. 3325
QUINLAN MOTORS, INC.—See AutoNation, Inc.; U.S. Public, pg. 237
QUIRK AUTO PARK; U.S. Private, pg. 3328
QUIRK CHEVROLET PORTLAND; U.S. Private, pg. 3328
RADLEY ACURA; U.S. Private, pg. 3345
RAFFERTY PONTIAC GMC, SUBARU; U.S. Private, pg. 3345
RAINBOW AUTOMOTIVE LLC; U.S. Private, pg. 3347
RALLYE MOTORS LLC; U.S. Private, pg. 3350
RALLY GM SUPERSTORE—See Rally Auto Group, Inc.; U.S. Private, pg. 3350
RALPH HONDA; U.S. Private, pg. 3350
RALPH THAYER CHEVROLET-TOYOTA INC.; U.S. Private, pg. 3350
RAM COUNTRY CHRYSLER DODGE INC.; U.S. Private, pg. 3350
RAMEY MOTORS INC.; U.S. Private, pg. 3351
RAMSEY AUTO GROUP; U.S. Private, pg. 3352
RAMSEY VOLVO; U.S. Private, pg. 3352
RANCHO FORD, INC.; U.S. Private, pg. 3352
RANCHO MOTOR COMPANY INC.; U.S. Private, pg. 3352
RANDALL MOTORS INC.; U.S. Private, pg. 3353
RANDALL NOE AUTO GROUP; U.S. Private, pg. 3353
RANDALL REED'S PRESTIGE LINCOLN MERCURY; U.S. Private, pg. 3353
RANDY MARION CHEVROLET-PONTIAC-BUICK, LLC—See Randy Marion Incorporated; U.S. Private, pg. 3354
RAPID CHEVROLET CO. INC.; U.S. Private, pg. 3355
RATH AUTO RESOURCES; U.S. Private, pg. 3357
RAVENNA MOTORS INC.; U.S. Private, pg. 3357
RAY BRANDT CHRYSLER DODGE JEEP—See Ray Brandt Nissan Inc.; U.S. Private, pg. 3358
RAY BRANDT NISSAN INC.; U.S. Private, pg. 3358
RAY BRANDT TOYOTA OF METAIRIE; U.S. Private, pg. 3358
RAY CATENA MOTOR CAR; U.S. Private, pg. 3358
RAY HUFFINES CHEVROLET PLANO; U.S. Private, pg. 3358
RAY LAETHEM BUICK-GMC, INC.—See Ray Laethem, Inc.; U.S. Private, pg. 3358
RAY LAETHEM CHRYSLER DODGE JEEP RAM—See Ray Laethem, Inc.; U.S. Private, pg. 3358
RAYMOND CHEVROLET; U.S. Private, pg. 3359
RAY PEARMAN LINCOLN, INC.; U.S. Private, pg. 3358
RAYS CHEVROLET OLDS INC.; U.S. Private, pg. 3359
RAY SERAPHIN FORD, INC.; U.S. Private, pg. 3358
RAY VARNER FORD, LLC.; U.S. Private, pg. 3359
RAZZARI DODGE CHRYSLER JEEP; U.S. Private, pg. 3360
RB CAR COMPANY; U.S. Private, pg. 3360
R. C. LACY, INC.; U.S. Private, pg. 3333
R.C. OLSEN CADILLAC; U.S. Private, pg. 3334
R&C SERVICES INC.; U.S. Private, pg. 3332
R.D. BANKS CHEVROLET, INC.; U.S. Private, pg. 3335
RDS MANAGEMENT, INC.—See LaFontaine Automotive Group, LLC; U.S. Private, pg. 2373
REBBEC MOTOR CO.; U.S. Private, pg. 3370
RECHTIEN INTERNATIONAL TRUCKS; U.S. Private, pg. 3370
RECTOR MOTOR CAR CO.; U.S. Private, pg. 3372
REDDELL HONDA; U.S. Private, pg. 3377
RED HOAGLAND HYUNDAI; U.S. Private, pg. 3374
RED MCCOMBS SUPERIOR HYUNDAI—See McCombs Enterprises; U.S. Private, pg. 2629
RED NOLAND CADILLAC; U.S. Private, pg. 3375
RED RIVER MOTOR COMPANY; U.S. Private, pg. 3375
REEDER CHEVROLET COMPANY; U.S. Private, pg. 3382
REED LALLIER CHEVROLET, INC.; U.S. Private, pg. 3382
REEDMAN TOLL AUTO WORLD; U.S. Private, pg. 3383
REE ENTERPRISES, INC.—See Rusty Eck Ford, Inc.; U.S. Private, pg. 3507
REEVES IMPORT MOTORCARS INC.; U.S. Private, pg. 3384
REGAL AUTOMOTIVE GROUP; U.S. Private, pg. 3385
REGAL NISSAN, INC.; U.S. Private, pg. 3385
REICHERT CHEVROLET BUICK OF WOODSTOCK; U.S. Private, pg. 3390
REINEKE FAMILY DEALERSHIPS; U.S. Private, pg. 3392
REINEKE FORD, INC.—See Reineke Family Dealerships; U.S. Private, pg. 3392
REINEKE LINCOLN MERCURY MAZDA INC.—See Reineke Family Dealerships; U.S. Private, pg. 3392
REINEKE MOTORS, INC.—See Reineke Family Dealerships; U.S. Private, pg. 3392

REINHARDT MOTORS, INC.; U.S. Private, pg. 3392
RELIABLE CHEVROLET; U.S. Private, pg. 3393
RENNER MOTORS, INC.; U.S. Private, pg. 3398
RENN KIRBY CHEVROLET BUICK, LLC.; U.S. Private, pg. 3398
RENN KIRBY MITSUBISHI INC.; U.S. Private, pg. 3398
RENO TOYOTA INC.; U.S. Private, pg. 3399
RENSSELAER HONDA; U.S. Private, pg. 3400
RENTON H IMPORTS, INC.—See AutoNation, Inc.; U.S. Public, pg. 237
REUTHER INVESTMENT CO. INC.; U.S. Private, pg. 3412
REUTHER JEEP CHRYSLER; U.S. Private, pg. 3412
REYNOLDS FORD INC.; U.S. Private, pg. 3418
REYNOLDS MOTOR COMPANY; U.S. Private, pg. 3418
R.F. INC.; U.S. Private, pg. 3336
RHC, INC.; U.S. Private, pg. 3421
RH FLORIDA, LLC—See Rosner Management Group, LLC; U.S. Private, pg. 3485
RHLI INC.; U.S. Private, pg. 3421
R&H MOTOR CARS LTD; U.S. Private, pg. 3332
RHODEN AUTO CENTER INC.; U.S. Private, pg. 3422
RI/BB ACQUISITION CORP.—See AutoNation, Inc.; U.S. Public, pg. 237
RICART FORD INC.; U.S. Private, pg. 3425
RICE BUICK-GMC, INC.—See Rice Automotive Group; U.S. Private, pg. 3425
RICE CHRYSLER DODGE, INC.—See Rice Automotive Group; U.S. Private, pg. 3425
RICE TOYOTA SCION & COLLISION CENTER; U.S. Private, pg. 3425
RICHARD KARR CADILLAC BUICK PONTIAC GMC; U.S. Private, pg. 3428
RICHARD KAY AUTOMOTIVE; U.S. Private, pg. 3428
RICHARDSON INVESTMENTS, INC.; U.S. Private, pg. 3429
RICH DEALERS; U.S. Private, pg. 3426
RICHLAND CHEVROLET COMPANY; U.S. Private, pg. 3430
RICH MORTONS GLEN BURNIE LINCOLN MERCURY; U.S. Private, pg. 3427
RICK BALL GM SUPERSTORE INC; U.S. Private, pg. 3431
RICK CASE ACURA—See Rick Case Enterprises, Inc.; U.S. Private, pg. 3431
RICK CASE HYUNDAI - FT. LAUDERDALE—See Rick Case Enterprises, Inc.; U.S. Private, pg. 3431
RICK HILL IMPORTS INC—See Don Hill Automotive Associates Inc.; U.S. Private, pg. 1257
RICK WEAVER BUICK-PONTIAC-GMC; U.S. Private, pg. 3431
RICO MOTOR COMPANY; U.S. Private, pg. 3431
RIDGEWAY CHEVROLET, INC.; U.S. Private, pg. 3433
RIESS FORD SALES INC.; U.S. Private, pg. 3434
RI/HOLLYWOOD NISSAN ACQUISITION CORP.—See AutoNation, Inc.; U.S. Public, pg. 237
RI/HOLLYWOOD NISSAN ACQUISITION CORP.—See AutoNation, Inc.; U.S. Public, pg. 237
RIKE, INC.; U.S. Private, pg. 3436
RI/LLC ACQUISITION CORP.—See AutoNation, Inc.; U.S. Public, pg. 237
RIMROCK AUTO GROUP, INC.; U.S. Private, pg. 3437
RIMROCK SUBURU, INC.—See Rimrock Auto Group, Inc.; U.S. Private, pg. 3437
RIO MOTOR CO.; U.S. Private, pg. 3438
RIPPY CADILLAC, LLC; U.S. Private, pg. 3440
RI/RMC ACQUISITION, LTD.—See AutoNation, Inc.; U.S. Public, pg. 237
RI/RMT ACQUISITION, LTD.—See AutoNation, Inc.; U.S. Public, pg. 237
RI/RMT ACQUISITION, LTD.—See AutoNation, Inc.; U.S. Public, pg. 237
RIVERSIDE ACURA; U.S. Private, pg. 3445
RIVERSIDE AUTO SALES INC.; U.S. Private, pg. 3445
RIVERSIDE FORD INC.; U.S. Private, pg. 3445
RIVERSIDE METRO AUTO GROUP LLC; U.S. Private, pg. 3445
RIVER STATES TRUCK & TRAILER—See Penske Automotive Group, Inc.; U.S. Public, pg. 1664
RIVERTON MOTOR COMPANY, INC.; U.S. Private, pg. 3448
RIVERVIEW INTERNATIONAL TRUCKS INC; U.S. Private, pg. 3448
R.K. AUTO GROUP, INC.; U.S. Private, pg. 3338
RKR MOTORS, INC.—See AutoNation, Inc.; U.S. Public, pg. 237
RKR MOTORS, INC.—See AutoNation, Inc.; U.S. Public, pg. 237
R.L. BROOKDALE MOTORS INC.—See Luther Holding Company; U.S. Private, pg. 2517
R.L. FRENCH CORPORATION; U.S. Private, pg. 3338
R.L. IMPORTS INC.—See Luther Holding Company; U.S. Private, pg. 2517
R.M. BURRITT MOTORS - BUICK CHEVROLET OSWEGO—See R.M. Burritt Motors, Inc.; U.S. Private, pg. 3339
R.M. BURRITT MOTORS, INC.; U.S. Private, pg. 3338
RNMC INC.; U.S. Private, pg. 3452
ROADSHOW BMW MINI; U.S. Private, pg. 3453

441110 — NEW CAR DEALERS

CORPORATE AFFILIATIONS

ROADSTER, INC.—See Brookfield Corporation; *Int'l*, pg. 1175
ROBERSON MOTORS INC.; *U.S. Private*, pg. 3457
ROBERT GREEN AUTO & TRUCK, INC.; *U.S. Private*, pg. 3458
ROBERT LARSON AUTOMOTIVE GROUP; *U.S. Private*, pg. 3458
ROBERTS CHEVROLET INC.; *U.S. Private*, pg. 3459
ROCKLAND AUTO PLAZA; *U.S. Private*, pg. 3467
ROCK OLDSMOBILE CADILLAC—See Gurley-Leep Buick-GMC Truck, Inc; *U.S. Private*, pg. 1819
ROCKWALL-H, INC.—See Lithia Motors, Inc.; *U.S. Public*, pg. 1326
ROCKY RIDGE TRUCKS, INC.—See Fox Factory Holding Corp.; *U.S. Public*, pg. 877
RODGERS CADILLAC, INC.; *U.S. Private*, pg. 3470
RODMAN LINCOLN-MERCURY INC.—See Rodman Ford Sales Inc.; *U.S. Private*, pg. 3470
ROGER BEASLEY MAZDA INC.; *U.S. Private*, pg. 3471
ROGER BURDICK AUTO SALES INC.; *U.S. Private*, pg. 3471
ROGER DEAN CHEVROLET, INC.; *U.S. Private*, pg. 3471
ROGERS-DABBS CHEVROLET, INC.; *U.S. Private*, pg. 3472
ROGERS FORD SALES INC.; *U.S. Private*, pg. 3472
ROGERS MOTORS, INC.; *U.S. Private*, pg. 3472
ROGERS & ROGERS; *U.S. Private*, pg. 3471
ROHRICH AUTOMOTIVE GROUP; *U.S. Private*, pg. 3473
ROHRICH CADILLAC, INC.—See Rohrich Automotive Group; *U.S. Private*, pg. 3473
ROHR-INDY MOTORS INC.; *U.S. Private*, pg. 3473
ROHR-LEX MOTORS INC.; *U.S. Private*, pg. 3473
ROLAND D. KELLY INFINITI INC.; *U.S. Private*, pg. 3473
ROLF LLC—See Delance Limited; *Int'l*, pg. 2010
ROLLING HILLS AUTO PLAZA; *U.S. Private*, pg. 3475
ROMAIN BUICK INC.; *U.S. Private*, pg. 3475
ROMANO FORD OF FAYETTEVILLE LTD.; *U.S. Private*, pg. 3476
ROMANO TOYOTA; *U.S. Private*, pg. 3476
ROMERO MOTORS CORPORATION; *U.S. Private*, pg. 3476
RON AND ANN ENTERPRISES INC.; *U.S. Private*, pg. 3477
RON BOUCHARD'S AUTO SALES, INC.; *U.S. Private*, pg. 3477
RON CARTER; *U.S. Private*, pg. 3477
RONNIE WATKINS FORD INC.; *U.S. Private*, pg. 3478
RON NORRIS BUICK GMC; *U.S. Private*, pg. 3477
RON SAYER'S CHRYSLER JEEP DODGE; *U.S. Private*, pg. 3477
RONSONET BUICK-GMC TRUCK, INC.; *U.S. Private*, pg. 3478
RON TIRAPELLI FORD; *U.S. Private*, pg. 3477
RON TONKIN CHEVROLET CO.; *U.S. Private*, pg. 3477
RON TONKIN TOYOTA INC.—See Ron Tonkin Chevrolet Co.; *U.S. Private*, pg. 3477
RON WESTPHAL CHEVROLET INC.; *U.S. Private*, pg. 3477
ROPER BUICK GMC, INC.; *U.S. Private*, pg. 3480
ROSEN MOTOR SALES; *U.S. Private*, pg. 3483
ROSENTHAL CORPORATE SERVICES, INC.; *U.S. Private*, pg. 3484
ROSEVILLE CHRYSLER PLYMOUTH JEEP INC.; *U.S. Private*, pg. 3484
ROSEVILLE MOTOR CORPORATION—See AutoNation, Inc.; *U.S. Public*, pg. 237
ROSS DOWNING CHEVROLET, INC.; *U.S. Private*, pg. 3485
ROTHROCK MOTOR SALES, INC.; *U.S. Private*, pg. 3487
ROTO SUBARU MAZDA, INC.; *U.S. Private*, pg. 3487
ROUNDTREE I VAN NUYS, LLC—See Roundtree Automotive Group, LLC; *U.S. Private*, pg. 3489
ROUNDTREE MOBILE, LLC—See AutoNation, Inc.; *U.S. Public*, pg. 237
ROUNDTREE N VAN NUYS, LLC—See Roundtree Automotive Group, LLC; *U.S. Private*, pg. 3489
ROUNTREE MOORE TOYOTA—See Morgan Auto Group, LLC; *U.S. Private*, pg. 2783
ROUNTREE MOTORS INC.; *U.S. Private*, pg. 3489
ROUSH EQUIPMENT COMPANY INC.; *U.S. Private*, pg. 3489
ROUTE 22 HONDA; *U.S. Private*, pg. 3490
ROUTE 22 TOYOTA; *U.S. Private*, pg. 3490
ROUTE 23 AUTO MALL; *U.S. Private*, pg. 3490
ROUTE 33 NISSAN—See Auto Mall 46, Inc.; *U.S. Private*, pg. 397
ROWE ENTERPRISES INC.; *U.S. Private*, pg. 3490
ROYAL AUTOMOTIVE COMPANY; *U.S. Private*, pg. 3491
ROYAL AUTOMOTIVE; *U.S. Private*, pg. 3491
ROYAL MOORE AUTO CENTER; *U.S. Private*, pg. 3492
ROYAL MOORE BUICK PONTIAC - GMC TRUCK—See Royal Moore Auto Center; *U.S. Private*, pg. 3492
ROYAL MOTOR SALES OF SAN FRANCISCO; *U.S. Private*, pg. 3492
ROYAL OAK FORD, INC.; *U.S. Private*, pg. 3493
ROYAL OAKS NISSAN, INC.; *U.S. Private*, pg. 3493
ROYAL SPEEDWAY, INC.; *U.S. Private*, pg. 3493
ROY O'BRIEN INC.; *U.S. Private*, pg. 3491

ROY ROBINSON, INC.—See Camping World Holdings, Inc.; *U.S. Public*, pg. 428
ROY'S GRAND DODGE, CHRYSLER, JEEP ON LOCUST, L.L.C.; *U.S. Private*, pg. 3491
RPM EQUIPMENT CO.; *U.S. Private*, pg. 3495
R & R AUTO GROUP; *U.S. Private*, pg. 3331
R&R INC.; *U.S. Private*, pg. 3333
RUDY LUTHER TOYOTA SCION—See Luther Holding Company; *U.S. Private*, pg. 2517
RUNDE CHEVROLET INC.; *U.S. Private*, pg. 3504
RUSH GMC TRUCK CENTER OF EL PASO, INC.—See Rush Enterprises, Inc.; *U.S. Public*, pg. 1826
RUSH TRUCK CENTERS OF FLORIDA, INC.—See Rush Enterprises, Inc.; *U.S. Public*, pg. 1826
RUSH TRUCK CENTERS OF TEXAS, L.P.—See Rush Enterprises, Inc.; *U.S. Public*, pg. 1827
RUSH TRUCK CENTER; *U.S. Private*, pg. 3505
RUSNAK AUTOMOTIVE GROUP; *U.S. Private*, pg. 3505
RUSNAK WESTLAKE; *U.S. Private*, pg. 3505
RUSS CHEVROLET; *U.S. Private*, pg. 3505
RUSS DARROW CHRYSLER & JEEP OF MADISON—See Russ Darrow Group, Inc.; *U.S. Private*, pg. 3505
RUSS DARROW CHRYSLER OF APPLETON—See Russ Darrow Group, Inc.; *U.S. Private*, pg. 3505
RUSS DARROW DODGE OF MILWAUKEE—See Russ Darrow Group, Inc.; *U.S. Private*, pg. 3505
RUSS DARROW GROUP, INC.; *U.S. Private*, pg. 3505
RUSS DARROW HONDA, NISSAN & SUZUKI OF MILWAUKEE—See Russ Darrow Group, Inc.; *U.S. Private*, pg. 3505
RUSS DARROW KIA OF APPLETON—See Russ Darrow Group, Inc.; *U.S. Private*, pg. 3505
RUSS DARROW KIA OF FOND DU LAC—See Russ Darrow Group, Inc.; *U.S. Private*, pg. 3505
RUSS DARROW KIA OF MADISON—See Russ Darrow Group, Inc.; *U.S. Private*, pg. 3505
RUSS DARROW KIA OF WAUKESHA—See Russ Darrow Group, Inc.; *U.S. Private*, pg. 3506
RUSS DARROW KIA—See Russ Darrow Group, Inc.; *U.S. Private*, pg. 3505
RUSS DARROW MAZDA OF GREENFIELD—See Russ Darrow Group, Inc.; *U.S. Private*, pg. 3506
RUSS DARROW OF WEST BEND—See Russ Darrow Group, Inc.; *U.S. Private*, pg. 3506
RUSSELL BARNETT CHRYSLER-DODGE-JEEP, INC.; *U.S. Private*, pg. 3506
RUSSELL CHEVROLET COMPANY; *U.S. Private*, pg. 3506
RUSSELL & SMITH FORD INC.; *U.S. Private*, pg. 3506
RUSTY ECK FORD, INC.; *U.S. Private*, pg. 3507
RUSTY WALLIS, INC.; *U.S. Private*, pg. 3507
RUXER FORD LINCOLN MERCURY; *U.S. Private*, pg. 3508
RYAN DODGE; *U.S. Private*, pg. 3510
RYAN LINCOLN MERCURY KIA; *U.S. Private*, pg. 3510
RYDELL CHEVROLET INC.; *U.S. Private*, pg. 3511
RYDELL COMPANY INC.; *U.S. Private*, pg. 3511
RYE FORD INC.; *U.S. Private*, pg. 3511
S.A. BILIA EMOND BELGIUM—See Bilia AB; *Int'l*, pg. 1029
SAFFORD AUTOMOTIVE GROUP; *U.S. Private*, pg. 3525
SAHARA IMPORTS, INC.—See AutoNation, Inc.; *U.S. Public*, pg. 237
SAHARA NISSAN, INC.—See AutoNation, Inc.; *U.S. Public*, pg. 237
SAHLING KENWORTH INC.; *U.S. Private*, pg. 3528
SAI AUTO GROUP LLC; *U.S. Private*, pg. 3528
SAIC GENERAL MOTORS SALES COMPANY LIMITED—See General Motors Company; *U.S. Public*, pg. 928
SAI CLEARWATER T, LLC—See Sonic Automotive, Inc.; *U.S. Public*, pg. 1902
SAI FORT MYERS H, LLC—See Sonic Automotive, Inc.; *U.S. Public*, pg. 1902
SAI ROCKVILLE L, LLC—See Graham Holdings Company; *U.S. Public*, pg. 956
SALE AUTO MALL; *U.S. Private*, pg. 3531
SALERNO DUANE INC.; *U.S. Private*, pg. 3531
SALISBURY MOTOR CO. INC.; *U.S. Private*, pg. 3533
SALMON RIVER MOTORS INC.; *U.S. Private*, pg. 3533
SALSBURY'S DODGE CITY, LLC; *U.S. Private*, pg. 3533
SALT LAKE VALLEY BUICK GMC; *U.S. Private*, pg. 3533
SALVADORE AUTO GROUP; *U.S. Private*, pg. 3535
SAMES FORD - CORPUS CHRISTI—See Sames Motor Co., Inc.; *U.S. Private*, pg. 3537
SAMES MOTOR CO., INC.; *U.S. Private*, pg. 3536
SAMES RED BARN MOTORS—See Sames Motor Co., Inc.; *U.S. Private*, pg. 3537
SAM GALLOWAY FORD, INC.; *U.S. Private*, pg. 3535
SAM LEMAN CHRYSLER-JEEP-DODGE OF PEORIA; *U.S. Private*, pg. 3535
SAM LEMAN CHRYSLER-PLYMOUTH-DODGE; *U.S. Private*, pg. 3535
SAM LINDER, INC.; *U.S. Private*, pg. 3535
SAM PACK'S FIVE STAR FORD; *U.S. Private*, pg. 3535
SAM SWOPE VOLKSWAGEN OF CLARKSVILLE; *U.S. Private*, pg. 3536
SAN ANTONIO ANUSA, LLC—See AutoNation, Inc.; *U.S. Public*, pg. 237
SANBORN CHEVROLET; *U.S. Private*, pg. 3542
SANDERS FORD INC.; *U.S. Private*, pg. 3543

SANDERSON FORD INC.; *U.S. Private*, pg. 3543
SANDIA BMW; *U.S. Private*, pg. 3543
SAN DIEGO VOLVO; *U.S. Private*, pg. 3540
SANDLIN MOTORS; *U.S. Private*, pg. 3544
SANDS BROS AUTO SALES, INC.; *U.S. Private*, pg. 3544
SANDS MOTOR COMPANY, INC.; *U.S. Private*, pg. 3545
SANDY SANSING NISSAN, INC.; *U.S. Private*, pg. 3545
SAN FERNANDO VALLEY AUTOMOTIVE, LLC—See General Motors Company; *U.S. Public*, pg. 929
SAN FRANCISCO-B, INC.—See Lithia Motors, Inc.; *U.S. Public*, pg. 1326
SANGERA BUICK, INC.; *U.S. Private*, pg. 3546
SANGSTER MOTORS, INC.; *U.S. Private*, pg. 3546
SANSONE AUTO MALL; *U.S. Private*, pg. 3546
SANTA CRUZ NISSAN DODGE; *U.S. Private*, pg. 3547
SANTA MARIA FORD INC.; *U.S. Private*, pg. 3547
SARASOTA 500 INC.; *U.S. Private*, pg. 3549
SARAT FORD SALES INC.; *U.S. Private*, pg. 3549
SARATOGA MOTORS INC.; *U.S. Private*, pg. 3549
SARCHIONE AUTOMOTIVE GROUP; *U.S. Private*, pg. 3550
SASKATOON MOTOR PRODUCTS LTD.—See Auto-Canada Inc.; *Int'l*, pg. 726
SATURN OF RICHMOND, INC.; *U.S. Private*, pg. 3553
SAVAGE DODGE CHRYSLER JEEP; *U.S. Private*, pg. 3555
SAVANNAH INTERNATIONAL MOTORS; *U.S. Private*, pg. 3556
SAX MOTOR COMPANY; *U.S. Private*, pg. 3558
SCAFFIDI MOTORS INC.; *U.S. Private*, pg. 3560
SCANLON AUTO GROUP; *U.S. Private*, pg. 3561
SCANLON LEXUS—See Scanlon Auto Group; *U.S. Private*, pg. 3561
SCAP AUTOMOTIVE; *U.S. Private*, pg. 3561
SCA PERFORMANCE, INC.—See Fox Factory Holding Corp.; *U.S. Public*, pg. 877
SCENIC CHEVROLET; *U.S. Private*, pg. 3562
SCHAFER INC.; *U.S. Private*, pg. 3563
SCHALLER AUTO WORLD, INC.; *U.S. Private*, pg. 3563
SCHIMMER CHEVROLET BUICK, INC.; *U.S. Private*, pg. 3565
SCHLOSSMANN DODGE CITY OF MILWAUKEE—See Schlossmann Investment Corp.; *U.S. Private*, pg. 3565
SCHLOSSMANN IMPORTS INC.—See Schlossmann Investment Corp.; *U.S. Private*, pg. 3565
SCHLOSSMANN'S DODGE CITY CHRYSLER JEEP, INC.—See Schlossmann Investment Corp.; *U.S. Private*, pg. 3565
SCHMIT FORD-MERCURY CORPORATION; *U.S. Private*, pg. 3566
SCHMITT'S AUDI VOLKSWAGEN OF BUFFALO; *U.S. Private*, pg. 3566
SCHOLFIELD BROS. INC.; *U.S. Private*, pg. 3567
SCHOLFIELD LEXUS LLC—See Scholfield Bros. Inc.; *U.S. Private*, pg. 3567
SCHUKEI CHEVROLET, INC.; *U.S. Private*, pg. 3570
SCOTT CLARK HONDA; *U.S. Private*, pg. 3576
SCOTT-CLARKS TOYOTA CITY INC.; *U.S. Private*, pg. 3577
SCOTT CRUMP TOYOTA SCION, INC.; *U.S. Private*, pg. 3576
SCOTT-MCRAE AUTOMOTIVE GROUP INC.; *U.S. Private*, pg. 3577
SCOTT ROBINSON HONDA INC.; *U.S. Private*, pg. 3577
SCOTTSBLUFF MOTOR COMPANY—See Rydell Company Inc.; *U.S. Private*, pg. 3511
SCOTTSDALE FERRARI, LLC—See Penske Automotive Group, Inc.; *U.S. Public*, pg. 1666
SCOTT SHERV HUMMER INCORPORATED; *U.S. Private*, pg. 3577
SDV INCORPORATED; *U.S. Private*, pg. 3582
SEACOAST VOLKSWAGEN, INC.; *U.S. Private*, pg. 3584
SEAVIEW BUICK GMC; *U.S. Private*, pg. 3592
SECOND FAMILY INC.; *U.S. Private*, pg. 3593
SECRET CITY CHRYSLER DODGE JEEP; *U.S. Private*, pg. 3593
SECURITY AUTO SALES INC.; *U.S. Private*, pg. 3594
SEEGER TOYOTA, INC.; *U.S. Private*, pg. 3597
SEEKINS FORD LINCOLN MERCURY; *U.S. Private*, pg. 3598
SEELYE WRIGHT KIA; *U.S. Private*, pg. 3598
SEELYE-WRIGHT OF SOUTH HAVEN; *U.S. Private*, pg. 3598
SELINSGROVE MOTORS INC.; *U.S. Private*, pg. 3602
SELLERS BUICK GMC; *U.S. Private*, pg. 3602
SELLERS-SEXTON INC.—See Morse Operations Inc.; *U.S. Private*, pg. 2790
SENTRY AUTO GROUP; *U.S. Private*, pg. 3610
SENTRY FORD LINCOLN, INC.; *U.S. Private*, pg. 3610
SENTRY FORD LINCOLN, INC.—See Sentry Auto Group; *U.S. Private*, pg. 3610
SENTRY WEST, INC.—See Sentry Auto Group; *U.S. Private*, pg. 3610
SERAFINI NISSAN VOLVO; *U.S. Private*, pg. 3613
SERRA CHEVROLET INC.; *U.S. Private*, pg. 3614
SERRA CHEVROLET, LLC—See Serra Automotive, Inc.; *U.S. Private*, pg. 3614
SERVCO PACIFIC INC.; *U.S. Private*, pg. 3614
SEWELL BMW MINI OF PLANO—See Sewell Motor Com-

N.A.I.C.S. INDEX 441110 — NEW CAR DEALERS

N.A.I.C.S. Index

pany; *U.S. Private*, pg. 3620
SEWELL CADILLAC CHEVROLET; *U.S. Private*, pg. 3620
SEWELL CADILLAC OF DALLAS—See Sewell Motor Company; *U.S. Private*, pg. 3620
SEWELL FORD—See Sewell Motor Company; *U.S. Private*, pg. 3620
SEWELL INFINITI OF DALLAS—See Sewell Motor Company; *U.S. Private*, pg. 3620
SEWELL LEXUS OF DALLAS—See Sewell Motor Company; *U.S. Private*, pg. 3620
SEWELL MOTOR COMPANY; *U.S. Private*, pg. 3620
SEXTON AUTOMOTIVE GROUP; *U.S. Private*, pg. 3620
SHAKOPEE CHEVROLET-OLDSMOBILE-PONTIAC-GEO, INC.; *U.S. Private*, pg. 3623
SHANGHAI BAOZEN AUTOMOBILE SALES AND SERVICES CO., LTD.—See China Yongda Automobiles Services Holdings Limited; *Int'l*, pg. 1564
SHANGHAI BAOZEN ZHONGHUAN AUTOMOBILE SALES AND SERVICES CO., LTD.—See China Yongda Automobiles Services Holdings Limited; *Int'l*, pg. 1564
SHANGHAI PUTUO BAOZEN AUTOMOBILE SALES AND SERVICES CO., LTD.—See China Yongda Automobiles Services Holdings Limited; *Int'l*, pg. 1564
SHANGHAI YONGDA AUTOMOBILE NANHUI SALES AND SERVICES CO., LTD.—See China Yongda Automobiles Services Holdings Limited; *Int'l*, pg. 1564
SHANGHAI YONGDA AUTOMOBILE PUDONG SALES AND SERVICES CO., LTD.—See China Yongda Automobiles Services Holdings Limited; *Int'l*, pg. 1564
SHANGHAI YONGDA AUTOMOBILE PUDONG TRADE CO., LTD.—See China Yongda Automobiles Services Holdings Limited; *Int'l*, pg. 1564
SHANGHAI YONGDA AUTOMOBILE SALES CO., LTD.—See China Yongda Automobiles Services Holdings Limited; *Int'l*, pg. 1564
SHANGHAI YONGDA AUTOMOBILE SONGJIANG SALES AND SERVICES CO., LTD.—See China Yongda Automobiles Services Holdings Limited; *Int'l*, pg. 1564
SHANGHAI YONGDA AUTOMOBILE TRADE CENTER CO., LTD.—See China Yongda Automobiles Services Holdings Limited; *Int'l*, pg. 1564
SHANGHAI YONGDA BAOYUNLAI AUTOMOBILE SALES AND SERVICES CO., LTD.—See China Yongda Automobiles Services Holdings Limited; *Int'l*, pg. 1565
SHANGHAI YONGDA BASHI AUTOMOBILE SALES AND SERVICES CO., LTD.—See China Yongda Automobiles Services Holdings Limited; *Int'l*, pg. 1565
SHANGHAI YONGDA HAOJIE AUTOMOBILE SALES AND SERVICES CO., LTD.—See China Yongda Automobiles Services Holdings Limited; *Int'l*, pg. 1565
SHANGHAI YONGDA INFINITI AUTOMOBILE SALES AND SERVICES CO., LTD.—See China Yongda Automobiles Services Holdings Limited; *Int'l*, pg. 1565
SHANGHAI YONGDA INFINITI QIBAO AUTOMOBILE SALES AND SERVICES CO., LTD.—See China Yongda Automobiles Services Holdings Limited; *Int'l*, pg. 1565
SHANGHAI YONGDA LUJIE AUTOMOBILE SALES AND SERVICES CO., LTD.—See China Yongda Automobiles Services Holdings Limited; *Int'l*, pg. 1565
SHANGHAI YONGDA QIDONG AUTOMOBILE SALES AND SERVICES CO., LTD.—See China Yongda Automobiles Services Holdings Limited; *Int'l*, pg. 1565
SHANGHAI YONGDA SHENLONG AUTOMOBILE SALES AND SERVICES CO., LTD.—See China Yongda Automobiles Services Holdings Limited; *Int'l*, pg. 1565
SHANGHAI YONGDA TONGBAO AUTOMOBILE SALES AND SERVICES CO., LTD.—See China Yongda Automobiles Services Holdings Limited; *Int'l*, pg. 1565
SHANGHAI YONGDA TONGNING AUTOMOBILE SALES AND SERVICES CO., LTD.—See China Yongda Automobiles Services Holdings Limited; *Int'l*, pg. 1565
SHANGHAI YONGDA TONGSHENG AUTOMOBILE SALES AND SERVICES CO., LTD.—See China Yongda Automobiles Services Holdings Limited; *Int'l*, pg. 1565
SHANGHAI YONGDA TOYOTA AUTOMOBILE SALES AND SERVICES CO., LTD.—See China Yongda Automobiles Services Holdings Limited; *Int'l*, pg. 1565
SHANGHAI YONGDA WEIRONG AUTOMOBILE SALES AND SERVICES CO., LTD.—See China Yongda Automobiles Services Holdings Limited; *Int'l*, pg. 1565
SHANGHAI YONGDA ZHONGXIN AUTOMOBILE SALES AND SERVICES CO., LTD.—See China Yongda Automobiles Services Holdings Limited; *Int'l*, pg. 1565
SHAOXING HECHENG HAICHANG AUTOMOBILE SALES AND SERVICE CO., LTD.—See China Yongda Automobiles Services Holdings Limited; *Int'l*, pg. 1565
SHAOXING YONGDA WUXIAN AUTOMOBILE SALES AND SERVICES CO., LTD.—See China Yongda Automobiles Services Holdings Limited; *Int'l*, pg. 1565
SHARRETT INC.; *U.S. Private*, pg. 3627
SHAVER AUTOMOTIVE GROUP, INC.; *U.S. Private*, pg. 3627
SHEALY'S TRUCK CENTER INC.; *U.S. Private*, pg. 3629
SHEBOYGAN CHEVROLET CADILLAC—See Rydell Company Inc.; *U.S. Private*, pg. 3511
SHEBOYGAN CHRYSLER CENTER—See Rydell Company Inc.; *U.S. Private*, pg. 3511
SHEEHAN BUICK PONTIAC GMC, INC.; *U.S. Private*, pg. 3629
SHEEHAN MOTORS INC.; *U.S. Private*, pg. 3629
SHEEHY ASHLAND, INC.—See Sheehy Auto Stores, Inc.; *U.S. Private*, pg. 3629
SHEEHY AUTO STORES, INC.; *U.S. Private*, pg. 3629
SHEEHY FORD OF SPRINGFIELD, INC.—See Sheehy Auto Stores, Inc.; *U.S. Private*, pg. 3629
SHEEHY FORD OF WARRENTON; *U.S. Private*, pg. 3630
SHEEHY WALDORF; *U.S. Private*, pg. 3630
SHELBY-REID, INC.; *U.S. Private*, pg. 3630
SHELOR MOTOR MILE; *U.S. Private*, pg. 3631
SHENGZHOU BAOZEN AUTO SALES & SERVICES CO., LTD.—See China Yongda Automobiles Services Holdings Limited; *Int'l*, pg. 1565
SHEPARD AUTO GROUP; *U.S. Private*, pg. 3632
SHEPARDS MOTOR; *U.S. Private*, pg. 3632
SHERIDAN NISSAN; *U.S. Private*, pg. 3633
SHERMAN AUTO RENTALS; *U.S. Private*, pg. 3634
SHERMAN DODGE, INC.; *U.S. Private*, pg. 3634
SHERMAN OAKS-A, INC.—See Lithia Motors, Inc.; *U.S. Public*, pg. 1326
SHERWOOD OF SALISBURY; *U.S. Private*, pg. 3635
SHIELDS AUTO CENTER INC.; *U.S. Private*, pg. 3635
SHIJIAZHUANG BAOHE AUTOMOTIVE SALES & SERVICE CO., LTD.—See China Yongda Automobiles Services Holdings Limited; *Int'l*, pg. 1565
SHILOH CORPORATION; *U.S. Private*, pg. 3636
SHIRNS PONTIAC-GMC INC.; *U.S. Private*, pg. 3637
SHIVELY MOTORS; *U.S. Private*, pg. 3638
SHORELINE VEHICLE SALES LLC—See Tesla, Inc.; *U.S. Public*, pg. 2021
SHORE TOYOTA INC.; *U.S. Private*, pg. 3641
SHOTTENKIRK INC.; *U.S. Private*, pg. 3643
SHOWALTER MOTOR COMPANY INC.; *U.S. Private*, pg. 3643
SHOWCASE MOTORS INC.; *U.S. Private*, pg. 3643
SHREWSBURY MOTORS INC—See US Auto Group Limited; *U.S. Private*, pg. 4317
SHULTS FORD, INC.; *U.S. Private*, pg. 3644
SHULTS FORD LINCOLN-MERCURY, INC.—See Shults Ford, Inc.; *U.S. Private*, pg. 3644
SIERRA ACURA OF ALHAMBRA; *U.S. Private*, pg. 3646
SIERRA AUTOCARS INCORPORATED; *U.S. Private*, pg. 3646
SIERRA BLANCA MOTOR CO.; *U.S. Private*, pg. 3646
SIERRA MAZDA; *U.S. Private*, pg. 3647
SIERRA VOLKSWAGEN INC.—See Bill Walsh Automotive Group; *U.S. Private*, pg. 558
SIGNATURE FORD OF PERRY, LLC—See Elder Automotive Group; *U.S. Private*, pg. 1350
SIGNER BUICK-CADILLAC; *U.S. Private*, pg. 3650
SILSBEE FORD LINCOLN MERCURY, INC.; *U.S. Private*, pg. 3653
SIMMONS-ROCKWELL, INC.; *U.S. Private*, pg. 3666
SIMMS CHEVROLET COMPANY INC.; *U.S. Private*, pg. 3666
SIMPSON GARDEN GROVE, INC.—See General Motors Company; *U.S. Public*, pg. 929
SIMS BUICK -GMC- TRUCK INC.; *U.S. Private*, pg. 3669
SIMS IMPORT INC.; *U.S. Private*, pg. 3669
SIOUX CITY FORD LINCOLN; *U.S. Private*, pg. 3671
SIOUX CITY MOTORCARS, LLC—See Vern Eide Motorcars, Inc.; *U.S. Private*, pg. 4367
SIOUX CITY TRUCK SALES INCORPORATED; *U.S. Private*, pg. 3671
SIOUX FALLS FORD INC.; *U.S. Private*, pg. 3671
SIOUX FALLS TRUCK & TRAILER, INC.—See North American Truck & Trailer, Inc.; *U.S. Private*, pg. 2941
SISBARRO DEALERSHIPS; *U.S. Private*, pg. 3675
SISK AUTO MALL; *U.S. Private*, pg. 3675
SITTON BUICK GMC SAAB; *U.S. Private*, pg. 3677
SKYLAND AUTOMOTIVE, INC.; *U.S. Private*, pg. 3685
SKYLINE SALES INC.; *U.S. Private*, pg. 3685
SLOANE TOYOTA OF GLENSIDE; *U.S. Private*, pg. 3689
SLOAN FORD; *U.S. Private*, pg. 3689
SLONE PONTIAC BUICK GMC TRUCK INC.; *U.S. Private*, pg. 3689
SMAIL LINCOLN MERCURY MAZDA; *U.S. Private*, pg. 3690
SMART CHEVROLET CO.; *U.S. Private*, pg. 3691
SMC ROVER—See Bestodeck Ltd.; *Int'l*, pg. 1000
SMITH-CAIRNS FORD INC.; *U.S. Private*, pg. 3696
SMITH CHEVROLET COMPANY INC.; *U.S. Private*, pg. 3694
SMITH & GRAY; *U.S. Private*, pg. 3694
SMITH HAVEN CORP.; *U.S. Private*, pg. 3695
SMITH MOTORS, INC.; *U.S. Private*, pg. 3695
SMITHTOWN NISSAN INC.; *U.S. Private*, pg. 3698
SMOKY JENNINGS CHEVROLET; *U.S. Private*, pg. 3698
SMOTHER'S MOTORS; *U.S. Private*, pg. 3698
SMYTHE EUROPEAN, INC.—See AutoNation, Inc.; *U.S. Public*, pg. 237
SNYDER CHEVROLET OLDSMOBILE, INC.; *U.S. Private*, pg. 3701
SOLOMON CHEVROLET CADILLAC; *U.S. Private*, pg. 3709
SOMERSET BUICK-GMC, INC.; *U.S. Private*, pg. 3711
SOMERSET MOTORS, INC.—See Penske Automotive Group, Inc.; *U.S. Public*, pg. 1666
SONIC AUTOMOTIVE F&I, LLC—See Sonic Automotive, Inc.; *U.S. Public*, pg. 1902
SONIC AUTOMOTIVE, INC.; *U.S. Public*, pg. 1902
SONIC-CREST CADILLAC, LLC—See Sonic Automotive, Inc.; *U.S. Public*, pg. 1902
SONIC DEVELOPMENT, LLC—See Sonic Automotive, Inc.; *U.S. Public*, pg. 1902
SONIC - LONE TREE CADILLAC, INC.—See Sonic Automotive, Inc.; *U.S. Public*, pg. 1902
SONIC - LUTE RILEY, LP—See Sonic Automotive, Inc.; *U.S. Public*, pg. 1902
SONIC MOMENTUM VWA, LP—See Sonic Automotive, Inc.; *U.S. Public*, pg. 1902
SONIC-NORTH CADILLAC, INC.—See Sonic Automotive, Inc.; *U.S. Public*, pg. 1902
SONIC - UNIVERSITY PARK A, LP—See Sonic Automotive, Inc.; *U.S. Public*, pg. 1902
SONJU TWO HARBORS LLC; *U.S. Private*, pg. 3714
SONNEN AUDI VOLKSWAGEN; *U.S. Private*, pg. 3714
SONNY CANNON AUTO PLAZA INC.; *U.S. Private*, pg. 3714
SONS ACURA; *U.S. Private*, pg. 3714
SORG DODGE INC.; *U.S. Private*, pg. 3715
SOUND FORD, INC.; *U.S. Private*, pg. 3717
SOUTH BAY LEXUS; *U.S. Private*, pg. 3719
SOUTH BAY MOTORS LLC; *U.S. Private*, pg. 3719
SOUTHBAY TOYOTA; *U.S. Private*, pg. 3724
SOUTH BROADWAY MOTORS, LLC—See AutoNation, Inc.; *U.S. Public*, pg. 237
SOUTHEAST AUTOMOTIVE GROUP PTY LTD—See Eagers Automotive Limited; *Int'l*, pg. 2263
SOUTHEAST TEXAS CLASSIC AUTOMOTIVE; *U.S. Private*, pg. 3726
SOUTHERN CASCADES FINANCE CORPORATION—See Lithia Motors, Inc.; *U.S. Public*, pg. 1326
SOUTHERN MOTORS HONDA; *U.S. Private*, pg. 3733
SOUTHERN STATES BDM, LLC; *U.S. Private*, pg. 3735
SOUTHFIELD CHRYSLER JEEP; *U.S. Private*, pg. 3736
SOUTHGATE FORD INC.; *U.S. Private*, pg. 3736
SOUTHGATE LINCOLN—See Southgate Ford Inc.; *U.S. Private*, pg. 3736
SOUTH HILLS HONDA; *U.S. Private*, pg. 3722
SOUTHLAND IMPORTS, INC.; *U.S. Private*, pg. 3736
SOUTH MOTOR COMPANY OF DADE COUNTY; *U.S. Private*, pg. 3723
SOUTH MOTORS INFINITI—See South Motor Company of Dade County; *U.S. Private*, pg. 3723
SOUTH OAK DODGE, INC.; *U.S. Private*, pg. 3723
SOUTH SHORE FORD INC.; *U.S. Private*, pg. 3723
SOUTH SHORE MOTORS CORP; *U.S. Private*, pg. 3724
SOUTHSIDE AUTOS (1981) PTY LTD—See Eagers Automotive Limited; *Int'l*, pg. 2263
SOUTHSIDE DODGE SALES INC.; *U.S. Private*, pg. 3737
SOUTHSIDE IMPORTS INC.; *U.S. Private*, pg. 3738
SOUTH VILLAGE FORD; *U.S. Private*, pg. 3724
SOUTHWAY FORD INC.; *U.S. Private*, pg. 3738
SOUTHWEST FORD INC.; *U.S. Private*, pg. 3739
SOUTHWEST INTERNATIONAL TRUCKS, INC.; *U.S. Private*, pg. 3739
SOUTHWEST MOTORS OF DENVER, LLC—See AutoNation, Inc.; *U.S. Public*, pg. 237
SOUTHWEST TRAILERS AND EQUIPMENT LLC; *U.S. Private*, pg. 3741
SOUTH WEYMOUTH DODGE; *U.S. Private*, pg. 3724
SOUTHWICK INC.; *U.S. Private*, pg. 3742
SOVEREIGN VOLKSWAGEN LLC.; *U.S. Private*, pg. 3743
SPARTA CHEVROLET, INC.; *U.S. Private*, pg. 3746
SPARTAN AUTOS INCORPORATED; *U.S. Private*, pg. 3746
SPIRE AUTOMOTIVE LIMITED—See Group 1 Automotive, Inc.; *U.S. Public*, pg. 972
SPIRIT CHRYSLER JEEP; *U.S. Private*, pg. 3758
SPIRIT FORD INC.; *U.S. Private*, pg. 3758
SPITZER AUTOWORLD HOMESTEAD, INC.—See Spitzer Management, Inc.; *U.S. Private*, pg. 3758
SPITZER CHEVROLET COMPANY; *U.S. Private*, pg. 3758
SPITZER CHEVY NORTHFIELD; *U.S. Private*, pg. 3758
SPONTE SALES, INC.—See Hawk Auto Group; *U.S. Private*, pg. 1882
SPORT CHEVROLET CO. INC.; *U.S. Private*, pg. 3760
SPRADLEY BARR FORD LINCOLN OF GREELEY INC.; *U.S. Private*, pg. 3762
SPRADLEY CHEVROLET-HYUNDAI; *U.S. Private*, pg. 3762
SPREEN, INC.; *U.S. Private*, pg. 3763
SPRINGFIELD HYUNDAI; *U.S. Private*, pg. 3764
SPURR CHEVROLET INC & COURTESY PONTIAC-GMC; *U.S. Private*, pg. 3765
SPX IBERICA S.A.—See Lone Star Funds; *U.S. Private*, pg. 2487
SSF INC.; *U.S. Private*, pg. 3768
STADIUM TOYOTA SCION; *U.S. Private*, pg. 3774
STAMFORD FORD LINCOLN, LLC; *U.S. Private*, pg. 3776
STAM-TERBERG AUTOBEDRIJVEN B. V.—See General Motors Company; *U.S. Public*, pg. 927
STAN KING CHEVROLET; *U.S. Private*, pg. 3777

441110 — NEW CAR DEALERS

STANLEY AUTOMOTIVE ENTERPRISES, INC.; *U.S. Private*, pg. 3782
STANLEY FORD - MCGREGOR—See Stanley Automotive Enterprises, Inc.; *U.S. Private*, pg. 3782
STANLEY NISSAN INC.; *U.S. Private*, pg. 3783
STAN MCNABB; *U.S. Private*, pg. 3777
STARBOARD MOTORS INC.; *U.S. Private*, pg. 3786
STAR BUICK GMC; *U.S. Private*, pg. 3784
STAR DODGE CHRYSLER JEEP HYUNDAI; *U.S. Private*, pg. 3784
STAR FORD; *U.S. Private*, pg. 3784
STARK AUTOMOTIVE GROUP; *U.S. Private*, pg. 3786
STAR MOTORS, LLC—See AutoNation, Inc.; *U.S. Public*, pg. 237
STAR MOTORS, LLC—See AutoNation, Inc.; *U.S. Public*, pg. 237
STATEN ISLAND NISSAN; *U.S. Private*, pg. 3793
ST. CLOUD TOYOTA INC.; *U.S. Private*, pg. 3771
STEAMBOAT MOTORS, L.L.C.; *U.S. Private*, pg. 3795
STEET-PONTE FORD; *U.S. Private*, pg. 3797
STEINGOLD VOLVO; *U.S. Private*, pg. 3798
STEPHEN PONTIAC-CADILLAC, INC.; *U.S. Private*, pg. 3802
STEPHEN WADE AUTO CENTER; *U.S. Private*, pg. 3802
STERLING-BM, LLC—See Lithia Motors, Inc.; *U.S. Public*, pg. 1326
STERLING HEIGHTS DODGE, INC.; *U.S. Private*, pg. 3805
STERLING MCCALL CADILLAC—See Group 1 Automotive, Inc.; *U.S. Public*, pg. 972
STERLING MCCALL TOYOTA GROUP—See Group 1 Automotive, Inc.; *U.S. Public*, pg. 972
STERLING PONTIAC BUICK GMC INC.; *U.S. Private*, pg. 3807
STERLING-RLM, LLC—See Lithia Motors, Inc.; *U.S. Public*, pg. 1326
STERNBERG CHRYSLER PLYMOUTH; *U.S. Private*, pg. 3807
STEVE BARRY BUICK INC.; *U.S. Private*, pg. 3807
STEVE COURY BUICK PONTIAC GMC; *U.S. Private*, pg. 3808
STEVE HOPKINS INC.; *U.S. Private*, pg. 3808
STEVE MOORE CHEVROLET DELRAY, LLC—See AutoNation, Inc.; *U.S. Public*, pg. 237
STEVE MOORE CHEVROLET, LLC—See AutoNation, Inc.; *U.S. Public*, pg. 237
STEVEN MOTOR GROUP; *U.S. Private*, pg. 3808
STEVENS CREEK LUXURY IMPORTS, INC.—See AutoNation, Inc.; *U.S. Public*, pg. 237
STEVENS CREEK MOTORS, INC.—See AutoNation, Inc.; *U.S. Public*, pg. 237
STEVENS CREEK VOLKSWAGEN; *U.S. Private*, pg. 3809
STEVEN TOYOTA SCION; *U.S. Private*, pg. 3808
STEVE RAYMAN CHEVROLET, LLC—See ZT Corporate; *U.S. Private*, pg. 4609
STEVES CHEVROLET-BUICK, INC.; *U.S. Private*, pg. 3810
STEVE'S CHEVROLET OF CHOWCHILL, LLC.; *U.S. Private*, pg. 3808
STEVE SCHMITT INC.—See Carriage Corporation; *U.S. Private*, pg. 772
STEVE WHITE MOTORS, INC.; *U.S. Private*, pg. 3808
STEVINSON AUTOMOTIVE INC.; *U.S. Private*, pg. 3810
STEVINSON CHEVROLET-WEST INC—See Stevinson Automotive Inc.; *U.S. Private*, pg. 3810
STEVINSON IMPORTS INC—See Stevinson Automotive Inc.; *U.S. Private*, pg. 3810
STEVINSON TOYOTA EAST SCION INC—See Stevinson Automotive Inc.; *U.S. Private*, pg. 3810
STEWART MANAGEMENT GROUP INC.; *U.S. Private*, pg. 3811
STEWART'S CLASSICS OF COLORADO LLC—See Lithia Motors, Inc.; *U.S. Public*, pg. 1326
STEW HANSEN HYUNDAI; *U.S. Private*, pg. 3810
STILLWELL MOTOR GROUP—See Autosports Group Limited; *Int'l*, pg. 732
STIVERS SUBARU; *U.S. Private*, pg. 3813
ST. JOHN NISSAN 7198; *U.S. Private*, pg. 3772
STOCKTON 12 AUTOMOTIVE, INC.; *U.S. Private*, pg. 3815
STODDARD NLA, LLC; *U.S. Private*, pg. 3815
STOHLMAN AUTOMOTIVE FAMILY; *U.S. Private*, pg. 3816
STOKES AUTOMOTIVE, INC.; *U.S. Private*, pg. 3816
STOKES BROWN TOYOTA OF HILTON HEAD—See Stokes Automotive, Inc.; *U.S. Private*, pg. 3816
STOKES CHEVROLET, INC.; *U.S. Private*, pg. 3816
STOKES-CRAVEN AUTOMOTIVE—See Stokes Automotive, Inc.; *U.S. Private*, pg. 3816
STONEHAM MOTOR CO. INC.; *U.S. Private*, pg. 3828
STONE MOTORS INC.; *U.S. Private*, pg. 3818
STONES TOWN & COUNTRY MOTORS; *U.S. Private*, pg. 3830
STOOPS BUICK, INC.—See Stoops Automotive Group, Inc.; *U.S. Private*, pg. 3830
STOOPS FREIGHTLINER QUALITY TRAILER; *U.S. Private*, pg. 3830
STORMS MOTORS, INC.; *U.S. Private*, pg. 3831
STOVESAND AUTO GROUP; *U.S. Private*, pg. 3832
STOWASSER BUICK GMC, INC.; *U.S. Private*, pg. 3832
STRAUB MOTORS, INC.; *U.S. Private*, pg. 3837
STREET TOYOTA, INC.; *U.S. Private*, pg. 3838

STRONG AUDI; *U.S. Private*, pg. 3840
STRONG VOLKSWAGON; *U.S. Private*, pg. 3840
STUART-BOWMAN AUTO CENTER; *U.S. Private*, pg. 3843
STUART CONKLIN BUICK INC—See Conklin Fangman Investment Co.; *U.S. Private*, pg. 1014
STUART NISSAN, LLC—See AutoNation, Inc.; *U.S. Public*, pg. 237
STUART POWELL FORD INC.; *U.S. Private*, pg. 3843
STU EMMERT CHEVROLET-BUICK-CADILLAC, INC.; *U.S. Private*, pg. 3843
STURGEON & BECK INC.; *U.S. Private*, pg. 3844
STURMAN & LARKIN FORD INC.; *U.S. Private*, pg. 3845
STYKEMAIN BUICK GMC, LTD.; *U.S. Private*, pg. 3846
SUBURBAN ANN ARBOR, LLC—See Suburban Motors Company, LLC; *U.S. Private*, pg. 3848
SUBURBAN CADILLAC OF LANSING, LLC—See Sonic Automotive, Inc.; *U.S. Public*, pg. 1903
SUBURBAN CHRYSLER JEEP DODGE, INC.—See Suburban Motors Company, LLC; *U.S. Private*, pg. 3848
SUBURBAN FORD OF FERNDALE, LLC—See Suburban Motors Company, LLC; *U.S. Private*, pg. 3848
SUBURBAN HAGGERTY IMPORTED CARS, LLC—See Suburban Motors Company, LLC; *U.S. Private*, pg. 3848
SUBURBAN OF WEST MICHIGAN, LLC—See Suburban Motors Company, LLC; *U.S. Private*, pg. 3848
SUGAR LOAF FORD; *U.S. Private*, pg. 3849
SULLIVAN BUICK GMC, INC.; *U.S. Private*, pg. 3851
SULLIVAN BUICK GMC—See Sullivan Cadillac; *U.S. Private*, pg. 3851
SULLIVAN CADILLAC; *U.S. Private*, pg. 3851
SULLIVAN INVESTMENT CORPORATION; *U.S. Private*, pg. 3851
SUN AUTOMOTIVE, INC.—See Morgan Auto Group, LLC; *U.S. Private*, pg. 2783
SUNBURY MOTOR COMPANY; *U.S. Private*, pg. 3865
SUNCOAST PORSCHE—See Sunset Automotive Group; *U.S. Private*, pg. 3871
SUNDANCE BUICK, GMC, INC.—See Sundance Chevrolet, Inc.; *U.S. Private*, pg. 3866
SUNDANCE CHEVROLET, INC.; *U.S. Private*, pg. 3866
SUN MOTORS BMW; *U.S. Private*, pg. 3863
SUNNYSIDE AUTOMOTIVE INC.; *U.S. Private*, pg. 3868
SUNRISE BUICK-PONTIAC-GMC-HUMMER WOLFCHASE; *U.S. Private*, pg. 3869
SUNRISE CHEVROLET—See Garber Management Group Inc.; *U.S. Private*, pg. 1642
SUNSET AUTOMOTIVE GROUP; *U.S. Private*, pg. 3871
SUNSET CHEVROLET, INC.—See Sunset Automotive Group; *U.S. Private*, pg. 3871
SUNSHINE TOYOTA INC.; *U.S. Private*, pg. 3872
SUN STATE FORD; *U.S. Private*, pg. 3864
SUNTRUP BUICK-PONTIAC-GMC TRUCK, INC.—See Southland Imports, Inc.; *U.S. Private*, pg. 3737
SUNTRUP FORD KIRKWOOD—See Southland Imports, Inc.; *U.S. Private*, pg. 3737
SUNTRUP VOLKSWAGEN—See Southland Imports, Inc.; *U.S. Private*, pg. 3737
SUOMEN TUKKUAUTOT OY—See Alma Media Corporation; *Int'l*, pg. 362
SUPERIOR AUTO GROUP; *U.S. Private*, pg. 3876
SUPERIOR AUTO MALL—See Superior Auto Group; *U.S. Private*, pg. 3876
SUPERIOR AUTOMOTIVE; *U.S. Private*, pg. 3876
SUPERIOR HONDA OF OMAHA; *U.S. Private*, pg. 3878
SUPERIOR MOTORS INC.; *U.S. Private*, pg. 3879
SUPPES FORD; *U.S. Private*, pg. 3881
SUPREME CHEVROLET, INC.; *U.S. Private*, pg. 3882
SUSAN SCHEIN AUTOMOTIVE; *U.S. Private*, pg. 3885
SUTHERLIN AUTOMOTIVE GROUP, LLC; *U.S. Private*, pg. 3886
SUTHERLIN H. IMPORTS, LLC—See AutoNation, Inc.; *U.S. Public*, pg. 237
SUTHERLIN H. IMPORTS, LLC—See AutoNation, Inc.; *U.S. Public*, pg. 237
SUTHERLIN IMPORTS, LLC—See AutoNation, Inc.; *U.S. Public*, pg. 237
SUTHERLIN NISSAN, LLC—See AutoNation, Inc.; *U.S. Public*, pg. 238
SUTLIFF BUICK GMC CADILLAC—See Sutliff Auto Group; *U.S. Private*, pg. 3887
SUTLIFF CHEVROLET CO.—See Sutliff Auto Group; *U.S. Private*, pg. 3887
SUTTLE MOTOR CORP.; *U.S. Private*, pg. 3887
SWANSON-FAHRNEY FORD SALES; *U.S. Private*, pg. 3891
SWEETEN TRUCK CENTER; *U.S. Private*, pg. 3892
SWIFTS SUPERSTORE; *U.S. Private*, pg. 3893
SWOPE VENTURES, INC.; *U.S. Private*, pg. 3895
SYMDON CHEVROLET; *U.S. Private*, pg. 3899
SYMES CADILLAC, INC.; *U.S. Private*, pg. 3899
SYTNER CARS LIMITED—See Penske Automotive Group, Inc.; *U.S. Public*, pg. 1666
SYTNER COVENTRY LIMITED—See Penske Automotive Group, Inc.; *U.S. Public*, pg. 1666
SYTNER OF LEICESTER LIMITED—See Penske Automotive Group, Inc.; *U.S. Public*, pg. 1666
SYTNER SHEFFIELD LIMITED—See Penske Automotive Group, Inc.; *U.S. Public*, pg. 1666

CORPORATE AFFILIATIONS

SZOTT M-59 CHRYSLER JEEP; *U.S. Private*, pg. 3908
TAFEL MOTORS INCORPORATED; *U.S. Private*, pg. 3921
TAG TRUCK CENTER; *U.S. Private*, pg. 3922
TAICANG BAOZEN AUTOMOBILE SALES AND SERVICES CO., LTD.—See China Yongda Automobiles Services Holdings Limited; *Int'l*, pg. 1565
TAIYUAN BAOZEN AUTOMOBILE SALES AND SERVICES CO., LTD.—See China Yongda Automobiles Services Holdings Limited; *Int'l*, pg. 1565
TAIZHOU BAOZEN AUTOMOBILE SALES AND SERVICES CO., LTD.—See China Yongda Automobiles Services Holdings Limited; *Int'l*, pg. 1565
TAIZHOU YONGDA AOCHENG AUTOMOBILE SALES AND SERVICES CO., LTD.—See China Yongda Automobiles Services Holdings Limited; *Int'l*, pg. 1565
TALLAHASSEE AUTOMOTIVE, LLC; *U.S. Private*, pg. 3926
TAMAROFF MOTORS, INC.; *U.S. Private*, pg. 3928
TANSKY'S SALES INC.; *U.S. Private*, pg. 3932
TANSKY'S SAWMILL TOYOTA INC.; *U.S. Private*, pg. 3932
TASCA LINCOLN MERCURY; *U.S. Private*, pg. 3934
TATE AUTOMOTIVE GROUP; *U.S. Private*, pg. 3935
TATE CHEVROLET—See Tate Automotive Group; *U.S. Private*, pg. 3935
TATE DODGE CHRYSLER JEEP, INC.; *U.S. Private*, pg. 3935
TATE'S AUTO CENTER; *U.S. Private*, pg. 3936
TAXIRAMA SAS—See G7 Entreprises; *Int'l*, pg. 2867
TAYLOR CHEVROLET COMPANY, INC.; *U.S. Private*, pg. 3937
TEAM CHEVROLET BUICK GMC CADILLAC; *U.S. Private*, pg. 3949
TEAM FORD LINCOLN; *U.S. Private*, pg. 3949
TEAM MOTOR SPORTS INC.; *U.S. Private*, pg. 3949
TEAM NISSAN INC.; *U.S. Private*, pg. 3949
TEAM ONE GM AUTO MALL; *U.S. Private*, pg. 3950
TEAM RAHAL OF MECHANICSBURG, INC.; *U.S. Private*, pg. 3950
TEAM SUPERSTORES OF VALLEJO; *U.S. Private*, pg. 3950
TEAM VOLKSWAGEN OF HAYWARD; *U.S. Private*, pg. 3950
TECHNOKAR S.A.—See AUTOHELLAS S.A.; *Int'l*, pg. 727
TED BRITT FORD SALES INC.; *U.S. Private*, pg. 3957
TED RUSSELL ENTERPRISES INC.; *U.S. Private*, pg. 3957
TEJAS TOYOTA INC.; *U.S. Private*, pg. 3958
TENNYSON CHEVROLET; *U.S. Private*, pg. 3968
TERRY SLIGH AUTOMOTIVE, INC.; *U.S. Private*, pg. 3972
TERRY YORK MOTOR CARS, LTD.—See AutoNation, Inc.; *U.S. Public*, pg. 238
TERRY YORK MOTOR CARS, LTD.—See AutoNation, Inc.; *U.S. Public*, pg. 238
TETON AUTO GROUP; *U.S. Private*, pg. 3973
TEXAN FORD, INC.—See AutoNation, Inc.; *U.S. Public*, pg. 238
TEXAN FORD SALES, LTD.—See AutoNation, Inc.; *U.S. Public*, pg. 238
TEXAN FORD SALES, LTD.—See AutoNation, Inc.; *U.S. Public*, pg. 238
TEXAS DODGE; *U.S. Private*, pg. 3975
THELEN INC.; *U.S. Private*, pg. 4141
THEORY ONE; *U.S. Private*, pg. 4142
THOMAS FORD SALES INC.; *U.S. Private*, pg. 4155
THOMAS MOTORS, INC.—See Morse Operations Inc.; *U.S. Private*, pg. 2790
THOMASVILLE FORD LINCOLN MERCURY—See Thomasville Toyota Used Cars; *U.S. Private*, pg. 4158
THOMASVILLE TOYOTA USED CARS; *U.S. Private*, pg. 4158
THOMPSON AUTOMOTIVE GROUP INC.; *U.S. Private*, pg. 4158
THOMPSON SALES CO.; *U.S. Private*, pg. 4160
THOMPSON'S HONDA; *U.S. Private*, pg. 4162
THOMPSON TOYOTA, INC.—See Thompson Automotive Group Inc.; *U.S. Private*, pg. 4158
THOMSON MACCONNELL CADILLAC, INC.; *U.S. Private*, pg. 4162
THOMSON MOTOR CENTRE INC.; *U.S. Private*, pg. 4162
THORNHILL GM SUPERSTORE INC.; *U.S. Private*, pg. 4162
THORNTON & STEFANOVICH INC.; *U.S. Private*, pg. 4163
THORSON GMC TRUCK BUICK MOTOR COMPANY, INC.; *U.S. Private*, pg. 4163
THORSTAD CHEVROLET INC.; *U.S. Private*, pg. 4163
THREE COUNTY VOLKSWAGEN CORP; *U.S. Private*, pg. 4163
THREE POINT MOTORS—See German Auto Import Network - Vancouver Island; *Int'l*, pg. 2943
THURSTON AUTO PLAZA; *U.S. Private*, pg. 4166
TIDELANDS FORD - LINCOLN; *U.S. Private*, pg. 4168
TIFFANY MOTOR COMPANY INC.; *U.S. Private*, pg. 4169
TIFFIN FORD-LINCOLN-MERCURY INC—See Reineke Family Dealerships; *U.S. Private*, pg. 3392
TILLEMAN MOTOR COMPANY; *U.S. Private*, pg. 4171
TILLERY CHEVROLET GMC INC.; *U.S. Private*, pg. 4171
TIM CASTELLAW AUTOMOTIVE; *U.S. Private*, pg. 4171
TIMMONS INTERNATIONAL INC.; *U.S. Private*, pg. 4173

N.A.I.C.S. INDEX

441110 — NEW CAR DEALERS

TIMONIUM TOYOTA INCORPORATED; *U.S. Private*, pg. 4173
TIM'S BUICK PONTIAC GMC TOYOTA; *U.S. Private*, pg. 4171
TIM WHITEHEAD CHRYSLER DODGE JEEP RAM; *U.S. Private*, pg. 4171
TINCHER-WILLIAMS CHEVROLET, INC.; *U.S. Private*, pg. 4173
TIPOTEX CHEVROLET, INC.; *U.S. Private*, pg. 4175
TIPTON HONDA; *U.S. Private*, pg. 4176
TJOD COMPANY INC.; *U.S. Private*, pg. 4177
TN CDJR MOTORS, LLC—See AutoNation, Inc.; *U.S. Public*, pg. 238
TODD WENZEL BUICK GMC OF WESTLAND—See General Motors Company; *U.S. Public*, pg. 929
TODD WENZEL CHEVROLET; *U.S. Private*, pg. 4181
TODEY MOTOR CO. INC.; *U.S. Private*, pg. 4181
TOM AHL BUICK GMC; *U.S. Private*, pg. 4182
TOMBELL CHEVROLET, INC.; *U.S. Private*, pg. 4183
TOM BUSH MOTORS INC.—See Tom Bush Regency Motors Inc.; *U.S. Private*, pg. 4182
TOM BUSH REGENCY MOTORS INC.; *U.S. Private*, pg. 4182
TOM BUSH VOLKSWAGEN INC.—See Tom Bush Regency Motors Inc.; *U.S. Private*, pg. 4182
TOM CLARK CHEVROLET INC.; *U.S. Private*, pg. 4182
TOM FORD INTERNATIONAL, LLC—See The Estee Lauder Companies Inc.; *U.S. Public*, pg. 2073
TOM GRADDY ENTERPRISES INC.; *U.S. Private*, pg. 4182
TOM HESSER AUTO GROUP; *U.S. Private*, pg. 4182
TOM HESSER CHEVROLET/BMW INC.—See Tom Hesser Auto Group; *U.S. Private*, pg. 4182
TOM JONES FORD; *U.S. Private*, pg. 4182
TOM LIGHT CHEVROLET; *U.S. Private*, pg. 4182
TOM MASANO INC.; *U.S. Private*, pg. 4183
TOMMIE VAUGHN MOTORS INC.; *U.S. Private*, pg. 4184
TOMMY'S QUALITY USED CARS; *U.S. Private*, pg. 4183
TOM NEHL TRUCK CO.; *U.S. Private*, pg. 4183
TOM O'BRIEN CHRYSLER JEEP GREENWOOD; *U.S. Private*, pg. 4183
TOM PECK FORD OF HUNTLEY, INC.; *U.S. Private*, pg. 4183
TOM ROUSH INC.; *U.S. Private*, pg. 4183
TOM'S FORD INC.; *U.S. Private*, pg. 4183
TOMS RIVER LINCOLN MERCURY MAZDA, INC.; *U.S. Private*, pg. 4184
TOM'S TRUCK CENTER INC.; *U.S. Private*, pg. 4183
TOM WHEAT LANDSCAPING; *U.S. Private*, pg. 4183
TONY DOMIANO AUTO DEALERSHIPS; *U.S. Private*, pg. 4185
TONY GULLO MOTORS OF TEXAS, INC.; *U.S. Private*, pg. 4185
TONY VOLKSWAGEN; *U.S. Private*, pg. 4185
TORONTO DODGE CHRYSLER LTD.—See AutoCanada Inc.; *Int'l*, pg. 726
TORRANCE NISSAN, LLC—See AutoNation, Inc.; *U.S. Public*, pg. 238
TOTAL AUTOS (1990) PTY LTD—See Eagers Automotive Limited; *Int'l*, pg. 2263
TOTH BUICK-GMC; *U.S. Private*, pg. 4192
TOUSLEY FORD, INC.—See AutoNation, Inc.; *U.S. Public*, pg. 238
TOWBIN AUTOMOTIVE ENTERPRISES; *U.S. Private*, pg. 4193
TOWER FORD; *U.S. Private*, pg. 4193
TOWER MOTOR CO. INC.; *U.S. Private*, pg. 4194
TOWN & COUNTRY CHRYSLER JEEP, INC.—See AutoNation, Inc.; *U.S. Public*, pg. 238
TOWN & COUNTRY FORD INC.; *U.S. Private*, pg. 4196
TOWN & COUNTRY HONDA; *U.S. Private*, pg. 4196
TOWNE HYUNDAI; *U.S. Private*, pg. 4198
TOWN MOTOR CAR CORPORATION; *U.S. Private*, pg. 4197
TOWN NORTH MAZDA; *U.S. Private*, pg. 4197
TOWNSEND FORD INC.; *U.S. Private*, pg. 4198
TOYOTA BILIA AS—See Bilia AB; *Int'l*, pg. 1029
TOYOTA CENTER; *U.S. Private*, pg. 4198
TOYOTA MAKATI, INC.—See GT Capital Holdings, Inc.; *Int'l*, pg. 3151
TOYOTA OF BOWLING GREEN; *U.S. Private*, pg. 4198
TOYOTA OF CLOVIS—See Penske Automotive Group, Inc.; *U.S. Public*, pg. 1666
TOYOTA OF DES MOINES; *U.S. Private*, pg. 4198
TOYOTA OF EASLEY; *U.S. Private*, pg. 4198
TOYOTA OF GLENDALE; *U.S. Private*, pg. 4199
TOYOTA OF HATTIESBURG, INC.; *U.S. Private*, pg. 4199
TOYOTA OF IRVING INC.; *U.S. Private*, pg. 4199
TOYOTA OF KIRKLAND—See Michael O'Brien Enterprises, Inc.; *U.S. Private*, pg. 2698
TOYOTA OF LOUISVILLE, INC.; *U.S. Private*, pg. 4199
TOYOTA OF MELBOURNE; *U.S. Private*, pg. 4199
TOYOTA OF MORRISTOWN; *U.S. Private*, pg. 4199
TOYOTA OF PASADENA; *U.S. Private*, pg. 4199
TOYOTA OF REDLANDS; *U.S. Private*, pg. 4199
TOYOTA OF RENTON—See Michael O'Brien Enterprises, Inc.; *U.S. Private*, pg. 2698
TOYOTA OF RIVERSIDE INC.; *U.S. Private*, pg. 4199
TOYOTA OF RUNNEMEDE; *U.S. Private*, pg. 4199
TOYOTA OF TRI-CITIES; *U.S. Private*, pg. 4199
TOYOTA ON NICHOLASVILLE; *U.S. Private*, pg. 4199
TOYOTA RENT-A-CAR; *U.S. Private*, pg. 4199
TOYOTA SAN FERNANDO PAMPANGA, INC.—See GT Capital Holdings, Inc.; *Int'l*, pg. 3151
TOYOTA SCION OF GOLDSBORO; *U.S. Private*, pg. 4199
TOYOTA SCION OF SAN BERNARDINO; *U.S. Private*, pg. 4199
TOYOTA SOUTH, INC.; *U.S. Private*, pg. 4199
TOYOTA SUBIC, INC.—See GT Capital Holdings, Inc.; *Int'l*, pg. 3151
TOYOTA TOWN OF STOCKTON; *U.S. Private*, pg. 4199
TOYOTA WALNUT CREEK, INC.; *U.S. Private*, pg. 4199
TRACY TOYOTA SCION; *U.S. Private*, pg. 4201
TRACY VOLKSWAGEN; *U.S. Private*, pg. 4201
TRAILER SOURCE INC.; *U.S. Private*, pg. 4203
TRANS-ATLANTIC MOTORS INC.; *U.S. Private*, pg. 4205
TRANSITOWNE HYUNDAI LLC—See West Herr Automotive Group, Inc.; *U.S. Private*, pg. 4485
TRANSOURCE INC.; *U.S. Private*, pg. 4210
TRANS-WEST INC.; *U.S. Private*, pg. 4206
TRANUM AUTO GROUP; *U.S. Private*, pg. 4212
TRAVERSE CITY AUTO PLAZA INC.; *U.S. Private*, pg. 4214
TREBOL MOTORS CORPORATION; *U.S. Private*, pg. 4216
TRECEK CHEVROLET OLDSMOBILE GEO; *U.S. Private*, pg. 4216
TRIANGLE AUTO CENTER, INC.; *U.S. Private*, pg. 4226
TRI-CITY FORD INC.; *U.S. Private*, pg. 4221
TRICKETT HONDA; *U.S. Private*, pg. 4229
TRI-FORD INC.; *U.S. Private*, pg. 4222
TRINITY TRAILER SALES & SERVICE, INC.—See Great Western Leasing & Sales, LLC; *U.S. Private*, pg. 1768
TRIPLE T PARTS & EQUIPMENT CO—See Matt Management Inc.; *U.S. Private*, pg. 2613
TRI-STAR FORD-MERCURY, INC.; *U.S. Private*, pg. 4223
TRI-STATE DIESEL INC.; *U.S. Private*, pg. 4223
TROPHY NISSAN, INC.; *U.S. Private*, pg. 4242
TROUTWINE AUTO SALES, INC.; *U.S. Private*, pg. 4243
TROY-ALAN CHEVROLET; *U.S. Private*, pg. 4243
TROY MOTORS, INC.—See Elder Automotive Group; *U.S. Private*, pg. 1350
TROY NISSAN INC.; *U.S. Private*, pg. 4243
TRUCK CENTER INCORPORATED; *U.S. Private*, pg. 4246
TRUCK ENTERPRISES INCORPORATED; *U.S. Private*, pg. 4246
TRUSTFORD - POTTERS BAR—See Ford Motor Company; *U.S. Public*, pg. 866
T&T MOTORS INC.; *U.S. Private*, pg. 3910
TT OF COLUMBIA, INC.; *U.S. Private*, pg. 4254
TUCKER CHRYSLER JEEP, INC.; *U.S. Private*, pg. 4256
TUCSON DODGE, INC.; *U.S. Private*, pg. 4256
TURAN-FOLEY MOTORS INC.; *U.S. Private*, pg. 4258
TURNER KIA; *U.S. Private*, pg. 4261
TURNERSVILLE AUTO MALL—See Penske Automotive Group, Inc.; *U.S. Public*, pg. 1666
TURNERSVILLE AUTO OUTLET, LLC—See Penske Automotive Group, Inc.; *U.S. Public*, pg. 1666
TURNPIKE FORD INC.; *U.S. Private*, pg. 4261
TURPIN DODGE OF DUBUQUE; *U.S. Private*, pg. 4261
TUSCALOOSA HYUNDAI, INC.; *U.S. Private*, pg. 4262
TUSTIN BUICK GMC; *U.S. Private*, pg. 4262
TUSTIN MOTORS INC.—See Lithia Motors, Inc.; *U.S. Public*, pg. 1326
TUSTIN TOYOTA; *U.S. Private*, pg. 4262
TUTTLE-CLICK AUTOMOTIVE GROUP; *U.S. Private*, pg. 4263
TUTTLE-CLICK COLLISION CENTER; *U.S. Private*, pg. 4263
T-WEST SALES & SERVICE, INC.—See AutoNation, Inc.; *U.S. Public*, pg. 238
TWIN CITY MAZDA; *U.S. Private*, pg. 4265
TWIN CITY MOTORS INC.—See Southeast Texas Classic Automotive; *U.S. Private*, pg. 3726
T&W OF KNOXVILLE INC.; *U.S. Private*, pg. 3910
TX ALLIANCE MOTORS, INC.—See AutoNation, Inc.; *U.S. Public*, pg. 238
TX MOTORS OF NORTH RICHLAND HILLS, INC.—See AutoNation, Inc.; *U.S. Public*, pg. 238
TX MOTORS ON KATY FREEWAY, INC.—See AutoNation, Inc.; *U.S. Public*, pg. 238
TX WEST HOUSTON MOTORS, INC.—See AutoNation, Inc.; *U.S. Public*, pg. 238
TYLER AUTOMOTIVE INC.; *U.S. Private*, pg. 4267
TYLER FORD; *U.S. Private*, pg. 4268
TYLERS AUTOMOTIVE INC.; *U.S. Private*, pg. 4268
TYLER'S JEFFERSON MOTORS; *U.S. Private*, pg. 4268
TYNAN'S VOLKSWAGEN, INC.; *U.S. Private*, pg. 4268
TYRRELL-DOYLE CHEVROLET CO.; *U.S. Private*, pg. 4269
TYRRELL MARXEN CHEVROLET & OLDSMOBILE CADILLAC INC.; *U.S. Private*, pg. 4269
UAG ATLANTA H1, LLC—See Penske Automotive Group, Inc.; *U.S. Public*, pg. 1666
UAG FAIRFIELD CA, LLC—See Penske Automotive Group, Inc.; *U.S. Public*, pg. 1666
UAG FAYETTEVILLE III, LLC—See Penske Automotive Group, Inc.; *U.S. Public*, pg. 1666
UAG LANDERS SPRINGDALE, LLC—See Penske Automotive Group, Inc.; *U.S. Public*, pg. 1666
UEBELHOR & SONS; *U.S. Private*, pg. 4274
UHL TRUCK SALES INC.; *U.S. Private*, pg. 4274
UKIAH FORD; *U.S. Private*, pg. 4275
ULRICH MOTOR COMPANY; *U.S. Private*, pg. 4277
UNDERRINER BUICK, INC.; *U.S. Private*, pg. 4279
UNDERWOOD CHEVROLET-BUICK, INC.; *U.S. Private*, pg. 4280
UNICARS HONDA; *U.S. Private*, pg. 4281
UNION CITY NISSAN INC.; *U.S. Private*, pg. 4284
UNION PARK AUTOMOTIVE GROUP, INC.; *U.S. Private*, pg. 4284
UNIVERSAL CHEVROLET CO. INC.; *U.S. Private*, pg. 4304
UNIVERSAL CITY NISSAN, INC.—See Sage Holding Company; *U.S. Private*, pg. 3526
UNIVERSITY CHRYSLER DODGE JEEP RAM OF FLORENCE; *U.S. Private*, pg. 4307
UNIVERSITY VOLKSWAGEN INC.; *U.S. Private*, pg. 4310
UPTOWN CHEVROLET-CADILLAC, INC.—See General Motors Company; *U.S. Public*, pg. 929
URBANDALE-S, LLC—See Lithia Motors, Inc.; *U.S. Public*, pg. 1326
US AUTO GROUP LIMITED; *U.S. Private*, pg. 4317
US AUTO GROUP OF MASSACHUSETTS—See US Auto Group Limited; *U.S. Private*, pg. 4317
USEM INC.; *U.S. Private*, pg. 4322
UTILITY/KEYSTONE TRAILER SALES; *U.S. Private*, pg. 4327
VACAVILLE HONDA; *U.S. Private*, pg. 4329
VALENCIA-A, INC.—See Lithia Motors, Inc.; *U.S. Public*, pg. 1326
VALENCIA B. IMPORTS, INC.—See AutoNation, Inc.; *U.S. Public*, pg. 238
VALENCIA H. IMPORTS, INC.—See AutoNation, Inc.; *U.S. Public*, pg. 238
VALENTI AUTO SALES, INC.; *U.S. Private*, pg. 4331
VALENTI MOTORS, INC.; *U.S. Private*, pg. 4331
VALENTI TOYOTA; *U.S. Private*, pg. 4331
VALKRY CORPORATION & EXOTIC CARS SOUTH; *U.S. Private*, pg. 4332
VALLEY AUTO WORLD INCORPORATED; *U.S. Private*, pg. 4332
THE VALLEY CADILLAC CORP.; *U.S. Private*, pg. 4130
VALLEY CADILLAC OLDSMOBILE; *U.S. Private*, pg. 4332
VALLEY CHEVROLET INC.; *U.S. Private*, pg. 4333
VALLEY CHRYSLER DODGE, INC.; *U.S. Private*, pg. 4333
VALLEY FORD SALES INC.; *U.S. Private*, pg. 4333
VALLEY FORD TRUCK SALES INCORPORATED; *U.S. Private*, pg. 4333
VALLEY FREIGHTLINER INC.; *U.S. Private*, pg. 4334
VALLEY-HI HONDA—See Dick Browning, Inc.; *U.S. Public*, pg. 1225
VALLEY-HI NISSAN—See Dick Browning, Inc.; *U.S. Public*, pg. 1225
VALLEY-HI TOYOTA SCION; *U.S. Private*, pg. 4336
VALLEY-HI TOYOTA—See Dick Browning, Inc.; *U.S. Public*, pg. 1225
VALLEY HONDA; *U.S. Private*, pg. 4334
VALLEY IMPORTS, INC.—See W.W. Wallwork, Inc.; *U.S. Private*, pg. 4423
VALLEY PONTIAC BUICK GMC, INC.; *U.S. Private*, pg. 4335
VALLEY STREAM LINCOLN MERCURY; *U.S. Private*, pg. 4335
VAL WARD CADILLAC, INC.; *U.S. Private*, pg. 4329
VAN ANDEL & FLIKKEMA MOTOR SALES, INC.; *U.S. Private*, pg. 4338
VAN BORTEL SUBARU; *U.S. Private*, pg. 4339
VAN BUREN TRUCK SALES CORP.; *U.S. Private*, pg. 4339
VAN CAMPEN MOTORS, INC.; *U.S. Private*, pg. 4339
VANDE HEY BRANTMEIER CHEVROLET-BUICK-PONTIAC-OLDSMOBILE, INC.—See Vande Hey Brantmeier Enterprises, Inc.; *U.S. Private*, pg. 4342
VANDERBEEK MOTORS, INC.—See AutoNation, Inc.; *U.S. Public*, pg. 238
VANDERBEEK MOTORS, INC.—See AutoNation, Inc.; *U.S. Public*, pg. 238
VANDERGRIFF CHEVROLET; *U.S. Private*, pg. 4342
VAN DRUNEN FORD; *U.S. Private*, pg. 4339
VAN DYKE DODGE INC.; *U.S. Private*, pg. 4339
VAN HORN HYUNDAI OF FOND DU LAC INC.; *U.S. Private*, pg. 4340
VAN NUYS-H, INC.—See Lithia Motors, Inc.; *U.S. Public*, pg. 1326
VANN YORK PONTIAC INC.; *U.S. Private*, pg. 4344
VAN'S HONDA; *U.S. Private*, pg. 4341
VAN SYCKLE KIA INC.; *U.S. Private*, pg. 4341
VAN-TROW TOYOTA; *U.S. Private*, pg. 4341
VARELA AUTO GROUP, LLC; *U.S. Private*, pg. 4346
VARSITY FORD LINCOLN MERCURY; *U.S. Private*, pg. 4347
VARSITY LINCOLN-MERCURY INC.; *U.S. Private*, pg. 4347
VAUGHN CHEVROLET; *U.S. Private*, pg. 4348
VENDETTI MOTORS INC.; *U.S. Private*, pg. 4356
VENTURCAP INVESTMENT GROUP V LLC; *U.S. Private*, pg. 4357
VER HOEF AUTOMOTIVE INC.; *U.S. Private*, pg. 4358

441110 — NEW CAR DEALERS

VERN EIDE MOTORCARS, INC.; *U.S. Private*, pg. 4367
VERTU MOTORS (CHINGFORD) LIMITED—See General Motors Company; *U.S. Public*, pg. 928
V&H, INC.; *U.S. Private*, pg. 4327
VIC BAILEY HONDA INC.; *U.S. Private*, pg. 4376
VIC BAILEY-LINCOLN MERCURY; *U.S. Private*, pg. 4376
VIC CANEVER CHEVROLET CO.; *U.S. Private*, pg. 4376
VICKSBURG CHRYSLER DODGE JEEP RAM; *U.S. Private*, pg. 4377
VICTORY LAYNE CHEVROLET; *U.S. Private*, pg. 4378
VICTORY MOTORS OF CRAIG; *U.S. Private*, pg. 4379
VIDMAR HONDA; *U.S. Private*, pg. 4381
VIKING BUICK GMC; *U.S. Private*, pg. 4382
VILLAGE AUTOMOTIVE GROUP; *U.S. Private*, pg. 4383
VILLAGE CAR COMPANY; *U.S. Private*, pg. 4383
VILLAGE CHEVROLET COMPANY - WAYZATA AUTO CENTER—See North American Automotive Services, Inc.; *U.S. Private*, pg. 2940
VILLAGE FORD INC.; *U.S. Private*, pg. 4383
VILLAGE LUXURY IMPORTS INC.—See North American Automotive Services, Inc.; *U.S. Private*, pg. 2940
VILLAGE MOTORS, LLC—See AutoNation, Inc.; *U.S. Public*, pg. 238
VILLAGE SUBARU—See Village Car Company; *U.S. Private*, pg. 4383
VINART ENTERPRISES INC.; *U.S. Private*, pg. 4384
VINCE WHIBBS PONTIAC-GMC TRUCKS; *U.S. Private*, pg. 4384
VINCE WIESE CHEVROLET, INC.—See AutoNation, Inc.; *U.S. Public*, pg. 238
VIN DEVERS INC.; *U.S. Private*, pg. 4384
VIP MOTOR CARS LTD.; *U.S. Private*, pg. 4386
VIRGINIA TRUCK CENTER INC.; *U.S. Private*, pg. 4388
VISION AUTO, INC.; *U.S. Private*, pg. 4390
VISTACAL LUXURY IMPORTS, INC.—See AutoNation, Inc.; *U.S. Public*, pg. 238
VISTA DIRECT; *U.S. Private*, pg. 4394
VISTA FORD; *U.S. Private*, pg. 4403
VITI, INC.; *U.S. Private*, pg. 4405
VOGLER MOTOR COMPANY, INC.; *U.S. Private*, pg. 4409
VOLKSWAGEN OF ALAMO HEIGHTS; *U.S. Private*, pg. 4410
VOLKSWAGEN OF OLD SAYBROOK; *U.S. Private*, pg. 4410
VOLKSWAGEN SANTA MONICA, INC.; *U.S. Private*, pg. 4410
VOLKSWAGEN VICTORIA—See German Auto Import Network - Vancouver Island; *Int'l*, pg. 2943
VOLKSWAGEN ZENTRUM AACHEN (VW) GMBH—See Penske Automotive Group, Inc.; *U.S. Public*, pg. 1666
VOLUME CHEVROLET BUICK; *U.S. Private*, pg. 4411
VOLUNTEER VOLVO AND GMC INC.—See Worldwide Equipment, Inc.; *U.S. Private*, pg. 4569
VOLVO OF EDISON; *U.S. Private*, pg. 4411
VOLVO OF FORT WASHINGTON; *U.S. Private*, pg. 4412
VOLVO OF LISLE; *U.S. Private*, pg. 4412
VOLVO OF THE TRIAD; *U.S. Private*, pg. 4412
VOLVO SALES & SERVICE CENTER; *U.S. Private*, pg. 4412
VON HOUSEN'S SACRAMENTO, INC.—See Von Housen's Motors; *U.S. Private*, pg. 4412
VORDERMAN MOTOR WERKS INC.; *U.S. Private*, pg. 4413
VOSS CHEVROLET, INC.; *U.S. Private*, pg. 4413
VT INC.; *U.S. Private*, pg. 4415
WACKERLI AUTO CENTER; *U.S. Private*, pg. 4424
WACONIA DODGE INC.; *U.S. Private*, pg. 4424
WAGNER CADILLAC CO., LP; *U.S. Private*, pg. 4426
WAGNER MOTORS; *U.S. Private*, pg. 4426
WAIKEM, GEORGE FORD, INC.; *U.S. Private*, pg. 4426
WALDORF FORD INC.; *U.S. Private*, pg. 4428
WALKER AUTO GROUP, INC.; *U.S. Private*, pg. 4428
WALKER AUTOMOTIVE; *U.S. Private*, pg. 4428
WALKER FORD CO., INC.; *U.S. Private*, pg. 4429
WALKER-JONES CHEVROLET-BUICK—See Jones Company, Inc.; *U.S. Private*, pg. 2232
WALKER MOTOR CO.; *U.S. Private*, pg. 4429
WALKER OLDSMOBILE COMPANY, INC.; *U.S. Private*, pg. 4429
WALLACE CHEVROLET, LLC—See Wallace Automotive Management Corporation, Inc.; *U.S. Private*, pg. 4430
WALLACE CHRYSLER JEEP, LLC—See Wallace Automotive Management Corporation, Inc.; *U.S. Private*, pg. 4430
WALLACE FORD, LLC—See AutoNation, Inc.; *U.S. Public*, pg. 238
WALLACE FORD, LLC—See AutoNation, Inc.; *U.S. Public*, pg. 238
WALLINGFORD AUTO COMPANY; *U.S. Private*, pg. 4431
WALLISMOTOR LJUBLJANA D.O.O.—See AutoWallis Public Limited Company; *Int'l*, pg. 732
WALLWORK FINANCIAL CORP.—See W.W. Wallwork, Inc.; *U.S. Private*, pg. 4423
WALLY MCCARTHY'S CADILLAC; *U.S. Private*, pg. 4431
WALNUT CREEK ASSOCIATES; *U.S. Private*, pg. 4432
WALSER BURNSVILLE M, LLC—See Walser Automotive Group, LLC; *U.S. Private*, pg. 4432
WALSER BURNSVILLE MOTORS, LLC—See Walser Automotive Group, LLC; *U.S. Private*, pg. 4432
WALSER H., LLC—See Walser Automotive Group, LLC; *U.S. Private*, pg. 4432
WALSER HY., LLC—See Walser Automotive Group, LLC; *U.S. Private*, pg. 4432
WALSH HONDA; *U.S. Private*, pg. 4433
WALT MASSEY AUTOMOTIVE, INC.; *U.S. Private*, pg. 4433
WALT SWEENEY; *U.S. Private*, pg. 4433
WANTAGH AUTO SALES INC.; *U.S. Private*, pg. 4436
WARD INTERNATIONAL TRUCKS INC.; *U.S. Private*, pg. 4441
WARD MUSCATELL AUTOMOTIVE GROUP; *U.S. Private*, pg. 4441
WARREN HENRY AUTOMOBILES INC.; *U.S. Private*, pg. 4444
WARREN MIDTOWN MOTORS INC.; *U.S. Private*, pg. 4444
WARREN MOTORS, INC.; *U.S. Private*, pg. 4444
WASCHKE FAMILY GM CENTER; *U.S. Private*, pg. 4445
WATERS TRUCK & TRACTOR INC.; *U.S. Private*, pg. 4454
WATERTOWN TRUCK & TRAILER INC.—See North American Truck & Trailer, Inc.; *U.S. Private*, pg. 2941
WATSEKA FORD-LINCOLN MERCURY, INC.; *U.S. Private*, pg. 4455
WATSON CHEVROLET, INC.; *U.S. Private*, pg. 4455
WATSON TRUCK & SUPPLY, INC.; *U.S. Private*, pg. 4456
WAYNE THOMAS CHEVROLET, INC.; *U.S. Private*, pg. 4460
WAYZATA NISSAN; *U.S. Private*, pg. 4461
W.C. MOTOR COMPANY, INC.—See Southland Imports, Inc.; *U.S. Private*, pg. 3737
WEBB AUTOMOTIVE GROUP, INC.—See AutoNation, Inc.; *U.S. Public*, pg. 238
WEBB CHEVROLET, INC.; *U.S. Private*, pg. 4464
WEBB FORD, INC.; *U.S. Private*, pg. 4464
WEBER GRANITE CITY CHEVROLET COMPANY; *U.S. Private*, pg. 4465
WEBSTER CHRYSLER JEEP, INC.; *U.S. Private*, pg. 4466
WEDEKIND MOTORS, INC.; *U.S. Private*, pg. 4468
WEHR FORD OF MOUNTAIN GROVE INC.; *U.S. Private*, pg. 4470
WEIL CADILLAC; *U.S. Private*, pg. 4471
WEIR CHEVROLET, INC.; *U.S. Private*, pg. 4472
WELD COUNTY GARAGE INC.; *U.S. Private*, pg. 4473
WENDLE MOTORS INC.; *U.S. Private*, pg. 4480
WENZHOU BAOZEN AUTOMOBILE SALES AND SERVICES CO., LTD.—See China Yongda Automobiles Services Holdings Limited; *Int'l*, pg. 1565
WENZHOU YONGDA LUJIE AUTOMOBILE SALES AND SERVICES CO., LTD.—See China Yongda Automobiles Services Holdings Limited; *Int'l*, pg. 1565
WESCOSVILLE AUTO SALES, INC.; *U.S. Private*, pg. 4482
WES FINCH AUTO PLAZA INC.; *U.S. Private*, pg. 4482
WES LASHER INC.—See Wesley B. Lasher Investment Corp.; *U.S. Private*, pg. 4482
WESLEY B. LASHER INVESTMENT CORP.; *U.S. Private*, pg. 4482
WESLEY CHAPEL-C, LLC—See Lithia Motors, Inc.; *U.S. Public*, pg. 1326
WESLEY CHAPEL-M, LLC—See Lithia Motors, Inc.; *U.S. Public*, pg. 1326
WESTBORN CHRYSLER JEEP, INC.; *U.S. Private*, pg. 4488
WESTBURY JEEP CHRYSLER DODGE, INC.; *U.S. Private*, pg. 4489
WEST CAROLINA FREIGHTLINER; *U.S. Private*, pg. 4483
WESTCHESTER BMW INC.—See Bayerische Motoren Werke Aktiengesellschaft; *Int'l*, pg. 912
WEST COLORADO MOTORS, LLC—See AutoNation, Inc.; *U.S. Public*, pg. 238
WESTCO TRUCK SALES PTY LTD.—See Great Western Corporation Pty. Ltd.; *Int'l*, pg. 3066
WESTERN MOTOR COMPANY INC.; *U.S. Private*, pg. 4494
WESTERN PETERBILT, INC.—See Greenbriar Equity Group, L.P.; *U.S. Private*, pg. 1776
WESTERN STAR TRUCK CENTRE PTY LTD.—See Penske Automotive Group, Inc.; *U.S. Public*, pg. 1666
WESTERN TRUCK EXCHANGE; *U.S. Private*, pg. 4497
WESTFALL-O'DELL GMC INC.; *U.S. Private*, pg. 4498
WESTGATE CHEVROLET, LTD.—See AutoNation, Inc.; *U.S. Public*, pg. 238
WEST GERMAN MOTOR IMPORTS, INCORPORATED; *U.S. Private*, pg. 4485
WEST HERR AUTOMOTIVE GROUP, INC.; *U.S. Private*, pg. 4485
WEST HERR CHEVROLET OF HAMBURG; *U.S. Private*, pg. 4485
WEST HOUSTON LUXURY IMPORTS, INC.—See AutoNation, Inc.; *U.S. Public*, pg. 238
WESTLEX INC.; *U.S. Private*, pg. 4499
WESTLIE MOTOR COMPANY; *U.S. Private*, pg. 4499
WESTLUND WARREN BUICK-GMC TRUCK; *U.S. Private*, pg. 4499
WESTMONT A. IMPORTS, INC.—See AutoNation, Inc.; *U.S. Public*, pg. 238
WESTMONT A. IMPORTS, INC.—See AutoNation, Inc.; *U.S. Public*, pg. 238
WESTMONT B. IMPORTS, INC.—See AutoNation, Inc.; *U.S. Public*, pg. 238
WESTMONT M. IMPORTS, INC.—See AutoNation, Inc.; *U.S. Public*, pg. 238
WEST MOTOR COMPANY INC.; *U.S. Private*, pg. 4486
WESTON PONTIAC BUICK GMC INC.; *U.S. Private*, pg. 4500
WESTRUX INTERNATIONAL; *U.S. Private*, pg. 4500
WEST SIDE GARAGE INC.; *U.S. Private*, pg. 4487
WEST SIDE MOTORS, INC.—See AutoNation, Inc.; *U.S. Public*, pg. 238
WESTSTAR AUTOPLEX, LLC—See Leif Johnson Ford Inc.; *U.S. Private*, pg. 2419
WEYMOUTH AUTO MALL; *U.S. Private*, pg. 4503
WF AUTOMOTIVE OF COLUMBUS, LLC; *U.S. Private*, pg. 4503
WHITAKER BUICK JEEP EAGLE CO.; *U.S. Private*, pg. 4507
WHITE BEAR LAKE SUPERSTORE; *U.S. Private*, pg. 4508
WHITE COUNTY FORD-CHRYSLER; *U.S. Private*, pg. 4508
THE WHITE FAMILY COMPANIES, INC.; *U.S. Private*, pg. 4135
WHITEMAN CHEVROLET, INC.; *U.S. Private*, pg. 4511
WHITE PLAINS HONDA; *U.S. Private*, pg. 4509
WHITE'S INTERNATIONAL TRUCKS—See White's International Trucks; *U.S. Private*, pg. 4510
WHITE'S MOUNTAIN MOTORS; *U.S. Private*, pg. 4510
WHITNEY'S VALUE FORD; *U.S. Private*, pg. 4513
WHITSON - MORGAN MOTOR COMPANY; *U.S. Private*, pg. 4513
WICKSTROM CHEVROLET; *U.S. Private*, pg. 4516
WICKSTROM FORD LINCOLN MERCURY; *U.S. Private*, pg. 4516
WIELAND SALES INC.; *U.S. Private*, pg. 4516
WIESE TOYOTA; *U.S. Private*, pg. 4516
WIESNER, INC.; *U.S. Private*, pg. 4517
WILBER DUCK CHEVROLET BUICK, INC.; *U.S. Private*, pg. 4517
WILBRAHAM IMPORT CARS, INC.—See Lia Auto Group; *U.S. Private*, pg. 2442
WILBUR-DUCK CHEVROLET & BUICK; *U.S. Private*, pg. 4517
WILCOX AUTOMOTIVE; *U.S. Private*, pg. 4518
WILCOXSON BUICK CADILLAC GMC TRUCK INC.; *U.S. Private*, pg. 4518
WILKINS BUICK, INC. & WILKINS SUBARU, LLC; *U.S. Private*, pg. 4520
WILLEY MOTORS INC.; *U.S. Private*, pg. 4522
WILLIAM FENTON INC.; *U.S. Private*, pg. 4523
WILLIAM LEHMAN & ASSOCIATES—See Lithia Motors, Inc.; *U.S. Public*, pg. 1323
WILLIAM LEHMAN BUICK INC.—See Lithia Motors, Inc.; *U.S. Public*, pg. 1323
WILLIAMS AUTO GROUP INC.; *U.S. Private*, pg. 4525
WILLIAMSBURG MOTORS, INC.—See Onity Group Inc.; *U.S. Public*, pg. 1605
WILLIAMSON MOTOR CO., INC; *U.S. Private*, pg. 4527
WILLIAMS VOLKSWAGEN INC.; *U.S. Private*, pg. 4527
WILMES CHEVROLET BUICK, INC.; *U.S. Private*, pg. 4529
WILMES FORD-LINCOLN, INC.; *U.S. Private*, pg. 4529
WILMES SUPERSTORE, INC.; *U.S. Private*, pg. 4529
WILSON AUTO GROUP, INC.; *U.S. Private*, pg. 4530
WILSON AUTO GROUP; *U.S. Private*, pg. 4530
WILSON COUNTY AUTOMOTIVE DEALER GROUP; *U.S. Private*, pg. 4530
WILSON MOTOR COMPANY; *U.S. Private*, pg. 4531
WIN CHEVROLET, INC.; *U.S. Private*, pg. 4532
WINDSOR AUTOMOTIVE INC.; *U.S. Private*, pg. 4539
WINFIELD MOTOR CO., INC.; *U.S. Private*, pg. 4540
WINNER AUTOMOTIVE GROUP, INC.; *U.S. Private*, pg. 4542
WINNER AUTOWORLD; *U.S. Private*, pg. 4542
WINNER CHEVROLET INC.; *U.S. Private*, pg. 4542
WINNER DOVER AUTOCENTER; *U.S. Private*, pg. 4542
WINTER CHEVROLET HONDA; *U.S. Private*, pg. 4545
WINTER HAVEN DODGE-CHRYSLER-JEEP INC.; *U.S. Private*, pg. 4545
WINTER & TAYLOR PTY LTD—See AMA Group Limited; *Int'l*, pg. 403
WISE AUTOMOTIVE, INC.; *U.S. Private*, pg. 4549
WISSLER MOTORS, INC.; *U.S. Private*, pg. 4550
WITHAM AUTO CENTERS, INC.; *U.S. Private*, pg. 4550
WITHNELL MOTOR COMPANY; *U.S. Private*, pg. 4550
WITT LINCOLN; *U.S. Private*, pg. 4551
WLOFM, CORP.; *U.S. Private*, pg. 4551
WMK, LLC—See Edwards Capital, LLC; *U.S. Private*, pg. 1342
WOBURN FOREIGN MOTORS INC.; *U.S. Private*, pg. 4553
WOLFE'S EVANSVILLE AUTO AUCTION INC—See Great Lakes Auto Auction, Inc.; *U.S. Private*, pg. 1764
WOLF MOTOR COMPANY INC.; *U.S. Private*, pg. 4553
WOLVERINE TRUCK SALES INC.; *U.S. Private*, pg. 4555
WOODBRIDGE BUICK GMC, INC.—See General Motors Company; *U.S. Public*, pg. 929
WOODHOUSE CHRYSLER DODGE JEEP RAM; *U.S. Private*, pg. 4558
WOODLAND MOTORS CORP.; *U.S. Private*, pg. 4559
WOOD MOTOR COMPANY INC.; *U.S. Private*, pg. 4557
WOODWORTH CHEVROLET-CADILLAC-BUICK; *U.S. Private*, pg. 4561

N.A.I.C.S. INDEX

441120 — USED CAR DEALERS

WOODY SANDER FORD INC.; *U.S. Private*, pg. 4561
WOOLWINE FORD LINCOLN, INC.; *U.S. Private*, pg. 4562
WORDEN MARTIN INC.; *U.S. Private*, pg. 4563
WORLD FORD PENSACOLA; *U.S. Private*, pg. 4565
WORLD FORD - STONE MOUNTAIN—See Group 1 Automotive, Inc.; *U.S. Public*, pg. 972
WORLD OF FORD SALES INC.; *U.S. Private*, pg. 4566
WORTHINGTON DEALERSHIP GROUP; *U.S. Private*, pg. 4570
WRAY FORD INC.; *U.S. Private*, pg. 4572
WRAY MAZDA VOLKSWAGEN; *U.S. Private*, pg. 4572
WRIGHT AUTOMOTIVE GROUP; *U.S. Private*, pg. 4572
WSMC INC.; *U.S. Private*, pg. 4574
WUXI BAOZEN AUTOMOBILE SALES AND SERVICES CO., LTD.—See China Yongda Automobiles Services Holdings Limited; *Int'l*, pg. 1565
WUXI YONGDA ORIENTAL AUTOMOBILE SALES AND SERVICES CO., LTD.—See China Yongda Automobiles Services Holdings Limited; *Int'l*, pg. 1565
W.W. WALLWORK, INC.; *U.S. Private*, pg. 4423
WYATT-JOHNSON BUICK, PONTIAC, GMC TRUCK, INC.; *U.S. Private*, pg. 4575
WYLIE MUSSER CHEVROLET CADILLAC; *U.S. Private*, pg. 4576
WYNNS SALES & SERVICE INC.; *U.S. Private*, pg. 4578
WYOMING VALLEY MOTORS; *U.S. Private*, pg. 4579
XIAMEN MEIDONG AUTO SALES & SERVICES CO., LTD.—See China MeiDong Auto Holdings Limited; *Int'l*, pg. 1519
XINYU DONGBU TOYOTA AUTO SALES & SERVICES CO., LTD.—See China MeiDong Auto Holdings Limited; *Int'l*, pg. 1519
XIPHIAS ENTERPRISES INC.; *U.S. Private*, pg. 4581
YALE EQUIPMENT & SERVICES INC.; *U.S. Private*, pg. 4585
YANCHENG BAOZEN AUTOMOBILE SALES AND SERVICES CO., LTD.—See China Yongda Automobiles Services Holdings Limited; *Int'l*, pg. 1565
YANGJIANG MEIBAOHANG AUTO SALES & SERVICES CO., LTD.—See China MeiDong Auto Holdings Limited; *Int'l*, pg. 1519
YATES BUICK GMC; *U.S. Private*, pg. 4587
YATES BUICK PONTIAC GMC, INC.; *U.S. Private*, pg. 4587
YIYANG DONGXIN AUTO SALES & SERVICES CO., LTD.—See China MeiDong Auto Holdings Limited; *Int'l*, pg. 1519
YIYI MOTORS INC.; *U.S. Private*, pg. 4589
YONGJIA BAOZEN AUTOMOBILE SALES AND SERVICES CO., LTD.—See China Yongda Automobiles Services Holdings Limited; *Int'l*, pg. 1565
YONKERS MOTORS CORP.; *U.S. Private*, pg. 4590
YORK AUTO GROUP; *U.S. Private*, pg. 4590
YORK CHRYSLER DODGE JEEP INC.; *U.S. Private*, pg. 4590
YORK FORD INC.—See Mcgovern Auto Group Corp Services, Inc.; *U.S. Private*, pg. 2635
YORKS OF HOULTON, INC.; *U.S. Private*, pg. 4591
YOUNG AUTOMOTIVE GROUP, INC.; *U.S. Private*, pg. 4592
YOUNG AUTOMOTIVE GROUP; *U.S. Private*, pg. 4592
YOUNG CHEVROLET COMPANY; *U.S. Private*, pg. 4592
YOUNG DAN TIPTON LLC; *U.S. Private*, pg. 4592
YOUNGER MOTOR CARS INC.; *U.S. Private*, pg. 4594
YOUNG TRUCK SALES INC.; *U.S. Private*, pg. 4593
YUCCA VALLEY CHRYSLER CENTER; *U.S. Private*, pg. 4595
YUCCA VALLEY FORD CENTER, INC.; *U.S. Private*, pg. 4595
YUEYANG MEIBAOHANG AUTO SALES & SERVICES CO., LTD.—See China MeiDong Auto Holdings Limited; *Int'l*, pg. 1519
ZECK FORD; *U.S. Private*, pg. 4599
ZEE AUTOMOTIVE; *U.S. Private*, pg. 4599
ZEIGLER CHRYSLER DODGE JEEP OF SCHAUMBURG; *U.S. Private*, pg. 4599
ZEISER MOTORS, INC.; *U.S. Private*, pg. 4599
ZELLER MOTOR COMPANY; *U.S. Private*, pg. 4600
ZHENGZHOU YONGDA HEXIE AUTOMOBILE SALES AND SERVICES CO., LTD.—See China Yongda Automobiles Services Holdings Limited; *Int'l*, pg. 1565
ZHUHAI MEIDONG LEXUS AUTO SALES & SERVICES CO., LTD.—See China MeiDong Auto Holdings Limited; *Int'l*, pg. 1519
ZHUZHOU MEIBAOHANG AUTO SALES & SERVICES CO., LTD.—See China MeiDong Auto Holdings Limited; *Int'l*, pg. 1519
ZIEMS FORD CORNERS, INC.; *U.S. Private*, pg. 4604
ZIMBRICK INC.; *U.S. Private*, pg. 4605
ZIMMERMAN FORD, INC.; *U.S. Private*, pg. 4605
ZIMMER MOTORS, INC.; *U.S. Private*, pg. 4605
ZONA FRANCA ALARI SEPAUTO S.A.—See CNH Industrial N.V.; *Int'l*, pg. 1676
ZT MOTORS HOLDING, L.P.—See ZT Corporate; *U.S. Private*, pg. 4609
ZUBOR BUICK GMC, INC.; *U.S. Private*, pg. 4609
ZUPPS ASPLEY PTY LTD—See Eagers Automotive Limited; *Int'l*, pg. 2264
ZUPPS MT GRAVATT PTY LTD—See Eagers Automotive Limited; *Int'l*, pg. 2264

441120 — USED CAR DEALERS

898984 ONTARIO INC; *Int'l*, pg. 15
ABC AUTOS, INC.; *U.S. Private*, pg. 35
AB INTERNATIONAL GROUP CORP.; *U.S. Public*, pg. 13
ADESA BELGIUM NV—See OPENLANE, Inc.; *U.S. Public*, pg. 1606
ADESA DEUTSCHLAND GMBH—See OPENLANE, Inc.; *U.S. Public*, pg. 1606
ADESA EUROPE NV—See OPENLANE, Inc.; *U.S. Public*, pg. 1606
ADESA FRANCE SAS—See OPENLANE, Inc.; *U.S. Public*, pg. 1606
ADESA ITALIA S.R.L.—See OPENLANE, Inc.; *U.S. Public*, pg. 1606
ADESA NEDERLAND B.V.—See OPENLANE, Inc.; *U.S. Public*, pg. 1606
ADESA NEW JERSEY, LLC—See OPENLANE, Inc.; *U.S. Public*, pg. 1606
ADESA OREGON, LLC—See OPENLANE, Inc.; *U.S. Public*, pg. 1606
ADESA SUBASTAS ESPANA, S.L.U.—See OPENLANE, Inc.; *U.S. Public*, pg. 1607
ADTRANS AUTOMOTIVE GROUP PTY. LTD.—See Eagers Automotive Limited; *Int'l*, pg. 2263
ADTRANS CORPORATE PTY. LTD.—See Eagers Automotive Limited; *Int'l*, pg. 2263
ALANT CORPORATION; *U.S. Private*, pg. 150
ALDERSON ENTERPRISES INC.; *U.S. Private*, pg. 159
AL-FUTTAIM AUTOMALL—See Al-Futtaim Private Company LLC; *Int'l*, pg. 285
ALINES AUTO GROUP; *U.S. Private*, pg. 168
AMAZING LUXURY CARS; *U.S. Private*, pg. 216
AMERICA'S AUTO AUCTION INC—See Trinity Hunt Management, L.P.; *U.S. Private*, pg. 4234
AMERICA'S CAR MART, INC.—See America's Car-Mart, Inc.; *U.S. Public*, pg. 95
ANDY MOHR BUICK GMC; *U.S. Private*, pg. 281
ANTHONY UNDERWOOD AUTOMOTIVE, INC.; *U.S. Private*, pg. 288
ANTILIA GROUP, CORP.; *Int'l*, pg. 483
ANTIOCH CHRYSLER JEEP DODGE; *U.S. Private*, pg. 288
APPLE INTERNATIONAL CO., LTD.; *Int'l*, pg. 520
ARAMIS GROUP SAS; *Int'l*, pg. 535
ARDEN MAIDSTONE LIMITED—See Lithia Motors, Inc.; *U.S. Public*, pg. 1321
AUCNET INC.; *Int'l*, pg. 699
AUTO1.COM GMBH—See AUTO1 Group SE; *Int'l*, pg. 725
AUTO1 CZECHIA S.R.O.—See AUTO1 Group SE; *Int'l*, pg. 725
AUTO1 GROUP SE; *Int'l*, pg. 725
AUTOHAUS BILIA GMBH & CO. KG—See Bilia AB; *Int'l*, pg. 1029
AUTOHAUS HEINRICH SENDEN GMBH; *Int'l*, pg. 726
AUTOHERO BELGIUM B.V.—See AUTO1 Group SE; *Int'l*, pg. 725
AUTOHERO GMBH—See AUTO1 Group SE; *Int'l*, pg. 725
AUTOHERO ITALIA S.R.L.—See AUTO1 Group SE; *Int'l*, pg. 725
AUTOHERO NL B.V.—See AUTO1 Group SE; *Int'l*, pg. 725
AUTOHERO OSTERREICH GMBH—See AUTO1 Group SE; *Int'l*, pg. 725
AUTOHERO PLUS SPAIN S.L.—See AUTO1 Group SE; *Int'l*, pg. 725
AUTOHERO POLAND SP. Z O.O.—See AUTO1 Group SE; *Int'l*, pg. 725
AUTOMARKET/LOTUS OF ORANGE COUNTY; *U.S. Private*, pg. 398
AUTONATION FORD EAST—See AutoNation, Inc.; *U.S. Public*, pg. 233
AUTOS ETC INC.; *U.S. Private*, pg. 401
AUTOTEILE SUPERMARKT GMBH—See LKQ Corporation; *U.S. Public*, pg. 1334
AUTOTRADER.COM INC.—See Cox Enterprises, Inc.; *U.S. Private*, pg. 1076
AVENUE CARS OF GLOUCESTER LIMITED; *Int'l*, pg. 739
AVIS CAR SALES, LLC—See Avis Budget Group, Inc.; *U.S. Public*, pg. 248
BACKLOTCARS, INC.—See OPENLANE, Inc.; *U.S. Public*, pg. 1607
BAODING AOZE AUTOMOBILE SALES SERVICES CO., LTD.—See China ZhengTong Auto Services Holdings Limited; *Int'l*, pg. 1566
BAOTOU LUZE AUTOMOBILE SALES SERVICES CO., LTD.—See China ZhengTong Auto Services Holdings Limited; *Int'l*, pg. 1566
BAOTOU ZHONGRUI AUTOMOBILE SALES SERVICE CO., LTD.—See China ZhengTong Auto Services Holdings Limited; *Int'l*, pg. 1566
BCS WEST LLC; *U.S. Private*, pg. 500
BEIJING ZHENGTONG BAOZEHANG AUTOMOBILE SALES SERVICES CO., LTD.—See China ZhengTong Auto Services Holdings Limited; *Int'l*, pg. 1566
BEIJING ZHENGTONG DINGWO AUTOMOBILE SALES SERVICES CO., LTD.—See China ZhengTong Auto Services Holdings Limited; *Int'l*, pg. 1566
BEN MYNATT MEGASTORE; *U.S. Private*, pg. 523
BENNETT TOYOTA; *U.S. Private*, pg. 527
BMW MADRID S.L.—See Bayerische Motoren Werke Aktiengesellschaft; *Int'l*, pg. 912
BOISE PETERBILT, INC.; *U.S. Private*, pg. 609
BROWNING CHEVROLET; *U.S. Private*, pg. 669
BTM CO.; *U.S. Private*, pg. 675
CALDWELL-AIR, LLC—See Lithia Motors, Inc.; *U.S. Public*, pg. 1321
CAR AUCTION CO., LTD.; *Int'l*, pg. 1319
CAREY COMPANY INC.; *U.S. Private*, pg. 754
CARGURUS IRELAND LIMITED, AN IRISH PRIVATE COMPANY LIMITED BY SHARES—See CarGurus, Inc.; *U.S. Public*, pg. 435
CARLOTZ, INC.—See Shift Technologies, Inc.; *U.S. Public*, pg. 1874
CARMAX AUTO—See CarMax, Inc.; *U.S. Public*, pg. 437
CARMAX AUTO SUPERSTORES, INC.—See CarMax, Inc.; *U.S. Public*, pg. 437
CARMAX AUTO SUPERSTORES WEST COAST, INC.—See CarMax, Inc.; *U.S. Public*, pg. 437
CAR PROS AUTOMOTIVE GROUP, INC.; *U.S. Private*, pg. 747
CAR QUALITY SERVICES GMBH—See OPENLANE, Inc.; *U.S. Public*, pg. 1607
CAR SENSE INC.—See Penske Automotive Group, Inc.; *U.S. Public*, pg. 1664
CARVANA CO.; *U.S. Public*, pg. 445
CAZOO GROUP LTD.; *Int'l*, pg. 1364
CHANGSHU YONGDA LUJIE AUTOMOBILE SALES & SERVICES CO., LTD.—See China Yongda Automobiles Services Holdings Limited; *Int'l*, pg. 1564
CHANGZHOU BAOZUN AUTOMOBILE SALES & SERVICES CO., LTD.—See China Yongda Automobiles Services Holdings Limited; *Int'l*, pg. 1564
CHENGDU QIBAO AUTOMOBILE SALES SERVICES CO., LTD.—See China ZhengTong Auto Services Holdings Limited; *Int'l*, pg. 1566
CHESAPEAKE-H, LLC—See Lithia Motors, Inc.; *U.S. Public*, pg. 1321
CLEAR LAKE-I, INC.—See Lithia Motors, Inc.; *U.S. Public*, pg. 1321
COLISEUM MOTOR COMPANY; *U.S. Private*, pg. 967
COPART CANADA, INC.—See Copart, Inc.; *U.S. Public*, pg. 575
COPART, INC.; *U.S. Public*, pg. 574
CORAL CADILLAC; *U.S. Private*, pg. 1046
CROOK MOTOR CO. INC.; *U.S. Private*, pg. 1103
DANBURY KIA; *U.S. Private*, pg. 1153
DANIEL BOONE AGENCY, LLC—See Shelter Mutual Insurance Company; *U.S. Private*, pg. 3631
DAVID RICE AUTO SALES; *U.S. Private*, pg. 1171
DCH CALIFORNIA MOTORS INC.—See Lithia Motors, Inc.; *U.S. Public*, pg. 1322
DCH CA LLC—See Lithia Motors, Inc.; *U.S. Public*, pg. 1322
DCH DEL NORTE, INC.—See Lithia Motors, Inc.; *U.S. Public*, pg. 1322
DCH KOREAN IMPORTS LLC—See Lithia Motors, Inc.; *U.S. Public*, pg. 1322
DCH MISSION VALLEY LLC—See Lithia Motors, Inc.; *U.S. Public*, pg. 1322
DCH OXNARD 1521 IMPORTS INC.—See Lithia Motors, Inc.; *U.S. Public*, pg. 1322
DCH (OXNARD) INC.—See Lithia Motors, Inc.; *U.S. Public*, pg. 1322
DCH TEMECULA IMPORTS LLC—See Lithia Motors, Inc.; *U.S. Public*, pg. 1322
DCH TEMECULA MOTORS LLC—See Lithia Motors, Inc.; *U.S. Public*, pg. 1322
DCH TORRANCE IMPORTS INC.—See Lithia Motors, Inc.; *U.S. Public*, pg. 1322
DEKRA AUSTRIA AUTOMOTIVE GMBH—See DEKRA e.V.; *Int'l*, pg. 2007
DEKRA AUTOMOTIVE MAROC S.A.—See DEKRA e.V.; *Int'l*, pg. 2007
DEKRA AUTOMOTIVE SOLUTIONS BELGIUM NV—See DEKRA e.V.; *Int'l*, pg. 2009
DEKRA AUTOMOTIVE SOLUTIONS PORTUGAL LDA.—See DEKRA e.V.; *Int'l*, pg. 2007
DEKRA AUTOMOTIVE SOLUTIONS S.A.S.U.—See DEKRA e.V.; *Int'l*, pg. 2007
DEKRA AUTOMOTIVE SOLUTIONS SPAIN S.L.—See DEKRA e.V.; *Int'l*, pg. 2007
DEKRA POLSKA SP. Z O.O.—See DEKRA e.V.; *Int'l*, pg. 2009
D & E MITSUBISHI; *U.S. Private*, pg. 1136
DONGGUAN AOZE AUTOMOBILE SALES SERVICES CO., LTD.—See China ZhengTong Auto Services Holdings Limited; *Int'l*, pg. 1566
DONGGUAN LIAOBU SCAS AUTOMOBILE SALES SERVICES CO., LTD.—See China ZhengTong Auto Services Holdings Limited; *Int'l*, pg. 1566
DONGGUAN SCAS AUTOMOBILE SALES SERVICES CO., LTD.—See China ZhengTong Auto Services Holdings Limited; *Int'l*, pg. 1566
DONGGUAN ZHENGTONG KAIDI AUTOMOBILE SALES

441120 — USED CAR DEALERS

SERVICES CO., LTD.—See China ZhengTong Auto Services Holdings Limited; *Int'l*, pg. 1566
DRIVETIME AUTOMOTIVE GROUP, INC.; *U.S. Private*, pg. 1278
DRIVEWAY MOTORS, LLC—See Lithia Motors, Inc.; *U.S. Public*, pg. 1322
DUNCAN HAMILTON & CO LIMITED; *Int'l*, pg. 2225
DUVAL MOTOR COMPANY INC.—See Scott-McRae Automotive Group Inc.; *U.S. Private*, pg. 3578
EARNHARDT'S AUTO CENTERS; *U.S. Private*, pg. 1314
EASTERNS AUTOMOTIVE GROUP; *U.S. Private*, pg. 1321
ECONOMY AUTO OUTLET; *U.S. Private*, pg. 1330
ED TILLMAN AUTO SALES INC.; *U.S. Private*, pg. 1332
EUROMOBIL SDN BHD—See DRB-HICOM Berhad; *Int'l*, pg. 2201
EWALD CHRYSLER JEEP DODGE, LLC—See Ewald Automotive Group, LLC; *U.S. Private*, pg. 1444
EXPRESS CREDIT AUTO, INC.; *U.S. Private*, pg. 1451
FAMILY RV GROUP—See Redwood Capital Investments, LLC; *U.S. Private*, pg. 3380
FARM & RANCH AUTO SALES, INC.; *U.S. Private*, pg. 1474
FERCO MOTORS, CORP.; *U.S. Private*, pg. 1496
FERGUSON BUICK GMC; *U.S. Private*, pg. 1496
FOSHAN DINGBAOHANG AUTOMOBILE SALES SERVICES CO., LTD.—See China ZhengTong Auto Services Holdings Limited; *Int'l*, pg. 1566
FRANK MYERS AUTO MAXX; *U.S. Private*, pg. 1595
FRANKS FOREIGN CAR SERVICE INC.; *U.S. Private*, pg. 1598
FUJIAN BAITAI AUTOMOBILE SALES & SERVICES CO., LTD.—See China Yongda Automobiles Services Holdings Limited; *Int'l*, pg. 1564
FUJIAN SCAS AUTOMOBILE SALES SERVICES CO., LTD.—See China ZhengTong Auto Services Holdings Limited; *Int'l*, pg. 1566
FUZHOU DINGWO AUTOMOBILE SALES SERVICES CO., LTD.—See China ZhengTong Auto Services Holdings Limited; *Int'l*, pg. 1566
FUZHOU EURO MOTORS SALES & SERVICES CO., LTD.—See G.A. Holdings Limited; *Int'l*, pg. 2865
G-7 CROWNTRADING CO., LTD.—See G-7 HOLDINGS Inc.; *Int'l*, pg. 2862
GANZHOU BAOZE AUTOMOBILE SALES SERVICES CO., LTD.—See China ZhengTong Auto Services Holdings Limited; *Int'l*, pg. 1566
GARBER BUICK COMPANY INC.—See Garber Management Group Inc.; *U.S. Private*, pg. 1642
GARDEN CITY-CJD, LLC—See Lithia Motors, Inc.; *U.S. Public*, pg. 1322
GENUINE MOTORCARS, INC.; *U.S. Private*, pg. 1680
G&L AUTO SALES INC.; *U.S. Private*, pg. 1629
GRAHAM CORNES MOTORS PTY. LTD.—See Eagers Automotive Limited; *Int'l*, pg. 2263
GUANGDONG SCAS AUTOMOBILE SALES SERVICES CO., LTD.—See China ZhengTong Auto Services Holdings Limited; *Int'l*, pg. 1566
GUANGZHOU BAOTAIHANG AUTOMOBILE SALES SERVICES CO., LTD.—See China ZhengTong Auto Services Holdings Limited; *Int'l*, pg. 1566
GUANGZHOU BAOZE AUTOMOBILE SALES SERVICES CO., LTD.—See China ZhengTong Auto Services Holdings Limited; *Int'l*, pg. 1566
GUELPH-S, LP—See Lithia Motors, Inc.; *U.S. Public*, pg. 1322
HAINAN SCAS AUTOMOBILE SALES SERVICES CO., LTD.—See China ZhengTong Auto Services Holdings Limited; *Int'l*, pg. 1566
HALDIMAND MOTORS LTD.—See AutoCanada Inc.; *Int'l*, pg. 726
HART FORD LINCOLN, INC.; *U.S. Private*, pg. 1873
HAWKES MOTORS; *U.S. Private*, pg. 1882
HAYLETT AUTO COMPANY, INC.—See Bish's RV, Inc.; *U.S. Private*, pg. 565
HEATHROW LIMITED—See Berjaya Corporation Berhad; *Int'l*, pg. 983
HENAN JINTANGSHENG AUTOMOBILE CO., LTD.—See China ZhengTong Auto Services Holdings Limited; *Int'l*, pg. 1566
HENDERSON ANUSA, LLC—See AutoNation, Inc.; *U.S. Public*, pg. 235
HENGYANG LUZE AUTOMOBILE SALES SERVICES CO., LTD.—See China ZhengTong Auto Services Holdings Limited; *Int'l*, pg. 1566
HOLCOMBE USA INC.; *U.S. Private*, pg. 1962
HOLMES MOTORS, INC.; *U.S. Private*, pg. 1967
HONDA U-TEC CO., LTD.—See Honda Motor Co., Ltd.; *Int'l*, pg. 3463
HOUSTON ANUSA, LLC—See AutoNation, Inc.; *U.S. Public*, pg. 235
HUBEI AOZE AUTOMOBILE SALES SERVICES CO., LTD.—See China ZhengTong Auto Services Holdings Limited; *Int'l*, pg. 1566
HUBEI CHANGZE AUTOMOBILE SALES SERVICES CO., LTD.—See China ZhengTong Auto Services Holdings Limited; *Int'l*, pg. 1566
HUNAN SCAS AUTOMOBILE SALES SERVICES CO.,

LTD.—See China ZhengTong Auto Services Holdings Limited; *Int'l*, pg. 1566
HYMAN LTD.; *U.S. Private*, pg. 2019
IDEAL CLASSIC CARS LLC; *U.S. Private*, pg. 2035
IDOM, INC.; *Int'l*, pg. 3595
INTELLICHOICE SOURCE INTERLINK MEDIA, INC.—See TEN: The Enthusiast Network, Inc.; *U.S. Private*, pg. 3964
JACOBS AUTO ENTERPRISES INC.; *U.S. Private*, pg. 2179
JD BYRIDER AUTOMAX LLC; *U.S. Private*, pg. 2195
JENSEN & SCHEELE BIL AS—See Bilia AB; *Int'l*, pg. 1029
JIANGXI ZHENGTONG ZETIAN AUTOMOBILE SALES SERVICES CO., LTD.—See China ZhengTong Auto Services Holdings Limited; *Int'l*, pg. 1566
JIANGYIN LEICHI AUTOMOBILE SALES & SERVICES CO., LTD.—See China Yongda Automobiles Services Holdings Limited; *Int'l*, pg. 1564
JIEYANG DINGJIE AUTOMOBILE SALES SERVICES CO., LTD.—See China ZhengTong Auto Services Holdings Limited; *Int'l*, pg. 1566
JIEYANG LUZE AUTOMOBILE SALES SERVICES CO., LTD.—See China ZhengTong Auto Services Holdings Limited; *Int'l*, pg. 1566
JINGMEN BAOZE AUTOMOBILE SALES SERVICES CO., LTD.—See China ZhengTong Auto Services Holdings Limited; *Int'l*, pg. 1566
JOHNSON MOTORS INC.; *U.S. Private*, pg. 2228
KATY ANUSA, LLC—See AutoNation, Inc.; *U.S. Public*, pg. 236
K-C EQUIPMENT FINANCE L.P.—See Kimberly-Clark Corporation; *U.S. Public*, pg. 1229
KEMNA MOTOR CO.; *U.S. Private*, pg. 2281
KEN DIXON AUTOMOTIVE GROUP; *U.S. Private*, pg. 2282
KIM'S TOYOTA; *U.S. Private*, pg. 2305
KUEHN MOTOR COMPANY; *U.S. Private*, pg. 2356
LAWSON CHEVROLET INC.; *U.S. Private*, pg. 2402
LEXINGTON-CJD, LLC—See Lithia Motors, Inc.; *U.S. Public*, pg. 1323
LITHIA DES MOINES-VW, LLC—See Lithia Motors, Inc.; *U.S. Public*, pg. 1324
LITHIA IDAHO FALLS-F, INC.—See Lithia Motors, Inc.; *U.S. Public*, pg. 1324
LITHIA OF WASILLA, LLC—See Lithia Motors, Inc.; *U.S. Public*, pg. 1325
LLOYD BELT AUTOMOTIVE; *U.S. Private*, pg. 2475
THE MAJOR AUTOMOTIVE COMPANIES, INC.; *U.S. Private*, pg. 4074
MANHEIM AUTO AUCTIONS LIMITED—See Cox Enterprises, Inc.; *U.S. Private*, pg. 1076
MANHEIM SOUTHERN CALIFORNIA—See Cox Enterprises, Inc.; *U.S. Private*, pg. 1077
MANHEIM TAMPA—See Cox Enterprises, Inc.; *U.S. Private*, pg. 1077
MARKHAM-B, LP—See Lithia Motors, Inc.; *U.S. Public*, pg. 1325
MARKHAM-P, LP—See Lithia Motors, Inc.; *U.S. Public*, pg. 1325
MARKQUART TOYOTA—See Markquart Inc.; *U.S. Private*, pg. 2582
MCCARTHY AUTO GROUP; *U.S. Private*, pg. 2626
MERCHANTS AUTOMOTIVE GROUP, LLC—See Abu Dhabi Investment Authority; *Int'l*, pg. 72
MHC TRUCK SOURCE INC.—See Murphy-Hoffman Company; *U.S. Private*, pg. 2816
MIAMI GARDENS-S, LLC—See Lithia Motors, Inc.; *U.S. Public*, pg. 1325
MIANYANG XINJINCHENG AUTOMOBILE SALES & SERVICES CO., LTD.—See China Yongda Automobiles Services Holdings Limited; *Int'l*, pg. 1564
MIKE DUMAN AUTO SALES, INC.; *U.S. Private*, pg. 2725
THE MORANDE AUTOMOTIVE GROUP; *U.S. Private*, pg. 4080
NELSON FORD MAZDA; *U.S. Private*, pg. 2883
NEWTON NISSAN OF GALLATIN, INC.; *U.S. Private*, pg. 2918
NICKEL CARS OF ABILENE, INC.; *U.S. Private*, pg. 2925
NORTH BAY IMPORTS, INC.; *U.S. Private*, pg. 2942
NORTHSIDE TRUCKS; *U.S. Private*, pg. 2957
NORTHWOOD AUTO PLAZA INC.; *U.S. Private*, pg. 2963
NY LNR LUXURY IMPORTS, INC.—See AutoNation, Inc.; *U.S. Public*, pg. 236
NY WHITE PLAINS LUXURY IMPORTS, INC.—See AutoNation, Inc.; *U.S. Public*, pg. 236
PAACO AUTOMOTIVE GROUP LP; *U.S. Private*, pg. 3062
PACIFIC TRUCK CENTERS—See Pacific Power Products Company; *U.S. Private*, pg. 3070
PALMEN DODGE CHRYSLER JEEP OF RACINE—See Palmen Automotive Group Inc.; *U.S. Private*, pg. 3080
PARSONS FORD LINCOLN MERCURY; *U.S. Private*, pg. 3100
PERKINS MOTOR COMPANY; *U.S. Private*, pg. 3151
PHILPOTT MOTORS, LLC—See Sonic Automotive, Inc.; *U.S. Public*, pg. 1902
PHOENIX ANUSA, LLC—See AutoNation, Inc.; *U.S. Public*, pg. 237
PLATTNER'S WINTER PARK SUPERSTORE—See Plattner Automotive Group, Inc.; *U.S. Private*, pg. 3212

PREFERRED AUTO INC.; *U.S. Private*, pg. 3247
PREMIUM MOTOR CARS LLC; *U.S. Private*, pg. 3252
PRESTIGE AUTO TRADERS AUSTRALIA PTY LTD—See Autosports Group Limited; *Int'l*, pg. 732
PRESTIGE CARS INTERNATIONAL, INC.; *U.S. Public*, pg. 1716
PRESTIGE MOTORS, INC.—See Prestige Motors, Inc.; *U.S. Private*, pg. 3256
PRO - M S.R.O.—See DEKRA e.V.; *Int'l*, pg. 2009
PUBLIC AUTOS LTD; *U.S. Private*, pg. 3298
QINGDAO AOZE AUTOMOBILE SALES SERVICES CO., LTD.—See China ZhengTong Auto Services Holdings Limited; *Int'l*, pg. 1566
RALPH SELLERS CHEVROLET—See Ralph Sellers Motor Co.; *U.S. Private*, pg. 3350
RAMEY AUTOMOTIVE INC.; *U.S. Private*, pg. 3351
REGAL MOTORS INC.; *U.S. Private*, pg. 3385
RESSLER MOTORS; *U.S. Private*, pg. 3408
RICHMOND HILL-H, LP—See Lithia Motors, Inc.; *U.S. Public*, pg. 1326
RIGHT WAY AUTO; *U.S. Private*, pg. 3436
ROSNER MOTORS, INC.—See Rosner Management Group, LLC; *U.S. Private*, pg. 3485
ROYAL AUTOMOTIVE GROUP INC.; *U.S. Private*, pg. 3491
ROYAL CAR CENTER; *U.S. Private*, pg. 3491
ROYAL MOTORS OF MIDDLEBURY, INC.—See Heritage Financial Group, Inc.; *U.S. Private*, pg. 1923
RUI'AN YONGDA NANYANG LUJIE AUTOMOBILE SALES & SERVICES CO., LTD.—See China Yongda Automobiles Services Holdings Limited; *Int'l*, pg. 1564
SALVADORE AUTO EXCHANGE INC.; *U.S. Private*, pg. 3535
SANDERSON LINCOLN; *U.S. Private*, pg. 3543
SCHOEPP MOTORS INC.; *U.S. Private*, pg. 3567
SHANGHAI AOHUI AUTOMOBILE SALES SERVICES CO., LTD.—See China ZhengTong Auto Services Holdings Limited; *Int'l*, pg. 1566
SHANGHAI LUDA AUTOMOBILE SALES SERVICES CO., LTD.—See China ZhengTong Auto Services Holdings Limited; *Int'l*, pg. 1567
SHANGHAI QIZE AUTOMOBILE SALES SERVICES CO., LTD.—See China ZhengTong Auto Services Holdings Limited; *Int'l*, pg. 1567
SHANGHAI SHENXIE AUTOMOBILE TRADING CO., LTD.—See China ZhengTong Auto Services Holdings Limited; *Int'l*, pg. 1567
SHANGHAI WEST SHANGHAI JIAWO AUTOMOBILE SALES & SERVICES CO., LTD.—See China Yongda Automobiles Services Holdings Limited; *Int'l*, pg. 1564
SHANGHAI WEST SHANGHAI SHENJIE AUTOMOBILE SALES & SERVICES CO., LTD.—See China Yongda Automobiles Services Holdings Limited; *Int'l*, pg. 1564
SHANGHAI YONGDA QIMING AUTOMOBILE SALES & SERVICES CO., LTD.—See China Yongda Automobiles Services Holdings Limited; *Int'l*, pg. 1565
SHANGRAO BAOZE AUTOMOBILE SALES SERVICES CO., LTD.—See China ZhengTong Auto Services Holdings Limited; *Int'l*, pg. 1567
SHANTOU BAOZE AUTOMOBILE SALES SERVICES CO., LTD.—See China ZhengTong Auto Services Holdings Limited; *Int'l*, pg. 1567
SHANTOU HONGXIANG MATERIALS CO., LTD.—See China ZhengTong Auto Services Holdings Limited; *Int'l*, pg. 1567
SHENGZHOU AOZE AUTOMOBILE SALES SERVICES CO., LTD.—See China ZhengTong Auto Services Holdings Limited; *Int'l*, pg. 1567
SHENZHEN AOZE AUTOMOBILE SALES SERVICES CO., LTD.—See China ZhengTong Auto Services Holdings Limited; *Int'l*, pg. 1567
SHENZHEN BAOTAIHANG AUTOMOBILE SALES SERVICES CO., LTD.—See China ZhengTong Auto Services Holdings Limited; *Int'l*, pg. 1567
SHENZHEN BAOZE AUTOMOBILE SALES SERVICES CO., LTD.—See China ZhengTong Auto Services Holdings Limited; *Int'l*, pg. 1567
SHENZHEN DINGWO AUTOMOBILE SALES SERVICES CO., LTD.—See China ZhengTong Auto Services Holdings Limited; *Int'l*, pg. 1567
SHENZHEN HUASHUNBAO AUTOMOBILE SALES SERVICES CO., LTD.—See China ZhengTong Auto Services Holdings Limited; *Int'l*, pg. 1567
SHENZHEN HUASHUNBAO AUTOMOBILE SERVICES CO., LTD.—See China ZhengTong Auto Services Holdings Limited; *Int'l*, pg. 1567
SHIFT TECHNOLOGIES, INC.; *U.S. Public*, pg. 1874
SINA S.P.A.—See Argo Finanziaria S.p.A.; *Int'l*, pg. 562
SKCO INVESTMENTS CORP.; *U.S. Private*, pg. 3681
SMYRNA-F, LLC—See Lithia Motors, Inc.; *U.S. Public*, pg. 1326
SOUTHERN AUTOMOTIVE GROUP PTY. LTD.—See Eagers Automotive Limited; *Int'l*, pg. 2264
SPORTS AND IMPORTS, INC.; *U.S. Private*, pg. 3761
SPRINGDALE TRACTOR COMPANY INC.; *U.S. Private*, pg. 3764
SS&KH CORPORATION; *U.S. Private*, pg. 3768
STEVINSON LEXUS OF LAKEWOOD—See Stevinson Automotive Inc.; *U.S. Private*, pg. 3810

N.A.I.C.S. INDEX

STROLID, INC.; *U.S. Private*, pg. 3840
SUPERIOR AUTO, INC.—See Parallel Investment Partners LLC; *U.S. Private*, pg. 3092
SUZHOU ANZHIXING AUTOMOBILE SALES SERVICES CO., LTD.—See China ZhengTong Auto Services Holdings Limited; *Int'l*, pg. 1567
TAIXING YONGDA ZHONGCHENG AUTOMOBILE SALES & SERVICES CO., LTD.—See China Yongda Automobiles Services Holdings Limited; *Int'l*, pg. 1565
TAYLOR'S AUTO MAX; *U.S. Private*, pg. 3941
TERRY'S LINCOLN MERCURY; *U.S. Private*, pg. 3972
TEXAS CAR-MART, INC.—See America's Car-Mart, Inc.; *U.S. Public*, pg. 95
TEXAS DIRECT AUTO—See Vroom, Inc.; *U.S. Public*, pg. 2312
TIANJIN SCAS AUTOMOBILE SALES SERVICES CO., LTD.—See China ZhengTong Auto Services Holdings Limited; *Int'l*, pg. 1567
TOYOTA OF GREENVILLE; *U.S. Private*, pg. 4199
TRACY VOLKSWAGEN, INC.; *U.S. Private*, pg. 4201
TRADEREV USA LLC—See OPENLANE, Inc.; *U.S. Public*, pg. 1607
TRICOLOR AUTO GROUP; *U.S. Private*, pg. 4229
TROY-I, LLC—See Lithia Motors, Inc.; *U.S. Public*, pg. 1326
UNIFLOTTE SRL—See Hera S.p.A.; *Int'l*, pg. 3357
UNIVERSAL TRUCK & TRAILER SALES II LLC; *U.S. Private*, pg. 4307
US AUTO SALES INC; *U.S. Private*, pg. 4317
VAN CHEVROLET; *U.S. Private*, pg. 4339
VAUGHAN-P, LP—See Lithia Motors, Inc.; *U.S. Public*, pg. 1326
VCT VOGEL GMBH—See Chart Industries, Inc.; *U.S. Public*, pg. 482
VEHIX, INC.—See Comcast Corporation; *U.S. Public*, pg. 542
VROOM, INC.; *U.S. Public*, pg. 2312
WAUKESHA-CJD, INC.—See Lithia Motors, Inc.; *U.S. Public*, pg. 1326
WEIHAI LUZE AUTOMOBILE SALES SERVICES CO., LTD.—See China ZhengTong Auto Services Holdings Limited; *Int'l*, pg. 1567
WESLEY CHAPEL-HY, LLC—See Lithia Motors, Inc.; *U.S. Public*, pg. 1326
WESLEY CHAPEL-MOTO, LLC—See Lithia Motors, Inc.; *U.S. Public*, pg. 1326
WEST ALLIS-T, INC.—See Lithia Motors, Inc.; *U.S. Public*, pg. 1326
WHOLESALE,INC—See RumbleON, Inc.; *U.S. Public*, pg. 1826
WHOLESALE OUTLET INC.; *U.S. Private*, pg. 4514
WINSLOW BMW; *U.S. Private*, pg. 4543
WKA B.V.—See AUTO1 Group SE; *Int'l*, pg. 725
WUHAN BAOZE AUTOMOBILE SALES SERVICES CO., LTD.—See China ZhengTong Auto Services Holdings Limited; *Int'l*, pg. 1567
WUHAN LUZE AUTOMOBILE SALES SERVICES CO., LTD.—See China ZhengTong Auto Services Holdings Limited; *Int'l*, pg. 1567
WUHAN ZHENGTONG YUECHI AUTOMOBILE SALES SERVICES CO., LTD.—See China ZhengTong Auto Services Holdings Limited; *Int'l*, pg. 1567
WUXI YICHENG AUTOMOBILE SALES & SERVICES CO., LTD.—See China Yongda Automobiles Services Holdings Limited; *Int'l*, pg. 1565
XIANGTAN BAOZE AUTOMOBILE SALES SERVICES CO., LTD.—See China ZhengTong Auto Services Holdings Limited; *Int'l*, pg. 1567
XIANGYANG BAOZE AUTOMOBILE SALES SERVICES CO., LTD.—See China ZhengTong Auto Services Holdings Limited; *Int'l*, pg. 1567
YICHANG BAOZE AUTOMOBILE SALES SERVICES CO., LTD.—See China ZhengTong Auto Services Holdings Limited; *Int'l*, pg. 1567
YICHUN BAOZE AUTOMOBILE SALES SERVICES CO., LTD.—See China ZhengTong Auto Services Holdings Limited; *Int'l*, pg. 1567
ZHANJIANG ZHENGTONG KAIDI AUTOMOBILE SALES SERVICES CO., LTD.—See China ZhengTong Auto Services Holdings Limited; *Int'l*, pg. 1567
ZHENGZHOU DINGWO AUTOMOBILE SALES SERVICES CO., LTD.—See China ZhengTong Auto Services Holdings Limited; *Int'l*, pg. 1567
ZHUHAI BAOZE AUTOMOBILE SALES SERVICES CO., LTD.—See China ZhengTong Auto Services Holdings Limited; *Int'l*, pg. 1567
ZHUHAI SCAS AUTOMOBILE SALES SERVICES CO., LTD.—See China ZhengTong Auto Services Holdings Limited; *Int'l*, pg. 1567

441210 — RECREATIONAL VEHICLE DEALERS

ALL SEASONS RV & MARINE—See Camping World Holdings, Inc.; *U.S. Public*, pg. 427
ALOHA R.V., INC.—See Redwood Capital Investments, LLC; *U.S. Private*, pg. 3380
ALPIN HAUS SKI SHOP INC.; *U.S. Private*, pg. 200
AMERICA CHOICE RV—See Camping World Holdings, Inc.; *U.S. Public*, pg. 427
AMERICAN MIDWEST FLEET SOLUTIONS—See Genstar Capital, LP; *U.S. Private*, pg. 1676
A & M MOTORS INC.; *U.S. Private*, pg. 18
ARIZONA STATE TRAILERS SALES, INC.; *U.S. Private*, pg. 324
BATES RV EXCHANGE; *U.S. Private*, pg. 486
BATES RV; *U.S. Private*, pg. 486
BELLINI NAUTICA S.P.A.; *Int'l*, pg. 967
BILL PLEMMONS RV; *U.S. Private*, pg. 558
BISH'S RV, INC.; *U.S. Private*, pg. 565
BOLEK INC.; *U.S. Private*, pg. 610
BOMBARDIER MOTOR CORPORATION OF AMERICA—See Bain Capital, LP; *U.S. Private*, pg. 431
BUDDY GREGG MOTOR HOMES INC.—See Lazydays Holdings, Inc.; *U.S. Public*, pg. 1294
BULLYAN TRAILER SALES INC.; *U.S. Private*, pg. 685
BUS SUPPLY COMPANY, INC.; *U.S. Private*, pg. 693
CAMPER COUNTRY RV—See Redwood Capital Investments, LLC; *U.S. Private*, pg. 3380
CAMPERS INN HOLDING CORP.; *U.S. Private*, pg. 731
CAMPERS INN OF KINGSTON INC—See Campers Inn Holding Corp.; *U.S. Private*, pg. 731
CAMPERS INN OF RAYNHAM INC—See Campers Inn Holding Corp.; *U.S. Private*, pg. 731
CAMPING WORLD OF DAVENPORT—See Camping World Holdings, Inc.; *U.S. Public*, pg. 427
CANDYS CAMPERS, INC.—See Redwood Capital Investments, LLC; *U.S. Private*, pg. 3380
CARAVANE 185 INC; *Int'l*, pg. 1320
CARPENTER'S CAMPERS INC.; *U.S. Private*, pg. 770
CENTURY RV, INC.—See Lazydays Holdings, Inc.; *U.S. Public*, pg. 1294
CHEYENNE CAMPING CENTER CO.; *U.S. Private*, pg. 876
CHILHOWEE TRAILER SALES, INC.—See Lazydays Holdings, Inc.; *U.S. Public*, pg. 1294
CHISOLM TRAIL RV; *U.S. Private*, pg. 887
COLAW RV SALES; *U.S. Private*, pg. 965
COLERAIN NORTHSIDE, LLC—See Redwood Capital Investments, LLC; *U.S. Private*, pg. 3380
COLERAIN RV AT ALUM CREEK, LLC—See Redwood Capital Investments, LLC; *U.S. Private*, pg. 3380
COLERAIN RV OF DAYTON, LLC—See Redwood Capital Investments, LLC; *U.S. Private*, pg. 3380
COLERAIN TRAILER CENTER, LLC—See Redwood Capital Investments, LLC; *U.S. Private*, pg. 3380
CURTIS TRAILERS INC.; *U.S. Private*, pg. 1127
CWI, INC.—See Camping World Holdings, Inc.; *U.S. Public*, pg. 428
DAN WYLIE'S DREAM ENTERPRISES, INC.; *U.S. Private*, pg. 1152
DAR-KIM, INC.—See Camping World Holdings, Inc.; *U.S. Public*, pg. 427
DEANS RV SUPERSTORE INC.; *U.S. Private*, pg. 1185
DELMARVA RV CENTER IN SEAFORD; *U.S. Private*, pg. 1197
DICK GORE'S RV WORLD INC.; *U.S. Private*, pg. 1226
DIXIE RV SUPERSTORE; *U.S. Private*, pg. 1245
EAGLE CREST HOMES, INC.—See Chief Industries, Inc.; *U.S. Private*, pg. 881
EAST BAY RV; *U.S. Private*, pg. 1315
ERWIN HYMER WORLD GMBH—See Thor Industries, Inc.; *U.S. Public*, pg. 2156
EVERGREEN RV CENTER, INC.; *U.S. Private*, pg. 1440
FLAGG RV CENTER; *U.S. Private*, pg. 1539
FUN COUNTRY RV'S & MARINE, INC.; *U.S. Private*, pg. 1622
GENERAL RV CENTER INC.; *U.S. Private*, pg. 1667
GIANT INLAND EMPIRE RV CENTER; *U.S. Private*, pg. 1695
GUARANTEE RV; *Int'l*, pg. 3169
GUARANTY CHEVROLET-PONTIAC; *U.S. Private*, pg. 1809
GUARANTY RV CENTERS; *U.S. Private*, pg. 1809
HART & VOGT INC.; *U.S. Private*, pg. 1872
HEARTLAND RECREATIONAL VEHICLES, LLC—See Thor Industries, Inc.; *U.S. Public*, pg. 2156
HOHL-FINDLAY, LTD.—See Lazydays Holdings, Inc.; *U.S. Public*, pg. 1295
HOLIDAY WORLD OF DALLAS LTD.; *U.S. Private*, pg. 1963
HYMER GMBH & CO. KG—See Thor Industries, Inc.; *U.S. Public*, pg. 2156
INDEPENDENCE RV SALES & SERVICES, INC—See General RV Center Inc.; *U.S. Private*, pg. 1667
JOHN BLEAKLEY RV CENTER INC.; *U.S. Private*, pg. 2220
JOHNNY KETELSEN RECREATIONAL VEHICLES INC.; *U.S. Private*, pg. 2226
KIBBI, LLC—See AIP, LLC; *U.S. Private*, pg. 135
LAIKA CARAVANS S.P.A.—See Thor Industries, Inc.; *U.S. Public*, pg. 2156
LAKE METROPARKS; *U.S. Private*, pg. 2375
LA MESA RV CENTER, INC.; *U.S. Private*, pg. 2369
LAZY DAYS' R.V. CENTER, INC.—See Lazydays Holdings, Inc.; *U.S. Public*, pg. 1295
LIVIN' LITE CORP.—See Thor Industries, Inc.; *U.S. Public*, pg. 2156

441222 — BOAT DEALERS

MARLIN INGRAM RV CENTER, LLC—See Redwood Capital Investments, LLC; *U.S. Private*, pg. 3380
MCCLAINS RV INC.; *U.S. Private*, pg. 2628
MCGEORGES ROLLING HILLS RV; *U.S. Private*, pg. 2634
MEDIA CAMPING CENTER INC.; *U.S. Private*, pg. 2651
MID-STATE RV CENTER, INC.—See Redwood Capital Investments, LLC; *U.S. Private*, pg. 3380
MIKE THOMPSON'S RECREATIONAL VEHICLES; *U.S. Private*, pg. 2725
MOVERA GMBH—See Thor Industries, Inc.; *U.S. Public*, pg. 2157
NATIONAL TRAVELERS INC.; *U.S. Private*, pg. 2864
NELSON'S RV'S, INC.—See Camping World Holdings, Inc.; *U.S. Public*, pg. 428
NOLAN'S RV CENTER INC.; *U.S. Private*, pg. 2934
NORTHTOWN MOTOR HOMES, INC.—See Fun Town RV LP; *U.S. Private*, pg. 1622
NVER ENTERPRISES INC.; *U.S. Private*, pg. 2975
OCEAN GROVE R.V. SALES INC., OF ST. AUGUSTINE—See Redwood Capital Investments, LLC; *U.S. Private*, pg. 3380
PAN PACIFIC RV CENTERS INC.; *U.S. Private*, pg. 3084
PAUL EVERTS RV COUNTRY; *U.S. Private*, pg. 3112
PAW-PAW'S CAMPER CITY INC.; *U.S. Private*, pg. 3115
PEDATA RESALES, INC.; *U.S. Private*, pg. 3127
PHARR R.V. 'S, INC.; *U.S. Private*, pg. 3166
PLEASURELAND INCORPORATED; *U.S. Private*, pg. 3213
POCONO RV SALES & SERVICE INC.; *U.S. Private*, pg. 3219
POLLARD ENTERPRISES INC.; *U.S. Private*, pg. 3224
PONTIAC RV INC.; *U.S. Private*, pg. 3227
RAPER, TOM, INC.; *U.S. Private*, pg. 3355
RECREATION WORLD INC.; *U.S. Private*, pg. 3372
RNR HOLIDAY RV INC.; *U.S. Private*, pg. 3453
RV CONNECTIONS, INC.; *U.S. Private*, pg. 3508
RV PEDDLER INC; *U.S. Private*, pg. 3508
RV RETAILER, LLC—See Redwood Capital Investments, LLC; *U.S. Private*, pg. 3380
RV'S NORTHWEST INC.; *U.S. Private*, pg. 3508
RV TRADERS; *U.S. Private*, pg. 3508
R V WORLD, INC.—See Markquart Inc.; *U.S. Private*, pg. 2582
RV WORLD OF GEORGIA, LLC—See Camping World Holdings, Inc.; *U.S. Public*, pg. 428
RV WORLD OF NOKOMIS INC.; *U.S. Private*, pg. 3508
SCENIC TRAVELER RV CENTERS; *U.S. Private*, pg. 3562
STALKUP'S RV SUPERSTORE, INC.; *U.S. Private*, pg. 3776
STEVE CASEY MOTORS INC.; *U.S. Private*, pg. 3808
STEVINSON TOYOTA-WEST INC—See Stevinson Automotive Inc.; *U.S. Private*, pg. 3810
SUN CITY RV, INC.; *U.S. Private*, pg. 3862
SUNLIGHT GMBH—See Thor Industries, Inc.; *U.S. Public*, pg. 2157
SYSTEM MANAGEMENT GROUP—See Cruise America, Inc.; *U.S. Private*, pg. 1114
TIMOTHY P. DE MARTINI AUTO SALES; *U.S. Private*, pg. 4173
TOM'S CAMPERLAND, INC.—See Redwood Capital Investments, LLC; *U.S. Private*, pg. 3380
TOM STINNETT HOLIDAY RV CENTER INC.; *U.S. Private*, pg. 4183
TOTAL VALUE RV; *U.S. Private*, pg. 4192
TRAILSIDE CAMPERS RV SALES, INC.; *U.S. Private*, pg. 4204
TRI-AM RV CENTER; *U.S. Private*, pg. 4221
TURNKEY INDUSTRIES, LLC—See K-Solv Group, LLC; *U.S. Private*, pg. 2251
WAKAZURU ENTERPRISES INC.; *U.S. Private*, pg. 4427
WELLS CARGO TRAILER SALES, LLC—See Corporate Partners LLC; *U.S. Private*, pg. 1055
WINDISH RV CENTER INC.; *U.S. Private*, pg. 4537
YOUNG'S RV CENTERS, INC.; *U.S. Private*, pg. 4593

441222 — BOAT DEALERS

ALASKA MINING & DIVING SUPPLY, INC.; *U.S. Private*, pg. 151
AMERITEX FABRIC SYSTEMS—See LCI Industries; *U.S. Public*, pg. 1295
ANGLERS MARINE; *U.S. Private*, pg. 283
APACHE INDUSTRIES, INC.—See Sinca Industries, Inc.; *U.S. Private*, pg. 3669
AQUAFAX LIMITED—See LKQ Corporation; *U.S. Public*, pg. 1333
BAERT MARINE INC.; *U.S. Private*, pg. 425
BARLETTA BOAT COMPANY, LLC—See Winnebago Industries, Inc.; *U.S. Public*, pg. 2374
BOATAMERICA INC.; *U.S. Private*, pg. 602
BOATIM, INC.; *U.S. Public*, pg. 366
BOATING GEAR CENTER, LLC—See MarineMax, Inc.; *U.S. Public*, pg. 1366
BOAT TREE INC.; *U.S. Private*, pg. 602
BON SECOUR MARINE SUPPLY INC.—See Bon Secour Fisheries Inc.; *U.S. Private*, pg. 612
BRADFORD MARINE, INC.; *U.S. Private*, pg. 631

441222 — BOAT DEALERS

BRETZ CAPITAL SPORTS SALES, INC.—See Bretz, Inc.; *U.S. Private*, pg. 646
BRETZ, INC.; *U.S. Private*, pg. 646
CAJUN OUTBOARDS INC.; *U.S. Private*, pg. 715
CAMPER & NICHOLSONS USA, INC.—See Camper & Nicholsons Marina Invst. Ltd.; *Int'l*, pg. 1274
CAPTAINS CHOICE MARINE, INC.—See OneWater Marine Holdings LLC; *U.S. Private*, pg. 3026
CARIBEE BOAT SALES & MARINA INC.; *U.S. Private*, pg. 761
CATAUMET BOATS, INC.; *U.S. Private*, pg. 788
CENTRAL BOATING (PTY) LTD—See Cullinan Holdings Limited; *Int'l*, pg. 1877
CLEWS & STRAWBRIDGE; *U.S. Private*, pg. 942
COZUMEL CORPORATION; *U.S. Private*, pg. 1079
CRYSTAL-PIERZ MARINE INC.; *U.S. Private*, pg. 1116
DENNY'S MARINA INC.—See Reeder-Trausch Marine; *U.S. Private*, pg. 3383
DORAL INTERNATIONAL INC.; *Int'l*, pg. 2175
D&R BOATS INC.; *U.S. Private*, pg. 1138
ENGLUND MARINE SUPPLY CO. INC.; *U.S. Private*, pg. 1400
ENG SOON INVESTMENT PTE LTD—See ES Group (Holdings) Limited; *Int'l*, pg. 2500
ENVIROWORKS, INC.—See Fiskars Oyj Abp; *Int'l*, pg. 2693
EXMAR YACHTING NV—See Exmar N.V.; *Int'l*, pg. 2585
FAWCETT MARINE SUPPLIES LLC; *U.S. Private*, pg. 1484
FISKARS BRANDS HUNGARY LTD.—See Fiskars Oyj Abp; *Int'l*, pg. 2693
FISKARS BRANDS OY AB—See Fiskars Oyj Abp; *Int'l*, pg. 2693
FISKARS OUTDOOR LEISURE PRODUCTS—See Fiskars Oyj Abp; *Int'l*, pg. 2693
FISKARS POLAND LTD.—See Fiskars Oyj Abp; *Int'l*, pg. 2694
FISKARS REAL ESTATE—See Fiskars Oyj Abp; *Int'l*, pg. 2694
FRANK L. BEIER RADIO INC.; *U.S. Private*, pg. 1595
FRASER YACHTS LIMITED—See MarineMax, Inc.; *U.S. Public*, pg. 1366
FRASER YACHTS MANAGEMENT & SERVICES LLC—See MarineMax, Inc.; *U.S. Public*, pg. 1366
FRASER YACHTS SPAIN SLU—See MarineMax, Inc.; *U.S. Public*, pg. 1366
GALATI YACHT SALES; *U.S. Private*, pg. 1636
GANDER, INC.; *U.S. Private*, pg. 1641
GILMAN YACHT SALES, INC.; *U.S. Private*, pg. 1701
GILMAN YACHTS OF FORT LAUDERDALE, INC.—See Gilman Yacht Sales, Inc.; *U.S. Private*, pg. 1701
GLEN COVE PROPERTIES LTD. INC.; *U.S. Private*, pg. 1709
GLOBAL MARINE BROKERAGE, LLC—See MarineMax, Inc.; *U.S. Public*, pg. 1366
GOODHUE HAWKINS NAVY YARD, LLC; *U.S. Private*, pg. 1739
GULF COAST YACHT SALES INCORPORATED; *U.S. Private*, pg. 1815
HANSE (DEUTSCHLAND) VERTRIEBS GMBH & CO. KG—See Aurelius Equity Opportunities SE & Co. KGaA; *Int'l*, pg. 708
HIGHWAY MARINE SERVICE INC.; *U.S. Private*, pg. 1942
HOBIE KAYAK EUROPE BV—See Hobie Cat Company; *U.S. Private*, pg. 1958
IRWIN CORPORATION; *U.S. Private*, pg. 2142
KENYON POWER BOATS INC.; *U.S. Private*, pg. 2290
LARSEN MARINE SERVICE INC.; *U.S. Private*, pg. 2393
LAS VEGAS BOAT HARBOR INC.; *U.S. Private*, pg. 2394
LMC MARINE CENTER; *U.S. Private*, pg. 2476
LONG BEACH YACHT SALES INC.; *U.S. Private*, pg. 2490
LOOKOUT MARINE SALES—See OneWater Marine Holdings LLC; *U.S. Private*, pg. 3026
LYNNHAVEN MARINE BOATEL INC.; *U.S. Private*, pg. 2522
MARCALI YACHT BROKERAGE & CONSULTING, LLC; *U.S. Private*, pg. 2571
MARINEMAX EAST, INC.—See MarineMax, Inc.; *U.S. Public*, pg. 1366
MARINEMAX, INC.; *U.S. Public*, pg. 1366
MARINEMAX NJ PARTNERS, INC.—See MarineMax, Inc.; *U.S. Public*, pg. 1366
MARINEMAX OF MINNESOTA, INC.—See MarineMax, Inc.; *U.S. Public*, pg. 1366
MARINEMAX OF NEW JERSEY HOLDINGS, INC.—See MarineMax, Inc.; *U.S. Public*, pg. 1366
MARINEMAX OF NORTH CAROLINA, INC.—See MarineMax, Inc.; *U.S. Public*, pg. 1366
MARINEMAX OF OHIO, INC.—See MarineMax, Inc.; *U.S. Public*, pg. 1367
MARINEMAX SERVICES, INC.—See MarineMax, Inc.; *U.S. Public*, pg. 1366
MARINEMAX VACATIONS, LTD—See MarineMax, Inc.; *U.S. Public*, pg. 1366
MARINE SPORTS LLC; *U.S. Private*, pg. 2575
MILLER MARINE—See Miller Enterprises; *U.S. Private*, pg. 2734
MILLER YACHT SALES, INC; *U.S. Private*, pg. 2735
NATIONAL MARINE SALES INC.—See AMCON Distributing Company; *U.S. Public*, pg. 92

NEW WAVE YACHTS; *U.S. Private*, pg. 2908
NISSWA MARINE, LLC—See MarineMax, Inc.; *U.S. Public*, pg. 1367
THE NORTH ATLANTIC MARINE GROUP; *U.S. Private*, pg. 4084
NORTHROP & JOHNSON MONACO S.A.M.—See MarineMax, Inc.; *U.S. Public*, pg. 1367
NORTHROP & JOHNSON YACHTS-SHIPS LLC—See MarineMax, Inc.; *U.S. Public*, pg. 1367
NXTLVL MARINE, LLC; *U.S. Private*, pg. 2976
OCEAN MARINE GROUP INC.; *U.S. Private*, pg. 2989
ONEWATER MARINE INC.; *U.S. Public*, pg. 1604
ORBETH, INC.—See MarineMax, Inc.; *U.S. Public*, pg. 1367
OYSTER YACHTS USA—See H.T.P. Investments BV; *Int'l*, pg. 3196
PETERSEN MARINE SUPPLY INC.; *U.S. Private*, pg. 3159
PHIL DILL BOATS, INC.—See Singleton Marine Group; *U.S. Private*, pg. 3670
PINMAR YACHT SUPPLY, S.L.—See GYG plc; *Int'l*, pg. 3191
PLANO MARINE SERVICE; *U.S. Private*, pg. 3197
P & L ENTERPRISES OF NAPLES, INC.; *U.S. Private*, pg. 3058
PORT HARBOR MARINE INC.; *U.S. Private*, pg. 3230
PRESTIGE YACHT SALES INC.; *U.S. Private*, pg. 3256
RAMBO MARINE, INC.—See OneWater Marine Holdings LLC; *U.S. Private*, pg. 3026
REBO INC.; *U.S. Private*, pg. 3370
RECREATIONAL PRODUCTS DIV.—See Bell Industries, Inc.; *U.S. Public*, pg. 295
REEDER-TRAUSCH MARINE; *U.S. Private*, pg. 3383
RENIX CORP.; *U.S. Private*, pg. 3398
REX MARINE CENTER, INC.; *U.S. Private*, pg. 3417
SAIL & SKI INC.—See NXTLVL Marine, LLC; *U.S. Private*, pg. 2976
SANDY HOOK YACHT SALES INC.; *U.S. Private*, pg. 3545
SAN RAMON BOAT CENTER INC.; *U.S. Private*, pg. 3542
SEA RAY SPORT YACHTS INC.; *U.S. Private*, pg. 3582
SILVER SEAS YACHTS OF CALIFORNIA, INC.—See MarineMax, Inc.; *U.S. Public*, pg. 1367
SINGLETON MARINE GROUP - BLUE CREEK MARINA AT LAKE MARTIN—See Singleton Marine Group; *U.S. Private*, pg. 3670
SINGLETON MARINE GROUP OF ATLANTA—See Singleton Marine Group; *U.S. Private*, pg. 3670
SINGLETON MARINE GROUP YACHT CENTER AT HOLIDAY MARINA—See Singleton Marine Group; *U.S. Private*, pg. 3670
THE SLALOM SHOP—See OneWater Marine Holdings LLC; *U.S. Private*, pg. 3026
SOUTH JERSEY MARINA INC.; *U.S. Private*, pg. 3722
STATEN ISLAND BOAT SALES INC.; *U.S. Private*, pg. 3793
STEVENS MARINE INC.; *U.S. Private*, pg. 3810
SUNDANCE MARINE, INC.; *U.S. Private*, pg. 3866
SUNDANCE MARINE NORTH, INC.—See OneWater Marine Holdings LLC; *U.S. Private*, pg. 3026
TAYLOR MARINE CENTER, INC.—See OneWater Marine Inc.; *U.S. Public*, pg. 1604
TCN ANTIBES S.A.R.L.—See MarineMax, Inc.; *U.S. Public*, pg. 1367
TECHNOMARINE YACHTS, INC.; *U.S. Private*, pg. 3956
THUNDER JET BOATS, INC.—See Brunswick Corporation; *U.S. Public*, pg. 408
TOM GEORGE YACHT GROUP; *U.S. Private*, pg. 4182
TRACKER BOAT CENTERS CORBIN—See The Great American Outdoors Group LLC; *U.S. Private*, pg. 4038
TRACKER BOATING CENTER - SNOWDEN—See The Great American Outdoors Group LLC; *U.S. Private*, pg. 4038
TRACKER MARINE - ARLINGTON—See The Great American Outdoors Group LLC; *U.S. Private*, pg. 4038
TRACKER MARINE - BEAUMONT—See The Great American Outdoors Group LLC; *U.S. Private*, pg. 4038
TRAVIS BOATS & MOTORS BATON ROUGE INC.—See The Great American Outdoors Group LLC; *U.S. Private*, pg. 4038
TREASURE COAST BOATING CENTER, INC.; *U.S. Private*, pg. 4216
TRENTON MARINE CENTER PERFORMANCE GROUP, INC.; *U.S. Private*, pg. 4218
US LIQUIDATORS, LLC—See MarineMax, Inc.; *U.S. Public*, pg. 1367
VAN ENTERPRISES INC.; *U.S. Private*, pg. 4340
VILLAGE MARINA; *U.S. Private*, pg. 4384
WAYZATA MARINE, INC.; *U.S. Private*, pg. 4461
WEST MARINE, INC.—See Monomoy Capital Partners LLC; *U.S. Private*, pg. 2772
WHER-RENA BOAT SALES INC.; *U.S. Private*, pg. 4506
WHITE ROCK OUTBOARD, INC.—See Portland Yacht Services, Inc.; *U.S. Private*, pg. 3233
WILSON MARINE CORPORATION; *U.S. Private*, pg. 4531
ZAO BALTIC TOOL—See Fiskars Oyj Abp; *Int'l*, pg. 2695
ZODIAC ESPANOLA S.A.—See The Carlyle Group Inc.; *U.S. Public*, pg. 2057

441227 — MOTORCYCLE, ATV, AND ALL OTHER MOTOR VEHICLE DEALERS

ADAMECS CYCLE SALES CO. INC.; *U.S. Private*, pg. 73
ADVANCED MAINTENANCE; *U.S. Private*, pg. 91
ADVANTAGE BMW CLEAR LAKE—See Group 1 Automotive, Inc.; *U.S. Public*, pg. 970
AERSALE CORP; *U.S. Public*, pg. 53
ALAMO CITY HARLEY-DAVIDSON; *U.S. Private*, pg. 149
AMERICA'S POWERSPORTS INC.; *U.S. Private*, pg. 221
AMSTRONG INDUSTRY CORPORATION—See Hota Industrial Mfg. Co., Ltd.; *Int'l*, pg. 3487
AN CADILLAC OF WPB, LLC—See AutoNation, Inc.; *U.S. Public*, pg. 231
AN/CF ACQUISITION CORP.—See AutoNation, Inc.; *U.S. Public*, pg. 232
AN CHEVROLET - ARROWHEAD, INC.—See AutoNation, Inc.; *U.S. Public*, pg. 231
AN COLLISION CENTER OF ADDISON, INC.—See AutoNation, Inc.; *U.S. Public*, pg. 231
AN CORPUS CHRISTI CHEVROLET, LP—See AutoNation, Inc.; *U.S. Public*, pg. 231
AN CORPUS CHRISTI MOTORS, INC.—See AutoNation, Inc.; *U.S. Public*, pg. 231
AN LUXURY IMPORTS OF SANFORD, INC.—See AutoNation, Inc.; *U.S. Public*, pg. 231
APACHE MOTORCYCLES INC.; *U.S. Private*, pg. 290
ARCTIC CAT GMBH—See Textron Inc.; *U.S. Public*, pg. 2028
ARCTIC CAT UK LTD—See Textron Inc.; *U.S. Public*, pg. 2028
ARROW TRUCK SALES INCORPORATED; *U.S. Private*, pg. 336
A&S BMW MOTORCYCLES; *U.S. Private*, pg. 21
ASC CONSTRUCTION EQUIPMENT USA, INC.—See AB Volvo; *Int'l*, pg. 43
ASIAN HONDA MOTOR CO., LTD.—See Honda Motor Co., Ltd.; *Int'l*, pg. 3460
ASTRA VEICOLI INDUSTRIALI S.P.A.—See CNH Industrial N.V.; *Int'l*, pg. 1675
ATHENS CHEVROLET, INC.—See General Motors Company; *U.S. Public*, pg. 923
ATLAS BANGLADESH LIMITED; *Int'l*, pg. 676
AUTO CAR, INC.—See AutoNation, Inc.; *U.S. Public*, pg. 232
AUTOHAUS AUGSBURG GMBH—See Penske Automotive Group, Inc.; *U.S. Public*, pg. 1664
AUTOHAUS G.V.O. GMBH—See General Motors Company; *U.S. Public*, pg. 926
AUTONATIONDIRECT.COM, INC.—See AutoNation, Inc.; *U.S. Public*, pg. 233
AUTONATION DODGE OF PEMBROKE PINES, INC.—See AutoNation, Inc.; *U.S. Public*, pg. 232
AUTONATION FORD BURLESON—See AutoNation, Inc.; *U.S. Public*, pg. 232
AUTONATION IMPORTS OF LITHIA SPRINGS, INC.—See AutoNation, Inc.; *U.S. Public*, pg. 233
AUTONATION IMPORTS OF LONGWOOD, INC.—See AutoNation, Inc.; *U.S. Public*, pg. 233
AUTONATION IMPORTS OF PALM BEACH, INC.—See AutoNation, Inc.; *U.S. Public*, pg. 233
AUTONATION NISSAN LEWISVILLE—See AutoNation, Inc.; *U.S. Public*, pg. 233
AUTONATION USA OF PERRINE, INC.—See HGreg.com; *U.S. Private*, pg. 1931
AUTOREVO, LTD; *U.S. Private*, pg. 401
AUTOWEB, INC.—See One Planet Group LLC; *U.S. Private*, pg. 3020
AVENTURE AVIATION; *U.S. Private*, pg. 405
AXESS LIMITED—See ENL Limited; *Int'l*, pg. 2441
BARGAIN RENT-A-CAR—See AutoNation, Inc.; *U.S. Public*, pg. 233
BARNETT HARLEY-DAVIDSON; *U.S. Private*, pg. 477
BARRETT-JACKSON AUCTION COMPANY LLC; *U.S. Private*, pg. 480
BATTLEY HARLEY-DAVIDSON INC.; *U.S. Private*, pg. 490
BAYLIS (GLOUCESTER) LIMITED—See General Motors Company; *U.S. Public*, pg. 927
BAYSHORE INTERNATIONAL TRUCKS; *U.S. Private*, pg. 497
BEECHMONT MOTORS, INC; *U.S. Private*, pg. 513
BELL AVIATION INC.; *U.S. Private*, pg. 518
BIG BARN HARLEY-DAVIDSON, INC.; *U.S. Private*, pg. 552
BIG TEX TRAILER WORLD, INC. - HOUSTON—See Bain Capital, LP; *U.S. Private*, pg. 436
BIG TEX TRAILER WORLD, INC.—See Bain Capital, LP; *U.S. Private*, pg. 436
BIG TEX TRAILER WORLD, INC. - TUCSON—See Bain Capital, LP; *U.S. Private*, pg. 436
BIKE O & COMPANY LTD.; *Int'l*, pg. 1022
BILIA AB; *Int'l*, pg. 1029
BILIA FORDON AB—See Bilia AB; *Int'l*, pg. 1029
BILIA PERSONBILAR AB—See Bilia AB; *Int'l*, pg. 1029
BILIA PERSONBIL AS—See Bilia AB; *Int'l*, pg. 1029
BLACKFOOT MOTORCYCLES LTD.; *Int'l*, pg. 1061
BLUE RIDGE HARLEY-DAVIDSON—See Scott Fischer Enterprises LLC; *U.S. Private*, pg. 3577
BOB TRACEY INC.; *U.S. Private*, pg. 605

N.A.I.C.S. INDEX

441227 — MOTORCYCLE, ATV, AN...

BOMBARDIER - LEARJET—See Bombardier Inc.; *Int'l*, pg. 1103
BOSTON HARLEY-DAVIDSON; *U.S. Private*, pg. 621
BOW CYCLE & MOTOR COMPANY LTD.; *Int'l*, pg. 1123
BRUCKNER TRUCK SALES, INC.; *U.S. Private*, pg. 671
BRUCKNER TRUCK SALES—See Bruckner Truck Sales, Inc.; *U.S. Private*, pg. 671
CADILLAC POLANCO, S.A. DE C.V.—See General Motors Company; *U.S. Public*, pg. 923
CANGO INC.; *Int'l*, pg. 1291
CAROLINA AIRCRAFT INC.; *U.S. Private*, pg. 767
CAROLINA INTERNATIONAL TRUCKS INC.; *U.S. Private*, pg. 768
CENTRAL FLYING SERVICE INC.; *U.S. Private*, pg. 821
CHICAGO HARLEY-DAVIDSON INC.; *U.S. Private*, pg. 877
CHICAGO INTERNATIONAL TRUCKS - CHICAGO, LLC—See FreightCar America, Inc.; *U.S. Public*, pg. 885
CHONGQING JIANSHE VEHICLE SYSTEM CO., LTD.; *Int'l*, pg. 1580
CHROME CAPITAL GROUP LLC—See Jefferies Financial Group Inc.; *U.S. Public*, pg. 1188
CITROEN UK LIMITED; *Int'l*, pg. 1626
CITY CYCLE, INC.—See Qurate Retail, Inc.; *U.S. Public*, pg. 1757
CLASSIC AUTO GROUP, INC.—See Penske Automotive Group, Inc.; *U.S. Public*, pg. 1664
CLASSIC IMPORTS, INC.—See Penske Automotive Group, Inc.; *U.S. Public*, pg. 1664
COLONIAL DEALERSHIP GROUP; *U.S. Private*, pg. 970
COLUMBUS TRACTOR, LLC—See SunSouth LLC; *U.S. Private*, pg. 3872
COMPETITION ACCESSORIES; *U.S. Private*, pg. 1000
COUNT'S KUSTOMS; *U.S. Private*, pg. 1066
CROWN EQUIPMENT CORPORATION; *U.S. Private*, pg. 1111
CYCLE BARN INC.; *U.S. Private*, pg. 1134
CYCLE GEAR INC.—See Prospect Hill Growth Partners, L.P.; *U.S. Private*, pg. 3288
DALLAS PETERBILT, INC.—See Rush Enterprises, Inc.; *U.S. Public*, pg. 1826
DAYTONA HARLEY DAVIDSON; *U.S. Private*, pg. 1178
DESTINATION HARLEY DAVIDSON LLC; *U.S. Private*, pg. 1215
DIAMOND INTERNATIONAL TRUCKS (GP) LTD.—See Diamond International Trucks Ltd.; *Int'l*, pg. 2105
DIAMOND INTERNATIONAL TRUCKS LTD.; *Int'l*, pg. 2105
DRIVE MOTOR RETAIL LIMITED—See General Motors Company; *U.S. Public*, pg. 928
DUCATI SEATTLE, LLC; *U.S. Private*, pg. 1283
EAST TEXAS MACK SALES LLC; *U.S. Private*, pg. 1318
EDARAN OTOMOBIL NASIONAL BERHAD—See DRB-HICOM Berhad; *Int'l*, pg. 2201
EDMONDS CHEVROLET BUICK GMC; *Int'l*, pg. 2313
EHLERDING MOTORSPORTS, INC.; *U.S. Private*, pg. 1346
ELLIOTT AVIATION, INC.; *U.S. Private*, pg. 1364
ENTERPRISE CAR SALES—See Enterprise Holdings, Inc.; *U.S. Private*, pg. 1403
EZ RAIDER, LLC—See EZRaider Co.; *U.S. Public*, pg. 818
FLEET SALES LLC—See FJ Management, Inc.; *U.S. Private*, pg. 1538
FLORIDA UTILITY TRAILERS INC.; *U.S. Private*, pg. 1551
FORD & SLATER LEICESTER; *Int'l*, pg. 2731
FOX POWERSPORTS LLC; *U.S. Private*, pg. 1584
G-7 BIKE WORLD CO., LTD.—See G-7 HOLDINGS Inc.; *Int'l*, pg. 2862
GAIL'S HARLEY-DAVIDSON INC; *U.S. Private*, pg. 1635
GALEANA AUTOMOTIVE GROUP; *U.S. Private*, pg. 1636
GARBER FORD MERCURY INC.—See Garber Management Group Inc.; *U.S. Private*, pg. 1642
GARY SURDYKE MOTORCYCLE INC.; *U.S. Private*, pg. 1646
GHOST-BIKES GMBH; *Int'l*, pg. 2960
GLOBAL USED TRUCK SALES, LLC; *U.S. Private*, pg. 1718
GM GLOBAL PURCHASING AND SUPPLY CHAIN ROMANIA SRL—See General Motors Company; *U.S. Public*, pg. 927
GOODING & COMPANY, INC.; *U.S. Private*, pg. 1739
GOODSON NORTH, LLC—See Penske Automotive Group, Inc.; *U.S. Public*, pg. 1665
GRAND JUNCTION HARLEY DAVIDSON—See Morse Operations, Inc.; *U.S. Private*, pg. 2790
GREAT LAKES PETERBILT, GMC; *U.S. Private*, pg. 1765
GREEN LINE EQUIPMENT, INC.; *U.S. Private*, pg. 1773
GREEN LINE EQUIPMENT - NORFOLK—See Green Line Equipment, Inc.; *U.S. Private*, pg. 1773
GREEN LINE EQUIPMENT - SPALDING—See Green Line Equipment, Inc.; *U.S. Private*, pg. 1773
GREENTECH TRANSPORTATION INDUSTRIES INC.; *U.S. Private*, pg. 1780
GREENWAY EQUIPMENT, INC.; *U.S. Private*, pg. 1781
HAGLUND & HELLBERG BIL I HANINGE AB—See Bilia AB; *Int'l*, pg. 1029
HAKA MOTORS—See HAK Algahtani Group of Companies; *Int'l*, pg. 3219
HANNUMS HARLEY-DAVIDSON SALES, INC.; *U.S. Private*, pg. 1855

HARLEY-DAVIDSON OF CHARLOTTE; *U.S. Private*, pg. 1865
HARLEY DAVIDSON OF FORT SMITH; *U.S. Private*, pg. 1865
HARLEY DAVIDSON OF GLENDALE; *U.S. Private*, pg. 1865
HARLEY-DAVIDSON OF MIAMI LLC; *U.S. Private*, pg. 1865
HARLEY DAVIDSON OF VICTORVILLE, INC.—See Wise Automotive, Inc.; *U.S. Private*, pg. 4549
HARLEY-DAVIDSON OF WASHINGTON, DC; *U.S. Private*, pg. 1865
HD AMERICAN ROAD LLC; *U.S. Private*, pg. 1890
HEARTLAND HONDA; *U.S. Private*, pg. 1900
HENRY FARM CENTER, INC.—See SunSouth LLC; *U.S. Private*, pg. 3872
HERWALDT AUTOMOTIVE GROUP, INC.; *U.S. Private*, pg. 1927
HITCHING POST INC.; *U.S. Private*, pg. 1953
HOJ FORKLIFT SYSTEMS—See Hoj Engineering & Sales Co., LLC; *U.S. Private*, pg. 1961
HOLLAND PARK LIMITED—See Berjaya Corporation Berhad; *Int'l*, pg. 983
HONDA AUSTRALIA PTY., LTD.—See Honda Motor Co., Ltd.; *Int'l*, pg. 3460
HONDA BELGIUM N.V.—See Honda Motor Co., Ltd.; *Int'l*, pg. 3460
HONDA CLIO SHIN TOKYO CO., LTD.—See Honda Motor Co., Ltd.; *Int'l*, pg. 3461
HONDA MOTOR EUROPE LIMITED—See Honda Motor Co., Ltd.; *Int'l*, pg. 3461
HONDA MOTOR EUROPE (NORTH) GMBH—See Honda Motor Co., Ltd.; *Int'l*, pg. 3461
HONDA NEDERLAND B.V.—See Honda Motor Co., Ltd.; *Int'l*, pg. 3462
HOOKSETT KAWASAKI, INC.; *U.S. Private*, pg. 1978
HOUSE OF HARLEY-DAVIDSON INC.; *U.S. Private*, pg. 1991
IMPERIAL COMMERCIALS LTD—See Dubai World Corporation; *Int'l*, pg. 2222
INTEGRAL AVTO D.O.O—See I Squared Capital Advisors (US) LLC; *U.S. Private*, pg. 2024
IRON PONY MOTORSPORTS GROUP, INC.; *U.S. Private*, pg. 2139
IVECO BELGIUM NV SA—See CNH Industrial N.V.; *Int'l*, pg. 1675
IVECO EST SAS—See CNH Industrial N.V.; *Int'l*, pg. 1675
JACK BARCLAY LIMITED—See Berjaya Corporation Berhad; *Int'l*, pg. 983
THE JACK OLSTA COMPANY; *U.S. Private*, pg. 4058
JETAVIVA; *U.S. Private*, pg. 2204
JOE MORGAN CHEVROLET CADILLAC, INC.—See General Motors Company; *U.S. Public*, pg. 926
KENWORTH OF JACKSONVILLE, INC.; *U.S. Private*, pg. 2289
KINEO S.A.—See AUTOHELLAS S.A.; *Int'l*, pg. 727
THE KRIETE GROUP; *U.S. Private*, pg. 4066
LANE AVIATION CORPORATION; *U.S. Private*, pg. 2387
THE LARSON GROUP; *U.S. Private*, pg. 4067
LONE STAR MOTORSPORTS INCORPORATED; *U.S. Private*, pg. 2489
LONGHORN HARLEY DAVIDSON; *U.S. Private*, pg. 2492
LUCKY'S TRAILER SALES, INC.; *U.S. Private*, pg. 2511
MALLOY AUTOMOTIVE OF WINCHESTER LLC; *U.S. Private*, pg. 2558
MCCUNE CYCLE WORLD, INC.—See Iron Pony Motorsports Group, Inc.; *U.S. Private*, pg. 2139
MCGUIRE HARLEY-DAVIDSON LLC; *U.S. Private*, pg. 2636
MECUM AUCTION, INC.; *U.S. Private*, pg. 2650
METRO CYCLES OF ATLANTA INC.; *U.S. Private*, pg. 2685
MICHIGAN IMPLEMENT INC. - DEVILS LAKE—See Michigan Implement Inc.; *U.S. Private*, pg. 2701
MICHIGAN IMPLEMENT INC.; *U.S. Private*, pg. 2701
MID CONTINENT AIRCRAFT CORP.; *U.S. Private*, pg. 2706
MONROE TRACTOR & IMPLEMENT CO., INC.; *U.S. Private*, pg. 2774
MOOSE LAKE IMPLEMENT & SPORT—See Northland Lawn Sport & Equipment; *U.S. Private*, pg. 2955
MOTOR CITY POWERSPORTS, LLC; *U.S. Private*, pg. 2797
MOTORIA BIL AB—See Bilia AB; *Int'l*, pg. 1029
MOTOSPORT, LLC—See Qurate Retail, Inc.; *U.S. Public*, pg. 1758
NAPLES HARLEY-DAVIDSON—See Scott Fischer Enterprises LLC; *U.S. Private*, pg. 3577
NASHVILLE PETERBILT INC.—See Rush Enterprises, Inc.; *U.S. Public*, pg. 1826
NAULTS ENTERPRISES INC.; *U.S. Private*, pg. 2868
NETBIL I SKANDINAVIEN AB—See Bilia AB; *Int'l*, pg. 1029
NEXTRAN CORPORATION; *U.S. Private*, pg. 2921
N.F. SHELDON INC.; *U.S. Private*, pg. 2828
NORTH AMERICAN TRAILER LLC; *U.S. Private*, pg. 2941
OHIO MACHINERY CO.; *U.S. Private*, pg. 3004
OHLINS USA, INC.—See Apollo Global Management, Inc.; *U.S. Public*, pg. 162
OLD FORT HARLEY DAVIDSON—See Hickenbotham Investments, Inc.; *U.S. Private*, pg. 1933

PAG SANTA ANA AVW, INC.—See Penske Automotive Group, Inc.; *U.S. Public*, pg. 1665
PAPE KENWORTH—See The Pape Group, Inc.; *U.S. Private*, pg. 4090
PATRIOT HARLEY-DAVIDSON, INC.—See Sheehy Auto Stores, Inc.; *U.S. Private*, pg. 3629
PEACOCK, LTD.—See Fox Powersports LLC; *U.S. Private*, pg. 1584
PENN-AIRE AVIATION INC.; *U.S. Private*, pg. 3135
PETERBILT CAROLINA INC.; *U.S. Private*, pg. 3159
PETERBILT OF LOUISIANA LLC; *U.S. Private*, pg. 3159
THE PETE STORE, LLC; *U.S. Private*, pg. 4093
PIEDMONT INTERNATIONAL TRUCKS, LLC—See Carolina International Trucks Inc.; *U.S. Private*, pg. 768
PIKES PEAK HARLEY DAVIDSON; *U.S. Private*, pg. 3180
POWER ASIA MOTORSPORT COMPANY LIMITED—See China Environmental Resources Group Limited; *Int'l*, pg. 1500
POWERSPORTS EAST; *U.S. Private*, pg. 3240
PRECISION SALES & SERVICE, INC.; *U.S. Private*, pg. 3246
RDK TRUCK SALES; *U.S. Private*, pg. 3364
RIDERS BIKE SHOP INC.; *U.S. Private*, pg. 3432
RIDESAFELY BULGARIA—See RideSafely.com, Inc.; *U.S. Private*, pg. 3432
RIDESAFELY CANADA, INC.—See RideSafely.com, Inc.; *U.S. Private*, pg. 3432
RIDESAFELY.COM, INC.; *U.S. Private*, pg. 3432
RIDESAFELY EUROPE GMBH—See RideSafely.com, Inc.; *U.S. Private*, pg. 3432
RIDESAFELY MIDDLE EAST—See RideSafely.com, Inc.; *U.S. Private*, pg. 3432
ROBERTS TRUCK CENTER, LTD. - ALBUQUERQUE—See Roberts Truck Center, Ltd.; *U.S. Private*, pg. 3460
ROBERTS TRUCK CENTER, LTD.; *U.S. Private*, pg. 3460
ROCKET HARLEY-DAVIDSON—See Scott Fischer Enterprises LLC; *U.S. Private*, pg. 3577
R STRATTON & CO LIMITED—See Penske Automotive Group, Inc.; *U.S. Public*, pg. 1666
SARASOTA FUN MACHINES INC.; *U.S. Private*, pg. 3549
SCOTT FISCHER ENTERPRISES LLC; *U.S. Private*, pg. 3577
SHASTA HARDEY-DAVIDSON, INC.—See Wise Automotive, Inc.; *U.S. Private*, pg. 4549
SIX BENDS HARLEY-DAVIDSON—See Scott Fischer Enterprises LLC; *U.S. Private*, pg. 3577
SK MOTORS, LLC—See Penske Automotive Group, Inc.; *U.S. Public*, pg. 1666
SKURRAYS LIMITED—See General Motors Company; *U.S. Public*, pg. 928
SKY POWERSPORTS OF LAKELAND, INC.—See Suzuki of Lake Wales, Inc.; *U.S. Private*, pg. 3887
SOGITEC INDUSTRIES—See Groupe Industriel Marcel Dassault S.A.; *Int'l*, pg. 3105
SOIL WATER SNOW, LLC; *U.S. Private*, pg. 3706
SOUTHEAST HARLEY-DAVIDSON, INC.; *U.S. Private*, pg. 3725
SOUTHERN NEVADA HARLEY-DAVIDSON SALES, INC.; *U.S. Private*, pg. 3734
SOUTH SEAS CYCLE EXCHANGE INC.; *U.S. Private*, pg. 3723
SRT-TAIWAN TRADING CORPORATION—See Hitachi Astemo, Ltd.; *Int'l*, pg. 3409
STADIUM INTERNATIONAL TRUCKS INC.; *U.S. Private*, pg. 3774
STEVENS' CYCLE SALES INC.; *U.S. Private*, pg. 3810
STILLWELL TRUCKS PTY LTD—See Eagers Automotive Limited; *Int'l*, pg. 2263
STURGIS MOTORCYCLE INC.; *U.S. Private*, pg. 3844
SUN ENTERPRISES INCORPORATED—See Sun Powersports Investments, LLC; *U.S. Private*, pg. 3863
SUN POWERSPORTS INVESTMENTS, LLC; *U.S. Private*, pg. 3863
SUNSOUTH - BLAKELY—See SunSouth LLC; *U.S. Private*, pg. 3872
SUNSOUTH - DOTHAN—See SunSouth LLC; *U.S. Private*, pg. 3872
SUNSOUTH - SAMSON—See SunSouth LLC; *U.S. Private*, pg. 3873
SUNSOUTH - TUSCALOOSA—See SunSouth LLC; *U.S. Private*, pg. 3873
SUN STATE INTERNATIONAL TRUCKS, LLC; *U.S. Private*, pg. 3864
SUZUKI OF LAKE WALES, INC.; *U.S. Private*, pg. 3887
SYTNER LIMITED—See Penske Automotive Group, Inc.; *U.S. Public*, pg. 1666
SYTNER RETAIL LIMITED—See Penske Automotive Group, Inc.; *U.S. Public*, pg. 1666
TCOM, L.P.; *U.S. Private*, pg. 3943
THOMPSON TRUCK GROUP, LLC—See Thompson Distribution, LLC; *U.S. Private*, pg. 4159
THUNDERBIRD HARLEY-DAVIDSON—See Scott Fischer Enterprises LLC; *U.S. Private*, pg. 3577
TM AVIATION INC.; *U.S. Private*, pg. 4179
TRAVELER'S RV SALES; *U.S. Private*, pg. 4214
TRUCKS-E-QUIP INC.; *U.S. Private*, pg. 4246
UAG WEST BAY IA, LLC—See Penske Automotive Group, Inc.; *U.S. Public*, pg. 1666

441227 — MOTORCYCLE, ATV, AN...

VOLVO TRUCKS CANADA—See AB Volvo; *Int'l*, pg. 47
VSSCO INCORPORATED; *U.S. Private*, pg. 4415
WAUKON YAMAHA, INC.; *U.S. Private*, pg. 4457
WENCO GROUP INCORPORATED—See SunSouth LLC; *U.S. Private*, pg. 3873
WERNER CYCLE WORKS, INC.—See Werner Enterprises, Inc.; *U.S. Public*, pg. 2349
WHITEHORSE TRUCKS PTY LTD—See Eagers Automotive Limited; *Int'l*, pg. 2263
WIGGINS AIRWAYS INC.; *U.S. Private*, pg. 4517
WILSON & CO. (MOTOR SALES) LIMITED—See General Motors Company; *U.S. Public*, pg. 928
WOLFINGTON BODY COMPANY, INC.; *U.S. Private*, pg. 4554
WORLD TOYOTA—See Group 1 Automotive, Inc.; *U.S. Public*, pg. 972
YAMAHA SUZUKI OF TEXAS; *U.S. Private*, pg. 4585
YANCEY BROS. CO.; *U.S. Private*, pg. 4585
YINGLING AIRCRAFT, LLC—See AE Industrial Partners, LP; *U.S. Private*, pg. 112

441330 — AUTOMOTIVE PARTS AND ACCESSORIES RETAILERS

3 D&V—See Fast Undercar Inc.; *U.S. Private*, pg. 1482
A&A AUTO PARTS STORES, INC.—See LKQ Corporation; *U.S. Public*, pg. 1334
ABC AUTOMOTIVE, INC.; *U.S. Private*, pg. 35
ACKLANDS-GRAINGER INC.—See W.W. Grainger, Inc.; *U.S. Public*, pg. 2319
AC MOBIL D.O.O.—See Honda Motor Co., Ltd.; *Int'l*, pg. 3459
ACTUANT ASIA PTE LTD—See Enerpac Tool Group Corp.; *U.S. Public*, pg. 765
ACTUANT AUSTRALIA LTD.—See Enerpac Tool Group Corp.; *U.S. Public*, pg. 765
ACTUANT CORPORATION JAPAN—See Enerpac Tool Group Corp.; *U.S. Public*, pg. 765
ADAMS AUTO PARTS, LLC—See Genuine Parts Company; *U.S. Public*, pg. 932
ADESA-TAMPA—See OPENLANE, Inc.; *U.S. Public*, pg. 1607
ADVANCE AUTO PARTS, INC.; *U.S. Public*, pg. 44
AEROVISION INTERNATIONAL, LLC—See LKQ Corporation; *U.S. Public*, pg. 1333
AETOS GROUP, INC.—See Mistras Group, Inc.; *U.S. Public*, pg. 1451
AIR RIDE TECHNOLOGIES, INC.—See Fox Factory Holding Corp.; *U.S. Public*, pg. 877
AISAN CORPORATION EUROPE S.A.—See Aisan Industry Co., Ltd.; *Int'l*, pg. 250
AISAN CORPORATION GAUANGZHOU CO., LTD—See Aisan Industry Co., Ltd.; *Int'l*, pg. 250
AISIN CHEMICAL CO., LTD.—See AISIN Corporation; *Int'l*, pg. 252
AISIN EUROPE S.A.—See AISIN Corporation; *Int'l*, pg. 252
AISIN SINWA CO., LTD.—See AISIN Corporation; *Int'l*, pg. 253
AISIN TAKAOKA CO., LTD.—See AISIN Corporation; *Int'l*, pg. 253
ALTROM AUTO GROUP LTD—See Genuine Parts Company; *U.S. Public*, pg. 932
AMERICAN VAN EQUIPMENT INC.; *U.S. Private*, pg. 258
A & P AUTO PARTS, INC.—See Stellex Capital Management LP; *U.S. Private*, pg. 3800
APM AUTOMOTIVE HOLDINGS BERHAD; *Int'l*, pg. 516
APM AUTOMOTIVE S.R.O.—See LKQ Corporation; *U.S. Public*, pg. 1333
APS B.V.—See LKQ Corporation; *U.S. Public*, pg. 1333
ARIZONA BRAKE & CLUTCH SUPPLY—See Platinum Equity, LLC; *U.S. Private*, pg. 3209
THE ARMOR ALL/STP PRODUCTS COMPANY—See Energizer Holdings, Inc.; *U.S. Public*, pg. 760
A.S.A.P. SUPPLIES LIMITED—See LKQ Corporation; *U.S. Public*, pg. 1333
ASHLEY IMPORTS, LLC; *U.S. Private*, pg. 350
AST BEARINGS LLC—See Genuine Parts Company; *U.S. Public*, pg. 933
ASTRO ALL ASIA NETWORKS PLC; *Int'l*, pg. 661
AUDIOSONIC—See KKR & Co. Inc.; *U.S. Public*, pg. 1261
AUDIOVOX SOUTHEAST—See VOXX International Corporation; *U.S. Public*, pg. 2311
AUSTEM CO., LTD. - SEJONG PLANT 1—See Austem Co., Ltd.; *Int'l*, pg. 717
AUSTEM CO., LTD. - SEJONG PLANT 2—See Austem Co., Ltd.; *Int'l*, pg. 717
AUTO ACCESSORIES GARAGE INC.; *U.S. Private*, pg. 396
AUTOANYTHING, INC.—See Kingswood Capital Management LLC; *U.S. Private*, pg. 2312
AUTODISTRIBUTION BENELUX B.V.—See LKQ Corporation; *U.S. Public*, pg. 1333
AUTO ELECTRA NAALDWIJK B.V.—See LKQ Corporation; *U.S. Public*, pg. 1333
AUTO KELLY A.S.—See LKQ Corporation; *U.S. Public*, pg. 1333

AUTO KELLY SLOVAKIA S.R.O.—See LKQ Corporation; *U.S. Public*, pg. 1333
AUTOLIGHTS, LLC—See Atlantic Street Capital Management LLC; *U.S. Private*, pg. 374
AUTOLIV DO BRASIL LTDA—See Autoliv, Inc.; *Int'l*, pg. 730
AUTOLIV ISODELTA SAS—See Autoliv, Inc.; *Int'l*, pg. 729
AUTOLIV KLE S.A.U.—See Autoliv, Inc.; *Int'l*, pg. 729
AUTOLIV (SHANGHAI) VEHICLE SAFETY SYSTEMS CO., LTD.—See Autoliv, Inc.; *Int'l*, pg. 728
AUTOLIV STEERING WHEELS MEXICO S. DE R.L. DE C.V.—See Autoliv, Inc.; *Int'l*, pg. 730
AUTO ONE AUSTRALIA PTY. LTD.; *Int'l*, pg. 725
AUTOPART INTERNATIONAL INC.—See Advance Auto Parts, Inc.; *U.S. Public*, pg. 44
AUTO PARTS 4LESS GROUP, INC.; *U.S. Public*, pg. 228
AUTO PARTS OF JUPITER, INC.—See Genuine Parts Company; *U.S. Public*, pg. 932
AUTOPARTS PROSEC NV—See LKQ Corporation; *U.S. Public*, pg. 1333
AUTO SAFETY HOUSE—See OEP Capital Advisors, L.P.; *U.S. Private*, pg. 3000
AUTOSALES, INC.; *U.S. Public*, pg. 401
AUTOSPORT WILLY SA—See LKQ Corporation; *U.S. Public*, pg. 1334
AUTO TRADER GROUP PLC—See Apax Partners LLP; *Int'l*, pg. 502
AUTO WESSEL B.V.—See LKQ Corporation; *U.S. Public*, pg. 1333
AUTOZONE.COM, INC.—See AutoZone, Inc.; *U.S. Public*, pg. 239
AUTOZONE DEVELOPMENT LLC—See AutoZone, Inc.; *U.S. Public*, pg. 239
AUTOZONE, INC.; *U.S. Public*, pg. 239
AUTOZONE NORTHEAST, INC.—See AutoZone, Inc.; *U.S. Public*, pg. 239
AUTOZONE PARTS, INC.—See AutoZone, Inc.; *U.S. Public*, pg. 239
AUTOZONE STORES, INC.—See AutoZone, Inc.; *U.S. Public*, pg. 239
AUTOZONE TEXAS, L.P.—See AutoZone, Inc.; *U.S. Public*, pg. 239
AVNET ELECTRONICS MARKETING—See Avnet, Inc.; *U.S. Public*, pg. 250
AVNET (NZ)—See Avnet, Inc.; *U.S. Public*, pg. 250
AVNET SILICA—See Avnet, Inc.; *U.S. Public*, pg. 250
AW DIRECT, INC.—See The Riverside Company; *U.S. Private*, pg. 4108
BALKAMP, INC.—See Genuine Parts Company; *U.S. Public*, pg. 932
BAPCOR LIMITED; *Int'l*, pg. 857
BARNES DISTRIBUTION (CANADA) LTD.—See MSC Industrial Direct Co., Inc.; *U.S. Public*, pg. 1483
BARNES GROUP (U.K.) LIMITED—See Barnes Group Inc.; *U.S. Public*, pg. 277
BAUER INDUSTRIES INC.; *U.S. Public*, pg. 490
BAUMOT AG—See Baumot Group AG; *Int'l*, pg. 895
BAUMOT UK LTD.—See Baumot Group AG; *Int'l*, pg. 895
BAXTER AUTO PARTS INC.; *U.S. Private*, pg. 491
B&B JOBBER SERVICES, INC.; *U.S. Private*, pg. 417
BCMZ PRECISION ENGINEERING LIMITED—See Bel Fuse Inc.; *U.S. Public*, pg. 292
BENNY'S INC.; *U.S. Private*, pg. 528
BENTELER ALUMINIUM SYSTEMS DENMARK AS—See Benteler International AG; *Int'l*, pg. 976
BENTELER ALUMINIUM SYSTEMS FRANCE SNC—See Benteler International AG; *Int'l*, pg. 976
BENTELER ALUMINIUM SYSTEMS KOREA LTD.—See Benteler International AG; *Int'l*, pg. 976
BENTELER ALUMINIUM SYSTEMS MICHIGAN, INC—See Benteler International AG; *Int'l*, pg. 976
BENTELER ALUMINIUM SYSTEMS NORWAY AS—See Benteler International AG; *Int'l*, pg. 976
BENTELER AUTOMOBILTECHNIK EISENACH GMBH—See Benteler International AG; *Int'l*, pg. 976
BENTELER AUTOMOBILTECHNIK NOWGOROD GMBH—See Benteler International AG; *Int'l*, pg. 975
BENTELER AUTOMOTIVE (FUZHOU) CO., LTD.—See Benteler International AG; *Int'l*, pg. 976
BENTELER AUTOMOTIVE INTERNATIONAL GMBH—See Benteler International AG; *Int'l*, pg. 976
BENTELER AUTOMOTIVE K.K.—See Benteler International AG; *Int'l*, pg. 976
BENTELER AUTOMOTIVE THAILAND LIMITED—See Benteler International AG; *Int'l*, pg. 975
BENTELER AUTOMOTIVE VIGO, S.L.—See Benteler International AG; *Int'l*, pg. 975
BENTELER BENELUX B.V—See Benteler International AG; *Int'l*, pg. 976
BENTELER COMPONENTES AUTOMOTIVOS LTDA.—See Benteler International AG; *Int'l*, pg. 976
BENTELER DISTRIBUCION IBERICA S.L.—See Benteler International AG; *Int'l*, pg. 975
BENTELER DISTRIBUTION AUSTRIA GMBH—See Benteler International AG; *Int'l*, pg. 976
BENTELER DISTRIBUTION BORU SAN. TIC. LTD. STI—See Benteler International AG; *Int'l*, pg. 975
BENTELER DISTRIBUTION BULGARIA S.R.L.—See Benteler International AG; *Int'l*, pg. 976

CORPORATE AFFILIATIONS

BENTELER DISTRIBUTION CSO-ES ACELKERESKEDELMI KFT.—See Benteler International AG; *Int'l*, pg. 975
BENTELER DISTRIBUTION CZECH REPUBLIC SPOL. S.R.O.—See Benteler International AG; *Int'l*, pg. 976
BENTELER DISTRIBUTION DEUTSCHLAND GMBH & CO. KG—See Benteler International AG; *Int'l*, pg. 976
BENTELER DISTRIBUTION ESTONIA OU—See Benteler International AG; *Int'l*, pg. 976
BENTELER DISTRIBUTION FRANCE S.A.R.L.—See Benteler International AG; *Int'l*, pg. 976
BENTELER DISTRIBUTION INDIA PRIVATE LIMITED—See Benteler International AG; *Int'l*, pg. 975
BENTELER DISTRIBUTION INTERNATIONAL GMBH—See Benteler International AG; *Int'l*, pg. 976
BENTELER DISTRIBUTION LIMITED—See Benteler International AG; *Int'l*, pg. 976
BENTELER DISTRIBUTION POLAND SP. Z.O.O.—See Benteler International AG; *Int'l*, pg. 976
BENTELER DISTRIBUTION ROMANIA SRL—See Benteler International AG; *Int'l*, pg. 975
BENTELER DISTRIBUTION SINGAPORE PTE LTD—See Benteler International AG; *Int'l*, pg. 976
BENTELER DISTRIBUTION SLOVAKIA S.R.O.—See Benteler International AG; *Int'l*, pg. 976
BENTELER DISTRIBUTION (THAILAND) COMPANY LIMITED—See Benteler International AG; *Int'l*, pg. 975
BENTELER DISTRIBUTION UKRAINE LLC—See Benteler International AG; *Int'l*, pg. 976
BENTELER DISTRIBUZIONE ITALIA S.P.A.—See Benteler International AG; *Int'l*, pg. 976
BENTELER TRADING INTERNATIONAL GMBH—See Benteler International AG; *Int'l*, pg. 977
BENTELER TRADING (SHANGHAI) CO., LTD.—See Benteler International AG; *Int'l*, pg. 977
BENTELER TRGOVINA D.O.O.—See Benteler International AG; *Int'l*, pg. 977
BENTELER TRGOVINA D.O.O.—See Benteler International AG; *Int'l*, pg. 977
BENTELER (U.K.) LTD.—See Benteler International AG; *Int'l*, pg. 976
BERTOLOTTI S.P.A.—See LKQ Corporation; *U.S. Public*, pg. 1334
BEST BUY TIRE CENTER, INC.; *U.S. Private*, pg. 542
BHATIA BROTHERS LLC - AUTOMOTIVE & INDUSTRIAL CHEMICALS—See Bhatia Brothers Group; *Int'l*, pg. 1013
BILDEMONTERING I HELSINGBORG AV—See LKQ Corporation; *U.S. Public*, pg. 1334
BLACKHAWK MODIFICATIONS INC.; *U.S. Private*, pg. 575
BLUE STREAK-HYGRADE MOTOR PRODUCTS, LTD.—See Standard Motor Products, Inc.; *U.S. Public*, pg. 1929
BOB HOOK OF SHELBYVILLE; *U.S. Private*, pg. 604
BOURNS KFT.—See Bourns, Inc.; *U.S. Private*, pg. 624
BOWERS ENTERPRISES, LLC; *U.S. Private*, pg. 625
BRATTAIN INTERNATIONAL TRUCKS, INC.; *U.S. Private*, pg. 640
BROADWAY TRUCK CENTERS; *U.S. Private*, pg. 660
THE BUS DEPOT, INC.—See GTJ REIT, Inc.; *U.S. Private*, pg. 1807
BUTLER AUTO SALES AND PARTS, INC.—See Stellex Capital Management LP; *U.S. Private*, pg. 3800
CALEX TRUCK SALES INC—See Calex Logistics Corp.; *U.S. Private*, pg. 717
CALIFORNIA MUSTANG SALES & PARTS, INC.—See Classic Industries Corp; *U.S. Private*, pg. 916
CAMPER CLINIC, INC.; *U.S. Private*, pg. 731
CANADIAN TIRE CORPORATION LIMITED; *Int'l*, pg. 1286
CAPITOL BEARING SERVICE; *U.S. Private*, pg. 743
CAPITOL CLUTCH & BRAKE, INC.; *U.S. Private*, pg. 743
CAR MONKEYS GROUP; *U.S. Private*, pg. 747
CARQUEST ALBUQUERQUE—See Advance Auto Parts, Inc.; *U.S. Public*, pg. 45
CARQUEST AUTO PARTS INC - CALIFORNIA—See Advance Auto Parts, Inc.; *U.S. Public*, pg. 45
CARQUEST AUTO PARTS OF CARO—See Advance Auto Parts, Inc.; *U.S. Public*, pg. 45
CARQUEST AUTO PARTS OF HATTIESBURG—See Advance Auto Parts, Inc.; *U.S. Public*, pg. 45
CARQUEST AUTO PARTS OF MCMINNVILLE—See Advance Auto Parts, Inc.; *U.S. Public*, pg. 45
CARQUEST CANADA, LTD.—See Advance Auto Parts, Inc.; *U.S. Public*, pg. 45
CARQUEST DISTRIBUTION CENTER - NEW MEXICO—See Advance Auto Parts, Inc.; *U.S. Public*, pg. 45
CARQUEST INC.—See Advance Auto Parts, Inc.; *U.S. Public*, pg. 45
CARQUEST WINCHESTER—See Advance Auto Parts, Inc.; *U.S. Public*, pg. 45
CAR STEREO CITY INC.; *U.S. Private*, pg. 747
CARTAL RIJSBERGEN AUTOMOTIVE B.V.—See LKQ Corporation; *U.S. Public*, pg. 1334
CAR TOYS INC.; *U.S. Private*, pg. 747
CELLI ENTERPRISES INC.; *U.S. Private*, pg. 807
CENTRAL GLASS MODULE CO., LTD.—See Central Glass Co., Ltd.; *Int'l*, pg. 1406

N.A.I.C.S. INDEX

441330 — AUTOMOTIVE PARTS AN...

CHAMPION MOTORSPORT; *U.S. Private*, pg. 846
CHARGEPOINT INC.—See ChargePoint Holdings, Inc.; *U.S. Public*, pg. 479
CHASE CHEVROLET CO., INC.; *U.S. Private*, pg. 859
CHRISTIE & SON SALES LTD; *Int'l*, pg. 1586
CHUHATSU HANBAI CO., LTD.—See Chuo Spring Co., Ltd.; *Int'l*, pg. 1599
CJ PONY PARTS, INC.; *U.S. Private*, pg. 908
CLASSIC INDUSTRIES CORP; *U.S. Private*, pg. 916
CMC METAL RECYCLING (AUGUSTA)—See Commercial Metals Company; *U.S. Public*, pg. 546
COLONIAL GARAGE AND DISTRIBUTORS LIMITED; *Int'l*, pg. 1702
CONN'S, INC.; *U.S. Public*, pg. 567
COOK AUTOMOTIVE; *U.S. Private*, pg. 1037
COPART OF HOUSTON, INC.—See Copart, Inc.; *U.S. Public*, pg. 574
CORP. CONSULTANTS PERFORMANCE, INC.—See Automatic Data Processing, Inc.; *U.S. Public*, pg. 230
COVENTRY GROUP LIMITED COVENTRYS DIVISION—See Coventry Group Limited; *Int'l*, pg. 1821
CROWN ACURA/NISSAN, LLC—See Asbury Automotive Group, Inc.; *U.S. Public*, pg. 209
CSGT (SHANGHAI) CO., LTD.—See China Steel Corporation; *Int'l*, pg. 1555
CSN PORTO REAL—See Companhia Siderurgica Nacional; *Int'l*, pg. 1748
CTS ELECTRO DE MATAMOROS S.A. DE C.V.—See Benchmark Electronics, Inc.; *U.S. Public*, pg. 295
CUSTOM ACCESSORIES ASIA LTD.—See Custom Accessories Inc.; *U.S. Private*, pg. 1128
CUSTOM ACCESSORIES EUROPE LTD.—See Custom Accessories Inc.; *U.S. Private*, pg. 1128
CUSTOM ACCESSORIES SCANDINAVIA OY—See Custom Accessories Inc.; *U.S. Private*, pg. 1128
CWD LLC—See Crowne Group LLC; *U.S. Private*, pg. 1112
DANA CORPORATION AUTOMOTIVE SYSTEMS GROUP—See Dana Incorporated; *U.S. Public*, pg. 622
DARBY GAS & OIL CO., INC.—See Steinhagen Oil Company, Inc.; *U.S. Private*, pg. 3798
DAY MOTOR SPORTS LLC—See Gen Cap America, Inc.; *U.S. Private*, pg. 1659
DC ENERGY GMBH—See Daiichi Jitsugyo Co. Ltd.; *Int'l*, pg. 1927
DEALERSHIP LIQUIDATIONS, INC.—See General Motors Company; *U.S. Public*, pg. 924
DEALERS TRUCK EQUIPMENT, INC.—See Manning Enterprises Inc.; *U.S. Private*, pg. 2565
DE BRUYN PROFESSIONAL COATINGS NV—See LKQ Corporation; *U.S. Public*, pg. 1334
DEINDESIGN GMBH—See CEWE Stiftung & Co. KGaA; *Int'l*, pg. 1425
DELFINGEN INDUSTRY, S.A.; *Int'l*, pg. 2012
DELPHI ENERGY CHASSIS SYSTEMS, ASIA HEADQUARTERS—See Aptiv PLC; *Int'l*, pg. 524
DELPHI ENERGY CHASSIS SYSTEMS, EUROPEAN REGIONAL HEADQUARTERS—See Aptiv PLC; *Int'l*, pg. 524
DELPHI ENERGY CHASSIS SYSTEMS, SOUTH AMERICAN REGIONAL HEADQUARTERS—See Aptiv PLC; *Int'l*, pg. 524
DELPHI PACKARD AUSTRIA GES.M.B.H.—See Aptiv PLC; *Int'l*, pg. 525
DENAPLES AUTO PARTS INC.; *U.S. Private*, pg. 1204
DENSO SOLUTION JAPAN CORPORATION—See Denso Corporation; *Int'l*, pg. 2032
DENT WIZARD S.A.S.—See Gridiron Capital, LLC; *U.S. Private*, pg. 1786
DIESEL PERFORMANCE INC.; *U.S. Private*, pg. 1229
DIFEO LEASING PARTNERSHIP—See Penske Automotive Group, Inc.; *U.S. Public*, pg. 1665
DIFEO PARTNERSHIP, LLC—See Penske Automotive Group, Inc.; *U.S. Public*, pg. 1665
DINARA A.D.; *Int'l*, pg. 2126
D MECATRONICS, INC.; *Int'l*, pg. 1899
DOWLAIS GROUP PLC; *Int'l*, pg. 2184
DUB PUBLISHING, INC. - DUB SHOP—See DUB Publishing, Inc.; *U.S. Private*, pg. 1283
THE EASTWOOD COMPANY—See Kian Capital Partners, LLC; *U.S. Private*, pg. 2302
ECOLOGY AUTO WRECKING INC.; *U.S. Private*, pg. 1329
EDDIES TIRE SERVICE INC.; *U.S. Private*, pg. 1332
E-LEAD ELECTRONIC CO., LTD.; *Int'l*, pg. 2248
EL FORGE LTD; *Int'l*, pg. 2340
ELIT CZ, SPOL S.R.O.—See LKQ Corporation; *U.S. Public*, pg. 1334
ELIT POLSKA SP. Z O.O.—See LKQ Corporation; *U.S. Public*, pg. 1334
ELIT SLOVAKIA S.R.O.—See LKQ Corporation; *U.S. Public*, pg. 1334
ELIT UKRAINE LLC—See LKQ Corporation; *U.S. Public*, pg. 1334
ENTEREX POLSKA SP. Z O.O.—See Enterex International Limited; *Int'l*, pg. 2451
ENTREPRISE ROBERT THIBERT INC.; *Int'l*, pg. 2453
EP MANUFACTURING BHD.; *Int'l*, pg. 2458
ERA S.P.A.—See LKQ Corporation; *U.S. Public*, pg. 1334
ERA S.R.L.—See LKQ Corporation; *U.S. Public*, pg. 1334

ESKIMOS, INC.—See Arctic Slope Regional Corporation; *U.S. Private*, pg. 316
EVIL EMPIRE DESIGNS, INC.; *U.S. Public*, pg. 803
FAURECIA INTERIEUR INDUSTRIE—See FORVIA SE; *Int'l*, pg. 2746
F.C.C. (NORTH CAROLINA), LLC—See F.C.C. Co., Ltd.; *Int'l*, pg. 2596
F.C.C. (THAILAND) CO.,LTD.—See F.C.C. Co., Ltd.; *Int'l*, pg. 2596
FCP GROTON LLC; *U.S. Private*, pg. 1486
FEDERAL-MOGUL AUTOMOTIVE—See Apollo Global Management, Inc.; *U.S. Public*, pg. 160
FEDERAL-MOGUL FRICTION PRODUCTS BARCELONA S.L.—See Apollo Global Management, Inc.; *U.S. Public*, pg. 161
FEDERAL-MOGUL POWERTRAIN SOLUTIONS INDIA PRIVATE LIMITED—See Apollo Global Management, Inc.; *U.S. Public*, pg. 161
FEDERAL-MOGUL POWERTRAIN SYSTEMS SA (PTY) LTD—See Apollo Global Management, Inc.; *U.S. Public*, pg. 161
FEDERAL-MOGUL SEALING SYSTEMS—See Apollo Global Management, Inc.; *U.S. Public*, pg. 161
FEINTOOL AUTOMOTIVE SYSTEM PARTS (TIANJIN) CO., LTD.—See Artemis Holding AG; *Int'l*, pg. 582
FELT AUTO PARTS COMPANY—See National Auto Parts Warehouse, LLC; *U.S. Private*, pg. 2847
FISKER INC.; *U.S. Public*, pg. 851
FLUKE ELECTRONICS CANADA LP—See Fortive Corporation; *U.S. Public*, pg. 870
FLYNN'S TIRE & AUTO SERVICE; *U.S. Private*, pg. 1553
FORD MOTOR COMPANY A/S—See Ford Motor Company; *U.S. Public*, pg. 865
FOSTER AUTO PARTS INC.; *U.S. Private*, pg. 1578
FOX INTERNATIONAL LLC—See Fox Corporation; *U.S. Public*, pg. 876
FREIGHT SALES INC.; *U.S. Private*, pg. 1607
FUJI CO., LTD.; *Int'l*, pg. 2809
G-7 AUTO SERVICE CO., LTD.—See G-7 HOLDINGS Inc.; *Int'l*, pg. 2862
GEMTOP MANUFACTURING, INC.—See Brand FX Body Company; *U.S. Private*, pg. 635
GENERAL MOTORS FINLAND OY—See General Motors Company; *U.S. Public*, pg. 927
GENERAL MOTORS (THAILAND) LIMITED—See General Motors Company; *U.S. Public*, pg. 924
GENUINE AUTO PARTS OF FAIRBANKS—See Genuine Parts Company; *U.S. Public*, pg. 932
GENUINE PARTS COMPANY; *U.S. Public*, pg. 932
GIA CAUCASIA LOGISTICS LTD.—See Endress+Hauser (International) Holding AG; *Int'l*, pg. 2408
GIGA GMBH—See Delticom AG; *Int'l*, pg. 2021
GLOTFELTY ENTERPRISES INC.; *U.S. Private*, pg. 1720
GMAC ADMINISTRADORA DE CONSORCIOS LTDA.—See General Motors Company; *U.S. Public*, pg. 925
GMAC SERVICIOS S.A.S.—See General Motors Company; *U.S. Public*, pg. 925
GMB NORTH AMERICA, INC.—See GMB Corp.; *Int'l*, pg. 3012
GMF LEASING LLC—See General Motors Company; *U.S. Public*, pg. 924
GNUTTI CARLO GERMANY GMBH—See Gnutti Carlo S.p.A.; *Int'l*, pg. 3017
GORDON AUTO BODY PARTS CO., LTD. - PLANT 2—See Gordon Auto Body Parts Co., Ltd.; *Int'l*, pg. 3042
GPB AFRICA (PTY) LTD—See Gazprombank JSC; *Int'l*, pg. 2892
GPC FINANCE COMPANY—See Genuine Parts Company; *U.S. Public*, pg. 932
GPIC LLC—See Genuine Parts Company; *U.S. Public*, pg. 932
GS MBIZ CO., LTD.—See GS Holdings Corp.; *Int'l*, pg. 3142
GURLEY-LEEP BUICK-GMC TRUCK, INC; *U.S. Private*, pg. 1819
GUYOUNG TECH. CO., LTD - ALABAMA FACTORY—See Guyoung Tech. Co., Ltd; *Int'l*, pg. 3189
GUYOUNG TECH. CO., LTD - DAEGU PLANT—See Guyoung Tech. Co., Ltd; *Int'l*, pg. 3189
GUYOUNG TECH. CO., LTD - YEONGCHEON PLANT—See Guyoung Tech. Co., Ltd; *Int'l*, pg. 3189
HARADA INDUSTRY CO., LTD.; *Int'l*, pg. 3269
HARREMS TOOLS B.V.—See LKQ Corporation; *U.S. Public*, pg. 1334
HARRISONBURG AUTO AUCTION—See Cox Enterprises, Inc.; *U.S. Private*, pg. 1076
HAVAM AUTOMOTIVE B.V.—See LKQ Corporation; *U.S. Public*, pg. 1334
HDTV SUPPLY, INC.; *U.S. Private*, pg. 1890
HEDBERGS BILSKROT AB—See Bilia AB; *Int'l*, pg. 1029
HEUTS HANDEL B.V.—See LKQ Corporation; *U.S. Public*, pg. 1334
HMS SERVICE CO. INC.; *U.S. Private*, pg. 1955
HONDA DE MEXICO, S.A. DE C.V.—See Honda Motor Co., Ltd.; *Int'l*, pg. 3463
HONDA EUROPE N.V.—See Honda Motor Co., Ltd.; *Int'l*, pg. 3461
HOPKINS AUTO SUPPLY INC.; *U.S. Private*, pg. 1979
HOTMAN CO., LTD.; *Int'l*, pg. 3489

ICAHN AUTOMOTIVE GROUP LLC—See Icahn Enterprises L.P.; *U.S. Public*, pg. 1084
INTERNATIONAL AUTOPARTS, INC.; *U.S. Private*, pg. 2114
IOWA 80.COM INC.—See Iowa 80 Group, Inc.; *U.S. Private*, pg. 2134
IPAR INDUSTRIAL PARTNERS B.V.—See LKQ Corporation; *U.S. Public*, pg. 1334
IRONMAN PARTS & SERVICES; *U.S. Private*, pg. 2140
JACKSON'S GARAGE INC.; *U.S. Private*, pg. 2179
J.C. MADIGAN INC.; *U.S. Private*, pg. 2160
J.C. WHITNEY & CO.; *U.S. Private*, pg. 2160
JGB INDUSTRIES, INC.; *U.S. Private*, pg. 2207
JIANGYIN DUAL AUTOMOTIVE TEXTILE CO., LTD.—See DUAL Co. Ltd; *Int'l*, pg. 2217
JO-DI'S INC.; *U.S. Private*, pg. 2217
JUST WHEELS & TIRES CO.—See Clearlake Capital Group, L.P.; *U.S. Public*, pg. 937
KARSTORP BILDEMONTERING AB—See LKQ Corporation; *U.S. Public*, pg. 1334
KENT CHAMOIS COMPANY LTD—See Spectrum Brands Holdings, Inc.; *U.S. Public*, pg. 1915
KEYSTONE AUTOMOTIVE INDUSTRIES - BUFFALO—See LKQ Corporation; *U.S. Public*, pg. 1334
KEYSTONE AUTOMOTIVE INDUSTRIES ON, INC.—See LKQ Corporation; *U.S. Public*, pg. 1334
K.K. RISING SUN—See Idemitsu Kosan Co., Ltd.; *Int'l*, pg. 3591
KNECHT'S OF SPRINGFIELD INC.; *U.S. Private*, pg. 2321
KOI AUTO PARTS; *U.S. Private*, pg. 2340
LANG KFT.—See LKQ Corporation; *U.S. Public*, pg. 1335
LAREDO GONZALEZ AUTO PARTS; *U.S. Private*, pg. 2392
LARTOM INC.; *U.S. Private*, pg. 2394
LEAR HOLDINGS (HUNGARY) KFT.—See Lear Corporation; *U.S. Public*, pg. 1297
LETHAL PERFORMANCE INC.; *U.S. Private*, pg. 2433
LIGHTNING AUDIO CORPORATION—See Patrick Industries, Inc.; *U.S. Public*, pg. 1653
LKQ AUTO PARTS OF NORTH TEXAS, L.P.—See LKQ Corporation; *U.S. Public*, pg. 1335
LKQ BELGIUM BVBA—See LKQ Corporation; *U.S. Public*, pg. 1335
LKQ CENTRAL, INC.—See LKQ Corporation; *U.S. Public*, pg. 1335
LKQ CRYSTAL RIVER, INC.—See LKQ Corporation; *U.S. Public*, pg. 1335
LKQ MIDWEST, INC.—See LKQ Corporation; *U.S. Public*, pg. 1335
LKQ ONLINE CORP.—See LKQ Corporation; *U.S. Public*, pg. 1335
LKQ PRECIOUS METALS, INC.—See LKQ Corporation; *U.S. Public*, pg. 1335
L&L PRODUCTS AUSTRALIA (PTY) LTD.—See L&L Products, Inc.; *U.S. Private*, pg. 2363
L&L PRODUCTS DO BRASIL LTDA.—See L&L Products, Inc.; *U.S. Private*, pg. 2363
L&L PRODUCTS OTOMOTIV LTD STI—See L&L Products, Inc.; *U.S. Private*, pg. 2363
LUMINAR TECHNOLOGIES, INC.; *U.S. Public*, pg. 1348
MAC TOOLS—See Stanley Black & Decker, Inc.; *U.S. Public*, pg. 1933
MANITEX VALLA S.R.L.—See Manitex International, Inc.; *U.S. Public*, pg. 1356
MANNING LIGHT TRUCK EQUIPMENT, LLC—See Manning Enterprises Inc.; *U.S. Private*, pg. 2565
MARANELLO CONCESSIONAIRES LIMITED—See Penske Automotive Group, Inc.; *U.S. Public*, pg. 1665
MASLACK SUPPLY LTD.—See LKQ Corporation; *U.S. Public*, pg. 1336
MCDAVID AUSTIN-ACRA, LLC—See Asbury Automotive Group, Inc.; *U.S. Public*, pg. 209
MIAMI BREEZE CAR CARE, INC.; *U.S. Public*, pg. 1436
MILLENNIUM AUTOMOTIVE LOGISTICS INC.; *U.S. Private*, pg. 2731
MOBILE-ONE AUTO SOUND INC.; *U.S. Private*, pg. 2757
MOLEX FRANCE—See Koch Industries, Inc.; *U.S. Private*, pg. 2334
MOLEX (MALAYSIA) SDN. BHD.—See Koch Industries, Inc.; *U.S. Private*, pg. 2334
MOLEX POLSKA SP. Z O.O.—See Koch Industries, Inc.; *U.S. Private*, pg. 2334
MYERSTIRESUPPLY.COM, INC.—See Myers Industries, Inc.; *U.S. Public*, pg. 1488
MYOTEK INDUSTRIES INC.—See New Water Capital, L.P.; *U.S. Private*, pg. 2908
NAPA AUTOMOTIVE PARTS DISTRIBUTION CENTER—See Genuine Parts Company; *U.S. Public*, pg. 932
NAPA AUTO PARTS GENUINE PARTS COMPANY—See Genuine Parts Company; *U.S. Public*, pg. 932
NAPA AUTO PARTS—See Genuine Parts Company; *U.S. Public*, pg. 932
NASHVILLE AUTO AUCTION—See Cox Enterprises, Inc.; *U.S. Public*, pg. 1077
NATIONAL PARTS DEPOT; *U.S. Private*, pg. 2860
NATIONAL PARTS SUPPLY COMPANY INC.; *U.S. Private*, pg. 2860

441330 — AUTOMOTIVE PARTS AN...

NATIONAL TYRE SERVICES LTD.—See Halfords Group plc; *Int'l*, pg. 3229
NEUTRONICS INC.—See FFL Partners, LLC; *U.S. Private*, pg. 1500
NEW WORLD INTERNATIONAL INC.—See United Commerce Centers Inc.; *U.S. Private*, pg. 4289
NORDGLASS SP. Z O.O.—See AGC Inc.; *Int'l*, pg. 202
NORWOOD AUTO PARTS—See Hahn Automotive Warehouse, Inc.; *U.S. Private*, pg. 1840
NYA CHRISTIANSTADS BILLACKERING AB—See LKQ Corporation; *U.S. Public*, pg. 1335
OFIRA ITALIANA S.R.L.—See Addtech AB; *Int'l*, pg. 134
OMEGA ENVIRONMENTAL TECHNOLOGIES, INC.—See River Associates Investments, LLC; *U.S. Private*, pg. 3443
OOO BENTELER DISTRIBUTION RUSSIA—See Benteler International AG; *Int'l*, pg. 977
O'REILLY AUTOMOTIVE STORES, INC.—See O'Reilly Automotive, Inc.; *U.S. Public*, pg. 1559
ORW IMPORT PARTS & MACHINE; *U.S. Private*, pg. 3046
PACIFIC SERVICES AND DEVELOPMENT CORPORATION—See Xerox Holdings Corporation; *U.S. Public*, pg. 2388
PALA HOLDING, B.V.—See LKQ Corporation; *U.S. Public*, pg. 1336
PALM BEACH MOTORING ACCESSORIES, INC.—See Vision Investments, LLC; *U.S. Private*, pg. 4391
PALMER (UK) LIMITED—See Palmer International, Inc.; *U.S. Private*, pg. 3081
PAPE KENWORTH—See The Pape Group, Inc.; *U.S. Private*, pg. 4090
PARKS AUTO PARTS INC.; *U.S. Private*, pg. 3098
THE PARTS PROS AUTOMOTIVE WAREHOUSE, INC.—See TPH Acquisition, LLLP; *U.S. Private*, pg. 4200
PEGASUS AUTO RACING SUPPLIES, INC.; *U.S. Private*, pg. 3129
THE PEP BOYS MANNY MOE & JACK OF CALIFORNIA—See Icahn Enterprises L.P.; *U.S. Public*, pg. 1085
THE PEP BOYS - MANNY, MOE & JACK—See Icahn Enterprises L.P.; *U.S. Public*, pg. 1085
PERFORMANCE TRUCK PRODUCTS; *U.S. Private*, pg. 3150
PICK-YOUR-PART AUTO WRECKING INC.—See LKQ Corporation; *U.S. Public*, pg. 1336
PIKA AUTOTEILE GMBH—See LKQ Corporation; *U.S. Public*, pg. 1336
POINT SPRING & DRIVESHAFT COMPANY; *U.S. Private*, pg. 3222
POS-AUSTEM KUNSHAN AUTOMOTIVE CO., LTD.—See Austem Co., Ltd.; *Int'l*, pg. 717
POS-AUSTEM SUZHOU AUTOMOTIVE CO., LTD.—See Austem Co., Ltd.; *Int'l*, pg. 717
POS-AUSTEM WUHAN AUTOMOTIVE CO., LTD.—See Austem Co., Ltd.; *Int'l*, pg. 717
POS-AUSTEM YANTAI AUTOMOTIVE CO., LTD.—See Austem Co., Ltd.; *Int'l*, pg. 717
POWER TRAIN SERVICES INC.—See Platinum Equity, LLC; *U.S. Private*, pg. 3209
PREMIER AUTO TRADE PTY LTD—See Bapcor Limited; *Int'l*, pg. 857
PT. IINO INDONESIA—See Daido Metal Corporation; *Int'l*, pg. 1922
Q-PARTS24 GMBH & CO. KG—See LKQ Corporation; *U.S. Public*, pg. 1336
QUALIS AUTOMOTIVE LLC—See Crowne Group LLC; *U.S. Private*, pg. 1112
R.A.C. GROUP INC.—See Mistras Group, Inc.; *U.S. Public*, pg. 1451
RAMEDER ANHANGERKUPPLUNGEN UND AUTOTEILE GMBH—See FSN Capital Partners AS; *Int'l*, pg. 2799
READING EQUIPMENT & DISTRIBUTION, INC.; *U.S. Private*, pg. 3366
RECOPART AB—See LKQ Corporation; *U.S. Public*, pg. 1336
REISTERSTOWN AUTO PARTS, INC.—See Genuine Parts Company; *U.S. Public*, pg. 933
RHIAG GROUP LTD.—See LKQ Corporation; *U.S. Public*, pg. 1336
RIDEGEAR.COM; *U.S. Private*, pg. 3432
THE RIDGE COMPANY; *U.S. Private*, pg. 4107
RIDGE-FORT WAYNE COMPANY, INC.; *U.S. Private*, pg. 3432
RIEBE'S AUTO PARTS; *U.S. Private*, pg. 3434
ROBBINS AUTO PARTS, INC.; *U.S. Private*, pg. 3456
RODI AUTOMOTIVE INC.; *U.S. Private*, pg. 3470
R.O.H. AUTO PRODUCTS PHILIPPINES, INC.—See Arrowcrest Group Pty. Ltd.; *Int'l*, pg. 580
ROPE ACCESS CALGARY, INC.—See Mistras Group, Inc.; *U.S. Public*, pg. 1451
ROWE TRUCK EQUIPMENT INC.; *U.S. Private*, pg. 3490
RUSH ACCESSORIES CORPORATION—See Rush Enterprises, Inc.; *U.S. Public*, pg. 1826
RUSH MEDIUM DUTY TRUCK CENTERS OF COLORADO, INC.—See Rush Enterprises, Inc.; *U.S. Public*, pg. 1826
SAI CHAMBLEE V, LLC—See Sonic Automotive, Inc.; *U.S. Public*, pg. 1902

SAI DENVER B, INC.—See Sonic Automotive, Inc.; *U.S. Public*, pg. 1902
SANEL AUTO PARTS CO.—See Automotive Supply Associates, Inc.; *U.S. Private*, pg. 401
SANTA ROSA CAMPWAY, INC.; *U.S. Private*, pg. 3547
SATOR HOLDING B.V.—See LKQ Corporation; *U.S. Public*, pg. 1336
SERGOYNE CAR-PARTS BVBA—See LKQ Corporation; *U.S. Public*, pg. 1336
SHANGHAI AAG AUTOMOTIVE PRODUCTS TRADING CO. LTD—See Energizer Holdings, Inc.; *U.S. Public*, pg. 760
SHERWIN-WILLIAMS AUTOMOTIVE FINISHES CORPORATION—See The Sherwin-Williams Company; *U.S. Public*, pg. 2128
SHOCK ABSORBER US INC—See Hanesbrands Inc.; *U.S. Public*, pg. 983
SHOWA DEUTSCHLAND GMBH—See Hitachi Astemo, Ltd.; *Int'l*, pg. 3409
SIGNALEN AB—See LKQ Corporation; *U.S. Public*, pg. 1336
SILICON VALLEY CONCEPTS; *U.S. Private*, pg. 3652
SIM IMPEX D.O.O.—See LKQ Corporation; *U.S. Public*, pg. 1336
SLP PERFORMANCE PARTS, INC.; *U.S. Private*, pg. 3689
SMART START, INC.; *U.S. Private*, pg. 3691
SMILE BUSINESS PRODUCTS INC.; *U.S. Private*, pg. 3693
SNAP-ON TOOLS LIMITED—See Snap-on Incorporated; *U.S. Public*, pg. 1898
SONOCO PRODUCTS COMPANY—See Sonoco Products Company; *U.S. Public*, pg. 1908
THE SPECIALISTS INC.; *U.S. Private*, pg. 4120
SPR PROCUREMENT COMPANY—See Genuine Parts Company; *U.S. Public*, pg. 933
STAHLGRUBER CZ S.R.O.—See LKQ Corporation; *U.S. Public*, pg. 1336
STAHLGRUBER D.O.O.—See LKQ Corporation; *U.S. Public*, pg. 1336
STAHLGRUBER GMBH—See LKQ Corporation; *U.S. Public*, pg. 1336
STAHLGRUBER TRGOVINA D.O.O.—See LKQ Corporation; *U.S. Public*, pg. 1336
STELLAR DISTRIBUTION LLC; *U.S. Private*, pg. 3799
STURDEVANTS INC.; *U.S. Private*, pg. 3844
SYRACUSE TRAILER SALES; *U.S. Private*, pg. 3905
TENNECO AUTOMOTIVE POLSKA SP. Z.O.O.—See Apollo Global Management, Inc.; *U.S. Public*, pg. 163
TENRYU SANGYO CO., LTD.—See F.C.C. Co., Ltd.; *Int'l*, pg. 2596
TEXAS INSTRUMENTS INTERNATIONAL TRADE CORPORATION—See Texas Instruments Incorporated; *U.S. Public*, pg. 2026
THOMASSONS.NU GRUPP AB—See LKQ Corporation; *U.S. Public*, pg. 1336
TIFORP INC.; *U.S. Private*, pg. 4169
TIGERGPS.COM, LTD.; *U.S. Private*, pg. 4170
TINT WORLD; *U.S. Private*, pg. 4175
TI POLAND SP Z O O.—See Bain Capital, LP; *U.S. Private*, pg. 447
TIRE DEN INC.; *U.S. Private*, pg. 4176
TOTAL TRUCK PARTS INC.; *U.S. Private*, pg. 4192
TOUCHUPDIRECT, LLC; *U.S. Private*, pg. 4193
TRACTOR TRAILER SUPPLY CO.; *U.S. Private*, pg. 4201
TRAILER WHEEL & FRAME COMPANY; *U.S. Private*, pg. 4204
TRANSAMERICAN AUTO PARTS CO.—See Polaris, Inc.; *U.S. Public*, pg. 1701
TRANSPORT SPECIALISTS INCORPORATED; *U.S. Private*, pg. 4211
TRI-CITY AUTO SALVAGE INC.—See Stellex Capital Management LP; *U.S. Private*, pg. 3800
TRIMAS CORPORATION; *U.S. Public*, pg. 2189
TRIMSOL CZECH S.R.O.—See DUAL Co. Ltd; *Int'l*, pg. 2217
TROMS BILDELSENTER AS—See LKQ Corporation; *U.S. Public*, pg. 1336
TRUCK CENTERS INC.; *U.S. Private*, pg. 4246
TUBIZE PARTS SERVICE S.R.L.—See LKQ Corporation; *U.S. Public*, pg. 1336
UAB BENTELER DISTRIBUTION LITHUANIA—See Benteler International AG; *Int'l*, pg. 977
UAPRO INC—See Genuine Parts Company; *U.S. Public*, pg. 933
UNITED COMMERCE CENTERS INC.; *U.S. Private*, pg. 4289
U.S. AUTOFORCE—See U.S. Venture, Inc.; *U.S. Private*, pg. 4272
UTILITY TRAILER SALES SOUTHEAST TEXAS INC.—See Utility Trailer Manufacturing Company, LLC; *U.S. Private*, pg. 4326
VAN BORTEL FORD; *U.S. Private*, pg. 4339
VAN HECK INTERPIECES N.V.—See LKQ Corporation; *U.S. Public*, pg. 1336
VANTAGE MOBILITY INTERNATIONAL, LLC—See Nautic Partners, LLC; *U.S. Private*, pg. 2872
VAXJO LACKCENTER AB—See LKQ Corporation; *U.S. Public*, pg. 1337

VEGE AUTOMOTIVE SPAIN, S.L.U.—See LKQ Corporation; *U.S. Public*, pg. 1337
VINTAGE PARTS, INC.—See GenNx360 Capital Partners, L.P.; *U.S. Private*, pg. 1672
VIP INC.—See The Edward S. Quirk Co., Inc.; *U.S. Private*, pg. 4025
VOVIS AUTOMOBILE GMBH—See AGRAVIS Raiffeisen AG; *Int'l*, pg. 216
WEB RIVER GROUP, INC.; *U.S. Private*, pg. 4464
WESCO GROUP, INC.; *U.S. Private*, pg. 4482
WESTBAY AUTO PARTS INC.; *U.S. Private*, pg. 4488
WHIRLPOOL BELUX N.V./S.A.—See Whirlpool Corporation; *U.S. Public*, pg. 2367
WHIRLPOOL ITALIA S.R.L.—See Whirlpool Corporation; *U.S. Public*, pg. 2368
WHIRLPOOL POLSKA APPLIANCES SP. Z O.O.—See Whirlpool Corporation; *U.S. Public*, pg. 2368
WHIRLPOOL RUS LLC—See Whirlpool Corporation; *U.S. Public*, pg. 2368
WHIRLPOOL SLOVAKIA HOME APPLIANCES SPOL. S.R.O.—See Whirlpool Corporation; *U.S. Public*, pg. 2368
WHIRLPOOL UK APPLIANCES LIMITED—See Whirlpool Corporation; *U.S. Public*, pg. 2368
WHITNEY AUTOMOTIVE GROUP, INC.—See CarParts.com, Inc.; *U.S. Public*, pg. 439
WOODSTOCK FARM & FLEET INC.—See Blain Supply, Inc.; *U.S. Private*, pg. 577
W.W. TIRE SERVICE, INC.; *U.S. Private*, pg. 4423
ZZ PERFORMANCE, LLC; *U.S. Private*, pg. 4611

441340 — TIRE DEALERS

AKH COMPANY, INC.; *U.S. Private*, pg. 145
ALLIED DISCOUNT TIRE & BRAKE; *U.S. Private*, pg. 185
ANTIOCH TIRE INC.; *U.S. Private*, pg. 288
A TO Z TIRE & BATTERY INC.; *U.S. Private*, pg. 19
ATWATER TIRE SERVICES INC.—See Delray Tire & Retreading Inc.; *U.S. Private*, pg. 1199
BANDEN DEPROOST BV—See Colruyt Group N.V.; *Int'l*, pg. 1705
BARNWELL HOUSE OF TIRES INC.; *U.S. Private*, pg. 478
BAUER BUILT, INC.; *U.S. Private*, pg. 490
BELLE TIRE DISTRIBUTOR INC.; *U.S. Private*, pg. 520
BELLE TIRE DISTRIBUTORS, INC.; *U.S. Private*, pg. 520
BEST DEAL SPRING INC.—See American Securities LLC; *U.S. Private*, pg. 248
BILL WILLIAMS TIRE CENTER; *U.S. Private*, pg. 558
BOB SUMEREL TIRE CO., INC.; *U.S. Private*, pg. 605
BOYD'S TIRE & SERVICE—See Greenbriar Equity Group, L.P.; *U.S. Private*, pg. 1776
BRIDGESTONE AIRCRAFT TIRE (EUROPE) S.A.—See Bridgestone Corporation; *Int'l*, pg. 1158
BRIDGESTONE AIRCRAFT TIRE (USA), INC.—See Bridgestone Corporation; *Int'l*, pg. 1156
BRIDGESTONE BENELUX B.V.—See Bridgestone Corporation; *Int'l*, pg. 1158
BRIDGESTONE DEUTSCHLAND GMBH—See Bridgestone Corporation; *Int'l*, pg. 1158
BRIDGESTONE EARTHMOVER TYRES PTY. LTD.—See Bridgestone Corporation; *Int'l*, pg. 1158
BRIDGESTONE EUROPE NV/SA—See Bridgestone Corporation; *Int'l*, pg. 1158
BRIDGESTONE/FIRESTONE OFF ROAD TIRE DIVISION—See Cox Enterprises, Inc.; *U.S. Private*, pg. 1075
BRIDGESTONE/FIRESTONE ORIGINAL EQUIPMENT DIVISION—See Cox Enterprises, Inc.; *U.S. Private*, pg. 1075
BRIDGESTONE PORTUGAL LDA.—See Bridgestone Corporation; *Int'l*, pg. 1159
BRIDGESTONE SWEDEN AB—See Bridgestone Corporation; *Int'l*, pg. 1159
BRIDGESTONE U.K. LTD.—See Bridgestone Corporation; *Int'l*, pg. 1159
BURT BROTHERS TIRE & SERVICE, INC.; *U.S. Private*, pg. 692
CERTIFIED TIRE & SERVICE CENTERS, INC.—See Monro, Inc.; *U.S. Public*, pg. 1465
CHENG SHIN RUBBER (XIAMEN) IND., LTD.; *Int'l*, pg. 1466
CITY TIRE CO. INC.; *U.S. Private*, pg. 907
CLARK TIRE & AUTO INCORPORATED; *U.S. Private*, pg. 914
COAST TIRE & AUTO SERVICE, INC.; *Int'l*, pg. 1681
COLONIAL TIRE DISTRIBUTOR INC—See Colonial Ford Truck Sales, Inc.; *U.S. Private*, pg. 971
COLONY TIRE CORPORATION; *U.S. Private*, pg. 972
COOPER TIRE & RUBBER COMPANY DE MEXICO S.A.—See The Goodyear Tire & Rubber Company; *U.S. Public*, pg. 2083
CROSS-MIDWEST TIRE, INC.; *U.S. Private*, pg. 1105
DANIELS TIRE SERVICE INC.; *U.S. Private*, pg. 1156
DELTICOM O.E. S.R.L.—See Delticom AG; *Int'l*, pg. 2021
DELTIQQ LTD.—See Delticom AG; *Int'l*, pg. 2021
DOBBS TIRE & AUTO CENTERS, INC.; *U.S. Private*, pg. 1250

N.A.I.C.S. INDEX

DUNN TIRE LLC; *U.S. Private*, pg. 1290
EARL W. COLVARD INC.; *U.S. Private*, pg. 1313
ELEMENT WHEELS; *U.S. Private*, pg. 1357
ELITE ROADS; *U.S. Private*, pg. 1361
EURORUBBER S.P.A.—See Certech SpA; *Int'l*, pg. 1423
EVANS TIRE & SERVICE CENTERS, INC.; *U.S. Private*, pg. 1435
EXPRESS TIRE AUTO SERVICE CENTERS; *U.S. Private*, pg. 1451
FIRESTONE BUILDING PRODUCTS-BEECH GROVE—See Bridgestone Corporation; *Int'l*, pg. 1156
FIRESTONE BUILDING PRODUCTS-KINGSTREE—See Bridgestone Corporation; *Int'l*, pg. 1156
FLEET TIRE INCORPORATED; *U.S. Private*, pg. 1542
FOUNTAIN TIRE CORP.; *Int'l*, pg. 2754
FRASIER TIRE SERVICE INC.; *U.S. Private*, pg. 1599
GOODGUYS TIRE CENTERS INC.; *U.S. Private*, pg. 1739
GOOD TIRE SERVICE INC.; *U.S. Private*, pg. 1738
GOODYEAR AUSTRALIA PTY LIMITED—See The Goodyear Tire & Rubber Company; *U.S. Public*, pg. 2083
GOODYEAR TYRES PTY LTD—See The Goodyear Tire & Rubber Company; *U.S. Public*, pg. 2083
HASLER OIL COMPANY INCORPORATED; *U.S. Private*, pg. 1878
HUBER TIRE INC.; *U.S. Private*, pg. 2001
INDY TIRE CENTERS, INC.; *U.S. Private*, pg. 2069
INTER CITY TIRE & AUTO CENTER; *U.S. Private*, pg. 2106
JACKIE COOPER TIRE DISTRIBUTORS; *U.S. Private*, pg. 2175
JACKS TIRE & OIL INC.—See Purcell Tire & Rubber Company Inc.; *U.S. Private*, pg. 3305
JACKS TIRE & OIL MANAGEMENT CO.—See Purcell Tire & Rubber Company Inc.; *U.S. Private*, pg. 3304
JACK WILLIAMS TIRE CO. INC.; *U.S. Private*, pg. 2175
JENNINGS TIRE COMPANY INC.; *U.S. Private*, pg. 2200
JOHNSON'S TIRE SERVICE; *U.S. Private*, pg. 2229
JUFFALI TYRES COMPANY—See E.A. Juffali & Brothers Company; *Int'l*, pg. 2251
LES SCHWAB TIRE CENTERS OF OREGON, INC.; *U.S. Private*, pg. 2432
MARTIN TIRE CO.; *U.S. Private*, pg. 2596
MAVIS TIRE EXPRESS SERVICES CORP.—See Golden Gate Capital Management II, LLC; *U.S. Private*, pg. 1731
MCCARTHY TIRE SERVICE COMPANY; *U.S. Private*, pg. 2627
MCLEA'S TIRE & AUTOMOTIVE CENTERS; *U.S. Private*, pg. 2640
MCMAHON TIRE, INC.; *U.S. Private*, pg. 2642
MICHELIN AMERICA DO SUL—See Compagnie Generale des Etablissements Michelin SCA; *Int'l*, pg. 1743
MICHELIN KOREA COMPANY LIMITED—See Compagnie Generale des Etablissements Michelin SCA; *Int'l*, pg. 1743
MICHELIN NORTH AMERICA (CANADA) INC.—See Compagnie Generale des Etablissements Michelin SCA; *Int'l*, pg. 1744
MIDWEST TIRE & MUFFLER, INC.; *U.S. Private*, pg. 2723
MIKE GATTO INC; *U.S. Private*, pg. 2725
MOBILEMECH GMBH—See Delticom AG; *Int'l*, pg. 2021
MYERS TIRE SUPPLY INTERNATIONAL, INC.—See Myers Industries, Inc.; *U.S. Public*, pg. 1488
MYERS TIRE SUPPLY—See Myers Industries, Inc.; *U.S. Public*, pg. 1488
NEBRASKALAND TIRE COMPANY; *U.S. Private*, pg. 2879
NORTHWEST TIRE & SERVICE INC.; *U.S. Private*, pg. 2962
OK TIRE STORE INC.; *U.S. Private*, pg. 3006
PARKHOUSE TIRE SERVICE INC.; *U.S. Private*, pg. 3098
PERRY BROTHERS TIRE SERVICE, INC.; *U.S. Private*, pg. 3153
PETE'S TIRE BARNS, INC.; *U.S. Private*, pg. 3157
RABEN TIRE CO. INC.—See The Goodyear Tire & Rubber Company; *U.S. Public*, pg. 2084
THE REINALT-THOMAS CORPORATION; *U.S. Private*, pg. 4103
ROAD-MART INC.; *U.S. Private*, pg. 3453
ROBERTSON TIRE CO. INC.—See Big Brand Tire & Service; *U.S. Private*, pg. 552
ROSSI'S TIRE & AUTO SERVICE; *U.S. Private*, pg. 3486
SAVANNAH TIRE & RUBBER COMPANY, INC.—See Golden Gate Capital Management II, LLC; *U.S. Private*, pg. 1731
SCHOETTLER TIRE INC.; *U.S. Private*, pg. 3567
SENTAIDA TIRE COMPANY LTD.; *U.S. Public*, pg. 1868
SHAUB-ELLISON CO; *U.S. Private*, pg. 3627
SIMPLETIRE, LLC; *U.S. Private*, pg. 3667
SNIDER FLEET SOLUTIONS; *U.S. Private*, pg. 3700
SOUTHERN TIRE MART, LLC; *U.S. Private*, pg. 3735
SUBURBAN TIRE COMPANY; *U.S. Private*, pg. 3848
SULLIVAN INVESTMENT CO. INC.—See Sullivan Tire Co. Inc.; *U.S. Private*, pg. 3852
SULLIVAN TIRE CO. INC.; *U.S. Private*, pg. 3852
TANDEM TIRE & AUTO SERVICE; *U.S. Private*, pg. 3930
TBC—See Golden Gate Capital Management II, LLC; *U.S. Private*, pg. 1731
TECNICENTROS MUNDIAL INC.—See Icahn Enterprises L.P.; *U.S. Public*, pg. 1084
TIRE DISCOUNTERS, INC.—See Four Corners Property Trust, Inc.; *U.S. Public*, pg. 875
TIRE GUYS INC.; *U.S. Private*, pg. 4176
TIRE KINGDOM, INC.—See Golden Gate Capital Management II, LLC; *U.S. Private*, pg. 1731
TIREMAN AUTO SERVICE CENTERS LTD.—See Belle Tire Distributors, Inc.; *U.S. Private*, pg. 520
TIREMAXX INC.; *U.S. Private*, pg. 4176
TIRENDO DEUTSCHLAND GMBH—See Delticom AG; *Int'l*, pg. 2021
TIRES PLUS TOTAL CAR CARE—See Bridgestone Corporation; *Int'l*, pg. 1160
TIRE'S WAREHOUSE, INC.; *U.S. Private*, pg. 4176
TIRE WAREHOUSE CENTRAL INC.—See Monro, Inc.; *U.S. Public*, pg. 1465
TOWN FAIR TIRE CENTERS INC.; *U.S. Private*, pg. 4197
TREDROC TIRE SERVICES; *U.S. Private*, pg. 4216
TREDROC TIRE SERVICES—See Tredroc Tire Services; *U.S. Private*, pg. 4216
TREDROC TIRE SERVICES—See Tredroc Tire Services; *U.S. Private*, pg. 4216
TREDROC TIRE SERVICES—See Tredroc Tire Services; *U.S. Private*, pg. 4216
TURBO WHOLESALE TIRES, INC.—See Kingswood Capital Management LLC; *U.S. Private*, pg. 2312
T&W TIRE COMPANY; *U.S. Private*, pg. 3910
TYRESNET GMBH—See Delticom AG; *Int'l*, pg. 2021
VALLEY TIRE CO., INC.; *U.S. Private*, pg. 4335
VULCAN TIRE & AUTOMOTIVE, INC.; *U.S. Private*, pg. 4416
WAYNES TIRE INC.; *U.S. Private*, pg. 4460
WEETING TYRES LIMITED—See The Goodyear Tire & Rubber Company; *U.S. Public*, pg. 2085
WESTERN TIRE CENTERS INC.; *U.S. Private*, pg. 4497
WHEELFIRE INC; *U.S. Private*, pg. 4506
WHITES TIRE SERVICE OF WILSON; *U.S. Private*, pg. 4511
WILSON WAY TIRE COMPANY INC.; *U.S. Private*, pg. 4531
YOUNGSTEDT INC.; *U.S. Private*, pg. 4594
ZIEGLER TIRE & SUPPLY COMPANY, INC.; *U.S. Private*, pg. 4604

444110 — HOME CENTERS

84 LUMBER COMPANY; *U.S. Private*, pg. 17
ACME ROLLING STEEL DOOR CORP.—See DuraServ Corp; *U.S. Private*, pg. 1293
ALLENSVILLE PLANING MILL INC.; *U.S. Private*, pg. 180
ASSOCIATED ALUMINUM PRODUCTS CO., LLC; *U.S. Private*, pg. 354
BANNER SUPPLY CO.; *U.S. Private*, pg. 469
BARR LUMBER CO. INC.; *U.S. Private*, pg. 479
BELLEVUE BUILDERS SUPPLY - US LBM, LLC—See Bain Capital, LP; *U.S. Private*, pg. 450
BERONIO LUMBER CO; *U.S. Private*, pg. 538
BHC MANAGEMENT SERVICES OF STREAMWOOD, LLC—See Universal Health Services, Inc.; *U.S. Public*, pg. 2256
BIG B LUMBERTERIA; *U.S. Private*, pg. 552
BIG CREEK LUMBER CO. INC.; *U.S. Private*, pg. 553
BLIFFERT LUMBER & FUEL CO. INC.; *U.S. Private*, pg. 581
BLOEDORN LUMBER COMPANY INC.; *U.S. Private*, pg. 583
BLUE BUG INC.—See Clayton, Dubilier & Rice, LLC; *U.S. Private*, pg. 930
BOLAND MALONEY ENTERPRISES INC.; *U.S. Private*, pg. 610
BOLIVAR INSULATION CO—See Quad-C Management, Inc.; *U.S. Private*, pg. 3315
BOWMAN INC.; *U.S. Private*, pg. 626
BUFFALO LUMBER CO; *U.S. Private*, pg. 681
BUILDERS GENERAL SUPPLY COMPANY; *U.S. Private*, pg. 682
BUSY BEAVER BUILDING CENTERS, INC.; *U.S. Private*, pg. 696
BYGGMAX GROUP AB—See Altor Equity Partners AB; *Int'l*, pg. 394
CANFOR PANEL & FIBRE—See Canfor Corporation; *Int'l*, pg. 1290
CAPE COD STONE & MASONRY SUPPLY, INC.—See SiteOne Landscape Supply, Inc.; *U.S. Public*, pg. 1888
CARLISLE WIDE PLANK FLOORS, INC.—See JMH Capital; *U.S. Private*, pg. 2215
CASCADE SALES—See Nature's Footprint, Inc.; *U.S. Private*, pg. 2867
CASSITY JONES LP; *U.S. Private*, pg. 784
CHENGDU FUSEN NOBLE-HOUSE INDSTRL CO LTD; *Int'l*, pg. 1467
CHESHIRE LUMBER CO. INC.—See The Lyon & Billard Co., Inc.; *U.S. Private*, pg. 4073
CHEVALIER (ALUMINIUM ENGINEERING) LIMITED—See Chevalier International Holdings Limited; *Int'l*, pg. 1473
CITY LUMBER & TRUSS COMPANY; *U.S. Private*, pg. 906
CLAY INGELS COMPANY, LLC; *U.S. Private*, pg. 917
COMFORT WINDOW CO. INC.; *U.S. Private*, pg. 981
CONCANNON LUMBER COMPANY—See Concannon Corporation; *U.S. Private*, pg. 1008

444110 — HOME CENTERS

CONTRACTORS BUILDING SUPPLY, INC.—See The Building Center, Inc.; *U.S. Private*, pg. 4002
COOPER TRADING, INC.; *U.S. Private*, pg. 1041
CORNING BUILDING CO. INC.; *U.S. Private*, pg. 1053
CRAMER'S HOME CENTERS, INC.; *U.S. Private*, pg. 1085
CURTIS LUMBER COMPANY, INC.; *U.S. Private*, pg. 1126
DAIYU EIGHT CO., LTD.—See Alleanza Holdings Co., Ltd.; *Int'l*, pg. 334
DCM KUROGANEYA CO., LTD.—See DCM Holdings Co., Ltd.; *Int'l*, pg. 1992
DECKS & DOCKS LUMBER COMPANY INC.—See CCMP Capital Advisors, LP; *U.S. Private*, pg. 800
DILLMAN & UPTON, INC.; *U.S. Private*, pg. 1231
DOOR PRO AMERICA, LLC—See Rotunda Capital Partners LLC; *U.S. Private*, pg. 3488
DUFFERIN CONCRETE - KITCHENER—See CRH plc; *Int'l*, pg. 1843
DUXBURY HARDWARE CORP.; *U.S. Private*, pg. 1295
EAST COLOMBIA S.A.—See Cencosud S.A.; *Int'l*, pg. 1400
ELITE HOME SUPPLIES—See Hendricks Holding Company, Inc.; *U.S. Private*, pg. 1914
ELLSWORTH FALLS LUMBER CO. INC.; *U.S. Private*, pg. 1375
FAIRVIEW MILLWORK INCORPORATED; *U.S. Private*, pg. 1465
FINGERLE LUMBER CO.; *U.S. Private*, pg. 1510
FLETCHER DISTRIBUTION LIMITED—See Fletcher Building Limited; *Int'l*, pg. 2701
FOGGS ACE HARDWARE BUILDING SUPPLIES; *U.S. Private*, pg. 1557
FOSTER LUMBER YARD INC. - FAIRFIELD—See Foster Lumber Yard Inc.; *U.S. Private*, pg. 1579
FOX HOME CENTER INC.; *U.S. Private*, pg. 1584
FRANK TAYLOR LUMBER & DEVELOPMENT CO.; *U.S. Private*, pg. 1595
GALLUP LUMBER & SUPPLY; *U.S. Private*, pg. 1640
GIBBS AND DANDY PLC—See Compagnie de Saint-Gobain SA; *Int'l*, pg. 1733
GO MODULAR, INC; *U.S. Private*, pg. 1723
GOODRICH LUMBER CO.—See Kodiak Building Partners LLC; *U.S. Private*, pg. 2336
THE GORDON LUMBER COMPANY; *U.S. Private*, pg. 4034
GROESBECK LUMBER & SUPPLY, INC.; *U.S. Private*, pg. 1791
GROUPE ADEO S.A.; *Int'l*, pg. 3091
GROVE LUMBER & BUILDING SUPPLIES INC.; *U.S. Private*, pg. 1794
GUADALUPE LUMBER & SUPPLY COMPANY, INC.; *U.S. Private*, pg. 1808
HABERSHAM HARDWARE & DISTRIBUTING COMPANY—See Tyndale Advisors, LLC; *U.S. Private*, pg. 4268
HACIENDA HOME CENTERS INC.; *U.S. Private*, pg. 1838
HAMILTON-PARKER COMPANY; *U.S. Private*, pg. 1848
HARDEL BUILDERS CENTER—See Hardel Mutual Plywood Corporation; *U.S. Private*, pg. 1862
HENSON TIMBER PRODUCTS CORP.—See Stonecutter Mills Corp.; *U.S. Private*, pg. 3828
H.G. PAGE REALTY CORPORATION—See Page Bros Enterprises Ltd.; *U.S. Private*, pg. 3074
H.G. PAGE & SONS INC.—See Page Bros Enterprises Ltd.; *U.S. Private*, pg. 3074
HIGGINBOTHAM BROS. & CO., LLC - GATESVILLE—See Bain Capital, LP; *U.S. Private*, pg. 450
HIGGINBOTHAM BROS. & CO., LLC—See Bain Capital, LP; *U.S. Private*, pg. 450
HIGGINBOTHAM BROS. & COMPANY; *U.S. Private*, pg. 1935
HILTON HOMES LTD.; *Int'l*, pg. 3395
HOLMQUIST LUMBER CO.; *U.S. Private*, pg. 1968
HOME DEPOT DIRECT—See The Home Depot, Inc.; *U.S. Public*, pg. 2089
HOME DEPOT MEXICO, S. DE R.L. DE C.V.—See The Home Depot, Inc.; *U.S. Public*, pg. 2089
HOME DEPOT OF CANADA INC.—See The Home Depot, Inc.; *U.S. Public*, pg. 2089
HOME DEPOT U.S.A., INC.—See The Home Depot, Inc.; *U.S. Public*, pg. 2089
HOME HARDWARE STORES LIMITED; *Int'l*, pg. 3454
HOMESTEAD BUILDING SYSTEMS INC.—See Bain Capital, LP; *U.S. Private*, pg. 451
HORNBACH BAUMARKT LUXEMBURG SARL—See Hornbach Holding AG & Co. KGaA; *Int'l*, pg. 3482
HOWARD LUMBER COMPANY; *U.S. Private*, pg. 1995
H.P. STARR LUMBER COMPANY LLC; *U.S. Private*, pg. 1835
H.R. HANNAPEL DOOR CO.; *U.S. Private*, pg. 1835
INTERSTATE LUMBER & MILL CORP.; *U.S. Private*, pg. 2125
JB WHOLESALE ROOFING & BUILDING SUPPLIES; *U.S. Private*, pg. 2193
KEENE LUMBER CO.—See Bain Capital, LP; *U.S. Private*, pg. 451
KIEFFER LUMBER CO., INC.—See RP Lumber Co. Inc.; *U.S. Private*, pg. 3495
KIGHT LUMBER CO. INC.; *U.S. Private*, pg. 2304
KITZMANS LTD.; *U.S. Private*, pg. 2317

444110 — HOME CENTERS

LAREDO RIDGE WIND, LLC—See BlackRock, Inc.; *U.S. Public*, pg. 345
LEADER HOME CENTERS INC.; *U.S. Private*, pg. 2406
LEINGANG HOME CENTER—See True Home Value, Inc.; *U.S. Private*, pg. 4247
LE NOBLE LUMBER CO. INC.; *U.S. Private*, pg. 2405
LESTER BUILDING SUPPLY CO.—See The Lester Group Inc.; *U.S. Private*, pg. 4069
THE LESTER GROUP INC.; *U.S. Private*, pg. 4069
LIC CO., LTD.—See Bengo4.com, Inc.; *Int'l*, pg. 974
L.J. STONE INC.; *U.S. Private*, pg. 2366
LL FLOORING HOLDINGS, INC.; *U.S. Public*, pg. 1337
LORENZI LUMBER CO. INC.; *U.S. Private*, pg. 2495
LOWE'S HOME CENTERS, LLC—See Lowe's Companies, Inc.; *U.S. Public*, pg. 1343
LOWE'S HOME CENTRES (CANADA) INC.—See Lowe's Companies, Inc.; *U.S. Public*, pg. 1343
LUMBERJACK BUILDING CENTERS—See Tyndale Advisors, LLC; *U.S. Private*, pg. 4268
LUMBER LIQUIDATORS SERVICES, LLC—See LL Flooring Holdings, Inc.; *U.S. Public*, pg. 1337
LUMBER MART INC.; *U.S. Private*, pg. 2513
MAHONING & TRUMBULL BUILDING TRADES INSURANCE FUND; *U.S. Private*, pg. 2550
MARINE HOME CENTER; *U.S. Private*, pg. 2575
MARION LUMBER CO. INC.—See Sequatchie Concrete Service Inc.; *U.S. Private*, pg. 3612
MARQUIS INDUSTRIES, INC.; *U.S. Private*, pg. 2587
MARSON & MARSON LUMBER, INC.—See TAL Holdings LLC; *U.S. Private*, pg. 3925
MARTIN BUILDING MATERIALS, LLC—See Lumber Investors LLC; *U.S. Private*, pg. 2513
MARVIN'S, LLC—See Tyndale Advisors, LLC; *U.S. Private*, pg. 4268
MATHEW HALL LUMBER CO; *U.S. Private*, pg. 2610
MAVERIC MINI MARTS INC.; *U.S. Private*, pg. 2615
MAXWELL PRODUCTS, INC.; *U.S. Private*, pg. 2619
MAZER'S DISCOUNT HOME CENTERS; *U.S. Private*, pg. 2623
MCBRIDE DOOR & HARDWARE, INC.—See Platinum Equity, LLC; *U.S. Private*, pg. 3209
MEEK'S, INC.—See Angeles Equity Partners, LLC; *U.S. Private*, pg. 282
MEEK'S, INC.—See Clearlake Capital Group, L.P.; *U.S. Private*, pg. 936
MEEK'S LUMBER COMPANY—See Angeles Equity Partners, LLC; *U.S. Private*, pg. 282
MEEK'S LUMBER COMPANY—See Clearlake Capital Group, L.P.; *U.S. Private*, pg. 936
MILWAUKIE LUMBER COMPANY; *U.S. Private*, pg. 2739
MODERNIZE, INC.—See QuinStreet, Inc.; *U.S. Public*, pg. 1757
MOONWORKS, INC.; *U.S. Private*, pg. 2779
MULLICAN BA LUMBER & MANUFACTURING CO. INC.—See Baillie Lumber Co., Inc.; *U.S. Private*, pg. 426
MUSSELMAN LUMBER INC.—See Bain Capital, LP; *U.S. Private*, pg. 451
NAGLE LUMBER CO.—See Alexander Lumber Co., Inc.; *U.S. Private*, pg. 163
NATIONAL LUMBER COMPANY—See Builders FirstSource, Inc.; *U.S. Public*, pg. 410
N.B. GOODWYN & SONS INC.; *U.S. Private*, pg. 2827
NEWPRO, INC.; *U.S. Private*, pg. 2916
NFL HOME CENTER—See Tyndale Advisors, LLC; *U.S. Private*, pg. 4268
NOFZIGER DOOR SALES, INC.; *U.S. Private*, pg. 2933
NOMI S.A.—See i4ventures Sp. z o.o.; *Int'l*, pg. 3567
NORTH COUNTRY WINDOWS & DOORS, LLC; *U.S. Private*, pg. 2944
NORTHEAST WINDOW & DOOR ASSOCIATION; *U.S. Private*, pg. 2951
NOTIFIER ESPANA S.L.—See Honeywell International Inc.; *U.S. Public*, pg. 1050
NU-SASH OF INDIANAPOLIS INCORPORATED; *U.S. Private*, pg. 2971
O.C. CLUSS LUMBER COMPANY; *U.S. Private*, pg. 2981
PARAMOUNT BUILDERS INC.; *U.S. Private*, pg. 3092
PLACOPLATRE SA—See Compagnie de Saint-Gobain SA; *Int'l*, pg. 1733
PROFESSIONAL BUILDERS SUPPLY, LLC; *U.S. Private*, pg. 3274
RAAB KARCHER BAUSTOFFE GMBH—See Compagnie de Saint-Gobain SA; *Int'l*, pg. 1733
RB LLC—See TopBuild Corp.; *U.S. Public*, pg. 2163
REED'S METALS, INC.—See Clayton, Dubilier & Rice, LLC; *U.S. Private*, pg. 921
REMODELERS SUPPLY CENTER—See Logan Square Aluminum Supply, Inc.; *U.S. Private*, pg. 2481
RENO LUMBER; *U.S. Private*, pg. 3399
RING'S END OF BETHEL INC.—See Rings End Inc.; *U.S. Private*, pg. 3438
RO-MAC LUMBER & SUPPLY INC.; *U.S. Private*, pg. 3453
RONA INC.—See Lowe's Companies, Inc.; *U.S. Public*, pg. 1343
ROYAL HOME CENTER CO., LTD.—See Daiwa House Industry Co., Ltd.; *Int'l*, pg. 1947
RP LUMBER CO. INC.; *U.S. Private*, pg. 3495
SACK LUMBER COMPANY; *U.S. Private*, pg. 3522

S & A HOMES INC.; *U.S. Private*, pg. 3511
SCHOENEMAN BROTHERS COMPANY; *U.S. Private*, pg. 3567
SHAW STEWART LUMBER CO. INC.; *U.S. Private*, pg. 3628
SHELLY ENTERPRISES, INC.—See Bain Capital, LP; *U.S. Private*, pg. 451
SIMONSON PROPERTIES COMPANY; *U.S. Private*, pg. 3666
SOUTHERN LUMBER & MILLWORK CORP.; *U.S. Private*, pg. 3733
SOUTHWEST BUILDER SUPPLY, INC.—See RP Lumber Co. Inc.; *U.S. Private*, pg. 3495
SPAHN & ROSE LUMBER CO., INC.; *U.S. Private*, pg. 3744
STANFORD LUMBER COMPANY INC.; *U.S. Private*, pg. 3782
STINE LUMBER COMPANY; *U.S. Private*, pg. 3813
STOCK BUILDING SUPPLY OF ARKANSAS, LLC—See Builders FirstSource, Inc.; *U.S. Public*, pg. 409
SUNNILAND CORP.—See Leonard Green & Partners, L.P.; *U.S. Private*, pg. 2429
SUTHERLAND BUILDING MATERIAL COMPANY; *U.S. Private*, pg. 3886
TANCO LUMBER, L.L.C.—See Bain Capital, LP; *U.S. Private*, pg. 450
TERRADEK LIGHTING INC.—See Great Plains Companies, Inc.; *U.S. Private*, pg. 1766
TISCHLER UND SOHN USA LIMITED; *U.S. Private*, pg. 4176
TOPTECH CO. LIMITED—See Great Eagle Holdings Limited; *Int'l*, pg. 3064
TRI-COUNTY BUILDING SUPPLIES; *U.S. Private*, pg. 4222
TRI-STATE BUILDING MATERIALS; *U.S. Private*, pg. 4223
TRI-STATE WINDOW & DOOR FACTORY, INC.; *U.S. Private*, pg. 4224
TRI-SUPPLY AND EQUIPMENT INC.—See Clayton, Dubilier & Rice, LLC; *U.S. Private*, pg. 930
TRUCKEE-TAHOE LUMBER CO; *U.S. Private*, pg. 4246
TUCKERTON LUMBER CO. INC.; *U.S. Private*, pg. 4256
TWIN CITY GARAGE DOOR COMPANY—See APi Group Corporation; *U.S. Public*, pg. 514
TW PERRY ENTERPRISES, INC.; *U.S. Private*, pg. 4263
UNIQUE WINDOWS & DOORS; *U.S. Private*, pg. 4286
UNITED STATES BUILDING SUPPLY; *U.S. Private*, pg. 4298
VAL PORT DISTRIBUTORS INC.; *U.S. Private*, pg. 4329
VALU HOME CENTERS INC.; *U.S. Private*, pg. 4337
VIC BOND SALES, INC.; *U.S. Private*, pg. 4376
VIRGINIA BUILDERS' SUPPLY, INC.—See American Securities LLC; *U.S. Private*, pg. 249
WETTERMAN INC.; *U.S. Private*, pg. 4502
WHEELWRIGHT LUMBER CO.; *U.S. Private*, pg. 4506
WHITES LUMBER INC.; *U.S. Private*, pg. 4511
WILLE BROS CO.; *U.S. Private*, pg. 4521
WILLIAMS LUMBER INC.; *U.S. Private*, pg. 4526
WINDOW AND DOOR FACTORY INC.; *U.S. Private*, pg. 4538
WINDOWIZARDS INC.; *U.S. Private*, pg. 4539
WINDOW PROS; *U.S. Private*, pg. 4538
WINDOWRAMA ENTERPRISES INC.; *U.S. Private*, pg. 4539
WOODHAVEN LUMBER & MILLWORK; *U.S. Private*, pg. 4558
W. S. KEEL LUMBER CO., INC.; *U.S. Private*, pg. 4418
W.S. TOWNSEND COMPANY; *U.S. Private*, pg. 4423
W.T. HARVEY LUMBER CO., INC.—See Tyndale Advisors, LLC; *U.S. Private*, pg. 4268
ZEELAND LUMBER & SUPPLY CO.; *U.S. Private*, pg. 4599
ZIP-RIB, INC.—See Merchant & Evans, Inc.; *U.S. Private*, pg. 2669
ZUERN BUILDING PRODUCTS INC.; *U.S. Private*, pg. 4610

444120 — PAINT AND WALLPAPER RETAILERS

COLORADO PEINTURES; *Int'l*, pg. 1704
COLOR CAULK INC.; *U.S. Private*, pg. 972
DIAMOND PRODUCTS COMPANY—See Diamond Vogel Paint, Inc.; *U.S. Private*, pg. 1224
DPNL BV—See DuPont de Nemours, Inc.; *U.S. Public*, pg. 692
ELLICOTT PAINT CO. INC.; *U.S. Private*, pg. 1363
E & S HOME OF COLOR, INC; *Int'l*, pg. 2245
FINE DECOR WALLCOVERINGS LIMITED—See Brewster Wallpaper Corp.; *U.S. Private*, pg. 647
HERZOG TRUE VALUE HOME CENTER INC.; *U.S. Private*, pg. 1927
INTERNATIONAL PAINT LLC—See Akzo Nobel N.V.; *Int'l*, pg. 271
J.P. MCDOUGALL & CO. LIMITED—See Akzo Nobel N.V.; *Int'l*, pg. 274
MINWAX COMPANY—See The Sherwin-Williams Company; *U.S. Public*, pg. 2128
NORDSJO BUTIKER AB—See Akzo Nobel N.V.; *Int'l*, pg. 274
PEINTURES COULEURS DECORATION S.A.S.—See Akzo Nobel N.V.; *Int'l*, pg. 274

RONSEAL LIMITED—See The Sherwin-Williams Company; *U.S. Public*, pg. 2128
SEVENS PAINT & WALLPAPER CO.; *U.S. Private*, pg. 3619
SHERWIN-WILLIAMS ARGENTINA I.Y C.S.A.—See The Sherwin-Williams Company; *U.S. Public*, pg. 2128
SHERWIN-WILLIAMS PAINT GROUP—See The Sherwin-Williams Company; *U.S. Public*, pg. 2128
STANDARD PAINT & WALLPAPER; *U.S. Private*, pg. 3781
VOGEL WEST INC.—See Diamond Vogel Paint, Inc.; *U.S. Private*, pg. 1224
WALLPAPERS-TO-GO, INC.; *U.S. Private*, pg. 4431

444140 — HARDWARE RETAILERS

ACA CORP.; *U.S. Private*, pg. 46
ACE HARDWARE BLUE RIDGE LLC; *U.S. Private*, pg. 56
ACE HARDWARE OF OAK FOREST; *U.S. Private*, pg. 57
ACE HOME CENTER DE MICHOACAN S.A. DE C.V—See Ace Hardware Corporation; *U.S. Private*, pg. 56
ACE MINERS HARDWARE, INC.; *U.S. Private*, pg. 57
ACHA TRADING CO. INC.; *U.S. Private*, pg. 58
ACO HARDWARE, INC.; *U.S. Private*, pg. 62
ADESSO, INC.; *U.S. Private*, pg. 78
AGENCE HAGUENAU POINT P—See Compagnie de Saint-Gobain SA; *Int'l*, pg. 1722
ALAMO LUMBER COMPANY—See Vaughan & Sons, Inc.; *U.S. Private*, pg. 4348
ALLIED SAFE & VAULT CO. INC.; *U.S. Private*, pg. 187
AMERICAN CONSTRUCTION SUPPLY & RENTAL INC.; *U.S. Private*, pg. 228
ARDILES IMPORT S.A.C.—See Einhell Germany AG; *Int'l*, pg. 2332
ASHBY LUMBER CO.; *U.S. Private*, pg. 349
AVDEL FRANCE SAS—See Stanley Black & Decker, Inc.; *U.S. Public*, pg. 1931
BAILEYS INC.; *U.S. Private*, pg. 426
BARBE—See Compagnie de Saint-Gobain SA; *Int'l*, pg. 1722
BARRETT INDUSTRIAL SUPPLY COMPANY; *U.S. Private*, pg. 479
BEOCIN A.D.; *Int'l*, pg. 978
BG AGRI SALES & SERVICE INC.—See Mid Valley Agricultural Services, Inc.; *U.S. Private*, pg. 2706
BLACK & DECKER AG—See Stanley Black & Decker, Inc.; *U.S. Public*, pg. 1936
BLACK & DECKER AKTIEBOLAG—See Stanley Black & Decker, Inc.; *U.S. Public*, pg. 1936
BLACK & DECKER ASIA PACIFIC PTE. LTD.—See Stanley Black & Decker, Inc.; *U.S. Public*, pg. 1936
BLACK & DECKER (BELGIUM) N.V.—See Stanley Black & Decker, Inc.; *U.S. Public*, pg. 1936
BLACK & DECKER CZECH SRO—See Stanley Black & Decker, Inc.; *U.S. Public*, pg. 1936
BLACK & DECKER DE COLOMBIA S.A.—See Stanley Black & Decker, Inc.; *U.S. Public*, pg. 1936
BLACK & DECKER (HELLAS) SA—See Stanley Black & Decker, Inc.; *U.S. Public*, pg. 1936
BLACK & DECKER (NEDERLAND) B.V.—See Stanley Black & Decker, Inc.; *U.S. Public*, pg. 1936
BLACK & DECKER (OVERSEAS) AG—See Stanley Black & Decker, Inc.; *U.S. Public*, pg. 1936
BLACK & DECKER SUZHOU POWER TOOLS CO. LTD.—See Stanley Black & Decker, Inc.; *U.S. Public*, pg. 1936
BOLD HARDWARE CO.; *U.S. Private*, pg. 610
BOURGEOIS—See Compagnie de Saint-Gobain SA; *Int'l*, pg. 1722
BRADFORDS BUILDING SUPPLIES LTD.; *Int'l*, pg. 1134
BREED & CO. INC.; *U.S. Private*, pg. 644
BRICORAMA S.A.; *Int'l*, pg. 1152
BUDCO, INC.; *U.S. Private*, pg. 679
BUIKEMAS ACE HARDWARE HOME CENTER; *U.S. Private*, pg. 681
BUILDERS SPECIALTIES & HARDWARE; *U.S. Private*, pg. 682
CAMPBELL SUPPLY COMPANY; *U.S. Private*, pg. 730
CARREFOUR ITALIA SPA—See Carrefour SA; *Int'l*, pg. 1344
CASHBUILD LIMITED; *Int'l*, pg. 1352
CEDEO—See Compagnie de Saint-Gobain SA; *Int'l*, pg. 1722
CKD CORPORATION—See CKD Corporation; *Int'l*, pg. 1639
COLES HARDWARE INC.; *U.S. Private*, pg. 967
CROWN HARDWARE, INC.; *U.S. Private*, pg. 1111
CUMMINGS TOOL—See Tap Enterprises Inc.; *U.S. Private*, pg. 3932
CUSTOM TOOL SUPPLY, LLC—See Incline MGMT Corp.; *U.S. Private*, pg. 2053
DB ENGINEERING, INC.—See Blue Sage Capital, L.P.; *U.S. Private*, pg. 592
DEERING LUMBER INC.—See Bain Capital, LP; *U.S. Private*, pg. 450
DELL FASTENER CORPORATION—See Bertram Capital Management, LLC; *U.S. Private*, pg. 540
DENAULTS HARDWARE-HOME CENTERS; *U.S. Private*, pg. 1204

N.A.I.C.S. INDEX 444180 — OTHER BUILDING MATE...

N.A.I.C.S. Index

DIXIELINE LUMBER & HOME CENTERS—See Builders FirstSource, Inc.; *U.S. Public*, pg. 410
DOLAN'S OF CONCORD; *U.S. Private*, pg. 1254
DORMAKABA AUSTRALIA PTY. LTD.—See dormakaba Holding AG; *Int'l*, pg. 2178
DOUGLAS LUMBER CORPORATION—See Builders FirstSource, Inc.; *U.S. Public*, pg. 410
DRILLSPOT; *U.S. Private*, pg. 1277
DUKES ACE HARDWARE INC.; *U.S. Private*, pg. 1286
EASTERS INC.; *U.S. Private*, pg. 1321
EDWARDS BUILDING CENTER, INC.—See Angeles Equity Partners, LLC; *U.S. Private*, pg. 282
EDWARDS BUILDING CENTER, INC.—See Clearlake Capital Group, L.P.; *U.S. Private*, pg. 934
ELLIOTT HARDWARE INC.; *U.S. Private*, pg. 1364
ELLIOTT'S HARDWARE, INC.—See Tyndale Advisors, LLC; *U.S. Private*, pg. 4268
EMIGH HARDWARE CO.; *U.S. Private*, pg. 1382
ENGTEX GROUP BERHAD; *Int'l*, pg. 2436
E.P. GERBER & SONS INC.; *U.S. Private*, pg. 1306
FAMILY CENTER OF HARRISONVILLE INC.; *U.S. Private*, pg. 1468
FASTENAL BRASIL IMPORTACAO, EXPORTACAO E DISTRIBUICAO LTDA.—See Fastenal Company; *U.S. Public*, pg. 823
FASTENAL CANADA, LTD.—See Fastenal Company; *U.S. Public*, pg. 823
FASTENAL COMPANY PURCHASING—See Fastenal Company; *U.S. Public*, pg. 823
FASTENAL EUROPE GMBH—See Fastenal Company; *U.S. Public*, pg. 824
FASTENAL EUROPE, KFT.—See Fastenal Company; *U.S. Public*, pg. 824
FASTENAL EUROPE, LTD.—See Fastenal Company; *U.S. Public*, pg. 824
FASTENAL EUROPE S.R.L.—See Fastenal Company; *U.S. Public*, pg. 824
FASTENAL EUROPE, S.R.O.—See Fastenal Company; *U.S. Public*, pg. 824
FASTENAL MALAYSIA SDN BHD—See Fastenal Company; *U.S. Public*, pg. 824
FASTENAL MEXICO SERVICES S. DE R.L. DE C.V.—See Fastenal Company; *U.S. Public*, pg. 824
FASTENAL PANAMA S.A.—See Fastenal Company; *U.S. Public*, pg. 824
FOCUS (DIY) GROUP LTD.; *Int'l*, pg. 2718
FOSTER LUMBER YARD INC.; *U.S. Private*, pg. 1578
FRONTIER FASTENER INC.—See Great Lakes Fasteners, Inc.; *U.S. Private*, pg. 1764
GIAQUINTO ASSOCIATES INC.; *U.S. Private*, pg. 1695
GODWIN HARDWARE, INC.; *U.S. Private*, pg. 1725
GRANQUARTZ, L.P.—See The Stephens Group, LLC; *U.S. Private*, pg. 4121
GRIMES ACE HARDWARE CO.; *U.S. Private*, pg. 1790
GRIZZLY INDUSTRIAL INC.; *U.S. Private*, pg. 1791
GUERRILLA RF OPERATING CORPORATION—See Guerrilla RF, Inc.; *U.S. Public*, pg. 974
HALLMAN WOOD PRODUCTS INC.; *U.S. Private*, pg. 1844
HARBOR FREIGHT TOOLS USA; *U.S. Private*, pg. 1859
HARDMAN SUPPLY COMPANY; *U.S. Private*, pg. 1863
HARD ROCK TOOL INC.; *U.S. Private*, pg. 1862
HARDWARE SALES INC.; *U.S. Private*, pg. 1863
HARRY'S HARDWARE INC.; *U.S. Private*, pg. 1872
HEP MATERIALS CORP.; *U.S. Private*, pg. 1920
H. GREENBERG & SON INC.; *U.S. Private*, pg. 1824
HIAWASSEE HARDWARE & BUILDING SUPPLY, INC.—See Tyndale Advisors, LLC; *U.S. Private*, pg. 4268
HIGHT ENTERPRISES, LTD. INC.; *U.S. Private*, pg. 1941
HIRU CORP.; *U.S. Public*, pg. 1042
HOMIER DISTRIBUTING COMPANY; *U.S. Private*, pg. 1976
HOUSE OF ANTIQUE HARDWARE; *U.S. Private*, pg. 1991
HURST STORES INCORPORATED; *U.S. Private*, pg. 2013
JELINEK HARDWARE CO.; *U.S. Private*, pg. 2198
JOHN J. DOODY & SON INC.; *U.S. Private*, pg. 2222
J.S. WEST & COMPANY; *U.S. Private*, pg. 2171
KABELIN HARDWARE COMPANY INC.; *U.S. Private*, pg. 2253
KENNAMETAL AUSTRALIA PTY. LTD.—See Kennametal Inc.; *U.S. Public*, pg. 1221
KENNAMETAL NEDERLAND B.V.—See Kennametal Inc.; *U.S. Public*, pg. 1222
KENNAMETAL (SINGAPORE) PTE. LTD.—See Kennametal Inc.; *U.S. Public*, pg. 1221
KETTLE-LAKES COOPERATIVE; *U.S. Private*, pg. 2292
KIM SENG HUAT HARDWARE PTE LTD—See CosmoSteel Holdings Limited; *Int'l*, pg. 1814
KIN-KO ACE STORES INC.; *U.S. Private*, pg. 2306
KITZ & PFEIL INC.; *U.S. Private*, pg. 2317
KWIK-SET FASTENERS, INC.; *U.S. Private*, pg. 2359
LAGUNA TOOLS INC.; *U.S. Private*, pg. 2373
LINCOLN STORES INC.; *U.S. Private*, pg. 2459
L&M SUPPLY INC.; *U.S. Private*, pg. 2363
LONG-LEWIS HARDWARE CO.—See House Hasson Hardware Company; *U.S. Private*, pg. 1992
MACPHERSON WESTERN TOOL & SUPPLY CO. INC.; *U.S. Private*, pg. 2538
MAPES 5 & 10 STORES LTD.; *U.S. Private*, pg. 2568
MAQUINAS Y HERRAMIENTAS BLACK & DECKER DE CHILE S.A.—See Stanley Black & Decker, Inc.; *U.S. Public*, pg. 1936
MAUI VARIETIES, LTD.; *U.S. Private*, pg. 2615
MCFEELY'S—See W.W. Grainger, Inc.; *U.S. Public*, pg. 2320
M&C HOME DEPOT LTD.—See Arthur J. Gallagher & Co.; *U.S. Public*, pg. 206
MCLENDON HARDWARE, INC.—See Tyndale Advisors, LLC; *U.S. Private*, pg. 4268
METROPOLITAN LUMBER & HARDWARE; *U.S. Private*, pg. 2688
MILLER HARDWARE COMPANY; *U.S. Private*, pg. 2734
MORTONS ASSOCIATES, INC.—See Sunshine Ace Hardware Inc.; *U.S. Private*, pg. 3871
MOUNT DORA ACE HARDWARE, INC.—See Ace Hardware Corporation; *U.S. Private*, pg. 56
MS BRICO—See Compagnie de Saint-Gobain SA; *Int'l*, pg. 1724
MUTUAL ACE HARDWARE—See Ace Hardware Corporation; *U.S. Private*, pg. 56
NACHON ENTERPRISES INC.; *U.S. Private*, pg. 2830
NATIONAL LADDER & SCAFFOLD COMPANY, INC.; *U.S. Private*, pg. 2858
NORTHERN TOOL & EQUIPMENT CO. LTD.—See Northern Tool & Equipment Company, Inc.; *U.S. Private*, pg. 2954
NORTHERN TOOL & EQUIPMENT COMPANY, INC.; *U.S. Private*, pg. 2954
NORTHWEST FASTENER SALES INC.—See AEA Investors LP; *U.S. Private*, pg. 114
ORCHARD SUPPLY COMPANY, LLC—See Lowe's Companies, Inc.; *U.S. Public*, pg. 1343
PARIS OXYGEN COMPANY—See BBHC, Inc.; *U.S. Public*, pg. 284
PARKROSE HARDWARE, INC.—See Tyndale Advisors, LLC; *U.S. Private*, pg. 4268
PARKROSE HARDWARE WASHINGTON, INC.—See Tyndale Advisors, LLC; *U.S. Private*, pg. 4268
PAUL B. ZIMMERMAN INC.; *U.S. Private*, pg. 3112
PAUL'S ACE HARDWARE STORES; *U.S. Private*, pg. 3113
POINT P—See Compagnie de Saint-Gobain SA; *Int'l*, pg. 1724
POINT P—See Compagnie de Saint-Gobain SA; *Int'l*, pg. 1724
POINT P TROUILLARD—See Compagnie de Saint-Gobain SA; *Int'l*, pg. 1725
PRESTA CONTRACTORS SUPPLY, INC.—See Leonard Green & Partners, L.P.; *U.S. Private*, pg. 2429
PROFESSIONAL EQUIPMENT—See W.W. Grainger, Inc.; *U.S. Public*, pg. 2320
PT BINA UNGGUL KENCANA—See Bukalapak.com PT Tbk; *Int'l*, pg. 1213
QUADCO INCORPORATED; *U.S. Private*, pg. 3315
QUALITY FASTENERS & SUPPLY CO.—See Kian Capital Partners, LLC; *U.S. Private*, pg. 2302
QUALITY FASTENERS & SUPPLY CO.—See Oakland Standard Co., LLC; *U.S. Private*, pg. 2985
RAND MATERIALS HANDLING EQUIPMENT—See W.W. Grainger, Inc.; *U.S. Public*, pg. 2320
RENO HARDWARE & SUPPLY INC.—See Clayton, Dubilier & Rice, LLC; *U.S. Private*, pg. 930
R.L. MORGAN COMPANY INC.; *U.S. Private*, pg. 3338
ROCKLER COMPANIES, INC.; *U.S. Private*, pg. 3467
ROCKY'S HARDWARE INCORPORATED; *U.S. Private*, pg. 3469
ROMMEL HOLDINGS INC.; *U.S. Private*, pg. 3476
ROWLEY COMPANY, LLC; *U.S. Private*, pg. 3490
RUNNING SUPPLY INC.; *U.S. Private*, pg. 3504
RUSSO HARDWARE, INC.; *U.S. Private*, pg. 3507
RYAN SUPPLY, INC.—See Ace Hardware Corporation; *U.S. Private*, pg. 57
SCHMIDT DISTRIBUTORS INC.; *U.S. Private*, pg. 3566
SFIC—See Compagnie de Saint-Gobain SA; *Int'l*, pg. 1728
SHELL LUMBER & HARDWARE INC.; *U.S. Private*, pg. 3631
SIERRA LUMBER, INC.—See Owens Corning; *U.S. Public*, pg. 1627
SIMONS HARDWARE & BATH, INC.; *U.S. Private*, pg. 3666
SPIRALOCK DO BRASIL LTDA—See Stanley Black & Decker, Inc.; *U.S. Public*, pg. 1935
STARTECH.COM USA LLP; *U.S. Private*, pg. 3788
SUNNY BUILDING AND DECORATION MATERIALS COMPANY LIMITED—See E. Bon Holdings Ltd; *Int'l*, pg. 2250
SUNSHINE ACE HARDWARE INC.; *U.S. Private*, pg. 3871
SUNSHINE HARDWARE INC.; *U.S. Private*, pg. 3871
TAP ENTERPRISES INC.; *U.S. Private*, pg. 3932
TAYLOR-FOSTER HARDWARE, INC.—See Tyndale Advisors, LLC; *U.S. Private*, pg. 4268
THUON SA—See Compagnie de Saint-Gobain SA; *Int'l*, pg. 1737
TOOLBOX.CO.UK—See Grafton Group plc; *Int'l*, pg. 3051
TOOL KING; *U.S. Private*, pg. 4185
TOWN & COUNTRY HARDWARE STORES, LLC—See Tyndale Advisors, LLC; *U.S. Private*, pg. 4268
TRUE VALUE COMPANY, L.L.C.—See ACON Investments, LLC; *U.S. Private*, pg. 63
VICSA STEELPRO S.A.—See Bunzl plc; *Int'l*, pg. 1220
VINE HILL HARDWARE INC.; *U.S. Private*, pg. 4385
VISION ACE HARDWARE, LLC; *U.S. Private*, pg. 4390
W.E. AUBUCHON CO., INC.; *U.S. Private*, pg. 4420
WESTLAKE HARDWARE, INC.—See Ace Hardware Corporation; *U.S. Private*, pg. 57
WOODCRAFT SUPPLY, LLC; *U.S. Private*, pg. 4557
WOODIE'S DIY—See Grafton Group plc; *Int'l*, pg. 3051
ZESKIND'S HARDWARE, INC.; *U.S. Private*, pg. 4602

444180 — OTHER BUILDING MATERIAL DEALERS

5C INVESTMENTS, LLC—See Campbell Soup Company; *U.S. Public*, pg. 427
ABB A/S—See ABB Ltd.; *Int'l*, pg. 49
ACCU-WELD, LLC—See H.I.G. Capital, LLC; *U.S. Private*, pg. 1831
ADVANTAGE SYSTEMS INC.—See NCH Corporation; *U.S. Private*, pg. 2875
AFFILIATED STEAM EQUIPMENT CO. INDIANAPOLIS—See Affiliated Steam Equipment Company; *U.S. Private*, pg. 122
AGRAVIS BAUSTOFFHANDEL GMBH—See AGRAVIS Raiffeisen AG; *Int'l*, pg. 214
AGROMEC TILEAGD SA; *Int'l*, pg. 220
AL AMANA BUILDING MATERIALS CO. L.L.C—See DAMAC Group; *Int'l*, pg. 1955
ALDACHANIE; *Int'l*, pg. 304
AL DANUBE BUILDING MATERIALS TRADING CO., LLC; *Int'l*, pg. 276
ALHAMRANI COMPANY FOR INDUSTRY—See Alhamrani Group; *Int'l*, pg. 319
ALLEY-CASSETTY BRICK BOWLING GREEN DIVISION—See Alley-Cassetty Companies; *U.S. Private*, pg. 180
AL-OULA COMPANY; *Int'l*, pg. 288
ALUMINIUM VERKOOP ZUID B.V.—See CRH plc; *Int'l*, pg. 1842
AMAZULU INC.; *U.S. Private*, pg. 216
AMERICAN RANGE CORPORATION—See Hatco Corporation; *U.S. Private*, pg. 1879
ANGELUS BLOCK CO. INC.; *U.S. Private*, pg. 282
ANN SACKS TILE & STONE, INC.—See Kohler Company; *U.S. Private*, pg. 2339
ANTARES GROUP, INC.; *U.S. Private*, pg. 287
ANTHONY SPECIALTY GLASS LLC—See Dover Corporation; *U.S. Public*, pg. 678
APACHE STONE LLC—See Trilantic Capital Management L.P.; *U.S. Private*, pg. 4231
APPLETON GROUP - FULLERTON—See Emerson Electric Co.; *U.S. Public*, pg. 740
APPLETON SUPPLY CO., INC.—See Gibraltar Industries, Inc.; *U.S. Public*, pg. 935
ARIZONA TILE SUPPLY, INC.; *U.S. Private*, pg. 325
ARMSTRONG WORLD INDUSTRIES (H.K.) LIMITED—See Armstrong World Industries, Inc.; *U.S. Public*, pg. 194
ARRAN ISLE LTD.—See ASSA ABLOY AB; *Int'l*, pg. 638
ARTISTIC TILE INC.; *U.S. Private*, pg. 343
ASSA ABLOY ENTRANCE SYSTEMS NORWAY AS—See ASSA ABLOY AB; *Int'l*, pg. 633
ASTRIMEX B.V.—See Blackstone Inc.; *U.S. Public*, pg. 356
AUTO GLASS NOW LLC—See Driven Brands Holdings Inc.; *U.S. Public*, pg. 688
A WORLD OF TILE LLC; *U.S. Private*, pg. 19
BALDAI1 UAB—See BHG Group AB; *Int'l*, pg. 1014
BARBER GLASS RETAIL; *Int'l*, pg. 858
BARRETTS OF BALLINASLOE LIMITED—See Grafton Group plc; *Int'l*, pg. 3050
BARRONS ENTERPRISES, INC.—See Bain Capital, LP; *U.S. Private*, pg. 450
BASF CONSTRUCTION CHEMICALS AUSTRALIA PTY. LTD.—See BASF SE; *Int'l*, pg. 874
BASF CONSTRUCTION CHEMICALS BELGIUM NV—See BASF SE; *Int'l*, pg. 874
BASF CONSTRUCTION CHEMICALS FRANCE S.A.S.—See BASF SE; *Int'l*, pg. 874
BASF CONSTRUCTION CHEMICALS (HONG KONG) LIMITED—See BASF SE; *Int'l*, pg. 874
BASF CONSTRUCTION CHEMICALS MALAYSIA SDN BHD—See BASF SE; *Int'l*, pg. 874
BASF CONSTRUCTION CHEMICALS SINGAPORE PTE LTD—See BASF SE; *Int'l*, pg. 874
BASF CONSTRUCTION CHEMICALS SWEDEN AB—See BASF SE; *Int'l*, pg. 874
BASF CONSTRUCTION CHEMICALS (TAIWAN) CO., LTD—See BASF SE; *Int'l*, pg. 874
BASF CONSTRUCTION CHEMICALS VENEZUELA, S.A.—See BASF SE; *Int'l*, pg. 875
BASF NEDERLAND B.V., CONSTRUCTION CHEMICALS—See BASF SE; *Int'l*, pg. 874
BAUMART HOLDINGS LIMITED; *Int'l*, pg. 895
BAY INSULATION OF MISSOURI INC.—See Bay Industries Inc.; *U.S. Private*, pg. 493
BEIJING BUILDING MATERIALS IMPORT AND EXPORT CO., LTD—See BBMG Corporation; *Int'l*, pg. 920
BELDEN BRICK & SUPPLY CO. INC.; *U.S. Private*, pg. 517
BILCO UK LTD.—See Quanex Building Products Corp.; *U.S. Public*, pg. 1749

444180 — OTHER BUILDING MATE...

BINGHAMTON MATERIAL HANDLING, INC.—See Win Win, Inc.; *U.S. Private*, pg. 4532
BISCA MATERIAUX SARL; *Int'l*, pg. 1048
BITUMENKA D.D.; *Int'l*, pg. 1050
BLACKWOOD BUILDING CENTRE LTD.; *Int'l*, pg. 1062
BLAIR BUILDING MATERIALS INC.—See GMS Inc.; *U.S. Public*, pg. 947
BMC WEST CORPORATION—See Builders FirstSource, Inc.; *U.S. Public*, pg. 410
BORGWARNER MASSACHUSETTS INC.—See BorgWarner Inc.; *U.S. Public*, pg. 369
BRILLOCA LIMITED—See Hindware Home Innovation Limited; *Int'l*, pg. 3400
BROOKSIDE LUMBER COMPANY; *U.S. Private*, pg. 665
BROOMFIELD LABORATORIES INC.; *U.S. Private*, pg. 665
BUCKWOLD WESTERN LTD.; *Int'l*, pg. 1210
THE BUILDERS CENTRE (SHEFFIELD) LIMITED—See Frank Key Group Limited; *Int'l*, pg. 2761
BULBS.COM INCORPORATED; *U.S. Private*, pg. 684
BURBAGE IRON CRAFT SERVICES LIMITED—See ARGENT INDUSTRIAL LIMITED; *Int'l*, pg. 560
BYGGMA ASA; *Int'l*, pg. 1235
BYGHJEMME.DK APS—See BHG Group AB; *Int'l*, pg. 1014
BYKO EHF—See Einhell Germany AG; *Int'l*, pg. 2332
CABINET DISCOUNTERS INC.; *U.S. Private*, pg. 710
CAMOLA APS—See BHG Group AB; *Int'l*, pg. 1014
CANCOS TILE CORP.; *U.S. Private*, pg. 733
CAPITOL INTERIOR PRODUCTS, INC.—See GMS Inc.; *U.S. Public*, pg. 947
CAPITOL MATERIALS COASTAL, INC.—See GMS Inc.; *U.S. Public*, pg. 948
CARDO DOOR INTERNATIONAL AG—See ASSA ABLOY AB; *Int'l*, pg. 634
CARLISLE CONSTRUCTION MATERIALS, LLC—See Carlisle Companies Incorporated; *U.S. Public*, pg. 436
CASA REDIMIX CONCRETE CORP.; *U.S. Private*, pg. 778
CEMENTOS LA UNION-SPAIN SA—See Arabian Cement Company; *Int'l*, pg. 533
CEMEX LATAM HOLDINGS SA—See CEMEX, S.A.B. de C.V.; *Int'l*, pg. 1398
CERAMICA AZULEJOS TERRAZZOS; *U.S. Private*, pg. 835
CHAMPION LUMBER CO.; *U.S. Private*, pg. 846
C.H. BRIGGS COMPANY; *U.S. Private*, pg. 707
CHIN HIN GROUP BERHAD; *Int'l*, pg. 1480
CHONBURI KANYONG CO., LTD.—See Chonburi Concrete Product Public Company Limited; *Int'l*, pg. 1578
CITY GLASS COMPANY—See Dothan Glass Co. Inc.; *U.S. Private*, pg. 1265
CLOSET & STORAGE CONCEPTS; *U.S. Private*, pg. 946
COCHEZ Y COMPANIA, S.A.; *Int'l*, pg. 1686
CONSOLIDATED ALLOYS (NZ) LTD—See Amalgamated Metal Corporation PLC; *Int'l*, pg. 408
COREAS HAZELLS INC.—See Goddard Enterprises Limited; *Int'l*, pg. 3018
CORK BUILDERS PROVIDERS LIMITED—See Grafton Group plc; *Int'l*, pg. 3050
COUNTRY FLOORS INC.; *U.S. Private*, pg. 1067
CRANE ENGINEERED MATERIALS—See Crane NXT, Co.; *U.S. Public*, pg. 590
CROWN C SUPPLY CO., INC.—See Leonard Green & Partners, L.P.; *U.S. Private*, pg. 2429
DAIMAN TRADING SDN. BHD.—See Daiman Development Berhad; *Int'l*, pg. 1938
DENVER GLASS INTERIORS, INC.—See Baymark Partners; *U.S. Private*, pg. 496
DESIGNKUPP AS—See Brodrene A & O Johansen A/S; *Int'l*, pg. 1173
DESIGN SPACE MODULAR BUILDINGS PNW, LP—See McGrath RentCorp.; *U.S. Public*, pg. 1407
DISCOUNT DRAINAGE SUPPLIES, LLC—See Winsupply, Inc.; *U.S. Private*, pg. 4545
DOUBLECOOL B.V.—See LCI Industries; *U.S. Public*, pg. 1296
DUGA A.D.; *Int'l*, pg. 2224
DUO-FAST, INC.; *U.S. Private*, pg. 1291
DYNAMIC ARCHITECTURAL WINDOWS & DOORS INC.; *Int'l*, pg. 2240
EAGLE ROCK AGGREGATES, INC.—See Vulcan Materials Company; *U.S. Public*, pg. 2314
EASY HEAT EUROPE B.V.—See Emerson Electric Co.; *U.S. Public*, pg. 740
E.B. MAWSON AND SONS PTY. LTD.—See CRH plc; *Int'l*, pg. 1842
ECOBUILD PRODUCTS PTE LTD—See GPS Alliance Holdings Limited; *Int'l*, pg. 3047
EDDY GROUP LIMITED; *Int'l*, pg. 2304
EFCO MALAYSIA SDN. BHD.—See Wilian Holding Co., Inc.; *U.S. Private*, pg. 4520
EMERSON ELECTRIC POLAND SP. Z.O.O.—See Emerson Electric Co.; *U.S. Public*, pg. 745
EMERSON ELECTRIC U.K. LTD.—See Emerson Electric Co.; *U.S. Public*, pg. 745
EMERSON PROCESS MANAGEMENT DISTRIBUTION LTD.—See Emerson Electric Co.; *U.S. Public*, pg. 747
EMERSON PROCESS MANAGEMENT—See Emerson Electric Co.; *U.S. Public*, pg. 746
EMIRATES BUILDING SYSTEMS COMPANY LLC—See Dubai Investments PJSC; *Int'l*, pg. 2219
EMIRATES EXTRUDED POLYSTYRENE LLC—See Dubai Investments PJSC; *Int'l*, pg. 2219
ENERPAC MIDDLE EAST FZE—See Enerpac Tool Group Corp.; *U.S. Public*, pg. 765
ESTAN ITALIA MINERALS SRL—See Eczacibasi Holding A.S.; *Int'l*, pg. 2301
ETR1 GROUP OU—See BHG Group AB; *Int'l*, pg. 1014
EUROPEAN BATH, KITCHEN, TILE & STONE—See Blackfriars Corp.; *U.S. Private*, pg. 575
EUROTRADE1 D.O.O.—See BHG Group AB; *Int'l*, pg. 1014
EUROTRADE1 SIA—See BHG Group AB; *Int'l*, pg. 1014
EXPI-DOOR SYSTEMS INC.—See Bay Industries Inc.; *U.S. Private*, pg. 493
THE FENCE STORE; *U.S. Private*, pg. 4028
FERGUSON VALVES & AUTOMATION CO.—See Ferguson plc; *Int'l*, pg. 2638
FERRELL BUILDER'S SUPPLY LTD.; *Int'l*, pg. 2640
FERTIG CABINET COMPANY INC.; *U.S. Private*, pg. 1498
FISKARS CONSUMER GOODS (SHANGHAI) CO., LTD.—See Fiskars Oyj Abp; *Int'l*, pg. 2694
FITTERS MARKETING SDN BHD—See FITTERS Diversified Berhad; *Int'l*, pg. 2695
FLETCHER BUILDING LIMITED; *Int'l*, pg. 2699
FLETCHER BUILDING PRODUCTS LIMITED—See Fletcher Building Limited; *Int'l*, pg. 2700
FRANK KEY GROUP LIMITED; *Int'l*, pg. 2761
FRANK KEY (NOTTINGHAM) LIMITED—See Frank Key Group Limited; *Int'l*, pg. 2761
FRONTLINE BLDG. PRODUCTS INC.—See Bay Industries Inc.; *U.S. Private*, pg. 493
F&T BUCKLEY (HOLDINGS) LIMITED—See Grafton Group plc; *Int'l*, pg. 3050
F&T BUCKLEY LIMITED—See Grafton Group plc; *Int'l*, pg. 3050
FURNITURE1 D.O.O.—See BHG Group AB; *Int'l*, pg. 1014
FURNITURE1 KFT—See BHG Group AB; *Int'l*, pg. 1014
FURNITURE1 UAB—See BHG Group AB; *Int'l*, pg. 1014
GALAXY GLASS & ALUMINUM INC.; *U.S. Private*, pg. 1636
GALLEHER LUMBER CO.—See Boyne Capital Management, LLC; *U.S. Private*, pg. 629
GARDEN SUPPLY HARDSCAPES—See Trilantic Capital Management L.P.; *U.S. Private*, pg. 4231
GARVEY BUILDERS PROVIDERS LIMITED—See Grafton Group plc; *Int'l*, pg. 3050
GEBR. KNAUF KG; *Int'l*, pg. 2906
GENESEE CUT STONE & MARBLE CO.; *U.S. Private*, pg. 1669
GEWISS DEUTSCHLAND GMBH—See Gewiss S.p.A.; *Int'l*, pg. 2955
GILEVE; *Int'l*, pg. 2975
GOLVPOOLEN HELSINGBORG AB—See BHG Group AB; *Int'l*, pg. 1015
GRAFTON MERCHANTING GB LIMITED - BUILDBASE SUPPORT CENTRE DIVISION—See Grafton Group plc; *Int'l*, pg. 3050
GRAFTON MERCHANTING GB LIMITED - CIVILS & LINTELS DIVISION—See Grafton Group plc; *Int'l*, pg. 3051
GRAFTON MERCHANTING ROI LIMITED—See Grafton Group plc; *Int'l*, pg. 3051
GRANITE PRECASTING & CONCRETE, INC.—See CRH plc; *Int'l*, pg. 1846
GREAT BRITAIN TILE, INC.; *U.S. Private*, pg. 1762
GREYSTONE AMBIENT & STYLE GMBH & CO. KG—See Heidelberg Materials AG; *Int'l*, pg. 3310
GREZDIS; *Int'l*, pg. 3082
GULF ROCKS K.S.C.; *Int'l*, pg. 3182
HALDANE FISHER LTD.; *Int'l*, pg. 3227
HALLMARK BUILDING SUPPLIES, INC.; *U.S. Private*, pg. 1844
HANEY BUILDERS' SUPPLIES (1971) LTD.; *Int'l*, pg. 3244
HARRELL HALL ENTERPRISES INC.; *U.S. Private*, pg. 1868
HARRISONS SARAWAK SDN BHD—See Harrisons Holdings (Malaysia) Berhad; *Int'l*, pg. 3279
HARRISONS TRADING (PENINSULAR) SDN BHD—See Harrisons Holdings (Malaysia) Berhad; *Int'l*, pg. 3279
HARRISONS TRADING (SABAH) SDN BHD—See Harrisons Holdings (Malaysia) Berhad; *Int'l*, pg. 3279
HARROD MANAGEMENT INC.; *U.S. Private*, pg. 1871
HASTINGS TILE & BATH, INC.; *U.S. Private*, pg. 1879
HATHAWAY & SONS, INC.—See GMS Inc.; *U.S. Public*, pg. 948
HAYWOOD BUILDERS SUPPLY COMPANY—See Building Industry Partners LLC; *U.S. Private*, pg. 683
HENDRICKS LOVELL LTD.—See Grafton Group plc; *Int'l*, pg. 3051
HESCO BASTION, INC.—See CVC Capital Partners SICAVFIS S.A.; *Int'l*, pg. 1886
H&H DOOR CO., INC.—See Platinum Equity, LLC; *U.S. Private*, pg. 3208
HILLS ACE HARDWARE & LUMBER CENTER; *U.S. Private*, pg. 1946
HIROSS ZANDER DIVISION—See Parker Hannifin Corporation; *U.S. Public*, pg. 1649
HIRSONDIS; *Int'l*, pg. 3406

HOME ACRES BUILDING SUPPLY CO., LLC; *U.S. Private*, pg. 1970
HORNBACH BAUMARKT CS SPOL S.R.O.—See Hornbach Holding AG & Co. KGaA; *Int'l*, pg. 3482
HORNBACH BAUMARKT (SCHWEIZ) AG—See Hornbach Holding AG & Co. KGaA; *Int'l*, pg. 3482
HORNBACH BOUWMARKT (NEDERLAND) B.V.—See Hornbach Holding AG & Co. KGaA; *Int'l*, pg. 3482
HORNBACH CENTRALA SRL—See Hornbach Holding AG & Co. KGaA; *Int'l*, pg. 3481
HOTEL VANITIES INTERNATIONAL, LLC; *U.S. Private*, pg. 1989
HUNZA TRADING SDN. BHD.—See Hunza Properties Berhad; *Int'l*, pg. 3537
HUTTIG, INC.—See Woodgrain, Inc.; *U.S. Private*, pg. 4558
HUTTIG TEXAS LIMITED PARTNERSHIP—See Woodgrain, Inc.; *U.S. Private*, pg. 4558
HYMETAL CONSTRUCTION PRODUCTS CO., LTD.; *Int'l*, pg. 3549
ICON UTILITY SERVICES, INC.; *U.S. Private*, pg. 2032
INNOVATIVE SURFACES, LLC; *U.S. Private*, pg. 2083
INTEGRATE MARKETING PTE LTD.—See Compact Metal Industries Ltd.; *Int'l*, pg. 1721
INTOWN DESIGN, INC.—See Littlejohn & Co., LLC; *U.S. Private*, pg. 2470
INTOWN DESIGN, INC.—See Platinum Equity, LLC; *U.S. Private*, pg. 3205
JENKINS BRICK COMPANY, INC. -ATTALLA—See Berkshire Hathaway Inc.; *U.S. Public*, pg. 298
J.E. TELFORD LIMITED—See Grafton Group plc; *Int'l*, pg. 3051
JEWETT-CAMERON TRADING COMPANY LTD.; *U.S. Public*, pg. 1189
JEWSON LTD.—See Compagnie de Saint-Gobain SA; *Int'l*, pg. 1733
JIM WATERS CORPORATION—See Richards Building Supply Company; *U.S. Private*, pg. 3428
JJ FERGUSON SAND & GRAVEL; *U.S. Private*, pg. 2211
JUNIOR'S BUILDING MATERIALS, INC.; *U.S. Private*, pg. 2244
KLEET LUMBER COMPANY, INC.—See Builders FirstSource, Inc.; *U.S. Public*, pg. 410
KNAUF AG—See Gebr. Knauf KG; *Int'l*, pg. 2906
KP BUILDING PRODUCTS LTD.—See Compagnie de Saint-Gobain SA; *Int'l*, pg. 1723
LA PLATEFORME DU BATIMENT—See Compagnie de Saint-Gobain SA; *Int'l*, pg. 1724
LASALLE BRISTOL CORP.—See ASSA ABLOY AB; *Int'l*, pg. 639
LEZZER LUMBER, INC.; *U.S. Private*, pg. 2441
LIBERTY LUMBER COMPANY—See Younger Brothers Group Inc.; *U.S. Private*, pg. 4593
LIFCO AB—See Carl Bennet AB; *Int'l*, pg. 1332
LUMBERJACK'S, INC.; *U.S. Private*, pg. 2513
L&W SUPPLY CORPORATION—See Hendricks Holding Company, Inc.; *U.S. Private*, pg. 1915
MANCHESTER SAND, GRAVEL & CEMENT CO. INC.—See Boston Sand & Gravel Company; *U.S. Public*, pg. 373
MANOR HOUSE KITCHENS INC.; *U.S. Private*, pg. 2566
MARKRAFT CABINETS INC.—See The Sterling Group, L.P.; *U.S. Private*, pg. 4122
MARTIN MARIETTA MATERIALS, INC.; *U.S. Public*, pg. 1389
MASCO CHILE LIMITADA—See Masco Corporation; *U.S. Public*, pg. 1391
MASSEY BUILDERS' SUPPLY CORP.—See Bain Capital, LP; *U.S. Private*, pg. 451
MATCO RAVARY INC.—See Groupe B.M.R. Inc.; *Int'l*, pg. 3092
M-D BUILDING PRODUCTS, INC.; *U.S. Private*, pg. 2525
MEBELI24 OOD—See BHG Group AB; *Int'l*, pg. 1015
MELTEC S.A.—See Gewiss S.p.A.; *Int'l*, pg. 2955
METRO TINT—See Solar Art Window Film, Inc.; *U.S. Private*, pg. 3707
METZ WOIPPY CEDEO—See Compagnie de Saint-Gobain SA; *Int'l*, pg. 1724
MFP SALES LTD.—See Grafton Group plc; *Int'l*, pg. 3051
MIDCO-BAY INSULATION INC.—See Bay Industries Inc.; *U.S. Private*, pg. 493
MISSOURI DRYWALL SUPPLY, INC.—See GMS Inc.; *U.S. Public*, pg. 948
MODULAR TECHNOLOGIES INC.; *U.S. Private*, pg. 2763
MORRISON TERREBONNE LUMBER CENTER—See Tyndale Advisors, LLC; *U.S. Private*, pg. 4268
MOUNTAIN LUMBER COMPANY, INC.—See The Building Center, Inc.; *U.S. Private*, pg. 4002
MTS SYSTEMS GMBH—See Amphenol Corporation; *U.S. Public*, pg. 131
NETRAUTA FINLAND OY—See BHG Group AB; *Int'l*, pg. 1015
NITTANY BUILDING SPECIALTIES, INC., FLOORING DIVISION—See Nittany Building Specialties, Inc.; *U.S. Private*, pg. 2929
NITTANY BUILDING SPECIALTIES, INC., GLASS DIVISION—See Nittany Building Specialties, Inc.; *U.S. Private*, pg. 2929

N.A.I.C.S. INDEX

444240 — NURSERY, GARDEN CEN...

NITTANY BUILDING SPECIALTIES, INC.; *U.S. Private*, pg. 2929
NOLAND PROPERTIES, INC.—See Winsupply Inc.; *U.S. Private*, pg. 4544
NORDISKA FONSTER I ANGELHOLM AB—See BHG Group AB; *Int'l*, pg. 1014
NOTIFIER (BENELUX) S.A.—See Honeywell International Inc.; *U.S. Public*, pg. 1050
NOTIFIER DEUTSCHLAND GMBH—See Honeywell International Inc.; *U.S. Public*, pg. 1050
NOTIFIER ITALIA S.R.L.—See Honeywell International Inc.; *U.S. Public*, pg. 1050
OK INTERNATIONAL, INC.—See Dover Corporation; *U.S. Public*, pg. 680
OLSHAN LUMBER CO.; *U.S. Private*, pg. 3011
OLYMPIA BUILDING SUPPLIES, LLC—See GMS Inc.; *U.S. Public*, pg. 948
OWENS-CORNING FIBERGLASS FRANCE S.A.—See Owens Corning; *U.S. Public*, pg. 1628
OWENS CORNING (SHANGHAI) TRADING CO., LTD.—See Owens Corning; *U.S. Public*, pg. 1627
PACIFIC ARCHITECTURAL PRODUCTS, INC.—See Tumac Lumber Co. Inc.; *U.S. Private*, pg. 4258
PACIFIC COAST SUPPLY, LLC - DIAMOND PACIFIC DIVISION—See Pacific Coast Building Products, Inc.; *U.S. Private*, pg. 3066
PACIFIC COAST SUPPLY, LLC - PACIFIC SUPPLY DIVISION—See Pacific Coast Building Products, Inc.; *U.S. Private*, pg. 3066
PACIFIC COAST SUPPLY, LLC—See Pacific Coast Building Products, Inc.; *U.S. Private*, pg. 3066
PACIFIC MOBILE STRUCTURES INC.; *U.S. Private*, pg. 3068
PARTIDIS S.A.S.—See Compagnie de Saint-Gobain SA; *Int'l*, pg. 1724
PCI AUGSBURG GMBH—See BASF SE; *Int'l*, pg. 875
PETER & COMPANY LIMITED—See Goddard Enterprises Limited; *Int'l*, pg. 3019
PIONEER SAND COMPANY INC.—See SiteOne Landscape Supply, Inc.; *U.S. Public*, pg. 1889
PIPE EXCHANGE INC.—See Corpac Steel Products Corp.; *U.S. Private*, pg. 1053
PLAKABETON FRANCE S.A.—See CRH plc; *Int'l*, pg. 1844
PLUMBLINE SUPPLIES LTD.—See Grafton Group plc; *Int'l*, pg. 3051
POINT P SA—See Compagnie de Saint-Gobain SA; *Int'l*, pg. 1724
POLY VINYL CREATIONS, INC.; *U.S. Private*, pg. 3225
PONTMEYER B.V.—See HAL Trust N.V.; *Int'l*, pg. 3224
PORCELANOSA NEW YORK INC.; *U.S. Private*, pg. 3229
PREMIX-MARBLETITE MFG. CO.—See Q.E.P. Co., Inc.; *U.S. Public*, pg. 1741
PROSPECT AGGREGATES, INC.—See CRH plc; *Int'l*, pg. 1847
PSI PRODUCTS GMBH—See Enpro Inc.; *U.S. Public*, pg. 775
RAAB KARCHER BOUWSTOFFEN—See Compagnie de Saint-Gobain SA; *Int'l*, pg. 1733
RGF INDUSTRIES INCORPORATED; *U.S. Private*, pg. 3420
RIDOUT LUMBER COS., INC.—See Bain Capital, LP; *U.S. Private*, pg. 451
RIVERHEAD BUILDING SUPPLY CORP.; *U.S. Private*, pg. 3444
R&K BUILDING SUPPLIES—See Farnsworth Development Companies; *U.S. Private*, pg. 1480
R.K. MILES; *U.S. Private*, pg. 3338
ROME BUILDING PRODUCTS INC.—See Hendricks Holding Company, Inc.; *U.S. Private*, pg. 1915
ROYAL COPENHAGEN KOREA LTD.—See Fiskars Oyj Abp; *Int'l*, pg. 2694
SAFETY FIRST—See O'Keeffe's, Inc.; *U.S. Private*, pg. 2978
SAINT-GOBAIN DISTRIBUCION CONSTRUCCION, S.L—See Compagnie de Saint-Gobain SA; *Int'l*, pg. 1732
SAMON'S TIGER STORES INC.; *U.S. Private*, pg. 3537
SAND & GRUS JEHANDER—See Heidelberg Materials AG; *Int'l*, pg. 3315
S&A SUPPLY COMPANY INC.—See Daikin Industries, Ltd.; *Int'l*, pg. 1935
SAX SANITAIR N.V.—See CRH plc; *Int'l*, pg. 1848
SBS/BISON BUILDING MATERIALS, LLC—See Builders FirstSource, Inc.; *U.S. Public*, pg. 409
SCREENMOBILE CORP.—See Apax Partners LLP; *U.S. Private*, pg. 502
SELCO TRADE CENTRES LIMITED—See Grafton Group plc; *Int'l*, pg. 3051
SELECT INTERIOR CONCEPTS, INC.—See Sun Capital Partners, Inc.; *U.S. Private*, pg. 3861
SERVICE PARTNERS OF FLORIDA, LLC—See Masco Corporation; *U.S. Public*, pg. 1392
SEWER TAP, INC.—See Advanced Drainage Systems, Inc.; *U.S. Public*, pg. 46
SHOSEKI KAKO K.K.—See Idemitsu Kosan Co., Ltd.; *Int'l*, pg. 3592
SIERRA READY MIX, LLC—See Summit Materials, Inc.; *U.S. Public*, pg. 1960

SILEX INTERIORS 2, LLC—See Silex Holdings, Inc.; *U.S. Private*, pg. 3652
SILVAN A/S—See Aurelius Equity Opportunities SE & Co. KGaA; *Int'l*, pg. 709
SIRAI DEUTSCHLAND VERTRIEB ELEKTROMECHANISCHER GERAETE GMBH—See Emerson Electric Co.; *U.S. Public*, pg. 752
SPOONFLOWER, INC.—See Apollo Global Management, Inc.; *U.S. Public*, pg. 159
STANDARD SUPPLIES—See Ernest Maier, Inc.; *U.S. Private*, pg. 1421
STARCREST OF CALIFORNIA—See Starcrest Products of California; *U.S. Private*, pg. 3786
STARK DANMARK A/S—See Lone Star Global Acquisitions, LLC; *U.S. Private*, pg. 2489
STARK DEUTSCHLAND GMBH—See Lone Star Global Acquisitions, LLC; *U.S. Private*, pg. 2489
STARK SUOMI OY—See Lone Star Global Acquisitions, LLC; *U.S. Private*, pg. 2489
STAR SHINE STEEL PRODUCTS SDN. BHD.—See BlueScope Steel Limited; *Int'l*, pg. 1074
STEELMASTER BUILDINGS, INC.; *U.S. Private*, pg. 3797
ST. MARYS SAND COMPANY, LLC—See Martin Marietta Materials, Inc.; *U.S. Public*, pg. 1389
STONE'S, INC.; *U.S. Private*, pg. 3826
STRUYK VERWO GROEP B.V.—See CRH plc; *Int'l*, pg. 1848
SUDWEST LACKE & FARBEN GMBH & CO. KG—See Buzzi SpA; *Int'l*, pg. 1231
SWIFTECH INTERNATIONAL LIMITED—See China Oral Industry Group Holdings Limited; *Int'l*, pg. 1538
TALOON YHTIOT OY—See BHG Group AB; *Int'l*, pg. 1015
TBSG, LLC—See Builders FirstSource, Inc.; *U.S. Public*, pg. 409
THERMAL ENERGY PRODUCTS, INC.—See HEICO Corporation; *U.S. Public*, pg. 1021
THEUT PRODUCTS INC.; *U.S. Private*, pg. 4143
TITAN CONSTRUCTION SUPPLY, INC.—See The Sterling Group, L.P.; *U.S. Private*, pg. 4122
TOPTECH (SHANGHAI) BUILDING MATERIAL LTD.—See Great Eagle Holdings Limited; *Int'l*, pg. 3064
TRIKEENAN TILEWORK, INC.—See Elgin-Butler Brick Company; *U.S. Private*, pg. 1359
TRUE HOME VALUE, INC.; *U.S. Private*, pg. 4247
TRUITT & WHITE; *U.S. Private*, pg. 4249
TUCKER MATERIALS, INC.—See GMS Inc.; *U.S. Public*, pg. 948
TYMAN PLC—See Quanex Building Products Corp.; *U.S. Public*, pg. 1749
UFP SHAWNEE, LLC—See UFP Industries, Inc.; *U.S. Public*, pg. 2220
ULBRINOX—See Ulbrich Stainless Steel & Special Metals, Inc.; *U.S. Private*, pg. 4276
UMICORE BUILDING PRODUCTS HUNGARY KFT.—See Fedrus International NV; *Int'l*, pg. 2631
UMICORE BUILDING PRODUCTS IBERICA S.L.—See Fedrus International NV; *Int'l*, pg. 2631
UMICORE BUILDING PRODUCTS ITALIA S.R.L.—See Fedrus International NV; *Int'l*, pg. 2631
UNITED BUILDING MATERIALS, INC.—See GMS Inc.; *U.S. Public*, pg. 948
UNITED CONSTRUCTION PRODUCTS, INC.—See GMS Inc.; *U.S. Public*, pg. 948
UNIVERSAL PROVIDERS LIMITED—See Grafton Group plc; *Int'l*, pg. 3051
US BUILDINGS LLC; *U.S. Private*, pg. 4318
VALDEYRON MATERIAUX SAS—See Bisca Materiaux SARL; *Int'l*, pg. 1048
VALLEY GLASS INC.; *U.S. Private*, pg. 4334
VANGUARD MODULAR BUILDING SYSTEMS, LLC; *U.S. Private*, pg. 4343
VITRA (UK) LTD.—See Eczacibasi Holding A.S.; *Int'l*, pg. 2301
VNS CORPORATION; *U.S. Private*, pg. 4408
WALDO BROS. COMPANY; *U.S. Private*, pg. 4428
WESCO DISTRIBUTION, INC.—See WESCO International, Inc.; *U.S. Public*, pg. 2351
WESTNY BUILDING PRODUCTS CO.; *U.S. Private*, pg. 4500
WEYMOUTH CONCRETE INC.—See Boston Sand & Gravel Company; *U.S. Public*, pg. 373
WILLIAM CHARLES CONSTRUCTION - MATERIALS DIVISION—See MasTec, Inc.; *U.S. Public*, pg. 1393
WRIGHT DO IT CENTER; *U.S. Private*, pg. 4573
XO WINDOWS, LLC—See Younger Brothers Group Inc.; *U.S. Private*, pg. 4593
YOUNGER BROTHERS BUILDERS EXPRESS LIBERTY LLC—See Younger Brothers Group Inc.; *U.S. Private*, pg. 4594
YOUNGER BROTHERS DOOR & TRIM, LLC—See Younger Brothers Group Inc.; *U.S. Private*, pg. 4594

444230 — OUTDOOR POWER EQUIPMENT RETAILERS

ALITE DESIGNS, INC.—See The Travel Hammock Inc.; *U.S. Private*, pg. 4128

ATWOOD DISTRIBUTING, INC.; *U.S. Private*, pg. 384
BARNETT IMPLEMENT CO; *U.S. Private*, pg. 477
BLUE MOUNTAIN AGRI SUPPORT, INC.—See AGCO Corporation; *U.S. Public*, pg. 58
BROOKSIDE EQUIPMENT SALES; *U.S. Private*, pg. 665
THE CRANDALL-HICKS COMPANY, INC.; *U.S. Private*, pg. 4016
E.P. BARRUS LIMITED—See E.P. Barrus Ltd.; *Int'l*, pg. 2260
HANDY TV INC.; *U.S. Private*, pg. 1853
INDUSTRIAS JOHN DEERE ARGENTINA S.A.—See Deere & Company; *U.S. Public*, pg. 647
INDUSTRIAS JOHN DEERE S.A. DE C.V.—See Deere & Company; *U.S. Public*, pg. 646
JAMES R. ROSENCRANTZ & SONS; *U.S. Private*, pg. 2185
JOHN DEERE INTERCONTINENTAL GMBH—See Deere & Company; *U.S. Public*, pg. 646
JOHN DEERE INTERNATIONAL GMBH—See Deere & Company; *U.S. Public*, pg. 646
JOHN DEERE LIMITED AUSTRALIA—See Deere & Company; *U.S. Public*, pg. 646
JOHN DEERE LTD.—See Deere & Company; *U.S. Public*, pg. 646
JOHN DEERE MEXICO S.A. DE C.V.—See Deere & Company; *U.S. Public*, pg. 647
JOHN DEERE S.A.S.—See Deere & Company; *U.S. Public*, pg. 647
KAN EQUIPMENT INC.; *U.S. Private*, pg. 2259
MINNESOTA EQUIPMENT, INC.; *U.S. Private*, pg. 2743
MOFFETT TURF EQUIPMENT, INC.; *U.S. Private*, pg. 2765
NORTHEAST BATTERY & ALTERNATOR INC.—See Colville Capital LLC; *U.S. Public*, pg. 979
PARAMOUNT EQUIPMENT LLC; *U.S. Private*, pg. 3092
PRODUCTION RESOURCE GROUP (AUSTRALIA) PTY LTD.—See The Jordan Company, L.P.; *U.S. Private*, pg. 4061
RITCHIE TRACTOR COMPANY, LLC.; *U.S. Private*, pg. 3441
SOUTH DAYTONA TRACTOR & MOWER, INC.—See Ag-Pro, LLC; *U.S. Private*, pg. 125
SOUTHEAST MOWER & SAW SHOP—See Ag-Pro, LLC; *U.S. Private*, pg. 125
STREACKER TRACTOR SALES INC.; *U.S. Private*, pg. 3838
TRIGREEN EQUIPMENT LLC; *U.S. Private*, pg. 4231
UNIPER ENERGY SALES GMBH—See Fortum Oyj; *Int'l*, pg. 2742
WEINGARTZ SUPPLY CO. INC.; *U.S. Private*, pg. 4472

444240 — NURSERY, GARDEN CENTER, AND FARM SUPPLY RETAILERS

ACROSS THE POND—See SiteOne Landscape Supply, Inc.; *U.S. Public*, pg. 1888
ADM COLLINGWOOD GRAIN, INC.—See Archer-Daniels-Midland Company; *U.S. Public*, pg. 181
ADM EDIBLE BEAN SPECIALTIES, INC.—See Archer-Daniels-Midland Company; *U.S. Public*, pg. 181
A. DUDA & SONS INC.; *U.S. Private*, pg. 23
ALICO CITRUS NURSERY, LLC—See Continental Grain Company; *U.S. Private*, pg. 1029
AL'S GARDEN CENTERS & GREENHOUSES, LLC.; *U.S. Private*, pg. 148
AMERICAN FOLIAGE MART—See Deli, Inc.; *U.S. Private*, pg. 1196
ANDREW HENDRIKS & SONS GREENHOUSES; *Int'l*, pg. 451
ARCHER DANIELS MIDLAND CO.—See Archer-Daniels-Midland Company; *U.S. Public*, pg. 183
ARMSTRONG GARDEN CENTERS, INC.; *U.S. Private*, pg. 331
BAMBOO PIPELINE, INC.; *U.S. Private*, pg. 463
BARNES NURSERY, INC.; *U.S. Private*, pg. 477
BARTON COUNTY IMPLEMENT CO; *U.S. Private*, pg. 483
BAYWA VORARLBERG HANDELSGMBH—See BayWa AG; *Int'l*, pg. 916
BEHNKE NURSERIES CO.; *U.S. Private*, pg. 515
BONSAI OUTLET; *U.S. Private*, pg. 615
BORGESTAD POLAND SP.Z.O.O—See Borgestad ASA; *Int'l*, pg. 1114
BRADLEY CALDWELL, INC.; *U.S. Private*, pg. 632
CALLOWAY'S NURSERY, INC.; *U.S. Private*, pg. 723
CANADA GARDENWORKS LTD.; *Int'l*, pg. 1278
CAPITAL NURSERY CO.; *U.S. Private*, pg. 741
CARDINAL CREST—See Deli, Inc.; *U.S. Private*, pg. 1196
CARGILL LIMITED—See Cargill, Inc.; *U.S. Private*, pg. 757
CARGILL LIMITED—See Cargill, Inc.; *U.S. Private*, pg. 757
CARGILL LIMITED—See Cargill, Inc.; *U.S. Private*, pg. 757
CARGILL LIMITED—See Cargill, Inc.; *U.S. Private*, pg. 757
CARGILL LIMITED—See Cargill, Inc.; *U.S. Private*, pg. 758
CARGILL LIMITED—See Cargill, Inc.; *U.S. Private*, pg. 758
CARGILL LIMITED—See Cargill, Inc.; *U.S. Private*, pg. 758
CENTRAL GARDEN & PET COMPANY; *U.S. Public*, pg. 473
CHS COUNTRY OPERATIONS CANADA, INC.—See CHS INC.; *U.S. Public*, pg. 491
CLEAN AIR GARDENING; *U.S. Private*, pg. 931

444240 — NURSERY, GARDEN CEN...

CORNELIUS NURSERIES—See Calloway's Nursery, Inc.; *U.S. Private*, pg. 723
DAVIS LANDSCAPE, LLC; *U.S. Private*, pg. 1173
DEAR GARDEN ASSOCIATES, INC.; *U.S. Private*, pg. 1185
DELHI HILLS FLOWER & GARDEN CENTER; *U.S. Private*, pg. 1196
DENSO AGRITECH SOLUTIONS, INC.—See Denso Corporation; *Int'l*, pg. 2029
DE VROOMEN BULB CO., INC.; *U.S. Private*, pg. 1181
THE DIRT DOCTORS, LLC—See SiteOne Landscape Supply, Inc.; *U.S. Public*, pg. 1889
DOBBIES GARDEN CENTRES LIMITED—See Hattington Capital LLP; *Int'l*, pg. 3285
DOBBIES GROVELANDS—See Hattington Capital LLP; *Int'l*, pg. 3285
DOUGLAS COUNTY FARMERS COOP; *U.S. Private*, pg. 1267
DRIFTWOOD GARDEN CENTER; *U.S. Private*, pg. 1277
DUNE COMPANY OF YUMA LLC; *U.S. Private*, pg. 1288
EARL MAY SEED & NURSERY L.C.; *U.S. Private*, pg. 1313
EDIBLE GARDEN CORP.—See Unrivaled Brands, Inc.; *U.S. Public*, pg. 2263
FIRST COOPERATIVE ASSOCIATION; *U.S. Private*, pg. 1516
FRUIT BASKET GARDENS INC.; *U.S. Private*, pg. 1617
GARDENMASTER—See PRO Group, Inc.; *U.S. Private*, pg. 3270
GEORGE W. PARK SEED COMPANY, INC.; *U.S. Private*, pg. 1683
GERTEN GREENHOUSES & GARDEN CENTER, INC.; *U.S. Private*, pg. 1688
GLOBAL AG ASSOCIATES INC.; *U.S. Private*, pg. 1712
GLOBAL LABORATORY SERVICES, INC.—See Universal Corporation; *U.S. Public*, pg. 2254
GRANNGARDEN AB—See Felleskjopet Agri SA; *Int'l*, pg. 2633
GREAT DANE POWER EQUIPMENT; *U.S. Private*, pg. 1762
GRIFFIN GREENHOUSE & NURSERY SUPPLIES, INC. - NEW YORK-CENTRAL—See Griffin Greenhouse & Nursery Supplies, Inc.; *U.S. Private*, pg. 1788
GRIFFIN GREENHOUSE & NURSERY SUPPLIES, INC. - NEW YORK-EAST—See Griffin Greenhouse & Nursery Supplies, Inc.; *U.S. Private*, pg. 1788
GRIFFIN GREENHOUSE & NURSERY SUPPLIES, INC. - PENNSYLVANIA—See Griffin Greenhouse & Nursery Supplies, Inc.; *U.S. Private*, pg. 1788
GRO-WELL BRANDS INC.; *U.S. Private*, pg. 1791
GROWGENERATION CORP.; *U.S. Public*, pg. 972
HICKORY CREEK NURSERY INC.; *U.S. Private*, pg. 1933
HIGH PLAINS COOPERATIVE; *U.S. Private*, pg. 1936
HOMESTEAD GARDENS INC.; *U.S. Private*, pg. 1974
HOUSTON PLANTS AND GARDEN WORLD; *U.S. Private*, pg. 1993
INDOOR GARDEN & LIGHTING INC.—See GrowGeneration Corp.; *U.S. Public*, pg. 972
J.W. JUNG SEED COMPANY; *U.S. Private*, pg. 2172
KING FARM CENTER, LLC—See Regency Centers Corporation; *U.S. Public*, pg. 1774
LAKE NORMAN TRACTOR COMPANY—See BobCon Inc.; *U.S. Private*, pg. 607
LILYPONS WATER GARDENS INC.; *U.S. Private*, pg. 2456
LIVING WHOLE FOODS, INC.; *U.S. Private*, pg. 2474
L.J. THALMANN COMPANY; *U.S. Private*, pg. 2366
MAHONEY'S ROCKY LEDGE FARM GARDEN; *U.S. Private*, pg. 2550
MCCLURE & ZIMMERMAN—See J.W. Jung Seed Company; *U.S. Private*, pg. 2172
MEADOWS FARMS INC.; *U.S. Private*, pg. 2647
MERRIFIELD GARDEN CENTER CORP.; *U.S. Private*, pg. 2676
MILAEGERS INC.; *U.S. Private*, pg. 2726
MOANA NURSERY INC.; *U.S. Private*, pg. 2756
MOLBAKS LLC; *U.S. Private*, pg. 2766
MONSANTO CANADA, INC.—See Bayer Aktiengesellschaft; *Int'l*, pg. 908
MOON VALLEY NURSERY, INC; *U.S. Private*, pg. 2779
MOSSER LEE CO.—See Deli, Inc.; *U.S. Private*, pg. 1196
NAVLETS GARDEN CENTERS INC.; *U.S. Private*, pg. 2873
NEW CENTURY FARM SERVICE INC.; *U.S. Private*, pg. 2893
NEW ENGLAND BONSAI GARDENS—See Bonsai Outlet; *U.S. Private*, pg. 615
OAKLAND NURSERY INC.; *U.S. Private*, pg. 2984
OHIGRO INC.; *U.S. Private*, pg. 3003
OXADIS S.L.—See Groupe Limagrain Holding SA; *Int'l*, pg. 3108
OXADIS S.R.L.—See Groupe Limagrain Holding SA; *Int'l*, pg. 3108
PACIFIC AGRICULTURAL SALES & SERVICES, INC.—See J.R. Simplot Company; *U.S. Private*, pg. 2171
PIKE NURSERIES ACQUISITION, LLC—See Armstrong Garden Centers, Inc.; *U.S. Private*, pg. 331
PIONEER HI-BRED INTERNATIONAL—See Corteva, Inc.; *U.S. Public*, pg. 583
PIONEER HI-BRED INTERNATIONAL—See Corteva, Inc.; *U.S. Public*, pg. 583

PIONEER HI-BRED INTERNATIONAL—See Corteva, Inc.; *U.S. Public*, pg. 583
PIONEER HI-BRED INTERNATIONAL—See Corteva, Inc.; *U.S. Public*, pg. 583
PIONEER HI-BRED INTERNATIONAL—See Corteva, Inc.; *U.S. Public*, pg. 583
PIONEER SEEDS INC.—See Corteva, Inc.; *U.S. Public*, pg. 583
PITTSBURGH POND CO.; *U.S. Private*, pg. 3191
PLANTRON, INC.; *U.S. Private*, pg. 3198
PRO GROUP, INC. - FARM MART DIVISION—See PRO Group, Inc.; *U.S. Private*, pg. 3270
QUALITY CHRISTMAS TREE CO. INC.; *U.S. Private*, pg. 3318
RAYMOND T. JOHNSON INC.; *U.S. Private*, pg. 3359
REYNOLDS ENTERPRISES OF BROOME, INC.; *U.S. Private*, pg. 3418
RF MORSE & SON INC.; *U.S. Private*, pg. 3419
SCHULTZ COMPANY—See Spectrum Brands Holdings, Inc.; *U.S. Public*, pg. 1916
SEED HOUSE, INC.—See Wilbur-Ellis Company; *U.S. Private*, pg. 4517
SEVIER FARMERS COOPERATIVE; *U.S. Private*, pg. 3619
SLOAT GARDEN CENTER INC.; *U.S. Private*, pg. 3689
STAUFFERS OF KISSEL HILL—See SKH Management Co. Inc.; *U.S. Private*, pg. 3681
STEIN GARDEN CENTERS, INC.; *U.S. Private*, pg. 3797
SUMMERWINDS GARDEN CENTERS INC.; *U.S. Private*, pg. 3853
SUMMERWINDS GARDEN CENTERS INC.—See Summerwinds Garden Centers Inc.; *U.S. Private*, pg. 3853
SYNAGRI—See Cargill, Inc.; *U.S. Private*, pg. 758
TALHER, S.A.—See ACS, Actividades de Construccion y Servicios, S.A.; *Int'l*, pg. 116
TRIANGLE LANDSCAPE SUPPLIES, INC.—See SiteOne Landscape Supply, Inc.; *U.S. Public*, pg. 1889
UNIPLUMO (IRELAND) LIMITED—See Dole plc; *Int'l*, pg. 2158
UNITED PACIFIC PET, LLC—See Pet Food Experts Inc.; *U.S. Private*, pg. 3156
VINTAGE NURSERIES LLC; *U.S. Private*, pg. 4386
VINTAGE NURSERIES—See Vintage Nurseries LLC; *U.S. Private*, pg. 4386
WARE MILLING, INC—See Kalmbach Feeds, Inc.; *U.S. Private*, pg. 2257
WATONWAN FARM SERVICE CO. INC.; *U.S. Private*, pg. 4455
WESTERN MILLING, LLC; *U.S. Private*, pg. 4494
WHITE FLOWER FARM; *U.S. Private*, pg. 4509
WHITTLESEY LANDSCAPE SUPPLIES & RECYCLING, INC.—See SiteOne Landscape Supply, Inc.; *U.S. Public*, pg. 1889

445110 — SUPERMARKETS AND OTHER GROCERY (EXCEPT CONVENIENCE) STORES

300 MAIN STREET REALTY, LLC—See United Natural Foods, Inc.; *U.S. Public*, pg. 2231
37TH AVE MARKET INC.—See Bogopa Enterprises Inc.; *U.S. Private*, pg. 609
8. NOVEMBAR A.D.; *Int'l*, pg. 15
99 ICHIBA CO., LTD.—See G-7 HOLDINGS Inc.; *Int'l*, pg. 2862
ABDULLAH AL-OTHAIM MARKETS COMPANY; *Int'l*, pg. 59
ABFB INC.; *U.S. Private*, pg. 38
ACME MARKETS, INC.—See Cerberus Capital Management, L.P.; *U.S. Private*, pg. 836
ADAMS FAIRACRE FARMS INC.; *U.S. Private*, pg. 74
ADITYA CONSUMER MARKETING LIMITED; *Int'l*, pg. 149
ADMINISTRADORA DE SERVICIOS PARIS LTDA.—See Cencosud S.A.; *Int'l*, pg. 1400
ADVANTAGE LOGISTICS - SOUTHEAST—See United Natural Foods, Inc.; *U.S. Public*, pg. 2231
AEON BIG (M) SDN. BHD.—See AEON Co., Ltd.; *Int'l*, pg. 176
AEON (CAMBODIA) CO., LTD.—See AEON Co., Ltd.; *Int'l*, pg. 176
AEON RYUKYU CO., LTD.—See AEON Co., Ltd.; *Int'l*, pg. 177
AEON SOUTH CHINA CO., LTD.—See AEON Co., Ltd.; *Int'l*, pg. 177
AEON SUPERCENTER CO., LTD.—See AEON Co., Ltd.; *Int'l*, pg. 177
AEON TOHOKU CO., LTD.—See AEON Co., Ltd.; *Int'l*, pg. 177
AEON TOPVALU (HONG KONG) CO., LIMITED—See AEON Co., Ltd.; *Int'l*, pg. 177
A&J SEABRA SUPERMARKET INC.; *U.S. Private*, pg. 20
ALASKA NATIVE INDUSTRIES COOP ASSOCIATION; *U.S. Private*, pg. 151
ALBECO INC.; *U.S. Private*, pg. 152
ALBERTSONS COMPANIES, INC.—See Cerberus Capital Management, L.P.; *U.S. Private*, pg. 836
ALBERTSONS, INC.-OREGON DIVISION—See Cerberus Capital Management, L.P.; *U.S. Private*, pg. 836
ALBERTSON'S, INC.-SOUTHERN CALIFORNIA DIVISION—See Cerberus Capital Management, L.P.; *U.S. Private*, pg. 836
ALBERTSON'S LLC—See Cerberus Capital Management, L.P.; *U.S. Private*, pg. 836
ALBIS CO., LTD.; *Int'l*, pg. 299
ALCAMPO—See Auchan Holding S.A.; *Int'l*, pg. 699
ALCYON BV—See Carrefour SA; *Int'l*, pg. 1344
ALDI EINKAUF SE & CO. OHG; *Int'l*, pg. 304
ALDI FOOD INC.—See Aldi Einkauf SE & Co. oHG; *Int'l*, pg. 304
ALEXANDRIA PETERSON CO. INC.; *U.S. Private*, pg. 164
ALEX FOOD INC.; *U.S. Private*, pg. 162
ALIANSCE MALL E MIDIA LTDA—See Allos SA; *Int'l*, pg. 359
ALIMENTATION DU FLORIVAL; *Int'l*, pg. 328
ALL AMERICAN MEAT INC.; *U.S. Private*, pg. 169
ALL AMERICAN QUALITY FOODS INC.; *U.S. Private*, pg. 170
ALLEGRO COFFEE CO.—See Amazon.com, Inc.; *U.S. Public*, pg. 91
ALLENS OF HASTINGS, INC.; *U.S. Private*, pg. 180
ALLEN SUPER SAVE MARKETS; *U.S. Private*, pg. 179
ALLIANCE FOODS INC.; *U.S. Private*, pg. 182
ALMSTED ENTERPRISES INC.; *U.S. Private*, pg. 195
ALOSRA SUPERMARKET W.L.L.—See BMMI B.S.C.; *Int'l*, pg. 1076
ALPENA SUPERMARKET INC.; *U.S. Private*, pg. 196
ALPHA FOODS INC.—See The Livekindly Company, Inc.; *U.S. Private*, pg. 4071
ALPINE COLONY ENTERPRISES INC.; *U.S. Private*, pg. 201
ALTAGHENY INC.; *U.S. Private*, pg. 204
AMANDO PENA INC.; *U.S. Private*, pg. 216
AMERICAN FOOD SERVICES INTERNATIONAL INC.—See Bellboy Corporation; *U.S. Private*, pg. 520
AMERICAN FROZEN FOODS, INC.; *U.S. Private*, pg. 234
AMERICAN SEAWAY FOODS, INC.—See Giant Eagle, Inc.; *U.S. Private*, pg. 1694
AMERIFRESH, INC.—See US Foods Holding Corp.; *U.S. Public*, pg. 2266
AML FOODS LTD.; *Int'l*, pg. 428
AMP WARRINGAH MALL PTY LTD—See AMP Limited; *Int'l*, pg. 432
ANDRONICO'S COMMUNITY MARKETS—See Renovo Capital, LLC; *U.S. Private*, pg. 3399
ANGELI-MENOMINEE INC.; *U.S. Private*, pg. 282
ANGELO'S FRESH FOOD MARKET, LLC—See Angelo's Fresh Market, Inc.; *U.S. Private*, pg. 282
ANGELO'S FRESH MARKET, INC.; *U.S. Private*, pg. 282
ANHUI ANFU BATTERY TECHNOLOGY CO., LTD.; *Int'l*, pg. 466
A&P MARKETS—See Williams, Inc.; *U.S. Private*, pg. 4527
APPLETREE MARKETS; *U.S. Private*, pg. 297
ARABIAN STORES COMPANY LTD.; *Int'l*, pg. 534
ARAB PALESTINIAN SHOPPING CENTERS—See Arab Palestinian Investment Company; *Int'l*, pg. 531
ARCS COMPANY LIMITED; *Int'l*, pg. 551
ARLAN'S MARKET INC.; *U.S. Private*, pg. 326
ARO-SYSTEMS INC.; *U.S. Private*, pg. 333
ARTHUR'S GARDEN DELI INC.; *U.S. Private*, pg. 342
ASNAS CO., LTD.—See H2O Retailing Corp.; *Int'l*, pg. 3200
ASPEN VISION CITY SDN. BHD.—See Aspen (Group) Holdings Limited; *Int'l*, pg. 628
ASSOCIATION DES CENTRES DISTRIBUTEURS E. LECLERC; *Int'l*, pg. 649
ATACADAO S.A.—See Carrefour SA; *Int'l*, pg. 1343
ATAC SAS—See Auchan Holding S.A.; *Int'l*, pg. 699
ATAK OOO—See Auchan Holding S.A.; *Int'l*, pg. 699
AT JAPAN CO., LTD—See AEON Co., Ltd.; *Int'l*, pg. 177
ATKINSON'S MARKET INC.; *U.S. Private*, pg. 369
ATLANTIC SUPER MARKET S.A.; *Int'l*, pg. 675
ATLANTIC WHOLESALERS LTD.—See George Weston Limited; *Int'l*, pg. 2938
AUCHAN (CHINA) INVESTMENT CO., LTD.—See Alibaba Group Holding Limited; *Int'l*, pg. 326
AUCHAN COORDINATION SERVICES S.A.—See Auchan Holding S.A.; *Int'l*, pg. 699
AUCHAN HUNGARY—See Auchan Holding S.A.; *Int'l*, pg. 699
AUCHAN POLSKA—See Auchan Holding S.A.; *Int'l*, pg. 699
AUCHAN ROMANIA S.A.—See Auchan Holding S.A.; *Int'l*, pg. 699
AUCHAN SHANGHAI HYPERMARKET—See Auchan Holding S.A.; *Int'l*, pg. 699
AUCHAN—See Auchan Holding S.A.; *Int'l*, pg. 699
AUCHAN—See Auchan Holding S.A.; *Int'l*, pg. 699
AUCHAN SPA; *Int'l*, pg. 699
AUCHAN UKRAINE—See Auchan Holding S.A.; *Int'l*, pg. 699
AUSSEE OATS MILLING (PRIVATE) LIMITED—See Future Corporate Resources Limited; *Int'l*, pg. 2853
AUSTRALIAN UNITED RETAILERS LIMITED; *Int'l*, pg. 722
AUTO POSTO IMPERIO LTDA.—See Companhia Brasileira de Distribuicao; *Int'l*, pg. 1746
AUTRY GREER & SONS, INC.; *U.S. Private*, pg. 402
AVA-RUHA CORP.; *U.S. Private*, pg. 402
AVENUE SUPERMARTS LIMITED; *Int'l*, pg. 739

N.A.I.C.S. INDEX

445110 — SUPERMARKETS AND OT...

AXFOOD SVERIGE AB—See Axel Johnson Gruppen AB; *Int'l*, pg. 764
AXIAL RETAILING INC.; *Int'l*, pg. 768
AYNOR FOODS INC.—See W. Lee Flowers & Company Inc.; *U.S. Private*, pg. 4418
BADGER INCORPORATED; *U.S. Private*, pg. 424
BAINES MANAGEMENT CO.; *U.S. Private*, pg. 453
BAJA RANCH MARKET; *U.S. Private*, pg. 454
BAKERS MANAGEMENT INC.; *U.S. Private*, pg. 457
BALDUCCI'S LLC—See Irving Place Capital Management, L.P.; *U.S. Private*, pg. 2141
BANANAR EHF.—See Hagar hf.; *Int'l*, pg. 3206
THE BARGAIN BARN INC—See Gen Cap America, Inc.; *U.S. Private*, pg. 1660
BASHAS' SUPERMARKETS; *U.S. Private*, pg. 484
BAY-DOVER INC.; *U.S. Private*, pg. 495
B&B CASH GROCERY STORES, INC.—See B&B Corporate Holdings, Inc.; *U.S. Private*, pg. 417
BEGLES DISTRIBUTION SA; *Int'l*, pg. 941
BEIJING AUCHAN HYPERMARKETS CO., LTD.—See Alibaba Group Holding Limited; *Int'l*, pg. 326
BEIJING HUALIAN HYPERMARKET CO., LTD.; *Int'l*, pg. 952
BEL AIR MARKETS—See Raley's Inc.; *U.S. Private*, pg. 3350
BELC CO., LTD.; *Int'l*, pg. 963
BELDEN'S SUPER MARKET INC.; *U.S. Private*, pg. 517
BELL'S FOOD MARKET INC.; *U.S. Private*, pg. 519
BELL'S OF ATHENS INC.—See Bell's Food Market Inc.; *U.S. Private*, pg. 519
BE-LO MARKETS INC.—See Camellia Food Stores, Inc.; *U.S. Private*, pg. 728
BERAT CORPORATION; *U.S. Private*, pg. 529
BERBERIAN ENTERPRISES INC.; *U.S. Private*, pg. 529
BERKOT LTD. INC.; *U.S. Private*, pg. 533
BEST DEAL FOOD COMPANY, INC.; *U.S. Private*, pg. 542
BEST DEAL FOOD COMPANY INC—See Best Deal Food Company, Inc.; *U.S. Private*, pg. 542
BEST DOORS AUSTRALIA PTY. LTD.—See dormakaba Holding AG; *Int'l*, pg. 2177
BEST YET MARKET INCORPORATED; *U.S. Private*, pg. 544
BETTER PLANT SCIENCES INC.; *Int'l*, pg. 1003
BHB INC.; *U.S. Private*, pg. 549
BIGG'S HYPER SHOPPES, INC.—See United Natural Foods, Inc.; *U.S. Public*, pg. 2231
BIG V SUPERMARKET INC.; *U.S. Private*, pg. 555
BIG Y FOODS, INC.; *U.S. Private*, pg. 555
BI-LO, LLC—See Aldi Einkauf SE & Co. oHG; *Int'l*, pg. 304
BIM BIRLESIK MAGAZALAR A.S.; *Int'l*, pg. 1031
BIO C' BON JAPON CO., LTD.—See AEON Co., Ltd.; *Int'l*, pg. 177
BIO-PLANET N.V.—See Colruyt Group N.V.; *Int'l*, pg. 1705
BIZIM TOPTAN SATIS MAGAZALARI A.S.; *Int'l*, pg. 1053
B&K ENTERPRISES INC.; *U.S. Private*, pg. 419
BKT ENTERPRISES INC.; *U.S. Private*, pg. 569
BLEWETT'S FOOD, INC.; *U.S. Private*, pg. 581
BLO DISTRIBUTION—See Carrefour SA; *Int'l*, pg. 1343
BLUE MOOSE OF BOULDER, INC.—See Sartori Company; *U.S. Private*, pg. 3551
BOB BAY & SONS INC.; *U.S. Private*, pg. 603
BOB'S KWIK SHOP FOODS CO; *U.S. Private*, pg. 605
BOB'S MARKETS, INC.; *U.S. Private*, pg. 605
BODEGA LATINA CORPORATION—See Grupo Comercial Chedraui S.A.B. de C.V.; *Int'l*, pg. 3125
BOLLIN GROUP LTD.; *Int'l*, pg. 1102
BONFARE MARKETS INC.—See Kapoor Enterprises; *U.S. Private*, pg. 2261
BONNER FOODS INC.; *U.S. Private*, pg. 614
BOROWIAK'S IGA FOODLINER, INC.; *U.S. Private*, pg. 619
BO'S FOOD STORES; *U.S. Private*, pg. 602
BOSKA RK A.D.; *Int'l*, pg. 1116
BOU KHALIL SOCIETE MODERNE SARL; *Int'l*, pg. 1119
BOULEVARD SHOPPING BELEM S.A—See Allos SA; *Int'l*, pg. 359
BOYER'S FOOD MARKETS INC.; *U.S. Private*, pg. 628
BRACEY'S SUPERMARKET INC.; *U.S. Private*, pg. 630
BRATSTVO A.D.; *Int'l*, pg. 1141
BREAUX MART INC.; *U.S. Private*, pg. 643
BREEN'S MARKET, INC.; *U.S. Private*, pg. 644
BRICOLAJE BRICOMAN S.L.U.—See Groupe Adeo S.A.; *Int'l*, pg. 3091
BRICOMAN ITALIA S.R.L.—See Groupe Adeo S.A.; *Int'l*, pg. 3091
BRICOMAN POLAND SP. Z O.O.—See Groupe Adeo S.A.; *Int'l*, pg. 3091
BRICOMAN S.A.—See Groupe Adeo S.A.; *Int'l*, pg. 3091
BROOKSHIRE BROTHERS, LTD.; *U.S. Private*, pg. 664
BROOKSHIRE GROCERY COMPANY; *U.S. Private*, pg. 664
BROULIMS SUPER MARKET INC.; *U.S. Private*, pg. 665
BROWNS SUPER STORES INC.; *U.S. Private*, pg. 670
B&R STORES INC.; *U.S. Private*, pg. 419
B&R SUPERMARKET INC.; *U.S. Private*, pg. 419
BUEHLER FOOD MARKETS INC.; *U.S. Private*, pg. 680
BUN PENNY INC.; *U.S. Private*, pg. 685

BURGESS LIGHTING & DISTRIBUTING CO.; *U.S. Private*, pg. 687
BURNSTAD BROTHERS, INC.; *U.S. Private*, pg. 691
BURTONS INC.; *U.S. Private*, pg. 693
BUSCHS INC.; *U.S. Private*, pg. 693
BUTERA FINER FOODS INC.; *U.S. Private*, pg. 696
BUURTWINKELS OKAY NV—See Colruyt Group N.V.; *Int'l*, pg. 1705
BUY-LO QUALITY FOOD STORES; *U.S. Private*, pg. 698
BUY-RITE FOODS INC.; *U.S. Private*, pg. 698
BYERLY'S INC.—See Lund Food Holdings, Inc.; *U.S. Private*, pg. 2515
CADAM BV—See Carrefour SA; *Int'l*, pg. 1344
C A FORTUNE & COMPANY—See Carlin O'Brien Inc.; *U.S. Private*, pg. 763
CALA CO.—See The Kroger Co.; *U.S. Public*, pg. 2107
CALANDROS SUPERMARKET, INC.; *U.S. Private*, pg. 716
CALHOUN ENTERPRISES INC.; *U.S. Private*, pg. 717
CALIFORNIA SUPERMARKET INC.; *U.S. Private*, pg. 720
CAMELLIA FOOD STORES, INC.; *U.S. Private*, pg. 728
CAMPIONI ENTERPRISES INC.; *U.S. Private*, pg. 731
CANADA SAFEWAY LIMITED—See Empire Company Limited; *Int'l*, pg. 2387
CANNATA'S CORPORATION; *U.S. Private*, pg. 734
CANNATA'S SUPER MARKET, INC.—See Cannata's Corporation; *U.S. Private*, pg. 734
CAP FOOD SERVICES CO.; *U.S. Private*, pg. 737
CAPRI FOODS INC.; *U.S. Private*, pg. 745
CARDADEL SA—See Carrefour SA; *Int'l*, pg. 1344
CARL'S SUPERMARKET INC.; *U.S. Private*, pg. 763
CARREFOUR ADMINISTRATIF FRANCE—See Carrefour SA; *Int'l*, pg. 1344
CARREFOUR ARGENTINA S.A.—See Carrefour SA; *Int'l*, pg. 1344
CARREFOUR ASIA LIMITED—See Carrefour SA; *Int'l*, pg. 1344
CARREFOUR BELGIUM SA—See Carrefour SA; *Int'l*, pg. 1344
CARREFOUR BRASIL—See Carrefour SA; *Int'l*, pg. 1344
CARREFOUR CANARIAS, S.A.—See Carrefour SA; *Int'l*, pg. 1345
CARREFOUR CESKA REPUBLIKA—See Carrefour SA; *Int'l*, pg. 1344
CARREFOUR FRANCE—See Carrefour SA; *Int'l*, pg. 1344
CARREFOUR HYPERMARCHES—See Carrefour SA; *Int'l*, pg. 1344
CARREFOUR MONACO—See Carrefour SA; *Int'l*, pg. 1344
CARREFOUR NAVARRA, S.L.—See Carrefour SA; *Int'l*, pg. 1345
CARREFOUR NEDERLAND B.V.—See Carrefour SA; *Int'l*, pg. 1344
CARREFOUR NORTE, S.L.—See Carrefour SA; *Int'l*, pg. 1345
CARREFOUR POLSKA PROPER SP. Z O.O.—See Carrefour SA; *Int'l*, pg. 1345
CARREFOUR POLSKA SP. Z O.O.—See Carrefour SA; *Int'l*, pg. 1345
CARREFOUR PROCUREMENT INTERNATIONAL AG & CO. KG—See Carrefour SA; *Int'l*, pg. 1345
CARREFOUR ROMANIA S.A.—See Carrefour SA; *Int'l*, pg. 1345
CARREFOUR SABANCI TICARET MERKEZI AS CARREFOURSA—See Carrefour SA; *Int'l*, pg. 1345
CARREFOUR SABANCI TICARET MERKEZI AS CARREFOURSA—See Haci Omer Sabanci Holding A.S.; *Int'l*, pg. 3203
CARREFOURSA CARREFOUR SABANCI TICARET MERKEZI A.S.; *Int'l*, pg. 1346
CARREFOURSA TURKIYE GENEL MUDURLUK—See Carrefour SA; *Int'l*, pg. 1345
CARREFOUR SINGAPORE PTE LTD—See Carrefour SA; *Int'l*, pg. 1344
CARREFOUR SLOVENSKO S.R.O.—See Carrefour SA; *Int'l*, pg. 1345
CARREFOUR SOUTH EAST ASIA PTE. LTD.—See Carrefour SA; *Int'l*, pg. 1344
CARREFOUR STATION SERVICE—See Carrefour SA; *Int'l*, pg. 1344
CARREFOUR WORLD TRADE SA—See Carrefour SA; *Int'l*, pg. 1345
CARSON PIRIE SCOTT II, INC.—See The Bon Ton Stores, Inc.; *U.S. Public*, pg. 2041
CARTER'S INC.; *U.S. Private*, pg. 776
CASEY'S FOODS INC.; *U.S. Private*, pg. 782
CASEY'S INC.; *U.S. Private*, pg. 782
CASINO GUICHARD-PERRACHON SA—See Finatis SA; *Int'l*, pg. 2670
CASTORAMA RUS LLC; *Int'l*, pg. 1357
CENCAR LIMITED (CARREFOUR THAILAND)—See Carrefour SA; *Int'l*, pg. 1344
CENCOSUD PERU S.A.—See Cencosud S.A.; *Int'l*, pg. 1400
CENCOSUD RETAIL S.A.—See Cencosud S.A.; *Int'l*, pg. 1400
CENCOSUD S.A.; *Int'l*, pg. 1400
CENCOSUD S.A.—See Cencosud S.A.; *Int'l*, pg. 1400
CENTRAL FOOD RETAIL COMPANY LIMITED—See Central Group Company Limited; *Int'l*, pg. 1407

CENTROISTOK A.D.; *Int'l*, pg. 1414
CENTRO MART INC.; *U.S. Private*, pg. 830
CENTROS COMERCIALES CARREFOUR, S.A.—See Carrefour SA; *Int'l*, pg. 1345
CHALLENGER SARL—See Carrefour SA; *Int'l*, pg. 1343
CHAMPION SUPERMARCHES FRANCE SAS—See Carrefour SA; *Int'l*, pg. 1345
CHANDIS; *Int'l*, pg. 1441
CHARLES SCATURRO & SONS INC.; *U.S. Private*, pg. 853
CHARTER HALL RETAIL REIT—See Charter Hall Limited; *Int'l*, pg. 1454
CHENGDU AUCHAN HYPERMARKETS CO., LTD.—See Alibaba Group Holding Limited; *Int'l*, pg. 326
CHENGDU YUSHENG INDUSTRIAL DEVELOPMENT CO LTD—See Carrefour SA; *Int'l*, pg. 1344
CHIEF SUPER MARKET, INC.—See Fresh Encounter Inc.; *U.S. Private*, pg. 1609
CHILIS OF KANASA, INC.—See Brinker International, Inc.; *U.S. Public*, pg. 384
CHINA RESOURCES VANGUARD CO., LTD.—See China Resources (Holdings) Co., Ltd.; *Int'l*, pg. 1548
CHINA RESOURCES VANGUARD (HONG KONG) CO., LTD.—See China Resources (Holdings) Co., Ltd.; *Int'l*, pg. 1548
CHIPREWARDS, INC.—See CVC Capital Partners SICAV-FIS S.A.; *Int'l*, pg. 1888
CHOICES MARKETS LTD.; *Int'l*, pg. 1577
CHOPPIES ENTERPRISES KENYA LIMITED—See Choppies Enterprises Ltd.; *Int'l*, pg. 1582
CHOPPIES SUPERMARKET MOZAMBIQUE LIMITADA—See Choppies Enterprises Ltd.; *Int'l*, pg. 1582
CHOPPIES SUPERMARKETS LIMITED—See Choppies Enterprises Ltd.; *Int'l*, pg. 1582
CHOPPIES SUPERMARKETS NAMIBIA (PTY) LTD—See Choppies Enterprises Ltd.; *Int'l*, pg. 1582
CHOPPIES SUPERMARKETS TANZANIA LIMITED—See Choppies Enterprises Ltd.; *Int'l*, pg. 1582
CIKER A.D.; *Int'l*, pg. 1607
CITARELLA; *U.S. Private*, pg. 901
CITY-ARKADEN WUPPERTAL KG—See Deutsche Euro-Shop AG; *Int'l*, pg. 2065
C&K MARKET, INC.; *U.S. Private*, pg. 703
CLAIRGUIL; *Int'l*, pg. 1641
CLARO'S ITALIAN MARKET, INC.; *U.S. Private*, pg. 915
CLIFFORD W. PERHAM, INC.—See United Natural Foods, Inc.; *U.S. Public*, pg. 2231
CLV DISTRIBUTION—See Carrefour SA; *Int'l*, pg. 1344
C MARKET A.D.; *Int'l*, pg. 1238
COBORN'S INCORPORATED; *U.S. Private*, pg. 958
CODI-FRANCE S.A.S.—See Colruyt Group N.V.; *Int'l*, pg. 1705
COFFS CENTRAL PTY. LTD.—See Gowing Brothers Limited; *Int'l*, pg. 3044
COLANDIS; *Int'l*, pg. 1697
COLES RETAIL GROUP PTY LTD—See Coles Group Limited; *Int'l*, pg. 1698
COLES SUPERMARKETS AUSTRALIA PTY. LTD.—See Coles Group Limited; *Int'l*, pg. 1698
COLRUYT LUXEMBOURG S.A.—See Colruyt Group N.V.; *Int'l*, pg. 1705
COLUMBIAN FOODS INCORPORATED; *U.S. Private*, pg. 978
COMALIMENT SA; *Int'l*, pg. 1707
COMMERCE QUALITY FOODS LLC; *U.S. Private*, pg. 982
COMPANHIA BRASILEIRA DE DISTRIBUICAO; *Int'l*, pg. 1746
CONDORUM SK, S.R.O.; *Int'l*, pg. 1766
CONGA FOODS PTY. LTD.; *Int'l*, pg. 1768
CONSUMERS COOP ASSOCIATION EAU CLAIRE; *U.S. Private*, pg. 1026
CONTINENT 2001—See Carrefour SA; *Int'l*, pg. 1344
COOKES FOOD STORE INC.; *U.S. Private*, pg. 1039
COOP NORGE SA; *Int'l*, pg. 1789
COOP SUPERMARKTEN B.V.; *Int'l*, pg. 1789
CORE-MARK DISTRIBUTORS, INC.—See Core-Mark Holding Co. Inc.; *U.S. Public*, pg. 576
CORPORACION LOS HERMANOS; *U.S. Private*, pg. 1054
CORRADO'S FAMILY AFFAIR; *U.S. Private*, pg. 1058
COSENTINO'S FOOD STORES; *U.S. Private*, pg. 1061
COSTCUTTER SUPERMARKETS GROUP LIMITED—See Bestway (Holdings) Limited; *Int'l*, pg. 1001
COST RIGHT NASSAU LIMITED—See AML Foods Ltd.; *Int'l*, pg. 428
COUSINS FOOD MARKET INC.; *U.S. Private*, pg. 1071
COX'S FOODARAMA INC.; *U.S. Private*, pg. 1078
C.P. LOTUS CORPORATION—See Charoen Pokphand Group Co., Ltd.; *Int'l*, pg. 1453
CRESCENT FOODS INC.; *U.S. Private*, pg. 1093
CROSBYS MARKETS INC.; *U.S. Private*, pg. 1104
CUB FOODS, INC.—See United Natural Foods, Inc.; *U.S. Public*, pg. 2232
CUB FOODS OF APPLETON INC.—See United Natural Foods, Inc.; *U.S. Public*, pg. 2232
CUB FOODS OF GREEN BAY INC.—See United Natural Foods, Inc.; *U.S. Public*, pg. 2232
CV'S FAMILY FOOD INC.; *U.S. Private*, pg. 1132

445110 — SUPERMARKETS AND OT...

CV'S FOODLINER INCORPORATED; *U.S. Private*, pg. 1132
D'AGOSTINO SUPERMARKETS INC.; *U.S. Private*, pg. 1138
DAIICHI CO., LTD.; *Int'l*, pg. 1927
DAIKOKUTENBUSSAN CO., LTD.; *Int'l*, pg. 1937
DAKOTA BROTHERS INC.; *U.S. Private*, pg. 1147
DALLO & CO. INC.; *U.S. Private*, pg. 1150
DANIELS SENTRY FOODS INC.; *U.S. Private*, pg. 1156
DANSK VINIMPORT VEJLE APS—See FDB Group; *Int'l*, pg. 2628
DAN'S SUPERMARKET INC.; *U.S. Private*, pg. 1152
DAN'S SUPREME SUPER MARKETS INC.; *U.S. Private*, pg. 1152
DAVE'S SUPERMARKET INC.; *U.S. Private*, pg. 1169
DAVIDSON HOLDING CO.; *U.S. Private*, pg. 1171
DAVIDS SUPERMARKETS INC.; *U.S. Private*, pg. 1171
DAVIS COUNTY CO-OPERATIVE SOCIETY; *U.S. Private*, pg. 1173
DAVIS FOODTOWN INC.; *U.S. Private*, pg. 1173
DAYTON FOODS LIMITED PARTNERSHIP; *U.S. Private*, pg. 1177
DC GRADACAC D.D.; *Int'l*, pg. 1989
D&D MANAGEMENT INC.; *U.S. Private*, pg. 1137
D&D OF LEE COUNTY INC.; *U.S. Private*, pg. 1137
DEHOFF ENTERPRISES INC.; *U.S. Private*, pg. 1191
DELAWARE SUPERMARKETS INC.; *U.S. Private*, pg. 1195
DELSEA DRIVE SUPERMARKET LLC; *U.S. Private*, pg. 1199
DEMOULAS SUPER MARKETS, INC.; *U.S. Private*, pg. 1204
DE RIDDER B.V—See Bunzl plc; *Int'l*, pg. 1218
DEVOTO HERMANOS S.A.—See Companhia Brasileira de Distribuicao; *Int'l*, pg. 1746
DHAMECHA GROUP, INC.; *Int'l*, pg. 2098
DIABLO FOODS; *U.S. Private*, pg. 1222
DIAMOND FOOD MARKETS INC.; *U.S. Private*, pg. 1223
DIAMOND LAKE 1994 L.L.C.—See United Natural Foods, Inc.; *U.S. Public*, pg. 2231
DIA PORTUGAL SUPERMERCADOS SA—See Carrefour SA; *Int'l*, pg. 1345
DIERBERGS MARKETS INC.; *U.S. Private*, pg. 1228
DILLON COMPANIES, INC.—See The Kroger Co.; *U.S. Public*, pg. 2107
DINO POLSKA SA; *Int'l*, pg. 2127
DISCO S.A.—See Cencosud S.A.; *Int'l*, pg. 1400
DISCOUNT FOODS INC.; *U.S. Private*, pg. 1237
DISMO; *Int'l*, pg. 2135
DLG EXHIBITIONS & EVENTS CORP LTD.; *Int'l*, pg. 2141
DOCS FOOD STORES INC.; *U.S. Private*, pg. 1251
DOKIC NTK A.D.; *Int'l*, pg. 2156
DOMPRO, S.A.S.—See Groupe Adeo S.A.; *Int'l*, pg. 3091
DONELAN'S SUPERMARKETS, INC.; *U.S. Private*, pg. 1260
DONG HUNG INVESTMENT DEVELOPMENT CONSULTANCY JOINT STOCK COMPANY LIMITED—See AEON Co., Ltd.; *Int'l*, pg. 177
DORIGNAC'S FOOD CENTER INC.; *U.S. Private*, pg. 1263
DOROTHY LANE MARKETS INC.; *U.S. Private*, pg. 1263
DOUBLE 8 FOODS INC.; *U.S. Private*, pg. 1265
DREAMLAND N.V.—See Colruyt Group N.V.; *Int'l*, pg. 1705
DREXELINE FOODS LLP; *U.S. Private*, pg. 1276
DUDLEY SUPERMARKET INC.; *U.S. Private*, pg. 1284
DURITZAS ENTERPRISES INC.; *U.S. Private*, pg. 1293
D-URSO ENTERPRISES INC.; *U.S. Private*, pg. 1139
DUSK NEW ZEALAND LIMITED—See Dusk Group Limited; *Int'l*, pg. 2234
DUVAN CACAK A.D.; *Int'l*, pg. 2236
DUVAN PROMET A.D.; *Int'l*, pg. 2236
E&A MARKETS INC.; *U.S. Private*, pg. 1301
EASTERN SHORE MARKETS, INC.—See Camellia Food Stores, Inc.; *U.S. Private*, pg. 728
EAST MAIN FOODS INC.; *U.S. Private*, pg. 1316
EAST SIDE MARKET PLACE INC.; *U.S. Private*, pg. 1317
EASY WAY FOOD STORES INC.; *U.S. Private*, pg. 1323
EBC INC.; *U.S. Private*, pg. 1323
EBJ FOODS CORP.; *U.S. Private*, pg. 1324
E.COLESGROUP PTY LTD—See Coles Group Limited; *Int'l*, pg. 1698
ECONOMICAL SUPER MARKET INCORPORATED; *U.S. Private*, pg. 1330
ECO'S CO., LTD.; *Int'l*, pg. 2293
EDDIE BRYANT ENTERPRISES INC.; *U.S. Private*, pg. 1332
EDEKA ZENTRALE AG & CO. KG; *Int'l*, pg. 2305
EDEN SHUR-FINE—See C&S Wholesale Grocers, Inc.; *U.S. Private*, pg. 704
ED SAS—See Carrefour SA; *Int'l*, pg. 1345
EKI RETAIL SERVICE HANKYU HANSHIN CO., LTD.—See Hankyu Hanshin Holdings Inc.; *Int'l*, pg. 3255
ELKHORN-LUEPTOW'S INC.; *U.S. Private*, pg. 1363
ELO—See Auchan Holding S.A.; *Int'l*, pg. 699
EL REY MEXICAN PRODUCTS INC.; *U.S. Private*, pg. 1349
EL TAPATIO MARKETS INCORPORATED; *U.S. Private*, pg. 1349
EMBRUDIS; *Int'l*, pg. 2376
EMMETSBURG FOOD PRIDE GROCERY & DELI INC.; *U.S. Private*, pg. 1383

ENNEN BROTHERS; *U.S. Private*, pg. 1401
EURAUCHAN SAS—See Auchan Holding S.A.; *Int'l*, pg. 699
EUROFASHION LTDA—See Cencosud S.A.; *Int'l*, pg. 1400
EURO SKLEP S.A.—See Emperia Holding S.A.; *Int'l*, pg. 2385
EVERETT FOODLINER INC.; *U.S. Private*, pg. 1438
E.W. JAMES & SONS INC.; *U.S. Private*, pg. 1307
E.WONG S.A.—See Cencosud S.A.; *Int'l*, pg. 1400
FACEMIRE FOODS INC.; *U.S. Private*, pg. 1459
FACTOR SALES, INC.; *U.S. Private*, pg. 1460
FAIRLAND MARKET INC.; *U.S. Private*, pg. 1464
FAIRPLAY INC.; *U.S. Private*, pg. 1464
FAIRVALUE SUPERMARKET INC.; *U.S. Private*, pg. 1464
FAIRWAY MARKET, INC.—See Sterling Investment Partners, L.P.; *U.S. Private*, pg. 3805
FAIRWAY STORES, INC.; *U.S. Private*, pg. 1465
FAKTA A/S—See FDB Group; *Int'l*, pg. 2628
FALDIS SA—See Carrefour SA; *Int'l*, pg. 1345
THE FALKLAND ISLANDS COMPANY LIMITED—See FIH group plc; *Int'l*, pg. 2661
FAMILY FOODS OF GATESVILLE; *U.S. Private*, pg. 1470
FAMILY MARKETS LLC; *U.S. Private*, pg. 1471
FANT'S FOODLAND; *U.S. Private*, pg. 1472
FAREWAY STORES, INC.; *U.S. Private*, pg. 1473
FARM BOY INC.; *Int'l*, pg. 2619
FARMERS FOODS CHASE CITY INCORPORATED; *U.S. Private*, pg. 1478
FE-MA ENTERPRISES INC.; *U.S. Private*, pg. 1486
FERRI SUPERMARKETS INC.; *U.S. Private*, pg. 1498
FESCO GROUP CO., LTD.; *Int'l*, pg. 2646
FETCHS ENTERPRISES INC.; *U.S. Private*, pg. 1500
FEZELL ENTERPRISES II INC.—See Fezell Enterprises Inc.; *U.S. Private*, pg. 1500
FEZELL ENTERPRISES INC.; *U.S. Private*, pg. 1500
FIESTA MART, LLC—See Grupo Comercial Chedraui S.A.B. de C.V.; *Int'l*, pg. 3125
FIESTA MEXICANA MARKET LTD. PARTNER; *U.S. Private*, pg. 1505
FISCHER HEIGHTS GIANT EAGLE; *U.S. Private*, pg. 1532
FISHER FOODS MARKETING INC.; *U.S. Private*, pg. 1534
FISHERS STORES CONSOLIDATED PTY. LTD.; *Int'l*, pg. 2693
FIVE STAR OF KNOX INC.; *U.S. Private*, pg. 1538
FLICK'S IGA LTD.; *U.S. Private*, pg. 1544
FLOCO FOODS INC.—See W. Lee Flowers & Company Inc.; *U.S. Private*, pg. 4418
FLORTINE—See Carrefour SA; *Int'l*, pg. 1345
FOCUS MALL ZIELONA GORA SP. Z O.O.—See Aviva plc; *Int'l*, pg. 746
FOGLES INC.; *U.S. Private*, pg. 1557
FOOD 4 LESS OF SOUTHERN CALIFORNIA, INC.—See The Kroger Co.; *U.S. Public*, pg. 2108
FOODARAMA INC—See United Natural Foods, Inc.; *U.S. Public*, pg. 2231
FOOD CIRCUS SUPERMARKETS INC.; *U.S. Private*, pg. 1560
FOOD COUNTRY USA INC.; *U.S. Private*, pg. 1560
FOOD & GAS, INC.; *U.S. Private*, pg. 1560
FOOD GIANT SUPERMARKETS, INC.—See Houchens Industries, Inc.; *U.S. Private*, pg. 1990
FOODHALL—See Future Corporate Resources Limited; *Int'l*, pg. 2853
FOODINVEST N.V.—See Colruyt Group N.V.; *Int'l*, pg. 1705
FOOD KING INC.; *U.S. Private*, pg. 1560
FOOD KING, INC.; *U.S. Private*, pg. 1561
FOODLAND SUPER MARKET LIMITED; *U.S. Private*, pg. 1562
FOODLAND WAREHOUSE FOODS INC.; *U.S. Private*, pg. 1562
FOODLINES B.V.B.A.—See Colruyt Group N.V.; *Int'l*, pg. 1705
FOODMASTER SUPER MARKETS INC.; *U.S. Private*, pg. 1562
FOOD PANTRY LTD. INC.; *U.S. Private*, pg. 1561
FOODTOWN, INC.; *U.S. Private*, pg. 1562
FOODTOWN SUPERMARKET INC.—See Foodtown, Inc.; *U.S. Private*, pg. 1562
FOODWORKS RETAIL PTY LTD—See Australian United Retailers Limited; *Int'l*, pg. 722
FOREVERGREEN INTERNATIONAL TAIWAN LTD—See ForeverGreen Worldwide Corporation; *U.S. Public*, pg. 867
FORSTER & HOWELL INCORPORATED; *U.S. Private*, pg. 1573
FORUM - PLASMAN A.D.; *Int'l*, pg. 2744
FORUM WETZLAR KG—See Deutsche EuroShop AG; *Int'l*, pg. 2065
FORWARD CORPORATION; *U.S. Private*, pg. 1577
FOURCAR BV—See Carrefour SA; *Int'l*, pg. 1345
FOURSOME FINER FOODS INC.; *U.S. Private*, pg. 1583
FOX BROS PIGGLY WIGGLY INC.; *U.S. Private*, pg. 1584
FRANCOFIN BV—See Carrefour SA; *Int'l*, pg. 1345
FRED MEYER, INC.—See The Kroger Co.; *U.S. Public*, pg. 2107
FRED MEYER STORES, INC.—See The Kroger Co.; *U.S. Public*, pg. 2107
THE FRED W. ALBRECHT GROCERY CO.; *U.S. Private*, pg. 4030

CORPORATE AFFILIATIONS

FRESH & EASY NEIGHBORHOOD MARKET INC—See The Yucaipa Companies LLC; *U.S. Private*, pg. 4140
THE FRESH MARKET, INC.—See Apollo Global Management, Inc.; *U.S. Public*, pg. 164
F.T. REYNOLDS COMPANY; *U.S. Private*, pg. 1457
FULLER MARKET BASKET INC.; *U.S. Private*, pg. 1621
FUTABA BUSINESS SYSTEM CO., LTD.—See Futaba Corporation; *Int'l*, pg. 2850
FUTUREBRANDS LTD.—See Future Corporate Resources Limited; *Int'l*, pg. 2853
FUTURE CONSUMER LIMITED—See Future Corporate Resources Limited; *Int'l*, pg. 2853
FUTURE LEARNING AND DEVELOPMENT LIMITED—See Future Corporate Resources Limited; *Int'l*, pg. 2853
G-7 AGRI JAPAN CO., LTD.—See G-7 HOLDINGS Inc.; *Int'l*, pg. 2862
G-7 SUPER MART CO., LTD.—See G-7 HOLDINGS Inc.; *Int'l*, pg. 2862
GAGMARS INC.; *U.S. Private*, pg. 1635
GALAPROM A.D.; *Int'l*, pg. 2871
GALATIAN INC.; *U.S. Private*, pg. 1636
GARRETT ENTERPRISES INC.; *U.S. Private*, pg. 1645
GATACKO POLJE A.D.; *Int'l*, pg. 2888
GATEWAY FOODS INC.; *U.S. Private*, pg. 1650
GATOR FOURE INC.; *U.S. Private*, pg. 1651
GCJ ENTERPRISES INC.; *U.S. Private*, pg. 1653
GEDEL SARL—See Carrefour SA; *Int'l*, pg. 1345
GEISSLER'S SUPERMARKET INCORPORATED; *U.S. Private*, pg. 1656
GELSON'S MARKETS—See TPG Capital, L.P.; *U.S. Public*, pg. 2168
GENEDIS SAS—See Carrefour SA; *Int'l*, pg. 1345
GENES THRIFTWAY INC.—See Garrett Enterprises Inc.; *U.S. Private*, pg. 1645
GENE STIMSON'S OF ARKANSAS; *U.S. Private*, pg. 1660
GERRITY'S SUPERMARKETS INC.; *U.S. Private*, pg. 1687
GEYERS MARKETS INC.; *U.S. Private*, pg. 1689
GF CAPITAL (THAILAND) CO., LTD.—See G-Factory Co., Ltd.; *Int'l*, pg. 2862
GIANT DISCOUNT FOOD INC.; *U.S. Private*, pg. 1694
GIANT EAGLE AMERICAN SEAWAY FOODS—See Giant Eagle, Inc.; *U.S. Private*, pg. 1694
GIANT EAGLE, INC.; *U.S. Private*, pg. 1694
GIANT EAGLE—See Giant Eagle, Inc.; *U.S. Private*, pg. 1694
GIUNTA BROTHERS INC.; *U.S. Private*, pg. 1703
GIZEH DISPOFORM SP. Z O.O.—See GIZEH Verpackungen GmbH & Co. KG; *Int'l*, pg. 2982
GIZEH EMBALLAGES ANGERS SAS—See GIZEH Verpackungen GmbH & Co. KG; *Int'l*, pg. 2982
GIZEH PACKAGING NA INC—See GIZEH Verpackungen GmbH & Co. KG; *Int'l*, pg. 2982
G&J BROOKS ENTERPRISE, INC.; *U.S. Private*, pg. 1629
GLACIER VILLAGE SUPERMARKET; *U.S. Private*, pg. 1704
GLASMEYER & CO. KG; *Int'l*, pg. 2989
GLASS GARDENS INC.; *U.S. Private*, pg. 1706
GLEN ELLEN VILLAGE MARKET—See Nugget Market Inc.; *U.S. Private*, pg. 2972
GLENS FOOD CENTER INCORPORATED; *U.S. Private*, pg. 1711
GL FOOD MARKET LTD.—See Goddard Enterprises Limited; *Int'l*, pg. 3019
GLN INC.; *U.S. Private*, pg. 1711
GONGCO FOODS; *U.S. Private*, pg. 1737
GONG VENTURES INC.—See Gong's Market of Sanger Inc.; *U.S. Private*, pg. 1737
GOOD FOODS GROCERY, INC.—See The Autism Program of Virginia, Inc.; *U.S. Private*, pg. 3990
GOODSONS SUPERMARKETS INC.; *U.S. Private*, pg. 1740
GORDY'S, INC.; *U.S. Private*, pg. 1743
GORMAN FOODS INC.; *U.S. Private*, pg. 1744
GOYA FOODS OF MADRID—See Goya Foods, Inc.; *U.S. Private*, pg. 1747
GRACE DISCOUNT FOODS INC.; *U.S. Private*, pg. 1748
GRADE A MARKET INC.; *U.S. Private*, pg. 1749
GRAND FOOD CENTER—See D&D Management Inc.; *U.S. Private*, pg. 1137
GRAVES SUPER MARKETS INC.; *U.S. Private*, pg. 1759
GRAY'S FOODS INC.; *U.S. Private*, pg. 1759
THE GREAT ATLANTIC & PACIFIC TEA COMPANY, INC.; *U.S. Private*, pg. 4038.
GREENWEEZ SAS—See Carrefour SA; *Int'l*, pg. 1345
GREGERSON'S FOODS INC.; *U.S. Private*, pg. 1782
GRISTEDES FOODS, INC.—See Red Apple Group, Inc.; *U.S. Private*, pg. 3372
GRISTEDES SUPERMARKETS, INC.—See Red Apple Group, Inc.; *U.S. Private*, pg. 3372
GROCERY OUTLET INC.—See Hellman & Friedman LLC; *U.S. Private*, pg. 1908
GROLMUS ENTERPRISES INC.; *U.S. Private*, pg. 1791
GROSZEK SP.Z.O.O—See Emperia Holding S.A.; *Int'l*, pg. 2385
GROUP SUPECO MAXOR SL—See Carrefour SA; *Int'l*, pg. 1345
GRUPO COMERCIAL CHEDRAUI S.A.B. DE C.V.; *Int'l*, pg. 3125

N.A.I.C.S. INDEX

445110 — SUPERMARKETS AND OT...

GRUPO EROSKI; *Int'l*, pg. 3128
GUANGDONG HNA LEWANJIA SUPERMARKET CO., LTD—See Hainan Traffic Administration Holding Co., Ltd.; *Int'l*, pg. 3213
GUILVIDIS—See Carrefour SA; *Int'l*, pg. 1345
GUYENNE ET GASCOGNE SA—See Carrefour SA; *Int'l*, pg. 1345
GW FOODS INC.; *U.S. Private*, pg. 1821
HADDENS IGA—See W. Lee Flowers & Company Inc.; *U.S. Private*, pg. 4418
HAGAR HF.; *Int'l*, pg. 3206
HAGGEN, INC.—See Comvest Group Holdings LLC; *U.S. Private*, pg. 1007
HALOWS CO., LTD; *Int'l*, pg. 3233
HANGZHOU AUCHAN HYPERMARKET CO., LTD.—See Alibaba Group Holding Limited; *Int'l*, pg. 326
HANKYU OASIS CO., LTD.—See H2O Retailing Corp.; *Int'l*, pg. 3200
THE HANOVER CONSUMER COOPERATIVE SOCIETY, INC.; *U.S. Private*, pg. 4043
HANSENS IGA INCORPORATED; *U.S. Private*, pg. 1856
HAPPY BELLY FOOD GROUP INC.; *Int'l*, pg. 3269
HAPPY FOODS, INC.; *U.S. Private*, pg. 1857
HARDING & HILL INC.; *U.S. Private*, pg. 1863
HARDINGS MARKET-WEST INC.; *U.S. Private*, pg. 1863
HARDINGS THOMAS MANAGEMENT; *U.S. Private*, pg. 1863
HARMON CITY, INC.; *U.S. Private*, pg. 1866
HARMON FOODS INC.; *U.S. Private*, pg. 1866
HAROLD FRIEDMAN INC.; *U.S. Private*, pg. 1867
HARPS FOOD STORES, INC.; *U.S. Private*, pg. 1868
HARRELL & HARRELL INC.; *U.S. Private*, pg. 1868
HARRIS TEETER, INC.—See The Kroger Co.; *U.S. Public*, pg. 2108
HARTER HOUSE-GLENSTONE, INC.; *U.S. Private*, pg. 1873
HARVEST FOODS—See URM Stores, Inc.; *U.S. Private*, pg. 4316
HARVEST, INC.; *U.S. Private*, pg. 1877
HARVEST SUPERMARKETS INC.; *U.S. Private*, pg. 1877
HAYS FOOD TOWN INC.; *U.S. Private*, pg. 1885
HAYS FOOD TOWN—See Hays Food Town Inc.; *U.S. Private*, pg. 1885
HEALTH FOOD ASSOCIATES, INC.—See AMCON Distributing Company; *U.S. Public*, pg. 93
H-E-B, LP; *U.S. Private*, pg. 1824
H.E. BUTT GROCERY COMPANY; *U.S. Private*, pg. 1826
HEINEN'S INC.; *U.S. Private*, pg. 1904
HEIWADO CO., LTD.; *Int'l*, pg. 3327
HELLO PRODUCTS LLC—See Colgate-Palmolive Company; *U.S. Public*, pg. 532
HEMKOPSKEDJAN AB—See Axel Johnson Gruppen AB; *Int'l*, pg. 764
HENCH ENTERPRISES INC.; *U.S. Private*, pg. 1913
HERITAGE DAIRY STORES INC.; *U.S. Private*, pg. 1922
HILLERS INC; *U.S. Private*, pg. 1946
HI NABOR SUPERMARKET INC.; *U.S. Private*, pg. 1931
HIPERCOR, S.A.—See El Corte Ingles, S.A.; *Int'l*, pg. 2340
HIPERMARC S.A.; *Int'l*, pg. 3402
HIT HANDELSGRUPPE GMBH & CO. KG—See Dohle Handelsgruppe Holding GmbH & Co. KG; *Int'l*, pg. 2155
HOKUYU LUCKY CO., LTD.; *Int'l*, pg. 3445
HOLIDAY FOODS & GROCERIES INC.; *U.S. Private*, pg. 1963
HOLIDAY QUALITY FOODS, INC.—See North State Grocery Inc.; *U.S. Private*, pg. 2948
HOLLISTER SUPER INCORPORATED; *U.S. Private*, pg. 1966
HOME FOOD SERVICE OF PA; *U.S. Private*, pg. 1970
HOMELAND STORES, INC.—See Associated Wholesale Grocers, Inc.; *U.S. Private*, pg. 357
HOMEMAKER MEGAMALL AUBURN PTY LTD—See AMP Limited; *Int'l*, pg. 432
HOMEPLUS CO., LIMITED—See Canada Pension Plan Investment Board; *Int'l*, pg. 1279
HOMESTEAD ENTERPRISES INC.; *U.S. Private*, pg. 1974
HOMOLJE A.D.; *Int'l*, pg. 3456
HONG KONG MARKET PLACE INC.; *U.S. Private*, pg. 1976
HONG KONG SUPERMARKET INC.; *U.S. Private*, pg. 1976
HORNBACHERS—See United Natural Foods, Inc.; *U.S. Public*, pg. 2231
HOUCHENS INDUSTRIES, INC.; *U.S. Private*, pg. 1989
HOUCHENS MARKETS—See Houchens Industries, Inc.; *U.S. Private*, pg. 1990
HOWS MARKETS LLC; *U.S. Private*, pg. 1996
H.P. NEMENZ FOOD STORES INC.; *U.S. Private*, pg. 1835
HUDSON'S SUPER MARKETS, INC.—See GW Foods Inc.; *U.S. Private*, pg. 1821
HUGO'S FAMILY MARKETPLACE—See Valley Markets, Incorporated; *U.S. Private*, pg. 4334
HUZHOU AUCHAN HYPERMARKETS CO., LTD.—See Alibaba Group Holding Limited; *Int'l*, pg. 326
HY LABONNE & SONS INC.; *U.S. Private*, pg. 2015
HYPARLO S.A.—See Carrefour SA; *Int'l*, pg. 1345
HYPCO; *Int'l*, pg. 3552
HYPERDEMA SA—See Carrefour SA; *Int'l*, pg. 1345
HY-VEE, INC.; *U.S. Private*, pg. 2015

IBAR A.D.; *Int'l*, pg. 3569
ICA SVERIGE AB—See ICA Gruppen AB; *Int'l*, pg. 3577
ICELAND FOODS LTD.; *Int'l*, pg. 3579
IGA, INC.; *U.S. Private*, pg. 2039
IMMOCO S.A.S.—See Colruyt Group N.V.; *Int'l*, pg. 1705
IMMODIS—See Carrefour SA; *Int'l*, pg. 1345
IMOREAL—See Carrefour SA; *Int'l*, pg. 1345
INDUS-LEAGUE CLOTHING LIMITED—See Future Corporate Resources Limited; *Int'l*, pg. 2853
INGLES MARKETS, INCORPORATED; *U.S. Public*, pg. 1122
INSERRA SUPERMARKETS, INC.; *U.S. Private*, pg. 2085
INSTASHOP DMCC—See Delivery Hero SE; *Int'l*, pg. 2013
INTERDIS SNC—See Carrefour SA; *Int'l*, pg. 1345
INVERSIONES PRYCA, S.A.—See Carrefour SA; *Int'l*, pg. 1345
IRMA A/S—See FDB Group; *Int'l*, pg. 2628
IVAN H. STEWART INC.; *U.S. Private*, pg. 2150
JADES SUPER FOOD; *U.S. Private*, pg. 2181
JA MARKETING CORP.; *U.S. Private*, pg. 2172
JAMES CHAPPEL; *U.S. Private*, pg. 2183
JAX MARKETS—See Macber Inc.; *U.S. Private*, pg. 2535
JAY PETROLEUM, INC.; *U.S. Private*, pg. 2192
J.B. SULLIVAN INC.; *U.S. Private*, pg. 2159
JENSENS COMPLETE SHOPPING; *U.S. Private*, pg. 2201
JERRY LEE'S GROCERY, INC.; *U.S. Private*, pg. 2202
JERRY'S ENTERPRISES INC.; *U.S. Private*, pg. 2202
JERRY'S SUPERMARKET INC.; *U.S. Private*, pg. 2202
JEWEL FOOD STORES, INC.—See Cerberus Capital Management, L.P.; *U.S. Private*, pg. 836
JGS SUPERMARKETS INC.; *U.S. Private*, pg. 2207
JHB INC.; *U.S. Private*, pg. 2207
J.H. HARVEY CO., LLC—See Aldi Einkauf SE & Co. oHG; *Int'l*, pg. 304
JIAXING AUCHAN HYPERMARKETS CO., LTD.—See Alibaba Group Holding Limited; *Int'l*, pg. 326
J&J FOODS INC.; *U.S. Private*, pg. 2154
JK FOODS INC.; *U.S. Private*, pg. 2211
J & L ENTERPRISES INC.; *U.S. Private*, pg. 2152
JOBAR INC.; *U.S. Private*, pg. 2217
JOHANNESON'S INC.; *U.S. Private*, pg. 2219
JOHNSONS MEGA SAN BERNARDO S.A.—See Cencosud S.A.; *Int'l*, pg. 1400
JORGENSEN'S INC.; *U.S. Private*, pg. 2236
J&T ENTERPRISES INC.; *U.S. Private*, pg. 2155
JUBA'S INC.; *U.S. Private*, pg. 2242
JUMBO RETAIL ARGENTINA S.A.—See Cencosud S.A.; *Int'l*, pg. 1400
KAMAL CORP.—See Trade Fair Corp.; *U.S. Private*, pg. 4201
KARNS PRIME AND FANCY FOOD; *U.S. Private*, pg. 2263
KASUMI CO., LTD.—See AEON Co., Ltd.; *Int'l*, pg. 177
KBANE SAS—See Groupe Adeo S.A.; *Int'l*, pg. 3091
K.E. MCKAY'S MARKET OF COOS BAY; *U.S. Private*, pg. 2252
KEMPSEY CENTRAL PTY. LTD.—See Gowing Brothers Limited; *Int'l*, pg. 3044
KENCO INC.; *U.S. Private*, pg. 2283
KENNIE'S MARKETS INC.; *U.S. Private*, pg. 2286
KEN'S SUPERFAIR FOODS; *U.S. Private*, pg. 2283
KENTCO INC.; *U.S. Private*, pg. 2288
THE KENT COMPANIES; *U.S. Private*, pg. 4065
KENYAN ENTERPRISES INC.; *U.S. Private*, pg. 2289
K-FOODS INC.; *U.S. Private*, pg. 2251
KING KULLEN GROCERY COMPANY, INC.; *U.S. Private*, pg. 2309
KING SOOPERS INC.—See The Kroger Co.; *U.S. Public*, pg. 2107
KINGS SUPER MARKETS, INC.—See MTN Capital Partners LLC; *U.S. Private*, pg. 2809
KINGS SUPER MARKETS, INC.—See TPG Capital, L.P.; *U.S. Public*, pg. 2168
KIRBY FOODS INC.; *U.S. Private*, pg. 2314
KIRKWOODS INC.; *U.S. Private*, pg. 2315
K KIOSK AG—See Fomento Economico Mexicano, S.A.B. de C.V.; *Int'l*, pg. 2724
KLEIN'S INC.; *U.S. Private*, pg. 2319
KLEINS SUPERMARKETS INC.—See Klein's Inc.; *U.S. Private*, pg. 2319
KNAPP FOODS INC.; *U.S. Private*, pg. 2321
KNIGHT'S INC.; *U.S. Private*, pg. 2322
KNOWLAN'S SUPER MARKETS INC.; *U.S. Private*, pg. 2323
KOHLERS INC.; *U.S. Private*, pg. 2340
KOWALSKI COMPANIES INC.; *U.S. Private*, pg. 2345
KOWALSKI'S WHITE BEAR LAKE MARKET—See Kowalski Companies Inc.; *U.S. Private*, pg. 2345
THE KROGER CO. OF MICHIGAN—See The Kroger Co.; *U.S. Public*, pg. 2109
THE KROGER CO.; *U.S. Public*, pg. 2107
KROGER LIMITED PARTNERSHIP I—See The Kroger Co.; *U.S. Public*, pg. 2108
KROGER SPECIALTY PHARMACY FL 2 LLC—See The Kroger Co.; *U.S. Public*, pg. 2108
K&S MARKET INC.; *U.S. Private*, pg. 2250
K-VA-T FOOD STORES, INC.; *U.S. Private*, pg. 2251
KV MART CO.; *U.S. Private*, pg. 2359

KWICKIE/FLASH FOODS, INC.—See Jones Company, Inc.; *U.S. Private*, pg. 2232
LA CADENA INVESTMENTS; *U.S. Private*, pg. 2368
LAKESHORE FOODS CORP.; *U.S. Private*, pg. 2377
LANDIS SUPER MARKET, INC.; *U.S. Private*, pg. 2385
LARRY'S MARKET, INC.; *U.S. Private*, pg. 2393
LARRY'S MARKETS, INC.; *U.S. Private*, pg. 2393
LASCARIS & SONS INC.; *U.S. Private*, pg. 2395
LA TIENDA FOODS INC.; *U.S. Private*, pg. 2370
LEELOWE INC.; *U.S. Private*, pg. 2415
LEEVERS FOODS INC.; *U.S. Private*, pg. 2415
LEEVERS SUPERMARKETS INC.; *U.S. Private*, pg. 2415
LEFAUBAS—See Carrefour SA; *Int'l*, pg. 1345
LEM MARKETS INC.; *U.S. Private*, pg. 2420
LEPPINKS INC.; *U.S. Private*, pg. 2431
LEROY MERLIN BRESIL LTDA—See Groupe Adeo S.A.; *Int'l*, pg. 3091
LEROY MERLIN BRICOLAJ ROMANIA SRL—See Groupe Adeo S.A.; *Int'l*, pg. 3091
LEROY MERLIN ESPANA S.L.U.—See Groupe Adeo S.A.; *Int'l*, pg. 3091
LEROY MERLIN ITALY S.R.L—See Groupe Adeo S.A.; *Int'l*, pg. 3091
LEROY MERLIN POLOGNE SP. Z.O.O.—See Groupe Adeo S.A.; *Int'l*, pg. 3091
LEWIATAN CZESTOCHOWA SP. Z O.O.—See Emperia Holding S.A.; *Int'l*, pg. 2385
LEWIATAN HOLDING S.A.—See Emperia Holding S.A.; *Int'l*, pg. 2385
LEWIATAN KUJAWY SP. Z O.O.—See Emperia Holding S.A.; *Int'l*, pg. 2385
LEWIATAN OPOLE SP. Z O.O.—See Emperia Holding S.A.; *Int'l*, pg. 2386
LEWIATAN-ORBITA SP.Z O.O.—See Emperia Holding S.A.; *Int'l*, pg. 2386
LEWIATAN PODKARPACIE SP. Z O.O.—See Eurocash S.A.; *Int'l*, pg. 2533
LEWIATAN PODLASIE SP. Z O.O.—See Eurocash S.A.; *Int'l*, pg. 2533
LEWIATAN POLNOC SP. Z O.O.—See Eurocash S.A.; *Int'l*, pg. 2533
LEWIATAN SLASK SP. Z O.O.—See Emperia Holding S.A.; *Int'l*, pg. 2386
LEWIATAN WIELKOPOLSKA SP. Z O.O.—See Emperia Holding S.A.; *Int'l*, pg. 2386
LEWIATAN ZACHOD SP. Z O.O.—See Eurocash S.A.; *Int'l*, pg. 2533
LEWIS FOOD TOWN INC.; *U.S. Private*, pg. 2438
LIANHUA SUPERMARKET HOLDINGS CO., LTD.—See Bailian Group Co., Ltd.; *Int'l*, pg. 802
THE LITTLE CLINIC LLC—See The Kroger Co.; *U.S. Public*, pg. 2109
LOBLAW BRANDS LIMITED—See George Weston Limited; *Int'l*, pg. 2938
LOBLAW COMPANIES LIMITED—See George Weston Limited; *Int'l*, pg. 2938
LOBLAW PROPERTIES WEST, INC.—See George Weston Limited; *Int'l*, pg. 2938
LODIAF S.A.—See Carrefour SA; *Int'l*, pg. 1345
LOGDIS SAS—See Carrefour SA; *Int'l*, pg. 1345
LOTUSS STORES (MALAYSIA) SDN. BHD.—See C.P. All Public Company Limited; *Int'l*, pg. 1244
LOUIS J. PARADIS INC.; *U.S. Private*, pg. 2498
LOWE'S FOOD STORES, INC.—See Alex Lee, Inc.; *U.S. Private*, pg. 163
LOWE'S PAY AND SAVE INC.; *U.S. Private*, pg. 2505
LUCERNE FOODS, INC.—See Cerberus Capital Management, L.P.; *U.S. Private*, pg. 836
LUEKEN'S FOOD STORE INC.; *U.S. Private*, pg. 2512
LUNARDI'S SUPER MARKET INC.; *U.S. Private*, pg. 2515
LUND FOOD HOLDINGS, INC.; *U.S. Private*, pg. 2515
LUND'S INC.—See Lund Food Holdings, Inc.; *U.S. Private*, pg. 2515
LYNNS MARKET INC.; *U.S. Private*, pg. 2522
MAASS CORPORATION; *U.S. Private*, pg. 2530
MACBER INC.; *U.S. Private*, pg. 2534
MACEY'S, INC.; *U.S. Private*, pg. 2535
MACFARLAND PICK & SAVE; *U.S. Private*, pg. 2535
MACY'S CORPORATE SERVICES, INC.—See Macy's, Inc.; *U.S. Public*, pg. 1353
MACY'S FLORIDA STORES, LLC—See Macy's, Inc.; *U.S. Public*, pg. 1353
MACY'S WEST STORES, INC.—See Macy's, Inc.; *U.S. Public*, pg. 1353
MACY'S WEST STORES, INC.—See Macy's, Inc.; *U.S. Public*, pg. 1353
MAGRUDER HOLDINGS INC.; *U.S. Private*, pg. 2549
MAGRUDERS—See Magruder Holdings Inc.; *U.S. Private*, pg. 2549
MAICHE DISTRIBUTION SA—See Carrefour SA; *Int'l*, pg. 1345
MAJOR MARKET, INC.; *U.S. Private*, pg. 2555
MAL ENTERPRISES, INC.; *U.S. Private*, pg. 2556
MALONE'S FOOD STORES, LLC; *U.S. Private*, pg. 2558
MAN-DELL FOOD STORES, INC.; *U.S. Private*, pg. 2559
MANNING, INC.; *U.S. Private*, pg. 2565
MARKET COMPANY, LTD.—See United Natural Foods, Inc.; *U.S. Public*, pg. 2231

445110 — SUPERMARKETS AND OT...

MARKETPLACE CENTER, INC.—See Regency Centers Corporation; *U.S. Public*, pg. 1774
MARKETPLACE FOODS, INC.—See Coborn's Incorporated; *U.S. Private*, pg. 958
MARKET PLACE INC.; *U.S. Private*, pg. 2579
THE MARKETS LLC—See Hancock Park Associates, LP; *U.S. Private*, pg. 1852
MARKFEST INC.; *U.S. Private*, pg. 2581
MARO MARKETY SP. Z O.O.—See Emperia Holding S.A; *Int'l*, pg. 2386
MARRAZZO'S THRIFTWAY; *U.S. Private*, pg. 2588
MARRICKVILLE METRO SHOPPING CENTRE PTY LIMITED—See AMP Limited; *Int'l*, pg. 432
MARROQUIN ORGANIC INTERNATIONAL, INC.—See AGRANA Beteiligungs-AG; *Int'l*, pg. 214
MARSH SUPERMARKETS, INC.—See Sun Capital Partners, Inc.; *U.S. Private*, pg. 3860
MARS SUPER MARKETS, INC.; *U.S. Private*, pg. 2588
MARTINS COUNTRY MARKET; *U.S. Private*, pg. 2597
MARTIN'S FARM MARKET, INC.—See Weis Markets, Inc.; *U.S. Public*, pg. 2342
THE MARUETSU INC.—See AEON Co., Ltd.; *Int'l*, pg. 178
MARUZ CORPORATION; *U.S. Private*, pg. 2597
MAR-VAL FOOD STORE 1 INC.; *U.S. Private*, pg. 2569
MARVIN'S FOODS; *U.S. Private*, pg. 2598
MARVIN'S FOOD WAREHOUSE, INC.; *U.S. Private*, pg. 2598
MAXI FOODS LLC; *U.S. Private*, pg. 2618
MAXVALU HOKKAIDO CO., LTD.—See AEON Co., Ltd.; *Int'l*, pg. 178
MAXVALU HOKURIKU CO., LTD.—See AEON Co., Ltd.; *Int'l*, pg. 178
MAXVALU KANTO CO., LTD.—See AEON Co., Ltd.; *Int'l*, pg. 178
MAXVALU KYUSHU CO., LTD.—See AEON Co., Ltd.; *Int'l*, pg. 178
MAXVALU MINAMI TOHOKU CO., LTD.—See AEON Co., Ltd.; *Int'l*, pg. 178
MAXVALU NISHINIHON CO., LTD.—See Fuji Co., Ltd.; *Int'l*, pg. 2809
MAXVALU TOHOKU CO., LTD.—See AEON Co., Ltd.; *Int'l*, pg. 178
MAXVALU TOKAI CO., LTD.—See AEON Co., Ltd.; *Int'l*, pg. 178
MAYFLOWER FOOD STORES INC.; *U.S. Private*, pg. 2622
MCALISTER'S DELI—See Four Corners Property Trust, Inc.; *U.S. Public*, pg. 875
MCDANIEL FOOD MANAGEMENT INC.; *U.S. Private*, pg. 2631
MCGINNIS SISTERS SPECIAL FOOD STORES; *U.S. Private*, pg. 2635
MCKEEVER ENTERPRISES INC.; *U.S. Private*, pg. 2638
MCLEMORE MARKETS; *U.S. Private*, pg. 2641
MEDFORD CO-OPERATIVE INC.; *U.S. Private*, pg. 2651
MEDIA MARKT BERGEN OP ZOOM B.V.—See Ceconomy AG; *Int'l*, pg. 1376
MEDIA MARKT CENTURY CENTER NV—See Ceconomy AG; *Int'l*, pg. 1373
MEDIA MARKT CORDOBA VIDEO-TV-ELEKTRO-COMPUTER-FOTO, S.A.—See Ceconomy AG; *Int'l*, pg. 1373
MEDIA MARKT CXXIX TV-HIFI-ELEKTRO GMBH INGOLSTADT—See Ceconomy AG; *Int'l*, pg. 1376
MEDIA MARKT DEVENTER B.V.—See Ceconomy AG; *Int'l*, pg. 1376
MEDIA MARKT ENSCHEDE B.V.—See Ceconomy AG; *Int'l*, pg. 1376
MEDIA MARKT GAVA VIDEO-TV-HIFI-ELEKTRO-COMPUTER-FOTO S.A.—See Ceconomy AG; *Int'l*, pg. 1373
MEDIA MARKT GOSSELIES/CHARLEROI N.V.—See Ceconomy AG; *Int'l*, pg. 1373
MEDIA MARKT GRONINGEN B.V.—See Ceconomy AG; *Int'l*, pg. 1376
MEDIA MARKT HEERLEN B.V.—See Ceconomy AG; *Int'l*, pg. 1376
MEDIA MARKT HENGELO B.V.—See Ceconomy AG; *Int'l*, pg. 1377
MEDIA MARKT LEEUWARDEN B.V.—See Ceconomy AG; *Int'l*, pg. 1377
MEDIA MARKT MATARO VIDEO-TV-HIFI-ELEKTRO-COMPUTER-FOTO, S.A.—See Ceconomy AG; *Int'l*, pg. 1373
MEDIA MARKT OOSTAKKER NV—See Ceconomy AG; *Int'l*, pg. 1377
MEDIA MARKT POLSKA SP. Z.O.O. BIELSKO-BIALA SPOLKA KOMANDYTOWA—See Ceconomy AG; *Int'l*, pg. 1379
MEDIA MARKT POLSKA SP. Z.O.O. KONIN SPOLKA KOMANDYTOWA—See Ceconomy AG; *Int'l*, pg. 1378
MEDIA MARKT POLSKA SP. Z.O.O. WROCLAW II SPOLKA KOMANDYTOWA—See Ceconomy AG; *Int'l*, pg. 1379
MEDIA MARKT POLUS CENTER VIDEO TV HIFI PHOTO COMPUTER KERESKEDELMI KFT—See Ceconomy AG; *Int'l*, pg. 1374
MEDIA MARKT RIJSWIJK B.V.—See Ceconomy AG; *Int'l*, pg. 1379
MEDIA MARKT ROERMOND B.V—See Ceconomy AG; *Int'l*, pg. 1379
MEDIA MARKT-SATURN BELGIUM N.V—See Ceconomy AG; *Int'l*, pg. 1375
MEDIA MARKT SATURN HOLDING NEDERLAND B.V.—See Ceconomy AG; *Int'l*, pg. 1379
MEDIA MARKT SATURN, S.A.—See Ceconomy AG; *Int'l*, pg. 1374
MEDIA MARKT SINT-PIETERS-LEEUW N.V.—See Ceconomy AG; *Int'l*, pg. 1374
MEDIA MARKT SPITTAL TV-HIFI-ELEKTRO GMBH—See Ceconomy AG; *Int'l*, pg. 1379
MEDIA MARKT ST. LORENZEN TV-HIFI-ELEKTRO GMBH—See Ceconomy AG; *Int'l*, pg. 1379
MEDIA MARKT TARRAGONA VIDEO-TV-HIFI-ELEKTRO-COMPUTER-FOTO S.A.—See Ceconomy AG; *Int'l*, pg. 1374
MEDIA MARKT TV-HIFI-ELEKTRO GMBH NEUSTADT AN DER WEINSTRASSE—See Ceconomy AG; *Int'l*, pg. 1383
MEDIA MARKT TV-HIFI-ELEKTRO GMBH POTSDAM—See Ceconomy AG; *Int'l*, pg. 1383
MEDIA MARKT TV-HIFI-ELEKTRO GMBH RAVENSBURG—See Ceconomy AG; *Int'l*, pg. 1383
MEDIA MARKT TV-HIFI-ELEKTRO GMBH TRAUNREUT—See Ceconomy AG; *Int'l*, pg. 1384
MEDIA MARKT TWEE TORENS HASSELT NV—See Ceconomy AG; *Int'l*, pg. 1375
MEDIA MARKT UMEA TV-HIFI-ELEKTRO AB—See Ceconomy AG; *Int'l*, pg. 1384
MEDIA MARKT VITORIA-GASTEIZ VIDEO-TV-HIFI-ELEKTRO-COMPUTER-FOTO, S.A.—See Ceconomy AG; *Int'l*, pg. 1375
MEDIA MARKT WIEN XXII TV-HIFI-ELEKTRO GMBH—See Ceconomy AG; *Int'l*, pg. 1384
MEDIA MARKT WORGL TV-HIFI-ELEKTRO GMBH—See Ceconomy AG; *Int'l*, pg. 1375
MEDIA-SATURN DEUTSCHLAND GMBH—See Ceconomy AG; *Int'l*, pg. 1385
MEDIA SATURN - SERVICOS DE APOIO ADMINSTRATIVO, LDA.—See Ceconomy AG; *Int'l*, pg. 1385
MEDIA-SATURN VERWALTUNG DEUTSCHLAND GMBH—See Ceconomy AG; *Int'l*, pg. 1385
MEGA JOHNSONS VINA DEL MAR S.A.—See Cencosud S.A.; *Int'l*, pg. 1401
MEIJER, INC.; *U.S. Private*, pg. 2660
MEIZHOU AUCHAN HYPERMARKETS CO., LTD.—See Alibaba Group Holding Limited; *Int'l*, pg. 326
METROPOLITAN MARKET LLC; *U.S. Private*, pg. 2688
MGV DISTRI-HIPER S.A. AUCHAN—See Auchan Holding S.A.; *Int'l*, pg. 699
MICHIGAN DAIRY, L.L.C.—See The Kroger Co.; *U.S. Public*, pg. 2108
MIDTOWN FOOD STORES INCORPORATION; *U.S. Private*, pg. 2718
MIDWEST PROFITS SDN. BHD.—See Bandar Raya Developments Berhad; *Int'l*, pg. 829
MIGROS TICARET A.S.—See AG Anadolu Grubu Holding A.S.; *Int'l*, pg. 197
MIGROS TICARET A.S.—See BC Partners LLP; *Int'l*, pg. 925
MIKES COLLIERVILLE BIG STAR 52; *U.S. Private*, pg. 2726
MILDEW BV—See Carrefour SA; *Int'l*, pg. 1345
MILFORD MARKETPLACE, LLC—See CBL & Associates Properties, Inc.; *U.S. Public*, pg. 458
MILLER BROTHERS GROCERY INC.; *U.S. Private*, pg. 2733
MINER'S INCORPORATED; *U.S. Private*, pg. 2741
MINGS SUPERMARKET INC.; *U.S. Private*, pg. 2742
MINI MART, INC.—See The Kroger Co.; *U.S. Public*, pg. 2108
MINYARD FOOD STORES, INC.; *U.S. Private*, pg. 2745
MITSUWA CORPORATION—See Wanoba Group Inc.; *U.S. Private*, pg. 4436
MODELO CONTINENTE, SGPA, SA—See Efanor Investimentos, SGPS, SA; *Int'l*, pg. 2318
MOHAR INCORPORATED; *U.S. Private*, pg. 2765
MOLSBERRY MARKETS INC.; *U.S. Private*, pg. 2767
MOODY'S MARKET INC.; *U.S. Private*, pg. 2778
MOTHERS NUTRITIONAL CENTER; *U.S. Private*, pg. 2795
MRS. GOOCH'S NATURAL FOOD MARKETS, INC.—See Amazon.com, Inc.; *U.S. Public*, pg. 91
MR. SPECIAL SUPERMARKETS INC.; *U.S. Private*, pg. 2805
MUNAFO INC.; *U.S. Private*, pg. 2813
MUSSERS INC.; *U.S. Private*, pg. 2818
NANAVAC INVESTMENTS (PVT) LTD—See Choppies Enterprises Ltd.; *Int'l*, pg. 1582
NANJING AUCHAN HYPERMARKETS CO., LTD.—See Alibaba Group Holding Limited; *Int'l*, pg. 326
NESTLE WATER CANADA LTD.—See Metropoulos & Co.; *U.S. Private*, pg. 2690
NESTLE WATER CANADA LTD.—See One Rock Capital Partners, LLC; *U.S. Private*, pg. 3021
NETTO MARKEN-DISCOUNT AG & CO. KG—See EDEKA Zentrale AG & Co. KG; *Int'l*, pg. 2305
NEW FRONTIERS HOLDINGS—See Northern Holdings Inc.; *U.S. Private*, pg. 2953
NEW LEAF COMMUNITY MARKETS INC.; *U.S. Private*, pg. 2898
NEW SAGAYA; *U.S. Private*, pg. 2906
NEWTON-DAVIS INC.; *U.S. Private*, pg. 2918
NIAGARA-LOCKPORT ENTERPRISES INC.—See Supermarket Management Inc.; *U.S. Private*, pg. 3881
NICHOLAS MARKETS INC.; *U.S. Private*, pg. 2925
NIEMANN FOODS INC.; *U.S. Private*, pg. 2927
NILGIRIS MECHANISED BAKERY PRIVATE LIMITED—See Future Corporate Resources Limited; *Int'l*, pg. 2853
NINGBO AUCHAN HYPERMARKETS CO., LTD.—See Alibaba Group Holding Limited; *Int'l*, pg. 326
NOB HILL FOODS, INC.—See Raley's Inc.; *U.S. Private*, pg. 3350
NO FRILLS SUPERMARKETS INC.; *U.S. Private*, pg. 2932
NORKUS ENTERPRISES INC.; *U.S. Private*, pg. 2938
NORRENBERNS FOODS; *U.S. Private*, pg. 2939
NORTH COAST COOPERATIVE INC.; *U.S. Private*, pg. 2944
NORTHEAST GROCERY, INC.; *U.S. Private*, pg. 2950
NORTHERN HOLDINGS INC.; *U.S. Private*, pg. 2953
NORTHERN LAKES COOPERATIVE; *U.S. Private*, pg. 2953
NORTHGATE GONZALEZ INC.; *U.S. Private*, pg. 2955
NORTH SNOHOMISH ENTERPRISES, INC.; *U.S. Private*, pg. 2947
NORTH STATE GROCERY INC.; *U.S. Private*, pg. 2948
NUGGET MARKET INC.; *U.S. Private*, pg. 2972
NUMERO UNO MARKETS—See Breco Holdings, Inc; *U.S. Private*, pg. 644
OBLONG FOOD CENTER INC.; *U.S. Private*, pg. 2987
OHIO VALLEY SUPERMARKET INC.; *U.S. Private*, pg. 3005
OLEAN WHOLESALE GROCERY COOPERATIVE INC.—See C&S Wholesale Grocers, Inc.; *U.S. Private*, pg. 704
OLESON'S FOODS INC.; *U.S. Private*, pg. 3010
O'MALIA FOOD MARKETS INC.—See Sun Capital Partners, Inc.; *U.S. Private*, pg. 3860
OOSHOP—See Carrefour SA; *Int'l*, pg. 1346
ORIGINAL AUSTIN'S GROCERY STORES; *U.S. Private*, pg. 3042
OV SMITH & SONS INC.; *U.S. Private*, pg. 3052
OZARK SUPERMARKET INC.; *U.S. Private*, pg. 3058
PACIFIC SUPERMARKET INC.; *U.S. Private*, pg. 3071
PAK 'N SAVE, INC.—See Cerberus Capital Management, L.P.; *U.S. Private*, pg. 836
PALCO LLC—See Rouse's Enterprises LLC; *U.S. Private*, pg. 3489
PALLIOS BROS. INC.; *U.S. Private*, pg. 3079
PAM PANORAMA S.P.A.—See GECOS S.p.A.; *Int'l*, pg. 2909
PAQ, INC.; *U.S. Private*, pg. 3088
PARAGON WHOLESALE FOODS CORP.—See Sysco Corporation; *U.S. Public*, pg. 1975
PARAMOUNT FOODS INC.; *U.S. Private*, pg. 3093
PARK LANE FOODS LLC; *U.S. Private*, pg. 3096
PARK & SHOP FOOD MART; *U.S. Private*, pg. 3095
PASARAYA JAYA GADING SDN. BHD.—See Cab Cakaran Corporation Berhad; *Int'l*, pg. 1245
PASTA SHOP; *U.S. Private*, pg. 3104
PATHMARK STORES, INC.—See The Great Atlantic & Pacific Tea Company, Inc.; *U.S. Private*, pg. 4038
PAULBECKS INC.; *U.S. Private*, pg. 3114
PAVILIONS—See Cerberus Capital Management, L.P.; *U.S. Private*, pg. 836
PEARL RIVER SHOP RITE ASSOCIATES INC.—See Glass Gardens Inc.; *U.S. Private*, pg. 1706
PEOPLES MARKET, INCORPORATED—See United Natural Foods, Inc.; *U.S. Public*, pg. 2232
PERLMART DRUGS OF LACEY INC.—See Perlmart Inc.; *U.S. Private*, pg. 3152
PERLMART INC.; *U.S. Private*, pg. 3152
PERLMART OF LACEY TOWNSHIP INC.—See Perlmart Inc.; *U.S. Private*, pg. 3152
PETE'S FRESH MARKET; *U.S. Private*, pg. 3157
PHIVETOL SA—See Carrefour SA; *Int'l*, pg. 1346
PICK QUICK FOODS; *U.S. Private*, pg. 3176
PIGGLY WIGGLY CAROLINA COMPANY; *U.S. Private*, pg. 3179
PIGGLY WIGGLY CENTRAL INC.; *U.S. Private*, pg. 3179
PIGGLY WIGGLY FOOD STORES OF JEFFERSON COUNTY, INC.; *U.S. Private*, pg. 3179
PIGGLY WIGGLY HALEYVILLE INC.; *U.S. Private*, pg. 3179
PIGGLY WIGGLY MIDWEST, LLC—See C&S Wholesale Grocers, Inc.; *U.S. Private*, pg. 704
PIGGLY WIGGLY OF CRYSTAL SPRING INC; *U.S. Private*, pg. 3179
PLAINBRIDGE LLC—See The Great Atlantic & Pacific Tea Company, Inc.; *U.S. Private*, pg. 4038
PLUMB INC.; *U.S. Private*, pg. 3214
POLLY'S FOOD SERVICE INC.; *U.S. Private*, pg. 3225
PONCE CASH & CARRY INC.; *U.S. Private*, pg. 3227
PONTIAC IGA FOOD CENTER; *U.S. Private*, pg. 3227
POTASH BROS INC.; *U.S. Private*, pg. 3235

N.A.I.C.S. INDEX

445110 — SUPERMARKETS AND OT...

POTTER & SIMS FOODS, INC.; *U.S. Private*, pg. 3235
PRENGER FOODS INC.; *U.S. Private*, pg. 3252
PRICE CHOPPER GOLUB CORPORATION—See Golub Corporation; *U.S. Private*, pg. 1736
PRICE CHOPPER OPERATING CO., INC.—See Golub Corporation; *U.S. Private*, pg. 1737
PRICE CHOPPER OPERATING CO. OF MASSACHUSETTS, INC.—See Golub Corporation; *U.S. Private*, pg. 1737
PRICE CHOPPER SUPERMARKET—See Golub Corporation; *U.S. Private*, pg. 1737
PRICESMART DOMINICANA, S.A.—See PriceSmart Inc.; *U.S. Public*, pg. 1716
PRICESMART PANAMA, S.A.—See PriceSmart Inc.; *U.S. Public*, pg. 1716
PRICESMART (TRINIDAD) LTD.—See PriceSmart Inc.; *U.S. Public*, pg. 1716
PROMOHYPERMARKT AG—See Carrefour SA; *Int'l*, pg. 1346
PROVIGO DISTRIBUTION—See George Weston Limited; *Int'l*, pg. 2939
PR SPRINGFIELD TOWN CENTER LLC—See Pennsylvania Real Estate Investment Trust; *U.S. Public*, pg. 1663
PRUITTS FOOD INC.; *U.S. Private*, pg. 3296
PSK SUPERMARKETS INC.; *U.S. Private*, pg. 3297
PT ALFA RETAILINDO TBK—See Carrefour SA; *Int'l*, pg. 1346
PT SRC INDONESIA SEMBILAN—See Philip Morris International Inc.; *U.S. Public*, pg. 1685
PUBLIX ALABAMA, LLC—See Publix Super Markets, Inc.; *U.S. Private*, pg. 3301
PUCKETT GROCERY CO. INC.; *U.S. Private*, pg. 3301
PUNA PLANTATION HAWAII LTD.; *U.S. Private*, pg. 3304
QINGDAO AEON DONGTAI CO., LTD.—See AEON Co., Ltd.; *Int'l*, pg. 178
QSI INC.; *U.S. Private*, pg. 3314
QUALITY FOODS CORPORATION; *U.S. Private*, pg. 3319
QUERCY—See Carrefour SA; *Int'l*, pg. 1346
QUIK-MART STORES INC.; *U.S. Private*, pg. 3327
QUIK THRIFT FOOD STORES, INC.; *U.S. Private*, pg. 3327
QUILLIN'S INC.; *U.S. Private*, pg. 3327
RAGLAND BROS. RETAIL COMPANIES INC.; *U.S. Private*, pg. 3346
RALEY'S INC.; *U.S. Private*, pg. 3350
RALPHS GROCERY COMPANY—See The Kroger Co.; *U.S. Public*, pg. 2107
RANDALLS FOOD & DRUGS, LP—See Cerberus Capital Management, L.P.; *U.S. Private*, pg. 836
RB PATEL GROUP LIMITED—See Fijian Holdings Limited; *Int'l*, pg. 2662
REAL HOLDING MANAGEMENT CORP.; *U.S. Private*, pg. 3367
REAM'S FOOD STORES; *U.S. Private*, pg. 3370
REASORS INC.; *U.S. Private*, pg. 3370
REDNER'S MARKETS INC.; *U.S. Private*, pg. 3379
REEBLE INC.; *U.S. Private*, pg. 3381
REMKE MARKETS INCORPORATED—See Fresh Encounter Inc.; *U.S. Private*, pg. 1609
REM MARKET LLC.; *U.S. Private*, pg. 3396
RENAISSANCE FOOD GROUP, LLC.—See Calavo Growers, Inc.; *U.S. Public*, pg. 422
RESCHOP CARRE HATTINGEN GMBH—See Aviva plc; *Int'l*, pg. 746
RESCHOP CARRE MARKETING GMBH—See Aviva plc; *Int'l*, pg. 746
RETAIL INVESTORS OF TEXAS, LTD.; *U.S. Private*, pg. 3411
RETAIL S.A.—See Cencosud S.A.; *Int'l*, pg. 1401
REYNALDOS MEXICAN FOOD COMPANY; *U.S. Private*, pg. 3418
RHODES GROCERY INC.; *U.S. Private*, pg. 3422
RICE EPICUREAN MARKET; *U.S. Private*, pg. 3425
RICHANN LLP; *U.S. Private*, pg. 3427
RIDLEYS FOOD CORP; *U.S. Private*, pg. 3434
RIESBECK FOOD MARKETS INC.; *U.S. Private*, pg. 3434
RISER FOODS COMPANY—See Giant Eagle, Inc.; *U.S. Private*, pg. 1694
RITE STUFF FOODS, INC.—See EMERAM Capital Partners GmbH; *Int'l*, pg. 2378
RIVERA FIGUEROA FRANCISCO INC.; *U.S. Private*, pg. 3444
ROCHE BROS. SUPERMARKETS INC.; *U.S. Private*, pg. 3463
ROCHESTER GIANT EAGLE; *U.S. Private*, pg. 3463
ROCKAWAY SHOPRITE ASSOCIATES, INC.—See Glass Gardens Inc.; *U.S. Private*, pg. 1706
RODHES MARKET INCORPORATED; *U.S. Private*, pg. 3470
ROLAND PARK-VICTOR'S MARKET INC.; *U.S. Private*, pg. 3474
RONETCO SUPERMARKETS INC.; *U.S. Private*, pg. 3478
ROSAUERS SUPERMARKETS, INC.—See URM Stores, Inc.; *U.S. Private*, pg. 4316
ROSE & ASSOCIATES LLC; *U.S. Private*, pg. 3481
ROSWIL INC.; *U.S. Private*, pg. 3486
ROTHIDI SA—See Carrefour SA; *Int'l*, pg. 1344
ROTH IGA FOODLINER INC.; *U.S. Private*, pg. 3487
ROTONDE—See Carrefour SA; *Int'l*, pg. 1346

ROUNDYS, INC.—See The Kroger Co.; *U.S. Public*, pg. 2109
ROUSE'S ENTERPRISES LLC; *U.S. Private*, pg. 3489
ROY D. GOODNER INC.; *U.S. Private*, pg. 3490
R-RANCH MARKET INC.; *U.S. Private*, pg. 3333
RUDDICK OPERATING COMPANY—See The Kroger Co.; *U.S. Public*, pg. 2108
RUDY'S MARKETS INC.; *U.S. Private*, pg. 3502
SAAR'S INC.; *U.S. Private*, pg. 3520
SAFEWAY SELECT GIFT SOURCE, INC.—See Cerberus Capital Management, L.P.; *U.S. Private*, pg. 836
SANTA ISABEL S.A.—See Cencosud S.A.; *Int'l*, pg. 1401
SANTANDER ENTERPRISES INC.; *U.S. Private*, pg. 3548
SANTONI'S INC.; *U.S. Private*, pg. 3548
SANTOS ENTERPRISES; *U.S. Private*, pg. 3548
S.A.S COLRUYT DISTRIBUTION FRANCE—See Colruyt Group N.V.; *Int'l*, pg. 1705
SATURN BUDA VIDEO TV HIFI ELEKTRO PHOTO COMPUTER KERESKEDELMI KFT.—See Ceconomy AG; *Int'l*, pg. 1385
SATURN ELECTRO-HANDELSGESELLSCHAFT MBH DARMSTADT—See Ceconomy AG; *Int'l*, pg. 1386
SATURN ELECTRO-HANDELSGESELLSCHAFT MBH DELMENHORST—See Ceconomy AG; *Int'l*, pg. 1386
SATURN ELECTRO-HANDELSGESELLSCHAFT MBH INGOLSTADT—See Ceconomy AG; *Int'l*, pg. 1386
SATURN ELECTRO-HANDELSGESELLSCHAFT MBH ISERNHAGEN—See Ceconomy AG; *Int'l*, pg. 1386
SATURN ELECTRO-HANDELSGESELLSCHAFT MBH KAISERSLAUTERN—See Ceconomy AG; *Int'l*, pg. 1386
SATURN ELECTRO-HANDELSGESELLSCHAFT MBH KARLSRUHE-DURLACH—See Ceconomy AG; *Int'l*, pg. 1386
SATURN ELECTRO-HANDELSGESELLSCHAFT MBH KASSEL—See Ceconomy AG; *Int'l*, pg. 1386
SATURN ELECTRO-HANDELSGESELLSCHAFT MBH KEMPTEN—See Ceconomy AG; *Int'l*, pg. 1386
SATURN ELECTRO-HANDELSGESELLSCHAFT MBH KOBLENZ—See Ceconomy AG; *Int'l*, pg. 1386
SATURN ELECTRO-HANDELSGESELLSCHAFT MBH KREFELD—See Ceconomy AG; *Int'l*, pg. 1386
SATURN ELECTRO-HANDELSGESELLSCHAFT MBH LANDSHUT—See Ceconomy AG; *Int'l*, pg. 1386
SATURN ELECTRO-HANDELSGESELLSCHAFT MBH LEIPZIG-HAUPTBAHNHOF—See Ceconomy AG; *Int'l*, pg. 1386
SATURN ELECTRO-HANDELSGESELLSCHAFT MBH LEIPZIG—See Ceconomy AG; *Int'l*, pg. 1386
SATURN ELECTRO-HANDELSGESELLSCHAFT MBH LUBECK—See Ceconomy AG; *Int'l*, pg. 1386
SATURN ELECTRO-HANDELSGESELLSCHAFT MBH LUDENSCHEID—See Ceconomy AG; *Int'l*, pg. 1387
SATURN ELECTRO-HANDELSGESELLSCHAFT MBH LUDWIGSBURG—See Ceconomy AG; *Int'l*, pg. 1387
SATURN ELECTRO-HANDELSGESELLSCHAFT MBH LUDWIGSHAFEN—See Ceconomy AG; *Int'l*, pg. 1387
SATURN ELECTRO-HANDELSGESELLSCHAFT MBH LUNEN—See Ceconomy AG; *Int'l*, pg. 1387
SATURN ELECTRO-HANDELSGESELLSCHAFT MBH MAGDEBURG—See Ceconomy AG; *Int'l*, pg. 1387
SATURN ELECTRO-HANDELSGESELLSCHAFT MBH MAINZ—See Ceconomy AG; *Int'l*, pg. 1387
SATURN ELECTRO-HANDELSGESELLSCHAFT MBH MARL—See Ceconomy AG; *Int'l*, pg. 1387
SATURN ELECTRO-HANDELSGESELLSCHAFT MBH MOERS—See Ceconomy AG; *Int'l*, pg. 1387
SATURN ELECTRO-HANDELSGESELLSCHAFT MBH MULHEIM—See Ceconomy AG; *Int'l*, pg. 1387
SATURN ELECTRO-HANDELSGESELLSCHAFT MBH NECKARSULM—See Ceconomy AG; *Int'l*, pg. 1387
SATURN ELECTRO-HANDELSGESELLSCHAFT MBH NEU-ISENBURG—See Ceconomy AG; *Int'l*, pg. 1387
SATURN ELECTRO-HANDELSGESELLSCHAFT MBH OBERHAUSEN—See Ceconomy AG; *Int'l*, pg. 1387
SATURN ELECTRO-HANDELSGESELLSCHAFT MBH PFORZHEIM—See Ceconomy AG; *Int'l*, pg. 1387
SATURN ELECTRO-HANDELSGESELLSCHAFT MBH REMSCHEID—See Ceconomy AG; *Int'l*, pg. 1387
SATURN ELECTRO-HANDELSGESELLSCHAFT MBH REUTLINGEN—See Ceconomy AG; *Int'l*, pg. 1387
SATURN ELECTRO-HANDELSGESELLSCHAFT MBH ROSTOCK—See Ceconomy AG; *Int'l*, pg. 1387
SATURN ELECTRO-HANDELSGESELLSCHAFT MBH SAARBRUCKEN—See Ceconomy AG; *Int'l*, pg. 1387
SATURN ELECTRO-HANDELSGESELLSCHAFT MBH SCHWEINFURT—See Ceconomy AG; *Int'l*, pg. 1387
SATURN GRAZ V VERTRIEBSGMBH—See Ceconomy AG; *Int'l*, pg. 1387
SATURN HAID ELECTRO-HANDELSGES .M.B.H—See Ceconomy AG; *Int'l*, pg. 1387
SATURN KLAGENFURT ELECTRO-HANDELSGES .M.B.H.—See Ceconomy AG; *Int'l*, pg. 1387
SATURN KORTRIJK N V—See Ceconomy AG; *Int'l*, pg. 1387
SATURN LIEGE MEDIACITE N.V.—See Ceconomy AG; *Int'l*, pg. 1385
SATURN MEIR ANTWERPEN—See Ceconomy AG; *Int'l*, pg. 1385

SATURN MONS N.V.—See Ceconomy AG; *Int'l*, pg. 1387
SATURN PLANET SP. Z O.O.—See Ceconomy AG; *Int'l*, pg. 1385
SATURN PLANET SP. Z O.O. WROCLAW II SPOLKA KOMANDYTOWA—See Ceconomy AG; *Int'l*, pg. 1388
SATURN TENERIFE 3 DE MAYO ELECTRO, S.A.—See Ceconomy AG; *Int'l*, pg. 1385
SATURN VOLKETSWIL AG—See Ceconomy AG; *Int'l*, pg. 1385
SATURN WIEN X VERTRIEBSGMBH—See Ceconomy AG; *Int'l*, pg. 1388
SATURN WIEN XXII ELECTRO-HANDELSGES .M.B.H.—See Ceconomy AG; *Int'l*, pg. 1388
SATURN WIEN XXIII ELECTRO-HANDELSGES .M.B.H.—See Ceconomy AG; *Int'l*, pg. 1388
SATURN WIEN XX VERTRIEBSGMBH—See Ceconomy AG; *Int'l*, pg. 1388
SATURN WILRIJK NV—See Ceconomy AG; *Int'l*, pg. 1385
SAV-A STEP FOOD MARTS INC.; *U.S. Private*, pg. 3555
SAVE-A-LOT—See Houchens Industries, Inc.; *U.S. Private*, pg. 1990
SAVE MART SUPERMARKETS—See Kingswood Capital Management LLC; *U.S. Private*, pg. 2312
SAVER SYSTEMS INC.; *U.S. Private*, pg. 3556
SAVER SYSTEMS OF OHIO, INC.—See Saver Systems Inc.; *U.S. Private*, pg. 3556
SCHNUCK MARKETS, INC.—See The Kroger Co.; *U.S. Public*, pg. 2109
SCHUETTE STORES, INC.; *U.S. Private*, pg. 3570
SCOLARI'S WAREHOUSE MARKETS; *U.S. Private*, pg. 3575
SCOTT'S FOOD AND PHARMACY—See The Kroger Co.; *U.S. Public*, pg. 2109
S.D.O.—See Carrefour SA; *Int'l*, pg. 1346
S&DS MARKET INC.; *U.S. Private*, pg. 3513
SEABRA GROUP; *U.S. Private*, pg. 3583
SEABREEZE PLAZA, LLC—See Saul Centers, Inc.; *U.S. Public*, pg. 1842
SEDANO'S SUPERMARKET MANAGEMENT, INC.; *U.S. Private*, pg. 3597
SELLERS BROS. INCORPORATED; *U.S. Private*, pg. 3602
SERVICE FOOD MARKET INC.; *U.S. Private*, pg. 3615
SERVICE FOODS; *U.S. Private*, pg. 3615
SHANGHAI BAILIAN GROUP CO., LTD.—See Bailian Group Co., Ltd.; *Int'l*, pg. 802
SHAW'S SUPERMARKETS, INC.—See Cerberus Capital Management, L.P.; *U.S. Private*, pg. 836
SHERMS THUNDERBIRD MARKET; *U.S. Private*, pg. 3634
SHOP-N-SAVE FOODS INC.; *U.S. Private*, pg. 3640
SHOP 'N SAVE ST. LOUIS, INC.—See United Natural Foods, Inc.; *U.S. Public*, pg. 2232
SHOPRITE OF BRISTOL LLC; *U.S. Private*, pg. 3640
SHOPRITE SUPERMARKETS, INC.—See Wakefern Food Corporation; *U.S. Private*, pg. 4427
SHOPRITE SUPERMARKETS, INC.—See Wakefern Food Corporation; *U.S. Private*, pg. 4427
SHOPS AT FAIRFAX LLC—See Saul Centers, Inc.; *U.S. Public*, pg. 1842
SIGNO INC.; *U.S. Private*, pg. 3651
S&J REED INC.; *U.S. Private*, pg. 3513
SKAG-WAY DISCOUNT DEPARTMENT STORES INC.; *U.S. Private*, pg. 3680
SMART & FINAL, INC.—See Apollo Global Management, Inc.; *U.S. Public*, pg. 160
SMART & FINAL STORES, LLC—See Apollo Global Management, Inc.; *U.S. Public*, pg. 160
SMITH'S FOOD & DRUG CENTERS, INC.—See The Kroger Co.; *U.S. Public*, pg. 2108
SMITHS FOOD & DRUGS, INC.—See The Kroger Co.; *U.S. Public*, pg. 2109
SO.BIO SAS—See Carrefour SA; *Int'l*, pg. 1346
SOBRECO—See Carrefour SA; *Int'l*, pg. 1346
SOCA BV—See Carrefour SA; *Int'l*, pg. 1345
SODITA—See Carrefour SA; *Int'l*, pg. 1346
SOESSARDIS SARL—See Carrefour SA; *Int'l*, pg. 1346
SOFO FOOD CO., INC.—See Antonio Sofo & Son Importing Co. Inc.; *U.S. Private*, pg. 288
SOLOMON'S FRESH MARKET LIMITED—See AML Foods Ltd.; *Int'l*, pg. 428
SOLOMON'S SUPERCENTRE (NASSAU) LIMITED—See AML Foods Ltd.; *Int'l*, pg. 428
SONOMA MARKET INC.—See Nugget Market Inc.; *U.S. Private*, pg. 2973
SOREDIS SA—See Carrefour SA; *Int'l*, pg. 1346
SOUQ COMPANY CO., LTD.—See H2O Retailing Corp.; *Int'l*, pg. 3201
SOUTHERN FAMILY MARKETS LLC—See C&S Wholesale Grocers, Inc.; *U.S. Private*, pg. 704
SOUTHERN OIL CO. INC.; *U.S. Private*, pg. 3734
SOUTHLAKE FOOD MART; *U.S. Private*, pg. 3736
SOVAL SA—See Carrefour SA; *Int'l*, pg. 1346
SPAR RETAIL NV—See Colruyt Group N.V.; *Int'l*, pg. 1705
SPENCER'S RETAIL LIMITED—See CESC Limited; *Int'l*, pg. 1424
SPROUTS FARMERS MARKETS, INC.; *U.S. Public*, pg. 1920
STAPLES FUTURE OFFICE PRODUCTS LIMITED—See Future Corporate Resources Limited; *Int'l*, pg. 2853

445110 — SUPERMARKETS AND OT...

STAR MARKETS COMPANY, INC.—See Cerberus Capital Management, L.P.; *U.S. Private*, pg. 836
STATER BROS. MARKETS—See La Cadena Investments; *U.S. Private*, pg. 2368
STAUFFERS OF KISSEL HILL—See SKH Management Co. Inc.; *U.S. Private*, pg. 3681
STAUFFERS OF ROHRERSTOWN INC.—See SKH Management Co. Inc.; *U.S. Private*, pg. 3681
STEIN BROS INC.; *U.S. Private*, pg. 3797
STEPHERSON INCORPORATED; *U.S. Private*, pg. 3803
STERKS SUPER FOODS INC.; *U.S. Private*, pg. 3804
STEVE DEYOUNG'S BIG TOP MARKET; *U.S. Private*, pg. 3808
STEWART'S FOOD STORE INC.; *U.S. Private*, pg. 3811
STEW LEONARD'S; *U.S. Private*, pg. 3810
STINKER STORES, INC.; *U.S. Private*, pg. 3813
STOKROTKA SP.Z.O.O—See Emperia Holding S.A; *Int'l*, pg. 2386
STORMANS INC.; *U.S. Private*, pg. 3831
STROFI SA—See Carrefour SA; *Int'l*, pg. 1346
SUN ART RETAIL GROUP LIMITED—See Alibaba Group Holding Limited; *Int'l*, pg. 326
SUNNYWAY FOODS INC.; *U.S. Private*, pg. 3869
SUNRISE SHOP RITE INC.; *U.S. Private*, pg. 3870
SUNSET FOOD MART INC.; *U.S. Private*, pg. 3871
SUPECO INVESTMENT SRL—See Carrefour SA; *Int'l*, pg. 1346
SUPER 1 FOODS; *U.S. Private*, pg. 3874
SUPER A FOODS INCORPORATED; *U.S. Private*, pg. 3874
SUPER CENTER CONCEPTS INC.; *U.S. Private*, pg. 3874
SUPER C MART INC.; *U.S. Private*, pg. 3874
SUPERCOR, S.A.—See El Corte Ingles, S.A.; *Int'l*, pg. 2340
SUPER FRESH COMPANY—See The Great Atlantic & Pacific Tea Company, Inc.; *U.S. Private*, pg. 4038
SUPER LOW FOODS—See Wayfield Foods Inc.; *U.S. Private*, pg. 4459
SUPERMARKET MANAGEMENT INC.; *U.S. Private*, pg. 3881
SUPERMARKET OPERATIONS INC.; *U.S. Private*, pg. 3881
SUPERMARKET OPERATORS OF AMERICA INC.—See United Natural Foods, Inc.; *U.S. Public*, pg. 2232
SUPERMERCADO AGUEYBANA INC.; *U.S. Private*, pg. 3881
SUPERMERCADO CONCHITA HATO REY; *U.S. Private*, pg. 3881
SUPERMERCADO FACUNDO INC.; *U.S. Private*, pg. 3881
SUPERMERCADO PLAZA GUAYAMA; *U.S. Private*, pg. 3881
SUPERTEST OIL COMPANY INC.; *U.S. Private*, pg. 3881
SUPER TIENDAS LA TAPCHULTECA; *U.S. Private*, pg. 3875
SUPERVALU FOUNDATION—See United Natural Foods, Inc.; *U.S. Public*, pg. 2232
SUPERVALU, INC., BISMARCK DIVISION—See United Natural Foods, Inc.; *U.S. Public*, pg. 2232
SUPERVALU, INC. - EASTON DISTRIBUTION CENTER—See United Natural Foods, Inc.; *U.S. Public*, pg. 2232
SUPERVALU, INC., FOOD MARKETING DIVISION—See United Natural Foods, Inc.; *U.S. Public*, pg. 2232
SUPERVALU, INC., PITTSBURGH DIVISION—See United Natural Foods, Inc.; *U.S. Public*, pg. 2232
SUZHOU AUCHAN HYPERMARKETS CO., LTD.—See Alibaba Group Holding Limited; *Int'l*, pg. 326
SWANSONS FOOD OF ABERDEEN; *U.S. Private*, pg. 3891
SYSCO LINCOLN, INC.—See Sysco Corporation; *U.S. Public*, pg. 1976
SYSCO SAN FRANCISCO, INC.—See Sysco Corporation; *U.S. Public*, pg. 1977
TACT HOLDING—See Aldi Einkauf SE & Co. oHG; *Int'l*, pg. 304
TAIZHOU AUCHAN HYPERMARKETS CO., LTD.—See Alibaba Group Holding Limited; *Int'l*, pg. 326
TAMURA SUPERETTE INC.; *U.S. Private*, pg. 3930
TANQUE VERDE ENTERPRISES, INC.—See United Flea Markets; *U.S. Public*, pg. 4292
TAPP'S SUPERMARKETS INC.; *U.S. Private*, pg. 3932
T.A. SOLBERG CO., INC.; *U.S. Private*, pg. 3911
TAWA SUPERMARKET INC.; *U.S. Private*, pg. 3937
T&C MARKETS IRON MOUNTAIN INC.; *U.S. Private*, pg. 3909
TEAM SLEDD, LLC—See AMCON Distributing Company; *U.S. Public*, pg. 93
TED'S & FRED'S INC.; *U.S. Private*, pg. 3957
TERUYA BROS., LTD.; *U.S. Private*, pg. 3972
TEXOMA PEANUT INN—See Texoma Peanut Company; *U.S. Private*, pg. 3978
TH MIDWEST, INC.—See The Kroger Co.; *U.S. Public*, pg. 2109
THORNE MANAGEMENT INC.; *U.S. Private*, pg. 4162
THRIFTY FOODS INC—See Empire Company Limited; *Int'l*, pg. 2387
TIETGENS ENTERPRISES INC.; *U.S. Private*, pg. 4169
TISCHLER FINER FOODS INC.; *U.S. Private*, pg. 4176
T&K FOODS INC.; *U.S. Private*, pg. 3909

TOKAI KIOSK COMPANY—See Central Japan Railway Company; *Int'l*, pg. 1408
TOM'S FOOD MARKETS INC.; *U.S. Private*, pg. 4183
TOM THUMB FOOD & PHARMACY—See Cerberus Capital Management, L.P.; *U.S. Private*, pg. 836
TOPS MARKETS, LLC—See Golub Corporation; *U.S. Private*, pg. 1737
TOTRAMA SUPERMARKET INC.; *U.S. Private*, pg. 4192
TOWN AND COUNTRY SUPERMARKETS, INC.; *U.S. Private*, pg. 4197
TOWN & COUNTRY MARKET INC.; *U.S. Private*, pg. 4196
TRADE FAIR CORP.; *U.S. Private*, pg. 4201
TRADER JOE'S CO.—See Aldi Einkauf SE & Co. oHG; *Int'l*, pg. 304
TRADING CO. STORES, FOOD & DRUG—See Bonner Foods Inc.; *U.S. Private*, pg. 614
TREASURE ISLAND FOOD MARTS INC.; *U.S. Private*, pg. 4216
TRIPLE V INC.; *U.S. Private*, pg. 4237
T&R MARKET INC.; *U.S. Private*, pg. 3910
T.R. MCTAGGART—See Forward Corporation; *U.S. Private*, pg. 1578
TRUCCHIS MARKETS; *U.S. Private*, pg. 4246
T&T FOODS INC.; *U.S. Private*, pg. 3910
T & T SUPERMARKET, INC.—See George Weston Limited; *Int'l*, pg. 2939
TYSENS COUNTRY GROCERY INC.; *U.S. Private*, pg. 4269
UAB KAROLINISKIU TURGUS—See City Service SE; *Int'l*, pg. 1628
UKAS BIG SAVER FOODS INC.; *U.S. Private*, pg. 4275
UNICENTER S.A.—See Cencosud S.A.; *Int'l*, pg. 1400
UNITED CORP.; *U.S. Private*, pg. 4290
UNITED SUPERMARKETS, LLC—See Cerberus Capital Management, L.P.; *U.S. Private*, pg. 836
UNITED SUPERMARKETS; *U.S. Private*, pg. 4300
UOEI SHOTEN CORPORATION—See Future Corporation; *Int'l*, pg. 2853
VALLERGAS DRIVE-IN MARKETS; *U.S. Private*, pg. 4332
VALLEY MARKETS, INCORPORATED; *U.S. Private*, pg. 4334
VALLI PRODUCE; *U.S. Private*, pg. 4336
VALMARK INC.; *U.S. Private*, pg. 4336
VALU DISCOUNT, INCORPORATED; *U.S. Private*, pg. 4337
VALU MART CO.—See KV Mart Co.; *U.S. Private*, pg. 2359
VIADIX SAS—See Carrefour SA; *Int'l*, pg. 1346
VIKING VILLAGE INC.; *U.S. Private*, pg. 4382
VILLAGE MARKET, INC; *U.S. Private*, pg. 4384
VILLAGE SUPER MARKET INC.; *U.S. Private*, pg. 2297
VONS A SAFEWAY COMPANY—See Cerberus Capital Management, L.P.; *U.S. Private*, pg. 836
THE VONS COMPANIES, INC.—See Cerberus Capital Management, L.P.; *U.S. Private*, pg. 836
WADES FOODS, INC.; *U.S. Private*, pg. 4424
WALMART CHILE S.A.—See Walmart Inc.; *U.S. Public*, pg. 2325
WAL-MART STORES TEXAS, LLC—See Walmart Inc.; *U.S. Public*, pg. 2325
WALTER LAGESTEE, INC.; *U.S. Private*, pg. 4434
WANOBA GROUP INC.; *U.S. Private*, pg. 4436
WAREHOUSE MARKET INC.; *U.S. Private*, pg. 4442
WAYFIELD FOODS INC.; *U.S. Private*, pg. 4459
WAYFIELD FOODS, INC.—See Wayfield Foods Inc.; *U.S. Private*, pg. 4459
WAYFIELD FOODS, INC.—See Wayfield Foods Inc.; *U.S. Private*, pg. 4459
WAYNE LEES GROCERY & MARKET; *U.S. Private*, pg. 4460
WEAVER MARKETS INC.; *U.S. Private*, pg. 4463
WEB & SONS INC.; *U.S. Private*, pg. 4463
WE CARE FOOD STORES INC.; *U.S. Private*, pg. 4462
WEDGE COMMUNITY CO-OP INC.; *U.S. Private*, pg. 4468
WEGMANS FOOD MARKETS, INC.; *U.S. Private*, pg. 4469
WEIS MARKETS, INC.; *U.S. Public*, pg. 2342
WELCOME MARKET, INC.; *U.S. Private*, pg. 4473
WELDOM FRANCE S.A.—See Groupe Adeo S.A.; *Int'l*, pg. 3091
WELPARK CO., LTD.—See AEON Co., Ltd.; *Int'l*, pg. 178
W.E. SALMON INC.; *U.S. Private*, pg. 4420
WESTERN BEEF, INC.; *U.S. Private*, pg. 4491
WESTERN PIONEER INC.; *U.S. Private*, pg. 4495
WESTERN SUPER MARKETS INC.; *U.S. Private*, pg. 4497
WEST POINT MARKET INC.; *U.S. Private*, pg. 4487
WESTWOOD UNITED SUPER INC.; *U.S. Private*, pg. 4502
WFM HAWAII, LLC—See Amazon.com, Inc.; *U.S. Public*, pg. 91
WFM PRIVATE LABEL, L.P.—See Amazon.com, Inc.; *U.S. Public*, pg. 91
WHITES KINGCO INC.; *U.S. Private*, pg. 4511
W.H. KOCH CO., LTD.; *U.S. Private*, pg. 4420
WHOLE FOODS MARKET CALIFORNIA, INC.—See Amazon.com, Inc.; *U.S. Public*, pg. 91
WHOLE FOODS MARKET CANADA, INC.—See Amazon.com, Inc.; *U.S. Public*, pg. 91
WHOLE FOODS MARKET - FLORIDA REGION—See Amazon.com, Inc.; *U.S. Public*, pg. 91
WHOLE FOODS MARKET, INC.—See Amazon.com, Inc.; *U.S. Public*, pg. 91

WHOLE FOODS MARKET - MID-ATLANTIC REGION—See Amazon.com, Inc.; *U.S. Public*, pg. 91
WHOLE FOODS MARKET - MIDWEST REGION—See Amazon.com, Inc.; *U.S. Public*, pg. 91
WHOLE FOODS MARKET NEBRASKA, LLC—See Amazon.com, Inc.; *U.S. Public*, pg. 91
WHOLE FOODS MARKET - NORTH ATLANTIC REGION—See Amazon.com, Inc.; *U.S. Public*, pg. 91
WHOLE FOODS MARKET - NORTHEAST REGION—See Amazon.com, Inc.; *U.S. Public*, pg. 91
WHOLE FOODS MARKET - NORTHERN CALIFORNIA REGION—See Amazon.com, Inc.; *U.S. Public*, pg. 91
WHOLE FOODS MARKET PACIFIC NORTHWEST, INC.—See Amazon.com, Inc.; *U.S. Public*, pg. 91
WHOLE FOODS MARKET - ROCKY MOUNTAIN REGION—See Amazon.com, Inc.; *U.S. Public*, pg. 91
WHOLE FOODS MARKET ROCKY MOUNTAIN/SOUTHWEST, L.P.—See Amazon.com, Inc.; *U.S. Public*, pg. 91
WHOLE FOODS MARKET - SOUTHERN PACIFIC REGION—See Amazon.com, Inc.; *U.S. Public*, pg. 91
WHOLE FOODS MARKET - SOUTHWEST REGION—See Amazon.com, Inc.; *U.S. Public*, pg. 91
WILLIAM A. STRAUB INC.; *U.S. Private*, pg. 4522
WILLIAM L. MARTIN JR.; *U.S. Private*, pg. 4523
WILLIAMS, INC.; *U.S. Private*, pg. 4527
WILLYS AB—See Axel Johnson Gruppen AB; *Int'l*, pg. 764
WILLYS HEMMA AB—See Axel Johnson Gruppen AB; *Int'l*, pg. 764
WILSONVILLE THRIFTWAY; *U.S. Private*, pg. 4532
WINCO FOODS, INC.; *U.S. Private*, pg. 4533
WINCO FOODS—See WinCo Foods, Inc.; *U.S. Private*, pg. 4533
WINEGAR'S SUPERMARKETS INC.; *U.S. Private*, pg. 4540
WINMARKT MANAGEMENT S.R.L.—See IGD SIIQ S.p.A; *Int'l*, pg. 3602
WINN-DIXIE STORES, INC. - JACKSONVILLE DIVISION—See Aldi Einkauf SE & Co. oHG; *Int'l*, pg. 304
WINN-DIXIE STORES, INC. - ORLANDO DIVISION—See Aldi Einkauf SE & Co. oHG; *Int'l*, pg. 304
WM MORRISON SUPERMARKETS PLC—See Clayton, Dubilier & Rice, LLC; *U.S. Private*, pg. 930
WOODMAN'S FOOD MARKET INC.; *U.S. Private*, pg. 4559
WOODSONS CASH STORE INC.; *U.S. Private*, pg. 4560
WOODS SUPER MARKET INC.; *U.S. Private*, pg. 4560
WRAY'S INC.; *U.S. Private*, pg. 4572
WRIGHT'S FOODLANE INC.; *U.S. Private*, pg. 4573
WRIGHT'S FOODLINER INC.; *U.S. Private*, pg. 4573
WUHAN HANFU SUPERMARKET CO. LTD—See Carrefour SA; *Int'l*, pg. 1344
XUZHOU YUEJIA COMMERCIAL CO., LTD.—See Carrefour SA; *Int'l*, pg. 1344
YANGZHOU AUCHAN HYPERMARKETS CO., LTD.—See Alibaba Group Holding Limited; *Int'l*, pg. 326
YOGURTLAND FRANCHISING, INC.; *U.S. Private*, pg. 4589
YOKE'S WASHINGTON FOODS INC.; *U.S. Private*, pg. 4589
ZANOTTO MARKET INC.; *U.S. Private*, pg. 4598
ZEHRMART INC.—See George Weston Limited; *Int'l*, pg. 2939
ZHENJIANG AUCHAN HYPERMARKETS CO., LTD.—See Alibaba Group Holding Limited; *Int'l*, pg. 326
Z INC.; *U.S. Private*, pg. 4596
ZODIO FRANCE—See Groupe Adeo S.A.; *Int'l*, pg. 3091
ZUPANCICH BROS INC.; *U.S. Private*, pg. 4610
ZUPAN ENTERPRISES INC.; *U.S. Private*, pg. 4610

445131 — CONVENIENCE RETAILERS

1ST STOP INC.; *U.S. Private*, pg. 4
4DDDD CORPORATION—See Gaseteria Oil Corp.; *U.S. Private*, pg. 1648
7-ELEVEN MALAYSIA HOLDINGS BERHAD; *Int'l*, pg. 14
7-ELEVEN STORES PTY. LTD.; *Int'l*, pg. 14
ABC STORES; *U.S. Private*, pg. 36
A.C.K. DEVELOPMENT, INC.; *U.S. Private*, pg. 25
ACTION PETROLEUM COMPANY LTD.; *U.S. Private*, pg. 67
AIMI INC.; *U.S. Private*, pg. 133
ALLEN OIL COMPANY INC.; *U.S. Private*, pg. 179
ALL STAR MARKETING INC.—See Morgan Distributing Company Inc.; *U.S. Private*, pg. 2783
ALLSUP ENTERPRISES INC.; *U.S. Private*, pg. 194
ALLSUP'S CONVENIENCE STORES INC.—See BW Gas & Convenience Holdings, LLC; *U.S. Private*, pg. 700
AL'S CORNER OIL CO.; *U.S. Private*, pg. 148
A M P M—See BP plc; *Int'l*, pg. 1126
ANCHOR GASOLINE CORPORATION; *U.S. Private*, pg. 273
A.O.C. FOODMARTS INC.—See R.K. Allen Oil Co., Inc.; *U.S. Private*, pg. 3338
ARCO AM PM—See BP plc; *Int'l*, pg. 1126
AREY COMPANY; *U.S. Private*, pg. 319
AVONDALE FOOD STORES LIMITED; *Int'l*, pg. 750

N.A.I.C.S. INDEX 445131 — CONVENIENCE RETAILE...

N.A.I.C.S. Index

BACON GROCERY CO., INC.—See Jones Company, Inc.; *U.S. Private*, pg. 2232
BEACH OIL COMPANY INC.; *U.S. Private*, pg. 503
BELL BROTHERS OIL CO. INC.; *U.S. Private*, pg. 518
BELLSTORES INC.—See Lykins Companies, Inc.; *U.S. Private*, pg. 2519
BERKLY ENTERPRISES INC.; *U.S. Private*, pg. 533
BETTIOL FUEL SERVICE INC.; *U.S. Private*, pg. 547
BGF CO., LTD.; *Int'l*, pg. 1007
BGF RETAIL CO. LTD.; *Int'l*, pg. 1007
BIGBY COMPANIES; *U.S. Private*, pg. 555
BOB BRANDI STATIONS, INC.—See Applegreen Plc; *Int'l*, pg. 521
BOWMAN ENTERPRISES INC.; *U.S. Private*, pg. 626
BOWMAN FARMS INC.—See Bowman Enterprises Inc.; *U.S. Private*, pg. 626
BREWER OIL CO.; *U.S. Private*, pg. 647
BROCK INVESTMENTS INC.; *U.S. Private*, pg. 660
BRO RETAIL GROUP INC.; *U.S. Private*, pg. 658
BRUCETON FARM SERVICE, INC.; *U.S. Private*, pg. 671
BUDDY'S MINI MARTS, INC.—See Pipeline Oil Sales Inc.; *U.S. Private*, pg. 3189
BW GAS & CONVENIENCE HOLDINGS, LLC; *U.S. Private*, pg. 700
BY-LO MARKETS INC.; *U.S. Private*, pg. 700
CALFEE COMPANY OF DALTON, INC.; *U.S. Private*, pg. 717
CAN DO CO., LTD.—See AEON Co., Ltd.; *Int'l*, pg. 177
CASEY'S GENERAL STORES, INC.; *U.S. Public*, pg. 446
CASEY'S RETAIL COMPANY—See Casey's General Stores, Inc.; *U.S. Public*, pg. 446
CASHION'S FOOD MART INC.; *U.S. Private*, pg. 783
CB MART INC.; *U.S. Private*, pg. 796
CDD SPA—See Bioera S.p.A.; *Int'l*, pg. 1037
CEFCO CONVENIENCE STORES; *U.S. Private*, pg. 805
C.E. TAYLOR OIL INC.; *U.S. Private*, pg. 706
CHASE OIL COMPANY INC.; *U.S. Private*, pg. 860
CHENGDU HONGQI CHAIN CO., LTD.; *Int'l*, pg. 1468
CHICO ENTERPRISES, INC.; *U.S. Private*, pg. 880
CHR CORP.; *U.S. Private*, pg. 889
CHRONISTER OIL COMPANY INC.; *U.S. Private*, pg. 893
CIRCLE K STORES INC.—See Alimentation Couche-Tard Inc.; *Int'l*, pg. 328
CLARK GAS & OIL COMPANY INC.; *U.S. Private*, pg. 913
CLIPPER PETROLEUM INC.; *U.S. Private*, pg. 945
COCO MART INC.; *U.S. Private*, pg. 959
COFFEE CUP FUEL STOP, INC.—See Coffee Cup Fuel Stops & Convenience Stores, Inc.; *U.S. Private*, pg. 961
CO-FREE INCORPORATED; *U.S. Private*, pg. 953
COGO'S CO.—See Coen Oil Company; *U.S. Private*, pg. 960
COLONIAL PANTRY LTD.; *U.S. Private*, pg. 971
CONSUN FOOD INDUSTRIES INCORPORATED; *U.S. Private*, pg. 1026
CONVENIENCE RETAIL ASIA LIMITED; *Int'l*, pg. 1787
CONVENIENCE SHOPPING (SABAH) SDN. BHD.—See 7-Eleven Malaysia Holdings Berhad; *Int'l*, pg. 14
COPA INC.; *U.S. Private*, pg. 1044
CORNER PANTRY INC.; *U.S. Private*, pg. 1051
COUNTRY CORNER INC.—See The Garden City Co-Op Inc.; *U.S. Private*, pg. 4032
COUNTRY FAIR INC.—See Red Apple Group, Inc.; *U.S. Private*, pg. 3373
COUNTRYSIDE MARTS INC.; *U.S. Private*, pg. 1067
CP ALL LAOS COMPANY LIMITED—See C.P. All Public Company Limited; *Int'l*, pg. 1243
CROWN COCO INC.; *U.S. Private*, pg. 1110
C&S INC.; *U.S. Private*, pg. 703
CUBBY'S INC.; *U.S. Private*, pg. 1120
CVS BAY AREA INC.; *Int'l*, pg. 1889
DAILYS—See Tri Star Energy, LLC; *U.S. Private*, pg. 4221
DANDY MINI MARTS INC.—See Williams Oil Company Inc.; *U.S. Private*, pg. 4526
DANNY & CLYDE'S FOOD STORE; *U.S. Private*, pg. 1157
DARI-MART STORES INC.; *U.S. Private*, pg. 1159
D&C INC.; *U.S. Private*, pg. 1137
DEE & DEE OIL CO.; *U.S. Private*, pg. 1188
DEGROOD OIL INC.; *U.S. Private*, pg. 1191
DELANO OIL COMPANY; *U.S. Private*, pg. 1193
DIXIE GAS & OIL CORPORATION; *U.S. Private*, pg. 1245
D&J ENTERPRISES INC.; *U.S. Private*, pg. 1137
DOUBLE QUICK INC.—See First Reserve Management, L.P.; *U.S. Private*, pg. 1526
DUNCAN OIL COMPANY; *U.S. Private*, pg. 1287
E.J. POPE & SON. INC.—See Haymaker Acquisition Corp.; *U.S. Private*, pg. 1885
ELDERS FINE FOODS (SHANGHAI) COMPANY—See Elders Limited; *Int'l*, pg. 2346
ELITE MARKET LLC; *U.S. Private*, pg. 1361
EUTAWVILLE IGA—See W. Lee Flowers & Company Inc.; *U.S. Private*, pg. 4418
EXPRESS LAINE CONVENIENCE STORES INC.; *U.S. Private*, pg. 1451
EXPRESS LANE INC.; *U.S. Private*, pg. 1451
EXXONMOBIL COAL AND MINERALS COMPANY—See Exxon Mobil Corporation; *U.S. Public*, pg. 815
E-Z MART STORES, INC.; *U.S. Private*, pg. 1303
FARM STORES; *U.S. Private*, pg. 1475
FAST POINT FOOD STORES INC.; *U.S. Private*, pg. 1482
FASTRAC MARKETS LLC; *U.S. Private*, pg. 1482
FCL ENTERPRISES LTD.—See Federated Co-operatives Limited; *Int'l*, pg. 2630
FEMSA COMERCIO, S.A. DE C.V.—See Fomento Economico Mexicano, S.A.B. de C.V.; *Int'l*, pg. 2724
FISHER STORES INC.; *U.S. Private*, pg. 1534
FLASH MARKETS INC.; *U.S. Private*, pg. 1540
FLEET MORRIS PETROLEUM INC.; *U.S. Private*, pg. 1542
FOOD FAST CORPORATION; *U.S. Private*, pg. 1560
FOOD-N-FUN, INC.; *U.S. Private*, pg. 1561
FORDE JOHNSON OIL COMPANY; *U.S. Private*, pg. 1565
FRITZ ENTERPRISES; *U.S. Private*, pg. 1612
FUEL MAN INC.—See NW Holding Co.; *U.S. Private*, pg. 2975
FUEL SERVICE - DJ'S MART LLC—See Pops Mart Fuels, LLC; *U.S. Private*, pg. 3229
FZ CORPORATION—See Rosemore Inc.; *U.S. Private*, pg. 3483
GARVIN OIL COMPANY INC.; *U.S. Private*, pg. 1646
GASMART USA INC.; *U.S. Private*, pg. 1648
GENERAL EQUITIES INC.; *U.S. Private*, pg. 1664
GERRY RED INC.; *U.S. Private*, pg. 1687
GIT-N-GO CONVENIENCE STORES; *U.S. Private*, pg. 1703
GOC LTD.; *U.S. Private*, pg. 1724
GO-MART, INC.; *U.S. Private*, pg. 1723
GPM INVESTMENTS, LLC—See Haymaker Acquisition Corp.; *U.S. Private*, pg. 1885
GPM SOUTHEAST, LLC—See Haymaker Acquisition Corp.; *U.S. Private*, pg. 1885
GREEN LANTERN, INC.—See Blue Beacon International, Inc.; *U.S. Private*, pg. 585
GREEN VALLEY GROCERIES; *U.S. Private*, pg. 1774
GRIFFIS INC.; *U.S. Private*, pg. 1788
GR VIETNAM INTERNATIONAL LIMITED—See Golden Resources Development International Limited; *Int'l*, pg. 3031
GS RETAIL CO., LTD.—See GS Holdings Corp.; *Int'l*, pg. 3142
HAMMER-WILLIAMS COMPANY; *U.S. Private*, pg. 1849
HANDEE MART FOOD STORES INC.; *U.S. Private*, pg. 1852
HANDY FOOD STORES INC.—See B&B Corporate Holdings, Inc.; *U.S. Private*, pg. 417
HANKYU RETAILS CORPORATION—See Hankyu Hanshin Holdings Inc.; *Int'l*, pg. 3255
HARRELL OIL CO. OF MOUNT AIRY; *U.S. Private*, pg. 1868
HIGH FALLS OIL COMPANY INC.; *U.S. Private*, pg. 1935
HILCONA CONVENIENCE AG—See Coop-Gruppe Genossenschaft; *Int'l*, pg. 1790
HINZE INC.; *U.S. Private*, pg. 1950
THE HOLLAR COMPANY INC.; *U.S. Private*, pg. 4054
HOLMES OIL COMPANY INC.; *U.S. Private*, pg. 1968
HONEY FARMS INC.; *U.S. Private*, pg. 1976
HUDSON FOOD STORES INCORPORATED; *U.S. Private*, pg. 2001
HUGLI NAHRMITTEL -ERZEUGUNG GES.M.B.H—See Coop-Gruppe Genossenschaft; *Int'l*, pg. 1790
HURST HARVEY OIL INC.; *U.S. Private*, pg. 2013
INDEPENDENT OIL & COAL COMPANY; *U.S. Private*, pg. 2060
INTER - PLANING GMBH—See Coop-Gruppe Genossenschaft; *Int'l*, pg. 1790
JAX ENTERPRISES INC.; *U.S. Private*, pg. 2191
JAYEN INC.; *U.S. Private*, pg. 2192
JET FOOD STORES OF GEORGIA INC; *U.S. Private*, pg. 2204
JOHNSON'S GENERAL STORES INC.; *U.S. Private*, pg. 2229
JOSEPH F. BOENTE SONS INC.; *U.S. Private*, pg. 2236
JOY FOOD STORES INC.—See Supertest Oil Company Inc.; *U.S. Private*, pg. 3881
J&P FLASH INC.; *U.S. Private*, pg. 2154
JR EAST RETAIL NET CO., LTD.—See East Japan Railway Company; *Int'l*, pg. 2270
JRS COUNTRY STORE INC.; *U.S. Private*, pg. 2240
KC MART INC.; *U.S. Private*, pg. 2269
KENT DISTRIBUTORS INC.; *U.S. Private*, pg. 2287
KERBS OIL COMPANY INC.; *U.S. Private*, pg. 2290
KINGSWAY ENTERPRISES INC.; *U.S. Private*, pg. 2312
KRAKOWSKI KREDENS SP. Z O.O.—See Alma Market S.A.; *Int'l*, pg. 361
KRAUSE GENTLE CORPORATION; *U.S. Private*, pg. 2350
LA AMAPOLA INC.; *U.S. Private*, pg. 2367
LANDHOPE CORPORATION; *U.S. Private*, pg. 2385
LAND O'SUN MANAGEMENT CORPORATION; *U.S. Private*, pg. 2383
LEWIS & RAULERSON, INC.; *U.S. Private*, pg. 2437
LIL THRIFT FOOD MARTS INC.—See Petroleum Marketing Group Inc.; *U.S. Private*, pg. 3162
LINN ENTERPRISES INC.; *U.S. Private*, pg. 2462
LIONS QUICK MARTS INC.; *U.S. Private*, pg. 2464
LITTLE GENERAL STORE, INC.; *U.S. Private*, pg. 2468
L&L STORES INCORPORATED; *U.S. Private*, pg. 2363
MAC'S CONVENIENCE STORES, INC.—See Alimentation Couche-Tard Inc.; *Int'l*, pg. 328
MACS MINIT MART; *U.S. Private*, pg. 2538
MARKET BASKET FOOD STORE, INC.; *U.S. Private*, pg. 2578
MARSHALL BROTHERS INC.; *U.S. Private*, pg. 2592
MARTIN & BAYLEY, INC.; *U.S. Private*, pg. 2594
MAX OIL COMPANY INC.; *U.S. Private*, pg. 2617
MELVIN L. DAVIS OIL CO. INC.; *U.S. Private*, pg. 2663
MICKEYS ENTERPRISES INC.; *U.S. Private*, pg. 2702
MID-KANSAS COOP—See Mid-Kansas Co-op Association; *U.S. Private*, pg. 2708
MID-WEST OIL COMPANY INCORPORATED; *U.S. Private*, pg. 2710
MILLER & HOLMES INC.; *U.S. Private*, pg. 2732
MILLER OIL CO., INC.; *U.S. Private*, pg. 2735
MINISTOP CO., LTD.—See AEON Co., Ltd.; *Int'l*, pg. 178
MINIT STOP; *U.S. Private*, pg. 2742
MISSISSIPPI OIL INC.—See Smith Petroleum Inc.; *U.S. Private*, pg. 3695
MOOVE AND OINK INC.; *U.S. Private*, pg. 2781
MORELANDS INC.; *U.S. Private*, pg. 2782
MORRIS CORPORATION; *U.S. Private*, pg. 2787
MWS ENTERPRISES INC.; *U.S. Private*, pg. 2822
NATIONAL FOOD STORES, INC.; *U.S. Private*, pg. 2854
NEEB CORPORATION; *U.S. Private*, pg. 2879
NELSONS OIL & GAS INCORPORATED; *U.S. Private*, pg. 2884
NUWAY COOPERATIVE INC.; *U.S. Private*, pg. 2975
OUTAGAMIE CO-OP SERVICES; *U.S. Private*, pg. 3051
PAR MAR OIL COMPANY—See Croton Holding Company; *U.S. Private*, pg. 1108
PATEL CONVENIENCE STORES INC.; *U.S. Private*, pg. 3105
PIC QUIK STORES INC.; *U.S. Private*, pg. 3176
PIEDMONT PETROLEUM CORP.; *U.S. Private*, pg. 3178
PLAID PANTRIES, INC.; *U.S. Private*, pg. 3194
PLEZ U STORES INC.; *U.S. Private*, pg. 3214
PRIDE CONVENIENCE INC.; *U.S. Private*, pg. 3259
PRI MAR PETROLEUM INC.; *U.S. Private*, pg. 3258
PUTNAM COMPANY; *U.S. Private*, pg. 3307
QUALITY FOODS INC.; *U.S. Private*, pg. 3319
QUICK CHANGE INC.—See Floco Unlimited Inc.; *U.S. Private*, pg. 1546
QUICK CHEK FOOD STORES INC.; *U.S. Private*, pg. 3326
RAM INC.; *U.S. Private*, pg. 3351
REED INC.; *U.S. Private*, pg. 3382
REOPCO INC.; *U.S. Private*, pg. 3400
R.L. JORDAN OIL CO; *U.S. Private*, pg. 3338
ROBINSON ENTERPRISES INC.; *U.S. Private*, pg. 3461
ROCKY MOUNT STOP & SHOP INC; *U.S. Private*, pg. 3468
ROETTGERS COMPANY INC.; *U.S. Private*, pg. 3471
ROSE MART INC.; *U.S. Private*, pg. 3481
SAC-N-PAC STORES, INC.—See Sunoco LP; *U.S. Public*, pg. 1965
SAVE TIME CONVENIENCE STORES INC.—See Melling Tool Company Inc.; *U.S. Private*, pg. 2662
SCAFF'S INC.; *U.S. Private*, pg. 3560
SCHIERL SALES CORP.—See Team Schierl Companies; *U.S. Private*, pg. 3950
SCULLIN OIL CO.; *U.S. Private*, pg. 3581
SHANGHAI HUALIAN LAWSON CO., LTD.—See AEON Co., Ltd.; *Int'l*, pg. 178
SHERO ENTERPRISES INC.; *U.S. Private*, pg. 3634
SHOP KWIK STORE LLC; *U.S. Private*, pg. 3640
SHOP RITE INC.; *U.S. Private*, pg. 3640
SOUTHERN FOOD PARK INCORPORATED; *U.S. Private*, pg. 3731
SOUTHERN OIL COMPANY INC.; *U.S. Private*, pg. 3734
SOUTHWEST CONVENIENCE STORES LLC; *U.S. Private*, pg. 3738
SPEEDY Q MARKETS; *U.S. Private*, pg. 3754
SPEEDY STOP FOOD STORES, LLC—See C.L. Thomas, Inc.; *U.S. Private*, pg. 708
SPIES CORPORATION; *U.S. Private*, pg. 3756
SPIVEY ENTERPRISES INC.; *U.S. Private*, pg. 3758
SPRINT OIL COMPANY; *U.S. Private*, pg. 3765
SSS DEVELOPMENT INC.; *U.S. Private*, pg. 3769
STACEY SMITH ENTERPRISES; *U.S. Private*, pg. 3774
STEINHAGEN OIL COMPANY, INC.; *U.S. Private*, pg. 3798
STEPHENSON OIL CO., INC.; *U.S. Private*, pg. 3803
STEWART'S SHOPS CORPORATION; *U.S. Private*, pg. 3811
ST. JOE PETROLEUM CO.; *U.S. Private*, pg. 3771
STOP IN FOOD STORES, INC.—See CrossAmerica Partners LP; *U.S. Public*, pg. 596
STOP N SAVE, INC.—See Kapoor Enterprises; *U.S. Private*, pg. 2261
STRIPES LLC—See Sunoco LP; *U.S. Public*, pg. 1965
SULLIVAN OIL COMPANY; *U.S. Private*, pg. 3851
SUNRISE STORES, LLC—See Foster Blue Water Oil, LLC; *U.S. Private*, pg. 1578
SUPER AMERICA; *U.S. Private*, pg. 3874
SWANSON SERVICES CORPORATION—See H.I.G. Capital, LLC; *U.S. Private*, pg. 1832
TAYLOR OIL COMPANY INCORPORATED; *U.S. Private*, pg. 3940
TEDESCHI FOOD SHOPS, INC.; *U.S. Private*, pg. 3957
TESORO ALASKA CO LLC—See Marathon Petroleum Corporation; *U.S. Public*, pg. 1363
TEXAN MARKETS INC.; *U.S. Private*, pg. 3974

445131 — CONVENIENCE RETAILE...

THOMPSON ENERGY; *U.S. Private*, pg. 4159
THORNTONS INC—See ArcLight Capital Holdings, LLC; *U.S. Private*, pg. 312
THORNTONS INC—See BP plc; *Int'l*, pg. 1131
TOM RANDALL DISTRIBUTING CO.; *U.S. Private*, pg. 4183
TOOT'N TOTUM FOOD STORES LLC; *U.S. Private*, pg. 4186
TWO FARMS, INC.; *U.S. Private*, pg. 4266
UNITED DAIRY FARMERS, INC.; *U.S. Private*, pg. 4290
UNITED FOOD STORE INC.; *U.S. Private*, pg. 4292
UPPY'S CONVENIENCE STORES INC.—See Sunoco LP; *U.S. Public*, pg. 1965
US ENTERPRISES INC.; *U.S. Private*, pg. 4318
VALDAK CORPORATION; *U.S. Private*, pg. 4330
VALLEY OIL CORPORATION; *U.S. Private*, pg. 4334
VERONA OIL CO., INC.; *U.S. Private*, pg. 4368
VIDCON ENTERPRISES, INC.; *U.S. Private*, pg. 4380
VILLAGE FARM DAIRY; *U.S. Private*, pg. 4383
V.R. PROPERTY MANAGEMENT; *U.S. Private*, pg. 4328
WARRENTON OIL CO.; *U.S. Private*, pg. 4444
WAWA, INC.; *U.S. Private*, pg. 4458
WEIGEL'S STORES INC.; *U.S. Private*, pg. 4471
WEST SIDE ONESTOP—See J&H Oil Company Inc.; *U.S. Private*, pg. 2154
WHITEHEAD OIL CO., INC.—See Whitehead Oil Co., Inc.; *U.S. Private*, pg. 4511
WILKERSON FUEL CO., INC.; *U.S. Private*, pg. 4520
WILSON BAKER INC.; *U.S. Private*, pg. 4530
WIND RIVER PETROLEUM; *U.S. Private*, pg. 4536
WYKSTRA OIL CO., INC.; *U.S. Private*, pg. 4576
YESWAY, INC.; *U.S. Private*, pg. 4588
YOSEMITE CONCESSION SERVICES MAIL ORDER DEPT—See Delaware North Companies, Inc.; *U.S. Private*, pg. 1194
ZABKA POLSKA SP. Z O. O.—See CVC Capital Partners SICAV-FIS S.A.; *Int'l*, pg. 1889

445132 — VENDING MACHINE OPERATORS

1.800.VENDING, INC.; *U.S. Private*, pg. 2
ACE COFFEE BAR, INC.; *U.S. Private*, pg. 56
A DRINK TRADE CO., LTD.—See Almedio, Inc.; *Int'l*, pg. 364
A.H. ENTERTAINERS INC.; *U.S. Private*, pg. 26
AIM SERVICES CO., LTD.—See Aramark; *U.S. Public*, pg. 177
AMERICAN BATTERY MATERIALS, INC.; *U.S. Public*, pg. 97
AMERICAN FOOD & VENDING CORP.; *U.S. Private*, pg. 234
ARAMARK CANADA LTD.—See Aramark; *U.S. Public*, pg. 176
ARAMARK GMBH—See Aramark; *U.S. Public*, pg. 176
ARAMARK NEDERLAND—See Aramark; *U.S. Public*, pg. 176
ARAMARK QUEBEC, INC.—See Aramark; *U.S. Public*, pg. 176
ARAMARK S.A.—See Aramark; *U.S. Public*, pg. 176
ASAHI CALPIS BEVERAGES CO., LTD.—See Asahi Group Holdings Ltd.; *Int'l*, pg. 593
ATLAS FOOD SYSTEMS & SERVICES, INC.; *U.S. Private*, pg. 376
AUTOBAR GROUP LTD.—See CVC Capital Partners SICAV-FIS S.A.; *Int'l*, pg. 1882
AUTOCRIB EMEA GMBH—See Snap-on Incorporated; *U.S. Public*, pg. 1897
AVI FOODSYSTEMS INC.; *U.S. Private*, pg. 406
BITTNER VENDING, INC.; *U.S. Private*, pg. 567
BURCH FOOD SERVICE INC.; *U.S. Private*, pg. 686
CANTEEN SERVICE CO. OF OWENSBORO, INC.—See Freeman Spogli & Co. Incorporated; *U.S. Private*, pg. 1606
CASCO BAY VENDING, LLC—See Casco Bay Vending Enterprises, LLC; *U.S. Private*, pg. 781
COCA-COLA WEST VENDING CO., LTD.—See Coca-Cola Bottlers Japan Holdings Inc.; *Int'l*, pg. 1684
COINSTAR LIMITED—See Apollo Global Management, Inc.; *U.S. Public*, pg. 150
COINSTAR, LLC—See Apollo Global Management, Inc.; *U.S. Public*, pg. 150
COMPASS GROUP USA, INC. - CANTEEN DIVISION—See Compass Group PLC; *Int'l*, pg. 1751
CONSOLIDATED VENDORS CORP.; *U.S. Private*, pg. 1022
COTT VENDING INC.—See Primo Water Corporation; *U.S. Public*, pg. 1718
CRH CATERING CO., INC.; *U.S. Private*, pg. 1100
CUSTOM FOOD GROUP, L.P.; *U.S. Private*, pg. 1129
DISPENSER SERVICES INC.; *U.S. Private*, pg. 1238
FIVE STAR FOOD SERVICE - CHATTANOOGA—See Freeman Spogli & Co. Incorporated; *U.S. Private*, pg. 1606
FIVE STAR FOOD SERVICE - COOKEVILLE—See Freeman Spogli & Co. Incorporated; *U.S. Private*, pg. 1606
FIVE STAR FOOD SERVICE INC.—See Freeman Spogli & Co. Incorporated; *U.S. Private*, pg. 1606
FIVE STAR FOOD SERVICE - KNOXVILLE—See Freeman Spogli & Co. Incorporated; *U.S. Private*, pg. 1606
FIVE STAR FOOD SERVICE - LAGRANGE—See Freeman Spogli & Co. Incorporated; *U.S. Private*, pg. 1606
FIVE STAR FOOD SERVICE - MARTINSVILLE—See Freeman Spogli & Co. Incorporated; *U.S. Private*, pg. 1606
FIVE STAR FOOD SERVICE - NASHVILLE—See Freeman Spogli & Co. Incorporated; *U.S. Private*, pg. 1606
FRANKS VENDING SERVICE, INC.—See Freeman Spogli & Co. Incorporated; *U.S. Private*, pg. 1606
FUN HOUSE LEISURE LIMITED—See Inspired Entertainment Inc; *U.S. Public*, pg. 1131
GATES CORP—See Blackstone Inc.; *U.S. Public*, pg. 353
GENERATION NEXT FRANCHISE BRANDS, INC.; *U.S. Private*, pg. 1668
GLORY LTD.; *Int'l*, pg. 3009
H. BETTI INDUSTRIES, INC.; *U.S. Private*, pg. 1824
HEROES, INC.; *U.S. Private*, pg. 1925
IMPERIAL, INC.; *U.S. Private*, pg. 2050
INTERNATIONAL BLENDS COFFEE CO—See Huron Capital Partners LLC; *U.S. Private*, pg. 2012
JEL-CAP VENDING INC.—See Legend Food Service LLC; *U.S. Private*, pg. 2418
KAFEVEND GROUP LIMITED—See Eden International SA; *U.S. Private*, pg. 2307
LAUREL FOODSYSTEMS INC.; *U.S. Private*, pg. 2398
MERCHANDISE VENDING COMPANY, INC.—See Freeman Spogli & Co. Incorporated; *U.S. Private*, pg. 1606
MERKUR DOSNIHA S.L.—See Gauselmann AG; *Int'l*, pg. 2890
METRO VENDING SERVICE, INC.—See Continental Services, Inc.; *U.S. Private*, pg. 1031
MODERN DISTRIBUTORS INC.; *U.S. Private*, pg. 2760
NATIONAL ENTERTAINMENT NETWORK, INC.; *U.S. Private*, pg. 2853
NEWZOOM, INC.—See Swyft, Inc.; *U.S. Private*, pg. 3895
NEXT GENERATION VENDING, LLC—See H.I.G. Capital, LLC; *U.S. Private*, pg. 1831
OLD FASHION FOODS, INC.; *U.S. Private*, pg. 3009
PATTON MUSIC CO., INC.; *U.S. Private*, pg. 3111
PIEDMONT BOTTLING & VENDING, INC.; *U.S. Private*, pg. 3177
PRESTIGE SERVICES INC.; *U.S. Private*, pg. 3256
PT. FUJI METEC SEMARANG—See Fuji Electric Co., Ltd.; *Int'l*, pg. 2812
REDBOX AUTOMATED RETAIL, LLC—See Apollo Global Management, Inc.; *U.S. Public*, pg. 150
SELECTA UK LTD.—See Allianz SE; *Int'l*, pg. 355
SEREX CORPORATION; *U.S. Private*, pg. 3613
SERVOMATION REFRESHMENTS INC.; *U.S. Private*, pg. 3617
SMARTBOX COMPANY; *U.S. Private*, pg. 3691
SPARTAN AUTOMATIC RETAILERS; *U.S. Private*, pg. 3746
STANSFIELD VENDING INC.; *U.S. Private*, pg. 3783
SWYFT, INC.; *U.S. Private*, pg. 3895
THEISEN VENDING INC.; *U.S. Private*, pg. 4141
THREE SQUARE MARKET, INC.—See Cantaloupe, Inc.; *U.S. Public*, pg. 430
THREE SQUARE MARKET LIMITED—See Cantaloupe, Inc.; *U.S. Public*, pg. 430
TREAT AMERICA FOOD SERVICES, INC. - INDIANAPOLIS—See Treat America Food Services, Inc.; *U.S. Private*, pg. 4216
TREAT AMERICA OMAHA—See Treat America Food Services, Inc.; *U.S. Private*, pg. 4216
VENDOMATIC INC.; *U.S. Private*, pg. 4356
VENDORS EXCHANGE INTERNATIONAL, INC.; *U.S. Private*, pg. 4356
VENDWEB.COM—See American Green, Inc.; *U.S. Public*, pg. 103
WEX CO., LTD.—See Coca-Cola Bottlers Japan Holdings Inc.; *Int'l*, pg. 1684
WJW ENTERPRISES SAN DIEGO INC.; *U.S. Private*, pg. 4551

445230 — FRUIT AND VEGETABLE MARKETS

AARTSENFRUIT BREDA B.V.—See Aartsenfruit Holding B.V.; *Int'l*, pg. 38
AARTSENFRUIT N.V.—See Aartsenfruit Holding B.V.; *Int'l*, pg. 38
AARTSENFRUIT VENLO B.V.—See Aartsenfruit Holding B.V.; *Int'l*, pg. 38
A&J SEABRA SUPERMARKET—See Seabra Group; *U.S. Private*, pg. 3583
ALBRITTON FRUIT COMPANY INC.; *U.S. Private*, pg. 153
ARC EUROBANAN, S.L.—See Dole plc; *Int'l*, pg. 2158
ARDO N.V.; *Int'l*, pg. 556
B.C. TREE FRUITS LTD.; *Int'l*, pg. 789
BORTON & SON'S INC.—See Altafresh LLC; *U.S. Private*, pg. 204
CALIFORNIA ORCHARDS CO.; *U.S. Public*, pg. 423
CHONGQING HONGJIU FRUIT CO., LTD.; *Int'l*, pg. 1579
DOLE FOODS OF CANADA LTD.—See Dole plc; *Int'l*, pg. 2157
DOMINION FARM PRODUCE LIMITED—See Dominion Holding Corporation; *Int'l*, pg. 2161
DUDA FARM FRESH FOOD—See A. Duda & Sons Inc.; *U.S. Private*, pg. 23
FORT BOISE PRODUCE; *U.S. Private*, pg. 1574
FRESHKO PRODUCE SERVICES, LLC—See C&S Wholesale Grocers, Inc.; *U.S. Private*, pg. 704
FRESHPOINT NORTH FLORIDA, INC.—See Sysco Corporation; *U.S. Public*, pg. 1974
FRESHPOINT SAN FRANCISCO, INC.—See Sysco Corporation; *U.S. Public*, pg. 1974
HEINRICH BRUNING GMBH—See BayWa AG; *Int'l*, pg. 918
I. KUNIK COMPANY—See The Wonderful Company LLC; *U.S. Private*, pg. 4138
JOHNSTON BROTHERS FARM; *U.S. Private*, pg. 2229
KULA PRODUCE CO, LTD—See Sysco Corporation; *U.S. Public*, pg. 1974
LEE CONSUMER PRODUCTS DIVISION—See Lee Pharmaceuticals; *U.S. Public*, pg. 1300
LITTLE GIANT FARMERS MARKET CORP.—See Mitchell Grocery Corp.; *U.S. Private*, pg. 2750
MILA S.A.—See Eurocash S.A.; *Int'l*, pg. 2533
NATURES BASKET LTD.—See CESC Limited; *Int'l*, pg. 1424
OAKVILLE PRODUCE PARTNERS, LLC—See The Chefs' Warehouse, Inc.; *U.S. Public*, pg. 2059
SOUTHERN FULFILLMENT SERVICES; *U.S. Private*, pg. 3732
SUBZI-MANDI—See House of Spices India Inc.; *U.S. Private*, pg. 1991
SUNDIA CORPORATION; *U.S. Private*, pg. 3866
SUNKIST GROWERS, INC.-EASTERN DIVISION—See Sunkist Growers, Inc.; *U.S. Private*, pg. 3867
SUNKIST GROWERS, INC.-SOUTHERN DIVISION—See Sunkist Growers, Inc.; *U.S. Private*, pg. 3868
SUNKIST GROWERS, INC.-WESTERN DIVISION—See Sunkist Growers, Inc.; *U.S. Private*, pg. 3868
SUNTRADE EXPORT SERVICES; *U.S. Private*, pg. 3873
TESTA PRODUCE INC—See Wind Point Advisors LLC; *U.S. Private*, pg. 4534
TEXASWEET CITRUS MARKETING INC.; *U.S. Private*, pg. 3978

445240 — MEAT RETAILERS

AFFCO EUROPE LIMITED—See AFFCO Holdings Limited; *Int'l*, pg. 185
AFFCO HOLDINGS LIMITED; *Int'l*, pg. 185
AFFCO NEW ZEALAND LIMITED—See AFFCO Holdings Limited; *Int'l*, pg. 186
ALDERFER, INC.; *U.S. Private*, pg. 159
CIXTA ENTERPRISES INC.; *U.S. Private*, pg. 908
DOLD FOODS—See Hormel Foods Corporation; *U.S. Public*, pg. 1054
ESS-FOOD AMBA—See Danish Crown AmbA; *Int'l*, pg. 1965
FEDERAL MARKET CO. INC.; *U.S. Private*, pg. 1489
FOODANE A/S—See Danish Crown AmbA; *Int'l*, pg. 1965
GALAXY INTERNATIONAL INC.; *U.S. Private*, pg. 1636
GREAT AMERICAN MARKETING CO.; *U.S. Private*, pg. 1762
HIGH COUNTRY INVESTOR, INC.; *U.S. Private*, pg. 1935
HONEYBAKED HAM CO. OF OHIO; *U.S. Private*, pg. 1976
INALCA ALGERIE S.A.R.L.—See Cremonini S.p.A.; *Int'l*, pg. 1838
ITALIA ALIMENTARI S.P.A.—See Cremonini S.p.A.; *Int'l*, pg. 1838
JACK'S FRUIT MARKET INC.; *U.S. Private*, pg. 2175
MARKET BASKET; *U.S. Private*, pg. 2578
MOO & OINK INC.; *U.S. Private*, pg. 2778
OMAHASTEAKS.COM, INC.—See Omaha Steaks International, Inc.; *U.S. Private*, pg. 3014
OMAHA STEAKS, INC.—See Omaha Steaks International, Inc.; *U.S. Private*, pg. 3014
OMAHA STEAKS-RETAIL STORES—See Omaha Steaks International, Inc.; *U.S. Private*, pg. 3014
OMEGA MEATS INC.; *U.S. Private*, pg. 3015
PERDIGAO AGROINDUSTRIAL S.A.—See BRF S.A.; *Int'l*, pg. 1151
PROGALIM—See Groupe Limagrain Holding SA; *Int'l*, pg. 3108
REUSS MEATS INC.—See Ellenbee-Leggett Company Inc.; *U.S. Private*, pg. 1363
T.F. KINNEALEY & CO., INC.—See Performance Food Group Company; *U.S. Public*, pg. 1676
TYSON EXPORT SALES, INC.—See Tyson Foods, Inc.; *U.S. Public*, pg. 2210

445250 — FISH AND SEAFOOD RETAILERS

APETIT KALA OY—See Apetit Plc; *Int'l*, pg. 509
ATLANTIC SEAFOOD AS—See Atlantic Group; *Int'l*, pg. 674
BAC LIEU FISHERIES JOINT STOCK COMPANY; *Int'l*, pg. 793
BAY N GULF INC.; *U.S. Private*, pg. 494
COASTAL PRIDE CO. INC.—See Blue Star Foods Corp.; *U.S. Public*, pg. 365
COPPER RIVER SEAFOODS, INC.; *U.S. Private*, pg. 1045
CREATIVE SALMON COMPANY LTD.; *Int'l*, pg. 1833

DAIKICHI CORPORATION—See Wanoba Group Inc.; *U.S. Private*, pg. 4436
FIRST CHOICE SEAFOOD, INC.; *U.S. Private*, pg. 1515
HIGASHIMARU CO., LTD.; *Int'l*, pg. 3385
HIGH LINER FOODS INCORPORATED; *Int'l*, pg. 3385
HOMEGROWN SHRIMP (USA), LLC—See Charoen Pokphand Foods Public Company Limited; *Int'l*, pg. 1452
ICELANDIC GERMANY GMBH—See Enterprise Investment Fund slhf.; *Int'l*, pg. 2451
ICELANDIC IBERICA SA—See Enterprise Investment Fund slhf.; *Int'l*, pg. 2451
ICELANDIC JAPAN KK—See Enterprise Investment Fund slhf.; *Int'l*, pg. 2451
ICELANDIC UK LIMITED—See Enterprise Investment Fund slhf.; *Int'l*, pg. 2451
LEROY SEAFOOD DANMARK A/S—See Austevoll Seafood ASA; *Int'l*, pg. 717
NORTH STAR SEAFOOD, LLC—See Sysco Corporation; *U.S. Public*, pg. 1975
PACIFIC SEAFOOD OF WASHINGTON—See Dulcich, Inc.; *U.S. Private*, pg. 1286
PIERLESS FISH CORP.—See Baldor Specialty Foods Inc.; *U.S. Private*, pg. 458
SCAN FISH DANMARK A/S—See Austevoll Seafood ASA; *Int'l*, pg. 718
TONY'S SEAFOOD LTD; *U.S. Private*, pg. 4185

445291 — BAKED GOODS RETAILERS

AUNTIE ANNE'S INC.—See Roark Capital Group Inc.; *U.S. Private*, pg. 3454
BACKWERK AT GMBH—See Fomento Economico Mexicano, S.A.B. de C.V.; *Int'l*, pg. 2724
BACKWERK NL B.V.—See Fomento Economico Mexicano, S.A.B. de C.V.; *Int'l*, pg. 2724
THE BONTE INC.—See AEON Co., Ltd.; *Int'l*, pg. 178
BRUEGGER'S ENTERPRISES—See Holding Le Duff SA; *Int'l*, pg. 3450
DONUT MANAGEMENT INC.; *U.S. Private*, pg. 1261
EARTHGRAINS BAKING CO. INC.—See Grupo Bimbo, S.A.B. de C.V.; *Int'l*, pg. 3122
EINSTEIN BROTHERS BAGELS; *U.S. Private*, pg. 1347
ELBISCO INDUSTRIAL & COMMERCIAL S.A.—See Elbisco Holding S.A.; *Int'l*, pg. 2344
ENTEMANN'S/OROWEAT—See Grupo Bimbo, S.A.B. de C.V.; *Int'l*, pg. 3122
HEALTHY HOLDINGS, INC.—See North Castle Partners, LLC; *U.S. Private*, pg. 2943
ISAMAX SNACKS, INC.; *U.S. Private*, pg. 2143
JUST BAKED SHOP LLC—See Tubby's Sub Shops, Inc.; *U.S. Private*, pg. 4255
KA INDUSTRIES INC.; *U.S. Private*, pg. 2253
MRS. BEASLEYS LLC—See KA Industries Inc.; *U.S. Private*, pg. 2253
NORTHEAST DONUT SHOP MANAGEMENT; *U.S. Private*, pg. 2950
PICCOLO SP. Z O.O.—See Emperia Holding S.A; *Int'l*, pg. 2386
RALCORP FROZEN BAKERY PRODUCTS—See Grupo Bimbo, S.A.B. de C.V.; *Int'l*, pg. 3122
TAI WO TONG COMPANY LIMITED—See Hin Sang Group (International) Holding Co. Ltd.; *Int'l*, pg. 3397
WILKINS-ROGERS, INC.; *U.S. Private*, pg. 4520
WINCHELL'S DONUT HOUSES OPERATING CO., LP—See Yum Yum Donut Shops, Inc.; *U.S. Private*, pg. 4595

445292 — CONFECTIONERY AND NUT RETAILERS

ACCREDITED DISTRIBUTORS PTY. LTD.; *Int'l*, pg. 93
CAKE BOX HOLDINGS PLC; *Int'l*, pg. 1260
CARGILL COTTON—See Cargill, Inc.; *U.S. Private*, pg. 756
CHARMS COMPANY—See Tootsie Roll Industries, Inc.; *U.S. Public*, pg. 2163
DAFFIN'S, INC.; *U.S. Private*, pg. 1144
DAN'S CHOCOLATES; *U.S. Private*, pg. 1152
EDWARD MARC BRANDS, LLC—See Promise Holdings, LLC; *U.S. Private*, pg. 3283
FAGRON HRVATSKA D.O.O.—See Fagron NV; *Int'l*, pg. 2603
FIRST SOURCE, LLC—See Slate Capital Group LLC; *U.S. Private*, pg. 3687
FREDERICKSBURG FUDGE CO.—See Fischer & Wieser Specialty Foods, Inc.; *U.S. Private*, pg. 1532
FUJIYA CO., LTD.; *Int'l*, pg. 2838
GORANT CANDIES INC.; *U.S. Private*, pg. 1741
HAYES DISTRIBUTING, INC.—See Alvarez & Marsal, Inc.; *U.S. Private*, pg. 213
HAYES DISTRIBUTING, INC.—See Highview Capital, LLC; *U.S. Private*, pg. 1942
HUSSEL SUSSWARENFACHGESCHAFTE GMBH—See EMERAM Capital Partners GmbH; *Int'l*, pg. 2378
IT'SUGAR LLC—See Hilton Grand Vacations Inc.; *U.S. Public*, pg. 1039

MARS IRELAND LTD.—See Mars, Incorporated; *U.S. Private*, pg. 2589
ONE BRANDS, LLC—See The Hershey Co.; *U.S. Public*, pg. 2089
PETERBROOKE CHOCOLATIER, INC.—See Hickory Foods, Inc.; *U.S. Private*, pg. 1933
RAMMKERR, INC.; *U.S. Private*, pg. 3351
RBV LEAF BELGIUM N.V.—See Cloetta AB; *Int'l*, pg. 1661
SEE'S CANDIES, INC.—See Berkshire Hathaway Inc.; *U.S. Public*, pg. 316
SQUIRREL BRAND, L.P.—See John B. Sanfilippo & Son, Inc.; *U.S. Public*, pg. 1190
THE SWEETS MIX COMPANY, INC.—See Tootsie Roll Industries, Inc.; *U.S. Public*, pg. 2163
VINTAGE FOOD CORP.—See Peak Rock Capital LLC; *U.S. Private*, pg. 3124

445298 — ALL OTHER SPECIALTY FOOD RETAILERS

AEON FOOD SUPPLY CO., LTD—See AEON Co., Ltd.; *Int'l*, pg. 176
AG ANADOLU GRUBU HOLDING ANONIM SIRKETI; *Int'l*, pg. 197
A.G. FERRARI FOODS; *U.S. Private*, pg. 25
AGUAS DANONE DE ARGENTINA—See Danone; *Int'l*, pg. 1967
A.K.A. GOURMET—See Baker Capital Partners, LLC; *U.S. Private*, pg. 455
ALIMENTA S.A.; *Int'l*, pg. 328
ALMA MARKET S.A.; *Int'l*, pg. 361
AL MEERA CONSUMER GOODS COMPANY Q.S.C.; *Int'l*, pg. 281
ALRESFORD SALADS LTD.—See Bakkavor Group plc; *Int'l*, pg. 805
AMANA COFFEE & TEA CO.—See Amana Society, Inc.; *U.S. Private*, pg. 216
AMERICAN ROLAND FOOD CORP.—See Vestar Capital Partners, LLC; *U.S. Private*, pg. 4371
ARROWHEAD MOUNTAIN SPRING WATER COMPANY—See Metropoulos & Co.; *U.S. Private*, pg. 2690
ARROWHEAD MOUNTAIN SPRING WATER COMPANY—See One Rock Capital Partners, LLC; *U.S. Private*, pg. 3021
A SOUTHERN SEASON INC.; *U.S. Private*, pg. 19
ASTRON CONNECT, INC.; *Int'l*, pg. 662
AUTO MANAGEMENT INC.; *U.S. Private*, pg. 397
BARNIE'S COFFEE & TEA COMPANY; *U.S. Private*, pg. 478
BEAN BOX, INC.; *U.S. Private*, pg. 506
BEEIO HONEY LTD; *Int'l*, pg. 939
BELCANTO FOODS, LLC—See The Chefs' Warehouse, Inc.; *U.S. Public*, pg. 2059
BERLINER SPECIALTY DISTRIBUTORS, INC.; *U.S. Private*, pg. 535
B&G FOODS SNACKS, INC.—See B&G Foods, Inc.; *U.S. Public*, pg. 260
BIMBO BAKERIES USA INC. - KNOXVILLE—See Grupo Bimbo, S.A.B. de C.V.; *Int'l*, pg. 3122
BLUE MARBLE BRANDS, LLC—See United Natural Foods, Inc.; *U.S. Public*, pg. 2231
BLUESKY SECURITIES JOINT STOCK COMPANY; *Int'l*, pg. 1074
BONVITO GMBH—See Shift4 Payments, Inc.; *U.S. Public*, pg. 1875
BOSTON PIZZA INTERNATIONAL, INC.; *Int'l*, pg. 1118
BRAUM'S ICE CREAM & DAIRY STORES INC.; *U.S. Private*, pg. 640
BREGAVA D.D.; *Int'l*, pg. 1144
BUCKS COUNTY COFFEE COMPANY; *U.S. Private*, pg. 678
BUGOJNOPROMET D.D.; *Int'l*, pg. 1211
BUSTELO COFFEE ROASTING CO.—See The J.M. Smucker Company; *U.S. Public*, pg. 2107
CAFE BRITT CHILE LTDA.—See Grupo Britt N.V.; *Int'l*, pg. 3123
CAFE BRITT PERU S.A.C.—See Grupo Britt N.V.; *Int'l*, pg. 3123
CAFE BRITT USA—See Grupo Britt N.V.; *Int'l*, pg. 3123
CAMPBELL JAPAN INCORPORATED—See Campbell Soup Company; *U.S. Public*, pg. 426
CAPRIOTTI'S SANDWICH SHOP; *U.S. Private*, pg. 745
CARDENAS MARKET, LLC—See KKR & Co. Inc.; *U.S. Public*, pg. 1242
CARDENAS MARKET, LLC—See Victory Park Capital Advisors, LLC; *U.S. Private*, pg. 4379
CAROLINA PURE WATER SYSTEMS LLC—See BDT Capital Partners, LLC; *U.S. Private*, pg. 502
CASA TRUCKING, INC.—See Post Holdings, Inc.; *U.S. Public*, pg. 1703
COASTAL COCKTAILS INC.; *U.S. Private*, pg. 955
COBB ANA DAMIZLIK TAVUKCULUK SANAYI VE TICARET LIMITED SIRKETI—See Tyson Foods, Inc.; *U.S. Public*, pg. 2209
THE COFFEE BEANERY LTD.; *U.S. Private*, pg. 4011
COFFEE INC.; *U.S. Public*, pg. 522

COLOMBO, INC.—See General Mills, Inc.; *U.S. Public*, pg. 921
COLORADO PRIME FOODS LLC; *U.S. Private*, pg. 974
COMPANIA AGROINDUSTRIAL DEL PERU SAC—See Ecom Agroindustrial Corporation Ltd.; *Int'l*, pg. 2296
CONVIVIALITY PLC; *Int'l*, pg. 1787
CO-OPERATIVE GROUP FOOD LIMITED—See Co-operative Group Limited; *Int'l*, pg. 1679
COOPERVISION S.A. (PTY) LIMITED—See The Cooper Companies, Inc.; *U.S. Public*, pg. 2066
COUNTRY FARMS SDN BHD—See Berjaya Corporation Berhad; *Int'l*, pg. 984
COURTESY PRODUCTS LLC—See Centric Group LLC; *U.S. Private*, pg. 830
COWGIRL CREAMERY—See Emmi AG; *Int'l*, pg. 2384
CREAMISTRY FRANCHISE, INC.; *U.S. Private*, pg. 1087
DAIRY BARN STORES INC.; *U.S. Private*, pg. 1145
DANIELE INTERNATIONAL, LLC—See Entrepreneurial Equity Partners, LLC; *U.S. Private*, pg. 1406
DANONE AS—See Danone; *Int'l*, pg. 1965
DANONE FINLAND—See Danone; *Int'l*, pg. 1967
DANONE SERDIKA S.A.—See Danone; *Int'l*, pg. 1968
DANONE WATER BRANDS BENELUX—See Danone; *Int'l*, pg. 1968
DANONE WATERS DEUTSCHLAND GMBH—See Danone; *Int'l*, pg. 1968
DANONE WATERS UK & IRELAND LTD.—See Danone; *Int'l*, pg. 1968
THE DARK STAR BREWING COMPANY LIMITED—See Asahi Group Holdings Ltd.; *Int'l*, pg. 594
DEEP FOODS, INC.; *U.S. Private*, pg. 1189
DORIA ENTERPRISES INC.; *U.S. Private*, pg. 1262
ECOM AGROTRADE LIMITED—See Ecom Agroindustrial Corporation Ltd.; *Int'l*, pg. 2296
ED & EDDIE'S ICE CREAM—See DeBartolo Holdings, LLC; *U.S. Private*, pg. 1186
EDITA FOOD INDUSTRIES SAE; *Int'l*, pg. 2311
ELDORADO ARTESIAN SPRINGS, INC.; *U.S. Private*, pg. 1351
EMPERIA HOLDING S.A; *Int'l*, pg. 2385
ESKIMO PIE CORPORATION—See Swisher Hygiene Inc.; *U.S. Private*, pg. 3894
FDB GROUP; *Int'l*, pg. 2628
FINALE DESSERTERIE & BAKERY; *U.S. Private*, pg. 1506
FJ FOODSERVICE, LLC—See Hormel Foods Corporation; *U.S. Public*, pg. 1054
FLANAGAN FOODSERVICE, INC.; *Int'l*, pg. 2698
FORBIDDEN FOODS LIMITED; *Int'l*, pg. 2729
FORTENOVA GROUP D.D.; *Int'l*, pg. 2738
FRAPORT CLEVELAND INC.—See Fraport AG; *Int'l*, pg. 2764
FRAPORT PITTSBURGH INC.—See Fraport AG; *Int'l*, pg. 2764
FREDDY'S FROZEN CUSTARD LLC—See Thompson Street Capital Manager LLC; *U.S. Private*, pg. 4161
FRESHPOINT IL PAESE, INC.—See Sysco Corporation; *U.S. Public*, pg. 1974
FRESHTIME UK LIMITED—See Greencore Group plc; *Int'l*, pg. 3074
GARCIA FOODS, INC.—See Mission Consumer Capital; *U.S. Private*, pg. 2747
GENERAL MILLS INTERNATIONAL SARL—See General Mills, Inc.; *U.S. Public*, pg. 921
GLACIERPOINT ENTERPRISES, INC.—See Guggenheim Partners, LLC; *U.S. Private*, pg. 1812
GLAS SRPSKI-TRGOVINA A.D.; *Int'l*, pg. 2988
GLENOAKS FARMS, INC.—See Lifeway Foods, Inc.; *U.S. Public*, pg. 1313
GLORIA JEAN'S, INC.—See Praise International North America, Inc.; *U.S. Private*, pg. 3243
GOLDEN BOY NUT CORPORATION—See Post Holdings, Inc.; *U.S. Public*, pg. 1703
GOLDEN ISLAND JERKY COMPANY, INC.—See Tyson Foods, Inc.; *U.S. Public*, pg. 2209
GOLLUCKE & ROTHFOS GMBH—See ED&F Man Holdings Limited; *Int'l*, pg. 2303
GOURMET GARAGE; *U.S. Private*, pg. 1746
GOURMET MASTER CO. LTD.; *Int'l*, pg. 3044
GRAND HAVANA INC.; *U.S. Private*, pg. 957
GRASSBURGER, LLC; *U.S. Private*, pg. 1758
GRUBMARKET, INC.; *U.S. Private*, pg. 1797
H2O HYDROPONICS, LLC—See GrowGeneration Corp.; *U.S. Public*, pg. 972
HAPPYFAMILY; *U.S. Private*, pg. 1857
HARRY & DAVID, LLC—See 1-800-FLOWERS.COM, Inc.; *U.S. Public*, pg. 1
HAWAIIAN COOL WATER, LLC; *U.S. Private*, pg. 1881
HF FOODS GROUP INC.; *U.S. Public*, pg. 1033
HICKORY FARMS, LLC—See Sun Capital Partners, Inc.; *U.S. Private*, pg. 3859
HIGH'S OF BALTIMORE INC.; *U.S. Private*, pg. 1937
HORMEL CANADA LTD.—See Hormel Foods Corporation; *U.S. Public*, pg. 1054
ICE MOUNTAIN SPRING WATER—See Metropoulos & Co.; *U.S. Private*, pg. 2690
ICE MOUNTAIN SPRING WATER—See One Rock Capital Partners, LLC; *U.S. Private*, pg. 3021
INKO'S TEA, LLC; *U.S. Private*, pg. 2078

445298 — ALL OTHER SPECIALTY...

INTERNATIONAL PRODUCE LTD.—See Bakkavor Group plc; *Int'l*, pg. 806
IRISH BISCUITS (N.I.) LIMITED—See CapVest Limited; *Int'l*, pg. 1318
JENNIE-O TURKEY STORE INTERNATIONAL INC.—See Hormel Foods Corporation; *U.S. Public*, pg. 1054
JORDANO'S FOOD SERVICE, INC.—See Jordano's, Inc.; *U.S. Private*, pg. 2236
JR CENTRAL PASSENGERS CO., LTD.—See Central Japan Railway Company; *Int'l*, pg. 1408
JR TOKAI FOOD SERVICE CO., LTD.—See Central Japan Railway Company; *Int'l*, pg. 1408
KELKIN LIMITED—See DCC plc; *Int'l*, pg. 1991
KEYSTONE COFFEE COMPANY; *U.S. Private*, pg. 2295
THE KITCHEN COLLECTION, LLC—See Hamilton Beach Brands Holding Company; *U.S. Public*, pg. 981
LAKEVIEW FARMS LLC; *U.S. Private*, pg. 2378
LES ALIMENTS DOMINION CITRUS—See Dominion Holding Corporation; *Int'l*, pg. 2161
LOLLICUP USA, INC.; *U.S. Private*, pg. 2483
LOTTE ASAHI CO., LTD.—See Asahi Group Holdings Ltd.; *Int'l*, pg. 594
MARS SNACKFOOD—See Mars, Incorporated; *U.S. Private*, pg. 2590
MCCORMICK (UK) LTD.—See McCormick & Company, Incorporated; *U.S. Public*, pg. 1404
MEADOWBROOK MEAT COMPANY, INC.—See Berkshire Hathaway Inc.; *U.S. Public*, pg. 312
MICHAEL FOODS OF DELAWARE, INC.—See Post Holdings, Inc.; *U.S. Public*, pg. 1703
MIDEAST AREA COUNCIL—See Dairy Farmers of America, Inc.; *U.S. Private*, pg. 1146
MIDWEST DAIRY ASSOCIATION; *U.S. Private*, pg. 2720
MONPI COFFEE EXPORTS LTD.—See Ecom Agroindustrial Corporation Ltd.; *Int'l*, pg. 2296
MONTEL DISTRIBUTION SA—See Carrefour SA; *Int'l*, pg. 1345
MSG DISTRIBUTORS, INC.; *U.S. Private*, pg. 2807
MY SECRET KITCHEN LTD.—See JRjr33, Inc.; *U.S. Private*, pg. 2240
NESTLE WATERS NORTH AMERICA INC. JACKSONVILLE—See Metropoulos & Co.; *U.S. Private*, pg. 2690
NESTLE WATERS NORTH AMERICA INC. JACKSONVILLE—See One Rock Capital Partners, LLC; *U.S. Private*, pg. 3021
NEWLY WEDS FOODS, LTD.—See Newly Weds Foods, Inc.; *U.S. Private*, pg. 2915
NORTHEAST AREA COUNCIL—See Dairy Farmers of America, Inc.; *U.S. Private*, pg. 1146
OOO AGROPROM VOSTOK—See Ecom Agroindustrial Corporation Ltd.; *Int'l*, pg. 2296
PALLAS FOODS—See Sysco Corporation; *U.S. Public*, pg. 1975
PATCON LIMITED—See Hadco Limited; *Int'l*, pg. 3205
PLZENSKY PRAZDROJ SLOVENSKO, A.S.—See Asahi Group Holdings Ltd.; *Int'l*, pg. 594
POPCORN PALACE; *U.S. Private*, pg. 3228
PRINCI UK LIMITED—See Starbucks Corporation; *U.S. Public*, pg. 1938
PRISXTRA AB—See Axel Johnson Gruppen AB; *Int'l*, pg. 764
PT INDO CAFCO (ROBUSTAS)—See Ecom Agroindustrial Corporation Ltd.; *Int'l*, pg. 2296
QUAIL MOUNTAIN INC.; *U.S. Private*, pg. 3316
QUALITY DAIRY COMPANY; *U.S. Private*, pg. 3318
QUIEVRAIN RETAIL ASSOCIATE NV—See Carrefour SA; *Int'l*, pg. 1344
R&A BAILEY & CO.—See Diageo plc; *Int'l*, pg. 2102
RAINBOW SHOKUHIN CO., LTD.—See Aohata Corporation; *Int'l*, pg. 487
R & C TRADING L.L.C.—See HF Foods Group Inc.; *U.S. Public*, pg. 1033
REGIO MOLKEREI BEIDER BASEL AG—See Emmi AG; *Int'l*, pg. 2385
ROWLAND COFFEE ROASTERS, INC.—See The J.M. Smucker Company; *U.S. Public*, pg. 2107
ROYAL CREST DAIRY INC.; *U.S. Private*, pg. 3492
SAPY DANONE—See Danone; *Int'l*, pg. 1968
SARGENTO FOODS INC.—See Sargento Foods Inc.; *U.S. Private*, pg. 3550
SCHWAN'S CONSUMER BRANDS, INC.—See The Schwan Food Company; *U.S. Private*, pg. 4115
SCHWAN'S HOME SERVICE, INC.—See The Schwan Food Company; *U.S. Private*, pg. 4115
SEDACO DMCC—See BayWa AG; *Int'l*, pg. 919
SGPY—See Danone; *Int'l*, pg. 1968
SHANDONG TYSON-DA LONG FOOD COMPANY LIMITED—See Tyson Foods, Inc.; *U.S. Public*, pg. 2210
THE SOUTH DAKOTA GREAT ATLANTIC & PACIFIC TEA CO., INC.—See The Great Atlantic & Pacific Tea Company, Inc.; *U.S. Private*, pg. 4038
SOUTO FOODS LLC—See Alex Lee, Inc.; *U.S. Private*, pg. 163
SPICEOLOGY, INC.; *U.S. Private*, pg. 3756
STARBUCKS COFFEE EMEA BV—See Starbucks Corporation; *U.S. Public*, pg. 1939
STARBUCKS COFFEE SWITZERLAND GMBH—See Starbucks Corporation; *U.S. Public*, pg. 1939
STARBUCKS COFFEE TRADING COMPANY S.A.R.L.—See Starbucks Corporation; *U.S. Public*, pg. 1939
STAR DUNKIN', LP—See Roark Capital Group Inc.; *U.S. Private*, pg. 3455
SUB ZERO ICE CREAM INC.; *U.S. Private*, pg. 3847
SUPER DOLLAR DISCOUNT FOODS—See K-VA-T Food Stores, Inc.; *U.S. Private*, pg. 2251
SYSCO CHICAGO, INC.—See Sysco Corporation; *U.S. Public*, pg. 1975
SYSCO INTERNATIONAL FOOD GROUP, INC.—See Sysco Corporation; *U.S. Public*, pg. 1976
SYSCO JACKSON, LLC—See Sysco Corporation; *U.S. Public*, pg. 1976
SYSCO WEST COAST FLORIDA, INC.—See Sysco Corporation; *U.S. Public*, pg. 1977
TAVA ORGANICS, LTD.; *U.S. Private*, pg. 3936
TC GLOBAL, INC.; *U.S. Private*, pg. 3942
TEAVANA CANADA, INC.—See Starbucks Corporation; *U.S. Public*, pg. 1939
TEAVANA HOLDINGS, INC.—See Starbucks Corporation; *U.S. Public*, pg. 1939
TRIBE 9 FOODS LLC; *U.S. Private*, pg. 4227
TULIP NORGE AS—See Danish Crown AmbA; *Int'l*, pg. 1965
VAN'S INTERNATIONAL FOODS—See Tyson Foods, Inc.; *U.S. Public*, pg. 2210
VITALITY BOWLS ENTERPRISES, LLC; *U.S. Private*, pg. 4405
VOLLRATH EUROPE B.V.—See The Vollrath Company LLC; *U.S. Private*, pg. 4132
WATERMILL EXPRESS LLC; *U.S. Private*, pg. 4454
WHOLE FOODS MARKET SERVICES, INC.—See Amazon.com, Inc.; *U.S. Public*, pg. 91
WM. WRIGLEY JR. COMPANY—See Mars, Incorporated; *U.S. Private*, pg. 2590
WWF OPERATING COMPANY LLC—See Danone; *Int'l*, pg. 1967
YARRA VALLEY CHOCOLATERIE & ICE CREAMERY—See PMC Capital Partners, LLC; *U.S. Private*, pg. 3218
YOUR INSPIRATION AT HOME PTY. LTD.—See JRjr33, Inc.; *U.S. Private*, pg. 2240
ZOUP!; *U.S. Private*, pg. 4609

445320 — BEER, WINE, AND LIQUOR RETAILERS

21ST AMENDMENT INC.; *U.S. Private*, pg. 5
ABC FINE WINES & SPIRITS; *U.S. Private*, pg. 35
ACKER MERRALL & CONDIT COMPANY, INC.; *U.S. Private*, pg. 59
AGIS SA—See CJSC Russian Standard Corporation; *Int'l*, pg. 1634
AMORIM AUSTRALASIA PTY. LTD.—See CORTICEIRA AMORIM, S.G.P.S., S.A.; *Int'l*, pg. 1807
ANHUI GUJING DISTILLERY CO., LTD.—See Anhui Gujing Group Co., Ltd.; *Int'l*, pg. 467
BBCK ENTERPRISES INC.; *U.S. Private*, pg. 498
BERRY BROS. & RUDD LIMITED; *Int'l*, pg. 989
BERRY BROS & RUDD SINGAPORE PTE. LTD.—See Berry Bros. & Rudd Limited; *Int'l*, pg. 989
BEVERAGES & MORE INC.—See goBrands, Inc.; *U.S. Private*, pg. 1724
BINNY'S INC.—See Gold Standard Enterprises Inc.; *U.S. Private*, pg. 1728
BINS CORPORATION; *U.S. Public*, pg. 561
BROWN DERBY STORES INC.; *U.S. Private*, pg. 667
CARLSBERG BREWING LIMITED—See Carlsberg A/S; *Int'l*, pg. 1339
CAVE SAINT-VERNY—See Groupe Limagrain Holding SA; *Int'l*, pg. 3107
COLORADO SUPERSTORES LLC—See Harco, LLC; *U.S. Private*, pg. 1862
CONSUMERS BEVERAGES INC.; *U.S. Private*, pg. 1026
COUNTRY VINTNER OF WV—See The Winebow Group, LLC; *U.S. Private*, pg. 4137
CROWN LIQUORS OF BROWARD INC.; *U.S. Private*, pg. 1111
DEARING & DEARING; *U.S. Private*, pg. 1185
DECCA DESIGN & DEVELOPMENT INC.; *U.S. Private*, pg. 1187
DIAGEO HOLDINGS LTD.—See Diageo plc; *Int'l*, pg. 2102
DONS & BENS INC.—See Gabriel's Holdings Ltd.; *U.S. Private*, pg. 1632
DRULEY ENTERPRISES INC.; *U.S. Private*, pg. 1279
EAST AFRICAN BREWERIES LIMITED—See Diageo plc; *Int'l*, pg. 2102
ENOTECA CO., LTD.—See Asahi Group Holdings Ltd.; *Int'l*, pg. 593
FIVE POINTS TITLE CO.—See The Deltona Corporation; *U.S. Public*, pg. 4020
FLANIGAN'S ENTERPRISES, INC.—See Flanigan's Enterprises, Inc.; *U.S. Public*, pg. 852
FLANIGAN'S ENTERPRISES, INC.—See Flanigan's Enterprises, Inc.; *U.S. Public*, pg. 852
FLANIGAN'S ENTERPRISES, INC.—See Flanigan's Enterprises, Inc.; *U.S. Public*, pg. 852
FLANIGAN'S RESTAURANTS—See Flanigan's Enterprises, Inc.; *U.S. Public*, pg. 852
FOLIO WINE COMPANY, LLC—See Compagnie Champenoise PH-CHPiper Heidsieck SAS; *Int'l*, pg. 1722
FTL CORPORATION; *U.S. Private*, pg. 1619
GARY'S WINE & MARKETPLACE; *U.S. Private*, pg. 1647
GEBRUDER JOSEF UND MATTHAUS ZIEGLER GMBH—See Hawesko Holding AG; *Int'l*, pg. 3288
GENERAL WHOLESALE COMPANY, INC.—See General Wholesale Company, Inc.; *U.S. Private*, pg. 1668
G&G BEVERAGES INC.—See Bergmann's Inc.; *U.S. Private*, pg. 531
GOLD STANDARD ENTERPRISES INC.; *U.S. Private*, pg. 1728
GORDONS WALTHAM LIQUOR STORES INC.; *U.S. Private*, pg. 1743
GRAND CRU SELECT WEINHANDELSGESELLSCHAFT MBH—See Hawesko Holding AG; *Int'l*, pg. 3288
GRAY MONK CELLARS LTD.—See Andrew Peller Limited; *Int'l*, pg. 451
G.R.H. MAIDEN INC.; *U.S. Private*, pg. 1631
GUINNESS NIGERIA PLC—See Diageo plc; *Int'l*, pg. 2102
HARCO; LLC; *U.S. Private*, pg. 1862
HIGH COUNTRY BEVERAGE CORP.; *U.S. Private*, pg. 1935
INTERNATIONAL DISTILLERS SOUTH ASIA—See Diageo plc; *Int'l*, pg. 2102
IOWA BEVERAGE SYSTEMS INC.; *U.S. Private*, pg. 2134
JACQUES WEIN-DEPOT WEIN-EINZELHANDEL GMBH—See Hawesko Holding AG; *Int'l*, pg. 3288
J&F ENTERPRISES INC.; *U.S. Private*, pg. 2154
JVC CORPORATION; *U.S. Private*, pg. 2246
KENWOOD LIQUORS; *U.S. Private*, pg. 2289
KOBRAND/WESTERN DIVISION—See Kobrand Corporation; *U.S. Private*, pg. 2326
KORKEN SCHIESSER GES.M.B.H.—See CORTICEIRA AMORIM, S.G.P.S., S.A.; *Int'l*, pg. 1808
LA CAVE WAREHOUSE—See Vino Vault, Inc.; *U.S. Private*, pg. 4386
LAGARDERE SERVICES DISTRIBUTION SAS—See Adriatic Media Investors LLC; *U.S. Private*, pg. 82
LAKE LOUIE BREWING LLC—See Wisconsin Brewing Company LLC; *U.S. Private*, pg. 4548
LEBAMOFF ENTERPRISES INC.; *U.S. Private*, pg. 2409
LEONARD KREUSCH GMBH & CO.—See Leonard Kreusch; *Int'l*, pg. 2430
MAJESTIC LIQUOR STORES INC.; *U.S. Private*, pg. 2554
MEL-JEN; *U.S. Private*, pg. 2661
MGM WINE & SPIRITS INC.; *U.S. Private*, pg. 2694
MY FAVORITE NEIGHBOR, LLC—See Constellation Brands, Inc.; *U.S. Public*, pg. 571
NEW HANOVER COUNTY ABC BOARD; *U.S. Private*, pg. 2896
PASADENA LIQUORS AND FINE WINES; *U.S. Private*, pg. 3103
P.E.L., INC.; *U.S. Private*, pg. 3060
PHOENIX VINTNERS, LLC; *U.S. Private*, pg. 3174
PINKIE'S INC.; *U.S. Private*, pg. 3184
PORTOCORK FRANCE, S.A.S.—See CORTICEIRA AMORIM, S.G.P.S., S.A.; *Int'l*, pg. 1808
QUIK-WAY FOODS OF DALLAS INC.; *U.S. Private*, pg. 3327
R.A. JEFFREYS DISTRIBUTING CO.; *U.S. Private*, pg. 3334
SHERRY-LEHMANN INC.; *U.S. Private*, pg. 3634
SIEGAL & SONS INVESTMENT LTD.; *U.S. Private*, pg. 3646
SIGELS BEVERAGES LP—See Twin Liquors; *U.S. Private*, pg. 4265
THE SMALL WINEMAKER'S COLLECTION INC.—See Andrew Peller Limited; *Int'l*, pg. 451
SOCIAL SPARKLING WINE, LLC; *U.S. Private*, pg. 3703
SPECS FAMILY PARTNERS LTD.; *U.S. Private*, pg. 3751
TINHORN CREEK VINEYARDS LTD.—See Andrew Peller Limited; *Int'l*, pg. 452
TRI - COUNTY BEVERAGE; *U.S. Private*, pg. 4220
UNIFREE DUTY FREE ISLETMECILIGI A.S.—See Bank of Georgia Group PLC; *Int'l*, pg. 843
VOGEL VINS SA—See Hawesko Holding AG; *Int'l*, pg. 3288
WAYNE GRETZKY ESTATES LIMITED—See Andrew Peller Limited; *Int'l*, pg. 452
WEINART HANDELSGESELLSCHAFT MBH—See Hawesko Holding AG; *Int'l*, pg. 3289
WEIN & CO. HANDELSGESELLSCHAFT M.B.H—See Hawesko Holding AG; *Int'l*, pg. 3288
WEIN & VINOS GMBH—See Hawesko Holding AG; *Int'l*, pg. 3288
WESTERN BEVERAGES INC.; *U.S. Private*, pg. 4491
WESTERN WHOLESALE LIQUOR CO.—See Johnson Brothers Liquor Company; *U.S. Private*, pg. 2227
THE WINE CLUB INC.; *U.S. Private*, pg. 4137
WINE.COM, INC.—See Baker Capital Partners, LLC; *U.S. Private*, pg. 455
THE WINE COMPANY HAWESKO GMBH—See Hawesko Holding AG; *Int'l*, pg. 3288

N.A.I.C.S. INDEX

449110 — FURNITURE RETAILERS

WINE DOCK GMBH—See Hawesko Holding AG; *Int'l*, pg. 3289
WINE WAREHOUSE, LLC—See Breakthru Beverage Group, LLC; *U.S. Private*, pg. 643
WIRWINZER GMBH—See Hawesko Holding AG; *Int'l*, pg. 3289
WITTS FOODS INC.; *U.S. Private*, pg. 4551
YANKEE SPIRITS INC.; *U.S. Private*, pg. 4586
YOUNG RANCH INC.—See Rod Fraser Enterprises Inc.; *U.S. Private*, pg. 3469

446130 —

LUXOTTICA RETAIL NORTH AMERICA INC.—See EssilorLuxottica SA; *Int'l*, pg. 2515

449110 — FURNITURE RETAILERS

AARON INVESTMENTS INC.; *U.S. Private*, pg. 32
ABBYSON LIVING; *U.S. Private*, pg. 35
ABC CARPET & HOME INC.; *U.S. Private*, pg. 35
A. BELANGER, LTEE.; *Int'l*, pg. 21
ADVANTAGE INC.—See C.S. Wo & Sons Ltd.; *U.S. Private*, pg. 709
AFC AQUISITION CORP.; *U.S. Private*, pg. 121
AFD CONTRACT FURNITURE, INC.; *U.S. Private*, pg. 121
AFFORDABLE RENT TO OWN LLC; *U.S. Private*, pg. 123
ALL MAKES OFFICE EQUIPMENT CO. INC.; *U.S. Private*, pg. 171
ALL MAKES OFFICE INTERIORS—See All Makes Office Equipment Co. Inc.; *U.S. Private*, pg. 171
AMERICA, THE BEAUTIFUL DREAMER, INC.; *U.S. Private*, pg. 221
AM SLEEP INC.; *U.S. Private*, pg. 214
ANDREAS FURNITURE COMPANY INC.; *U.S. Private*, pg. 279
ANGELUS FURNITURE OUTLET INC.; *U.S. Private*, pg. 283
A. POMERANTZ & COMPANY; *U.S. Private*, pg. 23
ARENSON OFFICE FURNISHINGS INC.; *U.S. Private*, pg. 318
BACON GALLERIES INC.; *U.S. Private*, pg. 423
BAD BOY FURNITURE WAREHOUSE LIMITED; *Int'l*, pg. 795
BADCOCK HOME FURNITURE & MORE OF SOUTH FLORIDA; *U.S. Private*, pg. 423
BAER'S FURNITURE CO. INC.; *U.S. Private*, pg. 425
BAILEYS FURNITURE OUTLET INC.; *U.S. Private*, pg. 426
BARCLAY DEAN, INC.; *U.S. Private*, pg. 473
BARN FURNITURE MART, INC.; *U.S. Private*, pg. 476
BARROW FINE FURNITURE INC.; *U.S. Private*, pg. 481
BECKS FURNITURE INC.; *U.S. Private*, pg. 511
BEDDING GALLERY; *U.S. Private*, pg. 512
THE BEDROOM STORE; *U.S. Private*, pg. 3992
BEITERS INC.; *U.S. Private*, pg. 516
B.F. MYERS FURNITURE COMPANY, INC.; *U.S. Private*, pg. 420
BIG SANDY FURNITURE INC.; *U.S. Private*, pg. 554
BKM TOTAL OFFICE TEXAS LP; *U.S. Private*, pg. 569
BOB MILLS FURNITURE CO. INC.; *U.S. Private*, pg. 604
BOB'S DISCOUNT FURNITURE INC.—See Bain Capital, LP; *U.S. Private*, pg. 436
BOCONCEPT HOLDING A/S—See 3i Group plc; *Int'l*, pg. 8
BOGRAD BROTHERS INC.; *U.S. Private*, pg. 609
BOLTON FURNITURE INC.—See Bertram Capital Management, LLC; *U.S. Private*, pg. 540
BOSTON INC.; *U.S. Private*, pg. 621
BOSTON INTERIORS INC.—See Castle Island Partners, LLC; *U.S. Private*, pg. 785
BROWN & SAENGER; *U.S. Private*, pg. 666
BURGESS CARRIAGE HOUSE INC.; *U.S. Private*, pg. 687
BUSINESS INTERIORS OF SEATTLE NORTH WEST INC.; *U.S. Private*, pg. 695
BX KOUN CO., LTD.—See Bunka Shutter Co., Ltd.; *Int'l*, pg. 1216
CARL'S PATIO, INC.—See Weinberg Capital Group, Inc.; *U.S. Private*, pg. 4471
CARLYLE CUSTOM CONVERTIBLES, LTD.; *U.S. Private*, pg. 765
CARRIAGE HOUSE INTERIORS SAN DIEGO; *U.S. Private*, pg. 772
CASA LINDA FURNITURE INC.; *U.S. Private*, pg. 778
CEDREX—See Azenta, Inc.; *U.S. Public*, pg. 258
THE CHAIR KING, INC.; *U.S. Private*, pg. 4007
CHERRY HOUSE INC.; *U.S. Private*, pg. 874
CHF HOME FURNISHINGS; *U.S. Private*, pg. 876
CIRCLE FURNITURE INC.; *U.S. Private*, pg. 899
CISCO HOME, INC.—See Cisco Bros. Corp.; *U.S. Private*, pg. 900
CITY FURNITURE INC.; *U.S. Private*, pg. 906
CITY MATTRESS INC.; *U.S. Private*, pg. 906
CITY STATIONERY INC.; *U.S. Private*, pg. 907
C.L. BARNES FURNITURE CO.; *U.S. Private*, pg. 708
THE CLEAN BEDROOM; *U.S. Private*, pg. 4010
CLEARWATER MATTRESS, INC.; *U.S. Private*, pg. 939
CLESTRA HAUSERMAN—See Clestra Hauserman S.A.; *Int'l*, pg. 1658
CLIVE DANIEL HOME - NAPLES, LLC; *U.S. Private*, pg. 945
COHEN FURNITURE COMPANY; *U.S. Private*, pg. 963
COHEN'S HOME FURNISHINGS LTD.; *Int'l*, pg. 1695
COLDER'S INC.; *U.S. Private*, pg. 966
COMEAUX FURNITURE & APPLIANCES INC.; *U.S. Private*, pg. 981
COMMERCIAL DESIGN SERVICES, INC.; *U.S. Private*, pg. 983
COMMERCIAL OFFICE FURNITURE CO.; *U.S. Private*, pg. 984
COMMON SENSE OFFICE FURNITURE; *U.S. Private*, pg. 986
COMPASS OFFICE SOLUTIONS LLC—See HNI Corporation; *U.S. Public*, pg. 1043
CONKLIN OFFICE SERVICES, INC.; *U.S. Private*, pg. 1014
CONLEASCO INC.; *U.S. Private*, pg. 1014
CONLIN'S FURNITURE INC.; *U.S. Private*, pg. 1014
CONVERTIBLE CASTLE, INC.; *U.S. Private*, pg. 1035
COPENHAGEN IMPORTS INC.; *U.S. Private*, pg. 1044
CORPORATE ENVIRONMENTS OF GEORGIA INC.; *U.S. Private*, pg. 1054
COST PLUS OF TEXAS, INC.—See Kingswood Capital Management LLC; *U.S. Private*, pg. 2312
COTTONWOOD TRADING, INC.—See Home Trends & Design, Inc.; *U.S. Private*, pg. 1972
COUNTRY ROAD ASSOCIATES, LTD.; *U.S. Private*, pg. 1067
CRAFTMATIC INDUSTRIES, INC.; *U.S. Private*, pg. 1082
CREST FURNITURE INC.; *U.S. Private*, pg. 1095
C.S. WO & SONS LTD.; *U.S. Private*, pg. 709
CUSTER OFFICE ENVIRONMENTS INC.; *U.S. Private*, pg. 1127
DALIA LTD.; *Int'l*, pg. 1951
DALLAS MIDWEST COMPANY—See Franz Haniel & Cie. GmbH; *Int'l*, pg. 2763
DANISH INSPIRATIONS CORPORATION; *U.S. Private*, pg. 1157
DANISH INSPIRATIONS, SHOWROOM—See Danish Inspirations Corporation; *U.S. Private*, pg. 1157
DANKER FURNITURE INC.; *U.S. Private*, pg. 1157
DARVIN FURNITURE; *U.S. Private*, pg. 1160
DDS CONTRACTS & INTERIOR SOLUTIONS PTE LTD—See Design Studio Group Ltd.; *Int'l*, pg. 2045
DDS CONTRACTS & INTERIOR SOLUTIONS SDN BHD—See Design Studio Group Ltd.; *Int'l*, pg. 2045
DDS CONTRACTS & INTERIOR SOLUTIONS (THAILAND) CO., LTD.—See Design Studio Group Ltd.; *Int'l*, pg. 2045
DEARDEN'S; *U.S. Private*, pg. 1185
DECORATOR'S OFFICE FURNITURE INC.; *U.S. Private*, pg. 1188
DEFYSUPPLY; *U.S. Private*, pg. 1191
DELTA ENTERPRISE CORPORATION; *U.S. Private*, pg. 1200
DENVER MATTRESS COMPANY—See Funiture Row LLC; *U.S. Private*, pg. 1623
DIAMOND FURNITURE INC.; *U.S. Private*, pg. 1223
DION'S QUIK MARTS INC.—See Alimentation Couche-Tard Inc.; *Int'l*, pg. 328
DIVERSIFIED CABINET DISTRIBUTORS—See Masco Corporation; *U.S. Public*, pg. 1390
DMITRIY & COMPANY LLC—See RH; *U.S. Public*, pg. 1796
DOCUSOURCE INC.; *U.S. Private*, pg. 1252
DOOR STORE FURNITURE; *U.S. Private*, pg. 1262
DOREL HOME PRODUCTS—See Dorel Industries, Inc.; *Int'l*, pg. 2176
DOREL NETHERLANDS—See Dorel Industries, Inc.; *Int'l*, pg. 2176
DOREL (UK) LTD.—See Dorel Industries, Inc.; *Int'l*, pg. 2176
DOROTHY LEO INC.; *U.S. Private*, pg. 1263
DREAMS LTD.—See Tempur Sealy International, Inc.; *U.S. Public*, pg. 1999
D-SCAN INC.—See Levi Strauss & Co.; *U.S. Public*, pg. 1309
DS PROJECT MANAGEMENT SDN BHD—See Design Studio Group Ltd.; *Int'l*, pg. 2045
D.T. MCCALL & SONS; *U.S. Private*, pg. 1142
DUNK & BRIGHT FURNITURE CO.; *U.S. Private*, pg. 1289
DUROCHER TV & APPLIANCE INC.; *U.S. Private*, pg. 1294
D. WALDNER COMPANY, INC.; *U.S. Private*, pg. 1140
EATON OFFICE SUPPLY CO., INC.; *U.S. Private*, pg. 1323
EBCO INC.; *U.S. Private*, pg. 1324
THE ELDER-BEERMAN STORES CORP.—See The Bon Ton Stores, Inc.; *U.S. Public*, pg. 2041
EL DORADO FURNITURE CORP.; *U.S. Private*, pg. 1349
EMERSON MATTRESS INC.; *U.S. Private*, pg. 1382
EMPRESAS BERRIOS INC.; *U.S. Private*, pg. 1388
ENNIS FURNITURE CO. INC.; *U.S. Private*, pg. 1401
ETHAN ALLEN (CANADA) INC.—See Ethan Allen Interiors Inc.; *U.S. Public*, pg. 797
ETHAN ALLEN DESIGN CENTER; *U.S. Private*, pg. 1431
EVERYTHING2GO COM, LLC; *U.S. Private*, pg. 1441
EVE SLEEP SASU—See Eve Sleep PLC; *Int'l*, pg. 2561
FAMILY FURNITURE CENTERS INC.; *U.S. Private*, pg. 1470
FINESSE HOME LIVING; *Int'l*, pg. 2674
FINGER FURNITURE COMPANY, INC.; *U.S. Private*, pg. 1509
FISH FURNITURE SHOP INC.; *U.S. Private*, pg. 1533
FLEGELS HOME FURNISHINGS; *U.S. Private*, pg. 1542
FORDS INC.; *U.S. Private*, pg. 1565
FOWLERS INC.; *U.S. Private*, pg. 1583
FREEDMAN OFFICE FURNITURE, LLC; *U.S. Private*, pg. 1603
FULLY EUROPE BVBA—See MillerKnoll, Inc.; *U.S. Public*, pg. 1447
FULTON OUTFITTERS, INC.; *U.S. Private*, pg. 1622
FUNITURE ROW LLC; *U.S. Private*, pg. 1623
FURNITURE DISTRIBUTORS INC.; *U.S. Private*, pg. 1624
FURNITURE ENTERPRISES OF ALASKA; *U.S. Private*, pg. 1624
FURNITURE FACTORY OUTLET, LLC—See B. Riley Financial, Inc.; *U.S. Public*, pg. 261
FURNITURE FACTORY OUTLET, LLC—See Irradiant Partners, LP; *U.S. Private*, pg. 2140
FURNITURE FAIR INC.; *U.S. Private*, pg. 1624
FURNITURELAND SOUTH, INC.; *U.S. Private*, pg. 1624
FURNITURE ON CONSIGNMENT INC.; *U.S. Private*, pg. 1624
FURNITURE OUTLETS USA; *U.S. Private*, pg. 1624
FURNITURE RENTAL ASSOCIATES; *U.S. Private*, pg. 1624
FURNITURE ROW; *U.S. Private*, pg. 1624
FURNITURE & THINGS INC.; *U.S. Private*, pg. 1624
THE FUTON SHOP; *U.S. Private*, pg. 4031
GABBERTS DESIGN STUDIO & FINE FURNISHINGS—See HOM Furniture, Inc.; *U.S. Private*, pg. 1969
GALLERY MODEL HOMES, INC.; *U.S. Private*, pg. 1639
GARDINERS HOME FURNISHING CENTER; *U.S. Private*, pg. 1643
GEORGETOWN MANOR INC.; *U.S. Private*, pg. 1684
GERDT FURNITURE & INTERIORS; *U.S. Private*, pg. 1686
GIORGI BROS; *U.S. Private*, pg. 1702
GLABMAN FURNITURE INC.; *U.S. Private*, pg. 1704
GODBY HOME FURNISHINGS INC.; *U.S. Private*, pg. 1724
GOODMANS INTERIOR STRUCTURES—See Goodmans, Inc.; *U.S. Private*, pg. 1739
GOODMANS OFFICE FURNITURE—See Goodmans, Inc.; *U.S. Private*, pg. 1739
GOODMANS OFFICE FURNITURE—See Goodmans, Inc.; *U.S. Private*, pg. 1740
GOODS FURNITURE HOUSE INC.; *U.S. Private*, pg. 1740
GORMAN'S FURNITURE INC.; *U.S. Private*, pg. 1744
GRAND FURNITURE DISCOUNT STORES; *U.S. Private*, pg. 1752
GRANGE FURNITURE INC.—See The Middleby Corporation; *U.S. Public*, pg. 2114
GRANGE LUXEMBOURG SARL—See The Middleby Corporation; *U.S. Public*, pg. 2114
GRANITE FURNITURE CO; *U.S. Private*, pg. 1755
THE GREAT AMERICAN HOME STORE, INC.—See Rooms To Go, Inc.; *U.S. Private*, pg. 3479
GREENBAUM HOME FURNISHINGS; *U.S. Private*, pg. 1774
GRUPO FAMSA S.A.B. DE C.V.; *Int'l*, pg. 3129
HABITAT INTERNATIONAL—See Cafom SA; *Int'l*, pg. 1250
HANK'S FURNITURE INC.; *U.S. Private*, pg. 1853
HART FURNITURE COMPANY INC.; *U.S. Private*, pg. 1873
HAVERTY FURNITURE COMPANIES, INC.; *U.S. Public*, pg. 988
HAYNES FURNITURE COMPANY INCORPORATED; *U.S. Private*, pg. 1885
HDM RETAIL, INC.—See Heritage Home Group, LLC; *U.S. Private*, pg. 1924
HENNEN FURNITURE; *U.S. Private*, pg. 1916
HINSON GALLERIES, INC.; *U.S. Private*, pg. 1950
HITCHCOCK CHAIR COMPANY LTD. - STILL RIVER ANTIQUES DIVISION—See Hitchcock Chair Company Ltd.; *U.S. Private*, pg. 1952
H.L. HUDSON FURNITURE INC.; *U.S. Private*, pg. 1835
HOME DECOR INNOVATIONS; *U.S. Private*, pg. 1970
HOME FURNITURE COMPANY INC.—See Home Furniture Company of Lafayette Inc.; *U.S. Private*, pg. 1971
HOME FURNITURE COMPANY OF LAFAYETTE INC.; *U.S. Private*, pg. 1971
HOME FURNITURE CO. OF LAKE CHARLES INC.—See Home Furniture Company of Lafayette Inc.; *U.S. Private*, pg. 1971
HOMEMAKERS PLAZA, INC.—See Berkshire Hathaway Inc.; *U.S. Public*, pg. 313
HOME TRENDS & DESIGN, INC.; *U.S. Private*, pg. 1972
HOMEWORKS INC.; *U.S. Private*, pg. 1976
HOMEWORLD—See C.S. Wo & Sons Ltd.; *U.S. Private*, pg. 709
HOM FURNITURE, INC.; *U.S. Private*, pg. 1969
HUMBLE ABODE, INC.; *U.S. Private*, pg. 2007
HURWITZ-MINTZ FINEST FURNITURE STORE SOUTH LLC; *U.S. Private*, pg. 2013
IMAGE BUSINESS INTERIORS; *U.S. Private*, pg. 2044
IMPERIAL HARDWARE COMPANY INC.; *U.S. Private*, pg. 2049
INNERPLAN; *U.S. Private*, pg. 2080

449110 — FURNITURE RETAILERS

INTERIOR DESIGN & ARCHITECTURE, INC.; *U.S. Private,* pg. 2111
INTRINSICS—See Barnhardt Manufacturing Company; *U.S. Private,* pg. 478
IVAN SMITH FURNITURE, LLC; *U.S. Private,* pg. 2150
JDW WRAP UP, INC.; *U.S. Private,* pg. 2196
JEROME'S FURNITURE WAREHOUSE; *U.S. Private,* pg. 2201
JESUP FURNITURE OUTLET INC.; *U.S. Private,* pg. 2203
JEUP INC.—See RH; *U.S. Public,* pg. 1796
J&J FURNITURE INCORPORATED; *U.S. Private,* pg. 2154
JMX INTERNATIONAL CORPORATION; *U.S. Private,* pg. 2216
JOHNNY JANOSIK INC.; *U.S. Private,* pg. 2226
JOHN V. SCHULTZ CO.; *U.S. Private,* pg. 2225
JOHN-WILLIAM FINE FURNITURE & INTERIORS INC.; *U.S. Private,* pg. 2225
JORDAN'S FURNITURE, INC.—See Berkshire Hathaway Inc.; *U.S. Public,* pg. 308
KANE FURNITURE CORPORATION; *U.S. Private,* pg. 2259
KEEPING TRADITIONS INC.; *U.S. Private,* pg. 2273
KEY CITY FURNITURE COMPANY; *U.S. Private,* pg. 2292
KIMBALL OFFICE, INC.—See HNI Corporation; *U.S. Public,* pg. 1043
KITCHEN KABOODLE II INC.; *U.S. Private,* pg. 2316
KITTLE'S HOME FURNISHINGS CENTER INC.; *U.S. Private,* pg. 2316
KML SALES INC.; *U.S. Private,* pg. 2321
KNOXVILLE WHOLESALE FURNITURE CO. INC.; *U.S. Private,* pg. 2325
KREISS COLLECTION ATLANTA INC.—See Kreiss Enterprises Inc.; *U.S. Private,* pg. 2351
KREISS COLLECTION FLORIDA INC.—See Kreiss Enterprises Inc.; *U.S. Private,* pg. 2351
LA CANASTA FURNISHINGS; *U.S. Private,* pg. 2368
LACK'S AARONSON, INC.; *U.S. Private,* pg. 2371
LACK'S VALLEY STORES LTD.—See Lack's Aaronson, Inc.; *U.S. Private,* pg. 2371
LANE HOME FURNITURE RETAIL, INC.—See Heritage Home Group, LLC; *U.S. Private,* pg. 1924
LA-Z-RECLINER SHOP INC.; *U.S. Private,* pg. 2370
LAZY-BOY FURNITURE GALLERIES; *U.S. Private,* pg. 2403
LBM CORP.; *U.S. Private,* pg. 2403
LEADER'S HOLDING COMPANY; *U.S. Private,* pg. 2406
LEATHER CREATIONS INC.; *U.S. Private,* pg. 2409
LINDER'S FURNITURE, INC.; *U.S. Private,* pg. 2460
LOUIS SHANKS OF TEXAS INC.; *U.S. Private,* pg. 2499
LZB FURNITURE GALLERIES OF PARAMUS, INC.—See La-Z-Boy Incorporated; *U.S. Public,* pg. 1285
MANCINI'S SLEEPWORLD INC.; *U.S. Private,* pg. 2562
MARLO FURNITURE CO., INC.; *U.S. Private,* pg. 2585
MATHIS BROS. FURNITURE CO. INC.; *U.S. Private,* pg. 2611
MATTRESS DEPOT USA; *U.S. Private,* pg. 2614
MATTRESS DISCOUNTERS CORP; *U.S. Private,* pg. 2614
MATTRESS KING, INC.—See Tempur Sealy International, Inc.; *U.S. Public,* pg. 1999
MATTRESS LAND SLEEPFIT; *U.S. Private,* pg. 2614
MAULDIN CORPORATION; *U.S. Private,* pg. 2615
MCGREGOR COMPANY; *U.S. Private,* pg. 2635
MEALEYS FURNITURE—See Parallel Investment Partners LLC; *U.S. Private,* pg. 3092
MISKELLY FURNITURE WAREHOUSE INC.; *U.S. Private,* pg. 2746
MISSOURI FURNITURE INC.; *U.S. Private,* pg. 2749
MITT HJEM NORGE AS—See Fortum Oyj; *Int'l,* pg. 2742
MOORADIANS INC.; *U.S. Private,* pg. 2779
MORE SPACE PLACE, INC.—See Closet & Storage Concepts; *U.S. Private,* pg. 946
MOR FURNITURE FOR LESS; *U.S. Private,* pg. 2781
MORRIS FURNITURE CO. INC.; *U.S. Private,* pg. 2787
MOSER CORPORATION; *U.S. Private,* pg. 2793
MY FAVORITE THINGS, LLC—See Forcht Group of Kentucky, Inc.; *U.S. Private,* pg. 1564
NASHVILLE STATIONERY CO. INC.; *U.S. Private,* pg. 2836
NATIONAL BUSINESS FURNITURE INC—See Franz Haniel & Cie. GmbH; *Int'l,* pg. 2763
NATIONAL RETAIL CORPORATION; *U.S. Private,* pg. 2862
NATURWOOD HOME FURNISHINGS, INC.; *U.S. Private,* pg. 2868
N.B. LIEBMAN & CO. INC.; *U.S. Private,* pg. 2827
ND FLUOROPOLYMER COATINGS DIVISION—See H.B. Fuller Company; *U.S. Public,* pg. 978
NEBRASKA FURNITURE MART, INC.—See Berkshire Hathaway Inc.; *U.S. Public,* pg. 313
NEST FEATHERINGS INC.; *U.S. Private,* pg. 2886
NEUVIE—See MichaelKate Interiors and Gallery; *U.S. Private,* pg. 2699
NEW DEAL MERCANTILE INC.; *U.S. Private,* pg. 2893
NEW TANGRAM, LLC - NEWPORT BEACH—See New Tangram, LLC; *U.S. Private,* pg. 2907
NFM OF KANSAS INC—See Berkshire Hathaway Inc.; *U.S. Public,* pg. 302
NOEL FURNITURE INC.; *U.S. Private,* pg. 2933
NORRIS FURNITURE INC.; *U.S. Private,* pg. 2939
OFFENBACHER AQUATICS INC.; *U.S. Private,* pg. 3001
OFFICE FURNITURE CENTER, INC.; *U.S. Private,* pg. 3001

OFFICEFURNITURE.COM—See Franz Haniel & Cie. GmbH; *Int'l,* pg. 2763
OFFICE FURNITURE & DESIGN CONCEPTS, INC.; *U.S. Private,* pg. 3001
OFFICE FURNITURE USA—See Business Interiors Inc.; *U.S. Private,* pg. 695
OFFICE RESOURCES, INC.; *U.S. Private,* pg. 3001
OKI FURNITURE FAIR INC.; *U.S. Private,* pg. 3007
OLINDE'S FURNITURE & APPLIANCES; *U.S. Private,* pg. 3010
ONESTOPERGONOMICS.COM; *U.S. Private,* pg. 3025
ONE WAY FURNITURE, INC.; *U.S. Private,* pg. 3024
OSKAR HUBER INC.; *U.S. Private,* pg. 3047
OSTERMANCRON, INC.; *U.S. Private,* pg. 3048
PANELLING CENTRE LIMITED—See Grafton Group plc; *Int'l,* pg. 3051
PARKE-BELL LTD., INC.; *U.S. Private,* pg. 3097
PARKER FURNITURE INCORPORATED; *U.S. Private,* pg. 3097
PATTON SALES CORPORATION; *U.S. Private,* pg. 3112
PETER ANDERSSON AB—See Addtech AB; *Int'l,* pg. 134
PIER 1 IMPORTS, INC.; *U.S. Public,* pg. 1690
PIERRE DEUX FRENCH COUNTRY; *U.S. Private,* pg. 3179
PILGRIM FURNITURE CITY; *U.S. Private,* pg. 3180
PLUMMERS INC.; *U.S. Private,* pg. 3215
POMPANOOSUC MILLS CORPORATION; *U.S. Private,* pg. 3227
POPPIN, INC.—See HNI Corporation; *U.S. Public,* pg. 1043
PORTICO BED & BATH INCORPORATED; *U.S. Private,* pg. 3232
POTTERY BARN OUTLET—See Williams-Sonoma, Inc.; *U.S. Public,* pg. 2371
PRICE MODERN LLC; *U.S. Private,* pg. 3258
QUATRINE FURNITURE COMPANY; *U.S. Private,* pg. 3324
RAYMOUR & FLANIGAN FURNITURE CO.; *U.S. Private,* pg. 3359
RAZMATAZ; *U.S. Private,* pg. 3359
R.C. WILLEY HOME FURNISHINGS—See Berkshire Hathaway Inc.; *U.S. Public,* pg. 315
REEDS & SON FURNITURE INC.; *U.S. Private,* pg. 3383
REFURBISHED OFFICE FURNITURE, INC.; *U.S. Private,* pg. 3385
RELAX THE BACK CORPORATION—See CI Capital Partners LLC; *U.S. Private,* pg. 895
RESTORATION HARDWARE, INC.—See RH; *U.S. Public,* pg. 1796
R.H. KUHN COMPANY, INC.; *U.S. Private,* pg. 3336
RIDGEWOOD—See Dorel Industries, Inc.; *Int'l,* pg. 2176
RITZ ASSOCIATES; *U.S. Private,* pg. 3442
ROOM & BOARD, INC.; *U.S. Private,* pg. 3479
ROOMS TO GO, INC.; *U.S. Private,* pg. 3479
ROOMSTORE, INC.; *U.S. Private,* pg. 3479
ROOMSTORES OF PHOENIX LLC; *U.S. Private,* pg. 3479
ROSE BROTHERS FURNITURE; *U.S. Private,* pg. 3481
ROTHMAN FURNITURE STORES, INC.; *U.S. Private,* pg. 3487
ROYAL FURNITURE COMPANY; *U.S. Private,* pg. 3492
RTA FURNITURE DISTRIBUTORS; *U.S. Private,* pg. 3498
SAM CLAR OFFICE FURNITURE, INC.; *U.S. Private,* pg. 3535
SAM LEVIN INC.—See Thomas H. Lee Partners, L.P.; *U.S. Private,* pg. 4156
SAM LEVITZ FURNITURE COMPANY; *U.S. Private,* pg. 3535
SAXON-CLARK INC.; *U.S. Private,* pg. 3558
SCHEWEL FURNITURE COMPANY, INC.; *U.S. Private,* pg. 3564
SCHMIDT-GOODMAN OFFICE PRODUCTS; *U.S. Private,* pg. 3566
SCHNEIDERMAN'S FURNITURE, INC.; *U.S. Private,* pg. 3567
SCS DIRECT INC.; *U.S. Private,* pg. 3580
SEASIDE FURNITURE SHOP INC.; *U.S. Private,* pg. 3591
SEASONAL CONCEPTS INC.—See HOM Furniture, Inc.; *U.S. Private,* pg. 1969
SEI/AARON'S, INC.—See Aaron's Company, Inc.; *U.S. Public,* pg. 13
SEIGERMANS FURNITURE SHOWPLACE LLC; *U.S. Private,* pg. 3599
SELDEN'S INTERIOR FURNISHINGS, INC.; *U.S. Private,* pg. 3600
SELECT COMFORT RETAIL CORPORATION—See Sleep Number Corporation; *U.S. Public,* pg. 1894
SENSING ENTERPRISES INC.; *U.S. Private,* pg. 3608
SEWCO INC.; *U.S. Private,* pg. 3620
SHARPS BEDROOMS LIMITED—See Sun Capital Partners, Inc.; *U.S. Private,* pg. 3862
SHENZHEN OULUO FURNITURE COMPANY LIMITED—See Hing Lee (HK) Holdings Limited; *Int'l,* pg. 3401
THE SHERIDAN GROUP INC; *U.S. Private,* pg. 4117
SHOFERS FURNITURE CO. INC.; *U.S. Private,* pg. 3639
SIMMONS JUVENILE FURNITURE—See Delta Enterprise Corporation; *U.S. Private,* pg. 1200
SK RETAIL, INC.—See Wayfair Inc.; *U.S. Public,* pg. 2338
SLEEPERS IN SEATTLE; *U.S. Private,* pg. 3688
SLEEP WELL INC.; *U.S. Private,* pg. 3688
SLUMBERLAND INC.; *U.S. Private,* pg. 3689

SLUMBERWORLD—See C.S. Wo & Sons Ltd.; *U.S. Private,* pg. 709
SMITH OFFICE EQUIPMENT INC.; *U.S. Private,* pg. 3695
SMULEKOFF FURNITURE COMPANY INC; *U.S. Private,* pg. 3699
SOFA MART, LLC—See Furniture Row; *U.S. Private,* pg. 1624
SPACE FURNITURE PTE LIMITED—See Harvey Norman Holdings Ltd; *Int'l,* pg. 3281
SPILLER FURNITURE COMPANY; *U.S. Private,* pg. 3757
SPRINTZ FURNITURE SHOWROOM INC.; *U.S. Private,* pg. 3765
STAR FURNITURE COMPANY; *U.S. Private,* pg. 3784
STAR FURNITURE COMPANY—See Berkshire Hathaway Inc.; *U.S. Public,* pg. 316
STEELCASE HONG KONG LTD.—See Steelcase Inc.; *U.S. Public,* pg. 1944
STEELCASE PLC—See Steelcase Inc.; *U.S. Public,* pg. 1944
STELAR INC.; *U.S. Private,* pg. 3799
STERLING FURNITURE CO; *U.S. Private,* pg. 3805
STEVENS OFFICE INTERIORS; *U.S. Private,* pg. 3810
STEWART'S SLEEP CENTER INC.; *U.S. Private,* pg. 3811
STOOL & DINETTE FACTORY INC.; *U.S. Private,* pg. 3830
STOWERS FURNITURE COMPANIES LTD; *U.S. Private,* pg. 3832
STRATASHOPS LLC; *U.S. Private,* pg. 3834
SUN HING POSH HOLDINGS LIMITED—See MillerKnoll, Inc.; *U.S. Public,* pg. 1448
SUNWAY (BENELUX) B.V.—See 3G Capital Partners L.P.; *U.S. Private,* pg. 13
THOMASVILLE HOME FURNISHINGS OF ARIZONA—See Heritage Home Group, LLC; *U.S. Private,* pg. 1924
TODAY'S OFFICE INC.; *U.S. Private,* pg. 4180
TOK & STOK LTDA.—See The Carlyle Group Inc.; *U.S. Public,* pg. 2056
TOMS-PRICE CO.; *U.S. Private,* pg. 4184
TRI COUNTY OFFICE FURNITURE; *U.S. Private,* pg. 4220
TUSCAN IMPORTS INC.—See Salt Creek Capital Management, LLC; *U.S. Private,* pg. 3533
UNCLAIMED FREIGHT COMPANY LLC; *U.S. Private,* pg. 4279
VALLEY FURNITURE SHOP, INC.; *U.S. Private,* pg. 4334
VATER'S OF OKLAHOMA CITY INC.; *U.S. Private,* pg. 4348
VIRCO INC.—See VIRCO MFG. CORPORATION; *U.S. Public,* pg. 2299
WALKER FURNITURE CO.; *U.S. Private,* pg. 4429
WALKERS FURNITURE INC.; *U.S. Private,* pg. 4429
WAREHOUSE HOME FURNISHINGS DISTRIBUTOR, INC.; *U.S. Private,* pg. 4441
WAYFAIR GMBH—See Wayfair Inc.; *U.S. Public,* pg. 2338
WAYFAIR STORES LIMITED—See Wayfair Inc.; *U.S. Public,* pg. 2338
WAYSIDE FURNITURE INC.; *U.S. Private,* pg. 4460
W.B. MASON COMPANY; *U.S. Private,* pg. 4419
WEEKENDS ONLY; *U.S. Private,* pg. 4469
WEIR'S FURNITURE VILLAGE; *U.S. Private,* pg. 4472
WELCOME TRAVELERS FURNITURE CO.; *U.S. Private,* pg. 4473
WESTERN CONTRACT FURNISHERS OF SACRAMENTO INC.; *U.S. Private,* pg. 4492
WEST MICHIGAN OFFICE INTERIORS INC.; *U.S. Private,* pg. 4486
WG&R FURNITURE CO., INC.; *U.S. Private,* pg. 4503
WILLIAM KAVANAGH FURNITURE CO.; *U.S. Private,* pg. 4523
WILLIAM M. BLOOMFIELD INC.; *U.S. Private,* pg. 4523
WILLIAM MORRIS HOME FASHIONS; *U.S. Private,* pg. 4524
WILSON BATES APPLIANCE STORES; *U.S. Private,* pg. 4530
WOODLEYS FINE FURNITURE INC.; *U.S. Private,* pg. 4559
WORKSCAPES INC.; *U.S. Private,* pg. 4564
WORKSPACE DYNAMICS, INC.—See Goodmans, Inc.; *U.S. Private,* pg. 1740
W.S. BADCOCK LLC—See Conn's, Inc.; *U.S. Public,* pg. 567
YOUNG'S FURNITURE COMPANY; *U.S. Private,* pg. 4593

449121 — FLOOR COVERING RETAILERS

ABBEY CARPET CO., INC.; *U.S. Private,* pg. 34
ACCOR RESERVATION—See Accor S.A.; *Int'l,* pg. 91
AIREA PLC; *Int'l,* pg. 247
ALADDIN MANUFACTURING OF ALABAMA, LLC—See Mohawk Industries, Inc.; *U.S. Public,* pg. 1457
AMERICAN CARPET ONE; *U.S. Private,* pg. 226
ATLANTA WEST CARPETS, LLC—See The Sterling Group, L.P.; *U.S. Private,* pg. 4121
BALTA GROUP NV; *Int'l,* pg. 811
BASSETT DIRECT NC, LLC—See Bassett Furniture Industries, Incorporated; *U.S. Public,* pg. 279
BASSETT DIRECT SC, LLC—See Bassett Furniture Industries, Incorporated; *U.S. Public,* pg. 279
BEATTY FLOORS LIMITED; *Int'l,* pg. 934

N.A.I.C.S. INDEX

449129 — ALL OTHER HOME FURN...

BETTER LIFE TECHNOLOGY, LLC—See Century Park Capital Partners, LLC; *U.S. Private*, pg. 833
BID4FLOORS.COM; *U.S. Private*, pg. 551
BOB WAGNER'S MILL CARPET INC.; *U.S. Private*, pg. 605
BODENHAUS GMBH—See Hornbach Holding AG & Co. KGaA; *Int'l*, pg. 3481
BOMBERGERS STORE INC.; *U.S. Private*, pg. 612
BRITT'S HOME FURNISHINGS, INC.; *U.S. Private*, pg. 657
BROADWAY FLOORS, INC.—See Bid4floors.com; *U.S. Private*, pg. 551
BUTLER CARPET COMPANY INC.; *U.S. Private*, pg. 697
CAL COAST CARPET WAREHOUSE, INC—See Live Ventures Incorporated; *U.S. Public*, pg. 1332
CAP CARPET, INC.; *U.S. Private*, pg. 737
CAROLINA CONVENIENCE CORP.; *U.S. Private*, pg. 767
CARPET BARN INC.; *U.S. Private*, pg. 770
CARPET CONCEPT OBJEKT-TEPPICHBODEN GMBH—See Egetaepper A/S; *Int'l*, pg. 2324
CARPET CONCEPT TEPPICHFABRIK GMBH & CO. KG—See Egetaepper A/S; *Int'l*, pg. 2324
CARPET CORNER INC.; *U.S. Private*, pg. 770
CARPET FACTORY OUTLET INC.; *U.S. Private*, pg. 770
CARPET FAIR, INC.; *U.S. Private*, pg. 770
CARPETLAND NV—See Carpetright plc; *Int'l*, pg. 1343
CARPET ONE BY VAN DRIE HOME FURNISHINGS; *U.S. Private*, pg. 770
CARPETRIGHT PLC; *Int'l*, pg. 1343
CARPETS PLUS OF WISCONSIN INC.; *U.S. Private*, pg. 770
CARPET WEAVERS INC.; *U.S. Private*, pg. 770
CC CARPET INC.; *U.S. Private*, pg. 799
CENTURY SUPPLY CO. INC.; *U.S. Private*, pg. 834
CHATEAU INTERIORS & DESIGN—See The Warmington Group; *U.S. Private*, pg. 4133
CMH SPACE FLOORING PRODUCTS, INC.—See J.J. Haines & Co. Inc.; *U.S. Private*, pg. 2167
CMH SPACE FLOORING—See J.J. Haines & Co. Inc.; *U.S. Private*, pg. 2167
COLEMAN FLOOR COMPANY—See Littlejohn & Co., LLC; *U.S. Private*, pg. 2470
COLEMAN FLOOR COMPANY—See Platinum Equity, LLC; *U.S. Private*, pg. 3205
COLES OF LA JOLLA INCORPORATED; *U.S. Private*, pg. 967
COMMERCIAL CONTRACTORS INC.; *U.S. Private*, pg. 983
DALTON CARPET ONE FLOOR & HOME; *U.S. Private*, pg. 1150
DOBSON FLOORS INC.; *U.S. Private*, pg. 1250
EASTSIDE FLOOR SERVICES LTD.; *U.S. Private*, pg. 1322
ECKARDS HOME IMPROVEMENTS; *U.S. Private*, pg. 1327
EGE CARPETS DACH GMBH—See Egetaepper A/S; *Int'l*, pg. 2324
EGE CARPETS NORWAY AS—See Egetaepper A/S; *Int'l*, pg. 2324
EGE CARPETS SWEDEN AB—See Egetaepper A/S; *Int'l*, pg. 2324
EGE CARPETS UK LTD.—See Egetaepper A/S; *Int'l*, pg. 2324
EGE CONTRACT A/S—See Egetaepper A/S; *Int'l*, pg. 2324
EMILAMERICA, INC.—See Mohawk Industries, Inc.; *U.S. Public*, pg. 1457
EMILCERAMICA S.R.L—See Mohawk Industries, Inc.; *U.S. Public*, pg. 1457
EMPIRE TODAY, LLC—See Charlesbank Capital Partners, LLC; *U.S. Private*, pg. 855
ENIA CARPETS NETHERLANDS B.V.—See Forbo Holding Ltd.; *Int'l*, pg. 2729
EXPANKO, INC.—See RPM International Inc.; *U.S. Public*, pg. 1818
EXPLORER S.R.L.—See Mohawk Industries, Inc.; *U.S. Public*, pg. 1457
FABER BROS. BROADLOOM CO.; *U.S. Private*, pg. 1458
FASHION CARPETS INC.; *U.S. Private*, pg. 1481
FIRED EARTH LIMITED—See The Middleby Corporation; *U.S. Public*, pg. 2114
FLOOR ASSOCIATES INCORPORATED; *U.S. Private*, pg. 1546
FLOORCRAFT INC.; *U.S. Private*, pg. 1546
FLOOR DECOR CENTER INC; *U.S. Private*, pg. 1546
FLOOR & DECOR HOLDINGS, INC.; *U.S. Public*, pg. 853
FLOOR & DECOR OUTLETS OF AMERICA, INC.—See Floor & Decor Holdings, Inc.; *U.S. Public*, pg. 853
FLOORING AMERICA, INC.—See CCA Global Partners, Inc.; *U.S. Private*, pg. 799
FLOORING GALLERY LLC; *U.S. Private*, pg. 1546
FLOORING LIQUIDATORS, INC.—See Live Ventures Incorporated; *U.S. Public*, pg. 1332
FLOORING XL B.V.—See Mohawk Industries, Inc.; *U.S. Public*, pg. 1457
FLOORSHOP.COM, INC.; *U.S. Private*, pg. 1546
FLOORS MY HOME LIMITED; *Int'l*, pg. 2707
FORBO CONTEL HANDELSGES. M.B.H.—See Forbo Holding Ltd.; *Int'l*, pg. 2729
FORBO FLOORCOVERINGS PTY. LTD.—See Forbo Holding Ltd.; *Int'l*, pg. 2729
FORBO FLOORING GMBH—See Forbo Holding Ltd.; *Int'l*, pg. 2729

FORBO FLOORING UK LTD.—See Forbo Holding Ltd.; *Int'l*, pg. 2729
FORBO FLOORING UK LTD.—See Forbo Holding Ltd.; *Int'l*, pg. 2729
FORBO FLORING OY AB—See Forbo Holding Ltd.; *Int'l*, pg. 2729
FORBO IRELAND LTD.—See Forbo Holding Ltd.; *Int'l*, pg. 2729
FORBO LINOLEUM A/S—See Forbo Holding Ltd.; *Int'l*, pg. 2729
FORBO LINOLEUM A/S—See Forbo Holding Ltd.; *Int'l*, pg. 2729
FORBO LINOLEUM, INC.—See Forbo Holding Ltd.; *Int'l*, pg. 2729
FORBO LINOLEUM—See Forbo Holding Ltd.; *Int'l*, pg. 2729
FORBO-NOVILON B.V.—See Forbo Holding Ltd.; *Int'l*, pg. 2730
FORBO PADLOBURKOLATOK KFT.—See Forbo Holding Ltd.; *Int'l*, pg. 2730
FORBO PAVIMENTOS SA—See Forbo Holding Ltd.; *Int'l*, pg. 2730
FORBO RESILIENTI S.R.L.—See Forbo Holding Ltd.; *Int'l*, pg. 2730
FORBO TAPIJT B.V.—See Forbo Holding Ltd.; *Int'l*, pg. 2730
GENERAL FLOOR INDUSTRIES INC.; *U.S. Private*, pg. 1665
G. FRIED FLOORING AMERICA; *U.S. Private*, pg. 1630
GIANT FLOOR & WALL COVERING CO., INC.; *U.S. Private*, pg. 1694
GREATMATS.COM CORPORATION; *U.S. Private*, pg. 1770
HADINGER CARPET INC.; *U.S. Private*, pg. 1839
HAGOPIAN WORLD OF RUGS INC.; *U.S. Private*, pg. 1840
HEADLAM GROUP PLC; *Int'l*, pg. 3301
HERITAGE INTERIORS, INC.; *U.S. Private*, pg. 1924
HESSLER'S, INC.; *U.S. Private*, pg. 1928
HMS ENTERPRISES INC.; *U.S. Private*, pg. 1955
HOME CENTER, INC.; *U.S. Private*, pg. 1970
HOME DESIGN STUDIO; *U.S. Private*, pg. 1970
IMPERIAL TRADING CO, INC.; *U.S. Private*, pg. 2049
IVC LUXEMBOURG S.A R.L.—See Mohawk Industries, Inc.; *U.S. Public*, pg. 1457
IVC US, INC.—See Mohawk Industries, Inc.; *U.S. Public*, pg. 1457
J.J. HAINES & CO. INC.; *U.S. Private*, pg. 2167
JOHNSON CARPET INC.; *U.S. Private*, pg. 2227
JOSEPH MCDONNELL ENTERPRISES; *U.S. Private*, pg. 2237
KAI MINING EOOD—See Mohawk Industries, Inc.; *U.S. Public*, pg. 1457
THE KELLOGG COLLECTION INC.; *U.S. Private*, pg. 4064
KERMANS FINE FLOORING, INC.; *U.S. Private*, pg. 2290
KHAN ASPARUH AD—See Mohawk Industries, Inc.; *U.S. Public*, pg. 1457
KW LEASING INC.; *U.S. Private*, pg. 2359
LEWIS FLOOR & HOME; *U.S. Private*, pg. 2438
MACADAM FLOOR & DESIGN; *U.S. Private*, pg. 2531
MANASOTA FLOORING INC.; *U.S. Private*, pg. 2561
MATTS CASH & CARRY BUILDING MATERIALS; *U.S. Private*, pg. 2614
MCI INC.; *U.S. Private*, pg. 2636
MCSWAIN CARPETS INC.; *U.S. Private*, pg. 2644
MERKEL BROTHERS INC.; *U.S. Private*, pg. 2675
MICHAEL'S CARPET INC.; *U.S. Private*, pg. 2699
MIKE'S FLOORING COMPANIES; *U.S. Private*, pg. 2726
MODULEO GMBH—See Mohawk Industries, Inc.; *U.S. Public*, pg. 1458
MOHAWK INTERNATIONAL SERVICES BVBA—See Mohawk Industries, Inc.; *U.S. Public*, pg. 1458
MONTAUK RUG & CARPET CORP.; *U.S. Private*, pg. 2775
NAIRN FLOORS BENELUX B.V.—See Forbo Holding Ltd.; *Int'l*, pg. 2730
N. GINSBURG & SON INCORPORATED; *U.S. Private*, pg. 2827
NOVILON LTD.—See Forbo Holding Ltd.; *Int'l*, pg. 2730
OLSON RUG COMPANY; *U.S. Private*, pg. 3011
PARK RUG COMPANY INC.; *U.S. Private*, pg. 3096
PIERCE FLOORING & DESIGN; *U.S. Private*, pg. 3178
PINO TILE HOLDINGS LLC; *U.S. Private*, pg. 3186
PUCKETT'S FLOORING COMPANY; *U.S. Private*, pg. 3301
QUALITY FLOORING 4 LESS; *U.S. Private*, pg. 3319
RAY'S FLOORING SPECIALIST, INC.; *U.S. Private*, pg. 3359
RITE RUG CO.; *U.S. Private*, pg. 3441
ROC SALES, INC.—See RPM International Inc.; *U.S. Public*, pg. 1817
RUCKER & SILL LTD. INC.; *U.S. Private*, pg. 3500
RUSMUR FLOORS, INC.; *U.S. Private*, pg. 3505
S&G CARPET AND MORE; *U.S. Private*, pg. 3513
SIERRA TILE SUPPLY, INC.; *U.S. Private*, pg. 3648
SMART CARPET, INC.; *U.S. Private*, pg. 3691
SOVEREIGN DISTRIBUTORS INC.; *U.S. Private*, pg. 3743
STAGESTEP INC.; *U.S. Private*, pg. 3775
STANTON CARPET CORPORATION—See Quad-C Management, Inc.; *U.S. Private*, pg. 3315
SUTTON'S WESTERN WHOLESALE FLOORING; *U.S. Private*, pg. 3887
SWISSTRAX CORPORATION—See Sentinel Capital Partners, L.L.C.; *U.S. Private*, pg. 3609

THERMOS PTY. LTD.—See Thermos L.L.C.; *U.S. Private*, pg. 4143
TILE & CARPET TOWN EAST INCORPORATED; *U.S. Private*, pg. 4170
TOLLEFSON'S RETAIL GROUP INC.; *U.S. Private*, pg. 4182
TRINITY CARPET BROKERS INC.; *U.S. Private*, pg. 4233
WAYNE WILES FLOOR COVERINGS, INC.; *U.S. Private*, pg. 4460
WCCV FLOOR COVERINGS, LLC—See The Sterling Group, L.P.; *U.S. Private*, pg. 4122
WEST COAST FLOORING CENTER; *U.S. Private*, pg. 4484
WILSONART LLC - TAMPA—See Clayton, Dubilier & Rice, LLC; *U.S. Private*, pg. 930
WINCHESTER CARPET & RUG, LLC—See L2 Capital Partners; *U.S. Private*, pg. 2367
WOLDE FLOORING, LLC; *U.S. Private*, pg. 4553
WORLD OF FLOORS, INC.—See Thomas H. Lee Partners, L.P.; *U.S. Private*, pg. 4156
WORLDWIDE WHOLESALE FLOOR COVERINGS; *U.S. Private*, pg. 4570

449122 — WINDOW TREATMENT RETAILERS

BLINDS CHALET; *U.S. Private*, pg. 581
BLINDS.COM; *U.S. Private*, pg. 581
BUDGET BLINDS, INC.—See JM Family Enterprises Inc.; *U.S. Private*, pg. 2214
CUTTING CORNERS INC.; *U.S. Private*, pg. 1132
DECEUNINCK GERMANY GMBH—See Deceuninck NV; *Int'l*, pg. 2000
EXTE - EXTRUDERTECHNIK GMBH; *Int'l*, pg. 2591
HOME FRANCHISE CONCEPTS, INC.—See JM Family Enterprises Inc.; *U.S. Private*, pg. 2214
IP DECORA EAST—See Decora S.A.; *Int'l*, pg. 2001
KUHNS & HELLER CUSTOM WINDOW TREATMENTS; *U.S. Private*, pg. 2356
MARBURN STORES INC.; *U.S. Private*, pg. 2571
PIERCE'S FLOORING; *U.S. Private*, pg. 3178
RISTAL INC.; *U.S. Private*, pg. 3441
ROLL-A-SHADE; *U.S. Private*, pg. 3474
SUNSHINE DRAPERY & INTERIOR FASHIONS; *U.S. Private*, pg. 3871

449129 — ALL OTHER HOME FURNISHINGS RETAILERS

131448 CANADA INC; *Int'l*, pg. 2
20230930-DK-BUTTERFLY-1, INC.; *U.S. Private*, pg. 5
ACCESSORY PLACE INC.; *U.S. Private*, pg. 53
ADAIRS LIMITED; *Int'l*, pg. 123
ALIRM, LLC; *U.S. Private*, pg. 168
ALL AROUND LIGHTING, INC.—See Revolution Lighting Technologies, Inc.; *U.S. Public*, pg. 1793
ALTMEYER HOME STORES INC.; *U.S. Private*, pg. 210
ANDREWS LIGHTING & HARDWARE GALLERY—See Ferguson plc; *Int'l*, pg. 2637
AUSTIN PRODUCTIONS INC.; *U.S. Private*, pg. 396
BACCARAT, INC.—See Fortune Fountain (Beijing) Holding Group Co., Ltd.; *U.S. Private*, pg. 2743
BED BATH & BEYOND CANADA L.P.—See 20230930-DK-Butterfly-1, Inc.; *U.S. Private*, pg. 5
BELLACOR, INC.; *U.S. Private*, pg. 519
BENIX & CO INC.; *Int'l*, pg. 974
BOUCLAIR INC.; *Int'l*, pg. 1119
BROWN JORDAN INTERNATIONAL INC.—See Littlejohn & Co., LLC; *U.S. Private*, pg. 2470
BUSH EQUITIES; *U.S. Private*, pg. 694
BUY HAPPIER, LLC; *U.S. Private*, pg. 698
CALIFORNIA ACRYLIC INDUSTRIES, INC.; *U.S. Private*, pg. 717
CALIFORNIA BACKYARD INC.; *U.S. Private*, pg. 718
CALIFORNIA CLOSET COMPANY, INC.—See FirstService Corporation; *Int'l*, pg. 2691
CAPITOL LIGHTING; *U.S. Private*, pg. 744
CAPITOL LIGHTING—See Capitol Lighting; *U.S. Private*, pg. 744
CARICO INTERNATIONAL INC.; *U.S. Private*, pg. 761
CDW GOVERNMENT, INC.—See CDW Corporation; *U.S. Public*, pg. 462
CHARABIA CO.—See ENL Limited; *Int'l*, pg. 2441
CHINTZ & COMPANY; *Int'l*, pg. 1571
CHRISTMAS LIGHTS, ETC.; *U.S. Private*, pg. 891
CLAS OHLSON AB; *Int'l*, pg. 1651
THE CONRAN SHOP LTD.—See Conran Holdings Limited; *Int'l*, pg. 1769
THE CONTAINER STORE INC.—See Leonard Green & Partners, L.P.; *U.S. Private*, pg. 2429
CO-OPERATIVE HOME STORES—See Co-operative Group Limited; *Int'l*, pg. 1679
CORNERSTONE BRANDS, INC.—See Qurate Retail, Inc.; *U.S. Public*, pg. 1758
CORNING JAPAN K.K.—See Corning Incorporated; *U.S. Public*, pg. 578
COSTCO CANADA HOLDINGS INC.—See Costco Wholesale Corporation; *U.S. Public*, pg. 586
COUNTRY CURTAINS RETAIL INC.—See Fitzpatrick Com-

449129 — ALL OTHER HOME FURN...

panies Inc.; *U.S. Private*, pg. 1536
CUISINART INC.—See American Securities LLC; *U.S. Private*, pg. 248
DAIKI REAL ESTATE INFORMATION CO., LTD.—See DCM Holdings Co., Ltd.; *Int'l*, pg. 1992
DAWN KITCHEN FITTINGS (PROPRIETARY) LIMITED—See DISTRIBUTION AND WAREHOUSING NETWORK LIMITED; *Int'l*, pg. 2136
DCM DAIKI CO., LTD.—See DCM Holdings Co., Ltd.; *Int'l*, pg. 1992
DCM HOLDINGS CO., LTD.; *Int'l*, pg. 1992
DCM HOMAC CORP.—See DCM Holdings Co., Ltd.; *Int'l*, pg. 1992
DCM KAHMA CO., LTD.—See DCM Holdings Co., Ltd.; *Int'l*, pg. 1992
DCM NICOT CO., LTD.—See DCM Holdings Co., Ltd.; *Int'l*, pg. 1992
DCM SANWA CO., LTD.—See DCM Holdings Co., Ltd.; *Int'l*, pg. 1992
DEL MAR DESIGNS, INC.; *U.S. Private*, pg. 1192
DESIGN TOSCANO, INC.; *U.S. Private*, pg. 1214
DOHOME PUBLIC COMPANY LIMITED; *Int'l*, pg. 2156
DSQUARED INTERNATIONAL, LLC; *U.S. Private*, pg. 1281
DUNELM (SOFT FURNISHINGS) LIMITED—See Dunelm Group plc; *Int'l*, pg. 2226
EARTH SENSE ENERGY SYSTEMS INC.; *U.S. Private*, pg. 1314
FARREY'S WHOLESALE HARDWARE CO., INC.; *U.S. Private*, pg. 1481
FIRESIDE HEARTH & HOME; *U.S. Private*, pg. 1512
FIRSTIME DESIGN LIMITED; *U.S. Public*, pg. 849
FITZPATRICK COMPANIES INC.; *U.S. Private*, pg. 1536
FORMATION BRANDS, LLC—See Pacific Market International, LLC; *U.S. Private*, pg. 3068
FRAMING ART CENTRE—See Franchise Concepts, Inc.; *U.S. Private*, pg. 1587
FRAN'S WICKER AND RATTAN INC.; *U.S. Private*, pg. 1586
FUEL FEED PLAZA HOME CENTERS; *U.S. Private*, pg. 1619
FURBAY ELECTRIC SUPPLY CO.; *U.S. Private*, pg. 1623
GANT HOME AB—See Gant Sweden; *Int'l*, pg. 2882
THE GUILD INC.; *U.S. Private*, pg. 4040
HABITAT FRANCE SA—See Cafom SA; *Int'l*, pg. 1250
HERMES CENTRE JOINT STOCK COMPANY; *Int'l*, pg. 3362
HOMAC NICOT CORP.—See DCM Holdings Co., Ltd.; *Int'l*, pg. 1992
HOMEBASE GROUP LTD.—See Hilco Trading, LLC; *U.S. Private*, pg. 1944
HOME CENTER SANKO CO., LTD.—See DCM Holdings Co., Ltd.; *Int'l*, pg. 1992
HOME DECORATORS COLLECTION INC.—See The Home Depot, Inc.; *U.S. Public*, pg. 2089
HOME DECOR LIQUIDATORS FURNITURE & FLOORING; *U.S. Private*, pg. 1970
HOME DESIGN OUTLET CENTER; *U.S. Private*, pg. 1970
HOMEGOODS, INC.—See The TJX Companies, Inc.; *U.S. Public*, pg. 2134
HOME OUTFITTERS—See Abrams Capital, LLC; *U.S. Private*, pg. 40
HOME OUTFITTERS—See Rhone Group, LLC; *U.S. Private*, pg. 3423
HOME OUTFITTERS—See WeWork Inc.; *U.S. Public*, pg. 2364
HOMESERVE ASSISTANCE LIMITED—See Brookfield Corporation; *Int'l*, pg. 1188
HOMESERVE GB LIMITED—See Brookfield Corporation; *Int'l*, pg. 1188
IENJOY HOME LLC; *U.S. Private*, pg. 2038
ILLUMS BOLIGHUS A/S—See Axcel Management A/S; *Int'l*, pg. 762
INNERSPACE LUXURY PRODUCTS, LLC—See FirsTime Design Limited; *U.S. Public*, pg. 849
INTERNATIONAL HOME SHOPPING—See Suarez Corporation Industries; *U.S. Private*, pg. 3847
JANE CHURCHILL LIMITED—See Colefax Group PLC; *Int'l*, pg. 1697
KAHYA CO., LTD.—See DCM Holdings Co., Ltd.; *Int'l*, pg. 1992
KHOURY INC.; *U.S. Private*, pg. 2301
KINGCOME SOFAS LIMITED—See Colefax Group PLC; *Int'l*, pg. 1697
KITCHEN STUFF PLUS, INC.—See Fairfax Financial Holdings Limited; *Int'l*, pg. 2607
KLAFF'S, INC.; *U.S. Private*, pg. 2317
KONINKLIJKE PEITSMAN B.V.—See Mohawk Industries, Inc.; *U.S. Public*, pg. 1457
LAMPS PLUS INC.; *U.S. Private*, pg. 2381
LEAF HOME, LLC; *U.S. Private*, pg. 2407
LIBERTY PROCUREMENT CO. INC.—See 20230930-DK-Butterfly-1, Inc.; *U.S. Public*, pg. 5
LIFETIME BRANDS GLOBAL LIMITED—See Lifetime Brands, Inc.; *U.S. Public*, pg. 1313
LIGHTING INCORPORATED; *U.S. Private*, pg. 2453
LINENS 'N THINGS, INC.—See The Carlyle Group Inc.; *U.S. Private*, pg. 2048
LIVING DIRECT, INC.; *U.S. Private*, pg. 2474

LTD. COMMODITIES LLC; *U.S. Private*, pg. 2509
LUBNER GROUP, LLC; *U.S. Private*, pg. 2510
MASTERCRAFT INTERNATIONAL LIMITED—See China Baofeng (International) Ltd.; *Int'l*, pg. 1485
ME BATH EXPERIENCE INC.—See Yellow Wood Partners LLC; *U.S. Private*, pg. 4587
METRO CARPETS, LLC—See The Sterling Group, L.P.; *U.S. Private*, pg. 4122
MICHAEL C. FINA CO. INC.; *U.S. Private*, pg. 2697
NEAT IDEAS LTD—See Sycamore Partners Management, LP; *U.S. Private*, pg. 3897
PATIOSHOPPERS INC.; *U.S. Private*, pg. 3109
THE PERFECTLY SAFE CATALOG—See Kids Stuff, Inc.; *U.S. Private*, pg. 2303
PIER 1 IMPORTS (U.S.), INC.—See Pier 1 Imports, Inc.; *U.S. Public*, pg. 1690
PLAN ONE (PTY) LTD—See Marriott International, Inc.; *U.S. Public*, pg. 1371
PRATESI LINENS INC.; *U.S. Private*, pg. 3243
REPLACEMENTS, LTD.; *U.S. Private*, pg. 3401
REVERE MILLS INTERNATIONAL GROUP; *U.S. Private*, pg. 3414
ROYAL PLUS INC.; *U.S. Private*, pg. 3493
SAFE STEP WALK IN TUB, LLC—See Ferguson plc; *Int'l*, pg. 2638
SANDER SALES ENTERPRISES LTD.; *U.S. Private*, pg. 3543
SHERIDAN U.K. LIMITED—See Hanesbrands Inc.; *U.S. Public*, pg. 983
SHOPPERSCHOICE.COM, LLC—See Brand Velocity Partners; *U.S. Private*, pg. 637
SIBYL COLEFAX & JOHN FOWLER LIMITED—See Colefax Group PLC; *Int'l*, pg. 1697
SMOKY MOUNTAIN KNIFE WORKS INC.; *U.S. Private*, pg. 3698
SOLSTICE SLEEP PRODUCTS, INC.; *U.S. Private*, pg. 3710
SPRINGS CANADA, LTD.—See Coteminas Companhia de Tecidos Norte de Minas; *Int'l*, pg. 1817
SPRINGS CANADA, LTD.—See Springs Global, Inc.; *U.S. Private*, pg. 3764
STANDARD ELECTRIC CO.—See Blackfriars Corp.; *U.S. Private*, pg. 575
STUDIO41—See Logan Square Aluminum Supply, Inc.; *U.S. Private*, pg. 2481
THE TILE SHOP, LLC—See Tile Shop Holdings, Inc.; *U.S. Public*, pg. 2159
TUESDAY MORNING CORPORATION; *U.S. Public*, pg. 2203
UPPERCASE LIVING, LLC—See JRjr33, Inc.; *U.S. Private*, pg. 2240
URBAN OUTFITTERS CANADA, INC.—See Urban Outfitters, Inc.; *U.S. Public*, pg. 2265
URBAN OUTFITTERS UK, LIMITED—See Urban Outfitters, Inc.; *U.S. Public*, pg. 2265
USA BABY; *U.S. Private*, pg. 4321
THE VENICE AUCTION COMPANY, INC.; *U.S. Private*, pg. 4130
VIKING DIREKT GESMBH—See Aurelius Equity Opportunities SE & Co. KGaA; *Int'l*, pg. 709
VIP INTERNATIONAL INC.; *U.S. Private*, pg. 4386
VIVRE, INC.; *U.S. Private*, pg. 4406
W.E. BEDDING CORPORATION; *U.S. Private*, pg. 4420
THE WECK CORPORATION; *U.S. Private*, pg. 4134
WILLIAMSBURG POTTERY FACTORY; *U.S. Private*, pg. 4527
WILLIAMS-SONOMA CANADA, INC.—See Williams-Sonoma, Inc.; *U.S. Public*, pg. 2371
WILLIAMS-SONOMA DELAWARE, LLC—See Williams-Sonoma, Inc.; *U.S. Public*, pg. 2371
WILLIAMS-SONOMA, INC.; *U.S. Public*, pg. 2371
WILLIAMS-SONOMA VIETNAM LLC—See Williams-Sonoma, Inc.; *U.S. Public*, pg. 2371
WINDY CITY PROMOTIONS, LLC; *U.S. Private*, pg. 4540
WORLD TABLEWARE INC.—See Libbey, Inc.; *U.S. Private*, pg. 2442
Z GALLERIE, LLC; *U.S. Private*, pg. 4596

449210 — ELECTRONICS AND APPLIANCE RETAILERS

1099 PRO, INC.—See HgCapital Trust plc; *Int'l*, pg. 3377
4SURE.COM, INC.—See The ODP Corporation; *U.S. Public*, pg. 2117
668824 ALBERTA LTD; *Int'l*, pg. 14
AAC ACOUSTIC TECHNOLOGIES (SHENZHEN) CO., LTD.—See AAC Technologies Holdings Inc.; *Int'l*, pg. 31
AAREON AG—See Advent International Corporation; *U.S. Private*, pg. 96
AAREON AG—See Centerbridge Partners, L.P.; *U.S. Private*, pg. 812
ABACO MOBILE INC; *U.S. Private*, pg. 33
ABC APPLIANCE INC.; *U.S. Private*, pg. 35
ABT ELECTRONICS, INC.; *U.S. Private*, pg. 45
A&B WIPER SUPPLY INC.; *U.S. Private*, pg. 19
ACMA COMPUTERS INC.; *U.S. Private*, pg. 60
ACTIVATE INC.; *U.S. Private*, pg. 68

ACUANT, INC.—See GB Group plc; *Int'l*, pg. 2892
ADAFRUIT INDUSTRIES, LLC; *U.S. Private*, pg. 72
ADAMATION—See Superior Equipment Solutions; *U.S. Private*, pg. 3878
ADOBE SYSTEMS BENELUX BV—See Adobe Inc.; *U.S. Public*, pg. 42
ADOBE SYSTEMS CO., LTD.—See Adobe Inc.; *U.S. Public*, pg. 42
ADOBE SYSTEMS FRANCE—See Adobe Inc.; *U.S. Public*, pg. 42
ADOBE SYSTEMS GMBH—See Adobe Inc.; *U.S. Public*, pg. 42
ADOBE SYSTEMS NORDIC AB—See Adobe Inc.; *U.S. Public*, pg. 42
ADOBE SYSTEMS UK—See Adobe Inc.; *U.S. Public*, pg. 42
ADORAMA CAMERA INC.; *U.S. Private*, pg. 82
ADVANCED BUSINESS SOLUTIONS—See Vista Equity Partners, LLC; *U.S. Private*, pg. 4394
ADVANCED COMMUNICATIONS SERVICE INC.; *U.S. Private*, pg. 88
ADVANCED DIGITAL SOLUTIONS INTERNATIONAL, INC.; *U.S. Private*, pg. 89
ADVANCED MICRO DEVICES GMBH—See Advanced Micro Devices, Inc.; *U.S. Public*, pg. 48
ADVANCED MICRO DEVICES, INC.—See Advanced Micro Devices, Inc.; *U.S. Public*, pg. 48
ADVANCED OFFICE SYSTEMS INC.; *U.S. Private*, pg. 91
ADVANCED WIRELESS COMMUNICATIONS; *U.S. Private*, pg. 93
THE ADVANTAGE COMPANY; *U.S. Private*, pg. 3982
ADVISORYWORLD—See LPL Financial Holdings Inc.; *U.S. Public*, pg. 1343
AEON CO., (M) BHD.—See AEON Co., Ltd.; *Int'l*, pg. 176
AF SERVICES, LLC—See Insight Enterprises, Inc.; *U.S. Public*, pg. 1130
AGA RAYBURN LTD—See The Middleby Corporation; *U.S. Public*, pg. 2113
AGFA-GEVAERT JAPAN, LTD.—See Agfa-Gevaert N.V.; *Int'l*, pg. 208
AICHI KOREA CORPORATION—See Aichi Steel Corporation; *Int'l*, pg. 230
AIR & WATER, INC.; *U.S. Private*, pg. 138
ALGORITHMIC IMPLEMENTATIONS, INC.—See Freedom Scientific Inc.; *U.S. Private*, pg. 1604
ALIVE COR INC.; *U.S. Private*, pg. 169
ALKAR-RAPIDPAK, INC.—See The Middleby Corporation; *U.S. Public*, pg. 2113
ALKIT PRO-CAMERA INC.; *U.S. Private*, pg. 169
ALPINE MANUFACTURING, INC.—See Alps Alpine Co., Ltd.; *Int'l*, pg. 375
ALTEK ELECTRONICS INC.—See Cyient Limited; *Int'l*, pg. 1896
AMANO SOFTWARE ENGINEERING (SHANGHAI) CO., LTD.—See Amano Corporation; *Int'l*, pg. 411
AMATEUR ELECTRONIC SUPPLY LLC; *U.S. Private*, pg. 216
AMAZON.COM, INC.; *U.S. Public*, pg. 90
AMERICAN TV & APPLIANCE OF MADISON, INC.; *U.S. Private*, pg. 257
AMERICAN WORDATA, INC.; *U.S. Private*, pg. 258
AMNET DATA SOLUTIONS INC.; *U.S. Private*, pg. 264
ANACOMP (NEDERLAND) B.V.—See Anacomp, Inc.; *U.S. Public*, pg. 134
ANALOG DEVICES AB—See Analog Devices, Inc.; *U.S. Public*, pg. 134
ANALOG DEVICES GMBH—See Analog Devices, Inc.; *U.S. Public*, pg. 134
ANALOG DEVICES GMBH—See Analog Devices, Inc.; *U.S. Public*, pg. 134
ANALOG DEVICES GMBH-TECHNISCHES BURO WEST—See Analog Devices, Inc.; *U.S. Public*, pg. 134
ANALOG DEVICES, (ISRAEL) LTD.—See Analog Devices, Inc.; *U.S. Public*, pg. 135
ANALOG DEVICES KOREA, LTD.—See Analog Devices, Inc.; *U.S. Public*, pg. 135
ANALOG DEVICES SRL—See Analog Devices, Inc.; *U.S. Public*, pg. 135
ANDERSON ELECTRICAL PRODUCTS—See Hubbell Incorporated; *U.S. Public*, pg. 1066
ANRITSU GMBH—See Anritsu Corporation; *Int'l*, pg. 475
ANTENNAS DIRECT; *U.S. Private*, pg. 287
AO DEUTSCHLAND LIMITED—See AO World PLC; *Int'l*, pg. 487
AO RECYCLING LIMITED—See AO World PLC; *Int'l*, pg. 487
APPLETON ELECTRIC, S.A. DE C.V.—See Emerson Electric Co.; *U.S. Public*, pg. 740
APPLIANCE FACTORY OUTLET & MATTRESSES, INC.; *U.S. Private*, pg. 297
APPLIANCESMART, INC.—See Live Ventures Incorporated; *U.S. Public*, pg. 1332
APPLIANCESMART—See Live Ventures Incorporated; *U.S. Public*, pg. 1332
APPLIANCESMART—See Live Ventures Incorporated; *U.S. Public*, pg. 1332
APPLIANCE WAREHOUSE OF EXETER; *U.S. Private*, pg. 298

N.A.I.C.S. INDEX

449210 — ELECTRONICS AND APP...

APSCO APPLIANCE & TV CENTERS, INC.; *U.S. Private*, pg. 302
ARCHIPELAGO LEARNING, INC.—See The Vistria Group, LP; *U.S. Private*, pg. 4131
ARISIT PTY LIMITED—See Harvey Norman Holdings Ltd; *Int'l*, pg. 3281
ARRIS GROUP B.V.—See CommScope Holding Company, Inc.; *U.S. Public*, pg. 548
ARROW ELECTRONICS COMPONENTS—See Arrow Electronics, Inc.; *U.S. Public*, pg. 197
ARROW ELECTRONICS HOLDINGS PTY LTD.—See Arrow Electronics, Inc.; *U.S. Public*, pg. 197
ARTIFEX SOFTWARE INC.—See Epapyrus, Inc.; *Int'l*, pg. 2458
ASAP SOLUTIONS GROUP, LLC; *U.S. Private*, pg. 345
ASIENS APPLIANCE, INC.—See 1847 Holdings LLC; *U.S. Public*, pg. 2
ASI SYSTEM INTEGRATION, INC.; *U.S. Private*, pg. 350
ASPEN ELECTRONICS LIMITED—See APC Technology Group plc; *Int'l*, pg. 508
ASSOCIATED SUPPLY COMPANY INC; *U.S. Private*, pg. 357
ATAI FUJI ELECTRIC CO., LTD.—See Fuji Electric Co., Ltd.; *Int'l*, pg. 2810
ATLANTIC RECORDS GROUP—See Access Industries, Inc.; *U.S. Private*, pg. 52
ATOM ENTERTAINMENT INC.—See National Amusements, Inc.; *U.S. Private*, pg. 2841
AUDIMATION SERVICES, INC.—See CaseWare International, Inc.; *Int'l*, pg. 1352
AUSTRIAMICROSYSTEMS JAPAN CO. LTD—See ams AG; *Int'l*, pg. 440
AVATECH OF FLORIDA INC.—See Rand Worldwide, Inc.; *U.S. Private*, pg. 1762
AVNET ELECTRONICS MARKETING—See Avnet, Inc.; *U.S. Public*, pg. 250
AVNET ELECTRONICS MARKETING—See Avnet, Inc.; *U.S. Public*, pg. 250
AVNET NORTEC AB—See Avnet, Inc.; *U.S. Public*, pg. 252
AVNET SILICA—See Avnet, Inc.; *U.S. Public*, pg. 251
AVNET TECHNOLOGY SOLUTIONS—See TD Synnex Corp; *U.S. Public*, pg. 1985
AVX DESIGN & INTEGRATION, INC.—See Focus Universal Inc.; *U.S. Public*, pg. 862
AVY PRECISION TECHNOLOGY, INC.; *Int'l*, pg. 751
AZARA HEALTHCARE LLC; *U.S. Private*, pg. 415
BAILLIO'S INC.; *U.S. Private*, pg. 426
BAND PRO FILM & DIGITAL INC.; *U.S. Private*, pg. 464
BANG & OLUFSEN FINANCE A/S—See Bang & Olufsen a/s; *Int'l*, pg. 831
BANG & OLUFSEN ITALIA S.P.A.—See Bang & Olufsen a/s; *Int'l*, pg. 831
BAY CITIES APPLIANCE INC.; *U.S. Private*, pg. 492
B&B APPLIANCE COMPANY INC.; *U.S. Private*, pg. 417
BCS PROSOFT; *U.S. Private*, pg. 500
BEC STUDIO CO., LTD.—See BEC World Public Company Limited; *Int'l*, pg. 936
BELDEN & HIRSCHMANN - FRANCE—See Belden, Inc.; *U.S. Public*, pg. 293
BEST BUY CO., INC.; *U.S. Public*, pg. 326
BEST BUY ENTERPRISES, S. DE R.L. DE C.V.—See Best Buy Co., Inc.; *U.S. Public*, pg. 326
BEST BUY STORES L.P.—See Best Buy Co., Inc.; *U.S. Public*, pg. 326
BEST BUY STORES, S. DE R.L. DE C.V.—See Best Buy Co., Inc.; *U.S. Public*, pg. 326
BEXEL CORPORATION—See The Carlyle Group Inc.; *U.S. Public*, pg. 2049
B&H FOTO & ELECTRONIC CORP.; *U.S. Private*, pg. 418
BIC CAMERA INC.; *Int'l*, pg. 1018
BILL SMITH INCORPORATED; *U.S. Private*, pg. 558
BIRNS TELECOMMUNICATIONS INC.; *U.S. Private*, pg. 565
BISSELL CANADA CORP.—See Bissell Homecare, Inc.; *U.S. Private*, pg. 566
B J S, INC.—See Pettus Office Products, Inc.; *U.S. Private*, pg. 3163
BONIAL SAS—See Axel Springer SE; *Int'l*, pg. 766
BOOKOFF WITH CO., LTD.—See Bookoff Group Holdings Ltd.; *Int'l*, pg. 1110
BOSE AG—See Bose Corporation; *U.S. Private*, pg. 619
BOSE A/S - SWEDEN REPRESENTATIVE OFFICE—See Bose Corporation; *U.S. Private*, pg. 619
BOSE GES.M.B.H.—See Bose Corporation; *U.S. Private*, pg. 620
BOSE SP. Z O.O.—See Bose Corporation; *U.S. Private*, pg. 620
BOSE UAE TRADING LLC—See Bose Corporation; *U.S. Private*, pg. 620
BOSE U.K., LTD.—See Bose Corporation; *U.S. Private*, pg. 620
BOURNS AG—See Bourns, Inc.; *U.S. Private*, pg. 624
BRAINSTORM CORPORATION; *U.S. Private*, pg. 634
BRANDSMART USA; *U.S. Private*, pg. 638
BRAY & SCARFF INC.; *U.S. Private*, pg. 641
BRENTHAVEN; *U.S. Private*, pg. 645
BREVILLE NEW ZEALAND LIMITED—See Breville Group Limited; *Int'l*, pg. 1150
BREVILLE PTY LIMITED—See Breville Group Limited; *Int'l*, pg. 1150
BREVILLE USA, INC.—See Breville Group Limited; *Int'l*, pg. 1150
BRG APPLIANCES LIMITED—See Breville Group Limited; *Int'l*, pg. 1150
BRISCOES (NEW ZEALAND) LIMITED—See Briscoe Group Limited; *Int'l*, pg. 1164
BROADLINE COMPONENTS, LLC; *U.S. Private*, pg. 659
BROADVISION FRANCE, S.A.—See ESW Capital, LLC; *U.S. Private*, pg. 1430
BROADVISION JAPAN K.K.—See ESW Capital, LLC; *U.S. Private*, pg. 1430
BUT SAS—See Clayton, Dubilier & Rice, LLC; *U.S. Private*, pg. 920
BUYITDIRECT.COM N.V.—See Bechtle AG; *Int'l*, pg. 937
BYGGHEMMA BUTIK I STHLM AB—See BHG Group AB; *Int'l*, pg. 1014
BYGGHEMMA SVERIGE AB—See BHG Group AB; *Int'l*, pg. 1014
BYGGHJEMMET NORGE AS—See BHG Group AB; *Int'l*, pg. 1014
CALUMET PHOTOGRAPHIC LTD.—See Aurelius Equity Opportunities SE & Co. KGaA; *Int'l*, pg. 708
C&A MARKETING, INC. - RITZ CAMERA & IMAGE DIVISION—See C&A Marketing, Inc.; *U.S. Private*, pg. 702
C&A MARKETING, INC.; *U.S. Private*, pg. 702
CAMBRIDGE SOUNDWORKS, INC.—See Creative Technology Ltd.; *Int'l*, pg. 1833
THE CAMERA COMPANY; *U.S. Private*, pg. 4003
CAMERA CORNER INC.; *U.S. Private*, pg. 728
CAMERA REPAIR INSTRUMENT SERVICE; *U.S. Private*, pg. 728
CAMETA CAMERA; *U.S. Private*, pg. 729
CANON AUSTRIA GMBH—See Canon Inc.; *Int'l*, pg. 1294
CANON ESPANA, S.A.—See Canon Inc.; *Int'l*, pg. 1294
CANON EUROPE LTD.—See Canon Inc.; *Int'l*, pg. 1294
CANON HONGKONG CO., LTD.—See Canon Inc.; *Int'l*, pg. 1295
CANON ITALIA S.P.A.—See Canon Inc.; *Int'l*, pg. 1294
CANON MARKETING (MALAYSIA) SDN. BHD.—See Canon Inc.; *Int'l*, pg. 1295
CANON MARKETING (THAILAND) CO., LTD.—See Canon Inc.; *Int'l*, pg. 1295
CANON MEXICANA, S. DE R.L. DE C.V.—See Canon Inc.; *Int'l*, pg. 1297
CANON NEW ZEALAND LTD.—See Canon Inc.; *Int'l*, pg. 1293
CANON NORGE A.S.—See Canon Inc.; *Int'l*, pg. 1294
CANON OY—See Canon Inc.; *Int'l*, pg. 1294
CANON PANAMA, S.A.—See Canon Inc.; *Int'l*, pg. 1297
CANON (SCHWEIZ) AG—See Canon Inc.; *Int'l*, pg. 1293
CANON SVENSKA AB—See Canon Inc.; *Int'l*, pg. 1295
CANON USA, INC.—See Canon Inc.; *Int'l*, pg. 1297
CAPTURE 3D, INC.—See Carl-Zeiss-Stiftung; *Int'l*, pg. 1334
CARRILLO BUSINESS TECHNOLOGIES; *U.S. Private*, pg. 772
CA SALES (THAILAND) CO., LTD—See Broadcom Inc.; *U.S. Public*, pg. 389
CASENET, LLC—See Zyter, Inc.; *U.S. Private*, pg. 4611
CASIO ELECTRONICS CO., LTD.—See Casio Computer Co., Ltd.; *Int'l*, pg. 1353
CCS ELECTRONICS (UK) LTD.—See Avnet, Inc.; *U.S. Public*, pg. 250
CCV ENGINEERING & MFG., INC.—See Aries Industries Inc.; *U.S. Private*, pg. 322
CD WAREHOUSE, INC.—See Magnolia Entertainment LLC; *U.S. Private*, pg. 2548
CDW CORPORATION; *U.S. Public*, pg. 462
CELL TRADE NY INC.; *U.S. Private*, pg. 807
THE CELLULAR CONNECTION, LLC—See Round Room LLC; *U.S. Private*, pg. 3488
CENTRAL COMPUTER SYSTEMS INC.; *U.S. Private*, pg. 819
CENTRAL HOSPITALITY CO., LTD.—See Home Pottery Public Company Limited; *Int'l*, pg. 3455
C-E (SINGAPORE) PTE. LTD.—See Citizen Watch Co., Ltd.; *Int'l*, pg. 1623
CHALLENGER TECHNOLOGIES LTD.; *Int'l*, pg. 1438
CHAMPION COMPUTER PRODUCTS INC.; *U.S. Private*, pg. 846
CHAMPION SOLUTIONS GROUP INC.—See CDW Corporation; *U.S. Public*, pg. 462
CHARLOTTE APPLIANCES INC.; *U.S. Private*, pg. 857
CHECK POINT SOFTWARE TECHNOLOGIES AUSTRALIA PTY LTD—See Check Point Software Technologies Ltd.; *Int'l*, pg. 1458
CHECK POINT SOFTWARE TECHNOLOGIES GMBH—See Check Point Software Technologies Ltd.; *Int'l*, pg. 1458
CHECK POINT SOFTWARE TECHNOLOGIES (JAPAN) LTD.—See Check Point Software Technologies Ltd.; *Int'l*, pg. 1458
CHECK POINT SOFTWARE TECHNOLOGIES LTD.—See Check Point Software Technologies Ltd.; *Int'l*, pg. 1458
CHECK POINT SOFTWARE TECHNOLOGIES (SINGAPORE) LTD.—See Check Point Software Technologies Ltd.; *Int'l*, pg. 1458
CHINA ELECTRONICS HOLDINGS, INC.; *Int'l*, pg. 1499
CHLORIDE KOEXA S.A.—See Emerson Electric Co.; *U.S. Public*, pg. 742
CHL S.P.A.; *Int'l*, pg. 1576
CIMPLEBOX INC.—See NCR Voyix Corporation.; *U.S. Public*, pg. 1502
CIRCLE MOBILE COMMUNICATIONS LIMITED—See HKC International Holdings Limited; *Int'l*, pg. 3428
C & K SYSTEMS, INC.; *U.S. Private*, pg. 701
CLARI, INC.; *U.S. Private*, pg. 911
CLBL, INC.; *U.S. Private*, pg. 930
CLEAR CHOICE TELEPHONES INC—See Medicus Solutions, LLC; *U.S. Private*, pg. 2656
CLEAR TECHNOLOGIES, INC.; *U.S. Private*, pg. 932
CLEARWATER SYSTEMS INC.; *U.S. Private*, pg. 939
CLICK CAMERA SHOP INCORPORATED; *U.S. Private*, pg. 942
COBRA ELECTRONICS (HK) LIMITED—See Monomoy Capital Partners LLC; *U.S. Private*, pg. 2772
CODIREP SNC—See Groupe Fnac S.A.; *Int'l*, pg. 3103
COM7 PUBLIC COMPANY LIMITED; *Int'l*, pg. 1706
COMMERCIAL DATA SYSTEMS INC.; *U.S. Private*, pg. 983
COMMLINK SYSTEMS—See Innovative, Inc.; *U.S. Private*, pg. 2083
COMPANY FINANCIERE DE CHAUSEY, S.A.—See Emerson Electric Co.; *U.S. Public*, pg. 742
COMPSOURCE, INC.; *U.S. Private*, pg. 1003
COMPUFIT, INC.—See Anatomy IT, LLC; *U.S. Private*, pg. 272
COMPUSA INC.—See Insight Enterprises, Inc.; *U.S. Public*, pg. 1130
COMPUTER ADVANTAGE INC.; *U.S. Private*, pg. 1004
COMPUTER BOULEVARD INC.; *Int'l*, pg. 1759
COMPUTER CONCEPTS INC.; *U.S. Private*, pg. 1004
COMPUTER DEDUCTIONS, INC.—See Futuris Company; *U.S. Public*, pg. 893
COMPUTEREASE SOFTWARE INC.—See Roper Technologies, Inc.; *U.S. Public*, pg. 1811
COMPUTER PARADISE INC.; *U.S. Private*, pg. 1005
COMPUTER PARTS INTERNATIONAL LTD.—See discoverIE Group plc; *Int'l*, pg. 2133
THE COMPUTER PLACE, INC.; *U.S. Private*, pg. 4013
COMPUTERS4SURE.COM, INC.—See The ODP Corporation; *U.S. Public*, pg. 2117
COMPUTER STORES NORTHWEST INC.; *U.S. Private*, pg. 1005
COMPUTERS UNLIMITED; *U.S. Private*, pg. 1005
COMPUTER SYSTEMS PLUS INC.—See Robert J. Young Company, LLC; *U.S. Private*, pg. 3458
COMPUTERUNIVERSE GMBH—See Hubert Burda Media Holding Kommanditgesellschaft; *Int'l*, pg. 3520
COMWORX INC.—See Advanced Imaging Solutions, Inc.; *U.S. Public*, pg. 90
CONFIGURE ONE EUROPE LIMITED—See Autodesk, Inc.; *U.S. Public*, pg. 229
CONFIGURE ONE, INC.—See Autodesk, Inc.; *U.S. Public*, pg. 229
CONSISTENT COMPUTER BARGAINS, INC.; *U.S. Private*, pg. 1020
CONSUMERS KITCHENS & BATHS; *U.S. Private*, pg. 1026
CO-OPERATIVES E-STORE LIMITED—See Co-operative Group Limited; *Int'l*, pg. 1679
COPPERWIRED PUBLIC COMPANY LIMITED; *Int'l*, pg. 1794
CORD CAMERA CENTERS INC.; *U.S. Private*, pg. 1047
COWBOY MALONEY APPLIANCE, AUDIO, VIDEO CENTERS, INC.; *U.S. Private*, pg. 1073
CPG INTERNATIONAL S.A.—See CPG International S.p.A.; *Int'l*, pg. 1824
CPS TECHNOLOGY SOLUTIONS INC.; *U.S. Private*, pg. 1081
CRAY CANADA ULC—See Hewlett Packard Enterprise Company; *U.S. Public*, pg. 1030
CREATIVE LABS (HK) LIMITED—See Creative Technology Ltd.; *Int'l*, pg. 1833
CREATIVE LABS IRELAND LTD.—See Creative Technology Ltd.; *Int'l*, pg. 1833
CREATIVE LABS N.V.—See Creative Technology Ltd.; *Int'l*, pg. 1833
CREATIVE LABS—See Creative Technology Ltd.; *Int'l*, pg. 1833
CREATIVE LABS—See Creative Technology Ltd.; *Int'l*, pg. 1833
CREATIVE LABS (SWEDEN)—See Creative Technology Ltd.; *Int'l*, pg. 1833
CREATIVE MEDIA K.K.—See Creative Technology Ltd.; *Int'l*, pg. 1833
CRESCENT MARKETING, INC.; *U.S. Private*, pg. 1094
CREVE COEUR CAMERA INC.; *U.S. Private*, pg. 1000
CRISS ENTERPRISES, INC.—See Leonard Green & Partners, L.P.; *U.S. Private*, pg. 2430
CROPS CORPORATION; *Int'l*, pg. 1855
CRUTCHFIELD CORPORATION; *U.S. Private*, pg. 1114
CTM SOFTWARE CORP.—See GI Manager L.P.; *U.S. Private*, pg. 1693

449210 — ELECTRONICS AND APP...

CTM SOFTWARE CORP.—See TA Associates, Inc.; *U.S. Private*, pg. 3914
CYBERADVISORS, INC.; *U.S. Private*, pg. 1133
CYBERIAN OUTPOST, INC.—See Fry's Electronics, Inc.; *U.S. Private*, pg. 1618
CYBERMAK INFORMATION SYSTEMS W.L.L.—See Hexagon AB; *Int'l*, pg. 3368
CYBERPORT SOLUTIONS GMBH—See Hubert Burda Media Holding Kommanditgesellschaft; *Int'l*, pg. 3520
CYCLING 74—See Ableton AG; *Int'l*, pg. 63
CYSTECH ELECTRONICS CORP.; *Int'l*, pg. 1897
DALIAN FUJI ELECTRIC MOTOR CO., LTD.—See Fuji Electric Co., Ltd.; *Int'l*, pg. 2810
DALTIX UNIPESSOAL LDA.—See Colruyt Group N.V.; *Int'l*, pg. 1705
DAN'S FAN CITY INC.; *U.S. Private*, pg. 1152
DATAVISION TECHNOLOGIES INC.—See myDigitalOffice Holdings Inc.; *U.S. Private*, pg. 2824
DATEL SYSTEMS INCORPORATED; *U.S. Private*, pg. 1167
DECKERWRIGHT CORPORATION—See Beringer Associates, Inc.; *U.S. Private*, pg. 532
DEERFIELD COMMUNICATIONS INC.; *U.S. Private*, pg. 1190
DELAWARE INTERACTIVE, LLC—See Tyler Technologies, Inc.; *U.S. Public*, pg. 2208
DELTA BUSINESS SYSTEMS, INC.—See LKCM Headwater Investments; *U.S. Private*, pg. 2475
DENMAR ASSOCIATES LLC; *U.S. Private*, pg. 1205
DESIGNER APPLIANCES; *U.S. Private*, pg. 1214
DEXXON GROUPE SA; *Int'l*, pg. 2093
DIAMOND WIRELESS LLC—See BCE Inc.; *Int'l*, pg. 927
DICK VANDYKE INCORPORATED; *U.S. Private*, pg. 1226
THE DIEBOLD COMPANY OF CANADA LIMITED—See Diebold Nixdorf, Inc.; *U.S. Public*, pg. 661
DIEBOLD NIXDORF GMBH—See Diebold Nixdorf, Inc.; *U.S. Public*, pg. 660
DIGITAL ENERGY WORLD; *U.S. Private*, pg. 1230
DIGITAL GATEWAY INC.; *U.S. Private*, pg. 1230
DIGITAL INSTINCT LLC—See Hellman & Friedman LLC; *U.S. Private*, pg. 1910
DIRECT SOURCE SPECIAL PRODUCTS, INC.; *Int'l*, pg. 2130
DISCOUNT ELECTRONICS; *U.S. Private*, pg. 1237
DISCOVERIE GROUP PLC; *Int'l*, pg. 2132
DISCOVERY COMPUTERS & WIRELESS INC.; *Int'l*, pg. 2134
DIT CORPORATION; *U.S. Private*, pg. 1240
DIXONS CARPHONE COE S.R.O.—See Currys plc; *Int'l*, pg. 1879
DK KOREA CO., LTD.—See DAIICHIKOUSHQ CO., LTD.; *Int'l*, pg. 1930
DNA INVESTMENT JOINT STOCK CORPORATION; *Int'l*, pg. 2147
DONPON; *Int'l*, pg. 2172
DON'S PHOTO SHOP LTD.; *Int'l*, pg. 2162
DRIESSEN WATER I INC.; *U.S. Private*, pg. 1277
DSG RETAIL LIMITED—See Currys plc; *Int'l*, pg. 1879
DTM SYSTEMS INC.; *Int'l*, pg. 2217
DUSTIN AB—See Altor Equity Partners AB; *Int'l*, pg. 394
DYKNOW; *U.S. Private*, pg. 1296
DYNABOOK - UK—See Hon Hai Precision Industry Co., Ltd.; *Int'l*, pg. 3457
EAGLE BUSINESS SOLUTIONS INC.; *U.S. Private*, pg. 1308
ECONOCOM TELECOM BV—See Econocom Group SA; *Int'l*, pg. 2298
ECOVACS ROBOTICS CO., LTD.; *Int'l*, pg. 2300
EDION CORPORATION; *Int'l*, pg. 2310
ED KELLUM & SON APPLIANCE CO.; *U.S. Private*, pg. 1331
EDUPOINT EDUCATIONAL SYSTEMS, LLC; *U.S. Private*, pg. 1340
EGS COMERCIALIZADORA MEXICO, S. DE R.L. DE C.V.—See Emerson Electric Co.; *U.S. Public*, pg. 740
ELECTRICAL APPLIANCE OUTLET LIMITED—See AO World PLC; *Int'l*, pg. 487
ELECTROLUX (HANGZHOU) DOMESTIC APPLIANCES CO. LTD—See AB Electrolux; *Int'l*, pg. 39
ELECTRONIC EVOLUTIONS, INC.—See Ultimate Technologies Group, Inc.; *U.S. Private*, pg. 4277
THE ELECTRONIC EXPRESS INC.; *U.S. Private*, pg. 4025
ELECTRONICPARTNER AUSTRIA GMBH—See ElectronicPartner Handel SE; *Int'l*, pg. 2354
ELECTRONICPARTNER BELGIE N.V.—See ElectronicPartner Handel SE; *Int'l*, pg. 2354
ELECTRONICPARTNER HANDEL SE; *Int'l*, pg. 2354
ELECTRONICPARTNER NEDERLAND B.V.—See ElectronicPartner Handel SE; *Int'l*, pg. 2354
ELECTRONICPARTNER SCHWEIZ AG—See ElectronicPartner Handel SE; *Int'l*, pg. 2354
ELECTRON MEC S.A.R.L; *Int'l*, pg. 2353
ELECTRON MEC S.A.R.L; *Int'l*, pg. 2354
ELEKDIRECT LIMITED—See AO World PLC; *Int'l*, pg. 487
ELEVAIR S.A.—See Emerson Electric Co.; *U.S. Public*, pg. 743
ELGIGANTEN AKTIEBOLAG—See Currys plc; *Int'l*, pg. 1879
ELGOOD OY—See Addtech AB; *Int'l*, pg. 133
ELKJOP NORDIC AS—See Currys plc; *Int'l*, pg. 1879
EL-O-MATIC LIMITED—See Emerson Electric Co.; *U.S. Public*, pg. 743
EL-O-MATIC VALVE ACTUATORS (F.E.) PTE. LTD.—See Emerson Electric Co.; *U.S. Public*, pg. 743
ELUMEO SE; *Int'l*, pg. 2371
EMC BRASIL SERVICOS DE TI LTDA—See Dell Technologies Inc.; *U.S. Public*, pg. 650
EMC CHILE S.A.—See Dell Technologies Inc.; *U.S. Public*, pg. 650
EMC COMPUTER SYSTEMS (BENELUX) B.V.—See Dell Technologies Inc.; *U.S. Public*, pg. 650
EMC CORPORATION OF CANADA—See Dell Technologies Inc.; *U.S. Public*, pg. 651
EMERSON CLIMATE TECHNOLOGIES (SHENYANG) REFRIGERATION CO., LTD.—See Emerson Electric Co.; *U.S. Public*, pg. 743
EMERSON CLIMATE TECHNOLOGIES - TRANSPORTATION SOLUTIONS APS—See Emerson Electric Co.; *U.S. Public*, pg. 743
EMERSON ERESOURCE (XI'AN) CO., LTD.—See Emerson Electric Co.; *U.S. Public*, pg. 749
EMERSON JUNKANG ENTERPRISE (SHANGHAI) CO., LTD.—See Emerson Electric Co.; *U.S. Public*, pg. 745
EMERSON NETWORK POWER (PHILIPPINES), INC.—See Emerson Electric Co.; *U.S. Public*, pg. 745
EMERSON NETWORK POWER SP. Z.O.O.—See Emerson Electric Co.; *U.S. Public*, pg. 745
EMERSON NETWORK POWER (VIETNAM) CO., LTD.—See Emerson Electric Co.; *U.S. Public*, pg. 745
EMERSON ORADEA S.R.L.—See Emerson Electric Co.; *U.S. Public*, pg. 745
EMERSON PROCESS MANAGEMENT MOROCCO SARL—See Emerson Electric Co.; *U.S. Public*, pg. 744
EMERSON PROCESS MANAGEMENT QATAR S.S.C.—See Emerson Electric Co.; *U.S. Public*, pg. 748
EMERSON PROCESS MANAGEMENT ROSEMOUNT & MICRO MOTION DIVISION—See Emerson Electric Co.; *U.S. Public*, pg. 747
EMERSON PROCESS MANAGEMENT SP. Z.O.O.—See Emerson Electric Co.; *U.S. Public*, pg. 747
EMERSON PROCESS MANAGEMENT TICARET LIMITED SIRKETI—See Emerson Electric Co.; *U.S. Public*, pg. 747
EMERSON PROCESS MANAGEMENT UAB—See Emerson Electric Co.; *U.S. Public*, pg. 747
EMERSON (THAILAND) LIMITED—See Emerson Electric Co.; *U.S. Public*, pg. 743
EMICO ASIA SDN. BHD.—See Emico Holdings Berhad; *Int'l*, pg. 2380
EMMY TECHNOLOGY DEVELOPMENT LIMITED—See China-Hong Kong Photo Products Holdings Limited; *Int'l*, pg. 1568
EMOTIVA PROFESSIONAL, LLC—See Jade Design, Inc.; *U.S. Private*, pg. 2181
E-NET JAPAN CORP.; *Int'l*, pg. 2249
ENSAMBLADORES ELECTRONICOS DE MEXICO, S. DE R.L. DE C.V.—See RTX Corporation; *U.S. Public*, pg. 1822
ENSEMBLE SYSTEMS INC.; *Int'l*, pg. 2446
ENTRE COMPUTER SERVICES INC.; *U.S. Private*, pg. 1406
EPHESOFT INC.—See Clearlake Capital Group, L.P.; *U.S. Private*, pg. 936
EPHESOFT INC.—See TA Associates, Inc.; *U.S. Private*, pg. 3916
EPICENTRE HOLDINGS LIMITED; *Int'l*, pg. 2460
E REVOLUTION VENTURES, INC.; *U.S. Private*, pg. 1301
ESO OUEST SARL—See Emerson Electric Co.; *U.S. Public*, pg. 743
ESO SUD OUEST—See Emerson Electric Co.; *U.S. Public*, pg. 743
ETRONICS, INC.—See Foto Electric Supply Co., Inc.; *U.S. Private*, pg. 1579
EURL GAMES WORKSHOP—See Games Workshop Group PLC; *Int'l*, pg. 2877
EURONICS AB—See EURONICS International BV; *Int'l*, pg. 2555
EURONICS AUSTRIA REG. GENOSSENSCHAFT M.B.H.—See EURONICS International BV; *Int'l*, pg. 2555
EURONICS BALTIC OU—See EURONICS International BV; *Int'l*, pg. 2555
EURONICS BELGIUM CVBA—See EURONICS International BV; *Int'l*, pg. 2555
EURONICS CR A.S.—See EURONICS International BV; *Int'l*, pg. 2555
EURONICS DEUTSCHLAND EG—See EURONICS International BV; *Int'l*, pg. 2555
EURONICS ESPANA—See EURONICS International BV; *Int'l*, pg. 2555
EURONICS FRANCE—See EURONICS International BV; *Int'l*, pg. 2555
EURONICS INTERNATIONAL BV; *Int'l*, pg. 2554
EURONICS IRELAND—See EURONICS International BV; *Int'l*, pg. 2555
EURONICS ITALIA S.P.A.—See EURONICS International BV; *Int'l*, pg. 2555
EURONICS KFT.—See EURONICS International BV; *Int'l*, pg. 2555
EURONICS LATVIA SIA—See EURONICS International BV; *Int'l*, pg. 2555
EURONICS NORGE AS—See EURONICS International BV; *Int'l*, pg. 2555
EURONICS PORTUGAL—See EURONICS International BV; *Int'l*, pg. 2555
EURONICS SCHWEIZ AG—See EURONICS International BV; *Int'l*, pg. 2555
EURONICS SK A.S.—See EURONICS International BV; *Int'l*, pg. 2555
EVANS & SUTHERLAND COMPUTER CORPORATION—See Elevate Entertainment, Inc.; *U.S. Private*, pg. 1358
EVERLIGHT ELECTRONICS (EUROPE) GMBH—See Everlight Electronics Co., Ltd.; *Int'l*, pg. 2567
EVERLIGHT OPTOELECTRONICS (M) SDN BHD—See Everlight Electronics Co., Ltd.; *Int'l*, pg. 2567
FACETS MULTI-MEDIA, INC.; *U.S. Private*, pg. 1459
FAMOUS TATE ELECTRIC CO., INC.; *U.S. Private*, pg. 1472
FEATURE FILMS FOR FAMILIES INC.; *U.S. Private*, pg. 1486
FILCO, INC.; *U.S. Private*, pg. 1505
FIRST SERVICE CAROLINA, INC.—See Pineland Telephone Cooperative, Inc.; *U.S. Private*, pg. 3183
FISCALSOFT CORP.—See Black Mountain Software, LLC; *U.S. Private*, pg. 572
FISHER & PAYKEL APPLIANCES LIMITED—See Haier Smart Home Co., Ltd.; *Int'l*, pg. 3210
FISHER & PAYKEL MANUFACTURING PTY LIMITED—See Haier Smart Home Co., Ltd.; *Int'l*, pg. 3210
FLANNERS AUDIO & VIDEO INC.; *U.S. Private*, pg. 1540
FNAC BRESIL SARL—See Groupe Fnac S.A.; *Int'l*, pg. 3103
FNAC SA—See Groupe Fnac S.A.; *Int'l*, pg. 3103
FNAC SUISSE SA—See Groupe Fnac S.A.; *Int'l*, pg. 3103
FOCUS HOME INTERACTIVE SAS; *Int'l*, pg. 2719
FOLLETT SOFTWARE COMPANY—See Follett Corporation; *U.S. Private*, pg. 1559
FONTSHOP INTERNATIONAL, INC.—See HGGC, LLC; *U.S. Private*, pg. 1930
FONUM OY—See Elisa Corporation; *Int'l*, pg. 2361
FORCE MOS TECHNOLOGY CO., LTD.; *Int'l*, pg. 2730
FORECAST HORIZON INC.—See Antuit, Inc.; *U.S. Private*, pg. 289
FOREGROUND SECURITY; *U.S. Private*, pg. 1565
FORENSIC LOGIC INC.—See SoundThinking, Inc.; *U.S. Public*, pg. 1910
FORTUNE INFORMATION SYSTEM INTERNATIONAL CO., LTD.—See Fortune Information Systems Corp.; *Int'l*, pg. 2743
FOSTER ELECTRIC (EUROPE) GMBH—See Foster Electric Co., Ltd.; *Int'l*, pg. 2749
FOTOMAX (F.E.) LTD.—See China-Hong Kong Photo Products Holdings Limited; *Int'l*, pg. 1568
FOTO-VIDEO SAUTER GMBH & CO. KG—See Aurelius Equity Opportunities SE & Co. KGaA; *Int'l*, pg. 708
FP1 STRATEGIES LLC—See Omnicom Group Inc.; *U.S. Public*, pg. 1589
FPT DIGITAL RETAIL JOINT STOCK COMPANY—See FPT Corporation; *Int'l*, pg. 2757
FREEDOM STORES INC.; *U.S. Private*, pg. 1604
FRY'S ELECTRONICS, INC.; *U.S. Private*, pg. 1618
FUJI ELECTRIC CO., LTD.; *Int'l*, pg. 2810
FUJI ELECTRIC FRANCE S.A.—See Fuji Electric Co., Ltd.; *Int'l*, pg. 2811
FUJIFILM MEDICAL SYSTEMS (CALIFORNIA), INC.—See FUJIFILM Holdings Corporation; *Int'l*, pg. 2822
FUJIFILM (NZ) LIMITED—See FUJIFILM Holdings Corporation; *Int'l*, pg. 2821
FUJIKURA ASIA LIMITED—See Fujikura Ltd.; *Int'l*, pg. 2827
FUJIKURA ASIA (MALAYSIA) SDN. BHD.—See Fujikura Ltd.; *Int'l*, pg. 2827
FUJIKURA HONG KONG LIMITED—See Fujikura Ltd.; *Int'l*, pg. 2828
FUJITSU AUSTRALIA SOFTWARE TECHNOLOGY PTY., LTD.—See Fujitsu Limited; *Int'l*, pg. 2835
FUJITSU CONSULTING (LUXEMBOURG) S.A.—See Fujitsu Limited; *Int'l*, pg. 2836
FUJITSU DEUTSCHLAND GMBH—See Fujitsu Limited; *Int'l*, pg. 2834
FUJITSU (MALAYSIA) SDN. BHD.—See Fujitsu Limited; *Int'l*, pg. 2835
FUJITSU SERVICES AB—See Fujitsu Limited; *Int'l*, pg. 2835
FUJITSU SERVICES—See Fujitsu Limited; *Int'l*, pg. 2836
FUJITSU TECHNOLOGIES SOLUTION INTERNATIONAL S.P.A.—See Fujitsu Limited; *Int'l*, pg. 2836
FUJITSU TECHNOLOGY SOLUTIONS GMBH—See Fujitsu Limited; *Int'l*, pg. 2836
FUJITSU TECHNOLOGY SOLUTIONS INTERNATIONAL AG—See Fujitsu Limited; *Int'l*, pg. 2837
FUJITSU TECHNOLOGY SOLUTIONS INTERNATIONAL N.V.—See Fujitsu Limited; *Int'l*, pg. 2837
FUJITSU TECHNOLOGY SOLUTIONS INTERNATIONAL SA—See Fujitsu Limited; *Int'l*, pg. 2837
FUTURE ELECTRONICS CORP, AUSTRALIA—See Future Electronics Inc.; *Int'l*, pg. 2854

449210 — ELECTRONICS AND APP...

FUTURE ELECTRONICS CORP., AUSTRALIA—See Future Electronics Inc.; *Int'l*, pg. 2854
FUTURE ELECTRONICS CORP., BELGIUM—See Future Electronics Inc.; *Int'l*, pg. 2854
FUTURE ELECTRONICS CORP., BULGARIA—See Future Electronics Inc.; *Int'l*, pg. 2854
FUTURE ELECTRONICS CORP., DENMARK—See Future Electronics Inc.; *Int'l*, pg. 2854
FUTURE ELECTRONICS CORP., ERFURT—See Future Electronics Inc.; *Int'l*, pg. 2854
FUTURE ELECTRONICS CORP., FINLAND—See Future Electronics Inc.; *Int'l*, pg. 2854
FUTURE ELECTRONICS CORP., FRANCE—See Future Electronics Inc.; *Int'l*, pg. 2855
FUTURE ELECTRONICS CORP., FRANCE—See Future Electronics Inc.; *Int'l*, pg. 2855
FUTURE ELECTRONICS CORP., FRANCE—See Future Electronics Inc.; *Int'l*, pg. 2855
FUTURE ELECTRONICS CORP., GERMANY—See Future Electronics Inc.; *Int'l*, pg. 2855
FUTURE ELECTRONICS CORP., HUNGARY—See Future Electronics Inc.; *Int'l*, pg. 2855
FUTURE ELECTRONICS CORP., IRELAND—See Future Electronics Inc.; *Int'l*, pg. 2855
FUTURE ELECTRONICS CORP., ISRAEL—See Future Electronics Inc.; *Int'l*, pg. 2855
FUTURE ELECTRONICS CORP., ITALY—See Future Electronics Inc.; *Int'l*, pg. 2855
FUTURE ELECTRONICS CORP., JAPAN—See Future Electronics Inc.; *Int'l*, pg. 2855
FUTURE ELECTRONICS CORP., KOREA—See Future Electronics Inc.; *Int'l*, pg. 2855
FUTURE ELECTRONICS CORP., MALAYSIA—See Future Electronics Inc.; *Int'l*, pg. 2855
FUTURE ELECTRONICS CORP., MEXICO—See Future Electronics Inc.; *Int'l*, pg. 2855
FUTURE ELECTRONICS CORP., MEXICO—See Future Electronics Inc.; *Int'l*, pg. 2855
FUTURE ELECTRONICS CORP., NEW ZEALAND—See Future Electronics Inc.; *Int'l*, pg. 2855
FUTURE ELECTRONICS CORP., NORWAY—See Future Electronics Inc.; *Int'l*, pg. 2855
FUTURE ELECTRONICS CORP., NORWAY—See Future Electronics Inc.; *Int'l*, pg. 2855
FUTURE ELECTRONICS CORP., POLAND—See Future Electronics Inc.; *Int'l*, pg. 2855
FUTURE ELECTRONICS CORP., SCOTLAND—See Future Electronics Inc.; *Int'l*, pg. 2855
FUTURE ELECTRONICS CORP., SINGAPORE—See Future Electronics Inc.; *Int'l*, pg. 2855
FUTURE ELECTRONICS CORP.—See Future Electronics Inc.; *Int'l*, pg. 2854
FUTURE ELECTRONICS CORP.—See Future Electronics Inc.; *Int'l*, pg. 2854
FUTURE ELECTRONICS CORP., SPAIN—See Future Electronics Inc.; *Int'l*, pg. 2855
FUTURE ELECTRONICS CORP., SPAIN—See Future Electronics Inc.; *Int'l*, pg. 2855
FUTURE ELECTRONICS CORP., SWEDEN—See Future Electronics Inc.; *Int'l*, pg. 2855
FUTURE ELECTRONICS CORP., SWEDEN—See Future Electronics Inc.; *Int'l*, pg. 2855
FUTURE ELECTRONICS CORP., SWEDEN—See Future Electronics Inc.; *Int'l*, pg. 2855
FUTURE ELECTRONICS CORP., TAIWAN—See Future Electronics Inc.; *Int'l*, pg. 2855
FUTURE ELECTRONICS CORP., TAIWAN—See Future Electronics Inc.; *Int'l*, pg. 2855
FUTURE ELECTRONICS CORP., THAILAND—See Future Electronics Inc.; *Int'l*, pg. 2855
FUTURE ELECTRONICS CORP., THE NETHERLANDS—See Future Electronics Inc.; *Int'l*, pg. 2855
FUTURE ELECTRONICS CORP., TURKEY—See Future Electronics Inc.; *Int'l*, pg. 2855
FUTURE ELECTRONICS DEUTSCHLAND—See Future Electronics Inc.; *Int'l*, pg. 2855
FUTURE ELECTRONICS HONG KONG LIMITED—See Future Electronics Inc.; *Int'l*, pg. 2855
FUTURE ELECTRONICS INC (DISTRIBUTION) PTE LTD.—See Future Electronics Inc.; *Int'l*, pg. 2855
FUTURE ELECTRONICS K.K.—See Future Electronics Inc.; *Int'l*, pg. 2855
FUTURE ELECTRONICS SERVICE MALAYSIA—See Future Electronics Inc.; *Int'l*, pg. 2855
FUTURE ELECTRONICS STUTTGART—See Future Electronics Inc.; *Int'l*, pg. 2856
GAME RETAIL LIMITED; *Int'l*, pg. 2877
GAMESTOP CORP.; *U.S. Public*, pg. 895
GAMESTOP GROUP LIMITED—See GameStop Corp.; *U.S. Public*, pg. 896
GAMESTOP, INC.—See GameStop Corp.; *U.S. Public*, pg. 896
GAMESTOP LTD.—See GameStop Corp.; *U.S. Public*, pg. 896
GAME STORES GROUP SWEDEN AB—See Game Retail Limited; *Int'l*, pg. 2877
GAMES WORKSHOP GOOD HOBBY (SHANGHAI) COMMERCIAL CO., LTD.—See Games Workshop Group PLC; *Int'l*, pg. 2877
GAMES WORKSHOP STOCKHOLM AB—See Games Workshop Group PLC; *Int'l*, pg. 2877
GAS CONNECTION, LLC—See Suburban Propane Partners, L.P.; *U.S. Public*, pg. 1958
GATEWAY EUROPE B.V.—See Acer Incorporated; *Int'l*, pg. 99
GE DRIVES & CONTROLS INC.—See General Electric Company; *U.S. Public*, pg. 919
GENERAL WIRELESS OPERATIONS INC.—See Standard General LP; *U.S. Private*, pg. 3778
THE GENE SCHICK COMPANY—See Viking Range, LLC; *U.S. Private*, pg. 4382
GENISYS GROUP INC.; *U.S. Private*, pg. 1671
GET PRICE PTY. LTD.; *Int'l*, pg. 2946
G-FIVE, INC.—See Xerox Holdings Corporation; *U.S. Public*, pg. 2389
GLASWEGIAN ENTERPRISES LTD; *Int'l*, pg. 2989
GOME RETAIL HOLDINGS LIMITED; *Int'l*, pg. 3037
GRADIANT CORPORATION—See Gradiant Corporation; *Int'l*, pg. 3049
GRAND WIRELESS INC.; *U.S. Private*, pg. 1753
GRAVIS COMPUTERVERTRIEBSGESELLSCHAF MBH—See freenet AG; *Int'l*, pg. 2770
GRAVIS-COMPUTERVERTRIEBSGESELLSCHAFT MBH—See Deutsche Post AG; *Int'l*, pg. 2080
GREAT LAKES COMPUTER CORP.; *U.S. Private*, pg. 1764
GREEN HILLS SOFTWARE AB—See Green Hills Software Inc.; *U.S. Private*, pg. 1773
GREEN HILLS SOFTWARE BV—See Green Hills Software Inc.; *U.S. Private*, pg. 1773
GREEN HILLS SOFTWARE GMBH—See Green Hills Software Inc.; *U.S. Private*, pg. 1773
GREEN HILLS SOFTWARE LTD.—See Green Hills Software Inc.; *U.S. Private*, pg. 1773
GREEN HILLS SOFTWARE, PALM HARBOR—See Green Hills Software Inc.; *U.S. Private*, pg. 1773
GREGG APPLIANCES, INC.—See hhgregg, Inc.; *U.S. Public*, pg. 1034
GRIDS INFORMATION TECHNOLOGIES, INC.—See Arlington Capital Partners LLC; *U.S. Private*, pg. 327
GROVE COLLABORATIVE, INC.—See Grove Collaborative Holdings, Inc.; *U.S. Public*, pg. 972
GST INFORMATION TECHNOLOGY SOLUTIONS; *U.S. Private*, pg. 1801
GUENTHER-VORRUCKEN INC.; *U.S. Private*, pg. 1810
GULF SOUTH TECHNOLOGY SOLUTIONS, LLC.; *U.S. Private*, pg. 1816
HAK ALGAHTANI GROUP OF COMPANIES; *Int'l*, pg. 3219
HARD DRIVES NORTHWEST, INC.; *U.S. Private*, pg. 1862
HART COMMUNICATIONS INC.—See Lintel Inc.; *U.S. Private*, pg. 2463
HARVEY NORMAN CROATIA D.O.O.—See Harvey Norman Holdings Ltd; *Int'l*, pg. 3281
HARVEY NORMAN SINGAPORE PTE. LIMITED—See Harvey Norman Holdings Ltd; *Int'l*, pg. 3281
HARVEY NORMAN TRADING D.O.O.—See Harvey Norman Holdings Ltd; *Int'l*, pg. 3281
HARVEY NORMAN TRADING (IRELAND) LIMITED—See Harvey Norman Holdings Ltd; *Int'l*, pg. 3281
HEWLETT-PACKARD BRASIL LTDA.—See Hewlett Packard Enterprise Company; *U.S. Public*, pg. 1032
HEWLETT-PACKARD ESPANOLA, S.A.—See HP Inc.; *U.S. Public*, pg. 1063
HEWLETT-PACKARD ESPANOLA, S.A.—See HP Inc.; *U.S. Public*, pg. 1063
HEWLETT-PACKARD ESPANOLA, S.A.—See HP Inc.; *U.S. Public*, pg. 1063
HEWLETT-PACKARD IRELAND LTD.—See HP Inc.; *U.S. Public*, pg. 1064
HEWLETT-PACKARD SINGAPORE (PRIVATE) LIMITED—See HP Inc.; *U.S. Public*, pg. 1064
HHG DISTRIBUTING LLC—See hhgregg, Inc.; *U.S. Public*, pg. 1034
HHGREGG, INC.; *U.S. Public*, pg. 1034
HITACHI DATA SYSTEMS INC.—See Hitachi, Ltd.; *Int'l*, pg. 3414
HMV CANADA, INC.—See Hilco Trading, LLC; *U.S. Private*, pg. 1944
HOBART NEDERLAND B.V.—See Illinois Tool Works Inc.; *U.S. Public*, pg. 1104
HOBBY HALL SUOMI OY—See Hansapost OU; *Int'l*, pg. 3259
HOME APPLIANCE MART INC.; *U.S. Private*, pg. 1970
HOUSEMARKET SA—See FOURLIS HOLDINGS S.A.; *Int'l*, pg. 2755
HOWARD'S TV & APPLIANCES, INC.; *U.S. Private*, pg. 1995
HRO INC.; *U.S. Private*, pg. 1998
HRR ENTERPRISES, INC.—See Kane-Miller Corp.; *U.S. Private*, pg. 2260
HT CONCEPTS, INCORPORATED; *U.S. Private*, pg. 1999
HUNGAROTON RECORDS KFT.—See Fotex Holding SE; *Int'l*, pg. 2752
HUPPIN'S HI-FI, PHOTO & VIDEO INC.—See Wipliance, LLC; *U.S. Private*, pg. 4546
HYPHEN SOLUTIONS, LLC; *U.S. Private*, pg. 2020
IFS CENTRAL & EASTERN EUROPE SP. Z.O.O.—See EQT AB; *Int'l*, pg. 2477
IHLAS PAZARLAMA A.S—See Ihlas Holding A.S.; *Int'l*, pg. 3606
IITS LLC; *U.S. Private*, pg. 2040
IITTALA BVBA—See Fiskars Oyj Abp; *Int'l*, pg. 2695
INCODE COMPUTER MANAGEMENT SERVICES—See Tyler Technologies, Inc.; *U.S. Public*, pg. 2208
INDEPENDENT DISTRIBUTORS, INC.—See Affiliated Distributors Inc.; *U.S. Private*, pg. 121
INDINERO INC.; *U.S. Private*, pg. 2064
INFRASOFT CORPORATION—See Bentley Systems, Inc.; *U.S. Public*, pg. 297
INGRAM MICRO ASIA LTD.—See Hainan Traffic Administration Holding Co., Ltd.; *Int'l*, pg. 3214
INNOVATIVE INFORMATION SOLUTIONS; *U.S. Private*, pg. 2082
INSIGMA INC.—See Futuris Company; *U.S. Public*, pg. 893
INSTAWARES, LLC—See ITC Holding Company, LLC; *U.S. Private*, pg. 2149
INSTITUTE FOR LANGUAGE STUDY—See Cortina Learning International, Inc.; *U.S. Private*, pg. 1061
INSYNC SOFTWARE, INC.—See ORBCOMM, Inc.; *U.S. Public*, pg. 1614
INTEGRATED ENGINEERING, PLLC—See NewHold Enterprises LLC; *U.S. Private*, pg. 2915
INTEGRATED IT SOLUTIONS, INC.; *U.S. Private*, pg. 2100
INTEGRATED SOLUTIONS GROUP, INC.; *U.S. Private*, pg. 2101
INTEL AUSTRALIA PTY. LTD.—See Intel Corporation; *U.S. Public*, pg. 1138
INTEL CORP. S.A.R.L.—See Intel Corporation; *U.S. Public*, pg. 1138
INTEL FINLAND OY—See Intel Corporation; *U.S. Public*, pg. 1138
INTELICLEAR, LLC—See Prometheum, Inc.; *U.S. Private*, pg. 3283
INTELISYS COMMUNICATIONS, INC.—See ScanSource, Inc.; *U.S. Public*, pg. 1843
INTEL KABUSHIKI KAISHA—See Intel Corporation; *U.S. Public*, pg. 1138
INTEL KOREA LTD.—See Intel Corporation; *U.S. Public*, pg. 1138
INTEL MICROELECTRONICS ASIA—See Intel Corporation; *U.S. Public*, pg. 1138
INTERACTIVE MEDIA GROUP INCORPORATED; *U.S. Private*, pg. 2108
INTERGRAPH BENELUX B.V.—See Hexagon AB; *Int'l*, pg. 3368
INTERGRAPH CANADA LTD.—See Hexagon AB; *Int'l*, pg. 3368
INTERGRAPH CONSULTING PVT LTD.—See Hexagon AB; *Int'l*, pg. 3368
INTERGRAPH EUROPEAN MANUFACTURING L.L.C.—See Hexagon AB; *Int'l*, pg. 3368
INTERGRAPH (FINLAND) OY—See Hexagon AB; *Int'l*, pg. 3368
INTERGRAPH ISRAEL SOFTWARE DEVELOPMENT CENTER LTD—See Hexagon AB; *Int'l*, pg. 3369
INTERGRAPH ITALIA LLC—See Hexagon AB; *Int'l*, pg. 3369
INTERGRAPH KOREA, LTD.—See Hexagon AB; *Int'l*, pg. 3369
INTERGRAPH NORGE AS—See Hexagon AB; *Int'l*, pg. 3369
INTERGRAPH (SVERIGE) A.B.—See Hexagon AB; *Int'l*, pg. 3368
INTERGRAPH (UK) LIMITED—See Hexagon AB; *Int'l*, pg. 3368
INVENGER TECHNOLOGIES, INC.—See Great Hill Partners, L.P.; *U.S. Private*, pg. 1763
IROBOT ITALIA S.R.L.—See iRobot Corp.; *U.S. Public*, pg. 1171
ISE LIMITED; *U.S. Private*, pg. 2143
JACK'S CAMERA INC.; *U.S. Private*, pg. 2175
JAVAN TECHNOLOGY INC; *U.S. Private*, pg. 2191
JETSON TV & APPLIANCE CENTERS; *U.S. Private*, pg. 2204
J.H. EVANS INC.; *U.S. Private*, pg. 2165
JIVE COMMUNICATIONS, INC.—See Elliott Management Corporation; *U.S. Public*, pg. 1368
JIVE COMMUNICATIONS, INC.—See Francisco Partners Management, LP; *U.S. Private*, pg. 1590
J & J TECHNICAL SERVICES, INC.—See Tonka Bay Equity Partners LLC; *U.S. Private*, pg. 4185
JMARK BUSINESS SOLUTIONS, INC.; *U.S. Private*, pg. 2215
JOSEPH BETH BOOKSELLERS LLC; *U.S. Private*, pg. 2236
JOURNEYED.COM, INC.—See Siris Capital Group, LLC; *U.S. Private*, pg. 3672
J&R FILM & MOVIOLA DIGITAL CO.; *U.S. Private*, pg. 2155
J&R MUSIC WORLD; *U.S. Private*, pg. 2155
JUNE LIFE, INC.—See BDT Capital Partners, LLC; *U.S. Private*, pg. 503
KANTONE PAGING COMPANY LIMITED—See Champion Technology Holdings Ltd; *Int'l*, pg. 1440
KAPP COMMUNICATIONS, INC.—See Interactive Services Network, Inc.; *U.S. Private*, pg. 2108

449210 — ELECTRONICS AND APP...

KASPIEN HOLDINGS INC.; *U.S. Public*, pg. 1214
KEY PUNCH COMPUTER TEMPORARIES; *U.S. Private*, pg. 2294
KIM'S HOME CENTER INC.; *U.S. Private*, pg. 2305
KING APPLIANCE CENTER INC.; *U.S. Private*, pg. 2308
KLARMOBIL GMBH—See freenet AG; *Int'l*, pg. 2770
KLUNGESS ELECTRONIC SUPPLY—See CCI Systems Inc.; *U.S. Private*, pg. 799
KOREA FA SYSTEMS CO., LTD.—See Fuji Electric Co., Ltd.; *Int'l*, pg. 2812
LARSONS APPLIANCE COMPANY; *U.S. Private*, pg. 2394
LEON SPEAKERS, INC.; *U.S. Private*, pg. 2423
LEWIS DIGITAL, INC.—See Robert J. Young Company, LLC; *U.S. Private*, pg. 3458
LFD, LLC; *U.S. Private*, pg. 2441
LIBERTY DATA PRODUCTS INC.; *U.S. Private*, pg. 2443
LIBSYS, INC.; *U.S. Private*, pg. 2448
LISTENUP.COM; *U.S. Private*, pg. 2466
LONG'S ELECTRONICS, INC.; *U.S. Private*, pg. 2492
LUFF RESEARCH INC.—See Ironwave Technologies LLC; *U.S. Private*, pg. 2140
MAGNOLIA AUDIO VIDEO—See Best Buy Co., Inc.; *U.S. Public*, pg. 326
MAGNOLIA HI-FI, LLC—See Best Buy Co., Inc.; *U.S. Public*, pg. 326
MAHAJAK INTERNATIONAL ELECTRIC CO., LTD.—See Fuji Electric Co., Ltd.; *Int'l*, pg. 2812
MANIFEST DISCS & TAPES INCORPORATED; *U.S. Private*, pg. 2564
MANNY'S TV AND APPLIANCES; *U.S. Private*, pg. 2566
MANTECH COMPUTER & TELECOMMUNICATIONS CO., LTD.—See Abdulla Fouad Holding Co.; *Int'l*, pg. 59
MARINE PARK COMPUTERS; *U.S. Private*, pg. 2575
MAXFAIR TECHNOLOGIES HOLDINGS LTD.—See Computer & Technologies Holdings Limited; *Int'l*, pg. 1758
MAXIM AUTOMOTIVE PRODUCTS LLC; *U.S. Private*, pg. 2618
MAZ MIKROELEKTRONIK-ANWENDUNGSZENTRUM GMBH IM LAND BRANDENBURG—See ELMOS Semiconductor AG; *Int'l*, pg. 2368
MCM ELECTRONICS INC.—See Avnet, Inc.; *U.S. Public*, pg. 254
MEDIAMARKET S. P. A.—See Ceconomy AG; *Int'l*, pg. 1385
MEDIA MARKT 14 - PRODUTOS ELECTRONICOS LDA—See Ceconomy AG; *Int'l*, pg. 1375
MEDIA MARKT 3 DE MAYO SANTA CRUZ DE TENERIFE S.A.—See Ceconomy AG; *Int'l*, pg. 1375
MEDIA MARKT AIGLE SA—See Ceconomy AG; *Int'l*, pg. 1375
MEDIA MARKT ALACANT VIDEO-TV-HIFI-ELEKTRO-COMPUTER-FOTO, S.A.—See Ceconomy AG; *Int'l*, pg. 1373
MEDIA MARKT ALCALA DE GUADAIRA VIDEO-TV-HIFI-ELEKTRO-COMPUTER-FOTO S.A.—See Ceconomy AG; *Int'l*, pg. 1373
MEDIA MARKT ALCALA DE HENARES VIDEO-TV-HIFI-ELEKTRO-COMPUTER-FOTO, S.A.—See Ceconomy AG; *Int'l*, pg. 1373
MEDIA MARKT ALCORCON VIDEO-TV-HIFI-ELEKTRO-COMPUTER-FOTO, S.A.—See Ceconomy AG; *Int'l*, pg. 1373
MEDIA MARKT ALEXANDRIUM B.V.—See Ceconomy AG; *Int'l*, pg. 1375
MEDIA MARKT ALFAFAR VIDEO-TV-HIFI-ELEKTRO-COMPUTER-FOTO, S.A.—See Ceconomy AG; *Int'l*, pg. 1373
MEDIA MARKT ALFRAGIDE - PRODUTOS INFORMATICOS E ELECTRONICOS, LDA—See Ceconomy AG; *Int'l*, pg. 1373
MEDIA MARKT ALKMAAR B.V.—See Ceconomy AG; *Int'l*, pg. 1375
MEDIA MARKT ALMERE B.V.—See Ceconomy AG; *Int'l*, pg. 1375
MEDIA MARKT ALPHEN AAN DEN RIJN B.V.—See Ceconomy AG; *Int'l*, pg. 1375
MEDIA MARKT AMERSFOORT B.V.—See Ceconomy AG; *Int'l*, pg. 1375
MEDIA MARKT AMSTERDAM CENTRUM B.V.—See Ceconomy AG; *Int'l*, pg. 1375
MEDIA MARKT AMSTERDAM NOORD B.V.—See Ceconomy AG; *Int'l*, pg. 1375
MEDIA MARKT AMSTERDAM WEST B.V.—See Ceconomy AG; *Int'l*, pg. 1375
MEDIA MARKT AMSTETTEN TV-HIFI-ELEKTRO GMBH—See Ceconomy AG; *Int'l*, pg. 1375
MEDIA MARKT APELDOORN B.V.—See Ceconomy AG; *Int'l*, pg. 1375
MEDIA MARKT ARENA B.V.—See Ceconomy AG; *Int'l*, pg. 1375
MEDIA MARKT ARNHEM B.V.—See Ceconomy AG; *Int'l*, pg. 1375
MEDIA MARKT ASSEN B.V.—See Ceconomy AG; *Int'l*, pg. 1375
MEDIA MARKT AUGSBURG-OBERHAUSEN—See Ceconomy AG; *Int'l*, pg. 1375
MEDIA MARKT AVEIRO - PRODUTOS INFORMATICOS E ELECTRONICOS, LDA—See Ceconomy AG; *Int'l*, pg. 1375

MEDIA MARKT BADAJOZ S.A.—See Ceconomy AG; *Int'l*, pg. 1375
MEDIA MARKT BADEN-BADEN—See Ceconomy AG; *Int'l*, pg. 1375
MEDIA MARKT BASEL AG—See Ceconomy AG; *Int'l*, pg. 1375
MEDIA MARKT BASILIX NV—See Ceconomy AG; *Int'l*, pg. 1375
MEDIA MARKT BEKESCSABA VIDEO TV HIFI ELEKTRO PHOTO COMPUTER KERESKEDELMI KFT.—See Ceconomy AG; *Int'l*, pg. 1375
MEDIA MARKT BENFICA - PRODUTOS INFORMATICOS E ELECTRONICOS, LDA—See Ceconomy AG; *Int'l*, pg. 1375
MEDIA MARKT BIEL-BRUGG AG—See Ceconomy AG; *Int'l*, pg. 1376
MEDIA MARKT BILBAO - ZUBIARTE, S.A.—See Ceconomy AG; *Int'l*, pg. 1376
MEDIA MARKT BORAS TV-HIFI-ELEKTRO AB—See Ceconomy AG; *Int'l*, pg. 1376
MEDIA MARKT BRAGA - PRODUTOS INFORMATICOS E ELECTRONICOS, LDA—See Ceconomy AG; *Int'l*, pg. 1376
MEDIA MARKT BRAINE-L'ALLEUD SA—See Ceconomy AG; *Int'l*, pg. 1373
MEDIA MARKT BREDA B.V.—See Ceconomy AG; *Int'l*, pg. 1376
MEDIA MARKT BRUGGE NV—See Ceconomy AG; *Int'l*, pg. 1376
MEDIA MARKT BRUSSEL DOCKS NV—See Ceconomy AG; *Int'l*, pg. 1376
MEDIA MARKT BRUXELLES RUE NEUVE - MEDIA MARKT BRUSSEL NIEUWSTRAAT SA—See Ceconomy AG; *Int'l*, pg. 1373
MEDIA MARKT - BUDAORS VIDEO TV HIFI ELEKTRO FOTO COMPUTER KERESKEDELMI KFT.—See Ceconomy AG; *Int'l*, pg. 1373
MEDIA MARKT BURS TV-HIFI-ELEKTRO GMBH—See Ceconomy AG; *Int'l*, pg. 1376
MEDIA MARKT CARTAGENA VIDEO-TV-ELEKTRO-COMPUTER-FOTO, S.A.—See Ceconomy AG; *Int'l*, pg. 1373
MEDIA MARKT CASTELLO DE LA PLANA VIDEO-TV-HIFI-ELEKTRO-COMPUTER-FOTO, S.A.—See Ceconomy AG; *Int'l*, pg. 1373
MEDIAMARKT CENTRAL WAREHOUSE N.V.—See Ceconomy AG; *Int'l*, pg. 1385
MEDIA MARKT CHUR AG—See Ceconomy AG; *Int'l*, pg. 1376
MEDIA MARKT COLLADO VILLALBA, S.A.—See Ceconomy AG; *Int'l*, pg. 1376
MEDIA MARKT CONTHEY SA—See Ceconomy AG; *Int'l*, pg. 1376
MEDIA MARKT CRISSIER SA—See Ceconomy AG; *Int'l*, pg. 1376
MEDIA MARKT CRUQUIUS B.V.—See Ceconomy AG; *Int'l*, pg. 1376
MEDIA MARKT DEBRECEN VIDEO-TV-HIFI-ELEKTRO-PHOTO-COMPUTER-KERESKEDELMI KFT.—See Ceconomy AG; *Int'l*, pg. 1373
MEDIA MARKT DEN BOSCH B.V.—See Ceconomy AG; *Int'l*, pg. 1376
MEDIA MARKT DEN HAAG B.V.—See Ceconomy AG; *Int'l*, pg. 1376
MEDIA MARKT DEURNE NV—See Ceconomy AG; *Int'l*, pg. 1376
MEDIA MARKT DIAGONAL MAR-BARCELONA VIDEO-TV-HIFI-ELEKTRO-COMPUTER-FOTO S.A.—See Ceconomy AG; *Int'l*, pg. 1376
MEDIA MARKT DOETINCHEM B.V.—See Ceconomy AG; *Int'l*, pg. 1376
MEDIA MARKT DONOSTI VIDEO-TV-HIFI-ELEKTRO-COMPUTER-FOTO, S.A.—See Ceconomy AG; *Int'l*, pg. 1373
MEDIA MARKT DORDRECHT B.V.—See Ceconomy AG; *Int'l*, pg. 1376
MEDIA MARKT DRACHTEN B.V.—See Ceconomy AG; *Int'l*, pg. 1376
MEDIA MARKT DUIVEN B.V.—See Ceconomy AG; *Int'l*, pg. 1376
MEDIA MARKT E-COMMERCE AG—See Ceconomy AG; *Int'l*, pg. 1376
MEDIA MARKT EDE B.V.—See Ceconomy AG; *Int'l*, pg. 1376
MEDIA MARKT EINDHOVEN B.V.—See Ceconomy AG; *Int'l*, pg. 1376
MEDIA MARKT EINDHOVEN EKKERSRIJT B.V.—See Ceconomy AG; *Int'l*, pg. 1376
MEDIA MARKT EMMEN B.V.—See Ceconomy AG; *Int'l*, pg. 1376
MEDIA MARKT ESKILSTUNA TV-HIFI-ELEKTRO AB—See Ceconomy AG; *Int'l*, pg. 1376
MEDIA MARKT ESPLUGUES, S.A.—See Ceconomy AG; *Int'l*, pg. 1376
MEDIA MARKT FELDKIRCH TV-HIFI-ELEKTRO GMBH—See Ceconomy AG; *Int'l*, pg. 1376
MEDIA MARKT FERROL, SA—See Ceconomy AG; *Int'l*, pg. 1376

CORPORATE AFFILIATIONS

MEDIA MARKT FINESTRAT S.A.U.—See Ceconomy AG; *Int'l*, pg. 1376
MEDIA MARKT GAIA - PRODUTOS INFORMATICOS E ELECTRONICOS, LDA—See Ceconomy AG; *Int'l*, pg. 1376
MEDIA MARKT GANDIA S.A.—See Ceconomy AG; *Int'l*, pg. 1376
MEDIA MARKT GAVLE TV-HIFI-ELEKTRO AB—See Ceconomy AG; *Int'l*, pg. 1376
MEDIA MARKT GIRONA VIDEO-TV-HIFI-ELEKTRO-COMPUTER-FOTO, S.A.—See Ceconomy AG; *Int'l*, pg. 1373
MEDIA MARKT GOTEBORG-BACKEBOL TV-HIFI-ELEKTRO AB—See Ceconomy AG; *Int'l*, pg. 1376
MEDIA MARKT GOTEBORG-HOGSBO TV-HIFI-ELEKTRO AB—See Ceconomy AG; *Int'l*, pg. 1376
MEDIA MARKT GOTEBORG-TORPAVALLEN TV-HIFI-ELEKTRO AB—See Ceconomy AG; *Int'l*, pg. 1376
MEDIA MARKT GRANADA - NEVADA, S.A.—See Ceconomy AG; *Int'l*, pg. 1376
MEDIA MARKT GRANCIA SA—See Ceconomy AG; *Int'l*, pg. 1376
MEDIA MARKT GRANGES-PACCOT AG—See Ceconomy AG; *Int'l*, pg. 1376
MEDIA MARKT GRONINGEN SONTPLEIN B.V.—See Ceconomy AG; *Int'l*, pg. 1376
MEDIA MARKT GYOR VIDEO TV HIFI ELEKTRO PHOTO COMPUTER KERESKEDELMI KFT.—See Ceconomy AG; *Int'l*, pg. 1376
MEDIA MARKT HELSINGBORG TV-HIFI-ELEKTRO AB—See Ceconomy AG; *Int'l*, pg. 1376
MEDIA MARKT HERSTAL SA—See Ceconomy AG; *Int'l*, pg. 1377
MEDIA MARKT HOOFDDORP B.V.—See Ceconomy AG; *Int'l*, pg. 1377
MEDIA MARKT HOORN B.V.—See Ceconomy AG; *Int'l*, pg. 1377
MEDIA MARKT IMST TV-HIFI-ELEKTRO GMBH—See Ceconomy AG; *Int'l*, pg. 1377
MEDIA MARKT JEMAPPES/MONS SA—See Ceconomy AG; *Int'l*, pg. 1377
MEDIA MARKT JONKOPING TV-HIFI- ELEKTRO AB—See Ceconomy AG; *Int'l*, pg. 1377
MEDIA MARKT KALMAR TV-HIFI-ELEKTRO AB—See Ceconomy AG; *Int'l*, pg. 1377
MEDIA MARKT KECSKEMET VIDEO TV HIFI ELEKTRO PHOTO COMPUTER KERESKEDELMI KFT.—See Ceconomy AG; *Int'l*, pg. 1377
MEDIA MARKT KISPEST VIDEO TV HIFI ELEKTRO PHOTO COMPUTER KERESKEDELMI KFT.—See Ceconomy AG; *Int'l*, pg. 1377
MEDIA MARKT KORTRIJK NV—See Ceconomy AG; *Int'l*, pg. 1377
MEDIA MARKT KRISTIANSTAD TV-HIFI-ELEKTRO AB—See Ceconomy AG; *Int'l*, pg. 1377
MEDIA MARKT LAS ARENAS S.A.—See Ceconomy AG; *Int'l*, pg. 1377
MEDIA MARKT LAS PALMAS DE GRAN CANARIA VIDEO-TV-HIFI-ELEKTRO-COMPUTER-FOTO, S.A.—See Ceconomy AG; *Int'l*, pg. 1373
MEDIA MARKT LEGANES VIDEO-TV- HIFI-ELEKTRO-COMPUTER-FOTO, S.A.—See Ceconomy AG; *Int'l*, pg. 1373
MEDIA MARKT LEIDSCHENDAM B.V.—See Ceconomy AG; *Int'l*, pg. 1377
MEDIA MARKT LEIRIA - PRODUTOS INFORMATICOS E ELECTRONICOS, LDA—See Ceconomy AG; *Int'l*, pg. 1377
MEDIA MARKT LEOBEN TV-HIFI-ELEKTRO GMBH—See Ceconomy AG; *Int'l*, pg. 1377
MEDIA MARKT LEON VIDEO-TV-HIFI-ELEKTRO-COMPUTER-FOTO, S.A.—See Ceconomy AG; *Int'l*, pg. 1373
MEDIA MARKT L HOSPITALET VIDEO-TV-HIFI-ELEKTRO-COMPUTER-FOTO S.A.—See Ceconomy AG; *Int'l*, pg. 1373
MEDIA MARKT LIEGE MEDIACITE SA—See Ceconomy AG; *Int'l*, pg. 1377
MEDIA MARKT LIEGE PLACE SAINT-LAMBERT SA—See Ceconomy AG; *Int'l*, pg. 1377
MEDIA MARKT LIEZEN TV-HIFI-ELEKTRO GMBH—See Ceconomy AG; *Int'l*, pg. 1377
MEDIA MARKT LINZ TV-HIFI-ELEKTRO GMBH—See Ceconomy AG; *Int'l*, pg. 1377
MEDIA MARKT LLEIDA, SA—See Ceconomy AG; *Int'l*, pg. 1377
MEDIA MARKT LOGRONO VIDEO-TV-HIFI-ELEKTRO-COMPUTER-FOTO, S.A.U.—See Ceconomy AG; *Int'l*, pg. 1373
MEDIA MARKT LORCA S.A.—See Ceconomy AG; *Int'l*, pg. 1377
MEDIA MARKT LUND TV-HIFI-ELEKTRO AB—See Ceconomy AG; *Int'l*, pg. 1377
MEDIA MARKT MAASTRICHT B.V.—See Ceconomy AG; *Int'l*, pg. 1377
MEDIA MARKT MACHELEN NV—See Ceconomy AG; *Int'l*, pg. 1377

N.A.I.C.S. INDEX

449210 — ELECTRONICS AND APP...

MEDIA MARKT MADRID BENLLIURE SA—See Ceconomy AG; *Int'l*, pg. 1377

MEDIA MARKT MADRID CASTELLANA SA—See Ceconomy AG; *Int'l*, pg. 1377

MEDIA MARKT MADRID - PLAZA DEL CARMEN S.A.U.—See Ceconomy AG; *Int'l*, pg. 1377

MEDIA MARKT MADRID PLENILUNIO VIDEO-TV-HIFI-ELEKTRO-COMPUTER-FOTO S.A.—See Ceconomy AG; *Int'l*, pg. 1377

MEDIA MARKT MADRID - VALLECAS S.A.—See Ceconomy AG; *Int'l*, pg. 1377

MEDIA MARKT MALAGA-CENTRO VFDEO-TV-HIFI-ELEKTRO-COMPUTER-FOTO, SA—See Ceconomy AG; *Int'l*, pg. 1377

MEDIA MARKT MALAGA-CENTRO VIDEO-TV-HIFI-ELEKTRO-COMPUTER-FOTO, S.A.—See Ceconomy AG; *Int'l*, pg. 1373

MEDIA MARKT MALAGA - PLAZA MAYOR S.A.—See Ceconomy AG; *Int'l*, pg. 1377

MEDIA MARKT MALMO-SVAGERTORP TV-HIFI-ELEKTRO AB—See Ceconomy AG; *Int'l*, pg. 1377

MEDIA MARKT MASSALFASSAR S.A.—See Ceconomy AG; *Int'l*, pg. 1377

MEDIA MARKT MEGAPARK VIDEO TV HIFI ELEKTRO PHOTO COMPUTER KERESKEDELMI KFT.—See Ceconomy AG; *Int'l*, pg. 1374

MEDIA MARKT MEYRIN SA—See Ceconomy AG; *Int'l*, pg. 1377

MEDIA MARKT MIDDELBURG B.V.—See Ceconomy AG; *Int'l*, pg. 1377

MEDIA MARKT MISKOLC VIDEO TV HIFI ELEKTRO PHOTO COMPUTER KERESKEDELMIT KFT—See Ceconomy AG; *Int'l*, pg. 1374

MEDIA MARKT MOLLET VIDEO-TV-HIFI-ELEKTRO-COMPUTER-FOTO, S.A.U.—See Ceconomy AG; *Int'l*, pg. 1374

MEDIA MARKT MURCIA NUEVA CONDOMINA VIDEO-TV-HIFI-ELEKTRO-COMPUTER-FOTO S.A.—See Ceconomy AG; *Int'l*, pg. 1377

MEDIA MARKT NIEUWEGEIN B.V.—See Ceconomy AG; *Int'l*, pg. 1377

MEDIA MARKT NORRKOPING TV-HIFI-ELEKTRO AB—See Ceconomy AG; *Int'l*, pg. 1377

MEDIA MARKT NYIREGYHAZA VIDEO TV HIFI ELEKTRO PHOTO COMPUTER KERESKEDELMI KFT.—See Ceconomy AG; *Int'l*, pg. 1377

MEDIA MARKT OBERWART TV-HIFI-ELEKTRO GMBH—See Ceconomy AG; *Int'l*, pg. 1377

MEDIA MARKT OFTRINGEN AG—See Ceconomy AG; *Int'l*, pg. 1377

MEDIA MARKT OOSTENDE NV—See Ceconomy AG; *Int'l*, pg. 1377

MEDIA MARKT OREBRO TV-HIFI-ELEKTRO AB—See Ceconomy AG; *Int'l*, pg. 1377

MEDIA MARKT ORIHUELA SA—See Ceconomy AG; *Int'l*, pg. 1378

MEDIA MARKT PALMA DE MALLORCA FAN SAU—See Ceconomy AG; *Int'l*, pg. 1378

MEDIA MARKT PALMA DE MALLORCA S.A.—See Ceconomy AG; *Int'l*, pg. 1378

MEDIA MARKTPARETS DEL VALLES SA—See Ceconomy AG; *Int'l*, pg. 1385

MEDIA MARKT PECS VIDEO TV HIFI ELEKTRO PHOTO COMPUTER KERESKEDELMIT KFT.—See Ceconomy AG; *Int'l*, pg. 1378

MEDIA MARKT PLACA DE CATALUNYA, S.A.U.—See Ceconomy AG; *Int'l*, pg. 1378

MEDIA MARKT POLSKA BIS SPOFKA Z OGRANICZONA ODPOWIEDZIALNOSCIA BYDGOSZCZ II SPOFKA KOMANDYTOWA—See Ceconomy AG; *Int'l*, pg. 1378

MEDIA MARKT POLSKA BIS SPOFKA Z OGRANICZONA ODPOWIEDZIALNOSCIA GDANSK IV SPOFKA KOMANDYTOWA—See Ceconomy AG; *Int'l*, pg. 1378

MEDIA MARKT POLSKA BIS SPOFKA Z OGRANICZONA ODPOWIEDZIALNOSCIA KATOWICE III SPOFKA KOMANDYTOWA—See Ceconomy AG; *Int'l*, pg. 1378

MEDIA MARKT POLSKA BIS SPOFKA Z OGRANICZONA ODPOWIEDZIALNOSCIA LUBIN SPOFKA KOMANDYTOWA—See Ceconomy AG; *Int'l*, pg. 1378

MEDIA MARKT POLSKA BIS SPOFKA Z OGRANICZONA ODPOWIEDZIALNOSCIA POZNAN III SPOFKA KOMANDYTOWA—See Ceconomy AG; *Int'l*, pg. 1378

MEDIA MARKT POLSKA BIS SPOFKA Z OGRANICZONA ODPOWIEDZIALNOSCIA POZNAN IV SPOFKA KOMANDYTOWA—See Ceconomy AG; *Int'l*, pg. 1378

MEDIA MARKT POLSKA BIS SPOFKA Z OGRANICZONA ODPOWIEDZIALNOSCIA SZCZECIN III SPOFKA KOMANDYTOWA—See Ceconomy AG; *Int'l*, pg. 1378

MEDIA MARKT POLSKA BIS SPOFKA Z OGRANICZONA ODPOWIEDZIALNOSCIA TYCHY SPOFKA KOMANDYTOWA—See Ceconomy AG; *Int'l*, pg. 1378

MEDIA MAHKI POLSKA BIS SP. Z O.O. WROOLAW V SPOFKA KOMANDYTOWA—See Ceconomy AG; *Int'l*, pg. 1378

MEDIA MARKT POLSKA SP. Z O.O. BIAFYSTOK SPOFKA KOMANDYTOWA—See Ceconomy AG; *Int'l*, pg. 1378

MEDIA MARKT POLSKA SP. Z O.O. BIELSKO-BIAFA SPOLKA KOMANDYTOWA—See Ceconomy AG; *Int'l*, pg. 1378

MEDIA MARKT POLSKA SP. Z O.O. CHORZOW SPOFKA KOMANDYTOWA—See Ceconomy AG; *Int'l*, pg. 1378

MEDIA MARKT POLSKA SP. Z O.O. CHORZOW SPOLKA KOMANDYTOWA—See Ceconomy AG; *Int'l*, pg. 1378

MEDIA MARKT POLSKA SP. Z.O.O. CZELADZ SPOFKA KOMANDYTOWA—See Ceconomy AG; *Int'l*, pg. 1379

MEDIA MARKT POLSKA SP. Z O.O. CZESTOCHOWA SPOFKA KOMANDYTOWA—See Ceconomy AG; *Int'l*, pg. 1379

MEDIA MARKT POLSKA SP. Z O.O. ELBLAG SPOFKA KOMANDYTOWA—See Ceconomy AG; *Int'l*, pg. 1378

MEDIA MARKT POLSKA SP. Z O.O. GDANSK II SPOFKA KOMANDYTOWA—See Ceconomy AG; *Int'l*, pg. 1378

MEDIA MARKT POLSKA SP. Z.O.O. GDANSK I SPOFKA KOMANDYTOWA—See Ceconomy AG; *Int'l*, pg. 1379

MEDIA MARKT POLSKA SP. Z.O.O. GDANSK I SPOLKA KOMANDYTOWA—See Ceconomy AG; *Int'l*, pg. 1379

MEDIA MARKT POLSKA SP. Z O.O. GDYNIA I SPOFKA KOMANDYTOWA—See Ceconomy AG; *Int'l*, pg. 1378

MEDIA MARKT POLSKA SP. Z O.O. GFOGOW SPOFKA KOMANDYTOWA—See Ceconomy AG; *Int'l*, pg. 1378

MEDIA MARKT POLSKA SP. Z O.O. GLIWICE SPOFKA KOMANDYTOWA—See Ceconomy AG; *Int'l*, pg. 1378

MEDIA MARKT POLSKA SP. Z O.O. GORZOW WIELKO-POLSKI SPOFKA KOMANDYTOWA—See Ceconomy AG; *Int'l*, pg. 1378

MEDIA MARKT POLSKA SP. Z O.O. KALISZ SPOFKA KOMANDYTOWA—See Ceconomy AG; *Int'l*, pg. 1378

MEDIA MARKT POLSKA SP. Z.O.O. KATOWICE I SPOFKA KOMANDYTOWA—See Ceconomy AG; *Int'l*, pg. 1379

MEDIA MARKT POLSKA SP. Z.O.O. KATOWICE I SPOLKA KOMANDYTOWA—See Ceconomy AG; *Int'l*, pg. 1379

MEDIA MARKT POLSKA SP. Z O.O. KIELCE SPOFKA KOMANDYTOWA—See Ceconomy AG; *Int'l*, pg. 1379

MEDIA MARKT POLSKA SP. Z O.O. KONIN SPOFKA KOMANDYTOWA—See Ceconomy AG; *Int'l*, pg. 1378

MEDIA MARKT POLSKA SP. Z O.O. KOSZALIN SPOFKA KOMANDYTOWA—See Ceconomy AG; *Int'l*, pg. 1378

MEDIA MARKT POLSKA SP. Z O.O. KRAKOW II SPOFKA KOMANDYTOWA—See Ceconomy AG; *Int'l*, pg. 1378

MEDIA MARKT POLSKA SP. Z O.O. KRAKOW II SPOLKA KOMANDYTOWA—See Ceconomy AG; *Int'l*, pg. 1378

MEDIA MARKT POLSKA SP. Z O.O. KRAKOW I SPOFKA KOMANDYTOWA—See Ceconomy AG; *Int'l*, pg. 1378

MEDIA MARKT POLSKA SP. Z O.O. LEGNICA SPOFKA KOMANDYTOWA—See Ceconomy AG; *Int'l*, pg. 1378

MEDIA MARKT POLSKA SP. Z.O.O. LUBLIN SPOFKA KOMANDYTOWA—See Ceconomy AG; *Int'l*, pg. 1379

MEDIA MARKT POLSKA SP. Z O.O. NOWY SACZ SPOFKA KOMANDYTOWA—See Ceconomy AG; *Int'l*, pg. 1378

MEDIA MARKT POLSKA SP. Z O.O. NOWY SACZ SPOLKA KOMANDYTOWA—See Ceconomy AG; *Int'l*, pg. 1378

MEDIA MARKT POLSKA SP. Z O.O. OLSZTYN SPOFKA KOMANDYTOWA—See Ceconomy AG; *Int'l*, pg. 1379

MEDIA MARKT POLSKA SP. Z O.O. OPOLE SPOFKA KOMANDYTOWA—See Ceconomy AG; *Int'l*, pg. 1378

MEDIA MARKT POLSKA SP. Z O.O. PFOCK SPOFKA KOMANDYTOWA—See Ceconomy AG; *Int'l*, pg. 1378

MEDIA MARKT POLSKA SP. Z O.O. PIOTRKOW TRYBU-NALSKI SPOLKA KOMANDYTOWA—See Ceconomy AG; *Int'l*, pg. 1378

MEDIA MARKT POLSKA SP. Z O.O. POZNAN II SPOFKA KOMANDYTOWA—See Ceconomy AG; *Int'l*, pg. 1378

MEDIA MARKT POLSKA SP. Z O.O. RADOM SPOFKA KOMANDYTOWA—See Ceconomy AG; *Int'l*, pg. 1378

MEDIA MARKT POLSKA SP. Z O.O. RYBNIK SPOFKA KOMANDYTOWA—See Ceconomy AG; *Int'l*, pg. 1378

MEDIA MARKT POLSKA SP. Z O.O. RZESZOW SPOFKA KOMANDYTOWA—See Ceconomy AG; *Int'l*, pg. 1379

MEDIA MARKT POLSKA SP. Z O O. SFUPSK SPOFKA KOMANDYTOWA—See Ceconomy AG; *Int'l*, pg. 1379

MEDIA MARKT POLSKA SP. Z O.O.—See Ceconomy AG; *Int'l*, pg. 1378

MEDIA MARKT POLSKA SP. Z O.O. TARNOW SPOFKA KOMANDYTOWA—See Ceconomy AG; *Int'l*, pg. 1378

MEDIA MARKT POLSKA SP. Z.O.O. TODZ II SPOFKA KOMANDYTOWA—See Ceconomy AG; *Int'l*, pg. 1379

MEDIA MARKT POLSKA SP. Z.O.O. TODZ I SPOFKA KOMANDYTOWA—See Ceconomy AG; *Int'l*, pg. 1379

MEDIA MARKT POLSKA SP. Z O.O. TORUN SPOFKA KOMANDYTOWA—See Ceconomy AG; *Int'l*, pg. 1378

MEDIA MARKT POLSKA SP. Z O.O. WAFBRZYCH SPOFKA KOMANDYTOWA—See Ceconomy AG; *Int'l*, pg. 1378

MEDIA MARKT POLSKA SP. Z.O.O. WARSCHAU III SPOFKA KOMANDYTOWA—See Ceconomy AG; *Int'l*, pg. 1379

MEDIA MARKT POLSKA SP. Z.O.O. WARSCHAU II SPOFKA KOMANDYTOWA—See Ceconomy AG; *Int'l*, pg. 1379

MEDIA MARKT POLSKA SP. Z.O.O. WARSCHAU IV SPOFKA KOMANDYTOWA—See Ceconomy AG; *Int'l*, pg. 1379

MEDIA MARKT POLSKA SP. Z.O.O. WROCLAW I SPOFKA KOMANDYTOWA—See Ceconomy AG; *Int'l*, pg. 1379

MEDIA MARKT POLSKA SP. Z.O.O. ZABRZE SPOFKA KOMANDYTOWA—See Ceconomy AG; *Int'l*, pg. 1379

MEDIA MARKT POLSKA SP. Z O.O. ZAMOSC SPOFKA KOMANDYTOWA—See Ceconomy AG; *Int'l*, pg. 1378

MEDIA MARKT PUERTO REAL VIDEO-TV-HIFI-ELEKTRO-COMPUTER-FOTO, S.A.—See Ceconomy AG; *Int'l*, pg. 1379

MEDIA MARKT QUART DE POBLET, S.A.—See Ceconomy AG; *Int'l*, pg. 1379

MEDIA MARKT REGION BERN AG—See Ceconomy AG; *Int'l*, pg. 1379

MEDIA MARKT RIED TV-HIFI-ELEKTRO GMBH—See Ceconomy AG; *Int'l*, pg. 1379

MEDIA MARKT RIVAS-VACIAMADRID VIDEO-TV-HIFI-ELEKTRO-COMPUTER-FOTO S.A.—See Ceconomy AG; *Int'l*, pg. 1379

MEDIA MARKT ROESELARE NV—See Ceconomy AG; *Int'l*, pg. 1379

MEDIA MARKT ROTTERDAM BEIJERLANDSELAAN B.V.—See Ceconomy AG; *Int'l*, pg. 1379

MEDIA MARKT SALAMANCA VIDEO-TV-HIFI-ELEKTRO-COMPUTER-FOTO, S.A.—See Ceconomy AG; *Int'l*, pg. 1374

MEDIA MARKT SAN JUAN DE AZNALFARACHE VIDEO-TV-HIFI-ELECTRO-COMPUTER-FOTO, S.A.—See Ceconomy AG; *Int'l*, pg. 1379

MEDIA MARKT SAN SEBASTIAN DE LOS REYES VIDEO-TV-HIFI-ELEKTRO-COMPUTER-FOTO, S.A.—See Ceconomy AG; *Int'l*, pg. 1374

MEDIA MARKT SANTANDER VIDEO-TV-HIFI-ELEKTRO-COMPUTER-FOTO, SA—See Ceconomy AG; *Int'l*, pg. 1379

MEDIA MARKT SANT CUGAT DEL VALLES VIDEO-TV-HIFI-ELEKTRO-COMPUTER-FOTO, S.A.—See Ceconomy AG; *Int'l*, pg. 1374

MEDIA MARKT SANTIAGO DE COMPOSTELA S.A.—See Ceconomy AG; *Int'l*, pg. 1379

MEDIA MARKT SATURN HOLDING MAGYARORSZAG KFT.—See Ceconomy AG; *Int'l*, pg. 1379

MEDIA MARKT SCHOTEN NV—See Ceconomy AG; *Int'l*, pg. 1379

MEDIA MARKT SETUBAL - PRODUTOS INFORMATICOS E ELECTRONICOS, LDA.—See Ceconomy AG; *Int'l*, pg. 1379

MEDIA MARKT SEVILLA-SANTA JUSTA VIDEO-TV-HIFI-ELEKTRO-COMPUTER-FOTO, S.A.—See Ceconomy AG; *Int'l*, pg. 1374

MEDIA MARKT SIERO VIDEO-TV-HIFI-ELEKTRO-COMPUTER-FOTO, S.A.—See Ceconomy AG; *Int'l*, pg. 1374

MEDIA MARKT SINGEN GMBH—See Ceconomy AG; *Int'l*, pg. 1379

MEDIA MARKT SINTRA - PRODUTOS INFORMATICOS E ELECTRONICOS, LDA—See Ceconomy AG; *Int'l*, pg. 1374

MEDIA MARKT SKOVDE TV-HIFI-ELEKTRO AB—See Ceconomy AG; *Int'l*, pg. 1379

MEDIA MARKT SOROKSAR VIDEO TV HIFI ELEKTRO PHOTO COMPUTER KERESKEDELMI KFT.—See Ceconomy AG; *Int'l*, pg. 1379

MEDIA MARKT STEYR TV-HIFI-ELEKTRO GMBH—See Ceconomy AG; *Int'l*, pg. 1379

MEDIA MARKT ST. GALLEN AG—See Ceconomy AG; *Int'l*, pg. 1379

MEDIA MARKT STOCKHOLM-BARKARBY TV-HIFI-ELEKTRO AB—See Ceconomy AG; *Int'l*, pg. 1380

MEDIA MARKT STOCKHOLM-GALLERIAN TV-HIFI-ELEKTRO AB—See Ceconomy AG; *Int'l*, pg. 1380

MEDIA MARKT STOCKHOLM-HERON CITY TV-HIFI-ELEKTRO AB—See Ceconomy AG; *Int'l*, pg. 1380

MEDIA MARKT STOCKHOLM-LANNA TV-HIFI-ELEKTRO AB—See Ceconomy AG; *Int'l*, pg. 1380

MEDIA MARKT STOCKHOLM-NACKA TV-HIFI-ELEKTRO AB—See Ceconomy AG; *Int'l*, pg. 1380

MEDIA MARKT STOCKHOLM-TABY TV-HIFI-ELEKTRO AB—See Ceconomy AG; *Int'l*, pg. 1380

MEDIA MARKT STOP SHOP VIDEO TV HIFI ELEKTRO PHOTO COMPUTER KERESKEDELMI KFT.—See Ceconomy AG; *Int'l*, pg. 1374

MEDIA MARKT SUNDSVALL TV-HIFI-ELEKTRO AB—See Ceconomy AG; *Int'l*, pg. 1380

MEDIA MARKT SZEGED VIDEO-TV-HIFI-ELEKTRO-PHOTO-COMPUTER-KERESKEDELMI KFT.—See Ceconomy AG; *Int'l*, pg. 1374

MEDIA MARKT SZEKESFEHERVAR VIDEO TV HIFI ELEKTRO PHOTO COMPUTER KERESKEDELMI KFT.—See Ceconomy AG; *Int'l*, pg. 1374

MEDIA MARKT SZOLNOK VIDEO TV HIFI ELEKTRO PHOTO COMPUTER KERESKEDELMI KFT.—See Ceconomy AG; *Int'l*, pg. 1380

MEDIA MARKT SZOMBATHELY VIDEO-TV-HIFI-ELEKTRO-PHOTO-COMPUTER-KERESKEDELMI KFT.—See Ceconomy AG; *Int'l*, pg. 1374

MEDIA MARKT TATABANYA VIDEO TV HIFI ELEKTRO PHOTO COMPUTER KERESKEDELMI KFT.—See Ceconomy AG; *Int'l*, pg. 1384

MEDIA MARKT TELDE VFDEO-TV- HIFI- ELEKTRO-COMPUTER- FOTO, SA—See Ceconomy AG; *Int'l*, pg. 1384

MEDIA MARKT TENERIFE VIDEO-TV-HIFI-ELEKTRO-

449210 — ELECTRONICS AND APP...   CORPORATE AFFILIATIONS

COMPUTER-FOTO, SA—See Ceconomy AG; *Int'l*, pg. 1384
MEDIA MARKT TERRASSA SA—See Ceconomy AG; *Int'l*, pg. 1384
MEDIA MARKT THE CORNER B.V.—See Ceconomy AG; *Int'l*, pg. 1384
MEDIA MARKT TOLEDO S.A.—See Ceconomy AG; *Int'l*, pg. 1384
MEDIA MARKT TURNHOUT NV—See Ceconomy AG; *Int'l*, pg. 1384
MEDIA MARKT TV-HIFI-ELEKTRO ATHENS I COMMERCIAL ANONYMI ETERIA—See Ceconomy AG; *Int'l*, pg. 1380
MEDIA MARKT TV-HIFI-ELEKTRO ATHENS II COMMERCIAL ANONYMI ETERIA—See Ceconomy AG; *Int'l*, pg. 1380
MEDIA-MARKT TV-HIFI-ELEKTRO GMBH AACHEN—See Ceconomy AG; *Int'l*, pg. 1375
MEDIA MARKT TV-HIFI-ELEKTRO GMBH AALEN—See Ceconomy AG; *Int'l*, pg. 1380
MEDIA MARKT TV-HIFI-ELEKTRO GMBH ALBSTADT—See Ceconomy AG; *Int'l*, pg. 1380
MEDIA MARKT TV-HIFI-ELEKTRO GMBH ALZEY—See Ceconomy AG; *Int'l*, pg. 1380
MEDIA MARKT TV-HIFI-ELEKTRO GMBH AMBERG—See Ceconomy AG; *Int'l*, pg. 1380
MEDIA MARKT TV-HIFI-ELEKTRO GMBH ANSBACH—See Ceconomy AG; *Int'l*, pg. 1380
MEDIA MARKT TV-HIFI-ELEKTRO GMBH ASCHAFFENBURG—See Ceconomy AG; *Int'l*, pg. 1375
MEDIA MARKT TV-HIFI-ELEKTRO GMBH AUGSBURG-GOGGINGEN—See Ceconomy AG; *Int'l*, pg. 1380
MEDIA MARKT TV-HIFI-ELEKTRO GMBH BAD KREUZNACH—See Ceconomy AG; *Int'l*, pg. 1374
MEDIA MARKT TV-HIFI-ELEKTRO GMBH BAYREUTH—See Ceconomy AG; *Int'l*, pg. 1375
MEDIA MARKT TV-HIFI-ELEKTRO GMBH BERLIN-BIESDORF—See Ceconomy AG; *Int'l*, pg. 1375
MEDIA MARKT TV-HIFI-ELEKTRO GMBH BERLIN-CHARLOTTENBURG—See Ceconomy AG; *Int'l*, pg. 1380
MEDIA MARKT TV-HIFI-ELEKTRO GMBH BERLIN-GROPIUSSTADT—See Ceconomy AG; *Int'l*, pg. 1375
MEDIA MARKT TV-HIFI-ELEKTRO GMBH BERLIN-HOHENSCHONHAUSEN—See Ceconomy AG; *Int'l*, pg. 1374
MEDIA MARKT TV-HIFI-ELEKTRO GMBH BERLIN-MITTE—See Ceconomy AG; *Int'l*, pg. 1380
MEDIA MARKT TV-HIFI-ELEKTRO GMBH BERLIN-NEUKOLLN—See Ceconomy AG; *Int'l*, pg. 1375
MEDIA MARKT TV-HIFI-ELEKTRO GMBH BERLIN-PRENZLAUER BERG—See Ceconomy AG; *Int'l*, pg. 1380
MEDIA MARKT TV-HIFI-ELEKTRO GMBH BERLIN-SCHONEWEIDE—See Ceconomy AG; *Int'l*, pg. 1380
MEDIA MARKT TV-HIFI-ELEKTRO GMBH BERLIN-SPANDAU—See Ceconomy AG; *Int'l*, pg. 1374
MEDIA MARKT TV-HIFI-ELEKTRO GMBH BERLIN-STEGLITZ—See Ceconomy AG; *Int'l*, pg. 1380
MEDIA MARKT TV-HIFI-ELEKTRO GMBH BERLIN-TEGEL—See Ceconomy AG; *Int'l*, pg. 1380
MEDIA MARKT TV-HIFI-ELEKTRO GMBH BERLIN-TEMPELHOF—See Ceconomy AG; *Int'l*, pg. 1380
MEDIA MARKT TV-HIFI-ELEKTRO GMBH BERLIN-WEDDING—See Ceconomy AG; *Int'l*, pg. 1374
MEDIA MARKT TV-HIFI-ELEKTRO GMBH BIELEFELD—See Ceconomy AG; *Int'l*, pg. 1380
MEDIA MARKT TV-HIFI-ELEKTRO GMBH BISCHOFSHEIM—See Ceconomy AG; *Int'l*, pg. 1380
MEDIA MARKT TV-HIFI-ELEKTRO GMBH BOCHUM-RUHRPARK—See Ceconomy AG; *Int'l*, pg. 1380
MEDIA MARKT TV-HIFI-ELEKTRO GMBH BOCHUM—See Ceconomy AG; *Int'l*, pg. 1380
MEDIA MARKT TV-HIFI-ELEKTRO GMBH BONN—See Ceconomy AG; *Int'l*, pg. 1380
MEDIA MARKT TV-HIFI-ELEKTRO GMBH BRANDENBURG AN DER HAVEL—See Ceconomy AG; *Int'l*, pg. 1380
MEDIA MARKT TV-HIFI-ELEKTRO GMBH BRAUNSCHWEIG—See Ceconomy AG; *Int'l*, pg. 1380
MEDIA MARKT TV-HIFI-ELEKTRO GMBH BREMEN—See Ceconomy AG; *Int'l*, pg. 1380
MEDIA MARKT TV-HIFI-ELEKTRO GMBH BREMEN-WATERFRONT—See Ceconomy AG; *Int'l*, pg. 1380
MEDIA MARKT TV-HIFI-ELEKTRO GMBH BUCHHOLZ IN DER NORDHEIDE—See Ceconomy AG; *Int'l*, pg. 1380
MEDIA MARKT TV-HIFI-ELEKTRO GMBH BUXTEHUDE—See Ceconomy AG; *Int'l*, pg. 1380
MEDIA MARKT TV-HIFI-ELEKTRO GMBH CASTROP-RAUXEL—See Ceconomy AG; *Int'l*, pg. 1374
MEDIA MARKT TV-HIFI-ELEKTRO GMBH CHEMNITZ-ROHRSDORF—See Ceconomy AG; *Int'l*, pg. 1380
MEDIA MARKT TV-HIFI-ELEKTRO GMBH CHEMNITZ—See Ceconomy AG; *Int'l*, pg. 1380
MEDIA MARKT TV-HIFI-ELEKTRO GMBH COBURG—See Ceconomy AG; *Int'l*, pg. 1380
MEDIA MARKT TV-HIFI-ELEKTRO GMBH & CO. KG BRUCHSAL—See Ceconomy AG; *Int'l*, pg. 1380
MEDIA MARKT TV-HIFI-ELEKTRO GMBH COTTBUS/GROB GAGLOW—See Ceconomy AG; *Int'l*, pg. 1380
MEDIA MARKT TV-HIFI-ELEKTRO GMBH DEGGENDORF—See Ceconomy AG; *Int'l*, pg. 1380
MEDIA MARKT TV-HIFI-ELEKTRO GMBH DESSAU—See Ceconomy AG; *Int'l*, pg. 1380
MEDIA MARKT TV-HIFI-ELEKTRO GMBH DIETZENBACH—See Ceconomy AG; *Int'l*, pg. 1374
MEDIA MARKT TV-HIFI-ELEKTRO GMBH DONAUWORTH—See Ceconomy AG; *Int'l*, pg. 1380
MEDIA MARKT TV-HIFI-ELEKTRO GMBH DORSTEN—See Ceconomy AG; *Int'l*, pg. 1380
MEDIA MARKT TV-HIFI-ELEKTRO GMBH DORTMUND-HORDE—See Ceconomy AG; *Int'l*, pg. 1380
MEDIA MARKT TV-HIFI-ELEKTRO GMBH DORTMUND-OESPEL—See Ceconomy AG; *Int'l*, pg. 1380
MEDIA MARKT TV-HIFI-ELEKTRO GMBH DRESDEN CENTRUM—See Ceconomy AG; *Int'l*, pg. 1380
MEDIA MARKT TV-HIFI-ELEKTRO GMBH DRESDEN-MICKTEN—See Ceconomy AG; *Int'l*, pg. 1374
MEDIA MARKT TV-HIFI-ELEKTRO GMBH DUISBURG-GROBENBAUM—See Ceconomy AG; *Int'l*, pg. 1381
MEDIA MARKT TV-HIFI-ELEKTRO GMBH DUISBURG—See Ceconomy AG; *Int'l*, pg. 1381
MEDIA MARKT TV-HIFI-ELEKTRO GMBH DUSSELDORF BILK—See Ceconomy AG; *Int'l*, pg. 1380
MEDIA MARKT TV-HIFI-ELEKTRO GMBH DUSSELDORF—See Ceconomy AG; *Int'l*, pg. 1381
MEDIA MARKT TV-HIFI-ELEKTRO GMBH EGELSBACH—See Ceconomy AG; *Int'l*, pg. 1381
MEDIA MARKT TV-HIFI-ELEKTRO GMBH EICHE—See Ceconomy AG; *Int'l*, pg. 1381
MEDIA MARKT TV-HIFI-ELEKTRO GMBH EISENACH—See Ceconomy AG; *Int'l*, pg. 1381
MEDIA MARKT TV-HIFI-ELEKTRO GMBH EISLINGEN—See Ceconomy AG; *Int'l*, pg. 1381
MEDIA MARKT TV-HIFI-ELEKTRO GMBH ELMSHORN—See Ceconomy AG; *Int'l*, pg. 1381
MEDIA MARKT TV-HIFI-ELEKTRO GMBH EMDEN—See Ceconomy AG; *Int'l*, pg. 1381
MEDIA MARKT TV-HIFI-ELEKTRO GMBH ERDING—See Ceconomy AG; *Int'l*, pg. 1381
MEDIA MARKT TV-HIFI-ELEKTRO GMBH ERFURT-DABERSTEDT—See Ceconomy AG; *Int'l*, pg. 1381
MEDIA MARKT TV-HIFI-ELEKTRO GMBH ERFURT THURINGEN-PARK—See Ceconomy AG; *Int'l*, pg. 1381
MEDIA MARKT TV-HIFI-ELEKTRO GMBH ERLANGEN—See Ceconomy AG; *Int'l*, pg. 1381
MEDIA MARKT TV-HIFI-ELEKTRO GMBH ESCHWEILER—See Ceconomy AG; *Int'l*, pg. 1381
MEDIA MARKT TV-HIFI-ELEKTRO GMBH ESSEN—See Ceconomy AG; *Int'l*, pg. 1381
MEDIA MARKT TV-HIFI-ELEKTRO GMBH ESSLINGEN—See Ceconomy AG; *Int'l*, pg. 1381
MEDIA MARKT TV-HIFI-ELEKTRO GMBH FELLBACH—See Ceconomy AG; *Int'l*, pg. 1381
MEDIA MARKT TV-HIFI-ELEKTRO GMBH FLENSBURG—See Ceconomy AG; *Int'l*, pg. 1381
MEDIA MARKT TV-HIFI-ELEKTRO GMBH FRANKFURT BORSIGALLEE—See Ceconomy AG; *Int'l*, pg. 1374
MEDIA MARKT TV-HIFI-ELEKTRO GMBH FRIEDRICHSHAFEN—See Ceconomy AG; *Int'l*, pg. 1374
MEDIA MARKT TV-HIFI-ELEKTRO GMBH FULDA—See Ceconomy AG; *Int'l*, pg. 1381
MEDIA MARKT TV-HIFI-ELEKTRO GMBH GIFHORN—See Ceconomy AG; *Int'l*, pg. 1381
MEDIA MARKT TV-HIFI-ELEKTRO GMBH GOSLAR—See Ceconomy AG; *Int'l*, pg. 1384
MEDIA MARKT TV-HIFI-ELEKTRO GMBH GOTTINGEN—See Ceconomy AG; *Int'l*, pg. 1381
MEDIA MARKT TV-HIFI-ELEKTRO GMBH GREIFSWALD—See Ceconomy AG; *Int'l*, pg. 1381
MEDIA MARKT TV-HIFI-ELEKTRO GMBH GRUNDAU-LIEBLOS—See Ceconomy AG; *Int'l*, pg. 1381
MEDIA MARKT TV-HIFI-ELEKTRO GMBH GUNTHERSDORF—See Ceconomy AG; *Int'l*, pg. 1381
MEDIA MARKT TV-HIFI-ELEKTRO GMBH GUTERSLOH—See Ceconomy AG; *Int'l*, pg. 1374
MEDIA MARKT TV-HIFI-ELEKTRO GMBH HALBERSTADT—See Ceconomy AG; *Int'l*, pg. 1381
MEDIA MARKT TV-HIFI-ELEKTRO GMBH HALSTENBEK—See Ceconomy AG; *Int'l*, pg. 1381
MEDIA MARKT TV-HIFI-ELEKTRO GMBH HAMBURG-ALTONA—See Ceconomy AG; *Int'l*, pg. 1381
MEDIA MARKT TV-HIFI-ELEKTRO GMBH HAMBURG-BILLSTEDT—See Ceconomy AG; *Int'l*, pg. 1381
MEDIA MARKT TV-HIFI-ELEKTRO GMBH HAMBURG-HARBURG—See Ceconomy AG; *Int'l*, pg. 1381
MEDIA MARKT TV-HIFI-ELEKTRO GMBH HAMBURG-HUMMELSBUTTEL—See Ceconomy AG; *Int'l*, pg. 1381
MEDIA MARKT TV-HIFI-ELEKTRO GMBH HAMBURG-NEDDERFELD—See Ceconomy AG; *Int'l*, pg. 1381
MEDIA MARKT TV-HIFI-ELEKTRO GMBH HAMBURG-WANDSBEK—See Ceconomy AG; *Int'l*, pg. 1381
MEDIA MARKT TV-HIFI-ELEKTRO GMBH HAMELN—See Ceconomy AG; *Int'l*, pg. 1381
MEDIA MARKT TV-HIFI-ELEKTRO GMBH HANNOVER-VAHRENHEIDE—See Ceconomy AG; *Int'l*, pg. 1381
MEDIA MARKT TV-HIFI-ELEKTRO GMBH HANNOVER-WULFEL—See Ceconomy AG; *Int'l*, pg. 1374
MEDIA MARKT TV-HIFI-ELEKTRO GMBH HEIDELBERG-ROHRBACH—See Ceconomy AG; *Int'l*, pg. 1381
MEDIA MARKT TV-HIFI-ELEKTRO GMBH HEIDELBERG—See Ceconomy AG; *Int'l*, pg. 1375
MEDIA MARKT TV-HIFI-ELEKTRO GMBH HEIDE—See Ceconomy AG; *Int'l*, pg. 1381
MEDIA MARKT TV-HIFI-ELEKTRO GMBH HEILBRONN—See Ceconomy AG; *Int'l*, pg. 1381
MEDIA MARKT TV-HIFI-ELEKTRO GMBH HENSTEDT-ULZBURG—See Ceconomy AG; *Int'l*, pg. 1381
MEDIA MARKT TV-HIFI-ELEKTRO GMBH HEPPENHEIM—See Ceconomy AG; *Int'l*, pg. 1381
MEDIA MARKT TV-HIFI-ELEKTRO GMBH HILDESHEIM—See Ceconomy AG; *Int'l*, pg. 1381
MEDIA MARKT TV-HIFI-ELEKTRO GMBH HOF—See Ceconomy AG; *Int'l*, pg. 1381
MEDIA MARKT TV-HIFI-ELEKTRO GMBH HOLZMINDEN—See Ceconomy AG; *Int'l*, pg. 1381
MEDIA MARKT TV-HIFI-ELEKTRO GMBH HOMBURG/SAAR—See Ceconomy AG; *Int'l*, pg. 1381
MEDIA MARKT TV-HIFI-ELEKTRO GMBH HUCKELHOVEN—See Ceconomy AG; *Int'l*, pg. 1382
MEDIA MARKT TV-HIFI-ELEKTRO GMBH IDAR-OBERSTEIN—See Ceconomy AG; *Int'l*, pg. 1382
MEDIA MARKT TV-HIFI-ELEKTRO GMBH ITZEHOE—See Ceconomy AG; *Int'l*, pg. 1382
MEDIA MARKT TV-HIFI-ELEKTRO GMBH JENA—See Ceconomy AG; *Int'l*, pg. 1382
MEDIA MARKT TV-HIFI-ELEKTRO GMBH KAISERSLAUTERN—See Ceconomy AG; *Int'l*, pg. 1382
MEDIA MARKT TV-HIFI-ELEKTRO GMBH KARLSFELD—See Ceconomy AG; *Int'l*, pg. 1382
MEDIA MARKT TV-HIFI-ELEKTRO GMBH KARLSRUHE-ETTLINGER TOR—See Ceconomy AG; *Int'l*, pg. 1382
MEDIA MARKT TV-HIFI-ELEKTRO GMBH KARLSRUHE—See Ceconomy AG; *Int'l*, pg. 1382
MEDIA MARKT TV-HIFI-ELEKTRO GMBH KASSEL—See Ceconomy AG; *Int'l*, pg. 1382
MEDIA MARKT TV-HIFI-ELEKTRO GMBH KEMPTEN—See Ceconomy AG; *Int'l*, pg. 1382
MEDIA MARKT TV-HIFI-ELEKTRO GMBH KIEL—See Ceconomy AG; *Int'l*, pg. 1382
MEDIA MARKT TV-HIFI-ELEKTRO GMBH KIRCHHEIM—See Ceconomy AG; *Int'l*, pg. 1382
MEDIA MARKT TV-HIFI-ELEKTRO GMBH KOBLENZ—See Ceconomy AG; *Int'l*, pg. 1382
MEDIA MARKT TV-HIFI-ELEKTRO GMBH KOLN-CHORWEILER—See Ceconomy AG; *Int'l*, pg. 1382
MEDIA MARKT TV-HIFI-ELEKTRO GMBH KOLN HOHE STRASSE—See Ceconomy AG; *Int'l*, pg. 1382
MEDIA MARKT TV-HIFI-ELEKTRO GMBH KOLN-KALK—See Ceconomy AG; *Int'l*, pg. 1382
MEDIA MARKT TV-HIFI-ELEKTRO GMBH KOLN-MARSDORF—See Ceconomy AG; *Int'l*, pg. 1382
MEDIA MARKT TV-HIFI-ELEKTRO GMBH KONSTANZ—See Ceconomy AG; *Int'l*, pg. 1382
MEDIA MARKT TV-HIFI-ELEKTRO GMBH KREFELD—See Ceconomy AG; *Int'l*, pg. 1382
MEDIA MARKT TV-HIFI-ELEKTRO GMBH KULMBACH—See Ceconomy AG; *Int'l*, pg. 1382
MEDIA MARKT TV-HIFI-ELEKTRO GMBH LAHR—See Ceconomy AG; *Int'l*, pg. 1382
MEDIA MARKT TV-HIFI-ELEKTRO GMBH LANDAU/PFALZ—See Ceconomy AG; *Int'l*, pg. 1382
MEDIA MARKT TV-HIFI-ELEKTRO GMBH LANDSBERG/LECH—See Ceconomy AG; *Int'l*, pg. 1382
MEDIA MARKT TV-HIFI-ELEKTRO GMBH LANDSHUT—See Ceconomy AG; *Int'l*, pg. 1382
MEDIA MARKT TV-HIFI-ELEKTRO GMBH LEIPZIG HOFE AM BRUHL—See Ceconomy AG; *Int'l*, pg. 1382
MEDIA MARKT TV-HIFI-ELEKTRO GMBH LEIPZIG PAUNSDORF—See Ceconomy AG; *Int'l*, pg. 1382
MEDIA MARKT TV-HIFI-ELEKTRO GMBH LIMBURG—See Ceconomy AG; *Int'l*, pg. 1374
MEDIA MARKT TV-HIFI-ELEKTRO GMBH LINGEN—See Ceconomy AG; *Int'l*, pg. 1382
MEDIA MARKT TV-HIFI-ELEKTRO GMBH LUBECK—See Ceconomy AG; *Int'l*, pg. 1382
MEDIA MARKT TV-HIFI-ELEKTRO GMBH LUDWIGSBURG—See Ceconomy AG; *Int'l*, pg. 1382
MEDIA MARKT TV-HIFI-ELEKTRO GMBH LUDWIGSHAFEN—See Ceconomy AG; *Int'l*, pg. 1382
MEDIA MARKT TV-HIFI-ELEKTRO GMBH MAGDEBURG-BORDEPARK—See Ceconomy AG; *Int'l*, pg. 1382
MEDIA MARKT TV-HIFI-ELEKTRO GMBH MAGDEBURG—See Ceconomy AG; *Int'l*, pg. 1374
MEDIA MARKT TV-HIFI-ELEKTRO GMBH MAIN-TAUNUS-ZENTRUM—See Ceconomy AG; *Int'l*, pg. 1382
MEDIA MARKT TV-HIFI-ELEKTRO GMBH MAINZ—See Ceconomy AG; *Int'l*, pg. 1382
MEDIA MARKT TV-HIFI-ELEKTRO GMBH MANNHEIM-SANDHOFEN—See Ceconomy AG; *Int'l*, pg. 1382
MEDIA MARKT TV-HIFI-ELEKTRO GMBH MANNHEIM—See Ceconomy AG; *Int'l*, pg. 1382
MEDIA MARKT TV-HIFI-ELEKTRO GMBH

N.A.I.C.S. INDEX

449210 — ELECTRONICS AND APP...

MEDIA MARKT TV-HIFI-ELEKTRO GMBH MARBURG—See Ceconomy AG; *Int'l*, pg. 1374
MEDIA MARKT TV-HIFI-ELEKTRO GMBH MARKTREDWITZ—See Ceconomy AG; *Int'l*, pg. 1382
MEDIA MARKT TV-HIFI-ELEKTRO GMBH MEERANE—See Ceconomy AG; *Int'l*, pg. 1382
MEDIA MARKT TV-HIFI-ELEKTRO GMBH MEMMINGEN—See Ceconomy AG; *Int'l*, pg. 1382
MEDIA MARKT TV-HIFI-ELEKTRO GMBH MONCHENGLADBACH—See Ceconomy AG; *Int'l*, pg. 1382
MEDIA MARKT TV-HIFI-ELEKTRO GMBH MUHLDORF/INN—See Ceconomy AG; *Int'l*, pg. 1382
MEDIA MARKT TV-HIFI-ELEKTRO GMBH MULHEIM—See Ceconomy AG; *Int'l*, pg. 1382
MEDIA MARKT TV-HIFI-ELEKTRO GMBH MUNCHEN-HAIDHAUSEN—See Ceconomy AG; *Int'l*, pg. 1382
MEDIA MARKT TV-HIFI-ELEKTRO GMBH MUNCHEN-PASING—See Ceconomy AG; *Int'l*, pg. 1382
MEDIA MARKT TV-HIFI-ELEKTRO GMBH MUNCHEN-SOLLN—See Ceconomy AG; *Int'l*, pg. 1382
MEDIA MARKT TV-HIFI-ELEKTRO GMBH MUNSTER—See Ceconomy AG; *Int'l*, pg. 1382
MEDIA MARKT TV-HIFI-ELEKTRO GMBH NAGOLD—See Ceconomy AG; *Int'l*, pg. 1384
MEDIA MARKT TV-HIFI-ELEKTRO GMBH NEUBRANDENBURG—See Ceconomy AG; *Int'l*, pg. 1383
MEDIA MARKT TV-HIFI-ELEKTRO GMBH NEUBURG AN DER DONAU—See Ceconomy AG; *Int'l*, pg. 1383
MEDIA MARKT TV-HIFI-ELEKTRO GMBH NEUMUNSTER—See Ceconomy AG; *Int'l*, pg. 1383
MEDIA MARKT TV-HIFI-ELEKTRO GMBH NEUNKIRCHEN—See Ceconomy AG; *Int'l*, pg. 1383
MEDIA MARKT TV-HIFI-ELEKTRO GMBH NEUSS—See Ceconomy AG; *Int'l*, pg. 1383
MEDIA MARKT TV-HIFI-ELEKTRO GMBH NEU-ULM—See Ceconomy AG; *Int'l*, pg. 1383
MEDIA MARKT TV-HIFI-ELEKTRO GMBH NEUWIED—See Ceconomy AG; *Int'l*, pg. 1383
MEDIA MARKT TV-HIFI-ELEKTRO GMBH NIENBURG—See Ceconomy AG; *Int'l*, pg. 1374
MEDIA MARKT TV-HIFI-ELEKTRO GMBH NORDHAUSEN—See Ceconomy AG; *Int'l*, pg. 1383
MEDIA MARKT TV-HIFI-ELEKTRO GMBH NORDHORN—See Ceconomy AG; *Int'l*, pg. 1383
MEDIA MARKT TV-HIFI-ELEKTRO GMBH NURNBERG-KLEINREUTH—See Ceconomy AG; *Int'l*, pg. 1375
MEDIA MARKT TV-HIFI-ELEKTRO GMBH NURNBERG-LANGWASSER—See Ceconomy AG; *Int'l*, pg. 1374
MEDIA MARKT TV-HIFI-ELEKTRO GMBH NURNBERG-SCHOPPERSHOF—See Ceconomy AG; *Int'l*, pg. 1384
MEDIA MARKT TV-HIFI-ELEKTRO GMBH OFFENBURG—See Ceconomy AG; *Int'l*, pg. 1383
MEDIA MARKT TV-HIFI-ELEKTRO GMBH OLDENBURG—See Ceconomy AG; *Int'l*, pg. 1383
MEDIA MARKT TV-HIFI-ELEKTRO GMBH OSTSTEINBEK—See Ceconomy AG; *Int'l*, pg. 1383
MEDIA MARKT TV-HIFI-ELEKTRO GMBH PADERBORN—See Ceconomy AG; *Int'l*, pg. 1383
MEDIA MARKT TV-HIFI-ELEKTRO GMBH PAPENBURG—See Ceconomy AG; *Int'l*, pg. 1383
MEDIA MARKT TV-HIFI-ELEKTRO GMBH PASSAU—See Ceconomy AG; *Int'l*, pg. 1383
MEDIA MARKT TV-HIFI-ELEKTRO GMBH PEINE—See Ceconomy AG; *Int'l*, pg. 1383
MEDIA MARKT TV-HIFI-ELEKTRO GMBH PFORZHEIM—See Ceconomy AG; *Int'l*, pg. 1383
MEDIA MARKT TV-HIFI-ELEKTRO GMBH PIRMASENS—See Ceconomy AG; *Int'l*, pg. 1383
MEDIA MARKT TV-HIFI-ELEKTRO GMBH PLAUEN—See Ceconomy AG; *Int'l*, pg. 1383
MEDIA MARKT TV-HIFI-ELEKTRO GMBH RECKLINGHAUSEN—See Ceconomy AG; *Int'l*, pg. 1383
MEDIA MARKT TV-HIFI-ELEKTRO GMBH REGENSBURG—See Ceconomy AG; *Int'l*, pg. 1383
MEDIA MARKT TV-HIFI-ELEKTRO GMBH RENDSBURG—See Ceconomy AG; *Int'l*, pg. 1383
MEDIA MARKT TV-HIFI-ELEKTRO GMBH REUTLINGEN—See Ceconomy AG; *Int'l*, pg. 1383
MEDIA MARKT TV-HIFI-ELEKTRO GMBH RHEINE—See Ceconomy AG; *Int'l*, pg. 1374
MEDIA MARKT TV-HIFI-ELEKTRO GMBH RODENTAL—See Ceconomy AG; *Int'l*, pg. 1374
MEDIA MARKT TV-HIFI-ELEKTRO GMBH ROSENHEIM—See Ceconomy AG; *Int'l*, pg. 1374
MEDIA MARKT TV-HIFI-ELEKTRO GMBH ROSTOCK-BRINCKMANSDORF—See Ceconomy AG; *Int'l*, pg. 1383
MEDIA MARKT TV-HIFI-ELEKTRO GMBH ROSTOCK—See Ceconomy AG; *Int'l*, pg. 1383
MEDIA MARKT TV-HIFI-ELEKTRO GMBH SAARBRUCKEN-SAARTERRASSEN—See Ceconomy AG; *Int'l*, pg. 1383
MEDIA MARKT TV-HIFI-ELEKTRO GMBH SAARBRUCKEN—See Ceconomy AG; *Int'l*, pg. 1374
MEDIA MARKT TV-HIFI-ELEKTRO GMBH SAARLOUIS—See Ceconomy AG; *Int'l*, pg. 1383
MEDIA MARKT TV-HIFI-ELEKTRO GMBH SCHIFFDORF-SPADEN—See Ceconomy AG; *Int'l*, pg. 1383
MEDIA MARKT TV-HIFI-ELEKTRO GMBH SCHWABACH—See Ceconomy AG; *Int'l*, pg. 1383
MEDIA MARKT TV-HIFI-ELEKTRO GMBH SCHWEDT—See Ceconomy AG; *Int'l*, pg. 1383
MEDIA MARKT TV-HIFI-ELEKTRO GMBH SCHWEINFURT—See Ceconomy AG; *Int'l*, pg. 1383
MEDIA MARKT TV-HIFI-ELEKTRO GMBH SCHWERIN—See Ceconomy AG; *Int'l*, pg. 1383
MEDIA MARKT TV-HIFI-ELEKTRO GMBH SIEGEN—See Ceconomy AG; *Int'l*, pg. 1383
MEDIA MARKT TV-HIFI-ELEKTRO GMBH SINDELFINGEN—See Ceconomy AG; *Int'l*, pg. 1383
MEDIA MARKT TV-HIFI-ELEKTRO GMBH SINGEN—See Ceconomy AG; *Int'l*, pg. 1374
MEDIA MARKT TV-HIFI-ELEKTRO GMBH SINSHEIM—See Ceconomy AG; *Int'l*, pg. 1383
MEDIA MARKT TV-HIFI-ELEKTRO GMBH—See Ceconomy AG; *Int'l*, pg. 1375
MEDIA MARKT TV-HIFI-ELEKTRO GMBH SPEYER—See Ceconomy AG; *Int'l*, pg. 1383
MEDIA MARKT TV-HIFI-ELEKTRO GMBH STADE—See Ceconomy AG; *Int'l*, pg. 1383
MEDIA MARKT TV-HIFI-ELEKTRO GMBH STRALSUND—See Ceconomy AG; *Int'l*, pg. 1383
MEDIA MARKT TV-HIFI-ELEKTRO GMBH STRAUBING—See Ceconomy AG; *Int'l*, pg. 1383
MEDIA MARKT TV-HIFI-ELEKTRO GMBH STUHR—See Ceconomy AG; *Int'l*, pg. 1374
MEDIA MARKT TV-HIFI-ELEKTRO GMBH STUTTGART-FEUERBACH—See Ceconomy AG; *Int'l*, pg. 1383
MEDIA MARKT TV-HIFI-ELEKTRO GMBH STUTTGART-VAIHINGEN—See Ceconomy AG; *Int'l*, pg. 1383
MEDIA MARKT TV-HIFI-ELEKTRO GMBH TRAUNSTEIN—See Ceconomy AG; *Int'l*, pg. 1384
MEDIA MARKT TV-HIFI-ELEKTRO GMBH TRIER—See Ceconomy AG; *Int'l*, pg. 1374
MEDIA MARKT TV-HIFI-ELEKTRO GMBH ULM—See Ceconomy AG; *Int'l*, pg. 1374
MEDIA MARKT TV-HIFI-ELEKTRO GMBH VELBERT—See Ceconomy AG; *Int'l*, pg. 1384
MEDIA MARKT TV-HIFI-ELEKTRO GMBH VIERNHEIM—See Ceconomy AG; *Int'l*, pg. 1384
MEDIA MARKT TV-HIFI-ELEKTRO GMBH WALTERSDORF BEI BERLIN—See Ceconomy AG; *Int'l*, pg. 1384
MEDIA MARKT TV-HIFI-ELEKTRO GMBH WEIDEN—See Ceconomy AG; *Int'l*, pg. 1384
MEDIA MARKT TV-HIFI-ELEKTRO GMBH WEILHEIM—See Ceconomy AG; *Int'l*, pg. 1384
MEDIA MARKT TV-HIFI-ELEKTRO GMBH WEITERSTADT—See Ceconomy AG; *Int'l*, pg. 1384
MEDIA MARKT TV-HIFI-ELEKTRO GMBH WETZLAR—See Ceconomy AG; *Int'l*, pg. 1384
MEDIA MARKT TV-HIFI-ELEKTRO GMBH WIESBADEN-APPELALLEE—See Ceconomy AG; *Int'l*, pg. 1384
MEDIA MARKT TV-HIFI-ELEKTRO GMBH WIESBADEN—See Ceconomy AG; *Int'l*, pg. 1384
MEDIA MARKT TV-HIFI-ELEKTRO GMBH WOLFSBURG—See Ceconomy AG; *Int'l*, pg. 1384
MEDIA MARKT TV-HIFI-ELEKTRO GMBH WORMS—See Ceconomy AG; *Int'l*, pg. 1384
MEDIA MARKT TV-HIFI-ELEKTRO GMBH WUPPERTAL—See Ceconomy AG; *Int'l*, pg. 1384
MEDIA MARKT TV-HIFI-ELEKTRO GMBH WURZBURG - ALFRED-NOBEL-STRASSE—See Ceconomy AG; *Int'l*, pg. 1384
MEDIA MARKT TV-HIFI-ELEKTRO GMBH WURZBURG—See Ceconomy AG; *Int'l*, pg. 1384
MEDIA MARKT TV-HIFI-ELEKTRO GMBH ZELLA-MEHLIS—See Ceconomy AG; *Int'l*, pg. 1375
MEDIA MARKT TV-HIFI-ELEKTRO GMBH ZWICKAU—See Ceconomy AG; *Int'l*, pg. 1384
MEDIA MARKT TV-HIFI-ELEKTRO LICHT GMBH INGOLSTADT—See Ceconomy AG; *Int'l*, pg. 1375
MEDIA MARKT TV-HIFI-ELEKTRO WIEN XI GESELLSCHAFT M.B.H.—See Ceconomy AG; *Int'l*, pg. 1375
MEDIA MARKT TV-HIFI-ELEKTRO WIEN XIII GMBH—See Ceconomy AG; *Int'l*, pg. 1375
MEDIA MARKT TV-HIFI-ELEKTRO WIEN XXI GESELLSCHAFT M.B.H.—See Ceconomy AG; *Int'l*, pg. 1384
MEDIA MARKT UPPSALA TV-HIFI-ELEKTRO AB—See Ceconomy AG; *Int'l*, pg. 1384
MEDIA MARKT UTRECHT B.V.—See Ceconomy AG; *Int'l*, pg. 1384
MEDIA MARKT UTRECHT THE WALL B.V.—See Ceconomy AG; *Int'l*, pg. 1384
MEDIA MARKT VALENCIA COLON SA—See Ceconomy AG; *Int'l*, pg. 1384
MEDIA MARKT VALLADOLID VFDEO-TV-HIFI-ELEKTRO-COMPUTER-FOTO, SA—See Ceconomy AG; *Int'l*, pg. 1384
MEDIA MARKT VASTERAS TV-HIFI-ELEKTRO AB—See Ceconomy AG; *Int'l*, pg. 1384
MEDIA MARKT VENLO B.V.—See Ceconomy AG; *Int'l*, pg. 1384
MEDIA MARKT VIDEO-TV-HIFI-ELEKTRO-COMPUTER-FOTO GRANCIA AG—See Ceconomy AG; *Int'l*, pg. 1384
MEDIA MARKT VIGO VIDEO-TV-HIFI-ELEKTRO-COMPUTER-FOTO S.A.—See Ceconomy AG; *Int'l*, pg. 1384
MEDIA MARKT VOCKLABRUCK TV-HIFI-ELEKTRO GMBH—See Ceconomy AG; *Int'l*, pg. 1384
MEDIA MARKT WELS TV-HIFI-ELEKTRO GMBH—See Ceconomy AG; *Int'l*, pg. 1384
MEDIA MARKT- WEST END VIDEO TV, HIFI ELEKTRO PHOTO COMPUTER KERESKEDELMI KFT.—See Ceconomy AG; *Int'l*, pg. 1375
MEDIA MARKT WIEN III TV-HIFI-ELEKTRO GMBH—See Ceconomy AG; *Int'l*, pg. 1384
MEDIA MARKT WIEN XV TV-HIFI-ELEKTRO GMBH—See Ceconomy AG; *Int'l*, pg. 1384
MEDIA MARKT ZAANDAM B.V.—See Ceconomy AG; *Int'l*, pg. 1385
MEDIA MARKT ZARAGOZA PUERTO VENECIA VIDEO-TV-HIFI-ELEKTRO-COMPUTER-FOTO, S.A.—See Ceconomy AG; *Int'l*, pg. 1375
MEDIA MARKT ZELL AM SEE TV-HIFI-ELEKTRO GMBH—See Ceconomy AG; *Int'l*, pg. 1385
MEDIA MARKT ZOETERMEER B.V.—See Ceconomy AG; *Int'l*, pg. 1385
MEDIA MARKT ZURICH AG—See Ceconomy AG; *Int'l*, pg. 1385
MEDIA MARKT ZWEI TV-HIFI-ELEKTRO GMBH DRESDEN-PROHLIS—See Ceconomy AG; *Int'l*, pg. 1385
MEDIA MARKT ZWIJNAARDE NV—See Ceconomy AG; *Int'l*, pg. 1385
MEDIA MARKT ZWOLLE B.V.—See Ceconomy AG; *Int'l*, pg. 1385
MEDIA - SATURN BETEILIGUNGSGES .M.B.H.—See Ceconomy AG; *Int'l*, pg. 1375
MEDIA-SATURN-HOLDING GMBH—See Ceconomy AG; *Int'l*, pg. 1385
MEDIA-SATURN HOLDING SWEDEN AB—See Ceconomy AG; *Int'l*, pg. 1385
MEDIA SATURN MULTICHANNEL SAU MADRID-ISLAZUL—See Ceconomy AG; *Int'l*, pg. 1385
MEDIA-SATURN (PORTUGAL), SGPS, UNIPESSOAL LDA—See Ceconomy AG; *Int'l*, pg. 1375
MERCURY APPLIANCES LIMITED—See The Middleby Corporation; *U.S. Public*, pg. 2114
MERITECH INC.; *U.S. Private*, pg. 2675
MERRICK ADVANCED PHOTOGRAMMETRY OF THE AMERICAS, S. DE. R.L. DE C.V.—See Merrick & Company Inc.; *U.S. Private*, pg. 2675
MICROMAN, INC.; *U.S. Private*, pg. 2703
MICRO SECURITY SOLUTIONS INC.—See Dunes Point Capital, LLC; *U.S. Private*, pg. 1289
MIDWAY APPLIANCE CENTER, INC.—See Howard's Appliances, Inc.; *U.S. Private*, pg. 1995
MIKE'S CAMERA INC.; *U.S. Private*, pg. 2726
MINTED LLC.; *U.S. Private*, pg. 2745
MISCO ITALY COMPUTER SUPPLIES S.P.A.—See Computacenter plc; *Int'l*, pg. 1758
MITEL NETWORKS ASIA PACIFIC LTD.—See Searchlight Capital Partners, L.P.; *U.S. Private*, pg. 3589
M & M VISIONS OY—See BHG Group AB; *Int'l*, pg. 1015
MOBILE SYSTEMS WIRELESS LLC; *U.S. Private*, pg. 2757
MOGAMI HONGKONG CO., LTD.—See EQT AB; *Int'l*, pg. 2470
MOLEX B.V. - ESPANA—See Koch Industries, Inc.; *U.S. Private*, pg. 2334
MOLEX B.V.—See Koch Industries, Inc.; *U.S. Private*, pg. 2334
MOLEX DE MEXICO S.A. DE C.V.—See Koch Industries, Inc.; *U.S. Private*, pg. 2335
MOLEX ELECTRONICS LTD.—See Koch Industries, Inc.; *U.S. Private*, pg. 2334
MOLEX (INDIA) LTD.—See Koch Industries, Inc.; *U.S. Private*, pg. 2334
MOLEX JAPAN CO., LTD.—See Koch Industries, Inc.; *U.S. Private*, pg. 2334
MOLEX KNUTSEN NORGE AS—See Koch Industries, Inc.; *U.S. Private*, pg. 2334
MOLEX SWEDEN—See Koch Industries, Inc.; *U.S. Private*, pg. 2334
MOLEX (THAILAND) LTD.—See Koch Industries, Inc.; *U.S. Private*, pg. 2334
MOLEX TURKEY—See Koch Industries, Inc.; *U.S. Private*, pg. 2335
MOOD MEDIA AB—See Vector Capital Management, L.P.; *U.S. Private*, pg. 4351
MOTEC GMBH—See AMETEK, Inc.; *U.S. Public*, pg. 121
MOVIES UNLIMITED INC.; *U.S. Private*, pg. 2802
M&S TECHNOLOGIES, INC.—See Windjammer Capital Investors, LLC; *U.S. Private*, pg. 4538
MTR GROUP LIMITED—See DCC plc; *Int'l*, pg. 1991
MULTIBAND NC INC.—See Goodman Networks, Inc.; *U.S. Private*, pg. 1739
MYERCONNEX; *U.S. Private*, pg. 2824
MY FAMILY CLUB LIMITED—See D.C. Thomson & Co. Ltd.; *Int'l*, pg. 1900
NATIONAL CAMERA EXCHANGE INC.; *U.S. Private*, pg. 2849

449210 — ELECTRONICS AND APP...

NATIONAL TELECONSULTANTS INC.—See Deloitte LLP; *U.S. Private,* pg. 1198
NATIONAL TELECONSULTANTS INC.—See Deloitte Touche Tohmatsu Limited; *Int'l,* pg. 2015
NEGRI ELECTRONICS; *U.S. Private,* pg. 2880
NEW AGE COMPUTER SOLUTIONS; *U.S. Private,* pg. 2892
NEWBURY COMICS INC.; *U.S. Private,* pg. 2914
NEXCOM GROUP; *U.S. Private,* pg. 2919
NEXT STAR COMMUNICATIONS, INC.; *U.S. Private,* pg. 2920
NEXTWORTH SOLUTIONS, INC.; *U.S. Private,* pg. 2921
NIEDERAUER INC.; *U.S. Private,* pg. 2926
NJOY ELECTRONIC CIGARETTE; *U.S. Private,* pg. 2931
NORTHEAST RURAL SERVICES INC.—See Northeast Oklahoma Electric Cooperative Inc.; *U.S. Private,* pg. 2950
NOTEBOOKSBILLIGER.DE AG—See ElectronicPartner Handel SE; *Int'l,* pg. 2354
OCEANSIDE PHOTO & TELESCOPE; *U.S. Private,* pg. 2990
OLUMS OF BINGHAMTON INC.; *U.S. Private,* pg. 3012
OMNI CORPORATION; *U.S. Private,* pg. 3016
ON APPROACH LLC—See Trellance, Inc.; *U.S. Private,* pg. 4217
ONEDIRECT SAS—See Groupe BPCE; *Int'l,* pg. 3095
OPEN-SILICON, INC—See SiFive, Inc.; *U.S. Private,* pg. 3648
ORACLE CANADA ULC - MARKHAM—See Oracle Corporation; *U.S. Public,* pg. 1611
PACE COMPUTER SOLUTIONS INC; *U.S. Private,* pg. 3063
PACEJET LOGISTICS, INC.—See Sumeru Equity Partners LLC; *U.S. Private,* pg. 3852
PALTALK; *U.S. Private,* pg. 3082
PARSEC COMPUTER CORP.; *U.S. Private,* pg. 3100
P.C. RICHARD & SON LONG ISLAND CORP.—See P.C. Richard & Son; *U.S. Private,* pg. 3060
P.C. RICHARD & SON; *U.S. Private,* pg. 3060
PC WAREHOUSE INVESTMENT INC.; *U.S. Private,* pg. 3119
PEACHMAC; *U.S. Private,* pg. 3123
PENNY AUCTION SOLUTIONS, INC.; *U.S. Private,* pg. 3137
P&F USA—See Funai Electric Co., Ltd.; *Int'l,* pg. 2844
PHOENIX TELECOMMUNICATIONS, INC.—See Level-4 Telcom; *U.S. Private,* pg. 2434
PLASS APPLIANCES AND FURNITURE INC.; *U.S. Private,* pg. 3198
PLAZA APPLIANCE MART INC.; *U.S. Private,* pg. 3212
POIRIER SERVICE CORPORATION; *U.S. Private,* pg. 3222
POLYCOM AG—See HP Inc.; *U.S. Public,* pg. 1064
POLYCOM GMBH—See HP Inc.; *U.S. Public,* pg. 1064
POWERON SERVICES, INC.; *U.S. Private,* pg. 3239
PRECISION CAMERA LP; *U.S. Private,* pg. 3244
PREZZYBOX.COM LTD—See Gift Universe Group Limited; *Int'l,* pg. 2970
PROGRESSIVE AUTO STEREO INC.; *U.S. Private,* pg. 3278
PRO SYSTEMS CORP; *U.S. Private,* pg. 3270
QINGDAO FU QIANG ELECTRONICS CO., LTD.—See Fu Yu Corporation Limited; *Int'l,* pg. 2801
QUIBIDS, LLC; *U.S. Private,* pg. 3326
RAC ENTERPRISES INC.; *U.S. Private,* pg. 3341
RACOM CORPORATION; *U.S. Private,* pg. 3342
RADIOSHACK DE MEXICO S.A. DE C.V.—See Grupo Gigante, S.A.B. de C.V.; *Int'l,* pg. 3130
RADIOSHACK DISTRIBUTION CENTER—See RS Legacy Corporation; *U.S. Private,* pg. 3496
RADIOSHACK (HK) LTD—See RS Legacy Corporation; *U.S. Private,* pg. 3496
RAM QUEST SOFTWARE, INC.—See Tyler Technologies, Inc.; *U.S. Public,* pg. 2209
RASPUTIN RECORDS INC.; *U.S. Private,* pg. 3357
RAYOVAC HONDURAS, SA—See Energizer Holdings, Inc.; *U.S. Public,* pg. 761
RECKER & BOERGER INC.; *U.S. Private,* pg. 3370
RECONSERVE, INC.—See ReConserve, Inc.; *U.S. Private,* pg. 3371
RECO TECHNOLOGY HONG KONG LIMITED—See General Interface Solution (GIS) Holding Ltd.; *Int'l,* pg. 2919
RECURSION SOFTWARE, INC.; *U.S. Private,* pg. 3372
REDLINE ENTERTAINMENT, INC.—See Best Buy Co., Inc.; *U.S. Public,* pg. 326
RELEVANCE INC.; *U.S. Private,* pg. 3393
RENA WARE DEL PERU, S.A.—See Rena-Ware Distributors Inc.; *U.S. Private,* pg. 3397
RENA WARE (THAILAND) LIMITED—See Rena-Ware Distributors Inc.; *U.S. Private,* pg. 3397
RENESAN SOFTWARE; *U.S. Private,* pg. 3397
RENO'S APPLIANCE INC.; *U.S. Private,* pg. 3399
RENUEVA COMERCIAL SAPI DE CV—See EZCORP, Inc.; *U.S. Public,* pg. 818
RESIDENTIAL SYSTEMS, INC.—See Presidio Investors LLC; *U.S. Private,* pg. 3255
REX RADIO AND TELEVISION, INC.—See REX American Resources Corporation; *U.S. Public,* pg. 1795
RICHARDSON ELECTRONICS GMBH—See Richardson Electronics, Ltd.; *U.S. Public,* pg. 1797
RICHARDSON ELECTRONICS ITALY, S.R.L.—See Richardson Electronics, Ltd.; *U.S. Public,* pg. 1798
RICHARDSON ELECTRONICS JAPAN CO., LTD.—See Richardson Electronics, Ltd.; *U.S. Public,* pg. 1798
RICHARDSON ELECTRONICS LTD.-NORTHEASTERN—See Richardson Electronics, Ltd.; *U.S. Public,* pg. 1798
RICHARDSON ELECTRONICS, LTD.—See Richardson Electronics, Ltd.; *U.S. Public,* pg. 1798
RICHARDSON ELECTRONICS, LTD. - SPAIN—See Richardson Electronics, Ltd.; *U.S. Public,* pg. 1798
RICHARDSON RFPD CANADA LTD.—See Arrow Electronics, Inc.; *U.S. Public,* pg. 200
RMI, LLC; *U.S. Private,* pg. 3452
ROCKWELL AUTOMATION PROPRIETARY LIMITED—See Rockwell Automation, Inc.; *U.S. Public,* pg. 1806
RODATA INC.; *U.S. Private,* pg. 3469
ROGERS JAPAN INC.—See Rogers Corporation; *U.S. Public,* pg. 1808
ROSETTA TECHNOLOGIES CORP.; *U.S. Private,* pg. 3484
ROXAR SOFTWARE SOLUTIONS AS—See Emerson Electric Co.; *U.S. Public,* pg. 752
ROXBURY TECHNOLOGY CORP; *U.S. Private,* pg. 3490
RS LEGACY CORPORATION; *U.S. Private,* pg. 3496
RW COOKWARE S.L.—See Rena-Ware Distributors Inc.; *U.S. Private,* pg. 3397
RW INOX DE RL DE C.V.—See Rena-Ware Distributors Inc.; *U.S. Private,* pg. 3397
SAGE APPLIANCES FRANCE SAS—See Breville Group Limited; *Int'l,* pg. 1150
SAGE APPLIANCES GMBH—See Breville Group Limited; *Int'l,* pg. 1150
SALEM GROUP INC.; *U.S. Private,* pg. 3531
SAMY'S CAMERA INC.; *U.S. Private,* pg. 3538
SANDERSON NI LIMITED—See TA Associates, Inc.; *U.S. Private,* pg. 3914
SARANTIS D.O.O.—See Gr. Sarantis S.A.; *Int'l,* pg. 3047
SARANTIS-SKOPJE D.O.O.—See Gr. Sarantis S.A.; *Int'l,* pg. 3048
SATURN BRUGGE NV—See Ceconomy AG; *Int'l,* pg. 1385
SATURN DUNA VIDEO TV HIFI ELEKTRO PHOTO COMPUTER KERESKEDELMI KFT.—See Ceconomy AG; *Int'l,* pg. 1385
SATURN ELECTRO-HANDELSGESELLSCHAFT MBH AUGSBURG—See Ceconomy AG; *Int'l,* pg. 1385
SATURN ELECTROHANDELSGESELLSCHAFT MBH BAD HOMBURG—See Ceconomy AG; *Int'l,* pg. 1385
SATURN ELECTRO-HANDELSGESELLSCHAFT MBH BAUNATAL—See Ceconomy AG; *Int'l,* pg. 1385
SATURN ELECTRO-HANDELSGESELLSCHAFT MBH BERLIN-KOPENICK—See Ceconomy AG; *Int'l,* pg. 1385
SATURN ELECTRO-HANDELSGESELLSCHAFT MBH BERLIN-LEIPZIGER PLATZ—See Ceconomy AG; *Int'l,* pg. 1385
SATURN ELECTRO-HANDELSGESELLSCHAFT MBH BERLIN-MARKISCHE ZEILE—See Ceconomy AG; *Int'l,* pg. 1385
SATURN ELECTRO-HANDELSGESELLSCHAFT MBH BERLIN-MARZAHN—See Ceconomy AG; *Int'l,* pg. 1385
SATURN ELECTRO-HANDELSGESELLSCHAFT MBH BERLIN-SCHLO15STRA15E—See Ceconomy AG; *Int'l,* pg. 1385
SATURN ELECTRO-HANDELSGESELLSCHAFT MBH BERLIN-TREPTOW—See Ceconomy AG; *Int'l,* pg. 1385
SATURN ELECTRO-HANDELSGESELLSCHAFT MBH BOCHOLT—See Ceconomy AG; *Int'l,* pg. 1385
SATURN ELECTRO-HANDELSGESELLSCHAFT MBH BOCHUM—See Ceconomy AG; *Int'l,* pg. 1385
SATURN ELECTRO-HANDELSGESELLSCHAFT MBH BRAUNSCHWEIG—See Ceconomy AG; *Int'l,* pg. 1385
SATURN ELECTRO-HANDELSGESELLSCHAFT MBH BREMEN-HABENHAUSEN—See Ceconomy AG; *Int'l,* pg. 1385
SATURN ELECTRO HANDELSGESELLSCHAFT MBH BREMEN—See Ceconomy AG; *Int'l,* pg. 1385
SATURN ELECTRO-HANDELSGESELLSCHAFT MBH CELLE—See Ceconomy AG; *Int'l,* pg. 1385
SATURN ELECTRO-HANDELSGESELLSCHAFT MBH CHEMNITZ—See Ceconomy AG; *Int'l,* pg. 1386
SATURN ELECTRO-HANDELSGESELLSCHAFT MBH CHEMNITZ-ZENTRUM—See Ceconomy AG; *Int'l,* pg. 1386
SATURN ELECTRO-HANDELSGESELLSCHAFT MBH DORTMUND-EVING—See Ceconomy AG; *Int'l,* pg. 1386
SATURN ELECTRO-HANDELSGESELLSCHAFT MBH DORTMUND—See Ceconomy AG; *Int'l,* pg. 1386
SATURN ELECTRO-HANDELSGESELLSCHAFT MBH DRESDEN—See Ceconomy AG; *Int'l,* pg. 1386
SATURN ELECTRO-HANDELSGESELLSCHAFT MBH DUISBURG—See Ceconomy AG; *Int'l,* pg. 1386
SATURN ELECTRO-HANDELSGESELLSCHAFT MBH ERFURT—See Ceconomy AG; *Int'l,* pg. 1386
SATURN ELECTRO-HANDELSGESELLSCHAFT MBH ERLANGEN—See Ceconomy AG; *Int'l,* pg. 1386
SATURN ELECTRO-HANDELSGESELLSCHAFT MBH ESSEN—See Ceconomy AG; *Int'l,* pg. 1386
SATURN ELECTRO-HANDELSGESELLSCHAFT MBH ESSLINGEN—See Ceconomy AG; *Int'l,* pg. 1386
SATURN ELECTRO-HANDELSGESELLSCHAFT MBH EUSKIRCHEN—See Ceconomy AG; *Int'l,* pg. 1386
SATURN ELECTRO-HANDELSGESELLSCHAFT MBH FLENSBURG—See Ceconomy AG; *Int'l,* pg. 1386
SATURN ELECTRO-HANDELSGESELLSCHAFT MBH FRANKFURT/MAIN—See Ceconomy AG; *Int'l,* pg. 1386
SATURN ELECTRO-HANDELSGESELLSCHAFT MBH FREIBURG—See Ceconomy AG; *Int'l,* pg. 1386
SATURN ELECTRO-HANDELSGESELLSCHAFT MBH FREISING—See Ceconomy AG; *Int'l,* pg. 1386
SATURN ELECTRO-HANDELSGESELLSCHAFT MBH FURTH—See Ceconomy AG; *Int'l,* pg. 1386
SATURN ELECTRO-HANDELSGESELLSCHAFT MBH GOTTINGEN—See Ceconomy AG; *Int'l,* pg. 1386
SATURN ELECTRO-HANDELSGESELLSCHAFT MBH GUMMERSBACH—See Ceconomy AG; *Int'l,* pg. 1386
SATURN ELECTRO-HANDELSGESELLSCHAFT MBH HAGEN—See Ceconomy AG; *Int'l,* pg. 1386
SATURN ELECTRO-HANDELSGESELLSCHAFT MBH HAMBURG-ALTSTADT—See Ceconomy AG; *Int'l,* pg. 1386
SATURN ELECTRO-HANDELSGESELLSCHAFT MBH HAMM—See Ceconomy AG; *Int'l,* pg. 1386
SATURN ELECTRO-HANDELSGESELLSCHAFT MBH HANAU—See Ceconomy AG; *Int'l,* pg. 1386
SATURN ELECTRO-HANDELSGESELLSCHAFT MBH HANNOVER—See Ceconomy AG; *Int'l,* pg. 1386
SATURN ELECTRO-HANDELSGESELLSCHAFT MBH HATTINGEN—See Ceconomy AG; *Int'l,* pg. 1386
SATURN ELECTRO-HANDELSGESELLSCHAFT MBH HILDEN—See Ceconomy AG; *Int'l,* pg. 1386
SATURN ELECTRO-HANDELSGESELLSCHAFT MBH JENA—See Ceconomy AG; *Int'l,* pg. 1386
SATURN ELECTRO-HANDELSGESELLSCHAFT MBH KERPEN—See Ceconomy AG; *Int'l,* pg. 1386
SATURN ELECTRO-HANDELSGESELLSCHAFT MBH KIEL—See Ceconomy AG; *Int'l,* pg. 1386
SATURN ELECTRO-HANDELSGESELLSCHAFT MBH KLEVE—See Ceconomy AG; *Int'l,* pg. 1386
SATURN ELECTRO-HANDELSGESELLSCHAFT MBH LEONBERG—See Ceconomy AG; *Int'l,* pg. 1386
SATURN ELECTRO-HANDELSGESELLSCHAFT MBH MANNHEIM—See Ceconomy AG; *Int'l,* pg. 1387
SATURN ELECTRO-HANDELSGESELLSCHAFT MBH MUNCHEN—See Ceconomy AG; *Int'l,* pg. 1387
SATURN ELECTRO-HANDELSGESELLSCHAFT MBH MUNSTER—See Ceconomy AG; *Int'l,* pg. 1387
SATURN ELECTRO-HANDELSGESELLSCHAFT MBH NORDERSTEDT—See Ceconomy AG; *Int'l,* pg. 1387
SATURN ELECTRO-HANDELSGESELLSCHAFT MBH NURNBERG—See Ceconomy AG; *Int'l,* pg. 1387
SATURN ELECTRO-HANDELSGESELLSCHAFT MBH OLDENBURG—See Ceconomy AG; *Int'l,* pg. 1387
SATURN ELECTRO-HANDELSGESELLSCHAFT MBH PADERBORN—See Ceconomy AG; *Int'l,* pg. 1387
SATURN ELECTRO-HANDELSGESELLSCHAFT MBH PASSAU—See Ceconomy AG; *Int'l,* pg. 1387
SATURN ELECTRO-HANDELSGESELLSCHAFT MBH POTSDAM—See Ceconomy AG; *Int'l,* pg. 1387
SATURN ELECTRO-HANDELSGESELLSCHAFT MBH REGENSBURG—See Ceconomy AG; *Int'l,* pg. 1387
SATURN ELECTRO-HANDELSGESELLSCHAFT MBH SENDEN—See Ceconomy AG; *Int'l,* pg. 1387
SATURN ELECTRO-HANDELSGESELLSCHAFT MBH STUTTGART-CITY—See Ceconomy AG; *Int'l,* pg. 1387
SATURN ELECTRO-HANDELSGESELLSCHAFT MBH TROISDORF—See Ceconomy AG; *Int'l,* pg. 1387
SATURN GERASDORF ELECTRO-HANDELSGES.M.B.H.—See Ceconomy AG; *Int'l,* pg. 1387
SATURN GRONINGEN B.V.—See Ceconomy AG; *Int'l,* pg. 1387
SATURN HEERHUGOWAARD B.V.—See Ceconomy AG; *Int'l,* pg. 1387
SATURN HOOFDDORP B.V.—See Ceconomy AG; *Int'l,* pg. 1387
SATURN INNSBRUCK ELECTRO-HANDELSGES.M.B.H.—See Ceconomy AG; *Int'l,* pg. 1387
SATURN LUXEMBOURG S.A.—See Ceconomy AG; *Int'l,* pg. 1387
SATURN MADRID-PLENILUNIO ELEKTRO, S.A.—See Ceconomy AG; *Int'l,* pg. 1385
SATURN-MEGA MARKT GMBH HALLE—See Ceconomy AG; *Int'l,* pg. 1388
SATURN-MEGA MARKT GMBH TRIER—See Ceconomy AG; *Int'l,* pg. 1388
SATURN MEGA MARKT GMBH WUPPERTAL—See Ceconomy AG; *Int'l,* pg. 1387
SATURN PLANET SP. Z O.O. KRAKOW I SPOLKA KOMANDYTOWA—See Ceconomy AG; *Int'l,* pg. 1387
SATURN PLANET SP. Z O.O. TYCHY SPOLKA KOMANDYTOWA—See Ceconomy AG; *Int'l,* pg. 1387
SATURN PLANET SP. Z O.O. WARSZAWA III SPOLKA KOMANDYTOWA—See Ceconomy AG; *Int'l,* pg. 1387
SATURN ROTTERDAM ZUIDPLEIN B.V.—See Ceconomy AG; *Int'l,* pg. 1388

N.A.I.C.S. INDEX

455110 — DEPARTMENT STORES

SATURN TECHNO-ELECTRO-HANDELSGESELLSCHAFT MBH—See Ceconomy AG; *Int'l*, pg. 1388
SATURN TECHNO-MARKT ELECTRO GMBH & CO. OHG—See Ceconomy AG; *Int'l*, pg. 1388
SATURN TECHNO-MARKT ELECTRO-HANDELSGESELLSCHAFT MBH DUSSELDORF - FLINGERN—See Ceconomy AG; *Int'l*, pg. 1388
SATURN TECHNO-MARKT ELECTRO-HANDELSGESELLSCHAFT MBH—See Ceconomy AG; *Int'l*, pg. 1388
SATURN TILBURG B.V.—See Ceconomy AG; *Int'l*, pg. 1388
SATURN WIEN XIV ELECTRO-HANDELSGES.M.B.H.—See Ceconomy AG; *Int'l*, pg. 1388
SEARS HOME APPLIANCE SHOWROOMS, LLC—See Sears Hometown and Outlet Stores, Inc.; *U.S. Public*, pg. 1855
SEATTLE COFFEE GEAR—See Sunrise Identity; *U.S. Private*, pg. 3870
SED INTERNATIONAL DE COLOMBIA LTDA.—See Paragon Technologies, Inc.; *U.S. Public*, pg. 1637
SENSOR SOLUTIONS INC.—See Standex International; *U.S. Public*, pg. 1930
S.G.M. DISTRIBUZIONE S.R.L.—See Rhone Group, LLC; *U.S. Private*, pg. 3424
SHERBOURN TECHNOLOGIES, LLC—See Jade Design, Inc.; *U.S. Private*, pg. 2181
SHERMAN'S PLACE INC.; *U.S. Private*, pg. 3634
SHOPJIMMY.COM, LLC; *U.S. Private*, pg. 3640
SHOWCASE INC.; *U.S. Private*, pg. 3643
SIGMATA ELECTRONICS, INC.; *U.S. Public*, pg. 1877
THE SIGNAL GROUP, LLC; *U.S. Private*, pg. 4118
SIGNAL; *U.S. Private*, pg. 3649
SILICA APPLIANCE & ELECTRONICS; *U.S. Private*, pg. 3652
SILKE COMMUNICATIONS, INC; *U.S. Private*, pg. 3652
SIMPLEXITY, LLC—See Independence Capital Partners, LLC; *U.S. Private*, pg. 2057
SIXTH AVENUE ELECTRONICS, INC.; *U.S. Private*, pg. 3677
SKIDATA AG—See ASSA ABLOY AB; *Int'l*, pg. 640
SKIDATA (SCHWEIZ) AG—See ASSA ABLOY AB; *Int'l*, pg. 640
SOFTMAN PRODUCTS COMPANY, LLC; *U.S. Private*, pg. 3705
SOFTWARE DESIGN SOLUTIONS INC.—See Applied Visions, Inc.; *U.S. Private*, pg. 300
SOUTHEAST ALASKA SMOKED SALMON CO., INC.; *U.S. Private*, pg. 3724
SPARCO.COM; *U.S. Private*, pg. 3745
SPARKFUN ELECTRONICS; *U.S. Private*, pg. 3745
SPENCER'S AIR CONDITIONING & APPLIANCE; *U.S. Private*, pg. 3755
SSB WIND ENERGY TECHNOLOGY (QINGDAO) CO., LTD.—See Emerson Electric Co.; *U.S. Public*, pg. 752
SSB WIND SYSTEMS GMBH & CO. KG—See Emerson Electric Co.; *U.S. Public*, pg. 752
STANDARD APPLIANCE INC.; *U.S. Private*, pg. 3777
STARMOUNT CO.—See Koch Industries, Inc.; *U.S. Private*, pg. 2331
STAT CREW SOFTWARE, INC.—See National Amusements, Inc.; *U.S. Private*, pg. 2843
STEALTHBITS TECHNOLOGIES, INC.—See TA Associates, Inc.; *U.S. Private*, pg. 3916
STERLING COMPUTERS; *U.S. Private*, pg. 3805
STEWARD CONSULTING INC.—See Bcs Prosoft; *U.S. Private*, pg. 500
STORMFRONT RETAIL LIMITED—See Compu B Ltd.; *Int'l*, pg. 1754
STRIGLOS COMPANIES INC.; *U.S. Private*, pg. 3840
STUART KITCHENS INC.; *U.S. Private*, pg. 3843
SUNGDOENG USA; *U.S. Private*, pg. 3867
SUN MICROSYSTEMS AUSTRALIA PTY. LTD.—See Oracle Corporation; *U.S. Public*, pg. 1611
SUN MICROSYSTEMS FRANCE, S.A.—See Oracle Corporation; *U.S. Public*, pg. 1611
SUN MICROSYSTEMS NEDERLAND, B.V.—See Oracle Corporation; *U.S. Public*, pg. 1611
SUNSHINE COMPUTERS & SOFTWARE; *U.S. Private*, pg. 3871
SUOMEN 3M OY—See 3M Company; *U.S. Public*, pg. 8
SUPERB SOUND CLARKSVILLE INC.—See Superb Sound Inc.; *U.S. Private*, pg. 3875
SUPERB SOUND INC.; *U.S. Private*, pg. 3875
SURGCENTER DEVELOPMENT; *U.S. Private*, pg. 3884
SUZHOU LANLIAN-FUJI INSTRUMENTS CO., LTD.—See Fuji Electric Co., Ltd.; *Int'l*, pg. 2813
SYNERGY CONSORTIUM SERVICES, LLC; *U.S. Private*, pg. 3904
SYNNEX CANADA LTD.—See TD Synnex Corp; *U.S. Public*, pg. 1984
SYSCOM TECHNOLOGIES; *U.S. Private*, pg. 3906
SYSTRONICS DEPOT—See Systronics Inc.; *U.S. Private*, pg. 3908
SYSTRONICS INC.; *U.S. Private*, pg. 3908
TAIWAN BROTHER INDUSTRIES, LTD.—See Brother Industries, Ltd.; *Int'l*, pg. 1198

TDS TELECOM—See Telephone & Data Systems, Inc.; *U.S. Public*, pg. 1997
TEAC CANADA LTD.—See Evolution Capital Management LLC; *U.S. Private*, pg. 1443
TECH ADVANCED COMPUTERS INC.; *U.S. Private*, pg. 3951
TECH DATA FRANCE SAS—See TD Synnex Corp; *U.S. Public*, pg. 1986
TECH DATA GMBH & CO. OHG—See TD Synnex Corp; *U.S. Public*, pg. 1985
TECH DATA GMBH & CO OHG—See TD Synnex Corp; *U.S. Public*, pg. 1986
TECH DATA MOBILE LIMITED—See TD Synnex Corp; *U.S. Public*, pg. 1986
TECHNOLOGY SUPPORT, INC.; *U.S. Private*, pg. 3955
TEKNOSA IC VE DIS TICARET A.S.—See Haci Omer Sabanci Holding A.S.; *Int'l*, pg. 3204
TEKTRONIX GMBH—See Fortive Corporation; *U.S. Public*, pg. 872
TELCO PROPERTIES—See Telalaska Inc.; *U.S. Private*, pg. 3959
THQ FRANCE S.A.R.L.—See THQ Inc.; *U.S. Private*, pg. 4163
THQ (UK) LIMITED—See THQ Inc.; *U.S. Private*, pg. 4163
TIGERDIRECT, INC.—See Insight Enterprises, Inc.; *U.S. Public*, pg. 1130
TIMERACK INC.; *U.S. Private*, pg. 4172
TJM ELECTRONICS WEST, INC.—See DarkPulse, Inc.; *U.S. Public*, pg. 633
TNT PAPERCRAFT, INC.—See The Millcraft Paper Company Inc.; *U.S. Private*, pg. 4079
TOKYO NISSAN COMPUTER SYSTEM CO., LTD.—See Canon Inc.; *U.S. Private*, pg. 1296
TORKIAN-ZARGARI TRADING CORP.—See B.H.T. Electronics Purchasing Inc.; *U.S. Private*, pg. 420
TRANSLATIONS.COM—See Translations.com; *U.S. Private*, pg. 4208
TRIAL SOLUTIONS OF TEXAS LLC; *U.S. Private*, pg. 4225
TSS-RADIO; *U.S. Private*, pg. 4254
TURNKEY COMPUTER SYSTEMS, LLC—See Patterson Companies, Inc.; *U.S. Public*, pg. 1654
TWIST SOLUTIONS, LP—See The Aldridge Company; *U.S. Private*, pg. 3983
ULTRA INC.; *U.S. Private*, pg. 4277
UMAX SYSTEMS GMBH—See Hiyes International Co., Ltd.; *Int'l*, pg. 3427
UNIEURO S.P.A.—See Rhone Group, LLC; *U.S. Private*, pg. 3424
UNISYS BELGIUM—See Unisys Corporation; *U.S. Public*, pg. 2228
UNISYS DEUTSCHLAND GMBH—See Unisys Corporation; *U.S. Public*, pg. 2228
UNISYS ESPANA S.A.—See Unisys Corporation; *U.S. Public*, pg. 2228
UNISYS ITALIA S.P.A.—See Unisys Corporation; *U.S. Public*, pg. 2228
UNISYS NEDERLAND N.V.—See Unisys Corporation; *U.S. Public*, pg. 2228
UNITED INDUSTRIES CORPORATION—See Spectrum Brands Holdings, Inc.; *U.S. Public*, pg. 1917
UN MONDE INTERNATIONAL LTD.; *U.S. Public*, pg. 2225
URNERS INC.; *U.S. Private*, pg. 4316
USA DISCOUNTERS, LTD.—See Parallel Investment Partners LLC; *U.S. Private*, pg. 3092
USI WIRELESS; *U.S. Private*, pg. 4323
USROBOTICS CORPORATION; *U.S. Private*, pg. 4324
VALUE MUSIC CONCEPTS INC.; *U.S. Private*, pg. 4337
VALU.NET CORPORATION; *U.S. Private*, pg. 4337
VANN'S INCORPORATED; *U.S. Private*, pg. 4344
VAN VREEDE TV & APPLIANCE INCORPORATED; *U.S. Private*, pg. 4341
VEECO INSTRUMENTS GMBH—See Veeco Instruments Inc.; *U.S. Public*, pg. 2277
VEECO INSTRUMENTS LTD.—See Veeco Instruments Inc.; *U.S. Public*, pg. 2277
VERIFONE ASIA PACIFIC—See British Columbia Investment Management Corp.; *Int'l*, pg. 1170
VERIFONE ASIA PACIFIC—See Francisco Partners Management, LP; *U.S. Private*, pg. 1592
VERIFONE DO BRASIL LTDA.—See British Columbia Investment Management Corp.; *Int'l*, pg. 1171
VERIFONE DO BRASIL LTDA.—See Francisco Partners Management, LP; *U.S. Private*, pg. 1593
VERIFONE SP. Z O.O—See British Columbia Investment Management Corp.; *Int'l*, pg. 1170
VERIFONE SP. Z O.O—See Francisco Partners Management, LP; *U.S. Private*, pg. 1592
VERINT SYSTEMS (ASIA PACIFIC) LIMITED—See Verint Systems Inc.; *U.S. Public*, pg. 2281
VERIZON WIRELESS - BUFFALO—See Verizon Communications Inc.; *U.S. Public*, pg. 2284
VERIZON WIRELESS - CHARLOTTE—See Verizon Communications Inc.; *U.S. Public*, pg. 2284
VERIZON WIRELESS - KNOXVILLE—See Verizon Communications Inc.; *U.S. Public*, pg. 2285
VERIZON WIRELESS - NORTHEAST—See Verizon Communications Inc.; *U.S. Public*, pg. 2284

VERLAGSGRUPPE WELTBILD GMBH—See Droege Group AG; *Int'l*, pg. 2205
VERSATILE MOBILE SYSTEMS (EUROPE) LTD.—See Versatile Systems Inc.; *U.S. Private*, pg. 4369
VERTMARKETS, INC.—See Jameson Publishing Inc.; *U.S. Private*, pg. 2185
VIA OPTRONICS LLC—See Ayala Corporation; *Int'l*, pg. 774
VIA VAREJO S.A.—See Companhia Brasileira de Distribuicao; *Int'l*, pg. 1746
VIDEO AND AUDIO CENTER; *U.S. Private*, pg. 4380
VIDEO CORPORATION OF AMERICA; *U.S. Private*, pg. 4380
VIDEOLAND, INC.; *U.S. Private*, pg. 4380
VIDEO ONLY INC.; *U.S. Private*, pg. 4380
VIKING RANGE CORPORATION DO BRASIL IMPORTACAO E COMERCIO LTDA.—See The Middleby Corporation; *U.S. Public*, pg. 2115
VIRTUE GROUP; *U.S. Private*, pg. 4389
VISHAY INTERTECHNOLOGY ASIA PTE., LTD.—See Vishay Intertechnology, Inc.; *U.S. Public*, pg. 2303
VISHAY JAPAN CO., LTD—See Vishay Intertechnology, Inc.; *U.S. Public*, pg. 2303
VISUAL APEX, INC.; *U.S. Private*, pg. 4404
VISUAL SOUND INC.; *U.S. Private*, pg. 4404
VITVARUEXPERTEN.COM NORDIC AB—See BHG Group AB; *Int'l*, pg. 1014
V.L.S SYSTEMS, INC.; *U.S. Private*, pg. 4328
VOXX AUTOMOTIVE CORPORATION—See VOXX International Corporation; *U.S. Public*, pg. 2311
WAREHOUSE EXPRESS LTD.—See Aurelius Equity Opportunities SE & Co. KGaA; *Int'l*, pg. 709
WARNER COMMUNICATIONS CORP.; *U.S. Private*, pg. 4442
WARNER'S STELLIAN CO., INC.; *U.S. Private*, pg. 4442
WATER HEATERS ONLY INCORPORATED; *U.S. Private*, pg. 4451
WAVE ELECTRONICS—See Kingswood Capital Management LLC; *U.S. Private*, pg. 2312
W.B. HUNT CO., INC.; *U.S. Private*, pg. 4419
WEB-HED TECHNOLOGIES, INC.; *U.S. Private*, pg. 4464
WESTCO INC.; *U.S. Private*, pg. 4489
WESTERN DIGITAL HONG KONG LIMITED—See Western Digital Corporation; *U.S. Public*, pg. 2355
WESTERN DIGITAL SE ASIA PTE. LTD.—See Western Digital Corporation; *U.S. Public*, pg. 2355
WETTSTEIN INVESTMENTS INC.; *U.S. Private*, pg. 4502
WETTSTEIN & SONS, INC.—See Wettstein Investments Inc.; *U.S. Private*, pg. 4502
WHIRLPOOL BALTIC UAB—See Whirlpool Corporation; *U.S. Public*, pg. 2367
WHIRLPOOL CANADA LP—See Whirlpool Corporation; *U.S. Public*, pg. 2367
WHIRLPOOL COLOMBIA S.A.—See Whirlpool Corporation; *U.S. Public*, pg. 2367
WHIRLPOOL OVERSEAS HONG KONG LIMITED—See Whirlpool Corporation; *U.S. Public*, pg. 2367
WHIRLPOOL PORTUGAL ELECTRODOMESTICOS, LDA.—See Whirlpool Corporation; *U.S. Public*, pg. 2368
WHIRLPOOL SOUTH AFRICA PROPRIETARY LIMITED—See Whirlpool Corporation; *U.S. Public*, pg. 2368
WHITE WESTINGHOUSE PUERTO RICO—See AB Electrolux; *Int'l*, pg. 40
WILLIAMS-SONOMA SINGAPORE PTE. LTD.—See Williams-Sonoma, Inc.; *U.S. Public*, pg. 2371
WING TAT STEREO COMPONENT LTD.—See Lasonic Electronics Corporation; *U.S. Private*, pg. 2395
WIN, LLC; *U.S. Private*, pg. 4532
WIRELESS ZONE LLC—See Round Room LLC; *U.S. Private*, pg. 3488
WORKPLACE TECHNOLOGY CENTER, INC.—See Direct Companies, LLC; *U.S. Private*, pg. 1234
@XI COMPUTER CORPORATION; *U.S. Private*, pg. 17
XIDAX, LLC; *U.S. Private*, pg. 4581
XP SOLUTIONS INC.—See EQT AB; *Int'l*, pg. 2481
YCY INTERNATIONAL LIMITED—See China-Hong Kong Photo Products Holdings Limited; *Int'l*, pg. 1568
YEC ELECTRONICS LIMITED—See AAC Technologies Holdings Inc.; *Int'l*, pg. 31
YOUNG & BEASLEY INCORPORATED; *U.S. Private*, pg. 4592
YUNG FU ELECTRICAL APPLIANCES CORP.—See Lasonic Electronics Corporation; *U.S. Private*, pg. 2395
ZOA CORPORATION—See Daiwabo Holdings Co., Ltd.; *Int'l*, pg. 1949

455110 — DEPARTMENT STORES

ADIR INTERNATIONAL EXPORT LTD.; *U.S. Private*, pg. 79
AEON HOKKAIDO CORPORATION—See AEON Co., Ltd.; *Int'l*, pg. 177
AHLENS AB—See Axel Johnson Gruppen AB; *Int'l*, pg. 765
ALIMENTATION COUCHE-TARD INC.; *Int'l*, pg. 328
ALMACENES PITUSA INC.; *U.S. Private*, pg. 195
AL-SAWANI GROUP; *Int'l*, pg. 288
AMMARS INC.; *U.S. Private*, pg. 264
ANN & HOPE INC.; *U.S. Private*, pg. 284

455110 — DEPARTMENT STORES

ANTTILA OY—See 4K Invest International; *Int'l*, pg. 12
APEX INCORPORATED; *U.S. Private*, pg. 292
ARNOTTS LTD.; *Int'l*, pg. 577
ATTICA DEPARTMENT STORES S.A.—See Folli Follie S.A.; *Int'l*, pg. 2721
AXSTORES AB—See Axel Johnson Gruppen AB; *Int'l*, pg. 764
BAIDA GROUP CO., LTD.; *Int'l*, pg. 801
THE BAY—See Abrams Capital, LLC; *U.S. Private*, pg. 40
THE BAY—See Rhone Group, LLC; *U.S. Private*, pg. 3424
THE BAY—See WeWork Inc.; *U.S. Public*, pg. 2364
BAZAR DE L'HOTEL DE VILLE—See Galeries Lafayette SA; *Int'l*, pg. 2872
B.C. MOORE & SON INC; *U.S. Private*, pg. 420
BEALE LIMITED; *Int'l*, pg. 932
BEALL'S DEPT. STORES—See Beall's, Inc.; *U.S. Private*, pg. 505
BEALL'S, INC.; *U.S. Private*, pg. 505
BEIJING CAPITAL RETAILING GROUP CO., LTD.; *Int'l*, pg. 947
BEIJING CUIWEI TOWER CO.,LTD.; *Int'l*, pg. 948
BELK, INC.—See Sycamore Partners Management, LP; *U.S. Private*, pg. 3895
BLOOMINGDALE'S, INC.—See Macy's, Inc.; *U.S. Public*, pg. 1353
BLUE SALON ESTABLISHMENT; *Int'l*, pg. 1069
BOMGAARS SUPPLY INC.; *U.S. Private*, pg. 612
THE BON-TON DEPARTMENT STORES, INC.—See The Bon Ton Stores, Inc.; *U.S. Public*, pg. 2041
THE BON-TON GIFTCO, INC.—See The Bon Ton Stores, Inc.; *U.S. Public*, pg. 2041
THE BON TON STORES, INC.; *U.S. Public*, pg. 2041
BOOHOO.COM UK LIMITED—See Boohoo Group Plc; *Int'l*, pg. 1110
BOSCOV'S DEPARTMENT STORE, LLC—See Boscov's Inc.; *U.S. Private*, pg. 619
BOSCOV'S INC.; *U.S. Private*, pg. 619
BOYERS & CO. LIMITED—See Arnotts Ltd.; *Int'l*, pg. 577
BOYNER BUYUK MAGAZACILIK A.S.; *Int'l*, pg. 1125
BURKE'S OUTLET STORES—See Beall's, Inc.; *U.S. Private*, pg. 505
BURLINGTON COAT FACTORY INVESTMENTS HOLDINGS, INC.—See Bain Capital, LP; *U.S. Private*, pg. 437
CAROLINA CAPRI INC.; *U.S. Private*, pg. 767
CARSON PIRIE SCOTT & CO.—See The Bon Ton Stores, Inc.; *U.S. Public*, pg. 2041
CCOOP GROUP CO., LTD.; *Int'l*, pg. 1369
CENTURY 21 INC.; *U.S. Private*, pg. 831
CHANG CHUN EURASIA GROUP CO., LTD.; *Int'l*, pg. 1441
CHONGQING DEPARTMENT STORE CO., LTD.; *Int'l*, pg. 1579
CHOSEN FOODS LLC—See Butterfly Equity LP; *U.S. Private*, pg. 698
CHRISTENSEN BROTHERS INC.; *U.S. Private*, pg. 890
C.K. TANG LIMITED; *Int'l*, pg. 1243
CLAS OHLSON AS—See Clas Ohlson AB; *Int'l*, pg. 1651
CLAS OHLSON OY—See Clas Ohlson AB; *Int'l*, pg. 1652
CONVENIENCE SHOPS, S.A.—See El Corte Ingles, S.A.; *Int'l*, pg. 2340
CONWAY ORGANIZATION; *U.S. Private*, pg. 1036
COOK BROS., INC.; *U.S. Private*, pg. 1037
COOP HOSTELLERIE AG—See Coop-Gruppe Genossenschaft; *Int'l*, pg. 1790
THE CORNERSTONE BRANDS GROUP, INC.—See Qurate Retail, Inc.; *U.S. Public*, pg. 1758
C.P. ALL PUBLIC COMPANY LIMITED; *Int'l*, pg. 1243
CR CHIANG MAI (THAILAND) CO., LTD.—See Central Group Company Limited; *Int'l*, pg. 1407
CR HAD YAI (THAILAND) CO., LTD.—See Central Group Company Limited; *Int'l*, pg. 1407
CR NAKORN SRI THAMMARAT (THAILAND) CO., LTD.—See Central Group Company Limited; *Int'l*, pg. 1407
CR PHUKET (THAILAND) CO., LTD.—See Central Group Company Limited; *Int'l*, pg. 1407
CR RATCHABURI (THAILAND) CO., LTD.—See Central Group Company Limited; *Int'l*, pg. 1407
CR UBON RATCHATHANI (THAILAND) CO., LTD.—See Central Group Company Limited; *Int'l*, pg. 1407
DAEGU DEPARTMENT STORE CO., LTD.; *Int'l*, pg. 1906
THE DAIEI, INC.—See AEON Co., Ltd.; *Int'l*, pg. 178
DAIWA CO., LTD.; *Int'l*, pg. 1944
DALIAN FRIENDSHIP (GROUP) CO., LTD.; *Int'l*, pg. 1951
DASHANG GROUP CO., LTD.; *Int'l*, pg. 1973
DE BIJENKORF—See KKR & Co. Inc.; *U.S. Public*, pg. 1261
DELONG COMPOSITE ENERGY GROUP CO., LTD.; *Int'l*, pg. 2015
DENNIS SALES CO. INC.; *U.S. Private*, pg. 1205
DEPARTMENTS & STORES NORWAY AS—See Coala-Life Group AB; *Int'l*, pg. 1680
DILLARD'S INC.; *U.S. Public*, pg. 666
DOLLARAMA INC.; *Int'l*, pg. 2158
DOLLAR GENERAL CORPORATION; *U.S. Public*, pg. 672
DOLLAR TREE STORES, INC.—See Dollar Tree, Inc.; *U.S. Public*, pg. 672
DUFRY SAMNAUN LTD.—See Avolta AG; *Int'l*, pg. 749
E.A. & H. HILDRETH INC.; *U.S. Private*, pg. 1304
EASYHOME NEW RETAIL GROUP CO., LTD.; *Int'l*, pg. 2276
EL CORTE INGLES, S.A.; *Int'l*, pg. 2340
EL PUERTO DE LIVERPOOL S.A.B. DE C.V.; *Int'l*, pg. 2341
EMPRESAS LA POLAR S.A.; *Int'l*, pg. 2391
ENERGYNET.COM, INC.; *U.S. Private*, pg. 1396
ESLITE SPECTRUM CORP.; *Int'l*, pg. 2504
FACTORY OUTLET AIRPORT S.A.—See Folli Follie S.A.; *Int'l*, pg. 2721
FALABELLA S.A.; *Int'l*, pg. 2610
FENWICK LTD.; *Int'l*, pg. 2635
FENWICK LTD.—See Fenwick Ltd.; *Int'l*, pg. 2635
FILENE'S BASEMENT, INC.—See Trinity Place Holdings, Inc.; *U.S. Public*, pg. 2194
FRED MEYER OF ALASKA—See The Kroger Co.; *U.S. Public*, pg. 2107
FRED MEYER STORES, INC.—See The Kroger Co.; *U.S. Public*, pg. 2107
FRED'S STORES OF TENNESSEE, INC—See Fred's Inc.; *U.S. Public*, pg. 883
FUJIAN DONGBAI (GROUP) CO., LTD.; *Int'l*, pg. 2817
GALERIES LAFAYETTE SA; *Int'l*, pg. 2872
GANSU GUOFANG INDUSTRY & TRADE GROUP CO., LTD.; *Int'l*, pg. 2881
GIFI SA; *Int'l*, pg. 2970
THE GLEN SHOPPING CENTRE—See Hyprop Investments Limited; *Int'l*, pg. 3554
GOLDEN EAGLE RETAIL GROUP LIMITED; *Int'l*, pg. 3029
GORDMANS STORES INC.—See Sun Capital Partners, Inc.; *U.S. Private*, pg. 3859
GRAND DEPARTMENT STORE CO., LTD.; *Int'l*, pg. 3054
GRAND OCEAN CLASSIC COMMERCIAL GROUP CO., LTD.—See Grand Ocean Retail Group Limited; *Int'l*, pg. 3055
GRAND OCEAN DEPARTMENT STORE GROUP CO., LTD.—See Grand Ocean Retail Group Limited; *Int'l*, pg. 3055
GRAND OCEAN RETAIL GROUP LIMITED; *Int'l*, pg. 3055
GRAND STORES—See GIBCA Limited; *Int'l*, pg. 2962
GRUPO PALACIO DE HIERRO S.A. DE C.V.—See Grupo BAL; *Int'l*, pg. 3121
GRUPO SANBORNS, S.A. DE C.V.—See Grupo Carso, S.A.B. de C.V.; *Int'l*, pg. 3123
GUANGZHOU FRIENDSHIP GROUP CO., LTD.; *Int'l*, pg. 3165
GUANGZHOU GRANDBUY CO., LTD.; *Int'l*, pg. 3165
H2O RETAILING CORP.; *Int'l*, pg. 3200
HAD YAI (THAILAND) CO., LTD.—See Central Group Company Limited; *Int'l*, pg. 1407
HALLS MERCHANDISING INC.—See Hallmark Cards, Inc.; *U.S. Private*, pg. 1844
HANGZHOU JIEBAI GROUP CO., LTD.; *Int'l*, pg. 3248
HANKYU HANSHIN DEPARTMENT STORES, INC.—See H2O Retailing Corp.; *Int'l*, pg. 3200
HANSAPOST OU; *Int'l*, pg. 3259
HANSHANG GROUP CO., LTD.; *Int'l*, pg. 3260
HANWHA GALLERIA CO., LTD.—See Hanwha Group; *Int'l*, pg. 3265
HANWHA GALLERIA TIMEWORLD CO., LTD.—See Hanwha Group; *Int'l*, pg. 3265
HANWHA STORES CO., LTD.—See Hanwha Group; *Int'l*, pg. 3266
HARBIN CHURIN GROUP JOINTSTOCK CO., LTD.; *Int'l*, pg. 3270
HARRIS SCARFE AUSTRALIA PTY LTD.; *Int'l*, pg. 3278
HARRODS LTD.; *Int'l*, pg. 3279
HART STORES INC.; *Int'l*, pg. 3279
HARVARD COOPERATIVE SOCIETY INC.; *U.S. Private*, pg. 1875
HEFEI DEPARTMENT STORE GROUP CO., LTD.; *Int'l*, pg. 3307
HERBERGER'S, INC.—See The Bon Ton Stores, Inc.; *U.S. Public*, pg. 2041
HICLASST, INC.; *Int'l*, pg. 3383
HOME OF ECONOMY INC.; *U.S. Private*, pg. 1972
HOUSE OF FRASER (STORES) LIMITED—See Frasers Group plc; *Int'l*, pg. 2765
HUDSON'S BAY COMPANY—See Abrams Capital, LLC; *U.S. Private*, pg. 40
HUDSON'S BAY COMPANY—See Rhone Group, LLC; *U.S. Private*, pg. 3423
HUDSON'S BAY COMPANY—See WeWork Inc.; *U.S. Public*, pg. 2364
HYDE PARK SHOPPING CENTRE—See Hyprop Investments Limited; *Int'l*, pg. 3554
HYUNDAI DEPARTMENT STORE CO., LTD.; *Int'l*, pg. 3555
IMPORT PARFUMERIEN AG—See Coop-Gruppe Genossenschaft; *Int'l*, pg. 1790
IN'S MERCATO S.P.A.—See GECOS S.p.A.; *Int'l*, pg. 2909
INTIME RETAIL (GROUP) COMPANY LIMITED—See Alibaba Group Holding Limited; *Int'l*, pg. 326
J.C. PENNEY CORPORATION, INC.—See J.C. Penney Company, Inc.; *U.S. Private*, pg. 2160
JM BULLION, INC.—See A-Mark Precious Metals, Inc.; *U.S. Public*, pg. 10
JR TOKAI TAKASHIMAYA CO., LTD.—See Central Japan Railway Company; *Int'l*, pg. 1408
KOHL'S CORPORATION; *U.S. Public*, pg. 1270
KOHL'S DEPARTMENT STORES—See Kohl's Corporation; *U.S. Public*, pg. 1270
KOHL'S INDIANA INC—See Kohl's Corporation; *U.S. Public*, pg. 1270
LE TOTE, INC.; *U.S. Private*, pg. 2405
LEWIS DRUG BRANDON—See Lewis Drug, Inc.; *U.S. Private*, pg. 2438
LEWIS DRUG HURON—See Lewis Drug, Inc.; *U.S. Private*, pg. 2438
LEWIS DRUG, INC.; *U.S. Private*, pg. 2438
LIBERTY RETAIL LIMITED—See BlueGem Capital Partners LLP; *Int'l*, pg. 1071
LORD & TAYLOR LLC—See Le Tote, Inc.; *U.S. Private*, pg. 2405
MACYS BACKSTAGE, INC.—See Macy's, Inc.; *U.S. Public*, pg. 1353
MACYS.COM, INC.—See Macy's, Inc.; *U.S. Public*, pg. 1353
MACY'S, INC.; *U.S. Public*, pg. 1353
MACY'S WEST STORES, INC. - HAWAII—See Macy's, Inc.; *U.S. Public*, pg. 1353
MARDEN'S, INC.; *U.S. Private*, pg. 2573
MARSHALLS OF IL, LLC—See The TJX Companies, Inc.; *U.S. Public*, pg. 2134
MARSHALLS OF MA, INC.—See The TJX Companies, Inc.; *U.S. Public*, pg. 2134
MASSMART HOLDINGS, LTD.—See Walmart Inc.; *U.S. Public*, pg. 2325
MAST GENERAL STORE INCORPORATED; *U.S. Private*, pg. 2607
MATSUYA CO., LTD. - ASAKUSA—See ALPICO Holdings Co., Ltd.; *Int'l*, pg. 371
MATSUYA CO., LTD. - GINZA—See ALPICO Holdings Co., Ltd.; *Int'l*, pg. 371
MATSUYA CO., LTD.—See ALPICO Holdings Co., Ltd.; *Int'l*, pg. 371
M.H. KING COMPANY INC.; *U.S. Private*, pg. 2529
NEIMAN MARCUS STORES—See Ares Management Corporation; *U.S. Public*, pg. 190
NEIMAN MARCUS STORES—See Canada Pension Plan Investment Board; *Int'l*, pg. 1281
THE NET-A-PORTER GROUP LTD.—See Compagnie Financiere Richemont S.A.; *Int'l*, pg. 1741
NEW SEASONS MARKET, LLC—See Good Food Holdings LLC; *U.S. Private*, pg. 1738
NEW WORLD DEPARTMENT STORE CHINA LIMITED—See Chow Tai Fook Enterprises Limited; *Int'l*, pg. 1585
NORTHWEST MALL, INC.—See Levcor, Inc.; *U.S. Private*, pg. 2434
POUNDWORLD RETAIL LIMITED—See TPG Capital, L.P.; *U.S. Public*, pg. 2175
PRICE MART INC.; *U.S. Private*, pg. 3258
R.H. RENY INC.; *U.S. Private*, pg. 3336
ROBINSON DEPARTMENT STORE PCL—See Central Group Company Limited; *Int'l*, pg. 1407
SAKS FIFTH AVENUE, INC.—See Abrams Capital, LLC; *U.S. Public*, pg. 40
SAKS FIFTH AVENUE, INC.—See Rhone Group, LLC; *U.S. Private*, pg. 3423
SAKS FIFTH AVENUE, INC.—See WeWork Inc.; *U.S. Public*, pg. 2364
SEARS ROEBUCK DE MEXICO, S. A. DE C. V.—See Grupo Carso, S.A.B. de C.V.; *Int'l*, pg. 3123
SELFRIDGES & CO.—See Central Group Company Limited; *Int'l*, pg. 1407
SHARPE DRY GOODS CO., INC.; *U.S. Private*, pg. 3627
STARCREST PRODUCTS OF CALIFORNIA; *U.S. Private*, pg. 3786
STEINFELS CLEANING SYSTEMS—See Coop-Gruppe Genossenschaft; *Int'l*, pg. 1790
STEIN MART BUYING CORP.—See Stein Mart, Inc.; *U.S. Private*, pg. 3798
TARGET STORES, INC.—See Target Corporation; *U.S. Public*, pg. 1982
T.J. MAXX—See The TJX Companies, Inc.; *U.S. Public*, pg. 2134
TJX DEUTSCHLAND LTD. & CO. KG—See The TJX Companies, Inc.; *U.S. Public*, pg. 2134
TJX EUROPE BUYING (DEUTSCHLAND) LTD—See The TJX Companies, Inc.; *U.S. Public*, pg. 2134
TJX EUROPE BUYING LTD—See The TJX Companies, Inc.; *U.S. Public*, pg. 2134
TJX EUROPE BUYING (POLSKA) LTD—See The TJX Companies, Inc.; *U.S. Public*, pg. 2134
TJX INCENTIVE SALES, INC.—See The TJX Companies, Inc.; *U.S. Public*, pg. 2134
TJX OESTERREICH LTD. & CO. KG—See The TJX Companies, Inc.; *U.S. Public*, pg. 2134
T.K. MAXX MANAGEMENT GMBH—See The TJX Companies, Inc.; *U.S. Public*, pg. 2134
TK MAXX—See The TJX Companies, Inc.; *U.S. Public*, pg. 2134
TOPTIP (R. MULLER AG)—See Coop-Gruppe Genossenschaft; *Int'l*, pg. 1790
TRANSFORM SR BRANDS LLC—See Transform Holdco LLC; *U.S. Private*, pg. 4208
VON MAUR INC.; *U.S. Private*, pg. 4412
VOXPOP COMMUNITIES, INC.—See Marlin Equity Part-

N.A.I.C.S. INDEX

455219 — ALL OTHER GENERAL M...

ners, LLC; *U.S. Private*, pg. 2584
WAL-MART CANADA CORP.—See Walmart Inc.; *U.S. Public*, pg. 2325
WALMART INC. - INTERNATIONAL DIVISION—See Walmart Inc.; *U.S. Public*, pg. 2325
WALMART INC.; *U.S. Public*, pg. 2324
WAL-MART REAL ESTATE BUSINESS TRUST—See Walmart Inc.; *U.S. Public*, pg. 2325
WAL-MART STORES EAST, LP—See Walmart Inc.; *U.S. Public*, pg. 2325
THE WORKS STORES LTD.—See Endless LLP; *Int'l*, pg. 2403
XS CARGO—See KarpReilly, LLC; *U.S. Private*, pg. 2263

455211 — WAREHOUSE CLUBS AND SUPERCENTERS

AL AHLIA ENTERPRISES PLC; *Int'l*, pg. 275
ANTEROS LAGERHANTERING AB—See Bjorn Borg AB; *Int'l*, pg. 1054
BIG C SUPERCENTER PUBLIC COMPANY LIMITED—See Berli Jucker Public Co. Ltd.; *Int'l*, pg. 985
BI-MART CORPORATION—See Bi-Mart Acquisition Corp.; *U.S. Private*, pg. 550
BJ'S WHOLESALE CLUB, INC.—See Leonard Green & Partners, L.P.; *U.S. Private*, pg. 2425
COSTCO WHOLESALE CANADA LTD.—See Costco Wholesale Corporation; *U.S. Public*, pg. 586
COSTCO WHOLESALE CORPORATION; *U.S. Public*, pg. 586
COSTCO WHOLESALE JAPAN, LTD.—See Costco Wholesale Corporation; *U.S. Public*, pg. 586
COSTCO WHOLESALE KOREA, LTD.—See Costco Wholesale Corporation; *U.S. Public*, pg. 586
COSTCO WHOLESALE UK LIMITED—See Costco Wholesale Corporation; *U.S. Public*, pg. 587
DIRECTBUY, INC.; *U.S. Private*, pg. 1236
ERA D.O.O.; *Int'l*, pg. 2488
L&J ENTERPRISES INC.; *U.S. Private*, pg. 2362
MCM (TN) LLC—See W.P. Carey Inc.; *U.S. Public*, pg. 2316
PRICESMART (GUATEMALA), S.A.—See PriceSmart Inc.; *U.S. Public*, pg. 1716
PRICESMART HONDURAS, S.A. DE C.V.—See PriceSmart Inc.; *U.S. Public*, pg. 1716
PRICESMART (JAMAICA) LIMITED—See PriceSmart Inc.; *U.S. Public*, pg. 1716
PRISMAR DE COSTA RICA, S.A.—See PriceSmart Inc.; *U.S. Public*, pg. 1716
PSMT (JAMAICA), LTD.—See PriceSmart Inc.; *U.S. Public*, pg. 1716
SAM'S CLUB—See Walmart Inc.; *U.S. Public*, pg. 2325
SAM'S EAST, INC.—See Walmart Inc.; *U.S. Public*, pg. 2325
SAM'S WEST, INC.—See Walmart Inc.; *U.S. Public*, pg. 2325
SHOPPERS FOOD WAREHOUSE CORP.—See United Natural Foods, Inc.; *U.S. Public*, pg. 2232
VIP WHOLESALE, INC.—See GrubMarket, Inc.; *U.S. Private*, pg. 1797
WUEST'S OF SAN MARCOS—See Wuest's Inc.; *U.S. Private*, pg. 4575
WUMART STORES, INC.—See Beijing Jingxi Culture & Tourism Co., Ltd.; *Int'l*, pg. 953

455219 — ALL OTHER GENERAL MERCHANDISE RETAILERS

32ND STREET 99 CENTS CORP.; *U.S. Private*, pg. 8
99 CENTS ONLY STORES LLC—See Ares Management Corporation; *U.S. Public*, pg. 187
99 CENTS ONLY STORES LLC—See Canada Pension Plan Investment Board; *Int'l*, pg. 1278
AEON GLOBAL SCM CO., LTD—See AEON Co., Ltd.; *Int'l*, pg. 176
AEON RETAIL CO., LTD—See AEON Co., Ltd.; *Int'l*, pg. 177
AEON STORES (HONG KONG) CO., LIMITED—See AEON Co., Ltd.; *Int'l*, pg. 177
AEON TOPVALU CO., LTD.—See AEON Co., Ltd.; *Int'l*, pg. 177
ALBUFEIRA RETAIL PARK LDA.—See Frey S.A.; *Int'l*, pg. 2791
ALGARVE SHOPPING - CENTRO COMERCIAL, SA—See Frey S.A.; *Int'l*, pg. 2791
AL JIMI MALL LLC—See ALDAR Properties PJSC; *Int'l*, pg. 304
AMAZON.DE GMBH—See Amazon.com, Inc.; *U.S. Public*, pg. 90
AMERICAN MERCHANDISE LIQUIDATORS, INC.; *U.S. Private*, pg. 241
AMERICAN SALE, INC.; *U.S. Private*, pg. 246
ARCTIC CO-OPERATIVES LIMITED; *Int'l*, pg. 551
ARIGATOU SERVICES CO., LTD.; *Int'l*, pg. 564
AUCFAN CO., LTD.; *Int'l*, pg. 698
AUCNET DIGITAL PRODUCTS INC.—See Aucnet Inc.; *Int'l*, pg. 700
AUCNET HK LIMITED—See Aucnet Inc.; *Int'l*, pg. 699
AXAS CORPORATION—See AXAS Holdings Co., Ltd.; *Int'l*, pg. 761

BARTLETT GRAIN COMPANY, L.P.—See Bartlett & Company; *U.S. Private*, pg. 483
BATTERIES PLUS, LLC—See Freeman Spogli & Co. Incorporated; *U.S. Private*, pg. 1606
BEIJING JINGKELONG COMPANY LIMITED; *Int'l*, pg. 953
BELLUNA CO. LTD.; *Int'l*, pg. 967
BEST IMPRESSIONS CATALOG COMPANY—See Malcolm Group Inc.; *U.S. Private*, pg. 2557
BHG GROUP AB; *Int'l*, pg. 1014
BIG LOTS, INC.; *U.S. Public*, pg. 330
BIG LOTS STORES, INC.—See Big Lots, Inc.; *U.S. Public*, pg. 330
BI-MART ACQUISITION CORP.; *U.S. Private*, pg. 550
BLUESTEM BRANDS, INC.; *U.S. Private*, pg. 598
B&M RETAIL LIMITED—See Clayton, Dubilier & Rice, LLC; *U.S. Private*, pg. 920
BOB'S DISCOUNT INC.; *U.S. Private*, pg. 605
BOWMAN PROMOTIONAL SPECIALTIES INC.—See Target Print & Mail; *U.S. Private*, pg. 3933
BRANDERS.COM INC.—See BEL USA LLC; *U.S. Private*, pg. 516
CAFOM SA; *Int'l*, pg. 1250
CALGARY CO-OPERATIVE ASSOCIATION LIMITED; *Int'l*, pg. 1263
CAMPONA SHOPPING CENTER KFT.—See CPI Property Group, S.A.; *Int'l*, pg. 1825
C. A. PERRY & SON INC.; *U.S. Private*, pg. 704
CASH CANADA GROUP LTD.; *Int'l*, pg. 1352
CCS—See Block Communications, Inc.; *U.S. Private*, pg. 582
CENTRAL ALBERTA CO-OP LTD.; *Int'l*, pg. 1404
CENTURION SERVICE GROUP, LLC—See Ascension Health Alliance; *U.S. Private*, pg. 346
CHINA NATIONAL NATIVE PRODUCE & ANIMAL BY-PRODUCTS IMPORT & EXPORT CORPORATION—See COFCO Limited; *Int'l*, pg. 1692
C.H. MARTIN, INC.; *U.S. Private*, pg. 707
CHRISTIE'S INC.—See Financiere Pinault SCA; *Int'l*, pg. 2668
CITY LIQUIDATORS INC.; *U.S. Private*, pg. 906
CODE ONE ENTERPRISES NJ CORP; *U.S. Private*, pg. 960
COLIBRI—See Carrefour SA; *Int'l*, pg. 1344
COLORADO OUTDOOR RETAIL GROUP; *U.S. Private*, pg. 974
COOP DANMARK A/S—See FDB Group; *Int'l*, pg. 2628
COOP NORGE GRORUD EIENDOM AS—See Coop Norge SA; *Int'l*, pg. 1789
COOP TRADING A/S—See Coop Norge SA; *Int'l*, pg. 1789
COOP TRADING A/S—See FDB Group; *Int'l*, pg. 2628
COSMO-ONE HELLAS MARKET SITE S.A.—See Hellenic Telecommunications Organization S.A.; *Int'l*, pg. 3333
COURTS (JAMAICA) LIMITED; *Int'l*, pg. 1819
CPI EAST, S.R.O.—See CPI Property Group, S.A.; *Int'l*, pg. 1825
CYPRUS AIRWAYS (DUTY FREE SHOPS) LTD.—See Cyprus Airways Public Limited; *Int'l*, pg. 1897
DELO PRODAJA, D.D.; *Int'l*, pg. 2014
DIMENSION SA—See Banque Cantonale de Geneve S.A.; *Int'l*, pg. 852
DISCOUNT DRUG MART INC.; *U.S. Private*, pg. 1237
DLF EMPORIO LIMITED—See DLF Limited; *Int'l*, pg. 2141
DLF PROMENADE LIMITED—See DLF Limited; *Int'l*, pg. 2141
DWW WOOLWORTH DEUTSCHLAND GMBH & CO. KG—See Argyll Partners Ltd.; *Int'l*, pg. 563
EBAY INC.; *U.S. Public*, pg. 1301
E&J LAWRENCE CORP.; *U.S. Private*, pg. 1301
ERT SALES OF HAWAII INC.; *U.S. Private*, pg. 1423
EUROCENTRUM OFFICES SP. Z O.O.—See CPI Property Group, S.A.; *Int'l*, pg. 1825
FAMILY DOLLAR, INC.—See Dollar Tree, Inc.; *U.S. Public*, pg. 672
FARM & FLEET OF DE KALB INC.; *U.S. Private*, pg. 1474
FARM KING SUPPLY INC.; *U.S. Private*, pg. 1475
FERNWAY LIMITED—See Searchlight Capital Partners, L.P.; *U.S. Private*, pg. 3589
FINS, FURS, FEATHERS, INC.; *U.S. Private*, pg. 1511
FIVE BELOW, INC.; *U.S. Public*, pg. 852
FIX PRICE GROUP PLC; *Int'l*, pg. 2696
FLAGS UNLIMITED; *Int'l*, pg. 2697
FLIPKART INTERNET PRIVATE LIMITED—See Walmart Inc.; *U.S. Public*, pg. 2325
FLOYDS STORES INC.; *U.S. Private*, pg. 1552
FRED'S INC.; *U.S. Public*, pg. 883
FUTURE ENTERPRISES LIMITED—See Future Corporate Resources Limited; *Int'l*, pg. 2853
THE GARDENS THEATRE SDN. BHD.—See IGB Berhad; *Int'l*, pg. 3602
GOODWILL INDUSTRIES INTERNATIONAL, INC.; *U.S. Private*, pg. 1740
GOODWILL OF GREATER WASHINGTON; *U.S. Private*, pg. 1740
G-P DISTRIBUTING INC.; *U.S. Private*, pg. 1630
GRUPPO TRADE SERVICE POLSKA SP. Z O.O.—See ASM Group S.A.; *Int'l*, pg. 625
GUMP'S BY MAIL, INC.—See Gump's Corp.; *U.S. Private*, pg. 1818

HALFORDS GROUP PLC; *Int'l*, pg. 3229
HAMMACHER SCHLEMMER & CO., INC.; *U.S. Private*, pg. 1849
HARVEY NORMAN HOLDINGS LTD; *Int'l*, pg. 3281
HIRAKI CO., LTD.; *Int'l*, pg. 3403
HONEST COMPANY, INC.; *U.S. Public*, pg. 1046
HSN IMPROVEMENTS, LLC—See Qurate Retail, Inc.; *U.S. Public*, pg. 1758
HUDSON INC.; *U.S. Private*, pg. 2002
HUDSON SALVAGE INC.; *U.S. Private*, pg. 2002
HUNAN FRIENDSHIP & APOLLO COMMERCIAL CO., LTD.; *Int'l*, pg. 3532
HYMAX, INC.—See Ship Supply of Florida, Inc.; *U.S. Private*, pg. 3637
IDEAL SHOPPING DIRECT LTD.—See Aurelius Equity Opportunities SE & Co. KGaA; *Int'l*, pg. 708
IDEAL WORLD HOME SHOPPING LTD.—See Aurelius Equity Opportunities SE & Co. KGaA; *Int'l*, pg. 708
IHUNT TECHNOLOGY IMPORT-EXPORT S.A.; *Int'l*, pg. 3607
ILLYCAFFE FRANCE BELUX SARL—See illycaffe S.p.A.; *Int'l*, pg. 3615
ILLYCAFFE NEDERLAND B.V.—See illycaffe S.p.A.; *Int'l*, pg. 3615
ILLYCAFFE NORTH AMERICA INC.—See illycaffe S.p.A.; *Int'l*, pg. 3615
ILLYCAFFE SHANGHAI CO. LTD.—See illycaffe S.p.A.; *Int'l*, pg. 3615
INFLIGHT SALES GROUP INC.; *U.S. Private*, pg. 2072
INVESTMENT INTERNATIONAL, D.O.O.E.L.—See Fortenova Group d.d.; *Int'l*, pg. 2738
IZUMIYA CO., LTD.—See H2O Retailing Corp.; *Int'l*, pg. 3200
JONES STORES INC.; *U.S. Private*, pg. 2234
JUST MY SHOPPING INC.; *U.S. Private*, pg. 2245
JUST RIGHT PRODUCTS, INC.—See ADM Endeavors, Inc.; *U.S. Public*, pg. 42
KESSLERS INTERNATIONAL LTD.—See Endless LLP; *Int'l*, pg. 2403
LEWIS DRUG SOUTHWEST—See Lewis Drug, Inc.; *U.S. Private*, pg. 2438
LILLIAN VERNON CORPORATION—See Regent, L.P.; *U.S. Private*, pg. 3387
THE LITTLE TRAVELER INC.; *U.S. Private*, pg. 4071
MAKRO-HABIB PAKISTAN LTD.—See House of Habib; *Int'l*, pg. 3491
MANDALAY PLACE—See MGM Resorts International; *U.S. Public*, pg. 1435
MARC GLASSMAN, INC.; *U.S. Private*, pg. 2571
MERCATOR - H, D.O.O.—See Fortenova Group d.d.; *Int'l*, pg. 2738
MERCATOR MAKEDONIJA D.O.O.E.L.—See Fortenova Group d.d.; *Int'l*, pg. 2738
MERCATOR - MEX, D.O.O.—See Fortenova Group d.d.; *Int'l*, pg. 2738
MERCATOR-S, D.O.O.—See Fortenova Group d.d.; *Int'l*, pg. 2738
MINER ELASTOMER PRODUCTS CORP.—See Miner Enterprises, Inc.; *U.S. Private*, pg. 2741
MONOPRIX S.A.—See Finatis SA; *Int'l*, pg. 2670
M&S BARGAIN HUNTER INC.; *U.S. Private*, pg. 2525
MULTIMERCADOS ZONALES S.A.—See Grupo Romero; *Int'l*, pg. 3134
MY EYE STORE—See Compulink Business Systems, Inc.; *U.S. Private*, pg. 1004
MYSALE GROUP PLC—See Frasers Group plc; *Int'l*, pg. 2765
NATIONAL PRODUCT SALES INC.; *U.S. Private*, pg. 2861
NATION REALTY INC.—See Cosco Capital, Inc.; *Int'l*, pg. 1809
NET DIRECT MERCHANTS; *U.S. Private*, pg. 2886
NEWTON WALL COMPANY; *U.S. Private*, pg. 2918
NISHINOMIYA MERCHANDISING CENTER—See Bain Capital, LP; *U.S. Private*, pg. 444
NS HOME SHOPPING CO., LTD.—See Harim Holdings Co., Ltd.; *Int'l*, pg. 3276
NS INTERNATIONAL CHINA CO., LTD—See Harim Holdings Co., Ltd.; *Int'l*, pg. 3276
OCEAN STATE JOBBERS INC.; *U.S. Private*, pg. 2990
OLLIE'S BARGAIN OUTLET, INC.—See CCMP Capital Advisors, LP; *U.S. Private*, pg. 801
OMNI ENTERPRISES INC.; *U.S. Private*, pg. 3016
ONQ SOLUTIONS, INC.; *U.S. Private*, pg. 3027
OREGON SCIENTIFIC TRADING (BEIJING) CO., LTD.—See IDT International Limited; *Int'l*, pg. 3597
OUTLET ARENA MORAVIA, S.R.O.—See CPI Property Group, S.A.; *Int'l*, pg. 1825
PARKER CASSIDY SUPPLY CO.; *U.S. Private*, pg. 3097
PLANET ACP, INC.; *U.S. Public*, pg. 3195
PLAZA HOUSE INC.—See Grandy House Corporation; *Int'l*, pg. 3058
PRICESMART COLOMBIA SAS—See PriceSmart Inc.; *U.S. Public*, pg. 1716
PRICESMART INC.; *U.S. Public*, pg. 1716
PROMOTIONAL SLIDEGUIDE CORP.; *U.S. Private*, pg. 3283
PROPERTYROOM.COM INC.; *U.S. Private*, pg. 3285
PUBLICIDENTITY INC.; *U.S. Private*, pg. 3300

455219 — ALL OTHER GENERAL M...

QUARTA-RAD, INC.; *U.S. Public*, pg. 1754
QVC CHESAPEAKE, INC.—See Qurate Retail, Inc.; *U.S. Public*, pg. 1758
QVC, INC.—See Qurate Retail, Inc.; *U.S. Public*, pg. 1758
RABIN WORLDWIDE, INC.; *U.S. Private*, pg. 3341
RICHARDS BROTHERS OF MOUNTAIN GROVE; *U.S. Private*, pg. 3428
ROYAL BUYING GROUP, INC.; *U.S. Private*, pg. 3491
SANTIAM DRUG INC.; *U.S. Private*, pg. 3548
S&A STORES INC.; *U.S. Private*, pg. 3512
SEARS AUTHORIZED HOMETOWN STORES, LLC—See Sears Hometown and Outlet Stores, Inc.; *U.S. Public*, pg. 1855
SEARS OUTLET STORES, LLC—See Sears Hometown and Outlet Stores, Inc.; *U.S. Public*, pg. 1855
SHANGHAI SMG-CJ HOMESHOPPING CO., LTD.—See CJ Corporation; *Int'l*, pg. 1634
SHILDAN USA, INC.; *U.S. Private*, pg. 3636
SOTHEBY'S—See Sotheby's; *U.S. Public*, pg. 1910
SOUTH COAST PLAZA; *U.S. Private*, pg. 3721
SPAR CANADA COMPANY—See SPAR Group, Inc.; *U.S. Public*, pg. 1914
SPAR CHINA LTD.—See SPAR Group, Inc.; *U.S. Public*, pg. 1914
SPECIALTY MERCHANDISE CORPORATION; *U.S. Private*, pg. 3750
SQO STADT QUARTIER OFFENBURG GMBH & CO. KG—See Helaba Landesbank Hessen-Thuringen; *Int'l*, pg. 3328
STAGER ENTERPRISES INC.; *U.S. Private*, pg. 3775
STELLAR PARTNERS INC.—See Avolta AG; *Int'l*, pg. 749
SUMMERWINDS GARDEN CENTERS OF CALIFORNIA INC.—See Summerwinds Garden Centers Inc.; *U.S. Private*, pg. 3853
TASMANIA FEEDLOT PTY. LTD.—See AEON Co., Ltd.; *Int'l*, pg. 178
TAYLOR & MARTIN INC.—See Taylor & Martin Enterprises Inc.; *U.S. Private*, pg. 3937
TDW INC.; *U.S. Private*, pg. 3944
TIANTIAN CJ HOME SHOPPING CO., LTD.—See CJ Corporation; *Int'l*, pg. 1634
TN MARKETING, LLC—See Apple Leisure Group; *U.S. Private*, pg. 297
TWIN TOWERS TRADING, INC.; *U.S. Private*, pg. 4266
TYRHOLM BIG R STORES; *U.S. Private*, pg. 4269
UNITED MARKETING GROUP LLC; *U.S. Private*, pg. 4294
VARIETY WHOLESALERS, INCORPORATED; *U.S. Private*, pg. 4347
VERIZON COMMUNICATIONS INC. - MONTGOMERYVILLE, PA—See Verizon Communications Inc.; *U.S. Public*, pg. 2285
VERMONT COUNTRY STORE, INC.; *U.S. Private*, pg. 4367
VF JEANSWEAR ESPANA S.L.—See Kontoor Brands, Inc.; *U.S. Public*, pg. 1271
VF OUTDOOR, INC.—See V. F. Corporation; *U.S. Public*, pg. 2269
VF SCANDINAVIA A/S—See V. F. Corporation; *U.S. Public*, pg. 2269
WAL-MART JAPAN HOLDINGS K.K.—See KKR & Co. Inc.; *U.S. Public*, pg. 1267
WEST COAST LIQUIDATORS, INC.—See Big Lots, Inc.; *U.S. Public*, pg. 331
WINMARK CORPORATION; *U.S. Public*, pg. 2374
WOOLRICH, INC. - STORE DIVISION—See Woolrich, Inc.; *U.S. Private*, pg. 4562
ZAKKAYA BULLDOG CO., LTD.—See AXAS Holdings Co., Ltd.; *Int'l*, pg. 761
ZULILY, LLC—See Regent, L.P.; *U.S. Public*, pg. 3388

456110 — PHARMACIES AND DRUG RETAILERS

ABBOTT-NORTHWESTERN MEDICAL BUILDING PHARMACY INC.—See Allina Health System, Inc.; *U.S. Private*, pg. 192
ACCREDO HEALTH GROUP, INC.—See The Cigna Group; *U.S. Public*, pg. 2062
ADVANCED CARE SCRIPS, INC.—See CVS Health Corporation; *U.S. Public*, pg. 616
AEGERION PHARMACEUTICALS S.A.S.—See Chiesi Farmaceutici SpA; *Int'l*, pg. 1477
AHF PHARMACY - SAN DIEGO—See AIDS Healthcare Foundation; *U.S. Private*, pg. 132
AIN HOLDINGS INC.; *Int'l*, pg. 234
AIN TOKAI INC.—See AIN Holdings Inc.; *Int'l*, pg. 234
AISEI PHARMACY CO., LTD.; *Int'l*, pg. 251
ALLEN'S PHARMASERV, INC.—See Procare LTC Holding LLC; *U.S. Private*, pg. 3271
ALLIANCE HEALTHCARE (DISTRIBUTION) LIMITED—See Walgreens Boots Alliance, Inc.; *U.S. Public*, pg. 2322
ALLIANCE HEALTHCARE NEDERLAND—See Walgreens Boots Alliance, Inc.; *U.S. Public*, pg. 2322
AMAVITA PHARMACY—See CSL Limited; *Int'l*, pg. 1866
AMBER ENTERPRISES, INC.—See Hy-Vee, Inc.; *U.S. Private*, pg. 2016
AMERICARX.COM; *U.S. Private*, pg. 259

APOTEK HJARTAT AB—See ICA Gruppen AB; *Int'l*, pg. 3577
APOTEKSTJANST SWEDEN AB—See Bonver AB; *Int'l*, pg. 1109
APOTHEEK HAGI B.V.—See Walgreens Boots Alliance, Inc.; *U.S. Public*, pg. 2322
APPEG SA—See Fagron NV; *Int'l*, pg. 2602
ARACOMA DRUG CO. INC.; *U.S. Private*, pg. 307
ARSEUS BV—See Fagron NV; *Int'l*, pg. 2603
ARX AUTOMATIZACION DE FARMACIAS, S.L.U.—See Becton, Dickinson & Company; *U.S. Public*, pg. 288
ASSURA PHARMACY LIMITED—See Assura plc; *Int'l*, pg. 649
ASTAREAL CO., LTD. - NAGOYA—See Fuji Chemical Industries Co., Ltd; *Int'l*, pg. 2809
ASTAREAL CO., LTD. - OSAKA—See Fuji Chemical Industries Co., Ltd; *Int'l*, pg. 2809
ASTAREAL CO., LTD. - TOYAMA—See Fuji Chemical Industries Co., Ltd; *Int'l*, pg. 2809
ASTRUP DRUGS, INC.; *U.S. Private*, pg. 362
AVITA DRUGS LLC—See Tailwind Capital Group, LLC; *U.S. Private*, pg. 3924
AXIUM HEALTHCARE PHARMACY, INC.—See The Kroger Co.; *U.S. Public*, pg. 2107
BAKER'S SUPERMARKETS, INC.—See The Kroger Co.; *U.S. Public*, pg. 2107
THE BARTELL DRUG COMPANY—See New Rite Aid, LLC; *U.S. Private*, pg. 2906
BAXTER DRUG, INC.—See Walgreens Boots Alliance, Inc.; *U.S. Public*, pg. 2323
BECCLES H.C.C. LIMITED—See Walgreens Boots Alliance, Inc.; *U.S. Public*, pg. 2322
BEIJING CANNY CONSULTING INC.—See Hangzhou Tigermed Consulting Co., Ltd.; *Int'l*, pg. 3251
BEIJING TONG REN TANG CHINESE MEDICINE COMPANY LIMITED; *Int'l*, pg. 958
BELMAR PHARMACY—See Webster Equity Partners, LLC; *U.S. Private*, pg. 4467
BERJAYA PHARMACY SDN BHD—See Berjaya Corporation Berhad; *Int'l*, pg. 984
BIG PHARMACY HEALTHCARE SDN. BHD; *Int'l*, pg. 1021
BIOCARE LIMITED—See Elder Pharmaceuticals Ltd.; *Int'l*, pg. 2346
BIOMATRIX SPECIALTY PHARMACY, LLC—See Frazier Management, LLC; *U.S. Private*, pg. 1600
BIOSCRIP PBM SERVICES, LLC—See Option Care Health, Inc.; *U.S. Public*, pg. 1609
BIOSCRIP PHARMACY, INC.—See Option Care Health, Inc.; *U.S. Public*, pg. 1609
BODYHEALTH.COM LLC; *U.S. Private*, pg. 608
BOND DRUG COMPANY OF ILLINOIS, LLC—See Walgreens Boots Alliance, Inc.; *U.S. Public*, pg. 2323
BOOTS NEDERLAND B.V.—See Walgreens Boots Alliance, Inc.; *U.S. Public*, pg. 2322
BOOTS UK LIMITED—See Walgreens Boots Alliance, Inc.; *U.S. Public*, pg. 2323
BRIOVARX, LLC—See UnitedHealth Group Incorporated; *U.S. Public*, pg. 2239
BRIOVARX OF CALIFORNIA, INC.—See UnitedHealth Group Incorporated; *U.S. Public*, pg. 2239
BRIOVARX OF FLORIDA, INC.—See UnitedHealth Group Incorporated; *U.S. Public*, pg. 2239
BRIOVARX OF INDIANA, LLC—See UnitedHealth Group Incorporated; *U.S. Public*, pg. 2239
BRIOVARX OF LOUISIANA, LLC—See UnitedHealth Group Incorporated; *U.S. Public*, pg. 2239
BRIOVARX OF MASSACHUSETTS, LLC—See UnitedHealth Group Incorporated; *U.S. Public*, pg. 2239
BRIOVARX OF NEVADA, LLC—See UnitedHealth Group Incorporated; *U.S. Public*, pg. 2239
BRIOVARX OF NEW YORK, INC.—See UnitedHealth Group Incorporated; *U.S. Public*, pg. 2239
BRIOVARX OF TEXAS, INC.—See UnitedHealth Group Incorporated; *U.S. Public*, pg. 2239
BUCKEYE DRUGS; *U.S. Private*, pg. 677
CACHET PHARMACEUTICAL CO., LTD.; *Int'l*, pg. 1247
CALIGOR PHARMACY—See Henry Schein, Inc.; *U.S. Public*, pg. 1025
CALIGOR RX, INC.—See Diversis Capital, LLC; *U.S. Private*, pg. 1244
CAMPUS-FOYER APOTHEKE GMBH—See Johnson & Johnson; *U.S. Public*, pg. 1194
CANADA DRUGS LTD.; *Int'l*, pg. 1278
CAREMARKPCS HEALTH LLC—See CVS Health Corporation; *U.S. Public*, pg. 615
CARING PHARMACY GROUP BHD—See BIG Pharmacy Healthcare Sdn. Bhd; *Int'l*, pg. 1021
CARLERBA - PRODUTOS QUIMICOS E FARMACEUTICOS, LDA.—See Pfizer Inc.; *U.S. Public*, pg. 1679
CARONDELET PHARMACY AT SAINT JOSEPH HEALTH CENTER INC.—See Ascension Health Alliance; *U.S. Private*, pg. 347
CASH WISE FLOWER SHOPPE INC.—See Coborn's Incorporated; *U.S. Private*, pg. 958
CCS MEDICAL, INC.—See CCS Medical Holdings, Inc.; *U.S. Private*, pg. 801
CEPD MANAGEMENT SP. Z O.O.—See CEPD N.V.; *Int'l*, pg. 1420

CEPD N.V.; *Int'l*, pg. 1420
CHARLES RIVER LABORATORIES PRECLINICAL SERVICES EDINBURGH LTD.—See Charles River Laboratories International, Inc.; *U.S. Public*, pg. 480
CHIBRET PHARMAZEUTISCHE GESELLSCHAFT MIT BESCHRANKTER HAFTUNG—See Merck & Co., Inc.; *U.S. Public*, pg. 1415
CHINA JO-JO DRUGSTORES, INC.; *Int'l*, pg. 1513
CHINA NEPSTAR CHAIN DRUGSTORE LTD.; *Int'l*, pg. 1534
CHUKYO IYAKUHIN CO., LTD.; *Int'l*, pg. 1595
CITY PHARMACY LTD; *Int'l*, pg. 1627
COLLIER DRUG STORES; *U.S. Private*, pg. 969
COLOMBO CITY HOLDINGS PLC; *Int'l*, pg. 1702
THE COMPOUNDING SHOP INC.; *U.S. Private*, pg. 4013
COMPSCRIPT, LLC—See CVS Health Corporation; *U.S. Public*, pg. 616
CORNERSTONE PHARMACY, INC.; *U.S. Private*, pg. 1052
COSMO PHARMACEUTICALS N.V.; *Int'l*, pg. 1813
COSMOS PHARMACEUTICAL CORPORATION; *Int'l*, pg. 1814
CREATE S.D. HOLDINGS CO., LTD.; *Int'l*, pg. 1832
C.T. STAMPS, INC.—See Fred's Inc.; *U.S. Public*, pg. 883
CURALEAF HOLDINGS, INC.; *U.S. Public*, pg. 610
DAITIKU CO., LTD.—See AIN Holdings Inc.; *Int'l*, pg. 234
DA RETAILGROEP B.V.; *Int'l*, pg. 1902
DAVIDSON HEALTH CARE, INC.; *U.S. Private*, pg. 1171
DENKA SEIKEN UK LIMITED—See Denki Company Limited; *Int'l*, pg. 2027
DIAMOND DRUGS, INC.; *U.S. Private*, pg. 1223
DIOSYNTH PRODUTOS FARMO-QUIMICOS LTDA.—See Merck & Co., Inc.; *U.S. Public*, pg. 1416
DIPLOMAT PHARMACY, INC.—See UnitedHealth Group Incorporated; *U.S. Public*, pg. 2247
DIS-CHEM PHARMACIES LTD.; *Int'l*, pg. 2130
DISCOUNT EMPORIUM INC.; *U.S. Private*, pg. 1237
DM-DROGERIE MARKT GMBH & CO. KG; *Int'l*, pg. 2142
DOCS DRUGS LTD.; *U.S. Private*, pg. 1251
DOHMEN CO.; *U.S. Private*, pg. 1253
DONGSUNG BIORANE CO., LTD.—See Dongsung Chemical Co., Ltd.; *Int'l*, pg. 2170
DOUGHERTY'S HOLDINGS, INC.—See Dougherty's Pharmacy, Inc.; *U.S. Private*, pg. 1266
DOUGHERTY'S PHARMACY, INC.—See Dougherty's Pharmacy, Inc.; *U.S. Private*, pg. 1266
THE DOW CHEMICAL COMPANY - MARIETTA—See Dow Inc.; *U.S. Public*, pg. 686
DRUG EMPORIUM—See Gibson Merchandise Group Inc.; *U.S. Private*, pg. 1696
DRUGSTORE.COM, INC.—See Walgreens Boots Alliance, Inc.; *U.S. Public*, pg. 2324
DS PHARMACY, INC.—See Walgreens Boots Alliance, Inc.; *U.S. Public*, pg. 2323
DUANE READE HOLDINGS, INC.—See Walgreens Boots Alliance, Inc.; *U.S. Public*, pg. 2323
DUANE READE, INC.—See Walgreens Boots Alliance, Inc.; *U.S. Public*, pg. 2323
DUANE READE INTERNATIONAL, LLC—See Walgreens Boots Alliance, Inc.; *U.S. Public*, pg. 2323
DUANE READE REALTY, INC.—See Walgreens Boots Alliance, Inc.; *U.S. Public*, pg. 2323
EASYSCRIPTS, LLC—See Elevance Health, Inc.; *U.S. Public*, pg. 730
E. MOSS, LIMITED—See Walgreens Boots Alliance, Inc.; *U.S. Public*, pg. 2322
EMPORIUM DRUG MART INC. OF AMARILLO—See Gibson Merchandise Group Inc.; *U.S. Private*, pg. 1696
EMPORIUM DRUG MART INC. OF LAFAYETTE—See Gibson Merchandise Group Inc.; *U.S. Private*, pg. 1696
EMPORIUM DRUG MART INC. OF LONGVIEW—See Gibson Merchandise Group Inc.; *U.S. Private*, pg. 1696
EMPORIUM DRUG MART INC. OF LUBBOCK—See Gibson Merchandise Group Inc.; *U.S. Private*, pg. 1696
EMPORIUM DRUG MART INC. OF SHREVEPORT—See Gibson Merchandise Group Inc.; *U.S. Private*, pg. 1696
EMPORIUM DRUG MART INC. OF TYLER—See Gibson Merchandise Group Inc.; *U.S. Private*, pg. 1696
EMPORIUM DRUG MART INC. OF WACO—See Gibson Merchandise Group Inc.; *U.S. Private*, pg. 1696
ESI CANADA—See The Cigna Group; *U.S. Public*, pg. 2061
EUROPA APOTHEEK VENLO BV; *Int'l*, pg. 2555
EVERSANA—See Water Street Healthcare Partners, LLC; *U.S. Private*, pg. 4452
EVIANA HEALTH CORPORATION, INC.; *Int'l*, pg. 2570
EXACT CARE PHARMACY, LLC; *U.S. Private*, pg. 1444
EXPRESS SCRIPTS ADMINISTRATORS, LLC—See The Cigna Group; *U.S. Public*, pg. 2061
EXPRESS SCRIPTS, INC.—See The Cigna Group; *U.S. Public*, pg. 2061
EXPRESS SCRIPTS—See The Cigna Group; *U.S. Public*, pg. 2061
FALCO PHARMACIES, LTD.—See FALCO Holdings Co., Ltd.; *Int'l*, pg. 2610
FANNIN LIMITED—See DCC plc; *Int'l*, pg. 1990
FARMACIAS BENAVIDES SAB DE CV—See Walgreens Boots Alliance, Inc.; *U.S. Public*, pg. 2323
FOUNDATION CARE, LLC—See Centene Corporation; *U.S. Public*, pg. 469

N.A.I.C.S. INDEX
456110 — PHARMACIES AND DRUG...

FRUTH, INC.; *U.S. Private*, pg. 1617
FUJI CHEMICAL INDUSTRIES CO., LTD. - OSAKA—See Fuji Chemical Industries Co., Ltd; *Int'l*, pg. 2809
FUJI YAKUHIN CO., LTD.; *Int'l*, pg. 2817
FUNDERBURK'S PHARMACY, INC.; *U.S. Private*, pg. 1623
GALFARM SP. Z O.O.—See Fagron NV; *Int'l*, pg. 2603
GEDEON RICHTER UKRFARM O.O.O—See Gedeon Richter Plc.; *Int'l*, pg. 2910
GENKY STORES, INC.; *Int'l*, pg. 2924
GENOA HEALTHCARE LLC; *U.S. Private*, pg. 1672
GIBSON MERCHANDISE GROUP INC.; *U.S. Private*, pg. 1696
GMC, LLC—See TREES Corporation; *U.S. Public*, pg. 2188
GRANITE ALLIANCE INSURANCE COMPANY—See Centene Corporation; *U.S. Public*, pg. 469
GRANULES USA INC—See Granules India Ltd; *Int'l*, pg. 3060
GUANGZHOU NEPSTAR CHAIN CO., LTD.—See China Nepstar Chain Drugstore Ltd.; *Int'l*, pg. 1534
GUARDIAN PHARMACY, LLC.; *U.S. Private*, pg. 1810
GUARDIAN PHARMACY OF DALLAS-FORT WORTH—See Guardian Pharmacy, LLC.; *U.S. Private*, pg. 1810
GULF CORPORATION FOR TECHNOLOGY; *Int'l*, pg. 3180
HAPPY HARRY'S INC.—See Walgreens Boots Alliance, Inc.; *U.S. Public*, pg. 2323
HARCO, INC.—See New Rite Aid, LLC; *U.S. Private*, pg. 2905
HARMON STORES, INC.—See 20230930-DK-Butterfly-1, Inc.; *U.S. Private*, pg. 5
HEALTH ADVANCE INC.; *U.S. Public*, pg. 1014
HEALTHNET INTERNATIONAL (PVT) LTD.—See Hemas Holdings PLC; *Int'l*, pg. 3340
HEALTHWAREHOUSE.COM, INC.; *U.S. Public*, pg. 1017
HEARTLAND PHARMACY OF ILLINOIS LLC—See CVS Health Corporation; *U.S. Public*, pg. 616
HEPITES SA; *Int'l*, pg. 3356
HINKLE'S PHARMACY; *U.S. Private*, pg. 1949
HIRELIFESCIENCE LLC—See Aequor Technologies, LLC; *U.S. Private*, pg. 117
HIRONS; *U.S. Private*, pg. 1950
HORNBACHER'S PHARMACIES, INC.—See United Natural Foods, Inc.; *U.S. Public*, pg. 2231
HUNT VALLEY PHARMACY, LLC—See Bond Pharmacy, Inc.; *U.S. Private*, pg. 613
IGB BERHAD; *Int'l*, pg. 3601
INTENSITY THERAPEUTICS, INC.; *U.S. Public*, pg. 1140
ITA, INC.—See The Kroger Co.; *U.S. Public*, pg. 2108
K&B MISSISSIPPI CORPORATION—See New Rite Aid, LLC; *U.S. Private*, pg. 2905
KINNEY DRUGS INC.; *U.S. Private*, pg. 2313
KROGER PRESCRIPTION PLANS, INC.—See The Kroger Co.; *U.S. Public*, pg. 2108
KROGER SPECIALTY INFUSION AL, LLC—See The Kroger Co.; *U.S. Public*, pg. 2108
KROGER SPECIALTY INFUSION CA, LLC—See The Kroger Co.; *U.S. Public*, pg. 2108
KROGER SPECIALTY INFUSION TX, LLC—See The Kroger Co.; *U.S. Public*, pg. 2108
KROGER SPECIALTY PHARMACY, INC.—See The Kroger Co.; *U.S. Public*, pg. 2108
KROGER SPECIALTY PHARMACY LA, LLC—See The Kroger Co.; *U.S. Public*, pg. 2108
LAWTONS DRUG STORES LIMITED—See Empire Company Limited; *Int'l*, pg. 2387
LEBARONBROWN SPECIALITIES LLC—See LeBaron-Brown Industries LLC; *U.S. Private*, pg. 2409
LEWIS & CLARK PHARMACEUTICALS, INC.—See REBUS HOLDINGS INC.; *U.S. Public*, pg. 1769
LEWIS DRUG EASTGATE—See Lewis Drug, Inc.; *U.S. Private*, pg. 2438
LEWIS DRUG SOUTHEAST—See Lewis Drug, Inc.; *U.S. Private*, pg. 2438
LEWIS DRUG SOUTHGATE—See Lewis Drug, Inc.; *U.S. Private*, pg. 2438
LEWIS DRUG WESTGATE—See Lewis Drug, Inc.; *U.S. Private*, pg. 2438
LIFEMED ALASKA, LLC—See CVS Health Corporation; *U.S. Public*, pg. 616
LONG'S DRUGS, INC.—See Tailwind Capital Group, LLC; *U.S. Private*, pg. 3924
MAXI DRUG SOUTH, L.P.—See New Rite Aid, LLC; *U.S. Private*, pg. 2905
MAXOR NATIONAL PHARMACY SERVICES CORPORATION; *U.S. Private*, pg. 2619
MCCRORY'S PHARMACY, INC.—See Dougherty's Pharmacy, Inc.; *U.S. Private*, pg. 1266
M&C DRUGSTORE LTD.—See Arthur J. Gallagher & Co.; *U.S. Public*, pg. 206
MEDCO HEALTH SOLUTIONS OF LAS VEGAS, LLC—See The Cigna Group; *U.S. Public*, pg. 2062
MEDCO HEALTH SOLUTIONS OF RICHMOND, LLC—See The Cigna Group; *U.S. Public*, pg. 2062
MEDCO HEALTH SOLUTIONS OF TEXAS, LLC—See The Cigna Group; *U.S. Public*, pg. 2062
MEDEXPRESS PHARMACY, LTD.; *U.S. Private*, pg. 2651
MEDICINE SHOPPE CANADA, INC.—See McKesson Corporation; *U.S. Public*, pg. 1408

MEDISYSTEM PHARMACY—See George Weston Limited; *Int'l*, pg. 2939
MEDTECH HOLDINGS, INC.—See Prestige Consumer Healthcare Inc.; *U.S. Public*, pg. 1716
MEMBERHEALTH LLC—See CVS Health Corporation; *U.S. Public*, pg. 616
MERCK SHARP & DOHME (CHILE) LTDA.—See Merck & Co., Inc.; *U.S. Public*, pg. 1419
MERCK SHARP & DOHME COLOMBIA S.A.S.—See Merck & Co., Inc.; *U.S. Public*, pg. 1420
MERCK SHARP & DOHME D.O.O. BELGRADE—See Merck & Co., Inc.; *U.S. Public*, pg. 1420
MERCK SHARP & DOHME D.O.O.—See Merck & Co., Inc.; *U.S. Public*, pg. 1420
MERCK SHARP DOHME ILACLARI LIMITED SIRKETI—See Merck & Co., Inc.; *U.S. Public*, pg. 1420
MERCK SHARP & DOHME (MALAYSIA) SDN. BHD.—See Merck & Co., Inc.; *U.S. Public*, pg. 1419
MERCK SHARP & DOHME RESEARCH GMBH—See Merck & Co., Inc.; *U.S. Public*, pg. 1420
MERIDIANRX, LLC—See Centene Corporation; *U.S. Public*, pg. 471
MOMS PHARMACY, INC.—See AIDS Healthcare Foundation; *U.S. Private*, pg. 131
MSD (L-SP) UNTERSTUTZUNGSKASSE GMBH—See Merck & Co., Inc.; *U.S. Public*, pg. 1417
NAVARRO DISCOUNT PHARMACIES, LLC—See CVS Health Corporation; *U.S. Public*, pg. 616
NCS HEALTHCARE OF MONTANA, INC.—See CVS Health Corporation; *U.S. Public*, pg. 616
NEIGHBORCARE OF INDIANA, LLC—See CVS Health Corporation; *U.S. Public*, pg. 616
NORTH COAST MEDICAL SUPPLY, INC.—See Court Square Capital Partners, L.P.; *U.S. Private*, pg. 1069
NORTHWEST PHARMACY SERVICES—See Prescryptive Health, Inc.; *U.S. Private*, pg. 3254
NUCLEAR PHARMACY SERVICES—See Cardinal Health, Inc.; *U.S. Public*, pg. 434
OMNICARE, INC.—See CVS Health Corporation; *U.S. Public*, pg. 616
OMNICARE PHARMACY OF PUEBLO, LLC—See CVS Health Corporation; *U.S. Public*, pg. 616
ONCOLOGY PLUS, INC.—See Avella of Deer Valley, Inc.; *U.S. Private*, pg. 405
OPTUM INFUSION SERVICES 551, LLC—See United-Health Group Incorporated; *U.S. Public*, pg. 2247
OPTUM INFUSION SERVICES 553, LLC—See United-Health Group Incorporated; *U.S. Public*, pg. 2247
OST JAPAN GROUP INC—See Fuji Yakuhin Co., Ltd.; *Int'l*, pg. 2817
PARTNERS PHARMACY, LLC; *U.S. Private*, pg. 3102
PEACE IN MEDICINE; *U.S. Private*, pg. 3122
PENNSYLVANIA CVS PHARMACY, L.L.C.—See CVS Health Corporation; *U.S. Public*, pg. 616
PERLMART DRUGS OF TOMS RIVER INC.—See Perlmart Inc.; *U.S. Private*, pg. 3152
PFIZER DOMINICANA, S.A.—See Pfizer Inc.; *U.S. Public*, pg. 1681
PFIZER GERMANY B.V. & CO. KG—See Pfizer Inc.; *U.S. Public*, pg. 1681
PFIZER TRADING POLSKA SP. Z.O.O.—See Pfizer Inc.; *U.S. Public*, pg. 1683
PHARMACA INTEGRATIVE PHARMACY INC.; *U.S. Private*, pg. 3165
PHARMACARE LLC; *U.S. Private*, pg. 3165
PHARMACEUTICAL CARE MANAGEMENT ASSOCIATION; *U.S. Private*, pg. 3165
PHARMACEUTICAL SPECIALTIES LLC—See Maxor National Pharmacy Services Corporation; *U.S. Private*, pg. 2619
PHARMACIA LLC—See Pfizer Inc.; *U.S. Public*, pg. 1683
PHARMAHEALTH; *U.S. Private*, pg. 3165
PHARMAPACKS, LLC—See Packable Holdings, LLC; *U.S. Private*, pg. 3072
PHARMERICA CORPORATION—See KKR & Co. Inc.; *U.S. Public*, pg. 1262
PIPELINERX; *U.S. Private*, pg. 3189
PLEASANT STREET APOTHECARY—See A C Center, Inc.; *U.S. Private*, pg. 18
PMC PHARMACY INC.—See Portage Pharma Ltd.; *U.S. Private*, pg. 3231
PORTAGE PHARMACY INC.—See Portage Pharma Ltd.; *U.S. Private*, pg. 3231
PRECISION LTC PHARMACY; *U.S. Private*, pg. 3245
PRECISIONRX—See Elevance Health, Inc.; *U.S. Public*, pg. 730
PRICE-LESS DRUG STORES INC.; *U.S. Private*, pg. 3258
PROGRESSIVE CARE, INC.—See NextPlat Corp.; *U.S. Public*, pg. 1526
REMEDI SENIORCARE OF OHIO - NORTHEAST, LLC—See Remedi SeniorCare Holding Corporation; *U.S. Private*, pg. 3306
REVELATION PHARMA CORPORATION LLC—See Osceola Capital Management, LLC; *U.S. Private*, pg. 3047
RICHLAND VILLAGE DRUG INC—See Portage Pharma Ltd.; *U.S. Private*, pg. 3231
RIDGEWAY PHARMACY; *U.S. Private*, pg. 3433

RITE AID CORPORATION—See New Rite Aid, LLC; *U.S. Private*, pg. 2905
RITE AID OF ILLINOIS, INC.—See New Rite Aid, LLC; *U.S. Private*, pg. 2905
RITE AID OF MARYLAND, INC.—See New Rite Aid, LLC; *U.S. Private*, pg. 2906
RITE AID OF NEW HAMPSHIRE, INC.—See New Rite Aid, LLC; *U.S. Private*, pg. 2906
RITE AID OF VIRGINIA, INC.—See New Rite Aid, LLC; *U.S. Private*, pg. 2906
RITE AID OF WASHINGTON, D.C., INC.—See New Rite Aid, LLC; *U.S. Private*, pg. 2906
RXAMERICA LLC—See CVS Health Corporation; *U.S. Public*, pg. 616
RX CARE SPECIALTY PHARMACY LLC—See Benzer Pharmacy Holding LLC; *U.S. Private*, pg. 529
RXSOLUTIONS, INC.—See Odyssey Investment Partners, LLC; *U.S. Private*, pg. 2996
RXUSA; *U.S. Private*, pg. 3509
SAVE DRUG CENTER CO., LTD.—See Bangkok Dusit Medical Services Public Company Limited; *Int'l*, pg. 834
SAV-ON DRUGS OF ARK, INC.; *U.S. Private*, pg. 3555
SENSIBLU S.R.L.—See A&D Pharma Holdings S.R.L.; *Int'l*, pg. 19
SERVICIOS OPERACIONALES BENAVIDES, S.A. DE C.V.—See Walgreens Boots Alliance, Inc.; *U.S. Public*, pg. 2323
SHANDONG TAIBANG BIOLOGICAL PRODUCTS CO. LTD.—See China Biologic Products Holdings, Inc.; *Int'l*, pg. 1486
SHELBOURN CHEMISTS, INC.—See Insulet Corporation; *U.S. Public*, pg. 1134
SHELDON'S EXPRESS PHARMACY—See Houchens Industries, Inc.; *U.S. Private*, pg. 1990
SHENZHEN NEPSTAR CHAIN CO., LTD.—See China Nepstar Chain Drugstore Ltd.; *Int'l*, pg. 1534
SHIRLEY PHARMACY LIMITED—See Green Cross Health Limited; *Int'l*, pg. 3070
SHOPPERS DRUG MART CORPORATION—See George Weston Limited; *Int'l*, pg. 2939
SHORE PHARMACEUTICAL PROVIDERS, INC.—See CVS Health Corporation; *U.S. Public*, pg. 616
SILVERSCRIPT INSURANCE COMPANY—See CVS Health Corporation; *U.S. Public*, pg. 616
SMITH'S BEVERAGE OF WYOMING—See The Kroger Co.; *U.S. Public*, pg. 2109
SORKIN'S RX, LTD.—See KKR & Co. Inc.; *U.S. Public*, pg. 1263
SOUTH MIAMI PHARMACY; *U.S. Private*, pg. 3723
STEPHEN L. LAFRANCE PHARMACY, INC.—See Walgreens Boots Alliance, Inc.; *U.S. Public*, pg. 2323
SUNSHINE PHARMACY, INC.; *U.S. Private*, pg. 3872
SUPERDRUG STORES PLC—See CK Hutchison Holdings Limited; *Int'l*, pg. 1636
SUPERPHARM LIMITED—See Agostini's Limited; *Int'l*, pg. 213
SUPERVALU PHARMACIES, INC.—See United Natural Foods, Inc.; *U.S. Public*, pg. 2232
SYSTEMFARMA B.V.—See Advent International Corporation; *U.S. Private*, pg. 104
TAMIMI PHARMACY LLC; *U.S. Private*, pg. 3928
TAXUS PHARMACEUTICALS HOLDINGS, INC.; *U.S. Private*, pg. 3937
TECH PHARMACY SERVICES, INC.—See Partners Pharmacy, LLC; *U.S. Private*, pg. 3103
TEL DRUG, INC.—See The Cigna Group; *U.S. Public*, pg. 2061
TEL DRUG OF PENNSYLVANIA, LLC—See The Cigna Group; *U.S. Public*, pg. 2061
TENEX HEALTH INC.—See Trice Medical, Inc; *U.S. Private*, pg. 4229
TRANSCRIPT PHARMACY, INC.; *U.S. Private*, pg. 4207
UNIPRIX INC.—See McKesson Corporation; *U.S. Public*, pg. 1408
UNITED STATES MEDICAL SUPPLY, INC.—See Court Square Capital Partners, L.P.; *U.S. Private*, pg. 1069
UPSTATE PHARMACY, LTD.; *U.S. Private*, pg. 4313
U-SAVE-IT PHARMACY, INC.; *U.S. Private*, pg. 4269
U-SAVE PHARMACY OF DAWSON COUNTY, LLC; *U.S. Private*, pg. 4269
US SCRIPT, INC.—See Centene Corporation; *U.S. Public*, pg. 471
VENTURA HEALTH PTY LTD—See EBOS Group Limited; *Int'l*, pg. 2286
VIFOR FRANCE SA—See CSL Limited; *Int'l*, pg. 1866
WALGREEN CO.—See Walgreens Boots Alliance, Inc.; *U.S. Public*, pg. 2323
WALGREEN EASTERN CO., INC.—See Walgreens Boots Alliance, Inc.; *U.S. Public*, pg. 2323
WALGREEN LOUISIANA CO., INC.—See Walgreens Boots Alliance, Inc.; *U.S. Public*, pg. 2323
WALGREEN MEDICAL SUPPLY, LLC—See Walgreens Boots Alliance, Inc.; *U.S. Public*, pg. 2324
WALGREEN MERCANTILE CORP.—See Walgreens Boots Alliance, Inc.; *U.S. Public*, pg. 2323
WALGREEN NATIONAL CORPORATION—See Walgreens Boots Alliance, Inc.; *U.S. Public*, pg. 2323
WALGREEN OF HAWAII, LLC—See Walgreens Boots Alli-

456110 — PHARMACIES AND DRUG...

ance, Inc.; *U.S. Public*, pg. 2324
WALGREEN OF MAUI, INC.—See Walgreens Boots Alliance, Inc.; *U.S. Public*, pg. 2324
WALGREEN OF PUERTO RICO, INC.—See Walgreens Boots Alliance, Inc.; *U.S. Public*, pg. 2324
WALGREEN OF SAN PATRICIO, INC.—See Walgreens Boots Alliance, Inc.; *U.S. Public*, pg. 2324
WALGREENS.COM, INC.—See Walgreens Boots Alliance, Inc.; *U.S. Public*, pg. 2324
WALGREENS MAIL SERVICE, INC.—See Walgreens Boots Alliance, Inc.; *U.S. Public*, pg. 2324
WALGREENS SPECIALTY PHARMACY HOLDINGS, INC.—See Walgreens Boots Alliance, Inc.; *U.S. Public*, pg. 2324
WALGREENS SPECIALTY PHARMACY, LLC—See Walgreens Boots Alliance, Inc.; *U.S. Public*, pg. 2324
WELLFOUNT CORP; *U.S. Private*, pg. 4475
WELLTEK INCORPORATED; *U.S. Private*, pg. 4478
WJ HOLDING COMPANY—See Hy-Vee, Inc.; *U.S. Private*, pg. 2016
WOMEN'S INTERNATIONAL PHARMACY; *U.S. Private*, pg. 4556
ZIP DRUG INC.—See Elevance Health, Inc.; *U.S. Public*, pg. 730

456120 — COSMETICS, BEAUTY SUPPLIES, AND PERFUME RETAILERS

AB&COMPANY CO., LTD.; *Int'l*, pg. 47
A. CHRISTENSSEN ENGROS A/S—See Aurelius Equity Opportunities SE & Co. KGaA; *Int'l*, pg. 709
ADACHI FACTORY INC.—See Beauty Garage Inc.; *Int'l*, pg. 935
ADORE BEAUTY GROUP LIMITED; *Int'l*, pg. 152
AEON BODY CO., LTD—See AEON Co., Ltd.; *Int'l*, pg. 176
AEON FOREST CO., LTD—See AEON Co., Ltd.; *Int'l*, pg. 176
ALEEDA INC.; *Int'l*, pg. 305
AL GHURAIR RETAIL LLC—See Al Ghurair Investment LLC; *Int'l*, pg. 278
ALLIED HEALTH ELEMENTS COMPANY LIMITED—See Deson Development International Holdings Ltd; *Int'l*, pg. 2045
ALOETTE COSMETICS OF CANADA—See Aloette Cosmetics, Inc.; *U.S. Private*, pg. 195
AMERIKAS, INC.; *U.S. Private*, pg. 260
AMWAY CANADA CORPORATION—See Alticor Inc.; *U.S. Private*, pg. 208
AMWAY DE ESPANA, S.A.—See Alticor Inc.; *U.S. Private*, pg. 209
AMWAY DE GUATEMALA, S.A.—See Alticor Inc.; *U.S. Private*, pg. 209
AMWAY FRANCE—See Alticor Inc.; *U.S. Private*, pg. 209
AMWAY GMBH—See Alticor Inc.; *U.S. Private*, pg. 209
AMWAY (JAPAN) LIMITED—See Alticor Inc.; *U.S. Private*, pg. 208
AMWAY KOREA, LTD.—See Alticor Inc.; *U.S. Private*, pg. 209
AMWAY (MALAYSIA) SDN. BHD.—See Alticor Inc.; *U.S. Private*, pg. 208
AMWAY NEDERLAND LTD.—See Alticor Inc.; *U.S. Private*, pg. 209
AMWAY OF AUSTRALIA—See Alticor Inc.; *U.S. Private*, pg. 209
AMWAY OF NEW ZEALAND—See Alticor Inc.; *U.S. Private*, pg. 209
AMWAY (THAILAND) LIMITED—See Alticor Inc.; *U.S. Private*, pg. 208
ANJAC SAS; *Int'l*, pg. 472
ANNEMARIE BORLIND SA—See Boerlind Gesellschaft fuer Erzeugnisse mbH; *Int'l*, pg. 1100
ANNICK GOUTAL S.A.S.—See Amorepacific Corp.; *Int'l*, pg. 430
APOLLO MED INNOVATIONS LLC; *U.S. Private*, pg. 295
ARATA (THAILAND) CO., LTD.—See Arata Corporation; *Int'l*, pg. 536
ARMSTRONG MCCALL, L.P.—See Sally Beauty Holdings, Inc.; *U.S. Public*, pg. 1838
AROMA AD; *Int'l*, pg. 577
AROMA COSMETICS AD; *Int'l*, pg. 577
AROMATHERAPY ASSOCIATES, INC—See Walgreens Boots Alliance, Inc.; *U.S. Public*, pg. 2322
ASTRAL BRANDS, INC.; *U.S. Private*, pg. 361
A.S. WATSON RETAIL (HK) LTD—See CK Hutchison Holdings Limited; *Int'l*, pg. 1636
AVROY SHLAIN COSMETICS (PTY.) LTD.—See Tupperware Brands Corporation; *U.S. Public*, pg. 2204
AYURA LABORATORIES INC—See AIN Holdings Inc.; *Int'l*, pg. 234
BATH & BODY WORKS, LLC—See Bath & Body Works, Inc.; *U.S. Public*, pg. 279
BEAUTY BAKERIE COSMETICS BRAND LLC; *U.S. Private*, pg. 508
BEAUTY BRANDS, INC.; *U.S. Private*, pg. 509
BEAUTY COMMUNITY PUBLIC COMPANY LIMITED; *Int'l*, pg. 935

BEAUTYFIRST INC.—See Regis Corporation; *U.S. Public*, pg. 1777
BEAUTY GARAGE SINGAPORE PTE. LTD.—See Beauty Garage Inc.; *Int'l*, pg. 935
BEAUTY GARAGE TAIWAN INC.—See Beauty Garage Inc.; *Int'l*, pg. 935
BEAUTY MANUFACTURING SOLUTIONS CORP.; *U.S. Private*, pg. 509
BEAUTY SYSTEMS GROUP (CANADA), INC.—See Sally Beauty Holdings, Inc.; *U.S. Public*, pg. 1838
BEAUTY SYSTEMS GROUP LLC—See Sally Beauty Holdings, Inc.; *U.S. Public*, pg. 1838
BG PARTNERS INC.—See Beauty Garage Inc.; *Int'l*, pg. 935
BG VENTURES INC.—See Beauty Garage Inc.; *Int'l*, pg. 935
BILLIE, INC.—See Edgewell Personal Care Company; *U.S. Public*, pg. 718
BIOEPIDERM GMBH—See Bio-Gate AG; *Int'l*, pg. 1035
BIRCHBOX, INC.—See FemTec Health, Inc.; *U.S. Private*, pg. 1494
BLUEMERCURY, INC.—See Macy's, Inc.; *U.S. Public*, pg. 1353
BOBBI BROWN PROFESSIONAL COSMETICS—See The Estee Lauder Companies Inc.; *U.S. Public*, pg. 2073
BODIM PORT OY—See Aurelius Equity Opportunities SE & Co. KGaA; *Int'l*, pg. 709
THE BODY SHOP A ISLANDI—See Aurelius Equity Opportunities SE & Co. KGaA; *Int'l*, pg. 710
THE BODY SHOP BETEILIGUNGS-GMBH—See Aurelius Equity Opportunities SE & Co. KGaA; *Int'l*, pg. 710
THE BODY SHOP CANADA LIMITED—See Aurelius Equity Opportunities SE & Co. KGaA; *Int'l*, pg. 710
THE BODY SHOP (FRANCE) SARL—See Aurelius Equity Opportunities SE & Co. KGaA; *Int'l*, pg. 710
THE BODY SHOP INTERNATIONAL INC.—See Aurelius Equity Opportunities SE & Co. KGaA; *Int'l*, pg. 710
THE BODY SHOP (SINGAPORE) PTE LTD—See Aurelius Equity Opportunities SE & Co. KGaA; *Int'l*, pg. 710
THE BODY SHOP SVENSKA AB—See Aurelius Equity Opportunities SE & Co. KGaA; *Int'l*, pg. 710
THE BODY SHOP SWITZERLAND AG—See Aurelius Equity Opportunities SE & Co. KGaA; *Int'l*, pg. 710
BOLDFACE GROUP, INC.; *U.S. Private*, pg. 610
BONJOUR HOLDINGS LIMITED; *Int'l*, pg. 1107
BOXY CHARM, INC.; *U.S. Private*, pg. 627
BS DENMARK A/S—See Aurelius Equity Opportunities SE & Co. KGaA; *Int'l*, pg. 709
BURT'S BEES INC.—See The Clorox Company; *U.S. Public*, pg. 2062
BUTTER LONDON LLC—See Astral Brands, Inc.; *U.S. Private*, pg. 361
BWX LIMITED; *Int'l*, pg. 1233
CAREGEN CO.,LTD.; *Int'l*, pg. 1324
CARIBBEAN FLAVOURS & FRAGRANCES LIMITED—See Derrimon Trading Co., Ltd.; *Int'l*, pg. 2043
CARL EDELMANN GMBH & CO. KG—See Edelmann GmbH; *Int'l*, pg. 2305
CARRIER COMMERCIAL REFRIGERATION, INC.—See Haier Smart Home Co., Ltd.; *Int'l*, pg. 3210
CASWELL-MASSEY CO. LTD.—See The Equitium Group, LLC; *U.S. Private*, pg. 4026
CHINA BOTON GROUP COMPANY LIMITED; *Int'l*, pg. 1487
CHUNGDAM GLOBAL CO., LTD.; *Int'l*, pg. 1597
CJ OLIVE YOUNG CO., LTD.—See CJ Corporation; *Int'l*, pg. 1632
CLARINS BELGIQUE—See Clarins S.A.; *Int'l*, pg. 1648
CLARINS CANADA INC.—See Clarins S.A.; *Int'l*, pg. 1648
CLARINS GMBH—See Clarins S.A.; *Int'l*, pg. 1648
CLARINS K.K.—See Clarins S.A.; *Int'l*, pg. 1648
CLARINS KOREA LTD.—See Clarins S.A.; *Int'l*, pg. 1648
CLARINS LTD.—See Clarins S.A.; *Int'l*, pg. 1648
CLARINS PARIS SA—See Clarins S.A.; *Int'l*, pg. 1648
CLARINS PTE. LTD.—See Clarins S.A.; *Int'l*, pg. 1649
CLARINS SA—See Clarins S.A.; *Int'l*, pg. 1649
CLARINS SDN BHD—See Clarins S.A.; *Int'l*, pg. 1649
CLARINS (U.K.) LTD.—See Clarins S.A.; *Int'l*, pg. 1648
CLICKS GROUP LIMITED; *Int'l*, pg. 1658
C.O. BIGELOW CHEMISTS, INC.; *U.S. Public*, pg. 708
COLGATE-PALMOLIVE SERVICES (BELGIUM) SA/NV—See Colgate-Palmolive Company; *U.S. Public*, pg. 532
COLOMER BEAUTY AND PROFESSIONAL PRODUCTS, S.L.—See MacAndrews & Forbes Incorporated; *U.S. Private*, pg. 2534
COMVITA LIMITED; *Int'l*, pg. 1763
COSMENATURA SA—See Aurelius Equity Opportunities SE & Co. KGaA; *Int'l*, pg. 709
COUNTER BRANDS LLC—See The Carlyle Group Inc.; *U.S. Public*, pg. 2046
CREME 21 GMBH—See Emami Ltd; *Int'l*, pg. 2374
CRYSTAL CLAIRE COSMETICS INC.; *Int'l*, pg. 1860
CUSTOM HBC, CORP.; *U.S. Private*, pg. 1129
DART INDUSTRIES (NEW ZEALAND) LIMITED—See Tupperware Brands Corporation; *U.S. Public*, pg. 2204
DELUVIA INC.; *U.S. Private*, pg. 1202
DERMOGROUP SRL—See Viatris Inc.; *U.S. Public*, pg. 2293
DEVITA INTERNATIONAL, INC.; *U.S. Private*, pg. 1218

THE DICKSON SHOP SDN. BHD.—See Dickson Concepts (International) Limited; *Int'l*, pg. 2112
DIGICELL INTERNATIONAL, INC.; *U.S. Private*, pg. 1229
DIGITAL HUB MIBE GMBH—See Dermapharm Holding SE; *Int'l*, pg. 2043
DIVABOX SAS—See Inter Parfums, Inc.; *U.S. Public*, pg. 1140
DO INFINITE DREAM COMPANY LIMITED—See Do Day Dream PCL; *Int'l*, pg. 2152
DOUGLAS COSMETICS GMBH—See CVC Capital Partners SICAV-FIS S.A.; *Int'l*, pg. 1883
DOUGLAS GMBH—See CVC Capital Partners SICAV-FIS S.A.; *Int'l*, pg. 1883
DOUGLAS PARFUMERIJE D.O.O.—See CVC Capital Partners SICAV-FIS S.A.; *Int'l*, pg. 1883
DOUGLAS POLSKA SP. Z O.O.—See CVC Capital Partners SICAV-FIS S.A.; *Int'l*, pg. 1883
DREAM DERMATOLOGY COMPANY LIMITED—See Do Day Dream PCL; *Int'l*, pg. 2152
DR. THEISS NATURWAREN SARL—See Dr. Theiss Naturwaren GmbH; *Int'l*, pg. 2195
DSWISS, INC.; *Int'l*, pg. 2216
ED BROWN DISTRIBUTORS—See EVI Industries, Inc.; *U.S. Public*, pg. 803
EDELMANN (BEIJING) CO., LTD.—See Edelmann GmbH; *Int'l*, pg. 2305
EDELMANN BITTERFELD GMBH—See Edelmann GmbH; *Int'l*, pg. 2305
EDELMANN BRAZIL EMBALAGENS LTDA.—See Edelmann GmbH; *Int'l*, pg. 2305
EDELMANN NORDERSTEDT GMBH—See Edelmann GmbH; *Int'l*, pg. 2305
EDELMANN WUPPERTAL GMBH—See Edelmann GmbH; *Int'l*, pg. 2306
EGYPT FREE SHOPS CO.; *Int'l*, pg. 2327
E.L.F. BEAUTY, INC.; *U.S. Public*, pg. 701
ELIZABETH ARDEN (AUSTRALIA) PTY LTD.—See MacAndrews & Forbes Incorporated; *U.S. Private*, pg. 2533
ELIZABETH ARDEN (CANADA) LIMITED—See MacAndrews & Forbes Incorporated; *U.S. Private*, pg. 2533
ENDLESS YOUTH AND LIFE LLC—See Suarez Corporation Industries; *U.S. Private*, pg. 3846
EO PRODUCTS; *U.S. Public*, pg. 1410
EOS INC.; *Int'l*, pg. 2458
EOS PRODUCTS, LLC; *U.S. Private*, pg. 1411
ESTEE LAUDER AG LACHEN—See The Estee Lauder Companies Inc.; *U.S. Public*, pg. 2073
ESTEE LAUDER COSMETICS LIMITED—See The Estee Lauder Companies Inc.; *U.S. Public*, pg. 2073
ESTEE LAUDER INC.—See The Estee Lauder Companies Inc.; *U.S. Public*, pg. 2073
EUROFRAGANCE SLU; *Int'l*, pg. 2552
FASHION FAIR COSMETICS, LLC—See Johnson Publishing Company, Inc.; *U.S. Private*, pg. 2228
FAVORINA CO., LTD.—See 4Cs Holdings Co., Ltd.; *Int'l*, pg. 11
FILORGA AMERICAS INC.—See Colgate-Palmolive Company; *U.S. Public*, pg. 532
FILORGA PORTUGAL, UNIPESSOAL, LDA.—See Colgate-Palmolive Company; *U.S. Public*, pg. 532
FIRMENICH S.P.A.—See Firmenich International SA; *Int'l*, pg. 2680
FLAMEFIGHTER CORRORATION—See South Park Corporation; *U.S. Private*, pg. 3723
FOREVER LIVING PRODUCTS INTERNATIONAL, INC.; *U.S. Private*, pg. 1567
FRAGRANCENET.COM, INC.; *U.S. Public*, pg. 877
FRAGRANCE OUTLET INC.; *U.S. Private*, pg. 1586
FSN E-COMMERCE VENTURES LIMITED; *Int'l*, pg. 2800
FUJI LIFE SCIENCE PRODUCTS LIMITED—See China-Hong Kong Photo Products Holdings Limited; *Int'l*, pg. 1568
FULLER COSMETICS S.A. DE C.V.—See Tupperware Brands Corporation; *U.S. Public*, pg. 2204
GENERIC VALUE PRODUCTS, INC.—See Sally Beauty Holdings, Inc.; *U.S. Public*, pg. 1838
GINGKO LTD.—See Aurelius Equity Opportunities SE & Co. KGaA; *Int'l*, pg. 709
GREENLEAF, INC.—See Grace Management Group, LLC; *U.S. Private*, pg. 1749
GREYSON INTERNATIONAL, INC.; *U.S. Public*, pg. 969
GROUPE ROCHER OPERATIONS SAS; *Int'l*, pg. 3110
GSM NATION LLC.; *U.S. Private*, pg. 1801
HARRELL'S CAR WASH SYSTEMS—See Generation Growth Capital; *U.S. Private*, pg. 1668
HATCHBEAUTY AGENCY LLC—See American Exchange Group; *U.S. Private*, pg. 232
HEALING SOLUTIONS (REMEDY) LLC—See Aterian, Inc.; *U.S. Public*, pg. 221
HEALTH & HAPPINESS (H&H) TRADING INDIA PRIVATE LIMITED—See Health and Happiness (H&H) International Holdings Limited; *Int'l*, pg. 3303
HIGH INTENSITY PRODUCTS, INC.—See Sally Beauty Holdings, Inc.; *U.S. Public*, pg. 1838
HI-TECH HEALTHCARE; *U.S. Private*, pg. 1932
HOUSE OF FULLER, S. DE RL DE CV—See Tupperware Brands Corporation; *U.S. Public*, pg. 2204
THE HOUSE OF KWONG SANG HONG LIMITED—See

N.A.I.C.S. INDEX

456130 — OPTICAL GOODS RETAI...

Chinese Estates Holdings Limited; *Int'l*, pg. 1569
HOUSE OF ROSE CO., LTD.; *Int'l*, pg. 3491
INTERNATIONAL FLAVOURS & FRAGRANCES I.F.F. (GREAT BRITAIN) LTD.—See International Flavors & Fragrances Inc.; *U.S. Public*, pg. 1153
INTER PARFUMS, INC.; *U.S. Public*, pg. 1140
INTERPARFUMS SINGAPORE PTE.—See Inter Parfums, Inc.; *U.S. Public*, pg. 1140
ITF GERMANY GMBH—See Angelini ACRAF S.p.A.; *Int'l*, pg. 460
ITF S.P.A.—See Angelini ACRAF S.p.A.; *Int'l*, pg. 460
JAFRA COSMETICS INTERNATIONAL, INC.—See Betterware de Mexico S.A.P.I. de C.V.; *U.S. Private*, pg. 1004
JAPAN EYELASH PRODUCTS INSTITUTE INC.—See Beauty Garage Inc.; *Int'l*, pg. 935
JAPAN TUPPERWARE CO., LTD.—See Tupperware Brands Corporation; *U.S. Public*, pg. 2204
JTG TRADING BV—See B&S Group S.A.; *Int'l*, pg. 784
KARBON BEAUTY LLC; *U.S. Public*, pg. 2262
KINESYS INC.; *U.S. Private*, pg. 2307
KRUIDVAT RETAIL BV—See CK Hutchison Holdings Limited; *Int'l*, pg. 1636
LABORATOIRES FILORGA COSMETIQUES ESPANA S.L.U.—See Colgate-Palmolive Company; *U.S. Public*, pg. 533
LABORATOIRES FILORGA COSMETIQUES S.A.—See Colgate-Palmolive Company; *U.S. Public*, pg. 533
LA FEMME PERFUMERY INC.; *U.S. Private*, pg. 2368
L'ARTISAN PARFUMEUR S.A.—See Paine Schwartz Partners, LLC; *U.S. Private*, pg. 3076
L'ARTISAN PARFUMEUR USA—See Paine Schwartz Partners, LLC; *U.S. Private*, pg. 3076
LBG LIMITED—See B. Grimm Group; *Int'l*, pg. 788
LEADING WAY APPAREL SHANGHAI LIMITED—See Dickson Concepts (International) Limited; *Int'l*, pg. 2112
LENDA, INC.—See Reali, Inc.; *U.S. Private*, pg. 3368
LIME CRIME INC.—See Tengram Capital Partners, Limited Partnership; *U.S. Private*, pg. 3967
LLC "MARY KAY (MOLDOVA) LIMITED"—See Mary Kay Holding Corporation; *U.S. Private*, pg. 2599
LUXE BRANDS, INC.; *U.S. Private*, pg. 2518
LUXURY BRANDS, LLC; *U.S. Private*, pg. 2518
MARC ANTHONY COSMETICS LTD.—See Nexus Capital Management LP; *U.S. Private*, pg. 2922
MARIANNA MEMPHIS INC.—See Marianna Imports Inc.; *U.S. Private*, pg. 2574
MARILYN MIGLIN, L.P.; *U.S. Private*, pg. 2574
MARY KAY ASIA SERVICES LIMITED—See Mary Kay Holding Corporation; *U.S. Private*, pg. 2599
MARY KAY (CHINA) COSMETICS CO., LTD.—See Mary Kay Holding Corporation; *U.S. Private*, pg. 2599
MARY KAY COSMETICOS DE MEXICO, S.A. DE C.V.—See Mary Kay Holding Corporation; *U.S. Private*, pg. 2599
MARY KAY COSMETICOS DO BRAZIL LTDA.—See Mary Kay Holding Corporation; *U.S. Private*, pg. 2599
MARY KAY COSMETICOS, S.A.—See Mary Kay Holding Corporation; *U.S. Private*, pg. 2599
MARY KAY COSMETICS GMBH—See Mary Kay Holding Corporation; *U.S. Private*, pg. 2599
MARY KAY COSMETICS (NEW ZEALAND) INC.—See Mary Kay Holding Corporation; *U.S. Private*, pg. 2599
MARY KAY CZECH REPUBLIC S.R.O.—See Mary Kay Holding Corporation; *U.S. Private*, pg. 2599
MARY KAY (KAZAKHSTAN) LLP—See Mary Kay Holding Corporation; *U.S. Private*, pg. 2599
MARY KAY KOREA, LTD.—See Mary Kay Holding Corporation; *U.S. Private*, pg. 2599
MARY KAY LITHUANIA—See Mary Kay Holding Corporation; *U.S. Private*, pg. 2599
MARY KAY (MALAYSIA) SDN BHD—See Mary Kay Holding Corporation; *U.S. Private*, pg. 2599
MARY KAY (SINGAPORE) PRIVATE LIMITED—See Mary Kay Holding Corporation; *U.S. Private*, pg. 2599
MAV BEAUTY BRANDS, INC.—See Nexus Capital Management LP; *U.S. Private*, pg. 2922
MAYFLOWER SALES CO.,LLC—See Gen Cap America, Inc.; *U.S. Private*, pg. 1660
MED STAR SURGICAL & BREATHING EQUIPMENT, INC.; *U.S. Private*, pg. 2650
MIGHTY OCEAN COMPANY LTD—See Aurelius Equity Opportunities SE & Co. KGaA; *Int'l*, pg. 710
MINERAL FUSION NATURAL BRANDS LLC—See BWX Limited; *Int'l*, pg. 1233
MODERN INDUSTRIES COMPANY—See The Procter & Gamble Company; *U.S. Public*, pg. 2120
MONARIMPORT S.P.A.—See Clarins S.A.; *Int'l*, pg. 1649
MORRIS FLAMINGO-STEPHAN, INC.—See The Stephan Company; *U.S. Public*, pg. 2132
MURAD SKIN RESEARCH LABS INC.; *U.S. Private*, pg. 2814
MY BEST FRIEND'S HAIR, LLC—See Sally Beauty Holdings, Inc.; *U.S. Public*, pg. 1839
NAMU LIFE PLUS COMPANY LIMITED—See Do Day Dream PCL; *Int'l*, pg. 2152
NAPLES SOAP COMPANY, INC.—See The GNS Group; *U.S. Private*, pg. 2075
NATIONAL DME, L.C.; *U.S. Private*, pg. 2852
NATIONAL MARKETING & TRADING CO LLC—See Aurelius Equity Opportunities SE & Co. KGaA; *Int'l*, pg. 710
NEOSTRATA COMPANY INC—See Kenvue Inc.; *U.S. Public*, pg. 1224
NOCIBE FRANCE SAS—See CVC Capital Partners SICAV-FIS S.A.; *Int'l*, pg. 1883
NORTH AMERICAN CORP.; *U.S. Private*, pg. 2940
NORVELL SKIN SOLUTIONS, LLC—See Castle Harlan, Inc.; *U.S. Private*, pg. 785
NU SKIN JAPAN CO., LTD.—See Nu Skin Enterprises, Inc.; *U.S. Public*, pg. 1552
NU SKIN PERU S.A.C.—See Nu Skin Enterprises, Inc.; *U.S. Public*, pg. 1552
OBON SAI COSMETICS LTD—See Aurelius Equity Opportunities SE & Co. KGaA; *Int'l*, pg. 710
OGEE LIMITED—See Sally Beauty Holdings, Inc.; *U.S. Public*, pg. 1838
ORLEANS COSMETICS PROPRIETARY LIMITED—See AYO Technology Solutions Ltd.; *Int'l*, pg. 775
OSMOTICS CORP.—See BHMS Investments LP; *U.S. Private*, pg. 549
PACIFIC WORLD CORPORATION—See Levine Leichtman Capital Partners, LLC; *U.S. Private*, pg. 2436
PARFUMERIE DOUGLAS AG—See CVC Capital Partners SICAV-FIS S.A.; *Int'l*, pg. 1883
PARFUMERIE DOUGLAS GES.M.B.H.—See CVC Capital Partners SICAV-FIS S.A.; *Int'l*, pg. 1883
PARFUMERIE DOUGLAS GMBH—See CVC Capital Partners SICAV-FIS S.A.; *Int'l*, pg. 1883
PARFUMERIE DOUGLAS INTERNATIONAL GMBH—See CVC Capital Partners SICAV-FIS S.A.; *Int'l*, pg. 1883
PARFUMERIE DOUGLAS MONACO S.A.M.—See CVC Capital Partners SICAV-FIS S.A.; *Int'l*, pg. 1883
PARFUMERIE DOUGLAS NEDERLAND B.V.—See CVC Capital Partners SICAV-FIS S.A.; *Int'l*, pg. 1883
PARFUMERIE DOUGLAS S.R.O.—See CVC Capital Partners SICAV-FIS S.A.; *Int'l*, pg. 1883
PENHALIGON'S LIMITED—See Paine Schwartz Partners, LLC; *U.S. Private*, pg. 3076
PERFUMANIA HOLDINGS, INC.; *U.S. Private*, pg. 3150
PERFUMANIA, INC.—See Perfumania Holdings, Inc.; *U.S. Private*, pg. 3150
PERFUMANIA PUERTO RICO, INC.—See Perfumania Holdings, Inc.; *U.S. Private*, pg. 3150
PERFUMARIA DOUGLAS PORTUGAL LDA.—See CVC Capital Partners SICAV-FIS S.A.; *Int'l*, pg. 1883
PERSONALIZED BEAUTY DISCOVERY, INC.; *U.S. Private*, pg. 3156
PRODUCTOS GILLETTE CHILE LIMITADA—See The Procter & Gamble Company; *U.S. Public*, pg. 2124
PRO-DUO DEUTSCHLAND GMBH—See Sally Beauty Holdings, Inc.; *U.S. Public*, pg. 1838
PRO-DUO NV—See Sally Beauty Holdings, Inc.; *U.S. Public*, pg. 1838
PRO-DUO SPAIN SL—See Sally Beauty Holdings, Inc.; *U.S. Public*, pg. 1838
PROFUMERIE DOUGLAS S.P.A.—See CVC Capital Partners SICAV-FIS S.A.; *Int'l*, pg. 1883
PROGUARD ACQUISITION CORP.; *U.S. Private*, pg. 3279
PT. APTAR B&H INDONESIA—See AptarGroup, Inc.; *U.S. Public*, pg. 174
RAMPAI-NIAGA SDN BHD—See Aurelius Equity Opportunities SE & Co. KGaA; *Int'l*, pg. 710
REBOUL SAS—See AptarGroup, Inc.; *U.S. Public*, pg. 175
RETAIL STORE OPERATIONS, INC.—See Bath & Body Works, Inc.; *U.S. Public*, pg. 279
REVLON, S.A.—See MacAndrews & Forbes Incorporated; *U.S. Private*, pg. 2533
SALLY BEAUTY NETHERLANDS BV—See Sally Beauty Holdings, Inc.; *U.S. Public*, pg. 1838
SALLY CHILE HOLDING SPA—See Sally Beauty Holdings, Inc.; *U.S. Public*, pg. 1838
SALLY HOLDINGS LLC—See Sally Beauty Holdings, Inc.; *U.S. Public*, pg. 1838
SALLY SALON SERVICES LTD—See Sally Beauty Holdings, Inc.; *U.S. Public*, pg. 1839
SALON PROFESSIONAL SERVICES, INC.; *U.S. Private*, pg. 3533
SALON SERVICES FRANCHISING LTD—See Sally Beauty Holdings, Inc.; *U.S. Public*, pg. 1839
SALON SUCCESS LIMITED—See Sally Beauty Holdings, Inc.; *U.S. Public*, pg. 1839
SBCBSG COMPANY DE MEXICO, S. DE R.I. DE C.V.—See Sally Beauty Holdings, Inc.; *U.S. Public*, pg. 1838
SCHOENEMAN BEAUTY SUPPLY INC—See Sally Beauty Holdings, Inc.; *U.S. Public*, pg. 1839
SIA DOUGLAS LATVIA—See CVC Capital Partners SICAV-FIS S.A.; *Int'l*, pg. 1883
SIAM ARATA CO., LTD.—See Arata Corporation; *Int'l*, pg. 536
SIBU BEAUTY; *U.S. Private*, pg. 3645
SILK ELEMENTS, INC.—See Sally Beauty Holdings, Inc.; *U.S. Public*, pg. 1839
SINELCO INTERNATIONAL BVBA—See Sally Beauty Holdings, Inc.; *U.S. Public*, pg. 1839
SINELCO ITALIANA SRL—See Sally Beauty Holdings, Inc.; *U.S. Public*, pg. 1839
SKINCARESTORE AUSTRALIA PTY LTD—See Walgreens Boots Alliance, Inc.; *U.S. Public*, pg. 2323
SKINSTORE.COM; *U.S. Private*, pg. 3682
SMITH ROBERTSON & COMPANY LIMITED—See Agostini's Limited; *Int'l*, pg. 213
SPECIALTY COMMERCE CORP.—See EdgeStone Capital Partners Inc.; *Int'l*, pg. 2309
SSG, INC.—See Great Range Capital, LLC; *U.S. Private*, pg. 1767
S & S SPRINKLER CO LLC—See Pye-Barker Fire & Safety, LLC; *U.S. Private*, pg. 3309
STANHOME FRANCE SAS—See Groupe Rocher Operations SAS; *Int'l*, pg. 3110
STEEL TECHNOLOGIES, LLC—See Helen of Troy Limited; *Int'l*, pg. 3329
SUPREME PAPER SUPPLIES LLC—See Bain Capital, LP; *U.S. Private*, pg. 441
SYNDERO, INC.; *U.S. Private*, pg. 3903
TOP CREATION LIMITED—See Dickson Concepts (International) Limited; *Int'l*, pg. 2112
TULA LIFE, INC.—See The Procter & Gamble Company; *U.S. Public*, pg. 2124
UAB DOUGLAS LT—See CVC Capital Partners SICAV-FIS S.A.; *Int'l*, pg. 1883
ULTA BEAUTY, INC.; *U.S. Public*, pg. 2223
USPA CORPORATION PTY. LTD.—See BWX Limited; *Int'l*, pg. 1233
VENIQUE, INC.—See Sally Beauty Holdings, Inc.; *U.S. Public*, pg. 1839
VICTORIA'S SECRET UK LIMITED—See Bath & Body Works, Inc.; *U.S. Public*, pg. 279
W3LL PEOPLE LLC—See e.l.f. Beauty, Inc.; *U.S. Public*, pg. 701
WARRENDER ENTERPRISE INC.; *U.S. Private*, pg. 4444
XTAVA LLC—See Aterian, Inc.; *U.S. Public*, pg. 221
XTREME LASHES, LLC; *U.S. Private*, pg. 4583
YOUNGBLOOD SKIN CARE PRODUCTS, LLC—See Luxury Brands, LLC; *U.S. Private*, pg. 2518

456130 — OPTICAL GOODS RETAILERS

1-800 CONTACTS, INC.—See AEA Investors LP; *U.S. Private*, pg. 113
ADO BUYING GROUP—See Walman Optical Company; *U.S. Private*, pg. 4432
AECC TOTAL VISION HEALTH PLAN OF TEXAS, INC.—See Centene Corporation; *U.S. Public*, pg. 467
AIGAN CO., LTD.; *Int'l*, pg. 232
ALLEGANY OPTICAL LLC; *U.S. Private*, pg. 175
ALTAIR EYEWEAR—See Vision Service Plan; *U.S. Private*, pg. 4391
AMERICA'S BEST CONTACTS & EYEGLASSES—See KKR & Co. Inc.; *U.S. Public*, pg. 1261
ARLINGTON CONTACT LENS SERVICE, INC.; *U.S. Private*, pg. 329
BAUR OPTIK GESCHAFTSFUHRUNGS-AG—See Fielmann Group AG; *Int'l*, pg. 2656
BAUSCH & LOMB POLSKA SP. Z.O.O.—See Bausch Health Companies Inc.; *Int'l*, pg. 896
BAUSCH & LOMB SCOTLAND LIMITED—See Bausch Health Companies Inc.; *Int'l*, pg. 896
BOOTS OPTICIANS PROFESSIONAL SERVICES LIMITED—See Walgreens Boots Alliance, Inc.; *U.S. Public*, pg. 2322
BRILLEN-BUNZEL GMBH—See Fielmann Group AG; *Int'l*, pg. 2656
BUFFALO OPTICAL COMPANY INC.; *U.S. Private*, pg. 681
CANUSA AUTOMOTIVE WAREHOUSING INC.; *Int'l*, pg. 1300
CARL ZEISS VISION IRELAND LTD.—See Carl-Zeiss-Stiftung; *Int'l*, pg. 1336
CARL ZEISS VISION IRELAND LTD.—See EQT AB; *Int'l*, pg. 2473
CARL ZEISS VISION—See Carl-Zeiss-Stiftung; *Int'l*, pg. 1335
CARL ZEISS VISION—See EQT AB; *Int'l*, pg. 2473
COHEN'S FASHION OPTICAL INC.—See Houchens Industries, Inc.; *U.S. Private*, pg. 1989
COOPERATIVE OPTICAL SERVICES; *U.S. Private*, pg. 1042
COOPERVISION S.A. (PTY) LIMITED—See The Cooper Companies, Inc.; *U.S. Public*, pg. 2066
CUSTOM OPTICAL—See EssilorLuxottica SA; *Int'l*, pg. 2513
DOCTER OPTICS INC.—See Hella GmbH & Co. KGaA; *Int'l*, pg. 3331
EMERGING VISION, INC.; *U.S. Private*, pg. 1381
EMPIRE VISION CTR. INC.—See Highmark Health; *U.S. Private*, pg. 1940
ENVOLVE OPTICAL, INC.—See Centene Corporation; *U.S. Public*, pg. 468
EYEBOBS, LLC—See Blue Point Capital Partners, LLC; *U.S. Private*, pg. 590
EYEGLASS SERVICE INDUSTRIES; *U.S. Private*, pg. 1453
EYEGLASS WORLD—See KKR & Co. Inc.; *U.S. Public*, pg. 1261
EYE-MART EXPRESS LTD.; *U.S. Private*, pg. 1453
EYETIQUE LLC—See Riata Capital Group LLC; *U.S. Private*, pg. 3424

456130 — OPTICAL GOODS RETAI...

FFN HOLDING AG—See Fielmann Group AG; *Int'l*, pg. 2656
FIELMANN AG & CO. AM KUGELBRUNNEN KG—See Fielmann Group AG; *Int'l*, pg. 2658
FIELMANN AG & CO. AM MARKT OHG—See Fielmann Group AG; *Int'l*, pg. 2658
FIELMANN AG & CO. BAD CANNSTATT OHG—See Fielmann Group AG; *Int'l*, pg. 2656
FIELMANN AG & CO. BARBAROSSAPLATZ OHG—See Fielmann Group AG; *Int'l*, pg. 2656
FIELMANN AG & CO. BARMEN OHG—See Fielmann Group AG; *Int'l*, pg. 2656
FIELMANN AG & CO. BERGEDORF OHG—See Fielmann Group AG; *Int'l*, pg. 2656
FIELMANN AG & CO. BILLSTEDT KG—See Fielmann Group AG; *Int'l*, pg. 2656
FIELMANN AG & CO. BONN-BAD GODESBERG OHG—See Fielmann Group AG; *Int'l*, pg. 2656
FIELMANN AG & CO. BORNHEIM KG—See Fielmann Group AG; *Int'l*, pg. 2656
FIELMANN AG & CO. BRAMFELD OHG—See Fielmann Group AG; *Int'l*, pg. 2656
FIELMANN AG & CO. BUER OHG—See Fielmann Group AG; *Int'l*, pg. 2656
FIELMANN AG & CO. CHORWEILER OHG—See Fielmann Group AG; *Int'l*, pg. 2656
FIELMANN AG & CO. DRESDEN ALTSTADT OHG—See Fielmann Group AG; *Int'l*, pg. 2656
FIELMANN AG & CO. DRESDEN NEUSTADT OHG—See Fielmann Group AG; *Int'l*, pg. 2656
FIELMANN AG & CO. EIMSBUTTEL OHG—See Fielmann Group AG; *Int'l*, pg. 2656
FIELMANN AG & CO. EKZ WESTPARK OHG—See Fielmann Group AG; *Int'l*, pg. 2656
FIELMANN AG & CO. EPPENDORF KG—See Fielmann Group AG; *Int'l*, pg. 2656
FIELMANN AG & CO. ERNST-AUGUST-GALERIE KG—See Fielmann Group AG; *Int'l*, pg. 2656
FIELMANN AG & CO. ESSEN-RUTTENSCHEID OHG—See Fielmann Group AG; *Int'l*, pg. 2656
FIELMANN AG & CO. ESSEN-STEELE OHG—See Fielmann Group AG; *Int'l*, pg. 2656
FIELMANN AG & CO. FRIEDRICHSTRASSE OHG—See Fielmann Group AG; *Int'l*, pg. 2656
FIELMANN AG & CO. HAIDHAUSEN OHG—See Fielmann Group AG; *Int'l*, pg. 2656
FIELMANN AG & CO. HAMBORN KG—See Fielmann Group AG; *Int'l*, pg. 2656
FIELMANN AG & CO. HILTRUP OHG—See Fielmann Group AG; *Int'l*, pg. 2656
FIELMANN AG & CO. HOCHST OHG—See Fielmann Group AG; *Int'l*, pg. 2656
FIELMANN AG & CO. IM DONAU-EINKAUFSZENTRUM KG—See Fielmann Group AG; *Int'l*, pg. 2658
FIELMANN AG & CO. KAUFPARK KG—See Fielmann Group AG; *Int'l*, pg. 2657
FIELMANN AG & CO. KLOSTERSTRASSE OHG—See Fielmann Group AG; *Int'l*, pg. 2657
FIELMANN AG & CO. LISTER MEILE OHG—See Fielmann Group AG; *Int'l*, pg. 2657
FIELMANN AG & CO. NEUMARKT KG—See Fielmann Group AG; *Int'l*, pg. 2657
FIELMANN AG & CO. NORDSTADT OHG—See Fielmann Group AG; *Int'l*, pg. 2657
FIELMANN AG & CO. NURNBERG-LANGWASSER OHG—See Fielmann Group AG; *Int'l*, pg. 2657
FIELMANN AG & CO. NURNBERG LORENZ OHG—See Fielmann Group AG; *Int'l*, pg. 2657
FIELMANN AG & CO. NURNBERG-SUD KG—See Fielmann Group AG; *Int'l*, pg. 2657
FIELMANN AG & CO. OBERHAUSEN OHG—See Fielmann Group AG; *Int'l*, pg. 2657
FIELMANN AG & CO. OBERKASSEL OHG—See Fielmann Group AG; *Int'l*, pg. 2657
FIELMANN AG & CO. OCHSENZOLL OHG—See Fielmann Group AG; *Int'l*, pg. 2657
FIELMANN AG & CO. OHG AN DER ROTHENBURG—See Fielmann Group AG; *Int'l*, pg. 2658
FIELMANN AG & CO. OHG BREMEN-NEUSTADT—See Fielmann Group AG; *Int'l*, pg. 2658
FIELMANN AG & CO. OHG KALK—See Fielmann Group AG; *Int'l*, pg. 2658
FIELMANN AG & CO. OHG KAVALIERSTRASSE—See Fielmann Group AG; *Int'l*, pg. 2658
FIELMANN AG & CO. OHG MUNCHEN PEP—See Fielmann Group AG; *Int'l*, pg. 2658
FIELMANN AG & CO. OHG NIENDORF—See Fielmann Group AG; *Int'l*, pg. 2658
FIELMANN AG & CO. OHG SENDLING—See Fielmann Group AG; *Int'l*, pg. 2658
FIELMANN AG & CO. OHG STERKRADE—See Fielmann Group AG; *Int'l*, pg. 2658
FIELMANN AG & CO. OHG WELLINGDORF—See Fielmann Group AG; *Int'l*, pg. 2658
FIELMANN AG & CO. OTTENSEN OHG—See Fielmann Group AG; *Int'l*, pg. 2657
FIELMANN AG & CO. PASING OHG—See Fielmann Group AG; *Int'l*, pg. 2657
FIELMANN AG & CO. PAUNSDORF-CENTER OHG—See Fielmann Group AG; *Int'l*, pg. 2657
FIELMANN AG & CO. RETHELSTRASSE OHG—See Fielmann Group AG; *Int'l*, pg. 2657
FIELMANN AG & CO. RHEINRUHRZENTRUM OHG—See Fielmann Group AG; *Int'l*, pg. 2657
FIELMANN AG & CO. ROLAND-CENTER KG—See Fielmann Group AG; *Int'l*, pg. 2657
FIELMANN AG & CO. ROSSMARKT OHG—See Fielmann Group AG; *Int'l*, pg. 2657
FIELMANN AG & CO. SCHILDERGASSE OHG—See Fielmann Group AG; *Int'l*, pg. 2657
FIELMANN AG & CO. SCHLOSS-ARKADEN KG—See Fielmann Group AG; *Int'l*, pg. 2657
FIELMANN AG & CO. SCHWARZER BAR OHG—See Fielmann Group AG; *Int'l*, pg. 2657
FIELMANN AG & CO. SCHWENNINGEN KG—See Fielmann Group AG; *Int'l*, pg. 2657
FIELMANN AG & CO. STERN CENTER OHG—See Fielmann Group AG; *Int'l*, pg. 2657
FIELMANN AG & CO. SUDENBURG OHG—See Fielmann Group AG; *Int'l*, pg. 2657
FIELMANN AG & CO. TAL KG—See Fielmann Group AG; *Int'l*, pg. 2657
FIELMANN AG & CO. THURINGEN-PARK OHG—See Fielmann Group AG; *Int'l*, pg. 2657
FIELMANN AG & CO. VEGESACK OHG—See Fielmann Group AG; *Int'l*, pg. 2658
FIELMANN AG & CO. VITA-CENTER KG—See Fielmann Group AG; *Int'l*, pg. 2658
FIELMANN AG & CO. VOLKSDORF OHG—See Fielmann Group AG; *Int'l*, pg. 2658
FIELMANN AG & CO. WATTENSCHEID KG—See Fielmann Group AG; *Int'l*, pg. 2658
FIELMANN AG & CO. WESTLICHE KAISERSTRASSE KG—See Fielmann Group AG; *Int'l*, pg. 2658
FIELMANN AUGENOPTIK AG & CO. HALLE-NEUSTADT OHG—See Fielmann Group AG; *Int'l*, pg. 2658
FIELMANN AUGENOPTIK AG & CO. OHG—See Fielmann Group AG; *Int'l*, pg. 2658
FIELMANN B.V.—See Fielmann Group AG; *Int'l*, pg. 2658
FIELMANN FINANZSERVICE GMBH—See Fielmann Group AG; *Int'l*, pg. 2658
FIELMANN HOLDING B.V.—See Fielmann Group AG; *Int'l*, pg. 2658
FIELMANN-OPTIC FIELMANN GMBH & CO. KG—See Fielmann Group AG; *Int'l*, pg. 2658
FIELMANN SCHWEIZ AG—See Fielmann Group AG; *Int'l*, pg. 2658
FIRSTSIGHT VISION SERVICES, INC.—See National Vision Holdings, Inc.; *U.S. Public*, pg. 1498
FOCUS OPTICS PTY. LTD.—See EYECARE PARTNERS LIMITED; *Int'l*, pg. 2593
FOCUS POINT VISION CARE GROUP SDN. BHD.—See Focus Point Holdings Berhad; *Int'l*, pg. 2719
FUJIFILM COLOMBIA S.A.S—See FUJIFILM Holdings Corporation; *Int'l*, pg. 2821
GAFFOS INC.; *U.S. Private*, pg. 1634
GENERAL OPTICA S.A.—See De Rigo S.p.A.; *Int'l*, pg. 1997
GOOCH & HOUSEGO (OHIO) LLC—See Gooch & Housego PLC; *Int'l*, pg. 3038
HAKIM OPTICAL LABORATORY LIMITED; *Int'l*, pg. 3219
HID HAMBURGER IMMOBILIENDIENSTE GMBH—See Fielmann Group AG; *Int'l*, pg. 2658
HORNER-RAUSCH EAST, INC.; *U.S. Private*, pg. 1983
JORGENSON OPTICAL SUPPLY CY.—See EssilorLuxottica SA; *Int'l*, pg. 2513
JS&A GROUP, INC.; *U.S. Private*, pg. 2241
KANSAS CITY OPTHALMICS LLC—See Carl-Zeiss-Stiftung; *Int'l*, pg. 1335
KANSAS CITY OPTHALMICS LLC—See EQT AB; *Int'l*, pg. 2473
THE LASIK VISION INSTITUTE, LLC; *U.S. Private*, pg. 4067
LOCHTE-OPTIK GMBH—See Fielmann Group AG; *Int'l*, pg. 2659
LUXOTTICA RETAIL AUSTRALIA PTY. LIMITED—See EssilorLuxottica SA; *Int'l*, pg. 2515
MARCHON GERMANY GMBH—See Vision Service Plan; *U.S. Private*, pg. 4391
MARCHON HELLAS S.A.—See Vision Service Plan; *U.S. Private*, pg. 4391
MAXX HD SUNGLASSES; *U.S. Private*, pg. 2619
MCGEE GROUP; *U.S. Private*, pg. 2634
MOSCOT OPTICAL CORP.; *U.S. Private*, pg. 2792
MYOPTIQUE GROUP LTD.—See EssilorLuxottica SA; *Int'l*, pg. 2515
NATIONAL VISION HOLDINGS, INC.; *U.S. Public*, pg. 1498
NATIONAL VISION, INC.—See KKR & Co. Inc.; *U.S. Public*, pg. 1261
NEOPHOTONICS (CHINA) CO., LTD.—See Lumentum Holdings, Inc.; *U.S. Public*, pg. 1348
OMNI OPTICAL LAB—See EssilorLuxottica SA; *Int'l*, pg. 2513
OPTICAL DISTRIBUTOR GROUP, LLC—See ABB/Concise Optical Group LLC; *U.S. Private*, pg. 34
OPTIK HESS GMBH—See Fielmann Group AG; *Int'l*, pg. 2659
OPTIK KAPERNICK GMBH & CO. KG—See Fielmann Group AG; *Int'l*, pg. 2659
OPTIK KLUTTERMANN VERWALTUNGS GMBH—See Fielmann Group AG; *Int'l*, pg. 2659
OPTIK SIMON GMBH—See Fielmann Group AG; *Int'l*, pg. 2659
OZARKS OPTICAL LABORATORIES INC—See EssilorLuxottica SA; *Int'l*, pg. 2513
RX OPTICAL LABORATORY INC.; *U.S. Private*, pg. 3509
SOLSTICE MARKETING CONCEPTS, LLC—See Solstice Marketing Corp.; *U.S. Private*, pg. 3710
STADT OPTIK FIELMANN LANGENTHAL AG—See Fielmann Group AG; *Int'l*, pg. 2659
STEPPER SOUTH AFRICA (PROPRIETARY) LIMITED—See Arts Optical International Holdings Ltd; *Int'l*, pg. 586
SUNLAND OPTICAL COMPANY INC.; *U.S. Private*, pg. 3868
SVS VISION, INC—See Fielmann Group AG; *Int'l*, pg. 2659
TASMANIAN OPTICAL CY PTY LTD—See EssilorLuxottica SA; *Int'l*, pg. 2516
THRALOW, INC.; *U.S. Private*, pg. 4163
TRAM DATA, LLC; *U.S. Private*, pg. 4204
TRI SUPREME OPTICAL LLC—See EssilorLuxottica SA; *Int'l*, pg. 2514
UNITED VISION GROUP INC.; *U.S. Private*, pg. 4301
U.S. VISION, INC.—See ACON Investments, LLC; *U.S. Private*, pg. 63
VISION DYNAMICS, LLC—See New England Low Vision & Blindness; *U.S. Private*, pg. 2894
VISIONWORKS OF AMERICA, INC.—See Vision Service Plan; *U.S. Private*, pg. 4391

456191 — FOOD (HEALTH) SUPPLEMENT RETAILERS

AAYUSH FOOD & HERBS LTD.; *Int'l*, pg. 38
ACCEL LIQUID GELS, INC.; *U.S. Private*, pg. 47
AGROLABS, INC.—See Integrated Biopharma, Inc.; *U.S. Public*, pg. 1136
ALLIANCE HEALTHCARE (IT SERVICES) LIMITED—See Walgreens Boots Alliance, Inc.; *U.S. Public*, pg. 2322
ALLOGA UK LIMITED—See Walgreens Boots Alliance, Inc.; *U.S. Public*, pg. 2322
ALLTECH FRANCE S.A.R.L.—See Standard Industries Holdings, Inc.; *U.S. Private*, pg. 3779
ALPHABET HOLDING COMPANY, INC.; *U.S. Private*, pg. 200
AMERICAN HEALTH PACKAGING—See Cencora, Inc.; *U.S. Public*, pg. 466
AMGEN AUSTRALIA PTY LTD.—See Amgen Inc.; *U.S. Public*, pg. 122
AMMD, LLC; *U.S. Private*, pg. 264
ANIMEDICA INTERNATIONAL GMBH—See AGRAVIS Raiffeisen AG; *Int'l*, pg. 216
ANIMEDICA LATINO AMERICA S.A. DE C.V.—See AGRAVIS Raiffeisen AG; *Int'l*, pg. 215
ARTSANA ARGENTINA S.A.—See BI-Invest Advisors S.A.; *Int'l*, pg. 1016
ARTSANA BELGIUM SA—See BI-Invest Advisors S.A.; *Int'l*, pg. 1016
ARTSANA FRANCE S.A.S.—See BI-Invest Advisors S.A.; *Int'l*, pg. 1016
ARTSANA GERMANY GMBH—See BI-Invest Advisors S.A.; *Int'l*, pg. 1016
ARTSANA PORTUGAL, S.A.—See BI-Invest Advisors S.A.; *Int'l*, pg. 1016
ARTSANA SPAIN S.A.U.—See BI-Invest Advisors S.A.; *Int'l*, pg. 1016
ARTSANA SUISSE S.A.—See BI-Invest Advisors S.A.; *Int'l*, pg. 1016
ARTSANA TURKEY BEBEK VE SAGLIK URUNLERI A.S.—See BI-Invest Advisors S.A.; *Int'l*, pg. 1016
ARTSANA USA, INC.—See BI-Invest Advisors S.A.; *Int'l*, pg. 1016
ASTAREAL (AUSTRALIA) PTY LTD—See Fuji Chemical Industries Co., Ltd; *Int'l*, pg. 2809
ASTAREAL PTE. LTD.—See Fuji Chemical Industries Co., Ltd; *Int'l*, pg. 2809
BARENTZ SPOL. S.R.O.—See Cinven Limited; *Int'l*, pg. 1611
BELLRING BRANDS, INC.—See Post Holdings, Inc.; *U.S. Public*, pg. 1703
BETANCOURT SPORTS NUTRITION, LLC—See B. Riley Financial, Inc.; *U.S. Public*, pg. 261
BETANCOURT SPORTS NUTRITION, LLC—See Irradiant Partners, LP; *U.S. Private*, pg. 2141
BETTER HEALTH; *U.S. Private*, pg. 546
BEWITAL GMBH & CO. KG; *Int'l*, pg. 1004
BIOCENTRIC HEALTH INC.; *U.S. Private*, pg. 561
BIOERA S.P.A.; *Int'l*, pg. 1037
BIO ESSENCE CORP.; *U.S. Public*, pg. 332
BIOFILM, INC.—See Combe Incorporated; *U.S. Private*, pg. 980
BIOFORCE NANOSCIENCES HOLDINGS, INC.; *U.S. Public*, pg. 335

N.A.I.C.S. INDEX

456191 — FOOD (HEALTH) SUPPL...

BIONUTRITIONAL RESEARCH GROUP, INC.; *U.S. Private*, pg. 562
BIORIGINAL FOOD & SCIENCE CORPORATION—See Cooke, Inc.; *Int'l*, pg. 1788
BOOST NUTRITION S.C./C.V.—See Ebro Foods S.A.; *Int'l*, pg. 2286
BRAIN SCIENTIFIC, INC.—See Piezo Motion Corp.; *U.S. Private*, pg. 3179
BROWNWOOD ACRES FOODS, INC.; *U.S. Private*, pg. 670
CARDINAL HEALTH EQUIPMENT MANAGEMENT SERVICES—See Cardinal Health, Inc.; *U.S. Public*, pg. 433
CARMICHAEL'S NUTRITIONAL DISTRIBUTOR, INC.—See SunLink Health Systems, Inc.; *U.S. Public*, pg. 1964
CBD GLOBAL SCIENCES, INC.; *U.S. Public*, pg. 455
CELLUCOR—See Woodbolt Distribution, LLC; *U.S. Private*, pg. 4557
CHAMBERLIN NATURAL FOODS INC.—See AMCON Distributing Company; *U.S. Public*, pg. 93
COMPLETE NUTRITION HOLDINGS INC.; *U.S. Private*, pg. 1001
THE COROMEGA COMPANY, INC.—See PlusPharma, Inc.; *U.S. Private*, pg. 3215
DESERET BIOLOGICALS; *U.S. Private*, pg. 1211
DREAMBRANDS, INC.; *U.S. Private*, pg. 1275
DXN INTERNATIONAL (AUSTRALIA) PTY. LTD.—See DXN Holdings Bhd.; *Int'l*, pg. 2237
EDOKO FOOD IMPORTERS LTD.; *Int'l*, pg. 2313
ELEVACITY U.S., LLC—See Sharing Services Global Corporation; *U.S. Public*, pg. 1873
FITLIFE FOODS; *U.S. Private*, pg. 1536
FLORENTAISE SA; *Int'l*, pg. 2707
FRANCO'S ATHLETIC CLUB; *U.S. Private*, pg. 1593
GENERAL MILLS DE MEXICO, S. DE R.L. DE C.V.—See General Mills, Inc.; *U.S. Public*, pg. 921
GENERAL NUTRITION CENTERS, INC.—See Ares Management Corporation; *U.S. Public*, pg. 189
GENERAL NUTRITION CENTRES COMPANY—See Ares Management Corporation; *U.S. Public*, pg. 189
GENESIS TODAY INC.; *U.S. Private*, pg. 1670
GEROLYMATOS GROUP OF COMPANIES; *Int'l*, pg. 2943
GLG LIFE TECH CORPORATION; *Int'l*, pg. 2992
GO EPIC HEALTH, INC.—See Leone Asset Management, Inc.; *U.S. Public*, pg. 1308
GOODY PRODUCTS, INC.—See ACON Investments, LLC; *U.S. Private*, pg. 62
GREEN BOX FOODS; *U.S. Private*, pg. 1771
GRUPO TAPER, S.A.—See Banco Santander, S.A.; *Int'l*, pg. 826
HEALTHE GOODS; *U.S. Private*, pg. 1896
HEALTHY LIFE GROUP PTY. LTD.—See Eu Yan Sang International Ltd.; *Int'l*, pg. 2525
HEALTHY NATURAL INC.—See RICEBRAN TECHNOLOGIES; *U.S. Public*, pg. 1797
HENDAYA S.A.—See Compania Electro Metalurgica S.A.; *Int'l*, pg. 1749
HERBALIFE AUSTRALASIA PTY. LTD.—See Herbalife Nutrition Ltd.; *Int'l*, pg. 3359
HERBALIFE DEL ECUADOR, S.A.—See Herbalife Nutrition Ltd.; *Int'l*, pg. 3359
HERBALIFE INTERNAITONAL (THAILAND), LTD.—See Herbalife Nutrition Ltd.; *Int'l*, pg. 3359
HERBALIFE INTERNATIONAL ARGENTINA, S.A.—See Herbalife Nutrition Ltd.; *Int'l*, pg. 3359
HERBALIFE INTERNATIONAL COMMUNICATIONS, INC.—See Herbalife Nutrition Ltd.; *Int'l*, pg. 3359
HERBALIFE INTERNATIONAL DO BRASIL LTDA.—See Herbalife Nutrition Ltd.; *Int'l*, pg. 3359
HERBALIFE INTERNATIONAL FINLAND OY—See Herbalife Nutrition Ltd.; *Int'l*, pg. 3359
HERBALIFE INTERNATIONAL GREECE S.A.—See Herbalife Nutrition Ltd.; *Int'l*, pg. 3359
HERBALIFE INTERNATIONAL ISRAEL LTD.—See Herbalife Nutrition Ltd.; *Int'l*, pg. 3360
HERBALIFE INTERNATIONAL LUXEMBOURG NETHERLANDS BRANCH—See Herbalife Nutrition Ltd.; *Int'l*, pg. 3360
HERBALIFE INTERNATIONAL OF HONG KONG LIMITED—See Herbalife Nutrition Ltd.; *Int'l*, pg. 3360
HERBALIFE INTERNATIONAL OF ISRAEL (1990) LTD.—See Herbalife Nutrition Ltd.; *Int'l*, pg. 3360
HERBALIFE INTERNATIONAL RS LLC—See Herbalife Nutrition Ltd.; *Int'l*, pg. 3359
HERBALIFE INTERNATIONAL SOUTH AFRICA, LTD.—See Herbalife Nutrition Ltd.; *Int'l*, pg. 3359
HERBALIFE ITALIA S.P.A.—See Herbalife Nutrition Ltd.; *Int'l*, pg. 3360
HERBALIFE KAZAKHSTAN LLP—See Herbalife Nutrition Ltd.; *Int'l*, pg. 3360
HERBALIFE NORWAY PRODUCTS AS—See Herbalife Nutrition Ltd.; *Int'l*, pg. 3360
HERBALIFE OF GHANA LIMITED—See Herbalife Nutrition Ltd.; *Int'l*, pg. 3360
HERBALIFE OF JAPAN K.K.—See Herbalife Nutrition Ltd.; *Int'l*, pg. 3360
HERBALIFE PARAGUAY S.R.L.—See Herbalife Nutrition Ltd.; *Int'l*, pg. 3360
HERBALIFE PERU S.R.L.—See Herbalife Nutrition Ltd.; *Int'l*, pg. 3360
HERBALIFE RO S.R.L.—See Herbalife Nutrition Ltd.; *Int'l*, pg. 3360
HERBALIFE TAIWAN, INC.—See Herbalife Nutrition Ltd.; *Int'l*, pg. 3360
HERBALIFE VIETNAM SMLLC—See Herbalife Nutrition Ltd.; *Int'l*, pg. 3360
HERBSPRO.COM—See Universal Herbs Inc.; *U.S. Private*, pg. 4305
HI-GREAT GROUP HOLDING CO.; *U.S. Public*, pg. 1034
HI-HEALTH SUPERMART CORPORATION; *U.S. Private*, pg. 1931
HI-HEALTH SUPERMART—See Hi-Health Supermart Corporation; *U.S. Private*, pg. 1931
HIN SANG HONG COMPANY LIMITED—See Hin Sang Group (International) Holding Co. Ltd.; *Int'l*, pg. 3397
HLF COLOMBIA LTD.—See Herbalife Nutrition Ltd.; *Int'l*, pg. 3359
HUNGARY CURT GEORGI KFT—See Curt Georgi GmbH & Co. KG; *Int'l*, pg. 1880
IBL HEALTHCARE LIMITED; *Int'l*, pg. 3576
INNOVATION1 BIOTECH INC.; *U.S. Public*, pg. 1126
JANSSEN-CILAG B.V.—See Johnson & Johnson; *U.S. Public*, pg. 1197
JANSSEN PHARMACEUTICAL K.K.—See Johnson & Johnson; *U.S. Public*, pg. 1197
JENNY CRAIG, INC.—See H.I.G. Capital, LLC; *U.S. Private*, pg. 1829
LABRADA BODYBUILDING NUTRITION INC.; *U.S. Private*, pg. 2370
LIFEPLUS EUROPE LTD.—See Lifeplus International; *U.S. Private*, pg. 2450
LIFEPLUS INTERNATIONAL; *U.S. Private*, pg. 2450
LIFES2GOOD INC.; *U.S. Private*, pg. 2451
LIVING WELLNESS PARTNERS LLC; *U.S. Private*, pg. 2474
LOVEBUG NUTRITION INC.; *U.S. Private*, pg. 2501
LUCKYVITAMIN LLC—See TSG Consumer Partners LLC; *U.S. Private*, pg. 4253
MANNATECH AUSTRALIA PTY LIMITED—See Mannatech, Incorporated; *U.S. Public*, pg. 1357
MILUPA N.V.—See Danone; *Int'l*, pg. 1966
MOTHERNATURE.COM, INC.; *U.S. Private*, pg. 2795
MOTHER'S COOKIE COMPANY, L.L.C.—See Ferrero International S.A.; *Int'l*, pg. 2641
MULTIPLE ORGANICS, INC.; *U.S. Private*, pg. 2813
MULTIVITA D.O.O.—See ATLANTIC GRUPA d.d.; *Int'l*, pg. 675
MUSTARD SEED HEALTH FOOD MARKET; *U.S. Private*, pg. 2819
MY NATURAL MARKET; *U.S. Private*, pg. 2823
MYOTCSTORE.COM; *U.S. Private*, pg. 2825
NATURAL ALTERNATIVES INTERNATIONAL EUROPE S.A.—See Natural Alternatives International, Inc.; *U.S. Public*, pg. 1499
NATURAL GROCERS BY VITAMIN COTTAGE, INC.; *U.S. Public*, pg. 1499
NATURAL LIVING, INC.—See Option Care Health, Inc.; *U.S. Public*, pg. 1499
NATURAL SPROUT COMPANY, LLC; *U.S. Private*, pg. 2867
NATURE'S SUNSHINE PRODUCTS DE MEXICO S.A. DE C.V.—See Nature's Sunshine Products, Inc.; *U.S. Public*, pg. 1499
NATURE'S SUNSHINE PRODUCTS, INC. - UK BRANCH—See Nature's Sunshine Products, Inc.; *U.S. Public*, pg. 1499
NATURE'S SUNSHINE PRODUCTS OF CANADA, LTD.—See Nature's Sunshine Products, Inc.; *U.S. Public*, pg. 1499
NEW FRONTIERS NATURAL FOODS V—See Northern Holdings Inc.; *U.S. Private*, pg. 2953
NORE NUTRITION AS—See Hofseth Biocare AS; *Int'l*, pg. 3440
NORTH AMERICAN SOLUTIONS INC.—See Big Lots, Inc.; *U.S. Public*, pg. 330
NORTH TEXAS FOOD BANK; *U.S. Private*, pg. 2948
NSE KOREA LTD.—See Nu Skin Enterprises, Inc.; *U.S. Public*, pg. 1551
NU SKIN BELGIUM, NV—See Nu Skin Enterprises, Inc.; *U.S. Public*, pg. 1552
NU SKIN CANADA, INC.—See Nu Skin Enterprises, Inc.; *U.S. Public*, pg. 1552
NU SKIN (CHINA) DAILY-USE AND HEALTH PRODUCTS CO., LTD.—See Nu Skin Enterprises, Inc.; *U.S. Public*, pg. 1552
NU SKIN ENTERPRISES AUSTRALIA, INC.—See Nu Skin Enterprises, Inc.; *U.S. Public*, pg. 1552
NU SKIN ENTERPRISES HONG KONG, INC.—See Nu Skin Enterprises, Inc.; *U.S. Public*, pg. 1552
NU SKIN ENTERPRISES NEW ZEALAND, INC.—See Nu Skin Enterprises, Inc.; *U.S. Public*, pg. 1552
NU SKIN ENTERPRISES SINGAPORE PTE. LTD.—See Nu Skin Enterprises, Inc.; *U.S. Public*, pg. 1552
NU SKIN FRANCE, SARL—See Nu Skin Enterprises, Inc.; *U.S. Public*, pg. 1552
NU SKIN GERMANY GMBH—See Nu Skin Enterprises, Inc.; *U.S. Public*, pg. 1552
NU SKIN ITALIA, S.R.L.—See Nu Skin Enterprises, Inc.; *U.S. Public*, pg. 1552
NU SKIN (MALAYSIA) SDN. BHD.—See Nu Skin Enterprises, Inc.; *U.S. Public*, pg. 1552
NU SKIN MEXICO, S.A. DE C.V.—See Nu Skin Enterprises, Inc.; *U.S. Public*, pg. 1552
NU SKIN NETHERLANDS, B.V.—See Nu Skin Enterprises, Inc.; *U.S. Public*, pg. 1552
NU SKIN PERSONAL CARE (THAILAND), LTD.—See Nu Skin Enterprises, Inc.; *U.S. Public*, pg. 1552
NU SKIN SCANDINAVIA A.S.—See Nu Skin Enterprises, Inc.; *U.S. Public*, pg. 1552
NU SKIN TAIWAN, LLC—See Nu Skin Enterprises, Inc.; *U.S. Public*, pg. 1552
NUTIVA; *U.S. Private*, pg. 2974
NUTRICAP LABS; *U.S. Private*, pg. 2974
NUTRICIA ITALIA S.P.A.—See Danone; *Int'l*, pg. 1966
NUTRICITY.COM LLC; *U.S. Private*, pg. 2974
OCEAN HEALTH PTE. LTD.—See Hyphens Pharma International Limited; *Int'l*, pg. 3553
ORGAIN, LLC—See Butterfly Equity LP; *U.S. Private*, pg. 698
OUTPOST NATURAL FOODS COOP; *U.S. Private*, pg. 3051
POLAND CURT GEORGI POLAND—See Curt Georgi GmbH & Co. KG; *Int'l*, pg. 1880
PREMIER NUTRITION COMPANY, LLC—See Post Holdings, Inc.; *U.S. Public*, pg. 1704
PRIMAL NUTRITION, LLC—See Berkshire Hathaway Inc.; *U.S. Public*, pg. 315
PRN PHYSICIAN RECOMMENDED NUTRICEUTICALS LLC—See ALPHAEON Corporation; *U.S. Private*, pg. 200
PROBIOTICA LABORATORIES LTDA.—See Bausch Health Companies Inc.; *Int'l*, pg. 897
PROLAB NUTRITION INC.—See Aurobindo Pharma Ltd.; *Int'l*, pg. 712
PRO NATURA B.V.—See Abattis Bioceuticals Corporation; *Int'l*, pg. 48
PRO-PARTNER INC.—See Grape King Bio Ltd.; *Int'l*, pg. 3060
PUREFORMULAS.COM; *U.S. Private*, pg. 3306
RELIV AUSTRALIA PTY, LIMITED—See Reliv International, Inc.; *U.S. Public*, pg. 1782
RELIV EUROPE LIMITED—See Reliv International, Inc.; *U.S. Public*, pg. 1782
RENEW LIFE FORMULAS, LLC—See The Clorox Company; *U.S. Public*, pg. 2062
RESERVEAGE, LLC.; *U.S. Private*, pg. 3405
RESERVE LIFE NUTRITION, L.L.C.—See Twinlab Consolidated Holdings, Inc.; *U.S. Public*, pg. 2207
RESERVE LIFE ORGANICS, LLC—See Twinlab Consolidated Holdings, Inc.; *U.S. Public*, pg. 2207
ROMANIA CURT GEORGI ROMANIA S.R.L.—See Curt Georgi GmbH & Co. KG; *Int'l*, pg. 1880
SAMBAZON BRAZIL—See Sambazon, Inc.; *U.S. Private*, pg. 3536
SCIVATION INC.—See Woodbolt Distribution, LLC; *U.S. Private*, pg. 4557
SERBIA CURT GEORGI NOVI SAD—See Curt Georgi GmbH & Co. KG; *Int'l*, pg. 1880
SHAKLEE MEXICO, S.A. DE C.V.—See Activated Holdings LLC; *U.S. Private*, pg. 69
SHAKLEE MEXICO, S.A. DE C.V.—See Ripplewood Holdings LLC; *U.S. Private*, pg. 3439
SHAKLEE PRODUCTS (MALAYSIA) SDN. BHD.—See Activated Holdings LLC; *U.S. Private*, pg. 69
SHAKLEE PRODUCTS (MALAYSIA) SDN. BHD.—See Ripplewood Holdings LLC; *U.S. Private*, pg. 3439
SMART FOR LIFE, INC.; *U.S. Public*, pg. 1895
SMARTYPANTS, INC.—See North Castle Partners, LLC; *U.S. Private*, pg. 2943
SPAIN CURT GEORGI AROMAS Y ESENCIAS S.A.—See Curt Georgi GmbH & Co. KG; *Int'l*, pg. 1880
STAFF OF LIFE NATURAL FOODS MARKET; *U.S. Private*, pg. 3775
STANDARD PROCESS INC.; *U.S. Private*, pg. 3781
STARLIGHT INTERNATIONAL LTD, LP; *U.S. Private*, pg. 3787
STOP AGING NOW, LLC—See The Clorox Company; *U.S. Public*, pg. 2062
SUN BROTHERS LLC; *U.S. Private*, pg. 3858
SUOMEN LISARAVINNE OY—See Celsius Holdings, Inc.; *U.S. Public*, pg. 466
SWANSON HEALTH PRODUCTS—See Swander Pace Capital, LLC; *U.S. Private*, pg. 3890
SWISSE WELLNESS PTY LTD—See Health and Happiness (H&H) International Holdings Limited; *Int'l*, pg. 3303
TAHITIAN NONI INTERNATIONAL—See NewAge Inc.; *U.S. Public*, pg. 1513
TAKE SHAPE FOR LIFE, INC—See Medifast, Inc.; *U.S. Public*, pg. 1412
TFSUPPLEMENTS; *U.S. Private*, pg. 3979
THURLAND REAY FAMILY INVESTMENT CO.; *U.S. Private*, pg. 4166

456191 — FOOD (HEALTH) SUPPL...

THUR MILCH RING AG—See HOCHDORF Holding AG; *Int'l*, pg. 3437
TIGER FITNESS INC.; *U.S. Private*, pg. 4169
UNIVERSAL HERBS INC.; *U.S. Private*, pg. 4305
VIDA HERBAL SUPLEMENTOS ALIMENTICIOS, C.A. (VENEZUELA)—See Herbalife Nutrition Ltd.; *Int'l*, pg. 3360
VITA HEALTH PRODUCTS, INC.—See KKR & Co. Inc.; *U.S. Public*, pg. 1264
VITAMIN DISCOUNT CENTER INC.—See Recommerce Holdings, LLC; *U.S. Private*, pg. 3371
VITAMIN EXPRESS, INC.; *U.S. Private*, pg. 4405
VITAMIN SHOPPE INDUSTRIES, INC.—See B. Riley Financial, Inc.; *U.S. Public*, pg. 261
VITAMIN SHOPPE INDUSTRIES, INC.—See Irradiant Partners, LP; *U.S. Private*, pg. 2141
THE VITAMIN STORE, LLC—See Healthier Choices Management Corp.; *U.S. Public*, pg. 1016
VITAMIN WORLD, INC.—See Centre Lane Partners, LLC; *U.S. Private*, pg. 828
VS DIRECT INC.—See B. Riley Financial, Inc.; *U.S. Public*, pg. 261
VS DIRECT INC.—See Irradiant Partners, LP; *U.S. Private*, pg. 2141
WELLNESS CENTER USA, INC.; *U.S. Public*, pg. 2342
WESTWOOD-INTRAFIN, S.A.—See Bristol-Myers Squibb Company; *U.S. Public*, pg. 387
YOR HEALTH; *U.S. Private*, pg. 4590
YOUNGEVITY NZ, LTD.—See Youngevity International Corp.; *U.S. Public*, pg. 2399

456199 — ALL OTHER HEALTH AND PERSONAL CARE RETAILERS

3TAILER, LLC; *U.S. Private*, pg. 14
ACCUQUEST HEARING CENTER LLC—See Demant A/S; *Int'l*, pg. 2022
AC MARCA, S.A; *Int'l*, pg. 74
ADENNA; *U.S. Private*, pg. 78
ADVANCED BEAUTY, INC.; *U.S. Private*, pg. 88
ALEVA STORES; *U.S. Private*, pg. 162
ALLIED INTEGRAL UNITED, INC.—See Clearday, Inc.; *U.S. Public*, pg. 512
ALLIED ORTHOPEDIC APPLIANCES, INC.—See WCA Hospital; *U.S. Private*, pg. 4461
AMERICA'S HEALTH CARE AT HOME, INC.—See AdaptHealth Corp.; *U.S. Public*, pg. 39
AMWAY ARGENTINA, INC.—See Alticor Inc.; *U.S. Private*, pg. 208
AMWAY CZECH REPUBLIC—See Alticor Inc.; *U.S. Private*, pg. 208
AMWAY DE PORTUGAL, INC.—See Alticor Inc.; *U.S. Private*, pg. 209
AMWAY HELLAS—See Alticor Inc.; *U.S. Private*, pg. 209
AMWAY HUNGARIA MARKETING KFT.—See Alticor Inc.; *U.S. Private*, pg. 208
AMWAY INDONESIA—See Alticor Inc.; *U.S. Private*, pg. 209
AMWAY ITALIA S.R.L.—See Alticor Inc.; *U.S. Private*, pg. 209
AMWAY PHILIPPINES—See Alticor Inc.; *U.S. Private*, pg. 209
AMWAY POLAND—See Alticor Inc.; *U.S. Private*, pg. 209
AMWAY SLOVENIA L.L.C.—See Alticor Inc.; *U.S. Private*, pg. 209
AMWAY SLOVENSKO, S.R.O.—See Alticor Inc.; *U.S. Private*, pg. 209
AMWAY URUGUAY—See Alticor Inc.; *U.S. Private*, pg. 209
APTARGROUP, INC.; *U.S. Public*, pg. 174
ARABI MEDICAL & SCIENTIFIC EQUIPMENT CO. W.L.L.—See Arabi Holding Group Company K.S.C.C.; *Int'l*, pg. 532
ASIAN CONSUMER CARE PRIVATE LIMITED—See Dabur India Ltd; *Int'l*, pg. 1903
ASTRID TM A.S.—See Gr. Sarantis S.A.; *Int'l*, pg. 3047
ATTENDO AB; *Int'l*, pg. 696
AUDIKA AG—See Demant A/S; *Int'l*, pg. 2023
AUDIONOVA FRANCE—See HAL Trust N.V.; *Int'l*, pg. 3223
AUDIOTECH HEALTHCARE CORPORATION; *Int'l*, pg. 702
AUDITZ, LLC—See TransUnion; *U.S. Public*, pg. 2184
AVANTEC HEALTHCARE LTD.—See Omnicell, Inc.; *U.S. Public*, pg. 1572
BANDAGES PLUS, INC.—See The Morrissey Group LLC; *U.S. Private*, pg. 4080
BANMEDICA S.A.—See UnitedHealth Group Incorporated; *U.S. Public*, pg. 2239
BAR-ALL, INC.; *U.S. Private*, pg. 471
BASTIDE LE CONFORT MEDICAL SA; *Int'l*, pg. 888
BEAUMONT HOME MEDICAL EQUIPMENT—See Beaumont Health; *U.S. Private*, pg. 508
BEST WORLD LIFESTYLE (HK) COMPANY LIMITED—See Best World International Ltd.; *Int'l*, pg. 1000
BEST WORLD LIFESTYLE SDN. BHD.—See Best World International Ltd.; *Int'l*, pg. 1000
BOD INTERNATIONAL PTY. LIMITED—See Eu Yan Sang International Ltd.; *Int'l*, pg. 2525
BONNE CO., LTD.; *Int'l*, pg. 1107

BRACE SHOP, LLC—See VeriTeQ Corporation; *U.S. Private*, pg. 4366
BRAINLAB FRANCE—See BrainLAB Inc.; *U.S. Private*, pg. 634
BTG INTERNATIONAL (HOLDINGS) LTD—See Boston Scientific Corporation; *U.S. Public*, pg. 373
CALIBRA MEDICAL, INC.—See Johnson & Johnson; *U.S. Public*, pg. 1194
CANADIAN HEARING CARE—See Audiotech Healthcare Corporation; *Int'l*, pg. 702
CARDINAL HEALTH SPAIN 219 S.L.—See Cardinal Health, Inc.; *U.S. Public*, pg. 433
CARE MEDICAL EQUIPMENT INCORPORATED; *U.S. Private*, pg. 751
CARENET; *U.S. Private*, pg. 753
CHEERWIN GROUP LIMITED; *Int'l*, pg. 1459
CNI ENTERPRISE (M) SDN. BHD.—See Citra Nusa Holdings Berhad; *Int'l*, pg. 1626
COLAN TOTTE.CO., LTD.; *Int'l*, pg. 1697
CONAIR CORPORATION; *U.S. Public*, pg. 564
CONCIERGE SERVICES OF ATLANTA, INC.—See GI Manager L.P.; *U.S. Private*, pg. 1694
COVAGEN AG—See Johnson & Johnson; *U.S. Public*, pg. 1194
CRYOLIFE EUROPA, LTD.—See Artivion, Inc.; *U.S. Public*, pg. 208
CUPID LTD.—See Columbia Petro Chem Pvt. Ltd.; *Int'l*, pg. 1706
CUSTOM MOBILITY INC.; *U.S. Private*, pg. 1129
DABUR (UK) LIMITED—See Dabur India Ltd; *Int'l*, pg. 1903
DAS HEALTH VENTURES, INC.; *U.S. Private*, pg. 1161
DENCO DIVISION—See Belcam Inc.; *U.S. Private*, pg. 516
DENTRIX DENTAL SYSTEMS, INC.-PMT—See Henry Schein, Inc.; *U.S. Public*, pg. 1025
DENTSPLY ITALIA S.R.L.—See DENTSPLY SIRONA Inc.; *U.S. Public*, pg. 654
DIABETICSUPPLIES.COM, INC.; *U.S. Private*, pg. 1222
DOCTOR DIABETIC SUPPLY, INC.—See Bertram Capital Management, LLC; *U.S. Private*, pg. 540
DORGE MEDIC SA—See Bastide le Confort Medical SA; *Int'l*, pg. 888
DR. LEONARD HEALTH CARE CATALOG; *U.S. Private*, pg. 1271
DXCM SWEDEN AB—See DexCom Inc; *U.S. Public*, pg. 657
E3 DIAGNOSTICS INC.—See Demant A/S; *Int'l*, pg. 2025
ECOSWAY MEXICO, S.A. DE C.V.—See Berjaya Corporation Berhad; *Int'l*, pg. 985
ECOSWAY RUS LLC—See Berjaya Corporation Berhad; *Int'l*, pg. 985
ELIZUR CORP.; *U.S. Private*, pg. 1362
EMAMI BANGLADESH LIMITED—See Emami Ltd; *Int'l*, pg. 2374
EMAMI INDO LANKA PVT LTD—See Emami Ltd; *Int'l*, pg. 2374
EMAMI OVERSEAS FZE—See Emami Ltd; *Int'l*, pg. 2374
EMAMI RUS LLC—See Emami Ltd; *Int'l*, pg. 2374
EVOLVENT TECHNOLOGIES INC.; *U.S. Private*, pg. 1444
FIT MY FEET ORTHOTIC LAB & SHOES, INC.; *U.S. Private*, pg. 1535
FOLICA, INC.; *U.S. Private*, pg. 1559
FULFORD (INDIA) LTD.—See Organon & Co.; *U.S. Public*, pg. 1616
GALIL MEDICAL INC.—See Boston Scientific Corporation; *U.S. Public*, pg. 373
GILLETTE INDIA LIMITED—See The Procter & Gamble Company; *U.S. Public*, pg. 2124
GILLETTE INDUSTRIES LIMITED—See The Procter & Gamble Company; *U.S. Public*, pg. 2124
GROUPE GILLETTE FRANCE S.A.—See The Procter & Gamble Company; *U.S. Public*, pg. 2124
GUIDEWELL INC.—See GuideWell Mutual Holding Corporation; *U.S. Private*, pg. 1813
HAEMONETICS (SHANGHAI) MANAGEMENT CO. LTD.—See Haemonetics Corporation; *U.S. Public*, pg. 979
HANGER CLINIC-MOBILE; *U.S. Private*, pg. 1853
HANWECK ASSOCIATES, LLC—See Cboe Global Markets, Inc.; *U.S. Public*, pg. 459
HEALTH-CHEM DIAGNOSTICS LLC—See PL Development, Inc.; *U.S. Private*, pg. 3194
HEALTH MANAGEMENT SERVICES INC.; *U.S. Private*, pg. 1894
HEAR ATLAST HOLDINGS, INC.; *Int'l*, pg. 3304
HENRY SCHEIN, INC. - COLUMBUS, OH—See Henry Schein, Inc.; *U.S. Public*, pg. 1026
HENRY SCHEIN, INC.-FLORIDA SOUTH—See Henry Schein, Inc.; *U.S. Public*, pg. 1027
HENRY SCHEIN, INC.-FT. WAYNE, INDIANA—See Henry Schein, Inc.; *U.S. Public*, pg. 1027
HENRY SCHEIN, INC. - GRAPEVINE, TX—See Henry Schein, Inc.; *U.S. Public*, pg. 1026
HENRY SCHEIN INC.-INDIANA—See Henry Schein, Inc.; *U.S. Public*, pg. 1025
HENRY SCHEIN, INC.-KANSAS—See Henry Schein, Inc.; *U.S. Public*, pg. 1027
HENRY SCHEIN, INC.-LOUISVILLE, KENTUCKY—See Henry Schein, Inc.; *U.S. Public*, pg. 1027

HENRY SCHEIN, INC. - MEMPHIS, TN—See Henry Schein, Inc.; *U.S. Public*, pg. 1026
HENRY SCHEIN, INC. - MILWAUKEE, WI—See Henry Schein, Inc.; *U.S. Public*, pg. 1026
HENRY SCHEIN, INC.-NEVADA SPARKS—See Henry Schein, Inc.; *U.S. Public*, pg. 1027
HENRY SCHEIN, INC.-NEW MEXICO—See Henry Schein, Inc.; *U.S. Public*, pg. 1027
HENRY SCHEIN, INC.-NEW YORK—See Henry Schein, Inc.; *U.S. Public*, pg. 1027
HENRY SCHEIN, INC.-NEW YORK—See Henry Schein, Inc.; *U.S. Public*, pg. 1027
HENRY SCHEIN, INC.-PENNSYLVANIA—See Henry Schein, Inc.; *U.S. Public*, pg. 1027
HENRY SCHEIN, INC. - PHILADELPHIA, PA—See Henry Schein, Inc.; *U.S. Public*, pg. 1026
HENRY SCHEIN, INC. - SAN FRANCISCO—See Henry Schein, Inc.; *U.S. Public*, pg. 1026
HENRY SCHEIN, INC. - SAN JOSE, CA—See Henry Schein, Inc.; *U.S. Public*, pg. 1026
HENRY SCHEIN, INC.-WILSONVILLE, OREGON—See Henry Schein, Inc.; *U.S. Public*, pg. 1027
HERBALIFE DENMARK APS—See Herbalife Nutrition Ltd.; *Int'l*, pg. 3359
HERBALIFE EUROPE LIMITED—See Herbalife Nutrition Ltd.; *Int'l*, pg. 3359
HERBALIFE INTERNATIONAL DE MEXICO, S.A.DE C.V.—See Herbalife Nutrition Ltd.; *Int'l*, pg. 3360
HERBALIFE INTERNATIONAL DEUTSCHLAND GMBH—See Herbalife Nutrition Ltd.; *Int'l*, pg. 3359
HERBALIFE INTERNATIONAL ESPANA, S.A.—See Herbalife Nutrition Ltd.; *Int'l*, pg. 3360
HERBALIFE INTERNATIONAL FRANCE S.A.—See Herbalife Nutrition Ltd.; *Int'l*, pg. 3360
HERBALIFE INTERNATIONAL-HONG KONG—See Herbalife Nutrition Ltd.; *Int'l*, pg. 3360
HERBALIFE INTERNATIONAL PHILIPPINES—See Herbalife Nutrition Ltd.; *Int'l*, pg. 3360
HERBALIFE INTERNATIONAL, S.A.-PORTUGAL—See Herbalife Nutrition Ltd.; *Int'l*, pg. 3360
HERBALIFE (N.Z.) LIMITED—See Herbalife Nutrition Ltd.; *Int'l*, pg. 3359
HERBALIFE OF CANADA LTD.—See Herbalife Nutrition Ltd.; *Int'l*, pg. 3360
HERBALIFE POLSKA SP.Z.O.O—See Herbalife Nutrition Ltd.; *Int'l*, pg. 3360
HERBALIFE (U.K.) LIMITED—See Herbalife Nutrition Ltd.; *Int'l*, pg. 3359
HIMS & HERS HEALTH, INC.; *U.S. Public*, pg. 1041
HOME CARE PULSE LLC—See In The Know, Inc.; *U.S. Private*, pg. 2052
HONG KONG WINALITE GROUP, INC.; *U.S. Private*, pg. 1052
HOZTORG LLC—See Gr. Sarantis S.A.; *Int'l*, pg. 3047
HUDSON HOME HEALTH CARE INC.; *U.S. Private*, pg. 2002
HYVE BEAUTY FUARCILIK AS—See Providence Equity Partners L.L.C.; *U.S. Private*, pg. 3292
HYVE BEAUTY FUARCILIK AS—See Searchlight Capital Partners, L.P.; *U.S. Private*, pg. 3587
IDEA ISITME SISTEMLERI SANAYI VE TICARET A.S.—See Demant A/S; *Int'l*, pg. 2024
ILEX MEDICAL LTD.; *Int'l*, pg. 3613
ILUMARK GMBH—See Fortive Corporation; *U.S. Public*, pg. 871
INGENESIS, INC.; *U.S. Private*, pg. 2075
INTEGRA BURLINGTON MA, INC.—See Integra LifeSciences Holdings Corporation; *U.S. Public*, pg. 1135
INTEGRA MICROFRANCE SAS—See Integra LifeSciences Holdings Corporation; *U.S. Public*, pg. 1136
INTEGRATED NEPHROLOGY NETWORK—See Cencora, Inc.; *U.S. Public*, pg. 467
INTRICON GMBH—See IntriCon Corporation; *U.S. Public*, pg. 1159
INVACARE FRANCE—See Invacare Corporation; *U.S. Private*, pg. 2130
JANSSEN-CILAG KFT.—See Johnson & Johnson; *U.S. Public*, pg. 1197
JANSSEN SCIENCES IRELAND UC—See Johnson & Johnson; *U.S. Public*, pg. 1197
JOHNSON & JOHNSON AG—See Johnson & Johnson; *U.S. Public*, pg. 1198
JOHNSON & JOHNSON INNOVATION LIMITED—See Johnson & Johnson; *U.S. Public*, pg. 1198
KAS DIRECT, LLC—See S.C. Johnson & Son, Inc.; *U.S. Private*, pg. 3516
KBK INSURANCE GROUP, INC.—See The Carlyle Group Inc.; *U.S. Public*, pg. 2050
KIMBERLY-CLARK OF SOUTH AFRICA (PTY) LTD.—See Kimberly-Clark Corporation; *U.S. Public*, pg. 1231
LIFESCAN—See Johnson & Johnson; *U.S. Public*, pg. 1199
LIFEWAVE, INC.; *U.S. Private*, pg. 2452
LINVATEC SWEDEN AB—See CONMED Corporation; *U.S. Public*, pg. 567
MCKESSON INFORMATION SOLUTIONS HOLDINGS LIMITED—See McKesson Corporation; *U.S. Public*, pg. 1408
MCKESSON MEDICAL-SURGICAL—See McKesson Cor-

N.A.I.C.S. INDEX

poration; *U.S. Public*, pg. 1408
MEDCO SUPPLY CO.—See Patterson Companies, Inc.; *U.S. Public*, pg. 1653
MEDICARE SUPPLY CENTERS INC—See Arcadian Healthcare Inc.; *U.S. Private*, pg. 310
METRO MEDICAL SUPPLY INC.; *U.S. Private*, pg. 2686
NATIVE PATHS LLC; *U.S. Private*, pg. 2866
THE NATURAL BABY CATALOG—See Kids Stuff, Inc.; *U.S. Private*, pg. 2303
NATURALLY YOU—See Southeastern Medequip, Inc.; *U.S. Private*, pg. 3728
NATURPRODUKT KFT—See Dr. Theiss Naturwaren GmbH; *Int'l*, pg. 2195
NEW BRITAIN MEDICAL SUPPLIES, INC.—See DENTSPLY SIRONA Inc.; *U.S. Public*, pg. 655
NEW ENGLAND LIFE CARE INC.; *U.S. Private*, pg. 2894
NOTTINGHAM REHAB LIMITED—See H2 Equity Partners B.V.; *Int'l*, pg. 3199
NOVAMED, LLC—See Bain Capital, LP; *U.S. Private*, pg. 446
OMNICELL GMBH—See Omnicell, Inc.; *U.S. Public*, pg. 1572
ORTHOPEDIC REHABILITATION PRODUCTS, LTD.—See Patient Square Capital, L.P.; *U.S. Private*, pg. 3107
PAZOO, INC.; *U.S. Public*, pg. 1657
THE PERFUME SHOP LIMITED—See CK Hutchison Holdings Limited; *Int'l*, pg. 1636
PHARMA DERM SAE CO.—See Emami Ltd; *Int'l*, pg. 2374
POLESTAR LABS, INC.; *U.S. Private*, pg. 3224
P&O SERVICES, INC.—See Select Medical Holdings Corporation; *U.S. Public*, pg. 1858
PPSC, INC.; *U.S. Private*, pg. 3240
PREMIER VISION, LLC—See Premier Exhibitions, Inc.; *U.S. Public*, pg. 1714
PROCARE HOME HEALTH SERVICES, INC.—See Progressive Health Systems Inc.; *U.S. Private*, pg. 3279
PROCARE LTC HOLDING LLC; *U.S. Private*, pg. 3271
PROCTER & GAMBLE OPERATIONS POLSKA-SPOLKA Z O.O.—See The Procter & Gamble Company; *U.S. Public*, pg. 2122
PT BERJAYA COSWAY INDONESIA—See Berjaya Corporation Berhad; *Int'l*, pg. 984
PT BEST WORLD INDONESIA—See Best World International Ltd.; *Int'l*, pg. 1000
RADIOMETER NEDERLAND B.V.—See Danaher Corporation; *U.S. Public*, pg. 631
RADIOMETER PACIFIC LTD.—See Danaher Corporation; *U.S. Public*, pg. 631
RADIOMETER S.A.—See Danaher Corporation; *U.S. Public*, pg. 631
RBC LIFE SCIENCES, INC.; *U.S. Public*, pg. 1766
SAFEGUARD MEDICAL, LLC—See Water Street Healthcare Partners, LLC; *U.S. Private*, pg. 4452
SANOMED SANITATSHAUS FUR ORTHOPADIE UND REHABILITATIONSTECHNIK GMBH—See Asklepios Kliniken GmbH & Co. KGaA; *Int'l*, pg. 624
SARANTIS BANJA LUKA D.O.O.—See Gr. Sarantis S.A.; *Int'l*, pg. 3047
SARANTIS ROMANIA S.A.—See Gr. Sarantis S.A.; *Int'l*, pg. 3047
SCAN MODUL ORGASYSTEM GMBH—See Stanley Black & Decker, Inc.; *U.S. Public*, pg. 1934
SCAN MODUL SYSTEM AG—See Stanley Black & Decker, Inc.; *U.S. Public*, pg. 1934
SENDAYCO, LLC; *U.S. Private*, pg. 3605
SG HOMECARE, INC.—See Sverica Capital Management LP; *U.S. Private*, pg. 3888
SHOPCBD.COM INC.—See Cannara Biotech, Inc.; *Int'l*, pg. 1292
SPIEGEL BRANDS, INC.—See Patriarch Partners, LLC; *U.S. Private*, pg. 3109
STARTUP HEALTH HOLDINGS, INC.; *U.S. Private*, pg. 3788
SUNLIGHTEN, INC.; *U.S. Private*, pg. 3868
SUPER CARE INC.; *U.S. Private*, pg. 3874
TAKE CARE HEALTH SYSTEMS, LLC—See Walgreens Boots Alliance, Inc.; *U.S. Public*, pg. 2324
TARSUS MEDICAL INC.—See Integra LifeSciences Holdings Corporation; *U.S. Public*, pg. 1136
TELEFLEX MEDICAL HELLAS A.E.E.—See Teleflex Incorporated; *U.S. Public*, pg. 1996
TNG WORLDWIDE, INC.; *U.S. Private*, pg. 4180
TRUHEARING, INC.—See EQT AB; *Int'l*, pg. 2480
VAN BOXTEL HOORWINKELS B.V.—See Demant A/S; *Int'l*, pg. 2025
VIELIFE LIMITED—See The Cigna Group; *U.S. Public*, pg. 2061
WELD SPEC, INC.—See Tailwind Capital Group, LLC; *U.S. Private*, pg. 3924
WELL.CA LLC—See McKesson Corporation; *U.S. Public*, pg. 1409
WEST HOME HEALTH CARE, INC.—See Quipt Home Medical Corp.; *U.S. Public*, pg. 1757
WOODBURY PRODUCTS, INC.—See MTS Health Partners, L.P.; *U.S. Private*, pg. 2810
WORLD MEDICAL RELIEF, INC.; *U.S. Private*, pg. 4566
ZILIS, LLC; *U.S. Private*, pg. 4604

457110 — GASOLINE STATIONS WITH CONVENIENCE STORES

AETOS CONSTRUCTION COMPANY—See Giant Eagle, Inc.; *U.S. Private*, pg. 1694
AMPOL METRO FUELS PTY LTD—See Ampol Limited; *Int'l*, pg. 436
AUCHAN—See Auchan Holding S.A.; *Int'l*, pg. 699
AUTOBAHN TANK & RAST GMBH—See Abu Dhabi Investment Authority; *Int'l*, pg. 71
AUTOBAHN TANK & RAST GMBH—See Allianz SE; *Int'l*, pg. 351
BOB'S SUPER SAVER INC; *U.S. Private*, pg. 606
BOWDEN OIL COMPANY, INC.—See Majors Management, LLC; *U.S. Private*, pg. 2555
BOWLIN TRAVEL CENTERS, INC.; *U.S. Public*, pg. 376
CALSTORES PTY LTD—See Ampol Limited; *Int'l*, pg. 436
CALTEX AUSTRALIA PETROLEUM PTY LTD—See Ampol Limited; *Int'l*, pg. 436
CARDINAL GAS STORAGE PARTNERS LLC—See Martin Midstream Partners LP; *U.S. Public*, pg. 1389
CARREFOUR TAIWAN—See Carrefour SA; *Int'l*, pg. 1344
COMPASS ENERGY HOLDINGS, INC.; *U.S. Private*, pg. 999
CONLEE OIL COMPANY; *U.S. Private*, pg. 1014
CORS - COMPANHIA DE EXPLORACAO DE ESTACOES DE SERVICO E RETALHO DE SERVICOS AUTOMOVEL, LDA.—See Galp Energia SGPS, S.A.; *Int'l*, pg. 2875
CROIX OIL COMPANY; *U.S. Private*, pg. 1103
CRYSTAL FLASH PETROLEUM CORP.—See Heritage Group; *U.S. Private*, pg. 1923
DASH IN FOOD STORES, INC.—See The Wills Group, Inc.; *U.S. Private*, pg. 4136
ESSO BRASILEIRA DE PETROLEO LIMITADA—See Cosan S.A.; *Int'l*, pg. 1809
EUROCASH S.A.; *Int'l*, pg. 2533
FESTI HF; *Int'l*, pg. 2646
FRY'S FOOD AND DRUG STORES—See The Kroger Co.; *U.S. Public*, pg. 2108
GESPEVESA, S.A.—See El Corte Ingles, S.A.; *Int'l*, pg. 2340
GOLUB CORPORATION; *U.S. Private*, pg. 1736
HAFFNER'S SERVICE STATIONS, INC.—See Energy North Incorporated; *U.S. Private*, pg. 1395
HERDRICH PETROLEUM CORP.; *U.S. Private*, pg. 1921
HIGGINBOTHAM OIL CO. INC.; *U.S. Private*, pg. 1935
HOLIDAY STATIONSTORES, LLC—See Alimentation Couche-Tard Inc.; *Int'l*, pg. 328
HY ENERGY GROUP CO., LTD.; *Int'l*, pg. 3543
ICA HANDLARNAS AB—See ICA Gruppen AB; *Int'l*, pg. 3577
INLAND OIL COMPANY INC.; *U.S. Private*, pg. 2079
JET-PEP INC.; *U.S. Private*, pg. 2204
JEWEL-OSCO—See Cerberus Capital Management, L.P.; *U.S. Private*, pg. 836
LEATHERS ENTERPRISES INC.—See S&S Petroleum Inc.; *U.S. Private*, pg. 3514
LIGHTNING QUICK GAS-N-GO; *U.S. Private*, pg. 2453
MAC'S CONVENIENCE STORES, INC.—See Alimentation Couche-Tard Inc.; *Int'l*, pg. 328
MAPCO EXPRESS, INC.—See Majors Management, LLC; *U.S. Private*, pg. 2555
MID-ATLANTIC CONVENIENCE STORES, LLC—See Sunoco LP; *U.S. Public*, pg. 926
MOBIL OIL CORPORATION—See Exxon Mobil Corporation; *U.S. Public*, pg. 817
MONROE GAS STORAGE COMPANY LLC; *U.S. Private*, pg. 2773
MOTOR FUEL LIMITED—See Clayton, Dubilier & Rice, LLC; *U.S. Private*, pg. 1965
NEWBERRY BP EXPRESS MARKET—See Autore Oil & Propane Company; *U.S. Private*, pg. 401
NORTHERN TIER RETAIL LLC—See Marathon Petroleum Corporation; *U.S. Public*, pg. 1363
NOURIA ENERGY CORP.; *U.S. Private*, pg. 2965
PACIFIC OIL COMPANY LLC; *U.S. Private*, pg. 3069
PARKER'S CORPORATION; *U.S. Private*, pg. 3097
PILOT TRAVEL CENTERS LLC—See Berkshire Hathaway Inc.; *U.S. Public*, pg. 313
POPS MART FUELS, LLC; *U.S. Private*, pg. 3229
PROVIGO INC.—See George Weston Limited; *Int'l*, pg. 2939
QUIKTRIP WEST, INC.—See QuikTrip Corporation; *U.S. Private*, pg. 3327
RACETRAC PETROLEUM, INC.; *U.S. Private*, pg. 3341
REFUEL, LLC—See First Reserve Management, L.P.; *U.S. Private*, pg. 1526
REFUEL OPERATING COMPANY, LLC—See First Reserve Management, L.P.; *U.S. Private*, pg. 1526
SHEETZ, INC.; *U.S. Private*, pg. 3630
SKYE PETROLEUM, INC.; *U.S. Public*, pg. 1892
SOBEYS ONTARIO DIVISION—See Empire Company Limited; *Int'l*, pg. 2387
SOBEYS WEST, INC.—See Empire Company Limited; *Int'l*, pg. 2387
SUPER CAMPARICO PITUSA; *U.S. Private*, pg. 3874
SUPERMERCADOS DEL ESTE INC.; *U.S. Private*, pg. 3881
TAMARKIN CO., INC.—See Giant Eagle, Inc.; *U.S. Private*, pg. 1694
TA OPERATING LLC—See BP plc; *Int'l*, pg. 1127
TULLOCH PETROLEUM SERVICES PTY LTD—See Ampol Limited; *Int'l*, pg. 437
U.S. VENTURE, INC. - EXPRESS CONVENIENCE CENTERS DIVISION—See U.S. Venture, Inc.; *U.S. Private*, pg. 4272
WALDBAUM'S SUPERMARKETS, INC.—See The Great Atlantic & Pacific Tea Company, Inc.; *U.S. Private*, pg. 4038

457120 — OTHER GASOLINE STATIONS

ABEL OIL CO. INC.; *U.S. Private*, pg. 37
A.G. LEE OIL COMPANY INC.; *U.S. Private*, pg. 25
AIRUL ENTERPRISES, INC.—See Roark Capital Group Inc.; *U.S. Private*, pg. 3454
ALFEN BELGIE BV—See Alfen N.V.; *Int'l*, pg. 315
AL-OSAIS PETROLEUM SERVICES CO.—See Al-Osais International Holding Company; *Int'l*, pg. 287
ANCHOR CNGO CORP.; *U.S. Private*, pg. 272
ARCO—See BP plc; *Int'l*, pg. 1126
ARFA ENTERPRISES INC.; *U.S. Private*, pg. 319
ARONSON ASSOCIATES INC.; *U.S. Private*, pg. 334
AUTOMATED PETROLEUM & ENERGY COMPANY, INC.; *U.S. Private*, pg. 399
A.W. HERNDON OIL CO. INC.; *U.S. Private*, pg. 28
AZTEX INTERNATIONAL; *U.S. Private*, pg. 416
BAILEY TIRE & AUTO SERVICE; *U.S. Private*, pg. 426
THE BALTUS COMPANY; *U.S. Private*, pg. 3991
BEACON BAY AUTO WASH; *U.S. Private*, pg. 504
BELL GAS, INC.; *U.S. Private*, pg. 518
BERNE COOPERATIVE ASSOCIATION INC.; *U.S. Private*, pg. 536
BESCHE OIL COMPANY, INC.; *U.S. Private*, pg. 541
BFS FOODS INC.—See Bruceton Farm Service, Inc.; *U.S. Private*, pg. 671
BLUELIB SAS—See Financiere de L'Odet; *Int'l*, pg. 2666
BLUELY SAS—See Financiere de L'Odet; *Int'l*, pg. 2666
BLUE POINT LONDON LTD.—See Financiere de L'Odet; *Int'l*, pg. 2665
BLUESG PTE. LTD.—See Goldbell Corporation; *Int'l*, pg. 3027
BP AUSTRIA MARKETING GMBH—See BP plc; *Int'l*, pg. 1128
BP LUXEMBOURG S.A.—See BP plc; *Int'l*, pg. 1129
BP ZIMBABWE (PVT) LIMITED—See BP plc; *Int'l*, pg. 1130
BUCK'S INC.; *U.S. Private*, pg. 676
BY-LO OIL COMPANY INC.; *U.S. Private*, pg. 700
CANADIAN ULTRAMAR COMPANY—See Valero Energy Corporation; *U.S. Public*, pg. 2272
CARDINAL STATES GATHERING COMPANY—See CNX Resources Corporation; *U.S. Public*, pg. 520
THE CARIOCA COMPANY INC.; *U.S. Private*, pg. 4005
CARQUEST DISTRIBUTION CENTER - MAINE—See Advance Auto Parts, Inc.; *U.S. Public*, pg. 45
CHARLES R. WOOD OIL CO. INC.; *U.S. Private*, pg. 853
CHICAGO PETROMARTS INC.; *U.S. Private*, pg. 878
CIRCLE K SVERIGE AB—See FUCHS SE; *Int'l*, pg. 2804
COFFEE CUP FUEL STOPS & CONVENIENCE STORES, INC.; *U.S. Private*, pg. 961
CONOCOPHILLIPS CO.—See ConocoPhillips; *U.S. Public*, pg. 568
CONSUMERS GASOLINE STATIONS, INC.—See Tri Star Energy, LLC; *U.S. Private*, pg. 4221
CONTROL TOWER TRUCK STOP INC.; *U.S. Private*, pg. 1034
CORRIGAN OIL CO.; *U.S. Private*, pg. 1059
COUNTRYWIDE PETROLEUM CO.—See Croton Holding Company; *U.S. Private*, pg. 1108
CROTON EQUITIES INC.—See Barrier Motor Fuels Inc.; *U.S. Private*, pg. 480
CW SERVICE—See Mercer Landmark Inc.; *U.S. Private*, pg. 2669
DELTA SONIC CAR WASH SYSTEMS INC.; *U.S. Private*, pg. 1201
DILMAR OIL COMPANY INC.; *U.S. Private*, pg. 1231
DOMINY OIL INC.; *U.S. Private*, pg. 1257
DON-A-VEE CHRYSLER JEEP INC.; *U.S. Private*, pg. 1259
DONNINI ENTERPRISES INC.; *U.S. Private*, pg. 1261
EKO SERBIA AD—See HELLENiQ ENERGY Holdings S.A.; *Int'l*, pg. 3334
ELLIOTT OIL CO. INC.; *U.S. Private*, pg. 1373
EMIRATES PETROLEUM PRODUCTS COMPANY LLC—See Emirates National Oil Company Limited; *Int'l*, pg. 2381
ENERGIELOSUNG GMBH—See E.ON SE; *Int'l*, pg. 2260
ENERGY RETAILERS INC.; *U.S. Private*, pg. 1396
ENGLEFIELD OIL COMPANY; *U.S. Private*, pg. 1399
ENMARK STATIONS, INC.—See Colonial Group, Inc.; *U.S. Private*, pg. 971
EQUINOR DANMARK A/S—See Equinor ASA; *Int'l*, pg. 2484
EQUINOR POLSKA SP.ZO.O.—See Equinor ASA; *Int'l*, pg. 2484

457120 — OTHER GASOLINE STAT...

EV CHARGING USA, INC.; *U.S. Private*, pg. 1434
EVERGREEN OIL COMPANY INC.; *U.S. Private*, pg. 1439
EVOLVE USA CHARGING CORPORATION—See JNS Holdings Corporation; *U.S. Private*, pg. 1190
EXXONMOBIL AIRCRAFT OPERATIONS—See Exxon Mobil Corporation; *U.S. Public*, pg. 814
EXXONMOBIL ITALIANA GAS S.R.L.—See Exxon Mobil Corporation; *U.S. Public*, pg. 815
EXXONMOBIL OIL CORPORATION—See Exxon Mobil Corporation; *U.S. Public*, pg. 815
FARMERS CO-OPERATIVE OIL CO.; *U.S. Private*, pg. 1476
FARMERS UNION COOP SUPPLY COMPANY; *U.S. Private*, pg. 1479
FASTNED DEUTSCHLAND GMBH & CO KG—See Fastned B.V.; *Int'l*, pg. 2622
FASTNED UK LTD.—See Fastned B.V.; *Int'l*, pg. 2622
FAST PETROLEUM, INC.; *U.S. Private*, pg. 1482
FCA COOP; *U.S. Private*, pg. 1485
FKG OIL COMPANY—See Moto, Inc.; *U.S. Private*, pg. 2796
FLINT HILLS RESOURCES, LLC—See Koch Industries, Inc.; *U.S. Private*, pg. 2327
F.L. ROBERTS & CO., INC.; *U.S. Private*, pg. 1456
FOLK OIL CO. INC.; *U.S. Private*, pg. 1559
FOUR SEASONS TRIANGLE STOP; *U.S. Private*, pg. 1582
FRANCOIS OIL COMPANY INC.; *U.S. Private*, pg. 1593
FREEDOM OIL COMPANY; *U.S. Private*, pg. 1604
FRIENDLY SERVICE STATION INC.; *U.S. Private*, pg. 1611
FRUITA CONSUMERS COOP ASSOCIATION; *U.S. Private*, pg. 1617
GAS DEPOT OIL CO.; *U.S. Private*, pg. 1647
GASETERIA OIL CORP.; *U.S. Private*, pg. 1648
GAS KING OIL CO. LTD.; *Int'l*, pg. 2887
GATE MARKETING—See Gate Petroleum Company; *U.S. Private*, pg. 1649
GATE PETROLEUM - DEVELOPMENT DIVISION—See Gate Petroleum Company; *U.S. Private*, pg. 1649
G&M OIL COMPANY INC.; *U.S. Private*, pg. 1629
GOLUB SERVICE STATIONS, INC.—See Golub Corporation; *U.S. Private*, pg. 1736
GREEN OIL CO. INC.; *U.S. Private*, pg. 1773
HALLUM INC.; *U.S. Private*, pg. 1845
HARDY ENTERPRISES INCORPORATED; *U.S. Private*, pg. 1864
HIGH POINT OIL CO.; *U.S. Private*, pg. 1936
HIGHWAY SERVICE VENTURES INC.; *U.S. Private*, pg. 1942
HILL CITY OIL COMPANY INC.; *U.S. Private*, pg. 1945
HI-LO FOOD STORES (JA) LTD.—See GraceKennedy Limited; *Int'l*, pg. 3049
HOLIDAY COMPANIES; *U.S. Private*, pg. 1962
HOLLY REFINING & MARKETING-TULSA LLC—See HF Sinclair Corporation; *U.S. Public*, pg. 1033
HOME OIL CO. INC.; *U.S. Private*, pg. 1972
HUNT & SONS, INC.; *U.S. Private*, pg. 2008
IOWA 80 GROUP, INC.; *U.S. Private*, pg. 2134
IOWA 80 TRUCKSTOP—See Iowa 80 Group, Inc.; *U.S. Private*, pg. 2134
JACO OIL; *U.S. Private*, pg. 2179
J & J MARTS INC.; *U.S. Private*, pg. 2152
JNS HOLDINGS CORPORATION; *U.S. Public*, pg. 1190
JONES COMPANY, INC.; *U.S. Private*, pg. 2232
JOPLIN PETRO—See Iowa 80 Group, Inc.; *U.S. Private*, pg. 2134
JR. FOOD STORES, INC.—See Houchens Industries, Inc.; *U.S. Private*, pg. 1990
JUBITZ CORPORATION; *U.S. Private*, pg. 2242
KELLEY-WILLIAMSON COMPANY INC.; *U.S. Private*, pg. 2276
KENJO OIL; *U.S. Private*, pg. 2284
KENTUCKY LAKE OIL CO. INC.; *U.S. Private*, pg. 2288
KNOX OIL OF TEXAS, INC.; *U.S. Private*, pg. 2324
KN PROPERTIES; *U.S. Private*, pg. 2321
KOCOLENE MARKETING, LLC; *U.S. Private*, pg. 2335
KUM & GO—See Krause Gentle Corporation; *U.S. Private*, pg. 2350
KWIK TRIP INC.; *U.S. Private*, pg. 2359
LASSUS BROS. OIL INC.; *U.S. Private*, pg. 2395
LEISZLER OIL CO., INC.; *U.S. Private*, pg. 2420
LIPSCOMB OIL CO. INC.; *U.S. Private*, pg. 2465
LITCO PETROLEUM INC.; *U.S. Private*, pg. 2467
LOVE'S TRAVEL STOPS & COUNTRY STORES, INC.; *U.S. Private*, pg. 2501
MARINE VENTURES LTD.—See Centerbridge Partners, L.P.; *U.S. Private*, pg. 815
MAVERIK COUNTRY STORES, INC.; *U.S. Private*, pg. 2616
MCCLURE OIL CORPORATION; *U.S. Private*, pg. 2629
MIDTEX OIL, LP; *U.S. Private*, pg. 2718
MIDWEST PETROLEUM CO.; *U.S. Private*, pg. 2722
M.M. FOWLER INC.; *U.S. Private*, pg. 2529
MON VALLEY PETROLEUM INC.; *U.S. Private*, pg. 2768
MORRIS OIL CO. INC.; *U.S. Private*, pg. 2788
MOTO, INC.; *U.S. Private*, pg. 2796
MOTOR EV, LLC—See The AES Corporation; *U.S. Public*, pg. 2032
MOUNTAIN EMPIRE OIL COMPANY INC.; *U.S. Private*, pg. 2799
MOYLE PETROLEUM COMPANY INC.; *U.S. Private*, pg. 2802

MYERS FAMILY LP; *U.S. Private*, pg. 2824
NEW HORIZON SUPPLY COOPERATIVE; *U.S. Private*, pg. 2897
OAK GROVE PETRO TRUCKSTOP—See Iowa 80 Group, Inc.; *U.S. Private*, pg. 2134
O'CONNOR OIL CORPORATION; *U.S. Private*, pg. 2978
O.K. PETROLEUM DISTRIBUTION CORP.; *U.S. Private*, pg. 2981
ON-SITE FUEL SERVICE; *U.S. Private*, pg. 3019
OPEN PANTRY FOOD MARTS OF WISCONSIN INC.; *U.S. Private*, pg. 3029
OTTAWA OIL COMPANY—See Jay Petroleum, Inc.; *U.S. Private*, pg. 2192
PAXTON & BALL INC.; *U.S. Private*, pg. 3115
PDQ FOOD STORES, INC.; *U.S. Private*, pg. 3122
PEAK ENERGY; *U.S. Private*, pg. 3123
PEERLESS TYRE CO.; *U.S. Private*, pg. 3129
PENN PRIDE INC—See Alexa Energy Ltd.; *U.S. Private*, pg. 163
PERFORMANCE COMPANIES, INC.; *U.S. Private*, pg. 3148
PETROCARD, INC.—See Bristol Bay Native Corporation; *U.S. Private*, pg. 656
PILOT CORPORATION; *U.S. Private*, pg. 3181
PLUGSURFING GMBH—See Corpay, Inc.; *U.S. Public*, pg. 580
PRAIRIE PRIDE COOPERATIVE; *U.S. Private*, pg. 3243
PROPEL INC.; *U.S. Private*, pg. 3285
PUGH MARINA—See Pugh Oil Company; *U.S. Private*, pg. 3303
PUGH OIL COMPANY; *U.S. Private*, pg. 3303
QUALITY OIL COMPANY LLC; *U.S. Private*, pg. 3320
QUARLES TRUCK STOP INC.—See Quarles Petroleum Incorporated; *U.S. Private*, pg. 3324
QUIK STOP QUIK WASH; *U.S. Private*, pg. 3327
QUIKTRIP CORPORATION; *U.S. Private*, pg. 3327
RAPID ROBERTS INC.; *U.S. Private*, pg. 3356
REID PETROLEUM CORP.; *U.S. Private*, pg. 3391
RIP GRIFFIN TRUCK SERVICE CENTER, INC.—See BP plc; *Int'l*, pg. 1127
ROBERTS OIL CO., INC.; *U.S. Private*, pg. 3460
ROBINSON OIL CORP.; *U.S. Private*, pg. 3462
ROCKY TOP MARKETS LLC; *U.S. Private*, pg. 3469
RUSSELL OIL COMPANY INC.; *U.S. Private*, pg. 3506
RUSSELL PETROLEUM CORPORATION; *U.S. Private*, pg. 3506
SAVINGS OIL COMPANY INC.; *U.S. Private*, pg. 3557
SAV-O-MAT, INC.—See Stinker Stores, Inc.; *U.S. Private*, pg. 3813
SAYLE OIL COMPANY INC.; *U.S. Private*, pg. 3558
SCHMUCKAL OIL COMPANY INC.—See True North Energy, LLC; *U.S. Private*, pg. 4248
SCULLY OIL CO., INC.—See Pops Mart Fuels, LLC; *U.S. Private*, pg. 3229
SERVICE OIL INC.; *U.S. Private*, pg. 3615
SHAY OIL COMPANY, INC.; *U.S. Private*, pg. 3628
SHOP-A-LOTT, INC.—See Lott Oil Company, Inc.; *U.S. Private*, pg. 2497
SING BROTHERS INC.; *U.S. Private*, pg. 3669
SITE OIL COMPANY OF MISSOURI; *U.S. Private*, pg. 3676
SJC INC.; *U.S. Private*, pg. 3678
SMITH & COFFMAN INCORPORATED; *U.S. Private*, pg. 3693
SNYDER AUTO WORKS INC.; *U.S. Private*, pg. 3701
THE SOMMERS COMPANY; *U.S. Private*, pg. 4119
SOUTHWEST GEORGIA OIL CO., INC.; *U.S. Private*, pg. 3739
THE SPINX COMPANY INC.; *U.S. Private*, pg. 4120
S/S/G CORPORATION; *U.S. Private*, pg. 3519
STOP-N-GO OF MADISON INC.—See Kwik Trip Inc.; *U.S. Private*, pg. 2359
SUNOCO MASCOT, INC.—See Energy Transfer LP; *U.S. Public*, pg. 764
SUPER-FLITE OIL CO. INC.; *U.S. Private*, pg. 3875
SUPER QUIK INC.; *U.S. Private*, pg. 3875
SWIFTY OIL, LLC; *U.S. Private*, pg. 3893
T&E OIL COMPANY INC.; *U.S. Private*, pg. 3909
TESORO ALASKA PIPELINE CO. LLC—See Marathon Petroleum Corporation; *U.S. Public*, pg. 1363
TEXAS PARIMUTUEL MANAGEMENT INC.—See Greene Group Inc.; *U.S. Private*, pg. 1776
TOWN PUMP, INC.; *U.S. Private*, pg. 4197
TRIPLETT INC.; *U.S. Private*, pg. 4237
TRISTATE PETROLEUM—See Exxon Mobil Corporation; *U.S. Public*, pg. 817
TRITON MARKETING COMPANY; *U.S. Private*, pg. 4239
TRUCK WORLD INC.; *U.S. Private*, pg. 4246
TRUE NORTH ENERGY, LLC; *U.S. Private*, pg. 4247
UNITECH SERVICES GROUP—See UniFirst Corporation; *U.S. Public*, pg. 2226
UPSTREAM TECHNICAL COMPUTING COMPANY—See Exxon Mobil Corporation; *U.S. Public*, pg. 817
VALERO TERMINALING & DISTRIBUTION COMPANY—See Valero Energy Corporation; *U.S. Public*, pg. 2273
VAN ZEELAND OIL CO., INC.; *U.S. Private*, pg. 4341
WADSWORTH OIL CO. OF CLANTON INC.; *U.S. Private*, pg. 4425

WALLIS COMPANIES, INC.; *U.S. Private*, pg. 4431
WALLIS OIL CO. INC.—See Wallis Companies, Inc.; *U.S. Private*, pg. 4431
THE WATKINS COMPANY INC.; *U.S. Private*, pg. 4133
WESTERN OIL INC.; *U.S. Private*, pg. 4495
WHITEHEAD OIL CO., INC.; *U.S. Private*, pg. 4511
WILCO FARMERS INC.; *U.S. Private*, pg. 4518
WILCO—See A.T. Williams Oil Company; *U.S. Private*, pg. 28
THE WILLS GROUP, INC.; *U.S. Private*, pg. 4136
WOODY'S ENTERPRISES LTD.; *U.S. Private*, pg. 4561
WORLD OIL CORP.; *U.S. Private*, pg. 4566

457210 — FUEL DEALERS

4REFUEL CANADA LP—See Finning International Inc.; *Int'l*, pg. 2676
941-2401 HEATING LIMITED; *Int'l*, pg. 16
ABBOTT & MILLS INC.; *U.S. Private*, pg. 34
ABILENE AERO INC.; *U.S. Private*, pg. 38
ADDITECH, INC.; *U.S. Private*, pg. 77
AEMETIS, INC.; *U.S. Public*, pg. 52
A.E. ROBINSON OIL CO. INC.; *U.S. Private*, pg. 25
AFC ENERGY PLC; *Int'l*, pg. 185
AIRPORT FUEL SERVICES PTY LTD—See Ampol Limited; *Int'l*, pg. 436
ALL AMERICAN PROPANE, INC.; *U.S. Private*, pg. 170
ALLGAS INC. OF MONTGOMERY—See Ergon, Inc.; *U.S. Private*, pg. 1418
ALLIANCE ENERGY LLC—See Global Partners LP; *U.S. Public*, pg. 1842
ALLIANCE PETROLEUM CORPORATION—See Van De Pol Enterprises, Inc.; *U.S. Private*, pg. 4339
ALVIN HOLLIS & CO. INC.; *U.S. Private*, pg. 214
AMERICAN COMPRESSED GASES INC.; *U.S. Private*, pg. 227
AMERIGAS PROPANE, L.P.—See UGI Corporation; *U.S. Public*, pg. 2221
ANDERSON OIL COMPANY INCORPORATED; *U.S. Private*, pg. 277
ANTARGAZ S.A.—See UGI Corporation; *U.S. Public*, pg. 2222
AO NNK-PRIMORNEFTEPRODUCT—See Alliance Oil Company Ltd.; *Int'l*, pg. 340
A.P. WOODSON CO.—See Star Group, L.P.; *U.S. Public*, pg. 1937
ASTOMOS ENERGY CORPORATION—See Idemitsu Kosan Co., Ltd.; *Int'l*, pg. 3590
AUTOMOTIVE SERVICE INC.; *U.S. Private*, pg. 401
BACKGROUND2 LIMITED—See Dover Corporation; *U.S. Public*, pg. 678
THE BANGCHAK GREEN NET CO. LTD—See Bangchak Corporation Public Company Limited; *Int'l*, pg. 832
BANGKOK AVIATION FUEL SERVICES PUBLIC COMPANY LIMITED; *Int'l*, pg. 832
BANLE ENERGY INTERNATIONAL LIMITED—See CBL International Limited; *Int'l*, pg. 1365
BANLE INTERNATIONAL (MALAYSIA) SDN. BHD.—See CBL International Limited; *Int'l*, pg. 1365
BANLE INTERNATIONAL MARKETING LIMITED—See CBL International Limited; *Int'l*, pg. 1365
BARROW PROPANE GAS—See Ferrellgas Partners, L.P.; *U.S. Public*, pg. 829
BASIN TRANSLOAD, LLC—See Global Partners LP; *U.S. Public*, pg. 942
BAY GAS SERVICE, INC.—See Paraco Gas Corporation; *U.S. Private*, pg. 3089
BEACON ENERGY CORPORATION—See EQM Technologies & Energy, Inc.; *U.S. Public*, pg. 784
BERICO HEATING AND AIR CONDITIONING, INC.; *U.S. Private*, pg. 531
THE BLOSSMAN COMPANIES INC.; *U.S. Private*, pg. 3995
BLOSSMAN GAS INC.—See The Blossman Companies Inc.; *U.S. Private*, pg. 3995
BLUE FLAME PROPANE, INC.—See Foster Blue Water Oil, LLC; *U.S. Private*, pg. 1578
BLUE RHINO GLOBAL SOURCING, INC.—See Ferrellgas Partners, L.P.; *U.S. Public*, pg. 829
BLUE STAR GAS; *U.S. Private*, pg. 593
BOSCO OIL, INC.; *U.S. Private*, pg. 619
BOTTINI FUEL COMPANY; *U.S. Private*, pg. 623
BP FUJIAN LIMITED—See China Resources (Holdings) Co., Ltd.; *Int'l*, pg. 1548
BP GAS AUSTRIA GMBH NFG. OHG—See BP plc; *Int'l*, pg. 1128
BRADCO INC.; *U.S. Private*, pg. 631
BRADENTON FUEL OIL; *U.S. Private*, pg. 631
BROBOT FUELS LTD.; *Int'l*, pg. 1172
BRONBERGER & KESSLER HANDELSGESELLSCHAFT GMBH—See Eni S.p.A.; *Int'l*, pg. 2437
BURKE FUEL & HEATING CO.—See Star Group, L.P.; *U.S. Public*, pg. 1937
BURNETT DAIRY COOP ASSOCIATION; *U.S. Private*, pg. 689
BURNS & MCBRIDE INC.—See Morgan Stanley; *U.S. Public*, pg. 1474

N.A.I.C.S. INDEX   457210 — FUEL DEALERS

CAMPBELL OIL, INC.—See Lykins Companies, Inc.; *U.S. Private*, pg. 2519
CAMPORA INC.; *U.S. Private*, pg. 731
CAPGAS PRIVATE LIMITED—See Attock Refinery Ltd; *Int'l*, pg. 697
CARBOIL SRL—See Eni S.p.A.; *Int'l*, pg. 2437
CARL KING INC.—See Star Group, L.P.; *U.S. Public*, pg. 1937
CARL'S OIL COMPANY; *U.S. Private*, pg. 763
CAROLANE PROPANE—See UGI Corporation; *U.S. Public*, pg. 2221
CASS COUNTY BUTANE CO., INC.—See Ferrellgas Partners, L.P.; *U.S. Public*, pg. 829
CENTRAL ENERGY K.K.—See Idemitsu Kosan Co., Ltd.; *Int'l*, pg. 3590
CENTRAL HUDSON ENTERPRISES CORPORATION—See Fortis Inc.; *Int'l*, pg. 2739
CENTRAL MONTANA PROPANE, LLC—See CHS INC.; *U.S. Public*, pg. 492
CENTRAL OIL & SUPPLY CORP SHREVEPORT—See Central Oil & Supply Corporation; *U.S. Private*, pg. 824
CHAMPION ENERGY CORPORATION—See Star Group, L.P.; *U.S. Public*, pg. 1937
CHESHIRE OIL COMPANY INC.; *U.S. Private*, pg. 875
CHEVRON BELGIUM NV/SA—See Chevron Corporation; *U.S. Public*, pg. 486
CHIEF ENERGY, INC.; *U.S. Private*, pg. 880
CHINA AVIATION OIL (SINGAPORE) CORPORATION LTD.—See China National Aviation Fuel Group Corporation; *Int'l*, pg. 1525
CHINA RESOURCES GAS (HOLDINGS) LTD.—See China Resources (Holdings) Co., Ltd.; *Int'l*, pg. 1548
C. HOFFBERGER COMPANY INC.—See Star Group, L.P.; *U.S. Public*, pg. 1937
CHRISTY-HALSEY MEENAN—See Star Group, L.P.; *U.S. Public*, pg. 1937
COC PROPERTIES, INC.; *U.S. Private*, pg. 958
COLT INTERNATIONAL DAS AMERICAS SERVICOS DE AVIACAO LTDA.—See World Kinect Corporation; *U.S. Public*, pg. 2380
COLT INTERNATIONAL EUROPE SARL—See World Kinect Corporation; *U.S. Public*, pg. 2380
COLT INTERNATIONAL HONG KONG LIMITED—See World Kinect Corporation; *U.S. Public*, pg. 2380
COLT INTERNATIONAL, L.L.C.—See World Kinect Corporation; *U.S. Public*, pg. 2380
CONSOLIDATED ENERGY COMPANY—See Hartland Fuel Products, LLC; *U.S. Private*, pg. 1874
CONTURA COAL SALES, LLC—See Alpha Metallurgical Resources, Inc.; *U.S. Public*, pg. 82
CORBIN GAS PROPANE—See UGI Corporation; *U.S. Public*, pg. 2222
CORTEZ GAS COMPANY INC.; *U.S. Private*, pg. 1060
COTA & COTA INC.; *U.S. Private*, pg. 1063
CRYSTAL FLASH LP OF MICHIGAN; *U.S. Private*, pg. 1115
CS MYERS & SON INC.; *U.S. Private*, pg. 1116
CUMBERLAND CONTURA, LLC—See Alpha Metallurgical Resources, Inc.; *U.S. Public*, pg. 82
CW PETROLEUM CORP.; *U.S. Public*, pg. 616
DAIGLE OIL COMPANY; *U.S. Private*, pg. 1145
DAVE REISDORF INC.; *U.S. Private*, pg. 1168
DEAD RIVER COMPANY - WEBBER ENERGY FUELS DIVISION—See Dead River Company; *U.S. Private*, pg. 1182
DEANS OIL COMPANY INC.; *U.S. Private*, pg. 1185
DELEK BENELUX BV—See Delek Group Ltd.; *Int'l*, pg. 2011
DELEK FRANCE BV—See Delek Group Ltd.; *Int'l*, pg. 2011
DELEK MARKETING & SUPPLY, INC.—See Delek Group Ltd.; *Int'l*, pg. 2011
DELEK THE ISRAEL FUEL CORPORATION LTD.—See Delek Group Ltd.; *Int'l*, pg. 2011
DELTA LIQUID ENERGY; *U.S. Private*, pg. 1201
DEVANEY ENERGY INC.; *U.S. Private*, pg. 1217
DF RICHARD INC.; *U.S. Private*, pg. 1220
DICKENSON-RUSSELL CONTURA, LLC—See Alpha Metallurgical Resources, Inc.; *U.S. Public*, pg. 82
DIXON BROS. INC.; *U.S. Private*, pg. 1245
DOMESTIC INDUSTRIES OF VIRGINIA INC.—See Domestic Industries Inc.; *U.S. Private*, pg. 1255
DQE COMMUNICATIONS LLC—See GI Manager L.P.; *U.S. Private*, pg. 1692
DUKE ENERGY NGL SERVICES LP—See Duke Energy Corporation; *U.S. Public*, pg. 690
EASTERN PROPANE GAS, INC.; *U.S. Private*, pg. 1321
EAST KANSAS AGRI ENERGY LLC; *U.S. Public*, pg. 703
E-CON GAS, INC—See UGI Corporation; *U.S. Public*, pg. 2221
ECONOMY PROPANE CORP.; *U.S. Private*, pg. 1330
ECUACENTAIR CIA. LTDA.—See World Kinect Corporation; *U.S. Public*, pg. 2380
E.E. WINE INC.; *U.S. Private*, pg. 1305
EMPRESAS LIPIGAS SA; *Int'l*, pg. 2391
ENERGYNORTH PROPANE, INC.—See UGI Corporation; *U.S. Public*, pg. 2221
ENERGY PETROLEUM CO. INC.; *U.S. Private*, pg. 1395
ENERGY TRANSFER LP; *U.S. Public*, pg. 762
ENERGY TRANSFER, LP—See Energy Transfer LP; *U.S. Public*, pg. 763

ENI ALGERIA PRODUCTION BV—See Eni S.p.A.; *Int'l*, pg. 2437
ENI FUEL NORD SPA—See Eni S.p.A.; *Int'l*, pg. 2437
E. OSTERMAN GAS SERVICE INC.; *U.S. Private*, pg. 1304
EPSILON TRADING, INC.—See Delta Air Lines, Inc.; *U.S. Public*, pg. 652
ESSO NEDERLAND B.V.—See Exxon Mobil Corporation; *U.S. Public*, pg. 814
ETHERIDGE OIL COMPANY; *U.S. Private*, pg. 1431
EXXONMOBIL MARINE LIMITED—See Exxon Mobil Corporation; *U.S. Public*, pg. 815
EXXONMOBIL OIL CORPORATION—See Exxon Mobil Corporation; *U.S. Public*, pg. 815
EXXONMOBIL SALES & SUPPLY LLC—See Exxon Mobil Corporation; *U.S. Public*, pg. 816
FAIRBANKS ENVIRONMENTAL LIMITED—See Dover Corporation; *U.S. Public*, pg. 681
FEDERAL PETROLEUM CO., INC.—See Ferrellgas Partners, L.P.; *U.S. Public*, pg. 829
FERRELLGAS, INC. - BOSSIER CITY—See Ferrellgas Partners, L.P.; *U.S. Public*, pg. 829
FERRELLGAS, INC. - HILLSBORO—See Ferrellgas Partners, L.P.; *U.S. Public*, pg. 829
FERRELLGAS, INC. - HOUSTON—See Ferrellgas Partners, L.P.; *U.S. Public*, pg. 829
FERRELLGAS PARTNERS, L.P.; *U.S. Public*, pg. 829
FIFTH WHEEL TRUCK STOPS; *Int'l*, pg. 2660
F K GAILEY—See UGI Corporation; *U.S. Public*, pg. 2222
FLEMING BROTHERS OIL COMPANY INC; *U.S. Private*, pg. 1542
FLOGAS IRELAND LIMITED—See DCC plc; *Int'l*, pg. 1990
FOUNDATION GAS—See Fauji Foundation; *Int'l*, pg. 2623
FREDERICKS FUEL & HEATING SERVICE; *U.S. Private*, pg. 1602
FRITCH INC.; *U.S. Private*, pg. 1612
FUEL DOCTOR HOLDINGS, INC.; *U.S. Public*, pg. 891
GAC BUNKER FUELS—See Gulf Agency Company Ltd.; *Int'l*, pg. 3178
GALP GAMBIA, LIMITED—See Galp Energia SGPS, S.A.; *Int'l*, pg. 2875
GALP SERVIEXPRESS - SERV. DE DISTRIB. E COMERCIALIZACAO DE PRODUTOS PETROLIFEROS, S.A.—See Galp Energia SGPS, S.A.; *Int'l*, pg. 2875
GANZ BIOFUELS SDN. BHD.—See Fintec Global Berhad; *Int'l*, pg. 2677
GAS INCORPORATED; *U.S. Private*, pg. 1647
GASPAL CO LTD—See Daito Trust Construction Co., Ltd.; *Int'l*, pg. 1943
GAS PLUS INC.; *Int'l*, pg. 2887
G.A. WILLIAMS & SONS INC.; *U.S. Private*, pg. 1630
GAY JOHNSON'S, INC.; *U.S. Private*, pg. 1652
GEORGE M. TAYLOR & SON, INC.; *U.S. Private*, pg. 1682
GEORGE'S GAS CO. INC.—See George's Inc.; *U.S. Private*, pg. 1683
GIBSON PROPANE—See UGI Corporation; *U.S. Public*, pg. 2221
GLOBAL MONTELLO GROUP CORPORATION—See Global Partners LP; *U.S. Public*, pg. 942
GLOBAL PARTNERS LP; *U.S. Public*, pg. 942
GOTT COMPANY INC.; *U.S. Private*, pg. 1745
GREAT PLAINS SERVICE, INC.; *U.S. Private*, pg. 1767
GRIFFITH ENERGY SERVICES, INC.—See Star Group, L.P.; *U.S. Public*, pg. 1937
GUILFORD GAS—See UGI Corporation; *U.S. Public*, pg. 2221
HALON BANKING SYSTEMS—See APi Group Corporation; *Int'l*, pg. 514
HARVEST LAND CO-OP INC.—See Harvest Land Co-Op Inc.; *U.S. Private*, pg. 1875
HELLENIC AVIATION FUEL COMPANY S.A.—See World Kinect Corporation; *U.S. Public*, pg. 2380
HELLENIC PETROLEUM CYPRUS LTD.—See HELLENiQ ENERGY Holdings S.A.; *Int'l*, pg. 3334
HENDELS INCORPORATED; *U.S. Private*, pg. 1913
HERITAGENERGY (NY) INC.; *U.S. Private*, pg. 1925
HERITAGE OPERATING, L.P.—See UGI Corporation; *U.S. Public*, pg. 2221
HERRING GAS COMPANY INC.; *U.S. Private*, pg. 1926
HIGHLAND FUELS LTD.; *Int'l*, pg. 3387
HI-HO PETROLEUM CO.—See D'Addario Industries Inc.; *U.S. Private*, pg. 1138
HIPOL A.D.; *Int'l*, pg. 3402
HOFFMAN FUEL COMPANY OF BRIDGEPORT INC.—See Star Group, L.P.; *U.S. Public*, pg. 1937
HOFFMAN FUEL COMPANY OF DANBURY INC.—See Star Group, L.P.; *U.S. Public*, pg. 1938
HOLTZMAN PROPANE LLC—See Holtzman Oil Corp.; *U.S. Private*, pg. 1969
HOME OIL COMPANY INCORPORATED; *U.S. Private*, pg. 1972
HOME SERVICE OIL CO. INC.; *U.S. Private*, pg. 1972
HOUSTON COUNTY PROPANE—See UGI Corporation; *U.S. Public*, pg. 2221
HUGHES OIL CO. INC.; *U.S. Private*, pg. 2003
HUHTALA OIL & TEMPLETON GARAGE; *U.S. Private*, pg. 2004
HURON SMITH OIL CO. INC.; *U.S. Private*, pg. 2012

HYDRATANE OF ATHENS—See UGI Corporation; *U.S. Public*, pg. 2221
INDEPENDENT PROPANE COMPANY—See Suburban Propane Partners, L.P.; *U.S. Public*, pg. 1958
INTERFOUNDRY, INC.; *U.S. Private*, pg. 1144
INTERSTATE ENERGY LLC; *U.S. Private*, pg. 2124
IRA WYMAN, INC.—See Suburban Propane Partners, L.P.; *U.S. Public*, pg. 1958
JACOBUS ENERGY - QUICKFLASH DIVISION—See Jacobus Energy, Inc.; *U.S. Private*, pg. 2180
JASPER ENGINE & TRANSMISSION EXCHANGE INC. - JASPER ALTERNATE FUELS—See Jasper Engine & Transmission Exchange Inc.; *U.S. Private*, pg. 2190
JAYSON OIL COMPANY INCORPORATED; *U.S. Private*, pg. 2192
JAYVEE PETROLEUM PTY LTD—See Ampol Limited; *Int'l*, pg. 436
JENKINS GAS & OIL CO., INC.—See Suburban Propane Partners, L.P.; *U.S. Public*, pg. 1958
J.H. BUHRMASTER COMPANY INC.; *U.S. Private*, pg. 2165
J.H. KASPAR OIL CO.—See Stinker Stores, Inc.; *U.S. Private*, pg. 3813
J.J. SKELTON OIL COMPANY INC.—See Star Group, L.P.; *U.S. Public*, pg. 1938
JOHN R. YOUNG & CO. INC.; *U.S. Private*, pg. 2224
J.W. PIERSON COMPANY INC.; *U.S. Private*, pg. 2172
KELLER OIL COMPANY—See Reading Anthracite Company; *U.S. Private*, pg. 3366
KEYSER ENERGY—See Delos Capital, LLC; *U.S. Private*, pg. 2296
KEYSTONE FUELS, INC.; *U.S. Private*, pg. 2296
KINGSTON PROPANE—See UGI Corporation; *U.S. Public*, pg. 2221
KOSAN GAS A/S—See UGI Corporation; *U.S. Public*, pg. 2222
KREISER FUEL SERVICE INC.; *U.S. Private*, pg. 2350
LACOX INC.—See Ergon, Inc.; *U.S. Private*, pg. 1418
LACOX PROPANE GAS COMPANY INC.—See Ergon, Inc.; *U.S. Private*, pg. 1418
LAKE COUNTY GAS—See UGI Corporation; *U.S. Public*, pg. 2221
LAKES GAS COMPANY; *U.S. Private*, pg. 2376
LAMPTON-LOVE, INC.—See Ergon, Inc.; *U.S. Private*, pg. 1418
LAMPTON-LOVE, INC.—See Ergon, Inc.; *U.S. Private*, pg. 1418
LAMPTON-LOVE, INC.—See Ergon, Inc.; *U.S. Private*, pg. 1418
LAMPTON-LOVE, INC.—See Ergon, Inc.; *U.S. Private*, pg. 1418
LANSING ICE AND FUEL COMPANY; *U.S. Private*, pg. 2390
LEE-MOORE CAPITAL COMPANY; *U.S. Private*, pg. 2414
LEIGHOW OIL COMPANY INCORPORATED; *U.S. Private*, pg. 2420
LIQAL, B.V.—See Dover Corporation; *U.S. Public*, pg. 681
LITTER INDUSTRIES INC.; *U.S. Private*, pg. 2468
LITTER QUALITY PROPANE COMPANY—See Litter Industries Inc.; *U.S. Private*, pg. 2468
LIVE OAK GAS CO.—See Suburban Propane Partners, L.P.; *U.S. Public*, pg. 1958
LORDEN OIL CO. INC.; *U.S. Private*, pg. 2495
LOTOS JASLO S.A.—See Grupa LOTOS S.A.; *Int'l*, pg. 3117
LYONS GAS—See UGI Corporation; *U.S. Public*, pg. 2221
MACK OIL CO. INC.; *U.S. Private*, pg. 2536
MAGNOLIA GAS INC.—See Ergon, Inc.; *U.S. Private*, pg. 1418
MAIN BROTHERS OIL COMPANY, INC.; *U.S. Private*, pg. 2551
MAJESTIC ENERGY (SINGAPORE) PTE. LTD.—See CBL International Limited; *Int'l*, pg. 1366
MANASSAS ICE & FUEL CO. INC.; *U.S. Private*, pg. 2561
MARITIME ENERGY, INC.; *U.S. Private*, pg. 2576
MARLEN GAS—See UGI Corporation; *U.S. Public*, pg. 2222
MARLIN COMPRESSION, LLC—See Chesapeake Utilities Corporation; *U.S. Public*, pg. 485
MARTIN LP GAS INC.—See Martin Resource Management Corporation; *U.S. Public*, pg. 2596
MARTIN MIDSTREAM PARTNERS LP; *U.S. Public*, pg. 1389
MARTIN OIL COMPANY; *U.S. Private*, pg. 2595
MASSEY WOOD & WEST INC.; *U.S. Private*, pg. 2606
MCMULLEN OIL CO. INC.; *U.S. Private*, pg. 2643
MEENAN HOLDINGS LOVE-EFFRON DIVISION—See Star Group, L.P.; *U.S. Public*, pg. 1937
MEENAN HOLDINGS OF NEW YORK, INC.—See Star Group, L.P.; *U.S. Public*, pg. 1937
MEENAN OIL CO., INC.—See Star Group, L.P.; *U.S. Public*, pg. 1938
MEENAN OIL PENNSYLVANIA DIVISION—See Star Group, L.P.; *U.S. Public*, pg. 1937
METRO FUEL INC.; *U.S. Private*, pg. 2685
M & J GAS COMPANY—See UGI Corporation; *U.S. Public*, pg. 2222
MJT ENTERPRISES INC.; *U.S. Private*, pg. 2753
MONMOUTH PETROLEUM CO. INC.; *U.S. Private*, pg. 2771

457210 — FUEL DEALERS

MOORE L.P. GAS—See UGI Corporation; *U.S. Public*, pg. 2222
NATIONAL FUEL OIL INC.; *U.S. Private*, pg. 2855
N.B. FAIRCLOUGH & SONS INC.; *U.S. Private*, pg. 2827
NEW HORIZON FARM SERVICE—See New Horizon F S Inc.; *U.S. Private*, pg. 2897
NICHOLAS CONTURA, LLC—See Alpha Metallurgical Resources, Inc.; *U.S. Public*, pg. 82
NOONAN ENERGY CORPORATION; *U.S. Private*, pg. 2935
NORBERT E. MITCHELL CO, INC.; *U.S. Private*, pg. 2935
NORTHERN ENERGY INC.; *U.S. Private*, pg. 2952
NORTHERN NECK OIL COMPANY—See Quarles Petroleum Incorporated; *U.S. Private*, pg. 3324
OPW FRANCE—See Dover Corporation; *U.S. Public*, pg. 682
ORTEP OF PENNSYLVANIA INC.—See Star Group, L.P.; *U.S. Public*, pg. 1937
PACER PROPANE LLC—See NGL Energy Partners LP; *U.S. Public*, pg. 1527
PAK PETROLEUM MARKETING INC.; *U.S. Private*, pg. 3076
PARAMONT CONTURA, LLC—See Alpha Metallurgical Resources, Inc.; *U.S. Public*, pg. 82
PARKER GAS COMPANY INC.; *U.S. Private*, pg. 3097
PARKER OIL COMPANY, INC.—See Parker Holding Company, Inc.; *U.S. Private*, pg. 3097
PARMAN ENERGY CORPORATION—See Parman Holding Corporation; *U.S. Private*, pg. 3099
PATTERSON FUEL OIL INC.; *U.S. Private*, pg. 3111
PEDLEY PROPANE—See UGI Corporation; *U.S. Public*, pg. 2222
PEP-UP, INC.; *U.S. Private*, pg. 3143
PERRY'S OIL SERVICE INC.—See NGL Energy Partners LP; *U.S. Public*, pg. 1527
PETRO FUEL CO. INC.—See Star Group, L.P.; *U.S. Public*, pg. 1937
PETRO HOLDINGS, INC.—See Star Group, L.P.; *U.S. Public*, pg. 1937
PETROLEUM HEAT & POWER CO. INC.—See Star Group, L.P.; *U.S. Public*, pg. 1938
PETROLEUM HEAT & POWER CO.—See Star Group, L.P.; *U.S. Public*, pg. 1938
PETROLEUM MARKETERS, INC.—See CrossAmerica Partners LP; *U.S. Public*, pg. 596
PETROLEUM SALES INC.; *U.S. Private*, pg. 3162
PETRO OIL INC.—See Star Group, L.P.; *U.S. Public*, pg. 1938
PETRO OIL—See Star Group, L.P.; *U.S. Public*, pg. 1938
PETRO—See Star Group, L.P.; *U.S. Public*, pg. 1937
P-FLEET INC.; *U.S. Private*, pg. 3059
PICKELNER FUEL CO. INC.; *U.S. Private*, pg. 3176
PIONEER PROPANE—See UGI Corporation; *U.S. Public*, pg. 2222
PLATINUM ENERGY SDN. BHD.—See Fintec Global Berhad; *Int'l*, pg. 2677
PM FOODS INC—See CrossAmerica Partners LP; *U.S. Public*, pg. 596
PM TERMINALS, INC.—See CrossAmerica Partners LP; *U.S. Public*, pg. 596
POWER MOUNTAIN CONTURA, LLC—See Alpha Metallurgical Resources, Inc.; *U.S. Public*, pg. 82
PROPEL FUELS, INC.; *U.S. Private*, pg. 3285
QUICK FUEL FLEET SERVICES, LLC—See Jacobus Energy, Inc.; *U.S. Private*, pg. 2180
RAIFFEISEN WAREN GMBH—See BayWa AG; *Int'l*, pg. 918
RED STAR OIL CO. INC.; *U.S. Private*, pg. 3376
REGIONOIL PLUMBING, HEATING & COOLING CO., INC.—See Star Group, L.P.; *U.S. Public*, pg. 1938
REINHARDT CORP; *U.S. Private*, pg. 3392
RICHLAND PARTNERS LLC—See Star Group, L.P.; *U.S. Public*, pg. 1938
RIGGINS, INC.; *U.S. Private*, pg. 3435
RINKER OIL CORPORATION; *U.S. Private*, pg. 3438
RIVERSIDE GAS & OIL CO. INC.; *U.S. Private*, pg. 3445
R. MCALLISTER SERVICE COMPANY; *U.S. Private*, pg. 3334
ROBINSON'S INDUSTRIAL GAS & EQUIPMENT CORP.; *U.S. Private*, pg. 3462
ROCKET SUPPLY CORP.—See Hicks Oil-Hicks Gas, Inc.; *U.S. Private*, pg. 1934
RTS OIL HOLDINGS, INC.; *U.S. Public*, pg. 1820
RYE FUEL COMPANY INC.—See Star Group, L.P.; *U.S. Public*, pg. 1938
SANDFORD PETROLEUM, INC.—See Sunoco LP; *U.S. Public*, pg. 1965
SANTA BUCKLEY ENERGY, INC.—See Santa Energy Corporation; *U.S. Private*, pg. 3547
SANTA FUEL, INC.—See Santa Energy Corporation; *U.S. Private*, pg. 3547
SANTORO OIL COMPANY INC—See Domestic Industries Inc.; *U.S. Private*, pg. 1255
SAVEWAY PETROLEUM INC.; *U.S. Private*, pg. 3557
SAWYER GAS—See UGI Corporation; *U.S. Public*, pg. 2222
SCHAGRIN GAS CO.; *U.S. Private*, pg. 3563
SCOTT ENERGY CO., INC.; *U.S. Private*, pg. 3576
S.C. SALGAS S.A.—See E.ON SE; *Int'l*, pg. 2259
SHARP ENERGY, INC—See Chesapeake Utilities Corporation; *U.S. Public*, pg. 486

SHAW L.P. GAS—See UGI Corporation; *U.S. Public*, pg. 2222
SHELBY COUNTY CO-OP; *U.S. Private*, pg. 3630
SHIPLEY ENERGY COMPANY; *U.S. Private*, pg. 3637
SHULTZ DISTRIBUTING, INC.; *U.S. Private*, pg. 3644
SJ FUEL CO., INC.; *U.S. Private*, pg. 3678
SKAGGS-WALSH, INC.; *U.S. Private*, pg. 3680
SLOMIN'S INC.; *U.S. Private*, pg. 3689
SNEDEKER OIL COMPANY INC.; *U.S. Private*, pg. 3700
SOURDOUGH FUEL, INC.—See Arctic Slope Regional Corporation; *U.S. Private*, pg. 316
SOUTH EAST QUEENSLAND FUELS PTY LTD—See Ampol Limited; *Int'l*, pg. 436
SOUTHSIDE OIL LLC—See Sunoco LP; *U.S. Public*, pg. 1965
SPENCE/BANKS INC.; *U.S. Private*, pg. 3754
SPENCER OIL COMPANY; *U.S. Private*, pg. 3755
STAFFORD OIL CO. INC.; *U.S. Private*, pg. 3775
STAR ENERGY—See Growmark, Inc.; *U.S. Private*, pg. 1795
STAR GAS CORPORATION—See Star Group, L.P.; *U.S. Public*, pg. 1938
STAR GROUP, L.P.; *U.S. Public*, pg. 1937
STARKVILLE LP GAS INC.—See Ergon, Inc.; *U.S. Private*, pg. 1418
STAR/PETRO, INC.—See Star Group, L.P.; *U.S. Public*, pg. 1938
STATEWOOD INCORPORATED; *U.S. Private*, pg. 3793
SUBURBAN PROPANE GROUP, INC.—See Suburban Propane Partners, L.P.; *U.S. Public*, pg. 1959
SUBURBAN PROPANE, L.P.—See Suburban Propane Partners, L.P.; *U.S. Public*, pg. 1959
SUBURBAN PROPANE PARTNERS, L.P.; *U.S. Public*, pg. 1958
SUPERIOR FUEL COMPANY; *U.S. Private*, pg. 3878
SUPREME ENERGY, INC.; *U.S. Private*, pg. 3882
SUPREME OIL COMPANY INC.; *U.S. Private*, pg. 3882
SWISS VALLEY OIL CO.—See Ullman Oil, Inc.; *U.S. Private*, pg. 4277
TENASKA BIOFUELS, LLC—See Tenaska, Inc.; *U.S. Private*, pg. 3965
THALER OIL COMPANY, INC.; *U.S. Private*, pg. 3979
THOELE INC.—See Warrenton Oil Co.; *U.S. Private*, pg. 4444
THOMAS GAS COMPANY—See UGI Corporation; *U.S. Public*, pg. 2222
TIMES OIL CORPORATION; *U.S. Private*, pg. 4172
TOPAZ ENERGY GROUP LIMITED—See Alimentation Couche-Tard Inc.; *Int'l*, pg. 328
TOWNSEND OIL CO. INC.; *U.S. Private*, pg. 4198
TRUAX CORPORATION; *U.S. Private*, pg. 4246
ULLMAN OIL, INC.; *U.S. Private*, pg. 4277
ULTRAMAR LTD.—See Valero Energy Corporation; *U.S. Public*, pg. 2272
UNITED PROPANE GAS COMPANIES INC.; *U.S. Private*, pg. 4296
UNITED PROPANE—See Suburban Propane Partners, L.P.; *U.S. Public*, pg. 1959
UNIVAR SOLUTIONS AS—See Apollo Global Management, Inc.; *U.S. Public*, pg. 166
UNIVAR SOLUTIONS DENMARK A/S—See Apollo Global Management, Inc.; *U.S. Public*, pg. 166
UNIVAR SOLUTIONS OY—See Apollo Global Management, Inc.; *U.S. Public*, pg. 166
UNIVERGAS ITALIA S.R.L.—See UGI Corporation; *U.S. Public*, pg. 2223
VALLEY PACIFIC PETROLEUM SERVICES, INC.; *U.S. Private*, pg. 4334
VETERANS OIL INC.; *U.S. Private*, pg. 4374
WAFI ENERGY CO.—See Asyad Holding Group; *Int'l*, pg. 664
WAVE SYNC CORP.; *U.S. Public*, pg. 2338
WAV WARME AUSTRIA VERTRIEBSGMBH—See BayWa AG; *Int'l*, pg. 919
WEVER PETROLEUM INC.; *U.S. Private*, pg. 4502
WFL (UK) LIMITED—See World Kinect Corporation; *U.S. Public*, pg. 2381
WISCONSIN RIVER CO-OP; *U.S. Private*, pg. 4549
WOODRUFF ENERGY; *U.S. Private*, pg. 4560
WORLD FUEL INTERNATIONAL S.R.L.—See World Kinect Corporation; *U.S. Public*, pg. 2381
WORLD FUEL SERVICES LTD.—See World Kinect Corporation; *U.S. Public*, pg. 2381
WORLD FUEL SERVICES MEXICO, S.A. DE C.V.—See World Kinect Corporation; *U.S. Public*, pg. 2381
WORLD FUEL SERVICES (SINGAPORE) PTE LTD—See World Kinect Corporation; *U.S. Public*, pg. 2381
WORLD FUEL SERVICES (SOUTH AFRICA) (PTY) LTD—See World Kinect Corporation; *U.S. Public*, pg. 2381
W.S. REICHENBACH & SON INC.; *U.S. Private*, pg. 4423
XERON, INC.—See Chesapeake Utilities Corporation; *U.S. Public*, pg. 486
YOUNGBLOOD OIL CO. INC.; *U.S. Private*, pg. 4593
YOUNG'S PROPANE—See UGI Corporation; *U.S. Public*, pg. 2222
YOUNICOS GMBH—See I Squared Capital Advisors (US) LLC; *U.S. Private*, pg. 2021

Z ENERGY LIMITED—See Ampol Limited; *Int'l*, pg. 437

458110 — CLOTHING AND CLOTHING ACCESSORIES RETAILERS

09WOMEN CO., LTD.; *Int'l*, pg. 1
1500 ROCKVILLE PIKE LLC—See Saul Centers, Inc.; *U.S. Public*, pg. 1842
18 MONTROSE RETAIL LIMITED—See Frasers Group plc; *Int'l*, pg. 2765
5.11, INC.—See Compass Diversified Holdings; *U.S. Public*, pg. 560
5.11 INTERNATIONAL A.B.—See Compass Diversified Holdings; *U.S. Public*, pg. 559
5.11 SOURCING, LIMITED—See Compass Diversified Holdings; *U.S. Public*, pg. 559
7NR RETAIL LIMITED; *Int'l*, pg. 15
7TH AVENUE SHOWCASE LTD—See The New York Look Inc.; *U.S. Private*, pg. 4083
ABERCROMBIE & FITCH CO.; *U.S. Public*, pg. 24
ABERCROMBIE & FITCH HOLDING CORP.—See Abercrombie & Fitch Co.; *U.S. Public*, pg. 25
ACNE CORP.—See Acne Studio AB; *Int'l*, pg. 107
ACQUI POLO ESPANA SL—See Ralph Lauren Corporation; *U.S. Public*, pg. 1761
ADDCN TECHNOLOGY CO., LTD.; *Int'l*, pg. 128
ADEN & ANAIS, INC—See Transom Capital Group, LLC; *U.S. Private*, pg. 4209
ADERANS HAIRGOODS, INC.—See Aderans Co., Ltd.; *Int'l*, pg. 143
ADIKA STYLE LTD.; *Int'l*, pg. 148
ADORABLE LINGERIE INC.; *Int'l*, pg. 152
A&D SPITZ (PTY) LIMITED—See AVI Limited; *Int'l*, pg. 740
AEFFE RETAIL S.P.A.—See Aeffe SpA; *Int'l*, pg. 173
AEO FOREIGN HOLD CO LLC—See American Eagle Outfitters, Inc.; *U.S. Public*, pg. 99
A&E STORES, INC.; *U.S. Private*, pg. 20
AFH AUSTRALIA PTY. LTD.—See Abercrombie & Fitch Co.; *U.S. Public*, pg. 25
AFH STORES UK LIMITED—See Abercrombie & Fitch Co.; *U.S. Public*, pg. 25
AGABANG & COMPANY; *Int'l*, pg. 199
A & G, INC.—See Gildan Activewear Inc.; *Int'l*, pg. 2973
AIJJ ENTERPRISES INC.; *U.S. Private*, pg. 132
ALBANY INTERNATIONAL JAPAN KABUSHIKI KAISHA—See Albany International Corp.; *U.S. Public*, pg. 72
AL DUCA D'AOSTA SPA; *Int'l*, pg. 276
ALEX & CO.—See Sun Capital Partners, Inc.; *U.S. Private*, pg. 3861
ALEXON INTERNATIONAL LIMITED—See Sun Capital Partners, Inc.; *U.S. Private*, pg. 3861
ALL SPORT COUTURE, LLC—See Lanco International Inc.; *U.S. Private*, pg. 2382
AL-RUBAIYAT COMPANY; *Int'l*, pg. 288
ALTERNATIVE APPAREL, INC.—See Hanesbrands Inc.; *U.S. Public*, pg. 982
ALWAYS FOR ME, LLC—See Waveland Investments, LLC; *U.S. Private*, pg. 4458
AMEREX GROUP—See Amerex Group, Inc.; *U.S. Private*, pg. 219
AMEREX LADIES—See Amerex Group, Inc.; *U.S. Private*, pg. 219
AMERICAN APPAREL CANADA RETAIL INC.—See American Apparel, Inc.; *U.S. Private*, pg. 222
AMERICAN APPAREL DEUTSCHLAND GMBH—See American Apparel, Inc.; *U.S. Private*, pg. 222
AMERICAN APPAREL (UK) LIMITED—See American Apparel, Inc.; *U.S. Private*, pg. 222
AMERICAN EAGLE OUTFITTERS DUTCH OP CO B.V.—See American Eagle Outfitters, Inc.; *U.S. Public*, pg. 99
AMERICAN EAGLE OUTFITTERS, INC.; *U.S. Public*, pg. 98
AMERICAN GOLF LTD.—See Sun Capital Partners, Inc.; *U.S. Private*, pg. 3861
AMS FULFILLMENT , INC.; *U.S. Private*, pg. 266
ANAP INC.; *Int'l*, pg. 447
ANN HARVEY DIVISION—See Sun Capital Partners, Inc.; *U.S. Private*, pg. 3861
ANNIL CO., LTD.; *Int'l*, pg. 474
ANNTAYLOR, INC.—See Sycamore Partners Management, LP; *U.S. Private*, pg. 3895
ANNTAYLOR RETAIL, INC.—See Sycamore Partners Management, LP; *U.S. Private*, pg. 3895
ANTHONY'S INC.; *U.S. Private*, pg. 288
ANTHROPOLOGIE, INC.—See Urban Outfitters, Inc.; *U.S. Public*, pg. 2265
APG & CO., PTY. LTD.; *Int'l*, pg. 512
APPLESEED'S, INC.—See Bluestem Brands, Inc.; *U.S. Private*, pg. 598
APRICA (SHANGHAI) TRADING CO., LTD.—See Newell Brands Inc.; *U.S. Public*, pg. 1513
ARAMARK UNIFORM & CAREER—See Vestis Corp; *U.S. Public*, pg. 2290
ARCADIA GROUP LIMITED; *Int'l*, pg. 540
AREZZO INDUSTRIA E COMERCIO S.A.; *Int'l*, pg. 560

N.A.I.C.S. INDEX

458110 — CLOTHING AND CLOTHI...

ARITZIA LP—See Aritzia, Inc.; *Int'l*, pg. 567
ARMY & NAVY DEPARTMENT STORES LIMITED; *Int'l*, pg. 575
ARTISTMSS INTERNATIONAL GROUP, INC.; *U.S. Public*, pg. 208
ASHLEY STEWART, INC.—See The Invus Group, LLC; *U.S. Private*, pg. 4057
ASTOR & BLACK CUSTOM CLOTHIERS, LTD.; *U.S. Private*, pg. 360
ATALLAH GROUP, INC.; *Int'l*, pg. 666
AT B.V.—See Excellent Retail Brands B.V.; *Int'l*, pg. 2578
ATHLEISURE INC.; *U.S. Private*, pg. 368
AULD PHILLIPS LTD.; *Int'l*, pg. 704
AUSTIN REED LIMITED—See Alteri Partners LLP; *Int'l*, pg. 391
AVENUE STORES, LLC—See Independence Capital Partners, LLC; *U.S. Private*, pg. 2057
AZAZIE, INC.; *U.S. Private*, pg. 415
AZULIS CAPITAL; *Int'l*, pg. 781
BABYHAVEN.COM INC.; *U.S. Private*, pg. 422
BACHRACH CLOTHING, INC.—See Sun Capital Partners, Inc.; *U.S. Private*, pg. 3858
BALLET MAKERS AUSTRALIA PTY LTD—See Capezio Ballet Makers Inc.; *U.S. Private*, pg. 738
BALLET MAKERS EUROPE LTD—See Capezio Ballet Makers Inc.; *U.S. Private*, pg. 738
BALL GROUP NORGE AS—See Axcel Management A/S; *Int'l*, pg. 762
BALL GROUP SVERIGE AB—See Axcel Management A/S; *Int'l*, pg. 762
BALL WHOLESALE APS—See Axcel Management A/S; *Int'l*, pg. 762
BANANA REPUBLIC—See The Gap, Inc.; *U.S. Public*, pg. 2074
BANANA REPUBLIC—See The Gap, Inc.; *U.S. Public*, pg. 2074
BARDOT PTY. LTD.; *Int'l*, pg. 864
BAROQUE JAPAN LIMITED; *Int'l*, pg. 867
BASEBALLISM, INC.; *U.S. Private*, pg. 484
BASIC VILLAGE S.P.A.—See BasicNet S.p.A.; *Int'l*, pg. 886
BATH & BODY WORKS, INC.; *U.S. Public*, pg. 279
B&B DEPARTMENT STORES SOUTH; *U.S. Private*, pg. 417
BCBG MAX AZRIA GROUP, INC.; *U.S. Private*, pg. 499
THE BEACH HOUSE SWIMWEAR, INC.; *U.S. Private*, pg. 3992
BEALL'S OUTLET INC.—See Beall's, Inc.; *U.S. Private*, pg. 505
THE BEAUFORT BONNET COMPANY, LLC—See Oxford Industries, Inc.; *U.S. Public*, pg. 1629
BEBE STORES, INC.—See B. Riley Financial, Inc.; *U.S. Public*, pg. 262
BELFEIN SLOVAKIA A.S.—See Hanesbrands Inc.; *U.S. Public*, pg. 982
BELLINDA CESKA REPUBLIKA, S.R.O.—See Hanesbrands Inc.; *U.S. Public*, pg. 982
BELLINDA HUNGARIA KFT.—See Hanesbrands Inc.; *U.S. Public*, pg. 982
BELLINDA SLOVENSKO S.R.O.—See Hanesbrands Inc.; *U.S. Public*, pg. 982
BEMIDJI WOOLEN MILLS; *U.S. Private*, pg. 522
BENDON LIMITED; *Int'l*, pg. 972
BENDON USA INC.—See Bendon Limited; *Int'l*, pg. 972
BENETTON ASIA PACIFIC LTD.—See Edizione S.r.l.; *Int'l*, pg. 2311
BERGDORF GOODMAN, INC.—See Ares Management Corporation; *U.S. Public*, pg. 190
BERGDORF GOODMAN, INC.—See Canada Pension Plan Investment Board; *Int'l*, pg. 1281
BERMO ENTERPRISES INC.; *U.S. Private*, pg. 535
BERNINI INC.; *U.S. Private*, pg. 537
BESTSELLER A/S; *Int'l*, pg. 1000
BEST UNIFORMS, LLC—See Charlesbank Capital Partners, LLC; *U.S. Private*, pg. 855
BEVERLY HILLS SHOE INC.; *U.S. Private*, pg. 547
BEZIERS POLYGONE SARL—See Guess? Inc.; *U.S. Public*, pg. 974
BHLDN LLC—See Urban Outfitters, Inc.; *U.S. Public*, pg. 2265
BIG BEAR STORES INC.; *U.S. Private*, pg. 552
BIG BUDDHA, INC.—See Steven Madden, Ltd.; *U.S. Public*, pg. 1947
BIG M, INC.; *U.S. Private*, pg. 553
BIOWORLD MERCHANDISING, INC.; *U.S. Private*, pg. 563
B.J. VINES INC.; *U.S. Private*, pg. 420
BKV TELLOS, INC.; *U.S. Private*, pg. 569
BLACKCRAFT CULT, INC.; *U.S. Private*, pg. 573
BLAIR, LLC—See Bluestem Brands, Inc.; *U.S. Private*, pg. 598
BLUEFLY, INC.—See Clearlake Capital Group, L.P.; *U.S. Private*, pg. 933
BLUE INC; *Int'l*, pg. 1068
BLUE SKY SCRUBS LLC; *U.S. Private*, pg. 590
BLUESTAR EXCHANGE LIMITED—See Giordano International Limited; *Int'l*, pg. 2977
BLUE TOMATO DEUTSCHLAND GMBH—See Zumiez Incorporated; *U.S. Public*, pg. 2411
BLUE TOMATO NETHERLANDS B.V.—See Zumiez Incorporated; *U.S. Public*, pg. 2411
B. MOSS CLOTHING COMPANY LTD.; *U.S. Private*, pg. 419
BOB MICKLER'S, INC.—See Timberfence Capital Partners, LLC; *U.S. Private*, pg. 4171
BOB'S STORES, LLC—See GoDigital Media Group, LLC; *U.S. Private*, pg. 1724
BODY ART AUSTRALIA PTY LIMITED—See PVH Corp.; *U.S. Public*, pg. 1739
BODY CENTRAL STORES, INC.—See WestView Capital Partners, L.P.; *U.S. Private*, pg. 4501
BODY GLOVE(M) SDN. BHD.—See BGT Corporation Public Company Limited; *Int'l*, pg. 1009
BODY SHOP OF AMERICA, INC.—See WestView Capital Partners, L.P.; *U.S. Private*, pg. 4501
BOHME; *U.S. Private*, pg. 609
BON FAME CO., LTD.; *Int'l*, pg. 1105
BONMARCHE HOLDINGS PLC; *Int'l*, pg. 1107
BONWORTH INC.; *U.S. Private*, pg. 615
BOOT BARN, INC.—See Boot Barn Holdings, Inc.; *U.S. Public*, pg. 368
BOOZT AB; *Int'l*, pg. 1111
BORA BORA INC.; *U.S. Private*, pg. 617
BOSTON PROPER LLC—See Brentwood Associates; *U.S. Private*, pg. 645
BOUTIQUE FITNESS, LLC—See Town Sports International Holdings, Inc.; *U.S. Private*, pg. 4197
BOUTIQUE JACOB INC.; *Int'l*, pg. 1121
BOUTIQUE LA VIE EN ROSE, INC.; *Int'l*, pg. 1121
BOUTIQUES, INC.; *Int'l*, pg. 1121
BOUTIQUE TERE, INC.; *U.S. Private*, pg. 624
BOYDS MEN'S STORE; *U.S. Private*, pg. 628
BRANCO ENTERPRISES INC.; *U.S. Private*, pg. 635
BRANDALLEY UK LIMITED; *Int'l*, pg. 1139
BRANDHOUSE RETAILS LTD; *Int'l*, pg. 1139
BRA SMYTH OF CALIFORNIA, INC.; *U.S. Private*, pg. 630
BRAS N THINGS PTY. LIMITED—See Hanesbrands Inc.; *U.S. Public*, pg. 982
BRAVADA INTERNATIONAL, LTD.; *Int'l*, pg. 380
BRAVE NEW WORLD; *U.S. Private*, pg. 641
BRAWN OF CALIFORNIA, INC.—See Chelsey Direct, LLC; *U.S. Private*, pg. 870
BRIGITTE FRANCE; *Int'l*, pg. 1163
BRIXTON USA CORPORATION—See Brixton Metals Corporation; *Int'l*, pg. 1171
BRODEUR CARVELL INC.; *U.S. Private*, pg. 661
BROOKS BROTHERS, INC.; *U.S. Private*, pg. 664
BROTHERS & SISTERS SVERIGE AB—See Coala-Life Group AB; *Int'l*, pg. 1680
THE BUCKLE, INC.; *U.S. Public*, pg. 2043
BUFFALO DAVID BITTON; *Int'l*, pg. 1211
BUMCITY SDN. BHD.—See Asia Brands Berhad; *Int'l*, pg. 610
BURBERRY GROUP PLC; *Int'l*, pg. 1220
BURBERRY LIMITED—See Burberry Group plc; *Int'l*, pg. 1220
BURBERRY (SHANGHAI) TRADING CO., LTD.—See Burberry Group plc; *Int'l*, pg. 1220
BUY BUY BABY, INC.—See 20230930-DK-Butterfly-1, Inc.; *U.S. Public*, pg. 5
C&A BELGIE COMM. V.—See COFRA Holding AG; *Int'l*, pg. 1694
CABIN CO., LTD.—See Fast Retailing Co., Ltd.; *Int'l*, pg. 2621
C&A (CHINA) CO., LTD.—See COFRA Holding AG; *Int'l*, pg. 1694
C&A - EUROPE HEAD OFFICE—See COFRA Holding AG; *Int'l*, pg. 1694
CALYPSO ST. BARTH INC.; *U.S. Private*, pg. 725
C&A MEXICO S. DE R.L.—See COFRA Holding AG; *Int'l*, pg. 1694
C&A MODAS S.A.; *Int'l*, pg. 1238
C&A MODA TRGOVINA D.O.O.—See COFRA Holding AG; *Int'l*, pg. 1694
C&A MODE AG—See COFRA Holding AG; *Int'l*, pg. 1694
C&A MODE GMBH & CO. KG—See COFRA Holding AG; *Int'l*, pg. 1694
C&A MODE S.A.—See COFRA Holding AG; *Int'l*, pg. 1694
CANTABIL RETAIL INDIA LIMITED; *Int'l*, pg. 1299
C&A POLSKA SP.Z.O.O.—See COFRA Holding AG; *Int'l*, pg. 1694
CARILOHA—See Pedersen Worldwide; *U.S. Private*, pg. 3128
CAROLINA FASHIONS INC.—See Rubie's Costume Company Inc.; *U.S. Private*, pg. 3500
CASALAGO CO., LTD.—See Credit Saison Co., Ltd.; *Int'l*, pg. 1836
CASUAL MALE DIRECT, LLC—See Destination XL Group, Inc.; *U.S. Public*, pg. 656
CASUAL MALE RBT, LLC—See Destination XL Group, Inc.; *U.S. Public*, pg. 656
CASUAL MALE RETAIL STORE, LLC—See Destination XL Group, Inc.; *U.S. Public*, pg. 656
CASUAL MALE STORE, LLC—See Destination XL Group, Inc.; *U.S. Public*, pg. 656
CATHERINES STORES CORPORATION—See Mahwah Bergen Retail Group, Inc.; *U.S. Private*, pg. 2550
CATOCORP.COM, LLC—See The Cato Corporation; *U.S. Public*, pg. 2058
THE CATO CORPORATION; *U.S. Public*, pg. 2057
CATO OF TEXAS L.P.—See The Cato Corporation; *U.S. Public*, pg. 2058
CATO SOUTHWEST, INC.—See The Cato Corporation; *U.S. Public*, pg. 2058
CAVE SPRINGS, INC.—See Destination Maternity Corporation; *U.S. Public*, pg. 656
CBL FAYETTE HOTEL MEMBER, LLC—See CBL & Associates Properties, Inc.; *U.S. Public*, pg. 458
CENOMI RETAIL; *Int'l*, pg. 1401
CETTIRE LIMITED; *Int'l*, pg. 1424
CHARMING CHARLIE USA CORP.; *U.S. Private*, pg. 858
CHARMING SHOPPES, INC.—See Mahwah Bergen Retail Group, Inc.; *U.S. Private*, pg. 2550
CHELSEA GROUP—See Simon Property Group, Inc.; *U.S. Public*, pg. 1881
CHELSEA & SCOTT, LTD.; *U.S. Private*, pg. 870
CHICK'S SPORTING GOODS INC.—See Dick's Sporting Goods, Inc.; *U.S. Public*, pg. 659
CHICO'S DISTRIBUTION SERVICES, LLC—See Sycamore Partners Management, LP; *U.S. Private*, pg. 3895
CHICO'S RETAIL SERVICES, INC.—See Sycamore Partners Management, LP; *U.S. Private*, pg. 3895
THE CHILDREN'S PLACE (CANADA), LP—See The Children's Place, Inc.; *U.S. Public*, pg. 2059
THE CHILDRENS PLACE (CANADA), LP—See The Children's Place, Inc.; *U.S. Public*, pg. 2059
THE CHILDREN'S PLACE (HONG KONG) LIMITED—See The Children's Place, Inc.; *U.S. Public*, pg. 2059
THE CHILDREN'S PLACE, INC.; *U.S. Public*, pg. 2059
THE CHILDREN'S PLACE (VIRGINIA), LLC—See The Children's Place, Inc.; *U.S. Public*, pg. 2059
CHINA VTV LIMITED; *Int'l*, pg. 1562
CHORI MODA CO., LTD.—See Chori Co., Ltd.; *Int'l*, pg. 1583
CHRISTOPHER & BANKS CORPORATION; *U.S. Public*, pg. 490
CHW LLC—See The Cato Corporation; *U.S. Public*, pg. 2058
CID RESOURCES, INC.—See Superior Group Of Companies, Inc.; *U.S. Public*, pg. 1966
CISALFA SPORT S.P.A.; *Int'l*, pg. 1618
CITI TRENDS INC.; *U.S. Public*, pg. 501
CITIZENS OF HUMANITY LLC—See Berkshire Partners LLC; *U.S. Private*, pg. 534
CITY BLUE INC.; *U.S. Private*, pg. 905
CITY CHIC COLLECTIVE LIMITED; *Int'l*, pg. 1626
CITY SPORTS—See Highland Capital Partners, LLC; *U.S. Private*, pg. 1938
CLAIRE'S BOUTIQUES, INC.—See Apollo Global Management, Inc.; *U.S. Public*, pg. 148
CLAIRE'S STORES, INC.—See Apollo Global Management, Inc.; *U.S. Public*, pg. 148
CLEAN ONES CORPORATION—See Bradshaw International, Inc.; *U.S. Private*, pg. 633
CLUB MONACO CORP.—See Ralph Lauren Corporation; *U.S. Public*, pg. 1761
CLUB MONACO INC.—See Ralph Lauren Corporation; *U.S. Public*, pg. 1761
CLUB MONACO U.S., LLC—See Ralph Lauren Corporation; *U.S. Public*, pg. 1761
CMJ ENTERPRISES INC.; *U.S. Private*, pg. 951
CMRG APPAREL, LLC—See Destination XL Group, Inc.; *U.S. Public*, pg. 656
COBALT SPORTSWEAR, LLC—See Malibu Boats, Inc.; *U.S. Public*, pg. 1355
COLETTE; *Int'l*, pg. 1698
COLIN'S BELARUS—See Eroglu Holding AS; *Int'l*, pg. 2496
COLIN'S RUSSIA—See Eroglu Holding AS; *Int'l*, pg. 2496
COLIN'S UKRAINE—See Eroglu Holding AS; *Int'l*, pg. 2496
COLLECTION CONRAD C; *Int'l*, pg. 1699
COLOR INC.; *U.S. Private*, pg. 972
COMBI KOREA CO., LTD.—See Combi Corporation; *Int'l*, pg. 1708
THE COMET CLOTHING COMPANY, LLC—See Kynetic LLC; *U.S. Private*, pg. 2360
COMMEND (H.K.) LTD.—See Collins Co., Ltd.; *Int'l*, pg. 1702
CREDO BRANDS MARKETING LIMITED; *Int'l*, pg. 1837
CRITICALTOOL INC.; *U.S. Private*, pg. 1102
CROCS STORES IRELAND—See Crocs, Inc.; *U.S. Public*, pg. 595
THE CRYPTO COMPANY; *U.S. Public*, pg. 2066
C'S MEN CO., LTD.; *Int'l*, pg. 1239
CUFFY CO. INCORPORATED; *U.S. Private*, pg. 1120
CWDKIDS INC.; *U.S. Private*, pg. 1132
DAI HOLDING, LLC; *U.S. Private*, pg. 1145
DASH DIVISION—See Sun Capital Partners, Inc.; *U.S. Private*, pg. 3861
DAVID & GOLIATH, INC.; *U.S. Private*, pg. 1169
DAVID'S BRIDAL, LLC—See CION Investment Corporation; *U.S. Public*, pg. 496
DAZZLE FASHION CO., LTD.; *Int'l*, pg. 1985
DBA BODYWEAR GERMANY GMBH—See Hanesbrands Inc.; *U.S. Public*, pg. 982
DBAPPAREL ITALIA SRL—See Hanesbrands Inc.; *U.S. Public*, pg. 982

458110 — CLOTHING AND CLOTHI...

DBAPPAREL SOUTH AFRICA (PTY) LIMITED—See Hanesbrands Inc.; *U.S. Public*, pg. 982
DBAPPAREL UK LTD—See Hanesbrands Inc.; *U.S. Public*, pg. 982
DBI HOLDINGS, INC.—See Mahwah Bergen Retail Group, Inc.; *U.S. Private*, pg. 2550
DEBENHAMS PLC; *Int'l*, pg. 1998
DEB SHOPS, INC.—See Lee Equity Partners LLC; *U.S. Private*, pg. 2412
DEFACTO OZON GIYIM SANAYI VE TICARET A.S.; *Int'l*, pg. 2004
DELTA MARKETING INC.; *U.S. Private*, pg. 1201
DEREK LAM INTERNATIONAL, LLC—See Public Clothing Company Inc.; *U.S. Private*, pg. 3298
DESTINATION XL GROUP, INC.; *U.S. Public*, pg. 656
DIESEL MARKETING SDN. BHD.—See Asia Brands Berhad; *Int'l*, pg. 610
DIESEL SPA; *Int'l*, pg. 2116
DIGITAL BRANDS GROUP, INC.; *U.S. Public*, pg. 662
DIM PORTUGAL - IMPORTACAO E COMERCIALIZACAO, LDA.—See Hanesbrands Inc.; *U.S. Public*, pg. 982
DISCOUNT DANCE SUPPLY; *U.S. Private*, pg. 1237
DISORDERLY KIDS, LLC; *U.S. Private*, pg. 1238
DIZZ FINANCE PLC; *Int'l*, pg. 2138
DK COMPANY A/S; *Int'l*, pg. 2138
DOCKERS BRAND—See Levi Strauss & Co.; *U.S. Public*, pg. 1308
THE DONNA KARAN COMPANY LLC—See G-III Apparel Group, Ltd.; *U.S. Public*, pg. 894
DONNA KARAN INTERNATIONAL INC.—See G-III Apparel Group, Ltd.; *U.S. Public*, pg. 893
DONNA KARAN (ITALY) SRL—See G-III Apparel Group, Ltd.; *U.S. Public*, pg. 893
DONNA KARAN SERVICE COMPANY BV—See G-III Apparel Group, Ltd.; *U.S. Public*, pg. 893
DOTS, INC.—See Irving Place Capital Management, L.P.; *U.S. Private*, pg. 2141
DRAPERS & DAMONS, LLC—See Bluestem Brands, Inc.; *U.S. Private*, pg. 598
DREAM VISION CO., LTD.; *Int'l*, pg. 2203
DRI ENTERPRISES LTD.; *U.S. Private*, pg. 1277
DR. JAY'S INC.; *U.S. Private*, pg. 1271
DRYSDALES INC.—See Boot Barn Holdings, Inc.; *U.S. Public*, pg. 368
DUFRY SHOP FINANCE LIMITED SRL.—See Avolta AG; *Int'l*, pg. 749
DULUTH HOLDINGS INC.; *U.S. Public*, pg. 691
DU PAREIL AU MEME SA; *Int'l*, pg. 2217
DYENOMITE, LLC; *U.S. Private*, pg. 1296
EAGLE CREEK EUROPE, LTD.—See V. F. Corporation; *U.S. Public*, pg. 2268
EASY PICKINS INC.; *U.S. Private*, pg. 1323
EBAY SINGAPORE SERVICES PRIVATE LIMITED—See eBay Inc.; *U.S. Public*, pg. 709
EBLENS LP—See Prospect Hill Growth Partners, L.P.; *U.S. Private*, pg. 3288
EDCON LIMITED—See Edcon Holdings Limited; *Int'l*, pg. 2304
EDELIGHT GMBH—See Hubert Burda Media Holding Kommanditgesellschaft; *Int'l*, pg. 3520
EDGARS STORES LIMITED; *Int'l*, pg. 2308
ED MITCHELL INC.; *U.S. Private*, pg. 1331
EDRIVING, LLC—See Vista Equity Partners, LLC; *U.S. Private*, pg. 4401
EDUCATIONAL OUTFITTERS, LLC; *U.S. Private*, pg. 1339
E-LAND FASHION CHINA HOLDINGS, LIMITED—See E-Land World Ltd.; *Int'l*, pg. 2248
EMBRY HOLDINGS LIMITED; *Int'l*, pg. 2376
EMICO MELAKA SDN. BHD.—See Emico Holdings Berhad; *Int'l*, pg. 2380
ERICA TANOV INC.; *U.S. Private*, pg. 1419
ERNSTING'S FAMILY GMBH & CO. KG; *Int'l*, pg. 2496
EROGLU GIYIM SAN. TIC. INC. - AKSARAY FACTORY—See Eroglu Holding AS; *Int'l*, pg. 2496
EROGLU GIYIM SAN. TIC. INC. - CORLU FACTORY—See Eroglu Holding AS; *Int'l*, pg. 2496
EROGLU GIYIM SAN. TIC. INC. - EGYPT FACTORY—See Eroglu Holding AS; *Int'l*, pg. 2496
ESKANDAR LTD.; *Int'l*, pg. 2503
ESP CLOTHING FINLAND OY—See Esprit Holdings Limited; *Int'l*, pg. 2506
ESPRIT ASIA (DISTRIBUTION) LIMITED—See Esprit Holdings Limited; *Int'l*, pg. 2507
ESPRIT BELGIE RETAIL N.V.—See Esprit Holdings Limited; *Int'l*, pg. 2507
ESPRIT CANADA WHOLESALE INC.—See Esprit Holdings Limited; *Int'l*, pg. 2507
ESPRIT CARD SERVICES GMBH—See Esprit Holdings Limited; *Int'l*, pg. 2507
ESPRIT DE CORP DANMARK A/S—See Esprit Holdings Limited; *Int'l*, pg. 2507
ESPRIT DE CORP (FAR EAST) LIMITED—See Esprit Holdings Limited; *Int'l*, pg. 2507
ESPRIT DE CORP FRANCE S.A.S.—See Esprit Holdings Limited; *Int'l*, pg. 2507
ESPRIT DE CORP. (SPAIN) S.L.—See Esprit Holdings Limited; *Int'l*, pg. 2507
ESPRIT DESIGN & PRODUCT DEVELOPMENT GMBH—See Esprit Holdings Limited; *Int'l*, pg. 2507
ESPRIT EUROPE B.V.—See Esprit Holdings Limited; *Int'l*, pg. 2507
ESPRIT GB LIMITED—See Esprit Holdings Limited; *Int'l*, pg. 2507
ESPRIT HANDELSGESELLSCHAFT MBH.—See Esprit Holdings Limited; *Int'l*, pg. 2507
ESPRIT (HONG KONG) LIMITED—See Esprit Holdings Limited; *Int'l*, pg. 2507
ESPRIT LUXEMBOURG S.A.R.L.—See Esprit Holdings Limited; *Int'l*, pg. 2507
ESPRIT MACAO COMMERCIAL OFFSHORE LIMITED—See Esprit Holdings Limited; *Int'l*, pg. 2507
ESPRIT REGIONAL SERVICES LIMITED—See Esprit Holdings Limited; *Int'l*, pg. 2507
ESPRIT RETAIL B.V. & CO. KG.—See Esprit Holdings Limited; *Int'l*, pg. 2507
ESPRIT RETAIL PTE. LTD.—See Esprit Holdings Limited; *Int'l*, pg. 2507
ESPRIT SWITZERLAND RETAIL AG—See Esprit Holdings Limited; *Int'l*, pg. 2507
ESPRIT US ONLINE SHOP LIMITED—See Esprit Holdings Limited; *Int'l*, pg. 2507
ESTNATION INC.; *Int'l*, pg. 2518
ETABLISSEMENTEN VAN MOER N.V.—See V. F. Corporation; *U.S. Public*, pg. 2268
ETAM ITALIA SRL—See Etam Developpement SCA; *Int'l*, pg. 2520
EVELYN & ARTHUR INC.; *U.S. Private*, pg. 1436
EVERGREEN INTERNATIONAL HOLDINGS LIMITED; *Int'l*, pg. 2565
EXPRESS FASHION OPERATIONS, LLC—See WHP Global; *U.S. Private*, pg. 4515
EXPRESS, INC.—See WHP Global; *U.S. Private*, pg. 4515
EXPRESS TOPCO LLC—See WHP Global; *U.S. Private*, pg. 4515
EZIBUY LTD.—See Alceon Group Pty Ltd; *Int'l*, pg. 300
FABRIC RETAIL GLBL AB—See H&M Hennes & Mauritz AB; *Int'l*, pg. 3192
FABRIC SALES A/S—See H&M Hennes & Mauritz AB; *Int'l*, pg. 3192
FABRIC SALES NORWAY AS—See H&M Hennes & Mauritz AB; *Int'l*, pg. 3192
FACTORY CONNECTION, LLC; *U.S. Private*, pg. 1460
FACTORY OUTLET S.A.—See Folli Follie S.A.; *Int'l*, pg. 2721
FACTORY STORE S.P.A.—See Giorgio Armani S.p.A.; *Int'l*, pg. 2978
FAMOUS HORSE INC.; *U.S. Private*, pg. 1472
FANATICS, INC.—See Kynetic LLC; *U.S. Private*, pg. 2360
FARFETCH LIMITED—See Coupang, Inc.; *Int'l*, pg. 1819
FARFETCH LIMITED—See Greenoaks Capital Partners LLC; *U.S. Private*, pg. 1779
FARFETCH PORTUGAL - UNIPESSOAL, LDA—See Coupang, Inc.; *Int'l*, pg. 1819
FARFETCH PORTUGAL - UNIPESSOAL, LDA—See Greenoaks Capital Partners LLC; *U.S. Private*, pg. 1779
FASHION B AIR S.A.; *Int'l*, pg. 2620
FASHION OUTLETS OF CHICAGO LLC—See The Macerich Company; *U.S. Public*, pg. 2109
FASHION SHOP OF KENTUCKY INC.; *U.S. Private*, pg. 1481
FASHION TO FIGURE, LLC—See RTW Retailwinds, Inc.; *U.S. Public*, pg. 1820
FAST RETAILING USA, INC.—See Fast Retailing Co.; *Int'l*, pg. 2621
FB DISTRO, INC.—See Mahwah Bergen Retail Group, Inc.; *U.S. Private*, pg. 2550
FELISSIMO CORPORATION; *Int'l*, pg. 2632
FENIX OUTDOOR AB—See Fenix Outdoor International AG; *Int'l*, pg. 2634
FENIX OUTDOOR AUSTRIA ITALY GMBH—See Fenix Outdoor International AG; *Int'l*, pg. 2634
FENIX OUTDOOR DANMARK APS—See Fenix Outdoor International AG; *Int'l*, pg. 2634
FENIX OUTDOOR FINLAND OY—See Fenix Outdoor International AG; *Int'l*, pg. 2634
FENIX OUTDOOR LOGISTICS B.V.—See Fenix Outdoor International AG; *Int'l*, pg. 2634
FENIX OUTDOOR LOGISTICS GMBH—See Fenix Outdoor International AG; *Int'l*, pg. 2634
FENIX OUTDOOR NORGE A/S—See Fenix Outdoor International AG; *Int'l*, pg. 2634
FENIX OUTDOOR S.R.O—See Fenix Outdoor International AG; *Int'l*, pg. 2634
FERAUD SARL; *Int'l*, pg. 2635
FILA HOLDINGS CORPORATION; *Int'l*, pg. 2662
FJALLRAVEN GMBH—See Fenix Outdoor International AG; *Int'l*, pg. 2634
FJALLRAVEN INTERNATIONAL AB—See Fenix Outdoor International AG; *Int'l*, pg. 2634
FJALLRAVEN USA LLC—See Fenix Outdoor International AG; *Int'l*, pg. 2634
F J BENJAMIN CONCEPTS PTE LTD—See FJ Benjamin Holdings Ltd.; *Int'l*, pg. 2697
F J BENJAMIN FASHIONS (U.S.) INC—See FJ Benjamin Holdings Ltd.; *Int'l*, pg. 2697
F J BENJAMIN LIFESTYLE SDN. BHD—See FJ Benjamin Holdings Ltd.; *Int'l*, pg. 2697
F J BENJAMIN LUXURY TIMEPIECES SDN. BHD—See FJ Benjamin Holdings Ltd.; *Int'l*, pg. 2697
F J BENJAMIN (SINGAPORE) PTE LTD—See FJ Benjamin Holdings Ltd.; *Int'l*, pg. 2697
F J BENJAMIN (TAIWAN) LTD—See FJ Benjamin Holdings Ltd.; *Int'l*, pg. 2697
FLEXFIT, LLC; *U.S. Private*, pg. 1544
FLYNN & O'HARA UNIFORMS INC.; *U.S. Private*, pg. 1553
FOOTLOCKER.COM, INC.—See Foot Locker, Inc.; *U.S. Public*, pg. 863
FOOT LOCKER SPECIALTY, INC.—See Foot Locker, Inc.; *U.S. Public*, pg. 863
FOREVER 21, INC.—See Brookfield Corporation; *Int'l*, pg. 1186
FOREVER 21, INC.—See Leonard Green & Partners, L.P.; *U.S. Private*, pg. 2424
FOREVER 21, INC.—See Simon Property Group, Inc.; *U.S. Public*, pg. 1881
FORMAN MILLS, INC.—See Cohesive Capital Partners; *U.S. Private*, pg. 963
FORMAN MILLS, INC.—See Goode Partners, LLC; *U.S. Private*, pg. 1739
FORT INC.; *U.S. Private*, pg. 1574
FORWARD BY ELYSE WALKER, LLC—See Revolve Group, Inc.; *U.S. Public*, pg. 1793
FOUR MARKETING LTD.; *Int'l*, pg. 2755
FRANCESCA'S COLLECTIONS, INC.—See TerraMar Capital LLC; *U.S. Private*, pg. 3971
FREEPEOPLE.COM LLC—See Urban Outfitters, Inc.; *U.S. Public*, pg. 2265
FRENCH CONNECTION GROUP, INC.—See French Connection Group plc; *Int'l*, pg. 2772
FRENCH CONNECTION (LONDON) LIMITED—See French Connection Group plc; *Int'l*, pg. 2772
FROGGER, LLC; *U.S. Private*, pg. 1613
FRUGAL FANNIE'S FASHION WAREHOUSE—See Retail Therapy LLC; *U.S. Private*, pg. 3411
FUJIKYU CORPORATION; *Int'l*, pg. 2829
FULLBEAUTY BRANDS, INC.—See Charlesbank Capital Partners, LLC; *U.S. Private*, pg. 855
FULLBEAUTY BRANDS, INC.—See Webster Equity Partners, LLC; *U.S. Private*, pg. 4467
FULLBEAUTY BRANDS, L.P.—See Charlesbank Capital Partners, LLC; *U.S. Private*, pg. 855
FULLBEAUTY BRANDS, L.P.—See Webster Equity Partners, LLC; *U.S. Private*, pg. 4467
FULLBEAUTY.COM—See Charlesbank Capital Partners, LLC; *U.S. Private*, pg. 855
FULLBEAUTY.COM—See Webster Equity Partners, LLC; *U.S. Private*, pg. 4467
FULLSUN INTERNATIONAL HOLDINGS GROUP CO., LIMITED; *Int'l*, pg. 2843
FUTURE LIFESTYLE FASHIONS LIMITED—See Future Corporate Resources Limited; *Int'l*, pg. 2853
FUZZIBUNZ LLC; *U.S. Private*, pg. 1627
GABRIEL BROTHERS, INC.—See Warburg Pincus LLC; *U.S. Private*, pg. 4438
GANT USA CORPORATION; *U.S. Private*, pg. 1641
GAP CANADA, INC.—See The Gap, Inc.; *U.S. Public*, pg. 2074
THE GAP, INC.; *U.S. Public*, pg. 2074
GAP INTERNATIONAL SOURCING LIMITED—See The Gap, Inc.; *U.S. Public*, pg. 2074
THE GAP—See The Gap, Inc.; *U.S. Public*, pg. 2074
GAP (UK HOLDINGS) LIMITED—See The Gap, Inc.; *U.S. Public*, pg. 2074
GARNET HILL, INC.—See Qurate Retail, Inc.; *U.S. Public*, pg. 1758
GARY'S & COMPANY NEWPORT BEACH; *U.S. Private*, pg. 1647
GAZAL CLOTHING COMPANY PTY LIMITED—See PVH Corp.; *U.S. Public*, pg. 1739
GAZAL (NZ) LIMITED—See PVH Corp.; *U.S. Public*, pg. 1739
GENC MAGAZALARI A.S.—See Fiba Holding A.S.; *Int'l*, pg. 2651
THE GENUINE CANADIAN CORP—See Carter's, Inc.; *U.S. Public*, pg. 445
GEORGETTE'S FASHIONS, INC.; *U.S. Private*, pg. 1684
GERRY WEBER BELGIEN GMBH—See GERRY WEBER International AG; *Int'l*, pg. 2944
GERRY WEBER FAR EAST LIMITED—See GERRY WEBER International AG; *Int'l*, pg. 2944
GERRY WEBER NORGE AS—See GERRY WEBER International AG; *Int'l*, pg. 2944
GERRY WEBER RETAIL GMBH—See GERRY WEBER International AG; *Int'l*, pg. 2944
GETZS, INC.; *U.S. Private*, pg. 1689
GILL NORTH AMERICA, LTD.—See POP Capital LLC; *U.S. Private*, pg. 3228
GILLY HICKS LLC—See Abercrombie & Fitch Co.; *U.S. Public*, pg. 25
GIORDANO (AUSTRALIA) PTY. LIMITED—See Giordano International Limited; *Int'l*, pg. 2977
GIORDANO FASHIONS (INDIA) PRIVATE LIMITED—See Giordano International Limited; *Int'l*, pg. 2977
GIORDANO INTERNATIONAL LIMITED; *Int'l*, pg. 2977

N.A.I.C.S. INDEX

458110 — CLOTHING AND CLOTHI...

GIORGIO ARMANI FRANCE SARL—See Giorgio Armani S.p.A.; *Int'l*, pg. 2978
GLASSONS LIMITED—See Hallenstein Glasson Holdings Limited; *Int'l*, pg. 3230
G. & L. CLOTHING, INC.—See Boot Barn Holdings, Inc.; *U.S. Public*, pg. 368
THE GLIK COMPANY; *U.S. Private*, pg. 4033
GM PLACE INC.; *U.S. Private*, pg. 1721
GO FASHION INDIA LIMITED; *Int'l*, pg. 3017
GOLDEN BRAND CLOTHING (CANADA) LTD.—See Tailored Brands, Inc.; *U.S. Public*, pg. 1979
GOLF & CO. LTD.—See Access Industries, Inc.; *U.S. Private*, pg. 51
GORDMANS, INC.—See Sun Capital Partners, Inc.; *U.S. Private*, pg. 3859
GORSUCH LTD.; *U.S. Private*, pg. 1744
GRACE HOLMES, INC.—See Leonard Green & Partners, L.P.; *U.S. Private*, pg. 2426
GRACE HOLMES, INC.—See TPG Capital, L.P.; *U.S. Public*, pg. 2174
GROUPE BEAUMANOIR; *Int'l*, pg. 3092
GROUPE CASPERA SA; *Int'l*, pg. 3101
GRUPO ESCADA ESPANA S.A.U.—See Regent, L.P.; *U.S. Private*, pg. 3388
GUANGDONG AEON TEEN STORES CO., LTD.—See AEON Co., Ltd.; *Int'l*, pg. 177
GUANGDONG BOBAOLON CO., LTD.; *Int'l*, pg. 3153
GUESS? ASIA LIMITED—See Guess? Inc.; *U.S. Public*, pg. 974
GUESS? CANADA CORPORATION—See Guess? Inc.; *U.S. Public*, pg. 974
GUESS.COM, INC.—See Guess? Inc.; *U.S. Public*, pg. 974
GUESS? DEUTSCHLAND GMBH—See Guess? Inc.; *U.S. Public*, pg. 974
GUESS? EUROPE SAGL—See Guess? Inc.; *U.S. Public*, pg. 974
GUESS? ITALIA, SRL—See Guess? Inc.; *U.S. Public*, pg. 974
GUESS? PORTUGAL, LDA—See Guess? Inc.; *U.S. Public*, pg. 974
GURU DENIM, INC.—See TowerBrook Capital Partners, L.P.; *U.S. Private*, pg. 4196
HALLENSTEIN BROS LIMITED—See Hallenstein Glasson Holdings Limited; *Int'l*, pg. 3230
HAMILTON'S UNIFORMS LLC; *U.S. Private*, pg. 1848
HAMMERS LLC; *U.S. Private*, pg. 1849
HAMRICK INC.; *U.S. Private*, pg. 1851
H AND M HENNES AND MAURITZ PROPRIETARY LIMITED—See H&M Hennes & Mauritz AB; *Int'l*, pg. 3192
HANESBRANDS BRAZIL TEXTIL LTDA.—See Hanesbrands Inc.; *U.S. Public*, pg. 983
HANES POLAND SP. Z O.O.—See Hanesbrands Inc.; *U.S. Public*, pg. 983
HANG UP SHOPPES INC.; *U.S. Private*, pg. 1853
HANNA ANDERSSON LLC—See Catterton Management Company, LLC; *U.S. Private*, pg. 793
HANSAEMK CO.,LTD.; *Int'l*, pg. 3259
HANSEL TEXTILROM SRL—See Freudenberg SE; *Int'l*, pg. 2789
HARRY ROSEN INC.; *Int'l*, pg. 3279
HARVEY NICHOLS GROUP LIMITED; *Int'l*, pg. 3281
THE HAT CLUB, LLC; *U.S. Private*, pg. 4043
HAT WORLD, INC.—See Genesco Inc.; *U.S. Public*, pg. 930
HAWAIIAN ISLAND CREATIONS; *U.S. Private*, pg. 1882
H&C HEADWEAR-ATLANTA CAPCO SPORTSWEAR—See H&C Headwear Inc.; *U.S. Private*, pg. 1822
HENIG FURS INC.; *U.S. Private*, pg. 1916
HERB PHILIPSON'S ARMY & NAVY; *U.S. Private*, pg. 1920
HERMANN LANGE GMBH & CO. KG; *Int'l*, pg. 3362
HERMES ARGENTINA SRL—See Hermes International SCA; *Int'l*, pg. 3362
HERMES ASIA PACIFIC LIMITED—See Hermes International SCA; *Int'l*, pg. 3362
HERMES BENELUX NORDICS SA—See Hermes International SCA; *Int'l*, pg. 3362
HERMES CHINA CO. LTD.—See Hermes International SCA; *Int'l*, pg. 3362
HERMES DENMARK APS—See Hermes International SCA; *Int'l*, pg. 3362
HERMES DE PARIS MEXICO, S.A. DE C.V.—See Hermes International SCA; *Int'l*, pg. 3363
HERMES DO BRASIL INDUSTRIA E COMERCIO LTDA.—See Hermes International SCA; *Int'l*, pg. 3362
HERMES GMBH—See Hermes International SCA; *Int'l*, pg. 3362
HERMES GRECE S.A.—See Hermes International SCA; *Int'l*, pg. 3362
HERMES IMMOBILIER GENEVE SA—See Hermes International SCA; *Int'l*, pg. 3362
HERMES INDIA RETAIL & DISTRIBUTORS PRIVATE LIMITED—See Hermes International SCA; *Int'l*, pg. 3362
HERMES INTERNACIONAL PORTUGAL LDA—See Hermes International SCA; *Int'l*, pg. 3362
HERMES ITALIE S.P.A.—See Hermes International SCA; *Int'l*, pg. 3363
HERMES JAPON CO., LTD.—See Hermes International SCA; *Int'l*, pg. 3363

HERMES PRAGUE, A.S.—See Hermes International SCA; *Int'l*, pg. 3363
H HERITAGE LICENSING, LLC—See XCel Brands, Inc.; *U.S. Public*, pg. 1739
HILFIGER STORES DENMARK APS—See PVH Corp.; *U.S. Public*, pg. 1739
HILFIGER STORES SPZOO—See PVH Corp.; *U.S. Public*, pg. 1739
HILFIGER STORES SRO—See PVH Corp.; *U.S. Public*, pg. 1739
HISTORICAL EMPORIUM, INC.; *U.S. Private*, pg. 1952
HLA CORP., LTD.; *Int'l*, pg. 3430
H&M HENNES LTD—See H&M Hennes & Mauritz AB; *Int'l*, pg. 3192
H&M HENNES & MAURITZ A.E.—See H&M Hennes & Mauritz AB; *Int'l*, pg. 3192
H&M HENNES & MAURITZ AS—See H&M Hennes & Mauritz AB; *Int'l*, pg. 3192
H&M HENNES & MAURITZ A/S—See H&M Hennes & Mauritz AB; *Int'l*, pg. 3192
H&M HENNES & MAURITZ BELGIUM NV—See H&M Hennes & Mauritz AB; *Int'l*, pg. 3192
H&M HENNES & MAURITZ B.V. & CO.KG—See H&M Hennes & Mauritz AB; *Int'l*, pg. 3192
H M HENNES & MAURITZ CZ, S.R.O.—See H&M Hennes & Mauritz AB; *Int'l*, pg. 3192
H&M HENNES & MAURITZ GESMBH—See H&M Hennes & Mauritz AB; *Int'l*, pg. 3192
H&M HENNES & MAURITZ INC.—See H&M Hennes & Mauritz AB; *Int'l*, pg. 3192
H & M HENNES & MAURITZ LLP—See H&M Hennes & Mauritz AB; *Int'l*, pg. 3192
H & M HENNES & MAURITZ MANAGEMENT B.V.—See H&M Hennes & Mauritz AB; *Int'l*, pg. 3192
H&M HENNES & MAURITZ NETHERLANDS BV—See H&M Hennes & Mauritz AB; *Int'l*, pg. 3192
H&M HENNES & MAURITZ OY—See H&M Hennes & Mauritz AB; *Int'l*, pg. 3192
H&M HENNES & MAURITZ SARL—See H&M Hennes & Mauritz AB; *Int'l*, pg. 3192
H&M HENNES & MAURITZ SA—See H&M Hennes & Mauritz AB; *Int'l*, pg. 3192
H & M HENNES & MAURITZ TR TEKSTIL LTD SIRKETI—See H&M Hennes & Mauritz AB; *Int'l*, pg. 3192
H & M HENNES & MAURITZ VIETNAM LLC—See H&M Hennes & Mauritz AB; *Int'l*, pg. 3192
HOLLIDAY'S GENERAL SERVICE CORP.; *U.S. Private*, pg. 1965
HOLLISTER CO.—See Abercrombie & Fitch Co.; *U.S. Public*, pg. 25
HOLLISTER FASHION L.L.C—See Abercrombie & Fitch Co.; *U.S. Public*, pg. 25
HONOLUA SURF CO. INTERNATIONAL LTD.—See Leonard Green & Partners, L.P.; *U.S. Private*, pg. 2424
HOTTOPIC.COM, INC.—See Sycamore Partners Management, LP; *U.S. Private*, pg. 3896
HOT TOPIC, INC.—See Sycamore Partners Management, LP; *U.S. Private*, pg. 3895
HOURGLASS ANGEL; *U.S. Private*, pg. 1991
H. SQUARED, INC.; *U.S. Private*, pg. 1825
IC COMPANYS CANADA INC.—See Friheden Invest A/S; *Int'l*, pg. 2792
IC COMPANYS FINLAND OY—See Friheden Invest A/S; *Int'l*, pg. 2792
IC COMPANYS FRANCE SARL—See Friheden Invest A/S; *Int'l*, pg. 2792
IC COMPANYS HONG KONG LTD.—See Friheden Invest A/S; *Int'l*, pg. 2792
IC COMPANYS HUNGARY KFT.—See Friheden Invest A/S; *Int'l*, pg. 2792
IC COMPANYS NEDERLAND B.V.—See Friheden Invest A/S; *Int'l*, pg. 2792
IC COMPANYS ROMANIA SRL—See Friheden Invest A/S; *Int'l*, pg. 2792
IC COMPANYS (SHANGHAI) LTD.—See Friheden Invest A/S; *Int'l*, pg. 2792
ICEBREAKER CZECH REPUBLIC S.R.O.—See V. F. Corporation; *U.S. Public*, pg. 2268
ICEBREAKER MERINO CLOTHING INC.—See V. F. Corporation; *U.S. Public*, pg. 2268
ICEBREAKER NEW ZEALAND LIMITED—See V. F. Corporation; *U.S. Public*, pg. 2268
ICHIHIRO CO., LTD.; *Int'l*, pg. 3580
IDEAL CORP.; *U.S. Private*, pg. 2035
IFG CORP.; *U.S. Private*, pg. 2038
IHEARTRAVES, LLC; *U.S. Private*, pg. 2040
INTERMIX (ITM) INC.—See Altamont Capital Partners; *U.S. Private*, pg. 205
INTERNATIONAL FASHION CONCEPTS, INC.; *U.S. Private*, pg. 2116
INTERSPORT ATHLETICS (CYPRUS) LTD.—See FOUR-LIS HOLDINGS S.A.; *Int'l*, pg. 2755
I PLAY, INC.; *U.S. Private*, pg. 2020
IRISA GROUP LIMITED—See Sun Capital Partners, Inc.; *U.S. Private*, pg. 3861
ISIS PARENTING, INC.; *U.S. Private*, pg. 2144
ISLAND COMPANY; *U.S. Private*, pg. 2145

JACK'S SURF & SPORT; *U.S. Private*, pg. 2175
JACK WOLFSKIN AUSTRIA GMBH—See Topgolf Callaway Brands Corp.; *U.S. Public*, pg. 2164
JACK WOLFSKIN BELGIUM BVBA—See Topgolf Callaway Brands Corp.; *U.S. Public*, pg. 2164
JACK WOLFSKIN ITALIA S.R.L.—See Topgolf Callaway Brands Corp.; *U.S. Public*, pg. 2164
JACK WOLFSKIN NETHERLANDS BV—See Topgolf Callaway Brands Corp.; *U.S. Public*, pg. 2164
JACK WOLFSKIN NORTH AMERICA, INC.—See Topgolf Callaway Brands Corp.; *U.S. Public*, pg. 2164
JACK WOLFSKIN UK LTD.—See Topgolf Callaway Brands Corp.; *U.S. Public*, pg. 2164
JACQUES VERT GROUP LIMITED—See Sun Capital Partners, Inc.; *U.S. Private*, pg. 3861
JANTZEN INC.—See Perry Ellis International, Inc.; *U.S. Private*, pg. 3153
J.CREW GROUP, INC.—See Leonard Green & Partners, L.P.; *U.S. Private*, pg. 2426
J.CREW GROUP, INC.—See TPG Capital, L.P.; *U.S. Public*, pg. 2174
J. CREW, INC.—See Leonard Green & Partners, L.P.; *U.S. Private*, pg. 2426
J. CREW, INC.—See TPG Capital, L.P.; *U.S. Public*, pg. 2174
J. CREW INTERNATIONAL, INC.—See Leonard Green & Partners, L.P.; *U.S. Private*, pg. 2426
J. CREW INTERNATIONAL, INC.—See TPG Capital, L.P.; *U.S. Public*, pg. 2174
J. CREW OPERATING CORP.—See Leonard Green & Partners, L.P.; *U.S. Private*, pg. 2426
J. CREW OPERATING CORP.—See TPG Capital, L.P.; *U.S. Public*, pg. 2174
J. CREW VIRGINIA, INC.—See Leonard Green & Partners, L.P.; *U.S. Private*, pg. 2426
J. CREW VIRGINIA, INC.—See TPG Capital, L.P.; *U.S. Public*, pg. 2174
JEANNE LANVIN SAS—See Fosun International Limited; *Int'l*, pg. 2751
JEANS.COM INC.; *U.S. Private*, pg. 2196
JEANS WAREHOUSE, INC.; *U.S. Private*, pg. 2196
JEANSWEST CORPORATION PTY. LTD.—See Glorious Sun Enterprises Limited; *Int'l*, pg. 3009
JEANSWEST INTERNATIONAL (H.K.) LIMITED—See Glorious Sun Enterprises Limited; *Int'l*, pg. 3009
J. HILBURN; *U.S. Private*, pg. 2156
JILL STUART INTERNATIONAL LLC; *U.S. Private*, pg. 2208
JINX, INC.; *U.S. Private*, pg. 2211
JOE BRAND INC.; *U.S. Private*, pg. 2218
JOHNNIE-O; *U.S. Private*, pg. 2225
JOHNNY CUPCAKES; *U.S. Private*, pg. 2225
JOMAR TEXTILES INC.; *U.S. Private*, pg. 2231
JOS. A. BANK CLOTHIERS, INC.—See Tailored Brands, Inc.; *U.S. Public*, pg. 1979
JOSEPH ABBOUD MANUFACTURING CORP.—See Tailored Brands, Inc.; *U.S. Public*, pg. 1979
JOYCE LESLIE INC.; *U.S. Private*, pg. 2239
JULIAN GOLD INC.; *U.S. Private*, pg. 2243
KAIKATSU FRONTIER INC.—See AOKI Holdings Inc.; *Int'l*, pg. 488
K&G MEN'S CENTER, INC.—See Tailored Brands, Inc.; *U.S. Public*, pg. 1979
K&G MEN'S COMPANY INC.—See Tailored Brands, Inc.; *U.S. Public*, pg. 1979
KIDPIK CORP.; *U.S. Public*, pg. 1227
KIDS FOOT LOCKER—See Foot Locker, Inc.; *U.S. Public*, pg. 863
KIP-CRAFT INCORPORATED; *U.S. Private*, pg. 2314
KNIGHTS APPAREL LLC—See Hanesbrands Inc.; *U.S. Public*, pg. 983
KODIAK GROUP HOLDINGS COMPANY—See V. F. Corporation; *U.S. Public*, pg. 2268
KOSTROMA LTD.—See G-III Apparel Group, Ltd.; *U.S. Public*, pg. 894
KOSUGI SANGYO CO., LTD.—See Asia Development Capital Co., Ltd.; *Int'l*, pg. 611
KRESS STORES OF PUERTO RICO; *U.S. Private*, pg. 2351
KUREIJI, INC.; *U.S. Private*, pg. 2357
LABELS BY ANDRES NV—See Damartex SA; *Int'l*, pg. 1956
LADY GRACE STORES INC.; *U.S. Private*, pg. 2372
LAFUMA HK LTD.—See Calida Holding AG; *Int'l*, pg. 1264
LANDS' END DIRECT MERCHANTS, INC.—See Lands' End, Inc.; *U.S. Public*, pg. 1292
LANE BRYANT, INC.—See Sycamore Partners Management, LP; *U.S. Private*, pg. 3896
LANGSTON COMPANY; *U.S. Private*, pg. 2390
LANVIN ASIA PACIFIC LTD.—See Fosun International Limited; *Int'l*, pg. 2751
LA REDOUTE PORTUGAL—See Galeries Lafayette SA; *Int'l*, pg. 2872
LA REDOUTE SA—See Galeries Lafayette SA; *Int'l*, pg. 2872
LAROHN INC.; *U.S. Private*, pg. 2392
LAURA ASHLEY ESPANA SA—See Gordon Brothers Group, LLC; *U.S. Private*, pg. 1742
LAURA ASHLEY, INC.—See Gordon Brothers Group, LLC; *U.S. Private*, pg. 1742

458110 — CLOTHING AND CLOTHI...

LAURA ASHLEY (IRELAND) LTD.—See Gordon Brothers Group, LLC; *U.S. Private,* pg. 1742
LAURA ASHLEY JAPAN CO., LTD.—See Gordon Brothers Group, LLC; *U.S. Private,* pg. 1742
LAURA ASHLEY NV—See Gordon Brothers Group, LLC; *U.S. Private,* pg. 1742
LAURA ASHLEY SA—See Gordon Brothers Group, LLC; *U.S. Private,* pg. 1742
LAURA ASHLEY SA—See Gordon Brothers Group, LLC; *U.S. Private,* pg. 1742
LAURA ASHLEY S.P.A.—See Gordon Brothers Group, LLC; *U.S. Private,* pg. 1742
LEEWRANGLER INTERNATIONAL SAGL—See V. F. Corporation; *U.S. Public,* pg. 2268
LEONISA USA; *U.S. Private,* pg. 2431
LERNER NEW YORK, INC.—See Irving Place Capital Management, L.P.; *U.S. Private,* pg. 2142
LEVI'S BRAND—See Levi Strauss & Co.; *U.S. Public,* pg. 1309
LEVI'S FOOTWEAR & ACCESSORIES SPAIN S.A.—See Levi Strauss & Co.; *U.S. Public,* pg. 1309
LEVI'S FOOTWEAR & ACCESSORIES (SWITZERLAND) S.A.—See Levi Strauss & Co.; *U.S. Public,* pg. 1309
LEVI STRAUSS & CO.—See Levi Strauss & Co.; *U.S. Public,* pg. 1308
LEVI STRAUSS & CO.—See Levi Strauss & Co.; *U.S. Public,* pg. 1308
LEVI STRAUSS GLOBAL TRADING COMPANY II, LIMITED—See Levi Strauss & Co.; *U.S. Public,* pg. 1309
LEVI STRAUSS INTERNATIONAL INC.—See Levi Strauss & Co;, *U.S. Public,* pg. 1309
LIBERTY LTD—See BlueGem Capital Partners LLP; *Int'l,* pg. 1071
LIFE UNIFORM COMPANY—See Scrubs & Beyond LLC; *U.S. Private,* pg. 3580
THE LIMITED STORES, INC.—See Sycamore Partners Management, LP; *U.S. Private,* pg. 3898
LIZ LANGE—See Bluestar Alliance LLC; *U.S. Private,* pg. 598
L&L WINGS INC.; *U.S. Private,* pg. 2363
LOEHMANN'S, INC.—See Dubai World Corporation; *Int'l,* pg. 2222
LOFT MAGAZACILIK INC.—See Eroglu Holding AS; *Int'l,* pg. 2496
LONG TALL SALLY LTD.—See AK Retail Holdings Limited; *Int'l,* pg. 259
LOVER'S LANE& CO.; *U.S. Private,* pg. 2504
LUCY ACTIVEWEAR, INC.—See V. F. Corporation; *U.S. Public,* pg. 2270
LUEMME, INC.—See Calida Holding AG; *Int'l,* pg. 1264
MADELEINE MODE GMBH—See Equistone Partners Europe Limited; *Int'l,* pg. 2487
MADEWELL, INC.—See Leonard Green & Partners, L.P.; *U.S. Private,* pg. 2426
MADEWELL, INC.—See TPG Capital, L.P.; *U.S. Public,* pg. 2174
MARCO DESTIN INC.; *U.S. Private,* pg. 2571
MARINEMAX TX, L.P.—See NXTLVL Marine, LLC; *U.S. Private,* pg. 2976
MARK SHALE DIRECT—See Mark Shale; *U.S. Private,* pg. 2578
MARK SHALE; *U.S. Private,* pg. 2578
MARKS WORK WEARHOUSE LTD.—See Canadian Tire Corporation Limited; *Int'l,* pg. 1286
MARKS WORK WEARHOUSE—See Canadian Tire Corporation Limited; *Int'l,* pg. 1286
MARY MAC APPAREL INC.—See Easyknit International Holdings Ltd.; *Int'l,* pg. 2277
MAUI CLOTHING CO. INC.; *U.S. Private,* pg. 2614
MAUS & HOFFMAN, INC.; *U.S. Private,* pg. 2615
MAXFIELD ENTERPRISES INC.; *U.S. Private,* pg. 2618
MCCAULOU'S, INC.; *U.S. Private,* pg. 2628
MECA SPORTSWEAR INC.; *U.S. Private,* pg. 2648
THE MENS WEARHOUSE, INC—See Tailored Brands, Inc.; *U.S. Public,* pg. 1979
ME SALVE ISABELA INC.; *U.S. Private,* pg. 2646
METROPARK USA, INC.; *U.S. Private,* pg. 2687
MEXX PAZARLAMA INC.—See Eroglu Holding AS; *Int'l,* pg. 2496
M. FREDRIC; *U.S. Private,* pg. 2526
MICHAEL KORS (AUSTRIA) GMBH—See Capri Holdings Limited; *Int'l,* pg. 1316
MICHAEL KORS BELGIUM BVBA—See Capri Holdings Limited; *Int'l,* pg. 1316
MICHAEL KORS (CANADA) CO.—See Capri Holdings Limited; *Int'l,* pg. 1316
MICHAEL KORS (CZECH REPUBLIC) S.R.O.—See Capri Holdings Limited; *Int'l,* pg. 1316
MICHAEL KORS (GERMANY) GMBH—See Capri Holdings Limited; *Int'l,* pg. 1316
MICHAEL KORS ITALY S.R.L.—See Capri Holdings Limited; *Int'l,* pg. 1316
MICHAEL KORS JAPAN K.K.—See Capri Holdings Limited; *Int'l,* pg. 1316
MICHAEL KORS LIMITED—See Capri Holdings Limited; *Int'l,* pg. 1316

MICHAEL KORS (NETHERLANDS) B.V.—See Capri Holdings Limited; *Int'l,* pg. 1316
MICHAEL KORS STORES (CALIFORNIA), INC.—See Capri Holdings Limited; *Int'l,* pg. 1316
MICHAEL KORS STORES, LLC—See Capri Holdings Limited; *Int'l,* pg. 1316
MICHAEL KORS (SWITZERLAND) GMBH—See Capri Holdings Limited; *Int'l,* pg. 1316
MICHAEL KORS (UK) LIMITED—See Capri Holdings Limited; *Int'l,* pg. 1316
MILLERS FASHION CLUB (QLD) PTY LIMITED—See City Chic Collective Limited; *Int'l,* pg. 1626
MILLERS FASHION CLUB (VIC) PTY LIMITED—See City Chic Collective Limited; *Int'l,* pg. 1626
MILLERS FASHION CLUB (WA) PTY LIMITED—See City Chic Collective Limited; *Int'l,* pg. 1626
MILTONS INC.; *U.S. Private,* pg. 2739
MK HOLETOWN (BARBADOS) INC.—See Capri Holdings Limited; *Int'l,* pg. 1316
M.L.F. & ASSOCIATES, INC.; *U.S. Private,* pg. 2529
MODASUITE INC.—See Unified Commerce Group; *U.S. Private,* pg. 4282
MODERN WOMAN, INC.—See Mahwah Bergen Retail Group, Inc.; *U.S. Private,* pg. 2550
MONKI—See H&M Hennes & Mauritz AB; *Int'l,* pg. 3192
MOORES CLOTHING FOR MEN—See Tailored Brands, Inc.; *U.S. Public,* pg. 1979
MORGAN & MILO, LLC—See Zutano Global Inc.; *U.S. Private,* pg. 4610
MOSCHINO FRANCE S.A.R.L—See Aeffe SpA; *Int'l,* pg. 173
MOSCHINO KOREA LTD.—See Aeffe SpA; *Int'l,* pg. 173
MOSCHINO RETAIL GMBH—See Aeffe SpA; *Int'l,* pg. 173
MOSCHINO S.P.A.—See Aeffe SpA; *Int'l,* pg. 173
MOTHERS WORK CANADA, INC.—See Destination Maternity Corporation; *U.S. Public,* pg. 656
MS MODE NEDERLAND B.V.—See B. Riley Financial, Inc.; *U.S. Public,* pg. 261
MUD PIE LLC.; *U.S. Private,* pg. 2810
MYNTRA DESIGNS PRIVATE LIMITED—See Walmart Inc.; *U.S. Public,* pg. 2325
NAME BRANDS INC.; *U.S. Private,* pg. 2831
NATIONAL STORES, INC.; *U.S. Private,* pg. 2863
NAT LANDAU HYMAN JEWELS LTD.—See Landau Direct; *U.S. Private,* pg. 2384
NATURKOMPANIET AB—See Fenix Outdoor International AG; *Int'l,* pg. 2634
NAUTICA RETAIL USA, INC.—See Leonard Green & Partners, L.P.; *U.S. Private,* pg. 2426
NBC APPAREL, INC.—See The TJX Companies, Inc.; *U.S. Public,* pg. 2134
NEW ERA ASIA PACIFIC LIMITED—See ACON Investments, LLC; *U.S. Private,* pg. 62
NEW ERA CAP COMPANY LTD.—See ACON Investments, LLC; *U.S. Private,* pg. 62
NEW ERA CAP S.R.L.—See ACON Investments, LLC; *U.S. Private,* pg. 62
NEW LOOK GROUP LIMITED—See Brait S.E.; *Int'l,* pg. 1137
NEW YORK & COMPANY, INC.—See Irving Place Capital Management, L.P.; *U.S. Private,* pg. 2142
NEWYORKER LTD.—See Daidoh Limited; *Int'l,* pg. 1924
NEW YORK LOOK AT FIFTH AVE INC.—See The New York Look Inc.; *U.S. Private,* pg. 4083
THE NEW YORK LOOK INC.; *U.S. Private,* pg. 4083
THE NEW YORK LOOK INC.—See The New York Look Inc.; *U.S. Private,* pg. 4083
NIKE (THAILAND) LIMITED—See NIKE, Inc.; *U.S. Public,* pg. 1528
NOA NOA APS—See Greystone Capital Partners A/S; *Int'l,* pg. 3082
NORDSTROM DIRECT—See Nordstrom, Inc.; *U.S. Public,* pg. 1535
NORDSTROM, INC.; *U.S. Public,* pg. 1535
NORTHERN REFLECTIONS LTD.—See York Management Services, Inc.; *U.S. Private,* pg. 4590
NORTH SAILS COLLECTION USA—See Windway Capital Corp.; *U.S. Private,* pg. 4539
NTY FRANCHISE COMPANY; *U.S. Private,* pg. 2971
OAK HALL INDUSTRIES LP; *U.S. Private,* pg. 2983
OLD NAVY (CANADA) INC.—See The Gap, Inc.; *U.S. Public,* pg. 2074
OLD NAVY—See The Gap, Inc.; *U.S. Public,* pg. 2074
OLIMPIAS GROUP S.R.L.—See Edizione S.r.l.; *Int'l,* pg. 2312
OLIVE & BETTE'S; *U.S. Private,* pg. 3010
ONLY THE BEST, INC.; *U.S. Private,* pg. 3027
OSHKOSH B'GOSH—See Carter's, Inc.; *U.S. Public,* pg. 445
OVERLAND SHEEPSKIN CO. INC; *U.S. Private,* pg. 3053
OXFORD CARIBBEAN, INC.—See Oxford Industries, Inc.; *U.S. Public,* pg. 1629
OXFORD GARMENT, INC.—See Oxford Industries, Inc.; *U.S. Public,* pg. 1629
PACIFIC POTENTIAL TRADING COMPANY LIMITED—See Glorious Sun Enterprises Limited; *Int'l,* pg. 3009
PACIFIC SPORTS INC.—See Peace Textile America Inc.; *U.S. Private,* pg. 3122

PACIFIC SUNWEAR OF CALIFORNIA, LLC—See Golden Gate Capital Management II, LLC; *U.S. Private,* pg. 1731
PACIFIC TRAIL CORPORATION—See Columbia Sportswear Company; *U.S. Public,* pg. 535
PACTIMO USA; *U.S. Private,* pg. 3073
PARADISE GROUP SP. Z O. O.—See Alma Market S.A.; *Int'l,* pg. 361
PATRICK JAMES INC.; *U.S. Private,* pg. 3110
PAULA YOUNG CATALOG—See EdgeStone Capital Partners Inc.; *Int'l,* pg. 2309
PAUL JARDIN OF USA INC.; *U.S. Private,* pg. 3113
PEDERSEN WORLDWIDE; *U.S. Private,* pg. 3127
PEI LICENSING, INC.—See Perry Ellis International, Inc.; *U.S. Private,* pg. 3154
PERUVIAN CONNECTION, LTD.; *U.S. Private,* pg. 3156
PETER HAHN GMBH—See Equistone Partners Europe Limited; *Int'l,* pg. 2487
PETER MILLAR INC.—See Compagnie Financiere Richemont S.A.; *Int'l,* pg. 1741
PETIT BATEAU UK LIMITED—See Groupe Rocher Operations SAS; *Int'l,* pg. 3110
PETRA FASHIONS INC.—See Pure Romance Parties, Inc.; *U.S. Private,* pg. 3306
PHAT FASHIONS, LLC—See Sun Capital Partners, Inc.; *U.S. Private,* pg. 3859
PICCOLLO S.R.O.—See Columbia Sportswear Company; *U.S. Public,* pg. 535
PIEDMONT APPAREL CORPORATION—See Oxford Industries, Inc.; *U.S. Public,* pg. 1629
PM RETAIL AS—See FSN Capital Partners AS; *Int'l,* pg. 2799
POHLAND-HERRENKLEIDUNG GMBH & CO. KG—See Aurelius Equity Opportunities SE & Co. KGaA; *Int'l,* pg. 709
POINT (SHANGHAI) CO., LTD.—See Adastria Co., Ltd.; *Int'l,* pg. 126
POLLINI FRANCE S.A.R.L.—See Aeffe SpA; *Int'l,* pg. 173
POMARE INTERNATIONAL CORP.—See Pomare Ltd.; *U.S. Private,* pg. 3226
POSH BOUTIQUE; *U.S. Private,* pg. 3233
PRENATAL RETAIL GROUP S.P.A.—See BI-Invest Advisors S.A.; *Int'l,* pg. 1016
PREP SPORTSWEAR; *U.S. Private,* pg. 3252
PRIMO ZRT.—See Fotex Holding SE; *Int'l,* pg. 2752
PRIVATE SALE GMBH—See Regent, L.P.; *U.S. Private,* pg. 3388
PRONOVIAS U.S.A., INC.—See BC Partners LLP; *Int'l,* pg. 925
PROTEC DIRECT—See Bunzl plc; *Int'l,* pg. 1217
PT. GIORDANO INDONESIA—See Giordano International Limited; *Int'l,* pg. 2978
PURITAN CLOTHING COMPANY OF CAPE COD; *U.S. Private,* pg. 3306
PVH NECKWEAR, INC.—See PVH Corp.; *U.S. Public,* pg. 1739
QUARTERMASTER, LLC—See Charlesbank Capital Partners, LLC; *U.S. Private,* pg. 855
THE QUEENSBORO SHIRT COMPANY; *U.S. Private,* pg. 4101
QUEST MARKETING, INC.—See OMNIQ Corp.; *U.S. Public,* pg. 1600
QUIKSILVER ASIA SOURCING LTD.—See Leonard Green & Partners, L.P.; *U.S. Private,* pg. 2424
RACHEL ALLAN, LLC; *U.S. Private,* pg. 3341
RAINBOW APPAREL COMPANIES INC.—See AIJJ Enterprises Inc.; *U.S. Private,* pg. 132
RALPH LAUREN BELGIUM S.P.R.L.—See Ralph Lauren Corporation; *U.S. Public,* pg. 1761
RALPH LAUREN GERMANY GMBH—See Ralph Lauren Corporation; *U.S. Public,* pg. 1761
RALPH LAUREN NETHERLANDS BV—See Ralph Lauren Corporation; *U.S. Public,* pg. 1761
THE RANCHER INC.—See White Construction Company Inc.; *U.S. Private,* pg. 4508
RASTACLAT, LLC; *U.S. Private,* pg. 3357
RCC WESTERN STORES, INC.—See Boot Barn Holdings, Inc.; *U.S. Public,* pg. 368
REAL AMERICAN CAPITAL CORPORATION; *U.S. Public,* pg. 1768
REFORM STUDIO CO., LTD.—See AEON Co., Ltd.; *Int'l,* pg. 178
REGSTAER-SP LLC—See Avolta AG; *Int'l,* pg. 749
REIMA OY—See The Riverside Company; *U.S. Private,* pg. 4110
RENEE CLAIRE, BEDHEAD PAJAMAS, INC.—See Charles Komar & Sons, Inc.; *U.S. Private,* pg. 852
RENGASLINJA OY—See Deutsche Bahn AG; *Int'l,* pg. 2052
RETAIL THERAPY LLC; *U.S. Private,* pg. 3411
REVOLUTION DANCEWEAR LLC—See Audax Group, Limited Partnership; *U.S. Private,* pg. 389
REVOLVE GROUP, INC.; *U.S. Public,* pg. 1793
REYN SPOONER, INC.—See Wedbush Capital Partners; *U.S. Private,* pg. 4468
RIGHTEOUS CLOTHING AGENCY; *U.S. Private,* pg. 3436
ROBERT FOX INC.; *U.S. Private,* pg. 3458
ROCK CREEK ATHLETICS, INC.—See Neff Motivation Inc.; *U.S. Private,* pg. 2880
RON HERMAN INC.; *U.S. Private,* pg. 3477

N.A.I.C.S. INDEX

458110 — CLOTHING AND CLOTHI...

RON JON SURF SHOP; *U.S. Private,* pg. 3477
ROSEMUNDE APS—See Boozt AB; *Int'l,* pg. 1111
ROSS STORES, INC.; *U.S. Public,* pg. 1814
ROYAL ROBBINS, LLC—See Fenix Outdoor International AG; *Int'l,* pg. 2634
RUBIE'S DEUTSCHLAND GMBH—See Rubie's Costume Company Inc.; *U.S. Private,* pg. 3500
RUBIE'S MASQUERADE LTD—See Rubie's Costume Company Inc.; *U.S. Private,* pg. 3500
RUE21, INC.—See Apax Partners LLP; *Int'l,* pg. 507
RUFFLEBUTTS, INC.; *U.S. Private,* pg. 3502
RUGGED WEARHOUSE INC.; *U.S. Private,* pg. 3502
THE RUNNING SPECIALTY GROUP, INC.—See Critical-Point Capital, LLC; *U.S. Private,* pg. 1102
SABAS BUNCH LIMITED PARTNERSHIP; *U.S. Private,* pg. 3520
SAGAMI GROUP HOLDINGS CO., LTD.—See BELLUNA CO. LTD.; *Int'l,* pg. 967
SAMOON-COLLECTION FASHION-CONCEPT GERRY WEBER GMBH—See GERRY WEBER International AG; *Int'l,* pg. 2945
SANDPIPER TOO, INC.; *U.S. Private,* pg. 3544
SAN JUAN TRADING CO. INC.; *U.S. Private,* pg. 3541
SAVED BY THE DRESS, INC.; *U.S. Private,* pg. 3556
SCHEELS ALL SPORTS INC.; *U.S. Private,* pg. 3564
SCHIESSER BODY FASHION CENTER S.R.O.—See GMM Capital LLC; *U.S. Private,* pg. 1722
SCHWESERS STORES INC.; *U.S. Private,* pg. 3573
SCOTCH & SODA B.V.—See Bluestar Alliance LLC; *U.S. Private,* pg. 598
SCOTTEVEST INC.; *U.S. Private,* pg. 3578
SCRUBS & BEYOND LLC; *U.S. Private,* pg. 3580
SCRUBS ON WHEELS—See Birch Swing Capital LLC; *U.S. Private,* pg. 564
SEA ISLAND CLOTHIERS, LLC—See Brentwood Associates; *U.S. Private,* pg. 646
SEE JANE RUN; *U.S. Private,* pg. 3597
SFERA JOVEN, S.A.—See El Corte Ingles, S.A.; *Int'l,* pg. 2340
SFO FORECAST INC.; *U.S. Private,* pg. 3621
SHANGHAI FIONA CHEN FASHION CO., LTD.—See Anzheng Fashion Group Co., Ltd.; *Int'l,* pg. 487
SHEFIT OPERATING COMPANY LLC; *U.S. Private,* pg. 3630
SHENZHEN TIGER GARMENT LTD—See Giordano International Limited; *Int'l,* pg. 2978
SHEPLERS, INC.—See Boot Barn Holdings, Inc.; *U.S. Public,* pg. 368
SIERRA TRADING POST INC.—See The TJX Companies, Inc.; *U.S. Public,* pg. 2134
SIMPLY FASHION STORES LTD.; *U.S. Private,* pg. 3668
SLATE ROCK SAFETY LLC; *U.S. Private,* pg. 3687
SNOW PEAK KOREA, INC.—See Bain Capital, LP; *U.S. Private,* pg. 436
SOMA INTIMATES, LLC—See Sycamore Partners Management, LP; *U.S. Private,* pg. 3895
THE SOURCE, LLC; *U.S. Private,* pg. 4119
SPECIALTY RETAILERS, INC.—See Stage Stores, Inc.; *U.S. Public,* pg. 1925
SPECTRATEX INC.—See Gildan Activewear Inc.; *Int'l,* pg. 2973
THE SPORTSMAN'S GUIDE, INC.—See Northern Tool & Equipment Company, Inc.; *U.S. Private,* pg. 2954
SPORTSMEMORABLIA.COM, LLC; *U.S. Private,* pg. 3761
SPREADSHIRT, INC.; *U.S. Private,* pg. 3762
STEIN MART INC. (ALABAMA)—See Stein Mart, Inc.; *U.S. Private,* pg. 3798
STEIN MART, INC. (CALIFORNIA)—See Stein Mart, Inc.; *U.S. Private,* pg. 3798
STEIN MART, INC. (FLORIDA)—See Stein Mart, Inc.; *U.S. Private,* pg. 3798
STEIN MART, INC. (NORTH CAROLINA)—See Stein Mart, Inc.; *U.S. Private,* pg. 3798
STEIN MART, INC.; *U.S. Private,* pg. 3798
STEIN MART, INC. (SOUTH CAROLINA)—See Stein Mart, Inc.; *U.S. Private,* pg. 3798
STEIN MART, INC. (TENNESSEE)—See Stein Mart, Inc.; *U.S. Private,* pg. 3798
STEIN MART, INC. (TEXAS)—See Stein Mart, Inc.; *U.S. Private,* pg. 3798
STITCH FIX, INC.; *U.S. Public,* pg. 1950
STREET MODA FOOTWEAR; *U.S. Private,* pg. 3838
SUPERFLY MANUFACTURING CO.; *U.S. Private,* pg. 3875
THE SWANK SHOP (BEIJING) LIMITED—See ENM Holdings Limited; *Int'l,* pg. 2442
THE SWANK SHOP LIMITED—See ENM Holdings Limited; *Int'l,* pg. 2442
SWAN RETAIL INC.; *U.S. Private,* pg. 3889
SWIM & SWEAT, INC.—See ALPHAGILITY LLC; *U.S. Private,* pg. 200
TAILORED BRANDS, INC.; *U.S. Public,* pg. 1978
TAKKO MODEMARKT GMBH & CO KG—See Apax Partners LLP; *Int'l,* pg. 507
TAKMOR LLC—See WHP Global; *U.S. Private,* pg. 4515
THE TALBOTS, INC.—See Sycamore Partners Management, LP; *U.S. Private,* pg. 3898
TALBOTS PRODUCT DEVELOPMENT CENTER—See Sycamore Partners Management, LP; *U.S. Private,* pg. 3898
TALON ZIPPER (SHENZHEN) CO. LTD.—See Talon International, Inc.; *U.S. Public,* pg. 1980
TANGER RIVERHEAD, LLC—See Tanger Inc.; *U.S. Public,* pg. 1981
TB FRASHION GERRY WEBER GMBH—See GERRY WEBER International AG; *Int'l,* pg. 2945
T&C HOLDING LTD; *U.S. Private,* pg. 3909
TEA COLLECTION; *U.S. Private,* pg. 3944
TEAM EDITION APPAREL, INC.—See Foot Locker, Inc.; *U.S. Public,* pg. 864
TED BAKER (FRANCE) SARL—See Leonard Green & Partners, L.P.; *U.S. Private,* pg. 2425
TED BAKER LIMITED—See Leonard Green & Partners, L.P.; *U.S. Private,* pg. 2425
TED BAKER NETHERLANDS B.V.—See Leonard Green & Partners, L.P.; *U.S. Private,* pg. 2425
THE TERRITORY AHEAD—See Qurate Retail, Inc.; *U.S. Public,* pg. 1758
TH DENMARK APS—See PVH Corp.; *U.S. Public,* pg. 1739
TIENDAS LA GRAN VIA INC.; *U.S. Private,* pg. 4168
TIERRA PRODUCTS AB—See Fenix Outdoor International AG; *Int'l,* pg. 2634
TIES.COM; *U.S. Private,* pg. 4169
TILLY'S, INC.; *U.S. Public,* pg. 2159
TIMBERLAND RETAIL, INC.—See V. F. Corporation; *U.S. Public,* pg. 2269
THE TJX COMPANIES, INC.; *U.S. Public,* pg. 2134
TJX DISTRIBUTION LTD. & CO. KG—See The TJX Companies, Inc.; *U.S. Public,* pg. 2134
TJX EUROPEAN DISTRIBUTION SP. Z O.O.—See The TJX Companies, Inc.; *U.S. Public,* pg. 2134
TJX EUROPE LIMITED—See The TJX Companies, Inc.; *U.S. Public,* pg. 2134
T.KAWABE & CO., LTD.—See Ichihiro Co., Ltd.; *Int'l,* pg. 3580
TK MAXX—See The TJX Companies, Inc.; *U.S. Public,* pg. 2134
TOAST (MAIL ORDER) LIMITED—See Bestseller A/S; *Int'l,* pg. 1000
THE TOG SHOP—See Bluestem Brands, Inc.; *U.S. Private,* pg. 598
TOM JAMES COMPANY—See Individualized Apparel Group; *U.S. Private,* pg. 2064
TOM JAMES OF ATLANTA, INC.—See Individualized Apparel Group; *U.S. Private,* pg. 2064
TOMMY BAHAMA AUSTRALIA PTY LTD—See Oxford Industries, Inc.; *U.S. Public,* pg. 1629
TOMMY BAHAMA CANADA ULC—See Oxford Industries, Inc.; *U.S. Public,* pg. 1629
TOMMY BAHAMA GROUP, INC.—See Oxford Industries, Inc.; *U.S. Public,* pg. 1629
TOMMY BAHAMA LIMITED—See Oxford Industries, Inc.; *U.S. Public,* pg. 1629
TOMMY BAHAMA SARASOTA LLC—See Oxford Industries, Inc.; *U.S. Public,* pg. 1629
TOMMY BAHAMA TEXAS BEVERAGES LLC—See Oxford Industries, Inc.; *U.S. Public,* pg. 1629
TOMMY HILFIGER ASIA-PACIFIC LIMITED—See Dickson Concepts (International) Limited; *Int'l,* pg. 2112
TOMMY HILFIGER EUROPE B.V.—See PVH Corp.; *U.S. Public,* pg. 1739
TOMMY HILFIGER (HK) LTD.—See PVH Corp.; *U.S. Public,* pg. 1739
TOMMY HILFIGER (SHANGHAI) APPAREL CO. LTD.—See PVH Corp.; *U.S. Public,* pg. 1739
TOPVALU COLLECTION CO., LTD.—See AEON Co., Ltd.; *Int'l,* pg. 178
TORY BURCH LLC; *U.S. Private,* pg. 4190
TOWN & COUNTRY SURF SHOP INC.—See T&C Holding Ltd; *U.S. Private,* pg. 3909
TRAVELSMITH OUTFITTERS, INC.—See DAI Holding, LLC; *U.S. Private,* pg. 1145
TRAVISMATHEW, LLC—See Topgolf Callaway Brands Corp.; *U.S. Public,* pg. 2164
TRES HERMANOS, INC.; *U.S. Private,* pg. 4218
TRUE RELIGION BRAND JEANS GERMANY GMBH—See TowerBrook Capital Partners, L.P.; *U.S. Private,* pg. 4196
TRUE RELIGION BRAND JEANS ITALY, S.R.L.—See TowerBrook Capital Partners, L.P.; *U.S. Private,* pg. 4196
TRUE RELIGION BRAND JEANS U.K. LIMITED—See TowerBrook Capital Partners, L.P.; *U.S. Private,* pg. 4196
TRUE RELIGION JAPAN K.K.—See TowerBrook Capital Partners, L.P.; *U.S. Private,* pg. 4196
TRUNK CLUB, INC.—See Nordstrom, Inc.; *U.S. Public,* pg. 1535
TWEEN BRANDS, INC.—See Mahwah Bergen Retail Group, Inc.; *U.S. Private,* pg. 2550
UJENA SWIMWEAR AND FASHION; *U.S. Private,* pg. 4275
ULLA POPKEN LTD.; *U.S. Private,* pg. 4276
UNCLE DANS, LTD.—See Gearhead Outfitters, Inc.; *U.S. Private,* pg. 1655
UNIFORMES DE SAN LUIS S.A. DE C.V.—See UniFirst Corporation; *U.S. Public,* pg. 2226
UNIFORMS UNLIMITED, INC.—See Charlesbank Capital Partners, LLC; *U.S. Private,* pg. 855
UNIQLO AUSTRALIA PTY LTD—See Fast Retailing Co., Ltd.; *Int'l,* pg. 2621
UNIQLO HONG KONG, LTD.—See Fast Retailing Co., Ltd.; *Int'l,* pg. 2621
UNITED FASHIONS OF TEXAS LTD.; *U.S. Private,* pg. 4292
UNITED LEGWEAR & APPAREL CO.; *U.S. Private,* pg. 4293
UNITED UNIFORM CO., INC.—See Kanders & Company, Inc.; *U.S. Private,* pg. 2259
UNZIPPED APPAREL LLC—See Iconix Acquisition LLC; *U.S. Private,* pg. 2033
URANUS INTERNATIONAL CO., LTD.—See Catcher Technology Co., Ltd.; *Int'l,* pg. 1359
URBAN OUTFITTERS BELGIUM BVBA—See Urban Outfitters, Inc.; *U.S. Public,* pg. 2265
URBAN OUTFITTERS, INC.; *U.S. Public,* pg. 2265
URBAN OUTFITTERS IRELAND LIMITED—See Urban Outfitters, Inc.; *U.S. Public,* pg. 2265
URBAN OUTFITTERS I SVERIGE AB—See Urban Outfitters, Inc.; *U.S. Public,* pg. 2265
URBN UK LIMITED—See Urban Outfitters, Inc.; *U.S. Public,* pg. 2265
US CAVALRY STORE INC.; *U.S. Private,* pg. 4318
UTEBUTIKEN I UMEA AB—See Fenix Outdoor International AG; *Int'l,* pg. 2634
VANITY FAIR BRANDS, LP—See Berkshire Hathaway Inc.; *U.S. Public,* pg. 319
VANITY SHOP OF GRAND FORKS INC.; *U.S. Private,* pg. 4344
VARAGE MOUNTAIN CO. INC.; *U.S. Private,* pg. 4345
V&D B.V.—See Sun Capital Partners, Inc.; *U.S. Private,* pg. 3862
VERLAG AENNE BURDA GMBH & CO. KG—See Hubert Burda Media Holding Kommanditgesellschaft; *Int'l,* pg. 3520
VERSACE AUSTRALIA PTY LIMITED—See Capri Holdings Limited; *Int'l,* pg. 1316
VERSACE AUSTRIA GMBH—See Capri Holdings Limited; *Int'l,* pg. 1316
VERSACE BELGIQUE SA—See Capri Holdings Limited; *Int'l,* pg. 1316
VERSACE CANADA, INC.—See Capri Holdings Limited; *Int'l,* pg. 1316
VERSACE DEUTSCHLAND GMBH—See Capri Holdings Limited; *Int'l,* pg. 1316
VERSACE FRANCE S.A.—See Capri Holdings Limited; *Int'l,* pg. 1316
VERSACE MONTE-CARLO S.A.M.—See Capri Holdings Limited; *Int'l,* pg. 1316
VF IMAGEWEAR CANADA CO.—See V. F. Corporation; *U.S. Public,* pg. 2269
VF IMAGEWEAR DE MEXICO, S. DE R.L. DE C.V.—See V. F. Corporation; *U.S. Public,* pg. 2269
VF INTERNACIONAL, S. DE R.L. DE C.V.—See V. F. Corporation; *U.S. Public,* pg. 2269
VF ISRAEL (APPAREL) LTD.—See V. F. Corporation; *U.S. Public,* pg. 2269
VF JEANSWEAR SALES, INC.—See Kontoor Brands, Inc.; *U.S. Public,* pg. 1271
VF OUTLET INC.—See Kontoor Brands, Inc.; *U.S. Public,* pg. 1271
VF POLSKA DISTRIBUTION SP.Z.O.O.—See V. F. Corporation; *U.S. Public,* pg. 2269
VFUSA MARKETING SDN. BHD.—See Asia Brands Berhad; *Int'l,* pg. 610
VICTORIA'S SECRET & CO.; *U.S. Public,* pg. 2296
VICTORIA'S SECRET STORES, LLC—See Victoria's Secret & Co.; *U.S. Public,* pg. 2296
VILEBREQUIN INTERNATIONAL SA—See G-III Apparel Group, Ltd.; *U.S. Public,* pg. 894
VILEBREQUIN SAINT MAARTEN—See G-III Apparel Group, Ltd.; *U.S. Public,* pg. 894
VILLA MODA LIFESTYLE COMPANY K.S.C.C.—See DIFC Investments LLC; *Int'l,* pg. 2118
WAKEFIELDS INC.; *U.S. Private,* pg. 4427
WB PROMOTIONS, INC.; *U.S. Private,* pg. 4461
WD EUROPE SAS—See V. F. Corporation; *U.S. Public,* pg. 2270
WEEKDAY BRANDS AB—See H&M Hennes & Mauritz AB; *Int'l,* pg. 3192
WEST COAST LEATHER; *U.S. Private,* pg. 4484
WEST MICHIGAN UNIFORM—See Wildman Business Group Inc.; *U.S. Private,* pg. 4519
THE WET SEAL, LLC—See Independence Capital Partners, LLC; *U.S. Private,* pg. 2057
WHEAT GROUP INC.—See United Legwear & Apparel Co.; *U.S. Private,* pg. 4293
WHITE HOUSE BLACK MARKET, INC.—See Sycamore Partners Management, LP; *U.S. Private,* pg. 3895
WHOLE EARTH PROVISION COMPANY; *U.S. Private,* pg. 4514
WILKES BASHFORD COMPANY; *U.S. Private,* pg. 4520
WILLIAMSON-DICKIE EUROPE HOLDINGS LIMITED—See V. F. Corporation; *U.S. Public,* pg. 2270
WINDSOR FASHIONS, INC.; *U.S. Private,* pg. 4539
WINNERS MERCHANTS INTERNATIONAL LP—See The TJX Companies, Inc.; *U.S. Public,* pg. 2134

458110 — CLOTHING AND CLOTHI...

WOMEN'S APPAREL GROUP, LLC—See Monomoy Capital Partners LLC; *U.S. Private*, pg. 2772
WORK WORLD AMERICA INC.—See The Gart Companies, Inc.; *U.S. Private*, pg. 4032
W&W WHOLESALE INCORPORATED; *U.S. Private*, pg. 4417
YM INTERNATIONAL INC.; *U.S. Private*, pg. 4589
YOOX NET-A-PORTER GROUP S.P.A—See Compagnie Financière Richemont S.A.; *Int'l*, pg. 1741
YOUNGWORLD STORES GROUP INC.; *U.S. Private*, pg. 4594
Y&S HANDBAG CO. INC.; *U.S. Private*, pg. 4584
ZUMIEZ INCORPORATED; *U.S. Public*, pg. 2411
ZUMIEZ SERVICES INC.—See Zumiez Incorporated; *U.S. Public*, pg. 2411
ZUTANO GLOBAL INC.; *U.S. Private*, pg. 4610

458210 — SHOE RETAILERS

ABC-MART, INC.; *Int'l*, pg. 57
ALLSHOES BENELUX B.V.—See Bunzl plc; *Int'l*, pg. 1217
AMAGASA CO., LTD.; *Int'l*, pg. 408
AMERICAN NIKE S.L.U.—See NIKE, Inc.; *U.S. Public*, pg. 1528
AM-PAT INCORPORATED; *U.S. Private*, pg. 215
B.A. MASON—See Mason Companies, Inc.; *U.S. Private*, pg. 2602
BARE FEET ENTERPRISES, INC.; *U.S. Private*, pg. 474
BARRATTS TRADING LIMITED; *Int'l*, pg. 868
BASKIN GROUP LIMITED; *U.S. Private*, pg. 485
BRANTANO RETAIL LIMITED—See Alteri Partners LLP; *Int'l*, pg. 391
BROWNS CHELTENHAM LLC—See Browns Super Stores Inc.; *U.S. Private*, pg. 670
CALERES ITALY S.R.L.—See Caleres, Inc.; *U.S. Public*, pg. 422
CANNING SHOES, INC.; *U.S. Private*, pg. 734
CAPEZIO BALLET MAKERS INC.; *U.S. Private*, pg. 738
CAVENDER'S; *U.S. Private*, pg. 795
CCC SHOES & BAGS D.O.O.—See CCC S.A.; *Int'l*, pg. 1366
CCC SHOES BULGARIA EOOD—See CCC S.A.; *Int'l*, pg. 1366
COCONUT ENTERPRISES INC.—See Unisa Holdings Incorporated; *U.S. Private*, pg. 4286
COCONUTS IN THE GROVE INC.—See Unisa Holdings Incorporated; *U.S. Private*, pg. 4286
COMPONENT FOOTWEAR DOMINICANA, S.A.—See V. F. Corporation; *U.S. Public*, pg. 2268
DAVID Z INTERNET, INC.; *U.S. Private*, pg. 1171
DEICHMANN OBUV S.R.O.—See Deichmann SE; *Int'l*, pg. 2005
DEICHMANN-OBUWIE SP.Z. O.O.—See Deichmann SE; *Int'l*, pg. 2005
DEICHMANN-SCHUHVERTRIEBSGESELLSCHAFT M.B.H.—See Deichmann SE; *Int'l*, pg. 2005
DEICHMANN-SHOES UK LTD.—See Deichmann SE; *Int'l*, pg. 2005
DEICHMANN SKO APS—See Deichmann SE; *Int'l*, pg. 2005
DESIGNER BRANDS, INC.—See Schottenstein Stores Corporation; *U.S. Private*, pg. 3569
DESMAZIERES SA; *Int'l*, pg. 2045
DINUCCIO LTD.—See The New York Look Inc.; *U.S. Private*, pg. 4083
DOSENBACH OCHSNER AG—See Deichmann SE; *Int'l*, pg. 2005
EBUYS, INC.—See Schottenstein Stores Corporation; *U.S. Private*, pg. 3569
EJ'S SHOES INC.; *U.S. Private*, pg. 1348
ESCO LTD.; *U.S. Private*, pg. 1425
FABCO ENTERPRISES INC.; *U.S. Private*, pg. 1458
FAMOUS FOOTWEAR—See Caleres, Inc.; *U.S. Public*, pg. 422
FARYLROBIN FOOTWEAR; *U.S. Private*, pg. 1481
FILA SPORT TAIWAN LTD.—See FILA Holdings Corporation; *Int'l*, pg. 2662
FLEET FEET, INC.; *U.S. Private*, pg. 1541
FLIP FLOP SHOPS; *U.S. Private*, pg. 1545
FOOT LOCKER AUSTRALIA, INC.—See Foot Locker, Inc.; *U.S. Public*, pg. 863
FOOT LOCKER BELGIUM B.V.B.A.—See Foot Locker, Inc.; *U.S. Public*, pg. 863
FOOT LOCKER EUROPE B.V.—See Foot Locker, Inc.; *U.S. Public*, pg. 863
FOOT LOCKER EUROPE.COM B.V.—See Foot Locker, Inc.; *U.S. Public*, pg. 863
FOOT LOCKER, INC.; *U.S. Public*, pg. 863
FOOT LOCKER ITALY S.R.L.—See Foot Locker, Inc.; *U.S. Public*, pg. 863
FOOT LOCKER NETHERLANDS B.V.—See Foot Locker, Inc.; *U.S. Public*, pg. 863
FOOT LOCKER RETAIL, INC.—See Foot Locker, Inc.; *U.S. Public*, pg. 863
FOOT LOCKER SWEDEN AKTIEBOLAG—See Foot Locker, Inc.; *U.S. Public*, pg. 863
FOOT LOCKER U.K. LIMITED—See Foot Locker, Inc.; *U.S. Public*, pg. 863

FOOTWAY GROUP AB; *Int'l*, pg. 2728
FREED OF LONDON LTD.—See Freed of London Ltd.; *Int'l*, pg. 2769
FUSION RETAIL BRANDS, PTY. LTD.; *Int'l*, pg. 2849
GENESCO BRANDS, LLC—See Genesco Inc.; *U.S. Public*, pg. 930
GENESCO INC.; *U.S. Public*, pg. 930
GENESCO MERGER COMPANY, INC.—See Genesco Inc.; *U.S. Public*, pg. 930
GERLER & SON, INC.—See Hardy Capital Corporation; *Int'l*, pg. 3273
G.H. BASS & CO.—See G-III Apparel Group, Ltd.; *U.S. Public*, pg. 894
GINZA YOSHINOYA CO., LTD.; *Int'l*, pg. 2977
GREATS BRAND, INC.—See Unified Commerce Group; *U.S. Private*, pg. 4282
HANIG'S FOOTWEAR INC.; *U.S. Private*, pg. 1853
H&F SHOES (THAILAND) CO., LTD.—See Aurelius Equity Opportunities SE & Co. KGaA; *Int'l*, pg. 708
HITCHCOCK SHOES, INC.; *U.S. Private*, pg. 1953
HOUSER SHOES INCORPORATED; *U.S. Private*, pg. 1992
HUSH PUPPIES RETAIL, LLC—See Wolverine World Wide, Inc.; *U.S. Public*, pg. 2377
JGEAR; *U.S. Private*, pg. 2207
JOHN REYER COMPANY; *U.S. Private*, pg. 2224
JOHNSTON & MURPHY CO.—See Genesco Inc.; *U.S. Public*, pg. 930
JOHNSTON & MURPHY RETAIL/WHOLESALE STORES—See Genesco Inc.; *U.S. Public*, pg. 930
KURT GEIGER LIMITED—See Cinven Limited; *Int'l*, pg. 1612
LADY FOOT LOCKER—See Foot Locker, Inc.; *U.S. Public*, pg. 863
LA FAVORITA INC.—See Novus Inc.; *U.S. Private*, pg. 2968
LC SUREFOOT, INC.; *U.S. Private*, pg. 2403
LEBOS SHOE STORE INC.; *U.S. Private*, pg. 2409
L&M FOOTWEAR INC.; *U.S. Private*, pg. 2363
MARTY SHOES, INC.; *U.S. Private*, pg. 2597
MATHERS SHOES PTY LTD.—See Fusion Retail Brands, Pty. Ltd.; *Int'l*, pg. 2849
MILROD ENTERPRISES; *U.S. Private*, pg. 2738
MR. ALAN'S MEN'S BOOTERY INC.—See Deichmann SE; *Int'l*, pg. 2005
MY BOOT STORE, INC.—See Northern Imports, Inc.; *U.S. Private*, pg. 2953
NEW BALANCE CANADA, INC.—See New Balance Athletic Shoe, Inc.; *U.S. Private*, pg. 2892
NFINITY ATHLETIC CORPORATION; *U.S. Private*, pg. 2923
NIKE CANADA LTD.—See NIKE, Inc.; *U.S. Public*, pg. 1529
NIKE DENMARK APS—See NIKE, Inc.; *U.S. Public*, pg. 1529
NIKE FRANCE S.A.R.L.—See NIKE, Inc.; *U.S. Public*, pg. 1529
NIKE GESELLSCHAFT M.B.H.—See NIKE, Inc.; *U.S. Public*, pg. 1529
NIKE ITALY S.R.L.—See NIKE, Inc.; *U.S. Public*, pg. 1529
NIKE RETAIL SERVICES INC.—See NIKE, Inc.; *U.S. Public*, pg. 1529
NIKE SWEDEN AB—See NIKE, Inc.; *U.S. Public*, pg. 1529
NIKE (U.K.) LIMITED—See NIKE, Inc.; *U.S. Public*, pg. 1529
NORTHERN IMPORTS, INC.; *U.S. Private*, pg. 2953
NOVUS INC.; *U.S. Private*, pg. 2968
OLYMPIA SPORTS INC.; *U.S. Private*, pg. 3012
ON A SHOESTRING, INC.; *U.S. Private*, pg. 3018
OPPEDISANO'S BOOTERY; *U.S. Private*, pg. 3033
PACIFIC SUNWEAR STORES LLC—See Golden Gate Capital Management II, LLC; *U.S. Private*, pg. 1731
PALM USA INC.; *U.S. Private*, pg. 3080
PAYLESS SHOESOURCE DE GUATEMALA LTDA.—See Payless Holdings LLC; *U.S. Private*, pg. 3117
PAYLESS SHOESOURCE, INC.—See Payless Holdings LLC; *U.S. Private*, pg. 3117
PLANET SHOES; *U.S. Private*, pg. 3196
RACK ROOM SHOES INC.—See Deichmann SE; *Int'l*, pg. 2005
RED'S SHOE BARN INC.; *U.S. Private*, pg. 3376
ROGAN SHOES INCORPORATED—See Shoe Carnival, Inc.; *U.S. Public*, pg. 1875
SAF-GARD SAFETY SHOE CO.; *U.S. Private*, pg. 3523
SAXON SHOES, INC.—See Comfort One Shoes L-1 Corporation; *U.S. Private*, pg. 981
SCHULER SHOES INC.; *U.S. Private*, pg. 3570
SERGIO ROSSI S.P.A.—See BI-Invest Advisors S.A.; *Int'l*, pg. 1017
SHIEKH LLC; *U.S. Private*, pg. 3635
SHOEBUY.COM, INC.—See CriticalPoint Capital, LLC; *U.S. Private*, pg. 1102
SHOE CARNIVAL, INC.; *U.S. Public*, pg. 1875
SHOE CITY G.P. INC.; *U.S. Private*, pg. 3639
SHOEDAZZLE.COM, INC.—See Just Fabulous, Inc.; *U.S. Private*, pg. 2245
SHOEME TECHNOLOGIES LTD.—See Hardy Capital Corporation; *Int'l*, pg. 3273
SHOE SENSATION, INC.—See Prospect Hill Growth Partners, L.P.; *U.S. Private*, pg. 3288
SHOE STATION INC.—See Shoe Carnival, Inc.; *U.S. Public*, pg. 1875

SHOEZOO.COM LLC; *U.S. Private*, pg. 3639
SHOPBOP.COM—See Amazon.com, Inc.; *U.S. Public*, pg. 91
SKECHERS COLOMBIA, S.A.S.—See Skechers U.S.A., Inc.; *U.S. Public*, pg. 1891
SKECHERS EDC S.P.R.L.—See Skechers U.S.A., Inc.; *U.S. Public*, pg. 1891
SKECHERS PERU, S.R.L.—See Skechers U.S.A., Inc.; *U.S. Public*, pg. 1891
SKECHERS S.A.R.L.—See Skechers U.S.A., Inc.; *U.S. Public*, pg. 1891
SKECHERS USA BENELUX B.V.—See Skechers U.S.A., Inc.; *U.S. Public*, pg. 1892
SKECHERS USA DEUTSCHLAND GMBH—See Skechers U.S.A., Inc.; *U.S. Public*, pg. 1892
SKECHERS USA FRANCE SAS—See Skechers U.S.A., Inc.; *U.S. Public*, pg. 1892
SKECHERS USA IBERIA, S.L.—See Skechers U.S.A., Inc.; *U.S. Public*, pg. 1892
SKECHERS USA ITALIA S.R.L.—See Skechers U.S.A., Inc.; *U.S. Public*, pg. 1892
SKECHERS USA LTD.—See Skechers U.S.A., Inc.; *U.S. Public*, pg. 1892
SKECHERS VIETNAM CO. LTD.—See Skechers U.S.A., Inc.; *U.S. Public*, pg. 1892
SNIPES SE—See Deichmann SE; *Int'l*, pg. 2005
SOUTHERN LEATHER COMPANY; *U.S. Private*, pg. 3732
SPORTSHOE CENTER, INC.; *U.S. Private*, pg. 3761
SPORTS ZONE INC.; *U.S. Private*, pg. 3761
THE STRIDE RITE CORPORATION—See Wolverine World Wide, Inc.; *U.S. Public*, pg. 2377
SUPER RUNNERS SHOP, INC.—See Surefoot Inc; *U.S. Private*, pg. 3883
TIENDAS LA GLORIA INC.; *U.S. Private*, pg. 4168
TO BOOT NEW YORK INC.; *U.S. Private*, pg. 4180
TOMS SHOES, LLC—See Bain Capital, LP; *U.S. Private*, pg. 447
TRADEHOME SHOE STORES, INC.; *U.S. Private*, pg. 4202
TREDEX GMBH—See Foot Locker, Inc.; *U.S. Public*, pg. 864
UNISA—See Unisa Holdings Incorporated; *U.S. Private*, pg. 4286
UNIVERSAL BOOT SHOPS, A CALIFORNIA GENERAL PARTNERSHIP—See Apartment Investment and Management Company; *U.S. Public*, pg. 144
THE WALKING COMPANY HOLDINGS, INC.; *U.S. Private*, pg. 4133
THE WALKING COMPANY, INC.—See The Walking Company Holdings, Inc.; *U.S. Private*, pg. 4133
WEXNER COMPANIES INC.; *U.S. Private*, pg. 4502
ZAPPOS.COM, INC.—See Amazon.com, Inc.; *U.S. Public*, pg. 91

458310 — JEWELRY RETAILERS

ABN INTERNATIONAL DIAMOND DIVISION—See ABN AMRO Group N.V.; *Int'l*, pg. 65
A.H. RIISE STORES; *U.S. Private*, pg. 26
ALEX & ANI LLC; *U.S. Private*, pg. 162
AL-FUTTAIM WATCHES AND JEWELLERY—See Al-Futtaim Private Company LLC; *Int'l*, pg. 285
AMERICAN FINDINGS CORPORATION; *U.S. Private*, pg. 234
ASIAN STAR JEWELS PRIVATE LIMITED—See Asian Star Company Ltd; *Int'l*, pg. 619
ASPIAL CORPORATION LIMITED; *Int'l*, pg. 630
ASPIAL-LEE HWA JEWELLERY PTE. LTD.—See Aspial Corporation Limited; *Int'l*, pg. 630
AURUM GROUP LIMITED—See Apollo Global Management, Inc.; *U.S. Public*, pg. 167
AWAD BROTHERS INC.; *U.S. Private*, pg. 410
BARED AND SONS INC.; *U.S. Private*, pg. 474
BARMAKIAN JEWELERS; *U.S. Private*, pg. 476
B.C. CLARK INC.; *U.S. Private*, pg. 420
THE BEN BRIDGE CORPORATION—See Berkshire Hathaway Inc.; *U.S. Public*, pg. 316
BEN BRIDGE JEWELER, INC.—See Berkshire Hathaway Inc.; *U.S. Public*, pg. 316
BERRICLE LLC; *U.S. Private*, pg. 538
BIJOUTERIE ADLER SA; *Int'l*, pg. 1022
BOONE & SONS INC.; *U.S. Private*, pg. 616
BORSHEIM JEWELRY COMPANY, INC.—See Berkshire Hathaway Inc.; *U.S. Public*, pg. 303
BRAUNSCHWEIGER BROS., INC.; *U.S. Private*, pg. 641
BROWNLEE JEWELERS OF THE CAROLINAS; *U.S. Private*, pg. 669
BURBERRY ANTWERP NV—See Burberry Group plc; *Int'l*, pg. 1220
BURBERRY (AUSTRIA) GMBH—See Burberry Group plc; *Int'l*, pg. 1220
BURBERRY CZECH REP S.R.O.—See Burberry Group plc; *Int'l*, pg. 1220
BURBERRY (DEUTSCHLAND) GMBH—See Burberry Group plc; *Int'l*, pg. 1220
BURBERRY (SUISSE) SA—See Burberry Group plc; *Int'l*, pg. 1220
CARDOW JEWELERS; *U.S. Private*, pg. 751

CASTLE JEWELRY; *U.S. Private*, pg. 785
CHINA NATIONAL GOLD GROUP GOLD JEWELLERY CO., LTD.; *Int'l*, pg. 1531
CHONG HING GOLDSMITH CORP.; *U.S. Private*, pg. 888
CHOPARD & CIE S.A.; *Int'l*, pg. 1582
CHOW TAI FOOK JEWELLERY CO., LTD.—See Chow Tai Fook Enterprises Limited; *Int'l*, pg. 1584
CITIZEN LATINAMERICA CORP.—See Citizen Watch Co., Ltd.; *Int'l*, pg. 1623
CITIZEN WATCHES AUSTRALIA PTY. LTD.—See Citizen Watch Co., Ltd.; *Int'l*, pg. 1625
CITIZEN WATCHES (H.K.) LTD.—See Citizen Watch Co., Ltd.; *Int'l*, pg. 1625
CITIZEN WATCH EUROPE GMBH—See Citizen Watch Co., Ltd.; *Int'l*, pg. 1624
CITIZEN WATCH ITALY S.P.A.—See Citizen Watch Co., Ltd.; *Int'l*, pg. 1625
CITIZEN WATCH (U.K.) LTD.—See Citizen Watch Co., Ltd.; *Int'l*, pg. 1624
CLEOPATRA'S BARGE FINE JEWELRY; *U.S. Private*, pg. 940
COMMERCIAL SERVICES INC.; *U.S. Private*, pg. 984
COOPER & COMPANY INC.; *U.S. Private*, pg. 1040
CTF WATCH LIMITED—See Chow Tai Fook Enterprises Limited; *Int'l*, pg. 1584
CUFFLINKS.COM; *U.S. Private*, pg. 1120
DAMIANI S.P.A.; *Int'l*, pg. 1957
DASWANI V. I. INC.; *U.S. Private*, pg. 1162
DAVID BIRNBAUM/RARE 1 CORPORATION; *U.S. Private*, pg. 1169
DE BEERS DIAMOND JEWELLERS US, INC.—See Anglo American PLC; *Int'l*, pg. 462
DE BEERS UK LIMITED—See Anglo American PLC; *Int'l*, pg. 462
DE VONS JEWELERS; *U.S. Private*, pg. 1181
DEXCLUSIVE; *U.S. Private*, pg. 1220
THE DIAMOND DISTRICT LLC; *U.S. Private*, pg. 4021
DIAMONDS DIRECT ONLINE USA, LLC; *U.S. Private*, pg. 1224
DIAMONDS DIRECT USA OF INDIANAPOLIS, INC.—See Diamonds Direct Online USA, LLC; *U.S. Private*, pg. 1224
DICKSON CONCEPTS (INTERNATIONAL) LIMITED; *Int'l*, pg. 2112
DON ROBERTO JEWELERS INC.; *U.S. Private*, pg. 1258
DOUBLE DIAMOND DELAWARE INC.; *U.S. Private*, pg. 1265
D. P. ABHUSHAN LTD.; *Int'l*, pg. 1900
D&Q JEWELLERY CO., LTD.—See Festaria Holdings Co., Ltd.; *Int'l*, pg. 2646
DUNKIN'S DIAMONDS INC.; *U.S. Private*, pg. 1289
E.B. HORN CO.; *U.S. Private*, pg. 1304
ELEGANT ILLUSIONS, INC.; *U.S. Private*, pg. 1356
ELINI BVBA; *Int'l*, pg. 2361
ELINI DESIGNS CORP.—See Elini BVBA; *Int'l*, pg. 2361
EMPEROR WATCH & JEWELLERY LIMITED; *Int'l*, pg. 2386
ENGELHARD METALS AG—See BASF SE; *Int'l*, pg. 875
ENGELHARD METALS LTD.—See BASF SE; *Int'l*, pg. 875
FACETS FINE JEWELRY, LLC—See Pohlad Companies; *U.S. Private*, pg. 3220
FASHION WORLD INC.; *U.S. Private*, pg. 1481
FINK'S JEWELERS INC.; *U.S. Private*, pg. 1510
FJ BENJAMIN FASHIONS (HK) LTD.—See FJ Benjamin Holdings Ltd.; *Int'l*, pg. 2697
FJ BENJAMIN SINGAPORE PTE. LTD.—See FJ Benjamin Holdings Ltd.; *Int'l*, pg. 2697
FOLLI FOLLIE JAPAN, LTD.—See Folli Follie S.A.; *Int'l*, pg. 2721
FOLLI FOLLIE UK LTD.—See Folli Follie S.A.; *Int'l*, pg. 2721
FOSSIL SWITZERLAND GMBH—See Fossil Group, Inc.; *U.S. Public*, pg. 875
FRED MEYER JEWELERS, INC.—See The Kroger Co.; *U.S. Public*, pg. 2107
FUJIAN IDEAL JEWELLERY INDUSTRIAL CO., LTD.; *Int'l*, pg. 2818
GEM JEWELRY INC.; *U.S. Private*, pg. 1657
GEM SHOPPING NETWORK, INC.—See Sun Capital Partners, Inc.; *U.S. Private*, pg. 3859
GLEIM THE JEWELER INC.; *U.S. Private*, pg. 1708
GOLD & DIAMOND SOURCE; *U.S. Private*, pg. 1726
GOLDENWEST DIAMOND CORPORATION; *U.S. Private*, pg. 1734
GOLDHEART BULLION PTE. LTD.—See Aspial Corporation Limited; *Int'l*, pg. 630
GOLDKART JEWELS LIMITED; *Int'l*, pg. 3033
GOLD & SILVER BUYERS; *U.S. Private*, pg. 1727
THE GRACE LIMITED—See Citizen Watch Co., Ltd.; *Int'l*, pg. 1625
GRAFF DIAMONDS (NEW YORK) INC.—See Graff Diamonds International Ltd.; *Int'l*, pg. 3050
GREENBERG'S JEWELERS INC.; *U.S. Private*, pg. 1775
GULFCOAST COIN & JEWELRY, LLC; *U.S. Private*, pg. 1817
GUNDERSON'S JEWELERS; *U.S. Private*, pg. 1818
HAIKOU PEACE BASE INDUSTRY DEVELOPMENT CO. LTD.—See CAQ Holdings Limited; *Int'l*, pg. 1319
HALTOM'S JEWELERS INC.; *U.S. Private*, pg. 1846

HANNOUSH JEWELERS INC.; *U.S. Private*, pg. 1855
HARRIS ORIGINALS OF NY., INC.; *U.S. Private*, pg. 1870
HARRY RITCHIE JEWELER INC.; *U.S. Private*, pg. 1872
HARTGERS DIAMONDS, LTD.; *U.S. Private*, pg. 1873
HELZBERG'S DIAMOND SHOPS, INC.—See Berkshire Hathaway Inc.; *U.S. Public*, pg. 306
H.E. MURDOCK CO. INC.; *U.S. Private*, pg. 1826
HISTOIRE D'OR S.A.S.—See Bridgepoint Group Plc; *Int'l*, pg. 1155
HITIT GOLD KUYUMCULUK VE MUCEVHERAT SAN. VE TIC. A.S.—See Hitit Holding A.S.; *Int'l*, pg. 3426
HITIT MODA TASARIM MAGAZACLK GIYIM MUCEVHERAT SAN.TIC.LTD.STI.—See Hitit Holding A.S.; *Int'l*, pg. 3427
HOFF DIAMONDS & GEMS; *U.S. Private*, pg. 1959
H. STERN JEWELERS, INC.—See H. Stern Com & Ind., S.A.; *Int'l*, pg. 3195
HYDE PARK INC.; *U.S. Private*, pg. 2017
INTERNATIONAL LUXURY PRODUCTS, INC.; *U.S. Public*, pg. 1154
J. B. HUDSON JEWELERS CO—See Pohlad Companies; *U.S. Private*, pg. 3220
JENSEN JEWELERS OF IDAHO LLC; *U.S. Private*, pg. 2200
JEWELERS INC.; *U.S. Private*, pg. 2204
THE JEWELERS; *U.S. Private*, pg. 4059
JEWELRY ASSET MANAGERS INC.—See Bookoff Group Holdings Ltd.; *Int'l*, pg. 1110
JEWELRY TO YOUR DOORSTEP; *U.S. Private*, pg. 2205
JUDITH RIPKA COMPANIES INC.; *U.S. Private*, pg. 2242
JUWELO ITALIA S.R.L.—See Elumeo SE; *Int'l*, pg. 2371
K BHINDI INTERNATIONAL; *U.S. Private*, pg. 2249
KMA SUNBELT TRADING CORP.; *U.S. Private*, pg. 2321
KRANICH'S JEWELERS, INC.; *U.S. Private*, pg. 2349
LAURA PEARCE, LTD.; *U.S. Private*, pg. 2398
LAZARE KAPLAN BELGIUM N.V.—See Lazare Kaplan International, Inc.; *U.S. Private*, pg. 2402
LEE HWA JEWELLERY PTE. LTD.—See Aspial Corporation Limited; *Int'l*, pg. 630
LEE MICHAELS JEWELERS INC.; *U.S. Private*, pg. 2413
LEVY JEWELERS INC.; *U.S. Private*, pg. 2437
LEXINGTON JEWELERS EXCHANGE; *U.S. Private*, pg. 2440
LITTLE SWITZERLAND, INC.—See NXP Corp.; *U.S. Private*, pg. 2975
LONG'S JEWELERS LTD.; *U.S. Private*, pg. 2492
LUCARDIE BV—See CVC Capital Partners SICAV-FIS S.A.; *Int'l*, pg. 1886
LUX BOND & GREEN INCORPORATED; *U.S. Private*, pg. 2518
LUXURY BRAND HOLDINGS; *U.S. Private*, pg. 2518
MAIDEN LANE JEWELRY, LTD.; *U.S. Private*, pg. 2551
MANFREDI OF GREENWICH, LTD.; *U.S. Private*, pg. 2563
MARKMANS DIAMOND BROKERS INC.; *U.S. Private*, pg. 2582
MAUI DIVERS OF HAWAII, LTD.; *U.S. Private*, pg. 2614
MAYOR'S JEWELERS OF FLORIDA, INC.—See Apollo Global Management, Inc.; *U.S. Public*, pg. 167
MGI LUXURY GROUP, S.A.—See Movado Group, Inc.; *U.S. Public*, pg. 1479
MICHAELS ENTERPRISES INC.; *U.S. Private*, pg. 2699
MICHAELS INC.—See Michaels Enterprises Inc.; *U.S. Private*, pg. 2699
MICHELSON JEWELERS; *U.S. Private*, pg. 2700
MONDERA.COM; *U.S. Private*, pg. 2769
MONEX DEPOSIT COMPANY; *U.S. Private*, pg. 2770
MOODY'S JEWELRY INC.; *U.S. Private*, pg. 2778
MORGAN JEWELERS OF SALT LAKE CITY; *U.S. Private*, pg. 2783
MRA INTERNATIONAL, INC.; *U.S. Private*, pg. 2805
NA HOKU, INC.; *U.S. Private*, pg. 2829
NANITAS INC.; *U.S. Private*, pg. 2833
NATIONAL PAWN—See Envela Corporation; *U.S. Public*, pg. 780
NXP CORP.; *U.S. Private*, pg. 2975
POLLACK CORPORATION; *U.S. Private*, pg. 3224
PROVIDENT JEWELRY & LOAN, INC.; *U.S. Private*, pg. 3295
REEDS JEWELERS, INC.; *U.S. Private*, pg. 3383
ROBBINS 8TH & WALNUT; *U.S. Private*, pg. 3456
ROBBINS BROTHERS; *U.S. Private*, pg. 3456
ROBBINS DIAMONDS; *U.S. Private*, pg. 3456
ROGER ENTERPRISES INC.—See Rogers & Hollands Enterprises Inc.; *U.S. Private*, pg. 3471
ROGERS & HOLLANDS ENTERPRISES INC.; *U.S. Private*, pg. 3471
ROGERS JEWELRY COMPANY; *U.S. Private*, pg. 3472
ROSS-SIMONS INC.—See Nonantum Capital Partners LLC; *U.S. Private*, pg. 2934
ROYAL HAWAIIAN HERITAGE JEWELRY LTD.; *U.S. Private*, pg. 3492
R&S ANTIQUES, INC.; *U.S. Private*, pg. 3333
SCHWARTZ JEWELERS; *U.S. Private*, pg. 3572
SCHWARZSCHILD JEWELERS, INC.; *U.S. Private*, pg. 3572
SETA CORPORATION OF BOCA, INC.; *U.S. Private*, pg. 3617
SHELDONS OF OCEANSIDE INC.; *U.S. Private*, pg. 3631

SHERWOOD MANAGEMENT CO. INC.—See Sheldons of Oceanside Inc.; *U.S. Private*, pg. 3631
SHREVE CRUMP & LOW COMPANY; *U.S. Private*, pg. 3643
SILPADA DESIGNS LLC—See Berkshire Hathaway Inc.; *U.S. Public*, pg. 316
SILVERBERG JEWELRY COMPANY; *U.S. Private*, pg. 3662
SISSY'S LOG CABIN, INC.; *U.S. Private*, pg. 3675
S. JOSEPH & SONS; *U.S. Private*, pg. 3515
SPARKLE, LLC; *U.S. Private*, pg. 3746
SUAREZ CORPORATION INDUSTRIES; *U.S. Private*, pg. 3846
TAPPER'S; *U.S. Private*, pg. 3932
THALHEIMER'S JEWELERS, INC.; *U.S. Private*, pg. 3979
TOKYO CITIZEN CORPORATION—See Citizen Watch Co., Ltd.; *Int'l*, pg. 1625
TOURNEAU, LLC—See Bucherer AG; *Int'l*, pg. 1209
TRADITIONAL JEWELERS INC.; *U.S. Private*, pg. 4203
VENTURA WATCH AG—See Herald Holdings Limited; *Int'l*, pg. 3358
VILLAGE JEWELERS GROUP INC.; *U.S. Private*, pg. 4384
WITH CLARITY INC.; *U.S. Private*, pg. 4550
YAMRON JEWELERS; *U.S. Private*, pg. 4585

458320 — LUGGAGE AND LEATHER GOODS RETAILERS

BAG N BAGGAGE; *U.S. Private*, pg. 425
BENTLEY GROUP; *Int'l*, pg. 977
BRIGGS & RILEY TRAVELWARE—See United States Luggage Company, LLC; *U.S. Private*, pg. 4299
BUXTON ACQUISITION CO., LLC; *U.S. Private*, pg. 698
COLORADO BAG N' BAGGAGE; *U.S. Private*, pg. 973
DESA DERI SANAYI VE TICARET A.S.; *Int'l*, pg. 2043
DGB LUGGAGE & LEATHER LLC; *U.S. Private*, pg. 1221
EXCELLED SHEEPSKIN & LEATHER COAT CORPORATION—See Excelled Sheepskin & Leather Coat Corporation; *U.S. Private*, pg. 1445
THE HIDE & LEATHER HOUSE; *U.S. Private*, pg. 4052
THE LEATHER FACTORY OF CANADA LTD.—See Tandy Leather Factory, Inc.; *U.S. Public*, pg. 1980
MORI LUGGAGE AND GIFTS INC.; *U.S. Private*, pg. 2785
SAMSARA LUGGAGE, INC.; *U.S. Public*, pg. 1839
SANDWALK FAR EAST LIMITED—See Elegance Optical International Holdings Ltd.; *Int'l*, pg. 2355
SANTA FE LEATHER CORPORATION; *U.S. Private*, pg. 3547
SENA CASES; *U.S. Private*, pg. 3605
T. ANTHONY LTD.; *U.S. Private*, pg. 3911

459110 — SPORTING GOODS RETAILERS

2ND WIND EXERCISE EQUIPMENT; *U.S. Private*, pg. 7
ACADEMY, LTD.—See Academy Sports and Outdoors, Inc.; *U.S. Public*, pg. 27
ACTIVE SPORTS LIFESTYLE USA, LLC; *U.S. Private*, pg. 70
ACTIVINSTINCT LTD.; *Int'l*, pg. 120
ADIDAS (IRELAND) LTD.—See adidas AG; *Int'l*, pg. 146
ADRENALINA; *U.S. Private*, pg. 82
ADVENTURE 16 INC.; *U.S. Private*, pg. 109
AERO TECH DESIGNS CYCLING APPAREL; *U.S. Private*, pg. 118
ALL3SPORTS, INC.—See C.C. Clark, Inc.; *U.S. Private*, pg. 706
AL'S GOLDFISH LURE CO.—See Stuart Sports Specialties, Inc.; *U.S. Private*, pg. 3843
ALTERITY INC.—See Symphony Technology Group, LLC; *U.S. Private*, pg. 3902
AMERSPORTS DEUTSCHLAND GMBH—See ANTA Sports Products Limited; *Int'l*, pg. 481
AMER SPORTS JAPAN, INC.—See ANTA Sports Products Limited; *Int'l*, pg. 481
AMER SPORTS NETHERLANDS—See ANTA Sports Products Limited; *Int'l*, pg. 480
AMER SPORTS UK LIMITED—See ANTA Sports Products Limited; *Int'l*, pg. 481
AMER SPORTS UK LTD. - LOGISTICS CENTER—See ANTA Sports Products Limited; *Int'l*, pg. 481
ANY MOUNTAIN LTD.; *U.S. Private*, pg. 289
ARISTOCRAT TECHNOLOGIES AUSTRALIA PTY. LTD.—See Aristocrat Leisure Limited; *Int'l*, pg. 566
ARISTOCRAT TECHNOLOGIES EUROPE LIMITED—See Aristocrat Leisure Limited; *Int'l*, pg. 566
ASICS TRADING CO., LTD.—See ASICS Corporation; *Int'l*, pg. 621
ATHLETA (ITM) INC.—See The Gap, Inc.; *U.S. Public*, pg. 2074
THE ATHLETE'S FOOT AUSTRALIA PTY LIMITED—See Accent Group Limited; *Int'l*, pg. 81
BABBOE B.V.—See Accell Group N.V.; *Int'l*, pg. 80
BASS PRO OUTDOORS ONLINE, LLC—See The Great American Outdoors Group LLC; *U.S. Private*, pg. 4037
BEIJING SANFO OUTDOOR PRODUCTS CO., LTD; *Int'l*, pg. 955

459110 — SPORTING GOODS RETA...

BIG 5 SPORTING GOODS CORPORATION; *U.S. Public,* pg. 330
BIKE AMERICA, INC.—See Barmer Enterprises LLC; *U.S. Private,* pg. 476
THE BIKE COOPERATIVE—See CCA Global Partners, Inc.; *U.S. Private,* pg. 799
BIKEEXCHANGE LIMITED; *Int'l,* pg. 1023
BIKE GROUP S.A.—See Giant Manufacturing Co., Ltd.; *Int'l,* pg. 2961
BILL JACKSON, INC.; *U.S. Private,* pg. 557
BLACK DIAMOND EQUIPMENT EUROPE GMBH—See Clarus Corporation; *U.S. Public,* pg. 508
BLUE RIDGE MOUNTAIN SPORTS LTD; *U.S. Private,* pg. 592
BOARDRIDERS CLUB BRATISLAVA S.R.O.—See Leonard Green & Partners, L.P.; *U.S. Private,* pg. 2424
BOB WARD & SONS INCORPORATED; *U.S. Private,* pg. 605
BODY BASICS FITNESS EQUIPMENT; *U.S. Private,* pg. 608
BODY BASICS, INC.; *U.S. Private,* pg. 608
BODYPOWER SPORTS PLC; *Int'l,* pg. 1099
BOLLE (N.Z.) LIMITED—See Alvarez & Marsal, Inc.; *U.S. Private,* pg. 212
BRAND ADDITION GMBH—See Caisse de Depot et Placement du Quebec; *Int'l,* pg. 1254
BRAND ADDITION GMBH—See Generation Investment Management LLP; *Int'l,* pg. 2920
BRISCOE GROUP LIMITED; *Int'l,* pg. 1164
BUSHNELL CORPORATION OF CANADA—See Vista Outdoor Inc.; *U.S. Public,* pg. 2304
BUS SPORT AG—See Fenix Outdoor International AG; *Int'l,* pg. 2634
CABELA'S LLC—See The Great American Outdoors Group LLC; *U.S. Private,* pg. 4038
CABELA'S RETAIL CANADA, INC.—See The Great American Outdoors Group LLC; *U.S. Private,* pg. 4038
CABELA'S RETAIL IL, INC.—See The Great American Outdoors Group LLC; *U.S. Private,* pg. 4038
CABELA'S RETAIL MO, LLC—See The Great American Outdoors Group LLC; *U.S. Private,* pg. 4038
CALLAWAY GOLF BALL OPERATIONS, INC.—See Topgolf Callaway Brands Corp.; *U.S. Public,* pg. 2164
CALLAWAY GOLF INTERACTIVE, INC.—See Topgolf Callaway Brands Corp.; *U.S. Public,* pg. 2164
CAMPMOR INC.; *U.S. Private,* pg. 731
CARTER'S SHOOTING CENTER INC.; *U.S. Private,* pg. 776
CENTURY MARTIAL ART SUPPLY LLC—See Century LLC; *U.S. Private,* pg. 833
CHAPTER 4 CORP.—See EssilorLuxottica SA; *Int'l,* pg. 2512
CHRISTY SPORTS LLC; *U.S. Private,* pg. 892
COLE SPORT, INC.; *U.S. Private,* pg. 966
CONNEXA SPORTS TECHNOLOGIES INC.; *U.S. Public,* pg. 568
COUNTRY CLUB SUPPLY, INC.—See Fore Supply Co.; *U.S. Private,* pg. 1565
CUTLER-OWENS INTERNATIONAL LTD. INC.—See UM Holdings Limited; *U.S. Private,* pg. 4278
CZ-USA; *U.S. Private,* pg. 1136
DACOME INTERNATIONAL LTD.; *Int'l,* pg. 1904
DAVE'S SPORTS CENTER, INC.; *U.S. Private,* pg. 1168
DECATHLON SA; *Int'l,* pg. 1999
DECATHLON USA—See Decathlon SA; *Int'l,* pg. 1999
DICK'S SPORTING GOODS, INC.; *U.S. Public,* pg. 659
THE DIVE SHOP, INC.; *U.S. Private,* pg. 4021
DOVER SADDLERY, INC.—See Webster Equity Partners, LLC; *U.S. Private,* pg. 4467
DUNHAM'S ATHLEISURE CORPORATION; *U.S. Private,* pg. 1289
DUNN'S SPORTING GOODS CO. INC.; *U.S. Private,* pg. 1290
EASTERN MOUNTAIN SPORTS, LLC—See GoDigital Media Group, LLC; *U.S. Private,* pg. 1724
EASTERN OUTFITTERS, INC.—See Frasers Group plc; *Int'l,* pg. 2765
EBERLESTOCK USA LLC; *U.S. Private,* pg. 1324
EDDIE BAUER JAPAN, INC.—See Leonard Green & Partners, L.P.; *U.S. Private,* pg. 2424
EDUARD KETTNER; *Int'l,* pg. 2315
EDWIN WATTS GOLF SHOPS, LLC—See Sun Capital Partners, Inc.; *U.S. Private,* pg. 3859
ESCALADE SPORTS INC; *U.S. Private,* pg. 1424
EUROPA SPORTS PRODUCTS, INC.; *U.S. Private,* pg. 1433
EVANS HOLDINGS LTD.—See Active Private Equity Advisory LLP; *Int'l,* pg. 120
EVOLUCION INNOVATIONS, INC.; *U.S. Private,* pg. 1442
FANCHEST, INC.; *U.S. Private,* pg. 1472
FANSEDGE INCORPORATED—See Kynetic LLC; *U.S. Private,* pg. 2360
FGL SPORTS LTD.—See Canadian Tire Corporation Limited; *Int'l,* pg. 1286
FINCH TURF EQUIPMENT INCORPORATED; *U.S. Private,* pg. 1508
FISHERMANS MARINE SUPPLY INC.; *U.S. Private,* pg. 1535

FITNESS GALLERY INC.; *U.S. Private,* pg. 1536
FLYKE INTERNATIONAL HOLDINGS LTD.; *Int'l,* pg. 2716
FOOTASYLUM PLC—See Aurelius Equity Opportunities SE & Co. KGaA; *Int'l,* pg. 708
FORE SUPPLY CO.; *U.S. Private,* pg. 1565
FRILUFTSLAND A/S—See Fenix Outdoor International AG; *Int'l,* pg. 2634
FRONT SIGHT MANAGEMENT LLC—See Nevada PF LLC; *U.S. Private,* pg. 2891
GAIAM PTY—See Sequential Brands Group, Inc.; *U.S. Public,* pg. 1868
GAMES WORKSHOP ITALIA SRL—See Games Workshop Group PLC; *Int'l,* pg. 2877
GANDER MOUNTAIN COMPANY; *U.S. Private,* pg. 1641
GEARHEAD OUTFITTERS, INC.; *U.S. Private,* pg. 1655
GENE TAYLOR'S SPORTSMEN SUPPLY, INC.; *U.S. Private,* pg. 1660
GIANT COLOMBIA DISANDINA S.A.—See Giant Manufacturing Co., Ltd.; *Int'l,* pg. 2961
GOLFBALLS.COM, INC.; *U.S. Private,* pg. 1736
GOLF DISCOUNT OF ST. LOUIS INCORPORATED; *U.S. Private,* pg. 1736
GOLFERS WAREHOUSE INC.—See Worldwide Golf Enterprises, Inc.; *U.S. Private,* pg. 4569
GOLF ETC. OF AMERICA, INC.; *U.S. Private,* pg. 1736
GOLF GALAXY, INC.—See Dick's Sporting Goods, Inc.; *U.S. Public,* pg. 659
GOLF HOUSE DIREKTVERSAND GMBH; *Int'l,* pg. 3035
GOLF MART INC.; *U.S. Private,* pg. 1736
GOLF & SKI WAREHOUSE INC.; *U.S. Private,* pg. 1735
GOLF TOWN LIMITED—See Fairfax Financial Holdings Limited; *Int'l,* pg. 2606
THE GOLF WAREHOUSE, INC.—See Northern Tool & Equipment Company, Inc.; *U.S. Private,* pg. 2954
GREAT OUTDOOR PROVISION CO.; *U.S. Private,* pg. 1766
THE GREEN MOUNTAIN CORPORATION; *U.S. Private,* pg. 4039
GREGG'S GREENLAKE CYCLE INC.; *U.S. Private,* pg. 1782
GRUPO WILSON, S.A. DE C.V.—See ANTA Sports Products Limited; *Int'l,* pg. 480
GT GOLF HOLDINGS, INC—See Kinzie Capital Partners LP; *U.S. Private,* pg. 2313
HALFORDS NEDERLAND BV; *Int'l,* pg. 3229
HAYWARD POOL EUROPE—See CCMP Capital Advisors, LP; *U.S. Private,* pg. 800
HAYWARD POOL EUROPE—See MSD Capital, L.P.; *U.S. Private,* pg. 2807
HENRY MODELL & COMPANY, INC.; *U.S. Private,* pg. 1919
H&H GUN RANGE-SHOOTING SPORTS OUTLET; *U.S. Private,* pg. 1822
HK SPORTS & GOLF AKTIEBOLAG—See Frasers Group plc; *Int'l,* pg. 2765
HOIGAARD'S, INC.—See Vail Resorts, Inc.; *U.S. Public,* pg. 2271
HOLIDAY DIVER INC.; *U.S. Private,* pg. 1963
HUDSON TRAIL OUTFITTERS LTD.; *U.S. Private,* pg. 2002
HYPERICE, INC.; *U.S. Private,* pg. 2019
ISLAND WATER SPORTS, INC.; *U.S. Private,* pg. 2145
JAY'S SPORTING GOODS, INC.; *U.S. Private,* pg. 2192
JIM FLETCHER ARCHERY AIDS, INC.—See Escalade, Incorporated; *U.S. Public,* pg. 793
JOHNNY MACS' SPORTING GOODS STORES; *U.S. Private,* pg. 2226
JOHNSON OUTDOORS CANADA, INC.—See Johnson Outdoors Inc.; *U.S. Public,* pg. 1200
JONATHAN'S LANDING, INC.; *U.S. Private,* pg. 2231
KBK TECHNOLOGIES, INC.; *U.S. Private,* pg. 2268
K.G. MOTORS, INC.—See The Zabel Companies, LLC; *U.S. Private,* pg. 4140
KYNETIC LLC; *U.S. Private,* pg. 2360
LIZARD SKINS, LLC—See Fox Factory Holding Corp.; *U.S. Public,* pg. 877
LONGSTRETH SPORTING GOODS, LLC—See Roebling Management Company, LLC; *U.S. Private,* pg. 3470
MCNETT EUROPE—See GEAR AID, Inc.; *U.S. Private,* pg. 1654
MEGA SPORTS CO., LTD—See AEON Co., Ltd.; *Int'l,* pg. 178
MICHIGAN SPORTING GOODS DISTRIBUTORS INC.; *U.S. Private,* pg. 2701
MICKEY FINN STORES INC.; *U.S. Private,* pg. 2701
MILTON TRANSPORTATION INC.; *U.S. Private,* pg. 2739
MITCHELL & NESS NOSTALGIA COMPANY—See Juggernaut Management, LLC; *U.S. Private,* pg. 2243
MODELL'S SPORTING GOODS INC.—See Henry Modell & Company, Inc.; *U.S. Private,* pg. 1919
MODERN EVERYDAY, INC.—See Live Ventures Incorporated; *U.S. Public,* pg. 1332
MOOSEJAW MOUNTAINEERING & BACKCOUNTRY TRAVEL, INC.—See Parallel Investment Partners LLC; *U.S. Private,* pg. 3092
MOUNTAIN SPORTS USA LLC—See Frasers Group plc; *Int'l,* pg. 2765
MYSTIC VALLEY WHEEL WORKS INCORPORATED; *U.S. Private,* pg. 2826
NEPTUNE MOUNTAINEERING, INC.—See The Ute Mountaineer, Ltd.; *U.S. Private,* pg. 4130

OMAREEF SPAIN SL—See Leonard Green & Partners, L.P.; *U.S. Private,* pg. 2424
OMEGA SPORTS INC.; *U.S. Private,* pg. 3015
THE ORVIS COMPANY, INC.; *U.S. Private,* pg. 4089
OUTDOOR WORLD INC.; *U.S. Private,* pg. 3051
OVERTON'S INC.—See Gander Mountain Company; *U.S. Private,* pg. 1641
PACHMAYR—See Lyman Products Corporation; *U.S. Private,* pg. 2520
PARTIOAITTA OY—See Fenix Outdoor International AG; *Int'l,* pg. 2634
PEACHTREE TENTS AND EVENTS, LLC—See Quest Events, LLC; *U.S. Private,* pg. 3325
PERFORMANCE CYCLING LIMITED—See Halfords Group plc; *Int'l,* pg. 3229
PERRY SPORT BV—See CVC Capital Partners SICAV-FIS S.A.; *Int'l,* pg. 1886
PING CANADA CORPORATION—See Karsten Manufacturing Corporation; *U.S. Private,* pg. 2263
PLAY IT AGAIN SPORTS; *U.S. Private,* pg. 3212
POLLINI AUSTRIA GMBH—See Aeffe SpA; *Int'l,* pg. 173
POLLINI RETAIL S.R.L.—See Aeffe SpA; *Int'l,* pg. 173
PPH.FORDEX SP.Z.O.O.—See Goldwin, Inc.; *Int'l,* pg. 3035
PRICE COSTCO CANADA HOLDINGS INC.—See Costco Wholesale Corporation; *U.S. Public,* pg. 587
PROACTIVE SPORTS INC.—See Kinzie Capital Partners LP; *U.S. Private,* pg. 2313
PRO SPORTS MEMORABILIA, INC.—See Kynetic LLC; *U.S. Private,* pg. 2360
PUSH PEDAL PULL, INC.; *U.S. Private,* pg. 3307
RAD POWER BIKES LLC; *U.S. Private,* pg. 3342
RAMSEY OUTDOOR STORE INC.; *U.S. Private,* pg. 3352
RANK + RALLY, LLC—See Compass Group PLC; *Int'l,* pg. 1752
REBEL SPORT LIMITED—See Briscoe Group Limited; *Int'l,* pg. 1164
RECREATIONAL EQUIPMENT, INC.; *U.S. Private,* pg. 3372
REDDEN MARINE SUPPLY INC.; *U.S. Private,* pg. 3377
RETAIL CONCEPTS, INC.; *U.S. Private,* pg. 3411
RIDE SPORTS ANZ PTY LTD—See Domino's Pizza Enterprises Ltd.; *Int'l,* pg. 2162
ROBINSON SPORTS INC.; *U.S. Private,* pg. 3462
ROCKBOTTOMGOLF.COM; *U.S. Private,* pg. 3465
ROCKTAPE, INC.—See Berkshire Partners LLC; *U.S. Private,* pg. 535
RUNNERS POINT ADMINISTRATION GMBH—See Foot Locker, Inc.; *U.S. Public,* pg. 864
RUNNERS POINT WARENHANDELSGESELLSCHAFT MBH—See Foot Locker, Inc.; *U.S. Public,* pg. 863
SIA SPORTLAND—See Frasers Group plc; *Int'l,* pg. 2765
SILVER DENKEN CO., LTD.—See Citizen Watch Co., Ltd.; *Int'l,* pg. 1625
THE SKI MARKET LTD. INC.; *U.S. Private,* pg. 4118
SMOOTH FITNESS—See InternetFitness.com, Inc.; *U.S. Private,* pg. 2122
SOLO BRANDS, INC.; *U.S. Public,* pg. 1901
SOUTHEAST AREA COUNCIL—See Dairy Farmers of America, Inc.; *U.S. Private,* pg. 1146
SPECIALTY SPORTS VENTURE LLC—See Vail Resorts, Inc.; *U.S. Public,* pg. 2271
SPORTAMORE AB—See Footway Group AB; *Int'l,* pg. 2728
SPORT CHALET, INC.—See Independence Capital Partners, LLC; *U.S. Private,* pg. 2057
SPORTING LIFE INC.—See Fairfax Financial Holdings Limited; *Int'l,* pg. 2608
SPORTLAND EESTIE A.S.—See Frasers Group plc; *Int'l,* pg. 2765
SPORTS DIRECT MST SDN. BHD.—See Frasers Group plc; *Int'l,* pg. 2765
SPORTS DIRECT SPAIN, S.L.U.—See Frasers Group plc; *Int'l,* pg. 2765
SPORT SEASONS LP; *U.S. Private,* pg. 3760
SPORTS ENDEAVORS INC.; *U.S. Private,* pg. 3761
THE SPORTSMAN'S GUIDE OUTLET, INC.—See Northern Tool & Equipment Company, Inc.; *U.S. Private,* pg. 2954
SPORTSMAN'S WAREHOUSE, INC.—See Sportsman's Warehouse Holdings, Inc.; *U.S. Public,* pg. 1919
SPRINT SPOL S.R.O.—See Goldwin, Inc.; *Int'l,* pg. 3035
STEAMBOAT SKI & RESORT CORPORATION—See KSL Capital Partners, LLC; *U.S. Public,* pg. 2354
SUMMIT SPORTS, INC.; *U.S. Private,* pg. 3857
SUN COMPANY, INC.; *U.S. Private,* pg. 3862
SURF ASSOCIATES, INC.; *U.S. Private,* pg. 3883
SURF HARDWARE INTERNATIONAL EUROPE SARL—See Gowing Brothers Limited; *Int'l,* pg. 3044
SUTHERLAND LUMBER & HOME CENTER INC.; *U.S. Private,* pg. 3886
TABLE TENNIS PRO EUROPE LTD.—See Frasers Group plc; *Int'l,* pg. 2765
TEAM EXPRESS DISTRIBUTING, LLC; *U.S. Private,* pg. 3949
TOTAL HOCKEY, INC.; *U.S. Private,* pg. 4191
TREDZ LIMITED—See Halfords Group plc; *Int'l,* pg. 3229
TRIGGER POINT TECHNOLOGIES; *U.S. Private,* pg. 4230
TRI-STATE DISTRIBUTORS INC.; *U.S. Private,* pg. 4223
TRYSPORTS, LLC; *U.S. Private,* pg. 4252
TURNER'S OUTDOORS, INC.; *U.S. Private,* pg. 4261

N.A.I.C.S. INDEX

459210 — BOOK RETAILERS AND ...

UAB SPORTLAND LT—See Frasers Group plc; *Int'l*, pg. 2765
ULTIMATE DIRECTION, INC.—See Exxel Outdoors, Inc.; *U.S. Private*, pg. 1453
US GOLF INC.; *U.S. Private*, pg. 4318
THE UTE MOUNTAINEER, LTD.; *U.S. Private*, pg. 4129
VAL SURF INC.; *U.S. Private*, pg. 4329
VAN'S PRO SHOP—See Worldwide Golf Enterprises, Inc.; *U.S. Private*, pg. 4569
WESTERN SADDLERY & SPORTING GOODS; *U.S. Private*, pg. 4496
WILSON FRANCE S.A.R.L.—See ANTA Sports Products Limited; *Int'l*, pg. 481
WILSON SPORTING GOODS COMPANY KAOHSIUNG BRANCH—See ANTA Sports Products Limited; *Int'l*, pg. 481
WILSON SPORTS EQUIPMENT CANADA SHIELDS—See ANTA Sports Products Limited; *Int'l*, pg. 481
WORLD CLASSICS—See Topco Holdings Inc.; *U.S. Private*, pg. 4187
ZEBCO—See W.C. Bradley Co.; *U.S. Private*, pg. 4419

459120 — HOBBY, TOY, AND GAME RETAILERS

7SEAS ENTERTAINMENT LIMITED; *Int'l*, pg. 15
AARON BROTHERS, INC.—See Apollo Global Management, Inc.; *U.S. Public*, pg. 164
A.C. MOORE ARTS & CRAFTS, INC.—See Sbar's, Inc.; *U.S. Private*, pg. 3559
AMUSE GROUP HOLDING LTD.; *Int'l*, pg. 442
ANGEL HOLDINGS GODO KAISHA; *Int'l*, pg. 459
ANIMAX DESIGNS INC.—See Cityneon Holdings Limited; *Int'l*, pg. 1629
ARISTOCRAT TECHNOLOGIES, INC.—See Aristocrat Leisure Limited; *Int'l*, pg. 566
BUILD-A-BEAR WORKSHOP, INC.; *U.S. Public*, pg. 409
CAP CANDY, INC.—See Hasbro, Inc.; *U.S. Public*, pg. 987
CHARISMA BRANDS, LLC; *U.S. Private*, pg. 850
DIAMOND TOOL AND ABRASIVES INC.—See Nautic Partners, LLC; *U.S. Private*, pg. 2871
DISCOUNT SCHOOL SUPPLY—See Brentwood Associates; *U.S. Private*, pg. 646
DREAMBABY N.V.—See Colruyt Group N.V.; *Int'l*, pg. 1705
DUNCAN TOYS COMPANY—See Nordic Group of Companies, Ltd.; *Int'l*, pg. 2936
EPIC GAMES INC.; *U.S. Private*, pg. 1412
GAME DIGITAL PLC—See Frasers Group plc; *Int'l*, pg. 2765
GAME DIGITAL PLC - SPAIN OFFICE—See Frasers Group plc; *Int'l*, pg. 2765
GAMESTOP UK LIMITED—See GameStop Corp.; *U.S. Public*, pg. 896
GAMES WORKSHOP RETAIL INC.—See Games Workshop Group PLC; *Int'l*, pg. 2877
GARDEN RIDGE POTTERY; *U.S. Private*, pg. 1643
GOLIATH GAMES, LLC—See Goliath International Holding BV; *Int'l*, pg. 3036
GORDON COMPANIES INC.; *U.S. Private*, pg. 1742
GROSNOR DISTRIBUTION INC.; *Int'l*, pg. 3088
GS MOBILE, INC.—See GameStop Corp.; *U.S. Public*, pg. 895
HEARTHSONG, INC.—See Evergreen Enterprises, Inc.; *U.S. Private*, pg. 1439
HOBBY LOBBY STORES INC.—See Hob-Lob Limited Partnership; *U.S. Private*, pg. 1958
HOBBY TOWN UNLIMITED, INC.; *U.S. Private*, pg. 1958
HOMESPAN REALTY CO., INC.—See Commerce Group Corp.; *U.S. Public*, pg. 545
JESON ENTERPRISES INC.; *U.S. Private*, pg. 2203
KAZOO & COMPANY; *U.S. Private*, pg. 2267
KIDS STUFF, INC.; *U.S. Private*, pg. 2303
LUKIE GAMES INC.; *U.S. Private*, pg. 2513
MANTECH CO., LTD.—See Abdulla Fouad Holding Co.; *Int'l*, pg. 59
MATTEL ASIA LTD.—See Mattel, Inc.; *U.S. Public*, pg. 1398
MATTEL AUSTRALIA PTY. LTD.—See Mattel, Inc.; *U.S. Public*, pg. 1398
MATTEL B.V. (NETHERLANDS)—See Mattel, Inc.; *U.S. Public*, pg. 1398
MATTEL CANADA, INC.—See Mattel, Inc.; *U.S. Public*, pg. 1398
MATTEL GMBH—See Mattel, Inc.; *U.S. Public*, pg. 1399
MATTEL INTERNATIONAL FINANCE B.V.—See Mattel, Inc.; *U.S. Public*, pg. 1399
MATTEL (UK) LTD.—See Mattel, Inc.; *U.S. Public*, pg. 1398
MGA ENTERTAINMENT (UK) LTD.—See MGA Entertainment, Inc.; *U.S. Private*, pg. 2694
MOBILEATION, INC.; *U.S. Private*, pg. 2757
MONDO TEES, LLC—See Funko Inc.; *U.S. Public*, pg. 893
PEBBLES IN MY POCKET, INC.; *U.S. Private*, pg. 3126
PHILIBERT SARL—See Carrefour SA; *Int'l*, pg. 1346
PLAYMOBIL FUNPARK ORLANDO—See Geobra Brandstatter GmbH & Co. KG; *Int'l*, pg. 2932
PLAYMOBIL USA INC.—See Geobra Brandstatter GmbH & Co. KG; *Int'l*, pg. 2932
SAX ARTS & CRAFTS, INC.—See School Specialty, Inc.; *U.S. Public*, pg. 1848

SMYK S.A.—See Bridgepoint Group Plc; *Int'l*, pg. 1155
STOCKDALE—See Tennessee Farmers Cooperative; *U.S. Private*, pg. 3967
STRAT-O-MATIC MEDIA, LLC; *U.S. Private*, pg. 3833
SUPERHEROSTUFF.COM—See eMerchandise Group LLC; *U.S. Private*, pg. 1380
TOYS "R" US (CANADA) LTD.—See Fairfax Financial Holdings Limited; *Int'l*, pg. 2608
TOYS "R" US JAPAN, LTD.—See WHP Global; *U.S. Private*, pg. 4515
TOYS "R" US PORTUGAL, LIMITADA—See WHP Global; *U.S. Private*, pg. 4515
TOYS "R" US S.A.R.L.—See Cyrus Capital Partners, L.P.; *U.S. Private*, pg. 1135
TOYSRUS.COM (JAPAN), LTD.—See WHP Global; *U.S. Private*, pg. 4515
TROLLANDTOAD.COM; *U.S. Private*, pg. 4241
UMSI INCORPORATED; *U.S. Private*, pg. 4279
WB GAMES INC.—See Warner Bros. Discovery, Inc.; *U.S. Public*, pg. 2328
ZAPF CREATION (POLSKA) SP. Z O.O.—See MGA Entertainment, Inc.; *U.S. Private*, pg. 2694

459130 — SEWING, NEEDLEWORK, AND PIECE GOODS RETAILERS

ACCUQUILT, LLC—See WILsquare Capital LLC; *U.S. Private*, pg. 4532
AMERICAN DORNIER MACHINERY CORPORATION—See Airbus SE; *Int'l*, pg. 242
CALICO CORNERS—See Everfast Inc.; *U.S. Private*, pg. 1438
CHECKER NOTIONS COMPANY INC.; *U.S. Private*, pg. 869
CRAFTS AMERICANA GROUP INC.—See Blue Point Capital Partners, LLC; *U.S. Private*, pg. 590
CRAFTS, ETC! LTD.—See Hob-Lob Limited Partnership; *U.S. Private*, pg. 1958
THE DMC CORPORATION—See Bernard Krief Consultants SA; *Int'l*, pg. 986
EASTMAN STAPLES LIMITED; *Int'l*, pg. 2274
EL TELAR INC.; *U.S. Private*, pg. 1349
EVERFAST INC.; *U.S. Private*, pg. 1438
FABRIC COM, INC.—See Amazon.com, Inc.; *U.S. Public*, pg. 90
GLENOIT FABRICS HG CORP.—See Haixin Group Company Ltd.; *Int'l*, pg. 3218
GLEN RAVEN CUSTOM FABRICS, L.L.C.—See Glen Raven, Inc.; *U.S. Private*, pg. 1709
G STREET FABRICS; *U.S. Private*, pg. 1628
HANCOCK FABRICS, INC.; *U.S. Private*, pg. 1852
HERRSCHNERS, INC.; *U.S. Private*, pg. 1926
JIMMY BEANS WOOL; *U.S. Private*, pg. 2210
JO-ANN STORES, INC.—See Leonard Green & Partners, L.P.; *U.S. Private*, pg. 2426
KEEPSAKE QUILTING, INC.—See The Riverside Company; *U.S. Private*, pg. 4109
MARY MAXIM, INC.; *U.S. Private*, pg. 2599
MARY MAXIM, LTD.—See Mary Maxim, Inc.; *U.S. Private*, pg. 2599
MEZ CRAFTS HUNGARY KFT.—See Aurelius Equity Opportunities SE & Co. KGaA; *Int'l*, pg. 709
MEZ CRAFTS LITHUANIA UAB—See Aurelius Equity Opportunities SE & Co. KGaA; *Int'l*, pg. 709
MEZ CRAFTS PORTUGAL LDA—See Aurelius Equity Opportunities SE & Co. KGaA; *Int'l*, pg. 709
MEZ CRAFTS TEKSTIL ANONIM SIRKET—See Aurelius Equity Opportunities SE & Co. KGaA; *Int'l*, pg. 709
MEZ CRAFTS UK LTD.—See Aurelius Equity Opportunities SE & Co. KGaA; *Int'l*, pg. 709
MEZ FABRA SPAIN S.A.—See Aurelius Equity Opportunities SE & Co. KGaA; *Int'l*, pg. 709
MEZ GMBH—See Aurelius Equity Opportunities SE & Co. KGaA; *Int'l*, pg. 709
MICHAELS STORES, INC.—See Apollo Global Management, Inc.; *U.S. Public*, pg. 164
NANCY'S NOTIONS—See Tacony Corporation; *U.S. Private*, pg. 3921
SEW WHAT, INC.; *U.S. Private*, pg. 3619
SPORTSWEAR STORE INC.; *U.S. Private*, pg. 3761

459140 — MUSICAL INSTRUMENT AND SUPPLIES RETAILERS

AMERICAN AUDIO & VIDEO—See DCC plc; *Int'l*, pg. 1990
AMERICAN MUSIC & SOUND LLC—See DCC plc; *Int'l*, pg. 1990
ANAHEIM BAND INSTRUMENTS, INC.—See Bain Capital, LP; *U.S. Private*, pg. 440
BACH TO ROCK MUSIC SCHOOL, INC.; *U.S. Private*, pg. 422
B.C. RICH GUITARS—See Hanser Holdings International; *U.S. Private*, pg. 1856
BRANDSPINS, LLC; *U.S. Private*, pg. 638
BROOK MAYS MUSIC COMPANY INC.; *U.S. Private*, pg. 663

CASIO BENELUX B.V.—See Casio Computer Co., Ltd.; *Int'l*, pg. 1353
CASIO CANADA, LTD.—See Casio Computer Co., Ltd.; *Int'l*, pg. 1353
CASIO ELECTRONIC TECHNOLOGY (ZHONGSHAN) CO., LTD.—See Casio Computer Co., Ltd.; *Int'l*, pg. 1353
CASIO ESPANA, S.L.—See Casio Computer Co., Ltd.; *Int'l*, pg. 1353
CASIO FRANCE S.A.—See Casio Computer Co., Ltd.; *Int'l*, pg. 1353
CASIO ITALIA S.R.L.—See Casio Computer Co., Ltd.; *Int'l*, pg. 1353
CASIO MEXICO MARKETING, S. DE R. L. DE C.V.—See Casio Computer Co., Ltd.; *Int'l*, pg. 1353
CASIO SCANDINAVIA AS—See Casio Computer Co., Ltd.; *Int'l*, pg. 1353
CASIO SINGAPORE PTE., LTD.—See Casio Computer Co., Ltd.; *Int'l*, pg. 1353
CASIO (THAILAND) CO., LTD.—See Casio Computer Co., Ltd.; *Int'l*, pg. 1353
DADDY'S JUNKY MUSIC STORES; *U.S. Private*, pg. 1144
ERNIE WILLIAMSON, INC.; *U.S. Private*, pg. 1422
EVOLA MUSIC CENTER INC.; *U.S. Private*, pg. 1442
FIRST ACT INC.—See Berkshire Hathaway Inc.; *U.S. Public*, pg. 298
FLETCHER MUSIC CENTERS INC.; *U.S. Private*, pg. 1542
FOX MUSIC, INC.—See Fox Corporation; *U.S. Public*, pg. 876
GENEVA INTERNATIONAL CORPORATION; *U.S. Private*, pg. 1670
GUITAR CENTER, INC.—See Bain Capital, LP; *U.S. Private*, pg. 440
HERMES MUSIC S.A. DE C.V.; *Int'l*, pg. 3363
HERMES TRADING CO. INC.—See Hermes Music S.A. de C.V.; *Int'l*, pg. 3363
HOSHINO BENELUX B.V.—See Hoshino Gakki Co., Ltd.; *Int'l*, pg. 3483
HOSHINO GAKKI HANBAI CO., LTD.—See Hoshino Gakki Co., Ltd.; *Int'l*, pg. 3483
HOSHINO (USA) INC.—See Hoshino Gakki Co., Ltd.; *Int'l*, pg. 3483
JORDAN-KITT MUSIC INC.; *U.S. Private*, pg. 2235
J.W. PEPPER & SON INC.; *U.S. Private*, pg. 2172
KAMAN MUSIC CORPORATION—See TPG Capital, L.P.; *U.S. Public*, pg. 2173
KEYBOARD CONCEPTS INC.; *U.S. Private*, pg. 2294
MARSHALL MUSIC CO.; *U.S. Private*, pg. 2593
MOOG MUSIC INC.—See inMusic, LLC; *U.S. Private*, pg. 2080
MUSIC & ARTS CENTER INC.—See Bain Capital, LP; *U.S. Private*, pg. 440
MUSIC CENTER, INC.; *U.S. Private*, pg. 2817
MUSICIAN'S FRIEND, INC.—See Bain Capital, LP; *U.S. Private*, pg. 440
MUSICNOTES, INC.; *U.S. Private*, pg. 2818
MUSICORP—See TPG Capital, L.P.; *U.S. Public*, pg. 2173
NAXOS DENMARK APS.—See HNH International Ltd.; *Int'l*, pg. 3434
NAXOS DEUTCHLAND GMBH—See HNH International Ltd.; *Int'l*, pg. 3434
NAXOS DEUTSCHLAND MUSIK UND VIDEO VERTRIEBS GMBH—See HNH International Ltd.; *Int'l*, pg. 3434
NAXOS GLOBAL DISTRIBUTION LIMITED—See HNH International Ltd.; *Int'l*, pg. 3434
NAXOS JAPAN INC—See HNH International Ltd.; *Int'l*, pg. 3434
NAXOS KOREA—See HNH International Ltd.; *Int'l*, pg. 3434
NAXOS NORWAY AS—See HNH International Ltd.; *Int'l*, pg. 3434
NAXOS OF CANADA LTD.—See HNH International Ltd.; *Int'l*, pg. 3434
NAXOS SWEDEN AB—See HNH International Ltd.; *Int'l*, pg. 3434
OY FG-NAXOS AB—See HNH International Ltd.; *Int'l*, pg. 3434
PAUL A. SCHMITT MUSIC COMPANY; *U.S. Private*, pg. 3112
ROBERT M. SIDES INC.; *U.S. Private*, pg. 3458
ROMEO MUSIC; *U.S. Private*, pg. 3476
SAM ASH MUSIC CORPORATION; *U.S. Private*, pg. 3535
SHERMAN, CLAY & CO.; *U.S. Private*, pg. 3634
STEINWAY RETAIL DEUTSCHLAND GMBH—See Paulson & Co. Inc.; *U.S. Private*, pg. 3114
SWEETWATER SOUND INC.; *U.S. Private*, pg. 3892
TED BROWN MUSIC COMPANY, INC.; *U.S. Private*, pg. 3957
WASHINGTON MUSIC SALES CENTER; *U.S. Private*, pg. 4447
WEST MUSIC CO.; *U.S. Private*, pg. 4486

459210 — BOOK RETAILERS AND NEWS DEALERS

ABEBOOKS INC.—See Amazon.com, Inc.; *U.S. Public*, pg. 90
AKATEEMINEN KIRJAKAUPPA—See Bonnier AB; *Int'l*, pg. 1108

4115

459210 — BOOK RETAILERS AND ...

AMERICAN COLLEGIATE MARKETING; *U.S. Private*, pg. 227
AUDIBLE GMBH—See Amazon.com, Inc.; *U.S. Public*, pg. 90
THE AUDIO PARTNERS, INC.—See Blackstone Audio, Inc.; *U.S. Private*, pg. 576
BANTAM DELL CANADA—See Bertelsmann SE & Co. KGaA; *Int'l*, pg. 990
BARNES & NOBLE BOOKSELLERS, INC.—See Elliott Management Corporation; *U.S. Private*, pg. 1364
BARNES & NOBLE COLLEGE BOOKSELLERS, LLC—See Barnes & Noble Education, Inc.; *U.S. Public*, pg. 276
BARNES & NOBLE EDUCATION, INC.; *U.S. Public*, pg. 276
BECKS BOOKSTORES INC.; *U.S. Private*, pg. 511
BEREAN CHRISTIAN STORES—See JMH Capital; *U.S. Private*, pg. 2215
BERJAYA BOOKS SDN BHD—See Berjaya Corporation Berhad; *Int'l*, pg. 982
BINH DINH BOOK & EQUIPMENT JOINT STOCK COMPANY; *Int'l*, pg. 1034
BLACKSTONE AUDIO, INC.; *U.S. Private*, pg. 576
BLUFF HOLDING COMPANY, LLC—See Churchill Downs, Inc.; *U.S. Public*, pg. 493
BOOK CLUB ASSOCIATES LTD.—See Bertelsmann SE & Co. KGaA; *Int'l*, pg. 992
BOOKOFF GROUP HOLDINGS LTD.; *Int'l*, pg. 1110
BOOK-OF-THE-MONTH CLUB, INC.—See Bertelsmann SE & Co. KGaA; *Int'l*, pg. 992
BOOKS-A-MILLION, INC.; *U.S. Private*, pg. 615
BOOKS INCORPORATED; *U.S. Private*, pg. 615
BOOKSPAN, LLC—See Bertelsmann SE & Co. KGaA; *Int'l*, pg. 992
BOOKSTORE1SARASOTA; *U.S. Private*, pg. 616
BOOK WORLD INC.; *U.S. Private*, pg. 615
CAL POLY POMONA FOUNDATION, INC.; *U.S. Private*, pg. 715
CARIBE GROLIER INC.—See Scholastic Corporation; *U.S. Public*, pg. 1847
CENTRAL MUTUAL INSURANCE CENTRAL REGIONAL OFFICE—See Central Mutual Insurance Company; *U.S. Private*, pg. 823
CHANDLER HOUSE PRESS—See Tatnuck Booksellers Inc.; *U.S. Private*, pg. 3936
CHRISTIAN SUPPLY CENTERS INC.—See R.B. Pamplin Corporation; *U.S. Private*, pg. 3334
CIRCULO DE LECTORES S.A.—See Bertelsmann SE & Co. KGaA; *Int'l*, pg. 992
COLLEGIATE RETAIL ALLIANCE; *U.S. Private*, pg. 968
COLUMBIA HOUSE—See Pride Tree Holdings, Inc.; *U.S. Private*, pg. 3260
CONSTRUCTION BOOK EXPRESS—See BNi Publications, Inc.; *U.S. Private*, pg. 602
CUSPIDE LIBROS S.A.—See Grupo Clarin S.A.; *Int'l*, pg. 3124
DARTMOUTH BOOKSTORE INC.; *U.S. Private*, pg. 1160
DELAWARE BOOK INC.; *U.S. Private*, pg. 1194
DE NORSKE BOKKLUBBENE AS—See H. Aschehoug & Co. W. Nygaard AS; *Int'l*, pg. 3194
DER CLUB GMBH—See Bertelsmann SE & Co. KGaA; *Int'l*, pg. 992
DICKENS BOOKS LTD.; *U.S. Private*, pg. 1226
DIRECT BRANDS, INC.—See Pride Tree Holdings, Inc.; *U.S. Private*, pg. 3260
DOUBLEDAY BOOK CLUB—See Bertelsmann SE & Co. KGaA; *Int'l*, pg. 992
EASTERN NATIONAL; *U.S. Private*, pg. 1320
E-COMMERCE CHINA DANGDANG INC.; *Int'l*, pg. 2247
EDUCATIONAL DEVELOPMENT CORPORATION - PUBLISHING DIVISION—See Educational Develop; *U.S. Public*, pg. 720
ENTITLE, INC.; *U.S. Private*, pg. 1405
FABER, COE & GREGG, INC.; *U.S. Private*, pg. 1458
FAMILY CHRISTIAN STORES INC.; *U.S. Private*, pg. 1469
FIREFIGHTERS BOOKSTORE, INC.—See L.N. Curtis & Sons; *U.S. Private*, pg. 2366
FOLLETT HIGHER EDUCATION GROUP, INC.—See Follett Corporation; *U.S. Private*, pg. 1559
FOLLETT OF CANADA INC.—See Follett Corporation; *U.S. Private*, pg. 1559
FRANCE LOISIRS SAS—See Bertelsmann SE & Co. KGaA; *Int'l*, pg. 992
GATHERING PLACE BOOKS & COFFEE INC.—See Family Christian Stores Inc.; *U.S. Private*, pg. 1469
GROUPE RENAUD-BRAY, INC.; *Int'l*, pg. 3110
HALF PRICE BOOKS RECORDS MAGAZINES INC.; *U.S. Private*, pg. 1842
HASLAM'S BOOK STORE, INC.; *U.S. Private*, pg. 1878
HIPARION DISTRIBUTION SA; *Int'l*, pg. 3402
HISTORY BOOK CLUB—See Bertelsmann SE & Co. KGaA; *Int'l*, pg. 992
HUMBOLDT STATE UNIVERSITY CENTER; *U.S. Private*, pg. 2007
ISLAND PERIODICALS INC.—See Periodical Management Group International Ltd.; *U.S. Private*, pg. 3150
JAY & SILENT BOB'S SECRET STASH; *U.S. Private*, pg. 2191
JOMIRA.COM—See Jomira/Advance; *U.S. Private*, pg. 2231

JUNKUDO CO., LTD.—See Dai Nippon Printing Co., Ltd.; *Int'l*, pg. 1915
LEBANON DISTRIBUTION CENTER—See The Maple-Vail Book Manufacturing Group; *U.S. Private*, pg. 4074
MAGAZINES.COM INC.; *U.S. Private*, pg. 2545
MAINE COAST BOOK SHOP, INC.—See Sherman's Books & Stationery, Inc.; *U.S. Private*, pg. 3634
MAJORS SCIENTIFIC BOOKS, INC.; *U.S. Private*, pg. 2555
MARUZEN BOOKSTORES CO., LTD.—See Dai Nippon Printing Co., Ltd.; *Int'l*, pg. 1915
MBS DIRECT, LLC—See Barnes & Noble Education, Inc.; *U.S. Public*, pg. 276
MCCOLLA ENTERPRISES LTD.; *U.S. Private*, pg. 2629
MCGRAW-HILL FINANCE (UK) LTD.—See S&P Global Inc.; *U.S. Public*, pg. 1830
MENNOMEDIA, INC.; *U.S. Private*, pg. 2666
MILITARY BOOK CLUB—See Bertelsmann SE & Co. KGaA; *Int'l*, pg. 992
MIRAIYA SHOTEN CO., LTD.—See AEON Co., Ltd.; *Int'l*, pg. 178
MR. PAPERBACK; *U.S. Private*, pg. 2805
MRS. NELSON'S BOOK FAIR COMPANY—See Scholastic Corporation; *U.S. Public*, pg. 1847
MVD MEDIEN VERTRIEB DRESDEN GMBH—See Bertelsmann SE & Co. KGaA; *Int'l*, pg. 993
MY PET CHICKEN LLC; *U.S. Private*, pg. 2823
NATIONAL BOOK NETWORK, INC.—See The Rowman & Littlefield Publishing Group, Inc.; *U.S. Private*, pg. 4112
NEBRASKA BOOK COMPANY, INC.—See Concise Capital Management LP; *U.S. Private*, pg. 1009
NEWSLINK GROUP, LLC.; *U.S. Private*, pg. 2917
NOOK DIGITAL, LLC—See Elliott Management Corporation; *U.S. Private*, pg. 1364
ODYSSEY INDIA LTD.—See Deccan Chronicle Holdings Ltd.; *Int'l*, pg. 1999
OREGON STATE UNIVERSITY BOOKSTORE; *U.S. Private*, pg. 3040
PARNASSUS BOOKS LLC; *U.S. Private*, pg. 3099
POSMAN COLLEGIATE STORES INC.; *U.S. Private*, pg. 3234
POWELL'S BOOKS INC.; *U.S. Private*, pg. 3237
PROMOVERSITY LLC—See Barnes & Noble Education, Inc.; *U.S. Public*, pg. 276
PUBLISHERS WAREHOUSE—See EBSCO Industries, Inc.; *U.S. Private*, pg. 1325
REAL ESTATE BUSINESS SERVICES, INC.—See California Association of Realtors; *U.S. Private*, pg. 718
SCHOLASTIC AT HOME INC.—See Scholastic Corporation; *U.S. Public*, pg. 1847
SCHOLASTIC BOOK CLUBS, INC.—See Scholastic Corporation; *U.S. Public*, pg. 1847
SCHULER BOOKS & MUSIC, INC.; *U.S. Private*, pg. 3570
SCRIBD, INC.; *U.S. Private*, pg. 3579
SEAGULL BOOK & TAPE INC.; *U.S. Private*, pg. 3584
SHERMAN'S BOOKS & STATIONERY, INC.; *U.S. Private*, pg. 3634
SHOWCASE NEW ENGLAND INC.; *U.S. Private*, pg. 3643
STUDENTS BOOK CORPORATION; *U.S. Private*, pg. 3843
STUDIO SBV, INC.; *U.S. Private*, pg. 3844
TATNUCK BOOKSELLERS INC.; *U.S. Private*, pg. 3936
TEXAS BOOK COMPANY INC.—See BibliU Ltd.; *Int'l*, pg. 1018
T&G CORP.—See GEO Holdings Corporation; *Int'l*, pg. 2932
TIS INC.; *U.S. Private*, pg. 4176
TXTB.COM LLC—See Barnes & Noble Education, Inc.; *U.S. Public*, pg. 276
UNIVERSITY BOOK STORE INC.; *U.S. Private*, pg. 4307
THE UNIVERSITY BOOK STORE; *U.S. Private*, pg. 4129
UNIVERSITY OF CONNECTICUT COOPERATIVE CORPORATION; *U.S. Private*, pg. 4309
UNIVERSITY OF KANSAS MEM CORP.; *U.S. Private*, pg. 4309
VALORA LUXEMBOURG S.A.R.L.—See Fomento Economico Mexicano, S.A.B. de C.V.; *Int'l*, pg. 2724
VALORE INC.—See Follett Corporation; *U.S. Private*, pg. 1559
WATERSTONES BOOKSELLERS LIMITED—See Elliott Management Corporation; *U.S. Private*, pg. 1365

459310 — FLORISTS

1-800-FLOWERS.COM FRANCHISE CO., INC.—See 1-800-FLOWERS.COM, Inc.; *U.S. Public*, pg. 1
1-800-FLOWERS.COM, INC.; *U.S. Public*, pg. 1
1-800-FLOWERS RETAIL, INC.—See 1-800-FLOWERS.COM, Inc.; *U.S. Public*, pg. 1
1-800-FLOWERS TEAM SERVICES, INC.—See 1-800-FLOWERS.COM, Inc.; *U.S. Public*, pg. 1
ALBERT F. AMLING, LLC; *U.S. Private*, pg. 152
ALL AMERICA-PHILLIP'S FLOWER SHOPS, INC.; *U.S. Private*, pg. 169
BACHMAN'S, INC.; *U.S. Private*, pg. 423
BENEVA FLOWERS AND GIFTS INC.; *U.S. Private*, pg. 525
BLOOM THAT, INC.—See FTD Companies, Inc.; *U.S. Private*, pg. 1619
BOTANICA INTERNATIONAL FLORIST, INC.; *U.S. Private*, pg. 622

BROWNS BROOKLAWN INC.; *U.S. Private*, pg. 669
CALYX & COROLLA, INC.—See The Mustang Group, LLC; *U.S. Private*, pg. 4081
COLIPAYS; *Int'l*, pg. 1698
DWF OF CINCINNATI, INC.—See Denver Wholesale Florists Company; *U.S. Private*, pg. 1208
EDIBLE ARRANGEMENTS INTERNATIONAL, INC.; *U.S. Private*, pg. 1336
EMOVA GROUP; *Int'l*, pg. 2385
ESPEC MIC CORP.—See ESPEC Corp.; *Int'l*, pg. 2505
FLOWERBUD.COM; *U.S. Private*, pg. 1552
INTERFLORA BRITISH UNIT—See The Wonderful Company LLC; *U.S. Private*, pg. 4138
LEHRER'S FLOWERS INC.; *U.S. Private*, pg. 2419
MYFLORIST.NET, LLC—See 1-800-FLOWERS.COM, Inc.; *U.S. Public*, pg. 1
NATIONAL FLORAL SUPPLY OF MARYLAND; *U.S. Private*, pg. 2854
PETALS NETWORK PTY. LTD.—See The Wonderful Company LLC; *U.S. Private*, pg. 4138
PROFLOWERS.COM—See Tenth Avenue Holdings LLC; *U.S. Private*, pg. 3968
SAN DIEGO HYDROPONICS & ORGANICS, INC.—See GrowGeneration Corp.; *U.S. Public*, pg. 972
STAR NURSERY INC.; *U.S. Private*, pg. 3785
STRANGE'S FLORIST & GREENHOUSES; *U.S. Private*, pg. 3833
TECHAU'S INC.; *U.S. Private*, pg. 3952
TELEFLORA LLC—See The Wonderful Company LLC; *U.S. Private*, pg. 4138
VELDKAMPS INC.; *U.S. Private*, pg. 4354
VINNYS GARDEN CENTER INC.; *U.S. Private*, pg. 4385

459410 — OFFICE SUPPLIES AND STATIONERY RETAILERS

AAA BUSINESS SUPPLIES LIMITED PARTNERSHIP; *U.S. Private*, pg. 30
ABDI COMPANY JSC; *Int'l*, pg. 58
ACCO AUSTRALIA PTY. LTD.—See ACCO Brands Corporation; *U.S. Public*, pg. 32
ADMIRAL EXPRESS, LLC—See The ODP Corporation; *U.S. Public*, pg. 2117
ADVANCED BUSINESS METHODS INC.; *U.S. Private*, pg. 88
AJ STATIONERS INC.; *U.S. Private*, pg. 143
AMERICAN LABORATORY PRODUCTS COMPANY, LTD.—See Ampersand Management LLC; *U.S. Private*, pg. 265
AMERICAS OFFICE SOURCE, INC.—See The ODP Corporation; *U.S. Public*, pg. 2117
ANKER INTERNATIONAL PLC—See IG Design Group Plc; *Int'l*, pg. 3600
APRICOT OFFICE SUPPLIES & FURNITURE, INC.; *U.S. Private*, pg. 301
ATLANTIC BUSINESS SYSTEMS—See Perpetual Capital, LLC; *U.S. Private*, pg. 3153
A-Z OFFICE RESOURCE, INC.; *U.S. Private*, pg. 22
BERTELSON BROTHERS, INC.—See The ODP Corporation; *U.S. Public*, pg. 2117
BINH THUAN BOOK & EQUIPMENT JOINT STOCK COMPANY; *Int'l*, pg. 1034
BLUMBERGEXCELSIOR INC.; *U.S. Private*, pg. 599
BRODART COMPANY—See Brodart Co.; *U.S. Private*, pg. 661
BUSINESS-SUPPLY.COM, INC.—See LoanSource Inc.; *U.S. Private*, pg. 2477
CALENDAR CLUB LLC—See Specialty Retail Ventures LLC; *U.S. Private*, pg. 3750
CANON AUSTRALIA PTY. LTD.—See Canon Inc.; *Int'l*, pg. 1293
CANON DEUTSCHLAND GMBH—See Canon Inc.; *Int'l*, pg. 1294
CANON FRANCE S.A.—See Canon Inc.; *Int'l*, pg. 1294
CANON SEMICONDUCTOR EQUIPMENT, INC.—See Canon Inc.; *Int'l*, pg. 1296
CEI PTY. LTD.—See Platinum Equity, LLC; *U.S. Private*, pg. 3210
CHAMPION INDUSTRIES, INC.—See Champion Industries, Inc.; *U.S. Public*, pg. 478
CHICAGO SCHOOL SUPPLY; *U.S. Private*, pg. 879
CHURCH & STAGG OFFICE SUPPLY INC; *U.S. Private*, pg. 894
COMPLETE OFFICE OF WISCONSIN, INC.—See The ODP Corporation; *U.S. Public*, pg. 2117
COMPUCOM SYSTEMS HOLDINGS LLC—See The ODP Corporation; *U.S. Public*, pg. 2117
COPY DUPLICATING SYSTEMS—See Dataflow Business Systems, Inc.; *U.S. Private*, pg. 1165
C.R. GIBSON, LLC—See IG Design Group Plc; *Int'l*, pg. 3600
CYGNUS TECHNOLOGIES, INC.—See GTCR LLC; *U.S. Private*, pg. 1805
DAHLE BUROTECHNIK GMBH—See Erwin Muller Gruppe GmbH; *Int'l*, pg. 2500
DANANG BOOKS & SCHOOL EQUIPMENT JOINT STOCK COMPANY; *Int'l*, pg. 1958

N.A.I.C.S. INDEX

459410 — OFFICE SUPPLIES AND...

DANCKER, SELLEW & DOUGLAS, INC.; *U.S. Private*, pg. 1153
DIRECT CHECKS UNLIMITED SALES, INC—See Deluxe Corporation; *U.S. Public*, pg. 653
DISCOUNT OFFICE ITEMS, INC.—See The ODP Corporation; *U.S. Public*, pg. 2117
DIXON EUROPE, LTD.—See F.I.L.A. - Fabbrica Italiana Lapis ed Affini S.p.A.; *Int'l*, pg. 2596
DLX INDUSTRIES, INC.—See Royal Industries, Inc.; *U.S. Private*, pg. 3492
EMO AS—See Sycamore Partners Management, LP; *U.S. Private*, pg. 3896
ERWIN MULLER GRUPPE GMBH; *Int'l*, pg. 2500
ESSELTE A/S—See ACCO Brands Corporation; *U.S. Public*, pg. 32
ESSELTE AS—See ACCO Brands Corporation; *U.S. Public*, pg. 32
ESSELTE BUSINESS BVBA—See ACCO Brands Corporation; *U.S. Public*, pg. 32
ESSELTE B.V.—See ACCO Brands Corporation; *U.S. Public*, pg. 32
ESSELTE KFT—See ACCO Brands Corporation; *U.S. Public*, pg. 33
ESSELTE LIMITED—See ACCO Brands Corporation; *U.S. Public*, pg. 33
ESSELTE OFFICE PRODUCTS OY—See ACCO Brands Corporation; *U.S. Public*, pg. 33
ESSELTE OOO—See ACCO Brands Corporation; *U.S. Public*, pg. 33
ESSELTE POLSKA SP.Z.O.O.—See ACCO Brands Corporation; *U.S. Public*, pg. 33
ESSELTE S.A. - PORTUGAL OFFICE—See ACCO Brands Corporation; *U.S. Public*, pg. 33
ESSELTE S.A.—See ACCO Brands Corporation; *U.S. Public*, pg. 33
ESSELTE SVERIGE AB—See ACCO Brands Corporation; *U.S. Public*, pg. 33
ESSENDANT MANAGEMENT SERVICES LLC—See Sycamore Partners Management, LP; *U.S. Private*, pg. 3897
FAISON OFFICE PRODUCTS, INC.—See Sycamore Partners Management, LP; *U.S. Private*, pg. 3897
FINE STATIONERY, INC.—See Regent, L.P.; *U.S. Private*, pg. 3388
FOREST CO., LTD.—See EDION Corporation; *Int'l*, pg. 2310
GAERNER GMBH—See Franz Haniel & Cie. GmbH; *Int'l*, pg. 2763
GARRISON BREWER—See Champion Industries, Inc.; *U.S. Public*, pg. 478
GERDMANS INREDNIGAR AB—See Franz Haniel & Cie. GmbH; *Int'l*, pg. 2763
GLOBAL OFFICE SOLUTIONS; *U.S. Private*, pg. 1716
GREATLAND CORPORATION; *U.S. Private*, pg. 1770
GRIEG KALENDERFORLAG AS—See Sycamore Partners Management, LP; *U.S. Private*, pg. 3897
GUERNSEY OFFICE PRODUCTS INC.; *U.S. Private*, pg. 1810
GUILBERT LUXEMBOURG S.A.R.L.—See Aurelius Equity Opportunities SE & Co. KGaA; *Int'l*, pg. 709
HC LAND COMPANY L.C.—See The ODP Corporation; *U.S. Public*, pg. 2117
HENDRIX BUSINESS SYSTEMS, INC.; *U.S. Private*, pg. 1915
HERALD OFFICE SUPPLY COMPANY; *U.S. Private*, pg. 1920
IMAGEX, INC.—See Hits, Inc; *U.S. Private*, pg. 1953
INSTRON PTY. LTD.—See Illinois Tool Works Inc.; *U.S. Public*, pg. 1108
INSTRON S.A.S.—See Illinois Tool Works Inc.; *U.S. Public*, pg. 1108
INTERMACO S.R.L.—See SED International Holdings, Inc.; *U.S. Private*, pg. 3597
INTERNATIONAL OFFICE SUPPLY; *U.S. Private*, pg. 2119
INTERNATIONAL PAPER COMPANY - COURTLAND—See International Paper Company; *U.S. Public*, pg. 1157
THE INTERNATIONAL PEN SHOP—See Arthur Brown & Bro., Inc.; *U.S. Private*, pg. 341
KEETON'S OFFICE & ART SUPPLY CO.; *U.S. Private*, pg. 2273
THE KNOWLEDGE TREE INC.; *U.S. Private*, pg. 4065
KWESTO—See Franz Haniel & Cie. GmbH; *Int'l*, pg. 2763
LAMB SIGN; *U.S. Private*, pg. 2379
LAMINATION DEPOT INC.; *U.S. Private*, pg. 2380
L.C. INDUSTRIES FOR THE BLIND INC.; *U.S. Private*, pg. 2365
LETTERFOLDERS.COM; *U.S. Private*, pg. 2433
LINDY OFFICE PRODUCTS, INC.; *U.S. Private*, pg. 2460
MARKE CREATIVE MERCHANDISE LTD.—See Sycamore Partners Management, LP; *U.S. Private*, pg. 3897
MCNALLY OPERATIONS LLC; *U.S. Private*, pg. 2643
MICHIGAN OFFICE SOLUTIONS; *U.S. Private*, pg. 2701
MONOTYPE ITC INC.—See HGGC, LLC; *U.S. Private*, pg. 1930
MYOFFICEPRODUCTS LLC; *U.S. Private*, pg. 2825
NATIONAL PEN PROMOTIONAL PRODUCTS LIMITED—See Cimpress plc; *Int'l*, pg. 1609
NEBS BUSINESS PRODUCTS LIMITED—See Deluxe Corporation; *U.S. Public*, pg. 652
NEXVUE INFORMATION SYSTEMS, INC.—See Net@Work, Inc.; *U.S. Private*, pg. 2886
NORTH CENTRAL INSTRUMENTS, INC.—See Thomas Scientific, LLC; *U.S. Private*, pg. 4157
NORTHERN BUSINESS PRODUCTS, INC.—See Innovative Office Solutions LLC; *U.S. Private*, pg. 2083
NOVUS DAHLE GMBH & CO. KG—See Erwin Muller Gruppe GmbH; *Int'l*, pg. 2500
OCE PORTUGAL EQUIPAMENTOS GRAFICOS S.A.—See Canon Inc.; *Int'l*, pg. 1295
OCE-RENTING S.A.—See Canon Inc.; *Int'l*, pg. 1294
THE ODP CORPORATION; *U.S. Public*, pg. 2117
OFFICECENTRE EQUIPAMENTOS DE ESCRITORIO LDA—See Sycamore Partners Management, LP; *U.S. Private*, pg. 3897
OFFICE DEPOT BS—See Aurelius Equity Opportunities SE & Co. KGaA; *Int'l*, pg. 709
OFFICE DEPOT B.V.—See Aurelius Equity Opportunities SE & Co. KGaA; *Int'l*, pg. 709
OFFICE DEPOT DE MEXICO S.A. DE C.V.—See Grupo Gigante, S.A.B. de C.V.; *Int'l*, pg. 3130
OFFICE DEPOT DEUTSCHLAND GMBH—See Aurelius Equity Opportunities SE & Co. KGaA; *Int'l*, pg. 709
OFFICE DEPOT FRANCE SNC—See Aurelius Equity Opportunities SE & Co. KGaA; *Int'l*, pg. 709
OFFICE DEPOT GMBH—See Aurelius Equity Opportunities SE & Co. KGaA; *Int'l*, pg. 709
OFFICE DEPOT INTERNATIONAL BVBA—See Aurelius Equity Opportunities SE & Co. KGaA; *Int'l*, pg. 709
OFFICE DEPOT INTERNATIONAL (UK) LTD—See Aurelius Equity Opportunities SE & Co. KGaA; *Int'l*, pg. 709
OFFICE DEPOT IRELAND LIMITED—See Aurelius Equity Opportunities SE & Co. KGaA; *Int'l*, pg. 709
OFFICE DEPOT KOREA CO., LTD.—See Excelsior Capital Asia (HK) Limited; *Int'l*, pg. 2578
OFFICE DEPOT NETHERLANDS B.V.—See Aurelius Equity Opportunities SE & Co. KGaA; *Int'l*, pg. 709
OFFICE DEPOT OVERSEAS LIMITED—See The ODP Corporation; *U.S. Public*, pg. 2117
OFFICE DEPOT PUERTO RICO, LLC—See The ODP Corporation; *U.S. Public*, pg. 2117
OFFICE DEPOT SERVICE- UND BETEILIGUNGS-GMBH & CO. KG—See Aurelius Equity Opportunities SE & Co. KGaA; *Int'l*, pg. 709
OFFICE DEPOT UK LIMITED—See Aurelius Equity Opportunities SE & Co. KGaA; *Int'l*, pg. 709
OFFICE EQUIPMENT COMPANY OF MOBILE, INC.; *U.S. Private*, pg. 3001
OFFICE EQUIPMENT & SUPPLY; *U.S. Private*, pg. 3001
OFFICEMATE OMNI FRANCHISES CO., LTD.—See COL Public Company Limited; *Int'l*, pg. 1697
OFFICEMAX AUSTRALIA LIMITED—See Platinum Equity, LLC; *U.S. Private*, pg. 3210
OFFICEMAX NEW ZEALAND LIMITED—See Platinum Equity, LLC; *U.S. Private*, pg. 3210
OFFICEMAX NORTH AMERICA, INC.—See The ODP Corporation; *U.S. Public*, pg. 2117
OFFICE SUPERSTORE WEST LLC—See Sycamore Partners Management, LP; *U.S. Private*, pg. 3897
OFFICESUPPLY.COM; *U.S. Private*, pg. 3002
OFFICE SYSTEMS CO.—See Loffler Companies, Inc.; *U.S. Private*, pg. 2480
OFFICE THREE SIXTY, INC.; *U.S. Private*, pg. 3002
OFFICEWORKS BUSINESSDIRECT PTY LTD—See Coles Group Limited; *Int'l*, pg. 1698
OFFICEWORKS LTD.—See Coles Group Limited; *Int'l*, pg. 1698
OFFICEXPRESS INC.; *U.S. Private*, pg. 3002
OFFICIA IMAGING INC; *U.S. Private*, pg. 3002
OHIO & MICHIGAN PAPER CO.—See Bain Capital, LP; *U.S. Private*, pg. 441
PELIKAN-ARTLINE PTY., LTD.—See ACCO Brands Corporation; *U.S. Public*, pg. 32
PENS N MORE; *U.S. Private*, pg. 3138
PERIMETER OFFICE PRODUCTS, INC.—See The ODP Corporation; *U.S. Public*, pg. 2117
PLANTIN BVBA—See CoBe Capital LLC; *U.S. Private*, pg. 957
POSTAL CONNECTIONS OF AMERICA, INC.; *U.S. Private*, pg. 3234
PREMIER OFFICE EQUIPMENT—See Xerox Holdings Corporation; *U.S. Public*, pg. 2388
PRESSEL POST B.V.B.A.—See Sycamore Partners Management, LP; *U.S. Private*, pg. 3897
PRESSEL SP.Z.O.O.—See Sycamore Partners Management, LP; *U.S. Private*, pg. 3897
PRESSEL VERSAND INTERNATIONAL GMBH—See Sycamore Partners Management, LP; *U.S. Private*, pg. 3897
PRINT IT 4 LESS; *U.S. Private*, pg. 3265
PVD PRODUCTS—See High Temperature Superconductors, Inc.; *U.S. Private*, pg. 1937
QUILL LINCOLNSHIRE, INC.—See Sycamore Partners Management, LP; *U.S. Private*, pg. 3897
QUILL LINCOLNSHIRE, INC.—See Sycamore Partners Management, LP; *U.S. Private*, pg. 3897
QUILL LLC—See Sycamore Partners Management, LP; *U.S. Private*, pg. 3897
QUILL LLC—See Sycamore Partners Management, LP; *U.S. Private*, pg. 3897
QUILL LLC—See Sycamore Partners Management, LP; *U.S. Private*, pg. 3897
QUILL LLC—See Sycamore Partners Management, LP; *U.S. Private*, pg. 3897
REGENCY OFFICE PRODUCTS, LLC—See The ODP Corporation; *U.S. Public*, pg. 2118
RICH ANDVORD GRAFISK AS—See Sycamore Partners Management, LP; *U.S. Private*, pg. 3897
ROBERT J. YOUNG COMPANY, LLC; *U.S. Private*, pg. 3458
SANDIA OFFICE SUPPLY; *U.S. Private*, pg. 3544
SCHOOLKIDZ.COM, LLC—See Skyview Capital, LLC; *U.S. Private*, pg. 3686
SMITH & BUTTERFIELD CO., INC.—See Champion Industries, Inc.; *U.S. Public*, pg. 478
SMITH CORONA CORPORATION—See Pubco Corporation; *U.S. Private*, pg. 3298
SOURCE OFFICE & TECHNOLOGY; *U.S. Private*, pg. 3718
STANDARD OFFICE SUPPLY; *U.S. Private*, pg. 3781
STAPLES ADVANTAGE IRELAND LTD.—See Sycamore Partners Management, LP; *U.S. Private*, pg. 3897
STAPLES BELGIUM BVBA—See Sycamore Partners Management, LP; *U.S. Private*, pg. 3897
STAPLES BUSINESS DEPOT—See Sycamore Partners Management, LP; *U.S. Private*, pg. 3897
STAPLES CANADA, ULC—See Sycamore Partners Management, LP; *U.S. Private*, pg. 3897
STAPLES DENMARK APS—See Sycamore Partners Management, LP; *U.S. Private*, pg. 3897
STAPLES DEUTSCHLAND GMBH & CO. KG—See Sycamore Partners Management, LP; *U.S. Private*, pg. 3898
STAPLES EUROPE B.V.—See Sycamore Partners Management, LP; *U.S. Private*, pg. 3897
STAPLES FINLAND OY—See Sycamore Partners Management, LP; *U.S. Private*, pg. 3898
STAPLES INTERNATIONAL GROUP SERVICES B.V.—See Sycamore Partners Management, LP; *U.S. Private*, pg. 3898
STAPLES NEDERLAND BV—See Sycamore Partners Management, LP; *U.S. Private*, pg. 3898
STAPLES NORWAY AS—See Sycamore Partners Management, LP; *U.S. Private*, pg. 3898
STAPLES POLSKA SP.Z.O.O.—See Sycamore Partners Management, LP; *U.S. Private*, pg. 3898
STAPLES PORTUGAL EQUIPAMENTO DE ESCRITORIA, SA—See Sycamore Partners Management, LP; *U.S. Private*, pg. 3898
STAPLES RETAIL NORWAY AS—See Sycamore Partners Management, LP; *U.S. Private*, pg. 3898
STAPLES SHARED SERVICE CENTER (EUROPE) II, BVBA—See Sycamore Partners Management, LP; *U.S. Private*, pg. 3897
STAPLES SWEDEN AB—See Sycamore Partners Management, LP; *U.S. Private*, pg. 3898
STAPLES UK LIMITED—See Sycamore Partners Management, LP; *U.S. Private*, pg. 3898
STAPLES VERWALTUNGS GMBH—See Sycamore Partners Management, LP; *U.S. Private*, pg. 3898
STAR PRINTING & SUPPLY CO., INC.—See Yellowstone Communications; *U.S. Private*, pg. 4588
STATELINE COPY PRODUCTS, INC.—See Stan's - LPS Midwest; *U.S. Private*, pg. 3777
STATIONERS, INC.—See Champion Industries, Inc.; *U.S. Public*, pg. 478
TAB PRODUCTS CO. LLC—See H.S. Morgan Limited Partnership; *U.S. Private*, pg. 1835
TAKKT AG—See Franz Haniel & Cie. GmbH; *Int'l*, pg. 2763
TARIFOLD S.A.—See ACCO Brands Corporation; *U.S. Public*, pg. 33
TONERS PLUS OFFICE PRODUCTS; *U.S. Private*, pg. 4184
TOPS PRODUCTS; *U.S. Private*, pg. 4188
UNIVERSITY OF OREGON BOOKSTORE; *U.S. Private*, pg. 4309
VERITIV—See Clayton, Dubilier & Rice, LLC; *U.S. Private*, pg. 929
VIKING DIRECT B.V.—See Aurelius Equity Opportunities SE & Co. KGaA; *Int'l*, pg. 709
VIKING DIRECT (HOLDINGS) LIMITED—See Aurelius Equity Opportunities SE & Co. KGaA; *Int'l*, pg. 709
VIKING DIRECT (IRELAND) LIMITED—See Aurelius Equity Opportunities SE & Co. KGaA; *Int'l*, pg. 709
VIKING NETHERLANDS B.V.—See Aurelius Equity Opportunities SE & Co. KGaA; *Int'l*, pg. 709
VIKING OFFICE PRODUCTS, INC.—See The ODP Corporation; *U.S. Public*, pg. 2118
WAREHOUSE DIRECT, INC; *U.S. Private*, pg. 4441
WINC AUSTRALIA PTY. LIMITED—See Platinum Equity, LLC; *U.S. Private*, pg. 3210
XEROX DE COLOMBIA S.A.—See Xerox Holdings Corporation; *U.S. Public*, pg. 2390
ZERBEE, LLC—See The ODP Corporation; *U.S. Public*, pg. 2118
ZONAL HOSPITALITY SYSTEMS INC.; *U.S. Private*, pg. 4607

459420 — GIFT, NOVELTY, AND SOUVENIR RETAILERS

ACCENTIV' KADEOS S.A.S.—See Edenred S.A.; *Int'l*, pg. 2307
ACV AUCTIONS INC.; *U.S. Public*, pg. 37
A&H STORES INC.; *U.S. Private*, pg. 20
ALL ABOUT GIFTS & BASKETS; *U.S. Private*, pg. 169
ALLCANES CORP.—See Follett Corporation; *U.S. Private*, pg. 1559
ARCHIES LIMITED; *Int'l*, pg. 548
ARTMARKET.COM; *Int'l*, pg. 585
ASHLEY AVERY'S COLLECTIBLES—See Franchise Concepts, Inc.; *U.S. Private*, pg. 1587
A&S, INC.; *U.S. Private*, pg. 21
BALLOONS ARE EVERYWHERE, INC.; *U.S. Private*, pg. 461
BALLOONS ARE EVERYWHERE, INC.—See Balloons Are Everywhere, Inc.; *U.S. Private*, pg. 461
BALOG AUCTION SERVICES INC.; *Int'l*, pg. 810
BANYAN TREE GALLERY (THAILAND) LIMITED—See Banyan Tree Holdings Ltd.; *Int'l*, pg. 855
BASKETRY BY PHINA, LLC; *U.S. Private*, pg. 485
BASKETRY INC.—See Basketry by Phina, LLC; *U.S. Private*, pg. 485
BECKY'S CARD & GIFTS INC.; *U.S. Private*, pg. 511
BERING HOME CENTER INC.; *U.S. Private*, pg. 532
BIRTHDAYEXPRESS.COM—See Rubie's Costume Company Inc.; *U.S. Private*, pg. 3500
BROOKSTONE COMPANY, INC.—See Bluestar Alliance LLC; *U.S. Private*, pg. 598
BROOKSTONE COMPANY, INC.—See B. Riley Financial, Inc.; *U.S. Public*, pg. 262
BROWNWOOD MEDICAL CENTER, LLC—See Community Health Systems, Inc.; *U.S. Public*, pg. 551
BUYSEASONS ENTERPRISES, LLC—See Rubie's Costume Company Inc.; *U.S. Private*, pg. 3500
CARLTON CARDS RETAIL, INC.—See Clayton, Dubilier & Rice, LLC; *U.S. Private*, pg. 919
CAR SPA INC.; *U.S. Private*, pg. 747
CBC GROUP; *U.S. Private*, pg. 797
CGIFT AG; *Int'l*, pg. 1434
CHRISTIAN BRANDS—See CBC Group; *U.S. Private*, pg. 797
CHRISTMAS TREE HILL INC.; *U.S. Private*, pg. 891
CONSTANTINE'S WOOD CENTER OF FLORIDA, INC.; *U.S. Private*, pg. 1023
DANBURY MINT—See MBI, Inc.; *U.S. Private*, pg. 2624
DECORA BALT UAB—See Decora S.A.; *Int'l*, pg. 2001
DECORA HUNGARIA KFT—See Decora S.A.; *Int'l*, pg. 2001
DECORA NOVA S.R.O.—See Decora S.A.; *Int'l*, pg. 2001
DECORA RU OOO—See Decora S.A.; *Int'l*, pg. 2001
DISNEY CONSUMER PRODUCTS, INC.—See The Walt Disney Company; *U.S. Public*, pg. 2138
DISNEY STORE INC.—See The Walt Disney Company; *U.S. Public*, pg. 2138
DOLLAR DAZE INC.; *U.S. Private*, pg. 1254
THE DOLPHIN—See Alden Global Capital LLC; *U.S. Private*, pg. 158
EAST MESA INDEPENDENT—See Independent Newspapers, Inc.; *U.S. Private*, pg. 2060
EDENRED FINLAND OY—See Edenred S.A.; *Int'l*, pg. 2307
ELECTRIC FETUS COMPANY; *U.S. Private*, pg. 1352
ELLIS POTTERY INC.; *U.S. Private*, pg. 1374
ENESCO CANADA CORPORATION—See Enesco, LLC; *U.S. Private*, pg. 1397
ENESCO LIMITED—See Enesco, LLC; *U.S. Private*, pg. 1397
EUROWRAP A/S—See Accent Equity Partners AB; *Int'l*, pg. 81
EUROWRAP LTD—See Accent Equity Partners AB; *Int'l*, pg. 81
FACTORY CARD OUTLET OF AMERICA LTD.—See Thomas H. Lee Partners, L.P.; *U.S. Private*, pg. 4156
FACTORY CARD & PARTY OUTLET CORP.—See Thomas H. Lee Partners, L.P.; *U.S. Private*, pg. 4156
FERRELS CARD SHOP INC.; *U.S. Private*, pg. 1498
FOSSIL (HONG KONG) LTD—See Fossil Group, Inc.; *U.S. Public*, pg. 874
FOSSIL INDIA PRIVATE LTD.—See Fossil Group, Inc.; *U.S. Public*, pg. 874
FOSSIL ITALIA, S.R.L.—See Fossil Group, Inc.; *U.S. Public*, pg. 875
FOSSIL MEXICO, S.A. DE C.V.—See Fossil Group, Inc.; *U.S. Public*, pg. 875
FOSSIL SINGAPORE PTE. LTD.—See Fossil Group, Inc.; *U.S. Public*, pg. 874
FOSSIL SWEDEN AB—See Fossil Group, Inc.; *U.S. Public*, pg. 875
FREED OF LONDON U.S.—See Freed of London Ltd.; *Int'l*, pg. 2769
FTD, INC.—See Tenth Avenue Holdings LLC; *U.S. Private*, pg. 3968
FTD INDIA PRIVATE LIMITED—See FTD Companies, Inc.; *U.S. Private*, pg. 1619
FUJISEY CO., LTD.—See ANA Holdings Inc.; *Int'l*, pg. 444
GAGS & GAMES INC.—See Thomas H. Lee Partners, L.P.; *U.S. Private*, pg. 4156
GAVEKORTET.DK A/S—See Egmont Fonden; *Int'l*, pg. 2326
GENERAL NOVELTY LTD.; *U.S. Private*, pg. 1666
GIFTCO, INC.—See Qurate Retail, Inc.; *U.S. Public*, pg. 1757
GIFTCRAFT LTD.; *Int'l*, pg. 2970
GIFTEE MEKONG COMPANY LTD.—See Giftee, Inc.; *Int'l*, pg. 2970
GIFTS BY DESIGN, INC.—See Superior Group Of Companies, Inc.; *U.S. Public*, pg. 1966
GIFT UNIVERSE GROUP LIMITED; *Int'l*, pg. 2970
GOURMETGIFTBASKETS.COM; *U.S. Private*, pg. 1746
GUMP'S CORP.; *U.S. Private*, pg. 1818
GVS GIFT VOUCHER SHOP LIMITED—See P2 Capital Partners, LLC; *U.S. Private*, pg. 3061
GVS GIFT VOUCHER SHOP LIMITED—See Silver Lake Group, LLC; *U.S. Private*, pg. 3656
THE HAMILTON COLLECTION, INC.—See The Bradford Group; *U.S. Private*, pg. 3999
HANOVER DIRECT, INC.—See Chelsey Direct, LLC; *U.S. Private*, pg. 870
HAPPINESS INC.; *U.S. Private*, pg. 1857
HARRIET CARTER GIFTS, INC.—See JH Partners LLC; *U.S. Private*, pg. 2207
HARRIET CARTER GIFTS, INC.—See Prudential Financial, Inc.; *U.S. Public*, pg. 1732
HARRY & DAVID OPERATIONS, INC.—See 1-800-FLOWERS.COM, Inc.; *U.S. Public*, pg. 1
THE HELMSLEY PARK LANE—See Helmsley Enterprises, Inc.; *U.S. Private*, pg. 1912
HERALD HOLDINGS LIMITED; *Int'l*, pg. 3358
IF IT'S PAPER (2) LLC; *U.S. Private*, pg. 2038
IF IT'S PAPER - GREENVILLE—See If It's Paper (2) LLC; *U.S. Private*, pg. 2038
INDEX NOTION COMPANY INC.; *U.S. Private*, pg. 2061
INTERNATIONAL GREETINGS ASIA LIMITED—See IG Design Group Plc; *Int'l*, pg. 3600
THE JAZZ STORE—See Musical Heritage Society Inc.; *U.S. Private*, pg. 2818
JHS INC.; *U.S. Private*, pg. 2208
J&J CARDS INC.; *U.S. Private*, pg. 2154
KIRKLAND OF CHATTANOOGA INC.—See Kirkland's Inc.; *U.S. Public*, pg. 1236
KIRKLAND'S INC.; *U.S. Public*, pg. 1236
KIRLIN'S INC.; *U.S. Private*, pg. 2315
LAMAJAK INC.; *U.S. Private*, pg. 2379
LEE HECHT HARRISON—See Adecco Group AG; *Int'l*, pg. 138
LSG-FOOD & NONFOOD HANDEL GMBH—See Deutsche Lufthansa AG; *Int'l*, pg. 2067
THE MADDEN CORPORATION; *U.S. Private*, pg. 4074
MADONNA ENTERPRISES; *U.S. Private*, pg. 2544
MARK-IT SMART INC.; *U.S. Private*, pg. 2578
MARK'S CARD SHOPS INC.; *U.S. Private*, pg. 2578
MAUI MAGNETS INC.; *U.S. Private*, pg. 2614
MAXIKARTY.PL. SP. Z O O—See Egmont Fonden; *Int'l*, pg. 2326
MBI, INC.; *U.S. Private*, pg. 2624
MERCHANDISE MANIA LIMITED—See HH Global Group Limited; *Int'l*, pg. 3379
M&K ENTERPRISE LLC; *U.S. Private*, pg. 2524
MVP GROUP INTERNATIONAL, INC.; *U.S. Private*, pg. 2821
MY FAVORITE THINGS, INC.—See Nu Skin Enterprises, Inc.; *U.S. Public*, pg. 1551
MYRON EVENSON'S CARDS & GIFTS; *U.S. Private*, pg. 2826
NATIONAL GIFT CARD CORPORATION—See LSCG Management, Inc.; *U.S. Private*, pg. 2508
NBO SYSTEMS, INC.; *U.S. Private*, pg. 2875
NEW PAPER LLC—See PA Acquisition Corp.; *U.S. Private*, pg. 3062
NORTHERN PLANET LLC; *U.S. Private*, pg. 2954
NOVELTEX MIAMI, INC.; *U.S. Private*, pg. 2968
OLD SALEM MUSEUMS & GARDENS; *U.S. Private*, pg. 3009
THE ORIGINAL HONEYBAKED HAM CO.; *U.S. Private*, pg. 4089
PA ACQUISITION CORP.; *U.S. Private*, pg. 3062
PACIFIC CONCEPT INDUSTRIES (USA) LLC—See Illinois Tool Works Inc.; *U.S. Public*, pg. 1110
PAPER STORE INCORPORATED; *U.S. Private*, pg. 3088
PARTY CITY CORPORATION—See Thomas H. Lee Partners, L.P.; *U.S. Private*, pg. 4156
PARTY CITY OF BIRMINGHAM INC.; *U.S. Private*, pg. 3103
PARTY CITY OF PUERTO RICO INC.; *U.S. Private*, pg. 3103
PARTY TIME RENTALS, INC.—See Premiere Events; *U.S. Private*, pg. 3251
PATIENCE BREWSTER, INC.—See EagleTree Capital, LP; *U.S. Private*, pg. 1311
PM PARTIES INC.; *U.S. Private*, pg. 3216
POGUE LABEL & SCREEN, INC.; *U.S. Private*, pg. 3220
POMARE LTD.; *U.S. Private*, pg. 3226
POSTAL COMMEMORATIVE SOCIETY COLLECTION—See MBI, Inc.; *U.S. Private*, pg. 2624
PRAIRIE GARDENS INC.; *U.S. Private*, pg. 3242
PRIMITIVES BY KATHY INC.; *U.S. Private*, pg. 3263
PURE ROMANCE PARTIES, INC.; *U.S. Private*, pg. 3306
PURPLE WAVE, INC; *U.S. Private*, pg. 3306
R&D CARY ENTERPRISES; *U.S. Private*, pg. 3332
REGAL GIFTS CORPORATION—See York Management Services, Inc.; *U.S. Private*, pg. 4591
REPUBLICAN & HERALD—See Alden Global Capital LLC; *U.S. Private*, pg. 157
RESORT INNS OF AMERICA INC.; *U.S. Private*, pg. 3406
SCHIFF ENTERPRISES; *U.S. Private*, pg. 3564
SCOOP DESIGNS LTD—See IG Design Group Plc; *Int'l*, pg. 3600
SENDONLINE.COM, INC.—See The Impex Group of Companies; *U.S. Private*, pg. 4055
SERVICE SYSTEMS ASSOCIATES; *U.S. Private*, pg. 3616
SIERRA AUCTION MANAGEMENT, INC.—See Liquidity Services, Inc.; *U.S. Public*, pg. 1321
SKYMALL HOLDINGS, LLC—See C&A Marketing, Inc.; *U.S. Private*, pg. 702
SPENCER GIFTS LLC—See ACON Investments, LLC; *U.S. Private*, pg. 62
ST. BERNARDINE MEDICAL CENTER—See Catholic Health Initiatives; *U.S. Private*, pg. 789
STELLE S.R.L.—See Gismondi 1754 S.p.A.; *Int'l*, pg. 2979
STUDIO RETAIL GROUP PLC—See Frasers Group plc; *Int'l*, pg. 2765
TANGO CARD, INC.—See Financial Technology Ventures Management Co. LLC; *U.S. Private*, pg. 1508
THINGS REMEMBERED, INC.—See Gordon Brothers Group, LLC; *U.S. Private*, pg. 1742
THINKGEEK, INC.—See GameStop Corp.; *U.S. Public*, pg. 896
TRENDSETTERS INC.—See May Trucking Company Inc.; *U.S. Private*, pg. 2620
TROPICAL SHELL & GIFTS INC—See Historic Tours of America Inc.; *U.S. Private*, pg. 1952
VANDOR, LLC—See BioWorld Merchandising, Inc.; *U.S. Private*, pg. 563
VINTAGE STOCK, INC.—See Live Ventures Incorporated; *U.S. Public*, pg. 1332
WALL DRUG STORE INC.; *U.S. Private*, pg. 4430
WILLIAM ASHLEY CHINA CORPORATION—See Fairfax Financial Holdings Limited; *Int'l*, pg. 2609
WINSLOWS INC.; *U.S. Private*, pg. 4543
WOODEN SOLDIER LTD.; *U.S. Private*, pg. 4557
YAMANDO GMBH—See Euronet Worldwide, Inc.; *U.S. Public*, pg. 798

459510 — USED MERCHANDISE RETAILERS

AMERICAN AUCTIONEERS LLC; *U.S. Private*, pg. 223
AMERICAN FURNITURE RENTAL; *U.S. Private*, pg. 234
AMERICAN JEWELRY & LOAN; *U.S. Private*, pg. 239
ANTEKS HOME FURNISHINGS INC.; *U.S. Private*, pg. 287
BLUE PLATE CATERING, LTD.; *U.S. Private*, pg. 590
BRASS ARMADILLO INC.; *U.S. Private*, pg. 640
BUFFALO EXCHANGE LTD.; *U.S. Private*, pg. 680
CASH CONVERTERS INTERNATIONAL LIMITED; *Int'l*, pg. 1352
COMPUTER PRODUCTS CORPORATION; *U.S. Private*, pg. 1005
CORT FURNITURE RENTALS & CLEARANCE CENTER—See Berkshire Hathaway Inc.; *U.S. Public*, pg. 303
DON PRESLEY AUCTIONS; *U.S. Private*, pg. 1258
EARLY AMERICAN HISTORY AUCTIONS, INC.; *U.S. Private*, pg. 1313
G-7 DEVELOPMENT CO., LTD.—See G-7 HOLDINGS Inc.; *Int'l*, pg. 2862
GALLERY 63, INC.; *U.S. Private*, pg. 1639
GOLD & SILVER COIN SHOP, INC.; *U.S. Public*, pg. 1727
GOODWILL OF NORTH FLORIDA; *U.S. Private*, pg. 1741
GREAT LAKES COMPUTER SOURCE, INC.; *U.S. Private*, pg. 1764
GUYETTE, SCHMIDT & DEETER; *U.S. Private*, pg. 1820
HARD OFF CORPORATION CO., LTD.; *Int'l*, pg. 3272
ICOLLECTOR.COM TECHNOLOGIES, INC.—See Hongli Clean Energy Technologies Corp.; *Int'l*, pg. 3471
IMC RETAIL, LLC—See Starwood Property Trust, Inc.; *U.S. Public*, pg. 1939
INTERGALACTIC INC.; *U.S. Private*, pg. 2110
J & J FLEA MARKET—See United Flea Markets; *U.S. Private*, pg. 4292
J. MANN INC.; *U.S. Private*, pg. 2156
KENO AUCTIONS LLC; *U.S. Private*, pg. 2287
LA FAMILIA PAWN & JEWELRY—See Simple Management Group, Inc.; *U.S. Private*, pg. 3666
LAMP WORKS—See ELK Group International, Inc.; *U.S. Private*, pg. 1362
THE LIGHTNING GROUP, INC.; *U.S. Private*, pg. 4070
METROPOLITAN ASSOCIATION FOR RETARDED CITIZENS, INC.; *U.S. Private*, pg. 2688
MIDDLE EAST EQUIPMENT & TRADING—See Al Jaber Group; *Int'l*, pg. 280
MINNEAPOLIS RAG STOCK CO. INC.; *U.S. Private*, pg. 2743
MYRIAD SUPPLY COMPANY, LLC; *U.S. Private*, pg. 2825

N.A.I.C.S. INDEX

NAIMAN GMBH—See G-III Apparel Group, Ltd.; *U.S. Public*, pg. 894
NANDORF INC.; *U.S. Private*, pg. 2833
NORQUIST SALVAGE CORPORATION; *U.S. Private*, pg. 2939
OBSCURA ANTIQUES & ODDITIES; *U.S. Private*, pg. 2987
OHIO VALLEY GOODWILL; *U.S. Private*, pg. 3005
PROFILES IN HISTORY; *U.S. Private*, pg. 3277
RANDY MERREN AUTO SALES INC.; *U.S. Private*, pg. 3354
REPRISE RECORDS, INC.—See Access Industries, Inc.; *U.S. Public*, pg. 52
SAVERS, INC.; *U.S. Private*, pg. 3556
SEATTLE GOODWILL INDUSTRIES; *U.S. Private*, pg. 3592
SKYWAY AUTO PARTS, INC.—See Metalico Inc.; *U.S. Private*, pg. 2681
STRAND BOOK STORE INC.; *U.S. Private*, pg. 3833
SUFFOLK JEWELERS INC.; *U.S. Private*, pg. 3849
TERRI'S CONSIGN & DESIGN HOLDING; *U.S. Private*, pg. 3972
TORTUGA TRADING INC.; *U.S. Private*, pg. 4190
UBID.COM, INC.—See Enable Holdings, Inc.; *U.S. Public*, pg. 754
UNITED FLEA MARKETS; *U.S. Private*, pg. 4292

459910 — PET AND PET SUPPLIES RETAILERS

ADM COLLINGWOOD GRAIN INC.—See Archer-Daniels-Midland Company; *U.S. Public*, pg. 181
ANIMALCARE GROUP PLC; *Int'l*, pg. 471
ANIMALCARE LIMITED—See Animalcare Group plc; *Int'l*, pg. 471
ANIMART INC.; *U.S. Private*, pg. 283
ANIPET ANIMAL SUPPLIES INC.; *Int'l*, pg. 472
ANISERCO S.A.; *Int'l*, pg. 472
BARKBOX, INC.—See BARK, Inc.; *U.S. Public*, pg. 276
BAY WALK—See The Sembler Company; *U.S. Private*, pg. 4116
BOSS PET PRODUCTS, INC.—See Boss Holdings, Inc.; *U.S. Public*, pg. 371
BULK REEF SUPPLY; *U.S. Private*, pg. 684
CAPITOL OFFICE SOLUTIONS—See Xerox Holdings Corporation; *U.S. Public*, pg. 2389
CARE-A-LOT PET SUPPLY; *U.S. Private*, pg. 752
CHEWY, INC.—See BC Partners LLP; *Int'l*, pg. 925
CHEWY, INC.—See Caisse de Depot et Placement du Quebec; *Int'l*, pg. 1254
CHEWY, INC.—See StepStone Group LP; *U.S. Private*, pg. 3804
COMPLETE PETMART INC.; *U.S. Private*, pg. 1001
DIRECT VET MARKETING, INC.—See Clayton, Dubilier & Rice, LLC; *U.S. Private*, pg. 921
DIRECT VET MARKETING, INC.—See TPG Capital, L.P.; *U.S. Public*, pg. 2170
DUBLIN DOG COMPANY, INC.—See Prospect Hill Growth Partners, L.P.; *U.S. Private*, pg. 3288
FEEDERS SUPPLY COMPANY INC.—See Houchens Industries, Inc.; *U.S. Private*, pg. 1990
FUTALIS GMBH—See CEWE Stiftung & Co. KGaA; *Int'l*, pg. 1425
HOLISTIC PET SOURCE—See Summit Partners, L.P.; *U.S. Private*, pg. 3855
HYGGE INTEGRATED BRANDS CORP.; *Int'l*, pg. 3549
HYPER PET, LLC; *U.S. Private*, pg. 2019
INTERNATIONAL PLAZA & BAY STREET—See Simon Property Group, Inc.; *U.S. Public*, pg. 1881
JACK'S AQUARIUM & PETS; *U.S. Private*, pg. 2175
KRISER'S; *U.S. Private*, pg. 2352
LEE'S PET CLUB INC.; *U.S. Private*, pg. 2414
LITTLE BIG CAT, INC.; *U.S. Private*, pg. 2468
LOVING PETS CORP.; *U.S. Private*, pg. 2504
MARK & CHAPPELL (IRELAND) LIMITED—See Bansk Group LLC; *U.S. Private*, pg. 469
MARK & CHAPPELL LIMITED—See Bansk Group LLC; *U.S. Private*, pg. 469
MARY FEED & SUPPLIES, INC.; *U.S. Private*, pg. 2598
MERKO B.V.—See Merck & Co., Inc.; *U.S. Public*, pg. 1420
MERKO NV—See Merck & Co., Inc.; *U.S. Public*, pg. 1420
MOBBY CO., LTD.—See Arata Corporation; *Int'l*, pg. 536
MOOCHIE & CO.—See Pet Stuff Illinois, LLC; *U.S. Private*, pg. 3156
MOTIVATION DESIGN LLC; *U.S. Private*, pg. 2796
MUNSON LAKES NUTRITION LLC; *U.S. Private*, pg. 2814
PENN-PLAX, INC.; *U.S. Private*, pg. 3135
PETCARERX.COM—See PetMed Express, Inc.; *U.S. Public*, pg. 1678
PETCO ANIMAL SUPPLIES, INC.—See Canada Pension Plan Investment Board; *Int'l*, pg. 1281
PETCO ANIMAL SUPPLIES, INC.—See CVC Capital Partners SICAV-FIS S.A.; *Int'l*, pg. 1885
PETCO WELLNESS, LLC—See Canada Pension Plan Investment Board; *Int'l*, pg. 1281
PETCO WELLNESS, LLC—See CVC Capital Partners SICAV-FIS S.A.; *Int'l*, pg. 1885
PETEDGE; *U.S. Private*, pg. 3157
PETFOODDIRECT.COM; *U.S. Private*, pg. 3161

PET HOUSE; *U.S. Private*, pg. 3156
PETLAND DISCOUNTS INC.; *U.S. Private*, pg. 3161
PET REPUBLIC SP. Z O.O.—See Charoen Pokphand Foods Public Company Limited; *Int'l*, pg. 1453
PETS AT HOME LTD.—See KKR & Co. Inc.; *U.S. Public*, pg. 1262
PETSENSE STORE—See Tractor Supply Company; *U.S. Public*, pg. 2178
PETSMART, INC.—See BC Partners LLP; *Int'l*, pg. 925
PETSMART, INC.—See Caisse de Depot et Placement du Quebec; *Int'l*, pg. 1254
PETSMART, INC.—See StepStone Group LP; *U.S. Private*, pg. 3803
PET SPECIALTIES LLC; *U.S. Private*, pg. 3156
PETSTAGES, INC.—See Prospect Hill Growth Partners, L.P.; *U.S. Private*, pg. 3288
PET STUFF ILLINOIS, LLC; *U.S. Private*, pg. 3156
PET SUPERMARKET INC.—See Roark Capital Group Inc.; *U.S. Private*, pg. 3455
PET VALU CANADA, INC.—See Roark Capital Group Inc.; *U.S. Private*, pg. 3455
PET VALU INC.—See Roark Capital Group Inc.; *U.S. Private*, pg. 3455
PET WORLD INC.; *U.S. Private*, pg. 3156
PREMIER PET PRODUCTS—See Radio Systems Corporation; *U.S. Private*, pg. 3344
PROVET HOLDINGS LIMITED—See Clayton, Dubilier & Rice, LLC; *U.S. Private*, pg. 921
PROVET HOLDINGS LIMITED—See TPG Capital, L.P.; *U.S. Public*, pg. 2170
PSP GROUP, LLC—See B. Riley Financial, Inc.; *U.S. Public*, pg. 261
PSP GROUP, LLC—See Irradiant Partners, LP; *U.S. Private*, pg. 2141
PSP STORES LLC—See B. Riley Financial, Inc.; *U.S. Public*, pg. 261
PSP STORES LLC—See Irradiant Partners, LP; *U.S. Private*, pg. 2141
RFG DISTRIBUTING INC.; *U.S. Private*, pg. 3420
SEABREEZE PROPERTIES, INC.—See Levy Group, Inc.; *U.S. Private*, pg. 2437
SUPERPETZ, LLC—See Weis Markets, Inc.; *U.S. Public*, pg. 2342
TABCOM, LLC; *U.S. Private*, pg. 3919
TRUPET LLC—See Better Choice Company, Inc.; *U.S. Public*, pg. 326
TSI; *U.S. Private*, pg. 4253
ULTRA PET COMPANY, INC.—See Oil-Dri Corporation of America; *U.S. Public*, pg. 1566
UNITED PET SUPPLY INC.; *U.S. Private*, pg. 4295
VALUEPETSUPPLIES.COM; *U.S. Private*, pg. 4338
VETDEPOT.COM; *U.S. Private*, pg. 4373
VETNIQUE LABS LLC—See Gryphon Investors, LLC; *U.S. Private*, pg. 1800
WILD CREATIONS; *U.S. Private*, pg. 4518
WORLDWISE, INC.—See Alvarez & Marsal, Inc.; *U.S. Private*, pg. 213
ZOETIS PHILIPPINES INC.—See Zoetis, Inc.; *U.S. Public*, pg. 2410

459920 — ART DEALERS

AMERICAN DESIGN LTD.; *U.S. Private*, pg. 230
ART FORCE LLC—See General Finance & Development, Inc.; *U.S. Public*, pg. 921
ARTNET AG; *Int'l*, pg. 585
ARTNET UK LTD.—See artnet AG; *Int'l*, pg. 585
ARTNEX INC.—See Aucnet Inc.; *Int'l*, pg. 700
ART VIVANT CO., LTD.; *Int'l*, pg. 580
BONHAMS 1793 LTD.—See Epiris Managers LLP; *Int'l*, pg. 2460
BONHAMS & BUTTERFIELDS—See Epiris Managers LLP; *Int'l*, pg. 2460
DANIEL SMITH, INC.; *U.S. Private*, pg. 1156
FRANKLIN BOWLES GALLERIES; *U.S. Private*, pg. 1596
GLOBE PHOTOST, INC.; *U.S. Public*, pg. 946
GUANGDONG POLY AUCTION CO., LTD—See China Poly Group Corporation; *Int'l*, pg. 1541
JESSE KALISHER GALLERY, INC.—See Longwater Opportunities LLC; *U.S. Private*, pg. 2493
MODERN ART MUSEUM OF FORT WORTH; *U.S. Private*, pg. 2759
NOVICA UNITED, INC.; *U.S. Private*, pg. 2968
OVERSTOCK ART, LLC; *U.S. Private*, pg. 3053
PETERS CORPORATION; *U.S. Private*, pg. 3159
PYRAMID TECHNOLOGIES INC.; *U.S. Private*, pg. 3310
SOCIETY6, LLC—See Graham Holdings Company; *U.S. Public*, pg. 956
SOICHER MARIN OF FLORIDA LLC; *U.S. Private*, pg. 3706
THE THOMAS KINKADE COMPANY; *U.S. Private*, pg. 4126
WALLY FINDLAY GALLERIES, INC.—See Wally Findlay Galleries International Inc; *U.S. Private*, pg. 4431
WALLY FINDLAY GALLERIES, INC.—See Wally Findlay Galleries International Inc; *U.S. Private*, pg. 4431
WALLY FINDLAY GALLERIES INTERNATIONAL INC; *U.S. Private*, pg. 4431

WENTWORTH GALLERY HOLDINGS INC.; *U.S. Private*, pg. 4481
WYLAND ENTERPRISES HAWAII LLC—See Wyland Worldwide LLC; *U.S. Private*, pg. 4576
WYLAND WORLDWIDE LLC; *U.S. Private*, pg. 4576

459930 — MANUFACTURED (MOBILE) HOME DEALERS

ADVANTAGE HOUSING INC.; *U.S. Private*, pg. 94
AFFORDABLE GREAT LOCATIONS; *U.S. Private*, pg. 123
AMEGA SALES INC.; *U.S. Private*, pg. 218
AMERICAN HOMES, INC.; *U.S. Private*, pg. 236
BAIRD HOME CORPORATION; *U.S. Private*, pg. 454
BAY MANUFACTURED HOMES INC.; *U.S. Private*, pg. 494
BRITT MOBILE HOMES INC.; *U.S. Private*, pg. 657
BYRDS MOBILE HOME SALES INC.; *U.S. Private*, pg. 700
CENTENNIAL HOMES, INC.; *U.S. Private*, pg. 809
CLIFF AVE ACCEPTANCE INC.; *U.S. Private*, pg. 943
CMH HOMES, INC.—See Berkshire Hathaway Inc.; *U.S. Public*, pg. 304
CMH MANUFACTURING, INC.—See Berkshire Hathaway Inc.; *U.S. Public*, pg. 304
CMH PARKS, INC.—See Berkshire Hathaway Inc.; *U.S. Public*, pg. 304
CONTINENTAL ESTATES INC.; *U.S. Private*, pg. 1028
CREST HOMES CORPORATION—See Berkshire Hathaway Inc.; *U.S. Public*, pg. 304
CRG HOLDINGS LLC—See Cavco Industries, Inc.; *U.S. Public*, pg. 455
DELTA HOUSING INVESTMENT INC.; *U.S. Private*, pg. 1200
DICK MOORE INC.; *U.S. Private*, pg. 1226
DOYLE MOBILE HOMES PARTS, INC.—See Berkshire Hathaway Inc.; *U.S. Public*, pg. 304
EAGLE HOMES INC.; *U.S. Private*, pg. 1309
EAGLE MOBILE HOME CENTER INC.; *U.S. Private*, pg. 1310
EDGEWOOD MOBILE HOMES INC.; *U.S. Private*, pg. 1335
EL DORADO MOBILE HOMES INC.; *U.S. Private*, pg. 1349
ELSEA INCORPORATED; *U.S. Private*, pg. 1377
FINANCIERE IMMOBILIERE ETANG BERRE MEDIT SA; *Int'l*, pg. 2668
FUTURES HOME INC.; *U.S. Private*, pg. 1627
GCP LAMPLIGHTER, LLC—See Sun Communities, Inc.; *U.S. Public*, pg. 1961
GEO. R. PIERCE INC.; *U.S. Private*, pg. 1680
G&I HOMES, INC.—See Berkshire Hathaway Inc.; *U.S. Public*, pg. 304
GOLDEN OFFICE TRAILERS INC.—See Pacific Mobile Structures Inc.; *U.S. Private*, pg. 3068
GOLDEN PACIFIC HOMES INC.; *U.S. Private*, pg. 1732
GOLDEN VILLA HOMES INC.; *U.S. Private*, pg. 1734
HAROLD ALLEN'S MOBILE HOMES INC.; *U.S. Private*, pg. 1867
HOLIDAY HOMES INC.; *U.S. Private*, pg. 1963
HOUSING MART INC.; *U.S. Private*, pg. 1992
J&M MOBILE HOMES INC.; *U.S. Private*, pg. 2154
KEITH BAKER HOMES INC.; *U.S. Private*, pg. 2274
LAKESHORE LANDINGS, LLC—See Sun Communities, Inc.; *U.S. Public*, pg. 1961
LEE CORP HOMES INC.; *U.S. Private*, pg. 2411
LITTLE VALLEY HOMES INC.; *U.S. Private*, pg. 2469
MAMMOTH INVESTMENTS INC.; *U.S. Private*, pg. 2559
MAPLE ISLAND ESTATES, INC.; *U.S. Private*, pg. 2568
MAPLE RIDGE MOBILE HOMES OF CALIFORNIA, INC.; *U.S. Private*, pg. 2568
MEADOWS HOMES INC; *U.S. Private*, pg. 2647
MIDDLETOWN HOME SALES; *U.S. Private*, pg. 2714
NATIONAL HOME COMMUNITIES LLC; *U.S. Private*, pg. 2856
NOBILITY HOMES, INC.; *U.S. Public*, pg. 1531
OWN A HOLIDAY HOME LIMITED—See Cox & Kings Limited; *Int'l*, pg. 1822
PACIFIC HOME SALES INC.—See Pacific Housing Group, LLC; *U.S. Public*, pg. 3067
PAUL & MARLENE INC.; *U.S. Private*, pg. 3112
PETERS MANUFACTURED HOMES; *U.S. Private*, pg. 3159
PRESTIGE HOME CENTERS, INC.—See Nobility Homes, Inc.; *U.S. Public*, pg. 1531
RIVER BIRCH HOMES INC.—See Berkshire Hathaway Inc.; *U.S. Public*, pg. 304
SKYCREST ENTERPRISES INC.; *U.S. Private*, pg. 3684
SOLITAIRE HOMES, INC.; *U.S. Private*, pg. 3709
SOLOMON HOMES, INC.; *U.S. Private*, pg. 3710
TAR HEEL HOUSING CENTER INC.; *U.S. Private*, pg. 3933
TRADING POST MANAGEMENT COMPANY, LLC; *U.S. Private*, pg. 4202
VALLEY QUALITY HOMES INC.; *U.S. Private*, pg. 4335
WASHINGTON HOME CENTER INC.; *U.S. Private*, pg. 4447
WAYNES MOBILE HOME SALES INC.; *U.S. Private*, pg. 4460
WEST GATE HOME SALES INC; *U.S. Private*, pg. 4485
WISDOM HOMES OF AMERICA, INC.; *U.S. Private*, pg. 4549

459991 — TOBACCO, ELECTRONIC CIGARETTE, AND OTHER SMOKING SUPPLIES RETAILERS

AGROEXPANSION, S.A.—See Agrosalga, S.L.; *Int'l*, pg. 220
ALLIANCE ONE ROTAG AG—See Pyxus International, Inc.; *U.S. Public*, pg. 1740
ALLIANCE ONE TABACO GUATEMALA S.A.—See Pyxus International, Inc.; *U.S. Public*, pg. 1740
ALLIANCE ONE TABACO MEXICO S.A. DE C.V.—See Pyxus International, Inc.; *U.S. Public*, pg. 1740
ALLIANCE ONETOBACCO ARGENTINA S.A.—See Pyxus International, Inc.; *U.S. Public*, pg. 1740
ALLIANCE ONE TOBACCO BULGARIA EOOD—See Pyxus International, Inc.; *U.S. Public*, pg. 1740
ALLIANCE ONE TOBACCO CANADA, INC.—See Pyxus International, Inc.; *U.S. Public*, pg. 1740
ALLIANCE ONE TUTUN A.S.—See Pyxus International, Inc.; *U.S. Public*, pg. 1740
ASHH, INC.; *U.S. Private*, pg. 349
BRITISH AMERICAN TOBACCO FINANCE BV—See British American Tobacco plc; *Int'l*, pg. 1165
BRITISH AMERICAN TOBACCO SWITZERLAND SA—See British American Tobacco plc; *Int'l*, pg. 1167
BRITISH AMERICAN TOBACCO THE NETHERLANDS B.V.—See British American Tobacco plc; *Int'l*, pg. 1165
CIGARS ON 6TH—See The Cigarette Store Corp.; *U.S. Private*, pg. 4010
DEUTSCH-HOLLANDISCHE TABAKGESELLSCHAFT MBH & CO. KG—See Blackstone Inc.; *U.S. Public*, pg. 356
DISCOUNT SMOKE SHOP MISSOURI INC.; *U.S. Private*, pg. 1237
DISCOUNT TOBACCO OUTLET INC.; *U.S. Private*, pg. 1237
FRIENDLY STRANGER HOLDINGS CORP.—See Fire & Flower Holdings Corp.; *Int'l*, pg. 2678
GOOD MEDS, INC.—See CRYOMASS TECHNOLOGIES INC.; *U.S. Public*, pg. 600
GOTHAM CIGARS, LLC; *U.S. Private*, pg. 1744
HOLT'S CIGAR HOLDINGS, INC.; *U.S. Private*, pg. 1969
J&W INC.; *U.S. Private*, pg. 2155
KAISER TOBACCO STORE—See Kaiser Wholesale, Inc.; *U.S. Private*, pg. 2256
MASHONALAND TOBACCO COMPANY—See Pyxus International, Inc.; *U.S. Public*, pg. 1740
NEAPOLITAN WAY SHOPPING CENTER, LLC—See Blackstone Inc.; *U.S. Public*, pg. 351
PHILIP MORRIS SABANCI PAZALARMA VE SATIS A.S.—See Philip Morris International Inc.; *U.S. Public*, pg. 1687
PHILIP MORRIS SA PHILIP MORRIS SABANCI PAZARLAMA VE SATIS A.S.—See Philip Morris International Inc.; *U.S. Public*, pg. 1686
P.T. MAYANGSARI—See Pyxus International, Inc.; *U.S. Public*, pg. 1741
SAHNI ENTERPRISES; *U.S. Private*, pg. 3528
SMOKER FRIENDLY INTERNATIONAL LLC—See The Cigarette Store Corp.; *U.S. Private*, pg. 4010
SMOKIN' JOES TOBACCO SHOP, INC.; *U.S. Private*, pg. 3698
STANDARD VAPE CORPORATION; *U.S. Public*, pg. 1929
THE TOBACCO HUT INC.; *U.S. Private*, pg. 4127
TOBACCO SUPERSTORES INC.; *U.S. Private*, pg. 4180
ULTOCO, S.A.—See Universal Corporation; *U.S. Private*, pg. 2254
THE VAPE STORE, INC.—See Healthier Choices Management Corp.; *U.S. Public*, pg. 1016

459999 — ALL OTHER MISCELLANEOUS RETAILERS

1STDIBS.COM, INC.; *U.S. Public*, pg. 3
22ND & BURN INC.—See Acreage Holdings, Inc.; *U.S. Public*, pg. 36
2CHECKOUT.COM, INC.—See British Columbia Investment Management Corp.; *Int'l*, pg. 1170
2CHECKOUT.COM, INC.—See Francisco Partners Management, LP; *U.S. Private*, pg. 1592
AAA FLAG & BANNER MANUFACTURING CO., INC.; *U.S. Private*, pg. 30
ABC-MART KOREA, INC.—See ABC-Mart, Inc.; *Int'l*, pg. 57
ACE COPY SYSTEMS, INC.—See Hon Hai Precision Industry Co., Ltd.; *Int'l*, pg. 3458
ADVANCED IMAGING SOLUTIONS INC.; *U.S. Private*, pg. 90
ADVANCED SYSTEMS INC.—See Gordon Flesch Company, Inc.; *U.S. Private*, pg. 1743
AEON KYUSHU CO., LTD.—See AEON Co., Ltd.; *Int'l*, pg. 176
AFORD AWARDS LIMITED—See CEPS PLC; *Int'l*, pg. 1420
AG-PRO, LLC; *U.S. Private*, pg. 125
AGRI-CHEM INC.; *U.S. Private*, pg. 129
ALARM TEAM, INC.; *U.S. Private*, pg. 150
AL & ED'S CORPORATION; *U.S. Private*, pg. 147
ALL COPY PRODUCTS LLC; *U.S. Private*, pg. 170
ALMACENES EXITO S.A.—See Calleja S.A. de C.V.; *Int'l*, pg. 1265
ALTERNATIVE ENERGY STORE, LLC; *U.S. Private*, pg. 207
AMANO MCGANN—See Amano Corporation; *Int'l*, pg. 411
AMERICANAS S.A.; *Int'l*, pg. 423
AMERITEL CORPORATION; *U.S. Private*, pg. 261
AMPLIFON COTE D'AZUR SAS—See Amplifon S.p.A.; *Int'l*, pg. 435
AMPLIFON IBERICA SA—See Amplifon S.p.A.; *Int'l*, pg. 435
AMPLIFON SUD OUEST SAS—See Amplifon S.p.A.; *Int'l*, pg. 435
AOKI SUPER CO., LTD.; *Int'l*, pg. 488
ARCLANDS CORP; *Int'l*, pg. 549
ARENDS-AWE INC.; *U.S. Private*, pg. 318
ART.COM INC.—See Trends International LLC; *U.S. Private*, pg. 4218
ASEL ART SUPPLY INC.; *U.S. Private*, pg. 348
ASSOCIATED RETAILERS LIMITED; *Int'l*, pg. 649
AT HOME GROUP INC.—See Hellman & Friedman LLC; *U.S. Private*, pg. 1907
AT HOME PROPERTIES LLC—See Hellman & Friedman LLC; *U.S. Private*, pg. 1907
ATLANTA WHIRLPOOL—See AGCO Inc.; *U.S. Private*, pg. 126
ATOMIC TATTOOS, LLC; *U.S. Private*, pg. 381
ATTARCO INC.; *U.S. Private*, pg. 383
AUGUSTA COOPERATIVE FARM BUREAU, INC.; *U.S. Private*, pg. 392
AUTOMATION-X CORPORATION; *U.S. Private*, pg. 400
AWARDS.COM LLC—See TWS Partnership LLC; *U.S. Private*, pg. 4267
BABY BUNTING GROUP LIMITED; *Int'l*, pg. 793
BABYSAM AMBA—See AAC Capital Partners Holding B.V.; *Int'l*, pg. 30
BACKCOUNTRY.COM, INC.—See TSG Consumer Partners LLC; *U.S. Private*, pg. 4252
BAILEY FEED MILL INC.; *U.S. Private*, pg. 425
BALLY, CORP.; *Int'l*, pg. 809
BALSAM BRANDS; *U.S. Private*, pg. 462
BALSAM HILL—See Balsam Brands; *U.S. Private*, pg. 462
BAOZUN INC.; *Int'l*, pg. 857
BATH & BODY WORKS BRAND MANAGEMENT, INC.—See Bath & Body Works, Inc.; *U.S. Public*, pg. 279
BAY CITY CABINETS; *U.S. Private*, pg. 492
BAYRU LLC; *U.S. Private*, pg. 496
BBQ FACTORY PTY. LTD.—See CapitalGroup Limited; *Int'l*, pg. 1314
BEACON LIGHTING GROUP LTD; *Int'l*, pg. 932
BEALL'S WESTGATE CORPORATION—See Beall's, Inc.; *U.S. Private*, pg. 505
BEDDEN & MATRASSEN B.V.—See Beter Bed Holding N.V.; *Int'l*, pg. 1002
BEENOS INC.; *Int'l*, pg. 939
BEL-AQUA POOL SUPPLY INC.; *U.S. Private*, pg. 516
BEN MEADOWS COMPANY—See The Riverside Company; *U.S. Private*, pg. 4108
BERCHTOLD EQUIPMENT COMPANY; *U.S. Private*, pg. 529
BEST INC.; *Int'l*, pg. 999
BESTNEST, INC.; *U.S. Private*, pg. 544
BETER BEHEER B.V.—See Beter Bed Holding N.V.; *Int'l*, pg. 1002
BETTER LIFE COMMERCIAL CHAIN SHARE CO., LTD.; *Int'l*, pg. 1003
THE BETTY MILLS COMPANY, INC.; *U.S. Private*, pg. 3994
BHG RETAIL TRUST MANAGEMENT PTE. LTD.; *Int'l*, pg. 1015
BIEDERMANN & SONS, INC.; *U.S. Private*, pg. 551
BIG 5 CORPORATION DISTRIBUTION CENTER—See Big 5 Sporting Goods Corporation; *U.S. Public*, pg. 330
BINSONS HOSPITAL SUPPLIES INC.; *U.S. Private*, pg. 561
BLUEBERRIES MEDICAL CORP.; *Int'l*, pg. 1070
BONDDESK GROUP LLC—See Tradeweb Markets Inc.; *U.S. Public*, pg. 2178
BOOHOO GROUP PLC; *Int'l*, pg. 1110
BORING BUSINESS SYSTEMS, INC.; *U.S. Private*, pg. 618
BOXLIGHT INC.; *U.S. Public*, pg. 626
BPA INTERNATIONAL; *U.S. Private*, pg. 629
BRACCO RESEARCH USA INC—See Bracco S.p.A.; *Int'l*, pg. 1134
BREWBILT MANUFACTURING, INC.; *U.S. Public*, pg. 381
THE BRIDGEWATER CANDLE COMPANY, LLC—See Grace Management Group, LLC; *U.S. Private*, pg. 1749
BRUCETON AG-SERVICES INC.—See Bruceton Farm Service, Inc.; *U.S. Private*, pg. 671
BTCS INC.; *U.S. Public*, pg. 409
BUFFALO CO., LTD.; *Int'l*, pg. 1211
BUFFALO WHEELCHAIR, INC.—See AdaptHealth Corp.; *U.S. Public*, pg. 38
BURDEN SALES COMPANY; *U.S. Private*, pg. 686
BURKES WESTGATE CORPORATION—See Beall's, Inc.; *U.S. Private*, pg. 505
CALEDONIA FARMERS ELEVATOR COMPANY INC.; *U.S. Private*, pg. 717
CALLEJA S.A. DE C.V.; *Int'l*, pg. 1265
CALL ONE, INC.—See Synergy Communications Management; *U.S. Private*, pg. 3904
CAL SPAS, INC.; *U.S. Private*, pg. 715
CALTRONICS BUSINESS SYSTEMS; *U.S. Private*, pg. 724
CANNA CABANA INC.—See High Tide, Inc.; *Int'l*, pg. 3386
CAPTURE TECHNOLOGIES, INC.; *U.S. Private*, pg. 747
CARPETLAND BV—See Carpetright plc; *Int'l*, pg. 1343
CARPETRIGHT OF LONDON LIMITED—See Carpetright plc; *Int'l*, pg. 1343
CARTA MUNDI UK LTD.—See Cartamundi N.V.; *Int'l*, pg. 1348
CASHMAN EQUIPMENT COMPANY; *U.S. Private*, pg. 783
CATALOG MARKETPLACE, INC.—See Capital Resource Partners, L.P.; *U.S. Private*, pg. 742
CAVE SHEPHERD & CO., LTD.; *Int'l*, pg. 1361
CDW MERCHANTS, INC.; *U.S. Private*, pg. 803
CEDARBROOK SAUNA & STEAM; *U.S. Private*, pg. 805
CELL BUSINESS EQUIPMENT; *U.S. Private*, pg. 807
CENCOSUD VIAJES ARGENTINA S.A.—See Cencosud S.A.; *Int'l*, pg. 1400
CENTRAL ILLINOIS AG INC.; *U.S. Private*, pg. 821
CENTURY NOVELTY COMPANY, INC.; *U.S. Private*, pg. 833
CHAI CANNABIS CO. INC.—See Captor Capital Corp.; *Int'l*, pg. 1317
CHAMPS SPORTS—See Foot Locker, Inc.; *U.S. Public*, pg. 863
CHARLOTTE OUTLETS, LLC—See Tanger Inc.; *U.S. Public*, pg. 1980
CHASING FIREFLIES, LLC—See DAI Holding, LLC; *U.S. Private*, pg. 1145
CHEMISTREE TECHNOLOGY, INC.; *Int'l*, pg. 1462
CHIEF CORPORATION; *U.S. Private*, pg. 880
CHRISTIANSEN IMPLEMENT COMPANY, INC.; *U.S. Private*, pg. 891
CJ ENM CO., LTD.—See CJ Corporation; *Int'l*, pg. 1632
CJ SPEEDEX LOGISTICS DEQING CO., LTD.—See CJ Corporation; *Int'l*, pg. 1633
CLASSICAL NUMISMATIC GROUP, INC.; *U.S. Private*, pg. 917
CLICKSHOPS INC.; *U.S. Private*, pg. 942
CLICKTOSHOP, LLC; *U.S. Private*, pg. 942
CMO CORPORATION; *Int'l*, pg. 1671
COASTAL FARM & HOME SUPPLY, LLC—See Nolan Capital, Inc.; *U.S. Private*, pg. 2934
COINS FOR ANYTHING, INC.; *U.S. Private*, pg. 965
COMMUNITY HOME SUPPLY CO. INC.; *U.S. Private*, pg. 994
COMPARENETWORKS, INC.; *U.S. Private*, pg. 998
COMPLEMAR PARTNERS; *U.S. Private*, pg. 1000
THE CONTAINER STORE GROUP, INC.—See Leonard Green & Partners, L.P.; *U.S. Private*, pg. 2429
COOKING ENTHUSIAST, LLC; *U.S. Private*, pg. 1039
CORNWELL COMMUNICATIONS, INC.—See Matrix Integration LLC; *U.S. Private*, pg. 2612
COSTUME CRAZE, LLC; *U.S. Private*, pg. 1063
COSWAY CORPORATION BERHAD—See Berjaya Corporation Berhad; *Int'l*, pg. 984
COURTS SINGAPORE LIMITED—See EQT AB; *Int'l*, pg. 2470
CPN PATTAYA CO., LTD.—See Central Pattana Public Company Limited; *Int'l*, pg. 1409
CREATE & CRAFT LTD.—See Aurelius Equity Opportunities SE & Co. KGaA; *Int'l*, pg. 708
CROWN POWER & EQUIPMENT CO.; *U.S. Private*, pg. 1112
CSWW INC.; *U.S. Private*, pg. 1118
CULTURE CONVENIENCE CLUB CO., LTD.; *Int'l*, pg. 1877
CUMMINS ROCKY MOUNTAIN—See Cummins Inc.; *U.S. Public*, pg. 607
CUTLER-DICKERSON COMPANY; *U.S. Private*, pg. 1131
CZERWONA TOREBKA SA; *Int'l*, pg. 1898
DAISO SANGYO CO., LTD.; *Int'l*, pg. 1942
DECORPLANET.COM; *U.S. Private*, pg. 1188
DELIVER NET LIMITED—See Bunzl plc; *Int'l*, pg. 1218
DEL'S FARM SUPPLY LLC—See Tractor Supply Company; *U.S. Public*, pg. 2178
DEODATO GALLERY S.P.A.; *Int'l*, pg. 2040
D&G EQUIPMENT INC.; *U.S. Private*, pg. 1137
DICK BLICK COMPANY—See Dick Blick Holdings Inc.; *U.S. Private*, pg. 1225
DIGITEL CORPORATION; *U.S. Private*, pg. 1231
DISA DIGITAL SAFETY PTE. LTD.—See DISA LIMITED; *Int'l*, pg. 2131
DISCOVER WELLNESS SOLUTIONS INC.; *Int'l*, pg. 2132
DODD DIESEL INC.; *U.S. Private*, pg. 1252
THE DONNA KARAN COMPANY STORE LLC—See G-III Apparel Group, Ltd.; *U.S. Public*, pg. 894
DRY ICE CORP.—See American Compressed Gases Inc.; *U.S. Private*, pg. 227
THE DUNE COMPANY OF IMPERIAL VALLEY INC.; *U.S. Private*, pg. 4023
DUTY FREE INTERNATIONAL LIMITED—See Atlan Holdings Berhad; *Int'l*, pg. 673
EBAY MARKETING (THAILAND) COMPANY LIMITED—See eBay Inc.; *U.S. Public*, pg. 709
EBAY TAIWAN COMPANY LTD.—See eBay Inc.; *U.S. Public*, pg. 709
E-CONCERT SOLUTIONS—See Apollo Global Manage-

N.A.I.C.S. INDEX

459999 — ALL OTHER MISCELLAN...

ment, Inc.; *U.S. Public,* pg. 151
EFORCITY CORPORATION; *U.S. Private,* pg. 1343
EFS INTERNATIONAL BV—See Econocom Group SA; *Int'l,* pg. 2297
EGP, INC.; *U.S. Private,* pg. 1345
ELECTRONIC INDUSTRIES CORPORATION; *U.S. Private,* pg. 1355
ELITE SPORTSWEAR & AWARDS LTD.; *Int'l,* pg. 2362
EMPRESAS HITES S.A.; *Int'l,* pg. 2390
EPIC STORES CORP.; *U.S. Private,* pg. 1412
EROTIK ABWICKLUNGSGES AG; *Int'l,* pg. 2497
EURO AUCTIONS (UK) LTD.—See Gardrum Holdings Limited; *Int'l,* pg. 2884
EVENT NETWORK, INC.; *U.S. Private,* pg. 1436
EVERGREEN IMPLEMENT INC.; *U.S. Private,* pg. 1439
EX A.D.; *Int'l,* pg. 2576
EXTRAKARE LLC; *U.S. Private,* pg. 1452
EZCORP, INC.; *U.S. Public,* pg. 817
FA. ANTON SCHLECKER; *Int'l,* pg. 2598
FARMER'S SUPPLY COOPERATIVE INC.; *U.S. Private,* pg. 1475
FASHIONPHILE; *U.S. Private,* pg. 1481
FIELDS EQUIPMENT CO. INC.; *U.S. Private,* pg. 1504
FINARTE SPA; *Int'l,* pg. 2669
FINGEN S.P.A.; *Int'l,* pg. 2674
FIRELINE CORPORATION; *U.S. Private,* pg. 1512
THE FIRESTATION 23 INC.—See Acreage Holdings, Inc.; *U.S. Public,* pg. 36
FISH & STILL EQUIPMENT CO. INC.; *U.S. Private,* pg. 1533
FIVERR INTERNATIONAL LTD.; *Int'l,* pg. 2696
FLAX ARTIST'S MATERIALS; *U.S. Private,* pg. 1541
FLORIDA COUNTRY STORES INC.—See John R. McKenzie Jobber, Inc.; *U.S. Private,* pg. 2223
FONE4 COMMUNICATIONS (INDIA) LIMITED; *Int'l,* pg. 2725
FOOTHILLS FARMERS COOPERATIVE; *U.S. Private,* pg. 1562
FOSTER WAYLAND INCORPORATED; *U.S. Private,* pg. 1579
FOUNTAIN SQUARE MANAGEMENT CO.—See Fifth Third Bancorp; *U.S. Public,* pg. 833
FRANCHISE CONCEPTS, INC.; *U.S. Private,* pg. 1587
FRONTLINE AG SOLUTIONS - LEWISTOWN—See Frontline AG LLC; *U.S. Private,* pg. 1616
GAITHERSBURG FARMERS SUPPLY; *U.S. Private,* pg. 1635
GALLERY OF HISTORY AUCTIONS, INC.—See GALLERY OF HISTORY, INC.; *U.S. Private,* pg. 1639
GALLERY OF HISTORY, INC.; *U.S. Private,* pg. 1639
GARTON TRACTOR INC.; *U.S. Private,* pg. 1646
GEBO DISTRIBUTING CO., INC.; *U.S. Private,* pg. 1655
GEBR. HEINEMANN SE & CO. KG; *Int'l,* pg. 2905
GEMPLER'S—See The Riverside Company; *U.S. Private,* pg. 4108
GIFTCARDRESCUE.COM, LLC; *U.S. Private,* pg. 1697
GIGACLOUD TECHNOLOGY, INC.; *Int'l,* pg. 2971
GILLIGAN & FERNEMAN, LLC; *U.S. Private,* pg. 1700
GINOP SALES INC.; *U.S. Private,* pg. 1702
GLOBAL TOP E-COMMERCE CO., LTD.; *Int'l,* pg. 3002
GOBINS INC.—See All Copy Products LLC; *U.S. Private,* pg. 170
GODLEY AUCTION COMPANY, INC.; *U.S. Private,* pg. 1724
GOLDMAN EQUIPMENT CO., LLC.; *U.S. Private,* pg. 1735
GOODSUITE; *U.S. Private,* pg. 1740
GOODY POINT, INC.—See Faith, Inc.; *Int'l,* pg. 2609
GRAND RIVER, INC.; *U.S. Private,* pg. 1753
GRANGE COOPERATIVE SUPPLY ASSOCIATION; *U.S. Private,* pg. 1754
GREAT AMERICAN DUCK RACES, INC.; *U.S. Private,* pg. 1762
GROUPE ARCHAMBAULT INC.—See Groupe Renaud-Bray, Inc.; *Int'l,* pg. 3110
GROUPE FNAC S.A.; *Int'l,* pg. 3102
GRUPO GIGANTE, S.A.B. DE C.V.; *Int'l,* pg. 3130
GUIRYS INC.; *U.S. Private,* pg. 1814
HANDSMAN CO., LTD.; *Int'l,* pg. 3243
HAPPINESS AND D CO., LTD.; *Int'l,* pg. 3268
HARRIS TECHNOLOGY GROUP LIMITED; *Int'l,* pg. 3278
HARROW STORES INC.; *U.S. Private,* pg. 1871
HARVEY & THOMPSON LTD.—See H&T Group Plc; *Int'l,* pg. 3193
HASEGAWA CO., LTD.; *Int'l,* pg. 3282
HAYNEEDLE, INC.; *U.S. Private,* pg. 1885
HAYWARD POOL PRODUCTS, INC.—See CCMP Capital Advisors, LP; *U.S. Public,* pg. 800
HAYWARD POOL PRODUCTS, INC.—See CCMP Capital Advisors, LP; *U.S. Public,* pg. 800
HAYWARD POOL PRODUCTS, INC.—See MSD Capital, L.P.; *U.S. Private,* pg. 2807
HAYWARD POOL PRODUCTS, INC.—See MSD Capital, L.P.; *U.S. Private,* pg. 2807
HEALTH CIRCLE, INC.—See Acreage Holdings, Inc.; *U.S. Public,* pg. 36
HIDEF LIFESTYLE; *U.S. Private,* pg. 1934
HOLMAN'S INCORPORATED; *U.S. Private,* pg. 1967

HOME BREW MART, INC.—See Kings & Convicts Brewing Co.; *U.S. Private,* pg. 2311
HOMEWETBAR; *U.S. Private,* pg. 1975
HOOBER INCORPORATED; *U.S. Private,* pg. 1977
HUNGERRUSH—See The CapStreet Group LLC; *U.S. Private,* pg. 4004
ICLICK INTERACTIVE ASIA GROUP LIMITED; *Int'l,* pg. 3581
THE INCREDIBLE CHRISTMAS PLACE; *U.S. Private,* pg. 4055
INDIAN VALLEY RECORD—See Feather Publishing Co., Inc.; *U.S. Private,* pg. 1486
INTERWORLD HIGHWAY, LLC—See Distribution Solutions Group, Inc.; *U.S. Public,* pg. 669
INVESTMENT RARITIES INCORPORATED; *U.S. Private,* pg. 2132
ISLAND EQUIPMENT INC; *U.S. Private,* pg. 2145
ISLAND RECREATIONAL; *U.S. Private,* pg. 2145
JAY INDUSTRIAL REPAIR, INC.; *U.S. Private,* pg. 2191
JD EQUIPMENT INC.; *U.S. Private,* pg. 2195
JENSEN AUDIO VISUAL; *U.S. Private,* pg. 2200
J&J DISTRIBUTING COMPANY; *U.S. Private,* pg. 2154
JOHN B. RUDY COMPANY INC.; *U.S. Private,* pg. 2220
JORDAN IMPLEMENTS CO.; *U.S. Private,* pg. 2235
KASPIEN, INC.—See Kaspien Holdings Inc.; *U.S. Public,* pg. 1214
KEEPRS, INC.; *U.S. Private,* pg. 2273
KEITH MONUMENT COMPANY, INC.—See PKDM Holdings, Inc.; *U.S. Private,* pg. 3193
LABORATOIRE D AUDITION DE ARCEAUX SARL—See Amplifon S.p.A.; *Int'l,* pg. 435
LAKESHORE LEARNING MATERIALS; *U.S. Private,* pg. 2377
LAMB & WEBSTER INC.; *U.S. Private,* pg. 2379
LANTANA COMMUNICATIONS CORP.; *U.S. Private,* pg. 2391
LAREDO OUTLET SHOPPES, LLC—See CBL & Associates Properties, Inc.; *U.S. Public,* pg. 458
LA SENZA CORPORATION—See Regent, L.P.; *U.S. Private,* pg. 3388
LASSETER IMPLEMENT COMPANY, LLC—See Lasseter Tractor Co.; *U.S. Private,* pg. 2395
LAWMEN'S SAFETY SUPPLY INC.—See Kanders & Company, Inc.; *U.S. Private,* pg. 2259
LAWMEN SUPPLY COMPANY OF NEW JERSEY, INC.; *U.S. Private,* pg. 2401
LESLIE'S POOLMART, INC.—See Leonard Green & Partners, L.P.; *U.S. Private,* pg. 2426
L. HARVEY & SON CO.—See Harvey Fertilizer & Gas Co.; *U.S. Private,* pg. 1878
LINTON SUPPLY CO.; *U.S. Private,* pg. 2463
LIPENWALD INC.; *U.S. Private,* pg. 2464
LITTLETON COIN CO., INC.; *U.S. Private,* pg. 2472
LIVING STREAM MINISTRY; *U.S. Private,* pg. 2474
LONS MEMORIALS—See Family Memorials Inc.; *Int'l,* pg. 2612
MAGIC ICE USA, INC.—See Everything Ice, Inc.; *U.S. Private,* pg. 1441
MARDEL INC.; *U.S. Private,* pg. 2573
MARSHALL RETAIL GROUP LLC—See Brentwood Associates; *U.S. Private,* pg. 646
MATRIX VISUAL SOLUTIONS, INC.—See Westminster Capital Inc.; *U.S. Public,* pg. 4499
MAX DAVIS ASSOCIATES INC.—See Adams Remco Inc.; *U.S. Private,* pg. 75
MCDOWELL & WALKER INC.; *U.S. Private,* pg. 2633
MFA INCORPORATED; *U.S. Private,* pg. 2693
MID CENTRAL ICE, LLC—See H.I.G. Capital, LLC; *U.S. Private,* pg. 1829
MODERN SUPPLY CO., INC.—See Modern Welding Company, Inc.; *U.S. Private,* pg. 2762
MODERN SUPPLY CO., INC.—See Modern Welding Company, Inc.; *U.S. Private,* pg. 2762
MODERN SUPPLY CO., INC.—See Modern Welding Company, Inc.; *U.S. Private,* pg. 2762
MONTGOMERY OFFICE EQUIPMENT CO.—See Pitney Bowes Inc.; *U.S. Public,* pg. 1694
MOVIETICKETS.COM, LLC—See Comcast Corporation; *U.S. Public,* pg. 540
MT. SHASTA MALL—See Brookfield Corporation; *Int'l,* pg. 1185
MYSTIC STAMP COMPANY; *U.S. Private,* pg. 2826
NAVAJO TRACTOR SALES INC.; *U.S. Private,* pg. 2872
NELSON WHITE SYSTEMS, INC.; *U.S. Private,* pg. 2884
NEWHERE, INC.; *U.S. Private,* pg. 2915
NEW YORK CENTRAL ART SUPPLY, INC.; *U.S. Private,* pg. 2920
NICHE RETAIL, LLC.; *U.S. Private,* pg. 2925
NM GROUP NETWORK MAPPING CORP.—See Trimble, Inc.; *U.S. Public,* pg. 2190
NOBU ARMANI SRL—See Giorgio Armani S.p.A.; *Int'l,* pg. 2978
NORTH AMERICAN HERITAGE SERVICES, INC.—See PKDM Holdings, Inc.; *U.S. Private,* pg. 3193
NORTH AMERICAN MARKETING CORPORATION; *U.S. Private,* pg. 2941
NORTHERN AG SERVICE INC.; *U.S. Private,* pg. 2951

NORTHERN BUSINESS MACHINES INC; *U.S. Private,* pg. 2952
THE NUANCE GROUP AG—See Avolta AG; *Int'l,* pg. 749
THE NUANCE GROUP (AUSTRALIA) PTY LTD—See Avolta AG; *Int'l,* pg. 749
OH MY CRAFTS, INC.; *U.S. Private,* pg. 3003
OLD TIME POTTERY INC.—See Warburg Pincus LLC; *U.S. Private,* pg. 4438
OM OF MEDICINE LLC—See 4Front Ventures Corp.; *U.S. Public,* pg. 9
ONDAS HOLDINGS, INC.; *U.S. Public,* pg. 1602
ONE CLICK VENTURES; *U.S. Private,* pg. 3020
ONE STOP BUSINESS CENTERS INC.; *U.S. Private,* pg. 3023
ONLINE STORES, INC.; *U.S. Private,* pg. 3027
OREGON SCIENTIFIC HONG KONG LIMITED—See IDT International Limited; *Int'l,* pg. 3597
OURNETT HOLDINGS, INC.; *U.S. Private,* pg. 3050
OUTLET MALL OF SAVANNAH, LLC—See Tanger Inc.; *U.S. Public,* pg. 1980
OUTLETS AT WESTGATE, LLC—See Tanger Inc.; *U.S. Public,* pg. 1980
OVERSTOCKDEALS LLC; *U.S. Private,* pg. 3053
PACIFIC OFFICE AUTOMATION, INC.; *U.S. Private,* pg. 3069
PARKLAND PLASTICS—See Patrick Industries, Inc.; *U.S. Public,* pg. 1653
P&C DISTRIBUTORS INC.; *U.S. Private,* pg. 3058
PEARL ARTIST & CRAFT SUPPLY; *U.S. Private,* pg. 3125
PEARL PAINT CO. INC.; *U.S. Private,* pg. 3125
PERRY CORPORATION; *U.S. Private,* pg. 3153
PIATT COUNTY SERVICE CO.; *U.S. Private,* pg. 3175
PILOTMALL.COM, INC.; *U.S. Private,* pg. 3181
PITTSBURGH PLUMBING & HEATING CORP.—See Famous Enterprises Inc.; *U.S. Private,* pg. 1472
POLO RALPH LAUREN MILAN S.R.L.—See Ralph Lauren Corporation; *U.S. Public,* pg. 1761
POOL CITY INC.; *U.S. Private,* pg. 3228
POOL COVERS, INC.; *U.S. Private,* pg. 3228
POSLOVNI SISTEM MERCATOR, D.D.—See Fortenova Group d.d.; *Int'l,* pg. 2738
PRISCO DIGITAL, LLC—See Printers' Service, Inc.; *U.S. Private,* pg. 3265
PRL PORTUGAL, UNIPESSOAL LDA—See Ralph Lauren Corporation; *U.S. Public,* pg. 1761
PRO-COPY TECHNOLOGIES, INC.; *U.S. Private,* pg. 3270
PROGRESSIVE TRACTOR & IMPLEMENT COMPANY; *U.S. Private,* pg. 3279
PROMOPEDDLER.COM; *U.S. Private,* pg. 3283
PROMOTIONS DISTRIBUTOR SERVICE CORPORATION—See eBay Inc.; *U.S. Public,* pg. 709
PROTECT ALARMS—See Pye-Barker Fire & Safety, LLC; *U.S. Private,* pg. 3309
PSA WORLDWIDE CORP.—See Dry Fly Capital LLC; *U.S. Private,* pg. 1280
PUCKETT RENTS INC—See Puckett Machinery Company Inc.; *U.S. Private,* pg. 3301
QC VENTURES LLC; *U.S. Private,* pg. 3312
QUALITY FARM EQUIPMENT CO. INC.; *U.S. Private,* pg. 3319
RALPH LAUREN LONDON LTD.—See Ralph Lauren Corporation; *U.S. Public,* pg. 1761
RANGER JOE'S COLUMBUS ARMY SURPLUS CO.; *U.S. Private,* pg. 3355
RHINEHART EQUIPMENT COMPANY; *U.S. Private,* pg. 3421
ROBELLE INDUSTRIES INC.; *U.S. Private,* pg. 3457
RUELALA, INC.—See Kynetic LLC; *U.S. Private,* pg. 2360
RUSHMORE COMMUNICATIONS INC.—See Rushmore Electric Power Cooperative Inc.; *U.S. Private,* pg. 3505
RUTHERFORD FARMERS COOPERATIVE INC.; *U.S. Private,* pg. 3508
SAN DIEGO SIGN COMPANY; *U.S. Private,* pg. 3539
SAVINGS.COM—See Platinum Equity, LLC; *U.S. Private,* pg. 3201
SCHOOL BOX INC.; *U.S. Private,* pg. 3568
SCRAP YOUR TRIP.COM; *U.S. Private,* pg. 3579
SERENITY WELLNESS CENTER, LLC—See CLS Holdings USA, Inc.; *U.S. Public,* pg. 515
SHOPRUNNER, INC.—See FedEx Corporation; *U.S. Public,* pg. 828
SILVER STATE RELIEF LLC—See C21 Investments Inc.; *Int'l,* pg. 1245
SLAAPGENOTEN—See Beter Bed Holding N.V.; *Int'l,* pg. 1002
SMARTSOLUTION TECHNOLOGIES, LP—See FOMO WORLDWIDE, INC.; *U.S. Public,* pg. 863
SMITH IMPLEMENTS INC.; *U.S. Private,* pg. 3695
SNYDER-DIAMOND; *U.S. Private,* pg. 3701
SOMERVILLE MEMORIALS LTD.—See Family Memorials Inc.; *Int'l,* pg. 2612
SONAE SGPS, SA—See Efanor Investimentos, SGPS, SA; *Int'l,* pg. 2318
SOTHEBY'S A.G.—See Sotheby's; *U.S. Public,* pg. 1910
SOTHEBY'S AMSTERDAM BV—See Sotheby's; *U.S. Public,* pg. 1910
SOTHEBY'S FRANCE S.A.S.—See Sotheby's; *U.S. Public,* pg. 1910

459999 — ALL OTHER MISCELLAN...

SOTHEBY'S GLOBAL TRADING—See Sotheby's; *U.S. Public*, pg. 1910
SOTHEBY'S ITALIA S.R.L.—See Sotheby's; *U.S. Public*, pg. 1910
SOUTH CENTRAL FS INC.; *U.S. Private*, pg. 3721
SOUTHEAST CONSTRUCTION PRODUCTS, INC.; *U.S. Private*, pg. 3725
SOUTHEASTERN ICE, INC.—See H.I.G. Capital, LLC; *U.S. Private*, pg. 1829
SOUTHEAST FARM EQUIPMENT CO. INC.—See ZV Pate Inc.; *U.S. Private*, pg. 4610
SPATIAL DIMENSION AUSTRALIA PTY. LTD.—See Trimble, Inc.; *U.S. Public*, pg. 2191
SPATIAL DIMENSION CANADA ULC—See Trimble, Inc.; *U.S. Public*, pg. 2191
SPATIAL DIMENSION SISTEMAS DO BRASIL LTDA.—See Trimble, Inc.; *U.S. Public*, pg. 2191
SPINK SHREVES GALLERIES, INC.; *U.S. Private*, pg. 3757
STARBAND COMMUNICATIONS INC.; *U.S. Private*, pg. 3786
STATE ALARM, INC.—See Redwire LLC; *U.S. Private*, pg. 3380
STEAL NETWORK, LLC.; *U.S. Private*, pg. 3794
STEWART BUSINESS SYTEMS—See Xerox Holdings Corporation; *U.S. Public*, pg. 2388
STRAINSFORPAINS, INC.; *U.S. Public*, pg. 1953
STROBES-R-US, INC.—See The Shyft Group, Inc.; *U.S. Public*, pg. 2130
SUNPLAY.COM; *U.S. Private*, pg. 3869
SUPERCO SPECIALTY PRODUCTS—See Momar, Inc.; *U.S. Private*, pg. 2768
TANGER GRAND RAPIDS, LLC—See Tanger Inc.; *U.S. Public*, pg. 1980
TANGER OUTLETS DEER PARK, LLC—See Tanger Inc.; *U.S. Public*, pg. 1981
TEACHING RESOURCE CENTER LLC; *U.S. Private*, pg. 3948
TEAM RETAIL SOLUTIONS LLC—See Teall Capital Partners, LLC; *U.S. Private*, pg. 3949
TECH GROUP MEDICAL PRODUCTS—See Valley Capital Corporation; *U.S. Private*, pg. 4333
TELTRONIC INC.; *U.S. Private*, pg. 3963
TENNESSEE FARMERS COOPERATIVE; *U.S. Private*, pg. 3967
TERRELL'S OFFICE MACHINES, INC.—See Fisher's Document Systems, Inc.; *U.S. Private*, pg. 1535
T&G INDUSTRIES INC.; *U.S. Private*, pg. 3909
THREDUP, INC.; *U.S. Public*, pg. 2157
THREE RIVERS FS COMPANY; *U.S. Private*, pg. 4164
TIENDAS CHEDRAUI S.A. DE C.V.—See Grupo Comercial Chedraui S.A.B. de C.V.; *Int'l*, pg. 3125
TITANIUM HOLDINGS GROUP, INC.; *U.S. Public*, pg. 2160
TITAN MACHINERY INC. - AGRICULTURAL DIVISION—See Titan Machinery Inc.; *U.S. Public*, pg. 2160
TITAN MACHINERY INC. - CONSTRUCTION DIVISION—See Titan Machinery Inc.; *U.S. Public*, pg. 2160
TITAN MACHINERY INC. - INTERNATIONAL MARKETS—See Titan Machinery Inc.; *U.S. Public*, pg. 2160
TITAN MACHINERY INC.; *U.S. Public*, pg. 2160
TOOLBARN.COM, INC.; *U.S. Private*, pg. 4186
TOPPS ARGENTINA SRL—See Madison Dearborn Partners, LLC; *U.S. Private*, pg. 2542
TREASURE GLOBAL, INC.; *U.S. Public*, pg. 2186
TREES N TRENDS INC.; *U.S. Private*, pg. 4217
TRIAD MARKETING INC.; *U.S. Private*, pg. 4225
TRI-STATE ELECTRIC OF JONESBORO—See Tri-State Armature & Electric Works, Inc.; *U.S. Private*, pg. 4223
TRULIEVE, INC.—See Trulieve Cannabis Corp.; *U.S. Public*, pg. 2201
TRUPOINT INC.; *U.S. Private*, pg. 4250
TS DOCK & LIFT SERVICES—See TS Recreational, Inc.; *U.S. Private*, pg. 4252
TS RECREATIONAL, INC.; *U.S. Private*, pg. 4252
UNICOVER CORPORATION; *U.S. Private*, pg. 4282
UNIVERSAL COIN & BULLION LTD.; *U.S. Private*, pg. 4304
UNIVERSAL POOL CO. INC.; *U.S. Private*, pg. 4306
URM DEVELOPMENT CORP.—See URM Stores, Inc.; *U.S. Private*, pg. 4316
VALENTINS GMBH—See Hubert Burda Media Holding Kommanditgesellschaft; *Int'l*, pg. 3520
VAN DYK BUSINESS SYSTEMS INC.; *U.S. Private*, pg. 4339
VICTORIA'S SECRET (CANADA) CORPORATION—See Victoria's Secret & Co.; *U.S. Public*, pg. 2296
VISUAL INNOVATIONS COMPANY INC; *U.S. Private*, pg. 4404
VMI, INC.; *U.S. Private*, pg. 4408
VOTIVO, LLC—See Grace Management Group, LLC; *U.S. Private*, pg. 1749
WALSON, INC.—See Elm Creek Partners; *U.S. Private*, pg. 1375
WDFG UK LIMITED—See Avolta AG; *Int'l*, pg. 749
THE WHITE BARN CANDLE CO.—See Bath & Body Works, Inc.; *U.S. Public*, pg. 279
WHITES FARM SUPPLY INC.; *U.S. Private*, pg. 4511

WHITE'S INTERNATIONAL TRUCKS; *U.S. Private*, pg. 4510
WHITEWATER WHIRLPOOL BATHS SYSTEMS; *U.S. Private*, pg. 4512
WILLIAMS DISTRIBUTING INC.; *U.S. Private*, pg. 4525
WINDRIDGE IMPLEMENTS LLC; *U.S. Private*, pg. 4539
WIRELESS EMPORIUM, INC.; *U.S. Private*, pg. 4547
WORLD DUTY FREE GROUP ESPANA S.A.—See Avolta AG; *Int'l*, pg. 749
WORLD OF WEED, INC.; *U.S. Public*, pg. 2381
XOXIDE, INC.; *U.S. Private*, pg. 4582
YANKEE RETAIL COMPANY LLC; *U.S. Private*, pg. 4586
YODER & FREY AUCTIONEERS LLC—See Gardrum Holdings Limited; *Int'l*, pg. 2884
ZAHM & MATSON INC.; *U.S. Private*, pg. 4597

481111 — SCHEDULED PASSENGER AIR TRANSPORTATION

ACNA—See Air France-KLM S.A.; *Int'l*, pg. 237
ADRIA AIRWAYS D.D.—See 4K Invest International; *Int'l*, pg. 12
AEGEAN AIRLINES S.A.; *Int'l*, pg. 173
AER ARANN EXPRESS LTD.; *Int'l*, pg. 179
AERODROM LJUBLJANA, LLC—See Fraport AG; *Int'l*, pg. 2763
AEROLITORAL, S.A. DE C.V.—See Grupo Aeromexico, S.A.B. de C.V.; *Int'l*, pg. 3118
AEROSVIT AIRLINES; *Int'l*, pg. 182
AEROVIAS DE MEXICO, S.A. DE C.V.—See Grupo Aeromexico, S.A.B. de C.V.; *Int'l*, pg. 3118
AIR ARABIA PJSC; *Int'l*, pg. 236
AIRASIA BERHAD—See Capital A Bhd; *Int'l*, pg. 1309
AIRASIA X BERHAD; *Int'l*, pg. 241
AIR ATLANTA ICELANDIC—See Eimskipafelag Islands Hf.; *Int'l*, pg. 2332
AIR BALTIC CORPORATION AS; *Int'l*, pg. 236
AIR BERLIN PLC & CO. LUFTVERKEHRS KG; *Int'l*, pg. 236
AIR BURKINA SA—See Aga Khan Development Network; *Int'l*, pg. 199
AIR CANADA EXPRESS—See Chorus Aviation Inc.; *Int'l*, pg. 1584
AIR CANADA EXPRESS—See Chorus Aviation Inc.; *Int'l*, pg. 1584
AIR CANADA; *Int'l*, pg. 236
AIR CHARTERS, INC.; *U.S. Private*, pg. 138
AIR CHINA LTD.—See China National Aviation Holding Company; *Int'l*, pg. 1525
AIR DOLOMITI S.P.A.—See Deutsche Lufthansa AG; *Int'l*, pg. 2066
AIR FRANCE C.S. PARTICIPATION—See Air France-KLM S.A.; *Int'l*, pg. 236
AIR FRANCE-KLM S.A.; *Int'l*, pg. 236
AIR FRANCE—See Air France-KLM S.A.; *Int'l*, pg. 236
AIR FRANCE, USA—See Air France-KLM S.A.; *Int'l*, pg. 236
AIR GEORGIAN LTD—See Georgian International Limited; *Int'l*, pg. 2939
AIR INDIA CHARTERS LTD.—See Air India Limited; *Int'l*, pg. 238
AIR INDIA LIMITED; *Int'l*, pg. 238
AIR JAPAN CO., LTD.—See ANA Holdings Inc.; *Int'l*, pg. 444
AIRKENYA AVIATION LTD.; *Int'l*, pg. 247
AIRLINE ALLIED SERVICES LIMITED—See Air India Limited; *Int'l*, pg. 238
AIR MACAU CO., LTD.—See China National Aviation Holding Company; *Int'l*, pg. 1525
AIR MALAWI LIMITED; *Int'l*, pg. 238
AIR MARSHALL ISLANDS, INC.; *Int'l*, pg. 238
AIR MAURITIUS LIMITED; *Int'l*, pg. 238
AIR NAMIBIA (PTY) LTD.; *Int'l*, pg. 238
AIR NEW ZEALAND CARGO SERVICES—See Air New Zealand Limited; *Int'l*, pg. 239
AIR NEW ZEALAND LIMITED; *Int'l*, pg. 238
AIR NIGERIA DEVELOPMENT LIMITED; *Int'l*, pg. 239
AIR NIPPON CO., LTD.—See ANA Holdings Inc.; *Int'l*, pg. 444
AIR ONE S.P.A.—See Alitalia - Compagnia Aerea Italiana S.p.A.; *Int'l*, pg. 329
AIR PACIFIC LIMITED; *Int'l*, pg. 239
AIR PARTNER HAVACILIK VE TASIMACILIK LTD.—See Wheels Up Experience Inc.; *U.S. Public*, pg. 2366
AIR SEYCHELLES LTD.; *Int'l*, pg. 239
AIR TAHITI; *Int'l*, pg. 239
AIRTRAN AIRWAYS, INC.—See Southwest Airlines Co.; *U.S. Public*, pg. 1913
AIR TRANSPORT INTERNATIONAL LIMITED LIABILITY COMPANY—See Air Transport Services Group, Inc.; *U.S. Public*, pg. 67
AIR VANUATU LTD; *Int'l*, pg. 239
AIR WISCONSIN AIRLINES CORPORATION; *U.S. Private*, pg. 140
ALASKA AIRLINES, INC.—See Alaska Air Group, Inc.; *U.S. Public*, pg. 71
ALITALIA - COMPAGNIA AEREA ITALIANA S.P.A.; *Int'l*, pg. 329
ALLEGIANT TRAVEL COMPANY; *U.S. Public*, pg. 78

ALLIANCE AIRLINES; *Int'l*, pg. 338
ALL NIPPON AIRWAYS WORLD TOURS CO., LTD.—See ANA Holdings Inc.; *Int'l*, pg. 444
AMADEUS CROATIA D.D.—See Croatia Airlines d.d.; *Int'l*, pg. 1851
AMADEUS FINLAND OY—See Finnair Plc; *Int'l*, pg. 2675
AMERICAN AIRLINES, INC. - PUERTO RICO OFFICE—See American Airlines Group Inc.; *U.S. Public*, pg. 95
AMERICAN AVIATION SUPPLY LLC—See American Airlines Group Inc.; *U.S. Public*, pg. 96
ANA HOLDINGS INC.; *Int'l*, pg. 443
ANA WINGS—See ANA Holdings Inc.; *Int'l*, pg. 444
ANGLO EUROPEAN AVIATION AG; *Int'l*, pg. 463
AREA TRAVEL AGENCY LTD.—See Finnair Plc; *Int'l*, pg. 2675
ASIA AVIATION PUBLIC COMPANY LIMITED; *Int'l*, pg. 610
ATLANTIC AIRWAYS; *Int'l*, pg. 674
AUSTRIAN AIRLINES AG—See Deutsche Lufthansa AG; *Int'l*, pg. 2066
AUSTRIAN MYHOLIDAY—See Deutsche Lufthansa AG; *Int'l*, pg. 2066
AZUL S.A.; *Int'l*, pg. 781
BAHAMASAIR HOLDINGS LIMITED; *Int'l*, pg. 799
BALTIA AIR LINES, INC.; *U.S. Private*, pg. 462
BANGKOK AIRWAYS PUBLIC COMPANY LIMITED; *Int'l*, pg. 832
BEARSKIN LAKE AIR SERVICE LTD.—See Exchange Income Corporation; *Int'l*, pg. 2579
BELAVIA NATSIONALYNAYA VIAKOMPANIYA R.U.P.; *Int'l*, pg. 963
BIMAN BANGLADESH AIRLINES; *Int'l*, pg. 1032
BINTER CANARIAS, S.A.; *Int'l*, pg. 1034
BLADE AIR MOBILITY, INC.; *U.S. Public*, pg. 361
BLUE PACIFIC TOURS—See Air New Zealand Limited; *Int'l*, pg. 239
BRAATHENS AVIATION—See Braganza AS; *Int'l*, pg. 1136
BRISTOW HELICOPTERS (AUSTRALIA PTY.) LTD—See Bristow Group, Inc.; *U.S. Public*, pg. 387
BUDDHA AIR PVT. LTD.; *Int'l*, pg. 1210
BULGARIA AIR AD—See Chimimport AD; *Int'l*, pg. 1479
CAL-DYNASTY INTERNATIONAL, INC.—See China Airlines Ltd.; *Int'l*, pg. 1481
CALM AIR INTERNATIONAL LTD.—See Exchange Income Corporation; *Int'l*, pg. 2579
CAMEROON AIRLINES SA; *Int'l*, pg. 1272
CAPE AIR; *U.S. Private*, pg. 737
CARIBBEAN AIRLINES LIMITED; *Int'l*, pg. 1329
CAYMAN AIRWAYS LTD.; *Int'l*, pg. 1363
CCAIR, INC.—See Mesa Air Group, Inc.; *U.S. Public*, pg. 1425
CENTRAL MOUNTAIN AIR LTD.; *Int'l*, pg. 1409
CHAUTAUQUA AIRLINES INC.—See Republic Airways Holdings Inc.; *U.S. Public*, pg. 3401
CHINA AIRLINES LTD.; *Int'l*, pg. 1481
CHINA EASTERN AIRLINES CORPORATION LTD.; *Int'l*, pg. 1498
CHINA SOUTHERN AIRLINES CO., LTD.; *Int'l*, pg. 1553
CHONGQING AIRLINES COMPANY LIMITED—See China Southern Airlines Co., Ltd.; *Int'l*, pg. 1553
COMPAGNIE AERIENNE INTER REGIONALE EXPRESS SA; *Int'l*, pg. 1722
CONTROLADORA VUELA COMPANIA DE AVIACION, S.A.B. DE C.V.; *Int'l*, pg. 1786
COPA HOLDINGS, S.A.; *Int'l*, pg. 1792
CORVUS AIRLINES—See J.F. Lehman & Company, Inc.; *U.S. Private*, pg. 2163
CREMONINI—See Air France-KLM S.A.; *Int'l*, pg. 237
CROATIA AIRLINES D.D.; *Int'l*, pg. 1851
CYPRUS AIRWAYS PUBLIC LIMITED; *Int'l*, pg. 1897
CZECH AIRLINES, A.S.; *Int'l*, pg. 1898
DELTA AIR LINES FRANCE—See Delta Air Lines, Inc.; *U.S. Public*, pg. 651
DELTA AIR LINES, INC.; *U.S. Public*, pg. 651
DELTA AIR LINES UK—See Delta Air Lines, Inc.; *U.S. Public*, pg. 651
DELTA PRIVATE JETS, INC.—See Wheels Up Experience Inc.; *U.S. Public*, pg. 2366
DOMICILE MANAGEMENT SERVICES, INC.—See United Airlines Holdings, Inc.; *U.S. Public*, pg. 2228
EAGLE AVIATION SERVICES, INC.—See American Airlines Group Inc.; *U.S. Public*, pg. 96
EASYJET AIRLINE COMPANY LIMITED—See easyJet plc; *Int'l*, pg. 2276
EBOOKERS LIMITED—See Expedia Group, Inc.; *U.S. Public*, pg. 810
EDELWEISS AIR AG—See Deutsche Lufthansa AG; *Int'l*, pg. 2070
EL AL AIRLINES LTD.; *Int'l*, pg. 2340
EL AL ISRAEL AIRLINES, LTD.—See El Al Airlines Ltd.; *Int'l*, pg. 2340
ENDEAVOR AIR, INC.—See Delta Air Lines, Inc.; *U.S. Public*, pg. 651
ENVOY AIR INC.—See American Airlines Group Inc.; *U.S. Public*, pg. 96
EOS AIRLINES, INC.; *U.S. Private*, pg. 1410
ESTRAVEL AS—See Finnair Plc; *Int'l*, pg. 2676
ETHIOPIAN AIRLINES ENTERPRISE; *Int'l*, pg. 2523

N.A.I.C.S. INDEX

481112 — SCHEDULED FREIGHT A...

ETIHAD AIRWAYS P.J.S.C.; *Int'l*, pg. 2523
EUROPEAN CATERING SERVICES INC.—See Air France-KLM S.A.; *Int'l*, pg. 237
EVA AIRWAYS CORPORATION—See Evergreen Marine Corporation (Taiwan) Ltd.; *Int'l*, pg. 2566
EVERGREEN HELICOPTERS INC.—See Erickson Incorporated; *U.S. Private*, pg. 1419
EXCEL AIRWAYS GROUP PLC—See Eimskipafelag Islands Hf.; *Int'l*, pg. 2332
EXPRESSJET AIRLINES INC.; *U.S. Private*, pg. 1451
EXPRESSJET AIRLINES, INC.—See ExpressJet Airlines Inc.; *U.S. Private*, pg. 1451
FALCON AIR EXPRESS INC.; *U.S. Private*, pg. 1466
FINNAIR OYJ-NEW YORK—See Finnair Plc; *Int'l*, pg. 2676
FINNAIR OYJ—See Finnair Plc; *Int'l*, pg. 2675
FINNAIR TRAVEL SERVICES OY—See Finnair Plc; *Int'l*, pg. 2676
FLIGHT RAJA MIDDLEEAST FZ LLC—See Ebix Inc.; *U.S. Public*, pg. 710
FLIGHT RAJA TRAVELS PHILIPPINES—See Ebix Inc.; *U.S. Public*, pg. 710
FORBES AIR SERVICES (PVT) LTD.—See Hemas Holdings PLC; *Int'l*, pg. 3340
FRONTIER AIRLINES, INC.—See Indigo Partners LLC; *U.S. Private*, pg. 2063
FRONTIER GROUP HOLDINGS, INC.; *U.S. Public*, pg. 887
GBT FINLAND OY—See Global Business Travel Group, Inc.; *U.S. Public*, pg. 941
GEORGIAN AIRWAYS LTD.; *Int'l*, pg. 2939
GERMANWINGS GMBH—See Deutsche Lufthansa AG; *Int'l*, pg. 2066
GIA-AIR HOLDINGS CORP.; *U.S. Private*, pg. 1694
GOL LINHAS AEREAS INTELIGENTES S.A.; *Int'l*, pg. 3023
GOL TRANSPORTES AEREOS—See Gol Linhas Aereas Inteligentes S.A.; *Int'l*, pg. 3023
GREAT LAKES AVIATION, LTD.; *U.S. Public*, pg. 961
GREAT SLAVE HELICOPTERS LTD.—See Clairvest Group Inc.; *Int'l*, pg. 1641
GUIZHOU AIRLINES COMPANY LIMITED—See China Southern Airlines Co., Ltd.; *Int'l*, pg. 1553
GULF AIR COMPANY B.S.C.; *Int'l*, pg. 3179
GULF AIR—See Gulf Air Company B.S.C.; *Int'l*, pg. 3179
HAINAN AIRLINES HOLDING CO., LTD.—See Hainan Traffic Administration Holding Co., Ltd.; *Int'l*, pg. 3215
HAINAN HNA DRINK CO., LTD—See Hainan Traffic Administration Holding Co., Ltd.; *Int'l*, pg. 3215
HARRODS AVIATION—See Harrods Ltd.; *Int'l*, pg. 3279
HAWAIIAN AIRLINES, INC.—See Alaska Air Group, Inc.; *U.S. Public*, pg. 72
HELICOPTERS INC.; *U.S. Private*, pg. 1906
HIFLY AIRLINES; *Int'l*, pg. 3385
HNA GROUP (HONG KONG) CO., LTD.—See Hainan Traffic Administration Holding Co., Ltd.; *Int'l*, pg. 3213
HONG KONG DRAGON AIRLINES LIMITED—See Cathay Pacific Airways Limited; *Int'l*, pg. 1360
HORIZON AIR INDUSTRIES—See Alaska Air Group, Inc.; *U.S. Public*, pg. 72
ICELANDAIR GROUP HF.; *Int'l*, pg. 3579
JAZZ AVIATION LP—See Chorus Aviation Inc.; *Int'l*, pg. 1584
JETBLUE AIRWAYS CORPORATION; *U.S. Public*, pg. 1189
JET ENGINE LEASING PTY LTD—See Alliance Airlines; *Int'l*, pg. 338
KEEWATIN AIR LP—See Exchange Income Corporation; *Int'l*, pg. 2579
KLM CITYHOPPER—See Air France-KLM S.A.; *Int'l*, pg. 237
KLM ROYAL DUTCH AIRLINES—See Air France-KLM S.A.; *Int'l*, pg. 237
KLM ROYAL DUTCH AIRLINES—See Air France-KLM S.A.; *Int'l*, pg. 237
KLM UK LTD.—See Air France-KLM S.A.; *Int'l*, pg. 237
LEFEBVRE COMPANIES, INC.; *U.S. Private*, pg. 2415
LOFTLEIOIR - ICELANDIC EHF.—See Icelandair Group hf.; *Int'l*, pg. 3579
LSG LUFTHANSA SERVICE ASIA LTD.—See Deutsche Lufthansa AG; *Int'l*, pg. 2067
LUFTHANSA AG—See Deutsche Lufthansa AG; *Int'l*, pg. 2068
LUFTHANSA CITYLINE GMBH—See Deutsche Lufthansa AG; *Int'l*, pg. 2068
LUFTHANSA GERMAN AIRLINES—See Deutsche Lufthansa AG; *Int'l*, pg. 2068
L.V.H. INC.—See Butz Enterprises, Inc.; *U.S. Private*, pg. 698
MALMO AVIATION AB—See Braganza AS; *Int'l*, pg. 1136
MANDARIN AIRLINES—See China Airlines Ltd.; *Int'l*, pg. 1482
MAXIMUS AIR L.L.C.—See Abu Dhabi Aviation; *Int'l*, pg. 70
MCCLASKEY ENTERPRISES; *U.S. Private*, pg. 2628
MESA AIRLINES, INC.—See Mesa Air Group, Inc.; *U.S. Public*, pg. 1425
MEXICANA DE AVIACION S.A. DE C.V.—See Grupo Posadas S.A.B. de C.V.; *Int'l*, pg. 3134
MIKKELIN MATKATOIMISTO OY—See Finnair Plc; *Int'l*, pg. 2676
MOLDAVIAN AIRLINES—See Carpatair SA; *Int'l*, pg. 1342
MONTANA ENTERPRISES, INC.—See Delta Air Lines, Inc.; *U.S. Public*, pg. 652

ORLY AIR TRAITEUR—See Air France-KLM S.A.; *Int'l*, pg. 237
OY AURINKOMATKAT-SUNTOURS LTD. AB—See Finnair Plc; *Int'l*, pg. 2676
PEGASUS HAVA TASIMACILIGI A.S.—See ESAS Holding A.S.; *Int'l*, pg. 2501
PENINSULA AIRWAYS INC.—See J.F. Lehman & Company, Inc.; *U.S. Private*, pg. 2163
PERIMETER AVIATION LP—See Exchange Income Corporation; *Int'l*, pg. 2579
P.J. HELICOPTERS, INC.—See Quanta Services, Inc.; *U.S. Public*, pg. 1752
REPUBLIC AIRLINE INC.—See Republic Airways Holdings Inc.; *U.S. Public*, pg. 3401
SENECA FLIGHT OPERATIONS—See Seneca Foods Corporation; *U.S. Public*, pg. 1864
SIBERIA AIRLINES PJSC—See CJSC S7 Group; *Int'l*, pg. 1634
SILVER AIRWAYS, LLC—See Independence Capital Partners, LLC; *U.S. Private*, pg. 2057
SKY SERVICE FBO INC.—See Exxon Mobil Corporation; *U.S. Public*, pg. 817
SKYWEST AIRLINES, INC.—See Skywest Inc.; *U.S. Public*, pg. 1893
SOCIETE DE RESTAURATION INDUSTRIELLE—See Air France-KLM S.A.; *Int'l*, pg. 237
SOUTHWEST AIRLINES CO.; *U.S. Public*, pg. 1913
SPIRIT AIRLINES, INC.; *U.S. Public*, pg. 1919
STAR AIRLINES—See Eimskipafelag Islands Hf.; *Int'l*, pg. 2332
STAR JETS INTERNATIONAL, INC.; *U.S. Public*, pg. 1938
SWISS INTERNATIONAL AIR LINES AG—See Deutsche Lufthansa AG; *Int'l*, pg. 2070
TEM ENTERPRISES; *U.S. Private*, pg. 3963
TOMISATO SHOJI KABUSHIKI KAISHA—See Delta Air Lines, Inc.; *U.S. Public*, pg. 652
TRANS STATES AIRLINES INC.; *U.S. Private*, pg. 4205
TYROLEAN AIRWAYS TIROLER LUFTFAHRT GMBH—See Deutsche Lufthansa AG; *Int'l*, pg. 2066
UNITED AIR LINES CREDIT UNION—See United Airlines Holdings, Inc.; *U.S. Public*, pg. 2229
UNITED AIRLINES, INC.—See United Airlines Holdings, Inc.; *U.S. Public*, pg. 2228
USA JET AIRLINES, INC.—See Roadrunner Transportation Systems, Inc.; *U.S. Public*, pg. 1802
VISION AIRLINES INC.; *U.S. Private*, pg. 4390
VOYAGEUR AIRWAYS LIMITED—See Chorus Aviation Inc.; *Int'l*, pg. 1584
XAEL CHARTERS INC.; *U.S. Private*, pg. 4579
XIAMEN AIRLINES CO., LTD.—See China Southern Airlines Co., Ltd.; *Int'l*, pg. 1553

481112 — SCHEDULED FREIGHT AIR TRANSPORTATION

ABX AIR, INC.—See Air Transport Services Group, Inc.; *U.S. Public*, pg. 67
ACCESS USA SHIPPING, LLC—See Aramex PJSC; *Int'l*, pg. 535
ACTIVE AERO GROUP, INC.—See Roadrunner Transportation Systems, Inc.; *U.S. Public*, pg. 1802
AERO EXPRESS DEL ECUADOR TRANSAM CIA LTD.—See Deutsche Post AG; *Int'l*, pg. 2071
AGILITY HOLDINGS INC.—See Agility; *Int'l*, pg. 209
AIRCO SERVICES, LLC—See Air T, Inc.; *U.S. Public*, pg. 67
AIR CREEBEC INC.; *Int'l*, pg. 236
AIR GREENLAND A/S; *Int'l*, pg. 238
AIR HARRODS LTD—See Harrods Ltd.; *Int'l*, pg. 3279
AIRNET II, LLC—See H.I.G. Capital, LLC; *U.S. Private*, pg. 1828
AIR TRANSPORT SERVICES GROUP, INC.; *U.S. Public*, pg. 67
ALPINE AVIATION INC—See AE Industrial Partners, LP; *U.S. Private*, pg. 111
AMERICAN INTERNATIONAL CARGO SERVICES (CHINA) LIMITED—See American Shipping Co. Inc.; *U.S. Private*, pg. 253
APC POSTAL LOGISTICS, LLC; *U.S. Private*, pg. 290
ARAMEX INTERNATIONAL EGYPT—See Aramex PJSC; *Int'l*, pg. 535
ARAMEX NEDERLAND BV—See Aramex PJSC; *Int'l*, pg. 535
ATLANTICA DE HANDLING—See Binter Canarias, S.A.; *Int'l*, pg. 1034
ATLAS AIR, INC.—See Apollo Global Management, Inc.; *U.S. Public*, pg. 148
ATLAS AIR, INC.—See J.F. Lehman & Company, Inc.; *U.S. Private*, pg. 2162
AUSTRALIAN AIR EXPRESS PTY. LTD.—See Australian Postal Corporation; *Int'l*, pg. 722
BINTERSWIFT—See Binter Canarias, S.A.; *Int'l*, pg. 1034
CAESARS INT'L SHIPPING & LOGISTICS CO. W.L.L.—See Caesars Group; *Int'l*, pg. 1249
CAMPBELL FREIGHT AGENCIES LIMITED—See DSV A/S; *Int'l*, pg. 2211
CARGOJET PARTNERSHIP LTD—See Cargojet Inc.; *Int'l*, pg. 1325

CARGOLUX AIRLINES INTERNATIONAL S.A.; *Int'l*, pg. 1325
CHELSEA SHIPPING CORPORATION—See Chelsea Logistics and Infrastructure Holdings Corp.; *Int'l*, pg. 1460
C.H. ROBINSON WORLDWIDE (UK) LTD.—See C.H. Robinson Worldwide, Inc.; *U.S. Public*, pg. 414
CITIFLIGHT, INC.—See Citigroup Inc.; *U.S. Public*, pg. 503
CJ GLS (S) AIRFREIGHT PTE. LTD.—See CJ Corporation; *Int'l*, pg. 1633
CN LOGISTICS FRANCE S.A.S.—See CN Logistics International Holdings Limited; *Int'l*, pg. 1673
CN LOGISTICS (JAPAN) LIMITED—See CN Logistics International Holdings Limited; *Int'l*, pg. 1673
CN LOGISTICS KOREA CO., LIMITED—See CN Logistics International Holdings Limited; *Int'l*, pg. 1673
CN LOGISTICS SA—See CN Logistics International Holdings Limited; *Int'l*, pg. 1673
CN LOGISTICS S.R.L.—See CN Logistics International Holdings Limited; *Int'l*, pg. 1673
COULSON AIRCRANE (U.S.A.), INC.—See Coulson Group of Companies; *Int'l*, pg. 1817
THE CROWN GROUP—See Crown Worldwide Holdings Ltd.; *Int'l*, pg. 1858
CROWN WORLDWIDE OY—See Crown Worldwide Holdings Ltd.; *Int'l*, pg. 1858
CROWN WORLDWIDE SRL—See Crown Worldwide Holdings Ltd.; *Int'l*, pg. 1858
DELTA AIR LINES FRANKFURT—See Delta Air Lines, Inc.; *U.S. Public*, pg. 651
DEUTSCHE POST GLOBAL MAIL (AUSTRALIA) PTY LTD.—See Deutsche Post AG; *Int'l*, pg. 2079
DEUTSCHE POST GLOBAL MAIL (FRANCE) SAS—See Deutsche Post AG; *Int'l*, pg. 2079
DHL AIR LIMITED—See Deutsche Post AG; *Int'l*, pg. 2073
DHL AIRWAYS GMBH—See Deutsche Post AG; *Int'l*, pg. 2073
DHL AVIATION (FRANCE) SAS—See Deutsche Post AG; *Int'l*, pg. 2072
DHL AVIATION (NIGERIA) LTD.—See Deutsche Post AG; *Int'l*, pg. 2072
DHL AVIATION NV / SA—See Deutsche Post AG; *Int'l*, pg. 2073
DHL EXPRESS (BRUNEI) SDN. BHD.—See Deutsche Post AG; *Int'l*, pg. 2074
DHL EXPRESS (LUXEMBOURG) S.A.—See Deutsche Post AG; *Int'l*, pg. 2074
DHL EXPRESS (PHILIPPINES) CORP.—See Deutsche Post AG; *Int'l*, pg. 2074
DHL EXPRESS (UK) LIMITED—See Deutsche Post AG; *Int'l*, pg. 2074
DHL GLOBAL FORWARDING (AUSTRIA) GMBH—See Deutsche Post AG; *Int'l*, pg. 2075
DHL GLOBAL FORWARDING (NETHERLANDS) B.V.—See Deutsche Post AG; *Int'l*, pg. 2075
DHL PAKISTAN (PRIVATE) LIMITED—See Deutsche Post AG; *Int'l*, pg. 2077
DLS-EURASIA TOO—See dls Land und See Speditionsgesellschaft mbH; *Int'l*, pg. 2141
DLS-RUSSIJA, LTD—See dls Land und See Speditionsgesellschaft mbH; *Int'l*, pg. 2141
DLS TRANS LTD. SP. Z O.O—See dls Land und See Speditionsgesellschaft mbH; *Int'l*, pg. 2141
DSV AIR & SEA AB—See DSV A/S; *Int'l*, pg. 2211
DSV AIR & SEA A/S—See DSV A/S; *Int'l*, pg. 2211
DSV AIR & SEA AS—See DSV A/S; *Int'l*, pg. 2211
DSV AIR & SEA AS—See DSV A/S; *Int'l*, pg. 2211
DSV AIR & SEA CO. LTD.—See DSV A/S; *Int'l*, pg. 2211
DSV AIR & SEA CO., LTD.—See DSV A/S; *Int'l*, pg. 2211
DSV AIR & SEA CO. LTD.—See DSV A/S; *Int'l*, pg. 2211
DSV AIR & SEA (HUNGARY) LTD.—See DSV A/S; *Int'l*, pg. 2211
DSV AIR & SEA LIMITED—See DSV A/S; *Int'l*, pg. 2211
DSV AIR & SEA LIMITED—See DSV A/S; *Int'l*, pg. 2211
DSV AIR & SEA LLC—See DSV A/S; *Int'l*, pg. 2211
DSV AIR & SEA LTD.—See DSV A/S; *Int'l*, pg. 2211
DSV AIR & SEA LTD.—See DSV A/S; *Int'l*, pg. 2211
DSV AIR & SEA LTD.—See DSV A/S; *Int'l*, pg. 2211
DSV AIR & SEA NV—See DSV A/S; *Int'l*, pg. 2211
DSV AIR & SEA OY—See DSV A/S; *Int'l*, pg. 2211
DSV AIR & SEA PTY. LTD.—See DSV A/S; *Int'l*, pg. 2211
DSV AIR & SEA PVT. LTD.—See DSV A/S; *Int'l*, pg. 2211
DSV AIR & SEA SAS—See DSV A/S; *Int'l*, pg. 2212
DSV AIR & SEA S.A.U.—See DSV A/S; *Int'l*, pg. 2212
DSV AIR & SEA SDN. BHD.—See DSV A/S; *Int'l*, pg. 2212
DSV AIR & SEA S.R.O—See DSV A/S; *Int'l*, pg. 2212
DSV HELLAS S.A.—See DSV A/S; *Int'l*, pg. 2212
ECU AIR N.V.—See Allcargo Logistics Limited; *Int'l*, pg. 333
EIMSKIPAFELAG ISLANDS HF.; *Int'l*, pg. 2332
EMO-TRANS GMBH—See Emo-Trans Inc.; *U.S. Private*, pg. 1383
ENRC MARKETING AG—See Eurasian Natural Resources Corporation Limited; *Int'l*, pg. 2527
F.C. (FLYING CARGO) INTERNATIONAL TRANSPORTATION LTD.—See Deutsche Post AG; *Int'l*, pg. 2080
FEDEX CROSS BORDER—See FedEx Corporation; *U.S. Public*, pg. 827
FLIGHT EXPRESS INCORPORATED—See H.I.G. Capital, LLC; *U.S. Private*, pg. 1827

481112 — SCHEDULED FREIGHT A... CORPORATE AFFILIATIONS

FM MULTIMODAL SERVICES SDN. BHD.—See FM Global Logistics Holdings Berhad; *Int'l*, pg. 2717
GKE FREIGHT PTE LTD—See GKE Corporation Limited; *Int'l*, pg. 2983
GLACIER WORLDWIDE, INC.; *U.S. Private*, pg. 1704
GROUND FREIGHT EXPEDITORS, LLC—See Allstates WorldCargo, Inc.; *U.S. Private*, pg. 193
GUANGZHOU BAIYUN INTERNATIONAL LOGISTIC COMPANY LIMITED—See China Southern Airlines Co., Ltd.; *Int'l*, pg. 1553
GUANGZHOU JIAHONG INTERNATIONAL FREIGHT FORWARDING CO., LTD.—See CN Logistics International Holdings Limited; *Int'l*, pg. 1673
HANDLING COUNTS GMBH—See Deutsche Lufthansa AG; *Int'l*, pg. 2066
HASSETT AIR EXPRESS; *U.S. Private*, pg. 1878
HEINRICH DEHN INTERNATIONALE SPEDITION GMBH; *Int'l*, pg. 3324
ITG INTERNATIONALE SPEDITION GMBH—See Deutsche Post AG; *Int'l*, pg. 2081
LUFTHANSA CARGO AG—See Deutsche Lufthansa AG; *Int'l*, pg. 2068
LUFTHANSA CARGO—See Deutsche Lufthansa AG; *Int'l*, pg. 2068
LUFTHANSA CARGO—See Deutsche Lufthansa AG; *Int'l*, pg. 2068
LUFTHANSA SHENZHEN MANAGEMENT COMPANY LIMITED—See Deutsche Lufthansa AG; *Int'l*, pg. 2069
LYNXS HOLDING LLC; *U.S. Private*, pg. 2522
MARTINAIR HOLLAND N.V.—See Air France-KLM S.A.; *Int'l*, pg. 238
MPG LOGISTICS, INC.; *U.S. Private*, pg. 2804
NGL CRUDE LOGISTICS, LLC—See NGL Energy Partners LP; *U.S. Public*, pg. 1527
NORTHERN AIR CARGO INC.; *U.S. Private*, pg. 2951
OLYMPIC AIR S.A.—See AEGEAN AIRLINES S.A.; *Int'l*, pg. 173
PACIFIC HELIPORT SERVICES—See Helijet International Inc.; *Int'l*, pg. 3330
PANALPINA ASIA-PACIFIC SERVICES (THAILAND) LTD.—See DSV A/S; *Int'l*, pg. 2214
PANALPINA A/S—See DSV A/S; *Int'l*, pg. 2214
PANALPINA BEVERWIJK B.V.—See DSV A/S; *Int'l*, pg. 2214
PANALPINA C.A.—See DSV A/S; *Int'l*, pg. 2214
PANALPINA CZECH SRO.—See DSV A/S; *Int'l*, pg. 2214
PANALPINA DENMARK—See DSV A/S; *Int'l*, pg. 2214
PANALPINA ECUADOR S.A.—See DSV A/S; *Int'l*, pg. 2214
PANALPINA GRIEG AS—See DSV A/S; *Int'l*, pg. 2214
PANALPINA MANAGEMENT LTD.—See DSV A/S; *Int'l*, pg. 2215
PANALPINA POLSKA SP. Z O.O.—See DSV A/S; *Int'l*, pg. 2215
PANALPINA TRANSPORT MONDIAUX SARL—See DSV A/S; *Int'l*, pg. 2215
PANALPINA WELTTRANSPORT GMBH—See DSV A/S; *Int'l*, pg. 2215
PANALPINA WORLD TRANSPORT (DUBAI) DWC-LLC—See DSV A/S; *Int'l*, pg. 2215
PANALPINA WORLD TRANSPORT LLP—See DSV A/S; *Int'l*, pg. 2216
PIEDMONT AIRLINES, INC.—See American Airlines Group Inc.; *U.S. Public*, pg. 96
POLAR AIR CARGO INC.—See Apollo Global Management, Inc.; *U.S. Private*, pg. 148
POLAR AIR CARGO INC.—See J.F. Lehman & Company, Inc.; *U.S. Private*, pg. 2163
POSTMATES INC.—See Uber Technologies, Inc.; *U.S. Public*, pg. 2217
PREMIER AVIATION SERVICES (PVT.) LTD.—See Akbar Group; *Int'l*, pg. 261
PT. FM GLOBAL LOGISTICS—See FM Global Logistics Holdings Berhad; *Int'l*, pg. 2717
SAIMA AVANDERO SPA—See DSV A/S; *Int'l*, pg. 2216
SHANTOU AIRLINES COMPANY LIMITED—See China Southern Airlines Co., Ltd.; *Int'l*, pg. 1553
SPACE CARGO SERVICES S.A.—See C.H. Robinson Worldwide, Inc.; *U.S. Public*, pg. 415
SUBURBAN AIR FREIGHT INC.—See AE Industrial Partners, LP; *U.S. Private*, pg. 111
SUN COUNTRY, INC.—See Sun Country Airlines Holdings, Inc.; *U.S. Public*, pg. 1963
TALLINK LATVIJA AS—See AS Infortar; *Int'l*, pg. 590
TBI CARGO INC.—See ACS, Actividades de Construccion y Servicios, S.A.; *Int'l*, pg. 112
TRANS-ASIA SHIPPING LINES, INCORPORATED—See Chelsea Logistics and Infrastructure Holdings Corp.; *Int'l*, pg. 1460
UNITED AIRLINES, INC.—See United Airlines Holdings, Inc.; *U.S. Public*, pg. 2228
U.S. AIRPORTS FLIGHT SUPPORT LLC; *U.S. Private*, pg. 4269
WORLDWIDE AIR LOGISTICS GROUP, INC.—See Apollo Global Management, Inc.; *U.S. Private*, pg. 148
WORLDWIDE AIR LOGISTICS GROUP, INC.—See J.F. Lehman & Company, Inc.; *U.S. Private*, pg. 2163
ZHUHAI AIRLINES COMPANY LIMITED—See China Southern Airlines Co., Ltd.; *Int'l*, pg. 1553

481211 — NONSCHEDULED CHARTERED PASSENGER AIR TRANSPORTATION

711 AIR CORP.—See Allen Holding Inc.; *U.S. Private*, pg. 179
AEROSHARES CHARTER, LLC; *U.S. Private*, pg. 119
AIRENKA HAVA TASIMACILIGI A.S.—See Enka Insaat ve Sanayi A.S.; *Int'l*, pg. 2440
AIR LAUREL, INC.—See Telephone Electronics Corporation; *U.S. Private*, pg. 3961
AIR MANAS AIR COMPANY LLC—See ESAS Holding A.S.; *Int'l*, pg. 2501
AIR PARTNER PLC—See Wheels Up Experience Inc.; *U.S. Public*, pg. 2366
AIRPORT SERVICES FRIEDRICHSHAFEN GMBH—See Deutsche Lufthansa AG; *Int'l*, pg. 2066
AIR RUTTER INTERNATIONAL, LLC; *U.S. Private*, pg. 139
AIR TRANSPORT INTERNATIONAL, INC.—See Air Transport Services Group, Inc.; *U.S. Public*, pg. 67
AIRWORKS LLC—See ATL Partners, LLC; *U.S. Private*, pg. 369
ALPINE AIR EXPRESS, INC.—See AE Industrial Partners, LP; *U.S. Private*, pg. 111
APOGEE JETS; *U.S. Private*, pg. 294
APOLLO JETS LLC; *U.S. Private*, pg. 295
BEIJING CAPITAL AIRLINES CO., LTD.—See Hainan Traffic Administration Holding Co., Ltd.; *Int'l*, pg. 3213
BRISTOW HOLDINGS U.S. INC.—See Bristow Group, Inc.; *U.S. Public*, pg. 387
BRISTOW NORWAY AS—See Bristow Group, Inc.; *U.S. Public*, pg. 387
CANADIAN HELICOPTERS LIMITED—See PHI, Inc.; *U.S. Private*, pg. 3168
CANJET AIRLINES LTD.—See I.M.P. Group International Inc.; *Int'l*, pg. 3566
CARPATAIR SA; *Int'l*, pg. 1342
CHARTERAUCTION.COM—See AeroShares Charter, LLC; *U.S. Private*, pg. 119
CITIGROUP CORPORATE AVIATION—See Citigroup Inc.; *U.S. Public*, pg. 503
CORPORATE FLIGHT MANAGEMENT INC.; *U.S. Private*, pg. 1055
CUSTOM HELICOPTERS LTD.—See Exchange Income Corporation; *Int'l*, pg. 2579
DASSAULT FALCON JET-WILMINGTON CORP.—See Groupe Industriel Marcel Dassault S.A.; *Int'l*, pg. 3105
DC AVIATION FLIGHT CREW LTD.—See ATON GmbH; *Int'l*, pg. 688
DC AVIATION LTD.—See ATON GmbH; *Int'l*, pg. 688
DEGOL AVIATION, INC.—See The DeGol Organization; *U.S. Private*, pg. 4019
DIRECTORS AIR CORPORATION—See Directors Investment Group Inc.; *U.S. Private*, pg. 1236
E.C. AVIATION SERVICES, INC.—See Gentex Corporation; *U.S. Public*, pg. 931
ELJET AVIATION SERVICES; *U.S. Private*, pg. 1362
EUROCOPTER UK LTD.—See Airbus SE; *Int'l*, pg. 244
EUROCYPRIA AIRLINES LTD—See Cyprus Airways Public Limited; *Int'l*, pg. 1897
EXECUJET CHARTER SERVICE, INC.; *U.S. Private*, pg. 1447
EXECUTIVE AIR TAXI CORP.; *U.S. Private*, pg. 1447
FLAIRJET LIMITED—See Directional Capital LLC; *U.S. Private*, pg. 1236
FLEXJET, LLC—See Directional Capital LLC; *U.S. Private*, pg. 1236
FLY VICTOR LTD.; *Int'l*, pg. 2716
GLOBAL CROSSING AIRLINES, INC.—See Global Crossing Airlines Group Inc.; *U.S. Public*, pg. 941
GLOBAL CROSSING AIRLINES OPERATIONS LLC—See Global Crossing Airlines Group Inc.; *U.S. Public*, pg. 941
GOLD AVIATION SERVICES, INC.; *U.S. Private*, pg. 1727
GRANT AVIATION INC.; *U.S. Private*, pg. 1756
HAINAN AIRLINES SALES CO., LTD.—See Hainan Traffic Administration Holding Co., Ltd.; *Int'l*, pg. 3215
HELIJET INTERNATIONAL INC.; *Int'l*, pg. 3330
HELIVIA AERO TAXI SA—See Greenwich AeroGroup, Inc.; *U.S. Private*, pg. 1781
HONG KONG AIRLINES LIMITED—See Hainan Traffic Administration Holding Co., Ltd.; *Int'l*, pg. 3215
HUNT & PALMER AIR CHARTER INDIA PVT. LTD.—See Hunt & Palmer plc.; *Int'l*, pg. 3536
HUNT & PALMER GERMANY GMBH—See Hunt & Palmer plc.; *Int'l*, pg. 3536
HUNT & PALMER HONG KONG LTD.—See Hunt & Palmer plc.; *Int'l*, pg. 3536
HUNT & PALMER PLC.; *Int'l*, pg. 3536
HUNT & PALMER (PTY) LTD.—See Hunt & Palmer plc.; *Int'l*, pg. 3536
JET-LINK AG—See ATON GmbH; *Int'l*, pg. 688
KALITTA CHARTERS, LLC—See Kalitta Air, LLC; *U.S. Private*, pg. 2257
KEYSTONE AVIATION, LLC—See Elevate Holdings, Inc.; *U.S. Private*, pg. 1358
LUCKY AIR CO., LTD.—See Hainan Traffic Administration Holding Co., Ltd.; *Int'l*, pg. 3215
MAGELLAN JETS LLC.; *U.S. Private*, pg. 2545

MAURITIUS HELICOPTER LTD.—See Air Mauritius Limited; *Int'l*, pg. 238
MIAMI AIR INTERNATIONAL, INC.—See TSI Holding Company; *U.S. Private*, pg. 4253
MORRO VERMELHO TAXI AEREO LTDA.—See Icon Aviation SA; *Int'l*, pg. 3583
MOUNT COOK AIRLINE LIMITED—See Air New Zealand Limited; *Int'l*, pg. 239
NATIONAL JETS, INC.—See Carolina Aircraft Corp.; *U.S. Private*, pg. 767
PARAMOUNT BUSINESS JETS; *U.S. Private*, pg. 3092
PIERCE ENTERPRISES INC.; *U.S. Private*, pg. 3178
RECTRIX AVIATION, INC.; *U.S. Private*, pg. 3372
ROCK-IT AIR CHARTER, INC.—See ATL Partners, LLC; *U.S. Private*, pg. 369
RUBLOFF JET EXPRESS, LLC—See Rubloff Development Group, Inc.; *U.S. Private*, pg. 3500
SOUTHERN AIRWAYS EXPRESS, LLC—See Surf Air Mobility Inc.; *U.S. Public*, pg. 1967
SOUTHERN JET INC.; *U.S. Private*, pg. 3732
SPOTLIGHT CAPITAL HOLDINGS, INC.; *U.S. Public*, pg. 1919
STERLING AVIATION, INC.; *U.S. Private*, pg. 3804
TALON AIR, INC.; *U.S. Private*, pg. 3927
TIANJIN AIRLINES CO., LTD.—See Hainan Traffic Administration Holding Co., Ltd.; *Int'l*, pg. 3216
WEST AIR CO., LTD.—See Hainan Traffic Administration Holding Co., Ltd.; *Int'l*, pg. 3216
XOJET, INC.; *U.S. Private*, pg. 4582
YOUNGJETS, LLC—See Fly Victor Ltd.; *Int'l*, pg. 2716

481212 — NONSCHEDULED CHARTERED FREIGHT AIR TRANSPORTATION

AAA AVIATION PRIVATE LIMITED—See Delta Corp Ltd.; *Int'l*, pg. 2016
AIR CARGO ASSOCIATES INC.; *U.S. Private*, pg. 138
AIR CARGO CARRIERS, LLC—See ACC Holding, Inc.; *U.S. Private*, pg. 47
AIRCON AIRFREIGHT CONTAINER MAINTENANCE GMBH—See Deufol SE; *Int'l*, pg. 2048
AIR FREIGHT NZ LIMITED—See Freightways Group Limited; *Int'l*, pg. 2771
AIR NEW ZEALAND AIRCRAFT HOLDINGS LIMITED—See Air New Zealand Limited; *Int'l*, pg. 239
AIR TRANSPORT INTERNATIONAL, LLC—See Air Transport Services Group, Inc.; *U.S. Public*, pg. 67
ALBERT COMPANIES, INC.—See ArcBest Corporation; *U.S. Public*, pg. 180
ALOHA AIR CARGO—See Saltchuk Resources Inc.; *U.S. Private*, pg. 3534
ALTA FLIGHTS (CHARTERS) INC.; *Int'l*, pg. 384
AMERICAN INTERNATIONAL RELOCATION SOLUTIONS LLC; *U.S. Private*, pg. 238
ANGLO-EUROPEAN (U.K.) LTD—See Anglo European Aviation AG; *Int'l*, pg. 463
ARIANESPACE, INC.—See Airbus SE; *Int'l*, pg. 245
ARIANESPACE SAS—See Airbus SE; *Int'l*, pg. 245
ARIANESPACE SINGAPORE PTE, LTD.—See Airbus SE; *Int'l*, pg. 245
ARMELLINI AIR EXPRESS, INC.—See Armellini Industries, Inc.; *U.S. Private*, pg. 330
ARROWHEAD INTERNATIONAL CORPORATION—See Chiyoda Corporation; *Int'l*, pg. 1574
CAPITAL CARGO INTERNATIONAL AIRLINES, INC.—See Air Transport Services Group, Inc.; *U.S. Public*, pg. 67
CARGO AIRCRAFT MANAGEMENT, INC.—See Air Transport Services Group, Inc.; *U.S. Public*, pg. 67
CARIBEX WORLDWIDE, INC.—See CaribEx Worldwide Inc.; *U.S. Private*, pg. 761
CELEBI HAVA SERVISI AS; *Int'l*, pg. 1391
CHC EUROPE (UK)—See First Reserve Management, L.P.; *U.S. Private*, pg. 1525
CHC HELICOPTER CORPORATION—See First Reserve Management, L.P.; *U.S. Private*, pg. 1525
CHC HELICOPTERS (AUSTRALIA)—See First Reserve Management, L.P.; *U.S. Private*, pg. 1525
CHC HELICOPTERS, INC.—See First Reserve Management, L.P.; *U.S. Private*, pg. 1525
CHINA EXPRESS AIRLINES CO., LTD.; *Int'l*, pg. 1501
CHINA STEEL EXPRESS CORPORATION—See China Steel Corporation; *Int'l*, pg. 1555
COMAIR REISE UND CHARTER GMBH—See BERGER Holding GmbH; *Int'l*, pg. 979
CONCORDIA INTERNATIONAL FORWARDING GMBH—See Concordia International Forwarding Inc.; *U.S. Private*, pg. 1010
CONCORDIA INTERNATIONAL FORWARDING PTE LTD—See Concordia International Forwarding Inc.; *U.S. Private*, pg. 1010
CONCORDIA INTERNATIONAL FORWARDING PTY. LTD.—See Concordia International Forwarding Inc.; *U.S. Private*, pg. 1010
CTI FREIGHT SYSTEMS PTY LTD—See CTI Logistics Limited; *Int'l*, pg. 1871
DESERT JET; *U.S. Private*, pg. 1212

N.A.I.C.S. INDEX

DEUFOL REMSCHEID GMBH—See Deufol SE; *Int'l*, pg. 2048
DEUTSCHE TRANSPORT-COMPAGNIE ERICH BOGDAN GMBH & CO. KG; *Int'l*, pg. 2085
DSV AIR & SEA INC.—See DSV A/S; *Int'l*, pg. 2211
DSV AIR & SEA INC.—See DSV A/S; *Int'l*, pg. 2211
DSV AIR & SEA PTE. LTD—See DSV A/S; *Int'l*, pg. 2211
DSV AIR & SEA S.A. DE C.V.—See DSV A/S; *Int'l*, pg. 2212
EAGLE AIR MAINTENANCE LIMITED—See Air New Zealand Limited; *Int'l*, pg. 239
EAGLE AIRWAYS LIMITED—See Air New Zealand Limited; *Int'l*, pg. 239
ENRC LOGISTICS LLP—See Eurasian Natural Resources Corporation Limited; *Int'l*, pg. 2527
EXPEDITORS INTERNATIONAL OF WASHINGTON, INC.; *U.S. Public*, pg. 810
FLYPRIVATE; *U.S. Private*, pg. 1553
GLOBAL VECTRA HELICORP LTD.; *Int'l*, pg. 3002
GRAND AIRE EXPRESS INC.; *U.S. Private*, pg. 1752
HELI-ONE EUROPE—See First Reserve Management, L.P.; *U.S. Private*, pg. 1525
INTERJET S.R.L.—See Cremonini S.p.A.; *Int'l*, pg. 1838
INTERNATIONAL CARGO MARKETING CONSULTANTS, INC.—See Alliance Ground International, LLC; *U.S. Private*, pg. 182
JET AIR (SINGAPORE) PRIVATE LIMITED—See China Best Group Holding Limited; *Int'l*, pg. 1486
LAND-MARINE CARGO, INC.—See ArcBest Corporation; *U.S. Public*, pg. 180
LYNDEN AIR CARGO, LLC—See Lynden Incorporated; *U.S. Private*, pg. 2521
MENZIES DISTRIBUTION LIMITED—See Endless LLP; *Int'l*, pg. 2403
MERCURY AIR CARGO, INC.—See Mercury Air Group Inc.; *U.S. Private*, pg. 2670
MOVING SOLUTIONS, INC.—See ArcBest Corporation; *U.S. Public*, pg. 180
NATIONAL AIR CARGO INC.; *U.S. Private*, pg. 2839
NEXUS LOGISTICS (INTERNATIONAL) LIMITED—See Heng Tai Consumables Group Limited; *Int'l*, pg. 3345
NORD HELIKOPTER AS—See Flakk Holding AS; *Int'l*, pg. 2698
PANALPINA LUXEMBOURG S.A.—See DSV A/S; *Int'l*, pg. 2214
PETROLEUM HELICOPTERS INTERNATIONAL, INC.—See PHI, Inc.; *U.S. Private*, pg. 3168
POLAR AIR CARGO WORLDWIDE, INC.—See Apollo Global Management, Inc.; *U.S. Public*, pg. 148
POLAR AIR CARGO WORLDWIDE, INC.—See J.F. Lehman & Company, Inc.; *U.S. Private*, pg. 2162
PREMIER TRUCK GROUP OF OSHAWA—See Penske Automotive Group, Inc.; *U.S. Public*, pg. 1666
R1 AIRLINES LTD.—See Avmax Group Inc.; *Int'l*, pg. 748
SINAER—See Corpfin Capital SA; *Int'l*, pg. 1802
TDS CORPORATE SERVICES LLC—See ITT Inc.; *U.S. Public*, pg. 1179
TRANSCOM LLP—See Eurasian Natural Resources Corporation Limited; *Int'l*, pg. 2527
UNIVERSAL SERVICE LLP—See Eurasian Natural Resources Corporation Limited; *Int'l*, pg. 2527
WORLDWIDE JET CHARTER, INC.; *U.S. Private*, pg. 4569
XPO AIR CHARTER, LLC—See XPO, Inc.; *U.S. Public*, pg. 2392

481219 — OTHER NONSCHEDULED AIR TRANSPORTATION

AERODYNAMICS, INCORPORATED; *U.S. Private*, pg. 118
AEROHOMEX, S.A. DE C.V.—See Desarrolladora Homex, S.A. de C.V.; *Int'l*, pg. 2043
AIRBORNE IMAGING INC.—See Barr Air Patrol, LLC; *U.S. Private*, pg. 479
AIR EVAC EMS, INC.—See KKR & Co. Inc.; *U.S. Public*, pg. 1251
AIR PARTNER SRL—See Wheels Up Experience Inc.; *U.S. Public*, pg. 2366
AIR ROYALE INTERNATIONAL INC.; *U.S. Private*, pg. 139
AIR SUNSHINE INC.; *U.S. Private*, pg. 139
AIR TINDI LTD.—See Clairvest Group Inc.; *Int'l*, pg. 1641
AMERISTAR JET CHARTER INC.; *U.S. Private*, pg. 260
ATIS IBERICA DERICHEBOURG ATIS AERONAUTIQUE SL—See Derichebourg S.A.; *Int'l*, pg. 2041
AVIATION CHARTER INC.; *U.S. Private*, pg. 406
AVJET CORPORATION; *U.S. Private*, pg. 409
BEST AVIATION—See Fieldale Farms Corporation; *U.S. Private*, pg. 1504
BRISTOW U.S. LLC—See Bristow Group, Inc.; *U.S. Public*, pg. 387
CAREFLITE; *U.S. Private*, pg. 753
CAROLINA AIRCRAFT CORP.; *U.S. Private*, pg. 767
CHAPMAN FREEBORN AIRCHARTERING BVBA—See Chapman Freeborn Airchartering Ltd.; *Int'l*, pg. 1447
CHAPMAN FREEBORN AIRCHARTERING (CHINA) LTD.—See Chapman Freeborn Airchartering Ltd.; *Int'l*, pg. 1447
CHAPMAN FREEBORN AIRCHARTERING FRETAMENTO E LOGISTICA DO BRASIL LTDA.—See Chapman Freeborn Airchartering Ltd.; *Int'l*, pg. 1447
CHAPMAN FREEBORN AIRCHARTERING, INC.—See Chapman Freeborn Airchartering Ltd.; *Int'l*, pg. 1447
CHAPMAN FREEBORN AIRCHARTERING, INC.—See Chapman Freeborn Airchartering Ltd.; *Int'l*, pg. 1448
CHAPMAN FREEBORN AIRCHARTERING (ITALIA) SRL—See Chapman Freeborn Airchartering Ltd.; *Int'l*, pg. 1447
CHAPMAN FREEBORN AIRCHARTERING LTD.; *Int'l*, pg. 1447
CHAPMAN FREEBORN AIRCHARTERING LTD.—See Chapman Freeborn Airchartering Ltd.; *Int'l*, pg. 1447
CHAPMAN FREEBORN AIRCHARTERING PTE LTD.—See Chapman Freeborn Airchartering Ltd.; *Int'l*, pg. 1447
CHAPMAN FREEBORN AIRCHARTERING PVT. LTD.—See Chapman Freeborn Airchartering Ltd.; *Int'l*, pg. 1447
CHAPMAN FREEBORN AIRCHARTERING (SHANGHAI) CO LTD.—See Chapman Freeborn Airchartering Ltd.; *Int'l*, pg. 1447
CHAPMAN FREEBORN AIRCHARTERING (SOUTH AFRICA) PTY LTD—See Chapman Freeborn Airchartering Ltd.; *Int'l*, pg. 1447
CHAPMAN FREEBORN AIRCHARTERING SP Z.O.O.—See Chapman Freeborn Airchartering Ltd.; *Int'l*, pg. 1447
CHAPMAN FREEBORN AIRMARKETING GMBH—See Chapman Freeborn Airchartering Ltd.; *Int'l*, pg. 1448
CHAPMAN FREEBORN AIRMARKETING GMBH—See Chapman Freeborn Airchartering Ltd.; *Int'l*, pg. 1448
CHAPMAN FREEBORN AIRMARKETING GMBH—See Chapman Freeborn Airchartering Ltd.; *Int'l*, pg. 1448
CHAPMAN FREEBORN AUSTRALIA—See Chapman Freeborn Airchartering Ltd.; *Int'l*, pg. 1448
CHAPMAN FREEBORN AVIATION SERVICES FZE—See Chapman Freeborn Airchartering Ltd.; *Int'l*, pg. 1448
CHAPMAN FREEBORN C/O COVIO SA—See Chapman Freeborn Airchartering Ltd.; *Int'l*, pg. 1448
CHAPMAN FREEBORN HANDCARRY LTD—See Chapman Freeborn Airchartering Ltd.; *Int'l*, pg. 1448
CHAPMAN FREEBORN HAVACILIK TASIMACILIK TIC. LTD. STI.—See Chapman Freeborn Airchartering Ltd.; *Int'l*, pg. 1448
CHERRY-AIR INC, CHARTERED AIR CARGO—See Cherry-Air; *U.S. Private*, pg. 874
CHERRY-AIR; *U.S. Private*, pg. 874
COULSON AIRCRANE LTD.—See Coulson Group of Companies; *Int'l*, pg. 1817
EAGLEMED LLC—See KKR & Co. Inc.; *U.S. Public*, pg. 1252
EDWARDS JET CENTER; *U.S. Private*, pg. 1342
EMPIRE AEROSPACE—See Empire Airlines; *U.S. Private*, pg. 1384
EMPIRE AIRLINES; *U.S. Private*, pg. 1384
ENTER AIR SP ZOO; *Int'l*, pg. 2450
EXECUTIVE FLIGHT CENTRE FUEL SERVICES LTD.; *Int'l*, pg. 2580
EXEL COMPOSITES N.V.—See Exel Composites Oyj; *Int'l*, pg. 2581
FLYING TANKERS, INC.—See Coulson Group of Companies; *Int'l*, pg. 1817
FREIGHT MANAGEMENT, INC; *U.S. Private*, pg. 1607
FRONTIER SERVICES GROUP LIMITED; *Int'l*, pg. 2796
GESELLSCHAFT FUR FLUGZIELDARSTELLUNG MBH—See Airbus SE; *Int'l*, pg. 242
GLOBAL LOAD CONTROL (PTY) LTD.—See Deutsche Lufthansa AG; *Int'l*, pg. 2066
GMR AVIATION PRIVATE LIMITED—See GMR Airports Infrastructure Limited; *Int'l*, pg. 3015
GUARDIAN FLIGHT, LLC—See KKR & Co. Inc.; *U.S. Public*, pg. 1252
HELINET AVIATION SERVICES LLC; *U.S. Private*, pg. 1906
JET AVIATION BUSINESS JETS DEUTSCHLAND GMBH—See General Dynamics Corporation; *U.S. Public*, pg. 916
JET AVIATION HOUSTON, INC.—See General Dynamics Corporation; *U.S. Public*, pg. 916
JET AVIATION SERVICES GMBH—See General Dynamics Corporation; *U.S. Public*, pg. 916
JETPOOL, LLC; *U.S. Private*, pg. 2204
JETSELECT, LLC—See Jet Edge International LLC; *U.S. Private*, pg. 2203
JETS MRO, LLC; *U.S. Private*, pg. 2204
KEYSTONE AERIAL SURVEYS, INC.—See Vexcel Holdings, Inc.; *U.S. Private*, pg. 4374
L-3 COMMUNICATIONS FLIGHT INTERNATIONAL AVIATION LLC—See L3Harris Technologies, Inc.; *U.S. Public*, pg. 1282
MARQUIS JET PARTNERS INC.—See Berkshire Hathaway Inc.; *U.S. Public*, pg. 313
MED-TRANS CORPORATION—See KKR & Co. Inc.; *U.S. Public*, pg. 1252
MIDAMERICA JET, INC.—See The Hines Group, Inc.; *U.S. Private*, pg. 4053
MID CAL AG AVIATION INC.—See TORtec Group Corp.; *U.S. Private*, pg. 2164
MILLIAN AIR CORP.—See Baton Rouge Jet Center LLC; *U.S. Private*, pg. 487
MOUNTAIN AVIATION, INC.—See Wheels Up Experience Inc.; *U.S. Public*, pg. 2366
NETJETS INC.—See Berkshire Hathaway Inc.; *U.S. Public*, pg. 313
NEW ENGLAND LIFE FLIGHT, INC.; *U.S. Private*, pg. 2894
NEW FLIGHT CHARTERS; *U.S. Private*, pg. 2896
OLDENBURG AVIATION INC.—See Oldenburg Group, Inc.; *U.S. Private*, pg. 3009
OOO EADS—See Airbus SE; *Int'l*, pg. 247
PAPILLON AIRWAYS INC.; *U.S. Private*, pg. 3088
PENTASTAR AVIATION LLC; *U.S. Private*, pg. 3140
PHI, INC.; *U.S. Private*, pg. 3168
PHOENIX AIR GROUP INC.; *U.S. Private*, pg. 3172
REW INVESTMENTS INCORPORATED; *U.S. Private*, pg. 3417
RICHMOR AVIATION INC.; *U.S. Private*, pg. 3430
SALT RIVER AVIATION, LLC—See Weinberg Capital Group, Inc.; *U.S. Private*, pg. 4471
STARJET AIR INC.—See Royal Street Corporation; *U.S. Private*, pg. 3493
TEMPUS JETS INC.—See Tempus Applied Solutions Holdings, Inc.; *U.S. Public*, pg. 2000
TRANSCONTINENTAL CORPORATION; *U.S. Private*, pg. 4207
WING AVIATION, LLC; *U.S. Private*, pg. 4541

482111 — LINE-HAUL RAILROADS

ALASKA RAILROAD CORPORATION; *U.S. Private*, pg. 151
AMEROPA-REISEN GMBH—See Deutsche Bahn AG; *Int'l*, pg. 2049
ARIZONA & CALIFORNIA RAILWAY COMPANY—See Brookfield Infrastructure Partners L.P.; *Int'l*, pg. 1190
ARIZONA & CALIFORNIA RAILWAY COMPANY—See GIC Pte. Ltd.; *Int'l*, pg. 2965
ARIZONA EASTERN RAILWAY COMPANY—See Brookfield Infrastructure Partners L.P.; *Int'l*, pg. 1190
ARIZONA EASTERN RAILWAY COMPANY—See GIC Pte. Ltd.; *Int'l*, pg. 2965
ARKANSAS MIDLAND RAILROAD—See Brookfield Infrastructure Partners L.P.; *Int'l*, pg. 1190
ARKANSAS MIDLAND RAILROAD—See GIC Pte. Ltd.; *Int'l*, pg. 2965
ARKANSAS & MISSOURI RAILROAD CO.; *U.S. Private*, pg. 325
ARRIVA CROYDON&NORTH SURREY LIMITED—See I Squared Capital Advisors (US) LLC; *U.S. Private*, pg. 2024
ARRIVA ITALIA S.R.L.—See I Squared Capital Advisors (US) LLC; *U.S. Private*, pg. 2024
ARRIVA RP SP. Z O.O.—See I Squared Capital Advisors (US) LLC; *U.S. Private*, pg. 2025
ARRIVA TRAINS WALES/TRENAU ARRIVA CYMRU LIMITED—See I Squared Capital Advisors (US) LLC; *U.S. Private*, pg. 2025
ARROWOOD-SOUTHERN COMPANY—See Norfolk Southern Corporation; *U.S. Public*, pg. 1535
AT&L RAILROAD—See Wheeler Brothers Grain Co.; *U.S. Private*, pg. 4505
AURIZON OPERATIONS LIMITED—See Aurizon Holdings Limited; *Int'l*, pg. 711
AXIOM RAIL COMPONENTS LIMITED—See Deutsche Bahn AG; *Int'l*, pg. 2050
BALTTRANSSERVIS, OOO—See Globaltrans Investment PLC; *Int'l*, pg. 3004
THE BAYLINE RAILROAD LLC—See Brookfield Infrastructure Partners L.P.; *Int'l*, pg. 1192
THE BAYLINE RAILROAD LLC—See GIC Pte. Ltd.; *Int'l*, pg. 2967
BNSF RAILWAY COMPANY—See Berkshire Hathaway Inc.; *U.S. Public*, pg. 303
BOSSDORF & KERSTAN GMBH—See Havellandische Eisenbahn AG; *Int'l*, pg. 3286
BUFFALO & PITTSBURGH RAILROAD, INC.—See Brookfield Infrastructure Partners L.P.; *Int'l*, pg. 1190
BUFFALO & PITTSBURGH RAILROAD, INC.—See GIC Pte. Ltd.; *Int'l*, pg. 2965
BURLINGTON NORTHERN (MANITOBA) LIMITED—See Berkshire Hathaway Inc.; *U.S. Public*, pg. 303
CAMP LEJEUNE RAILROAD COMPANY—See Norfolk Southern Corporation; *U.S. Public*, pg. 1535
CANADIAN NATIONAL RAILWAY COMPANY; *Int'l*, pg. 1284
CANADIAN NATIONAL RAILWAY COMPANY—See Canadian National Railway Company; *Int'l*, pg. 1284
CANADIAN NATIONAL RAILWAY COMPANY—See Canadian National Railway Company; *Int'l*, pg. 1284
CANADIAN PACIFIC KANSAS CITY LIMITED; *Int'l*, pg. 1285
CAPE FEAR RAILWAYS INC.—See Seaboard Corporation; *U.S. Public*, pg. 1850
CAROLINA AND NORTHWESTERN RAILWAY COMPANY—See Norfolk Southern Corporation; *U.S. Public*, pg. 1536
CAROLINA PIEDMONT RAILROAD—See Brookfield Infrastructure Partners L.P.; *Int'l*, pg. 1191
CAROLINA PIEDMONT RAILROAD—See GIC Pte. Ltd.; *Int'l*, pg. 2965

482111 — LINE-HAUL RAILROADS

CASCADE & COLUMBIA RIVER RAILROAD COMPANY—See Brookfield Infrastructure Partners L.P.; *Int'l*, pg. 1191
CASCADE & COLUMBIA RIVER RAILROAD COMPANY—See GIC Pte. Ltd.; *Int'l*, pg. 2965
CENTRAL JAPAN RAILWAY COMPANY; *Int'l*, pg. 1408
CENTRAL OF GEORGIA RAILROAD COMPANY—See Norfolk Southern Corporation; *U.S. Public*, pg. 1536
THE CENTRAL RAILROAD COMPANY OF INDIANA—See Brookfield Infrastructure Partners L.P.; *Int'l*, pg. 1192
THE CENTRAL RAILROAD COMPANY OF INDIANA—See GIC Pte. Ltd.; *Int'l*, pg. 2967
CHATTAHOOCHEE INDUSTRIAL RAILROAD—See Brookfield Infrastructure Partners L.P.; *Int'l*, pg. 1191
CHATTAHOOCHEE INDUSTRIAL RAILROAD—See GIC Pte. Ltd.; *Int'l*, pg. 2965
CHATTOOGA & CHICKAMAUGA RAILWAY CO.—See Brookfield Infrastructure Partners L.P.; *Int'l*, pg. 1191
CHATTOOGA & CHICKAMAUGA RAILWAY CO.—See GIC Pte. Ltd.; *Int'l*, pg. 2965
CHESAPEAKE & ALBEMARLE RAILROAD—See Brookfield Infrastructure Partners L.P.; *Int'l*, pg. 1192
CHESAPEAKE & ALBEMARLE RAILROAD—See GIC Pte. Ltd.; *Int'l*, pg. 2966
CHICAGO RAIL LINK—See The Broe Companies, Inc.; *U.S. Private*, pg. 4001
THE CHILTERN RAILWAY COMPANY LIMITED—See Deutsche Bahn AG; *Int'l*, pg. 2054
CHINA RAILWAY TIELONG CONTAINER LOGISTICS CO., LTD.; *Int'l*, pg. 1544
THE CINCINNATI, NEW ORLEANS & TEXAS PACIFIC RAILWAY CO.—See Norfolk Southern Corporation; *U.S. Public*, pg. 1536
COMBOIOS DE PORTUGAL; *Int'l*, pg. 1709
CONSOLIDATED RAIL CORPORATION—See CSX Corporation; *U.S. Public*, pg. 602
CONSOLIDATED RAIL CORPORATION—See Norfolk Southern Corporation; *U.S. Public*, pg. 1535
CRC PROPERTIES INC.—See CSX Corporation; *U.S. Public*, pg. 602
CRC PROPERTIES INC.—See Norfolk Southern Corporation; *U.S. Public*, pg. 1535
CSX REAL PROPERTY INC.—See CSX Corporation; *U.S. Public*, pg. 602
DAKOTA, MINNESOTA & EASTERN RAILROAD CORPORATION—See Canadian Pacific Kansas City Limited; *Int'l*, pg. 1285
DAQIN RAILWAY CO., LTD.; *Int'l*, pg. 1971
DB CARGO RUSSIJA OOO—See Deutsche Bahn AG; *Int'l*, pg. 2050
DB SCHENKER RAIL DEUTSCHLAND AG—See Deutsche Bahn AG; *Int'l*, pg. 2050
DB SCHENKER RAIL ITALIA S.R.L.—See Deutsche Bahn AG; *Int'l*, pg. 2050
DB SCHENKER RAIL NEDERLAND N. V.—See Deutsche Bahn AG; *Int'l*, pg. 2050
DB SCHENKER RAIL POLSKA S.A.—See Deutsche Bahn AG; *Int'l*, pg. 2050
DB SCHENKER RAIL ROMANIA S.R.L.—See Deutsche Bahn AG; *Int'l*, pg. 2050
DB SCHENKER RAIL SCHWEIZ GMBH—See Deutsche Bahn AG; *Int'l*, pg. 2050
DB SCHENKER RAIL SPEDKOL SP. Z O.O.—See Deutsche Bahn AG; *Int'l*, pg. 2051
DELAWARE & HUDSON RAILWAY COMPANY, INC.—See Canadian Pacific Kansas City Limited; *Int'l*, pg. 1285
DELAWARE OTSEGO CORP.; *U.S. Private*, pg. 1195
D & I RAILROAD—See L.G. Everist Inc.; *U.S. Private*, pg. 2366
EL CHICO RESTAURANTS, INC.—See Cracken, Harkey & Co., LLC; *U.S. Private*, pg. 1081
ERS RAILWAYS B.V.—See Brookfield Infrastructure Partners L.P.; *Int'l*, pg. 1191
ERS RAILWAYS B.V.—See GIC Pte. Ltd.; *Int'l*, pg. 2965
ESCANABA & LAKE SUPERIOR RAILROAD CO.; *U.S. Private*, pg. 1424
EURO CARGO RAIL SAS—See Deutsche Bahn AG; *Int'l*, pg. 2051
EUROPORTE—See Getlink SE; *Int'l*, pg. 2952
EUROSTAR INTERNATIONAL LTD; *Int'l*, pg. 2558
FIRM TRANSGARANT LLC—See Far Eastern Shipping Company OJSC; *Int'l*, pg. 2617
FIRST SCOTRAIL LIMITED—See FirstGroup plc; *Int'l*, pg. 2689
FIRST TRANSPENNINE EXPRESS LIMITED—See FirstGroup plc; *Int'l*, pg. 2689
FLORIDA EAST COAST RAILWAY, LLC—See Grupo Mexico, S.A.B. de C.V.; *Int'l*, pg. 3132
FORDYCE AND PRINCETON R.R. CO.—See Brookfield Infrastructure Partners L.P.; *Int'l*, pg. 1191
FORDYCE AND PRINCETON R.R. CO.—See GIC Pte. Ltd.; *Int'l*, pg. 2965
FREIGHTLINER LIMITED—See Brookfield Infrastructure Partners L.P.; *Int'l*, pg. 1191
FREIGHTLINER LIMITED—See GIC Pte. Ltd.; *Int'l*, pg. 2966
GARDEN CITY WESTERN RAILWAY, INC.—See Pioneer Railcorp; *U.S. Private*, pg. 3188
GB RAILFREIGHT LIMITED—See EQT AB; *Int'l*, pg. 2475

GENESEE & WYOMING INC.—See Brookfield Infrastructure Partners L.P.; *Int'l*, pg. 1190
GENESEE & WYOMING INC.—See GIC Pte. Ltd.; *Int'l*, pg. 2965
GENESEE & WYOMING RAILROAD COMPANY—See Brookfield Infrastructure Partners L.P.; *Int'l*, pg. 1191
GENESEE & WYOMING RAILROAD COMPANY—See GIC Pte. Ltd.; *Int'l*, pg. 2966
GIBELA RAIL TRANSPORT CONSORTIUM (PTY) LTD—See Alstom S.A.; *Int'l*, pg. 383
GUANGSHEN RAILWAY COMPANY LIMITED; *Int'l*, pg. 3162
GWI ACQUISITIONS PTY LTD—See Brookfield Infrastructure Partners L.P.; *Int'l*, pg. 1191
GWI ACQUISITIONS PTY LTD—See GIC Pte. Ltd.; *Int'l*, pg. 2966
HAVELLANDISCHE EISENBAHN AG; *Int'l*, pg. 3286
HEART OF GEORGIA RAILROAD, INC.—See Brookfield Infrastructure Partners L.P.; *Int'l*, pg. 1191
HEART OF GEORGIA RAILROAD, INC.—See GIC Pte. Ltd.; *Int'l*, pg. 2966
HECTOR RAIL AB—See EQT AB; *Int'l*, pg. 2475
HHLA INTERMODAL GMBH—See Hamburger Hafen und Logistik AG; *Int'l*, pg. 3236
HIGH POINT, RANDLEMAN, ASHEBORO AND SOUTHERN RAILROAD CO.—See Norfolk Southern Corporation; *U.S. Public*, pg. 1536
HURON CENTRAL RAILWAY INC.—See Brookfield Infrastructure Partners L.P.; *Int'l*, pg. 1191
HURON CENTRAL RAILWAY INC.—See GIC Pte. Ltd.; *Int'l*, pg. 2966
ILLINOIS & MIDLAND RAILROAD, INC.—See Brookfield Infrastructure Partners L.P.; *Int'l*, pg. 1192
ILLINOIS & MIDLAND RAILROAD, INC.—See GIC Pte. Ltd.; *Int'l*, pg. 2966
THE INDIANA & OHIO RAILWAY COMPANY—See Brookfield Infrastructure Partners L.P.; *Int'l*, pg. 1192
THE INDIANA & OHIO RAILWAY COMPANY—See GIC Pte. Ltd.; *Int'l*, pg. 2967
IOWA INTERSTATE RAILROAD, LTD.—See Railroad Development Corp.; *U.S. Private*, pg. 3346
IOWA NORTHERN RAILWAY CO., INC.; *U.S. Private*, pg. 2135
THE KANSAS CITY SOUTHERN RAILWAY COMPANY—See Canadian Pacific Kansas City Limited; *Int'l*, pg. 1285
KETTLE FALLS INTERNATIONAL RAILWAY, LLC—See The Broe Companies, Inc.; *U.S. Private*, pg. 4001
KOMBITERMINAL BURGHAUSEN GMBH—See Deutsche Bahn AG; *Int'l*, pg. 2051
KOMPETENZNETZ RAIL BERLIN BRANDENBURG GMBH—See Havellandische Eisenbahn AG; *Int'l*, pg. 3286
LENORD S.R.L.—See FNM S.p.A.; *Int'l*, pg. 2718
LIVONIA, AVON & LAKEVILLE RAILROAD CORP.; *U.S. Private*, pg. 2474
LONDON AND NORTH WESTERN RAILWAY COMPANY LIMITED—See Deutsche Bahn AG; *Int'l*, pg. 2052
LOS ANGELES JUNCTION RAILWAY COMPANY—See Berkshire Hathaway Inc.; *U.S. Public*, pg. 303
M & B RAILROAD L.L.C.—See Brookfield Infrastructure Partners L.P.; *Int'l*, pg. 1192
M & B RAILROAD L.L.C.—See GIC Pte. Ltd.; *Int'l*, pg. 2966
MERIDIAN SPEEDWAY, LLC—See Canadian Pacific Kansas City Limited; *Int'l*, pg. 1285
MID-MICHIGAN RAILROAD, INC.—See Brookfield Infrastructure Partners L.P.; *Int'l*, pg. 1192
MID-MICHIGAN RAILROAD, INC.—See GIC Pte. Ltd.; *Int'l*, pg. 2966
MISSION MOUNTAIN RAILROAD—See Kinder Morgan, Inc.; *U.S. Public*, pg. 1233
MITTELDEUTSCHE EISENBAHN GMBH—See Deutsche Bahn AG; *Int'l*, pg. 2051
MOBILE & BIRMINGHAM RAILROAD CO.—See Norfolk Southern Corporation; *U.S. Public*, pg. 1536
MONTANA RAIL LINK, INC.—See Washington Corporations; *U.S. Private*, pg. 4446
MOUNT STEPHEN PROPERTIES INC.—See Canadian Pacific Kansas City Limited; *Int'l*, pg. 1285
NATIONAL RAILROAD PASSENGER CORPORATION; *U.S. Private*, pg. 2861
NIC FREIGHT CO., LTD.—See Dynic Corporation; *Int'l*, pg. 2243
NORDCARGO S.R.L.—See Deutsche Bahn AG; *Int'l*, pg. 2050
NORFOLK AND PORTSMOUTH BELT LINE RAILROAD COMPANY—See Norfolk Southern Corporation; *U.S. Public*, pg. 1536
NORFOLK SOUTHERN INTERMODAL—See Norfolk Southern Corporation; *U.S. Public*, pg. 1535
NORFOLK SOUTHERN RAILWAY COMPANY—See Norfolk Southern Corporation; *U.S. Public*, pg. 1535
NORTHERN OHIO & WESTERN RAILWAY, LLC—See The Broe Companies, Inc.; *U.S. Private*, pg. 4001
ONTARIO MIDLAND RAILROAD CORP.—See Livonia, Avon & Lakeville Railroad Corp.; *U.S. Private*, pg. 2474
PABTEX, INC.—See Canadian Pacific Kansas City Limited; *Int'l*, pg. 1285

PADUCAH & LOUISVILLE RAILWAY, INC.; *U.S. Private*, pg. 3074
PAN AM RAILWAYS, INC.—See CSX Corporation; *U.S. Public*, pg. 602
PANHANDLE NORTHERN RAILROAD—See The Broe Companies, Inc.; *U.S. Private*, pg. 4001
PENN CENTRAL COMMUNICATIONS CORP.—See CSX Corporation; *U.S. Public*, pg. 602
PENN CENTRAL COMMUNICATIONS CORP.—See Norfolk Southern Corporation; *U.S. Public*, pg. 1535
PERMIAN BASIN RAILWAYS—See Iowa Pacific Holdings, LLC; *U.S. Private*, pg. 2135
PINSLY RAILROAD CO. INC.; *U.S. Private*, pg. 3186
PIONEER RAILCORP; *U.S. Private*, pg. 3188
PORTLAND & WESTERN RAILROAD INC—See Brookfield Infrastructure Partners L.P.; *Int'l*, pg. 1192
PORTLAND & WESTERN RAILROAD INC—See GIC Pte. Ltd.; *Int'l*, pg. 2966
THE PRESCOTT & NORTHWESTERN RAILROAD CO.—See PotlatchDeltic Corporation; *U.S. Public*, pg. 1704
RAILROAD DEVELOPMENT CORP.; *U.S. Private*, pg. 3346
RAILROAD DISTRIBUTION SERVICES, INC.—See Brookfield Infrastructure Partners L.P.; *Int'l*, pg. 1192
RAILROAD DISTRIBUTION SERVICES, INC.—See GIC Pte. Ltd.; *Int'l*, pg. 2967
RAPID CITY, PIERRE & EASTERN RAILROAD, INC.—See Brookfield Infrastructure Partners L.P.; *Int'l*, pg. 1192
RAPID CITY, PIERRE & EASTERN RAILROAD, INC.—See GIC Pte. Ltd.; *Int'l*, pg. 2967
ROCK & RAIL LLC—See Martin Marietta Materials, Inc.; *U.S. Public*, pg. 1389
SAND SPRINGS RAILWAY, CO.—See The Broe Companies, Inc.; *U.S. Private*, pg. 4001
SOMERSET RAILROAD CORPORATION—See The AES Corporation; *U.S. Public*, pg. 2032
SOO LINE CORPORATION—See Canadian Pacific Kansas City Limited; *Int'l*, pg. 1285
SOUTH CENTRAL FLORIDA EXPRESS, INC.—See United States Sugar Corporation; *U.S. Private*, pg. 4300
SOUTHERN RAIL TERMINALS OF NORTH CAROLINA, INC.—See Norfolk Southern Corporation; *U.S. Public*, pg. 1536
SOUTHERN RAILWAY OF BRITISH COLUMBIA LIMITED (SRY)—See Washington Corporations; *U.S. Private*, pg. 4446
SOUTHERN REGION COAL TRANSPORT, INC.—See Norfolk Southern Corporation; *U.S. Public*, pg. 1536
THE SOUTH WESTERN RAILROAD CO.—See Norfolk Southern Corporation; *U.S. Public*, pg. 1536
STATE UNIVERSITY RAILROAD CO.—See Norfolk Southern Corporation; *U.S. Public*, pg. 1536
STRAITS CORPORATION; *U.S. Private*, pg. 3833
TENNESSEE, ALABAMA & GEORGIA RAILWAY CO.—See Norfolk Southern Corporation; *U.S. Public*, pg. 1536
TENNESSEE RAILWAY CO.—See Norfolk Southern Corporation; *U.S. Public*, pg. 1536
THE TEXAS MEXICAN RAILWAY COMPANY—See Canadian Pacific Kansas City Limited; *Int'l*, pg. 1285
TEXAS-NEW MEXICO RAILROAD—See Iowa Pacific Holdings, LLC; *U.S. Private*, pg. 2135
TEXAS SOUTH-EASTERN RAILROAD COMPANY—See International Paper Company; *U.S. Public*, pg. 1158
TOMAHAWK RAILWAY LIMITED PARTNERSHIP—See Brookfield Infrastructure Partners L.P.; *Int'l*, pg. 1193
TOMAHAWK RAILWAY LIMITED PARTNERSHIP—See GIC Pte. Ltd.; *Int'l*, pg. 2967
TOTAL MOMENTUM PTY. LTD.—See Engenco Limited; *Int'l*, pg. 2427
TRANSFESA PORTUGAL LDA.—See Deutsche Bahn AG; *Int'l*, pg. 2051
TRANSFESA UK LTD—See Deutsche Bahn AG; *Int'l*, pg. 2051
TRENITALIA C2C LIMITED—See Ferrovie dello Stato Italiane S.p.A.; *Int'l*, pg. 2645
TRIPLE CROWN SERVICES, CO.—See Norfolk Southern Corporation; *U.S. Public*, pg. 1536
UNION PACIFIC RAILROAD COMPANY—See Union Pacific Corporation; *U.S. Public*, pg. 2227
VERKEHRSVERBUND ROTTWEIL GMBH—See Deutsche Bahn AG; *Int'l*, pg. 2055
VERMONT RAILWAY INC.; *U.S. Private*, pg. 4367
VIRGINIA & SOUTHWESTERN RAILWAY CO.—See Norfolk Southern Corporation; *U.S. Public*, pg. 1536
WFEC RAILROAD CO., INC.—See Western Farmers Electric Cooperative, Inc.; *U.S. Private*, pg. 4493
THE WHEELING CORPORATION INC.; *U.S. Private*, pg. 4134
WHEELING & LAKE ERIE RAILWAY CO., INC.—See The Wheeling Corporation Inc.; *U.S. Private*, pg. 4134
WHITE PASS & YUKON ROUTE—See Carnival Corporation; *U.S. Public*, pg. 438
WIREGRASS CENTRAL RAILWAY, L.L.C.—See Brookfield Infrastructure Partners L.P.; *Int'l*, pg. 1193
WIREGRASS CENTRAL RAILWAY, L.L.C.—See GIC Pte. Ltd.; *Int'l*, pg. 2967
WISCONSIN & SOUTHERN RAILROAD COMPANY—See Kinder Morgan, Inc.; *U.S. Public*, pg. 1233

N.A.I.C.S. INDEX

WISCONSIN & SOUTHERN RAILROAD COMPANY—See Kinder Morgan, Inc.; *U.S. Public*, pg. 1233

WISCONSIN & SOUTHERN RAILROAD COMPANY—See Kinder Morgan, Inc.; *U.S. Public*, pg. 1233

XC TRAINS LIMITED—See Deutsche Bahn AG; *Int'l*, pg. 2055

YADKIN RAILROAD CO.—See Norfolk Southern Corporation; *U.S. Public*, pg. 1536

YORK RAILWAY COMPANY—See Brookfield Infrastructure Partners L.P.; *Int'l*, pg. 1193

YORK RAILWAY COMPANY—See GIC Pte. Ltd.; *Int'l*, pg. 2967

ZENTRAL-OMNIBUSBAHNHOF BERLIN GMBH—See Deutsche Bahn AG; *Int'l*, pg. 2055

482112 — SHORT LINE RAILROADS

THE ALIQUIPPA & OHIO RIVER RAILROAD CO.—See Brookfield Infrastructure Partners L.P.; *Int'l*, pg. 1192

THE ALIQUIPPA & OHIO RIVER RAILROAD CO.—See GIC Pte. Ltd.; *Int'l*, pg. 2967

ALLEGHENY & EASTERN RAILROAD, LLC—See Brookfield Infrastructure Partners L.P.; *Int'l*, pg. 1190

ALLEGHENY & EASTERN RAILROAD, LLC—See GIC Pte. Ltd.; *Int'l*, pg. 2965

ALPHA TRAINS—See Arcus Infrastructure Partners LLP; *Int'l*, pg. 552

ARKANSAS LOUISIANA & MISSISSIPPI RAILROAD CO.—See Brookfield Infrastructure Partners L.P.; *Int'l*, pg. 1190

ARKANSAS LOUISIANA & MISSISSIPPI RAILROAD CO.—See GIC Pte. Ltd.; *Int'l*, pg. 2965

ATLAS RAILROAD CONSTRUCTION CO., INC.—See Brookfield Infrastructure Partners L.P.; *Int'l*, pg. 1190

ATLAS RAILROAD CONSTRUCTION CO., INC.—See GIC Pte. Ltd.; *Int'l*, pg. 2965

BAUXITE & NORTHERN RAILWAY COMPANY—See Brookfield Infrastructure Partners L.P.; *Int'l*, pg. 1190

BAUXITE & NORTHERN RAILWAY COMPANY—See GIC Pte. Ltd.; *Int'l*, pg. 2965

THE BELT RAILWAY COMPANY OF CHICAGO—See Berkshire Hathaway Inc.; *U.S. Public*, pg. 303

BRISA—See Arcus Infrastructure Partners LLP; *Int'l*, pg. 552

CALIFORNIA NORTHERN RAILROAD COMPANY—See Brookfield Infrastructure Partners L.P.; *Int'l*, pg. 1191

CALIFORNIA NORTHERN RAILROAD COMPANY—See GIC Pte. Ltd.; *Int'l*, pg. 2965

CAPE BRETON & CENTRAL NOVA SCOTIA RAILWAY LIMITED—See Brookfield Infrastructure Partners L.P.; *Int'l*, pg. 1191

CAPE BRETON & CENTRAL NOVA SCOTIA RAILWAY LIMITED—See GIC Pte. Ltd.; *Int'l*, pg. 2965

CENTRAL OREGON & PACIFIC RAILROAD, INC.—See Brookfield Infrastructure Partners L.P.; *Int'l*, pg. 1191

CENTRAL OREGON & PACIFIC RAILROAD, INC.—See GIC Pte. Ltd.; *Int'l*, pg. 2965

CENTRAL RAILROAD COMPANY OF INDIANAPOLIS—See Brookfield Infrastructure Partners L.P.; *Int'l*, pg. 1191

CENTRAL RAILROAD COMPANY OF INDIANAPOLIS—See GIC Pte. Ltd.; *Int'l*, pg. 2965

CG RAILWAY, LLC—See AIP, LLC; *U.S. Private*, pg. 136

CG RAILWAY, LLC—See Brookfield Infrastructure Partners L.P.; *Int'l*, pg. 1191

CG RAILWAY, LLC—See GIC Pte. Ltd.; *Int'l*, pg. 2965

COLORADO & WYOMING RAILWAY COMPANY—See Evraz plc; *Int'l*, pg. 2574

COLUMBUS & CHATTAHOOCHEE RAILROAD, INC.—See Brookfield Infrastructure Partners L.P.; *Int'l*, pg. 1191

COLUMBUS & CHATTAHOOCHEE RAILROAD, INC.—See GIC Pte. Ltd.; *Int'l*, pg. 2965

CONECUH VALLEY RAILWAY, L.L.C.—See Brookfield Infrastructure Partners L.P.; *Int'l*, pg. 1191

CONECUH VALLEY RAILWAY, L.L.C.—See GIC Pte. Ltd.; *Int'l*, pg. 2965

CONNECTICUT SOUTHERN RAILROAD, INC.—See Brookfield Infrastructure Partners L.P.; *Int'l*, pg. 1191

CONNECTICUT SOUTHERN RAILROAD, INC.—See GIC Pte. Ltd.; *Int'l*, pg. 2965

DALLAS, GARLAND & NORTHEASTERN RAILROAD, INC.—See Brookfield Infrastructure Partners L.P.; *Int'l*, pg. 1191

DALLAS, GARLAND & NORTHEASTERN RAILROAD, INC.—See GIC Pte. Ltd.; *Int'l*, pg. 2965

EASTERN ALABAMA RAILWAY, LLC—See Brookfield Infrastructure Partners L.P.; *Int'l*, pg. 1191

EASTERN ALABAMA RAILWAY, LLC—See GIC Pte. Ltd.; *Int'l*, pg. 2965

EASTERN IDAHO RAILROAD—See Kinder Morgan, Inc.; *U.S. Public*, pg. 1233

EAST PENN RAILROAD, LLC—See 3i Group plc; *Int'l*, pg. 9

EAST TENNESSEE RAILWAY, L.P.—See Brookfield Infrastructure Partners L.P.; *Int'l*, pg. 1191

EAST TENNESSEE RAILWAY, L.P.—See GIC Pte. Ltd.; *Int'l*, pg. 2965

FIRST COAST RAILROAD INC.—See Brookfield Infrastructure Partners L.P.; *Int'l*, pg. 1191

FIRST COAST RAILROAD INC.—See GIC Pte. Ltd.; *Int'l*, pg. 2965

FORT WORTH & WESTERN RAILROAD INC.—See Davoil Inc.; *U.S. Private*, pg. 1175

FREIGHTLINER AUSTRALIA PTY LTD—See Brookfield Infrastructure Partners L.P.; *Int'l*, pg. 1191

FREIGHTLINER AUSTRALIA PTY LTD—See GIC Pte. Ltd.; *Int'l*, pg. 2966

FREIGHTLINER DE GMBH—See Brookfield Infrastructure Partners L.P.; *Int'l*, pg. 1191

FREIGHTLINER DE GMBH—See GIC Pte. Ltd.; *Int'l*, pg. 2966

FREIGHTLINER HEAVY HAUL LIMITED—See Brookfield Infrastructure Partners L.P.; *Int'l*, pg. 1191

FREIGHTLINER HEAVY HAUL LIMITED—See GIC Pte. Ltd.; *Int'l*, pg. 2966

GENESEE & WYOMING AUSTRALIA PTY LTD—See Brookfield Infrastructure Partners L.P.; *Int'l*, pg. 1191

GENESEE & WYOMING AUSTRALIA PTY LTD—See GIC Pte. Ltd.; *Int'l*, pg. 2966

GENESEE & WYOMING CANADA INC.—See Brookfield Infrastructure Partners L.P.; *Int'l*, pg. 1191

GENESEE & WYOMING CANADA INC.—See GIC Pte. Ltd.; *Int'l*, pg. 2966

GENESEE & WYOMING RAILROAD SERVICES, INC.—See Brookfield Infrastructure Partners L.P.; *Int'l*, pg. 1191

GENESEE & WYOMING RAILROAD SERVICES, INC.—See GIC Pte. Ltd.; *Int'l*, pg. 2966

GEORGIA CENTRAL RAILWAY, L.P.—See Brookfield Infrastructure Partners L.P.; *Int'l*, pg. 1191

GEORGIA CENTRAL RAILWAY, L.P.—See GIC Pte. Ltd.; *Int'l*, pg. 2966

GEORGIA & FLORIDA RAILWAY, LLC—See The Broe Companies, Inc.; *U.S. Private*, pg. 4001

GODERICH-EXETER RAILWAY COMPANY LIMITED—See Brookfield Infrastructure Partners L.P.; *Int'l*, pg. 1191

GODERICH-EXETER RAILWAY COMPANY LIMITED—See GIC Pte. Ltd.; *Int'l*, pg. 2966

GOLDEN ISLES TERMINAL RAILROAD, INC.—See Brookfield Infrastructure Partners L.P.; *Int'l*, pg. 1191

GOLDEN ISLES TERMINAL RAILROAD, INC.—See GIC Pte. Ltd.; *Int'l*, pg. 2966

GWI HOLDING BV—See Brookfield Infrastructure Partners L.P.; *Int'l*, pg. 1191

GWI HOLDING BV—See GIC Pte. Ltd.; *Int'l*, pg. 2966

HURON & EASTERN RAILWAY COMPANY, INC.—See Brookfield Infrastructure Partners L.P.; *Int'l*, pg. 1191

HURON & EASTERN RAILWAY COMPANY, INC.—See GIC Pte. Ltd.; *Int'l*, pg. 2966

INDIANA SOUTHERN RAILROAD, LLC—See Brookfield Infrastructure Partners L.P.; *Int'l*, pg. 1192

INDIANA SOUTHERN RAILROAD, LLC—See GIC Pte. Ltd.; *Int'l*, pg. 2966

KANSAS CITY SOUTHERN DE MEXICO S.A. DE C.V.—See Canadian Pacific Kansas City Limited; *Int'l*, pg. 1285

KIAMICHI RAILROAD COMPANY L.L.C.—See Brookfield Infrastructure Partners L.P.; *Int'l*, pg. 1192

KIAMICHI RAILROAD COMPANY L.L.C.—See GIC Pte. Ltd.; *Int'l*, pg. 2966

KYLE RAILROAD COMPANY—See Brookfield Infrastructure Partners L.P.; *Int'l*, pg. 1192

KYLE RAILROAD COMPANY—See GIC Pte. Ltd.; *Int'l*, pg. 2966

LAKELAND & WATERWAYS RAILWAY—See Canadian National Railway Company; *Int'l*, pg. 1284

LOTOS KOLEJ SP. Z O.O.—See Grupa LOTOS S.A.; *Int'l*, pg. 3117

LOUISIANA & DELTA RAILROAD, INC.—See Brookfield Infrastructure Partners L.P.; *Int'l*, pg. 1192

LOUISIANA & DELTA RAILROAD, INC.—See GIC Pte. Ltd.; *Int'l*, pg. 2966

MACKENZIE NORTHERN RAILWAY—See Canadian National Railway Company; *Int'l*, pg. 1284

MAPTELLIGENT INC., *U.S. Public*, pg. 1363

MARQUETTE RAIL, LLC—See Brookfield Infrastructure Partners L.P.; *Int'l*, pg. 1192

MARQUETTE RAIL, LLC—See GIC Pte. Ltd.; *Int'l*, pg. 2966

MARYLAND MIDLAND RAILWAY, INC.—See Brookfield Infrastructure Partners L.P.; *Int'l*, pg. 1192

MARYLAND MIDLAND RAILWAY, INC.—See GIC Pte. Ltd.; *Int'l*, pg. 2966

MICHIGAN SHORE RAILROAD—See Brookfield Infrastructure Partners L.P.; *Int'l*, pg. 1192

MICHIGAN SHORE RAILROAD—See GIC Pte. Ltd.; *Int'l*, pg. 2966

MISSOURI & NORTHERN ARKANSAS RAILROAD COMPANY, INC.—See Brookfield Infrastructure Partners L.P.; *Int'l*, pg. 1192

MISSOURI & NORTHERN ARKANSAS RAILROAD COMPANY, INC.—See GIC Pte. Ltd.; *Int'l*, pg. 2966

NEBRASKA, KANSAS & COLORADO RAILWAY, LLC—See The Broe Companies, Inc.; *U.S. Private*, pg. 4001

NEWBURGH & SOUTH SHORE RAILROAD COMPANY—See The Broe Companies, Inc.; *U.S. Private*, pg. 4001

NEW ENGLAND CENTRAL RAILROAD, INC.—See Brookfield Infrastructure Partners L.P.; *Int'l*, pg. 1192

482112 — SHORT LINE RAILROAD...

NEW ENGLAND CENTRAL RAILROAD, INC.—See GIC Pte. Ltd.; *Int'l*, pg. 2966

NORTH CAROLINA & VIRGINIA RAILROAD COMPANY, LLC—See Brookfield Infrastructure Partners L.P.; *Int'l*, pg. 1192

NORTH CAROLINA & VIRGINIA RAILROAD COMPANY, LLC—See GIC Pte. Ltd.; *Int'l*, pg. 2966

OHIO CENTRAL RAILROAD, INC.—See Brookfield Infrastructure Partners L.P.; *Int'l*, pg. 1192

OHIO CENTRAL RAILROAD, INC.—See GIC Pte. Ltd.; *Int'l*, pg. 2966

OHIO SOUTHERN RAILROAD, INC.—See Brookfield Infrastructure Partners L.P.; *Int'l*, pg. 1192

OHIO SOUTHERN RAILROAD, INC.—See GIC Pte. Ltd.; *Int'l*, pg. 2966

OLD AUGUSTA RAILROAD COMPANY—See Koch Industries, Inc.; *U.S. Private*, pg. 2329

OMNITRAX, INC.—See The Broe Companies, Inc.; *U.S. Private*, pg. 4001

OTTAWA VALLEY RAILWAY—See Brookfield Infrastructure Partners L.P.; *Int'l*, pg. 1192

OTTAWA VALLEY RAILWAY—See GIC Pte. Ltd.; *Int'l*, pg. 2966

OTTER TAIL VALLEY RAILROAD COMPANY, INC.—See Brookfield Infrastructure Partners L.P.; *Int'l*, pg. 1192

OTTER TAIL VALLEY RAILROAD COMPANY, INC.—See GIC Pte. Ltd.; *Int'l*, pg. 2966

PANAMA CANAL RAILWAY COMPANY—See Canadian Pacific Kansas City Limited; *Int'l*, pg. 1285

THE PITTSBURGH & OHIO CENTRAL RAILROAD COMPANY—See Brookfield Infrastructure Partners L.P.; *Int'l*, pg. 1193

THE PITTSBURGH & OHIO CENTRAL RAILROAD COMPANY—See GIC Pte. Ltd.; *Int'l*, pg. 2967

PROVIDENCE & WORCESTER RAILROAD COMPANY—See Brookfield Infrastructure Partners L.P.; *Int'l*, pg. 1192

PROVIDENCE & WORCESTER RAILROAD COMPANY—See GIC Pte. Ltd.; *Int'l*, pg. 2966

PUGET SOUND & PACIFIC RAILROAD—See Brookfield Infrastructure Partners L.P.; *Int'l*, pg. 1192

PUGET SOUND & PACIFIC RAILROAD—See GIC Pte. Ltd.; *Int'l*, pg. 2967

QUEBEC GATINEAU RAILWAY—See Brookfield Infrastructure Partners L.P.; *Int'l*, pg. 1191

QUEBEC GATINEAU RAILWAY—See GIC Pte. Ltd.; *Int'l*, pg. 2966

RAILAMERICA, INC.—See Brookfield Infrastructure Partners L.P.; *Int'l*, pg. 1192

RAILAMERICA, INC.—See GIC Pte. Ltd.; *Int'l*, pg. 2967

RAILAMERICA TRANSPORTATION CORP.—See Brookfield Infrastructure Partners L.P.; *Int'l*, pg. 1192

RAILAMERICA TRANSPORTATION CORP.—See GIC Pte. Ltd.; *Int'l*, pg. 2967

RAILCARE INC.—See Brookfield Infrastructure Partners L.P.; *Int'l*, pg. 1192

RAILCARE INC.—See GIC Pte. Ltd.; *Int'l*, pg. 2967

RAIL LINK, INC.—See Brookfield Infrastructure Partners L.P.; *Int'l*, pg. 1192

RAIL LINK, INC.—See GIC Pte. Ltd.; *Int'l*, pg. 2967

REGIONAL RAIL, LLC—See 3i Group plc; *Int'l*, pg. 9

ROCKDALE, SANDOW & SOUTHERN RAILROAD COMPANY—See Brookfield Infrastructure Partners L.P.; *Int'l*, pg. 1192

ROCKDALE, SANDOW & SOUTHERN RAILROAD COMPANY—See GIC Pte. Ltd.; *Int'l*, pg. 2967

ROGUE VALLEY TERMINAL RAILROAD CORPORATION—See CCT Rail System Corporation; *U.S. Private*, pg. 801

SABINE RIVER & NORTHERN RAILROAD COMPANY—See International Paper Company; *U.S. Public*, pg. 1158

SALT LAKE CITY SOUTHERN RAILROAD COMPANY, INC.—See Brookfield Infrastructure Partners L.P.; *Int'l*, pg. 1192

SALT LAKE CITY SOUTHERN RAILROAD COMPANY, INC.—See GIC Pte. Ltd.; *Int'l*, pg. 2967

SAN DIEGO & IMPERIAL VALLEY RAILROAD COMPANY, INC.—See Brookfield Infrastructure Partners L.P.; *Int'l*, pg. 1192

SAN DIEGO & IMPERIAL VALLEY RAILROAD COMPANY, INC.—See GIC Pte. Ltd.; *Int'l*, pg. 2967

SAN JOAQUIN VALLEY RAILROAD CO.—See Brookfield Infrastructure Partners L.P.; *Int'l*, pg. 1192

SAN JOAQUIN VALLEY RAILROAD CO.—See GIC Pte. Ltd.; *Int'l*, pg. 2967

SAVANNAH PORT TERMINAL RAILROAD, INC.—See Brookfield Infrastructure Partners L.P.; *Int'l*, pg. 1192

SAVANNAH PORT TERMINAL RAILROAD, INC.—See GIC Pte. Ltd.; *Int'l*, pg. 2967

SHERE GROUP LIMITED—See Cellnex Telecom, S.A.; *Int'l*, pg. 1394

SOUTH CAROLINA CENTRAL RAILROAD COMPANY, LLC—See Brookfield Infrastructure Partners L.P.; *Int'l*, pg. 1192

SOUTH CAROLINA CENTRAL RAILROAD COMPANY, LLC—See GIC Pte. Ltd.; *Int'l*, pg. 2967

482112 — SHORT LINE RAILROAD...

SOUTHERN ONTARIO RAILWAY—See Brookfield Infrastructure Partners L.P.; *Int'l*, pg. 1192
SOUTHERN ONTARIO RAILWAY—See GIC Pte. Ltd.; *Int'l*, pg. 2967
STILLWATER CENTRAL RAILROAD, LLC—See Kinder Morgan, Inc.; *U.S. Public*, pg. 1233
ST. LAWRENCE & ATLANTIC RAILROAD COMPANY—See Brookfield Infrastructure Partners L.P.; *Int'l*, pg. 1192
ST. LAWRENCE & ATLANTIC RAILROAD COMPANY—See GIC Pte. Ltd.; *Int'l*, pg. 2967
ST. LAWRENCE & ATLANTIC RAILROAD (QUEBEC) INC.—See Brookfield Infrastructure Partners L.P.; *Int'l*, pg. 1191
ST. LAWRENCE & ATLANTIC RAILROAD (QUEBEC) INC.—See Brookfield Infrastructure Partners L.P.; *Int'l*, pg. 1193
ST. LAWRENCE & ATLANTIC RAILROAD (QUEBEC) INC.—See GIC Pte. Ltd.; *Int'l*, pg. 2966
ST. LAWRENCE & ATLANTIC RAILROAD (QUEBEC) INC.—See GIC Pte. Ltd.; *Int'l*, pg. 2967
ST. MARIES RIVER RAILROAD COMPANY—See Williams Group LLC; *U.S. Private*, pg. 4526
TARANTULA CORPORATION—See Davoil Inc.; *U.S. Private*, pg. 1175
TARANTULA MERCANTILE CORPORATION—See Davoil Inc.; *U.S. Private*, pg. 1175
TAZEWELL & PEORIA RAILROAD, INC.—See Brookfield Infrastructure Partners L.P.; *Int'l*, pg. 1192
TAZEWELL & PEORIA RAILROAD, INC.—See GIC Pte. Ltd.; *Int'l*, pg. 2967
TEXAS NORTHEASTERN RAILROAD—See Brookfield Infrastructure Partners L.P.; *Int'l*, pg. 1191
TEXAS NORTHEASTERN RAILROAD—See GIC Pte. Ltd.; *Int'l*, pg. 2965
TOLEDO, PEORIA & WESTERN RAILWAY CORP.—See Brookfield Infrastructure Partners L.P.; *Int'l*, pg. 1193
TOLEDO, PEORIA & WESTERN RAILWAY CORP.—See GIC Pte. Ltd.; *Int'l*, pg. 2967
TRINITY INDUSTRIES—See Trinity Industries, Inc.; *U.S. Public*, pg. 2194
VENTURA COUNTY RAILROAD COMPANY—See Brookfield Infrastructure Partners L.P.; *Int'l*, pg. 1193
VENTURA COUNTY RAILROAD COMPANY—See GIC Pte. Ltd.; *Int'l*, pg. 2967
VIRGINIA SOUTHERN RAILROAD—See Brookfield Infrastructure Partners L.P.; *Int'l*, pg. 1193
VIRGINIA SOUTHERN RAILROAD—See GIC Pte. Ltd.; *Int'l*, pg. 2966
VIRGIN TRAINS USA INC.; *U.S. Private*, pg. 4387
WELLSBORO & CORNING RAILROAD, LLC—See Brookfield Infrastructure Partners L.P.; *Int'l*, pg. 1193
WELLSBORO & CORNING RAILROAD, LLC—See GIC Pte. Ltd.; *Int'l*, pg. 2967
WESTERN LABRADOR RAIL SERVICES INC.—See Brookfield Infrastructure Partners L.P.; *Int'l*, pg. 1191
WESTERN LABRADOR RAIL SERVICES INC.—See GIC Pte. Ltd.; *Int'l*, pg. 2966
WILMINGTON TERMINAL RAILROAD, LIMITED PARTNERSHIP—See Brookfield Infrastructure Partners L.P.; *Int'l*, pg. 1193
WILMINGTON TERMINAL RAILROAD, LIMITED PARTNERSHIP—See GIC Pte. Ltd.; *Int'l*, pg. 2967
YORK RAIL LOGISTICS, INC.—See Brookfield Infrastructure Partners L.P.; *Int'l*, pg. 1193
YORK RAIL LOGISTICS, INC.—See GIC Pte. Ltd.; *Int'l*, pg. 2967
YOUNGSTOWN & AUSTINTOWN RAILROAD, INC.—See Brookfield Infrastructure Partners L.P.; *Int'l*, pg. 1193
YOUNGSTOWN & AUSTINTOWN RAILROAD, INC.—See GIC Pte. Ltd.; *Int'l*, pg. 2967

483111 — DEEP SEA FREIGHT TRANSPORTATION

2020 BULKERS LTD.; *Int'l*, pg. 4
AB DFDS SEAWAYS—See DFDS A/S; *Int'l*, pg. 2094
ACOMAR—See CMA CGM S.A.; *Int'l*, pg. 1666
ADMINISTRACION PORTUARIA INTEGRAL DE ACAPULCO, S.A. DE C.V.—See Grupo TMM, S.A.B.; *Int'l*, pg. 3137
ADRIATIKAGENT INTERNATIONLA SHIPPING AGENCY D.O.O.—See Albert Ballin KG; *Int'l*, pg. 294
AGEMAR S.A. DE C.V.-VERACRUZ, VER.—See Grupo TMM, S.A.B.; *Int'l*, pg. 3137
AGENCIA MARITIMA MEXICANA, S.A. DE C.V.—See Grupo TMM, S.A.B.; *Int'l*, pg. 3137
AGENCIA MARITIMA MEXICANA, S.A. DE C.V.—See Grupo TMM, S.A.B.; *Int'l*, pg. 3137
AGENCIA MARITIMA MEXICANA, S.A. DE C.V.—See Grupo TMM, S.A.B.; *Int'l*, pg. 3137
AGENCIA MARITIMA MEXICANA, S.A. DE C.V.—See Grupo TMM, S.A.B.; *Int'l*, pg. 3137
AGENCIA MARITIMA MEXICANA, S.A. DE C.V.—See Grupo TMM, S.A.B.; *Int'l*, pg. 3137
AGENCIA MARITIMA REMAR S.R.L.—See Albert Ballin KG; *Int'l*, pg. 294

AGENCIA NAVIERA EUROPA S.A.—See Albert Ballin KG; *Int'l*, pg. 294
AGENCIAS CONTINENTAL S.A.—See Albert Ballin KG; *Int'l*, pg. 294
ALGOMA TANKERS—See Algoma Central Corporation; *Int'l*, pg. 318
ALMA MARITIME LIMITED; *Int'l*, pg. 361
ALSON'S SHIPPING LTD.—See Albert Ballin KG; *Int'l*, pg. 294
ALTERA INFRASTRUCTURE L.P.—See Brookfield Corporation; *Int'l*, pg. 1175
AMERICAN PETROLEUM TANKERS LLC—See Kinder Morgan, Inc.; *U.S. Public*, pg. 1232
AMNAV MARITIME SERVICES—See Saltchuk Resources Inc.; *U.S. Private*, pg. 3534
AMSC ASA; *Int'l*, pg. 441
ANANGEL-AMERICAN SHIPHOLDINGS LIMITED; *Int'l*, pg. 447
ANL (CHINA) LIMITED—See CMA CGM S.A.; *Int'l*, pg. 1666
ANL CONTAINER LINE PTY LIMITED—See CMA CGM S.A.; *Int'l*, pg. 1666
ANL SINGAPORE—See CMA CGM S.A.; *Int'l*, pg. 1666
ANTILLEAN MARINE SHIPPING CORP.; *U.S. Private*, pg. 288
API CIUDAD DE MEXICO—See Grupo TMM, S.A.B.; *Int'l*, pg. 3137
APL MARITIME, LTD.—See CMA CGM S.A.; *Int'l*, pg. 1668
AQUAMARINE SHIPPING CO. LTD.—See Albert Ballin KG; *Int'l*, pg. 294
ARCTIC LEASING LLC—See AIP, LLC; *U.S. Private*, pg. 136
ARDMORE SHIPPING CORPORATION; *Int'l*, pg. 556
ARKAS ALGERIE S.P.A.—See Albert Ballin KG; *Int'l*, pg. 294
ARKAS SHIPPING & TRANSPORT S.A.—See Albert Ballin KG; *Int'l*, pg. 294
AVANCE GAS HOLDING LTD.; *Int'l*, pg. 734
AVIATION INVENTORY RESOURCES, INC.; *U.S. Private*, pg. 406
AWILCO LNG 1 AS—See Awilco LNG ASA; *Int'l*, pg. 753
AWILCO LNG 2 AS—See Awilco LNG ASA; *Int'l*, pg. 753
AWILCO LNG 3 AS—See Awilco LNG ASA; *Int'l*, pg. 753
AWILCO LNG 4 AS—See Awilco LNG ASA; *Int'l*, pg. 753
AWILCO LNG 5 AS—See Awilco LNG ASA; *Int'l*, pg. 753
AWILCO LNG 6 AS—See Awilco LNG ASA; *Int'l*, pg. 753
AWILCO LNG 7 AS—See Awilco LNG ASA; *Int'l*, pg. 753
BALTIC REEFERS LTD.; *Int'l*, pg. 812
BALTIC TRADING LIMITED—See Genco Shipping & Trading Limited; *U.S. Public*, pg. 911
BEIBU GULF PORT CO., LTD.; *Int'l*, pg. 942
B+H OCEAN CARRIERS LTD.; *Int'l*, pg. 784
BIANCHI & CO. (1916) LTD.—See Albert Ballin KG; *Int'l*, pg. 294
BIBBY MARITIME LIMITED—See Bibby Line Group Limited; *Int'l*, pg. 1018
BINEX LINE CORP.; *U.S. Private*, pg. 560
BLUE FUNNELL ANGOLA—See Albert Ballin KG; *Int'l*, pg. 294
BOCIMAR INTERNATIONAL N.V.—See Compagnie Maritime Belge S.A.; *Int'l*, pg. 1746
BOC INTERNATIONAL, INC.; *U.S. Private*, pg. 607
BOECKMANS BELGIE NV—See Banco Safra S.A.; *Int'l*, pg. 824
BOECKMANS NEDERLAND B.V.—See Banco Safra S.A.; *Int'l*, pg. 824
BOHAI FERRY GROUP CO., LTD.; *Int'l*, pg. 1100
BOSKALIS OFFSHORE HEAVY MARINE TRANSPORT B.V.—See HAL Trust N.V.; *Int'l*, pg. 3225
BOX SHIPS, INC.; *Int'l*, pg. 1124
BRAEMAR QUINCANNON PTE LIMITED—See Braemar PLC; *Int'l*, pg. 1135
BRAEMAR QUINCANNON PTE LIMITED—See Quincannon Associates, Inc.; *U.S. Private*, pg. 3327
BRAEMAR STEEGE INC—See ABL Group ASA; *Int'l*, pg. 62
BULK PARTNERS (BERMUDA) LTD.—See Pangaea Logistics Solutions Ltd.; *U.S. Public*, pg. 1635
BUMI ARMADA BERHAD; *Int'l*, pg. 1215
BW FLEET MANAGEMENT PTE LTD—See BW Group Ltd.; *Int'l*, pg. 1231
BW SHIPPING PHILIPPINES INC.—See BW Group Ltd.; *Int'l*, pg. 1231
CANAL BARGE COMPANY INC.; *U.S. Private*, pg. 732
CARAVELLE INTERNATIONAL GROUP; *Int'l*, pg. 1320
CARGO MARINE LTD.—See Albert Ballin KG; *Int'l*, pg. 294
CATONI 7 CO.—See Albert Ballin KG; *Int'l*, pg. 294
CELTIC MARINE CORPORATION; *U.S. Private*, pg. 808
CHENG LIE NAVIGATION CO., LTD.—See CMA CGM S.A.; *Int'l*, pg. 1668
CHEVRON SHIPPING COMPANY LLC—See Chevron Corporation; *U.S. Public*, pg. 486
CHINA CHENGTONG DEVELOPMENT GROUP LIMITED; *Int'l*, pg. 1488
CHINA MERCHANTS ENERGY SHIPPING CO., LTD.—See China Merchants Group Limited; *Int'l*, pg. 1520
CHIQUITA BRANDS LLC - FREEPORT—See Banco Safra S.A.; *Int'l*, pg. 824
CHOICE REEFER SYSTEMS—See Eassons Transport Limited; *Int'l*, pg. 2269
CHOWGULE STEAMSHIPS LIMITED—See Chowgule & Company Pvt. Ltd.; *Int'l*, pg. 1585

CHUAN HUP HOLDINGS LIMITED; *Int'l*, pg. 1589
CLARKSON MELBOURNE PTY LIMITED—See Clarkson PLC; *Int'l*, pg. 1650
CLARKSON SHIPPING SERVICES INDIA PRIVATE LIMITED—See Clarkson PLC; *Int'l*, pg. 1650
C-LIFT LLC—See AIP, LLC; *U.S. Private*, pg. 136
CMA CGM ALGERIA—See CMA CGM S.A.; *Int'l*, pg. 1667
CMA CGM AMERICA LLC—See CMA CGM S.A.; *Int'l*, pg. 1667
CMA CGM AND ANL HONG KONG—See CMA CGM S.A.; *Int'l*, pg. 1667
CMA CGM AND ANL MALAYSIA SDN BHD—See CMA CGM S.A.; *Int'l*, pg. 1667
CMA CGM ANTILLES GUYANE—See CMA CGM S.A.; *Int'l*, pg. 1667
CMA CGM AUSTRALIA—See CMA CGM S.A.; *Int'l*, pg. 1667
CMA CGM BELGIUM NV—See CMA CGM S.A.; *Int'l*, pg. 1667
CMA CGM BOLIVIA—See CMA CGM S.A.; *Int'l*, pg. 1667
CMA CGM CANADA—See CMA CGM S.A.; *Int'l*, pg. 1667
CMA CGM CENTRAL ASIA—See CMA CGM S.A.; *Int'l*, pg. 1667
CMA CGM CHILE SA—See CMA CGM S.A.; *Int'l*, pg. 1667
CMA CGM COLOMBIA S.A.S.—See CMA CGM S.A.; *Int'l*, pg. 1667
CMA CGM COSTA RICA—See CMA CGM S.A.; *Int'l*, pg. 1667
CMA CGM CROATIA—See CMA CGM S.A.; *Int'l*, pg. 1667
CMA CGM DELMAS NIGERIA—See CMA CGM S.A.; *Int'l*, pg. 1667
CMA CGM DEUTSCHLAND—See CMA CGM S.A.; *Int'l*, pg. 1667
CMA CGM DO BRASIL AGENCIA MARITIMA LTDA—See CMA CGM S.A.; *Int'l*, pg. 1667
CMA CGM DOMINICANA—See CMA CGM S.A.; *Int'l*, pg. 1667
CMA CGM ECUADOR—See CMA CGM S.A.; *Int'l*, pg. 1667
CMA CGM ESTONIA LTD—See CMA CGM S.A.; *Int'l*, pg. 1667
CMA CGM FINLAND—See CMA CGM S.A.; *Int'l*, pg. 1667
CMA CGM GLOBAL INDIA—See CMA CGM S.A.; *Int'l*, pg. 1667
CMA CGM GREECE—See CMA CGM S.A.; *Int'l*, pg. 1667
CMA CGM HOLLAND BV—See CMA CGM S.A.; *Int'l*, pg. 1667
CMA CGM HUNGARY—See CMA CGM S.A.; *Int'l*, pg. 1667
CMA CGM IBERICA SAU—See CMA CGM S.A.; *Int'l*, pg. 1667
CMA CGM ITALY S.R.L.—See CMA CGM S.A.; *Int'l*, pg. 1667
CMA CGM JAMAICA LTD—See CMA CGM S.A.; *Int'l*, pg. 1667
CMA CGM JAPAN—See CMA CGM S.A.; *Int'l*, pg. 1667
CMA CGM KENYA—See CMA CGM S.A.; *Int'l*, pg. 1667
CMA CGM MADAGASCAR—See CMA CGM S.A.; *Int'l*, pg. 1667
CMA CGM MAROC—See CMA CGM S.A.; *Int'l*, pg. 1667
CMA CGM MEXICO—See CMA CGM S.A.; *Int'l*, pg. 1668
CMA CGM MOZAMBIQUE—See CMA CGM S.A.; *Int'l*, pg. 1668
CMA CGM NOUMEA—See CMA CGM S.A.; *Int'l*, pg. 1668
CMA CGM PAKISTAN (PVT) LTD—See CMA CGM S.A.; *Int'l*, pg. 1668
CMA CGM PANAMA—See CMA CGM S.A.; *Int'l*, pg. 1668
CMA CGM PAPEETE—See CMA CGM S.A.; *Int'l*, pg. 1668
CMA CGM POLSKA LTD—See CMA CGM S.A.; *Int'l*, pg. 1668
CMA CGM PORTUGAL—See CMA CGM S.A.; *Int'l*, pg. 1668
CMA CGM REUNION—See CMA CGM S.A.; *Int'l*, pg. 1668
CMA CGM ROMANIA—See CMA CGM S.A.; *Int'l*, pg. 1668
CMA CGM S.A.; *Int'l*, pg. 1666
CMA CGM SCANDINAVIA AS—See CMA CGM S.A.; *Int'l*, pg. 1668
CMA CGM SERBIA—See CMA CGM S.A.; *Int'l*, pg. 1668
CMA CGM SHIPPING AGENCIES UKRAINE LTD—See CMA CGM S.A.; *Int'l*, pg. 1668
CMA CGM SLOVENIA—See CMA CGM S.A.; *Int'l*, pg. 1668
CMA CGM ST LUCIA LTD—See CMA CGM S.A.; *Int'l*, pg. 1668
CMA CGM ST MARTEEN—See CMA CGM S.A.; *Int'l*, pg. 1668
CMA CGM SUDAN—See CMA CGM S.A.; *Int'l*, pg. 1668
CMA CGM TRINIDAD LTD—See CMA CGM S.A.; *Int'l*, pg. 1668
CMA CGM TURKEY—See CMA CGM S.A.; *Int'l*, pg. 1668
CMA CGM UK SHIPPING LTD—See CMA CGM S.A.; *Int'l*, pg. 1668
CMA CGM VENEZUELA—See CMA CGM S.A.; *Int'l*, pg. 1668
COCONUT PRODUCTS LTD.—See Albert Ballin KG; *Int'l*, pg. 294
COECLERICI BULK TERMINAL TORRES S.P.A.—See Coeclerici S.p.A.; *Int'l*, pg. 1688
COECLERICI SHIPPING S.P.A.—See Coeclerici S.p.A.; *Int'l*, pg. 1689
COMANAV—See CMA CGM S.A.; *Int'l*, pg. 1668
COMPAGNIE GENERALE MARITIME—See CMA CGM S.A.; *Int'l*, pg. 1668

N.A.I.C.S. INDEX

483111 — DEEP SEA FREIGHT TR...

COMPAGNIE MARITIME BELGE S.A.; *Int'l*, pg. 1745
CONG TY CO PHAN LOGISTICS VINALINK; *Int'l*, pg. 1768
CONSORCIO NAVIERO PERUANO S.A.—See Grupo Romero; *Int'l*, pg. 3134
COOL CARRIERS AB—See Baltic Reefers Ltd.; *Int'l*, pg. 812
COOL CARRIERS CHILE S.A.—See Baltic Reefers Ltd.; *Int'l*, pg. 812
COOL CARRIERS NEW ZEALAND LTD—See Baltic Reefers Ltd.; *Int'l*, pg. 812
COOL CARRIERS USA INC.—See Baltic Reefers Ltd.; *Int'l*, pg. 812
COSCO CONTAINER LINES NORTH AMERICA INC.—See China COSCO Shipping Corporation Limited; *Int'l*, pg. 1494
COSCO SHIPPING INTERNATIONAL (SINGAPORE) CO., LTD.—See China COSCO Shipping Corporation Limited; *Int'l*, pg. 1492
COSCO SHIPPING LINES CO., LTD.—See China COSCO Shipping Corporation Limited; *Int'l*, pg. 1494
COSCO SHIPPING LOGISTICS (WEST ASIA) L.L.C.—See China COSCO Shipping Corporation Limited; *Int'l*, pg. 1493
COSCO SHIPPING SPECIALIZED CARRIERS CO., LTD.—See China COSCO Shipping Corporation Limited; *Int'l*, pg. 1493
COSTAMARE INC.; *Int'l*, pg. 1815
COURAGE MARINE (HK) COMPANY LIMITED—See Courage Investment Group Limited; *Int'l*, pg. 1819
COURAGE - NEW AMEGO SHIPPING AGENCY CO. LTD.—See Courage Investment Group Limited; *Int'l*, pg. 1819
CROWLEY MARITIME CORPORATION; *U.S. Private*, pg. 1109
DAIICHI CHUO KISEN KAISHA; *Int'l*, pg. 1927
D'AMICO INTERNATIONAL SHIPPING S.A.; *Int'l*, pg. 1899
D'AMICO TANKERS LTD—See d'Amico International Shipping S.A.; *Int'l*, pg. 1899
D'AMICO TANKERS MONACO SAM—See d'Amico International Shipping S.A.; *Int'l*, pg. 1899
D'AMICO TANKERS UK LTD—See d'Amico International Shipping S.A.; *Int'l*, pg. 1899
DANAOS CORPORATION; *Int'l*, pg. 1958
DELMAS—See CMA CGM S.A.; *Int'l*, pg. 1668
DELMAS (UK) LIMITED—See CMA CGM S.A.; *Int'l*, pg. 1668
DELTA TRANSPORT (PVT.) LTD.—See Albert Ballin KG; *Int'l*, pg. 294
DET NORSKE VERITAS PUERTO RICO—See DNV GL Group AS; *Int'l*, pg. 2151
DFDS A/S; *Int'l*, pg. 2094
DFDS SEAWAYS AB—See DFDS A/S; *Int'l*, pg. 2095
DFDS SEAWAYS AS—See DFDS A/S; *Int'l*, pg. 2095
DFDS SEAWAYS BALTIC GMBH—See DFDS A/S; *Int'l*, pg. 2095
DFDS SEAWAYS GMBH—See DFDS A/S; *Int'l*, pg. 2095
DFDS SEAWAYS IJMUIDEN BV—See DFDS A/S; *Int'l*, pg. 2095
DFDS SEAWAYS LTD—See DFDS A/S; *Int'l*, pg. 2095
DFDS SEAWAYS NEWCASTLE LTD—See DFDS A/S; *Int'l*, pg. 2095
DFDS SEAWAYS OU—See DFDS A/S; *Int'l*, pg. 2095
DFDS SEAWAYS S.A.S.—See DFDS A/S; *Int'l*, pg. 2095
DFDS SEAWAYS SIA—See DFDS A/S; *Int'l*, pg. 2095
DFDS SEAWAYS TERMINALS BV—See DFDS A/S; *Int'l*, pg. 2095
DHL INTERNATIONAL (GAMBIA) LTD.—See Deutsche Post AG; *Int'l*, pg. 2076
DHT HOLDINGS, INC.; *Int'l*, pg. 2100
DIANA SHIPPING INC.; *Int'l*, pg. 2106
DM SHIPPING LTD—See d'Amico International Shipping S.A.; *Int'l*, pg. 1899
DOCKWISE LTD.—See HAL Trust N.V.; *Int'l*, pg. 3226
DOF ASA; *Int'l*, pg. 2153
DOF MANAGEMENT AUSTRALIA PTY LTD—See DOF ASA; *Int'l*, pg. 2154
DOF SUBSEA AS—See DOF ASA; *Int'l*, pg. 2154
DOF SUBSEA AUSTRALIAN PTY.—See DOF ASA; *Int'l*, pg. 2154
DOF SUBSEA US INC.—See DOF ASA; *Int'l*, pg. 2154
DORIAN LPG (DK) APS—See Dorian LPG Ltd.; *U.S. Public*, pg. 677
DORIAN LPG LTD.; *U.S. Public*, pg. 677
EIMSKIP USA INC.—See Eimskipafelag Islands Hf.; *Int'l*, pg. 2332
ENETI INC.—See Cadeler A/S; *Int'l*, pg. 1247
EPDC COALTECH AND MARINE CO., LTD.—See Electric Power Development Co., Ltd.; *Int'l*, pg. 2349
ESSAR SHIPPING LIMITED; *Int'l*, pg. 2508
EURONAV LUXEMBOURG SA—See Euronav NV; *Int'l*, pg. 2554
EURONAV MI II INC.—See Euronav NV; *Int'l*, pg. 2554
EURONAV SAS—See Euronav NV; *Int'l*, pg. 2554
EURONAV SHIP MANAGEMENT (HELLAS) LTD—See Euronav NV; *Int'l*, pg. 2554
EURONAV SHIP MANAGEMENT SAS—See Euronav NV; *Int'l*, pg. 2554
EUROSEAS LTD.; *Int'l*, pg. 2558
EVERGREEN AGENCY (SOUTH AFRICA) (PTY) LTD.—See Evergreen Marine Corporation (Taiwan) Ltd.; *Int'l*, pg. 2566
EVERGREEN SHIPPING AGENCY (AUSTRALIA) PTY. LTD.—See Evergreen Marine Corporation (Taiwan) Ltd.; *Int'l*, pg. 2566
EVERGREEN SHIPPING AGENCY (DEUTSCHLAND) GMBH—See Evergreen Marine Corporation (Taiwan) Ltd.; *Int'l*, pg. 2566
EVERGREEN SHIPPING AGENCY FRANCE S.A.—See Evergreen Marine Corporation (Taiwan) Ltd.; *Int'l*, pg. 2566
EVERGREEN SHIPPING AGENCY (IRELAND) LTD.—See Evergreen Marine Corporation (Taiwan) Ltd.; *Int'l*, pg. 2566
EVERGREEN SHIPPING AGENCY (NETHERLANDS) B.V.—See Evergreen Marine Corporation (Taiwan) Ltd.; *Int'l*, pg. 2566
EVERGREEN SHIPPING AGENCY (POLAND) SP. ZO.O—See Evergreen Marine Corporation (Taiwan) Ltd.; *Int'l*, pg. 2566
EVERGREEN SHIPPING AGENCY (UK) LIMITED—See Evergreen Marine Corporation (Taiwan) Ltd.; *Int'l*, pg. 2566
EVERGREEN SHIPPING AGENCY (VIETNAM) CORP.—See Evergreen Marine Corporation (Taiwan) Ltd.; *Int'l*, pg. 2566
EVERGREEN SHIPPING (SPAIN) S.L.—See Evergreen Marine Corporation (Taiwan) Ltd.; *Int'l*, pg. 2566
EXCEL MARITIME CARRIERS LTD.; *Int'l*, pg. 2577
EXMAR LUX SA—See Exmar N.V.; *Int'l*, pg. 2585
EXMAR MARINE N.V.—See Exmar N.V.; *Int'l*, pg. 2585
EXMAR N.V.; *Int'l*, pg. 2585
EXMAR SHIPMANAGEMENT INDIA, PVT. LTD.—See Exmar N.V.; *Int'l*, pg. 2585
EXMAR SHIPMANAGEMENT N.V.—See Exmar N.V.; *Int'l*, pg. 2585
EXMAR SHIPPING N.V.—See Exmar N.V.; *Int'l*, pg. 2585
FAIRSTAR HEAVY TRANSPORT N.V.—See HAL Trust N.V.; *Int'l*, pg. 3226
FAR EASTERN SHIPPING COMPANY OJSC; *Int'l*, pg. 2617
FEDERAL OFFSHORE SERVICES PTE LTD—See Federal International (2000) Ltd; *Int'l*, pg. 2630
FEDNAV ASIA LTD.—See Fednav Limited; *Int'l*, pg. 2631
FEDNAV (BELGIUM) N.V.—See Fednav Limited; *Int'l*, pg. 2631
FEDNAV BRASIL AGENCIA MARITIMA LTDA—See Fednav Limited; *Int'l*, pg. 2631
FEDNAV EUROPE LIMITED—See Fednav Limited; *Int'l*, pg. 2631
FEDNAV (HAMBURG) GMBH—See Fednav Limited; *Int'l*, pg. 2631
FEDNAV INTERNATIONAL LTD.—See Fednav Limited; *Int'l*, pg. 2631
FEDNAV LIMITED; *Int'l*, pg. 2631
FEDNAV SINGAPORE PTE. LTD.—See Fednav Limited; *Int'l*, pg. 2631
FESCO AGENCIES N.A, INC.—See Far Eastern Shipping Company OJSC; *Int'l*, pg. 2617
FIRST STEAMSHIP CO., LTD.; *Int'l*, pg. 2688
FLEX LNG LTD.; *Int'l*, pg. 2701
FM GLOBAL LOGISTICS HOLDINGS BERHAD; *Int'l*, pg. 2716
FOSS MARITIME CO.—See Saltchuk Resources Inc.; *U.S. Private*, pg. 3534
FREIGHTOS LIMITED; *Int'l*, pg. 2771
FRONTLINE PLC; *Int'l*, pg. 2796
FRONTLINE SHIPPING SINGAPORE PTE LTD—See Frontline plc; *Int'l*, pg. 2796
FRT INTERNATIONAL INCORPORATED; *U.S. Private*, pg. 1617
GAC CARGO SYSTEMS (MALAYSIA) SDN. BHD—See Gulf Agency Company Ltd.; *Int'l*, pg. 3178
GAC DENMARK A/S—See Gulf Agency Company Ltd.; *Int'l*, pg. 3178
GAC DO BRASIL LTDA—See Gulf Agency Company Ltd.; *Int'l*, pg. 3179
GAC ENERGY AND MARINE SERVICES LTD—See Gulf Agency Company Ltd.; *Int'l*, pg. 3178
GAC FORWARDING & SHIPPING (SHANGHAI) LTD—See Gulf Agency Company Ltd.; *Int'l*, pg. 3178
GAC GHANA—See Gulf Agency Company Ltd.; *Int'l*, pg. 3178
GAC KAZAKHSTAN LLP—See Gulf Agency Company Ltd.; *Int'l*, pg. 3178
GAC LASER INTERNATIONAL LOGISTICS (PTY) LIMITED—See Gulf Agency Company Ltd.; *Int'l*, pg. 3178
GAC LOGISTICS (UK) LTD—See Gulf Agency Company Ltd.; *Int'l*, pg. 3178
GAC MARINE L.L.C.—See Gulf Agency Company Ltd.; *Int'l*, pg. 3178
GAC MARINE LOGISTICS INC.—See Gulf Agency Company Ltd.; *Int'l*, pg. 3178
GAC MARINE—See Gulf Agency Company Ltd.; *Int'l*, pg. 3178
GAC NETHERLANDS LTD—See Gulf Agency Company Ltd.; *Int'l*, pg. 3178
GAC NORWAY AS—See Gulf Agency Company Ltd.; *Int'l*, pg. 3178
GAC PHILIPPINES, INC—See Gulf Agency Company Ltd.; *Int'l*, pg. 3178
GAC (POLAND) SP. Z.O.O—See Gulf Agency Company Ltd.; *Int'l*, pg. 3178
GAC SERVICES (JAPAN) LIMITED—See Gulf Agency Company Ltd.; *Int'l*, pg. 3178
GAC SHIPPING AND LOGISTICS LIMITED—See Gulf Agency Company Ltd.; *Int'l*, pg. 3178
GAC SHIPPING (INDIA) PVT. LTD.—See Gulf Agency Company Ltd.; *Int'l*, pg. 3178
GAC SHIPPING LIMITED—See Gulf Agency Company Ltd.; *Int'l*, pg. 3178
GAC SHIPPING NIGERIA LIMITED—See Albert Ballin KG; *Int'l*, pg. 294
GAC SHIPPING (S.A.) (PTY) LIMITED—See Gulf Agency Company Ltd.; *Int'l*, pg. 3178
GAC SHIPPING SA—See Gulf Agency Company Ltd.; *Int'l*, pg. 3178
GAC SHIPPING SERVICES (NIGERIA) LTD.—See Gulf Agency Company Ltd.; *Int'l*, pg. 3178
GAC SHIPPING (USA) INC.—See Gulf Agency Company Ltd.; *Int'l*, pg. 3179
GAC SWEDEN AB—See Gulf Agency Company Ltd.; *Int'l*, pg. 3179
GAC (TAIWAN) LTD.—See Gulf Agency Company Ltd.; *Int'l*, pg. 3178
GAC TRANSFER SERVICES S.A.—See Gulf Agency Company Ltd.; *Int'l*, pg. 3179
GAC USA—See Gulf Agency Company Ltd.; *Int'l*, pg. 3179
GASMAR - TRANSPORTES MARITIMOS, LDA.—See Galp Energia SGPS, S.A.; *Int'l*, pg. 2875
GBX LOGISTICS LTD.—See Albert Ballin KG; *Int'l*, pg. 294
GENCO SHIPPING PTE. LIMITED—See Genco Shipping & Trading Limited; *U.S. Public*, pg. 911
GLOBAL CARRIERS BHD; *Int'l*, pg. 2994
GLOBAL MARITIME SERVICES LTD.—See Albert Ballin KG; *Int'l*, pg. 294
GLOBAL SHIP LEASE, INC.; *Int'l*, pg. 3001
GLOBAL TS SDN. BHD.—See Global Carriers Bhd; *Int'l*, pg. 2994
GOLAR MANAGEMENT (UK) LIMITED—See Golar LNG Limited; *Int'l*, pg. 3023
GOLDENPORT HOLDINGS INC.; *Int'l*, pg. 3033
GRAHAM GULF, INC.; *U.S. Private*, pg. 1751
GRANPORTUARIA S.A.—See Grupo TMM, S.A.B.; *Int'l*, pg. 3137
GRANUMIX B.V.—See Group de Cloedt SA; *Int'l*, pg. 3088
GREAT HARVEST MAETA HOLDINGS LIMITED; *Int'l*, pg. 3064
GRIMALDI GROUP SPA; *Int'l*, pg. 3085
GRINDROD SHIPS AGENCIES LDA—See Albert Ballin KG; *Int'l*, pg. 294
GRUPO TMM CIUDAD DEL CARMEN—See Grupo TMM, S.A.B.; *Int'l*, pg. 3137
GULF AGENCY CO. (BAHRAIN) W.L.L.—See Gulf Agency Company Ltd.; *Int'l*, pg. 3179
GULF AGENCY COMPANY (CYPRUS) LTD—See Gulf Agency Company Ltd.; *Int'l*, pg. 3179
GULF AGENCY COMPANY (EGYPT) LTD—See Gulf Agency Company Ltd.; *Int'l*, pg. 3179
GULF AGENCY COMPANY (FUJAIRAH) PVT. WLL.—See Gulf Agency Company Ltd.; *Int'l*, pg. 3179
GULF AGENCY COMPANY (HONG KONG) LTD.—See Gulf Agency Company Ltd.; *Int'l*, pg. 3179
GULF AGENCY COMPANY (JORDAN) LTD—See Gulf Agency Company Ltd.; *Int'l*, pg. 3179
GULF AGENCY COMPANY (OMAN) L.L.C.—See Gulf Agency Company Ltd.; *Int'l*, pg. 3179
GULF AGENCY COMPANY QATAR (W.L.L.)—See Gulf Agency Company Ltd.; *Int'l*, pg. 3179
GULF AGENCY COMPANY (RAS AL KHAIMAH) L.L.C.—See Gulf Agency Company Ltd.; *Int'l*, pg. 3179
GULF AGENCY COMPANY SAUDI ARABIA—See Gulf Agency Company Ltd.; *Int'l*, pg. 3179
GULF AGENCY CO. SHARJAH W.L.L.—See Gulf Agency Company Ltd.; *Int'l*, pg. 3179
GULF AGENCY DENIZCILIK A.S.—See Gulf Agency Company Ltd.; *Int'l*, pg. 3179
GULF OFFSHORE NORGE AS—See Tidewater Inc.; *U.S. Public*, pg. 2158
HAFNIA LIMITED—See BW Group Ltd.; *Int'l*, pg. 1231
HAJI ABDULLAH ALIREZA & CO. LTD.—See Albert Ballin KG; *Int'l*, pg. 294
HAMBURG SUDAMERIKANISCHE DAMPFSCHIFFFAHRTS-GESELLSCHAFT A/S & CO KG—See A.P. Moller-Maersk A/S; *Int'l*, pg. 27
HAPAC-LLOYD (SCHWEIZ) AG—See Albert Ballin KG; *Int'l*, pg. 294
HAPAG-LLOYD (AFRICA) PTY. LTD.—See Albert Ballin KG; *Int'l*, pg. 294
HAPAG-LLOYD AGENCY LLC—See Albert Ballin KG; *Int'l*, pg. 295
HAPAG-LLOYD AG—See Albert Ballin KG; *Int'l*, pg. 294
HAPAG-LLOYD (AMERICA) INC.—See Albert Ballin KG; *Int'l*, pg. 294
HAPAG-LLOYD ANTWERPEN—See Albert Ballin KG; *Int'l*, pg. 295

483111 — DEEP SEA FREIGHT TR...

HAPAG-LLOYD ARGENTINA S.R.L.—See Albert Ballin KG; *Int'l*, pg. 295
HAPAG-LLOYD (AUSTRALIA) PTY. LTD.—See Albert Ballin KG; *Int'l*, pg. 294
HAPAG-LLOYD AUSTRIA GMBH—See Albert Ballin KG; *Int'l*, pg. 295
HAPAG-LLOYD BRAZIL—See Albert Ballin KG; *Int'l*, pg. 295
HAPAG-LLOYD (CANADA) INC.—See Albert Ballin KG; *Int'l*, pg. 294
HAPAG-LLOYD CHILE AG. MAR. LTDA.—See Albert Ballin KG; *Int'l*, pg. 295
HAPAG-LLOYD (CHINA) SHIPPING LTD.—See Albert Ballin KG; *Int'l*, pg. 294
HAPAG-LLOYD COLOMBIA LTDA.—See Albert Ballin KG; *Int'l*, pg. 295
HAPAG-LLOYD COSTA RICA S.A.—See Albert Ballin KG; *Int'l*, pg. 295
HAPAG-LLOYD DENAMRK—See Albert Ballin KG; *Int'l*, pg. 295
HAPAG-LLOYD (FRANCE) SAS—See Albert Ballin KG; *Int'l*, pg. 295
HAPAG-LLOYD GUATAMALA S.A.—See Albert Ballin KG; *Int'l*, pg. 295
HAPAG-LLOYD (IRELAND) LTD.—See Albert Ballin KG; *Int'l*, pg. 295
HAPAG-LLOYD (JAPAN) K.K.—See Albert Ballin KG; *Int'l*, pg. 295
HAPAG-LLOYD (KOREA) LTD.—See Albert Ballin KG; *Int'l*, pg. 295
HAPAG-LLOYD LANKA (PVT.) LTD.—See Albert Ballin KG; *Int'l*, pg. 295
HAPAG-LLOYD (MALAYSIA) SDN. BHD.—See Albert Ballin KG; *Int'l*, pg. 295
HAPAG-LLOYD MEXICO S.A. DE C.V.—See Albert Ballin KG; *Int'l*, pg. 295
HAPAG-LLOYD OVERSEAS TRANSPORT (HELLAS) SA—See Albert Ballin KG; *Int'l*, pg. 295
HAPAG-LLOYD OVERSEAS TRANSPORT S.A.—See Albert Ballin KG; *Int'l*, pg. 295
HAPAG-LLOYD PERU S.A.C.—See Albert Ballin KG; *Int'l*, pg. 295
HAPAG-LLOYD (PHILIPPINES) INC.—See Albert Ballin KG; *Int'l*, pg. 295
HAPAG-LLOYD POLSKA SP. Z.O.O.—See Albert Ballin KG; *Int'l*, pg. 295
HAPAG-LLOYD PORTUGAL LDA.—See Albert Ballin KG; *Int'l*, pg. 295
HAPAG-LLOYD PTE. LTD.—See Albert Ballin KG; *Int'l*, pg. 295
HAPAG-LLOYD ROTTERDAM—See Albert Ballin KG; *Int'l*, pg. 295
HAPAG-LLOYD SPAIN S.L.—See Albert Ballin KG; *Int'l*, pg. 295
HAPAG-LLOYD SWEDEN AB—See Albert Ballin KG; *Int'l*, pg. 295
HAPAG-LLOYD TAIWAN LTD.—See Albert Ballin KG; *Int'l*, pg. 295
HAPAG-LLOYD (THAILAND) LTD.—See Albert Ballin KG; *Int'l*, pg. 295
HAPAG-LLOYD VENEZUELA, C.A.—See Albert Ballin KG; *Int'l*, pg. 295
HAPAG-LLOYD (VIETNAM)—See Albert Ballin KG; *Int'l*, pg. 295
HARBOUR AGENCIES (SARAWAK) SDN. BHD.—See Harbour-Link Group Berhad; *Int'l*, pg. 3272
HARBOUR AGENCIES (SIBU) SDN. BHD.—See Harbour-Link Group Berhad; *Int'l*, pg. 3272
HARBOUR-LINK LOGISTICS SDN. BHD.—See Harbour-Link Group Berhad; *Int'l*, pg. 3272
HARBOUR-LINK LOGISTICS (S) SDN. BHD.—See Harbour-Link Group Berhad; *Int'l*, pg. 3272
HARBOUR LINK SHIPPING SDN. BHD.—See Albert Ballin KG; *Int'l*, pg. 295
HARBOUR SERVICES CORPORATION SDN. BHD.—See Harbour-Link Group Berhad; *Int'l*, pg. 3272
HARRISONS HOLDINGS (MALAYSIA) BERHAD; *Int'l*, pg. 3278
HAVILA SHIPPING ASA—See Havila Holding AS; *Int'l*, pg. 3287
HC SHIPPING AND CHARTERING LTD—See Clarkson PLC; *Int'l*, pg. 1651
HELNAN MARINA HOTEL—See Helnan International Hotels A/S; *Int'l*, pg. 3338
HERMITAGE OFFSHORE SERVICES LTD.; *Int'l*, pg. 3363
HEUNG-A LOGISTICS (SHANGHAI) CO., LTD.—See Heung-A Shipping Company Limited; *Int'l*, pg. 3366
HEUNG-A (M) SDN. BHD.—See Heung-A Shipping Company Limited; *Int'l*, pg. 3366
HEUNG-A SHIPPING (CHINA) CO.,LTD.—See Heung-A Shipping Company Limited; *Int'l*, pg. 3366
HEUNG-A SHIPPING COMPANY LIMITED; *Int'l*, pg. 3366
HEUNG-A SHIPPING (THAILAND) CO., LTD.—See Heung-A Shipping Company Limited; *Int'l*, pg. 3366
HEUNG-A SHIPPING VIETNAM CO., LTD.—See Heung-A Shipping Company Limited; *Int'l*, pg. 3366
HEUNG-A (SINGAPORE) PTE LTD.—See Heung-A Shipping Company Limited; *Int'l*, pg. 3366

HIGHLINE QUEST SDN. BHD.—See Hubline Berhad; *Int'l*, pg. 3520
HIGH POOL TANKERS LTD—See d'Amico International Shipping S.A.; *Int'l*, pg. 1899
HMM CO., LTD.; *Int'l*, pg. 3432
THE HONGKONG AND YAUMATI FERRY COMPANY LIMITED—See Henderson Land Development Co. Ltd.; *Int'l*, pg. 3345
HONG KONG MING WAH SHIPPING CO., LTD.—See China Merchants Group Limited; *Int'l*, pg. 1521
HORN INTERNATIONAL FORWARDING—See Horn Packaging Corporation; *U.S. Private*, pg. 1983
HOS PORT, LLC—See Hornbeck Offshore Services, Inc.; *U.S. Private*, pg. 1983
HUB DACIA S.R.L.—See Albert Ballin KG; *Int'l*, pg. 295
HUB DUNAV D.O.O.—See Albert Ballin KG; *Int'l*, pg. 295
HUB LEVANT LIMITED—See Albert Ballin KG; *Int'l*, pg. 295
HUB MARINE PTE. LTD.—See Hubline Berhad; *Int'l*, pg. 3520
HUDSON BAY PORT COMPANY—See The Broe Companies, Inc.; *U.S. Private*, pg. 4001
HULL BLYTH & CO LTD—See Deutsche Post AG; *Int'l*, pg. 2080
HUMBERTO ALVAREZ SUCESORES DE NICARAGUA S.A.—See Albert Ballin KG; *Int'l*, pg. 295
HYOKI KAIUN KAISHA LTD.; *Int'l*, pg. 3550
HYUNDAI MERCHANT MARINE (CHINA) CO., LTD.—See HMM Co., Ltd.; *Int'l*, pg. 3432
HYUNDAI MERCHANT MARINE (HONG KONG) LTD.—See HMM Co., Ltd.; *Int'l*, pg. 3432
HYUNDAI MERCHANT MARINE (SINGAPORE) PTE. LTD.—See HMM Co., Ltd.; *Int'l*, pg. 3432
IBEX MARITIME LTD—See Erria A/S; *Int'l*, pg. 2497
IINO KAIUN KAISHA LTD.; *Int'l*, pg. 3607
IINO SINGAPORE PTE. LTD.—See Iino Kaiun Kaisha Ltd.; *Int'l*, pg. 3608
IINO UK LTD.—See Iino Kaiun Kaisha Ltd.; *Int'l*, pg. 3608
IMPERIAL MOBILITY DEUTSCHLAND BETEILIGUNGS GMBH—See Dubai World Corporation; *Int'l*, pg. 2221
INCHCAPE SHIPPING SERVICES (CAMBODIA) LTD.—See Albert Ballin KG; *Int'l*, pg. 295
INCHCAPE SHIPPING SERVICES LLC—See Albert Ballin KG; *Int'l*, pg. 295
INCHCAPE SHIPPING SERVICES WLL—See Albert Ballin KG; *Int'l*, pg. 295
ING RUGGERO VIO—See Coeclerici S.p.A.; *Int'l*, pg. 1689
INTERMARINE, INC.; *U.S. Private*, pg. 2112
INTERNATIONAL SHIPHOLDING CORPORATION—See AIP, LLC; *U.S. Private*, pg. 136
ISS SHIPPING INDIA PVT. LTD.—See Albert Ballin KG; *Int'l*, pg. 295
KAPLAN AUTO GROUP; *U.S. Private*, pg. 2261
KOOLE TANKTRANSPORT B.V.—See JPMorgan Chase & Co.; *U.S. Public*, pg. 1209
LINEAR MARITIME MEXICANA S.A. DE C.V.—See Grupo TMM, S.A.B.; *Int'l*, pg. 3137
LUIS A. AYALA COLON SUCRS INC.—See Albert Ballin KG; *Int'l*, pg. 297
MACANDREWS & COMPANY LIMITED—See CMA CGM S.A.; *Int'l*, pg. 1668
MAERSK AUSTRALIA PTY. LTD.—See A.P. Moller-Maersk A/S; *Int'l*, pg. 26
MAERSK BRASIL LTDA.—See A.P. Moller-Maersk A/S; *Int'l*, pg. 26
MAERSK (HONG KONG) LTD.—See A.P. Moller-Maersk A/S; *Int'l*, pg. 26
MAERSK ITALIA SPA—See A.P. Moller-Maersk A/S; *Int'l*, pg. 27
MAERSK KENYA LTD.—See A.P. Moller-Maersk A/S; *Int'l*, pg. 27
MAERSK KENYA LTD.—See A.P. Moller-Maersk A/S; *Int'l*, pg. 27
MAERSK K.K.—See A.P. Moller-Maersk A/S; *Int'l*, pg. 27
MAERSK MALAYSIA SDN BHD—See A.P. Moller-Maersk A/S; *Int'l*, pg. 27
MAERSK NEW ZEALAND LTD.—See A.P. Moller-Maersk A/S; *Int'l*, pg. 27
MAERSK SINGAPORE PTE. LTD.—See A.P. Moller-Maersk A/S; *Int'l*, pg. 27
MAERSK SUPPLY SERVICE UK LIMITED—See A.P. Moller-Maersk A/S; *Int'l*, pg. 27
MARINE TRADING LTD.—See Albert Ballin KG; *Int'l*, pg. 295
MARINE TRANSPORT CORPORATION—See Crowley Maritime Corporation; *U.S. Private*, pg. 1110
MARITIMA MEXICANA, S.A. DE C.V., MORGAN CITY—See Grupo TMM, S.A.B.; *Int'l*, pg. 3137
MARITIMA MEXICANA, S.A. DE C.V.—See Grupo TMM, S.A.B.; *Int'l*, pg. 3137
MARITIMA MEXICANA, S.A. DE C.V.—See Grupo TMM, S.A.B.; *Int'l*, pg. 3137
MARYVILLE MARITIME INC.—See EXCEL MARITIME CARRIERS LTD.; *Int'l*, pg. 2577
MASTER LINE SHIPPING CO.; *U.S. Private*, pg. 2607
MATSON NAVIGATION COMPANY, INC.—See Matson, Inc.; *U.S. Public*, pg. 1398
MATSON TERMINALS, INC.—See Matson, Inc.; *U.S. Public*, pg. 1398
MC SHIPPING, INC.—See Irving Place Capital Management, L.P.; *U.S. Private*, pg. 2141

MC SHIPPING LTD.—See Irving Place Capital Management, L.P.; *U.S. Private*, pg. 2142
MC SHIPPING PTE LTD—See Irving Place Capital Management, L.P.; *U.S. Private*, pg. 2142
MC SHIPPING S.A.M.—See Irving Place Capital Management, L.P.; *U.S. Private*, pg. 2141
METRANS (DANUBIA) A.S.—See Hamburger Hafen und Logistik AG; *Int'l*, pg. 3237
MILLENIUM FREIGHT SERVICES—See H.H.V. Whitchurch & Co. Ltd.; *Int'l*, pg. 3195
MINOAN LINES SHIPPING S.A.—See Grimaldi Group SpA; *Int'l*, pg. 3085
MORMAC MARINE GROUP, INC.; *U.S. Private*, pg. 2785
NATIONAL GAS SHIPPING COMPANY LTD. (NGSCO)—See Abu Dhabi National Oil Company; *Int'l*, pg. 73
NATIONAL SHIPPING GULF AGENCY COMPANY (ABU DHABI) LTD. L.L.C.—See Gulf Agency Company Ltd.; *Int'l*, pg. 3179
NAVIERA DEL PACIFICO, S.A. DE C.V.—See Grupo TMM, S.A.B.; *Int'l*, pg. 3137
NEPTUNE PACIFIC AGENCY AUSTRALIA PTY. LIMITED—See The Wonderful Company LLC; *U.S. Private*, pg. 4138
NHM BRUGES NV—See Group de Cloedt SA; *Int'l*, pg. 3088
NHM NIEUWPOORT NV—See Group de Cloedt SA; *Int'l*, pg. 3088
NIPPON MARINE CO., LTD.—See ENEOS Holdings, Inc.; *Int'l*, pg. 2416
NOLIS-SPA—See Cevital S.p.A.; *Int'l*, pg. 1425
NORDEN SHIPPING (SINGAPORE) PTE. LTD—See Dampskibsselskabet NORDEN A/S; *Int'l*, pg. 1957
NORDEN TANKERS & BULKERS INDIA PVT. LTD.—See Dampskibsselskabet NORDEN A/S; *Int'l*, pg. 1957
NORDIC BULK CARRIERS SINGAPORE PTE. LTD.—See Pangaea Logistics Solutions Ltd.; *U.S. Public*, pg. 1635
NT PORT & MARINE PTY. LTD.—See AusGroup Limited; *Int'l*, pg. 716
OCEAN CONTAINER SERVICE (OCS)—See Albert Ballin KG; *Int'l*, pg. 296
OCEANLINK LTD.—See Fred. Olsen & Co.; *Int'l*, pg. 2769
OCS KALININGRAD—See Albert Ballin KG; *Int'l*, pg. 296
OCS OCEAN CONTAINER SERVICES LTD.—See Albert Ballin KG; *Int'l*, pg. 296
OCS OCEAN CONTAINER SERVICES LTD.—See Albert Ballin KG; *Int'l*, pg. 296
OIL AND MARINE AGENCIES (GHANA) LTD.—See Albert Ballin KG; *Int'l*, pg. 296
OIL AND MARINE AGENCIES SARL—See Albert Ballin KG; *Int'l*, pg. 296
OIL & MARINE AGENCIES (O.M.A.) SARL—See Albert Ballin KG; *Int'l*, pg. 296
OOCL (BENELUX) NV—See China COSCO Shipping Corporation Limited; *Int'l*, pg. 1495
OOCL (ITALY) S.R.L.—See China COSCO Shipping Corporation Limited; *Int'l*, pg. 1495
OOCL (KOREA) LTD—See China COSCO Shipping Corporation Limited; *Int'l*, pg. 1495
OOCL (PHILIPPINES) INC.—See China COSCO Shipping Corporation Limited; *Int'l*, pg. 1495
OOCL (PORTUGAL) LDA—See China COSCO Shipping Corporation Limited; *Int'l*, pg. 1495
OOCL (RUSSIA) LTD—See China COSCO Shipping Corporation Limited; *Int'l*, pg. 1495
OOCL (SINGAPORE) PTE LTD—See China COSCO Shipping Corporation Limited; *Int'l*, pg. 1495
OOCL (SWEDEN) AB—See China COSCO Shipping Corporation Limited; *Int'l*, pg. 1495
OOCL (TAIWAN) CO LTD—See China COSCO Shipping Corporation Limited; *Int'l*, pg. 1495
OOCL (UK) LTD—See China COSCO Shipping Corporation Limited; *Int'l*, pg. 1495
ORIENT OVERSEAS CONTAINER LINE (CHINA) CO. LTD - GUANGZHOU BRANCH—See China COSCO Shipping Corporation Limited; *Int'l*, pg. 1495
ORIENT OVERSEAS CONTAINER LINE (MALAYSIA) SDN. BHD.—See China COSCO Shipping Corporation Limited; *Int'l*, pg. 1495
ORIENT OVERSEAS CONTAINER LINE (SPAIN) S.L.—See China COSCO Shipping Corporation Limited; *Int'l*, pg. 1495
OSG LIGHTERING LLC—See Saltchuk Resources Inc.; *U.S. Private*, pg. 3534
OSG SHIP MANAGEMENT INC.—See Saltchuk Resources Inc.; *U.S. Private*, pg. 3534
OSG SHIP MANAGEMENT, MANILA INC.—See Saltchuk Resources Inc.; *U.S. Private*, pg. 3534
OSG SHIP MANAGEMENT (UK) LTD.—See Saltchuk Resources Inc.; *U.S. Private*, pg. 3534
OT HAPAG-LLOYD FINLAND AB—See Albert Ballin KG; *Int'l*, pg. 296
OVERSEAS CONTAINER LINE LIMITED - JAPAN BRANCH—See China COSCO Shipping Corporation Limited; *Int'l*, pg. 1495
OVERSEAS SHIPHOLDING GROUP, INC.—See Saltchuk Resources Inc.; *U.S. Private*, pg. 3534

N.A.I.C.S. INDEX

483113 — COASTAL AND GREAT L...

OVERSEAS TRANSPORT UKRAINE LTD.—See Albert Ballin KG; *Int'l*, pg. 296
PAPEETE SEIRLAND TRANSPORTS (PST)—See Albert Ballin KG; *Int'l*, pg. 296
PELICAN OFFSHORE SERVICES PTE LTD—See Dymon Asia Capital (Singapore) Pte. Ltd; *Int'l*, pg. 2238
PERDANA MARINE OFFSHORE PTE LTD—See Dayang Enterprise Holdings Berhad; *Int'l*, pg. 1985
PEREZ Y CIA JAMAICA LTD.—See Albert Ballin KG; *Int'l*, pg. 296
PETROMAR LIMITED—See Saltchuk Resources Inc.; *U.S. Private*, pg. 3534
PORT & TERMINAL MULTISERVICES LIMITED—See Grimaldi Group SpA; *Int'l*, pg. 3085
POSEIDON CONTAINERS HOLDINGS LLC—See Global Ship Lease, Inc.; *Int'l*, pg. 3001
PRINCIPAL MARITIME TANKERS CORPORATION; *U.S. Private*, pg. 3264
PROMAR INSTITUCION CULTURAL MARITIMA MEXICANA, A.C.—See Grupo TMM, S.A.B.; *Int'l*, pg. 3137
PT OCEAN GLOBAL SHIPPING—See China COSCO Shipping Corporation Limited; *Int'l*, pg. 1496
PT SAMUDERA INDONESIA, TBK.—See Albert Ballin KG; *Int'l*, pg. 296
PT TARUNACIPTA KENCANA—See Golden Agri-Resources Ltd.; *Int'l*, pg. 3028
QATAR MARITIME & MERCANTILE INTL. CO.—See Albert Ballin KG; *Int'l*, pg. 296
QUAY CARGO SERVICES LTD.—See Albert Ballin KG; *Int'l*, pg. 296
RAHI SHIPPING PTE. LTD.—See Adani Enterprises Limited; *Int'l*, pg. 125
REDERIET A.P. MOLLER A/S—See A.P. Moller-Maersk A/S; *Int'l*, pg. 27
REMINGTON SHIPPING INC.—See Sealift Holdings Inc.; *U.S. Private*, pg. 3585
RIJNAARDE B.V.—See Dubai World Corporation; *Int'l*, pg. 2221
SAFMARINE CONTAINER LINES N.V.—See A.P. Moller-Maersk A/S; *Int'l*, pg. 27
SAFMARINE (PTY) LTD.—See A.P. Moller-Maersk A/S; *Int'l*, pg. 27
SAGET MAROC/WORMS S.M. GROUP—See Albert Ballin KG; *Int'l*, pg. 296
SAKAIDE COSMO KOSAN CO., LTD.—See Cosmo Energy Holdings Co., Ltd.; *Int'l*, pg. 1812
SAM SHIPPING & CLEARING CO. LTD.—See Albert Ballin KG; *Int'l*, pg. 296
SEABOARD MARINE LTD. INC.—See Seaboard Corporation; *U.S. Public*, pg. 1851
SEABULK INTERNATIONAL, INC.—See AIP, LLC; *U.S. Private*, pg. 136
SEABULK TANKERS, INC.—See AIP, LLC; *U.S. Private*, pg. 137
SEACOR AMH LLC—See AIP, LLC; *U.S. Private*, pg. 136
SEACOR HOLDINGS INC.—See AIP, LLC; *U.S. Private*, pg. 136
SEALIFT CHEMICAL INCORPORATED—See Sealift Holdings Inc.; *U.S. Private*, pg. 3585
SEALIFT HOLDINGS INC.; *U.S. Private*, pg. 3585
SEALIFT INCORPORATED OF DELAWARE—See Sealift Holdings Inc.; *U.S. Private*, pg. 3585
SEALIFT TANKSHIPS INCORPORATED—See Sealift Holdings Inc.; *U.S. Private*, pg. 3585
SEAPEAK LLC—See Stonepeak Partners L.P.; *U.S. Private*, pg. 3829
SEASPAN FERRIES CORPORATION—See Washington Corporations; *U.S. Private*, pg. 4446
SEA TRADE INTERNATIONAL, INC.—See China COSCO Shipping Corporation Limited; *Int'l*, pg. 1494
SERVICIOS DEDICADOS DE TRANSPORTACION, S.A. DE C.V.—See Grupo TMM, S.A.B.; *Int'l*, pg. 3137
SFL CORPORATION LTD.—See Frontline plc; *Int'l*, pg. 2796
SHORELAND TRANSPORT INC.—See Cooke, Inc.; *Int'l*, pg. 1788
SINOTRANS CONTAINER LINES COMPANY LIMITED—See China Merchants Group Limited; *Int'l*, pg. 1522
SOCIETE MARITIME GENMAR SARL—See Albert Ballin KG; *Int'l*, pg. 296
SOLVTRANS AS—See Brookfield Corporation; *Int'l*, pg. 1183
SOLVTRANS CHILE S.A.—See Brookfield Corporation; *Int'l*, pg. 1183
SOMOCAR OVERSEAS N.V.—See Coeclerici S.p.A.; *Int'l*, pg. 1689
SUNMAR SHIPPING, INC.; *U.S. Private*, pg. 3868
SUN YEE GODOWN&TRANSPORTATION CO. LTD—See China Merchants Group Limited; *Int'l*, pg. 1523
SUPERFAST DEKA MC.—See Attica Group; *Int'l*, pg. 696
SUPREME VOYAGER PTE. LTD.—See Hoe Leong Corporation Ltd.; *Int'l*, pg. 3439
TAL INTERNATIONAL GROUP, INC—See Brookfield Infrastructure Partners L.P.; *Int'l*, pg. 1190
TEAM TANKERS MANAGEMENT AS—See Team Tankers International Ltd.; *U.S. Private*, pg. 3950
TEAM TANKERS MANAGEMENT A/S—See Team Tankers International Ltd.; *U.S. Private*, pg. 3950

TEAM TANKERS MANAGEMENT LLC—See Team Tankers International Ltd.; *U.S. Private*, pg. 3950
TEAM TANKERS MANAGEMENT PTE. LTD.—See Team Tankers International Ltd.; *U.S. Private*, pg. 3950
TEAM TANKERS MANAGEMENT S.A.—See Team Tankers International Ltd.; *U.S. Private*, pg. 3950
TEAM TANKERS (USA) LLC—See Team Tankers International Ltd.; *U.S. Private*, pg. 3950
TERAS 336 PTE LTD—See Ezion Holdings Limited; *Int'l*, pg. 2594
TERAS CONQUEST 2 PTE LTD—See Ezion Holdings Limited; *Int'l*, pg. 2594
TERAS OFFSHORE PTE LTD—See Ezion Holdings Limited; *Int'l*, pg. 2594
TERMINAL ESPECIALIZADA DE CONTENEDORES—See Grupo TMM, S.A.B.; *Int'l*, pg. 3138
TEXTAINER EQUIPMENT RESALE—See Stonepeak Partners L.P.; *U.S. Private*, pg. 3829
THUN TANKERS B.V.—See Erik Thun AB; *Int'l*, pg. 2493
TMM AGENCIAS ACAPULCO—See Grupo TMM, S.A.B.; *Int'l*, pg. 3137
TMM AGENCIAS COATZACOALCOS—See Grupo TMM, S.A.B.; *Int'l*, pg. 3137
TMM AGENCIAS DOS BOCAS—See Grupo TMM, S.A.B.; *Int'l*, pg. 3137
TMM CAR CARRIER CIUDAD DE MEXICO—See Grupo TMM, S.A.B.; *Int'l*, pg. 3138
TMM LOGISTICS CIUDAD DE MEXICO—See Grupo TMM, S.A.B.; *Int'l*, pg. 3138
TMM LOGISTICS MONTERREY—See Grupo TMM, S.A.B.; *Int'l*, pg. 3138
TOLLO SHIPPING CO. S.A.—See Compania Sudamericana de Vapores, S.A.; *Int'l*, pg. 1749
TOURISM & SHIPPING SERVICES SARL—See Albert Ballin KG; *Int'l*, pg. 296
TRANS GLOBAL S.R.L.—See Albert Ballin KG; *Int'l*, pg. 296
TRANSLINK SHIPPING INC.; *U.S. Private*, pg. 4208
TRANSMERES S.A. DE C.V.—See Albert Ballin KG; *Int'l*, pg. 296
TRANSOCEANA CIA. LTDA.—See Albert Ballin KG; *Int'l*, pg. 296
TRANSPORCIAN MARITIMA MEXICANA, S.A. DE C.V.—See Grupo TMM, S.A.B.; *Int'l*, pg. 3137
TROPICAL SHIPPING & CONSTRUCTION COMPANY LIMITED—See Saltchuk Resources Inc.; *U.S. Private*, pg. 3534
UNITED ARAB SHIPPING AGENCIES COMPANY (EMIRATES)—See Albert Ballin KG; *Int'l*, pg. 296
UNITED ARAB SHIPPING AGENCY COMPANY (SINGAPORE)—See Albert Ballin KG; *Int'l*, pg. 297
U.N. RO-RO ISLETMELERI A.S.—See DFDS A/S; *Int'l*, pg. 2095
US LINES—See CMA CGM S.A.; *Int'l*, pg. 1666
UTC OVERSEAS, INC.; *U.S. Private*, pg. 4325
VANSHI SHIPPING PTE. LTD—See Adani Enterprises Limited; *Int'l*, pg. 125
VASSILOPOULOS SHIPPING LTD.—See Albert Ballin KG; *Int'l*, pg. 297
VICTORY MARITIME INC.—See Sealift Holdings Inc.; *U.S. Private*, pg. 3585
VR SHIPPING (ARUBA) N.V.—See Albert Ballin KG; *Int'l*, pg. 297
VR SHIPPING NV—See Albert Ballin KG; *Int'l*, pg. 297
WASHINGTON MARINE GROUP—See Washington Corporations; *U.S. Private*, pg. 4446
WATERMAN STEAMSHIP CORPORATION—See AIP, LLC; *U.S. Private*, pg. 136
WIJGULA B.V.—See Dubai World Corporation; *Int'l*, pg. 2221
WSS ALARBAB SHIPPING CO.—See Albert Ballin KG; *Int'l*, pg. 297
YOUNG BROTHERS, LIMITED—See Saltchuk Resources Inc.; *U.S. Private*, pg. 3534
ZHANJIANG PORT (GROUP) CO., LTD.—See China Merchants Group Limited; *Int'l*, pg. 1523

483112 — DEEP SEA PASSENGER TRANSPORTATION

ANEK LINES SA—See Attica Group; *Int'l*, pg. 696
AS TALLINK BALTIC—See AS Infortar; *Int'l*, pg. 590
ATTICA GROUP; *Int'l*, pg. 696
BLUE LAGOON CRUISES HOLDINGS PTE LIMITED—See Fijian Holdings Limited; *Int'l*, pg. 2662
BLUE STAR MARITIME S.A.—See Attica Group; *Int'l*, pg. 696
BOHAI FERRY (QINGDAO) INTERNATIONAL TRAVEL SERVICE CO., LTD.—See Bohai Ferry Group Co., Ltd.; *Int'l*, pg. 1100
CARNIVAL CRUISE LINES—See Carnival Corporation; *U.S. Public*, pg. 438
CARNIVAL (UK) LIMITED—See Carnival Corporation; *U.S. Public*, pg. 437
CLIPPER NAVIGATION LTD.—See FRS GmbH & Co. KG; *Int'l*, pg. 2797
COSTA CRUISE LINES INC.—See Carnival Corporation; *U.S. Public*, pg. 438
COSTA CRUZEIROS AGENCIA MARITIMA E TURISMO LTDA.—See Carnival Corporation; *U.S. Public*, pg. 438
CRYSTAL CRUISES, LLC—See Genting Hong Kong Limited; *Int'l*, pg. 2929
CUNARD LINE LTD.—See Carnival Corporation; *U.S. Public*, pg. 438
DFDS (DEUTSCHLAND) GMBH—See DFDS A/S; *Int'l*, pg. 2094
ENCORE CRUISES—See H.I.S. Co., Ltd.; *Int'l*, pg. 3195
FLOATEL INTERNATIONAL AB—See Floatel International Ltd.; *Int'l*, pg. 2707
FRED. OLSEN CRUISE LINES LTD.—See Fred. Olsen & Co.; *Int'l*, pg. 2768
GRANDI NAVI VELOCI S.P.A.; *Int'l*, pg. 3058
HAPAG-LLOYD KREUZFAHRTEN GMBH—See Royal Caribbean Cruises Ltd.; *U.S. Public*, pg. 1815
HCC HANSEATIC CRUISE CENTERS GMBH—See Hamburger Hafen und Logistik AG; *Int'l*, pg. 3236
HOLLAND AMERICA LINE N.V.—See Carnival Corporation; *U.S. Public*, pg. 438
KOSMAS GROUP INTERNATIONAL INC.; *U.S. Private*, pg. 2344
MOSQUITO FLEET, LLC—See FRS GmbH & Co. KG; *Int'l*, pg. 2797
MS DEUTSCHLAND BETEILIGUNGSGESELLSCHAFT MBH—See Callista Private Equity GmbH & Co. KG; *Int'l*, pg. 1265
MS HAMMONIA MASSILIA SCHIFFAHRTS GMBH & CO. KG—See HCI Hammonia Shipping AG; *Int'l*, pg. 3297
NCL (BAHAMAS) LTD.—See Norwegian Cruise Line Holdings Ltd.; *U.S. Public*, pg. 1543
NORFOLKLINE B.V.—See DFDS A/S; *Int'l*, pg. 2095
ODYSSEY MARINE EXPLORATION, INC.; *U.S. Public*, pg. 1564
OOO TALLINK-RU—See AS Infortar; *Int'l*, pg. 590
ORION EXPEDITION CRUISES PTY. LTD.—See KSL Capital Partners, LLC; *U.S. Private*, pg. 2355
OU HT LAEVATEENINDUS—See AS Infortar; *Int'l*, pg. 590
PACIFIC MARINE & SUPPLY CO. LTD. INC.; *U.S. Private*, pg. 3068
P&O PRINCESS CRUISES INTERNATIONAL LIMITED—See Carnival Corporation; *U.S. Public*, pg. 438
PRESTIGE CRUISES INTERNATIONAL, INC.—See Norwegian Cruise Line Holdings Ltd.; *U.S. Public*, pg. 1543
PRINCESS CRUISES—See Carnival Corporation; *U.S. Public*, pg. 438
PULLMANTUR SA—See Royal Caribbean Cruises Ltd.; *U.S. Public*, pg. 1815
RCL CRUISES LTD.—See Royal Caribbean Cruises Ltd.; *U.S. Public*, pg. 1815
REEDEREI PETER DEILMANN GMBH—See Callista Private Equity GmbH & Co. KG; *Int'l*, pg. 1265
ROYAL CARIBBEAN CRUISES (ASIA) PTE. LTD.—See Royal Caribbean Cruises Ltd.; *U.S. Public*, pg. 1815
ROYAL CARIBBEAN CRUISES (AUSTRALIA) PTY. LTD—See Royal Caribbean Cruises Ltd.; *U.S. Public*, pg. 1815
ROYAL CARIBBEAN CRUISES LTD.; *U.S. Public*, pg. 1815
ROYAL HYWAY TOURS, INC.—See Carnival Corporation; *U.S. Public*, pg. 438
SEACOR MARINE LLC—See AIP, LLC; *U.S. Private*, pg. 136
SEADREAM YACHT CLUB, INC.; *U.S. Private*, pg. 3584
SIA HT SHIPMANAGEMENT—See AS Infortar; *Int'l*, pg. 590
SILVERSEA CRUISES LTD.—See Royal Caribbean Cruises Ltd.; *U.S. Public*, pg. 1815
SILVERSEA CRUISES LTD. - THE AMERICAS REGIONAL OFFICE—See Royal Caribbean Cruises Ltd.; *U.S. Public*, pg. 1815
STAZIONI MARITIME S.P.A.—See Carnival Corporation; *U.S. Public*, pg. 438
TALLINK SILJA GMBH—See AS Infortar; *Int'l*, pg. 590
TALLINK SILJA OY—See AS Infortar; *Int'l*, pg. 590
TERMINAL NAPOLI S.P.A.—See Carnival Corporation; *U.S. Public*, pg. 438

483113 — COASTAL AND GREAT LAKES FREIGHT TRANSPORTATION

ALASKA MARINE LINES, INC.—See Lynden Incorporated; *U.S. Private*, pg. 2521
ALASKAN MARINE LINES, INC.—See Lynden Incorporated; *U.S. Private*, pg. 2521
AMERICAN STEAMSHIP COMPANY—See AIP, LLC; *U.S. Private*, pg. 135
ANDRIE, INC.—See Auxo Investment Partners, LLC; *U.S. Private*, pg. 402
BP OIL SHIPPING COMPANY—See BP plc; *Int'l*, pg. 1127
BP OIL SHIPPING COMPANY USA—See BP plc; *Int'l*, pg. 1127
BP OIL SHIPPING COMPANY USA—See BP plc; *Int'l*, pg. 1127
CEMEX UK MARINE LTD.—See CEMEX, S.A.B. de C.V.; *Int'l*, pg. 1399
CHELSEA LOGISTICS AND INFRASTRUCTURE HOLDINGS CORP.; *Int'l*, pg. 1460
CLEAN PRODUCTS INTERNATIONAL LTD.—See Saltchuk

483113 — COASTAL AND GREAT L...

Resources Inc.; *U.S. Private*, pg. 3534
DEALER'S AUTO AUCTION GROUP; *U.S. Private*, pg. 1182
DET NORSKE VERITAS EIENDOM AS—See DNV GL Group AS; *Int'l*, pg. 2151
DET NORSKE VERITAS EIENDOM AS - TRONDHEIM—See DNV GL Group AS; *Int'l*, pg. 2151
DET NORSKE VERITAS TECHNOLOGY SERVICES—See DNV GL Group AS; *Int'l*, pg. 2151
DNV ALESUND—See DNV GL Group AS; *Int'l*, pg. 2148
DNV BERGEN—See DNV GL Group AS; *Int'l*, pg. 2148
DNV CERTIFICATION—See DNV GL Group AS; *Int'l*, pg. 2151
DNV EIENDOM—See DNV GL Group AS; *Int'l*, pg. 2148
DNV FLORO—See DNV GL Group AS; *Int'l*, pg. 2148
DNV FORDE—See DNV GL Group AS; *Int'l*, pg. 2148
DNV FREDRIKSTAD—See DNV GL Group AS; *Int'l*, pg. 2148
DNV GL—See DNV GL Group AS; *Int'l*, pg. 2151
DNV HAUGESUND—See DNV GL Group AS; *Int'l*, pg. 2150
DNV KRISTIANSAND S—See DNV GL Group AS; *Int'l*, pg. 2150
DNV KRISTIANSUND N—See DNV GL Group AS; *Int'l*, pg. 2150
DNV MARITIME NORTH AMERICA NEW ORLEANS—See DNV GL Group AS; *Int'l*, pg. 2151
DNV PORSGRUNN—See DNV GL Group AS; *Int'l*, pg. 2150
DNV REGION NORGE AS—See DNV GL Group AS; *Int'l*, pg. 2150
DNV REGION NORGE AS—See DNV GL Group AS; *Int'l*, pg. 2150
DNV STORD—See DNV GL Group AS; *Int'l*, pg. 2151
DNV TROMSO—See DNV GL Group AS; *Int'l*, pg. 2151
DNV ULSTEINVIK—See DNV GL Group AS; *Int'l*, pg. 2151
DYER AUTO AUCTION INC.; *U.S. Private*, pg. 1296
FINNLINES DEUTSCHLAND GMBH—See Grimaldi Group SpA; *Int'l*, pg. 3085
FINNLINES UK LIMITED—See Grimaldi Group SpA; *Int'l*, pg. 3085
GC RIEBER SHIPPING ASA—See GC Rieber AS; *Int'l*, pg. 2894
GRAND RIVER NAVIGATION COMPANY, INC.—See AIP, LLC; *U.S. Private*, pg. 135
GULF NAVIGATION HOLDING PJSC; *Int'l*, pg. 3181
HARBOUR-LINK GROUP BERHAD; *Int'l*, pg. 3272
INLAND LAKES MANAGEMENT INC.; *U.S. Private*, pg. 2078
KEYSTONE SHIPPING CO.; *U.S. Private*, pg. 2300
LOWER LAKES TOWING LTD.—See AIP, LLC; *U.S. Private*, pg. 135
MARBULK SHIPPING INC.—See Algoma Central Corporation; *Int'l*, pg. 318
MARINE TRANSPORTATION SERVICES, INC.; *U.S. Private*, pg. 2575
MARITIME NORTH AMERICA JACKSONVILLE—See DNV GL Group AS; *Int'l*, pg. 2151
MEDLEVANT SHIPPING S.A.E.—See Albert Ballin KG; *Int'l*, pg. 295
MO I RANA—See DNV GL Group AS; *Int'l*, pg. 2151
MORAN TOWING OF TEXAS INC.—See Moran Towing Corporation; *U.S. Private*, pg. 2782
MULTISERV LOGISTICS LIMITED—See Enviri Corporation; *U.S. Public*, pg. 781
MYKONOS TANKER LLC—See Saltchuk Resources Inc.; *U.S. Private*, pg. 3534
NORTHLAND HOLDINGS INC.; *U.S. Private*, pg. 2955
NORTHLAND SERVICES, INC.—See Lynden Incorporated; *U.S. Private*, pg. 2521
OLD DOMINION FREIGHT LINE, INC.; *U.S. Public*, pg. 1566
THE PASHA GROUP; *U.S. Private*, pg. 4091
PENGUIN MARINE BOATS SERVICES L.L.C.—See Dymon Asia Capital (Singapore) Pte. Ltd; *Int'l*, pg. 2238
PIRAEUS PORT AUTHORITY S.A.—See China COSCO Shipping Corporation Limited; *Int'l*, pg. 1496
POLAR TANKERS, INC.—See ConocoPhillips; *U.S. Public*, pg. 569
TOTEM OCEAN TRAILER EXPRESS—See Saltchuk Resources Inc.; *U.S. Private*, pg. 3534
UNION PACIFIC RAILROAD—See Union Pacific Corporation; *U.S. Public*, pg. 2227
UPS SUPPLY CHAIN SOLUTIONS, INC.—See United Parcel Service, Inc.; *U.S. Public*, pg. 2234
VITUS MARINE LLC; *U.S. Private*, pg. 4406

483114 — COASTAL AND GREAT LAKES PASSENGER TRANSPORTATION

AS TALLINK GRUPP—See AS Infortar; *Int'l*, pg. 590
BEAUFORD MARINE PTE LTD—See Chuan Hup Holdings Limited; *Int'l*, pg. 1589
COMPANIA TRASMEDITERRANEA, S.A.—See Anarafe SL; *Int'l*, pg. 447
COSTA CROCIERE S.P.A.—See Carnival Corporation; *U.S. Public*, pg. 438
CUNARD LINE LTD. - UK OFFICE—See Carnival Corporation; *U.S. Public*, pg. 438

GOSPORT FERRY LIMITED—See FIH group plc; *Int'l*, pg. 2661
HELLENIC SEAWAYS SINGLE MEMBER MARITIME S.A.—See Attica Group; *Int'l*, pg. 696
LAKE TAHOE CRUISES, INC.—See Aramark; *U.S. Public*, pg. 176
OSG AMERICA, L.P.—See Saltchuk Resources Inc.; *U.S. Private*, pg. 3534
P&O FERRIES HOLDINGS LIMITED—See Dubai World Corporation; *Int'l*, pg. 2220
PORTSEA HARBOUR COMPANY LIMITED—See FIH group plc; *Int'l*, pg. 2661
STAR CRUISES (HK) LIMITED—See Genting Hong Kong Limited; *Int'l*, pg. 2929
SUPERFAST FERRIES SINGLE MEMBER MARITIME S.A.—See Attica Group; *Int'l*, pg. 696
WIGHTLINK LIMITED—See Colliers International Group Inc.; *Int'l*, pg. 1700
WINDSTAR CRUISES, LLC—See The Anschutz Corporation; *U.S. Private*, pg. 3987

483211 — INLAND WATER FREIGHT TRANSPORTATION

ALABAMA BULK TERMINAL INC.—See Hunt Consolidated, Inc.; *U.S. Private*, pg. 2008
ALTA TRANSPORTATION, LLC—See World Kinect Corporation; *U.S. Public*, pg. 2380
ALTER BARGE LINE INC.; *U.S. Private*, pg. 206
ALTER COMPANIES; *U.S. Private*, pg. 206
AMERICAN COMMERCIAL LINES INC.—See Platinum Equity, LLC; *U.S. Private*, pg. 3201
AMERICAN RIVER TRANSPORTATION COMPANY—See Archer-Daniels-Midland Company; *U.S. Public*, pg. 183
ANTWERP TOWAGE NV—See Fairplay Schleppdampfschiffs-Reederei Richard Borchard GmbH; *Int'l*, pg. 2609
BEIJING GLOVIS WAREHOUSING & TRANSPORTATION CO., LTD.—See Hyundai Glovis Co., Ltd.; *Int'l*, pg. 3556
B+H EQUIMAR SINGAPORE PTE. LTD.—See B+H Ocean Carriers Ltd.; *Int'l*, pg. 784
BOCS BREMEN OVERSEAS CHARTERING AND SHIPPING GMBH; *Int'l*, pg. 1097
BRAEMAR SEASCOPE LIMITED—See Braemar PLC; *Int'l*, pg. 1135
CHASEN SINO-SIN (BEIJING) HI TECH SERVICES PTE LTD—See Chasen Holdings Limited; *Int'l*, pg. 1457
CHATHAM TOWING COMPANY, INC.—See Colonial Group, Inc.; *U.S. Private*, pg. 971
COMPANIA DE NAVIGATIE FLUVIALA ROMANA NAVROM S.A. GALATI; *Int'l*, pg. 1749
CROUNSE CORPORATION; *U.S. Private*, pg. 1108
DIAMOND'S TRANSFER LTD—See Armour Transportation Systems; *Int'l*, pg. 575
ECU-LINE N.V.—See Allcargo Logistics Limited; *Int'l*, pg. 334
FRANCESCO PARISI GMBH - COLOGNE—See Francesco Parisi S.p.A.; *Int'l*, pg. 2759
FRANCESCO PARISI GMBH—See Francesco Parisi S.p.A.; *Int'l*, pg. 2759
FRANCESCO PARISI S.A.G.L.—See Francesco Parisi S.p.A.; *Int'l*, pg. 2759
FRANCESCO PARISI S.P.A. - MONFALCONE—See Francesco Parisi S.p.A.; *Int'l*, pg. 2759
FRANCESCO PARISI S.P.A. - PONTEBBA—See Francesco Parisi S.p.A.; *Int'l*, pg. 2759
FRANCESCO PARISI S.P.A. - RONCHI DEI LEGIONARI—See Francesco Parisi S.p.A.; *Int'l*, pg. 2759
FRANCESCO PARISI S.P.A. - SEDICO—See Francesco Parisi S.p.A.; *Int'l*, pg. 2759
FRANCESCO PARISI S.P.A. - VENEZIA-MESTRE—See Francesco Parisi S.p.A.; *Int'l*, pg. 2759
FRONTLINE MANAGEMENT AS—See Frontline plc; *Int'l*, pg. 2796
GENCO SHIPPING A/S—See Genco Shipping & Trading Limited; *U.S. Public*, pg. 911
GENCO SHIPPING & TRADING LIMITED; *U.S. Public*, pg. 911
GIURGIU NAV SA; *Int'l*, pg. 2979
GLOBAL AUTO PROCESSING SERVICES GEORGIA LLC—See Hyundai Glovis Co., Ltd.; *Int'l*, pg. 3557
GLOBAL AUTO PROCESSING SERVICES, LLC—See Hyundai Glovis Co., Ltd.; *Int'l*, pg. 3557
GLOBAL AUTO PROCESSING SERVICES—See Hyundai Glovis Co., Ltd.; *Int'l*, pg. 3557
GLOBAL LOGISTICS NEW JERSEY, LLC—See Hyundai Glovis Co., Ltd.; *Int'l*, pg. 3557
GLOVIS AMERICA INC.—See Hyundai Glovis Co., Ltd.; *Int'l*, pg. 3556
GLOVIS AUSTRALIA PTY. LTD.—See Hyundai Glovis Co., Ltd.; *Int'l*, pg. 3556
GLOVIS BRAZIL LOGISTICA LTDA.—See Hyundai Glovis Co., Ltd.; *Int'l*, pg. 3556
GLOVIS CANADA INC.—See Hyundai Glovis Co., Ltd.; *Int'l*, pg. 3556
GLOVIS CZECH REPUBLIC S.R.O.—See Hyundai Glovis Co., Ltd.; *Int'l*, pg. 3556

GLOVIS EUROPE GMBH—See Hyundai Glovis Co., Ltd.; *Int'l*, pg. 3556
GLOVIS GEORGIA, LLC—See Hyundai Glovis Co., Ltd.; *Int'l*, pg. 3556
GLOVIS HOLDINGS MONGOL—See Hyundai Glovis Co., Ltd.; *Int'l*, pg. 3556
GLOVIS INDIA PVT. LTD.—See Hyundai Glovis Co., Ltd.; *Int'l*, pg. 3556
GLOVIS RUSSIA, LLC—See Hyundai Glovis Co., Ltd.; *Int'l*, pg. 3557
GLOVIS SLOVAKIA S.R.O.—See Hyundai Glovis Co., Ltd.; *Int'l*, pg. 3557
GLOVIS TURKEY LOJISTIK TIC. SAN. VE TIC. LTD. STI.—See Hyundai Glovis Co., Ltd.; *Int'l*, pg. 3557
GREEN MANAGEMENT SP. Z O.O.—See Caiano AS; *Int'l*, pg. 1252
HANIEL REEDEREI HOLDING GMBH—See Franz Haniel & Cie. GmbH; *Int'l*, pg. 2763
HARLEY MARINE SERVICES INC.; *U.S. Private*, pg. 1865
HORNBECK OFFSHORE SERVICES, INC.; *U.S. Private*, pg. 1983
INGRAM BARGE COMPANY—See Ingram Industries, Inc.; *U.S. Private*, pg. 2076
INTERLAKE STEAMSHIP COMPANY INC.—See Mormac Marine Group, Inc.; *U.S. Private*, pg. 2785
INTERMARINE DENMARK APS—See Intermarine, Inc.; *U.S. Private*, pg. 2112
INTERMARINE PROJECT SERVICES S.L.—See Intermarine, Inc.; *U.S. Private*, pg. 2112
KIRBY INLAND MARINE, LP—See Kirby Corporation; *U.S. Public*, pg. 1235
KIRBY INLAND MARINE—See Kirby Corporation; *U.S. Public*, pg. 1235
LA. CARRIERS, L.L.C.; *U.S. Private*, pg. 2370
LAMBERT'S POINT BARGE COMPANY, INC.—See Norfolk Southern Corporation; *U.S. Public*, pg. 1536
LOWER LAKES TOWING (17) LTD.—See AIP, LLC; *U.S. Private*, pg. 135
MAERSK SUPPLY SERVICE A/S—See DOF Group ASA; *Int'l*, pg. 2154
MARQUETTE TRANSPORTATION CO.; *U.S. Private*, pg. 2587
M/G TRANSPORT SERVICES, INC.—See Auxo Investment Partners, LLC; *U.S. Private*, pg. 402
NAVROM BAC S.R.L.—See Compania de Navigatie Fluviala Romana NAVROM S.A. Galati; *Int'l*, pg. 1749
NAVROM CENTRU DE AFACERI S.R.L.—See Compania de Navigatie Fluviala Romana NAVROM S.A. Galati; *Int'l*, pg. 1749
NAVROM DELTA S.A.—See Compania de Navigatie Fluviala Romana NAVROM S.A. Galati; *Int'l*, pg. 1749
NAVROM SHIPYARD S.R.L.—See Compania de Navigatie Fluviala Romana NAVROM S.A. Galati; *Int'l*, pg. 1749
OSPREY LINE, LLC—See Kirby Corporation; *U.S. Public*, pg. 1236
PAN MARINE DO BRASIL LTDA.—See Tidewater Inc.; *U.S. Public*, pg. 2158
REDERIJ CEMENT-TANKVAART B.V.—See Heidelberg Materials AG; *Int'l*, pg. 3319
REINAUER TRANSPORTATION COMPANIES; *U.S. Private*, pg. 3391
RIVERLAND RESOURCES INC.; *U.S. Private*, pg. 3444
SCF MARINE INC.—See AIP, LLC; *U.S. Private*, pg. 136
SEAFREIGHT AGENCIES INC.; *U.S. Private*, pg. 3584
SULPHUR CARRIERS, INC.—See AIP, LLC; *U.S. Private*, pg. 136
TERRAL RIVERSERVICE, INC.; *U.S. Private*, pg. 3971
THEODOR BUSCHMANN GMBH & CO KG—See Fairplay Schleppdampfschiffs-Reederei Richard Borchard GmbH; *Int'l*, pg. 2609
TIANJIN GLOVIS AUTOMOTIVE PARTS CO., LTD.—See Hyundai Glovis Co., Ltd.; *Int'l*, pg. 3557
TIDEWATER BARGE LINES INC.—See Tidewater Holdings, Inc.; *U.S. Private*, pg. 4168
TIDEWATER DE MEXICO, S.A. DE C.V.—See Tidewater Inc.; *U.S. Public*, pg. 2158
TIDEWATER HOLDINGS, INC.; *U.S. Private*, pg. 4168
TIDEWATER INC.; *U.S. Public*, pg. 2158
TIDEWATER (INDIA) PRIVATE LIMITED—See Tidewater Inc.; *U.S. Public*, pg. 2158
TIDEWATER MARINE INTERNATIONAL PTE. LTD.—See Tidewater Inc.; *U.S. Public*, pg. 2158
TRANSMODE LTD.—See Infinera Corporation; *U.S. Public*, pg. 1117
TROMS OFFSHORE FLEET 2 AS—See Tidewater Inc.; *U.S. Public*, pg. 2158
WILSON ASA—See Caiano AS; *Int'l*, pg. 1252
WINDCAT WORKBOATS B.V.—See AIP, LLC; *U.S. Private*, pg. 137

483212 — INLAND WATER PASSENGER TRANSPORTATION

ANARAFE SL; *Int'l*, pg. 447
BINTAN RESORT FERRIES PRIVATE LIMITED—See Gallant Venture Ltd.; *Int'l*, pg. 2874
BRAEMAR SEASCOPE INDIA PRIVATE LIMITED—See

N.A.I.C.S. INDEX

484110 — GENERAL FREIGHT TRU...

Braemar PLC; *Int'l*, pg. 1135
BRITISH COLUMBIA FERRY SERVICES INC; *Int'l*, pg. 1169
CROSS-SOUND FERRY SERVICES; *U.S. Private*, pg. 1105
DAMEN MARINE SERVICES BV—See Damen Shipyards Group; *Int'l*, pg. 1956
FINANGLIA FERRIES LIMITED—See Grimaldi Group SpA; *Int'l*, pg. 3085
FRS GMBH & CO. KG; *Int'l*, pg. 2797
GCI OUTDOOR, INC.—See Centre Partners Management LLC; *U.S. Private*, pg. 828
HAINAN STRAIT SHIPPING CO., LTD.; *Int'l*, pg. 3212
HONG KONG FERRY (HOLDINGS) CO. LTD.—See Henderson Land Development Co. Ltd.; *Int'l*, pg. 3344
PRECISION DOORS & HARDWARE FREDERICKSBURG—See Platinum Equity, LLC; *U.S. Private*, pg. 3209
THE STEAMSHIP AUTHORITY; *U.S. Private*, pg. 4121
WEISSE FLOTTE GMBH—See FRS GmbH & Co. KG; *Int'l*, pg. 2797
WIJKOPENAUTOS B.V.—See AUTO1 Group SE; *Int'l*, pg. 725

484110 — GENERAL FREIGHT TRUCKING, LOCAL

1-800-PACK-RAT, LLC; *U.S. Private*, pg. 1
A&A MACHINERY MOVING, INC.—See Olympus Partners; *U.S. Private*, pg. 3013
ABF GLOBAL SUPPLY CHAIN, INC.—See ArcBest Corporation; *U.S. Public*, pg. 180
ACTION RESOURCES INC.; *U.S. Private*, pg. 67
ADAMS ENTERPRISES (1993) LTD; *Int'l*, pg. 124
ADDICKS & KREYE CONTAINER SERVICE GMBH & CO. KG—See A.P. Moller-Maersk A/S; *Int'l*, pg. 26
ADDICKS & KREYE HOLDING GMBH; *Int'l*, pg. 128
A. DUIE PYLE INC.; *U.S. Private*, pg. 23
AIR BUSINESS LTD—See An Post LLC; *Int'l*, pg. 443
AKROTEX TRUCKING INC—See Akrotex, Inc.; *U.S. Private*, pg. 146
ALBERT SCHUCK GMBH & CO. KG; *Int'l*, pg. 297
ALL PRO FREIGHT SYSTEMS INC.; *U.S. Private*, pg. 171
ALL-STATE EXPRESS, INC.; *U.S. Private*, pg. 173
AL MUHAIDIB LAND TRANSPORT COMPANY—See A.K. Al-Muhaidib & Sons Group of Companies; *Int'l*, pg. 24
AL-TA'ALUF GENERAL TRANSPORTATION CO. LTD.—See Eng. Shabah Al-Shammery & Partners Co.; *Int'l*, pg. 2426
AMBASSADOR WORLDWIDE MOVING, INC.—See Interstate Group Holdings, Inc.; *U.S. Private*, pg. 2125
AMERICAN BULK COMMODITIES INC.; *U.S. Private*, pg. 225
AMERICAN TERMINALS DISTRIBUTION CORP—See H&M International Transportation Inc.; *U.S. Private*, pg. 1823
AMWAT MOVING WAREHOUSING & STORAGE; *U.S. Private*, pg. 269
ANCON KOT LOGISTICS—See Ancon Marine, LLC; *U.S. Private*, pg. 274
ANCON MARINE, LLC; *U.S. Private*, pg. 274
ARG TRUCKING CORP—See Wadhams Enterprises Inc.; *U.S. Private*, pg. 4424
ARL NETWORK—See US 1 Industries, Inc.; *U.S. Private*, pg. 4316
ARR CRAIB TRANSPORT LTD.—See Gregory Distribution (Holdings) Limited; *Int'l*, pg. 3078
ASAFFA LOGISTICS LLC—See A'Saffa Foods S.A.O.G; *Int'l*, pg. 19
ASAGAMI CORPORATION; *Int'l*, pg. 592
ASKUL LOGIST CORPORATION—See ASKUL Corporation; *Int'l*, pg. 625
ASSOCIATED TRANSFER & STORAGE INC.; *U.S. Private*, pg. 357
ASSURED AGGREGATES COMPANY; *U.S. Private*, pg. 359
ASSURED TRANSPORTATION SERVICES; *U.S. Private*, pg. 359
ASTA AG—See Arbonia AG; *Int'l*, pg. 538
AWESOME TRANSPORTATION, INC.—See Western Beef, Inc.; *U.S. Private*, pg. 4491
AZUMA LOGITEC CO., LTD.—See Azuma Shipping Co., Ltd.; *Int'l*, pg. 781
AZUMA TRANSPORT SERVICES (THAILAND) CO., LTD.—See Azuma Shipping Co., Ltd.; *Int'l*, pg. 782
BEDFORD LOGISTICS, LLC—See Ryder System, Inc.; *U.S. Public*, pg. 1828
BEKINS MOVING SOLUTIONS, INC.; *U.S. Private*, pg. 516
BELSHIPS ASA; *Int'l*, pg. 968
BEST CARTAGE INC.—See Best Logistics Group, Inc.; *U.S. Private*, pg. 543
BEST COURIER & DELIVERY SERVICE—See NewSpring Capital LLC; *U.S. Private*, pg. 2918
BEST DISTRIBUTION; *U.S. Private*, pg. 542
BEST MAYFLOWER—See UniGroup, Inc.; *U.S. Private*, pg. 4283
BEVERLY HILLS TRANSFER & STORAGE CO.; *U.S. Private*, pg. 547

B-H TRANSFER CO; *U.S. Private*, pg. 419
BIG CHILL DISTRIBUTION LIMITED—See Freightways Group Limited; *Int'l*, pg. 2771
BIG RED EXPRESS TRUCKING LLC; *U.S. Private*, pg. 553
B.J. CECIL TRUCKING INC.; *U.S. Private*, pg. 420
BOOKER TRANSPORTATION SERVICES, INC.; *U.S. Private*, pg. 615
BRASSEUR TRANSPORT INC.; *Int'l*, pg. 1140
BRINK'S CHILE, S.A.—See The Brink's Company; *U.S. Public*, pg. 2042
BRINK'S GLOBAL SERVICES KOREA LIMITED—See The Brink's Company; *U.S. Public*, pg. 2042
BROWN TRANSFER COMPANY; *U.S. Private*, pg. 669
BT INCORPORATED; *U.S. Private*, pg. 675
BTR INCORPORATED; *U.S. Private*, pg. 675
BUD INDUSTRIES—See Bud Industries, Inc.; *U.S. Private*, pg. 679
BWP TRANSPORT, INC.—See Wind Point Advisors LLC; *U.S. Private*, pg. 4535
CABARAN PERSPEKTIF SDN. BHD.—See HPI Resources Berhad; *Int'l*, pg. 3500
CABLE ENTERPRISES INC.; *U.S. Private*, pg. 711
CAPITAL DELIVERY SYSTEM INC.—See NewSpring Capital LLC; *U.S. Private*, pg. 2918
CARDINAL LOGISTICS MANAGEMENT CORP—See Ryder System, Inc.; *U.S. Public*, pg. 1828
CARGO CARRIERS LTD.; *Int'l*, pg. 1325
CB TRANSPORT, INC.—See Banco Bilbao Vizcaya Argentaria, S.A.; *Int'l*, pg. 817
C. COAKLEY RELOCATION SYSTEMS, INC.; *U.S. Private*, pg. 705
CENTENNIAL, COLORADO STORAGE & MOVING—See Johnson Storage & Moving Company; *U.S. Private*, pg. 2229
CENTRAL MOVING & STORAGE CO.; *U.S. Private*, pg. 822
CENTRO DE FOMENTO PARA INCLUSION, S. DE R.L. DE C.V.—See Cummins Inc.; *U.S. Public*, pg. 605
CENTROTRANS-TRANZIT D.D.; *Int'l*, pg. 1415
CENTURY MOVING & STORAGE INC—See Johnson Storage & Moving Company; *U.S. Private*, pg. 2229
CHALLENGER MOTOR FREIGHT INC.; *Int'l*, pg. 1438
CHAMBERS & COOK FREIGHT LTD.; *Int'l*, pg. 1439
CHARGEPOINT TECHNOLOGY LTD.; *Int'l*, pg. 1448
CHEVALLIER SUD; *Int'l*, pg. 1474
C.H. ROBINSON FREIGHT SERVICES (VIETNAM) COMPANY LIMITED—See C.H. Robinson Worldwide, Inc.; *Int'l*, pg. 415
CIRCLE A CONSTRUCTION INC.; *U.S. Private*, pg. 899
COASTAL PACIFIC XPRESS INC.—See Bay Grove Capital LLC; *U.S. Private*, pg. 493
COMCAST OF SOUTHERN NEW ENGLAND, INC.—See Comcast Corporation; *U.S. Public*, pg. 538
COMPLETE TRANSPORT SYSTEMS, LLC—See Expolanka Holdings PLC; *Int'l*, pg. 2589
COMTRAN INC.—See Mid-South Milling Company, Inc.; *U.S. Private*, pg. 2709
CONSOLIDATED FASTFRATE INC.; *Int'l*, pg. 1770
CONTAINERFREIGHT/EIT LLC; *U.S. Private*, pg. 1027
CONWELL CORP.—See Frozen Food Express Industries, Inc.; *U.S. Private*, pg. 1617
COVANTA INDIANAPOLIS, INC.—See EQT AB; *Int'l*, pg. 2474
CROSSCOUNTRY FREIGHT SOLUTIONS, INC.; *U.S. Private*, pg. 1106
CRYSTAL MOTOR EXPRESS INC.; *U.S. Private*, pg. 1115
C-SYSTEMS INTERNATIONAL CORPORATION; *U.S. Private*, pg. 704
CTS ADVANTAGE LOGISTICS INC.; *U.S. Private*, pg. 1119
CUSHING TRANSPORTATION INC.; *U.S. Private*, pg. 1127
C&W TRUCKING INC.; *U.S. Private*, pg. 704
CYPRESS TRUCK LEASING COMPANY, INC.—See Cypress Truck Lines, Inc.; *Int'l*, pg. 1135
DALTON TRUCKING INC.; *U.S. Private*, pg. 1150
DART INTERNATIONAL; *U.S. Private*, pg. 1160
DATS TRUCKING INC.; *U.S. Private*, pg. 1167
DECO LOGISTICS, INC.—See Universal Logistics Holdings, Inc.; *U.S. Public*, pg. 2261
DEDICATED FLEET SYSTEMS, INC.—See The Osterkamp Group; *U.S. Private*, pg. 4089
DEMON TRUCKING INC.—See Phoenix Beverages, Inc.; *U.S. Private*, pg. 3172
DEN HARTOGH ASIA PACIFIC PTE LTD.—See Den Hartogh Holding BV; *Int'l*, pg. 2026
DILLON TRANSPORT INC.; *U.S. Private*, pg. 1231
DISTRIBUTION MARCEL DION INC.; *Int'l*, pg. 2136
DIVERSIFIED AUTOMOTIVE INC.; *U.S. Private*, pg. 1241
DMT SERVICES INC.; *U.S. Private*, pg. 1249
DOLPHIN DELIVERY LTD.; *Int'l*, pg. 2159
DOMINIQUE PRUDENT SAS; *Int'l*, pg. 2161
DON E. KEITH TRANSPORTATION, LLC; *U.S. Private*, pg. 1257
DSV AIR & SEA OOD—See DSV A/S; *Int'l*, pg. 2211
DSV COMMERCIALS LTD.—See DSV A/S; *Int'l*, pg. 2212
DSV HRVATSKA D.O.O.—See DSV A/S; *Int'l*, pg. 2212
DSV LOGISTICS CO., LTD.—See DSV A/S; *Int'l*, pg. 2212
DSV LOGISTICS SA—See DSV A/S; *Int'l*, pg. 2212

DSV OSTERREICH SPEDITION GMBH—See DSV A/S; *Int'l*, pg. 2212
DSV ROAD A.S.—See DSV A/S; *Int'l*, pg. 2212
DSV ROAD A/S—See DSV A/S; *Int'l*, pg. 2212
DSV ROAD AS—See DSV A/S; *Int'l*, pg. 2212
DSV ROAD EOOD—See DSV A/S; *Int'l*, pg. 2212
DSV ROAD GMBH—See DSV A/S; *Int'l*, pg. 2212
DSV ROAD HOLDING A/S—See DSV A/S; *Int'l*, pg. 2212
DSV ROAD, INC.—See DSV A/S; *Int'l*, pg. 2213
DSV ROAD LIMITED—See DSV A/S; *Int'l*, pg. 2212
DSV ROAD LTD.—See DSV A/S; *Int'l*, pg. 2212
DSV ROAD NV—See DSV A/S; *Int'l*, pg. 2212
DSV ROAD OY—See DSV A/S; *Int'l*, pg. 2212
DSV ROAD S.A.—See DSV A/S; *Int'l*, pg. 2212
DSV ROAD S.A.U.—See DSV A/S; *Int'l*, pg. 2212
DSV ROAD & SOLUTIONS A.S.—See DSV A/S; *Int'l*, pg. 2212
DSV ROAD SP. Z.O.O—See DSV A/S; *Int'l*, pg. 2212
DSV S.A.—See DSV A/S; *Int'l*, pg. 2213
DSV SGPS, LDA.—See DSV A/S; *Int'l*, pg. 2213
DSV SOLUTIONS AB—See DSV A/S; *Int'l*, pg. 2213
DSV SOLUTIONS A/S—See DSV A/S; *Int'l*, pg. 2213
DSV SOLUTIONS (AUTOMOTIVE) NV—See DSV A/S; *Int'l*, pg. 2213
DSV SOLUTIONS GROUP GMBH—See DSV A/S; *Int'l*, pg. 2213
DSV SOLUTIONS NV—See DSV A/S; *Int'l*, pg. 2213
DSV SOLUTIONS OOO—See DSV A/S; *Int'l*, pg. 2213
DSV SOLUTIONS PUURS NV—See DSV A/S; *Int'l*, pg. 2213
DSV STUTTGART GMBH & CO. KG—See DSV A/S; *Int'l*, pg. 2213
DSV TRANSITARIOS LDA.—See DSV A/S; *Int'l*, pg. 2213
DSV TRANSPORT AS—See DSV A/S; *Int'l*, pg. 2213
DSV TRANSPORT D.O.O.—See DSV A/S; *Int'l*, pg. 2213
DSV TRANSPORT LTD.—See DSV A/S; *Int'l*, pg. 2213
DSV TRANSPORT SIA—See DSV A/S; *Int'l*, pg. 2213
DSV TRANSPORT UAB—See DSV A/S; *Int'l*, pg. 2213
DSV UKRAINE—See DSV A/S; *Int'l*, pg. 2213
DULUTH STORAGE, LLC—See Nelnet, Inc.; *U.S. Public*, pg. 1504
DW DISTRIBUTION L.L.C.—See National Amusements, Inc.; *U.S. Private*, pg. 2842
DYNAMIC INTERNATIONAL USA, INC.; *U.S. Private*, pg. 1298
EAGLE VAN LINES INC.—See Coleman American Companies, Inc.; *U.S. Private*, pg. 967
EARL T. WADHAMS INC.—See Wadhams Enterprises Inc.; *U.S. Private*, pg. 4424
EARTH INC.; *U.S. Private*, pg. 1314
E B TRANS SA; *Int'l*, pg. 2246
ECU TRUCKING, INC.—See Allcargo Logistics Limited; *Int'l*, pg. 333
EGIS ROAD OPERATION PORTUGAL S.A.—See Groupe Egis S.A.; *Int'l*, pg. 3102
ELECTRONIC DATA CARRIERS INC.; *U.S. Private*, pg. 1355
E.L. HOLLINGSWORTH & CO.; *U.S. Private*, pg. 1306
EMME INC.—See SimpleHealth, Inc.; *U.S. Private*, pg. 3667
EMPIRE TRANSPORT—See Empire Southwest LLC; *U.S. Private*, pg. 1385
ENG KONG CONTAINER SERVICES (SHENZHEN) COMPANY LIMITED—See Eng Kong Holdings Pte Ltd.; *Int'l*, pg. 2426
EVO TRANSPORTATION & ENERGY SERVICES, INC.; *U.S. Public*, pg. 803
E.W. WYLIE CORPORATION—See Daseke, Inc.; *U.S. Private*, pg. 1161
EXCEL TRANSPORTATION INC.; *Int'l*, pg. 2577
EXPRESS 2000, INC.—See CrossCountry Freight Solutions, Inc.; *U.S. Private*, pg. 1106
EXTRA MILE TRANSPORTATION LLC; *U.S. Private*, pg. 1452
FAIRRINGTON TRANSPORTATION CORP.—See Atlas Holdings, LLC; *U.S. Private*, pg. 377
FEDEX EXPRESS GREECE SINGLE MEMBER L.L.C.—See FedEx Corporation; *U.S. Public*, pg. 827
FEDEX EXPRESS TRANSPORTATION & SUPPLY CHAIN SERVICES (INDIA) PVT. LTD.—See FedEx Corporation; *U.S. Public*, pg. 827
FGV TRANSPORT SERVICES SDN. BHD.—See FGV Holdings Bhd; *Int'l*, pg. 2649
FIRST CLASS SERVICES INC.; *U.S. Private*, pg. 1515
FISTER INCORPORATED; *U.S. Private*, pg. 1535
FISTER MOVING & STORAGE—See Fister Incorporated; *U.S. Private*, pg. 1535
FLASH, INC.; *U.S. Private*, pg. 1540
FLAT RATE MOVING NEW YORK; *U.S. Private*, pg. 1541
FLORIDA GIFT FRUIT SHIPPERS ASSOCIATION INC.; *U.S. Private*, pg. 1548
FLORIDA ROCK & TANK LINES, INC.—See FRP Holdings, Inc.; *U.S. Public*, pg. 888
FLOWER TRANSFER INC.—See Delaware Valley Wholesale Florist Inc.; *U.S. Private*, pg. 1196
FLUKE TRANSPORTATION GROUP; *Int'l*, pg. 2714
F. MURPF AG; *Int'l*, pg. 2595
FOOD EXPRESS INC.; *U.S. Private*, pg. 1560
FREIGHT FORCE, INC.—See Wind Point Advisors LLC; *U.S. Private*, pg. 4535

484110 — GENERAL FREIGHT TRU...

F.R.F. SYSTEMS INC.; U.S. Private, pg. 1457
FRONTIER TRANSPORTATION INC.—See The Osterkamp Group; U.S. Private, pg. 4089
FSA NETWORK INC.—See Forward Air Corporation; U.S. Public, pg. 874
FST LOGISTICS INC.; U.S. Private, pg. 1618
FTS INTERNATIONAL EXPRESS INC.; U.S. Private, pg. 1619
FU DA TRANSPORTATION CO., LTD.—See Asia Cement Corporation; Int'l, pg. 611
FU-MING TRANSPORTATION CO. LTD.—See Asia Cement Corporation; Int'l, pg. 611
FUNABASHI KIKO CO., LTD.—See Godo Steel, Ltd.; Int'l, pg. 3020
GALASSO TRUCKING, INC.; U.S. Private, pg. 1636
GEBRUDER WEISS, INC.—See Gebruder Weiss Gesellschaft m.b.H.; Int'l, pg. 2909
GENESIS TRANSPORTATION INC.; U.S. Private, pg. 1670
GENTLE GIANT MOVING CO. INC.; U.S. Private, pg. 1679
GENTNER INC.; U.S. Private, pg. 1679
GILLESPIE, INC.—See The Interpublic Group of Companies, Inc.; U.S. Public, pg. 2093
GOLDEN EAGLE EXPRESS INC.; U.S. Private, pg. 1730
GOSSELIN EXPRESS; Int'l, pg. 3043
GOTETSU OSAKA BUTURYU CO., LTD.—See Godo Steel, Ltd.; Int'l, pg. 3020
GRAND PACIFIC WAREHOUSE LIMITED—See Eng Kong Holdings Pte Ltd.; Int'l, pg. 2426
GRANE TRANSPORTATION LINES; U.S. Private, pg. 1754
GRIMM BROS. TRUCKING INC.—See Peoria Disposal Company/Area Disposal Service, Inc.; U.S. Private, pg. 3143
GROUPE GARNIER; Int'l, pg. 3103
GUARDIAN MOVING & STORAGE CO., INC.; U.S. Private, pg. 1810
GYPSUM EXPRESS LTD.; U.S. Private, pg. 1821
HAI MINH CORPORATION; Int'l, pg. 3208
HAMAKYOREX CO., LTD.; Int'l, pg. 3235
HANEY TRUCK LINE LLC - PORTLAND—See Evergreen Pacific Partners Management Co., Inc.; U.S. Private, pg. 1440
HANEY TRUCK LINE LLC—See Evergreen Pacific Partners Management Co., Inc.; U.S. Private, pg. 1440
HANKYU INTERNATIONAL TRANSPORT (DEUTSCHLAND) GMBH—See Hankyu Hanshin Holdings Inc.; Int'l, pg. 3255
HARAM TRANSPORTATION CO. S.A.E.—See Ghabbour Auto S.A.E.; Int'l, pg. 2958
HAWAII TRANSFER CO. LTD.; U.S. Private, pg. 1881
HAZEN TRANSPORT INC.—See Storage & Transportation Co., Inc.; U.S. Private, pg. 3831
HBIS GROUP SUPPLY CHAIN MANAGEMENT CO., LTD.—See HBIS Group Co., Ltd.; Int'l, pg. 3296
HCCR HAMBURGER CONTAINER- UND CHASSIS-REPARATUR-GESELLSCHAFT MBH—See Hamburger Hafen und Logistik AG; Int'l, pg. 3236
HEARTLAND EXPRESS, INC.; U.S. Public, pg. 1017
HERITAGE LOGISTICS, LLC—See Vulcan Materials Company; U.S. Public, pg. 2314
HIGH PLAINS TRANSPORT LLC—See Seaboard Corporation; U.S. Public, pg. 1850
HODOGAYA LOGISTICS CO., LTD.—See Hodogaya Chemical Co., Ltd.; Int'l, pg. 3438
HOPSON HOLDINGS INCORPORATED; U.S. Private, pg. 1979
HOT SHOT DELIVERY INC.; U.S. Private, pg. 1988
HOYER ESPANA, S.A.—See Hoyer GmbH; Int'l, pg. 3498
HOYER GLOBAL SHANGHAI BV—See Hoyer GmbH; Int'l, pg. 3498
HOYER GLOBAL TRANSPORT BV—See Hoyer GmbH; Int'l, pg. 3498
HOYER GLOBAL TRANSPORT FZE—See Hoyer GmbH; Int'l, pg. 3498
HOYER HUNGARIA KFT—See Hoyer GmbH; Int'l, pg. 3499
HOYER LUXEMBOURG S.A.R.L—See Hoyer GmbH; Int'l, pg. 3498
HOYER MEDNARODNA SPEDICIJA D.O.O.—See Hoyer GmbH; Int'l, pg. 3498
HOYER NEDERLAND B.V.—See Hoyer GmbH; Int'l, pg. 3498
HOYER SLOVENSKA REPUBLIKA S.R.O.—See Hoyer GmbH; Int'l, pg. 3498
HOYER SVENSKA AB—See Hoyer GmbH; Int'l, pg. 3498
HOYER (SVIZZERA) SA—See Hoyer GmbH; Int'l, pg. 3498
HOYER UKRAINE TOV—See Hoyer GmbH; Int'l, pg. 3498
HUB GROUP TRUCKING—See Hub Group, Inc.; U.S. Public, pg. 1065
HUGHES RELOCATION SERVICE INC.; U.S. Private, pg. 2004
HUTECH NORIN CO., LTD.—See Chilled & Frozen Logis; Int'l, pg. 1479
HYGRADE DISTRIBUTION & DELIVERY SYSTEMS; U.S. Private, pg. 2018
IBP ASSET, LLC—See Installed Building Products, Inc.; U.S. Public, pg. 1132
ICE DELIVERY SYSTEMS INC.; U.S. Private, pg. 2030
INTEGRATED SERVICES INC.—See Roadrunner Transportation Systems, Inc.; U.S. Public, pg. 1802

INTERNATIONAL EXPRESS TRUCKING, INC.—See Bluejay Capital Partners, LLC; U.S. Private, pg. 597
J.A. FRATE TRANSPORT SERVICES, INC.; U.S. Private, pg. 2157
JDL MOTOR EXPRESS—See John Lenore & Company, Inc.; U.S. Private, pg. 2223
JETCO DELIVERY, INC.—See GTI Transport Solutions, Inc.; Int'l, pg. 3151
JET EXPRESS INC.; U.S. Private, pg. 2203
JNJ EXPRESS INC.; U.S. Private, pg. 2216
JONES LOGISTICS, LLC—See Jones Capital, LLC; U.S. Private, pg. 2232
JOYAU S.A.—See Deutsche Bahn AG; Int'l, pg. 2052
JUAREZ BROTHERS TRUCKING INC.; U.S. Private, pg. 2242
JUNGS TRUCKING, INC.; U.S. Private, pg. 2244
KAHULUI TRUCKING & STORAGE, INC.—See Alexander & Baldwin, Inc.; U.S. Public, pg. 75
THE KANE COMPANY; U.S. Private, pg. 4064
KANE TRANSPORT, INC.—See Transwood Carriers Inc.; U.S. Private, pg. 4211
KAPLAN TRUCKING—See Kaplan Trucking Company; U.S. Private, pg. 2261
KARLSHAMN EXPRESS AB—See DFDS A/S; Int'l, pg. 2095
KAWAICHI SANGYO CO., LTD.—See Daido Steel Co., Ltd.; Int'l, pg. 1923
K-B CORPORATION; U.S. Private, pg. 2250
KC TRANSPORTATION INC.; U.S. Private, pg. 2269
KEEP ON TRUCKING COMPANY INCORPORATED; U.S. Private, pg. 2272
KELLEY TRUCKING, INC.; U.S. Private, pg. 2276
KEYSTONE FREIGHT CORP.—See National Retail Systems, Inc.; U.S. Private, pg. 2862
K.H. CHAN TRADING SDN. BHD.—See HPI Resources Berhad; Int'l, pg. 3501
KING LOGISTICS, INC.; U.S. Private, pg. 2309
KNIGHT TRANSPORTATION, INC.—See Knight-Swift Transportation Holdings Inc.; U.S. Public, pg. 1269
KNIGHT TRUCK & TRAILER SALES, LLC—See Knight-Swift Transportation Holdings Inc.; U.S. Public, pg. 1269
KUNTZMAN TRUCKING INC.; U.S. Private, pg. 2357
LAND AIR EXPRESS OF NEW ENGLAND; U.S. Private, pg. 2382
LAND BRIDGE TERMINALS, INC.—See Pyramid Industries, Inc.; U.S. Private, pg. 3310
LA ROSA DEL MONTE EXPRESS INC.; U.S. Private, pg. 2369
LEFEBVRE & SONS INC.—See LeFebvre Companies, Inc.; U.S. Private, pg. 2415
LEGACY TRANSPORTATION SERVICES; U.S. Private, pg. 2417
LEONARD'S EXPRESS INC.; U.S. Private, pg. 2430
LILE INTERNATIONAL COMPANIES; U.S. Private, pg. 2455
LINDSAY TRANSPORTATION, INC.—See Lindsay Corporation; U.S. Public, pg. 1320
LINKS FREIGHT MANAGEMENT LLC; U.S. Private, pg. 2462
L&J TRANSPORTATION COMPANIES, INC.; U.S. Private, pg. 2362
LKS TRANSPORTATION, LLC—See Installed Building Products, Inc.; U.S. Public, pg. 1133
LLL TRANSPORT, INC.—See Great Range Capital, LLC; U.S. Private, pg. 1767
LOAD ONE TRANSPORTATION & LOGISTICS; U.S. Private, pg. 2476
LOUDON COUNTY TRUCKING, LLC—See OEP Capital Advisors, L.P.; U.S. Private, pg. 2999
LYNDEN LOGISTICS, INC.—See Lynden Incorporated; U.S. Private, pg. 2521
MATERIAL TRANSFER, INC.—See LPX, Inc.; U.S. Private, pg. 2507
M A T PARCEL EXPRESS, INC.; U.S. Private, pg. 2523
MATS, INC.—See Moran Transportation Corp.; U.S. Private, pg. 2782
MAXXON LOGISTICS LLC—See Legend Oil and Gas, Ltd.; U.S. Public, pg. 1301
MAYFIELD TRANSFER COMPANY INCORPORATED; U.S. Private, pg. 2621
MCCLYMONDS SUPPLY & TRANSIT CO. INC.; U.S. Private, pg. 2629
MCO TRANSPORT, INC.; U.S. Private, pg. 2644
MEDICAL DELIVERY SERVICES, INC.—See HCI Equity Management, L.P.; U.S. Private, pg. 1889
MEITO TRANSPORTATION CO., LTD.—See Chilled & Frozen Logis; Int'l, pg. 1479
METRANS A.S.—See Hamburger Hafen und Logistik AG; Int'l, pg. 3237
METRANS RAIL (DEUTSCHLAND) GMBH—See Hamburger Hafen und Logistik AG; Int'l, pg. 3237
METRO FILM EXPRESS INC.; U.S. Private, pg. 2685
MILAN EXPRESS CO., INC.; U.S. Private, pg. 2726
MILLARD TRUCKING LTD.—See Enerchem International, Inc.; Int'l, pg. 2418
M&M CARTAGE CO. INC.; U.S. Private, pg. 2524
MODERN MARKET MASTER INC.; U.S. Private, pg. 2761
MODERN TRANSPORTATION SERVICES INC.; U.S. Private, pg. 2762

CORPORATE AFFILIATIONS

MONROE TRANSPORTATION SERVICES; U.S. Private, pg. 2774
MORAN TRANSPORTATION CORP.; U.S. Private, pg. 2782
MOUNTCREST LTD—See Dragon Ukrainian Properties & Development Plc; Int'l, pg. 2199
MSM LOGISTICS SDN. BHD.—See FGV Holdings Bhd; Int'l, pg. 2649
NATIONAL DELIVERY SYSTEMS; U.S. Private, pg. 2852
NATIONAL TRANSFER & STORAGE, INC.—See Chipman Corporation; U.S. Private, pg. 886
NELSON WESTERBERG ATLAS—See Nelson Westerberg, Inc.; U.S. Private, pg. 2884
NELSON WESTERBERG ATLAS—See Nelson Westerberg, Inc.; U.S. Private, pg. 2884
NELSON WESTERBERG OF ILLINOIS—See Nelson Westerberg, Inc.; U.S. Private, pg. 2884
NINGBO CIMC CONTAINER SERVICE CO., LTD.—See China International Marine Containers (Group) Co., Ltd.; Int'l, pg. 1512
N&M TRANSFER CO., INC.; U.S. Private, pg. 2827
NORCO DELIVERY SERVICES; U.S. Private, pg. 2935
NORTHERN FREIGHT SERVICE, INC.—See Allen Lund Company, LLC; U.S. Private, pg. 179
NORTH SHORE MOVERS, INC.; U.S. Private, pg. 2946
NORTHSTAR VAN LINES—See UniGroup, Inc.; U.S. Private, pg. 4283
OFFICE MOVERS INC.—See The Kane Company; U.S. Private, pg. 4064
OHIO TRANSPORT CORPORATION; U.S. Private, pg. 3005
OKADA TRUCKING CO. LTD.; U.S. Private, pg. 3006
ON TIME TRUCKING, INC.—See The RK Logistics Group, Inc.; U.S. Private, pg. 4110
OOO DSV TRANSPORT—See DSV A/S; Int'l, pg. 2214
OOO HOYER RUS—See Hoyer GmbH; Int'l, pg. 3499
ORBCOMM DEUTSCHLAND SATELLITENKOMMUNIKATION AG—See Hiscox Ltd.; Int'l, pg. 3407
OSBORN TRANSPORTATION, INC.; U.S. Private, pg. 3046
OZARK TRUCKING INC.; U.S. Private, pg. 3058
PACIFIC TRANS ENVIRONMENTAL SERVICES, INC.—See Aurora Capital Group, LLC; U.S. Private, pg. 394
PACORINI METALS ITALIA S.R.L.—See B. Pacorini S.p.A.; Int'l, pg. 789
THE PADDED WAGON INC.; U.S. Private, pg. 4090
PANTHER II TRANSPORTATION, INC.—See ArcBest Corporation; U.S. Public, pg. 180
PANTHER PREMIUM LOGISTICS, INC.—See ArcBest Corporation; U.S. Public, pg. 180
PATTERSON TRUCK LINE, INC.—See RPC, Inc.; U.S. Public, pg. 1816
PAXTON VAN LINES INCORPORATED; U.S. Private, pg. 3116
PB EXPRESS INC.; U.S. Private, pg. 3118
PB INDUSTRIES INC.; U.S. Private, pg. 3118
PCC TRANSLOAD SYSTEM—See PCC Logistics; U.S. Private, pg. 3120
PEGASUS TRANSPORTATION GROUP, INC.; U.S. Private, pg. 3129
PENINSULA TRUCK LINES INC.; U.S. Private, pg. 3133
PERFORMANCE TEAM, LLC—See A.P. Moller-Maersk A/S; Int'l, pg. 26
PINTAIL CORPORATION—See Tech Agricultural, Inc.; U.S. Private, pg. 3951
P&L TRANSPORTATION, INC.; U.S. Private, pg. 3059
POLE STAR TRANSPORT INC—See Armour Transportation Systems; Int'l, pg. 575
POP GESELLSCHAFT FUR PROZESSLOGISTIK MBH—See DSV A/S; Int'l, pg. 2214
POWER TRANSPORTATION, LLC—See DNOW Inc.; U.S. Public, pg. 671
PRICE TRANSFER INC.; U.S. Private, pg. 3258
PRIORITY-1 INC—See Priority Wire & Cable Inc.; U.S. Private, pg. 3267
PRIORITY DISPATCH INC.; U.S. Private, pg. 3266
PRITCHETT TRUCKING INC.; U.S. Private, pg. 3268
PVS TRANSPORTATION, INC.—See PVS Chemicals, Inc.; U.S. Private, pg. 3308
PYLE TRANSPORT SERVICES INC.—See A. Duie Pyle Inc.; U.S. Private, pg. 23
PYRAMID INDUSTRIES, INC.; U.S. Private, pg. 3310
QINGDAO SINOTRANS-AZUMA LOGISTICS CO., LTD.—See Azuma Shipping Co., Ltd.; Int'l, pg. 782
QUICK DELIVERY SERVICE, INC.—See Peoples Services Inc.; U.S. Private, pg. 3142
QUICKSILVER EXPRESS COURIER INC.; U.S. Private, pg. 3326
QUICKSILVER EXPRESS COURIER OF MINNESOTA INC.—See Quicksilver Express Courier Inc.; U.S. Private, pg. 3327
QUICKSILVER EXPRESS COURIER OF MISSOURI INC.—See Quicksilver Express Courier Inc.; U.S. Private, pg. 3327
QUICKSILVER EXPRESS COURIER OF WISCONSIN, INC.—See Quicksilver Express Courier Inc.; U.S. Private, pg. 3327
QUICKWAY EXPRESS INC.; U.S. Private, pg. 3327
RAC TRANSPORT COMPANY INC.; U.S. Private, pg. 3341

N.A.I.C.S. INDEX

484121 — GENERAL FREIGHT TRU...

RAPID RESPONSE DELIVERY INC.—See H.I.G. Capital, LLC; *U.S. Private*, pg. 1827
RELAY EXPRESS; *U.S. Private*, pg. 3393
RELIANT TRANSPORTATION, INC.; *U.S. Private*, pg. 3395
RESOURCES TRUCKING, INC.—See Pyramid Industries, Inc.; *U.S. Private*, pg. 3310
RIST TRANSPORT LTD.—See Wadhams Enterprises Inc.; *U.S. Private*, pg. 4425
R & J TRUCKING INC.—See American Bulk Commodities Inc.; *U.S. Private*, pg. 225
ROAD SCHOLAR TRANSPORT INC.; *U.S. Private*, pg. 3453
ROCK HILL CONCRETE; *U.S. Private*, pg. 3464
RODGERS TRUCKING CO.; *U.S. Private*, pg. 3470
RODOBAN SEGURANCA E TRANPSORTE DE VALORES LTDA.—See The Brink's Company; *U.S. Public*, pg. 2043
ROSE MOVING AND STORAGE CO.—See Corporate Installation Services; *U.S. Private*, pg. 1055
ROY MILLER FREIGHT LINES LLC; *U.S. Private*, pg. 3490
RPM TRANSPORTATION INC.—See RPM Consolidated Services, Inc.; *U.S. Private*, pg. 3495
RUBIN GMBH—See Bijou Brigitte modische Accessoires AG; *Int'l*, pg. 1022
RUSH TRUCK CENTERS OF NEW MEXICO, INC.—See Rush Enterprises, Inc.; *U.S. Public*, pg. 1827
RUSH TRUCKING CORPORATION; *U.S. Private*, pg. 3505
RUSSELL REID WASTE HAULING; *U.S. Private*, pg. 3506
RYAN TRANSPORTATION INC.—See Auto Expediting Inc.; *U.S. Private*, pg. 397
SAL-SON LOGISTICS, INC.—See Saybrook Corporate Opportunity Fund LP; *U.S. Private*, pg. 3558
SAM BROUSSARD TRUCKING COMPANY INC.; *U.S. Private*, pg. 3535
SANDTORP THERMOTRANSPORT AS—See DSV A/S; *Int'l*, pg. 2216
S.C. TRANSPORTER S.R.L.—See CHS INC.; *U.S. Public*, pg. 493
SENTINEL TRANSPORTATION LLC - LOUISVILLE—See Phillips 66 Company; *U.S. Public*, pg. 1688
SENTINEL TRANSPORTATION LLC—See Phillips 66 Company; *U.S. Public*, pg. 1688
SENTINEL TRANSPORTATION LLC - WASHINGTON—See Phillips 66 Company; *U.S. Public*, pg. 1688
SERVICE TRANSFER INC.; *U.S. Private*, pg. 3616
SHANGHAI ENG KONG CONTAINER SERVICES LTD.—See Eng Kong Holdings Pte Ltd.; *Int'l*, pg. 2426
SHYPDIRECT, LLC—See Transportation and Logistics Systems, Inc.; *U.S. Public*, pg. 2184
SIBONEY CONTRACTING CO.; *U.S. Private*, pg. 3645
SICHUAN YALI TRANSPORT CO., LTD.—See Asia Cement Corporation; *Int'l*, pg. 611
SINCLAIR CASPER REFINERY—See HF Sinclair Corporation; *U.S. Public*, pg. 1034
SLAY INDUSTRIES INC.; *U.S. Private*, pg. 3687
SMISC HOLDINGS, INC.—See Sonic Financial Corporation; *U.S. Private*, pg. 3713
S&M MOVING SYSTEMS WEST INC.; *U.S. Private*, pg. 3513
SOUTHEAST LOGISTICS, INC.—See OEP Capital Advisors, L.P.; *U.S. Private*, pg. 2999
SOUTH PARK MOTOR LINES LLC; *U.S. Private*, pg. 3723
S.P.C. TRANSPORT; *U.S. Private*, pg. 3518
SPECIALIZED CARRIER CO. INC.—See General Equipment & Supplies Inc.; *U.S. Private*, pg. 1664
SPECIALIZED RAIL SERVICE, INC.—See Universal Logistics Holdings, Inc.; *U.S. Public*, pg. 2261
SPEE-DEE DELIVERY SERVICE INC.; *U.S. Private*, pg. 3753
START TRUCKING, INC.; *U.S. Private*, pg. 3788
STONE BELT FREIGHT LINES INC.; *U.S. Private*, pg. 3816
STORAGE & TRANSPORTATION CO., INC.; *U.S. Private*, pg. 3831
SUDDATH RELOCATION SYSTEMS OF ARIZONA LLC—See The Suddath Companies; *U.S. Private*, pg. 4124
SULLIVAN MOVING AND STORAGE CO; *U.S. Private*, pg. 3851
SUNBELT TRANSPORT, LLC—See Cypress Truck Lines, Inc.; *U.S. Private*, pg. 1135
SUNSET PACIFIC TRANSPORTATION, INC.—See Granite Creek Capital Partners, LLC; *U.S. Private*, pg. 1755
SUNSET PACIFIC TRANSPORTATION, INC.—See Red Arts Capital; *U.S. Private*, pg. 3373
TAX AIRFREIGHT INC.; *U.S. Private*, pg. 3937
TECHNI-CON CONTAINER SURVEY LIMITED—See Eng Kong Holdings Pte Ltd.; *Int'l*, pg. 2426
THREE WAY; *U.S. Private*, pg. 4164
THRIFT TRUCKING INCORPORATED—See Assured Transportation Services; *U.S. Private*, pg. 359
THUNDERBIRD TRUCKING INC.—See Omni Holding Company; *U.S. Private*, pg. 3016
TIME MOVING & STORAGE INC.; *U.S. Private*, pg. 4172
TNS OCEAN LINES (S) PTE. LTD.—See GKE Corporation Limited; *Int'l*, pg. 2983
TNT AUSTRALIA PTY. LIMITED—See FedEx Corporation; *U.S. Public*, pg. 828
TNT NEDERLAND B.V.—See FedEx Corporation; *U.S. Public*, pg. 828

TNT UK LIMITED—See FedEx Corporation; *U.S. Public*, pg. 828
TOTAL DISTRIBUTION—See Peoples Services Inc.; *U.S. Private*, pg. 3142
TRANSALL AG—See Bystronic AG; *Int'l*, pg. 1236
TRANSCEND LOGISTICS, INC.—See P.A.M. Transportation Services, Inc.; *U.S. Public*, pg. 1630
TRANSERVICE LOGISTICS INC.—See ZS Fund L.P.; *U.S. Private*, pg. 4609
TRANSPORTATION GENERAL INC.; *U.S. Private*, pg. 4211
THE TRANSPORTER, INC.—See Ridgemont Partners Management LLC; *U.S. Private*, pg. 3433
TRANSPORTIQ, INC.—See TraQiQ, Inc.; *U.S. Public*, pg. 2185
TRANSVIARIA - GESTAO DE TRANSPORTES S.A.—See Camargo Correa S.A.; *Int'l*, pg. 1268
TRANSWOOD INC.—See Transwood Carriers Inc.; *U.S. Private*, pg. 4211
TRANSWOOD LOGISTICS INC—See Transwood Carriers Inc.; *U.S. Private*, pg. 4212
TRANSYSTEMS LLC; *U.S. Private*, pg. 4212
TRATEL S.A.S—See E B Trans SA; *Int'l*, pg. 2246
TRATEL S.A.S—See Groupe GARNIER; *Int'l*, pg. 3103
TRI-MODAL DISTRIBUTION SERVICES; *U.S. Private*, pg. 4222
TRI-VALLEY TRANSPORT & STORAGE; *U.S. Private*, pg. 4224
TRUCK LEASE SERVICES, INC.; *U.S. Private*, pg. 4246
T&S TRUCKING COMPANY; *U.S. Private*, pg. 3910
TUNNEL NETWORK SERVICES PTY LTD—See Groupe Egis S.A.; *Int'l*, pg. 3102
TWO MEN & A TRUCK/INTERNATIONAL INC.—See Roark Capital Group Inc.; *U.S. Private*, pg. 3456
TX LOGISTIK AB—See Ferrovie dello Stato Italiane S.p.A.; *Int'l*, pg. 2645
TX LOGISTIK A/S—See Ferrovie dello Stato Italiane S.p.A.; *Int'l*, pg. 2645
TX LOGISTIK GMBH—See Ferrovie dello Stato Italiane S.p.A.; *Int'l*, pg. 2645
TX LOGISTIK TRANSALPINE GMBH—See Ferrovie dello Stato Italiane S.p.A.; *Int'l*, pg. 2645
UNITED HOLDINGS LLC—See Kirby Corporation; *U.S. Public*, pg. 1235
UNITED MAYFLOWER CONTAINER SERVICES, LLC—See UniGroup, Inc.; *U.S. Private*, pg. 4283
VALLEY COURIERS; *U.S. Private*, pg. 4333
VAN PLYCON LINES INC.; *U.S. Private*, pg. 4340
VENEZIA HAULING INC.; *U.S. Private*, pg. 4356
WAAGAN BIL AS—See DSV A/S; *Int'l*, pg. 2216
WADHAMS ENTERPRISES INC.; *U.S. Private*, pg. 4424
WAKEFIELD DISTRIBUTION SYSTEMS; *U.S. Private*, pg. 4427
WANNEMACHER ENTERPRISES INC.; *U.S. Private*, pg. 4435
WEBER DISTRIBUTION WAREHOUSES, LLC; *U.S. Private*, pg. 4465
WERNER GLOBAL LOGISTICS AUSTRALIA PTY. LTD—See Werner Enterprises, Inc.; *U.S. Public*, pg. 2349
WESTERN TRANSPORTATION, INC.—See Energy Transfer LP; *U.S. Public*, pg. 765
WEST OK TRUCKING, INC.—See Energy Spectrum Securities Corporation; *U.S. Private*, pg. 1396
WILLIAM C. HUFF COMPANIES; *U.S. Private*, pg. 4522
WINCANTON GROUP LIMITED—See GXO Logistics, Inc.; *U.S. Public*, pg. 976
WINCANTON UK LIMITED—See GXO Logistics, Inc.; *U.S. Public*, pg. 976
WJW ASSOCIATES, LTD.; *U.S. Private*, pg. 4551
WORLD WAREHOUSE & DISTRIBUTION INC.—See NFI Industries, Inc.; *U.S. Private*, pg. 2923
YRC INC.—See Yellow Corporation; *U.S. Public*, pg. 2398
YRC REGIONAL TRANSPORTATION, INC.—See Yellow Corporation; *U.S. Public*, pg. 2398

484121 — GENERAL FREIGHT TRUCKING, LONG-DISTANCE, TRUCKLOAD

1507953 ONTARIO INC.; *Int'l*, pg. 2
4-H TRANSPORTATION CO. INC.; *U.S. Private*, pg. 14
4. JULI A.D.; *Int'l*, pg. 10
591182 ONTARIO LIMITED; *Int'l*, pg. 13
615315 SASKATCHEWAN LTD; *Int'l*, pg. 14
AAA COOPER TRANSPORTATION, INC.—See Knight-Swift Transportation Holdings Inc.; *U.S. Public*, pg. 1269
A&A EXPRESS, LLC—See Roadrunner Transportation Systems, Inc.; *U.S. Public*, pg. 1802
AAT CARRIERS, INC.—See Covenant Logistics Group, Inc.; *U.S. Public*, pg. 588
ABF FREIGHT SYSTEM, INC.—See ArcBest Corporation; *U.S. Public*, pg. 180
ACE DORAN HAULING & RIGGING COMPANY; *U.S. Private*, pg. 56
A-C LOGISTICS—See Am-Can Transport Service Inc.; *U.S. Private*, pg. 215
ACME TRUCK LINE, INC.; *U.S. Private*, pg. 61
ACTION CARRIER; *U.S. Private*, pg. 67

ACTION TRANSPORT, INC.—See Heritage Home Group, LLC; *U.S. Private*, pg. 1924
A.C. WHITE TRANSFER & STORAGE CO.; *U.S. Private*, pg. 25
ADM TRUCKING COMPANY—See Archer-Daniels-Midland Company; *U.S. Public*, pg. 183
ADM TRUCKING INC.—See Archer-Daniels-Midland Company; *U.S. Public*, pg. 183
AGWAY SYSTEMS; *U.S. Private*, pg. 130
AIME BELLAVANCE & SONS INCORPORATED; *U.S. Private*, pg. 133
AIR CONTACT TRANSPORT INC.; *U.S. Private*, pg. 138
AIR GROUND XPRESS, INC.; *U.S. Private*, pg. 138
AIR-RIDE INC.; *U.S. Private*, pg. 140
ALABAMA CARRIERS, INC.—See Daseke, Inc.; *U.S. Private*, pg. 1161
ALABAMA MOTOR EXPRESS INC.; *U.S. Private*, pg. 148
ALCO TRANSPORTATION INC.; *U.S. Private*, pg. 154
ALEXANDER'S MOBILITY SERVICES; *U.S. Private*, pg. 164
ALEXANDER'S MOBILITY SERVICES—See Alexander's Mobility Services; *U.S. Private*, pg. 164
ALL CHEMICAL TRANSPORT—See All Chemical Leasing, Inc.; *U.S. Private*, pg. 170
ALL CHICAGOLAND MOVING & STORAGE CO.; *U.S. Private*, pg. 170
ALL FREIGHT SYSTEMS INC.; *U.S. Private*, pg. 171
ALLIANCE TRANSPORTATION, INC.—See GCC, S.A.B. de C.V.; *Int'l*, pg. 2894
ALPS LOGISTICS CO., LTD.; *Int'l*, pg. 377
ALTL INC.; *U.S. Private*, pg. 209
ALTON BEAN TRUCKING INC.; *U.S. Private*, pg. 210
AMA TRANSPORTATION COMPANY, INC.—See Wadhams Enterprises Inc.; *U.S. Private*, pg. 4425
AMBASSADOR VAN LINES INC.; *U.S. Private*, pg. 217
AMBROISE BOUVIER TRANSPORTS; *Int'l*, pg. 415
AM-CAN TRANSPORT SERVICE INC.; *U.S. Private*, pg. 215
AMERICA 1, LLC—See US 1 Industries, Inc.; *U.S. Private*, pg. 4317
AMERICAN CENTRAL TRANSPORT, INC.—See The Kretsinger Group, Inc.; *U.S. Private*, pg. 4066
AMERICAN ROAD LINE, INC.; *U.S. Private*, pg. 246
AMERICAN TRUCKING ASSOCIATION; *U.S. Private*, pg. 257
AMERICAN WEST WORLDWIDE EXPRESS INC.; *U.S. Private*, pg. 258
AMSTAN LOGISTICS INC.—See Sun Capital Partners, Inc.; *U.S. Private*, pg. 3858
AM TRANS EXPEDITE, INC.—See Hudson Hill Capital LLC; *U.S. Private*, pg. 2002
AM TRANSPORT SERVICES, INC.; *U.S. Private*, pg. 215
ANDERSON TRUCKING SERVICE INC.; *U.S. Private*, pg. 277
A.N. WEBBER INC.; *U.S. Private*, pg. 27
ARCTIC EXPRESS INC.; *U.S. Private*, pg. 315
ARGIX DIRECT INC.; *U.S. Private*, pg. 320
ARLINGTON SALVAGE & WRECKER CO.; *U.S. Private*, pg. 329
ARL TRANSPORT, LLC.—See US 1 Industries, Inc.; *U.S. Private*, pg. 4316
ARMELLINI EXPRESS LINES INC.—See Armellini Industries, Inc.; *U.S. Private*, pg. 330
ARMELLINI INDUSTRIES, INC.; *U.S. Private*, pg. 330
ARNOLD BROS. TRANSPORT LTD; *Int'l*, pg. 576
ARNOLD J THOMAS & SON INC—See Thomas & Sons Distributors, Inc.; *U.S. Private*, pg. 4154
A&R TRANSPORT, INC.; *U.S. Private*, pg. 20
ATLAS TRANSFER & STORAGE CO.; *U.S. Private*, pg. 380
ATS SPECIALIZED, INC.—See Anderson Trucking Service Inc.; *U.S. Private*, pg. 277
AUBRY LOGISTIQUE; *Int'l*, pg. 698
AUTO EXPEDITING INC.; *U.S. Private*, pg. 397
AUTOMOTIVE COMPONENT CARRIER LLC—See Penske Corporation; *U.S. Private*, pg. 3138
AUTOTRANSPORT A.D.; *Int'l*, pg. 732
AVAIL RESOURCE MANAGEMENT, INC.—See Atlas World Group, Inc.; *U.S. Private*, pg. 380
AVERITT EXPRESS INC.; *U.S. Private*, pg. 405
AZ-COM MARUWA HOLDINGS INC.; *Int'l*, pg. 776
BADGER STATE WESTERN INC.; *U.S. Private*, pg. 424
BAGGETT TRANSPORTATION COMPANY; *U.S. Private*, pg. 425
BARR-NUNN ENTERPRISES LTD. - OHIO ORIENTATION FACILITY—See Barr-Nunn Enterprises Ltd.; *U.S. Private*, pg. 479
BARR-NUNN ENTERPRISES LTD.; *U.S. Private*, pg. 479
BARR-NUNN TRANSPORTATION, INC.—See Knight-Swift Transportation Holdings Inc.; *U.S. Public*, pg. 1269
BAY & BAY TRANSFER COMPANY INC.; *U.S. Private*, pg. 491
BAYLOR TRUCKING, INC.—See Werner Enterprises, Inc.; *U.S. Public*, pg. 2349
B.B.X. INC.; *U.S. Private*, pg. 420
BEAVER EXPRESS SERVICE, LLC; *U.S. Private*, pg. 509
BELMONT ENTERPRISES, INC.—See Daseke, Inc.; *U.S. Private*, pg. 1161
BELTMANN GROUP INC.; *U.S. Private*, pg. 521

484121 — GENERAL FREIGHT TRU...

CORPORATE AFFILIATIONS

N.A.I.C.S. Index

BEN FLEET SERVICES GMBH—See EnBW Energie Baden-Wurttemberg AG; *Int'l*, pg. 2398
BENGAL TRANSPORTATION SERVICES, LLC.; *U.S. Private*, pg. 526
BENNETT INTERNATIONAL GROUP, INC.; *U.S. Private*, pg. 527
BENNETT MOTOR EXPRESS INC.—See Bennett International Group, Inc.; *U.S. Private*, pg. 527
BENNETT TRUCK TRANSPORT—See Bennett International Group, Inc.; *U.S. Private*, pg. 527
BEOTRANS A.D.; *Int'l*, pg. 978
THE BESL TRANSFER CO. INC.—See CRST International, Inc.; *U.S. Private*, pg. 1113
BEST-WAY MOTOR LINES INC.; *U.S. Private*, pg. 544
BESTWAY SYSTEMS, INC. - MEMPHIS DIVISION—See RJW, Inc.; *U.S. Private*, pg. 3450
BESTWAY SYSTEMS, INC.—See RJW, Inc.; *U.S. Private*, pg. 3449
BETTENDORF ENTERPRISES INC.; *U.S. Private*, pg. 546
BHX INC.; *U.S. Private*, pg. 549
BIAGI BROS INC.; *U.S. Private*, pg. 550
BIG E TRANSPORTATION LLC—See Estes Express Lines, Inc.; *U.S. Private*, pg. 1429
BIRCHWOOD FOODS—See Kenosha Beef International Ltd. Inc.; *U.S. Private*, pg. 2287
BITTERROOT INTERNATIONAL SYSTEMS, LTD.; *U.S. Private*, pg. 567
BJJ COMPANY INC.; *U.S. Private*, pg. 568
BLACKHAWK TRANSPORT INC.—See Hendricks Holding Company, Inc.; *U.S. Private*, pg. 1915
BLACK HILLS TRUCKING CO.—See True Companies; *U.S. Private*, pg. 4247
BOB'S TRANSPORT STORAGE CO; *U.S. Private*, pg. 606
BOHREN'S MOVING & STORAGE INC.; *U.S. Private*, pg. 609
BONDED CARRIERS INC.; *U.S. Private*, pg. 613
BORA KECIC ATP A.D.; *Int'l*, pg. 1112
BOWLING GREEN FREIGHT INC.; *U.S. Private*, pg. 626
BOYD BROS. TRANSPORTATION INC.—See Daseke, Inc.; *U.S. Private*, pg. 1161
BRANDT TRUCK LINE INC.; *U.S. Private*, pg. 639
BRAUNS EXPRESS INC.; *U.S. Private*, pg. 641
BRELET TRANSPORT SAS—See Groupement FLO; *Int'l*, pg. 3112
BRIAN KURTZ TRUCKING LTD.; *Int'l*, pg. 1151
BRIDGE LOGISTICS, INC.; *U.S. Private*, pg. 649
BRINK'S GLOBAL SERVICES (BGS) BOTSWANA (PROPRIETARY) LIMITED—See The Brink's Company; *U.S. Public*, pg. 2042
BRINK'S GLOBAL SERVICES KOREA LIMITED - YUNAN HOESA BRINK'S GLOBAL—See The Brink's Company; *U.S. Public*, pg. 2042
BRINK'S SOUTHERN AFRICA PTY LTD.—See The Brink's Company; *U.S. Public*, pg. 2043
BRINK'S TAIWAN SECURITY LIMITED—See The Brink's Company; *U.S. Public*, pg. 2043
BRINK'S VIETNAM, INCORPORATED—See The Brink's Company; *U.S. Public*, pg. 2043
BSP TRANSPORTATION INC.; *U.S. Private*, pg. 675
B&T EXPRESS INC.; *U.S. Private*, pg. 419
B-T INC.—See The Decker Companies Inc.; *U.S. Private*, pg. 4019
BT-TWISS TRANSPORT LLC—See Bulova Technologies Group, Inc.; *U.S. Private*, pg. 685
BUDDY MOORE TRUCKING, INC.—See OEP Capital Advisors, L.P.; *U.S. Private*, pg. 2999
BUDWAY ENTERPRISES INC.; *U.S. Private*, pg. 679
BUFFALO FUEL CORP.; *U.S. Private*, pg. 680
BUILDERS TRANSPORTATION CO., LLC—See Daseke, Inc.; *U.S. Private*, pg. 1161
BUILDING SYSTEMS TRANSPORTATION CO.; *U.S. Private*, pg. 683
BULKMATIC TRANSPORT COMPANY INC.; *U.S. Private*, pg. 684
BULK TRANSIT CORPORATION; *U.S. Private*, pg. 684
BULK TRANSPORTATION; *U.S. Private*, pg. 684
BULLDOG HIWAY EXPRESS INC.—See Daseke, Inc.; *U.S. Private*, pg. 1161
BULLOCKS EXPRESS TRANSPORTATION; *U.S. Private*, pg. 685
BUNCH TRANSPORT INC.; *U.S. Private*, pg. 685
BURNS MOTOR FREIGHT INC.; *U.S. Private*, pg. 691
BUSKE LINES, INC.—See Fourshore Capital LLC; *U.S. Private*, pg. 1583
BUTLER TRUCKING COMPANY; *U.S. Private*, pg. 697
BUTTON TRANSPORTATION INC.; *U.S. Private*, pg. 698
CABARAN MINDA SDN. BHD.—See HPI Resources Berhad; *Int'l*, pg. 3500
CALAC TRUCKING LTD.; *Int'l*, pg. 1261
CAL-ARK INC.; *U.S. Private*, pg. 715
CAL-CLEVE LIMITED; *U.S. Private*, pg. 715
CALDWELL FREIGHT LINES INC.—See CF Holding Company, Inc.; *U.S. Private*, pg. 843
CALEX LOGISTICS CORP.; *U.S. Private*, pg. 717
CALIFORNIA TANK LINES INC.—See Chemical Transfer Company; *U.S. Private*, pg. 871
CARDINAL TRANSPORT INC.; *U.S. Private*, pg. 751
CARGILL LOGISTICS—See Cargill, Inc.; *U.S. Private*, pg. 758
CARGO CONSOLIDATION SERVICES—See CT Group; *U.S. Private*, pg. 1118
CARGO LOGISTICS BY J. CIOFFI INC.; *U.S. Private*, pg. 760
CARGO TRANSPORTATION SERVICES INC.; *U.S. Private*, pg. 760
CARGO TRANSPORTERS, INC.—See CT Group; *U.S. Private*, pg. 1118
CARROLL FULMER LOGISTICS CORPORATION; *U.S. Private*, pg. 773
CASCADES TRANSPORT INC.—See Cascades Inc.; *Int'l*, pg. 1351
CATAWBA TRUCK RENTAL—See CT Group; *U.S. Private*, pg. 1118
C.C. SOUTHERN INC.—See CenTra, Inc.; *U.S. Private*, pg. 818
CELADON TRUCKING SERVICES, INC.—See Celadon Group, Inc.; *U.S. Public*, pg. 464
CENTRA, INC.; *U.S. Private*, pg. 818
CENTRAL ALABAMA TRANSPORT, INC.—See Coral Industries, Inc.; *U.S. Private*, pg. 1046
CENTRAL FREIGHT LINES, INC.; *U.S. Private*, pg. 821
CENTRAL PLAINS AG SERVICES LLC—See CHS INC.; *U.S. Public*, pg. 492
CENTRAL STATES TRUCKING CO.—See Forward Air Corporation; *U.S. Public*, pg. 874
CENTRAL TRANSPORTATION INTERNATIONAL INC—See CenTra, Inc.; *U.S. Private*, pg. 818
CENTRAL TRANSPORT INTERNATIONAL INC.—See CenTra, Inc.; *U.S. Private*, pg. 818
CENTRAL TRANSPORT INTERNATIONAL—See CenTra, Inc.; *U.S. Private*, pg. 818
CENTRAL TRANSPORT—See CenTra, Inc.; *U.S. Private*, pg. 818
CENTRAL TRUCKING INC.; *U.S. Private*, pg. 825
CHEMICAL TRANSFER COMPANY; *U.S. Private*, pg. 871
CHEMICAL TRANSPORTATION, INC.—See One Rock Capital Partners, LLC; *U.S. Private*, pg. 3022
CH ROBINSON FREIGHT SERVICES (MALAYSIA) SDN. BHD.—See C.H. Robinson Worldwide, Inc.; *U.S. Public*, pg. 415
C.H. ROBINSON FREIGHT SERVICES (THAILAND) LTD.—See C.H. Robinson Worldwide, Inc.; *U.S. Public*, pg. 415
CHURCHILL TRANSPORTATION INC.; *U.S. Private*, pg. 895
CIMARRON EXPRESS INC.; *U.S. Private*, pg. 897
CITY LINK EXPRESS, INC.; *U.S. Private*, pg. 906
CLARK FREIGHT LINES INC.; *U.S. Private*, pg. 913
THE CLARK GROUP, INC.—See Atlas Holdings, LLC; *U.S. Private*, pg. 376
CLARK & REID COMPANY, INC.—See Wheaton Van Lines, Inc.; *U.S. Private*, pg. 4505
CLARK TRANSFER INC.; *U.S. Private*, pg. 914
CLASSIC CARRIERS, INC.; *U.S. Private*, pg. 916
CLIFF VIESSMAN INC.; *U.S. Private*, pg. 943
CLOVERLEAF TRANSPORTATION, INC.; *U.S. Private*, pg. 948
COLONIAL FREIGHT SYSTEMS INC.; *U.S. Private*, pg. 971
COMBI MARITIME CORPORATION—See Roadrunner Transportation Systems, Inc.; *U.S. Public*, pg. 1802
COMBISPED HANSEATISCHE SPEDITION GMBH—See Hamburger Hafen und Logistik AG; *Int'l*, pg. 3236
COMCAR INDUSTRIES, INC.; *U.S. Private*, pg. 981
COMMERCIAL WORKS INC.; *U.S. Private*, pg. 985
CONNER TRANSPORT, INC.—See Conner Industries, Inc.; *U.S. Private*, pg. 1017
CONTAINER PORT GROUP—See World Shipping, Inc.; *U.S. Private*, pg. 4567
CONTINENTAL VAN LINES INC.; *U.S. Private*, pg. 1031
CONTRACT TRANSPORT INC.; *U.S. Private*, pg. 1032
COOKE TRUCKING COMPANY INC.; *U.S. Private*, pg. 1039
COOK MOVING SYSTEMS, INC. (ILLINOIS CORPORATION)—See Cook Moving Systems, Inc.; *U.S. Private*, pg. 1038
COPE BESTWAY EXPRESS INC.; *U.S. Private*, pg. 1044
CORCORAN TRUCKING INC.; *U.S. Private*, pg. 1047
CORRIGAN MOVING SYSTEMS; *U.S. Private*, pg. 1059
COUNTRYWIDE TRANSPORTATION, INC.; *U.S. Private*, pg. 1068
COVENANT LOGISTICS GROUP, INC.; *U.S. Public*, pg. 587
COVENANT TRANSPORT, INC.—See Covenant Logistics Group, Inc.; *U.S. Public*, pg. 588
COWAN SYSTEMS INC.; *U.S. Private*, pg. 1073
CRAIG TRANSPORTATION CO.; *U.S. Private*, pg. 1083
CRESCO LINES INC.; *U.S. Private*, pg. 1094
CROWN ENTERPRISES INC.—See CenTra, Inc.; *U.S. Private*, pg. 818
CRST FLATBED INC.—See CRST International, Inc.; *U.S. Private*, pg. 1113
CRST FLATBED, INC.—See CRST International, Inc.; *U.S. Private*, pg. 1113
CRST INTERNATIONAL, INC.; *U.S. Private*, pg. 1113
CRW FREIGHT MANAGEMENT SERVICES, INC.—See CRW, Inc.; *U.S. Private*, pg. 1114
CSC TRANSPORTATION LLC—See Commodity Specialists Company Inc.; *U.S. Private*, pg. 985
CTD CONTAINER-TRANSPORT-DIENST GMBH—See Hamburger Hafen und Logistik AG; *Int'l*, pg. 3236
CT GROUP; *U.S. Private*, pg. 1118
CTI CORP.; *U.S. Private*, pg. 1118
CTW TRANSPORT INC.—See HCI Equity Management, L.P.; *U.S. Private*, pg. 1889
CUMMINGS MOVING SYSTEMS—See Cummings Transfer Co.; *U.S. Private*, pg. 1123
CYPRESS TRUCK LINES, INC.; *U.S. Private*, pg. 1135
DAF TRUCKS DEUTSCHLAND GMBH—See PACCAR Inc.; *U.S. Public*, pg. 1630
DAILY EXPRESS, INC.; *U.S. Private*, pg. 1145
DAIO LOGISTICS CO., LTD.—See Daio Paper Corporation; *Int'l*, pg. 1939
DAKOTA CARTAGE COMPANY INC—See Lewis Transportation Systems; *U.S. Private*, pg. 2439
DAKOTA LINE, INC.; *U.S. Private*, pg. 1147
DANA TRANSPORT INC.; *U.S. Private*, pg. 1152
DANNY HERMAN TRUCKING INC.; *U.S. Private*, pg. 1157
DANNY NICHOLSON INC.; *U.S. Private*, pg. 1157
DART TRANSIT COMPANY; *U.S. Private*, pg. 1160
DAVIS CARTAGE CO.; *U.S. Private*, pg. 1173
DAVIS TRANSFER CO. INC.; *U.S. Private*, pg. 1174
DAVIS TRANSPORT INC.; *U.S. Private*, pg. 1174
DAVIS TRUCKING, LLC; *U.S. Private*, pg. 1174
DAWN ENTERPRISES INCORPORATED; *U.S. Private*, pg. 1175
DAYLIGHT TRANSPORT; *U.S. Private*, pg. 1177
DAYTON FREIGHT LINES INC.; *U.S. Private*, pg. 1177
DDI TRANSPORTATION, INC.—See Ridgemont Partners Management LLC; *U.S. Private*, pg. 3433
DEBOER TRANSPORTATION, INC.—See Schneider National, Inc.; *U.S. Public*, pg. 1847
DEDICATED LOGISTICS INC.; *U.S. Private*, pg. 1188
DEDICATED TRANSPORT LLC; *U.S. Private*, pg. 1188
DELTA STAR CORPORATION—See Collins Brothers Corporation; *U.S. Private*, pg. 969
DEN HARTOGH LOGISTICS LATIN AMERICA LTDA.—See Den Hartogh Holding BV; *Int'l*, pg. 2026
DEPENDABLE HIGHWAY EXPRESS INC.; *U.S. Private*, pg. 1209
DESERT COASTAL TRANSPORT INCORPORATION; *U.S. Private*, pg. 1212
D&E TRANSPORT INC.—See Roadrunner Transportation Systems, Inc.; *U.S. Public*, pg. 1802
DEVINE & PETERS INTERMODAL; *U.S. Private*, pg. 1218
DIAMOND GROUP INC.; *U.S. Private*, pg. 1223
DIAMOND STATE TRUCKING, INC.—See OEP Capital Advisors, L.P.; *U.S. Private*, pg. 2999
DIAMOND TRANSPORTATION SYSTEMS; *U.S. Private*, pg. 1224
DICKEY INC.; *U.S. Private*, pg. 1226
DILIGENT DELIVERY SYSTEMS; *U.S. Private*, pg. 1231
DILLON TRANSPORT INC—See Dillon Transport Inc.; *U.S. Private*, pg. 1231
DISTRIBUTION TRUCKING COMPANY—See The Kroger Co.; *U.S. Public*, pg. 2107
DIXON BROTHERS INC.; *U.S. Private*, pg. 1245
D.M. BOWMAN INCORPORATED—See Bowman Group LLP; *U.S. Private*, pg. 626
DODGE MOVING & STORAGE COMPANY INCORPORATED; *U.S. Private*, pg. 1252
DOHRN TRANSFER COMPANY; *U.S. Private*, pg. 1254
DOLPHIN LINE INCORPORATED; *U.S. Private*, pg. 1255
DRUG TRANSPORT INC.; *U.S. Private*, pg. 1279
D&S DISTRIBUTION INC.; *U.S. Private*, pg. 1138
DSV ROAD TRANSPORT, INC.—See DSV A/S; *Int'l*, pg. 2212
DTL TRANSPORTATION INC.; *U.S. Private*, pg. 1282
EAGLE SYSTEMS INC.; *U.S. Private*, pg. 1311
EARL R. MARTIN, INC.; *U.S. Private*, pg. 1313
EAST COAST TRANSPORT AND LOGISTICS, LLC—See P.A.M. Transportation Services, Inc.; *U.S. Public*, pg. 1629
ECM TRANSPORTATION, INC.; *U.S. Private*, pg. 1328
EDDIE STOBART LIMITED—See DBAY Advisors Limited; *Int'l*, pg. 1986
E&H TRANSPORT NETWORK INC.; *U.S. Private*, pg. 1301
EMPIRE TRUCK LINES, INC.—See IMC Holding, LLC; *U.S. Private*, pg. 2046
ENTERPRISE DISTRIBUTION INC.; *U.S. Private*, pg. 1403
EN-WAY ENTERPRISES INC.; *U.S. Private*, pg. 1389
EPES CARRIERS INC.; *U.S. Private*, pg. 1412
EPES TRANSPORT SYSTEM, INC.—See EPES Carriers Inc.; *U.S. Private*, pg. 1412
EPIKA FLEET SERVICES, INC.; *U.S. Private*, pg. 1413
EQUITY TRANSPORTATION CO.; *U.S. Private*, pg. 1416
ERICKSON TRANSPORT CORPORATION; *U.S. Private*, pg. 1420
ESSENTIAL FREIGHT SYSTEMS INC.; *U.S. Private*, pg. 1427
ESTES—See Estes Express Lines, Inc.; *U.S. Private*, pg. 1429
ETABLISSEMENTS R. BLANCHET; *Int'l*, pg. 2519
EVERFRESH BEVERAGES INC.—See National Beverage

N.A.I.C.S. INDEX 484121 — GENERAL FREIGHT TRU...

N.A.I.C.S. Index

Corp.; *U.S. Public*, pg. 1494
EVER GLORY LOGISTICS PTE. LTD.; *Int'l*, pg. 2562
EVERGREEN TRANSPORT, LLC; *U.S. Private*, pg. 1440
EXPEDITED FREIGHT SYSTEMS, LLC—See Roadrunner Transportation Systems, Inc.; *U.S. Public*, pg. 1802
EXPLOITATIEMAATSCHAPPIJ INTRAPROGRES B.V—See China International Marine Containers (Group) Co., Ltd.; *Int'l*, pg. 1511
EXPOLANKA FREIGHT (PRIVATE) LIMITED—See Expolanka Holdings PLC; *Int'l*, pg. 2589
EXPRESS LEASING INC.; *U.S. Private*, pg. 1451
EXXACT EXPRESS INC.; *U.S. Private*, pg. 1453
EZZELL TRUCKING INC.; *U.S. Private*, pg. 1454
FALCON TRANSPORT CO.; *U.S. Private*, pg. 1467
FAST TRUCKING SERVICE LTD .; *Int'l*, pg. 2621
FCD ENTERPRISES, INC.—See Kottke Trucking, Inc.; *U.S. Private*, pg. 2345
FEDERAL TRANSPORT, INC.—See Greif Inc.; *U.S. Public*, pg. 966
FEDEX FREIGHT CORPORATION—See FedEx Corporation; *U.S. Public*, pg. 827
FEDEX TRADE NETWORKS TRANSPORT & BROKERAGE (HONG KONG) LIMITED—See FedEx Corporation; *U.S. Public*, pg. 828
FIKES TRUCK LINE INC.; *U.S. Private*, pg. 1505
FINE ARTS ENTERPRISES, INC.; *U.S. Private*, pg. 1509
FIREBIRD BULK CARRIERS, INC.—See Adams Resources & Energy, Inc.; *U.S. Public*, pg. 38
FIRSTEXPRESS; *U.S. Private*, pg. 1531
FIRSTFLEET INC.; *U.S. Private*, pg. 1532
FLEETMASTER EXPRESS INC.; *U.S. Private*, pg. 1542
FLEET MOVERS, INC.—See Daseke, Inc.; *U.S. Private*, pg. 1161
FLINT SPECIAL SERVICES, INC.—See Universal Logistics Holdings, Inc.; *U.S. Public*, pg. 2261
FLOYD & BEASLEY TRANSFER CO. INC.; *U.S. Private*, pg. 1552
FOREWAY TRANSPORTATION INC.—See En-Way Enterprises Inc.; *U.S. Private*, pg. 1389
FORT WORTH CARRIER CORPORATION; *U.S. Private*, pg. 1575
FOUR STAR TRANSPORTATION CO.; *U.S. Private*, pg. 1582
FOX TRANSPORT CO.; *U.S. Private*, pg. 1585
FRANK'S VACUUM TRUCK SERVICE, INC.—See EQT AB; *Int'l*, pg. 2482
FREDERICK-THOMPSON CO.; *U.S. Private*, pg. 1602
FREEHOLD CARTAGE INC.; *U.S. Private*, pg. 1604
FREEPORT TRANSPORT INDUSTRIES, INC.; *U.S. Private*, pg. 1607
FREIGHT ALL KINDS INC.; *U.S. Private*, pg. 1607
FREMONT CONTRACT CARRIERS—See HMN Inc.; *U.S. Private*, pg. 1955
FRONTIER LOGISTICS, LP; *U.S. Private*, pg. 1615
FRONTIER TEMPERATURE CONTROL—See Online Transport System, Inc.; *U.S. Private*, pg. 3027
FRONTIER TRANSPORT CORPORATION—See Online Transport System, Inc.; *U.S. Private*, pg. 3027
FRY-WAGNER SYSTEMS INC.; *U.S. Private*, pg. 1618
GAINES MOTOR LINES INCORPORATED; *U.S. Private*, pg. 1635
GANGLOFF INDUSTRIES, INC.; *U.S. Private*, pg. 1641
GARDNER TRUCKING, INC.—See CRST International, Inc.; *U.S. Private*, pg. 1113
GARNER TRANSPORTATION GROUP, INC.; *U.S. Private*, pg. 1645
GARRY MERCER TRUCKING INC.; *Int'l*, pg. 2886
GARY AMOTH TRUCKING, INC.; *U.S. Private*, pg. 1646
GATEWAY DISTRIPARKS LTD.; *Int'l*, pg. 2889
GATEWAY TRANSPORT; *U.S. Private*, pg. 1651
GB MANAGEMENT SYSTEMS, INC.; *U.S. Private*, pg. 1653
G & D INTEGRATED; *U.S. Private*, pg. 1628
GEBRUDER WEISS GESELLSCHAFT M.B.H.; *Int'l*, pg. 2909
G JACQUEMMOZ ET FILS; *Int'l*, pg. 2861
GLASSCOCK COMPANY INC.—See Summit Materials, Inc.; *U.S. Public*, pg. 1959
GLEN RAVEN TRANSPORTATION INC.—See Glen Raven, Inc.; *U.S. Private*, pg. 1709
GLOBAL TRANSPORT LOGISTICS, INC.—See Hudson Hill Capital LLC; *U.S. Private*, pg. 2002
GOLDEN CARRIERS INC.; *U.S. Private*, pg. 1730
GO NORTH WEST LIMITED—See GLOBALVIA Inversiones, S.A.U.; *Int'l*, pg. 3005
GOOD TRANSPORT SERVICES, INC.; *U.S. Private*, pg. 1738
GOPETRO TRANSPORT LLC—See Sunoco LP; *U.S. Public*, pg. 1965
GPSI, INC.—See Ryman Hospitality Properties, Inc.; *U.S. Public*, pg. 1829
G&P TRUCKING COMPANY, INC.—See NFI Industries, Inc.; *U.S. Private*, pg. 2923
GRAMMER INDUSTRIES INC.—See Stellex Capital Management LP; *U.S. Private*, pg. 3800
GRAND ISLAND EXPRESS INC.; *U.S. Private*, pg. 1753
GRAY TRANSPORTATION INC.; *U.S. Private*, pg. 1759
GREAT AMERICAN LINES, INC.—See Universal Logistics Holdings, Inc.; *U.S. Public*, pg. 2261
GREEN LINES TRANSPORTATION; *U.S. Private*, pg. 1773
GREENWOOD MOTOR LINES INC.—See R & L Carriers, Inc.; *U.S. Private*, pg. 3331
GROCERY HAULERS INC.; *U.S. Private*, pg. 1791
GROENDYKE TRANSPORT, INC.; *U.S. Private*, pg. 1791
GROUP ONE, INC.—See Daseke, Inc.; *U.S. Private*, pg. 1161
GULLY TRANSPORTATION INC.; *U.S. Private*, pg. 1818
HAAS CARRIAGE INC.—See Haas Cabinet Co. Inc.; *U.S. Private*, pg. 1837
HAHN HOLDING CO.; *U.S. Private*, pg. 1840
HALLAMORE CORPORATION; *U.S. Private*, pg. 1844
HANNA TRUCK LINE, INC.—See Hanna Steel Corporation; *U.S. Private*, pg. 1855
HARBOR BRIDGE INTERMODAL INC—See US 1 Industries, Inc.; *U.S. Private*, pg. 4317
HARDINGER TRANSFER CO. INC.; *U.S. Private*, pg. 1863
HARNUM INDUSTRIES, LTD.—See Olympus Partners; *U.S. Private*, pg. 3013
HARRIS & SON TRUCKING CO. INC.; *U.S. Private*, pg. 1869
HARSCO METALS OOSTELIJK STAAL INTERNATIONAL B.V.—See Enviri Corporation; *U.S. Public*, pg. 781
HARTE HANKS LOGISTICS, LLC—See Harte Hanks, Inc.; *U.S. Public*, pg. 986
HAZMAT ENVIRONMENTAL GROUP, INC.; *U.S. Private*, pg. 1886
HEMMERLIN POLSKA SP. Z O.O.—See Hemmerlin S.A.; *Int'l*, pg. 3341
HEMMERLIN ROMANIA DUNAROM SPED. S.R.L.—See Hemmerlin S.A.; *Int'l*, pg. 3341
HEMMERLIN SWISS AG—See Hemmerlin S.A.; *Int'l*, pg. 3341
HENDRICKSON TRUCKING, INC.; *U.S. Private*, pg. 1915
HENIFF TRANSPORTATION SYSTEMS INC.; *U.S. Private*, pg. 1916
HERMAN R. EWELL INC.; *U.S. Private*, pg. 1925
HEYL TRUCK LINES INC.; *U.S. Private*, pg. 1928
HFCS TRANSPORT INC.—See P&S Investment Company Inc.; *U.S. Private*, pg. 3059
HHLA CONTAINER TERMINALS GMBH—See Hamburger Hafen und Logistik AG; *Int'l*, pg. 3236
HI-BOY GROUP INC.; *U.S. Private*, pg. 1931
HIGHLAND WATER COMPANY, INC.—See Pinnacle West Capital Corporation; *U.S. Public*, pg. 1692
HILL BROTHERS, INC.; *U.S. Private*, pg. 1945
HILLDRUP TRANSFER & STORAGE, INC.; *U.S. Private*, pg. 1946
HILLMAN'S TRANSFER LIMITED—See Armour Transportation Systems; *Int'l*, pg. 575
HILLSBORO TRANSPORTATION CO.; *U.S. Private*, pg. 1947
HINER TRANSPORT, INC.—See Service First Corporation; *U.S. Private*, pg. 3615
HIRSCHBACH MOTOR LINES, INC.; *U.S. Private*, pg. 1951
HMN INC.; *U.S. Private*, pg. 1955
HOFFMAN TRANSPORT INC.; *U.S. Private*, pg. 1960
HOLMES COMPANY OF JACKSON; *U.S. Private*, pg. 1967
HORIZON FREIGHT SYSTEM INC.; *U.S. Private*, pg. 1980
HORIZON FREIGHT SYSTEM—See Horizon Freight System Inc.; *U.S. Private*, pg. 1980
HORIZON TANK LINES, INC.—See Heniff Transportation Systems Inc.; *U.S. Private*, pg. 1916
HORIZON TRANSPORT INC.; *U.S. Private*, pg. 1982
HORNADY TRANSPORTATION, LLC—See Daseke, Inc.; *U.S. Private*, pg. 1161
HOUFF TRANSFER INC.; *U.S. Private*, pg. 1990
HOUG SPECIAL SERVICES, INC.; *U.S. Private*, pg. 1990
HOWARD SHEPPARD INC.; *U.S. Private*, pg. 1995
HOWARD TRANSPORTATION, INC.—See Howard Industries, Inc.; *U.S. Private*, pg. 1995
H&S TRANSPORTATION CO. INC.—See EverArc Holdings Limited; *Int'l*, pg. 2563
HVH TRANSPORTATION INC.; *U.S. Private*, pg. 2015
HYNDMAN TRANSPORT (1972) LIMITED—See Celadon Group, Inc.; *U.S. Public*, pg. 464
IMC HOLDING, LLC; *U.S. Private*, pg. 2046
INDIANA WESTERN EXPRESS INC.; *U.S. Private*, pg. 2063
INFINITY GROUP MANAGEMENT SERVICES, INC.; *U.S. Private*, pg. 2071
INTEGRATED FREIGHT CORPORATION; *U.S. Private*, pg. 2100
INTERLOAD SERVICES LTD.—See Caron Transportation Systems Partnership; *Int'l*, pg. 1342
INTERMODAL CARTAGE CO. INC.; *U.S. Private*, pg. 2112
INTERSTATE PERSONNEL SERVICES, INC.; *U.S. Private*, pg. 2125
IOWA TANKLINES INC.; *U.S. Private*, pg. 2136
JACK HOOD TRANSPORTATION INC.; *U.S. Private*, pg. 2174
JAMES BROWN CONTRACTING INC.—See Navigation Capital Partners, Inc.; *U.S. Private*, pg. 2873
JAMES J. WILLIAMS BULK SERVICE TRANSPORT, INC.—See Trans-System Inc.; *U.S. Private*, pg. 4206
JANCO LTD.; *U.S. Private*, pg. 2186
JAS WORLDWIDE, INC.; *U.S. Private*, pg. 2188
J.B. HUNT TRANSPORT, INC.—See J.B. Hunt Transport Services, Inc.; *U.S. Public*, pg. 1180
J.B. HUNT TRANSPORT SERVICES, INC.; *U.S. Public*, pg. 1180
J.D. & BILLY HINES TRUCKING, INC.; *U.S. Private*, pg. 2160
JEFFCO LEASING COMPANY INC.; *U.S. Private*, pg. 2197
JERRY W. BAILEY TRUCKING, INC.; *U.S. Private*, pg. 2202
J. GRADY RANDOLPH, INC.—See Daseke, Inc.; *U.S. Private*, pg. 1161
JHOC INC.; *U.S. Private*, pg. 2208
J.H. WALKER INC.; *U.S. Private*, pg. 2166
JIM PALMER TRUCKING INC.; *U.S. Private*, pg. 2209
J&J DRIVE AWAY SYSTEMS, LLC—See Evanston Partners, LLC; *U.S. Private*, pg. 1435
J.L. ROTHROCK INC.; *U.S. Private*, pg. 2167
J&M TANK LINES INC.; *U.S. Private*, pg. 2154
JOHN BUNNING TRANSFER COMPANY; *U.S. Private*, pg. 2220
JOHN CHRISTNER TRUCKING INC.; *U.S. Private*, pg. 2220
JOHNSON FEED INCORPORATED; *U.S. Private*, pg. 2227
JOSEPH ELETTO TRANSFER INCORPORATED; *U.S. Private*, pg. 2236
J.P. JENKS, INC.—See R.W. Sidley, Incorporated; *U.S. Private*, pg. 3340
J.P. NOONAN TRANSPORTATION; *U.S. Private*, pg. 2170
J&R SCHUGEL TRUCKING INC.; *U.S. Private*, pg. 2155
JRS TRUCKING SERVICE, INC.; *U.S. Private*, pg. 2240
J. SUPOR & SON TRUCKING & RIGGING CO., INC.; *U.S. Private*, pg. 2157
JUNKLUGGERS, LLC—See Apax Partners LLP; *Int'l*, pg. 502
JUST LOGISTICS, INC.—See Daiwa House Industry Co., Ltd.; *Int'l*, pg. 1946
KANE IS ABLE, INC.; *U.S. Private*, pg. 2260
KANSAI MARUWA LOGISTICS CO., LTD.—See AZ-COM MARUWA Holdings Inc.; *Int'l*, pg. 776
KAPLAN TRUCKING COMPANY; *U.S. Private*, pg. 2261
KARRIERS INC.; *U.S. Private*, pg. 2263
K&B TRANSPORTATION; *U.S. Private*, pg. 2249
KEIM TS INC.; *U.S. Private*, pg. 2274
KEITH TITUS CORPORATION; *U.S. Private*, pg. 2274
KENNEDY TRANSPORTATION; *U.S. Private*, pg. 2285
KENNEDY TRANSPORTATION—See Kennedy Transportation; *U.S. Private*, pg. 2285
KENOSHA BEEF INTERNATIONAL LTD. INC.; *U.S. Private*, pg. 2287
KEPHART TRUCKING COMPANY; *U.S. Private*, pg. 2290
KERNS TRUCKING INC.; *U.S. Private*, pg. 2291
KEYSTONE LINES, INC.—See US 1 Industries, Inc.; *U.S. Private*, pg. 4317
KKW TRUCKING, INC.; *U.S. Private*, pg. 2317
KLLM TRANSPORT SERVICES, INC.; *U.S. Private*, pg. 2320
KORUTRANS INTERNATIONAL INC.; *U.S. Private*, pg. 2344
KRAMME CONSOLIDATED INC.; *U.S. Private*, pg. 2349
KREILKAMP TRUCKING INC.; *U.S. Private*, pg. 2350
KYUSHU MARUWA LOGISTICS CO., LTD.—See AZ-COM MARUWA Holdings Inc.; *Int'l*, pg. 776
L.A. INC.—See J.B. Hunt Transport Services, Inc.; *U.S. Public*, pg. 1180
LAKEWAY TRUCKING INCORPORATED; *U.S. Private*, pg. 2378
LANDAIR TRANSPORT, INC.; *U.S. Private*, pg. 2384
LANDIS EXPRESS, INC.—See S&H Express, Inc.; *U.S. Private*, pg. 3513
LAND SPAN INC.—See Watkins Associated Industries Inc.; *U.S. Private*, pg. 4454
LANDSTAR LIGON, INC.—See Landstar System, Inc.; *U.S. Public*, pg. 1292
LANDSTAR RANGER, INC.—See Landstar System, Inc.; *U.S. Public*, pg. 1292
LANDSTAR TRANSPORTATION LOGISTICS, INC.—See Landstar System, Inc.; *U.S. Public*, pg. 1292
LAND TRUCKING CO. INC.—See Laney & Duke Terminal Warehouse Co. Inc.; *U.S. Private*, pg. 2388
LANGER TRANSPORT; *U.S. Private*, pg. 2389
LAUREL TRUCKING COMPANY INC.—See Laurel Grocery Company LLC; *U.S. Private*, pg. 2398
LAWRENCE TRANSPORTATION COMPANY—See Rihm Motor Company; *U.S. Private*, pg. 3436
L&B TRANSPORT INC.—See L&B Transport Inc.; *U.S. Private*, pg. 2362
LCL BULK TRANSPORT INC.—See P&S Investment Company Inc.; *U.S. Private*, pg. 3059
LCL TRANSIT COMPANY—See P&S Investment Company Inc.; *U.S. Private*, pg. 3059
LEGACY SUPPLY CHAIN SERVICES - ONTARIO—See LEGACY Supply Chain Services; *U.S. Private*, pg. 2417
LEON JONES FEED AND GRAIN INC.; *U.S. Private*, pg. 2423
LESAINT LOGISTICS TRANSPORTATION, INC.—See LeSaint Logistics LLC; *U.S. Private*, pg. 2432
LIBERTY TRANSPORTATION, INC.; *U.S. Private*, pg. 2447
LIEDTKA TRUCKING INCORPORATED; *U.S. Private*, pg. 2448

N.A.I.C.S. Index
484121 — GENERAL FREIGHT TRU... CORPORATE AFFILIATIONS

LIGHTNING TRANSPORTATION INC.; *U.S. Private*, pg. 2453
LINCOLN SECURITIES CORP.; *U.S. Private*, pg. 2458
LINDEN BULK TRANSPORTATION CO., LLC—See KKR & Co. Inc.; *U.S. Public*, pg. 1241
LIQUID TRANSPORT CORP.—See Dana Transport Inc.; *U.S. Private*, pg. 1152
LIQUID TRANSPORT INC.—See Dana Transport Inc.; *U.S. Private*, pg. 1152
LISK TRUCKING INC.; *U.S. Private*, pg. 2466
LMD INTEGRATED LOGISTIC SERVICES, INC.; *U.S. Private*, pg. 2476
LOCHER EVERS INTERNATIONAL, INC.—See Expolanka Holdings PLC; *Int'l*, pg. 2589
LOCKWOOD BROTHERS, INC.; *U.S. Private*, pg. 2478
LONGHORN PRODUCE COMPANY; *U.S. Private*, pg. 2492
LOUISIANA TRANSPORTATION, INC.—See Universal Logistics Holdings, Inc.; *U.S. Public*, pg. 2261
L&P TRANSPORTATION, LLC—See Leggett & Platt, Incorporated; *U.S. Public*, pg. 1302
LTI, INC.—See Lynden Incorporated; *U.S. Private*, pg. 2521
LUMIKKO TECHNOLOGIES OY—See BITZER SE; *Int'l*, pg. 1052
L.W. MILLER TRANSPORTATION; *U.S. Private*, pg. 2367
LYNDEN INCORPORATED; *U.S. Private*, pg. 2521
LYNDEN TRANSPORT, INC.—See Lynden Incorporated; *U.S. Private*, pg. 2521
MACON TRADING POST INC.—See HI-Boy Group Inc.; *U.S. Private*, pg. 1931
MAGNUM, LTD.; *U.S. Private*, pg. 2549
MAG TRANSPORT, LLC—See Mid Western Automotive LLC; *U.S. Private*, pg. 2707
MANUEL HUERTA TRUCKING INC.; *U.S. Private*, pg. 2567
MARINE CONTAINER SERVICES, INC.—See Saybrook Corporate Opportunity Fund LP; *U.S. Private*, pg. 3558
MARISOL INTERNATIONAL, LLC—See Roadrunner Transportation Systems, Inc.; *U.S. Public*, pg. 1802
MARJENN TRUCKING COMPANY INC.—See Frank Calandra, Inc.; *U.S. Private*, pg. 1594
MARKET TRANSPORT LTD.; *U.S. Private*, pg. 2579
MARTIN TRANSPORT, INC.—See Martin Resource Management Corporation; *U.S. Private*, pg. 2596
MASON DIXON INTERMODAL, INC.—See Universal Logistics Holdings, Inc.; *U.S. Public*, pg. 2261
MATHESON TRUCKING, INC.; *U.S. Private*, pg. 2610
MAUST CORPORATION; *U.S. Private*, pg. 2615
MAVERICK USA, INC. - NC FACILITY—See Maverick USA, Inc.; *U.S. Private*, pg. 2616
MAWSON & MAWSON INC.; *U.S. Private*, pg. 2616
MAYFLOWER INTERNATIONAL FORWARDING INC.—See UniGroup, Inc.; *U.S. Private*, pg. 4283
MAYFLOWER MILITARY MOVERS, LLC—See UniGroup, Inc.; *U.S. Private*, pg. 4283
MAYFLOWER TRANSIT, LLC—See UniGroup, Inc.; *U.S. Private*, pg. 4283
MAY TRUCKING COMPANY INC.; *U.S. Private*, pg. 2620
M. BRUENGER & CO., INC.—See Roadrunner Transportation Systems, Inc.; *U.S. Public*, pg. 1802
MCCOLLISTER MOVING & STORAGE OF NEW YORK—See McCollister's Transportation Group Inc.; *U.S. Private*, pg. 2629
MCCOY GROUP, INC.; *U.S. Private*, pg. 2630
MCELROY TRUCK LINES INC.; *U.S. Private*, pg. 2633
MCILVAINE TRUCKING INC.; *U.S. Private*, pg. 2637
MEGALIFT PTY LTD—See Lampson International, LLC; *U.S. Private*, pg. 2381
MELTON TRUCK LINES INC.; *U.S. Private*, pg. 2663
MERCER TRANSPORTATION COMPANY; *U.S. Private*, pg. 2669
MERGENTHALER TRANSFER & STORAGE CO.—See Mesa Systems, Inc.; *U.S. Private*, pg. 2678
MESILLA VALLEY TRANSPORTATION SERVICES INC.; *U.S. Private*, pg. 2678
METEOR EXPRESS, INC.; *U.S. Private*, pg. 2683
METRANS ADRIA D.O.O.—See Hamburger Hafen und Logistik AG; *Int'l*, pg. 3237
METROPOLITAN TRUCKING, INC.—See P.A.M. Transportation Services, Inc.; *U.S. Public*, pg. 1629
METROPOLITAN TRUCKING INC.—See P.A.M. Transportation Services, Inc.; *U.S. Public*, pg. 1629
MHF INC.; *U.S. Private*, pg. 2695
MIDNITE EXPRESS INC.—See MME Inc.; *U.S. Private*, pg. 2754
MID SOUTH TRANSPORT INC.; *U.S. Private*, pg. 2706
MIDWEST MOTOR EXPRESS INC.—See MME Inc.; *U.S. Private*, pg. 2754
MIDWEST SPECIALIZED TRANSPORTATION, INC.; *U.S. Private*, pg. 2723
MILLER BROTHERS EXPRESS LLC; *U.S. Private*, pg. 2733
MILLER HOLDING CORP.; *U.S. Private*, pg. 2734
MILLER TRUCK LINES INC.—See Miller Holding Corp.; *U.S. Private*, pg. 2734
MILLER TRUCK LINES INC. - TULSA—See Miller Holding Corp.; *U.S. Private*, pg. 2734
MILLIS TRANSFER INC.—See Heartland Express, Inc.; *U.S. Public*, pg. 1017
MISSOULA CARTAGE CO. INC.; *U.S. Private*, pg. 2748
MIZAR MOTORS, INC.—See Centaur, Inc.; *U.S. Private*, pg. 809
MMC TRANSPORT, INC.—See The Mennel Milling Company; *U.S. Private*, pg. 4077
MMC TRANSPORT OF VIRGINIA, INC.—See The Mennel Milling Company; *U.S. Private*, pg. 4077
MME INC.; *U.S. Private*, pg. 2754
MODE GLOBAL, LLC; *U.S. Private*, pg. 2759
MODERN GAS SALES INC.; *U.S. Private*, pg. 2760
MONROE PACKAGING BVBA—See Apollo Global Management, Inc.; *U.S. Public*, pg. 162
MORGAN SOUTHERN, INC.—See Universal Logistics Holdings, Inc.; *U.S. Public*, pg. 2261
MORRISTOWN DRIVERS SERVICE INC.; *U.S. Private*, pg. 2790
MOUNTAIN VALLEY EXPRESS CO; *U.S. Private*, pg. 2800
M & W HOT OIL INC; *U.S. Private*, pg. 2523
NAM PHAT LTD—See Hai Minh Corporation; *Int'l*, pg. 3209
NATIONAL COMMODITY EXCHANGE, INC.—See Custom Protein Corporation; *U.S. Private*, pg. 1129
NATIONAL DISTRIBUTORS INC.; *U.S. Private*, pg. 2852
NATIONAL FLEET MANAGEMENT, INC.; *U.S. Private*, pg. 2854
NATIONAL RETAIL TRANSPORTATION—See National Retail Systems, Inc.; *U.S. Private*, pg. 2862
NATIONAL TRANSPORT SERVICES CO.—See Wakefern Food Corporation; *U.S. Private*, pg. 4427
NATIONWIDE EXPRESS INC.—See Jones Capital, LLC; *U.S. Private*, pg. 2232
NATIONWIDE MAGAZINE & BOOK DISTRIBUTORS; *U.S. Private*, pg. 2866
NATIONWIDE SOUTHEAST INC.; *U.S. Private*, pg. 2866
NATIONWIDE TRUCK BROKERS INC.; *U.S. Private*, pg. 2866
NED BARD & SON CO.; *U.S. Private*, pg. 2879
NEW LEGEND, INC.; *U.S. Private*, pg. 2898
NEW YORK CAROLINA EXPRESS; *U.S. Private*, pg. 2908
NEXUS DISTRIBUTION CORPORATION; *U.S. Private*, pg. 2922
NFI INDUSTRIES, INC.; *U.S. Private*, pg. 2922
NFT DISTRIBUTION OPERATIONS LIMITED—See EmergeVest Limited; *Int'l*, pg. 2378
NICK STRIMBU INC.; *U.S. Private*, pg. 2925
NORTH AMERICAN BULK TRANSPORT INC.—See Tankstar USA, Inc.; *U.S. Private*, pg. 3931
NORTH AMERICAN VAN LINES—See Madison Dearborn Partners, LLC; *U.S. Private*, pg. 2542
NORTH CANTON TRANSFER COMPANY—See Rhone Group, LLC; *U.S. Private*, pg. 3424
NORTH CANTON TRANSFER COMPANY—See The Goldman Sachs Group, Inc.; *U.S. Public*, pg. 2080
NORTH DALLAS MOVING & STORAGE COMPANY CO., INC.; *U.S. Private*, pg. 2945
NORTHERN STEEL TRANSPORT CO.; *U.S. Private*, pg. 2954
NORTH PARK TRANSPORTATION CO. INC.; *U.S. Private*, pg. 2946
NORTH STAR TRANSPORTATION INC.—See Armellini Industries, Inc.; *U.S. Private*, pg. 330
NORTHWEST CONTAINER SERVICES INC.; *U.S. Private*, pg. 2959
NS MARUWA LOGISTICS CO., LTD.—See AZ-COM MARUWA Holdings Inc.; *Int'l*, pg. 776
OAK HARBOR FREIGHT LINES, INC.; *U.S. Private*, pg. 2983
OAK HARBOR FREIGHT LINES—See Oak Harbor Freight Lines, Inc.; *U.S. Private*, pg. 2983
OAKLEY TRANSPORT, INC.—See Oakley Groves Inc.; *U.S. Private*, pg. 2985
ONLINE TRANSPORT SYSTEM, INC.; *U.S. Private*, pg. 3027
ONO TRANSPORT SERVICES, INC.; *U.S. Private*, pg. 3027
ORLANDO COGEN LIMITED, L.P.—See I Squared Capital Advisors (US) LLC; *U.S. Private*, pg. 2025
ORMSBY TRUCKING INC.; *U.S. Private*, pg. 3044
OST TRUCKING COMPANY INC.; *U.S. Private*, pg. 3048
OZARK MOTOR LINES INC.; *U.S. Private*, pg. 3057
PACE MOTOR LINES INC.; *U.S. Private*, pg. 3063
PACIFIC COAST SEAFOODS COMPANY, INC.—See Dulcich, Inc.; *U.S. Private*, pg. 1286
PACIFIC GROUP TRANSPORT CO., INC.—See Dulcich, Inc.; *U.S. Private*, pg. 1286
PACIFIC MOTOR TRUCKING COMPANY INC.—See Jack Cooper Transport Co., Inc.; *U.S. Private*, pg. 2173
PACKARD TRANSPORT INC.; *U.S. Private*, pg. 3073
PAGE TRANSPORTATION INC.—See Keith Titus Corporation; *U.S. Private*, pg. 2274
PALMER MOVING & STORAGE CO.; *U.S. Private*, pg. 3081
P.A.M. TRANSPORT, INC.—See P.A.M. Transportation Services, Inc.; *U.S. Public*, pg. 1630
PAN AMERICAN EXPRESS INC.; *U.S. Private*, pg. 3083
PATRICK GALLAGHER TRUCKING INC.; *U.S. Private*, pg. 3110
PATRIOT ENVIRONMENTAL SERVICES, INC.—See J.F. Lehman & Company, Inc.; *U.S. Private*, pg. 2163
PAT SALMON & SONS, INC.; *U.S. Private*, pg. 3105
PAUL ARPIN VAN LINES, INC.; *U.S. Private*, pg. 3112
PEGASUS TRANSPORTATION, INC.—See CRST International, Inc.; *U.S. Private*, pg. 1113
PEI LOGISTICS, INC.—See PEI, Inc.; *U.S. Private*, pg. 3130
P.E. KRAMME INC.—See Kramme Consolidated Inc.; *U.S. Private*, pg. 2349
PENN'S BEST INC.; *U.S. Private*, pg. 3135
PHOENIX TRANSPORTATION SERVICES LLC; *U.S. Private*, pg. 3174
PINOLE VALLEY TRUCKING, INC.; *U.S. Private*, pg. 3186
PLAINS TRANSPORTATION INC.; *U.S. Private*, pg. 3195
PLANES MOVING & STORAGE COMPANY OF COLUMBUS—See Planes Moving & Storage, Inc.; *U.S. Private*, pg. 3195
PLANES MOVING & STORAGE, INC.; *U.S. Private*, pg. 3195
PLANES MOVING & STORAGE OF INDIANAPOLIS, INC.—See Planes Moving & Storage, Inc.; *U.S. Private*, pg. 3195
PORTLAND AIR FREIGHT, INC.; *U.S. Private*, pg. 3232
POTPOURRI GROUP INC.—See Northlane Capital Partners, LLC; *U.S. Private*, pg. 2956
PREMIER TRANSPORTATION & WAREHOUSES; *U.S. Private*, pg. 3251
PRICE TRUCK LINES INC.; *U.S. Private*, pg. 3258
PRIORITY AMERICA, INC.; *U.S. Private*, pg. 3266
PRODUCT DISTRIBUTION COMPANY—See General Electric Company; *U.S. Public*, pg. 920
P&S INVESTMENT COMPANY INC.; *U.S. Private*, pg. 3059
P&S TRANSPORTATION, INC.; *U.S. Private*, pg. 3059
PURDY BROTHERS TRUCKING COMPANY—See P&S Transportation, Inc.; *U.S. Private*, pg. 3059
QUALITY CARRIERS, INC. - RIVER FALLS—See Apax Partners LLP; *Int'l*, pg. 505
QUEST LINER INC.; *U.S. Private*, pg. 3326
RAINBOW MOVERS INC.; *U.S. Private*, pg. 3347
RAVEN TRANSPORT COMPANY INC.—See Raven Transport Holding, Inc.; *U.S. Private*, pg. 3357
RAVEN TRANSPORT HOLDING, INC.; *U.S. Private*, pg. 3357
REDDING LUMBER TRANSPORT, INC.; *U.S. Private*, pg. 3378
REEVE TRUCKING CO.; *U.S. Private*, pg. 3384
R. E. GARRISON TRUCKING INC.; *U.S. Private*, pg. 3333
REGENCY TRANSPORTATION INC.; *U.S. Private*, pg. 3386
RELCO SYSTEMS INC.; *U.S. Private*, pg. 3393
RELIABLE TANK LINE, LLC—See Quality Oil Company LLC; *U.S. Private*, pg. 3320
RELIABLE VAN & STORAGE CO., INC.; *U.S. Private*, pg. 3394
R E WEST INC.; *U.S. Private*, pg. 3331
REXIUS FOREST BY-PRODUCTS; *U.S. Private*, pg. 3417
RIISER TRANSPORTATION—See Riiser Oil Company Inc.; *U.S. Private*, pg. 3436
RISINGER BROS TRANSFER INC.; *U.S. Private*, pg. 3440
RITTER TRANSPORT, INC.—See EVO Transportation & Energy Services, Inc.; *U.S. Public*, pg. 804
RIVERSIDE TRANSPORT INC.; *U.S. Private*, pg. 3446
R & L CARRIERS, INC.; *U.S. Private*, pg. 3331
ROADRUNNER CARRIERS, LLC—See Roadrunner Transportation Systems, Inc.; *U.S. Public*, pg. 1802
ROADRUNNER TRANSPORTATION SYSTEMS, INC.—See Roadrunner Transportation Systems, Inc.; *U.S. Public*, pg. 1802
ROBERT M. NEFF INC.; *U.S. Private*, pg. 3458
ROEHL TRANSPORT, INC.; *U.S. Private*, pg. 3470
ROSS TRANSPORTATION SERVICES, INC.—See Ross Consolidated Corp.; *U.S. Private*, pg. 3485
ROYAL TRUCKING COMPANY; *U.S. Private*, pg. 3494
R.R. DONNELLEY LOGISTICS—See Chatham Asset Management, LLC; *U.S. Private*, pg. 865
RSC TRANSPORTATION INC.; *U.S. Private*, pg. 3496
RSD TRANSPORTATION INC.; *U.S. Private*, pg. 3496
RSK TRANSPORT LLC; *U.S. Private*, pg. 3497
RUAN TRANSPORTATION MANAGEMENT SYSTEMS, INC.; *U.S. Private*, pg. 3498
RUSSELL TRANSPORT, INC.; *U.S. Private*, pg. 3507
RYDER INTEGRATED LOGISTICS, INC.—See Ryder System, Inc.; *U.S. Public*, pg. 1828
SAIA, INC.; *U.S. Public*, pg. 1835
SAIA MOTOR FREIGHT LINE, INC.—See Saia, Inc.; *U.S. Public*, pg. 1835
SAIA MOTOR FREIGHT LINE, INC.—See Saia, Inc.; *U.S. Public*, pg. 1835
SAIA MOTOR FREIGHT LINE, INC.—See Saia, Inc.; *U.S. Public*, pg. 1835
SAIA MOTOR FREIGHT LINE, INC.—See Saia, Inc.; *U.S. Public*, pg. 1835
SAIA TL PLUS—See Saia, Inc.; *U.S. Public*, pg. 1835
SAKAE UNYU COMPANY LIMITED—See KKR & Co. Inc.; *U.S. Public*, pg. 1259
SAMMONS TRUCKING, INC.; *U.S. Private*, pg. 3537
SARGENT TRUCKING INC.; *U.S. Private*, pg. 3550
SAVAGE INLAND MARINE, LLC—See Savage Services Corporation; *U.S. Private*, pg. 3555
SAVAGE SERVICES CORPORATION; *U.S. Private*, pg. 3555
SCALES EXPRESS INC.; *U.S. Private*, pg. 3560
SCAN-VINO INC.; *U.S. Private*, pg. 3561

N.A.I.C.S. INDEX

484121 — GENERAL FREIGHT TRU...

SCARLET & GRAY CORP.—See Gray America Corp.; *U.S. Private*, pg. 1759
SCHLUMBERGER WIRELINE & TESTING—See Schlumberger Limited; *U.S. Public*, pg. 1846
SCHWERMAN TRUCKING CO. INC.—See Tankstar USA, Inc.; *U.S. Private*, pg. 3931
SCILLI SPECIALIZED FLATBED DIVISION, INC.—See Daseke, Inc.; *U.S. Private*, pg. 1161
SENTINEL TRANSPORTATION LLC - BELLE—See Phillips 66 Company; *U.S. Public*, pg. 1688
SENTINEL TRANSPORTATION LLC - WESTLAKE—See Phillips 66 Company; *U.S. Public*, pg. 1688
SERVICE CENTER BURCHARDKAI GMBH—See Hamburger Hafen und Logistik AG; *Int'l*, pg. 3237
SERVICE FIRST CORPORATION; *U.S. Private*, pg. 3615
SERVICE TRUCKING INC.; *U.S. Private*, pg. 3616
SEWARD MOTOR FREIGHT, INC.; *U.S. Private*, pg. 3619
SHAFFER TRUCKING COMPANY—See Crete Carrier Corp.; *U.S. Private*, pg. 1099
SHAFFER TRUCKING COMPANY—See Crete Carrier Corp.; *U.S. Private*, pg. 1099
SHARP TRANSPORT INC.; *U.S. Private*, pg. 3627
SHELBA D. JOHNSON TRUCKING, INC.; *U.S. Private*, pg. 3630
SHERMAN BROS TRUCKING; *U.S. Private*, pg. 3634
S&H EXPRESS, INC.; *U.S. Private*, pg. 3513
SHONAN VANTEC CORPORATION—See KKR & Co. Inc.; *U.S. Public*, pg. 1259
SITTON MOTOR LINES, INC.; *U.S. Private*, pg. 3677
SKINNER TRANSFER CORP.; *U.S. Private*, pg. 3682
SKY TRANSPORTATION SERVICES—See Warehouse Services Inc.; *U.S. Private*, pg. 4442
SLAY TRANSPORTATION CO INC—See Slay Industries Inc.; *U.S. Private*, pg. 3687
SMALL BUSINESS TRANSPORTATION; *U.S. Private*, pg. 3690
SMITH TRANSPORT, INC.—See Heartland Express, Inc.; *U.S. Public*, pg. 1017
S&M TRANSPORTATION INC; *U.S. Private*, pg. 3513
SNL DISTRIBUTION INC.; *U.S. Private*, pg. 3700
SODREL TRUCK LINES INC.; *U.S. Private*, pg. 3704
SOUTHEASTERN FREIGHT LINES, INC.; *U.S. Private*, pg. 3728
SOUTHERN AG CARRIERS, INC.; *U.S. Private*, pg. 3729
SOUTHLAND TRANSPORTATION CO.; *U.S. Private*, pg. 3737
SOUTH SHORE TRANSPORTATION CO.; *U.S. Private*, pg. 3724
SOUTHWESTERN MOTOR TRANSPORT INCORPORATED; *U.S. Private*, pg. 3741
SOUTHWEST FREIGHT DISTRIBUTORS, INC.—See Forward Air Corporation; *U.S. Public*, pg. 874
SOUTHWEST FREIGHT INC.; *U.S. Private*, pg. 3739
SOUTHWEST TRAILERS INC.—See Pan American Express Inc.; *U.S. Private*, pg. 3083
SPECIALIZED TRANSPORTATION SERVICE; *U.S. Private*, pg. 3749
SPECTRAL ENTERPRISES, INC.; *U.S. Private*, pg. 3751
SSS TRUCKING INC.—See Structural Steel Holding Inc.; *U.S. Private*, pg. 3842
STACEY MOVING & STORAGE, INC.; *U.S. Private*, pg. 3774
STAMPEDE TRANSPORTATION, LLC—See AET Holdings, LLC; *U.S. Private*, pg. 120
STANDARD FORWARDING CO. INC.—See Deutsche Post AG; *Int'l*, pg. 3814
STAN KOCH & SONS TRUCKING; *U.S. Private*, pg. 3777
STAR TRANSPORTATION, LLC—See Covenant Logistics Group, Inc.; *U.S. Public*, pg. 588
STC TRANSPORATION INC.—See Myers Container, LLC; *U.S. Private*, pg. 2824
STEALTH MAYFLOWER—See UniGroup, Inc.; *U.S. Private*, pg. 4283
STEEL & MACHINERY TRANSPORTATION; *U.S. Private*, pg. 3795
STEELMAN TRANSPORTATION, INC.—See Daseke, Inc.; *U.S. Private*, pg. 1162
STEVENS TRANSPORT INC.; *U.S. Private*, pg. 3810
STIDHAM TRUCKING INC.; *U.S. Private*, pg. 3812
STILES TRUCK LINE INC.; *U.S. Private*, pg. 3812
STOCK TRANSPORT INC.; *U.S. Private*, pg. 3814
STONE TRANSPORT INC.; *U.S. Private*, pg. 3826
STYLINE TRANSPORTATION INC.—See Styline Industries Inc.; *U.S. Private*, pg. 3846
SUDDATH RELOCATION SYSTEMS OF OREGON LLC—See The Suddath Companies; *U.S. Private*, pg. 4124
SUDDATH VAN LINES, INC. - KENT—See The Suddath Companies; *U.S. Private*, pg. 4124
SUMMIT TRUCKING, INC.; *U.S. Private*, pg. 3857
SUNBELT FURNITURE XPRESS, INC.—See Anderson Trucking Service Inc.; *U.S. Private*, pg. 277
SUPER SERVICE, LLC - KENTUCKY OFFICE—See Wayzata Investment Partners LLC; *U.S. Private*, pg. 4461
SUPER SERVICE, LLC—See Wayzata Investment Partners LLC; *U.S. Private*, pg. 4461

SUTTLES TRUCK LEASING INC.—See Dana Transport Inc.; *U.S. Private*, pg. 1152
SWIFT LOGISTICS, LLC—See Knight-Swift Transportation Holdings Inc.; *U.S. Public*, pg. 1269
SWIFT TRANSPORTATION CO., LLC—See Knight-Swift Transportation Holdings Inc.; *U.S. Public*, pg. 1269
SWING TRANSPORT INC.; *U.S. Private*, pg. 3894
SYSTEM FREIGHT INC.; *U.S. Private*, pg. 3906
SYSTEM TRANSPORT INC.—See Trans-System Inc.; *U.S. Private*, pg. 4206
TANDEM TRANSPORT INC.—See Prolog Services; *U.S. Private*, pg. 3282
TANKSTAR USA, INC.; *U.S. Private*, pg. 3931
TANTARA TRANSPORTATION GROUP; *U.S. Private*, pg. 3932
TAYLOR-MADE TRANSPORTATION INC.; *U.S. Private*, pg. 3941
TCSI/TRANSLAND INC.; *U.S. Private*, pg. 3943
TEDDY'S TRANSPORT; *U.S. Private*, pg. 3957
TEDI TRANSLOGIC EXPRESS DEDICATED INC.—See Deutsche Post AG; *Int'l*, pg. 2082
TENNESSEE STEEL HAULERS, INC.—See Daseke, Inc.; *U.S. Private*, pg. 1161
TERMINAL TRANSPORT INC.; *U.S. Private*, pg. 3969
TERRA FLUID MANAGEMENT, LLC—See Great Lakes Dredge & Dock Corporation; *U.S. Public*, pg. 962
TESORO LOGISTICS OPERATIONS LLC—See Marathon Petroleum Corporation; *U.S. Public*, pg. 1364
TEXAS STAR EXPRESS—See EPES Carriers Inc.; *U.S. Private*, pg. 1412
THREE RIVERS TRUCKING, INC.; *U.S. Private*, pg. 4164
TIDEWATER TRANSIT CO., INC.; *U.S. Private*, pg. 4168
TIONA TRUCK LINE INC.; *U.S. Private*, pg. 4175
T. M. INC.; *U.S. Private*, pg. 3911
TOHOKU MARUWA LOGISTICS CO., LTD.—See AZ-COM MARUWA Holdings Inc.; *Int'l*, pg. 776
TOKIWA KAIUN COMPANY LIMITED—See KKR & Co. Inc.; *U.S. Public*, pg. 1259
TOTAL TRANSPORTATION OF MISSISSIPPI LLC—See Knight-Swift Transportation Holdings Inc.; *U.S. Public*, pg. 1269
TOWNE AIR FREIGHT INC.—See Towne Holdings Inc.; *U.S. Private*, pg. 4198
TOWNE HOLDINGS INC.; *U.S. Private*, pg. 4198
TP OF MACON, INC.—See HI-Boy Group Inc.; *U.S. Private*, pg. 1931
TP TRUCKING LLC—See Timber Products Company, LP; *U.S. Private*, pg. 4171
TRANS AMERICAN TRUCKING SERVICE; *U.S. Private*, pg. 4205
TRANSAM TRUCKING INC.; *U.S. Private*, pg. 4207
TRANS-CARRIERS INC.—See Daco Corporation; *U.S. Private*, pg. 1144
TRANSCO LEASING INC.; *U.S. Private*, pg. 4207
TRANSCORR LLC; *U.S. Private*, pg. 4207
TRANSFLO CORPORATION—See CSX Corporation; *U.S. Public*, pg. 602
TRANS-LEASE GROUP; *U.S. Private*, pg. 4206
TRANSPORTATION GROUP—See Van Eerden Trucking Company; *U.S. Private*, pg. 4340
TRANSPORTATION SERVICES, INC.; *U.S. Private*, pg. 4211
TRANSPORTATION SPECIALISTS LTD.—See TSL Companies; *U.S. Private*, pg. 4254
TRANSPORT LEASING SYSTEMS, LLC—See US 1 Industries, Inc.; *U.S. Private*, pg. 4317
TRANSPORT SERVICE CO.—See Caisse de Depot et Placement du Quebec; *Int'l*, pg. 1255
TRANSPORT SERVICE CO.—See The Goldman Sachs Group, Inc.; *U.S. Public*, pg. 2081
TRANSPORT SERVICES, INC.—See Bennett International Group, Inc.; *U.S. Private*, pg. 527
TRANSPORTS GAZEAU SAS—See Groupement FLO; *Int'l*, pg. 3112
TRANS-SYSTEM INC.; *U.S. Private*, pg. 4206
TRANSWOOD CARRIERS INC.; *U.S. Private*, pg. 4211
TRANSYOKI - TRANSPORTES YOKI LTDA—See General Mills, Inc.; *U.S. Public*, pg. 922
TRANSYSTEMS INC.—See Little Brownie Properties Inc.; *U.S. Private*, pg. 2468
TRANSYSTEMS LLC - IDAHO DIVISION—See Transystems LLC; *U.S. Private*, pg. 4212
TRANSYSTEMS LLC - MINNESOTA DIVISION—See Transystems LLC; *U.S. Private*, pg. 4212
TRANSYSTEMS LLC - RED RIVER VALLEY DIVISION—See Transystems LLC; *U.S. Private*, pg. 4212
TRIAD TRANSPORT INC.; *U.S. Private*, pg. 4225
TRINITY TRANSPORTATION—See Trinity Industries, Inc.; *U.S. Public*, pg. 2194
TRIO TRUCKING INC.; *U.S. Private*, pg. 4236
TRI-STATE MOTOR TRANSIT CO.; *U.S. Private*, pg. 4224
TRUCK ONE, INC.; *U.S. Private*, pg. 4246
TRUCKS FOR YOU, INC.; *U.S. Private*, pg. 4246
TTI, INC.; *U.S. Private*, pg. 4255
T&T TRUCKING INCORPORATED; *U.S. Private*, pg. 3910
TURNER BROS TRUCKING LLC; *U.S. Private*, pg. 4260
TWISS TRANSPORT—See Bulova Technologies Group, Inc.; *U.S. Private*, pg. 685
T-W TRANSPORT, INC.—See Trans-System Inc.; *U.S. Private*, pg. 4206
UNIGROUP RELOCATION—See UniGroup, Inc.; *U.S. Private*, pg. 4283
UNISHIPPERS GLOBAL LOGISTICS, LLC—See Ridgemont Partners Management LLC; *U.S. Private*, pg. 3433
UNITED PARCEL SERVICE, INC.; *U.S. Public*, pg. 2233
UNITED VISION LOGISTICS HOLDING CORP.—See Welsh, Carson, Anderson & Stowe; *U.S. Private*, pg. 4480
UNITED VISION LOGISTICS MEXICO—See Welsh, Carson, Anderson & Stowe; *U.S. Private*, pg. 4480
UNITRANS CORPORATION, INC.—See Q International Courier, LLC; *U.S. Private*, pg. 3312
UNIVERSITY MOVING & STORAGE CO.; *U.S. Private*, pg. 4308
USA TRUCK, INC.—See Deutsche Bahn AG; *Int'l*, pg. 2054
US BULK TRANSPORT INC.; *U.S. Private*, pg. 4318
USHER TRANSPORT INC.; *U.S. Private*, pg. 4323
U.S. LIME COMPANY-TRANSPORTATION—See United States Lime & Minerals, Inc.; *U.S. Public*, pg. 2236
U.S. XPRESS, INC.—See Knight-Swift Transportation Holdings Inc.; *U.S. Public*, pg. 1269
VALLEY TRUCKING CO., INC.; *U.S. Private*, pg. 4335
VAN EERDEN TRUCKING COMPANY; *U.S. Private*, pg. 4340
VAN-PAK INC.; *U.S. Private*, pg. 4341
VANTEC CENTRAL CORPORATION—See KKR & Co. Inc.; *U.S. Public*, pg. 1259
VANTEC CENTRAL LOGISTICS CORPORATION—See KKR & Co. Inc.; *U.S. Public*, pg. 1259
VANTEC EAST LOGISTICS CORPORATION—See KKR & Co. Inc.; *U.S. Public*, pg. 1259
VANTEC TOKAI LOGISTICS CORPORATION—See KKR & Co. Inc.; *U.S. Public*, pg. 1259
VAN WYK INC.; *U.S. Private*, pg. 4341
VENTURE EXPRESS, INC.; *U.S. Private*, pg. 4357
VINCENT FISTER INC.—See Fister Incorporated; *U.S. Private*, pg. 1535
VOLUNTEER EXPRESS, INC.—See Central Freight Lines, Inc.; *U.S. Private*, pg. 821
V&S MIDWEST CARRIERS CORP.; *U.S. Private*, pg. 4327
THE WAGGONERS TRUCKING; *U.S. Private*, pg. 4132
WALBON AND COMPANY INC.; *U.S. Private*, pg. 4427
WALLACE CASCADE TRANSPORT, INC.; *U.S. Private*, pg. 4430
WALPOLE INC.; *U.S. Private*, pg. 4432
WALPOLE LEASING COMPANY—See Walpole Inc.; *U.S. Private*, pg. 4432
WALSH TRUCKING CO. LTD; *U.S. Private*, pg. 4433
WANDO TRUCKING, LLC—See Universal Logistics Holdings, Inc.; *U.S. Public*, pg. 2261
WARD TRUCKING CORP.; *U.S. Private*, pg. 4441
WARREN TRUCKING COMPANY INC.—See Worldwide Logistics, Inc.; *U.S. Private*, pg. 4569
WATTS FREIGHT SYSTEMS, INC.—See Watts Trucking Service, Inc.; *U.S. Private*, pg. 4456
WAYNE TRANSPORTS INC.; *U.S. Private*, pg. 4460
WAY'S TRANSPORT LTD.—See Armour Transportation Systems; *Int'l*, pg. 575
W.C. MCQUAIDE INC.; *U.S. Private*, pg. 4419
WEBER DISTRIBUTION, LLC; *U.S. Private*, pg. 4465
WEBSTER TRUCKING CORPORATION; *U.S. Private*, pg. 4467
W.E. GRAHAM, INC.—See EVO Transportation & Energy Services, Inc.; *U.S. Public*, pg. 804
WERNER ENTERPRISES CANADA CORPORATION—See Werner Enterprises, Inc.; *U.S. Public*, pg. 2349
WERNER ENTERPRISES, INC.; *U.S. Public*, pg. 2349
WESTERN EXPRESS HOLDINGS, INC.; *U.S. Private*, pg. 4493
WESTERN EXPRESS, INC.—See Western Express Holdings, Inc.; *U.S. Private*, pg. 4493
WESTERN STAR TRANSPORTATION; *U.S. Private*, pg. 4496
WEST SIDE TRANSPORT, INC.—See West Side Unlimited Corporation; *U.S. Private*, pg. 4487
WHELAN & ASSOCIATES INC.; *U.S. Private*, pg. 4506
WHITELINE EXPRESS LTD.—See Plastipak Holdings, Inc.; *U.S. Private*, pg. 3200
WILEY SANDERS TRUCK LINES INC.; *U.S. Private*, pg. 4520
WILLIAMS BROTHERS TRUCKING; *U.S. Private*, pg. 4525
WILLS TRUCKING INC.—See Total Recovery Group, LLC; *U.S. Private*, pg. 4191
WILSEY BENNETT COMPANY; *U.S. Private*, pg. 4529
WILSON TRUCKING CORPORATION; *U.S. Private*, pg. 4531
WINN-DIXIE LOGISTICS, INC.—See Aldi Einkauf SE & Co. oHG; *Int'l*, pg. 304
WISEWAY MOTOR FREIGHT INC.; *U.S. Private*, pg. 4550
WITHERS/SUDDATH VAN LINES, INC.—See The Suddath Companies; *U.S. Private*, pg. 4125
WITTE BROTHERS EXCHANGE INC.; *U.S. Private*, pg. 4551
WOODFIELD INC.; *U.S. Private*, pg. 4558

484121 — GENERAL FREIGHT TRU...

WORLDBRIDGE LOGISTICS INC.—See V. Alexander & Co. Inc.; *U.S. Private*, pg. 4328
WORLD SHIPPING, INC.; *U.S. Private*, pg. 4567
WORLDWIDE LOGISTICS, INC.; *U.S. Private*, pg. 4569
W.S. THOMAS TRANSFER, INC.—See Online Transport System, Inc.; *U.S. Private*, pg. 3027
W.W. TRANSPORT, INC.; *U.S. Private*, pg. 4423
WYNNE TRANSPORT SERVICE INC.; *U.S. Private*, pg. 4578
XONEX INC.; *U.S. Private*, pg. 4582
XPO NLM, INC.—See XPO, Inc.; *U.S. Public*, pg. 2392
YARNALL WAREHOUSE, INC.; *U.S. Private*, pg. 4586
YOSEMITE EXPRESS CO.—See Kingswood Capital Management LLC; *U.S. Private*, pg. 2312

484122 — GENERAL FREIGHT TRUCKING, LONG-DISTANCE, LESS THAN TRUCKLOAD

ABF FREIGHT SYSTEM (B.C.), LTD.—See ArcBest Corporation; *U.S. Public*, pg. 180
ABF FREIGHT SYSTEM CANADA, LTD.—See ArcBest Corporation; *U.S. Public*, pg. 180
ACE DORAN BROKERAGE CO.—See Ace Doran Hauling & Rigging Company; *U.S. Private*, pg. 56
AL-AMIN BROTHERS TRANSPORTATION, LLC.; *U.S. Private*, pg. 148
ALASKA WEST EXPRESS, INC.—See Lynden Incorporated; *U.S. Private*, pg. 2521
AM CAN—See Frozen Food Express Industries, Inc.; *U.S. Private*, pg. 1617
AMERICAN GROUP, LLC.; *U.S. Private*, pg. 235
AVENUE MOVING AND STORAGE LIMITED; *Int'l*, pg. 739
AYR MOTOR EXPRESS INC.; *Int'l*, pg. 775
BDR TRANSPORT, INC.; *U.S. Private*, pg. 502
BLUE & GREY TRANSPORTATION—See US 1 Industries, Inc.; *U.S. Private*, pg. 4317
CAROLINA NATIONAL TRANSPORTATION LLC—See US 1 Industries, Inc.; *U.S. Private*, pg. 4317
CARRIER INDUSTRIES—See New England Motor Freight, Inc.; *U.S. Private*, pg. 2894
CELADON CANADA INC.—See Celadon Group, Inc.; *U.S. Public*, pg. 464
CENTRAL TRANSPORT INTERNATIONAL - GIBSONIA—See CenTra, Inc.; *U.S. Private*, pg. 818
CHEESMAN LLC; *U.S. Private*, pg. 869
CONWELL, LLC—See Frozen Food Express Industries, Inc.; *U.S. Private*, pg. 1617
COOPER POWER SYSTEMS TRANSPORTATION COMPANY—See Eaton Corporation plc; *Int'l*, pg. 2278
DTS COMPANIES INC.; *U.S. Private*, pg. 1282
ESTES EXPRESS LINES, INC.; *U.S. Private*, pg. 1429
EXEL AUTOMOCION S.A. DE C.V.—See Deutsche Post AG; *Int'l*, pg. 2080
FEDEX FREIGHT CANADA CORP.—See FedEx Corporation; *U.S. Public*, pg. 827
FEDEX FREIGHT, INC.—See FedEx Corporation; *U.S. Public*, pg. 828
FORBES-HEWLETT TRANSPORT INC.; *Int'l*, pg. 2729
FREIGHTVALUE INC.—See ArcBest Corporation; *U.S. Public*, pg. 180
FROZEN FOOD EXPRESS INDUSTRIES, INC.; *U.S. Private*, pg. 1617
GRAEBEL DENVER MOVERS, INC.; *U.S. Private*, pg. 1750
GULF LINE TRANSPORTATION—See US 1 Industries, Inc.; *U.S. Private*, pg. 4317
H & R TRANSPORT LTD.; *Int'l*, pg. 3191
HYWAY TRUCKING COMPANY—See FST Logistics Inc.; *U.S. Private*, pg. 1618
JOINT RETAIL LOGISTICS LIMITED—See Deutsche Post AG; *Int'l*, pg. 2081
KIMBALL INTERNATIONAL TRANSIT, INC.—See HNI Corporation; *U.S. Public*, pg. 1043
LAKEVILLE MOTOR EXPRESS INC.—See Wren Corporation; *U.S. Private*, pg. 4572
LANDSTAR GEMINI, INC.—See Landstar System, Inc.; *U.S. Public*, pg. 1292
L & N TRUCK SERVICE OF ELLENWOOD, LLC—See American Securities LLC; *U.S. Private*, pg. 248
LONDON GENERAL TRANSPORT SERVICES LIMITED—See GLOBALVIA Inversiones, S.A.U.; *Int'l*, pg. 3005
MAGNUM LTL, INC.—See Magnum, Ltd.; *U.S. Private*, pg. 2549
MILKY WAY—See Lynden Incorporated; *U.S. Private*, pg. 2521
NEBRASKA TRANSPORT CO. INC.; *U.S. Private*, pg. 2879
NEW ENGLAND MOTOR FREIGHT, INC.; *U.S. Private*, pg. 2894
NEW PENN MOTOR EXPRESS, INC.—See Yellow Corporation; *U.S. Public*, pg. 2398
NICK BARBIERI TRUCKING, LLC—See AIP, LLC; *U.S. Private*, pg. 136
NORTHERN PLAINS TRUCKING, LLC—See Superior Energy Services, Inc.; *U.S. Private*, pg. 3877
PITT-OHIO EXPRESS INC.; *U.S. Private*, pg. 3191
PREMIUM TRANSPORTATION SERVICES, INC.—See Saybrook Corporate Opportunity Fund LP; *U.S. Private*, pg. 3558
ROADMASTER TRANSPORTATION, INC.—See Daseke, Inc.; *U.S. Private*, pg. 1161
ROCKWELL TRANSPORTATION, INC.—See Rockwell Medical, Inc.; *U.S. Public*, pg. 1807
SCHENKER AB—See Deutsche Bahn AG; *Int'l*, pg. 2053
SERVICIOS DE TRANSPORTACION JAGUAR, S.A DE C.V.—See Lilium Group LLC; *U.S. Private*, pg. 2455
SERVICIOS DE TRANSPORTACION JAGUAR, S.A DE C.V.—See Luminus Management, LLC; *U.S. Private*, pg. 2514
SINOTRANS AIR TRANSPORTATION DEVELOPMENT CO., LTD.—See China Merchants Group Limited; *Int'l*, pg. 1522
SMOKEY POINT DISTRIBUTING, INC.—See Daseke, Inc.; *U.S. Private*, pg. 1161
T.J. MCGEEHAN'S SALES & SERVICE LTD.; *U.S. Private*, pg. 3912
TONY'S EXPRESS INC.; *U.S. Private*, pg. 4185
UNITED PARCEL SERVICE CO.—See United Parcel Service, Inc.; *U.S. Public*, pg. 2233
UNITED PARCEL SERVICE GENERAL SERVICES CO.—See United Parcel Service, Inc.; *U.S. Public*, pg. 2234
UNITED PARCEL SERVICE OF AMERICA, INC.—See United Parcel Service, Inc.; *U.S. Public*, pg. 2234
USF HOLLAND INC.—See Yellow Corporation; *U.S. Public*, pg. 2398
USF REDDAWAY INC.—See Yellow Corporation; *U.S. Public*, pg. 2398
US SPECIAL DELIVERY INC.; *U.S. Private*, pg. 4320
WILSON LOGISTICS, INC.; *U.S. Private*, pg. 4531

484210 — USED HOUSEHOLD AND OFFICE GOODS MOVING

A-1 FREEMAN MOVING & STORAGE INC.; *U.S. Private*, pg. 21
AACTION MOVERS; *U.S. Private*, pg. 31
A. ARNOLD MOVING COMPANY, INC. - INDIANAPOLIS DIVISION—See A. Arnold Moving Company, Inc.; *U.S. Private*, pg. 22
A. ARNOLD MOVING COMPANY, INC.; *U.S. Private*, pg. 22
A. ARNOLD OF KANSAS CITY, LLC—See A. Arnold Moving Company, Inc.; *U.S. Private*, pg. 22
ABC MOVING & STORAGE INC.; *U.S. Private*, pg. 36
ACE RELOCATION SYSTEMS INC.; *U.S. Private*, pg. 57
ACE VAN LINES INC.—See Stevens Group, Inc.; *U.S. Private*, pg. 3809
ACE WORLD WIDE MOVING & STORAGE CO. INC.; *U.S. Private*, pg. 57
ADVANTAGE FORWARDERS INC.—See Stevens Group, Inc.; *U.S. Private*, pg. 3809
ALBERT MOVING & STORAGE, INC.; *U.S. Private*, pg. 153
ALL-AMERICAN MOVING GROUP LLC; *U.S. Private*, pg. 173
ALLIED PICKFORDS—See Madison Dearborn Partners, LLC; *U.S. Private*, pg. 2542
ALLIED VAN LINES, INC.—See Madison Dearborn Partners, LLC; *U.S. Private*, pg. 2542
AMERICAN INTERNATIONAL MOVERS—See HI-Boy Group Inc.; *U.S. Private*, pg. 1931
AMERICAN RED BALL TRANSIT CO. INC.—See Interstate Group Holdings, Inc.; *U.S. Private*, pg. 2125
AMJ CAMPBELL, INC.; *Int'l*, pg. 428
THE ANDREWS MOVING & STORAGE COMPANY INC.; *U.S. Private*, pg. 3986
ARCBEST CORPORATION; *U.S. Public*, pg. 179
ARMSTRONG MOVING & STORAGE INC.; *U.S. Private*, pg. 332
ATLANTIC RELOCATION SYSTEMS; *U.S. Private*, pg. 374
ATLAS VAN LINES (CANADA) LTD.—See Atlas World Group, Inc.; *U.S. Private*, pg. 380
ATLAS VAN LINES, INC.—See Atlas World Group, Inc.; *U.S. Private*, pg. 380
BAILEY'S MOVING AND STORAGE; *U.S. Private*, pg. 426
BANDSTRA TRANSPORTATION SYSTEMS LTD.; *Int'l*, pg. 831
BEKINS MOVING & STORAGE CO.; *U.S. Private*, pg. 516
BEKINS VAN LINES, LLC—See Wheaton Van Lines, Inc.; *U.S. Private*, pg. 4505
BUDD VAN LINES, INC.; *U.S. Private*, pg. 679
BULLDOG MOVERS, INC.; *U.S. Private*, pg. 685
BURNHAM WORLD FORWARDERS INC.—See Stevens Group, Inc.; *U.S. Private*, pg. 3809
CARLYLE VAN LINES INC.; *U.S. Private*, pg. 765
CENTRAL TRANSPORTATION SYSTEMS, INC.; *U.S. Private*, pg. 825
CENTRAL VAN & STORAGE, INC.—See Madison Dearborn Partners, LLC; *U.S. Private*, pg. 2542
CHHJ FRANCHISING LLC; *U.S. Private*, pg. 876
CHIPMAN CORPORATION; *U.S. Private*, pg. 886
CHUNG LIEN TRANSPORTATION CO., LTD.; *Int'l*, pg. 1597
CLANCY'S TRANSFER & STORAGE, INC.—See Bekins Moving & Storage Co.; *U.S. Private*, pg. 516
COLEMAN AMERICAN ALLIED—See Coleman American Companies, Inc.; *U.S. Private*, pg. 967
COLEMAN AMERICAN COMPANIES, INC.; *U.S. Private*, pg. 966
COLEMAN AMERICAN MOVING SERVICES INC.—See Coleman American Companies, Inc.; *U.S. Private*, pg. 967
COLLEGEBOXES, LLC—See U-Haul Holding Company; *U.S. Public*, pg. 2211
COMMERCIAL RECORD CENTER—See Nelson Westerberg, Inc.; *U.S. Private*, pg. 2884
CONNECT NOW PTY. LTD.—See AGL Energy Limited; *Int'l*, pg. 211
COOK MOVING SYSTEMS, INC.; *U.S. Private*, pg. 1038
CORNERSTONE RELOCATION GROUP, LLC.—See Atlas World Group, Inc.; *U.S. Private*, pg. 381
COROVAN CORPORATION; *U.S. Private*, pg. 1053
COROVAN MOVING & STORAGE CO.—See Corovan Corporation; *U.S. Private*, pg. 1053
COVAN INTERNATIONAL INC.—See Coleman American Companies, Inc.; *U.S. Private*, pg. 967
COVAN WORLDWIDE MOVING INC.—See Coleman American Companies, Inc.; *U.S. Private*, pg. 967
COVENANT STORAGE INC.—See HI-Boy Group Inc.; *U.S. Private*, pg. 1931
CROWN MOVING & STORAGE INC.—See Wheaton Van Lines, Inc.; *U.S. Private*, pg. 4505
DARYL FLOOD RELOCATION & LOGISTICS; *U.S. Private*, pg. 1160
DEARBORN MOVING & STORAGE INC.; *U.S. Private*, pg. 1185
DOPPELMAYR NEW ZEALAND LTD.—See Doppelmayr Group; *Int'l*, pg. 2174
DOPPELMAYR TRANSPORT TECHNOLOGY GMBH—See Doppelmayr Group; *Int'l*, pg. 2174
DRS DILIP ROADLINES LTD.; *Int'l*, pg. 2206
ECYCLERS, LLC—See The Kane Company; *U.S. Private*, pg. 4064
E.H. HAMILTON TRUCKING SERVICE; *U.S. Private*, pg. 1305
ESTES EXPRESS LINES, INC. - ESTES SUREMOVE DIVISION—See Estes Express Lines, Inc.; *U.S. Private*, pg. 1429
EXECUTIVE RELOCATION CORPORATION—See Madison Dearborn Partners, LLC; *U.S. Private*, pg. 2542
FIRST CLASS MOVING SYSTEMS, INC.; *U.S. Private*, pg. 1515
GATEKEEPER INTELLIGENT SECURITY UK LTD.—See OSI Systems, Inc.; *U.S. Public*, pg. 1621
GATEKEEPER SECURITY MIDDLE EAST FTZ—See OSI Systems, Inc.; *U.S. Public*, pg. 1621
GEORGE B. HOLMAN & CO. INC.—See Xonex Inc.; *U.S. Private*, pg. 4582
GLOBE STORAGE & MOVING CO. INC.; *U.S. Private*, pg. 1720
HAZEL'S HOT SHOT, INC.; *U.S. Private*, pg. 1886
HI-LINE MOVING SERVICES INC.; *U.S. Private*, pg. 1931
HIREAHELPER LLC; *U.S. Private*, pg. 1950
HORSELESS CARRIAGE CARRIERS, INC.—See McCollister's Transportation Group Inc.; *U.S. Private*, pg. 2629
HUCK FINN GMBH—See Ekosem-Agrar GmbH; *Int'l*, pg. 2339
HUTCHCRAFT VAN SERVICE, INC.; *U.S. Private*, pg. 2014
IMLACH MOVERS INC.; *U.S. Private*, pg. 2047
INTERSTATE INTERNATIONAL, INC.—See Interstate Group Holdings, Inc.; *U.S. Private*, pg. 2125
ISLAND MOVERS INC.; *U.S. Private*, pg. 2145
JOHN FAYARD MOVING AND WAREHOUSING; *U.S. Private*, pg. 2221
JOHNSON STORAGE & MOVING COMPANY; *U.S. Private*, pg. 2229
JOYCE BROS STORAGE & VAN CO.; *U.S. Private*, pg. 2238
LA GROU MOTOR SERVICE INCORPORATED; *U.S. Private*, pg. 2368
LAWRENCE TRANSPORTATION SYSTEMS INC.; *U.S. Private*, pg. 2402
LEWIS & MICHAEL, INC.; *U.S. Private*, pg. 2437
L & L VAN LINES INC.—See HI-Boy Group Inc.; *U.S. Private*, pg. 1931
MEATHEAD MOVERS; *U.S. Private*, pg. 2648
MESA SYSTEMS, INC.; *U.S. Private*, pg. 2678
METROPOLITAN MOVING & STORAGE; *U.S. Private*, pg. 2688
MOVEDYNAMICS—See EAC Invest AS; *Int'l*, pg. 2262
MOVE-PRO USA INC.—See HI-Boy Group Inc.; *U.S. Private*, pg. 1931
MOVE SOLUTIONS LTD.; *U.S. Private*, pg. 2801
MOVING.COM, INC.—See News Corporation; *U.S. Public*, pg. 1519
NATIONAL VAN LINES, INC.; *U.S. Private*, pg. 2864
NAVL LLC—See Madison Dearborn Partners, LLC; *U.S. Private*, pg. 2542
NELSON WESTERBERG, INC.; *U.S. Private*, pg. 2883
NILSON VAN & STORAGE INC.; *U.S. Private*, pg. 2927
NOR-CAL MOVING SERVICES; *U.S. Private*, pg. 2935
NORTH AMERICAN VAN LINES, INC.—See Madison Dearborn Partners, LLC; *U.S. Private*, pg. 2542

N.A.I.C.S. INDEX

484230 — SPECIALIZED FREIGHT...

PATRIOT FORWARDERS INC.—See Stevens Group, Inc.; *U.S. Private*, pg. 3809
PILGRIM VAN LINES, LLC—See UniGroup, Inc.; *U.S. Private*, pg. 4283
PITZER TRANSFER & STORAGE—See Peoples Services Inc.; *U.S. Private*, pg. 3142
PLANES MOVING & STORAGE OF CHICAGO, LLC—See Planes Moving & Storage, Inc.; *U.S. Private*, pg. 3195
PLUS RELOCATION SERVICES, INC.; *U.S. Private*, pg. 3215
RAIL DELIVERY SERVICES, INC.; *U.S. Private*, pg. 3346
RANGER LIFT TRUCKS; *U.S. Private*, pg. 3355
RBAB, INC.—See Riverstone Logistics, LLC; *U.S. Private*, pg. 3448
ROGER WARD INC.; *U.S. Private*, pg. 3471
ROYAL HAWAIIAN MOVERS, INC.; *U.S. Private*, pg. 3492
SAFEWAY MOVING & STORAGE INC—See Fister Incorporated; *U.S. Private*, pg. 1535
SANTA FE WRIDGWAYS—See EAC Invest AS; *Int'l*, pg. 2262
SCOBEY MOVING & STORAGE LTD; *U.S. Private*, pg. 3575
SECURITY VAN LINES—See Johnson Storage & Moving Company; *U.S. Private*, pg. 2229
SIRVA CANADA LP—See Madison Dearborn Partners, LLC; *U.S. Private*, pg. 2542
SIRVA PTY. LTD—See Madison Dearborn Partners, LLC; *U.S. Private*, pg. 2542
SIRVA RELOCATION LLC—See Madison Dearborn Partners, LLC; *U.S. Private*, pg. 2542
SMITH DRAY LINE & STORAGE CO.; *U.S. Private*, pg. 3694
SML RELOCATION, LLC—See Porch Group, Inc.; *U.S. Public*, pg. 1702
SORENSEN MOVING & STORAGE COMPANY, INC.—See The Advance Group; *U.S. Private*, pg. 3982
STANDARD OFFICE SYSTEMS ATLANTIC INC.; *U.S. Private*, pg. 3781
STARVING STUDENTS MOVING COMPANY; *U.S. Private*, pg. 3788
STERLING INTERNATIONAL, INC.—See A. Arnold Moving Company, Inc.; *U.S. Private*, pg. 22
STEVENS GROUP, INC.; *U.S. Private*, pg. 3809
STEVENS TRANSPORTATION CO. INC.—See Stevens Group, Inc.; *U.S. Private*, pg. 3809
STEVENS VAN LINES INC.—See Stevens Group, Inc.; *U.S. Private*, pg. 3809
THE SUDDATH COMPANIES; *U.S. Private*, pg. 4124
SUDDATH RELOCATION SYSTEMS INC—See The Suddath Companies; *U.S. Private*, pg. 4124
SUDDATH RELOCATION SYSTEMS OF ARIZONA - PHOENIX—See The Suddath Companies; *U.S. Private*, pg. 4124
SUDDATH RELOCATION SYSTEMS OF FT. LAUDERDALE, INC.—See The Suddath Companies; *U.S. Private*, pg. 4124
SUDDATH RELOCATION SYSTEMS OF THE TWIN CITIES, LLC—See The Suddath Companies; *U.S. Private*, pg. 4124
SUDDATH VAN LINES INC.—See The Suddath Companies; *U.S. Private*, pg. 4124
TEXAS MOVING COMPANY INC.—See Willis Permian Movers, Inc.; *U.S. Private*, pg. 4528
TRANSPORT DISTRIBUTION COMPANY; *U.S. Private*, pg. 4210
TRC GLOBAL SOLUTIONS, INC.; *U.S. Private*, pg. 4215
TRI STAR FREIGHT SYSTEM INC.; *U.S. Private*, pg. 4221
UNIGROUP, INC.; *U.S. Private*, pg. 4283
UNIGROUP WORLDWIDE, INC.—See UniGroup, Inc.; *U.S. Private*, pg. 4283
UNITED VAN LINES, LLC—See UniGroup, Inc.; *U.S. Private*, pg. 4283
VALLEY RELOCATION & STORAGE; *U.S. Private*, pg. 4335
VAN KING & STORAGE INC.; *U.S. Private*, pg. 4340
VICTORY WORLDWIDE TRANSPORTATION; *U.S. Private*, pg. 4379
WELESKI TRANSFER INC.; *U.S. Private*, pg. 4474
WHEATON VAN LINES, INC.; *U.S. Private*, pg. 4505
WILLIAM B. MEYER INC.; *U.S. Private*, pg. 4522
WILLIS PERMIAN MOVERS, INC.; *U.S. Private*, pg. 4528

484220 — SPECIALIZED FREIGHT (EXCEPT USED GOODS) TRUCKING, LOCAL

ABLE MACHINERY MOVERS, INC.; *U.S. Private*, pg. 39
AG EXPRESS, INC.; *U.S. Private*, pg. 124
ALTER TRUCKING AND TERMINAL CORP.—See Alter Companies; *U.S. Private*, pg. 206
ANE (CAYMAN) INC.; *Int'l*, pg. 457
APEX BULK COMMODITIES INC.; *U.S. Private*, pg. 291
AT+S N.V.—See Deufol SE; *Int'l*, pg. 2048
AVEDA TRANSPORTATION AND ENERGY SERVICES INC.—See Daseke, Inc.; *U.S. Private*, pg. 1161
BED ROCK, INC.—See Daseke, Inc.; *U.S. Private*, pg. 1161
BF SPA; *Int'l*, pg. 1006
BIRD GLOBAL, INC.; *U.S. Public*, pg. 339
BRAY TRUCKING INC.; *U.S. Private*, pg. 642
BRENNER OIL COMPANY INC.; *U.S. Private*, pg. 645
BROOK LEDGE INC—See Gotwals Inc.; *U.S. Private*, pg. 1745
BRT INC.; *U.S. Private*, pg. 670
BULLDOG HIWAY LOGISTICS, LLC—See Daseke, Inc.; *U.S. Private*, pg. 1161
BUNGE ASIA PTE. LTD—See Bunge Limited; *U.S. Public*, pg. 411
CARGO SIGNAL SOLUTIONS, LLC—See Expeditors International of Washington, Inc.; *U.S. Public*, pg. 810
THE CARPHONE WAREHOUSE LIMITED—See Currys plc; *Int'l*, pg. 1879
CARRY-ALL INC.—See Robert's Hawaii Inc.; *U.S. Private*, pg. 3459
CHINA AGRI PRODUCTS EXCHANGE LIMITED; *Int'l*, pg. 1481
CLARK DISTRIBUTION SYSTEMS, INC.-MECHANICSBURG—See Atlas Holdings, LLC; *U.S. Private*, pg. 377
CLARK DISTRIBUTION SYSTEMS, INC.—See Atlas Holdings, LLC; *U.S. Private*, pg. 376
COASTAL TRANSPORT CO. INC.; *U.S. Private*, pg. 957
COAST INTERNATIONAL SERVICES, INC.—See Olympus Partners; *U.S. Private*, pg. 3013
COLLINS BROTHERS MOVING CORP.; *U.S. Private*, pg. 969
COMET SA; *Int'l*, pg. 1711
COMPAGNIE AGRICOLE DE LA CRAU SA; *Int'l*, pg. 1722
CORD MOVING & STORAGE CO.; *U.S. Private*, pg. 1047
CROSS STREET SERVICE INC.; *U.S. Private*, pg. 1105
DAVIDSON OIL COMPANY INC.; *U.S. Private*, pg. 1172
DCV INC.; *U.S. Private*, pg. 1180
ELMER BUCHTA TRUCKING, INC.; *U.S. Private*, pg. 1376
FEDERAL EXPRESS ASIA PACIFIC—See FedEx Corporation; *U.S. Public*, pg. 828
FRANK C. ALEGRE TRUCKING INC.; *U.S. Private*, pg. 1594
FREIGHTLINER MANITOBA LTD.; *Int'l*, pg. 2771
FREIGHTLINER OF RED DEER INC; *Int'l*, pg. 2771
GAS LAND TRUCKING INC.—See Gas Land Petroleum Inc.; *U.S. Private*, pg. 1647
G.D.C., INC.; *U.S. Private*, pg. 1630
GOTWALS INC.; *U.S. Private*, pg. 1745
GREGMAR, INC.; *U.S. Private*, pg. 1782
HARTWIG TRANSIT INC.; *U.S. Private*, pg. 1874
HORNADY TRUCK LINE, INC.—See Daseke, Inc.; *U.S. Private*, pg. 1161
HURD HAULAGE PTY. LTD.—See CRH plc; *Int'l*, pg. 1842
IDDINGS TRUCKING, INC.; *U.S. Private*, pg. 2035
JASA TRANSIT, INC.; *U.S. Private*, pg. 2189
JASON'S HAULING, LLC.; *U.S. Private*, pg. 2190
JET STAR INC.; *U.S. Private*, pg. 2204
J.P. DONMOYER, INC.—See Ono Transport Services, Inc.; *U.S. Private*, pg. 3027
KARL R. JOHNSON TRUCKING, INC.; *U.S. Private*, pg. 2262
KATZ & KATZ TRANSFER, INC.; *U.S. Private*, pg. 2265
KENTUCKY HAULING, INC.—See Summit Materials, Inc.; *U.S. Public*, pg. 1960
KPS CEE S.R.O.—See Dover Corporation; *U.S. Public*, pg. 681
KPS FRANCE SARL—See Dover Corporation; *U.S. Public*, pg. 681
KPS UK LIMITED—See Dover Corporation; *U.S. Public*, pg. 681
LEE TRANSPORT INC.; *U.S. Private*, pg. 2414
LTI, INC.—See Lynden Incorporated; *U.S. Private*, pg. 2521
MAIL CONTRACTORS OF AMERICA, INC.—See Pat Salmon & Sons, Inc.; *U.S. Private*, pg. 3105
MAIN PASS OIL GATHERING COMPANY—See ArcLight Capital Holdings, LLC; *U.S. Private*, pg. 312
MANITO TRANSIT LLC—See Growmark, Inc.; *U.S. Private*, pg. 1795
MARGIE WOOD TRUCKING INC.; *U.S. Private*, pg. 2573
MCKEE FOODS TRANSPORTATION, LLC—See McKee Foods Corporation; *U.S. Private*, pg. 2637
MIDSTREAM LOGISTICS, LLC—See Energy Transfer LP; *U.S. Public*, pg. 764
MORGAN BUILDING TRANSPORT CORP.—See GHM Corp.; *U.S. Private*, pg. 1691
N.W. WHITE & COMPANY; *U.S. Private*, pg. 2828
OPTIMODAL, INC.—See Odyssey Logistics & Technology Corp.; *U.S. Private*, pg. 2996
OPW SWEDEN AB—See Dover Corporation; *U.S. Public*, pg. 682
PERISHABLE SHIPPING SOLUTIONS, LLC—See Bay Grove Capital LLC; *U.S. Private*, pg. 493
PETROLEUM TRANSPORT COMPANY; *U.S. Private*, pg. 3162
PRO OIL INC.; *U.S. Private*, pg. 3270
PROSPECT TRANSPORTATION INC.; *U.S. Private*, pg. 3288
PURNELL FURNITURE SERVICES, INC.—See Fidelitone, Inc.; *U.S. Private*, pg. 1502
RELIABLE TRUCKING INC.; *U.S. Private*, pg. 3394
RIVERTON TRUCKERS, INC.—See Gohmann Asphalt & Construction LLC; *U.S. Private*, pg. 1726
ROAD RUNNER MOVING & STORAGE INC.—See Wheaton Van Lines, Inc.; *U.S. Private*, pg. 4505
ROCK-IT SAND & GRAVEL, INC.; *U.S. Private*, pg. 3465
RON BOWERS, INC.; *U.S. Private*, pg. 3477
SAMUEL CORALUZZO CO. INC.; *U.S. Private*, pg. 3538
SARTIN LEE TRUCKING CO. INC.; *U.S. Private*, pg. 3551
SCHILLI NATIONAL TRUCK LEASING & SALES, INC.—See Daseke, Inc.; *U.S. Private*, pg. 1162
SCHILLI SPECIALIZED OF TEXAS, INC.—See Daseke, Inc.; *U.S. Private*, pg. 1162
SCHILLI TRANSPORTATION SERVICES, INC.—See Daseke, Inc.; *U.S. Private*, pg. 1162
SEILER TANK TRUCK SERVICE INC.—See Elkin Co.; *U.S. Private*, pg. 1363
SF TRANSPORT LTD.—See Vita Plus Corporation; *U.S. Private*, pg. 4405
SHEEHY MAIL CONTRACTORS, INC.—See EVO Transportation & Energy Services, Inc.; *U.S. Public*, pg. 804
SOURCE ONE TRANSPORTATION, LLC—See Guttman Holdings, Inc.; *U.S. Private*, pg. 1820
SOUTHWEST TRAILS; *U.S. Private*, pg. 3741
SPD TRUCKING, LLC—See Daseke, Inc.; *U.S. Private*, pg. 1162
THUNDER RIDGE TRANSPORT, INC.—See EVO Transportation & Energy Services, Inc.; *U.S. Public*, pg. 804
TRIMBLE NV—See Trimble, Inc.; *U.S. Public*, pg. 2192
TWT REFRIGERATED SERVICE—See Trans-System Inc.; *U.S. Private*, pg. 4206
UNITED PETROLEUM TRANSPORTS, INC.—See Gregmar, Inc.; *U.S. Private*, pg. 1782
UOP CH SARL—See Honeywell International Inc.; *U.S. Public*, pg. 1052
UOP LIMITED—See Honeywell International Inc.; *U.S. Public*, pg. 1052
WBC CORP.—See Wells Concrete Products Company Inc.; *U.S. Private*, pg. 4476
WEAVERTOWN TRANSPORT LEASING, INC.; *U.S. Private*, pg. 4463
WEGENER POST BV—See DPG Media Group NV; *Int'l*, pg. 2189
WESTERN PORTS TRANSPORTATION, INC.; *U.S. Private*, pg. 4496
WHOLESALE EXPRESS, LLC—See RumbleON, Inc.; *U.S. Public*, pg. 1826
WITHERS WORLDWIDE; *U.S. Private*, pg. 4550
YES TRANS, INC.—See Roadrunner Transportation Systems, Inc.; *U.S. Public*, pg. 1802

484230 — SPECIALIZED FREIGHT (EXCEPT USED GOODS) TRUCKING, LONG-DISTANCE

A&A LOGISTICS, LLC—See Roadrunner Transportation Systems, Inc.; *U.S. Public*, pg. 1802
ABILENE MOTOR EXPRESS, LLC—See Knight-Swift Transportation Holdings Inc.; *U.S. Public*, pg. 1269
ADM/CHS, LLC—See CHS Inc.; *U.S. Public*, pg. 491
AIR RIDE TECHNOLOGIES LLC; *U.S. Private*, pg. 139
AMERICAN EAGLE LOGISTICS, LLC—See Bennett International Group, Inc.; *U.S. Private*, pg. 527
AMERICA'S SERVICE LINE, LLC—See Rosens Diversified, Inc.; *U.S. Private*, pg. 3484
ANDREWS LOGISTICS, INC.; *U.S. Private*, pg. 280
ANDREWS TRANSPORTATION, INC.—See Andrews Logistics, Inc.; *U.S. Private*, pg. 280
ASSOCIATED PETROLEUM CARRIERS; *U.S. Private*, pg. 356
BAVARIAN MOTOR TRANSPORT INC.; *U.S. Private*, pg. 491
BENCHMARK LOGISTICS, INC.—See ACI Capital Co. LLC; *U.S. Private*, pg. 59
BIGGE CRANE AND RIGGING CO.—See Bigge Crane & Rigging Company; *U.S. Private*, pg. 555
BIG ROCK TRANSPORTATION, LLC—See Roadrunner Transportation Systems, Inc.; *U.S. Public*, pg. 1802
BIRCHWOOD TRANSPORT INC.—See Kenosha Beef International Ltd. Inc.; *U.S. Private*, pg. 2287
BULLOCH & BULLOCH, INC.; *U.S. Private*, pg. 685
CAPITAL CITY COMPANIES INC.; *U.S. Private*, pg. 739
CARRIER TRANSICOLD FRANCE—See Carrier Global Corporation; *U.S. Public*, pg. 443
CASSENS TRANSPORT COMPANY; *U.S. Private*, pg. 784
CENTRAL CAL TRANSPORTATION, LLC—See Universal Logistics Holdings, Inc.; *U.S. Public*, pg. 2261
CENTRAL CRUDE INC.; *U.S. Private*, pg. 820
CENTURION AUTO TRANSPORT—See Centurion Auto Logistics; *U.S. Private*, pg. 831
CERTIFIED FREIGHT LINES INC.; *U.S. Private*, pg. 841
CHARLES G. LAWSON TRUCKING; *U.S. Private*, pg. 852
COASTAL CARRIERS, LLC—See AIP, LLC; *U.S. Private*, pg. 136
CONSOLIDATED TRANSPORTATION WORLD, LLC—See Roadrunner Transportation Systems, Inc.; *U.S. Public*, pg. 1802
C.R. ENGLAND, INC.; *U.S. Private*, pg. 708
CRETE CARRIER CORP.; *U.S. Private*, pg. 1099
CROSSETT INC.; *U.S. Private*, pg. 1106

484230 — SPECIALIZED FREIGHT...

CSX INTERMODAL, INC.—See CSX Corporation; *U.S. Public*, pg. 602
CTL TRANSPORTATION LLC—See Comcar Industries, Inc.; *U.S. Private*, pg. 981
CTS SPEDITION GMBH; *Int'l*, pg. 1874
CUSTOM PRO LOGISTICS, LLC; *U.S. Private*, pg. 1129
DAVISON TRANSPORT INC.; *U.S. Private*, pg. 1175
THE DECKER COMPANIES INC.; *U.S. Private*, pg. 4019
DECKER TRUCK LINE INC.—See The Decker Companies Inc.; *U.S. Private*, pg. 4019
DEPENDABLE AUTO SHIPPERS, INC.; *U.S. Private*, pg. 1208
DEWEY CORPORATION; *U.S. Private*, pg. 1219
DIRCKS MOVING SERVICES, INC.; *U.S. Private*, pg. 1234
DUBAI AL AHLIA TRANSPORT L.L.C—See Gulf General Investment Company PSC; *Int'l*, pg. 3180
EAGLE TRANSPORT CORPORATION; *U.S. Private*, pg. 1311
EAST COAST AUTO TRANSPORT INCORPORATED; *U.S. Private*, pg. 1316
EASTEX CRUDE COMPANY; *U.S. Private*, pg. 1321
ERGON TRUCKING, INC.—See Ergon, Inc.; *U.S. Private*, pg. 1418
EVANS DEDICATED SYSTEMS, INC.; *U.S. Private*, pg. 1435
FFE TRANSPORTATION SERVICES, INC.—See Frozen Food Express Industries, Inc.; *U.S. Private*, pg. 1617
FIRST CHOICE LOGISTICS INC.—See Wind Point Advisors LLC; *U.S. Private*, pg. 4535
FLEET CAR LEASE INC.; *U.S. Private*, pg. 1541
FLYING J TRANSPORTATION (FUEL DISTRIBUTION)—See FJ Management, Inc.; *U.S. Private*, pg. 1538
FLYING STAR TRANSPORT LLC—See Davidson Oil Company Inc.; *U.S. Private*, pg. 1172
GEMINI MOTOR TRANSPORT, LP—See Love's Travel Stops & Country Stores, Inc.; *U.S. Private*, pg. 2501
GLYECO ACQUISITION CORP #7—See GlyEco, Inc.; *U.S. Private*, pg. 1721
GOODBULK LTD.; *Int'l*, pg. 3039
GREAT NORTHERN TRANSPORTATION SERVICES, LLC—See Roadrunner Transportation Systems, Inc.; *U.S. Public*, pg. 1802
GREAT WHITE FLEET, LTD.—See Banco Safra S.A.; *Int'l*, pg. 824
GREATWIDE CHEETAH TRANSPORTATION INC.—See Centerbridge Partners, L.P.; *U.S. Private*, pg. 815
GRINDROD LIMITED - GRINDROD LOGISTICS AUTO CARRIERS DIVISION—See Grindrod Limited; *Int'l*, pg. 3086
GRINDROD TANK TERMINALS SA (PTY) LTD—See Grindrod Limited; *Int'l*, pg. 3086
GROUP TRANSPORTATION SERVICES, INC.—See Roadrunner Transportation Systems, Inc.; *U.S. Public*, pg. 1802
HAMM MANAGEMENT CO.; *U.S. Private*, pg. 1849
HAMM & PHILLIPS SERVICE COMPANY—See Hamm Management Co.; *U.S. Private*, pg. 1849
HEAVY TRANSPORT, INC.—See Bragg Investment Company, Inc.; *U.S. Private*, pg. 634
HEMMERLIN S.A.; *Int'l*, pg. 3341
HERCULES TRANSPORT INC.; *U.S. Private*, pg. 1921
HERITAGE TRANSPORT LLC—See EQT AB; *Int'l*, pg. 2482
HILCO TRANSPORT INC.; *U.S. Private*, pg. 1944
HOLIDAY EXPRESS CORPORATION; *U.S. Private*, pg. 1963
HO-RO TRUCKING COMPANY INC.; *U.S. Private*, pg. 1957
ICS LOGISTICS, INC.; *U.S. Private*, pg. 2033
INDIAN RIVER TRANSPORT CO.; *U.S. Private*, pg. 2061
JACK COOPER TRANSPORT CO., INC.; *U.S. Private*, pg. 2173
JACK COOPER TRANSPORT-TEAM AUTO PROCESSING INC.—See Jack Cooper Transport Co., Inc.; *U.S. Private*, pg. 2173
JASON JONES TRUCKING, INC.—See OEP Capital Advisors, L.P.; *U.S. Private*, pg. 2999
J.F. LOMMA INC.; *U.S. Private*, pg. 2164
JH ROSE LOGISTICS INC.; *U.S. Private*, pg. 2207
JKC TRUCKING INC.; *U.S. Private*, pg. 2211
KANE FREIGHT LINES INC.—See Kane Is Able, Inc.; *U.S. Private*, pg. 2260
KELSEY-TRAIL TRUCKING LTD.—See Daseke, Inc.; *U.S. Private*, pg. 1161
KLEMM TANK LINES, INC.—See The Goldman Sachs Group, Inc.; *U.S. Public*, pg. 2080
KMT BRRR!—See Americold Realty Trust, Inc.; *U.S. Public*, pg. 113
KOTTKE TRUCKING, INC.; *U.S. Private*, pg. 2345
LANDSTAR INWAY, INC.—See Landstar System, Inc.; *U.S. Public*, pg. 1292
L&B TRANSPORT INC.; *U.S. Private*, pg. 2362
LEAVITTS FREIGHT SERVICE, INC.—See Daseke, Inc.; *U.S. Private*, pg. 1161
LEIVERS BROTHERS LTD.—See Danish Crown AmbA; *Int'l*, pg. 1965
LEWIS TRANSPORT INC.; *U.S. Private*, pg. 2439
LISA MOTOR LINES, INC.—See Frozen Food Express Industries, Inc.; *U.S. Private*, pg. 1617

L&L TRANSPORTATION, LLC—See Crestwood Equity Partners LP; *U.S. Public*, pg. 594
LOGISTIC DYNAMICS, INC.; *U.S. Private*, pg. 2481
MAGIC VALLEY TRUCK BROKERS INC.—See Allen Lund Company, LLC; *U.S. Private*, pg. 179
MARTEN TRANSPORT, LTD.; *U.S. Public*, pg. 1388
MAVERICK USA, INC.; *U.S. Private*, pg. 2616
MCKENZIE TANK LINES, INC.—See Groendyke Transport, Inc.; *U.S. Private*, pg. 1791
MCLANE LIVESTOCK TRANSPORT; *U.S. Private*, pg. 2640
MCTYRE TRUCKING COMPANY, INC.—See ACI Capital Co. LLC; *U.S. Private*, pg. 59
THE MEADOWLARK GROUP, LLC—See Roadrunner Transportation Systems, Inc.; *U.S. Public*, pg. 1802
MERCHANTS TRANSPORT OF HICKORY—See Alex Lee, Inc.; *U.S. Private*, pg. 163
MIDWEST CARRIERS, LLC—See Roadrunner Transportation Systems, Inc.; *U.S. Public*, pg. 1802
MIDWEST TRANSIT, INC.—See Roadrunner Transportation Systems, Inc.; *U.S. Public*, pg. 1802
MILLER TRANSPORTERS, INC.—See Dewey Corporation; *U.S. Private*, pg. 1219
MISSION PETROLEUM CARRIERS, INC.—See TETCO Inc.; *U.S. Private*, pg. 3973
NAVAJO EXPRESS INC.—See Navajo Shippers Inc.; *U.S. Private*, pg. 2872
NAVAJO SHIPPERS INC.; *U.S. Private*, pg. 2872
NORTHERN REFRIGERATED TRANSPORTATION INC.; *U.S. Private*, pg. 2954
OCCIDENTAL ENERGY TRANSPORTATION LLC—See Occidental Petroleum Corporation; *U.S. Public*, pg. 1561
THE OSTERKAMP GROUP; *U.S. Private*, pg. 4089
OSTERKAMP TRUCKING INC.—See The Osterkamp Group; *U.S. Private*, pg. 4089
P.A.M. TRANSPORTATION SERVICES, INC.; *U.S. Public*, pg. 1629
PENN TANK LINES INC.; *U.S. Private*, pg. 3135
PETE & PETE CONTAINER SERVICE, INC.; *U.S. Private*, pg. 3157
PETROLEOS DE VALENCIA, S.A.—See Galp Energia SGPS, S.A.; *Int'l*, pg. 2875
PETRON, LLC—See Lykins Companies, Inc.; *U.S. Private*, pg. 2520
P&H TRANSPORTATION—See Bradford Oil Company, Inc.; *U.S. Private*, pg. 632
PITTSBURGH LOGISTICS SYSTEMS, INC.—See Quadrivius, Inc.; *U.S. Private*, pg. 3316
PRIME, INC.; *U.S. Private*, pg. 3262
PRO ADVANTAGE; *U.S. Private*, pg. 3269
PROFICIENT AUTO LOGISTICS, INC.; *U.S. Public*, pg. 1724
PROGRESSIVE LOGISTICS INC.; *U.S. Private*, pg. 3279
QUICKWAY CARRIERS INC.—See Quickway Distribution Services LLC; *U.S. Private*, pg. 3327
QUICKWAY DISTRIBUTION SERVICES LLC; *U.S. Private*, pg. 3327
RADIANT ROAD & RAIL, INC.—See Radiant Logistics, Inc.; *U.S. Public*, pg. 1760
REFRIGERATED FOOD EXPRESS INC.; *U.S. Private*, pg. 3384
RELIABLE CARRIERS INC.; *U.S. Private*, pg. 3393
RIECHMANN TRANSPORT INC.—See OEP Capital Advisors, L.P.; *U.S. Private*, pg. 2999
ROADRUNNER INTERMODAL SERVICES, LLC—See Universal Logistics Holdings, Inc.; *U.S. Public*, pg. 2261
ROBERT'S TRUCKING—See Wavepoint 3PI Expedite LLC; *U.S. Private*, pg. 4458
R&O TRANSPORTATION LLC—See Castellini Company, Inc.; *U.S. Private*, pg. 784
RWI TRANSPORTATION LLC—See Castellini Company, Inc.; *U.S. Private*, pg. 784
SAFEWAY TRANSPORTATION INC.; *U.S. Private*, pg. 3525
SCHNEIDER NATIONAL BULK CARRIERS, INC.—See Schneider National, Inc.; *U.S. Public*, pg. 1847
SEA-CAP INC.; *U.S. Private*, pg. 3583
SELLAND AUTO TRANSPORT INC.; *U.S. Private*, pg. 3602
SERVICE TRANSPORT COMPANY—See Adams Resources & Energy, Inc.; *U.S. Public*, pg. 38
SILK ROAD TRANSPORT, INC.—See ACI Capital Co. LLC; *U.S. Private*, pg. 59
SIRVA, INC.—See Madison Dearborn Partners, LLC; *U.S. Private*, pg. 2542
SNOLINE EXPRESS, INC.; *U.S. Private*, pg. 3700
SORENSON TRANSPORTATION CO; *U.S. Private*, pg. 3715
SOUTHERN AUTO TRANSPORT SERVICES, INC.; *U.S. Private*, pg. 3729
SOUTHERN COUNTIES EXPRESS, INC.—See Universal Logistics Holdings, Inc.; *U.S. Public*, pg. 2261
SOUTHERN REFRIGERATED TRANSPORT—See Covenant Logistics Group, Inc.; *U.S. Public*, pg. 588
STARDUST TRANSPORTATION; *U.S. Private*, pg. 3786
SUPERIOR BULK LOGISTICS, INC.—See Heniff Transportation Systems Inc.; *U.S. Private*, pg. 1916
SUPERIOR CARRIERS, INC.—See Heniff Transportation Systems Inc.; *U.S. Private*, pg. 1916
SUPERIOR TRUCKING SERVICES—See First Reserve

Management, L.P.; *U.S. Private*, pg. 1526
SWIFT REFRIGERATED SERVICE, LLC—See Knight-Swift Transportation Holdings Inc.; *U.S. Public*, pg. 1269
TEXAS TRANSEASTERN INC.; *U.S. Private*, pg. 3977
TRAILINER CORP.; *U.S. Private*, pg. 4204
TRAILWOOD TRANSPORTATION INC.; *U.S. Private*, pg. 4204
TRANSPORT INDIANA, LLC—See Patrick Industries, Inc.; *U.S. Public*, pg. 1653
TRINITY LOGISTICS GROUP, INC.—See Trinity Industries, Inc.; *U.S. Public*, pg. 2194
TRINITY LOGISTICS—See Trinity Industries, Inc.; *U.S. Public*, pg. 2194
TRINITY LOGISTICS—See Trinity Industries, Inc.; *U.S. Public*, pg. 2194
TRINITY LOGISTICS—See Trinity Industries, Inc.; *U.S. Public*, pg. 2194
TRISTAR TRANSPORT LLC—See Agility; *Int'l*, pg. 210
UFP TRANSPORTATION, INC.—See UFP Industries, Inc.; *U.S. Public*, pg. 2220
UNITED ROAD SERVICES, INC.—See The Carlyle Group Inc.; *U.S. Public*, pg. 2056
US 1 INDUSTRIES, INC.; *U.S. Private*, pg. 4316
US TRANSPORT; *U.S. Private*, pg. 4320
WEL COMPANIES INC.; *U.S. Private*, pg. 4473
WHEELS CLIPPER INC.—See Radiant Logistics, Inc.; *U.S. Public*, pg. 1759
WILLIAMS TANK LINES; *U.S. Private*, pg. 4526
WM TRANSLOGISTICS (PTY) LTD—See Grindrod Limited; *Int'l*, pg. 3086
WORLD TRANSPORT SERVICES, LLC—See Roadrunner Transportation Systems, Inc.; *U.S. Public*, pg. 1802
WORLDWIDE PERISHABLES ENTERPRISE INC.—See American Holdco Inc.; *U.S. Private*, pg. 236
XPRESS GLOBAL SYSTEMS, LLC—See Aterian Investment Management, L.P.; *U.S. Private*, pg. 367
ZENITH FREIGHT LINES INC.—See Bassett Furniture Industries, Incorporated; *U.S. Public*, pg. 279

485111 — MIXED MODE TRANSIT SYSTEMS

ALPICO KOTSU CO., LTD.—See ALPICO Holdings Co., Ltd.; *Int'l*, pg. 371
BETAO LIZ S.A.—See Camargo Correa S.A.; *Int'l*, pg. 1267
EGGED BULGARIA—See Egged Israel Transport Cooperative Society Ltd.; *Int'l*, pg. 2324
EGGED HOLDING—See Egged Israel Transport Cooperative Society Ltd.; *Int'l*, pg. 2324
JOMATEL - EMPRESA DE MATERIAIS DE CONSTRUCAO S.A.—See Camargo Correa S.A.; *Int'l*, pg. 1268

485112 — COMMUTER RAIL SYSTEMS

ALSTOM NEDERLAND BV—See Alstom S.A.; *Int'l*, pg. 381
AMEY RAIL LTD.—See Ferrovial S.A.; *Int'l*, pg. 2644
ASCIANO LIMITED—See BlackRock, Inc.; *U.S. Public*, pg. 345
ASCIANO LIMITED—See Canada Pension Plan Investment Board; *Int'l*, pg. 1279
ASCIANO LIMITED—See China Investment Corporation; *Int'l*, pg. 1513
BERCHTESGADENER BERGBAHN AG; *Int'l*, pg. 978
FIRST CAPITAL CONNECT LIMITED—See FirstGroup plc; *Int'l*, pg. 2689
GRAND CANYON RAILWAY INC.; *U.S. Private*, pg. 1752
GYOR-SOPRON-EBENFURTI VASUT RT.; *Int'l*, pg. 3191
HANKYU CORPORATION—See Hankyu Hanshin Holdings Inc.; *Int'l*, pg. 3255
LONDON MIDLAND—See GLOBALVIA Inversiones, S.A.U.; *Int'l*, pg. 3005
LONDON & SOUTH EASTERN RAILWAY LIMITED—See GLOBALVIA Inversiones, S.A.U.; *Int'l*, pg. 3005
THE NEW YORK SUSQUEHANNA & WESTERN RAILWAY CORP—See Delaware Otsego Corp.; *U.S. Private*, pg. 1195
NORTHEAST ILLINOIS REGIONAL COMMUTER RAILROAD CORPORATION—See Regional Transportation Authority; *U.S. Private*, pg. 3389
PORT AUTHORITY TRANS-HUDSON CORP.—See Port Authority of New York & New Jersey; *U.S. Private*, pg. 3229
PORT AUTHORITY TRANSIT CORP. OF PENNSYLVANIA AND NEW JERSEY INC.—See Delaware River Port Authority of Pennsylvania & New Jersey; *U.S. Private*, pg. 1195
SOUTHERN CALIFORNIA REGIONAL RAIL AUTHORITY; *U.S. Private*, pg. 3730
SOUTHERN RAILWAY LIMITED—See GLOBALVIA Inversiones, S.A.U.; *Int'l*, pg. 3005
STRUKTON RAILINFRA N.V.—See Centric Holding B.V.; *Int'l*, pg. 1412
TRENITALIA S.P.A.—See Ferrovie dello Stato Italiane S.p.A.; *Int'l*, pg. 2645

N.A.I.C.S. INDEX

485113 — BUS AND OTHER MOTOR VEHICLE TRANSIT SYSTEMS

ALAMEDA-CONTRA COSTA TRANSIT DISTRICT; *U.S. Private*, pg. 149
AMS PUBLIC TRANSPORT HOLDINGS LIMITED; *Int'l*, pg. 441
ARRIVA LONDON LTD—See I Squared Capital Advisors (US) LLC; *U.S. Private*, pg. 2024
ARRIVA MIDLANDS LIMITED—See I Squared Capital Advisors (US) LLC; *U.S. Private*, pg. 2024
ARRIVA NEDERLAND B.V.—See I Squared Capital Advisors (US) LLC; *U.S. Private*, pg. 2024
ARRIVA NITRA A.S—See I Squared Capital Advisors (US) LLC; *U.S. Private*, pg. 2024
ARRIVA NOROESTE SL—See I Squared Capital Advisors (US) LLC; *U.S. Private*, pg. 2024
ARRIVA NORTH EAST LIMITED—See I Squared Capital Advisors (US) LLC; *U.S. Private*, pg. 2025
ARRIVA NORTH EAST - NEWCASTLE UPON TYNE—See I Squared Capital Advisors (US) LLC; *U.S. Private*, pg. 2025
ARRIVA NORTH WEST & WALES—See I Squared Capital Advisors (US) LLC; *U.S. Private*, pg. 2025
ARRIVA NOVE ZAMKY, A.S.—See I Squared Capital Advisors (US) LLC; *U.S. Private*, pg. 2025
ARRIVA PLC—See I Squared Capital Advisors (US) LLC; *U.S. Private*, pg. 2024
ARRIVA PORTUGAL - TRANSPORTES LDA—See I Squared Capital Advisors (US) LLC; *U.S. Private*, pg. 2024
ARRIVA SOUTHERN COUNTIES—See I Squared Capital Advisors (US) LLC; *U.S. Private*, pg. 2025
ARRIVA STAJERSKA, DRUZBA ZA PREVOZ POTNIKOV, D.D.—See I Squared Capital Advisors (US) LLC; *U.S. Private*, pg. 2025
ARRIVA TEPLICE S.R.O—See I Squared Capital Advisors (US) LLC; *U.S. Private*, pg. 2025
ARRIVA THE SHIRES—See I Squared Capital Advisors (US) LLC; *U.S. Private*, pg. 2025
ARRIVA VYCHODNI CECHY A.S.—See I Squared Capital Advisors (US) LLC; *U.S. Private*, pg. 2025
ARRIVA YORKSHIRE LTD.—See I Squared Capital Advisors (US) LLC; *U.S. Private*, pg. 2025
ARRIVA YORKSHIRE NORTH LTD—See I Squared Capital Advisors (US) LLC; *U.S. Private*, pg. 2025
ARRIVA YORKSHIRE WEST LTD—See I Squared Capital Advisors (US) LLC; *U.S. Private*, pg. 2025
AUTOKRAFT GMBH—See Deutsche Bahn AG; *Int'l*, pg. 2049
BANGKOK MASS TRANSIT SYSTEM PUBLIC COMPANY LIMITED—See BTS Group Holdings Public Company Limited; *Int'l*, pg. 1205
BAYERN EXPRESS&P. KUHN BERLIN GMBH—See Deutsche Bahn AG; *Int'l*, pg. 2049
BBH BAHNBUS HOCHSTIFT GMBH—See Deutsche Bahn AG; *Int'l*, pg. 2049
BRIGHTON & HOVE BUS & COACH COMPANY LIMITED—See GLOBALVIA Inversiones, S.A.U.; *Int'l*, pg. 3005
BUSVERKEHR MARKISCH-ODERLAND GMBH—See Deutsche Bahn AG; *Int'l*, pg. 2049
BUSVERKEHR ODER-SPREE GMBH—See Deutsche Bahn AG; *Int'l*, pg. 2049
BVO BUSVERKEHR OSTWESTFALEN GMBH—See Deutsche Bahn AG; *Int'l*, pg. 2049
BVR BUSVERKEHR RHEINLAND GMBH—See Deutsche Bahn AG; *Int'l*, pg. 2049
CENTRAL FLORIDA REGIONAL TRANSPORT AUTHORITY; *U.S. Private*, pg. 821
CENTRO CALL-A-BUS INC.—See Central New York Regional Transportation Authority; *U.S. Private*, pg. 823
CLARK COUNTY PUBLIC TRANSPORTATION BENEFIT AREA; *U.S. Private*, pg. 912
C.N.Y CENTRO INC.—See Central New York Regional Transportation Authority; *U.S. Private*, pg. 823
COBUS INDUSTRIES GMBH; *Int'l*, pg. 1683
COMFORTDELGRO CABCHARGE PTY. LTD.—See ComfortDelGro Corporation Limited; *Int'l*, pg. 1712
DAIWA MOTOR TRANSPORTATION CO., LTD.; *Int'l*, pg. 1947
DALLAS AREA RAPID TRANSIT INC.; *U.S. Private*, pg. 1149
DB ZUGBUS REGIONALVERKEHR ALB-BODENSEE GMBH—See Deutsche Bahn AG; *Int'l*, pg. 2051
EASTON COACH CO.; *U.S. Private*, pg. 1322
EUROPART HOLDING GMBH—See Alpha Associes Conseil SAS; *Int'l*, pg. 366
FIRSTGROUP PLC; *Int'l*, pg. 2688
FLIXMOBILITY GMBH; *Int'l*, pg. 2706
GIRARDIN BLUE BIRD COMPANY; *Int'l*, pg. 2979
GO NORTH EAST LIMITED—See GLOBALVIA Inversiones, S.A.U.; *Int'l*, pg. 3005
HALLER BUSBETRIEB GMBH—See Deutsche Bahn AG; *Int'l*, pg. 2051
HANEKAMP BUSREISEN GMBH—See Deutsche Bahn AG; *Int'l*, pg. 2051

INTERNATIONAL FREIGHT SYSTEMS LLC.; *U.S. Private*, pg. 2117
KOB GMBH—See Deutsche Bahn AG; *Int'l*, pg. 2052
LAZYDAYS HOLDINGS, INC.; *U.S. Public*, pg. 1294
LONDON CENTRAL—See GLOBALVIA Inversiones, S.A.U.; *Int'l*, pg. 3005
LONDON GENERAL—See GLOBALVIA Inversiones, S.A.U.; *Int'l*, pg. 3005
LONG BEACH PUBLIC TRANSPORTATION CO.; *U.S. Private*, pg. 2490
LOS ANGELES COUNTY METROPOLITAN TRANSPORTATION AUTHORITY; *U.S. Private*, pg. 2496
METROBUS LIMITED—See GLOBALVIA Inversiones, S.A.U.; *Int'l*, pg. 3005
METROPOLITAN ATLANTA RAPID TRANSIT AUTHORITY; *U.S. Private*, pg. 2688
METROPOLITAN TRANSIT AUTHORITY OF HARRIS COUNTY; *U.S. Private*, pg. 2689
METROPOLITAN TRANSIT SYSTEM; *U.S. Private*, pg. 2689
MONTEREY-SALINAS TRANSIT; *U.S. Private*, pg. 2776
NIAGARA FRONTIER TRANSIT & METRO SYSTEM—See Niagara Frontier Transportation Authority; *U.S. Private*, pg. 2924
OAHU TRANSIT SERVICES INC.; *U.S. Private*, pg. 2983
OMNIBUSVERKEHR FRANKEN GMBH—See Deutsche Bahn AG; *Int'l*, pg. 2052
OMNITRANS; *U.S. Private*, pg. 3017
ORANGE COUNTY TRANSPORTATION AUTHORITY; *U.S. Private*, pg. 3037
ORN OMNIBUSVERKEHR RHEIN-NAHE GMBH—See Deutsche Bahn AG; *Int'l*, pg. 2052
THE OXFORD BUS COMPANY LTD—See GLOBALVIA Inversiones, S.A.U.; *Int'l*, pg. 3005
PACE—See Regional Transportation Authority; *U.S. Private*, pg. 3389
PACE SUBURBAN BUS; *U.S. Private*, pg. 3064
PARKVIEW TRANSIT—See Caisse de Depot et Placement du Quebec; *Int'l*, pg. 1255
PARKVIEW TRANSIT—See Ullico Inc.; *U.S. Private*, pg. 4276
PIERCE COUNTY PUBLIC TRANSPORTATION BENEFIT AREA CORPORATION; *U.S. Private*, pg. 3178
PKS OSTROLEKA S.A.—See Egged Israel Transport Cooperative Society Ltd.; *Int'l*, pg. 2324
PKS PLOCK S.A.—See Egged Israel Transport Cooperative Society Ltd.; *Int'l*, pg. 2324
PKS TARNOBRZEG SP. Z O.O.—See Accor S.A.; *Int'l*, pg. 92
PLYMOUTH CITYBUS LIMITED—See GLOBALVIA Inversiones, S.A.U.; *Int'l*, pg. 3005
POSTAUTO LIECHTENSTEIN ANSTALT—See Die Schweizerische Post AG; *Int'l*, pg. 2113
PROTRANS BC OPERATIONS LTD.—See AtkinsRealis Group Inc.; *Int'l*, pg. 671
RED BUS LTD—See Christchurch City Holdings Ltd.; *Int'l*, pg. 1586
REGIONAL TRANSIT AUTHORITY; *U.S. Private*, pg. 3389
REGIONAL TRANSPORTATION DISTRICT INC.; *U.S. Private*, pg. 3389
RITEWAY BUS SERVICE, INC.; *U.S. Private*, pg. 3442
SAN DIEGO TRANSIT CORPORATION—See Metropolitan Transit System; *U.S. Private*, pg. 2689
SBS TRANSIT LTD.—See ComfortDelGro Corporation Limited; *Int'l*, pg. 1713
SNC-LAVALIN ROMANIA S.A.—See AtkinsRealis Group Inc.; *Int'l*, pg. 673
SOLENT BLUE LINE LTD.—See GLOBALVIA Inversiones, S.A.U.; *Int'l*, pg. 3005
SOUTHERN VECTIS OMNIBUS COMPANY LTD.—See GLOBALVIA Inversiones, S.A.U.; *Int'l*, pg. 3005
SOUTHWEST OHIO REGIONAL TRANSIT AUTHORITY; *U.S. Private*, pg. 3740
TAMIMI & SAIHAITI TRANSPORT CO.—See Ali Abdullah Al Tamimi Company; *Int'l*, pg. 319
TBL GROUP, INC.; *U.S. Private*, pg. 3941
TGMGROUP LIMITED—See I Squared Capital Advisors (US) LLC; *U.S. Private*, pg. 2025
TOP OF THE WORLD HOTEL—See Arctic Slope Regional Corporation; *U.S. Private*, pg. 316
TRAM OPERATIONS LIMITED—See FirstGroup plc; *Int'l*, pg. 2689
TRANSDEV NORTH AMERICA, INC.—See Caisse des Depots et Consignations; *Int'l*, pg. 1258
TRANSIT MANAGEMENT OF VOLUSIA, INC.—See FirstGroup plc; *Int'l*, pg. 2689
TRANSPORTATION CLAIMS LIMITED—See FirstGroup plc; *Int'l*, pg. 2689
TRANSPORTES SUL DO TEJO S.A.—See Deutsche Bahn AG; *Int'l*, pg. 2055
TRI-MET; *U.S. Private*, pg. 4222
TUF-TRANSPORTES URBANOS DE FAMALICAO, LDA—See Deutsche Bahn AG; *Int'l*, pg. 2054
TUNDRA TOURS, INC.—See Arctic Slope Regional Corporation; *U.S. Private*, pg. 316
UBB USEDOMER BADERBAHN GMBH—See Deutsche Bahn AG; *Int'l*, pg. 2055
UTAH TRANSIT AUTHORITY; *U.S. Private*, pg. 4324

485210 — INTERURBAN AND RURA...

VIA METROPOLITAN TRANSIT; *U.S. Private*, pg. 4375
VVW VERKEHRSVERBUND WARNOW GMBH—See Deutsche Bahn AG; *Int'l*, pg. 2055
WB WESTFALEN BUS GMBH—See Deutsche Bahn AG; *Int'l*, pg. 2055
WHITE ROSE BUS COMPANY LIMITED—See Deutsche Bahn AG; *Int'l*, pg. 2055
WILTS AND DORSET BUS COMPANY LTD.—See GLOBALVIA Inversiones, S.A.U.; *Int'l*, pg. 3005
XI'AN SILVER BUS CORPORATION—See AB Volvo; *Int'l*, pg. 47

485119 — OTHER URBAN TRANSIT SYSTEMS

BATTLES TRANSPORTATION INC.; *U.S. Private*, pg. 490
CHINA HIGH-SPEED RAILWAY TECHNOLOGY CO., LTD.; *Int'l*, pg. 1508
GREATER CLEVELAND REGIONAL TRANSIT AUTHORITY; *U.S. Private*, pg. 1769
GREYHOUND LINES, INC.—See FlixMobility GmbH; *Int'l*, pg. 2706
LONG ISLAND RAIL ROAD—See Metropolitan Transportation Authority; *U.S. Private*, pg. 2689
METROPOLITAN TRANSPORTATION AUTHORITY; *U.S. Private*, pg. 2689
MIDWEST PARATRANSIT SERVICES INC.—See Audax Group, Limited Partnership; *U.S. Private*, pg. 386
MURPHY TRANSPORTATION INC.; *U.S. Private*, pg. 2816
MV TRANSPORTATION INC.; *U.S. Private*, pg. 2821
NORTH SAN DIEGO COUNTY TRANSIT; *U.S. Private*, pg. 2946
SAN DIEGO TROLLEY INC.—See Metropolitan Transit System; *U.S. Private*, pg. 2689
SAN MATEO COUNTY TRANSIT; *U.S. Private*, pg. 3542
SOUTHEASTERN PENNSYLVANIA TRANSPORTATION AUTHORITY; *U.S. Private*, pg. 3728
SUPERSHUTTLE INTERNATIONAL, INC.—See Caisse des Depots et Consignations; *Int'l*, pg. 1258
WASHINGTON METROPOLITAN AREA TRANSIT AUTHORITY; *U.S. Private*, pg. 4447
WORCESTER REGIONAL TRANSIT AUTHORITY; *U.S. Private*, pg. 4562

485210 — INTERURBAN AND RURAL BUS TRANSPORTATION

AEROSERVICE CONSULTORIA E ENGENHARIA DE PROJETO LTDA—See Caisse des Depots et Consignations; *Int'l*, pg. 1257
ARRIVA CITY S.R.O.—See Deutsche Bahn AG; *Int'l*, pg. 2049
ARRIVA GALICIA S.L.—See Deutsche Bahn AG; *Int'l*, pg. 2049
ARRIVA MADRID MOVILIDAD S.L.—See Deutsche Bahn AG; *Int'l*, pg. 2049
BOLT BUS—See Peter Pan Bus Lines, Inc.; *U.S. Private*, pg. 3159
BRITISH COLUMBIA TRANSIT; *Int'l*, pg. 1171
CENTREWEST LONDON BUSES LIMITED—See FirstGroup plc; *Int'l*, pg. 2688
CENTRO OF OSWEGO, INC.—See Central New York Regional Transportation Authority; *U.S. Private*, pg. 824
CHUNIL EXPRESS CO., LTD.; *Int'l*, pg. 1598
CITY OF OXFORD MOTOR SERVICES LIMITED—See GLOBALVIA Inversiones, S.A.U.; *Int'l*, pg. 3005
DONGYANG EXPRESS CORP.; *Int'l*, pg. 2171
EGIS ALGERIE S.P.A.—See Caisse des Depots et Consignations; *Int'l*, pg. 1257
EGIS AVIA SA—See Caisse des Depots et Consignations; *Int'l*, pg. 1257
EGIS BDPA SA—See Caisse des Depots et Consignations; *Int'l*, pg. 1257
EGIS BEIJING INDUSTRIAL TECHNICAL CO., LTD.—See Caisse des Depots et Consignations; *Int'l*, pg. 1257
EGIS CAMEROUN—See Caisse des Depots et Consignations; *Int'l*, pg. 1257
EGIS EASYTRIP SERVICES SA—See Caisse des Depots et Consignations; *Int'l*, pg. 1257
EGIS EAU SA—See Caisse des Depots et Consignations; *Int'l*, pg. 1257
EGIS EYSER SA—See Caisse des Depots et Consignations; *Int'l*, pg. 1257
EGIS GEOPLAN PVT. LTD.—See Caisse des Depots et Consignations; *Int'l*, pg. 1257
EGIS INDIA CONSULTING ENGINEERS PRIVATE LIMITED—See Caisse des Depots et Consignations; *Int'l*, pg. 1257
EGIS INTERNATIONAL S.A.—See Caisse des Depots et Consignations; *Int'l*, pg. 1257
EGIS KENYA LIMITED—See Caisse des Depots et Consignations; *Int'l*, pg. 1257
EGIS POLAND SP. Z O.O.—See Caisse des Depots et Consignations; *Int'l*, pg. 1257
EGIS PROJECTS ASIA PACIFIC PTY LTD—See Caisse des Depots et Consignations; *Int'l*, pg. 1257
EGIS PROJECTS CANADA INC.—See Caisse des Depots

485210 — INTERURBAN AND RURA...

et Consignations; *Int'l*, pg. 1258
EGIS PROJECTS IRELAND LTD—See Caisse des Depots et Consignations; *Int'l*, pg. 1258
EGIS PROJECTS PHILIPPINES, INC.—See Caisse des Depots et Consignations; *Int'l*, pg. 1258
EGIS PROJECTS POLSKA SP. Z O.O.—See Caisse des Depots et Consignations; *Int'l*, pg. 1258
EGIS RAIL S.A.—See Caisse des Depots et Consignations; *Int'l*, pg. 1258
EGIS ROAD OPERATION CROATIA D.O.O.—See Caisse des Depots et Consignations; *Int'l*, pg. 1258
EGIS ROAD OPERATION INDIA PRIVATE LIMITED—See Caisse des Depots et Consignations; *Int'l*, pg. 1258
EGIS UKRAINA LLC—See Caisse des Depots et Consignations; *Int'l*, pg. 1258
EMPIRE BUS SALES, LLC—See Beam Mack Sales & Service, Inc.; *U.S. Private*, pg. 506
ENGLAND TIR GROUP—See Caisse des Depots et Consignations; *Int'l*, pg. 1258
ENVIRITE TRANSPORTATION, LLC—See Republic Services, Inc.; *U.S. Public*, pg. 1788
GOLD LINE INC.—See Frank Martz Coach Company Inc.; *U.S. Private*, pg. 1595
GREYHOUND CANADA TRANSPORTATION CORP.—See FlixMobility GmbH; *Int'l*, pg. 2706
INSTITUTE FOR TRANSPORTATION & DEVELOPMENT POLICY; *U.S. Private*, pg. 2093
INTERCITY TRANSIT; *U.S. Private*, pg. 2109
INTERMODAL TRANSPORTATION CENTER, INC.—See Central New York Regional Transportation Authority; *U.S. Private*, pg. 824
IRISBUS IVECO—See CNH Industrial N.V.; *Int'l*, pg. 1675
KONECTBUS LIMITED—See GLOBALVIA Inversiones, S.A.U.; *Int'l*, pg. 3005
LAKESIDE TRANSPORTATION INC.—See Cook-Illinois Corp.; *U.S. Private*, pg. 1038
LIBERTY LINES TRANSIT, INC.—See Liberty Systems, Inc.; *U.S. Private*, pg. 2447
LONDON UNITED BUSWAYS—See Caisse des Depots et Consignations; *Int'l*, pg. 1259
MILWAUKEE COUNTY TRANSIT SYSTEM; *U.S. Private*, pg. 2739
NEW JERSEY TRANSIT BUS OPERATIONS—See NJ Transit Corporation; *U.S. Private*, pg. 2930
NEW JERSEY TRANSIT RAIL OPERATIONS—See NJ Transit Corporation; *U.S. Private*, pg. 2930
NORTH SHORE TRANSIT, INC.—See Cook-Illinois Corp.; *U.S. Private*, pg. 1038
PAIGE BUS ENTERPRISES INC.—See Cook-Illinois Corp.; *U.S. Private*, pg. 1039
PETER PAN BUS LINES, INC.; *U.S. Private*, pg. 3159
PORT AUTHORITY OF ALLEGHENY COUNTY INC.; *U.S. Private*, pg. 3229
PT EGIS INDONESIA—See Caisse des Depots et Consignations; *Int'l*, pg. 1258
REALIZE INFORMATION TECHNOLOGY LLC—See Tonka Bay Equity Partners LLC; *U.S. Private*, pg. 4185
THAMES TRAVEL (WALLINGFORD) LIMITED—See GLOBALVIA Inversiones, S.A.U.; *Int'l*, pg. 3005
TRANSPASS B.V.—See Caisse des Depots et Consignations; *Int'l*, pg. 1258
VEOLIA TRANSPORT AUSTRALIA PTY LTD—See Caisse des Depots et Consignations; *Int'l*, pg. 1259
VEOLIA TRANSPORT RATP INDIA PVT. LTD.—See Caisse des Depots et Consignations; *Int'l*, pg. 1259

485310 — TAXI AND RIDESHARING SERVICES

13CABS INNOVATIONS PTY. LTD.—See ComfortDelGro Corporation Limited; *Int'l*, pg. 1712
AJIGAURA DAIICHI TRAFFIC LTD—See Daiichi Koutsu Sangyo Co., Ltd.; *Int'l*, pg. 1928
AKASHINA DAIICHI TRAFFIC CO., LTD.—See Daiichi Koutsu Sangyo Co., Ltd.; *Int'l*, pg. 1928
ALPICO TAXI CO., LTD.—See ALPICO Holdings Co., Ltd.; *Int'l*, pg. 371
ATAMI DAIICHI TRAFFIC CO., LTD.—See Daiichi Koutsu Sangyo Co., Ltd.; *Int'l*, pg. 1928
BAWAG LEASING & FLEET S.R.O.—See BAWAG Group AG; *Int'l*, pg. 900
BLACK CABS COMBINED PTY LTD—See ComfortDelGro Corporation Limited; *Int'l*, pg. 1712
COMBINED COMMUNICATIONS NETWORK PTY LTD—See ComfortDelGro Corporation Limited; *Int'l*, pg. 1712
CTI RECORDS MANAGEMENT PTY LTD—See CTI Logistics Limited; *Int'l*, pg. 1871
DAIICHI KOUTSU SANGYO CO., LTD. - FUKUOKA BRANCH—See Daiichi Koutsu Sangyo Co., Ltd.; *Int'l*, pg. 1928
DAIICHI KOUTSU SANGYO CO., LTD. - KAGOSHIMA BRANCH—See Daiichi Koutsu Sangyo Co., Ltd.; *Int'l*, pg. 1928
DAIICHI KOUTSU SANGYO CO., LTD. - KITAKYUSHU HEADQUARTERS TRAFFIC ENTERPRISE DIVISION—See Daiichi Koutsu Sangyo Co., Ltd.; *Int'l*, pg. 1928
DAIICHI KOUTSU SANGYO CO., LTD. - MIYAZAKI BANCH—See Daiichi Koutsu Sangyo Co., Ltd.; *Int'l*, pg. 1928
DAZHONG TRANSPORTATION (GROUP) CO., LTD.; *Int'l*, pg. 1985
DIVERSIFIED PARATRANSIT INC.; *U.S. Private*, pg. 1243
DRESDNER CHAUFFEUR SERVICE 8X8 GMBH—See Bertelsmann SE & Co. KGaA; *Int'l*, pg. 992
EDENRED MAGYARORSZAG KFT—See Edenred S.A.; *Int'l*, pg. 2308
EMPIRECLS WORLDWIDE CHAUFFEURED SERVICES—See GTS Holdings, Inc.; *U.S. Private*, pg. 1807
FINTAXI, SEC; *Int'l*, pg. 2677
FUJI DAIICHI TRAFFIC CO., LTD.—See Daiichi Koutsu Sangyo Co., Ltd.; *Int'l*, pg. 1928
FUKUGAWA DAIICHI TRAFFIC LTD—See Daiichi Koutsu Sangyo Co., Ltd.; *Int'l*, pg. 1928
FUYO DAIICHI TRAFFIC CO., LTD.—See Daiichi Koutsu Sangyo Co., Ltd.; *Int'l*, pg. 1928
GOBO DAIICHI TRAFFIC CO., LTD.—See Daiichi Koutsu Sangyo Co., Ltd.; *Int'l*, pg. 1928
GUNHOKU DAIICHI TRAFFIC CO., LTD.—See Daiichi Koutsu Sangyo Co., Ltd.; *Int'l*, pg. 1928
HANKYU TAXI INC.—See Hankyu Hanshin Holdings Inc.; *Int'l*, pg. 3255
HANSHIN TAXI CO., LTD.—See Hankyu Hanshin Holdings Inc.; *Int'l*, pg. 3256
HIGO DAIICHI TRAFFIC LTD—See Daiichi Koutsu Sangyo Co., Ltd.; *Int'l*, pg. 1928
HIMEJI DAIICHI TRAFFIC CO., LTD.—See Daiichi Koutsu Sangyo Co., Ltd.; *Int'l*, pg. 1928
HIRATSUKA DAIICHI TRAFFIC & CO., LTD.—See Daiichi Koutsu Sangyo Co., Ltd.; *Int'l*, pg. 1928
HIROSHIMA DAIICHI TRAFFIC CO., LTD.—See Daiichi Koutsu Sangyo Co., Ltd.; *Int'l*, pg. 1928
IBARAKI DAIICHI TRAFFIC CO., LTD.—See Daiichi Koutsu Sangyo Co., Ltd.; *Int'l*, pg. 1928
IDSUMO DAIICHI TRAFFIC CO., LTD.—See Daiichi Koutsu Sangyo Co., Ltd.; *Int'l*, pg. 1928
IWAKUNI DAIICHI TRAFFIC LTD—See Daiichi Koutsu Sangyo Co., Ltd.; *Int'l*, pg. 1928
IZU DAIICHI TRAFFIC CO., LTD.—See Daiichi Koutsu Sangyo Co., Ltd.; *Int'l*, pg. 1928
JIANGXI YALI TRANSPORT CO., LTD.—See Asia Cement Corporation; *Int'l*, pg. 611
KAGA FIRST TRANSPORT SERVICE CO. LTD.—See Daiichi Koutsu Sangyo Co., Ltd.; *Int'l*, pg. 1928
KANKO DAIICHI TRAFFIC CO., LTD.—See Daiichi Koutsu Sangyo Co., Ltd.; *Int'l*, pg. 1928
KAPTYN, INC.; *U.S. Private*, pg. 2262
KENTO DAIICHI TRAFFIC CO., LTD.—See Daiichi Koutsu Sangyo Co., Ltd.; *Int'l*, pg. 1928
KINGSCLIFF TWEED COAST TAXIS PTY. LTD.—See ComfortDelGro Corporation Limited; *Int'l*, pg. 1712
KOA DAIICHI TRAFFIC CO., LTD.—See Daiichi Koutsu Sangyo Co., Ltd.; *Int'l*, pg. 1928
KOBE DAIICHI TRAFFIC CO., LTD.—See Daiichi Koutsu Sangyo Co., Ltd.; *Int'l*, pg. 1928
KOSHU DAIICHI TRAFFIC LTD—See Daiichi Koutsu Sangyo Co., Ltd.; *Int'l*, pg. 1928
KUMAMOTO DAIICHI TRAFFIC LTD—See Daiichi Koutsu Sangyo Co., Ltd.; *Int'l*, pg. 1928
KUMANO DAIICHI TRAFFIC CO., LTD.—See Daiichi Koutsu Sangyo Co., Ltd.; *Int'l*, pg. 1928
(KUSHIKINO) DAIICHI TRAFFIC CO., LTD.—See Daiichi Koutsu Sangyo Co., Ltd.; *Int'l*, pg. 1928
KYOE DAIICHI TRAFFIC INDUSTRIAL LTD—See Daiichi Koutsu Sangyo Co., Ltd.; *Int'l*, pg. 1928
LOUISVILLE TRANSPORTATION—See Interlock Industries, Inc.; *U.S. Private*, pg. 2111
(MASUDA) DAIICHI TRAFFIC CO., LTD.—See Daiichi Koutsu Sangyo Co., Ltd.; *Int'l*, pg. 1928
MATSUE DAIICHI TRAFFIC LTD—See Daiichi Koutsu Sangyo Co., Ltd.; *Int'l*, pg. 1928
(MATSUMOTO) DAIICHI TRAFFIC CO., LTD.—See Daiichi Koutsu Sangyo Co., Ltd.; *Int'l*, pg. 1928
MATSUSHIMA WAKABA DAIICHI TRAFFIC LTD.—See Daiichi Koutsu Sangyo Co., Ltd.; *Int'l*, pg. 1928
MEARS TRANSPORTATION GROUP, LLC—See Palm Beach Capital Partners LLC; *U.S. Private*, pg. 3079
MIKAGE DAIICHI CO., LTD.—See Daiichi Koutsu Sangyo Co., Ltd.; *Int'l*, pg. 1928
MINATO DAIICHI TRAFFIC CO., LTD.—See Daiichi Koutsu Sangyo Co., Ltd.; *Int'l*, pg. 1928
MOBILE TECHNOLOGIES INTERNATIONAL PTY. LTD.—See ComfortDelGro Corporation Limited; *Int'l*, pg. 1712
NAGOYA DAIICHI TRAFFIC CO., LTD.—See Daiichi Koutsu Sangyo Co., Ltd.; *Int'l*, pg. 1928
NEWCASTLE TAXIS LTD—See ComfortDelGro Corporation Limited; *Int'l*, pg. 1712
NIKOSAX A/S—See Edenred S.A.; *Int'l*, pg. 2308
NUMAZU DAIICHI TRAFFIC CO., LTD.—See Daiichi Koutsu Sangyo Co., Ltd.; *Int'l*, pg. 1929
OKUBO DAIICHI TRAFFIC CO., LTD.—See Daiichi Koutsu Sangyo Co., Ltd.; *Int'l*, pg. 1929
OSAKA DAIICHI TRAFFIC CO., LTD.—See Daiichi Koutsu Sangyo Co., Ltd.; *Int'l*, pg. 1929
PROCARENT—See Interlock Industries, Inc.; *U.S. Private*, pg. 2112
SAITAMA DAIICHI TRAFFIC CO., LTD.—See Daiichi Koutsu Sangyo Co., Ltd.; *Int'l*, pg. 1929
SAKAI DAIICHI TRAFFIC CO., LTD.—See Daiichi Koutsu Sangyo Co., Ltd.; *Int'l*, pg. 1929
(SAKU) DAIICHI TRAFFIC LTD.—See Daiichi Koutsu Sangyo Co., Ltd.; *Int'l*, pg. 1928
SAN DAIICHI TRAFFIC LTD.—See Daiichi Koutsu Sangyo Co., Ltd.; *Int'l*, pg. 1929
SAPPORO DAIICHI TRAFFIC CO., LTD.—See Daiichi Koutsu Sangyo Co., Ltd.; *Int'l*, pg. 1929
SAWARA DAIICHI TRAFFIC CO., LTD.—See Daiichi Koutsu Sangyo Co., Ltd.; *Int'l*, pg. 1929
SENDAI DAIICHI TRAFFIC CO., LTD.—See Daiichi Koutsu Sangyo Co., Ltd.; *Int'l*, pg. 1929
SEN NARI DAIICHI TRAFFIC CO., LTD.—See Daiichi Koutsu Sangyo Co., Ltd.; *Int'l*, pg. 1929
SHIMABARA DAIICHI TRAFFIC CO., LTD.—See Daiichi Koutsu Sangyo Co., Ltd.; *Int'l*, pg. 1929
SHIRAHAMA DAIICHI TRAFFIC CO., LTD.—See Daiichi Koutsu Sangyo Co., Ltd.; *Int'l*, pg. 1929
SHUNAN DAIICHI TRAFFIC CO., LTD.—See Daiichi Koutsu Sangyo Co., Ltd.; *Int'l*, pg. 1929
SUWA DAIICHI TRAFFIC LTD.—See Daiichi Koutsu Sangyo Co., Ltd.; *Int'l*, pg. 1929
TAIYO DAIICHI TRAFFIC CO., LTD.—See Daiichi Koutsu Sangyo Co., Ltd.; *Int'l*, pg. 1929
TAKASAKI DAIICHI TRAFFIC CO., LTD.—See Daiichi Koutsu Sangyo Co., Ltd.; *Int'l*, pg. 1929
(TAKASHIMA) DAIICHI TRAFFIC LTD.—See Daiichi Koutsu Sangyo Co., Ltd.; *Int'l*, pg. 1928
TAXI COMBINED SERVICES PTY LTD—See ComfortDelGro Corporation Limited; *Int'l*, pg. 1712
TOBATA DAIICHI TRAFFIC INDUSTRIAL CO., LTD.—See Daiichi Koutsu Sangyo Co., Ltd.; *Int'l*, pg. 1929
TOHOKU DAIICHI TRAFFIC CO., LTD.—See Daiichi Koutsu Sangyo Co., Ltd.; *Int'l*, pg. 1929
TOKUSHIMA DAIICHI TRAFFIC CO., LTD.—See Daiichi Koutsu Sangyo Co., Ltd.; *Int'l*, pg. 1929
TOKUYAMA DAIICHI TRAFFIC LTD.—See Daiichi Koutsu Sangyo Co., Ltd.; *Int'l*, pg. 1929
TOKYO DAIICHI HIRE(CHAUFFEUR DRIVEN HIRED CAR) LTD—See Daiichi Koutsu Sangyo Co., Ltd.; *Int'l*, pg. 1929
(TOKYO) DAIICHI TRAFFIC CO., LTD.—See Daiichi Koutsu Sangyo Co., Ltd.; *Int'l*, pg. 1928
TWEED HEADS COOLANGATTA TAXI SERVICE PTY. LTD.—See ComfortDelGro Corporation Limited; *Int'l*, pg. 1712
WAAH TAXIS PRIVATE LIMITED—See Ebix Inc.; *U.S. Public*, pg. 710
WARPSPEED TAXI INC.; *U.S. Public*, pg. 2329
WORLD WIRELESS COMMUNICATIONS INC; *U.S. Private*, pg. 4568
YAMANAKA DAIICHI TRAFFIC CO., LTD.—See Daiichi Koutsu Sangyo Co., Ltd.; *Int'l*, pg. 1929
YAMANASHI DAIICHI TRAFFIC CO., LTD.—See Daiichi Koutsu Sangyo Co., Ltd.; *Int'l*, pg. 1929
YAMASHIRO DAIICHI TRAFFIC CO., LTD.—See Daiichi Koutsu Sangyo Co., Ltd.; *Int'l*, pg. 1929
YELLOW CAB COMPANY OF TAMPA, INC.; *U.S. Private*, pg. 4587
YELLOW CABS OF SYDNEY PTY. LTD.—See ComfortDelGro Corporation Limited; *Int'l*, pg. 1712

485320 — LIMOUSINE SERVICE

A1A AIRPORT & LIMOUSINE SERVICE; *U.S. Private*, pg. 29
A-1 LIMOUSINE INC.; *U.S. Private*, pg. 21
AMBASSADOR LIMOUSINE, INC.; *U.S. Private*, pg. 217
ATLANTIC SERVICES GROUP, INC.—See Propark, Inc.; *U.S. Private*, pg. 3284
AT YOUR SERVICE LIMOUSINES, INC.—See Unique Limousine, Inc.; *U.S. Private*, pg. 4286
BAYVIEW LIMOUSINE SERVICE, INC.; *U.S. Private*, pg. 497
BIG APPLE CAR INC.; *U.S. Private*, pg. 552
BLS LIMOUSINE SERVICE; *U.S. Private*, pg. 585
BOSTONCOACH—See Marcou Transportation Group LLC; *U.S. Private*, pg. 2572
CAREY INTERNATIONAL, INC.—See Avis Budget Group, Inc.; *U.S. Public*, pg. 249
CAREY INTERNATIONAL, INC.—See Chartwell Investments; *U.S. Private*, pg. 859
CAREY INTERNATIONAL, INC.—See Ford Motor Company; *U.S. Public*, pg. 864
CHARGE & RIDE INC.; *U.S. Private*, pg. 850
CIRCA DESTINATION MANAGEMENT COMPANY—See The RK Group, LLC; *U.S. Private*, pg. 4110
COMMONWEALTH WORLDWIDE CHAUFFEURED TRANSPORTATION; *U.S. Private*, pg. 987
CONCORD LIMOUSINE, INC.; *U.S. Private*, pg. 1010
CORPORATE CAR LTD. INC.—See Communicar Corp.; *U.S. Private*, pg. 987

N.A.I.C.S. INDEX

DAV-EL LOS ANGELES, INC.—See Marcou Transportation Group LLC; *U.S. Private*, pg. 2572
DAV-EL SERVICES, INC.—See Marcou Transportation Group LLC; *U.S. Private*, pg. 2572
DAV-EL TRANSPORTATION, INC.—See Marcou Transportation Group LLC; *U.S. Private*, pg. 2572
DIVA LIMOUSINE LTD.; *U.S. Private*, pg. 1240
FINCH TRANSPORTATION, LLC; *U.S. Private*, pg. 1508
FORTIS RIDERS; *U.S. Private*, pg. 1576
FUGAZY INTERNATIONAL CORPORATION; *U.S. Private*, pg. 1619
FUGAZY TRANSPORTATION INC—See Fugazy International Corporation; *U.S. Private*, pg. 1620
FUGAZY TRAVEL—See Fugazy International Corporation; *U.S. Private*, pg. 1620
GBJ, INC.—See TBL Group, Inc.; *U.S. Private*, pg. 3941
GRACE LIMOUSINE, LLC; *U.S. Private*, pg. 1749
GUANGZHOU PARKLANE LIMOUSINE SERVICE LTD—See Brockman Mining Limited; *Int'l*, pg. 1173
HARRISON TRANSPORTATION SERVICES, INC.—See Marcou Transportation Group LLC; *U.S. Private*, pg. 2572
HURLEY LIMOUSINE INC.; *U.S. Private*, pg. 2011
INTERNATIONAL LIMOUSINE SERVICE, INC.—See Errands Plus, Inc.; *U.S. Private*, pg. 1423
IZZY'S FRANCHISE SYSTEMS INC.; *U.S. Private*, pg. 2152
KISMET INTERNATIONAL LIMOUSINE SERVICE INC.; *U.S. Private*, pg. 2315
LIMORES LIMOS; *U.S. Private*, pg. 2456
METROPOLITAN LIMOUSINE, INC.—See Marcou Transportation Group LLC; *U.S. Private*, pg. 2572
MUV, INC.; *U.S. Private*, pg. 2820
O'HARE-MIDWAY LIMOUSINE SERVICE INC.; *U.S. Private*, pg. 2978
PARKLANE LIMOUSINE SERVICE LIMITED—See Brockman Mining Limited; *Int'l*, pg. 1173
PARKLANE LIMOUSINE SERVICE (SHANGHAI) LTD—See Brockman Mining Limited; *Int'l*, pg. 1173
RESTON LIMOUSINE & TRAVEL SERVICE, INC.; *U.S. Private*, pg. 3409
REZMAN EXPRESS INC.—See Kismet International Limousine Service Inc.; *U.S. Private*, pg. 2315
SKYLINE CREDIT RIDE INC.; *U.S. Private*, pg. 3685
TEDDY'S TRANSPORTATION SYSTEM, INC.; *U.S. Private*, pg. 3957
TORREY PINES TRANSPORTATION—See Marcou Transportation Group LLC; *U.S. Private*, pg. 2572
VALERA GLOBAL; *U.S. Private*, pg. 4331
WASHINGTONIAN LIMOUSINE COACH CORP.; *U.S. Private*, pg. 4449
WINDY CITY LIMOUSINE; *U.S. Private*, pg. 4540
WORLDWIDE GROUND TRANSPORTATION SOLUTIONS INC.; *U.S. Private*, pg. 4569

485410 — SCHOOL AND EMPLOYEE BUS TRANSPORTATION

ALPHA SCHOOL BUS COMPANY INC.—See Cook-Illinois Corp.; *U.S. Private*, pg. 1038
ANTELOPE VALLEY SCHOOL TRANSPORTATION AGENCY; *U.S. Private*, pg. 287
APPLE BUS COMPANY; *U.S. Private*, pg. 296
BAUMANN & SONS BUSES, INC.; *U.S. Private*, pg. 490
BEACON MOBILITY CORP.—See Audax Group, Limited Partnership; *U.S. Private*, pg. 386
BLUE STAR BUS SALES, LTD.—See A-Z Bus Sales, Inc.; *U.S. Private*, pg. 22
COOK COUNTY SCHOOL BUS INC.—See Cook-Illinois Corp.; *U.S. Private*, pg. 1038
COOK-ILLINOIS CORP.; *U.S. Private*, pg. 1038
FIRSTBUS CANADA—See FirstGroup plc; *Int'l*, pg. 2689
FIRSTGROUP AMERICA INC.—See FirstGroup plc; *Int'l*, pg. 2689
FIRST STUDENT CANADA—See FirstGroup plc; *Int'l*, pg. 2689
FIRST STUDENT INC.—See FirstGroup plc; *Int'l*, pg. 2689
FIRST STUDENT—See FirstGroup plc; *Int'l*, pg. 2689
FIRST STUDENT—See FirstGroup plc; *Int'l*, pg. 2689
GRAND PRAIRIE TRANSIT—See Cook-Illinois Corp.; *U.S. Private*, pg. 1038
GTJ CO. INC.; *U.S. Private*, pg. 1807
ILLINOIS SCHOOL BUS CO. INC.—See Cook-Illinois Corp.; *U.S. Private*, pg. 1038
MAGNETAR CAPITAL, LLC; *U.S. Private*, pg. 2547
MONROE SCHOOL TRANSPORTATION INC.—See Penske Automotive Group, Inc.; *U.S. Public*, pg. 1665
MONROE SCHOOL TRANSPORTATION INC.—See Penske Corporation; *U.S. Private*, pg. 3139
PIONEER TRANSPORTATION CORP.; *U.S. Private*, pg. 3188
RICHLEE VANS INC.—See Cook-Illinois Corp.; *U.S. Private*, pg. 1039
STAR BUS SALES INC.—See Velocity Vehicle Group; *U.S. Private*, pg. 4355
STUDENT TRANSPORTATION INC.—See Caisse de Depot et Placement du Quebec; *Int'l*, pg. 1255

STUDENT TRANSPORTATION INC.—See Ullico Inc.; *U.S. Private*, pg. 4276
STUDENT TRANSPORTATION OF AMERICA, INC.—See Caisse de Depot et Placement du Quebec; *Int'l*, pg. 1255
STUDENT TRANSPORTATION OF AMERICA, INC.—See Ullico Inc.; *U.S. Private*, pg. 4276
STUDENT TRANSPORTATION OF CANADA, INC.—See Caisse de Depot et Placement du Quebec; *Int'l*, pg. 1255
STUDENT TRANSPORTATION OF CANADA, INC.—See Ullico Inc.; *U.S. Private*, pg. 4276
VPSI INC.; *U.S. Private*, pg. 4414
WESTWAY COACH INC.—See Cook-Illinois Corp.; *U.S. Private*, pg. 1039
WE TRANSPORT, INC.; *U.S. Private*, pg. 4462

485510 — CHARTER BUS INDUSTRY

ALL WEST COACHLINES, INC.—See Variant Equity Advisors, LLC; *U.S. Private*, pg. 4346
ARROW COACH LINES, INC.—See Village Charters, Inc.; *U.S. Private*, pg. 4383
BUSCO INC.; *U.S. Private*, pg. 693
CARDINAL BUSES, INC.—See Riteway Bus Service, Inc.; *U.S. Private*, pg. 3442
CENTRO AUBURN—See Central New York Regional Transportation Authority; *U.S. Private*, pg. 823
CROSWELL BUS LINES, INC.; *U.S. Private*, pg. 1108
DEACON TRANSPORTATION INC.—See Historic Tours of America Inc.; *U.S. Private*, pg. 1952
DRINA TRANS A.D.; *Int'l*, pg. 2204
EL CAMINO TRAILWAYS; *U.S. Private*, pg. 1348
FIRST MANCHESTER LIMITED—See FirstGroup plc; *Int'l*, pg. 2689
FIRST MIDLAND RED BUSES LIMITED—See FirstGroup plc; *Int'l*, pg. 2689
FIRST POTTERIES LIMITED—See FirstGroup plc; *Int'l*, pg. 2689
FLORIDA TRAILS, INC.; *U.S. Private*, pg. 1550
FRANK MARTZ COACH COMPANY INC.; *U.S. Private*, pg. 1595
GRAY LINE OF ALASKA—See Carnival Corporation; *U.S. Public*, pg. 438
GRAY LINE OF SEATTLE—See Carnival Corporation; *U.S. Public*, pg. 438
GREYHOUND AUSTRALIA PTY. LTD.; *Int'l*, pg. 3082
H & L BLOOM, INC.; *U.S. Private*, pg. 1822
JAMES RIVER TRANSPORTATION; *U.S. Private*, pg. 2185
KICKERT SCHOOL BUS LINES, INC.—See Cook-Illinois Corp.; *U.S. Private*, pg. 1038
KRAPF'S COACHES INC.; *U.S. Private*, pg. 2349
LEWIS STAGES INC.; *U.S. Private*, pg. 2439
LONE STAR COACHES, INC.; *U.S. Private*, pg. 2484
MERIDIAN TRANSPORTATION RESOURCES, LLC; *U.S. Private*, pg. 2673
NATIONAL BUS SALES & LEASING, INC.—See Creative Bus Sales Inc.; *U.S. Private*, pg. 1088
NITETRAIN COACH CO INC.—See Encore Luxury Coach Leasing LLC; *U.S. Private*, pg. 1391
OLD TOWN TROLLEY TOURS—See Historic Tours of America Inc.; *U.S. Private*, pg. 1952
RAZ TRANSPORTATION INC.—See Variant Equity Advisors, LLC; *U.S. Private*, pg. 4346
RICK BUS COMPANY, INC.—See Caisse de Depot et Placement du Quebec; *Int'l*, pg. 1255
RICK BUS COMPANY, INC.—See Ullico Inc.; *U.S. Private*, pg. 4276
SAVDA AUTOSERVIZI VALLE D'AOSTA S.P.A.—See Deutsche Bahn AG; *Int'l*, pg. 2052
SILVERADO STAGES, INC.; *U.S. Private*, pg. 3662
SPRINGBOK ATLAS NAMIBIA (PTY) LTD—See Cullinan Holdings Limited; *Int'l*, pg. 1877
STARR TRANSIT CO. INC.; *U.S. Private*, pg. 3787
TRANS-BRIDGE LINES, INC.; *U.S. Private*, pg. 4205
TRI-CITY CHARTER OF BOSSIER, INC.—See Lone Star Coaches, Inc.; *U.S. Private*, pg. 2484

485991 — SPECIAL NEEDS TRANSPORTATION

DELVAG VERSICHERUNGS-AG—See Deutsche Lufthansa AG; *Int'l*, pg. 2066
FIRST TRANSIT, INC.—See EQT AB; *Int'l*, pg. 2475
HELTOR LIMITED; *Int'l*, pg. 3338
LOGISTICARE SOLUTIONS LLC—See ModivCare, Inc.; *U.S. Public*, pg. 1455
PROTRANSPORT-1; *U.S. Private*, pg. 3290
SM DEUTSCHLAND GMBH—See Philip Morris International Inc.; *U.S. Public*, pg. 1687
VEYO, LLC; *U.S. Private*, pg. 4374

485999 — ALL OTHER TRANSIT AND GROUND PASSENGER TRANSPORTATION

482 JOINT STOCK COMPANY; *Int'l*, pg. 11
ADDISON LEE LIMITED—See ComfortDelGro Corporation Limited; *Int'l*, pg. 1712

AIRPORT SHUTTLE SERVICES LIMITED—See Brockman Mining Limited; *Int'l*, pg. 1173
AL FAHED VALUABLE ASSETS IN TRANSIT UNITED CO. LTD.—See Bank of Khartoum; *Int'l*, pg. 845
AL GHAZAL TRANSPORT CO.—See Abu Dhabi National Hotels PJSC; *Int'l*, pg. 72
ALLIANCE BUS GROUP, INC.—See Creative Bus Sales Inc.; *U.S. Private*, pg. 1088
ALPHA FLYING, INC.; *U.S. Private*, pg. 197
ARRIVA LIORBUS, A. S.—See Deutsche Bahn AG; *Int'l*, pg. 2049
ARRIVA PRAHA S.R.O.—See I Squared Capital Advisors (US) LLC; *U.S. Private*, pg. 2025
ARRIVA RAIL LONDON LIMITED—See Deutsche Bahn AG; *Int'l*, pg. 2049
ARRIVA SLOVAKIA A.S.—See Deutsche Bahn AG; *Int'l*, pg. 2049
ARRIVA STREDNI CECHY S.R.O.—See Deutsche Bahn AG; *Int'l*, pg. 2049
ARRIVA TRNAVA, A. S.—See Deutsche Bahn AG; *Int'l*, pg. 2049
ATAF GESTIONI S.R.L.—See Ferrovie dello Stato Italiane S.p.A.; *Int'l*, pg. 2645
ATI JET, INC.; *U.S. Private*, pg. 368
AURIZON PORT SERVICES PTY LTD—See Aurizon Holdings Limited; *Int'l*, pg. 711
AUTOKOMERC A.D.; *Int'l*, pg. 727
AUTOPREVOZ GORNJI MILANOVAC A.D.; *Int'l*, pg. 732
AUTOPREVOZ JANJUSEVIC A.D.; *Int'l*, pg. 732
AUTOPROMETNO PODUZECE D.D.—See Deutsche Bahn AG; *Int'l*, pg. 2049
AUTOTRANS D.D.—See Deutsche Bahn AG; *Int'l*, pg. 2049
AUTOTRANSPORT A.D.; *Int'l*, pg. 732
AUTOTRANSPORT A.D.; *Int'l*, pg. 732
AUTOTRANSPORTES MIGUEL MEZA SANCHEZ, S. A. P. I. DE C. V.—See Grupo Traxion, S. A. B. de C. V.; *Int'l*, pg. 3138
BEIJING JIN JIAN TAXI SERVICES CO., LTD.—See ComfortDelGro Corporation Limited; *Int'l*, pg. 1712
BEOGRADSKA AUTOBUSKA STANICA A.D.; *Int'l*, pg. 978
BLACK TIE LIMOUSINE INC.—See Grace Limousine, LLC; *U.S. Private*, pg. 1749
BLUE MOUNTAINS TRANSIT PTY. LTD.—See ComfortDelGro Corporation Limited; *Int'l*, pg. 1713
BLUFERRIES S.R.L.—See Ferrovie dello Stato Italiane S.p.A.; *Int'l*, pg. 2645
BLU JET S.R.L.—See Ferrovie dello Stato Italiane S.p.A.; *Int'l*, pg. 2645
BOREAL NORGE AS—See Caisse des Depots et Consignations; *Int'l*, pg. 1259
BOSTON CAR SERVICE, INC.; *U.S. Private*, pg. 621
BRIDGE HOLDINGS USA, LLC; *U.S. Private*, pg. 649
BURG TRAILER SERVICE B.V.—See CIMC Vehicle (Group) Co., Ltd.; *Int'l*, pg. 1608
BUSITALIA CAMPANIA S.P.A.—See Ferrovie dello Stato Italiane S.p.A.; *Int'l*, pg. 2645
BUSITALIA VENETO S.P.A.—See Ferrovie dello Stato Italiane S.p.A.; *Int'l*, pg. 2645
CARRIER COACH INC.; *U.S. Private*, pg. 772
CDC VICTORIA PTY. LTD.—See ComfortDelGro Corporation Limited; *Int'l*, pg. 1712
CEVOTRANS BV—See Mohawk Industries, Inc.; *U.S. Public*, pg. 1457
CHENGDU COMFORTDELGRO QINGYANG DRIVING SCHOOL CO., LTD.—See ComfortDelGro Corporation Limited; *Int'l*, pg. 1712
CHENGDU COMFORTDELGRO TAXI CO., LTD.—See ComfortDelGro Corporation Limited; *Int'l*, pg. 1712
CHICAGO TRANSIT AUTHORITY—See Regional Transportation Authority; *U.S. Private*, pg. 3389
C.H. ROBINSON SHANGHAI TRADING CO.—See C.H. Robinson Worldwide, Inc.; *U.S. Public*, pg. 415
C.H. ROBINSON TECHNOLOGY LLC—See C.H. Robinson Worldwide, Inc.; *U.S. Public*, pg. 415
C.H. ROBINSON WORLDWIDE FREIGHT LANKA (PRIVATE) LIMITED—See C.H. Robinson Worldwide, Inc.; *U.S. Public*, pg. 415
CITYCAB PTE. LTD.—See ComfortDelGro Corporation Limited; *Int'l*, pg. 1712
CITYCAB (SHENYANG) CO., LTD.—See ComfortDelGro Corporation Limited; *Int'l*, pg. 1712
CITYFLEET NETWORKS LIMITED—See ComfortDelGro Corporation Limited; *Int'l*, pg. 1712
CLINICAL NETWORK G.K.—See H.U. Group Holdings, Inc.; *Int'l*, pg. 3196
CLOSE BROTHERS VEHICLE HIRE LIMITED—See Close Brothers Group plc; *Int'l*, pg. 1661
COLORADO MOUNTAIN EXPRESS LLC—See Vail Resorts, Inc.; *U.S. Public*, pg. 2271
COMFORTDELGRO BUS PTE LTD—See ComfortDelGro Corporation Limited; *Int'l*, pg. 1712
COMFORTDELGRO CORPORATION AUSTRALIA PTY. LTD.—See ComfortDelGro Corporation Limited; *Int'l*, pg. 1712
COMFORTDELGRO CORPORATION LIMITED; *Int'l*, pg. 1711
COMFORTDELGRO ENGINEERING PTE LTD—See ComfortDelGro Corporation Limited; *Int'l*, pg. 1713

485999 — ALL OTHER TRANSIT A...

COMFORTDELGRO INSURANCE BROKERS PTE. LTD.—See ComfortDelGro Corporation Limited; *Int'l*, pg. 1713
COMFORTDELGRO IRISH CITYLINK LIMITED—See ComfortDelGro Corporation Limited; *Int'l*, pg. 1713
COMFORTDELGRO RENT-A-CAR (CHENGDU) CO., LTD.—See ComfortDelGro Corporation Limited; *Int'l*, pg. 1713
COMFORTDELGRO SWAN PTY. LTD.—See ComfortDelGro Corporation Limited; *Int'l*, pg. 1713
COMFORT TRANSPORTATION PTE LTD—See ComfortDelGro Corporation Limited; *Int'l*, pg. 1712
COMMUNICAR CORP.; *U.S. Private*, pg. 987
COMPAGNIE AERIENNE DU MALI—See Aga Khan Development Network; *Int'l*, pg. 199
COMPUTER CAB PLC—See ComfortDelGro Corporation Limited; *Int'l*, pg. 1712
CONNEX TCT LLC—See Caisse des Depots et Consignations; *Int'l*, pg. 1258
CTM SA; *Int'l*, pg. 1872
CT TRANSPORTATION LLC—See Comcar Industries, Inc.; *U.S. Private*, pg. 981
DALLAH ALMUTAQDMAH BUSES & EQUIPMENT CO. LTD.; *Int'l*, pg. 1954
DB REGIO BUS MITTE GMBH—See Deutsche Bahn AG; *Int'l*, pg. 2050
D. D. LITVATRANS BANOVICI; *Int'l*, pg. 1900
DUNAVPREVOZ A.D.; *Int'l*, pg. 2225
EGGED ISRAEL TRANSPORT COOPERATIVE SOCIETY LTD.; *Int'l*, pg. 2324
EMPRESA DE BLAS Y COMPANIA S.A.—See Deutsche Bahn AG; *Int'l*, pg. 2051
ENCORE LUXURY COACH LEASING LLC; *U.S. Private*, pg. 1391
ENGELBERG TRANSPORTES INTERNACIONALES C.A.—See Deutsche Bahn AG; *Int'l*, pg. 2051
ERRANDS PLUS, INC.; *U.S. Private*, pg. 1423
ESFERA BUS S.L.—See Deutsche Bahn AG; *Int'l*, pg. 2051
ESSA LIMITED—See ESAS Holding A.S.; *Int'l*, pg. 2501
EXPRESS TRANSPORT SA; *Int'l*, pg. 2590
FINGER LAKES AMBULANCE EMS INC—See G.W. Lisk Company, Inc.; *U.S. Private*, pg. 1631
FIRST ABERDEEN LIMITED—See FirstGroup plc; *Int'l*, pg. 2688
FIRST BEELINE BUSES LIMITED—See FirstGroup plc; *Int'l*, pg. 2688
FIRST BRISTOL LIMITED—See FirstGroup plc; *Int'l*, pg. 2688
FIRST CAPITAL NORTH LIMITED—See FirstGroup plc; *Int'l*, pg. 2689
FIRST CORPORATE SEDANS INC.—See Elite Limousine Plus, Inc.; *U.S. Private*, pg. 1361
FIRST DEVON & CORNWALL LIMITED—See FirstGroup plc; *Int'l*, pg. 2689
FIRST EASTERN COUNTIES BUSES LIMITED—See FirstGroup plc; *Int'l*, pg. 2689
FIRST GLASGOW (NO. 1) LIMITED—See FirstGroup plc; *Int'l*, pg. 2689
FIRST GLASGOW (NO. 2) LIMITED—See FirstGroup plc; *Int'l*, pg. 2689
FIRST SCOTLAND EAST LIMITED—See FirstGroup plc; *Int'l*, pg. 2689
FIRST SOMERSET & AVON LIMITED—See FirstGroup plc; *Int'l*, pg. 2689
FIRST SOUTH YORKSHIRE LIMITED—See FirstGroup plc; *Int'l*, pg. 2689
FIRST WEST YORKSHIRE LIMITED—See FirstGroup plc; *Int'l*, pg. 2689
FLIGHTLINK INTERNATIONAL LIMITED—See ComfortDelGro Corporation Limited; *Int'l*, pg. 1712
FLORIDA BEAUTY FLORA, INC.—See MOGUL ENERGY INTERNATIONAL, INC.; *U.S. Public*, pg. 1457
FOREST COACH LINES PTY. LIMITED—See ComfortDelGro Corporation Limited; *Int'l*, pg. 1713
FRANBO LINES CORP.; *Int'l*, pg. 2759
FREIGHTCENTER INC.; *U.S. Private*, pg. 1607
GENERAL TRANSPORT SA; *Int'l*, pg. 2920
GOLDEN TOUCH TRANSPORTATION OF NEW YORK—See Caisse des Depots et Consignations; *Int'l*, pg. 1258
GOTCHA MOBILITY, LLC—See Bolt Mobility Corp.; *U.S. Private*, pg. 611
GRAND CENTRAL TRANS-SERVICES SDN. BHD.—See Grand Central Enterprises Bhd.; *Int'l*, pg. 3054
GUANGZHOU XIN TIAN WEI TRANSPORTATION DEVELOPMENT CO., LTD.—See ComfortDelGro Corporation Limited; *Int'l*, pg. 1713
HANSEA NV—See Deutsche Bank Aktiengesellschaft; *Int'l*, pg. 2057
HELLMANN WORLDWIDE LOGISTICS N.V.—See Hellmann Worldwide Logistics GmbH & Co. KG; *Int'l*, pg. 3336
HILLSBUS CO PTY. LTD.—See ComfortDelGro Corporation Limited; *Int'l*, pg. 1713
HOANGHA JOINT STOCK COMPANY; *Int'l*, pg. 3436
HOKKAIDO CHUO BUS CO., LTD.; *Int'l*, pg. 3442
HUBEI THREE GORGES TOURISM GROUP CO., LTD.; *Int'l*, pg. 3518

IHY IZMIR HAVAYOLLARI A.S.—See ESAS Holding A.S.; *Int'l*, pg. 2501
INDIANA TRANSPORT, INC.—See Patrick Industries, Inc.; *U.S. Public*, pg. 1652
INTERCAMBIADOR DE TRANSPORTES DE PRINCIPIO, S.A.—See ACS, Actividades de Construccion y Servicios, S.A.; *Int'l*, pg. 115
J.B. HUNT LOGISTICS, INC.—See J.B. Hunt Transport Services, Inc.; *U.S. Public*, pg. 1180
JIC INSPECTION SERVICES PTE. LTD.—See ComfortDelGro Corporation Limited; *Int'l*, pg. 1713
JILIN COMFORTDELGRO TAXI CO., LTD.—See ComfortDelGro Corporation Limited; *Int'l*, pg. 1713
JMT PROPERTY CORP.—See Warburg Pincus LLC; *U.S. Private*, pg. 4438
JOLLEY TROLLEY TRANSPORTATION OF CLEARWATER, INC.; *U.S. Private*, pg. 2230
JR TOKAI BUS COMPANY—See Central Japan Railway Company; *Int'l*, pg. 1408
KAM-BUS DD—See I Squared Capital Advisors (US) LLC; *U.S. Private*, pg. 2024
KD SERVIS A.S.—See Deutsche Bahn AG; *Int'l*, pg. 2052
LGM ENTERPRISES LLC—See flyExclusive, Inc.; *U.S. Public*, pg. 861
MANAGED CHIROPRACTICS INC.—See NCMIC Group Inc.; *U.S. Private*, pg. 2876
MERCITALIA INTERMODAL S.P.A.—See Ferrovie dello Stato Italiane S.p.A.; *Int'l*, pg. 2645
METROLINE LIMITED—See ComfortDelGro Corporation Limited; *Int'l*, pg. 1713
METRO PARKING MANAGEMENT (PHILIPPINES) INC.—See Damansara Realty Berhad; *Int'l*, pg. 1955
MOOVE MEDIA PTE. LTD.—See ComfortDelGro Corporation Limited; *Int'l*, pg. 1713
MTA BUS COMPANY—See Metropolitan Transportation Authority; *U.S. Private*, pg. 2689
MVT CANADIAN BUS, INC.—See MV Transportation Inc.; *U.S. Private*, pg. 2821
MY HOME LINER CO., LTD.—See Hoosiers Holdings; *Int'l*, pg. 3472
NANJING COMFORTDELGRO DAJIAN TAXI CO., LTD.—See ComfortDelGro Corporation Limited; *Int'l*, pg. 1713
NANJING COMFORTDELGRO XIXIA DRIVER TRAINING CO., LTD.—See ComfortDelGro Corporation Limited; *Int'l*, pg. 1713
NANNING COMFORT TRANSPORTATION CO., LTD.—See ComfortDelGro Corporation Limited; *Int'l*, pg. 1713
NATIONAL MEDTRANS NETWORK INC.—See UnitedHealth Group Incorporated; *U.S. Public*, pg. 2242
NATIONAL PATIENT TRANSPORT PTY. LTD.—See ComfortDelGro Corporation Limited; *Int'l*, pg. 1713
NEW ADVENTURE TRAVEL LIMITED—See ComfortDelGro Corporation Limited; *Int'l*, pg. 1713
NEW YORK CITY TRANSIT AUTHORITY—See Metropolitan Transportation Authority; *U.S. Private*, pg. 2689
NORTHAMPTON TRANSPORT LIMITED—See FirstGroup plc; *Int'l*, pg. 2689
OATS, INC.; *U.S. Private*, pg. 2986
OFJ AIRLINKS LIMITED—See ABM Industries, Inc.; *U.S. Public*, pg. 26
OLYMPUS WORLDWIDE CHAUFFEURED SERVICES; *U.S. Private*, pg. 3014
THE ORIGINAL LONDON SIGHTSEEING TOUR LTD.—See I Squared Capital Advisors (US) LLC; *U.S. Private*, pg. 2025
PARATRANSIT SERVICES; *U.S. Private*, pg. 3093
PETRELOCATION INC.; *U.S. Private*, pg. 3161
PHT INC.—See Kobayashi Travel Service Ltd. Inc.; *U.S. Private*, pg. 2326
PINELLAS SUNCOAST TRANSIT AUTHORITY; *U.S. Private*, pg. 3183
PLANETTRAN; *U.S. Private*, pg. 3196
POLYNESIAN ADVENTURE TOURS INC.—See Norwegian Cruise Line Holdings Ltd.; *U.S. Public*, pg. 1543
PORT AUTHORITY OF NEW YORK & NEW JERSEY; *U.S. Private*, pg. 3229
QCITY TRANSIT PTY. LTD.—See ComfortDelGro Corporation Limited; *Int'l*, pg. 1713
REGIONALVERKEHRE START DEUTSCHLAND GMBH—See Deutsche Bahn AG; *Int'l*, pg. 2052
RYAN'S EXPRESS TRANSPORTATION SERVICES, INC.—See Century Park Capital Partners, LLC; *U.S. Private*, pg. 834
SADEM - SOCIETA PER AZIONI—See Deutsche Bahn AG; *Int'l*, pg. 2052
SAVIT S.R.L.—See Ferrovie dello Stato Italiane S.p.A.; *Int'l*, pg. 2645
SBS TRANSIT DTL PTE. LTD.—See ComfortDelGro Corporation Limited; *Int'l*, pg. 1713
SEI MOBIL VERKEHRSGESELLSCHAFT MBH—See Ferrovie dello Stato Italiane S.p.A.; *Int'l*, pg. 2645
SETSCO CONSULTANCY INTERNATIONAL PTE. LTD.—See ComfortDelGro Corporation Limited; *Int'l*, pg. 1713
SETSCO SERVICES (M) SDN. BHD.—See ComfortDelGro Corporation Limited; *Int'l*, pg. 1713
SHANGHAI CITY QI AI TAXI SERVICES CO., LTD.—See ComfortDelGro Corporation Limited; *Int'l*, pg. 1713
SHENYANG COMFORTDELGRO TAXI CO., LTD.—See ComfortDelGro Corporation Limited; *Int'l*, pg. 1713
SIPPEL-TRAVEL GMBH—See Ferrovie dello Stato Italiane S.p.A.; *Int'l*, pg. 2645
SUZHOU COMFORT TAXI CO., LTD.—See ComfortDelGro Corporation Limited; *Int'l*, pg. 1713
SWAN TAXIS PTY. LTD.—See ComfortDelGro Corporation Limited; *Int'l*, pg. 1713
TIANJIN NEW UNIVERSAL SCIENCE & TECHNOLOGY CO., LTD.—See Beijing New Universal Science and Technology Co., Ltd.; *Int'l*, pg. 954
TRAD SCAFFOLDING COMPANY LTD—See Altrad Investment Authority SAS; *Int'l*, pg. 398
TRAINOSE SA—See Ferrovie dello Stato Italiane S.p.A.; *Int'l*, pg. 2645
TRANSCOR AMERICA, LLC—See Corecivic, Inc.; *U.S. Public*, pg. 577
TRANSDEV GROUP S.A.—See Caisse des Depots et Consignations; *Int'l*, pg. 1258
TRANSDEV PLC—See Caisse des Depots et Consignations; *Int'l*, pg. 1259
TRANSDEV S.A.—See Caisse des Depots et Consignations; *Int'l*, pg. 1258
TRANSDEV SVERIGE AB—See Caisse des Depots et Consignations; *Int'l*, pg. 1258
TRANSDEV SYDNEY PTY LTD—See Caisse des Depots et Consignations; *Int'l*, pg. 1259
TRAVEL SECURITY S.A.—See Grupo Security S.A.; *Int'l*, pg. 3135
TVG-ZIMSEN EHF.—See Eimskipafelag Islands Hf.; *Int'l*, pg. 2332
UNITED RAIL, INC.; *U.S. Public*, pg. 2234
VEOLIA TRANSPORTATION, INC.—See Caisse des Depots et Consignations; *Int'l*, pg. 1258
VEOLIA TRANSPORT AUSTRALASIA—See Caisse des Depots et Consignations; *Int'l*, pg. 1259
VEOLIA TRANSPORT FINLAND OY—See Caisse des Depots et Consignations; *Int'l*, pg. 1259
VEOLIA TRANSPORT IRELAND—See Caisse des Depots et Consignations; *Int'l*, pg. 1259
VEOLIA TRANSPORT NEDERLAND BV—See Caisse des Depots et Consignations; *Int'l*, pg. 1259
VEOLIA TRANSPORT POLSKA SP. Z O.O. UL.—See Caisse des Depots et Consignations; *Int'l*, pg. 1259
VEOLIA VERKHER GMBH—See Caisse des Depots et Consignations; *Int'l*, pg. 1259
VERKEHRSGESELLSCHAFT START NRW MBH—See Deutsche Bahn AG; *Int'l*, pg. 2055
VERKEHRSTRIEBE BILS GMBH—See Ferrovie dello Stato Italiane S.p.A.; *Int'l*, pg. 2645
VGI GLOBAL MEDIA (MALAYSIA) SDN. BHD.—See BTS Group Holdings Public Company Limited; *Int'l*, pg. 1206
VIET NAM RENEWABLE ENERGY GROUP JSC—See Duc Long Gia Lai Group JSC; *Int'l*, pg. 2222
VIETNAM TAXI CO., LTD.—See ComfortDelGro Corporation Limited; *Int'l*, pg. 1713
VT-ARRIVA SZEMELYSZALLITO ES SZOLGALTATO KFT.—See Deutsche Bahn AG; *Int'l*, pg. 2055
WESTBUS COACH SERVICES LIMITED—See ComfortDelGro Corporation Limited; *Int'l*, pg. 1712
WORKPLACE INSTALL NETWORK, INC.; *U.S. Private*, pg. 4564
XANTERRA SOUTH RIM, LLC—See The Anschutz Corporation; *U.S. Private*, pg. 3987
XPRESSPA AMSTERDAM AIRPORT B.V.—See XWELL, Inc.; *U.S. Public*, pg. 2393

486110 — PIPELINE TRANSPORTATION OF CRUDE OIL

ALYESKA PIPELINE SERVICE COMPANY; *U.S. Private*, pg. 214
AMERICAN PETROLEUM TANKERS II LLC—See Kinder Morgan, Inc.; *U.S. Public*, pg. 1232
AP MARINE, LLC—See Genesis Energy, L.P.; *U.S. Public*, pg. 930
BAKKENLINK PIPELINE LLC—See Marathon Petroleum Corporation; *U.S. Public*, pg. 1363
BELLE FOURCHE PIPELINE CO.—See True Companies; *U.S. Private*, pg. 4247
BP OIL PIPELINE—See BP plc; *Int'l*, pg. 1127
BP PIPELINES (ALASKA) INC.—See BP plc; *Int'l*, pg. 1127
CAPLINE PIPELINE COMPANY LLC—See Plains All American Pipeline, L.P.; *U.S. Public*, pg. 1696
CDE PIPELINE LLC—See Kinder Morgan, Inc.; *U.S. Public*, pg. 1232
CENIT TRANSPORTE Y LOGISTICA DE HIDROCARBUROS S.A.S.—See Ecopetrol S.A.; *Int'l*, pg. 2298
CENTURION PIPELINE—See Occidental Petroleum Corporation; *U.S. Public*, pg. 1561
CHEVRON PIPE LINE COMPANY—See Chevron Corporation; *U.S. Public*, pg. 486
CINCINNATI BIOREFINING CORP.—See Marathon Petroleum Corporation; *U.S. Public*, pg. 1364
CONOCOPHILLIPS ALASKA, INC.—See ConocoPhillips; *U.S. Public*, pg. 568

N.A.I.C.S. INDEX

486210 — PIPELINE TRANSPORTA...

COSMO OIL (SHANGHAI) CO., LTD.—See Cosmo Energy Holdings Co., Ltd.; *Int'l*, pg. 1812
DELEK LOGISTICS PARTNERS, LP—See Delek Group Ltd.; *Int'l*, pg. 2011
ENBRIDGE PIPELINES, INC.—See Enbridge Inc.; *Int'l*, pg. 2397
ENERGY TRANSFER CRUDE MARKETING LLC—See Energy Transfer LP; *U.S. Public*, pg. 763
ENTERPRISE CRUDE PIPELINE LLC—See Enterprise Products Partners L.P.; *U.S. Public*, pg. 778
EXPRESS PIPELINE LTD.—See Enbridge Inc.; *Int'l*, pg. 2397
EXXONMOBIL PIPELINE COMPANY—See Exxon Mobil Corporation; *U.S. Public*, pg. 816
EXXONMOBIL PIPELINE COMPANY—See Exxon Mobil Corporation; *U.S. Public*, pg. 816
EXXONMOBIL PIPELINE COMPANY—See Exxon Mobil Corporation; *U.S. Public*, pg. 816
EXXONMOBIL PIPELINE COMPANY—See Exxon Mobil Corporation; *U.S. Public*, pg. 816
EXXONMOBIL PIPELINE COMPANY—See Exxon Mobil Corporation; *U.S. Public*, pg. 816
EXXONMOBIL PIPELINE COMPANY—See Exxon Mobil Corporation; *U.S. Public*, pg. 816
EXXONMOBIL PIPELINE COMPANY—See Exxon Mobil Corporation; *U.S. Public*, pg. 816
EXXONMOBIL PIPELINE COMPANY—See Exxon Mobil Corporation; *U.S. Public*, pg. 816
EXXONMOBIL PIPELINE COMPANY—See Exxon Mobil Corporation; *U.S. Public*, pg. 816
FRONTIER PIPELINE LLC—See HF Sinclair Corporation; *U.S. Public*, pg. 1033
GAZELLE TRANSPORTATION INC.; *U.S. Private*, pg. 1652
GENER8 MARITIME MANAGEMENT LLC—See Euronav NV; *Int'l*, pg. 2554
GULFMARK ENERGY, INC.—See Adams Resources & Energy, Inc.; *U.S. Public*, pg. 38
GULF STATE PIPE LINE COMPANY—See Balmoral Funds LLC; *U.S. Private*, pg. 462
HAWTHORN OIL TRANSPORTATION, INC.—See EOG Resources, Inc.; *U.S. Public*, pg. 782
HOLLY ENERGY PARTNERS, L.P.—See HF Sinclair Corporation; *U.S. Public*, pg. 1033
KINDER MORGAN ENERGY PARTNERS, L.P.—See Kinder Morgan, Inc.; *U.S. Public*, pg. 1233
KOCH ALASKA PIPELINE COMPANY, LLC—See Koch Industries, Inc.; *U.S. Private*, pg. 2331
KOCH PIPELINE COMPANY, L.P—See Koch Industries, Inc.; *U.S. Private*, pg. 2333
LPC CRUDE OIL MARKETING LLC—See Devon Energy Corporation; *U.S. Public*, pg. 657
M3 MIDSTREAM LLC; *U.S. Private*, pg. 2530
MARATHON PIPE LINE LLC—See Marathon Petroleum Corporation; *U.S. Public*, pg. 1364
MARKWEST MICHIGAN PIPELINE COMPANY, L.L.C.—See Marathon Petroleum Corporation; *U.S. Public*, pg. 1364
MARKWEST TEXAS LPG PIPELINE, L.L.C.—See Marathon Petroleum Corporation; *U.S. Public*, pg. 1364
MCMURREY PIPE LINE COMPANY—See Rosemore Inc.; *U.S. Private*, pg. 3483
MONROE PIPELINE LLC—See Antero Resources Corporation; *U.S. Public*, pg. 140
MONTREAL PIPE LINE LIMITED—See Exxon Mobil Corporation; *U.S. Public*, pg. 816
MPLX LP—See Marathon Petroleum Corporation; *U.S. Public*, pg. 1364
NAPP-GRECCO COMPANY; *U.S. Private*, pg. 2835
NAVAJO PIPELINE CO., L.P.—See HF Sinclair Corporation; *U.S. Public*, pg. 1034
OLEODUCTO BICENTENARIO DE COLOMBIA S.A.S.—See Ecopetrol S.A.; *Int'l*, pg. 2299
PORTLAND PIPE LINE CORPORATION—See Exxon Mobil Corporation; *U.S. Public*, pg. 816
POSEIDON OIL PIPELINE COMPANY, LLC—See Enterprise Products Partners L.P.; *U.S. Public*, pg. 779
POSEIDON OIL PIPELINE COMPANY, LLC—See Genesis Energy, L.P.; *U.S. Public*, pg. 930
RANGELAND ENERGY—See EnCap Investments L.P.; *U.S. Private*, pg. 1390
SABINE PIPE LINE LLC—See Chevron Corporation; *U.S. Public*, pg. 488
SANDRIDGE CO2, LLC—See SandRidge Energy, Inc.; *U.S. Public*, pg. 1839
TRANSMONTAIGNE PARTNERS LLC—See ArcLight Capital Holdings, LLC; *U.S. Private*, pg. 312
TRANSMONTAIGNE TRANSPORT INC.—See NGL Energy Partners LP; *U.S. Public*, pg. 1527
TRINITY PIPELINE, L.P.—See Morgan Stanley; *U.S. Public*, pg. 1474
TRUE COMPANIES; *U.S. Private*, pg. 4247
VARDAX S.A.—See HELLENIQ ENERGY Holdings S.A.; *Int'l*, pg. 3334
VIKING GAS TRANSMISSION COMPANY—See ONEOK, Inc.; *U.S. Public*, pg. 1603
WESTERN REFINING COMPANY, L.P.—See Marathon Petroleum Corporation; *U.S. Public*, pg. 1364
THE WILLIAMS COMPANIES, INC. - WASHINGTON—See The Williams Companies, Inc.; *U.S. Public*, pg. 2142
WILLIAMS GAS PIPELINE—See The Williams Companies, Inc.; *U.S. Public*, pg. 2143
WILLIAMS GAS PIPELINE TRANSCO—See The Williams Companies, Inc.; *U.S. Public*, pg. 2144

486210 — PIPELINE TRANSPORTATION OF NATURAL GAS

ACADIAN GAS, LLC—See Enterprise Products Partners L.P.; *U.S. Public*, pg. 778
ACADIAN GAS PIPELINE SYSTEM—See Enterprise Products Partners L.P.; *U.S. Public*, pg. 778
ADISTRIBUZIONEGAS S.R.L.—See ACEA S.p.A.; *Int'l*, pg. 95
AGGERENERGIE GMBH—See E.ON SE; *Int'l*, pg. 2251
ALGONQUIN GAS TRANSMISSION, LLC—See Enbridge Inc.; *Int'l*, pg. 2397
ALLIANCE PIPELINE LIMITED PARTNERSHIP—See Enbridge Inc.; *Int'l*, pg. 2397
ALTAGAS UTILITIES, INC.—See AltaGas Ltd.; *Int'l*, pg. 384
AMERICAN MIDSTREAM (MISSISSIPPI), LLC—See ArcLight Capital Holdings, LLC; *U.S. Private*, pg. 312
APA GASNET AUSTRALIA (OPERATIONS) PTY. LTD.—See APA Group; *Int'l*, pg. 500
APA GASNET AUSTRALIA PTY LIMITED—See APA Group; *Int'l*, pg. 500
APPALACHIA MIDSTREAM SERVICES, L.L.C.—See The Williams Companies, Inc.; *U.S. Public*, pg. 2143
APT FACILITY MANAGEMENT PTY. LTD.—See APA Group; *Int'l*, pg. 500
APT O&M SERVICES PTY LTD.—See APA Group; *Int'l*, pg. 500
APT PARMELIA PTY. LTD.—See APA Group; *Int'l*, pg. 500
APT PIPELINES (QLD) PTY LIMITED—See APA Group; *Int'l*, pg. 500
ARG MBH & CO. KG; *Int'l*, pg. 560
ATCO GAS AUSTRALIA PTY. LTD.—See ATCO Ltd.; *Int'l*, pg. 666
ATCO PIPELINES—See ATCO Ltd.; *Int'l*, pg. 667
ATLAS GROWTH PARTNERS, L.P.; *U.S. Private*, pg. 376
AUX SABLE CANADA LTD.—See Enbridge Inc.; *Int'l*, pg. 2397
AZURE MIDSTREAM ENERGY LLC—See Clearfork Midstream LLC; *U.S. Private*, pg. 933
BITTER CREEK PIPELINES, LLC—See MDU Resources Group, Inc.; *U.S. Public*, pg. 1410
BLACK WARRIOR TRANSMISSION CORP.—See Atlas Energy Group, LLC; *U.S. Public*, pg. 223
BLACK WARRIOR TRANSMISSION CORP.—See Warrior Met Coal, Inc; *U.S. Public*, pg. 2329
BLACKWATER NEW ORLEANS, LLC—See ArcLight Capital Holdings, LLC; *U.S. Private*, pg. 312
BNP PARIBAS ENERGY TRADING CANADA CORP—See BNP Paribas SA; *Int'l*, pg. 1083
BOARDWALK FIELD SERVICES, LLC—See Loews Corporation; *U.S. Public*, pg. 1339
CANADIAN UTILITY CONSTRUCTION LIMITED—See Quanta Services, Inc.; *U.S. Public*, pg. 1750
CARBON CALIFORNIA OPERATING COMPANY, LLC—See Carbon Energy Corporation; *U.S. Public*, pg. 432
CARBON ENERGY CORPORATION; *U.S. Public*, pg. 432
CARDINAL PIPELINE CO.—See The Williams Companies, Inc.; *U.S. Public*, pg. 2143
CENTRAL RANGES PIPELINE PTY. LTD.—See APA Group; *Int'l*, pg. 500
CERITAS ENERGY, LLC—See Energy Spectrum Securities Corporation; *U.S. Private*, pg. 1396
CERITAS ENERGY, LLC—See Quantum Energy Partners, LLC; *U.S. Private*, pg. 3323
CHENIERE CORPUS CHRISTI PIPELINE, L.P.—See Cheniere Corpus Christi Holdings, LLC; *U.S. Private*, pg. 872
CHENIERE CREOLE TRAIL PIPELINE, L.P.—See Cheniere Energy, Inc.; *U.S. Public*, pg. 485
CHEYENNE PLAINS GAS PIPELINE COMPANY, L.L.C.—See Kinder Morgan, Inc.; *U.S. Public*, pg. 1232
CNX MIDSTREAM OPERATING COMPANY LLC—See CNX Resources Corporation; *U.S. Public*, pg. 520
COLORADO INTERSTATE GAS COMPANY, L.L.C.—See Kinder Morgan, Inc.; *U.S. Public*, pg. 1232
COMMISSIONERS OF PUBLIC WORKS; *U.S. Private*, pg. 985
CONNECTICUT NATURAL GAS CORPORATION—See Iberdrola, S.A.; *Int'l*, pg. 3571
CONTROL DEVICES, INC.—See Sensata Technologies Holding plc; *U.S. Public*, pg. 1866
CORPUS CHRISTI LIQUEFACTION, LLC—See Cheniere Corpus Christi Holdings, LLC; *U.S. Private*, pg. 873
CORPUS CHRISTI PIPELINE GP, LLC—See Cheniere Corpus Christi Holdings, LLC; *U.S. Private*, pg. 873
CRESTWOOD APPALACHIA PIPELINE LLC—See Crestwood Equity Partners LP; *U.S. Public*, pg. 594
CRESTWOOD ARKANSAS PIPELINE LLC—See Crestwood Equity Partners LP; *U.S. Public*, pg. 594
CRESTWOOD CRUDE TRANSPORTATION LLC—See Crestwood Equity Partners LP; *U.S. Public*, pg. 594
CRESTWOOD DAKOTA PIPELINES LLC—See Crestwood Equity Partners LP; *U.S. Public*, pg. 594
CRESTWOOD GAS SERVICES OPERATING LLC—See Crestwood Equity Partners LP; *U.S. Public*, pg. 594
CRESTWOOD PANHANDLE PIPELINE LLC—See Crestwood Equity Partners LP; *U.S. Public*, pg. 594
DANA GAS PJSC; *Int'l*, pg. 1957
DBNGP (WA) NOMINEES PTY LIMITED—See CK Hutchison Holdings Limited; *Int'l*, pg. 1636
DEPOMURES SA—See ENGIE SA; *Int'l*, pg. 2434
DIXIE PIPELINE COMPANY LLC—See Enterprise Products Partners L.P.; *U.S. Public*, pg. 778
DOMINION COVE POINT LNG LP—See Dominion Energy, Inc.; *U.S. Public*, pg. 673
DUKE ENERGY ROYAL, LLC—See Duke Energy Corporation; *U.S. Public*, pg. 691
DYNNIQ ENERGY B.V.—See Heijmans N.V.; *Int'l*, pg. 3322
EL PASO CGP COMPANY, L.L.C.—See Kinder Morgan, Inc.; *U.S. Public*, pg. 1232
EL PASO CNG COMPANY, L.L.C.—See Kinder Morgan, Inc.; *U.S. Public*, pg. 1232
EL PASO PIPELINE PARTNERS, L.P.—See Kinder Morgan, Inc.; *U.S. Public*, pg. 1232
EMERA BRUNSWICK PIPELINE CO LTD—See Emera, Inc.; *Int'l*, pg. 2377
ENAGAS, S.A.; *Int'l*, pg. 2396
ENBRIDGE PIPELINES (ATHABASCA) INC.—See Enbridge Inc.; *Int'l*, pg. 2397
ENLINK MIDSTREAM, INC.—See EnLink Midstream, LLC; *U.S. Public*, pg. 768
ENSTOR INC.—See Iberdrola, S.A.; *Int'l*, pg. 3570
ENSTOR OPERATING COMPANY, LLC—See Iberdrola, S.A.; *Int'l*, pg. 3570
ENTERPRISE GTM HOLDINGS L.P.—See Enterprise Products Partners L.P.; *U.S. Public*, pg. 778
ENTERPRISE PRODUCTS PARTNERS L.P.; *U.S. Public*, pg. 778
E.ON DISTRIBUCIJA PLINA D.O.O.—See E.ON SE; *Int'l*, pg. 2252
E.ON GASIFICATION DEVELOPMENT AB—See E.ON SE; *Int'l*, pg. 2255
E.ON GAS SVERIGE AB—See E.ON SE; *Int'l*, pg. 2255
EQUINOR DEUTSCHLAND GMBH—See Equinor ASA; *Int'l*, pg. 2484
EQUITRANS, LP—See EQT Corporation; *U.S. Public*, pg. 785
EQUITRANS MIDSTREAM CORPORATION—See EQT Corporation; *U.S. Public*, pg. 784
ERMEWA GENEVE—See Ermewa Interservices Sarl; *Int'l*, pg. 2494
EWE GASSPEICHER GMBH—See EWE Aktiengesellschaft; *Int'l*, pg. 2575
FAYETTEVILLE EXPRESS PIPELINE LLC—See Energy Transfer LP; *U.S. Public*, pg. 763
FLAME PROPANE—See UGI Corporation; *U.S. Public*, pg. 2222
GASLOG ASIA PTE. LTD.—See GasLog Ltd.; *Int'l*, pg. 2888
GASLOG LNG SERVICES LTD.—See GasLog Ltd.; *Int'l*, pg. 2888
GASNETZ HAMBURG GMBH; *Int'l*, pg. 2888
GASODUCTO GASANDES S.A.—See The AES Corporation; *U.S. Public*, pg. 2031
GASODUCTO NOR ANDINO ARGENTINA—See ENGIE SA; *Int'l*, pg. 2434
GASODUCTO NOR ANDINO CHILE S.A.—See ENGIE SA; *Int'l*, pg. 2434
GASSCO AS; *Int'l*, pg. 2888
GASTRANSPORT NORD GMBH—See EWE Aktiengesellschaft; *Int'l*, pg. 2575
GATEWAY ENERGY COMPANY, LLC; *U.S. Private*, pg. 1650
GENESIS ALKALI WYOMING, LP—See Genesis Energy, L.P.; *U.S. Public*, pg. 930
GNL CHILE S.A.—See Enel S.p.A.; *Int'l*, pg. 2414
GNL ITALIA S.P.A.—See Eni S.p.A.; *Int'l*, pg. 2438
GOLDFIELDS GAS TRANSMISSION PTY. LTD.—See APA Group; *Int'l*, pg. 500
GRANITE STATE GAS TRANSMISSION, INC.—See Unitil Corporation; *U.S. Public*, pg. 2253
GRTGAZ DEUTSCHLAND GMBH—See ENGIE SA; *Int'l*, pg. 2434
GUIZHOU GAS GROUP CORPORATION, LTD.; *Int'l*, pg. 3174
GULF COAST EXPRESS PIPELINE LLC; *U.S. Private*, pg. 1815
GULF SOUTH PIPELINE COMPANY, LP—See Loews Corporation; *U.S. Public*, pg. 1339
GVG RHEIN-ERFT GMBH—See E.ON SE; *Int'l*, pg. 2257
HAMPSHIRE GAS COMPANY—See AltaGas Ltd.; *Int'l*, pg. 384
HARLAND & WOLFF GROUP HOLDINGS PLC; *Int'l*, pg. 3277
HERITAGE ETC GP, L.L.C.—See Energy Transfer LP; *U.S. Public*, pg. 763
HESS MIDSTREAM LP; *U.S. Public*, pg. 1030
HIGH POINT GAS TRANSMISSION, LLC—See ArcLight Capital Holdings, LLC; *U.S. Private*, pg. 312
HNG STORAGE LP; *U.S. Private*, pg. 1955

486210 — PIPELINE TRANSPORTA...

HOUSTON PIPE LINE COMPANY, L.P.—See Energy Transfer LP; *U.S. Public*, pg. 763
INTERNATIONAL SEAWAYS, INC.; *U.S. Public*, pg. 1158
IROQUOIS GAS TRANSMISSION SYSTEM, LP—See Dominion Energy, Inc.; *U.S. Public*, pg. 674
IROQUOIS GAS TRANSMISSION SYSTEM, LP—See Iberdrola, S.A.; *Int'l*, pg. 3570
KB PIPELINE COMPANY—See Northwest Natural Holding Company; *U.S. Public*, pg. 1542
KERN RIVER GAS TRANSMISSION COMPANY—See Berkshire Hathaway Inc.; *U.S. Public*, pg. 300
KINDER MORGAN TEXAS PIPELINE, LP—See Kinder Morgan, Inc.; *U.S. Public*, pg. 1233
KINDER MORGAN TEXAS TERMINALS, L.P.—See Kinder Morgan, Inc.; *U.S. Public*, pg. 1233
KINDER MORGAN TREATING LP—See Kinder Morgan, Inc.; *U.S. Public*, pg. 1233
LIBERTY PIPELINE GROUP, LLC—See Energy Transfer LP; *U.S. Public*, pg. 763
LIBERTY UTILITIES ENERGY SOLUTIONS (APPLIANCE) CORP.—See Algonquin Power & Utilities Corp.; *Int'l*, pg. 319
LNG SHIPPING SPA—See Eni S.p.A.; *Int'l*, pg. 2438
LUBMIN-BRANDOV GASTRANSPORT GMBH—See E.ON SE; *Int'l*, pg. 2255
MARLIN GAS SERVICES, LLC—See Chesapeake Utilities Corporation; *U.S. Public*, pg. 485
MATERIAL DE AIREACION S.A.—See Aliaxis S.A./N.V.; *Int'l*, pg. 325
MEGAL MITTEL-EUROPAISCHE-GASLEITUNGSGESELLSCHAFT MBH & CO. KG—See British Columbia Investment Management Corp.; *Int'l*, pg. 1169
MEGAL MITTEL-EUROPAISCHE-GASLEITUNGSGESELLSCHAFT MBH & CO. KG—See ENGIE SA; *Int'l*, pg. 2431
MID AMERICA PIPELINE CO., LLC—See Enterprise Products Partners L.P.; *U.S. Public*, pg. 779
MID-AMERICA PIPELINE CO., LLC—See Enterprise Products Partners L.P.; *U.S. Public*, pg. 779
MID-AMERICA PIPELINE CO., LLC—See Enterprise Products Partners L.P.; *U.S. Public*, pg. 779
MID-AMERICA PIPELINE CO., LLC—See Enterprise Products Partners L.P.; *U.S. Public*, pg. 779
MID-AMERICA PIPELINE CO., LLC—See Enterprise Products Partners L.P.; *U.S. Public*, pg. 779
MID-AMERICA PIPELINE CO., LLC—See Enterprise Products Partners L.P.; *U.S. Public*, pg. 779
MIDCO LLC—See Kinder Morgan, Inc.; *U.S. Public*, pg. 1233
MILLENNIUM PIPELINE COMPANY, LLC—See DT Midstream, Inc.; *U.S. Public*, pg. 689
MITTELRHEINISCHE ERDGASTRANSPORTLEI-TUNGSGESELLSCHAFT MBH—See British Columbia Investment Management Corp.; *Int'l*, pg. 1169
MOJAVE PIPELINE COMPANY, L.L.C.—See Kinder Morgan, Inc.; *U.S. Public*, pg. 1232
MOJAVE PIPELINE OPERATING COMPANY—See Kinder Morgan, Inc.; *U.S. Public*, pg. 1233
MONARCH PIPELINE, LLC—See The Williams Companies, Inc.; *U.S. Public*, pg. 2142
MOUNTAINWEST OVERTHRUST PIPELINE, LLC—See The Williams Companies, Inc.; *U.S. Public*, pg. 2142
MOUNTAINWEST PIPELINE, LLC—See The Williams Companies, Inc.; *U.S. Public*, pg. 2142
NATIONAL GAS & OIL COMPANY—See The Energy Cooperative, Inc.; *U.S. Private*, pg. 4026
NATURAL GAS PIPELINE COMPANY OF AMERICA LLC—See Brookfield Infrastructure Partners L.P.; *Int'l*, pg. 1193
NATURAL GAS PIPELINE COMPANY OF AMERICA LLC—See Kinder Morgan, Inc.; *U.S. Public*, pg. 1234
NATURGAS ENERGIA TRANSPORTE, S.A.U.—See Enagas, S.A.; *Int'l*, pg. 2396
NAVIERA TRANS GAS, A.I.E.—See Banco Santander, S.A.; *Int'l*, pg. 826
NET4GAS, S.R.O.—See Allianz SE; *Int'l*, pg. 344
NEXTBRIDGE INFRASTRUCTURE LP—See Enbridge Inc.; *Int'l*, pg. 2397
NFG MIDSTREAM COVINGTON, LLC—See National Fuel Gas Company; *U.S. Public*, pg. 1494
NGO DEVELOPMENT CORPORATION—See The Energy Cooperative, Inc.; *U.S. Private*, pg. 4026
NGO TRANSMISSION, INC.—See The Energy Cooperative, Inc.; *U.S. Private*, pg. 4026
NOORDGASTRANSPORT B.V.—See ENGIE SA; *Int'l*, pg. 2434
NORTHERN NATURAL GAS COMPANY—See Berkshire Hathaway Inc.; *U.S. Public*, pg. 301
NORTHWEST PIPELINE CORPORATION—See The Williams Companies, Inc.; *U.S. Public*, pg. 2144
NORTHWEST PIPELINE CORPORATION—See The Williams Companies, Inc.; *U.S. Public*, pg. 2144
NORTHWEST PIPELINE LLC—See The Williams Companies, Inc.; *U.S. Public*, pg. 2143
OASIS PIPE LINE COMPANY; *U.S. Public*, pg. 2986
OMEGA PIPELINE COMPANY, LLC—See Spire, Inc; *U.S. Public*, pg. 1918

ONEOK GAS PROCESSING, LLC—See ONEOK, Inc.; *U.S. Public*, pg. 1603
ONEOK GAS STORAGE, LLC—See ONEOK, Inc.; *U.S. Public*, pg. 1603
ONEOK GAS TRANSPORTATION, LLC—See ONEOK, Inc.; *U.S. Public*, pg. 1603
ONEOK LEASING COMPANY—See ONEOK, Inc.; *U.S. Public*, pg. 1603
ONSTREAM PIPELINE INSPECTION SERVICES INC.—See Mistras Group, Inc.; *U.S. Public*, pg. 1451
OPAL NEL TRANSPORT GMBH—See BASF SE; *Int'l*, pg. 884
OPEN GRID SERVICE GMBH—See E.ON SE; *Int'l*, pg. 2258
OVERLAND PASS PIPELINE COMPANY LLC—See The Williams Companies, Inc.; *U.S. Public*, pg. 2142
PARADEE GAS COMPANY—See UGI Corporation; *U.S. Public*, pg. 2222
PEOPLES GAS SYSTEM (FLORIDA), INC.—See Emera, Inc.; *Int'l*, pg. 2377
PETROBRAS GAS S.A.—See Cosan S.A.; *Int'l*, pg. 1809
PINE NEEDLE OPERATING COMPANY—See The Williams Companies, Inc.; *U.S. Public*, pg. 2143
PORTLAND NATURAL GAS TRANSMISSION SYSTEM—See BlackRock, Inc.; *U.S. Public*, pg. 346
PORTLAND NATURAL GAS TRANSMISSION SYSTEM—See Morgan Stanley; *U.S. Public*, pg. 1475
ROSE ROCK FINANCE CORPORATION—See Energy Transfer LP; *U.S. Public*, pg. 764
SABINE PASS LIQUEFACTION, LLC; *U.S. Private*, pg. 3521
SAGE REFINED PRODUCTS, LTD.—See Kinder Morgan, Inc.; *U.S. Public*, pg. 1234
SEMGAS, L.P.—See Energy Transfer LP; *U.S. Public*, pg. 764
SEMINOLE PIPELINE COMPANY—See Enterprise Products Partners L.P.; *U.S. Public*, pg. 779
SEMINOLE PIPELINE COMPANY—See Enterprise Products Partners L.P.; *U.S. Public*, pg. 779
SEMPRA PIPELINES & STORAGE CORP.—See Sempra; *U.S. Public*, pg. 1863
SHORELINE GAS INC.; *U.S. Private*, pg. 3641
SIERRITA GAS PIPELINE LLC—See Kinder Morgan, Inc.; *U.S. Public*, pg. 1234
SITI ENERGY LIMITED—See Essel Corporate Resources Pvt. Ltd.; *Int'l*, pg. 2510
SNAM RETE GAS S.P.A.—See Eni S.p.A.; *Int'l*, pg. 2438
SOCIEDAD GNL MEJILLONES S.A.—See ENGIE SA; *Int'l*, pg. 2431
SONGAS LIMITED—See General Atlantic Service Company, L.P.; *U.S. Private*, pg. 1661
SOUTHCROSS ENERGY GP LLC—See Charlesbank Capital Partners, LLC; *U.S. Private*, pg. 856
SOUTHCROSS ENERGY GP LLC—See EIG Global Energy Partners, LLC; *U.S. Private*, pg. 1347
SOUTHCROSS ENERGY GP LLC—See Tailwater Capital LLC; *U.S. Private*, pg. 3923
SOUTHCROSS MISSISSIPPI PIPELINE, L.P.—See Charlesbank Capital Partners, LLC; *U.S. Private*, pg. 856
SOUTHCROSS MISSISSIPPI PIPELINE, L.P.—See EIG Global Energy Partners, LLC; *U.S. Private*, pg. 1347
SOUTHCROSS MISSISSIPPI PIPELINE, L.P.—See Tailwater Capital LLC; *U.S. Private*, pg. 3923
SOUTHCROSS NGL PIPELINE LTD.—See Charlesbank Capital Partners, LLC; *U.S. Private*, pg. 856
SOUTHCROSS NGL PIPELINE LTD.—See EIG Global Energy Partners, LLC; *U.S. Private*, pg. 1347
SOUTHCROSS NGL PIPELINE LTD.—See Tailwater Capital LLC; *U.S. Private*, pg. 3923
SOUTH EAST AUSTRALIA GAS PTY LTD—See APA Group; *Int'l*, pg. 500
SOUTHERN GULF LNG COMPANY, L.L.C.—See Kinder Morgan, Inc.; *U.S. Public*, pg. 1232
SOUTHERN NATURAL GAS COMPANY, L.L.C.—See Kinder Morgan, Inc.; *U.S. Public*, pg. 1232
SOUTHERN STAR CENTRAL CORP.—See Caisse de Depot et Placement du Quebec; *Int'l*, pg. 1255
SOUTHERN STAR CENTRAL GAS PIPELINE, INC.—See Morgan Stanley; *U.S. Public*, pg. 1475
SOUTHWESTERN ENERGY PIPELINE SERVICES—See Expand Energy Corporation; *U.S. Public*, pg. 809
SPECTRA ENERGY CANADA EXCHANGECO INC.—See Enbridge Inc.; *Int'l*, pg. 2397
SPECTRA ENERGY PARTNERS, L.P.—See Enbridge Inc.; *Int'l*, pg. 2397
STANCHION ENERGY, LLC—See Blackstone Inc.; *U.S. Public*, pg. 359
ST. LAWRENCE GAS COMPANY, INC.—See Algonquin Power & Utilities Corp.; *Int'l*, pg. 319
STOREGY DEUTSCHLAND GMBH—See ENGIE SA; *Int'l*, pg. 2435
STOREGY SA—See ENGIE SA; *Int'l*, pg. 2435
STOREGY UK LTD—See ENGIE SA; *Int'l*, pg. 2435
SUPERIOR NATURAL GAS CORP.; *U.S. Private*, pg. 3879
TAQA NORTH LTD.—See Abu Dhabi Water & Electricity Authority; *Int'l*, pg. 73
TARGA DOWNSTREAM LLC—See Targa Resources Corp.; *U.S. Public*, pg. 1982

TARGA GAS MARKETING LLC—See Targa Resources Corp.; *U.S. Public*, pg. 1982
TARGA INTRASTATE PIPELINE LLC—See Targa Resources Corp.; *U.S. Public*, pg. 1982
TARGA LOUISIANA INTRASTATE LLC—See Targa Resources Corp.; *U.S. Public*, pg. 1982
TARGA MIDSTREAM SERVICES LLC—See Targa Resources Corp.; *U.S. Public*, pg. 1982
TARGA PIPELINE MID-CONTINENT LLC—See Targa Resources Corp.; *U.S. Public*, pg. 1982
TARGA RESOURCES OPERATING LLC—See Targa Resources Corp.; *U.S. Public*, pg. 1982
TARGA RESOURCES PARTNERS LP—See Targa Resources Corp.; *U.S. Public*, pg. 1981
TENGASCO PIPELINE CORPORATION—See Riley Exploration Permian, Inc.; *U.S. Public*, pg. 1798
TENNESSEE GAS PIPELINE COMPANY, L.L.C.—See Kinder Morgan, Inc.; *U.S. Public*, pg. 1233
TEXAS GAS TRANSMISSION, LLC—See Loews Corporation; *U.S. Public*, pg. 1339
THYSSENGAS GMBH—See DIF Management Holding B.V.; *Int'l*, pg. 2118
THYSSENGAS GMBH—See Electricite de France S.A.; *Int'l*, pg. 2352
TOTAL INFRASTRUCTURES GAZ FRANCE SA—See Electricite de France S.A.; *Int'l*, pg. 2352
TOTAL INFRASTRUCTURES GAZ FRANCE SA—See Eni S.p.A.; *Int'l*, pg. 2438
TOTAL INFRASTRUCTURES GAZ FRANCE SA—See GIC Pte. Ltd.; *Int'l*, pg. 2965
TRANS AUSTRIA GASLEITUNG GMBH—See Eni S.p.A.; *Int'l*, pg. 2438
TRANSCO GAS PIPE LINE CORPORATION—See The Williams Companies, Inc.; *U.S. Public*, pg. 2143
TRANSCO GAS PIPE LINE CORPORATION—See The Williams Companies, Inc.; *U.S. Public*, pg. 2143
TRANSCO GAS PIPE LINE CORP.—See The Williams Companies, Inc.; *U.S. Public*, pg. 2143
TRANSCO GAS PIPE LINE CORP.—See The Williams Companies, Inc.; *U.S. Public*, pg. 2143
TRANSPORT 4, L.L.C.—See Enterprise Products Partners L.P.; *U.S. Public*, pg. 779
TRANS QUEBEC & MARITIMES PIPELINE INC.—See Caisse de Depot et Placement du Quebec; *Int'l*, pg. 1256
TRANSWESTERN PIPELINE COMPANY, LLC—See Energy Transfer LP; *U.S. Public*, pg. 764
TRUNKLINE GAS COMPANY—See Energy Transfer LP; *U.S. Public*, pg. 763
VECTOR PIPELINE, L.P.—See DTE Energy Company; *U.S. Public*, pg. 689
VECTOR PIPELINE, L.P.—See Enbridge Inc.; *Int'l*, pg. 2397
WBI ENERGY TRANSMISSION, INC.—See MDU Resources Group, Inc.; *U.S. Public*, pg. 1410
WEST TEXAS LPG PIPELINE LIMITED PARTNERSHIP—See ONEOK, Inc.; *U.S. Public*, pg. 1603
WILCO TRANSPORTATION LLC—See Marathon Petroleum Corporation; *U.S. Public*, pg. 1364
THE WILLIAMS COMPANIES, INC. - HOUSTON—See The Williams Companies, Inc.; *U.S. Public*, pg. 2142
THE WILLIAMS COMPANIES, INC.; *U.S. Public*, pg. 2142
WILLIAMS ENERGY CO.—See The Williams Companies, Inc.; *U.S. Public*, pg. 2142
WILLIAMS ENERGY SERVICES—See The Williams Companies, Inc.; *U.S. Public*, pg. 2142
WILLIAMS ENERGY SERVICES—See The Williams Companies, Inc.; *U.S. Public*, pg. 2142
WILLIAMS FOUR CORNERS LLC—See The Williams Companies, Inc.; *U.S. Public*, pg. 2142
WILLIAMS GAS PIPELINE COMPANY LLC—See The Williams Companies, Inc.; *U.S. Public*, pg. 2143
WILLIAMS GAS PIPELINE PLYMOUTH DISTRICT—See The Williams Companies, Inc.; *U.S. Public*, pg. 2144
WILLIAMS GAS PIPELINE—See The Williams Companies, Inc.; *U.S. Public*, pg. 2143
WILLIAMS GAS PIPELINE—See The Williams Companies, Inc.; *U.S. Public*, pg. 2143
WILLIAMS GAS PIPELINE—See The Williams Companies, Inc.; *U.S. Public*, pg. 2144
WILLIAMS GAS PIPELINE WEST—See The Williams Companies, Inc.; *U.S. Public*, pg. 2144
WILLIAMS NORTHWEST PIPELINE—See The Williams Companies, Inc.; *U.S. Public*, pg. 2144
WILLIAMS PIPELINE PARTNERS, L.P.—See The Williams Companies, Inc.; *U.S. Public*, pg. 2144
WILLIAMS PIPELINE SERVICES—See The Williams Companies, Inc.; *U.S. Public*, pg. 2144
WILLIAMS WPC INTERNATIONAL COMPANY—See The Williams Companies, Inc.; *U.S. Public*, pg. 2144
WINGAS TRANSPORT GMBH & CO. KG—See BASF SE; *Int'l*, pg. 885
WYOMING INTERSTATE COMPANY, L.L.C.—See Kinder Morgan, Inc.; *U.S. Public*, pg. 1232
YOUNG GAS STORAGE COMPANY—See Colorado Springs Utilities, Inc.; *U.S. Private*, pg. 974
YOUNG GAS STORAGE COMPANY—See Kinder Morgan, Inc.; *U.S. Public*, pg. 1232

N.A.I.C.S. INDEX

YOUNG GAS STORAGE COMPANY—See Xcel Energy Inc.; *U.S. Public,* pg. 2385

486910 — PIPELINE TRANSPORTATION OF REFINED PETROLEUM PRODUCTS

ABU DHABI NATIONAL ENERGY COMPANY PJSC—See Abu Dhabi Water & Electricity Authority; *Int'l,* pg. 73
ABU DHABI NATIONAL TANKER COMPANY—See Abu Dhabi National Oil Company; *Int'l,* pg. 73
BARAKAH OFFSHORE PETROLEUM BERHAD; *Int'l,* pg. 858
BOARDWALK PIPELINE PARTNERS, LP—See Loews Corporation; *U.S. Public,* pg. 1339
BP PIPELINES NORTH AMERICA INC.—See BP plc; *Int'l,* pg. 1126
BP PIPELINES NORTH AMERICA INC.—See BP plc; *Int'l,* pg. 1127
BP PIPELINES NORTH AMERICA INC.—See BP plc; *Int'l,* pg. 1127
BP PIPELINES NORTH AMERICA INC.—See BP plc; *Int'l,* pg. 1127
BP PRODUCTS NORTH AMERICA INC.—See BP plc; *Int'l,* pg. 1127
COLONIAL PIPELINE COMPANY; *U.S. Private,* pg. 971
COMPANHIA LOGISTICA DE COMBUSTIVEIS, S.A.—See Galp Energia SGPS, S.A.; *Int'l,* pg. 2875
DELAWARE PIPELINE COMPANY LLC—See PBF Energy Inc.; *U.S. Public,* pg. 1657
DELEK CRUDE LOGISTICS, LLC—See Delek Group Ltd.; *Int'l,* pg. 2011
DELEK MARKETING & SUPPLY, LP—See Delek Group Ltd.; *Int'l,* pg. 2011
DOW PIPE LINE COMPANY—See Dow Inc.; *U.S. Public,* pg. 684
DOW PIPE LINE COMPANY—See Dow Inc.; *U.S. Public,* pg. 684
DOW PIPE LINE COMPANY—See Dow Inc.; *U.S. Public,* pg. 684
ENTERPRISE CRUDE OIL LLC—See Enterprise Products Partners L.P.; *U.S. Public,* pg. 778
EXPLORER PIPELINE COMPANY; *U.S. Private,* pg. 1450
EXXONMOBIL OIL CORPORATION—See Exxon Mobil Corporation; *U.S. Public,* pg. 815
EXXONMOBIL PIPELINE COMPANY LLC—See Exxon Mobil Corporation; *U.S. Public,* pg. 816
EXXONMOBIL PIPELINE COMPANY—See Exxon Mobil Corporation; *U.S. Public,* pg. 816
HAVRE PIPELINE COMPANY, LLC—See NorthWestern Corporation; *U.S. Public,* pg. 1543
HB CONSTRUCTION COMPANY LTD.—See The Williams Companies, Inc.; *U.S. Public,* pg. 2142
HOFFMAN FUEL COMPANY OF STAMFORD—See Star Group, L.P.; *U.S. Public,* pg. 1937
INLAND CORPORATION—See Energy Transfer LP; *U.S. Public,* pg. 764
INTER PIPELINE LTD. - COCHRANE EXTRACTION PLANT—See Brookfield Infrastructure Partners L.P.; *Int'l,* pg. 1193
KAW PIPE LINE COMPANY—See CHS INC.; *U.S. Public,* pg. 491
KINDER MORGAN ENERGY PARTNERS, L.P. - PACIFIC OPERATIONS—See Kinder Morgan, Inc.; *U.S. Public,* pg. 1233
LACLEDE PIPELINE COMPANY—See Spire, Inc; *U.S. Public,* pg. 1918
LION OIL TRADING & TRANSPORTATION, LLC—See Delek Group Ltd.; *Int'l,* pg. 2012
MAGELLAN PIPELINE COMPANY, L.P.—See ONEOK, Inc.; *U.S. Public,* pg. 1603
MAGELLAN PIPELINE LP—See ONEOK, Inc.; *U.S. Public,* pg. 1603
MARATHON PETROLEUM COMPANY LLC—See Marathon Petroleum Corporation; *U.S. Public,* pg. 1364
MCCHORD PIPELINE COMPANY—See Par Pacific Holdings, Inc.; *U.S. Public,* pg. 1636
MOGAS PIPELINE, LLC—See Spire, Inc; *U.S. Public,* pg. 1918
NORTHERN TIER OIL TRANSPORT LLC—See Marathon Petroleum Corporation; *U.S. Public,* pg. 1363
NUSTAR ENERGY L.P.—See Sunoco LP; *U.S. Public,* pg. 1964
NUSTAR ENERGY L.P. - WICHITA—See Sunoco LP; *U.S. Public,* pg. 1964
NUSTAR PIPELINE COMPANY, LLC—See Sunoco LP; *U.S. Public,* pg. 1964
PALINE PIPELINE COMPANY, LLC—See Delek Group Ltd.; *Int'l,* pg. 2012
THE PIPELINES OF PUERTO RICO, INC.—See Chevron Corporation; *U.S. Public,* pg. 488
PLANTATION PIPE LINE COMPANY—See Kinder Morgan, Inc.; *U.S. Public,* pg. 1233
THE PREMCOR PIPELINE CO.—See Valero Energy Corporation; *U.S. Public,* pg. 2272
TAIWAN MARKETING & TRANSPORTATION DIVISION—See CPC Corporation; *Int'l,* pg. 1824
TOWNGAS INTERNATIONAL COMPANY LIMITED—See Henderson Land Development Co. Ltd.; *Int'l,* pg. 3344
TRANS LOUISIANA GAS PIPELINE, INC.—See Atmos Energy Corporation; *U.S. Public,* pg. 224
VALERO MARKETING & SUPPLY COMPANY—See Valero Energy Corporation; *U.S. Public,* pg. 2272
WEST SHORE PIPE LINE COMPANY—See Energy Transfer LP; *U.S. Public,* pg. 764
WILLIAMS PURITY PIPELINES, LLC—See The Williams Companies, Inc.; *U.S. Public,* pg. 2144
WOLVERINE PIPE LINE COMPANY; *U.S. Private,* pg. 4555

486990 — ALL OTHER PIPELINE TRANSPORTATION

ADVANCED VALVE SOLUTIONS B.V.—See Addtech AB; *Int'l,* pg. 131
ALLIANCE PIPELINE L.P.—See Enbridge Inc.; *Int'l,* pg. 2397
AQUALINE LTD.; *Int'l,* pg. 527
AUX SABLE CANADA L.P.—See Enbridge Inc.; *Int'l,* pg. 2397
AUX SABLE LIQUID PRODUCTS INC.—See The Williams Companies, Inc.; *U.S. Public,* pg. 2142
BAFS PIPELINE TRANSPORTATION LTD—See Bangkok Aviation Fuel Services Public Company Limited; *Int'l,* pg. 832
BJ TUBULAR SERVICES B.V.—See Baker Hughes Company; *U.S. Public,* pg. 264
BOMBARD MECHANICAL, LLC—See MDU Resources Group, Inc.; *U.S. Public,* pg. 1409
BP MIDSTREAM PARTNERS LP; *U.S. Public,* pg. 378
CARON TRANSPORTATION SYSTEMS PARTNERSHIP; *Int'l,* pg. 1342
CONTROL CUTTER AS—See Addtech AB; *Int'l,* pg. 132
CSE-SERVELEC S.R.O.—See CSE Global Ltd.; *Int'l,* pg. 1863
ENTERPRISE PIPELINE COMPANY INC.—See Enterprise Group, Inc.; *Int'l,* pg. 2451
ESSO ITALIANA S.R.L.—See Exxon Mobil Corporation; *U.S. Public,* pg. 814
FRIATEC AG-CERAMICS DIVISION—See Aliaxis S.A./N.V.; *Int'l,* pg. 324
FRIATEC AG—See Aliaxis S.A./N.V.; *Int'l,* pg. 324
FRIATEC AG-TECHNICAL PLASTICS DIVISION—See Aliaxis S.A./N.V.; *Int'l,* pg. 324
FRIATEC BUILDING SERVICES—See Aliaxis S.A./N.V.; *Int'l,* pg. 324
FRIATEC DPL—See Aliaxis S.A./N.V.; *Int'l,* pg. 324
INTER PIPELINE LTD.—See Brookfield Infrastructure Partners L.P.; *Int'l,* pg. 1193
MEARS CANADA CORP.—See Quanta Services, Inc.; *U.S. Public,* pg. 1752
MID-VALLEY PIPELINE COMPANY—See Energy Transfer LP; *U.S. Public,* pg. 764
MIPC, LLC—See Delta Air Lines, Inc.; *U.S. Public,* pg. 652
MONTREAL PIPE LINE LIMITED—See Exxon Mobil Corporation; *U.S. Public,* pg. 816
NORTH SHORE GAS COMPANY—See WEC Energy Group, Inc.; *U.S. Public,* pg. 2342
PETRO PROGRESS, INC.—See Fuji Oil Company, Ltd.; *Int'l,* pg. 2815
SALTVILLE GAS STORAGE COMPANY L.L.C.—See Enbridge Inc.; *Int'l,* pg. 2397
SED FLOW CONTROL GMBH—See Aliaxis S.A./N.V.; *Int'l,* pg. 324
SEMINOLE PIPELINE COMPANY—See Enterprise Products Partners L.P.; *U.S. Public,* pg. 779
STRIKE LLC—See AIP, LLC; *U.S. Private,* pg. 137
TALLGRASS MIDSTREAM, LLC—See Blackstone Inc.; *U.S. Public,* pg. 359
TALLGRASS MLP OPERATIONS, LLC—See Blackstone Inc.; *U.S. Public,* pg. 359
TEXAS BRINE COMPANY LLC—See United Salt Corporation; *U.S. Private,* pg. 4297
THAI AVIATION REFUELLING COMPANY LIMITED—See Bangkok Aviation Fuel Services Public Company Limited; *Int'l,* pg. 832
TRANSCO GAS PIPELINES—See The Williams Companies, Inc.; *U.S. Public,* pg. 2143
TRANSLOAD SERVICES, LLC—See Kinder Morgan, Inc.; *U.S. Public,* pg. 1233
TRANS TUNISIAN PIPELINE CO LTD—See Eni S.p.A.; *Int'l,* pg. 2438
WBI ENERGY SERVICES, INC.—See MDU Resources Group, Inc.; *U.S. Public,* pg. 1411
WILLIAMS INTERNATIONAL VENTURES COMPANY—See The Williams Companies, Inc.; *U.S. Public,* pg. 2142

487110 — SCENIC AND SIGHTSEEING TRANSPORTATION, LAND

CANGGANG RAILWAY LIMITED; *Int'l,* pg. 1291
CAPORIN VOYAGES SARL—See Die Schweizerische Post AG; *Int'l,* pg. 2112
CARPOSTAL AGDE SAS—See Die Schweizerische Post AG; *Int'l,* pg. 2112
CARPOSTAL DOLE SAS—See Die Schweizerische Post AG; *Int'l,* pg. 2112
CARPOSTAL MACON SAS—See Die Schweizerische Post AG; *Int'l,* pg. 2112
CARPOSTAL MEDITERRANEE SAS—See Die Schweizerische Post AG; *Int'l,* pg. 2112
CROSS SOUND CABLE COMPANY, LLC—See Argo Infrastructure Partners LLC; *U.S. Private,* pg. 320
EAGLE TRANSPORTATION LLC—See Gryphon Investors, LLC; *U.S. Private,* pg. 1799
HOTARD COACHES, INC.; *U.S. Public,* pg. 1999
NAPA VALLEY WINE TRAIN, INC.—See Noble House Hotels & Resorts, Ltd.; *U.S. Private,* pg. 2932
NORTHERN SOUND & LIGHT, INC—See Alarmax Distributors Inc.; *U.S. Private,* pg. 150
PRINCESS TOURS—See Carnival Corporation; *U.S. Public,* pg. 438
ROBERT'S HAWAII INC.; *U.S. Private,* pg. 3459
ROBERT'S HAWAII TOURS AND TRANSPORTATION—See Robert's Hawaii Inc.; *U.S. Private,* pg. 3459
SOCIETE D'AFFRETEMENT ET DE TRANSIT S.A.T. SAS—See Die Schweizerische Post AG; *Int'l,* pg. 2113

487210 — SCENIC AND SIGHTSEEING TRANSPORTATION, WATER

BATEAUX NANTAIS; *Int'l,* pg. 889
BLOUNT SMALL SHIP ADVENTURES, INC.; *U.S. Private,* pg. 584
BLUE & GOLD FLEET INC.—See PIER 39 L.P.; *U.S. Private,* pg. 3178
CALYPSO REEF CHARTERS PTY. LTD.—See Experience Co Limited; *Int'l,* pg. 2588
CATALINA CHANNEL EXPRESS INC.; *U.S. Private,* pg. 786
CLIPPER NAVIGATION, INC.—See FRS GmbH & Co. KG; *Int'l,* pg. 2797
CROISIERES AUSTRALES LTEE—See ENL Limited; *Int'l,* pg. 2441
DISNEY CRUISE VACATIONS INC.—See The Walt Disney Company; *U.S. Public,* pg. 2138
ENTERTAINMENT CRUISES INC.—See The Pritzker Group - Chicago, LLC; *U.S. Private,* pg. 4098
GIANT NETWORK GROUP CO., LTD.; *Int'l,* pg. 2961
GLACIER PARK MARINE SERVICES INC.—See Gold Belt Incorporated; *U.S. Private,* pg. 1727
GOLD BELT INCORPORATED; *U.S. Private,* pg. 1727
HORNBLOWER CRUISES & EVENTS; *U.S. Private,* pg. 1983
INTERYACHTING—See Francoudi & Stephanou Ltd.; *Int'l,* pg. 2761
LADY ANN CRUISES INC.; *U.S. Private,* pg. 2372
LAKE COEUR D'ALENE CRUISES INC.—See The Hagadone Corporation; *U.S. Private,* pg. 4041
LINDBLAD EXPEDITIONS, LLC—See Lindblad Expeditions Holdings, Inc.; *U.S. Public,* pg. 1319
MAID OF THE MIST CORPORATION; *U.S. Private,* pg. 2550
ODYSSEY MARINE ENTERTAINMENT, INC.—See Odyssey Marine Exploration, Inc.; *U.S. Public,* pg. 1564
OU HT MEELELAHUTUS—See AS Infortar; *Int'l,* pg. 590
PARADISE CRUISES LTD.; *U.S. Private,* pg. 3090
REGENT SEVEN SEAS CRUISES UK LTD—See Norwegian Cruise Line Holdings Ltd.; *U.S. Public,* pg. 1543
ROBERT'S HAWAII CRUISES INC.—See Robert's Hawaii Inc.; *U.S. Private,* pg. 3459
ROYAL CARIBBEAN CRUISE LINES AS—See Royal Caribbean Cruises Ltd.; *U.S. Public,* pg. 1815
SHM ANACAPA ISLE, LLC—See Sun Communities, Inc.; *U.S. Public,* pg. 1961
SHM ANNAPOLIS, LLC—See Sun Communities, Inc.; *U.S. Public,* pg. 1961
SHM AQUALAND, LLC—See Sun Communities, Inc.; *U.S. Public,* pg. 1961
SHM AQUA YACHT, LLC—See Sun Communities, Inc.; *U.S. Public,* pg. 1961
SHM BAHIA BLEU, LLC—See Sun Communities, Inc.; *U.S. Public,* pg. 1961
SHM BALLENA ISLE, LLC—See Sun Communities, Inc.; *U.S. Public,* pg. 1961
SHM BEAUFORT, LLC—See Sun Communities, Inc.; *U.S. Public,* pg. 1961
SHM BEAVER CREEK, LLC—See Sun Communities, Inc.; *U.S. Public,* pg. 1961
SHM BELLE MAER, LLC—See Sun Communities, Inc.; *U.S. Public,* pg. 1961
SHM BOHEMIA VISTA, LLC—See Sun Communities, Inc.; *U.S. Public,* pg. 1961
SHM BRADY MOUNTAIN, LLC—See Sun Communities, Inc.; *U.S. Public,* pg. 1961
SHM BRUCE & JOHNSON, LLC—See Sun Communities, Inc.; *U.S. Public,* pg. 1961
SHM BURNSIDE, LLC—See Sun Communities, Inc.; *U.S. Public,* pg. 1961
SHM CABRILLO ISLE, LLC—See Sun Communities, Inc.; *U.S. Public,* pg. 1961

487210 — SCENIC AND SIGHTSEE...

SHM CAPE HARBOUR, LLC—See Sun Communities, Inc.; *U.S. Public*, pg. 1961
SHM CAPRI, LLC—See Sun Communities, Inc.; *U.S. Public*, pg. 1961
SHM CARROLL ISLAND, LLC—See Sun Communities, Inc.; *U.S. Public*, pg. 1961
SHM CHARLESTON BOATYARD, LLC—See Sun Communities, Inc.; *U.S. Public*, pg. 1962
SHM CHARLESTON CITY MARINA, LLC—See Sun Communities, Inc.; *U.S. Public*, pg. 1962
SHM COVE HAVEN, LLC—See Sun Communities, Inc.; *U.S. Public*, pg. 1962
SHM COWESETT, LLC—See Sun Communities, Inc.; *U.S. Public*, pg. 1962
SHM CRYSTAL POINT, LLC—See Sun Communities, Inc.; *U.S. Public*, pg. 1962
SHM DAUNTLESS, LLC—See Sun Communities, Inc.; *U.S. Public*, pg. 1962
SHM DEEP RIVER, LLC—See Sun Communities, Inc.; *U.S. Public*, pg. 1962
SHM DETROIT RIVER, LLC—See Sun Communities, Inc.; *U.S. Public*, pg. 1962
SHM EAGLE COVE, LLC—See Sun Communities, Inc.; *U.S. Public*, pg. 1962
SHM EMERALD COAST, LLC—See Sun Communities, Inc.; *U.S. Public*, pg. 1962
SHM EMERALD POINT, LLC—See Sun Communities, Inc.; *U.S. Public*, pg. 1962
SHM EMERYVILLE, LLC—See Sun Communities, Inc.; *U.S. Public*, pg. 1962
SHM FERRY POINT, LLC—See Sun Communities, Inc.; *U.S. Public*, pg. 1962
SHM FIDDLER'S COVE, LLC—See Sun Communities, Inc.; *U.S. Public*, pg. 1962
SHM GAINES, LLC—See Sun Communities, Inc.; *U.S. Public*, pg. 1962
SHM GLEN COVE, LLC—See Sun Communities, Inc.; *U.S. Public*, pg. 1962
SHM GRAND ISLE, LLC—See Sun Communities, Inc.; *U.S. Public*, pg. 1962
SHM GREAT ISLAND, LLC—See Sun Communities, Inc.; *U.S. Public*, pg. 1962
SHM GREAT LAKES, LLC—See Sun Communities, Inc.; *U.S. Public*, pg. 1962
SHM GREAT OAK LANDING, LLC—See Sun Communities, Inc.; *U.S. Public*, pg. 1962
SHM GREEN HARBOR, LLC—See Sun Communities, Inc.; *U.S. Public*, pg. 1962
SHM GREENPORT, LLC—See Sun Communities, Inc.; *U.S. Public*, pg. 1962
SHM GREENWICH BAY, LLC—See Sun Communities, Inc.; *U.S. Public*, pg. 1962
SHM GRIDER HILL, LLC—See Sun Communities, Inc.; *U.S. Public*, pg. 1962
SHM HACKS POINT, LLC—See Sun Communities, Inc.; *U.S. Public*, pg. 1962
SHM HARBORAGE YC, LLC—See Sun Communities, Inc.; *U.S. Public*, pg. 1962
SHM HARBORS VIEW, LLC—See Sun Communities, Inc.; *U.S. Public*, pg. 1962
SHM HARBORTOWN, LLC—See Sun Communities, Inc.; *U.S. Public*, pg. 1962
SHM HAVERSTRAW, LLC—See Sun Communities, Inc.; *U.S. Public*, pg. 1962
SHM HAWTHORNE COVE, LLC—See Sun Communities, Inc.; *U.S. Public*, pg. 1962
SHM HIDEAWAY BAY, LLC—See Sun Communities, Inc.; *U.S. Public*, pg. 1962
SHM HOLLY CREEK, LLC—See Sun Communities, Inc.; *U.S. Public*, pg. 1962
SHM ISLAMORADA, LLC—See Sun Communities, Inc.; *U.S. Public*, pg. 1962
SHM ISLAND PARK, LLC—See Sun Communities, Inc.; *U.S. Public*, pg. 1962
SHM JAMESTOWN BOATYARD, LLC—See Sun Communities, Inc.; *U.S. Public*, pg. 1962
SHM JAMESTOWN, LLC—See Sun Communities, Inc.; *U.S. Public*, pg. 1962
SHM JEFFERSON BEACH, LLC—See Sun Communities, Inc.; *U.S. Public*, pg. 1962
SHM KING'S POINT, LLC—See Sun Communities, Inc.; *U.S. Public*, pg. 1962
SHM LAKEFRONT, LLC—See Sun Communities, Inc.; *U.S. Public*, pg. 1962
SHM LOCH LOMOND, LLC—See Sun Communities, Inc.; *U.S. Public*, pg. 1962
SHM MANASQUAN, LLC—See Sun Communities, Inc.; *U.S. Public*, pg. 1962
SHM MARINA BAY, LLC—See Sun Communities, Inc.; *U.S. Public*, pg. 1962
SHM MYSTIC, LLC—See Sun Communities, Inc.; *U.S. Public*, pg. 1962
SHM NARROWS POINT, LLC—See Sun Communities, Inc.; *U.S. Public*, pg. 1962
SHM NEW PORT COVE, LLC—See Sun Communities, Inc.; *U.S. Public*, pg. 1962
SHM NORTH PALM BEACH, LLC—See Sun Communities, Inc.; *U.S. Public*, pg. 1962
SHM OLD PORT COVE, LLC—See Sun Communities, Inc.; *U.S. Public*, pg. 1962
SHM ONSET BAY, LLC—See Sun Communities, Inc.; *U.S. Public*, pg. 1962
SHM PIER 121, LLC—See Sun Communities, Inc.; *U.S. Public*, pg. 1962
SHM PILOTS POINT, LLC—See Sun Communities, Inc.; *U.S. Public*, pg. 1962
SHM PINELAND, LLC—See Sun Communities, Inc.; *U.S. Public*, pg. 1962
SHM PLYMOUTH, LLC—See Sun Communities, Inc.; *U.S. Public*, pg. 1962
SHM PORT ROYAL, LLC—See Sun Communities, Inc.; *U.S. Public*, pg. 1962
SHM POST ROAD, LLC—See Sun Communities, Inc.; *U.S. Public*, pg. 1962
SHM PUERTO DEL REY, LLC—See Sun Communities, Inc.; *U.S. Public*, pg. 1962
SHM REGATTA POINTE, LLC—See Sun Communities, Inc.; *U.S. Public*, pg. 1962
SHM RESERVE HARBOR, LLC—See Sun Communities, Inc.; *U.S. Public*, pg. 1962
SHM ROCKLAND, LLC—See Sun Communities, Inc.; *U.S. Public*, pg. 1962
SHM RYBOVICH WPB TRS, LLC—See Sun Communities, Inc.; *U.S. Public*, pg. 1962
SHM SAKONNET, LLC—See Sun Communities, Inc.; *U.S. Public*, pg. 1962
SHM SANDUSKY, LLC—See Sun Communities, Inc.; *U.S. Public*, pg. 1962
SHM SHELBURNE, LLC—See Sun Communities, Inc.; *U.S. Public*, pg. 1962
SHM SHELTER ISLAND, LLC—See Sun Communities, Inc.; *U.S. Public*, pg. 1962
SHM SILVER SPRING, LLC—See Sun Communities, Inc.; *U.S. Public*, pg. 1963
SHM SKIPPERS LANDING, LLC—See Sun Communities, Inc.; *U.S. Public*, pg. 1963
SHM SKULL CREEK, LLC—See Sun Communities, Inc.; *U.S. Public*, pg. 1963
SHM SOUTH BAY, LLC—See Sun Communities, Inc.; *U.S. Public*, pg. 1963
SHM SPORTSMAN, LLC—See Sun Communities, Inc.; *U.S. Public*, pg. 1963
SHM STRATFORD, LLC—See Sun Communities, Inc.; *U.S. Public*, pg. 1963
SHM SUNROAD, LLC—See Sun Communities, Inc.; *U.S. Public*, pg. 1963
SHM SUNSET BAY, LLC—See Sun Communities, Inc.; *U.S. Public*, pg. 1963
SHM TOLEDO BEACH, LLC—See Sun Communities, Inc.; *U.S. Public*, pg. 1963
SHM TRADE WINDS, LLC—See Sun Communities, Inc.; *U.S. Public*, pg. 1963
SHM VENTURA ISLE, LLC—See Sun Communities, Inc.; *U.S. Public*, pg. 1963
SHM VINEYARD HAVEN, LLC—See Sun Communities, Inc.; *U.S. Public*, pg. 1963
SHM WALDEN, LLC—See Sun Communities, Inc.; *U.S. Public*, pg. 1963
SHM WENTWORTH, LLC—See Sun Communities, Inc.; *U.S. Public*, pg. 1963
SHM WESTPORT, LLC—See Sun Communities, Inc.; *U.S. Public*, pg. 1963
SHM WICKFORD COVE, LLC—See Sun Communities, Inc.; *U.S. Public*, pg. 1963
SHM WISDOM DOCK, LLC—See Sun Communities, Inc.; *U.S. Public*, pg. 1963
SHM YACHT HAVEN, LLC—See Sun Communities, Inc.; *U.S. Public*, pg. 1963
SHM ZAHNISERS, LLC—See Sun Communities, Inc.; *U.S. Public*, pg. 1963
SPIRIT CRUISES LLC—See The Pritzker Group - Chicago, LLC; *U.S. Private*, pg. 4098
SPIRIT OF BOSTON—See The Pritzker Group - Chicago, LLC; *U.S. Private*, pg. 4098
SPIRIT OF CHICAGO—See The Pritzker Group - Chicago, LLC; *U.S. Private*, pg. 4099
SPIRIT OF NEW YORK—See The Pritzker Group - Chicago, LLC; *U.S. Private*, pg. 4099
SPIRIT OF NORFOLK—See The Pritzker Group - Chicago, LLC; *U.S. Private*, pg. 4099
SPIRIT OF PHILADELPHIA—See The Pritzker Group - Chicago, LLC; *U.S. Private*, pg. 4099
SPIRIT OF WASHINGTON—See The Pritzker Group - Chicago, LLC; *U.S. Private*, pg. 4099
STAR & CRESCENT BOAT COMPANY; *U.S. Private*, pg. 3784
ZEPHYR COVE RESORT—See Aramark; *U.S. Public*, pg. 176

487990 — SCENIC AND SIGHTSEEING TRANSPORTATION, OTHER

APICAL INDUSTRIES—See Bristow Group, Inc.; *U.S. Public*, pg. 387
BURSCH TRAVEL AGENCY, INC.; *U.S. Private*, pg. 692
DSC/PURGATORY LLC; *U.S. Private*, pg. 1281
EDWARDS ROTORCRAFT SOLUTIONS INC—See Textron Inc.; *U.S. Public*, pg. 2028
ERA FLIGHTSEEING LLC—See Bristow Group, Inc.; *U.S. Public*, pg. 387
HELICOPTER CONSULTANTS OF MAUI, LLC—See American Securities LLC; *U.S. Private*, pg. 247
KILLINGTON LIMITED—See Powdr Corp.; *U.S. Private*, pg. 3236
MOUNT HOOD MEADOWS OREGON LTD. PARTNERSHIP; *U.S. Private*, pg. 2798
PRIVATE BALLOON FLIGHTS LLC—See Rainbow Ryders Inc.; *U.S. Private*, pg. 3347
RAINBOW RYDERS INC.; *U.S. Private*, pg. 3347
RAUSCHBERGBAHN GESELLSCHAFT MIT BESCHRANKTER HAFTUNG—See E.ON SE; *Int'l*, pg. 2259
SUNDANCE HELICOPTERS, INC.—See American Securities LLC; *U.S. Private*, pg. 247
TAOS SKI VALLEY, INC.; *U.S. Private*, pg. 3932
TELLURIDE SKI & GOLF COMPANY LLP; *U.S. Private*, pg. 3962

488111 — AIR TRAFFIC CONTROL

AERODROM NIKOLA TESLA A.D.; *Int'l*, pg. 181
AVIATION BLADE SERVICES, INC.—See First Equity Group, Inc.; *U.S. Private*, pg. 1517
CARDNO EPPELL OLSEN PTY. LTD.—See Cardno Limited; *Int'l*, pg. 1322
ENAV S.P.A.; *Int'l*, pg. 2396
INTERIM SOLUTIONS FOR GOVERNMENT, LLC; *U.S. Private*, pg. 2110
METRON AVIATION, INC.—See Airbus SE; *Int'l*, pg. 244
MIDWEST AIR TRAFFIC CONTROL SERVICE; *U.S. Private*, pg. 2719
Q-FREE AMERICA INC.—See Guardian Capital Group Limited; *Int'l*, pg. 3170
Q-FREE ESPANA S.L.U.—See Guardian Capital Group Limited; *Int'l*, pg. 3170
Q-FREE TRAFFIC DESIGN D.O.O.—See Guardian Capital Group Limited; *Int'l*, pg. 3170

488119 — OTHER AIRPORT OPERATIONS

1ST CHOICE AEROSPACE, INC.—See VSE Corporation; *U.S. Public*, pg. 2312
AAR AIRCRAFT COMPONENT SERVICES-LONDON—See AAR Corp.; *U.S. Public*, pg. 13
AAR AIRLIFT GROUP, INC.—See AAR Corp.; *U.S. Public*, pg. 13
ABERDEEN AIRPORT LTD.—See Ferrovial S.A.; *Int'l*, pg. 2644
ABERTIS AIRPORTS S.A.—See ACS, Actividades de Construccion y Servicios, S.A.; *Int'l*, pg. 112
ACCIONA AIRPORT SERVICES, S.A.—See Acciona, S.A.; *Int'l*, pg. 90
ACNA—See Air France-KLM S.A.; *Int'l*, pg. 237
ADANI ENTERPRISES LIMITED; *Int'l*, pg. 124
ADAPTALIA OUTSOURCING SL—See Groupe Crit, S.A.; *Int'l*, pg. 3101
ADB AIRFIELD SOLUTIONS—See The Carlyle Group Inc.; *U.S. Public*, pg. 2043
ADB SAFEGATE AMERICAS, LLC—See The Carlyle Group Inc.; *U.S. Public*, pg. 2043
ADB SAFEGATE BVBA—See The Carlyle Group Inc.; *U.S. Public*, pg. 2043
ADPI LIBYA—See Artelia Holding SA; *Int'l*, pg. 581
ADP INGENIERIE—See Artelia Holding SA; *Int'l*, pg. 581
AEROCAR B.V.—See Deutsche Post AG; *Int'l*, pg. 2071
AERO EXPRESS DEL ECUADOR (TRANSAM) LTDA.—See Deutsche Post AG; *Int'l*, pg. 2071
AEROFORM—See Air France-KLM S.A.; *Int'l*, pg. 237
AEROPLEX OF CENTRAL EUROPE LTD.; *Int'l*, pg. 181
AEROPORTI DI ROMA S.P.A.—See Edizione S.r.l.; *Int'l*, pg. 2312
AEROPORTO DI GENOVA S.P.A.—See Edizione S.r.l.; *Int'l*, pg. 2311
AEROPORTO GUGLIELMO MARCONI DI BOLOGNA S.P.A.; *Int'l*, pg. 181
AEROPORTS DE MONTREAL; *Int'l*, pg. 181
AEROPORTS DE PARIS S.A.; *Int'l*, pg. 181
AEROPUERTO ACAPULCO S.A. DE C.V.—See Empresas ICA S.A.B. de C.V.; *Int'l*, pg. 2390
AEROPUERTO CHIHUAHUA, S.A. DE C.V.—See Empresas ICA S.A.B. de C.V.; *Int'l*, pg. 2390
AEROPUERTO CIUDAD JUAREZ, S.A. DE C.V.—See Empresas ICA S.A.B. de C.V.; *Int'l*, pg. 2390
AEROPUERTO CULIACAN, S.A. DE C.V.—See Empresas ICA S.A.B. de C.V.; *Int'l*, pg. 2390
AEROPUERTO DE AGUASCALIENTES, S.A. DE C.V.—See Grupo Aeroportuario del Pacifico, S.A.B. de C.V.; *Int'l*, pg. 3118
AEROPUERTO DE COZUMEL S.A. DE C.V.—See Grupo Aeroportuario del Sureste, S.A.B. de C.V.; *Int'l*, pg. 3119
AEROPUERTO DE HERMOSILLO, S.A. DE C.V.—See

N.A.I.C.S. INDEX
488119 — OTHER AIRPORT OPERA...

Grupo Aeroportuario del Pacifico, S.A.B. de C.V.; *Int'l*, pg. 3118
AEROPUERTO DE HUATULCO S.A. DE C.V.—See Grupo Aeroportuario del Sureste, S.A.B. de C.V.; *Int'l*, pg. 3119
AEROPUERTO DE LA PAZ, S.A. DE C.V.—See Grupo Aeroportuario del Pacifico, S.A.B. de C.V.; *Int'l*, pg. 3118
AEROPUERTO DEL BAJIO, S.A. DE C.V.—See Grupo Aeroportuario del Pacifico, S.A.B. de C.V.; *Int'l*, pg. 3118
AEROPUERTO DE LOS MOCHIS, S.A. DE C.V.—See Grupo Aeroportuario del Pacifico, S.A.B. de C.V.; *Int'l*, pg. 3118
AEROPUERTO DE MEXICALI, S.A. DE C.V.—See Grupo Aeroportuario del Pacifico, S.A.B. de C.V.; *Int'l*, pg. 3118
AEROPUERTO DE MORELIA, S.A. DE C.V.—See Grupo Aeroportuario del Pacifico, S.A.B. de C.V.; *Int'l*, pg. 3118
AEROPUERTO DE PUERTO VALLARTA, S.A. DE C.V.—See Grupo Aeroportuario del Pacifico, S.A.B. de C.V.; *Int'l*, pg. 3118
AEROPUERTO DE PUNTA DEL ESTE—See Corporacion America S.A.; *Int'l*, pg. 1803
AEROPUERTO DE TIJUANA, S.A. DE C.V.—See Grupo Aeroportuario del Pacifico, S.A.B. de C.V.; *Int'l*, pg. 3118
AEROPUERTO DE VERACRUZ S.A. DE C.V.—See Grupo Aeroportuario del Sureste, S.A.B. de C.V.; *Int'l*, pg. 3119
AEROPUERTO DURANGO—See Empresas ICA S.A.B. de C.V.; *Int'l*, pg. 2390
AEROPUERTO INTERNACIONAL DE TOCUMEN S.A.; *Int'l*, pg. 181
AEROPUERTO MAZATLAN, S.A. DE C.V.—See Empresas ICA S.A.B. de C.V.; *Int'l*, pg. 2390
AEROPUERTO MONTERREY—See Empresas ICA S.A.B. de C.V.; *Int'l*, pg. 2390
AEROPUERTO REYNOSA SA DE CV—See Empresas ICA S.A.B. de C.V.; *Int'l*, pg. 2390
AEROPUERTOS ARGENTINA 2000—See Corporacion America S.A.; *Int'l*, pg. 1803
AEROPUERTOS DEL NEUQUEN S.A.—See Corporacion America S.A.; *Int'l*, pg. 1803
AEROPUERTO TAMPICO, S. A. DE C. V.—See Empresas ICA S.A.B. de C.V.; *Int'l*, pg. 2390
AEROPUERTO TORREON S.A. DE C.V.—See Empresas ICA S.A.B. de C.V.; *Int'l*, pg. 2390
AEROPUERTO ZACATECAS, S.A. DE C.V.—See Empresas ICA S.A.B. de C.V.; *Int'l*, pg. 2390
AGILITY DGS UK LTD.—See Agility; *Int'l*, pg. 209
AIR ALLIANCE GMBH.—See DPE Deutsche Private Equity GmbH; *Int'l*, pg. 2187
AIR CHINA CARGO CO., LTD.—See China National Aviation Holding Company; *Int'l*, pg. 1525
AIR GENERAL INC.; *U.S. Private*, pg. 138
AIRGEST S.P.A.—See Corporacion America S.A.; *Int'l*, pg. 1803
AIRIT AIRPORT IT SERVICES HAHN AG—See Fraport AG; *Int'l*, pg. 2764
AIRLINE ACCOUNTING CENTER SP. Z O.O—See Deutsche Lufthansa AG; *Int'l*, pg. 2069
AIRMATE LTD—See Air Mauritius Limited; *Int'l*, pg. 238
AIR NEW ZEALAND ENGINEERING SERVICES—See Air New Zealand Limited; *Int'l*, pg. 239
AIRPORT AUTHORITY WASHOE COUNTY; *U.S. Private*, pg. 142
AIRPORT MEDICAL SERVICES C.V.—See Air France-KLM S.A.; *Int'l*, pg. 236
AIRPORT SERVICES DRESDEN GMBH—See Deutsche Lufthansa AG; *Int'l*, pg. 2066
AIRPORTS OF THAILAND PUBLIC COMPANY LIMITED; *Int'l*, pg. 248
AIRPORTS VANUATU LTD; *Int'l*, pg. 248
AIR SERV CORPORATION—See ABM Industries, Inc.; *U.S. Public*, pg. 26
AIR SERVICE HAWAII; *U.S. Private*, pg. 139
AIR SERVICES INC.—See 1100 Holdings LLC; *U.S. Private*, pg. 2
ALATOSCANA SPA—See Corporacion America Airports S.A.; *Int'l*, pg. 1803
ALYZIA—See Aeroports de Paris S.A.; *Int'l*, pg. 181
AMERICAN AIRLINES, INC.—See American Airlines Group Inc.; *U.S. Public*, pg. 95
AMERICAN AIRPORTS CORPORATION; *U.S. Private*, pg. 222
ANA AIR SERVICE MATSUYAMA CO., LTD.—See ANA Holdings Inc.; *Int'l*, pg. 444
ANCRA INTERNATIONAL LLC - CARGO DIVISION—See The Heico Companies, L.L.C.; *U.S. Private*, pg. 4050
ARENDAL LUFTHAVN GULLKNAPP AS—See Arendals Fossekompani ASA; *Int'l*, pg. 558
ASG AIRPORT SERVICE GESELLSCHAFT MBH—See Fraport AG; *Int'l*, pg. 2763
ASSOCIATED HANGAR INC.; *U.S. Private*, pg. 356
ATHENS INTERNATIONAL AIRPORT S.A.; *Int'l*, pg. 670
ATIAC—See Groupe Crit, S.A.; *Int'l*, pg. 3101
AUCKLAND INTERNATIONAL AIRPORT LIMITED; *Int'l*, pg. 699
AURORA JET CENTER—See The Sterling Group, L.P.; *U.S. Private*, pg. 4122
AVCON INDUSTRIES, INC.—See Butler National Corporation; *U.S. Public*, pg. 413
AVIATION GROUND EQUIPMENT CORP.—See Nexus Capital Management LP; *U.S. Private*, pg. 2922
AVIATION LOGISTICS CORP.—See The Boeing Company; *U.S. Public*, pg. 2041
AVIATION SERVICE SERVIS LETAL, DOO, LJUBLJANA—See Textron Inc.; *U.S. Public*, pg. 2028
AVIATOR AIRPORT ALLIANCE EUROPE AB—See Avia Solutions Group AB; *Int'l*, pg. 741
AVIATOR DENMARK A/S—See Avia Solutions Group AB; *Int'l*, pg. 741
AVINCO LTD.; *Int'l*, pg. 743
AVINODE GROUP AB—See The Hearst Corporation; *U.S. Private*, pg. 4044
AVINOR AS; *Int'l*, pg. 744
AVJET ASIA CO., LTD.—See Avjet Corporation; *U.S. Private*, pg. 409
AVPLAN TRIP SUPPORT—See Avfuel Corporation; *U.S. Private*, pg. 406
BABCOCK AIRPORTS—See Babcock International Group PLC; *Int'l*, pg. 792
BALTIMORE WASHINGTON THURGOOD MARSHALL INTERNATIONAL AIRPORT; *U.S. Private*, pg. 463
BASEOPS INTERNATIONAL INC.—See World Kinect Corporation; *U.S. Public*, pg. 2380
BCS AIRPORT SYSTEMS PTY LIMITED—See Daifuku Co., Ltd.; *Int'l*, pg. 1924
BCS INTEGRATION SOLUTIONS SDN. BHD.—See Daifuku Co., Ltd.; *Int'l*, pg. 1924
BEIJING AIRPORT FOODS SERVICE CO., LTD.—See Capital Airports Holding Company (CAH); *Int'l*, pg. 1309
BEIJING CAPITAL INTERNATIONAL AIRPORT COMPANY LIMITED; *Int'l*, pg. 947
BELFAST INTERNATIONAL AIRPORT LTD.—See ACS, Actividades de Construccion y Servicios, S.A.; *Int'l*, pg. 112
BERMUDA SKYPORT CORPORATION LIMITED—See Aecon Group Inc.; *Int'l*, pg. 172
BERRY AVIATION INC.—See Acorn Growth Companies, LC; *U.S. Private*, pg. 63
BLUELINK INTERNATIONAL CZ S. R. O.—See Air France-KLM S.A.; *Int'l*, pg. 237
BLUELINK—See Air France-KLM S.A.; *Int'l*, pg. 237
BOB HOPE AIRPORT, *U.S. Private*, pg. 604
THE BOEING CO. - ELECTRONIC SYSTEMS—See The Boeing Company; *U.S. Public*, pg. 2040
BOEING DISTRIBUTION SERVICES—See The Boeing Company; *U.S. Public*, pg. 2040
BRISBANE AIRPORT FUEL SERVICES PTY LTD—See Ampol Limited; *Int'l*, pg. 436
CAIRO AIRPORT COMPANY—See Fraport AG; *Int'l*, pg. 2764
CARDIFF INTERNATIONAL AIRPORT LTD.; *Int'l*, pg. 1321
CARIBBEAN DISPATCH SERVICES LTD.—See Goddard Enterprises Limited; *Int'l*, pg. 3019
CATHAY PACIFIC SERVICES LIMITED—See Cathay Pacific Airways Limited; *Int'l*, pg. 1360
CELEBI DELHI CARGO TERMINAL MANAGEMENT INDIA PVT. LTD.—See Celebi Holding A.S.; *Int'l*, pg. 1391
CELEBI GROUND HANDLING HUNGARY KFT.—See Celebi Holding A.S.; *Int'l*, pg. 1391
CELEBI GROUND HANDLING INC.—See Celebi Holding A.S.; *Int'l*, pg. 1391
CELEBI GROUND SERVICES AUSTRIA GMBH—See Celebi Holding A.S.; *Int'l*, pg. 1391
CENTRE DE FORMATION AERONAUTIQUE ICARE—See Air France-KLM S.A.; *Int'l*, pg. 237
CESSNA ZURICH CITATION SERVICE CENTER GMBH—See Textron Inc.; *U.S. Public*, pg. 2028
CHARLESTON COUNTY AVIATION AUTHORITY; *U.S. Private*, pg. 856
CHINA AIR EXPRESS CO., LIMITED—See China National Aviation Holding Company; *Int'l*, pg. 1525
CHRISTCHURCH INTERNATIONAL AIRPORT LTD—See Christchurch City Holdings Ltd.; *Int'l*, pg. 1585
CITIC OFFSHORE HELICOPTER CO., LIMITED; *Int'l*, pg. 1621
CITY AIR TERMINAL BETRIEBSGESELLSCHAFT M.B.H.—See Flughafen Wien Aktiengesellschaft; *Int'l*, pg. 2712
CLAY LACY AVIATION INC.; *U.S. Private*, pg. 917
COBALT GROUND SOLUTIONS LTD—See Groupe Crit, S.A.; *Int'l*, pg. 3101
COBHAM AVIATION SERVICES PTY LIMITED—See Advent International Corporation; *U.S. Private*, pg. 99
COLORADO JETCENTER, INC.—See Cordillera Corporation; *U.S. Private*, pg. 1047
COLUMBUS AIRPORT AUTHORITY; *U.S. Private*, pg. 978
COMPAGNIE D'EXPLOITATION DES SERVICES AUXILIAIRES AERIENS—See Air France-KLM S.A.; *Int'l*, pg. 237
CONCORDE AIR LOGISTICS LTD.—See Deutsche Post AG; *Int'l*, pg. 2072
CORPORACION AMERICA AIRPORTS S.A.; *Int'l*, pg. 1803
CORPORATE WINGS—See Directional Capital LLC; *U.S. Private*, pg. 1236
DAE AIRPORTS—See Dubai Aerospace Enterprise Ltd; *Int'l*, pg. 2218
DANANG AIRPORT SERVICES COMPANY; *Int'l*, pg. 1958
DANZAS KIEV LTD.—See Deutsche Post AG; *Int'l*, pg. 2079
DAYTON INTERNATIONAL AIRPORT; *U.S. Private*, pg. 1177
DC AVIATION GMBH—See ATON GmbH; *Int'l*, pg. 688
DEFENSE CONTRACT SERVICES, INC.; *U.S. Private*, pg. 1191
DENVER JETCENTER, INC.—See Cordillera Corporation; *U.S. Private*, pg. 1048
DES MOINES FLYING SERVICE, INC.—See Muncie Aviation Co.; *U.S. Private*, pg. 2813
DESTIN JET—See The Sterling Group, L.P.; *U.S. Private*, pg. 4122
DISCOVERY AIR INC.—See Clairvest Group Inc.; *Int'l*, pg. 1641
DREAMFOLKS SERVICES LTD.; *Int'l*, pg. 2203
DUBAI AEROSPACE ENTERPRISE LTD; *Int'l*, pg. 2218
DU PAGE AIRPORT AUTHORITY; *U.S. Private*, pg. 1282
ECUACENTAIR S.A.—See World Kinect Corporation; *U.S. Public*, pg. 2380
EDINBURGH AIRPORT LIMITED—See BlackRock, Inc.; *U.S. Public*, pg. 346
EGYPTAIR CARGO—See EgyptAir Holding Company; *Int'l*, pg. 2327
ETS INTERNATIONAL; *U.S. Private*, pg. 1432
ETTYL LIMITED; *Int'l*, pg. 2525
EUROTRADIA INTERNATIONAL—See Groupe Industriel Marcel Dassault S.A.; *Int'l*, pg. 3105
EXECUTIVE AVIATION INC.—See Baton Rouge Jet Center LLC; *U.S. Private*, pg. 487
FALCON TRAINING CENTRE—See Groupe Industriel Marcel Dassault S.A.; *Int'l*, pg. 3105
FERROVIAL AEROPUERTOS S.A.—See Ferrovial S.A.; *Int'l*, pg. 2644
FINNAIR CARGO TERMINAL OPERATIONS OY—See Finnair Plc; *Int'l*, pg. 2676
FLUGHAFEN FRANKFURT-HAHN GMBH—See Hainan Traffic Administration Holding Co., Ltd.; *Int'l*, pg. 3213
FLUGHAFEN PARKEN GMBH—See Flughafen Wien Aktiengesellschaft; *Int'l*, pg. 2712
FLUGHAFEN SAARBRUECKEN GMBH—See Fraport AG; *Int'l*, pg. 2764
FLUGHAFEN WIEN AKTIENGESELLSCHAFT; *Int'l*, pg. 2712
FLUGHAFEN ZURICH AG; *Int'l*, pg. 2713
FLYING COLOURS CORPORATION—See Directional Capital LLC; *U.S. Private*, pg. 1236
FOUAD TRAVEL & CARGO AGENCY—See Abdulla Fouad Holding Co.; *Int'l*, pg. 59
FRACARESERVICES GMBH—See Fraport AG; *Int'l*, pg. 2764
FRAPORT AG; *Int'l*, pg. 2763
FRAPORT IC ICTAS HAVALIMAN YER HIZMETLERI AS—See Fraport AG; *Int'l*, pg. 2764
FRAPORT OBJEKT MONCHHOF GMBH—See Fraport AG; *Int'l*, pg. 2764
FRAPORT SAUDI ARABIA LTD.—See Fraport AG; *Int'l*, pg. 2764
FRAPORT TWIN STAR AIRPORT MANAGEMENT AD—See Fraport AG; *Int'l*, pg. 2764
GANSU AIRPORT GROUP CO., LTD.—See Hainan Traffic Administration Holding Co., Ltd.; *Int'l*, pg. 3213
GAT AIRLINE GROUND SUPPORT, INC.—See Atlantic Street Capital Management LLC; *U.S. Private*, pg. 374
GCG GROUND SERVICES (BARBADOS) LIMITED—See Goddard Enterprises Limited; *Int'l*, pg. 3019
GCG GROUND SERVICES, LLC—See Goddard Enterprises Limited; *Int'l*, pg. 3019
GETSERVICE-FLUGHAFEN-SICHERHEITS- UND SERVICEDIENST GMBH—See Flughafen Wien Aktiengesellschaft; *Int'l*, pg. 2712
GLASGOW AIRPORT LTD.—See Ferrovial S.A.; *Int'l*, pg. 2644
GLASGOW PRESTWICK AIRPORT LIMITED; *Int'l*, pg. 2989
GLOBAL LOGISTICS SYSTEM (HK) COMPANY LIMITED—See Cathay Pacific Airways Limited; *Int'l*, pg. 1360
GREATER ORLANDO AVIATION AUTHORITY INC.; *U.S. Private*, pg. 1770
GREAT SOUTHWEST AVIATION, INC.—See Leonard Green & Partners, L.P.; *U.S. Private*, pg. 2424
GROUPE EUROPE HANDLING—See Groupe Crit, S.A.; *Int'l*, pg. 3101
GRUPO AEROPORTUARIO CENTRO NORTE, S.A. DE C.V.—See Empresas ICA S.A.B. de C.V.; *Int'l*, pg. 2390
GRUPO AEROPORTUARIO DEL CENTRO NORTE, S.A.B. DE C.V.; *Int'l*, pg. 3118
GRUPO AEROPORTUARIO DEL PACIFICO, S.A.B. DE C.V.; *Int'l*, pg. 3118
GRUPO AEROPORTUARIO DEL SURESTE, S.A.B. DE C.V.; *Int'l*, pg. 3118
GSC AIR LOGISTICS INC.—See GSC Logistics Inc.; *U.S. Private*, pg. 1800
GSP INTERNATIONAL AIRPORT; *U.S. Private*, pg. 1801
GUANGZHOU BAIYUN INTERNATIONAL AIRPORT COMPANY LIMITED; *Int'l*, pg. 3164
HAINAN MEILAN INTERNATIONAL AIRPORT COMPANY LIMITED; *Int'l*, pg. 3212
HAWKER PACIFIC AEROSPACE—See Deutsche Lufthansa AG; *Int'l*, pg. 2070
HEATHROW AIRPORT HOLDINGS LIMITED—See Ferrovial S.A.; *Int'l*, pg. 2644

488119 — OTHER AIRPORT OPERA...   CORPORATE AFFILIATIONS

HEATHROW AIRPORT LTD.—See Ferrovial S.A.; *Int'l*, pg. 2644
HILLSBOROUGH COUNTY AVIATION AUTHORITY; *U.S. Private*, pg. 1947
HILLTOP AVIATION SERVICES; *U.S. Private*, pg. 1947
HMA BAYFLITE SERVICES, LLC—See Community Health Systems, Inc.; *U.S. Public*, pg. 553
HUNTSVILLE-MADISON COUNTY AIRPORT AUTHORITY; *U.S. Private*, pg. 2011
IAP WORLD SERVICES INC.—See IAP Worldwide Services, Inc.; *U.S. Private*, pg. 2028
ICM AIRPORT TECHNICS AUSTRALIA PTY. LTD.—See Amadeus IT Group, S.A.; *Int'l*, pg. 407
ICM AIRPORT TECHNICS LLC—See Amadeus IT Group, S.A.; *Int'l*, pg. 407
ICM AIRPORT TECHNICS SINGAPORE PTE. LTD.—See Amadeus IT Group, S.A.; *Int'l*, pg. 407
ICM AIRPORT TECHNICS UK LTD.—See Amadeus IT Group, S.A.; *Int'l*, pg. 407
ICON AVIATION SA; *Int'l*, pg. 3583
IFR FRANCE S.A.S.—See Airbus SE; *Int'l*, pg. 246
IGS EHF.—See Icelandair Group hf.; *Int'l*, pg. 3579
INTEGRATED AIRLINE SERVICES, INC.; *U.S. Private*, pg. 2098
INTERNATIONAL AIRPORT UTILITY CO., LTD—See ANA Holdings Inc.; *Int'l*, pg. 444
INTERNATIONAL GROUND SERVICES, S.A. DE C.V.—See American Airlines Group Inc.; *U.S. Public*, pg. 96
IR (MIDDLE EAST) LLC—See CIMC-TianDa Holdings Company Limited; *Int'l*, pg. 1608
JACKSONVILLE JETPORT LLC; *U.S. Private*, pg. 2179
JAMAICA DISPATCH SERVICES LIMITED—See Goddard Enterprises Limited; *Int'l*, pg. 3019
JAPAN TURBINE TECHNOLOGIES CO., LTD.—See RTX Corporation; *U.S. Public*, pg. 1823
JET AVIATION AUSTRALIA PTY LTD—See General Dynamics Corporation; *U.S. Public*, pg. 916
JETCORP TECHNICAL SERVICES INC.—See Directional Capital LLC; *U.S. Private*, pg. 1236
JET YARD SOLUTIONS, LLC—See Air T, Inc.; *U.S. Public*, pg. 67
KENMORE AIR HARBOR INC.; *U.S. Private*, pg. 2284
KFS INC.; *U.S. Private*, pg. 2301
LATELEC—See Searchlight Capital Partners, L.P.; *U.S. Private*, pg. 3588
LETISKO KOSICE - AIRPORT KOSICE, A.S.—See Flughafen Wien Aktiengesellschaft; *Int'l*, pg. 2712
LIMA AIRPORT PARTNERS S.R.L.—See Fraport AG; *Int'l*, pg. 2764
LINSTOL LLC—See The Hoffmann Family of Companies; *U.S. Private*, pg. 4053
LOCKHEED MIDDLE EAST SERVICES—See Lockheed Martin Corporation; *U.S. Public*, pg. 1338
LOGAIR—See Air France-KLM S.A.; *Int'l*, pg. 237
LOGAN TELEFLEX (FRANCE) S.A.—See Daifuku Co., Ltd.; *Int'l*, pg. 1926
LOGAN TELEFLEX, INC.—See Daifuku Co., Ltd.; *Int'l*, pg. 1925
LONDON CITY AIRPORT LIMITED—See Alberta Investment Management Corporation; *Int'l*, pg. 297
LONDON LUTON AIRPORT OPERATIONS LIMITED—See Ardian SAS; *Int'l*, pg. 556
LONDON LUTON AIRPORT OPERATIONS LIMITED—See ENAIRE; *Int'l*, pg. 2396
LONDON SOUTHEND AIRPORT COMPANY LIMITED—See Esken Limited; *Int'l*, pg. 2503
LUFTHANSA CARGO INDIA (PRIV) LTD.—See Deutsche Lufthansa AG; *Int'l*, pg. 2068
LUFTHANSA ENGINEERING AND OPERATIONAL SERVICES GMBH—See Deutsche Lufthansa AG; *Int'l*, pg. 2070
LUFTHANSA SERVICES (THAILAND) LTD.—See Deutsche Lufthansa AG; *Int'l*, pg. 2069
LUX AIR JET CENTERS; *U.S. Private*, pg. 2518
MADISON HUNTSVILLE COUNTY AIRPORT AUTHORITY; *U.S. Private*, pg. 2543
MALTA INTERNATIONAL AIRPORT PLC—See Flughafen Wien Aktiengesellschaft; *Int'l*, pg. 2712
MANZHOULI XIJIAO AIRPORT CO., LTD.—See Hainan Traffic Administration Holding Co., Ltd.; *Int'l*, pg. 3215
MASSACHUSETTS PORT AUTHORITY; *U.S. Private*, pg. 2606
MAVERICK AIR CENTER LLC—See Sanford Health; *U.S. Private*, pg. 3545
MEDIA FRANKFURT GMBH—See Fraport AG; *Int'l*, pg. 2764
MEGGITT AIRCRAFT BRAKING SYSTEMS CORPORATION - DANVILLE FACILITY—See Parker Hannifin Corporation; *U.S. Public*, pg. 1642
MEMPHIS SHELBY COUNTY AIRPORT AUTHORITY, INC.; *U.S. Private*, pg. 2665
METROPOLITAN KNOXVILLE AIRPORT AUTHORITY; *U.S. Private*, pg. 2688
METROPOLITAN WASHINGTON AIRPORTS AUTHORITY; *U.S. Private*, pg. 2689
MH AVIATION SERVICES (PTY) LTD—See World Kinect Corporation; *U.S. Public*, pg. 2380
MIAMI INTERNATIONAL AIRPORT; *U.S. Private*, pg. 2696

MIDWAY AIRLINES' TERMINAL CONSORTIUM; *U.S. Private*, pg. 2718
MIDWEST CORPORATE AVIATION, INC.—See Clemens Aviation LLC; *U.S. Private*, pg. 939
MINNEAPOLIS-SAINT PAUL INTERNATIONAL AIRPORT; *U.S. Private*, pg. 2743
MOBILE AIRPORT AUTHORITY; *U.S. Private*, pg. 2756
MOUNTAIN WEST AVIATION, LLC; *U.S. Private*, pg. 2800
MULTI-AERO, INC.—See Surf Air Mobility Inc.; *U.S. Public*, pg. 1967
MULTI SERVICE AERO B.V.—See World Kinect Corporation; *U.S. Public*, pg. 2380
MUNCIE AVIATION CO.; *U.S. Private*, pg. 2813
MYTECHNIC MRO TECHNIC SERVIS A.S.—See Hainan Traffic Administration Holding Co., Ltd.; *Int'l*, pg. 3216
NATIONAL AIRWAYS CORPORATION—See Dubai World Corporation; *Int'l*, pg. 2221
NATIONAL AVIATION SERVICES COMPANY W.L.L.—See Agility; *U.S. Private*, pg. 210
N*ICE AIRCRAFT SERVICE & SUPPORTS GMBH—See Fraport AG; *Int'l*, pg. 2764
THE NUANCE GROUP (MALTA) LIMITED—See Avolta AG; *Int'l*, pg. 749
OOO JET AVIATION VNUKOVO—See General Dynamics Corporation; *U.S. Public*, pg. 916
ORLANDO SANFORD INTERNATIONAL INC.—See ACS, Actividades de Construccion y Servicios, S.A.; *Int'l*, pg. 112
OSLO LUFTHAVN AS—See Avinor AS; *Int'l*, pg. 744
OTESSA—See Groupe Crit, S.A.; *Int'l*, pg. 1368
P2, INC.—See Markel Group Inc.; *U.S. Public*, pg. 1368
PACIFIC AVIATION CORPORATION—See Woodlawn Partners, Inc.; *U.S. Private*, pg. 4559
PASSERELLE—See Air France-KLM S.A.; *Int'l*, pg. 237
PEGASUS AVIATION SERVICES, LLC—See Nana Regional Corporation, Inc.; *U.S. Private*, pg. 2832
PENINSULAR AVIATION SERVICES CO. LTD.—See BP plc; *Int'l*, pg. 1131
PERISHABLE CENTER GMBH + CO. BETRIEBS KG—See Fraport AG; *Int'l*, pg. 2764
PHOENIX AVIATION LIMITED—See Frontier Services Group Limited; *Int'l*, pg. 2796
PHOENIX MANAGEMENT INC.; *U.S. Private*, pg. 3173
PHOENIX RISING AVIATION INC.—See Saker Aviation Services, Inc.; *U.S. Public*, pg. 1836
POS AVIATION SDN. BHD.—See DRB-HICOM Berhad; *Int'l*, pg. 2202
PRESTINTER—See Groupe Crit, S.A.; *Int'l*, pg. 3101
PRIMKOP AIRPORT MANAGEMENT (PTY) LTD—See ABB Ltd.; *Int'l*, pg. 55
PROJET AVIATION; *U.S. Private*, pg. 3281
PROPULSION CONTROLS COMPANY—See NFS Holdings Inc.; *U.S. Private*, pg. 2923
PTERIS GLOBAL (BEIJING) LTD.—See CIMC-TianDa Holdings Company Limited; *Int'l*, pg. 1609
PTERIS GLOBAL LIMITED—See CIMC-TianDa Holdings Company Limited; *Int'l*, pg. 1608
PTERIS GLOBAL SDN BHD—See CIMC-TianDa Holdings Company Limited; *Int'l*, pg. 1609
QUALITY AIR FORWARDING, INC.—See Littlejohn & Co., LLC; *U.S. Private*, pg. 2470
REGIONAL AIRPORT AUTHORITY; *U.S. Private*, pg. 3388
RHODE ISLAND AIRPORT CORP; *U.S. Private*, pg. 3422
RICHARDSON AVIATION—See Sid Richardson Carbon & Energy Ltd.; *U.S. Private*, pg. 3645
SAFE FUEL SYSTEMS, INC.—See Arlington Capital Partners LLC; *U.S. Private*, pg. 327
SANYA PHOENIX INTERNATIONAL AIRPORT CO., LTD.—See Hainan Traffic Administration Holding Co., Ltd.; *Int'l*, pg. 3216
SATS HK LIMITED—See Hainan Traffic Administration Holding Co., Ltd.; *Int'l*, pg. 3215
SCARABEE AVIATION GROUP - JAPAN CO., LTD.—See Daifuku Co., Ltd.; *Int'l*, pg. 1926
SCIS AIR SECURITY CORPORATION—See Deutsche Lufthansa AG; *Int'l*, pg. 2068
SERVANTAGE—See Air France-KLM S.A.; *Int'l*, pg. 237
SERVICIOS A LA INFRAESTRUCTURA AEROPORTUARIA DEL PACIFICO, S.A. DE C.V.—See Grupo Aeroportuario del Pacifico, S.A.B. de C.V.; *Int'l*, pg. 3118
SIGNATURE FLIGHT SUPPORT CORP.—See BlackRock, Inc.; *U.S. Public*, pg. 346
SIGNATURE FLIGHT SUPPORT CORP.—See Blackstone Inc.; *U.S. Public*, pg. 358
SIGNATURE FLIGHT SUPPORT CORP.—See Cascade Investment LLC; *U.S. Private*, pg. 780
SIGNATURE FLIGHT SUPPORT - MKE—See BlackRock, Inc.; *U.S. Public*, pg. 346
SIGNATURE FLIGHT SUPPORT - MKE—See Blackstone Inc.; *U.S. Public*, pg. 358
SIGNATURE FLIGHT SUPPORT - MKE—See Cascade Investment LLC; *U.S. Private*, pg. 780
SIGNATURE FLIGHT SUPPORT - MMU—See BlackRock, Inc.; *U.S. Public*, pg. 346
SIGNATURE FLIGHT SUPPORT - MMU—See Blackstone Inc.; *U.S. Public*, pg. 358
SIGNATURE FLIGHT SUPPORT - MMU—See Cascade Investment LLC; *U.S. Private*, pg. 780

SIGNATURE FLIGHT SUPPORT - PIE—See BlackRock, Inc.; *U.S. Public*, pg. 346
SIGNATURE FLIGHT SUPPORT - PIE—See Blackstone Inc.; *U.S. Public*, pg. 358
SIGNATURE FLIGHT SUPPORT - PIE—See Cascade Investment LLC; *U.S. Private*, pg. 780
SIGNATURE FLIGHT SUPPORT - PWK—See BlackRock, Inc.; *U.S. Public*, pg. 346
SIGNATURE FLIGHT SUPPORT - PWK—See Blackstone Inc.; *U.S. Public*, pg. 358
SIGNATURE FLIGHT SUPPORT - PWK—See Cascade Investment LLC; *U.S. Private*, pg. 781
SIGNATURE FLIGHT SUPPORT - STL—See BlackRock, Inc.; *U.S. Public*, pg. 346
SIGNATURE FLIGHT SUPPORT - STL—See Blackstone Inc.; *U.S. Public*, pg. 358
SIGNATURE FLIGHT SUPPORT - STL—See Cascade Investment LLC; *U.S. Private*, pg. 781
SKY HANDLING PARTNER—See Groupe Crit, S.A.; *Int'l*, pg. 3101
SKY HANDLING PARTNER UK LIMITED—See Groupe Crit, S.A.; *Int'l*, pg. 3101
SKY HELICOPTERS, INC.; *U.S. Private*, pg. 3684
SOCIEDAD CONCESIONARIA OPERADORA AEROPORTUARIA INTERNACIONAL S.A.-OPAIN S.A.—See Grupo Argos S.A.; *Int'l*, pg. 3121
SOCIETE DE CONSTRUCTION ET DE REPARATION DE MATERIEL AERONAUTIQUE—See Air France-KLM S.A.; *Int'l*, pg. 238
SOCIETE NOUVELLE AIR IVOIRE S.A.—See Air France-KLM S.A.; *Int'l*, pg. 238
SOUTHAMPTON INTERNATIONAL—See Ferrovial S.A.; *Int'l*, pg. 2644
SPOKANE INTERNATIONAL AIRPORT; *U.S. Private*, pg. 3759
SR TECHNICS SPAIN SA—See Hainan Traffic Administration Holding Co., Ltd.; *Int'l*, pg. 3216
STANDARDAERO BUSINESS AVIATION SERVICES LLC—See The Carlyle Group Inc.; *U.S. Public*, pg. 2054
STOBART AIR (UK) LIMITED—See Esken Limited; *Int'l*, pg. 2503
STOCKHOLM SKAVSTA FLYGPLATS AB—See ACS, Actividades de Construccion y Servicios, S.A.; *Int'l*, pg. 112
SUMMIT AVIATION, INC.—See TransMedics Group, Inc.; *U.S. Public*, pg. 2183
SWISSPORT AMSTERDAM B.V.—See Hainan Traffic Administration Holding Co., Ltd.; *Int'l*, pg. 3216
SWISSPORT BELGIUM N. V.—See Hainan Traffic Administration Holding Co., Ltd.; *Int'l*, pg. 3216
SWISSPORT CARGO SERVICES, L.P.—See Hainan Traffic Administration Holding Co., Ltd.; *Int'l*, pg. 3216
SWISSPORT FUELING, INC.—See Hainan Traffic Administration Holding Co., Ltd.; *Int'l*, pg. 3216
SWISSPORT INTERNATIONAL LTD.—See Hainan Traffic Administration Holding Co., Ltd.; *Int'l*, pg. 3216
SWISSPORT TANZANIA PLC.—See Hainan Traffic Administration Holding Co., Ltd.; *Int'l*, pg. 3216
SWISSPORT USA, INC.—See Hainan Traffic Administration Holding Co., Ltd.; *Int'l*, pg. 3216
SWISS PRIVATE AVIATION AG—See Deutsche Lufthansa AG; *Int'l*, pg. 2070
SWISS WORLDCARGO (INDIA) PRIVATE LIMITED—See Deutsche Lufthansa AG; *Int'l*, pg. 2070
TANGSHAN SANNVHE AIRPORT CO., LTD.—See Hainan Traffic Administration Holding Co., Ltd.; *Int'l*, pg. 3216
TBI AIRPORT MANAGEMENT INC.—See ACS, Actividades de Construccion y Servicios, S.A.; *Int'l*, pg. 112
TBI PLC—See ACS, Actividades de Construccion y Servicios, S.A.; *Int'l*, pg. 112
TEAM ACCESSORIES LIMITED—See Moog Inc.; *U.S. Public*, pg. 1471
TERMINAL DE CARGAS ARGENTINA—See Corporacion America S.A.; *Int'l*, pg. 1803
TERMINAL DE CARGAS URUGUAY S.A.—See Corporacion America S.A.; *Int'l*, pg. 1803
TIRANA INTERNATIONAL AIRPORT SHPK—See China Everbright Group Limited; *Int'l*, pg. 1501
TOSCANA AEROPORTI S.P.A.—See Corporacion America Airports S.A.; *Int'l*, pg. 1803
TRACE AVIATION, INC.—See GenNx360 Capital Partners, L.P.; *U.S. Private*, pg. 1672
TRADEPORT FRANKFURT GMBH—See Fraport AG; *Int'l*, pg. 2764
TRISTAR ELECTRIC INC.—See Aecon Group Inc.; *Int'l*, pg. 172
TRIUMPH AVIATION SERVICES - NAAS DIVISION—See STS Aviation Group; *U.S. Private*, pg. 3842
TUCSON AIRPORT AUTHORITY INC.; *U.S. Private*, pg. 4256
TULSA AIRPORT AUTHORITY; *U.S. Private*, pg. 4258
ULTIMATE JETCHARTERS, INC.; *U.S. Private*, pg. 4277
UNIQUE BETRIEBSSYSTEME AG—See Flughafen Zurich AG; *Int'l*, pg. 2713
UNITED AIRLINES OPERATIONS CENTER—See United Airlines Holdings, Inc.; *U.S. Public*, pg. 2229
VIENNA INTERNATIONAL AIRPORT SECURITY SERVICES GES.M.B.H.—See Flughafen Wien Aktiengesellschaft; *Int'l*, pg. 2713

N.A.I.C.S. INDEX

488190 — OTHER SUPPORT ACTIV...

VOLATO GROUP, INC.; *U.S. Public*, pg. 2308
WEIFANG NANYUAN AIRPORT CO., LTD.—See Hainan Traffic Administration Holding Co., Ltd.; *Int'l*, pg. 3216
WHELEN AEROSPACE TECHNOLOGIES LLC—See Whelen Engineering Company, Inc.; *U.S. Private*, pg. 4506
WISCONSIN AVIATION INC.; *U.S. Private*, pg. 4548
WOODLAND AVIATION INC.; *U.S. Private*, pg. 4559
YICHANG SANXIA AIRPORT CO., LTD.—See Hainan Traffic Administration Holding Co., Ltd.; *Int'l*, pg. 3216
YINGKOU AIRPORT CO., LTD.—See Hainan Traffic Administration Holding Co., Ltd.; *Int'l*, pg. 3216
ZENIT SERVICIOS INTEGRALES, S.A.—See ACS, Actividades de Construccion y Servicios, S.A.; *Int'l*, pg. 117
ZENTRUM FUR INTEGRIERTE VERKEHRSSYSTEME GMBH—See Fraport AG; *Int'l*, pg. 2764

488190 — OTHER SUPPORT ACTIVITIES FOR AIR TRANSPORTATION

3S ENGINEERING—See Sierra Nevada Corporation; *U.S. Private*, pg. 3647
AAR AIRCRAFT SERVICES - MIAMI—See AAR Corp.; *U.S. Public*, pg. 13
AAR AIRCRAFT SERVICES - OKLAHOMA—See AAR Corp.; *U.S. Public*, pg. 13
ABSOLUTE AVIATION SERVICES, LLC—See HEICO Corporation; *U.S. Public*, pg. 1021
ACP JETS, LLC—See Air Rutter International, LLC; *U.S. Private*, pg. 139
ACTION RESEARCH CORPORATION—See HEICO Corporation; *U.S. Public*, pg. 1021
ADA MILLENNIUM CONSULTING-OWNED BY ABU DHABI AVIATION SOLE PROPRIETORSHIP L.L.C.—See Abu Dhabi Aviation; *Int'l*, pg. 70
AERO AVIATION LTD.; *Int'l*, pg. 180
AERO-CARE PTY LTD.—See Archer Capital Pty. Ltd.; *Int'l*, pg. 547
AERODROME GROUP LTD.; *Int'l*, pg. 181
AERONAVDATA, INC.—See Garmin Ltd.; *Int'l*, pg. 2884
AEROPUERTO DE LOS CABOS, S.A. DE C.V.—See Grupo Aeroportuario del Pacifico, S.A.B. de C.V.; *Int'l*, pg. 3118
AEROPUERTO DE SAN LUIS POTOSI, S.A. DE C.V.—See Grupo Aeroportuario del Centro Norte, S.A.B. de C.V.; *Int'l*, pg. 3118
AEROPUERTO DE ZIHUATANEJO, S.A. DE C.V.—See Grupo Aeroportuario del Centro Norte, S.A.B. de C.V.; *Int'l*, pg. 3118
AEROREPAIR—See GenNx360 Capital Partners, L.P.; *U.S. Private*, pg. 1672
AEROREPUBLICA, S.A.—See Copa Holdings, S.A.; *Int'l*, pg. 1792
AEROSPACE ASSET TRADING, LLC; *U.S. Private*, pg. 119
AEROSTAR S.A.; *Int'l*, pg. 181
AIRBORNE MAINTENANCE AND ENGINEERING SERVICES, INC.—See Air Transport Services Group, Inc.; *U.S. Public*, pg. 67
AIRBUS CORPORATE JET CENTRE S.A.S.—See Airbus SE; *Int'l*, pg. 244
AIRBUS HELICOPTERS MALAYSIA SDN BHD—See Airbus SE; *Int'l*, pg. 243
AIRBUS HELICOPTERS ROMANIA SA—See Airbus SE; *Int'l*, pg. 243
AIRBUS TRANSPORT INTERNATIONAL S.N.C.—See Airbus SE; *Int'l*, pg. 244
AIRCRAFT MAINTENANCE & ENGINEERING CORP.—See China National Aviation Holding Company; *Int'l*, pg. 1525
AIRCRAFT MAINTENANCE & ENGINEERING CORP.—See Deutsche Lufthansa AG; *Int'l*, pg. 2069
AIR FAYRE CA INC.—See Harwood Capital LLP; *Int'l*, pg. 3282
AIR FAYRE USA INC.—See Harwood Capital LLP; *Int'l*, pg. 3282
AIR FRANCE SA—See Air France-KLM S.A.; *Int'l*, pg. 236
AIRINMAR LTD.—See AAR Corp.; *U.S. Public*, pg. 13
AIRLINE CARGO RESOURCES FZCO—See Expolanka Holdings PLC; *Int'l*, pg. 2589
AIR MAURITIUS SOUTH AFRICA (PTY) LIMITED—See Air Mauritius Limited; *Int'l*, pg. 238
AIR NELSON LIMITED—See Air New Zealand Limited; *Int'l*, pg. 238
AIR NEW ZEALAND (AUSTRALIA) PTY LIMITED—See Air New Zealand Limited; *Int'l*, pg. 238
AIR NEXT CO., LTD.—See ANA Holdings Inc.; *Int'l*, pg. 444
AIRPLANES, INC.—See STS Holdings, Inc.; *U.S. Private*, pg. 3842
AIRPORT SERVICES LEIPZIG GMBH—See Deutsche Lufthansa AG; *Int'l*, pg. 2066
AIR SAFETY EQUIPMENT INC.; *U.S. Private*, pg. 139
AIR TRANSPORT COMPONENTS, LLC; *U.S. Private*, pg. 140
AIR WISCONSIN, INC.—See United Airlines Holdings, Inc.; *U.S. Public*, pg. 2228
AIR'ZONA AIRCRAFT SERVICES, INC.—See Air T, Inc.; *U.S. Public*, pg. 67
AKIMA TECHNICAL SOLUTIONS, LLC—See Nana Regional Corporation, Inc.; *U.S. Private*, pg. 2832

ALGOMA CENTRAL PROPERTIES, INC.—See Algoma Central Corporation; *Int'l*, pg. 318
ALLIANCE GROUND INTERNATIONAL, LLC; *U.S. Private*, pg. 182
ALLIEDSIGNAL AEROSPACE SERVICE CORPORATION—See Honeywell International Inc.; *U.S. Public*, pg. 1047
ALPINE AEROTECH LTD.; *Int'l*, pg. 371
ALYZIA SURETE—See Aeroports de Paris S.A.; *Int'l*, pg. 181
AMETEK AIRCRAFT PARTS & ACCESSORIES, INC.—See AMETEK, Inc.; *U.S. Public*, pg. 117
AMETEK MRO FLORIDA, INC.—See AMETEK, Inc.; *U.S. Public*, pg. 117
AMSTERDAM SCHIPHOL PIJPLEIDING C.V.—See Air France-KLM S.A.; *Int'l*, pg. 236
ANA AERO SUPPLY SYSTEMS CO., LTD.—See ANA Holdings Inc.; *Int'l*, pg. 443
ANA AIRCRAFT MAINTENANCE CO., LTD.—See ANA Holdings Inc.; *Int'l*, pg. 443
ANA AIR SERVICE FUKUSHIMA CO., LTD.—See ANA Holdings Inc.; *Int'l*, pg. 444
ANA AIR SERVICE SAGA CO., LTD.—See ANA Holdings Inc.; *Int'l*, pg. 444
ANA BASE MAINTENANCE TECHNICS CO., LTD.—See ANA Holdings Inc.; *Int'l*, pg. 444
ANA BUSINESS CREATE CO., LTD.—See ANA Holdings Inc.; *Int'l*, pg. 444
ANA BUSINESS JET INC.—See ANA Holdings Inc.; *Int'l*, pg. 444
ANA CATERING SERVICE CO., LTD.—See ANA Holdings Inc.; *Int'l*, pg. 444
ANA COMPONENT TECHNICS CO., LTD.—See ANA Holdings Inc.; *Int'l*, pg. 444
ANA ENGINE TECHNICS CO., LTD.—See ANA Holdings Inc.; *Int'l*, pg. 444
ANA FOODS CO., LTD.—See ANA Holdings Inc.; *Int'l*, pg. 444
ANA LINE MAINTENANCE TECHNICS CO., LTD.—See ANA Holdings Inc.; *Int'l*, pg. 444
ANA SKY BUILDING SERVICE CO., LTD.—See ANA Holdings Inc.; *Int'l*, pg. 444
ANA TRADING DUTY FREE CO., LTD.—See ANA Holdings Inc.; *Int'l*, pg. 444
ANQING TIANZHUSHAN AIRPORT CO., LTD.—See Hainan Traffic Administration Holding Co., Ltd.; *Int'l*, pg. 3212
APSYS UK—See Airbus SE; *Int'l*, pg. 246
ARCHER DANIELS MIDLAND CO.—See Archer-Daniels-Midland Company; *U.S. Public*, pg. 183
ASCENT AVIATION SERVICES CORP.—See Marana Aerospace Solutions, Inc.; *U.S. Private*, pg. 2569
ASIA DIGITAL ENGINEERING SDN. BHD.—See Capital A Bhd; *Int'l*, pg. 1309
ASIA JET PARTNERS MALAYSIA SDN BHD—See Berjaya Corporation Berhad; *Int'l*, pg. 982
ASKARI AVIATION SERVICES PVT LTD.—See Army Welfare Trust LLC; *Int'l*, pg. 575
A. SORIANO AIR CORPORATION—See A. Soriano Corporation; *Int'l*, pg. 22
ASSOCIATED PAINTERS, INC.—See Vance Street Capital LLC; *U.S. Private*, pg. 4342
ASTRIUM SPACE TRANSPORTATION—See Airbus SE; *Int'l*, pg. 245
ATFIN GMBH—See Camellia Plc; *Int'l*, pg. 1271
AUSTRALIAN AEROSPACE COMPOSITES PTY LTD.—See Airbus SE; *Int'l*, pg. 243
AVIACION INTERCONTINENTAL, A.I.E.—See Banco Santander, S.A.; *Int'l*, pg. 825
AVIAQ AB—See AVTECH Sweden AB; *Int'l*, pg. 751
AVIA SOLUTIONS GROUP AB; *Int'l*, pg. 741
AVIATIONPOWER TECHNICAL SERVICES GMBH—See ManpowerGroup Inc.; *U.S. Public*, pg. 1357
AVIATIONPOWER UK LTD.—See ManpowerGroup Inc.; *U.S. Public*, pg. 1357
AVIATION TECHNICAL SERVICES INC.—See JLL Partners, LLC; *U.S. Private*, pg. 2212
AVMAX ENGINEERING—See Avmax Group Inc.; *Int'l*, pg. 748
AVMAX GROUP INC.; *Int'l*, pg. 748
AVMAX MONTANA, INC.—See Avmax Group Inc.; *Int'l*, pg. 748
AVTECH FRANCE SARL—See AVTECH Sweden AB; *Int'l*, pg. 751
AVTECH MIDDLE EAST LLC—See AVTECH Sweden AB; *Int'l*, pg. 751
AVTECH SWEDEN AB; *Int'l*, pg. 751
AYALA AVIATION CORPORATION—See Ayala Corporation; *Int'l*, pg. 773
BAE SYSTEMS REGIONAL AIRCRAFT—See BAE Systems plc; *Int'l*, pg. 796
BAMA AIR, INC.—See Moelis Asset Management LP; *U.S. Private*, pg. 2764
BANYAN AIR SERVICE INC.; *U.S. Private*, pg. 470
BATON ROUGE JET CENTER LLC; *U.S. Private*, pg. 487
BELL TEXTRON ASIA (PTE) LTD.—See Textron Inc.; *U.S. Public*, pg. 2028
BELL TEXTRON PRAGUE, A.S.—See Textron Inc.; *U.S. Public*, pg. 2028
BFS CARGO DMK CO., LTD.—See Bangkok Airways Public Company Limited; *Int'l*, pg. 832

BINTERTECHNIC—See Binter Canarias, S.A.; *Int'l*, pg. 1034
BLUE AEROSPACE LLC—See HEICO Corporation; *U.S. Public*, pg. 1021
BLUE CROWN B.V.—See Air France-KLM S.A.; *Int'l*, pg. 236
BOEING COMMERCIAL AVIATION SERVICES—See The Boeing Company; *U.S. Public*, pg. 2039
BOMBARDIER AEROSPACE—See Bombardier Inc.; *Int'l*, pg. 1103
BOTTOM LINE AVIATION, LLC—See Nexstar Media Group, Inc.; *U.S. Public*, pg. 1524
CALSPAN SYSTEMS CORPORATION—See TransDigm Group Incorporated; *U.S. Public*, pg. 2180
CAMP EUROPE SAS—See The Hearst Corporation; *U.S. Private*, pg. 4044
CAMP SYSTEMS INTERNATIONAL, INC.—See The Hearst Corporation; *U.S. Private*, pg. 4044
CAMP SYSTEMS INTERNATIONAL, INC. - WICHITA—See The Hearst Corporation; *U.S. Private*, pg. 4044
CARGOJET INC.; *Int'l*, pg. 1325
CARSON HELICOPTERS INC.; *U.S. Private*, pg. 774
CAV INTERNATIONAL, INC.; *U.S. Private*, pg. 794
CHC GROUP LTD.—See First Reserve Management, L.P.; *U.S. Private*, pg. 1525
CHINA NATIONAL AVIATION FUEL GROUP CORPORATION; *Int'l*, pg. 1525
CHITOSE AIRPORT MOTOR SERVICE CO., LTD.—See ANA Holdings Inc.; *Int'l*, pg. 444
C&L AEROSPACE PTY LTD.; *Int'l*, pg. 1239
CLEMENS AVIATION LLC; *U.S. Private*, pg. 939
COLLINS AEROSPACE - AEROSTRUCTURES, PRESTWICK SERVICE CENTER—See RTX Corporation; *U.S. Public*, pg. 1821
COMMERCIAL AIRCRAFT INTERIORS, LLC; *U.S. Private*, pg. 983
COMPANIA PANAMENA DE AVIACION, S.A.—See Copa Holdings, S.A.; *Int'l*, pg. 1792
CONSOLIDATED TURBINE SPECIALISTS CANADA, LLP—See Kratos Defense & Security Solutions, Inc.; *U.S. Public*, pg. 1276
CONSOLIDATED TURBINE SPECIALISTS, LLC—See Kratos Defense & Security Solutions, Inc.; *U.S. Public*, pg. 1276
COOK AVIATION INC.—See Cook Group Incorporated; *U.S. Private*, pg. 1037
CORPORATE WINGS INC.—See Directional Capital LLC; *U.S. Private*, pg. 1236
CORPORATE WINGS SERVICES CORP.—See Directional Capital LLC; *U.S. Private*, pg. 1236
CSC TRANSPORT INC.—See Altice USA, Inc.; *U.S. Public*, pg. 87
CTS ENGINES, LLC—See J.F. Lehman & Company, Inc.; *U.S. Private*, pg. 2163
CUTTER AVIATION ALBUQUERQUE, INC.—See Cutter Holding Co.; *U.S. Private*, pg. 1131
CUTTER AVIATION COLORADO SPRINGS, LLC—See Cutter Holding Co.; *U.S. Private*, pg. 1131
CUTTER AVIATION DALLAS-ADDISON, LLC—See Cutter Holding Co.; *U.S. Private*, pg. 1131
CUTTER AVIATION DEER VALLEY, INC.—See Cutter Holding Co.; *U.S. Private*, pg. 1131
CUTTER AVIATION EL PASO LIMITED PARTNERSHIP—See Cutter Holding Co.; *U.S. Private*, pg. 1131
CUTTER AVIATION PHOENIX, INC.—See Cutter Holding Co.; *U.S. Private*, pg. 1131
CUTTER AVIATION SAN ANTONIO, INC.—See Cutter Holding Co.; *U.S. Private*, pg. 1131
DART HELICOPTER SERVICES CANADA, INC.—See Bristow Group, Inc.; *U.S. Public*, pg. 387
DART HELICOPTER SERVICES CANADA, INC.—See Eagle Copters Ltd.; *Int'l*, pg. 2264
DERICHEBOURG AERONAUTICS SERVICES GERMANY GMBH—See Derichebourg S.A.; *Int'l*, pg. 2041
DHL FREIGHT FINLAND OY—See Deutsche Post AG; *Int'l*, pg. 2075
DLH FUEL COMPANY MBH—See Deutsche Lufthansa AG; *Int'l*, pg. 2066
DONCASTER CITATION SERVICE CENTRE LIMITED—See Textron Inc.; *U.S. Public*, pg. 2028
DOSS AVIATION, INC.—See L3Harris Technologies, Inc.; *U.S. Public*, pg. 1281
DRAKE AIR, INC.—See AMETEK, Inc.; *U.S. Public*, pg. 117
DYNASTY AEROTECH INTERNATIONAL CORP.—See China Airlines Ltd.; *Int'l*, pg. 1482
EADS ATR S.A.—See Airbus SE; *Int'l*, pg. 246
EAGLE COPTERS LTD.; *Int'l*, pg. 2264
EAGLE COPTERS SOUTH AMERICA S.A.—See Eagle Copters Ltd.; *Int'l*, pg. 2264
EC SERVICES—See Danbury AeroSpace, Inc.; *U.S. Private*, pg. 1153
EGYPTAIR MAINTENANCE & ENGINEERING—See EgyptAir Holding Company; *Int'l*, pg. 2327
EMBRAER AIRCRAFT MAINTENANCE SERVICES, INC.—See Embraer S.A.; *Int'l*, pg. 2375
EMBRAER AVIATION EUROPE SAS—See Embraer S.A.; *Int'l*, pg. 2375

488190 — OTHER SUPPORT ACTIV...

EMBRAER AVIATION INTERNATIONAL SAS—See Embraer S.A.; *Int'l*, pg. 2375
ENCOMPASS SUPPLY CHAIN MANAGEMENT (CANADA) INC.—See Harwood Capital LLP; *Int'l*, pg. 3282
EUROAVIONICS USA LLC—See HENSOLDT AG; *Int'l*, pg. 3355
EVE HOLDING, INC.; *U.S. Public*, pg. 799
EXPRESSJET SERVICES, LLC—See ExpressJet Airlines Inc.; *U.S. Private*, pg. 1451
FFC SERVICES INC.—See Linden Street Capital Corp.; *U.S. Private*, pg. 2460
FLIGHTSTAR AIRCRAFT SERVICES, LLC—See MRO Holdings LP; *U.S. Private*, pg. 2805
FLYERTECH LIMITED—See Gama Aviation plc; *Int'l*, pg. 2876
FLYING COLOURS CORPORATION - SINGAPORE FACILITY—See Directional Capital LLC; *U.S. Private*, pg. 1236
FLY LEASING LIMITED—See The Carlyle Group Inc.; *U.S. Public*, pg. 2047
FPS FRANKFURT PASSENGER SERVICES GMBH—See Fraport AG; *Int'l*, pg. 2764
FRAPORT CARGO SERVICES GMBH—See Cerberus Capital Management, L.P.; *U.S. Private*, pg. 840
FRAPORT MALTA BUSINESS SERVICES LTD.—See Fraport AG; *Int'l*, pg. 2764
FSL FLUGPLATZ SPEYER/LUDWIGSHAFEN GMBH—See BASF SE; *Int'l*, pg. 883
FTI ENGINEERING NETWORK GMBH—See Eckelmann AG; *Int'l*, pg. 2290
GAMA AVIATION LLC—See Wheels Up Experience Inc.; *U.S. Public*, pg. 2366
GAMA AVIATION PLC; *Int'l*, pg. 2876
GAMA AVIATION SA—See Gama Aviation plc; *Int'l*, pg. 2876
GAMA SUPPORT SERVICES FZE—See Gama Aviation plc; *Int'l*, pg. 2876
GARDNER AVIATION SPECIALIST, INC.—See GenNx360 Capital Partners, L.P.; *U.S. Private*, pg. 1672
GA TELESIS COMPOSITE REPAIR GROUP SOUTHEAST—See GA Telesis LLC; *U.S. Private*, pg. 1632
GA TELESIS UK LTD.—See GA Telesis LLC; *U.S. Private*, pg. 1632
GENERAL AVIATION MAINTENANCE & ENGINEERING CO., LTD—See Airbus SE; *Int'l*, pg. 243
GLOBAL AIRCRAFT SERVICE, INC.; *U.S. Private*, pg. 1712
GLOBAL AVIATION SERVICES, LLC—See The Carlyle Group Inc.; *U.S. Public*, pg. 2052
GLOBAL LOGISTICS SYSTEM EUROPE COMPANY FOR CARGO INFORMATION SERVICES GMBH—See Air France-KLM S.A.; *Int'l*, pg. 237
GLOBAL LOGISTICS SYSTEM EUROPE COMPANY FOR CARGO INFORMATION SERVICES GMBH—See Deutsche Lufthansa AG; *Int'l*, pg. 2066
GMR AERO TECHNIC LIMITED—See GMR Airports Infrastructure Limited; *Int'l*, pg. 3015
GOLDEN ISLES AVIATION—See Quantem FBO Group LLC; *U.S. Private*, pg. 3322
GOODRICH AEROSTRUCTURES SERVICE CENTER - ASIA PTE. LTD.—See RTX Corporation; *U.S. Public*, pg. 1821
GREAT CIRCLE FLIGHT SERVICES, LLC—See Vitus Marine LLC; *U.S. Private*, pg. 4406
GREENWICH KAHALA AVIATION LTD.; *Int'l*, pg. 3077
HAINAN HNA ZHONGMIAN DUTY FREE CO., LTD—See Hainan Traffic Administration Holding Co., Ltd.; *Int'l*, pg. 3215
HAINAN TECHNIK CO., LTD.—See Hainan Traffic Administration Holding Co., Ltd.; *Int'l*, pg. 3215
HANGAR 8 MANAGEMENT LIMITED—See Gama Aviation plc; *Int'l*, pg. 2876
HANTZ AIR, LLC—See Hantz Group, Inc.; *U.S. Private*, pg. 1857
HAWTHORNE GLOBAL AVIATION SERVICES, LLC—See Moelis Asset Management LP; *U.S. Private*, pg. 2764
HEARTLAND AVIATION—See Moelis Asset Management LP; *U.S. Private*, pg. 2764
HELEX, LLC—See PHI, Inc.; *U.S. Public*, pg. 3168
HELI-ONE COLORADO—See First Reserve Management, L.P.; *U.S. Private*, pg. 1525
HELI-ONE—See First Reserve Management, L.P.; *U.S. Private*, pg. 1525
HIGHLAND HELICOPTERS LTD.; *Int'l*, pg. 3387
HONDA AIRWAYS CO., LTD.—See Honda Motor Co., Ltd.; *Int'l*, pg. 3460
HWA HSIA COMPANY LTD.—See China Airlines Ltd.; *Int'l*, pg. 1482
INTEGRATED DEICING SERVICES, LLC; *U.S. Private*, pg. 2099
INTERNATIONAL AIR CONSOLIDATORS; *U.S. Private*, pg. 2114
INTERNATIONAL AIRLINE SERVICES AMERICAS L.P.—See Air France-KLM S.A.; *Int'l*, pg. 237
INTERNATIONAL AIRLINE SERVICES EUROPE LIMITED—See Air France-KLM S.A.; *Int'l*, pg. 237
INTERNATIONAL AIRLINE SERVICES LIMITED—See Air France-KLM S.A.; *Int'l*, pg. 237

INTERNATIONAL LEASE FINANCE CORPORATION—See AerCap Holdings N.V.; *Int'l*, pg. 179
INTERNATIONAL MARINE AIRLINE SERVICES LIMITED—See Air France-KLM S.A.; *Int'l*, pg. 237
I-SEC ITALIA SERVICES S.R.L.—See ICTS International, N.V.; *Int'l*, pg. 3587
ISLAND AVIATION, INC.—See A. Soriano Corporation; *Int'l*, pg. 22
JET AVIATION MANAGEMENT—See General Dynamics Corporation; *U.S. Public*, pg. 913
JET AVIATION ST. LOUIS, INC.—See General Dynamics Corporation; *U.S. Public*, pg. 913
JET YARD, LLC—See Air T, Inc.; *U.S. Public*, pg. 67
J&J MAINTENANCE INC.—See CBRE Group, Inc.; *U.S. Public*, pg. 460
JORDAN AIRCRAFT MAINTENANCE LIMITED—See Dubai Aerospace Enterprise Ltd; *Int'l*, pg. 2218
JORMAC AEROSPACE, INC.; *U.S. Private*, pg. 2236
JOURNEY GROUP PLC—See Harwood Capital LLP; *Int'l*, pg. 3282
KOREAN HELICOPTER DEVELOPMENT SUPPORT LTD.—See Airbus SE; *Int'l*, pg. 247
L-3 COMMUNICATIONS INTEGRATED SYSTEMS L.P.—See L3Harris Technologies, Inc.; *U.S. Public*, pg. 1282
LEADING EDGE AVIATION SERVICES INC.—See Vance Street Capital LLC; *U.S. Private*, pg. 4342
LEGACY AVIATION SERVICES INC.; *U.S. Private*, pg. 2416
LGSTX SERVICES, INC.—See Air Transport Services Group, Inc.; *U.S. Public*, pg. 67
LINDEN STREET CAPITAL CORP.; *U.S. Private*, pg. 2460
LONDON LUTON AIRPORT GROUP LIMITED—See Ardian SAS; *Int'l*, pg. 556
LONDON LUTON AIRPORT GROUP LIMITED—See ENAIRE; *Int'l*, pg. 2396
LUFTHANSA TECHNIK AG—See Deutsche Lufthansa AG; *Int'l*, pg. 2069
LUFTHANSA TECHNIK PHILIPPINES INC.—See Deutsche Lufthansa AG; *Int'l*, pg. 2070
LUFTHANSA TECHNIK PUERTO RICO LLC—See Deutsche Lufthansa AG; *Int'l*, pg. 2070
MACH MONUMENT AVIATION FUELLING CO. LTD.—See BP plc; *Int'l*, pg. 1131
MARANA AEROSPACE SOLUTIONS, INC.; *U.S. Private*, pg. 2569
MAYTAG AIRCRAFT CORP.—See Mercury Air Group Inc.; *U.S. Private*, pg. 2670
MCGEE AIR SERVICES, INC.—See Alaska Air Group, Inc.; *U.S. Public*, pg. 72
MERCURY AIR GROUP INC.; *U.S. Private*, pg. 2670
MIDWAY AIRCRAFT INSTRUMENT CORP.—See Groupe Industriel Marcel Dassault S.A.; *Int'l*, pg. 3105
MILLENNIUM TRANSPORTATION PVT LTD—See Hayleys PLC; *Int'l*, pg. 3292
MOOG DUBLIN LTD.—See Moog Inc.; *U.S. Public*, pg. 1470
MOORABBIN AIRPORT CORPORATION PTY LTD—See Goodman Limited; *Int'l*, pg. 3041
MUSASHI NO MORI COUNTRY CLUB CO., LTD.—See ANA Holdings Inc.; *Int'l*, pg. 444
NAMPA VALLEY HELICOPTERS INC.—See PHI, Inc.; *U.S. Private*, pg. 3168
NATIONAL FLIGHT SERVICES INC—See NFS Holdings Inc.; *U.S. Private*, pg. 2923
NFS HOLDINGS INC.; *U.S. Private*, pg. 2923
NORTHROP GRUMMAN TECHNICAL SERVICES-NORFOLK—See Northrop Grumman Corporation; *U.S. Public*, pg. 1541
PANNESMA COMPANY LTD.—See Atheeb Group; *Int'l*, pg. 669
PATTERSON-ERIE CORPORATION; *U.S. Private*, pg. 3111
PEMCO WORLD AIR SERVICES INC.—See Air Transport Services Group, Inc.; *U.S. Public*, pg. 67
PERFORMANCE AVIATION AUSTRALIA—See Experience Co Limited; *Int'l*, pg. 2588
PHS/MWA—See HEICO Corporation; *U.S. Public*, pg. 1021
PRECISION AVIATION GROUP, INC.—See GenNx360 Capital Partners, L.P.; *U.S. Private*, pg. 1672
PREMIAIR AVIATION MAINTENANCE PTY LTD—See Textron Inc.; *U.S. Public*, pg. 2028
PRIMEFLIGHT AVIATION SERVICES, INC.—See The Carlyle Group Inc.; *U.S. Public*, pg. 2052
PRIOR AVIATION SERVICE, INC.—See OnCore Aviation LLC; *U.S. Private*, pg. 3019
PROSPECT AIRPORT SERVICES INC.; *U.S. Private*, pg. 3287
PSA AIRLINES, INC.—See American Airlines Group Inc.; *U.S. Public*, pg. 96
REVIMA SASU—See Ardian SAS; *Int'l*, pg. 556
ROCKWELL COLLINS SOUTHEAST ASIA PTE. LTD.—See RTX Corporation; *U.S. Public*, pg. 1823
ROROS FLYSERVICE AS—See Avia Solutions Group AB; *Int'l*, pg. 741
ROSS AVIATION INC—See Pierce Enterprises Inc.; *U.S. Private*, pg. 3178
ROTOR BLADES LIMITED—See Textron Inc.; *U.S. Public*, pg. 2028
RVA INC.—See Robinson Aviation (RVA) Inc.; *U.S. Private*, pg. 3461

SABRE AIRLINE SOLUTIONS—See Sabre Corporation; *U.S. Public*, pg. 1833
SABRELINER CORPORATION; *U.S. Private*, pg. 3521
SAFEAIR TECHNICAL SDN. BHD.—See Destini Berhad; *Int'l*, pg. 2046
SAKER AVIATION SERVICES, INC.; *U.S. Public*, pg. 1835
SCR AIR SERVICES, INC.—See NFI Industries, Inc.; *U.S. Private*, pg. 2923
SERVICIOUS AEROTECNICOS INSULARES SL—See Binter Canarias, S.A.; *Int'l*, pg. 1034
SFS MUNICH GMBH & CO. KG—See BlackRock, Inc.; *U.S. Public*, pg. 346
SFS MUNICH GMBH & CO. KG—See Blackstone Inc.; *U.S. Public*, pg. 358
SFS MUNICH GMBH & CO. KG—See Cascade Investment LLC; *U.S. Private*, pg. 780
SHANNON AEROSPACE LTD.—See Deutsche Lufthansa AG; *Int'l*, pg. 2070
SIGNATURE FLIGHT SUPPORT - BED—See BlackRock, Inc.; *U.S. Public*, pg. 346
SIGNATURE FLIGHT SUPPORT - BED—See Blackstone Inc.; *U.S. Public*, pg. 358
SIGNATURE FLIGHT SUPPORT - BED—See Cascade Investment LLC; *U.S. Private*, pg. 780
SIGNATURE FLIGHT SUPPORT PARIS SA—See BlackRock, Inc.; *U.S. Public*, pg. 346
SIGNATURE FLIGHT SUPPORT PARIS SA—See Blackstone Inc.; *U.S. Public*, pg. 358
SIGNATURE FLIGHT SUPPORT PARIS SA—See Cascade Investment LLC; *U.S. Private*, pg. 781
SIGNATURE FLIGHT SUPPORT WASHINGTON NATIONAL, INC.—See BlackRock, Inc.; *U.S. Public*, pg. 346
SIGNATURE FLIGHT SUPPORT WASHINGTON NATIONAL, INC.—See Blackstone Inc.; *U.S. Public*, pg. 358
SIGNATURE FLIGHT SUPPORT WASHINGTON NATIONAL, INC.—See Cascade Investment LLC; *U.S. Private*, pg. 781
SKY HARBOUR GROUP CORPORATION; *U.S. Public*, pg. 1892
SKYSTAR AIRPORT SERVICES PTY. LTD.—See Agility; *Int'l*, pg. 210
SOUNDAIR AVIATION SERVICES, LLC—See HEICO Corporation; *U.S. Public*, pg. 1021
SOUTHERN AEROPARTS, INC.—See AMETEK, Inc.; *U.S. Public*, pg. 117
SPRINGFIELD FLYING SERVICE INCORPORATED—See Harry Cooper Supply Company; *U.S. Private*, pg. 1871
SR TECHNICS AIRFOIL SERVICES LTD.—See Hainan Traffic Administration Holding Co., Ltd.; *Int'l*, pg. 3216
SR TECHNICS AMERICA INC.—See Hainan Traffic Administration Holding Co., Ltd.; *Int'l*, pg. 3216
SR TECHNICS AUSTRALIA PTY LTD—See Hainan Traffic Administration Holding Co., Ltd.; *Int'l*, pg. 3216
SR TECHNICS MALAYSIA SDN BHD—See Hainan Traffic Administration Holding Co., Ltd.; *Int'l*, pg. 3216
SR TECHNICS MALTA LTD.—See Hainan Traffic Administration Holding Co., Ltd.; *Int'l*, pg. 3216
SR TECHNICS SWITZERLAND AG—See Hainan Traffic Administration Holding Co., Ltd.; *Int'l*, pg. 3216
STRAIGHT FLIGHT, INC.—See Sierra Nevada Corporation; *U.S. Private*, pg. 3647
SWISS EUROPEAN AIR LINES AG—See Deutsche Lufthansa AG; *Int'l*, pg. 2070
SWISSPORT CANADA HANDLING INC.—See Hainan Traffic Administration Holding Co., Ltd.; *Int'l*, pg. 3216
SWISSPORT CHILE—See Hainan Traffic Administration Holding Co., Ltd.; *Int'l*, pg. 3216
SWISSPORT DENMARK—See Hainan Traffic Administration Holding Co., Ltd.; *Int'l*, pg. 3216
SWISSPORT FINLAND OY—See Hainan Traffic Administration Holding Co., Ltd.; *Int'l*, pg. 3216
SWISSPORT PORTUGAL—See Hainan Traffic Administration Holding Co., Ltd.; *Int'l*, pg. 3216
SWISSPORT TRINIDAD & TOBAGO—See Hainan Traffic Administration Holding Co., Ltd.; *Int'l*, pg. 3216
TAIWAN AIR CARGO TERMINAL LTD.—See China Airlines Ltd.; *Int'l*, pg. 1482
TAIWAN AIRCRAFT MAINTENANCE & ENGINEERING CO., LTD.—See China Airlines Ltd.; *Int'l*, pg. 1482
TRANSAVIA AIRLINES B.V.—See Air France-KLM S.A.; *Int'l*, pg. 238
TRANSAVIA AIRLINES C.V.—See Air France-KLM S.A.; *Int'l*, pg. 238
TRANSAVIA FRANCE S.A.S.—See Air France-KLM S.A.; *Int'l*, pg. 238
TRIUMPH ACTUATION SYSTEMS, LLC—See Triumph Group, Inc.; *U.S. Public*, pg. 2196
TRIUMPH AFTERMARKET SERVICES GROUP, LLC—See Triumph Group, Inc.; *U.S. Public*, pg. 2197
TRIUMPH FABRICATIONS-ST. LOUIS, INC.—See Triumph Group, Inc.; *U.S. Public*, pg. 2196
TRU SIMULATION + TRAINING LLC—See Textron Inc.; *U.S. Public*, pg. 2029
UNITED ROTORCRAFT SOLUTIONS, LLC—See American Securities LLC; *U.S. Private*, pg. 247
UNITPOOL AG—See Brambles Limited; *Int'l*, pg. 1139
UNIVERSAL ASSET MANAGEMENT, INC.—See China Air-

N.A.I.C.S. INDEX

craft Leasing Group Holdings Limited; *Int'l*, pg. 1481
UNIVERSAL WEATHER & AVIATION, INC.; *U.S. Private*, pg. 4307
UTC AEROSPACE SYSTEMS - AEROSTRUCTURES, TIANJIN—See RTX Corporation; *U.S. Public*, pg. 1821
UTC AEROSPACE SYSTEMS - LANDING GEAR, BURLINGTON—See RTX Corporation; *U.S. Public*, pg. 1821
VOYAGEUR AVIATION CORP.—See Chorus Aviation Inc.; *Int'l*, pg. 1584
WESCO AIRCRAFT FRANCE SAS—See Platinum Equity, LLC; *U.S. Private*, pg. 3210
WEST STAR AVIATION LLC—See The Sterling Group, L.P.; *U.S. Private*, pg. 4123
WFS ASIA PACIFIC, AFRICA & MIDDLE EAST—See Cerberus Capital Management, L.P.; *U.S. Private*, pg. 840
WFS EUROPE—See Cerberus Capital Management, L.P.; *U.S. Private*, pg. 840
WHEELS UP EXPERIENCE INC.; *U.S. Public*, pg. 2366
WHEELTUG PLC—See Borealis Exploration Limited; *Int'l*, pg. 1114
WORLDWIDE FLIGHT SERVICES BANGKOK AIR GROUND HANDLING CO., LTD.—See Bangkok Airways Public Company Limited; *Int'l*, pg. 832
ZHENJIANG BELL TEXTRON AVIATION SERVICES LIMITED—See Textron Inc.; *U.S. Public*, pg. 2029

488210 — SUPPORT ACTIVITIES FOR RAIL TRANSPORTATION

ABERTIS INFRAESTRUCTURAS, S.A.—See ACS, Actividades de Construccion y Servicios, S.A.; *Int'l*, pg. 112
ACTREN MANTENIMIENTO FERROVIARIO, S.A.—See Construcciones y Auxiliar de Ferrocarriles S.A.; *Int'l*, pg. 1776
AIRPORT LINK CO. PTY LTD.—See CP2 Group Limited; *Int'l*, pg. 1823
AKRON BARBERTON CLUSTER RAILWAY COMPANY, INC.—See The Wheeling Corporation Inc.; *U.S. Private*, pg. 4134
ALABAMA & TENNESSEE RIVER RAILWAY, LLC—See The Broe Companies, Inc.; *U.S. Private*, pg. 4001
ALBANY PORT RAILROAD CO.—See CSX Corporation; *U.S. Public*, pg. 602
ALBANY PORT RAILROAD CO.—See Norfolk Southern Corporation; *U.S. Public*, pg. 1535
ALGHANIM GROUP OF SHIPPING & TRANSPORT W.L.L.—See Fouad Alghanim & Sons Group of Companies; *Int'l*, pg. 2753
ALLEGHENY & WESTERN RAILWAY CO.—See CSX Corporation; *U.S. Public*, pg. 602
ALLIANCE CASTINGS COMPANY, LLC—See The Greenbrier Companies, Inc.; *U.S. Public*, pg. 2085
ALLPRESS & MOORE RAILROAD SIGNAL CONTRACTORS INC.—See CDL Electric Company, Inc.; *U.S. Private*, pg. 802
ALSTOM TRANSPORT REGIONAL TRAINS—See Alstom S.A.; *Int'l*, pg. 380
AMERICAN INTERNATIONAL CARGO SERVICE—See American Shipping Co. Inc.; *U.S. Private*, pg. 253
AM GENERAL CONTRACTORS SPA—See Westinghouse Air Brake Technologies Corporation; *U.S. Public*, pg. 2356
AMP GERMAN CANNABIS GROUP INC.; *Int'l*, pg. 431
ANSALDO STS FRANCE SAS—See Hitachi, Ltd.; *Int'l*, pg. 3417
ANSALDO STS IRELAND—See Hitachi, Ltd.; *Int'l*, pg. 3417
ANSALDO STS SWEDEN AB—See Hitachi, Ltd.; *Int'l*, pg. 3417
ATLANTIC AND WESTERN RAILWAY LP—See Brookfield Infrastructure Partners L.P.; *Int'l*, pg. 1190
ATLANTIC AND WESTERN RAILWAY LP—See GIC Pte. Ltd.; *Int'l*, pg. 2965
AXIOM RAIL LIMITED—See Deutsche Bahn AG; *Int'l*, pg. 2050
BAY WORX INDUSTRIES, LLC—See Trinity Industries, Inc.; *U.S. Public*, pg. 2193
BCPL RAILWAY INFRASTRUCTURE LIMITED; *Int'l*, pg. 929
BEIJING CSR TIMES LOCOMOTIVE AND ROLLING STOCK MECHANICS CO., LTD.—See CRRC Corporation Limited; *Int'l*, pg. 1858
BEML LIMITED - INTERNATIONAL BUSINESS DIVISION—See BEML Limited; *Int'l*, pg. 969
BERCHTESGARDENER LAND BAHN GMBH—See Ferrovie dello Stato Italiane S.p.A.; *Int'l*, pg. 2645
B. GRIMM TRANSPORT LTD.—See B. Grimm Group; *Int'l*, pg. 788
BIRMINGHAM TERMINAL RAILWAY—See Kinder Morgan, Inc.; *U.S. Public*, pg. 1233
BOATRIGHT RAILROAD COMPANIES, INC.; *U.S. Private*, pg. 603
BOMBARDIER TRANSPAORTATION ISRAEL LTD.—See Alstom S.A.; *Int'l*, pg. 381
BOMBARDIER TRANSPORTATION AUSTRALIA PTY. LTD.—See Alstom S.A.; *Int'l*, pg. 382
BOMBARDIER TRANSPORTATION (ZWUS) POLSKA SP. Z O.O.—See Alstom S.A.; *Int'l*, pg. 382
BROOKFIELD RAIL PTY. LTD.—See Brookfield Infrastructure Partners L.P.; *Int'l*, pg. 1190
BRUSH BARCLAY LTD.—See Westinghouse Air Brake Technologies Corporation; *U.S. Public*, pg. 2357
BRUSH TRACTION LTD.—See Westinghouse Air Brake Technologies Corporation; *U.S. Public*, pg. 2357
BUSITALIA RAIL SERVICE S.R.L.—See Ferrovie dello Stato Italiane S.p.A.; *Int'l*, pg. 2645
B & V DELITZSCH GMBH—See Duroc AB; *Int'l*, pg. 2229
CAF FRANCIA, S.A.S.—See Construcciones y Auxiliar de Ferrocarriles S.A.; *Int'l*, pg. 1776
CAF ITALIA, S.R.L.—See Construcciones y Auxiliar de Ferrocarriles S.A.; *Int'l*, pg. 1776
CAF MEXICO, S.A. DE C.V.—See Construcciones y Auxiliar de Ferrocarriles S.A.; *Int'l*, pg. 1776
CAF USA, INC.—See Construcciones y Auxiliar de Ferrocarriles S.A.; *Int'l*, pg. 1777
CALIFORNIA RAIL BUILDERS, LLC—See Ferrovial S.A.; *Int'l*, pg. 2644
CARLTON TRAIL RAILWAY COMPANY—See The Broe Companies, Inc.; *U.S. Private*, pg. 4001
CBSL TRANSPORTATION SERVICES, INC.; *U.S. Private*, pg. 797
CE CIDEON ENGINEERING GMBH & CO. KG—See CRCC High-tech Equipment Corporation Limited; *Int'l*, pg. 1830
CE CIDEON ENGINEERING SCHWEIZ AG—See CRCC High-tech Equipment Corporation Limited; *Int'l*, pg. 1830
CENTRAL CALIFORNIA TRACTION COMPANY—See Berkshire Hathaway Inc.; *U.S. Public*, pg. 303
CENTRO DE ENSAYOS Y ANALISIS CETEST, S.L.—See Construcciones y Auxiliar de Ferrocarriles S.A.; *Int'l*, pg. 1777
CENTUM ADETEL TRANSPORTATION SYSTEM SAS—See Centum Electronics Ltd.; *Int'l*, pg. 1416
CHICAGO FREIGHT CAR LEASING CO.—See Sasser Family Holdings, Inc.; *U.S. Private*, pg. 3552
CHICAGO UNION STATION COMPANY—See National Railroad Passenger Corporation; *U.S. Public*, pg. 2861
CHICHIBU RAILWAY CO., LTD.; *Int'l*, pg. 1476
CIRCULAR AGENCY SDN. BHD.—See Batu Kawan Berhad; *Int'l*, pg. 891
CN WORLDWIDE NORTH AMERICA—See Canadian National Railway Company; *Int'l*, pg. 1284
COLONIAL EQUIPMENT COMPANY; *U.S. Private*, pg. 970
CONSTRUCCIONES Y AUXILIAR DE FERROCARRILES ARGENTINA, S.A.—See Construcciones y Auxiliar de Ferrocarriles S.A.; *Int'l*, pg. 1777
CONSTRURAIL, S.A.—See ACS, Actividades de Construccion y Servicios, S.A.; *Int'l*, pg. 111
CP FINANCE SWITZERLAND AG—See Canadian Pacific Kansas City Limited; *Int'l*, pg. 1285
CRCC HIGH-TECH EQUIPMENT CORPORATION LIMITED; *Int'l*, pg. 1830
CSR QISHUYAN LOCOMOTIVE CO., LTD—See CRRC Corporation Limited; *Int'l*, pg. 1858
DANA RAILCARE, INC.—See Dana Transport Inc.; *U.S. Private*, pg. 1152
DB CARGO BELGIUM BV—See Deutsche Bahn AG; *Int'l*, pg. 2050
DB CARGO BULGARIA EOOD—See Deutsche Bahn AG; *Int'l*, pg. 2050
DB CARGO EURASIA GMBH—See Deutsche Bahn AG; *Int'l*, pg. 2050
DB CARGO HUNGARIA KFT.—See Deutsche Bahn AG; *Int'l*, pg. 2050
DB CARGO ITALIA SERVICES S.R.L.—See Deutsche Bahn AG; *Int'l*, pg. 2050
DB CARGO ITALIA S.R.L.—See Deutsche Bahn AG; *Int'l*, pg. 2050
DB FAHRWEGDIENSTE GMBH—See Deutsche Bahn AG; *Int'l*, pg. 2050
DB NETZ AG—See Deutsche Bahn AG; *Int'l*, pg. 2050
DB SICHERHEIT GMBH—See Deutsche Bahn AG; *Int'l*, pg. 2051
DELRAY CONNECTING RAILROAD COMPANY—See United States Steel Corporation; *U.S. Public*, pg. 2236
DEUTSCHE BAHN CONNECT GMBH—See Deutsche Bahn AG; *Int'l*, pg. 2051
DEUTSCHE BAHN INTERNATIONAL OPERATIONS GMBH—See Deutsche Bahn AG; *Int'l*, pg. 2051
DIE LANDERBAHN CZ S.R.O.—See Ferrovie dello Stato Italiane S.p.A.; *Int'l*, pg. 2645
DOWNER EDI RAIL PTY LTD—See Downer EDI Limited; *Int'l*, pg. 2185
DRIVE VAUXHALL ALDERSHOT—See DRIVE Motor Retail Limited; *Int'l*, pg. 2204
DRIVE VAUXHALL CLEVEDON—See DRIVE Motor Retail Limited; *Int'l*, pg. 2204
DRIVE VAUXHALL HAVERHILL—See DRIVE Motor Retail Limited; *Int'l*, pg. 2204
DUROC RAIL AB—See Duroc AB; *Int'l*, pg. 2229
ENYSE ENCLAVAMIENTOS Y SENALIZACION FERROVIARIA, S.A.—See ACS, Actividades de Construccion y Servicios, S.A.; *Int'l*, pg. 111
ERIXX GMBH—See Ferrovie dello Stato Italiane S.p.A.; *Int'l*, pg. 2645
EUROMAINT AB—See Construcciones y Auxiliar de Ferrocarriles S.A.; *Int'l*, pg. 1777
EUROMAINT RAIL AB—See Construcciones y Auxiliar de Ferrocarriles S.A.; *Int'l*, pg. 1777
EUROP MAINTENANCE—See Hiolle Industries S.A.; *Int'l*, pg. 3401
EUROPORTE PROXIMIT SAS—See Getlink SE; *Int'l*, pg. 2952
EVERSHOLT UK RAILS LIMITED—See CK Hutchison Holdings Limited; *Int'l*, pg. 1637
FERROCARRIL MEXICANO, S.A. DE C.V.—See Grupo Mexico, S.A.B. de C.V.; *Int'l*, pg. 3132
FERROSUR, SA DE CV—See Grupo Mexico, S.A.B. de C.V.; *Int'l*, pg. 3132
FIRST FINANCIAL RESOURCES INC.; *U.S. Private*, pg. 1519
FLORIDA CENTRAL RAILROAD—See Pinsly Railroad Co. Inc.; *U.S. Private*, pg. 3186
FLORIDA MIDLAND RAILROAD—See Pinsly Railroad Co. Inc.; *U.S. Private*, pg. 3186
FLORIDA NORTHERN RAILROAD—See Pinsly Railroad Co. Inc.; *U.S. Private*, pg. 3186
FORESTIERE EQUATORIALE SA; *Int'l*, pg. 2732
FORTUNE MARITIME INC.—See Sealift Holdings Inc.; *U.S. Private*, pg. 3585
FRASER MARINE & INDUSTRIAL—See Algoma Central Corporation; *Int'l*, pg. 318
FREIGHTLINER PL SP. Z O. O.—See Brookfield Infrastructure Partners L.P.; *Int'l*, pg. 1191
FREIGHTLINER PL SP. Z O. O.—See GIC Pte. Ltd.; *Int'l*, pg. 2966
FREIGHTLINER SCOTLAND LTD—See Brookfield Infrastructure Partners L.P.; *Int'l*, pg. 1191
FREIGHTLINER SCOTLAND LTD—See GIC Pte. Ltd.; *Int'l*, pg. 2966
FRIT CAR INC.—See Frit Incorporated; *U.S. Private*, pg. 1612
FS SISTEMI URBANI S.R.L.—See Ferrovie dello Stato Italiane S.p.A.; *Int'l*, pg. 2645
FULTON COUNTY RAILWAY, LLC—See The Broe Companies, Inc.; *U.S. Private*, pg. 4001
GATEWAY RAIL FREIGHT LTD.—See Gateway Distriparks Ltd.; *Int'l*, pg. 2889
GEMCO RAIL PTY. LTD.—See Engenco Limited; *Int'l*, pg. 2427
GEORGIA WOODLANDS RAILROAD—See The Broe Companies, Inc.; *U.S. Private*, pg. 4001
GERKEN SAS—See Westinghouse Air Brake Technologies Corporation; *U.S. Public*, pg. 2358
GETLINK SE; *Int'l*, pg. 2952
GLOBALTRANS INVESTMENT PLC; *Int'l*, pg. 3004
GREAT WESTERN RAILWAY OF COLORADO, LLC—See The Broe Companies, Inc.; *U.S. Private*, pg. 4001
GRUPA AZOTY KOLTAR SP. Z O.O.—See Grupa Azoty S.A.; *Int'l*, pg. 3115
GRUPO TMM, S.A.B.; *Int'l*, pg. 3137
HANGARTNER TERMINAL S.R.L.—See Deutsche Bahn AG; *Int'l*, pg. 2051
HANNING & KAHL GMBH & CO KG; *Int'l*, pg. 3257
HARSCO RAIL LTDA.—See Enviri Corporation; *U.S. Public*, pg. 781
HENAN SPLENDOR SCIENCE & TECHNOLOGY CO., LTD.; *Int'l*, pg. 3343
HITACHI RAIL ESPANA, S.L.U.—See Hitachi, Ltd.; *Int'l*, pg. 3421
HITACHI RAIL ITALY S.P.A—See Hitachi, Ltd.; *Int'l*, pg. 3420
HITACHI RAIL STS—See Hitachi, Ltd.; *Int'l*, pg. 3417
HITACHI RAIL STS USA—See Hitachi, Ltd.; *Int'l*, pg. 3417
HOKUSHINKYUKO RAILWAY CO., LTD.—See Hankyu Hanshin Holdings Inc.; *Int'l*, pg. 3256
HUDSON BAY RAILWAY COMPANY—See The Broe Companies, Inc.; *U.S. Private*, pg. 4001
HULL TRAINS COMPANY LIMITED—See FirstGroup plc; *Int'l*, pg. 2689
HYLIION HOLDINGS CORP.; *U.S. Public*, pg. 1079
IMC EXPLORATION GROUP PLC; *Int'l*, pg. 3620
INDIANA HARBOR BELT RAILROAD CO.—See CSX Corporation; *U.S. Public*, pg. 602
INDIANA HARBOR BELT RAILROAD CO.—See Norfolk Southern Corporation; *U.S. Public*, pg. 1535
IOKI GMBH—See Deutsche Bahn AG; *Int'l*, pg. 2055
IRVIA MANTENIMIENTO FERROVIARIO, S.A.—See Alstom S.A.; *Int'l*, pg. 383
ITALCERTIFER S.P.A.—See Ferrovie dello Stato Italiane S.p.A.; *Int'l*, pg. 2645
JRL ENTERPRISES INC.; *U.S. Private*, pg. 2240
KAISER & KRAFT EUROPA—See Franz Haniel & Cie. GmbH; *Int'l*, pg. 2763
KAISER & KRAFT GMBH—See Franz Haniel & Cie. GmbH; *Int'l*, pg. 2763
KITA-OSAKA KYUKO RAILWAY CO., LTD.—See Hankyu Hanshin Holdings Inc.; *Int'l*, pg. 3256
KOPPERS RAILROAD STRUCTURES INC.—See Koppers Holdings Inc.; *U.S. Public*, pg. 1272
KWT RAILWAY, INC.—See Brookfield Infrastructure Partners L.P.; *Int'l*, pg. 1192
KWT RAILWAY, INC.—See GIC Pte. Ltd.; *Int'l*, pg. 2966
THE LAKE TERMINAL RAILROAD COMPANY—See United

488210 — SUPPORT ACTIVITIES ...

States Steel Corporation; *U.S. Public*, pg. 2236
LONDON AND BIRMINGHAM RAILWAY LIMITED—See GLOBALVIA Inversiones, S.A.U.; *Int'l*, pg. 3005
LORAM MAINTENANCE OF WAY INC.; *U.S. Private*, pg. 2494
MALMO-LIMHAMNS JARNVAGSAKTIEBOLAG—See Heidelberg Materials AG; *Int'l*, pg. 3318
MANUFACTURERS' JUNCTION RAILWAY, LLC—See The Broe Companies, Inc.; *U.S. Private*, pg. 4001
MANUFACTURERS RAILWAY COMPANY—See Anheuser-Busch InBev SA/NV; *Int'l*, pg. 465
MAST LOGISTICS SERVICES, INC.—See Bath & Body Works, Inc.; *U.S. Public*, pg. 279
MERCITALIA SHUNTING & TERMINAL S.R.L.—See Ferrovie dello Stato Italiane S.p.A.; *Int'l*, pg. 2645
METRANS DYKO RAIL REPAIR SHOP S.R.O.—See Hamburger Hafen und Logistik AG; *Int'l*, pg. 3237
METRANS RAILPROFI AUSTRIA GMBH—See Hamburger Hafen und Logistik AG; *Int'l*, pg. 3237
METRONOM EISENBAHNGESELLSCHAFT MBH—See Ferrovie dello Stato Italiane S.p.A.; *Int'l*, pg. 2645
MINNESOTA COMMERCIAL RAILWAY CO.; *U.S. Private*, pg. 2743
MONTANA RAIL LINK, INC. - LIVINGSTON—See Washington Corporations; *U.S. Private*, pg. 4446
NEW HAMPSHIRE NORTHCOAST CORP.—See Boston Sand & Gravel Company; *U.S. Public*, pg. 373
NOMAD DIGITAL BV—See Alstom S.A.; *Int'l*, pg. 381
NOMAD DIGITAL GMBH—See Alstom S.A.; *Int'l*, pg. 381
NOMAD DIGITAL INC.—See Alstom S.A.; *Int'l*, pg. 381
NOSE ELECTRIC RAILWAY CO., LTD.—See Hankyu Hanshin Holdings Inc.; *Int'l*, pg. 3256
NSH NAHVERKEHR SCHLESWIG-HOLSTEIN GMBH—See Deutsche Bahn AG; *Int'l*, pg. 2052
OCEANOGATE ITALIA S.P.A.—See EUROKAI GmbH & Co. KGaA; *Int'l*, pg. 2553
PACIFIC RAIL SERVICES LLC; *U.S. Private*, pg. 3070
PCC DIRECT DELIVERY—See PCC Logistics; *U.S. Private*, pg. 3119
PCC LOGISTICS; *U.S. Private*, pg. 3119
PCC LOGISTICS—See PCC Logistics; *U.S. Private*, pg. 3119
PCC LOGISTICS—See PCC Logistics; *U.S. Private*, pg. 3119
PCC LOGISTICS—See PCC Logistics; *U.S. Private*, pg. 3119
PCC LOGISTICS—See PCC Logistics; *U.S. Private*, pg. 3119
PCC LOGISTICS - WATSON CENTER RD. FACILITY—See PCC Logistics; *U.S. Private*, pg. 3119
PEORIA & PEKIN UNION RAILWAY CO.—See CSX Corporation; *U.S. Public*, pg. 602
PEORIA & PEKIN UNION RAILWAY CO.—See Norfolk Southern Corporation; *U.S. Public*, pg. 1535
PICKFORDS LIMITED—See Madison Dearborn Partners, LLC; *U.S. Private*, pg. 2542
PLUREL BV—See DEKRA e.V.; *Int'l*, pg. 2008
THE PRESCOTT AND NORTHWESTERN RAILROAD COMPANY—See Brookfield Infrastructure Partners L.P.; *Int'l*, pg. 1193
THE PRESCOTT AND NORTHWESTERN RAILROAD COMPANY—See GIC Pte. Ltd.; *Int'l*, pg. 2967
PROGRESS RAIL SERVICES CORPORATION—See Caterpillar, Inc.; *U.S. Public*, pg. 453
PROGRESS RAIL SWITCHING SERVICES LLC—See Caterpillar, Inc.; *U.S. Public*, pg. 453
PROKAR, INC.—See Aurora Capital Group, LLC; *U.S. Private*, pg. 394
PROKAR, INC.—See The Jordan Company, L.P.; *U.S. Private*, pg. 4061
QUALITY TERMINAL SERVICES, L.L.C.—See The Broe Companies, Inc.; *U.S. Private*, pg. 4001
QUANTEM AVIATION SERVICES; *U.S. Private*, pg. 3322
RAILMAINT GMBH—See Iberia Industry Capital Group SARL; *Int'l*, pg. 3574
RAILROAD CONTROLS, LP—See Westinghouse Air Brake Technologies Corporation; *U.S. Public*, pg. 2359
RAILSERVE INC.—See Berkshire Hathaway Inc.; *U.S. Public*, pg. 311
RAILWAY APPROVALS GERMANY GMBH—See Deutsche Bahn AG; *Int'l*, pg. 2052
RAILWORKS CORP.—See Wind Point Advisors LLC; *U.S. Private*, pg. 4535
RETE FERROVIARIA ITALIANA - RFI S.P.A.—See Ferrovie dello Stato Italiane S.p.A.; *Int'l*, pg. 2645
ROM RAIL S.R.L.—See Ferrovie dello Stato Italiane S.p.A.; *Int'l*, pg. 2645
RSI LEASING INC.—See Trinity Industries, Inc.; *U.S. Public*, pg. 2193
SERMANFER, S.A.U.—See Construcciones y Auxiliar de Ferrocarriles S.A.; *Int'l*, pg. 1777
SINOTRANS LIMITED—See China Merchants Group Limited; *Int'l*, pg. 1522
SIRVA WORLDWIDE, INC.—See Madison Dearborn Partners, LLC; *U.S. Private*, pg. 2542
SOCORAIL SAS—See Getlink SE; *Int'l*, pg. 2953
SOUTHERN AERO PARTNERS, INC.—See AMETEK, Inc.; *U.S. Public*, pg. 117

SOUTHERN RAIL TERMINALS, INC.—See Norfolk Southern Corporation; *U.S. Public*, pg. 1536
SOUTHERN RAILWAY OF VANCOUVER ISLAND LIMITED—See Washington Corporations; *U.S. Private*, pg. 4446
STOBART RAIL FREIGHT LIMITED—See DBAY Advisors Limited; *Int'l*, pg. 1986
STRUKTON RAIL SHORT LINE BV—See Centric Holding B.V.; *Int'l*, pg. 1412
STUCKI DO BRASIL LTDA—See Stone Canyon Industries, LLC; *U.S. Private*, pg. 3817
TERMINAL RAILROAD ASSOCIATION; *U.S. Private*, pg. 3969
THELLO SAS—See Ferrovie dello Stato Italiane S.p.A.; *Int'l*, pg. 2645
TOKAI ROLLING STOCK & MACHINERY CO., LTD.—See Central Japan Railway Company; *Int'l*, pg. 1408
TOKAI TRANSPORT SERVICE COMPANY—See Central Japan Railway Company; *Int'l*, pg. 1408
TRADINSA INDUSTRIAL, S.L.—See Construcciones y Auxiliar de Ferrocarriles S.A.; *Int'l*, pg. 1777
TRAINELEC, S.L.—See Construcciones y Auxiliar de Ferrocarriles S.A.; *Int'l*, pg. 1777
TRANSCO RAILWAY PRODUCTS, INC.—See Transco Inc.; *U.S. Private*, pg. 4207
TRANSPORTATION TECHNOLOGY SERVICES, INC.—See Berkshire Hathaway Inc.; *U.S. Public*, pg. 303
TRENITALIA TPER SCARL—See Ferrovie dello Stato Italiane S.p.A.; *Int'l*, pg. 2645
TRINITYRAIL MAINTENANCE SERVICES, INC.—See Trinity Industries, Inc.; *U.S. Public*, pg. 2194
TTX CO.; *U.S. Private*, pg. 4255
UGL RAIL SERVICES PTY LIMITED—See ACS, Actividades de Construccion y Servicios, S.A.; *Int'l*, pg. 113
UNION RAILROAD COMPANY—See United States Steel Corporation; *U.S. Public*, pg. 2237
UNION STATION REDEVELOPMENT CORPORATION; *U.S. Private*, pg. 4285
USD PARTNERS LP; *U.S. Public*, pg. 2267
VERKEHRSGESELLSCHAFT START UNTERELBE MBH—See Deutsche Bahn AG; *Int'l*, pg. 2055
VGT VORBEREITUNGSGESELLSCHAFT TRANSPORTTECHNIK GMBH—See Alstom S.A.; *Int'l*, pg. 383
VLEXX GMBH—See Ferrovie dello Stato Italiane S.p.A.; *Int'l*, pg. 2645
VTG RAIL—See Morgan Stanley; *U.S. Public*, pg. 1476
WABTEC AUSTRALIA PTY LTD—See Westinghouse Air Brake Technologies Corporation; *U.S. Public*, pg. 2359
WABTEC GLOBAL SERVICES—See Westinghouse Air Brake Technologies Corporation; *U.S. Public*, pg. 2359
WABTEC RAIL LIMITED—See Westinghouse Air Brake Technologies Corporation; *U.S. Public*, pg. 2359
WASHINGTON TERMINAL COMPANY—See National Railroad Passenger Corporation; *U.S. Private*, pg. 2861
WHEELERSBURG TERMINAL LLC—See Norfolk Southern Corporation; *U.S. Public*, pg. 1536
WINCHESTER & WESTERN RAILROAD COMPANY—See The Broe Companies, Inc.; *U.S. Private*, pg. 4001
WISCONSIN & SOUTHERN RAILROAD COMPANY—See Kinder Morgan, Inc.; *U.S. Public*, pg. 1233

488310 — PORT AND HARBOR OPERATIONS

ABP HULL—See GIC Pte. Ltd.; *Int'l*, pg. 2964
ABP HULL—See The Goldman Sachs Group, Inc.; *U.S. Public*, pg. 2076
ADANI PORTS AND SPECIAL ECONOMIC ZONE LIMITED—See Adani Enterprises Limited; *Int'l*, pg. 125
AD PORT OF ADRIA-BAR—See Global Yatirim Holding A.S.; *Int'l*, pg. 3002
ALEXANDRIA INTERNATIONAL CONTAINER TERMINALS COMPANY S.A.E.—See CK Hutchison Holdings Limited; *Int'l*, pg. 1636
ANGELICA RIVERFRONT REDEVELOPMENT INC.—See Lange-Stegmann Co., Inc.; *U.S. Private*, pg. 2389
APAPA BULK TERMINAL LIMITED—See Flour Mills of Nigeria Plc.; *Int'l*, pg. 2709
ASIAN TERMINALS, INC.; *Int'l*, pg. 619
BINH DUONG PORT CORPORATION—See Gemadept Corporation; *Int'l*, pg. 2915
CAGLIARI CRUISE PORT SRL—See Global Yatirim Holding A.S.; *Int'l*, pg. 3002
CATANIA CRUISE TERMINAL SRL—See Global Yatirim Holding A.S.; *Int'l*, pg. 3002
CHINA CONTAINER TERMINAL CORP.; *Int'l*, pg. 1491
CHINA INFRASTRUCTURE & LOGISTICS GROUP LTD.; *Int'l*, pg. 1510
C.L.T.- COMPANHIA LOGISTICA DE TERM. MARITIMOS, LDA.—See Galp Energia SGPS, S.A.; *Int'l*, pg. 2875
CREUERS DEL PORT DE BARCELONA, S.A.—See Global Yatirim Holding A.S.; *Int'l*, pg. 3002
CSP ZEEBRUGGE TERMINAL NV—See COSCO Shipping Holdings Co., Ltd.; *Int'l*, pg. 1810
DA NANG PORT JSC; *Int'l*, pg. 1901
DC INDUSTRIAL N.V.—See Group de Cloedt SA; *Int'l*, pg. 3088
DONG NAI PORT; *Int'l*, pg. 2164

CORPORATE AFFILIATIONS

DP WORLD AMERICAS RO, INC.—See Dubai World Corporation; *Int'l*, pg. 2220
DP WORLD AUSTRALIA LIMITED—See Corsair Capital, LLC; *U.S. Private*, pg. 1059
DP WORLD LIMITED—See Dubai World Corporation; *Int'l*, pg. 2220
DP WORLD PLC—See Dubai World Corporation; *Int'l*, pg. 2220
DP WORLD PRIVATE LIMITED—See Dubai World Corporation; *Int'l*, pg. 2220
EGE LIMAN ISLETMELERI A.S.—See Global Yatirim Holding A.S.; *Int'l*, pg. 3002
ESSAR INTERNATIONAL LTD.—See Essar Global Limited; *Int'l*, pg. 2508
ESSAR PORTS LIMITED—See Essar Global Limited; *Int'l*, pg. 2508
ESSAR PORT & TERMINALS LTD.—See Essar Global Limited; *Int'l*, pg. 2508
EUROPEAN BULK SERVICES (E.B.S.) B.V.—See H.E.S. Beheer N.V.; *Int'l*, pg. 3195
FAUJI AKBAR PORTIA MARINE TERMINALS LIMITED—See Akbar Group; *Int'l*, pg. 261
FAUJI AKBAR PORTIA MARINE TERMINALS LIMITED—See Fauji Foundation; *Int'l*, pg. 2623
FIJI PORTS TERMINAL LTD.—See Aitken Spence PLC; *Int'l*, pg. 254
FORTH PORTS PLC—See Arcus Infrastructure Partners LLP; *Int'l*, pg. 552
FRS SHIP MANAGEMENT LTD.—See FRS GmbH & Co. KG; *Int'l*, pg. 2797
GATEWAY TRADE CENTER, INC.—See New Enterprise Stone & Lime Co., Inc.; *U.S. Private*, pg. 2895
GEMADEPT DUNG QUAT INTERNATIONAL PORT J.S.C.—See Gemadept Corporation; *Int'l*, pg. 2915
GEMADEPT (MALAYSIA) SDN. BHD.—See Gemadept Corporation; *Int'l*, pg. 2915
GHL GESELLSCHAFT FUR HAFEN- UND LAGEREIIMMOBILIEN-VERWALTUNG BLOCK D MBH—See Hamburger Hafen und Logistik AG; *Int'l*, pg. 3236
GLADSTONE PORTS CORPORATION LIMITED; *Int'l*, pg. 2987
GLOBAL LIMAN ISLETMELERI A.S.—See Global Yatirim Holding A.S.; *Int'l*, pg. 3002
GRUPO EMPRESAS NAVIERAS S.A.; *Int'l*, pg. 3128
GUANGZHOU PORT GROUP CO., LTD.; *Int'l*, pg. 3167
GUJARAT PIPAVAV PORT LIMITED—See A.P. Moller-Maersk A/S; *Int'l*, pg. 25
GULFTAINER COMPANY LIMITED; *Int'l*, pg. 3182
HAI MINH PORT SERVICE JOINT STOCK COMPANY—See Hai Minh Corporation; *Int'l*, pg. 3209
HARWICH INTERNATIONAL PORT LIMITED—See CK Hutchison Holdings Limited; *Int'l*, pg. 1637
HHLA PLT ITALY S.R.L.—See Hamburger Hafen und Logistik AG; *Int'l*, pg. 3236
HOEGH LNG ASIA PTE. LTD.—See Hoegh LNG Holding Ltd.; *Int'l*, pg. 3439
HOEGH LNG COLOMBIA S.A.S.—See Hoegh LNG Holding Ltd.; *Int'l*, pg. 3439
HOEGH LNG EGYPT LCC.—See Hoegh LNG Holding Ltd.; *Int'l*, pg. 3439
HUTCHISON AJMAN INTERNATIONAL TERMINALS LIMITED - F.Z.E.—See CK Hutchison Holdings Limited; *Int'l*, pg. 1637
HUTCHISON KOREA TERMINALS LIMITED—See CK Hutchison Holdings Limited; *Int'l*, pg. 1637
HUTCHISON LAEMCHABANG TERMINAL LIMITED—See CK Hutchison Holdings Limited; *Int'l*, pg. 1637
HUTCHISON PORT HOLDINGS LIMITED—See CK Hutchison Holdings Limited; *Int'l*, pg. 1637
HUTCHISON PORTS SWEDEN AB—See CK Hutchison Holdings Limited; *Int'l*, pg. 1637
INTERCRUISES SHORESIDE & PORT SERVICES INC.—See Canada Pension Plan Investment Board; *Int'l*, pg. 1279
INTERCRUISES SHORESIDE & PORT SERVICES INC.—See Cinven Limited; *Int'l*, pg. 1612
INVER PORT SERVICES PTY. LTD.—See Cargotec Corporation; *Int'l*, pg. 1328
JACINTOPORT INTERNATIONAL LLC—See Seaboard Corporation; *U.S. Public*, pg. 1850
THE JACKSONVILLE PORT AUTHORITY; *U.S. Private*, pg. 4058
KASHIMA BERTH CO., LTD.—See AGC Inc.; *Int'l*, pg. 204
KINGSTON FREEPORT TERMINAL LTD.—See CMA CGM S.A.; *Int'l*, pg. 1668
KUANTAN PORT CONSORTIUM SDN BHD—See IJM Corporation Berhad; *Int'l*, pg. 3609
LEIF HOEGH (U.K.) LIMITED—See Hoegh LNG Holding Ltd.; *Int'l*, pg. 3439
LLC KALININGRADCEMENT—See Heidelberg Materials AG; *Int'l*, pg. 3318
LLC UKRAINIAN INTERMODAL COMPANY—See Hamburger Hafen und Logistik AG; *Int'l*, pg. 3236
LONG BEACH CONTAINER TERMINAL LLC—See China COSCO Shipping Corporation Limited; *Int'l*, pg. 1495
LOOP, LLC—See Marathon Petroleum Corporation; *U.S. Public*, pg. 1364

N.A.I.C.S. INDEX

488320 — MARINE CARGO HANDLI...

MAILIAO HARBOR ADMINISTRATION CORPORATION—See Formosa Petrochemical Corporation; *Int'l*, pg. 2735

MANATEE COUNTY PORT AUTHORITY; *U.S. Private*, pg. 2561

METRANS (DANUBIA) KFT.—See Hamburger Hafen und Logistik AG; *Int'l*, pg. 3237

MOSS CONTAINER TERMINAL AS—See DFDS A/S; *Int'l*, pg. 2095

NAM DINH VU PORT JOINT STOCK COMPANY—See Gemadept Corporation; *Int'l*, pg. 2915

NAM HAI DINH VU PORT J.S.C.—See Gemadept Corporation; *Int'l*, pg. 2915

NAM HAI ICD JOINT STOCK COMPANY—See Gemadept Corporation; *Int'l*, pg. 2915

NASSAU CRUISE PORT LTD.—See Global Yatirim Holding A.S.; *Int'l*, pg. 3003

OMAN INTERNATIONAL CONTAINER TERMINAL L.L.C.—See CK Hutchison Holdings Limited; *Int'l*, pg. 1638

OY RAUMA STEVEDORING LTD.—See Brookfield Infrastructure Partners L.P.; *Int'l*, pg. 1190

PANAMA PORTS COMPANY, S.A.—See CK Hutchison Holdings Limited; *Int'l*, pg. 1638

PD PORT SERVICES LTD.—See Brookfield Infrastructure Partners L.P.; *Int'l*, pg. 1190

PHUOC LONG PORT CO., LTD.—See Gemadept Corporation; *Int'l*, pg. 2915

PORT OF FELIXSTOWE LIMITED—See CK Hutchison Holdings Limited; *Int'l*, pg. 1638

PORT OF GALVESTON; *U.S. Private*, pg. 3230

PORT OF HOUSTON AUTHORITY; *U.S. Private*, pg. 3230

PORTS AMERICA, INC.—See Canada Pension Plan Investment Board; *Int'l*, pg. 1281

PRUMO LOGISTICA S.A.—See EIG Global Energy Partners, LLC; *U.S. Private*, pg. 1347

QSL QUEBEC INC.—See Mistras Group, Inc.; *U.S. Public*, pg. 1451

RAVENNA TERMINALI PASSEGERI SRL—See Global Yatirim Holding A.S.; *Int'l*, pg. 3003

SC CONTAINER TERMINAL ODESSA—See Hamburger Hafen und Logistik AG; *Int'l*, pg. 3237

SMIT INTERNATIONALE N.V.—See HAL Trust N.V.; *Int'l*, pg. 3226

SOCIEDAD MATRIZ SAAM S.A.—See Compania Sudamericana de Vapores, S.A.; *Int'l*, pg. 1749

SOUTH CAROLINA STATE PORTS AUTHORITY; *U.S. Private*, pg. 3720

SOUTHERN TOWING COMPANY—See Henry Crown & Company; *U.S. Private*, pg. 1918

SVITZER A/S—See A.P. Moller-Maersk A/S; *Int'l*, pg. 27

SVITZER AUSTRALASIA—See A.P. Moller-Maersk A/S; *Int'l*, pg. 27

TAMPA PORT AUTHORITY INC.; *U.S. Private*, pg. 3929

TANQUISADO - TERMINAIS MARITIMOS, S.A.—See Galp Energia SGPS, S.A.; *Int'l*, pg. 2876

TERMINAL INTERNACIONAL DEL SUR S.A.—See Grupo Romero; *Int'l*, pg. 3135

TIP ZILINA, S.R.O.—See Hamburger Hafen und Logistik AG; *Int'l*, pg. 3237

TRABAJOS MARITIMOS S.A.—See Grupo Romero; *Int'l*, pg. 3135

ULSAN PORT OPERATING CO., LTD.—See CJ Corporation; *Int'l*, pg. 1634

VALLETTA CRUISE PORT PLC—See Global Yatirim Holding A.S.; *Int'l*, pg. 3003

VENEZIA TERMINAL PASSEGGERI S.P.A.—See Carnival Corporation; *U.S. Public*, pg. 438

ZADAR INTERNATIONAL PORT OPERATIONS D.O.O.—See Global Yatirim Holding A.S.; *Int'l*, pg. 3003

488320 — MARINE CARGO HANDLING

ABP AYR—See GIC Pte. Ltd.; *Int'l*, pg. 2964
ABP AYR—See The Goldman Sachs Group, Inc.; *U.S. Public*, pg. 2076
ABP BARROW—See GIC Pte. Ltd.; *Int'l*, pg. 2964
ABP BARROW—See The Goldman Sachs Group, Inc.; *U.S. Public*, pg. 2076
ABP CARDIFF—See GIC Pte. Ltd.; *Int'l*, pg. 2964
ABP CARDIFF—See The Goldman Sachs Group, Inc.; *U.S. Public*, pg. 2076
ABP FLEETWOOD—See GIC Pte. Ltd.; *Int'l*, pg. 2964
ABP FLEETWOOD—See The Goldman Sachs Group, Inc.; *U.S. Public*, pg. 2076
ABP GARSTON—See GIC Pte. Ltd.; *Int'l*, pg. 2964
ABP GARSTON—See The Goldman Sachs Group, Inc.; *U.S. Public*, pg. 2076
ABP GOOLE—See GIC Pte. Ltd.; *Int'l*, pg. 2964
ABP GOOLE—See The Goldman Sachs Group, Inc.; *U.S. Public*, pg. 2076
ABP IPSWICH—See GIC Pte. Ltd.; *Int'l*, pg. 2964
ABP IPSWICH—See The Goldman Sachs Group, Inc.; *U.S. Public*, pg. 2076
ABP PLYMOUTH—See GIC Pte. Ltd.; *Int'l*, pg. 2964
ABP PLYMOUTH—See The Goldman Sachs Group, Inc.; *U.S. Public*, pg. 2076

ACCESS WORLD AG; *Int'l*, pg. 89
ACK FORANKRA SAS—See Axel Johnson Gruppen AB; *Int'l*, pg. 763
ADDICKS & TALLY UNION GMBH & CO—See Addicks & Kreye Holding GmbH; *Int'l*, pg. 128
ADS MARITIME HOLDING PLC; *Int'l*, pg. 153
AES KALAELOA VENTURE, L.L.C.—See The AES Corporation; *U.S. Public*, pg. 2031
AG SHIP MAINTENANCE CORP.; *U.S. Private*, pg. 125
AI PORTS AND TERMINALS COMPANY LIMITED—See AI Energy Public Company Limited; *Int'l*, pg. 226
ALEXANDRIA CONTAINER & CARGO HANDLING COMPANY; *Int'l*, pg. 307
AL JABER HEAVY LIFT & TRANSPORT LLC—See AI Jaber Group; *Int'l*, pg. 279
ALLIANCE SUPPLY MANAGEMENT, LTD.—See Ship Supply of Florida, Inc.; *U.S. Private*, pg. 3637
ALL SET MARINE LASHING AB—See Cargotec Corporation; *Int'l*, pg. 1326
ALPHA ADRIATIC D.D.; *Int'l*, pg. 366
ALPS LOGISTICS (GUANG DONG) CO., LTD.—See Alps Alpine Co., Ltd.; *Int'l*, pg. 376
AMERIJET INTERNATIONAL INC.—See ZS Fund L.P.; *U.S. Private*, pg. 4609
AMPORTS ATLANTIC TERMINAL—See AGF Management Limited; *Int'l*, pg. 206
AMPORTS, INC.—See AGF Management Limited; *Int'l*, pg. 206
AMPORTS MEXICO ALTAMIRA TERMINAL—See AGF Management Limited; *Int'l*, pg. 207
APM TERMINALS - CARGO SERVICE A/S—See A.P. Moller-Maersk A/S; *Int'l*, pg. 25
ARAMBHAN GROUP; *Int'l*, pg. 535
ARCELORMITTAL SHIPPING LTD.—See ArcelorMittal S.A.; *Int'l*, pg. 545
ASIAN MARINE SERVICES PUBLIC COMPANY LIMITED; *Int'l*, pg. 618
ASSOCIATED TERMINALS LLC; *U.S. Private*, pg. 357
AZUMA SHIPPING CO., LTD.; *Int'l*, pg. 781
BALMORAL MARINE LTD.—See Balmoral Group Ltd.; *Int'l*, pg. 810
BALTICON SA; *Int'l*, pg. 812
BANGLADESH SHIPPING CO., LTD. BSC; *Int'l*, pg. 836
BEGISTICS PUBLIC COMPANY LIMITED; *Int'l*, pg. 941
BENICIA PORT TERMINAL COMPANY—See AGF Management Limited; *Int'l*, pg. 207
BIO GREEN ENERGY TECH PUBLIC COMPANY; *Int'l*, pg. 1035
BMT DE BEER BV—See BMT Group Limited; *Int'l*, pg. 1077
BOCIMAR NV—See Compagnie Maritime Belge S.A.; *Int'l*, pg. 1746
BRAEMAR SEASCOPE (DRY CARGO) PTE LIMITED—See Braemar PLC; *Int'l*, pg. 1135
BRILLIANT TOP IN LOGISTICS LIMITED—See Daido Group Ltd; *Int'l*, pg. 1920
C3 LIMITED—See BlackRock, Inc.; *U.S. Public*, pg. 345
C3 LIMITED—See Canada Pension Plan Investment Board; *Int'l*, pg. 1279
C3 LIMITED—See China Investment Corporation; *Int'l*, pg. 1513
CARGOTEC ARGENTINA S.R.L.—See Cargotec Corporation; *Int'l*, pg. 1326
CARGOTEC AUSTRALIA PTY. LTD.—See Cargotec Corporation; *Int'l*, pg. 1326
CARGOTEC BRAZIL INDUSTRIA E COMERCIO DE EQUIPAMENTOS PARA MOVIMENTACAO DE CARGAS LTDA—See Cargotec Corporation; *Int'l*, pg. 1326
CARGOTEC BRAZIL LTDA—See Cargotec Corporation; *Int'l*, pg. 1326
CARGOTEC CHILE - S.A.—See Cargotec Corporation; *Int'l*, pg. 1326
CARGOTEC CHS ASIA PACIFIC PTE LTD—See Cargotec Corporation; *Int'l*, pg. 1326
CARGOTEC CORPORATION; *Int'l*, pg. 1326
CARGOTEC CRANE & ELECTRICAL SERVICES INC.—See Cargotec Corporation; *Int'l*, pg. 1326
CARGOTEC CYPRUS LTD.—See Cargotec Corporation; *Int'l*, pg. 1326
CARGOTEC CZECH REPUBLIC S.R.O—See Cargotec Corporation; *Int'l*, pg. 1326
CARGOTEC DE MEXICO, S.A. DE C.V.—See Cargotec Corporation; *Int'l*, pg. 1327
CARGOTEC DENMARK A/S—See Cargotec Corporation; *Int'l*, pg. 1328
CARGOTEC ENGINEERING ITALY S.R.L.—See Cargotec Corporation; *Int'l*, pg. 1326
CARGOTEC FINLAND OY—See Cargotec Corporation; *Int'l*, pg. 1326
CARGOTEC GERMANY GMBH—See Cargotec Corporation; *Int'l*, pg. 1327
CARGOTEC INDIA PRIVATE LIMITED—See Cargotec Corporation; *Int'l*, pg. 1327
CARGOTEC INDUSTRIES (CHINA) CO., LTD.—See Cargotec Corporation; *Int'l*, pg. 1327
CARGOTEC ITALIA S.R.L.—See Cargotec Corporation; *Int'l*, pg. 1326
CARGOTEC KOREA LIMITED—See Cargotec Corporation; *Int'l*, pg. 1327

CARGOTEC NETHERLANDS B.V.—See Cargotec Corporation; *Int'l*, pg. 1326
CARGOTEC (SHANGHAI) TRADING COMPANY LIMITED—See Cargotec Corporation; *Int'l*, pg. 1326
CARGOTEC SOLUTIONS OY—See Cargotec Corporation; *Int'l*, pg. 1327
CARGOTEC TERMINAL SOLUTIONS (MALAYSIA) SDN BHD—See Cargotec Corporation; *Int'l*, pg. 1327
CARGOTEC UK LTD.—See Cargotec Corporation; *Int'l*, pg. 1327
CARGOTEC UKRAINE, LLC—See Cargotec Corporation; *Int'l*, pg. 1327
CARISBROOKE SHIPPING LIMITED; *Int'l*, pg. 1331
CARPAT CEMTRANS S.R.L.—See Heidelberg Materials AG; *Int'l*, pg. 3309
CASPIAN SERVICES INC.; *Int'l*, pg. 1354
CBL INTERNATIONAL LIMITED; *Int'l*, pg. 1365
CELEBI BANDIRMA ULUSLARARASI LIMANI ISLETMECILIGI A.S.—See Celebi Holding A.S.; *Int'l*, pg. 1391
CERES TERMINALS INCORPORATED—See Carrix, Inc.; *U.S. Private*, pg. 772
CERES TERMINALS INC.—See Carrix, Inc.; *U.S. Private*, pg. 773
CHIMPEX S.A.—See Ameropa AG; *Int'l*, pg. 424
CHINA MERCHANTS PORT HOLDINGS COMPANY LIMITED—See China Merchants Group Limited; *Int'l*, pg. 1521
CHINA SPECIAL ARTICLE LOGISTICS CO., LTD.—See CTS International Logistics Corporation Limited; *Int'l*, pg. 1874
CHONGQING PORT CO., LTD.; *Int'l*, pg. 1580
CHU KONG SHIPPING ENTERPRISES (GROUP) COMPANY LIMITED—See Chu Kong Shipping Enterprises (Holding) Co. Ltd.; *Int'l*, pg. 1589
CLARKSON (HELLAS) LIMITED—See Clarkson PLC; *Int'l*, pg. 1650
CLARKSON INVESTMENT SERVICES (DIFC) LIMITED—See Clarkson PLC; *Int'l*, pg. 1650
CMB JAPAN LIMITED—See Compagnie Maritime Belge S.A.; *Int'l*, pg. 1746
CMB NV—See Compagnie Maritime Belge S.A.; *Int'l*, pg. 1746
COMAN S.A.—See A.P. Moller-Maersk A/S; *Int'l*, pg. 26
COMVEX S.A.; *Int'l*, pg. 1763
CONFORCE 1 CONTAINER TERMINALS INC.—See Conforce International, Inc.; *Int'l*, pg. 1768
CONTANDA STEEL, LLC—See EQT AB; *Int'l*, pg. 2473
COOPER/T. SMITH CORPORATION; *U.S. Private*, pg. 1041
COOS BAY SHIPPING TERMINAL—See Roseburg Forest Products; *U.S. Private*, pg. 3482
COPENHAGEN MALMO PORT—See Copenhagen Malmo Port; *Int'l*, pg. 1793
CORDSTRAP (MIDDLE EAST) LTD.—See Cordstrap Netherlands B.V.; *Int'l*, pg. 1796
CORDSTRAP (THAILAND) CO., LTD.—See Cordstrap Netherlands B.V.; *Int'l*, pg. 1796
COSMO KAIUN CO., LTD.—See Cosmo Energy Holdings Co., Ltd.; *Int'l*, pg. 1812
COURAGE INVESTMENT GROUP LIMITED; *Int'l*, pg. 1819
CROSSGLOBE TRANSPORT, LTD.—See Blue Wolf Capital Partners LLC; *U.S. Private*, pg. 595
CUXPORT GMBH—See Hamburger Hafen und Logistik AG; *Int'l*, pg. 3236
DAIUN CO., LTD.; *Int'l*, pg. 1944
DAMPSKIBSSELSKABET NORDEN A/S; *Int'l*, pg. 1957
DANZAS AEI S.A. DE C.V.—See Deutsche Post AG; *Int'l*, pg. 2073
DELAWARE RIVER STEVEDORES INC.; *U.S. Private*, pg. 1195
DENSO LOGITEM CORPORATION—See Denso Corporation; *Int'l*, pg. 2029
DHL QUALITY CARGO AS—See Deutsche Post AG; *Int'l*, pg. 2077
DIALOG SERVICES, INC.—See Dialog Group Berhad; *Int'l*, pg. 2104
DONG DO MARINE JOINT STOCK COMPANY; *Int'l*, pg. 2163
EAGLE MARINE INDUSTRIES INC.; *U.S. Private*, pg. 1310
EDISON CHOUEST OFFSHORE, LLC; *U.S. Private*, pg. 1336
EIMSKIP—See Eimskipafelag Islands Hf.; *Int'l*, pg. 2332
ELIZABETH RIVER TERMINALS LLC—See Kinder Morgan, Inc.; *U.S. Public*, pg. 1233
EM SHIPPING SDN. BHD.; *Int'l*, pg. 2372
ERIK THUN AB; *Int'l*, pg. 2493
ERRIA A/S; *Int'l*, pg. 2497
ES GROUP (HOLDINGS) LIMITED; *Int'l*, pg. 2500
ESL SHIPPING LTD—See Aspo Oyj; *Int'l*, pg. 631
EUROPE CONTAINERS TERMINALS B.V.—See CK Hutchison Holdings Limited; *Int'l*, pg. 1637
EVERGREEN SHIPPING AGENCY LANKA (PVT) LTD.—See Hemas Holdings PLC; *Int'l*, pg. 3340
EXEL SPORTS NA—See Exel Composites Oyj; *Int'l*, pg. 2581
FAIRSTAR MARITIME SERVICES BV—See HAL Trust N.V.; *Int'l*, pg. 3226
FAL SHIPPING CO., LTD.—See FAL Group of Companies; *Int'l*, pg. 2610

488320 — MARINE CARGO HANDLI...   CORPORATE AFFILIATIONS

FAPS INC.; *U.S. Private*, pg. 1473
FINNLINES OYJ—See Grimaldi Group SpA; *Int'l*, pg. 3085
FOREST PRODUCTS TERMINAL CORPORATION LTD. (FORTERM)—See Blue Wolf Capital Partners LLC; *U.S. Private*, pg. 594
FRASER RIVER PILE & DREDGE (GP) INC.; *Int'l*, pg. 2765
FRASER SURREY DOCKS LP—See Dubai World Corporation; *Int'l*, pg. 2221
FRED. OLSEN MARINE SERVICES AS—See Fred. Olsen & Co.; *Int'l*, pg. 2768
FUSHIKI KAIRIKU UNSO CO.,LTD.; *Int'l*, pg. 2849
G.A.P VASSILOPOULOS PUBLIC LIMITED; *Int'l*, pg. 2865
GATI ASIA PACIFIC PTE LTD.—See Gati Ltd.; *Int'l*, pg. 2889
GENERAL MARINE COMPANY LIMITED—See Asian Marine Services Public Company Limited; *Int'l*, pg. 618
GERMANISCHER LLOYD IRELAND LTD.—See DNV GL Group AS; *Int'l*, pg. 2150
GJ LEASING COMPANY INC.—See Slay Industries Inc.; *U.S. Private*, pg. 3687
GLOBAL PORTS HOLDING PLC—See Global Yatirim Holding A.S.; *Int'l*, pg. 3002
GLOBAL PORTS INVESTMENTS PLC—See Delo Group; *Int'l*, pg. 2014
GLOBAL TERMINAL & CONTAINER SERVICES INC.—See China COSCO Shipping Corporation Limited; *Int'l*, pg. 1495
G-MARINE SERVICE CO., LTD.—See Hyundai Motor Company; *Int'l*, pg. 3558
GOLAR MANAGEMENT OSLO—See Golar LNG Limited; *Int'l*, pg. 3023
GORMAN CORY SHIPPING LIMITED—See Braemar PLC; *Int'l*, pg. 1135
GREYSTONES CARGO SYSTEMS—See Carrix, Inc.; *U.S. Private*, pg. 773
GRINDROD LIMITED - GRINDROD INTERMODAL DIVISION—See Grindrod Limited; *Int'l*, pg. 3086
GULF STREAM MARINE INC.—See Blue Wolf Capital Partners LLC; *U.S. Private*, pg. 595
HALIFAX PORT AUTHORITY; *Int'l*, pg. 3229
HANKYU INTERNATIONAL TRANSPORT (TAIWAN) LTD.—See Hankyu Hanshin Holdings Inc.; *Int'l*, pg. 3255
HAWAIIAN TUG & BARGE—See Saltchuk Resources Inc.; *U.S. Private*, pg. 3534
HEMAS MARITIME (PVT) LTD.—See Hemas Holdings PLC; *Int'l*, pg. 3340
HHLA CONTAINER-TERMINAL ALTENWERDER GMBH—See Hamburger Hafen und Logistik AG; *Int'l*, pg. 3236
HHLA CONTAINER TERMINAL BURCHARDKAI GMBH—See Hamburger Hafen und Logistik AG; *Int'l*, pg. 3236
HHLA CONTAINER TERMINAL TOLLERORT GMBH—See Hamburger Hafen und Logistik AG; *Int'l*, pg. 3236
HHLA TK ESTONIA AS—See Hamburger Hafen und Logistik AG; *Int'l*, pg. 3236
HHLA TK ESTONIA AS—See Hamburger Hafen und Logistik AG; *Int'l*, pg. 3236
HIAB AUSTRIA GMBH—See Cargotec Corporation; *Int'l*, pg. 1327
HIAB GMBH—See Cargotec Corporation; *Int'l*, pg. 1326
HIGHLINE SHIPPING SDN. BHD.—See Hubline Berhad; *Int'l*, pg. 3520
HOKUTO KOGYO CO.,LTD.—See Cosmo Energy Holdings Co., Ltd.; *Int'l*, pg. 1812
HONG KONG CHAOSHANG GROUP LIMITED; *Int'l*, pg. 3465
HORNBECK OFFSHORE OPERATORS, LLC—See Hornbeck Offshore Services, Inc.; *U.S. Private*, pg. 1983
HORNBECK OFFSHORE SERVICES, LLC—See Hornbeck Offshore Services, Inc.; *U.S. Private*, pg. 1983
HTG STEVEDORING OY—See AS Infortar; *Int'l*, pg. 590
HUB SHIPPING SDN. BHD.—See Hubline Berhad; *Int'l*, pg. 3520
IINO GAS TRANSPORT CO., LTD.—See Iino Kaiun Kaisha Ltd.; *Int'l*, pg. 3608
IMPERIAL SHIPPING ROTTERDAM B.V.—See Dubai World Corporation; *Int'l*, pg. 2221
INDUSTRIAL TERMINALS, L.P.—See Intermarine, Inc.; *U.S. Private*, pg. 2112
JACK GRAY TRANSPORT, INC.; *U.S. Private*, pg. 2174
JACKSON KEARNEY GROUP; *U.S. Private*, pg. 2177
JBG CORPORATION; *U.S. Private*, pg. 2193
KALMAR AUSTRIA GMBH—See Cargotec Corporation; *Int'l*, pg. 1328
KALMAR ITALIA S.R.L.—See Cargotec Corporation; *Int'l*, pg. 1328
KALMAR LTD.—See Cargotec Corporation; *Int'l*, pg. 1327
KALMAR MIDDLE EAST DMCC—See Cargotec Corporation; *Int'l*, pg. 1328
KALMAR NORWAY AS—See Cargotec Corporation; *Int'l*, pg. 1327
KALMAR SPAIN CARGO HANDLING SOLUTIONS S.A.—See Cargotec Corporation; *Int'l*, pg. 1328
KINKI TRANSPORT & TERMINAL CO., LTD.—See Azuma Shipping Co., Ltd.; *Int'l*, pg. 782
LAKEHEAD SHIPPING COMPANY LIMITED—See Blue Wolf Capital Partners LLC; *U.S. Private*, pg. 594
LAKES & RIVERS TRANSFER DIV.—See Jack Gray Transport, Inc.; *U.S. Private*, pg. 2174
LA LUZ, S.A.—See Grupo Boluda; *Int'l*, pg. 3123
LEVIN ENTERPRISES INC.; *U.S. Private*, pg. 2435
LIGHTERING LLC—See International Seaways, Inc.; *U.S. Public*, pg. 1158
LIHAI INTERNATIONAL SHIPPING CO., LTD.—See COFCO Limited; *Int'l*, pg. 1692
LOGISTEC CORPORATION—See Blue Wolf Capital Partners LLC; *U.S. Private*, pg. 594
LOGISTEC MARINE AGENCIES INC.—See Blue Wolf Capital Partners LLC; *U.S. Private*, pg. 594
LOGISTEC STEVEDORING (ATLANTIC) INC.—See Blue Wolf Capital Partners LLC; *U.S. Private*, pg. 594
LOGISTEC STEVEDORING INC. - CHURCHILL—See Blue Wolf Capital Partners LLC; *U.S. Private*, pg. 595
LOGISTEC STEVEDORING INC. - CONTRECOEUR—See Blue Wolf Capital Partners LLC; *U.S. Private*, pg. 595
LOGISTEC STEVEDORING INC. - MONTREAL, LAURIER TERMINAL—See Blue Wolf Capital Partners LLC; *U.S. Private*, pg. 595
LOGISTEC STEVEDORING INC. - QUEBEC—See Blue Wolf Capital Partners LLC; *U.S. Private*, pg. 595
LOGISTEC STEVEDORING INC. - SEPT-ILES—See Blue Wolf Capital Partners LLC; *U.S. Private*, pg. 595
LOGISTEC STEVEDORING INC.—See Blue Wolf Capital Partners LLC; *U.S. Private*, pg. 594
LOGISTEC STEVEDORING INC. - TROIS-RIVIERES—See Blue Wolf Capital Partners LLC; *U.S. Private*, pg. 595
LOGISTEC STEVEDORING (NEW BRUNSWICK) INC.—See Blue Wolf Capital Partners LLC; *U.S. Private*, pg. 594
LOGISTEC STEVEDORING (NOVA SCOTIA) INC.—See Blue Wolf Capital Partners LLC; *U.S. Private*, pg. 595
LOGISTEC STEVEDORING (NOVA SCOTIA) INC. - SYDNEY—See Blue Wolf Capital Partners LLC; *U.S. Private*, pg. 595
LOGISTEC STEVEDORING (ONTARIO) INC.—See Blue Wolf Capital Partners LLC; *U.S. Private*, pg. 595
LOGISTEC USA INC. - PORT MANATEE—See Blue Wolf Capital Partners LLC; *U.S. Private*, pg. 595
LOGISTEC USA INC.—See Blue Wolf Capital Partners LLC; *U.S. Private*, pg. 595
LONHAM GROUP LIMITED—See The Hanover Insurance Group, Inc.; *U.S. Public*, pg. 2087
LUIS A. AYALA COLON SUCRS. INC.; *U.S. Private*, pg. 2512
LYTTELTON PORT COMPANY LIMITED—See Christchurch City Holdings Ltd.; *Int'l*, pg. 1586
MACGREGOR (ARE) LLC—See Cargotec Corporation; *Int'l*, pg. 1328
MACGREGOR (AUS) PTY. LTD.—See Cargotec Corporation; *Int'l*, pg. 1328
MACGREGOR BLRT BALTIC OU—See BLRT Grupp AS; *Int'l*, pg. 1066
MACGREGOR BLRT BALTIC OU—See Cargotec Corporation; *Int'l*, pg. 1328
MACGREGOR CONVER GMBH—See Cargotec Corporation; *Int'l*, pg. 1328
MACGREGOR CROATIA D.O.O.—See Cargotec Corporation; *Int'l*, pg. 1328
MACGREGOR FRANCE S.A.S—See Cargotec Corporation; *Int'l*, pg. 1329
MACGREGOR (GBR) LTD.—See Cargotec Corporation; *Int'l*, pg. 1328
MACGREGOR GERMANY GMBH—See Cargotec Corporation; *Int'l*, pg. 1328
MACGREGOR GREECE LTD—See Cargotec Corporation; *Int'l*, pg. 1328
MACGREGOR (HONG KONG) LTD.—See Cargotec Corporation; *Int'l*, pg. 1328
MACGREGOR JAPAN LTD.—See Cargotec Corporation; *Int'l*, pg. 1329
MACGREGOR (NOR) A/S—See Cargotec Corporation; *Int'l*, pg. 1328
MACGREGOR OY—See Cargotec Corporation; *Int'l*, pg. 1329
MACGREGOR PLIMSOLL OFFSHORE SERVICES PTE LTD—See Cargotec Corporation; *Int'l*, pg. 1329
MACGREGOR PLIMSOLL SDN BHD—See Cargotec Corporation; *Int'l*, pg. 1329
MACGREGOR (SGP) PTE. LTD.—See Cargotec Corporation; *Int'l*, pg. 1328
MACGREGOR (UKR) A.O.—See Cargotec Corporation; *Int'l*, pg. 1328
MANZANILLO INTERNATIONAL TERMINAL, PANAMA S.A.—See Carrix, Inc.; *U.S. Private*, pg. 773
MARIETTA INDUSTRIAL ENTERPRISES; *U.S. Private*, pg. 2574
MARSH MARINE & ENERGY AB—See Marsh & McLennan Companies, Inc.; *U.S. Public*, pg. 1383
MARUTA TRANSPORT CO., LTD.—See Daido Steel Co., Ltd.; *Int'l*, pg. 1923
MCCABE HAMILTON & RENNY COMPANY LTD.—See JBG Corporation; *U.S. Private*, pg. 2193
MID-SHIP GROUP LLC—See Kinder Morgan, Inc.; *U.S. Public*, pg. 1233
MINMETAL S.R.L.—See Archer-Daniels-Midland Company; *U.S. Public*, pg. 185
MS HAMMONIA ROMA SCHIFFAHRTS GMBH & CO. KG—See HCI Hammonia Shipping AG; *Int'l*, pg. 3297
MULTI-LINK TERMINALS LTD OY—See Delo Group; *Int'l*, pg. 2014
NASSAU TERMINALS LLC—See Worldwide Terminals Fernandina, LLC; *U.S. Private*, pg. 4570
NAVIERA DEL MERCOSUR S.A.—See Grupo Boluda; *Int'l*, pg. 3123
NESSKIP HF.—See Caiano AS; *Int'l*, pg. 1252
NORDIC BULK CARRIERS A/S—See Pangaea Logistics Solutions Ltd.; *U.S. Public*, pg. 1635
NORTH STAR TERMINAL & STEVEDORE COMPANY, LLC; *U.S. Private*, pg. 2948
NSA SCHIFFFAHRT UND TRANSPORT GMBH—See Caiano AS; *Int'l*, pg. 1252
OCEANIC TANKERS AGENCY LTD.—See Valero Energy Corporation; *U.S. Public*, pg. 2272
OCEANSHIP OWNERS LIMITED—See DryShips Inc.; *Int'l*, pg. 2207
OCEANVENTURE OWNERS LIMITED—See DryShips Inc.; *Int'l*, pg. 2207
O'CONNOR CONTAINER TRANSPORT LIMITED—See DBAY Advisors Limited; *Int'l*, pg. 1986
OFFSHORE SERVICE VESSELS, LLC.; *U.S. Private*, pg. 3003
OJSC PETROLESPORT—See Delo Group; *Int'l*, pg. 2014
OKAYAMA KOYU CO., LTD.—See Dowa Holdings Co., Ltd.; *Int'l*, pg. 2183
OMEGA SHIPYARD, INC.—See Cooke, Inc.; *Int'l*, pg. 1788
OPERADORA PORTUARIA DEL GOLFO, S.A. DE C.V.—See Grupos TMM, S.A.B.; *Int'l*, pg. 3137
ORIENT OVERSEAS CONTAINER LINE LIMITED—See China COSCO Shipping Corporation Limited; *Int'l*, pg. 1495
PACORINI VLISSINGEN B.V.—See B. Pacorini S.p.A.; *Int'l*, pg. 789
PASHA STEVEDORING & TERMINALS L.P.—See The Pasha Group; *U.S. Private*, pg. 4091
PEEPLES INDUSTRIES INC.; *U.S. Private*, pg. 3128
PENTALVER TRANSPORT LIMITED—See Brookfield Infrastructure Partners L.P.; *Int'l*, pg. 1192
PENTALVER TRANSPORT LIMITED—See GIC Pte. Ltd.; *Int'l*, pg. 2966
P&O FERRYMASTERS LIMITED—See Dubai World Corporation; *Int'l*, pg. 2220
PORTLINE-TRANSPORTES MARITIMOS INTERNACIONAIS SA—See Compagnie Maritime Belge S.A.; *Int'l*, pg. 1746
PORT OF EVERETT; *U.S. Private*, pg. 3230
PORT OF MIAMI TERMINAL OPERATING COMPANY, LC; *U.S. Private*, pg. 3230
PREMUDA S.P.A.—See KKR & Co. Inc.; *U.S. Public*, pg. 1263
PRODUCT TRANSPORT (S) PTE. LTD.—See B+H Ocean Carriers Ltd.; *Int'l*, pg. 784
PT MACGREGOR PLIMSOLL INDONESIA—See Cargotec Corporation; *Int'l*, pg. 1329
RAMSEY GREIG & CO. LTD.—See Blue Wolf Capital Partners LLC; *U.S. Private*, pg. 595
SAKURA INTERNATIONAL KK—See Compagnie Maritime Belge S.A.; *Int'l*, pg. 1746
SC CONTAINER TERMINAL ODESSA—See Hamburger Hafen und Logistik AG; *Int'l*, pg. 3237
SEACOR MARINE (ASIA) PTE. LTD.—See AIP, LLC; *U.S. Private*, pg. 136
SEACOR MARINE (INTERNATIONAL) LTD.—See AIP, LLC; *U.S. Private*, pg. 136
SEACOR OFFSHORE DUBAI (L.L.C.)—See AIP, LLC; *U.S. Private*, pg. 136
SEA FREIGHT AGENCIES & STEVEDORING LIMITED—See Goddard Enterprises Limited; *Int'l*, pg. 3019
SERVICIOS CORPORATIVOS PORTUARIOS S.A. DE C.V.—See Albert Ballin KG; *Int'l*, pg. 296
SIA CORDSTRAP BALTIC—See Cordstrap Netherlands B.V.; *Int'l*, pg. 1797
SIGNET MARITIME CORP.; *U.S. Private*, pg. 3650
SIWERTELL AB—See Cargotec Corporation; *Int'l*, pg. 1329
SOCIEDAD PORTUARIA GOLFO DE MORROSQUILLO S.A.—See Grupo Argos S.A.; *Int'l*, pg. 3121
SOCIEDAD PORTUARIA PUERTO BAHIA S.A.—See Frontera Energy Corporation; *U.S. Private*, pg. 2794
SOKHNA PORT DEVELOPMENT COMPANY—See Carrix, Inc.; *U.S. Private*, pg. 773
SOREL MARITIME AGENCIES INC.—See Blue Wolf Capital Partners LLC; *U.S. Private*, pg. 595
SOUTHERN CROSS STEVEDORING—See Carrix, Inc.; *U.S. Private*, pg. 773
SOUTH JERSEY PORT CORPORATION; *U.S. Private*, pg. 3723
SSA BANGLADESH LTD.—See Carrix, Inc.; *U.S. Private*, pg. 773
SSA MARINE, INC.—See Carrix, Inc.; *U.S. Private*, pg. 773
SSA MEXICO S.A. DE C.V.—See Carrix, Inc.; *U.S. Private*, pg. 773
STI-SAN ANTONIO TERMINAL INTERNACIONAL—See Carrix, Inc.; *U.S. Private*, pg. 773
SUMMIT TERMINAL, LLC—See HALLADOR ENERGY

COMPANY; *U.S. Public*, pg. 980
SVTI-SAN VICENTE TERMINAL INTERNACIONAL—See Carrix, Inc.; *U.S. Private*, pg. 773
TALLINK SILJA AB—See AS Infortar; *Int'l*, pg. 590
TALLY-UNION GMBH & CO. KG—See Addicks & Kreye Holding GmbH; *Int'l*, pg. 128
TERAS CARGO TRANSPORT (AMERICA) LLC—See Ezion Holdings Limited; *Int'l*, pg. 2594
TERMINAL DE CONTENEDORES DE ALGECIRAS, S.A.—See Acciona, S.A.; *Int'l*, pg. 90
TERMINAL DE CONTENEDORES DE TENERIFE, S.A—See Grupo Villar Mir, S.A.U.; *Int'l*, pg. 3139
TERMINAL PUERTO ARICA S.A.—See Empresa Constructora Belfi SA; *Int'l*, pg. 2388
TERMONT MONTREAL INC.—See Blue Wolf Capital Partners LLC; *U.S. Private*, pg. 595
TEXTAINER GROUP HOLDINGS LIMITED—See Stonepeak Partners L.P.; *U.S. Private*, pg. 3829
TEXTAINER MARINE CONTAINERS LTD.—See BNP Paribas SA; *Int'l*, pg. 1093
TONIC PHARMA SDN. BHD.—See 7-Eleven Malaysia Holdings Berhad; *Int'l*, pg. 14
TRANSPORT NANUK INC.—See Blue Wolf Capital Partners LLC; *U.S. Private*, pg. 595
TRICO MARINE ASSETS, INC.—See Trico Marine Services, Inc.; *U.S. Private*, pg. 4229
TRICO MARINE INTERNATIONAL, INC.—See Trico Marine Services, Inc.; *U.S. Private*, pg. 4229
TRICO MARINE OPERATORS, INC.—See Trico Marine Services, Inc.; *U.S. Private*, pg. 4229
TRICO MARINE SERVICES, INC.; *U.S. Private*, pg. 4229
TRI PAK, INC.—See Saybrook Corporate Opportunity Fund LP; *U.S. Private*, pg. 3558
TTS MARINE AS—See Cargotec Corporation; *Int'l*, pg. 1329
TTS VIETNAM—See Cargotec Corporation; *Int'l*, pg. 1329
UNIKAI HAFENBETRIEB GMBH—See Hamburger Hafen und Logistik AG; *Int'l*, pg. 3237
UNITED STATES MARITIME ALLIANCE, LTD.; *U.S. Private*, pg. 4299
U.S. SHIPPING CORP.—See AIP, LLC; *U.S. Private*, pg. 137
VIRGINIA INTERNATIONAL TERMINALS INC.; *U.S. Private*, pg. 4387
VOSTOCHNAYA STEVEDORING COMPANY—See Delo Group; *Int'l*, pg. 2014
WILSON AGENCY B.V.—See Caiano AS; *Int'l*, pg. 1252
WILSON AGENCY NORGE AS—See Caiano AS; *Int'l*, pg. 1252
WILSON CREWING AGENCY LTD.—See Caiano AS; *Int'l*, pg. 1252
WILSON CREWING AGENCY ODESSA LTD.—See Caiano AS; *Int'l*, pg. 1252
WILSON EUROCARRIERS AS—See Caiano AS; *Int'l*, pg. 1252
WILSON MANAGEMENT AS—See Caiano AS; *Int'l*, pg. 1252
WILSON MURMANSK LTD.—See Caiano AS; *Int'l*, pg. 1252
WILSON NRL TRANSPORT GMBH—See Caiano AS; *Int'l*, pg. 1252
WILSON SHIP MANAGEMENT AS—See Caiano AS; *Int'l*, pg. 1252
YANTIAN INTERNATIONAL CONTAINER TERMINALS LIMITED—See Hutchison Port Holdings Trust; *Int'l*, pg. 3540
ZEN CARGO MOVERS PVT. LTD.—See Gati Ltd.; *Int'l*, pg. 2889

488330 — NAVIGATIONAL SERVICES TO SHIPPING

ALAM MARITIM RESOURCES BERHAD; *Int'l*, pg. 289
ALSTONS SHIPPING LIMITED—See ANSA McAL Limited; *Int'l*, pg. 477
AL WASL MARINE LLC—See Tidewater Inc.; *U.S. Public*, pg. 2158
ANTA NETHERLANDS B.V.—See ANTA Sports Products Limited; *Int'l*, pg. 479
A.P. MOLLER SINGAPORE PTE. LTD.—See A.P. Moller-Maersk A/S; *Int'l*, pg. 25
ARABIAN CHEMICAL CARRIERS LTD. CO.—See Albert Ballin KG; *Int'l*, pg. 296
ARVIND & COMPANY SHIPPING AGENCIES LIMITED; *Int'l*, pg. 587
AVINOR FLYSIKRING AS—See Avinor AS; *Int'l*, pg. 744
AZUMA SHIPPING CO., LTD. - CHUBU BUSINESS DIVISION—See Azuma Shipping Co., Ltd.; *Int'l*, pg. 781
AZUMA SHIPPING CO., LTD. - KANTO BUSINESS DIVISION—See Azuma Shipping Co., Ltd.; *Int'l*, pg. 781
AZUMA SHIPPING CO., LTD. - KANTO BUSINESS DIVISION—See Azuma Shipping Co., Ltd.; *Int'l*, pg. 781
AZUMA SHIPPING CO., LTD. - KEIHIN BUSINESS DIVISION—See Azuma Shipping Co., Ltd.; *Int'l*, pg. 587
AZUMA SHIPPING CO., LTD. - KEIHIN BUSINESS DIVISION—See Azuma Shipping Co., Ltd.; *Int'l*, pg. 781
AZUMA SHIPPING CO., LTD. - KYUSHU BUSINESS DIVISION—See Azuma Shipping Co., Ltd.; *Int'l*, pg. 781
AZUMA SHIPPING CO., LTD. - MARITIME TRANSPORTATION DIVISION—See Azuma Shipping Co., Ltd.; *Int'l*, pg. 782
AZUMA SHIPPING MONGOLIA LLC—See Azuma Shipping Co., Ltd.; *Int'l*, pg. 782
BERGESEN D.Y. PHILIPPINES, INC.—See BW Group Ltd.; *Int'l*, pg. 1231
BERNHARD SCHULTE SHIPMANAGEMENT (CHINA) COMPANY LIMITED—See Bernhard Schulte Shipmanagement (Cyprus) Ltd.; *Int'l*, pg. 988
BERNHARD SCHULTE SHIPMANAGEMENT (CYPRUS) LTD.; *Int'l*, pg. 988
BERNHARD SCHULTE SHIPMANAGEMENT (DEUTSCHLAND) GMBH & CO. KG—See Bernhard Schulte Shipmanagement (Cyprus) Ltd.; *Int'l*, pg. 988
BERNHARD SCHULTE SHIPMANAGEMENT (HELLAS) SPLLC.—See Bernhard Schulte Shipmanagement (Cyprus) Ltd.; *Int'l*, pg. 988
BERNHARD SCHULTE SHIPMANAGEMENT (HONG KONG) LTD.—See Bernhard Schulte Shipmanagement (Cyprus) Ltd.; *Int'l*, pg. 988
BERNHARD SCHULTE SHIPMANAGEMENT (INDIA) PVT. LIMITED—See Bernhard Schulte Shipmanagement (Cyprus) Ltd.; *Int'l*, pg. 988
BERNHARD SCHULTE SHIPMANAGEMENT (ISLE OF MAN) LTD.—See Bernhard Schulte Shipmanagement (Cyprus) Ltd.; *Int'l*, pg. 988
BERNHARD SCHULTE SHIPMANAGEMENT (UK) LTD.—See Bernhard Schulte Shipmanagement (Cyprus) Ltd.; *Int'l*, pg. 989
BJORGUN EHF—See Heidelberg Materials AG; *Int'l*, pg. 3309
BLUE DANUBE INCORPORATED; *U.S. Private*, pg. 588
BRAEMAR SEASCOPE PTY LIMITED—See Braemar PLC; *Int'l*, pg. 1135
BSM CREW SERVICE CENTRE (ESTONIA) LTD.—See Bernhard Schulte Shipmanagement (Cyprus) Ltd.; *Int'l*, pg. 988
BW GAS ASA—See BW Group Ltd.; *Int'l*, pg. 1231
CESKY LODNI A PRUMYSLOVY REGISTR, S.R.O.—See DNV GL Group AS; *Int'l*, pg. 2149
CHEMRING AUSTRALIA PTY LTD—See Chemring Group PLC; *Int'l*, pg. 1463
CHINESE MARITIME TRANSPORT (S) PTE. LTD.—See Chinese Maritime Transport Ltd.; *Int'l*, pg. 1569
CIVITANAVI SYSTEMS UK LTD.—See Civitanavi Systems SpA; *Int'l*, pg. 1630
CJ GLS (S) SHIPPING PTE. LTD.—See CJ Corporation; *Int'l*, pg. 1633
CLARKSON PORT SERVICES LIMITED—See Clarkson PLC; *Int'l*, pg. 1651
CLARKSON SOUTH AFRICA (PTY) LIMITED—See Clarkson PLC; *Int'l*, pg. 1651
COMPAGNIE NATIONALE DU RHONE—See ENGIE SA; *Int'l*, pg. 2428
CONCEPT SYSTEMS LTD.—See ION Geophysical Corporation; *U.S. Public*, pg. 1166
CORY BROTHERS—See Braemar PLC; *Int'l*, pg. 1135
CSAV INVERSIONES NAVIERAS S.A.—See Compania Sudamericana de Vapores, S.A.; *Int'l*, pg. 1749
DAMEN VEROLME ROTTERDAM B.V.—See Damen Shipyards Group; *Int'l*, pg. 1956
DANAOS GERMANY—See Danaos Corporation; *Int'l*, pg. 1958
DANAOS NORDIC A.S.—See Danaos Corporation; *Int'l*, pg. 1958
DANAOS SEAROUTES LTD.—See Danaos Corporation; *Int'l*, pg. 1958
DANAOS SOFTWARE SERVICES PTE LTD.—See Danaos Corporation; *Int'l*, pg. 1958
DANAOS SYSTEMS (CYPRUS) LTD.—See Danaos Corporation; *Int'l*, pg. 1958
DBB JACK-UP SERVICES A/S—See BWB Partners P/S; *Int'l*, pg. 1232
DNV GL BUSINESS ASSURANCE DENMARK A/S—See DNV GL Group AS; *Int'l*, pg. 2149
DNV GL CYPRUS LTD.—See DNV GL Group AS; *Int'l*, pg. 2149
DNV GL - LITHUANIA—See DNV GL Group AS; *Int'l*, pg. 2149
DNV GL SE - HAMBURG—See DNV GL Group AS; *Int'l*, pg. 2149
DOF GROUP ASA; *Int'l*, pg. 2154
EIDESVIK OFFSHORE ASA; *Int'l*, pg. 2329
EURONAV HONG KONG LTD—See Euronav NV; *Int'l*, pg. 2554
EVERGREEN SHIPPING AGENCY (ITALY) S.P.A.—See Evergreen Marine Corporation (Taiwan) Ltd.; *Int'l*, pg. 2566
EVERGREEN SHIPPING AGENCY (SINGAPORE) PTE. LTD.—See Evergreen Marine Corporation (Taiwan) Ltd.; *Int'l*, pg. 2566
FAIRPLAY SCHLEPPDAMPFSCHIFFS-REEDEREI RICHARD BORCHARD GMBH; *Int'l*, pg. 2609
FLINDERS PORTS PTY LTD; *Int'l*, pg. 2706
FUGRO MARINE SERVICES B.V.—See Fugro N.V.; *Int'l*, pg. 2807
FUGRO SEASTAR AS—See Fugro N.V.; *Int'l*, pg. 2807
GENCHEM HOLDINGS LIMITED—See Clarkson PLC; *Int'l*, pg. 1651
GERMANISCHER LLOYD ARGENTINA S.A.—See DNV GL Group AS; *Int'l*, pg. 2149
GERMANISCHER LLOYD (AUSTRALIA) PTY. LTD.—See DNV GL Group AS; *Int'l*, pg. 2149
GERMANISCHER LLOYD AUSTRIA GMBH—See DNV GL Group AS; *Int'l*, pg. 2149
GERMANISCHER LLOYD BANGLADESH LTD.—See DNV GL Group AS; *Int'l*, pg. 2149
GERMANISCHER LLOYD BELGIUM N.V.—See DNV GL Group AS; *Int'l*, pg. 2149
GERMANISCHER LLOYD BULGARIA LTD.—See DNV GL Group AS; *Int'l*, pg. 2149
GERMANISCHER LLOYD CANADA LTD.—See DNV GL Group AS; *Int'l*, pg. 2149
GERMANISCHER LLOYD CERTIFICATION GMBH—See DNV GL Group AS; *Int'l*, pg. 2149
GERMANISCHER LLOYD CERTIFICATION SERVICES, S.L.—See DNV GL Group AS; *Int'l*, pg. 2149
GERMANISCHER LLOYD (CHILE) LTDA.—See DNV GL Group AS; *Int'l*, pg. 2149
GERMANISCHER LLOYD COLOMBIA LTDA.—See DNV GL Group AS; *Int'l*, pg. 2149
GERMANISCHER LLOYD COLOMBO PVT. LTD.—See DNV GL Group AS; *Int'l*, pg. 2149
GERMANISCHER LLOYD DE PANAMA, LTD.—See DNV GL Group AS; *Int'l*, pg. 2150
GERMANISCHER LLOYD DO BRASIL LTDA.—See DNV GL Group AS; *Int'l*, pg. 2150
GERMANISCHER LLOYD ENGINEERING SERVICES EAST ASIA (ESEA)—See DNV GL Group AS; *Int'l*, pg. 2149
GERMANISCHER LLOYD ESPANA, S.L.—See DNV GL Group AS; *Int'l*, pg. 2149
GERMANISCHER LLOYD ESTONIA OU—See DNV GL Group AS; *Int'l*, pg. 2149
GERMANISCHER LLOYD FINLAND OY—See DNV GL Group AS; *Int'l*, pg. 2149
GERMANISCHER LLOYD FRANCE SARL—See DNV GL Group AS; *Int'l*, pg. 2149
GERMANISCHER LLOYD GLM SDN. BHD.—See DNV GL Group AS; *Int'l*, pg. 2149
GERMANISCHER LLOYD-HAVANA—See DNV GL Group AS; *Int'l*, pg. 2150
GERMANISCHER LLOYD HELLAS SURVEY E.P.E.—See DNV GL Group AS; *Int'l*, pg. 2149
GERMANISCHER LLOYD HONG KONG LTD.—See DNV GL Group AS; *Int'l*, pg. 2149
GERMANISCHER LLOYD HUNGARY KFT.—See DNV GL Group AS; *Int'l*, pg. 2149
GERMANISCHER LLOYD ICELAND LTD.—See DNV GL Group AS; *Int'l*, pg. 2149
GERMANISCHER LLOYD INDUSTRIAL SERVICES CO.,LTD.—See DNV GL Group AS; *Int'l*, pg. 2149
GERMANISCHER LLOYD INDUSTRIAL SERVICES DO BRASIL LTDA.—See DNV GL Group AS; *Int'l*, pg. 2150
GERMANISCHER LLOYD INDUSTRIAL SERVICES ITALIA S.R.L.—See DNV GL Group AS; *Int'l*, pg. 2150
GERMANISCHER LLOYD INDUSTRIE SERVICES RUSSLAND (LCC)—See DNV GL Group AS; *Int'l*, pg. 2150
GERMANISCHER LLOYD ISRAEL LTD.—See DNV GL Group AS; *Int'l*, pg. 2150
GERMANISCHER LLOYD (KAOHSIUNG) TAIWAN PTE LTD.—See DNV GL Group AS; *Int'l*, pg. 2149
GERMANISCHER LLOYD (KOREA) PTY LTD.—See DNV GL Group AS; *Int'l*, pg. 2149
GERMANISCHER LLOYD - LEBANON S.A.R.L.—See DNV GL Group AS; *Int'l*, pg. 2149
GERMANISCHER LLOYD (MALAYSIA) SDN. BHD.—See DNV GL Group AS; *Int'l*, pg. 2149
GERMANISCHER LLOYD MALTA LTD.—See DNV GL Group AS; *Int'l*, pg. 2150
GERMANISCHER LLOYD MOROCCO S.A.R.L.—See DNV GL Group AS; *Int'l*, pg. 2150
GERMANISCHER LLOYD NETHERLANDS B.V.—See DNV GL Group AS; *Int'l*, pg. 2150
GERMANISCHER LLOYD NEW ZEALAND LTD.—See DNV GL Group AS; *Int'l*, pg. 2150
GERMANISCHER LLOYD NORGE AS—See DNV GL Group AS; *Int'l*, pg. 2150
GERMANISCHER LLOYD OFFSHORE & INDUSTRIAL SERVICES KOREA LTD. CO.—See DNV GL Group AS; *Int'l*, pg. 2150
GERMANISCHER LLOYD PERU S.A.C.—See DNV GL Group AS; *Int'l*, pg. 2150
GERMANISCHER LLOYD PHILIPPINES, INC.—See DNV GL Group AS; *Int'l*, pg. 2150
GERMANISCHER LLOYD POLEN SP. Z O.O.—See DNV GL Group AS; *Int'l*, pg. 2150
GERMANISCHER LLOYD PORTUGAL INSPECCAO DE NAVIOS, LDA.—See DNV GL Group AS; *Int'l*, pg. 2150
GERMANISCHER LLOYD PRUFLABOR GMBH—See DNV GL Group AS; *Int'l*, pg. 2150
GERMANISCHER LLOYD ROMANIA S.R.L.—See DNV GL Group AS; *Int'l*, pg. 2150
GERMANISCHER LLOYD SANKT PETERSBURG GMBH—See DNV GL Group AS; *Int'l*, pg. 2150
GERMANISCHER LLOYD SHANGHAI CO.,LTD.—See DNV GL Group AS; *Int'l*, pg. 2150

488330 — NAVIGATIONAL SERVIC...

GERMANISCHER LLOYD SINGAPORE PTE. LTD.—See DNV GL Group AS; *Int'l*, pg. 2150
GERMANISCHER LLOYD SLOVENIJA D.O.O.—See DNV GL Group AS; *Int'l*, pg. 2150
GERMANISCHER LLOYD SOUTH AFRICA (PTY) LTD.—See DNV GL Group AS; *Int'l*, pg. 2150
GERMANISCHER LLOYD SPLIT D.O.O.—See DNV GL Group AS; *Int'l*, pg. 2150
GERMANISCHER LLOYD TEKNIK HIZMETLER LTD. STI.—See DNV GL Group AS; *Int'l*, pg. 2150
GERMANISCHER LLOYD (THAILAND) CO., LTD.—See DNV GL Group AS; *Int'l*, pg. 2149
GERMANISCHER LLOYD UKRAINE—See DNV GL Group AS; *Int'l*, pg. 2150
GERMANISCHER LLOYD UNIVERSAL INDUSTRIAL SERVICES LTD.—See DNV GL Group AS; *Int'l*, pg. 2150
GERMANISCHER LLOYD (USA), INC.—See DNV GL Group AS; *Int'l*, pg. 2149
GL GARRAD HASSAN DEUTSCHLAND GMBH—See DNV GL Group AS; *Int'l*, pg. 2149
GL LUXEMBOURG GMBH—See DNV GL Group AS; *Int'l*, pg. 2149
GL STATION NINGBO CO.,LTD.—See DNV GL Group AS; *Int'l*, pg. 2149
GWC MARINE SERVICES W.L.L.—See Gulf Warehousing Company QSC; *Int'l*, pg. 3182
HARBOUR-LINK LINES (PK) SDN. BHD.—See Harbour-Link Group Berhad; *Int'l*, pg. 3272
H CLARKSON & COMPANY LIMITED—See Clarkson PLC; *Int'l*, pg. 1651
HEBEI SERCEL-JUNFENG GEOPHYSICAL PROSPECTING EQUIPMENT CO., LTD.—See CGG; *Int'l*, pg. 1432
HERM. DAUELSBERG GMBH & CO. KG; *Int'l*, pg. 3362
HIGMAN MARINE INC.; *U.S. Private*, pg. 1943
HORIZON SHIPPING LIMITED—See GraceKennedy Limited; *Int'l*, pg. 3049
HOUSTON PILOTS; *U.S. Private*, pg. 1993
ICAP SHIPPING (GERMANY) GMBH—See CME Group, Inc.; *U.S. Public*, pg. 517
ICAP SHIPPING (GIBRALTAR) LIMITED—See CME Group, Inc.; *U.S. Public*, pg. 517
ICAP SHIPPING (HONG KONG) LIMITED—See CME Group, Inc.; *U.S. Public*, pg. 517
ICAP SHIPPING INTERNATIONAL LIMITED—See CME Group, Inc.; *U.S. Public*, pg. 517
ICAP SHIPPING SINGAPORE PTE LIMITED—See CME Group, Inc.; *U.S. Public*, pg. 517
ICAP SHIPPING USA INC—See CME Group, Inc.; *U.S. Public*, pg. 517
IMBV B.V.—See IHI Corporation; *Int'l*, pg. 3605
INTERNATIONAL ASSOCIATED CARGO CARRIER S.A.E.—See Abu Dhabi Developmental Holding Company PJSC; *Int'l*, pg. 71
L-3 MARITIME SYSTEMS—See L3Harris Technologies, Inc.; *U.S. Public*, pg. 1283
LLOYD GERMANICO DE MEXICO, S. DE R.L. DE C.V.—See DNV GL Group AS; *Int'l*, pg. 2150
LLOYD GERMAN IRAN KISH, LTD.—See DNV GL Group AS; *Int'l*, pg. 2150
MAERSK LINE PERU S.A.C.—See A.P. Moller-Maersk A/S; *Int'l*, pg. 27
MAERSK SUPPLY SERVICE CANADA LTD.—See A.P. Moller-Maersk A/S; *Int'l*, pg. 27
MAERSK VIETNAM LTD.—See A.P. Moller-Maersk A/S; *Int'l*, pg. 27
MARINE TOWING OF TAMPA, LLC; *U.S. Private*, pg. 2575
MORAN TOWING AND TRANSPORTATION, LLC—See Moran Towing Corporation; *U.S. Private*, pg. 2781
MORAN TOWING OF PENNSYLVANIA—See Moran Towing Corporation; *U.S. Private*, pg. 2782
MORAN TOWING OF VIRGINIA INC.—See Moran Towing Corporation; *U.S. Private*, pg. 2782
PARKER MARITIME AS—See Parker Hannifin Corporation; *U.S. Public*, pg. 1649
PREMUDA (MONACO) SAM—See KKR & Co. Inc.; *U.S. Public*, pg. 1263
PROVINCIAL AEROSPACE LTD.—See Exchange Income Corporation; *Int'l*, pg. 2579
P.T. EVERGREEN SHIPPING AGENCY INDONESIA—See Evergreen Marine Corporation (Taiwan) Ltd.; *Int'l*, pg. 2566
P.T. GERMANISCHER LLOYD NUSANTARA—See DNV GL Group AS; *Int'l*, pg. 2150
P.T. GL- INDONESIA - STATION BATAM—See DNV GL Group AS; *Int'l*, pg. 2150
PUGET SOUND PILOTS; *U.S. Private*, pg. 3302
SAG ARCADIA, LP—See National Storage Affiliates Trust; *U.S. Public*, pg. 1498
SAMALAJU INDUSTRIAL PORT SDN. BHD.—See Bintulu Port Holdings Berhad; *Int'l*, pg. 1035
SEABOARD DE COLOMBIA, S.A.—See Seaboard Corporation; *U.S. Public*, pg. 1851
SEABOARD DE NICARAGUA, S.A.—See Seaboard Corporation; *U.S. Public*, pg. 1851
SEABOARD MARINE OF FLORIDA, INC.—See Seaboard Corporation; *U.S. Public*, pg. 1851
SEABOARD OVERSEAS TRADING AND SHIPPING (PTY) LTD.—See Seaboard Corporation; *U.S. Public*, pg. 1851
SEABULK TOWING—See AIP, LLC; *U.S. Private*, pg. 137
SEA TOW SERVICES INTERNATIONAL INC.; *U.S. Private*, pg. 3582
SHIPPING, TRADING & LIGHTERAGE CO. LLC—See Chugoku Marine Paints, Ltd.; *Int'l*, pg. 1595
SKELTON TRUCK LINES, INC.—See Andlauer Healthcare Group, Inc.; *Int'l*, pg. 451
SONATIDE MARINE, LTD—See Tidewater Inc.; *U.S. Public*, pg. 2158
SUDAMERICANA, AGENCIAS AEREAS Y MARITIMAS S.A.—See Compania Sudamericana de Vapores, S.A.; *Int'l*, pg. 1749
TAIWAN TERMINAL SERVICE CORPORATION LTD.—See Evergreen Marine Corporation (Taiwan) Ltd.; *Int'l*, pg. 2567
TIDEWATER SUPPORT SERVICES LIMITED—See Tidewater Inc.; *U.S. Public*, pg. 2158
WINDTEST IBERICA S.L.—See DNV GL Group AS; *Int'l*, pg. 2150
WORLDWIDE EXPRESS OPERATIONS, LLC—See Ridgemont Partners Management LLC; *U.S. Private*, pg. 3433

488390 — OTHER SUPPORT ACTIVITIES FOR WATER TRANSPORTATION

3. MAJ BRODOGRADILISTE D.D.; *Int'l*, pg. 6
ADVANCED MARINE PRESERVATION, LLC—See Stellex Capital Management LP; *U.S. Private*, pg. 3800
ALGOMA CENTRAL CORPORATION; *Int'l*, pg. 318
ALIANCA NAVEGACAO E LOGISTICA LTDA.—See A.P. Moller-Maersk A/S; *Int'l*, pg. 26
AL SHIPS GMBH—See Commerzbank AG; *Int'l*, pg. 1718
AMATHUS MARITIME LTD.—See Amathus Public Limited; *Int'l*, pg. 413
AMERICAN PETROLEUM TANKERS PARTNERS LP; *U.S. Private*, pg. 243
AMOS EUROPE (UK) LIMITED—See AMOS Group Limited; *Int'l*, pg. 430
APM TERMINALS - AARHUS A/S—See A.P. Moller-Maersk A/S; *Int'l*, pg. 25
APM TERMINALS APAPA LTD.—See A.P. Moller-Maersk A/S; *Int'l*, pg. 25
APM TERMINALS BAHRAIN B.S.C.—See A.P. Moller-Maersk A/S; *Int'l*, pg. 25
APM TERMINALS CALLAO S.A.—See A.P. Moller-Maersk A/S; *Int'l*, pg. 25
APM TERMINALS GOTHENBURG AB—See A.P. Moller-Maersk A/S; *Int'l*, pg. 25
APM TERMINALS INDIA PVT. LTD.—See A.P. Moller-Maersk A/S; *Int'l*, pg. 25
APM TERMINALS LAZARO CARDENAS S.A. DE C.V.—See A.P. Moller-Maersk A/S; *Int'l*, pg. 25
APM TERMINALS MAASVLAKTE II B.V.—See A.P. Moller-Maersk A/S; *Int'l*, pg. 25
APM TERMINALS MOBILE, LLC—See A.P. Moller-Maersk A/S; *Int'l*, pg. 25
APM TERMINALS TANGIER SA—See A.P. Moller-Maersk A/S; *Int'l*, pg. 25
ARAMO SHIPPING (SINGAPORE) PTE LTD—See Fuji Oil Company, Ltd.; *Int'l*, pg. 2815
ARMADA MARINE CONTRACTORS CASPIAN PTE. LTD.—See Bumi Armada Berhad; *Int'l*, pg. 1215
A-SONIC LOGISTICS (UK) LTD.—See A-Sonic Aerospace Limited; *Int'l*, pg. 21
BAGGERWERKEN DECLOEDT EN ZOON N.V.—See Ackermans & van Haaren NV; *Int'l*, pg. 105
BERGEN GROUP HANOYTANGEN AS—See Endur ASA; *Int'l*, pg. 2409
BIBBY MARINE LIMITED—See Bibby Line Group Limited; *Int'l*, pg. 1018
B & J MARINE PTE. LTD.—See Beng Kuang Marine Limited; *Int'l*, pg. 973
BOCIMAR BELGIUM NV—See Compagnie Maritime Belge S.A.; *Int'l*, pg. 1745
BOCIMAR HONG KONG LIMITED—See Compagnie Maritime Belge S.A.; *Int'l*, pg. 1746
BROSTROM TANKERS AB—See A.P. Moller-Maersk A/S; *Int'l*, pg. 26
BUMI ARMADA CASPIAN LLC—See Bumi Armada Berhad; *Int'l*, pg. 1215
BUMI ARMADA NAVIGATION LABUAN LIMITED—See Bumi Armada Berhad; *Int'l*, pg. 1215
BUMI ARMADA NAVIGATION SDN. BHD.—See Bumi Armada Berhad; *Int'l*, pg. 1215
BUMI ARMADA (SINGAPORE) PTE. LTD.—See Bumi Armada Berhad; *Int'l*, pg. 1215
BUMI ARMADA UK LIMITED—See Bumi Armada Berhad; *Int'l*, pg. 1215
BWT AKTIENGESELLSCHAFT; *Int'l*, pg. 1232
BWT BELGIUM N.V.—See BWT Aktiengesellschaft; *Int'l*, pg. 1232
CADELER A/S; *Int'l*, pg. 1247
CALS LOGISTICS, INC.—See A-Sonic Aerospace Limited; *Int'l*, pg. 21
CENTRAL GLOBAL CARGO GMBH; *Int'l*, pg. 1407
CIMPRESS - TRANSPORTES MARITIMOS, S.A.—See Camargo Correa S.A.; *Int'l*, pg. 1267

CORPORATE AFFILIATIONS

CLARKSON OVERSEAS SHIPBROKING LIMITED—See Clarkson PLC; *Int'l*, pg. 1650
CLARKSON PARIS SAS—See Clarkson PLC; *Int'l*, pg. 1651
CLARKSON RESEARCH SERVICES LIMITED—See Clarkson PLC; *Int'l*, pg. 1651
CLARKSONS PLATOU AS—See Clarkson PLC; *Int'l*, pg. 1650
CMA SHIPS LANKA (PVT) LTD.—See Hayleys PLC; *Int'l*, pg. 3291
CMB SERVICES SA—See Compagnie Maritime Belge S.A.; *Int'l*, pg. 1746
CONTAINERSHIPS-CMA CGM GMBH—See CMA CGM S.A.; *Int'l*, pg. 1668
CP MARINE, INC.—See Gold Belt Incorporated; *U.S. Private*, pg. 1727
CRAWFORD & COMPANY INTERNATIONAL PTE LTD—See Crawford & Company; *U.S. Public*, pg. 592
CTC SERVICES (MALAYSIA) SDN BHD—See Lovell Minnick Partners LLC; *U.S. Private*, pg. 2502
C.U. TRANSPORT INC.; *U.S. Private*, pg. 709
DESTINI SHIPBUILDING & ENGINEERING SDN. BHD.—See Destini Berhad; *Int'l*, pg. 2046
DLS LAND UND SEE SPEDITIONSGESELLSCHAFT MBH; *Int'l*, pg. 2141
DNV GL SE—See DNV GL Group AS; *Int'l*, pg. 2148
DREW AMEROID (SINGAPORE) PTE. LTD.—See Court Square Capital Partners, L.P.; *U.S. Private*, pg. 1068
DREW MARINE GERMANY GMBH—See Court Square Capital Partners, L.P.; *U.S. Private*, pg. 1068
DREW MARINE INTERNATIONAL B.V.—See Court Square Capital Partners, L.P.; *U.S. Private*, pg. 1069
DREW MARINE JAPAN G.K.—See Court Square Capital Partners, L.P.; *U.S. Private*, pg. 1069
DYNAGAS LNG PARTNERS LP; *Int'l*, pg. 2239
DYN MARINE SERVICES OF VIRGINIA LLC—See Cerberus Capital Management, L.P.; *U.S. Private*, pg. 838
EASTWIND MARITIME SA INC.; *U.S. Private*, pg. 1322
EIDESVIK AS—See Eidesvik Holding A/S; *Int'l*, pg. 2329
EKK EAGLE ASIA PACIFIC PTE. LTD.—See Eagle Industry Co., Ltd.; *Int'l*, pg. 2265
ELCOME INTERNATIONAL LLC—See Daeyang Electric Co., Ltd.; *Int'l*, pg. 1911
ENDUR MARITIME AS—See Endur ASA; *Int'l*, pg. 2410
ESSAR OILFIELDS SERVICES LIMITED—See Essar Shipping Limited; *Int'l*, pg. 2509
ESVAGT A/S—See 3i Group plc; *Int'l*, pg. 8
ESVAGT A/S—See AMP Limited; *Int'l*, pg. 432
EXMAR HONG KONG LTD.—See Exmar N.V.; *Int'l*, pg. 2585
EXMAR OFFSHORE SERVICES SA—See Exmar N.V.; *Int'l*, pg. 2585
EXMAR SHIPPING USA INC.—See Exmar N.V.; *Int'l*, pg. 2585
EXMAR SINGAPORE PTE. LTD.—See Exmar N.V.; *Int'l*, pg. 2585
EXMAR (UK) SHIPPING COMPANY LTD.—See Exmar N.V.; *Int'l*, pg. 2585
EXPLORATION VESSEL RESOURCES AS—See CGG; *Int'l*, pg. 1431
FINNLINES DANMARK A/S—See Grimaldi Group SpA; *Int'l*, pg. 3085
FRANSHIP OFFSHORE LUX SA—See Exmar N.V.; *Int'l*, pg. 2585
FUMA-TECH GMBH—See BWT Aktiengesellschaft; *Int'l*, pg. 1233
GLOBAL OFFSHORE SERVICES B.V.—See Global Offshore Services Ltd.; *Int'l*, pg. 2999
GODO MARINE INDUSTRY CO., LTD.—See Iino Kaiun Kaisha Ltd.; *Int'l*, pg. 3607
GULF NAVIGATION POLIMAR MARITIME LLC—See Gulf Navigation Holding PJSC; *Int'l*, pg. 3181
HAMBURG SUDAMERIKANISCHE DAMPFSCHIFFFAHRTS-GESELLSCHAFT A/S & CO KG—See A.P. Moller-Maersk A/S; *Int'l*, pg. 26
HARBOR STAR SHIPPING SERVICES INC.; *Int'l*, pg. 3271
HAYLEYS ADVANTIS LTD—See Hayleys PLC; *Int'l*, pg. 3292
HENDRICKS RIVER LOGISTICS, LLC—See Hendricks Holding Company, Inc.; *U.S. Private*, pg. 1915
HGIM HOLDINGS, LLC—See The Jordan Company, L.P.; *U.S. Private*, pg. 4061
HONDA LOGISTICS INC.—See Honda Motor Co., Ltd.; *Int'l*, pg. 3461
HORIZON SURVEY COMPANY (FZE)—See HAL Trust N.V.; *Int'l*, pg. 3226
ICAP SHIPPING LIMITED—See CME Group, Inc.; *U.S. Public*, pg. 517
IINO SHIPPING ASIA PTE. LTD.—See Iino Kaiun Kaisha Ltd.; *Int'l*, pg. 3608
INTERNATIONAL MARINE & INDUSTRIAL APPLICATORS, LLC—See Stellex Capital Management LP; *U.S. Private*, pg. 3800
I.T.N. CONSOLIDATORS—See ZS Fund L.P.; *U.S. Private*, pg. 4609
JONRIE INTERTECH LLC—See Markey Machine LLC; *U.S. Private*, pg. 2581
LANCE SHIPPING S.A.—See Dynagas LNG Partners LP; *Int'l*, pg. 2239

N.A.I.C.S. INDEX

488490 — OTHER SUPPORT ACTIV...

MACGREGOR GROUP AB—See Cargotec Corporation; *Int'l*, pg. 1328
MAERSK LINE, LIMITED—See A.P. Moller-Maersk A/S; *Int'l*, pg. 27
MAIN INDUSTRIES, INC.—See Stellex Capital Management LP; *U.S. Private*, pg. 3800
MARKEY MACHINE LLC; *U.S. Private*, pg. 2581
MCDONOUGH MARINE SERVICE, INC.—See McDonough Corporation; *U.S. Private*, pg. 2632
MCKEIL MARINE LIMITED—See Astatine Investment Partners LLC; *U.S. Private*, pg. 360
MICLYN EXPRESS OFFSHORE LIMITED—See CHAMP Private Equity Pty. Ltd.; *Int'l*, pg. 1439
MORAN TOWING OF CHARLESTON—See Moran Towing Corporation; *U.S. Private*, pg. 2781
MORAN TOWING OF MARYLAND—See Moran Towing Corporation; *U.S. Private*, pg. 2781
MORAN TOWING OF MIAMI—See Moran Towing Corporation; *U.S. Private*, pg. 2781
MORAN TOWING OF NEW HAMPSHIRE—See Moran Towing Corporation; *U.S. Private*, pg. 2781
MPW INDUSTRIAL WATER SERVICES, INC.—See MPW Industrial Services Group, Inc.; *U.S. Private*, pg. 2804
MTM ENGINEERING PTE. LTD.—See Beng Kuang Marine Limited; *Int'l*, pg. 973
NEW YORK STATE CANAL CORPORATION—See New York State Thruway Authority; *U.S. Private*, pg. 2912
PAYETTE SHIPS INC.—See Payette Associates Inc.; *U.S. Private*, pg. 3117
PENN MARITIME INC.—See Kirby Corporation; *U.S. Public*, pg. 1236
PICCO ENTERPRISE PTE. LTD.—See Beng Kuang Marine Limited; *Int'l*, pg. 973
POINT MARINE, L.L.C.—See Tidewater Inc.; *U.S. Public*, pg. 2158
PRODUCED WATER ABSORBENTS, INC.—See AQUANEX, Servicio Domiciliario del Agua de EXTREMADURA SA; *Int'l*, pg. 527
PROGECO—See CMA CGM S.A.; *Int'l*, pg. 1668
PURONICS, INC.—See Franklin Electric Co., Inc.; *U.S. Public*, pg. 879
REDERI AB NORDO-LINK—See Grimaldi Group SpA; *Int'l*, pg. 3085
RMC WATER & ENVIRONMENT—See Woodard & Curran Inc.; *U.S. Private*, pg. 4557
SAYBOLT (SINGAPORE) PTE LTD.—See China Leon Inspection Holding Limited; *Int'l*, pg. 1514
SEAFARER EXPLORATION CORP.; *U.S. Public*, pg. 1851
SEATEC UK LTD.—See Ackermans & van Haaren NV; *Int'l*, pg. 106
SMITH MARITIME LLC—See Kirby Corporation; *U.S. Public*, pg. 1236
SMIT INTERNATIONAL (AMERICAS) INC.—See HAL Trust N.V.; *Int'l*, pg. 3227
SNC-LAVALIN DOMINICANA S.A.—See AtkinsRealis Group Inc.; *Int'l*, pg. 672
THAIDEN MARITIME CO., LTD.—See BIO GREEN ENERGY TECH HOLDING PLC COMPANY; *Int'l*, pg. 1035
TIDEWATER MARINE AS—See Tidewater Inc.; *U.S. Public*, pg. 2158
TIDEWATER MARINE, L.L.C.—See Tidewater Inc.; *U.S. Public*, pg. 2158
TITAN MARITIME, LLC—See Crowley Maritime Corporation; *U.S. Private*, pg. 1110
T T BARGE SERVICES MILE 237, LLC; *U.S. Private*, pg. 3909
UBI LOGISTICS (CHINA) LIMITED—See A-Sonic Aerospace Limited; *Int'l*, pg. 21
UNITED ARAB SHIPPING AGENCIES CO. (SAUDIA) LTD.—See Albert Ballin KG; *Int'l*, pg. 296
UNITED ARAB SHIPPING AGENCIES CO. (SAUDIA) LTD.—See Albert Ballin KG; *Int'l*, pg. 296
UNITED ARAB SHIPPING AGENCIES CO. (SAUDIA) LTD.—See Albert Ballin KG; *Int'l*, pg. 296
UNITED ARAB SHIPPING COMPANY (S.A.G.)—See Albert Ballin KG; *Int'l*, pg. 296
UNITED ARAB SHIPPING COMPANY—See Albert Ballin KG; *Int'l*, pg. 297
UNITED ARAB SHIPPING COMPANY—See Albert Ballin KG; *Int'l*, pg. 297
UNITED ARAB SHIPPING COMPANY—See Albert Ballin KG; *Int'l*, pg. 297
UNITED ARAB SHIPPING COMPANY—See Albert Ballin KG; *Int'l*, pg. 297
UNITED ARAB SHIPPING COMPANY—See Albert Ballin KG; *Int'l*, pg. 297
UNITED ARAB SHIPPING COMPANY—See Albert Ballin KG; *Int'l*, pg. 297
UNITED ARAB SHIPPING COMPANY—See Albert Ballin KG; *Int'l*, pg. 297
V.SHIPS GROUP LTD.—See Ackermans & van Haaren NV; *Int'l*, pg. 106
V.SHIPS LEISURE LTD.—See Ackermans & van Haaren NV; *Int'l*, pg. 106
V.SHIPS LEISURE (USA) LLC—See Ackermans & van Haaren NV; *Int'l*, pg. 106
V.SHIPS UK LTD.—See Ackermans & van Haaren NV; *Int'l*, pg. 106
WEST AFRICA CONTAINER TERMINAL NIGERIA LTD.—See A.P. Moller-Maersk A/S; *Int'l*, pg. 28

488410 — MOTOR VEHICLE TOWING

ASAP TOWING & STORAGE COMPANY; *U.S. Private*, pg. 345
BONIFACE ENGINEERING, LTD.—See Miller Industries, Inc.; *U.S. Public*, pg. 1446
BUCKHORN SERVICES, INC.—See Myers Industries, Inc.; *U.S. Public*, pg. 1488
CENTURION AUTO LOGISTICS; *U.S. Private*, pg. 831
DUTCH VALLEY AUTO WORKS; *U.S. Private*, pg. 1294
G&M TOWING & RECOVERY, LLC—See Total Recovery Group, LLC; *U.S. Private*, pg. 4191
HENRY'S WRECKER SERVICE FAIRFAX COUNTY; *U.S. Private*, pg. 1919
JUNK MY CAR, LLC; *U.S. Private*, pg. 2244
KANSAS CITY AUTO AUCTION INC.—See Cox Enterprises, Inc.; *U.S. Private*, pg. 1076
KITSAP PUBLIC SERVICES, INC.—See Kitsap Towing; *U.S. Private*, pg. 2316
KITSAP TOWING; *U.S. Private*, pg. 2316
MARIETTA WRECKER SERVICE LLC; *U.S. Private*, pg. 2574
MASTERNAUT B.V.—See Corpay, Inc.; *U.S. Public*, pg. 580
MASTERNAUT IBERICA SL—See Corpay, Inc.; *U.S. Public*, pg. 580
NEW IMAGE TOWING & RECOVERY, LLC—See Marietta Wrecker Service LLC; *U.S. Private*, pg. 2574
RFE HOLDING (CANADA) CORP.—See Fox Factory Holding Corp.; *U.S. Public*, pg. 877
TOTAL RECOVERY GROUP, LLC; *U.S. Private*, pg. 4191
UNITED ROAD TOWING, INC.—See Guggenheim Partners, LLC; *U.S. Private*, pg. 1812

488490 — OTHER SUPPORT ACTIVITIES FOR ROAD TRANSPORTATION

ABC TRANSPORT PLC; *Int'l*, pg. 57
ADAMPOL CZECH REPUBLIC CORPORATION—See Hyundai Glovis Co., Ltd.; *Int'l*, pg. 3556
ADAMPOL S.A. CORPORATION—See Hyundai Glovis Co., Ltd.; *Int'l*, pg. 3556
ADAMPOL SLOVAKIA CORPORATION—See Hyundai Glovis Co., Ltd.; *Int'l*, pg. 3556
AL AHLIAH TRANSPORT COMPANY; *Int'l*, pg. 275
ALLSTATE MOTOR CLUB, INC.—See The Allstate Corporation; *U.S. Public*, pg. 2032
AMERICAN ROADS, LLC—See DIF Management Holding B.V.; *Int'l*, pg. 2117
AMEY INFRASTRUCTURE SERVICES LTD.—See Ferrovial S.A.; *Int'l*, pg. 2644
ANCRA INTERNATIONAL LLC—See The Heico Companies, L.L.C.; *U.S. Private*, pg. 4050
ARCTIC SNOW & ICE CONTROL INC.; *U.S. Private*, pg. 316
ARRIVA HUNGARY ZRT.—See I Squared Capital Advisors (US) LLC; *U.S. Private*, pg. 2024
ARRIVA MICHALOVCE, A.S.—See I Squared Capital Advisors (US) LLC; *U.S. Private*, pg. 2024
ARRIVA MIDDLE EAST FZE—See I Squared Capital Advisors (US) LLC; *U.S. Private*, pg. 2024
ARRIVA MIDLANDS NORTH LIMITED—See I Squared Capital Advisors (US) LLC; *U.S. Private*, pg. 2024
ARRIVA OSTGOTAPENDELN AB—See I Squared Capital Advisors (US) LLC; *U.S. Private*, pg. 2025
ARRIVA SERVICE S.R.O.—See I Squared Capital Advisors (US) LLC; *U.S. Private*, pg. 2025
ARRIVA TOG A/S—See I Squared Capital Advisors (US) LLC; *U.S. Private*, pg. 2025
ARRIVA TRANSPORT SOLUTIONS LIMITED—See I Squared Capital Advisors (US) LLC; *U.S. Private*, pg. 2025
ASHOKA REFINERIES LIMITED; *Int'l*, pg. 608
ATLANTIC CONTAINER SERVICE INC.; *U.S. Private*, pg. 372
AUDECA, S.L.U.—See Elecnor, S.A.; *Int'l*, pg. 2347
AUTOCARES MALLORCA, S.L.—See Deutsche Bahn AG; *Int'l*, pg. 2049
AUTOMOTIVE MEDIA, LLC—See Penske Automotive Group, Inc.; *U.S. Public*, pg. 1664
BAGHDAD OF IRAQ COMPANY FOR PUBLIC TRANSPORT & REAL ESTATE INVESTMENTS—See Baghdad Soft Drinks Co.; *Int'l*, pg. 799
BERGAMO TRASPORTI EST S.C.A.R.L.—See Deutsche Bahn AG; *Int'l*, pg. 2049
BFLABS CO.,LTD.; *Int'l*, pg. 1006
BMC TRANSPORTATION CO.—See Behlen Mfg. Co.; *U.S. Private*, pg. 515
BOTNIATAG AB—See Deutsche Bahn AG; *Int'l*, pg. 2049
BRING TRANSPORT INDUSTRIES PTY LTD—See CTI Logistics Limited; *Int'l*, pg. 1871
BUCHER MUNICIPAL GMBH—See Bucher Industries AG; *Int'l*, pg. 1207
BUCHER MUNICIPAL LLC—See Bucher Industries AG; *Int'l*, pg. 1207
BUTLER BROS, INC.; *U.S. Private*, pg. 697
CEDAR FAIR, L.P.—See Six Flags Entertainment Corporation; *U.S. Public*, pg. 1890

CEMEX PAVING SOLUTIONS LIMITED—See CEMEX, S.A.B. de C.V.; *Int'l*, pg. 1399
CENTRAL OREGON TRUCK COMPANY, INC.—See Daseke, Inc.; *U.S. Private*, pg. 1161
CENTRAL VALLEY SWEEPING, INC.—See Warburg Pincus LLC; *U.S. Private*, pg. 4440
CENTROTRANS-EUROLINES D.D.; *Int'l*, pg. 1415
CENTROTRANS TRANSPORT ROBE D.D. SARAJEVO; *Int'l*, pg. 1415
CHARTERED LOGISTICS LTD.; *Int'l*, pg. 1454
CIA MARITIMA CHILENA SA; *Int'l*, pg. 1602
CINTRA INFRAESTRUCTURAS, S.A.U.—See Ferrovial S.A.; *Int'l*, pg. 2644
CITY PARK D.D.; *Int'l*, pg. 1627
CONGLOBAL INDUSTRIES INC.—See AMP Limited; *Int'l*, pg. 432
CONNECTEAST PTY. LIMITED—See CP2 Group Limited; *Int'l*, pg. 1823
CONSOLIDATED TRANSPORT INDUSTRIES PTY LTD—See CTI Logistics Limited; *Int'l*, pg. 1871
CONTIPARK PARKGARAGENGESELLSCHAFT MBH—See Ageas SA/NV; *Int'l*, pg. 204
CRUZ ENERGY SERVICES LLC—See Cook Inlet Region, Inc.; *U.S. Private*, pg. 1038
CTI BUSINESS INVESTMENT COMPANY PTY LTD—See CTI Logistics Limited; *Int'l*, pg. 1871
CTI TRANSPORT SYSTEMS PTY LTD—See CTI Logistics Limited; *Int'l*, pg. 1871
CTS NATIONAL CORPORATION—See The Sherwin-Williams Company; *U.S. Public*, pg. 2127
DARTCO, INC.—See Dart Transit Company; *U.S. Private*, pg. 1160
DCH DUSSELDORFER CONTAINER-HAFEN GMBH—See Deutsche Bahn AG; *Int'l*, pg. 2051
DEKRA AUTOMOBIL GMBH—See DEKRA e.V.; *Int'l*, pg. 2008
DEKRA SE—See DEKRA e.V.; *Int'l*, pg. 2007
DELAWARE RIVER & BAY AUTHORITY; *U.S. Private*, pg. 1195
DELAWARE RIVER JOINT TOLL BRIDGE COMMISSION; *U.S. Private*, pg. 1195
DETROIT INTERNATIONAL BRIDGE CO. INC.—See Centra, Inc.; *U.S. Private*, pg. 818
DIGITAL TRAFFIC SYSTEMS, INC.—See Sterling Partners; *U.S. Private*, pg. 3806
EFENDOS GLOBAL, INC.; *U.S. Private*, pg. 1343
EKB CONTAINER LOGISTIK GMBH & CO. KG—See CTS Spedition GmbH; *Int'l*, pg. 1874
ENVIROTECH SERVICES INC.—See Monomoy Capital Partners LLC; *U.S. Private*, pg. 2772
EROAD LIMITED; *Int'l*, pg. 2496
EUROTUNNELPLUS LIMITED—See Getlink SE; *Int'l*, pg. 2953
FOREST TRAFFIC SERVICES LIMITED—See Forest Support Services Plc; *Int'l*, pg. 2732
GATI LTD.; *Int'l*, pg. 2889
G CAPITAL BERHAD; *Int'l*, pg. 2861
GIPS D.D.; *Int'l*, pg. 2979
GOLDEN ARROW BUS SERVICES (PROPRIETARY) LIMITED—See Hosken Consolidated Investments Limited; *Int'l*, pg. 3485
GOLDEN GATE BRIDGE HIGHWAY & TRANSPORTATION DISTRICT; *U.S. Private*, pg. 1730
GRINDROD TERMINALS (PTY) LTD - BAY STEVEDORES DIVISION—See Grindrod Limited; *Int'l*, pg. 3086
GRINDROD TERMINALS (PTY) LTD—See Grindrod Limited; *Int'l*, pg. 3086
GROUPE GUILBAULT LTEE; *Int'l*, pg. 3103
GUANGDONG PROVINCIAL EXPRESSWAY DEVELOPMENT CO., LTD.; *Int'l*, pg. 3159
GUANGXI WUZHOU COMMUNICATIONS CO., LTD.; *Int'l*, pg. 3164
HAINAN EXPRESSWAY CO., LTD.; *Int'l*, pg. 3212
HANKYU BUS CO., LTD.—See Hankyu Hanshin Holdings Inc.; *Int'l*, pg. 3255
HENAN ZHONGYUAN EXPRESSWAY COMPANY LIMITED; *Int'l*, pg. 3344
HIAB BENELUX B.V.—See Cargotec Corporation; *Int'l*, pg. 1327
HIROSHIMA ELECTRIC RAILWAY CO.,LTD.; *Int'l*, pg. 3405
HOLLYBERRY PROPS 12 (PROPRIETARY) LIMITED—See Hosken Consolidated Investments Limited; *Int'l*, pg. 3485
HOYER DANMARK A/S—See Hoyer GmbH; *Int'l*, pg. 3498
HOYER FINLAND OY—See Hoyer GmbH; *Int'l*, pg. 3498
HOYER FRANCE S.A.—See Hoyer GmbH; *Int'l*, pg. 3499
HOYER GASLOG GMBH—See Hoyer GmbH; *Int'l*, pg. 3499
HOYER GLOBAL SINGAPORE PTE LTD.—See Hoyer GmbH; *Int'l*, pg. 3499
HOYER IRELAND LTD.—See Hoyer GmbH; *Int'l*, pg. 3499
HUNAN INVESTMENT GROUP CO., LTD.; *Int'l*, pg. 3532
HUNT TRANSPORTATION, INC.—See Crete Carrier Corp.; *U.S. Private*, pg. 1099
INGAL CIVIL PRODUCTS PTY LTD.—See Valmont Industries, Inc.; *U.S. Public*, pg. 2273
INTERPARKING FRANCE SA—See Ageas SA/NV; *Int'l*, pg. 204
INTERVIAL CHILE SA—See Ecopetrol S.A.; *Int'l*, pg. 2299

488490 — OTHER SUPPORT ACTIV...

IRAQI LAND TRANSPORT CO.—See Baghdad Soft Drinks Co.; *Int'l*, pg. 799
ISE FLEET SERVICES, LLC—See Trimble, Inc.; *U.S. Public*, pg. 2190
J. HVIDTVED LARSEN A/S—See Bucher Industries AG; *Int'l*, pg. 1209
KANSAS TURNPIKE AUTHORITY; *U.S. Private*, pg. 2261
KANTO AIR CARGO CO., LTD.—See Azuma Shipping Co., Ltd.; *Int'l*, pg. 782
KENCO LOGISTIC SERVICES INC.—See Kenco Group Inc.; *U.S. Private*, pg. 2283
KIINTEISTO OY TIR-TRANS—See Deutsche Bahn AG; *Int'l*, pg. 2052
K+M FAHRLEITUNGSTECHNIK GMBH—See Alpiq Holding AG; *Int'l*, pg. 372
KOZARAPUTEVI D.O.O. BANJA LUKA—See Grupa Fortis d.o.o. Banja Luka; *Int'l*, pg. 3116
LECCO TRASPORTI S.C.A.R.L.—See Deutsche Bahn AG; *Int'l*, pg. 2052
MAINE TURNPIKE AUTHORITY; *U.S. Private*, pg. 2552
MAPUTO CAR TERMINAL LIMITADA—See Grindrod Limited; *Int'l*, pg. 3086
MAQUIASFALT SL—See Bucher Industries AG; *Int'l*, pg. 1209
MDL DISTRIBUCION Y LOGISTICA S.A.—See Deutsche Bahn AG; *Int'l*, pg. 2051
MEGAHUB LEHRTE BETREIBERGESELLSCHAFT MBH—See Deutsche Bahn AG; *Int'l*, pg. 2052
MID SEVEN TRANSPORTATION CO.—See Daseke, Inc.; *U.S. Private*, pg. 1161
MOBOTREX, INC.—See Warren Equity Partners, LLC; *U.S. Private*, pg. 4443
MOTOR CAR AUTO CARRIERS, INC.; *U.S. Private*, pg. 2796
MUBARRAD HOLDING COMPANY (K.S.C)—See A'ayan Leasing and Investment Company KSCC; *Int'l*, pg. 19
MUNDYS S.P.A—See Edizione S.r.l.; *Int'l*, pg. 2312
NEWELL BRIDGE & RAILWAY COMPANY—See The Homer Laughlin China Company; *U.S. Private*, pg. 4054
NEW HONG KONG TUNNEL COMPANY LIMITED—See CITIC Group Corporation; *Int'l*, pg. 1621
NEW JERSEY TURNPIKE AUTHORITY INC.; *U.S. Private*, pg. 2898
NEW YORK STATE BRIDGE AUTHORITY; *U.S. Private*, pg. 2912
NEW YORK STATE THRUWAY AUTHORITY; *U.S. Private*, pg. 2912
NORVIAL S.A.—See Aenza S.A.A.; *Int'l*, pg. 176
NPA DE MEXICO S DE RL DE CV—See Jabil Inc.; *U.S. Public*, pg. 1181
NVO NAHVERKEHR OSTWESTFALEN GMBH—See Deutsche Bahn AG; *Int'l*, pg. 2052
OKLAHOMA TRANSPORTATION AUTHORITY; *U.S. Private*, pg. 3007
OSCEOLA COUNTY EXPRESSWAY AUTHORITY; *U.S. Private*, pg. 3047
PENGANGKUTAN COGENT SDN. BHD.—See Ancom Logistics Berhad; *Int'l*, pg. 449
PENTALVER CANNOCK LIMITED—See Brookfield Infrastructure Partners L.P.; *Int'l*, pg. 1192
PENTALVER CANNOCK LIMITED—See GIC Pte. Ltd.; *Int'l*, pg. 2966
PET FOOD EXPERTS INC.; *U.S. Private*, pg. 3156
PLESO PRIJEVOZ D.O.O.—See Croatia Airlines d.d.; *Int'l*, pg. 1851
PROLOG SERVICES; *U.S. Private*, pg. 3282
Q-FREE AUSTRALIA PTY. LTD.—See Guardian Capital Group Limited; *Int'l*, pg. 3170
Q-FREE MALAYSIA SDN. BHD.—See Guardian Capital Group Limited; *Int'l*, pg. 3170
Q-FREE PORTUGAL LDA.—See Guardian Capital Group Limited; *Int'l*, pg. 3170
ROADSAFE TRAFFIC SYSTEMS, INC.—See Trilantic Capital Management L.P.; *U.S. Private*, pg. 4231
RTC NEVADA, LLC—See Rush Enterprises, Inc.; *U.S. Public*, pg. 1826
SAFE TECHNOLOGIES, INC.—See Lindsay Corporation; *U.S. Public*, pg. 1320
SANEF—See ACS, Actividades de Construccion y Servicios, S.A.; *Int'l*, pg. 112
SCHARRER & ANDRESEN GMBH—See Hoyer GmbH; *Int'l*, pg. 3499
SCHILLI SPECIALIZED, INC.—See Daseke, Inc.; *U.S. Private*, pg. 1161
SCOTLAND TRANSERV—See Balfour Beatty plc; *Int'l*, pg. 808
SNOLINE S.P.A.—See Lindsay Corporation; *U.S. Public*, pg. 1320
SOCIEDAD CONCESIONARIA AUTOPISTA CENTRAL S.A.—See ACS, Actividades de Construccion y Servicios, S.A.; *Int'l*, pg. 112
SOUTHERNAG CARRIERS, INC.—See HCI Equity Management, L.P.; *U.S. Private*, pg. 1889
SWIFT TRANSPORTATION SERVICES, LLC—See Knight-Swift Transportation Holdings Inc.; *U.S. Public*, pg. 1269
TC SERVICES, INC.—See US 1 Industries, Inc.; *U.S. Private*, pg. 4317

TIS LOGISTICS, INC.—See Toll Brothers, Inc.; *U.S. Public*, pg. 2162
TMS MANAGEMENT GROUP, INC.; *U.S. Private*, pg. 4179
TRINITY SHORING PRODUCTS, INC.—See Trinity Industries, Inc.; *U.S. Public*, pg. 2194
UNIVERSAL INTERMODAL SERVICES, INC.—See Universal Logistics Holdings, Inc.; *U.S. Public*, pg. 2261
VERKEHRSGESELLSCHAFT MBH UNTERMAIN-VU—See Deutsche Bahn AG; *Int'l*, pg. 2055
VIALIVRE, S.A.—See Ferrovial S.A.; *Int'l*, pg. 2645
WAYMO LLC—See Alphabet Inc.; *U.S. Public*, pg. 84

488510 — FREIGHT TRANSPORTATION ARRANGEMENT

24/7 EXPRESS LOGISTICS, INC.; *U.S. Private*, pg. 6
AAA TRANSPORTATION GROUP LTD.; *U.S. Private*, pg. 30
A & A CONTRACT CUSTOMS BROKERS LTD.; *Int'l*, pg. 17
AALCO FORWARDING INC.; *U.S. Private*, pg. 31
ABETRANS LOGISTICS LTD.; *Int'l*, pg. 60
ABLE FREIGHT SERVICES INC.; *U.S. Private*, pg. 39
ABU DHABI AVIATION; *Int'l*, pg. 70
ACCELERATED INTERNATIONAL FORWARDERS LLC; *U.S. Private*, pg. 49
ACCURACY SHIPPING LIMITED; *Int'l*, pg. 94
ACCURISTIX HEALTHCARE LOGISTICS INC.—See Andlauer Healthcare Group, Inc.; *Int'l*, pg. 451
ACX INTERNATIONAL (PTE) LTD—See Hemas Holdings PLC; *Int'l*, pg. 3340
ADCOM EXPRESS, INC.—See Radiant Logistics, Inc.; *U.S. Public*, pg. 1759
ADMIRAL AIR EXPRESS INC.—See ALG Admiral Inc; *U.S. Private*, pg. 166
ADS LOGISTICS CO, LLC—See Odyssey Logistics & Technology Corp.; *U.S. Private*, pg. 2996
ADVANCE INTERNATIONAL FREIGHT SDN. BHD.—See FM Global Logistics Holdings Berhad; *Int'l*, pg. 2717
ADVANTAGE TRANSPORT, INC.—See The Jordan Company, L.P.; *U.S. Private*, pg. 4061
AERONET WORLDWIDE INC.; *U.S. Private*, pg. 119
AEROPORT INTERNATIONAL SERVICES, INC.—See PriceSmart Inc.; *U.S. Public*, pg. 1716
AES LOGISTICS, INC.; *U.S. Private*, pg. 120
AETNA FREIGHT LINES, INC.—See Transport Investments, Inc.; *U.S. Private*, pg. 4210
AFC WORLDWIDE EXPRESS INC.—See R & L Carriers, Inc.; *U.S. Private*, pg. 3331
AFS LOGISTICS, LLC; *U.S. Private*, pg. 124
AGENCIAS UNIVERSALES SA—See Grupo Empresas Navieras S.A.; *Int'l*, pg. 3128
AGILITY COMPANY L.L.C.—See Agility; *Int'l*, pg. 209
AGILITY LOGISTICS LLC—See Agility; *Int'l*, pg. 210
AGILITY PROJECT LOGISTICS INC.—See Agility; *Int'l*, pg. 210
AGIT - AGENCIJA ZA INTEGRALNI TRANSPORT D.O.O.—See HZ Hrvatske Zeljeznice Holding d.o.o.; *Int'l*, pg. 3561
AGRI FUTURA GMBH—See AGRAVIS Raiffeisen AG; *Int'l*, pg. 215
AGRIHOLDING INC.; *U.S. Private*, pg. 129
AGRI PORT SERVICES, LLC—See Archer-Daniels-Midland Company; *U.S. Public*, pg. 183
AICHI STEEL LOGISTICS CO., LTD.—See Aichi Steel Corporation; *Int'l*, pg. 230
AIR CHARTER OF OHIO, INC.—See A.P. Moller-Maersk A/S; *Int'l*, pg. 27
AIR-CITY INC.—See Greenbriar Equity Group, L.P.; *U.S. Private*, pg. 1776
AIRES; *U.S. Private*, pg. 141
AIR-SEA FORWARDERS INC.; *U.S. Private*, pg. 140
AIR TRANSPORT, INC.—See Transport Investments, Inc.; *U.S. Private*, pg. 4210
AIT CORPORATION; *Int'l*, pg. 254
AITKEN SPENCE CARGO (PVT) LTD.—See Aitken Spence PLC; *Int'l*, pg. 254
AITKEN SPENCE SHIPPING LTD.—See Aitken Spence PLC; *Int'l*, pg. 254
AIT WORLDWIDE LOGISTICS, INC.; *U.S. Private*, pg. 142
AKTIFSPED ULUSLARARASI NAKLIYAT VE TIC. LTD. STI—See Hoyer GmbH; *Int'l*, pg. 3498
ALASKA LOGISTICS, LLC; *U.S. Private*, pg. 151
ALASKA TANKER COMPANY LLC—See Saltchuk Resources Inc.; *U.S. Private*, pg. 3534
ALBANIAN FERRY TERMINAL OPERATOR SHPK—See FRS GmbH & Co. KG; *Int'l*, pg. 2797
ALBA WHEELS UP INTERNATIONAL, INC.—See Southfield Capital Advisors, LLC; *U.S. Private*, pg. 3736
ALBA WHEELS UP INTERNATIONAL, INC.—See Southfield Capital Advisors, LLC; *U.S. Private*, pg. 3736
ALBA WHEELS UP INTERNATIONAL, INC.—See Southfield Capital Advisors, LLC; *U.S. Private*, pg. 3736
ALBERT & ASSOCIATES INC.; *U.S. Private*, pg. 152
ALBINI & PITIGLIANI S.P.A.; *Int'l*, pg. 298
ALBINI & PITIGLIANI SVERIGE AB—See Albini & Pitigliani S.p.A.; *Int'l*, pg. 298

ALDREES PETROLEUM & TRANSPORT SERVICES COMPANY; *Int'l*, pg. 305
ALG ADMIRAL INC; *U.S. Private*, pg. 166
ALGOMA SHIPPING INC.—See Algoma Central Corporation; *Int'l*, pg. 318
AL JABER HEAVY LIFT—See Al Jaber Group; *Int'l*, pg. 279
AL JABER HEAVY LIFT & TRANSPORT PTE.LTD—See Al Jaber Group; *Int'l*, pg. 279
ALLCARGO LOGISTICS LIMITED; *Int'l*, pg. 333
ALLEN LUND COMPANY, LLC; *U.S. Private*, pg. 179
ALLIANCE INTERNATIONAL FORWARDERS, INC.; *U.S. Private*, pg. 183
ALLIANCE SHIPPERS, INC.; *U.S. Private*, pg. 184
ALLIANCE SHIPPERS TRANSPORTATION BROKER—See Alliance Shippers, Inc.; *U.S. Private*, pg. 184
ALLMODES TRANSPORT INC.; *U.S. Private*, pg. 192
ALL NIPPON AIRWAYS TRADING CO., LTD.—See ANA Holdings Inc.; *Int'l*, pg. 444
ALLSTATES WORLDCARGO, INC.; *U.S. Private*, pg. 193
ALLY LOGISTICS LLC; *U.S. Private*, pg. 194
AL MADINA LOGISTICS SERVICE S.A.O.C—See Global Financial Investments Holding SAOG; *Int'l*, pg. 2996
ALOHA FREIGHT FORWARDERS, INC.; *U.S. Private*, pg. 195
ALPHONSE CHARPIOT ET COMPAGNIE; *Int'l*, pg. 370
ALPI ADRIATICA SRL—See Albini & Pitigliani S.p.A.; *Int'l*, pg. 298
ALPI AIR & SEA A/S—See Albini & Pitigliani S.p.A.; *Int'l*, pg. 298
ALPI BELGIUM N.V.S.A.—See Albini & Pitigliani S.p.A.; *Int'l*, pg. 298
ALPI EESTI OU—See Albini & Pitigliani S.p.A.; *Int'l*, pg. 298
ALPI EXPRESS NORD SRL—See Albini & Pitigliani S.p.A.; *Int'l*, pg. 298
ALPI EXPRESS S.R.L.—See Albini & Pitigliani S.p.A.; *Int'l*, pg. 298
ALPI KOREA LTD—See Albini & Pitigliani S.p.A.; *Int'l*, pg. 298
ALPI LAGHI S.R.L.—See Albini & Pitigliani S.p.A.; *Int'l*, pg. 298
ALPI LATVIA SIA—See Albini & Pitigliani S.p.A.; *Int'l*, pg. 298
ALPI LEVANTE SRL—See Albini & Pitigliani S.p.A.; *Int'l*, pg. 298
ALPI LISBOA LDA—See Albini & Pitigliani S.p.A.; *Int'l*, pg. 298
ALPI LOGISTICS INC—See Albini & Pitigliani S.p.A.; *Int'l*, pg. 298
ALPI LUCCA SRL—See Albini & Pitigliani S.p.A.; *Int'l*, pg. 298
ALPI NORD EST S.R.L.—See Albini & Pitigliani S.p.A.; *Int'l*, pg. 298
ALPI PADANA S.R.L.—See Albini & Pitigliani S.p.A.; *Int'l*, pg. 298
ALPI PORTUGAL LDA.—See Albini & Pitigliani S.p.A.; *Int'l*, pg. 298
ALPI SERVIZIO MODA S.R.L.—See Albini & Pitigliani S.p.A.; *Int'l*, pg. 298
ALPI SUISSE S.A.—See Albini & Pitigliani S.p.A.; *Int'l*, pg. 298
ALPI SUOMI OY—See Albini & Pitigliani S.p.A.; *Int'l*, pg. 298
ALPI TIRRENICA S.R.L.—See Albini & Pitigliani S.p.A.; *Int'l*, pg. 298
ALPI UK LTD—See Albini & Pitigliani S.p.A.; *Int'l*, pg. 298
ALPI USA, INC.—See Albini & Pitigliani S.p.A.; *Int'l*, pg. 298
ALPI USA PACIFIC INC—See Albini & Pitigliani S.p.A.; *Int'l*, pg. 298
ALSO SWEDEN AB—See Droege Group AG; *Int'l*, pg. 2205
AMAC LOGISTICS, LLC.—See ABRY Partners, LLC; *U.S. Private*, pg. 41
AMAN FREIGHT (MALAYSIA) SDN. BHD.—See DRB-HICOM Berhad; *Int'l*, pg. 2201
AMATHUS CORPORATION LTD.—See Amathus Public Limited; *Int'l*, pg. 413
AMERICAN CARGO EXPRESS, INC.—See LDI Ltd., LLC; *U.S. Private*, pg. 2404
AMERICAN FAST FREIGHT, INC.—See The Jordan Company, L.P.; *U.S. Private*, pg. 4060
AMERICAN FREIGHT, LLC—See B. Riley Financial, Inc.; *U.S. Public*, pg. 261
AMERICAN FREIGHT, LLC—See Irradiant Partners, LP; *U.S. Private*, pg. 2140
AMERICAN PACKAGE EXPRESS—See Heritage Partners, Inc.; *U.S. Private*, pg. 1924
AMERICAN SHIPPING CO. INC.; *U.S. Private*, pg. 253
AMERICAN VANPAC CARRIERS, INC.—See Atlas World Group, Inc.; *U.S. Private*, pg. 380
AMERI-CO CARRIERS, INC.—See Minerals Technologies, Inc.; *U.S. Public*, pg. 1448
AMERICO LOGISTICS, INC.—See Minerals Technologies, Inc.; *U.S. Public*, pg. 1448
AMERIQUEST BUSINESS SERVICES; *U.S. Private*, pg. 260
A.M. LOGISTICS, INC.; *U.S. Private*, pg. 27
AMTREX, INC.; *U.S. Private*, pg. 268
A.N. DERINGER, INC.; *U.S. Private*, pg. 27
ANDERSON CARGO SERVICES, LLC—See Argosy Capital Group, LLC; *U.S. Private*, pg. 321

N.A.I.C.S. INDEX

488510 — FREIGHT TRANSPORTAT...

ANDERSON CARGO SERVICES, LLC—See Headhaul Capital Partners LLC; *U.S. Private*, pg. 1891
AOE FREIGHT (HK) LTD.—See Beijing Sports & Entertainment Industry Group Limited; *Int'l*, pg. 957
AOE FREIGHT (SHENZHEN) LTD.—See Beijing Sports & Entertainment Industry Group Limited; *Int'l*, pg. 957
AOE FREIGHT (SHENZHEN) LTD.—See Beijing Sports & Entertainment Industry Group Limited; *Int'l*, pg. 957
AOE FREIGHT (SHENZHEN) LTD.—See Beijing Sports & Entertainment Industry Group Limited; *Int'l*, pg. 957
AOE FREIGHT (SHENZHEN) LTD.—See Beijing Sports & Entertainment Industry Group Limited; *Int'l*, pg. 957
AOE FREIGHT (SHENZHEN) LTD.—See Beijing Sports & Entertainment Industry Group Limited; *Int'l*, pg. 957
APEX FREIGHT SERVICES, INC.—See ABRY Partners, LLC; *U.S. Private*, pg. 41
APL (AMERICA) LLC—See CMA CGM S.A.; *Int'l*, pg. 1668
APL BANGLADESH PVT. LTD.—See CMA CGM S.A.; *Int'l*, pg. 1668
APL CO. PTE. LTD. - EUROPE OFFICE—See CMA CGM S.A.; *Int'l*, pg. 1668
APL CO. PTE. LTD. - MIDDLE EAST OFFICE—See CMA CGM S.A.; *Int'l*, pg. 1668
APL CO. PTE. LTD.—See CMA CGM S.A.; *Int'l*, pg. 1668
APL-NOL (M) SDN. BHD.—See CMA CGM S.A.; *Int'l*, pg. 1668
APL VIETNAM LIMITED—See CMA CGM S.A.; *Int'l*, pg. 1668
APM TERMINAL PACIFIC LTD.—See A.P. Moller-Maersk A/S; *Int'l*, pg. 25
APM TERMINALS INTERNATIONAL B.V.—See A.P. Moller-Maersk A/S; *Int'l*, pg. 25
APM TERMINALS NORTH AMERICA, INC.—See A.P. Moller-Maersk A/S; *Int'l*, pg. 25
APOLLO INTERNATIONAL FORWARDERS, INC.; *U.S. Private*, pg. 295
ARAB AMERICAN INTERNATIONAL EXPRESS COMPANY—See Aramex PJSC; *Int'l*, pg. 535
ARAMEX EMIRATES LLC—See Aramex PJSC; *Int'l*, pg. 535
ARAMEX KUWAIT KSE—See Aramex PJSC; *Int'l*, pg. 535
ARASCO TRANSPORT, HANDLING AND SHIPPING CO.—See Arabian Agricultural Services Co.; *Int'l*, pg. 533
ARB MIDSTREAM, LLC; *U.S. Private*, pg. 308
ARCBEST INTERNATIONAL, INC.—See ArcBest Corporation; *U.S. Public*, pg. 180
ARCHGATE TMS SOLUTIONS LLC; *U.S. Private*, pg. 311
ARGENTS EXPRESS GROUP LTD; *U.S. Private*, pg. 320
ARIES GLOBAL LOGISTICS, INC.; *U.S. Private*, pg. 322
ARLAN WAGONS LLP; *Int'l*, pg. 573
ARROWPAC INCORPORATED; *U.S. Private*, pg. 336
A.R. SAVAGE & SON, LLC; *U.S. Private*, pg. 27
ARTISAN CONTAINER SERVICE LLC—See NLM Inc.; *U.S. Private*, pg. 2931
ART SHIPPING INTERNATIONAL SAS—See Clasquin S.A.; *Int'l*, pg. 1652
ASCO FREIGHT MANAGEMENT LTD.—See Endless LLP; *Int'l*, pg. 2403
ASCO FREIGHT MANAGEMENT—See Endless LLP; *Int'l*, pg. 2403
A & S GROUP (HOLDINGS) LIMITED; *Int'l*, pg. 17
ASIA LOGISTICS (CHINA) LIMITED; *Int'l*, pg. 613
ASIA PACIFIC FREIGHT SYSTEM SDN. BHD.—See DRB-HICOM Berhad; *Int'l*, pg. 2201
ASPINWALL & CO. LTD., - LOGISTICS DIVISION—See Aspinwall & Co. Ltd.,; *Int'l*, pg. 630
ASTRA INC.; *U.S. Private*, pg. 361
ATEC SYSTEMS, LTD.—See Armada Group, Ltd.; *U.S. Private*, pg. 329
ATLANTIC SHIPPERS OF TEXAS, INC.—See Animalfeeds International Corporation; *U.S. Private*, pg. 283
ATLAS VAN LINES INTL—See Atlas World Group, Inc.; *U.S. Private*, pg. 380
ATOBATC SHIPPING AB—See Aspo Oyj; *Int'l*, pg. 631
ATS-HELLMANN WORLDWIDE LOGISTICS LTD.—See Hellmann Worldwide Logistics GmbH & Co. KG; *Int'l*, pg. 3335
AURORA TANKERS USA INC.—See IMC Pan Asia Alliance Pte. Ltd.; *Int'l*, pg. 3621
AUTO EXPRESS FRONTERA NORTE, S. A. DE C. V.—See Grupo Traxion, S. A. B. de C. V.; *Int'l*, pg. 3138
AVG LOGISTICS LTD.; *Int'l*, pg. 740
AVS CARGO MANAGEMENT SERVICES PRIVATE LIMITED—See Expolanka Holdings PLC; *Int'l*, pg. 2589
AWILCO LNG ASA; *Int'l*, pg. 753
AXIS GLOBAL SYSTEMS LLC; *U.S. Private*, pg. 413
AXIS GROUP, INC.—See Jack Cooper Transport Co., Inc.; *U.S. Private*, pg. 2173
AZUMA CIS, LLC—See Azuma Shipping Co., Ltd.; *Int'l*, pg. 781
AZUMA SHIPPING (QINGDAO) CO., LTD.—See Azuma Shipping Co., Ltd.; *Int'l*, pg. 781
BANSARD BANGLADESH—See Bansard International; *Int'l*, pg. 854
BARRE LOGISTIQUE SERVICES; *Int'l*, pg. 869
BARR-NUNN LOGISTICS, INC.—See Barr-Nunn Enterprises Ltd.; *U.S. Private*, pg. 479

BCB INTERNATIONAL INC.; *U.S. Private*, pg. 499
BDP INTERNATIONAL INC.; *U.S. Private*, pg. 501
BEAR TRANSPORTATION SERVICES, L.P.—See ArcBest Corporation; *U.S. Public*, pg. 180
BEDROCK LOGISTICS LLC; *U.S. Private*, pg. 512
BELLAIR EXPEDITING NORTHWEST, INC.—See Bellair Expediting Service Inc.; *U.S. Private*, pg. 519
BELLAIR EXPEDITING SERVICE INC.; *U.S. Private*, pg. 519
BENNETT INTERNATIONAL TRANSPORT INC.—See Bennett International Group, Inc.; *U.S. Private*, pg. 527
BERGER TRANSFER & STORAGE, INC.; *U.S. Private*, pg. 530
BERTLING LOGISTICS INC.; *U.S. Private*, pg. 539
BEST DRIVERS; *U.S. Private*, pg. 542
BESTWAY REFRIGERATED SERVICE, INC.; *U.S. Private*, pg. 544
BETT-A-WAY TRAFFIC SYSTEMS, INC.; *U.S. Private*, pg. 546
BIBBY LINE LIMITED—See Bibby Line Group Limited; *Int'l*, pg. 1018
BIBBY LINE LIMITED—See Bibby Line Group Limited; *Int'l*, pg. 1018
BIBBY MARITIME LIMITED—See Bibby Line Group Limited; *Int'l*, pg. 1018
BIDVEST PANALPINA LOGISTICS—See DSV A/S; *Int'l*, pg. 2214
BIEHL & CO. L.P.—See Biehl International Corporation; *U.S. Private*, pg. 551
BIEHL INTERNATIONAL CORPORATION; *U.S. Private*, pg. 551
BIG FREIGHT SYSTEMS INC.—See Daseke, Inc.; *U.S. Private*, pg. 1161
BISCHOF GESELLSCHAFT MBH.—See Deutsche Bahn AG; *Int'l*, pg. 2049
BIS INDUSTRIES LIMITED—See KKR & Co. Inc.; *U.S. Public*, pg. 1239
BLADCENTRALEN ANS—See Egmont Fonden; *Int'l*, pg. 2325
BLG AUTOTERMINAL GDANSK SP. Z O. O.—See Bremer Lagerhaus-Gesellschaft; *Int'l*, pg. 1145
BLG LOGISTICS AUTOMOBILE SPB—See Bremer Lagerhaus-Gesellschaft; *Int'l*, pg. 1145
BLG LOGISTICS INC.—See Bremer Lagerhaus-Gesellschaft; *Int'l*, pg. 1145
BLG LOGISTICS SOLUTIONS ITALIA S.R.L.—See Bremer Lagerhaus-Gesellschaft; *Int'l*, pg. 1145
BLUEBIRD EXPRESS, LLC—See Cryoport, Inc.; *U.S. Public*, pg. 600
BLUE DART EXPRESS LIMITED; *Int'l*, pg. 1067
BLUE-GRACE LOGISTICS, LLC; *U.S. Private*, pg. 596
BLUE RIBBON TRANSPORT, INC.; *U.S. Private*, pg. 591
BNSF LOGISTICS INTERNATIONAL—See Berkshire Hathaway Inc.; *U.S. Public*, pg. 303
BNX SHIPPING INC.; *U.S. Private*, pg. 602
BOHAI LEASING CO., LTD.—See Hainan Traffic Administration Holding Co., Ltd.; *Int'l*, pg. 3213
BOLLORE ENERGIE—See Financiere de L'Odet; *Int'l*, pg. 2667
BOLT EXPRESS LLC; *U.S. Private*, pg. 611
BOMBARDIER TRANSPORTATION UK LTD.—See Alstom S.A.; *Int'l*, pg. 383
BOUNCE LOGISTICS, INC.—See XPO, Inc.; *U.S. Public*, pg. 2392
BOYD LOGISTICS, LLC—See Daseke, Inc.; *U.S. Private*, pg. 1161
BRAEMAR ACM SHIPBROKING PTY LIMITED—See Braemar PLC; *Int'l*, pg. 1135
BRAEMAR ACM SHIPBROKING (USA) INC.—See Braemar PLC; *Int'l*, pg. 1135
BRAEMAR HOLDINGS (USA) INC.—See Braemar PLC; *Int'l*, pg. 1135
BRAEMAR SEASCOPE ITALIA SRL—See Braemar PLC; *Int'l*, pg. 1135
BRAEMAR SEASCOPE (SHANGHAI) LIMITED—See Braemar PLC; *Int'l*, pg. 1135
BRIGHT KEY; *U.S. Private*, pg. 651
BRUZZONE SHIPPING, INC.; *U.S. Private*, pg. 673
B-T BROKERAGE INC.—See The Decker Companies Inc.; *U.S. Private*, pg. 4019
BT TRUCKING, INC.; *U.S. Private*, pg. 675
BUCKLAND CUSTOMS BROKERS LTD.; *Int'l*, pg. 1210
BURKINA LOGISTICS & MINING SERVICES SA—See Financiere de L'Odet; *Int'l*, pg. 2667
BUZEN KUBOTA KAIUN CO., LTD.—See Azuma Shipping Co., Ltd.; *Int'l*, pg. 782
B-X NORTH CHELMSFORD LLC—See Welltower Inc.; *U.S. Public*, pg. 2347
B-X QUINCY LLC—See Welltower Inc.; *U.S. Public*, pg. 2347
B-X TRUMBULL LLC—See Welltower Inc.; *U.S. Public*, pg. 2347
B-X YARMOUTH LLC—See Welltower Inc.; *U.S. Public*, pg. 2347
CAI-CHARLESTON—See CAI International, Inc.; *U.S. Public*, pg. 421
CAI CHILE S.P.A—See CAI International, Inc.; *U.S. Public*, pg. 421

CAI INTERNATIONAL, INC.; *U.S. Public*, pg. 421
CALBEE LOGISTICS, INC.—See Calbee, Inc.; *Int'l*, pg. 1261
CAMPOSTANO GROUP S.P.A.; *Int'l*, pg. 1275
CAPCO U.S.A., INC.—See Central Automotive Products Ltd.; *Int'l*, pg. 1404
CAPITAL TRANSPORTATION LOGISTICS, LLC—See Roadrunner Transportation Systems, Inc.; *U.S. Public*, pg. 1802
CAP LOGISTICS INC.; *U.S. Private*, pg. 737
CARGOBARN INC.—See SheerTrans Solutions, LLC; *U.S. Private*, pg. 3630
CARGO-LINK INTERNATIONAL, INC.—See Gebruder Weiss Gesellschaft m.b.H.; *Int'l*, pg. 2909
CARGO LOGISTICS GROUP, INC—See Littlejohn & Co., LLC; *U.S. Public*, pg. 2470
CARGOPORT LOGISTICS, C.A.; *Int'l*, pg. 1326
CARGOTRANS MARITIME LIMITED; *Int'l*, pg. 1329
CARIBBEAN SHIPPING SERVICES, INC.—See The Jordan Company, L.P.; *U.S. Private*, pg. 4060
CARIBE FREIGHT—See CaribEx Worldwide Inc.; *U.S. Private*, pg. 761
CARIBEX WORLDWIDE INC.; *U.S. Private*, pg. 761
CARIBEX WORLDWIDE—See CaribEx Worldwide Inc.; *U.S. Private*, pg. 761
CARISBROOKE SHIPPING BV—See Carisbrooke Shipping Limited; *Int'l*, pg. 1331
CARISBROOKE SHIPPING (GERMANY) GMBH—See Carisbrooke Shipping Limited; *Int'l*, pg. 1331
CARISBROOKE SHIPPING GMBH—See Carisbrooke Shipping Limited; *Int'l*, pg. 1331
CAROLINA LOGISTICS—See US 1 Industries, Inc.; *U.S. Private*, pg. 4317
CAROLINA SHIPPING CO. INC.—See Biehl International Corporation; *U.S. Private*, pg. 551
CARRY TRANSPORT INC.—See Heniff Transportation Systems Inc.; *U.S. Private*, pg. 1916
CARTWRIGHT INTERNATIONAL VAN LINES INC.—See Centre Limited Inc.; *U.S. Private*, pg. 828
CARTWRIGHT VAN LINES INC.—See Centre Limited Inc.; *U.S. Private*, pg. 828
CASCADE TRANSPORTATION, INC.—See Radiant Logistics, Inc.; *U.S. Public*, pg. 1759
CASTOR MARITIME INC.; *Int'l*, pg. 1357
CAVALIER LOGISTICS INC; *U.S. Private*, pg. 794
CDS GLOBAL LOGISTICS INC.; *U.S. Private*, pg. 803
CELADON LOGISTICS SERVICES, INC.—See Celadon Group, Inc.; *U.S. Private*, pg. 464
CELEBI CARGO GMBH—See Celebi Holding A.S.; *Int'l*, pg. 1391
CELTIC INTERNATIONAL, LLC—See TPG Capital, L.P.; *U.S. Public*, pg. 2177
CENTENARY INTERNATIONAL CORP.; *Int'l*, pg. 1402
CENTRE LIMITED INC.; *U.S. Private*, pg. 828
CERES TRANSPORTATION GROUP, INC.; *U.S. Private*, pg. 841
CERTUSPACT, LLC—See Expeditors International of Washington, Inc.; *U.S. Public*, pg. 810
CEVA AUTOMOTIVE LOGISTICS POLAND—See CMA CGM S.A.; *Int'l*, pg. 1667
CEVA CONTAINER LOGISTICS—See CMA CGM S.A.; *Int'l*, pg. 1667
CEVA FREIGHT MANAGEMENT—See CMA CGM S.A.; *Int'l*, pg. 1667
CEVA LOGISTICS AG—See CMA CGM S.A.; *Int'l*, pg. 1666
CEVA LOGISTICS AUSTRALIA—See CMA CGM S.A.; *Int'l*, pg. 1666
CEVA LOGISTICS FRANCE—See CMA CGM S.A.; *Int'l*, pg. 1666
CEVA LOGISTICS GERMANY—See CMA CGM S.A.; *Int'l*, pg. 1666
CEVA LOGISTICS GREECE—See CMA CGM S.A.; *Int'l*, pg. 1666
CEVA LOGISTICS HUNGARY—See CMA CGM S.A.; *Int'l*, pg. 1666
CEVA LOGISTICS INDONESIA—See CMA CGM S.A.; *Int'l*, pg. 1666
CEVA LOGISTICS ITALY—See CMA CGM S.A.; *Int'l*, pg. 1667
CEVA LOGISTICS MALAYSIA—See CMA CGM S.A.; *Int'l*, pg. 1667
CEVA LOGISTICS SINGAPORE—See CMA CGM S.A.; *Int'l*, pg. 1667
CEVA LOGISTICS SPAIN—See CMA CGM S.A.; *Int'l*, pg. 1667
CEVA LOGISTICS THAILAND—See CMA CGM S.A.; *Int'l*, pg. 1667
CEVA LOGISTICS TURKEY—See CMA CGM S.A.; *Int'l*, pg. 1667
CEVA LOGISTICS UNITED KINGDOM—See CMA CGM S.A.; *Int'l*, pg. 1667
C&F WORLDWIDE AGENCY CORP.; *U.S. Private*, pg. 703
CHALLENGER OVERSEAS LLC—See CAI International, Inc.; *U.S. Public*, pg. 421
CHAMPION FERRIES L.T.D.—See Attica Group; *Int'l*, pg. 696
CHAMPION TRANSPORTATION SERVICES, INC.; *U.S. Private*, pg. 847
CHARLES NAVASKY & COMPANY; *U.S. Private*, pg. 853

CHIEN SHING HARBOUR SERVICE CO., LTD.; *Int'l*, pg. 1477
CHINA LOGISTICS GROUP, INC.; *Int'l*, pg. 1515
CHINA MACHINERY ENGINEERING YINCHUAN FREE TRADE ZONE CO., LTD.—See China Machinery Engineering Corporation; *Int'l*, pg. 1516
CHINA MARINE SHIPPING AGENCY COMPANY LIMITED—See China Merchants Group Limited; *Int'l*, pg. 1522
CHINA MARINE SHIPPING AGENCY GUANGDONG CO., LTD.—See China Merchants Group Limited; *Int'l*, pg. 1522
CHINA MARINE SHIPPING AGENCY, JIANGSU COMPANY LIMITED—See China Merchants Group Limited; *Int'l*, pg. 1522
CHINA MARINE SHIPPING AGENCY, NANTONG COMPANY LIMITED—See China Merchants Group Limited; *Int'l*, pg. 1522
CHINA MARINE SHIPPING AGENCY RUGAO CO., LTD.—See China Merchants Group Limited; *Int'l*, pg. 1522
CHINA MARINE SHIPPING AGENCY, TAICANG COMPANY LIMITED—See China Merchants Group Limited; *Int'l*, pg. 1522
CHINA MARINE SHIPPING AGENCY, TAIZHOU COMPANY LIMITED—See China Merchants Group Limited; *Int'l*, pg. 1522
CHINA MARINE SHIPPING AGENCY, ZHANGJIAGANG COMPANY LIMITED—See China Merchants Group Limited; *Int'l*, pg. 1522
CHINA MARINE SHIPPING AGENCY ZHENJIANG CO., LTD.—See China Merchants Group Limited; *Int'l*, pg. 1522
CHINA RAILWAY MATERIAL GROUP CO., LTD.—See China Railway Construction Corporation Limited; *Int'l*, pg. 1543
CHINA SHIPBUILDING TRADING CO., LTD.—See China State Shipbuilding Corporation; *Int'l*, pg. 1554
CHINA SHIPPING AGENCY CO., LTD.—See China COSCO Shipping Corporation Limited; *Int'l*, pg. 1494
CHINA SHIPPING BULK CARRIER CO., LTD.—See China COSCO Shipping Corporation Limited; *Int'l*, pg. 1494
CHINESE MARITIME TRANSPORT LTD.; *Int'l*, pg. 1569
CHIQUITA BRANDS LLC - GULFPORT—See Banco Safra S.A.; *Int'l*, pg. 824
CHOPTANK TRANSPORT INC—See Hub Group, Inc.; *U.S. Public*, pg. 1065
CHOWGULE BROTHERS PVT. LTD—See Chowgule & Company Pvt. Ltd.; *Int'l*, pg. 1585
C.H. POWELL COMPANY; *U.S. Private*, pg. 707
C.H. ROBINSON COMPANY—See C.H. Robinson Worldwide, Inc.; *U.S. Public*, pg. 414
C.H. ROBINSON FRANCE SAS—See C.H. Robinson Worldwide, Inc.; *U.S. Public*, pg. 415
C.H. ROBINSON FREIGHT SERVICES, LTD.—See C.H. Robinson Worldwide, Inc.; *U.S. Public*, pg. 414
C.H. ROBINSON HUNGARIA KFT.—See C.H. Robinson Worldwide, Inc.; *U.S. Public*, pg. 414
C.H. ROBINSON INTERNATIONAL COLUMBIA SAS—See C.H. Robinson Worldwide, Inc.; *U.S. Public*, pg. 415
C.H. ROBINSON INTERNATIONAL ITALY, SRL—See C.H. Robinson Worldwide, Inc.; *U.S. Public*, pg. 414
C.H. ROBINSON-SHANNON INTERNATIONAL—See C.H. Robinson Worldwide, Inc.; *U.S. Public*, pg. 414
C.H. ROBINSON (UK) LTD.—See C.H. Robinson Worldwide, Inc.; *U.S. Public*, pg. 414
C.H. ROBINSON WORLDWIDE FREIGHT INDIA PRIVATE LIMITED—See C.H. Robinson Worldwide, Inc.; *U.S. Public*, pg. 415
C.H. ROBINSON WORLDWIDE GMBH—See C.H. Robinson Worldwide, Inc.; *U.S. Public*, pg. 415
C.H. ROBINSON WORLDWIDE (IRELAND) LTD.—See C.H. Robinson Worldwide, Inc.; *U.S. Public*, pg. 414
CHUNICHI TRANSPORTATION CO., LTD.—See Howa Machinery, Ltd.; *Int'l*, pg. 3493
CHURCHILL FREIGHT SERVICES INC.—See Churchill Transportation Inc.; *U.S. Private*, pg. 895
CHU-SHIKOKU MARUWA LOGISTICS CO., LTD.—See AZ-COM MARUWA Holdings Inc.; *Int'l*, pg. 776
CIMC MODERN LOGISTIC DEVELOPMENT CO., LTD.—See China International Marine Containers (Group) Co., Ltd.; *Int'l*, pg. 1511
CIRCLE 8 LOGISTICS, LLC—See Providence Equity Partners L.L.C.; *U.S. Private*, pg. 3292
CITY POSTAL, INC.; *U.S. Private*, pg. 906
CITY SELF-STORAGE A/S—See Teachers Insurance Association - College Retirement Fund; *U.S. Private*, pg. 3945
CITY SELF-STORAGE NORGE AS—See Teachers Insurance Association - College Retirement Fund; *U.S. Private*, pg. 3945
CIVARO LANKA (PVT) LIMITED.—See Hayleys PLC; *Int'l*, pg. 3292
CJ GLS AMERICA, INC.—See CJ Corporation; *Int'l*, pg. 1632
CJ GLS CORPORATION—See CJ Corporation; *Int'l*, pg. 1632
CJ GLS FORWARDING MALAYSIA SDN. BHD.—See CJ Corporation; *Int'l*, pg. 1633

CLARKSON ASIA LTD.—See Clarkson PLC; *Int'l*, pg. 1650
CLARKSON ASIA PTE LTD.—See Clarkson PLC; *Int'l*, pg. 1650
CLARKSON AUSTRALIA (PTY) LIMITED—See Clarkson PLC; *Int'l*, pg. 1650
CLARKSON ITALIA SRL—See Clarkson PLC; *Int'l*, pg. 1650
CLARKSON PLC; *Int'l*, pg. 1650
CLARKSON RESEARCH HOLDINGS LIMITED—See Clarkson PLC; *Int'l*, pg. 1651
CLARKSON SHIPBROKING (SHANGHAI) CO. LIMITED—See Clarkson PLC; *Int'l*, pg. 1651
CLARKSON SHIPPING SERVICES USA INC.—See Clarkson PLC; *Int'l*, pg. 1651
CLARKSONS MARTANKERS, S.L.U.—See Clarkson PLC; *Int'l*, pg. 1651
CLARKSONS PLATOU ASIA LIMITED—See Clarkson PLC; *Int'l*, pg. 1651
CLARKSONS PLATOU ASIA PTE. LIMITED—See Clarkson PLC; *Int'l*, pg. 1651
CLARKSONS PLATOU (AUSTRALIA) PTY LIMITED—See Clarkson PLC; *Int'l*, pg. 1651
CLARKSONS PLATOU (BRASIL) LTDA.—See Clarkson PLC; *Int'l*, pg. 1651
CLARKSONS PLATOU (DENMARK) APS—See Clarkson PLC; *Int'l*, pg. 1651
CLARKSONS PLATOU DMCC—See Clarkson PLC; *Int'l*, pg. 1651
CLARKSONS PLATOU GMBH—See Clarkson PLC; *Int'l*, pg. 1651
CLARKSONS PLATOU JAPAN K.K.—See Clarkson PLC; *Int'l*, pg. 1651
CLARKSONS PLATOU (KOREA) COMPANY LIMITED—See Clarkson PLC; *Int'l*, pg. 1651
CLARKSONS PLATOU (NEDERLAND) B.V.—See Clarkson PLC; *Int'l*, pg. 1651
CLARKSONS PLATOU SHIPBROKING (SWITZERLAND) SA—See Clarkson PLC; *Int'l*, pg. 1651
CLARKSONS PLATOU (SOUTH AFRICA) (PTY) LIMITED—See Clarkson PLC; *Int'l*, pg. 1651
CLARKSONS PLATOU (SWEDEN) AB—See Clarkson PLC; *Int'l*, pg. 1651
CLARKSONS PLATOU (USA) INC.—See Clarkson PLC; *Int'l*, pg. 1651
CLASQUIN AUSTRALIA PTY LTD—See Clasquin S.A.; *Int'l*, pg. 1652
CLASQUIN BURKINA FASO LTD.—See Clasquin S.A.; *Int'l*, pg. 1652
CLASQUIN CHILE SPA—See Clasquin S.A.; *Int'l*, pg. 1652
CLASQUIN ESPANA S.L.—See Clasquin S.A.; *Int'l*, pg. 1652
CLASQUIN (FAR EAST) LTD.—See Clasquin S.A.; *Int'l*, pg. 1652
CLASQUIN FAR EAST LTD.—See Clasquin S.A.; *Int'l*, pg. 1652
CLASQUIN INDIA PVT. LTD.—See Clasquin S.A.; *Int'l*, pg. 1652
CLASQUIN INTERNATIONAL TAIWAN LTD.—See Clasquin S.A.; *Int'l*, pg. 1652
CLASQUIN ITALIA S.R.L.—See Clasquin S.A.; *Int'l*, pg. 1652
CLASQUIN JAPAN CO. LTD.—See Clasquin S.A.; *Int'l*, pg. 1652
CLASQUIN KOREA CO. LTD.—See Clasquin S.A.; *Int'l*, pg. 1652
CLASQUIN MALAYSIA SDN BHD—See Clasquin S.A.; *Int'l*, pg. 1652
CLASQUIN PORTUGAL LDA.—See Clasquin S.A.; *Int'l*, pg. 1652
CLASQUIN S.A.; *Int'l*, pg. 1652
CLASQUIN SINGAPORE PTE. LTD.—See Clasquin S.A.; *Int'l*, pg. 1652
CLASQUIN THAILAND (CO.) LTD.—See Clasquin S.A.; *Int'l*, pg. 1652
CLASQUIN USA INC.—See Clasquin S.A.; *Int'l*, pg. 1652
CLASQUIN VIETNAM LTD.—See Clasquin S.A.; *Int'l*, pg. 1652
CLASSIC FORWARDING INC.; *U.S. Private*, pg. 916
CLASSIC TRANSPORT, INC.; *U.S. Private*, pg. 917
CLOVER INTERNACIONAL, C.A.—See Clover Systems Inc.; *U.S. Private*, pg. 947
CLOVER INTERNACIONAL LLC—See Clover Systems Inc.; *U.S. Private*, pg. 947
CLOVER SYSTEMS INC.; *U.S. Private*, pg. 947
CMA CGM DENIZ ACENTELIGI A.S.—See CMA CGM S.A.; *Int'l*, pg. 1667
CMA CGM SOUTH AFRICA (PTY) LTD.—See CMA CGM S.A.; *Int'l*, pg. 1668
CMEC COMTRANS INTERNATIONAL CO., LTD.—See China Machinery Engineering Corporation; *Int'l*, pg. 1515
COASTAL CONTAINERS LTD.—See GrainCorp Limited; *Int'l*, pg. 3052
COASTAL INLAND MARINE SERVICES LTD.—See Trico Marine Services, Inc.; *U.S. Private*, pg. 4229
COECLERICI COAL & FUELS S.P.A—See Coeclerici S.p.A.; *Int'l*, pg. 1688
COLDIRON COMPANIES, INC.; *U.S. Private*, pg. 966
COLORADO TRUCK EQUIPMENT & PARTS INC—See North American Truck & Trailer, Inc.; *U.S. Private*, pg. 2941
COMBINED EXPRESS INC.; *U.S. Private*, pg. 980

COMBINED TRANSPORT INC.; *U.S. Private*, pg. 980
COMMITTED CARGO CARE LIMITED; *Int'l*, pg. 1719
COMMODITY SERVICES INC.; *U.S. Private*, pg. 985
COMPAGNIE DU CAMBODGE SA; *Int'l*, pg. 1740
COMPANHIA LIBRA DE NAVEGACAO S.A.—See Albert Ballin KG; *Int'l*, pg. 294
COMPANIA SUDAMERICANA DE VAPORES, S.A.; *Int'l*, pg. 1749
COMPASS FORWARDING CO., INC.; *U.S. Private*, pg. 999
CONCERT GROUP LOGISTICS, INC.—See XPO, Inc.; *U.S. Public*, pg. 2392
CONCORDIA INTERNATIONAL FORWARDING INC.; *U.S. Private*, pg. 1010
CONCORDIA INTERNATIONAL FORWARDING LTD.—See Concordia International Forwarding Inc.; *U.S. Private*, pg. 1010
CONECLI INTERNATIONAL S.A.—See Allcargo Logistics Limited; *Int'l*, pg. 333
CONTINENTAL RAIL, S.A.—See ACS, Actividades de Construccion y Servicios, S.A.; *Int'l*, pg. 111
CONTINENTAL TRUCK BROKERS INC.; *U.S. Private*, pg. 1031
CONTSHIP ITALIA S.P.A.—See EUROKAI GmbH & Co. KGaA; *Int'l*, pg. 2553
COPPERSMITH CORPORATION; *U.S. Private*, pg. 1045
COREA & CO. (1988) LIMITED—See Goddard Enterprises Limited; *Int'l*, pg. 3018
CORNERSTONE SYSTEMS, INC.; *U.S. Private*, pg. 1053
CORPORATIVO DE NEGOCIOS DE COMERCIO EXTERIOR, S.A. DE C.V.—See Accel, S.A.B. de C.V.; *Int'l*, pg. 79
CORY BROTHERS SHIPPING AGENCY LIMITED—See Braemar PLC; *Int'l*, pg. 1135
CORY BROTHERS SHIPPING PTE LIMITED—See Braemar PLC; *Int'l*, pg. 1135
CORY BROTHERS (THE NETHERLANDS) B.V.—See Braemar PLC; *Int'l*, pg. 1136
COSCO AGENCIES (LOS ANGELES) INC.—See China COSCO Shipping Corporation Limited; *Int'l*, pg. 1493
COSCO ANQING CONTAINER SHIPPING AGENCY CO., LTD.—See China COSCO Shipping Corporation Limited; *Int'l*, pg. 1491
COSCO BRASIL S.A.—See China COSCO Shipping Corporation Limited; *Int'l*, pg. 1493
COSCO CHILE S.A.—See China COSCO Shipping Corporation Limited; *Int'l*, pg. 1494
COSCO CHONGQING INTERNATIONAL FREIGHT CO., LTD.—See China COSCO Shipping Corporation Limited; *Int'l*, pg. 1491
COSCO CONTAINER LINES VIETNAM COMPANY LTD.—See China COSCO Shipping Corporation Limited; *Int'l*, pg. 1494
COSCO GUANGZHOU MARINE SERVICE CO., LTD.—See China COSCO Shipping Corporation Limited; *Int'l*, pg. 1493
COSCO HEBEI INTERNATIONAL FREIGHT CO., LTD.—See China COSCO Shipping Corporation Limited; *Int'l*, pg. 1491
COSCO (H.K.) SHIPPING CO., LIMITED—See China COSCO Shipping Corporation Limited; *Int'l*, pg. 1491
COSCO HUNAN INTERNATIONAL FREIGHT CO., LTD.—See China COSCO Shipping Corporation Limited; *Int'l*, pg. 1491
COSCO HUZHOU INTERNATIONAL FREIGHT CO., LTD.—See China COSCO Shipping Corporation Limited; *Int'l*, pg. 1491
COSCO JIANGXI INTERNATIONAL FREIGHT CO., LTD.—See China COSCO Shipping Corporation Limited; *Int'l*, pg. 1491
COSCO JIAXING INTERNATIONAL FREIGHT CO., LTD.—See China COSCO Shipping Corporation Limited; *Int'l*, pg. 1496
COSCO LANKA (PVT) LTD.—See China COSCO Shipping Corporation Limited; *Int'l*, pg. 1494
COSCO LOGISTICS (DALIAN) CO LTD.—See China COSCO Shipping Corporation Limited; *Int'l*, pg. 1493
COSCO MANNING COOPERATION INC.—See China COSCO Shipping Corporation Limited; *Int'l*, pg. 1491
COSCO NEIMENGGU INTERNATIONAL FREIGHT CO., LTD.—See China COSCO Shipping Corporation Limited; *Int'l*, pg. 1492
COSCO NINGXIA INTERNATIONAL FREIGHT CO., LTD.—See China COSCO Shipping Corporation Limited; *Int'l*, pg. 1492
COSCO PERU S.A.—See China COSCO Shipping Corporation Limited; *Int'l*, pg. 1494
COSCO QINGDAO INTERNATIONAL FREIGHT CO., LTD.—See China COSCO Shipping Corporation Limited; *Int'l*, pg. 1492
COSCO QINGHAI INTERNATIONAL FREIGHT CO., LTD.—See China COSCO Shipping Corporation Limited; *Int'l*, pg. 1492
COSCO SHANXI INTERNATIONAL FREIGHT CO., LTD.—See China COSCO Shipping Corporation Limited; *Int'l*, pg. 1493
COSCO SHAOXING INTERNATIONAL FREIGHT CO., LTD.—See China COSCO Shipping Corporation Limited; *Int'l*, pg. 1493

N.A.I.C.S. INDEX

488510 — FREIGHT TRANSPORTAT...

COSCO SHENZHEN INTERNATIONAL FREIGHT CO., LTD.—See China COSCO Shipping Corporation Limited; *Int'l*, pg. 1493

COSCOSHIP BEIJING COMPANY LIMITED—See China COSCO Shipping Corporation Limited; *Int'l*, pg. 1492

COSCO SHIPPING AGENCY (GREECE) S.A.—See China COSCO Shipping Corporation Limited; *Int'l*, pg. 1494

COSCO SHIPPING ARGENTINA—See China COSCO Shipping Corporation Limited; *Int'l*, pg. 1494

COSCO SHIPPING CONTAINER LINE AGENCIES LIMITED—See COSCO Shipping Holdings Co., Ltd.; *Int'l*, pg. 1810

COSCO SHIPPING DEVELOPMENT CO., LTD.—See China COSCO Shipping Corporation Limited; *Int'l*, pg. 1492

COSCO SHIPPING ENERGY TRANSPORTATION CO., LTD.—See China COSCO Shipping Corporation Limited; *Int'l*, pg. 1492

COSCO SHIPPING GUANGXI INTERNATIONAL FREIGHT CO., LTD.—See China COSCO Shipping Corporation Limited; *Int'l*, pg. 1493

COSCO SHIPPING GUANGZHOU INTERNATIONAL FREIGHT CO., LTD.—See China COSCO Shipping Corporation Limited; *Int'l*, pg. 1493

COSCO SHIPPING GUIZHOU INTERNATIONAL FREIGHT CO., LTD.—See China COSCO Shipping Corporation Limited; *Int'l*, pg. 1493

COSCO SHIPPING HEAVY INDUSTRY CO., LTD.—See China COSCO Shipping Corporation Limited; *Int'l*, pg. 1496

COSCO SHIPPING HEAVY TRANSPORT (EUROPE) B.V.—See China COSCO Shipping Corporation Limited; *Int'l*, pg. 1493

COSCO SHIPPING (HONG KONG) SHIP TRADING COMPANY LIMITED—See China COSCO Shipping Corporation Limited; *Int'l*, pg. 1492

COSCO SHIPPING JIANGSU INTERNATIONAL FREIGHT CO., LTD.—See China COSCO Shipping Corporation Limited; *Int'l*, pg. 1493

COSCO SHIPPING JIANGSU INTERNATIONAL FREIGHT CO., LTD.—See China COSCO Shipping Corporation Limited; *Int'l*, pg. 1493

COSCOSHIPPING KOREA CO., LTD.—See China COSCO Shipping Corporation Limited; *Int'l*, pg. 1493

COSCO SHIPPING LINES (BELGIUM) NV—See China COSCO Shipping Corporation Limited; *Int'l*, pg. 1494

COSCO SHIPPING LINES (CANADA) INC.—See China COSCO Shipping Corporation Limited; *Int'l*, pg. 1493

COSCO SHIPPING LINES (CENTRAL EUROPE) S.R.O.—See China COSCO Shipping Corporation Limited; *Int'l*, pg. 1494

COSCO SHIPPING LINES EMIRATES LLC—See China COSCO Shipping Corporation Limited; *Int'l*, pg. 1494

COSCO SHIPPING LINES (FRANCE) S.A.S.—See China COSCO Shipping Corporation Limited; *Int'l*, pg. 1493

COSCO SHIPPING LINES (INDIA) PVT. LTD.—See China COSCO Shipping Corporation Limited; *Int'l*, pg. 1494

COSCO SHIPPING LINES (JAPAN) CO.—See China COSCO Shipping Corporation Limited; *Int'l*, pg. 1494

COSCO SHIPPING LINES (MALAYSIA) SDN. BHD.—See China COSCO Shipping Corporation Limited; *Int'l*, pg. 1494

COSCO SHIPPING LINES (MYANMAR) CO.—See China COSCO Shipping Corporation Limited; *Int'l*, pg. 1494

COSCO SHIPPING LINES (NEW ZEALAND) LTD—See China COSCO Shipping Corporation Limited; *Int'l*, pg. 1494

COSCO SHIPPING LINES (OCEANIA) PTY. LTD.—See China COSCO Shipping Corporation Limited; *Int'l*, pg. 1493

COSCO SHIPPING LINES PAKISTAN PVT. LTD.—See China COSCO Shipping Corporation Limited; *Int'l*, pg. 1494

COSCO SHIPPING LINES (POLAND) SP. Z OO—See China COSCO Shipping Corporation Limited; *Int'l*, pg. 1494

COSCO SHIPPING LINES (ROMANIA) CO. LTD. SRL—See China COSCO Shipping Corporation Limited; *Int'l*, pg. 1494

COSCO SHIPPING LINES (SPAIN) S.A.—See China COSCO Shipping Corporation Limited; *Int'l*, pg. 1493

COSCO SHIPPING LOGISTICS (BEIJING) CO., LTD.—See China COSCO Shipping Corporation Limited; *Int'l*, pg. 1493

COSCO SHIPPING LOGISTICS CO., LTD.—See China COSCO Shipping Corporation Limited; *Int'l*, pg. 1493

COSCO SHIPPING LOGISTICS (HONG KONG) CO., LTD.—See China COSCO Shipping Corporation Limited; *Int'l*, pg. 1493

COSCO SHIPPING LOGISTICS (NANJING) CO., LTD—See China COSCO Shipping Corporation Limited; *Int'l*, pg. 1493

COSCO SHIPPING LOGISTICS (NINGBO) CO., LTD.—See China COSCO Shipping Corporation Limited; *Int'l*, pg. 1493

COSCO SHIPPING LOGISTICS (QINGDAO) CO., LTD.—See China COSCO Shipping Corporation Limited; *Int'l*, pg. 1493

COSCO SHIPPING NETWORK LIMITED—See China COSCO Shipping Corporation Limited; *Int'l*, pg. 1493

COSCO SHIPPING (UK) COMPANY LIMITED—See China COSCO Shipping Corporation Limited; *Int'l*, pg. 1493

COSCO SHIPPING URUGUAY—See China COSCO Shipping Corporation Limited; *Int'l*, pg. 1494

COSCO SHIPPING YUNNAN INTERNATIONAL FREIGHT CO., LTD.—See China COSCO Shipping Corporation Limited; *Int'l*, pg. 1494

COSCO SUZHOU INTERNATIONAL FREIGHT FORWARDING CO., LTD.—See China COSCO Shipping Corporation Limited; *Int'l*, pg. 1494

COSCO TAICANG INTERNATIONAL FREIGHT CO., LTD.—See China COSCO Shipping Corporation Limited; *Int'l*, pg. 1494

COSCO TIANJIN INTERNATIONAL FREIGHT CO., LTD.—See China COSCO Shipping Corporation Limited; *Int'l*, pg. 1494

COSCO WENZHOU INTERNATIONAL FREIGHT CO., LTD.—See China COSCO Shipping Corporation Limited; *Int'l*, pg. 1494

COSCO WUXI INTERNATIONAL FREIGHT CO., LTD.—See China COSCO Shipping Corporation Limited; *Int'l*, pg. 1494

COSCO YANGPU SHIPPING AGENCY LTD.—See China COSCO Shipping Corporation Limited; *Int'l*, pg. 1494

COSCO YANGZHOU INTERNATIONAL FREIGHT CO., LTD.—See China COSCO Shipping Corporation Limited; *Int'l*, pg. 1494

COSCO ZHEJIANG INTERNATIONAL FREIGHT CO., LTD.—See China COSCO Shipping Corporation Limited; *Int'l*, pg. 1494

COSCO ZHENJIANG INTERNATIONAL FREIGHT CO., LTD.—See China COSCO Shipping Corporation Limited; *Int'l*, pg. 1494

COSKOR SHIPPING CO., LTD.—See China COSCO Shipping Corporation Limited; *Int'l*, pg. 1494

COSTAMARE PARTICIPATIONS PLC—See Costamare Inc.; *Int'l*, pg. 1815

COSTAMARE PARTNERS LP—See Costamare Inc.; *Int'l*, pg. 1815

COUGAR LOGISTICS (MALAYSIA) SDN. BHD.—See DRB-HICOM Berhad; *Int'l*, pg. 2201

COURAGE - NEW AMEGO SHIPPING CORP.—See Courage Investment Group Limited; *Int'l*, pg. 1819

COURIER HOLDINGS LTD.—See Intuit Inc.; *U.S. Public*, pg. 1160

COX TRUCK BROKERAGE INC.; *U.S. Private*, pg. 1078

COYOTE LOGISTICS, LLC—See RXO Inc.; *U.S. Public*, pg. 1827

CPA INTERNATIONAL, INC.—See Gryphon Investors, LLC; *U.S. Private*, pg. 1799

CROWN RELOCATIONS—See Crown Worldwide Holdings Ltd.; *Int'l*, pg. 1858

CROWN WORLDWIDE MOVING & STORAGE COMPANY; *U.S. Private*, pg. 1112

CROZIER SCHWEIZ AG—See Iron Mountain Incorporated; *U.S. Public*, pg. 1172

CRR INDUSTRIES, INC.—See CSX Corporation; *U.S. Public*, pg. 602

CRR INDUSTRIES, INC.—See Norfolk Southern Corporation; *U.S. Public*, pg. 1535

CRST LOGISTICS INC.—See CRST International, Inc.; *U.S. Private*, pg. 1113

CRYO EXPRESS GMBH—See Cryoport, Inc.; *U.S. Public*, pg. 600

CRYO EXPRESS SP. Z O.O.—See Cryoport, Inc.; *U.S. Public*, pg. 600

CSAV AGENCIAMIENTO MARITIMO SPA—See Albert Ballin KG; *Int'l*, pg. 294

CSAV AGENCY FRANCE S.A.S.—See Albert Ballin KG; *Int'l*, pg. 294

CSAV AGENCY ITALY, S.P.A.—See Albert Ballin KG; *Int'l*, pg. 294

CSAV AGENCY LLC—See Albert Ballin KG; *Int'l*, pg. 294

CSAV AGENCY LTD.—See Albert Ballin KG; *Int'l*, pg. 294

CSAV ARGENTINA S.A.—See Albert Ballin KG; *Int'l*, pg. 294

CSAV DENIZCILIK ACENTASI A.S.—See Albert Ballin KG; *Int'l*, pg. 294

CSAV GROUP AGENCIES (INDIA) PVT LTD—See Albert Ballin KG; *Int'l*, pg. 294

CSAV GROUP AGENCIES (TAIWAN) LTD.—See Albert Ballin KG; *Int'l*, pg. 294

CSAV GROUP AGENCIES URUGUAY S.A.—See Albert Ballin KG; *Int'l*, pg. 294

CSAV GROUP AGENCY COLOMBIA LTDA.—See Albert Ballin KG; *Int'l*, pg. 294

CSAV GROUP (CHINA) SHIPPING CO. LTD.—See Albert Ballin KG; *Int'l*, pg. 294

CSAV GROUP (HONG KONG) LTD.—See Albert Ballin KG; *Int'l*, pg. 294

CSAV NORTH & CENTRAL EUROPE GMBH—See Albert Ballin KG; *Int'l*, pg. 294

CSAV NORTH & CENTRAL EUROPE N.V.—See Albert Ballin KG; *Int'l*, pg. 294

CSAV UK & IRELAND LIMITED—See Albert Ballin KG; *Int'l*, pg. 294

CSX TRANSPORTATION, INC.—See CSX Corporation; *U.S. Public*, pg. 602

CTE LOGISTICS; *U.S. Private*, pg. 1118

CTG US LLC; *U.S. Private*, pg. 1118

CTI FREIGHTLINES PTY LTD—See CTI Logistics Limited; *Int'l*, pg. 1871

CTI LOGISTICS LIMITED; *Int'l*, pg. 1871

CTX INC.—See Universal Logistics Holdings, Inc.; *U.S. Public*, pg. 2261

CUSTINO ENTERPRISES; *U.S. Private*, pg. 1127

CUSTOM SERVICES INTERNATIONAL LTD.—See CenTra, Inc.; *U.S. Private*, pg. 818

CV INTERNATIONAL, INC.; *U.S. Private*, pg. 1132

CWT GLOBELINK PTE LTD—See CWT International Limited; *Int'l*, pg. 1891

CYBERLOGITEC GLOBAL PTE. LTD.—See Eusu Holdings Co., Ltd.; *Int'l*, pg. 2559

CYBERLOGITEC SHANGHAI CO., LTD.—See Eusu Holdings Co., Ltd.; *Int'l*, pg. 2559

CYBERLOGITEC SPAIN S.L.U.—See Eusu Holdings Co., Ltd.; *Int'l*, pg. 2559

CYBERLOGITEC VIETNAM CO., LTD.—See Eusu Holdings Co., Ltd.; *Int'l*, pg. 2559

DACHSER GMBH & CO.; *Int'l*, pg. 1903

DACHSER TRANSPORT OF AMERICA INC.—See Dachser GmbH & Co.; *Int'l*, pg. 1904

DAFENG PORT HESHUN TECHNOLOGY COMPANY LIMITED; *Int'l*, pg. 1911

DAIICHI SANKYO LOGISTICS CO., LTD.—See Daiichi Sankyo Co., Ltd.; *Int'l*, pg. 1930

DAIKO SANGYO CO., LTD.—See Hanwa Co., Ltd.; *Int'l*, pg. 3261

DAIWA LOGISTICS VIETNAM CO., LTD.—See Daiwa House Industry Co., Ltd.; *Int'l*, pg. 1946

DAMCO A/S—See A.P. Moller-Maersk A/S; *Int'l*, pg. 26

DAMCO AUSTRALIA PTY. LTD.—See A.P. Moller-Maersk A/S; *Int'l*, pg. 26

DAMCO CHINA LIMITED—See A.P. Moller-Maersk A/S; *Int'l*, pg. 26

DAMCO CUSTOMS SERVICES, INC.—See A.P. Moller-Maersk A/S; *Int'l*, pg. 26

DAMCO FRANCE S.A.S.—See A.P. Moller-Maersk A/S; *Int'l*, pg. 26

DAMCO INDIA PRIVATE LIMITED—See A.P. Moller-Maersk A/S; *Int'l*, pg. 26

DAMCO INTERNATIONAL A/S—See A.P. Moller-Maersk A/S; *Int'l*, pg. 26

DAMCO ITALY S.R.L.—See A.P. Moller-Maersk A/S; *Int'l*, pg. 26

DAMCO UK LTD.—See A.P. Moller-Maersk A/S; *Int'l*, pg. 26

DANBOR SERVICE AS—See A.P. Moller-Maersk A/S; *Int'l*, pg. 26

DANIEL B. HASTINGS INC.; *U.S. Private*, pg. 1153

DANIEL F. YOUNG, INC.; *U.S. Private*, pg. 1153

DANZAS ABU DHABI LLC—See Deutsche Post AG; *Int'l*, pg. 2079

DANZAS BAHRAIN WLL—See Deutsche Post AG; *Int'l*, pg. 2079

DANZAS ECUADOR S.A.—See Deutsche Post AG; *Int'l*, pg. 2073

DANZAS FASHION SERVICE CENTERS B.V.—See Deutsche Post AG; *Int'l*, pg. 2079

DANZAS S.A.—See Deutsche Post AG; *Int'l*, pg. 2073

DATA2LOGISTICS EUROPE BV—See Platinum Equity, LLC; *U.S. Private*, pg. 3202

DATA2LOGISTICS, LLC—See Platinum Equity, LLC; *U.S. Private*, pg. 3202

DAVAO GULF MARINE SERVICES, INC.—See Chelsea Logistics and Infrastructure Holdings Corp.; *Int'l*, pg. 1460

DAVIS CARGO LLC; *U.S. Private*, pg. 1173

DAYTON & MICHIGAN RAILROAD CO.—See CSX Corporation; *U.S. Public*, pg. 602

DBA DISTRIBUTION SERVICES, INC.—See Radiant Logistics, Inc.; *U.S. Public*, pg. 1759

DB CARGO LOGISTICS GMBH—See Deutsche Bahn AG; *Int'l*, pg. 2050

DB CARGO NEDERLAND N.V.—See Deutsche Bahn AG; *Int'l*, pg. 2050

DB CARGO SCHWEIZ GMBH—See Deutsche Bahn AG; *Int'l*, pg. 2050

DB CARGO SPEDKOL SP. Z O.O.—See Deutsche Bahn AG; *Int'l*, pg. 2050

DBPORT SZCZECIN SP. Z O.O.—See Deutsche Bahn AG; *Int'l*, pg. 2051

D&D TRANSPORTATION SERVICES; *U.S. Private*, pg. 1137

DEDOLA GLOBAL LOGISTICS; *U.S. Private*, pg. 1188

DELL WILL CUSTOMS BROKERS (U.S.A.) INC.—See ATL Partners, LLC; *U.S. Private*, pg. 369

DEOLIX S.A.—See Allcargo Logistics Limited; *Int'l*, pg. 333

DEPENDABLE GLOBAL EXPRESS—See Dependable Highway Express Inc.; *U.S. Private*, pg. 1209

DEPENDABLE HAWAIIAN EXPRESS—See Dependable Highway Express Inc.; *U.S. Private*, pg. 1209

DERBY INDUSTRIES, LLC; *U.S. Private*, pg. 1209

DES MOINES TRUCK BROKERS, INC.—See Allen Lund Company, LLC; *U.S. Private*, pg. 179

488510 — FREIGHT TRANSPORTAT...

DESPRED PLC; *Int'l*, pg. 2046
DESTICON TRANSPORTATION SERVICES INC; *Int'l*, pg. 2046
DEUFOL AUSTRIA SUPPLY CHAIN SOLUTIONS GMBH—See Deufol SE; *Int'l*, pg. 2048
DEUFOL CESKA REPUBLIKA A.S.—See Deufol SE; *Int'l*, pg. 2048
DEUFOL CZ PRODUCTION S. R. O.—See Deufol SE; *Int'l*, pg. 2048
DEUFOL LIER NV—See Deufol SE; *Int'l*, pg. 2048
DEUFOL PORT OF ANTWERP NV—See Deufol SE; *Int'l*, pg. 2048
DEUFOL (SUZHOU) PACKAGING CO., LTD.—See Deufol SE; *Int'l*, pg. 2048
DEUFOL TECHNICS NV—See Deufol SE; *Int'l*, pg. 2049
DEUTSCHE BAHN CARGO ROMANIA S.R.L.—See Deutsche Bahn AG; *Int'l*, pg. 2051
DFDS DENIZCILIK VE TASIMACILIK A.S.—See DFDS A/S; *Int'l*, pg. 2094
DFDS LOGISTICS AB—See DFDS A/S; *Int'l*, pg. 2094
DFDS LOGISTICS AS—See DFDS A/S; *Int'l*, pg. 2094
DFDS LOGISTICS BV—See DFDS A/S; *Int'l*, pg. 2094
DFDS LOGISTICS GMBH—See DFDS A/S; *Int'l*, pg. 2094
DFDS LOGISTICS INTERMODAL A/S—See DFDS A/S; *Int'l*, pg. 2094
DFDS LOGISTICS (IRELAND) LTD.—See DFDS A/S; *Int'l*, pg. 2094
DFDS LOGISTICS NIJMEGEN B.V.—See DFDS A/S; *Int'l*, pg. 2094
DFDS LOGISTICS NV—See DFDS A/S; *Int'l*, pg. 2094
DFDS LOGISTICS OY—See DFDS A/S; *Int'l*, pg. 2094
DFDS LOGISTICS S.P.A.—See DFDS A/S; *Int'l*, pg. 2094
DFDS LOGISTICS WIJCHEN B.V.—See DFDS A/S; *Int'l*, pg. 2095
DFDS LOGISTICS WINTERSWIJK B.V.—See DFDS A/S; *Int'l*, pg. 2095
DFDS POLSKA SP. Z.O.O.—See DFDS A/S; *Int'l*, pg. 2095
DFDS SEAWAYS HISPANIA S.L—See DFDS A/S; *Int'l*, pg. 2095
DFDS SEAWAYS NV—See DFDS A/S; *Int'l*, pg. 2095
DFDS STEVEDORING A/S—See DFDS A/S; *Int'l*, pg. 2095
DF YOUNG AUSTRALIA PTY LTD—See Daniel F. Young, Inc.; *U.S. Private*, pg. 1154
DHL (COSTA RICA) S.A.—See Deutsche Post AG; *Int'l*, pg. 2073
DHL CUSTOMS BROKERAGE LTD.—See Deutsche Post AG; *Int'l*, pg. 2073
DHL DANZAS AIR & OCEAN (CANADA) INC.—See Deutsche Post AG; *Int'l*, pg. 2073
DHL DANZAS AIR & OCEAN—See Deutsche Post AG; *Int'l*, pg. 2073
DHL EKSPRES (SLOVENIJA), D.O.O.—See Deutsche Post AG; *Int'l*, pg. 2073
DHL EXPRESS (SCHWEIZ) AG—See Deutsche Post AG; *Int'l*, pg. 2074
DHL FINLAND—See Deutsche Post AG; *Int'l*, pg. 2073
DHL FREIGHT (BELGIUM) NV—See Deutsche Post AG; *Int'l*, pg. 2075
DHL FREIGHT GERMANY HOLDING GMBH—See Deutsche Post AG; *Int'l*, pg. 2072
DHL FREIGHT GMBH—See Deutsche Post AG; *Int'l*, pg. 2075
DHL FREIGHT HUNGARY FORWARDING AND LOGISTICS LTD.—See Deutsche Post AG; *Int'l*, pg. 2075
DHL FREIGHT (NETHERLANDS) B.V.—See Deutsche Post AG; *Int'l*, pg. 2075
DHL FREIGHT SERVICES (NETHERLANDS) B.V.—See Deutsche Post AG; *Int'l*, pg. 2075
DHL FREIGHT SPAIN, S.L.—See Deutsche Post AG; *Int'l*, pg. 2075
DHL FREIGHT (SWEDEN) AB—See Deutsche Post AG; *Int'l*, pg. 2075
DHL GLOBAL FORWARDING ADUANAS PERU S.A.—See Deutsche Post AG; *Int'l*, pg. 2075
DHL GLOBAL FORWARDING (ARGENTINA) S.A.—See Deutsche Post AG; *Int'l*, pg. 2072
DHL GLOBAL FORWARDING (AUSTRALIA) PTY LTD.—See Deutsche Post AG; *Int'l*, pg. 2075
DHL GLOBAL FORWARDING (BELGIUM) NV—See Deutsche Post AG; *Int'l*, pg. 2075
DHL GLOBAL FORWARDING (CAMEROON) PLC—See Deutsche Post AG; *Int'l*, pg. 2075
DHL GLOBAL FORWARDING (CANADA) INC.—See Deutsche Post AG; *Int'l*, pg. 2075
DHL GLOBAL FORWARDING (CHILE) S.A.—See Deutsche Post AG; *Int'l*, pg. 2075
DHL GLOBAL FORWARDING & CO. LLC—See Deutsche Post AG; *Int'l*, pg. 2075
DHL GLOBAL FORWARDING (COLOMBIA) LTDA.—See Deutsche Post AG; *Int'l*, pg. 2075
DHL GLOBAL FORWARDING COTE D'IVOIRE SA—See Deutsche Post AG; *Int'l*, pg. 2079
DHL GLOBAL FORWARDING (CZ) S. R. O.—See Deutsche Post AG; *Int'l*, pg. 2075
DHL GLOBAL FORWARDING (DENMARK) A /. S—See Deutsche Post AG; *Int'l*, pg. 2075
DHL GLOBAL FORWARDING (ECUADOR) S.A.—See Deutsche Post AG; *Int'l*, pg. 2075
DHL GLOBAL FORWARDING EGYPT S.A.E.—See Deutsche Post AG; *Int'l*, pg. 2075
DHL GLOBAL FORWARDING (FINLAND) OY—See Deutsche Post AG; *Int'l*, pg. 2075
DHL GLOBAL FORWARDING (GABON) SA—See Deutsche Post AG; *Int'l*, pg. 2075
DHL GLOBAL FORWARDING GMBH—See Deutsche Post AG; *Int'l*, pg. 2075
DHL GLOBAL FORWARDING (GUATEMALA) S.A.—See Deutsche Post AG; *Int'l*, pg. 2075
DHL GLOBAL FORWARDING HELLAS S.A.—See Deutsche Post AG; *Int'l*, pg. 2075
DHL GLOBAL FORWARDING (HONG KONG) LIMITED—See Deutsche Post AG; *Int'l*, pg. 2075
DHL GLOBAL FORWARDING HUNGARY KFT.—See Deutsche Post AG; *Int'l*, pg. 2075
DHL GLOBAL FORWARDING (IRELAND) LIMITED—See Deutsche Post AG; *Int'l*, pg. 2075
DHL GLOBAL FORWARDING (ITALY) S. P. A.—See Deutsche Post AG; *Int'l*, pg. 2075
DHL GLOBAL FORWARDING (KUWAIT) COMPANY WLL—See Deutsche Post AG; *Int'l*, pg. 2075
DHL GLOBAL FORWARDING LANKA (PRIVATE) LIMITED—See Deutsche Post AG; *Int'l*, pg. 2075
DHL GLOBAL FORWARDING LEBANON S.A.L.—See Deutsche Post AG; *Int'l*, pg. 2075
DHL GLOBAL FORWARDING (LUXEMBOURG) S.A.—See Deutsche Post AG; *Int'l*, pg. 2075
DHL GLOBAL FORWARDING MANAGEMENT (ASIA PACIFIC) PTE. LTD.—See Deutsche Post AG; *Int'l*, pg. 2076
DHL GLOBAL FORWARDING (MEXICO) S.A. DE C.V.—See Deutsche Post AG; *Int'l*, pg. 2075
DHL GLOBAL FORWARDING (NEW ZEALAND) LIMITED—See Deutsche Post AG; *Int'l*, pg. 2075
DHL GLOBAL FORWARDING (NICARAGUA) S.A.—See Deutsche Post AG; *Int'l*, pg. 2075
DHL GLOBAL FORWARDING NIGERIA LIMITED—See Deutsche Post AG; *Int'l*, pg. 2072
DHL GLOBAL FORWARDING PAKISTAN (PRIVATE) LIMITED—See Deutsche Post AG; *Int'l*, pg. 2076
DHL GLOBAL FORWARDING PERU S.A.—See Deutsche Post AG; *Int'l*, pg. 2076
DHL GLOBAL FORWARDING (PHILIPPINES) INC.—See Deutsche Post AG; *Int'l*, pg. 2075
DHL GLOBAL FORWARDING PORTUGAL, LDA.—See Deutsche Post AG; *Int'l*, pg. 2076
DHL GLOBAL FORWARDING (SENEGAL) S.A.—See Deutsche Post AG; *Int'l*, pg. 2075
DHL GLOBAL FORWARDING SP. Z.O.O.—See Deutsche Post AG; *Int'l*, pg. 2076
DHL GLOBAL FORWARDING (SWEDEN) AB—See Deutsche Post AG; *Int'l*, pg. 2075
DHL GLOBAL FORWARDING TASIMACILIK A.S.—See Deutsche Post AG; *Int'l*, pg. 2076
DHL GLOBAL FORWARDING (THAILAND) LIMITED—See Deutsche Post AG; *Int'l*, pg. 2072
DHL GLOBAL FORWARDING (UGANDA) LIMITED—See Deutsche Post AG; *Int'l*, pg. 2075
DHL GLOBAL FORWARDING (UK) LIMITED—See Deutsche Post AG; *Int'l*, pg. 2075
DHL GLOBAL FORWARDING VENEZUELA, C.A.—See Deutsche Post AG; *Int'l*, pg. 2076
DHL HUB LEIPZIG GMBH—See Deutsche Post AG; *Int'l*, pg. 2076
DHL LOGISTICS (CAMBODIA) LTD.—See Deutsche Post AG; *Int'l*, pg. 2077
DHL LOGISTICS (SCHWEIZ) AG—See Deutsche Post AG; *Int'l*, pg. 2077
DHL SOLUTIONS RETAIL GMBH—See Deutsche Post AG; *Int'l*, pg. 2077
DHL SUPPLY CHAIN (AUSTRALIA) PTY LIMITED—See Deutsche Post AG; *Int'l*, pg. 2077
DHL SUPPLY CHAIN (BELGIUM) NV—See Deutsche Post AG; *Int'l*, pg. 2077
DHL SUPPLY CHAIN (CHILE) S.A.—See Deutsche Post AG; *Int'l*, pg. 2077
DHL SUPPLY CHAIN (IRELAND) LIMITED—See Deutsche Post AG; *Int'l*, pg. 2077
DHL SUPPLY CHAIN K. K.—See Deutsche Post AG; *Int'l*, pg. 2078
DHL SUPPLY CHAIN (NORWAY) AS—See Deutsche Post AG; *Int'l*, pg. 2078
DHL SUPPLY CHAIN SINGAPORE PTE. LTD.—See Deutsche Post AG; *Int'l*, pg. 2078
DHX INCORPORATED; *U.S. Private*, pg. 1221
DIAMOND S SHIPPING GROUP, INC.; *U.S. Private*, pg. 1224
DIESEL RECON COMPANY—See Cummins Inc.; *U.S. Public*, pg. 607
DIETL INTERNATIONAL SERVICES, INC.—See ATL Partners, LLC; *U.S. Private*, pg. 369
DIMERCO EXPRESS CORPORATION; *Int'l*, pg. 2126
DIMERCO EXPRESS (TAIWAN) CORPORATION—See Dimerco Express Corporation; *Int'l*, pg. 2126
DIMERCO EXPRESS (TAIWAN) CORPORATION—See Dimerco Express Corporation; *Int'l*, pg. 2126
DIMERCO EXPRESS (TAIWAN) CORPORATION—See Dimerco Express Corporation; *Int'l*, pg. 2126
DIMERCO EXPRESS (TAIWAN) CORPORATION—See Dimerco Express Corporation; *Int'l*, pg. 2126
DIMERCO EXPRESS USA CORP.—See Dimerco Express Corporation; *Int'l*, pg. 2126
DISPATCH TRANSPORTATION INC.; *U.S. Private*, pg. 1238
DIVERSIFIED FREIGHT SYSTEM CORPORATION—See Dimerco Express Corporation; *Int'l*, pg. 2126
D.J. POWERS COMPANY INC.; *U.S. Private*, pg. 1142
DJS INTERNATIONAL SERVICES INC.—See BDP International Inc.; *U.S. Private*, pg. 502
DOAN XA PORT JSC; *Int'l*, pg. 2152
DOGUS DIDIM MARINA ISLETMELERI VE TICARET A.S.—See Dogus Holding AS; *Int'l*, pg. 2154
DOKER-PORT SP. Z O.O.—See Deutsche Bahn AG; *Int'l*, pg. 2051
DON CAMERON & ASSOCIATES, INC.—See Radiant Logistics, Inc.; *U.S. Public*, pg. 1759
DONG BANG TRANSPORT LOGISTICS CO., LTD.; *Int'l*, pg. 2163
DONGGUAN DHL SUPPLY CHAIN CO., LTD.—See Deutsche Post AG; *Int'l*, pg. 2078
DONG NAI MARITIME SERVICES JOINT STOCK COMPANY—See Dong Nai Port; *Int'l*, pg. 2164
DSV AIR & SEA CO., LTD.—See DSV A/S; *Int'l*, pg. 2211
DSV AIR & SEA CO., LTD.—See DSV A/S; *Int'l*, pg. 2211
DSV AIR & SEA GMBH—See DSV A/S; *Int'l*, pg. 2211
DSV AIR & SEA INC.—See DSV A/S; *Int'l*, pg. 2211
DSV AIR & SEA LIMITED—See DSV A/S; *Int'l*, pg. 2211
DSV AIR & SEA LIMITED—See DSV A/S; *Int'l*, pg. 2211
DSV AIR & SEA LIMITED—See DSV A/S; *Int'l*, pg. 2211
DSV AIR & SEA LTD—See DSV A/S; *Int'l*, pg. 2211
DSV AIR & SEA LTD—See DSV A/S; *Int'l*, pg. 2211
DSV AIR & SEA LTD.—See DSV A/S; *Int'l*, pg. 2211
DSV AIR & SEA PAKISTAN (SMC-PRIVATE) LIMITED—See DSV A/S; *Int'l*, pg. 2211
DSV AIR & SEA (PTY) LIMITED—See DSV A/S; *Int'l*, pg. 2211
DSV AIR & SEA SP. Z.O.O—See DSV A/S; *Int'l*, pg. 2212
DSV PANALPINA MARINE SHIPPING W.L.L.—See DSV A/S; *Int'l*, pg. 2212
DSV SOLUTIONS LDA.—See DSV A/S; *Int'l*, pg. 2213
DSV SOUTH AFRICA (PTY) LTD.—See DSV A/S; *Int'l*, pg. 2213
DSV TRANSPORT INTERNATIONAL S.A.—See DSV A/S; *Int'l*, pg. 2213
DSV TRANSPORT (US), INC.—See DSV A/S; *Int'l*, pg. 2213
DSV-UTI EGYPT LTD.—See DSV A/S; *Int'l*, pg. 2213
DTS LOGISTICS LLC—See DTS Companies Inc.; *U.S. Private*, pg. 1282
EAGLE MOVING SYSTEMS INC.—See Ambassador Van Lines Inc.; *U.S. Private*, pg. 217
EASTCOMTRANS LLP; *Int'l*, pg. 2271
E.A TECHNIQUE (M) BHD; *Int'l*, pg. 2250
E.C.B N.V.—See Allcargo Logistics Limited; *Int'l*, pg. 333
ECI TAIWAN CO., LTD.—See Expeditors International of Washington, Inc.; *U.S. Public*, pg. 810
ECONOCARIBE CONSOLIDATORS INC.—See Allcargo Logistics Limited; *Int'l*, pg. 334
ECONOQUALITY FREIGHT FORWARDERS, INC.—See M.B.R. Industries, Inc.; *U.S. Private*, pg. 2528
ECU AUSTRALIA PTY LTD.—See Allcargo Logistics Limited; *Int'l*, pg. 333
ECU INTERNATIONAL N.V.—See Allcargo Logistics Limited; *Int'l*, pg. 333
ECU LINE ABU DHABI LLC—See Allcargo Logistics Limited; *Int'l*, pg. 333
ECU LINE ALGERIE S.A.R.L.—See Allcargo Logistics Limited; *Int'l*, pg. 333
ECU-LINE CANADA INC.—See Allcargo Logistics Limited; *Int'l*, pg. 334
ECU LINE CHILE S.A.—See Allcargo Logistics Limited; *Int'l*, pg. 333
ECU LINE CHINA LTD.—See Allcargo Logistics Limited; *Int'l*, pg. 333
ECU LINE COTE D'IVOIRE SARL—See Allcargo Logistics Limited; *Int'l*, pg. 333
ECU-LINE CZECH S.R.O.—See Allcargo Logistics Limited; *Int'l*, pg. 334
ECU-LINE DE COLOMBIA S.A—See Allcargo Logistics Limited; *Int'l*, pg. 334
ECU LINE DEL ECUADOR S.A.—See Allcargo Logistics Limited; *Int'l*, pg. 333
ECU LINE DOHA W.L.L.—See Allcargo Logistics Limited; *Int'l*, pg. 333
ECU LINE EGYPT LTD.—See Allcargo Logistics Limited; *Int'l*, pg. 333
ECU-LINE (GERMANY) GMBH—See Allcargo Logistics Limited; *Int'l*, pg. 334
ECU-LINE GUANGZHOU LTD.—See Allcargo Logistics Limited; *Int'l*, pg. 334
ECU LINE GUATEMALA S.A.—See Allcargo Logistics Limited; *Int'l*, pg. 333
ECU-LINE HONG KONG LTD.—See Allcargo Logistics Limited; *Int'l*, pg. 334
ECU-LINE MALTA LTD.—See Allcargo Logistics Limited; *Int'l*, pg. 334

N.A.I.C.S. INDEX

488510 — FREIGHT TRANSPORTAT...

ECU LINE MAROC S.A.—See Allcargo Logistics Limited; *Int'l*, pg. 333
ECU LINE MIDDLEEAST LLC—See Allcargo Logistics Limited; *Int'l*, pg. 333
ECU-LINE PANAMA S.A.—See Allcargo Logistics Limited; *Int'l*, pg. 334
ECU-LINE PERU S.A.—See Allcargo Logistics Limited; *Int'l*, pg. 334
ECU LINE PHILIPPINES INC.—See Allcargo Logistics Limited; *Int'l*, pg. 334
ECU LINE ROMANIA S.R.L.—See Allcargo Logistics Limited; *Int'l*, pg. 333
ECU LINE ROTTERDAM B.V.—See Allcargo Logistics Limited; *Int'l*, pg. 333
ECU LINE S.A. (PTY) LTD.—See Allcargo Logistics Limited; *Int'l*, pg. 333
ECU LINE SINGAPORE PTE. LTD.—See Allcargo Logistics Limited; *Int'l*, pg. 333
ECU LINE SPAIN S.L.—See Allcargo Logistics Limited; *Int'l*, pg. 333
ECU LINE (THAILAND) CO.LTD.—See Allcargo Logistics Limited; *Int'l*, pg. 333
ECU LOGISTICS S.A.—See Allcargo Logistics Limited; *Int'l*, pg. 333
ECU NORDIC OY—See Allcargo Logistics Limited; *Int'l*, pg. 333
ECU WORLDWIDE (MALAYSIA) SDN BHD—See Allcargo Logistics Limited; *Int'l*, pg. 334
EFESANPORT—See Efesan Group; *Int'l*, pg. 2319
EFL EXPRESS PRIVATE LIMITED—See Expolanka Holdings PLC; *Int'l*, pg. 2589
EFL GLOBAL B.V.—See Expolanka Holdings PLC; *Int'l*, pg. 2589
EFL MALAYSIA SDN. BHD.—See Expolanka Holdings PLC; *Int'l*, pg. 2589
EIDAI STAFF SERVICE CO., LTD.—See Eidai Co., Ltd.; *Int'l*, pg. 2328
EIMSKIP UK LTD.—See Eimskipafelag Islands Hf.; *Int'l*, pg. 2332
ELFS BROKERAGE LLC—See Janel Corporation; *U.S. Public*, pg. 1187
ELV MULTIMODAL C.A.—See Allcargo Logistics Limited; *Int'l*, pg. 333
ELWA GHANA LTD.—See Allcargo Logistics Limited; *Int'l*, pg. 334
EMERALD AIRWAYS LTD.; *Int'l*, pg. 2377
EMILIA DEVELOPMENT LTD.; *Int'l*, pg. 2380
EMO-TRANS INC.; *U.S. Private*, pg. 1383
ENGLAND LOGISTICS, INC.—See C.R. England, Inc.; *U.S. Private*, pg. 708
ENTERPRISE TMS LLC—See C.H. Robinson Worldwide, Inc.; *U.S. Public*, pg. 415
ENTERTAINMENT TRANSPORTATION SPECIALISTS; *U.S. Private*, pg. 1405
EPES LOGISTICS SERVICES, INC.—See EPES Carriers Inc.; *U.S. Private*, pg. 1412
ERIN INTERNATIONAL CO., LTD.—See Dynam Japan Holdings Co., Ltd.; *Int'l*, pg. 2239
ERMEWA FRANCE—See Ermewa Interservices Sarl; *Int'l*, pg. 2494
ERMEWA INTERSERVICES SARL; *Int'l*, pg. 2494
ESTENSON LOGISTICS LLC—See Hub Group, Inc.; *U.S. Public*, pg. 1065
ESTES FORWARDING WORLDWIDE LLC—See Estes Express Lines, Inc.; *U.S. Private*, pg. 1429
ETC INC. INTERNATIONAL LOGISTICS; *U.S. Private*, pg. 1431
ETERNITY SHIPPING COMPANY—See Euroseas Ltd.; *Int'l*, pg. 2558
EUROFINS ENVIRONNEMENT LOGISTIQUE FRANCE SAS—See Eurofins Scientific S.E.; *Int'l*, pg. 2541
EURONAV NV; *Int'l*, pg. 2554
EURONAV SINGAPORE PTE. LTD.—See Euronav NV; *Int'l*, pg. 2554
EURONAV (UK) AGENCIES LTD.—See Euronav NV; *Int'l*, pg. 2554
EUROPORTE FRANCE SAS—See Getlink SE; *Int'l*, pg. 2953
EUROTAINER SA—See Ermewa Interservices Sarl; *Int'l*, pg. 2494
EUSU LOGISTICS CO., LTD.—See Eusu Holdings Co., Ltd.; *Int'l*, pg. 2559
EUSU LOGISTICS (HONG KONG) CO., LTD.—See Eusu Holdings Co., Ltd.; *Int'l*, pg. 2559
EUSU LOGISTICS JAPAN CO., LTD.—See Eusu Holdings Co., Ltd.; *Int'l*, pg. 2559
EUSU LOGISTICS LLC—See Eusu Holdings Co., Ltd.; *Int'l*, pg. 2559
EUSU LOGISTICS (M) SDN. BHD.—See Eusu Holdings Co., Ltd.; *Int'l*, pg. 2559
EUSU LOGISTICS (SHANGHAI) CO., LTD.—See Eusu Holdings Co., Ltd.; *Int'l*, pg. 2559
EUSU LOGISTICS (SHENZHEN) CO., LTD.—See Eusu Holdings Co., Ltd.; *Int'l*, pg. 2559
EUSU LOGISTICS SINGAPORE PTE. LTD.—See Eusu Holdings Co., Ltd.; *Int'l*, pg. 2559
EUSU LOGISTICS SPAIN S.A.—See Eusu Holdings Co., Ltd.; *Int'l*, pg. 2559

EUSU LOGISTICS THAILAND CO., LTD.—See Eusu Holdings Co., Ltd.; *Int'l*, pg. 2559
EVANS DELIVERY COMPANY, INC.—See Calera Capital Management, Inc.; *U.S. Private*, pg. 717
EVERGREEB SHIPPING AGENCY (CHILE) SPA.—See Evergreen Marine Corporation (Taiwan) Ltd.; *Int'l*, pg. 2566
EVERGREEB SHIPPING AGENCY (MEXICO) S.A. DE C.V.—See Evergreen Marine Corporation (Taiwan) Ltd.; *Int'l*, pg. 2566
EVERGREEN MARINE CORP. (MALAYSIA) SDN. BHD.—See Evergreen Marine Corporation (Taiwan) Ltd.; *Int'l*, pg. 2566
EVERGREEN MARINE CORPORATION (TAIWAN) LTD.; *Int'l*, pg. 2566
EVERGREEN MARINE (HONG KONG) LIMITED—See Evergreen Marine Corporation (Taiwan) Ltd.; *Int'l*, pg. 2566
EVERGREEN SHIPPING AGENCY (COLOMBIA) S.A.S.—See Evergreen Marine Corporation (Taiwan) Ltd.; *Int'l*, pg. 2566
EVERGREEN SHIPPING AGENCY (INDIA) PVT. LTD.—See Evergreen Marine Corporation (Taiwan) Ltd.; *Int'l*, pg. 2566
EVERGREEN SHIPPING AGENCY (KOREA) CORPORATION—See Evergreen Marine Corporation (Taiwan) Ltd.; *Int'l*, pg. 2566
EVERGREEN SHIPPING AGENCY (PERU) S.A.C.—See Evergreen Marine Corporation (Taiwan) Ltd.; *Int'l*, pg. 2566
EVERGREEN SHIPPING AGENCY (RUSSIA) LTD.—See Evergreen Marine Corporation (Taiwan) Ltd.; *Int'l*, pg. 2566
EVERGREEN SHIPPING AGENCY (THAILAND) CO., LTD.—See Evergreen Marine Corporation (Taiwan) Ltd.; *Int'l*, pg. 2566
EVERGREEN SHIPPING SERVICE (CAMBODIA) CO., LTD.—See Evergreen Marine Corporation (Taiwan) Ltd.; *Int'l*, pg. 2566
EVER HARVEST GROUP HOLDINGS LIMITED; *Int'l*, pg. 2562
EVO LOGISTICS, LLC—See EVO Transportation & Energy Services, Inc.; *U.S. Public*, pg. 804
EXEL SUPPLY CHAIN SOLUTIONS LTD.—See Deutsche Post AG; *Int'l*, pg. 2080
EXPECT DISTRIBUTION; *Int'l*, pg. 2586
EXPEDITED LOGISTICS & FREIGHT SERVICES, LTD.—See Janel Corporation; *U.S. Public*, pg. 1187
EXPEDITORS CAMBODIA LTD.—See Expeditors International of Washington, Inc.; *U.S. Public*, pg. 810
EXPEDITORS CANADA, INC.—See Expeditors International of Washington, Inc.; *U.S. Public*, pg. 810
EXPEDITORS DE COLOMBIA LTDA.—See Expeditors International of Washington, Inc.; *U.S. Public*, pg. 812
EXPEDITORS GUATEMALA S.A.—See Expeditors International of Washington, Inc.; *U.S. Public*, pg. 810
EXPEDITORS INTERNATIONAL BAHRAIN (SPC)—See Expeditors International of Washington, Inc.; *U.S. Public*, pg. 811
EXPEDITORS INTERNATIONAL B.V.—See Expeditors International of Washington, Inc.; *U.S. Public*, pg. 811
EXPEDITORS INTERNATIONAL CARGO CO. LTD.—See Expeditors International of Washington, Inc.; *U.S. Public*, pg. 811
EXPEDITORS INTERNATIONAL DE MEXICO, S.A. DE C.V.—See Expeditors International of Washington, Inc.; *U.S. Public*, pg. 811
EXPEDITORS INTERNATIONAL DO BRASIL LTDA.—See Expeditors International of Washington, Inc.; *U.S. Public*, pg. 811
EXPEDITORS INTERNATIONAL ESPANA, S.A.—See Expeditors International of Washington, Inc.; *U.S. Public*, pg. 811
EXPEDITORS INTERNATIONAL FORWARDING AND CLEARING, LLC—See Expeditors International of Washington, Inc.; *U.S. Public*, pg. 811
EXPEDITORS INTERNATIONAL FRANCE, SAS—See Expeditors International of Washington, Inc.; *U.S. Public*, pg. 811
EXPEDITORS INTERNATIONAL GMBH—See Expeditors International of Washington, Inc.; *U.S. Public*, pg. 811
EXPEDITORS INTERNATIONAL (HELLAS) S.A.—See Expeditors International of Washington, Inc.; *U.S. Public*, pg. 810
EXPEDITORS INTERNATIONAL HUNGARY KFT.—See Expeditors International of Washington, Inc.; *U.S. Public*, pg. 811
EXPEDITORS INTERNATIONAL ITALIA S.R.L.—See Expeditors International of Washington, Inc.; *U.S. Public*, pg. 811
EXPEDITORS INTERNATIONAL-JORDAN—See Expeditors International of Washington, Inc.; *U.S. Public*, pg. 811
EXPEDITORS INTERNATIONAL - LEBANON (S.A.L.)—See Expeditors International of Washington, Inc.; *U.S. Public*, pg. 811
EXPEDITORS INTERNATIONAL NORWAY AS—See Expeditors International of Washington, Inc.; *U.S. Public*, pg. 811
EXPEDITORS INTERNATIONAL N.V.—See Expeditors International of Washington, Inc.; *U.S. Public*, pg. 811
EXPEDITORS INTERNATIONAL (NZ) LTD.—See Expeditors International of Washington, Inc.; *U.S. Public*, pg. 810
EXPEDITORS INTERNATIONAL PTY. LIMITED—See Expeditors International of Washington, Inc.; *U.S. Public*, pg. 811
EXPEDITORS INTERNATIONAL (PUERTO RICO) INC.—See Expeditors International of Washington, Inc.; *U.S. Public*, pg. 811
EXPEDITORS INTERNATIONAL ROMANIA S.R.L.—See Expeditors International of Washington, Inc.; *U.S. Public*, pg. 811
EXPEDITORS INTERNATIONAL SVERIGE AB—See Expeditors International of Washington, Inc.; *U.S. Public*, pg. 811
EXPEDITORS INTERNATIONAL (SWITZERLAND) SAGL—See Expeditors International of Washington, Inc.; *U.S. Public*, pg. 811
EXPEDITORS INTERNATIONAL TRADING (SHANGHAI) CO., LTD—See Expeditors International of Washington, Inc.; *U.S. Public*, pg. 811
EXPEDITORS INTERNATIONAL (UK) LTD.—See Expeditors International of Washington, Inc.; *U.S. Public*, pg. 811
EXPEDITORS IRELAND LIMITED—See Expeditors International of Washington, Inc.; *U.S. Public*, pg. 811
EXPEDITORS JAPAN KK—See Expeditors International of Washington, Inc.; *U.S. Public*, pg. 811
EXPEDITORS MAR Y TIERRA S.A.—See Expeditors International of Washington, Inc.; *U.S. Public*, pg. 811
EXPEDITORS PERU S.A.C.—See Expeditors International of Washington, Inc.; *U.S. Public*, pg. 811
EXPEDITORS POLSKA SP. Z O. O.—See Expeditors International of Washington, Inc.; *U.S. Public*, pg. 811
EXPEDITORS (PORTUGAL) TRANSITARIOS INTERNACIONAIS LDA.—See Expeditors International of Washington, Inc.; *U.S. Public*, pg. 810
EXPEDITORS SPEDITIONS GMBH—See Expeditors International of Washington, Inc.; *U.S. Public*, pg. 811
EXPO FREIGHT (SHANGHAI) LIMITED—See Expolanka Holdings PLC; *Int'l*, pg. 2589
EXPRESS AIR FREIGHT UNLIMITED, INC.; *U.S. Private*, pg. 1451
EXPRESS CUSTOMS CLEARANCE (USA), INC.—See A-Sonic Aerospace Limited; *Int'l*, pg. 21
FARRELL FORWARDING CO. INC.; *U.S. Private*, pg. 1481
FAR SHIPPING LANKA (PVT) LTD.—See Hemas Holdings PLC; *Int'l*, pg. 3340
FARWEST FREIGHT SYSTEMS INC.; *U.S. Private*, pg. 1481
FASHIONPARTNER GROUP SAS—See Holding Financiere Dimotrans SA; *Int'l*, pg. 3450
FASTFRATE HOLDINGS INC. - CALGARY DIVISION—See Fenway Partners, LLC; *U.S. Private*, pg. 1496
FEDEX CUSTOM CRITICAL, INC.—See FedEx Corporation; *U.S. Public*, pg. 827
FEDEX TRADE NETWORKS, INC.—See FedEx Corporation; *U.S. Public*, pg. 828
FEDEX TRADE NETWORKS—See FedEx Corporation; *U.S. Public*, pg. 828
FEDEX TRADE NETWORKS TRADE SERVICES, INC.—See FedEx Corporation; *U.S. Public*, pg. 828
FEDEX TRADE NETWORKS TRANSPORT & BROKERAGE (CANADA), INC—See FedEx Corporation; *U.S. Public*, pg. 828
FEDEX TRADE NETWORKS TRANSPORT & BROKERAGE, INC.—See FedEx Corporation; *U.S. Public*, pg. 828
FEDEX UK LIMITED—See FedEx Corporation; *U.S. Public*, pg. 828
FERROCARRILES CHIAPAS-MAYAB, S.A. DE C.V.—See Brookfield Infrastructure Partners L.P.; *Int'l*, pg. 1191
FERROCARRILES CHIAPAS-MAYAB, S.A. DE C.V.—See GIC Pte. Ltd.; *Int'l*, pg. 2965
FERSPED A.D.; *Int'l*, pg. 2646
FERTIMPORT S.A.—See Bunge Limited; *U.S. Public*, pg. 412
FERTRADE D.O.O.—See Ferspred A.D.; *Int'l*, pg. 2646
FESCO LINES MANAGEMENT LTD.—See Far Eastern Shipping Company OJSC; *Int'l*, pg. 2617
FESCO LOGISTIC LLC—See Far Eastern Shipping Company OJSC; *Int'l*, pg. 2617
FETCH LOGISTICS, INC.; *U.S. Private*, pg. 1499
FINNAIR CARGO OY—See Finnair Plc; *Int'l*, pg. 2676
FINNLINES BELGIUM N.V.—See Grimaldi Group SpA; *Int'l*, pg. 3085
FINNLINES POLSKA SP.Z.O.O—See Grimaldi Group SpA; *Int'l*, pg. 3085
FINNLINK AB—See Grimaldi Group SpA; *Int'l*, pg. 3085
FINNSTEVE OY—See Grimaldi Group SpA; *Int'l*, pg. 3085
FINNWEST N.V.—See Grimaldi Group SpA; *Int'l*, pg. 3085
FIRST-DDSG LOGISTICS HOLDING GMBH—See Ferrexpo plc; *Int'l*, pg. 2641
FIRST OLSEN AS—See Fred. Olsen & Co.; *Int'l*, pg. 2768
FISTER DISTRIBUTION INC.—See Fister Incorporated; *U.S. Private*, pg. 1535

488510 — FREIGHT TRANSPORTAT...

FITZMARK, INC.—See Calera Capital Management, Inc.; *U.S. Private*, pg. 717
FLAMINGO LINE EL SALVADOR S.A. DE C.V.—See Allcargo Logistics Limited; *Int'l*, pg. 334
FLEETWOOD TRANSPORTATION SERVICES INC.; *U.S. Private*, pg. 1542
FLEXPORT INC.; *U.S. Private*, pg. 1544
FLORIDA VESSEL MANAGEMENT LLC—See Albert Ballin KG; *Int'l*, pg. 294
FM GLOBAL LOGISTICS (IPOH) SDN. BHD.—See FM Global Logistics Holdings Berhad; *Int'l*, pg. 2717
FM GLOBAL LOGISTICS (M) SDN. BHD.—See FM Global Logistics Holdings Berhad; *Int'l*, pg. 2717
FM GLOBAL LOGISTICS (M) SDN. BHD.—See FM Global Logistics Holdings Berhad; *Int'l*, pg. 2717
FM GLOBAL LOGISTICS PTY LTD.—See FM Global Logistics Holdings Berhad; *Int'l*, pg. 2717
FM-HELLMANN WORLDWIDE LOGISTICS SDN. BHD.—See FM Global Logistics Holdings Berhad; *Int'l*, pg. 2717
FMI EXPRESS CORP.; *U.S. Private*, pg. 1554
FNS, INC.; *U.S. Private*, pg. 1556
FONUA LTD.; *Int'l*, pg. 2726
FORDE REEDEREI SEETOURISTIK IBERIA S.L.U.—See FRS GmbH & Co. KG; *Int'l*, pg. 2797
FORTE TRANSPORTATION LOGISTICS; *U.S. Private*, pg. 1575
FORTIS TUGS CORPORATION—See Chelsea Logistics and Infrastructure Holdings Corp.; *Int'l*, pg. 1460
FORT PITT CONSOLIDATORS INC.; *U.S. Private*, pg. 1574
FORU WORLDWIDE INC.; *Int'l*, pg. 2744
FORWARD AIR CORPORATION; *U.S. Public*, pg. 874
FORWARD AIR, INC.—See Forward Air Corporation; *U.S. Public*, pg. 874
FOUR WINDS TRUCK BROKERS, INC.; *U.S. Private*, pg. 1583
FRANCESCO PARISI S.P.A.; *Int'l*, pg. 2759
FRAPORT SLOVENIJA D.O.O—See Fraport AG; *Int'l*, pg. 2764
FRED. OLSEN FREIGHT LIMITED—See Braemar PLC; *Int'l*, pg. 1136
FREESEAS INC.; *Int'l*, pg. 2771
FREIGHQUOTE.COM, INC.—See C.H. Robinson Worldwide, Inc.; *U.S. Public*, pg. 415
FREIGHT 4U LOGISTICS NV-SA—See bpost NV/SA; *Int'l*, pg. 1133
FREIGHT-BASE CUSTOMS BROKERS INC.—See Freight-Base Services Inc.; *U.S. Private*, pg. 1607
FREIGHT-BASE SERVICES INC.; *U.S. Private*, pg. 1607
FREIGHTLINER OF NEW HAMPSHIRE; *U.S. Private*, pg. 1608
FREIGHT MANAGEMENT (PENANG) SDN. BHD.—See FM Global Logistics Holdings Berhad; *Int'l*, pg. 2717
FREIGHT MANAGEMENT TEAM INC; *U.S. Private*, pg. 1607
FREIGHTQUOTE.COM—See C.H. Robinson Worldwide, Inc.; *U.S. Public*, pg. 414
FREIGHT SOLUTION PROVIDERS; *U.S. Private*, pg. 1607
FREIGHTWISE, INC.—See Berkshire Hathaway Inc.; *U.S. Public*, pg. 303
FRIDENSON LOGISTIC SERVICES LTD.; *Int'l*, pg. 2791
FRONTLINE FREIGHT, INC.; *U.S. Private*, pg. 1616
FRS HELGOLINE GMBH & CO. KG—See FRS GmbH & Co. KG; *Int'l*, pg. 2797
FRS OFFSHORE GMBH & CO. KG—See FRS GmbH & Co. KG; *Int'l*, pg. 2797
FTAI INFRASTRUCTURE, INC.; *U.S. Public*, pg. 888
FUJITRANS CORPORATION; *Int'l*, pg. 2832
FUJITRANS U.S.A., INC.—See Fujitrans Corporation; *Int'l*, pg. 2832
FULMER LOGISTICS SERVICES, INC.; *U.S. Private*, pg. 1621
GAC-NURMINEN NAVIS OY—See Gulf Agency Company Ltd.; *Int'l*, pg. 3179
GAHTANI INTERNATIONAL MARITIME AGENCY—See HAK Algahtani Group of Companies; *Int'l*, pg. 3219
GATEWAYS INTERNATIONAL INC.—See The Pasha Group; *U.S. Private*, pg. 4091
GATEWAY TERMINALS INDIA PVT. LTD.—See A.P. Moller-Maersk A/S; *Int'l*, pg. 26
GEMADEPT CORPORATION; *Int'l*, pg. 2915
GEMADEPT HAI PHONG ONE MEMBER COMPANY LIMITED—See CJ Corporation; *Int'l*, pg. 1633
GENERAL STEAMSHIP AGENCIES; *U.S. Private*, pg. 1667
GENERAL TRANSPORTATION, INC.; *U.S. Private*, pg. 1667
GENERAL TRANSPORTATION SERVICES; *U.S. Private*, pg. 1667
GENPRO TRANSPORTATION INC.; *U.S. Private*, pg. 1673
GEOLOGISTICS CORPORATION—See Agility; *Int'l*, pg. 210
GEORG FISCHER PTE. LTD.—See Georg Fischer AG; *Int'l*, pg. 2936
GH TRANSPORT LIMITED—See HAK Algahtani Group of Companies; *Int'l*, pg. 3219
GIBUNCO SHIP AGENCY SL—See Gibunco Group Limited; *Int'l*, pg. 2963
GIF SERVICES INC.; *U.S. Private*, pg. 1697
GIORGIO GORI INTERNATIONAL FREIGHT FORWARDS (PTY) LTD.—See Deutsche Post AG; *Int'l*, pg. 2080
GKN FREIGHT SERVICES LTD., EDGWARE—See GKN plc; *Int'l*, pg. 2985
GLOBAL CLEARING HOUSE SYSTEMS K.S.C.C.—See Agility; *Int'l*, pg. 210
GLOBAL FORWARDING ENTERPRISES LIMITED LIABILITY COMPANY; *U.S. Private*, pg. 1714
GLOBAL FREIGHT SOURCE—See Providence Equity Partners L.L.C.; *U.S. Private*, pg. 3292
GLOBAL TRADING RESOURCES, INC.—See Janel Corporation; *U.S. Public*, pg. 1187
GLOBAL TRANSPORTATION SERVICES, INC.—See The Jordan Company, L.P.; *U.S. Private*, pg. 4060
GLOBALTRANZ ENTERPRISES, INC.—See Providence Equity Partners L.L.C.; *U.S. Private*, pg. 3292
GLOBE EXPRESS SERVICES LTD.; *U.S. Private*, pg. 1719
GLOBELINK-TRANS (TIANJIN) INTERNATIONAL FORWARDING CO., LTD.—See CWT International Limited; *Int'l*, pg. 1891
GLOBUS MARITIME LIMITED; *Int'l*, pg. 3008
GLSG GERSTHOFER LOGISTIK- UND SPEDITIONSGESELLSCHAFT MBH; *Int'l*, pg. 3011
GODDARDS SHIPPING & TOURS LIMITED—See Goddard Enterprises Limited; *Int'l*, pg. 3019
GOLDEN HOUR DATA SYSTEMS, INC.—See Asahi Kasei Corporation; *Int'l*, pg. 597
GOLDEN OCEAN MANAGEMENT ASIA PTE. LTD.—See Golden Ocean Group Ltd.; *Int'l*, pg. 3030
GOLDEN OCEAN MANAGEMENT AS—See Golden Ocean Group Ltd.; *Int'l*, pg. 3030
GOLD STAR TRANSPORTATION INC.; *U.S. Private*, pg. 1728
GOODNIGHT INTERNATIONAL, LLC; *U.S. Private*, pg. 1740
GOTHENBURG RO/RO TERMINAL AB—See DFDS A/S; *Int'l*, pg. 2095
GRAF AIR FREIGHT INCORPORATION; *U.S. Private*, pg. 1750
GRAMPET SA; *Int'l*, pg. 3053
GRAMPIAN INTERNATIONAL FREIGHT B.V.—See DSV A/S; *Int'l*, pg. 2214
GREATWIDE AMERICAN TRANS-FREIGHT, LLC—See Centerbridge Partners, L.P.; *U.S. Private*, pg. 815
GREATWIDE LOGISTICS SERVICES, INC.—See Centerbridge Partners, L.P.; *U.S. Private*, pg. 815
GREENTREE TRANSPORTATION COMPANY—See Transport Investments, Inc.; *U.S. Private*, pg. 4210
GREENWAY TRANSPORTATION SERVICES; *U.S. Private*, pg. 1781
GRIEG TRIANGLE LOGISTICS B.V.—See DSV A/S; *Int'l*, pg. 2214
GRINDROD LIMITED - ISLAND VIEW SHIPPING DIVISION—See Grindrod Limited; *Int'l*, pg. 3086
GRINDROD LIMITED - UNICORN SHIPPING DIVISION—See Grindrod Limited; *Int'l*, pg. 3086
GRINDROD MARINE SERVICES—See Grindrod Limited; *Int'l*, pg. 3086
GRINDROD SHIPPING SERVICES UK LIMITED—See Grindrod Shipping Holdings Ltd.; *Int'l*, pg. 3087
GRINDROD SHIPPING (SOUTH AFRICA) PTY. LTD.—See Grindrod Shipping Holdings Ltd.; *Int'l*, pg. 3087
GRINDROD SHIPS AGENCIES (PTY) LIMITED - KING & SONS DIVISION—See Grindrod Limited; *Int'l*, pg. 3086
GRINDROD SHIPS AGENCIES (PTY) LIMITED—See Grindrod Limited; *Int'l*, pg. 3086
GRINDROD (SOUTH AFRICA) (PTY) LTD - GRINDROD PCA DIVISION—See Grindrod Limited; *Int'l*, pg. 3086
GRINDROD (SOUTH AFRICA) (PTY) LTD - MITCHELL COTTS MARITIME DIVISION—See Grindrod Limited; *Int'l*, pg. 3086
GTO 2000, INC.—See Calera Capital Management, Inc.; *U.S. Private*, pg. 717
GUANGDONG ETERNAL WAY INTERNATIONAL FREIGHT CO., LTD.—See China Merchants Group Limited; *Int'l*, pg. 1522
GUANGDONG TRANSPORT CO., LTD.—See China Merchants Group Limited; *Int'l*, pg. 1522
GUANGZHOU HOYER BULK TRANSPORT CO. LTD.—See Hoyer GmbH; *Int'l*, pg. 3498
GULF AGENCY COMPANY (AUSTRALIA) PTY LTD—See Gulf Agency Company Ltd.; *Int'l*, pg. 3179
GULF AGENCY COMPANY LTD.; *Int'l*, pg. 3178
GULF MARINE FAR EAST PTE. LTD.—See Tidewater Inc.; *U.S. Public*, pg. 2158
GULF OFFSHORE N.S. LTD.—See Tidewater Inc.; *U.S. Public*, pg. 2158
G.W. PALMER LOGISTICS, LLC; *U.S. Private*, pg. 1631
GW TRANSPORTATION SERVICES—See Stan Koch & Sons Trucking; *U.S. Private*, pg. 3777
HAAS INDUSTRIES, INC.—See Lynden Incorporated; *U.S. Private*, pg. 2521
HA LOGISTICS, INC.; *U.S. Private*, pg. 1837
HANJIN ARKAS LOGISTICS & TRADING S.A.—See Eusu Holdings Co., Ltd.; *Int'l*, pg. 2559
HANKYU HANSHIN EXPRESS SOUTHEAST ASIA PTE. LTD.—See Hankyu Hanshin Holdings Inc.; *Int'l*, pg. 3255
HANKYU HANSHIN EXPRESS (USA) INC.—See Hankyu Hanshin Holdings Inc.; *Int'l*, pg. 3255

CORPORATE AFFILIATIONS

HANKYU INTERNATIONAL TRANSPORT (NETHERLANDS) B.V.—See Hankyu Hanshin Holdings Inc.; *Int'l*, pg. 3255
HANWA LOGISTICS OSAKA CO., LTD.—See Hanwa Co., Ltd.; *Int'l*, pg. 3262
HAPAG-LLOYD(AMERICA) LLC—See Albert Ballin KG; *Int'l*, pg. 294
HAPAG-LLOYD (CHINA) LTD.—See Albert Ballin KG; *Int'l*, pg. 294
HAPAG-LLOYD DENIZASIRI NAKLIYAT A.S.—See Albert Ballin KG; *Int'l*, pg. 295
HAPAG-LLOYD (EASTWIND) PTE. LTD.—See Albert Ballin KG; *Int'l*, pg. 295
HAPAG-LLOYD GLOBAL SERVICES PVT. LTD.—See Albert Ballin KG; *Int'l*, pg. 295
HAPAG-LLOYD (ITALY) S.R.L.—See Albert Ballin KG; *Int'l*, pg. 295
HAPAG-LLOYD (NEW ZEALAND) LTD.—See Albert Ballin KG; *Int'l*, pg. 295
HAPAG-LLOYD (UK) LTD.—See Albert Ballin KG; *Int'l*, pg. 295
HARBOUR AGENCIES (SABAH) SDN. BHD.—See Harbour-Link Group Berhad; *Int'l*, pg. 3272
HARBOUR-LINK LINES (JB) SDN. BHD.—See Harbour-Link Group Berhad; *Int'l*, pg. 3272
HARTWICK O'SHEA & CARTWRIGHT LIMITED; *Int'l*, pg. 3280
HASLER & COMPANY INCORPORATED; *U.S. Private*, pg. 1878
HASSETT AIR EXPRESS—See Hassett Air Express; *U.S. Private*, pg. 1879
HAVILA KYSTRUTEN AS; *Int'l*, pg. 3287
HAWAIIAN EXPRESS SERVICE INC.; *U.S. Private*, pg. 1881
HAWAIIAN OCEAN TRANSPORT, INC.—See The Jordan Company, L.P.; *U.S. Private*, pg. 4060
HAYASHI SHIPPING, CO., LTD.—See Daicel Corporation; *Int'l*, pg. 1919
HCI HAMMONIA SHIPPING AG; *Int'l*, pg. 3297
HECNY TRANSPORTATION INC.; *U.S. Private*, pg. 1903
HELLMANN EAST EUROPE LLC—See Hellmann Worldwide Logistics GmbH & Co. KG; *Int'l*, pg. 3335
HELLMANN EAST EUROPE OVERSEAS LTD—See Hellmann Worldwide Logistics GmbH & Co. KG; *Int'l*, pg. 3335
HELLMANN EAST EUROPE SOOO—See Hellmann Worldwide Logistics GmbH & Co. KG; *Int'l*, pg. 3335
HELLMANN NETWORK INC.—See Hellmann Worldwide Logistics GmbH & Co. KG; *Int'l*, pg. 3335
HELLMANN PERISHABLE LOGISTICS INC.—See Hellmann Worldwide Logistics GmbH & Co. KG; *Int'l*, pg. 3336
HELLMANN PERISHABLE LOGISTICS—See Hellmann Worldwide Logistics GmbH & Co. KG; *Int'l*, pg. 3335
HELLMANN PERISHABLE LOGISTICS—See Hellmann Worldwide Logistics GmbH & Co. KG; *Int'l*, pg. 3335
HELLMANN PERISHABLE LOGISTICS—See Hellmann Worldwide Logistics GmbH & Co. KG; *Int'l*, pg. 3336
HELLMANN PERISHABLE LOGISTICS—See Hellmann Worldwide Logistics GmbH & Co. KG; *Int'l*, pg. 3336
HELLMANN PERISHABLE LOGISTICS—See Hellmann Worldwide Logistics GmbH & Co. KG; *Int'l*, pg. 3336
HELLMANN SAUDI ARABIA LLC—See Hellmann Worldwide Logistics GmbH & Co. KG; *Int'l*, pg. 3335
HELLMANN WORLDWIDE LOGISTICS AS—See Hellmann Worldwide Logistics GmbH & Co. KG; *Int'l*, pg. 3335
HELLMANN WORLDWIDE LOGISTICS A/S—See Hellmann Worldwide Logistics GmbH & Co. KG; *Int'l*, pg. 3335
HELLMANN WORLDWIDE LOGISTICS B.V.—See Hellmann Worldwide Logistics GmbH & Co. KG; *Int'l*, pg. 3335
HELLMANN WORLDWIDE LOGISTICS (CAMBODIA) LLC—See Hellmann Worldwide Logistics GmbH & Co. KG; *Int'l*, pg. 3335
HELLMANN WORLDWIDE LOGISTICS (CHINA) LTD.—See Hellmann Worldwide Logistics GmbH & Co. KG; *Int'l*, pg. 3335
HELLMANN WORLDWIDE LOGISTICS CO., LTD.—See Hellmann Worldwide Logistics GmbH & Co. KG; *Int'l*, pg. 3335
HELLMANN WORLDWIDE LOGISTICS (CUBA) GMBH—See Hellmann Worldwide Logistics GmbH & Co. KG; *Int'l*, pg. 3335
HELLMANN WORLDWIDE LOGISTICS DO BRASIL LTDA.—See Hellmann Worldwide Logistics GmbH & Co. KG; *Int'l*, pg. 3335
HELLMANN WORLDWIDE LOGISTICS GMBH & CO. KG; *Int'l*, pg. 3335
HELLMANN WORLDWIDE LOGISTICS GMBH—See Hellmann Worldwide Logistics GmbH & Co. KG; *Int'l*, pg. 3335
HELLMANN WORLDWIDE LOGISTICS INC.—See Hellmann Worldwide Logistics GmbH & Co. KG; *Int'l*, pg. 3335
HELLMANN WORLDWIDE LOGISTICS INC.—See Hellmann Worldwide Logistics GmbH & Co. KG; *Int'l*, pg. 3335
HELLMANN WORLDWIDE LOGISTICS, INC.—See Hell-

mann Worldwide Logistics GmbH & Co. KG; *Int'l*, pg. 3336
HELLMANN WORLDWIDE LOGISTICS INDIA PRIVATE LIMITED—See Hellmann Worldwide Logistics GmbH & Co. KG; *Int'l*; pg. 3335
HELLMANN WORLDWIDE LOGISTICS KAZAKHSTAN LLP—See Hellmann Worldwide Logistics GmbH & Co. KG; *Int'l*; pg. 3335
HELLMANN WORLDWIDE LOGISTICS KFT.—See Hellmann Worldwide Logistics GmbH & Co. KG; *Int'l*, pg. 3335
HELLMANN WORLDWIDE LOGISTICS LIMITED—See Hellmann Worldwide Logistics GmbH & Co. KG; *Int'l*, pg. 3336
HELLMANN WORLDWIDE LOGISTICS LLC—See Hellmann Worldwide Logistics GmbH & Co. KG; *Int'l*, pg. 3336
HELLMANN WORLDWIDE LOGISTICS LLP—See Hellmann Worldwide Logistics GmbH & Co. KG; *Int'l*, pg. 3336
HELLMANN WORLDWIDE LOGISTICS LTDA.—See Hellmann Worldwide Logistics GmbH & Co. KG; *Int'l*, pg. 3336
HELLMANN WORLDWIDE LOGISTICS LTD.—See Hellmann Worldwide Logistics GmbH & Co. KG; *Int'l*, pg. 3336
HELLMANN WORLDWIDE LOGISTICS LTD.—See Hellmann Worldwide Logistics GmbH & Co. KG; *Int'l*, pg. 3336
HELLMANN WORLDWIDE LOGISTICS LTD.—See Hellmann Worldwide Logistics GmbH & Co. KG; *Int'l*, pg. 3336
HELLMANN WORLDWIDE LOGISTICS LTD.—See Hellmann Worldwide Logistics GmbH & Co. KG; *Int'l*, pg. 3336
HELLMANN WORLDWIDE LOGISTICS LTD.—See Hellmann Worldwide Logistics GmbH & Co. KG; *Int'l*, pg. 3336
HELLMANN WORLDWIDE LOGISTICS LTD.—See Hellmann Worldwide Logistics GmbH & Co. KG; *Int'l*, pg. 3336
HELLMANN WORLDWIDE LOGISTICS LTD.—See Hellmann Worldwide Logistics GmbH & Co. KG; *Int'l*, pg. 3336
HELLMANN WORLDWIDE LOGISTICS LTD.—See Hellmann Worldwide Logistics GmbH & Co. KG; *Int'l*, pg. 3336
HELLMANN WORLDWIDE LOGISTICS LTD. STI—See Hellmann Worldwide Logistics GmbH & Co. KG; *Int'l*, pg. 3336
HELLMANN WORLDWIDE LOGISTICS MADAGASCAR SARL—See Hellmann Worldwide Logistics GmbH & Co. KG; *Int'l*; pg. 3336
HELLMANN WORLDWIDE LOGISTICS OU—See Hellmann Worldwide Logistics GmbH & Co. KG; *Int'l*, pg. 3336
HELLMANN WORLDWIDE LOGISTICS POLSKA SPOLKA Z OGRANICZONA ODPOWIEDZIALNOSCIA—See Hellmann Worldwide Logistics GmbH & Co. KG; *Int'l*, pg. 3336
HELLMANN WORLDWIDE LOGISTICS (PTY) LTD—See Hellmann Worldwide Logistics GmbH & Co. KG; *Int'l*, pg. 3335
HELLMANN WORLDWIDE LOGISTICS (PTY) LTD.—See Hellmann Worldwide Logistics GmbH & Co. KG; *Int'l*, pg. 3336
HELLMANN WORLDWIDE LOGISTICS PTY LTD—See Hellmann Worldwide Logistics GmbH & Co. KG; *Int'l*, pg. 3336
HELLMANN WORLDWIDE LOGISTICS (PVT) LTD—See Hellmann Worldwide Logistics GmbH & Co. KG; *Int'l*, pg. 3335
HELLMANN WORLDWIDE LOGISTICS (PVT) LTD—See Hellmann Worldwide Logistics GmbH & Co. KG; *Int'l*, pg. 3335
HELLMANN WORLDWIDE LOGISTICS S.A.C.—See Hellmann Worldwide Logistics GmbH & Co. KG; *Int'l*, pg. 3336
HELLMANN WORLDWIDE LOGISTICS S.A. DE C.V.—See Hellmann Worldwide Logistics GmbH & Co. KG; *Int'l*, pg. 3336
HELLMANN WORLDWIDE LOGISTICS SARL—See Hellmann Worldwide Logistics GmbH & Co. KG; *Int'l*, pg. 3336
HELLMANN WORLDWIDE LOGISTICS S.A.—See Hellmann Worldwide Logistics GmbH & Co. KG; *Int'l*, pg. 3336
HELLMANN WORLDWIDE LOGISTICS S.A.—See Hellmann Worldwide Logistics GmbH & Co. KG; *Int'l*, pg. 3336
HELLMANN WORLDWIDE LOGISTICS SDN. BHD.—See Hellmann Worldwide Logistics GmbH & Co. KG; *Int'l*, pg. 3336
HELLMANN WORLDWIDE LOGISTICS (SHANGHAI) LTD.—See Hellmann Worldwide Logistics GmbH & Co. KG; *Int'l*, pg. 3335
HELLMANN WORLDWIDE LOGISTICS SIA—See Hellmann Worldwide Logistics GmbH & Co. KG; *Int'l*, pg. 3336
HELLMANN WORLDWIDE LOGISTICS S.P.A.—See Hellmann Worldwide Logistics GmbH & Co. KG; *Int'l*, pg. 3336
HELLMANN WORLDWIDE LOGISTICS SRL—See Hellmann Worldwide Logistics GmbH & Co. KG; *Int'l*, pg. 3336
HELLMANN WORLDWIDE LOGISTICS S.R.O.—See Hellmann Worldwide Logistics GmbH & Co. KG; *Int'l*, pg. 3336
HELLMANN WORLDWIDE LOGISTICS (T) LTD.—See Hellmann Worldwide Logistics GmbH & Co. KG; *Int'l*, pg. 3336
HELLMANN WORLDWIDE LOGISTICS UAB—See Hellmann Worldwide Logistics GmbH & Co. KG; *Int'l*, pg. 3336
HELLMANN WORLDWIDE LOGISTICS (VIETNAM) CO., LTD—See Hellmann Worldwide Logistics GmbH & Co. KG; *Int'l*, pg. 3335
HELLMANN WORLDWIDE LOGISTICS WLL—See Hellmann Worldwide Logistics GmbH & Co. KG; *Int'l*, pg. 3336
HELLMANN WORLDWIDE LOGISTICS ZAMBIA LIMITED—See Hellmann Worldwide Logistics GmbH & Co. KG; *Int'l*, pg. 3336
HENDERSON COMBINED GROUP OF COMPANIES, INC.; *U.S. Private*, pg. 1913
HEYL LOGISTICS—See Heyl Truck Lines Inc.; *U.S. Private*, pg. 1928
H.F. LONG AND ASSOCIATES, INC.; *U.S. Private*, pg. 1826
HHE (DEUTSCHLAND) GMBH—See Hankyu Hanshin Holdings Inc.; *Int'l*, pg. 3255
H&H INT'L LOGISTICS (FUJIAN) CO., LTD.—See Eusu Holdings Co., Ltd.; *Int'l*, pg. 2559
HICHAIN LOGISTICS CO., LTD.; *Int'l*, pg. 3383
HIGHLAND FORWARDING, INC.; *U.S. Private*, pg. 1938
HIGH SEAS MARINE & INDUSTRIAL SERVICES CO. LTD.—See Ali Abdullah Al Tamimi Company; *Int'l*, pg. 319
HIGHWAYS & SKYWAYS, INC.—See Radiant Logistics, Inc.; *U.S. Public*, pg. 1759
HIGHWAYS & SKYWAYS OF NC, INC.—See Radiant Logistics, Inc.; *U.S. Public*, pg. 1759
HILL BROTHERS INTERMODAL LOGISTICS INC.—See Hill Brothers, Inc.; *U.S. Private*, pg. 1945
HIMALAYA SHIPPING LTD.; *Int'l*, pg. 3396
HINDUSTAN CARGO LTD.—See Allcargo Logistics Limited; *Int'l*, pg. 334
HIOLLE LOGISTICS JSC—See Hiolle Industries S.A.; *Int'l*, pg. 3401
H&M INTERNATIONAL TRANSPORTATION INC.; *U.S. Private*, pg. 1823
HOC USA INC.—See Hartwick O'shea & Cartwright Limited; *Int'l*, pg. 3280
HOGANAS HAMNBYGGNADS AB—See Hoganas AB; *Int'l*, pg. 3441
HOLLAND TRANSPORTATION MANAGEMENT INC.; *U.S. Private*, pg. 1964
HOLLYWOOD TRUCKS, LLC—See Base Craft LLC; *U.S. Private*, pg. 484
HOLMES FREIGHT LINES INC.; *Int'l*, pg. 3453
HONOLULU FREIGHT SERVICE INC.; *U.S. Private*, pg. 1977
HOYER BITUMEN-LOGISTIK GMBH—See Hoyer GmbH; *Int'l*, pg. 3498
HOYER DEEPSEA MALAYSIA SDN. BHD.—See Hoyer GmbH; *Int'l*, pg. 3498
HOYER ESTONIA OU—See Hoyer GmbH; *Int'l*, pg. 3498
HOYER GLOBAL (BRASIL) TRANSPORTES LTDA.—See Hoyer GmbH; *Int'l*, pg. 3499
HOYER LIQUID DRUMMING B.V.—See Hoyer GmbH; *Int'l*, pg. 3499
HOYER LOGISTICS AUSTRALIA PTY. LTD.—See Hoyer GmbH; *Int'l*, pg. 3499
HOYER MIDDLE EAST LTD.—See Hoyer GmbH; *Int'l*, pg. 3499
HOYER-ODFJELL INC.—See Hoyer GmbH; *Int'l*, pg. 3499
HOYER POLSKA SP.Z O.O.—See Hoyer GmbH; *Int'l*, pg. 3499
HOYER PORTUGAL UNIPESSOAL LDA.—See Hoyer GmbH; *Int'l*, pg. 3499
HOYT, SHEPSTON & SCIARONI INC.; *U.S. Private*, pg. 1996
HSF BETEILIGUNGS GMBH—See DFDS A/S; *Int'l*, pg. 2095
HUB GROUP CANADA, L.P—See Hub Group, Inc.; *U.S. Public*, pg. 1065
HUB GROUP, INC.; *U.S. Public*, pg. 1065
HUB GROUP TRUCKING, INC.—See Hub Group, Inc.; *U.S. Public*, pg. 1065
HUBLINE BERHAD; *Int'l*, pg. 3520
HUGHES GROUP LLC; *U.S. Private*, pg. 2003
HULL BLYTH GHANA LTD—See Deutsche Post AG; *Int'l*, pg. 2080
HULL BLYTH SOUTH AFRICA PTY LTD—See Deutsche Post AG; *Int'l*, pg. 2081
HYBRID LOGISTICS, INC.—See CAI International, Inc.; *U.S. Public*, pg. 421
HYOSUNG TRANS-WORLD CO., LTD.—See Hyosung Corporation; *Int'l*, pg. 3552
HYUNDAI MERCHANT MARINE (AMERICA), INC.—See HMM Co., Ltd.; *Int'l*, pg. 3432
HYUNDAI MERCHANT MARINE (EUROPE) LTD.—See HMM Co., Ltd.; *Int'l*, pg. 3432
HYUNDAI MERCHANT MARINE (JAPAN) CO., LTD.—See HMM Co., Ltd.; *Int'l*, pg. 3432
ICAT LOGISTICS, INC.—See KCM Capital Partners, LLC; *U.S. Private*, pg. 2270
ICAT LOGISTICS, INC.—See MMF Capital Management LLC; *U.S. Private*, pg. 2754
ICON FREIGHT SERVICES CO. LTD.—See FM Global Logistics Holdings Berhad; *Int'l*, pg. 2717
ICS CUSTOMS SERVICE INC.; *U.S. Private*, pg. 2033
ICT HOLDINGS INC.; *U.S. Private*, pg. 2033
IKEDA UNYU COMPANY LIMITED—See KKR & Co. Inc.; *U.S. Public*, pg. 1259
IMC SHIPPING (CHINA) COMPANY LIMITED—See IMC Pan Asia Alliance Pte. Ltd.; *Int'l*, pg. 3621
IMC SHIPPING SERVICES CO. PTE. LTD.—See IMC Pan Asia Alliance Pte. Ltd.; *Int'l*, pg. 3621
IMPACT LOGISTICS, INC.; *U.S. Private*, pg. 2048
IMPERIAL SASFIN LOGISTICS—See Dubai World Corporation; *Int'l*, pg. 2221
IMPEX SERVICES INC.; *U.S. Private*, pg. 2050
INGRAM MICRO CFS BENELUX B.V.—See Hainan Traffic Administration Holding Co., Ltd.; *Int'l*, pg. 3214
INGRAM MICRO CFS ESERVICES B.V.—See Hainan Traffic Administration Holding Co., Ltd.; *Int'l*, pg. 3214
INTEGRATED FORWARDING & SHIPPING BERHAD—See ILB Group Berhad; *Int'l*, pg. 3613
INTEGRATED FREIGHT SERVICES SDN. BHD.—See ILB Group Berhad; *Int'l*, pg. 3613
INTEGRITY CARGO SOLUTIONS, INC.; *U.S. Private*, pg. 2102
INTEGRITY EXPRESS LOGISTICS; *U.S. Private*, pg. 2102
INTELLIGENT LOGISTICS, LLC—See AIT Worldwide Logistics, Inc.; *U.S. Private*, pg. 142
INTELLITRANS, LLC—See Roper Technologies, Inc.; *U.S. Public*, pg. 1813
INTERACTIVE LOGISTICS INC.—See NFI Industries, Inc.; *U.S. Private*, pg. 2923
INTERDEAN INTERNATIONAL LTD.—See EAC Invest AS; *Int'l*, pg. 2262
INTERDOM LLC—See Odyssey Logistics & Technology Corp.; *U.S. Private*, pg. 2996
INTERMODAL MEXICO, S.A. DE C.V.—See Grupo Mexico, S.A.B. de C.V.; *Int'l*, pg. 3132
INTERMODAL SALES CORPORATION; *U.S. Private*, pg. 2112
INTERNATIONAL CHECKOUT, INC.; *U.S. Private*, pg. 2115
INTERNATIONAL FORWARDERS, INC.—See Odyssey Logistics & Technology Corp.; *U.S. Private*, pg. 2996
INTERNATIONAL FREIGHT FORWARDING, INC.; *U.S. Private*, pg. 2117
INTERNATIONAL FREIGHT SYSTEMS (OF OREGON), INC.—See Radiant Logistics, Inc.; *U.S. Public*, pg. 1759
INTERNATIONAL PORT SERVICES, INC.; *U.S. Private*, pg. 2119
INTERSTATE MOVING SYSTEMS, INC.—See Interstate Group Holdings, Inc.; *U.S. Private*, pg. 2125
INTERSTATE RELOCATION SERVICES, INC.—See Interstate Group Holdings, Inc.; *U.S. Private*, pg. 2125
INTERSTATE VAN LINES, INC.—See Interstate Group Holdings, Inc.; *U.S. Private*, pg. 2125
INTRANSIT INC.; *U.S. Private*, pg. 2129
ITG GMBH INTERNATIONALE SPEDITION UND LOGISTIK—See Carl Bennet AB; *Int'l*, pg. 1331
ITS LOGISTICS, INC.—See GHK Capital Partners LP; *U.S. Private*, pg. 1690
ITS TECHNOLOGIES & LOGISTICS, LLC—See AMP Limited; *Int'l*, pg. 432
JA FLOWERS SERVICES INC.—See Armellini Industries, Inc.; *U.S. Private*, pg. 330
JAMCO INTERNATIONAL INC.—See Littlejohn & Co., LLC; *U.S. Private*, pg. 2470
JAMES J. BOYLE & CO.; *U.S. Private*, pg. 2184
JANEL GROUP, INC.—See Janel Corporation; *U.S. Public*, pg. 1187
THE JANEL GROUP OF GEORGIA, INC.—See Janel Corporation; *U.S. Public*, pg. 1187
JAPAN AIRCARGO FORWARDERS ASSOCIATION—See Azuma Shipping Co., Ltd.; *Int'l*, pg. 782
JAPAN INTERNATIONAL FREIGHT FORWARDERS ASSOCIATION, INC.—See Azuma Shipping Co., Ltd.; *Int'l*, pg. 782
JAS FORWARDING INCORPORATED; *U.S. Private*, pg. 2188
JAS OCEAN SERVICES INC.—See JAS Forwarding Incorporated; *U.S. Private*, pg. 2188
J.A .TUCKER COMPANY; *U.S. Private*, pg. 2157
JBS LOGISTIC INC.; *U.S. Private*, pg. 2194
JEM FINCO LIMITED—See American Securities LLC; *U.S. Private*, pg. 252
JET DISPATCH LIMITED—See China Best Group Holding Limited; *Int'l*, pg. 1486
JF HILLEBRAND ARGENTINA SA—See Deutsche Post AG; *Int'l*, pg. 2081
JF HILLEBRAND BRASIL LTDA—See Deutsche Post AG; *Int'l*, pg. 2081

488510 — FREIGHT TRANSPORTAT...   CORPORATE AFFILIATIONS

JF HILLEBRAND CANADA INC.—See Deutsche Post AG; *Int'l*, pg. 2081
JF HILLEBRAND CENTRAL EUROPE GMBH—See Deutsche Post AG; *Int'l*, pg. 2081
JF HILLEBRAND CHILE LTDA—See Deutsche Post AG; *Int'l*, pg. 2081
JF HILLEBRAND CHINA CO. LTD—See Deutsche Post AG; *Int'l*, pg. 2081
JF HILLEBRAND DEUTSCHLAND GMBH—See Deutsche Post AG; *Int'l*, pg. 2081
JF HILLEBRAND FINLAND OY—See Deutsche Post AG; *Int'l*, pg. 2081
JF HILLEBRAND FRANCE SAS—See Deutsche Post AG; *Int'l*, pg. 2081
JF HILLEBRAND GROUP AG—See Deutsche Post AG; *Int'l*, pg. 2081
JF HILLEBRAND GROUP MANAGEMENT SERVICES—See Deutsche Post AG; *Int'l*, pg. 2081
JF HILLEBRAND IRELAND LTD—See Deutsche Post AG; *Int'l*, pg. 2081
JF HILLEBRAND ITALIA SPA—See Deutsche Post AG; *Int'l*, pg. 2081
JF HILLEBRAND JAPAN KK—See Deutsche Post AG; *Int'l*, pg. 2081
JF HILLEBRAND KOREA LTD.—See Deutsche Post AG; *Int'l*, pg. 2081
JF HILLEBRAND MALAYSIA SDN BHD—See Deutsche Post AG; *Int'l*, pg. 2081
JF HILLEBRAND MEXICO SA DE CV—See Deutsche Post AG; *Int'l*, pg. 2081
JF HILLEBRAND MIDDLE EAST LLC—See Deutsche Post AG; *Int'l*, pg. 2081
JF HILLEBRAND NETHERLANDS—See Deutsche Post AG; *Int'l*, pg. 2081
JF HILLEBRAND PHILIPPINES INC—See Deutsche Post AG; *Int'l*, pg. 2081
JF HILLEBRAND PORTUGAL-TRANSITARIOS LDA—See Deutsche Post AG; *Int'l*, pg. 2081
JF HILLEBRAND RUSSIA (OOO)—See Deutsche Post AG; *Int'l*, pg. 2081
JF HILLEBRAND SCANDINAVIA A/S—See Deutsche Post AG; *Int'l*, pg. 2081
J.F. HILLEBRAND SCOTLAND LIMITED—See Deutsche Post AG; *Int'l*, pg. 2081
JF HILLEBRAND SINGAPORE PTE LTD—See Deutsche Post AG; *Int'l*, pg. 2081
JF HILLEBRAND SOUTH AFRICA (PTY) LTD—See Deutsche Post AG; *Int'l*, pg. 2081
JF HILLEBRAND SPAIN SA—See Deutsche Post AG; *Int'l*, pg. 2081
JF HILLEBRAND SWEDEN AB—See Deutsche Post AG; *Int'l*, pg. 2081
JF HILLEBRAND (THAILAND) LIMITED—See Deutsche Post AG; *Int'l*, pg. 2081
JF HILLEBRAND UK LIMITED—See Deutsche Post AG; *Int'l*, pg. 2081
JF HILLEBRAND URUGUAY—See Deutsche Post AG; *Int'l*, pg. 2081
JF HILLEBRAND USA INC—See Deutsche Post AG; *Int'l*, pg. 2081
JF HILLEBRAND VIETNAM CO., LTD—See Deutsche Post AG; *Int'l*, pg. 2081
J&H TRANSPORTATION INC.; *U.S. Private*, pg. 2154
JLE INDUSTRIES, LLC; *U.S. Private*, pg. 2212
JOHANSON TRANSPORTATION SERVICE; *U.S. Private*, pg. 2219
JOHN S. JAMES CO.; *U.S. Private*, pg. 2224
JONES MOTOR CO., INC.—See Transport Investments, Inc.; *U.S. Private*, pg. 4210
JP LOGISTICS & MOTORSPORTS, INC.; *U.S. Private*, pg. 2239
JRC LOGISTICS; *U.S. Private*, pg. 2239
JSI SHIPPING; *U.S. Private*, pg. 2241
KANE TRAFFIC SERVICES INC.—See Kane Is Able, Inc.; *U.S. Private*, pg. 2260
KEM KREST CORPORATION; *U.S. Private*, pg. 2281
KEPPEL LOGISTICS (HONG KONG) LTD—See China Merchants Group Limited; *Int'l*, pg. 1522
KERRY ROCKFORD ENTERPRISES INC.—See A.P. Moller-Maersk A/S; *Int'l*, pg. 27
KEYSTONE DEDICATED LOGISTICS; *U.S. Private*, pg. 2296
KIMRAD TRANSPORT, LP.; *U.S. Private*, pg. 2306
KINGSGATE TRANSPORTATION SERVICES, LLC; *U.S. Private*, pg. 2311
KING SOLUTIONS, INC.; *U.S. Private*, pg. 2310
K&K EXPRESS LLC; *U.S. Private*, pg. 2249
K&L FREIGHT MANAGEMENT, INC.; *U.S. Private*, pg. 2249
KLM EQUIPMENT SERVICES BV—See Air, France-KLM S.A.; *Int'l*, pg. 238
KNICHEL LOGISTICS; *U.S. Private*, pg. 2322
KNOCK TANKERS LTD.—See Fred. Olsen & Co.; *Int'l*, pg. 2769
KOREA EXPRESS EUROPE GMBH—See CJ Corporation; *Int'l*, pg. 1633
KOREA EXPRESS HONG KONG CO., LTD.—See CJ Corporation; *Int'l*, pg. 1633

KOREA EXPRESS JAPAN CO., LTD.—See CJ Corporation; *Int'l*, pg. 1633
KOREA EXPRESS TIANJIN CO., LTD.—See CJ Corporation; *Int'l*, pg. 1633
K&R TRANSPORTATION, LLC—See California Cartage Company LLC; *U.S. Private*, pg. 718
LABAY-SUMMERS INTERNATIONAL INC.; *U.S. Private*, pg. 2370
LAMBERT'S POINT DOCKS, INC.—See Norfolk Southern Corporation; *U.S. Public*, pg. 1535
LANDSTAR EXPRESS AMERICA, INC.—See Landstar System, Inc.; *U.S. Public*, pg. 1292
LANDSTAR GLOBAL LOGISTICS, INC.—See Landstar System, Inc.; *U.S. Public*, pg. 1292
LANDSTAR SYSTEM, INC. - ROCKFORD SERVICE CENTER—See Landstar System, Inc.; *U.S. Public*, pg. 1292
LA SPEZIA CONTAINER TERMINAL S.P.A.—See EUROKAI GmbH & Co. KGaA; *Int'l*, pg. 2553
LAUFER GROUP INTERNATIONAL LTD.; *U.S. Private*, pg. 2397
LAURITZEN KOSAN A/S—See BW Epic Kosan Ltd.; *Int'l*, pg. 1231
LA-Z-BOY LOGISTICS, INC.—See La-Z-Boy Incorporated; *U.S. Public*, pg. 1285
LCI CLASQUIN SA—See Clasquin S.A.; *Int'l*, pg. 1652
LCL LOGISTIX (INDIA) PVT. LTD.—See CMA CGM S.A.; *Int'l*, pg. 1668
L.E. COPPERSMITH INC.; *U.S. Private*, pg. 2365
LEGACY SUPPLY CHAIN SERVICES - GARDEN GROVE—See LEGACY Supply Chain Services; *U.S. Private*, pg. 2417
LETICA RESOURCES INC.—See Berry Global Group, Inc; *U.S. Public*, pg. 322
LEXICON RELOCATION LTD.—See The Suddath Companies; *U.S. Private*, pg. 4124
LEXICON RELOCATION—See The Suddath Companies; *U.S. Private*, pg. 4124
LF LOGISTICS (HONG KONG) LIMITED—See A.P. Moller-Maersk A/S; *Int'l*, pg. 26
LGI LOGISTICS GROUP INTERNATIONAL GMBH—See Carl Bennet AB; *Int'l*, pg. 1331
LGSTX DISTRIBUTION SERVICES, INC.—See Air Transport Services Group, Inc.; *U.S. Public*, pg. 67
LHP TRANSPORTATION SERVICES—See Prime, Inc.; *U.S. Private*, pg. 3262
LIGHTEN THE LOAD, INC.; *U.S. Private*, pg. 2452
LILLY AND ASSOCIATES INTERNATIONAL; *U.S. Private*, pg. 2456
LIMITLESS INTERNATIONAL INC.; *U.S. Private*, pg. 2456
LINKEX, INC.—See Saia, Inc.; *U.S. Public*, pg. 1835
LIVINGSTON INTERNATIONAL INC.—See Platinum Equity, LLC; *U.S. Private*, pg. 3205
LIVINGSTON INTERNATIONAL, INC.—See Platinum Equity, LLC; *U.S. Private*, pg. 3205
L&M TRANSPORTATION SERVICES, INC.; *U.S. Private*, pg. 2363
LOADMATCH LOGISTICS INC.; *U.S. Private*, pg. 2476
LOGIMAR SRL—See DSV A/S; *Int'l*, pg. 2214
LOGISTICS MANAGEMENT SOLUTIONS LLC—See TPG Capital, L.P.; *U.S. Public*, pg. 2177
LOGISTICS PLUS, INC.; *U.S. Private*, pg. 2482
LOGWIN AIR AND OCEAN KENYA LIMITED—See Delton AG; *Int'l*, pg. 2022
LOGWIN AIR AND OCEAN LOJISTIK HIZMETLERI VE TICARET LIMITED SIRKETI—See Delton AG; *Int'l*, pg. 2022
LOGWIN AIR + OCEAN AUSTRALIA PTY. LTD.—See Delton AG; *Int'l*, pg. 2021
LOGWIN AIR + OCEAN AUSTRIA GMBH—See Delton AG; *Int'l*, pg. 2021
LOGWIN AIR + OCEAN BELGIUM N.V.—See Delton AG; *Int'l*, pg. 2021
LOGWIN AIR + OCEAN BRAZIL LTDA—See Delton AG; *Int'l*, pg. 2021
LOGWIN AIR + OCEAN CHILE S.A.—See Delton AG; *Int'l*, pg. 2021
LOGWIN AIR + OCEAN CHINA LTD.—See Delton AG; *Int'l*, pg. 2021
LOGWIN AIR + OCEAN DEUTSCHLAND GMBH—See Delton AG; *Int'l*, pg. 2021
LOGWIN AIR & OCEAN FAR EAST LTD.—See Delton AG; *Int'l*, pg. 2021
LOGWIN AIR + OCEAN HUNGARY KFT.—See Delton AG; *Int'l*, pg. 2022
LOGWIN AIR & OCEAN INDIA PVT. LTD.—See Delton AG; *Int'l*, pg. 2021
LOGWIN AIR + OCEAN INDONESIA P.T.—See Delton AG; *Int'l*, pg. 2021
LOGWIN AIR + OCEAN INTERNATIONAL GMBH—See Delton AG; *Int'l*, pg. 2022
LOGWIN AIR + OCEAN ITALY S.R.L.—See Delton AG; *Int'l*, pg. 2022
LOGWIN AIR & OCEAN KOREA CO. LTD.—See Delton AG; *Int'l*, pg. 2021
LOGWIN AIR & OCEAN MIDDLE EAST (LLC)—See Delton AG; *Int'l*, pg. 2021

LOGWIN AIR + OCEAN PHILIPPINES INC.—See Delton AG; *Int'l*, pg. 2022
LOGWIN AIR + OCEAN POLAND SP. Z O.O.—See Delton AG; *Int'l*, pg. 2022
LOGWIN AIR + OCEAN SHANGHAI LTD.—See Delton AG; *Int'l*, pg. 2022
LOGWIN AIR + OCEAN SINGAPORE PTE. LTD.—See Delton AG; *Int'l*, pg. 2022
LOGWIN AIR + OCEAN SOUTH AFRICA (PTY.) LTD.—See Delton AG; *Int'l*, pg. 2022
LOGWIN AIR & OCEAN SPAIN S.L.—See Delton AG; *Int'l*, pg. 2021
LOGWIN AIR + OCEAN SWITZERLAND AG—See Delton AG; *Int'l*, pg. 2022
LOGWIN AIR + OCEAN TAIWAN LTD.—See Delton AG; *Int'l*, pg. 2022
LOGWIN AIR + OCEAN (THAILAND) LTD.—See Delton AG; *Int'l*, pg. 2021
LOGWIN AIR + OCEAN THE NETHERLANDS B.V.—See Delton AG; *Int'l*, pg. 2022
LOGWIN AIR + OCEAN UK LIMITED—See Delton AG; *Int'l*, pg. 2022
LOGWIN AIR + OCEAN VIETNAM COMPANY LTD.—See Delton AG; *Int'l*, pg. 2022
LOGWIN CROATIA D.O.O.—See Delton AG; *Int'l*, pg. 2022
LOGWIN ROAD + RAIL TRIER GMBH—See Delton AG; *Int'l*, pg. 2022
LOGWIN SOLUTIONS LIECHTENSTEIN AG—See Delton AG; *Int'l*, pg. 2022
LOGWIN SOLUTIONS LOGISTICS SERVICES GMBH—See Delton AG; *Int'l*, pg. 2022
LOGWIN SOLUTIONS NECKARTENZLINGEN GMBH—See Delton AG; *Int'l*, pg. 2022
LOGWIN SOLUTIONS SPAIN S.A.—See Delton AG; *Int'l*, pg. 2022
LONGZHU OILFIELD SERVICES (S) PTE. LTD.—See Falcon Energy Group Limited; *Int'l*, pg. 2611
LTS SHIPPING CORPORATION—See Alliance International Forwarders, Inc.; *U.S. Private*, pg. 183
LUCEY TRANSPORT LOGISTICS LTD.—See DFDS A/S; *Int'l*, pg. 2095
LUFTHANSA TECHNIK LOGISTIK OF AMERICA LLC—See Deutsche Lufthansa AG; *Int'l*, pg. 2070
LUFTHANSA TECHNIK LOGISTIK SERVICES GMBH—See Deutsche Lufthansa AG; *Int'l*, pg. 2070
LUGGAGE FORWARD, INC.; *U.S. Private*, pg. 2512
LYNC LOGISTICS, LLC; *U.S. Private*, pg. 2520
LYNDEN AIR FREIGHT, INC.—See Lynden Incorporated; *U.S. Private*, pg. 2521
LYNDEN INTERNATIONAL—See Lynden Incorporated; *U.S. Private*, pg. 2521
MACKINNON MACKENZIE & CO. OF PAKISTAN (PVT.) LTD.—See Dubai World Corporation; *Int'l*, pg. 2221
MAERSK (CHINA) SHIPPING COMPANY LTD.—See A.P. Moller-Maersk A/S; *Int'l*, pg. 26
THE MAERSK COMPANY LIMITED—See A.P. Moller-Maersk A/S; *Int'l*, pg. 28
MAERSK DEUTSCHLAND A/S & CO.KG—See A.P. Moller-Maersk A/S; *Int'l*, pg. 26
MAERSK FRANCE S.A.—See A.P. Moller-Maersk A/S; *Int'l*, pg. 26
MAERSK INC.—See A.P. Moller-Maersk A/S; *Int'l*, pg. 27
MAERSK TANKERS A/S—See A.P. Moller Holding A/S; *Int'l*, pg. 25
MAGNUM LOGISTICS, INC.; *U.S. Private*, pg. 2549
MALAYSIAN SHIPPING AGENCIES SDN. BHD.—See DRB-HICOM Berhad; *Int'l*, pg. 2201
MALLORY ALEXANDER INTERNATIONAL LOGISTICS, LLC; *U.S. Private*, pg. 2557
MANNA DISTRIBUTION; *U.S. Private*, pg. 2565
MANNA FREIGHT SYSTEMS, INC.—See A.P. Moller-Maersk A/S; *Int'l*, pg. 27
MAP CARGO INTERNATIONAL INC.; *U.S. Private*, pg. 2568
MARATHON TRANSPORT, INC.—See Transport Investments, Inc.; *U.S. Private*, pg. 4210
MARIAN SHIPPING LTD.; *U.S. Private*, pg. 2574
MARINA BORIK D.O.O.—See Dogus Holding AS; *Int'l*, pg. 2155
MARINA DALMACIJA D.O.O—See Dogus Holding AS; *Int'l*, pg. 2155
MARINE TRANSPORT INC.; *U.S. Private*, pg. 2575
MARKEN LLP—See United Parcel Service, Inc.; *U.S. Public*, pg. 2233
MARK WESTBY & ASSOCIATES, INC.; *U.S. Private*, pg. 2578
MASTERPIECE INTERNATIONAL LIMITED—See Littlejohn & Co., LLC; *U.S. Private*, pg. 2470
MATSON LOGISTICS, INC.—See Matson, Inc.; *U.S. Public*, pg. 1398
MATSUOKA KOZAI CO., LTD.—See Hanwa Co., Ltd.; *Int'l*, pg. 3263
MAX TRANS LOGISTICS OF CHATTANOOGA, LLC; *U.S. Private*, pg. 2617
MAZU SHIPPING (PVT) LTD.—See Hemas Holdings PLC; *Int'l*, pg. 3340
M&C SHIPPING DEPARTMENT—See Arthur J. Gallagher & Co.; *U.S. Public*, pg. 206

N.A.I.C.S. INDEX

488510 — FREIGHT TRANSPORTAT...

MELLER FLOW TRANS LIMITED—See Axel Johnson Gruppen AB; *Int'l*, pg. 763

MEMO EXPRESS SERVICES LLC—See Aramex PJSC; *Int'l*, pg. 535

MERIDIAN WORLDWIDE TRANSPORTATION GROUP; *U.S. Private*, pg. 2674

MESCA FREIGHT SERVICES; *U.S. Private*, pg. 2678

METROPOLITAN LOGISTIC SERVICES INC.—See Mangino Holding Corp.; *U.S. Private*, pg. 2563

MID-AMERICA OVERSEAS (CHINA) LTD.—See Mid-America Overseas Inc.; *U.S. Private*, pg. 2707

MID-AMERICA OVERSEAS DE VENEZUELA, C.A.—See Mid-America Overseas Inc.; *U.S. Private*, pg. 2707

MID-AMERICA OVERSEAS INC.; *U.S. Private*, pg. 2707

MID-AMERICA OVERSEAS, LTD.—See Mid-America Overseas Inc.; *U.S. Private*, pg. 2707

MID-AMERICA OVERSEAS (M) SDN. BHD.—See Mid-America Overseas Inc.; *U.S. Private*, pg. 2707

MID-AMERICA OVERSEAS (S) PTE. LTD.—See Mid-America Overseas Inc.; *U.S. Private*, pg. 2707

MID-AMERICA OVERSEAS (THE NETHERLANDS) B.V.—See Mid-America Overseas Inc.; *U.S. Private*, pg. 2707

MIDDLE EAST SHIPPING COMPANY LTD.—See Hayel Saeed Anam Group of Companies; *Int'l*, pg. 3290

MINMETALS DEVELOPMENT CO., LTD.—See China Rare Earth Resources And Technology Co., Ltd.; *Int'l*, pg. 1546

MINMETALS SHIPPING (SINGAPORE) PTE. LTD.—See China Rare Earth Resources And Technology Co., Ltd.; *Int'l*, pg. 1546

MIRACLE TRANSPORTATION, INC.; *U.S. Private*, pg. 2746

MJN SERVICES INC.; *U.S. Private*, pg. 2753

MNS1 EXPRESS, INC.; *U.S. Private*, pg. 2756

MODE FREIGHT SERVICES, LLC—See Hub Group, Inc.; *U.S. Public*, pg. 1065

MOORE FREIGHT SERVICE—See Daseke, Inc.; *U.S. Private*, pg. 1161

MORRISON EXPRESS CORPORATION USA; *U.S. Private*, pg. 2789

M.O.T. INTERMODAL SHIPPING USA INC.—See C.H. Robinson Worldwide, Inc.; *U.S. Public*, pg. 415

MOVIANTO TRANSPORT SOLUTIONS LTD.—See Owens & Minor, Inc.; *U.S. Private*, pg. 1626

MS HAMMONIA BAVARIA SCHIFFAHRTS GMBH & CO. KG—See HCI Hammonia Shipping AG; *Int'l*, pg. 3297

MS HAMMONIA TEUTONICA SCHIFFAHRTS GMBH & CO. KG—See HCI Hammonia Shipping AG; *Int'l*, pg. 3297

MSI INTERNATIONAL (THAILAND) LTD.—See IMC Pan Asia Alliance Pte. Ltd.; *Int'l*, pg. 3621

MSI SHIP MANAGEMENT PTE. LTD.—See IMC Pan Asia Alliance Pte. Ltd.; *Int'l*, pg. 3621

MSI SHIP MANAGEMENT (QINGDAO) CO. LTD.—See IMC Pan Asia Alliance Pte. Ltd.; *Int'l*, pg. 3621

MTLLINK MULTIMODAL SOLUTIONS INC.—See Blue Wolf Capital Partners LLC; *U.S. Private*, pg. 595

MUSCULAR MOVING MEN, LLC; *U.S. Private*, pg. 2817

MY FREIGHTWORLD TECHNOLOGIES, INC.; *U.S. Public*, pg. 1487

NACA LOGISTICS (USA), INC.; *U.S. Private*, pg. 2829

NAL MAROC LTD.—See Eusu Holdings Co., Ltd.; *Int'l*, pg. 2559

NATIONAL CONSOLIDATION SERVICES, LLC—See Menasha Corporation; *U.S. Private*, pg. 2665

NATIONAL TRANSPORTATION & LOGISTICS, INC.; *U.S. Private*, pg. 2864

NELSON WESTERBERG INTERNATIONAL INC.—See Nelson Westerberg, Inc.; *U.S. Private*, pg. 2884

NEPTUNE ORIENT LINES LIMITED—See CMA CGM S.A.; *Int'l*, pg. 1668

NEPW LOGISTICS, INC.—See Hyde Park Holdings LLC; *U.S. Private*, pg. 2017

NEWGISTICS, INC.—See Pitney Bowes Inc.; *U.S. Public*, pg. 1694

NEW GOLDEN SEA SHIPPING PTE., LTD.—See China COSCO Shipping Corporation Limited; *Int'l*, pg. 1494

NEXUS SEALAND TRADING PTE. LTD.—See Beng Kuang Marine Limited; *Int'l*, pg. 973

NFI LOGISTICS—See NFI Industries, Inc.; *U.S. Private*, pg. 2923

NISSHIN TRANSPORTATION CO., LTD.—See AIT Corporation; *Int'l*, pg. 254

NISSHO SHIPPING CO., LTD.—See ENEOS Holdings, Inc.; *Int'l*, pg. 2417

N&K SPEDITION SPAIN S.L.—See DFDS A/S; *Int'l*, pg. 2095

NLM INC.; *U.S. Private*, pg. 2931

NONSTOPDELIVERY, LLC—See Hub Group, Inc.; *U.S. Public*, pg. 1066

NORDDEUTSCHER LLOYD GMBH—See Albert Ballin KG; *Int'l*, pg. 295

NORRA SKEPPNINGS GRUPPEN AB—See Aspo Oyj; *Int'l*, pg. 631

NORSTEVE A/S—See Grimaldi Group SpA; *Int'l*, pg. 3085

NORSTEVE DRAMMEN A/S—See Grimaldi Group SpA; *Int'l*, pg. 3085

NORTH AMERICAN TRANSPORT CONCEPTS; *U.S. Private*, pg. 2941

NORTHWEST LOGISTICS INC.; *U.S. Private*, pg. 2961

NORTON LILLY INTERNATIONAL INC.; *U.S. Private*, pg. 2964

NORVANCO INTERNATIONAL, INC.; *U.S. Private*, pg. 2964

NTS INTERNATIONAL TRANSPORT SERVICES CO. LTD.—See A.P. Moller-Maersk A/S; *Int'l*, pg. 27

NUNAVUT SEALINK & SUPPLY INCORPORATED—See Arctic Co-Operatives Limited; *Int'l*, pg. 551

OCEANAIR INC.; *U.S. Private*, pg. 2990

OCEAN AIR INTERNATIONAL, INC.; *U.S. Private*, pg. 2988

OCEANIA LEASING AGENCIES—See CAI International, Inc.; *U.S. Public*, pg. 421

OCEANLAND SERVICE INC.; *U.S. Private*, pg. 2990

OCEANSTAR INTERNATIONAL INC.; *U.S. Private*, pg. 2992

ODYSSEY INTERNATIONAL LLC—See Odyssey Logistics & Technology Corp.; *U.S. Private*, pg. 2996

ODYSSEY LOGISTICS EUROPE BVBA—See Odyssey Logistics & Technology Corp.; *U.S. Private*, pg. 2996

ODYSSEY LOGISTICS & TECHNOLOGY CORP.; *U.S. Private*, pg. 2996

ODYSSEY OVERLAND, LLC—See Odyssey Logistics & Technology Corp.; *U.S. Private*, pg. 2996

OEC GROUP INC.; *U.S. Private*, pg. 2997

OL&T INTERNATIONAL (SHANGHAI) COMPANY LTD.—See Odyssey Logistics & Technology Corp.; *U.S. Private*, pg. 2996

OMNITRAX CANADA, INC.—See The Broe Companies, Inc.; *U.S. Private*, pg. 4001

ON TARGET PROFESSIONALS; *U.S. Private*, pg. 3018

ON TIME EXPRESS, INC.—See Radiant Logistics, Inc.; *U.S. Public*, pg. 1759

OOCL (ASIA PACIFIC) LTD—See China COSCO Shipping Corporation Limited; *Int'l*, pg. 1495

OOCL AUSTRALIA PTY LTD—See China COSCO Shipping Corporation Limited; *Int'l*, pg. 1495

OOCL (CANADA) INC.—See China COSCO Shipping Corporation Limited; *Int'l*, pg. 1495

OOCL CHINA DOMESTICS LTD—See China COSCO Shipping Corporation Limited; *Int'l*, pg. 1495

OOCL (DENMARK) A/S—See China COSCO Shipping Corporation Limited; *Int'l*, pg. 1495

OOCL (DEUTSCHLAND) GMBH—See China COSCO Shipping Corporation Limited; *Int'l*, pg. 1495

OOCL (FINLAND) LTD OY—See China COSCO Shipping Corporation Limited; *Int'l*, pg. 1495

OOCL (FRANCE) S.A.—See China COSCO Shipping Corporation Limited; *Int'l*, pg. 1495

OOCL (INDIA) PRIVATE LTD—See China COSCO Shipping Corporation Limited; *Int'l*, pg. 1495

OOCL (USA) INC.—See China COSCO Shipping Corporation Limited; *Int'l*, pg. 1495

OOO HELLMANN EAST EUROPE—See Hellmann Worldwide Logistics GmbH & Co. KG; *Int'l*, pg. 3336

OREGON INTERNATIONAL AIR FREIGHT COMPANY INC.; *U.S. Private*, pg. 3040

OSHKOSH LOGISTICS CORPORATION—See Oshkosh Corporation; *U.S. Public*, pg. 1621

OVAIR FREIGHT SERVICE, INC.—See Bruzzone Shipping, Inc.; *U.S. Private*, pg. 673

OVERSEAS WIBORG CHARTERING CO.—See Clarkson PLC; *Int'l*, pg. 1651

OWANO SHOTEN CO., LTD.—See Hanwa Co., Ltd.; *Int'l*, pg. 3263

OY INTERCARRIERS AB—See Grimaldi Group SpA; *Int'l*, pg. 3085

PACIFIC TRANSPORTATION LINES, INC.; *U.S. Private*, pg. 3071

PACORINI CUSTOMS & FORWARDING LLC—See B. Pacorini S.p.A.; *Int'l*, pg. 789

PACORINI DMCC—See B. Pacorini S.p.A.; *Int'l*, pg. 789

PACORINI FORWARDING S.R.L.—See Crane Worldwide Logistics LLC; *U.S. Private*, pg. 1085

PACORINI GLOBAL SERVICES LLC—See B. Pacorini S.p.A.; *Int'l*, pg. 789

PACORINI METALS USA LLC—See B. Pacorini S.p.A.; *Int'l*, pg. 789

PACORINI TOLL PTE. LTD.—See B. Pacorini S.p.A.; *Int'l*, pg. 789

PACORINI TOLL (SHANGHAI) WAREHOUSING LIMITED—See B. Pacorini S.p.A.; *Int'l*, pg. 789

PALLETWAYS GROUP LIMITED—See Dubai World Corporation; *Int'l*, pg. 2221

PANALPINA AB—See DSV A/S; *Int'l*, pg. 2214

PANALPINA AG—See DSV A/S; *Int'l*, pg. 2214

PANALPINA ASIA-PACIFIC SERVICES LTD.—See DSV A/S; *Int'l*, pg. 2214

PANALPINA BAHRAIN W.L.L.—See DSV A/S; *Int'l*, pg. 2214

PANALPINA CENTRAL ASIA AZERBAIJAN—See DSV A/S; *Int'l*, pg. 2214

PANALPINA CHILE TRANSPORTES MUNDIALES LTDA.—See DSV A/S; *Int'l*, pg. 2214

PANALPINA CHINA LIMITED—See DSV A/S; *Int'l*, pg. 2214

PANALPINA FINLAND—See DSV A/S; *Int'l*, pg. 2214

PANALPINA FREIGHT LLC—See DSV A/S; *Int'l*, pg. 2214

PANALPINA (GHANA) LIMITED—See DSV A/S; *Int'l*, pg. 2214

PANALPINA GULF LLC—See DSV A/S; *Int'l*, pg. 2214

PANALPINA HASSI MESSAOUD—See DSV A/S; *Int'l*, pg. 2214

PANALPINA, INC.—See DSV A/S; *Int'l*, pg. 2216

PANALPINA, INC.—See DSV A/S; *Int'l*, pg. 2216

PANALPINA KOREA LTD.—See DSV A/S; *Int'l*, pg. 2214

PANALPINA LTDA.—See DSV A/S; *Int'l*, pg. 2214

PANALPINA MACAU EMPRESA TRANSITARIA LIMITADA—See DSV A/S; *Int'l*, pg. 2214

PANALPINA MAGYARORSZAG KFT.—See DSV A/S; *Int'l*, pg. 2214

PANALPINA QATAR W.L.L.—See DSV A/S; *Int'l*, pg. 2215

PANALPINA S.A.—See DSV A/S; *Int'l*, pg. 2215

PANALPINA SLOVAKIA S.R.O.—See DSV A/S; *Int'l*, pg. 2215

PANALPINA TAIWAN LTD.—See DSV A/S; *Int'l*, pg. 2215

PANALPINA TRANSPORTES MUNDIAIS LDA.—See DSV A/S; *Int'l*, pg. 2215

PANALPINA TRANSPORTES MUNDIAIS, NAVEGACAO & TRANSISTOS S.A.R.L.—See DSV A/S; *Int'l*, pg. 2215

PANALPINA TRANSPORTES MUNDIALES C.A.—See DSV A/S; *Int'l*, pg. 2215

PANALPINA TRANSPORTES MUNDIALES S.A. DE C.V.—See DSV A/S; *Int'l*, pg. 2215

PANALPINA TRANSPORTES MUNDIALES S.A.—See DSV A/S; *Int'l*, pg. 2215

PANALPINA TRANSPORTES MUNDIALES S.A.—See DSV A/S; *Int'l*, pg. 2215

PANALPINA TRANSPORTES MUNDIALES S.A.—See DSV A/S; *Int'l*, pg. 2215

PANALPINA TRANSPORTES MUNDIALES S.A.—See DSV A/S; *Int'l*, pg. 2215

PANALPINA TRANSPORTES MUNDIALES S.A.—See DSV A/S; *Int'l*, pg. 2215

PANALPINA TRANSPORTI MONDIALI S.P.A.—See DSV A/S; *Int'l*, pg. 2215

PANALPINA TRANSPORT (MALAYSIA) SDN. BHD.—See DSV A/S; *Int'l*, pg. 2215

PANALPINA TRANSPORTS INTERNATIONAUX S.A.—See DSV A/S; *Int'l*, pg. 2215

PANALPINA TRANSPORTS MONDIAUX CAMEROON S.A.—See DSV A/S; *Int'l*, pg. 2215

PANALPINA TRANSPORTS MONDIAUX CONGO S.A.R.L.—See DSV A/S; *Int'l*, pg. 2215

PANALPINA TRANSPORTS MONDIAUX GABON S.A.—See DSV A/S; *Int'l*, pg. 2215

PANALPINA URUGUAY TRANSPORTES MUNDIALES S.A.—See DSV A/S; *Int'l*, pg. 2215

PANALPINA WELTTRANSPORT (DEUTSCHLAND) GMBH—See DSV A/S; *Int'l*, pg. 2215

PANALPINA WELTTRANSPORT GMBH—See DSV A/S; *Int'l*, pg. 2215

PANALPINA WELTTRANSPORT GMBH—See DSV A/S; *Int'l*, pg. 2215

PANALPINA WELTTRANSPORT GMBH—See DSV A/S; *Int'l*, pg. 2215

PANALPINA WELTTRANSPORT GMBH—See DSV A/S; *Int'l*, pg. 2215

PANALPINA WELTTRANSPORT GMBH—See DSV A/S; *Int'l*, pg. 2215

PANALPINA WELTTRANSPORT GMBH—See DSV A/S; *Int'l*, pg. 2215

PANALPINA WORLD TRANSPORT B.V.—See DSV A/S; *Int'l*, pg. 2216

PANALPINA WORLD TRANSPORT GMBH—See DSV A/S; *Int'l*, pg. 2216

PANALPINA WORLD TRANSPORT HOLDING LTD.—See DSV A/S; *Int'l*, pg. 2214

PANALPINA WORLD TRANSPORT (INDIA) PVT. LTD.—See DSV A/S; *Int'l*, pg. 2215

PANALPINA WORLD TRANSPORT (IRELAND) LTD.—See DSV A/S; *Int'l*, pg. 2215

PANALPINA WORLD TRANSPORT (JAPAN) LTD.—See DSV A/S; *Int'l*, pg. 2215

PANALPINA WORLD TRANSPORT LTD.—See DSV A/S; *Int'l*, pg. 2216

PANALPINA WORLD TRANSPORT LTD.—See DSV A/S; *Int'l*, pg. 2216

PANALPINA WORLD TRANSPORT LTD.—See DSV A/S; *Int'l*, pg. 2216

PANALPINA WORLD TRANSPORT NAKLIYAT LTD. STI.—See DSV A/S; *Int'l*, pg. 2216

PANALPINA WORLD TRANSPORT NIGERIA LTD.—See DSV A/S; *Int'l*, pg. 2216

PANALPINA WORLD TRANSPORT N.V.—See DSV A/S; *Int'l*, pg. 2216

PANALPINA WORLD TRANSPORT N.V.—See DSV A/S; *Int'l*, pg. 2216

PANALPINA WORLD TRANSPORT (PHILS.) INC.—See DSV A/S; *Int'l*, pg. 2215

PANALPINA WORLD TRANSPORT (PRC) LTD.—See DSV A/S; *Int'l*, pg. 2215

PANALPINA WORLD TRANSPORT PTY. LTD.—See DSV A/S; *Int'l*, pg. 2216

PANALPINA WORLD TRANSPORT PTY. LTD.—See DSV A/S; *Int'l*, pg. 2216

PANALPINA WORLD TRANSPORT (SAUDI ARABIA) LTD.—See DSV A/S; *Int'l*, pg. 2216

PANALPINA WORLD TRANSPORT (SINGAPORE) PTE.

488510 — FREIGHT TRANSPORTAT...

LTD.—See DSV A/S; *Int'l*, pg. 2216
PANALPINA WORLD TRANSPORT (THAILAND) LIMITED—See DSV A/S; *Int'l*, pg. 2216
PANALPINA WORLD TRANSPORT ZAO—See DSV A/S; *Int'l*, pg. 2216
PAN PACIFIC EXPRESS CORP.; *U.S. Private*, pg. 3084
PANTHER EXPEDITED SERVICES, INC.—See ArcBest Corporation; *U.S. Public*, pg. 180
PAOLETTI AMERICA S.A.—See Corporacion America Airports S.A.; *Int'l*, pg. 1803
PARKER & COMPANY INC.; *U.S. Private*, pg. 3097
PATHMARK TRANSPORTATION MARKETING CO.; *U.S. Private*, pg. 3106
PAUL BELLACK INC.; *U.S. Private*, pg. 3112
PELICAN SHIP MANAGEMENT SERVIES PTE LTD—See Dymon Asia Capital (Singapore) Pte. Ltd; *Int'l*, pg. 2238
PENTAGON FREIGHT SERVICES, INC.; *U.S. Private*, pg. 3140
PERISHIP LLC—See VerifyMe, Inc.; *U.S. Public*, pg. 2280
PHOENIX BULK CARRIERS (US) LLC—See Pangaea Logistics Solutions Ltd.; *U.S. Public*, pg. 1635
PHOENIX INDUSTRIES, LLC; *U.S. Private*, pg. 3173
PIASA OIL TRANSPORT LLC—See Piasa Motor Fuels LLC; *U.S. Private*, pg. 3175
PILOT AIR FREIGHT, LLC—See A.P. Moller-Maersk A/S; *Int'l*, pg. 27
PIONEER TRANSFER, LLC—See Refrigerated Food Express Inc.; *U.S. Private*, pg. 3395
PIONEER VALLEY RAILROAD—See Pinsly Railroad Co. Inc.; *U.S. Private*, pg. 3186
PJSC CENTER FOR CARGO CONTAINER TRAFFIC TRANSCONTAINER—See Delo Group; *Int'l*, pg. 2014
P&J TEAM AMERICA INC.; *U.S. Private*, pg. 3059
PLANETWIDE LIMITED—See Braemar PLC; *Int'l*, pg. 1135
PLS LOGISTICS SERVICES; *U.S. Private*, pg. 3214
PMG WORLDWIDE INC.; *U.S. Private*, pg. 3218
P&O FERRIES LTD.—See Dubai World Corporation; *Int'l*, pg. 2220
POINT TO POINT TRANSPORTATION SERVICES INC.; *U.S. Private*, pg. 3222
POLAMER INC.; *U.S. Private*, pg. 3223
PORT OF DUNDEE LTD—See Arcus Infrastructure Partners LLP; *Int'l*, pg. 553
PORT OF TILBURY LONDON LIMITED—See Arcus Infrastructure Partners LLP; *Int'l*, pg. 553
PORT TO PORT INTERNATIONAL CORP.; *U.S. Private*, pg. 3231
POS LOGISTICS BERHAD—See DRB-HICOM Berhad; *Int'l*, pg. 2202
POTEN & PARTNERS, INC.—See BGC Group, Inc.; *U.S. Public*, pg. 330
PRIMARY FREIGHT SERVICES INC.; *U.S. Private*, pg. 3260
PRIMERAIL GMBH—See DFDS A/S; *Int'l*, pg. 2095
PRIORITY AIR EXPRESS, LLC—See Thermo Fisher Scientific Inc.; *U.S. Public*, pg. 2151
PRODUCT TRANSPORT (US) INC—See B+H Ocean Carriers Ltd.; *Int'l*, pg. 784
PROJECT LOGISTICS INTERNATIONAL—See Emo-Trans Inc.; *U.S. Private*, pg. 1383
PROTRANS INTERNATIONAL INC.; *U.S. Private*, pg. 3290
PT DANZAS SARANA PERKASA—See Deutsche Post AG; *Int'l*, pg. 2082
PT DHL GLOBAL FORWARDING INDONESIA—See Deutsche Post AG; *Int'l*, pg. 2078
PT. EUSU LOGISTICS INDONESIA—See Eusu Holdings Co., Ltd.; *Int'l*, pg. 2559
PT. JF HILLEBRAND INDONESIA—See Deutsche Post AG; *Int'l*, pg. 2081
PT KIM SEAH SHIPYARD INDONESIA—See Dymon Asia Capital (Singapore) Pte. Ltd; *Int'l*, pg. 2238
P.T. MULTI BINA PURA INTERNATIONAL—See Evergreen Marine Corporation (Taiwan) Ltd.; *Int'l*, pg. 2566
P.T. MULTI BINA TRANSPORT—See Evergreen Marine Corporation (Taiwan) Ltd.; *Int'l*, pg. 2566
P.T. PANALPINA NUSAJAYA TRANSPORT—See DSV A/S; *Int'l*, pg. 2214
PT. PELITA SAMUDERA SHIPPING—See IMC Pan Asia Alliance Pte. Ltd.; *Int'l*, pg. 3621
PT TELEPORTASI BISNIS INDONESIA—See Capital A Bhd; *Int'l*, pg. 1309
PT. UNIQUE LOGISTICS INTERNATIONAL INDONESIA—See Unique Logistics International Inc.; *U.S. Public*, pg. 2227
PULSAR SHIPPING AGENCIES (PRIVATE) LIMITED—See Expolanka Holdings PLC; *Int'l*, pg. 2589
PWC TRANSPORT COMPANY W.L.L.—See Agility; *Int'l*, pg. 210
QUADRIVIUS, INC.; *U.S. Private*, pg. 3316
QUALITY CARRIERS, INC.—See Apax Partners LLP; *Int'l*, pg. 505
QUALITY CUSTOMS BROKER INC.; *U.S. Private*, pg. 3318
QUANTIX SCS, INC.—See Wind Point Advisors LLC; *U.S. Private*, pg. 4535
QUICK BOX, LLC; *U.S. Private*, pg. 3326
QUINCANNON ASSOCIATES, INC.; *U.S. Private*, pg. 3327
RADIANT GLOBAL LOGISTICS (CA), INC.—See Radiant Logistics, Inc.; *U.S. Public*, pg. 1760

RADIANT GLOBAL LOGISTICS (HK) LIMITED—See Radiant Logistics, Inc.; *U.S. Public*, pg. 1759
RADIANT GLOBAL LOGISTICS, INC.—See Radiant Logistics, Inc.; *U.S. Public*, pg. 1759
RADIX GROUP INTERNATIONAL, INC.—See Deutsche Post AG; *Int'l*, pg. 2082
RAIL INTERMODEL SPECIALISTS—See TSL Companies; *U.S. Private*, pg. 4254
RAILROAD DISTRIBUTION SERVICES, INC.—See Pinsly Railroad Co. Inc.; *U.S. Private*, pg. 3186
RAM INTERNATIONAL INC.; *U.S. Private*, pg. 3351
RAVISA DISTRIBUTION CENTER LLC.; *U.S. Private*, pg. 3358
RAYMOND EXPRESS INTERNATIONAL CORPORATION; *U.S. Private*, pg. 3359
RECON LOGISTICS; *U.S. Private*, pg. 3371
RED ARROW LOGISTICS INC.; *U.S. Private*, pg. 3373
REDCOON LOGISTICS GMBH—See Ceconomy AG; *Int'l*, pg. 1388
REDHAWK GLOBAL, LLC; *U.S. Private*, pg. 3378
RED RIVER INTERMODAL INC.; *U.S. Private*, pg. 3375
REICH LOGISTICS SERVICES INC.—See Best Logistics Group, Inc.; *U.S. Private*, pg. 543
THE RELOCATION FREIGHT CORPORATION OF AMERICA—See Prudential Financial, Inc.; *U.S. Public*, pg. 1734
RELOCATION SERVICES INTERNATIONAL; *U.S. Private*, pg. 3395
REV IT LOGISTICS LLC; *U.S. Private*, pg. 3412
RHEIN LOGISTICS GMBH—See Dubai Islamic Bank PSJ; *Int'l*, pg. 2220
RICH SHIPPING (USA) INC.; *U.S. Private*, pg. 3427
RIM LOGISTICS LTD; *U.S. Private*, pg. 3437
RIVERSTONE LOGISTICS, LLC; *U.S. Private*, pg. 3448
RIZHAO COSCO LOGISTICS LIMITED—See China COSCO Shipping Corporation Limited; *Int'l*, pg. 1493
RLI & HAWAII PRODUCT LINES—See RLI Corp.; *U.S. Public*, pg. 1801
R.L. JONES CUSTOMHOUSE BROKERS INC.; *U.S. Private*, pg. 3338
ROCK-IT CARGO USA LLC - LOS ANGELES-RIC—See ATL Partners, LLC; *U.S. Private*, pg. 369
ROCK-IT CARGO USA LLC—See ATL Partners, LLC; *U.S. Private*, pg. 369
ROCKY MOUNTAIN EXPRESS CORP; *U.S. Private*, pg. 3468
ROGERS & BROWN CUSTOM BROKERS, INC. - GREER—See Rogers & Brown Custom Brokers, Inc.; *U.S. Private*, pg. 3471
ROGERS & BROWN CUSTOM BROKERS, INC.; *U.S. Private*, pg. 3471
ROGERS SHIPPING LTD.—See ENL Limited; *Int'l*, pg. 2442
RO-MAR TRANSPORTATION SYSTEMS INC.; *U.S. Private*, pg. 3453
ROSEDALE GROUP INC.; *U.S. Private*, pg. 3482
ROTRA, LLC—See Delmar International, Inc.; *Int'l*, pg. 2014
ROTTERDAM FREIGHT STATION B.V.—See Allcargo Logistics Limited; *Int'l*, pg. 334
ROYAL GLOBAL EXPRESS INC—See RPM Consolidated Services, Inc.; *U.S. Private*, pg. 3495
RPM CONSOLIDATED SERVICES, INC.; *U.S. Private*, pg. 3495
RSI LOGISTICS INC.—See Trinity Industries, Inc.; *U.S. Public*, pg. 2193
RT&T GROUP, INC.; *U.S. Private*, pg. 3497
RXO INC.; *U.S. Public*, pg. 1827
SACOR MARITIMA, S.A.—See Galp Energia SGPS, S.A.; *Int'l*, pg. 2875
SALERNO CONTAINER TERMINAL S.P.A.—See EUROKAI GmbH & Co. KGaA; *Int'l*, pg. 2553
SALLY AB—See AS Infortar; *Int'l*, pg. 590
SAMUEL SHAPIRO & COMPANY INC.; *U.S. Private*, pg. 3538
SANDUSKY DOCK CORPORATION—See Norfolk Southern Corporation; *U.S. Public*, pg. 1535
SAN MATEO FORWARDING; *U.S. Private*, pg. 3542
SANTANDREA TERMINALI SPECIALIZZATI S.R.L.—See B. Pacorini S.p.A.; *Int'l*, pg. 789
SASKATCHEWAN TRANSPORTATION COMPANY—See Crown Investments Corporation of Saskatchewan; *Int'l*, pg. 1857
SATURN FREIGHT SYSTEMS INC.; *U.S. Private*, pg. 3553
SCANDFIBRE LOGISTICS AB—See Billerud AB; *Int'l*, pg. 1030
SCARBROUGH INTERNATIONAL, LTD.; *U.S. Private*, pg. 3561
SCHAEFER TRANS INC.; *U.S. Private*, pg. 3563
SCHENKER AG—See Deutsche Bahn AG; *Int'l*, pg. 2052
SCHENKER ARGENTINA S.A.—See Deutsche Bahn AG; *Int'l*, pg. 2053
SCHENKER & CO AG—See Deutsche Bahn AG; *Int'l*, pg. 2053
SCHENKER DEUTSCHLAND AG—See Deutsche Bahn AG; *Int'l*, pg. 2053
SCHENKER DO BRASIL TRANSPORTES INTERNACIONAIS LTDA.—See Deutsche Bahn AG; *Int'l*, pg. 2054
SCHENKER, INC.—See Deutsche Bahn AG; *Int'l*, pg. 2054
SCHENKER, INC.—See Deutsche Bahn AG; *Int'l*, pg. 2054

CORPORATE AFFILIATIONS

SCHENKER INTERNATIONAL HK LIMITED—See Deutsche Bahn AG; *Int'l*, pg. 2053
SCHENKER INTERNATIONAL (HK) LTD.—See Deutsche Bahn AG; *Int'l*, pg. 2054
SCHENKER JINBEI LOGISTICS (SHENYANG) CO. LTD.—See Deutsche Bahn AG; *Int'l*, pg. 2054
SCHENKER KAZAKHSTAN TOO—See Deutsche Bahn AG; *Int'l*, pg. 2054
SCHENKER LOGISTICS (BANGLADESH) LIMITED—See Deutsche Bahn AG; *Int'l*, pg. 2054
SCHENKER LOGISTICS (JIAXING) CO., LTD.—See Deutsche Bahn AG; *Int'l*, pg. 2054
SCHENKER LOGISTICS (KUNSHAN) CO., LTD.—See Deutsche Bahn AG; *Int'l*, pg. 2054
SCHENKER LOGISTICS ROMANIA S.A.—See Deutsche Bahn AG; *Int'l*, pg. 2054
SCHENKER MYANMAR CO., LTD.—See Deutsche Bahn AG; *Int'l*, pg. 2054
SCHENKER OF CANADA LIMITED—See Deutsche Bahn AG; *Int'l*, pg. 2054
SCHENKER PHILIPPINES, INC.—See Deutsche Bahn AG; *Int'l*, pg. 2054
SCHENKER PHILIPPINES, INC.—See Deutsche Bahn AG; *Int'l*, pg. 2054
SCHENKER SCHWEIZ AG—See Deutsche Bahn AG; *Int'l*, pg. 2054
SCHENKER SINGAPORE (PTE) LTD.—See Deutsche Bahn AG; *Int'l*, pg. 2054
SCHERBAUER SPEDITION GMBH—See Deutsche Post AG; *Int'l*, pg. 2082
SCHILLI TRANSPORTATION SERVICES, INC.—See Daseke, Inc.; *U.S. Private*, pg. 1161
SCHNEIDER LOGISTICS, INC.—See Schneider National, Inc.; *U.S. Public*, pg. 1847
SCHNEIDER TRANSPORT, INC.—See Schneider National, Inc.; *U.S. Public*, pg. 1847
SCOTT LOGISTICS CORP.—See ABRY Partners, LLC; *U.S. Private*, pg. 41
SD - KOLEJOVA DOPRAVA, A.S.—See CEZ, a.s.; *Int'l*, pg. 1428
SDV (USA) INC.—See Financiere de L'Odet; *Int'l*, pg. 2667
SEABOARD TRANSPORT LLC—See Seaboard Corporation; *U.S. Public*, pg. 1851
SEALAND EUROPE A/S—See A.P. Moller-Maersk A/S; *Int'l*, pg. 27
SEAMATES INTERNATIONAL INC.; *U.S. Private*, pg. 3585
SEA STAR LINE, LLC; *U.S. Private*, pg. 3582
SEKO ENTERPRISES, LLC—See Greenbriar Equity Group, L.P.; *U.S. Private*, pg. 1776
SENATE FORWARDING INC—See Ambassador Van Lines Inc.; *U.S. Private*, pg. 217
SENDEREX CARGO INC.; *U.S. Private*, pg. 3606
SENTRY HOUSEHOLD SHIPPING INC—See The Suddath Companies; *U.S. Private*, pg. 4124
SERNAM CENTRE S.A.—See Butler Capital Partners SA; *Int'l*, pg. 1229
SERNAM EST S.A.—See Butler Capital Partners SA; *Int'l*, pg. 1229
SERNAM IDF S.A.—See Butler Capital Partners SA; *Int'l*, pg. 1229
SERNAM NORD S.A.—See Butler Capital Partners SA; *Int'l*, pg. 1229
SERNAM OUEST S.A.—See Butler Capital Partners SA; *Int'l*, pg. 1229
SERRA INTERNATIONAL INC.; *U.S. Private*, pg. 3614
SERVICE BY AIR, INC.—See Radiant Logistics, Inc.; *U.S. Public*, pg. 1760
SERVICE TERMINAL ROTTERDAM B.V.—See iCON Infrastructure LLP; *Int'l*, pg. 3583
SERVICIOS DE APOYO MARITIMO DE MEXICO, S. DE R.L. DE C.V.—See Trico Marine Services, Inc.; *U.S. Private*, pg. 4229
SERVILOGISTICS DE MEXICO, S.A. DE C.V.—See Accel, S.A.B. de C.V.; *Int'l*, pg. 79
SETHMAR TRANSPORTATION INC.; *U.S. Private*, pg. 3617
SHANDONG JIAJIA INTERNATIONAL FREIGHT & FORWARDING CO., LTD.—See China Logistics Group, Inc.; *Int'l*, pg. 1515
SHANGHAI HOYER SINOBULK TRANSPORT CO., LTD.—See Hoyer GmbH; *Int'l*, pg. 3499
SHANGHAI OCEAN SHIPPING CO., LTD.—See China COSCO Shipping Corporation Limited; *Int'l*, pg. 1496
SHANGHAI PAN ASIA SHIPPING COMPANY LIMITED—See China COSCO Shipping Corporation Limited; *Int'l*, pg. 1494
SHENZHEN COSCO INTERNATIONAL SHIPMANAGEMENT CO., LTD.—See China COSCO Shipping Corporation Limited; *Int'l*, pg. 1492
SHENZHEN COSCO LOGISTICS CO., LTD.—See China COSCO Shipping Corporation Limited; *Int'l*, pg. 1493
SHENZHEN GREENTRANS TRANSPORTATION CO., LTD.—See Evergreen Marine Corporation (Taiwan) Ltd.; *Int'l*, pg. 2567
SHIP SUPPLY OF FLORIDA, INC.; *U.S. Private*, pg. 3637
SHO-AIR INTERNATIONAL INC.; *U.S. Private*, pg. 3639
SHOWA NITTAN CORP.—See ENEOS Holdings, Inc.; *Int'l*, pg. 2418

N.A.I.C.S. INDEX

488510 — FREIGHT TRANSPORTAT...

SHOW GROUP ENTERPRISES PTY LTD—See Helloworld Travel Limited; *Int'l*, pg. 3337
SIAM AZUMA MULTI-TRANS CO., LTD.—See Azuma Shipping Co., Ltd.; *Int'l*, pg. 782
SIMPLEXITY TECHNOLOGY & OPERATIONS CENTER—See Independence Capital Partners, LLC; *U.S. Private*, pg. 2057
SINGULARITY FUTURE TECHNOLOGY LTD.; *U.S. Public*, pg. 1888
SINO-GLOBAL SHIPPING AGENCY LIMITED—See Singularity Future Technology Ltd.; *U.S. Public*, pg. 1888
SINO-GLOBAL SHIPPING CANADA INC.—See Singularity Future Technology Ltd.; *U.S. Public*, pg. 1888
SINO-GLOBAL SHIPPING (HK) LTD.—See Singularity Future Technology Ltd.; *U.S. Public*, pg. 1888
SINOMART TRANSPORT CO., LTD.—See China Merchants Group Limited; *Int'l*, pg. 1522
SINOTRANS AGENCIES (S) PTE LTD.—See China Merchants Group Limited; *Int'l*, pg. 1522
SINOTRANS CANADA INC.—See China Merchants Group Limited; *Int'l*, pg. 1521
SINOTRANS CHONGQING COMPANY LIMITED—See China Merchants Group Limited; *Int'l*, pg. 1522
SINOTRANS FOSHAN EXPRESS MANAGMENT AND CUSTOM BROKERAGE CO., LTD.—See China Merchants Group Limited; *Int'l*, pg. 1522
SINOTRANS FOSHAN SHIPPING CO., LTD.—See China Merchants Group Limited; *Int'l*, pg. 1523
SINOTRANS (GERMANY) GMBH—See China Merchants Group Limited; *Int'l*, pg. 1522
SINOTRANS GUANGDONG COMPANY LIMITED—See China Merchants Group Limited; *Int'l*, pg. 1522
SINOTRANS GUANGDONG CUSTOMS BROKER CO., LTD.—See China Merchants Group Limited; *Int'l*, pg. 1523
SINOTRANS GUANGDONG INTERNATIONAL FREIGHT FORWARDING CO., LTD.—See China Merchants Group Limited; *Int'l*, pg. 1523
SINOTRANS GUANGDONG PROPERTY MANAGEMENT CO., LTD.—See China Merchants Group Limited; *Int'l*, pg. 1523
SINOTRANS GUANGDONG SHIPPING CO., LTD.—See China Merchants Group Limited; *Int'l*, pg. 1523
SINOTRANS HEAVY-LIFT LOGISTICS COMPANY LIMITED—See China Merchants Group Limited; *Int'l*, pg. 1523
SINOTRANS KOREA SHIPPING CO., LTD.—See China Merchants Group Limited; *Int'l*, pg. 1522
SINOTRANS LANDBRIDGE TRANSPORTATION COMPANY LIMITED—See China Merchants Group Limited; *Int'l*, pg. 1523
SINOTRANS MACAO CO., LTD.—See China Merchants Group Limited; *Int'l*, pg. 1523
SINOTRANS NETHERLANDS B.V.—See China Merchants Group Limited; *Int'l*, pg. 1522
SINOTRANS SHANDONG COMPANY LIMITED—See China Merchants Group Limited; *Int'l*, pg. 1523
SINOTRANS SHANTOU CO. LTD.—See China Merchants Group Limited; *Int'l*, pg. 1523
SINOTRANS SHENZHEN CUSTOMS BROKER CO., LTD.—See China Merchants Group Limited; *Int'l*, pg. 1523
SINOTRANS ZHONGSHAN CUSTOMS BROKER CO., LTD.—See China Merchants Group Limited; *Int'l*, pg. 1523
SKY COUNTRY TRANSPORTATION SERVICE; *U.S. Private*, pg. 3684
SKY LOGISTICS AND DISTRIBUTION; *U.S. Private*, pg. 3684
SMIT HARBOUR TOWAGE ROTTERDAM B.V.—See HAL Trust N.V.; *Int'l*, pg. 3227
SMIT LOGISTICS B.V.—See HAL Trust N.V.; *Int'l*, pg. 3227
SNAP GLOBAL, LLC—See Hemisphere Media Group, Inc.; *U.S. Private*, pg. 1913
SNS LOGISTICS, INC.; *U.S. Private*, pg. 3701
SOETERMEER FEKKES - ZWIJNDRECHT—See Carisbrooke Shipping Limited; *Int'l*, pg. 1331
SOGEMAR S.P.A.—See EUROKAI GmbH & Co. KGaA; *Int'l*, pg. 2553
SOLAS SHIPPING AGENCY S.R.L.—See Coeclerici S.p.A.; *Int'l*, pg. 1689
SOLVTRANS REDERI AS—See Brookfield Corporation; *Int'l*, pg. 1183
SOMERSET MARINE LINES, LLC—See Littlejohn & Co., LLC; *U.S. Private*, pg. 2470
SOS GLOBAL EXPRESS INC.—See ATL Partners, LLC; *U.S. Private*, pg. 369
SPAN ALASKA TRANSPORTATION, INC.—See Matson, Inc.; *U.S. Public*, pg. 1398
SPECTRUM TRANSPORTATION; *U.S. Private*, pg. 3753
SPEEDMARK TRANSPORTATION INC.; *U.S. Private*, pg. 3754
STAGECOACH CARTAGE & DISTRIBUTION, LLC.—See JH Rose Logistics Inc.; *U.S. Private*, pg. 2207
STANDARD FREIGHT, LLC; *U.S. Private*, pg. 3778
STANDARD TRANSPORTATION SERVICES, INC.; *U.S. Private*, pg. 3782

STARLITE SERVICES, INC.—See Distribution 2000 Inc.; *U.S. Private*, pg. 1239
STAR TRACK EXPRESS PTY. LTD.—See Australian Postal Corporation; *Int'l*, pg. 722
STERIPLUS AG—See Die Schweizerische Post AG; *Int'l*, pg. 2113
STEVENS FORWARDERS INC.—See Stevens Group, Inc.; *U.S. Private*, pg. 3809
STEWART CORPORATION; *U.S. Private*, pg. 3811
STOTT & DAVIS MOTOR EXPRESS; *U.S. Private*, pg. 3832
STRIVE LOGISTICS, LLC—See AEA Investors LP; *U.S. Private*, pg. 115
STYLINE BROKERAGE SERVICE INC.—See Styline Industries Inc.; *U.S. Private*, pg. 3846
SUDDATH TRANSPORTATION SERVICES, INC.—See The Suddath Companies; *U.S. Private*, pg. 4125
SUNSET TRANSPORTATION, LLC—See Armada Group, Ltd.; *U.S. Private*, pg. 329
SUNTECK TRANSPORT GROUP, INC.—See Comvest Group Holdings LLC; *U.S. Private*, pg. 1007
SUPERIOR FREIGHT SERVICES INC.; *U.S. Private*, pg. 3878
SUPERIOR LOGISTICS SOLUTIONS LLC; *U.S. Private*, pg. 3878
SUPERVALU, INC., QUINCY DIVISION—See United Natural Foods, Inc.; *U.S. Public*, pg. 2232
SWAIM LOGISTICS LLC; *U.S. Private*, pg. 3889
TACISA TRANSITARIA S.L.—See DSV A/S; *Int'l*, pg. 2216
TAICANG CIMC CONTAINERS CO., LTD.—See China International Marine Containers (Group) Co., Ltd.; *Int'l*, pg. 1512
TAIMEN TRANSPORT, LLC; *U.S. Private*, pg. 3924
TAMARIND CONSOLIDATED, INC.—See Crowley Maritime Corporation; *U.S. Private*, pg. 1110
TANDEM GLOBAL LOGISTICS (HK) LIMITED—See Azuma Shipping Co., Ltd.; *Int'l*, pg. 782
TANDEM GLOBAL LOGISTICS (INDIA) PVT. LTD.—See Azuma Shipping Co., Ltd.; *Int'l*, pg. 782
TANDEM GLOBAL LOGISTICS JAPAN CO., LTD.—See Azuma Shipping Co., Ltd.; *Int'l*, pg. 782
TANDEM GLOBAL LOGISTICS NETHERLANDS B.V.—See Azuma Shipping Co., Ltd.; *Int'l*, pg. 782
TANDEM GLOBAL LOGISTICS (SHANGHAI) CO., LTD.—See Azuma Shipping Co., Ltd.; *Int'l*, pg. 782
TANGSHAN COSCO SHIPPING LINES LOGISTICS CO., LTD.—See China COSCO Shipping Corporation Limited; *Int'l*, pg. 1494
TANTARA SERVICES INC.—See Tantara Transportation Group; *U.S. Private*, pg. 3932
TARGET FREIGHT MANAGEMENT; *U.S. Private*, pg. 3933
TARGET INTERSTATE SYSTEMS INC.; *U.S. Private*, pg. 3933
TA SERVICES, INC.—See P&S Transportation, Inc.; *U.S. Private*, pg. 3059
TBB GLOBAL LOGISTICS INC.; *U.S. Private*, pg. 3941
TBB GLOBAL LOGISTICS INC., TRUCKLOAD DIVISION—See TBB Global Logistics Inc.; *U.S. Private*, pg. 3941
TEAM DRIVE-AWAY, INC.—See The Carlyle Group Inc.; *U.S. Public*, pg. 2056
TEAM WORLDWIDE; *U.S. Private*, pg. 3950
TECHNICAL TRANSPORTATION INC.; *U.S. Private*, pg. 3954
TECTO CYPRUS LIMITED—See Exmar N.V.; *Int'l*, pg. 2585
TENNESSEE COMMERCIAL WAREHOUSE INC.; *U.S. Private*, pg. 3967
TERMINAL ALPTRANSIT S.R.L.—See Ferrovie dello Stato Italiane S.p.A.; *Int'l*, pg. 2645
TERMINAL CONSOLIDATION CO. INC.; *U.S. Private*, pg. 3969
TERMINAL CONTAINER RAVENNA S.P.A.—See EUROKAI GmbH & Co. KGaA; *Int'l*, pg. 2553
TFG TRANSFRACHT GMBH—See Deutsche Bahn AG; *Int'l*, pg. 2054
THOMAS & SONS DISTRIBUTORS; *U.S. Private*, pg. 4154
THOROUGHBRED DIRECT INTERMODAL SERVICES, INC.—See Norfolk Southern Corporation; *U.S. Public*, pg. 1536
THUN TANKERS B.V.—See Erik Thun AB; *Int'l*, pg. 2493
TIANJIN YUANHUA SHIPPING CO., LTD—See COSCO Shipping Holdings Co., Ltd.; *Int'l*, pg. 1810
TIDAL LOGISTICS, INC.—See Select Water Solutions, Inc.; *U.S. Public*, pg. 1862
TIGERS GLOBAL LOGISTICS PTY LTD—See JAS Worldwide, Inc.; *U.S. Private*, pg. 2189
TIGERS GLOBAL LOGISTICS—See JAS Worldwide, Inc.; *U.S. Private*, pg. 2189
TIGERS (HK) CO., LTD.—See JAS Worldwide, Inc.; *U.S. Private*, pg. 2189
TIGERS (USA) GLOBAL LOGISTICS, INC.—See JAS Worldwide, Inc.; *U.S. Private*, pg. 2189
TIMAR SA—See Clasquin S.A.; *Int'l*, pg. 1652
TIME DEFINITE SERVICES INC.; *U.S. Private*, pg. 4172
TIME MATTERS GMBH—See Deutsche Lufthansa AG; *Int'l*, pg. 2071
TITAN LANSING, LLC—See The Andersons Incorporated; *U.S. Public*, pg. 2035
TMI TRANSPORTGESELLSCHAFT DER MOBELINDUSTRIE MBH—See G. Peter Reber Mobel-Logistik GmbH; *Int'l*, pg. 2864
TMT LOGISTICS INC.; *U.S. Private*, pg. 4180
TNT INC.; *U.S. Private*, pg. 4180
TOMASSEN TRANSPORT B.V.—See Bangkok Ranch Public Company Limited; *Int'l*, pg. 835
THE TOPOCEAN GROUP; *U.S. Private*, pg. 4127
TOTAL QUALITY, INC.—See Forward Air Corporation; *U.S. Public*, pg. 874
TOTAL QUALITY LOGISTICS INC.; *U.S. Private*, pg. 4191
TOTAL TRANSPORTATION CONCEPT; *U.S. Private*, pg. 4192
TRAILER BRIDGE, INC.; *U.S. Private*, pg. 4203
TRANSAMERICA EXPRESS LOGISTICS, LLC; *U.S. Private*, pg. 4207
TRANS AMERICAN CUSTOMHOUSE BROKERS, INC.—See Expolanka Holdings PLC; *Int'l*, pg. 2589
TRANSCORE LINK LOGISTICS CORPORATION—See Roper Technologies, Inc.; *U.S. Public*, pg. 1814
TRANSEAWAYS SHIPPING SDN. BHD.—See Asdion Berhad.; *Int'l*, pg. 604
TRANS EXPEDITE, INC.; *U.S. Private*, pg. 4205
TRANSFESA LOGISTICS, S.A.—See Deutsche Bahn AG; *Int'l*, pg. 2054
TRANSFREIGHT, LLC—See Penske Corporation; *U.S. Private*, pg. 3138
TRANSIT FREIGHT FORWARDING PROPRIETARY LIMITED—See Frontier Services Group Limited; *Int'l*, pg. 2796
TRANSIT SYSTEMS INC.; *U.S. Private*, pg. 4208
TRANS-OVERSEAS CORPORATION; *U.S. Private*, pg. 4206
TRANS PACIFIC SHIPPING LIMITED—See Singularity Future Technology Ltd.; *U.S. Public*, pg. 1888
TRANSPLACE CANADA - LAKESIDE DIVISION—See TPG Capital, L.P.; *U.S. Public*, pg. 2177
TRANSPLACE, LLC—See TPG Capital, L.P.; *U.S. Public*, pg. 2177
TRANSPORTATION INSIGHT, LLC—See Gryphon Investors, LLC; *U.S. Private*, pg. 1799
TRANSPORTATION SOLUTIONS GROUP, LLC.; *U.S. Private*, pg. 4211
TRANSPORTATION WORLDWIDE INC.; *U.S. Private*, pg. 4211
TRANSPORT EXPRESS LLC; *U.S. Private*, pg. 4210
TRANS-TRADE, INC.; *U.S. Private*, pg. 4206
TRANS-TRADE, INC.—See Trans-Trade, Inc.; *U.S. Private*, pg. 4206
TRICO SERVICOS MARITIMOS LTDA.—See Trico Marine Services, Inc.; *U.S. Private*, pg. 4229
TRI-COUNTY TRUCK COMPANY; *U.S. Private*, pg. 4222
TRIDENT TRANSPORT, LLC; *U.S. Private*, pg. 4230
TRINITY TRANSPORT, INC.; *U.S. Private*, pg. 4236
TRIPLE B FORWARDERS, INC.; *U.S. Private*, pg. 4236
TRIPLE T TRANSPORT, INC.; *U.S. Private*, pg. 4237
TRIPUL - SOC. DE GESTAO DE NAVIOS, LDA.—See Galp Energia SGPS, S.A.; *Int'l*, pg. 2875
TRIWAYS LOGISTICS USA INC.; *U.S. Private*, pg. 4241
TRUCK TRACK LOGISTICS LTD.—See TSL Companies; *U.S. Private*, pg. 4254
TRUMP CARD, LLC—See Littlejohn & Co., LLC; *U.S. Private*, pg. 2470
TSL COMPANIES; *U.S. Private*, pg. 4254
TS TRANSPORT & SERVICES SPEDITIONS GMBH—See G. Peter Reber Mobel-Logistik GmbH; *Int'l*, pg. 2864
TWI GROUP, INC.; *U.S. Private*, pg. 4264
TWI GROUP INC.—See TWI Group, Inc.; *U.S. Private*, pg. 4264
TWISS LOGISTICS INC.—See Bulova Technologies Group, Inc.; *U.S. Private*, pg. 685
UAA DENMARK—See Albert Ballin KG; *Int'l*, pg. 296
UAA FINLAND—See Albert Ballin KG; *Int'l*, pg. 296
UAASC NORWAY—See Albert Ballin KG; *Int'l*, pg. 296
UASAC CEE (AUSTRIA) GMBH—See Albert Ballin KG; *Int'l*, pg. 296
UASAC CEE (HUNGARY) KFT.—See Albert Ballin KG; *Int'l*, pg. 296
UASAC CEE (SLOVAKIA) S.R.O.—See Albert Ballin KG; *Int'l*, pg. 296
UASAC DENIZCILIK NAKLIYAT A.S.—See Albert Ballin KG; *Int'l*, pg. 296
UASAC FRANCE SAS—See Albert Ballin KG; *Int'l*, pg. 296
UASAC IBERIA S.L.—See Albert Ballin KG; *Int'l*, pg. 296
UASAC (ITALY) SRL—See Albert Ballin KG; *Int'l*, pg. 296
UASAC POLSKA—See Albert Ballin KG; *Int'l*, pg. 296
UASAC (UK) LTD.—See Albert Ballin KG; *Int'l*, pg. 296
UASC AGENCIES GHANA—See Albert Ballin KG; *Int'l*, pg. 296
UASC AGENCIES NIGERIA—See Albert Ballin KG; *Int'l*, pg. 296
U-FREIGHT AMERICA INC.; *U.S. Private*, pg. 4269
ULI INTERNATIONAL CO., LTD.—See Unique Logistics International Inc.; *U.S. Public*, pg. 2227
ULI (NORTH & EAST CHINA) CO. LTD.—See Unique Logistics International Inc.; *U.S. Public*, pg. 2227
ULS EXPRESS—See Universal Warehouse Co.; *U.S. Private*, pg. 4307
UNIKAI LAGEREI- UND SPEDITIONSGESELLSCHAFT

488510 — FREIGHT TRANSPORTAT...

MBH—See Hamburger Hafen und Logistik AG; *Int'l*, pg. 3237
UNION PACIFIC DISTRIBUTION SERVICES—See Union Pacific Corporation; *U.S. Public*, pg. 2227
UNIQUE INTERNATIONAL LOGISTICS (M) SDN BHD—See Unique Logistics International Inc.; *U.S. Public*, pg. 2227
UNIQUE LOGISTICS INTERNATIONAL (ATL) LLC—See Unique Logistics International Inc.; *U.S. Public*, pg. 2227
UNIQUE LOGISTICS INTERNATIONAL (CAMBODIA) CO., LTD.—See Unique Logistics International Inc.; *U.S. Public*, pg. 2227
UNIQUE LOGISTICS INTERNATIONAL (H.K.) LTD.—See Unique Logistics International Inc.; *U.S. Public*, pg. 2227
UNIQUE LOGISTICS INTERNATIONAL (LAX), INC.—See Unique Logistics International Inc.; *U.S. Public*, pg. 2227
UNIQUE LOGISTICS INTERNATIONAL (NYC), LLC—See Unique Logistics International Inc.; *U.S. Public*, pg. 2227
UNIQUE LOGISTICS INTERNATIONAL PHILIPPINES INC.—See Unique Logistics International Inc.; *U.S. Public*, pg. 2227
UNIQUE LOGISTICS INTERNATIONAL (S) PTE LTD—See Unique Logistics International Inc.; *U.S. Public*, pg. 2227
UNIQUE LOGISTICS INTERNATIONAL (THAILAND) CO., LTD.—See Unique Logistics International Inc.; *U.S. Public*, pg. 2227
UNIQUE LOGISTICS INTERNATIONAL (VIETNAM) LTD.—See Unique Logistics International Inc.; *U.S. Public*, pg. 2227
UNIQUE LOGISTICS (KOREA) CO., LTD.—See Unique Logistics International Inc.; *U.S. Public*, pg. 2227
UNIQUE REGULUS SUPPLY CHAIN SOLUTIONS INDIA PRIVATE LIMITED—See Unique Logistics International Inc.; *U.S. Public*, pg. 2227
UNITED ARAB AGENCIES AB—See Albert Ballin KG; *Int'l*, pg. 296
UNITED ARAB AGENCIES AUSTRALIA PTY LTD—See Albert Ballin KG; *Int'l*, pg. 296
UNITED ARAB AGENCIES, INC.—See Albert Ballin KG; *Int'l*, pg. 296
UNITED ARAB SHIPPING AGENCIES COMPANY—See Albert Ballin KG; *Int'l*, pg. 296
UNITED ARAB SHIPPING AGENCIES COMPANY W.L.L.—See Albert Ballin KG; *Int'l*, pg. 296
UNITED ARAB SHIPPING AGENCIES (PAKISTAN) PVT. LTD.—See Albert Ballin KG; *Int'l*, pg. 296
UNITED ARAB SHIPPING AGENCY COMPANY (BENELUX) B.V.—See Albert Ballin KG; *Int'l*, pg. 297
UNITED ARAB SHIPPING AGENCY COMPANY (DEUTSCHLAND) GMBH—See Albert Ballin KG; *Int'l*, pg. 297
UNITED ARAB SHIPPING AGENCY COMPANY (HONG KONG) LIMITED—See Albert Ballin KG; *Int'l*, pg. 297
UNITED ARAB SHIPPING AGENCY COMPANY (NINGBO) LTD.—See Albert Ballin KG; *Int'l*, pg. 297
UNITED ARAB SHIPPING AGENCY COMPANY, (QATAR) WLL—See Albert Ballin KG; *Int'l*, pg. 297
UNITED ARAB SHIPPING AGENCY COMPANY (SHANGHAI) LTD.—See Albert Ballin KG; *Int'l*, pg. 297
UNITED ARAB SHIPPING AGENCY COMPANY (SHENZHEN) LTD.—See Albert Ballin KG; *Int'l*, pg. 297
UNITED ARAB SHIPPING AGENCY COMPANY (TAIWAN) LTD.—See Albert Ballin KG; *Int'l*, pg. 297
UNITED ARAB SHIPPING AGENCY COMPANY (THAILAND) LTD.—See Albert Ballin KG; *Int'l*, pg. 297
UNITED ARAB SHIPPING AGENCY COMPANY (VIETNAM) LIMITED—See Albert Ballin KG; *Int'l*, pg. 297
UNITED ARAB SHIPPING AGENCY CO. (M) SDN BHD—See Albert Ballin KG; *Int'l*, pg. 297
UNITED ARAB SHIPPING AGENCY (INDIA) PVT LTD—See Albert Ballin KG; *Int'l*, pg. 296
UNITED CUSTOMHOUSE BROKERS; *U.S. Private*, pg. 4290
UNITED EXPRESS SERVICE, INC.—See NFI Industries, Inc.; *U.S. Private*, pg. 2923
UNITED PARCEL SERVICE ITALIA SRL—See United Parcel Service, Inc.; *U.S. Public*, pg. 2233
UNITED SHIPPING AGENCIES LTD—See Albert Ballin KG; *Int'l*, pg. 297
UNITED SHIPPING CO. LTD.—See Albert Ballin KG; *Int'l*, pg. 297
UNITED SHIPPING SOLUTIONS; *U.S. Private*, pg. 4297
UNITED THAI SHIPPING CORP LIMITED—See IMC Pan Asia Alliance Pte. Ltd.; *Int'l*, pg. 3621
UNITHAI SHIPYARD AND ENGINEERING LIMITED—See IMC Pan Asia Alliance Pte. Ltd.; *Int'l*, pg. 3621
UNITRANS INTERNATIONAL CORP.—See AIT Worldwide Logistics, Inc.; *U.S. Private*, pg. 143
UNIVERSAL CAPACITY SOLUTIONS, LLC—See Universal Logistics Holdings, Inc.; *U.S. Public*, pg. 2261
UNIVERSAL TRAFFIC SERVICE; *U.S. Private*, pg. 4307
UPS ASIA GROUP PTE. LTD.—See United Parcel Service, Inc.; *U.S. Public*, pg. 2233
UPS CUSTOMER SERVICE CENTER—See United Parcel Service, Inc.; *U.S. Public*, pg. 2233
UPS HUNGARY LTD.—See United Parcel Service, Inc.; *U.S. Public*, pg. 2233
UPS LIMITED—See United Parcel Service, Inc.; *U.S. Public*, pg. 2233
UPS PARCEL DELIVERY SERVICE LTD.—See United Parcel Service, Inc.; *U.S. Public*, pg. 2233
UPS SCS, INC.—See United Parcel Service, Inc.; *U.S. Public*, pg. 2234
UPS SUPPLY CHAIN SOLUTIONS, INC. - COPPELL—See United Parcel Service, Inc.; *U.S. Public*, pg. 2234
URGENT.LY, INC.; *U.S. Public*, pg. 2266
US 1 LOGISTICS, LLC—See US 1 Industries, Inc.; *U.S. Private*, pg. 4317
U.S. EXPRESS, INC.—See U.S. Logistics, Inc.; *U.S. Private*, pg. 4271
US LOGISTICS LLC; *U.S. Private*, pg. 4319
U.S. WORLDWIDE LOGISTICS, INC.—See LDI Ltd., LLC; *U.S. Public*, pg. 2404
UTC OVERSEAS INC.—See UTC Overseas, Inc.; *U.S. Private*, pg. 4325
UTI EGYPT/JORDAN LTD.—See DSV A/S; *Int'l*, pg. 2216
UTILICRAFT AEROSPACE INDUSTRIES, INC.; *U.S. Public*, pg. 2267
UTI PERSHIP (PVT) LIMITED—See DSV A/S; *Int'l*, pg. 2216
UTI WORLDWIDE INC.—See DSV A/S; *Int'l*, pg. 2216
UTXL, INC.—See Knight-Swift Transportation Holdings Inc.; *U.S. Public*, pg. 1269
V. ALEXANDER & CO. INC.; *U.S. Private*, pg. 4328
VALLEY EXPRESS INC.; *U.S. Private*, pg. 4333
VALLEY MANAGEMENT GROUP, INC.; *U.S. Private*, pg. 4334
VANDEGRIFT FORWARDING CO, INC.—See A.P. Moller-Maersk A/S; *Int'l*, pg. 28
VAN GEND & LOOS - EURO EXPRESS NV—See Deutsche Post AG; *Int'l*, pg. 2083
VANGUARD LOGISTICS SERVICES—See NACA Logistics (USA), Inc.; *U.S. Private*, pg. 2829
VECV SOUTH AFRICA (PTY) LTD.—See Eicher Motors Limited; *Int'l*, pg. 2328
VERON GRAUER AG—See Deutsche Post AG; *Int'l*, pg. 2083
VETSCH AG, INTERNATIONALE TRANSPORTE—See Deutsche Post AG; *Int'l*, pg. 2083
VICTORY TRANSPORTATION SYSTEMS, INC.; *U.S. Private*, pg. 4379
VOUK TRANSPORTATION INC.; *U.S. Private*, pg. 4413
VTG RAIL ESPANA S.L.—See Morgan Stanley; *U.S. Public*, pg. 1476
V T MANCUSI, INC.—See Southfield Capital Advisors, LLC; *U.S. Private*, pg. 3736
WAGNER INDUSTRIES, INC.; *U.S. Private*, pg. 4426
WASHITA VALLEY LOGISTICS, LLC—See Arcosa, Inc.; *U.S. Public*, pg. 186
WATKINS AND SHEPARD TRUCKING, INC.—See Schneider National, Inc.; *U.S. Public*, pg. 1847
WEMCO, INC.—See Randa Corp.; *U.S. Private*, pg. 3353
WERNER GLOBAL LOGISTICS (SHANGHAI) CO., LTD.—See Werner Enterprises, Inc.; *U.S. Public*, pg. 2349
WEST COAST DISTRIBUTING, INC.—See Leonard's Express Inc.; *U.S. Private*, pg. 2430
WESTERN OVERSEAS CORPORATION; *U.S. Private*, pg. 4495
WHEELS LOGISTICS INC.—See Radiant Logistics, Inc.; *U.S. Public*, pg. 1760
WHEELS MSM CANADA INC.—See Radiant Logistics, Inc.; *U.S. Public*, pg. 1760
WILDERNEST LOGISTICS SOLUTIONS INCORPORATED; *U.S. Private*, pg. 4519
WIMMER TRANSPORTDIENST GMBH—See Hoyer GmbH; *Int'l*, pg. 3499
W.J. BYRNES & CO. - ARIZONA-PHOENIX—See Janel Corporation; *U.S. Public*, pg. 1187
W.J. BYRNES & CO. - OREGON—See Janel Corporation; *U.S. Public*, pg. 1187
W.J. BYRNES & CO.—See Janel Corporation; *U.S. Public*, pg. 1187
W.J. BYRNES & CO. - WISCONSIN—See Janel Corporation; *U.S. Public*, pg. 1187
WOOTTON TRANSPORTATION SERVICES; *U.S. Private*, pg. 4562
WORKLINK SERVICES, INC.—See Chelsea Logistics and Infrastructure Holdings Corp.; *Int'l*, pg. 1460
WORLDBRIDGE SECURE LOGISTICS CO., LTD.—See The Brink's Company; *U.S. Public*, pg. 2043
WORLD EXPRESS LOGISTICS LTD.—See Attard & Co. Ltd.; *Int'l*, pg. 696
WORLDWIDE LOGISTICS LIMITED; *U.S. Private*, pg. 4569
XING YUAN (SINGAPORE) PTE. LTD.—See China COSCO Shipping Corporation Limited; *Int'l*, pg. 1492
XPO BULK UK LTD.—See XPO, Inc.; *U.S. Public*, pg. 2392
XPO EXPRESS, INC.—See XPO, Inc.; *U.S. Public*, pg. 2392
XPO GLOBAL FORWARDING, INC.—See XPO, Inc.; *U.S. Public*, pg. 2392
XPO GLOBAL LOGISTICS INC.—See XPO, Inc.; *U.S. Public*, pg. 2392
XPO HOLDING TRANSPORT SOLUTIONS EUROPE—See XPO, Inc.; *U.S. Public*, pg. 2392
XPO INTERMODAL, INC.—See XPO, Inc.; *U.S. Public*, pg. 2392
XPO LOGISTICS EXPRESS, LLC—See XPO, Inc.; *U.S. Public*, pg. 2392
XPO LOGISTICS, LLC—See XPO, Inc.; *U.S. Public*, pg. 2392
XPO SUPPLY CHAIN ITALY S.P.A.—See XPO, Inc.; *U.S. Public*, pg. 2392
XPO TRANSPORT SOLUTIONS ITALY S.R.L.—See XPO, Inc.; *U.S. Public*, pg. 2392
XPO TRANSPORT SOLUTIONS PORTUGAL, LDA.—See XPO, Inc.; *U.S. Public*, pg. 2392
YANG MING MARINE TRANSPORT CORPORATION; *U.S. Private*, pg. 4585
YAO YANG ENTERPRISE LLC; *U.S. Private*, pg. 4586
YINSON POWER MARINE SDN. BHD.—See Hwa Tai Industries Berhad; *Int'l*, pg. 3541
THE YOKOHAMA CHAMBER OF COMMERCE & INDUSTRY—See Azuma Shipping Co., Ltd.; *Int'l*, pg. 782
YUME CORPORATION CO., LTD.—See Dynam Japan Holdings, Co., Ltd.; *Int'l*, pg. 2239
YUSEN LOGISTICS—See TPG Capital, L.P.; *U.S. Public*, pg. 2177
ZEN CONTINENTAL CO., INC.; *U.S. Private*, pg. 4601
ZHANJIANG COSCO LOGISTICS CO., LTD.—See China COSCO Shipping Corporation Limited; *Int'l*, pg. 1493
ZIPLINE LOGISTICS LLC; *U.S. Private*, pg. 4606
Z TRANSPORTATION INC.; *U.S. Private*, pg. 4596

488991 — PACKING AND CRATING

ADVANTAGE MEDIA SERVICES, INC.—See Fort Point Capital, LLC; *U.S. Private*, pg. 1574
ALDELANO PACKAGING CORPORATION; *U.S. Private*, pg. 155
ARLA FOODS UK PLC-OSWESTRY PACKING FACILITY—See Arla Foods amba; *Int'l*, pg. 573
BURGMANN PACKINGS GMBH—See Freudenberg SE; *Int'l*, pg. 2783
CSS DISTRIBUTION GROUP, INC.; *U.S. Private*, pg. 1117
CUMMINGS MOVING SYSTEMS L.L.C.—See Cummings Transfer Co.; *U.S. Private*, pg. 1123
DYSART CORPORATION; *U.S. Private*, pg. 1300
ELANDERS LTD—See Carl Bennet AB; *Int'l*, pg. 1331
EXPORT PACKAGING CO. INC.; *U.S. Private*, pg. 1450
FAPCO INC.; *U.S. Private*, pg. 1473
FULFILLMENT STRATEGIES INTERNATIONAL; *U.S. Private*, pg. 1620
GEORGIA PERFECT PACKERS—See Hi-Boy Group Inc.; *U.S. Private*, pg. 1931
HOWARD TERNES PACKAGING CO.; *U.S. Private*, pg. 1995
INTERNATIONAL PAPER TAIWAN LTD.—See International Paper Company; *U.S. Public*, pg. 1157
KNILAM PACKAGING (PTY) LTD—See Berry Global Group, Inc; *U.S. Public*, pg. 324
LA HABRA RELOCATIONS, INC.—See Wheaton Van Lines, Inc.; *U.S. Private*, pg. 4505
MACMILLAN-PIPER LLC—See GSC Logistics Inc.; *U.S. Private*, pg. 1800
MANAGEMENT CONSULTING, INC.; *U.S. Private*, pg. 2560
MASTHEAD INTERNATIONAL, INC.—See Performance Contracting Group; *U.S. Private*, pg. 3148
MOMART LIMITED—See FIH group plc; *Int'l*, pg. 2661
MYOFFICE, INC.; *U.S. Private*, pg. 2825
PACK2PACK GROUP N.V.—See Greif Inc.; *U.S. Public*, pg. 969
THE PACKAGING CAFE—See Lawrence Paper Company; *U.S. Private*, pg. 2401
PACK-LINE HOLDINGS (PTY) LTD—See Berry Global Group, Inc; *U.S. Public*, pg. 324
PACKRITE, LLC; *U.S. Private*, pg. 3073
PAK 2000 (PTY) LTD—See Berry Global Group, Inc; *U.S. Public*, pg. 324
PIERCE PACKAGING CO.; *U.S. Private*, pg. 3178
PRO-PAC INTERNATIONAL, INC.—See Olympus Partners; *U.S. Private*, pg. 3013
RIVERFRONT PACKING COMPANY, LLC; *U.S. Private*, pg. 3444
SAFLITE PACKAGING (PTY) LTD—See Berry Global Group, Inc; *U.S. Public*, pg. 324
SEATTLE BOX CO.; *U.S. Private*, pg. 3591
SIMPAK INTERNATIONAL, LLC; *U.S. Private*, pg. 3666
STARCHTECH, INC.; *U.S. Private*, pg. 3786
STEPHEN GOULD OF PENNSYLVANIA CORP.—See Stephen Gould Corporation; *U.S. Private*, pg. 3802
SUNTREAT PACKING & SHIPPING CO.; *U.S. Private*, pg. 3874
SUPERIOR PACKAGING INC.; *U.S. Private*, pg. 3879
UNIFIED AIRCRAFT SERVICES INC.; *U.S. Private*, pg. 4282

488999 — ALL OTHER SUPPORT ACTIVITIES FOR TRANSPORTATION

N.A.I.C.S. INDEX

488999 — ALL OTHER SUPPORT A...

1520 SIGNAL LTD.—See 1520 Group of Companies; *Int'l*, pg. 2
A2B AUSTRALIA LIMITED—See ComfortDelGro Corporation Limited; *Int'l*, pg. 1712
ACP MARKETING, INC.; *Int'l*, pg. 108
ACP MARKETING UK LTD.—See ACP Marketing, Inc.; *Int'l*, pg. 108
AEP RIVER TRANSPORTATION—See American Electric Power Company, Inc.; *U.S. Public*, pg. 99
AFMS LOGISTICS MANAGEMENT GROUP; *U.S. Private*, pg. 123
AGARWAL INDUSTRIAL CORPORATION LTD.; *Int'l*, pg. 200
AGILITY; *Int'l*, pg. 209
AGROTECHIMPEX JOINT STOCK COMPANY; *Int'l*, pg. 221
AHT SERVICES, LLC—See World Kinect Corporation; *U.S. Public*, pg. 2380
AISIN TECHNICAL CENTER OF AMERICA, INC.—See AISIN Corporation; *Int'l*, pg. 252
AL BADIA FOR GENERAL TRANSPORTATION; *Int'l*, pg. 275
AL RAJHI DEVELOPMENT COMPANY LTD.—See Al Rajhi Bank; *Int'l*, pg. 282
AMERICA MIDWEST TRANSPORTATION, LLC.; *U.S. Private*, pg. 220
AMERICAN EXPRESS CORPORATE TRAVEL A/S—See American Express Company; *U.S. Public*, pg. 101
AMERICAN TRAFFIC SOLUTIONS, INC.—See Platinum Equity, LLC; *U.S. Private*, pg. 3201
AMEY UK PLC—See Ferrovial S.A.; *Int'l*, pg. 2644
ANAHEIM TRANSPORTATION NETWORK; *U.S. Private*, pg. 271
ANDRADE GUTIERREZ PARTICIPACOES S.A.—See Andrade Gutierrez Concessoes S.A.; *Int'l*, pg. 451
ANGLO-EASTERN UNIVAN GROUP; *Int'l*, pg. 463
ARAMEX INTERNATIONAL LIMITED—See Aramex PJSC; *Int'l*, pg. 535
ARC LOGISTICS LLC—See Warburg Pincus LLC; *U.S. Private*, pg. 4440
ARTUR EXPRESS, INC.; *U.S. Private*, pg. 344
ASL DISTRIBUTION SERVICES LIMITED—See Consolidated Fastfrate Inc.; *Int'l*, pg. 1770
ASTROTECH SPACE OPERATIONS, INC. - VANDENBERG AIR FORCE BASE—See Lockheed Martin Corporation; *U.S. Public*, pg. 1338
ASTROTECH SPACE OPERATIONS, INC.—See Lockheed Martin Corporation; *U.S. Public*, pg. 1338
ATG TRANSPORTATION LLC—See Palladium Equity Partners, LLC; *U.S. Private*, pg. 3078
ATL PUEBLA—See Grupo TMM, S.A.B.; *Int'l*, pg. 3137
ATUL AUTO LTD.; *Int'l*, pg. 697
AUTOPREVOZ AD BANJA LUKA; *Int'l*, pg. 731
AUTOROUTES PARIS-RHIN-RHONE—See Eiffage S.A.; *Int'l*, pg. 2331
AZN CAPITAL CORP.; *Int'l*, pg. 780
BAGGAGE AIRLINE GUEST SERVICES, INC.—See Eldridge Industries LLC; *U.S. Private*, pg. 1351
BALURGHAT TECHNOLOGIES LTD.; *Int'l*, pg. 812
BANSARD INTERNATIONAL; *Int'l*, pg. 854
BESTPASS, INC.; *U.S. Private*, pg. 544
BEST TRANSPORTATION OF ST. LOUIS; *U.S. Private*, pg. 543
BLUEJAY CAPITAL PARTNERS, LLC; *U.S. Private*, pg. 597
BMT ASIA PACIFIC LTD.—See BMT Group Limited; *Int'l*, pg. 1077
BMT ASIA PACIFIC PTE. LTD.—See BMT Group Limited; *Int'l*, pg. 1077
BMT CONSULTANTS (INDIA) PVT. LTD.—See BMT Group Limited; *Int'l*, pg. 1077
BMT FLEET TECHNOLOGY LIMITED—See BMT Group Limited; *Int'l*, pg. 1077
BMT FLEET TECHNOLOGY LIMITED—See BMT Group Limited; *Int'l*, pg. 1077
BMT FLEET TECHNOLOGY LIMITED—See BMT Group Limited; *Int'l*, pg. 1078
BMT FLEET TECHNOLOGY LIMITED—See BMT Group Limited; *Int'l*, pg. 1078
BOMBARDIER (MAURITIUS) LTD—See Bombardier Inc.; *Int'l*, pg. 1103
BOMBARDIER TRANSPORTATION (MALAYSIA) SDN. BHD.—See Alstom S.A.; *Int'l*, pg. 382
BOMBARDIER TRANSPORTATION (NETHERLAND) B.V.—See Alstom S.A.; *Int'l*, pg. 382
BOMBARDIER TRANSPORTATION NORTH AMERICA INC.—See Alstom S.A.; *Int'l*, pg. 382
BOMBARDIER TRANSPORTATION ROMANIA SRL—See Alstom S.A.; *Int'l*, pg. 383
BOMBARDIER TRANSPORTATION SHARED SERVICES ROMANIA SRL—See Alstom S.A.; *Int'l*, pg. 383
BOMBARDIER TRANSPORTATION SOUTH AFRICA (PTY.) LTD—See Alstom S.A.; *Int'l*, pg. 383
BOSS CHAIR, INC.; *Int'l*, pg. 620
BREWSTER INC.—See Viad Corp.; *U.S. Public*, pg. 2291
BRISA ASSISTENCIA RODOVIARIA, S.A.—See APG Asset Management NV; *Int'l*, pg. 512
BRUCE R SMITH LIMITED; *Int'l*, pg. 1199
BRUIN EXPRESS INTERMODAL LLC—See US 1 Industries, Inc.; *U.S. Private*, pg. 4317
BUDAMAR LOGISTICS AS; *Int'l*, pg. 1210
BULGARIAN RIVER SHIPPING J.S.CO.; *Int'l*, pg. 1213
CANADA CARTAGE CORPORATION.; *Int'l*, pg. 1277
CANADIAN COMMERCIAL VEHICLES CORPORATION—See The Eastern Company; *U.S. Public*, pg. 2069
CBOCS DISTRIBUTION, INC.—See Cracker Barrel Old Country Store, Inc.; *U.S. Public*, pg. 589
CB TRANSPORTATION; *U.S. Private*, pg. 796
CG TRANSPORTATION, LLC—See Walgreens Boots Alliance, Inc.; *U.S. Public*, pg. 2323
CHANTLER TRANSPORT; *Int'l*, pg. 1447
CHASEN (SHANGHAI) HI TECH MACHINERY SERVICES PTE LTD—See Chasen Holdings Limited; *Int'l*, pg. 1457
C.H. ROBINSON COMPANY (CANADA) LTD.—See C.H. Robinson Worldwide, Inc.; *U.S. Public*, pg. 414
C.H. ROBINSON DE MEXICO, S.A. DE C.V.—See C.H. Robinson Worldwide, Inc.; *U.S. Public*, pg. 415
C.H. ROBINSON WORLDWIDE ARGENTINA, S.A.—See C.H. Robinson Worldwide, Inc.; *U.S. Public*, pg. 415
C.H. ROBINSON WORLDWIDE SINGAPORE PTE. LTD—See C.H. Robinson Worldwide, Inc.; *U.S. Public*, pg. 415
CIMC BURG B.V.—See China International Marine Containers (Group) Co., Ltd.; *Int'l*, pg. 1511
CINTRA DEVELOPMENTS, LLC—See Ferrovial S.A.; *Int'l*, pg. 2644
CITY GROUP COMPANY KSCP; *Int'l*, pg. 1626
CMS TRAFFIC SYSTEMS LIMITED—See CMS Computers Ltd.; *Int'l*, pg. 1672
CRANE WORLDWIDE LOGISTICS LLC; *U.S. Private*, pg. 1085
CREW TRANSPORTATION SPECIALISTS, INC.—See Corpay, Inc.; *U.S. Public*, pg. 579
CRT GROUP PTY. LTD.—See Aurizon Holdings Limited; *Int'l*, pg. 711
CRYOGENIC INDUSTRIAL SOLUTIONS, INC.; *U.S. Private*, pg. 1115
CSI-GMBH; *Int'l*, pg. 1865
CWT ASIA PACIFIC—See Carlson Companies Inc.; *U.S. Private*, pg. 765
DAKOTA BULK TERMINAL, INC.—See Kinder Morgan, Inc.; *U.S. Public*, pg. 1233
DARJEELING ROPEWAY COMPANY LTD.; *Int'l*, pg. 1972
DAT SOLUTIONS, LLC—See Roper Technologies, Inc.; *U.S. Public*, pg. 1811
DCT CHAMBERS TRUCKING LTD.; *Int'l*, pg. 1993
DELEK TRANSPORTATION LTD.—See Delek Group Ltd.; *Int'l*, pg. 2012
DHL SOLUTIONS FASHION GMBH—See Deutsche Post AG; *Int'l*, pg. 2077
DONGHWA CONTAINER TRANSPORTATION SERVICE CO., LTD.—See China International Marine Containers (Group) Co., Ltd.; *Int'l*, pg. 1511
DOPPELMAYR A/S—See Doppelmayr Group; *Int'l*, pg. 2174
DOWA-TSUUN CO., LTD.—See Dowa Holdings Co., Ltd.; *Int'l*, pg. 2183
DSV ROAD AB—See DSV A/S; *Int'l*, pg. 2212
DSV ROAD, INC.—See DSV A/S; *Int'l*, pg. 2213
EASSONS TRANSPORT LIMITED; *Int'l*, pg. 2269
ENERGETIC SERVICES INC.; *Int'l*, pg. 2419
ENTERPRISE GATHERING LLC—See Enterprise Products Partners L.P.; *U.S. Public*, pg. 778
ERDEMIR LOJISTIK A.S.—See Eregli Demir Ve Celik Fabrikalari T.A.S.; *Int'l*, pg. 2490
EVERGREEN INTERNATIONAL STORAGE & TRANSPORT CORP.; *Int'l*, pg. 2565
EZ PAY PAYMENT CENTERS INC.; *U.S. Private*, pg. 1454
FARGLORY F T Z INVESTMENT HOLDING CO., LTD.; *Int'l*, pg. 2618
FASTTRAC TRANSPORTATION, INC.; *U.S. Private*, pg. 1483
FERROVIAL S.A.; *Int'l*, pg. 2644
FIRST CLASS SERVICE, INC.—See Fox Corporation; *U.S. Public*, pg. 875
FORD SMART MOBILITY LLC—See Ford Motor Company; *U.S. Public*, pg. 866
FORNET, INC.—See H.U. Group Holdings, Inc.; *Int'l*, pg. 3197
FOSS MARITIME CO.—See Saltchuk Resources Inc.; *U.S. Private*, pg. 3534
FRADENA TRANSPORT—See Derichebourg S.A.; *Int'l*, pg. 2042
FRIGOSPED GMBH; *Int'l*, pg. 2792
FRONTLINE CARRIER SYSTEMS INC.; *Int'l*, pg. 2796
FT TECHNO OF AMERICA, LLC—See AISIN Corporation; *Int'l*, pg. 253
FUJITEC VIETNAM CO., LTD.—See Fujitec Co., Ltd.; *Int'l*, pg. 2831
F.W. NEUKIRCH (GMBH & CO.) KG; *Int'l*, pg. 2597
GEORG H. LUH FARBEN- UND CHEMIKALIEN GROSSHANDELSGES GMBH; *Int'l*, pg. 2938
G&H TOWING CO. INC.; *U.S. Private*, pg. 1629
GIORGIO GORI (FRANCE) SAS—See Deutsche Post AG; *Int'l*, pg. 2080
GIORGIO GORI S.R.L.—See Deutsche Post AG; *Int'l*, pg. 2080
GLOBALVIA INVERSIONES, S.A.U.; *Int'l*, pg. 3005
GOLAR CAMEROON SASU—See Golar LNG Limited; *Int'l*, pg. 3023
GOLAR VIKING MANAGEMENT D.O.O.—See Golar LNG Limited; *Int'l*, pg. 3023
GORI ARGENTINA S.A.—See Deutsche Post AG; *Int'l*, pg. 2080
GORI AUSTRALIA PTY LTD.—See Deutsche Post AG; *Int'l*, pg. 2080
GORI IBERIA S.L.—See Deutsche Post AG; *Int'l*, pg. 2080
GORI IBERIA TRANSITARIOS, LIMITADA—See Deutsche Post AG; *Int'l*, pg. 2080
GRAND BRANDS (M) SDN. BHD.—See Hai-O Enterprise Berhad; *Int'l*, pg. 3209
GREAT LAKES FASTENERS, INC.; *U.S. Private*, pg. 1764
GREAT NORTH EASTERN RAILWAY COMPANY LTD—See Deutsche Bahn AG; *Int'l*, pg. 2051
HANJIN GLOBAL LOGISTICS (DALIAN) CO., LIMITED—See Hanjin Transportation Co., Ltd.; *Int'l*, pg. 3253
HANJIN GLOBAL LOGISTICS (GUANGZHOU) CO., LIMITED—See Hanjin Transportation Co., Ltd.; *Int'l*, pg. 3253
HANJIN GLOBAL LOGISTICS (HONG KONG) LIMITED—See Hanjin Transportation Co., Ltd.; *Int'l*, pg. 3253
HANJIN GLOBAL LOGISTICS (SHANGHAI) CO., LIMITED—See Hanjin Transportation Co., Ltd.; *Int'l*, pg. 3253
HANJIN GLOBAL LOGISTICS (SHENZHEN) CO., LIMITED—See Hanjin Transportation Co., Ltd.; *Int'l*, pg. 3253
HANKYU HANSHIN EXPRESS CO., LTD.—See Hankyu Hanshin Holdings Inc.; *Int'l*, pg. 3255
HEKINAN UNSO CO., LTD.—See AISIN Corporation; *Int'l*, pg. 253
HIGMAN BARGE LINES INC.—See Higman Marine Inc.; *U.S. Private*, pg. 1943
HOYER BULK TRANSPORT CO. LTD. GUANGZHOU—See Hoyer GmbH; *Int'l*, pg. 3498
HUBEI CHUTIAN SMART COMMUNICATION CO., LTD.; *Int'l*, pg. 3517
HUNT'S TRANSPORT LTD.; *Int'l*, pg. 3536
HYBRID TRANSIT SYSTEMS, INC.; *U.S. Private*, pg. 2016
I J MCGILL TRANSPORT LTD; *Int'l*, pg. 3561
ILLINOIS RAILWAY, LLC—See The Broe Companies, Inc.; *U.S. Private*, pg. 4001
INTERGIS CO., LTD.—See Dongkuk Steel Mill Co., Ltd.; *Int'l*, pg. 2169
INTERNET TRUCKSTOP GROUP, LLC; *U.S. Private*, pg. 2122
INTERPARKING NEDERLAND B.V.—See Ageas SA/NV; *Int'l*, pg. 204
INTERPARKING SA—See Ageas SA/NV; *Int'l*, pg. 204
ISLAND TUG & BARGE CO.; *U.S. Private*, pg. 2145
KELLY'S INDUSTRIAL SERVICES, INC.—See Vantage Contractors, LLC; *U.S. Private*, pg. 4345
KIRBY MARINE TRANSPORT CORPORATION—See Kirby Corporation; *U.S. Public*, pg. 1235
KIRBY OCEAN TRANSPORT COMPANY—See Kirby Corporation; *U.S. Public*, pg. 1236
KOLD TRANS, LLC—See Knight-Swift Transportation Holdings Inc.; *U.S. Public*, pg. 1269
KRAFTVERKEHRSGESELLSCHAFT PADERBORN MBH—See E.ON SE; *Int'l*, pg. 2253
KUMMLER+MATTER AG—See Bouygues S.A.; *Int'l*, pg. 1123
LAGTA GROUP TRAINING LIMITED—See SPX Technologies, Inc.; *U.S. Public*, pg. 1921
LAWRENCE TRANSPORTATION SERVICES, INC.; *U.S. Private*, pg. 2402
LIMOUSINE SERVICE OF WESTCHESTER; *U.S. Private*, pg. 2456
LOAD DELIVERED LOGISTICS LLC; *U.S. Private*, pg. 2476
LOCKHEED MARTIN MISSILES & FIRE CONTROL - ORLANDO—See Lockheed Martin Corporation; *U.S. Public*, pg. 1338
LONE STAR TRANSPORTATION, LLC—See Daseke, Inc.; *U.S. Private*, pg. 1161
MACY'S LOGISTICS & OPERATIONS—See Macy's, Inc.; *U.S. Public*, pg. 1353
MARKETING & ENGINEERING SOLUTIONS INC.; *U.S. Private*, pg. 2580
MARTI TECHNOLOGIES, INC.; *U.S. Public*, pg. 1389
MEDAIRE INC.; *U.S. Private*, pg. 2650
MEDAIRE LTD.—See MedAire Inc.; *U.S. Private*, pg. 2650
MERIDIAN LOGISTICS LLC—See Gryphon Investors, LLC; *U.S. Private*, pg. 1799
ACERTUS—See Tailwind Capital Group, LLC; *U.S. Private*, pg. 3924
MORAN TOWING CORPORATION; *U.S. Private*, pg. 2781
MORAN TOWING OF FLORIDA—See Moran Towing Corporation; *U.S. Private*, pg. 2781
MORAN TOWING OF SAVANNAH—See Moran Towing Corporation; *U.S. Private*, pg. 2782

488999 — ALL OTHER SUPPORT A...

MOVEX, INC.; *U.S. Private*, pg. 2802
MULTIVANS INC.—See J.B. Poindexter & Co., Inc.; *U.S. Private*, pg. 2158
NEOVIA LOGISTICS SERVICES INTERNATIONAL NV—See Rhone Group, LLC; *U.S. Private*, pg. 3424
NEOVIA LOGISTICS SERVICES INTERNATIONAL NV—See The Goldman Sachs Group, Inc.; *U.S. Public*, pg. 2080
NEOVIA LOGISTICS SERVICES (U.K.) LTD.—See Rhone Group, LLC; *U.S. Private*, pg. 3424
NEOVIA LOGISTICS SERVICES (U.K.) LTD.—See The Goldman Sachs Group, Inc.; *U.S. Public*, pg. 2080
NOLAN TRANSPORTATION GROUP, INC.—See Gryphon Investors, LLC; *U.S. Private*, pg. 1799
OAKCREEK GOLF & TURF LP—See Connor, Clark & Lunn Financial Group; *Int'l*, pg. 1769
OPW ENGINEERED SYSTEMS, INC.—See Dover Corporation; *U.S. Public*, pg. 679
ORIENT OVERSEAS (INTERNATIONAL) LIMITED—See China COSCO Shipping Corporation Limited; *Int'l*, pg. 1495
ORION TRANSPORTATION SERVICES INC.; *U.S. Private*, pg. 3043
PACIFIC LOGISTICS CORP.; *U.S. Private*, pg. 3068
PACWEST DISTRIBUTING, INC.; *U.S. Private*, pg. 3073
PADERBORNER TRANSPORT-BETON-GESELLSCHAFT MIT BESCHRANKTER HAFTUNG & CO. K.-G.—See Heidelberg Materials AG; *Int'l*, pg. 3318
PARAGON SOFTWARE SYSTEMS PLC—See TA Associates, Inc.; *U.S. Private*, pg. 3914
PARKER TOWING COMPANY, INC.; *U.S. Private*, pg. 3097
PCM-LOGISTICS, LLC—See Insight Enterprises, Inc.; *U.S. Public*, pg. 1130
POWDERLY TRANSPORTATION, INC.—See Martin Marietta Materials, Inc.; *U.S. Public*, pg. 1389
PROLERIDE TRANSPORT SYSTEMS, INC.—See Radius Recycling, Inc.; *U.S. Public*, pg. 1760
QC ENERGY RESOURCES, LLC—See Apax Partners LLP; *Int'l*, pg. 505
QINGDAO HANJIN LUHAI INTERNATIONAL LOGISTICS CO., LTD.—See Hanjin Transportation Co., Ltd.; *Int'l*, pg. 3253
QUANTUM MEDICAL TRANSPORT, INC.; *U.S. Public*, pg. 1754
R2 LOGISTICS, INC.; *U.S. Private*, pg. 3340
RAILCARE AG—See Coop-Gruppe Genossenschaft; *Int'l*, pg. 1790
REFLEX KFT—See Gedeon Richter Plc.; *Int'l*, pg. 2910
RUMO S.A.—See Cosan S.A.; *Int'l*, pg. 1809
RYDER SYSTEM HOLDINGS (UK) LIMITED—See Ryder System, Inc.; *U.S. Public*, pg. 1828
SALTCHUK RESOURCES INC.; *U.S. Private*, pg. 3534
SANETSU TRANSPORT CO., LTD.—See AISIN Corporation; *Int'l*, pg. 253
SANHE DOPPELMAYR TRANSPORT SYSTEMS CO., LTD.—See Doppelmayr; *Int'l*, pg. 2175
SAUSE BROS INC.—See Sause Bros. Ocean Towing Co. Inc.; *U.S. Private*, pg. 3555
SAUSE BROS. OCEAN TOWING CO. INC.; *U.S. Private*, pg. 3555
SEABULK TOWING SERVICES, INC.—See AIP, LLC; *U.S. Private*, pg. 137
SHEERTRANS SOLUTIONS, LLC; *U.S. Private*, pg. 3630
SNC-LAVALIN TRANSPORTATION KOREA INC.—See AtkinsRealis Group Inc.; *Int'l*, pg. 673
STARBROKER AG—See Deutsche Post AG; *Int'l*, pg. 2082
SUPERVALU TRANSPORTATION INC.—See United Natural Foods, Inc.; *U.S. Public*, pg. 2232
TAKARA CHOUUN CO., LTD—See Aspirant Group, Inc.; *Int'l*, pg. 631
TBG TRANSPORTBETON SAALFELD VERWALTUNGS-GMBH—See Heidelberg Materials AG; *Int'l*, pg. 3320
TESORO HIGH PLAINS PIPELINE COMPANY LLC—See Marathon Petroleum Corporation; *U.S. Public*, pg. 1364
THERMO KING OF HOUSTON, LP—See Kirby Corporation; *U.S. Public*, pg. 1235
TIDEWATER MARINE WESTERN, INC.—See Tidewater Inc.; *U.S. Public*, pg. 2158
TRANSYSTEMS CORP.—See OceanSound Partners, LP; *U.S. Private*, pg. 2991
TTS, LLC; *U.S. Private*, pg. 4255
UNITED BRINE PIPELINE COMPANY LLC—See United Salt Corporation; *U.S. Private*, pg. 4297
UNITEK SERVICIOS DE ASESOIRIA ESPECIALIZAD S.A.—See Quaker Chemical Corporation; *U.S. Public*, pg. 1747
URBAN INSIGHTS ASSOCIATES, INC.—See Elliott Management Corporation; *U.S. Private*, pg. 1368
URBAN INSIGHTS ASSOCIATES, INC.—See Veritas Capital Fund Management, LLC; *U.S. Private*, pg. 4362
US SERVICE GROUP, LLC; *U.S. Private*, pg. 4320
UTLX COMPANY—See Berkshire Hathaway Inc.; *U.S. Public*, pg. 319
VERO BEACH AVIONICS, INC.—See Sun Aviation, Inc.; *U.S. Private*, pg. 3858

491110 — POSTAL SERVICE

AN POST LLC; *Int'l*, pg. 443
ARTISTDIRECT, INC.—See Relativity Media, LLC; *U.S. Private*, pg. 3393
ASENDIA MANAGEMENT SAS—See Die Schweizerische Post AG; *Int'l*, pg. 2112
ASENDIA USA—See Die Schweizerische Post AG; *Int'l*, pg. 2112
AUSTRALIAN POSTAL CORPORATION; *Int'l*, pg. 722
BELGIAN POST INTERNATIONAL SA/NV—See bpost NV/SA; *Int'l*, pg. 1133
BPOST NV/SA; *Int'l*, pg. 1133
CANADA POST CORPORATION; *Int'l*, pg. 1282
CHINA POST GROUP CORPORATION LIMITED; *Int'l*, pg. 1541
CITIPOST DIRECT DISTRIBUTION LTD.—See Citipost Group; *Int'l*, pg. 1623
CITIPOST DSA LTD.—See Citipost Group; *Int'l*, pg. 1622
CITIPOST GROUP; *Int'l*, pg. 1622
CITIPOST UK LTD.—See Citipost Group; *Int'l*, pg. 1623
COMPANIA NATIONALA POSTA ROMANA S.A.; *Int'l*, pg. 1749
COVIUS DOCUMENT SERVICES, LLC—See Covius Holdings, Inc.; *U.S. Private*, pg. 1073
CTT - CORREIOS DE PORTUGAL SA; *Int'l*, pg. 1874
DEUTSCHE POST SHOP HANNOVER GMBH—See Deutsche Post AG; *Int'l*, pg. 2079
DEUTSCHE POST ZAHLUNGSDIENSTE GMBH—See Deutsche Post AG; *Int'l*, pg. 2079
DHL EXPRESS HUNGARY FORWARDING AND SERVICES LLC—See Deutsche Post AG; *Int'l*, pg. 2074
DHL GLOBAL MAIL—See Deutsche Post AG; *Int'l*, pg. 2076
DIE SCHWEIZERISCHE POST AG; *Int'l*, pg. 2112
ELECTRONIC BUSINESS SYSTEM; *Int'l*, pg. 2354
EMIRATES POST; *Int'l*, pg. 2382
FRANCOTYP-POSTALIA GMBH—See Francotyp-Postalia Holding AG; *Int'l*, pg. 2761
LIVEWORLD, INC.; *U.S. Public*, pg. 1333
POINTS.COM INC.—See General Atlantic Service Company, L.P.; *U.S. Private*, pg. 1663
QUOTEMEDIA, INC.; *Int'l*, pg. 1757
SECAP GROUPE PITNEY BOWES—See Pitney Bowes Inc.; *U.S. Public*, pg. 1694
STAMPS.COM INC.—See Thoma Bravo, L.P.; *U.S. Private*, pg. 4153
TAXIPOST SA/NV—See bpost NV/SA; *Int'l*, pg. 1133
TNT EXPRESS N.V.—See FedEx Corporation; *U.S. Public*, pg. 828
UNITED COURIERS S.A.R.L.—See United Parcel Service, Inc.; *U.S. Public*, pg. 2234
UNITED PARCEL SERVICE (BY)—See United Parcel Service, Inc.; *U.S. Public*, pg. 2234
UNITED PARCEL SERVICE (RUS) LLC—See United Parcel Service, Inc.; *U.S. Public*, pg. 2234
UNITED STATES POSTAL SERVICE; *U.S. Public*, pg. 4299
THE UPS STORE, INC.—See United Parcel Service, Inc.; *U.S. Public*, pg. 2233

492110 — COURIERS AND EXPRESS DELIVERY SERVICES

13TEN LIMITED—See Citipost Group; *Int'l*, pg. 1622
A-1 EXPRESS DELIVERY SERVICE, INC.; *U.S. Private*, pg. 21
A-1 INTERNATIONAL, INC.; *U.S. Private*, pg. 21
AEROPUERTO DE MERIDA S.A. DE C.V.—See Grupo Aeroportuario del Sureste, S.A.B. de C.V.; *Int'l*, pg. 3119
AIR MENZIES INTERNATIONAL (CAPE) PROPRIETARY LTD.—See Agility; *Int'l*, pg. 210
AIR MENZIES INTERNATIONAL (INDIA) PRIVATE LTD.—See Agility; *Int'l*, pg. 210
AIR MENZIES INTERNATIONAL (NZ) LTD.—See Agility; *Int'l*, pg. 210
AIR MENZIES INTERNATIONAL SA PROPRIETARY LTD.—See Agility; *Int'l*, pg. 210
AIR MENZIES INTERNATIONAL—See Agility; *Int'l*, pg. 210
AMBRY HILLS TECHNOLOGIES, LLC—See Air T, Inc.; *U.S. Public*, pg. 67
APPLE EXPRESS COURIER INC.—See bpost NV/SA; *Int'l*, pg. 1133
APPLE EXPRESS COURIER LTD.—See bpost NV/SA; *Int'l*, pg. 1133
ARAMEX HONG KONG LIMITED—See Aramex PJSC; *Int'l*, pg. 535
ARAMEX INTERNATIONAL EGYPT FOR AIR & LOCAL SERVICES (S.A.E)—See Aramex PJSC; *Int'l*, pg. 535
ARAMEX INTERNATIONAL HAVA KARGO VE KERYE ANONIM SIRKETI—See Aramex PJSC; *Int'l*, pg. 535
ARAMEX INTERNATIONAL LOGISTICS PRIVATE LTD.—See Aramex PJSC; *Int'l*, pg. 535
ARAMEX JORDAN LTD.—See Aramex PJSC; *Int'l*, pg. 535
ARAMEX PJSC; *Int'l*, pg. 535
ARAMEX SAUDI LIMITED COMPANY—See Aramex PJSC; *Int'l*, pg. 535
ARAMEX SOUTH AFRICA PTY LTD—See Aramex PJSC; *Int'l*, pg. 535
ARAMEX (UK) LIMITED—See Aramex PJSC; *Int'l*, pg. 535
ARMOUR COURIER SERVICES INC.—See Armour Transportation Systems; *Int'l*, pg. 575
ASAP EXPEDITING & LOGISTICS, LLC—See Littlejohn & Co., LLC; *U.S. Private*, pg. 2470
A TOUTE VITESSE SA; *Int'l*, pg. 18
AZBIL YAMATAKE FRIENDLY CO., LTD.—See Azbil Corporation; *Int'l*, pg. 777
BEAVEX; *Int'l*, pg. 509
BESTGOFER INC.; *U.S. Private*, pg. 544
BLUEGRASS SUPPLY CHAIN SERVICES; *U.S. Private*, pg. 596
CASTLE PARCELS - CHRISTCHURCH—See Freightways Group Limited; *Int'l*, pg. 2771
CASTLE PARCELS LIMITED—See Freightways Group Limited; *Int'l*, pg. 2771
CASTLE PARCELS - WELLINGTON—See Freightways Group Limited; *Int'l*, pg. 2771
CITYCON NORWAY AS—See Citycon Oyj; *Int'l*, pg. 1629
CITY DASH, LLC—See Brixey & Meyer, Inc.; *U.S. Private*, pg. 658
CITYSPRINT (UK) LIMITED; *Int'l*, pg. 1630
CORPORATE AIR; *U.S. Private*, pg. 1054
CRISIS COURIER SOLUTIONS LTD—See CitySprint (UK) Limited; *Int'l*, pg. 1630
CROSSCOUNTRY COURIER; *U.S. Private*, pg. 1106
CSA AIR INC.—See Air T, Inc.; *U.S. Public*, pg. 67
CTI COURIERS PTY LTD—See CTI Logistics Limited; *Int'l*, pg. 1871
CTI XPRESS SYSTEMS PTY LTD—See CTI Logistics Limited; *Int'l*, pg. 1871
CYC LOGISTICS LTD—See CitySprint (UK) Limited; *Int'l*, pg. 1630
DELGADO COURIER INC.—See Delgado Travel Agency Corporation; *U.S. Private*, pg. 1196
DEUTSCHE POST AG; *Int'l*, pg. 2071
DEUTSCHE POST GLOBAL MAIL B.V.—See Deutsche Post AG; *Int'l*, pg. 2079
DEUTSCHE POST GLOBAL MAIL GMBH—See Deutsche Post AG; *Int'l*, pg. 2079
DEUTSCHE POST GLOBAL MAIL LTD.—See Deutsche Post AG; *Int'l*, pg. 2079
DEUTSCHE POST GLOBAL MAIL (SWITZERLAND) AG—See Deutsche Post AG; *Int'l*, pg. 2079
DEUTSCHE POST GLOBAL MAIL (UK) LTD.—See Deutsche Post AG; *Int'l*, pg. 2079
DHL ASIA PACIFIC SHARED SERVICES SDN. BHD.—See Deutsche Post AG; *Int'l*, pg. 2073
DHL DANZAS AIR & OCEAN NORTH AMERICA—See Deutsche Post AG; *Int'l*, pg. 2073
DHL DE EL SALVADOR S.A. DE C.V.—See Deutsche Post AG; *Int'l*, pg. 2076
DHL DOMINICANA S.A.—See Deutsche Post AG; *Int'l*, pg. 2076
DHL EGYPT W.L.L.—See Deutsche Post AG; *Int'l*, pg. 2073
DHL EXPRESS A/S—See Deutsche Post AG; *Int'l*, pg. 2074
DHL EXPRESS (AUSTRALIA) PTY LTD.—See Deutsche Post AG; *Int'l*, pg. 2073
DHL EXPRESS CYPRUS—See Deutsche Post AG; *Int'l*, pg. 2074
DHL EXPRESS (CZECH REPUBLIC) S.R.O.—See Deutsche Post AG; *Int'l*, pg. 2074
DHL EXPRESS GERMANY GMBH—See Deutsche Post AG; *Int'l*, pg. 2073
DHL EXPRESS (HONG KONG) LTD—See Deutsche Post AG; *Int'l*, pg. 2074
DHL EXPRESS HUNGARY LTD.—See Deutsche Post AG; *Int'l*, pg. 2074
DHL EXPRESS INTERNATIONAL (THAILAND) LTD.—See Deutsche Post AG; *Int'l*, pg. 2074
DHL EXPRESS (IRELAND) LTD.—See Deutsche Post AG; *Int'l*, pg. 2074
DHL EXPRESS MEXICO, S.A. DE C.V.—See Deutsche Post AG; *Int'l*, pg. 2074
DHL EXPRESS (POLAND) SP.ZO.O.—See Deutsche Post AG; *Int'l*, pg. 2074
DHL EXPRESS (SINGAPORE) PTE LTD.—See Deutsche Post AG; *Int'l*, pg. 2074
DHL EXPRESS S.R.L.—See Deutsche Post AG; *Int'l*, pg. 2074
DHL EXPRESS (SWEDEN) AB—See Deutsche Post AG; *Int'l*, pg. 2074
DHL EXPRESS (TAIWAN) CORP.—See Deutsche Post AG; *Int'l*, pg. 2074
DHL EXPRESS (THAILAND) LIMITED—See Deutsche Post AG; *Int'l*, pg. 2074
DHL EXPRESS VALENCIA SPAIN S.L.—See Deutsche Post AG; *Int'l*, pg. 2074
DHL FLETES AEREOS, C.A.—See Deutsche Post AG; *Int'l*, pg. 2074
DHL GLOBAL MAIL (JAPAN) K. K.—See Deutsche Post AG; *Int'l*, pg. 2076
DHL GLOBAL MAIL (SINGAPORE) PTE. LTD.—See Deutsche Post AG; *Int'l*, pg. 2076
DHL HOLDINGS (USA), INC.—See Deutsche Post AG; *Int'l*, pg. 2076
DHL HRADFLUTNINGAR EHF—See Deutsche Post AG; *Int'l*, pg. 2076
DHL INTERNATIONAL (ALGERIE) S.A.R.L.—See Deutsche Post AG; *Int'l*, pg. 2076

N.A.I.C.S. INDEX

492210 — LOCAL MESSENGERS AN...

DHL INTERNATIONAL (BEOGRADE) D.O.O.—See Deutsche Post AG; *Int'l*, pg. 2076
DHL INTERNATIONAL BOTSWANA (PTY) LTD.—See Deutsche Post AG; *Int'l*, pg. 2073
DHL INTERNATIONAL B.V.—See Deutsche Post AG; *Int'l*, pg. 2076
DHL INTERNATIONAL D.O.O.—See Deutsche Post AG; *Int'l*, pg. 2077
DHL INTERNATIONAL GMBH—See Deutsche Post AG; *Int'l*, pg. 2073
DHL INTERNATIONAL HELLAS S.A.—See Deutsche Post AG; *Int'l*, pg. 2076
DHL INTERNATIONAL LTD.—See Deutsche Post AG; *Int'l*, pg. 2076
DHL INTERNATIONAL MAURITANIE SARL—See Deutsche Post AG; *Int'l*, pg. 2073
DHL INTERNATIONAL (NIGERIA) LTD.—See Deutsche Post AG; *Int'l*, pg. 2076
DHL INTERNATIONAL (PTY) LTD.—See Deutsche Post AG; *Int'l*, pg. 2076
DHL INTERNATIONAL REUNION SARL—See Deutsche Post AG; *Int'l*, pg. 2073
DHL INTERNATIONAL ROMANIA SRL—See Deutsche Post AG; *Int'l*, pg. 2077
DHL INTERNATIONAL S.A./N.V.—See Deutsche Post AG; *Int'l*, pg. 2073
DHL INTERNATIONAL S.R.L.—See Deutsche Post AG; *Int'l*, pg. 2077
DHL INTERNATIONAL (THAILAND) LTD.—See Deutsche Post AG; *Int'l*, pg. 2073
DHL INTERNATIONAL (UK) LTD.—See Deutsche Post AG; *Int'l*, pg. 2076
DHL INTL (BULGARIA) E.O.O.D.—See Deutsche Post AG; *Int'l*, pg. 2077
DHL INTL (SLOVAKIA) SPOL. S R.O.—See Deutsche Post AG; *Int'l*, pg. 2077
DHL JAPAN, INC.—See Deutsche Post AG; *Int'l*, pg. 2077
DHL KOREA LTD.—See Deutsche Post AG; *Int'l*, pg. 2077
DHL KUWAIT CO. LTD—See Deutsche Post AG; *Int'l*, pg. 2077
DHL (LATVIA) SIA—See Deutsche Post AG; *Int'l*, pg. 2073
DHL (MAURITIUS) LTD.—See Deutsche Post AG; *Int'l*, pg. 2073
DHL OF CURACAO N.V.—See Deutsche Post AG; *Int'l*, pg. 2079
DHL-SINOTRANS INTERNATIONAL AIR COURIER LTD.—See China Merchants Group Limited; *Int'l*, pg. 1522
DHL (TANZANIA) LTD.—See Deutsche Post AG; *Int'l*, pg. 2072
DHL-TRANSPORTADORES RAPIDOS INTERNACIONAIS LDA.—See Deutsche Post AG; *Int'l*, pg. 2078
DHL WORLDWIDE EXPRESS (BANGLADESH) PRIVATE LIMITED—See Deutsche Post AG; *Int'l*, pg. 2078
DHL WORLDWIDE EXPRESS CARGO LLC—See Deutsche Post AG; *Int'l*, pg. 2078
DHL WORLDWIDE EXPRESS KENYA LTD.—See Deutsche Post AG; *Int'l*, pg. 2078
DHL WORLDWIDE EXPRESS (PH) CORP.—See Deutsche Post AG; *Int'l*, pg. 2078
DHL WORLDWIDE EXPRESS (PNG) LTD.—See Deutsche Post AG; *Int'l*, pg. 2078
DHL WORLDWIDE EXPRESS TASIMACILIK VE TICARET A.S.—See Deutsche Post AG; *Int'l*, pg. 2078
DHL YEMEN LTD.—See Deutsche Post AG; *Int'l*, pg. 2078
DJ MEDIAPRINT & LOGISTICS LTD.; *Int'l*, pg. 2138
DRIVEN DELIVERIES, INC.—See Stem Holdings, Inc.; *U.S. Public*, pg. 1945
DROPOFF, INC.; *U.S. Private*, pg. 1279
DUNHAM EXPRESS CORPORATION; *U.S. Private*, pg. 1289
ECOURIER UK LTD.; *Int'l*, pg. 2300
EPSILON SA—See Die Schweizerische Post AG; *Int'l*, pg. 2113
EURO-SPRINTERS SA/NV—See bpost NV/SA; *Int'l*, pg. 1133
EXPRESS COURIER INTERNATIONAL, INC.—See Diligent Delivery Systems; *U.S. Private*, pg. 1231
FALKLAND ISLANDS SHIPPING LIMITED—See FIH group plc; *Int'l*, pg. 2661
FEDERAL EXPRESS CANADA CORPORATION—See FedEx Corporation; *U.S. Public*, pg. 828
FEDERAL EXPRESS EUROPE, INC.—See FedEx Corporation; *U.S. Public*, pg. 828
FEDERAL EXPRESS JAPAN G.K.—See FedEx Corporation; *U.S. Public*, pg. 828
FEDERAL EXPRESS KOREA LLC—See FedEx Corporation; *U.S. Public*, pg. 828
FEDERAL EXPRESS PACIFIC, INC.—See FedEx Corporation; *U.S. Public*, pg. 828
FEDEX CROSS BORDER TECHNOLOGIES, INC.—See FedEx Corporation; *U.S. Public*, pg. 827
FEDEX EXPRESS GERMANY GMBH—See FedEx Corporation; *U.S. Public*, pg. 827
FEDEX EXPRESS SVERIGE AB—See FedEx Corporation; *U.S. Public*, pg. 827
FEDEX GROUND PACKAGE SYSTEM, INC.—See FedEx Corporation; *U.S. Public*, pg. 828

FEDEX SMARTPOST, INC.—See FedEx Corporation; *U.S. Public*, pg. 828
FEDEX SUPPLY CHAIN DISTRIBUTION SYSTEM, INC.—See FedEx Corporation; *U.S. Public*, pg. 828
FMC INSIGHTS LIMITED—See Die Schweizerische Post AG; *Int'l*, pg. 2113
FOXLINE LOGISTICS PTY LTD—See CTI Logistics Limited; *Int'l*, pg. 1871
FREIGHTWAYS GROUP LIMITED; *Int'l*, pg. 2771
FRESH DIRECT (UK) LIMITED—See Sysco Corporation; *U.S. Public*, pg. 1973
FRONTLINE CORPORATE SERVICES LIMITED—See Frontline plc; *Int'l*, pg. 2796
GENERAL AVIATION FLYING SERVICES, INC.—See BlackRock, Inc.; *U.S. Public*, pg. 346
GENERAL AVIATION FLYING SERVICES, INC.—See Blackstone Inc.; *U.S. Public*, pg. 358
GENERAL AVIATION FLYING SERVICES, INC.—See Cascade Investment LLC; *U.S. Private*, pg. 780
GHS CLASSIC DRINKS LIMITED—See Sysco Corporation; *U.S. Public*, pg. 1974
GLOBAL MAIL (AUSTRIA) GES. M.B.H.—See Deutsche Post AG; *Int'l*, pg. 2079
GLOBAL PARCEL DELIVERY (PVT) LTD.—See Aitken Spence PLC; *Int'l*, pg. 254
GOBRANDS, INC.; *U.S. Private*, pg. 1724
HACKBARTH DELIVERY SERVICE, INC.; *U.S. Private*, pg. 1838
HANJIN TRANSPORTATION CO., LTD.; *Int'l*, pg. 3252
HBL, LTD.—See Herbalife Nutrition Ltd.; *Int'l*, pg. 3359
HERMES AVIATION, INC.—See Mercury Air Group Inc.; *U.S. Private*, pg. 2670
IMEX GLOBAL SOLUTIONS LLC—See bpost NV/SA; *Int'l*, pg. 1133
INNOVATIVE COURIER SOLUTIONS INC.; *U.S. Private*, pg. 2082
INTERNATIONAL BONDED COURIERS INC.; *U.S. Private*, pg. 2114
INTERNATIONAL DELIVERY SOLUTIONS; *U.S. Private*, pg. 2116
JANEL CORPORATION; *U.S. Public*, pg. 1187
JORDAN & CO INTERNATIONAL LIMITED—See An Post LLC; *Int'l*, pg. 443
KALITTA AIR, LLC; *U.S. Private*, pg. 2257
KIWI EXPRESS—See Freightways Group Limited; *Int'l*, pg. 2771
KOREA EXPRESS U.S.A. INC.—See CJ Corporation; *Int'l*, pg. 1633
KRUSE WORLDWIDE COURIER, LTD.; *U.S. Private*, pg. 2353
LAND AIR EXPRESS INC.; *U.S. Private*, pg. 2382
LLC DHL INTERNATIONAL KAZAKHSTAN—See Deutsche Post AG; *Int'l*, pg. 2078
LONE STAR HOLDINGS, LLC; *U.S. Private*, pg. 2489
MANCHESTER MILLS, LLC—See Sysco Corporation; *U.S. Public*, pg. 1974
MAPLEBEAR INC; *U.S. Public*, pg. 1362
MEDIA LOGISTIK GMBH—See Bertelsmann SE & Co. KGaA; *Int'l*, pg. 993
MEDICAL LOGISTIC SOLUTIONS, INC.—See United Parcel Service, Inc.; *U.S. Public*, pg. 2233
MENZIES AVIATION GROUP—See Agility; *Int'l*, pg. 210
MERCURY MESSENGERS PTY LTD—See CTI Logistics Limited; *Int'l*, pg. 1871
MESSENGER SERVICES LIMITED—See Freightways Group Limited; *Int'l*, pg. 2771
ML MULTISERVICE EXPRESS, INC.; *U.S. Public*, pg. 2753
MOBILE AIR TRANSPORT, INC.; *U.S. Private*, pg. 2756
MOBILE ONE COURIER CARGO & LOGISTICS; *U.S. Private*, pg. 2757
MOUNTAIN AIR CARGO INC.—See Air T, Inc.; *U.S. Public*, pg. 67
MYANMAR DHL LIMITED—See Deutsche Post AG; *Int'l*, pg. 2078
NATIONWIDE LOGISTICS INC—See Van Plycon Lines Inc.; *U.S. Private*, pg. 4340
NEEDSPLUS INC—See Amana Inc.; *Int'l*, pg. 409
NETWORK COURIER SERVICES INC.; *U.S. Private*, pg. 2889
NETWORK LOGISTICS UK LTD—See CitySprint (UK) Limited; *Int'l*, pg. 1630
NEW ZEALAND COURIERS LIMITED—See Freightways Group Limited; *Int'l*, pg. 2771
NOW COURIERS LIMITED—See Freightways Group Limited; *Int'l*, pg. 2771
PARTSFLEET, INC.—See Harbour Group Industries, Inc.; *U.S. Private*, pg. 1860
PEGASUS LOGISTICS GROUP; *U.S. Private*, pg. 3129
PELICAN DELIVERS, INC.; *U.S. Private*, pg. 3130
PGED CORP.—See Fire & Flower Holdings Corp.; *Int'l*, pg. 2678
PINEAPPLE EXPRESS DELIVERY INC.—See Fire & Flower Holdings Corp.; *Int'l*, pg. 2678
POST HASTE LIMITED—See Freightways Group Limited; *Int'l*, pg. 2772
PRESTIGE DELIVERY SYSTEMS INC.; *U.S. Private*, pg. 3256

PRIORITY EXPRESS COURIER INC.—See H.I.G. Capital, LLC; *U.S. Private*, pg. 1827
P.T. BIROTIKA SEMESTA/DHL—See Deutsche Post AG; *Int'l*, pg. 2078
QUICK INTERNATIONAL COURIER UK LIMITED—See Q International Courier, LLC; *U.S. Private*, pg. 3311
R.B. MATHESON TRUCKING INC.; *U.S. Private*, pg. 3334
RENNEL LIMITED—See ENL Limited; *Int'l*, pg. 2441
ROYALE INTERNATIONAL COURIERS INC.; *U.S. Private*, pg. 3494
SECUREXPRESS SERVICES SDN BHD—See Berjaya Corporation Berhad; *Int'l*, pg. 984
SECURITY EXPRESS LTD—See Freightways Group Limited; *Int'l*, pg. 2772
SELECT EXPRESS & LOGISTICS LLC—See AIT Worldwide Logistics, Inc.; *U.S. Private*, pg. 142
SERNAM S.A.—See Butler Capital Partners SA; *Int'l*, pg. 1229
SKY BLUE COURIERS LTD—See CitySprint (UK) Limited; *Int'l*, pg. 1630
SKY COURIER, INC.—See Deutsche Post AG; *Int'l*, pg. 2082
SKYNET WORLDWIDE EXPRESS (PVT.) LTD.—See Hemas Holdings PLC; *Int'l*, pg. 3341
SKYSHOP LOGISTICS, INC.; *U.S. Public*, pg. 1892
SKYWEST AIRLINES, INC. - IDAHO—See Skywest Inc.; *U.S. Public*, pg. 1893
SODEXI—See Air France-KLM S.A.; *Int'l*, pg. 238
SUB60—See Freightways Group Limited; *Int'l*, pg. 2772
SYSCO FRANCE SAS—See Sysco Corporation; *U.S. Public*, pg. 1976
SYSCO LABS PVT. LTD.—See Sysco Corporation; *U.S. Public*, pg. 1976
TNT EXPRESS NEDERLAND B.V.—See FedEx Corporation; *U.S. Public*, pg. 828
TNT EXPRESS ROAD NETWORK B.V.—See FedEx Corporation; *U.S. Public*, pg. 828
TOPHAT LOGISTICAL SOLUTIONS, LLC—See Atlas World Group, Inc.; *U.S. Private*, pg. 380
TRICOR AMERICA, INC.; *U.S. Private*, pg. 4229
UNITED PARCEL SERVICE CANADA LTD.—See United Parcel Service, Inc.; *U.S. Public*, pg. 2234
UNITED PARCEL SERVICE CZECH REPUBLIC, S.R.O.—See United Parcel Service, Inc.; *U.S. Public*, pg. 2234
UNITED PARCEL SERVICE DEUTSCHLAND S.A.R.L. & CO. OHG—See United Parcel Service, Inc.; *U.S. Public*, pg. 2233
UNITED STATES CARGO & COURIER SERVICE, INC.—See U.S. Cargo, Inc.; *U.S. Private*, pg. 4270
UPS PARCEL DELIVERY (GUANGDONG) CO., LTD.—See United Parcel Service, Inc.; *U.S. Public*, pg. 2233
UPS SUPPLY CHAIN SOLUTIONS GENERAL SERVICES, INC.—See United Parcel Service, Inc.; *U.S. Public*, pg. 2234
U.S. CARGO, INC.; *U.S. Private*, pg. 4270
WEB TO DOOR, INC.; *U.S. Public*, pg. 2341
WEGENER TRANSPORT BV—See DPG Media Group NV; *Int'l*, pg. 2189
WESSIN TRANSPORT INC.; *U.S. Private*, pg. 4483
WORLD COURIER INC.—See Cencora, Inc.; *U.S. Public*, pg. 467
WORLD COURIER MANAGEMENT INC.—See Cencora, Inc.; *U.S. Public*, pg. 467
ZAO DHL INTERNATIONAL RUSSIA—See Deutsche Post AG; *Int'l*, pg. 2078

492210 — LOCAL MESSENGERS AND LOCAL DELIVERY

AEROPOST COLOMBIA, SAS—See PriceSmart Inc.; *U.S. Public*, pg. 1716
ARCHER DANIELS MIDLAND ASIA PACIFIC, LIMITED—See Archer-Daniels-Midland Company; *U.S. Public*, pg. 183
CARGUS INTERNATIONAL S.R.L.—See Abris Capital Partners Sp. z o.o.; *Int'l*, pg. 69
CITIPOST AMP LTD.—See Citipost Group; *Int'l*, pg. 1622
CITY TRANSFER CO. INC.; *U.S. Private*, pg. 907
COBORNS DELIVERS LLC—See Coborn's Incorporated; *U.S. Private*, pg. 958
DA NIANG DUMPLINGS HOLDINGS LIMITED—See CVC Capital Partners SICAV-FIS S.A.; *Int'l*, pg. 1885
DHL AVIATION (UK) LIMITED—See Deutsche Post AG; *Int'l*, pg. 2073
DHL EXPRESS IBERIA S.L.—See Deutsche Post AG; *Int'l*, pg. 2074
DHL EXPRESS (USA), INC.—See Deutsche Post AG; *Int'l*, pg. 2074
DHL HOME DELIVERY GMBH—See Deutsche Post AG; *Int'l*, pg. 2076
DHL INTERNATIONAL (CONGO) SPRL—See Deutsche Post AG; *Int'l*, pg. 2076
DHL INTERNATIONAL SENEGAL SARL—See Deutsche Post AG; *Int'l*, pg. 2077
DHL KEELLS (PRIVATE) LIMITED—See Deutsche Post AG; *Int'l*, pg. 2077

492210 — LOCAL MESSENGERS AN...

DHL (NAMIBIA) (PTY) LTD.—See Deutsche Post AG; *Int'l*, pg. 2073
DHL PANAMA S.A.—See Deutsche Post AG; *Int'l*, pg. 2077
DONESI D.O.O.—See Delivery Hero SE; *Int'l*, pg. 2013
DONESI D.O.O.—See Delivery Hero SE; *Int'l*, pg. 2013
DOORDASH, INC.; *U.S. Public*, pg. 677
DRAGONTAIL SYSTEMS LIMITED—See Dragontail Systems Limited; *Int'l*, pg. 2200
DRAGONTAIL SYSTEMS USA INC.—See Dragontail Systems Limited; *Int'l*, pg. 2200
E-FREIGHT COURIER, LLC—See MED-STAT USA LLC; *U.S. Private*, pg. 2650
E-STYLE, LLC—See Qurate Retail, Inc.; *U.S. Public*, pg. 1758
EV LOGISTICS LTD. - AMBIENT FACILITY—See Deutsche Post AG; *Int'l*, pg. 2080
EV LOGISTICS LTD. - PERISHABLES FACILITY—See Deutsche Post AG; *Int'l*, pg. 2080
EXECUTIVE EXPRESS, INC.; *U.S. Private*, pg. 1447
FINKLE TRANSPORT, INC.—See EVO Transportation & Energy Services, Inc.; *U.S. Public*, pg. 804
FOODORA AB—See Delivery Hero SE; *Int'l*, pg. 2013
FOODORA NORWAY AS—See Delivery Hero SE; *Int'l*, pg. 2013
FUNDELY CO., LTD.; *Int'l*, pg. 2845
GANGNAM KITCHEN PTE. LTD.—See E-Station Green Technology Group Co., Limited; *Int'l*, pg. 2249
GLOBAL MAIL, INC.—See Deutsche Post AG; *Int'l*, pg. 2080
KRAFT FOODS COLOMBIA LTDA.—See Mondelez International, Inc.; *U.S. Public*, pg. 1461
LETCHWORTH COURIERS LTD.—See CitySprint (UK) Limited; *Int'l*, pg. 1630
LLC DHL EXPRESS—See Deutsche Post AG; *Int'l*, pg. 2078
LYKES CARTAGE COMPANY, INC.; *U.S. Private*, pg. 2519
MEDIFLEET, INC.—See Harbour Group Industries, Inc.; *U.S. Private*, pg. 1860
MEDITRUST PHARMACY—See McKesson Corporation; *U.S. Public*, pg. 1408
ORDERMATE PTY LTD.—See FirstRand Limited; *Int'l*, pg. 2690
PLAZA FOOD SYSTEMS—See Plaza Provision Company; *U.S. Private*, pg. 3213
PLOTUN D.O.O.—See Delivery Hero SE; *Int'l*, pg. 2013
PPL CZ S. R. O.—See Deutsche Post AG; *Int'l*, pg. 2082
PRICESMART EL SALVADOR, S.A. DE C.V.—See PriceSmart Inc.; *U.S. Public*, pg. 1716
PRICESMART (GUATELMALA), S.A.—See PriceSmart Inc.; *U.S. Public*, pg. 1716
QUICKSILVER EXPRESS COURIER OF COLORADO, INC.—See Quicksilver Express Courier Inc.; *U.S. Private*, pg. 3326
QUIKORDER, LLC—See Yum! Brands, Inc.; *U.S. Public*, pg. 2400
REINHART FOODSERVICE, LLC - ATLANTA DIVISION—See Performance Food Group Company; *U.S. Public*, pg. 1675
REINHART FOODSERVICE, LLC - CEDAR RAPIDS DIVISION—See Performance Food Group Company; *U.S. Public*, pg. 1675
REINHART FOODSERVICE, LLC - CHICAGO DIVISION—See Performance Food Group Company; *U.S. Public*, pg. 1675
REINHART FOODSERVICE, LLC - CINCINNATI DIVISION—See Performance Food Group Company; *U.S. Public*, pg. 1675
REINHART FOODSERVICE, LLC - DETROIT DIVISION—See Performance Food Group Company; *U.S. Public*, pg. 1675
REINHART FOODSERVICE, LLC - EASTERN PENNSYLVANIA DIVISION—See Performance Food Group Company; *U.S. Public*, pg. 1675
REINHART FOODSERVICE, LLC - JACKSONVILLE DIVISION—See Performance Food Group Company; *U.S. Public*, pg. 1675
REINHART FOODSERVICE, LLC - JOHNSON CITY DIVISION—See Performance Food Group Company; *U.S. Public*, pg. 1675
REINHART FOODSERVICE, LLC - KANSAS CITY DIVISION—See Performance Food Group Company; *U.S. Public*, pg. 1675
REINHART FOODSERVICE, LLC - KNOXVILLE DIVISION—See Performance Food Group Company; *U.S. Public*, pg. 1675
REINHART FOODSERVICE, LLC - LA CROSSE DIVISION—See Performance Food Group Company; *U.S. Public*, pg. 1675
REINHART FOODSERVICE, LLC - LAFAYETTE DIVISION—See Performance Food Group Company; *U.S. Public*, pg. 1675
REINHART FOODSERVICE, LLC - LOUISVILLE DIVISION—See Performance Food Group Company; *U.S. Public*, pg. 1675
REINHART FOODSERVICE, LLC - MARQUETTE DIVISION—See Performance Food Group Company; *U.S. Public*, pg. 1675
REINHART FOODSERVICE, LLC - MILWAUKEE DIVISION—See Performance Food Group Company; *U.S. Public*, pg. 1675
REINHART FOODSERVICE, LLC - NEW BEDFORD DIVISION—See Performance Food Group Company; *U.S. Public*, pg. 1675
REINHART FOODSERVICE, LLC - NEW ORLEANS DIVISION—See Performance Food Group Company; *U.S. Public*, pg. 1675
REINHART FOODSERVICE, LLC - PITTSBURGH DIVISION—See Performance Food Group Company; *U.S. Public*, pg. 1675
REINHART FOODSERVICE, LLC - SHAWANO DIVISION—See Performance Food Group Company; *U.S. Public*, pg. 1675
REINHART FOODSERVICE, LLC - VALDOSTA DIVISION—See Performance Food Group Company; *U.S. Public*, pg. 1676
RELISH LABS LLC—See The Kroger Co.; *U.S. Public*, pg. 2109
SCM SP. Z O.O.—See AmRest Holdings SE; *Int'l*, pg. 437
SCRIPTFLEET, INC.—See Harbour Group Industries, Inc.; *U.S. Private*, pg. 1860
SPECIAL DISPATCH OF SAN ANTONIO, INC.—See J.B. Hunt Transport Services, Inc.; *U.S. Public*, pg. 1180
TALABAT ELECTRONIC & DELIVERY SERVICES LLC—See Delivery Hero SE; *Int'l*, pg. 2013
TALABAT GENERAL TRADING & CONTRACTING COMPANY W.L.L.—See Delivery Hero SE; *Int'l*, pg. 2013
TALABAT SERVICES COMPANY L.L.C.—See Delivery Hero SE; *Int'l*, pg. 2013
UK MAIL LTD—See Deutsche Post AG; *Int'l*, pg. 2083
UPS EUROPE SA/NV—See United Parcel Service, Inc.; *U.S. Public*, pg. 2233
UPS WORLDWIDE FORWARDING, INC.—See United Parcel Service, Inc.; *U.S. Public*, pg. 2234
VIVENO GROUP GMBH—See Bertelsmann SE & Co. KGaA; *Int'l*, pg. 995
WOOWA BROTHERS CORP.—See Delivery Hero SE; *Int'l*, pg. 2013
ZIFTY COM, INC.; *U.S. Private*, pg. 4604

493110 — GENERAL WAREHOUSING AND STORAGE

4WHEELS SERVICE + LOGISTIK GMBH—See CAPCELLENCE Mittelstandspartner GmbH; *Int'l*, pg. 1302
ACME DELIVERY SERVICE INC.; *U.S. Private*, pg. 60
ADL DELIVERY; *U.S. Private*, pg. 80
AG STOCK CENTER CORPORATION—See AIFUL Corporation; *Int'l*, pg. 231
AHC WAREHOUSE & TRADING (SHENZHEN) CO., LTD.—See Audix Corporation; *Int'l*, pg. 702
AHI ELECTRONICS WAREHOUSE (SHANGHAI) CO., LTD.—See Audix Corporation; *Int'l*, pg. 702
AJIS HOKKAIDO CO., LTD.—See AJIS Co., Ltd.; *Int'l*, pg. 258
AJIS KYUSHU CO., LTD.—See AJIS Co., Ltd.; *Int'l*, pg. 258
AJIS RETAIL SUPPORT CO., LTD.—See AJIS Co., Ltd.; *Int'l*, pg. 258
AJIS SHIKOKU CO., LTD.—See AJIS Co., Ltd.; *Int'l*, pg. 258
AKRON SERVICES, BRIMFIELD—See Akron Services Inc.; *U.S. Private*, pg. 146
ALGOL CHEMICALS SIA—See Algol Oy; *Int'l*, pg. 318
ALLEN DISTRIBUTION; *U.S. Private*, pg. 178
ALMACENAJES, S.A.; *Int'l*, pg. 363
AL-PI POLONIA SP. Z O.O.—See Albini & Pitigliani S.p.A.; *Int'l*, pg. 298
AMAZON.COM.DEDC, LLC—See Amazon.com, Inc.; *U.S. Public*, pg. 90
ANA LOGISTIC SERVICE CO., LTD—See ANA Holdings Inc.; *Int'l*, pg. 444
APM TERMINALS B.V.—See A.P. Moller-Maersk A/S; *Int'l*, pg. 25
APM TERMINALS—See A.P. Moller-Maersk A/S; *Int'l*, pg. 25
A&R BULK-PAK, INC.—See Nova Infrastructure Management, LLC; *U.S. Private*, pg. 2965
ARMADA SUPPLY CHAIN SOLUTIONS, LLC—See Armada Group, Ltd.; *U.S. Private*, pg. 329
A&R PACKAGING & DISTRIBUTION SERVICES, INC.—See A&R Transport, Inc.; *U.S. Private*, pg. 20
ASA APPLE INC.; *U.S. Private*, pg. 345
ASW LOGISTICS INC.; *U.S. Private*, pg. 363
ATLANTIC DETROIT DIESEL-ALLISON—See Atlantic Detroit Diesel-Allison, LLC; *U.S. Private*, pg. 373
ATLANTIC SHIPPERS INC.—See Animalfeeds International Corporation; *U.S. Private*, pg. 283
ATS LOGISTICS, INC.—See Nova Infrastructure Management, LLC; *U.S. Private*, pg. 2965
ATTO TECHNOLOGY, INC.; *U.S. Private*, pg. 383
BARRETT DISTRIBUTION CENTERS, INC.; *U.S. Private*, pg. 479
BEAM STORAGE PTE LTD—See Fatfish Group Ltd.; *Int'l*, pg. 2623
BEARDSELL LIMITED; *Int'l*, pg. 933
BENDER WAREHOUSE CO.; *U.S. Private*, pg. 524
BERGEN SHIPPERS CORP.—See Carl Bennet AB; *Int'l*, pg. 1331
BIG YELLOW (BATTERSEA) LIMITED—See Big Yellow Group plc; *Int'l*, pg. 1022
BINNY LIMITED; *Int'l*, pg. 1034
BROKERS LOGISTICS, LTD.; *U.S. Private*, pg. 662
BROOKVALE INTERNATIONAL CORPORATION—See California Cartage Company LLC; *U.S. Private*, pg. 718
CAFECO ARMAZENS GERAIS LTDA—See B. Pacorini S.p.A.; *Int'l*, pg. 789
CALIFORNIA CARTAGE COMPANY LLC; *U.S. Private*, pg. 718
CAPACITY LLC; *U.S. Private*, pg. 737
CBS CANADA CO.—See National Amusements, Inc.; *U.S. Private*, pg. 2840
CERES MARINE TERMINALS INC.—See Carrix, Inc.; *U.S. Private*, pg. 772
CHANNEL DISTRIBUTION CORPORATION—See Wind Point Advisors LLC; *U.S. Private*, pg. 4535
CHASEN LOGISTICS SDN BHD—See Chasen Holdings Limited; *Int'l*, pg. 1457
CHASEN LOGISTICS SERVICES LIMITED—See Chasen Holdings Limited; *Int'l*, pg. 1457
C.H. COAKLEY & CO.; *U.S. Private*, pg. 707
CHESTER CARTAGE LTD.; *Int'l*, pg. 1473
CHS-LCC CO-OP—See CHS INC.; *U.S. Public*, pg. 492
CHUO WAREHOUSE CO., LTD.; *Int'l*, pg. 1600
CHURCH & DWIGHT (UK) LTD.—See Church & Dwight Co., Inc.; *U.S. Public*, pg. 493
CJ CENTURY LOGISTICS HOLDINGS BERHAD; *Int'l*, pg. 1630
CJ LOGISTICS AMERICA, LLC—See CJ Corporation; *Int'l*, pg. 1633
CLH AVIACION, S.A.—See Compania Logistica de Hidrocarburos CLH, S.A.; *Int'l*, pg. 1749
CMT LOGISTICS CO., LTD.—See Chinese Maritime Transport Ltd.; *Int'l*, pg. 1569
COAKLEY BROS. COMPANY INC.; *U.S. Private*, pg. 953
COLONIAL TERMINALS, INC.—See Colonial Group, Inc.; *U.S. Private*, pg. 971
COMMANDER TERMINALS; *U.S. Private*, pg. 982
COMMERCIAL WAREHOUSE & CARTAGE, INC.; *U.S. Private*, pg. 985
COMPUTER SOLUTIONS INTERNATIONAL; *U.S. Private*, pg. 1005
COOPERVISION DO BRASIL LTDA—See The Cooper Companies, Inc.; *U.S. Public*, pg. 2066
COREY OIL LTD; *U.S. Private*, pg. 1050
COURIER SYSTEM INC.; *U.S. Private*, pg. 1068
CROSSGLOBE DISTRIBUTION SERVICES, INC.—See Blue Wolf Capital Partners LLC; *U.S. Private*, pg. 595
CROZIER FINE ARTS LIMITED—See Iron Mountain Incorporated; *U.S. Public*, pg. 1172
CTI RP, INC.—See Ridgemont Partners Management LLC; *U.S. Private*, pg. 3433
DAICEL LOGISTICS SERVICE CO., LTD.—See Daicel Corporation; *Int'l*, pg. 1919
DAIWA SHIKO CO., LTD.—See Daio Paper Corporation; *Int'l*, pg. 1940
DART WAREHOUSE CORPORATION; *U.S. Private*, pg. 1160
DATA SECURITY DEVELOPMENT, INC; *U.S. Private*, pg. 1163
D&D DISTRIBUTION SERVICES; *U.S. Private*, pg. 1137
DEI LOGISTICS (USA) CORP.—See Delta Electronics, Inc.; *Int'l*, pg. 2016
DEPENDABLE DISTRIBUTION CENTERS—See Dependable Highway Express Inc.; *U.S. Private*, pg. 1209
DEPOTS PETROLIERS DE FOS; *Int'l*, pg. 2041
DEUFOL BELGIE N.V.—See Deufol SE; *Int'l*, pg. 2048
DEUFOL PACKAGING TIENEN N.V.—See Deufol SE; *Int'l*, pg. 2048
DIS SERVICE & SUPPORT CO., LTD.—See Daiwabo Holdings Co., Ltd.; *Int'l*, pg. 1949
DISTRIBUTION ALTERNATIVES, INC.; *U.S. Private*, pg. 1239
DISTRIBUTION & MARKING SERVICES, INC.; *U.S. Private*, pg. 1239
DISTRIBUTION SERVICES OF AMERICA, INC.; *U.S. Private*, pg. 1239
DISTRIBUTION UNLIMITED, INC.—See Galesi Group; *U.S. Private*, pg. 1637
DKK LOGISTICS CORPORATION—See Daiichi Kigenso Kagaku Kogyo Co., Ltd.; *Int'l*, pg. 1928
DNP LOGISTICS CO., LTD.—See Dai Nippon Printing Co., Ltd.; *Int'l*, pg. 1915
DOLLAR TREE DISTRIBUTION, INC.—See Dollar Tree, Inc.; *U.S. Public*, pg. 672
DOMINION WAREHOUSING & DISTRIBUTION SERVICES LTD.; *Int'l*, pg. 2161
DOT FOODS, INC.; *U.S. Private*, pg. 1264
DRY STORAGE CORPORATION; *U.S. Private*, pg. 1280
DSV SOLUTIONS 2 BV—See DSV A/S; *Int'l*, pg. 2213
DSV SOLUTIONS LTD.—See DSV A/S; *Int'l*, pg. 2213
DSV SOLUTIONS S.A.S.—See DSV A/S; *Int'l*, pg. 2213
DSV SOLUTIONS SP. Z O.O.—See DSV A/S; *Int'l*, pg. 2213
EAST COAST WAREHOUSE & DISTRIBUTION CORP.—See Romark Logistics, Inc.; *U.S. Private*, pg. 3476
EASYDIS—See Finatis SA; *Int'l*, pg. 2670
ELITE LOGISTICS, LLC; *U.S. Private*, pg. 1361
ELM GLOBAL LOGISTICS; *U.S. Private*, pg. 1375

N.A.I.C.S. INDEX
493110 — GENERAL WAREHOUSING...

ELSTON RICHARDS, INC.; *U.S. Private*, pg. 1377
ENCOMPASS PARTS DISTRIBUTION, INC.—See Bain Capital, LP; *U.S. Private*, pg. 444
ENG KONG CONTAINER AGENCIES (PTE) LTD—See Eng Kong Holdings Pte Ltd; *Int'l*, pg. 2426
ENLINX, LLC—See Port Logistics Group, Inc.; *U.S. Private*, pg. 3230
EXXONMOBIL OIL CORPORATION—See Exxon Mobil Corporation; *U.S. Public*, pg. 815
EZSTORAGE CORP. OF MARYLAND—See Public Storage; *U.S. Public*, pg. 1736
FALCON PACKAGING, INC.; *U.S. Private*, pg. 1466
FASTFETCH CORP.—See ABCO Systems LLC; *U.S. Private*, pg. 36
FEDERAL WAREHOUSE COMPANY; *U.S. Private*, pg. 1491
FERDINAND GROSS GMBH & CO. KG; *Int'l*, pg. 2637
FIFTH GEAR, INC.-MISSOURI—See Speed Commerce, Inc.; *U.S. Public*, pg. 1917
FIRST FITNESS INTERNATIONAL; *U.S. Private*, pg. 1519
FLASH LOGISTICS SERVICES INC.; *U.S. Private*, pg. 1540
FM RETAIL SERVICES INC.—See The Kroger Co.; *U.S. Public*, pg. 2107
FORMS DISTRIBUTION CORP.; *U.S. Private*, pg. 1572
FOXBORO TERMINALS CO. INC.—See Distribution Services of America, Inc.; *U.S. Private*, pg. 1239
FRASERS PROPERTY INDUSTRIAL (THAILAND) COMPANY LIMITED—See Frasers Property Limited; *Int'l*, pg. 2766
FREIGHT DISTRIBUTION MANAGEMENT SYSTEMS PTY LTD—See bpost NV/SA; *Int'l*, pg. 1133
FULFILLMENT WORKS, LLC—See Stord, Inc.; *U.S. Private*, pg. 3831
GENCO DISTRIBUTION SYSTEM, INC.—See FedEx Corporation; *U.S. Public*, pg. 828
GENERAL PENCIL CO.—See General Pencil Company; *U.S. Private*, pg. 1666
GENOVA-INDIANA, INC.—See Genova Products, Inc.; *U.S. Private*, pg. 1673
GEORGIA KAOLIN TERMINALS, INC.—See Colonial Group, Inc.; *U.S. Private*, pg. 971
GFA INCORPORATED; *U.S. Private*, pg. 1689
GKE METAL LOGISTICS PTE. LTD.—See GKE Corporation Limited; *Int'l*, pg. 2983
GKE (SHANGHAI) METAL LOGISTICS CO., LTD.—See GKE Corporation Limited; *Int'l*, pg. 2983
GKE WAREHOUSING & LOGISTICS PTE LTD—See GKE Corporation Limited; *Int'l*, pg. 2983
GLENWAY DISTRIBUTION; *U.S. Private*, pg. 1711
GLOBAL HOLDINGS (BOTSWANA) (PTY) LIMITED—See CIC Holdings Limited; *Int'l*, pg. 1602
G & M WAREHOUSING ENTERPRISES LIMITED—See Hadco Limited; *Int'l*, pg. 3205
GOINDUSTRY DOVEBID ASSET MANAGEMENT (H.K.) LTD.—See Liquidity Services, Inc.; *U.S. Public*, pg. 1320
GOLDEN STATE FOODS-SOUTH CAROLINA DIVISION—See Golden State Foods Corp.; *U.S. Private*, pg. 1733
GOLIK GODOWN LIMITED—See Golik Holdings Limited; *Int'l*, pg. 3036
GORDON CORPORATION—See PBI/Gordon Corporation; *U.S. Private*, pg. 3118
GRAND WORLDWIDE LOGISTICS CORP.—See The Jordan Company, L.P.; *U.S. Private*, pg. 4060
GRAYMONT LIMITED PLEASANT GAP PLANT—See Graymont Limited; *Int'l*, pg. 3063
GSC LOGISTICS INC.; *U.S. Private*, pg. 1800
GUANGDONG CHANGTONG WAREHOUSE & TERMINAL CO., LTD.—See China Merchants Group Limited; *Int'l*, pg. 1522
GULF WAREHOUSING COMPANY QSC; *Int'l*, pg. 3182
GULF WINDS INTERNATIONAL INC.; *U.S. Private*, pg. 1817
GUTHRIE MARKETING (S) PTE LTD—See Guthrie GTS Limited; *Int'l*, pg. 3188
HALLS WAREHOUSE CORP.; *U.S. Private*, pg. 1845
HANDL-IT INC.; *U.S. Private*, pg. 1852
HAN EXPRESS VIETNAM CO., LTD.—See HANEXPRESS CO, LTD.; *Int'l*, pg. 3244
HANWA LOGISTICS GROUP CO., LTD.—See Hanwa Co., Ltd.; *Int'l*, pg. 3262
HAPILOGI, INC.—See CRE, Inc.; *Int'l*, pg. 1830
HENAN XINNING MODERN LOGISICS CO., LTD.; *Int'l*, pg. 3343
HENSON LUMBER LTD.; *U.S. Private*, pg. 1920
HERMANN SERVICES INCORPORATED; *U.S. Private*, pg. 1925
HOLMAN DISTRIBUTION CENTER OF OREGON; *U.S. Private*, pg. 1967
HOLMAN DISTRIBUTION CENTER OF WASHINGTON; *U.S. Private*, pg. 1967
HOYER POLSKA SP. Z O. O.—See Hoyer GmbH; *Int'l*, pg. 3499
HUNTER PIPE LINE COMPANY PTY LTD—See Ampol Limited; *Int'l*, pg. 436
HY-PAC SELF STORAGE—See Yamada Group USA Ltd.; *U.S. Private*, pg. 4585

IEMOLI TRASPORTI SA—See Die Schweizerische Post AG; *Int'l*, pg. 2113
INDUSTRIAL FABRICATORS INC.—See Williams Enterprises of Georgia, Inc.; *U.S. Private*, pg. 4525
INLAND STAR DISTRIBUTION CENTERS; *U.S. Private*, pg. 2079
INTEGRATED SHUN HING LOGISTICS (LINGANG) CO. LTD.—See ILB Group Berhad; *Int'l*, pg. 3613
INTEGRATED SHUN HING LOGISTICS (SHANGHAI) LTD.—See ILB Group Berhad; *Int'l*, pg. 3613
INTEGRATED SHUN HING LOGISTICS (SHENZHEN) CO. LTD.—See ILB Group Berhad; *Int'l*, pg. 3613
INTERNATIONAL MARINE PRODUCTS NEVADA INC.—See Eiwa International Inc.; *U.S. Private*, pg. 1348
INTERPORTO DI VADO I.O.S.C.P.A.—See B. Pacorini S.p.A.; *Int'l*, pg. 789
INTRALOG HERMES AG—See Die Schweizerische Post AG; *Int'l*, pg. 2113
INTRALOG OVERSEAS AG—See Die Schweizerische Post AG; *Int'l*, pg. 2113
JACKSON SALES & STORAGE CO.—See National Presto Industries, Inc; *U.S. Public*, pg. 1497
J.A. LOGISTICS, INC.—See J.A. Frate Transport Services, Inc.; *U.S. Private*, pg. 2157
JENNY CRAIG DISTRIBUTION CENTER—See H.I.G. Capital, LLC; *U.S. Private*, pg. 1830
JERALD R. BREKKE, INC.—See McGrath RentCorp.; *U.S. Public*, pg. 1407
JOHN WILEY & SONS, INC. - SOMERSET—See John Wiley & Sons, Inc.; *U.S. Public*, pg. 1193
JOSEPH CORY HOLDINGS LLC—See J.B. Hunt Transport Services, Inc.; *U.S. Public*, pg. 1180
JTR & CO. INC.; *U.S. Private*, pg. 2242
KANE WAREHOUSING INC.—See Kane Is Able, Inc.; *U.S. Private*, pg. 2260
KAYHAN INTERNATIONAL LIMITED—See Business Office Systems Inc.; *U.S. Private*, pg. 695
KEMCO KNOXVILLE—See GSK plc; *Int'l*, pg. 3149
KENCO GROUP INC.; *U.S. Private*, pg. 2283
KOREA EXPRESS SHANGHAI CO., LTD.—See CJ Corporation; *Int'l*, pg. 1633
KRAEFT LOGISTIK GMBH—See HELM AG; *Int'l*, pg. 3338
KYOEI SHOJI CO LTD.—See AGC Inc.; *Int'l*, pg. 204
LANEY & DUKE TERMINAL WAREHOUSE CO. INC.; *U.S. Private*, pg. 2388
LEICHT TRANSFER & STORAGE COMPANY; *U.S. Private*, pg. 2419
LESAINT CHEMICAL LOGISTICS—See LeSaint Logistics LLC; *U.S. Private*, pg. 2432
LINDEN WAREHOUSE & DISTRIBUTION CO., INC.—See KKR & Co. Inc.; *U.S. Public*, pg. 1241
LINDO INDUSTRIPARK A/S—See A.P. Moller-Maersk A/S; *Int'l*, pg. 26
LITEN LOGISTICS SERVICES PTE LTD—See Chasen Holdings Limited; *Int'l*, pg. 1457
LOGISTIC SERVICES, INC.—See Hormel Foods Corporation; *U.S. Public*, pg. 1054
LOGWIN AIR + OCEAN CZECH S.R.O.—See Delton AG; *Int'l*, pg. 2021
LUFKIN INDUSTRIES LLC - POWER TRANSMISSION DIVISION—See KPS Capital Partners, LP; *U.S. Private*, pg. 2348
MAGAZZINI GENERALI DELLE TAGLIATE (M.G.T.) SPA—See Credito Emiliano S.p.A.; *Int'l*, pg. 1836
MAGNUM WAREHOUSING, INC.—See Magnum, Ltd.; *U.S. Private*, pg. 2549
MANHATTAN MINI STORAGE—See Edison Properties, LLC; *U.S. Private*, pg. 1337
MAXZONE AUTO PARTS CORP.—See DEPO AUTO PARTS IND. CO., LTD.; *Int'l*, pg. 2041
MCCORMICK-HUNT VALLEY PLANT—See McCormick & Company, Incorporated; *U.S. Public*, pg. 1404
MEDALTUS, LLC—See HealthEdge Investment Partners, LLC; *U.S. Private*, pg. 1896
METALINOX BILBAO, S.A.—See Acerinox, S.A.; *Int'l*, pg. 101
MIDWEST WAREHOUSE & DISTRIBUTION SYSTEMS; *U.S. Private*, pg. 2723
MILWHITE INC.; *U.S. Private*, pg. 2740
MINI-PAC INC.—See Decurion Corp.; *U.S. Private*, pg. 1188
MNP STEEL SERVICES & WAREHOUSING DIVISION—See MNP Corporation; *U.S. Private*, pg. 2756
MOBILE MINI CANADA ULC—See WillScot Mobile Mini Holdings Corp.; *U.S. Public*, pg. 2372
MOBILE MINI, LLC—See WillScot Mobile Mini Holdings Corp.; *U.S. Public*, pg. 2372
MOBILE MINI UK LTD.—See WillScot Mobile Mini Holdings Corp.; *U.S. Public*, pg. 2372
MODENA TERMINAL S.R.L.—See BPER BANCA S.p.A; *Int'l*, pg. 1132
MORGAN & BROTHER MANHATTAN STORAGE INC.; *U.S. Private*, pg. 2783
MURPHY WAREHOUSE COMPANY; *U.S. Private*, pg. 2816
NANNING BULK COMMODITIES EXCHANGE CORPORATION LIMITED—See Forlink Software Corporation, Inc.; *Int'l*, pg. 2733
NATIONAL DISTRIBUTION—See Public Investment Corporation; *U.S. Private*, pg. 3299
NFI WAREHOUSING & DISTRIBUTION—See NFI Industries, Inc.; *U.S. Private*, pg. 2923
NORDSTROM DISTRIBUTION #89—See Nordstrom, Inc.; *U.S. Public*, pg. 1535
NORTEX MIDSTREAM PARTNERS, LLC—See The Williams Companies, Inc.; *U.S. Public*, pg. 2143
NORTHSTAR MOVING CORP.; *U.S. Private*, pg. 2958
NTS EUROPEAN DISTRIBUTION AB—See DSV A/S; *Int'l*, pg. 2214
ODW LOGISTICS INC.; *U.S. Private*, pg. 2993
OFFICE MOVERS OF FLORIDA LLC; *U.S. Private*, pg. 3001
OFFICEWORKS LLC; *U.S. Private*, pg. 3002
OHNAMI CORPORATION—See Hitachi Zosen Corporation; *Int'l*, pg. 3412
OREGON TRANSFER CO.; *U.S. Private*, pg. 3040
ORION GLOBAL CORP.; *U.S. Private*, pg. 3043
OTTO SCHMIDT AG—See Die Schweizerische Post AG; *Int'l*, pg. 2113
PACIFIC COAST WAREHOUSE CO—See Weber Distribution, LLC; *U.S. Private*, pg. 4465
PACORINI KOPER D.O.O—See B. Pacorini S.p.A.; *Int'l*, pg. 789
PACORINI SILOCAF S.R.L.—See B. Pacorini S.p.A.; *Int'l*, pg. 789
PACORINI VIETNAM LTD—See B. Pacorini S.p.A.; *Int'l*, pg. 789
PALMER DISTRIBUTION SERVICES, INC.; *U.S. Private*, pg. 3081
PARKER HANNIFIN KIT OPERATIONS—See Parker Hannifin Corporation; *U.S. Public*, pg. 1646
PARKER SEAL O-RING DIVISION—See Parker Hannifin Corporation; *U.S. Public*, pg. 1643
PAUL SUSTEK COMPANY INC.; *U.S. Private*, pg. 3113
PCL CONTAINER SERVICES LIMITED—See Eng Kong Holdings Pte Ltd.; *Int'l*, pg. 2426
PD LOGISTICS—See Brookfield Infrastructure Partners L.P.; *Int'l*, pg. 1190
PEOPLES CARTAGE INC—See Peoples Services Inc.; *U.S. Private*, pg. 3142
PEOPLES SERVICES INC.; *U.S. Private*, pg. 3142
PETERSON SPRING-PACKAGING & DISTRIBUTION—See MiddleGround Management, LP; *U.S. Private*, pg. 2712
PIER RESTAURANTS L.P.—See PIER 39 L.P.; *U.S. Private*, pg. 3178
PUBLIC INVESTMENT CORPORATION; *U.S. Private*, pg. 3299
PUGET SOUND INTERNATIONAL, INC.; *U.S. Private*, pg. 3302
QUEEN CITY TERMINALS, INC.—See Kinder Morgan, Inc.; *U.S. Public*, pg. 1233
RADIAL ITALY SRL—See bpost NV/SA; *Int'l*, pg. 1133
RAUMA TERMINAL SERVICES OY—See Aspo Oyj; *Int'l*, pg. 631
RETAILERS & MANUFACTURERS DISTRIBUTION MARKETING SERVICES INC.; *U.S. Private*, pg. 3411
RICHMOND BONDED WAREHOUSE CORP.; *U.S. Private*, pg. 3430
RIDGE SERVICES INC.; *U.S. Private*, pg. 3432
ROADRUNNER STORAGE LLC—See Enel S.p.A.; *Int'l*, pg. 2414
ROBINSON TERMINAL WAREHOUSE LLC—See Nash Holdings LLC; *U.S. Private*, pg. 2835
ROMARK LOGISTICS, INC.; *U.S. Private*, pg. 3476
R.S. HUGHES CO.—See R.S. Hughes Co., Inc.; *U.S. Private*, pg. 3339
RUKERT TERMINALS CORPORATION; *U.S. Private*, pg. 3503
RWA RAIFFEISEN WARE AUSTRIA AKTIENGESELLSCHAFT—See BayWa AG; *Int'l*, pg. 919
SADDLE CREEK CORPORATION; *U.S. Private*, pg. 3522
SAFEGUARD SELF STORAGE; *U.S. Private*, pg. 3524
SANTA FE (THAILAND) LTD.—See EAC Invest AS; *Int'l*, pg. 2262
SCHICK MANUFACTURING INC.—See Edgewell Personal Care Company; *U.S. Public*, pg. 718
SCISAFE, INC.—See 1315 Capital LLC; *U.S. Private*, pg. 3
S.C. SILOTRANS S.R.L.—See CHS INC.; *U.S. Public*, pg. 492
SEA JET INDUSTRIES DE CORP.; *U.S. Private*, pg. 3582
SHANGHAI CIMC YANGSHAN CONTAINER SERVICE CO., LTD.—See China International Marine Containers (Group) Co., Ltd.; *Int'l*, pg. 1512
SHIPPERS WAREHOUSE, INC.; *U.S. Private*, pg. 3637
SHIPPERS WAREHOUSE OF GEORGIA—See Shippers Warehouse, Inc.; *U.S. Private*, pg. 3637
SIMON TANKLAGER GESELLSCHAFT MBH—See Brookfield Infrastructure Partners L.P.; *Int'l*, pg. 1193
SINGAPORE WAREHOUSE COMPANY (PRIVATE) LTD.—See Hwa Hong Corporation Limited; *Int'l*, pg. 3541
SINOTRANS FOSHAN WAREHOUSE & TERMINAL CO., LTD.—See China Merchants Group Limited; *Int'l*, pg. 1523
SINOTRANS GUANGDONG DONGJIANG WAREHOUSE &

493110 — GENERAL WAREHOUSING...

TERMINAL CO., LTD.—See China Merchants Group Limited; *Int'l*, pg. 1523
SINOTRANS GUANGDONG HUANGPU WAREHOUSE & TERMINAL CO., LTD.—See China Merchants Group Limited; *Int'l*, pg. 1523
SINOTRANS JIANGMEN WAREHOUSE & TERMINAL CO., LTD.—See China Merchants Group Limited; *Int'l*, pg. 1523
SINOTRANS SHENZHEN LOGISTICS CO., LTD.—See China Merchants Group Limited; *Int'l*, pg. 1523
SINOTRANS ZHONGSHAN WAREHOUSE & TERMINAL CO., LTD.—See China Merchants Group Limited; *Int'l*, pg. 1523
SI WAREHOUSING COMPANY INC.—See Slay Industries Inc.; *U.S. Private*, pg. 3687
SOURCE LOGISTICS CENTER CORP.—See Palladium Equity Partners, LLC; *U.S. Private*, pg. 3078
SRC LOGISTICS, INC.—See SRC Holdings Corporation; *U.S. Private*, pg. 3767
ST GEORGE LOGISTICS CORP.—See Wind Point Advisors LLC; *U.S. Private*, pg. 4535
ST. GEORGE WAREHOUSE TRUCKING OF CALIFORNIA; *U.S. Private*, pg. 3771
ST. GEORGE WAREHOUSE TRUCKING OF TEXAS INC.—See St. George Warehouse Trucking of California; *U.S. Private*, pg. 3771
STORAGE EXPRESS MANAGEMENT, LLC—See Extra Space Storage, Inc.; *U.S. Public*, pg. 813
STRYKER EMEA SUPPLY CHAIN SERVICES BV—See Stryker Corporation; *U.S. Public*, pg. 1957
STS TRUCK EQUIPMENT; *U.S. Private*, pg. 3842
SWAFFORD WAREHOUSING, INC.—See Peoples Services Inc.; *U.S. Private*, pg. 3142
SYDNEY COAL RAILWAY INC.—See Blue Wolf Capital Partners LLC; *U.S. Private*, pg. 595
TAIHO MARINE CO., LTD.—See Iino Kaiun Kaisha Ltd.; *Int'l*, pg. 3608
TEGRA CORPORATION; *U.S. Private*, pg. 3958
TERMINAL CORPORATION; *U.S. Private*, pg. 3969
TERMINALS PTY. LTD—See Sunoco LP; *U.S. Public*, pg. 1965
TERMINAL WAREHOUSE, INC.—See Peoples Services Inc.; *U.S. Private*, pg. 3142
THETFORD CORP. - WAREHOUSING DIV—See The Dyson-Kissner-Moran Corporation; *U.S. Private*, pg. 4024
TIGHE WAREHOUSING & DISTRIBUTION; *U.S. Private*, pg. 4170
TINDALL RECORD STORAGE LTD.—See Berkshire Partners LLC; *U.S. Private*, pg. 534
TITUS—See Canada Pension Plan Investment Board; *Int'l*, pg. 1278
TOTAL DISTRIBUTION INC.—See Peoples Services Inc.; *U.S. Private*, pg. 3142
TRANSCARE SUPPLY CHAIN MANAGEMENT INC.—See Deutsche Post AG; *Int'l*, pg. 2082
TRIDENT STEEL INTELLECTUAL PROPERTY (PTY) LIMITED—See Aveng Limited; *Int'l*, pg. 738
TYLER DISTRIBUTION CENTERS—See Port Jersey Logistics; *U.S. Private*, pg. 3230
UAB ALGOL CHEMICALS—See Algol Oy; *Int'l*, pg. 318
UNITED FACILITIES, INC.; *U.S. Private*, pg. 4292
UNITED WAREHOUSE CO. INC.; *U.S. Private*, pg. 4301
UNITED WAREHOUSE COMPANY; *U.S. Private*, pg. 4301
UNIVERSAL WAREHOUSE CO.; *U.S. Private*, pg. 4307
UNSER LAGERHAUS WARENHANDELSGESELLSCHAFT M.B.H.—See BayWa AG; *Int'l*, pg. 919
UPS SUPPLY CHAIN SOLUTIONS, INC. - SOUTH SAN FRANCISCO—See United Parcel Service, Inc.; *U.S. Public*, pg. 2234
U-STORE-IT MINI WAREHOUSE CO.—See CubeSmart; *U.S. Public*, pg. 604
THE VAN HOOF COMPANIES; *U.S. Private*, pg. 4130
VANTAGE GODOWN COMPANY LIMITED—See Hong Kong Shanghai Alliance Holdings Limited; *Int'l*, pg. 3467
VERITIV—See Clayton, Dubilier & Rice, LLC; *U.S. Private*, pg. 929
VERITIV—See Clayton, Dubilier & Rice, LLC; *U.S. Private*, pg. 929
VERST GROUP LOGISTICS, INC.; *U.S. Private*, pg. 4369
VICTORY VAN CORP.; *U.S. Private*, pg. 4379
WAGNER ENTERPRISES; *U.S. Private*, pg. 4426
WAITEX INTERNATIONAL CO. LTD; *U.S. Private*, pg. 4427
WAL-MART DISTRIBUTION CENTER—See Walmart Inc.; *U.S. Public*, pg. 2325
WAL-MART DISTRIBUTION CENTER—See Walmart Inc.; *U.S. Public*, pg. 2325
WAL-MART DISTRIBUTION CENTER—See Walmart Inc.; *U.S. Public*, pg. 2325
WAL-MART DISTRIBUTION CENTER—See Walmart Inc.; *U.S. Public*, pg. 2325
WAL-MART DISTRIBUTION CENTER—See Walmart Inc.; *U.S. Public*, pg. 2325
WAL-MART DISTRIBUTION CENTER—See Walmart Inc.; *U.S. Public*, pg. 2325
WAREHOUSE SERVICES INC.; *U.S. Private*, pg. 4442
WAREHOUSE SPECIALISTS, INC.—See The Van Hoof Companies; *U.S. Private*, pg. 4130
WATERLOO INDUSTRIES, INC.—See Fortune Brands Innovations, Inc.; *U.S. Public*, pg. 873
WATERTOWN CROP NUTRIENTS LLC—See CHS INC.; *U.S. Public*, pg. 493
WEST BROTHERS TRANSFER & STORAGE; *U.S. Private*, pg. 4483
WESTCO MULTITEMP DISTRIBUTION CENTRES INC.—See Congebec Capital Ltee.; *Int'l*, pg. 1768
WESTERN CARRIERS INC.; *U.S. Private*, pg. 4491
WESTROCK COMPANY - CHINO DISTRIBUTION CENTER—See WestRock Company; *U.S. Public*, pg. 2362
WOLVERINE WAREHOUSING & DISTRIBUTION LIMITED—See 591182 ONTARIO LIMITED; *Int'l*, pg. 13
WOODBURY AUTO WHOLESALER ENTERPRISE LLC; *U.S. Private*, pg. 4557
WOW LOGISTICS COMPANY; *U.S. Private*, pg. 4571
XIAMEN BONDED AREA AIRPORT LOGISTICS PARK CONSTRUCTION CO., LTD.—See BES Engineering Corporation; *Int'l*, pg. 998
YONGMA LOGIS CO., LTD.—See Dong-A Socio Holdings Co., Ltd.; *Int'l*, pg. 2165
ZAO ALGOL CHEMICALS—See Algol Oy; *Int'l*, pg. 318
ZENITH LOGISTICS INC.—See Deutsche Post AG; *Int'l*, pg. 2083

493120 — REFRIGERATED WAREHOUSING AND STORAGE

ACCEL LOGISTICA S.A. DE C.V.—See Accel, S.A.B. de C.V.; *Int'l*, pg. 79
ACOMMERCE GROUP PUBLIC COMPANY LIMITED; *Int'l*, pg. 108
AERIS BIOLOGICAL SYSTEMS PTY LTD.—See Aeris Environmental Ltd; *Int'l*, pg. 180
AEROFREEZE, INC.—See GEA Group Aktiengesellschaft; *Int'l*, pg. 2897
AJC INTERNATIONAL, INC.—See AJC International, Inc.; *U.S. Private*, pg. 143
ALCOR CORP.—See Wavepoint 3Pl Expedite LLC; *U.S. Private*, pg. 4458
A&M COLD STORAGE, LLC—See WillScot Mobile Mini Holdings Corp.; *U.S. Public*, pg. 2372
AMERICAN COLD STORAGE; *U.S. Private*, pg. 227
AMERICOLD CASCADE COLD INC.—See Americold Realty Trust, Inc.; *U.S. Public*, pg. 113
AMERICOLD LOGISTICS, LLC—See Americold Realty Trust, Inc.; *U.S. Public*, pg. 113
AMERICOLD REALTY LLC—See Americold Realty Trust, Inc.; *U.S. Public*, pg. 113
ARASCO COLD STORE CO.—See Arabian Agricultural Services Co.; *Int'l*, pg. 533
ATLANTA BONDED WAREHOUSE CORPORATION; *U.S. Private*, pg. 370
ATLANTIC REEFER TERMINALS INC.—See F.W. Bryce, Inc.; *U.S. Private*, pg. 1457
BHATIA COLD STORAGE & TRADING CO., LLC—See Bhatia Brothers Group; *Int'l*, pg. 1013
BLA SERVICIOS, S.A.—See Bunge Limited; *U.S. Public*, pg. 410
BLUE STAR GROWERS INC.; *U.S. Private*, pg. 593
BRAHMANAND HIMGHAR LIMITED; *Int'l*, pg. 1136
BRILLIANT COLD STORAGE MANAGEMENT LIMITED—See Daido Group Ltd; *Int'l*, pg. 1920
BUNGE FERTILIZANTES S.A.—See Bunge Limited; *U.S. Public*, pg. 411
BUNGE MILLING, LLC—See Bunge Limited; *U.S. Public*, pg. 411
BUNGE-SCF GRAIN, LLC—See Bunge Limited; *U.S. Public*, pg. 411
CARRIER TRANSICOLD AUSTRIA, GMBH—See Carrier Global Corporation; *U.S. Public*, pg. 443
CARRIER TRANSICOLD BELGIUM BVBA—See Carrier Global Corporation; *U.S. Public*, pg. 443
CARRIER TRANSICOLD ESPANA, S.A.—See Carrier Global Corporation; *U.S. Public*, pg. 443
CARRIER TRANSICOLD ITALIA S.R.L.—See Carrier Global Corporation; *U.S. Public*, pg. 443
CARRIER TRANSICOLD NETHERLANDS B.V.—See Carrier Global Corporation; *U.S. Public*, pg. 443
CARRIER TRANSICOLD POLSKA SP. Z O.O.—See Carrier Global Corporation; *U.S. Public*, pg. 443
CARRIER TRANSICOLD SWEDEN AB—See Carrier Global Corporation; *U.S. Public*, pg. 443
CHEVALIER COLD STORAGE & LOGISTICS LIMITED—See Chevalier International Holdings Limited; *Int'l*, pg. 1473
CLOVERLEAF COLD STORAGE CO. INC. - PLANT 1—See Americold Realty Trust, Inc.; *U.S. Public*, pg. 113
CLOVERLEAF COLD STORAGE CO. INC. - PLANT 6—See Americold Realty Trust, Inc.; *U.S. Public*, pg. 113
CLOVERLEAF COLD STORAGE CO. INC.—See Americold Realty Trust, Inc.; *U.S. Public*, pg. 113
COLD BOX INC.—See WillScot Mobile Mini Holdings Corp.; *U.S. Public*, pg. 2372

COMMERCIAL COLD STRORAGE GROUP LTD.—See African Infrastructure Investment Managers; *Int'l*, pg. 191
CONESTOGA COLD STORAGE; *Int'l*, pg. 1767
CONGEBEC CAPITAL LTEE.; *Int'l*, pg. 1768
COOL-PAK SOLUTIONS LP—See Americold Realty Trust, Inc.; *U.S. Public*, pg. 113
CRYOPORT, INC.; *U.S. Public*, pg. 600
CRYOPORT SYSTEMS, INC.—See Cryoport, Inc.; *U.S. Public*, pg. 600
CRYSTAL DISTRIBUTION SERVICES; *U.S. Private*, pg. 1115
CUSTOMIZED DISTRIBUTION SERVICES; *U.S. Private*, pg. 1130
DONG SUH COMPANIES INC.; *Int'l*, pg. 2164
ECKART COLD STORAGE CO. INC.; *U.S. Private*, pg. 1327
EMERGENT COLD LP—See Bay Grove Capital LLC; *U.S. Private*, pg. 492
EMIRATES COLD STORAGE COMPANY—See Bhatia Brothers Group; *Int'l*, pg. 1014
EUGENE FREEZING & STORAGE CO.; *U.S. Private*, pg. 1433
FINLAY COLD STORAGE (PVT) LIMITED—See Bay Grove Capital LLC; *U.S. Private*, pg. 492
FLINT RIVER SERVICES INC.—See Bay Grove Capital LLC; *U.S. Private*, pg. 492
FRIGORIFERI MILANESI S.P.A.—See Bastogi S.p.A.; *Int'l*, pg. 888
HANSON COLD STORAGE, LLC—See Bay Grove Capital LLC; *U.S. Private*, pg. 493
HANSON LOGISTICS; *U.S. Private*, pg. 1856
HENNINGSEN COLD STORAGE COMPANY; *U.S. Private*, pg. 1917
HENRY'S FOODS, INC.—See AMCON Distributing Company; *U.S. Public*, pg. 93
HHLA FRUCHT- UND KUHL-ZENTRUM GMBH—See Hamburger Hafen und Logistik AG; *Int'l*, pg. 3236
HLADNJACA A.D.; *Int'l*, pg. 3430
HOYER BALTIC EXPEDITION UAB—See Hoyer GmbH; *Int'l*, pg. 3498
IGLO (SHANGHAI) CO., LTD.—See Haisan Resources Berhad; *Int'l*, pg. 3217
INDUSTRIAL COLD STORAGE INC.—See ICS Logistics, Inc.; *U.S. Private*, pg. 2033
INTERSTATE WAREHOUSING INC.; *U.S. Private*, pg. 2126
LINEAGE LOGISTICS - ALGONA—See Bay Grove Capital LLC; *U.S. Private*, pg. 492
LINEAGE LOGISTICS - MIDWEST REGIONAL OFFICE—See Bay Grove Capital LLC; *U.S. Private*, pg. 492
MHC KENWORTH-OKLAHOMA CITY—See Murphy-Hoffman Company; *U.S. Private*, pg. 2816
MID-FLORIDA FREEZER WAREHOUSES, LTD.; *U.S. Private*, pg. 2708
MILWAUKEE CENTER FOR INDEPENDENCE, INC.; *U.S. Private*, pg. 2739
NEWPORT-ST. PAUL COLD STORAGE CO.—See Americold Realty Trust, Inc.; *U.S. Public*, pg. 113
NORDIC COLD STORAGE, LLC; *U.S. Private*, pg. 2936
NORTHLAND COLD STORAGE, INC.; *U.S. Private*, pg. 2955
NOVAOL AUSTRIA G.M.B.H.—See Bunge Limited; *U.S. Public*, pg. 412
OCEANA COUNTY FREEZER STORAGE, INC.—See Peterson Farms, Inc.; *U.S. Private*, pg. 3160
PACE TRANSPORTATION—See Warren Distribution, Inc.; *U.S. Private*, pg. 4443
PACORINI BEO D.O.O.—See B. Pacorini S.p.A.; *Int'l*, pg. 789
PACORINI MONTENEGRO D.O.O.—See B. Pacorini S.p.A.; *Int'l*, pg. 789
PACORINI ROTTERDAM B.V.—See B. Pacorini S.p.A.; *Int'l*, pg. 789
PREFERRED FREEZER SERVICES INC.—See Bay Grove Capital LLC; *U.S. Private*, pg. 493
PREFERRED FREEZER SERVICES MIAMI, INC.—See Bay Grove Capital LLC; *U.S. Private*, pg. 493
PREFERRED FREEZER SERVICES OF HO CHI MINH CITY—See Bay Grove Capital LLC; *U.S. Private*, pg. 493
PREFERRED FREEZER SERVICES OF LINGANG LOGISTICS PARK—See Bay Grove Capital LLC; *U.S. Private*, pg. 493
PREFERRED FREEZER SERVICES OF PERTH AMBOY, LLC—See Bay Grove Capital LLC; *U.S. Private*, pg. 493
PREFERRED FREEZER SERVICES OF WAI GAO QIAO—See Bay Grove Capital LLC; *U.S. Private*, pg. 493
PRIMUS BUILDERS, INC.; *U.S. Private*, pg. 3263
PRIO BIOCOMBUSTIBIL SRL—See Bunge Limited; *U.S. Public*, pg. 412
PURCHASES SALES INC.; *U.S. Private*, pg. 3305
REPROTECH LIMITED; *U.S. Private*, pg. 3401
SNOWMAN LOGISTICS LTD.—See Adani Enterprises Limited; *Int'l*, pg. 124
STAR DISTRIBUTION SYSTEMS INC.; *U.S. Private*, pg. 3784
SUNMAC HAWAII, LTD.—See Sunkist Growers, Inc.; *U.S. Private*, pg. 3867

N.A.I.C.S. INDEX

493190 — OTHER WAREHOUSING A...

SUN ORCHARD FRUIT COMPANY, INC.; *U.S. Private*, pg. 3863
SUNRAY ELECTRIC SUPPLY CO., INC.; *U.S. Private*, pg. 3869
TERMINAL DE FERTILIZANTES ARGENTINOS SA—See Bunge Limited; *U.S. Public*, pg. 412
TERMINAL FREEZERS, INC.—See Bay Grove Capital LLC; *U.S. Private*, pg. 493
TOTAL QUALITY, INC. - MECOSTA TERMINAL—See Forward Air Corporation; *U.S. Public*, pg. 874
UNION ICE LTD.; *U.S. Private*, pg. 4284
UNIVERSAL FINANCIAL SERVICES, L.P.—See Bunge Limited; *U.S. Public*, pg. 412
US GROWERS COLD STORAGE INC.; *U.S. Private*, pg. 4318
VERSACOLD INTERNATIONAL CORPORATION—See Bay Grove Capital LLC; *U.S. Private*, pg. 493
VERSACOLD LOGISTICS, LLC—See Americold Realty Trust, Inc.; *U.S. Public*, pg. 113
ZERO MOUNTAIN, INC.—See Americold Realty Trust, Inc.; *U.S. Public*, pg. 113

493130 — FARM PRODUCT WAREHOUSING AND STORAGE

ADM ALFRED C. TOEPFER INTERNATIONAL BV—See Archer-Daniels-Midland Company; *U.S. Public*, pg. 184
ADM EDIBLE BEAN SPECIALTIES, INC.—See Archer-Daniels-Midland Company; *U.S. Public*, pg. 181
ADM-GRAIN—See Archer-Daniels-Midland Company; *U.S. Public*, pg. 182
AFC CO., LTD.—See Aohata Corporation; *Int'l*, pg. 487
AGCO GSI ASIA SDN BHD—See AGCO Corporation; *U.S. Public*, pg. 58
AGRI MARKETING INC.; *U.S. Private*, pg. 129
ARCHER DANIELS MIDLAND CO.—See Archer-Daniels-Midland Company; *U.S. Public*, pg. 183
ARCHER DANIELS MIDLAND CO.—See Archer-Daniels-Midland Company; *U.S. Public*, pg. 183
AWB GRAINFLOW PTY. LTD.—See Cargill, Inc.; *U.S. Private*, pg. 755
BEST WAREHOUSING & TRANSPORTATION CENTER INC.—See Bluejay Capital Partners, LLC; *U.S. Private*, pg. 597
BROADGRAIN COMMODITIES INC.; *Int'l*, pg. 1172
BUNGE LIMITED; *U.S. Public*, pg. 410
CALCOT, LTD. - THE GLENDALE FACILITY—See Calcot, Ltd.; *U.S. Private*, pg. 716
CARGILL COTTON—See Cargill, Inc.; *U.S. Private*, pg. 756
CHIEF INDUSTRIES UK LTD—See Chief Industries, Inc.; *U.S. Private*, pg. 881
COMO GRAIN—See Green Plains Inc.; *U.S. Public*, pg. 963
CONSUMERS OIL AND SUPPLY CO; *U.S. Private*, pg. 1026
COUNTRY VISIONS COOPERATIVE; *U.S. Private*, pg. 1067
C&S CAPITAL MANAGEMENT; *U.S. Private*, pg. 703
DELMAR COMMODITIES LTD. - BEAUSEJOUR FACILITY—See Ceres Global Ag Corp.; *U.S. Public*, pg. 475
DELMAR COMMODITIES LTD.—See Ceres Global Ag Corp.; *U.S. Public*, pg. 475
DOLNOSLASKIE CENTRUM HURTU ROLNO-SPOZYWCZEGO SA; *Int'l*, pg. 2159
DUMAS COTTON WAREHOUSE INC.; *U.S. Private*, pg. 1287
DYER GRAIN—See Green Plains Inc.; *U.S. Public*, pg. 963
THE ELKHART COOPERATIVE EQUITY EXCHANGE; *U.S. Private*, pg. 4025
EUGENE B. SMITH & CO. INC.; *U.S. Private*, pg. 1433
EURALIS COOP; *Int'l*, pg. 2527
FARMERS COOPERATIVE COMPRESS INC.; *U.S. Private*, pg. 1477
FARMERS GRAIN TERMINAL INC.; *U.S. Private*, pg. 1478
FEDERAL COMPRESS & WAREHOUSE COMPANY, INC.; *U.S. Private*, pg. 1487
GENERAL MILLS OPERATIONS, INC.—See General Mills, Inc.; *U.S. Public*, pg. 922
GENERAL MILLS - WELLSTON PLANT—See General Mills, Inc.; *U.S. Public*, pg. 922
G.F. VAUGHAN TOBACCO CO. INC.; *U.S. Private*, pg. 1631
GRAINCORP OPERATIONS LIMITED—See GrainCorp Limited; *Int'l*, pg. 3052
GREAT-SUN FOODS CO.,LTD.; *Int'l*, pg. 3066
GREEN PLAINS ESSEX INC.—See Green Plains Inc.; *U.S. Public*, pg. 963
GREEN PLAINS GRAIN COMPANY TN LLC—See Green Plains Inc.; *U.S. Public*, pg. 963
THE GSI ASIA GROUP SDN. BHD.—See AGCO Corporation; *U.S. Public*, pg. 59
GULF COMPRESS; *U.S. Private*, pg. 1816
JORDAN MILLS INC—See Ceres Global Ag Corp.; *U.S. Public*, pg. 475
KOREA SILO CO., LTD.—See Daehan Flour Mills co., Ltd; *Int'l*, pg. 1907
LAKESIDE FOODS, INC. - SEYMOUR PLANT—See Lakeside Foods, Inc.; *U.S. Private*, pg. 2377

LANDMARK SERVICES COOPERATIVE; *U.S. Private*, pg. 2386
LLC AGROTECHNOLOGY—See Gruppa Kompaniy Rusagro OOO; *Int'l*, pg. 3140
MAPLEHURST FARMS INC.; *U.S. Private*, pg. 2568
THE MENNEL MILLING COMPANY OF INDIANA INC.—See The Mennel Milling Company; *U.S. Private*, pg. 4077
NEW COOPERATIVE, INC.; *U.S. Private*, pg. 2893
ODESSA UNION WAREHOUSE CO-OP; *U.S. Private*, pg. 2993
PABOR ARCHER DANIELS MIDLAND COMPANY—See Archer-Daniels-Midland Company; *U.S. Public*, pg. 185
PICKENS COUNTY PORTS INC.—See Parker Towing Company, Inc.; *U.S. Private*, pg. 3097
PLAINS COTTON COOPERATIVE ASSOCIATION - ALTUS WAREHOUSE—See Plains Cotton Cooperative Association; *U.S. Private*, pg. 3195
PLAINS COTTON COOPERATIVE ASSOCIATION - SWEETWATER WAREHOUSE—See Plains Cotton Cooperative Association; *U.S. Private*, pg. 3195
POINSETT RICE & GRAIN, INC. - CHERRY VALLEY—See Poinsett Rice & Grain, Inc.; *U.S. Private*, pg. 3221
POINSETT RICE & GRAIN, INC. - MARKED TREE—See Poinsett Rice & Grain, Inc.; *U.S. Private*, pg. 3221
POINSETT RICE & GRAIN, INC.; *U.S. Private*, pg. 3221
PREMIER COOPERATIVE, INC.; *U.S. Private*, pg. 3250
SCAFCO CORPORATION; *U.S. Private*, pg. 3560
SILOS GRANARI DELLA SICILIA S.R.L.—See Heidelberg Materials AG; *Int'l*, pg. 3317
SKYLAND GRAIN, LLC—See The Andersons Incorporated; *U.S. Public*, pg. 2034
THCG GROUP CO., LTD.—See Gunkul Engineering Co., Ltd.; *Int'l*, pg. 3184
ULRICH STEIN GESELLSCHAFT MIT BESCHRANKTER HAFTUNG—See Hamburger Hafen und Logistik AG; *Int'l*, pg. 3237
UNION SERVICE INDUSTRIES INC.; *U.S. Private*, pg. 4285
WILD JUICE B.V.—See Archer-Daniels-Midland Company; *U.S. Public*, pg. 185

493190 — OTHER WAREHOUSING AND STORAGE

AB ARCHYVU SISTEMOS—See Iron Mountain Incorporated; *U.S. Public*, pg. 1171
AB ARCHYVU SISTEMOS—See Iron Mountain Incorporated; *U.S. Public*, pg. 1171
AB ARCHYVU SISTEMOS—See Iron Mountain Incorporated; *U.S. Public*, pg. 1171
ABLE SALES COMPANY, INC.; *U.S. Private*, pg. 39
ACCEL DISTRIBUCION, S. A. DE C. V.—See Accel, S.A.B. de C.V.; *Int'l*, pg. 79
AD JAVNA SKLADISTA SUBOTICA; *Int'l*, pg. 122
AERIS HYGIENE SERVICES PTY LTD—See Aeris Environmental Ltd; *Int'l*, pg. 180
AGRO MERCHANTS NORTH AMERICA HOLDINGS LLC—See Americold Realty Trust, Inc.; *U.S. Public*, pg. 113
AIFUL STOCK CENTER CORPORATION—See AIFUL Corporation; *Int'l*, pg. 231
A.L.C.Z A.S—See Iron Mountain Incorporated; *U.S. Public*, pg. 1172
ALGOL-EESTI OU—See Algol Oy; *Int'l*, pg. 318
ALMACENADORA ACCEL, S. A.—See Accel, S.A.B. de C.V.; *Int'l*, pg. 79
ALPHALOGIC INDUSTRIES LIMITED; *Int'l*, pg. 370
APM TERMINALS ALGECIRAS S.A.—See A.P. Moller-Maersk A/S; *Int'l*, pg. 25
APM TERMINALS LIBERIA LTD—See A.P. Moller-Maersk A/S; *Int'l*, pg. 25
APM TERMINALS MANAGEMENT B.V.—See A.P. Moller-Maersk A/S; *Int'l*, pg. 25
APM TERMINALS NORTH AMERICA B.V.—See A.P. Moller-Maersk A/S; *Int'l*, pg. 25
APM TERMINALS ROTTERDAM B.V.—See A.P. Moller-Maersk A/S; *Int'l*, pg. 25
ARCHIVES CORP.—See Berkshire Partners LLC; *U.S. Private*, pg. 534
ARKIVE INFORMATION MANAGEMENT LLC—See SPP Management Services, LLC; *U.S. Private*, pg. 3762
AUTOPORT LIMITED—See Canadian National Railway Company; *Int'l*, pg. 1284
BIG YELLOW SELF STORAGE COMPANY 6 LIMITED—See Big Yellow Group plc; *Int'l*, pg. 1022
BIG YELLOW SELF STORAGE COMPANY 8 LIMITED—See Big Yellow Group plc; *Int'l*, pg. 1022
BIG YELLOW SELF STORAGE COMPANY LIMITED—See Big Yellow Group plc; *Int'l*, pg. 1022
BIG YELLOW SELF STORAGE (GP) LIMITED—See Big Yellow Group plc; *Int'l*, pg. 1022
BONDED SERVICES (INTERNATIONAL) B.V.—See Iron Mountain Incorporated; *U.S. Public*, pg. 1172
BOURY ENTERPRISES; *U.S. Private*, pg. 624
BUSINESS RECORDS MANAGEMENT, INC.; *U.S. Private*, pg. 695
BWC TERMINALS LLC; *U.S. Private*, pg. 700

BYSSCO LIMITED—See Big Yellow Group plc; *Int'l*, pg. 1022
CAESARS CARGO CO. W.L.L.—See Caesars Group; *Int'l*, pg. 1249
CANSO CHEMICALS LIMITED—See Olin Corporation; *U.S. Public*, pg. 1570
CANTON SALES & STORAGE CO.—See National Presto Industries, Inc; *U.S. Public*, pg. 1497
CAPITAL RELOCATION SERVICES LLC—See JK Moving & Storage Inc.; *U.S. Private*, pg. 2211
CAPITAL TERMINAL COMPANY—See Capital Properties, Inc.; *U.S. Public*, pg. 432
CATERPILLAR UK HOLDINGS LIMITED—See Caterpillar, Inc.; *U.S. Public*, pg. 452
CAYTHORPE GAS STORAGE LIMITED—See Centrica plc; *Int'l*, pg. 1413
CIRCUIT LOGISTICS INC.—See Deutsche Post AG; *Int'l*, pg. 2072
COFCO SHENZHEN CO., LTD.—See COFCO Limited; *Int'l*, pg. 1692
CONSTRUCTOR DEXION ITALIA SRL—See Corporacion Gestamp SL; *Int'l*, pg. 1804
CONSTRUCTOR FINLAND OY—See Corporacion Gestamp SL; *Int'l*, pg. 1804
CONTAINER OPERATORS S.A.—See A.P. Moller-Maersk A/S; *Int'l*, pg. 26
CONTAINER PRODUCTS CORPORATION; *U.S. Private*, pg. 1026
CORTECO GMBH—See Freudenberg SE; *Int'l*, pg. 2783
CUMMINGS TRANSFER CO.; *U.S. Private*, pg. 1123
DAIDO LOGITECH CO., LTD.—See Daido Metal Corporation; *Int'l*, pg. 1921
DATASAFE, INC.; *U.S. Private*, pg. 1166
DEXION POLSKA SP. Z.O.O.—See Corporacion Gestamp SL; *Int'l*, pg. 1804
DISTRIBUTION 2000 INC.; *U.S. Private*, pg. 1239
DISTRIBUTION COOPERATIVE INC; *U.S. Private*, pg. 1239
DOCUMENT STORAGE CORPORATION—See Berkshire Partners LLC; *U.S. Private*, pg. 534
DOCUTAR IRATRENDEZO ES TAROLO SZOLGALTATO KFT.—See Iron Mountain Incorporated; *U.S. Public*, pg. 1173
DUPUY STORAGE & FORWARDING LLC—See Ridgewood Infrastructure LLC; *U.S. Private*, pg. 3433
DUPUY STORAGE & FORWARDING LLC—See Savage Services Corporation; *U.S. Private*, pg. 3555
ED&F MAN LIQUID PRODUCTS LLC—See ED&F Man Holdings Limited; *Int'l*, pg. 2303
ED&F MAN TERMINALS UK LIMITED—See ED&F Man Holdings Limited; *Int'l*, pg. 2303
ETHANOL MANAGEMENT COMPANY LLC—See HF Sinclair Corporation; *U.S. Public*, pg. 1033
EVOLUTION LIGHTING LLC-TUPELO—See Boyne Capital Management, LLC; *U.S. Private*, pg. 628
FGV JOHOR BULKERS SDN. BHD.—See FGV Holdings Bhd; *Int'l*, pg. 2649
FGV JOHORE BULKERS SDN. BHD.—See FGV Holdings Bhd; *Int'l*, pg. 2649
FIFTH GEAR, INC.-PENNSYLVANIA—See Speed Commerce, Inc.; *U.S. Public*, pg. 1917
FILE KEEPERS, LLC—See Raleigh Enterprises; *U.S. Private*, pg. 3349
THE FORTRESS CORPORATION; *U.S. Private*, pg. 4030
FRANCESCO PARISI S.P.A. - FERNETTI—See Francesco Parisi S.p.A.; *Int'l*, pg. 2759
FRANCESCO PARISI S.P.A. - GENOA—See Francesco Parisi S.p.A.; *Int'l*, pg. 2759
FRANCESCO PARISI S.P.A. - GORIZIA—See Francesco Parisi S.p.A.; *Int'l*, pg. 2759
FRANCESCO PARISI S.P.A. - LIVORNO—See Francesco Parisi S.p.A.; *Int'l*, pg. 2759
FRANCESCO PARISI S.P.A. - MILANO—See Francesco Parisi S.p.A.; *Int'l*, pg. 2759
GAMBRO S.A.—See Baxter International Inc.; *U.S. Public*, pg. 282
GATEWAY TERMINALS LLC—See Harvestone Group LLC; *U.S. Private*, pg. 1877
GKN CEDU LIMITED—See GKN plc; *Int'l*, pg. 2984
GLT INC.; *U.S. Private*, pg. 1721
GO MINI'S LLC; *U.S. Private*, pg. 1723
GRM INFORMATION MANAGEMENT SERVICES; *U.S. Private*, pg. 1791
GUANGDONG (PANYU) PETROCHEMICAL STORAGE & TRANSPORTATION LTD.—See Guangzhou Development Group Incorporated; *Int'l*, pg. 3164
HITACHI PLANT MECHANICS CO., LTD.—See Hitachi, Ltd.; *Int'l*, pg. 3420
HOEGH LNG PARTNERS LP—See Hoegh LNG Holding Ltd.; *Int'l*, pg. 3439
HOLFORD GAS STORAGE LIMITED—See E.ON SE; *Int'l*, pg. 2256
HONEY-CAN-DO INTERNATIONAL; *U.S. Private*, pg. 1076
HOUSTON FUEL OIL TERMINAL COMPANY LLC—See Energy Transfer LP; *U.S. Public*, pg. 764
IMTT-NTL, LTD—See Riverstone Holdings LLC; *U.S. Private*, pg. 3447
IMTT QUEBEC INC.—See Riverstone Holdings LLC; *U.S. Private*, pg. 3447

493190 — OTHER WAREHOUSING A...

INTERACTIVE MARKETING SERVICES, INC.; *U.S. Private*, pg. 2108
INTERCONTINENTAL TERMINALS COMPANY; *U.S. Private*, pg. 2109
INTERENVASES, S.A.—See ACS, Actividades de Construccion y Servicios, S.A.; *Int'l*, pg. 115
INTERNATIONAL DATA DEPOSITORY—See Berkshire Partners LLC; *U.S. Private*, pg. 534
IRON MOUNTAIN CANADA OPERATIONS ULC—See Iron Mountain Incorporated; *U.S. Public*, pg. 1172
IRON MOUNTAIN DIMS LTD.—See Iron Mountain Incorporated; *U.S. Public*, pg. 1173
IRON MOUNTAIN DO BRASIL LTDA.—See Iron Mountain Incorporated; *U.S. Public*, pg. 1173
IRON MOUNTAIN D.O.O.—See Iron Mountain Incorporated; *U.S. Public*, pg. 1173
IRON MOUNTAIN ESPANA, S.A.—See Iron Mountain Incorporated; *U.S. Public*, pg. 1173
IRON MOUNTAIN IRELAND LTD.—See Iron Mountain Incorporated; *U.S. Public*, pg. 1173
IRON MOUNTAIN MAGYARORSZAG KERESKEDELMI ES SZOLGALTATO KFT.—See Iron Mountain Incorporated; *U.S. Public*, pg. 1173
IRON MOUNTAIN MAGYARORSZAQ KFT—See Iron Mountain Incorporated; *U.S. Public*, pg. 1173
IRON MOUNTAIN PERU S.A.—See Iron Mountain Incorporated; *U.S. Public*, pg. 1173
IRON MOUNTAIN SHANGHAI CO. LTD—See Iron Mountain Incorporated; *U.S. Public*, pg. 1173
IRON MOUNTAIN SOUTH AFRICA (PTY) LTD—See Iron Mountain Incorporated; *U.S. Public*, pg. 1173
IRON MOUNTAIN SRL—See Iron Mountain Incorporated; *U.S. Public*, pg. 1173
IRON MOUNTAIN UKRAINE LLC—See Iron Mountain Incorporated; *U.S. Public*, pg. 1173
IRON MOUNTAIN (UK) SERVICES LIMITED—See Iron Mountain Incorporated; *U.S. Public*, pg. 1173
IRON TRUST DOO BEOGRAD—See Iron Mountain Incorporated; *U.S. Public*, pg. 1173
ISLANDMAGEE STORAGE LIMITED—See Harland & Wolff Group Holdings plc; *Int'l*, pg. 3277
IWC MEDIA SERVICES—See Windjammer Capital Investors, LLC; *U.S. Private*, pg. 4538
JINGTANG INTERNATIONAL CONTAINER TERMINAL CO. LTD.—See ACS, Actividades de Construccion y Servicios, S.A.; *Int'l*, pg. 115
JK MOVING & STORAGE INC.; *U.S. Private*, pg. 2211
KEEPERS BRASIL LTDA—See Iron Mountain Incorporated; *U.S. Public*, pg. 1173
L&P MATERIALS MANUFACTURING, INC.—See Leggett & Platt, Incorporated; *U.S. Public*, pg. 1302
MAERSK A/S—See A.P. Moller-Maersk A/S; *Int'l*, pg. 26
MAERSK DENIZCILIK A.S.—See A.P. Moller-Maersk A/S; *Int'l*, pg. 26
MAERSK GLOBAL SERVICE CENTRES (INDIA) PRIVATE LIMITED—See A.P. Moller-Maersk A/S; *Int'l*, pg. 27
MAERSK SPAIN, S.L.U.—See A.P. Moller-Maersk A/S; *Int'l*, pg. 27
MAERSK TANKERS SINGAPORE PTE. LTD—See A.P. Moller-Maersk A/S; *Int'l*, pg. 27
MILWAUKEE BULK TERMINALS LLC—See Kinder Morgan, Inc.; *U.S. Public*, pg. 1233
MOBILE MINI, INC.—See WillScot Mobile Mini Holdings Corp.; *U.S. Public*, pg. 2372
MOSS BLUFF HUB, LLC—See Enbridge Inc.; *Int'l*, pg. 2397
MP STORAGE & BLENDING—See Banner Chemicals Limited; *Int'l*, pg. 851
NATIONAL BOOK COMPANY INC.—See W.W. Norton & Company, Inc.; *U.S. Private*, pg. 4423
NELSON WESTERBERG/ATLAS VAN LINES—See Nelson Westerberg, Inc.; *U.S. Private*, pg. 2884
NUSTAR EASTHAM LIMITED—See Brookfield Infrastructure Partners L.P.; *Int'l*, pg. 1193
NUSTAR GRANGEMOUTH LIMITED—See Brookfield Infrastructure Partners L.P.; *Int'l*, pg. 1193
NUSTAR TERMINALS CANADA PARTNERSHIP—See Sunoco LP; *U.S. Public*, pg. 1965
OEC RECORDS MANAGEMENT COMPANY PRIVATE LIMITED—See Iron Mountain Incorporated; *U.S. Public*, pg. 1174
OLIVER WAREHOUSE INC.—See BASF SE; *Int'l*, pg. 876
PANALPINA S.A.—See DSV A/S; *Int'l*, pg. 2215
PANHANDLE ENERGY—See Energy Transfer LP; *U.S. Public*, pg. 763
PETON DISTRIBUTORS INC.—See Roark Capital Group Inc.; *U.S. Private*, pg. 3455
PLANES MOVING & STORAGE OF DAYTON, INC.—See Planes Moving & Storage, Inc.; *U.S. Private*, pg. 3195
PORT JERSEY LOGISTICS; *U.S. Private*, pg. 3230
PROGRESSIVE DISTRIBUTION SERVICES, INC.; *U.S. Private*, pg. 3278
PT SANTA FE PROPERTIES—See Iron Mountain Incorporated; *U.S. Public*, pg. 1174
REED & GRAHAM, INC. - GEOSYNTHETICS DIVISION-SAN JOSE—See Reed & Graham Inc.; *U.S. Private*, pg. 3381
ROYAL WOLF HOLDINGS LIMITED—See United Rentals, Inc.; *U.S. Public*, pg. 2235
RSL N.V.—See Bio-Rad Laboratories, Inc.; *U.S. Public*, pg. 334
SAVANNAH RIVER NUCLEAR SOLUTIONS, LLC—See Fluor Corporation; *U.S. Public*, pg. 859
SAVANNAH RIVER NUCLEAR SOLUTIONS, LLC—See Huntington Ingalls Industries, Inc.; *U.S. Public*, pg. 1072
THE SHERWIN-WILLIAMS CO. - DISTRIBUTION SERVICE CENTER - WACO—See The Sherwin-Williams Company; *U.S. Public*, pg. 2129
SOCIEDADE ACOREANA DE ARMAZENAGEM DE GAS, S.A.—See Galp Energia SGPS, S.A.; *Int'l*, pg. 2875
SOPAKCO INC.—See Unaka Company Inc.; *U.S. Private*, pg. 4279
SOURCE MANAGEMENT INC.; *U.S. Private*, pg. 3718
STEVENS & STEVENS BUSINESS RECORDS MANAGEMENT, INC.; *U.S. Private*, pg. 3809
ST. MARY'S/WESTSIDE FOOD BANK ALLIANCE; *U.S. Private*, pg. 3773
STORAGE PLUS CORP.—See Warburg Pincus LLC; *U.S. Private*, pg. 4439
TAP PLASTICS INC.; *U.S. Private*, pg. 3932
TERADATA EGYPT WLL—See Teradata Corporation; *U.S. Public*, pg. 2017
TERADATA GOVERNMENT SYSTEMS LLC—See Teradata Corporation; *U.S. Public*, pg. 2017
TERADATA LLC—See Teradata Corporation; *U.S. Public*, pg. 2017
TERADATA TAIWAN LLC—See Teradata Corporation; *U.S. Public*, pg. 2017
TERMINAL 4 S.A.—See A.P. Moller-Maersk A/S; *Int'l*, pg. 28
TIDEWATER TERMINAL COMPANY INC.—See Tidewater Holdings, Inc.; *U.S. Private*, pg. 4168
TJX UK—See The TJX Companies, Inc.; *U.S. Public*, pg. 2134
TOTAL DISTRIBUTION SERVICES, INC. (TDSI)—See CSX Corporation; *U.S. Public*, pg. 602
TRANSCONTINENTAL DEPOSITORY SERVICES, LLC—See A-Mark Precious Metals, Inc.; *U.S. Public*, pg. 10
ULSHOFER IT GMBH & CO. KG.—See Iron Mountain Incorporated; *U.S. Public*, pg. 1174
UNITED FREIGHT SERVICE INC.; *U.S. Private*, pg. 4292
VERITIV—See Clayton, Dubilier & Rice, LLC; *U.S. Private*, pg. 929
VITAL RECORDS INC.; *U.S. Private*, pg. 4405
WAKAMATSU KONPOU UNYU SOKO, INC.—See Daiwa House Industry Co., Ltd.; *Int'l*, pg. 1947
WAL-MART DISTRIBUTION CENTER 6012—See Walmart Inc.; *U.S. Public*, pg. 2325
WAL-MART DISTRIBUTION CENTER—See Walmart Inc.; *U.S. Public*, pg. 2325
WAL-MART DISTRIBUTION CENTER—See Walmart Inc.; *U.S. Public*, pg. 2325
WARNERS MOTOR EXPRESS INC.; *U.S. Private*, pg. 4443
WESTPORT DISTRIPARK (M) SDN. BHD.—See DRB-HICOM Berhad; *Int'l*, pg. 2202
WESTWAY TERMINAL COMPANY LLC—See EQT AB; *Int'l*, pg. 2473
THE WINE LOCKER, INC.—See Vino Vault, Inc.; *U.S. Private*, pg. 4386
WORLDWIDE TERMINALS FERNANDINA, LLC; *U.S. Private*, pg. 4570
Y.S. LOGISTICS SERVICE CO., LTD.—See Daicel Corporation; *Int'l*, pg. 1920

512110 — MOTION PICTURE AND VIDEO PRODUCTION

2929 PRODUCTIONS LLC—See 2929 Entertainment LP; *U.S. Private*, pg. 6
3ALITY TECHNICA; *U.S. Private*, pg. 8
4BY4 INC.; *Int'l*, pg. 11
8VIC JOOY MEDIA SDN. BHD.—See 8VI Holdings Limited; *Int'l*, pg. 16
99 PRO MEDIA GMBH—See Bertelsmann SE & Co. KGaA; *Int'l*, pg. 989
A24 FILMS LLC; *U.S. Private*, pg. 29
ABC LIBRA CO., LTD.—See Asahi Broadcasting Group Holdings Corporation; *Int'l*, pg. 592
ABC NEWS INTERCONTINENTAL, INC.—See The Walt Disney Company; *U.S. Public*, pg. 2137
ACOUSTIGUIDE GMBH—See Espro Information Technologies Ltd.; *Int'l*, pg. 2507
ACOUSTIGUIDE INC.—See Espro Information Technologies Ltd.; *Int'l*, pg. 2507
ACOUSTIGUIDE LTD.—See Espro Information Technologies Ltd.; *Int'l*, pg. 2507
ADVANCED DIGITAL SERVICES; *U.S. Private*, pg. 89
AKATSUKI ENTERTAINMENT USA, INC.—See Akatsuki, Inc.; *Int'l*, pg. 260
ALLIED ARTIST INTERNATIONAL, INC.; *U.S. Private*, pg. 185
ALMOST NEVER FILMS INC.; *U.S. Private*, pg. 195
ALTA PRODUCTIONS GROUP, INC.—See GMA Holdings, Inc.; *Int'l*, pg. 3012
AMBIENT, LLC—See PAR Capital Management, Inc.; *U.S. Private*, pg. 3089

CORPORATE AFFILIATIONS

AMERICAN BROADCASTING COMPANIES, INC.—See The Walt Disney Company; *U.S. Public*, pg. 2137
AMERICAN FILMS, INC.; *U.S. Public*, pg. 102
AMS PICTURES; *U.S. Public*, pg. 267
AMUSE SOFT ENTERTAINMENT, INC.—See Amuse Inc.; *Int'l*, pg. 442
ANGELVISION TECHNOLOGIES, INC.; *U.S. Private*, pg. 283
ANIMEIGO INC.; *U.S. Private*, pg. 283
ANTENA 3 FILMS S.L.U.—See Atresmedia Corporacion de Medios de Comunicacion, S.A.; *Int'l*, pg. 693
APPASIA STREAM SDN. BHD.—See AppAsia Berhad; *Int'l*, pg. 519
ARCHIE COMIC PUBLICATIONS INC.; *U.S. Private*, pg. 311
ARNOLD SHAPIRO PRODUCTIONS, INC.; *U.S. Private*, pg. 333
ASAHI BROADCASTING GROUP HOLDINGS CORPORATION; *Int'l*, pg. 592
ASKANIA MEDIA FILMPRODUKTION GMBH—See Bavaria Film GmbH; *Int'l*, pg. 899
ASTRO SHAW SDN. BHD.—See Astro Malaysia Holdings Bhd; *Int'l*, pg. 662
THE ASYLUM; *U.S. Private*, pg. 3989
ATLANTIC VIDEO INC.—See Family Federation for World Peace & Unification; *U.S. Private*, pg. 1469
ATM GRUPA S.A.; *Int'l*, pg. 687
ATM STUDIO SP. Z.O.O.—See ATM Grupa S.A.; *Int'l*, pg. 687
ATTIC LIGHT ENTERTAINMENT, INC.; *U.S. Private*, pg. 383
AUDIENCE PRODUCTIONS, INC.; *U.S. Private*, pg. 391
AUTOMAT PICTURES, INC.; *U.S. Private*, pg. 398
AVATAR STUDIOS; *U.S. Private*, pg. 404
AVVENTA WORLDWIDE, LLC—See Accenture plc; *Int'l*, pg. 86
AYNGARAN INTERNATIONAL LTD.; *Int'l*, pg. 775
AYNGARAN INTERNATIONAL MEDIA PVT. LTD.—See Ayngaran International Ltd.; *Int'l*, pg. 775
AZTECA AMERICA, INC.—See Grupo Salinas, S.A. de C.V.; *Int'l*, pg. 3135
BABA ARTS LTD.; *Int'l*, pg. 792
BACKYARD PRODUCTIONS INC.; *U.S. Private*, pg. 423
B.A.G. FILMS & MEDIA LIMITED; *Int'l*, pg. 789
BALAJI MOTION PICTURES LTD—See Balaji Telefilms Ltd.; *Int'l*, pg. 806
BANDAI CHANNEL CO., LTD.—See BANDAI NAMCO Holdings Inc.; *Int'l*, pg. 828
BAVARIA FERNSEHPRODUKTION GMBH—See Bavaria Film GmbH; *Int'l*, pg. 899
BAVARIA FILM GMBH; *Int'l*, pg. 899
BAVARIA FILMVERLEIH- UND PRODUKTIONS GMBH—See Bavaria Film GmbH; *Int'l*, pg. 899
BAVARIA MEDIA ITALIA S.R.L.—See Bavaria Film GmbH; *Int'l*, pg. 899
BAVARIA PICTURES GMBH—See Bavaria Film GmbH; *Int'l*, pg. 899
BAVARIA PRODUCTION SERVICES GMBH—See Bavaria Film GmbH; *Int'l*, pg. 899
BAYERISCHES FILMZENTRUM WIRTSCHAFTSFORDERUNGS GMBH—See Bavaria Film GmbH; *Int'l*, pg. 899
BBC WORLDWIDE AMERICA INC.—See British Broadcasting Corporation; *Int'l*, pg. 1169
BBTV PRODUCTIONS CO., LTD.—See Bangkok Broadcasting & TV Co., Ltd.; *Int'l*, pg. 833
BEACHBODY, LLC; *U.S. Private*, pg. 503
BEACON COMMUNICATIONS LLC; *U.S. Private*, pg. 504
BEIJING BAINATION PICTURES CO., LTD.; *Int'l*, pg. 946
BEIJING ENLIGHT MEDIA CO., LTD.; *Int'l*, pg. 949
BEIJING GALLOPING HORSE FILM & TV PRODUCTION CO., LTD.; *Int'l*, pg. 950
BEIJING GDC MEDIA TECHNOLOGIES CO., LTD.—See Global Digital Creations Holdings Limited; *Int'l*, pg. 2994
BET SERVICES, INC.—See National Amusements, Inc.; *U.S. Private*, pg. 2839
BETTY TV LIMITED—See Warner Bros. Discovery, Inc.; *U.S. Public*, pg. 2326
BEYOND HOME PRODUCTIONS; *U.S. Private*, pg. 548
BFA EDUCATIONAL MEDIA—See The Phoenix Learning Group, Inc.; *U.S. Private*, pg. 4095
BFI (BIG SCREEN) LIMITED—See British Film Institute; *Int'l*, pg. 1171
BIG IDEA, INC.; *U.S. Private*, pg. 553
BIG SCREEN ENTERTAINMENT GROUP, INC.; *U.S. Public*, pg. 331
BIG SCREEN ENTERTAINMENT PVT. LIMITED—See Eros International Plc; *Int'l*, pg. 2496
BIG TICKET PRODUCTIONS INC.—See National Amusements, Inc.; *U.S. Private*, pg. 2839
BINGO GROUP HOLDINGS LIMITED; *Int'l*, pg. 1033
BLAST! FILMS LIMITED—See Comcast Corporation; *U.S. Public*, pg. 537
BLINDLIGHT LLC—See Canada Pension Plan Investment Board; *Int'l*, pg. 1280
BLINDLIGHT LLC—See EQT AB; *Int'l*, pg. 2482
BLUE MARBLE MEDIA INC.; *U.S. Private*, pg. 589
BMB MUSIC & MAGNETICS LIMITED; *Int'l*, pg. 1076

N.A.I.C.S. INDEX 512110 — MOTION PICTURE AND ...

BMG PRODUCTION MUSIC, INC.—See Bertelsmann SE & Co. KGaA; *Int'l*, pg. 990
BOAT ROCKER MEDIA; *Int'l*, pg. 1095
BODHI TREE MULTIMEDIA LIMITED; *Int'l*, pg. 1097
BOOK MAKER CO., LTD.—See Bangkok Broadcasting & TV Co., Ltd.; *Int'l*, pg. 833
BOOMERANG PLUS PLC; *Int'l*, pg. 1110
BOOM EXTREME PUBLISHING LIMITED—See Boomerang Plus plc; *Int'l*, pg. 1110
BOOM FILMS LIMITED—See Boomerang Plus plc; *Int'l*, pg. 1110
BOSSDOM DIGIINNOVATION CO., LTD.; *Int'l*, pg. 1118
BOULDER MEDIA LIMITED—See Hasbro, Inc.; *U.S. Public*, pg. 987
BOX TV LIMITED—See DCD Media plc; *Int'l*, pg. 1991
BRAD!BRYAN MULTIMEDIA INC.; *U.S. Private*, pg. 631
BRAINPOOL TV GMBH—See National Amusements, Inc.; *U.S. Private*, pg. 2839
BRANDED PRODUCTIONS, INC.—See National Amusements, Inc.; *U.S. Private*, pg. 2839
BREMEDIA PRODUKTION GMBH—See Bavaria Film GmbH; *Int'l*, pg. 899
BRILLSTEIN ENTERTAINMENT PARTNERS, LLC—See Wasserman Media Group, LLC; *U.S. Private*, pg. 4450
BRISTOL BAY PRODUCTIONS, LLC—See The Anschutz Corporation; *U.S. Private*, pg. 3987
BROADWAY SOUND—See Broadway Video Inc.; *U.S. Private*, pg. 660
BROADWAY VIDEO INC.; *U.S. Private*, pg. 660
BUENA VISTA HOME ENTERTAINMENT, INC.—See The Walt Disney Company; *U.S. Public*, pg. 2138
BUENA VISTA INTERNATIONAL, INC.—See The Walt Disney Company; *U.S. Public*, pg. 2138
BUENA VISTA THEATRICAL GROUP LLC—See The Walt Disney Company; *U.S. Public*, pg. 2138
CAMERON THOMSON ENTERTAINMENT LTD.—See Cameron Thomson Group Ltd.; *Int'l*, pg. 1272
CAMP KAZ PRODUCTIONS INC.—See AOI TYO Holdings Inc.; *Int'l*, pg. 488
CAPTURED LIGHT STUDIO INC.—See Edify Multimedia Group LLC; *U.S. Private*, pg. 1336
CARNIVAL FILM & TELEVISION LIMITED—See Comcast Corporation; *U.S. Public*, pg. 537
CARRIESOFT CO., LTD.; *Int'l*, pg. 1346
CASTLE ROCK ENTERTAINMENT, INC.—See Warner Bros. Discovery, Inc.; *U.S. Public*, pg. 2328
CBD OF DENVER, INC.; *U.S. Public*, pg. 456
CBS-CSI INTERNATIONAL B.V.—See National Amusements, Inc.; *U.S. Private*, pg. 2841
CBS FILMS INC.—See National Amusements, Inc.; *U.S. Private*, pg. 2840
CBS STUDIOS INC.—See National Amusements, Inc.; *U.S. Private*, pg. 2840
CELESTIAL FILMED ENTERTAINMENT LIMITED—See Astro All Asia Networks plc; *Int'l*, pg. 662
CELESTIAL PICTURES LIMITED—See Astro All Asia Networks plc; *Int'l*, pg. 662
CENTRAL PARK MEDIA CORP.; *U.S. Private*, pg. 824
CHANNEL NINE ENTERTAINMENT LTD; *Int'l*, pg. 1446
CHAOS VISUAL PRODUCTIONS LLC—See The Jordan Company, L.P.; *U.S. Private*, pg. 4061
CHINA CREATIVE DIGITAL ENTERTAINMENT LIMITED; *Int'l*, pg. 1496
CHINA FILM CO., LTD.; *Int'l*, pg. 1502
CHINA NATIONAL CULTURE GROUP LTD.; *Int'l*, pg. 1531
CHINA STAR ENTERTAINMENT HOLDING COMPANY—See China Star Entertainment Limited; *Int'l*, pg. 1553
CHINA STAR ENTERTAINMENT LIMITED; *Int'l*, pg. 1553
CHINA STAR HK DISTRIBUTION LIMITED—See China Star Entertainment Limited; *Int'l*, pg. 1553
CHINA STAR INTERNATIONAL DISTRIBUTION LIMITED—See China Star Entertainment Limited; *Int'l*, pg. 1553
CHINA TELEVISION MEDIA, LTD.; *Int'l*, pg. 1558
CINEMARK USA, INC.—See Cinemark Holdings, Inc.; *U.S. Public*, pg. 495
CINEMATIC ARTS B.V.—See National Amusements, Inc.; *U.S. Private*, pg. 2842
CINEMA TRUSTS INVESTMENTS IN MOVIES LP; *Int'l*, pg. 1610
CINEMEDIA AG; *Int'l*, pg. 1610
CINEPLEX COMPANY LIMITED—See Charoen Pokphand Group Co., Ltd.; *Int'l*, pg. 1453
CINERAD COMMUNICATIONS LIMITED; *Int'l*, pg. 1610
CITY PULSE MULTIPLEX LIMITED; *Int'l*, pg. 1627
COASTAL SATELLITE, INC.—See Live Media Group, LLC; *U.S. Private*, pg. 2473
COCA-COLA REFRESHMENTS USA, INC. - KANSAS—See The Coca-Cola Company; *U.S. Public*, pg. 2064
COLOGNE BROADCASTING CENTER—See Bertelsmann SE & Co. KGaA; *Int'l*, pg. 994
COLORCHIPS NEWS MEDIA LTD.; *Int'l*, pg. 1704
COLUMBUS CIRCLE FILMS LLC—See National Amusements, Inc.; *U.S. Private*, pg. 2842
THE COMEDY UNIT—See De Agostini S.p.A.; *Int'l*, pg. 1994

COMPUTER GRAPHICS INTERNATIONAL INC.; *Int'l*, pg. 1759
CONDE NAST ENTERTAINMENT—See Advance Publications, Inc.; *U.S. Private*, pg. 86
CONSTANTIN ENTERTAINMENT GMBH—See Highlight Communications AG; *Int'l*, pg. 3388
CONSTANTIN FILM AG—See Highlight Communications AG; *Int'l*, pg. 3388
COOLABI LIMITED—See Edge Group Limited; *Int'l*, pg. 2309
COOLFIRE MEDIA, LLC; *U.S. Private*, pg. 1040
COOLFIRE WEST—See Coolfire Media, LLC; *U.S. Private*, pg. 1040
CORAL MINT LTD.—See Daily Mail & General Trust plc; *Int'l*, pg. 1937
CORE MEDIA GROUP., INC.—See Apollo Global Management, Inc.; *U.S. Public*, pg. 148
CORONET/MTI—See The Phoenix Learning Group, Inc.; *U.S. Private*, pg. 4095
CORPLEX, INC.—See The Carlyle Group Inc.; *U.S. Public*, pg. 2050
CRAIG MURRAY PRODUCTIONS LLC; *U.S. Private*, pg. 1083
CREATIVE ASSOCIATES LTD.—See Dentsu Group Inc.; *Int'l*, pg. 2034
CREATIVE CHINA HOLDINGS LIMITED; *Int'l*, pg. 1832
CREATIVE EYE LIMITED; *Int'l*, pg. 1832
CRM LEARNING LP; *U.S. Private*, pg. 1102
CROSSROADS FILM INC.; *U.S. Private*, pg. 1108
CRYSTAL CATHEDRAL MINISTRIES INC.; *U.S. Private*, pg. 1115
CURIOSITYSTREAM INC.; *U.S. Public*, pg. 610
CYNHYRCHIADAU ALFRESCO PRODUCTIONS CYFYNGEDIG—See Boomerang Plus plc; *Int'l*, pg. 1110
DANJAQ LLC; *U.S. Private*, pg. 1157
DCD MEDIA PLC; *Int'l*, pg. 1991
DE AGOSTINI COMMUNICATIONS S.P.A—See De Agostini S.p.A.; *Int'l*, pg. 1994
DEFY MEDIA, LLC - LOS ANGELES—See ZelnickMedia Corp.; *U.S. Private*, pg. 4600
DEMETER CORPORATION PUBLIC COMPANY LIMITED; *Int'l*, pg. 2025
DENTSU OKINAWA INC.—See Dentsu Group Inc.; *Int'l*, pg. 2038
DESCRIPTIVE VIDEO WORKS INC.—See Canada Pension Plan Investment Board; *Int'l*, pg. 1280
DESCRIPTIVE VIDEO WORKS INC.—See EQT AB; *Int'l*, pg. 2482
DESTINATION CINEMA INC.; *U.S. Private*, pg. 1215
DEXTER STUDIOS CO., LTD; *Int'l*, pg. 2093
DHX MEDIA LTD. - TORONTO—See DHX Media Ltd.; *Int'l*, pg. 2101
DHX MEDIA LTD. - VANCOUVER—See DHX Media Ltd.; *Int'l*, pg. 2101
DIAMANTE FILMS; *U.S. Private*, pg. 1222
DIGITAL DOMAIN PRODUCTIONS 3.0 (BC), LTD.—See Digital Domain Holdings Limited; *Int'l*, pg. 2121
DISHOLDER 3, INC.—See The Walt Disney Company; *U.S. Public*, pg. 2138
DISNEY ENTERPRISES, INC.—See The Walt Disney Company; *U.S. Public*, pg. 2138
DLE INC.; *Int'l*, pg. 2140
DNP PLANNING NETWORK CO., LTD.—See Dai Nippon Printing Co., Ltd.; *Int'l*, pg. 1915
DONE+DUSTED INC—See Done & Dusted Group Limited; *Int'l*, pg. 2163
DORI MEDIA CONTENIDOS S.A.—See Dori Media Group Ltd.; *Int'l*, pg. 2176
DORI MEDIA DISTRIBUTION ARGENTINA S.A.—See Dori Media Group Ltd.; *Int'l*, pg. 2176
D.P.S.I. DIGITAL PRODUCTION SOLUTIONS ISRAEL LTD.—See IDT Corporation; *U.S. Public*, pg. 1093
DRAMMEN KINO AS—See Egmont Fonden; *Int'l*, pg. 2325
DREAMFLY PRODUCTIONS CORPORATION; *U.S. Private*, pg. 1275
DREAMWORKS ANIMATION, LLC—See Comcast Corporation; *U.S. Public*, pg. 539
DREAMWORKS LLC—See National Amusements, Inc.; *U.S. Private*, pg. 2842
DW FILMS L.L.C.—See National Amusements, Inc.; *U.S. Private*, pg. 2842
DW STUDIOS PRODUCTIONS L.L.C.—See National Amusements, Inc.; *U.S. Private*, pg. 2842
DYNAMO AMUSEMENT, INC.; *Int'l*, pg. 2241
EASTMAN KODAK HOLDINGS B.V.—See Eastman Kodak Company; *U.S. Public*, pg. 706
EASY TIGER PRODUCTIONS PTY LTD.—See Bertelsmann SE & Co. KGaA; *Int'l*, pg. 992
ECCHO RIGHTS AB—See CJ Corporation; *Int'l*, pg. 1633
EDIFY MULTIMEDIA GROUP LLC; *U.S. Private*, pg. 1336
EGMONT IMAGINATION A/S—See Egmont Fonden; *Int'l*, pg. 2325
EGYPTIAN MEDIA PRODUCTION CITY SAE; *Int'l*, pg. 2327
ELECTROSONIC, INC.; *U.S. Public*, pg. 1356
EMERGING MEDIA CORP.—See The Movie Studio, Inc.; *U.S. Public*, pg. 2116
EMPIRE POST MEDIA, INC.; *U.S. Private*, pg. 1385
ENCASH ENTERTAINMENT LIMITED; *Int'l*, pg. 2401

ENERGY HOLDINGS, INC; *U.S. Public*, pg. 762
ENTERTAINMENT STUDIOS MOTION PICTURES, LLC—See Entertainment Studios, Inc.; *U.S. Private*, pg. 1405
EROS ENTERTAINMENT, INC.—See Eros International Plc; *Int'l*, pg. 2496
EROS INTERNATIONAL LTD.—See Eros International Plc; *Int'l*, pg. 2496
EROS INTERNATIONAL MEDIA LTD.—See Eros International Plc; *Int'l*, pg. 2496
EROS NETWORK LIMITED—See Eros International Plc; *Int'l*, pg. 2496
EROS (PACIFIC) PVT. LTD.—See Eros International Plc; *Int'l*, pg. 2496
EROS WORLDWIDE FZ LLC—See Eros International Plc; *Int'l*, pg. 2497
ESPRO ACOUSTIGUIDE SAS—See Espro Information Technologies Ltd.; *Int'l*, pg. 2507
ESPRO INFORMATION TECHNOLOGIES LTD.; *Int'l*, pg. 2507
EURO BROADCAST HIRE A/S—See Egmont Fonden; *Int'l*, pg. 2325
EUROFINS DIGITAL MEDIA SERVICES, LLC—See Eurofins Scientific S.E.; *Int'l*, pg. 2539
EUROPACORP; *Int'l*, pg. 2555
EUSTON FILMS LIMITED—See Bertelsmann SE & Co. KGaA; *Int'l*, pg. 992
EVOLUTION FILM & TAPE, INC.—See Metro-Goldwyn-Mayer Inc.; *U.S. Private*, pg. 2687
EXPECTING PRODUCTIONS, LLC—See Stagwell, Inc.; *U.S. Public*, pg. 1926
EYEQUBE STUDIOS PVT. LTD.—See Eros International Plc; *Int'l*, pg. 2497
FAMILY ROOM ENTERTAINMENT CORPORATION; *U.S. Public*, pg. 821
FASTEC IMAGING CORP.—See SFW Capital Partners LLC; *U.S. Private*, pg. 3622
F.C. PORTOMULTIMEDIA - EDICOES MULTIMEDIA, S.A.—See Futebol Clube do Porto; *Int'l*, pg. 2852
FEARLESS FILMS, INC.; *Int'l*, pg. 2629
FFLIC CYFYNGEDIG—See Boomerang Plus plc; *Int'l*, pg. 1110
THE FILM DEPARTMENT HOLDINGS, INC.; *U.S. Private*, pg. 4028
FILMS FOR THE HUMANITIES & SCIENCES, INC.—See Veronis Suhler Stevenson Partners LLC; *U.S. Private*, pg. 4368
FILMS PARAMOUNT S.A.—See National Amusements, Inc.; *U.S. Private*, pg. 2842
FILMWEB AS—See Egmont Fonden; *Int'l*, pg. 2325
FIRST LOOK STUDIOS, INC.—See Nu Image, Inc.; *U.S. Private*, pg. 2971
FOCUS FEATURES LLC - NEW YORK—See Comcast Corporation; *U.S. Public*, pg. 540
FOCUS FEATURES LLC—See Comcast Corporation; *U.S. Public*, pg. 540
FORTISSIMO FILM SALES; *Int'l*, pg. 2740
THE FOUNDATION—See De Agostini S.p.A.; *Int'l*, pg. 1994
FOX PRODUCTION SERVICES PTY LIMITED—See Fox Corporation; *U.S. Public*, pg. 876
FOXTELECOMBIA, S.A.—See Fox Corporation; *U.S. Public*, pg. 876
FRAMESTORE LIMITED—See Cultural Investment Holdings Co., Ltd.; *Int'l*, pg. 1877
FREEFORM TV—See The Walt Disney Company; *U.S. Public*, pg. 2137
FREMANTLEMEDIA LTD—See Bertelsmann SE & Co. KGaA; *Int'l*, pg. 994
FREMANTLE PRODUCTIONS ASIA PTE. LTD.—See Bertelsmann SE & Co. KGaA; *Int'l*, pg. 992
FTL VENTURES CORP.; *Int'l*, pg. 2800
FUBOTV INC.; *U.S. Public*, pg. 891
FUNNELBOX INC.; *U.S. Private*, pg. 1623
FUTA B.V.—See National Amusements, Inc.; *U.S. Private*, pg. 2843
FUTURE FILM GROUP PLC; *Int'l*, pg. 2856
GAUMONT S.A.; *Int'l*, pg. 2890
GDH 559 COMPANY LIMITED—See GMM Grammy Public Company Limited; *Int'l*, pg. 3012
GEAR HEAD CO., LTD.—See Bangkok Broadcasting & TV Co., Ltd.; *Int'l*, pg. 833
GHY CULTURE & MEDIA (MALAYSIA) SDN. BHD.—See GHY Culture & Media Holding Co., Limited; *Int'l*, pg. 2960
GIANTSTEP INC.; *Int'l*, pg. 2962
GLOBAL ENTERTAINMENT HOLDINGS, INC.; *U.S. Public*, pg. 942
GMO ENGINE INC.—See GMO Internet Group, Inc.; *Int'l*, pg. 3013
GOODY FILM (THAILAND) CO., LTD.—See Bangkok Broadcasting & TV Co., Ltd.; *Int'l*, pg. 833
GOTHAM IMAGE WORKS INC.—See Wiegers Capital Partners; *U.S. Private*, pg. 4510
GRAVITY PRODUCTIONS INC.—See National Amusements, Inc.; *U.S. Private*, pg. 2841
GUIDEDRAW LTD.; *Int'l*, pg. 3173
GV FILMS LTD; *Int'l*, pg. 3189
HAGER MOSS FILM GMBH—See Highlight Communications AG; *Int'l*, pg. 3388

512110 — MOTION PICTURE AND ...   CORPORATE AFFILIATIONS

HAKSAN PUBLISHING CO., LTD.—See Daewon Media Co., Ltd.; *Int'l*, pg. 1910
HANK PRODUCTIONS LLC—See Dolphin Entertainment, Inc.; *U.S. Public*, pg. 673
HANNOVER HOUSE, INC.—See Crimson Forest Entertainment Group Inc.; *U.S. Private*, pg. 1100
HAPPINET PHANTOM STUDIOS CORPORATION—See Happinet Corporation; *Int'l*, pg. 3269
HBO VIDEO—See Warner Bros. Discovery, Inc.; *U.S. Public*, pg. 2327
HCF HOLDINGS INC.—See Big Fresh Media, Inc.; *U.S. Private*, pg. 553
HEARST ENTERTAINMENT, INC.—See The Hearst Corporation; *U.S. Private*, pg. 4045
HEAVY IRON STUDIOS, INC.—See Canada Pension Plan Investment Board; *Int'l*, pg. 1280
HEAVY IRON STUDIOS, INC.—See EQT AB; *Int'l*, pg. 2482
HELLO!; *U.S. Private*, pg. 1911
HENGDIAN ENTERTAINMENT CO., LTD.; *Int'l*, pg. 3346
HIGH GROUND ENTERPRISE LIMITED; *Int'l*, pg. 3385
HIGH VOLTAGE SOFTWARE, INC.—See Canada Pension Plan Investment Board; *Int'l*, pg. 1280
HIGH VOLTAGE SOFTWARE, INC.—See EQT AB; *Int'l*, pg. 2482
HIT ENTERTAINMENT, INC.—See Mattel, Inc.; *U.S. Public*, pg. 1398
HIT ENTERTAINMENT LTD.—See Mattel, Inc.; *U.S. Public*, pg. 1398
HUAYI BROTHERS MEDIA CORP.; *Int'l*, pg. 3515
HUNGRY MAN LLC; *U.S. Private*, pg. 2008
ICE ANIMATIONS (PRIVATE) LIMITED—See COLGATE-PALMOLIVE (PAKISTAN) LTD; *Int'l*, pg. 1698
IDOMOO LTD.; *Int'l*, pg. 3595
IDREAM FILM INFRASTRUCTURE COMPANY LIMITED; *Int'l*, pg. 3596
IFC COMPANIES—See AMC Networks Inc.; *U.S. Public*, pg. 92
IG PORT, INC.; *Int'l*, pg. 3601
IHQ, INC.; *Int'l*, pg. 3607
ILUSTRATO PICTURES INTERNATIONAL INC.; *Int'l*, pg. 3616
IM360 ENTERTAINMENT INC.—See Digital Domain Holdings Limited; *Int'l*, pg. 2121
IMAGE CHAIN GROUP LIMITED, INC.; *Int'l*, pg. 3617
IMAGICA GROUP INC.; *Int'l*, pg. 3618
IMAGI INTERNATIONAL HOLDINGS LTD.; *Int'l*, pg. 3618
IMAGINARY FORCES LLC; *U.S. Private*, pg. 2045
IMAGINEAR INC.; *Int'l*, pg. 3619
IMAGINE ASIA CO., LTD.—See Ascendio Co., Ltd.; *Int'l*, pg. 601
IMAGINE ENTERTAINMENT; *U.S. Private*, pg. 2045
IMATX, INC.—See restor3d, Inc.; *U.S. Private*, pg. 3409
IMMERSIVE MEDIA COMPANY—See Digital Domain Holdings Limited; *Int'l*, pg. 2121
IMMERSIVE VENTURES INC.—See Digital Domain Holdings Limited; *Int'l*, pg. 2121
INDEPENDENT MEDIA; *U.S. Private*, pg. 2060
INDIGO PEARL LIMITED—See Canada Pension Plan Investment Board; *Int'l*, pg. 1280
INDIGO PEARL LIMITED—See EQT AB; *Int'l*, pg. 2482
INDUS FILMS LIMITED—See Boomerang Plus plc; *Int'l*, pg. 1110
IN ENTERTAINMENT INDIA LTD.—See Hinduja Group Ltd.; *Int'l*, pg. 3399
INNOVATIVE DESIGNS—See Barco N.V.; *Int'l*, pg. 864
INSTANT KARMA FILMS, LLC—See Beijing Galloping Horse Film & TV Production Co., Ltd.; *Int'l*, pg. 950
INSTITUTE OF DIGITAL MEDIA TECHNOLOGY (SHENZHEN) LIMITED—See Global Digital Creations Holdings Limited; *Int'l*, pg. 2994
INTERNATIONAL PICTURES CORP.; *U.S. Private*, pg. 2119
IWC MEDIA—See De Agostini S.p.A.; *Int'l*, pg. 1994
JAFFE/BRAUNSTEIN FILMS, LTD.; *U.S. Private*, pg. 2181
JAPAN LAIM CO., LTD.—See Ichishin Holdings Co., Ltd.; *Int'l*, pg. 3581
J.C. VIRAMONTES INC.; *U.S. Private*, pg. 2160
JERRY BRUCKHEIMER FILMS INC.; *U.S. Private*, pg. 2202
THE JIM HENSON COMPANY; *U.S. Private*, pg. 4059
JINGLEBELL S.R.L.—See Canada Pension Plan Investment Board; *Int'l*, pg. 1280
JINGLEBELL S.R.L.—See EQT AB; *Int'l*, pg. 2482
JULIA JAPAN CO., LTD.—See GENDAI AGENCY INC.; *Int'l*, pg. 2917
JWM PRODUCTIONS, LLC; *U.S. Private*, pg. 2247
KARGA SEVEN PICTURES, LLC; *U.S. Private*, pg. 2262
KARTOON STUDIOS, INC.; *U.S. Public*, pg. 1214
KILLER FILMS INC.; *U.S. Private*, pg. 2304
KING & MAXWELL PRODUCTIONS INC.—See National Amusements, Inc.; *U.S. Private*, pg. 2841
KINOPLEX SP. Z O.O—See Agora S.A.; *Int'l*, pg. 212
KNOCK, INC.; *U.S. Private*, pg. 2323
L37 LLC—See BCD Holdings N.V.; *Int'l*, pg. 926
LAIKA, INC.; *U.S. Private*, pg. 2373
LAKESHORE ENTERTAINMENT CORP.; *U.S. Private*, pg. 2377
LAKESIDE PRODUCTIONS INC.; *U.S. Private*, pg. 2378

LASER INFOMEDIA LTD.—See CDI International Limited; *Int'l*, pg. 1371
LEFTFIELD PICTURES; *U.S. Private*, pg. 2415
LEGENDARY PICTURES PRODUCTIONS, LLC—See Dalian Wanda Group Corporation Ltd.; *Int'l*, pg. 1953
LEGENDARY TELEVISION, LLC—See Dalian Wanda Group Corporation Ltd.; *Int'l*, pg. 1953
LEITMOTIF CREATORS GMBH—See Highlight Communications AG; *Int'l*, pg. 3388
LIFETIME TELEVISION—See The Hearst Corporation; *U.S. Private*, pg. 4045
LIFETIME TELEVISION—See The Walt Disney Company; *U.S. Public*, pg. 2137
LINGNER GROUP PRODUCTIONS, INC.; *U.S. Private*, pg. 2461
LMG, LLC—See Entertainment Technology Partners LLC; *U.S. Private*, pg. 1405
LOCATION ONE LTD.—See Facilities by ADF Plc; *Int'l*, pg. 2600
LORD GLOBAL CORPORATION; *U.S. Public*, pg. 1342
LOVE PRODUCTIONS USA, INC.—See Comcast Corporation; *U.S. Public*, pg. 538
LUCASFILM LTD.—See The Walt Disney Company; *U.S. Public*, pg. 2139
LYON VIDEO, INC.—See Live Media Group, LLC; *U.S. Private*, pg. 2473
MANDALAY PICTURES, LLC—See Mandalay Entertainment Group; *U.S. Private*, pg. 2562
MANKIN MEDIA SYSTEMS, INC.; *U.S. Private*, pg. 2564
MARITIME NORTH AMERICA SEATTLE—See DNV GL Group AS; *Int'l*, pg. 2151
MARVEL ANIMATION, INC.—See The Walt Disney Company; *U.S. Public*, pg. 2139
THE MASLOW MEDIA GROUP, INC.—See Reliability Incorporated; *U.S. Public*, pg. 1778
MASS HYSTERIA ENTERTAINMENT COMPANY, INC.; *U.S. Private*, pg. 2603
MATCHBOX PICTURES PTY LTD.—See Comcast Corporation; *U.S. Public*, pg. 538
MATCHING ENTERTAINMENT CO., LTD.—See Bangkok Broadcasting & TV Co., Ltd.; *Int'l*, pg. 833
MATCHING MAXIMIZE SOLUTION PLC—See Bangkok Broadcasting & TV Co., Ltd.; *Int'l*, pg. 833
MATCHING MOTION PICTURES CO., LTD.—See Bangkok Broadcasting & TV Co., Ltd.; *Int'l*, pg. 833
MATCHING MOVIE TOWN CO., LTD.—See Bangkok Broadcasting & TV Co., Ltd.; *Int'l*, pg. 833
MATILA ROHR PRODUCTIONS (MRP)—See Egmont Fonden; *Int'l*, pg. 2326
MAVERICK MEDIA LIMITED—See Canada Pension Plan Investment Board; *Int'l*, pg. 1280
MAVERICK MEDIA LIMITED—See EQT AB; *Int'l*, pg. 2483
MAZRI INC.—See AOI TYO Holdings Inc.; *Int'l*, pg. 488
MEDCOM INC—See Chicago City Capitol Group; *U.S. Private*, pg. 877
MEDIA CITY ATELIER (MCA) GMBH—See Bavaria Film GmbH; *Int'l*, pg. 899
MEDIA DIRECT NORGE AS—See Egmont Fonden; *Int'l*, pg. 2326
MEDIA GARDEN INC.—See AOI TYO Holdings Inc.; *Int'l*, pg. 488
MEDIA MANAGEMENT, LLC—See Ebiquity plc; *Int'l*, pg. 2285
MEDIAMOTION—See Chepri Holding B.V.; *Int'l*, pg. 1471
MEDIA POST INC.—See ProFromGo Internet Marketing, LLC; *U.S. Private*, pg. 3277
MEDIA RIGHTS CAPITAL II L.P.—See Valence Media Group; *U.S. Private*, pg. 4330
MEGA-VISION PICTURES LIMITED—See Emperor Culture Group Limited; *Int'l*, pg. 2386
MET/HODDER INC.; *U.S. Private*, pg. 2679
METRO-GOLDWYN-MAYER HOME ENTERTAINMENT LLC—See Amazon.com, Inc.; *U.S. Public*, pg. 91
METRO-GOLDWYN-MAYER PICTURES INC.—See Amazon.com, Inc.; *U.S. Public*, pg. 91
METRO-GOLDWYN-MAYER STUDIOS, INC.—See Amazon.com, Inc.; *U.S. Public*, pg. 90
MGM TELEVISION ENTERTAINMENT INC.—See Amazon.com, Inc.; *U.S. Public*, pg. 90
MIKE VASILINDA PRODUCTIONS, INC.; *U.S. Private*, pg. 2725
MILLENNIUM FILMS, INC.—See Nu Image, Inc.; *U.S. Private*, pg. 2971
MILNER-FENWICK, INC.—See Interactivation Health Networks LLC; *U.S. Private*, pg. 2108
MINDFIRE ENTERTAINMENT; *U.S. Private*, pg. 2740
MISO FILM APS—See Bertelsmann SE & Co. KGaA; *Int'l*, pg. 995
MISO FILM NORGE AS—See Bertelsmann SE & Co. KGaA; *Int'l*, pg. 995
MISO FILM SVERIGE AB—See Bertelsmann SE & Co. KGaA; *Int'l*, pg. 995
MOBILE TV GROUP; *U.S. Private*, pg. 2757
MONKEY KINGDOM LIMITED—See Comcast Corporation; *U.S. Public*, pg. 539
MONSTER ULTRA INC.—See AOI TYO Holdings Inc.; *Int'l*, pg. 488

MOTIONWORKS GMBH—See Bavaria Film GmbH; *Int'l*, pg. 899
THE MOVIE STUDIO, INC.; *U.S. Public*, pg. 2116
MOVIE TAVERN, INC.—See The Marcus Corporation; *U.S. Public*, pg. 2112
M SS NG P ECES; *U.S. Private*, pg. 2523
MTV CHANNEL ESPANA S.L.U.—See National Amusements, Inc.; *U.S. Private*, pg. 2841
MULTI IMAGE GROUP INC.; *U.S. Private*, pg. 2812
MULTIMEDIA PLUS, INC.; *U.S. Private*, pg. 2813
MYTHOS FILM PRODUKTIONS-GMBH & CO. KG—See Highlight Communications AG; *Int'l*, pg. 3388
NEOFILM AS—See Egmont Fonden; *Int'l*, pg. 2326
NEP BROADCASTING, LLC—See The Carlyle Group Inc.; *U.S. Public*, pg. 2049
NETWORK AFFILIATES INC.; *U.S. Private*, pg. 2888
NEW CENTURY PRODUCTIONS, INC.—See The Carlyle Group Inc.; *U.S. Public*, pg. 2050
NEW HORIZONS PICTURE CORP.; *U.S. Private*, pg. 2897
NEW LINE CINEMA CORPORATION—See Warner Bros. Discovery, Inc.; *U.S. Public*, pg. 2327
NEW LINE CINEMA—See Warner Bros. Discovery, Inc.; *U.S. Public*, pg. 2327
NEW LINE PRODUCTIONS, INC.—See Warner Bros. Discovery, Inc.; *U.S. Public*, pg. 2327
NEW REGENCY PRODUCTIONS INC.; *U.S. Private*, pg. 2905
NFL FILMS, INC.—See National Football League; *U.S. Private*, pg. 2854
NICE SHOES, LLC; *U.S. Private*, pg. 2925
NICKELODEON INDIA PVT. LTD.—See National Amusements, Inc.; *U.S. Private*, pg. 2842
NIGHTINGALE-CONANT RECORDING & TAPE DUPLICATING DIVISION—See Nightingale-Conant Corporation; *U.S. Private*, pg. 2927
NO PICTURES PLEASE PRODUCTIONS B.V.—See Bertelsmann SE & Co. KGaA; *Int'l*, pg. 993
NORDISK FILM AB—See Egmont Fonden; *Int'l*, pg. 2326
NORDISK FILM A/S—See Egmont Fonden; *Int'l*, pg. 2326
NORDISK FILM AS—See Egmont Fonden; *Int'l*, pg. 2326
NORDISK FILM POST PRODUCTION A/S—See Egmont Fonden; *Int'l*, pg. 2326
NORDISK FILM POST PRODUCTION STOCKHOLM AB—See Egmont Fonden; *Int'l*, pg. 2326
NORDISK FILM PRODUCTION SVERIGE AB—See Egmont Fonden; *Int'l*, pg. 2326
NORDISK FILM SHORTCUT AB—See Egmont Fonden; *Int'l*, pg. 2326
NORDISK FILM SHORTCUT A/S—See Egmont Fonden; *Int'l*, pg. 2326
NORDISK FILM SHORTCUT AS—See Egmont Fonden; *Int'l*, pg. 2326
NORSK FILMDISTRIBUSJON AS—See Egmont Fonden; *Int'l*, pg. 2326
NORTHERN ENTERTAINMENT PRODUCTIONS LLC—See Comcast Corporation; *U.S. Public*, pg. 541
NORTH SHORE PRODUCTIONS INC.—See National Amusements, Inc.; *U.S. Private*, pg. 2842
NU IMAGE, INC.; *U.S. Private*, pg. 2971
NYHETSBOLAGET SVERIGE AB—See Bonnier AB; *Int'l*, pg. 1109
OLGA FILM GMBH—See Highlight Communications AG; *Int'l*, pg. 3388
OLM DIGITAL, INC.—See Imagica Group Inc.; *Int'l*, pg. 3618
OLYMPUS PICTURES, LLC—See Olympus Holdings, LLC; *U.S. Private*, pg. 3013
OPEN DOOR PRODUCTIONS INC.—See National Amusements, Inc.; *U.S. Private*, pg. 2842
ORIGINAL PRODUCTIONS LLC—See Bertelsmann SE & Co. KGaA; *Int'l*, pg. 994
OTTONIA MEDIA GMBH—See Bavaria Film GmbH; *Int'l*, pg. 899
OY NORDISK FILM AB—See Egmont Fonden; *Int'l*, pg. 2326
PANTELION, LLC—See Grupo Televisa, S.A.B.; *Int'l*, pg. 3137
PARAMOUNT BRITISH PICTURES LIMITED—See National Amusements, Inc.; *U.S. Private*, pg. 2843
PARAMOUNT COMEDY CHANNEL ESPANA S.L.—See National Amusements, Inc.; *U.S. Private*, pg. 2842
PARAMOUNT HOME ENTERTAINMENT (FINLAND) OY—See National Amusements, Inc.; *U.S. Private*, pg. 2843
PARAMOUNT HOME ENTERTAINMENT (MEXICO) S. DE R.L. DE C.V.—See National Amusements, Inc.; *U.S. Private*, pg. 2843
PARAMOUNT PICTURES CORPORATION—See National Amusements, Inc.; *U.S. Private*, pg. 2842
PARAMOUNT PRODUCTION SUPPORT INC.—See National Amusements, Inc.; *U.S. Private*, pg. 2843
PARTICIPANT PRODUCTIONS, LLC; *U.S. Private*, pg. 3100
PHOENIX FILMS & VIDEO—See The Phoenix Learning Group, Inc.; *U.S. Private*, pg. 4095
THE PHOENIX LEARNING GROUP, INC.; *U.S. Private*, pg. 4095
PHOENIX PICTURES INC.; *U.S. Private*, pg. 3173
P.I.C.S. CO., LTD.—See Imagica Group Inc.; *Int'l*, pg. 3618
PICT INC.—See Dentsu Group Inc.; *Int'l*, pg. 2039

N.A.I.C.S. INDEX

512120 — MOTION PICTURE AND ...

PIKSIK, LLC—See Nana Regional Corporation, Inc.; *U.S. Private*, pg. 2833
PINEWOOD GROUP LIMITED—See Aermont Capital LLP; *Int'l*, pg. 180
PINEWOOD STUDIOS LIMITED—See Aermont Capital LLP; *Int'l*, pg. 180
PIXAR—See The Walt Disney Company; *U.S. Public*, pg. 2139
PLAYBOY FRANCHISINGS INC.—See PLBY Group, Inc.; *U.S. Public*, pg. 1698
PLAYBOY TV & VIDEO ENTERPRISES, INC.—See PLBY Group, Inc.; *U.S. Public*, pg. 1698
POL-KA PRODUCCIONES S.A.—See Grupo Clarin S.A.; *Int'l*, pg. 3125
PONY CANYON PLANNING INC.—See Fuji Media Holdings, Inc.; *Int'l*, pg. 2814
POPULAR PRODUCTIONS, INC.—See The Walt Disney Company; *U.S. Public*, pg. 2140
POW! ENTERTAINMENT, INC.—See Camsing International Holding Limited; *Int'l*, pg. 1275
PREMIUM AGENCY INC.—See Digital Hearts Holdings Co., Ltd.; *Int'l*, pg. 2122
PRODUCTION RESOURCE GROUP AG—See The Jordan Company, L.P.; *U.S. Private*, pg. 4061
PROSAAR MEDIENPRODUKTION GMBH—See Bavaria Film GmbH; *Int'l*, pg. 899
PROSPECT PICTURES LIMITED—See DCD Media plc; *Int'l*, pg. 1991
PSSST FILM GMBH—See Highlight Event & Entertainment AG; *Int'l*, pg. 3388
PSYCHOTHERAPY.NET LLC—See Moelis Asset Management LP; *U.S. Private*, pg. 2764
PT DUNIA VISITAMA—See Bertelsmann SE & Co. KGaA; *Int'l*, pg. 995
PT. FRONTIER INTERNATIONAL INDONESIA—See Frontier International, Inc.; *Int'l*, pg. 2795
PULSE FILMS LIMITED—See Monroe Capital LLC; *U.S. Private*, pg. 2773
PULSE FILMS LIMITED—See Soros Fund Management LLC; *U.S. Private*, pg. 3716
QUALITRON OY AB—See Helvar Merca Oy AB; *Int'l*, pg. 3339
RALEIGH STUDIOS, INC.—See Raleigh Enterprises; *U.S. Private*, pg. 3349
RAT PACK FILMPRODUKTION GMBH—See Highlight Communications AG; *Int'l*, pg. 3388
RED 212; *U.S. Private*, pg. 3372
RELATIVITY MEDIA, LLC; *U.S. Private*, pg. 3392
RENAVOTIO, INC.; *U.S. Private*, pg. 1783
REVOLUTION STUDIOS—See Content Partners LLC; *U.S. Private*, pg. 1027
RGB VENTURES LLC—See Blend Images, LLC; *U.S. Private*, pg. 580
RHYTHM AND HUES INC.; *U.S. Private*, pg. 3424
ROBOT COMMUNICATIONS INC.—See Imagica Group Inc.; *Int'l*, pg. 3619
ROGER TV; *U.S. Private*, pg. 3471
RSA FILMS INC.; *U.S. Private*, pg. 3496
SAMUEL GOLDWYN FILMS, LLC - NEW YORK—See Samuel Goldwyn Films, LLC; *U.S. Private*, pg. 3538
SAMUEL GOLDWYN FILMS, LLC; *U.S. Private*, pg. 3538
SASANI FILMS CORP.; *U.S. Private*, pg. 3552
SATEL FERNSEH- UND FILMPRODUKTIONS GMBH—See Bavaria Film GmbH; *Int'l*, pg. 899
SAXONIA MEDIA FILMPRODUKTION GMBH—See Bavaria Film GmbH; *Int'l*, pg. 899
SCANDINAVIAN STUDIOS AB—See Bonnier AB; *Int'l*, pg. 1109
SCANLINE VFX; *U.S. Private*, pg. 3561
SCHOLASTIC ENTERTAINMENT INC.—See Scholastic Corporation; *U.S. Public*, pg. 1847
SCOTT RESOURCES—See Geneve Holdings Corp.; *U.S. Private*, pg. 1671
SCREENWORKS LLC - OPERATIONS & TECHNICAL SUPPORT—See The Carlyle Group Inc.; *U.S. Public*, pg. 2049
SEARCHLIGHT PICTURES, INC.—See The Walt Disney Company; *U.S. Public*, pg. 2140
SEPTEMBER FILMS LIMITED—See DCD Media plc; *Int'l*, pg. 1991
SEPTEMBER FILMS USA, INC.—See DCD Media plc; *Int'l*, pg. 1991
SESAME WORKSHOP; *U.S. Private*, pg. 3617
SEVEN ARTS ENTERTAINMENT INC.; *U.S. Public*, pg. 1873
SHED MEDIA SCOTLAND LIMITED—See Warner Bros. Discovery, Inc.; *U.S. Public*, pg. 2329
SHED MEDIA US—See Warner Bros. Discovery, Inc.; *U.S. Public*, pg. 2329
SHEPPERTON STUDIOS LIMITED—See Aermont Capital LLP; *Int'l*, pg. 100
SHOOTERS, INC.; *U.S. Private*, pg. 3640
SMASHING IDEAS, INC.—See Bertelsmann SE & Co. KGaA; *Int'l*, pg. 991
SMOKE AND MIRRORS PRODUCTIONS LIMITED - SHANGHAI UNIT—See Deutsche Post AG; *Int'l*, pg. 2082
SMOKE AND MIRRORS PRODUCTIONS LIMITED—See Deutsche Post AG; *Int'l*, pg. 2082
SOLID ANGLE LIMITED—See Autodesk, Inc.; *U.S. Public*, pg. 229
SOLID ANGLE, S.L.U.—See Autodesk, Inc.; *U.S. Public*, pg. 229
SONAR ENTERTAINMENT, LLC—See Chicken Soup for the Soul Entertainment, Inc.; *U.S. Public*, pg. 488
SOTSU CO.,LTD.—See BANDAI NAMCO Holdings Inc.; *Int'l*, pg. 829
SOULPANCAKE—See Participant Productions, LLC; *U.S. Private*, pg. 3100
SOVRN HOLDINGS, INC.; *U.S. Private*, pg. 3743
SPARK STUDIOS—See SPARK; *U.S. Private*, pg. 3745
SPLASHLIGHT LLC; *U.S. Private*, pg. 3759
SPOV LTD.—See Canada Pension Plan Investment Board; *Int'l*, pg. 1280
SPOV LTD.—See EQT AB; *Int'l*, pg. 2483
SPYGLASS ENTERTAINMENT GROUP, LLC—See Cerberus Capital Management, L.P.; *U.S. Private*, pg. 839
STARGAZE ENTERTAINMENT GROUP, INC.; *U.S. Public*, pg. 1939
STEINER STUDIOS LLC—See Steiner Equities Group LLC; *U.S. Private*, pg. 3798
STONEY ROAD PRODUCTION INC.; *U.S. Private*, pg. 3830
STORY HOUSE PRODUCTION, INC.; *U.S. Private*, pg. 3832
STORY HOUSE PRODUCTIONS GMBH—See STORY HOUSE Production, Inc.; *U.S. Private*, pg. 3832
STUDIONOW, INC.; *U.S. Private*, pg. 3844
STU SEGALL PRODUCTIONS INC.; *U.S. Private*, pg. 3843
SYNTREND CREATIVE PARK CO., LTD.—See Hon Hai Precision Industry Co., Ltd.; *Int'l*, pg. 3459
TANTALUS MEDIA PTY. LIMITED—See Canada Pension Plan Investment Board; *Int'l*, pg. 1280
TANTALUS MEDIA PTY. LIMITED—See EQT AB; *Int'l*, pg. 2483
TEATRO DE LOS INSURGENTES, S.A. DE C.V.—See Grupo Televisa, S.A.B.; *Int'l*, pg. 3136
TELEDU APOLLO CYFYNGEDIG—See Boomerang Plus plc; *Int'l*, pg. 1110
TELEPICTURES PRODUCTION INC.—See Warner Bros. Discovery, Inc.; *U.S. Public*, pg. 2328
TELE TIPS DIGITAL, S.A. DE C.V.—See Grupo Televisa, S.A.B.; *Int'l*, pg. 3136
TELEVISA ENTRETENIMIENTO, S.A. DE C.V.—See Grupo Televisa, S.A.B.; *Int'l*, pg. 3137
TELEVISA INTERNACIONAL, LLC—See Grupo Televisa, S.A.B.; *Int'l*, pg. 3137
TIME WARNER CABLE ENTERPRISES LLC—See Charter Communications, Inc.; *U.S. Public*, pg. 483
TOKYO BIJUTSU CO., LTD.—See Citizen Watch Co., Ltd.; *Int'l*, pg. 1625
TOUCHPAPER TELEVISION—See De Agostini S.p.A.; *Int'l*, pg. 1994
TRAQIQ, INC.; *U.S. Public*, pg. 2185
TRIFECTA MULTIMEDIA, LLC—See Leonard Green & Partners, L.P.; *U.S. Private*, pg. 2430
TROMA ENTERTAINMENT INC.; *U.S. Private*, pg. 4241
TRUE NORTH PRODUCTIONS LIMITED—See Comcast Corporation; *U.S. Public*, pg. 542
TRUMP MEDIA & TECHNOLOGY GROUP CORP.; *U.S. Public*, pg. 2201
TSN WEST, LLC—See Bunzl plc; *Int'l*, pg. 1219
TSUBURAYA PRODUCTIONS CO., LTD.—See BANDAI NAMCO Holdings Inc.; *Int'l*, pg. 828
TTT WEST COAST INC.; *U.S. Private*, pg. 4255
TURNER ENTERTAINMENT NETWORKS INCORPORATED—See Warner Bros. Discovery, Inc.; *U.S. Public*, pg. 2328
TWENTIETH CENTURY FOX FILM CORPORATION—See The Walt Disney Company; *U.S. Public*, pg. 2140
TWISTED SCHOLAR, INC.; *U.S. Private*, pg. 4266
UFA FILM UND FERNSEH GMBH—See Bertelsmann SE & Co. KGaA; *Int'l*, pg. 996
UFA SHOW GMBH—See Bertelsmann SE & Co. KGaA; *Int'l*, pg. 995
UNIVERSAL CITY TRAVEL PARTNERS—See Comcast Corporation; *U.S. Public*, pg. 540
UNIVERSUM FILM GMBH—See KKR & Co. Inc.; *U.S. Public*, pg. 1266
VCT VIDEOCATION CREATIVE TOOLS GMBH—See Avemio AG; *Int'l*, pg. 738
VIACOM GLOBAL HUNGARY KFT.—See National Amusements, Inc.; *U.S. Private*, pg. 2844
VIA PRODUCTION—See Groupe AB S.A.; *Int'l*, pg. 3091
VIDEOCINE, S.A. DE C.V.—See Grupo Televisa, S.A.B.; *Int'l*, pg. 3137
VIDEOLAND, INC.—See Grand Pacific Petrochemical Corporation; *Int'l*, pg. 3055
VIDEOPOLIS, S.A.S.—See Amadeus IT Group, S.A.; *Int'l*, pg. 407
VIEWMARKET INC.; *U.S. Private*, pg. 4381
VISUAL DOMAIN AUSTRALIA PTY LIMITED—See News Corporation; *U.S. Public*, pg. 1521
VJII PRODUCTIONS AG—See Allgeier SE; *Int'l*, pg. 338
VULCAN PRODUCTIONS INC.—See Vulcan Inc.; *U.S. Private*, pg. 4416
WALDEN MEDIA, LLC—See The Anschutz Corporation; *U.S. Private*, pg. 3987
WALL TO WALL MEDIA LIMITED—See Warner Bros. Discovery, Inc.; *U.S. Public*, pg. 2329
THE WALT DISNEY COMPANY (FRANCE) S.A.S.—See The Walt Disney Company; *U.S. Public*, pg. 2139
THE WALT DISNEY COMPANY (GERMANY) GMBH—See The Walt Disney Company; *U.S. Public*, pg. 2139
THE WALT DISNEY COMPANY LTD.—See The Walt Disney Company; *U.S. Public*, pg. 2140
THE WALT DISNEY COMPANY (SOUTHEAST ASIA) PTE LTD.—See The Walt Disney Company; *U.S. Public*, pg. 2139
WALT DISNEY ENTERPRISES OF JAPAN LTD.—See The Walt Disney Company; *U.S. Public*, pg. 2140
WALT DISNEY INTERNATIONAL LTD.—See The Walt Disney Company; *U.S. Public*, pg. 2138
WARNER BROS. ANIMATION INC.—See Warner Bros. Discovery, Inc.; *U.S. Public*, pg. 2328
WARNER BROS. ENTERTAINMENT UK LIMITED—See Warner Bros. Discovery, Inc.; *U.S. Public*, pg. 2329
WARNER BROS. SINGAPORE PTE LTD.—See Warner Bros. Discovery, Inc.; *U.S. Public*, pg. 2329
WARNER BROS. TELEVISION PRODUCTION, INC.—See Warner Bros. Discovery, Inc.; *U.S. Public*, pg. 2329
WARNER BROS. TELEVISION PRODUCTIONS UK LTD—See Warner Bros. Discovery, Inc.; *U.S. Public*, pg. 2329
WARNER BROS. TELEVISION PRODUCTION UK—See Warner Bros. Discovery, Inc.; *U.S. Public*, pg. 2329
WARREN MILLER ENTERTAINMENT—See Bonnier AB; *Int'l*, pg. 1108
WGBH EDUCATIONAL FOUNDATION; *U.S. Private*, pg. 4503
WHITES LOCATION EQUIPMENT SUPPLY INC.—See Ashtead Group Plc; *Int'l*, pg. 609
WILDSIDE S.R.L.—See Bertelsmann SE & Co. KGaA; *Int'l*, pg. 996
WILLIAMS/GERARD PRODUCTIONS INC.; *U.S. Private*, pg. 4527
WINNAN CORP.; *U.S. Private*, pg. 4542
WINNERCOMM, INC.—See Kroenke Sports & Entertainment, LLC; *U.S. Private*, pg. 2352
WORKING TITLE FILMS LIMITED—See Comcast Corporation; *U.S. Public*, pg. 542
WORLD ENTERTAINMENT SERVICES, LLC—See Bonnier AB; *Int'l*, pg. 1109
WORLD EVENTS PRODUCTIONS, LTD.—See Koplar Communications International, Inc.; *U.S. Private*, pg. 2343
THE WOW FACTOR, INC.; *U.S. Private*, pg. 4139
WOW UNLIMITED MEDIA INC.—See Kartoon Studios, Inc.; *U.S. Public*, pg. 1214
WRIT MEDIA GROUP, INC.; *U.S. Public*, pg. 2383
WWE MIDDLE EAST FZ-LLC—See Silver Lake Group, LLC; *U.S. Private*, pg. 3654
WWE STUDIOS, INC.—See Silver Lake Group, LLC; *U.S. Private*, pg. 3654
YORKTEL, INC.; *U.S. Private*, pg. 4591
YORKTEL, INC.—See Yorktel, Inc.; *U.S. Private*, pg. 4591
YORKTEL, INC.—See Yorktel, Inc.; *U.S. Private*, pg. 4591
YORKTEL, INC.—See Yorktel, Inc.; *U.S. Private*, pg. 4591
YORKTEL—See Yorktel, Inc.; *U.S. Private*, pg. 4591
ZODIAK MEDIA GROUP - LONDON—See De Agostini S.p.A.; *Int'l*, pg. 1994

512120 — MOTION PICTURE AND VIDEO DISTRIBUTION

ADK EMOTIONS INC.—See Bain Capital, LP; *U.S. Private*, pg. 428
ALLIANCE ENTERTAINMENT, LLC—See Alliance Entertainment Holding Corporation; *U.S. Public*, pg. 79
AVE S.A.; *Int'l*, pg. 737
BLACKOUT PRODUCTIONS INC.—See National Amusements, Inc.; *U.S. Private*, pg. 2842
BLAIR & ASSOCIATES, LTD.; *U.S. Private*, pg. 578
BONA FILM GROUP LIMITED; *Int'l*, pg. 1105
BRIDGESTONE MULTIMEDIA GROUP; *U.S. Private*, pg. 649
BRITISH FILM INSTITUTE; *Int'l*, pg. 1171
BUENA VISTA TELEVISION, LLC—See The Walt Disney Company; *U.S. Public*, pg. 2138
CBS INTERNATIONAL TELEVISION AUSTRALIA PTY LIMITED—See National Amusements, Inc.; *U.S. Private*, pg. 2840
CHINA 3D DIGITAL DISTRIBUTION LIMITED—See China Creative Digital Entertainment Limited; *Int'l*, pg. 1496
CINEDIGM ENTERTAINMENT CORP.—See Cineverse Corp.; *U.S. Public*, pg. 495
CINESITE (EUROPE) LIMITED—See Endless LLP; *Int'l*, pg. 2403
CINEVERSE CORP.; *U.S. Public*, pg. 495
CONTINENTAL FILM D.O.O.; *Int'l*, pg. 1783
CRIMSON FOREST ENTERTAINMENT GROUP INC.; *U.S. Public*, pg. 1100
DEUCE ENTERTAINMENT, LLC; *U.S. Private*, pg. 1217

512120 — MOTION PICTURE AND ...

DISCOVERY COMMUNICATIONS, LLC—See Warner Bros. Discovery, Inc.; *U.S. Public*, pg. 2326
DISTRIBUTION VIDEO & AUDIO, INC.; *U.S. Private*, pg. 1239
ENTERTAINMENT STUDIOS, INC.; *U.S. Private*, pg. 1405
EROS AUSTRALIA PVT. LTD.—See Eros International Plc; *Int'l*, pg. 2496
EROS DIGITAL FZ LLC—See Eros International Plc; *Int'l*, pg. 2497
EROS INTERNATIONAL PTE LTD.—See Eros International Plc; *Int'l*, pg. 2496
FOOTAGE FIRM, INC.—See Great Hill Partners, L.P.; *U.S. Private*, pg. 1763
FORTISSIMO FILM SALES—See Fortissimo Film Sales; *Int'l*, pg. 2740
FOX STUDIO LOT LLC—See Fox Corporation; *U.S. Public*, pg. 876
FREECAST, INC.; *U.S. Private*, pg. 1602
FREMANTLEMEDIA NORTH AMERICA INC.—See Bertelsmann SE & Co. KGaA; *Int'l*, pg. 994
FUTURE FILMS LIMITED—See Future Film Group plc; *Int'l*, pg. 2856
FUTURE FILMS USA LLC—See Future Film Group plc; *Int'l*, pg. 2856
GC PRODUCTIONS INC.—See National Amusements, Inc.; *U.S. Private*, pg. 2843
GMA WORLDWIDE (PHILIPPINES), INC.—See GMA Holdings, Inc.; *Int'l*, pg. 3012
GOLDEN HARVEST ENTERTAINMENT (HOLDINGS) LTD.; *Int'l*, pg. 3029
GOLIATH FILM & MEDIA HOLDINGS, INC.; *U.S. Public*, pg. 951
GRACE PRODUCTIONS LLC—See National Amusements, Inc.; *U.S. Private*, pg. 2843
HBO FILMS—See Warner Bros. Discovery, Inc.; *U.S. Public*, pg. 2327
HBO INTERNATIONAL DISTRIBUTION—See Warner Bros. Discovery, Inc.; *U.S. Public*, pg. 2327
HBO INTERNATIONAL—See Warner Bros. Discovery, Inc.; *U.S. Public*, pg. 2327
HEALTH EMPIRE CORPORATION PUBLIC COMPANY LIMITED; *Int'l*, pg. 3303
HITACHI KOKUSAI ELECTRIC AMERICA, LTD.—See KKR & Co. Inc.; *U.S. Public*, pg. 1257
HOLLYWALL ENTERTAINMENT INC.; *U.S. Public*, pg. 1044
HOLOGRAM USA NETWORKS INC.; *U.S. Private*, pg. 1968
INCEPTION MEDIA GROUP, LLC; *U.S. Private*, pg. 2053
INGRAM ENTERTAINMENT INC. - INDIANAPOLIS—See Ingram Entertainment Inc.; *U.S. Private*, pg. 2076
INGRAM ENTERTAINMENT INC.; *U.S. Private*, pg. 2076
KING WORLD PRODUCTIONS, INC.—See National Amusements, Inc.; *U.S. Private*, pg. 2840
KINO INTERNATIONAL CORP.; *U.S. Private*, pg. 2313
LBS COMMUNICATIONS INC—See Bertelsmann SE & Co. KGaA; *Int'l*, pg. 995
LIGHTNING ENTERTAINMENT GROUP, INC.—See L.F.P., Inc.; *U.S. Private*, pg. 2365
MAESTRO FILMWORKS LLC; *U.S. Private*, pg. 2544
METRO-GOLDWYN-MAYER DISTRIBUTION CO.—See Amazon.com, Inc.; *U.S. Public*, pg. 90
MRG ENTERTAINMENT, INC.—See L.F.P., Inc.; *U.S. Private*, pg. 2365
M THIRTY COMMUNICATIONS INC.—See DGTL Holdings Inc.; *Int'l*, pg. 2097
MTI HOME VIDEO; *U.S. Private*, pg. 2809
MTV NETWORKS AFRICA (PTY) LIMITED—See National Amusements, Inc.; *U.S. Private*, pg. 2841
MTV NETWORKS B.V.—See National Amusements, Inc.; *U.S. Private*, pg. 2841
MTV OWNERSHIP (PORTUGAL), LDA—See National Amusements, Inc.; *U.S. Private*, pg. 2842
ODYSSEY PICTURES CORPORATION; *U.S. Private*, pg. 2996
OPEN 4 BUSINESS PRODUCTIONS LLC—See Comcast Corporation; *U.S. Public*, pg. 541
OPEN ROAD FILMS, LLC—See MetLife, Inc.; *U.S. Public*, pg. 1430
PARAMOUNT HOME ENTERTAINMENT (BRAZIL) LIMITADA—See National Amusements, Inc.; *U.S. Private*, pg. 2843
PARAMOUNT HOME ENTERTAINMENT (GERMANY) GMBH—See National Amusements, Inc.; *U.S. Private*, pg. 2843
PARAMOUNT HOME ENTERTAINMENT (SWEDEN) AB—See National Amusements, Inc.; *U.S. Private*, pg. 2843
PARAMOUNT INTERNATIONAL NETHERLANDS B.V.—See National Amusements, Inc.; *U.S. Private*, pg. 2843
PARAMOUNT PICTURES AUSTRALIA PTY.—See National Amusements, Inc.; *U.S. Private*, pg. 2843
PARAMOUNT PICTURES FRANCE SARL—See National Amusements, Inc.; *U.S. Private*, pg. 2843
PARAMOUNT PICTURES INTERNATIONAL LIMITED—See National Amusements, Inc.; *U.S. Private*, pg. 2843
PARAMOUNT PICTURES MEXICO S. DE R.L. DE C.V.—See National Amusements, Inc.; *U.S. Private*, pg. 2843
PARAMOUNT PICTURES NZ—See National Amusements, Inc.; *U.S. Private*, pg. 2843
PARAMOUNT SPAIN S.L.—See National Amusements, Inc.; *U.S. Private*, pg. 2843
REBOOT MARKETING LLC; *U.S. Private*, pg. 3370
REGENT ENTERTAINMENT, INC.—See Regent Entertainment Partnership, L.P.; *U.S. Private*, pg. 3387
SCREEN MEDIA VENTURES LLC—See Chicken Soup for the Soul Entertainment, Inc.; *U.S. Public*, pg. 488
SECTION EIGHT, INC.; *U.S. Private*, pg. 3593
SE DISTRIBUTION INC.—See Scholastic Corporation; *U.S. Public*, pg. 1847
SONAR ENTERTAINMENT DISTRIBUTION, LLC—See Chicken Soup for the Soul Entertainment, Inc.; *U.S. Public*, pg. 488
SONIA FRIEDMAN PRODUCTIONS LTD—See Ambassador Theatre Group Limited; *Int'l*, pg. 414
SPEED COMMERCE, INC. - CANADA—See Speed Commerce, Inc.; *U.S. Public*, pg. 1917
SUPER D, INC.; *U.S. Private*, pg. 3874
SUPERSTAR PRODUCTIONS USA INC.—See National Amusements, Inc.; *U.S. Private*, pg. 2843
TWENTIETH CENTURY FOX FILM DISTRIBUTORS PTY LIMITED—See The Walt Disney Company; *U.S. Public*, pg. 2141
TWENTIETH CENTURY FOX HOME ENTERTAINMENT FRANCE S.A.—See The Walt Disney Company; *U.S. Public*, pg. 2140
TWENTIETH CENTURY FOX HOME ENTERTAINMENT GERMANY GMBH—See The Walt Disney Company; *U.S. Public*, pg. 2140
TWENTIETH CENTURY FOX HOME ENTERTAINMENT JAPAN K.K.—See The Walt Disney Company; *U.S. Public*, pg. 2140
TWENTIETH CENTURY FOX HOME ENTERTAINMENT LIMITED—See The Walt Disney Company; *U.S. Public*, pg. 2140
TWENTIETH CENTURY FOX HOME ENTERTAINMENT LLC—See The Walt Disney Company; *U.S. Public*, pg. 2140
TWENTIETH CENTURY FOX HOME ENTERTAINMENT SOUTH PACIFIC PTY. LIMITED—See The Walt Disney Company; *U.S. Public*, pg. 2140
UNITED ARTISTS CORPORATION—See Amazon.com, Inc.; *U.S. Public*, pg. 91
UNITED INTERNATIONAL PICTURES OF PANAMA, INC.—See Comcast Corporation; *U.S. Public*, pg. 542
UNITED INTERNATIONAL PICTURES—See Comcast Corporation; *U.S. Public*, pg. 541
UNITED INTERNATIONAL PICTURES—See National Amusements, Inc.; *U.S. Private*, pg. 2843
UNIVERSAL PICTURES HOME ENTERTAINMENT LLC—See Comcast Corporation; *U.S. Public*, pg. 542
UNIVERSAL STUDIOS HOME ENTERTAINMENT LLC—See Comcast Corporation; *U.S. Public*, pg. 541
UNIVERSAL STUDIOS INTERNATIONAL B.V.—See Comcast Corporation; *U.S. Public*, pg. 541
VIACOM A.G.—See National Amusements, Inc.; *U.S. Private*, pg. 2844
VIACOM INTERNATIONAL PTY. LIMITED—See National Amusements, Inc.; *U.S. Private*, pg. 2844
VIVA ENTERTAINMENT GROUP INC.; *U.S. Public*, pg. 2307
THE WALT DISNEY COMPANY ITALIA S.R.L.—See The Walt Disney Company; *U.S. Public*, pg. 2140
WALT DISNEY STUDIOS MOTION PICTURES, INC—See The Walt Disney Company; *U.S. Public*, pg. 2140
WARNER BROS. DISTRIBUTING INC.—See Warner Bros. Discovery, Inc.; *U.S. Public*, pg. 2328
WARNER BROS. DOMESTIC TELEVISION DISTRIBUTION—See Warner Bros. Discovery, Inc.; *U.S. Public*, pg. 2329
WARNER BROS. ENTERTAINMENT CANADA INC.—See Warner Bros. Discovery, Inc.; *U.S. Public*, pg. 2328
WARNER BROS. HOME ENTERTAINMENT GROUP—See Warner Bros. Discovery, Inc.; *U.S. Public*, pg. 2328
WARNER BROS. INTERNATIONAL TELEVISION DISTRIBUTION INC.—See Warner Bros. Discovery, Inc.; *U.S. Public*, pg. 2329
WARNER ENTERTAINMENT JAPAN INC.—See Warner Bros. Discovery, Inc.; *U.S. Public*, pg. 2329
WARNER HOME VIDEO INC.—See Warner Bros. Discovery, Inc.; *U.S. Public*, pg. 2329
WEPOST S.R.L.—See Iervolino & Lady Bacardi Entertainment S.p.A.; *Int'l*, pg. 3597
WORLD WRESTLING ENTERTAINMENT (INTERNATIONAL) LIMITED—See Silver Lake Group, LLC; *U.S. Private*, pg. 3654

512131 — MOTION PICTURE THEATERS (EXCEPT DRIVE-INS)

AB CINEMAS NY, INC.—See AB International Group Corp.; *U.S. Public*, pg. 13
ADELPHI-CARLTON LIMITED—See Cineworld Group plc; *Int'l*, pg. 1610
ALL FOR ONE MEDIA CORP.; *U.S. Public*, pg. 78
ALL JOB POLAND SP. Z O.O.—See Cineworld Group plc; *Int'l*, pg. 1610
AMBASSADOR THEATRE GROUP LIMITED; *Int'l*, pg. 414
AMC ENTERTAINMENT INC.—See Dalian Wanda Group Corporation Ltd.; *Int'l*, pg. 1953
ARCLIGHT CINEMA COMPANY; *U.S. Private*, pg. 312
BAHRAIN CINEMA COMPANY B.S.C.; *Int'l*, pg. 800
BEIJING VIGOR TIANBAO INTERNATIONAL STUDIOS CO., LTD—See Hainan Traffic Administration Holding Co., Ltd.; *Int'l*, pg. 3213
BOW TIE CINEMAS, LLC; *U.S. Private*, pg. 625
BRENDEN THEATRE CORPORATION; *U.S. Private*, pg. 645
CARIBBEAN CINEMAS; *U.S. Private*, pg. 760
CATHAY CINEPLEXES SDN BHD—See Cathay Organisation Holdings Ltd; *Int'l*, pg. 1360
CATHAY-KERIS FILMS PTE LTD—See Cathay Organisation Holdings Ltd; *Int'l*, pg. 1360
CENTURY THEATRES OF CANADA, ULC—See Cinemark Holdings, Inc.; *U.S. Public*, pg. 495
CENTURY THEATRES SUMMIT SIERRA, L.L.C.—See Cinemark Holdings, Inc.; *U.S. Public*, pg. 495
CHERRYLANE THEATRE—See A24 Films LLC; *U.S. Private*, pg. 29
CINEMA ENTERTAINMENT CORP.; *U.S. Private*, pg. 898
CINEMARK ARGENTINA, S.R.L.—See Cinemark Holdings, Inc.; *U.S. Public*, pg. 495
CINEMARK DE MEXICO, S.A. DE C.V.—See Entretenimiento GM de Mexico SA de CV; *Int'l*, pg. 2453
CINEMARK, INC.—See Cinemark Holdings, Inc.; *U.S. Public*, pg. 495
CINEMARK INTERNATIONAL, LLC—See Cinemark Holdings, Inc.; *U.S. Public*, pg. 495
CINEMARK MEDIA, INC.—See Cinemark Holdings, Inc.; *U.S. Public*, pg. 495
CINEMEX HOLDINGS USA, INC.—See Entretenimiento GM de Mexico SA de CV; *Int'l*, pg. 2453
CINEPLEX ENTERTAINMENT LP—See Cineplex Inc.; *Int'l*, pg. 1610
CINERGY ENTERTAINMENT GROUP, INC.; *U.S. Private*, pg. 898
CINESYSTEM S.A.; *Int'l*, pg. 1610
CINEWORLD GROUP PLC; *Int'l*, pg. 1610
CJ 4DPLEX CO., LTD.—See CJ Corporation; *Int'l*, pg. 1631
COHEN MEDIA GROUP, LLC; *U.S. Public*, pg. 963
CONSOLIDATED AMUSEMENT CO. LTD. INC.—See Decurion Corp.; *U.S. Private*, pg. 1188
CONSOLIDATED ENTERTAINMENT, INC.—See Reading International, Inc.; *U.S. Public*, pg. 1768
DICKINSON THEATRES INC.; *U.S. Private*, pg. 1227
DIGITAL CINEMA IMPLEMENTATION PARTNERS, LLC—See Cineworld Group plc; *Int'l*, pg. 1611
DOUGLAS THEATRE CO.; *U.S. Private*, pg. 1267
EASTERN FEDERAL CORP.; *U.S. Private*, pg. 1319
EMS ENTERTAINMENT (M) SDN BHD—See Event Marketing Service GmbH; *Int'l*, pg. 2562
EMS EXHIBITS LAS VEGAS, INC.—See Event Marketing Service GmbH; *Int'l*, pg. 2562
EMS EXHIBITS MIAMI, LLC.—See Event Marketing Service GmbH; *Int'l*, pg. 2562
EMS EXHIBITS ORLANDO, LLC.—See Event Marketing Service GmbH; *Int'l*, pg. 2562
EMS LIVE ENTERTAINMENT GMBH—See Event Marketing Service GmbH; *Int'l*, pg. 2562
EPIC THEATRES, INC.; *U.S. Private*, pg. 1413
EVERYMAN MEDIA GROUP PLC; *Int'l*, pg. 2570
THE EYES CO., LTD—See CMO Public Company Limited; *Int'l*, pg. 1671
FORUM FILM CZECH S.R.O.—See Cineworld Group plc; *Int'l*, pg. 1610
FORUM FILM SLOVAKIA S.R.O.—See Cineworld Group plc; *Int'l*, pg. 1610
FRANK THEATRES, LLC; *U.S. Private*, pg. 1595
GALAXY ENTERTAINMENT INC.—See Cineplex Inc.; *Int'l*, pg. 1610
GOODRICH QUALITY THEATERS INC.—See Goodrich Radio and Theaters Inc.; *U.S. Private*, pg. 1740
GOODRICH RADIO AND THEATERS INC.; *U.S. Private*, pg. 1740
GREAT ESCAPE THEATRES OF NEW ALBANY, LLC—See Cineworld Group plc; *Int'l*, pg. 1611
GRUPO CINEMEX SA DE CV—See Entretenimiento GM de Mexico SA de CV; *Int'l*, pg. 2453
GUANGZHOU JINYI MEDIA CORPORATION; *Int'l*, pg. 3166
HARKINS THEATRES, INC.—See Harkins Amusement Enterprises, Inc.; *U.S. Private*, pg. 1864
HELIOS S.A.—See Agora S.A.; *Int'l*, pg. 212
HNA YAJEE PERFORMING ARTS INTERNATIONAL CO., LTD.—See Hainan Traffic Administration Holding Co., Ltd.; *Int'l*, pg. 3215
IMAX (SHANGHAI) MULTIMEDIA TECHNOLOGY CO., LTD.—See Imax Corporation; *Int'l*, pg. 3620
IPIC ENTERTAINMENT INC.; *U.S. Public*, pg. 1167
KINO.DK A/S—See Egmont Fonden; *Int'l*, pg. 2325

N.A.I.C.S. INDEX

512199 — OTHER MOTION PICTUR...

LOCKWOOD MCKINNON CO. INC.; *U.S. Private*, pg. 2479
LOEKS THEATRES, INC.; *U.S. Private*, pg. 2480
MALCO THEATRES INC.; *U.S. Private*, pg. 2557
MANN THEATERS INC.; *U.S. Private*, pg. 2564
MARCUS THEATRES CORP.—See The Marcus Corporation; *U.S. Public*, pg. 2112
METROPOLITAN THEATRES CORPORATION; *U.S. Private*, pg. 2689
MINETTA LIVE, LLC—See Reading International, Inc.; *U.S. Public*, pg. 1768
NEW AGE MEDIA ROMANIA SRL—See Cineworld Group plc; *Int'l*, pg. 1610
NORDISK FILM BIOGRAFER A/S—See Egmont Fonden; *Int'l*, pg. 2326
NORDISK FILM KINO AS—See Egmont Fonden; *Int'l*, pg. 2326
OSLO KINO AS—See Egmont Fonden; *Int'l*, pg. 2326
PACIFIC THEATERS ENTERTAINMENT CORP.—See Decurion Corp.; *U.S. Private*, pg. 1188
PARAMOUNT WORLDWIDE PRODUCTIONS INC.—See National Amusements, Inc.; *U.S. Private*, pg. 2843
PATAGONIK FILM GROUP S.A.—See Grupo Clarin S.A.; *Int'l*, pg. 3125
PICTUREHOUSE CINEMAS LIMITED—See Cineworld Group plc; *Int'l*, pg. 1610
RAGAINS ENTERPRISES LLC—See Cineworld Group plc; *Int'l*, pg. 1611
R.C.COBB, INC.—See Cineworld Group plc; *Int'l*, pg. 1611
READING ROUSE HILL PTY LTD—See Reading International, Inc.; *U.S. Public*, pg. 1768
REALD EUROPE LIMITED—See Rizvi Traverse Management LLC; *U.S. Private*, pg. 3449
R.L. FRIDLEY THEATRES INC.; *U.S. Private*, pg. 3338
SCALA BIO NYKOBONG F. APS—See Egmont Fonden; *Int'l*, pg. 2326
SILVER CINEMAS ACQUISITION CO.—See Cohen Media Group, LLC; *U.S. Private*, pg. 963
SPECTRUM 8 THEATRES—See Cohen Media Group, LLC; *U.S. Private*, pg. 963
STER CINEMAS A.E.—See AVE S.A.; *Int'l*, pg. 737
TAKARAZUKA STAGE CO., LTD.—See Hankyu Hanshin Holdings Inc.; *Int'l*, pg. 3255
TEATRO MANZONI SPA—See Fininvest S.p.A.; *Int'l*, pg. 2675
THEATRE MANAGEMENT INC.; *U.S. Private*, pg. 4141
TIVOLI ENTERPRISES INC.; *U.S. Private*, pg. 4177
UMEDA ARTS THEATER CO., LTD.—See Hankyu Hanshin Holdings Inc.; *Int'l*, pg. 3256
UNITED ARTISTS THEATRE CIRCUIT, INC.—See Cineworld Group plc; *Int'l*, pg. 1611
UNITED CINEMAS CO., LTD.—See Advantage Partners LLP; *Int'l*, pg. 164
VICI PROPERTIES INC.; *U.S. Public*, pg. 2295
WESTLAKES CINEMA PTY LTD—See Reading International, Inc.; *U.S. Public*, pg. 1768

512132 — DRIVE-IN MOTION PICTURE THEATERS

AEON CINEMAS CO., LTD.—See AEON Co., Ltd.; *Int'l*, pg. 176
CINEPLEX S.A.; *Int'l*, pg. 1610
EMPIRE THEATERS LIMITED—See Empire Company Limited; *Int'l*, pg. 2387

512191 — TELEPRODUCTION AND OTHER POSTPRODUCTION SERVICES

3PLAY MEDIA, INC.—See Riverside Partners, LLC; *U.S. Private*, pg. 3445
ACORN PRODUCTIONS LTD—See AMC Networks Inc.; *U.S. Public*, pg. 92
ACTAS INC.—See BANDAI NAMCO Holdings Inc.; *Int'l*, pg. 828
ADAPTIVE MEDIA, INC.—See Adaptive Ad Systems, Inc.; *U.S. Public*, pg. 39
ASCENT MEDIA GROUP, LLC—See Ascent Capital Group, Inc.; *U.S. Private*, pg. 348
ASPECT RATIO INC.; *U.S. Private*, pg. 351
AVAIL-TVN; *U.S. Private*, pg. 403
BABY COW PRODUCTIONS LIMITED—See British Broadcasting Corporation; *Int'l*, pg. 1169
BBC STUDIOWORKS LIMITED—See British Broadcasting Corporation; *Int'l*, pg. 1169
BGIL FILMS & TECHNOLOGIES LTD.; *Int'l*, pg. 1008
BRAVES PRODUCTIONS LLC—See Atlanta Braves Holdings, Inc.; *U.S. Public*, pg. 222
BTI STUDIO3 AB—See The Carlylo Group Inc.; *U.S. Public*, pg. 2045
BTI STUDIOS - ROMANIA—See The Carlyle Group Inc.; *U.S. Public*, pg. 2045
BTI STUDIOS SP. Z O.O—See The Carlyle Group Inc.; *U.S. Public*, pg. 2045
CAPITAL VISION SAS—See Iron Mountain Incorporated; *U.S. Public*, pg. 1172
CAVENA IMAGE PRODUCTS AB—See Edgeware AB; *Int'l*, pg. 2309
CDI INTERNATIONAL LIMITED; *Int'l*, pg. 1371
CINETECH—See Ascent Capital Group, Inc.; *U.S. Private*, pg. 348
COMMUNITY PHARMACY OF RANDOLPH; *U.S. Private*, pg. 996
COMPANIA DE MEDIOS DIGITALES S.A.—See Grupo Clarin S.A.; *Int'l*, pg. 3125
COMPANY 3 LA—See Deluxe Corporation; *U.S. Public*, pg. 652
CREST NATIONAL FILM LABORATORIES; *U.S. Private*, pg. 1096
CREW CUTS INC.; *U.S. Private*, pg. 1099
DAEWON MEDIA CO., LTD.; *Int'l*, pg. 1910
DELUXE LABORATORIES, INC.—See MacAndrews & Forbes Incorporated; *U.S. Private*, pg. 2532
DELUXE LABORATORIES, LTD.—See MacAndrews & Forbes Incorporated; *U.S. Private*, pg. 2532
DHX MEDIA LTD.; *Int'l*, pg. 2100
DIGIFEX AB—See AFRY AB; *Int'l*, pg. 194
DIGITAL GARDEN INC.—See AOI TYO Holdings Inc.; *Int'l*, pg. 488
DORI MEDIA OT LTD.—See Dori Media Group Ltd.; *Int'l*, pg. 2176
DU-ART FILM LABORATORIES INC.; *U.S. Private*, pg. 1282
DWARF INC.—See AOI TYO Holdings Inc.; *Int'l*, pg. 488
ENCORE HOLLYWOOD—See Deluxe Corporation; *U.S. Public*, pg. 653
GORILLA GROUP LTD.—See Boomerang Plus plc; *Int'l*, pg. 1110
GRASS VALLEY GERMANY GMBH—See Black Dragon Capital LLC; *U.S. Private*, pg. 475
HENNINGER D.C., L.L.C.—See Henninger Media Services Inc.; *U.S. Private*, pg. 1917
HENNINGER MEDIA SERVICES INC.; *U.S. Private*, pg. 1917
HUAIZHONG HEALTH GROUP, INC.; *Int'l*, pg. 3512
HUDSON AND SUNSET MEDIA LLC—See Stagwell, Inc.; *U.S. Public*, pg. 1927
IMAGN CONTENT SERVICES, LLC—See Gannett Co., Inc.; *U.S. Public*, pg. 906
INFRONT ITALY S.R.L.—See Dalian Wanda Group Corporation Ltd.; *Int'l*, pg. 1953
INNOVATIVE SCIENCE SOLUTIONS, LLP—See Arsenal Capital Management LP; *U.S. Private*, pg. 338
ISPOT.TV, INC.; *U.S. Private*, pg. 2146
IYUNO UK III LTD.—See The Carlyle Group Inc.; *U.S. Public*, pg. 2045
LASER-PACIFIC MEDIA CORPORATION—See Eastman Kodak Company; *U.S. Public*, pg. 708
LEVEL THREE POST—See Deluxe Corporation; *U.S. Public*, pg. 653
LOOKOUT POINT LIMITED—See British Broadcasting Corporation; *Int'l*, pg. 1169
LUDENS CO., LTD.—See AOI TYO Holdings Inc.; *Int'l*, pg. 488
MACKEVISION CG TECHNOLOGY & SERVICE (SHANGHAI) CO. LTD.—See Accenture plc; *Int'l*, pg. 87
MACKEVISION CORPORATION—See Accenture plc; *Int'l*, pg. 87
MACKEVISION JAPAN CO., LTD.—See Accenture plc; *Int'l*, pg. 87
MACKEVISION MEDIEN DESIGN GMBH - STUTTGART—See Accenture plc; *Int'l*, pg. 87
MAGNO SOUND INC.; *U.S. Public*, pg. 2548
MARATHON MEDIA—See De Agostini S.p.A.; *Int'l*, pg. 1994
MATTHEWS INSTORE SOLUTIONS EUROPE GMBH—See Matthews International Corporation; *U.S. Public*, pg. 1399
MIGOM GLOBAL CORP.; *U.S. Public*, pg. 1446
MUSIC SALES WEST—See Music Sales Corporation; *U.S. Private*, pg. 2818
NATIONAL CAPTIONING INSTITUTE; *U.S. Private*, pg. 2850
NELVANA LIMITED—See Corus Entertainment Inc.; *Int'l*, pg. 1808
OPTIC NERVE STUDIOS, INC.; *U.S. Private*, pg. 3034
PERFORMANCE CAPTURE STUDIOS—See Motion Analysis Corporation; *U.S. Private*, pg. 2795
PHENOMENA MOTION PICTURES CO. LTD—See GMM Grammy Public Company Limited; *Int'l*, pg. 3013
PLASTIC RESEARCH AND DEVELOPMENT CORPORATION - COMMONWEALTH PRODUCTIONS DIVISION—See EBSCO Industries, Inc.; *U.S. Private*, pg. 1325
THE POST GROUP PRODUCTION SUITES; *U.S. Private*, pg. 4097
POST MODERN EDIT, LLC—See PAR Capital Management, Inc.; *U.S. Private*, pg. 3089
RFX INCORPORATED; *U.S. Private*, pg. 3420
RIOT—See Ascent Capital Group, Inc.; *U.S. Private*, pg. 348
RUSHES POSTPRODUCTION LTD—See Deluxe Corporation; *U.S. Public*, pg. 653
SDI MEDIA A/S—See Imagica Group Inc.; *Int'l*, pg. 3619
SDI MEDIA GROUP, INC.—See Imagica Group Inc.; *Int'l*, pg. 3619
SDI MEDIA HOLDINGS GERMANY GMBH—See Imagica Group Inc.; *Int'l*, pg. 3619
SDI MEDIA LTD.—See Imagica Group Inc.; *Int'l*, pg. 3619
SDI MEDIA SWEDEN AB—See Imagica Group Inc.; *Int'l*, pg. 3619
SHENZHEN GLOBAL DIGITAL CREATIONS TECHNOLOGY LIMITED—See Global Digital Creations Holdings Limited; *Int'l*, pg. 2994
SID GENTLE FILMS LIMITED—See British Broadcasting Corporation; *Int'l*, pg. 1169
SOUNDELUX—See Empire Investment Holdings, LLC; *U.S. Private*, pg. 1385
STOCK POINT, INC.—See Credit Saison Co., Ltd.; *Int'l*, pg. 1836
SUNSHINE MEDIA GROUP, INC—See Gladstone Management Corporation; *U.S. Private*, pg. 1705
TRIBUNE ENTERTAINMENT COMPANY—See Nexstar Media Group, Inc.; *U.S. Public*, pg. 1524
TUPELO-HONEY RAYCOM, LLC—See Gray Television, Inc.; *U.S. Public*, pg. 959
TWENTIETH TELEVISION, INC.—See The Walt Disney Company; *U.S. Public*, pg. 2140
WACKY WORLD STUDIOS, LLC—See Court Square Capital Partners, L.P.; *U.S. Private*, pg. 1070
WARNER BROS. INTERNATIONAL TELEVISION PRODUCTION HOLDING B.V.—See Warner Bros. Discovery, Inc.; *U.S. Public*, pg. 2329
WARNER BROS. INTERNATIONAL TELEVISION PRODUCTION NEW ZEALAND LIMITED—See Warner Bros. Discovery, Inc.; *U.S. Public*, pg. 2329

512199 — OTHER MOTION PICTURE AND VIDEO INDUSTRIES

ACADEMY OF MOTION PICTURE ARTS & SCIENCES; *U.S. Private*, pg. 46
ALTIA SYSTEMS INC.—See GN Store Nord A/S; *Int'l*, pg. 3015
AMWELL INC.—See The Walt Disney Company; *U.S. Public*, pg. 2140
AUSTRALIAN FILM INSTITUTE; *Int'l*, pg. 721
BAVARIA FILM INTERACTIVE GMBH—See Bavaria Film GmbH; *Int'l*, pg. 899
BEACH HOUSE PICTURES PTE LIMITED—See Bertelsmann SE & Co. KGaA; *Int'l*, pg. 994
BEBOP CHANNEL CORPORATION; *U.S. Public*, pg. 288
BETTER COLLECTIVE A/S; *Int'l*, pg. 1003
BIG TICKET PICTURES INC.—See National Amusements, Inc.; *U.S. Private*, pg. 2839
BRAVURA INC.—See The Walt Disney Company; *U.S. Public*, pg. 2140
CARSEY-WERNER LLC; *U.S. Private*, pg. 774
CATHAY ORGANISATION HOLDINGS LTD; *Int'l*, pg. 1360
CDI MEDIA INC.; *U.S. Private*, pg. 802
CD PROJEKT S.A.; *Int'l*, pg. 1370
CD SERVICES INC.—See The Walt Disney Company; *U.S. Public*, pg. 2140
CELESTIAL MOVIE CHANNEL LIMITED—See Astro All Asia Networks plc; *Int'l*, pg. 662
CINE MAGNETICS VIDEO & DIGITAL LABORATORIES—See Cine Magnetics, Inc.; *U.S. Private*, pg. 898
CINEVISTA CORP.; *Int'l*, pg. 1610
CLIKIA CORP.; *U.S. Public*, pg. 514
COLORLAND ANIMATION LTD.; *Int'l*, pg. 1704
COOLFIRE MEDIA ORIGINALS, LLC—See Coolfire Media, LLC; *U.S. Private*, pg. 1040
THE CULVER STUDIOS—See Pacific Coast Capital Partners, LLC; *U.S. Private*, pg. 3066
DAVID KEIGHLEY PRODUCTIONS 70MM INC.—See Imax Corporation; *Int'l*, pg. 3620
DET DANSKE FILMINSTITUT; *Int'l*, pg. 2047
DICAPTA CORP.; *U.S. Private*, pg. 1225
DIGIKORE STUDIOS LTD.—See Grauer & Weil India Limited; *Int'l*, pg. 3061
DLO CORP.—See The Walt Disney Company; *U.S. Public*, pg. 2140
EMPORIUM PRESENTS, LLC—See Live Nation Entertainment, Inc.; *U.S. Public*, pg. 1328
EUE/SCREEN GEMS LTD.; *U.S. Private*, pg. 1433
FTA FILM- UND THEATERAUSSTATTUNG GMBH—See Bavaria Film GmbH; *Int'l*, pg. 899
GAMESTOP IBERIA S.L.—See GameStop Corp.; *U.S. Public*, pg. 896
GMM TAI HUB CO., LTD.—See GMM Grammy Public Company Limited; *Int'l*, pg. 3012
HIBINO USA, INC.—See Hibino Corporation; *Int'l*, pg. 3383
HUZUR RADYO TELEVIZYON AS—See The Walt Disney Company; *U.S. Public*, pg. 2140
IMAGICA CORP.; *Int'l*, pg. 3618
JEFF BURGESS & ASSOCIATES, INC.—See DCC plc; *Int'l*, pg. 1990
KROSSOVER INTELLIGENCE INC.—See Agile Sports Technologies, Inc.; *U.S. Private*, pg. 128
LOOP MEDIA, INC.; *U.S. Public*, pg. 1342
MARAN FILM GMBH—See Bavaria Film GmbH; *Int'l*, pg. 899

512199 — OTHER MOTION PICTUR...

MOTOR TREND GROUP, LLC—See Warner Bros. Discovery, Inc.; *U.S. Public*, pg. 2327
NEWS (UK) LIMITED—See The Walt Disney Company; *U.S. Public*, pg. 2141
NEW WORLD VIDEO—See The Walt Disney Company; *U.S. Public*, pg. 2141
OPENFILM, LLC—See Enerfund, LLC; *U.S. Private*, pg. 1393
PANAVISION (CANADA) CORP.—See Cerberus Capital Management, L.P.; *U.S. Private*, pg. 839
PARAMOUNT PRODUCTION SUPPORT INC.—See National Amusements, Inc.; *U.S. Private*, pg. 2843
POINT.360; *U.S. Public*, pg. 1700
POST WORKS; *U.S. Private*, pg. 3234
RIALTO DISTRIBUTION LTD—See Reading International, Inc.; *U.S. Public*, pg. 1768
SCOUT PUBLISHING, LLC—See The Walt Disney Company; *U.S. Public*, pg. 2141
SHINE TV LIMITED—See The Walt Disney Company; *U.S. Public*, pg. 2141
STARVISION HONG KONG LIMITED—See National Amusements, Inc.; *U.S. Private*, pg. 2844
TAG GERMANY GMBH—See Dentsu Group Inc.; *Int'l*, pg. 2039
TAG INDIA PRIVATE LIMITED—See Dentsu Group Inc.; *Int'l*, pg. 2039
TAG WORLDWIDE (SINGAPORE) PTE. LTD.—See Dentsu Group Inc.; *Int'l*, pg. 2039
TAMPA DIGITAL STUDIOS, INC.; *U.S. Private*, pg. 3929
THE TODD-AO CORPORATION—See Empire Investment Holdings, LLC; *U.S. Private*, pg. 1385
TRIBECA FILM INSTITUTE INC.; *U.S. Private*, pg. 4227
VASC CO., LTD.—See Fuji Media Holdings, Inc.; *Int'l*, pg. 2814
VERTICE 360 S.A.—See Grupo Ezentis S.A.; *Int'l*, pg. 3129
VIXEN STUDIOS, LLC—See The Walt Disney Company; *U.S. Public*, pg. 2141
XDC S.A.—See EVS Broadcast Equipment S.A.; *Int'l*, pg. 2574

512230 — MUSIC PUBLISHERS

AFFILIATED PUBLISHERS, INC.; *U.S. Private*, pg. 122
A GEN EVENT AGENCY CO., LTD.—See GMM Grammy Public Company Limited; *Int'l*, pg. 3012
APACE MUSIC LIMITED—See Content Ventures Limited; *Int'l*, pg. 1779
ASSOCIATED MUSIC PUBLISHERS—See Music Sales Corporation; *U.S. Private*, pg. 2817
ASYLUM RECORDS LLC—See Access Industries, Inc.; *U.S. Private*, pg. 52
AVEX ENTERTAINMENT INC.—See Avex Inc.; *Int'l*, pg. 740
BELIEVE SAS; *Int'l*, pg. 964
THE BICYCLE MUSIC COMPANY—See Massachusetts Mutual Life Insurance Company; *U.S. Private*, pg. 2605
BINYL RECORDS INC.—See Avex Inc.; *Int'l*, pg. 740
BMG PRODUCTION MUSIC (FRANCE) SAS—See Bertelsmann SE & Co. KGaA; *Int'l*, pg. 990
BMG PRODUCTION MUSIC (GERMANY) GMBH—See Bertelsmann SE & Co. KGaA; *Int'l*, pg. 990
BMG RIGHTS MANAGEMENT SERVICES (UK) LIMITED—See Bertelsmann SE & Co. KGaA; *Int'l*, pg. 990
BMG RIGHTS MANAGEMENT (US) LLC—See Bertelsmann SE & Co. KGaA; *Int'l*, pg. 990
BOOSEY & HAWKES BOTE & BOCK GMBH & CO.—See HgCapital Trust plc; *Int'l*, pg. 3376
BOOSEY & HAWKES, INC.—See HgCapital Trust plc; *Int'l*, pg. 3376
BOOSEY & HAWKES MUSIC PUBLISHERS LTD.—See HgCapital Trust plc; *Int'l*, pg. 3376
BOSWORTH GMBH—See Music Sales Corporation; *U.S. Private*, pg. 2817
CARL FISCHER, LLC; *U.S. Private*, pg. 762
CHESTER MUSICE FRANCE—See Music Sales Corporation; *U.S. Private*, pg. 2818
CHESTER MUSIC—See Music Sales Corporation; *U.S. Private*, pg. 2817
CINQ MUSIC PUBLISHING, LLC—See GoDigital Media Group, LLC; *U.S. Private*, pg. 1724
CLEAN KARAOKE CO., LTD.—See GMM Grammy Public Company Limited; *Int'l*, pg. 3012
CULTURE PUBLISHERS INC—See Culture Convenience Club Co., Ltd.; *Int'l*, pg. 1877
CURB RECORDS, INC.; *U.S. Private*, pg. 1124
DEAG MUSIC GMBH—See DEAG Deutsche Entertainment AG; *Int'l*, pg. 1998
DEX MEDIA BRE LLC—See Thryv Holdings, Inc.; *U.S. Public*, pg. 2157
EDEL SE & CO. KGAA; *Int'l*, pg. 2305
EDITION WILHELM HANSEN—See Music Sales Corporation; *U.S. Private*, pg. 2818
EMI MUSIC PUBLISHING CANADA—See Blackstone Inc.; *U.S. Public*, pg. 349
EMI MUSIC PUBLISHING CESKA REPUBLIKA, A.S.—See Blackstone Inc.; *U.S. Public*, pg. 349
EMI MUSIC PUBLISHING DENMARK A/S—See Blackstone Inc.; *U.S. Public*, pg. 349
EMI MUSIC PUBLISHING (GREECE) LLC—See Blackstone Inc.; *U.S. Public*, pg. 349
EMI MUSIC PUBLISHING LTD.—See Blackstone Inc.; *U.S. Public*, pg. 349
EMI MUSIC PUBLISHING MEXICO—See Blackstone Inc.; *U.S. Public*, pg. 349
EMI MUSIC PUBLISHING—See Blackstone Inc.; *U.S. Public*, pg. 349
FUJIPACIFIC MUSIC INC—See Fuji Media Holdings, Inc.; *Int'l*, pg. 2814
GMM MUSIC PUBLISHING INTERNATIONAL CO., LTD—See GMM Grammy Public Company Limited; *Int'l*, pg. 3013
GOTEE RECORDS, INC.—See Zealot Networks, Inc.; *U.S. Private*, pg. 4599
G. SCHIRMER, INC.—See Music Sales Corporation; *U.S. Private*, pg. 2818
HAL LEONARD CORPORATION—See Francisco Partners Management, LP; *U.S. Private*, pg. 1590
HARPO PRODUCTIONS, INC.—See Harpo, Inc.; *U.S. Private*, pg. 1868
THE HARRY FOX AGENCY, INC.—See Blackstone Inc.; *U.S. Public*, pg. 357
HIM INTERNATIONAL MUSIC, INC.; *Int'l*, pg. 3395
HYBE CO., LTD.; *Int'l*, pg. 3544
IMAGE PUBLISHING CO. LTD.—See GMM Grammy Public Company Limited; *Int'l*, pg. 3012
KONTOR RECORDS GMBH—See Edel SE & Co. KGaA; *Int'l*, pg. 2305
LANTIS CO., LTD.—See BANDAI NAMCO Holdings Inc.; *Int'l*, pg. 829
MAKEMUSIC, INC.—See LaunchEquity Partners, LLC; *U.S. Private*, pg. 2398
MCGINNIS & MARX MUSIC PUBLISHERS; *U.S. Private*, pg. 2634
MERCURY MUSIC CORPORATION—See Theodore Presser Co.; *U.S. Private*, pg. 4141
MUSICAL HERITAGE SOCIETY INC.; *U.S. Private*, pg. 2818
MUSIC SALES CORPORATION; *U.S. Private*, pg. 2817
MUSIC SALES LIMITED—See Music Sales Corporation; *U.S. Private*, pg. 2818
MUSIC SALES PTY. LIMITED—See Music Sales Corporation; *U.S. Private*, pg. 2818
MUSIC WORLD RETAIL LIMITED—See CESC Limited; *Int'l*, pg. 1424
NAXOS RIGHTS INTERNATIONAL LIMITED—See HNH International Ltd.; *Int'l*, pg. 3434
NIPPON CROWN CO., LTD.—See DAIICHIKOUSHO CO., LTD.; *Int'l*, pg. 1930
NOVELLO & CO. LTD.—See Music Sales Corporation; *U.S. Private*, pg. 2818
THE ORCHARD MEDIA, INC.—See JDS Capital Management, Inc.; *U.S. Private*, pg. 2196
ORIGINAL SOURCE MUSIC, INC.; *U.S. Private*, pg. 3042
PARLOPHONE RECORDS LIMITED—See Access Industries, Inc.; *U.S. Public*, pg. 52
PONY CANYON INC.—See Fuji Media Holdings, Inc.; *Int'l*, pg. 2814
PRO MUSIC RIGHTS INC.—See Nuvus Gro Corp.; *U.S. Private*, pg. 2975
RIVERFRONT MUSIC PUBLISHING CO., INC.—See The Procter & Gamble Company; *U.S. Public*, pg. 2123
RTL AUDIO CENTER BERLIN GMBH—See Bertelsmann SE & Co. KGaA; *Int'l*, pg. 993
RTL MUSIC PUBLISHING GMBH—See Bertelsmann SE & Co. KGaA; *Int'l*, pg. 996
SONGTRADR, INC.; *U.S. Private*, pg. 3713
SOUNDEXCHANGE, INC.; *U.S. Private*, pg. 3717
SUNRISE MUSIC PUBLISHING CO., LTD.—See BANDAI NAMCO Holdings Inc.; *Int'l*, pg. 829
TELAMO MUSIK & UNTERHALTUNG GMBH—See Bertelsmann SE & Co. KGaA; *Int'l*, pg. 996
THEODORE PRESSER CO.; *U.S. Private*, pg. 4141
TRUE BLUE HOLDINGS, INC.; *U.S. Public*, pg. 2198
TYPHOON TOUCH TECHNOLOGIES, INC.; *U.S. Private*, pg. 4269
UNION MUSICAL EDICIONES SL—See Music Sales Corporation; *U.S. Private*, pg. 2818
VERSE MUSIC GROUP LLC—See Bertelsmann SE & Co. KGaA; *Int'l*, pg. 990
WARNER/CHAPPELL MUSIC, INC.—See Access Industries, Inc.; *U.S. Public*, pg. 52
WARNER MUSIC DENMARK—See Access Industries, Inc.; *U.S. Public*, pg. 52
WARNER MUSIC FRANCE—See Access Industries, Inc.; *U.S. Public*, pg. 52
WARNER MUSIC GROUP CORP.—See Access Industries, Inc.; *U.S. Public*, pg. 51
WELK MUSIC GROUP INC.; *U.S. Private*, pg. 4474
WIND-UP RECORDS—See Wind-up Entertainment, Inc.; *U.S. Private*, pg. 4537
XING MUSIC ENTERTAINMENT, INC.—See Brother Industries, Ltd.; *Int'l*, pg. 1198

512240 — SOUND RECORDING STUDIOS

AFTERMASTER, INC.; *U.S. Public*, pg. 57
BINARI SONORI S.R.L.—See Canada Pension Plan Investment Board; *Int'l*, pg. 1280
BINARI SONORI S.R.L.—See EQT AB; *Int'l*, pg. 2482
COOKE OPTICS LTD.—See Caledonia Investments plc; *Int'l*, pg. 1262
DELI ART CO., LTD.—See Fullcast Holdings Co., Ltd.; *Int'l*, pg. 2842
ELIAS ARTS LLC—See Seaport Capital, LLC; *U.S. Private*, pg. 3586
FILMS AT 59; *Int'l*, pg. 2663
FUNDAMENTAL ACOUSTIC RESEARCH (FAR)—See EVS Broadcast Equipment S.A.; *Int'l*, pg. 2574
GELLMAN MANAGEMENT LLC—See Live Nation Entertainment, Inc.; *U.S. Public*, pg. 1328
LEARNING ALLY, INC.; *U.S. Private*, pg. 2408
LIQUID VIOLET LIMITED—See Canada Pension Plan Investment Board; *Int'l*, pg. 1280
LIQUID VIOLET LIMITED—See EQT AB; *Int'l*, pg. 2483
MANHATTAN CENTER STUDIOS INC.—See Family Federation for World Peace & Unification; *U.S. Private*, pg. 1469
MOBILE MARK, INC.; *U.S. Private*, pg. 2757
NO SLEEP PRODUCTIONS LLC—See Stagwell, Inc.; *U.S. Public*, pg. 1927
RON ROSE PRODUCTIONS LTD; *U.S. Private*, pg. 3477
SAMA SOUND INC.—See Hibino Corporation; *Int'l*, pg. 3383
THINGMAGIC INC.—See Novanta Inc.; *U.S. Public*, pg. 1548
TODD SOUNDELUX—See Empire Investment Holdings, LLC; *U.S. Private*, pg. 1385
TV+SYNCHRON BERLIN GMBH—See Canada Pension Plan Investment Board; *Int'l*, pg. 1280
TV+SYNCHRON BERLIN GMBH—See EQT AB; *Int'l*, pg. 2483
WIND-UP ENTERTAINMENT, INC.; *U.S. Private*, pg. 4537

512250 — RECORD PRODUCTION AND DISTRIBUTION

24-7 ENTERTAINMENT APS—See Ceconomy AG; *Int'l*, pg. 1373
ANTENNA GROUP; *Int'l*, pg. 482
ARVATO DE MEXICO, S.A. DE C.V.—See Bertelsmann SE & Co. KGaA; *Int'l*, pg. 990
BUCKET STUDIO CO., LTD.; *Int'l*, pg. 1209
BUSHIROAD MUSIC, INC.—See Bushiroad, Inc.; *Int'l*, pg. 1227
CINQ MUSIC GROUP, LLC—See GoDigital Media Group, LLC; *U.S. Private*, pg. 1724
CLEANTECH BIOFUELS, INC.; *U.S. Private*, pg. 931
COLUMBIA HOUSE CANADA—See Pride Tree Holdings, Inc.; *U.S. Private*, pg. 3260
CONCORD BICYCLE MUSIC—See Massachusetts Mutual Life Insurance Company; *U.S. Private*, pg. 2605
CONCORD MUSIC GROUP, INC.—See Massachusetts Mutual Life Insurance Company; *U.S. Private*, pg. 2605
CRONA CORP.; *Int'l*, pg. 1854
DOMO RECORDS, INC.; *U.S. Private*, pg. 1257
EASY SOUND RECORDING CO.—See Welk Music Group Inc.; *U.S. Private*, pg. 4474
EMI MUSIC PUBLISHING (BELGIUM) SA NV—See Blackstone Inc.; *U.S. Public*, pg. 349
EMI MUSIC PUBLISHING CHILE—See Blackstone Inc.; *U.S. Public*, pg. 349
EMI MUSIC PUBLISHING (HOLLAND) B.V.—See Blackstone Inc.; *U.S. Public*, pg. 349
EMI MUSIC PUBLISHING HONG KONG—See Blackstone Inc.; *U.S. Public*, pg. 349
EMI MUSIC PUBLISHING ITALIA SRL—See Blackstone Inc.; *U.S. Public*, pg. 349
EMI MUSIC PUBLISHING MALAYSIA SDN BHD—See Blackstone Inc.; *U.S. Public*, pg. 349
EMI MUSIC PUBLISHING PORTUGAL—See Blackstone Inc.; *U.S. Public*, pg. 349
EMI MUSIC PUBLISHING SCANDINAVIA AB—See Blackstone Inc.; *U.S. Public*, pg. 349
EMI MUSIC PUBLISHING SPAIN—See Blackstone Inc.; *U.S. Public*, pg. 349
FIRST LEVEL ENTERTAINMENT GROUP, INC.; *U.S. Private*, pg. 1520
FNC ENTERTAINMENT CO., LTD.; *Int'l*, pg. 2717
GAIAM AMERICAS, INC.—See Sequential Brands Group, Inc.; *U.S. Public*, pg. 1868
GVH MANAGEMENT; *U.S. Private*, pg. 1820
MOOD MEDIA CORPORATION—See Vector Capital Management, L.P.; *U.S. Private*, pg. 4351
MUSIC DEALERS, LLC—See BrandSpins, LLC; *U.S. Private*, pg. 638
ORCHARD INC.; *U.S. Private*, pg. 3039
PLAYGROUND MUSIC SCANDINAVIA AB - COPENHAGEN BRANCH—See Edel SE & Co. KGaA; *Int'l*, pg. 2305
PLAYGROUND MUSIC SCANDINAVIA AB - OSLO BRANCH—See Edel SE & Co. KGaA; *Int'l*, pg. 2305

N.A.I.C.S. INDEX

PLAYGROUND MUSIC SCANDINAVIA AB—See Edel SE & Co. KGaA; *Int'l*, pg. 2305
RECORDED BOOKS, INC.—See Shamrock Holdings, Inc.; *U.S. Private*, pg. 3624
RIMAGE EUROPE GMBH—See Equus Holdings, Inc.; *U.S. Private*, pg. 1417
ROUNDER RECORDS CORPORATION—See Massachusetts Mutual Life Insurance Company; *U.S. Private*, pg. 2605
SDMS, INC.; *U.S. Private*, pg. 3581
SOTSU MUSIC PUBLISHING CO., LTD.—See BANDAI NAMCO Holdings Inc.; *Int'l*, pg. 829
SPAWN LABS, INC.—See GameStop Corp.; *U.S. Public*, pg. 896
SUB POP LTD.; *U.S. Private*, pg. 3847
SUGAR HILL RECORDS, INC.—See Massachusetts Mutual Life Insurance Company; *U.S. Private*, pg. 2605
TAKARAZUKA CREATIVE ARTS CO., LTD.—See Hankyu Hanshin Holdings Inc.; *Int'l*, pg. 3255
TANTOR MEDIA, INC.—See Shamrock Holdings, Inc.; *U.S. Private*, pg. 3624
TEICHIKU MUSIC, INC.—See Brother Industries, Ltd.; *Int'l*, pg. 1198
UNITED RECORD PRESSING LLC; *U.S. Private*, pg. 4296
VANGUARD RECORDS—See Massachusetts Mutual Life Insurance Company; *U.S. Private*, pg. 2605
WARNER MUSIC BENELUX N.V.—See Access Industries, Inc.; *U.S. Private*, pg. 52
WARNER MUSIC NORWAY—See Access Industries, Inc.; *U.S. Private*, pg. 52
WARNER MUSIC SWEDEN—See Access Industries, Inc.; *U.S. Private*, pg. 52

512290 — OTHER SOUND RECORDING INDUSTRIES

ALL ACCESS MUSIC GROUP, INC.—See iHeartMedia, Inc.; *U.S. Public*, pg. 1095
AUDIONAMIX SA—See Eurovestech Plc; *Int'l*, pg. 2558
AUDIOVALLEY; *Int'l*, pg. 702
CONSTANTIN MUSIC GMBH—See Highlight Communications AG; *Int'l*, pg. 3388
DISCMAKERS, INC.; *U.S. Private*, pg. 1237
EDEL MUSICA VERTRIEBS GMBH—See Edel SE & Co. KGaA; *Int'l*, pg. 2305
EDEL MUSIC S.A.—See Edel SE & Co. KGaA; *Int'l*, pg. 2305
EDEL RECORDS FINLAND OY—See Edel SE & Co. KGaA; *Int'l*, pg. 2305
EDEL RECORDS GMBH—See Edel SE & Co. KGaA; *Int'l*, pg. 2305
EDEL RECORDS (SWITZERLAND) AG—See Edel SE & Co. KGaA; *Int'l*, pg. 2305
EDEL UK RECORDS LTD.—See Edel SE & Co. KGaA; *Int'l*, pg. 2305
EMUSIC.COM INC.—See TriPlay, Inc.; *U.S. Private*, pg. 4236
EVENTEQ, LLC; *U.S. Private*, pg. 1437
FISHBOWL INVENTORY; *U.S. Private*, pg. 1533
HUNAN ELECTRONIC & AUDIO-VISUAL PUBLISHING HOUSE CO., LTD.—See China South Publishing & Media Group Co., Ltd.; *Int'l*, pg. 1553
LIQUID DIGITAL MEDIA—See Anderson Companies, Inc.; *U.S. Private*, pg. 276
MEDIA VISION (1994) CO. LTD.—See GMM Grammy Public Company Limited; *Int'l*, pg. 3013
MEGATRAX PRODUCTION MUSIC, INC.; *U.S. Private*, pg. 2660
MUZAK HOLDINGS LLC—See Vector Capital Management, L.P.; *U.S. Private*, pg. 4351
MUZAK LLC—See Vector Capital Management, L.P.; *U.S. Private*, pg. 4351
NATIONAL CAPITOL CONTRACTING; *U.S. Private*, pg. 2850
OUR DAILY BREAD MINISTRIES; *U.S. Private*, pg. 3050
PHONAG RECORDS AG—See Edel SE & Co. KGaA; *Int'l*, pg. 2305
SIRE RECORDS—See Access Industries, Inc.; *U.S. Private*, pg. 52
SMC ENTERTAINMENT INC.; *U.S. Private*, pg. 3693
TAIT TOWERS INC.; *U.S. Private*, pg. 3925
TELEVISORA PENINSULAR, S.A. DE C.V.—See Grupo Televisa, S.A.B.; *Int'l*, pg. 3137
TM STUDIOS, INC.—See Brookfield Corporation; *Int'l*, pg. 1184
VARESE SARABANDE RECORDS, INC.; *U.S. Private*, pg. 4346
WARNER BROS. RECORDS, INC.—See Access Industries, Inc.; *U.S. Private*, pg. 52
WARNER SPECIAL PRODUCTS—See Access Industries, Inc.; *U.S. Private*, pg. 52
WATERFRONT CONFERENCE COMPANY LIMITED—See Freshwater UK PLC; *Int'l*, pg. 2782

513110 — NEWSPAPER PUBLISHERS

10/13 COMMUNICATIONS LLC; *U.S. Private*, pg. 2

1105 MEDIA GOVERNMENT INFORMATION GROUP—See Alta Communications, Inc.; *U.S. Private*, pg. 203
1105 MEDIA GOVERNMENT INFORMATION GROUP—See Nautic Partners, LLC; *U.S. Private*, pg. 2868
1FORM ONLINE PTY LTD—See News Corporation; *U.S. Public*, pg. 1518
20 MINUTOS ESPANA S.L.—See Henneo Media, SA; *Int'l*, pg. 3354
AARGAUER ZEITUNG AG—See BT Holding AG; *Int'l*, pg. 1204
ABERDEEN NEWS COMPANY—See Gannett Co., Inc.; *U.S. Public*, pg. 901
ABILENE REPORTER-NEWS, LLC—See Gannett Co., Inc.; *U.S. Public*, pg. 898
ABINGTON MARINER—See Gannett Co., Inc.; *U.S. Public*, pg. 901
ACTION ADVERTISING, INC.—See Gannett Co., Inc.; *U.S. Public*, pg. 896
ADAMS PUBLISHING GROUP, LLC; *U.S. Private*, pg. 74
ADIRONDACK PUBLISHING CO. INC.—See The Nutting Company, Inc.; *U.S. Private*, pg. 4086
AD NIEUWSMEDIA BV—See DPG Media Group NV; *Int'l*, pg. 2188
ADVANCE PUBLICATIONS—See Advance Publications, Inc.; *U.S. Private*, pg. 84
THE ADVERTISER COMPANY—See Gannett Co., Inc.; *U.S. Public*, pg. 900
ADVERTISING AGE—See Crain Communications, Inc.; *U.S. Private*, pg. 1084
ADVISOR-SOURCE NEWSPAPERS—See Alden Global Capital LLC; *U.S. Private*, pg. 155
THE ADVOCATE—See Alden Global Capital LLC; *U.S. Private*, pg. 157
THE ADVOCATE—See Gannett Co., Inc.; *U.S. Public*, pg. 900
THE ADVOCATE—See The Hearst Corporation; *U.S. Private*, pg. 4048
AHC CALIFORNIA DISPOSITIONS, INC.—See DallasNews Corporation; *U.S. Public*, pg. 621
AHWATUKEE FOOTHILLS NEWS—See EOS Publishing, LLC; *U.S. Private*, pg. 1411
AIKEN STANDARD—See Evening Post Publishing Co.; *U.S. Private*, pg. 1436
AKRON BEACON JOURNAL—See Gannett Co., Inc.; *U.S. Public*, pg. 904
AKRON NEWS-REPORTER—See Alden Global Capital LLC; *U.S. Private*, pg. 157
ALAMEDA JOURNAL—See Alden Global Capital LLC; *U.S. Private*, pg. 155
ALAMEDA TIMES-STAR—See Alden Global Capital LLC; *U.S. Private*, pg. 155
ALAMOGORDO DAILY NEWS—See Gannett Co., Inc.; *U.S. Public*, pg. 899
ALAMOSA NEWSPAPERS INC.—See News Media Corporation; *U.S. Private*, pg. 2916
ALASKA DISPATCH PUBLISHING LLC; *U.S. Private*, pg. 150
ALASKA HIGHWAY NEWS—See Glacier Media Inc.; *Int'l*, pg. 2987
ALASKA STAR—See Shivers Trading & Operating Company; *U.S. Private*, pg. 3638
THE ALBANY DEMOCRAT-HERALD—See Lee Enterprises, Incorporated; *U.S. Public*, pg. 1300
THE ALBANY HERALD PUBLISHING CO.—See Southern Community Newspapers Inc.; *U.S. Private*, pg. 3730
AL DIA, INC.—See DallasNews Corporation; *U.S. Public*, pg. 621
ALEXANDRIA NEWSPAPERS, INC.—See Gannett Co., Inc.; *U.S. Public*, pg. 896
ALICE ECHO-NEWS, INC.—See American Consolidated Media LP; *U.S. Private*, pg. 228
ALLIANCE PUBLISHING COMPANY INC., LLC—See Gannett Co., Inc.; *U.S. Public*, pg. 901
ALLSTON-BRIGHTON TAB—See Gannett Co., Inc.; *U.S. Public*, pg. 901
ALMA 360 CUSTOM MEDIA—See Alma Media Corporation; *Int'l*, pg. 361
ALMA MEDIA VENTURES OY—See Alma Media Corporation; *Int'l*, pg. 361
THE ALPENA NEWS PUBLISHING CO. INC.—See The Nutting Company, Inc.; *U.S. Private*, pg. 4086
ALPRESS OY—See Alma Media Corporation; *Int'l*, pg. 362
ALPRINT ROVANIEMI—See Alma Media Corporation; *Int'l*, pg. 362
ALTA NEWSPAPER GROUP LIMITED PARTNERSHIP—See GVIC Communications Corp.; *Int'l*, pg. 3189
THE (ALTON) TELEGRAPH—See Independence Capital Partners, LLC; *U.S. Private*, pg. 2057
ALVARADO STAR—See Alden Global Capital LLC; *U.S. Private*, pg. 156
AMARILLO GLOBE-NEWS—See Gannett Co., Inc.; *U.S. Public*, pg. 901
AMERICAN CITY BUSINESS JOURNALS, INC.—See Advance Publications, Inc.; *U.S. Private*, pg. 84
AMESBURY NEWS—See Gannett Co., Inc.; *U.S. Public*, pg. 901
AM NEW YORK—See Altice USA, Inc.; *U.S. Public*, pg. 87

513110 — NEWSPAPER PUBLISHER...

ANDERSON INDEPENDENT MAIL, LLC—See Gannett Co., Inc.; *U.S. Public*, pg. 898
ANTELOPE VALLEY NEWSPAPER INC.; *U.S. Private*, pg. 287
APACHE JUNCTION INDEPENDENT—See Independent Newspapers, Inc.; *U.S. Private*, pg. 2060
APM PRINT D.O.O.—See Axel Springer SE; *Int'l*, pg. 765
APN MEDIA (NZ) LIMITED—See ARN Media Limited; *Int'l*, pg. 576
APN SUPERANNUATION PTY LTD—See ARN Media Limited; *Int'l*, pg. 576
APPEAL-DEMOCRAT—See Horizon Publications Inc.; *U.S. Private*, pg. 1982
ARCOM PUBLISHING INC.; *U.S. Private*, pg. 315
AREAWIDE MEDIA INC.—See Rust Communications; *U.S. Private*, pg. 3507
ARGUS-COURIER—See Gannett Co., Inc.; *U.S. Public*, pg. 905
ARGUS LEADER—See Gannett Co., Inc.; *U.S. Public*, pg. 897
THE ARGUS—See Alden Global Capital LLC; *U.S. Private*, pg. 155
ARIPAEV, AS—See Bonnier AB; *Int'l*, pg. 1108
THE ARIZONA DAILY STAR—See Gannett Co., Inc.; *U.S. Public*, pg. 899
THE ARIZONA DAILY STAR—See Lee Enterprises, Incorporated; *U.S. Public*, pg. 1300
ARIZONA DAILY SUN—See Lee Enterprises, Incorporated; *U.S. Public*, pg. 1298
THE ARIZONA REPUBLIC—See Gannett Co., Inc.; *U.S. Public*, pg. 899
THE ARKANSAS CITY TRAVELER—See Winfield Publishing Co.; *U.S. Private*, pg. 4540
THE ARLINGTON ADVOCATE—See Gannett Co., Inc.; *U.S. Public*, pg. 903
ARMADA TIMES—See Alden Global Capital LLC; *U.S. Private*, pg. 159
ARN MEDIA LIMITED; *Int'l*, pg. 576
ARROWHEAD RANCH INDEPENDENT—See Independent Newspapers, Inc.; *U.S. Private*, pg. 2060
ARSEDITION GMBH—See Bonnier AB; *Int'l*, pg. 1108
ARTE GRAFICO EDITORIAL ARGENTINO S.A.—See Grupo Clarin S.A.; *Int'l*, pg. 3124
ASBURY PARK PRESS—See Gannett Co., Inc.; *U.S. Public*, pg. 897
AS EKSPRESS GRUPP; *Int'l*, pg. 589
ASHEVILLE CITIZEN-TIMES—See Gannett Co., Inc.; *U.S. Public*, pg. 897
ASHLAND DAILY TIDINGS—See Rosebud Media, LLC; *U.S. Private*, pg. 3482
ASHLAND PUBLISHING CO., LLC—See Gannett Co., Inc.; *U.S. Public*, pg. 901
ASHLAND TAB—See Gannett Co., Inc.; *U.S. Public*, pg. 901
ASIAN AGE HOLDINGS LTD.—See Deccan Chronicle Holdings Ltd.; *Int'l*, pg. 1999
ASIAN WEEK FOUNDATION—See AsianWeek; *U.S. Private*, pg. 351
ASIANWEEK; *U.S. Private*, pg. 351
ASP WESTWARD, L.P.—See American Securities LLC; *U.S. Private*, pg. 247
ASSOCIATED NEWSPAPERS LTD.—See Daily Mail & General Trust plc; *Int'l*, pg. 1937
ATHENS BANNER-HERALD—See Gannett Co., Inc.; *U.S. Public*, pg. 901
THE ATHENS MESSENGER—See American Consolidated Media LP; *U.S. Private*, pg. 228
THE ATLANTA JOURNAL-CONSTITUTION—See Apollo Global Management, Inc.; *U.S. Public*, pg. 163
THE ATLANTIC ADVERTISING SALES—See National Journal Group; *U.S. Private*, pg. 2858
ATTICA PUBLICATIONS S.A.; *Int'l*, pg. 696
AUBURN JOURNAL INC.—See Brehm Communications Inc.; *U.S. Private*, pg. 644
AUBURN TRADER—See Brehm Communications Inc.; *U.S. Private*, pg. 644
THE AUGUSTA CHRONICLE—See Gannett Co., Inc.; *U.S. Public*, pg. 904
AUSTRALIAN PROVINCIAL NEWSPAPERS INTERNATIONAL PTY LIMITED—See ARN Media Limited; *Int'l*, pg. 576
AUSTRALIAN PROVINCIAL NEWSPAPERS LTD—See ARN Media Limited; *Int'l*, pg. 576
AUTOMOBILWOCHE—See Crain Communications, Inc.; *U.S. Private*, pg. 1083
AUTOMOTIVE NEWS—See Crain Communications, Inc.; *U.S. Private*, pg. 1083
AVANT PUBLICATIONS LLC; *U.S. Private*, pg. 404
AVERY JOURNAL-TIMES—See Adams Publishing Group, LLC; *U.S. Private*, pg. 75
AXEL SPRINGER BUDAPEST GMBH—See Axel Springer SE; *Int'l*, pg. 766
AXEL SPRINGER CORPORATE SOLUTIONS GMBH & CO. KG—See Axel Springer SE; *Int'l*, pg. 766
AXEL SPRINGER ESPANA S.A.—See Axel Springer SE; *Int'l*, pg. 766
AXEL SPRINGER POLSKA SP.Z O.O.—See Axel Springer SE; *Int'l*, pg. 766
AZ ANZEIGER AG—See BT Holding AG; *Int'l*, pg. 1204

513110 — NEWSPAPER PUBLISHER... CORPORATE AFFILIATIONS

AZUSA HIGHLANDER—See Alden Global Capital LLC; *U.S. Private*, pg. 158
THE BAKER CITY HERALD—See Western Communications Inc.; *U.S. Private*, pg. 4491
THE BAKERSFIELD CALIFORNIAN; *U.S. Private*, pg. 3991
BALTIMORE BUSINESS JOURNAL—See Advance Publications, Inc.; *U.S. Private*, pg. 84
THE BALTIMORE SUN COMPANY—See Tribune Publishing Company; *U.S. Private*, pg. 4228
BALTIMORE SUN MEDIA GROUP—See Tribune Publishing Company; *U.S. Private*, pg. 4228
BANGKOK POST PUBLIC COMPANY LIMITED; *Int'l*, pg. 835
BANGOR PUBLISHING COMPANY; *U.S. Private*, pg. 466
BANNER-GRAPHIC—See Rust Communications; *U.S. Private*, pg. 3507
BANNER NEWS PUBLISHING CO. INC.—See Wehco Media, Inc.; *U.S. Private*, pg. 4469
BARANSKI PUBLISHING COMPANY—See Barancorp, Ltd.; *U.S. Private*, pg. 471
BATTLE CREEK ENQUIRER—See Gannett Co., Inc.; *U.S. Public*, pg. 897
BAUER SICHUAN CULTURE SERVICE CO.LTD.—See Heinrich Bauer Verlag KG; *Int'l*, pg. 3324
BAUER VERTRIEBS KG—See Heinrich Bauer Verlag KG; *Int'l*, pg. 3324
THE BAXTER BULLETIN—See Gannett Co., Inc.; *U.S. Public*, pg. 897
BAXTER COUNTY NEWSPAPERS, INC.—See Gannett Co., Inc.; *U.S. Public*, pg. 897
THE BEACH REPORTER—See Alden Global Capital LLC; *U.S. Private*, pg. 158
THE BEACON JOURNAL PUBLISHING COMPANY—See Gannett Co., Inc.; *U.S. Public*, pg. 904
THE BEACON—See Gannett Co., Inc.; *U.S. Public*, pg. 903
THE BEACON-VILLAGER—See Gannett Co., Inc.; *U.S. Public*, pg. 903
THE BEAUFORT GAZETTE—See Chatham Asset Management, LLC; *U.S. Private*, pg. 866
BEAUMONT ENTERPRISE—See The Hearst Corporation; *U.S. Private*, pg. 4047
BEAVER NEWSPAPERS INC.—See Gannett Co., Inc.; *U.S. Public*, pg. 901
BEDFORD MINUTEMAN—See Gannett Co., Inc.; *U.S. Public*, pg. 901
BELLEVILLE INTELLIGENCER—See Chatham Asset Management, LLC; *U.S. Private*, pg. 861
BELLEVILLE NEWS-DEMOCRAT—See Chatham Asset Management, LLC; *U.S. Private*, pg. 866
THE BELLINGHAM HERALD—See Chatham Asset Management, LLC; *U.S. Private*, pg. 866
BELLOWS FALLS TOWN CRIER—See Alden Global Capital LLC; *U.S. Private*, pg. 155
BELMONT CITIZEN-HERALD—See Gannett Co., Inc.; *U.S. Public*, pg. 901
BELO ENTERPRISES, INC.—See DallasNews Corporation; *U.S. Public*, pg. 621
BELTON PUBLISHING COMPANY—See Chatham Asset Management, LLC; *U.S. Private*, pg. 866
THE BENNINGTON BANNER—See Alden Global Capital LLC; *U.S. Private*, pg. 158
BENTON COUNTY DAILY RECORD—See Wehco Media, Inc.; *U.S. Private*, pg. 4470
BERJAYA MEDIA BERHAD—See Berjaya Corporation Berhad; *Int'l*, pg. 983
THE BERKSHIRE EAGLE—See Alden Global Capital LLC; *U.S. Private*, pg. 158
BERLINGSKE MEDIA A/S—See DPG Media Group NV; *Int'l*, pg. 2188
BEVERLY CITIZEN—See Gannett Co., Inc.; *U.S. Public*, pg. 902
THE B. F. SHAW PRINTING COMPANY; *U.S. Private*, pg. 3990
BH MEDIA GROUP—See Lee Enterprises, Incorporated; *U.S. Public*, pg. 1298
BIFFIN PTY LIMITED—See ARN Media Limited; *Int'l*, pg. 576
BIG MAGAZINES LIMITED PARTNERSHIP—See GVIC Communications Corp.; *Int'l*, pg. 3189
BIG SKY PUBLISHING CO. INC.—See Pioneer Newspapers Inc.; *U.S. Private*, pg. 3187
BILANZ DEUTSCHLAND WIRTSCHAFTSMAGAZIN GMBH—See Axel Springer SE; *Int'l*, pg. 766
BILLERICA MINUTEMAN—See Gannett Co., Inc.; *U.S. Public*, pg. 902
THE BILLINGS GAZETTE—See Lee Enterprises, Incorporated; *U.S. Public*, pg. 1300
BIRMINGHAM NEWS—See Advance Publications, Inc.; *U.S. Private*, pg. 85
THE BISMARCK TRIBUNE—See Lee Enterprises, Incorporated; *U.S. Public*, pg. 1300
BLACK MOUNTAIN NEWS—See Gannett Co., Inc.; *U.S. Public*, pg. 897
BLACK PRESS GROUP LTD.; *Int'l*, pg. 1059
THE BLADE CO.—See Block Communications, Inc.; *U.S. Private*, pg. 582
BLETHEN CORPORATION; *U.S. Private*, pg. 580
BLOCK COMMUNICATIONS, INC.; *U.S. Private*, pg. 582

THE BLOWING ROCKET—See Adams Publishing Group, LLC; *U.S. Private*, pg. 75
BONITA BANNER—See Gannett Co., Inc.; *U.S. Public*, pg. 898
BONNIER BUSINESS FORUM OY—See Bonnier AB; *Int'l*, pg. 1108
BONNIER BUSINESS MEDIA SWEDEN AB—See Bonnier AB; *Int'l*, pg. 1108
BONNIER BUSINESS PRESS, ZAO—See Bonnier AB; *Int'l*, pg. 1108
BONNIER NEWSPAPERS—See Bonnier AB; *Int'l*, pg. 1109
BOOTH NEWSPAPERS, INC.—See Advance Publications, Inc.; *U.S. Private*, pg. 85
BOOTH NEWSPAPERS—See Advance Publications, Inc.; *U.S. Private*, pg. 85
BOOTH NEWSPAPERS—See Advance Publications, Inc.; *U.S. Private*, pg. 85
BOSTON BUSINESS JOURNAL—See Advance Publications, Inc.; *U.S. Private*, pg. 84
BOSTON GLOBE ELECTRONIC PUBLISHING LLC—See NE Media Group, Inc.; *U.S. Private*, pg. 2877
THE BOSTON GLOBE—See NE Media Group, Inc.; *U.S. Private*, pg. 2877
THE BRADENTON HERALD—See Chatham Asset Management, LLC; *U.S. Private*, pg. 866
BRAINERD DISPATCH—See Forum Communications Company; *U.S. Private*, pg. 1577
BRAINTREE FORUM—See Gannett Co., Inc.; *U.S. Public*, pg. 902
THE BRANTFORD EXPOSITOR—See Chatham Asset Management, LLC; *U.S. Private*, pg. 861
BRATTLEBORO REFORMER—See Alden Global Capital LLC; *U.S. Private*, pg. 155
THE BRAZIL TIMES—See Rust Communications; *U.S. Private*, pg. 3507
THE BRECKENRIDGE AMERICAN—See Alden Global Capital LLC; *U.S. Private*, pg. 156
THE BREEZE CORPORATION—See The Nutting Company, Inc.; *U.S. Private*, pg. 4086
BRIDGEPORT NEWS—See Hersam Acorn Newspapers LLC; *U.S. Private*, pg. 1926
BRISTOL HERALD COURIER—See Lee Enterprises, Incorporated; *U.S. Public*, pg. 1298
BRITISH PATHE PLC—See Daily Mail & General Trust plc; *Int'l*, pg. 1937
BROAD STREET MEDIA, LLC - CHERRY HILL—See Broad Street Media, LLC; *U.S. Private*, pg. 658
BROAD STREET MEDIA, LLC; *U.S. Private*, pg. 658
BROOKINGS NEWSPAPERS LLC—See News Media Corporation; *U.S. Private*, pg. 2916
BROOMFIELD ENTERPRISE—See Alden Global Capital LLC; *U.S. Private*, pg. 157
BROWN CITY BANNER—See JAMS Media LLC; *U.S. Private*, pg. 2186
BROWN COUNTY DEMOCRAT—See Home News Enterprises, LLC; *U.S. Private*, pg. 1971
THE BROWNSVILLE HERALD—See AIM Media Texas, LLC; *U.S. Private*, pg. 132
BROWNWOOD NEWSPAPERS, INC.—See American Consolidated Media LP; *U.S. Private*, pg. 228
BRUNSWICK NEWS, INC.—See Chatham Asset Management, LLC; *U.S. Private*, pg. 860
BRUSH NEWS TRIBUNE—See Alden Global Capital LLC; *U.S. Private*, pg. 157
BRYAN-COLLEGE STATION COMMUNICATIONS, INC.—See Berkshire Hathaway Inc.; *U.S. Public*, pg. 303
BUCYRUS TELEGRAPH-FORUM—See Gannett Co., Inc.; *U.S. Public*, pg. 897
BUFFALO LAW JOURNAL—See Advance Publications, Inc.; *U.S. Private*, pg. 84
THE BUFFALO NEWS—See Lee Enterprises, Incorporated; *U.S. Public*, pg. 1300
BUILDER MEDIA SOLUTIONS, LLC—See Tribune Publishing Company; *U.S. Private*, pg. 4227
THE BULLETIN—See Gannett Co., Inc.; *U.S. Public*, pg. 904
THE BULLETIN—See Western Communications Inc.; *U.S. Private*, pg. 4491
BURBANK LEADER—See Los Angeles Times Communications, LLC; *U.S. Private*, pg. 2497
THE BUREAU OF NATIONAL AFFAIRS, INC.—See Bloomberg L.P.; *U.S. Private*, pg. 583
BURLESON STAR—See Alden Global Capital LLC; *U.S. Private*, pg. 156
BURLINGTON FREE PRESS—See Gannett Co., Inc.; *U.S. Public*, pg. 897
THE BURLINGTON RECORD—See Alden Global Capital LLC; *U.S. Private*, pg. 157
BURLINGTON TIMES, INC.—See Gannett Co., Inc.; *U.S. Public*, pg. 901
BURLINGTON UNION—See Gannett Co., Inc.; *U.S. Public*, pg. 902
BURNS TIMES-HERALD—See Survival Media LLC; *U.S. Private*, pg. 3885
BUSINESS FIRST OF COLUMBUS—See Advance Publications, Inc.; *U.S. Private*, pg. 84
BUSINESS FIRST OF LOUISVILLE—See Advance Publications, Inc.; *U.S. Private*, pg. 84

BUSINESS INSURANCE—See Crain Communications, Inc.; *U.S. Private*, pg. 1084
BUSINESS OBSERVER—See Observer Media Group, Inc.; *U.S. Private*, pg. 2988
THE BUSINESS REVIEW—See Advance Publications, Inc.; *U.S. Private*, pg. 85
CACHE VALLEY PUBLISHING COMPANY—See Pioneer Newspapers Inc.; *U.S. Private*, pg. 3187
CALGARY HERALD—See Chatham Asset Management, LLC; *U.S. Private*, pg. 861
THE CALGARY SUN—See Chatham Asset Management, LLC; *U.S. Private*, pg. 861
CALIFORNIA DEMOCRAT—See Wehco Media, Inc.; *U.S. Private*, pg. 4469
CAMBRIDGE CHRONICLE—See Gannett Co., Inc.; *U.S. Public*, pg. 902
CAMDEN NEWS PUBLISHING COMPANY—See Wehco Media, Inc.; *U.S. Private*, pg. 4469
CANON CITY DAILY RECORD—See Alden Global Capital LLC; *U.S. Private*, pg. 157
THE CANTON REPOSITORY—See Gannett Co., Inc.; *U.S. Public*, pg. 904
CAPE CODDER—See Gannett Co., Inc.; *U.S. Public*, pg. 902
CAPE COD TIMES—See Gannett Co., Inc.; *U.S. Public*, pg. 904
CAPE PUBLICATIONS, INC.—See TEGNA Inc.; *U.S. Public*, pg. 1990
CAPITAL CITY PRESS; *U.S. Private*, pg. 739
CAPITAL GAZETTE COMMUNICATIONS INC.—See Irish Times; *U.S. Private*, pg. 2138
THE CAPITAL TIMES COMPANY; *U.S. Private*, pg. 4004
THE CAPITAL TIMES—See Lee Enterprises, Incorporated; *U.S. Public*, pg. 1299
THE CAPITAL TIMES—See The Capital Times Company; *U.S. Private*, pg. 4004
CAPITOL CITY PUBLISHING COMPANY, INC.—See Alden Global Capital LLC; *U.S. Private*, pg. 156
CAPITOL NEWS COMPANY, LLC—See Sinclair, Inc.; *U.S. Public*, pg. 1585
CARLSBAD CURRENT-ARGUS—See Gannett Co., Inc.; *U.S. Public*, pg. 899
CARROLL COUNTY TIMES—See Irish Times; *U.S. Private*, pg. 2138
CASIANO COMMUNICATIONS INC.; *U.S. Private*, pg. 783
CASNIK FINANCE, D.O.O.—See Bonnier AB; *Int'l*, pg. 1108
CASS COUNTY PUBLISHING COMPANY, INC.—See Chatham Asset Management, LLC; *U.S. Private*, pg. 866
CHAMPION PUBLISHING, INC.—See Champion Industries, Inc.; *U.S. Public*, pg. 478
CHAPEL HILL PUBLISHING CO.—See Chatham Asset Management, LLC; *U.S. Private*, pg. 866
THE CHARIHO TIMES—See R.I.S.N. Operations Inc.; *U.S. Private*, pg. 3336
CHARLESTON DAILY MAIL—See Alden Global Capital LLC; *U.S. Private*, pg. 156
THE CHARLESTON MERCURY—See Evening Post Publishing Co.; *U.S. Private*, pg. 1436
CHARLOTTE BUSINESS JOURNAL—See Advance Publications, Inc.; *U.S. Private*, pg. 84
THE CHARLOTTE OBSERVER PUBLISHING CO.—See Chatham Asset Management, LLC; *U.S. Private*, pg. 867
CHARLOTTE SUN—See Sun Coast Media Group, Inc.; *U.S. Private*, pg. 3862
THE CHATHAM DAILY NEWS—See Chatham Asset Management, LLC; *U.S. Private*, pg. 861
CHATTANOOGA PUBLISHING CO. INC.—See Wehco Media, Inc.; *U.S. Private*, pg. 4469
CHATTANOOGA TIMES FREE PRESS COMPANY—See Wehco Media, Inc.; *U.S. Private*, pg. 4469
CHESAPEAKE PUBLISHING & PRINTING—See American Consolidated Media LP; *U.S. Private*, pg. 228
CHESTER PROGRESSIVE—See Feather Publishing Co., Inc.; *U.S. Private*, pg. 1486
CHICAGO READER—See Chicago Public Media, Inc.; *U.S. Private*, pg. 879
CHICAGO SUN-TIMES MEDIA, INC.—See Chicago Public Media, Inc.; *U.S. Private*, pg. 879
CHICAGO SUN-TIMES—See Chicago Public Media, Inc.; *U.S. Private*, pg. 879
CHICAGO TRIBUNE—See Tribune Publishing Company; *U.S. Private*, pg. 4227
CHIIKISHINBUNSHA CO., LTD.; *Int'l*, pg. 1478
CHILLICOTHE GAZETTE—See Gannett Co., Inc.; *U.S. Public*, pg. 897
CHINA MEDIA GROUP; *Int'l*, pg. 1518
CHINA TOPREACH INC.; *Int'l*, pg. 1560
CHIPPEWA VALLEY ETHANOL COMPANY, LLC—See Chippewa Valley Agrafuels Cooperative; *U.S. Private*, pg. 886
CHRONICLE OF HIGHER EDUCATION; *U.S. Private*, pg. 893
THE CHRONICLE—See Community Media Group; *U.S. Private*, pg. 995
CHRONICLE-TRIBUNE—See Paxton Media Group LLC; *U.S. Private*, pg. 3116
CHUNICHI SHIMBUN CO., LTD.; *Int'l*, pg. 1598
CINCINNATI BUSINESS COURIER—See Advance Publica-

N.A.I.C.S. INDEX
513110 — NEWSPAPER PUBLISHER...

tions, Inc.; *U.S. Private*, pg. 84
THE CINCINNATI ENQUIRER—See Gannett Co., Inc.; *U.S. Public*, pg. 900
CITIZEN PUBLISHING COMPANY—See Gannett Co., Inc.; *U.S. Public*, pg. 896
CITRUS COUNTY CHRONICLE—See Irish Times; *U.S. Private*, pg. 2138
CIVITAS MEDIA, LLC—See Independence Capital Partners, LLC; *U.S. Private*, pg. 2057
THE CLARION-LEDGER—See Gannett Co., Inc.; *U.S. Public*, pg. 900
CLASS EDITORI S.P.A.; *Int'l*, pg. 1652
CLEAR LAKE OBSERVER AMERICAN—See Alden Global Capital LLC; *U.S. Private*, pg. 156
CLEVELAND SCENE PUBLISHING LLC—See Great Lakes Publishing Company; *U.S. Private*, pg. 1765
CLEWISTON NEWS—See Independent Newspapers, Inc.; *U.S. Private*, pg. 2060
CLOVIS MEDIA, INC.; *U.S. Private*, pg. 948
CNHI, LLC—See The Retirement Systems of Alabama; *U.S. Private*, pg. 4105
THE COALINGA RECORD—See Lee Enterprises, Incorporated; *U.S. Public*, pg. 1300
THE COASTAL JOURNAL—See MaineToday Media, Inc.; *U.S. Private*, pg. 2553
COBOURG DAILY STAR—See Chatham Asset Management, LLC; *U.S. Private*, pg. 861
COFINA SGPS, S.A.; *Int'l*, pg. 1692
COHASSET MARINER—See Gannett Co., Inc.; *U.S. Public*, pg. 902
COLORADO COMMUNITY MEDIA—See Macari-Healey Publishing Company, LLC; *U.S. Private*, pg. 2534
COLORADO DAILY—See Alden Global Capital LLC; *U.S. Private*, pg. 157
COLORADO HOMETOWN WEEKLY—See Alden Global Capital LLC; *U.S. Private*, pg. 157
COLUMBIA BASIN PUBLISHING CO., INC.—See The Hagadone Corporation; *U.S. Private*, pg. 4041
THE COLUMBIA COUNTY NEWS-TIMES—See Shivers Trading & Operating Company; *U.S. Private*, pg. 3638
THE COLUMBUS LEDGER-ENQUIRER—See Chatham Asset Management, LLC; *U.S. Private*, pg. 867
COLUMBUS TELEGRAM—See Lee Enterprises, Incorporated; *U.S. Public*, pg. 1299
COMET-PRESS NEWSPAPERS, INC.—See Gannett Co., Inc.; *U.S. Public*, pg. 905
COMMERCIAL-NEWS—See The Retirement Systems of Alabama; *U.S. Private*, pg. 4105
COMMONWEALTH JOURNAL INC.—See The Retirement Systems of Alabama; *U.S. Private*, pg. 4105
COMMUNITY HOLDINGS OF KENTUCKY LLC—See The Retirement Systems of Alabama; *U.S. Private*, pg. 4105
COMMUNITY NEWSPAPERS INC.; *U.S. Private*, pg. 996
CONNECTICUT POST—See The Hearst Corporation; *U.S. Private*, pg. 4047
CONNERSVILLE NEWS EXAMINER—See Paxton Media Group LLC; *U.S. Private*, pg. 3116
CONTRA COSTA NEWSPAPERS, INC.—See Alden Global Capital LLC; *U.S. Private*, pg. 155
CONTRA COSTA TIMES—See Alden Global Capital LLC; *U.S. Private*, pg. 155
COOKE COMMUNICATIONS FLORIDA, LLC; *U.S. Private*, pg. 1039
COOKE COMMUNICATIONS NORTH CAROLINA, LLC—See Cooke Communications Florida, LLC; *U.S. Private*, pg. 1039
CORNWALL STANDARD-FREEHOLDER—See Chatham Asset Management, LLC; *U.S. Private*, pg. 861
CORPUS CHRISTI CALLER-TIMES LLC—See Gannett Co., Inc.; *U.S. Public*, pg. 898
CORRIERE ADRIATICO SRL—See Caltagirone Editore S.p.A.; *Int'l*, pg. 1265
CORVALLIS GAZETTE-TIMES—See Lee Enterprises, Incorporated; *U.S. Public*, pg. 1299
COTTAGE GROVE SENTINEL—See News Media Corporation; *U.S. Private*, pg. 2916
COULTER PRESS—See Gannett Co., Inc.; *U.S. Public*, pg. 906
COUNTRY GAZETTE—See Gannett Co., Inc.; *U.S. Public*, pg. 902
THE COURIER-JOURNAL, INC.—See Gannett Co., Inc.; *U.S. Public*, pg. 900
COURIER NEWSPAPER HOLDINGS PTY LIMITED—See News Corporation; *U.S. Public*, pg. 1519
THE COURIER NEWS—See Chicago Public Media, Inc.; *U.S. Private*, pg. 879
COURIER NEWS—See Gannett Co., Inc.; *U.S. Public*, pg. 897
COURIER-POST—See Gannett Co., Inc.; *U.S. Public*, pg. 897
THE COURIER—See Gannett Co., Inc.; *U.S. Public*, pg. 904
COURIER TIMES, INC.—See Gannett Co., Inc.; *U.S. Public*, pg. 901
COURIER TIMES NEWSPAPER—See Paxton Media Group LLC; *U.S. Private*, pg. 3116
THE COVENTRY COURIER—See R.I.S.N. Operations Inc.; *U.S. Private*, pg. 3336
COVINA PRESS-COURIER HIGHLANDER—See Alden Global Capital LLC; *U.S. Private*, pg. 158
COWLES PUBLISHING COMPANY—See Cowles Company; *U.S. Private*, pg. 1073
COX ENTERPRISES, INC.; *U.S. Private*, pg. 1074
COX NEWSPAPERS, INC.—See Apollo Global Management, Inc.; *U.S. Public*, pg. 163
CRAIG DAILY PRESS—See The World Company; *U.S. Private*, pg. 4139
CRAIN COMMUNICATIONS GMBH—See Crain Communications, Inc.; *U.S. Private*, pg. 1083
CRAIN COMMUNICATIONS, INC. - AUTOMOTIVE NEWS CHINA UNIT—See Crain Communications, Inc.; *U.S. Private*, pg. 1083
CRAIN'S CHICAGO BUSINESS—See Crain Communications, Inc.; *U.S. Private*, pg. 1084
CRAIN'S CLEVELAND BUSINESS—See Crain Communications, Inc.; *U.S. Private*, pg. 1084
CRAIN'S DETROIT BUSINESS—See Crain Communications, Inc.; *U.S. Private*, pg. 1084
CRAIN'S NEW YORK BUSINESS—See Crain Communications, Inc.; *U.S. Private*, pg. 1084
CRANBROOK DAILY TOWNSMAN—See Black Press Group Ltd.; *Int'l*, pg. 1059
CREATIVE LOAFING ATLANTA, INC.—See SouthComm, Inc.; *U.S. Private*, pg. 3724
CREATIVE LOAFING-CHARLOTTE—See Womack Publishing Company, Inc.; *U.S. Private*, pg. 4555
CREATIVE LOAFING TAMPA, LLC—See SouthComm, Inc.; *U.S. Private*, pg. 3724
CRISFIELD TIMES—See Independent Newspapers, Inc.; *U.S. Private*, pg. 2060
CROWLEY STAR—See Alden Global Capital LLC; *U.S. Private*, pg. 156
CULPEPER STAR-EXPONENT—See Lee Enterprises, Incorporated; *U.S. Public*, pg. 1298
CULTUREMAP LLC—See ViewMarket Inc.; *U.S. Private*, pg. 4381
CURRY COASTAL PILOT—See Western Communications Inc.; *U.S. Private*, pg. 4491
CYNTHIANA PUBLISHING CO.—See Irish Times; *U.S. Private*, pg. 2138
CYPRESS MEDIA, INC.—See Chatham Asset Management, LLC; *U.S. Private*, pg. 866
CYPRESS MEDIA, LLC—See Chatham Asset Management, LLC; *U.S. Private*, pg. 866
D.A. BARANSKI & CO.—See Barancorp, Ltd.; *U.S. Private*, pg. 471
DAGBLADET BORSEN A/S—See Bonnier AB; *Int'l*, pg. 1108
DAGENS INDUSTRI AB—See Bonnier AB; *Int'l*, pg. 1108
DAGENS MEDICIN A/S—See Bonnier AB; *Int'l*, pg. 1108
DAGENS MEDISIN AS—See Bonnier AB; *Int'l*, pg. 1108
DAGENS NAERINGSLIV AS—See Fred. Olsen & Co.; *Int'l*, pg. 2768
DAGENS NAERINGSLIV-BERGEN—See Fred. Olsen & Co.; *Int'l*, pg. 2768
DAGENS NAERINGSLIV-KRISTIANSAND—See Fred. Olsen & Co.; *Int'l*, pg. 2768
DAGENS NAERINGSLIV-LILLEHAMMER—See Fred. Olsen & Co.; *Int'l*, pg. 2768
DAGENS NAERINGSLIV-STAVANGER—See Fred. Olsen & Co.; *Int'l*, pg. 2768
DAGENS NAERINGSLIV-TELEMARK/VESTFOLD—See Fred. Olsen & Co.; *Int'l*, pg. 2768
DAGENS NAERINGSLIV-TROMSO—See Fred. Olsen & Co.; *Int'l*, pg. 2768
DAGENS NAERINGSLIV-TRONDHEIM—See Fred. Olsen & Co.; *Int'l*, pg. 2768
THE DAILY ARDMOREITE—See Gannett Co., Inc.; *U.S. Public*, pg. 904
THE DAILY BEAST—See IAC Inc.; *U.S. Public*, pg. 1083
THE DAILY BREEZE—See Alden Global Capital LLC; *U.S. Private*, pg. 158
DAILY CAMERA—See Alden Global Capital LLC; *U.S. Private*, pg. 157
DAILY CAMERA—See Alden Global Capital LLC; *U.S. Private*, pg. 157
THE DAILY CHRONICLE—See Shaw Suburban Media Group, Inc.; *U.S. Private*, pg. 3628
THE DAILY DEMOCRAT—See Alden Global Capital LLC; *U.S. Private*, pg. 156
THE DAILY DISPATCH—See Paxton Media Group LLC; *U.S. Private*, pg. 3116
DAILY GAZETTE CO. INC.; *U.S. Private*, pg. 1145
THE DAILY HERALD COMPANY—See Black Press Group Ltd.; *Int'l*, pg. 1059
THE DAILY HERALD—See Lee Enterprises, Incorporated; *U.S. Public*, pg. 1300
THE DAILY INDEPENDENT, INC.—See Gannett Co., Inc.; *U.S. Public*, pg. 906
THE DAILY ITEM; *U.S. Private*, pg. 4017
THE DAILY ITEM—See The Retirement Systems of Alabama; *U.S. Private*, pg. 4105
DAILY JOURNAL CORPORATION; *U.S. Public*, pg. 620
THE DAILY JOURNAL—See Gannett Co., Inc.; *U.S. Public*, pg. 900
DAILY JOURNAL—See Home News Enterprises, LLC; *U.S. Private*, pg. 1971
THE DAILY JOURNAL—See Lee Enterprises, Incorporated; *U.S. Public*, pg. 1300
THE DAILY LOCAL NEWS—See Alden Global Capital LLC; *U.S. Private*, pg. 158
DAILY MAIL & GENERAL TRUST PLC; *Int'l*, pg. 1937
THE DAILY NEWS - JACKSONVILLE, NC—See Gannett Co., Inc.; *U.S. Public*, pg. 906
DAILY NEWS, L.P.; *U.S. Private*, pg. 1145
THE DAILY NEWS—See Alden Global Capital LLC; *U.S. Private*, pg. 158
THE DAILY NEWS—See The Nutting Company, Inc.; *U.S. Private*, pg. 4086
DAILY NEWS-SUN - SURPRISE TODAY - GLENDALE/PEORIA TODAY—See 10/13 Communications LLC; *U.S. Private*, pg. 2
DAILY NEWS TRIBUNE INC.—See The B. F. Shaw Printing Company; *U.S. Private*, pg. 3990
THE DAILY OAKLAND PRESS—See Alden Global Capital LLC; *U.S. Private*, pg. 158
THE DAILY PRESS, INC.—See Tribune Publishing Company; *U.S. Public*, pg. 4228
THE DAILY PRESS—See American Consolidated Media LP; *U.S. Private*, pg. 228
DAILY PRESS—See Gannett Co., Inc.; *U.S. Public*, pg. 904
THE DAILY PROGRESS—See Lee Enterprises, Incorporated; *U.S. Public*, pg. 1299
DAILY RACING FORM, LLC—See Z Capital Group, LLC; *U.S. Private*, pg. 4595
DAILY RECORD NEWSPAPER—See Pioneer Newspapers Inc.; *U.S. Private*, pg. 3187
DAILY RECORD—See Gannett Co., Inc.; *U.S. Public*, pg. 897
DAILY REPORTER PUBLISHING COMPANY—See The Dolan Company; *U.S. Private*, pg. 4022
THE DAILY REPORTER—See Gannett Co., Inc.; *U.S. Public*, pg. 904
DAILY REPORTER—See Home News Enterprises, LLC; *U.S. Private*, pg. 1971
DAILY REPUBLICAN REGISTER—See Brehm Communications Inc.; *U.S. Private*, pg. 644
THE DAILY REVIEW—See Alden Global Capital LLC; *U.S. Private*, pg. 155
THE DAILY SOUTHERNER—See The Retirement Systems of Alabama; *U.S. Private*, pg. 4105
THE DAILY STAR—See The Retirement Systems of Alabama; *U.S. Private*, pg. 4105
THE DAILY TELEGRAM—See Forum Communications Company; *U.S. Private*, pg. 1577
DAILY TIMES LEADER—See Horizon Publications Inc.; *U.S. Private*, pg. 1982
THE DAILY TIMES—See Gannett Co., Inc.; *U.S. Public*, pg. 900
THE DAILY TIMES—See Gannett Co., Inc.; *U.S. Public*, pg. 900
THE DAILY TRIBUNE—See Alden Global Capital LLC; *U.S. Private*, pg. 158
DAILY TRIBUNE—See Gannett Co., Inc.; *U.S. Public*, pg. 897
DAILY WORLD—See Gannett Co., Inc.; *U.S. Public*, pg. 897
THE DALLAS MORNING NEWS, INC.—See DallasNews Corporation; *U.S. Public*, pg. 621
DALLAS OBSERVER, LP—See Village Voice Media Holdings, LLC; *U.S. Private*, pg. 4384
DANVERS HERALD—See Gannett Co., Inc.; *U.S. Public*, pg. 902
DANVILLE REGISTER & BEE—See Lee Enterprises, Incorporated; *U.S. Public*, pg. 1298
DAVIE COUNTY ENTERPRISE-RECORD—See Evening Post Publishing Co.; *U.S. Private*, pg. 1436
THE DAY PUBLISHER COMPANY; *U.S. Private*, pg. 4019
THE DAY PUBLISHING COMPANY INC.—See The Day Publisher Company; *U.S. Private*, pg. 4019
DAYTONA BEACH NEWS-JOURNAL CORP.—See Gannett Co., Inc.; *U.S. Public*, pg. 905
DAYTON BUSINESS JOURNAL—See Advance Publications, Inc.; *U.S. Private*, pg. 84
DAYTON NEWSPAPERS, INC.—See Apollo Global Management, Inc.; *U.S. Public*, pg. 163
DB CORP LIMITED; *Int'l*, pg. 1986
D B CORP LTD.; *Int'l*, pg. 1899
D.C. THOMSON & CO. LTD.; *Int'l*, pg. 1900
DEFIANCE PUBLISHING COMPANY, LLC—See Adams Publishing Group, LLC; *U.S. Private*, pg. 75
DELAWARE PRINTING COMPANY—See Independent Newspapers, Inc.; *U.S. Private*, pg. 2060
DELAWARE STATE NEWS—See Independent Newspapers, Inc.; *U.S. Private*, pg. 2060
DELFI AS—See AS Ekspress Grupp; *Int'l*, pg. 589
DELFI UAB—See AS Ekspress Grupp; *Int'l*, pg. 590
THE DEL NORTE TRIPLICATE—See Western Communications Inc.; *U.S. Private*, pg. 4492
DELPHOS HERALD INC.; *U.S. Private*, pg. 1199
DELTA DEFENSE, LLC; *U.S. Public*, pg. 1199
THE DEMING HEADLIGHT—See Gannett Co., Inc.; *U.S. Public*, pg. 900
DEMOCRAT & CHRONICLE—See Gannett Co., Inc.; *U.S. Public*, pg. 897

THE DEMOCRAT CO.—See Brehm Communications Inc.; *U.S. Private*, pg. 644
DEMOCRAT NEWS—See Lee Enterprises, Incorporated; *U.S. Public*, pg. 1299
DEN BLA AVIS A/S—See eBay Inc.; *U.S. Public*, pg. 709
DENVER BUSINESS JOURNAL—See Advance Publications, Inc.; *U.S. Private*, pg. 84
THE DENVER POST CORPORATION—See Alden Global Capital LLC; *U.S. Private*, pg. 158
DENVER WESTWORD, LLC—See Village Voice Media Holdings, LLC; *U.S. Private*, pg. 4384
DE PERSGROEP PRINTING B.V.—See DPG Media Group NV; *Int'l*, pg. 2188
DERRICK PUBLISHING CO.; *U.S. Private*, pg. 1210
DERRY PUBLISHING CO. INC.—See The Retirement Systems of Alabama; *U.S. Private*, pg. 4105
DESERET MORNING NEWS—See Deseret Management Corporation; *U.S. Private*, pg. 1212
DESERT DISPATCH—See Gannett Co., Inc.; *U.S. Public*, pg. 904
THE DESERT SUN PUBLISHING COMPANY—See Gannett Co., Inc.; *U.S. Public*, pg. 900
THE DESERT SUN—See Gannett Co., Inc.; *U.S. Public*, pg. 900
DES MOINES REGISTER AND TRIBUNE COMPANY—See Gannett Co., Inc.; *U.S. Public*, pg. 897
DESOTO SUN—See Sun Coast Media Group, Inc.; *U.S. Private*, pg. 3862
THE DESTIN LOG—See Gannett Co., Inc.; *U.S. Public*, pg. 906
DETROIT FREE PRESS, INC.—See Gannett Co., Inc.; *U.S. Public*, pg. 897
DETROIT LEGAL NEWS COMPANY; *U.S. Public*, pg. 657
DETROIT LEGAL NEWS PUBLISHING LLC—See Detroit Legal News Company; *U.S. Public*, pg. 657
THE DETROIT NEWS, INC.—See Alden Global Capital LLC; *U.S. Private*, pg. 158
DETROIT NEWSPAPER PARTNERSHIP, L.P.—See Gannett Co., Inc.; *U.S. Public*, pg. 897
DFW PRINTING COMPANY, INC.—See DallasNews Corporation; *U.S. Public*, pg. 621
DIAMOND BAR HIGHLANDER—See Alden Global Capital LLC; *U.S. Private*, pg. 158
DILIGENT MEDIA CORPORATION LIMITED; *Int'l*, pg. 2125
DIRECT MATIN PLUS—See Financiere de L'Odet; *Int'l*, pg. 2667
THE DISPATCH PUBLISHING COMPANY, INC.—See Gannett Co., Inc.; *U.S. Public*, pg. 905
DISPATCH PUBLISHING COMPANY, INC.—See Paxton Media Group LLC; *U.S. Private*, pg. 3116
DISTRIBUTION SERVICES, INC.—See Chatham Asset Management, LLC; *U.S. Private*, pg. 860
DODGE CITY DAILY GLOBE—See Gannett Co., Inc.; *U.S. Public*, pg. 901
DOGAN GAZETECILIK A.S.—See Adil Bey Holding A.S.; *Int'l*, pg. 148
DORCHESTER BANNER—See Independent Newspapers, Inc.; *U.S. Private*, pg. 2060
THE DOTHAN EAGLE—See Lee Enterprises, Incorporated; *U.S. Public*, pg. 1299
DOVER-SHERBORN PRESS—See Gannett Co., Inc.; *U.S. Public*, pg. 902
DOW JONES & COMPANY, INC.—See News Corporation; *U.S. Public*, pg. 1518
DOW JONES PUBLISHING COMPANY (ASIA), INC.—See News Corporation; *U.S. Public*, pg. 1518
DULUTH NEWS TRIBUNE—See Forum Communications Company; *U.S. Private*, pg. 1577
THE DURHAM HERALD CO.—See Paxton Media Group LLC; *U.S. Private*, pg. 3116
EAGLE HERALD PUBLISHING LLC—See Adams Publishing Group, LLC; *U.S. Private*, pg. 74
EAGLE NEWSPAPERS INC.; *U.S. Private*, pg. 1310
EAGLE PRINTING COMPANY; *U.S. Private*, pg. 1310
EAGLE PUBLISHING INC. - THE HUMAN EVENTS GROUP DIVISION—See Eagle Publishing Inc.; *U.S. Private*, pg. 1310
EAGLE-TRIBUNE PUBLISHING COMPANY INC.—See The Retirement Systems of Alabama; *U.S. Private*, pg. 4105
EASTERN PENNSYLVANIA BUSINESS JOURNAL—See Journal Publications, Inc.; *U.S. Private*, pg. 2238
THE EAST GREENWICH PENDULUM—See R.I.S.N. Operations Inc.; *U.S. Private*, pg. 3336
EASTON JOURNAL—See Gannett Co., Inc.; *U.S. Public*, pg. 902
EASTON PUBLISHING CO.—See Advance Publications, Inc.; *U.S. Private*, pg. 86
EASTON PUBLISHING CO.—See Advance Publications, Inc.; *U.S. Private*, pg. 86
EAST OREGONIAN PUBLISHING CO.; *U.S. Private*, pg. 1317
EAST OREGONIAN—See East Oregonian Publishing Co.; *U.S. Private*, pg. 1317
EAST VALLEY TRIBUNE—See EOS Publishing, LLC; *U.S. Private*, pg. 1411
EAU CLAIRE PRESS COMPANY—See Adams Publishing Group, LLC; *U.S. Private*, pg. 75
ECHO PUBLISHING & PRINTING—See Shivers Trading & Operating Company; *U.S. Private*, pg. 3638
ECHO PUBLISHING & PRINTING—See Shivers Trading & Operating Company; *U.S. Private*, pg. 3638
ECM PUBLISHERS, INC.—See Adams Publishing Group, LLC; *U.S. Private*, pg. 75
ECM-SUN GROUP, LLC—See Adams Publishing Group, LLC; *U.S. Private*, pg. 75
ECO LOG ENVIRONMENTAL RISK INFORMATION SERVICES LTD.—See GVIC Communications Corp.; *Int'l*, pg. 3189
ECO PRINT CENTER NV—See DPG Media Group NV; *Int'l*, pg. 2188
EDEN DAILY NEWS—See Lee Enterprises, Incorporated; *U.S. Public*, pg. 1299
EDIPRESSE SA; *Int'l*, pg. 2310
EDITORIAL C&P S.A.S.—See Grupo Televisa, S.A.B.; *Int'l*, pg. 3136
EDITORIALE FVG SPA—See Giovanni Agnelli B.V.; *Int'l*, pg. 2978
EDITORIALE LA NUOVA SARDEGNA SPA—See Giovanni Agnelli B.V.; *Int'l*, pg. 2978
EDITORIAL LA RAZON S.A.—See Grupo Clarin S.A.; *Int'l*, pg. 3125
EDMONTON JOURNAL—See Chatham Asset Management, LLC; *U.S. Private*, pg. 861
THE EDMONTON SUN—See Chatham Asset Management, LLC; *U.S. Private*, pg. 861
EDWARDS PUBLICATIONS INC.; *U.S. Private*, pg. 1342
EDWARDSVILLE PUBLISHING COMPANY, LLC—See The Hearst Corporation; *U.S. Private*, pg. 4047
EESTI AJALEHED AS—See AS Ekspress Grupp; *Int'l*, pg. 590
EINDHOVENS DAGBLAD B.V.—See DPG Media Group NV; *Int'l*, pg. 2189
ELAUWIT LLC; *U.S. Private*, pg. 1350
EL CLASIFICADO; *U.S. Private*, pg. 1348
EL DORADO NEWSPAPERS—See Chatham Asset Management, LLC; *U.S. Private*, pg. 866
EL DORADO NEWS-TIMES—See Wehco Media, Inc.; *U.S. Private*, pg. 4470
EL DORADO TIMES—See Gannett Co., Inc.; *U.S. Public*, pg. 901
ELKINS INTER-MOUNTAIN CO. INC.—See The Nutting Company, Inc.; *U.S. Private*, pg. 4086
ELMSHORNER NACHRICHTEN—See Axel Springer SE; *Int'l*, pg. 766
EL NUEVO HERALD—See Chatham Asset Management, LLC; *U.S. Private*, pg. 867
EL PASO TIMES—See Gannett Co., Inc.; *U.S. Public*, pg. 899
EL TIEMPO LATINO LLC—See Nash Holdings LLC; *U.S. Private*, pg. 2835
EMMETSBURG PUBLISHING CO.—See The Nutting Company, Inc.; *U.S. Private*, pg. 4086
ENIRO NORGE AS—See Eniro Group AB; *Int'l*, pg. 2439
ENIRO NORWAY—See Eniro Group AB; *Int'l*, pg. 2439
ENTERPRISE LEDGER—See Lee Enterprises, Incorporated; *U.S. Public*, pg. 1299
ENTERPRISE NEWSMEDIA, LLC—See Gannett Co., Inc.; *U.S. Public*, pg. 896
ENTERPRISE PUBLISHING COMPANY, LLC—See Gannett Co., Inc.; *U.S. Public*, pg. 902
ENTERPRISE-RECORD—See Alden Global Capital LLC; *U.S. Private*, pg. 155
EOS PUBLISHING, LLC; *U.S. Private*, pg. 1411
ESTES PARK TRAIL-GAZETTE—See Alden Global Capital LLC; *U.S. Private*, pg. 157
ESTHERVILLE PUBLICATIONS INC.—See The Nutting Company, Inc.; *U.S. Private*, pg. 4086
EVANSVILLE COURIER COMPANY, INC.—See Gannett Co., Inc.; *U.S. Public*, pg. 898
THE EVENING CALL PUBLISHING COMPANY—See R.I.S.N. Operations Inc.; *U.S. Private*, pg. 3337
EVENING POST DIGITAL—See Evening Post Publishing Co.; *U.S. Private*, pg. 1436
EVENING STANDARD LTD.; *Int'l*, pg. 2562
THE EVENING SUN—See Gannett Co., Inc.; *U.S. Public*, pg. 900
THE E.W. SCRIPPS COMPANY; *U.S. Public*, pg. 2067
THE EXAMINER—See Gannett Co., Inc.; *U.S. Public*, pg. 904
EXPRESS TIMES—See Advance Publications, Inc.; *U.S. Private*, pg. 86
FAIRBANKS DAILY NEWS-MINER INC.; *U.S. Private*, pg. 1462
FAIRFIELD COUNTY WEEKLY—See Tribune Publishing Company; *U.S. Private*, pg. 4228
FAYETTEVILLE PUBLISHING CO.—See Gannett Co., Inc.; *U.S. Public*, pg. 902
FEATHER PUBLISHING CO., INC.; *U.S. Private*, pg. 1486
FEATHER RIVER BULLETIN—See Feather Publishing Co., Inc.; *U.S. Private*, pg. 1486
FINANCE AND COMMERCE, INC.—See The Dolan Company; *U.S. Private*, pg. 4022
FINGER LAKES TIMES—See Community Media Group; *U.S. Private*, pg. 995
FLAGSTAFF PUBLISHING CO.—See Lee Enterprises, Incorporated; *U.S. Public*, pg. 1299
FLOOR COVERING WEEKLY—See The Hearst Corporation; *U.S. Private*, pg. 4048
FLORIDA HEALTH CARE NEWS, INC.; *U.S. Private*, pg. 1548
THE FLORIDA TIMES-UNION—See Gannett Co., Inc.; *U.S. Public*, pg. 904
FMMX S. DE R.L. DE C.V.—See Graham Holdings Company; *U.S. Public*, pg. 954
FOOTHILLS TRADER INC.—See Alden Global Capital LLC; *U.S. Private*, pg. 156
FORNEY MAQUILA, LLC—See Graham Holdings Company; *U.S. Public*, pg. 954
FORSALEBYOWNER.COM, LLC, INC.—See ROCKET Homes Real Estate LLC; *U.S. Private*, pg. 3466
FORT BRAGG ADVOCATE-NEWS—See Alden Global Capital LLC; *U.S. Private*, pg. 156
FORT COLLINS COLORADOAN—See Gannett Co., Inc.; *U.S. Public*, pg. 897
THE FORT MORGAN TIMES—See Alden Global Capital LLC; *U.S. Private*, pg. 157
FORT WAYNE NEWSPAPERS, INC.—See The Nutting Company, Inc.; *U.S. Private*, pg. 4086
FORT WORTH STAR-TELEGRAM—See Chatham Asset Management, LLC; *U.S. Private*, pg. 866
FORUM COMMUNICATIONS COMPANY; *U.S. Private*, pg. 1577
FORUM PUBLISHING GROUP, INC.—See Tribune Publishing Company; *U.S. Private*, pg. 4228
FOUNTAIN COUNTY NEIGHBOR INC.—See Community Media Group; *U.S. Private*, pg. 995
FOUR CORNERS BUSINESS JOURNAL—See Gannett Co., Inc.; *U.S. Public*, pg. 900
FP CANADIAN NEWSPAPERS LIMITED PARTNERSHIP—See FP Newspapers Inc.; *Int'l*, pg. 2757
FP NEWSPAPERS INC.; *Int'l*, pg. 2757
THE FRAMINGHAM TAB—See Gannett Co., Inc.; *U.S. Public*, pg. 903
FRANKFURTER ALLGEMEINE ZEITUNG GMBH; *Int'l*, pg. 2761
FRANK MAYBORN ENTERPRISES; *U.S. Private*, pg. 1595
THE FREE LANCE-STAR PUBLISHING CO.; *U.S. Private*, pg. 4030
THE FREELANCE-STAR RADIO GROUPS—See The Free Lance-Star Publishing Co.; *U.S. Private*, pg. 4030
FREEMAN NEWSPAPERS LLC—See Conley Publishing Group Ltd.; *U.S. Private*, pg. 1014
THE FREE PRESS—See Gannett Co., Inc.; *U.S. Public*, pg. 906
THE FREE WEEKLY—See Wehco Media, Inc.; *U.S. Private*, pg. 4470
THE FRESNO BEE—See Chatham Asset Management, LLC; *U.S. Private*, pg. 867
THE GABBER; *U.S. Private*, pg. 4031
THE GADSDEN TIMES—See Gannett Co., Inc.; *U.S. Public*, pg. 905
GAINESVILLE SUN PUBLISHING COMPANY—See Gannett Co., Inc.; *U.S. Public*, pg. 905
GANNETT MISSOURI PUBLISHING, INC.—See Gannett Co., Inc.; *U.S. Public*, pg. 897
GANNETT VERMONT PUBLISHING, INC.—See Gannett Co., Inc.; *U.S. Public*, pg. 897
GARDNER NEWS INC.; *U.S. Private*, pg. 1644
THE GASTON GAZETTE—See Gannett Co., Inc.; *U.S. Public*, pg. 906
GATEHOUSE MEDIA, LLC—See Gannett Co., Inc.; *U.S. Public*, pg. 901
GATEHOUSE MEDIA NEW ENGLAND—See Gannett Co., Inc.; *U.S. Public*, pg. 901
GATEHOUSE MEDIA OHIO HOLDINGS II, INC.—See Gannett Co., Inc.; *U.S. Public*, pg. 903
GATTON STAR PTY LTD—See ARN Media Limited; *Int'l*, pg. 576
GAZETTE COMMUNICATIONS, INC.—See The Gazette Company; *U.S. Private*, pg. 4032
GAZETTE NEWSPAPERS—See Alden Global Capital LLC; *U.S. Private*, pg. 156
THE GAZETTE—See The Anschutz Corporation; *U.S. Private*, pg. 3987
GEDI GRUPPO EDITORIALE S.P.A.—See Giovanni Agnelli B.V.; *Int'l*, pg. 2978
GEELONG ADVERTISER—See News Corporation; *U.S. Public*, pg. 1520
GE FABBRI PHOENIX SP. Z .O.O. LTD.—See Eaglemoss Publications Ltd; *Int'l*, pg. 2266
GEORGE J. FOSTER CO. INC.; *U.S. Private*, pg. 1682
GEORGETOWN COMMUNICATIONS, INC.—See Evening Post Publishing Co.; *U.S. Private*, pg. 1436
GEORGE W. PRESCOTT PUBLISHING COMPANY, LLC—See Gannett Co., Inc.; *U.S. Public*, pg. 905
GILROY DISPATCH—See Metro Publishing, Inc.; *U.S. Private*, pg. 2686
GLACIER MEDIA INC.; *Int'l*, pg. 2987
GLADES COUNTY DEMOCRAT—See Independent Newspapers, Inc.; *U.S. Private*, pg. 2060
GLADSTONE NEWSPAPER COMPANY PTY LTD—See ARN Media Limited; *Int'l*, pg. 576
THE GLADWIN COUNTY RECORD—See American Con-

N.A.I.C.S. INDEX 513110 — NEWSPAPER PUBLISHER...

solidated Media LP; *U.S. Private*, pg. 228
GLAS PODRINJA A.D.; *Int'l*, pg. 2988
GLENDORA HIGHLANDER—See Alden Global Capital LLC; *U.S. Private*, pg. 158
GLOBE-GAZETTE—See Lee Enterprises, Incorporated; *U.S. Public*, pg. 1299
THE GOLD COAST PRESS PTY LIMITED—See ARN Media Limited; *Int'l*, pg. 576
GOOD TIMES—See Metro Publishing, Inc.; *U.S. Private*, pg. 2686
GOTA MEDIA AB; *Int'l*, pg. 3043
THE GRAHAM LEADER—See Alden Global Capital LLC; *U.S. Private*, pg. 156
GRAND FORKS GAZETTE—See Black Press Group Ltd.; *Int'l*, pg. 1059
GRAND FORKS HERALD—See Forum Communications Company; *U.S. Private*, pg. 1577
THE GRAND ISLAND DAILY INDEPENDENT—See Lee Enterprises, Incorporated; *U.S. Public*, pg. 1298
GRAND JUNCTION NEWSPAPERS, INC.—See Apollo Global Management, Inc.; *U.S. Public*, pg. 163
GRASSROOTS ENTERPRISE, INC.; *U.S. Private*, pg. 1758
GREATER BELOIT PUBLISHING CO.—See Adams Publishing Group, LLC; *U.S. Private*, pg. 75
GREATER WASHINGTON PUBLISHING, LLC—See Nash Holdings LLC; *U.S. Private*, pg. 2835
GREAT FALLS TRIBUNE—See Gannett Co., Inc.; *U.S. Public*, pg. 897
GREEN BAY PRESS-GAZETTE—See Gannett Co., Inc.; *U.S. Public*, pg. 897
THE GREENEVILLE SUN—See Adams Publishing Group, LLC; *U.S. Private*, pg. 75
THE GREENFIELD TOWN CRIER—See Alden Global Capital LLC; *U.S. Private*, pg. 155
GREENVILLE NEWS—See Gannett Co., Inc.; *U.S. Public*, pg. 897
GREENWICH TIME—See The Hearst Corporation; *U.S. Private*, pg. 4047
GRESHAM OUTLOOK; *U.S. Private*, pg. 1783
GROTON LANDMARK—See Alden Global Capital LLC; *U.S. Private*, pg. 157
GROUPE LE FIGARO—See Groupe Industriel Marcel Dassault S.A.; *Int'l*, pg. 3105
GRUPA RADIOWA AGORY SP. Z O.O.—See Agora S.A.; *Int'l*, pg. 212
GUAM PUBLICATIONS, INCORPORATED—See Gannett Co., Inc.; *U.S. Public*, pg. 897
GUARD PUBLISHING COMPANY; *U.S. Private*, pg. 1809
GULF COAST NEWSPAPERS, LLC—See Osteen Publishing Company; *U.S. Private*, pg. 3048
GULF PUBLISHING COMPANY, INC.—See Chatham Asset Management, LLC; *U.S. Private*, pg. 866
GULGONG PTY LIMITED—See ARN Media Limited; *Int'l*, pg. 576
GVIC COMMUNICATIONS CORP.; *Int'l*, pg. 3189
GWINNETT DAILY POST—See Southern Community Newspapers Inc.; *U.S. Private*, pg. 3730
HACHETTE FILIPACCHI PRESSE SA—See Czech Media Invest as; *Int'l*, pg. 1898
HACIENDA HEIGHTS HIGHLANDER—See Alden Global Capital LLC; *U.S. Private*, pg. 158
HAMILTON-WENHAM CHRONICLE—See Gannett Co., Inc.; *U.S. Public*, pg. 902
HAMMOND DAILY STAR PUBLISHING CO. INC.—See Paxton Media Group LLC; *U.S. Private*, pg. 3116
THE HAMPTON COUNTY GUARDIAN—See Shivers Trading & Operating Company; *U.S. Private*, pg. 3638
HANFORD SENTINEL, INC.—See Lee Enterprises, Incorporated; *U.S. Public*, pg. 1299
HANNIBAL COURIER-POST—See Gannett Co., Inc.; *U.S. Public*, pg. 903
HANOVER MARINER—See Gannett Co., Inc.; *U.S. Public*, pg. 902
HARTFORD ADVOCATE—See Tribune Publishing Company; *U.S. Private*, pg. 4228
HARTFORD CITY NEWS TIMES INC.—See Community Media Group; *U.S. Private*, pg. 995
THE HARTFORD COURANT COMPANY—See Tribune Publishing Company; *U.S. Private*, pg. 4228
HARTMAN NEWSPAPERS INC.; *U.S. Private*, pg. 1874
HARVARD HILLSIDE—See Alden Global Capital LLC; *U.S. Private*, pg. 157
HARWICH ORACLE—See Gannett Co., Inc.; *U.S. Public*, pg. 902
HASWELL PTY LIMITED—See ARN Media Limited; *Int'l*, pg. 576
HATTIESBURG AMERICAN—See Gannett Co., Inc.; *U.S. Public*, pg. 898
HAVASU NEWSPAPERS INC.—See Western Newspapers, Inc.; *U.S. Private*, pg. 4495
HAVELOCK NEWS—See Gannett Co., Inc.; *U.S. Public*, pg. 906
HAVERHILL GAZETTE—See The Retirement Systems of Alabama; *U.S. Public*, pg. 4105
HAVRE DAILY NEWS INC.—See Pioneer Newspapers Inc.; *U.S. Private*, pg. 3187
HAWAII TRIBUNE HERALD—See Gannett Co., Inc.; *U.S. Public*, pg. 903

HAWKER SIDDELEY CANADA INC.—See GVIC Communications Corp.; *Int'l*, pg. 3189
HAZLETON STANDARD-SPEAKER INC.; *U.S. Private*, pg. 1886
HD MEDIA COMPANY, LLC; *U.S. Private*, pg. 1890
HEARST NEWSPAPERS—See The Hearst Corporation; *U.S. Private*, pg. 4047
HEARST NEWS SERVICE—See The Hearst Corporation; *U.S. Private*, pg. 4047
HEARTLAND PUBLICATIONS, LLC; *U.S. Private*, pg. 1900
HEINRICH BAUER EDICIONES S.L.—See Hubert Burda Media Holding Kommanditgesellschaft; *Int'l*, pg. 3519
HELEN GORDON INTERESTS LTD.; *U.S. Private*, pg. 1905
HENDERSONVILLE NEWSPAPER CORPORATION—See Gannett Co., Inc.; *U.S. Public*, pg. 905
THE HERALD-DISPATCH—See HD Media Company, LLC; *U.S. Private*, pg. 1890
HERALD MEDIA INC.; *U.S. Private*, pg. 1920
THE HERALD NEWS—See Gannett Co., Inc.; *U.S. Public*, pg. 903
HERALDO DE ARAGON SA—See Henneo Media, SA; *Int'l*, pg. 3354
HERALD & REVIEW—See Lee Enterprises, Incorporated; *U.S. Public*, pg. 1299
THE HERALD—See Chatham Asset Management, LLC; *U.S. Private*, pg. 867
HERALD TIMES REPORTER—See Gannett Co., Inc.; *U.S. Public*, pg. 898
HERALD-TRIBUNE COMPANY—See Gannett Co., Inc.; *U.S. Public*, pg. 905
THE HERALD & WEEKLY TIMES LTD.—See News Corporation; *U.S. Public*, pg. 1520
HERITAGE NEWSPAPERS, INC.—See Alden Global Capital LLC; *U.S. Private*, pg. 156
HERMISTON HERALD—See East Oregonian Publishing Co.; *U.S. Private*, pg. 1317
HERSAM ACORN NEWSPAPERS LLC; *U.S. Private*, pg. 1926
HERSAM ACORN NEWSPAPERS—See Hersam Acorn Newspapers LLC; *U.S. Private*, pg. 1926
HET PAROOL B.V.—See DPG Media Group NV; *Int'l*, pg. 2188
HIBBING DAILY TRIBUNE—See American Consolidated Media LP; *U.S. Private*, pg. 228
HICKORY DAILY RECORD—See Lee Enterprises, Incorporated; *U.S. Public*, pg. 1298
HI-DESERT PUBLISHING CO. INC.—See Brehm Communications Inc.; *U.S. Private*, pg. 644
HIGGS INTERNATIONAL PUBLISHING LOGISTICS LTD—See Deutsche Post AG; *Int'l*, pg. 2080
HIGHLAND NEWS-LEADER—See Chatham Asset Management, LLC; *U.S. Private*, pg. 866
THE HIGHLANDS NEWS-SUN—See Sun Coast Media Group, Inc.; *U.S. Private*, pg. 3862
HIGH POINT ENTERPRISE; *U.S. Private*, pg. 1936
HIGHWAY MAIL (PTY) LTD.—See Caxton and CTP Publishers and Printers Ltd.; *Int'l*, pg. 1363
HILLSDALE DAILY NEWS—See Gannett Co., Inc.; *U.S. Public*, pg. 903
HINDUSTAN MEDIA VENTURES LIMITED; *Int'l*, pg. 3400
HINGHAM JOURNAL—See Gannett Co., Inc.; *U.S. Public*, pg. 902
HOLBROOK SUN—See Gannett Co., Inc.; *U.S. Public*, pg. 902
THE HOLLAND SENTINEL—See Gannett Co., Inc.; *U.S. Public*, pg. 904
HOLLISTER FREE LANCE—See Metro Publishing, Inc.; *U.S. Private*, pg. 2686
HOLLISTON TAB—See Gannett Co., Inc.; *U.S. Public*, pg. 902
HOME NEWS ENTERPRISES, LLC; *U.S. Private*, pg. 1971
HOME NEWS TRIBUNE—See Gannett Co., Inc.; *U.S. Public*, pg. 898
HOMER NEWS, LLC—See Gannett Co., Inc.; *U.S. Public*, pg. 903
HOMESTEAD PUBLISHING CO.—See Tribune Publishing Company; *U.S. Private*, pg. 4228
HONG KONG ECONOMIC TIMES HOLDINGS LTD; *Int'l*, pg. 3465
HONG KONG ECONOMIC TIMES LIMITED—See Hong Kong Economic Times Holdings Ltd; *Int'l*, pg. 3466
HONOLULU STAR-ADVERTISER—See Black Press Group Ltd.; *Int'l*, pg. 1059
HOOSIER-TIMES, INC.—See Gannett Co., Inc.; *U.S. Public*, pg. 903
HOPKINTON CRIER—See Gannett Co., Inc.; *U.S. Public*, pg. 902
HORIZON NORTH DAKOTA PUBLICATIONS INC.—See Horizon Publications Inc.; *U.S. Private*, pg. 1982
HORIZON PUBLICATIONS INC.; *U.S. Private*, pg. 1982
THE HOUMA COURIER NEWSPAPER CORPORATION—See Gannett Co., Inc.; *U.S. Public*, pg. 905
HOUR PUBLISHING COMPANY; *U.S. Private*, pg. 1991
HOUSATONIC PUBLICATIONS INC.—See Warburg Pincus LLC; *U.S. Private*, pg. 4438
HOUSTON BUSINESS JOURNAL, INC.—See Advance Publications, Inc.; *U.S. Private*, pg. 84

HOUSTON CHRONICLE—See The Hearst Corporation; *U.S. Private*, pg. 4047
HOUSTON COMMUNITY NEWSPAPERS—See The Hearst Corporation; *U.S. Private*, pg. 4047
HOY PUBLICATIONS, LLC—See Tribune Publishing Company; *U.S. Private*, pg. 4228
H.S. GERE & SONS INCORPORATED; *U.S. Private*, pg. 1835
HT MEDIA LIMITED; *Int'l*, pg. 3508
HUCKLE MEDIA, LLC.; *U.S. Private*, pg. 2001
HUDSON SUN—See Gannett Co., Inc.; *U.S. Public*, pg. 902
HUMBOLDT BEACON—See Alden Global Capital LLC; *U.S. Private*, pg. 156
HUNAN XIAOXIANG MORNING HERALD MEDIA MANAGEMENT CO., LTD.—See China South Publishing & Media Group Co., Ltd.; *Int'l*, pg. 1553
HUNTINGTON BEACH INDEPENDENT—See Los Angeles Times Communications, LLC; *U.S. Private*, pg. 2497
HUNTSVILLE TIMES—See Advance Publications, Inc.; *U.S. Private*, pg. 86
HURON DAILY TRIBUNE—See The Hearst Corporation; *U.S. Private*, pg. 4047
HURON NEWSPAPERS LLC—See News Media Corporation; *U.S. Private*, pg. 2916
HURRIYET GAZETECILIK VE MATBAACILIK A.S.—See Adil Bey Holding A.S.; *Int'l*, pg. 148
IDAHO BUSINESS REVIEW, LLC—See The Dolan Company; *U.S. Private*, pg. 4022
IDAHO PRESS-TRIBUNE INC.—See Pioneer Newspapers Inc.; *U.S. Private*, pg. 3187
IDAHO STATESMAN—See Chatham Asset Management, LLC; *U.S. Private*, pg. 866
IHLAS GAZETECILIK A.S.—See Ihlas Holding A.S.; *Int'l*, pg. 3606
THE ILE CAMERA—See Alden Global Capital LLC; *U.S. Private*, pg. 158
IL GAZZETTINO SPA—See Caltagirone Editore S.p.A.; *Int'l*, pg. 1265
ILKKA YHTYMAE OYJ; *Int'l*, pg. 3615
IL MATTINO SPA—See Caltagirone Editore S.p.A.; *Int'l*, pg. 1266
IMMOKALEE BULLETIN—See Independent Newspapers, Inc.; *U.S. Private*, pg. 2060
IMPACTO USA—See Alden Global Capital LLC; *U.S. Private*, pg. 158
IMPRESE TIPOGRAFICHE VENETE SPA—See Caltagirone Editore S.p.A.; *Int'l*, pg. 1266
INDEPENDENT NEWSPAPERS, INC.; *U.S. Private*, pg. 2060
INDEPENDENT PRINT LIMITED—See Evening Standard Ltd.; *Int'l*, pg. 2562
INDEPENDENT PUBLICATIONS, INC.; *U.S. Private*, pg. 2061
THE INDEPENDENT RECORD—See Lee Enterprises, Incorporated; *U.S. Public*, pg. 1300
INDEPENDENT TRIBUNE—See Lee Enterprises, Incorporated; *U.S. Public*, pg. 1299
INDIANA NEWSPAPERS, LLC—See Gannett Co., Inc.; *U.S. Public*, pg. 898
INDIANAPOLIS STAR—See Gannett Co., Inc.; *U.S. Public*, pg. 898
INDIAN RIVER PRESS JOURNAL—See Gannett Co., Inc.; *U.S. Public*, pg. 898
INLAND MEDIA COMPANY—See Inland Industries, Inc.; *U.S. Private*, pg. 2078
INLAND VALLEY DAILY BULLETIN—See Alden Global Capital LLC; *U.S. Private*, pg. 157
INN PARTNERS, L.C.—See Lee Enterprises, Incorporated; *U.S. Public*, pg. 1299
INQUIRER & MIRROR, INC.—See Gannett Co., Inc.; *U.S. Public*, pg. 904
INSIDE BUSINESS INC.—See Irish Times; *U.S. Private*, pg. 2138
INTERNATIONAL HERALD TRIBUNE LTD.—See The New York Times Company; *U.S. Public*, pg. 2116
INTERNATIONAL HERALD TRIBUNE S.A.S.—See The New York Times Company; *U.S. Public*, pg. 2116
INTERNATIONAL HERALD TRIBUNE U.S. INC.—See The New York Times Company; *U.S. Public*, pg. 2116
INTERNATIONAL MEDIA CONCEPTS, INC.—See The New York Times Company; *U.S. Public*, pg. 2117
INTERNATIONAL NEW YORK TIMES—See The New York Times Company; *U.S. Public*, pg. 2116
INTERNEWS NETWORK; *U.S. Private*, pg. 2122
INTRAFISH MEDIA AS—See Fred. Olsen & Co.; *Int'l*, pg. 2768
INVESTMENTNEWS LLC—See Bonhill Group PLC; *Int'l*, pg. 1107
IOWA FARMER TODAY—See Lee Enterprises, Incorporated; *U.S. Public*, pg. 1299
IPSWICH CHRONICLE—See Gannett Co., Inc.; *U.S. Public*, pg. 902
THE ISLAND PACKET—See Chatham Asset Management, LLC; *U.S. Private*, pg. 867
THE ITHACA JOURNAL—See Gannett Co., Inc.; *U.S. Public*, pg. 900
JACKALOPE PUBLISHING, INC.—See Macari-Healey Publishing Company, LLC; *U.S. Private*, pg. 2534

513110 — NEWSPAPER PUBLISHER... CORPORATE AFFILIATIONS

THE JACK COUNTY HERALD—See Alden Global Capital LLC; *U.S. Private*, pg. 156
JACKSBORO GAZETTE-NEWS—See Alden Global Capital LLC; *U.S. Private*, pg. 156
JACKSON COUNTY FLORIDAN—See Lee Enterprises, Incorporated; *U.S. Public*, pg. 1299
THE JACKSON SUN—See Gannett Co., Inc.; *U.S. Public*, pg. 900
JACKSONVILLE BUSINESS JOURNAL—See Advance Publications, Inc.; *U.S. Private*, pg. 84
THE JAMESTOWN SUN—See Forum Communications Company; *U.S. Private*, pg. 1577
JASPER NEWS-BOY—See The Hearst Corporation; *U.S. Private*, pg. 4047
J.BEE NP PUBLISHING, LTD.—See EOS Publishing, LLC; *U.S. Private*, pg. 1411
JEFFERSON COUNTY ADVERTISER—See Gannett Co., Inc.; *U.S. Public*, pg. 898
THE JEFFERSONIAN COMPANY, LLC—See Gannett Co., Inc.; *U.S. Public*, pg. 904
JERSEY JOURNAL NEWSPAPER—See Advance Publications, Inc.; *U.S. Private*, pg. 86
JOHNSON CITY PRESS—See Sandusky Newspapers Inc.; *U.S. Private*, pg. 3545
JOHNSON NEWSPAPER CORPORATION; *U.S. Private*, pg. 2228
JONES MEDIA, INC.—See Adams Publishing Group, LLC; *U.S. Private*, pg. 75
JOSHUA STAR—See Alden Global Capital LLC; *U.S. Private*, pg. 156
JOURNAL ADVOCATE—See Alden Global Capital LLC; *U.S. Private*, pg. 157
JOURNAL COMMUNITY PUBLISHING GROUP, INC.—See Gannett Co., Inc.; *U.S. Public*, pg. 898
JOURNAL & COURIER—See Gannett Co., Inc.; *U.S. Public*, pg. 898
THE JOURNAL-COURIER—See Independence Capital Partners, LLC; *U.S. Private*, pg. 2057
THE JOURNAL GAZETTE—See The Nutting Company, Inc.; *U.S. Private*, pg. 4086
THE JOURNAL NEWS—See Gannett Co., Inc.; *U.S. Public*, pg. 900
JOURNAL PUBLISHING CO. INC.—See CREATE Foundation; *U.S. Private*, pg. 1087
THE JOURNAL PUBLISHING CO. INC.—See The Nutting Company, Inc.; *U.S. Private*, pg. 4086
THE JOURNAL RECORD PUBLISHING CO., LLC—See The Dolan Company; *U.S. Private*, pg. 4022
THE JOURNAL-REGISTER—See The Retirement Systems of Alabama; *U.S. Private*, pg. 4106
JOURNAL SENTINEL, INC.—See Gannett Co., Inc.; *U.S. Public*, pg. 898
JOURNAL STAR, INC.—See Gannett Co., Inc.; *U.S. Public*, pg. 903
JOURNAL-STAR PRINTING CO.—See Lee Enterprises, Incorporated; *U.S. Public*, pg. 1299
THE JOURNAL TIMES—See Lee Enterprises, Incorporated; *U.S. Public*, pg. 1300
JULESBURG ADVOCATE—See Alden Global Capital LLC; *U.S. Private*, pg. 157
JUNEAU EMPIRE—See Gannett Co., Inc.; *U.S. Public*, pg. 903
JUPITER COURIER NEWSWEEKLY—See Gannett Co., Inc.; *U.S. Public*, pg. 898
JWP PUBLISHING LIMITED PARTNERSHIP—See GVIC Communications Corp.; *Int'l*, pg. 3189
THE KAMLOOPS DAILY NEWS—See Glacier Media Inc.; *Int'l*, pg. 2987
KANKAKEE DAILY JOURNAL COMPANY LLC—See Small Newspaper Group Inc.; *U.S. Private*, pg. 3690
THE KANSAS CITY STAR COMPANY—See Chatham Asset Management, LLC; *U.S. Private*, pg. 867
KAUPPALEHTI OY—See Alma Media Corporation; *Int'l*, pg. 362
KEARNEY HUB PUBLISHING COMPANY INC.—See Lee Enterprises, Incorporated; *U.S. Public*, pg. 1298
KEARNS-TRIBUNE, LLC; *U.S. Private*, pg. 2271
KEENE STAR—See Alden Global Capital LLC; *U.S. Private*, pg. 156
KENDALL COUNTY RECORD, INC.—See The B. F. Shaw Printing Company; *U.S. Private*, pg. 3990
KENNEBEC JOURNAL—See MaineToday Media, Inc.; *U.S. Private*, pg. 2553
KENT COUNTY DAILY TIMES—See R.I.S.N. Operations Inc.; *U.S. Private*, pg. 3336
KEYNOTER PUBLISHING COMPANY, INC.—See Chatham Asset Management, LLC; *U.S. Public*, pg. 866
KICKSERV, INC.—See Gannett Co., Inc.; *U.S. Public*, pg. 898
KIMBERLY-CLARK CORPORATION - HOUSEHOLD PRODUCTS SECTOR—See Kimberly-Clark Corporation; *U.S. Public*, pg. 1229
KIMBERLY-CLARK CORPORATION - PERSONAL CARE SECTOR—See Kimberly-Clark Corporation; *U.S. Public*, pg. 1230
KINGMAN DAILY MINER—See Western Newspapers, Inc.; *U.S. Private*, pg. 4495

KINGSTON REPORTER—See Gannett Co., Inc.; *U.S. Public*, pg. 902
KINGSTON WHIG-STANDARD—See Chatham Asset Management, LLC; *U.S. Public*, pg. 861
KINGSVILLE PUBLISHING COMPANY—See King Ranch, Inc.; *U.S. Private*, pg. 2310
KITSAP SUN, LLC—See Gannett Co., Inc.; *U.S. Public*, pg. 898
KLAMATH PUBLISHING CO. INC.—See Pioneer Newspapers Inc.; *U.S. Private*, pg. 3187
KNOXVILLE NEWS SENTINEL, LLC—See Gannett Co., Inc.; *U.S. Public*, pg. 898
KODIAK DAILY MIRROR—See Fairbanks Daily News-Miner Inc.; *U.S. Private*, pg. 1462
KONINKLIJKE WEGENER N.V.—See DPG Media Group NV; *Int'l*, pg. 2188
KONYA KAGIT SAN. VE TIC. A.S.—See Bera Holding A.S.; *Int'l*, pg. 978
KUSTANNUSOSAKEYHTIO ILTALEHTI—See Alma Media Corporation; *Int'l*, pg. 362
LA CROSSE TRIBUNE—See Lee Enterprises, Incorporated; *U.S. Public*, pg. 1299
LA GRANDE OBSERVER—See Western Communications Inc.; *U.S. Private*, pg. 4491
LAKE CITY REPORTER—See Community Newspapers Inc.; *U.S. Private*, pg. 996
THE LAKE COUNTRY SUN—See Alden Global Capital LLC; *U.S. Private*, pg. 156
LAKE COUNTY RECORD-BEE—See Alden Global Capital LLC; *U.S. Private*, pg. 156
LAKE GENEVA REGIONAL NEWS—See Lee Enterprises, Incorporated; *U.S. Public*, pg. 1299
LAKELAND LEDGER PUBLISHING CORPORATION—See Gannett Co., Inc.; *U.S. Public*, pg. 905
LAKELAND PRINTING CO INC; *U.S. Private*, pg. 2376
LAKE SHORE NEWSPAPERS INC.; *U.S. Private*, pg. 2376
THE LAKE TODAY—See Wehco Media, Inc.; *U.S. Private*, pg. 4470
LAKEWAY PUBLISHERS INCORPORATED; *U.S. Private*, pg. 2378
LAMAR ADVERTISING CO. - RICHMOND BRANCH—See Lamar Advertising Company; *U.S. Public*, pg. 1290
LAMAR LEDGER—See Alden Global Capital LLC; *U.S. Private*, pg. 157
LANCASTER COUNTY WEEKLIES INC.—See Lancaster Newspapers Inc.; *U.S. Private*, pg. 2381
LANCASTER NEWSPAPERS INC.; *U.S. Private*, pg. 2381
LANDMARK MEDIA ENTERPRISES, LLC—See Irish Times; *U.S. Private*, pg. 2138
LANSING STATE JOURNAL—See Gannett Co., Inc.; *U.S. Public*, pg. 897
LAPEER COUNTY PRESS—See JAMS Media LLC; *U.S. Private*, pg. 2186
LAPORTE HERALD ARGUS—See Paxton Media Group LLC; *U.S. Private*, pg. 3116
LA PRENSA LIBRE—See Wehco Media, Inc.; *U.S. Private*, pg. 4470
LA PUENTE HIGHLANDER—See Alden Global Capital LLC; *U.S. Private*, pg. 158
LAREDO MORNING TIMES—See The Hearst Corporation; *U.S. Private*, pg. 4047
LAS CRUCES SUN-NEWS—See Gannett Co., Inc.; *U.S. Public*, pg. 899
LAS VEGAS SUN, INC.—See The Greenspun Corporation; *U.S. Private*, pg. 4039
LAS VEGAS WEEKLY—See The Greenspun Corporation; *U.S. Private*, pg. 4039
THE LAUREL OUTLOOK—See Yellowstone Communications; *U.S. Private*, pg. 4588
LAVERNE HIGHLANDER—See Alden Global Capital LLC; *U.S. Private*, pg. 158
LA WEEKLY, LP—See Semanal Media, LLC; *U.S. Private*, pg. 3603
LAWRENCE COUNTY NEWSPAPERS, INC.; *U.S. Private*, pg. 2401
LEADER & KALKASKIAN—See Alden Global Capital LLC; *U.S. Private*, pg. 156
LEADER POST—See Chatham Asset Management, LLC; *U.S. Public*, pg. 861
THE LEAF-CHRONICLE—See Gannett Co., Inc.; *U.S. Public*, pg. 900
LEBANON DAILY NEWS—See Gannett Co., Inc.; *U.S. Public*, pg. 900
LEBANON EXPRESS—See Lee Enterprises, Incorporated; *U.S. Public*, pg. 1299
LEBANON PUBLISHING COMPANY INC.—See Sandusky Newspapers Inc.; *U.S. Private*, pg. 3545
LEDGER DISPATCH—See Alden Global Capital LLC; *U.S. Private*, pg. 155
LEE FOUNDATION—See Lee Enterprises, Incorporated; *U.S. Public*, pg. 1299
LEE PROCUREMENT SOLUTIONS CO.—See Lee Enterprises, Incorporated; *U.S. Public*, pg. 1299
LEE PUBLICATIONS, INC.—See Lee Enterprises, Incorporated; *U.S. Public*, pg. 1299
LEE'S SUMMIT JOURNAL—See Chatham Asset Management, LLC; *U.S. Public*, pg. 866
LEGGO SRL—See Caltagirone Editore S.p.A.; *Int'l*, pg. 1266

LEWISTON DAILY SUN; *U.S. Private*, pg. 2440
LEWISTOWN NEWS-ARGUS—See Yellowstone Communications; *U.S. Private*, pg. 4587
LEXINGTON HERALD-LEADER—See Chatham Asset Management, LLC; *U.S. Public*, pg. 866
LEXINGTON H-L SERVICES, INC.—See Chatham Asset Management, LLC; *U.S. Public*, pg. 866
LEXINGTON MINUTEMAN—See Gannett Co., Inc.; *U.S. Public*, pg. 902
LIBERTY ALLIANCE; *U.S. Private*, pg. 2443
THE LIMA NEWS—See Independence Capital Partners, LLC; *U.S. Private*, pg. 2057
LINCOLN JOURNAL, INC.—See HD Media Company, LLC; *U.S. Private*, pg. 1890
LINCOLN JOURNAL—See Gannett Co., Inc.; *U.S. Public*, pg. 902
LINCOLN JOURNAL-STAR—See Lee Enterprises, Incorporated; *U.S. Public*, pg. 1299
LINCOLN NEWS MESSENGER—See Brehm Communications, Inc.; *U.S. Private*, pg. 644
LIVINGSTON ENTERPRISE—See Yellowstone Communications; *U.S. Private*, pg. 4587
LMG NETHERLANDS II B.V.—See Concentra nv; *Int'l*, pg. 1763
LMG STOCKTON, INC.—See Gannett Co., Inc.; *U.S. Public*, pg. 904
LOCAL MEDIA GROUP, INC.—See Gannett Co., Inc.; *U.S. Public*, pg. 904
THE LOCK HAVEN EXPRESS—See The Nutting Company, Inc.; *U.S. Private*, pg. 4086
LOCKPORT UNION SUN & JOURNAL—See The Retirement Systems of Alabama; *U.S. Private*, pg. 4105
THE LOGAN BANNER—See HD Media Company, LLC; *U.S. Private*, pg. 1890
LOG CABIN DEMOCRAT, LLC—See Paxton Media Group LLC; *U.S. Private*, pg. 3116
LOKALTIDNINGEN MITT I STOCKHOLM AB—See Ge-Te Media AB; *Int'l*, pg. 2897
THE LONDON FREE PRESS—See Chatham Asset Management, LLC; *U.S. Public*, pg. 861
LONG BEACH PUBLISHING COMPANY—See Alden Global Capital LLC; *U.S. Private*, pg. 158
LONG ISLAND BUSINESS NEWS, LLC—See The Dolan Company; *U.S. Private*, pg. 4022
LONGMONT TIMES-CALL—See Alden Global Capital LLC; *U.S. Private*, pg. 157
LONGVIEW NEWS-JOURNAL—See Texas Community Media LLC; *U.S. Private*, pg. 3975
THE LORAIN JOURNAL COMPANY-THE MORNING JOURNAL—See Alden Global Capital LLC; *U.S. Private*, pg. 159
LOS ALAMOS MONITOR—See Irish Times; *U.S. Private*, pg. 2139
LOS ANGELES DAILY NEWS PUBLISHING COMPANY—See Alden Global Capital LLC; *U.S. Private*, pg. 158
LOS ANGELES TIMES COMMUNICATIONS, LLC; *U.S. Private*, pg. 2497
LOVELAND REPORTER-HERALD—See Alden Global Capital LLC; *U.S. Private*, pg. 157
THE LUBBOCK AVALANCHE-JOURNAL—See Gannett Co., Inc.; *U.S. Public*, pg. 904
MACKENZIE TIMES NEWSPAPER—See Chatham Asset Management, LLC; *U.S. Public*, pg. 861
MACOMB COUNTY LEGAL NEWS—See Detroit Legal News Company; *U.S. Public*, pg. 657
THE MACOMB DAILY—See Alden Global Capital LLC; *U.S. Private*, pg. 159
THE MACON TELEGRAPH PUBLISHING CO.—See Chatham Asset Management, LLC; *U.S. Private*, pg. 867
MADISON NEWSPAPERS, INC.—See Lee Enterprises, Incorporated; *U.S. Public*, pg. 1299
MADISON NEWSPAPERS, INC.—See The Capital Times Company; *U.S. Private*, pg. 4004
MAFRA, A.S.—See Agrofert Holding, a.s.; *Int'l*, pg. 219
THE MAIL TRIBUNE, INC.—See Rosebud Media, LLC; *U.S. Private*, pg. 3482
MAINETODAY MEDIA, INC.; *U.S. Private*, pg. 2553
MALDEN OBSERVER—See Gannett Co., Inc.; *U.S. Public*, pg. 902
MALVERN DAILY RECORD—See Horizon Publications Inc.; *U.S. Private*, pg. 1982
THE MANCHESTER JOURNAL—See Alden Global Capital LLC; *U.S. Private*, pg. 159
THE MANISTEE NEWS ADVOCATE—See The Pioneer Group, Inc.; *U.S. Private*, pg. 4096
MANNEY'S SHOPPER, INC.; *U.S. Private*, pg. 2565
MANSFIELD NEWS JOURNAL—See Gannett Co., Inc.; *U.S. Public*, pg. 898
MANSFIELD NEWS—See Gannett Co., Inc.; *U.S. Public*, pg. 902
MARBLEHEAD REPORTER—See Gannett Co., Inc.; *U.S. Public*, pg. 902
MARCO ISLAND EAGLE—See Gannett Co., Inc.; *U.S. Public*, pg. 898
THE MARIETTA TIMES—See The Nutting Company, Inc.; *U.S. Private*, pg. 4086
MARIN INDEPENDENT JOURNAL—See Alden Global

N.A.I.C.S. INDEX
513110 — NEWSPAPER PUBLISHER...

Capital LLC; *U.S. Private*, pg. 155
THE MARION STAR—See Gannett Co., Inc.; *U.S. Public*, pg. 900
THE MARSHALL NEWS MESSENGER—See Texas Community Media LLC; *U.S. Private*, pg. 3975
MARSHALLTOWN NEWSPAPER INC.—See The Nutting Company, Inc.; *U.S. Private*, pg. 4086
MARSHFIELD MARINER—See Gannett Co., Inc.; *U.S. Public*, pg. 902
MASSACHUSETTS LAWYERS WEEKLY, INC.—See The Dolan Company; *U.S. Private*, pg. 4022
MCALESTER NEWS-CAPITAL & DEMOCRAT—See The Retirement Systems of Alabama; *U.S. Private*, pg. 4105
THE MCCLATCHY COMPANY—See Chatham Asset Management, LLC; *U.S. Private*, pg. 866
MCCLATCHY INTERACTIVE—See Chatham Asset Management, LLC; *U.S. Private*, pg. 866
MCCLATCHY NEWSPAPERS, INC.—See Chatham Asset Management, LLC; *U.S. Private*, pg. 866
MCCLATCHY NEWSPRINT COMPANY—See Chatham Asset Management, LLC; *U.S. Private*, pg. 867
MEDIANEWS GROUP, INC.—See Alden Global Capital LLC; *U.S. Private*, pg. 155
MEDIAONE OF UTAH; *U.S. Private*, pg. 2653
MEDICINE HAT NEWS—See Glacier Media Inc.; *Int'l*, pg. 2987
MEDICINE TODAY POLAND SP. Z O.O.—See Bonnier AB; *Int'l*, pg. 1108
MELBOURNE INDEPENDENT NEWSPAPERS PTY LTD—See ARN Media Limited; *Int'l*, pg. 576
MELROSE FREE PRESS—See Gannett Co., Inc.; *U.S. Public*, pg. 902
MEMPHIS PUBLISHING COMPANY—See Gannett Co., Inc.; *U.S. Public*, pg. 898
THE MENDOCINO BEACON—See Alden Global Capital LLC; *U.S. Private*, pg. 159
MENDOTA PUBLISHING CORPORATION—See News Media Corporation; *U.S. Private*, pg. 2916
METRO GROUP, INC.—See Strategic Publications, LLC; *U.S. Private*, pg. 3835
METRO NEWSPAPERS—See Metro Publishing, Inc.; *U.S. Private*, pg. 2686
METRO PHILADELPHIA—See Metro USA Inc.; *U.S. Private*, pg. 2686
METRO PUBLISHING, INC.; *U.S. Private*, pg. 2686
METRO USA INC.; *U.S. Private*, pg. 2686
METROWEST DAILY NEWS—See Gannett Co., Inc.; *U.S. Public*, pg. 902
MF DOW JONES NEWS S.R.L.—See Class Editori S.p.A.; *Int'l*, pg. 1652
THE MIAMI HERALD MEDIA COMPANY—See Chatham Asset Management, LLC; *U.S. Private*, pg. 867
THE MIAMI HERALD—See Chatham Asset Management, LLC; *U.S. Private*, pg. 867
MIAMI NEWSPAPERS, INC.—See American Consolidated Media LP; *U.S. Private*, pg. 228
MIAMI NEW TIMES, LLC—See Village Voice Media Holdings, LLC; *U.S. Private*, pg. 4384
THE MIDDLETOWN PRESS—See Alden Global Capital LLC; *U.S. Private*, pg. 159
MIDLAND DAILY NEWS—See The Hearst Corporation; *U.S. Private*, pg. 4047
MIDLAND REPORTER-TELEGRAM—See The Hearst Corporation; *U.S. Private*, pg. 4047
MID-SOUTH MANAGEMENT CO. INC.; *U.S. Private*, pg. 2709
THE MID VALLEY TOWN CRIER—See AIM Media Texas, LLC; *U.S. Private*, pg. 132
MIDWEST SUBURBAN PUBLISHING—See Chicago Public Media, Inc.; *U.S. Private*, pg. 879
MIDWEST SUBURBAN PUBLISHING—See Chicago Public Media, Inc.; *U.S. Private*, pg. 879
MILES CITY STAR—See Yellowstone Communications; *U.S. Private*, pg. 4587
MILFORD CHRONICLE—See Independent Newspapers, Inc.; *U.S. Private*, pg. 2060
MILPITAS POST—See Alden Global Capital LLC; *U.S. Private*, pg. 155
MINERAL DAILY NEWS TRIBUNE, INC.—See Gannett Co., Inc.; *U.S. Public*, pg. 904
MINERAL WELLS INDEX INC.—See The Retirement Systems of Alabama; *U.S. Private*, pg. 4105
MINOT DAILY NEWS—See The Nutting Company, Inc.; *U.S. Private*, pg. 4086
MISSILE RANGER—See Gannett Co., Inc.; *U.S. Public*, pg. 900
THE MISSOULIAN—See Lee Enterprises, Incorporated; *U.S. Public*, pg. 1300
MISSOURI LAWYERS MEDIA, INC.—See The Dolan Company; *U.S. Private*, pg. 4022
THE MODESTO BEE—See Chatham Asset Management, LLC; *U.S. Private*, pg. 867
MOLINE DISPATCH PUBLISHING CO. LLC—See Lee Enterprises, Incorporated; *U.S. Public*, pg. 1300
THE MONITOR—See AIM Media Texas, LLC; *U.S. Private*, pg. 132
MONROE CABLEVISION INC.—See Block Communications, Inc.; *U.S. Private*, pg. 582

MONROE PUBLISHING COMPANY LLC—See Adams Publishing Group, LLC; *U.S. Private*, pg. 74
THE MONTANA STANDARD—See Lee Enterprises, Incorporated; *U.S. Public*, pg. 1300
MONTEREY NEWSPAPERS, LLC—See Alden Global Capital LLC; *U.S. Private*, pg. 156
THE MONTGOMERY ADVERTISER—See Gannett Co., Inc.; *U.S. Public*, pg. 900
MONTREAL GAZETTE—See Chatham Asset Management, LLC; *U.S. Private*, pg. 861
MORGAN COUNTY CITIZEN—See Times Journal Inc.; *U.S. Private*, pg. 4172
MORGAN HILL TIMES—See Metro Publishing, Inc.; *U.S. Private*, pg. 2686
THE MORNING CALL, INC.—See Tribune Publishing Company; *U.S. Private*, pg. 4228
MORNING JOURNAL—See The Nutting Company, Inc.; *U.S. Private*, pg. 4086
MORNING NEWS—See Lee Enterprises, Incorporated; *U.S. Public*, pg. 1298
MORNING SENTINEL—See MaineToday Media, Inc.; *U.S. Private*, pg. 2553
THE MORNING SUN—See Gannett Co., Inc.; *U.S. Public*, pg. 904
MORRIS COMMUNICATIONS COMPANY, LLC—See Shivers Trading & Operating Company; *U.S. Private*, pg. 3638
MORRIS MULTIMEDIA, INC.; *U.S. Private*, pg. 2788
MORRIS NEWSPAPER CORPORATION—See Morris Multimedia, Inc.; *U.S. Private*, pg. 2788
MOSCOW PULLMAN DAILY NEWS—See TPC Holdings, Inc.; *U.S. Private*, pg. 4200
MOTORSPORT.COM, INC.—See Enerfund, LLC; *U.S. Private*, pg. 1393
THE MOUNTAIN TIMES—See Adams Publishing Group, LLC; *U.S. Private*, pg. 75
MOUNT AIRY GAZETTE—See Nash Holdings LLC; *U.S. Private*, pg. 2835
MT. CARMEL REGISTER COMPANY—See Brehm Communications Inc.; *U.S. Private*, pg. 644
MT. PLEASANT NEWS—See Inland Industries, Inc.; *U.S. Private*, pg. 2078
MULTI MEDIA CHANNELS, LLC; *U.S. Private*, pg. 2812
MULTIMEDIA HOLDINGS CORPORATION—See TEGNA Inc.; *U.S. Public*, pg. 1990
MUSCATINE JOURNAL—See Lee Enterprises, Incorporated; *U.S. Public*, pg. 1300
NANAIMO DAILY NEWS—See Glacier Media Inc.; *Int'l*, pg. 2987
NAPA VALLEY PUBLISHING CO.—See Lee Enterprises, Incorporated; *U.S. Public*, pg. 1300
NAPLES DAILY NEWS, LLC—See Gannett Co., Inc.; *U.S. Public*, pg. 898
NARRAGANSETT TIMES—See R.I.S.N. Operations Inc.; *U.S. Private*, pg. 3336
NASHOBA PUBLISHING—See Alden Global Capital LLC; *U.S. Private*, pg. 157
NASHUA TELEGRAPH—See Independent Publications, Inc.; *U.S. Private*, pg. 2061
NATICK BULLETIN & TAB—See Gannett Co., Inc.; *U.S. Public*, pg. 902
NATIONAL POST, INC.—See Chatham Asset Management, LLC; *U.S. Private*, pg. 861
NATIONWIDE NEWS PTY. LIMITED—See News Corporation; *U.S. Public*, pg. 1520
NAUTISK FORLAG AS—See EQT AB; *Int'l*, pg. 2478
NEEDHAM TIMES—See Gannett Co., Inc.; *U.S. Public*, pg. 902
NEWARK MORNING LEDGER COMPANY—See Advance Publications, Inc.; *U.S. Private*, pg. 86
NEW FOREST POST LIMITED—See Gannett Co., Inc.; *U.S. Public*, pg. 898
NEW HAVEN REGISTER, INC.—See Alden Global Capital LLC; *U.S. Private*, pg. 157
NEWHOUSE NEWS SERVICE—See Advance Publications, Inc.; *U.S. Private*, pg. 86
NEW JERSEY HERALD INC.—See Gray Television, Inc.; *U.S. Public*, pg. 961
NEW ORLEANS PUBLISHING GROUP, L.L.C.—See The Dolan Company; *U.S. Private*, pg. 4022
NEWPORT NEWS TIMES—See News Media Corporation; *U.S. Private*, pg. 2916
THE NEWS & ADVANCE—See Lee Enterprises, Incorporated; *U.S. Public*, pg. 1299
THE NEWS AND OBSERVER PUBLISHING COMPANY—See Chatham Asset Management, LLC; *U.S. Private*, pg. 867
NEWS CHIEF—See Gannett Co., Inc.; *U.S. Public*, pg. 905
NEWS COMMUNICATIONS, INC.; *U.S. Private*, pg. 2916
NEWS CORP AUSTRALIA PTY. LIMITED—See News Corporation; *U.S. Public*, pg. 1519
NEWS-ENTERPRISE CORPORATION—See Irish Times; *U.S. Private*, pg. 2139
THE NEWS-ENTERPRISE—See Irish Times; *U.S. Private*, pg. 2138
THE NEWS EXAMINER—See Gannett Co., Inc.; *U.S. Public*, pg. 900
NEWS GAZETTE INC.; *U.S. Private*, pg. 2916

THE NEWS-HERALD (LAKE COUNTY)—See Alden Global Capital LLC; *U.S. Private*, pg. 159
THE NEWS-HERALD—See Alden Global Capital LLC; *U.S. Private*, pg. 159
NEWS HERALD—See Gannett Co., Inc.; *U.S. Public*, pg. 906
NEWS-JOURNAL CORPORATION; *U.S. Private*, pg. 2917
THE NEWS JOURNAL—See Gannett Co., Inc.; *U.S. Public*, pg. 900
NEWS LEADER, INC.—See Gannett Co., Inc.; *U.S. Public*, pg. 904
NEWS-LEADER—See Community Newspapers Inc.; *U.S. Private*, pg. 996
THE NEWS LEADER—See Gannett Co., Inc.; *U.S. Public*, pg. 900
NEWS MEDIA CORPORATION; *U.S. Private*, pg. 2916
THE NEWS-MESSENGER—See Gannett Co., Inc.; *U.S. Public*, pg. 900
THE NEWS & OBSERVER—See Chatham Asset Management, LLC; *U.S. Private*, pg. 867
THE NEWS-PRESS—See Gannett Co., Inc.; *U.S. Public*, pg. 900
NEWSQUEST MEDIA GROUP LTD.—See Gannett Co., Inc.; *U.S. Public*, pg. 899
NEWSQUEST (NORTH EAST) LIMITED—See Gannett Co., Inc.; *U.S. Public*, pg. 898
NEWSQUEST PLC—See TEGNA Inc.; *U.S. Public*, pg. 1990
NEWSQUEST SPECIALIST MEDIA LIMITED—See Gannett Co., Inc.; *U.S. Public*, pg. 898
NEWS & RECORD—See Irish Times; *U.S. Private*, pg. 2139
THE NEWS-SENTINEL—See The Nutting Company, Inc.; *U.S. Private*, pg. 4086
THE NEWS—See Evening Post Publishing Co.; *U.S. Private*, pg. 1436
THE NEWS-STAR—See Gannett Co., Inc.; *U.S. Public*, pg. 900
THE NEWS SUN—See Chicago Public Media, Inc.; *U.S. Private*, pg. 879
NEWS-TIMES PUBLISHING COMPANY INC.—See Wehco Media, Inc.; *U.S. Private*, pg. 4469
THE NEWS-TIMES—See The Hearst Corporation; *U.S. Private*, pg. 4048
NEWS TRIBUNE CO.; *U.S. Private*, pg. 2917
NEWS TRIBUNE—See Chatham Asset Management, LLC; *U.S. Private*, pg. 866
THE NEWS TRIBUNE—See Chatham Asset Management, LLC; *U.S. Private*, pg. 866
NEWS UK & IRELAND LIMITED—See News Corporation; *U.S. Public*, pg. 1521
THE NEWS VIRGINIAN—See Lee Enterprises, Incorporated; *U.S. Public*, pg. 1299
NEWS WEST PUBLISHING COMPANY INC.—See Brehm Communications Inc.; *U.S. Private*, pg. 644
NEW TIMES BPB, LLC—See Village Voice Media Holdings, LLC; *U.S. Private*, pg. 4384
NEWTON COUNTY ENTERPRISES INC.—See Community Media Group; *U.S. Private*, pg. 995
THE NEWTON KANSAN—See Gannett Co., Inc.; *U.S. Public*, pg. 904
NEWTON TAB—See Gannett Co., Inc.; *U.S. Public*, pg. 902
NEW WEST NEWSPAPERS INC.; *U.S. Private*, pg. 2908
THE NEW YORK LAW PUBLISHING COMPANY—See Apax Partners LLP; *Int'l*, pg. 504
THE NEW YORK POST—See Charlesbank Capital Partners, LLC; *U.S. Private*, pg. 855
THE NEW YORK TIMES COMPANY; *U.S. Public*, pg. 2116
THE NEW YORK TIMES—See The New York Times Company; *U.S. Public*, pg. 2117
THE NEW YORK TIMES SYNDICATION SALES CORPORATION—See The New York Times Company; *U.S. Public*, pg. 2117
NHST MEDIA GROUP AS—See Fred. Olsen & Co.; *Int'l*, pg. 2768
NICKEL NIK, WHEEL DEALS & DRIVELINE—See Digital Air Strike Inc.; *U.S. Private*, pg. 1230
THE NICKEL OF MEDFORD, INC.—See Gannett Co., Inc.; *U.S. Public*, pg. 904
NITTANY PRINTING & PUBLISHING CO.—See Chatham Asset Management, LLC; *U.S. Private*, pg. 866
NJBIZ—See Journal Publications, Inc.; *U.S. Private*, pg. 2238
NORSK HELSEINFORMATIKK AS—See Bonnier AB; *Int'l*, pg. 1108
NOR-TEX PUBLISHING, INC.—See Chatham Asset Management, LLC; *U.S. Private*, pg. 866
NORTH ADAMS TRANSCRIPT—See Alden Global Capital LLC; *U.S. Private*, pg. 157
NORTH ANDOVER CITIZEN—See Gannett Co., Inc.; *U.S. Public*, pg. 902
THE NORTH BAY NUGGET—See Chatham Asset Management, LLC; *U.S. Private*, pg. 861
NORTHCLIFFE MEDIA HOLDINGS LIMITED—See Daily Mail & General Trust plc; *Int'l*, pg. 1938
NORTHDALE OIL INC.; *U.S. Private*, pg. 2949
THE NORTHERNER—See Glacier Media Inc.; *Int'l*, pg. 2987
NORTHERN LIGHT—See Chatham Asset Management, LLC; *U.S. Private*, pg. 861
NORTHERN MINER—See Glacier Media Inc.; *Int'l*, pg. 2987

513110 — NEWSPAPER PUBLISHER...   CORPORATE AFFILIATIONS

THE NORTHERN NEWS—See Chatham Asset Management, LLC; *U.S. Private*, pg. 861
NORTHERN VIRGINIA MEDIA SERVICES; *U.S. Private*, pg. 2955
NORTH GEORGIA NEWSPAPER GROUP—See The Retirement Systems of Alabama; *U.S. Private*, pg. 4105
NORTH JERSEY MEDIA GROUP, INC.—See Gannett Co., Inc.; *U.S. Public*, pg. 899
NORTH SHORE NEWS—See Glacier Media Inc.; *Int'l*, pg. 2987
NORTH SHORE SUNDAY—See Gannett Co., Inc.; *U.S. Public*, pg. 902
NORTHWEST ARKANSAS NEWSPAPERS LLC—See Wehco Media, Inc.; *U.S. Private*, pg. 4470
NORTHWEST BUSINESS PRESS INC.—See Cowles Company; *U.S. Private*, pg. 1074
NORTHWEST FLORIDA DAILY NEWS—See Gannett Co., Inc.; *U.S. Public*, pg. 906
THE NORTHWOODS RIVER NEWS—See Lakeland Printing Co Inc; *U.S. Private*, pg. 2376
NORTON MIRROR—See Gannett Co., Inc.; *U.S. Public*, pg. 902
NORWELL MARINER—See Gannett Co., Inc.; *U.S. Public*, pg. 902
NOTICIAS LIBRES SURESTE DE TENNESSEE—See Wehco Media, Inc.; *U.S. Private*, pg. 4470
NUTRITION DIMENSION, INC.—See TEGNA Inc.; *U.S. Public*, pg. 1990
NYT CAPITAL, LLC—See The New York Times Company; *U.S. Public*, pg. 2116
NYT SHARED SERVICE CENTER, INC.—See The New York Times Company; *U.S. Public*, pg. 2117
NYT SINGAPORE PTE. LTD.—See The New York Times Company; *U.S. Public*, pg. 2117
OAHU PUBLICATIONS INC.—See Black Press Group Ltd.; *Int'l*, pg. 1059
THE OAKLAND TRIBUNE—See Alden Global Capital LLC; *U.S. Private*, pg. 155
THE OAK RIDGER, LLC—See Gannett Co., Inc.; *U.S. Public*, pg. 904
THE OBSERVER-DISPATCH—See Gannett Co., Inc.; *U.S. Public*, pg. 904
OBSERVER MEDIA GROUP, INC.; *U.S. Private*, pg. 2988
OBSERVER PUBLISHING COMPANY—See The Nutting Company, Inc.; *U.S. Private*, pg. 4086
THE OBSERVER (SARNIA)—See Chatham Asset Management, LLC; *U.S. Private*, pg. 861
OCONEE PUBLISHING INC.—See Edwards Publications Inc.; *U.S. Private*, pg. 1342
OC WEEKLY, LP—See Village Voice Media Holdings, LLC; *U.S. Private*, pg. 4384
THE ODESSA AMERICAN—See AIM Media Texas, LLC; *U.S. Private*, pg. 133
O'FALLON PROGRESS—See Chatham Asset Management, LLC; *U.S. Private*, pg. 866
OGDEN NEWSPAPERS OF OHIO INC.—See The Nutting Company, Inc.; *U.S. Private*, pg. 4086
OGDEN NEWSPAPERS OF PENNSYLVANIA INC.—See The Nutting Company, Inc.; *U.S. Private*, pg. 4086
OGDEN PUBLISHING CORPORATION—See Sandusky Newspapers Inc.; *U.S. Private*, pg. 3545
OHIO CUMMUNITY MEDIA LLC—See Independence Capital Partners, LLC; *U.S. Private*, pg. 2057
THE OKEECHOBEE NEWS—See Independent Newspapers, Inc.; *U.S. Private*, pg. 2060
THE OKLAHOMAN—See The Anschutz Corporation; *U.S. Private*, pg. 3987
THE OKLAHOMA PUBLISHING COMPANY—See The Anschutz Corporation; *U.S. Private*, pg. 3987
THE OLATHE NEWS—See Chatham Asset Management, LLC; *U.S. Private*, pg. 867
THE OLNEY ENTERPRISE—See Alden Global Capital LLC; *U.S. Private*, pg. 156
THE OLYMPIAN—See Chatham Asset Management, LLC; *U.S. Private*, pg. 867
OLYMPIC-CASCADE PUBLISHING, INC.—See Chatham Asset Management, LLC; *U.S. Private*, pg. 867
OMAHA WORLD HERALD COMPANY—See Lee Enterprises, Incorporated; *U.S. Public*, pg. 1298
ONION, INC.; *U.S. Private*, pg. 3026
OOO MUSIC1—See Enerfund, LLC; *U.S. Private*, pg. 1393
OPELIKA-AUBURN NEWS—See Lee Enterprises, Incorporated; *U.S. Public*, pg. 1298
THE ORANGE COUNTY REGISTER—See Alden Global Capital LLC; *U.S. Private*, pg. 159
OREGONIAN PUBLISHING CO.—See Advance Publications, Inc.; *U.S. Private*, pg. 86
OREGONIAN V 5—See Advance Publications, Inc.; *U.S. Private*, pg. 86
ORLANDO SENTINEL COMMUNICATIONS COMPANY—See Tribune Publishing Company; *U.S. Private*, pg. 4228
OROVILLE MERCURY-REGISTER—See Alden Global Capital LLC; *U.S. Private*, pg. 156
OSCEOLA NEWS-GAZETTE—See West End Holdings LLC; *U.S. Private*, pg. 4485
OSHKOSH NORTHWESTERN—See Gannett Co., Inc.; *U.S. Public*, pg. 899

OSTEEN PUBLISHING COMPANY; *U.S. Private*, pg. 3048
THE OTTAWA CITIZEN—See Chatham Asset Management, LLC; *U.S. Private*, pg. 861
OTTAWA PUBLISHING CO., LLC—See Small Newspaper Group Inc.; *U.S. Private*, pg. 3690
THE OTTAWA SUN—See Chatham Asset Management, LLC; *U.S. Private*, pg. 861
OTTUMWA COURIER—See The Retirement Systems of Alabama; *U.S. Private*, pg. 4105
PACIFICA TRIBUNE—See Alden Global Capital LLC; *U.S. Private*, pg. 155
PACIFIC DAILY NEWS—See Gannett Co., Inc.; *U.S. Public*, pg. 898
PACIFIC NEWSPAPER GROUP INC.—See Chatham Asset Management, LLC; *U.S. Private*, pg. 861
PACIFIC PALISADES POST INC.—See Small Newspaper Group Inc.; *U.S. Private*, pg. 3690
PACKET NEWSPAPERS LIMITED—See Gannett Co., Inc.; *U.S. Public*, pg. 899
PADDOCK PUBLICATIONS, INC.; *U.S. Private*, pg. 3073
PAGEMASTERS PTY LTD.—See Australian Associated Press Pty Ltd; *Int'l*, pg. 721
PALATKA DAILY NEWS—See Community Newspapers Inc.; *U.S. Private*, pg. 996
PALLADIUM-ITEM—See Gannett Co., Inc.; *U.S. Public*, pg. 899
PALM BEACH NEWSPAPERS, LLC—See Gannett Co., Inc.; *U.S. Public*, pg. 906
PA-MORNING CALL, LLC—See Nexstar Media Group, Inc.; *U.S. Public*, pg. 1524
THE PANOLA WATCHMAN—See Texas Community Media LLC; *U.S. Private*, pg. 3975
PANTAGRAPH PUBLISHING CO.—See Lee Enterprises, Incorporated; *U.S. Public*, pg. 1300
PARADISE POST—See Alden Global Capital LLC; *U.S. Private*, pg. 156
PARAGOULD DAILY PRESS—See Paxton Media Group LLC; *U.S. Private*, pg. 3116
PASADENA STAR-NEWS—See Alden Global Capital LLC; *U.S. Private*, pg. 156
THE PATRIOT LEDGER—See Gannett Co., Inc.; *U.S. Public*, pg. 899
PATRIOT-NEWS CO. INC.—See Advance Publications, Inc.; *U.S. Private*, pg. 86
PATRIOT-NEWS CO—See Advance Publications, Inc.; *U.S. Private*, pg. 86
PAXTON MEDIA GROUP LLC; *U.S. Private*, pg. 3115
PAYSON ROUNDUP—See The World Company; *U.S. Private*, pg. 4139
PEMBROKE MARINER & REPORTER—See Gannett Co., Inc.; *U.S. Public*, pg. 902
PENCOR SERVICES INC.; *U.S. Private*, pg. 3132
THE PENINSULA CLARION—See Gannett Co., Inc.; *U.S. Public*, pg. 905
PENINSULA NEWS—See Alden Global Capital LLC; *U.S. Private*, pg. 158
PENSACOLA NEWS-JOURNAL—See Gannett Co., Inc.; *U.S. Public*, pg. 899
PENSIONS & INVESTMENTS—See Crain Communications, Inc.; *U.S. Private*, pg. 1084
THE PEOPLE-SENTINEL—See Shivers Trading & Operating Company; *U.S. Private*, pg. 3638
PEORIA INDEPENDENT—See Independent Newspapers, Inc.; *U.S. Private*, pg. 2060
THE PEORIA JOURNAL STAR, INC.—See Gannett Co., Inc.; *U.S. Public*, pg. 905
PEPPERELL NEWS—See Alden Global Capital LLC; *U.S. Private*, pg. 157
PERU DAILY TRIBUNE PUBLISHING CO. INC.—See Paxton Media Group LLC; *U.S. Private*, pg. 3116
PG PUBLISHING COMPANY—See Block Communications, Inc.; *U.S. Private*, pg. 582
PHILADELPHIA DAILY NEWS—See Philadelphia Media Holdings, LLC; *U.S. Private*, pg. 3169
THE PHILADELPHIA INQUIRER—See Philadelphia Media Holdings, LLC; *U.S. Private*, pg. 3169
PHILADELPHIA NEWSPAPERS, LLC—See Philadelphia Media Holdings, LLC; *U.S. Private*, pg. 3169
PHILADELPHIA WEEKLY—See Broad Street Media, LLC; *U.S. Private*, pg. 658
PHOENIX BUSINESS JOURNAL—See Advance Publications, Inc.; *U.S. Private*, pg. 84
THE PHOENIX MEDIA/COMMUNICATIONS GROUP; *U.S. Private*, pg. 4095
PHOENIX NEWSPAPERS, INC.—See Gannett Co., Inc.; *U.S. Public*, pg. 899
PHOENIX NEW TIMES, LLC—See Village Voice Media Holdings, LLC; *U.S. Private*, pg. 4384
PHOENIX PRESS LTD L.P.—See Heinrich Bauer Verlag KG; *Int'l*, pg. 3324
PHOENIXVILLE NEWSPAPERS, INC.—See Alden Global Capital LLC; *U.S. Private*, pg. 157
THE PILOT LLC; *U.S. Private*, pg. 4095
PINELLAS HEALTH CARE NEWS—See Florida Health Care News, Inc.; *U.S. Private*, pg. 1548
THE PIONEER GROUP, INC.; *U.S. Private*, pg. 4096
PIONEER NEWSPAPERS INC.; *U.S. Private*, pg. 3187

THE PIONEER NEWSPAPER—See The Pioneer Group, Inc.; *U.S. Private*, pg. 4096
PIONEER NEWSPAPERS—See Chicago Public Media, Inc.; *U.S. Private*, pg. 879
PIONEER PRESS - WEST GROUP—See Chicago Public Media, Inc.; *U.S. Private*, pg. 879
PITTSBURGH BUSINESS TIMES—See Advance Publications, Inc.; *U.S. Private*, pg. 84
PLAIN DEALER PUBLISHING CO.—See Advance Publications, Inc.; *U.S. Private*, pg. 87
PLAIN DEALER PUBLISHING CO.—See Advance Publications, Inc.; *U.S. Private*, pg. 87
PLAIN DEALER PUBLISHING CO.—See Advance Publications, Inc.; *U.S. Private*, pg. 87
PLAIN DEALER PUBLISHING CO.—See Advance Publications, Inc.; *U.S. Private*, pg. 87
PLAINVIEW DAILY HERALD—See The Hearst Corporation; *U.S. Private*, pg. 4047
PLASTICS NEWS—See Crain Communications, Inc.; *U.S. Private*, pg. 1084
THE PLATTSMOUTH JOURNAL—See Lee Enterprises, Incorporated; *U.S. Public*, pg. 1299
POINT PLEASANT REGISTER—See Heartland Publications, LLC; *U.S. Private*, pg. 1900
PORTERVILLE RECORDER—See Horizon Publications Inc.; *U.S. Private*, pg. 1982
PORT HOPE EVENING GUIDE—See Chatham Asset Management, LLC; *U.S. Private*, pg. 861
PORTLAND PRESS HERALD—See MaineToday Media, Inc.; *U.S. Private*, pg. 2553
POST-ATHENIAN COMPANY LLC—See Adams Publishing Group, LLC; *U.S. Private*, pg. 75
POST BULLETIN COMPANY LLC—See Forum Communications Company; *U.S. Private*, pg. 1577
THE POST COMPANY; *U.S. Private*, pg. 4097
THE POST & COURIER, LLC—See Evening Post Publishing Co.; *U.S. Private*, pg. 1436
THE POST-CRESCENT—See Gannett Co., Inc.; *U.S. Public*, pg. 900
POSTMEDIA NETWORK INC.—See Chatham Asset Management, LLC; *U.S. Private*, pg. 861
POST-NEWSWEEK MEDIA, LLC—See Nash Holdings LLC; *U.S. Private*, pg. 2835
THE POST PUBLISHING COMPANY LTD.—See GMM Grammy Public Company Limited; *Int'l*, pg. 3012
POST PUBLISHING COMPANY—See Evening Post Publishing Co.; *U.S. Private*, pg. 1436
THE POST—See Chatham Asset Management, LLC; *U.S. Private*, pg. 861
THE POST-TRIBUNE—See Chicago Public Media, Inc.; *U.S. Private*, pg. 879
POUGHKEEPSIE JOURNAL—See Gannett Co., Inc.; *U.S. Public*, pg. 899
PPI MEDIA US, INC.—See Allianz SE; *Int'l*, pg. 356
PRAIRIE MOUNTAIN PUBLISHING COMPANY LLP—See Alden Global Capital LLC; *U.S. Private*, pg. 157
PRESCOTT NEWSPAPERS INC.—See Western Newspapers, Inc.; *U.S. Private*, pg. 4495
PRESS-CITIZEN COMPANY INC.—See Gannett Co., Inc.; *U.S. Public*, pg. 899
THE PRESS DEMOCRAT—See Gannett Co., Inc.; *U.S. Public*, pg. 905
PRESS-ENTERPRISE INC.; *U.S. Private*, pg. 3255
THE PRESS-ENTERPRISE—See Alden Global Capital LLC; *U.S. Private*, pg. 158
PRESS & GUIDE—See Alden Global Capital LLC; *U.S. Private*, pg. 157
PRESS-REPUBLICAN—See The Retirement Systems of Alabama; *U.S. Private*, pg. 4105
PRESS & SUN-BULLETIN—See Gannett Co., Inc.; *U.S. Public*, pg. 899
THE PRESS-TRIBUNE—See Brehm Communications Inc.; *U.S. Private*, pg. 644
PRESTO PRESSE-VERTRIEBS AG—See Die Schweizerische Post AG; *Int'l*, pg. 2113
PRIME TIMES NEWSPAPER—See Aegon N.V.; *Int'l*, pg. 175
THE PRINCE GEORGE CITIZEN—See Glacier Media Inc.; *Int'l*, pg. 2987
PRINCETON PACKET INC.; *U.S. Private*, pg. 3264
PRINCETON PUBLISHING INC.—See Brehm Communications Inc.; *U.S. Private*, pg. 644
PRINTWEST COMMUNICATIONS LTD.—See GVIC Communications Corp.; *Int'l*, pg. 3189
PRODUCT DEVELOPMENT CORPORATION AUSTRALIA PTY LTD—See Product Development Corporation; *U.S. Private*, pg. 3273
PRO FOOTBALL WEEKLY, LLC; *U.S. Private*, pg. 3269
THE PROGRESS-INDEX—See Gannett Co., Inc.; *U.S. Public*, pg. 905
PROVIDENCE BUSINESS NEWS INC.—See Woodward Communications, Inc.; *U.S. Private*, pg. 4561
THE PROVIDENCE JOURNAL COMPANY—See Gannett Co., Inc.; *U.S. Public*, pg. 905
THE PROVINCE—See Chatham Asset Management, LLC; *U.S. Private*, pg. 861
PUBLIC OPINION—See Gannett Co., Inc.; *U.S. Public*, pg. 900
PUBLIC SPIRIT-AYER—See Alden Global Capital LLC; *U.S. Private*, pg. 157

N.A.I.C.S. INDEX

513110 — NEWSPAPER PUBLISHER...

THE PUGET SOUND BUSINESS JOURNAL—See Advance Publications, Inc.; *U.S. Private*, pg. 85

PULITZER INC.—See Lee Enterprises, Incorporated; *U.S. Public*, pg. 1300

THE PUYALLUP HERALD—See Chatham Asset Management, LLC; *U.S. Private*, pg. 867

QUAD-CITY TIMES—See Lee Enterprises, Incorporated; *U.S. Public*, pg. 1300

QUAY COUNTY SUN—See Clovis Media, Inc.; *U.S. Private*, pg. 948

RANNIE PUBLICATIONS INC.—See Chatham Asset Management, LLC; *U.S. Private*, pg. 861

RAPID CITY JOURNAL—See Lee Enterprises, Incorporated; *U.S. Public*, pg. 1300

RAVALLI REPUBLIC—See Lee Enterprises, Incorporated; *U.S. Public*, pg. 1300

REA AUSTIN PTY LTD.—See News Corporation; *U.S. Public*, pg. 1521

THE READING ADVOCATE—See Gannett Co., Inc.; *U.S. Public*, pg. 905

READING EAGLE COMPANY; *U.S. Private*, pg. 3366

RECORDER PUBLISHING CO.; *U.S. Private*, pg. 3371

THE RECORD-JOURNAL PUBLISHING COMPANY; *U.S. Private*, pg. 4103

RECORD PUBLISHING COMPANY—See Gannett Co., Inc.; *U.S. Public*, pg. 904

THE RECORD—See Gannett Co., Inc.; *U.S. Public*, pg. 904

RED BLUFF DAILY NEWS—See Alden Global Capital LLC; *U.S. Private*, pg. 156

REDDING RECORD SEARCHLIGHT, LLC—See Gannett Co., Inc.; *U.S. Public*, pg. 898

REDLANDS DAILY FACTS—See Alden Global Capital LLC; *U.S. Private*, pg. 158

REDMOND SPOKESMAN—See Western Communications Inc.; *U.S. Private*, pg. 4491

REDWING REPUBLICAN EAGLE—See Forum Communications Company; *U.S. Private*, pg. 1577

REDWOOD TIMES—See Alden Global Capital LLC; *U.S. Private*, pg. 157

THE REGISTER CITIZEN—See Alden Global Capital LLC; *U.S. Private*, pg. 159

THE REGISTER MAIL—See Gannett Co., Inc.; *U.S. Public*, pg. 905

THE REGISTER STAR—See Johnson Newspaper Corporation; *U.S. Private*, pg. 2228

THE REIDSVILLE REVIEW—See Lee Enterprises, Incorporated; *U.S. Public*, pg. 1299

RELIGION NEWS LLC; *U.S. Private*, pg. 3395

RENO GAZETTE-JOURNAL—See Gannett Co., Inc.; *U.S. Public*, pg. 899

RENO NEWSPAPERS, INC.—See Gannett Co., Inc.; *U.S. Public*, pg. 899

THE REPORTER PUBLISHING CO.—See Alden Global Capital LLC; *U.S. Private*, pg. 159

THE REPORTER—See Alden Global Capital LLC; *U.S. Private*, pg. 155

THE REPORTER—See Gannett Co., Inc.; *U.S. Public*, pg. 900

REPUBLICAN COMPANY INC.—See Advance Publications, Inc.; *U.S. Private*, pg. 87

REPUBLICAN COMPANY INC.—See Advance Publications, Inc.; *U.S. Private*, pg. 87

THE REPUBLIC—See Home News Enterprises, LLC; *U.S. Private*, pg. 1971

RETAIL SALES, LLC—See NE Media Group, Inc.; *U.S. Private*, pg. 2877

RHODE ISLAND MONTHLY COMMUNICATIONS, INC.—See Gannett Co., Inc.; *U.S. Public*, pg. 905

THE RICHFIELD REAPER—See Brehm Communications Inc.; *U.S. Private*, pg. 644

RICHMOND TIMES-DISPATCH—See Lee Enterprises, Incorporated; *U.S. Public*, pg. 1299

RICHNER COMMUNICATIONS, INC.; *U.S. Private*, pg. 3430

RINGIER AXEL SPRINGER MAGYARORSZAG KFT—See Axel Springer SE; *Int'l*, pg. 766

RIVERFRONT TIMES, LLC—See Village Voice Media Holdings, LLC; *U.S. Private*, pg. 4384

THE ROANOKE TIMES—See Irish Times; *U.S. Private*, pg. 2139

THE ROBESONIAN—See Heartland Publications, LLC; *U.S. Private*, pg. 1900

ROCKFORD REGISTER STAR—See Gannett Co., Inc.; *U.S. Public*, pg. 904

ROGERS MORNING NEWS—See Wehco Media, Inc.; *U.S. Private*, pg. 4470

ROWLAND HEIGHTS HIGHLANDER—See Alden Global Capital LLC; *U.S. Private*, pg. 158

RUBBER & PLASTICS NEWS—See Crain Communications, Inc.; *U.S. Private*, pg. 1084

RUIDOSO NEWS—See Gannett Co., Inc.; *U.S. Public*, pg. 900

RUST COMMUNICATIONS; *U.S. Private*, pg. 3507

THE SACRAMENTO BEE—See Chatham Asset Management, LLC; *U.S. Private*, pg. 867

SALES IMPACT GMBH—See Axel Springer SE; *Int'l*, pg. 766

SALINAS NEWSPAPERS LLC—See Gannett Co., Inc.; *U.S. Public*, pg. 899

THE SAMPSON INDEPENDENT, INC.—See Heartland Publications, LLC; *U.S. Private*, pg. 1900

SAN ANGELO STANDARD-TIMES, LLC—See Gannett Co., Inc.; *U.S. Public*, pg. 898

SAN ANTONIO BUSINESS JOURNAL—See Advance Publications, Inc.; *U.S. Private*, pg. 85

SAN ANTONIO EXPRESS NEWS—See The Hearst Corporation; *U.S. Private*, pg. 4047

THE SAN BERNARDINO COUNTY SUN—See Alden Global Capital LLC; *U.S. Private*, pg. 158

THE SAN DIEGO UNION-TRIBUNE, LLC—See Alden Global Capital LLC; *U.S. Private*, pg. 159

SAN DIMAS HIGHLANDER—See Alden Global Capital LLC; *U.S. Private*, pg. 158

SANDUSKY NEWSPAPERS INC.; *U.S. Private*, pg. 3545

THE SANFORD HERALD INC.—See Paxton Media Group LLC; *U.S. Private*, pg. 3116

SAN FRANCISCO BUSINESS TIMES—See Advance Publications, Inc.; *U.S. Private*, pg. 85

SAN FRANCISCO CHRONICLE—See The Hearst Corporation; *U.S. Private*, pg. 4048

SAN GABRIEL VALLEY TRIBUNE—See Alden Global Capital LLC; *U.S. Private*, pg. 158

SAN JOSE BUSINESS JOURNAL—See Advance Publications, Inc.; *U.S. Private*, pg. 85

SAN JOSE MERCURY NEWS—See Alden Global Capital LLC; *U.S. Private*, pg. 155

SAN LUIS OBISPO TRIBUNE, LLC—See Chatham Asset Management, LLC; *U.S. Private*, pg. 867

SAN MATEO COUNTY TIMES—See Alden Global Capital LLC; *U.S. Private*, pg. 155

SANOMA DIGITAL THE NETHERLANDS B.V.—See DPG Media Group NV; *Int'l*, pg. 2188

SANTA BARBARA NEWS-PRESS; *U.S. Private*, pg. 3547

THE SANTA CRUZ COUNTY SENTINEL, INC.—See Gannett Co., Inc.; *U.S. Public*, pg. 905

SANTA CRUZ SENTINEL—See Alden Global Capital LLC; *U.S. Private*, pg. 155

SANTA MARIA TIMES, INC.—See Lee Enterprises, Incorporated; *U.S. Public*, pg. 1300

SAUGUS ADVERTISER—See Gannett Co., Inc.; *U.S. Public*, pg. 903

THE SAULT STAR—See Chatham Asset Management, LLC; *U.S. Private*, pg. 861

SAVANNAH MORNING NEWS—See Gannett Co., Inc.; *U.S. Public*, pg. 904

SCITUATE MARINER—See Gannett Co., Inc.; *U.S. Public*, pg. 903

SCRANTON TIMES TRIBUNE—See Alden Global Capital LLC; *U.S. Private*, pg. 157

SEACOAST NEWSPAPERS, INC.—See Gannett Co., Inc.; *U.S. Public*, pg. 904

SEATTLEPI.COM—See The Hearst Corporation; *U.S. Private*, pg. 4048

SEATTLE POST-INTELLIGENCER—See The Hearst Corporation; *U.S. Private*, pg. 4048

SEATTLE TIMES COMPANY—See Blethen Corporation; *U.S. Private*, pg. 581

SEATTLE TIMES COMPANY—See Chatham Asset Management, LLC; *U.S. Private*, pg. 867

THE SEDALIA DEMOCRAT—See Independence Capital Partners, LLC; *U.S. Private*, pg. 2057

SELPI SPA—See Giovanni Agnelli B.V.; *Int'l*, pg. 2978

SENTINEL & ENTERPRISE—See Alden Global Capital LLC; *U.S. Private*, pg. 157

SENTINEL-RECORD INC.—See Wehco Media, Inc.; *U.S. Private*, pg. 4469

SF NEWSPAPER COMPANY, LLC—See The Anschutz Corporation; *U.S. Private*, pg. 3628

SHARON ADVOCATE—See Gannett Co., Inc.; *U.S. Public*, pg. 903

SHAWNEE NEWS-STAR—See Gannett Co., Inc.; *U.S. Public*, pg. 904

SHAW SUBURBAN MEDIA GROUP, INC.; *U.S. Private*, pg. 3628

SHEARMAN CORPORATION; *U.S. Private*, pg. 3629

THE SHEBOYGAN PRESS—See Gannett Co., Inc.; *U.S. Public*, pg. 900

SHERMAN PUBLICATIONS, INC.—See JAMS Media LLC; *U.S. Private*, pg. 2186

THE SHOPPER'S GUIDE—See The Nutting Company, Inc.; *U.S. Private*, pg. 4087

SHORE LINE NEWSPAPER—See Alden Global Capital LLC; *U.S. Private*, pg. 157

SHREWSBURY CHRONICLE—See Gannett Co., Inc.; *U.S. Public*, pg. 903

SILICON VALLEY COMMUNITY NEWSPAPERS—See Alden Global Capital LLC; *U.S. Private*, pg. 155

THE SILOAM SPRINGS HERALD LEADER—See Wehco Media, Inc.; *U.S. Private*, pg. 4470

SIOUX CITY NEWSPAPERS, INC.—See Lee Enterprises, Incorporated; *U.S. Public*, pg. 1300

THE SLATE GROUP LLC—See Graham Holdings Company; *U.S. Public*, pg. 956

SMALL NEWSPAPER GROUP INC.; *U.S. Private*, pg. 3690

SNOWMASS VILLAGE SUN—See Swift Communications, Inc.; *U.S. Private*, pg. 3893

SOCIETA EDITRICE PADANA SPA—See Caltagirone Editore S.p.A.; *Int'l*, pg. 1266

SOLOTHURNER ZEITUNG AG—See BT Holding AG; *Int'l*, pg. 1204

SOMERVILLE JOURNAL—See Gannett Co., Inc.; *U.S. Public*, pg. 903

SOUND PUBLISHING, INC.—See Black Press Group Ltd.; *Int'l*, pg. 1059

SOUTH CHINA MORNING POST PUBLISHERS LTD—See Alibaba Group Holding Limited; *Int'l*, pg. 326

THE SOUTH CHINA MORNING POST PUBLISHERS LTD.—See News Corporation; *U.S. Public*, pg. 1520

SOUTHCOMM COMMUNICATIONS, INC.—See SouthComm, Inc.; *U.S. Private*, pg. 3724

SOUTH DADE NEWS, INC.; *U.S. Private*, pg. 3722

SOUTHERN CALIFORNIA NEWS GROUP—See Alden Global Capital LLC; *U.S. Private*, pg. 157

SOUTHERN COMMUNITY NEWSPAPERS INC.; *U.S. Private*, pg. 3730

THE SOUTHERN ILLINOISAN—See Paxton Media Group LLC; *U.S. Private*, pg. 3116

SOUTHERN MARYLAND NEWSPAPERS—See Nash Holdings LLC; *U.S. Private*, pg. 2835

SOUTHERN NEWSPAPERS INC.; *U.S. Private*, pg. 3734

SOUTHERN RHODE ISLAND NEWSPAPERS—See R.I.S.N. Operations Inc.; *U.S. Private*, pg. 3336

SOUTH FLORIDA MEDIA GROUP, LLC; *U.S. Private*, pg. 3722

SOUTHWESTERN OREGON PUBLISHING CO.—See Lee Enterprises, Incorporated; *U.S. Public*, pg. 1300

SPARTANBURG HERALD-JOURNAL—See Gannett Co., Inc.; *U.S. Public*, pg. 905

THE SPECTRUM—See Gannett Co., Inc.; *U.S. Public*, pg. 900

THE SPIRIT PUBLISHING COMPANY—See Horizon Publications Inc.; *U.S. Private*, pg. 1982

THE SPORTING NEWS—See Advance Publications, Inc.; *U.S. Private*, pg. 85

SPRINGDALE MORNING NEWS—See Wehco Media, Inc.; *U.S. Private*, pg. 4470

SPRINGFIELD NEWSPAPERS, INC.—See Apollo Global Management, Inc.; *U.S. Public*, pg. 163

STADSNIEUWS BV—See DPG Media Group NV; *Int'l*, pg. 2189

THE STANDARD-TIMES—See R.I.S.N. Operations Inc.; *U.S. Private*, pg. 3337

STAR COURIER—See Gannett Co., Inc.; *U.S. Public*, pg. 904

STAR-GAZETTE—See Gannett Co., Inc.; *U.S. Public*, pg. 899

THE STAR-JOURNAL PUBLISHING CORP.; *U.S. Private*, pg. 4121

THE STAR-LEDGER—See Advance Publications, Inc.; *U.S. Private*, pg. 87

STAR LOCAL MEDIA—See 10/13 Communications LLC; *U.S. Private*, pg. 2

THE STARPHOENIX—See Chatham Asset Management, LLC; *U.S. Private*, pg. 861

THE STAR PRESS—See Gannett Co., Inc.; *U.S. Public*, pg. 900

STAR PUBLISHING COMPANY—See Lee Enterprises, Incorporated; *U.S. Public*, pg. 1300

THE STAR—See Gannett Co., Inc.; *U.S. Public*, pg. 906

STAR-TELEGRAM, INC.—See Chatham Asset Management, LLC; *U.S. Private*, pg. 867

THE STAR TRIBUNE COMPANY—See Star Tribune Media Company LLC; *U.S. Private*, pg. 3785

THE STATE JOURNAL-REGISTER—See Gannett Co., Inc.; *U.S. Public*, pg. 905

THE STATE MEDIA COMPANY—See Chatham Asset Management, LLC; *U.S. Private*, pg. 868

STATEN ISLAND ADVANCE—See Advance Publications, Inc.; *U.S. Private*, pg. 87

THE STATE-RECORD COMPANY—See Chatham Asset Management, LLC; *U.S. Private*, pg. 867

STATESMAN JOURNAL—See Gannett Co., Inc.; *U.S. Public*, pg. 899

THE ST. AUGUSTINE RECORD—See Gannett Co., Inc.; *U.S. Public*, pg. 905

ST. CLOUD TIMES—See Gannett Co., Inc.; *U.S. Public*, pg. 899

STEAMBOAT PILOT & TODAY—See The World Company; *U.S. Private*, pg. 4139

STEVENS POINT JOURNAL—See Gannett Co., Inc.; *U.S. Public*, pg. 899

ST. LOUIS BUSINESS JOURNAL CORPORATION—See Advance Publications, Inc.; *U.S. Private*, pg. 85

ST. LOUIS COUNTIAN—See The Dolan Company; *U.S. Private*, pg. 4022

ST. LOUIS POST-DISPATCH LLC—See Lee Enterprises, Incorporated; *U.S. Public*, pg. 1300

STOCKTON NEWSPAPERS INC.—See Lee Enterprises, Incorporated; *U.S. Public*, pg. 1299

STONEHAM SUN—See Gannett Co., Inc.; *U.S. Public*, pg. 903

STOUGHTON JOURNAL—See Gannett Co., Inc.; *U.S. Public*, pg. 903

STP PUBLICATIONS LIMITED PARTNERSHIP—See GVIC

513110 — NEWSPAPER PUBLISHER...

Communications Corp.; *Int'l*, pg. 3189
STRATEGIC PUBLICATIONS, LLC; *U.S. Private*, pg. 3835
STREET & SMITH SPORTS GROUP—See Advance Publications, Inc.; *U.S. Private*, pg. 85
THE STUART NEWS—See Gannett Co., Inc.; *U.S. Public*, pg. 898
STYLE WEEKLY INC.—See Irish Times; *U.S. Private*, pg. 2139
SUBURBAN JOURNALS OF GREATER ST. LOUIS LLC—See Lee Enterprises, Incorporated; *U.S. Public*, pg. 1300
SUBURBAN NEWSPAPERS OF GREATER ST. LOUIS—See Lee Enterprises, Incorporated; *U.S. Public*, pg. 1300
THE SUDBURY STAR—See Chatham Asset Management, LLC; *U.S. Private*, pg. 861
THE SUDBURY TOWN CRIER—See Gannett Co., Inc.; *U.S. Public*, pg. 903
SUMMERVILLE COMMUNICATIONS, INC.—See Evening Post Publishing Co.; *U.S. Private*, pg. 1436
SUN CITIES INDEPENDENT—See Independent Newspapers, Inc.; *U.S. Private*, pg. 2060
SUN COAST MEDIA GROUP, INC.; *U.S. Private*, pg. 3862
SUN CURRENT/SUN NEWSPAPERS—See Adams Publishing Group, LLC; *U.S. Private*, pg. 75
SUN-GAZETTE COMPANY INC.—See The Nutting Company, Inc.; *U.S. Private*, pg. 4086
THE SUN HERALD—See Chatham Asset Management, LLC; *U.S. Private*, pg. 867
SUN JOURNAL—See Gannett Co., Inc.; *U.S. Public*, pg. 906
THE SUN NEWS—See Chatham Asset Management, LLC; *U.S. Private*, pg. 866
SUN PUBLISHING COMPANY, INC.—See Chatham Asset Management, LLC; *U.S. Private*, pg. 866
SUNRISE PUBLICATIONS, INC.—See GameStop Corp.; *U.S. Public*, pg. 896
SUN-SENTINEL COMPANY—See Tribune Publishing Company; *U.S. Private*, pg. 4228
SUNSHINE COAST REPORTER PARTNERSHIP—See GVIC Communications Corp.; *Int'l*, pg. 3189
SUNSHINE NEWPAPER PRINTING—See Independent Newspapers, Inc.; *U.S. Private*, pg. 2060
THE SUN—See Alden Global Capital LLC; *U.S. Private*, pg. 156
THE SUN—See Alden Global Capital LLC; *U.S. Private*, pg. 159
THE SUN—See Independent Newspapers, Inc.; *U.S. Private*, pg. 2060
THE SUN—See News Corporation; *U.S. Public*, pg. 1521
THE SUN TIMES—See Chatham Asset Management, LLC; *U.S. Private*, pg. 861
THE SUN-TIMES—See Gannett Co., Inc.; *U.S. Public*, pg. 905
SUPERIOR PUBLISHING, INC.—See American Consolidated Media LP; *U.S. Private*, pg. 228
SUREWEST DIRECTORIES—See Gannett Co., Inc.; *U.S. Public*, pg. 906
SURPRISE INDEPENDENT—See Independent Newspapers, Inc.; *U.S. Private*, pg. 2060
SURVIVAL MEDIA LLC; *U.S. Private*, pg. 3885
SUSSEX POST—See Independent Newspapers, Inc.; *U.S. Private*, pg. 2060
THE SWAMPSCOTT REPORTER—See Gannett Co., Inc.; *U.S. Public*, pg. 903
SWIFT COMMUNICATIONS, INC.; *U.S. Private*, pg. 3893
SYLVANIA TELEPHONE—See Gannett Co., Inc.; *U.S. Public*, pg. 904
TACOMA NEWS, INC.—See Chatham Asset Management, LLC; *U.S. Private*, pg. 867
TALLAHASSEE DEMOCRAT—See Gannett Co., Inc.; *U.S. Public*, pg. 899
TAMPA BAY BUSINESS JOURNAL—See Advance Publications, Inc.; *U.S. Private*, pg. 85
TAMPA BAY NEWSPAPERS, INC.—See Times Holding Co.; *U.S. Private*, pg. 4172
TAMPA BAY TIMES—See Times Holding Co.; *U.S. Private*, pg. 4172
THE TAUNTON GAZETTE—See Gannett Co., Inc.; *U.S. Public*, pg. 903
TELEVISIONWEEK—See Crain Communications, Inc.; *U.S. Private*, pg. 1084
THE TENNESSEAN—See Gannett Co., Inc.; *U.S. Public*, pg. 900
TENNESSEE VALLEY PRINTING CO.; *U.S. Private*, pg. 3968
TEWKSBURY ADVOCATE—See Gannett Co., Inc.; *U.S. Public*, pg. 903
TEXARKANA GAZETTE—See Wehco Media, Inc.; *U.S. Private*, pg. 4470
TEXARKANA NEWSPAPER INC.—See Wehco Media, Inc.; *U.S. Private*, pg. 4469
TEXAS COMMUNITY MEDIA LLC; *U.S. Private*, pg. 3975
TEXAS-NEW MEXICO NEWSPAPERS, LLC—See Gannett Co., Inc.; *U.S. Public*, pg. 899
THISWEEK COMMUNITY NEWS—See Gannett Co., Inc.; *U.S. Public*, pg. 903
TIME MAGAZINE EUROPE LIMITED—See Warner Bros. Discovery, Inc.; *U.S. Public*, pg. 2328

TIMES COLONIST—See Glacier Media Inc.; *Int'l*, pg. 2987
TIMES COMMUNITY NEWS—See Los Angeles Times Communications, LLC; *U.S. Private*, pg. 2497
TIMES COMMUNITY NEWS - SOUTH—See Los Angeles Times Communications, LLC; *U.S. Private*, pg. 2497
TIMESDAILY—See Tennessee Valley Printing Co.; *U.S. Private*, pg. 3968
THE TIMES HERALD COMPANY—See Gannett Co., Inc.; *U.S. Public*, pg. 901
TIMES HERALD-RECORD—See Gannett Co., Inc.; *U.S. Public*, pg. 904
TIMES-HERALD—See Alden Global Capital LLC; *U.S. Private*, pg. 155
THE TIMES HERALD—See Alden Global Capital LLC; *U.S. Private*, pg. 159
THE TIMES INC.—See Paxton Media Group LLC; *U.S. Private*, pg. 3116
THE TIMES INC.—See Small Newspaper Group Inc.; *U.S. Private*, pg. 3690
TIMES JOURNAL INC.; *U.S. Private*, pg. 4172
THE TIMES LEADER—See The Nutting Company, Inc.; *U.S. Private*, pg. 4087
TIMES NEWSPAPERS LTD.—See News Corporation; *U.S. Public*, pg. 1521
THE TIMES-NEWS—See Gannett Co., Inc.; *U.S. Public*, pg. 906
THE TIMES OF INDIA—See Bennett, Coleman & Co. Ltd.; *Int'l*, pg. 975
THE TIMES OF TRENTON—See Advance Publications, Inc.; *U.S. Private*, pg. 87
THE TIMES-PICAYUNE PUBLISHING CORP.—See Advance Publications, Inc.; *U.S. Private*, pg. 87
TIMES-POST—See Home News Enterprises, LLC; *U.S. Private*, pg. 1971
TIMES PUBLISHING COMPANY—See Times Holding Co.; *U.S. Private*, pg. 4172
TIMES PUBLISHING CO.—See Gannett Co., Inc.; *U.S. Public*, pg. 906
TIMES PUBLISHING NEWSPAPERS INC.—See O'Rourke Media Group, LLC; *U.S. Public*, pg. 2980
TIMES RECORDER—See Gannett Co., Inc.; *U.S. Public*, pg. 901
THE TIMES REPORTER—See Gannett Co., Inc.; *U.S. Public*, pg. 905
THE TIMES—See Gannett Co., Inc.; *U.S. Public*, pg. 901
TIMES-STANDARD—See Alden Global Capital LLC; *U.S. Private*, pg. 156
TIMMINS DAILY PRESS—See Chatham Asset Management, LLC; *U.S. Private*, pg. 861
TNI PARTNERS—See Gannett Co., Inc.; *U.S. Public*, pg. 899
TNI PARTNERS—See Lee Enterprises, Incorporated; *U.S. Public*, pg. 1300
THE TOPSAIL ADVERTISER—See Gannett Co., Inc.; *U.S. Public*, pg. 906
THE TORONTO SUN PUBLISHING CORPORATION—See Chatham Asset Management, LLC; *U.S. Private*, pg. 861
TOWANDA PRINTING CO.—See Times-Shamrock, Inc.; *U.S. Private*, pg. 4173
TOWN OF PARADISE VALLEY INDEPENDENT—See Independent Newspapers, Inc.; *U.S. Private*, pg. 2060
TOWNSEND TIMES—See Alden Global Capital LLC; *U.S. Private*, pg. 157
THE TOWN TALK—See Gannett Co., Inc.; *U.S. Public*, pg. 896
TRADER.COM (POLSKA) SP. Z O.O—See Agora S.A.; *Int'l*, pg. 213
TRADEWINDS A/S—See Fred. Olsen & Co.; *Int'l*, pg. 2768
TRADEWINDS-ATHENS—See Fred. Olsen & Co.; *Int'l*, pg. 2768
TRADEWINDS-ITALY—See Fred. Olsen & Co.; *Int'l*, pg. 2768
TRADEWINDS-LONDON—See Fred. Olsen & Co.; *Int'l*, pg. 2768
TRADEWINDS-NEW DELHI—See Fred. Olsen & Co.; *Int'l*, pg. 2768
TRANSPORT TOPICS PUBLISHING GROUP; *U.S. Private*, pg. 4211
TRAVERSE CITY RECORD-EAGLE—See The Retirement Systems of Alabama; *U.S. Private*, pg. 4106
TREASURE COAST NEWSPAPERS, LLC—See Gannett Co., Inc.; *U.S. Public*, pg. 898
TRIBE MEDIA CORP.; *U.S. Private*, pg. 4227
TRIBUNE CONTENT AGENCY, LLC—See Tribune Publishing Company; *U.S. Private*, pg. 4228
THE TRIBUNE-DEMOCRAT—See The Retirement Systems of Alabama; *U.S. Private*, pg. 4106
TRIBUNE PUBLISHING COMPANY, LLC—See Tribune Publishing Company; *U.S. Private*, pg. 4228
TRIBUNE PUBLISHING COMPANY—See TPC Holdings, Inc.; *U.S. Private*, pg. 4200
TRIBUNE-REVIEW PUBLISHING COMPANY; *U.S. Private*, pg. 4228
THE TRIBUNE—See Chatham Asset Management, LLC; *U.S. Private*, pg. 867
THE TRIBUNE—See Home News Enterprises, LLC; *U.S. Private*, pg. 1971
TRIBUNE WASHINGTON BUREAU, LLC—See Tribune

CORPORATE AFFILIATIONS

Publishing Company; *U.S. Private*, pg. 4228
TRI-CITY WEEKLY—See Alden Global Capital LLC; *U.S. Private*, pg. 156
TRINIDAD PUBLISHING COMPANY LIMITED—See ANSA McAl Limited; *Int'l*, pg. 477
TRITON DIGITAL CANADA, INC.—See The E.W. Scripps Company; *U.S. Public*, pg. 2069
TRI-VALLEY HERALD—See Alden Global Capital LLC; *U.S. Private*, pg. 155
TROY DAILY NEWS—See Independence Capital Partners, LLC; *U.S. Private*, pg. 2057
TRUE NORTH REAL ESTATE LLC—See DallasNews Corporation; *U.S. Public*, pg. 621
TRUTH PUBLISHING COMPANY INC.—See Federated Media Inc.; *U.S. Private*, pg. 1492
TUCSON EXPLORER—See 10/13 Communications LLC; *U.S. Private*, pg. 2
THE TUKWILA REPORTER—See Black Press Group Ltd.; *Int'l*, pg. 1059
TULARE ADVANCE-REGISTER—See Gannett Co., Inc.; *U.S. Public*, pg. 901
TURLEY PUBLICATIONS INC.; *U.S. Private*, pg. 4259
TWEAKERS.NET B.V.—See DPG Media Group NV; *Int'l*, pg. 2188
TWIN STATES PUBLISHING CO. INC.—See Community Media Group; *U.S. Private*, pg. 995
THE UKIAH DAILY JOURNAL—See Alden Global Capital LLC; *U.S. Private*, pg. 156
THE UNION DEMOCRAT—See Western Communications Inc.; *U.S. Private*, pg. 4492
UNION LEADER CORPORATION; *U.S. Private*, pg. 4284
THE UNION-RECORDER—See The Retirement Systems of Alabama; *U.S. Private*, pg. 4106
UNIONTOWN NEWSPAPERS INC.—See The Nutting Company, Inc.; *U.S. Private*, pg. 4087
UNITED COMMUNICATIONS CORPORATION; *U.S. Private*, pg. 4289
UNITED WEHCO INC.—See Wehco Media, Inc.; *U.S. Private*, pg. 4469
UPSTREAM AS—See Fred. Olsen & Co.; *Int'l*, pg. 2768
UPSTREAM LONDON—See Fred. Olsen & Co.; *Int'l*, pg. 2768
UPSTREAM SINGAPORE—See Fred. Olsen & Co.; *Int'l*, pg. 2768
USA TODAY—See Gannett Co., Inc.; *U.S. Public*, pg. 901
USA TODAY—See Gannett Co., Inc.; *U.S. Public*, pg. 901
USA TODAY SPORTS MEDIA GROUP, LLC—See Gannett Co., Inc.; *U.S. Public*, pg. 901
UTAH MEDIA, INC.—See Alden Global Capital LLC; *U.S. Private*, pg. 159
VALLEY ADVOCATE—See Tribune Publishing Company; *U.S. Private*, pg. 4228
VALLEY MORNING STAR—See AIM Media Texas, LLC; *U.S. Private*, pg. 133
VALLEY NEWSPAPERS—See Independent Newspapers, Inc.; *U.S. Private*, pg. 2060
THE VANCOUVER SUN—See Chatham Asset Management, LLC; *U.S. Private*, pg. 861
VENICE GONDOLIER SUN—See Sun Coast Media Group, Inc.; *U.S. Private*, pg. 3862
VENTURA COUNTY STAR, LLC—See Gannett Co., Inc.; *U.S. Public*, pg. 898
VERDE VALLEY NEWSPAPERS INC.—See Western Newspapers, Inc.; *U.S. Private*, pg. 4495
VERSLO ZINIOS, UAB—See Bonnier AB; *Int'l*, pg. 1108
VERTICAL MEDIA GMBH—See Axel Springer SE; *Int'l*, pg. 767
VERTICORE COMMUNICATIONS LTD.—See TEGNA Inc.; *U.S. Public*, pg. 1991
VICTORIA ADVOCATE PUBLISHING COMPANY; *U.S. Private*, pg. 4378
THE VILLAGER—See Gannett Co., Inc.; *U.S. Public*, pg. 903
VILLAGE VOICE, LLC; *U.S. Private*, pg. 4384
VINCENNES NEWSPAPERS, INC.—See Paxton Media Group LLC; *U.S. Private*, pg. 3116
VIRGINIA GAZETTE COMPANIES, LLC—See Tribune Publishing Company; *U.S. Private*, pg. 4228
THE VIRGINIAN-PILOT—See Tribune Publishing Company; *U.S. Private*, pg. 4228
VISALIA NEWSPAPERS LLC—See Gannett Co., Inc.; *U.S. Public*, pg. 901
VISALIA TIMES-DELTA—See Gannett Co., Inc.; *U.S. Public*, pg. 901
VOICE COMMUNICATIONS CORP.—See Alden Global Capital LLC; *U.S. Private*, pg. 159
WABASH PLAIN DEALER COMPANY INC.—See Paxton Media Group LLC; *U.S. Private*, pg. 3116
WAKEFIELD OBSERVER—See Gannett Co., Inc.; *U.S. Public*, pg. 903
WALLA WALLA UNION BULLETIN INC.—See Blethen Corporation; *U.S. Private*, pg. 581
THE WALL STREET JOURNAL ASIA—See News Corporation; *U.S. Public*, pg. 1518
THE WALL STREET JOURNAL EUROPE S.P.R.L.—See News Corporation; *U.S. Public*, pg. 1519
THE WALL STREET JOURNAL—See News Corporation; *U.S. Public*, pg. 1518

WALNUT HIGHLANDER—See Alden Global Capital LLC; *U.S. Private*, pg. 158
WALTHAM NEWS TRIBUNE—See Gannett Co., Inc.; *U.S. Public*, pg. 903
THE WALTON SUN—See Gannett Co., Inc.; *U.S. Public*, pg. 906
WARRICK PUBLISHING CO. INC.—See Brehm Communications Inc.; *U.S. Private*, pg. 644
WASHINGTON COUNTY ENTERPRISE-LEADER—See Wehco Media, Inc.; *U.S. Private*, pg. 4470
THE WASHINGTON EVENING JOURNAL—See Inland Industries, Inc.; *U.S. Private*, pg. 2078
THE WASHINGTON NEWSPAPER PUBLISHING COMPANY, LLC—See The Anschutz Corporation; *U.S. Private*, pg. 3987
WASTE NEWS—See Crain Communications, Inc.; *U.S. Private*, pg. 1084
WATAUGA DEMOCRAT NEWSPAPERS, INC.—See Adams Publishing Group, LLC; *U.S. Private*, pg. 75
WAUSAU DAILY HERALD—See Gannett Co., Inc.; *U.S. Public*, pg. 901
WAXAHACHIE NEWSPAPERS, INC.—See American Consolidated Media LP; *U.S. Private*, pg. 228
WAYLAND TOWN CRIER—See Gannett Co., Inc.; *U.S. Public*, pg. 903
THE WEEKLY VISTA—See Wehco Media, Inc.; *U.S. Private*, pg. 4470
WEGENER HUIS-AAN-HUISKRANTEN BV—See DPG Media Group NV; *Int'l*, pg. 2189
WEGENER NIEUWSDRUK—See DPG Media Group NV; *Int'l*, pg. 2189
WEHCO MEDIA, INC.; *U.S. Private*, pg. 4469
WEHCO NEWSPAPERS, INC.—See Wehco Media, Inc.; *U.S. Private*, pg. 4470
WEISS MEDIEN AG—See BT Holding AG; *Int'l*, pg. 1204
WELLSVILLE DAILY REPORTER—See Gannett Co., Inc.; *U.S. Public*, pg. 905
WESTBOROUGH NEWS—See Gannett Co., Inc.; *U.S. Public*, pg. 903
WEST COUNTY TIMES—See Alden Global Capital LLC; *U.S. Private*, pg. 155
WEST COVINA HIGHLANDER—See Alden Global Capital LLC; *U.S. Private*, pg. 158
WESTERN COMMUNICATIONS INC.; *U.S. Private*, pg. 4491
WESTERN NEWSPAPERS, INC.; *U.S. Private*, pg. 4495
WESTERN OUTDOORS PUBLICATIONS; *U.S. Private*, pg. 4495
WESTERN PRODUCER PUBLICATIONS PARTNERSHIP—See GVIC Communications Corp.; *Int'l*, pg. 3189
WESTFORD EAGLE—See Gannett Co., Inc.; *U.S. Public*, pg. 903
WESTMINSTER HOLDING; *U.S. Private*, pg. 4499
WEST ROXBURY TRANSCRIPT—See Gannett Co., Inc.; *U.S. Public*, pg. 903
WESTSIDE EAGLE OBSERVER—See Wehco Media, Inc.; *U.S. Private*, pg. 4470
WEST VIRGINIA NEWSPAPER PUBLISHING COMPANY—See Greer Industries Inc.; *U.S. Private*, pg. 1782
WESTWOOD PRESS—See Gannett Co., Inc.; *U.S. Public*, pg. 903
WETZEL CHRONICLE—See The Nutting Company, Inc.; *U.S. Private*, pg. 4087
WEYMOUTH NEWS—See Gannett Co., Inc.; *U.S. Public*, pg. 903
WHEELING NEWSPAPERS, INC.—See The Nutting Company, Inc.; *U.S. Private*, pg. 4087
WHITTIER DAILY NEWS—See Alden Global Capital LLC; *U.S. Private*, pg. 158
THE WIARTON ECHO—See Chatham Asset Management, LLC; *U.S. Private*, pg. 861
WICHITA BUSINESS JOURNAL, INC.—See Advance Publications, Inc.; *U.S. Private*, pg. 85
THE WICHITA EAGLE—See Chatham Asset Management, LLC; *U.S. Private*, pg. 867
WICHITA FALLS TIMES RECORD NEWS, LLC—See Gannett Co., Inc.; *U.S. Public*, pg. 898
WICK COMMUNICATIONS CO., INC.—See Wick News Corporation; *U.S. Private*, pg. 4515
WICK NEWS CORPORATION; *U.S. Private*, pg. 4515
WILKES-BARRE PUBLISHING COMPANY, INC.—See Independence Capital Partners, LLC; *U.S. Private*, pg. 2057
WILKES-BARRE TIMES LEADER—See Independence Capital Partners, LLC; *U.S. Private*, pg. 2057
WILLIAM B. COLLINS CO., INC.—See The Nutting Company, Inc.; *U.S. Private*, pg. 4087
WILLIAMS GO NEWSPAPERS INC.—See Western Newspapers, Inc.; *U.S. Private*, pg. 4495
WILLIAMSON DAILY NEWS—See HD Media Company, LLC; *U.S. Private*, pg. 1890
THE WILLITS NEWS—See Alden Global Capital LLC; *U.S. Private*, pg. 159
WILMINGTON ADVOCATE—See Gannett Co., Inc.; *U.S. Public*, pg. 903

WILMINGTON STAR-NEWS, INC.—See Gannett Co., Inc.; *U.S. Public*, pg. 906
THE WILSON GROUP KW23, LLC; *U.S. Private*, pg. 4136
WINCHESTER STAR—See Gannett Co., Inc.; *U.S. Public*, pg. 903
THE WINDSOR STAR—See Chatham Asset Management, LLC; *U.S. Private*, pg. 861
WINFIELD DAILY COURIER—See Winfield Publishing Co.; *U.S. Private*, pg. 4541
WINFIELD PUBLISHING CO.; *U.S. Private*, pg. 4540
WINONA DAILY NEWS—See Lee Enterprises, Incorporated; *U.S. Public*, pg. 1300
WINSTON-SALEM JOURNAL—See Lee Enterprises, Incorporated; *U.S. Public*, pg. 1299
WISCONSIN STATE JOURNAL—See Lee Enterprises, Incorporated; *U.S. Public*, pg. 1299
WISCONSIN STATE JOURNAL—See The Capital Times Company; *U.S. Private*, pg. 4004
WOBURN ADVOCATE—See Gannett Co., Inc.; *U.S. Public*, pg. 903
WOMACK PUBLISHING COMPANY, INC.; *U.S. Private*, pg. 4555
WOODWARD COMMUNICATIONS, INC.; *U.S. Private*, pg. 4561
WOOSTER DAILY RECORD, INC., LLC—See Gannett Co., Inc.; *U.S. Public*, pg. 905
WORCESTER TELEGRAM & GAZETTE CORPORATION—See Gannett Co., Inc.; *U.S. Public*, pg. 906
THE WORLD COMPANY; *U.S. Private*, pg. 4139
THE WORLD NEWSPAPER—See Lee Enterprises, Incorporated; *U.S. Public*, pg. 1300
WORLDWEST LIMITED LIABILITY COMPANY—See The World Company; *U.S. Private*, pg. 4139
WP COMPANY LLC—See Nash Holdings LLC; *U.S. Private*, pg. 2835
WYOMING NEWSPAPERS INC.—See News Media Corporation; *U.S. Private*, pg. 2917
WYOMING NEWSPAPERS INC.—See News Media Corporation; *U.S. Private*, pg. 2917
YANKTON DAILY PRESS & DAKOTAN—See Yankton Media, Inc.; *U.S. Private*, pg. 4586
YANKTON MEDIA, INC.; *U.S. Private*, pg. 4586
YELLOWSTONE NEWSPAPERS—See Yellowstone Communications; *U.S. Private*, pg. 4587
YIELDREPORT PTY LTD—See Finexia Financial Group Ltd.; *Int'l*, pg. 2674
YORK DAILY RECORD-YORK SUNDAY NEWS LLC—See Gannett Co., Inc.; *U.S. Public*, pg. 900
YORK DISPATCH LLC—See Gannett Co., Inc.; *U.S. Public*, pg. 901
YORK NEWSPAPER COMPANY—See Gannett Co., Inc.; *U.S. Public*, pg. 901
THE YORK NEWS-TIMES—See Lee Enterprises, Incorporated; *U.S. Public*, pg. 1298
YUMA SUN—See Horizon Publications Inc.; *U.S. Private*, pg. 1982
ZULULAND OBSERVER (PTY) LTD.—See Caxton and CTP Publishers and Printers Ltd.; *Int'l*, pg. 1363
ZULULAND OBSERVER (PTY) LTD.—See Caxton and CTP Publishers and Printers Ltd.; *Int'l*, pg. 1363
ZULULAND OBSERVER (PTY) LTD.—See Caxton and CTP Publishers and Printers Ltd.; *Int'l*, pg. 1363
ZULULAND OBSERVER (PTY) LTD.—See Caxton and CTP Publishers and Printers Ltd.; *Int'l*, pg. 1363

513120 — PERIODICAL PUBLISHERS

1105 MEDIA, INC.—See Alta Communications, Inc.; *U.S. Private*, pg. 203
1105 MEDIA, INC.—See Nautic Partners, LLC; *U.S. Private*, pg. 2868
500VOLT INC; *Int'l*, pg. 12
ABOARD PUBLISHING, INC.—See Chatham Asset Management, LLC; *U.S. Private*, pg. 866
ACCESS INTELLIGENCE, LLC—See Veronis Suhler Stevenson Partners LLC; *U.S. Private*, pg. 4368
ACCESS PUBLISHING CO. LTD.—See Access Co., Ltd.; *Int'l*, pg. 88
ACTIVE INTEREST MEDIA, INC.; *U.S. Private*, pg. 69
ADVANCE PUBLICATIONS, INC.; *U.S. Private*, pg. 84
ADVANTAGE BUSINESS MEDIA LLC—See Owner Resource Group, LLC; *U.S. Private*, pg. 3055
ADVOCATE MEDIA; *U.S. Private*, pg. 111
ADWEEK, LLC—See Shamrock Capital Advisors, LLC; *U.S. Private*, pg. 3624
AHC MEDIA LLC—See Bertelsmann SE & Co. KGaA; *Int'l*, pg. 991
AIR CARGO WORLD MAGAZINE—See Royal Media Group, Inc.; *U.S. Private*, pg. 3492
AIRLINE TARIFF PUBLISHING COMPANY; *U.S. Private*, pg. 141
ALASKA JOURNAL OF COMMERCE—See Shivers Trading & Operating Company; *U.S. Private*, pg. 3638
ALBANY TIMES UNION—See The Hearst Corporation; *U.S. Private*, pg. 4047
A-LEHDET OY; *Int'l*, pg. 20

AL GHURAIR PRINTING AND PUBLISHING LLC—See Al Ghurair Investment LLC; *Int'l*, pg. 278
ALLEN PRESS INC.; *U.S. Private*, pg. 179
ALLERS FAMILIE-JOURNAL A/S—See Aller Holding A/S; *Int'l*, pg. 336
ALLURED PUBLISHING CORPORATION; *U.S. Private*, pg. 194
ALMANAC PUBLISHING CO.—See Geiger Brothers; *U.S. Private*, pg. 1656
ALMA TALENT OY—See Alma Media Corporation; *Int'l*, pg. 361
AMERICAN BABY MAGAZINE—See Meredith Corporation; *U.S. Public*, pg. 1422
AMERICAN CITY BUSINESS JOURNALS—See Advance Publications, Inc.; *U.S. Private*, pg. 84
AMERICAN FIELD PUBLISHING COMPANY, INC.—See United Kennel Club, Inc.; *U.S. Private*, pg. 4293
AMERICAN INSTITUTE OF PHYSICS INC.; *U.S. Private*, pg. 238
AMERICAN JEWISH CONGRESS INC.; *U.S. Private*, pg. 239
AMERICAN LAWYER MEDIA, INC.—See Apax Partners LLP; *Int'l*, pg. 504
THE AMERICAN LEGION MAGAZINE; *U.S. Private*, pg. 3986
AMERICAN METAL MARKET—See Astorg Partners S.A.S.; *Int'l*, pg. 656
AMERICAN METAL MARKET—See Epiris Managers LLP; *Int'l*, pg. 2460
AMERICAN PHYSICAL SOCIETY; *U.S. Private*, pg. 243
AMERICAN POLICE BEAT—See Regent, L.P.; *U.S. Private*, pg. 3388
AMERICAS TEST KITCHEN LIMITED PARTNERSHIP—See Marquee Brands LLC; *U.S. Private*, pg. 2586
AMOS CRAFT PUBLISHING—See Amos Press, Inc.; *U.S. Private*, pg. 264
AMOS PRESS, INC.; *U.S. Private*, pg. 264
ANNEX PUBLISHING & PRINTING INC.; *Int'l*, pg. 474
ANNIE'S PUBLISHING, LLC—See Dynamic Resource Group, Inc.; *U.S. Private*, pg. 1298
A.PLUS GROUP HOLDINGS LIMITED; *Int'l*, pg. 28
APPAREL MAGAZINE—See RFE Investment Partners; *U.S. Private*, pg. 3419
ARBEIT-TIMES CO., LTD.; *Int'l*, pg. 537
ARCHITECTURAL DIGEST—See Advance Publications, Inc.; *U.S. Private*, pg. 85
ARCHITECTURAL RECORD—See BNP Media, Inc.; *U.S. Private*, pg. 602
ARIP PUBLIC COMPANY LIMITED; *Int'l*, pg. 565
ARMY TIMES PUBLISHING COMPANY—See Regent, L.P.; *U.S. Private*, pg. 3388
ARNOLD BERNHARD & CO.; *U.S. Private*, pg. 333
ARNOLDO MONDADORI EDITORE S.P.A.—See Fininvest S.p.A.; *Int'l*, pg. 2675
ARTFORUM INTERNATIONAL MAGAZINE, INC.—See Penske Media Corporation; *U.S. Private*, pg. 3139
ARTHUR L DAVIS PUBLISHING AGENCY, INC.—See Ziff Davis, Inc.; *U.S. Public*, pg. 2404
ASCEND INTEGRATED MEDIA, LLC; *U.S. Private*, pg. 346
ASIMOV'S SCIENCE FICTION MAGAZINE—See Penny Publications, LLC; *U.S. Private*, pg. 3137
ASSOCIATED CONSTRUCTION PUBLICATIONS LLC; *U.S. Private*, pg. 355
ASTORIA D.O.O.—See Adris Grupa d.d.; *Int'l*, pg. 153
ASTRO DIGITAL PUBLICATIONS SDN BHD—See Astro Malaysia Holdings Bhd; *Int'l*, pg. 662
ATHLON SPORTS COMMUNICATIONS, INC.—See Athlon Holdings, Inc.; *U.S. Private*, pg. 368
ATLANTA BUSINESS CHRONICLE—See Advance Publications, Inc.; *U.S. Private*, pg. 84
THE ATLANTIC MONTHLY GROUP, INC.—See National Journal Group; *U.S. Private*, pg. 2858
AUDUBON MAGAZINE—See National Audubon Society, Inc.; *U.S. Private*, pg. 2847
AUGUST HOME PUBLISHING COMPANY; *U.S. Private*, pg. 392
AUTOMOBILE MAGAZINE—See TEN: The Enthusiast Network, Inc.; *U.S. Private*, pg. 3964
AUTOWEEK—See Crain Communications, Inc.; *U.S. Private*, pg. 1083
AXEL SPRINGER MEDIAHOUSE BERLIN GMBH—See Axel Springer SE; *Int'l*, pg. 766
AXEL SPRINGER SE; *Int'l*, pg. 765
AZ FACHVERLAGE AG—See BT Holding AG; *Int'l*, pg. 1204
BABCOX PUBLICATIONS INC.; *U.S. Private*, pg. 422
BACKSTAGE LLC—See Guggenheim Partners, LLC; *U.S. Private*, pg. 1811
BACUI TECHNOLOGIES INTERNATIONAL LTD.; *Int'l*, pg. 795
BALL PUBLISHING—See Ball Horticultural Company; *U.S. Private*, pg. 400
BANTAM PAPERBACKS UK—See Bertelsmann SE & Co. KGaA; *Int'l*, pg. 991
BANTAM PRESS UK—See Bertelsmann SE & Co. KGaA; *Int'l*, pg. 991
BARRON'S—See News Corporation; *U.S. Public*, pg. 1518
BASEBALL AMERICA, INC.; *U.S. Private*, pg. 484

BASELINE—See Ziff Davis Enterprise, Inc.; *U.S. Private*, pg. 4604
B.A.S.S., INC.—See The Walt Disney Company; *U.S. Public*, pg. 2138
BASSMASTER MAGAZINE—See The Walt Disney Company; *U.S. Public*, pg. 2138
B.A.S.S. TIMES—See The Walt Disney Company; *U.S. Public*, pg. 2138
BASTEI LUBBE AG; *Int'l*, pg. 888
BAUER CONSUMER MEDIA LTD.—See Heinrich Bauer Verlag KG; *Int'l*, pg. 3323
BAUER MEDIA GROUP—See Heinrich Bauer Verlag KG; *Int'l*, pg. 3323
BAUER MEDIA NEW ZEALAND—See Heinrich Bauer Verlag KG; *Int'l*, pg. 3324
BAUER MEDIA POLSKA SP. Z O.O.—See Heinrich Bauer Verlag KG; *Int'l*, pg. 3324
BAUER MEDIA SK V.O.S.—See Heinrich Bauer Verlag KG; *Int'l*, pg. 3324
BAUER MEDIA V.O.S.—See Heinrich Bauer Verlag KG; *Int'l*, pg. 3324
BAUER PUBLISHING USA—See Heinrich Bauer Verlag KG; *Int'l*, pg. 3324
BAUER SPECIALIST MEDIA—See Heinrich Bauer Verlag KG; *Int'l*, pg. 3323
BAUER TRADER MEDIA—See Heinrich Bauer Verlag KG; *Int'l*, pg. 3324
BAYARD CANADA, INC.—See Bayard-Presse S.A.; *Int'l*, pg. 901
BAYARD PRESSE ASIA—See Bayard-Presse S.A.; *Int'l*, pg. 901
BAYARD-PRESSE S.A.; *Int'l*, pg. 901
BAYARD REVISTAS S.A.—See Bayard-Presse S.A.; *Int'l*, pg. 901
BBC WORLDWIDE LIMITED—See British Broadcasting Corporation; *Int'l*, pg. 1169
BDV BETEILIGUNGEN GMBH & CO. KG—See Hubert Burda Media Holding Kommanditgesellschaft; *Int'l*, pg. 3519
BECKETT MEDIA LLC; *U.S. Private*, pg. 511
BELLEROPHON PUBLICATIONS, INC.—See Sandow Media LLC; *U.S. Private*, pg. 3544
BELLINGHAM HERALD PUBLISHING, LLC—See Chatham Asset Management, LLC; *U.S. Private*, pg. 866
BELVOIR PUBLICATIONS INC.; *U.S. Private*, pg. 522
BERLINER PRESSE VERTRIEB GMBH & CO. KG—See Bertelsmann SE & Co. KGaA; *Int'l*, pg. 994
BETTER HOMES & GARDENS BOOKS—See Meredith Corporation; *U.S. Public*, pg. 1422
BGR MEDIA, LLC—See Penske Media Corporation; *U.S. Private*, pg. 3139
BIG STONE PUBLISHING, INC.—See Pocket Outdoor Media, Inc.; *U.S. Private*, pg. 3219
BILLBOARD—See Valence Media Group; *U.S. Private*, pg. 4330
BILLIAN PUBLISHING INC.; *U.S. Private*, pg. 559
BIOONE; *U.S. Private*, pg. 562
BIZBASH MEDIA INC.; *U.S. Private*, pg. 567
BIZJOURNALS.COM—See Advance Publications, Inc.; *U.S. Private*, pg. 84
BLEACHER REPORT, INC.—See Warner Bros. Discovery, Inc.; *U.S. Public*, pg. 2328
BLOOD-HORSE PUBLICATIONS; *U.S. Private*, pg. 583
BLOOMBERG BUSINESSWEEK—See Bloomberg L.P.; *U.S. Private*, pg. 583
BLUE OCEAN ENTERTAINMENT AG—See Hubert Burda Media Holding Kommanditgesellschaft; *Int'l*, pg. 3519
BNA INTERNATIONAL INC.—See Bloomberg L.P.; *U.S. Private*, pg. 584
BNP MEDIA, INC.; *U.S. Private*, pg. 602
BNP MEDIA—See BNP Media, Inc.; *U.S. Private*, pg. 602
BOARDROOM INCORPORATED; *U.S. Private*, pg. 602
BOBIT BUSINESS MEDIA INC.; *U.S. Private*, pg. 607
BON APPETIT MAGAZINE—See Advance Publications, Inc.; *U.S. Private*, pg. 85
BONHILL GROUP PLC; *Int'l*, pg. 1107
BONNIER ACTIVE MEDIA, INC.—See Bonnier AB; *Int'l*, pg. 1108
BONNIER CORPORATION—See Bonnier AB; *Int'l*, pg. 1108
BOUNTY SERVICES PTY LTD.—See Apax Partners LLP; *Int'l*, pg. 507
BOWHUNTER MAGAZINE—See InterMedia Advisors, LLC; *U.S. Private*, pg. 2112
BOWTIE PRESS—See Fancy Publications Inc.; *U.S. Private*, pg. 1472
BOYS' LIFE MAGAZINE—See Boy Scouts of America; *U.S. Private*, pg. 627
BRANT PUBLICATIONS, INC.; *U.S. Private*, pg. 640
BRASS MEDIA INC.; *U.S. Private*, pg. 640
BTOB—See Crain Communications, Inc.; *U.S. Private*, pg. 1084
BUNTE VERLAG GMBH—See Hubert Burda Media Holding Kommanditgesellschaft; *Int'l*, pg. 3519
BURDA COMMUNICATIONS SP. Z O.O.—See Hubert Burda Media Holding Kommanditgesellschaft; *Int'l*, pg. 3519
BURDA DRUCK NURNBERG GMBH & CO. KG—See Hubert Burda Media Holding Kommanditgesellschaft; *Int'l*, pg. 3519

BURDA PRAHA SPOL. S R.O.—See Hubert Burda Media Holding Kommanditgesellschaft; *Int'l*, pg. 3519
BURDA SERVICE AG—See Hubert Burda Media Holding Kommanditgesellschaft; *Int'l*, pg. 3519
BURDA SINGAPORE PTE. LTD.—See Hubert Burda Media Holding Kommanditgesellschaft; *Int'l*, pg. 3520
BURDA TAIWAN CO. LTD.—See Hubert Burda Media Holding Kommanditgesellschaft; *Int'l*, pg. 3520
BURDA (THAILAND) CO., LTD.—See Hubert Burda Media Holding Kommanditgesellschaft; *Int'l*, pg. 3519
THE BUSINESS JOURNAL OF PORTLAND, INC.—See Advance Publications, Inc.; *U.S. Private*, pg. 85
BUSINESS LEADER MEDIA; *U.S. Private*, pg. 695
BUSINESS & LEGAL RESOURCES INC.; *U.S. Private*, pg. 694
BUYERS LABORATORY LLC—See SFW Capital Partners LLC; *U.S. Private*, pg. 3622
BUY & EZ SELL RECYCLER CORPORATION—See Digital Air Strike Inc.; *U.S. Private*, pg. 1230
BY DESIGN PUBLISHING—See CARDON Group Inc.; *Int'l*, pg. 1323
CAMBRIDGE HEALTHTECH MEDIA GROUP—See Cambridge Healthtech Institute; *U.S. Private*, pg. 727
CAPITOL INFORMATION GROUP, INC.; *U.S. Private*, pg. 744
CAR AND DRIVER—See The Hearst Corporation; *U.S. Private*, pg. 4046
CAROLINA PARENTING, INC.—See Shivers Trading & Operating Company; *U.S. Private*, pg. 3638
CASINO JOURNAL PUBLISHING GROUP; *U.S. Private*, pg. 783
CATCHA DIGITAL BERHAD; *Int'l*, pg. 1359
CDC PUBLISHING LLC; *U.S. Private*, pg. 802
CDG NAPOLI SRL—See Gambero Rosso S.p.A.; *Int'l*, pg. 2877
CDG TORINO E PIEMONTE SRL—See Gambero Rosso S.p.A.; *Int'l*, pg. 2877
CENTRO STAMPA VENETO SPA—See Caltagirone Editore S.p.A.; *Int'l*, pg. 1265
CFM RELIGION PUBLISHING GROUP, LLC—See The Wicks Group of Companies, LLC; *U.S. Private*, pg. 4135
CFQ MEDIA, LLC—See Mindfire Entertainment; *U.S. Private*, pg. 2740
CHARISMA MEDIA; *U.S. Private*, pg. 850
CHARTER FINANCIAL PUBLISHING NETWORK; *U.S. Private*, pg. 858
CHEMICAL WEEK ASSOCIATES—See Veronis Suhler Stevenson Partners LLC; *U.S. Private*, pg. 4368
CHICAGOLAND PUBLISHING COMPANY—See Tribune Publishing Company; *U.S. Private*, pg. 4227
CHICAGO MAGAZINE—See Tribune Publishing Company; *U.S. Private*, pg. 4227
CHILDREN'S BETTER HEALTH INSTITUTE—See Saturday Evening Post Society; *U.S. Private*, pg. 3553
CHIP COMMUNICATIONS GMBH—See Hubert Burda Media Holding Kommanditgesellschaft; *Int'l*, pg. 3520
CHIP HOLDING GMBH—See Hubert Burda Media Holding Kommanditgesellschaft; *Int'l*, pg. 3520
CHOICE PUBLISHING LTD—See Heinrich Bauer Verlag KG; *Int'l*, pg. 3323
CHRISTIANITY TODAY INTERNATIONAL; *U.S. Private*, pg. 891
CHUCO CO., LTD.; *Int'l*, pg. 1594
CIO INSIGHT—See Ziff Davis Enterprise, Inc.; *U.S. Private*, pg. 4604
CIRRUS MEDIA PTY. LIMITED—See Catalyst Investment Managers Pty. Limited; *Int'l*, pg. 1358
CITICOMICS LIMITED—See Culturecom Holdings Ltd; *Int'l*, pg. 1877
CITIES WEST PUBLISHING; *U.S. Private*, pg. 901
CITYWIRE FINANCIAL PUBLISHERS LTD.—See Citywire Holdings Ltd.; *Int'l*, pg. 1630
CNN MONEY—See Warner Bros. Discovery, Inc.; *U.S. Public*, pg. 2328
COMCORP FACTORS, INC.—See Kennington Ltd., Inc.; *U.S. Private*, pg. 2286
COMPLEX MAGAZINE—See Complex Media, Inc.; *U.S. Private*, pg. 1001
COMPLEX MEDIA, INC.; *U.S. Private*, pg. 1001
COMPUTERWORLD, INC.—See China Oceanwide Holdings Group Co., Ltd.; *Int'l*, pg. 1536
COMPUTERWORLD, INC.—See IDG Capital; *Int'l*, pg. 3593
CONDE NAST, INC. - LOS ANGELES—See Advance Publications, Inc.; *U.S. Private*, pg. 86
CONDE NAST, INC. - SAN FRANCISCO—See Advance Publications, Inc.; *U.S. Private*, pg. 86
CONDE NAST, INC.—See Advance Publications, Inc.; *U.S. Private*, pg. 85
CONDE NAST JOHANSENS LTD.—See Advance Publications, Inc.; *U.S. Private*, pg. 86
CONDE NAST TRAVELER—See Advance Publications, Inc.; *U.S. Private*, pg. 86
CONNELL COMMUNICATIONS INC.—See China Oceanwide Holdings Group Co., Ltd.; *Int'l*, pg. 1536
CONNELL COMMUNICATIONS INC.—See IDG Capital; *Int'l*, pg. 3593
CONSTRUCTION BUSINESS MEDIA, LLC—See Endeavor Business Media LLC; *U.S. Private*, pg. 1391

CONSTRUCTION RESEARCH COMMUNICATIONS LTD.—See Apax Partners LLP; *Int'l*, pg. 507
CONSUMER GOODS TECHNOLOGY—See RFE Investment Partners; *U.S. Private*, pg. 3419
CONTINUING EDUCATION NETWORK, INC.—See Moelis Asset Management LP; *U.S. Private*, pg. 2764
CORGI BOOKS LTD.—See Bertelsmann SE & Co. KGaA; *Int'l*, pg. 991
COUNTRY HOME MAGAZINE—See Meredith Corporation; *U.S. Public*, pg. 1422
COUNTRY SAMPLER, LLC—See Dynamic Resource Group, Inc.; *U.S. Private*, pg. 1299
COYNE & BLANCHARD, INC.; *U.S. Private*, pg. 1079
CRAIN COMMUNICATIONS, INC. - AKRON—See Crain Communications, Inc.; *U.S. Private*, pg. 1084
CRAIN COMMUNICATIONS, INC. - CHICAGO—See Crain Communications, Inc.; *U.S. Private*, pg. 1084
CRAIN COMMUNICATIONS, INC. - NEW YORK—See Crain Communications, Inc.; *U.S. Private*, pg. 1084
CRAIN COMMUNICATIONS, INC.; *U.S. Private*, pg. 1083
CRAIN COMMUNICATIONS LTD.—See Crain Communications, Inc.; *U.S. Private*, pg. 1083
CREATIVE AGE PUBLICATIONS, INC.—See Allured Publishing Corporation; *U.S. Private*, pg. 194
CREATIVE CRAFTS GROUP LLC—See Tinicum Enterprises, Inc.; *U.S. Private*, pg. 4174
CREEK & RIVER KOREA CO., LTD.—See CREEK & RIVER Co., Ltd.; *Int'l*, pg. 1837
CRICKET MAGAZINE GROUP—See Cricket Media Group Ltd.; *U.S. Private*, pg. 1100
CRM MEDIA, LLC—See Information Today Inc.; *U.S. Private*, pg. 2073
CULTURECOM HOLDINGS LTD; *Int'l*, pg. 1877
CURTCO MEDIA LABS LLC; *U.S. Private*, pg. 1126
CURTCO ROBB MEDIA, LLC—See RockBridge Growth Equity, LLC; *U.S. Private*, pg. 3465
CYBER MEDIA INDIA LTD.; *Int'l*, pg. 1892
CYBERPORT SERVICES GMBH—See Hubert Burda Media Holding Kommanditgesellschaft; *Int'l*, pg. 3520
CYGNUS BUSINESS MEDIA INC.—See ABRY Partners, LLC; *U.S. Private*, pg. 41
DAGENS MEDIA SVERIGE AB—See Bonnier AB; *Int'l*, pg. 1108
THE DAILY BEAST COMPANY LLC—See IAC Inc.; *U.S. Public*, pg. 1083
DAILY RACING FORM, INC.—See Arlington Capital Partners LLC; *U.S. Private*, pg. 327
DALLAS BUSINESS JOURNAL—See Advance Publications, Inc.; *U.S. Private*, pg. 84
DANCE MAGAZINE—See MacFadden Communications Group, LLC; *U.S. Private*, pg. 2535
DARK HORSE COMICS, INC.; *U.S. Private*, pg. 1159
DAVID & CHARLES PLC—See RDA Holding Co.; *U.S. Private*, pg. 3363
DAVLER MEDIA GROUP, LLC; *U.S. Private*, pg. 1175
DC COMICS, INC.—See Warner Bros. Discovery, Inc.; *U.S. Public*, pg. 2328
DEADLINE BUSINESS MEDIA, LLC—See Penske Media Corporation; *U.S. Private*, pg. 3139
DECCAN CHRONICLE HOLDINGS LTD.; *Int'l*, pg. 1999
DENNIS PUBLISHING LTD.—See Future plc; *Int'l*, pg. 2857
DEPARTURES MAGAZINE—See Meredith Corporation; *U.S. Public*, pg. 1422
DESERT PUBLICATIONS INC.; *U.S. Private*, pg. 1213
DESIGN COST DATA—See BNi Publications, Inc.; *U.S. Private*, pg. 602
DETAILS MAGAZINE—See Advance Publications, Inc.; *U.S. Private*, pg. 86
DET BESTE A/S—See RDA Holding Co.; *U.S. Private*, pg. 3363
DETEMEDIEN, DEUTSCHE TELEKOM MEDIEN GMBH—See Deutsche Telekom AG; *Int'l*, pg. 2083
DIME MAGAZINE PUBLISHING CO., INC.—See Woven Digital, Inc.; *U.S. Private*, pg. 4571
DISCOVER MAGAZINE—See Kalmbach Publishing Co.; *U.S. Private*, pg. 2257
DISTRIBUIDORA BOLIVARIANA, S.A.—See Grupo Televisa, S.A.B.; *Int'l*, pg. 3136
DISTRIBUIDORA LOS ANDES, S.A.—See Grupo Televisa, S.A.B.; *Int'l*, pg. 3136
DISTRIMEDIA SERVICES B.V.—See RDA Holding Co.; *U.S. Private*, pg. 3363
DOGAN BURDA DERGI YAYINCILIK VE PAZARLAMA A.S.; *Int'l*, pg. 2154
DOTDASH MEREDITH, INC.—See IAC Inc.; *U.S. Public*, pg. 1082
DR. OETKER VERLAG KG—See Dr. August Oetker KG; *Int'l*, pg. 2190
DUBICKI ROBNI MAGAZIN A.D.; *Int'l*, pg. 2222
DUB PUBLISHING, INC.; *U.S. Private*, pg. 1283
DUPONT PUBLISHING, INC.—See GMF Capital LLC; *U.S. Private*, pg. 1722
DUPONT REGISTRY—See GMF Capital LLC; *U.S. Private*, pg. 1722
DYNAMIC RESOURCE GROUP, INC.; *U.S. Private*, pg. 1298
EAGLE OPERATING CORP.—See RFE Investment Partners; *U.S. Private*, pg. 3419

N.A.I.C.S. INDEX

513120 — PERIODICAL PUBLISHE...

EARL G. GRAVES PUBLISHING CO., INC.—See Earl G. Graves Ltd.; *U.S. Private*, pg. 1312
EASTERN PUBLISHING PTE LTD—See Eastern Holdings Ltd.; *Int'l*, pg. 2272
EASTERN TRADE MEDIA PTE LTD—See Eastern Holdings Ltd.; *Int'l*, pg. 2272
EASYRIDERS, LLC—See Paisano Publications, LLC; *U.S. Private*, pg. 3076
EDIPRESSE AS ROMANIA SRL—See Edipresse SA; *Int'l*, pg. 2310
EDIPRESSE POLSKA SA—See Edipresse SA; *Int'l*, pg. 2310
EDIPRESSE UKRAINE LLC—See Edipresse SA; *Int'l*, pg. 2310
EDITORIALE METROPOLI SPA—See Giovanni Agnelli B.V.; *Int'l*, pg. 2978
EDITORIAL MOTORPRESS-TELEVISA, S.A. DE C.V.—See Grupo Televisa, S.A.B.; *Int'l*, pg. 3136
EDITORIAL TELEVISA COLOMBIA CULTURAL, S.A.—See Grupo Televisa, S.A.B.; *Int'l*, pg. 3136
EDITORIAL TELEVISA INTERNATIONAL, S.A.—See Grupo Televisa, S.A.B.; *Int'l*, pg. 3136
EDITORIAL TELEVISA S.A. DE C.V.—See Grupo Televisa, S.A.B.; *Int'l*, pg. 3136
E.D. PUBLICATIONS, INC.—See RCI Hospitality Holdings, Inc.; *U.S. Public*, pg. 1767
E. D. PUBLICATIONS, INC.—See RCI Hospitality Holdings, Inc.; *U.S. Public*, pg. 1767
EGMONT BULGARIA EAD—See Egmont Fonden; *Int'l*, pg. 2325
EGMONT CREATIVE A/S—See Egmont Fonden; *Int'l*, pg. 2325
EGMONT CREATIVE CENTER A/S—See Egmont Fonden; *Int'l*, pg. 2325
EGMONT CR S.R.O.—See Egmont Fonden; *Int'l*, pg. 2325
EGMONT D.O.O.—See Egmont Fonden; *Int'l*, pg. 2325
EGMONT EHAPA COMIC COLLECTION GMBH—See Egmont Fonden; *Int'l*, pg. 2325
EGMONT EHAPA MEDIA GMBH—See Egmont Fonden; *Int'l*, pg. 2325
EGMONT EHAPA VERLAG GMBH—See Egmont Fonden; *Int'l*, pg. 2325
EGMONT ESTONIA AS—See Egmont Fonden; *Int'l*, pg. 2325
EGMONT HUNGARY KFT.—See Egmont Fonden; *Int'l*, pg. 2325
EGMONT KARNAN AB—See Egmont Fonden; *Int'l*, pg. 2325
EGMONT KIDS MEDIA NORDIC AS—See Egmont Fonden; *Int'l*, pg. 2326
EGMONT LATVIJA SIA—See Egmont Fonden; *Int'l*, pg. 2325
EGMONT POLSKA SP. Z O.O.—See Egmont Fonden; *Int'l*, pg. 2325
EGMONT PRINTING SERVICE A/S—See Egmont Fonden; *Int'l*, pg. 2326
EGMONT PUBLISHING KIDS AB—See Egmont Fonden; *Int'l*, pg. 2326
EGMONT PUBLISHING MAGASINER A/S—See Egmont Fonden; *Int'l*, pg. 2325
EGMONT PUBLISHING SUBSIDIARY AB—See Egmont Fonden; *Int'l*, pg. 2326
EGMONT SERBIA—See Egmont Fonden; *Int'l*, pg. 2326
EGMONT SERIEFORLAGET A/S—See Egmont Fonden; *Int'l*, pg. 2325
EGMONT SOURCING (HK) LTD.—See Egmont Fonden; *Int'l*, pg. 2325
EGMONT TIDSKRIFTER AB—See Egmont Fonden; *Int'l*, pg. 2325
EGMONT TIDSKRIFTER BM AB—See Egmont Fonden; *Int'l*, pg. 2325
EGMONT UK LTD.—See Charlesbank Capital Partners, LLC; *U.S. Private*, pg. 854
EGMONT UKRAINE LLC—See Egmont Fonden; *Int'l*, pg. 2325
EGMONT US INC.—See Egmont Fonden; *Int'l*, pg. 2325
EGMONT VERLAGSGESELLSCHAFTEN MBH—See Egmont Fonden; *Int'l*, pg. 2325
EH PUBLISHING, INC.; *U.S. Private*, pg. 1346
ELECTRIC WORD PLC; *Int'l*, pg. 2349
ELI RESEARCH, LLC—See Eli Global, LLC; *U.S. Private*, pg. 1359
ELLE DECOR—See The Hearst Corporation; *U.S. Private*, pg. 4046
ELLE—See The Hearst Corporation; *U.S. Private*, pg. 4046
EMAP COMMUNICATIONS BV—See Apax Partners LLP; *Int'l*, pg. 507
EMAP CONSTRUCTION NETWORKS LTD.—See Apax Partners LLP; *Int'l*, pg. 507
EMAP CONSTRUCT LTD.—See Apax Partners LLP; *Int'l*, pg. 507
EMAP LIMITED—See Apax Partners LLP; *Int'l*, pg. 507
EMAP MACLAREN—See Apax Partners LLP; *Int'l*, pg. 507
EMAP PUBLIC SECTOR MANAGEMENT LTD.—See Apax Partners LLP; *Int'l*, pg. 507
EMMIS MEADOWLANDS CORPORATION—See Emmis Communications Corporation; *U.S. Public*, pg. 753
EMMIS PUBLISHING, L.P.—See Emmis Communications Corporation; *U.S. Public*, pg. 753
ENGINEERING NEWS-RECORD MAGAZINE—See BNP Media, Inc.; *U.S. Private*, pg. 602
ENTERTAINMENT WEEKLY INC.—See Meredith Corporation; *U.S. Public*, pg. 1422
ENTREPRENDRE SA; *Int'l*, pg. 2453
ENTREPRENEUR MEDIA, INC.; *U.S. Private*, pg. 1406
ENTREPRENEUR MEDIA SA (PTY) LTD.—See Entrepreneur Media, Inc.; *U.S. Private*, pg. 1406
EQUINE JOURNAL—See Shivers Trading & Operating Company; *U.S. Private*, pg. 3638
THE EQUINE NETWORK—See Active Interest Media, Inc.; *U.S. Private*, pg. 69
E.REPUBLIC, INC.; *U.S. Private*, pg. 1307
ESQUIRE—See The Hearst Corporation; *U.S. Private*, pg. 4046
ESSENCE COMMUNICATIONS INC.; *U.S. Private*, pg. 1427
ESSENCE MAGAZINE—See Essence Communications Inc.; *U.S. Private*, pg. 1427
ET PUBLISHING INTERNATIONAL, LLC—See Grupo Televisa, S.A.B.; *Int'l*, pg. 3136
EUROPEAN RUBBER JOURNAL—See Crain Communications, Inc.; *U.S. Private*, pg. 1083
EWEEK—See Ziff Davis Enterprise, Inc.; *U.S. Private*, pg. 4604
EXCERPTA MEDICA MEDICAL COMMUNICATIONS BV—See Omnicom Group Inc.; *U.S. Public*, pg. 1583
EXTREMETECH—See Ziff Davis, Inc.; *U.S. Public*, pg. 2404
FACES MAGAZINE INC.; *U.S. Private*, pg. 1459
FANCY PUBLICATIONS INC.; *U.S. Private*, pg. 1472
FARM JOURNAL, INC.; *U.S. Private*, pg. 1475
FAST COMPANY MAGAZINE—See Mansueto Ventures LLC; *U.S. Private*, pg. 2566
FASTLINE PUBLICATIONS INC.; *U.S. Private*, pg. 1482
FG FITNESS & MEDIA GROUP, INC.; *U.S. Public*, pg. 830
FIELD & STREAM MAGAZINE—See Bonnier AB; *Int'l*, pg. 1108
FILMFAX, INC.; *U.S. Private*, pg. 1506
FIT FOR FUN VERLAG GMBH—See Hubert Burda Media Holding Kommanditgesellschaft; *Int'l*, pg. 3520
FITNESS MAGAZINE—See Meredith Corporation; *U.S. Public*, pg. 1422
FLASHES PUBLISHERS—See Gannett Co., Inc.; *U.S. Public*, pg. 901
FOCUS MAGAZIN VERLAG—See Hubert Burda Media Holding Kommanditgesellschaft; *Int'l*, pg. 3520
FOOD NETWORK MAGAZINE—See The Hearst Corporation; *U.S. Private*, pg. 4046
FOOD & WINE—See Meredith Corporation; *U.S. Public*, pg. 1422
FOOTWEAR NEWS—See Penske Media Corporation; *U.S. Private*, pg. 3139
FORBES CHINA—See Forbes Media LLC; *U.S. Private*, pg. 1563
FORBES INVESTORS ADVISORY INSTITUTE INC.—See Forbes Media LLC; *U.S. Private*, pg. 1563
FORBES MAGAZINE—See Forbes Media LLC; *U.S. Private*, pg. 1563
FORECAST INTERNATIONAL INC.; *U.S. Private*, pg. 1565
FORTUNE; *U.S. Private*, pg. 1577
FREEDREAMS B.V.—See Hubert Burda Media Holding Kommanditgesellschaft; *Int'l*, pg. 3520
FRIEZE EVENTS INC.—See Silver Lake Group, LLC; *U.S. Private*, pg. 3654
FRIEZE EVENTS LIMITED—See Silver Lake Group, LLC; *U.S. Private*, pg. 3654
FRONTLINE LIMITED—See Heinrich Bauer Verlag KG; *Int'l*, pg. 3324
FRONTLINE MEDICAL COMMUNICATIONS INC.—See KKR & Co. Inc.; *U.S. Public*, pg. 1253
FTM FREIZEIT- UND TRENDMARKETING GMBH & CO. KG—See Hubert Burda Media Holding Kommanditgesellschaft; *Int'l*, pg. 3520
FUSOSHA PUBLISHING INC.—See Fuji Media Holdings, Inc.; *Int'l*, pg. 2814
FUTURE FRANCE SA—See Future plc; *Int'l*, pg. 2857
FUTURE PUBLISHING LTD. - LONDON OFFICE—See Future plc; *Int'l*, pg. 2857
FUTURE PUBLISHING LTD.—See Future plc; *Int'l*, pg. 2857
FUTURES MAGAZINE GROUP—See Summit Business Media, LLC; *U.S. Private*, pg. 3853
FUTURE US, INC.—See Future plc; *Int'l*, pg. 2857
GAMBERO ROSSO S.P.A.; *Int'l*, pg. 2877
GANNETT HEALTHCARE GROUP—See Bertelsmann SE & Co. KGaA; *Int'l*, pg. 990
GARDEN & GUN—See Evening Post Publishing Co.; *U.S. Private*, pg. 1436
GARDNER BUSINESS MEDIA INC.; *U.S. Private*, pg. 1643
GARLINGHOUSE COMPANY; *U.S. Private*, pg. 1644
G&C PALERMO SRL; *Int'l*, pg. 2862
GENOMEWEB, LLC—See Crain Communications, Inc.; *U.S. Private*, pg. 1084
GIRLS' LIFE, INC.—See Monarch Services, Inc.; *U.S. Public*, pg. 1460
G+J ESPANA S.A.—See Bertelsmann SE & Co. KGaA; *Int'l*, pg. 992
G+J / KLAMBT STYLE-VERLAG GMBH & CO. KG—See Bertelsmann SE & Co. KGaA; *Int'l*, pg. 994
GLAMOUR—See Advance Publications, Inc.; *U.S. Private*, pg. 86
GOD'S WORLD PUBLICATIONS INC.; *U.S. Private*, pg. 1724
GOINGPUBLIC MEDIA AG; *Int'l*, pg. 3022
GOLD COAST PUBLICATIONS PTY. LIMITED—See News Corporation; *U.S. Public*, pg. 1520
GOLD KEY MEDIA—See Advance Publications, Inc.; *U.S. Private*, pg. 85
GOLD KEY MEDIA—See The Hearst Corporation; *U.S. Private*, pg. 4047
GOLF DIGEST PUBLICATIONS—See Advance Publications, Inc.; *U.S. Private*, pg. 86
GOLF MAGAZINE—See Meredith Corporation; *U.S. Public*, pg. 1423
GOLF WORLD BUSINESS—See Advance Publications, Inc.; *U.S. Private*, pg. 86
GO MEDIA, INC.—See Great Hill Partners, L.P.; *U.S. Private*, pg. 1763
GOOD HOUSEKEEPING—See The Hearst Corporation; *U.S. Private*, pg. 4046
GOVERNING MAGAZINE—See e.Republic, Inc.; *U.S. Private*, pg. 1307
GOVERNMENT EXECUTIVE MEDIA GROUP LLC—See Growth Catalyst Partners, LLC; *U.S. Private*, pg. 1796
GRAPHIC DESIGN USA—See Kaye Publishing Corporation; *U.S. Private*, pg. 2266
GREAT LAKES PUBLISHING COMPANY; *U.S. Private*, pg. 1765
GREENSPRING MEDIA LLC—See Hour Media Group, LLC; *U.S. Private*, pg. 1990
GREENSPUN MEDIA GROUP, LLC—See The Greenspun Corporation; *U.S. Private*, pg. 4039
GRINDMEDIA, LLC—See TEN: The Enthusiast Network, Inc.; *U.S. Private*, pg. 3964
GROUPE HOMMELL; *Int'l*, pg. 3104
GROUPE TERRITORIAL—See Bridgepoint Group Plc; *Int'l*, pg. 1155
GROUP MONITEUR—See Bridgepoint Group Plc; *Int'l*, pg. 1155
GRUNER + JAHR AG (SCHWEIZ)—See Bertelsmann SE & Co. KGaA; *Int'l*, pg. 992
GRUNER + JAHR GMBH—See Bertelsmann SE & Co. KGaA; *Int'l*, pg. 992
GUIDEPOSTS ASSOCIATES, INC.; *U.S. Private*, pg. 1813
GULF ENERGY INFORMATION; *U.S. Private*, pg. 1816
GULF PUBLISHING COMPANY—See Main Street Capital Corporation; *U.S. Public*, pg. 1355
GULFSHORE BUSINESS—See Open Sky Media Inc.; *U.S. Private*, pg. 3029
GULFSHORE LIFE—See Open Sky Media Inc.; *U.S. Private*, pg. 3029
HACHETTE FILIPACCHI NORGE A/S—See Hjemmet Mortensen As; *Int'l*, pg. 3428
HAIGHTS CROSS COMMUNICATIONS, INC.; *U.S. Private*, pg. 1840
HAPPENINGS COMMUNICATIONS GROUP, INC.—See JRjr33, Inc.; *U.S. Private*, pg. 2240
HARDWOOD MARKET REPORT L.P.—See Astorg Partners S.A.S.; *Int'l*, pg. 656
HARPER'S BAZAAR—See The Hearst Corporation; *U.S. Private*, pg. 4046
HARPER'S MAGAZINE FOUNDATION; *U.S. Private*, pg. 1868
HARVARD BUSINESS SCHOOL PUBLISHING CORPORATION; *U.S. Private*, pg. 1874
HAYMARKET MEDIA GROUP LTD.—See Haymarket Group Limited; *Int'l*, pg. 3292
HAYMARKET MEDIA, INC.—See Haymarket Group Limited; *Int'l*, pg. 3293
H. BAUER PUBLISHING LTD.—See Heinrich Bauer Verlag KG; *Int'l*, pg. 3323
HEALTH MEDIA VENTURES INC. - LOS ANGELES—See Meredith Corporation; *U.S. Public*, pg. 1423
HEALTH MEDIA VENTURES INC.—See Meredith Corporation; *U.S. Public*, pg. 1422
HEARST BUSINESS MEDIA—See The Hearst Corporation; *U.S. Private*, pg. 4044
HEARST BUSINESS PUBLISHING, INC.—See The Hearst Corporation; *U.S. Private*, pg. 4045
HEARST COMMUNICATIONS, INC.—See The Hearst Corporation; *U.S. Private*, pg. 4045
HEARST ELECTRONICS GROUP—See The Hearst Corporation; *U.S. Private*, pg. 4045
HEARST INTERACTIVE MEDIA—See The Hearst Corporation; *U.S. Private*, pg. 4046
HEARST MAGAZINES DIGITAL MEDIA—See The Hearst Corporation; *U.S. Private*, pg. 4046
HEARST MAGAZINES INTERNATIONAL—See The Hearst Corporation; *U.S. Private*, pg. 4046
HEARST MAGAZINES—See The Hearst Corporation; *U.S. Private*, pg. 4046
HGTV MAGAZINE—See The Hearst Corporation; *U.S. Private*, pg. 4046

513120 — PERIODICAL PUBLISHE...

HIGHLIGHTS FOR CHILDREN, INC.; *U.S. Private*, pg. 1940
HISPANIC BUSINESS INC.; *U.S. Private*, pg. 1951
HISPANIC BUSINESS MAGAZINE—See Hispanic Business Inc.; *U.S. Private*, pg. 1951
HISTORYNET, LLC—See Regent, L.P.; *U.S. Private*, pg. 3388
HOLLYWOOD LIFE MEDIA, LLC—See Peńske Media Corporation; *U.S. Private*, pg. 3139
THE HOLLYWOOD REPORTER, LLC—See Valence Media Group; *U.S. Private*, pg. 4330
HOLYROOD COMMUNICATIONS LTD.—See Biteback Publishing Ltd.; *Int'l*, pg. 1050
HOME SERVICE PUBLICATIONS, INC.—See RDA Holding Co.; *U.S. Private*, pg. 3363
HORIZON HOUSE PUBLICATIONS INC.; *U.S. Private*, pg. 1981
HORSECITY.COM—See Shivers Trading & Operating Company; *U.S. Private*, pg. 3638
HORSE & RIDER—See Active Interest Media, Inc.; *U.S. Private*, pg. 69
HOSPITALITY TECHNOLOGY—See RFE Investment Partners; *U.S. Private*, pg. 3419
HOSPITAL PRACTICE—See JTE Multimedia, LLC; *U.S. Private*, pg. 2241
HOT SPRINGS ON THE GO!—See Wehco Media, Inc.; *U.S. Private*, pg. 4470
HOUR MEDIA, LLC—See Hour Media Group, LLC; *U.S. Private*, pg. 1991
HOUSE BEAUTIFUL—See The Hearst Corporation; *U.S. Private*, pg. 4046
H.O. ZIMMAN, INC.; *U.S. Private*, pg. 1835
HUBERT BURDA MEDIA HONG KONG LIMITED—See Hubert Burda Media Holding Kommanditgesellschaft; *Int'l*, pg. 3520
HUNAN LITERATURE & ART PUBLISHING HOUSE CO., LTD.—See China South Publishing & Media Group Co., Ltd.; *Int'l*, pg. 1553
THE H.W. WILSON CO.—See EBSCO Industries, Inc.; *U.S. Private*, pg. 1325
IBT MEDIA INC.; *U.S. Private*, pg. 2028
ICC CHICAGO—See International Code Council, Inc.; *U.S. Private*, pg. 2115
ICC EVALUATION SERVICE—See International Code Council, Inc.; *U.S. Private*, pg. 2115
ICC EVALUATION SERVICE—See International Code Council, Inc.; *U.S. Private*, pg. 2115
ICT MEDIA LTD.—See Economedia; *Int'l*, pg. 2298
IDC ASIA PACIFIC (SINGAPORE)—See China Oceanwide Holdings Group Co., Ltd.; *Int'l*, pg. 1536
IDC ASIA PACIFIC (SINGAPORE)—See IDG Capital; *Int'l*, pg. 3593
IDC BENELUX—See China Oceanwide Holdings Group Co., Ltd.; *Int'l*, pg. 1536
IDC BENELUX—See IDG Capital; *Int'l*, pg. 3593
IDC CENTRAL EUROPE GMBH—See China Oceanwide Holdings Group Co., Ltd.; *Int'l*, pg. 1537
IDC CENTRAL EUROPE GMBH—See IDG Capital; *Int'l*, pg. 3593
IDC FRANCE—See China Oceanwide Holdings Group Co., Ltd.; *Int'l*, pg. 1537
IDC FRANCE—See IDG Capital; *Int'l*, pg. 3593
IDC TURKEY—See China Oceanwide Holdings Group Co., Ltd.; *Int'l*, pg. 1537
IDC TURKEY—See IDG Capital; *Int'l*, pg. 3594
IDC VENEZUELA—See China Oceanwide Holdings Group Co., Ltd.; *Int'l*, pg. 1537
IDC VENEZUELA—See IDG Capital; *Int'l*, pg. 3594
IDEAL MEDIA LLC—See Schofield Media Ltd.; *U.S. Private*, pg. 3567
IDG BUSINESS VERLAG GMBH—See China Oceanwide Holdings Group Co., Ltd.; *Int'l*, pg. 1537
IDG BUSINESS VERLAG GMBH—See IDG Capital; *Int'l*, pg. 3594
IDG CHINA CO., LTD.—See China Oceanwide Holdings Group Co., Ltd.; *Int'l*, pg. 1537
IDG CHINA CO., LTD.—See IDG Capital; *Int'l*, pg. 3594
IDG COMMUNICATIONS, INC.—See Eagle Publishing Inc.; *U.S. Private*, pg. 1310
IDG COMMUNICATIONS MEDIA AG—See China Oceanwide Holdings Group Co., Ltd.; *Int'l*, pg. 1537
IDG COMMUNICATIONS MEDIA AG—See IDG Capital; *Int'l*, pg. 3594
IDG COMMUNICATIONS NORGE AS—See China Oceanwide Holdings Group Co., Ltd.; *Int'l*, pg. 1537
IDG COMMUNICATIONS NORGE AS—See IDG Capital; *Int'l*, pg. 3594
IDG COMMUNICATIONS PTY. LTD.—See China Oceanwide Holdings Group Co., Ltd.; *Int'l*, pg. 1537
IDG COMMUNICATIONS PTY. LTD.—See IDG Capital; *Int'l*, pg. 3594
IDG COMMUNICATIONS PUBLISHING GROUP SRL—See China Oceanwide Holdings Group Co., Ltd.; *Int'l*, pg. 1537
IDG COMMUNICATIONS PUBLISHING GROUP SRL—See IDG Capital; *Int'l*, pg. 3594
IDG COMMUNICATIONS, S.A.U.—See China Oceanwide Holdings Group Co., Ltd.; *Int'l*, pg. 1537

IDG COMMUNICATIONS, S.A.U.—See IDG Capital; *Int'l*, pg. 3594
IDG COMMUNICATIONS UK, LTD.—See China Oceanwide Holdings Group Co., Ltd.; *Int'l*, pg. 1537
IDG COMMUNICATIONS UK, LTD.—See IDG Capital; *Int'l*, pg. 3594
IDG COMPUTERWORLD DO BRAZIL—See China Oceanwide Holdings Group Co., Ltd.; *Int'l*, pg. 1537
IDG COMPUTERWORLD DO BRAZIL—See IDG Capital; *Int'l*, pg. 3594
IDG CZECH REPUBLIC, A.S.—See China Oceanwide Holdings Group Co., Ltd.; *Int'l*, pg. 1537
IDG CZECH REPUBLIC, A.S.—See IDG Capital; *Int'l*, pg. 3594
IDG ENTERPRISE—See China Oceanwide Holdings Group Co., Ltd.; *Int'l*, pg. 1536
IDG ENTERPRISE—See IDG Capital; *Int'l*, pg. 3593
IDG ENTERTAINMENT MEDIA GMBH—See China Oceanwide Holdings Group Co., Ltd.; *Int'l*, pg. 1537
IDG ENTERTAINMENT MEDIA GMBH—See IDG Capital; *Int'l*, pg. 3594
IDG JAPAN, INC.—See China Oceanwide Holdings Group Co., Ltd.; *Int'l*, pg. 1537
IDG JAPAN, INC.—See IDG Capital; *Int'l*, pg. 3594
IDG MAGAZINES NORGE AS—See China Oceanwide Holdings Group Co., Ltd.; *Int'l*, pg. 1537
IDG MAGAZINES NORGE AS—See IDG Capital; *Int'l*, pg. 3594
IDG MEDIA PRIVATE LIMITED—See China Oceanwide Holdings Group Co., Ltd.; *Int'l*, pg. 1537
IDG MEDIA PRIVATE LIMITED—See IDG Capital; *Int'l*, pg. 3594
IDG NETHERLANDS—See China Oceanwide Holdings Group Co., Ltd.; *Int'l*, pg. 1538
IDG NETHERLANDS—See IDG Capital; *Int'l*, pg. 3594
IDG POLAND S.A.—See China Oceanwide Holdings Group Co., Ltd.; *Int'l*, pg. 1538
IDG POLAND S.A.—See IDG Capital; *Int'l*, pg. 3594
IDG SWEDEN AB—See China Oceanwide Holdings Group Co., Ltd.; *Int'l*, pg. 1538
IDG SWEDEN AB—See IDG Capital; *Int'l*, pg. 3594
IDG TAIWAN—See China Oceanwide Holdings Group Co., Ltd.; *Int'l*, pg. 1538
IDG TAIWAN—See IDG Capital; *Int'l*, pg. 3594
I.D. MAGAZINE—See Tinicum Enterprises, Inc.; *U.S. Private*, pg. 4174
IHI PRESS TECHNOLOGY AMERICA, INC.—See IHI Corporation; *Int'l*, pg. 3604
IL MESSAGGERO SPA—See Caltagirone Editore S.p.A.; *Int'l*, pg. 1266
IMAGE COMICS INC.; *U.S. Private*, pg. 2044
IMAGINATION PUBLISHING, LLC; *U.S. Private*, pg. 2045
INC.COM LLC—See Mansueto Ventures LLC; *U.S. Private*, pg. 2567
INCENTIVE MAGAZINE—See EagleTree Capital, LP; *U.S. Private*, pg. 1312
INCISIVE MEDIA LIMITED—See Apax Partners LLP; *Int'l*, pg. 504
INC. MAGAZINE—See Mansueto Ventures LLC; *U.S. Private*, pg. 2566
INDEPENDENT PUBLISHER ONLINE—See Jenkins Group, Inc.; *U.S. Private*, pg. 2199
IN-FISHERMAN—See InterMedia Advisors, LLC; *U.S. Private*, pg. 2112
INFORMATION TODAY INC.; *U.S. Private*, pg. 2073
INFORMATION TODAY, LTD—See Information Today Inc.; *U.S. Private*, pg. 2073
IN-MEDIA AG—See Die Schweizerische Post AG; *Int'l*, pg. 2113
INSIDE EDITION INC.—See National Amusements, Inc.; *U.S. Private*, pg. 2841
INSIDER, INC.—See Axel Springer SE; *Int'l*, pg. 766
INSTYLE MAGAZINE—See Meredith Corporation; *U.S. Public*, pg. 1423
INTEGRATED DIRECT MARKETING SOLUTIONS, INC.—See Arthur J. Gallagher & Co.; *U.S. Public*, pg. 206
INTERMEDIA OUTDOORS, INC.—See InterMedia Advisors, LLC; *U.S. Private*, pg. 2112
INTESCIA GROUP SAS—See Andera Partners SCA; *Int'l*, pg. 450
INTIME MEDIA SERVICES GMBH—See Hubert Burda Media Holding Kommanditgesellschaft; *Int'l*, pg. 3520
INVIARCO SAS—See China Oceanwide Holdings Group Co., Ltd.; *Int'l*, pg. 1538
INVIARCO SAS—See IDG Capital; *Int'l*, pg. 3594
IPC INSPIRE—See Meredith Corporation; *U.S. Public*, pg. 1423
IPC MEDIA LIMITED—See Meredith Corporation; *U.S. Public*, pg. 1423
ISLANDS MAGAZINE—See Bonnier AB; *Int'l*, pg. 1108
ISSUE MEDIA GROUP, LLC; *U.S. Private*, pg. 2147
ITI REFERENCE GROUP - NJ—See Information Today Inc.; *U.S. Private*, pg. 2073
JAMESON PUBLISHING INC.; *U.S. Private*, pg. 2185
J.B. DOLLAR STRETCHER MAGAZINE; *U.S. Private*, pg. 2158
JENKINS GROUP, INC.; *U.S. Private*, pg. 2199

CORPORATE AFFILIATIONS

JHI OPTICAL GROUP—See The Wicks Group of Companies, LLC; *U.S. Private*, pg. 4135
JOBSON HEALTHCARE INFORMATION LLC—See The Wicks Group of Companies, LLC; *U.S. Private*, pg. 4135
JOBSON MEDICAL INFORMATION LLC—See The Wicks Group of Companies, LLC; *U.S. Private*, pg. 4135
JOHNSON PUBLISHING COMPANY, INC.; *U.S. Private*, pg. 2228
JOURNAL PUBLICATIONS, INC.; *U.S. Private*, pg. 2238
JTE MULTIMEDIA, LLC; *U.S. Private*, pg. 2241
J.V. ROCKWELL PUBLISHING INC.; *U.S. Private*, pg. 2171
KALMBACH PUBLISHING CO.; *U.S. Private*, pg. 2257
KANSAS CITY BUSINESS JOURNAL—See Advance Publications, Inc.; *U.S. Private*, pg. 84
KAPPA PUBLISHING GROUP, INC.; *U.S. Private*, pg. 2262
KATES-BOYLSTON PUBLICATIONS—See United Communications Group; *U.S. Private*, pg. 4289
KAYE PUBLISHING CORPORATION; *U.S. Private*, pg. 2266
KELLEY BLUE BOOK CO., INC.—See Cox Enterprises, Inc.; *U.S. Private*, pg. 1076
KEY COMMUNICATIONS, INC.; *U.S. Private*, pg. 2292
KEY PROFESSIONAL MEDIA, INC.; *U.S. Private*, pg. 2293
THE KIPLINGER WASHINGTON EDITORS, INC.—See Future plc; *Int'l*, pg. 2857
KMWORLD—See Information Today Inc.; *U.S. Private*, pg. 2073
KRAUSE PUBLICATIONS, INC.—See Tinicum Enterprises, Inc.; *U.S. Private*, pg. 4174
LAGARDERE PUBLICITE SAS—See Czech Media Invest as; *Int'l*, pg. 1898
LAKE SHORE PRESS, INC.—See PLBY Group, Inc.; *U.S. Public*, pg. 1698
LANDMARK PUBLISHING—See Irish Times; *U.S. Private*, pg. 2139
LAS VEGAS MAGAZINE—See The Greenspun Corporation; *U.S. Private*, pg. 4039
LATINA MEDIA VENTURES, LLC; *U.S. Private*, pg. 2397
LAURIN PUBLISHING CO., INC.; *U.S. Private*, pg. 2400
LE POINT—See Financiere Pinault SCA; *Int'l*, pg. 2668
LESSITER PUBLICATIONS, INC.; *U.S. Private*, pg. 2432
L.F.P., INC.; *U.S. Private*, pg. 2365
LIBERTY MEDIA FOR WOMEN, LLC; *U.S. Private*, pg. 2444
LINDHARDT OG RINGHOF FORLAG A/S—See Egmont Fonden; *Int'l*, pg. 2325
LOS ANGELES MAGAZINE, LLC—See Hour Media Group, LLC; *U.S. Private*, pg. 1991
LRP PUBLICATIONS; *U.S. Private*, pg. 2508
MACFADDEN COMMUNICATIONS GROUP, LLC; *U.S. Private*, pg. 2535
MADAVOR MEDIA, LLC—See BeBop Channel Corporation; *U.S. Public*, pg. 288
MAD MAGAZINE/E.C. PUBLICATIONS, INC.—See Warner Bros. Discovery, Inc.; *U.S. Public*, pg. 2328
MANOR HOUSE PUBLISHING CO, INC.; *U.S. Private*, pg. 2566
MANSUETO VENTURES LLC; *U.S. Private*, pg. 2566
MARIAH MEDIA INC.; *U.S. Private*, pg. 2573
MARIE CLAIRE MAGAZINE—See Meredith Corporation; *U.S. Public*, pg. 1423
MARIE CLAIRE US—See Future plc; *Int'l*, pg. 2857
MARKETFORCE (UK) LIMITED—See Meredith Corporation; *U.S. Public*, pg. 1423
MARKHAM WOODS PRESS PUBLISHING CO., INC.; *U.S. Private*, pg. 2582
MARVEL PUBLISHING, INC.—See The Walt Disney Company; *U.S. Public*, pg. 2139
MAXIM INC.—See Biglari Holdings Inc.; *U.S. Public*, pg. 331
MCKNIGHT'S LONG TERM CARE NEWS & ASSISTED LIVING—See Haymarket Group Limited; *U.S. Private*, pg. 3293
MCLEAN COMMUNICATIONS—See Yankee Publishing Inc.; *U.S. Private*, pg. 4586
MCMAHON PUBLISHING COMPANY; *U.S. Private*, pg. 2642
MEDIA CORPORATION PUBLISHING (M)—See Apax Partners LLP; *Int'l*, pg. 507
MEDIAFY AB—See Bonnier AB; *Int'l*, pg. 1109
MEDIAFY MAGAZINES AS—See Bonnier AB; *Int'l*, pg. 1109
MEDIATEAM LTD.—See China Oceanwide Holdings Group Co., Ltd.; *Int'l*, pg. 1538
MEDIATEAM LTD.—See IDG Capital; *Int'l*, pg. 3594
MEDIA TRANS ASIA LIMITED—See China Oceanwide Holdings Group Co., Ltd.; *Int'l*, pg. 1538
MEDIA TRANS ASIA LIMITED—See IDG Capital; *Int'l*, pg. 3594
MEDIA VISTA GROUP, LLC; *U.S. Private*, pg. 2653
MEDICAL EDUCATION AND RESEARCH FOUNDATION—See Saturday Evening Post Society; *U.S. Private*, pg. 3553
MEDIENFABRIK GUTERSLOH GMBH—See Bertelsmann SE & Co. KGaA; *Int'l*, pg. 995
MEISTER MEDIA WORLDWIDE INC.; *U.S. Private*, pg. 2661
MEREDITH CORPORATION; *U.S. Public*, pg. 1422
METROPARENT WEST MAGAZINE—See Gannett Co., Inc.; *U.S. Public*, pg. 898
METROSOURCE PUBLISHING, INC.—See Davler Media

Group, LLC; *U.S. Private*, pg. 1175
MIDWEST LIVING MAGAZINE—See Meredith Corporation; *U.S. Public*, pg. 1423
MIDWEST PUBLISHING, INC.; *U.S. Private*, pg. 2722
MILLER PUBLISHING GROUP, LLC; *U.S. Private*, pg. 2735
MILLER SPORTS GROUP—See Miller Publishing Group, LLC; *U.S. Private*, pg. 2735
MODERN BRIDE GROUP—See IAC Inc.; *U.S. Public*, pg. 1081
MODERN LUXURY MEDIA, LLC—See Clarity Partners, L.P.; *U.S. Private*, pg. 912
MONDADORI SCIENZA S.P.A.—See Fininvest S.p.A.; *Int'l*, pg. 2675
MONTGOMERY MEDIA INTERNATIONAL, LLC—See mThink LLC; *U.S. Private*, pg. 2809
MORAVSKA BASTEI MOBA S.R.O.—See Bastei Lubbe AG; *Int'l*, pg. 888
MOTHER EARTH NEWS—See The Nutting Company, Inc.; *U.S. Private*, pg. 4086
MOTHERHOOD PTE LTD—See Eastern Holdings Ltd.; *Int'l*, pg. 2272
MOTOR INFORMATION SYSTEMS—See The Hearst Corporation; *U.S. Private*, pg. 4045
MOTOR MAGAZINE—See The Hearst Corporation; *U.S. Private*, pg. 4045
MOTOR TREND—See TEN: The Enthusiast Network, Inc.; *U.S. Private*, pg. 3964
MS. MAGAZINE—See Liberty Media for Women, LLC; *U.S. Private*, pg. 2445
MTHINK LLC; *U.S. Private*, pg. 2809
NATIONAL AUTO RESEARCH—See The Hearst Corporation; *U.S. Private*, pg. 4045
THE NATIONAL ENQUIRER—See Chatham Asset Management, LLC; *U.S. Private*, pg. 860
NATIONAL GEOGRAPHIC MAGAZINE GROUP—See National Geographic Society; *U.S. Private*, pg. 2855
NATIONAL JOURNAL GROUP; *U.S. Private*, pg. 2858
THE NATIONAL MAGAZINE COMPANY LTD.—See The Hearst Corporation; *U.S. Private*, pg. 4046
NATIONAL REVIEW, INC.; *U.S. Private*, pg. 2862
THE NATIONAL UNDERWRITER COMPANY—See Summit Business Media, LLC; *U.S. Private*, pg. 3853
NATURAL HEALTH MAGAZINE—See Meredith Corporation; *U.S. Public*, pg. 1423
THE NATURAL MARKETING INSTITUTE INC—See Research America, Inc.; *U.S. Private*, pg. 3403
NEIGHBORHOOD NETWORKS PUBLISHING; *U.S. Private*, pg. 2881
NERVE.COM, INC.—See This Life, Inc.; *U.S. Private*, pg. 4145
NETWORK WORLD, INC.—See China Oceanwide Holdings Group Co., Ltd.; *Int'l*, pg. 1538
NETWORK WORLD, INC.—See IDG Capital; *Int'l*, pg. 3594
NEWBAY MEDIA, LLC—See Future plc; *Int'l*, pg. 2857
THE NEW ENGLAND JOURNAL OF MEDICINE—See Massachusetts Medical Society; *U.S. Private*, pg. 2604
NEW JERSEY MONTHLY; *U.S. Private*, pg. 2898
THE NEW LEADER; *U.S. Private*, pg. 4083
NEW LINE DISTRIBUTION, INC.—See Warner Bros. Discovery, Inc.; *U.S. Public*, pg. 2327
NEW LINE HOME ENTERTAINMENT, INC.—See Warner Bros. Discovery, Inc.; *U.S. Public*, pg. 2327
NEW LINE INTERNATIONAL RELEASING, INC.—See Warner Bros. Discovery, Inc.; *U.S. Public*, pg. 2327
NEWMEDIAROCKSTARS, INC.—See Zealot Networks, Inc.; *U.S. Private*, pg. 4599
NEWPOINT FRANCHISOR, LLC—See Lion Equity Partners, LLC; *U.S. Private*, pg. 2463
THE NEW REPUBLIC INC.; *U.S. Private*, pg. 4083
NEWSWEEK LLC—See IBT Media Inc.; *U.S. Private*, pg. 2029
THE NEW YORKER MAGAZINE, INC.—See Advance Publications, Inc.; *U.S. Private*, pg. 86
THE NEW YORKER MAGAZINE—See Advance Publications, Inc.; *U.S. Private*, pg. 86
NEW YORK MAGAZINE—See New York Media, LLC; *U.S. Private*, pg. 2911
NEW YORK MEDIA, LLC; *U.S. Private*, pg. 2911
NEW YORK SPACES, INC.—See MOD Media LLC; *U.S. Private*, pg. 2759
NEXT STEP EDUCATION GROUP, INC.; *U.S. Private*, pg. 2920
NORTH AMERICAN PUBLISHING CO.—See Specialty Graphic Imag; *U.S. Private*, pg. 3750
NORTHBROOK PUBLISHING—See Aurora Capital Group, LLC; *U.S. Private*, pg. 394
NORTH COAST MEDIA, LLC; *U.S. Private*, pg. 2944
NORTHSTAR TRAVEL MEDIA LLC—See EagleTree Capital, LP; *U.S. Private*, pg. 1312
NYI ON, LLC—See Diversis Capital, LLC; *U.S. Private*, pg. 1244
ODYSSEY MAGAZINE PUBLISHING GROUP INC.—See Chatham Asset Management, LLC; *U.S. Private*, pg. 860
OGDEN PUBLICATIONS, INC.—See The Nutting Company, Inc.; *U.S. Private*, pg. 4086
OK! MAGAZINE—See Chatham Asset Management, LLC; *U.S. Private*, pg. 860

O'MEARA-BROWN PUBLICATIONS, INC.; *U.S. Private*, pg. 2979
ONLINE—See Information Today Inc.; *U.S. Private*, pg. 2073
OPEN SKY MEDIA INC.; *U.S. Private*, pg. 3029
ORANGE COAST MAGAZINE, LLC—See Hour Media Group, LLC; *U.S. Private*, pg. 1991
O, THE OPRAH MAGAZINE—See The Hearst Corporation; *U.S. Private*, pg. 4046
OUR SUNDAY VISITOR, INC.; *U.S. Private*, pg. 3050
OY VALITUT PALAT - READER'S DIGEST AB—See CIL Group SL; *Int'l*, pg. 1607
PACE COMMUNICATIONS INC.; *U.S. Private*, pg. 3063
PACIFIC MAGAZINES PTY. LTD.—See Heinrich Bauer Verlag KG; *Int'l*, pg. 3324
PACIFIC PRESS PUBLISHING ASSOCIATION; *U.S. Private*, pg. 3070
PACIFIC STANDARD—See Grist Magazine, Inc.; *U.S. Private*, pg. 1790
PAISANO PUBLICATIONS, LLC; *U.S. Private*, pg. 3076
PALM BEACH ILLUSTRATED—See Hour Media Group, LLC; *U.S. Private*, pg. 1991
PALM BEACH MEDIA GROUP INC.—See Hour Media Group, LLC; *U.S. Private*, pg. 1991
PARADE MAGAZINE—See Advance Publications, Inc.; *U.S. Private*, pg. 86
PARADE PUBLICATIONS INC.—See Advance Publications, Inc.; *U.S. Private*, pg. 86
PARAMOUNT RESEARCH, INC.—See Colgate-Palmolive Company; *U.S. Public*, pg. 533
THE PARENTING GROUP, INC.—See Bonnier AB; *Int'l*, pg. 1109
PARENTS MAGAZINE—See Meredith Corporation; *U.S. Public*, pg. 1423
PC MAGAZINE—See Ziff Davis, Inc.; *U.S. Public*, pg. 2404
PENNY PUBLICATIONS, LLC; *U.S. Private*, pg. 3137
PENSKE MEDIA CORPORATION; *U.S. Private*, pg. 3139
PEOPLE MAGAZINE—See Meredith Corporation; *U.S. Public*, pg. 1423
PERSONAL SELLING POWER INC.; *U.S. Private*, pg. 3155
PETER LI EDUCATION GROUP; *U.S. Private*, pg. 3158
THE PETROLEUM ECONOMIST LIMITED—See Main Street Capital Corporation; *U.S. Public*, pg. 1355
THE PHYSICIAN & SPORTSMEDICINE—See JTE Multimedia, LLC; *U.S. Private*, pg. 2242
PLAYBILL INCORPORATED; *U.S. Private*, pg. 3212
PLAYBOY SPECIAL EDITIONS—See PLBY Group, Inc.; *U.S. Public*, pg. 1698
POPULAR SCIENCE MAGAZINE—See Bonnier AB; *Int'l*, pg. 1108
POST GRADUATE INSTITUTE FOR MEDICINE (PIM)—See The Wicks Group of Companies, LLC; *U.S. Private*, pg. 4135
POSTGRADUATE MEDICINE—See JTE Multimedia, LLC; *U.S. Private*, pg. 2242
POST INDEPENDENT—See Swift Communications, Inc.; *U.S. Private*, pg. 3893
POWER & MOTORYACHT—See TEN: The Enthusiast Network, Inc.; *U.S. Private*, pg. 3964
PREMIER ASIAN AUTO PUBLICATIONS (M) SDN BHD—See Delloyd Ventures Sdn Bhd; *Int'l*, pg. 2014
PRESSE-SERVICE GULL GMBH—See Deutsche Post AG; *Int'l*, pg. 2082
PRINCETON UNIVERSITY PRESS; *U.S. Private*, pg. 3264
PRINT MARKETING CONCEPTS INC.—See Cowles Company; *U.S. Private*, pg. 1074
PRISMA PRESSE & CIE—See Bertelsmann SE & Co. KGaA; *Int'l*, pg. 993
PRISMA VERLAG GMBH & CO. KG—See Bertelsmann SE & Co. KGaA; *Int'l*, pg. 993
PRO PUBLICA INC.; *U.S. Private*, pg. 3270
PSYCHOLOGY TODAY—See Sussex Publishers, LLC; *U.S. Private*, pg. 3886
PT PRIMA INFOSARANA MEDIA—See China Oceanwide Holdings Group Co., Ltd.; *Int'l*, pg. 1538
PT PRIMA INFOSARANA MEDIA—See IDG Capital; *Int'l*, pg. 3594
PUBLICACIONES AQUARIO, S. DE R.L. DE C.V.—See Grupo Televisa, S.A.B.; *Int'l*, pg. 3136
PUBLICATIONS & COMMUNICATIONS, INC.; *U.S. Private*, pg. 3300
QUESTEX MEDIA GROUP LLC—See MidOcean Partners, LLP; *U.S. Public*, pg. 2717
RAILWAY EDUCATIONAL BUREAU—See Simmons-Boardman Publishing Corp.; *U.S. Private*, pg. 3665
RANDOM LENGTHS PUBLICATIONS, INC.—See Astorg Partners S.A.S.; *Int'l*, pg. 656
RANDOM LENGTHS PUBLICATIONS, INC.—See Epiris Managers LLP; *Int'l*, pg. 2461
RD PUBLICATIONS, INC.—See RDA Holding Co.; *U.S. Private*, pg. 3363
READER'S DIGEST AB—See CIL Group SL; *Int'l*, pg. 1607
THE READER'S DIGEST ASSOCIATION, INC.—See RDA Holding Co.; *U.S. Private*, pg. 3363
THE READER'S DIGEST ASSOCIATION PTY LIMITED—See RDA Holding Co.; *U.S. Private*, pg. 3364
THE READER'S DIGEST ASSOCIATION (RUSSIA) INC.—See RDA Holding Co.; *U.S. Private*, pg. 3363
READER'S DIGEST (AUSTRALIA) PTY LTD.—See RDA Holding Co.; *U.S. Private*, pg. 3364
READER'S DIGEST CHILDREN'S PUBLISHING, INC.—See RDA Holding Co.; *U.S. Private*, pg. 3363
READER'S DIGEST CHILDREN'S PUBLISHING LIMITED—See RDA Holding Co.; *U.S. Private*, pg. 3363
READER'S DIGEST COLOMBIA, LTDA—See RDA Holding Co.; *U.S. Private*, pg. 3363
READER'S DIGEST CONSUMER SERVICES, INC.—See RDA Holding Co.; *U.S. Private*, pg. 3363
READER'S DIGEST ENTERTAINMENT, INC.—See RDA Holding Co.; *U.S. Private*, pg. 3363
READER'S DIGEST EUROPE LIMITED—See RDA Holding Co.; *U.S. Private*, pg. 3363
READER'S DIGEST KIADO KFT—See RDA Holding Co.; *U.S. Private*, pg. 3363
READER'S DIGEST (MALAYSIA) SDN. BHD—See RDA Holding Co.; *U.S. Private*, pg. 3363
READER'S DIGEST MEXICO S.A. DE C.V.—See RDA Holding Co.; *U.S. Private*, pg. 3363
THE READER'S DIGEST (NEW ZEALAND) LIMITED—See RDA Holding Co.; *U.S. Private*, pg. 3363
READER'S DIGEST N.V. S.A.—See RDA Holding Co.; *U.S. Private*, pg. 3363
READER'S DIGEST (PHILIPPINES) INC.—See RDA Holding Co.; *U.S. Private*, pg. 3363
READER'S DIGEST PRZEGLAD SP.Z.O.O.—See RDA Holding Co.; *U.S. Private*, pg. 3363
READER'S DIGEST S.A.—See RDA Holding Co.; *U.S. Private*, pg. 3363
READER'S DIGEST SELECCIONES S.A.—See RDA Holding Co.; *U.S. Private*, pg. 3363
READER'S DIGEST (THAILAND) LIMITED—See RDA Holding Co.; *U.S. Private*, pg. 3363
READER'S DIGEST VYBER S.R.O.—See RDA Holding Co.; *U.S. Private*, pg. 3363
READER'S DIGEST WORLD SERVICES, S.A.—See RDA Holding Co.; *U.S. Private*, pg. 3363
READEX—See NewsBank, Inc.; *U.S. Private*, pg. 2917
READYMADE MAGAZINE—See Meredith Corporation; *U.S. Public*, pg. 1423
RED 7 MEDIA, LLC; *U.S. Private*, pg. 3372
RED HAND MEDIA, LLC—See The Pilot LLC; *U.S. Private*, pg. 4095
RED HERRING, INC.; *U.S. Private*, pg. 3374
REIMAN MEDIA GROUP, INC.—See RDA Holding Co.; *U.S. Private*, pg. 3363
RESOURCE RECYCLING, INC.—See The Association of Plastic Recyclers; *U.S. Private*, pg. 3989
RESTAURANT BUSINESS—See Schofield Media Ltd.; *U.S. Private*, pg. 3567
REVENUE—See mThink LLC; *U.S. Private*, pg. 2809
REVIEW PUBLISHING COMPANY LIMITED—See News Corporation; *U.S. Public*, pg. 1518
RHODE ISLAND MONTHLY COMMUNICATIONS, INC—See Gannett Co., Inc.; *U.S. Public*, pg. 905
RISK & INSURANCE MANAGEMENT SOCIETY, INC.; *U.S. Private*, pg. 3440
RIS NEWS—See RFE Investment Partners; *U.S. Private*, pg. 3419
RIZZOLI LIBRI S.P.A.—See Fininvest S.p.A.; *Int'l*, pg. 2675
ROAD & TRACK—See The Hearst Corporation; *U.S. Private*, pg. 4046
ROBB REPORT - NEW YORK—See RockBridge Growth Equity, LLC; *U.S. Private*, pg. 3465
ROLLING STONE MAGAZINE—See Penske Media Corporation; *U.S. Private*, pg. 3139
THE ROTARIAN MAGAZINE—See Rotary International; *U.S. Private*, pg. 3486
THE ROUGH NOTES COMPANY, INC.; *U.S. Private*, pg. 4112
ROWLAND PUBLISHING, INC.; *U.S. Private*, pg. 3490
R.R. DONNELLEY & SONS CO. - CHICAGO (111 WACKER) OFFICE—See Chatham Asset Management, LLC; *U.S. Private*, pg. 865
SAGE PUBLICATIONS, INC.; *U.S. Private*, pg. 3526
SAIL MAGAZINE—See TEN: The Enthusiast Network, Inc.; *U.S. Private*, pg. 3964
SALEM PUBLISHING, INC.—See Salem Media Group, Inc.; *U.S. Public*, pg. 1836
SAN ANTONIO MAGAZINE—See The Hearst Corporation; *U.S. Private*, pg. 4045
SAN DIEGO BUSINESS JOURNAL; *U.S. Private*, pg. 3539
SANDOW MEDIA LLC; *U.S. Private*, pg. 3544
SANOMA MAGAZINES FINLAND CORPORATION—See DPG Media Group NV; *Int'l*, pg. 2188
SANOMA MAGAZINES INTERNATIONAL B.V.—See DPG Media Group NV; *Int'l*, pg. 2188
SANOMA MEDIA UKRAINE—See DPG Media Group NV; *Int'l*, pg. 2188
SATURDAY EVENING POST SOCIETY; *U.S. Private*, pg. 3553
SCHOFIELD MEDIA LTD.; *U.S. Private*, pg. 3567
SCHOLASTIC INC. INFORMATION CENTER—See Scholastic Corporation; *U.S. Public*, pg. 1847
SCHOLASTIC INC.—See Scholastic Corporation; *U.S. Public*, pg. 1847
SCRANTON GILLETTE COMMUNICATIONS, INC.; *U.S. Private*, pg. 3579

513120 — PERIODICAL PUBLISHE...

SELDON SYSTEMS, INC.—See EnerSys; *U.S. Public*, pg. 768
SELECCOES DO READER'S DIGEST (PORTUGAL) S.A.—See RDA Holding Co.; *U.S. Private*, pg. 3363
SELECTION DU READER'S DIGEST S.A.—See CIL Group SL; *Int'l*, pg. 1607
SELF MAGAZINE—See Advance Publications, Inc.; *U.S. Private*, pg. 86
SELLING HALLOWEEN—See RFE Investment Partners; *U.S. Private*, pg. 3419
SENIOR MARKET ADVISOR—See Wiesner Publishing, LLC; *U.S. Private*, pg. 4517
SEVENTEEN MAGAZINE—See The Hearst Corporation; *U.S. Private*, pg. 4046
SGC HORIZON LLC—See Scranton Gillette Communications, Inc.; *U.S. Private*, pg. 3579
SHOTGUN NEWS—See InterMedia Advisors, LLC; *U.S. Private*, pg. 2112
SHUFUNOTOMO CO., LTD.—See Dai Nippon Printing Co., Ltd.; *Int'l*, pg. 1916
SIEBTER HIMMEL BASTEI LUBBE GMBH—See Bastei Lubbe AG; *Int'l*, pg. 888
SILVERCHAIR INFORMATION SYSTEMS; *U.S. Private*, pg. 3662
SIMMONS-BOARDMAN PUBLISHING CORP.; *U.S. Private*, pg. 3665
SLATE MAGAZINE—See Graham Holdings Company; *U.S. Public*, pg. 956
SMARTBRIEF, INC.—See Future plc; *Int'l*, pg. 2857
SMITHSONIAN MAGAZINE; *U.S. Private*, pg. 3698
SOAP OPERA DIGEST—See Chatham Asset Management, LLC; *U.S. Private*, pg. 860
SOAP OPERA WEEKLY—See TEN: The Enthusiast Network, Inc.; *U.S. Private*, pg. 3964
SOUTH FLORIDA BUSINESS JOURNAL—See Advance Publications, Inc.; *U.S. Private*, pg. 85
SOUTH FLORIDA BUSINESS LEADER—See Business Leader Media; *U.S. Private*, pg. 695
SOUTH FLORIDA PARENTING—See Tribune Publishing Company; *U.S. Private*, pg. 4228
SPAFINDER, INC.; *U.S. Private*, pg. 3744
SPEECH TECHNOLOGY MEDIA—See Information Today Inc.; *U.S. Private*, pg. 2073
SPORTS CAR CLUB OF AMERICA; *U.S. Private*, pg. 3761
SPORTS ILLUSTRATED—See Meredith Corporation; *U.S. Public*, pg. 1423
SPRINGER MEDIA B.V.—See BC Partners LLP; *Int'l*, pg. 925
STAR MAGAZINE—See Chatham Asset Management, LLC; *U.S. Private*, pg. 860
STEALS N DEALS—See Digital Air Strike Inc.; *U.S. Private*, pg. 1230
STOREROTICA MAGAZINE, INC.—See RCI Hospitality Holdings, Inc.; *U.S. Public*, pg. 1767
STREETWISE MAPS, INC.—See Compagnie Generale des Etablissements Michelin SCA; *Int'l*, pg. 1744
SUBCO INC.; *U.S. Private*, pg. 3847
SUCCESSFUL FARMING MAGAZINE—See Meredith Corporation; *U.S. Public*, pg. 1423
SUMNER COMMUNICATIONS INC.; *U.S. Private*, pg. 3857
SUNSET PUBLISHING CORPORATION—See Regent, L.P.; *U.S. Private*, pg. 3388
SUOMEN RAKENNUSLEHTI OY—See DPG Media Group NV; *Int'l*, pg. 2188
SURFER MAGAZINE—See TEN: The Enthusiast Network, Inc.; *U.S. Private*, pg. 3964
SUSSEX PUBLISHERS, LLC; *U.S. Private*, pg. 3886
SYS-CON MEDIA, INC.; *U.S. Private*, pg. 3905
TAMPA BAY MAGAZINE—See Tampa Bay Publications, Inc.; *U.S. Private*, pg. 3929
TAMPA BAY PUBLICATIONS, INC.; *U.S. Private*, pg. 3929
TARGET MEDIA PARTNERS—See Digital Air Strike Inc.; *U.S. Private*, pg. 1230
TAUNTON, INC.; *U.S. Private*, pg. 3936
THE TAUNTON PRESS, INC.—See Active Interest Media, Inc.; *U.S. Private*, pg. 69
TAX ANALYSTS; *U.S. Private*, pg. 3937
TEDDY BEAR AND FRIENDS MAGAZINES—See BeBop Channel Corporation; *U.S. Private*, pg. 288
TENNIS MAGAZINE—See Miller Publishing Group, LLC; *U.S. Private*, pg. 2735
TEN: THE ENTHUSIAST NETWORK, LLC—See TEN: The Enthusiast Network, Inc.; *U.S. Private*, pg. 3964
TEXAS MONTHLY, INC.; *U.S. Private*, pg. 3976
THIS OLD HOUSE MAGAZINE—See Roku, Inc.; *U.S. Public*, pg. 1808
THOMAS INDUSTRIAL MEDIA GMBH—See Thomas Publishing Company LLC; *U.S. Private*, pg. 4157
TI INC. AFFLUENT MEDIA GROUP—See Meredith Corporation; *U.S. Public*, pg. 1423
TI MEDIA LIMITED—See Epiris Managers LLP; *Int'l*, pg. 2461
TIME INC. (UK) PROPERTY INVESTMENTS LTD—See Epiris Managers LLP; *Int'l*, pg. 2461
TIME USA, LLC—See Meredith Corporation; *U.S. Public*, pg. 1423
THE TOPEKA CAPITAL-JOURNAL—See Gannett Co., Inc.; *U.S. Public*, pg. 905
TOWN & COUNTRY—See The Hearst Corporation; *U.S. Private*, pg. 4047
TRADE ONLY LIMITED—See Altitude Group plc; *Int'l*, pg. 393
TRADE PRESS PUBLISHING CORP.; *U.S. Private*, pg. 4202
TRADITIONAL HOME—See Meredith Corporation; *U.S. Public*, pg. 1423
TRANSACTION PUBLISHERS, INC.; *U.S. Private*, pg. 4206
TRANSWORLD PUBLISHERS—See Bertelsmann SE & Co. KGaA; *Int'l*, pg. 991
TRAVEL + LEISURE—See Travel & Leisure Co.; *U.S. Public*, pg. 2185
TREND MAGAZINES, INC.—See Times Holding Co.; *U.S. Private*, pg. 4172
TRIANGLE BUSINESS JOURNALS OF NORTH CAROLINA, LLC—See Advance Publications, Inc.; *U.S. Private*, pg. 85
TRUCKER PUBLICATIONS INC.—See Digital Air Strike Inc.; *U.S. Private*, pg. 1230
TURNSTILE PUBLISHING COMPANY; *U.S. Private*, pg. 4261
TV GUIDE MAGAZINE GROUP, INC.—See OpenGate Capital Management, LLC; *U.S. Private*, pg. 3031
TV GUIDE—See NTVB Media, Inc.; *U.S. Private*, pg. 2971
TVLINE MEDIA, LLC—See Penske Media Corporation; *U.S. Private*, pg. 3139
UAB EGMONT LIETUVA—See Egmont Fonden; *Int'l*, pg. 2326
UITGEVERSMAATSCHAPPIJ THE READER'S DIGEST N.V.—See RDA Holding Co.; *U.S. Private*, pg. 3364
UNITED COMMUNICATIONS GROUP; *U.S. Private*, pg. 4289
UNITED KENNEL CLUB, INC.; *U.S. Private*, pg. 4293
UNITED READERS SERVICE LTD.; *U.S. Private*, pg. 4296
THE UPPER ROOM; *U.S. Private*, pg. 4129
UPSTREAM HOUSTON—See Fred. Olsen & Co.; *Int'l*, pg. 2768
URBANDADDY, INC.; *U.S. Private*, pg. 4315
URETHANES TECHNOLOGY INTERNATIONAL—See Crain Communications, Inc.; *U.S. Private*, pg. 1083
U.S. NEWS & WORLD REPORT, L.P.; *U.S. Private*, pg. 4271
US WEEKLY MAGAZINE—See Chatham Asset Management, LLC; *U.S. Private*, pg. 860
VAGABOND MEDIA AB—See Egmont Fonden; *Int'l*, pg. 2326
VALUE LINE, INC.—See Arnold Bernhard & Co.; *U.S. Private*, pg. 333
VALUE LINE PUBLISHING LLC—See Arnold Bernhard & Co.; *U.S. Private*, pg. 333
VANCE PUBLISHING CORPORATION; *U.S. Private*, pg. 4342
VANITY FAIR—See Advance Publications, Inc.; *U.S. Private*, pg. 86
VARIETY MEDIA, LLC—See Penske Media Corporation; *U.S. Private*, pg. 3139
VECTEUR PLUS—See Bridgepoint Group Plc; *Int'l*, pg. 1155
VEGAS INC—See The Greenspun Corporation; *U.S. Private*, pg. 4039
VEGETARIAN TIMES—See Active Interest Media, Inc.; *U.S. Private*, pg. 69
VENDING TIMES INC.—See Networld Alliance, LLC; *U.S. Private*, pg. 2889
VENDOME GROUP, LLC—See Conversion Capital Partners Ltd.; *Int'l*, pg. 1787
VERANDA—See The Hearst Corporation; *U.S. Private*, pg. 4047
VERLAG DAS BESTE GES.M.B.H.—See RDA Holding Co.; *U.S. Private*, pg. 3364
VERLEGERDIENST MUNCHEN GMBH—See Bertelsmann SE & Co. KGaA; *Int'l*, pg. 996
VERTICAL WEB MEDIA LLC; *U.S. Private*, pg. 4370
VERWALTUNGSGESELLSCHAFT MAX VERLAG MBH—See Hubert Burda Media Holding Kommanditgesellschaft; *Int'l*, pg. 3520
VIANOVA GEOSUITE AB—See Trimble, Inc.; *U.S. Public*, pg. 2193
VIANOVA SYSTEMS SWEDEN AB—See Trimble, Inc.; *U.S. Public*, pg. 2193
VICE MEDIA LLC—See Monroe Capital LLC; *U.S. Private*, pg. 2773
VICE MEDIA LLC—See Soros Fund Management LLC; *U.S. Private*, pg. 3715
VICON BUSINESS MEDIA, INC.—See Owner Resource Group, LLC; *U.S. Private*, pg. 3055
VICTORY MEDIA INC.; *U.S. Private*, pg. 4379
VIRGO PUBLISHING, LLC—See Arlington Capital Partners LLC; *U.S. Private*, pg. 328
VNU BUSINESS PUBLICATIONS LIMITED—See Apax Partners LLP; *Int'l*, pg. 504
VOGUE MAGAZINE—See Advance Publications, Inc.; *U.S. Private*, pg. 86
WASHINGTON BUSINESS INFORMATION, INC.—See Leonard Green & Partners, L.P.; *U.S. Private*, pg. 2430
WASHINGTON BUSINESS JOURNAL, INC.—See Advance Publications, Inc.; *U.S. Private*, pg. 85
WATT PUBLISHING COMPANY; *U.S. Private*, pg. 4456
W.D. HOARD & SONS COMPANY INC.; *U.S. Private*, pg. 4419
WEALTHPIRE INC; *U.S. Private*, pg. 4462
WEAVER PUBLICATIONS INC.; *U.S. Private*, pg. 4463
WEB2CARZ.COM LTD; *U.S. Private*, pg. 4464
WEBSITE MAGAZINE INCORPORATED; *U.S. Private*, pg. 4466
THE WEEK LTD.—See Future plc; *Int'l*, pg. 2857
WEEKLY READER CORPORATION—See RDA Holding Co.; *U.S. Private*, pg. 3364
WEIDER PUBLICATIONS, LLC—See Chatham Asset Management, LLC; *U.S. Private*, pg. 860
WEISS RESEARCH, INC.—See Weiss Group, LLC; *U.S. Private*, pg. 4473
WENNER MEDIA LLC—See Penske Media Corporation; *U.S. Private*, pg. 3139
WHERE INTERNATIONAL LP—See Miller Publishing Group, LLC; *U.S. Private*, pg. 2735
WIESNER PUBLISHING, LLC; *U.S. Private*, pg. 4517
THE WINE ADVOCATE, INC.—See Compagnie Generale des Etablissements Michelin SCA; *Int'l*, pg. 1745
WINE COUNTRY PUBLICATIONS, INC.—See Brehm Communications Inc.; *U.S. Private*, pg. 644
WIRED—See Advance Publications, Inc.; *U.S. Private*, pg. 86
WOMANS DAY—See The Hearst Corporation; *U.S. Private*, pg. 4047
WOMENSFORUM.COM, INC.—See ForgeLight, LLC; *U.S. Private*, pg. 1568
WOMENSFORUM.COM, INC.—See Searchlight Capital Partners, L.P.; *U.S. Private*, pg. 3591
WOMEN'S WEAR DAILY—See Penske Media Corporation; *U.S. Private*, pg. 3139
WORKFORCE MANAGEMENT—See Crain Communications, Inc.; *U.S. Private*, pg. 1084
WORKING MOTHER MEDIA, INC.—See Bonnier AB; *Int'l*, pg. 1109
WORTH GROUP, LLC—See Curtco Media Labs LLC; *U.S. Private*, pg. 1126
WYOMING BUSINESS REPORT—See Adams Publishing Group, LLC; *U.S. Private*, pg. 75
XCONOMY, INC.; *U.S. Private*, pg. 4580
XING NETWORKING SPAIN, S.L.—See Hubert Burda Media Holding Kommanditgesellschaft; *Int'l*, pg. 3520
YANKEE PUBLISHING INC.; *U.S. Private*, pg. 4585
YOGA JOURNAL—See Active Interest Media, Inc.; *U.S. Private*, pg. 69
YOUR BIG BACKYARD—See National Wildlife Federation; *U.S. Private*, pg. 2865
YOUR HOME MAGAZINE—See Your Home Publishing, Inc.; *U.S. Private*, pg. 4594
YOUR HOME PUBLISHING, INC.; *U.S. Private*, pg. 4594
ZAO EGMONT RUSSIA LTD.—See Egmont Fonden; *Int'l*, pg. 2326
ZIFF DAVIS ENTERPRISE, INC.; *U.S. Private*, pg. 4604
ZIFF DAVIS, LLP—See Ziff Davis, Inc.; *U.S. Public*, pg. 2404

513130 — BOOK PUBLISHERS

2DFACTO, INC.—See Dai Nippon Printing Co., Ltd.; *Int'l*, pg. 1914
AAP LEHRERFACHVERLAGE GMBH—See Ernst Klett AG; *Int'l*, pg. 2495
ABC-CLIO; *U.S. Private*, pg. 36
ABRAMS & COMPANY PUBLISHERS, INC.—See Learning Trends, LLC; *U.S. Private*, pg. 2408
A&C BLACK PUBLISHERS LTD.—See Bloomsbury Publishing Plc; *Int'l*, pg. 1065
ACCELERATED CHRISTIAN EDUCATION INC.; *U.S. Private*, pg. 49
ACE SOFTWARE EXPORTS LTD.; *Int'l*, pg. 95
ADAMS MEDIA CORPORATION—See Tinicum Enterprises, Inc.; *U.S. Private*, pg. 4174
ADVANTAGE MEDIA GROUP, INC.; *U.S. Private*, pg. 94
THE AEP GROUP; *U.S. Private*, pg. 3982
ALADIN VERLAG GMBH—See Bonnier AB; *Int'l*, pg. 1108
ALBERT BONNIERS FORLAG AB—See Bonnier AB; *Int'l*, pg. 1108
ALBRECHT KNAUS VERLAG—See Bertelsmann SE & Co. KGaA; *Int'l*, pg. 989
ALFRED A. KNOPF, INC.—See Bertelsmann SE & Co. KGaA; *Int'l*, pg. 990
ALINEA—See Egmont Fonden; *Int'l*, pg. 2326
ALLER TRYK A/S—See Aller Holding A/S; *Int'l*, pg. 336
ALLIGATOR BOOKS LIMITED—See IG Design Group Plc; *Int'l*, pg. 3600
ALPHAPOLIS CO., LTD.; *Int'l*, pg. 370
AMAR CHITRA KATHA PRIVATE LIMITED—See Future Corporate Resources Limited; *Int'l*, pg. 2853
AMERICAN GIRL LLC—See Mattel, Inc.; *U.S. Public*, pg. 1398
AMERICAN QUILTER'S SOCIETY—See Schroeder Publishing Company; *U.S. Private*, pg. 3569
AMERICAN TECHNICAL PUBLISHERS, INC.; *U.S. Private*, pg. 256
AMSCO SCHOOL PUBLICATIONS, INC.; *U.S. Private*, pg. 267

N.A.I.C.S. INDEX

513130 — BOOK PUBLISHERS

ANDERSON PRESS INC; *U.S. Private*, pg. 277
ANDREWS MCMEEL UNIVERSAL; *U.S. Private*, pg. 280
ANGEL CITY PRESS—See Los Angeles Public Library Docents; *U.S. Private*, pg. 2497
ANHUI XINHUA MEDIA CO., LTD.; *Int'l*, pg. 470
ANOTEROS, INC.; *U.S. Private*, pg. 285
APN EDUCATIONAL MEDIA (NZ) LIMITED—See ARN Media Limited; *Int'l*, pg. 576
ARCADIA PUBLISHING, INC.; *U.S. Private*, pg. 309
ART DESIGN & COMMUNICATION JOINT STOCK COMPANY; *Int'l*, pg. 580
ASTARA, INC.; *U.S. Private*, pg. 360
ASTRO-CENTURY EDUCATION & TECHNOLOGY CO., LTD.; *Int'l*, pg. 662
ATLANTIC BOOKS—See Grove/Atlantic, Inc.; *U.S. Private*, pg. 1794
AUGSBURG FORTRESS CANADA—See Augsburg Fortress; *U.S. Private*, pg. 392
AUGSBURG FORTRESS; *U.S. Private*, pg. 392
BAKER PUBLISHING GROUP; *U.S. Private*, pg. 456
THE BALLANTINE PUBLISHING GROUP—See Bertelsmann SE & Co. KGaA; *Int'l*, pg. 991
BALMER BUCHERDIENST AG—See Ernst Klett AG; *Int'l*, pg. 2495
BANTAM BOOKS LTD.—See Bertelsmann SE & Co. KGaA; *Int'l*, pg. 991
BANTAM DELL PUBLISHING GROUP—See Bertelsmann SE & Co. KGaA; *Int'l*, pg. 990
BAREFOOT BOOKS, INC.; *U.S. Private*, pg. 474
BARRINGTON STOKE LIMITED—See News Corporation; *U.S. Public*, pg. 1518
BARRON'S EDUCATIONAL SERIES, INC.; *U.S. Private*, pg. 481
BAYARD, INC.—See Bayard-Presse S.A.; *Int'l*, pg. 901
BEDRIFTSKATALOGEN AS—See Eniro Group AB; *Int'l*, pg. 2439
BENDON, INC.—See Irving Place Capital Management, L.P.; *U.S. Private*, pg. 2141
BERTELSMANN LEXIKOTHEK VERLAG GMBH—See Bertelsmann SE & Co. KGaA; *Int'l*, pg. 991
BEST PERSONALIZED BOOKS, INC.; *U.S. Private*, pg. 543
BETHANY HOUSE PUBLISHERS—See Baker Publishing Group; *U.S. Private*, pg. 456
BIGZ PUBLISHING A.D.; *Int'l*, pg. 1022
BITEBACK PUBLISHING LTD.; *Int'l*, pg. 1050
BLACK BALLOON PUBLISHING, LLC; *U.S. Private*, pg. 569
BLACKWELL MUNKSGAARD—See John Wiley & Sons, Inc.; *U.S. Public*, pg. 1193
BLACKWELL VERLAG GMBH—See John Wiley & Sons, Inc.; *U.S. Public*, pg. 1192
BLANVALET VERLAG GMBH—See Bertelsmann SE & Co. KGaA; *Int'l*, pg. 992
BLASTWORKS INC.—See Gaming Realms plc; *Int'l*, pg. 2878
BLOOMSBURY BOOK PUBLISHING COMPANY LIMITED—See Bloomsbury Publishing Plc; *Int'l*, pg. 1065
BLOOMSBURY INDIA UK LIMITED—See Bloomsbury Publishing Plc; *Int'l*, pg. 1065
BLOOMSBURY INFORMATION LIMITED—See Bloomsbury Publishing Plc; *Int'l*, pg. 1065
BLOOMSBURY PROFESSIONAL LIMITED—See Bloomsbury Publishing Plc; *Int'l*, pg. 1065
BLOOMSBURY PUBLISHING INC.—See Bloomsbury Publishing Plc; *Int'l*, pg. 1065
BLOOMSBURY PUBLISHING INDIA PVT LIMITED—See Bloomsbury Publishing Plc; *Int'l*, pg. 1065
BLOOMSBURY PUBLISHING PLC; *Int'l*, pg. 1065
BLOOMSBURY PUBLISHING PTY LTD—See Bloomsbury Publishing Plc; *Int'l*, pg. 1065
BLURB, INC.—See Reischling Press, Inc.; *U.S. Private*, pg. 3392
BNET MEDIA GROUP, INC.; *U.S. Public*, pg. 366
BNI PUBLICATIONS, INC.; *U.S. Private*, pg. 602
BONNIERFORLAGEN AB—See Bonnier AB; *Int'l*, pg. 1108
BONNIER MEDIA DEUTSCHLAND GMBH—See Bonnier AB; *Int'l*, pg. 1108
BOOKANDSMILE GMBH—See Heinrich Bauer Verlag KG; *Int'l*, pg. 3324
THE BOOK SERVICE LIMITED—See Bertelsmann SE & Co. KGaA; *Int'l*, pg. 996
BOYDS MILLS PRESS, INC.—See Highlights for Children, Inc.; *U.S. Private*, pg. 1940
BRIDGE PUBLICATIONS INC.; *U.S. Private*, pg. 649
BROADVIEW PRESS INC.; *Int'l*, pg. 1172
BROMBERGS BOKFORLAG; *Int'l*, pg. 1173
BUCHGEMEINSCHAFT DONAULAND KREMAYR & SCHERIAU KG—See Bertelsmann SE & Co. KGaA; *Int'l*, pg. 992
BUCHVERTRIEB BLANK GMBH—See Bonnier AB; *Int'l*, pg. 1108
BUNKEIDO CO., LTD.; *Int'l*, pg. 1216
BUSHIROAD MEDIA, INC.—See Bushiroad, Inc.; *Int'l*, pg. 1227
CAIRO COMMUNICATION S.P.A.; *Int'l*, pg. 1253
CAMBRIDGE UNIVERSITY PRESS INDIA PRIVATE LIMITED—See Cambridge University Press; *Int'l*, pg. 1270
CAMBRIDGE UNIVERSITY PRESS JAPAN K.K.—See Cambridge University Press; *Int'l*, pg. 1270
CAMBRIDGE UNIVERSITY PRESS, NORTH AMERICA—See Cambridge University Press; *Int'l*, pg. 1270
CAMBRIDGE UNIVERSITY PRESS; *Int'l*, pg. 1269
CAMPE BILDUNGSZENTRUM HANNOVER GGMBH—See Ernst Klett AG; *Int'l*, pg. 2495
CAPPELEN DAMM AS—See Egmont Fonden; *Int'l*, pg. 2325
CAPSTONE PRESS, INC.—See Coughlan Companies, Inc.; *U.S. Private*, pg. 1064
CARLSEN VERLAG GMBH—See Bonnier AB; *Int'l*, pg. 1108
CARNEGIE LEARNING, INC.—See CIP Capital Fund, L.P.; *U.S. Private*, pg. 899
CAROLRHODA BOOKS, INC.; *U.S. Private*, pg. 769
CARUS PUBLISHING COMPANY—See Cricket Media Group Ltd.; *U.S. Private*, pg. 1100
CASTLE CONNOLLY MEDICAL LTD.—See Ziff Davis, Inc.; *U.S. Public*, pg. 2404
C. BANGE VERLAG GMBH—See Ernst Klett AG; *Int'l*, pg. 2495
CENGAGE HIGHER EDUCATION—See Apax Partners LLP; *Int'l*, pg. 503
CENGAGE HIGHER EDUCATION—See Apollo Global Management, Inc.; *U.S. Public*, pg. 168
CENGAGE HIGHER EDUCATION—See KKR & Co. Inc.; *U.S. Public*, pg. 1256
CENGAGE HIGHER EDUCATION—See Searchlight Capital Partners, L.P.; *U.S. Public*, pg. 3587
CENGAGE LEARNING ASIA—See Apax Partners LLP; *Int'l*, pg. 503
CENGAGE LEARNING ASIA—See Apollo Global Management, Inc.; *U.S. Public*, pg. 168
CENGAGE LEARNING ASIA—See KKR & Co. Inc.; *U.S. Public*, pg. 1256
CENGAGE LEARNING ASIA—See Searchlight Capital Partners, L.P.; *U.S. Private*, pg. 3587
CENGAGE LEARNING AUSTRALIA PTY. LIMITED—See Apax Partners LLP; *Int'l*, pg. 503
CENGAGE LEARNING AUSTRALIA PTY. LIMITED—See Apollo Global Management, Inc.; *U.S. Public*, pg. 168
CENGAGE LEARNING AUSTRALIA PTY. LIMITED—See KKR & Co. Inc.; *U.S. Public*, pg. 1256
CENGAGE LEARNING AUSTRALIA PTY. LIMITED—See Searchlight Capital Partners, L.P.; *U.S. Private*, pg. 3587
CENGAGE LEARNING, INC.—See Apax Partners LLP; *Int'l*, pg. 502
CENGAGE LEARNING, INC.—See Apollo Global Management, Inc.; *U.S. Public*, pg. 168
CENGAGE LEARNING, INC.—See KKR & Co. Inc.; *U.S. Public*, pg. 1256
CENGAGE LEARNING, INC.—See Searchlight Capital Partners, L.P.; *U.S. Private*, pg. 3587
CENTERWATCH—See Leonard Green & Partners, L.P.; *U.S. Private*, pg. 2429
CENTRAL CHINA LAND MEDIA CO., LTD.; *Int'l*, pg. 1405
CHANGJIANG PUBLISHING & MEDIA CO., LTD.; *Int'l*, pg. 1443
CHANNING BETE CO., INC.; *U.S. Private*, pg. 849
CHICKEN HOUSE PUBLISHING LTD.—See Scholastic Corporation; *U.S. Public*, pg. 1848
CHINA LITERATURE LTD.; *Int'l*, pg. 1515
CHINA PUBLISHING & MEDIA HOLDINGS CO., LTD.; *Int'l*, pg. 1542
CHINA SCIENCE PUBLISHING & MEDIA LTD.; *Int'l*, pg. 1550
CHINA SOUTH PUBLISHING & MEDIA GROUP CO., LTD.; *Int'l*, pg. 1552
CHINESE UNIVERSE PUBLISHING AND MEDIA GROUP CO., LTD.; *Int'l*, pg. 1569
CHUOKEIZAI-SHA HOLDINGS, INC.; *Int'l*, pg. 1600
CIDER MILL PRESS BOOK PUBLISHERS LLC—See News Corporation; *U.S. Public*, pg. 1518
CITIC PRESS CORPORATION; *Int'l*, pg. 1622
CJ FALLON LIMITED—See Levine Leichtman Capital Partners, LLC; *U.S. Private*, pg. 2435
CLASSBOOK.COM; *U.S. Private*, pg. 916
CLAUSEN & BOSSE GMBH—See Chevrillon Philippe Industrie; *Int'l*, pg. 1474
CLIFFSNOTES, INC.—See John Wiley & Sons, Inc.; *U.S. Public*, pg. 1193
COLLINS LEARNING—See News Corporation; *U.S. Public*, pg. 1519
COLUMBIA UNIVERSITY PRESS; *U.S. Private*, pg. 978
CONCORDIA PUBLISHING HOUSE; *U.S. Private*, pg. 1010
CONTINENTAL PRESS INC.; *U.S. Private*, pg. 1030
CONTRACTORS REGISTER INC.—See Symphony Technology Group, LLC; *U.S. Private*, pg. 3900
COOKBOOK PUBLISHERS INC.; *U.S. Private*, pg. 1039
CORA VERLAG GMBH & CO. KG—See Charlesbank Capital Partners, LLC; *U.S. Private*, pg. 854
CORNELL UNIVERSITY PRESS; *U.S. Private*, pg. 1051
COUNTERPOINT, LLC—See Black Balloon Publishing, LLC; *U.S. Private*, pg. 569
CPI COLOUR—See Chevrillon Philippe Industrie; *Int'l*, pg. 1474
CRAIN COMMUNICATIONS, INC. - AUTOMOTIVE NEWS EUROPE UNIT—See Crain Communications, Inc.; *U.S. Private*, pg. 1083
CRANBURY INTERNATIONAL LLC—See ProBility Media Corporation; *U.S. Public*, pg. 1723
CREATIVE TEACHING PRESS INC.; *U.S. Private*, pg. 1090
CRISIL IREVNA POLAND SP. Z.O.O.—See S&P Global Inc.; *U.S. Public*, pg. 1831
THE CROWN PUBLISHING GROUP—See Bertelsmann SE & Co. KGaA; *Int'l*, pg. 991
DAEWON C.I. INC.—See Daewon Media Co., Ltd.; *Int'l*, pg. 1910
DALMATIAN PRESS LLC; *U.S. Private*, pg. 1150
DANANG EDUCATION INVESTMENT & DEVELOPMENT JOINT STOCK COMPANY; *Int'l*, pg. 1958
DE AGOSTINI EDITORE S.P.A.—See De Agostini S.p.A.; *Int'l*, pg. 1994
DE AGOSTINI LIBRI S.P.A.—See De Agostini S.p.A.; *Int'l*, pg. 1994
DE AGOSTINI PUBLISHING ITALIA S.P.A.—See De Agostini S.p.A.; *Int'l*, pg. 1994
DELL PUBLISHING—See Bertelsmann SE & Co. KGaA; *Int'l*, pg. 990
DELMAR CENGAGE LEARNING—See Apax Partners LLP; *Int'l*, pg. 503
DELMAR CENGAGE LEARNING—See Apollo Global Management, Inc.; *U.S. Public*, pg. 168
DELMAR CENGAGE LEARNING—See KKR & Co. Inc.; *U.S. Public*, pg. 1256
DELMAR CENGAGE LEARNING—See Searchlight Capital Partners, L.P.; *U.S. Public*, pg. 3587
DEMOS MEDICAL PUBLISHING, LLC—See Mannheim, LLC; *U.S. Private*, pg. 2565
DIALOGUE SYSTEM INC.; *U.S. Private*, pg. 1222
DIFUSION CENTRO DE INVESTIGACION Y PUBLICACIONES DE IDIOMAS, S.L.—See Ernst Klett AG; *Int'l*, pg. 2495
DISNEY PUBLISHING WORLDWIDE, INC.—See The Walt Disney Company; *U.S. Public*, pg. 2138
DITT DISTRIKT AS—See Eniro Group AB; *Int'l*, pg. 2439
DK PUBLISHING—See Bertelsmann SE & Co. KGaA; *Int'l*, pg. 991
DNC MEDIA CO., LTD.; *Int'l*, pg. 2148
DNP CHUBU CO., LTD.—See Dai Nippon Printing Co., Ltd.; *Int'l*, pg. 1914
DNP ENGINEERING CO., LTD.—See Dai Nippon Printing Co., Ltd.; *Int'l*, pg. 1914
DNP FINE CHEMICALS UTSUNOMIYA CO., LTD.—See Dai Nippon Printing Co., Ltd.; *Int'l*, pg. 1914
DNP HUMAN SERVICES CO., LTD.—See Dai Nippon Printing Co., Ltd.; *Int'l*, pg. 1914
DNP MEDIA SUPPORT CO., LTD.—See Dai Nippon Printing Co., Ltd.; *Int'l*, pg. 1915
DNP PHOTO IMAGING CO., LTD.—See Dai Nippon Printing Co., Ltd.; *Int'l*, pg. 1915
DNP PHOTO IMAGING JAPAN CO., LTD.—See Dai Nippon Printing Co., Ltd.; *Int'l*, pg. 1915
DNP PHOTO IMAGING RUSSIA LLC—See Dai Nippon Printing Co., Ltd.; *Int'l*, pg. 1915
DODGE DATA & ANALYTICS LLC—See Symphony Technology Group, LLC; *U.S. Private*, pg. 3900
DORCHESTER PUBLISHING CO., INC.; *U.S. Private*, pg. 1262
DORLING KINDERSLEY LTD.—See Bertelsmann SE & Co. KGaA; *Int'l*, pg. 991
DORLING KINDERSLEY PUBLISHING PRIVATE LIMITED—See Bertelsmann SE & Co. KGaA; *Int'l*, pg. 992
DOUBLEDAY AUSTRALIA PTY LTD—See Bertelsmann SE & Co. KGaA; *Int'l*, pg. 992
DOUBLEDAY NEW ZEALAND LTD.—See Bertelsmann SE & Co. KGaA; *Int'l*, pg. 992
DOUBLEDAY—See Bertelsmann SE & Co. KGaA; *Int'l*, pg. 990
DOVER PUBLICATIONS, INC.—See Atlas Holdings, LLC; *U.S. Private*, pg. 377
DR. JOSEF RAABE SLOVENSKO, S. R. O.—See Ernst Klett AG; *Int'l*, pg. 2495
DR JOSEF RAABE SPOLKA WYDAWNICZA SP. Z O.O.—See Ernst Klett AG; *Int'l*, pg. 2495
DUZHE PUBLISHING & MEDIA CO., LTD.; *Int'l*, pg. 2236
EAGLEMOSS PUBLICATIONS LTD; *Int'l*, pg. 2266
EAGLE PUBLISHING INC. - EAGLES FINANCIAL PUBLICATIONS DIVISION—See Eagle Publishing Inc.; *U.S. Private*, pg. 1310
EAGLE PUBLISHING INC.; *U.S. Private*, pg. 1310
EASTON PRESS—See MBI, Inc.; *U.S. Private*, pg. 2624
E-BOOK SYSTEMS K. K.—See E-Book Systems Pte. Ltd.; *Int'l*, pg. 2247
EDITIONS ATLAS (FRANCE) S.A.S.—See De Agostini S.p.A.; *Int'l*, pg. 1994
EDITIONS BORDAS—See Czech Media Invest as; *Int'l*, pg. 1898
EDITIONS DU MONITEUR—See Bridgepoint Group Plc; *Int'l*, pg. 1155
EDITIONS DU SIGNE SA; *Int'l*, pg. 2311
EDITIONS GRANADA SA; *Int'l*, pg. 2311

513130 — BOOK PUBLISHERS

EDITIONS MAISON DES LANGUES S.A.R.L.—See Ernst Klett AG; *Int'l*, pg. 2495
EDITIONS NATHAN—See Czech Media Invest as; *Int'l*, pg. 1898
EDITIONS PRIVAT SA; *Int'l*, pg..2311
EDITIONS RAABE S.A.R.L.—See Ernst Klett AG; *Int'l*, pg. 2495
EDITIS SAS—See Czech Media Invest as; *Int'l*, pg. 1898
EDITORA ATICA S.A.—See Cogna Educacao S.A.; *Int'l*, pg. 1695
EDITORIAL PLANETA DE AGOSTINI, SA—See De Agostini S.p.A.; *Int'l*, pg. 1994
EDITORIUM AS—See Eniro Group AB; *Int'l*, pg. 2439
EDUCATIONAL BOOK JSC; *Int'l*, pg. 2315
EDUCATIONAL BOOK JSC; *Int'l*, pg. 2315
EDUCATIONAL BOOK JSC; *Int'l*, pg. 2315
EDUCAUSE; *U.S. Private*, pg. 1340
EGMONT AS—See Egmont Fonden; *Int'l*, pg. 2325
EGMONT SERIEFORLAGET AS—See Egmont Fonden; *Int'l*, pg. 2325
ELF ON THE SHELF, LLC; *U.S. Private*, pg. 1359
EMC PUBLISHING, LLC; *U.S. Private*, pg. 1379
ENCODE PACKAGING INDIA LIMITED; *Int'l*, pg. 2402
ENCYCLOPAEDIA BRITANNICA, INC.; *U.S. Private*, pg. 1391
ENIRO EMFAS AB—See Eniro Group AB; *Int'l*, pg. 2439
ENTERTAINMENT PUBLICATIONS, LLC—See Afin Technologies Limited; *Int'l*, pg. 189
ERNST KLETT AG; *Int'l*, pg. 2495
ERNST KLETT VERTRIEBSGESELLSCHAFT—See Ernst Klett AG; *Int'l*, pg. 2495
F.A. DAVIS PUBLISHING COMPANY; *U.S. Private*, pg. 1455
FAMOUS ARTIST SCHOOL—See Cortina Learning International, Inc.; *U.S. Private*, pg. 1061
FAMOUS WRITERS SCHOOL—See Cortina Learning International, Inc.; *U.S. Private*, pg. 1061
FANTAGRAPHICS BOOKS, INC.; *U.S. Private*, pg. 1472
FASTPENCIL, INC.; *U.S. Private*, pg. 1482
FINDEXA FORLAG AS—See Eniro Group AB; *Int'l*, pg. 2439
FIREFLY BOOKS; *Int'l*, pg. 2679
FODOR'S TRAVEL PUBLICATIONS, INC.—See Bertelsmann SE & Co. KGaA; *Int'l*, pg. 991
FONDS MERCATOR—See Dexia SA; *Int'l*, pg. 2092
FORBES INDIA—See Forbes Media LLC; *U.S. Private*, pg. 1563
FORBES ISRAEL—See Forbes Media LLC; *U.S. Private*, pg. 1563
FORBES ROMANIA—See Forbes Media LLC; *U.S. Private*, pg. 1563
FORBES RUSSIA—See Forbes Media LLC; *U.S. Private*, pg. 1563
FORBES UKRAINE—See Forbes Media LLC; *U.S. Private*, pg. 1563
FORLAGSHUSET VIGMOSTAD & BJORKE AS; *Int'l*, pg. 2733
FRANK W. CAWOOD & ASSOCIATES; *U.S. Private*, pg. 1595
FRECHVERLAG GMBH—See Bertelsmann SE & Co. KGaA; *Int'l*, pg. 992
FREDERICK FELL PUBLISHERS, INC.; *U.S. Private*, pg. 1602
FRIEDL BUSINESS INFORMATION LIMITED; *Int'l*, pg. 2792
F+W MEDIA, INC.—See Tinicum Enterprises, Inc.; *U.S. Private*, pg. 4174
F&W PUBLICATIONS - BOOKS—See Tinicum Enterprises, Inc.; *U.S. Private*, pg. 4174
THE GABLES PUBLISHING COMPANY—See Chatham Asset Management, LLC; *U.S. Private*, pg. 867
GENTLE PATH PRESS—See International Institute for Trauma and Addiction Professionals; *U.S. Private*, pg. 2118
GEORGE BRAZILLER, INC.; *U.S. Private*, pg. 1681
GIULIO EINAUDI EDITORE S.P.A.—See Fininvest S.p.A.; *Int'l*, pg. 2675
GLENCOE/MCGRAW-HILL—See Platinum Equity, LLC; *U.S. Private*, pg. 3205
THE GLOBE PEQUOT PRESS, INC.—See Shivers Trading & Operating Company; *U.S. Private*, pg. 3638
THE GOODHEART-WILLCOX CO., INC.; *U.S. Public*, pg. 2082
GOOD WILL PUBLISHERS INC.; *U.S. Private*, pg. 1738
GOOSEBERRY PATCH—See The Rowman & Littlefield Publishing Group, Inc.; *U.S. Private*, pg. 4112
GOSPEL LIGHT PUBLICATIONS; *U.S. Private*, pg. 1744
GRANTHAM BOOK SERVICES LIMITED—See Bertelsmann SE & Co. KGaA; *Int'l*, pg. 992
GRATISFILM PHOTOCOLQR CLUB SA—See CIL Group SL; *Int'l*, pg. 1607
GREENLEAF BOOK GROUP, LLC; *U.S. Private*, pg. 1778
GRENSEGUIDEN AS—See Eniro Group AB; *Int'l*, pg. 2439
GROLIER INCORPORATED—See Scholastic Corporation; *U.S. Public*, pg. 1847
GROUP PUBLISHING INC.; *U.S. Private*, pg. 1794
GROVE/ATLANTIC, INC.; *U.S. Private*, pg. 1794
GRUPO NELSON—See Charlesbank Capital Partners, LLC; *U.S. Private*, pg. 854

GRUPO QUMMA, S.A. DE C.V.; *Int'l*, pg. 3134
GULE SIDER AS—See Eniro Group AB; *Int'l*, pg. 2439
GULE SIDER INTERNETT AS—See Eniro Group AB; *Int'l*, pg. 2439
GYLDENDAL A/S; *Int'l*, pg. 3191
HARDIE GRANT PUBLISHING PTY. LTD.; *Int'l*, pg. 3273
HARLEQUIN ENTERPRISES (AUSTRALIA) PTY LTD—See News Corporation; *U.S. Public*, pg. 1519
HARLEQUIN ENTERPRISES LIMITED—See Charlesbank Capital Partners, LLC; *U.S. Private*, pg. 854
HARLEQUIN KFT. (AKA HARLEQUIN MAGYARORSZAG KORLATOLT FELELOSSEGU TARSASAG)—See News Corporation; *U.S. Public*, pg. 1519
HARLEQUIN MAGAZINES INC—See Charlesbank Capital Partners, LLC; *U.S. Private*, pg. 854
HARLEQUIN S.A.—See News Corporation; *U.S. Public*, pg. 1519
HARLEQUIN (UK) LIMITED—See Charlesbank Capital Partners, LLC; *U.S. Private*, pg. 854
HARPERCOLLINS CHILDREN'S BOOKS GROUP - U.S.—See Charlesbank Capital Partners, LLC; *U.S. Private*, pg. 854
HARPERCOLLINS CHRISTIAN PUBLISHING, INC.—See News Corporation; *U.S. Public*, pg. 1519
HARPERCOLLINS GENERAL BOOKS GROUP - U.S.—See Charlesbank Capital Partners, LLC; *U.S. Private*, pg. 854
HARPERCOLLINS ITALIA S.P.A.—See Charlesbank Capital Partners, LLC; *U.S. Private*, pg. 854
HARPERCOLLINS PUBLISHERS AUSTRALIA PTY. LIMITED—See News Corporation; *U.S. Public*, pg. 1519
HARPERCOLLINS PUBLISHERS (HOLDINGS) PTY. LIMITED—See News Corporation; *U.S. Public*, pg. 1519
HARPERCOLLINS PUBLISHERS INDIA LIMITED—See News Corporation; *U.S. Public*, pg. 1519
HARPERCOLLINS PUBLISHERS LIMITED—See News Corporation; *U.S. Public*, pg. 1519
HARPERCOLLINS PUBLISHERS L.L.C.—See Charlesbank Capital Partners, LLC; *U.S. Private*, pg. 854
HARPERCOLLINS PUBLISHERS LTD—See News Corporation; *U.S. Public*, pg. 1519
HARPERONE—See Charlesbank Capital Partners, LLC; *U.S. Private*, pg. 854
HARRISON HOUSE; *U.S. Private*, pg. 1870
HARVARD UNIVERSITY PRESS - LONDON—See Harvard University Press; *U.S. Private*, pg. 1875
HARVARD UNIVERSITY PRESS; *U.S. Private*, pg. 1875
H. ASCHEHOUG & CO. W. NYGAARD AS; *Int'l*, pg. 3194
HAY HOUSE, LLC—See Bertelsmann SE & Co. KGaA; *Int'l*, pg. 990
HAYNES NORTH AMERICA, INC—See Apax Partners LLP; *Int'l*, pg. 502
HAYNES NORTH AMERICA, INC—See TowerBrook Capital Partners, L.P.; *U.S. Private*, pg. 4195
HAYNES PUBLISHING GROUP PLC—See Apax Partners LLP; *Int'l*, pg. 502
HAYNES PUBLISHING GROUP PLC—See TowerBrook Capital Partners, L.P.; *U.S. Private*, pg. 4195
HEALTHSTYLE PRESS—See Interactivation Health Networks LLC; *U.S. Private*, pg. 2108
HEA LUGU OU—See AS Ekspress Grupp; *Int'l*, pg. 590
HEARST BOOKS—See The Hearst Corporation; *U.S. Private*, pg. 4046
HEINEMANN-RAINTREE—See Coughlan Companies, Inc.; *U.S. Private*, pg. 1065
HEINEMANN—See Veritas Capital Fund Management, LLC; *U.S. Private*, pg. 4363
THE HISTORY PRESS, INC.—See Arcadia Publishing, Inc.; *U.S. Private*, pg. 309
HMH PUBLISHERS LLC—See Veritas Capital Fund Management, LLC; *U.S. Private*, pg. 4363
HOLIDAY HOUSE, INC.; *U.S. Private*, pg. 1963
HOT OFF THE PRESS, INC.; *U.S. Private*, pg. 1988
HOUGHTON MIFFLIN COMPANY INTERNATIONAL, INC.—See Veritas Capital Fund Management, LLC; *U.S. Private*, pg. 4363
HOUGHTON MIFFLIN HARCOURT INTERNATIONAL PUBLISHERS—See Veritas Capital Fund Management, LLC; *U.S. Private*, pg. 4363
HOUGHTON MIFFLIN HARCOURT PUBLISHING CO. - AUSTIN—See Veritas Capital Fund Management, LLC; *U.S. Private*, pg. 4363
HOUGHTON MIFFLIN HARCOURT PUBLISHING COMPANY—See Veritas Capital Fund Management, LLC; *U.S. Private*, pg. 4363
HOUGHTON MIFFLIN HARCOURT PUBLISHING CO. - ORLANDO—See Veritas Capital Fund Management, LLC; *U.S. Private*, pg. 4363
HOUGHTON MIFFLIN HARCOURT TRADE & REFERENCE PUBLISHERS—See Veritas Capital Fund Management, LLC; *U.S. Private*, pg. 4363
HOUGHTON MIFFLIN HARCOURT TRADE & REFERENCE PUBLISHERS—See Veritas Capital Fund Management, LLC; *U.S. Private*, pg. 4363
HSP EPI ACQUISITIONS, LLC—See Augeo Affinity Marketing, Inc.; *U.S. Private*, pg. 392
HUMAN KINETICS AUSTRALIA—See Human Kinetics Publishers Inc.; *U.S. Private*, pg. 2005
HUMAN KINETICS CANADA—See Human Kinetics Publish-

ers Inc.; *U.S. Private*, pg. 2005
HUMAN KINETICS EUROPE—See Human Kinetics Publishers Inc.; *U.S. Private*, pg. 2005
HUMAN KINETICS NEW ZEALAND—See Human Kinetics Publishers Inc.; *U.S. Private*, pg. 2005
HUMAN KINETICS PUBLISHERS INC.; *U.S. Private*, pg. 2005
HUNAN CHILDREN & JUVENILE'S PUBLISHING HOUSE CO., LTD.—See China South Publishing & Media Group Co., Ltd.; *Int'l*, pg. 1552
HUNAN PEOPLE'S PUBLISHING HOUSE CO., LTD.—See China South Publishing & Media Group Co., Ltd.; *Int'l*, pg. 1553
HUNAN SCIENCE & TECHNOLOGY PRESS CO., LTD.—See China South Publishing & Media Group Co., Ltd.; *Int'l*, pg. 1553
HUNAN TIANWEN XINHUA PRINTING CO., LTD.—See China South Publishing & Media Group Co., Ltd.; *Int'l*, pg. 1553
HUNAN YUELU PUBLISHING HOUSE CO., LTD.—See China South Publishing & Media Group Co., Ltd.; *Int'l*, pg. 1553
IBH BOOKS AND MAGAZINES DISTRIBUTORS LIMITED—See Future Corporate Resources Limited; *Int'l*, pg. 2853
IDEAS BOX ENTERTAINMENT LIMITED—See Future Corporate Resources Limited; *Int'l*, pg. 2853
IDW MEDIA HOLDINGS, INC.; *U.S. Public*, pg. 1094
IEXALT, INC.; *U.S. Public*, pg. 1094
IL SOLE 24 ORE SPA; *Int'l*, pg. 3613
IMAGINEENGINE—See Foundation 9 Entertainment, Inc.; *U.S. Private*, pg. 1579
INCISIVE MEDIA INVESTMENT LIMITED—See Apax Partners LLP; *Int'l*, pg. 504
INCISIVE RWG LIMITED—See Apax Partners LLP; *Int'l*, pg. 504
INDEX PUBLISHING AS—See Eniro Group AB; *Int'l*, pg. 2439
INDICATOR - FL MEMO LTD.—See Editions Lefebvre Sarrut SA; *Int'l*, pg. 2311
INFOBASE HOLDINGS, LLC—See Centre Lane Partners, LLC; *U.S. Private*, pg. 827
INGRAM BOOK COMPANY—See Ingram Industries, Inc.; *U.S. Private*, pg. 2076
INGRAM CONTENT GROUP INC.—See Ingram Industries, Inc.; *U.S. Private*, pg. 2076
INNER TRADITIONS INTERNATIONAL; *U.S. Private*, pg. 2080
INSIGHT EDITIONS, LP; *U.S. Private*, pg. 2085
INTERSENTIA LTD.—See Editions Lefebvre Sarrut SA; *Int'l*, pg. 2311
IN TOUCH WEEKLY—See Heinrich Bauer Verlag KG; *Int'l*, pg. 3324
ITI REFERENCE GROUP - FL—See Information Today Inc.; *U.S. Private*, pg. 2073
J H HAYNES & CO LTD—See Apax Partners LLP; *Int'l*, pg. 502
J H HAYNES & CO LTD—See TowerBrook Capital Partners, L.P.; *U.S. Private*, pg. 4195
JOBSON PROFESSIONAL PUBLICATIONS GROUP—See The Wicks Group of Companies, LLC; *U.S. Private*, pg. 4135
THE JOHNS HOPKINS UNIVERSITY PRESS—See Johns Hopkins University; *U.S. Private*, pg. 2226
JOHN WILEY & SONS (ASIA) PTE. LTD.—See John Wiley & Sons, Inc.; *U.S. Public*, pg. 1192
JOHN WILEY & SONS AUSTRALIA, LTD.—See John Wiley & Sons, Inc.; *U.S. Public*, pg. 1192
JOHN WILEY & SONS AUSTRALIA, LTD.—See John Wiley & Sons, Inc.; *U.S. Public*, pg. 1193
JOHN WILEY & SONS CANADA, LTD.—See John Wiley & Sons, Inc.; *U.S. Public*, pg. 1192
JOHN WILEY & SONS GMBH—See John Wiley & Sons, Inc.; *U.S. Public*, pg. 1192
JOHN WILEY & SONS (HK) LIMITED—See John Wiley & Sons, Inc.; *U.S. Public*, pg. 1192
JOHN WILEY & SONS, INC.; *U.S. Public*, pg. 1192
JOHN WILEY & SONS INTERNATIONAL RIGHTS, INC.—See John Wiley & Sons, Inc.; *U.S. Public*, pg. 1193
JOHN WILEY & SONS LTD A/S—See John Wiley & Sons, Inc.; *U.S. Public*, pg. 1193
JOMIRA/ADVANCE; *U.S. Private*, pg. 2231
JONES & BARTLETT LEARNING, LLC—See Blackstone Group; *U.S. Private*, pg. 348
JONES & BARTLETT LEARNING, LLC—See Canada Pension Plan Investment Board; *Int'l*, pg. 1279
JOSSEY-BASS, INC.—See John Wiley & Sons, Inc.; *U.S. Public*, pg. 1193
J.S. PALUCH CO. INC.; *U.S. Private*, pg. 2171
THE JUDAICA PRESS, INC.; *U.S. Private*, pg. 4063
KAPPA BOOKS PUBLISHERS LLC—See Kappa Publishing Group, Inc.; *U.S. Private*, pg. 2262
KARADI TALES COMPANY PRIVATE LIMITED—See Future Corporate Resources Limited; *Int'l*, pg. 2853
KENDALL/HUNT PUBLISHING COMPANY INC.; *U.S. Private*, pg. 2283
KENSINGTON PUBLISHING CORP.; *U.S. Private*, pg. 2287

N.A.I.C.S. INDEX
513130 — BOOK PUBLISHERS

KEY CURRICULUM PRESS, INC.—See Platinum Equity, LLC; *U.S. Private*, pg. 3205
K.LAB EDUCMEDIA GMBH—See Ernst Klett AG; *Int'l*, pg. 2495
KLAMATH PUBLISHING CO. LLC—See Pioneer Newspapers Inc.; *U.S. Private*, pg. 3187
KLETT BULGARIA EOOD—See Ernst Klett AG; *Int'l*, pg. 2495
KLETT HELLAS E.M.E.—See Ernst Klett AG; *Int'l*, pg. 2495
KLETT IZDAVACKA KUCA D.O.O.—See Ernst Klett AG; *Int'l*, pg. 2495
KLETT NAKLADATELSTVI S.R.O.—See Ernst Klett AG; *Int'l*, pg. 2495
KLETT UND BALMER AG—See Ernst Klett AG; *Int'l*, pg. 2495
LADYBIRD BOOKS LTD.—See Bertelsmann SE & Co. KGaA; *Int'l*, pg. 991
LEARNING TRENDS, LLC; *U.S. Private*, pg. 2408
LECKIE & LECKIE LIMITED—See News Corporation; *U.S. Public*, pg. 1519
LEGACY PUBLICATIONS INC.—See Pace Communications Inc.; *U.S. Private*, pg. 3063
LITERARY CLASSICS OF THE UNITED STATES, INC.; *U.S. Private*, pg. 2467
LIVERIGHT PUBLISHING CORP.—See W.W. Norton & Company, Inc.; *U.S. Private*, pg. 4423
LLEWELLYN WORLDWIDE LIMITED; *U.S. Private*, pg. 2475
LONELY PLANET PUBLICATIONS LIMITED—See NC2 Media, LLC; *U.S. Private*, pg. 2875
LONELY PLANET PUBLICATIONS PTY. LIMITED—See NC2 Media, LLC; *U.S. Private*, pg. 2875
LRP PUBLICATIONS - PENNSYLVANIA—See LRP Publications Inc.; *U.S. Private*, pg. 2508
MACH 2 LIBRI S.P.A.—See Fininvest S.p.A.; *Int'l*, pg. 2675
MACMILLAN REFERENCE USA—See Apax Partners LLP; *Int'l*, pg. 503
MACMILLAN REFERENCE USA—See Apollo Global Management, Inc.; *U.S. Public*, pg. 168
MACMILLAN REFERENCE USA—See KKR & Co. Inc.; *U.S. Public*, pg. 1256
MACMILLAN REFERENCE USA—See Searchlight Capital Partners, L.P.; *U.S. Private*, pg. 3587
MAITLAND PRIMROSE GROUP; *U.S. Private*, pg. 2554
MARKET SELF S.A.—See Bertelsmann SE & Co. KGaA; *Int'l*, pg. 993
MARLIN COMPANY; *U.S. Private*, pg. 2583
MARSILIO EDITORI S.P.A.—See GEM S.r.l.; *Int'l*, pg. 2915
MARUZEN KYOEI PRINCE—See Dai Nippon Printing Co., Ltd.; *Int'l*, pg. 1915
MARUZEN PUBLISHING CO., LTD.—See Dai Nippon Printing Co., Ltd.; *Int'l*, pg. 1916
MARUZEN-YUSHODO COMPANY, LIMITED—See Dai Nippon Printing Co., Ltd.; *Int'l*, pg. 1915
MARVEL ENTERTAINMENT, LLC—See The Walt Disney Company; *U.S. Public*, pg. 2139
MARVEL WORLDWIDE, INC.—See The Walt Disney Company; *U.S. Public*, pg. 2139
MCFARLAND & COMPANY, INC.; *U.S. Private*, pg. 2633
MCGRAW-HILL AUSTRALIA PTY LTD—See S&P Global Inc.; *U.S. Public*, pg. 1830
MCGRAW-HILL BOOK PUBLISHING COMPANY—See S&P Global Inc.; *U.S. Public*, pg. 1830
THE MCGRAW-HILL COMPANIES, S.R.L.—See S&P Global Inc.; *U.S. Public*, pg. 1832
MCGRAW-HILL EDUCATION INDIA PRIVATE LIMITED—See Platinum Equity, LLC; *U.S. Private*, pg. 3205
MCGRAW-HILL (GERMANY) GMBH—See S&P Global Inc.; *U.S. Public*, pg. 1830
MCGRAW-HILL HIGHER EDUCATION—See Platinum Equity, LLC; *U.S. Private*, pg. 3205
MCGRAW-HILL/INTERAMERICANA DE CHILE LIMITADA—See S&P Global Inc.; *U.S. Public*, pg. 1831
MCGRAW-HILL INTERAMERICANA DO BRASIL LTDA.—See S&P Global Inc.; *U.S. Public*, pg. 1830
MCGRAW-HILL/INTERAMERICANA, S.A.—See S&P Global Inc.; *U.S. Public*, pg. 1831
MCGRAW-HILL INTERNATIONAL (U.K.) LIMITED—See S&P Global Inc.; *U.S. Public*, pg. 1830
MCGRAW-HILL KOREA, INC.—See S&P Global Inc.; *U.S. Public*, pg. 1830
MCGRAW-HILL PROFESSIONAL—See S&P Global Inc.; *U.S. Public*, pg. 1830
MCGRAW-HILL RYERSON LIMITED—See Platinum Equity, LLC; *U.S. Private*, pg. 3206
MCGRAW-HILL—See Platinum Equity, LLC; *U.S. Private*, pg. 3205
MEDIA SOURCE, INC.; *U.S. Private*, pg. 2652
MERRIAM-WEBSTER, INC.—See Encyclopaedia Britannica, Inc.; *U.S. Private*, pg. 1391
MOBILEBOOK.JP, INC.—See Dai Nippon Printing Co., Ltd.; *Int'l*, pg. 1916
MODERN PUBLISHING, INC.—See Kappa Publishing Group, Inc.; *U.S. Private*, pg. 2262
MONDADORI ELECTA S.P.A.—See Fininvest S.p.A.; *Int'l*, pg. 2675

MONDADORI FRANCHISING S.P.A.—See Fininvest S.p.A.; *Int'l*, pg. 2675
MONDOLIBRI S.P.A.—See Bertelsmann SE & Co. KGaA; *Int'l*, pg. 992
MONDOLIBRI S.P.A.—See Fininvest S.p.A.; *Int'l*, pg. 2675
MONDO PUBLISHING, INC.—See CIP Capital Fund, L.P.; *U.S. Private*, pg. 899
MOVIE FACTS INC.; *U.S. Private*, pg. 2802
NAICS ASSOCIATION, LLC; *U.S. Private*, pg. 2831
NAKLADATELSTVI DR. JOSEF RAABE, S.R.O.—See Ernst Klett AG; *Int'l*, pg. 2495
NATIONAL GEOGRAPHIC BOOKS GROUP—See National Geographic Society; *U.S. Private*, pg. 2855
NATIONAL PUBLISHING COMPANY—See Atlas Holdings, LLC; *U.S. Private*, pg. 377
NAZARENE PUBLISHING HOUSE; *U.S. Private*, pg. 2874
NCH ROMANIA PRODUSE DE INTRETINERE SRL—See NCH Corporation; *U.S. Private*, pg. 2876
NELSON EDUCATION LTD.—See Apax Partners LLP; *Int'l*, pg. 503
NELSON EDUCATION LTD.—See Apollo Global Management, Inc.; *U.S. Public*, pg. 168
NELSON EDUCATION LTD.—See KKR & Co. Inc.; *U.S. Public*, pg. 1256
NELSON EDUCATION LTD.—See Searchlight Capital Partners, L.P.; *U.S. Private*, pg. 3587
NEMZETI TANKONYVKIADO ZRT—See DPG Media Group NV; *Int'l*, pg. 2188
NETWORLD ALLIANCE, LLC; *U.S. Private*, pg. 2889
NEUMANN PRESS—See Saint Benedict Press; *U.S. Private*, pg. 3529
OAKSTONE PUBLISHING, LLC—See Ebix Inc.; *U.S. Public*, pg. 710
OBV OSTERREICHISCHER BUNDESVERLAG SCHULBUCH GMBH & CO. KG—See Ernst Klett AG; *Int'l*, pg. 2495
OFFSET PAPERBACK MFRS., INC. (BPMC)—See Bertelsmann SE & Co. KGaA; *Int'l*, pg. 990
OFUP—See ADLPartner SA; *Int'l*, pg. 151
OMNIGRAPHICS, INC.—See Centre Lane Partners, LLC; *U.S. Private*, pg. 827
ON-DEMAND PUBLISHING, LLC—See Amazon.com, Inc.; *U.S. Public*, pg. 91
ONE UP ENTERPRISES INC.—See Family Federation for World Peace & Unification; *U.S. Private*, pg. 1469
OPTIMUS PROFESSIONAL PUBLISHING LIMITED—See Electric Word Plc; *Int'l*, pg. 2349
ORCHARD BOOKS, INC.—See Scholastic Corporation; *U.S. Public*, pg. 1847
O'REILLY CHINA—See O'Reilly Media, Inc.; *U.S. Private*, pg. 2980
O'REILLY JAPAN—See O'Reilly Media, Inc.; *U.S. Private*, pg. 2980
O'REILLY MEDIA, INC.; *U.S. Private*, pg. 2980
O'REILLY UK—See O'Reilly Media, Inc.; *U.S. Private*, pg. 2980
O'REILLY VERLAG—See O'Reilly Media, Inc.; *U.S. Private*, pg. 2980
OSBORNE BOOKS LIMITED—See Graham Holdings Company; *U.S. Public*, pg. 956
OSPREY PUBLISHING LIMITED—See Bloomsbury Publishing Plc; *Int'l*, pg. 1065
OUTSKIRTS PRESS INC.; *U.S. Private*, pg. 3052
PARRAGON BOOKS LTD—See D.C. Thomson & Co. Ltd.; *Int'l*, pg. 1900
PAVILION BOOKS COMPANY LIMITED—See News Corporation; *U.S. Public*, pg. 1521
PAXEN LEARNING CORPORATION; *U.S. Private*, pg. 3115
PENGUIN AUSTRALIA PTY LTD—See Bertelsmann SE & Co. KGaA; *Int'l*, pg. 991
PENGUIN BOOKS BENELUX BV—See Bertelsmann SE & Co. KGaA; *Int'l*, pg. 991
PENGUIN BOOKS DEUTSCHLAND GMBH—See Bertelsmann SE & Co. KGaA; *Int'l*, pg. 991
PENGUIN BOOKS LTD—See Bertelsmann SE & Co. KGaA; *Int'l*, pg. 991
PENGUIN GROUP UK—See Bertelsmann SE & Co. KGaA; *Int'l*, pg. 991
PENGUIN GROUP (USA) INC.—See Bertelsmann SE & Co. KGaA; *Int'l*, pg. 991
PENGUIN IRELAND—See Bertelsmann SE & Co. KGaA; *Int'l*, pg. 991
PENGUIN RANDOM HOUSE GRUPO EDITORIAL S.A.—See Bertelsmann SE & Co. KGaA; *Int'l*, pg. 993
PENGUIN RANDOM HOUSE GRUPO EDITORIAL—See Bertelsmann SE & Co. KGaA; *Int'l*, pg. 991
PENGUIN RANDOM HOUSE LLC - CANADA—See Bertelsmann SE & Co. KGaA; *Int'l*, pg. 991
PENGUIN RANDOM HOUSE LLC—See Bertelsmann SE & Co. KGaA; *Int'l*, pg. 990
PENGUIN RANDOM HOUSE SOUTH AFRICA (PTY) LTD.—See Bertelsmann SE & Co. KGaA; *Int'l*, pg. 993
PENGUIN RANDOM HOUSE VERLAGSGRUPPE GMBH—See Bertelsmann SE & Co. KGaA; *Int'l*, pg. 993
PERFECTION LEARNING CORPORATION; *U.S. Private*, pg. 3148
PERSEUS BOOKS, INC.—See Perseus Books, LLC; *U.S. Private*, pg. 3155

PETER COLLIN PUBLISHING LIMITED—See Bloomsbury Publishing Plc; *Int'l*, pg. 1065
PETERSON'S NELNET, LLC—See Nelnet, Inc.; *U.S. Public*, pg. 1504
PHOENIX LEARNING RESOURCES—See The Phoenix Learning Group, Inc.; *U.S. Private*, pg. 4095
PLANDIT CO., LTD.—See EQT AB; *Int'l*, pg. 2467
POWER LEISURE BOOKMAKERS LTD.—See Flutter Entertainment plc; *Int'l*, pg. 2715
PRACTICE MANAGEMENT INFORMATION CORPORATION; *U.S. Private*, pg. 3241
PRESBYTERIAN PUBLISHING CORPORATION; *U.S. Private*, pg. 3253
PRESTEL PUBLISHING LIMITED—See Bertelsmann SE & Co. KGaA; *Int'l*, pg. 993
PRIMA GAMES—See Asteri Holdings; *U.S. Private*, pg. 360
PROFF AS—See Enento Group Plc; *Int'l*, pg. 2415
PROGRESSIVE BUSINESS PUBLICATIONS; *U.S. Private*, pg. 3278
PSC PRINT SERVICE CENTER GMBH—See Bertelsmann SE & Co. KGaA; *Int'l*, pg. 995
P.T. DAI NIPPON PRINTING INDONESIA—See Dai Nippon Printing Co., Ltd.; *Int'l*, pg. 1916
PUBLICATIONS INTERNATIONAL, LTD.; *U.S. Private*, pg. 3300
PUBLIC UTILITIES REPORTS, INC.; *U.S. Private*, pg. 3300
PUZZLER MEDIA LIMITED—See D.C. Thomson & Co. Ltd.; *Int'l*, pg. 1900
RAABE BULGARIEN EOOD—See Ernst Klett AG; *Int'l*, pg. 2495
RAABE TANACSADO ES KIADO KFT.—See Ernst Klett AG; *Int'l*, pg. 2495
RANDOM HOUSE ADULT TRADE GROUP—See Bertelsmann SE & Co. KGaA; *Int'l*, pg. 991
RANDOM HOUSE CHILDREN'S BOOKS—See Bertelsmann SE & Co. KGaA; *Int'l*, pg. 991
RANDOM HOUSE LLC—See Bertelsmann SE & Co. KGaA; *Int'l*, pg. 990
RANDOM HOUSE TRADE PUBLISHING GROUP—See Bertelsmann SE & Co. KGaA; *Int'l*, pg. 991
REEDS NAUTICAL ALMANAC—See Bloomsbury Publishing Plc; *Int'l*, pg. 1065
REGNERY PUBLISHING, INC.—See Skyhorse Publishing Co., Inc.; *U.S. Private*, pg. 3684
RESEARCH & EDUCATION ASSOCIATION, INC.—See Atlas Holdings, LLC; *U.S. Private*, pg. 377
THE RIVERSIDE PUBLISHING CO.—See Veritas Capital Fund Management, LLC; *U.S. Private*, pg. 4363
RIVERSIDE WORLD PUBLISHING, INC.; *U.S. Private*, pg. 3446
ROWMAN & LITTLEFIELD PUBLISHERS, INC.—See The Rowman & Littlefield Publishing Group, Inc.; *U.S. Private*, pg. 4112
R. PIPER & CO VERLAG GMBH—See Bonnier AB; *Int'l*, pg. 1108
R.R. BOWKER LLC—See Cambridge Information Group, Inc.; *U.S. Private*, pg. 727
R.R. DONNELLEY & SONS CO.—See Chatham Asset Management, LLC; *U.S. Private*, pg. 865
SAFARI BOOKS ONLINE, LLC—See O'Reilly Media, Inc.; *U.S. Private*, pg. 2980
SAINT BENEDICT PRESS; *U.S. Private*, pg. 3529
SAMUEL FRENCH INC.—See Massachusetts Mutual Life Insurance Company; *U.S. Private*, pg. 2605
SANOMA PRO OY—See Bonnier AB; *Int'l*, pg. 1108
SARAL PUBLICATIONS, INC.—See Grupo Televisa, S.A.B.; *Int'l*, pg. 3136
SASQUATCH BOOKS LLC—See Bertelsmann SE & Co. KGaA; *Int'l*, pg. 996
SCARECROW PRESS, INC.—See The Rowman & Littlefield Publishing Group, Inc.; *U.S. Private*, pg. 4112
SCHOCKEN BOOKS—See Bertelsmann SE & Co. KGaA; *Int'l*, pg. 991
SCHOLASTIC AUSTRALIA PTY. LTD.—See Scholastic Corporation; *U.S. Public*, pg. 1847
SCHOLASTIC BOOKFAIRS CANADA LTD.—See Scholastic Corporation; *U.S. Public*, pg. 1847
SCHOLASTIC CANADA LTD.—See Scholastic Corporation; *U.S. Public*, pg. 1847
SCHOLASTIC HONG KONG LIMITED—See Scholastic Corporation; *U.S. Public*, pg. 1847
SCHOLASTIC LIBRARY PUBLISHING INC.—See Scholastic Corporation; *U.S. Public*, pg. 1847
SCHOLASTIC LIMITED—See Scholastic Corporation; *U.S. Public*, pg. 1848
SCHOLASTIC NEW ZEALAND LTD.—See Scholastic Corporation; *U.S. Public*, pg. 1847
THE SCHOLASTIC STORE, INC.—See Scholastic Corporation; *U.S. Public*, pg. 1848
SCHOLASTIC UK LIMITED—See Scholastic Corporation; *U.S. Public*, pg. 1847
SCHROEDER PUBLISHING COMPANY - COLLECTOR BOOKS—See Schroeder Publishing Company; *U.S. Private*, pg. 3569
SCHROEDER PUBLISHING COMPANY; *U.S. Private*, pg. 3569
SDI INNOVATIONS, INC.; *U.S. Private*, pg. 3581

4207

513130 — BOOK PUBLISHERS

SDU UITGEVERS B.V.—See Editions Lefebvre Sarrut SA; *Int'l*, pg. 2311
SEEDLING PUBLICATIONS—See Continental Press Inc.; *U.S. Private*, pg. 1030
SHAMBHALA PUBLICATIONS INC.; *U.S. Private*, pg. 3623
SHANGHAI DONNELLEY PREMEDIA TECHNOLOGY CO., LTD.—See Chatham Asset Management, LLC; *U.S. Private*, pg. 865
SHUFUNOTOMO INFOS CO., LTD.—See Imagica Group Inc.; *Int'l*, pg. 3619
SIMON & SCHUSTER CHILDREN'S PUBLISHING—See KKR & Co. Inc.; *U.S. Public*, pg. 1264
SIMON & SCHUSTER, INC.—See KKR & Co. Inc.; *U.S. Public*, pg. 1263
SIMON & SCHUSTER (UK) LIMITED—See National Amusements, Inc.; *U.S. Public*, pg. 1243
SKIRA EDITORE S.P.A.—See Chargeurs SA; *Int'l*, pg. 1450
SKYHORSE PUBLISHING CO., INC.; *U.S. Private*, pg. 3684
SOFT SKULL PRESS—See Black Balloon Publishing, LLC; *U.S. Private*, pg. 569
SOMOS EDUCACAO S.A.—See Cogna Educacao S.A.; *Int'l*, pg. 1695
SOUTH-WESTERN CENGAGE LEARNING—See Apax Partners LLP; *Int'l*, pg. 503
SOUTH-WESTERN CENGAGE LEARNING—See Apollo Global Management, Inc.; *U.S. Public*, pg. 168
SOUTH-WESTERN CENGAGE LEARNING—See KKR & Co. Inc.; *U.S. Public*, pg. 1256
SOUTH-WESTERN CENGAGE LEARNING—See Searchlight Capital Partners, L.P.; *U.S. Private*, pg. 3587
SPARKHOUSE—See Augsburg Fortress; *U.S. Private*, pg. 392
SPERLING & KUPFER EDITORI S.P.A.—See Fininvest S.p.A.; *Int'l*, pg. 2675
SPRINGER PUBLISHING COMPANY, LLC—See Mannheim, LLC; *U.S. Private*, pg. 2565
SRA/MCGRAW HILL—See Platinum Equity, LLC; *U.S. Private*, pg. 3206
STANDARD & POOR'S (AUSTRALIA) PTY LTD.—See S&P Global Inc.; *U.S. Public*, pg. 1831
STANDARD & POOR'S CREDIT MARKET SERVICES ITALY S.R.L.—See S&P Global Inc.; *U.S. Public*, pg. 1831
STANDARD PUBLISHING GROUP LLC—See The Wicks Group of Companies, LLC; *U.S. Private*, pg. 4136
THE STATIONERY OFFICE ENTERPRISES LIMITED—See Deutsche Post AG; *Int'l*, pg. 2082
THE STATIONERY OFFICE LIMITED—See Advent International Corporation; *U.S. Private*, pg. 107
THE STAYWELL COMPANY, LLC—See KKR & Co. Inc.; *U.S. Public*, pg. 1254
STENHOUSE PUBLISHERS—See Highlights for Children, Inc.; *U.S. Private*, pg. 1940
STERLING PUBLISHING CO., INC.—See Elliott Management Corporation; *U.S. Private*, pg. 1365
SUNDANCE PUBLISHING—See Carolrhoda Books, Inc.; *U.S. Private*, pg. 769
SYRACUSE UNIVERSITY PRESS; *U.S. Private*, pg. 3905
TAIWAN RATINGS CORPORATION—See S&P Global Inc.; *U.S. Public*, pg. 1832
TAN BOOKS & PUBLISHERS—See Saint Benedict Press; *U.S. Private*, pg. 3529
TAXBRIEFS LIMITED—See Centaur Media plc; *Int'l*, pg. 1402
TAYLOR PUBLISHING CO.—See Fenway Partners, LLC; *U.S. Private*, pg. 1495
TEKNO BOOKS—See NovelStem International Corp.; *U.S. Public*, pg. 1549
TELEFONKATALOGENS GULE SIDER AS—See Eniro Group AB; *Int'l*, pg. 2439
TFH PUBLICATIONS, INC.—See Central Garden & Pet Company; *U.S. Public*, pg. 473
THIENEMANN VERLAG GMBH—See Bonnier AB; *Int'l*, pg. 1108
THOMAS ENDUSTRIYEL MEDYA YAYINCILIK VE PAZ. LTD.—See Thomas Publishing Company LLC; *U.S. Private*, pg. 4157
THOMAS INDUSTRIAL MEDIA SARL—See Thomas Publishing Company LLC; *U.S. Private*, pg. 4157
THOMAS INDUSTRIAL MEDIA SRL—See Thomas Publishing Company LLC; *U.S. Private*, pg. 4157
THOMAS INTERNATIONAL PUBLISHING COMPANY, INC.—See Thomas Publishing Company LLC; *U.S. Private*, pg. 4157
THOMAS NELSON, INC.—See Charlesbank Capital Partners, LLC; *U.S. Private*, pg. 854
THOMSON-SHORE, INC.—See CJK Group, Inc.; *U.S. Private*, pg. 909
TIEN WAH PRESS (PTE.) LTD.—See Dai Nippon Printing Co., Ltd.; *Int'l*, pg. 1916
TINTA FRESCA EDICIONES S.A.—See Grupo Clarin S.A.; *Int'l*, pg. 3125
TSO HOLDINGS A LIMITED—See Deutsche Post AG; *Int'l*, pg. 2082
TSO HOLDINGS B LIMITED—See Deutsche Post AG; *Int'l*, pg. 2082
TUNDRA BOOKS INC.—See Bertelsmann SE & Co. KGaA; *Int'l*, pg. 991

TYNDALE HOUSE PUBLISHERS, INC.; *U.S. Private*, pg. 4268
UCG INFORMATION SERVICES LLC—See United Communications Group; *U.S. Private*, pg. 4289
UITGEVERIJ VAN IN N.V.—See DPG Media Group NV; *Int'l*, pg. 2188
ULLSTEIN BUCHVERLAGE GMBH—See Bonnier AB; *Int'l*, pg. 1108
UNITED EDUCATORS INC.; *U.S. Private*, pg. 4291
UNITED METHODIST PUBLISHING HOUSE; *U.S. Private*, pg. 4294
UNIVERSITY PRESS OF AMERICA, INC.—See The Rowman & Littlefield Publishing Group, Inc.; *U.S. Private*, pg. 4112
U.S. NAVAL INSTITUTE; *U.S. Private*, pg. 4271
VANTAGE PRESS, INC.; *U.S. Private*, pg. 4345
VAULT.COM, INC.—See Veronis Suhler Stevenson Partners LLC; *U.S. Private*, pg. 4368
VERLAGSGRUPPE HARPERCOLLINS DEUTSCHLAND GMBH—See News Corporation; *U.S. Public*, pg. 1521
VICTOR GRAPHICS INC.; *U.S. Private*, pg. 4377
VIRGINIA BUSINESS MAGAZINE—See Lee Enterprises, Incorporated; *U.S. Public*, pg. 1299
WADSWORTH CENGAGE LEARNING—See Apax Partners LLP; *Int'l*, pg. 503
WADSWORTH CENGAGE LEARNING—See Apollo Global Management, Inc.; *U.S. Public*, pg. 168
WADSWORTH CENGAGE LEARNING—See KKR & Co. Inc.; *U.S. Public*, pg. 1256
WADSWORTH CENGAGE LEARNING—See Searchlight Capital Partners, L.P.; *U.S. Private*, pg. 3587
WARNER PRESS, INC.; *U.S. Private*, pg. 4442
WELBERT PINKUS; *U.S. Private*, pg. 4473
WELDON OWEN, INC.—See Insight Editions, LP; *U.S. Private*, pg. 2085
WELDON OWEN PUBLISHING, INC.—See Bonnier AB; *Int'l*, pg. 1109
WELLESLEY INFORMATION SERVICES, LLC—See United Communications Group; *U.S. Private*, pg. 4289
WERNER SODERSTROM OSAKEYHTION—See Bonnier AB; *Int'l*, pg. 1108
WESTCHESTER PUBLISHING SERVICES, LLC; *U.S. Private*, pg. 4489
WHITE HOUSE HISTORICAL ASSOCIATION; *U.S. Private*, pg. 4509
WILDSTORM PRODUCTIONS—See Warner Bros. Discovery, Inc.; *U.S. Public*, pg. 2328
WILEY BLACKWELL PUBLISHING LTD.—See John Wiley & Sons, Inc.; *U.S. Public*, pg. 1193
WILEY BLACKWELL PUBLISHING—See John Wiley & Sons, Inc.; *U.S. Public*, pg. 1193
WILEY EUROPE LIMITED—See John Wiley & Sons, Inc.; *U.S. Public*, pg. 1193
WILEY HIGHER EDUCATION PUBLISHING—See John Wiley & Sons, Inc.; *U.S. Public*, pg. 1193
WILEY INDIA PRIVATE LTD.—See John Wiley & Sons, Inc.; *U.S. Public*, pg. 1193
WILEY JAPAN KK—See John Wiley & Sons, Inc.; *U.S. Public*, pg. 1193
WILEY PROFESSIONAL/TRADE PUBLISHING—See John Wiley & Sons, Inc.; *U.S. Public*, pg. 1193
WILEY PUBLISHING AUSTRALIA PTY LTD.—See John Wiley & Sons, Inc.; *U.S. Public*, pg. 1193
WILEY PUBLISHING, INC.—See John Wiley & Sons, Inc.; *U.S. Public*, pg. 1193
WILEY PUBLISHING JAPAN KK—See John Wiley & Sons, Inc.; *U.S. Public*, pg. 1193
WILEY PUBLISHING SERVICES, INC.—See John Wiley & Sons, Inc.; *U.S. Public*, pg. 1193
WILEY SCIENTIFIC, TECHNICAL & MEDICAL PUBLISHING—See John Wiley & Sons, Inc.; *U.S. Public*, pg. 1193
WILEY-VCH VERLAG GMBH & CO. KGAA—See John Wiley & Sons, Inc.; *U.S. Public*, pg. 1193
WILEY-VHCA AG—See John Wiley & Sons, Inc.; *U.S. Public*, pg. 1193
WILHELM ERNST & SOHN GMBH & CO. KG—See John Wiley & Sons, Inc.; *U.S. Public*, pg. 1193
WILHELM GOLDMANN VERLAG GMBH—See Bertelsmann SE & Co. KGaA; *Int'l*, pg. 996
WILLIAM H. SADLIER, INC.; *U.S. Public*, pg. 2371
WILLIAM S. HEIN & CO., INC.; *U.S. Private*, pg. 4525
WORLD ALMANAC EDUCATION GROUP, INC.—See Centre Lane Partners, LLC; *U.S. Private*, pg. 827
WORLD BOOK/SCOTT FETZER COMPANY, INC.—See Berkshire Hathaway Inc.; *U.S. Public*, pg. 300
WORLD JOINT CORP.; *U.S. Private*, pg. 4566
THE WRIGHT GROUP; *U.S. Private*, pg. 4139
W.W. NORTON & COMPANY, INC. - COUNTRYMAN PRESS DIVISION—See W.W. Norton & Company, Inc.; *U.S. Private*, pg. 4423
W.W. NORTON & COMPANY, INC.; *U.S. Private*, pg. 4423
W.W. NORTON & COMPANY, INC.—See W.W. Norton & Company, Inc.; *U.S. Private*, pg. 4423
WYDAWNICTWA SZKOLNE I PEDAGOGICZNE SA—See Central Group; *Int'l*, pg. 1407
WYDAWNICTWO LEKTORKLETT SP. Z O.O.—See Ernst Klett AG; *Int'l*, pg. 2495

YUSHODO (KYOTO) CO., LTD.—See Dai Nippon Printing Co., Ltd.; *Int'l*, pg. 1916
ZALOZBA ROKUS KLETT, D.O.O.—See Ernst Klett AG; *Int'l*, pg. 2495
THE ZONDERVAN CORPORATION—See Charlesbank Capital Partners, LLC; *U.S. Private*, pg. 854

513140 — DIRECTORY AND MAILING LIST PUBLISHERS

2GM CORPORATION; *U.S. Private*, pg. 6
ALLRECIPES.COM, INC.—See Meredith Corporation; *U.S. Public*, pg. 1422
AMERICAN REGISTRY FOR INTERNET NUMBERS, LTD.; *U.S. Private*, pg. 245
ANCESTRY.COM EUROPE S.A R.L.—See Blackstone Inc.; *U.S. Public*, pg. 348
APN SPECIALIST PUBLICATIONS NZ LIMITED—See ARN Media Limited; *Int'l*, pg. 576
ARTSONIA, LLC; *U.S. Private*, pg. 344
ASSOCIATED PUBLISHING COMPANY—See The Hearst Corporation; *U.S. Private*, pg. 4047
AUSTRALIAN LOCAL SEARCH PTY. LTD.—See Thryv Holdings, Inc.; *U.S. Public*, pg. 2157
AVID DATING LIFE INC.—See Avid Life Media Inc.; *Int'l*, pg. 743
AVVO, INC.—See KKR & Co. Inc.; *U.S. Public*, pg. 1253
AXESA SERVICIOS DE INFORMACION, S. EN C.—See Caribe Media, Inc.; *U.S. Private*, pg. 761
BEEKMAN MUSIC, INC.—See Theodore Presser Co.; *U.S. Private*, pg. 4141
BREAD FINANCIAL HOLDINGS INC.; *U.S. Public*, pg. 380
BTG INTERNATIONAL INC.—See Boston Scientific Corporation; *U.S. Public*, pg. 373
BUREAU VAN DIJK ELECTRONIC PUBLISHING BV—See Moody's Corporation; *U.S. Public*, pg. 1467
BUSINESS MONITOR INTERNATIONAL LTD.—See The Hearst Corporation; *U.S. Private*, pg. 4044
CANADIAN ART PRINTS, INC.—See Encore Art Group; *Int'l*, pg. 2402
CAPTERRA, INC.—See Gartner, Inc.; *U.S. Public*, pg. 906
CATCH—See Catalyst Investment Managers Pty. Limited; *Int'l*, pg. 1358
CAVEGUIAS—See Compania Anonima Nacional Telefonos de Venezuela; *Int'l*, pg. 1748
CELLINK BIOPRINTING AB—See BICO Group AB; *Int'l*, pg. 1019
CELLINK KK—See BICO Group AB; *Int'l*, pg. 1019
CHAMBERS & PARTNERS MEDIA LTD.—See ABRY Partners, LLC; *U.S. Private*, pg. 41
CITIZEN INFOLINE LIMITED; *Int'l*, pg. 1623
COLE INFORMATION SERVICES, INC.—See 424 Capital, LLC; *U.S. Private*, pg. 15
COLE INFORMATION SERVICES, INC.—See Eagle Private Capital, LLC; *U.S. Private*, pg. 1310
COLE INFORMATION SERVICES, INC.—See Resolute Administration, Inc.; *U.S. Private*, pg. 3406
COMPORIUM PUBLISHING—See Comporium Group; *U.S. Private*, pg. 1002
COOKPAD INC.; *Int'l*, pg. 1788
CORELOGIC NATIONAL BACKGROUND DATA, LLC—See Insight Venture Management, LLC; *U.S. Private*, pg. 2088
CORELOGIC NATIONAL BACKGROUND DATA, LLC—See Stone Point Capital LLC; *U.S. Private*, pg. 3822
COUGAR LIFE INC.—See Avid Life Media Inc.; *Int'l*, pg. 743
CVM SOLUTIONS, LLC—See Supplier.io, Inc.; *U.S. Private*, pg. 3882
DEX MEDIA - DENVER—See Thryv Holdings, Inc.; *U.S. Public*, pg. 2157
DEX MEDIA, INC. - EVERETT—See Thryv Holdings, Inc.; *U.S. Public*, pg. 2157
DEX MEDIA, INC. - FORT WAYNE—See Thryv Holdings, Inc.; *U.S. Public*, pg. 2157
DIN DEL AB—See Eniro Group AB; *Int'l*, pg. 2439
DIP CORPORATION; *Int'l*, pg. 2128
DOCTORDIRECTORY.COM, LLC—See Ziff Davis, Inc.; *U.S. Public*, pg. 2404
DUN & BRADSTREET (AUSTRALIA) PTY. LTD.—See Archer Capital Pty. Ltd.; *Int'l*, pg. 547
DUN & BRADSTREET (NEW ZEALAND) LTD.—See Archer Capital Pty. Ltd.; *Int'l*, pg. 547
EASYCALL COMMUNICATIONS PHILIPPINES, INC.; *Int'l*, pg. 2276
EDMUNDS, INC.; *U.S. Private*, pg. 1338
ELKAN-VOGEL INC.—See Theodore Presser Co.; *U.S. Private*, pg. 4141
ELTA - EMPRESA DE LISTAS TELEFONICAS DE ANGOLA—See Altice Europe N.V.; *Int'l*, pg. 393
ENGINEERING.COM INCORPORATED; *Int'l*, pg. 2435
ENIRO DANMARK A/S—See Eniro Group AB; *Int'l*, pg. 2439
ENIRO GROUP AB; *Int'l*, pg. 2439
ENIRO GULA SIDORNA AB—See Eniro Group AB; *Int'l*, pg. 2439
ENIRO SENTRAALI OY—See Eniro Group AB; *Int'l*, pg. 2439
ENTREPARTICULIERS.COM SA; *Int'l*, pg. 2453

N.A.I.C.S. INDEX

513199 — ALL OTHER PUBLISHER...

EUROPEAN DIRECTORIES S.A.; *Int'l*, pg. 2556
FAULKNER INFORMATION SERVICES—See Information Today Inc.; *U.S. Private*, pg. 2073
FIJI DIRECTORIES LIMITED—See Fiji National Provident Fund; *Int'l*, pg. 2661
FIRST DATABANK EUROPE LTD.—See The Hearst Corporation; *U.S. Private*, pg. 4045
FIRST DATABANK, INC.—See The Hearst Corporation; *U.S. Private*, pg. 4044
FIRST DATABANK—See The Hearst Corporation; *U.S. Private*, pg. 4045
FOUNDATION CENTER; *U.S. Private*, pg. 1579
FREELANCE.COM SA; *Int'l*, pg. 2770
GALE GROUP INC.—See Apax Partners LLP; *Int'l*, pg. 503
GALE GROUP INC.—See Apollo Global Management, Inc.; *U.S. Public*, pg. 168
GALE GROUP INC.—See KKR & Co. Inc.; *U.S. Public*, pg. 1256
GALE GROUP INC.—See Searchlight Capital Partners, L.P.; *U.S. Private*, pg. 3587
GFK MEDIAMARK RESEARCH & INTELLIGENCE, LLC—See Advent International Corporation; *U.S. Private*, pg. 105
GLOBAL AI, INC.; *U.S. Public*, pg. 940
GOCOMPARE.COM LIMITED—See Future plc; *Int'l*, pg. 2857
GOUDEN GIDS B.V.—See Apax Partners LLP; *Int'l*, pg. 507
GOUDEN GIDS B.V.—See Cinven Limited; *Int'l*, pg. 1615
GUIDESTAR USA, INC.; *U.S. Private*, pg. 1813
HAGADONE DIRECTORIES INC.—See The Hagadone Corporation; *U.S. Private*, pg. 4041
HAINES & COMPANY, INC.; *U.S. Private*, pg. 1840
HANSON DIRECTORY SERVICE, INC.—See DirecTech LLC; *U.S. Private*, pg. 1236
HARRIS CONNECT, LLC; *U.S. Private*, pg. 1869
HIBU INC.—See H.I.G. Capital, LLC; *U.S. Private*, pg. 1834
HIBU (UK) LIMITED—See hibu Group 2013 Limited; *Int'l*, pg. 3383
HOMEPAGES, LLC—See BV Investment Partners, LLC; *U.S. Private*, pg. 699
HOPPENSTEDT FIRMENINFORMATIONEN GMBH; *Int'l*, pg. 3473
IFAP SERVICE-INSTITUT FUR ARZTE UND APOTHEKER GMBH—See CompuGroup Medical SE & Co. KGaA; *Int'l*, pg. 1757
INCOM CO., LTD.—See Thomas Publishing Company LLC; *U.S. Private*, pg. 4157
INFOCANADA CORP.—See CCMP Capital Advisors, LP; *U.S. Private*, pg. 800
INFOCORE, INC.; *U.S. Private*, pg. 2072
INFOGROUP TARGETING SOLUTIONS—See CCMP Capital Advisors, LP; *U.S. Private*, pg. 800
INTERNATIONAL EXHIBITIONS, INC.; *U.S. Private*, pg. 2116
IPROPERTY GROUP LIMITED—See News Corporation; *U.S. Public*, pg. 1521
ISTOCKPHOTO LP—See CC Capital Partners, LLC; *U.S. Private*, pg. 797
JOHN CHURCH CO.—See Theodore Presser Co.; *U.S. Private*, pg. 4141
KHERA COMMUNICATIONS INC.; *U.S. Private*, pg. 2301
KNOVEL CORPORATION; *U.S. Private*, pg. 2323
KOMPASS INTERNATIONAL NEUENSCHWANDER SA—See Axon Active AG; *Int'l*, pg. 770
KOTIKOKKI.NET OY—See Alma Media Corporation; *Int'l*, pg. 362
LEAFBUYER TECHNOLOGIES, INC.; *U.S. Public*, pg. 1296
LEGACY PUBLISHING COMPANY; *U.S. Private*, pg. 2416
LETA INFORMATION ENIRO AB—See Eniro Group AB; *Int'l*, pg. 2439
LIST SOLUTIONS, INC.; *U.S. Private*, pg. 2466
LIVE VENTURES INCORPORATED; *U.S. Public*, pg. 1332
LIVINGSOCIAL, LLC—See Groupon Inc.; *U.S. Public*, pg. 972
MAILERMAILER, LLC—See Khera Communications Inc.; *U.S. Private*, pg. 2301
MANTA MEDIA, INC.; *U.S. Private*, pg. 2567
MANUFACTURERS' NEWS, INC.; *U.S. Private*, pg. 2567
MARKETFISH INC.; *U.S. Private*, pg. 2579
MARTINDALE, LLC—See KKR & Co. Inc.; *U.S. Public*, pg. 1253
MCMILLION RESEARCH; *U.S. Private*, pg. 2642
MECALUX SA—See Acerolux SL; *Int'l*, pg. 102
METAL BULLETIN JAPAN—See Astorg Partners S.A.S.; *Int'l*, pg. 656
METAL BULLETIN JAPAN—See Epiris Managers LLP; *Int'l*, pg. 2461
METAL BULLETIN LIMITED—See Astorg Partners S.A.S.; *Int'l*, pg. 656
METAL BULLETIN LIMITED—See Epiris Managers LLP; *Int'l*, pg. 2460
METAL BULLETIN SINGAPORE—See Astorg Partners S.A.S.; *Int'l*, pg. 656
METAL BULLETIN SINGAPORE—See Epiris Managers LLP; *Int'l*, pg. 2461
MOMONDO GROUP LIMITED—See Booking Holdings, Inc.; *U.S. Public*, pg. 368
MONSTER OY—See Alma Media Corporation; *Int'l*, pg. 362

MYLIFE.COM, INC.; *U.S. Private*, pg. 2825
NEWPOINT MEDIA GROUP, LLC—See Lion Equity Partners, LLC; *U.S. Private*, pg. 2463
NEXUS ENTERPRISE SOLUTIONS, INC.; *U.S. Public*, pg. 1527
THE NUMBER UK LTD.—See kgb USA, Inc.; *U.S. Private*, pg. 2301
OIL PRICE INFORMATION SERVICE LLC—See News Corporation; *U.S. Public*, pg. 1521
OLIVER DITSON CO.—See Theodore Presser Co.; *U.S. Private*, pg. 4141
PETRODATA AS—See Halliburton Company; *U.S. Public*, pg. 980
PETRODATA AS—See International Business Machines Corporation; *U.S. Public*, pg. 1149
PHONE DIRECTORIES COMPANY—See Kainos Capital, LLC; *U.S. Private*, pg. 2255
PRIVCO MEDIA LLC; *U.S. Private*, pg. 3268
PROFESSIONAL DIVERSITY NETWORK, INC.; *U.S. Public*, pg. 1724
PROQUEST, LLC—See Clarivate PLC; *Int'l*, pg. 1649
PUBLISHERS CLEARING HOUSE, INC.; *U.S. Private*, pg. 3301
PUBLITEC B.V.—See Apax Partners LLP; *Int'l*, pg. 507
PUBLITEC B.V.—See Cinven Limited; *Int'l*, pg. 1615
REALINFO, L.L.C.—See Fidelity National Financial, Inc.; *U.S. Public*, pg. 831
REDVISION SYSTEMS INC.; *U.S. Private*, pg. 3380
RX TECHNOLOGIES CORP.; *U.S. Private*, pg. 3509
SITTERCITY INC.—See Bain Capital, LP; *U.S. Private*, pg. 437
SNAGAJOB.COM, INC.; *U.S. Private*, pg. 3699
SNAPNAMES WEB.COM, LLC—See Siris Capital Group, LLC; *U.S. Private*, pg. 3675
SRDS, INC.—See Bain Capital, LP; *U.S. Private*, pg. 448
STAT RESOURCE GROUP, INC.—See The Alesco Group, LLC; *U.S. Private*, pg. 3983
TELEINFO MEDIA PUBLIC COMPANY LIMITED—See Advanced Info Service Plc; *Int'l*, pg. 160
THEDIRECTORY.COM, INC.; *U.S. Private*, pg. 4141
THOMAS INDUSTRIAL NETWORK ADVERTISING—See Thomas Publishing Company LLC; *U.S. Private*, pg. 4157
THOMAS INTERNATIONAL ADVERTISING CO. (BEIJING), LTD.—See Thomas Publishing Company LLC; *U.S. Private*, pg. 4157
THOMAS INTERNATIONAL PUBLISHING CO. INDIA PRIVATE LIMITED—See Thomas Publishing Company LLC; *U.S. Private*, pg. 4157
THOMAS/LUND PUBLICACOES INDUSTRIAIS LTDA.—See Thomas Publishing Company LLC; *U.S. Private*, pg. 4157
THOMAS PUBLISHING COMPANY LLC; *U.S. Private*, pg. 4157
THOMSON DIRECTORIES LTD.—See Foster Denovo Limited; *Int'l*, pg. 2749
THORPE-BOWKER—See Cambridge Information Group, Inc.; *U.S. Private*, pg. 727
THUMBTACK, INC.; *U.S. Private*, pg. 4165
TOKYO IPO—See FinanTec Co., Ltd.; *Int'l*, pg. 2669
TOTAL BRAIN LIMITED; *U.S. Public*, pg. 2164
TRADE DIMENSIONS INTERNATIONAL, INC.—See Brookfield Corporation; *Int'l*, pg. 1180
TRADE DIMENSIONS INTERNATIONAL, INC.—See Elliott Management Corporation; *U.S. Private*, pg. 1373
TRUVEN HEALTH ANALYTICS INC.—See International Business Machines Corporation; *U.S. Public*, pg. 1151
TRUVO NV/SA—See Apax Partners LLP; *Int'l*, pg. 507
TRUVO NV/SA—See Cinven Limited; *Int'l*, pg. 1615
TURBOMED EDV GMBH—See CompuGroup Medical SE & Co. KGaA; *Int'l*, pg. 1757
TYLOON, INC.—See 2GM Corporation; *U.S. Private*, pg. 6
UNIVERSITY DIRECTORIES—See The AroundCampus Group; *U.S. Private*, pg. 3988
U.S. STORAGE SEARCH, INC.—See B2 Interactive; *U.S. Private*, pg. 421
VERIZON YELLOW PAGES—See Verizon Communications Inc.; *U.S. Public*, pg. 2286
VICKERS STOCK RESEARCH CORPORATION—See The Argus Research Group, Inc.; *U.S. Private*, pg. 3988
WASHINGTONPOST.NEWSWEEK INTERACTIVE COMPANY, LLC—See Nash Holdings LLC; *U.S. Private*, pg. 2836
WHITEPAGES.COM INC.; *U.S. Private*, pg. 4511
YELP INC.; *U.S. Public*, pg. 2398
YOUVIA B.V.—See European Directories S.A.; *Int'l*, pg. 2556
YP LLC—See Thryv Holdings, Inc.; *U.S. Public*, pg. 2157
ZETA EMAIL SOLUTIONS; *U.S. Private*, pg. 4602
ZETA EMAIL SOLUTIONS—See Zeta Email Solutions; *U.S. Private*, pg. 4602
ZOOM INFORMATION INC.—See TA Associates, Inc.; *U.S. Private*, pg. 3915

513191 — GREETING CARD PUBLISHERS

AMERICAN GREETINGS CORP. - NORTH AMERICAN SOCIAL EXPRESSION PRODUCTS—See Clayton, Dubilier & Rice, LLC; *U.S. Private*, pg. 919
AMERICAN GREETINGS CORPORATION—See Clayton, Dubilier & Rice, LLC; *U.S. Private*, pg. 919
AMERICAN GREETINGS CORP. - RIPLEY FACILITY—See Clayton, Dubilier & Rice, LLC; *U.S. Private*, pg. 919
BELARTO LTD—See HAL Trust N.V.; *Int'l*, pg. 3224
CARLTON CARDS LIMITED—See Clayton, Dubilier & Rice, LLC; *U.S. Private*, pg. 919
CSS INDUSTRIES, INC.—See IG Design Group Plc; *Int'l*, pg. 3600
DAYSPRING CARDS, INC.—See Hallmark Cards, Inc.; *U.S. Private*, pg. 1844
EXCELSIOR PRINTING COMPANY - OATMEAL STUDIOS DIVISION—See Excelsior Printing Company; *U.S. Private*, pg. 1446
EXKLUSIV KARTENVERLAG GMBH—See HAL Trust N.V.; *Int'l*, pg. 3224
EXPOSURES ONLINE—See Crosby Rock LLC; *U.S. Private*, pg. 1104
HALLMARK CARDS BELGIUM NV—See Hallmark Cards, Inc.; *U.S. Private*, pg. 1844
HALLMARK CARDS, INC. - LAWRENCE PRODUCTION CENTER—See Hallmark Cards, Inc.; *U.S. Private*, pg. 1844
HALLMARK CARDS, INC. - LEAVENWORTH PRODUCTION CENTER—See Hallmark Cards, Inc.; *U.S. Private*, pg. 1844
HALLMARK CARDS, INC.; *U.S. Private*, pg. 1844
HALLMARK CARDS NEW ZEALAND LTD.—See Hallmark Cards, Inc.; *U.S. Private*, pg. 1844
HEALTHY PLANET PRODUCTS PUBLISHING, INC.; *U.S. Private*, pg. 1898
IG DESIGN GROUP PLC; *Int'l*, pg. 3600
LEANIN' TREE, INC.; *U.S. Private*, pg. 2407
MARIAN HEATH GREETING CARDS LLC; *U.S. Private*, pg. 2573
MARIAN HEATH GREETING CARDS—See Marian Heath Greeting Cards LLC; *U.S. Private*, pg. 2573
MASTERPIECE STUDIOS, INC.—See Taylor Corporation; *U.S. Private*, pg. 3938
MERCARD INTERCARD BV—See HAL Trust N.V.; *Int'l*, pg. 3224
MERCARD INTERCARD SA—See HAL Trust N.V.; *Int'l*, pg. 3224
NARBONI HOLDINGS, SARL—See Taylor Corporation; *U.S. Private*, pg. 3939
PAPER MAGIC GROUP, INC.—See IG Design Group Plc; *Int'l*, pg. 3600
PAPYRUS-RECYCLED GREETINGS, INC.—See Clayton, Dubilier & Rice, LLC; *U.S. Private*, pg. 919
THE PEACEABLE KINGDOM PRESS, INC.—See GL Group, Inc.; *U.S. Private*, pg. 1704
PLUS MARK LLC—See Clayton, Dubilier & Rice, LLC; *U.S. Private*, pg. 919
SHENZHEN GIFT INTENATIONAL GREETINGS COMPANY LTD—See IG Design Group Plc; *Int'l*, pg. 3601
SILVER STAR BRANDS, INC.—See Crosby Rock LLC; *U.S. Private*, pg. 1104
SPS STUDIOS, INC.; *U.S. Private*, pg. 3765
STARLINE PRINTING COMPANY, LLLP—See Gannett Co., Inc.; *U.S. Public*, pg. 906
STUDIO CALICO; *U.S. Private*, pg. 3843
SUNRISE GREETINGS—See Hallmark Cards, Inc.; *U.S. Private*, pg. 1845
UK GREETINGS LIMITED—See Clayton, Dubilier & Rice, LLC; *U.S. Private*, pg. 919

513199 — ALL OTHER PUBLISHERS

ACORN MEDIA GROUP, INC.—See AMC Networks Inc.; *U.S. Public*, pg. 92
ACTIFIO, INC.—See Alphabet Inc.; *U.S. Public*, pg. 83
ADVFN PLC; *Int'l*, pg. 167
AGILE CONTENT SA; *Int'l*, pg. 209
AG INTERACTIVE—See Clayton, Dubilier & Rice, LLC; *U.S. Private*, pg. 919
AGI PUBLISHING, INC; *U.S. Private*, pg. 127
AIO ACQUISITIONS INC.; *U.S. Private*, pg. 133
ALFRED MAINZER, INC.—See CBC Group; *U.S. Private*, pg. 797
ALFRED MUSIC CO. (UK) LTD.—See Alfred Publishing Company Inc.; *U.S. Private*, pg. 166
ALFRED MUSIC GMBH—See Alfred Publishing Company Inc.; *U.S. Private*, pg. 166
ALFRED MUSIC (S) PTE LTD—See Alfred Publishing Company Inc.; *U.S. Private*, pg. 166
ALFRED PUBLISHING COMPANY INC.; *U.S. Private*, pg. 165
ALLBUSINESS.COM, INC.—See Cannae Holdings, Inc.; *U.S. Public*, pg. 429
ALLBUSINESS.COM, INC.—See CC Capital Partners, LLC; *U.S. Private*, pg. 798
ALLBUSINESS.COM, INC.—See Intercontinental Exchange, Inc.; *U.S. Public*, pg. 1141
ALMON, INC.; *U.S. Private*, pg. 195
ALPHA OMEGA PUBLICATIONS—See Silver Lake Group, LLC; *U.S. Private*, pg. 3661

513199 — ALL OTHER PUBLISHER...

AMERICAN FUTURE SYSTEMS INC.; *U.S. Private*, pg. 235
AMERICAN HERITAGE PUBLISHING COMPANY; *U.S. Private*, pg. 236
AMERICAN JOURNAL EXPERTS, LLC; *U.S. Private*, pg. 239
A PASS EDUCATIONAL GROUP LLC; *U.S. Private*, pg. 18
APN ONLINE (AUSTRALIA) PTY LIMITED—See ARN Media Limited; *Int'l*, pg. 576
APPLIED COMPUTER RESEARCH, INC.—See Wired Real Estate Group Inc.; *U.S. Private*, pg. 4546
ARCAMAX PUBLISHING, INC.; *U.S. Private*, pg. 310
ARGUS MEDIA, INC. - NEW YORK—See General Atlantic Service Company, L.P.; *U.S. Private*, pg. 1662
ARGUS MEDIA, INC. - NEW YORK—See HgCapital Trust plc; *Int'l*, pg. 3376
ARGUS MEDIA, INC.—See General Atlantic Service Company, L.P.; *U.S. Private*, pg. 1662
ARGUS MEDIA, INC.—See HgCapital Trust plc; *Int'l*, pg. 3376
ARGYLE EXECUTIVE FORUM, LLC; *U.S. Private*, pg. 322
ASAHI NET, INC.; *Int'l*, pg. 598
ASMALLWORLD AG; *Int'l*, pg. 627
ATLANTIC COMMUNICATIONS-HOUSTON OFFICE—See International Exhibitions, Inc.; *U.S. Private*, pg. 2116
AUTHOR SOLUTIONS, LLC—See Najafi Companies, LLC; *U.S. Private*, pg. 2831
AUTOWEB.COM, INC.—See One Planet Group LLC; *U.S. Private*, pg. 3020
AVALON DOCUMENTS SERVICES; *U.S. Private*, pg. 403
AXEL SPRINGER SYNDICATION GMBH—See Axel Springer SE; *Int'l*, pg. 766
BDG MEDIA, INC.; *U.S. Private*, pg. 500
BEAGLEE, INC.; *Int'l*, pg. 932
BELCARO GROUP, INC.; *U.S. Private*, pg. 516
BELIEFNET, INC.—See BN Media LLC; *U.S. Private*, pg. 601
BELO INTERACTIVE, INC.—See DallasNews Corporation; *U.S. Public*, pg. 621
BENCHMARK BROADCAST SYSTEMS (P) LIMITED—See Benchmark Telecast Integration Pte Ltd; *Int'l*, pg. 970
BENESSE CORPORATION—See EQT AB; *Int'l*, pg. 2467
BESTOFMEDIA, LLC—See Purch Group, Inc.; *U.S. Private*, pg. 3305
BITPIPE, INC.—See TechTarget, Inc.; *U.S. Public*, pg. 1989
BLADE URBAN AIR MOBILITY, INC.—See Blade Air Mobility, Inc.; *U.S. Public*, pg. 361
BLOCKHOLD CAPITAL CORPORATION; *U.S. Public*, pg. 362
BOOKPAL, L.L.C.; *U.S. Private*, pg. 615
BOOKRAGS, INC.; *U.S. Private*, pg. 615
BOXCEIPTS.COM, INC.; *U.S. Private*, pg. 626
BOYAA INTERACTIVE INTERNATIONAL LTD; *Int'l*, pg. 1124
BRIEFING MEDIA LTD.—See Horizon Capital LLP; *Int'l*, pg. 3479
BRILLIENT CORPORATION; *U.S. Private*, pg. 654
BROADBAND SECURITY, INC.; *Int'l*, pg. 1172
THE BROADCASTER—See Yankton Media, Inc.; *U.S. Private*, pg. 4586
BULL ALGERIE—See Atos SE; *Int'l*, pg. 691
BUSBY WEB SOLUTIONS PTY. LTD.—See Hire Intelligence International Limited; *Int'l*, pg. 3404
BUSINESS MANAGEMENT DAILY—See Capitol Information Group, Inc.; *U.S. Private*, pg. 744
BUSINESS SPECTATOR PTY LTD—See News Corporation; *U.S. Public*, pg. 1518
BUYRITE CLUB CORP.; *U.S. Private*, pg. 699
CAESARS INTERACTIVE ENTERTAINMENT, LLC—See Caesars Entertainment, Inc.; *U.S. Public*, pg. 420
CAIRO EDITORE S.P.A.—See Cairo Communication S.p.A.; *Int'l*, pg. 1253
CAIRO PUBLISHING SRL—See Cairo Communication S.p.A.; *Int'l*, pg. 1253
CARE.COM, INC.—See IAC Inc.; *U.S. Public*, pg. 1082
CATALOG360 LIMITED—See HCA Healthcare, Inc.; *U.S. Public*, pg. 992
CHIHULY WORKSHOP—See Chihuly Inc.; *U.S. Private*, pg. 881
CITIC PUBLISHING HOUSE—See CITIC Group Corporation; *Int'l*, pg. 1621
CLEMENT COMMUNICATIONS INC.—See Brady Corporation; *U.S. Public*, pg. 379
COFINA MEDIA, SGPS, S.A.—See Cofina SGPS, S.A.; *Int'l*, pg. 1692
COL GROUP CO., LTD.; *Int'l*, pg. 1697
COLLEGE NETWORK INC.; *U.S. Private*, pg. 968
COLLEGE PROWLER, INC.; *U.S. Private*, pg. 968
COMPANY WEBCAST B.V.—See Euronext N.V.; *Int'l*, pg. 2554
COMPRINT MILITARY PUBLICATIONS—See Nash Holdings LLC; *U.S. Private*, pg. 2835
CONNECTURE, INC.—See Francisco Partners Management, LP; *U.S. Private*, pg. 1589
CONSUMERREVIEW, INC.—See Invenda Corporation; *U.S. Private*, pg. 2131
CONSUMER SOURCE INC.—See Redfin Corporation; *U.S. Public*, pg. 1770

CONSUMERS PRESS—See Gannett Co., Inc.; *U.S. Public*, pg. 897
COUNSELING INTERNATIONAL, INC.; *U.S. Private*, pg. 1066
COX CUSTOM MEDIA INC.—See Apollo Global Management, Inc.; *U.S. Public*, pg. 163
CRAFTSY INC.; *U.S. Private*, pg. 1082
CREATELIVE, INC.; *U.S. Private*, pg. 1087
CRESTEC (ASIA) LIMITED—See Crestec Inc.; *Int'l*, pg. 1841
CRESTEC INC. - SURABAYA FACTORY—See Crestec Inc.; *Int'l*, pg. 1841
CRESTEC PRINTING (DONGGUAN) LIMITED—See Crestec Inc.; *Int'l*, pg. 1841
CRESTEC (THAILAND) CO., LTD.—See Crestec Inc.; *Int'l*, pg. 1841
CRESTEC USA INC.—See Crestec Inc.; *Int'l*, pg. 1841
CRESTEC VIETNAM CO., LTD.—See Crestec Inc.; *Int'l*, pg. 1841
CRICKET MEDIA, INC.—See Cricket Media Group Ltd.; *U.S. Private*, pg. 1100
CROSSKNOWLEDGE GROUP LIMITED—See John Wiley & Sons, Inc.; *U.S. Public*, pg. 1192
CROWDWORKS INC.; *Int'l*, pg. 1857
CYGER MEDIA; *U.S. Private*, pg. 1134
CYTAGLOBAL HELLAS AE—See Cyprus Telecommunications Authority; *Int'l*, pg. 1897
DAILYCANDY, LLC—See Comcast Corporation; *U.S. Public*, pg. 540
DAILY JOURNAL OF COMMERCE, INC.—See The Dolan Company; *U.S. Private*, pg. 4022
THE DAILY RECORD COMPANY, LLC—See The Dolan Company; *U.S. Private*, pg. 4022
DASKOCHREZEPT.DE GMBH—See Hubert Burda Media Holding Kommanditgesellschaft; *Int'l*, pg. 3520
DEDRAX AD—See Billboard JSC; *Int'l*, pg. 1030
DELTATRE SPA—See Bruins Sports Capital, LLC; *U.S. Private*, pg. 671
DE PERSGROEP PUBLISHING NV—See DPG Media Group NV; *Int'l*, pg. 2188
DESERET DIGITAL MEDIA—See Deseret Management Corporation; *U.S. Private*, pg. 1212
DEWBERRY REDPOINT LTD; *Int'l*, pg. 2091
DEX MEDIA - CHICAGO—See Thryv Holdings, Inc.; *U.S. Public*, pg. 2157
DIGITAL PUBLISHING SOLUTIONS, INC.—See Diversified Global Graphics Group, LLC; *U.S. Private*, pg. 1242
DIRECT MEDICAL DATA MARKETING CORP.—See DMD-Connects Services Inc.; *U.S. Private*, pg. 2143
DIRECT RESPONSE DECKS INC.—See Marketshare Publications, Inc.; *U.S. Private*, pg. 2581
DISTRIBUTECH—See Redfin Corporation; *U.S. Public*, pg. 1770
DOCU GROUP DEUTSCHE HOLDING GMBH—See Apax Partners LLP; *Int'l*, pg. 502
DOCU GROUP DEUTSCHE HOLDING GMBH—See Towerbrook Capital Partners, L.P.; *U.S. Private*, pg. 4195
DOMAIN MEDIA CORP.; *U.S. Private*, pg. 1255
DONUTS INC.—See Ethos Capital, LLC; *U.S. Private*, pg. 1432
DOZ S.A.—See CEPD N.V.; *Int'l*, pg. 1420
DPREVIEW.COM LTD.—See Amazon.com, Inc.; *U.S. Public*, pg. 91
DRAGON INNOVATION, INC.—See Avnet, Inc.; *U.S. Public*, pg. 252
EASY BUY PLUS, INC.; *U.S. Private*, pg. 1323
E-BOOK SYSTEMS EUROPE—See E-Book Systems Pte. Ltd.; *Int'l*, pg. 2247
E-BOOK SYSTEMS INC.—See E-Book Systems Pte. Ltd.; *Int'l*, pg. 2247
E-BOOK SYSTEMS PTE. LTD.; *Int'l*, pg. 2247
EBSCO INDUSTRIES, INC. - EBSCO RESEARCH DIVISION—See EBSCO Industries, Inc.; *U.S. Private*, pg. 1325
EBTH, INC.; *U.S. Private*, pg. 1326
EDICO HOLDINGS LIMITED; *Int'l*, pg. 2309
EDIPRESSE ASIA LTD—See Edipresse SA; *Int'l*, pg. 2310
EDIPRESSE-KONLIGA ZAO—See Edipresse SA; *Int'l*, pg. 2310
EDITIONS LEFEBVRE SARRUT SA; *Int'l*, pg. 2311
EDITORIALE GIORGIO MONDADORI SPA—See Cairo Communication S.p.A.; *Int'l*, pg. 1253
EJ4, LLC—See Waud Capital Partners LLC; *U.S. Private*, pg. 4457
E-LEARNING SAS—See John Wiley & Sons, Inc.; *U.S. Public*, pg. 1192
ELEMENT K PRESS LLC—See Charterhouse Capital Partners LLP; *Int'l*, pg. 1456
EMAP COMMUNICATIONS USA—See Apax Partners LLP; *Int'l*, pg. 507
EMBARK CORPORATION; *U.S. Private*, pg. 1378
EMEDIA INVESTMENTS PROPRIETARY LIMITED—See E Media Holdings Limited; *Int'l*, pg. 2246
ENABLE MEDIA LIMITED—See Siris Capital Group, LLC; *U.S. Private*, pg. 3675
ENCORE ART GROUP; *Int'l*, pg. 2402
ENTOURAGE YEARBOOKS; *U.S. Private*, pg. 1405
EPRICE S.P.A.; *Int'l*, pg. 2465

ESQUIRE MAGAZINE JAPAN, INC.—See Culture Convenience Club Co., Ltd.; *Int'l*, pg. 1877
ETACTICS INC.; *U.S. Private*, pg. 1431
ETHERNITY NETWORKS LTD.; *Int'l*, pg. 2523
EVOLVI RAIL SYSTEMS LIMITED—See Capita plc; *Int'l*, pg. 1309
EZEE FIBER TEXAS LLC—See I Squared Capital Advisors (US) LLC; *U.S. Private*, pg. 2025
EZTD INC.; *Int'l*, pg. 2594
FILM SCORE MONTHLY; *U.S. Private*, pg. 1506
FIRE SOLUTIONS, INC.—See Compliance Science, Inc.; *U.S. Private*, pg. 1001
FIRST RESEARCH, INC.—See Cannae Holdings, Inc.; *U.S. Public*, pg. 429
FIRST RESEARCH, INC.—See CC Capital Partners, LLC; *U.S. Private*, pg. 798
FIRST RESEARCH, INC.—See Intercontinental Exchange, Inc.; *U.S. Public*, pg. 1142
FLAG PUBLICATION, INC; *U.S. Private*, pg. 1539
FLASH NETWORKS LTD.—See Constellation Software Inc.; *Int'l*, pg. 1775
FLAVORPILL PRODUCTIONS LLC—See BDG Media, Inc.; *U.S. Private*, pg. 500
FOODMAVEN CORPORATION; *U.S. Private*, pg. 1562
FRANKLIN COVEY CATALOG SALES INC.—See Franklin Covey Company; *U.S. Public*, pg. 877
FRANKLIN COVEY PRINTING, INC.—See Franklin Covey Company; *U.S. Public*, pg. 877
FRANKLIN COVEY PRODUCT SALES, INC.—See Franklin Covey Company; *U.S. Public*, pg. 877
FRANKLIN COVEY—See Franklin Covey Company; *U.S. Public*, pg. 877
FRANKLIN COVEY TRAVEL, INC.—See Franklin Covey Company; *U.S. Public*, pg. 878
FRANKLIN DEVELOPMENT CORP.—See Franklin Covey Company; *U.S. Public*, pg. 878
FREEDOM MARKETING LIMITED—See Red Ventures, LLC; *U.S. Private*, pg. 3376
GAKKEN SHUPPAN HOLDINGS CO., LTD.—See Gakken Holdings Co., Ltd.; *Int'l*, pg. 2869
GARLIK LIMITED—See Experian plc; *Int'l*, pg. 2588
THE GEELONG ADVERTISER PTY. LIMITED—See News Corporation; *U.S. Public*, pg. 1521
GENR8 DIGITAL MEDIA PTY LTD—See Ausmani Limited; *Int'l*, pg. 716
GENSCAPE INTERNATIONAL, INC.—See Verisk Analytics, Inc.; *U.S. Public*, pg. 2282
GEOCENTER TOURISTIK MEDIENSERVICE GMBH; *Int'l*, pg. 2932
GEOLOCATION TECHNOLOGY, INC.; *Int'l*, pg. 2933
GIB CAPITAL GROUP, INC.; *Int'l*, pg. 2962
GIFTCERTIFICATES.COM CORPORATION—See Financial Technology Ventures Management Co. LLC; *U.S. Private*, pg. 1508
GIUFFRE FRANCIS LEFEBVRE SPA—See Editions Lefebvre Sarrut SA; *Int'l*, pg. 2311
GLOBENEWSWIRE UK LIMITED—See Apollo Global Management, Inc.; *U.S. Public*, pg. 152
GOFBA, INC.; *U.S. Private*, pg. 1726
GRAND VIEW MEDIA GROUP—See EBSCO Industries, Inc.; *U.S. Private*, pg. 1325
GROUPE PLUS VALUES SA; *Int'l*, pg. 3109
GROUPON GMBH—See Groupon Inc.; *U.S. Public*, pg. 972
HANOVER COMPANY STORE, LLC—See Chelsey Direct, LLC; *U.S. Private*, pg. 870
HARTE-HANKS TAMPA FLYER INC.—See Harte Hanks, Inc.; *U.S. Public*, pg. 986
HART ENERGY PUBLISHING LP—See Wiegers Capital Partners; *U.S. Private*, pg. 4516
HATCH, INC.—See Wall Family Enterprise, Inc.; *U.S. Private*, pg. 4430
HCPRO, INC.; *U.S. Private*, pg. 1890
HEALTHY DIRECTIONS, LLC—See Helen of Troy Limited; *Int'l*, pg. 3328
HERFF JONES CANADA—See Bain Capital, LP; *U.S. Private*, pg. 452
HERFF JONES, INC. - YEARBOOKS—See Bain Capital, LP; *U.S. Private*, pg. 452
HI-MEDIA BELGIUM SPRL—See AdUX SA; *Int'l*, pg. 155
HI-MEDIA LTD—See AdUX SA; *Int'l*, pg. 155
HI-MEDIA NETWORK INTERNET ESPANA SL—See AdUX SA; *Int'l*, pg. 155
HI-MEDIA PORTUGAL LDA—See AdUX SA; *Int'l*, pg. 155
HI-MEDIA SALES AB—See AdUX SA; *Int'l*, pg. 155
HITRON TECHNOLOGIES INC.; *Int'l*, pg. 3427
HOBSONS PLC—See Daily Mail & General Trust plc; *Int'l*, pg. 1937
HOLIDAYCHECK AG—See Hubert Burda Media Holding Kommanditgesellschaft; *Int'l*, pg. 3520
HOLMEN ENERGI ELNAT AB—See Holmen AB; *Int'l*, pg. 3452
HOLMEN FRANCE S.A.S.—See Holmen AB; *Int'l*, pg. 3452
HOOPS SCOUTING USA; *U.S. Public*, pg. 1052
HORBUCH HAMBURG HHV GMBH—See Bonnier AB; *Int'l*, pg. 1108
HOUSE 2 HOME SHOWCASE—See MacAndrews & Forbes Incorporated; *U.S. Private*, pg. 2532

N.A.I.C.S. INDEX

HOWSTUFFWORKS, INC.—See Genstar Capital, LLC; *U.S. Private,* pg. 1676
H&R CENTURY UNION CORPORATION; *Int'l,* pg. 3192
HYTEXTS INTERACTIVE CO., LTD.—See COL Public Company Limited; *Int'l,* pg. 1697
IGAMING BUSINESS LIMITED—See Blackstone Inc.; *U.S. Public,* pg. 360
IIOT-OXYS, INC.; *U.S. Public,* pg. 1100
I MEDIA CORP LTD.—See DB Corp Limited; *Int'l,* pg. 1986
INCISIVE FINANCIAL PUBLISHING LIMITED—See Apax Partners LLP; *Int'l,* pg. 504
INEDIT—See Agence France-Presse; *Int'l,* pg. 205
INFOMEDIA A/S—See DPG Media Group NV; *Int'l,* pg. 2188
INFORMATION, INC.—See SmithBucklin Corporation; *U.S. Private,* pg. 3697
INKD LLC—See IAC Inc.; *U.S. Public,* pg. 1082
INSIDEMETALS.COM—See Itronics Inc.; *U.S. Public,* pg. 1177
INSURANCENOODLE LLC—See Insureon; *U.S. Private,* pg. 2095
INTERFORUM CANADA INC.—See Czech Media Invest as; *Int'l,* pg. 1898
INTERNATIONAL CODE COUNCIL, INC.; *U.S. Private,* pg. 2115
INTERNATIONAL IMAGE SERVICES INC.—See Sonic Foundry, Inc.; *U.S. Public,* pg. 1903
INVESTING DAILY—See Capitol Information Group, Inc.; *U.S. Private,* pg. 744
INVESTOPEDIA.COM—See IAC Inc.; *U.S. Public,* pg. 1082
INVESTORPLACE MEDIA, LLC—See Avista Capital Partners, L.P.; *U.S. Private,* pg. 408
IRISH STUDIO, LLC; *U.S. Private,* pg. 2138
ISID FAIRNESS, LTD.—See Dentsu Group Inc.; *Int'l,* pg. 2038
IUNIVERSE, LLC—See Najafi Companies, LLC; *U.S. Private,* pg. 2831
IWIN, INC.—See Flipside, Inc.; *U.S. Private,* pg. 1546
J-AD GRAPHICS INC.; *U.S. Private,* pg. 2155
JAMEDA GMBH—See DocPlanner Group; *Int'l,* pg. 2153
J.J. KELLER & ASSOCIATES, INC.; *U.S. Private,* pg. 2167
JU-SEE PUBLISHING CO., LTD.—See Daito Trust Construction Co., Ltd.; *Int'l,* pg. 1944
KABOODLE, INC.—See StyleSpot, Inc.; *U.S. Private,* pg. 3846
KAPP ADVERTISING SERVICE INCORPORATED; *U.S. Private,* pg. 2262
KEESING MEDIA GROUP B.V.—See Groupe Bruxelles Lambert SA; *Int'l,* pg. 3099
KE&G DEVELOPMENT LLC; *U.S. Private,* pg. 2270
KEN COOK CO.; *U.S. Private,* pg. 2282
KIDSPOT.COM.AU PTY LIMITED—See News Corporation; *U.S. Public,* pg. 1519
KIT DIGITAL PRAGUE A.S.—See Piksel, Inc.; *U.S. Private,* pg. 3180
KNOBIAS, INC.; *U.S. Private,* pg. 2323
LADAS DOMAINS LLC—See Ladas & Parry; *U.S. Private,* pg. 2372
LAW BULLETIN PUBLISHING COMPANY; *U.S. Private,* pg. 2400
LEFT BEHIND GAMES, INC.; *U.S. Private,* pg. 2415
LEGENDARY ENTERTAINMENT, LLC—See Dalian Wanda Group Corporation Ltd.; *Int'l,* pg. 1953
LET'S GO PUBLICATIONS, INC.—See Harvard Student Agencies, Inc.; *U.S. Private,* pg. 1875
LIBREDIGITAL, INC.—See Atlas Holdings, LLC; *U.S. Private,* pg. 377
LIFESCRIPT, INC.; *U.S. Private,* pg. 2451
LINKOFFERS, LLC—See Red Ventures, LLC; *U.S. Private,* pg. 3376
LITURGICAL PUBLICATIONS, INC.; *U.S. Private,* pg. 2472
LIVINGLY MEDIA, INC.—See Axel Springer SE; *Int'l,* pg. 766
LIVINGSOCIAL LTD.—See Groupon Inc.; *U.S. Public,* pg. 972
LOCAL MEDIA LINK; *U.S. Private,* pg. 2477
LUDICORP RESEARCH & DEVELOPMENT LTD.—See SmugMug, Inc.; *U.S. Private,* pg. 3699
LULU INC.; *U.S. Private,* pg. 2513
MAKING EVERLASTING MEMORIES, L.L.C.—See Service Corporation International; *U.S. Public,* pg. 1870
MANAGING AUTOMATION—See Thomas Publishing Company LLC; *U.S. Private,* pg. 4157
MAP OF MEDICINE LTD.—See The Hearst Corporation; *U.S. Private,* pg. 4048
MARCOA PUBLISHING INC.; *U.S. Private,* pg. 2572
MARKETWATCH, INC.—See News Corporation; *U.S. Public,* pg. 1518
MARQUIS WHO'S WHO, LLC; *U.S. Private,* pg. 2588
THE MAZER CORPORATION; *U.S. Private,* pg. 4076
MCGRAW-HILL EDUCATION, INC.—See Platinum Equity, LLC; *U.S. Private,* pg. 3205
MD BUYLINE, INC.—See Clearlake Capital Group, L.P.; *U.S. Private,* pg. 937
MD BUYLINE, INC.—See SkyKnight Capital LLC; *U.S. Private,* pg. 3685
MECOM GROUP PLC—See DPG Media Group NV; *Int'l,* pg. 2188
MEDX PUBLISHING INC.; *U.S. Private,* pg. 2659

MEN'S JOURNAL—See Penske Media Corporation; *U.S. Private,* pg. 3139
MENTORING MINDS LP; *U.S. Private,* pg. 2667
MILL POND HOLDINGS LLC; *U.S. Private,* pg. 2730
MITCHELL REPAIR INFORMATION COMPANY, LLC—See Snap-on Incorporated; *U.S. Public,* pg. 1897
MLB ADVANCED MEDIA, L.P.—See Major League Baseball; *U.S. Private,* pg. 2555
MOD MEDIA LLC; *U.S. Private,* pg. 2759
MOMONDO A/S—See Booking Holdings, Inc.; *U.S. Public,* pg. 368
MORRIS VISITOR PUBLICATION—See Shivers Trading & Operating Company; *U.S. Private,* pg. 3638
MOSAIC MEDIA VENTURES PVT. LTD.—See HT Media Limited; *Int'l,* pg. 3508
THE MOTLEY FOOL, INC.; *U.S. Private,* pg. 4081
MULTI-AD, INC.; *U.S. Private,* pg. 2812
MULTI-AD RECAS—See Multi-Ad, Inc.; *U.S. Private,* pg. 2812
MULTI-HEALTH SYSTEMS, INC.; *U.S. Private,* pg. 2812
MY RECEPTIONIST, INC.; *U.S. Private,* pg. 2823
NATIONAL TAXNET—See Fidelity National Financial, Inc.; *U.S. Public,* pg. 831
NC TRANSACTION, INC.—See News Corporation; *U.S. Public,* pg. 1519
NETCOM LEARNING; *U.S. Private,* pg. 2887
NEWBRIDGE EDUCATIONAL PUBLISHING—See The Rowman & Littlefield Publishing Group, Inc.; *U.S. Private,* pg. 4112
NEWSCRED, INC.—See Insight Venture Management, LLC; *U.S. Private,* pg. 2090
NEWSMAX MEDIA, INC.; *U.S. Private,* pg. 2917
NINIAN SOLUTIONS LTD.—See HgCapital Trust plc; *Int'l,* pg. 3377
NXGN, INC.; *U.S. Private,* pg. 2975
NYSTROM EDUCATION—See Social Studies School Service; *U.S. Private,* pg. 3703
NZCH CORPORATION—See Spectrum Brands Holdings, Inc.; *U.S. Public,* pg. 1915
O'NEIL & ASSOCIATES INCORPORATED; *U.S. Private,* pg. 2979
ONEPLACE LLC—See Salem Media Group, Inc.; *U.S. Public,* pg. 1836
OOKA ISLAND INC.—See Scholastic Corporation; *U.S. Public,* pg. 1847
OPPRTUNITY, INC.; *U.S. Private,* pg. 3033
OVERDRIVE, INC.—See KKR & Co. Inc.; *U.S. Public,* pg. 1262
PAIZO PUBLISHING LLC; *U.S. Private,* pg. 3076
PARTICIPANT MEDIA, LLC—See Apollo Global Management, Inc.; *U.S. Public,* pg. 167
PATRON SOLUTIONS, L.P.—See Comcast Corporation; *U.S. Public,* pg. 541
PAWTUCKET TIMES—See R.I.S.N. Operations Inc.; *U.S. Private,* pg. 3336
PAYSCALE, INC.—See Francisco Partners Management, LP; *U.S. Private,* pg. 1590
PENNYSAVER GROUP INC.—See SV Investment Partners; *U.S. Private,* pg. 3888
PEOPLE2PEOPLE GROUP INC.—See The Phoenix Media/Communications Group; *U.S. Private,* pg. 4095
PLATINUM STUDIOS, INC.; *U.S. Public,* pg. 1697
PLAYSCRIPTS INC.; *U.S. Private,* pg. 3212
PLJ INFORMATION SYSTEMS, INC.; *U.S. Private,* pg. 3214
POCKET OUTDOOR MEDIA, INC.; *U.S. Private,* pg. 3219
PRACTICE FUSION, INC.—See Veradigm Inc.; *U.S. Public,* pg. 2280
PROPERTY TAX DIRECT, INC—See Fidelity National Financial, Inc.; *U.S. Public,* pg. 831
PROSPER FUNDING LLC—See Prosper Marketplace, Inc.; *U.S. Private,* pg. 3288
PROTOTYPE INDUSTRIES, INC.; *U.S. Private,* pg. 3290
PROVATION MEDICAL, INC.—See Fortive Corporation; *U.S. Public,* pg. 871
PRUDENT PUBLISHING COMPANY, INC.; *U.S. Private,* pg. 3295
PSYCHOLOGICAL ASSESSMENT RESOURCES, INC.; *U.S. Private,* pg. 3298
PUBLISHING GROUP OF AMERICA; *U.S. Private,* pg. 3301
PUNTERS PARADISE PTY LIMITED—See News Corporation; *U.S. Public,* pg. 1520
RADIOIO, INC.; *U.S. Public,* pg. 1760
RAND MCNALLY & COMPANY—See Patriarch Partners, LLC; *U.S. Private,* pg. 3109
REALAGE, INC.—See Altaris Capital Partners, LLC; *U.S. Private,* pg. 206
RIGDATA—See Hellman & Friedman LLC; *U.S. Private,* pg. 1908
RIMAGE CORPORATION—See Equus Holdings, Inc.; *U.S. Private,* pg. 1417
RP DATA VALUATION SERVICES PTY LTD—See Insight Venture Management, LLC; *U.S. Private,* pg. 2089
RP DATA VALUATION SERVICES PTY LTD—See Stone Point Capital LLC; *U.S. Private,* pg. 3823
R.S. MEANS COMPANY LLC—See Fortive Corporation; *U.S. Public,* pg. 872

RUSH PRESS—See Chatham Asset Management, LLC; *U.S. Private,* pg. 863
THE SANBORN MAP COMPANY, INC.; *U.S. Private,* pg. 4113
SANDHILLS PUBLISHING COMPANY; *U.S. Private,* pg. 3543
SANOMA BUDAPEST ZRT—See DPG Media Group NV; *Int'l,* pg. 2188
SANOMA MAGAZINES BELGIUM NV—See DPG Media Group NV; *Int'l,* pg. 2188
SANOMA MEDIA B.V.—See DPG Media Group NV; *Int'l,* pg. 2188
SAVVYPHONE, LLC; *U.S. Private,* pg. 3557
SEAS INDUSTRIES INC.; *U.S. Private,* pg. 3591
SHAREDXPERTISE MEDIA, LLC; *U.S. Private,* pg. 3626
SIMPLICITY PATTERN CO. INC.—See Conso International Corporation; *U.S. Private,* pg. 1020
SKY PUBLICATIONS LIMITED—See Comcast Corporation; *U.S. Public,* pg. 541
SMART AWARDS LTD.—See Hexatronic Group AB; *Int'l,* pg. 3371
SMARTERTRAVEL.COM—See Cognius, Inc.; *U.S. Private,* pg. 962
SNAP-ON BUSINESS SOLUTIONS INDIA PRIVATE LIMITED—See Snap-on Incorporated; *U.S. Public,* pg. 1898
SNAP-ON BUSINESS SOLUTIONS S.L.—See Snap-on Incorporated; *U.S. Public,* pg. 1898
SOCIAL STUDIES SCHOOL SERVICE; *U.S. Private,* pg. 3703
SOMERSET HOUSE PUBLISHING INC.; *U.S. Private,* pg. 3712
SONIC FOUNDRY MEDIA SYSTEMS, INC.—See Sonic Foundry, Inc.; *U.S. Public,* pg. 1903
SORENSON MEDIA—See Brookfield Corporation; *Int'l,* pg. 1180
SORENSON MEDIA—See Elliott Management Corporation; *U.S. Private,* pg. 1372
SOUTHERN GRAPHIC SYSTEMS, LLC—See Summit Partners, L.P.; *U.S. Private,* pg. 3856
SOUTHERN GRAPHIC SYSTEMS, LLC—See The Jordan Company, L.P.; *U.S. Private,* pg. 4062
SPARKNOTES, LLC—See Elliott Management Corporation; *U.S. Private,* pg. 1365
SPIDELL PUBLISHING, INC.—See Leeds Equity Partners, LLC; *U.S. Private,* pg. 2414
SPORTS AFIELD, INC.; *U.S. Private,* pg. 3761
STEPSTONE SERVICES SP. Z O.O.—See Axel Springer SE; *Int'l,* pg. 767
STEVVA CORPORATION; *U.S. Private,* pg. 3810
STYLEHAUL, INC.—See Bertelsmann SE & Co. KGaA; *Int'l,* pg. 991
STYLESPOT, INC.; *U.S. Private,* pg. 3846
SUCCEED CORPORATION; *U.S. Private,* pg. 3848
SUNCOAST DIGITAL PRESS INC.; *U.S. Private,* pg. 3865
SUZHOU CRESTEC PRINTING CO., LTD.—See Crestec Inc.; *Int'l,* pg. 1841
TARGET PROGRAMS, LLC—See W.R. Berkley Corporation; *U.S. Public,* pg. 2318
TAX MANAGEMENT, INC.—See Bloomberg L.P.; *U.S. Private,* pg. 584
TECHNO-GRAPHICS & TRANSLATIONS, INC.; *U.S. Private,* pg. 3955
THEHUFFINGTONPOST.COM, INC.—See BuzzFeed, Inc.; *U.S. Public,* pg. 413
THEORIA COMMUNICATIONS INC.—See AOI TYO Holdings Inc.; *Int'l,* pg. 488
THESTREET, INC.—See The Arena Group Holdings, Inc; *U.S. Public,* pg. 2035
THIS OLD HOUSE VENTURES, LLC—See Roku, Inc.; *U.S. Public,* pg. 1808
THOMPSON MEDIA GROUP LLC; *U.S. Private,* pg. 4160
THOMPSON PUBLISHING GROUP—See Thompson Media Group LLC; *U.S. Private,* pg. 4160
THRILLIST MEDIA GROUP, INC.; *U.S. Private,* pg. 4165
TOTAL BEAUTY MEDIA, INC.—See Evolve Media, LLC; *U.S. Private,* pg. 1444
TOUCH LOCAL LIMITED—See Siris Capital Group, LLC; *U.S. Private,* pg. 3675
TRADER CORPORATION—See Thoma Bravo, L.P.; *U.S. Private,* pg. 4154
TRAKKER MIDDLE EAST LLC—See Al Jaber Group; *Int'l,* pg. 280
TRAVELHOST, INC.; *U.S. Private,* pg. 4214
TRELLO, INC—See Atlassian Corporation; *Int'l,* pg. 686
TRENDS INTERNATIONAL LLC; *U.S. Private,* pg. 4218
TRIUMPH LEARNING, LLC—See School Specialty, Inc.; *U.S. Public,* pg. 1848
TWENTSCHE COURANT TUBANTIA BV—See DPG Media Group NV; *Int'l,* pg. 2189
UITGEVERIJ BN/DE STEM B.V.—See DPG Media Group NV; *Int'l,* pg. 2189
UNITED ADVERTISING PUBLICATIONS, INC.—See Irish Times; *U.S. Private,* pg. 2138
UNIVERSITY OF CHICAGO PRESS—See University of Chicago; *U.S. Private,* pg. 4308
VENETEL SERVICIOS PUBLICITARIOS, S.A.—See Grupo Televisa, S.A.B.; *Int'l,* pg. 3136

513199 — ALL OTHER PUBLISHER...

VERTIGO COMICS—See Warner Bros. Discovery, Inc.; *U.S. Public*, pg. 2328
VIATOR, INC.—See TripAdvisor, Inc.; *U.S. Public*, pg. 2195
VICTORY PRODUCTIONS, INC.—See A Pass Educational Group LLC; *U.S. Private*, pg. 18
VISTAPRINT TUNISIE SARL—See Cimpress plc; *Int'l*, pg. 1609
VITAL SOURCE TECHNOLOGIES INC.—See Ingram Industries, Inc.; *U.S. Private*, pg. 2076
VIX, INC.—See ForgeLight, LLC; *U.S. Private*, pg. 1568
VIX, INC.—See Searchlight Capital Partners, L.P.; *U.S. Private*, pg. 3591
WALSWORTH PUBLISHING COMPANY, INC.; *U.S. Private*, pg. 4433
THE WASHINGTON TIMES, LLC—See Family Federation for World Peace & Unification; *U.S. Private*, pg. 1469
WEBS, INC.—See Cimpress plc; *Int'l*, pg. 1609
WEGENER BEDRIJFSVASTGOED BV—See DPG Media Group NV; *Int'l*, pg. 2189
WEGENER NEDERLAND BV—See DPG Media Group NV; *Int'l*, pg. 2189
WHAT ON EARTH; *U.S. Private*, pg. 4504
WIKIMEDIA FOUNDATION INC.; *U.S. Private*, pg. 4517
WILD WINGS INC.; *U.S. Private*, pg. 4519
WINN DEVON ART GROUP—See Encore Art Group; *Int'l*, pg. 2402
WIRELESS INNOVATION LTD.—See Horizon Capital LLP; *Int'l*, pg. 3479
WOW MEDIA PRODUCTS, INC.; *U.S. Private*, pg. 4571
WRIGHT'S MEDIA, LLC; *U.S. Private*, pg. 4573
ZAGAT SURVEY, LLC; *U.S. Private*, pg. 4597
ZINIO, LLC—See Vista Equity Partners, LLC; *U.S. Private*, pg. 4399
ZITIZ AB—See Duroc AB; *Int'l*, pg. 2229
ZONZIA MEDIA, INC.; *U.S. Private*, pg. 4608
ZUBRA, INC.; *U.S. Private*, pg. 4609

513210 — SOFTWARE PUBLISHERS

01 COMMUNIQUE LABORATORY INC.; *Int'l*, pg. 1
1010DATA, INC.—See Symphony Innovation, LLC; *U.S. Private*, pg. 3899
1SPATIAL PLC; *Int'l*, pg. 3
1SYNC INC.; *U.S. Private*, pg. 4
1WORLDSYNC, INC.—See Battery Ventures, L.P.; *U.S. Private*, pg. 488
24 MOBILE ADVERTISING SOLUTIONS AB; *Int'l*, pg. 4
2FA, INC.—See Identity Automation, LP; *U.S. Private*, pg. 2037
2K CZECH, S.R.O.—See Take-Two Interactive Software, Inc.; *U.S. Public*, pg. 1979
2K GAMES, INC.—See Take-Two Interactive Software, Inc.; *U.S. Public*, pg. 1979
2K GAMES WEST—See Take-Two Interactive Software, Inc.; *U.S. Public*, pg. 1979
2K PLAY, INC.—See Take-Two Interactive Software, Inc.; *U.S. Public*, pg. 1979
2K VEGAS, INC.—See Take-Two Interactive Software, Inc.; *U.S. Public*, pg. 1979
2U, INC.; *U.S. Public*, pg. 3
3DC, INC.; *U.S. Public*, pg. 3
360INSIGHTS.COM CANADA, INC.; *Int'l*, pg. 6
3965546 CANADA INC; *Int'l*, pg. 7
3CINTERACTIVE CORP.; *U.S. Private*, pg. 9
3CLOUD, LLC—See Gryphon Investors, LLC; *U.S. Private*, pg. 1798
3C SOFTWARE INC.; *U.S. Private*, pg. 8
3DCART SHOPPING CARTS; *U.S. Private*, pg. 9
3D PLM SOFTWARE SOLUTIONS LIMITED—See Dassault Systemes S.A.; *Int'l*, pg. 1974
3D-P—See Epiroc AB; *Int'l*, pg. 2463
3D-P—See Epiroc AB; *Int'l*, pg. 2463
3D REALMS ENTERTAINMENT APS—See Embracer Group AB; *Int'l*, pg. 2375
3D SYSTEMS CORPORATION; *U.S. Public*, pg. 4
3D SYSTEMS KOREA, INC.—See 3D Systems Corporation; *U.S. Public*, pg. 4
3D SYSTEMS SOFTWARE GMBH—See Battery Ventures, L.P.; *U.S. Private*, pg. 438
3P LEARNING LIMITED; *Int'l*, pg. 9
3Q HOLDINGS LIMITED; *Int'l*, pg. 9
3VR SECURITY, INC.—See Identiv, Inc.; *U.S. Public*, pg. 1089
4CLICKS SOLUTIONS, LLC—See Fortive Corporation; *U.S. Public*, pg. 872
4-TELL INC.—See Scaleworks, Inc.; *U.S. Private*, pg. 3561
505 GAMES LTD—See Digital Bros SpA; *Int'l*, pg. 2120
5AM SOLUTIONS INC.; *U.S. Private*, pg. 16
5TH PLANET GAMES A/S; *Int'l*, pg. 14
66DEGREES INC.—See Sunstone Partners Management LLC; *U.S. Private*, pg. 3373
6CONNEX CHINA—See Dura Software Series A Qof LLC; *U.S. Private*, pg. 1292
6CONNEX INC.—See Dura Software Series A Qof LLC; *U.S. Private*, pg. 1292
7FC LLP; *Int'l*, pg. 15
7THSENSE DESIGN LIMITED; *Int'l*, pg. 15

8COMMON LIMITED; *Int'l*, pg. 16
8TH LIGHT, INC.; *U.S. Private*, pg. 17
8X8 INTERNATIONAL PTY LTD.—See 8x8, Inc.; *U.S. Public*, pg. 10
8X8 INTERNATIONAL SRL—See 8x8, Inc.; *U.S. Public*, pg. 10
8X8 UK LIMITED—See 8x8, Inc.; *U.S. Public*, pg. 10
ABALANCE CORPORATION LTD.; *Int'l*, pg. 48
ABAXX TECHNOLOGIES INC.; *Int'l*, pg. 48
ABC DISTRIBUTION AND RETAIL SOLUTIONS GMBH—See Electronic Arts Inc.; *U.S. Public*, pg. 723
ABC SOFTWARE GMBH—See Electronic Arts Inc.; *U.S. Public*, pg. 723
ABILA, INC.—See Insight Venture Management, LLC; *U.S. Private*, pg. 2088
ABILITY COMMERCE, INC.; *U.S. Private*, pg. 38
ABL DIAGNOSTICS S.A.—See Advanced Biological Laboratories (ABL) S.A.; *Int'l*, pg. 157
ABLENET, INC.; *U.S. Private*, pg. 39
ABLETON AG; *Int'l*, pg. 63
ABSENTYS, LLC—See The Carlyle Group Inc.; *U.S. Public*, pg. 2053
ABS MARITIME SERVICES - HELLAS—See American Bureau of Shipping; *U.S. Private*, pg. 225
ABS NAUTICAL SYSTEMS ASIA PACIFIC—See American Bureau of Shipping; *U.S. Private*, pg. 225
ABS NAUTICAL SYSTEMS CHILE—See American Bureau of Shipping; *U.S. Private*, pg. 225
ABS NAUTICAL SYSTEMS LLC—See American Bureau of Shipping; *U.S. Private*, pg. 225
ABS NAUTICAL SYSTEMS MALAYSIA—See American Bureau of Shipping; *U.S. Private*, pg. 225
ABSOLUTE IT SOLUTIONS, LLC; *U.S. Private*, pg. 44
ABSOLUTE IT SOLUTIONS, SRL—See Absolute IT Solutions, LLC; *U.S. Private*, pg. 44
ABSORB SOFTWARE INC.—See Welsh, Carson, Anderson & Stowe; *U.S. Private*, pg. 4479
ACADIASOFT, INC.; *U.S. Private*, pg. 47
ACADIASOFT (UK) LTD.—See AcadiaSoft, Inc.; *U.S. Private*, pg. 47
ACCELA INC.; *U.S. Private*, pg. 49
ACCELERA INNOVATIONS, INC.; *U.S. Public*, pg. 32
ACCELLION, INC.; *U.S. Private*, pg. 49
ACCELLOS, INC.; *U.S. Private*, pg. 50
ACCELOPS, INC.—See Fortinet, Inc.; *U.S. Public*, pg. 869
ACCELRYS K.K.—See Dassault Systemes S.A.; *Int'l*, pg. 1974
ACCELRYS LIMITED—See Dassault Systemes S.A.; *Int'l*, pg. 1974
ACCELRYS SARL—See Dassault Systemes S.A.; *Int'l*, pg. 1974
ACCELRYS SOFTWARE INCORPORATED—See Dassault Systemes S.A.; *Int'l*, pg. 1974
ACCENTURE A/S—See Accenture plc; *Int'l*, pg. 82
ACCENTURE SOLUTIONS PRIVATE LIMITED—See Accenture plc; *Int'l*, pg. 86
ACCESSDATA GROUP, LLC—See Leeds Equity Partners, LLC; *U.S. Private*, pg. 2414
ACCESS TECHNOLOGY GROUP LIMITED; *Int'l*, pg. 89
THE ACCOUNTABLE CARE ORGANIZATION LTD.—See Evolent Health, Inc.; *U.S. Public*, pg. 804
ACCOUNTING SYSTEMS, INC.—See Eide Bailly LLP; *U.S. Private*, pg. 1347
ACCRUENT, LLC—See Fortive Corporation; *U.S. Public*, pg. 870
ACCUFUND INC.—See i3 Verticals, Inc.; *U.S. Public*, pg. 1081
ACCULYNK, INC.—See Fiserv, Inc.; *U.S. Public*, pg. 850
ACCURENCE, INC.—See Insight Venture Management, LLC; *U.S. Private*, pg. 2089
ACCURENCE, INC.—See Stone Point Capital LLC; *U.S. Private*, pg. 3834
ACCUSOFT CORPORATION—See Pegasus Imaging Corporation; *U.S. Public*, pg. 3129
ACCUSOFT CORPORATION—See Pegasus Imaging Corporation; *U.S. Public*, pg. 3129
ACENDRE PTY. LTD.—See Strattam Capital, LLC; *U.S. Private*, pg. 3837
ACEP FRANCE; *Int'l*, pg. 98
ACER CLOUD TECHNOLOGY CO.—See Acer Incorporated; *Int'l*, pg. 98
ACI WORLDWIDE (ASIA) PTE. LTD.—See ACI Worldwide, Inc.; *U.S. Public*, pg. 34
ACI WORLDWIDE CORP. - AUSTIN OFFICE—See ACI Worldwide, Inc.; *U.S. Public*, pg. 34
ACI WORLDWIDE CORP.—See ACI Worldwide, Inc.; *U.S. Public*, pg. 34
ACI WORLDWIDE CORP. - WEST HILLS OFFICE—See ACI Worldwide, Inc.; *U.S. Public*, pg. 34
ACI WORLDWIDE (EMEA) LIMITED—See ACI Worldwide, Inc.; *U.S. Public*, pg. 34
ACI WORLDWIDE (JAPAN) K.K.—See ACI Worldwide, Inc.; *U.S. Public*, pg. 34
ACI WORLDWIDE KOREA YUHAN HOESA—See ACI Worldwide, Inc.; *U.S. Public*, pg. 34
ACI WORLDWIDE (THAILAND) LIMITED—See ACI Worldwide, Inc.; *U.S. Public*, pg. 34
ACI WORLDWIDE (UK DEVELOPMENT) LIMITED—See ACI Worldwide, Inc.; *U.S. Public*, pg. 34

ACLARA SOFTWARE—See Hubbell Incorporated; *U.S. Public*, pg. 1067
ACL SERVICES LTD.—See Insight Venture Management, LLC; *U.S. Private*, pg. 2090
ACQUIA AUSTRALIA—See Vista Equity Partners, LLC; *U.S. Private*, pg. 4394
ACQUIA INC.—See Vista Equity Partners, LLC; *U.S. Private*, pg. 4394
ACQUIA UK—See Vista Equity Partners, LLC; *U.S. Private*, pg. 4394
ACQUISIO INC.—See Siris Capital Group, LLC; *U.S. Private*, pg. 3675
ACRONIS INC.; *U.S. Private*, pg. 65
ACTIANCE EUROPE LIMITED—See K1 Investment Management, LLC; *U.S. Private*, pg. 2252
ACTIANCE, INC.—See K1 Investment Management, LLC; *U.S. Private*, pg. 2252
ACTIANCE INDIA PVT. LTD.—See K1 Investment Management, LLC; *U.S. Private*, pg. 2252
ACTIAN CORPORATION—See HCL Technologies Ltd.; *Int'l*, pg. 3298
ACTIAN EUROPE LIMITED—See HCL Technologies Ltd.; *Int'l*, pg. 3298
ACTIAN GERMANY GMBH—See HCL Technologies Ltd.; *Int'l*, pg. 3298
ACTIO SOFTWARE CORP.—See Thoma Bravo, L.P.; *U.S. Private*, pg. 4146
ACTIVATE NETWORKS INC.—See Clarivate PLC; *Int'l*, pg. 1649
ACTIVELOGIX LLC—See Building Controls & Solutions; *U.S. Private*, pg. 682
ACTIVE NETWORK, LLC—See Global Payments Inc.; *U.S. Public*, pg. 943
ACTIVESTRATEGY, INC.—See UnitedHealth Group Incorporated; *U.S. Public*, pg. 2248
ACTIVEVIDEO NETWORKS, INC.—See CommScope Holding Company, Inc.; *U.S. Public*, pg. 548
ACTIVIDENTITY AUSTRALIA PTY. LTD.—See ASSA ABLOY AB; *Int'l*, pg. 637
ACTIVIDENTITY CORPORATION—See ASSA ABLOY AB; *Int'l*, pg. 637
ACTIVIDENTITY EUROPE S.A.—See ASSA ABLOY AB; *Int'l*, pg. 637
ACTIVIDENTITY JAPAN K.K.—See ASSA ABLOY AB; *Int'l*, pg. 637
ACTIVIDENTITY UK LTD.—See ASSA ABLOY AB; *Int'l*, pg. 637
ACTIVISION BLIZZARD UK LIMITED—See Microsoft Corporation; *U.S. Public*, pg. 1438
ACTIVISION PUBLISHING MINNEAPOLIS, INC—See Microsoft Corporation; *U.S. Public*, pg. 1438
ACTIVU CORPORATION; *U.S. Private*, pg. 70
ACT-ON SOFTWARE, INC.; *U.S. Private*, pg. 66
ACT-ON SOFTWARE INDIA PRIVATE LIMITED—See Act-On Software, Inc.; *U.S. Private*, pg. 66
ACTSOFT, INC.; *U.S. Private*, pg. 70
ACTUAL EXPERIENCE PLC; *Int'l*, pg. 121
ACTURIS LTD.; *Int'l*, pg. 121
A.D.A.M., INC.—See Ebix Inc.; *U.S. Public*, pg. 710
ADAPTIT HOLDINGS LIMITED—See Constellation Software Inc.; *Int'l*, pg. 1775
ADAPTIVE COMPUTING ENTERPRISES INC.—See ALA Services LLC; *U.S. Private*, pg. 148
ADAPTIVE CORP.; *U.S. Private*, pg. 76
ADAPTIVE INSIGHTS CO., LTD.—See Workday, Inc.; *U.S. Public*, pg. 2378
ADAPTIVE INSIGHTS LLC—See Workday, Inc.; *U.S. Public*, pg. 2378
ADAPT SOFTWARE APPLICATIONS, INC.; *U.S. Private*, pg. 76
ADDTHIS, INC.—See Oracle Corporation; *U.S. Public*, pg. 1610
ADDTRONICS BUSINESS SYSTEMS, INC.—See ID Group, Inc.; *U.S. Private*, pg. 2034
ADERANT HOLDINGS, INC.—See Roper Technologies, Inc.; *U.S. Public*, pg. 1810
ADGOOROO, LLC—See Adthena Ltd.; *Int'l*, pg. 154
ADHESION WEALTH ADVISOR SOLUTIONS, INC.—See GTCR LLC; *U.S. Private*, pg. 1802
ADMEREX (SINGAPORE) PTE LIMITED—See CB Australia Limited; *Int'l*, pg. 1364
ADOBE INC.; *U.S. Public*, pg. 42
ADOBE SYSTEMS HONG KONG LIMITED—See Adobe Inc.; *U.S. Public*, pg. 42
ADOBE SYSTEMS ITALIA SRL—See Adobe Inc.; *U.S. Public*, pg. 42
ADOBE SYSTEMS PTY. LTD.—See Adobe Inc.; *U.S. Public*, pg. 42
ADOBE SYSTEMS ROMANIA SRL—See Adobe Inc.; *U.S. Public*, pg. 42
ADOBE SYSTEMS SOFTWARE IRELAND LIMITED—See Adobe Inc.; *U.S. Public*, pg. 42
ADPAY, INC.—See Blackstone Inc.; *U.S. Public*, pg. 348
ADTOLLO AB—See Addnode Group AB; *Int'l*, pg. 130
THE ADTRACK CORPORATION; *U.S. Private*, pg. 3982
AD VALOREM RECORDS, INC.—See i3 Verticals, Inc.; *U.S. Public*, pg. 1081

N.A.I.C.S. INDEX

513210 — SOFTWARE PUBLISHERS

ADVANCED COMPUTER SOFTWARE GROUP LIMITED—See Vista Equity Partners, LLC; *U.S. Private*, pg. 4394
ADVANCED FRAUD SOLUTIONS; *U.S. Private*, pg. 89
ADVANCED HEALTH & CARE—See Vista Equity Partners, LLC; *U.S. Private*, pg. 4394
ADVANCED HEALTH INTELLIGENCE LTD; *Int'l*, pg. 159
ADVANCED INSTRUCTIONAL SYSTEMS, INC.—See Apax Partners LLP; *Int'l*, pg. 502
ADVANCED INSTRUCTIONAL SYSTEMS, INC.—See Apollo Global Management, Inc.; *U.S. Public*, pg. 168
ADVANCED INSTRUCTIONAL SYSTEMS, INC.—See KKR & Co. Inc.; *U.S. Public*, pg. 1256
ADVANCED INSTRUCTIONAL SYSTEMS, INC.—See Searchlight Capital Partners, L.P.; *U.S. Private*, pg. 3587
ADVANCED LEISURE TECHNOLOGIES PLC; *Int'l*, pg. 160
ADVANCEDMD, INC.—See Global Payments Inc.; *U.S. Public*, pg. 943
ADVANCED MICRO DEVICES, INC.—See Advanced Micro Devices, Inc.; *U.S. Public*, pg. 48
ADVANCED NEW TECHNOLOGIES LTD—See L3Harris Technologies, Inc.; *U.S. Public*, pg. 1280
ADVANCED RESPONSE CONCEPTS CORPORATION—See WidePoint Corporation; *U.S. Public*, pg. 2370
ADVANCED SOLUTIONS INTERNATIONAL, INC.; *U.S. Private*, pg. 92
ADVANCED VISUAL SYSTEMS INC.; *U.S. Private*, pg. 93
ADVANCED VOICE RECOGNITION SYSTEMS, INC.; *U.S. Public*, pg. 49
ADVANET INC.—See Eurotech S.p.A.; *Int'l*, pg. 2558
ADVANTAGE COMPUTING SYSTEMS INC.; *U.S. Private*, pg. 94
ADVANTAGE DATA INC.—See Solve Advisors Inc.; *U.S. Private*, pg. 3711
ADVANTAGE TECHNOLOGIES CONSULTING, INC.; *U.S. Private*, pg. 95
ADVANT-E CORPORATION; *U.S. Public*, pg. 49
ADVANTEDGE HEALTHCARE SOLUTIONS, INC.; *U.S. Private*, pg. 95
ADVANTIVE LLC; *U.S. Private*, pg. 95
ADVENT SOFTWARE APS—See SS&C Technologies Holdings, Inc.; *U.S. Public*, pg. 1922
ADVENT SOFTWARE (SINGAPORE) PTE. LTD—See SS&C Technologies Holdings, Inc.; *U.S. Public*, pg. 1922
ADVENT SWITZERLAND AG—See SS&C Technologies Holdings, Inc.; *U.S. Public*, pg. 1922
THE ADVERTISING SPECIALTY INSTITUTE; *U.S. Private*, pg. 3982
ADVIZOR SOLUTIONS, INC.—See Allegiance Fundraising LLC; *U.S. Private*, pg. 176
ADYEN INTERNATIONAL B.V.—See Adyen N.V.; *Int'l*, pg. 169
AEGIS ANALYTICAL CORPORATION—See Dassault Systemes S.A.; *Int'l*, pg. 1974
AERIES TECHNOLOGY, INC.; *U.S. Public*, pg. 52
AERVA, INC.—See H.I.G. Capital, LLC; *U.S. Private*, pg. 1834
AETHER CONSULTING INC.—See BrainSell Technologies, LLC; *U.S. Private*, pg. 634
AETHERPAL INC.—See Broadcom Inc.; *U.S. Public*, pg. 390
AETHERPAL (INDIA) PRIVATE LIMITED—See Broadcom Inc.; *U.S. Public*, pg. 390
AFAS ERP SOFTWARE B.V.; *Int'l*, pg. 185
AFFINNOVA, INC.—See Brookfield Corporation; *Int'l*, pg. 1178
AFFINNOVA, INC.—See Elliott Management Corporation; *U.S. Private*, pg. 1370
AFFIRMED NETWORKS, INC.; *U.S. Private*, pg. 123
AFIN TECHNOLOGIES, INC.—See Afin Technologies Limited; *Int'l*, pg. 189
AFIN TECHNOLOGIES LIMITED; *Int'l*, pg. 189
AFS TECHNOLOGIES, INC.—See Court Square Capital Partners, L.P.; *U.S. Private*, pg. 1068
AGC NETWORKS PTE. LIMITED—See Black Box Limited; *Int'l*, pg. 1056
AGENCYBLOC—See Resurgens Technology Partners, LLC; *U.S. Private*, pg. 3410
AGILAIRE LLC; *U.S. Private*, pg. 127
AGILE DEFENSE, INC.—See Enlightenment Capital LLC; *U.S. Private*, pg. 1400
AGILE SPORTS TECHNOLOGIES, INC.; *U.S. Private*, pg. 127
AGILITY INC.; *Int'l*, pg. 210
AGILITY MULTICHANNEL LTD.—See TA Associates, Inc.; *U.S. Private*, pg. 3915
AGILOFT, INC.—See Salesforce, Inc.; *U.S. Public*, pg. 1838
AGILONE INC.—See Vista Equity Partners, LLC; *U.S. Private*, pg. 4394
AGITAL HOLDINGS, LLC; *U.S. Private*, pg. 128
AGTRAX TECHNOLOGIES—See Integrated Solutions Group, Inc.; *U.S. Private*, pg. 2101
AIMING GLOBAL SERVICE, INC.—See Aiming Inc.; *Int'l*, pg. 234
AIMING INC.; *Int'l*, pg. 234
AINS—See Gemspring Capital Management, LLC; *U.S. Private*, pg. 1658

AIRCRAFT TECHNICAL PUBLISHERS—See ParkerGale, LLC; *U.S. Private*, pg. 3098
AIRTIGHT NETWORKS, INC.; *U.S. Private*, pg. 142
AISAN TECHNOLOGY CO., LTD.; *Int'l*, pg. 251
AKADEMOS, INC.—See Ingram Industries, Inc.; *U.S. Private*, pg. 2076
AKAMAI JAPAN K.K.—See Akamai Technologies, Inc.; *U.S. Public*, pg. 68
AKAMAI TECHNOLOGIES HONG KONG LIMITED—See Akamai Technologies, Inc.; *U.S. Public*, pg. 68
AKCELERANT HOLDINGS LLC; *U.S. Private*, pg. 144
AKRITIV TECHNOLOGIES, INC.—See Genpact Limited; *Int'l*, pg. 2926
AKTION ASSOCIATES, INC.; *U.S. Private*, pg. 147
A LA MODE, INC.—See Insight Venture Management, LLC; *U.S. Private*, pg. 2089
A LA MODE, INC.—See Stone Point Capital LLC; *U.S. Private*, pg. 3823
ALA SERVICES LLC; *U.S. Private*, pg. 148
ALAYA CARE INC.; *Int'l*, pg. 292
ALBUMPRINTER SERVICES B.V.—See Cimpress plc; *Int'l*, pg. 1609
ALCHEMER LLC—See KKR & Co. Inc.; *U.S. Public*, pg. 1239
ALDON COMPUTER GROUP—See Marlin Equity Partners, LLC; *U.S. Private*, pg. 2583
ALD SOFTWARE LTD.—See HUB Cyber Security Ltd.; *Int'l*, pg. 3516
ALEGIS REVENUE GROUP LLC—See MEDNAX, Inc.; *U.S. Public*, pg. 1413
ALEGRI INTERNATIONAL AUSTRIA GMBH—See Devoteam SA; *Int'l*, pg. 2089
ALEGRI INTERNATIONAL SERVICE GMBH—See Devoteam SA; *Int'l*, pg. 2089
ALEKS CORPORATION—See Platinum Equity, LLC; *U.S. Private*, pg. 3205
ALFRESCO SOFTWARE, INC.—See Thoma Bravo, L.P.; *U.S. Private*, pg. 4148
ALFRESCO SOFTWARE LIMITED—See Thoma Bravo, L.P.; *U.S. Private*, pg. 4148
ALIANZA INC.; *U.S. Private*, pg. 167
ALIBRE, INC.—See 3D Systems Corporation; *U.S. Public*, pg. 4
ALIENVAULT, INC.—See AT&T Inc.; *U.S. Public*, pg. 219
ALINEAN, INC.—See Boathouse Capital Management, LLC; *U.S. Private*, pg. 603
ALI SOLUTIONS, INC.—See Vector Capital Management, L.P.; *U.S. Private*, pg. 4350
ALLDATA LLC—See AutoZone, Inc.; *U.S. Public*, pg. 239
ALLEN SYSTEMS GROUP, INC.; *U.S. Private*, pg. 180
ALLIANCE HEALTHCARE SOLUTIONS, INC.—See Quatris Health LLC; *U.S. Private*, pg. 3324
ALLIED INFORMATICS INC.; *U.S. Private*, pg. 186
ALLIED SOFT LLC; *U.S. Private*, pg. 187
ALLOCATE SOFTWARE PLC—See TA Associates, Inc.; *U.S. Private*, pg. 3917
ALLOCATE SOFTWARE PTY. LTD.—See TA Associates, Inc.; *U.S. Private*, pg. 3917
ALLOCATION NETWORK GMBH—See Thoma Bravo, L.P.; *U.S. Private*, pg. 4151
ALLOT COMMUNICATIONS INC.—See Allot Ltd.; *Int'l*, pg. 360
ALLOT LTD.; *Int'l*, pg. 359
ALLOY SOFTWARE, INC.; *U.S. Private*, pg. 193
ALLSCRIPTS—See Veradigm Inc.; *U.S. Public*, pg. 2279
ALLURE GLOBAL SOLUTIONS, INC.—See Creative Realities, Inc.; *U.S. Public*, pg. 593
ALLURESOFT, INC.; *U.S. Private*, pg. 194
ALPHA AND OMEGA SEMICONDUCTOR INCORPORATED—See Alpha and Omega Semiconductor Limited; *Int'l*, pg. 366
ALPHACOM HOLDINGS, INC.; *Int'l*, pg. 370
ALPHA II, LLC - MONTGOMERY—See Alpha II, LLC; *U.S. Private*, pg. 197
ALPHAWEST SERVICES PTY LTD; *Int'l*, pg. 370
ALT 5 SIGMA INC.—See ALT5 Sigma Corporation; *U.S. Public*, pg. 85
ALTADYN CORP.; *U.S. Private*, pg. 204
ALTADYN SA—See Altadyn Corp.; *U.S. Private*, pg. 204
ALTAIR ENGINEERING FRANCE, SARL—See Altair Engineering, Inc.; *U.S. Public*, pg. 86
ALTAIR ENGINEERING GMBH—See Altair Engineering, Inc.; *U.S. Public*, pg. 86
ALTAIR ENGINEERING, INC.; *U.S. Public*, pg. 86
ALTAIR ENGINEERING INDIA PVT. LTD.—See Altair Engineering, Inc.; *U.S. Public*, pg. 86
ALTECH IT INC.—See Altech Co., Ltd.; *Int'l*, pg. 388
ALTERYX CZECH REPUBLIC S.R.O.—See Clearlake Capital Group, L.P.; *U.S. Private*, pg. 933
ALTERYX CZECH REPUBLIC S.R.O.—See Insight Venture Management, LLC; *U.S. Private*, pg. 2087
ALTERYX GMBH—See Clearlake Capital Group, L.P.; *U.S. Private*, pg. 933
ALTERYX GMBH—See Insight Venture Management, LLC; *U.S. Private*, pg. 2087
ALTERYX, INC.—See Clearlake Capital Group, L.P.; *U.S. Private*, pg. 933

ALTERYX, INC.—See Insight Venture Management, LLC; *U.S. Private*, pg. 2087
ALTICAST CORP.; *Int'l*, pg. 392
ALTIMATE GROUP SAS—See Arrow Electronics, Inc.; *U.S. Public*, pg. 195
ALTIMATE UK DISTRIBUTION LIMITED—See Arrow Electronics, Inc.; *U.S. Public*, pg. 195
ALTIUM LIMITED; *Int'l*, pg. 393
ALTIUM NETHERLANDS BV—See Altium Limited; *Int'l*, pg. 393
ALTIUM UK LIMITED—See Altium Limited; *Int'l*, pg. 393
ALTPLUS INC.; *Int'l*, pg. 397
ALZCHEM GROUP AG; *Int'l*, pg. 402
AMANO CORPORATION—See Amano Corporation; *Int'l*, pg. 410
AMAZING CHARTS LLC—See Constellation Software Inc.; *Int'l*, pg. 1773
AMDOCS B.V.—See Amdocs Limited; *Int'l*, pg. 419
AMDOCS CANADIAN MANAGED SERVICES, INC.—See Amdocs Limited; *Int'l*, pg. 419
AMDOCS CHAMPAIGN, INC.—See Amdocs Limited; *Int'l*, pg. 419
AMDOCS CHILE SPA—See Amdocs Limited; *Int'l*, pg. 419
AMDOCS INC. - SEATTLE—See Amdocs Limited; *Int'l*, pg. 419
AMDOCS INC.—See Amdocs Limited; *Int'l*, pg. 419
AMDOCS (ITALY) SRL—See Amdocs Limited; *Int'l*, pg. 419
AMDOCS MEXICO S. DE R.L. DE C.V.—See Amdocs Limited; *Int'l*, pg. 419
AMDOCS PHILIPPINES INC.—See Amdocs Limited; *Int'l*, pg. 419
AMDOCS (PORTUGAL) SOFTWARE, UNIPESSOAL LDA.—See Amdocs Limited; *Int'l*, pg. 419
AMDOCS QPASS INC.—See Amdocs Limited; *Int'l*, pg. 419
AMDOCS SYSTEMS EUROPE LIMITED—See Amdocs Limited; *Int'l*, pg. 419
AMDOCS SYSTEMS GROUP LIMITED—See Amdocs Limited; *Int'l*, pg. 419
AMDOCS SYSTEMS LIMITED—See Amdocs Limited; *Int'l*, pg. 419
AMDOCS VIETNAM COMPANY LIMITED—See Amdocs Limited; *Int'l*, pg. 420
AMERICAN CADASTRE, LLC—See Riverside Partners, LLC; *U.S. Private*, pg. 3445
AMERICAN WELL CORPORATION; *U.S. Public*, pg. 112
AMERICOMMERCE, L.P.—See Cart.Com, Inc.; *U.S. Private*, pg. 775
AMIVOICE THAI CO., LTD.—See Advanced Media, Inc.; *Int'l*, pg. 160
AMJ GLOBAL TECHNOLOGY; *U.S. Public*, pg. 124
AMOEBA TECHNOLOGIES INC.—See Keysight Technologies, Inc.; *U.S. Public*, pg. 1226
AMPERO GMBH—See BayWa AG; *Int'l*, pg. 915
AMPHORA, INC.; *U.S. Private*, pg. 266
AMPLIFY EDUCATION, INC.—See News Corporation; *U.S. Public*, pg. 1518
AMPLYFI LTD; *Int'l*, pg. 436
AMSI PROPERTY MANAGEMENT—See Koch Industries, Inc.; *U.S. Private*, pg. 2330
AMTDIRECT, LLC—See GI Manager L.P.; *U.S. Private*, pg. 1693
AMX INTERNATIONAL, INC.; *U.S. Private*, pg. 270
AMZUR TECHNOLOGIES, INC.; *U.S. Private*, pg. 270
AMZUR TECHNOLOGIES (I) PRIVATE LIMITED—See Amzur Technologies, Inc.; *U.S. Private*, pg. 271
ANALYTICS8, LLC; *U.S. Private*, pg. 271
ANAQUA, INC.—See Insight Venture Management, LLC; *U.S. Private*, pg. 2087
ANCHORFREE, INC.; *U.S. Private*, pg. 274
ANCHOR SOFTWARE LLC—See Anchor Computer Inc.; *U.S. Private*, pg. 272
ANEVIA SA—See ATEME S.A.; *Int'l*, pg. 668
AN GLOBAL I.T. S.A.P.I. DE C.V.; *U.S. Private*, pg. 271
ANIMOCA BRANDS CORPORATION LIMITED; *Int'l*, pg. 471
ANJU SOFTWARE, INC.—See ABRY Partners, LLC; *U.S. Private*, pg. 40
ANKAMA SAS; *Int'l*, pg. 472
ANSYS BELGIUM SA—See ANSYS, Inc.; *U.S. Public*, pg. 138
ANSYS CANADA LTD.—See ANSYS, Inc.; *U.S. Public*, pg. 138
ANSYS FLUENT INDIA PVT. LTD.—See ANSYS, Inc.; *U.S. Public*, pg. 138
ANSYS FLUENT SHANGHAI ENGINEERING SOFTWARE TRADING COMPANY LTD.—See ANSYS, Inc.; *U.S. Public*, pg. 138
ANSYS FRANCE SAS—See ANSYS, Inc.; *U.S. Public*, pg. 138
ANSYS GERMANY GMBH—See ANSYS, Inc.; *U.S. Public*, pg. 138
ANSYS HONG KONG LTD.—See ANSYS, Inc.; *U.S. Public*, pg. 138
ANSYS IBERIA S.L.—See ANSYS, Inc.; *U.S. Public*, pg. 138
ANSYS, INC.; *U.S. Public*, pg. 138
ANSYS ITALIA, S.R.L.—See ANSYS, Inc.; *U.S. Public*, pg. 138
ANSYS OOO—See ANSYS, Inc.; *U.S. Public*, pg. 138

513210 — SOFTWARE PUBLISHERS

ANSYS SOFTWARE PVT. LTD.—See ANSYS, Inc.; *U.S. Public*, pg. 138
ANSYS SWEDEN AB—See ANSYS, Inc.; *U.S. Public*, pg. 138
ANTENNA SOFTWARE, LLC—See Pegasystems Inc.; *U.S. Public*, pg. 1660
THE ANTHONY ROBBINS COMPANY—See Robbins Research International; *U.S. Private*, pg. 3457
ANTS SOFTWARE INC.; *U.S. Private*, pg. 288
ANVATO, INC.—See Alphabet Inc.; *U.S. Public*, pg. 83
APACHE DESIGN SOLUTIONS K.K.—See ANSYS, Inc.; *U.S. Public*, pg. 139
APACHE POWER SOLUTIONS ISRAEL LTD.—See ANSYS, Inc.; *U.S. Public*, pg. 139
APAMA (UK) LIMITED—See Progress Software Corporation; *U.S. Public*, pg. 1725
APERE ENTERPRISE STORAGE SOLUTIONS INDIA PVT. LTD.—See Elliott Management Corporation; *U.S. Private*, pg. 1366
APERE ENTERPRISE STORAGE SOLUTIONS INDIA PVT. LTD.—See Vista Equity Partners, LLC; *U.S. Private*, pg. 4395
APERTURE TECHNOLOGIES INC.—See Vertiv Holdings Co; *U.S. Public*, pg. 2288
APEX ANALYTIX, LLC—See KKR & Co. Inc.; *U.S. Public*, pg. 1239
APEX INFORMATION TECHNOLOGIES; *U.S. Private*, pg. 292
APEXSQL, LLC—See Francisco Partners Management, LP; *U.S. Private*, pg. 1591
APIGEE CORPORATION—See Alphabet Inc.; *U.S. Public*, pg. 83
API HEALTHCARE CORPORATION—See Clearlake Capital Group, L.P.; *U.S. Public*, pg. 937
API HEALTHCARE CORPORATION—See SkyKnight Capital LLC; *U.S. Private*, pg. 3685
APLIX CORPORATION; *Int'l*, pg. 516
APLIX KOREA CORPORATION—See Aplix Corporation; *Int'l*, pg. 516
APOLLO BELL INTERNATIONAL PLC; *Int'l*, pg. 517
APPAREO SYSTEMS, LLC; *U.S. Private*, pg. 295
APPCELERATOR INC.—See Axway Software SA; *Int'l*, pg. 772
APPCENTRAL, INC.—See BlueRun Ventures; *U.S. Private*, pg. 597
APPDIRECT INC.; *U.S. Private*, pg. 296
APP-DNA, INC.—See Elliott Management Corporation; *U.S. Private*, pg. 1366
APP-DNA, INC.—See Vista Equity Partners, LLC; *U.S. Private*, pg. 4395
APPDYNAMICS INTERNATIONAL LTD.—See Cisco Systems, Inc.; *U.S. Public*, pg. 497
APPDYNAMICS TECHNOLOGIES INDIA PRIVATE LIMITED—See Cisco Systems, Inc.; *U.S. Public*, pg. 497
APPERIAN, INC.—See TPG Capital, L.P.; *U.S. Public*, pg. 2173
APPFOLIO, INC.; *U.S. Public*, pg. 168
APP INCLINE CORPORATION; *U.S. Private*, pg. 295
APPLIED INFORMATION GROUP INC.—See Aquiline Capital Partners LLC; *U.S. Private*, pg. 304
APPLIED INTUITION, INC.; *U.S. Private*, pg. 299
APPLIED PREDICTIVE TECHNOLOGIES, INC.—See Mastercard Incorporated; *U.S. Public*, pg. 1394
APPLIED SYSTEMS, INC.—See Hellman & Friedman LLC; *U.S. Private*, pg. 1907
APPLIED SYSTEMS INC.—See JMI Services, Inc.; *U.S. Private*, pg. 2215
APPLIED TECHNOLOGIES INTERNET SAS; *Int'l*, pg. 521
APPLIED VISUAL SCIENCES, INC.; *U.S. Public*, pg. 173
APPLIED WEATHER TECHNOLOGY, INC.—See Alfa Laval AB; *Int'l*, pg. 312
APPLOVIN CORP.; *U.S. Public*, pg. 173
APPRISS RETAIL—See Appriss Holdings, Inc.; *U.S. Public*, pg. 300
APPROXY INC.—See Numecent Holdings Ltd.; *U.S. Private*, pg. 2973
APPSENSE LTD.; *Int'l*, pg. 522
APPTENTIVE, INC.—See KKR & Co. Inc.; *U.S. Public*, pg. 1239
APPTIO, INC.—See International Business Machines Corporation; *U.S. Public*, pg. 1145
APPWORX LLC; *U.S. Private*, pg. 300
APPYEA, INC.; *U.S. Public*, pg. 174
APRIMA MEDICAL SOFTWARE, INC.—See CompuGroup Medical SE & Co. KGaA; *Int'l*, pg. 1757
APTARIS LLC; *U.S. Private*, pg. 302
APTEAN, INC.—See TA Associates, Inc.; *U.S. Private*, pg. 3914
APTEAN - MADE2MANAGE ERP—See TA Associates, Inc.; *U.S. Private*, pg. 3914
APTEAN - TRADEBEAM SCM—See TA Associates, Inc.; *U.S. Private*, pg. 3914
APTIFY—See Insight Venture Management, LLC; *U.S. Private*, pg. 2088
APT SYSTEMS, INC.; *U.S. Public*, pg. 174
AQUILA SOFTWARE—See Constellation Software Inc.; *Int'l*, pg. 1775
ARAB SEA INFORMATION SYSTEM CO; *Int'l*, pg. 531

ARALIA SYSTEMS, INC.—See Aralia Systems Ltd.; *Int'l*, pg. 535
ARALIA SYSTEMS LTD.; *Int'l*, pg. 535
ARAS CORP; *U.S. Private*, pg. 307
ARBOL INC.; *U.S. Private*, pg. 308
ARCHITECTURAL COMPUTER SERVICES, INC.—See Alpine Investors; *U.S. Private*, pg. 201
ARCHON INFORMATION SYSTEMS, L.L.C.; *U.S. Private*, pg. 312
ARCOT R&D SOFTWARE PRIVATE LTD.—See Broadcom Inc.; *U.S. Public*, pg. 388
ARCSERVE (USA) LLC—See Marlin Equity Partners, LLC; *U.S. Private*, pg. 2583
ARDEN SOFTWARE LTD.; *Int'l*, pg. 554
ARES INTERNATIONAL CORPORATION; *Int'l*, pg. 559
ARGUS SOFTWARE, INC.—See Altus Group Limited; *Int'l*, pg. 399
ARGUS WORLDWIDE CORP.; *U.S. Public*, pg. 191
ARI EUROPE B.V.—See True Wind Capital Management, L.P.; *U.S. Private*, pg. 4248
ARISTA NETWORKS, INC.; *U.S. Public*, pg. 192
ARISTOCRAT TECHNOLOGIES MACAU LIMITED—See Aristocrat Leisure Limited; *Int'l*, pg. 566
ARITHMETIC INC.—See Aeria Inc.; *Int'l*, pg. 179
THE ARLEN GROUP, INC.—See Stone Point Capital LLC; *U.S. Private*, pg. 3819
THE ARMADA GROUP, INC.—See Stone Point Capital LLC; *U.S. Private*, pg. 3823
ARMORIZE TECHNOLOGIES, INC.—See Thoma Bravo, L.P.; *U.S. Private*, pg. 4151
AROBS TRANSILVANIA SOFTWARE S.A.; *Int'l*, pg. 577
ARRAYCOMM, INC.—See Ygomi LLC; *U.S. Private*, pg. 4589
ARREVA LLC; *U.S. Private*, pg. 334
ARROWPOINTE CORP.—See The Ascent Group LLC; *U.S. Private*, pg. 3988
ARTEC TECHNOLOGIES AG; *Int'l*, pg. 581
ARTICAD LTD—See COFRA Holding AG; *Int'l*, pg. 1693
ARTIFICIAL LIFE, INC.; *Int'l*, pg. 584
ARTIFICIAL MIND & MOVEMENT; *Int'l*, pg. 584
ARTILIUM PLC—See Pareteum Corporation; *U.S. Public*, pg. 1637
ARTISAN INFRASTRUCTURE INC.; *U.S. Private*, pg. 343
ARX INC.—See DocuSign, Inc.; *U.S. Public*, pg. 672
ASCADE MIDDLE EAST FZ-LLC—See CSG Systems International, Inc.; *U.S. Public*, pg. 601
ASCEND FUNDRAISING SOLUTIONS—See Orange Capital Ventures GP, LLC; *U.S. Private*, pg. 3036
ASCENDIA INC.—See Future Corporation; *Int'l*, pg. 2853
ASCENTIS CORPORATION—See Hellman & Friedman LLC; *U.S. Private*, pg. 1910
ASCON HOSTING FACILITIES B.V.—See CompuGroup Medical SE & Co. KGaA; *Int'l*, pg. 1755
ASCON SOFTWARE B.V.—See CompuGroup Medical SE & Co. KGaA; *Int'l*, pg. 1755
ASGARD CORPORATION—See Aeria Inc.; *Int'l*, pg. 179
ASIAN BUSINESS SOFTWARE SOLUTIONS SDN. BHD.—See Bain Capital, LP; *U.S. Private*, pg. 441
ASIASOFT ONLINE PTE. LTD—See Asphere Innovations Public Company Limited; *Int'l*, pg. 630
ASIGNET USA, INC.; *U.S. Private*, pg. 351
ASL ACQUISITION, INC.—See NetXposure, Inc.; *U.S. Private*, pg. 2890
AS ONLINE SDN. BHD.—See Asphere Innovations Public Company Limited; *Int'l*, pg. 629
ASPARITY DECISION SOLUTIONS, INC.—See Automatic Data Processing, Inc.; *U.S. Public*, pg. 230
ASPECT SOFTWARE GROUP HOLDINGS LTD.; *U.S. Private*, pg. 351
ASPECT SOFTWARE, INC.—See Vector Capital Management, L.P.; *U.S. Private*, pg. 4350
ASPENWARE, INC.; *U.S. Private*, pg. 352
ASPERA, INC.—See International Business Machines Corporation; *U.S. Public*, pg. 1148
ASPYR MEDIA, INC.—See Embracer Group AB; *Int'l*, pg. 2375
ASSECO BUSINESS SOLUTIONS S.A.—See Asseco Poland S.A.; *Int'l*, pg. 641
ASSECO SEE SH.P.K.—See Asseco Poland S.A.; *Int'l*, pg. 641
ASSEMBLA INC.—See HGGC, LLC; *U.S. Private*, pg. 1929
ASSET INTELLIGENCE, LLC—See PowerFleet, Inc.; *U.S. Public*, pg. 1706
ASSET INTERTECH, INC.; *U.S. Private*, pg. 354
ASSET REALTY GROUP; *U.S. Private*, pg. 354
ASSET VANTAGE SYSTEMS PVT. LTD.; *Int'l*, pg. 642
ASSETWORKS, INC.—See Constellation Software Inc.; *Int'l*, pg. 1775
ASSIMA CANADA, INC.—See Fonds de Solidarite des Travailleurs du Quebec; *Int'l*, pg. 2725
ASSIMA, INC.—See Fonds de Solidarite des Travailleurs du Quebec; *Int'l*, pg. 2725
ASSIMA PLC—See Fonds de Solidarite des Travailleurs du Quebec; *Int'l*, pg. 2725
ASSIST DIGITAL S.P.A.—See Ardian SAS; *Int'l*, pg. 555
ASSURANCE SOFTWARE, INC.—See Resurgens Technology Partners, LLC; *U.S. Private*, pg. 3410

CORPORATE AFFILIATIONS

ASSURECARE, LLC—See Vora Ventures LLC; *U.S. Private*, pg. 4412
ASSURESIGN LLC—See TPG Capital, L.P.; *U.S. Public*, pg. 2175
ASTA DEVELOPMENT GMBH—See Eleco Plc; *Int'l*, pg. 2348
ASTEA INTERNATIONAL AUSTRALIAN PTY LTD.—See EQT AB; *Int'l*, pg. 2477
ASTEA INTERNATIONAL INC.—See EQT AB; *Int'l*, pg. 2477
ASTEA INTERNATIONAL JAPAN, INC.—See EQT AB; *Int'l*, pg. 2477
ASTEA (UK) LTD.—See EQT AB; *Int'l*, pg. 2477
ASTERIA CORPORATION; *Int'l*, pg. 654
ASTRIX TECHNOLOGY GROUP, INC.; *U.S. Private*, pg. 361
ASTUTE, INC.; *U.S. Private*, pg. 362
ATALASOFT, INC.—See Clearlake Capital Group, L.P.; *U.S. Private*, pg. 935
ATALASOFT, INC.—See TA Associates, Inc.; *U.S. Private*, pg. 3916
ATEAM INC.; *Int'l*, pg. 667
ATEGO GROUP LTD.—See PTC Inc.; *U.S. Public*, pg. 1734
ATEGO SAS—See PTC Inc.; *U.S. Public*, pg. 1734
ATEMPO DEUTSCHLAND GMBH—See Atempo S.A.; *Int'l*, pg. 668
ATEMPO, INC.—See Atempo S.A.; *Int'l*, pg. 668
ATHENIUM ANALYTICS LLC; *U.S. Private*, pg. 367
ATHENIUM, LLC—See Athenium Analytics LLC; *U.S. Private*, pg. 367
ATHOC, INC.—See BlackBerry Limited; *Int'l*, pg. 1060
AT INTERNET BRAZIL—See Applied Technologies Internet SAS; *Int'l*, pg. 521
AT INTERNET GMBH—See Applied Technologies Internet SAS; *Int'l*, pg. 521
AT INTERNET INC.—See Applied Technologies Internet SAS; *Int'l*, pg. 521
AT INTERNET LTD.—See Applied Technologies Internet SAS; *Int'l*, pg. 521
AT INTERNET PTE. LTD.—See Applied Technologies Internet SAS; *Int'l*, pg. 521
AT INTERNET SL—See Applied Technologies Internet SAS; *Int'l*, pg. 521
ATKA US, LLC—See Salesforce, Inc.; *U.S. Public*, pg. 1836
ATLAS CONSULTING—See Atlas Development Corporation; *U.S. Private*, pg. 376
ATLAS DEVELOPMENT CORPORATION; *U.S. Private*, pg. 375
ATLAS MEDICAL—See Atlas Development Corporation; *U.S. Private*, pg. 376
ATLAS PUBLIC HEALTH—See Atlas Development Corporation; *U.S. Private*, pg. 376
ATLAS RFID SOLUTIONS, INC.; *U.S. Private*, pg. 379
ATLASSIAN B.V.—See Atlassian Corporation; *Int'l*, pg. 686
ATLASSIAN, INC.—See Atlassian Corporation; *Int'l*, pg. 686
ATLASSIAN K.K.—See Atlassian Corporation; *Int'l*, pg. 686
ATLASSIAN PHILIPPINES, INC.—See Atlassian Corporation; *Int'l*, pg. 686
ATLASSIAN PTY. LTD.—See Atlassian Corporation; *Int'l*, pg. 686
ATOS CONVERGENCE CREATORS GMBH—See Atos SE; *Int'l*, pg. 690
ATOS CONVERGENCE CREATORS SRL—See Atos SE; *Int'l*, pg. 690
ATOS ORIGIN BRASIL LTDA—See Atos SE; *Int'l*, pg. 691
ATTENSITY CORPORATION—See Attensity Group, Inc.; *U.S. Private*, pg. 383
ATTRAQT GROUP PLC—See CrownPeak Technology, Inc.; *U.S. Private*, pg. 1112
ATTUNITY LTD.—See Thoma Bravo, L.P.; *U.S. Private*, pg. 4152
ATTURRA HOLDINGS PTY LTD—See Atturra Ltd.; *Int'l*, pg. 697
ATTURRA LTD.; *Int'l*, pg. 697
ATW TECH INC.; *Int'l*, pg. 697
ATYATI TECHNOLOGIES PRIVATE LIMITED—See Genpact Limited; *Int'l*, pg. 2926
ATYPON SYSTEMS JORDAN—See John Wiley & Sons, Inc.; *U.S. Public*, pg. 1192
ATYPON SYSTEMS, LLC—See John Wiley & Sons, Inc.; *U.S. Public*, pg. 1192
ATYPON SYSTEMS UK—See John Wiley & Sons, Inc.; *U.S. Public*, pg. 1192
AUCTIVA CORPORATION—See Alibaba Group Holding Limited; *Int'l*, pg. 326
AUDATEX AUSTRALIA PTY LTD.—See Vista Equity Partners, LLC; *U.S. Private*, pg. 4399
AUDATEX DATEN INTERNATIONALE DATENENTWICKLUNGSGESELLSCHAFT MBH—See Vista Equity Partners, LLC; *U.S. Private*, pg. 4399
AUDATEX ESPANA S.A.—See Vista Equity Partners, LLC; *U.S. Private*, pg. 4399
AUDATEX INFORMATION SYSTEM (CHINA) CO., LTD.—See Vista Equity Partners, LLC; *U.S. Private*, pg. 4399
AUDATEX LTN S. DE R.L. DE C.V.—See Vista Equity Partners, LLC; *U.S. Private*, pg. 4400
AUDATEX NETWORK SERVICES NETHERLANDS

N.A.I.C.S. INDEX
513210 — SOFTWARE PUBLISHERS

B.V.—See Vista Equity Partners, LLC; *U.S. Private*, pg. 4400
AUDATEX OSTERREICH GES.MBH—See Vista Equity Partners, LLC; *U.S. Private*, pg. 4400
AUDATEX PORTUGAL PERITAGENS INFORMATIZADAS DERIVADAS DE ACIDENTES, S.A.—See Vista Equity Partners, LLC; *U.S. Private*, pg. 4400
AUDATEX SERVICES SRL—See Vista Equity Partners, LLC; *U.S. Private*, pg. 4400
AUDATEX SINGAPORE PTE LTD—See Vista Equity Partners, LLC; *U.S. Private*, pg. 4400
AUDATEX SLOVAKIA S.R.O.—See Vista Equity Partners, LLC; *U.S. Private*, pg. 4400
AUDATEX SYSTEMS BILGI TEKNOLOJILERI HIZMETLERI LIMTED SIRKETI—See Vista Equity Partners, LLC; *U.S. Private*, pg. 4400
AUDATEX SYSTEMS S.R.O.—See Vista Equity Partners, LLC; *U.S. Private*, pg. 4400
AUDIOEYE, INC.; *U.S. Public*, pg. 227
AUDIOTEL CORPORATION—See Jack Henry & Associates, Inc.; *U.S. Public*, pg. 1182
AUDITUDE, INC.—See Adobe Inc.; *U.S. Public*, pg. 42
AUDIUS AG; *Int'l*, pg. 702
AUGE TECHNOLOGY CORPORATION; *Int'l*, pg. 703
AUGURE SA; *Int'l*, pg. 703
AUNALYTICS, INC., *U.S. Private*, pg. 393
AUREA SOFTWARE GMBH—See ESW Capital, LLC; *U.S. Private*, pg. 1429
AUREA SOFTWARE, INC.—See ESW Capital, LLC; *U.S. Private*, pg. 1429
AURIONPRO SOLUTIONS (HK) LTD.—See Aurionpro Solutions Limited; *Int'l*, pg. 711
AURUM PROPTECH LTD.; *Int'l*, pg. 715
AUTOAGENT DATA SOLUTIONS, LLC—See Stella Point Capital, LP; *U.S. Private*, pg. 3799
AUTOBASE, INC.—See Irish Times; *U.S. Private*, pg. 2138
AUTO DATA, INC.; *U.S. Private*, pg. 397
AUTODATA SOLUTIONS, INC.—See Thoma Bravo, L.P.; *U.S. Private*, pg. 4146
AUTODEMO LLC; *U.S. Private*, pg. 398
AUTODESK AB—See Autodesk, Inc.; *U.S. Public*, pg. 228
AUTODESK APS—See Autodesk, Inc.; *U.S. Public*, pg. 228
AUTODESK BENELUX B.V.—See Autodesk, Inc.; *U.S. Public*, pg. 228
AUTODESK CANADA CO.—See Autodesk, Inc.; *U.S. Public*, pg. 229
AUTODESK CANADA CO.—See Autodesk, Inc.; *U.S. Public*, pg. 229
AUTODESK GESMBH—See Autodesk, Inc.; *U.S. Public*, pg. 228
AUTODESK GMBH—See Autodesk, Inc.; *U.S. Public*, pg. 228
AUTODESK, INC.; *U.S. Public*, pg. 228
AUTODESK, INC. - UK—See Autodesk, Inc.; *U.S. Public*, pg. 229
AUTODESK INDIA PRIVATE LIMITED—See Autodesk, Inc.; *U.S. Public*, pg. 228
AUTODESK LIMITED—See Autodesk, Inc.; *U.S. Public*, pg. 228
AUTODESK SOFTWARE (CHINA) CO., LTD.—See Autodesk, Inc.; *U.S. Public*, pg. 228
AUTOMATED FINANCIAL SYSTEMS INC.; *U.S. Private*, pg. 399
AUTOMATED HEALTHCARE SOLUTIONS, LLC; *U.S. Private*, pg. 399
AUTOMATED MEDICAL SYSTEMS INC.—See DAS Health Ventures, Inc.; *U.S. Private*, pg. 1161
AUTOMATED PAYMENT HIGHWAY, INC—See Lovell Minnick Partners LLC; *U.S. Private*, pg. 2501
AUTO/MATE, INC.—See Vista Equity Partners, LLC; *U.S. Private*, pg. 4400
AUTOMATTIC INC.; *U.S. Private*, pg. 400
AUTOMIC SOFTWARE GMBH—See Broadcom Inc.; *U.S. Public*, pg. 388
AUTOMIC SOFTWARE, INC.—See Broadcom Inc.; *U.S. Public*, pg. 388
AUTOMOTIVE LEASE GUIDE (ALG), INC.—See TrueCar, Inc.; *U.S. Public*, pg. 2199
AUTONAVI SOFTWARE CO., LTD.—See Alibaba Group Holding Limited; *Int'l*, pg. 326
AUTOONLINE OTOMOTIV BILGI ISLEM ANONIM SIRKETI—See Vista Equity Partners, LLC; *U.S. Private*, pg. 4399
AUTOONLINE SISTEME INFORMATICE SRL—See Vista Equity Partners, LLC; *U.S. Private*, pg. 4399
AUTO POINT, INC.—See Vista Equity Partners, LLC; *U.S. Private*, pg. 4400
AUTOTASK CORPORATION—See Vista Equity Partners, LLC; *U.S. Private*, pg. 4395
AUTOTASK (UK) LIMITED—See Vista Equity Partners, LLC; *U.S. Private*, pg. 4395
AUTOTEC LLC; *U.S. Private*, pg. 401
AVALARA, INC.—See Vista Equity Partners, LLC; *U.S. Private*, pg. 4395
AVALARA TECHNOLOGIES PVT. LTD.—See Vista Equity Partners, LLC; *U.S. Private*, pg. 4395
AVANADE IRELAND LIMITED—See Accenture plc; *Int'l*, pg. 86

AVANADE OSTERREICH GMBH—See Accenture plc; *Int'l*, pg. 86
AVANADE POLAND SP. Z O.O.—See Accenture plc; *Int'l*, pg. 86
AVANGATE B.V.—See Francisco Partners Management, LP; *U.S. Private*, pg. 1588
AVANGATE INC.—See Francisco Partners Management, LP; *U.S. Private*, pg. 1588
AVANQUEST CHINA—See Claranova SA; *Int'l*, pg. 1642
AVANQUEST FRANCE—See Claranova SA; *Int'l*, pg. 1642
AVANQUEST ITALIA SRL—See Claranova SA; *Int'l*, pg. 1642
AVANQUEST PUBLISHING USA—See Claranova SA; *Int'l*, pg. 1642
AVANQUEST SOFTWARE USA—See Claranova SA; *Int'l*, pg. 1642
AVANQUEST UK LTD—See Claranova SA; *Int'l*, pg. 1642
AVANTAS, LLC—See AMN Healthcare Services, Inc.; *U.S. Public*, pg. 125
AVANT CORPORATION; *Int'l*, pg. 735
AVAST SOFTWARE, INC.—See Gen Digital Inc.; *U.S. Public*, pg. 910
AVAST SOFTWARE S.R.O.—See Gen Digital Inc.; *U.S. Public*, pg. 910
AVATAR INTEGRATED SYSTEMS, INC.; *U.S. Private*, pg. 404
AVATAR SYSTEMS, INC.; *U.S. Public*, pg. 242
AVENZA SYSTEMS INC.—See Avenza Holdings Inc.; *Int'l*, pg. 739
AVEPOINT, INC.; *U.S. Public*, pg. 243
AVETTA, LLC—See Welsh, Carson, Anderson & Stowe; *U.S. Private*, pg. 4479
AVG TECHNOLOGIES B.V.—See Gen Digital Inc.; *U.S. Public*, pg. 910
AVG TECHNOLOGIES CZ S.R.O.—See Gen Digital Inc.; *U.S. Public*, pg. 910
AVIDIAN TECHNOLOGIES, INC.; *U.S. Private*, pg. 407
AVIDXCHANGE, INC.—See AvidXchange Holdings, Inc.; *U.S. Public*, pg. 246
AVISTA INCORPORATED—See AE Industrial Partners, LP; *U.S. Private*, pg. 111
AVIT LTD.; *Int'l*, pg. 745
AVITRU, LLC—See Roper Technologies, Inc.; *U.S. Public*, pg. 1810
AVIZIA INC.—See American Well Corporation; *U.S. Public*, pg. 112
AWARENESS CANADA—See Awareness, Inc.; *U.S. Private*, pg. 410
AWARENESS, INC.; *U.S. Private*, pg. 410
AWAREPOINT CORP.; *U.S. Private*, pg. 410
AWEBER COMMUNICATIONS, INC.; *U.S. Private*, pg. 411
AWR-APLAC CORPORATION—See Cadence Design Systems, Inc.; *U.S. Public*, pg. 418
AWR CORPORATION—See Cadence Design Systems, Inc.; *U.S. Public*, pg. 418
AXIANS INFORMA GMBH—See Electricite de France S.A.; *Int'l*, pg. 2351
AX INC.—See Axell Corporation; *Int'l*, pg. 767
AXIS INFORMATION SYSTEMS; *Int'l*, pg. 770
AXIS RISK CONSULTING SERVICES PVT. LTD.—See Genpact Limited; *Int'l*, pg. 2926
AXIUM XTS CORPORATION; *U.S. Private*, pg. 414
AXWAY BELGIUM SA—See Axway Software SA; *Int'l*, pg. 772
AXWAY BULGARIA—See Axway Software SA; *Int'l*, pg. 772
AXWAY GMBH—See Axway Software SA; *Int'l*, pg. 772
AXWAY LIMITED—See Axway Software SA; *Int'l*, pg. 772
AXWAY PTE. LTD.—See Axway Software SA; *Int'l*, pg. 772
AXWAY SOFTWARE CHINA—See Axway Software SA; *Int'l*, pg. 772
AXWAY SOFTWARE GMBH—See Axway Software SA; *Int'l*, pg. 772
AXWAY SOFTWARE MALAYSIA SDN BHD—See Axway Software SA; *Int'l*, pg. 772
AXWAY SOFTWARE SA; *Int'l*, pg. 772
AXXESS TECHNOLOGY SOLUTIONS, INC; *U.S. Private*, pg. 414
AYU TECHNOLOGY SOLUTIONS LLC; *U.S. Private*, pg. 415
AZALEA HEALTH INNOVATIONS, INC.; *U.S. Private*, pg. 415
AZEUS PTY LTD—See Azeus Systems Holdings Ltd.; *Int'l*, pg. 778
AZEUS SYSTEMS (DALIAN) CO., LTD.—See Azeus Systems Holdings Ltd.; *Int'l*, pg. 778
AZEUS SYSTEMS HOLDINGS LTD.; *Int'l*, pg. 778
AZEUS SYSTEMS LIMITED—See Azeus Systems Holdings Ltd.; *Int'l*, pg. 778
AZEUS UK LIMITED—See Azeus Systems Holdings Ltd.; *Int'l*, pg. 778
B2X CARE SOLUTIONS GMBH—See Barkawi Holding GmbH; *Int'l*, pg. 865
B7 INTERACTIVE, LLC—See Scaleworks, Inc.; *U.S. Private*, pg. 3561
BABYLON LTD.; *Int'l*, pg. 793
BACKBONE ENTERTAINMENT—See Foundation 9 Entertainment, Inc.; *U.S. Private*, pg. 1579

BAE SYSTEMS APPLIED INTELLIGENCE—See BAE Systems plc; *Int'l*, pg. 798
BAIOO FAMILY INTERACTIVE LIMITED; *Int'l*, pg. 803
BAIWANG HOLDING CO., LTD.—See Beijing Watertek Information Technology Co., Ltd.; *Int'l*, pg. 960
BAKKT, LLC—See Intercontinental Exchange, Inc.; *U.S. Public*, pg. 1141
BALAJI TELEFILMS LTD.; *Int'l*, pg. 806
BALIHOO, INC.; *U.S. Private*, pg. 459
BANDAI NAMCO ENTERTAINMENT AMERICA INC.—See BANDAI NAMCO Holdings Inc.; *Int'l*, pg. 829
BANKER'S TOOLBOX, INC.—See The Carlyle Group Inc.; *U.S. Public*, pg. 2045
BANYAN SOFTWARE, INC.; *U.S. Private*, pg. 470
BAOFENG GROUP CO., LTD.; *Int'l*, pg. 856
BARISTA SOFTWARE BVBA—See CompuGroup Medical SE & Co. KGaA; *Int'l*, pg. 1755
BARKING APPLICATIONS CORPORATION; *Int'l*, pg. 865
BARRACUDA MSP—See KKR & Co. Inc.; *U.S. Public*, pg. 1241
BARRACUDA NETWORKS (HONG KONG) LIMITED—See KKR & Co. Inc.; *U.S. Public*, pg. 1241
BARRACUDA NETWORKS (INDIA) PRIVATE LIMITED—See KKR & Co. Inc.; *U.S. Public*, pg. 1241
BARRACUDA NETWORKS, LIMITED—See KKR & Co. Inc.; *U.S. Public*, pg. 1241
BARRACUDA NETWORKS SINGAPORE PTE LTD.—See KKR & Co. Inc.; *U.S. Public*, pg. 1241
BASICSOFT INC.—See Leeds Equity Partners, LLC; *U.S. Private*, pg. 2415
BASSETTI GROUP SAS; *Int'l*, pg. 888
BASWARE OYJ—See Accel Partners L.P.; *U.S. Private*, pg. 47
BASWARE OYJ—See KKR & Co. Inc.; *U.S. Public*, pg. 1237
BASWARE OYJ—See Long Path Partners, LP; *U.S. Private*, pg. 2491
BAY ACQUISITION CORP.; *U.S. Private*, pg. 491
BAYANAT AI PLC; *Int'l*, pg. 901
BAZAARVOICE, INC.—See Marlin Equity Partners, LLC; *U.S. Private*, pg. 2584
BCC SOFTWARE, LLC—See Platinum Equity, LLC; *U.S. Private*, pg. 3202
BD DIAGNOSTIC SYSTEMS-INFORMATICS—See Becton, Dickinson & Company; *U.S. Public*, pg. 288
BEARWARE, INC.; *U.S. Private*, pg. 507
BECOME, INC.—See Symphony Technology Group, LLC; *U.S. Private*, pg. 3900
BECRYPT LIMITED; *Int'l*, pg. 938
BECUAI INC.; *Int'l*, pg. 938
BEELINE.COM, INC.—See Stone Point Capital LLC; *U.S. Private*, pg. 3821
BEIJING ACOINFO INFORMATION TECHNOLOGY CO. LTD.—See Beijing Watertek Information Technology Co., Ltd.; *Int'l*, pg. 960
BEIJING CEE TECHNOLOGY CO., LTD.—See Celartem Technology Inc.; *Int'l*, pg. 1391
BEIJING CENTURY TECHNOLOGY CO., LTD.; *Int'l*, pg. 947
BEIJING CLOUDNET TECHNOLOGY CO., LTD.—See Beijing Watertek Information Technology Co., Ltd.; *Int'l*, pg. 960
BEIJING CORE SOFTWARE CO., LTD.—See Core Corporation; *Int'l*, pg. 1797
BEIJING FOREVER TECHNOLOGY COMPANY LIMITED; *Int'l*, pg. 950
BEIJING HANDRUN TECHNOLOGY CO., LTD.—See Beijing Watertek Information Technology Co., Ltd.; *Int'l*, pg. 960
BEIJING NAVISTAR CLOUD SCIENCE & TECHNOLOGY CO., LTD.—See Beijing Watertek Information Technology Co., Ltd.; *Int'l*, pg. 960
BEIJING SHIJI INFORMATION TECHNOLOGY CO., LTD.; *Int'l*, pg. 956
BEIJING TELLHOW INTELLIGENT ENGINEERING CO., LTD.—See Beijing Watertek Information Technology Co., Ltd.; *Int'l*, pg. 960
BEIJING THUNISOFT CORPORATION LIMITED; *Int'l*, pg. 958
BEIJING TONGTECH COMPANY LIMITED; *Int'l*, pg. 959
BEIJING TRS INFORMATION TECHNOLOGY CO., LTD.; *Int'l*, pg. 959
BEIJING VRV SOFTWARE CORPORATION LIMITED; *Int'l*, pg. 960
BEIJING WATERTEK FUXI BIG DATA TECHNOLOGY CO., LTD.—See Beijing Watertek Information Technology Co., Ltd.; *Int'l*, pg. 960
BEIJING WATERTEK_SINDA TECHNOLOGY CO., LTD.—See Beijing Watertek Information Technology Co., Ltd.; *Int'l*, pg. 960
BEIJING ZHUNGHUAN JINKA INFORMATION TECHNOLOGY CO., LTD.—See Beijing Watertek Information Technology Co., Ltd.; *Int'l*, pg. 960
BEING CO., LTD.; *Int'l*, pg. 962
BELVEDERE MARKETING GROUP LLC—See 424 Capital, LLC; *U.S. Private*, pg. 15
BELVEDERE MARKETING GROUP LLC—See HealthEdge Investment Partners, LLC; *U.S. Private*, pg. 1896
BEMAP, INC.; *Int'l*, pg. 968

513210 — SOFTWARE PUBLISHERS

BENCHMARK BROADCAST SYSTEMS (S) PTE LTD—See Benchmark Telecast Integration Pte Ltd; *Int'l*, pg. 970
BENCHMARK DIGITAL PARTNERS LLC—See Vista Equity Partners, LLC; *U.S. Private*, pg. 4395
BENEFIT SYSTEMS SA; *Int'l*, pg. 972
BENO TNR, INC.; *Int'l*, pg. 975
BENSATA CORPORATION; *U.S. Private*, pg. 528
BENTLEY SYSTEMS AUSTRIA GMBH—See Bentley Systems, Inc.; *U.S. Public*, pg. 296
BENTLEY SYSTEMS EUROPE B.V.—See Bentley Systems, Inc.; *U.S. Public*, pg. 296
BENTLEY SYSTEMS FRANCE SARL—See Bentley Systems, Inc.; *U.S. Public*, pg. 296
BENTLEY SYSTEMS, INC. - CARLSBAD—See Bentley Systems, Inc.; *U.S. Public*, pg. 297
BENTLEY SYSTEMS, INC.; *U.S. Public*, pg. 296
BENTLEY SYSTEMS KOREA, INC.—See Bentley Systems, Inc.; *U.S. Public*, pg. 296
BENTLEY SYSTEMS PTY. LTD.—See Bentley Systems, Inc.; *U.S. Public*, pg. 296
BENTLEY SYSTEMS SWITZERLAND AG—See Bentley Systems, Inc.; *U.S. Public*, pg. 296
BERNOULLI ENTERPRISE, INC.—See Francisco Partners Management, LP; *U.S. Private*, pg. 1589
BEST WONDERS SCIENCE & TECHNOLOGY CO., LTD—See Beijing Watertek Information Technology Co., Ltd.; *Int'l*, pg. 960
BE TEAM S.R.L.—See Devoteam SA; *Int'l*, pg. 2089
BEYOND LIMITS, INC.; *U.S. Private*, pg. 548
BEYONDTRUST SOFTWARE, INC.—See Francisco Partners Management, LP; *U.S. Private*, pg. 1589
BIBLIOLABS, LLC—See LYRASIS Inc.; *U.S. Private*, pg. 2522
BI CONSULTING GROUP; *U.S. Private*, pg. 549
BIDSYNC INC.—See KKR & Co. Inc.; *U.S. Public*, pg. 1267
BIGBEN INTERACTIVE SA; *Int'l*, pg. 1022
BIGCOMMERCE, INC.; *U.S. Private*, pg. 555
BIGFIX, INC.—See HCL Technologies Ltd.; *Int'l*, pg. 3298
BIG SKY TECHNOLOGIES INC.—See Fortive Corporation; *U.S. Public*, pg. 872
BIGTIME SOFTWARE, INC.—See Vista Equity Partners, LLC; *U.S. Private*, pg. 4395
BIO-KEY INTERNATIONAL, INC.; *U.S. Public*, pg. 332
BIOTEKNO; *Int'l*, pg. 1043
BIOTRICITY INC.; *U.S. Public*, pg. 339
BIOWARE AUSTIN, LLC—See Electronic Arts Inc.; *U.S. Public*, pg. 723
BIOWARE ULC—See Electronic Arts Inc.; *U.S. Public*, pg. 723
BIRDDOG SOFTWARE CORPORATION; *U.S. Private*, pg. 564
BIT9, INC.; *U.S. Private*, pg. 566
BIT COMPUTER CO., LTD.; *Int'l*, pg. 1049
BITDEFENDER LLC—See BitDefender S.R.L.; *Int'l*, pg. 1049
BITDEFENDER S.R.L.; *Int'l*, pg. 1049
BITNIX, INC.—See Bit Computer Co., Ltd.; *Int'l*, pg. 1049
BITTUBE INTERNATIONAL SE; *Int'l*, pg. 1050
BIZIBLE INC.—See Adobe Inc.; *U.S. Public*, pg. 42
BIZ TECHNOLOGY SOLUTIONS, INC.—See Oval Partners; *U.S. Private*, pg. 3052
BIZVIZ AUDIENCE ANALYTICS, INC.; *U.S. Private*, pg. 567
BLACKBAUD, INC.; *U.S. Public*, pg. 341
BLACK BELT SOLUTIONS LLC; *U.S. Private*, pg. 569
BLACKBOARD COLLABORATE—See Class Technologies Inc.; *U.S. Private*, pg. 915
BLACKBOARD INC.—See Class Technologies Inc.; *U.S. Private*, pg. 915
BLACKBOXSTOCKS INC.; *U.S. Public*, pg. 341
BLACK CREEK INTEGRATED SYSTEMS CORPORATION; *U.S. Private*, pg. 570
BLACKICE ENTERPRISE RISK MANAGEMENT INC.; *Int'l*, pg. 1061
BLACKLINE SYSTEMS; *U.S. Private*, pg. 576
BLACKSTRATUS, INC.; *U.S. Private*, pg. 576
BLANCHARD SYSTEMS, INC.; *U.S. Private*, pg. 579
BLASCHKO COMPUTERS, INC.—See Open Systems, Inc.; *U.S. Private*, pg. 3030
BLEND LABS, INC.; *U.S. Public*, pg. 361
BLIZZARD ENTERTAINMENT—See Microsoft Corporation; *U.S. Public*, pg. 1438
BLOMESYSTEM GMBH—See GUS Group AG & Co KG; *Int'l*, pg. 3188
BLOOMERANG, LLC; *U.S. Private*, pg. 584
BLUECAT NETWORKS, INC.—See Madison Dearborn Partners, LLC; *U.S. Private*, pg. 2540
BLUECAVA, INC.; *U.S. Private*, pg. 596
BLUE CLOUD SOFTECH SOLUTIONS LTD.; *Int'l*, pg. 1067
BLUEDON INFORMATION SECURITY TECHNOLOGIES CO., LTD.; *Int'l*, pg. 1071
BLUE PLANET—See Ciena Corporation; *U.S. Public*, pg. 494
BLUE RIBBON SOFTWARE MALTA LIMITED—See DraftKings Inc.; *U.S. Public*, pg. 687
BLUERIDGE ANALYTICS INC.—See Bentley Systems, Inc.; *U.S. Public*, pg. 296
BLUESIGHT, INC.—See Thoma Bravo, L.P.; *U.S. Private*, pg. 4146

BLUE SKY STUDIOS INC.—See The Walt Disney Company; *U.S. Public*, pg. 2140
BLUESPACE SOFTWARE CORP—See Sterling Computers; *U.S. Private*, pg. 3805
BLUE SPHERE SOLUTIONS, INC.—See Conway, Dierking & Hillman, Inc.; *U.S. Private*, pg. 1037
BLUEWARE, INC.; *U.S. Private*, pg. 598
BLUE WHALE WEB SOLUTIONS, INC.; *U.S. Private*, pg. 594
BLUEWOLF, INC.; *U.S. Private*, pg. 599
BLUEWOLF UK—See Bluewolf, Inc.; *U.S. Private*, pg. 599
BMC SOFTWARE, INC.—See KKR & Co. Inc.; *U.S. Public*, pg. 1239
BMC SOFTWARE (NEW ZEALAND) LTD.—See KKR & Co. Inc.; *U.S. Public*, pg. 1239
BNA SOFTWARE—See Bloomberg L.P.; *U.S. Private*, pg. 584
BNN TECHNOLOGY PLC; *Int'l*, pg. 1079
BOARDVANTAGE, INC.—See Nasdaq, Inc.; *U.S. Public*, pg. 1491
BOARDWALKTECH, INC.—See Boardwalktech Software Corp.; *U.S. Public*, pg. 366
BODY AND MIND INC.; *Int'l*, pg. 1097
BOLD INTERNATIONAL SA—See Devoteam SA; *Int'l*, pg. 2089
BOLT SOLUTIONS, INC.—See CVC Capital Partners SICAV-FIS S.A.; *Int'l*, pg. 1885
BOMGAR CORPORATION—See Francisco Partners Management, LP; *U.S. Private*, pg. 1589
BOND INTERNATIONAL SOFTWARE, INC.—See Symphony Technology Group, LLC; *U.S. Private*, pg. 3900
BONITASOFT, S.A.—See Fortino Capital Partners; *Int'l*, pg. 2739
BONZI TECHNOLOGY INC.; *U.S. Private*, pg. 615
BOOMI, INC.—See Dell Technologies Inc.; *U.S. Public*, pg. 649
BOOMTOWN, LLC; *U.S. Private*, pg. 616
BORIS FX, INC.; *U.S. Private*, pg. 618
BOSTON TECHNOLOGY CORPORATION; *U.S. Private*, pg. 622
BOTTOMLINE TECHNOLOGIES INC.—See Thoma Bravo, L.P.; *U.S. Private*, pg. 4146
BOUNDARY SYSTEMS, LTD; *U.S. Private*, pg. 623
BOX, INC.; *U.S. Public*, pg. 377
BOX UK LIMITED; *Int'l*, pg. 1124
BOX UK LIMITED—See Box UK Limited; *Int'l*, pg. 1124
BPA CORPORATE FACILITATION LTD.—See Verint Systems Inc.; *U.S. Public*, pg. 2281
BPLI HOLDINGS INC.; *Int'l*, pg. 1132
BPO SYSTEMS INC.; *U.S. Private*, pg. 630
BQE SOFTWARE, INC.; *U.S. Private*, pg. 630
BRADMARK TECHNOLOGIES INC.; *U.S. Private*, pg. 633
BRAD SYSTEMS, INC.—See Lawrence Paper Company; *U.S. Private*, pg. 2401
BRADY ENERGY AG—See Brady plc; *Int'l*, pg. 1135
BRADY ENERGY NORWAY AS—See Brady plc; *Int'l*, pg. 1135
BRADY SWITZERLAND SA—See Brady plc; *Int'l*, pg. 1135
BRADY USA, INC.—See Brady plc; *Int'l*, pg. 1135
BRAINCHIP RESEARCH INSTITUTE PTY LTD—See Brainchip Holdings Ltd.; *Int'l*, pg. 1137
BRAIN FORCE GMBH—See Cegeka Groep NV; *Int'l*, pg. 1391
BRAIN FORCE SOFTWARE S.R.O.—See Cegeka Groep NV; *Int'l*, pg. 1391
BRAIN FORCE S.P.A.—See Cegeka Groep NV; *Int'l*, pg. 1390
BRANDBANK LIMITED—See Brookfield Corporation; *Int'l*, pg. 1178
BRANDBANK LIMITED—See Elliott Management Corporation; *U.S. Private*, pg. 1370
BRAND ENGAGEMENT NETWORK, INC.; *U.S. Public*, pg. 380
BRANDT INFORMATION SERVICES, INC.; *U.S. Private*, pg. 639
BRAVATEK SOLUTIONS, INC.; *U.S. Public*, pg. 380
BRAVO PASSENGER SOLUTION PTE LIMITED; *Int'l*, pg. 1142
BRAVOSOLUTION S.P.A.—See Accel Partners L.P.; *U.S. Private*, pg. 48
BRAVOSOLUTION S.P.A.—See KKR & Co. Inc.; *U.S. Public*, pg. 1238
BREATHOMETER, INC.; *U.S. Private*, pg. 643
BRIDGE CORE LLC—See NewSpring Capital LLC; *U.S. Private*, pg. 2917
BRIDGELINE DIGITAL, INC.; *U.S. Public*, pg. 382
BRIDGELINE DIGITAL, INC. - TAMPA—See Bridgeline Digital, Inc.; *U.S. Public*, pg. 382
BRIDGEPORT NETWORKS, INC.—See Alianza Inc.; *U.S. Private*, pg. 167
BRIDGES TRANSITIONS INC.—See Xap Corporation; *U.S. Private*, pg. 4580
BRIGHTEDGE TECHNOLOGIES, INC.; *U.S. Private*, pg. 651
BRIGHT MARKET, LLC; *U.S. Private*, pg. 651
BRIGHTREE PATIENT COLLECTIONS INC.—See ResMed Inc.; *U.S. Public*, pg. 1790

CORPORATE AFFILIATIONS

BRIGHTTALK INC.—See TechTarget, Inc.; *U.S. Public*, pg. 1989
BRIGHTTALK LIMITED—See TechTarget, Inc.; *U.S. Public*, pg. 1989
BRILLIANCE TECHNOLOGY CO LTD; *Int'l*, pg. 1163
BRILLIANT TELECOMMUNICATIONS, INC.; *U.S. Private*, pg. 654
BRITESKIES, LLC; *U.S. Private*, pg. 657
BROADCAST SOFTWARE INTERNATIONAL INC.—See Cumulus Media Inc.; *U.S. Public*, pg. 609
BROADLEAF CO., LTD.; *Int'l*, pg. 1172
BROADPOINT, INC.—See Velosio, LLC; *U.S. Private*, pg. 4355
BROADRIDGE FX & LIQUIDITY SOLUTIONS, LLC—See Broadridge Financial Solutions, Inc.; *U.S. Public*, pg. 391
BROADRIDGE MANAGED SOLUTIONS, INC.—See Broadridge Financial Solutions, Inc.; *U.S. Public*, pg. 391
BROADSOFT, INC.—See Cisco Systems, Inc.; *U.S. Public*, pg. 497
BROADSOFT JAPAN KK—See Cisco Systems, Inc.; *U.S. Public*, pg. 497
BROADVISION SYSTEM PVT LTD.—See ESW Capital, LLC; *U.S. Private*, pg. 1430
BROADVISION UK, LTD.—See ESW Capital, LLC; *U.S. Private*, pg. 1430
BROADWAY TECHNOLOGY, LLC—See Bloomberg L.P.; *U.S. Private*, pg. 583
BROCCOLI CO., LTD.; *Int'l*, pg. 1172
BROMIUM, INC.; *U.S. Private*, pg. 662
BRONTO SOFTWARE, LLC—See Oracle Corporation; *U.S. Public*, pg. 1611
BRQ SOLUCOES EM INFORMATICA S.A.; *Int'l*, pg. 1199
B-SCADA, INC.; *U.S. Public*, pg. 419
BTS ALLIANCE, LLC—See AvidXchange Holdings, Inc; *U.S. Public*, pg. 246
BUBBLES INTERGROUP LTD; *Int'l*, pg. 1206
BUDDY MEDIA, INC.—See Salesforce, Inc; *U.S. Public*, pg. 1836
BUDDY PLATFORM, INC.—See Buddy Platform Ltd.; *Int'l*, pg. 1211
BUILDERFUSION, INC.—See Greenridge Investment Partners; *U.S. Private*, pg. 1779
BUILDERMT, INC.—See Berkshire Hathaway Inc.; *U.S. Public*, pg. 312
BUILDFIRE, INC.; *U.S. Private*, pg. 682
BUILDING ENGINES, INC.; *U.S. Private*, pg. 682
BUILDOUT, INC.—See The Riverside Company; *U.S. Private*, pg. 4108
BULK STORAGE SOFTWARE, INC.; *U.S. Private*, pg. 684
BUNCEE, LLC—See Coughlan Companies, Inc.; *U.S. Private*, pg. 1064
BUNCHBALL, INC.—See Schoeneckers Inc.; *U.S. Private*, pg. 3567
BUREAU VAN DIJK EDITIONS ELECTRONIQUES SAS—See Moody's Corporation; *U.S. Public*, pg. 1467
BUREAU VAN DIJK EDIZIONI ELETTRONICHE SPA—See Moody's Corporation; *U.S. Public*, pg. 1467
BUREAU VAN DIJK ELECTRONIC PUBLISHING AB—See Moody's Corporation; *U.S. Public*, pg. 1467
BUREAU VAN DIJK ELECTRONIC PUBLISHING APS—See Moody's Corporation; *U.S. Public*, pg. 1467
BUREAU VAN DIJK ELECTRONIC PUBLISHING (BEIJING) CO. LIMITED—See Moody's Corporation; *U.S. Public*, pg. 1467
BUREAU VAN DIJK ELECTRONIC PUBLISHING HONG KONG LIMITED—See Moody's Corporation; *U.S. Public*, pg. 1467
BUREAU VAN DIJK ELECTRONIC PUBLISHING KK—See Moody's Corporation; *U.S. Public*, pg. 1467
BUREAU VAN DIJK ELECTRONIC PUBLISHING LLC—See Moody's Corporation; *U.S. Public*, pg. 1467
BUREAU VAN DIJK ELECTRONIC PUBLISHING LTD—See Moody's Corporation; *U.S. Public*, pg. 1467
BUREAU VAN DIJK ELECTRONIC PUBLISHING PTE LTD—See Moody's Corporation; *U.S. Public*, pg. 1467
BUREAU VAN DIJK ELECTRONIC PUBLISHING PTY LIMITED—See Moody's Corporation; *U.S. Public*, pg. 1467
BUREAU VAN DIJK ELECTRONIC PUBLISHING SA DE CV—See Moody's Corporation; *U.S. Public*, pg. 1467
BUREAU VAN DIJK ELECTRONIQ PUBLISHING SA (PTY) LTD.—See Moody's Corporation; *U.S. Public*, pg. 1467
BUSINESS SEARCH TECHNOLOGIES CORPORATION—See Geniee, Inc.; *Int'l*, pg. 2923
BUSINESS SOFTWARE, INC.; *U.S. Private*, pg. 695
BUSINESS SOLUTIONS BUILDERS (BELGIUM) SA—See BSB SA; *Int'l*, pg. 1202
BUZZTABLE INC.; *U.S. Private*, pg. 699
BYTEMOBILE EUROPEAN DEVELOPMENT CENTER MEPE—See Elliott Management Corporation; *U.S. Private*, pg. 1366
BYTEMOBILE EUROPEAN DEVELOPMENT CENTER MEPE—See Vista Equity Partners, LLC; *U.S. Private*, pg. 4395
BYTE POWER (HONG KONG) LIMITED—See Byte Power Group Limited; *Int'l*, pg. 1236
BYTE POWER TECHNOLOGIES PTY LTD—See Byte Power Group Limited; *Int'l*, pg. 1237

N.A.I.C.S. INDEX

513210 — SOFTWARE PUBLISHERS

C2 DESIGN AUTOMATION—See Cadence Design Systems, Inc.; *U.S. Public*, pg. 418
CA ARABIA FZ-LLC—See Broadcom Inc.; *U.S. Public*, pg. 388
CA BELGIUM SA—See Broadcom Inc.; *U.S. Public*, pg. 389
CADAC GROUP B.V.—See Cadac Group Holding B.V.; *Int'l*, pg. 1247
CADD EDGE INC.; *U.S. Private*, pg. 712
CADENCE DESIGN (ISRAEL) II LTD.—See Cadence Design Systems, Inc.; *U.S. Public*, pg. 418
CADENCE DESIGN SYSTEMS AB—See Cadence Design Systems, Inc.; *U.S. Public*, pg. 418
CADENCE DESIGN SYSTEMS GMBH—See Cadence Design Systems, Inc.; *U.S. Public*, pg. 418
CADENCE DESIGN SYSTEMS, INC.; *U.S. Public*, pg. 418
CADENCE DESIGN SYSTEMS (IRELAND) LIMITED—See Cadence Design Systems, Inc.; *U.S. Public*, pg. 418
CADENCE DESIGN SYSTEMS (ISRAEL) LIMITED—See Cadence Design Systems, Inc.; *U.S. Public*, pg. 418
CADENCE DESIGN SYSTEMS (JAPAN) B.V.—See Cadence Design Systems, Inc.; *U.S. Public*, pg. 418
CADENCE DESIGN SYSTEMS S.A.S.—See Cadence Design Systems, Inc.; *U.S. Public*, pg. 418
CADENCE DESIGN SYSTEMS (S) PTE LTD.—See Cadence Design Systems, Inc.; *U.S. Public*, pg. 418
CADENCE KOREA LTD.—See Cadence Design Systems, Inc.; *U.S. Public*, pg. 418
CADENT TECHNOLOGY, INC.—See Cross Mediaworks, Inc.; *U.S. Private*, pg. 1105
CADUCEUS SOFTWARE SYSTEMS CORP.; *Int'l*, pg. 1248
CA (HONG KONG) LIMITED—See Broadcom Inc.; *U.S. Public*, pg. 388
CA, INC.—See Broadcom Inc.; *U.S. Public*, pg. 388
CA (INDIA) TECHNOLOGIES PRIVATE LIMITED—See Broadcom Inc.; *U.S. Public*, pg. 388
CA INVESTMENT HOLDING, INC.—See Broadcom Inc.; *U.S. Public*, pg. 389
CAI SOFTWARE, LLC—See Symphony Technology Group, LLC; *U.S. Private*, pg. 3902
CA KOREA INC.—See Broadcom Inc.; *U.S. Public*, pg. 389
CALERO SOFTWARE, LLC—See Riverside Partners, LLC; *U.S. Private*, pg. 3445
CALLMINER, INC.; *U.S. Private*, pg. 722
CALLMINER UK—See CallMiner, Inc.; *U.S. Private*, pg. 722
CALYPSO TECHNOLOGY, INC.—See Thoma Bravo, L.P.; *U.S. Private*, pg. 4146
CALYSTENE; *Int'l*, pg. 1266
CALYX TECHNOLOGY, INC.; *U.S. Private*, pg. 725
CAM2 SRL—See FARO Technologies, Inc.; *U.S. Public*, pg. 823
CA MARKETING CORPORATION—See Broadcom Inc.; *U.S. Public*, pg. 389
CAM COMMERCE SOLUTIONS, INC.—See Celerant Technology Corp.; *U.S. Private*, pg. 806
CAMELEON SOFTWARE SA—See PROS Holdings, Inc.; *U.S. Public*, pg. 1728
CAMPAIGNERCRM—See Ziff Davis, Inc.; *U.S. Public*, pg. 2403
CAMPAIGN MONITOR PTY LTD; *Int'l*, pg. 1274
CAMPUSCLARITY—See EverFi, Inc.; *U.S. Private*, pg. 1438
CAMPUSLOGIC, INC.—See e.Bricks Ventures; *Int'l*, pg. 2251
CANCOM FINANCIAL SERVICES GMBH—See CANCOM SE; *Int'l*, pg. 1288
CANCOM ICT SERVICE GMBH—See CANCOM SE; *Int'l*, pg. 1288
CANCOM, INC.—See CANCOM SE; *Int'l*, pg. 1289
CANCOM ON LINE GMBH—See CANCOM SE; *Int'l*, pg. 1289
CANCOM PHYSICAL INFRASTRUCTURE GMBH—See CANCOM SE; *Int'l*, pg. 1289
CANCOM PUBLIC BV—See CANCOM SE; *Int'l*, pg. 1289
CANCOM VVM GMBH—See CANCOM SE; *Int'l*, pg. 1289
CANON HI-TECH (THAILAND) LTD.—See Canon Inc.; *Int'l*, pg. 1295
CANONICAL GROUP LIMITED; *Int'l*, pg. 1298
CANON SOFTWARE, INC.—See Canon Inc.; *Int'l*, pg. 1296
CAPCOM INC—See Capcom Co., Ltd.; *Int'l*, pg. 1302
CAPCOM INTERACTIVE CANADA, INC—See Capcom Co., Ltd.; *Int'l*, pg. 1302
CAPE CLEAR SOFTWARE, INC.; *U.S. Private*, pg. 737
CAP HPI LIMITED—See Vista Equity Partners, LLC; *U.S. Private*, pg. 4401
THE CAPITAL MARKETS COMPANY (UK) LIMITED—See Clayton, Dubilier & Rice, LLC; *U.S. Private*, pg. 927
CA PROGRAMAS DE COMPUTADOR PARTICIPACOAS SERVICOS LTDA.—See Broadcom Inc.; *U.S. Public*, pg. 389
CAPSPIRE, INC.; *U.S. Private*, pg. 746
CAPTIRA ANALYTICAL, LLC—See General Catalyst Partners; *U.S. Private*, pg. 1664
CAPTIRA ANALYTICAL, LLC—See iSubscribed Inc.; *U.S. Private*, pg. 2147
CAPTIRA ANALYTICAL, LLC—See WndrCo Holdings, LLC; *U.S. Private*, pg. 4552
CAR360, INC.—See Carvana Co.; *U.S. Public*, pg. 445
CARBON FIVE INC.—See West Monroe Partners, LLC; *U.S. Private*, pg. 4486

CARBONMETA TECHNOLOGIES, INC.; *U.S. Public*, pg. 432
CARDINUS RISK MANAGEMENT LIMITED—See AmWINS Group, Inc.; *U.S. Private*, pg. 270
CARDIOCOMM SOLUTIONS, INC.; *Int'l*, pg. 1321
CARDIOVIEW INC.—See CardioComm Solutions, Inc.; *Int'l*, pg. 1321
CARDLYTICS, INC; *U.S. Public*, pg. 434
CARECLOUD CORPORATION—See CareCloud, Inc.; *U.S. Public*, pg. 434
CARECLOUD, INC.; *U.S. Public*, pg. 434
CARELINX INC.—See Altaris Capital Partners, LLC; *U.S. Private*, pg. 206
CARIDEN TECHNOLGOIES LLC—See Cisco Systems, Inc.; *U.S. Public*, pg. 497
CARINGO, INC.—See DataCore Software Corp.; *U.S. Private*, pg. 1165
CARL DATA SOLUTIONS, INC.; *Int'l*, pg. 1332
CARLY HOLDINGS LIMITED; *Int'l*, pg. 1341
CARPIO SOLUTIONS INC.—See Palladium Equity Partners, LLC; *U.S. Private*, pg. 3077
CARRIER MANAGEMENT SYSTEMS, INC.—See Constellation Software Inc.; *Int'l*, pg. 1774
CAR SYSTEMS B.V.—See LKQ Corporation; *U.S. Public*, pg. 1334
CARTEGRAPH SYSTEMS, LLC—See Pamlico Capital Management, L.P.; *U.S. Private*, pg. 3083
CASAMBA, LLC—See Level Equity Management, LLC; *U.S. Private*, pg. 2434
CASAMBA, LLC—See Silversmith Management, L.P.; *U.S. Private*, pg. 3664
CASAMBA, LLC—See The Carlyle Group Inc.; *U.S. Public*, pg. 2050
CA SERVICES, LLC—See Broadcom Inc.; *U.S. Public*, pg. 389
CASEWARE INTERNATIONAL, INC.; *Int'l*, pg. 1352
CA SOFTWARE B.V.—See Broadcom Inc.; *U.S. Public*, pg. 389
CA SOFTWARE DE COLOMBIA S.A.—See Broadcom Inc.; *U.S. Public*, pg. 389
CA SOFTWARE DE PERU S.A.—See Broadcom Inc.; *U.S. Public*, pg. 389
CA SOFTWARE FINLAND OY—See Broadcom Inc.; *U.S. Public*, pg. 389
CA SOFTWARE ISRAEL LTD.—See Broadcom Inc.; *U.S. Public*, pg. 389
CA SOFTWARE NORWAY A/S—See Broadcom Inc.; *U.S. Public*, pg. 389
CA SOFTWARE OSTERREICH GMBH—See Broadcom Inc.; *U.S. Public*, pg. 389
CA SOFTWARE SWEDEN AB—See Broadcom Inc.; *U.S. Public*, pg. 389
CA S.R.L.—See Broadcom Inc.; *U.S. Public*, pg. 389
CAS SEVERN INC; *U.S. Private*, pg. 777
CASSIDIAN CYBERSECURITY SAS—See Airbus SE; *Int'l*, pg. 242
CASTLIGHT HEALTH, INC.; *U.S. Public*, pg. 447
CATAVOLT, INC.—See Hexagon AB; *Int'l*, pg. 3367
CA TECHNOLOGIES—See Broadcom Inc.; *U.S. Public*, pg. 389
CA TECHNOLOGIES—See Broadcom Inc.; *U.S. Public*, pg. 389
CA TECHNOLOGIES—See Broadcom Inc.; *U.S. Public*, pg. 389
CA TECHNOLOGIES—See Broadcom Inc.; *U.S. Public*, pg. 389
CAUSEWAY TECHNOLOGIES LIMITED; *Int'l*, pg. 1361
CAVERN TECHNOLOGIES INC.—See GI Manager L.P.; *U.S. Private*, pg. 1692
CBIZ TECHNOLOGIES, LLC—See CBIZ, Inc.; *U.S. Public*, pg. 457
THE CBORD GROUP INC.—See Roper Technologies, Inc.; *U.S. Public*, pg. 1813
CBR ASSOCIATES INC.—See Clearlake Capital Group, L.P.; *U.S. Private*, pg. 937
CBR ASSOCIATES INC.—See SkyKnight Capital LLC; *U.S. Private*, pg. 3685
CBRE SERVICEINSIGHT GROUP—See CBRE Group, Inc.; *U.S. Public*, pg. 460
CBT CAMPUS, LLC; *U.S. Private*, pg. 797
CCK FINANCIAL SOLUTIONS PTY LIMITED; *Int'l*, pg. 1367
CD GROUP, INC.—See TAC Partners, Inc.; *U.S. Private*, pg. 3920
CDNETWORKS, INC.—See ChinaNetCenter Co., Ltd.; *Int'l*, pg. 1568
CDYNE CORPORATION; *U.S. Private*, pg. 803
CECON AB—See AFRY AB; *Int'l*, pg. 194
CEELOX, INC.; *U.S. Private*, pg. 805
CEGEDIM LOGICIELS MEDICAUX SAS—See Cegedim S.A.; *Int'l*, pg. 1390
CEGEDIM SANTE SASU—See Cegedim S.A.; *Int'l*, pg. 1390
CEGEKA DEUTSCHLAND GMBH—See Cegeka Groep NV; *Int'l*, pg. 1390
CEGID GROUP SA—See Silver Lake Group, LLC; *U.S. Private*, pg. 3656
CEGID LTD.—See Silver Lake Group, LLC; *U.S. Private*, pg. 3656
CEGID U.S.—See Silver Lake Group, LLC; *U.S. Private*, pg. 3656

CEIBA SOLUTIONS, INC.—See Revvity, Inc.; *U.S. Public*, pg. 1793
CEIPAL CORP.; *U.S. Private*, pg. 806
CELEBROS, INC.; *U.S. Private*, pg. 806
CELEBROS LTD.—See Celebros, Inc.; *U.S. Private*, pg. 806
CELEBROS LTD.—See Celebros, Inc.; *U.S. Private*, pg. 806
CELEBROS LTD.—See Celebros, Inc.; *U.S. Private*, pg. 806
CELEBROS LTD.—See Celebros, Inc.; *U.S. Private*, pg. 806
CELEBROS LTD.—See Celebros, Inc.; *U.S. Private*, pg. 806
CELERANT TECHNOLOGY CORP.; *U.S. Private*, pg. 806
CELERITY SOLUTIONS, INC.; *U.S. Private*, pg. 806
CELLCURA SOLUTIONS A/S—See Dag Dvergsten AS; *Int'l*, pg. 1912
CELLFIRE, INC.—See Berkshire Partners LLC; *U.S. Private*, pg. 534
CELLFISH MEDIA, INC.—See Cellfish Media LLC; *U.S. Private*, pg. 807
CELLFISH MEDIA LLC; *U.S. Private*, pg. 807
CELLNOVO GROUP SA; *Int'l*, pg. 1394
CELOXICA INC.—See Celoxica Holdings plc; *Int'l*, pg. 1395
CELOXICA LTD.—See Celoxica Holdings plc; *Int'l*, pg. 1395
CEMAGID SAS—See Silver Lake Group, LLC; *U.S. Private*, pg. 3656
CENDUIT (INDIA) SERVICES PRIVATE COMPANY LIMITED—See IQVIA Holdings Inc.; *U.S. Public*, pg. 1168
CENDYN CORP.; *U.S. Private*, pg. 808
CENGEA SOLUTIONS INC—See Trimble, Inc.; *U.S. Public*, pg. 2190
CENSOF HOLDINGS BERHAD; *Int'l*, pg. 1401
CENTAGE CORPORATION—See Scaleworks, Inc.; *U.S. Private*, pg. 3561
CENTARA EHF; *Int'l*, pg. 1402
CENTRAL LOGIC INC.—See Rubicon Technology Partners, LLC; *U.S. Private*, pg. 3499
CENTRALSQUARE TECHNOLOGIES, LLC—See Vista Equity Partners, LLC; *U.S. Private*, pg. 4395
CENTRIC SOFTWARE, INC.; *U.S. Private*, pg. 830
CENTRIFY CORP.—See TPG Capital, L.P.; *U.S. Public*, pg. 2169
CENTURION SYSTEMS, INC.—See Tier 1 Performance Solutions, LLC; *U.S. Private*, pg. 4168
CEON CORPORATION—See Concentrix Corporation; *U.S. Public*, pg. 564
CERASIS, INC.—See Providence Equity Partners L.L.C.; *U.S. Private*, pg. 3292
CERENCE DEUTSCHLAND GMBH—See Microsoft Corporation; *U.S. Public*, pg. 1442
CERNER DEUTSCHLAND GMBH—See Oracle Corporation; *U.S. Public*, pg. 1610
CERNER FRANCE SAS—See Oracle Corporation; *U.S. Public*, pg. 1610
CERTAIN, INC.; *U.S. Private*, pg. 841
CERTIF-ICE, INC.—See ANSYS, Inc.; *U.S. Public*, pg. 139
CERTIFY, LLC—See K1 Investment Management, LLC; *U.S. Private*, pg. 2252
CERTIVE SOLUTIONS INC.; *U.S. Public*, pg. 476
CEVA D.S.P. LIMITED—See CEVA, Inc.; *U.S. Public*, pg. 476
CGG JASON (U.S.) INC.—See CGG; *Int'l*, pg. 1431
CGM ARZTSYSTEME OSTERREICH GMBH—See CompuGroup Medical SE & Co. KGaA; *Int'l*, pg. 1755
CGM BILGI SISTEMLERI A.S.—See CompuGroup Medical SE & Co. KGaA; *Int'l*, pg. 1755
CGM CLINICAL OSTERREICH GMBH—See CompuGroup Medical SE & Co. KGaA; *Int'l*, pg. 1755
CGM LAB BELGIUM SA—See CompuGroup Medical SE & Co. KGaA; *Int'l*, pg. 1755
CGM LAB DEUTSCHLAND GMBH—See CompuGroup Medical SE & Co. KGaA; *Int'l*, pg. 1755
CGM LAB FRANCE SAS—See CompuGroup Medical SE & Co. KGaA; *Int'l*, pg. 1755
CGM MOBILE SOFTWARE GMBH—See CompuGroup Medical SE & Co. KGaA; *Int'l*, pg. 1756
CGM SOFTWARE RO SRL—See CompuGroup Medical SE & Co. KGaA; *Int'l*, pg. 1756
CGM SOUTH AFRICA (PTY) LTD.—See CompuGroup Medical SE & Co. KGaA; *Int'l*, pg. 1755
CGM XDENT SOFTWARE S.R.L.—See CompuGroup Medical SE & Co. KGaA; *Int'l*, pg. 1756
CGS NORTH AMERICA INC.—See C&G SYSTEMS INC.; *Int'l*, pg. 1238
CHALLENGER TECHNOLOGIES (M) SDN BHD—See Challenger Technologies Ltd.; *Int'l*, pg. 1438
CHAMPION TECHNOLOGY HOLDINGS LTD; *Int'l*, pg. 1440
CHANGE HEALTHCARE CORPORATION—See McKesson Corporation; *U.S. Public*, pg. 1407
CHANGZHOU MINGJING IOT SENSING CO., LTD.—See China Security Co., Ltd.; *Int'l*, pg. 1550
CHANJET INFORMATION TECHNOLOGY COMPANY LIMITED; *Int'l*, pg. 1446
CHANNELADVISOR ASIA-PACIFIC—See Insight Venture Management, LLC; *U.S. Private*, pg. 2088
CHANNELADVISOR CORPORATION—See Insight Venture Management, LLC; *U.S. Private*, pg. 2087
CHANNELADVISOR EMEA—See Insight Venture Management, LLC; *U.S. Private*, pg. 2088
CHANNELADVISOR GERMANY—See Insight Venture Management, LLC; *U.S. Private*, pg. 2088

513210 — SOFTWARE PUBLISHERS

CHANNELADVISOR IRELAND—See Insight Venture Management, LLC; *U.S. Private*, pg. 2088
CHAPSVISION SASU—See CHAPS Holding SAS; *Int'l*, pg. 1448
CHARGIFY LLC; *U.S. Private*, pg. 850
CHARTBEAT INC.—See Cuadrilla Capital LLC; *U.S. Private*, pg. 1119
CHARTIO INC.; *U.S. Private*, pg. 859
CHARTWISE MEDICAL SYSTEMS, INC.—See Iodine Software, LLC; *U.S. Private*, pg. 2133
THE CHATFIELD GROUP, INC., *U.S. Private*, pg. 4007
CHECK POINT SOFTWARE TECHNOLOGIES, INC.—See Check Point Software Technologies Ltd.; *Int'l*, pg. 1458
CHECK POINT SOFTWARE TECHNOLOGIES (ITALIA) SRL—See Check Point Software Technologies Ltd.; *Int'l*, pg. 1458
CHECK POINT SOFTWARE TECHNOLOGIES LTD.; *Int'l*, pg. 1458
CHECK POINT SOFTWARE TECHNOLOGIES (UK) LTD.—See Check Point Software Technologies Ltd.; *Int'l*, pg. 1458
CHECKSTER, INC.—See Rubicon Technology Partners, LLC; *U.S. Private*, pg. 3499
CHEMSTATIONS, INC.—See Datacor, Inc.; *U.S. Private*, pg. 1165
CHEMSW, INC.—See Dassault Systemes S.A.; *Int'l*, pg. 1974
CHEMWARE INC.—See Dohmen Co.; *U.S. Private*, pg. 1254
CHENGDU IXONOS TECHNOLOGY CO., LTD.—See Digitalist Group Oyj; *Int'l*, pg. 2123
CHENGDU JIAFAANTAI EDUCATION TECHNOLOGY CO., LTD.; *Int'l*, pg. 1468
CHENGDU VANTRON TECHNOLOGY INC.—See Eurotech S.p.A.; *Int'l*, pg. 2558
CHENGDU WATER STAR-SOURCE INFORMATION TECHNOLOGY CO., LTD.—See Beijing Watertek Information Technology Co., Ltd.; *Int'l*, pg. 960
CHENGDU WATERTEK INFORMATION TECHNOLOGY CO., LTD.—See Beijing Watertek Information Technology Co., Ltd.; *Int'l*, pg. 960
CHILDREN'S PROGRESS, INC.; *U.S. Private*, pg. 885
CHILLINGO LIMITED—See Electronic Arts Inc.; *U.S. Public*, pg. 723
CHINA INTELLIGENCE INFORMATION SYSTEMS, INC.; *Int'l*, pg. 1510
CHINA NATIONAL SOFTWARE & SERVICE CO., LTD—See China Electronics Corporation; *Int'l*, pg. 1499
CHINA TREASURE MINE TECHNOLOGY HOLDINGS CO., LTD.; *Int'l*, pg. 1560
CHITA INC.—See Dassault Systemes S.A.; *Int'l*, pg. 1975
CHITRCHATR COMMUNICATIONS INC.; *Int'l*, pg. 1574
CHOOSE NETWORKS, INC.—See Frontenac Company LLC; *U.S. Private*, pg. 1614
CHROME RIVER TECHNOLOGIES, INC.—See K1 Investment Management, LLC; *U.S. Private*, pg. 2252
CHUCK ATKINSON, INC.—See Crimson Solutions, LLC; *U.S. Private*, pg. 1101
CHUGACH GOVERNMENT SOLUTIONS, LLC—See Chugach Alaska Corporation; *U.S. Private*, pg. 893
CHUKONG HOLDINGS LIMITED; *Int'l*, pg. 1595
CHYRONHEGO AB—See Vector Capital Management, L.P.; *U.S. Private*, pg. 4350
CHYRONHEGO CHILE LIMITADA—See Vector Capital Management, L.P.; *U.S. Private*, pg. 4350
CHYRONHEGO CORPORATION—See Vector Capital Management, L.P.; *U.S. Private*, pg. 4350
CHYRONHEGO CZECH S.R.O.—See Vector Capital Management, L.P.; *U.S. Private*, pg. 4350
CHYRONHEGO DANMARK APS—See Vector Capital Management, L.P.; *U.S. Private*, pg. 4350
CHYRONHEGO FINLAND OY—See Vector Capital Management, L.P.; *U.S. Private*, pg. 4350
CHYRONHEGO GMBH—See Vector Capital Management, L.P.; *U.S. Private*, pg. 4350
CHYRONHEGO NORGE A/S—See Vector Capital Management, L.P.; *U.S. Private*, pg. 4350
CHYRONHEGO SLOVAKIA S.R.O.—See Vector Capital Management, L.P.; *U.S. Private*, pg. 4350
CHYRONHEGO UK LTD.—See Vector Capital Management, L.P.; *U.S. Private*, pg. 4350
CIB DEVELOPMENT SDN. BHD.—See Asphere Innovations Public Company Limited; *Int'l*, pg. 630
CIBOODLE LTD.—See Verint Systems Inc.; *U.S. Public*, pg. 2281
CI GAMES S.A.; *Int'l*, pg. 1601
CIMETRIX INCORPORATED—See PDF Solutions, Inc.; *U.S. Public*, pg. 1658
CINCINNATI TIME SYSTEMS, INC.—See Hellman & Friedman LLC; *U.S. Private*, pg. 1910
CIPHERCLOUD, INC.—See Lookout, Inc.; *U.S. Private*, pg. 2494
CIPHER TECH SOLUTIONS, INC.; *U.S. Private*, pg. 899
CIRATA PLC.; *Int'l*, pg. 1617
CIRCLEUP NETWORK INC.—See Brightflow.AI, Inc.; *U.S. Private*, pg. 652
CIRCUIT VISION INC.; *U.S. Private*, pg. 900

CISCO WEBEX LLC—See Cisco Systems, Inc.; *U.S. Public*, pg. 499
CISION LTD.—See Platinum Equity, LLC; *U.S. Private*, pg. 3201
CITATION GLOBAL, INC.; *U.S. Private*, pg. 901
CITRIX ONLINE AUS PTY LTD.—See Elliott Management Corporation; *U.S. Private*, pg. 1366
CITRIX ONLINE AUS PTY LTD.—See Vista Equity Partners, LLC; *U.S. Private*, pg. 4395
CITRIX R&D INDIA PRIVATE LIMITED—See Elliott Management Corporation; *U.S. Private*, pg. 1366
CITRIX R&D INDIA PRIVATE LIMITED—See Vista Equity Partners, LLC; *U.S. Private*, pg. 4395
CITRIX SISTEMAS DE ARGENTINA, S.R.L.—See Elliott Management Corporation; *U.S. Private*, pg. 1366
CITRIX SISTEMAS DE ARGENTINA, S.R.L.—See Vista Equity Partners, LLC; *U.S. Private*, pg. 4396
CITRIX SISTEMAS DO BRASIL LTDA.—See Elliott Management Corporation; *U.S. Private*, pg. 1366
CITRIX SISTEMAS DO BRASIL LTDA.—See Vista Equity Partners, LLC; *U.S. Private*, pg. 4396
CITRIX SYSTEMS ASIA PACIFIC PTY LTD.—See Elliott Management Corporation; *U.S. Private*, pg. 1366
CITRIX SYSTEMS ASIA PACIFIC PTY LTD.—See Vista Equity Partners, LLC; *U.S. Private*, pg. 4396
CITRIX SYSTEMS CANADA, INC.—See Elliott Management Corporation; *U.S. Private*, pg. 1366
CITRIX SYSTEMS CANADA, INC.—See Vista Equity Partners, LLC; *U.S. Private*, pg. 4396
CITRIX SYSTEMS CZECH REPUBLIC SRO—See Elliott Management Corporation; *U.S. Private*, pg. 1366
CITRIX SYSTEMS CZECH REPUBLIC SRO—See Vista Equity Partners, LLC; *U.S. Private*, pg. 4396
CITRIX SYSTEMS DENMARK APS—See Elliott Management Corporation; *U.S. Private*, pg. 1366
CITRIX SYSTEMS DENMARK APS—See Vista Equity Partners, LLC; *U.S. Private*, pg. 4396
CITRIX SYSTEMS FINLAND OY—See Elliott Management Corporation; *U.S. Private*, pg. 1366
CITRIX SYSTEMS FINLAND OY—See Vista Equity Partners, LLC; *U.S. Private*, pg. 4396
CITRIX SYSTEMS FRANCE SARL—See Elliott Management Corporation; *U.S. Private*, pg. 1367
CITRIX SYSTEMS FRANCE SARL—See Vista Equity Partners, LLC; *U.S. Private*, pg. 4396
CITRIX SYSTEMS GMBH—See Elliott Management Corporation; *U.S. Private*, pg. 1367
CITRIX SYSTEMS GMBH—See Elliott Management Corporation; *U.S. Private*, pg. 1367
CITRIX SYSTEMS GMBH—See Vista Equity Partners, LLC; *U.S. Private*, pg. 4396
CITRIX SYSTEMS GMBH—See Vista Equity Partners, LLC; *U.S. Private*, pg. 4396
CITRIX SYSTEMS INFORMATION TECHNOLOGY (BEIJING) LTD—See Elliott Management Corporation; *U.S. Private*, pg. 1367
CITRIX SYSTEMS INFORMATION TECHNOLOGY (BEIJING) LTD—See Vista Equity Partners, LLC; *U.S. Private*, pg. 4396
CITRIX SYSTEMS NETHERLANDS, B.V.—See Elliott Management Corporation; *U.S. Private*, pg. 1367
CITRIX SYSTEMS NETHERLANDS, B.V.—See Vista Equity Partners, LLC; *U.S. Private*, pg. 4396
CITRIX SYSTEMS NORWAY AS—See Elliott Management Corporation; *U.S. Private*, pg. 1367
CITRIX SYSTEMS NORWAY AS—See Vista Equity Partners, LLC; *U.S. Private*, pg. 4396
CITRIX SYSTEMS UK LIMITED—See Elliott Management Corporation; *U.S. Private*, pg. 1367
CITRIX SYSTEMS UK LIMITED—See Vista Equity Partners, LLC; *U.S. Private*, pg. 4396
CITYTECH, INC.—See ICF International, Inc.; *U.S. Public*, pg. 1085
CITYXPRESS CORPORATION; *Int'l*, pg. 1630
CIVICA EDUCATION PTY LIMITED - MELBOURNE—See Blackstone Inc.; *U.S. Public*, pg. 352
CIVICA EDUCATION PTY LIMITED—See Blackstone Inc.; *U.S. Public*, pg. 352
CIVICA GROUP LIMITED—See Blackstone Inc.; *U.S. Public*, pg. 352
CIVICA PTY. LTD.—See Blackstone Inc.; *U.S. Public*, pg. 352
CIVICORE, LLC—See Neon One LLC; *U.S. Private*, pg. 2885
CIVIQ SMARTSCAPES—See JMC Capital Partners LLC; *U.S. Private*, pg. 2215
CIVITAS LEARNING, INC.—See Warburg Pincus LLC; *U.S. Private*, pg. 4437
CLAIRVOYANT TECHNOSOLUTIONS INC; *U.S. Private*, pg. 910
CLANCY SYSTEMS INTERNATIONAL, INC.; *U.S. Private*, pg. 910
CLARANOVA SA; *Int'l*, pg. 1642
CLARITY RETAIL SYSTEMS PLC—See Heritage Group Ltd.; *Int'l*, pg. 3361
CLARITYSOFT LLC; *U.S. Private*, pg. 912
CLARIZEN, INC.—See K1 Investment Management, LLC; *U.S. Private*, pg. 2252

CLASS TECHNOLOGIES INC.; *U.S. Private*, pg. 915
CLAUSAL COMPUTING OY; *Int'l*, pg. 1653
CLAVISTER HOLDING AB; *Int'l*, pg. 1653
CLAXSON INTERACTIVE GROUP, INC.; *Int'l*, pg. 1653
CLEAR C2, INC.; *U.S. Private*, pg. 932
CLEARPLAN, LLC—See OPENLANE, Inc.; *U.S. Public*, pg. 1607
CLEARSENSE, LLC; *U.S. Private*, pg. 938
CLEARSLIDE, INC.—See Bigtincan Holdings Limited; *U.S. Public*, pg. 331
CLEARSTAR, INC.; *U.S. Private*, pg. 938
CLEARSTRUCTURE FINANCIAL TECHNOLOGY, LLC—See Broadridge Financial Solutions, Inc.; *U.S. Public*, pg. 391
CLEO COMMUNICATIONS, INC.; *U.S. Private*, pg. 940
CLEVERBRIDGE AG—See EMH Partners GmbH; *Int'l*, pg. 2380
CLEVERBRIDGE, INC.—See EMH Partners GmbH; *Int'l*, pg. 2380
CLEVERSAFE, INC.—See International Business Machines Corporation; *U.S. Public*, pg. 1148
CLEVERTECH; *U.S. Private*, pg. 942
CLICKSOFTWARE AUSTRALIA PTY LIMITED—See Salesforce, Inc.; *U.S. Public*, pg. 1836
CLICKSOFTWARE CENTRAL EUROPE GMBH—See Salesforce, Inc.; *U.S. Public*, pg. 1837
CLICKSOFTWARE EUROPE LIMITED—See Salesforce, Inc.; *U.S. Public*, pg. 1837
CLICKSOFTWARE, INC.—See Salesforce, Inc.; *U.S. Public*, pg. 1837
CLICKSOFTWARE TECHNOLOGIES LTD.—See Salesforce, Inc.; *U.S. Public*, pg. 1836
CLICKSQUARED INC.—See Zeta Interactive Corporation; *U.S. Private*, pg. 4602
CLICKTALE LTD.—See Content Square SAS; *Int'l*, pg. 1779
CLINICAL COMPUTING PLC; *Int'l*, pg. 1659
CLINICAL INK INC.—See GI Manager L.P.; *U.S. Private*, pg. 1691
CLINIGENCE, LLC—See NUTEX HEALTH INC.; *U.S. Public*, pg. 1555
CLIOSOFT, INC.—See Keysight Technologies, Inc.; *U.S. Public*, pg. 1226
CLIQ DIGITAL AG; *Int'l*, pg. 1660
CLOUDBEES EUROPE—See CloudBees, Inc.; *U.S. Private*, pg. 947
CLOUDBEES, INC.; *U.S. Private*, pg. 947
CLOUDBUY INDIA PRIVATE LTD.—See cloudBuy PLC; *Int'l*, pg. 1662
CLOUDBUY PLC; *Int'l*, pg. 1662
CLOUDCALL GROUP LIMITED; *Int'l*, pg. 1662
CLOUDCALL, INC.—See CloudCall Group Limited; *Int'l*, pg. 1662
CLOUDERA INC.—See Clayton, Dubilier & Rice, LLC; *U.S. Private*, pg. 920
CLOUDERA INC.—See KKR & Co. Inc.; *U.S. Public*, pg. 1243
CLOUDERA K.K.—See Clayton, Dubilier & Rice, LLC; *U.S. Private*, pg. 920
CLOUDERA K.K.—See KKR & Co. Inc.; *U.S. Public*, pg. 1243
CLOUDGENIX INC.—See Palo Alto Networks, Inc.; *U.S. Public*, pg. 1635
CLOUDHEALTH TECHNOLOGIES INC.—See Broadcom Inc.; *U.S. Public*, pg. 390
CLOUDPASSAGE INC.—See Fonds de Solidarite des Travailleurs du Quebec; *Int'l*, pg. 2725
CLOUDPAY; *Int'l*, pg. 1662
CLOUDPHYSICS, INC.—See Hewlett Packard Enterprise Company; *U.S. Public*, pg. 1030
CLOUD SERVICE PARTNERS, INC.; *U.S. Private*, pg. 946
CLOUD TECHNOLOGY PARTNERS, INC.—See Hewlett Packard Enterprise Company; *U.S. Public*, pg. 1030
CLOUDYN LTD.; *Int'l*, pg. 1662
CLUSTRIX, INC.—See California Technology Ventures, LLC; *U.S. Private*, pg. 721
CMI-MANAGEMENT SERVICES INC.; *U.S. Private*, pg. 951
COACTION.COM LLC—See Cannae Holdings, Inc.; *U.S. Public*, pg. 430
COACTION.COM LLC—See CC Capital Partners, LLC; *U.S. Private*, pg. 799
COACTION.COM LLC—See Intercontinental Exchange, Inc.; *U.S. Public*, pg. 1142
COBHAM GAISLER AB—See Advent International Corporation; *U.S. Private*, pg. 99
CODE 42 SOFTWARE, INC.; *U.S. Private*, pg. 960
CODE GREEN NETWORKS, INC.—See Fairhaven Capital Management, LLC; *U.S. Private*, pg. 1464
CODENOMICON LTD.—See Synopsys, Inc.; *U.S. Public*, pg. 1970
CODENOMICON OY—See Synopsys, Inc.; *U.S. Public*, pg. 1970
CODERYTE, INC.—See 3M Company; *U.S. Public*, pg. 8
CODESMITH TOOLS, LLC; *U.S. Private*, pg. 960
CODESPEAR, LLC—See Federal Signal Corporation; *U.S. Public*, pg. 826
COFFEECUP SOFTWARE INC.; *U.S. Private*, pg. 961
COGNITEC SYSTEMS GMBH; *Int'l*, pg. 1695
COGNIZANT TECHNOLOGY SOLUTIONS (NETHER-

513210 — SOFTWARE PUBLISHERS

LANDS) B.V.—See Cognizant Technology Solutions Corporation; *U.S. Public,* pg. 523
COGNIZANT TECHNOLOGY SOLUTIONS SWEDEN AB—See Cognizant Technology Solutions Corporation; *U.S. Public,* pg. 524
COGSDALE CORPORATION—See Constellation Software Inc.; *Int'l,* pg. 1774
COHERIS SA; *Int'l,* pg. 1695
COLDLIGHT SOLUTIONS, LLC—See PTC Inc.; *U.S. Public,* pg. 1734
COLLABNET, INC.—See TPG Capital, L.P.; *U.S. Public,* pg. 2173
COLLABORATEMD; *U.S. Private,* pg. 968
COLLABOS CORPORATION; *Int'l,* pg. 1698
COLLABRASPACE, INC.—See Arlington Capital Partners LLC; *U.S. Private,* pg. 327
COLOPL INC.; *Int'l,* pg. 1702
COLUMBUS A/S; *Int'l,* pg. 1706
COLUMN5 CONSULTING; *U.S. Private,* pg. 979
COM2US CORPORATION; *Int'l,* pg. 1706
COM2US HOLDINGS; *Int'l,* pg. 1706
COMARCH CHILE SPA—See ComArch S.A.; *Int'l,* pg. 1707
COMARCH JAPAN KK—See ComArch S.A.; *Int'l,* pg. 1707
COMARCH LLC—See ComArch S.A.; *Int'l,* pg. 1707
COMARCH LUXEMBOURG S.A R.L.—See ComArch S.A.; *Int'l,* pg. 1707
COMARCH MALAYSIA SDN. BHD.—See ComArch S.A.; *Int'l,* pg. 1707
COMARCH MIDDLE EAST FZ-LLC—See ComArch S.A.; *Int'l,* pg. 1707
COMARCH PANAMA INC.—See ComArch S.A.; *Int'l,* pg. 1707
COMARCH S.A.; *Int'l,* pg. 1707
COMARCH SISTEMAS LTDA—See ComArch S.A.; *Int'l,* pg. 1707
COMARCH TECHNOLOGIES OY—See ComArch S.A.; *Int'l,* pg. 1707
COMARCH UK LTD.—See ComArch S.A.; *Int'l,* pg. 1707
COMMAND CONTROL CENTER CORP.—See Znergy, Inc.; *U.S. Private,* pg. 4607
COMMENCE CORPORATION; *U.S. Private,* pg. 982
COMMERCE TECHNOLOGIES, LLC—See Insight Venture Management, LLC; *U.S. Private,* pg. 2088
COMMODITIES SOFTWARE (UK) LIMITED—See Brady plc; *Int'l,* pg. 1135
COMMURE, INC—See HCA Healthcare, Inc.; *U.S. Public,* pg. 994
COMMVAULT SYSTEMS AB—See CommVault Systems, Inc.; *U.S. Public,* pg. 559
COMMVAULT SYSTEMS (AUSTRALIA) PTY. LTD.—See CommVault Systems, Inc.; *U.S. Public,* pg. 559
COMMVAULT SYSTEMS (CANADA) INC.—See CommVault Systems, Inc.; *U.S. Public,* pg. 559
COMMVAULT SYSTEMS GMBH—See CommVault Systems, Inc.; *U.S. Public,* pg. 559
COMMVAULT SYSTEMS, INC.; *U.S. Public,* pg. 558
COMMVAULT SYSTEMS (INDIA) PRIVATE LIMITED—See CommVault Systems, Inc.; *U.S. Public,* pg. 559
COMM VAULT SYSTEMS INTERNATIONAL B.V.—See CommVault Systems, Inc.; *U.S. Public,* pg. 559
COMMVAULT SYSTEMS ITALIA S.R.L.—See CommVault Systems, Inc.; *U.S. Public,* pg. 559
COMMVAULT SYSTEMS LIMITED—See CommVault Systems, Inc.; *U.S. Public,* pg. 559
COMMVAULT SYSTEMS MEXICO S. DE R.L. DE C.V.—See CommVault Systems, Inc.; *U.S. Public,* pg. 559
COMMVAULT SYSTEMS NETHERLANDS B.V.—See CommVault Systems, Inc.; *U.S. Public,* pg. 559
COMMVAULT SYSTEMS (NEW ZEALAND) LIMITED—See CommVault Systems, Inc.; *U.S. Public,* pg. 559
COMMVAULT SYSTEMS SARL—See CommVault Systems, Inc.; *U.S. Public,* pg. 559
COMMVAULT SYSTEMS (SINGAPORE) PRIVATE LIMITED—See CommVault Systems, Inc.; *U.S. Public,* pg. 559
COMODO GROUP, INC.; *U.S. Private,* pg. 998
COMPANHIA IBM PORTUGUESA, S.A.—See International Business Machines Corporation; *U.S. Public,* pg. 1145
COMPASS HRM, INC.—See Asure Software, Inc.; *U.S. Public,* pg. 218
COMPASSMSP LLC; *U.S. Private,* pg. 999
COMPAX SOFTWARE DEVELOPMENT GMBH; *Int'l,* pg. 1753
COMPELLON, INC.—See Clearsense, LLC; *U.S. Private,* pg. 938
COMPILE, INC.—See Teladoc Health, Inc.; *U.S. Public,* pg. 1992
COMPONENTSOURCE HOLDING CORPORATION; *U.S. Private,* pg. 1002
COMPOSITE SOFTWARE, INC.—See Cisco Systems, Inc.; *U.S. Public,* pg. 499
COMPRESSUS, INC.—See ESW Capital, LLC; *U.S. Private,* pg. 1430
COMPUFIT BVBA—See CompuGroup Medical SE & Co. KGaA; *Int'l,* pg. 1755
COMPUGROUP MEDICAL BELGIUM BVBA—See CompuGroup Medical SE & Co. KGaA; *Int'l,* pg. 1755
COMPUGROUP MEDICAL BILGI SISTEMLERI A.S.—See CompuGroup Medical SE & Co. KGaA; *Int'l,* pg. 1756
COMPUGROUP MEDICAL CEE GMBH—See CompuGroup Medical SE & Co. KGaA; *Int'l,* pg. 1755
COMPUGROUP MEDICAL CESKA REPUBLIKA S.R.O.—See CompuGroup Medical SE & Co. KGaA; *Int'l,* pg. 1755
COMPUGROUP MEDICAL DENMARK A/S—See CompuGroup Medical SE & Co. KGaA; *Int'l,* pg. 1755
COMPUGROUP MEDICAL DEUTSCHLAND AG—See CompuGroup Medical SE & Co. KGaA; *Int'l,* pg. 1756
COMPUGROUP MEDICAL FRANCE SAS—See CompuGroup Medical SE & Co. KGaA; *Int'l,* pg. 1756
COMPUGROUP MEDICAL INC.—See CompuGroup Medical SE & Co. KGaA; *Int'l,* pg. 1756
COMPUGROUP MEDICAL ITALIA HOLDING S.R.L.—See CompuGroup Medical SE & Co. KGaA; *Int'l,* pg. 1756
COMPUGROUP MEDICAL ITALIA S.P.A.—See CompuGroup Medical SE & Co. KGaA; *Int'l,* pg. 1756
COMPUGROUP MEDICAL MALAYSIA SDN BHD—See CompuGroup Medical SE & Co. KGaA; *Int'l,* pg. 1756
COMPUGROUP MEDICAL POLSKA SP. Z O.O.—See CompuGroup Medical SE & Co. KGaA; *Int'l,* pg. 1756
COMPUGROUP MEDICAL SCHWEIZ AG—See CompuGroup Medical SE & Co. KGaA; *Int'l,* pg. 1756
COMPUGROUP MEDICAL SLOVENSKO S.R.O.—See CompuGroup Medical SE & Co. KGaA; *Int'l,* pg. 1756
COMPUGROUP MEDICAL SOLUTIONS SAS—See CompuGroup Medical SE & Co. KGaA; *Int'l,* pg. 1756
COMPUGROUP MEDICAL SWEDEN AB—See CompuGroup Medical SE & Co. KGaA; *Int'l,* pg. 1756
COMPUGROUP OSTERREICH GMBH—See CompuGroup Medical SE & Co. KGaA; *Int'l,* pg. 1756
COMPULINK BUSINESS SYSTEMS, INC.; *U.S. Private,* pg. 1003
COMPULIT INC.—See Pitney Bowes Inc.; *U.S. Public,* pg. 1694
COMPUSOFT INTEGRATED SOLUTIONS INC.; *U.S. Private,* pg. 1004
COMPUTATIONAL ENGINEERING INTERNATIONAL, INC.—See ANSYS, Inc.; *U.S. Public,* pg. 139
COMPUTER AUTOMATION SYSTEMS, INC.; *U.S. Private,* pg. 1004
COMPUWARE CORPORATION—See KKR & Co. Inc.; *U.S. Public,* pg. 1240
COMS INTERACTIVE, LLC; *U.S. Private,* pg. 1006
COMSOFT CORPORATION; *U.S. Private,* pg. 1006
COMUTO SA; *Int'l,* pg. 1763
CONCEP GROUP LIMITED—See Freedom Solutions Group, L.L.C.; *U.S. Private,* pg. 1604
CONCEP INC.—See Freedom Solutions Group, L.L.C.; *U.S. Private,* pg. 1604
CONCEP PTY LTD—See Freedom Solutions Group, L.L.C.; *U.S. Private,* pg. 1604
CONCEPTS NREC, INC.; *U.S. Private,* pg. 1009
CONDUENT PARKING ENFORCEMENT SOLUTIONS LIMITED—See Conduent Incorporated; *U.S. Public,* pg. 566
CONDUENT PAYMENT INTEGRITY SOLUTIONS, INC.—See Conduent Incorporated; *U.S. Public,* pg. 566
CONDUENT TRANSPORT SOLUTIONS, INC.—See Conduent Incorporated; *U.S. Public,* pg. 566
CONDUSIV TECHNOLOGIES CORPORATION; *U.S. Private,* pg. 1012
CONDUSIV TECHNOLOGIES CORPORATION—See Condusiv Technologies Corporation; *U.S. Private,* pg. 1012
CONFIGERO; *U.S. Private,* pg. 1013
CONFLUENCE TECHNOLOGIES, INC.—See TA Associates, Inc.; *U.S. Private,* pg. 3914
CONNECT FIRST, INC.—See RingCentral, Inc.; *U.S. Public,* pg. 1799
CONNECTIVA SYSTEMS, INC.; *U.S. Private,* pg. 1016
CONNEXION MOBILITY LTD; *Int'l,* pg. 1769
CONNEXITY, INC.—See Symphony Technology Group, LLC; *U.S. Private,* pg. 3900
CONNOTATE, INC.—See Import-io Corporation; *U.S. Private,* pg. 2050
CONSILIENCE SOFTWARE, INC.—See Conduent Incorporated; *U.S. Public,* pg. 566
CONSTELLATION SOFTWARE INC.; *Int'l,* pg. 1772
CONSTELLATION TECHNOLOGIES LIMITED; *Int'l,* pg. 1776
CONSUMERSOFT; *U.S. Private,* pg. 1026
CONTACTLAB; *Int'l,* pg. 1778
CONTACTUAL, INC.—See 8x8, Inc.; *U.S. Public,* pg. 10
CONTAGIOUS GAMING INC.; *Int'l,* pg. 1778
CONTENT4ALL B.V.—See Bayerische Motoren Werke Aktiengesellschaft; *Int'l,* pg. 912
CONTENT SQUARE SAS; *Int'l,* pg. 1779
CONTINUUM PERFORMANCE SYSTEMS INC.—See MedHOK HealthCare Solutions, LLC; *U.S. Private,* pg. 2651
CONVENE UK LIMITED—See Azeus Systems Holdings Ltd.; *Int'l,* pg. 778
CONVERGEONE ADVANCED SERVICES—See CVC Capital Partners SICAV-FIS S.A.; *Int'l,* pg. 1883
CONVERSA SOLUTIONS, LLC—See Vertex Wireless LLC; *U.S. Private,* pg. 4370
COOPERATIE ACTIVISION BLIZZARD INTERNATIONAL U.A—See Microsoft Corporation; *U.S. Public,* pg. 1439
COPITRAK INC.; *Int'l,* pg. 1793
COPYTALK, LLC; *U.S. Private,* pg. 1046
CORACENT INC.; *U.S. Private,* pg. 1046
CORASWORKS CORPORATION—See HumanTouch, LLC; *U.S. Public,* pg. 2007
COREL UK LIMITED—See KKR & Co. Inc.; *U.S. Public,* pg. 1243
COREMEDIA AG; *Int'l,* pg. 1799
COREMEDIA ASIA PACIFIC PTE. LTD.—See CoreMedia AG; *Int'l,* pg. 1799
COREMEDIA CORPORATION—See CoreMedia AG; *Int'l,* pg. 1799
COREMEDIA UK LTD.—See CoreMedia AG; *Int'l,* pg. 1799
CORERO NETWORK SECURITY PLC; *Int'l,* pg. 1799
CORE SECURITY SDI CORPORATION; *U.S. Private,* pg. 1049
CORESENSE INC.—See Constellation Software Inc.; *Int'l,* pg. 1773
CORE TECHNOLOGY CORP.—See Constellation Software Inc.; *Int'l,* pg. 1774
CORETRAC, INC.—See TA Associates, Inc.; *U.S. Private,* pg. 3914
CORITY SOFTWARE INC.—See Thoma Bravo, L.P.; *U.S. Private,* pg. 4146
CORNERSTONE CONSULTING, INC.; *U.S. Private,* pg. 1052
CORNERSTONE ONDEMAND, INC.—See Clearlake Capital Group, L.P.; *U.S. Private,* pg. 933
CORNERSTONE ONDEMAND LIMITED—See Clearlake Capital Group, L.P.; *U.S. Private,* pg. 933
CORONA LABS INC.; *U.S. Private,* pg. 1053
CORPORACION MICROSOFT DEL ECUADOR S.A.—See Microsoft Corporation; *U.S. Public,* pg. 1440
CORPTAX, INC.—See Corporation Service Company; *U.S. Private,* pg. 1058
CORRIGO INCORPORATED—See Jones Lang LaSalle Incorporated; *U.S. Public,* pg. 1201
CORRISOFT LLC; *U.S. Private,* pg. 1059
CORTERA, INC.—See Moody's Corporation; *U.S. Public,* pg. 1467
CORTICON TECHNOLOGIES, INC.—See Progress Software Corporation; *U.S. Public,* pg. 1725
CORVISA SERVICES LLC—See Novation Companies, Inc.; *U.S. Public,* pg. 1548
COSM, INC—See Elevate Entertainment, Inc.; *U.S. Private,* pg. 1358
COSOL LTD.; *Int'l,* pg. 1814
COSYTEC SA—See Cegedim S.A.; *Int'l,* pg. 1390
COUCHBASE, INC.; *U.S. Public,* pg. 587
COUNTERPATH CORPORATION—See Alianza Inc.; *U.S. Private,* pg. 167
COUPA EMEA—See Thoma Bravo, L.P.; *U.S. Private,* pg. 4147
COUPA SOFTWARE INCORPORATED—See Thoma Bravo, L.P.; *U.S. Private,* pg. 4146
COVALENT METROLOGY SERVICES, INC.; *U.S. Private,* pg. 1071
COVENANT EYES, INC.; *U.S. Private,* pg. 1071
COVENTOR, INC.—See Lam Research Corporation; *U.S. Public,* pg. 1289
COX AUTOMOTIVE, INC.—See Cox Enterprises, Inc.; *U.S. Private,* pg. 1074
CPA GLOBAL SOFTWARE SOLUTIONS AUSTRALIA PTY. LTD.—See Clarivate PLC; *Int'l,* pg. 1649
CPR TOOLS, INC.; *U.S. Private,* pg. 1080
CPU, LLC—See Life's Time Capsule Services, Inc.; *U.S. Public,* pg. 1312
CPU SOFTWAREHOUSE AG; *Int'l,* pg. 1826
CRADLE SOLUTION INC.; *U.S. Private,* pg. 1081
CRAMER SYSTEMS INTERNATIONAL LIMITED—See Amdocs Limited; *Int'l,* pg. 419
CRANEWARE, INC.—See Craneware plc; *Int'l,* pg. 1828
CRANEWARE PLC; *Int'l,* pg. 1828
CRANK MEDIA INC.; *Int'l,* pg. 1828
CRAWFORD TECHNOLOGIES, INC.; *Int'l,* pg. 1829
CREATIVE AGENCY SERVICES TEAM, INC.; *U.S. Private,* pg. 1087
CREDO INTERACTIVE INC.; *Int'l,* pg. 1837
CREDO REFERENCE, INC.; *U.S. Private,* pg. 1092
CRESTWOOD ASSOCIATES LLC; *U.S. Private,* pg. 1099
CREXENDO, INC.; *U.S. Public,* pg. 594
CR GROUP NORDIC AB—See Formica Capital Holding AB; *Int'l,* pg. 2734
CRICKET TECHNOLOGIES, LLC; *U.S. Private,* pg. 1100
CRI MIDDLEWARE CO., LTD.; *Int'l,* pg. 1849
CRISP MEDIA INC.—See Charlesbank Capital Partners, LLC; *U.S. Private,* pg. 855
CROCKER DATA PROCESSING PTY LTD—See Weatherford International plc; *U.S. Public,* pg. 2339
CROOZ, INC.; *Int'l,* pg. 1855
CROWDCOMPASS, L.L.C.—See Blackstone Inc.; *U.S. Public,* pg. 353
CROWDSTAR, INC.—See Electronic Arts Inc.; *U.S. Public,* pg. 724
CROWNPEAK TECHNOLOGY, INC.; *U.S. Private,* pg. 1112
CROWNPEAK TECHNOLOGY UK—See CrownPeak Technology, Inc.; *U.S. Private,* pg. 1113
CRYSTAL COMPUTER CORPORATION—See LTN Global

Communications, Inc.; *U.S. Private*, pg. 2509
CSC AGILITY PLATFORM, INC.—See DXC Technology Company; *U.S. Public*, pg. 695
CSG INTERNATIONAL COLOMBIA SAS—See CSG Systems International, Inc.; *U.S. Public*, pg. 601
CSG INTERNATIONAL DP, INC.—See CSG Systems International, Inc.; *U.S. Public*, pg. 601
CSIDENTITY CORPORATION—See Experian plc; *Int'l*, pg. 2586
CS STARS LLC—See Marsh & McLennan Companies, Inc.; *U.S. Public*, pg. 1380
C TECHNOLOGIES AB—See Anoto Group AB; *Int'l*, pg. 474
CUC SOFTWARE INC.—See ServiceTitan, Inc.; *U.S. Private*, pg. 3617
CUMULUS SYSTEMS INCORPORATED—See Hitachi, Ltd.; *Int'l*, pg. 3412
CURALATE, INC.—See Marlin Equity Partners, LLC; *U.S. Private*, pg. 2584
CURA RISK MANAGEMENT SOFTWARE (PTY) LIMITED—See Cura Technologies Ltd.; *Int'l*, pg. 1878
CUREATR, INC.—See Vora Ventures LLC; *U.S. Private*, pg. 4412
CUR MEDIA INC.; *U.S. Private*, pg. 1124
CUSCAPI BEIJING CO. LTD.—See Cuscapi Berhad; *Int'l*, pg. 1880
CUSCAPI BERHAD; *Int'l*, pg. 1880
CUSCAPI SUZHOU CO. LTD.—See Cuscapi Berhad; *Int'l*, pg. 1880
CUTTING EDGE SOLUTIONS LTD.—See Accenture plc; *Int'l*, pg. 87
CVISION TECHNOLOGIES, INC.—See Foxit Software Inc.; *U.S. Private*, pg. 1585
CV SIMPANA SOFTWARE (PROPRIETARY) LIMITED—See CommVault Systems, Inc.; *U.S. Public*, pg. 558
CYAN AG; *Int'l*, pg. 1891
CYBER ADAPT, INC.; *U.S. Private*, pg. 1133
CYBERARK SOFTWARE, INC.—See CyberArk Software Ltd.; *Int'l*, pg. 1892
CYBERARK SOFTWARE LTD.; *Int'l*, pg. 1892
CYBER_FOLKS S.A.; *Int'l*, pg. 1892
CYBERFORT SOFTWARE, INC.; *U.S. Public*, pg. 617
CYBERGRANTS, LLC; *U.S. Private*, pg. 1133
CYBERLINK CORP.; *Int'l*, pg. 1893
CYBERLINK EUROPE B.V.—See CyberLink Corp.; *Int'l*, pg. 1893
CYBERLINKS CO., LTD.; *Int'l*, pg. 1893
CYBERLOQ TECHNOLOGIES, INC.; *U.S. Public*, pg. 617
CYBERSTEP, INC.; *Int'l*, pg. 1894
CYBOZU INC.; *Int'l*, pg. 1894
CYCLOPS TECHNOLOGIES, INC.; *U.S. Private*, pg. 1134
CYGNET SOFTWARE, INC.—See Weatherford International plc; *U.S. Public*, pg. 2339
CYIENT GMBH—See Cyient Limited; *Int'l*, pg. 1896
CYLANCE, INC.—See BlackBerry Limited; *Int'l*, pg. 1060
CYREN LTD.—See Warburg Pincus LLC; *U.S. Private*, pg. 4437
D3PUBLISHER INC.—See BANDAI NAMCO Holdings Inc.; *Int'l*, pg. 829
D3PUBLISHER OF AMERICA, INC.—See Digital Bros SpA; *Int'l*, pg. 2120
DAEDALIC ENTERTAINMENT GMBH—See Bastei Lubbe AG; *Int'l*, pg. 888
DAIICHIKOUSHO CO., LTD.; *Int'l*, pg. 1930
D.A. KOPP & ASSOCIATES, INC.—See Milestone Partners Ltd.; *U.S. Private*, pg. 2728
DALIAN MORNINGSTAR NETWORK TECHNOLOGY CO., LTD.; *Int'l*, pg. 1952
DALIAN ZEUS ENTERTAINMENT CO., LTD.; *Int'l*, pg. 1953
DAMARIS SA; *Int'l*, pg. 1955
DANGER INC.—See Microsoft Corporation; *U.S. Public*, pg. 1440
DANLAW TECHNOLOGIES INDIA LIMITED—See Danlaw, Inc.; *U.S. Private*, pg. 1157
DANMAGI GROUP APS; *Int'l*, pg. 1965
DARKPULSE, INC.; *U.S. Public*, pg. 633
DASHBOX INC.—See FilmTrack Inc.; *U.S. Private*, pg. 1506
DAS, INC.; *U.S. Private*, pg. 1161
DASSAULT SYSTEMES S.A.; *Int'l*, pg. 1974
DATA ADVANTAGE GROUP, INC.—See Toro Data Labs, Inc.; *U.S. Private*, pg. 4189
DATA AGE BUSINESS SYSTEMS, INC.; *U.S. Private*, pg. 1162
DATABASE PUBLISHING CONSULTANTS, INC.; *U.S. Private*, pg. 1164
DATA BEST PRACTICES, LLC—See Incline MGMT Corp.; *U.S. Private*, pg. 2054
DATA DEPOSIT BOX INC.—See HostPapa, Inc.; *U.S. Private*, pg. 3487
DATADIRECT TECHNOLOGIES, INC.; *U.S. Private*, pg. 1165
DATA INTENSITY, LLC—See EQT AB; *Int'l*, pg. 2474
DATALAB TEHNOLOGIJE D.D.; *Int'l*, pg. 1977
DATALOT INC.—See Platinum Equity, LLC; *U.S. Private*, pg. 3201
DATAMAXX GROUP, INC.; *U.S. Private*, pg. 1166
DATAMEER INC.; *U.S. Private*, pg. 1166
DATAMENTORS, LLC; *U.S. Private*, pg. 1166

DATA PRESSE SAS—See Platinum Equity, LLC; *U.S. Private*, pg. 3201
DATA PRO ACCOUNTING SOFTWARE, INC.; *U.S. Private*, pg. 1163
DATARPM LLC—See Progress Software Corporation; *U.S. Public*, pg. 1725
DATASCAN TECHNOLOGIES LLC—See JM Family Enterprises Inc.; *U.S. Private*, pg. 2214
DATASERV, INCORPORATED—See American CyberSystems, Inc.; *U.S. Private*, pg. 229
DATASITE LLC—See CapVest Limited; *Int'l*, pg. 1318
DATASPHERE TECHNOLOGIES, INC.—See Sinclair, Inc.; *U.S. Public*, pg. 1885
DATASTAX, INC.; *U.S. Private*, pg. 1166
DATA STREAMS CORPORATION; *Int'l*, pg. 1976
DATA SYSTEMS OF TEXAS, INC.; *U.S. Private*, pg. 1163
DATATRAX PUBLISHING SYSTEMS, INC.; *U.S. Private*, pg. 1166
DATAVANT, INC.—See New Mountain Capital, LLC; *U.S. Private*, pg. 2900
DATAWATCH AB—See Altair Engineering, Inc.; *U.S. Public*, pg. 86
DATAWATCH CORPORATION—See Altair Engineering, Inc.; *U.S. Public*, pg. 86
DATAWORDS DATASIA SARL; *Int'l*, pg. 1981
DATEV EG; *Int'l*, pg. 1982
DATIX, INC.; *U.S. Private*, pg. 1167
DATSTAT, INC.—See R1 RCM Inc.; *U.S. Public*, pg. 1758
DAVALEN, LLC; *U.S. Private*, pg. 1168
DAVID CORPORATION—See TA Associates, Inc.; *U.S. Private*, pg. 3918
DAXKO, LLC—See GI Manager L.P.; *U.S. Private*, pg. 1692
DAYFORCE, INC.; *U.S. Public*, pg. 645
DAYSMART SOFTWARE, INC.—See Independence Capital Partners, LLC; *U.S. Private*, pg. 2056
DAYSMART SOFTWARE, INC.—See PCP Enterprise, L.P.; *U.S. Private*, pg. 3121
DB BEST TECHNOLOGIES, LLC; *U.S. Private*, pg. 1178
DCG, INC.—See DFNN, Inc.; *Int'l*, pg. 2096
DEALERSOCKET, INC.—See Vista Equity Partners, LLC; *U.S. Private*, pg. 4400
DEALERTRACK DIGITAL SERVICES, INC.—See Cox Enterprises, Inc.; *U.S. Private*, pg. 1074
DEALERTRACK, INC.—See Cox Enterprises, Inc.; *U.S. Private*, pg. 1074
DEALERTRACK REGISTRATION AND TITLING SOLUTIONS, INC.—See Cox Enterprises, Inc.; *U.S. Private*, pg. 1074
DEALERTRACK REGISTRATION & TITLING SERVICES-LOUISIANA, LLC—See Cox Enterprises, Inc.; *U.S. Private*, pg. 1074
DEALERTRACK SYSTEMS, INC.—See Cox Enterprises, Inc.; *U.S. Private*, pg. 1074
DEAN EVANS & ASSOCIATES, INC.; *U.S. Private*, pg. 1183
DEBT RESOLVE, INC.; *U.S. Public*, pg. 645
DEDALUS S.P.A.—See Ardian SAS; *Int'l*, pg. 555
DEEPMATTER GROUP PLC; *Int'l*, pg. 2003
DEFENSEWEB TECHNOLOGIES, INC.—See Humana, Inc.; *U.S. Public*, pg. 1069
DEFI SOLUTIONS, INC.; *U.S. Private*, pg. 1191
DEFRAN SYSTEMS, INC.; *U.S. Private*, pg. 1191
DELCAM INDONESIA—See Autodesk, Inc.; *U.S. Public*, pg. 229
DELHIVERY PRIVATE LIMITED; *Int'l*, pg. 2013
DELL MESSAGEONE—See Dell Technologies Inc.; *U.S. Public*, pg. 650
DELORME PUBLISHING COMPANY, INC.—See Garmin Ltd.; *Int'l*, pg. 2884
DELTA HEALTH TECHNOLOGIES, LLC—See Alaya Care Inc.; *Int'l*, pg. 292
DELTEK DANMARK A/S—See Roper Technologies, Inc.; *U.S. Public*, pg. 1811
DELTEK NEDERLAND B.V.—See Roper Technologies, Inc.; *U.S. Public*, pg. 1811
DELTEK SYSTEMS (PHILIPPINES) LTD.—See Roper Technologies, Inc.; *U.S. Public*, pg. 1811
DEMAND ENERGY NETWORKS, INC.—See Enel S.p.A.; *Int'l*, pg. 2413
DEMANDFORCE, INC.—See KKR & Co. Inc.; *U.S. Public*, pg. 1253
DEMAND MANAGEMENT, INC.—See American Software, Inc.; *U.S. Public*, pg. 109
DEMATIC REDDWERKS—See KKR & Co. Inc.; *U.S. Public*, pg. 1254
DEMATIC REDDWERKS—See The Goldman Sachs Group, Inc.; *U.S. Public*, pg. 2079
DEMATIC RETROTECH—See Egemin Automation Inc.; *U.S. Private*, pg. 1344
DEMIBOOKS INC.—See Educational Develop; *U.S. Public*, pg. 720
DEMIURGE STUDIOS, LLC—See Embracer Group AB; *Int'l*, pg. 2375
DENA GLOBAL, INC.—See DeNA Co., Ltd.; *Int'l*, pg. 2026
DESCO, INC.; *U.S. Private*, pg. 1211
DESTINY MEDIA TECHNOLOGIES, INC.; *Int'l*, pg. 2047
DESTINY SOLUTIONS, INC.; *Int'l*, pg. 2047
DETERMINE, INC.—See Corcentric, Inc.; *U.S. Private*, pg. 1047

DETICA SOLUTIONS, INC.—See BAE Systems plc; *Int'l*, pg. 798
DEVELOPINTELLIGENCE LLC—See Pluralsight, Inc.; *U.S. Private*, pg. 1699
DEVICELOCK, INC.—See Acronis Inc.; *U.S. Private*, pg. 66
DEVMYND SOFTWARE INC.; *U.S. Private*, pg. 1218
DEVOTEAM A/S—See Devoteam SA; *Int'l*, pg. 2089
DEVOTEAM INFORMATION TECHNOLOGY & CONSULTANCY AS—See Devoteam SA; *Int'l*, pg. 2090
DEVOTEAM MEXICO, S.A. DE C.V.—See Devoteam SA; *Int'l*, pg. 2090
DEVOTEAM NETHERLANDS BV—See Devoteam SA; *Int'l*, pg. 2090
DEVOTEAM NV—See Devoteam SA; *Int'l*, pg. 2090
DEVOTEAM SA—See Devoteam SA; *Int'l*, pg. 2090
DEVOTEAM TECHNOLOGY CONSULTING SARL—See Devoteam SA; *Int'l*, pg. 2090
DEVSISTERS CO., LTD.; *Int'l*, pg. 2090
DEVSOURCE TECHNOLOGY SOLUTIONS, LLC; *U.S. Private*, pg. 1219
DHC SOFTWARE CO., LTD.; *Int'l*, pg. 2099
DHISCO ELECTRONIC DISTRIBUTION, INC.—See H.I.G. Capital, LLC; *U.S. Private*, pg. 1829
DIAMOND LANE, INC.; *U.S. Private*, pg. 1223
DICENTRAL CORP.—See Welsh, Carson, Anderson & Stowe; *U.S. Private*, pg. 4480
DI COM SOFTWARE CORP.—See The Carlyle Group Inc.; *U.S. Public*, pg. 2045
DIEBOLD BOLIVIA S.R. L.—See Diebold Nixdorf, Inc.; *U.S. Public*, pg. 660
DIEBOLD BRASIL LTDA—See Diebold Nixdorf, Inc.; *U.S. Public*, pg. 660
DIEBOLD MEXICO, S.A. DE C.V.—See Diebold Nixdorf, Inc.; *U.S. Public*, pg. 660
DIEBOLD NIXDORF AB—See Diebold Nixdorf, Inc.; *U.S. Public*, pg. 660
DIEBOLD NIXDORF SAS—See Diebold Nixdorf, Inc.; *U.S. Public*, pg. 660
DIEBOLD PACIFIC, LIMITED—See Diebold Nixdorf, Inc.; *U.S. Public*, pg. 660
DIEBOLD SELF-SERVICE SOLUTIONS INDUSTRIAL AND SERVICING ROM SRL—See Diebold Nixdorf, Inc.; *U.S. Public*, pg. 660
DIEBOLD URUGUAY S.A.—See Diebold Nixdorf, Inc.; *U.S. Public*, pg. 661
DIGIASIA CORP; *Int'l*, pg. 2118
DIGICAP CO., LTD.; *Int'l*, pg. 2118
DIGICERT, INC.—See Clearlake Capital Group, L.P.; *U.S. Private*, pg. 934
DIGICERT, INC.—See Crosspoint Capital Partners LP; *U.S. Private*, pg. 1107
DIGICERT, INC.—See TA Associates, Inc.; *U.S. Private*, pg. 3915
DIGICHART INC.—See Constellation Software Inc.; *Int'l*, pg. 1774
DIGILANT BRASIL—See Digilant, Inc.; *U.S. Private*, pg. 1229
DIGILANT B.V.—See Digilant, Inc.; *U.S. Private*, pg. 1229
DIGILANT, INC.; *U.S. Private*, pg. 1229
DIGILANT MADRID—See Digilant, Inc.; *U.S. Private*, pg. 1229
DIGILANT MEXICO—See Digilant, Inc.; *U.S. Private*, pg. 1229
DIGITAL.AI SOFTWARE, INC.—See TPG Capital, L.P.; *U.S. Public*, pg. 2173
DIGITAL ARTS INC.; *Int'l*, pg. 2120
DIGITAL BROS IBERIA S.L.—See Digital Bros SpA; *Int'l*, pg. 2120
DIGITAL CHINA INFORMATION SERVICE GROUP CO., LTD.; *Int'l*, pg. 2121
DIGITAL CHOCOLATE, INC.; *U.S. Private*, pg. 1230
DIGITAL FILING SOLUTIONS, INC.—See Shazam, Inc.; *U.S. Private*, pg. 3628
DIGITAL HOLLYWOOD INTERACTIVE LIMITED; *Int'l*, pg. 2122
DIGITAL ILLUSIONS CE AB—See Electronic Arts Inc.; *U.S. Public*, pg. 724
DIGITAL INFORMATION TECHNOLOGIES CORPORATION; *Int'l*, pg. 2122
DIGITAL INSIGHT CORPORATION-PRODUCT DEVELOPMENT—See NCR Voyix Corporation.; *U.S. Public*, pg. 1502
DIGITAL INSIGHT CORPORATION—See NCR Voyix Corporation.; *U.S. Public*, pg. 1502
DIGITAL KEYSTONE LIMITED—See Dunstan Thomas Group Limited; *Int'l*, pg. 2227
DIGITAL LEARNING MARKETPLACE PLC; *Int'l*, pg. 2122
DIGITAL NAUTIC SAS—See Beneteau S.A; *Int'l*, pg. 972
DIGITALPOST INTERACTIVE, INC.; *U.S. Private*, pg. 1231
DIGITAL RIVER ONLINE GAMES—See Siris Capital Group, LLC; *U.S. Private*, pg. 3672
DIGITAL VIRGO S.A.—See Digital Virgo Group SAS; *Int'l*, pg. 2123
DIGITAL VIRGO SAS—See Digital Virgo Group SAS; *Int'l*, pg. 2123
DIGITALX LIMITED; *Int'l*, pg. 2123
DIGITECH SA; *Int'l*, pg. 2123
DIGIWIN SOFTWARE CO., LTD.; *Int'l*, pg. 2124

N.A.I.C.S. INDEX

513210 — SOFTWARE PUBLISHERS

DIGNITAS TECHNOLOGIES, LLC; *U.S. Private*, pg. 1231
DIH HOLDING US, INC.; *U.S. Public*, pg. 666
DILIGENT CORPORATION—See Insight Venture Management, LLC; *U.S. Private*, pg. 2089
DILLISTONE GROUP PLC; *Int'l*, pg. 2125
DIMELO, SA—See RingCentral, Inc.; *U.S. Public*, pg. 1799
DIMENSIONAL INSIGHT, INC.; *U.S. Private*, pg. 1233
DION GLOBAL SOLUTIONS LIMITED; *Int'l*, pg. 2127
DION TRANSACTION SOLUTIONS GMBH—See DPE Deutsche Private Equity GmbH; *Int'l*, pg. 2188
DIRECT COMPANIES, LLC; *U.S. Private*, pg. 1234
DIRTT ENVIRONMENTAL SOLUTIONS LTD.; *Int'l*, pg. 2130
DISPUTESUITE.COM, LLC; *U.S. Private*, pg. 1239
DISQUS, INC.—See Zeta Interactive Corporation; *U.S. Private*, pg. 4603
DISTIMO HOLDING B.V.—See App Annie Ltd.; *Int'l*, pg. 519
DISTRIBION, INC.—See DallasNews Corporation; *U.S. Public*, pg. 621
DISTRIBUTION TECHNOLOGY LTD.; *Int'l*, pg. 2136
DITO, LLC; *U.S. Private*, pg. 1240
DIVERSE SOLUTIONS, INC.—See Zillow Group, Inc.; *U.S. Public*, pg. 2405
DL SOFTWARE; *Int'l*, pg. 2140
DMG MORI B.U.G. CO., LTD.—See DMG MORI Co., Ltd.; *Int'l*, pg. 2144
DMI INTERNATIONAL B.V.—See Aebi Schmidt Holding AG; *Int'l*, pg. 170
DNN CORP.—See ESW Capital, LLC; *U.S. Private*, pg. 1430
DNP HYPERTECH CO., LTD—See Dai Nippon Printing Co., Ltd.; *Int'l*, pg. 1914
DOBA LLC; *U.S. Private*, pg. 1250
DOCIRCLE INC.; *U.S. Private*, pg. 1251
DOCKER, INC.; *U.S. Private*, pg. 1251
DOCPHIN, INC.—See HealthTap, Inc.; *U.S. Private*, pg. 1898
DOCTORBASE, INC.—See Kareo, Inc.; *U.S. Private*, pg. 2262
DOCULYNX, INC.—See The HiGro Group LLC; *U.S. Private*, pg. 4052
DOCUPACE TECHNOLOGIES LLC—See Financial Technology Ventures Management Co. LLC; *U.S. Private*, pg. 1508
DOCUPHASE LLC—See LoneTree Capital LLC; *U.S. Private*, pg. 2490
DOCUSIGN BRASIL SOLUCOES EM TECNOLOGIA LTDA.—See DocuSign, Inc.; *U.S. Public*, pg. 672
DOMO, INC.; *U.S. Public*, pg. 675
DOORBOT; *U.S. Private*, pg. 1262
DOOVLE LIMITED; *Int'l*, pg. 2174
DOOZER SOFTWARE, INC.—See Management Analysis & Utilization, Inc.; *U.S. Private*, pg. 2560
DORADO CORPORATION; *U.S. Private*, pg. 1262
DORSETT TECHNOLOGIES INC.—See MMF Capital Management LLC; *U.S. Private*, pg. 2754
DOSH SOFTWARE LTD—See Bain Capital, LP; *U.S. Private*, pg. 442
DOTCMS INC.; *U.S. Private*, pg. 1265
DOTMATICS, INC.—See Insight Venture Management, LLC; *U.S. Private*, pg. 2090
THE DOT NET FACTORY LLC; *U.S. Private*, pg. 4023
DOUBLEDOWN INTERACTIVE CO., LTD.—See DoubleUGames Co., Ltd.; *Int'l*, pg. 2181
DOUBLE DOWN INTERACTIVE LLC—See DoubleUGames Co., Ltd.; *Int'l*, pg. 2181
DOUBLE FINE PRODUCTIONS—See Microsoft Corporation; *U.S. Public*, pg. 1439
DOUBLEUGAMES CO., LTD.; *Int'l*, pg. 2181
DOVEL TECHNOLOGIES, INC.—See Veritas Capital Fund Management, LLC; *U.S. Private*, pg. 4362
DOWLING CONSULTING GROUP, INC.—See Technology Recovery Group Ltd.; *U.S. Private*, pg. 3955
DOXEE CZECH S.R.O.—See Doxee S.p.A; *Int'l*, pg. 2187
DPSI INC.; *U.S. Private*, pg. 1271
DRAGONFLY GF CO., LTD.; *Int'l*, pg. 2199
DRAGOS, INC.; *U.S. Private*, pg. 1272
DRAKE ENTERPRISES LTD.; *U.S. Private*, pg. 1272
DREAM BOX LEARNING INC.—See Clearlake Capital Group, L.P.; *U.S. Private*, pg. 934
DRESSER & ASSOCIATES, INC.—See Net@Work, Inc.; *U.S. Private*, pg. 2886
DRFIRST.COM, INC.; *U.S. Private*, pg. 1277
DRIVEWAY SOFTWARE CORP.—See Earnix Ltd.; *Int'l*, pg. 2267
DROPBOX, INC.; *U.S. Public*, pg. 688
DROPLETS, INC.—See Vivox, Inc.; *U.S. Private*, pg. 4406
DSI-ITI, LLC—See American Securities LLC; *U.S. Private*, pg. 249
DS MEDIALABS; *U.S. Private*, pg. 1281
DSS ADMINISTRATIVE GROUP, INC.—See DSS, Inc.; *U.S. Public*, pg. 689
DSS DIGITAL INC.—See Proof Authentication Corporation; *U.S. Private*, pg. 3284
DST GLOBAL SOLUTIONS LLC—See SS&C Technologies Holdings, Inc.; *U.S. Public*, pg. 1923
DST SYSTEMS, INC.—See SS&C Technologies Holdings, Inc.; *U.S. Public*, pg. 1923
DUBBER CORPORATION LIMITED; *Int'l*, pg. 2222
DUCK CREEK TECHNOLOGIES, INC.—See Vista Equity Partners, LLC; *U.S. Private*, pg. 4396
DUCK DUCK MOOSE, INC.—See Khan Academy, Inc.; *U.S. Private*, pg. 2301
DUDA MOBILE INC.; *U.S. Private*, pg. 1284
DUNDAS DATA VISUALIZATION, INC.—See TA Associates, Inc.; *U.S. Private*, pg. 3915
DUNSTAN THOMAS ENERGY LIMITED—See Dunstan Thomas Group Limited; *Int'l*, pg. 2227
DUNSTAN THOMAS HOLDINGS LIMITED—See Dunstan Thomas Group Limited; *Int'l*, pg. 2227
DUO SECURITY LLC—See Cisco Systems, Inc.; *U.S. Public*, pg. 499
DURA SOFTWARE, INC.—See Dura Software Series A Qof LLC; *U.S. Private*, pg. 1292
DURA SOFTWARE SERIES A QOF LLC; *U.S. Private*, pg. 1291
DVHP INC.; *U.S. Private*, pg. 1295
D-WAVE QUANTUM INC.; *Int'l*, pg. 1900
D-WAVE SYSTEMS INC.—See D-Wave Quantum Inc.; *Int'l*, pg. 1900
DWOLLA INC.; *U.S. Private*, pg. 1296
DYN365, INC.; *U.S. Private*, pg. 1296
DYNAMIC NETWORK SERVICES, INC.—See Oracle Corporation; *U.S. Public*, pg. 1611
DYNASYS S.A.S.—See Thoma Bravo, L.P.; *U.S. Private*, pg. 4151
DYNATRACE AUSTRIA GMBH—See Dynatrace, Inc.; *U.S. Public*, pg. 700
DYNATRACE BV—See Dynatrace, Inc.; *U.S. Public*, pg. 700
DYNATRACE LLC—See Dynatrace, Inc.; *U.S. Public*, pg. 700
E2B TEKNOLOGIES; *U.S. Private*, pg. 1308
E2OPEN AG—See Insight Venture Management, LLC; *U.S. Private*, pg. 2090
E2OPEN CHINA—See Insight Venture Management, LLC; *U.S. Private*, pg. 2090
E2OPEN, LLC—See Insight Venture Management, LLC; *U.S. Private*, pg. 2090
E2OPEN LTD.—See Insight Venture Management, LLC; *U.S. Private*, pg. 2090
E2OPEN MALAYSIA—See Insight Venture Management, LLC; *U.S. Private*, pg. 2090
EA DIGITAL ILLUSIONS CE AB—See Electronic Arts Inc.; *U.S. Public*, pg. 724
EAGLE ADVANTAGE SOLUTIONS, INC.—See Constellation Software Inc.; *Int'l*, pg. 1774
EAGLE EYE SOLUTIONS LTD.—See Eagle Eye Solutions Group PLC; *Int'l*, pg. 2264
EAGLE EYE SOLUTIONS (NORTH) LTD.—See Eagle Eye Solutions Group PLC; *Int'l*, pg. 2264
EAGLES INVESTMENT SYSTEMS LLC—See The Bank of New York Mellon Corporation; *U.S. Public*, pg. 2037
EA SWISS SARL—See Electronic Arts Inc.; *U.S. Public*, pg. 724
EASY APIOMAT GMBH—See Easy Software AG; *Int'l*, pg. 2275
EASYIO ENGINEERING PTE LTD.; *Int'l*, pg. 2276
EASY SOFTWARE AG; *Int'l*, pg. 2275
EASY SOFTWARE (ASIA PACIFIC) PTE. LTD.—See Easy Software AG; *Int'l*, pg. 2275
EASY SOFTWARE DEUTSCHLAND GMBH—See Easy Software AG; *Int'l*, pg. 2275
EASY SOFTWARE TURKIYE LTD. STI.—See Easy Software AG; *Int'l*, pg. 2276
EASYVISTA GMBH—See Eurazeo SE; *Int'l*, pg. 2528
EASYVISTA, S.A.—See Eurazeo SE; *Int'l*, pg. 2528
EASYVISTA SL—See Eurazeo SE; *Int'l*, pg. 2528
EASYVISTA SRL—See Eurazeo SE; *Int'l*, pg. 2528
EBIX AUSTRALIA PTY,. LTD.—See Ebix Inc.; *U.S. Public*, pg. 710
EBIX AUSTRALIA (VIC) PTY. LTD.—See Ebix Inc.; *U.S. Public*, pg. 710
EBIX BPO DIVISION—See Ebix Inc.; *U.S. Public*, pg. 710
EBIX LATIN AMERICA TECHNOLOGIA E CONSULTORIA LTDA—See Ebix Inc.; *U.S. Public*, pg. 710
EBIXLIFE INC.—See Ebix Inc.; *U.S. Public*, pg. 710
EBIX NEW ZEALAND—See Ebix Inc.; *U.S. Public*, pg. 710
EBIX SINGAPORE PTE LTD—See Ebix Inc.; *U.S. Public*, pg. 710
EBOOK TECHNOLOGIES, INC.—See Alphabet Inc.; *U.S. Public*, pg. 84
E-BUILDER, INC.—See Trimble, Inc.; *U.S. Public*, pg. 2193
ECHANNELING PLC; *Int'l*, pg. 2289
ECHO—See HealthStream, Inc.; *U.S. Public*, pg. 1017
ECI SOFTWARE SOLUTIONS, INC.—See Apax Partners LLP; *Int'l*, pg. 503
ECLINICALWORKS, LLC; *U.S. Private*, pg. 1328
ECOMPEX, INC.; *U.S. Private*, pg. 1329
ECRYPT TECHNOLOGIES, INC.; *U.S. Private*, pg. 1331
EDGE CENTRES PTY LTD; *Int'l*, pg. 2309
EDGE DATA SOLUTIONS, INC.; *U.S. Public*, pg. 717
EDGEWATER TECHNOLOGY-RANZAL & ASSOCIATES—See Alithya Group, Inc.; *Int'l*, pg. 329
EDGEWAVE INC.—See GoSecure Inc.; *U.S. Private*, pg. 1744
EDIA CO., LTD.; *Int'l*, pg. 2309
EDITEK, INC.; *U.S. Private*, pg. 1337
EDITION LTD.; *Int'l*, pg. 2311
EDITSHARE, LLC—See ParkerGale, LLC; *U.S. Private*, pg. 3098
EDMENTUM, INC.—See The Vistria Group, LP; *U.S. Private*, pg. 4131
EDO INTERACTIVE, INC.—See Augeo Affinity Marketing, Inc.; *U.S. Private*, pg. 392
EDRAN BERHAD; *Int'l*, pg. 2315
E.D.S. INTERNATIONAL LIMITED—See Veritas Capital Fund Management, LLC; *U.S. Private*, pg. 4364
EDVANCE TECHNOLOGY (HONG KONG) LIMITED—See Edvance International Holdings Limited; *Int'l*, pg. 2316
EDVANCE TECHNOLOGY (SINGAPORE) PTE. LTD.—See Edvance International Holdings Limited; *Int'l*, pg. 2316
EDX WIRELESS, INC.; *U.S. Private*, pg. 1342
EFFEPIEFFE S.R.L.—See CompuGroup Medical SE & Co. KGaA; *Int'l*, pg. 1756
EFFICIENT COLLABORATIVE RETAIL MARKETING COMPANY LLC—See TruArc Partners, L.P.; *U.S. Private*, pg. 4245
EFFICIENT WORKFLOW SOLUTIONS LLC—See Constellation Software Inc.; *Int'l*, pg. 1773
EFFICIO SOLUTIONS, INC.—See ShareBuilders, Inc.; *U.S. Private*, pg. 3626
EFFIZIENZCLOUD GMBH—See EnBW Energie Baden-Wurttemberg AG; *Int'l*, pg. 2401
EFOLDER, INC.; *U.S. Private*, pg. 1343
EFRONT FINANCIAL SOLUTIONS INC.—See BlackRock, Inc.; *U.S. Public*, pg. 347
EFRONT SASU—See BlackRock, Inc.; *U.S. Public*, pg. 347
EFULFILLMENT SERVICE, INC.; *U.S. Private*, pg. 1344
EGAIN COMMUNICATIONS LTD.—See eGain Corporation; *U.S. Public*, pg. 721
EGAIN COMMUNICATIONS PVT. LTD.—See eGain Corporation; *U.S. Public*, pg. 721
EGENERA, INC.; *U.S. Private*, pg. 1344
EGGPLANT—See Keysight Technologies, Inc.; *U.S. Public*, pg. 1227
EGLS CO., LTD.; *Int'l*, pg. 2324
EGOV STRATEGIES LLC—See Wonderware, Inc.; *U.S. Private*, pg. 4556
EGYM GMBH; *Int'l*, pg. 2327
EHEALTH SOLUTIONS, INC.—See ResMed Inc.; *U.S. Public*, pg. 1790
EINSTRUCTION CORP.—See Centre Lane Partners, LLC; *U.S. Private*, pg. 828
EIQNETWORKS, INC.; *U.S. Private*, pg. 1347
EKOTROPE INC.; *U.S. Private*, pg. 1348
ELASTICBOX INC.—See Lumen Technologies, Inc.; *U.S. Public*, pg. 1346
ELATERAL LTD.; *Int'l*, pg. 2343
ELCOM TECHNOLOGY PTY LTD; *Int'l*, pg. 2345
ELECO SOFTWARE GMBH—See Eleco Plc; *Int'l*, pg. 2348
ELECO SOFTWARE LIMITED—See Eleco Plc; *Int'l*, pg. 2347
ELECTRIC CLOUD INC.; *U.S. Private*, pg. 1352
ELECTRONIC ARTS BELGIUM—See Electronic Arts Inc.; *U.S. Public*, pg. 724
ELECTRONIC ARTS NORWAY AS—See Electronic Arts Inc.; *U.S. Public*, pg. 724
ELECTRONIC ARTS PUBLISHING SARL—See Electronic Arts Inc.; *U.S. Public*, pg. 724
ELECTRONIC ARTS ROMANIA SRL—See Electronic Arts Inc.; *U.S. Public*, pg. 724
ELECTRONIC ARTS SWEDEN AB—See Electronic Arts Inc.; *U.S. Public*, pg. 724
ELECTRONIC DATA SYSTEMSBELGIUM BVBA—See HP Inc.; *U.S. Public*, pg. 1062
ELECTRONIC DATA SYSTEMS INTERNATIONAL B.V.—See Veritas Capital Fund Management, LLC; *U.S. Private*, pg. 4364
ELEKTROBIT AUTOMOTIVE SOFTWARE (SHANGHAI) CO., LTD.—See Continental Aktiengesellschaft; *Int'l*, pg. 1783
ELEMENT SOLUTIONS, LLC—See Hinduja Global Solutions Ltd.; *Int'l*, pg. 3398
ELITE EMAIL INC.; *Int'l*, pg. 2362
ELLIE MAE, INC.—See Intercontinental Exchange, Inc.; *U.S. Public*, pg. 1142
ELLUCIAN COMPANY L.P.—See Blackstone Inc.; *U.S. Public*, pg. 353
ELLUCIAN COMPANY L.P.—See Vista Equity Partners, LLC; *U.S. Private*, pg. 4396
ELM CORPORATION—See Future Corporation; *Int'l*, pg. 2853
ELOQUA, INC.—See Oracle Corporation; *U.S. Public*, pg. 1611
ELYPSIS, INC.—See WineDirect, Inc.; *U.S. Private*, pg. 4540
EMAINT ENTERPRISES, LLC—See Fortive Corporation; *U.S. Public*, pg. 870
EMASON, INC.; *U.S. Private*, pg. 1378
EMDS, INC.—See CompuGroup Medical SE & Co. KGaA; *Int'l*, pg. 1757
EMERGE IT SOLUTIONS, LLC; *U.S. Private*, pg. 1380
EMERSON PARADIGM HOLDING LLC—See Emerson Electric Co.; *U.S. Public*, pg. 746
EMONEY ADVISOR, LLC—See FMR LLC; *U.S. Private*, pg. 1555

513210 — SOFTWARE PUBLISHERS

EMPIRED LTD; *Int'l*, pg. 2387.
EMPOWER SOFTWARE SOLUTIONS, INC.—See Hellman & Friedman LLC; *U.S. Private*, pg. 1910.
EMPOWER TECHNOLOGIES, INC.—See EMR Technology Solutions, Inc.; *U.S. Private*, pg. 1388.
EMPTORIS, INC.—See International Business Machines Corporation; *U.S. Public*, pg. 1145.
EMR TECHNOLOGY SOLUTIONS, INC.; *U.S. Private*, pg. 1388.
ENCOURAGE TECHNOLOGIES CO., LTD.; *Int'l*, pg. 2402.
ENDAVA, LLC—See Endava plc; *Int'l*, pg. 2402.
ENDGAME SYSTEMS, LLC; *U.S. Private*, pg. 1391.
ENEA AB; *Int'l*, pg. 2410.
ENEL X NORTH AMERICA, INC.—See Enel S.p.A.; *Int'l*, pg. 2413.
ENERGYCAP, LLC—See Resurgens Technology Partners, LLC; *U.S. Private*, pg. 3411.
ENERGY INTELLIGENCE WORLDWIDE CORP, INC.; *U.S. Private*, pg. 1395.
ENERGY & POWER SOLUTIONS, INC.; *U.S. Private*, pg. 1393.
ENEXOMA AG; *Int'l*, pg. 2425.
ENFO AB—See Enfo Oyj; *Int'l*, pg. 2425.
ENGHOUSE INTERACTIVE—See Enghouse Systems Limited; *Int'l*, pg. 2427.
ENGHOUSE INTERACTIVE—See Enghouse Systems Limited; *Int'l*, pg. 2427.
ENGINEERING & COMPUTER SIMULATIONS, INC.; *U.S. Private*, pg. 1398.
ENGINE YARD, INC.—See GFI Software S.A.; *Int'l*, pg. 2957.
ENISH INC.; *Int'l*, pg. 2439.
ENLYTE GROUP, LLC—See Stone Point Capital LLC; *U.S. Private*, pg. 3823.
ENPORION, INC.—See NB Ventures, Inc.; *U.S. Private*, pg. 2874.
ENSIGHTEN, INC.; *U.S. Private*, pg. 1402.
ENSPIRE LEARNING, INC.; *U.S. Private*, pg. 1402.
ENTERPRISE JBILLING SOFTWARE LTD.—See AppDirect Inc.; *U.S. Private*, pg. 296.
ENTERPRISE PERFORMANCE SYSTEMS, INC.—See Roper Technologies, Inc.; *U.S. Public*, pg. 1813.
ENTERPRISE SERVICES BELGIUM BVBA—See Veritas Capital Fund Management, LLC; *U.S. Private*, pg. 4364.
ENTERPRISE SERVICES FRANCE SAS—See Veritas Capital Fund Management, LLC; *U.S. Private*, pg. 4364.
ENTERPRISE SERVICES (HONG KONG) LIMITED—See Veritas Capital Fund Management, LLC; *U.S. Private*, pg. 4363.
ENTERPRISE SERVICES ITALIA S.R.L.—See Veritas Capital Fund Management, LLC; *U.S. Private*, pg. 4364.
ENTERPRISE SERVICES JAPAN, LTD.—See Veritas Capital Fund Management, LLC; *U.S. Private*, pg. 4364.
ENTERPRISE SERVICES, LLC—See Veritas Capital Fund Management, LLC; *U.S. Private*, pg. 4363.
ENTERPRISE SERVICES SVERIGE AB—See Veritas Capital Fund Management, LLC; *U.S. Private*, pg. 4364.
ENTERRA SOLUTIONS LLC—See glendonTodd Capital LLC; *U.S. Private*, pg. 1710.
ENTERTAINMENT ARTS RESEARCH, INC.; *U.S. Public*, pg. 779.
ENTERWORKS, INC.—See Symphony Technology Group, LLC; *U.S. Private*, pg. 3902.
ENTOMO, INC.—See Insight Venture Management, LLC; *U.S. Private*, pg. 2090.
ENTREDA, INC.—See K1 Investment Management, LLC; *U.S. Private*, pg. 2252.
ENTRUST (EUROPE) LTD.—See DataCard Corporation; *U.S. Private*, pg. 1165.
ENTRUST, INC.—See DataCard Corporation; *U.S. Private*, pg. 1165.
ENVIANCE, INC.—See Thoma Bravo, L.P.; *U.S. Private*, pg. 4146.
EPAM SYSTEMS CANADA, LTD.—See EPAM Systems, Inc.; *U.S. Public*, pg. 783.
EPAM SYSTEMS GMBH—See EPAM Systems, Inc.; *U.S. Public*, pg. 783.
EPAM SYSTEMS, INC.; *U.S. Public*, pg. 783.
EPAM SYSTEMS KFT—See EPAM Systems, Inc.; *U.S. Public*, pg. 783.
EPAM SYSTEMS LLC—See EPAM Systems, Inc.; *U.S. Public*, pg. 783.
EPAM SYSTEMS LTD.—See EPAM Systems, Inc.; *U.S. Public*, pg. 783.
EPAM SYSTEMS NORDIC AB—See EPAM Systems, Inc.; *U.S. Public*, pg. 783.
EPAM SYSTEMS (POLAND) SP. Z O.O.—See EPAM Systems, Inc.; *U.S. Public*, pg. 783.
EPAM SYSTEMS (SWITZERLAND) GMBH—See EPAM Systems, Inc.; *U.S. Public*, pg. 783.
EPAPYRUS, INC.; *Int'l*, pg. 2458.
EPAZZ, INC.; *U.S. Public*, pg. 1411.
EPCSOLUTIONS; *U.S. Private*, pg. 1411.
EPICOR EDI SOURCE, INC.—See Clayton, Dubilier & Rice, LLC; *U.S. Private*, pg. 922.
EPICOR SOFTWARE CORPORATION-MINNEAPOLIS—See Clayton, Dubilier & Rice, LLC; *U.S. Private*, pg. 922.
EPIC SYSTEMS CORPORATION; *U.S. Private*, pg. 1413.

EPION HEALTH, INC.—See Kyruus, Inc.; *U.S. Private*, pg. 2360.
EPISERVER GROUP AB—See Insight Venture Management, LLC; *U.S. Private*, pg. 2090.
EPLAN SERVICES, INC.; *U.S. Private*, pg. 1414.
EPRO SYSTEMS (HK) LIMITED—See Hang Tai Yue Group Holdings Limited; *Int'l*, pg. 3245.
EPTURA, INC.; *U.S. Private*, pg. 1414.
EQ INC.; *Int'l*, pg. 2466.
EQUBE GAMING LIMITED; *Int'l*, pg. 2484.
EQUICARE HEALTH INC.; *Int'l*, pg. 2484.
EQUITRAC CORPORATION—See Microsoft Corporation; *U.S. Public*, pg. 1442.
EQUIVIO INC.—See Microsoft Corporation; *U.S. Public*, pg. 1439.
EQUUS SOFTWARE, LLC; *U.S. Private*, pg. 1417.
ERECORDING PARTNERS NETWORK, LLC—See Old Republic International Corporation; *U.S. Public*, pg. 1569.
ERESEARCHTECHNOLOGY GMBH—See Astorg Partners S.A.S.; *Int'l*, pg. 657.
ERESEARCHTECHNOLOGY, INC. - BRIDGEWATER—See Astorg Partners S.A.S.; *Int'l*, pg. 657.
ERESEARCHTECHNOLOGY, INC.—See Astorg Partners S.A.S.; *Int'l*, pg. 657.
ERESEARCHTECHNOLOGY LIMITED—See Astorg Partners S.A.S.; *Int'l*, pg. 657.
ESA CO., LTD.; *Int'l*, pg. 2500.
ESALESTRACK—See Soleran, Inc.; *U.S. Private*, pg. 3709.
ESCALATE RETAIL, INC.—See Golden Gate Capital Management II, LLC; *U.S. Private*, pg. 1731.
ESCHER GROUP LIMITED; *U.S. Private*, pg. 1425.
ESC, INC.—See QXO, Inc.; *U.S. Public*, pg. 1758.
ESET, LLC; *U.S. Private*, pg. 1425.
ESET, SPOL. S.R.O.—See ESET, LLC; *U.S. Private*, pg. 1425.
ESHA RESEARCH INC.—See The Riverside Company; *U.S. Private*, pg. 4108.
ESI ACQUISITION, INC.; *U.S. Private*, pg. 1425.
ESIGN SOFTWARE GMBH—See Eleco Plc; *Int'l*, pg. 2348.
ESIGNSYSTEMS—See DocMagic, Inc.; *U.S. Private*, pg. 1251.
ESKER S.A.; *Int'l*, pg. 2503.
ESKO-GRAPHICS BVBA—See Danaher Corporation; *U.S. Public*, pg. 626.
ESKO-GRAPHICS PTE LTD.—See Danaher Corporation; *U.S. Public*, pg. 626.
ESO SOLUTIONS, INC.; *U.S. Private*, pg. 1426.
ESPIAL GROUP INC.—See Enghouse Systems Limited; *Int'l*, pg. 2427.
ESP TECHONOLOGIES CORP.; *U.S. Private*, pg. 1426.
ESTEREL TECHNOLOGIES, INC.—See ANSYS, Inc.; *U.S. Public*, pg. 139.
ESTEREL TECHNOLOGIES, S.A.—See ANSYS, Inc.; *U.S. Public*, pg. 139.
E-TECHNOLOGIES GROUP, LLC—See The Graham Group, Inc.; *U.S. Private*, pg. 4036.
ET EUROPE HOLDING BV—See Pareteum Corporation; *U.S. Public*, pg. 1637.
ETHERSTACK PLC; *Int'l*, pg. 2523.
E-TRANZACT INTERNATIONAL PLC.; *Int'l*, pg. 2249.
ETRIGUE CORPORATION; *U.S. Private*, pg. 1432.
E-TRON CO., LTD; *Int'l*, pg. 2249.
EUCLYDE DATA CENTERS SAS—See I Squared Capital Advisors (US) LLC; *U.S. Private*, pg. 2025.
EUDA HEALTH HOLDINGS LIMITED; *Int'l*, pg. 2525.
EUROFINS DIGITAL TESTING UK HOLDING LIMITED—See Eurofins Scientific S.E.; *Int'l*, pg. 2539.
EVALYTICA, LLC—See Veradigm Inc.; *U.S. Public*, pg. 2280.
EVD BERHAD; *Int'l*, pg. 2561.
EVENTBRITE, INC.; *U.S. Public*, pg. 799.
EVENTINVENTORY.COM, INC.—See Live Nation Entertainment, Inc.; *U.S. Public*, pg. 1328.
EVER.AG CORPORATION—See Dairy, LLC; *U.S. Private*, pg. 1146.
EVEREST SOFTWARE INC.—See ESW Capital, LLC; *U.S. Private*, pg. 1430.
EVERFI, INC.; *U.S. Private*, pg. 1438.
E-VERIFILE.COM, INC.; *U.S. Private*, pg. 1303.
EVERNOTE CORPORATION; *U.S. Private*, pg. 1440.
EVERYMATRIX LTD.; *Int'l*, pg. 2570.
EVESTMENT ALLIANCE, LLC—See Nasdaq, Inc.; *U.S. Public*, pg. 1492.
EVESTMENT, INC.—See Nasdaq, Inc.; *U.S. Public*, pg. 1492.
EVGO RECARGO, LLC—See EVgo Inc.; *U.S. Public*, pg. 802.
EVIDENT SOFTWARE, INC.; *U.S. Private*, pg. 1441.
EVIIVO LTD.; *Int'l*, pg. 2570.
EVIVE HEALTH, LLC; *U.S. Private*, pg. 1442.
EVOCATIVE, INC.; *U.S. Private*, pg. 1442.
EVOLENT HEALTH, INC.; *U.S. Public*, pg. 804.
EVOLIT CONSULTING GMBH—See DZ BANK AG Deutsche Zentral-Genossenschaftsbank; *Int'l*, pg. 2244.
EVOLUTION1, INC.—See WEX, Inc.; *U.S. Public*, pg. 2364.
EVOLUTIONARY TECHNOLOGIES INTERNATIONAL, INC.—See ESW Capital, LLC; *U.S. Private*, pg. 1430.
EVOLVING SYSTEMS LIMITED—See CCUR Holdings Inc.; *U.S. Public*, pg. 461.

EVOLVING SYSTEMS LIMITED—See CCUR Holdings Inc.; *U.S. Public*, pg. 461.
EWINWIN, INC.; *U.S. Private*, pg. 1444.
EX2 SOLUTIONS, INC.—See Builder Homesite, Inc.; *U.S. Private*, pg. 681.
EXACT ESPANA SL—See KKR & Co. Inc.; *U.S. Public*, pg. 1250.
EXACT SOFTWARE BELGIUM N.V.—See KKR & Co. Inc.; *U.S. Public*, pg. 1250.
EXACT SOFTWARE FRANCE SARL—See KKR & Co. Inc.; *U.S. Public*, pg. 1250.
EXACT SOFTWARE (MALAYSIA) SDN. BHD.—See KKR & Co. Inc.; *U.S. Public*, pg. 1250.
EXACT SOFTWARE NEDERLAND B.V. - EINDHOVEN—See KKR & Co. Inc.; *U.S. Public*, pg. 1250.
EXACT SOFTWARE NORTH AMERICA LLC—See KKR & Co. Inc.; *U.S. Public*, pg. 1251.
EXACT SOFTWARE POLAND SP. Z O.O.—See KKR & Co. Inc.; *U.S. Public*, pg. 1250.
EXACT SOFTWARE (UK) LTD.—See KKR & Co. Inc.; *U.S. Public*, pg. 1250.
EXACTTARGET, INC.—See Salesforce, Inc.; *U.S. Public*, pg. 1837.
EXALEAD INC.—See Dassault Systemes S.A.; *Int'l*, pg. 1975.
EXALEAD S.A.—See Dassault Systemes S.A.; *Int'l*, pg. 1975.
EXAMSOFT WORLDWIDE, INC.—See Advance Publications, Inc.; *U.S. Private*, pg. 87.
EXAN ENTERPRISES INC.—See Henry Schein, Inc.; *U.S. Public*, pg. 1025.
EXARI GROUP, INC.—See Thoma Bravo, L.P.; *U.S. Private*, pg. 4147.
EXCEL SYSTEM (BEIJING) LIMITED; *Int'l*, pg. 2577.
EXCHEQUER ENTERPRISE SOFTWARE (NEW ZEALAND) LIMITED—See HgCapital Trust plc; *Int'l*, pg. 3376.
EXCHEQUER SOFTWARE LTD—See HgCapital Trust plc; *Int'l*, pg. 3376.
EXECUTIVE BUSINESS SERVICES, INC.—See Roper Technologies, Inc.; *U.S. Public*, pg. 1811.
EXECUTIVE INFORMATION SYSTEMS, LLC; *U.S. Private*, pg. 1447.
EXELIS VISUAL INFORMATION SOLUTIONS, INC.—See L3Harris Technologies, Inc.; *U.S. Public*, pg. 1280.
EXEM CO., LTD.; *Int'l*, pg. 2583.
EXHEDRA SOLUTIONS, INC.; *U.S. Private*, pg. 1448.
EXIM A.S.—See Hitay Investment Holdings A.S.; *Int'l*, pg. 3425.
EXINI DIAGNOSTICS AB—See Avista Capital Partners, L.P.; *U.S. Private*, pg. 408.
EX LIBRIS ASIA PTE LTD.—See Clarivate PLC; *Int'l*, pg. 1650.
EX LIBRIS (AUSTRALIA) PTY LTD—See Clarivate PLC; *Int'l*, pg. 1649.
EX LIBRIS ITALY S.R.L.—See Clarivate PLC; *Int'l*, pg. 1650.
EX LIBRIS LTD.—See Clarivate PLC; *Int'l*, pg. 1649.
EX LIBRIS (UK) LIMITED—See Clarivate PLC; *Int'l*, pg. 1649.
EX LIBRIS (USA) INC.—See Clarivate PLC; *Int'l*, pg. 1649.
EXONY INC.—See eGain Corporation; *U.S. Public*, pg. 721.
EXONY LTD.—See eGain Corporation; *U.S. Public*, pg. 721.
EXPERIAN HEALTHCARE—See Experian plc; *Int'l*, pg. 2587.
EXPERIOR GROUP LTD.—See QualiTest Group; *U.S. Private*, pg. 3317.
EXPERT.AI S.P.A.; *Int'l*, pg. 2588.
EXPERTICITY, INC.; *U.S. Private*, pg. 1450.
EXPLEO SOLUTIONS LIMITED—See Assystem S.A.; *Int'l*, pg. 650.
EXPOSOFT SOLUTIONS INC.; *Int'l*, pg. 2590.
EXPRESS DIGITAL GRAPHICS, INC.—See Photoreflect, LLC; *U.S. Private*, pg. 3174.
EXPRIVIA SPA; *Int'l*, pg. 2590.
EXTREME CO., LTD.; *Int'l*, pg. 2592.
EYEVIEW, INC.; *U.S. Private*, pg. 1453.
EZLINKS GOLF LLC—See Comcast Corporation; *U.S. Public*, pg. 539.
EZSHIELD, INC.—See The Wicks Group of Companies, LLC; *U.S. Private*, pg. 4135.
EZ SYSTEMS AS; *Int'l*, pg. 2593.
EZ SYSTEMS CHINA—See eZ Systems AS; *Int'l*, pg. 2593.
EZ SYSTEMS FRANCE—See eZ Systems AS; *Int'l*, pg. 2593.
EZ SYSTEMS GERMANY—See eZ Systems AS; *Int'l*, pg. 2593.
EZ SYSTEMS ITALY—See eZ Systems AS; *Int'l*, pg. 2593.
EZ SYSTEMS JAPAN—See eZ Systems AS; *Int'l*, pg. 2593.
EZ SYSTEMS NORDICS—See eZ Systems AS; *Int'l*, pg. 2593.
EZ SYSTEMS SPAIN—See eZ Systems AS; *Int'l*, pg. 2593.
EZUCE, INC.—See Thompson Street Capital Manager LLC; *U.S. Private*, pg. 4160.
F5, INC.; *U.S. Public*, pg. 818.
F5 NETWORKS BENELUX B.V.—See F5, Inc.; *U.S. Public*, pg. 819.
F5 NETWORKS CHINA—See F5, Inc.; *U.S. Public*, pg. 819.
F5 NETWORKS IBERIA SL—See F5, Inc.; *U.S. Public*, pg. 819.

513210 — SOFTWARE PUBLISHERS

FAAC, INCORPORATED—See Greenbriar Equity Group, L.P.; *U.S. Private*, pg. 1775
FACEPHI BIOMETRIA SA; *Int'l*, pg. 2600
FACTOR—See W.R. Hess Company; *U.S. Private*, pg. 4422
FACTSET DIGITAL SOLUTIONS AG—See FactSet Research Systems Inc.; *U.S. Public*, pg. 819
FACTSET DIGITAL SOLUTIONS, LLC—See FactSet Research Systems Inc.; *U.S. Public*, pg. 819
FACTSET PACIFIC, INC.—See FactSet Research Systems Inc.; *U.S. Public*, pg. 820
FACTSET SINGAPORE PTE LTD—See FactSet Research Systems Inc.; *U.S. Public*, pg. 820
FACTSET UK LIMITED—See FactSet Research Systems Inc.; *U.S. Public*, pg. 820
FACTUAL INC.—See Foursquare Labs, Inc.; *U.S. Private*, pg. 1583
FAIRCOM CORPORATION; *U.S. Private*, pg. 1462
FAIR ISAAC ADEPTRA, INC.—See Fair Isaac Corporation; *U.S. Public*, pg. 820
FAIR ISAAC CHILE SOFTWARE & SERVICES LTDA.—See Fair Isaac Corporation; *U.S. Public*, pg. 820
FAIR ISAAC GERMANY GMBH—See Fair Isaac Corporation; *U.S. Public*, pg. 820
FAIR ISAAC SOUTH AFRICA (PTY) LTD.—See Fair Isaac Corporation; *U.S. Public*, pg. 820
FAIRWARNING LLC—See Thoma Bravo, L.P.; *U.S. Private*, pg. 4148
FAIRWARNING SARL—See Thoma Bravo, L.P.; *U.S. Private*, pg. 4148
FALCON SOCIAL APS; *Int'l*, pg. 2611
FALCON-SOFTWARE COMPANY, INC.; *Int'l*, pg. 2611
FALCONSTOR SOFTWARE, INC.; *U.S. Public*, pg. 821
FALCONSTOR SOFTWARE (KOREA), INC.—See FalconStor Software, Inc.; *U.S. Public*, pg. 821
FAMILY ZONE CYBER SAFETY LIMITED; *Int'l*, pg. 2612
FARMA3TEC S.R.L.—See CompuGroup Medical SE & Co. KGaA; *Int'l*, pg. 1756
FARMAGES SOFTWARE S.L.—See CompuGroup Medical SE & Co. KGaA; *Int'l*, pg. 1757
FASHION GPS, INC.—See Augure SA; *Int'l*, pg. 703
FASOO CO.,LTD.; *Int'l*, pg. 2621
FASOO USA INC.—See FASOO Co.,Ltd.; *Int'l*, pg. 2621
FAST ENTERPRISES, LLC; *U.S. Private*, pg. 1481
FAST—See Microsoft Corporation; *U.S. Public*, pg. 1439
FASTVUE INC.; *U.S. Private*, pg. 1483
FAST WHITE CAT S.A.—See Digitree Group S.A.; *Int'l*, pg. 2124
FDM SOFTWARE LTD.—See TA Associates, Inc.; *U.S. Private*, pg. 3914
FD TECHNOLOGIES PLC; *Int'l*, pg. 2628
FEDMINE LLC—See Endicott Group Equity Partners, L.P.; *U.S. Private*, pg. 1391
FEDMINE LLC—See Thompson Street Capital Manager LLC; *U.S. Private*, pg. 4161
FEEDHENRY (IRELAND) LIMITED—See International Business Machines Corporation; *U.S. Public*, pg. 1150
FEEDHENRY LLC—See International Business Machines Corporation; *U.S. Public*, pg. 1150
FEEDHENRY LTD.—See International Business Machines Corporation; *U.S. Public*, pg. 1150
FEI HOUSTON, INC.—See Thermo Fisher Scientific Inc.; *U.S. Public*, pg. 2147
FEIYU TECHNOLOGY INTERNATIONAL COMPANY LTD.; *Int'l*, pg. 2632
FENICS FX, LLC—See BGC Group, Inc.; *U.S. Public*, pg. 328
FFRI SECURITY, INC.; *Int'l*, pg. 2649
FIDELIO CRUISE SOFTWARE GMBH—See Oracle Corporation; *U.S. Public*, pg. 1612
FIDELITY INFORMATION SERVICES KORDOBA GMBH—See Fidelity National Infor; *U.S. Public*, pg. 832
FIELDVIEW SOLUTIONS, INC.—See Nlyte Software Americas Limited; *U.S. Private*, pg. 2931
FILEMAKER, INC.—See Apple Inc.; *U.S. Public*, pg. 169
FILEMAKER JAPAN INC.—See Apple Inc.; *U.S. Public*, pg. 169
FILMTRACK INC.; *U.S. Private*, pg. 1506
FINAL DRAFT, INC.—See EQT AB; *Int'l*, pg. 2473
FINANCE EXPRESS, LLC—See Vista Equity Partners, LLC; *U.S. Private*, pg. 4400
FINDEX.COM, INC.; *U.S. Public*, pg. 834
FINDEX INC.; *Int'l*, pg. 2672
FINGERMOTION, INC.; *U.S. Public*, pg. 834
FINICITY CORPORATION—See Mastercard Incorporated; *U.S. Public*, pg. 1394
FINTECH CHAIN LIMITED; *Int'l*, pg. 2677
FIREHOST INC.; *U.S. Private*, pg. 1511
FIREMON LLC—See Insight Venture Management, LLC; *U.S. Private*, pg. 2090
FIRSTINVISION GESMBH; *Int'l*, pg. 2689
FIRSTLIGHT MEDIA LTD—See Highview Capital, LLC; *U.S. Private*, pg. 1942
FISCALNOTE HOLDINGS, INC.; *U.S. Public*, pg. 850
FISCHER INTERNATIONAL SYSTEMS CORPORATION; *U.S. Private*, pg. 1532
FIS FINANCIAL SYSTEMS LLC—See Fidelity National Infor; *U.S. Public*, pg. 832

FIT TRACKING SOLUTIONS—See Alcea Technologies Inc.; *Int'l*, pg. 300
FIVE9, INC.; *U.S. Public*, pg. 852
FIVE POINTS TECHNOLOGY GROUP, INC.; *U.S. Private*, pg. 1537
FIXNETIX LTD.—See DXC Technology Company; *U.S. Public*, pg. 695
FIXSTARS CORPORATION; *Int'l*, pg. 2696
FKAUBI, INC.—See Harvard Bioscience, Inc.; *U.S. Public*, pg. 987
FLEXERA SOFTWARE LLC—See TA Associates, Inc.; *U.S. Private*, pg. 3915
FLEXERA SOFTWARE LTD.—See TA Associates, Inc.; *U.S. Private*, pg. 3915
FLIMP MEDIA INC.; *U.S. Private*, pg. 1545
FLOWPLAY, INC.—See PCI Gaming Authority; *U.S. Private*, pg. 3120
FLUITEC INTERNATIONAL EUROPE—See Fluitec International LLC; *U.S. Private*, pg. 1552
FLUITEC INTERNATIONAL LLC; *U.S. Private*, pg. 1552
FNC, INC.—See Insight Venture Management, LLC; *U.S. Private*, pg. 2089
FNC, INC.—See Stone Point Capital LLC; *U.S. Private*, pg. 3822
FOCUS LEARNING CORPORATION—See The Brydon Group LLC; *U.S. Private*, pg. 4001
FOCUS SOLUTIONS GROUP LTD.—See abrdn PLC; *Int'l*, pg. 68
FOCUS SYSTEMS CORPORATION; *Int'l*, pg. 2720
FOCUSVISION WORLDWIDE, INC.—See EQT AB; *Int'l*, pg. 2475
FOG SOFTWARE GROUP—See Constellation Software Inc.; *Int'l*, pg. 1772
FOLIATEAM SASU; *Int'l*, pg. 2721
FOODLOGIQ, LLC—See The Riverside Company; *U.S. Private*, pg. 4108
FORCEPOINT DEUTSCHLAND GMBH—See Francisco Partners Management, LP; *U.S. Private*, pg. 1590
FORCEPOINT FRANCE—See Francisco Partners Management, LP; *U.S. Private*, pg. 1590
FORCEPOINT INTERNATIONAL TECHNOLOGY LIMITED—See Francisco Partners Management, LP; *U.S. Private*, pg. 1590
FORCEPOINT ITALY S.R.L.—See Francisco Partners Management, LP; *U.S. Private*, pg. 1590
FORCEPOINT JAPAN KK—See Francisco Partners Management, LP; *U.S. Private*, pg. 1590
FORCEPOINT LLC—See Francisco Partners Management, LP; *U.S. Private*, pg. 1589
FORCEPOINT UK LIMITED—See Francisco Partners Management, LP; *U.S. Private*, pg. 1590
FORCEWORKS LLC; *U.S. Private*, pg. 1563
FORCS CO., LTD.; *Int'l*, pg. 2730
FOREFLIGHT LLC—See The Boeing Company; *U.S. Public*, pg. 2041
FORESIGHT SOFTWARE, LLC; *U.S. Private*, pg. 1566
FORGAME HOLDINGS LIMITED; *Int'l*, pg. 2733
FORLINK SOFTWARE CORPORATION, INC.; *Int'l*, pg. 2733
FORMPIPE SOFTWARE AB; *Int'l*, pg. 2736
FORMSCAN LIMITED; *Int'l*, pg. 2736
FORMSTACK, LLC—See PSG Equity L.L.C.; *U.S. Private*, pg. 3297
FORMSTACK, LLC—See Silversmith Management, L.P.; *U.S. Private*, pg. 3663
FORMULA TELECOM SOLUTIONS LIMITED; *Int'l*, pg. 2737
FORSTA INC.—See Ares Management Corporation; *U.S. Public*, pg. 190
FORSTA INC.—See Leonard Green & Partners, L.P.; *U.S. Private*, pg. 2427
FORTINET GMBH—See Fortinet, Inc.; *U.S. Public*, pg. 869
FORTINET INFORMATION TECHNOLOGY (BEIJING) CO., LTD.—See Fortinet, Inc.; *U.S. Public*, pg. 869
FORTINET JAPAN CO. LTD.—See Fortinet, Inc.; *U.S. Public*, pg. 869
FORTINET MEXICO, S. DE R.L. DE C.V.—See Fortinet, Inc.; *U.S. Public*, pg. 869
FORTINET S.A.R.L.—See Fortinet, Inc.; *U.S. Public*, pg. 869
FORTINET SECURITY ISRAEL LTD.—See Fortinet, Inc.; *U.S. Public*, pg. 869
FORTINET SECURITY KOREA LTD.—See Fortinet, Inc.; *U.S. Public*, pg. 869
FORTINET SECURITY SPAIN S.L—See Fortinet, Inc.; *U.S. Public*, pg. 869
FORTINET SINGAPORE PRIVATE LIMITED—See Fortinet, Inc.; *U.S. Public*, pg. 869
FORTINET TECHNOLOGIES (CANADA), INC.—See Fortinet, Inc.; *U.S. Public*, pg. 869
FORTINET TECHNOLOGIES INDIA PRIVATE LIMITED—See Fortinet, Inc.; *U.S. Public*, pg. 869
FORTINET TURKEY GUVENLIK SISTEMLERI LIMITED SIRKETI—See Fortinet, Inc.; *U.S. Public*, pg. 869
FORTINET (UK) LTD.—See Fortinet, Inc.; *U.S. Public*, pg. 869
FOUNDATION 9 ENTERTAINMENT, INC.; *U.S. Private*, pg. 1579

FOUNDATION SOFTWARE, INC.—See Thoma Bravo, L.P.; *U.S. Private*, pg. 4148
FOUNDER INTERNATIONAL (BEIJING) CO., LTD.—See Founder Technology Group Corp.; *Int'l*, pg. 2753
FOUNDER INTERNATIONAL (CHANGCHUN) CO., LTD.—See Founder Technology Group Corp.; *Int'l*, pg. 2753
FOUNDER INTERNATIONAL CO., LTD.—See Founder Technology Group Corp.; *Int'l*, pg. 2753
FOUNDER INTERNATIONAL (GUANGZHOU) CO., LTD.—See Founder Technology Group Corp.; *Int'l*, pg. 2753
FOUNDER INTERNATIONAL (JIANGSU) CO., LTD.—See Founder Technology Group Corp.; *Int'l*, pg. 2753
FOUNDER INTERNATIONAL (WUHAN) CO., LTD.—See Founder Technology Group Corp.; *Int'l*, pg. 2753
THE FOUNDRY VISIONMONGERS LIMITED—See Roper Technologies, Inc.; *U.S. Public*, pg. 1813
FOURTH LTD.—See Marlin Equity Partners, LLC; *U.S. Private*, pg. 2584
FOUR WINDS INTERACTIVE LLC; *U.S. Private*, pg. 1582
FOXINSIGHTS GMBH—See EnBW Energie Baden-Wurttemberg AG; *Int'l*, pg. 2399
FOXIT SOFTWARE INC.; *U.S. Private*, pg. 1585
FPX, LLC; *U.S. Private*, pg. 1586
FRACTURECODE CORPORATION APS; *Int'l*, pg. 2758
FRAMEHAWK, INC.—See Elliott Management Corporation; *U.S. Private*, pg. 1367
FRAMEHAWK, INC.—See Vista Equity Partners, LLC; *U.S. Private*, pg. 4396
FRANKLIN ELECTRONIC PUBLISHERS (AUST) PTY. LTD.—See Franklin Electronic Publishers, Inc.; *U.S. Private*, pg. 1597
FRANKLIN ELECTRONIC PUBLISHERS DEUTSCHLAND GMBH—See Franklin Electronic Publishers, Inc.; *U.S. Private*, pg. 1597
FRANKLIN ELECTRONIC PUBLISHERS FRANCE—See Franklin Electronic Publishers, Inc.; *U.S. Private*, pg. 1597
FRANKLIN ELECTRONIC PUBLISHERS, LTD.—See Franklin Electronic Publishers, Inc.; *U.S. Private*, pg. 1597
FRANKLIN PUBLISHERS DE MEXICO—See Franklin Electronic Publishers, Inc.; *U.S. Private*, pg. 1597
FRANKLIN U.K.—See Franklin Electronic Publishers, Inc.; *U.S. Private*, pg. 1597
FREEWHEEL MEDIA INC.—See Comcast Corporation; *U.S. Public*, pg. 538
FREEZE TAG, INC.; *U.S. Public*, pg. 884
FREQUENTIS AG; *Int'l*, pg. 2773
FREUDENBERG VILENE TELA SAN. VE TIC. A.S.—See Freudenberg SE; *Int'l*, pg. 2788
FRIENDWORKS GMBH—See Easy Software AG; *Int'l*, pg. 2276
FRIMO GROUP GMBH—See Deutsche Beteiligungs AG; *Int'l*, pg. 2062
FRONTIER COMMUNICATIONS CORPORATION; *U.S. Private*, pg. 1615
FRONTIER DEVELOPMENTS INC.—See Frontier Developments plc; *Int'l*, pg. 2795
FRONTIER DEVELOPMENTS PLC; *Int'l*, pg. 2795
FRONTLINE TECHNOLOGIES GROUP LLC—See Roper Technologies, Inc.; *U.S. Public*, pg. 1811
FTEN, INC.—See Nasdaq, Inc.; *U.S. Public*, pg. 1491
FTI GROUPS, INC.—See ArcBest Corporation; *U.S. Public*, pg. 180
FUJIAN APEX SOFTWARE CO., LTD.; *Int'l*, pg. 2817
FUJIAN BOSS SOFTWARE CORP.; *Int'l*, pg. 2817
FUJIAN RONGJI SOFTWARE CO., LTD.; *Int'l*, pg. 2819
FULLCONTACT, INC.; *U.S. Private*, pg. 1621
FUNBOX COMPANY LIMITED—See Asphere Innovations Public Company Limited; *Int'l*, pg. 630
FUNDABLE LLC; *U.S. Private*, pg. 1622
FUNDAMO (PTY) LTD.—See Visa, Inc.; *U.S. Public*, pg. 2301
FUNDLY INC.—See NonProfitEasy, Inc.; *U.S. Private*, pg. 2934
FUNMOBILITY, INC.; *U.S. Private*, pg. 1623
FUNNY SOFTWARE LIMITED; *Int'l*, pg. 2846
FURSTPERSON, INC.—See Rubicon Technology Partners, LLC; *U.S. Private*, pg. 3500
FUSEBILL INC.; *Int'l*, pg. 2849
FUSIONEX INTERNATIONAL PLC; *Int'l*, pg. 2849
FUSION PPT LLC; *U.S. Private*, pg. 1625
FUTONG TECHNOLOGY DEVELOPMENT HOLDINGS LIMITED; *Int'l*, pg. 2852
FUTUREMARK CORPORATION—See Underwriters Laboratories Inc.; *U.S. Private*, pg. 4280
FUTUREMARK OY—See Underwriters Laboratories Inc.; *U.S. Private*, pg. 4280
FUYO NETWORK SERVICE CO., LTD.—See Fuyo General Lease Co., Ltd.; *Int'l*, pg. 2859
FUZZY LOGIX, LLC; *U.S. Private*, pg. 1627
F.W. DAVISON & COMPANY, INC.; *U.S. Private*, pg. 1457
FYBER N.V.—See Digital Turbine, Inc.; *U.S. Public*, pg. 664
G5 ENTERTAINMENT AB; *Int'l*, pg. 2866
GAEASOFT; *Int'l*, pg. 2868
GALA INCORPORATED; *Int'l*, pg. 2870

513210 — SOFTWARE PUBLISHERS

GALA LAB CORP.—See GALA INCORPORATED; *Int'l*, pg. 2870
GALE TECHNOLOGIES, INC.—See Dell Technologies Inc.; *U.S. Public*, pg. 650
THE GAME AGENCY LLC—See Fundos Group LLC; *U.S. Private*, pg. 1623
THE GAME AGENCY LLC—See Trinity Private Equity Group, LLC; *U.S. Private*, pg. 4235
GAMEFORGE AG; *Int'l*, pg. 2877
GAME HOUSE EUROPE B.V.—See RealNetworks, Inc.; *U.S. Private*, pg. 3369
GAMESIM, INC.—See Canada Pension Plan Investment Board; *Int'l*, pg. 1280
GAMESIM, INC.—See EQT AB; *Int'l*, pg. 2482
GAMEVIL USA, INC.—See Com2uS Holdings; *Int'l*, pg. 1706
GAMEZEBO, INC.—See Flipside, Inc.; *U.S. Private*, pg. 1546
GAMZIO MOBILE INC.; *U.S. Private*, pg. 1641
GAN PLC; *Int'l*, pg. 2880
GATHID LTD.; *Int'l*, pg. 2889
GBT TECHNOLOGIES INC.; *U.S. Public*, pg. 908
GE INTELLIGENT PLATFORMS EMBEDDED SYSTEMS, INC.—See General Electric Company; *U.S. Public*, pg. 917
GENERAL ASP INC.; *U.S. Private*, pg. 1660
GENERATION PASS CO., LTD.; *Int'l*, pg. 2920
GENERIX GROUP FRANCE SA; *Int'l*, pg. 2921
GENESIS NETWORKS ENTERPRISES, LLC; *U.S. Private*, pg. 1669
GENIUS.COM, INCORPORATED; *U.S. Private*, pg. 1671
GENIUS.COM UK—See Genius.com, Incorporated; *U.S. Private*, pg. 1671
GENOME COMPILER CORPORATION—See Twist Bioscience Corporation; *U.S. Public*, pg. 2207
GENPACT HUNGARY PROCESS SZOLGALTATO KFT.—See Genpact Limited; *Int'l*, pg. 2927
GENPACT INTERNATIONAL, INC.—See Genpact Limited; *Int'l*, pg. 2926
GENPACT NL B.V—See Genpact Limited; *Int'l*, pg. 2927
GENPACT PL SP. Z O.O.—See Genpact Limited; *Int'l*, pg. 2927
GENPACT REGULATORY AFFAIRS UK LIMITED—See Genpact Limited; *Int'l*, pg. 2927
GENPACT ROMANIA SRL—See Genpact Limited; *Int'l*, pg. 2927
GENPACT SERVICES HUNGARY KFT—See Genpact Limited; *Int'l*, pg. 2927
GENPACT SINGAPORE PTE. LTD.—See Genpact Limited; *Int'l*, pg. 2927
GENPACT WB LLC—See Genpact Limited; *Int'l*, pg. 2927
GENTICS SOFTWARE GMBH—See APA-Austria Presse Agentur eG; *Int'l*, pg. 500
GENTRACK LIMITED; *Int'l*, pg. 2929
GENTRACK LTD.—See Gentrack Limited; *Int'l*, pg. 2929
GENTRACK PTY. LTD.—See Gentrack Limited; *Int'l*, pg. 2929
GEOCONCEPT SA; *Int'l*, pg. 2932
GEODIGITAL SOLUTIONS, INC.—See GeoDigital International Inc.; *U.S. Private*, pg. 2933
GEOFIELDS, INC.—See Emerson Electric Co.; *U.S. Public*, pg. 749
GEOFORCE, INC.—See Independence Capital Partners, LLC; *U.S. Private*, pg. 2056
GEOGRAPHIC INFORMATION SERVICES, INC.—See Bluestone Investment Partners, LLC; *U.S. Private*, pg. 598
GEOGRAPHIC SOLUTIONS, INC.; *U.S. Private*, pg. 1680
GEOKNOWLEDGE AS—See Schlumberger Limited; *U.S. Public*, pg. 1844
GEOKNOWLEDGE USA, INC.—See Schlumberger Limited; *U.S. Public*, pg. 1844
GEOMETRIC AMERICAS, INC. - SCOTTSDALE—See HCL Technologies Ltd.; *Int'l*, pg. 3298
GEOMETRIC AMERICAS, INC.—See HCL Technologies Ltd.; *Int'l*, pg. 3298
GEOMETRIC CHINA INC.—See HCL Technologies Ltd.; *Int'l*, pg. 3298
GEOMETRIC EUROPE GMBH—See HCL Technologies Ltd.; *Int'l*, pg. 3298
GEOMETRIC JAPAN K.K.—See HCL Technologies Ltd.; *Int'l*, pg. 3298
GEOPOLIS SP. Z O.O.—See ComArch S.A.; *Int'l*, pg. 1707
GEOSOFT INC.—See Bentley Systems, Inc.; *U.S. Public*, pg. 297
GEOSPIZA, INC.—See Revvity, Inc.; *U.S. Public*, pg. 1794
GEOWAGGLE, LLC; *U.S. Private*, pg. 1685
GES LTD.; *Int'l*, pg. 2945
GETFEEDBACK, INC.—See Symphony Technology Group, LLC; *U.S. Private*, pg. 3901
GETSWIFT LIMITED—See GetSwift Technologies Limited; *U.S. Public*, pg. 935
GETWELLNETWORK, INC.; *U.S. Private*, pg. 1689
GEYSERS INTERNATIONAL INC.—See Banco de Sabadell, S.A.; *Int'l*, pg. 821
GFI ASIA PACIFIC PTY LTD—See GFI Software S.A.; *Int'l*, pg. 2957
GFI SOFTWARE S.A.; *Int'l*, pg. 2957
GHOST STORY GAMES, LLC—See Take-Two Interactive Software, Inc.; *U.S. Public*, pg. 1979
GIACOM (CLOUD) LIMITED—See Giacom (Cloud) Holdings Limited; *Int'l*, pg. 2961
GIFTS SOFTWARE, INC.—See Fidelity National Infor; *U.S. Public*, pg. 833
GIGAMEDIA LIMITED; *Int'l*, pg. 2971
GIGAMON INC.—See Elliott Management Corporation; *U.S. Private*, pg. 1368
GILLILAND GOLD YOUNG CONSULTING INC.—See Moody's Corporation; *U.S. Public*, pg. 1467
GIMMAL LLC—See Gimmal Group, Inc.; *U.S. Private*, pg. 1701
GINT SOFTWARE, INC.—See Bentley Systems, Inc.; *U.S. Public*, pg. 297
GIRO INC.; *Int'l*, pg. 2979
GITA TECHNOLOGIES LTD.—See Verint Systems Inc.; *U.S. Public*, pg. 2281
GIVEGAB INC.—See Insight Venture Management, LLC; *U.S. Private*, pg. 2090
GIVING.COM LIMITED; *Int'l*, pg. 2982
GK SOFTWARE SE—See Fujitsu Limited; *Int'l*, pg. 2837
G-LABS SAGL—See Guess? Inc.; *U.S. Public*, pg. 974
GLOBAL ACCESS (PTY) LTD.; *Int'l*, pg. 2993
GLOBAL COMPLIANCE APPLICATIONS CORP.; *Int'l*, pg. 2994
GLOBAL DATA MANAGEMENT SYSTEMS, LLC; *U.S. Private*, pg. 1713
GLOBAL DOMINION ACCESS SA; *Int'l*, pg. 2995
GLOBAL GRAPHICS KK—See Hybrid Software Group PLC; *Int'l*, pg. 3544
GLOBAL GRAPHICS SOFTWARE (INDIA) PVT LTD—See Hybrid Software Group PLC; *Int'l*, pg. 3544
GLOBAL INFOTECH CO., LTD.; *Int'l*, pg. 2997
GLOBAL INTELLISYSTEMS, LLC; *U.S. Private*, pg. 1715
GLOBALIZATION PARTNERS INTERNATIONAL; *U.S. Private*, pg. 1719
GLOBALLOGIC INC.—See Hitachi, Ltd.; *Int'l*, pg. 3413
GLOBAL MANAGEMENT TECHNOLOGIES CORPORATION—See Verint Systems Inc.; *U.S. Public*, pg. 2281
GLOBAL PROFIT TECHNOLOGIES, INC.; *U.S. Public*, pg. 945
GLOBALSCAPE INC.—See HGGC, LLC; *U.S. Private*, pg. 1929
GLOBAL SMART CAPITAL CORP.; *Int'l*, pg. 3001
GLOBAL SOFTWARE, LLC—See TA Associates, Inc.; *U.S. Private*, pg. 3915
GLOBALSPACE TECHNOLOGIES LIMITED; *Int'l*, pg. 3004
GLOBALVIEW SOFTWARE, INC.—See Hellman & Friedman LLC; *U.S. Private*, pg. 1908
GLOBANT S.A.; *Int'l*, pg. 3005
GLOBERANGER CORPORATION—See Fujitsu Limited; *Int'l*, pg. 2836
GLOBOFORCE GROUP PLC; *Int'l*, pg. 3007
GLOBYS INC.; *U.S. Private*, pg. 1720
GLODON CO., LTD.; *Int'l*, pg. 3008
GLORY SUN LAND GROUP LIMITED—See Glory Sun Financial Group Limited; *Int'l*, pg. 3011
GLU EMEA-GLU MOBILE LTD.—See Electronic Arts Inc.; *U.S. Public*, pg. 724
GLU MOBILE TECHNOLOGY (BEIJING) CO. LTD.—See Electronic Arts Inc.; *U.S. Public*, pg. 724
GMO PEPABO, INC.—See GMO Internet Group, Inc.; *Int'l*, pg. 3014
GODLAN, INC. - REGIONAL OFFICE—See Godlan, Inc.; *U.S. Private*, pg. 1724
GODLAN, INC.; *U.S. Private*, pg. 1724
GOECART; *U.S. Private*, pg. 1725
GOGO AIR INTERNATIONAL SARL—See Gogo Inc.; *U.S. Public*, pg. 949
GOGO INC.; *U.S. Public*, pg. 949
GOGO LLC—See Gogo Inc.; *U.S. Public*, pg. 949
GOLFZON NEWDIN HOLDINGS CO., LTD.; *Int'l*, pg. 3036
GOLO, INC.; *Int'l*, pg. 3036
GOMSPACE GROUP AB; *Int'l*, pg. 3037
GOOGLE LLC—See Alphabet Inc.; *U.S. Public*, pg. 83
GO-PAGE CORPORATION; *U.S. Public*, pg. 949
GOSTATS; *U.S. Private*, pg. 3043
GPSHOPPER LLC—See Synchrony Financial; *U.S. Public*, pg. 1970
GRABTAXI PTE. LTD.; *Int'l*, pg. 3048
GRANICUS INC.—See Vista Equity Partners, LLC; *U.S. Private*, pg. 4397
GRAPHICODE INC.; *U.S. Private*, pg. 1758
GRAPHON CORPORATION—See hopTo Inc.; *U.S. Public*, pg. 1052
GRAVITANT, INC.—See International Business Machines Corporation; *U.S. Public*, pg. 1145
GREAT FRIDAYS LIMITED—See EPAM Systems, Inc.; *U.S. Public*, pg. 783
GREEN AGREVOLUTION PVT LTD.; *Int'l*, pg. 3069
GREEN RADAR (HONG KONG) LIMITED—See Edvance International Holdings Limited; *Int'l*, pg. 2316
GREENROPE, LLC; *U.S. Private*, pg. 1779
GREENSHADES SOFTWARE, INC.—See WayPoint Capital Partners; *U.S. Private*, pg. 4460
GREENWAVE REALITY, INC.; *U.S. Private*, pg. 1781
GREENWAVE TECHNOLOGY SOLUTIONS, INC.; *U.S. Public*, pg. 965
GREENWAY MEDICAL TECHNOLOGIES, INC.—See Vista Equity Partners, LLC; *U.S. Private*, pg. 4398
GREY MATTER LTD.; *Int'l*, pg. 3082
GRINDR INC.; *U.S. Public*, pg. 969
GROUNDLINK, INC.—See Comvest Group Holdings LLC; *U.S. Private*, pg. 1007
GROUP LOGIC, INC.; *U.S. Private*, pg. 1793
GROUPSYSTEMS CORPORATION; *U.S. Private*, pg. 1794
GROWTHZONE, INC.—See Greenridge Investment Partners; *U.S. Private*, pg. 1779
GRUPA NOKAUT S.A.; *Int'l*, pg. 3117
GRUPPO FORMULA S.P.A.; *Int'l*, pg. 3140
GTS SERVICES, LLC—See Vista Equity Partners, LLC; *U.S. Private*, pg. 4400
GUARDIAN TRACKING, LLC—See Envisage Technologies, LLC; *U.S. Private*, pg. 1410
GUIDESPARK, INC.; *U.S. Private*, pg. 1813
GUIDEWIRE SOFTWARE ASIA LTD.—See Guidewire Software, Inc.; *U.S. Public*, pg. 974
GUIDEWIRE SOFTWARE CANADA LTD.—See Guidewire Software, Inc.; *U.S. Public*, pg. 974
GUIDEWIRE SOFTWARE DENMARK APS—See Guidewire Software, Inc.; *U.S. Public*, pg. 974
GUIDEWIRE SOFTWARE FRANCE SAS—See Guidewire Software, Inc.; *U.S. Public*, pg. 974
GUIDEWIRE SOFTWARE GMBH—See Guidewire Software, Inc.; *U.S. Public*, pg. 974
GUIDEWIRE SOFTWARE, INC.; *U.S. Public*, pg. 974
GUIDEWIRE SOFTWARE (IRELAND) LIMITED—See Guidewire Software, Inc.; *U.S. Public*, pg. 974
GUIDEWIRE SOFTWARE JAPAN K.K.—See Guidewire Software, Inc.; *U.S. Public*, pg. 974
GUIDEWIRE SOFTWARE LTD.—See Guidewire Software, Inc.; *U.S. Public*, pg. 974
GUIDEWIRE SOFTWARE (MALAYSIA) SDN. BHD—See Guidewire Software, Inc.; *U.S. Public*, pg. 974
GUIDEWIRE SOFTWARE PTY. LTD.—See Guidewire Software, Inc.; *U.S. Public*, pg. 974
GUMI INC.; *Int'l*, pg. 3183
GUNGHO ONLINE ENTERTAINMENT AMERICA, INC.—See GungHo Online Entertainment, Inc.; *Int'l*, pg. 3183
GUNGHO ONLINE ENTERTAINMENT, INC.; *Int'l*, pg. 3183
GUNOSY INC.; *Int'l*, pg. 3185
GURUM COMPANY INC.; *Int'l*, pg. 3188
GUS GROUP AG & CO KG; *Int'l*, pg. 3188
HABA COMPUTER AKTIENGESELLSCHAFT—See CompuGroup Medical SE & Co. KGaA; *Int'l*, pg. 1756
HADAPT INC.—See Teradata Corporation; *U.S. Public*, pg. 2017
HAIVISION NETWORK VIDEO - INTERNET MEDIA DIVISION—See HaiVision Systems, Inc.; *Int'l*, pg. 3218
HAMEE CORP.; *Int'l*, pg. 3237
HANBIT SOFT INC.; *Int'l*, pg. 3241
HANCOM, INC.; *Int'l*, pg. 3242
HANCOM INTERFREE, INC.—See Hancom, Inc.; *Int'l*, pg. 3243
HANCOM TALKAFE INC.—See Hancom, Inc.; *Int'l*, pg. 3243
HANCOM WITH INC.; *Int'l*, pg. 3242
HANDYSOFT, INC.; *Int'l*, pg. 3244
HANGZHOU ELECTRONIC SOUL NETWORK TECHNOLOGY CO., LTD.; *Int'l*, pg. 3247
HANGZHOU LIANLUO INTERACTIVE INFORMATION TECHNOLOGY CO., LTD.; *Int'l*, pg. 3249
HANNON HILL CORPORATION; *U.S. Private*, pg. 1855
HANSEN CORPORATION PTY. LTD.—See Hansen Technologies Limited; *Int'l*, pg. 3260
HAOYUN TECHNOLOGY CO., LTD.; *Int'l*, pg. 3268
HARBINGER GROUP INC.; *Int'l*, pg. 3271
HARBINGER KNOWLEDGE PRODUCTS, INC.—See Harbinger Group Inc.; *Int'l*, pg. 3271
HARBINGER KNOWLEDGE PRODUCTS PVT. LTD.—See Harbinger Group Inc.; *Int'l*, pg. 3271
HARMON.IE CORP. - ISRAEL OFFICE—See Cukierman & Co. Investment House Ltd.; *Int'l*, pg. 1876
HARMON.IE CORPORATION—See Cukierman & Co. Investment House Ltd.; *Int'l*, pg. 1876
HARRIS GEOSPATIAL SOLUTIONS GMBH—See L3Harris Technologies, Inc.; *U.S. Public*, pg. 1280
HARRIS GEOSPATIAL SOLUTIONS, INC.—See L3Harris Technologies, Inc.; *U.S. Public*, pg. 1280
HARRIS GEOSPATIAL SOLUTIONS ITALIA SRL—See L3Harris Technologies, Inc.; *U.S. Public*, pg. 1280
HARRIS GEOSPATIAL SOLUTIONS SARL—See L3Harris Technologies, Inc.; *U.S. Public*, pg. 1280
HARRIS GEOSPATIAL SOLUTIONS UK LIMITED—See L3Harris Technologies, Inc.; *U.S. Public*, pg. 1280
HART SYSTEMS, INC.—See Zebra Technologies Corporation; *U.S. Public*, pg. 2401
HART SYSTEMS UK LTD.—See Zebra Technologies Corporation; *U.S. Public*, pg. 2401
HARVER B.V.—See Rubicon Technology Partners, LLC; *U.S. Private*, pg. 3500
HARVEST TECHNOLOGY GROUP LTD.; *Int'l*, pg. 3281
HASHAVSHEVET LTD.—See Hilan Ltd.; *Int'l*, pg. 3390
HATTON POINT, INC.; *U.S. Private*, pg. 1880

N.A.I.C.S. INDEX

513210 — SOFTWARE PUBLISHERS

HCS - HEALTH COMMUNICATION SERVICE GMBH—See CompuGroup Medical SE & Co. KGaA; *Int'l*, pg. 1757
HCSS, INC.; *U.S. Private*, pg. 1890
HEADSPACE INC.; *U.S. Private*, pg. 1891
HEADSTREAM INC; *U.S. Private*, pg. 1891
HEADSTRONG BUSINESS SERVICES, INC.—See Genpact Limited; *Int'l*, pg. 2927
HEADSTRONG CORPORATION—See Genpact Limited; *Int'l*, pg. 2927
HEADSTRONG PHILIPPINES, INC.—See Genpact Limited; *Int'l*, pg. 2927
HEALTHCAREFIRST, INC.—See ResMed Inc.; *U.S. Public*, pg. 1790
HEALTHDATIX, INC.—See NUTEX HEALTH INC.; *U.S. Public*, pg. 1555
HEALTHEDGE SOFTWARE, INC.—See Blackstone Inc.; *U.S. Public*, pg. 354
HEALTH FIDELITY, INC.—See Edifecs, Inc.; *U.S. Private*, pg. 1336
HEALTHFUSION, INC.—See Thoma Bravo, L.P.; *U.S. Private*, pg. 4150
HEALTH INNOVATION TECHNOLOGIES INC.; *U.S. Private*, pg. 1893
HEALTHLAND, INC. - GLENWOOD—See TruBridge, Inc.; *U.S. Public*, pg. 2198
HEALTHLAND, INC.—See TruBridge, Inc.; *U.S. Public*, pg. 2198
HEALTH SYSTEMS SOLUTIONS, INC.—See Sandata Holdings, Inc.; *U.S. Private*, pg. 3542
HEALTHTAP, INC.; *U.S. Private*, pg. 1898
HEALTHWYSE, LLC; *U.S. Private*, pg. 1898
HEALTHY EXTRACTS INC.; *U.S. Public*, pg. 1017
HEARMEOUT LIMITED; *Int'l*, pg. 3304
HEARSAY SOCIAL, INC.—See Yext, Inc.; *U.S. Public*, pg. 2398
HEAT SOFTWARE USA INC.—See Clearlake Capital Group, L.P.; *U.S. Private*, pg. 935
HEAVYWATER, INC.—See Intercontinental Exchange, Inc.; *U.S. Public*, pg. 1141
HECTO INNOVATION CO., LTD; *Int'l*, pg. 3307
HEDGE CONNECTION INC.; *U.S. Private*, pg. 1903
HELLO GROUP INC.; *Int'l*, pg. 3336
HELP/SYSTEMS, LLC—See HGGC, LLC; *U.S. Private*, pg. 1929
HEMPLIFE TODAY; *U.S. Public*, pg. 1025
HEROKU, INC.—See Salesforce, Inc.; *U.S. Public*, pg. 1837
HETROGENOUS, INC.—See Infospectrum, Inc.; *U.S. Private*, pg. 2074
HEWLETT PACKARD ENTERPRISE GLOBALSOFT PRIVATE LIMITED—See Hewlett Packard Enterprise Company; *U.S. Public*, pg. 1031
HEXAGON PPM - CADWORX & ANALYSIS SOLUTIONS—See Hexagon AB; *Int'l*, pg. 3368
HEXAGON PPM—See Hexagon AB; *Int'l*, pg. 3368
HEXATIER LTD.—See Huawei Investment & Holding Co., Ltd.; *Int'l*, pg. 3515
HEYWIRE, INC.—See Salesforce, Inc.; *U.S. Public*, pg. 1837
HG DATA CO.—See Clarion Capital Partners, LLC; *U.S. Private*, pg. 911
HIGHER LOGIC, LLC; *U.S. Private*, pg. 1937
HIGHJUMP SOFTWARE INC.—See Accellos, Inc.; *U.S. Private*, pg. 50
HIGHPOINT TECHNOLOGY SOLUTIONS, INC.; *U.S. Private*, pg. 1941
HIGHRADIUS CORPORATION; *U.S. Private*, pg. 1941
HIGHWINDS NETWORK GROUP INC.—See ABRY Partners, LLC; *U.S. Private*, pg. 42
HILAN LTD.; *Int'l*, pg. 3390
HIL MEDIC SDN. BHD.—See HIL Industris Berhad; *Int'l*, pg. 3390
HIPEROS, LLC—See Thoma Bravo, L.P.; *U.S. Private*, pg. 4147
HITACHI ENERGY UK LIMITED—See ABB Ltd.; *Int'l*, pg. 52
HITACHI ENERGY USA INC.—See ABB Ltd.; *Int'l*, pg. 52
HITACHI SOLUTIONS AMERICA - BUSINESS SOLUTIONS GROUP—See Hitachi, Ltd.; *Int'l*, pg. 3421
HITEC SYSTEMS CORPORATION—See CAC Holdings Corporation; *Int'l*, pg. 1247
HMIS, INC.—See Hillenbrand, Inc.; *U.S. Public*, pg. 1035
HOGIA AB; *Int'l*, pg. 3441
HOLADOCTOR, INC.—See Pan-American Life Insurance Group, Inc.; *U.S. Private*, pg. 3084
HOMECARE HOMEBASE, LLC—See The Hearst Corporation; *U.S. Private*, pg. 4045
HOMENET AUTOMOTIVE LLC—See Cox Enterprises, Inc.; *U.S. Private*, pg. 1076
HOOKED MEDIA, LLC; *U.S. Private*, pg. 1978
HOOTSUITE MEDIA, INC.; *Int'l*, pg. 3472
HOPTO INC.; *U.S. Public*, pg. 1052
HORIZON BUSINESS SERVICES, INC.; *U.S. Private*, pg. 1980
HORTONWORKS INC.—See Clayton, Dubilier & Rice, LLC; *U.S. Private*, pg. 920
HORTONWORKS INC.—See KKR & Co. Inc.; *U.S. Public*, pg. 1243
HOST ANALYTICS, INC.—See Vector Capital Management, L.P.; *U.S. Private*, pg. 4351

HOUGHTON MIFFLIN HARCOURT LEARNING TECHNOLOGY—See Veritas Capital Fund Management, LLC; *U.S. Private*, pg. 4363
HPE SECURITY - DATA SECURITY—See Veritas Capital Fund Management, LLC; *U.S. Private*, pg. 4364
HRANSWERLINK; *U.S. Private*, pg. 1998
HR FOCAL POINT, LLC; *U.S. Private*, pg. 1998
HUBB SYSTEMS LLC.—See Vislink Technologies Inc.; *U.S. Public*, pg. 2304
HUBER + SUHNER INC.—See Huber + Suhner AG; *Int'l*, pg. 3519
HUBSPOT AUSTRALIA PTY. LTD.—See HubSpot, Inc.; *U.S. Public*, pg. 1068
HUBSPOT, INC.; *U.S. Public*, pg. 1067
HUBSPOT IRELAND LIMITED—See HubSpot, Inc.; *U.S. Public*, pg. 1068
HUBSPOT LATIN AMERICA S.A.S.—See HubSpot, Inc.; *U.S. Public*, pg. 1068
HULBEE AG; *Int'l*, pg. 3528
HUM WORLD INC.—See Hum Network Limited; *Int'l*, pg. 3528
HUNAN CREATOR INFORMATION TECHNOLOGIES CO., LTD.; *Int'l*, pg. 3532
HURIX SYSTEMS PVT. LTD.; *Int'l*, pg. 3538
HWA INTERNATIONAL, INC.—See Banyan Software, Inc.; *U.S. Private*, pg. 470
HYDRIX LIMITED; *Int'l*, pg. 3546
HYLAND LLC—See Thoma Bravo, L.P.; *U.S. Private*, pg. 4148
HYLAND SOFTWARE, INC.—See Thoma Bravo, L.P.; *U.S. Private*, pg. 4148
HYPEMARKS, INC.; *U.S. Private*, pg. 2019
HYPHA LABS, INC.; *U.S. Public*, pg. 1079
HYTRUST, INC.—See DataCard Corporation; *U.S. Private*, pg. 1165
HYUNDAI EZWEL CO.,LTD; *Int'l*, pg. 3556
I2 INC.—See Constellation Software Inc.; *Int'l*, pg. 1774
I2 LTD.—See Constellation Software Inc.; *Int'l*, pg. 1774
I3-LL, LLC—See i3 Verticals, Inc.; *U.S. Public*, pg. 1081
I95DEV; *U.S. Private*, pg. 2027
I-9 ADVANTAGE, LLC—See Equifax Inc.; *U.S. Public*, pg. 786
IAR SYSTEMS GROUP AB; *Int'l*, pg. 3569
IASOLUTION INC.—See Aplix Corporation; *Int'l*, pg. 516
IATRIC SYSTEMS, INC.—See Constellation Software Inc.; *Int'l*, pg. 1774
IBM FINANS NORGE AS—See International Business Machines Corporation; *U.S. Public*, pg. 1146
IBM GLOBAL FINANCING SWEDEN AB—See International Business Machines Corporation; *U.S. Public*, pg. 1147
IBM GLOBAL SERVICES ESPANA, S.A.—See International Business Machines Corporation; *U.S. Public*, pg. 1147
IBM-INTERNATIONAL BUSINESS MACHINES D.O.O., BELGRADE—See International Business Machines Corporation; *U.S. Public*, pg. 1149
IBM MAROC—See International Business Machines Corporation; *U.S. Public*, pg. 1147
IBM SOFTWARE - ENTERPRISE CONTENT MANAGEMENT—See International Business Machines Corporation; *U.S. Public*, pg. 1148
IBM SOFTWARE GROUP—See International Business Machines Corporation; *U.S. Public*, pg. 1148
IBM TANZANIA LIMITED—See International Business Machines Corporation; *U.S. Public*, pg. 1148
IBQ SYSTEMS LLC—See Clearlake Capital Group, L.P.; *U.S. Private*, pg. 938
IBS AB—See Marlin Equity Partners, LLC; *U.S. Private*, pg. 2584
IBS OPENSYSTEMS (UK) LIMITED—See Capita plc; *Int'l*, pg. 1309
IBS SOFTWARE PRIVATE LIMITED; *Int'l*, pg. 3576
IBS SOFTWARE SERVICES AMERICAS, INC.—See IBS Software Private Limited; *Int'l*, pg. 3577
IBS TECHNICS, INC.—See IBS Software Private Limited; *Int'l*, pg. 3577
ICARE.COM LLC; *U.S. Private*, pg. 2029
ICE MESSAGING PTE. LTD.—See Touchpoint Group Holdings, Inc.; *U.S. Private*, pg. 2165
ICLICK, INC.; *U.S. Private*, pg. 2031
I-COM SOFTWARE—See Global Industrial Company; *U.S. Public*, pg. 942
ICONTACT LLC—See Ziff Davis, Inc.; *U.S. Public*, pg. 2404
IC SOLUTIONS, INC.; *U.S. Private*, pg. 2029
ICS TRIPLEX ISAGRAF INC.—See Rockwell Automation, Inc.; *U.S. Public*, pg. 1805
IDDRIVEN, INC.; *U.S. Public*, pg. 1088
IDEAGEN PLC—See HgCapital Trust plc; *Int'l*, pg. 3377
IDEMIA IDENTITY & SECURITY GERMANY AG—See Advent International Corporation; *U.S. Private*, pg. 102
IDENTITY AUTOMATION, LP; *U.S. Private*, pg. 2037
IDENTROPY, INC.—See Robert Half Inc.; *U.S. Public*, pg. 1803
IDENTRUST, INC.—See ASSA ABLOY AB; *Int'l*, pg. 637
I-DESIGN GROUP LTD—See NCR Voyix Corporation.; *U.S. Public*, pg. 1502
I-DESIGN MULTIMEDIA LTD.—See NCR Voyix Corporation.; *U.S. Public*, pg. 1502

IDEXX COMPUTER SYSTEMS—See IDEXX Laboratories, Inc.; *U.S. Public*, pg. 1092
IDIMENSION MSC PTE LTD—See Evd Berhad; *Int'l*, pg. 2561
IDLE MEDIA, INC.; *U.S. Public*, pg. 1093
IDNOW GMBH; *Int'l*, pg. 3595
IDREAMSKY TECHNOLOGY LIMITED; *Int'l*, pg. 3596
IDS SCHEER AG—See Silver Lake Group, LLC; *U.S. Private*, pg. 3658
IDS SCHEER AUSTRIA GMBH—See Silver Lake Group, LLC; *U.S. Private*, pg. 3658
IDS SCHEER CANADA—See Silver Lake Group, LLC; *U.S. Private*, pg. 3658
IDS SCHEER SCHWEIZ AG—See Silver Lake Group, LLC; *U.S. Private*, pg. 3658
IDS SCHEER SINGAPORE PTE. LTD.—See Silver Lake Group, LLC; *U.S. Private*, pg. 3658
IENTERTAINMENT NETWORK, INC.; *U.S. Private*, pg. 2038
I:FAO AG—See Amadeus IT Group, S.A.; *Int'l*, pg. 407
IFAX SOLUTIONS, INC.; *U.S. Private*, pg. 2038
IFDS LUXEMBOURG S.A.—See SS&C Technologies Holdings, Inc.; *U.S. Public*, pg. 1923
IFS AMERICAS, INC.—See EQT AB; *Int'l*, pg. 2477
IFS BENELUX B.V.—See EQT AB; *Int'l*, pg. 2477
IFS FRANCE SA—See EQT AB; *Int'l*, pg. 2477
IFS INDUSTRIAL FINANCIAL SYSTEMS CANADA, INC—See EQT AB; *Int'l*, pg. 2477
IFS JAPAN K.K.—See EQT AB; *Int'l*, pg. 2477
IFS MIDDLE EAST FZ-LLC—See EQT AB; *Int'l*, pg. 2478
IFS NORGE AS—See EQT AB; *Int'l*, pg. 2478
IFS NORTH AMERICA INC.—See EQT AB; *Int'l*, pg. 2478
IGG INC.; *Int'l*, pg. 3602
IGLOO CORPORATION; *Int'l*, pg. 3602
IGNIS LTD; *Int'l*, pg. 3602
IGNITE RMSA RETAIL SOLUTIONS, LLC—See ESW Capital, LLC; *U.S. Private*, pg. 1430
IGNITE SCALEARC SOLUTIONS, INC.—See ESW Capital, LLC; *U.S. Private*, pg. 1430
IGNITIONONE, INC. - AKRON—See IgnitionOne, Inc.; *U.S. Private*, pg. 2039
I-HUMAN PATIENTS, INC.—See Graham Holdings Company; *U.S. Public*, pg. 956
ILS TECHNOLOGY LLC—See DBAY Advisors Limited; *Int'l*, pg. 1988
IL TROVATORE SRL—See Cairo Communication S.p.A.; *Int'l*, pg. 1253
IMAGETAG, INC.—See Aldrich Capital Partners, LLC; *U.S. Private*, pg. 160
IMAGINE COMMUNICATIONS - AUSTRALIA—See The Gores Group, LLC; *U.S. Private*, pg. 4035
IMAGINE COMMUNICATIONS CORP.—See The Gores Group, LLC; *U.S. Private*, pg. 4034
IMAGINE COMMUNICATIONS - SINGAPORE—See The Gores Group, LLC; *U.S. Private*, pg. 4035
IMAGINEEASY SOLUTIONS, LLC; *U.S. Private*, pg. 2045
IMAGINE EDITIONS SAS—See CompuGroup Medical SE & Co. KGaA; *U.S. Private*, pg. 1757
IMAGINEER CO., LTD.; *Int'l*, pg. 3619
IMAGINE THAT, INC.—See ANDRITZ AG; *Int'l*, pg. 453
IMAKENEWS, INC.—See The Reynolds & Reynolds Company; *U.S. Private*, pg. 4106
IMDSOFT—See TPG Capital, L.P.; *U.S. Public*, pg. 2177
IMEDX, INC.; *U.S. Private*, pg. 2046
IMEET CENTRAL—See Siris Capital Group, LLC; *U.S. Private*, pg. 3674
IMMEDIATEK INC.; *U.S. Public*, pg. 1112
IMPAC GLOBAL SYSTEMS—See Elekta AB; *Int'l*, pg. 2356
IMPAC MEDICAL SYSTEMS, INC.—See Elekta AB; *Int'l*, pg. 2356
IMPACT MOBILE INC.—See Cisco Systems, Inc.; *U.S. Public*, pg. 499
IMPREV, INC.—See Vector Capital Management, L.P.; *U.S. Private*, pg. 4351
IMPROMED, LLC—See Clayton, Dubilier & Rice, LLC; *U.S. Private*, pg. 921
IMPROMED, LLC—See TPG Capital, L.P.; *U.S. Public*, pg. 2170
IMX SOFTWARE SOUTH AFRICA—See Holley Holland Limited; *Int'l*, pg. 3451
IMX SOFTWARE UK LIMITED—See Holley Holland Limited; *Int'l*, pg. 3451
INAUTH, INC.—See American Express Company; *U.S. Public*, pg. 102
INCADEA (BEIJING) ITC LTD.—See Cox Enterprises, Inc.; *U.S. Private*, pg. 1078
INCADEA GMBH—See Cox Enterprises, Inc.; *U.S. Private*, pg. 1077
INCADEA GMBH—See Cox Enterprises, Inc.; *U.S. Private*, pg. 1077
INCADEA GREECE INFORMATICS SYSTEMS S.A.—See Cox Enterprises, Inc.; *U.S. Private*, pg. 1078
INCADEA INDIA PRIVATE LIMITED—See Cox Enterprises, Inc.; *U.S. Private*, pg. 1078
INCADEA NEW ZEALAND LIMITED—See Cox Enterprises, Inc.; *U.S. Private*, pg. 1078
INCADEA SL—See Cox Enterprises, Inc.; *U.S. Private*, pg. 1078

513210 — SOFTWARE PUBLISHERS

INCADEA TAIWAN—See Cox Enterprises, Inc.; *U.S. Private*, pg. 1078
INCA SOFTWARE LIMITED—See Datatec Limited; *Int'l*, pg. 1980
INCEDO, INC.; *U.S. Private*, pg. 2053
INCIPIO TECHNOLOGIES, INC.—See Incipio, LLC; *U.S. Private*, pg. 2053
INCODE TECHNOLOGIES, INC.; *U.S. Private*, pg. 2054
INDUSTRY DIVE, LLC—See Falfurrias Capital Partners, LP; *U.S. Private*, pg. 1467
INDUSTRY IDS, INC.; *U.S. Private*, pg. 2069
INDUSTRY IDS, INC.—See Industry IDS, Inc.; *U.S. Private*, pg. 2069
INDUSTRY WEAPON, INC.—See The Jordan Company, L.P.; *U.S. Private*, pg. 4062
INET SOLUTIONS GROUP, INC.—See Myriad Mobile LLC; *U.S. Private*, pg. 2825
I-NEW UNIFIED MOBILE SOLUTIONS AG—See cyan AG; *Int'l*, pg. 1891
INFINATA, INC.—See GlobalData Plc; *Int'l*, pg. 3003
INFLECTION LLC; *U.S. Private*, pg. 2072
INFOGIX, INC.—See Clearlake Capital Group, L.P.; *U.S. Private*, pg. 936
INFOGIX, INC.—See TA Associates, Inc.; *U.S. Private*, pg. 3917
INFOGLIDE SOFTWARE CORPORATION—See Fair Isaac Corporation; *U.S. Public*, pg. 820
INFOMATICS SOFTWARE SOLUTIONS INDIA—See Infomatics, Inc; *U.S. Private*, pg. 2072
INFONIQA HOLDING GMBH—See Warburg Pincus LLC; *U.S. Private*, pg. 4438
INFOOBJECTS INC; *U.S. Private*, pg. 2072
INFOPRO DIGITAL SAS—See Apax Partners LLP; *Int'l*, pg. 501
INFOPRO DIGITAL SAS—See TowerBrook Capital Partners, L.P.; *U.S. Private*, pg. 4195
INFOR ENTERPRISE ASSET MANAGEMENT—See Koch Industries, Inc.; *U.S. Private*, pg. 2330
INFOR GLOBAL SOLUTIONS, INC. - DALLAS—See Koch Industries, Inc.; *U.S. Private*, pg. 2330
INFOR LIBRARY & INFORMATION SOLUTIONS - USA—See Koch Industries, Inc.; *U.S. Private*, pg. 2331
INFORMATICA AUSTRALIA PTY. LTD. - ASIA/PACIFIC HEADQUARTERS—See Canada Pension Plan Investment Board; *Int'l*, pg. 1279
INFORMATICA (BEIJING) INFORMATION TECHNOLOGY CO., LTD.—See Canada Pension Plan Investment Board; *Int'l*, pg. 1279
INFORMATICA BUSINESS SOLUTIONS PVT. LTD.—See Canada Pension Plan Investment Board; *Int'l*, pg. 1279
INFORMATICA CORPORATION—See Canada Pension Plan Investment Board; *Int'l*, pg. 1279
INFORMATICA CZ, S.R.O.—See Canada Pension Plan Investment Board; *Int'l*, pg. 1279
INFORMATICA DE EUSKADI S.L—See Accenture plc; *Int'l*, pg. 87
INFORMATICA FRANCE S.A.S.—See Canada Pension Plan Investment Board; *Int'l*, pg. 1279
INFORMATICA GMBH—See Canada Pension Plan Investment Board; *Int'l*, pg. 1280
INFORMATICA HONG KONG—See Canada Pension Plan Investment Board; *Int'l*, pg. 1279
INFORMATICA INTERNATIONAL DO BRAZIL LTD. - LATIN AMERICA REGION HEADQUARTERS—See Canada Pension Plan Investment Board; *Int'l*, pg. 1279
INFORMATICA JAPAN K.K—See Canada Pension Plan Investment Board; *Int'l*, pg. 1279
INFORMATICA KOREA CORPORATION—See Canada Pension Plan Investment Board; *Int'l*, pg. 1279
INFORMATICA MIDDLE EAST FZ-LLC—See Canada Pension Plan Investment Board; *Int'l*, pg. 1280
INFORMATICA NEDERLAND B.V. - EMEA HEADQUARTERS—See Canada Pension Plan Investment Board; *Int'l*, pg. 1279
INFORMATICA - RIO DE JANEIRO—See Canada Pension Plan Investment Board; *Int'l*, pg. 1279
INFORMATICA S.E.A. PTE., LTD.—See Canada Pension Plan Investment Board; *Int'l*, pg. 1279
INFORMATICA SOFTWARE ITALIA S.R.L.—See Canada Pension Plan Investment Board; *Int'l*, pg. 1280
INFORMATICA SOFTWARE LTD.—See Canada Pension Plan Investment Board; *Int'l*, pg. 1280
INFORMATICA SOFTWARE (SCHWEIZ) AG—See Canada Pension Plan Investment Board; *Int'l*, pg. 1280
INFORMATICA SOFTWARE SERVICES DE MEXICO S.A. DE C.V.—See Canada Pension Plan Investment Board; *Int'l*, pg. 1279
INFORMATICA SOUTH AFRICA—See Canada Pension Plan Investment Board; *Int'l*, pg. 1280
INFORMATICA TAIWAN CO. LTD.—See Canada Pension Plan Investment Board; *Int'l*, pg. 1279
INFORMATICA TURKEY—See Canada Pension Plan Investment Board; *Int'l*, pg. 1280
INFORMATICS GROUP; *U.S. Private*, pg. 2073
INFORMATION ACCESS TECHNOLOGY, INC.—See Enghouse Systems Limited; *Int'l*, pg. 2427
INFORMATION TECHNOLOGY SERVICES (ITS) LTD—See HgCapital Trust plc; *Int'l*, pg. 3376

INFORMEX S.A.—See Vista Equity Partners, LLC; *U.S. Private*, pg. 4400
INFOR S.A.—See Koch Industries, Inc.; *U.S. Private*, pg. 2331
INFOSPECTRUM, INC.; *U.S. Private*, pg. 2074
INFOTECH ENTERPRISES AMERICA INC.—See Cyient Limited; *Int'l*, pg. 1896
INFOTECH ENTERPRISES EUROPE LTD—See Cyient Limited; *Int'l*, pg. 1896
INFOTECH ENTERPRISES EUROPE LTD.—See Cyient Limited; *Int'l*, pg. 1896
INFOTECH ENTERPRISES GMBH FRANCE—See Cyient Limited; *Int'l*, pg. 1896
INFOTECH ENTERPRISES JAPAN KK—See Cyient Limited; *Int'l*, pg. 1896
INFOTECH ENTERPRISES LTD - SOFTWARE & ENGINEERING DIVISIONS—See Cyient Limited; *Int'l*, pg. 1896
INFOTECH ENTERPRISES LTD.—See Cyient Limited; *Int'l*, pg. 1896
INFOTECH ENTERPRISES LTD—See Cyient Limited; *Int'l*, pg. 1896
INFOTECH SOFTWARE SOLUTIONS CANADA INC—See Cyient Limited; *Int'l*, pg. 1896
INFOVISION TECHNOLOGIES INC.; *U.S. Private*, pg. 2074
INFOVISION TECHNOLOGIES—See Infovision Technologies Inc.; *U.S. Private*, pg. 2074
INFUSIONSOFT, INC.; *U.S. Private*, pg. 2075
INFUSION SOFTWARE, INC.—See Thryv Holdings, Inc.; *U.S. Private*, pg. 2157
INGENIUX CORP.; *U.S. Private*, pg. 2075
INKLING SYSTEMS, INC.—See Marlin Equity Partners, LLC; *U.S. Private*, pg. 2584
INLOG—See Haemonetics Corporation; *U.S. Public*, pg. 979
INMOMENT MISSISSAUGA—See Mindshare Technologies, Inc.; *U.S. Private*, pg. 2741
INNER RANGE PTY. LTD.—See WESCO International, Inc.; *U.S. Public*, pg. 2351
INNFLUX LLC—See TZP Group LLC; *U.S. Private*, pg. 4269
INNOBYTE ZRT.—See 4iG Nyrt.; *Int'l*, pg. 12
INNOFACTOR PLC—See CapMan PLC; *Int'l*, pg. 1315
INNOFACTOR PLC—See Osprey Capital LLC; *U.S. Private*, pg. 3048
INNOMED GESELLSCHAFT FUR MEDIZINISCHE SOFTWAREANWENDUNGEN GMBH—See CompuGroup Medical SE & Co. KGaA; *Int'l*, pg. 1757
INNOPATH SOFTWARE, INC.; *U.S. Private*, pg. 2080
INNOPRISE SOFTWARE, INC.—See Constellation Software Inc.; *Int'l*, pg. 1774
INNOVARO, INC.; *U.S. Private*, pg. 2081
INNOVATIVE AUTOMATION, INC.—See Paragon Technologies, Inc.; *U.S. Public*, pg. 1637
INNOVATIVE BANKING SOLUTIONS AG—See DXC Technology Company; *U.S. Public*, pg. 695
INNOVATIVE COMPUTER SOLUTIONS, INC.—See Constellation Software Inc.; *Int'l*, pg. 1773
INNOVATIVE INTERFACES INC.—See HGGC, LLC; *U.S. Private*, pg. 1930
INNOVATIVE INTERFACES INC.—See JMI Services, Inc.; *U.S. Private*, pg. 2216
INNOVATIVE SOFTWARE ENGINEERING, LLC—See Trimble, Inc.; *U.S. Public*, pg. 2190
INNOVATIVE SOFTWARE SOLUTIONS, INC.—See Advanced Solutions International Inc.; *U.S. Private*, pg. 92
INOVALON, INC.—See Inovalon Holdings, Inc.; *U.S. Public*, pg. 1128
INOVELAN S.A.—See Agfa-Gevaert N.V.; *Int'l*, pg. 208
INRULE TECHNOLOGY INC.—See OpenGate Capital Management, LLC; *U.S. Private*, pg. 3030
INSALA, LLC; *U.S. Private*, pg. 2085
INSIDESALES.COM, INC.; *U.S. Private*, pg. 2085
INSIDEVIEW TECHNOLOGIES (INDIA) PVT LTD—See Demandbase, Inc.; *U.S. Private*, pg. 1203
INSIGHT SOFTWARE, LLC; *U.S. Private*, pg. 2086
INSIGHT TECHNOLOGY SOLUTIONS, INC.—See Insight Enterprises, Inc.; *U.S. Public*, pg. 1130
INSITE SOFTWARE SOLUTIONS, INC.—See Insight Venture Management, LLC; *U.S. Private*, pg. 2090
INSOURCE SOFTWARE SOLUTIONS LLC; *U.S. Private*, pg. 2092
INSPECTIONXPERT CORPORATION—See HgCapital Trust plc; *Int'l*, pg. 3377
INSPECTTECH SYSTEMS, INC.—See Bentley Systems, Inc.; *U.S. Public*, pg. 297
INSPERITY TIME AND ATTENDANCE—See Insperity, Inc.; *U.S. Public*, pg. 1131
INSPIRED GAMING (GIBRALTAR) LIMITED—See Inspired Entertainment Inc; *U.S. Public*, pg. 1131
INSPIRED GAMING (ITALY) LIMITED—See Inspired Entertainment Inc; *U.S. Public*, pg. 1131
INSPIRED TECHNOLOGY UK LIMITED—See Inspired Entertainment Inc; *U.S. Public*, pg. 1131
INSPRO TECHNOLOGIES CORPORATION—See Thoma Bravo, L.P.; *U.S. Private*, pg. 4149
INSTEM LIFE SCIENCE SYSTEMS, LTD.—See ArchiMed SAS; *Int'l*, pg. 548
INSTEM PLC—See ArchiMed SAS; *Int'l*, pg. 548

INSTRUCTURE GLOBAL LIMITED—See Thoma Bravo, L.P.; *U.S. Private*, pg. 4148
INSURANCE TECHNOLOGIES CORPORATION—See Clearlake Capital Group, L.P.; *U.S. Private*, pg. 938
INSURANCE TECHNOLOGIES CORP. TURBORATER—See Clearlake Capital Group, L.P.; *U.S. Private*, pg. 938
INSURITY, INC.—See GI Manager L.P.; *U.S. Private*, pg. 1692
INSYNC INFORMATION SYSTEMS, PVT. LTD.—See ORBCOMM, Inc.; *U.S. Public*, pg. 1614
INSYNQ INC.—See Summit Hosting LLC; *U.S. Private*, pg. 3854
INTALIQ APAC—See Intalio, Inc.; *U.S. Private*, pg. 2097
INTALIO EMEA—See Intalio, Inc.; *U.S. Private*, pg. 2097
INTALIO, INC.; *U.S. Private*, pg. 2097
INTALIO INDIA—See Intalio, Inc.; *U.S. Private*, pg. 2097
INTALIO LATIN AMERICA—See Intalio, Inc.; *U.S. Private*, pg. 2097
INTAPP, INC.; *U.S. Public*, pg. 1134
INTEGRATED BUSINESS SYSTEMS, INC.; *U.S. Private*, pg. 2099
INTEGRATED BUSINESS SYSTEMS INC.—See Comcast Corporation; *U.S. Public*, pg. 539
INTEGRATED BUSINESS SYSTEMS & SERVICES, INC.; *U.S. Public*, pg. 1136
INTEGRATED COMPUTER SYSTEMS, INC.—See Banneker Partners, LLC; *U.S. Private*, pg. 469
INTEGRATED ENERGY SERVICES LLC—See Gainline Capital Partners LP; *U.S. Private*, pg. 1635
INTEGRATED SOFTWARE SOLUTIONS, INC.; *U.S. Private*, pg. 2101
INTEGRATED VENTURES, INC.; *U.S. Public*, pg. 1136
INTELERAD MEDICAL SYSTEMS INC.—See HgCapital Trust plc; *Int'l*, pg. 3376
INTELISHIFT TECHNOLOGIES; *U.S. Private*, pg. 2104
INTELLECTUAL TECHNOLOGY, INC.—See Arlington Capital Partners LLC; *U.S. Private*, pg. 328
INTELLICHECK, INC.; *U.S. Public*, pg. 1139
INTELLIFLO LIMITED—See HgCapital Trust plc; *Int'l*, pg. 3376
INTELLIGENT SOFTWARE SOLUTIONS—See Intelligraphics Inc.; *U.S. Private*, pg. 2106
INTELLINETICS, INC.; *U.S. Public*, pg. 1140
INTER-ACTIVE ENTERTAINMENT SOLUTIONS TECHNOLOGIES, INC.—See DFNN, Inc.; *Int'l*, pg. 2096
INTERACTIVE FINANCIAL SOLUTIONS, INC.—See Sandata Holdings, Inc.; *U.S. Private*, pg. 3543
INTERACTIVE IDEAS, LLC—See Condeco Ltd.; *Int'l*, pg. 1766
INTERACT PUBLIC SAFETY SYSTEMS; *U.S. Private*, pg. 2108
INTERACTYX LIMITED; *U.S. Private*, pg. 2109
INTERACTYX LIMITED—See Interactyx Limited; *U.S. Private*, pg. 2109
INTERAPPTIVE, INC.—See Thoma Bravo, L.P.; *U.S. Private*, pg. 4153
INTERCLOUD SYSTEMS, INC.; *U.S. Public*, pg. 1141
INTERGRAPH CORPORATION—See Hexagon AB; *Int'l*, pg. 3368
INTERLEAF GMBH—See ESW Capital, LLC; *U.S. Private*, pg. 1430
INTERMEDIX CESKA REPUBLIKA S.R.O.—See CompuGroup Medical SE & Co. KGaA; *Int'l*, pg. 1757
INTERNATIONAL AUTOMATED SYSTEMS, INC.; *U.S. Private*, pg. 2114
INTERNATIONAL CARD ESTABLISHMENT, INC.; *U.S. Public*, pg. 1151
INTERNATIONAL DECISION SYSTEMS, INC.—See TA Associates, Inc.; *U.S. Private*, pg. 3916
INTERNATIONAL DIRECT SELLING TECHNOLOGY CORP.; *U.S. Private*, pg. 2116
INTERNATIONAL FINANCIAL DATA SERVICES (IRELAND) LIMITED—See SS&C Technologies Holdings, Inc.; *U.S. Public*, pg. 1923
INTERNATIONAL TRUSS SYSTEMS PROPRIETARY LIMITED—See Illinois Tool Works Inc.; *U.S. Public*, pg. 1108
INTERNET PIPELINE, INC.—See Roper Technologies, Inc.; *U.S. Public*, pg. 1812
INTERNET PRODUCTION INC.; *U.S. Private*, pg. 2122
INTERNSHIPS.COM, LLC—See Chegg Inc.; *U.S. Public*, pg. 483
INTERPLAY ENTERTAINMENT CORP.; *U.S. Public*, pg. 1158
INTERPLAY OEM, INC.—See Interplay Entertainment Corp.; *U.S. Public*, pg. 1158
INTERSTELLAR, INC.—See Stellar Development, Inc.; *U.S. Private*, pg. 3799
INTERSYSTEMS AUSTRALIA PTY LIMITED—See InterSystems Corporation; *U.S. Private*, pg. 2126
INTERSYSTEMS AUSTRALIA PTY LIMITED—See InterSystems Corporation; *U.S. Private*, pg. 2126
INTERSYSTEMS B.V. - BELGIUM BRANCH—See InterSystems Corporation; *U.S. Private*, pg. 2126
INTERSYSTEMS B.V. - CZECH REPUBLIC BRANCH—See InterSystems Corporation; *U.S. Private*, pg. 2126
INTERSYSTEMS B.V. - FINLAND BRANCH—See InterSys-

513210 — SOFTWARE PUBLISHERS

tems Corporation; *U.S. Private*, pg. 2126
INTERSYSTEMS B.V. - ISRAEL BRANCH—See InterSystems Corporation; *U.S. Private*, pg. 2126
INTERSYSTEMS B.V. - SAUDI ARABIA BRANCH—See InterSystems Corporation; *U.S. Private*, pg. 2126
INTERSYSTEMS B.V.—See InterSystems Corporation; *U.S. Private*, pg. 2126
INTERSYSTEMS CHILE—See InterSystems Corporation; *U.S. Private*, pg. 2126
INTERSYSTEMS CHILE—See InterSystems Corporation; *U.S. Private*, pg. 2126
INTERSYSTEMS CORPORATION; *U.S. Private*, pg. 2126
INTERSYSTEMS DO BRASIL LTDA.—See InterSystems Corporation; *U.S. Private*, pg. 2127
INTERSYSTEMS DO BRASIL LTDA.—See InterSystems Corporation; *U.S. Private*, pg. 2127
INTERSYSTEMS DUBAI—See InterSystems Corporation; *U.S. Private*, pg. 2126
INTERSYSTEMS GMBH—See InterSystems Corporation; *U.S. Private*, pg. 2126
INTERSYSTEMS IBERIA, S.L.—See InterSystems Corporation; *U.S. Private*, pg. 2126
INTERSYSTEMS IBERIA, S.L.—See InterSystems Corporation; *U.S. Private*, pg. 2126
INTERSYSTEMS ITALIA S.R.L.—See InterSystems Corporation; *U.S. Private*, pg. 2126
INTERSYSTEMS ITALIA S.R.L.—See InterSystems Corporation; *U.S. Private*, pg. 2126
INTERSYSTEMS JAPAN KK—See InterSystems Corporation; *U.S. Private*, pg. 2126
INTERSYSTEMS JAPAN KK—See InterSystems Corporation; *U.S. Private*, pg. 2126
INTERSYSTEMS KOREA—See InterSystems Corporation; *U.S. Private*, pg. 2126
INTERSYSTEMS RUSSIA—See InterSystems Corporation; *U.S. Private*, pg. 2126
INTERSYSTEMS SA—See InterSystems Corporation; *U.S. Private*, pg. 2126
INTERSYSTEMS SAS—See InterSystems Corporation; *U.S. Private*, pg. 2127
INTERSYSTEMS SHANGHAI—See InterSystems Corporation; *U.S. Private*, pg. 2127
INTERSYSTEMS SOFTWARE (BEIJING) CO., LTD.—See InterSystems Corporation; *U.S. Private*, pg. 2127
INTERSYSTEMS SOFTWARE (THAILAND) LTD.—See InterSystems Corporation; *U.S. Private*, pg. 2127
INTERSYSTEMS UK—See InterSystems Corporation; *U.S. Private*, pg. 2127
INTERSYSTEMS UK—See InterSystems Corporation; *U.S. Private*, pg. 2127
INTERTECH INC.; *U.S. Private*, pg. 2127
INTERVALZERO INC.; *U.S. Private*, pg. 2128
INTRALINKS INDIA SOLUTIONS PVT. LIMITED—See SS&C Technologies Holdings, Inc.; *U.S. Public*, pg. 1923
INTRALINKS SERVICIOS DE TECNOLOGIA DE MEXICO, S DE R.L. DE C.V.—See SS&C Technologies Holdings, Inc.; *U.S. Public*, pg. 1923
INTRALINKS SRL—See SS&C Technologies Holdings, Inc.; *U.S. Public*, pg. 1923
INTRINSYC SOFTWARE (BARBADOS) INC.—See Lantronix, Inc.; *U.S. Public*, pg. 1293
INTRINSYC TECHNOLOGIES CORPORATION—See Lantronix, Inc.; *U.S. Public*, pg. 1293
INTTRA, INC.—See Insight Venture Management, LLC; *U.S. Private*, pg. 2090
INTUIT CANADA LIMITED—See Intuit Inc.; *U.S. Public*, pg. 1160
INTUIT GREENPOINT—See Intuit Inc.; *U.S. Public*, pg. 1160
INTUIT INC.-CONSUMER TAX GROUP—See Intuit Inc.; *U.S. Public*, pg. 1160
INTUIT INC.-CUSTOMER CONTACT CENTER—See Intuit Inc.; *U.S. Public*, pg. 1160
INTUIT INC.; *U.S. Public*, pg. 1159
INTUIT LIMITED—See Intuit Inc.; *U.S. Public*, pg. 1160
INTUIT TECHNOLOGY SERVICES PRIVATE LIMITED—See Intuit Inc.; *U.S. Public*, pg. 1160
INTY LTD.—See Giacom (Cloud) Holdings Limited; *Int'l*, pg. 2961
INUVO, INC.; *U.S. Public*, pg. 1161
INVESTMENT METRICS LLC—See Resurgens Technology Partners, LLC; *U.S. Private*, pg. 3411
INVESTOR FORCE HOLDINGS, INC.—See Resurgens Technology Partners, LLC; *U.S. Private*, pg. 3411
INVESTOR FORCE, INC.—See Resurgens Technology Partners, LLC; *U.S. Private*, pg. 3411
INVINCEA, INC.—See Apax Partners LLP; *Int'l*, pg. 506
INVOTECH SYSTEMS, INC.—See ASSA ABLOY AB; *Int'l*, pg. 637
INXILE ENTERTAINMENT, INC.—See Microsoft Corporation; *U.S. Public*, pg. 1440
IODINE SOFTWARE, LLC; *U.S. Private*, pg. 2133
I-ON INTERACTIVE, INC.—See e.Bricks Ventures; *Int'l*, pg. 2251
IONQ, INC.; *U.S. Public*, pg. 1166
IPARADIGMS, LLC—See Insight Venture Management, LLC; *U.S. Private*, pg. 2091
IPAYABLES, INC.—See LoneTree Capital LLC; *U.S. Private*, pg. 2490

IPCOS NV—See ATS Corporation; *Int'l*, pg. 695
IP FUSION, INC.—See Access Co., Ltd.; *Int'l*, pg. 88
IPKEYS POWER PARTNERS, INC—See Parsons Corporation; *U.S. Public*, pg. 1651
IPM SOFTWARE, INC.—See GI Manager L.P.; *U.S. Private*, pg. 1693
IP NETWORKS, INC.; *U.S. Private*, pg. 2136
IPROFILE, LLC.—See TA Associates, Inc.; *U.S. Private*, pg. 3915
IPRO TECH, LLC—See K1 Investment Management, LLC; *U.S. Private*, pg. 2252
IPSWITCH, INC.—See Progress Software Corporation; *U.S. Public*, pg. 1725
IQNAVIGATOR, INC.; *U.S. Private*, pg. 2137
IQUEST GMBH & CO KG—See Allgeier SE; *Int'l*, pg. 338
IQVIA INC.—See IQVIA Holdings Inc.; *U.S. Public*, pg. 1168
IRIS ENTERPRISE SOFTWARE (AUSTRALIA) PTY LTD—See HgCapital Trust plc; *Int'l*, pg. 3376
IRIS SOFTWARE GROUP LTD.—See HgCapital Trust plc; *Int'l*, pg. 3376
IRN PAYMENT SYSTEMS LLC—See Shift4 Payments, Inc.; *U.S. Public*, pg. 1874
IROC TECHNOLOGIES—See BNP Paribas SA; *Int'l*, pg. 1089
IRTH SOLUTIONS, INC.; *U.S. Private*, pg. 2141
IRTH SOLUTIONS LLC—See Blackstone Inc.; *U.S. Public*, pg. 355
ISC SOFTWARE PVT. LTD.—See CoreCard Corporation; *U.S. Public*, pg. 577
ISG GROUP LLC—See Clearlake Capital Group, L.P.; *U.S. Private*, pg. 937
ISG GROUP LLC—See SkyKnight Capital LLC; *U.S. Private*, pg. 3685
ISGN SOLUTIONS, INC.—See CESC Limited; *Int'l*, pg. 1424
ISIGN SOLUTIONS INC.; *U.S. Public*, pg. 1174
IS INFORMATIK SYSTEME GESELLSCHAFT FUR INFORMATIONSTECHNIK MBH—See CompuGroup Medical SE & Co. KGaA; *Int'l*, pg. 1757
ISIRONA, LLC; *U.S. Public*, pg. 2144
ISLAND PACIFIC—See 3Q Holdings Limited; *Int'l*, pg. 9
ISLAND SOFTWARE, INC.—See CP Software Group, Inc.; *U.S. Private*, pg. 1079
ISP INTERNATIONAL SOFTWARE PARTNERS, INC.—See Climb Global Solutions, Inc.; *U.S. Public*, pg. 515
ISS GROUP (ASIA) PTE. LTD.—See Advent International Corporation; *U.S. Private*, pg. 105
ISS GROUP EUROPE LIMITED—See Advent International Corporation; *U.S. Private*, pg. 105
ISSUETRAK, INC.; *U.S. Private*, pg. 2147
ISSUU, INC.—See Bending Spoons S.p.A.; *Int'l*, pg. 971
ITA SOFTWARE, INC.—See Alphabet Inc.; *U.S. Public*, pg. 83
IT FIRST SOURCE; *U.S. Private*, pg. 2148
ITG SOFTWARE SOLUTIONS, INC.—See Virtu Financial, Inc.; *U.S. Public*, pg. 2300
ITIVITI GROUP AB—See Broadridge Financial Solutions, Inc.; *U.S. Public*, pg. 391
ITRAC LLC—See 424 Capital, LLC; *U.S. Public*, pg. 15
ITRAC LLC—See HealthEdge Investment Partners, LLC; *U.S. Private*, pg. 1896
ITRADEFAIR.COM, INC.; *U.S. Private*, pg. 2150
ITRENEW, INC.—See Iron Mountain Incorporated; *U.S. Public*, pg. 1172
IT RETAIL, INC.—See Dura Software Series A Qof LLC; *U.S. Private*, pg. 1292
ITRON, INC. - OAKLAND—See Itron, Inc.; *U.S. Private*, pg. 1176
ITRS GROUP LTD.—See TA Associates, Inc.; *U.S. Private*, pg. 3916
IVALUA, INC.; *U.S. Private*, pg. 2150
IVANTI SOFTWARE, INC.—See Clearlake Capital Group, L.P.; *U.S. Private*, pg. 935
IVINEX; *U.S. Private*, pg. 2151
IVIZ GROUP, INC.; *U.S. Private*, pg. 2151
IVOLUTION MEDICAL SYSTEMS, INC.; *U.S. Private*, pg. 2151
IVONA SOFTWARE SP. Z O.O.—See Amazon.com, Inc.; *U.S. Public*, pg. 90
IWAVE INFORMATION SYSTEMS INC—See Incline MGMT Corp.; *U.S. Private*, pg. 2054
IXL LEARNING, INC.; *U.S. Private*, pg. 2152
IX PARTNERS LTD.—See Genpact Limited; *Int'l*, pg. 2927
IXREVEAL, INC.—See Springboard Capital, LLC; *U.S. Private*, pg. 3763
IXRF SYSTEMS, INC.; *U.S. Private*, pg. 2152
JAC COMPUTER SERVICES LTD.—See Leonard Green & Partners, L.P.; *U.S. Private*, pg. 2430
JAC COMPUTER SERVICES LTD.—See TPG Capital, L.P.; *U.S. Public*, pg. 2177
JADESTONE GROUP AB—See Light & Wonder, Inc.; *U.S. Public*, pg. 1315
JAGEX LTD.—See The Carlyle Group Inc.; *U.S. Public*, pg. 2047
JAGGED PEAK, INC.—See ID Logistics SAS; *Int'l*, pg. 3587
JAGUAR CONSULTING, INC.—See FilmTrack Inc.; *U.S. Private*, pg. 1506
JAMA SOFTWARE INC.; *U.S. Private*, pg. 2182

JAMCRACKER, INC.—See Actua Corporation; *U.S. Private*, pg. 71
JANRAIN, INC.—See Akamai Technologies, Inc.; *U.S. Public*, pg. 69
JANRAIN UK LIMITED—See Akamai Technologies, Inc.; *U.S. Public*, pg. 69
JASPERSOFT CORPORATION—See Vista Equity Partners, LLC; *U.S. Private*, pg. 4402
JCAC TECHNOLOGIES INC—See Epiroc AB; *Int'l*, pg. 2463
JCS COMPUTER RESOURCE CORP.—See QXO, Inc.; *U.S. Public*, pg. 1758
JDA SOFTWARE ASIA PTE. LTD.—See New Mountain Capital, LLC; *U.S. Private*, pg. 2902
JDA SOFTWARE, INC. - AKRON—See New Mountain Capital, LLC; *U.S. Private*, pg. 2902
JDA SOFTWARE, INC. - ROCKVILLE—See New Mountain Capital, LLC; *U.S. Private*, pg. 2902
JDA SOFTWARE, INC.—See New Mountain Capital, LLC; *U.S. Private*, pg. 2902
JDA SOFTWARE, INC. - WEST DES MOINES—See New Mountain Capital, LLC; *U.S. Private*, pg. 2902
JDA SOFTWARE, INC. - WESTLAKE VILLAGE—See New Mountain Capital, LLC; *U.S. Private*, pg. 2902
JDA SOFTWARE NORDIC AB—See New Mountain Capital, LLC; *U.S. Private*, pg. 2902
JENARK BUSINESS SYSTEMS, INC.—See Insight Venture Management, LLC; *U.S. Private*, pg. 2089
JENARK BUSINESS SYSTEMS, INC.—See Stone Point Capital LLC; *U.S. Private*, pg. 3822
JET.AI INC.; *U.S. Public*, pg. 1189
JHJ SOFTWARE, INC.—See Eli Global, LLC; *U.S. Private*, pg. 1360
JIVE SOFTWARE, INC.—See ESW Capital, LLC; *U.S. Private*, pg. 1430
J.K. GROUP, INC.—See CyberGrants, LLC; *U.S. Private*, pg. 1133
JOBCASE, INC.; *U.S. Private*, pg. 2217
THE JOBSCOPE CORPORATION—See Gower Corporation; *U.S. Private*, pg. 1747
JOLT ONLINE GAMING LIMITED (IRELAND)—See GameStop Corp.; *U.S. Public*, pg. 896
JONAS COMPUTING (UK) LTD.—See Constellation Software Inc.; *Int'l*, pg. 1773
JONES CYBER SOLUTIONS, LTD.—See Jones International University; *U.S. Private*, pg. 2233
JOURNAL TECHNOLOGIES, INC.—See Daily Journal Corporation; *U.S. Public*, pg. 620
JTECH COMMUNICATIONS INC.—See HM Electronics Incorporated; *U.S. Public*, pg. 1954
JULY SYSTEMS, LLC—See Cisco Systems, Inc.; *U.S. Public*, pg. 499
JUNCTION SOLUTIONS, INC.; *U.S. Private*, pg. 2244
JUNXURE; *U.S. Private*, pg. 2245
JWORD, INC.—See GMO Internet Group, Inc.; *Int'l*, pg. 3013
K2 DESIGN & STRATEGY; *U.S. Private*, pg. 2253
KABADDI GAMES INC.—See Greenbank Capital Inc.; *Int'l*, pg. 3073
KABUSHIKI KAISHA VASCO DATA SECURITY JAPAN—See OneSpan Inc.; *U.S. Public*, pg. 1603
KAHOOT! ASA—See The Goldman Sachs Group, Inc.; *U.S. Public*, pg. 2082
KAIROS AR, INC.; *U.S. Private*, pg. 2255
KALIBRATE TECHNOLOGIES LTD.—See Hanover Investors Management LLP; *Int'l*, pg. 3258
KALLIDUS INC.; *U.S. Private*, pg. 2257
KANA SOFTWARE—See Verint Systems Inc.; *U.S. Public*, pg. 2281
KANA SOLUTIONS LTD—See Verint Systems Inc.; *U.S. Public*, pg. 2281
KAPLAN (INDIA) PRIVATE LIMITED—See Graham Holdings Company; *U.S. Public*, pg. 955
KARMA SCIENCE, INC—See Meta Platforms, Inc.; *U.S. Public*, pg. 1427
KARMASPHERE, INC.; *U.S. Private*, pg. 2263
KASHFLOW SOFTWARE LTD—See HgCapital Trust plc; *Int'l*, pg. 3376
KAYAKO LIMITED—See ESW Capital, LLC; *U.S. Private*, pg. 1430
KCENTRIC TECHNOLOGIES, INC.—See KKR & Co. Inc.; *U.S. Public*, pg. 1267
K-ECOMMERCE—See KKR & Co. Inc.; *U.S. Public*, pg. 1267
KENEXA—See International Business Machines Corporation; *U.S. Public*, pg. 1148
KENEXA TECHNOLOGIES PRIVATE LIMITED—See International Business Machines Corporation; *U.S. Public*, pg. 1148
KEWEGO DEUTSCHLAND GMBH—See Piksel, Inc.; *U.S. Private*, pg. 3180
KEWILL INC.—See Francisco Partners Management, LP; *U.S. Public*, pg. 1589
KEYMARK, INC.; *U.S. Private*, pg. 2294
KHOROS INTERNATIONAL, LLC—See Vista Equity Partners, LLC; *U.S. Private*, pg. 4398
KHOROS, LLC - AUSTRALIA OFFICE—See Vista Equity Partners, LLC; *U.S. Private*, pg. 4398
KHOROS, LLC - FRANCE OFFICE—See Vista Equity Partners, LLC; *U.S. Private*, pg. 4398

513210 — SOFTWARE PUBLISHERS

KHOROS, LLC—See Vista Equity Partners, LLC; *U.S. Private*, pg. 4398
KIBO COMMERCE LTD.—See Vista Equity Partners, LLC; *U.S. Private*, pg. 4398
KIBO - PETALUMA—See Vista Equity Partners, LLC; *U.S. Private*, pg. 4398
KIBO - SAN LUIS OBISPO—See Vista Equity Partners, LLC; *U.S. Private*, pg. 4398
KIBO SOFTWARE, INC.—See Vista Equity Partners, LLC; *U.S. Private*, pg. 4398
KINETIC; *U.S. Private*, pg. 2308
KING.COM LIMITED—See Microsoft Corporation; *U.S. Public*, pg. 1439
KINGLAND SYSTEMS CORP.; *U.S. Private*, pg. 2311
KINNSER SOFTWARE, INC.; *U.S. Private*, pg. 2313
KITWARE, INC.; *U.S. Private*, pg. 2317
KIVATI SOFTWARE, LLC—See Resolute Solutions Corporation; *U.S. Private*, pg. 3406
KLAUS TECH, INC.; *U.S. Public*, pg. 1269
KLDISCOVERY ONTRACK CANADA CO.—See Pivotal Acquisition Corp.; *U.S. Private*, pg. 3192
KLOUT, INC.—See Vista Equity Partners, LLC; *U.S. Private*, pg. 4398
KNOWLEDGEADVISORS, INC.—See eXplorance, Inc.; *Int'l*, pg. 2588
KNOWLEDGE MARKETING, LLC—See ESW Capital, LLC; *U.S. Private*, pg. 1430
KODAK RAHOLA, INC.—See Eastman Kodak Company; *U.S. Public*, pg. 708
KOFAX AUSTRALIA PTY. LTD.—See Clearlake Capital Group, L.P.; *U.S. Private*, pg. 936
KOFAX AUSTRALIA PTY. LTD.—See TA Associates, Inc.; *U.S. Private*, pg. 3916
KOFAX BENELUX NV—See Clearlake Capital Group, L.P.; *U.S. Private*, pg. 936
KOFAX BENELUX NV—See TA Associates, Inc.; *U.S. Private*, pg. 3916
KOFAX DANMARK A/S—See Clearlake Capital Group, L.P.; *U.S. Private*, pg. 936
KOFAX DANMARK A/S—See TA Associates, Inc.; *U.S. Private*, pg. 3916
KOFAX DEUTSCHLAND AG—See Clearlake Capital Group, L.P.; *U.S. Private*, pg. 936
KOFAX DEUTSCHLAND AG—See TA Associates, Inc.; *U.S. Private*, pg. 3916
KOFAX INC.—See Clearlake Capital Group, L.P.; *U.S. Private*, pg. 935
KOFAX INC.—See TA Associates, Inc.; *U.S. Private*, pg. 3916
KOFAX ITALIA S.R.L.—See Clearlake Capital Group, L.P.; *U.S. Private*, pg. 936
KOFAX ITALIA S.R.L.—See TA Associates, Inc.; *U.S. Private*, pg. 3916
KOFAX JAPAN CO. LTD.—See Clearlake Capital Group, L.P.; *U.S. Private*, pg. 936
KOFAX JAPAN CO. LTD.—See TA Associates, Inc.; *U.S. Private*, pg. 3916
KOFAX MALAYSIA SDN. BHD.—See Clearlake Capital Group, L.P.; *U.S. Private*, pg. 936
KOFAX MALAYSIA SDN. BHD.—See TA Associates, Inc.; *U.S. Private*, pg. 3916
KOFAX NETHERLANDS BV—See Clearlake Capital Group, L.P.; *U.S. Private*, pg. 936
KOFAX NETHERLANDS BV—See TA Associates, Inc.; *U.S. Private*, pg. 3916
KOFAX PORTUGAL, S.A.—See Clearlake Capital Group, L.P.; *U.S. Private*, pg. 936
KOFAX PORTUGAL, S.A.—See TA Associates, Inc.; *U.S. Private*, pg. 3916
KOFAX PRODUTOS DE IMAGEM DO BRASIL LTDA—See Clearlake Capital Group, L.P.; *U.S. Private*, pg. 936
KOFAX PRODUTOS DE IMAGEM DO BRASIL LTDA—See TA Associates, Inc.; *U.S. Private*, pg. 3916
KOFAX SCHWEIZ AG—See Clearlake Capital Group, L.P.; *U.S. Private*, pg. 936
KOFAX SCHWEIZ AG—See TA Associates, Inc.; *U.S. Private*, pg. 3916
KOFAX SINGAPORE PTE. LTD.—See Clearlake Capital Group, L.P.; *U.S. Private*, pg. 936
KOFAX SINGAPORE PTE. LTD.—See TA Associates, Inc.; *U.S. Private*, pg. 3916
KOFAX SOFTWARE IBERICA S.A.U.—See Clearlake Capital Group, L.P.; *U.S. Private*, pg. 936
KOFAX SOFTWARE IBERICA S.A.U.—See TA Associates, Inc.; *U.S. Private*, pg. 3916
KOFAX SVERIGE AB—See Clearlake Capital Group, L.P.; *U.S. Private*, pg. 936
KOFAX SVERIGE AB—See TA Associates, Inc.; *U.S. Private*, pg. 3916
KOFAX UK LTD.—See Clearlake Capital Group, L.P.; *U.S. Private*, pg. 936
KOFAX UK LTD.—See TA Associates, Inc.; *U.S. Private*, pg. 3916
KOFAX VIETNAM CO., LTD.—See Clearlake Capital Group, L.P.; *U.S. Private*, pg. 936
KOFAX VIETNAM CO., LTD.—See TA Associates, Inc.; *U.S. Private*, pg. 3916
KOLDWATER TECHNOLOGIES LLC—See Business Industrial Network; *U.S. Private*, pg. 695
KOLOGIK CAPITAL, LLC—See Kologik LLC; *U.S. Private*, pg. 2341
KOLOGIK LLC; *U.S. Private*, pg. 2341
KOMODO HEALTH, INC.; *U.S. Private*, pg. 2342
KONTAGENT INC.; *U.S. Private*, pg. 2342
KONY SOLUTIONS, INC.; *U.S. Private*, pg. 2343
KOUNT INC.—See Equifax Inc.; *U.S. Public*, pg. 786
KOVAIR SOFTWARE, INC.—See Surge Ventures, LLC; *U.S. Private*, pg. 3884
KOVA SOLUTIONS, INC.—See Berkshire Hathaway Inc.; *U.S. Public*, pg. 312
KREG CORPORATION - CONNECTICUT OFFICE—See Vizient, Inc.; *U.S. Private*, pg. 4407
KROLL ONTRACK GMBH—See Pivotal Acquisition Corp.; *U.S. Private*, pg. 3192
KROLL ONTRACK (HK) LTD.—See Pivotal Acquisition Corp.; *U.S. Private*, pg. 3192
KROLL ONTRACK PTY LTD.—See Pivotal Acquisition Corp.; *U.S. Private*, pg. 3192
KROLL ONTRACK (SWITZERLAND) GMBH—See Pivotal Acquisition Corp.; *U.S. Private*, pg. 3192
KRONOS AUSTRALIA PTY LTD—See Hellman & Friedman LLC; *U.S. Private*, pg. 1910
KRONOS DE MEXICO SA DE CV—See Hellman & Friedman LLC; *U.S. Private*, pg. 1911
KRONOS, INCORPORATED - HIRING SOLUTIONS GROUP—See Hellman & Friedman LLC; *U.S. Private*, pg. 1911
KRONOS, INCORPORATED—See Hellman & Friedman LLC; *U.S. Private*, pg. 1910
KRONOS, INCORPORATED - TELESTAFF SOLUTIONS GROUP—See Hellman & Friedman LLC; *U.S. Private*, pg. 1911
KRONOS SINGAPORE PTE. LTD—See Hellman & Friedman LLC; *U.S. Private*, pg. 1910
KRONOS SYSTEMS B.V.—See Hellman & Friedman LLC; *U.S. Private*, pg. 1910
KRONOS SYSTEMS INDIA PRIVATE LIMITED—See Hellman & Friedman LLC; *U.S. Private*, pg. 1910
K.TEK SYSTEMS, INC.; *U.S. Private*, pg. 2252
KURTZMAN CARSON CONSULTANTS LLC—See GCP Capital Partners Holdings LLC; *U.S. Private*, pg. 1654
LAB ESCAPE, INC.—See Teikametrics LLC; *U.S. Private*, pg. 3958
LABTECH SOFTWARE, LLC; *U.S. Private*, pg. 2371
LABTECH SOFTWARE—See LabTech Software, LLC; *U.S. Private*, pg. 2371
LACERTE SOFTWARE CORPORATION—See Intuit Inc.; *U.S. Public*, pg. 1160
LAMBDA TD SOFTWARE, INC.; *U.S. Private*, pg. 2379
LANCOPE, LLC—See Cisco Systems, Inc.; *U.S. Public*, pg. 499
LANDACORP, INC.—See ExlService Holdings, Inc.; *U.S. Public*, pg. 808
LANDMARK GRAPHICS CORPORATION—See Halliburton Company; *U.S. Public*, pg. 980
LANDTECH DATA CORP.—See AccuTitle LLC; *U.S. Private*, pg. 55
LANWORKS PTE LTD—See HgCapital Trust plc; *Int'l*, pg. 3377
LAPIS SOFTWARE ASSOCIATES LLC—See Light & Wonder, Inc.; *U.S. Public*, pg. 1314
LATTICE ENGINES, INC.—See Cannae Holdings, Inc.; *U.S. Public*, pg. 430
LATTICE ENGINES, INC.—See CC Capital Partners, LLC; *U.S. Private*, pg. 798
LATTICE ENGINES, INC.—See Intercontinental Exchange, Inc.; *U.S. Public*, pg. 1142
LAUER-FISCHER GMBH—See CompuGroup Medical SE & Co. KGaA; *Int'l*, pg. 1757
LAUNCHROCK, INC.—See Fundable LLC; *U.S. Private*, pg. 1622
LA-WELL SYSTEMS GMBH—See CompuGroup Medical SE & Co. KGaA; *Int'l*, pg. 1756
LAWLOGIX GROUP, INC.—See Equifax Inc.; *U.S. Public*, pg. 786
LAWROOM—See EverFi, Inc.; *U.S. Private*, pg. 1438
LAWSON TRAVELS & TOURS (INDIA) PRIVATE LIMITED—See Ebix Inc.; *U.S. Public*, pg. 710
LDISCOVERY, LLC - FORT LAUDERDALE—See Pivotal Acquisition Corp.; *U.S. Private*, pg. 3192
LEADLIFE SOLUTIONS INC.; *U.S. Private*, pg. 2406
LEADS360 INC.; *U.S. Private*, pg. 2406
LEARNING OBJECTS, INC.—See Apax Partners LLP; *Int'l*, pg. 503
LEARNING OBJECTS, INC.—See Apollo Global Management, Inc.; *U.S. Public*, pg. 168
LEARNING OBJECTS, INC.—See KKR & Co. Inc.; *U.S. Public*, pg. 1256
LEARNING OBJECTS, INC.—See Searchlight Capital Partners, L.P.; *U.S. Private*, pg. 3587
LECORPIO, LLC—See Insight Venture Management, LLC; *U.S. Private*, pg. 2087
LEGATIO TECHNOLOGIES LTD.—See GTCR LLC; *U.S. Private*, pg. 1804
LEGIC IDENTSYSTEMS AG—See dormakaba Holding AG; *Int'l*, pg. 2179
LETTUCE INC.—See Intuit Inc.; *U.S. Public*, pg. 1160
LEVELBLOX, INC.; *U.S. Public*, pg. 1308
LEVEL UP! (PHILIPPINES), INC.—See Asphere Innovations Public Company Limited; *Int'l*, pg. 630
LGBTQ LOYALTY HOLDINGS, INC.; *U.S. Public*, pg. 1309
LHP SOFTWARE LLC; *U.S. Private*, pg. 2442
LIAISON INTERNATIONAL, INC.; *U.S. Private*, pg. 2442
LIBER ENTERTAINMENT INC.—See Aeria Inc.; *Int'l*, pg. 179
LIBRATO, INC.—See Silver Lake Group, LLC; *U.S. Private*, pg. 3661
LIBRATO, INC.—See Thoma Bravo, L.P.; *U.S. Private*, pg. 4153
LICENSE MONITOR, INC.—See Vista Equity Partners, LLC; *U.S. Private*, pg. 4400
LIFEIMAGE, INC.—See HgCapital Trust plc; *Int'l*, pg. 3376
LIFELOCK, INC.—See Gen Digital Inc.; *U.S. Public*, pg. 910
LIFERAY AUSTRALIA PTY. LTD.—See Liferay, Inc.; *U.S. Private*, pg. 2450
LIFERAY BRASIL—See Liferay, Inc.; *U.S. Private*, pg. 2450
LIFERAY DALIAN SOFTWARE CO., LTD.—See Liferay, Inc.; *U.S. Private*, pg. 2450
LIFERAY FRANCE—See Liferay, Inc.; *U.S. Private*, pg. 2450
LIFERAY GMBH—See Liferay, Inc.; *U.S. Private*, pg. 2450
LIFERAY HUNGARY KFT.—See Liferay, Inc.; *U.S. Private*, pg. 2451
LIFERAY, INC.; *U.S. Private*, pg. 2450
LIFERAY INDIA PVT. LTD.—See Liferay, Inc.; *U.S. Private*, pg. 2451
LIFERAY IRELAND—See Liferay, Inc.; *U.S. Private*, pg. 2451
LIFERAY JAPAN K. K.—See Liferay, Inc.; *U.S. Private*, pg. 2451
LIFERAY S.L.—See Liferay, Inc.; *U.S. Private*, pg. 2451
LIFERAY UK—See Liferay, Inc.; *U.S. Private*, pg. 2451
LIFE'S TIME CAPSULE SERVICES, INC.; *U.S. Public*, pg. 1312
LIGHTSIDE LABS, LLC—See Advance Publications, Inc.; *U.S. Private*, pg. 87
LIMEADE, INC.—See KKR & Co. Inc.; *U.S. Public*, pg. 1254
LINEWIZE LIMITED—See Family Zone Cyber Safety Limited; *Int'l*, pg. 2612
LINKSMART, INC.—See sovrn Holdings, Inc.; *U.S. Private*, pg. 3743
LINK-SYSTEMS INTERNATIONAL, INC.; *U.S. Private*, pg. 2462
LINOMA SOFTWARE; *U.S. Private*, pg. 2462
LIQUID AIR LAB GMBH—See 24 Mobile Advertising Solutions AB; *Int'l*, pg. 4
LIQUID HOLDINGS GROUP, INC.; *U.S. Private*, pg. 2465
LIQUIT B.V.—See Recast Software Inc.; *U.S. Private*, pg. 3370
LISTENLOGIC, LLC—See Guggenheim Partners, LLC; *U.S. Private*, pg. 1811
LISTRAK, INC.; *U.S. Private*, pg. 2467
LITTLE ORBIT EUROPE LTD.—See Little Orbit LLC; *U.S. Private*, pg. 2469
LITTLE ORBIT LLC; *U.S. Private*, pg. 2469
LITTLESEA S.R.L.—See Doxee S.p.A; *Int'l*, pg. 2187
LIVEOFFICE LLC—See Gen Digital Inc.; *U.S. Public*, pg. 910
LIVEPERSON, INC.; *U.S. Public*, pg. 1332
LIVETILES CORPORATION—See LiveTiles Limited; *U.S. Private*, pg. 2473
LIZARDTECH—See Celartem Technology Inc.; *Int'l*, pg. 1391
LLAMASOFT INC.—See Thoma Bravo, L.P.; *U.S. Private*, pg. 4147
LLC AUDATEX UKRAINE—See Vista Equity Partners, LLC; *U.S. Private*, pg. 4400
LOADSPRING SOLUTIONS, INC.; *U.S. Private*, pg. 2476
LOCAL MATTERS, INC.; *U.S. Private*, pg. 2477
LOCALYTICS COMPANY; *U.S. Private*, pg. 2477
LOCATION LABS, INC.—See Gen Digital Inc.; *U.S. Public*, pg. 910
LOCKBOX LINK INC.; *U.S. Private*, pg. 2478
LOCKPATH, INC.—See BC Partners LLP; *Int'l*, pg. 925
LOCUS ENERGY, LLC—See Also Energy Inc.; *U.S. Private*, pg. 203
LOGGLY, INC.—See Silver Lake Group, LLC; *U.S. Private*, pg. 3661
LOGGLY, INC.—See Thoma Bravo, L.P.; *U.S. Private*, pg. 4153
LOGI ANALYTICS, INC.—See TA Associates, Inc.; *U.S. Private*, pg. 3915
LOGIBEC INC.—See GI Manager L.P.; *U.S. Private*, pg. 1693
LOGICAL IMAGES, INC.; *U.S. Private*, pg. 2481
LOGICARE CORPORATION—See Interactivation Health Networks LLC; *U.S. Private*, pg. 2108
LOGICEASE SOLUTIONS, INC.; *U.S. Private*, pg. 2481
LOGICMARK, INC.; *U.S. Public*, pg. 1340
LOGICMONITOR, INC.—See Vista Equity Partners, LLC; *U.S. Private*, pg. 4398
LOGILITY, INC.—See American Software, Inc.; *U.S. Public*, pg. 109
LOGILITY SOLUTIONS PVT. LTD.—See American Software, Inc.; *U.S. Public*, pg. 109
LOGIQ, INC.; *U.S. Public*, pg. 1341

N.A.I.C.S. INDEX
513210 — SOFTWARE PUBLISHERS

LOGISTICS BUSINESS SYSTEMS LIMITED—See PTC Inc.; *U.S. Public*, pg. 1734

LOGMEIN EUROPE B.V.—See Elliott Management Corporation; *U.S. Private*, pg. 1368

LOGMEIN EUROPE B.V.—See Francisco Partners Management, LP; *U.S. Private*, pg. 1590

LOGRHYTHM, INC.—See Thoma Bravo, L.P.; *U.S. Private*, pg. 4149

LOG SYSTEM SARL—See Clasquin S.A.; *Int'l*, pg. 1652

LONGVIEW EUROPE GMBH—See TA Associates, Inc.; *U.S. Private*, pg. 3915

LOOKER DATA SCIENCES INC—See Alphabet Inc.; *U.S. Public*, pg. 83

LOOKINGGLASS CYBER SOLUTIONS, LLC—See Whanau Interests LLC.; *U.S. Private*, pg. 4504

LOOKOUT, INC.; *U.S. Private*, pg. 2493

LOOP, LLC; *U.S. Private*, pg. 2494

LOQUENDO S.P.A.—See Microsoft Corporation; *U.S. Public*, pg. 1442

LORENSBERGS COMMUNICATION AB—See CompuGroup Medical SE & Co. KGaA; *Int'l*, pg. 1756

LOUDCLOUD SYSTEMS, INC.—See Barnes & Noble Education, Inc.; *U.S. Public*, pg. 276

LTN GLOBAL COMMUNICATIONS, INC.; *U.S. Private*, pg. 2509

LUCIAD, INC.—See Hexagon AB; *Int'l*, pg. 3369

LUCIAD NV—See Hexagon AB; *Int'l*, pg. 3369

LUCIDWORKS INC.; *U.S. Private*, pg. 2511

LUMENDATA, INC.—See LumenData, Inc.; *U.S. Private*, pg. 2514

LUMENTUM INTERNATIONAL (THAILAND) CO., LTD.—See Lumentum Holdings Inc.; *U.S. Public*, pg. 1348

LUMENTUM SWITZERLAND AG—See Lumentum Holdings Inc.; *U.S. Public*, pg. 1348

LUMENTUM TAIWAN CO., LTD.—See Lumentum Holdings Inc.; *U.S. Public*, pg. 1348

LUMESSE, INC.—See Clearlake Capital Group, L.P.; *U.S. Private*, pg. 934

LUMESSE LIMITED—See Clearlake Capital Group, L.P.; *U.S. Private*, pg. 934

LUMINE GROUP INC.—See Constellation Software Inc.; *Int'l*, pg. 1773

LUNEXA, LLC; *U.S. Private*, pg. 2515

LUXOFT HOLDING, INC.—See DXC Technology Company; *U.S. Public*, pg. 696

LYFT, INC.; *U.S. Public*, pg. 1350

LYRASIS INC.; *U.S. Private*, pg. 2522

M2 SYSTEMS CORPORATION—See Digital Payments PLC; *Int'l*, pg. 2123

M3 ACCOUNTING SERVICES INC.; *U.S. Private*, pg. 2530

MACH7 TECHNOLOGIES, INC.—See Mach7 Technologies Limited; *U.S. Public*, pg. 1352

MACROBRIGHT LLC; *U.S. Private*, pg. 2538

MACROVISION KOREA CO., LTD.—See Adeia Inc.; *U.S. Public*, pg. 41

MADCAP SOFTWARE, INC.—See Battery Ventures, L.P.; *U.S. Private*, pg. 489

MAESTRO LLC; *U.S. Private*, pg. 2544

MAG+ AB—See Bonnier AB; *Int'l*, pg. 1109

MAGENIC TECHNOLOGIES, INC.—See Cognizant Technology Solutions Corporation; *U.S. Public*, pg. 524

MAGIC SOFTWARE ENTERPRISES GMBH—See Asseco Poland S.A.; *Int'l*, pg. 642

MAGIC SOFTWARE ENTERPRISES INC.—See Asseco Poland S.A.; *Int'l*, pg. 642

MAGIC SOFTWARE ENTERPRISES LTD.—See Asseco Poland S.A.; *Int'l*, pg. 642

MAGNETIC VARIATION SERVICES, LLC—See Helmerich & Payne, Inc.; *U.S. Public*, pg. 1024

MAGNOLIA AMERICAS, INC.—See Genui GmbH; *Int'l*, pg. 2930

MAGNOLIA ESPANA SOFTWARE AND COMPUTER APPLICATIONS S.L.—See Genui GmbH; *Int'l*, pg. 2930

MAGNOLIA INTERNATIONAL LTD.—See Genui GmbH; *Int'l*, pg. 2930

MAGNOLIA SOFTWARE & SERVICES CZ S.R.O.—See Genui GmbH; *Int'l*, pg. 2930

MAGZTER INC.—See VerSe Innovation Private Limited; *U.S. Private*, pg. 4369

MAILIGEN CHINA—See Pipedrive Inc.; *U.S. Private*, pg. 3189

MAILIGEN EUROPE—See Pipedrive Inc.; *U.S. Private*, pg. 3189

MAILIGEN LIMITED—See Pipedrive Inc.; *U.S. Private*, pg. 3189

MAILIGEN RUSSIA—See Pipedrive Inc.; *U.S. Private*, pg. 3189

MAINTENANCENET, INC.—See Cisco Systems, Inc.; *U.S. Public*, pg. 499

MAKING SENSE LLC—See Internet Cowboy Ventures LLC; *U.S. Private*, pg. 2122

MAM SOFTWARE GROUP, INC.—See KKR & Co. Inc.; *U.S. Public*, pg. 1256

MANAGED HEALTH CARE ASSOCIATES, INC.—See Roper Technologies, Inc.; *U.S. Public*, pg. 1812

MANAGEMENT MENTORS, INC.—See Engagedly, Inc.; *U.S. Private*, pg. 1397

MANAGERPLUS SOLUTIONS, LLC—See iOffice, LLC; *U.S. Private*, pg. 2133

MANDIANT AUSTRALIA PTY LTD—See Alphabet Inc.; *U.S. Public*, pg. 84

MANDIANT CORPORATION—See Alphabet Inc.; *U.S. Public*, pg. 84

MANDIANT CYBERSECURITY PRIVATE LIMITED—See Alphabet Inc.; *U.S. Public*, pg. 84

MANDIANT DEUTSCHLAND GMBH—See Alphabet Inc.; *U.S. Public*, pg. 84

MANDIANT, INC.—See Alphabet Inc.; *U.S. Public*, pg. 83

MANDIANT IRELAND LIMITED—See Alphabet Inc.; *U.S. Public*, pg. 84

MANDIANT K.K.—See Alphabet Inc.; *U.S. Public*, pg. 84

MANDIANT KOREA LIMITED—See Alphabet Inc.; *U.S. Public*, pg. 84

MANDIANT SINGAPORE PRIVATE LIMITED—See Alphabet Inc.; *U.S. Public*, pg. 84

MANDIANT UK LTD.—See Alphabet Inc.; *U.S. Public*, pg. 84

MANHATTAN ASSOCIATES, INC.; *U.S. Public*, pg. 1356

MANHATTAN ASSOCIATES PTY LTD—See Manhattan Associates, Inc.; *U.S. Public*, pg. 1356

MANHATTAN ASSOCIATES SOFTWARE PTE LTD.—See Manhattan Associates, Inc.; *U.S. Public*, pg. 1356

MANSELL GROUP, INC.—See The Riverside Company; *U.S. Private*, pg. 4109

MAPR TECHNOLOGIES, INC.—See Hewlett Packard Enterprise Company; *U.S. Public*, pg. 1032

MAPSYS INC.; *U.S. Private*, pg. 2569

MAQ SOFTWARE; *U.S. Private*, pg. 2569

MARIADB CORPORATION AB—See California Technology Ventures, LLC; *U.S. Private*, pg. 721

MARIN SOFTWARE INC.; *U.S. Public*, pg. 1366

MARITECH AS—See Symphony Technology Group, LLC; *U.S. Private*, pg. 3902

MARKETNET SERVICES, LLC; *U.S. Private*, pg. 2581

MARKETO AUSTRALIA PTY LTD—See Adobe Inc.; *U.S. Public*, pg. 42

MARKETO EMEA LTD.—See Adobe Inc.; *U.S. Public*, pg. 42

MARKETO, INC.—See Adobe Inc.; *U.S. Public*, pg. 42

MARKETPATH, INC.; *U.S. Private*, pg. 2581

MARKET VELOCITY, INC.—See KKR & Co. Inc.; *U.S. Public*, pg. 1267

MASERGY COMMUNICATIONS, INC.—See Berkshire Partners LLC; *U.S. Private*, pg. 535

MASTERNAUT INTERNATIONAL S.A.S.—See Compagnie Generale des Etablissements Michelin SCA; *Int'l*, pg. 1743

MASTERNAUT LIMITED—See Compagnie Generale des Etablissements Michelin SCA; *Int'l*, pg. 1743

THE MATHWORKS, INC.; *U.S. Private*, pg. 4075

MATORIT DATA AB—See LKQ Corporation; *U.S. Public*, pg. 1335

MATRIXCARE, INC.—See ResMed Inc.; *U.S. Public*, pg. 1790

MATROX ELECTRONIC SYSTEMS GMBH—See Zebra Technologies Corporation; *U.S. Public*, pg. 2401

MATROX GRAPHICS, INC.—See Zebra Technologies Corporation; *U.S. Public*, pg. 2401

MATROX VIDEO AND IMAGING TECHNOLOGY EUROPE LIMITED—See Zebra Technologies Corporation; *U.S. Public*, pg. 2401

MATTERMARK, INC.—See FullContact, Inc.; *U.S. Private*, pg. 1621

MAXIMUM SOLUTIONS, LLC—See Global Payments Inc.; *U.S. Public*, pg. 943

MAXIS STUDIO—See Electronic Arts Inc.; *U.S. Public*, pg. 724

MAXPOINT INTERACTIVE INC.—See MacAndrews & Forbes Incorporated; *U.S. Private*, pg. 2532

MAXYMISER GMBH—See Maxymiser Inc.; *U.S. Private*, pg. 2620

MAXYMISER INC.; *U.S. Private*, pg. 2620

MAXYMISER TECHNICAL CENTER—See Maxymiser Inc.; *U.S. Private*, pg. 2620

MAZDA COMPUTING; *U.S. Private*, pg. 2623

MBS/NET, INC.—See Medsphere Systems Corp.; *U.S. Private*, pg. 2658

MCAFEE CO., LTD.—See Advent International Corporation; *U.S. Private*, pg. 104

MCAFEE CO., LTD.—See Crosspoint Capital Partners LP; *U.S. Private*, pg. 1107

MCAFEE INTERNATIONAL BV—See Advent International Corporation; *U.S. Private*, pg. 104

MCAFEE INTERNATIONAL BV—See Crosspoint Capital Partners LP; *U.S. Private*, pg. 1107

MCAFEE, LLC—See Advent International Corporation; *U.S. Private*, pg. 104

MCAFEE, LLC—See Crosspoint Capital Partners LP; *U.S. Private*, pg. 1107

MCCORMICK SYSTEMS, INC.—See Thoma Bravo, L.P.; *U.S. Private*, pg. 4148

MC HOLOGRAM INC.—See MicroCloud Hologram Inc.; *U.S. Public*, pg. 1437

MCKESSON HEALTH SOLUTIONS LLC—See McKesson Corporation; *U.S. Public*, pg. 1408

MCLANE ADVANCED TECHNOLOGIES, LLC; *U.S. Private*, pg. 2640

MCPC INC.; *U.S. Private*, pg. 2644

MCX TECHNOLOGIES CORPORATION; *U.S. Private*, pg. 1409

MD ON-LINE INC.; *U.S. Private*, pg. 2646

MDSAVE, INC.—See Tendo Systems Inc.; *U.S. Private*, pg. 3966

MDT SOFTWARE—See Desco Corporation; *U.S. Private*, pg. 1211

MEASURABL, INC.; *U.S. Private*, pg. 2648

MEASUREFUL INC.—See Chirpify, Inc.; *U.S. Private*, pg. 887

MECHANICAL DATA INC—See Trimble, Inc.; *U.S. Public*, pg. 2192

MECHANICAL SIMULATION CORP.—See Applied Intuition, Inc.; *U.S. Private*, pg. 299

MED3000 GROUP, INC. - OLDSMAR—See McKesson Corporation; *U.S. Public*, pg. 1407

MED3000 GROUP, INC.—See McKesson Corporation; *U.S. Public*, pg. 1407

MEDALLIA ARGENTINA—See Thoma Bravo, L.P.; *U.S. Private*, pg. 4149

MEDALLIA AUSTRALIA PTY. LTD.—See Thoma Bravo, L.P.; *U.S. Private*, pg. 4149

MEDALLIA DIGITAL LTD.—See Thoma Bravo, L.P.; *U.S. Private*, pg. 4149

MEDALLIA FRANCE SARL—See Thoma Bravo, L.P.; *U.S. Private*, pg. 4149

MEDALLIA GMBH—See Thoma Bravo, L.P.; *U.S. Private*, pg. 4149

MEDALLIA, INC.—See Thoma Bravo, L.P.; *U.S. Private*, pg. 4149

MEDALLIA SINGAPORE PTE. LTD.—See Thoma Bravo, L.P.; *U.S. Private*, pg. 4149

MEDALLIA UK—See Thoma Bravo, L.P.; *U.S. Private*, pg. 4149

MEDAPTUS, INC.—See Constellation Software Inc.; *Int'l*, pg. 1775

MEDATA INC.—See The Carlyle Group Inc.; *U.S. Public*, pg. 2049

MEDEANALYTICS, INC.—See Thoma Bravo, L.P.; *U.S. Private*, pg. 4150

MEDHOK HEALTHCARE SOLUTIONS, LLC; *U.S. Private*, pg. 2651

MEDHUB, LLC—See Blackstone Inc.; *U.S. Public*, pg. 348

MEDHUB, LLC—See Canada Pension Plan Investment Board; *Int'l*, pg. 1279

MEDIA CYBERNETICS INC.—See Roper Technologies, Inc.; *U.S. Public*, pg. 1812

MEDIAFLY, INC.—See Boathouse Capital Management, LLC; *U.S. Private*, pg. 603

MEDIALON INC.—See 7thSense Design Limited; *Int'l*, pg. 15

MEDIARADAR, INC.—See Thompson Street Capital Manager LLC; *U.S. Private*, pg. 4161

MEDIA SENTIMENT, INC.; *U.S. Public*, pg. 1411

MEDIAVALET INC.—See Symphony Technology Group, LLC; *U.S. Private*, pg. 3902

MEDICAL DIAGNOSTIC EXCHANGE CORP—See DXStorm.com Inc.; *Int'l*, pg. 2237

MEDICAL NUMERICS, INC.—See Textron Inc.; *U.S. Public*, pg. 2028

MEDICAL OUTCOMES RESEARCH ANALYTICS, LLC—See Forian Inc.; *U.S. Public*, pg. 868

MEDICAT LLC—See Banyan Software, Inc.; *U.S. Private*, pg. 470

MEDIGAIN, INC.—See CareCloud, Inc.; *U.S. Public*, pg. 435

MEDIGEST CONSULTORES S.L.—See CompuGroup Medical SE & Co. KGaA; *Int'l*, pg. 1757

MEDIQUAL SYSTEMS, INC.—See Quantros, Inc.; *U.S. Private*, pg. 3322

MEDISOLUTION LTD.—See Brookfield Corporation; *Int'l*, pg. 1189

MEDIVO, INC.; *U.S. Private*, pg. 2657

MEDNET TECHNOLOGIES, INC.—See Advice Media LLC; *U.S. Private*, pg. 110

MEDSPHERE SYSTEMS CORP.; *U.S. Private*, pg. 2658

MEDSTREAMING, LLC; *U.S. Private*, pg. 2659

MEDTRAN DIRECT, INC.—See Leonard Green & Partners, L.P.; *U.S. Private*, pg. 2430

MEDTRAN DIRECT, INC.—See TPG Capital, L.P.; *U.S. Public*, pg. 2177

MELTWATER NEWS US INC.; *U.S. Private*, pg. 2663

MEMBERCLICKS LLC—See Pamlico Capital Management, L.P.; *U.S. Private*, pg. 3083

MEMPHIS AREA TRANSIT AUTHORITY; *U.S. Private*, pg. 2664

MENLO INNOVATIONS LLC; *U.S. Private*, pg. 2666

MERAKI LLC—See Cisco Systems, Inc.; *U.S. Public*, pg. 499

MERCATOR SOLUTIONS FZE—See Warburg Pincus LLC; *U.S. Private*, pg. 4439

MERCHANT E-SOLUTIONS, INC.—See Cielo S.A.; *Int'l*, pg. 1605

MERCHANTRY, INC.—See Tradeshift Inc.; *U.S. Private*, pg. 4202

MERCURY NETWORK, LLC—See Insight Venture Management, LLC; *U.S. Private*, pg. 2089

513210 — SOFTWARE PUBLISHERS

MERCURY NETWORK, LLC—See Stone Point Capital LLC; *U.S. Private*, pg. 3822
MERCURY NEW MEDIA, INC.; *U.S. Private*, pg. 2671
MERCURY TECHNOLOGY GROUP, INC.—See Accenture plc; *Int'l*, pg. 87
MERLIN BUSINESS SOFTWARE LIMITED—See TA Associates, Inc.; *U.S. Private*, pg. 3914
MERLINONE, INC.—See Canto Software, Inc.; *U.S. Private*, pg. 735
MERRICK SYSTEMS, INC.—See HitecVision AS; *Int'l*, pg. 3426
META DATA SOFTWARE, INC.; *U.S. Private*, pg. 2679
META HEALTH TECHNOLOGY, INC.—See Streamline Health Solutions, Inc.; *U.S. Public*, pg. 1954
METAMAP, INC.—See Incode Technologies, Inc.; *U.S. Private*, pg. 2054
METAPACK LTD—See Thoma Bravo, L.P.; *U.S. Private*, pg. 4153
METHODFACTORY, INC.; *U.S. Private*, pg. 2683
METIER, LTD.; *U.S. Private*, pg. 2684
METISENTRY LLC; *U.S. Private*, pg. 2684
METOVA, INC.; *U.S. Private*, pg. 2684
METRICSTREAM-ASIA REGIONAL OFFICE—See MetricStream, Inc.; *U.S. Private*, pg. 2685
METRICSTREAM-ATLANTA REGIONAL OFFICE—See MetricStream, Inc.; *U.S. Private*, pg. 2685
METRICSTREAM, INC.; *U.S. Private*, pg. 2685
METRIX INC.; *U.S. Private*, pg. 2685
M-FINANCE LIMITED—See DTXS Silk Road Investment Holdings Company Limited; *Int'l*, pg. 2217
MFORMATION TECHNOLOGIES, INC.; *U.S. Private*, pg. 2693
MFOUNDRY, INC.—See Fidelity National Infor; *U.S. Public*, pg. 833
MHC SOFTWARE LLC—See Strattam Capital, LLC; *U.S. Private*, pg. 3837
MI9 RETAIL, INC.; *U.S. Private*, pg. 2696
MICELLO, INC.; *U.S. Private*, pg. 2697
MICRIUM, INC.—See Silicon Laboratories Inc.; *U.S. Public*, pg. 1879
MICROEDGE, LLC—See Blackbaud, Inc.; *U.S. Public*, pg. 341
MICROGEN APTITUDE LIMITED—See Aptitude Software Group Plc; *Int'l*, pg. 523
MICROGEN LIMITED—See Aptitude Software Group Plc; *Int'l*, pg. 523
MICROMAX, INC.—See Danlaw, Inc.; *U.S. Private*, pg. 1157
MICROSOFT AB—See Microsoft Corporation; *U.S. Public*, pg. 1439
MICROSOFT BELGIUM & LUXEMBOURG—See Microsoft Corporation; *U.S. Public*, pg. 1439
MICROSOFT BILGISAYAR YAZILIM HIZMETLERI LIMITED SIRKETI—See Microsoft Corporation; *U.S. Public*, pg. 1439
MICROSOFT BUSINESS DIVISION—See Microsoft Corporation; *U.S. Public*, pg. 1439
MICROSOFT B.V.—See Microsoft Corporation; *U.S. Public*, pg. 1439
MICROSOFT CANADA CO.—See Microsoft Corporation; *U.S. Public*, pg. 1439
MICROSOFT CHILE S.A.—See Microsoft Corporation; *U.S. Public*, pg. 1440
MICROSOFT (CHINA) CO., LTD.—See Microsoft Corporation; *U.S. Public*, pg. 1439
MICROSOFT CO., LTD.—See Microsoft Corporation; *U.S. Public*, pg. 1439
MICROSOFT CORP. - DENVER OFFICE—See Microsoft Corporation; *U.S. Public*, pg. 1439
MICROSOFT CORP. - FARGO OFFICE—See Microsoft Corporation; *U.S. Public*, pg. 1439
MICROSOFT CORPORATION (I) PVT. LTD.—See Microsoft Corporation; *U.S. Public*, pg. 1439
MICROSOFT CORPORATION; *U.S. Public*, pg. 1438
MICROSOFT COSTA RICA—See Microsoft Corporation; *U.S. Public*, pg. 1440
MICROSOFT DANMARK APS—See Microsoft Corporation; *U.S. Public*, pg. 1439
MICROSOFT DEUTSCHLAND GMBH—See Microsoft Corporation; *U.S. Public*, pg. 1439
MICROSOFT FRANCE S.A.R.L.—See Microsoft Corporation; *U.S. Public*, pg. 1440
MICROSOFT HELLAS S.A.—See Microsoft Corporation; *U.S. Public*, pg. 1440
MICROSOFT HUNGARY—See Microsoft Corporation; *U.S. Public*, pg. 1440
MICROSOFT IBERICA S.R.L.—See Microsoft Corporation; *U.S. Public*, pg. 1440
MICROSOFT INFORMATICA LTDA.—See Microsoft Corporation; *U.S. Public*, pg. 1441
MICROSOFT IRELAND OPERATIONS LIMITED—See Microsoft Corporation; *U.S. Public*, pg. 1440
MICROSOFT ISRAEL LTD.—See Microsoft Corporation; *U.S. Public*, pg. 1440
MICROSOFT KOREA—See Microsoft Corporation; *U.S. Public*, pg. 1440
MICROSOFT LATIN AMERICA—See Microsoft Corporation; *U.S. Public*, pg. 1440
MICROSOFT LIMITED—See Microsoft Corporation; *U.S. Public*, pg. 1440
MICROSOFT MEXICO, S.A. DE C.V.—See Microsoft Corporation; *U.S. Public*, pg. 1441
MICROSOFT NIGERIA LIMITED—See Microsoft Corporation; *U.S. Public*, pg. 1441
MICROSOFT NORGE AS—See Microsoft Corporation; *U.S. Public*, pg. 1440
MICROSOFT ONLINE SERVICES DIVISION—See Microsoft Corporation; *U.S. Public*, pg. 1441
MICROSOFT OSTERREICH GMBH—See Microsoft Corporation; *U.S. Public*, pg. 1440
MICROSOFT OY SUOMI—See Microsoft Corporation; *U.S. Public*, pg. 1440
MICROSOFT PUERTO RICO S.A.—See Microsoft Corporation; *U.S. Public*, pg. 1441
MICROSOFT SCHWEIZ GMBH—See Microsoft Corporation; *U.S. Public*, pg. 1440
MICROSOFT SLOVAKIA S.R.O.—See Microsoft Corporation; *U.S. Public*, pg. 1440
MICROSOFT SP. Z O.O.—See Microsoft Corporation; *U.S. Public*, pg. 1440
MICROSOFT S.R.L.—See Microsoft Corporation; *U.S. Public*, pg. 1440
MICROSOFT WINDOWS & WINDOWS LIVE DIVISION—See Microsoft Corporation; *U.S. Public*, pg. 1441
MICROSTRATEGY JAPAN KABUSHIKI KAISHA—See MicroStrategy, Inc.; *U.S. Public*, pg. 1444
MICROSTRATEGY SWEDEN AB—See MicroStrategy, Inc.; *U.S. Public*, pg. 1444
MICROSYSTEMS; *U.S. Private*, pg. 2704
MICROTECH SYSTEMS, INC.—See Middough, Inc.; *U.S. Private*, pg. 2714
MIDWAY GAMES INC.; *U.S. Private*, pg. 2718
MILE HIGH INSIGHTS, LLC—See IAC Inc.; *U.S. Public*, pg. 1082
MILES 33 LIMITED—See Vista Equity Partners, LLC; *U.S. Private*, pg. 4399
MILES SOFTWARE SOLUTIONS PVT. LTD.—See Ebix Inc.; *U.S. Public*, pg. 710
MILESTONE SISTEMAS DO BRASIL—See Canon Inc.; *Int'l*, pg. 1297
MILESTONE SYSTEMS A/S—See Canon Inc.; *Int'l*, pg. 1297
MILESTONE SYSTEMS (AUSTRALIA) PTY LIMITED—See Canon Inc.; *Int'l*, pg. 1297
MILESTONE SYSTEMS BULGARIA—See Canon Inc.; *Int'l*, pg. 1297
MILESTONE SYSTEMS FRANCE SARL—See Canon Inc.; *Int'l*, pg. 1297
MILESTONE SYSTEMS GERMANY GMBH—See Canon Inc.; *Int'l*, pg. 1297
MILESTONE SYSTEMS INC.—See Canon Inc.; *Int'l*, pg. 1297
MILESTONE SYSTEMS ITALIA S.R.L.—See Canon Inc.; *Int'l*, pg. 1298
MILESTONE SYSTEMS K.K.—See Canon Inc.; *Int'l*, pg. 1298
MILESTONE SYSTEMS PTE. LTD.—See Canon Inc.; *Int'l*, pg. 1298
MILESTONE SYSTEMS SPAIN S.L.—See Canon Inc.; *Int'l*, pg. 1298
MILESTONE SYSTEMS UAE—See Canon Inc.; *Int'l*, pg. 1298
MILESTONE SYSTEMS UK LTD.—See Canon Inc.; *Int'l*, pg. 1298
MILSOFT UTILITY SOLUTIONS, INC.; *U.S. Private*, pg. 2738
MINDBODY, INC.—See Vista Equity Partners, LLC; *U.S. Private*, pg. 4398
MINDPETAL SOFTWARE SOLUTIONS, INC.; *U.S. Private*, pg. 2741
MINDSEYE SOLUTIONS LLC—See K1 Investment Management, LLC; *U.S. Private*, pg. 2252
MINDSHARE TECHNOLOGIES, INC.; *U.S. Private*, pg. 2741
MINDSPEED TECHNOLOGIES INDIA PRIVATE LTD.—See MACOM Technology Solutions Holdings, Inc.; *U.S. Public*, pg. 1352
MINTEC, INC.—See Hexagon AB; *Int'l*, pg. 3368
MIRIA SYSTEMS, INC.—See Aquiline Capital Partners LLC; *U.S. Private*, pg. 304
MIRO TECHNOLOGIES, INC.—See The Boeing Company; *U.S. Public*, pg. 2040
MISSISSIPPI POLYMERS, INC.; *U.S. Private*, pg. 2748
MITEL COMMUNICATIONS PRIVATE LIMITED—See Searchlight Capital Partners, L.P.; *U.S. Private*, pg. 3589
MITEL NETHERLANDS B.V.—See Searchlight Capital Partners, L.P.; *U.S. Private*, pg. 3589
MITEL NETWORKS (NEW ZEALAND) LIMITED—See Searchlight Capital Partners, L.P.; *U.S. Private*, pg. 3589
MITEL NETWORKS SOUTH AFRICA (PTY) LIMITED—See Searchlight Capital Partners, L.P.; *U.S. Private*, pg. 3589
MIX TELEMATICS LIMITED—See PowerFleet, Inc.; *U.S. Public*, pg. 1706
MIZE INC.; *U.S. Private*, pg. 2752
MLM INFORMATION SERVICES, LLC—See Corporation Service Company; *U.S. Private*, pg. 1058
MMODAL GLOBAL SERVICES PVT. LTD.—See Solventum Corporation; *U.S. Public*, pg. 1902
MMODAL INC.—See Solventum Corporation; *U.S. Public*, pg. 1902
MOAI TECHNOLOGIES INC.; *U.S. Private*, pg. 2756
MOBAOKU CO., LTD.—See DeNA Co., Ltd.; *Int'l*, pg. 2026
MOBI CORP.—See Geotab, Inc.; *U.S. Private*, pg. 2941
MOBIFUSION, INC.; *U.S. Private*, pg. 2756
MOBILEDATAFORCE, INC.; *U.S. Private*, pg. 2757
MOBILESMITH, INC.; *U.S. Public*, pg. 1454
MOBILESTORM, INC.; *U.S. Private*, pg. 2758
MOBILEUM, INC.—See H.I.G. Capital, LLC; *U.S. Private*, pg. 1833
MOBILEYE INC.—See Intel Corporation; *U.S. Public*, pg. 1139
MOBILEYE JAPAN LTD.—See Intel Corporation; *U.S. Public*, pg. 1139
MOBILEYE N.V.—See Intel Corporation; *U.S. Public*, pg. 1139
MOBILEYE VISION TECHNOLOGIES LTD.—See Intel Corporation; *U.S. Public*, pg. 1139
MOBIMEO GMBH—See Deutsche Bahn AG; *Int'l*, pg. 2052
MOBIQUITY, INC.—See EQT AB; *Int'l*, pg. 2470
MOBIUS MANAGEMENT SYSTEMS, AUSTRALIA—See Allen Systems Group, Inc.; *U.S. Private*, pg. 180
MOBIVITY HOLDINGS CORP.; *U.S. Public*, pg. 1454
MOCANA CORPORATION—See Clearlake Capital Group, L.P.; *U.S. Private*, pg. 934
MOCANA CORPORATION—See Crosspoint Capital Partners LP; *U.S. Private*, pg. 1107
MOCANA CORPORATION—See TA Associates, Inc.; *U.S. Private*, pg. 3915
MOCANA SOLUTIONS PRIVATE LIMITED—See Clearlake Capital Group, L.P.; *U.S. Private*, pg. 934
MOCANA SOLUTIONS PRIVATE LIMITED—See Crosspoint Capital Partners LP; *U.S. Private*, pg. 1107
MOCANA SOLUTIONS PRIVATE LIMITED—See TA Associates, Inc.; *U.S. Private*, pg. 3915
MODAXO INC.—See Constellation Software Inc.; *Int'l*, pg. 1775
MODEL N, INC.; *U.S. Public*, pg. 1454
MODERNE COMMUNICATIONS INC.; *U.S. Private*, pg. 2763
MODERNIZING MEDICINE, INC.; *U.S. Private*, pg. 2763
MODFIN SYSTEMS PTY LTD—See HgCapital Trust plc; *Int'l*, pg. 3377
MODULEMD LLC; *U.S. Private*, pg. 2764
MOJANG AB—See Microsoft Corporation; *U.S. Public*, pg. 1440
MOJOTECH—See MojoTech, LLC; *U.S. Public*, pg. 2766
MOJOTECH—See MojoTech, LLC; *U.S. Private*, pg. 2766
MONDEE INC.—See Mondee Holdings, Inc.; *U.S. Public*, pg. 1460
MONDOFARMA S.R.L.—See CompuGroup Medical SE & Co. KGaA; *Int'l*, pg. 1756
MONETRA TECHNOLOGIES, LLC—See i3 Verticals, Inc.; *U.S. Public*, pg. 1081
MONGODB, INC.; *U.S. Public*, pg. 1464
MONITISE LIMITED—See Fiserv, Inc.; *U.S. Public*, pg. 851
MONK DEVELOPMENT, INC.; *U.S. Private*, pg. 2771
MONSTER ARTS, INC.; *U.S. Public*, pg. 1465
MONTAVISTA SOFTWARE JAPAN, INC.—See MontaVista Software LLC; *U.S. Private*, pg. 2775
MONTAVISTA SOFTWARE KOREA LLC—See MontaVista Software LLC; *U.S. Private*, pg. 2775
MONTAVISTA SOFTWARE LLC; *U.S. Private*, pg. 2775
MONTAVO, INC.; *U.S. Private*, pg. 2775
MONTICELLO SOFTWARE, INC.—See Platinum Equity, LLC; *U.S. Private*, pg. 3202
MOODY'S ANALYTICS SINGAPORE PTE LTD.—See Moody's Corporation; *U.S. Public*, pg. 1468
MOPUB, INC.—See AppLovin Corp.; *U.S. Public*, pg. 173
MORTECH, INC.—See Zillow Group, Inc.; *U.S. Public*, pg. 2405
MORTGAGE BUILDER SOFTWARE, INC.—See Constellation Software Inc.; *Int'l*, pg. 1774
MORTGAGE RETURNS, LLC—See Intercontinental Exchange, Inc.; *U.S. Public*, pg. 1142
MOTIONPORTRAIT, INC.—See Axell Corporation; *Int'l*, pg. 767
MOTIVITY SOLUTIONS LLC—See Intercontinental Exchange, Inc.; *U.S. Public*, pg. 1141
MOTIVUS—See AN Global I.T. S.A.P.I. de C.V.; *U.S. Private*, pg. 271
MOTRICITY, INC.—See Voltari Corporation; *U.S. Private*, pg. 4411
MOVELLA HOLDINGS INC.; *U.S. Public*, pg. 1480
MOVISTA INC.; *U.S. Private*, pg. 2802
MOXIWORKS, LLC—See Vector Capital Management, L.P.; *U.S. Private*, pg. 4351
MRI SOFTWARE LIMITED—See GI Manager L.P.; *U.S. Private*, pg. 1693
MRI SOFTWARE, LLC—See GI Manager L.P.; *U.S. Private*, pg. 1693
MSCRIPTS, LLC—See Cardinal Health, Inc.; *U.S. Public*, pg. 434

513210 — SOFTWARE PUBLISHERS

MSC.SOFTWARE BENELUX B.V.—See Hexagon AB; *Int'l*, pg. 3369
MSC.SOFTWARE CORP. - ANN ARBOR—See Hexagon AB; *Int'l*, pg. 3369
MSC SOFTWARE CORPORATION—See Hexagon AB; *Int'l*, pg. 3369
MSC SOFTWARE GMBH—See Hexagon AB; *Int'l*, pg. 3369
MSC.SOFTWARE JAPAN LTD. - OSAKA OFFICE—See Hexagon AB; *Int'l*, pg. 3369
MSC.SOFTWARE JAPAN LTD.—See Hexagon AB; *Int'l*, pg. 3369
MSC.SOFTWARE LTD. - CHENGDU OFFICE—See Hexagon AB; *Int'l*, pg. 3369
MSC.SOFTWARE LTD.—See Hexagon AB; *Int'l*, pg. 3369
MSC.SOFTWARE SARL - SAINT-FONS—See Hexagon AB; *Int'l*, pg. 3369
MSC.SOFTWARE SARL—See Hexagon AB; *Int'l*, pg. 3369
MSC.SOFTWARE SIMULATING REALITY S.A.—See Hexagon AB; *Int'l*, pg. 3369
MSC.SOFTWARE S.R.L.—See Hexagon AB; *Int'l*, pg. 3369
MSI ENGINEERING SOFTWARE LTD.—See Hexagon AB; *Int'l*, pg. 3369
MS PORTUGAL—See Microsoft Corporation; *U.S. Public*, pg. 1439
MTELLIGENCE CORPORATION—See Emerson Electric Co.; *U.S. Public*, pg. 742
MTI SYSTEMS INC.; *U.S. Private*, pg. 2809
MULESOFT ARGENTINA—See Salesforce, Inc.; *U.S. Public*, pg. 1837
MULESOFT AUSTRALIA—See Salesforce, Inc.; *U.S. Public*, pg. 1837
MULESOFT INC.—See Salesforce, Inc.; *U.S. Public*, pg. 1837
MULTI-SYSTEMS INC.—See Constellation Software Inc.; *Int'l*, pg. 1773
MULTIVIEW INC.—See Stagwell, Inc.; *U.S. Public*, pg. 1928
MUSEGLOBAL, INC.; *U.S. Private*, pg. 2817
MY G SAS—See Devoteam SA; *Int'l*, pg. 2090
MYOB ASIA SDN BHD—See Bain Capital, LP; *U.S. Private*, pg. 442
MYOB AUSTRALIA PTY LTD—See Bain Capital, LP; *U.S. Private*, pg. 442
MYOB GROUP LIMITED—See KKR & Co. Inc.; *U.S. Public*, pg. 1259
MYOB LIMITED—See Bain Capital, LP; *U.S. Private*, pg. 441
MYOB SINGAPORE PTE LIMITED—See Bain Capital, LP; *U.S. Private*, pg. 442
MYRIAD MOBILE LLC; *U.S. Private*, pg. 2825
MYSQL AB—See Oracle Corporation; *U.S. Public*, pg. 1611
MY-VILLAGES, INC.; *U.S. Private*, pg. 2823
MZINGA, INC.; *U.S. Private*, pg. 2826
MZINGA—See Mzinga, Inc.; *U.S. Private*, pg. 2826
N-ABLE, INC.; *U.S. Public*, pg. 1489
NAMELY, INC.; *U.S. Private*, pg. 2832
NANIGANS, INC.; *U.S. Private*, pg. 2833
NANOTECH ENTERTAINMENT, INC.; *U.S. Public*, pg. 1490
NATIONAL INSTRUMENTS AUSTRALIA CORPORATION—See National Instruments Corporation; *U.S. Private*, pg. 2857
NATIONAL INSTRUMENTS BELGIUM N.V.—See National Instruments Corporation; *U.S. Private*, pg. 2857
NATIONAL INSTRUMENTS INSTRUMENTACIJA, AVTOMATIZACIJA IN UPRAVLJANJE PROCESOV D.O.O.—See National Instruments Corporation; *U.S. Private*, pg. 2857
NATIONAL INSTRUMENTS SWITZERLAND CORPORATION—See National Instruments Corporation; *U.S. Private*, pg. 2857
NATURALMOTION LIMITED—See Zynga Inc.; *U.S. Private*, pg. 4611
NAVBLUE—See Airbus SE; *Int'l*, pg. 247
NAVBLUE UK—See Airbus SE; *Int'l*, pg. 247
NAVICURE, INC.—See Canada Pension Plan Investment Board; *Int'l*, pg. 1282
NAVICURE, INC.—See EQT AB; *Int'l*, pg. 2481
NAVIGA INC.—See Vista Equity Partners, LLC; *U.S. Private*, pg. 4398
NAVISYS, INC.—See Accenture plc; *Int'l*, pg. 86
NAYA P.A.I.TECHNOLOGIES LTD.—See EPAM Systems, Inc.; *U.S. Public*, pg. 783
NC4 PUBLIC SECTOR, LLC—See Thoma Bravo, L.P.; *U.S. Private*, pg. 4147
NCM FINANCIAL, INC.; *U.S. Private*, pg. 2876
NDS.TS CO., LTD.—See COMSYS Holdings Corporation; *Int'l*, pg. 1762
NEDGRAPHICS B.V.—See Cadac Group Holding B.V.; *Int'l*, pg. 1247
NEDGRAPHICS, INC.—See Constellation Software Inc.; *Int'l*, pg. 1773
NEDSENSE NEDGRAPHICS B.V.—See Constellation Software Inc.; *Int'l*, pg. 1773
NEEDLE, INC.—See The Stage Fund, LLC; *U.S. Private*, pg. 4120
NELNET TECHNOLOGY SERVICES LLC—See Nelnet, Inc.; *U.S. Public*, pg. 1504
NEOLANE, INC.—See Adobe Inc.; *U.S. Public*, pg. 43
NEOLANE NORDIC—See Adobe Inc.; *U.S. Public*, pg. 43
NEOLANE S.A.—See Adobe Inc.; *U.S. Public*, pg. 42
NEOMEDIA EUROPE AG—See NeoMedia Technologies, Inc.; *U.S. Public*, pg. 1506
NEONET AB—See Hay Tor Capital LLP; *Int'l*, pg. 3289
NEON ONE LLC; *U.S. Private*, pg. 2885
NET ATLANTIC, INC.; *U.S. Private*, pg. 2886
NETBASE SOLUTIONS, INC.; *U.S. Private*, pg. 2887
NETBRIEFINGS, INC.; *U.S. Private*, pg. 2887
NETCOM3 INC.; *U.S. Private*, pg. 2887
NETDIRECTOR; *U.S. Private*, pg. 2887
NETFABB GMBH—See Autodesk, Inc.; *U.S. Public*, pg. 229
NETFACILITIES, INC.—See GI Manager L.P.; *U.S. Private*, pg. 1693
NETMAP ANALYTICS—See Verisk Analytics, Inc.; *U.S. Public*, pg. 2283
NET MEDICAL XPRESS SOLUTIONS, INC.; *U.S. Public*, pg. 1506
NETMOTION SOFTWARE, INC.—See Crosspoint Capital Partners LP; *U.S. Private*, pg. 1107
NETMOTION WIRELESS GMBH—See Crosspoint Capital Partners LP; *U.S. Private*, pg. 1107
NETMOTION WIRELESS, LTD.—See Crosspoint Capital Partners LP; *U.S. Private*, pg. 1107
NETSMART TECHNOLOGIES, INC. - MISSOURI—See GI Manager L.P.; *U.S. Private*, pg. 1693
NETSMART TECHNOLOGIES, INC. - MISSOURI—See TA Associates, Inc.; *U.S. Private*, pg. 3916
NETSMART TECHNOLOGIES, INC.—See GI Manager L.P.; *U.S. Private*, pg. 1693
NETSMART TECHNOLOGIES, INC.—See TA Associates, Inc.; *U.S. Private*, pg. 3916
NETSOL-ABRAXAS AUSTRALIA PTY LTD—See NetSol Technologies, Inc.; *U.S. Public*, pg. 1509
NETSOL TECHNOLOGIES, INC.; *U.S. Public*, pg. 1509
NETSUITE AUSTRALIA PTY. LTD.—See Oracle Corporation; *U.S. Public*, pg. 1611
NETSUITE INC.—See Oracle Corporation; *U.S. Public*, pg. 1611
NETSUITE PHILIPPINES INC.—See Oracle Corporation; *U.S. Public*, pg. 1611
NETWORK SYSTEMS INTERNATIONAL, INC.; *U.S. Private*, pg. 2889
NEURODIMENSION, INC.; *U.S. Private*, pg. 2890
NEUROPATHIX, INC.; *U.S. Public*, pg. 1510
NEVERFAIL GROUP LTD.—See Artisan Infrastructure Inc.; *U.S. Private*, pg. 343
NEVERFAIL, INC.—See Schurz Communications, Inc.; *U.S. Private*, pg. 3571
NEVERSOFT ENTERTAINMENT, INC—See Microsoft Corporation; *U.S. Public*, pg. 1439
NEW CENTURY SOFTWARE, INC.—See Mistras Group, Inc.; *U.S. Public*, pg. 1451
NEWFORMA, INC.—See Ethos Capital, LLC; *U.S. Private*, pg. 1432
NEW GENERATION COMPUTING—See American Software, Inc.; *U.S. Public*, pg. 109
NEWLEADS, INC.; *U.S. Private*, pg. 2915
NEWMARKET INTERNATIONAL, INC. - MTECH DIVISION—See Amadeus IT Group, S.A.; *Int'l*, pg. 406
NEWMARKET INTERNATIONAL, INC.—See Amadeus IT Group, S.A.; *Int'l*, pg. 406
NEWMARKET INTERNATIONAL SOFTWARE (SHANGHAI) CO., LTD.—See Amadeus IT Group, S.A.; *Int'l*, pg. 406
NEW RELIC, INC.—See Francisco Partners Management, LP; *U.S. Private*, pg. 1590
NEW RELIC, INC.—See TPG Capital, L.P.; *U.S. Public*, pg. 2175
NEWSCYCLE SOLUTIONS AB—See Vista Equity Partners, LLC; *U.S. Private*, pg. 4399
NEWSCYCLE SOLUTIONS AMERICAS, LLC—See Vista Equity Partners, LLC; *U.S. Private*, pg. 4399
NEWSCYCLE SOLUTIONS A/S—See Vista Equity Partners, LLC; *U.S. Private*, pg. 4399
NEWSCYCLE SOLUTIONS AS—See Vista Equity Partners, LLC; *U.S. Private*, pg. 4399
NEWSCYCLE SOLUTIONS—See Vista Equity Partners, LLC; *U.S. Private*, pg. 4399
NEWSGATOR TECHNOLOGIES, INC.; *U.S. Private*, pg. 2917
NEWSGATOR TECHNOLOGIES—See NewsGator Technologies, Inc.; *U.S. Private*, pg. 2917
NEWSGATOR TECHNOLOGIES—See NewsGator Technologies, Inc.; *U.S. Private*, pg. 2917
NEWSGATOR TECHNOLOGIES—See NewsGator Technologies, Inc.; *U.S. Private*, pg. 2917
NEWSGATOR TECHNOLOGIES—See NewsGator Technologies, Inc.; *U.S. Private*, pg. 2917
NEWSGATOR TECHNOLOGIES—See NewsGator Technologies, Inc.; *U.S. Private*, pg. 2917
NEXGENIX, INC.; *U.S. Private*, pg. 2919
NEXTERNAL SOLUTIONS INC.—See Accellos, Inc.; *U.S. Private*, pg. 50
NEXT GEAR SOLUTIONS, LLC—See Insight Venture Management, LLC; *U.S. Private*, pg. 2089
NEXT GEAR SOLUTIONS, LLC—See Stone Point Capital LLC; *U.S. Private*, pg. 3823
NEXTGEN HEALTHCARE INFORMATION SYSTEMS, LLC - ATLANTA—See Thoma Bravo, L.P.; *U.S. Private*, pg. 4150
NEXTGEN HEALTHCARE INFORMATION SYSTEMS, LLC—See Thoma Bravo, L.P.; *U.S. Private*, pg. 4150
NEXTOPIA SOFTWARE CORPORATION—See Scaleworks, Inc.; *U.S. Private*, pg. 3561
NEXTSOURCE INC.—See Asseco Poland S.A.; *Int'l*, pg. 642
NEXTTRIP, INC.—See NextTrip Holdings, Inc.; *U.S. Public*, pg. 2921
NGMOCO INC.—See DeNA Co., Ltd.; *Int'l*, pg. 2026
NGP VAN, INC.; *U.S. Private*, pg. 2924
NIANDC SOFT INC.—See International Business Machines Corporation; *U.S. Public*, pg. 1147
NIANTIC, INC.; *U.S. Private*, pg. 2924
NICE-BUSINESS SOLUTIONS - BRIGHTON—See Fujitsu Limited; *Int'l*, pg. 2837
NIHON SYNOPSYS G.K.—See Synopsys, Inc.; *U.S. Public*, pg. 1970
NIHON SYNOPSYS GK—See Synopsys, Inc.; *U.S. Public*, pg. 1971
NIK SOFTWARE GMBH—See Alphabet Inc.; *U.S. Public*, pg. 83
NIK SOFTWARE, INC.—See Alphabet Inc.; *U.S. Public*, pg. 83
NIMBO INC.—See Equinix, Inc.; *U.S. Public*, pg. 788
NIRVANIX, INC.; *U.S. Private*, pg. 2928
NI SOLUTIONS (PROPRIETARY) LIMITED—See National Instruments Corporation; *U.S. Private*, pg. 2857
NITRO MOBILE SOLUTIONS LLC; *U.S. Private*, pg. 2929
NITRO SOFTWARE, INC.; *U.S. Private*, pg. 2929
NLP LOGIX, LLC; *U.S. Private*, pg. 2931
NLYTE SOFTWARE AMERICAS LIMITED; *U.S. Private*, pg. 2931
NLYTE SOFTWARE LIMITED—See Carrier Global Corporation; *U.S. Public*, pg. 440
NOETIX CORPORATION—See TA Associates, Inc.; *U.S. Private*, pg. 3916
NONPROFITEASY, INC.; *U.S. Private*, pg. 2934
NORMAN ASA—See FSN Capital Partners AS; *Int'l*, pg. 2799
NORTHGATEARINSO BRAZIL INFORMATICA LTDA.—See Alight, Inc.; *U.S. Public*, pg. 77
NOTABLE SOLUTIONS, INC.—See Microsoft Corporation; *U.S. Public*, pg. 1442
NOTEVAULT, INC.—See Bentley Systems, Inc.; *U.S. Public*, pg. 297
NOTION ONE, LLC—See DVHP Inc.; *U.S. Private*, pg. 1295
NOVATEL WIRELESS TECHNOLOGIES, LTD.—See Inseego Corp.; *U.S. Public*, pg. 1129
NOVATIME TECHNOLOGY, INC.—See Hellman & Friedman LLC; *U.S. Private*, pg. 1910
NOVEDA TECHNOLOGIES, INC.; *U.S. Private*, pg. 2967
NOVII PTY. LTD.—See News Corporation; *U.S. Public*, pg. 1519
NOVITECH TECHNOLOGIA E SERVICOS LTDA.—See Microsoft Corporation; *U.S. Public*, pg. 1442
NSI EUROPE GMBH—See Microsoft Corporation; *U.S. Public*, pg. 1442
NSI TECHNOLOGIES, LLC—See Premier Oilfield Laboratories LLC; *U.S. Public*, pg. 3250
NTELX, INC.; *U.S. Private*, pg. 2970
NUANCE COMMUNICATIONS HUNGARY KFT—See Microsoft Corporation; *U.S. Public*, pg. 1442
NUANCE COMMUNICATIONS INTERNATIONAL BVBA—See Microsoft Corporation; *U.S. Public*, pg. 1442
NUANCE COMMUNICATIONS ISRAEL, LTD.—See Microsoft Corporation; *U.S. Public*, pg. 1442
NUANCE COMMUNICATONS HONG KONG LIMITED—See Microsoft Corporation; *U.S. Public*, pg. 1442
NUANCE DICTAPHONE HEALTHCARE SOLUTIONS—See Microsoft Corporation; *U.S. Public*, pg. 1442
NUANCE ENTERPRISE SOLUTIONS & SERVICES CORPORATION—See Microsoft Corporation; *U.S. Public*, pg. 1443
NUANCE FRANCE—See Microsoft Corporation; *U.S. Public*, pg. 1443
NUANCE JAPAN K.K.—See Microsoft Corporation; *U.S. Public*, pg. 1443
NUANCE RECOGNITA CORP.—See Microsoft Corporation; *U.S. Public*, pg. 1443
NUESOFT TECHNOLOGIES, INC.—See Global Payments Inc.; *U.S. Public*, pg. 943
NUMBERFIRE, INC.—See Flutter Entertainment plc; *Int'l*, pg. 2715
NUMECENT HOLDINGS LTD.; *U.S. Private*, pg. 2973
NUMERICAL APPLICATIONS, INC.—See Zachry Holdings, Inc.; *U.S. Private*, pg. 4596
NUSPHERE CORPORATION—See Progress Software Corporation; *U.S. Public*, pg. 1725
NUTSHELL, INC.—See Web FX Inc.; *U.S. Private*, pg. 4463
NUWAVE SOLUTIONS LLC—See AE Industrial Partners, LP; *U.S. Private*, pg. 112
NUXEO—See The Goldman Sachs Group, Inc.; *U.S. Public*, pg. 2080
NXTBOOK MEDIA, LLC; *U.S. Private*, pg. 2976
NXTSOFT LLC; *U.S. Private*, pg. 2976
NYX GAMING GROUP LLC—See Light & Wonder, Inc.; *U.S. Public*, pg. 1314
OAKLEAF SOFTWARE, INC.; *U.S. Private*, pg. 2985

513210 — SOFTWARE PUBLISHERS

OAKTREE ENTERPRISE SOLUTIONS, INC.; *U.S. Private,* pg. 2985
OATES & COMPANY, LLC.—See QXO, Inc.; *U.S. Public,* pg. 1758
OBERON MEDIA, INC.; *U.S. Private,* pg. 2987
OBJECTIVA CHINA—See Allgeier SE; *Int'l,* pg. 337
OCEANHOUSE MEDIA, INC.; *U.S. Private,* pg. 2990
OCEANWIDE INC.—See GI Manager L.P.; *U.S. Private,* pg. 1692
OCTO TECHNOLOGY PTY. LTD.—See Accenture plc; *Int'l,* pg. 87
OCTO TECHNOLOGY SA—See Accenture plc; *Int'l,* pg. 87
ODDCAST, INC.; *U.S. Private,* pg. 2993
ODYSSEY INTERACTIVE LIMITED—See Hasgrove plc; *Int'l,* pg. 3283
ODYSSEYWARE—See Silver Lake Group, LLC; *U.S. Private,* pg. 3661
OGSYSTEMS LLC—See Parsons Corporation; *U.S. Public,* pg. 1651
THE OLB GROUP, INC.; *U.S. Public,* pg. 2118
OLIVE SOFTWARE, INC.—See ESW Capital, LLC; *U.S. Private,* pg. 1430
OMEDA COMMUNICATIONS, INC.; *U.S. Private,* pg. 3015
OMEGA LEGAL SYSTEMS, INC.; *U.S. Private,* pg. 3015
OMEGA VISION 2000 S.A.—See Hexagon AB; *Int'l,* pg. 3369
OMNICOMM SYSTEMS, INC.—See ABRY Partners, LLC; *U.S. Private,* pg. 41
OMNIQ CORP.; *U.S. Public,* pg. 1600
OMTOOL, LTD.—See Upland Software, Inc.; *U.S. Public,* pg. 2264
ONCONTACT SOFTWARE CORP.—See WorkWise, LLC; *U.S. Private,* pg. 4564
ONEADVANCED, INC.—See HgCapital Trust plc; *Int'l,* pg. 3377
ONELOGIN, INC.; *U.S. Private,* pg. 3025
ONEMETA, INC.; *U.S. Private,* pg. 1602
ONESHIELD, INC.; *U.S. Private,* pg. 3025
ONESTOP INTERNET, INC.; *U.S. Private,* pg. 3025
ONETRUST LLC; *U.S. Private,* pg. 3026
ONETRUST TECHNOLOGY LIMITED—See OneTrust LLC; *U.S. Private,* pg. 3026
ONE WORLD PRODUCTS, INC.; *U.S. Public,* pg. 1602
ONSET TECHNOLOGY INC.—See Cukierman & Co. Investment House Ltd.; *Int'l,* pg. 1876
ONTARIO SYSTEMS, LLC—See New Mountain Capital, LLC; *U.S. Private,* pg. 2903
ONTRAPORT; *U.S. Private,* pg. 3028
OOMA, INC.; *U.S. Public,* pg. 1605
OOO AUDATEX—See Vista Equity Partners, LLC; *U.S. Private,* pg. 4401
OOO MSC.SOFTWARE RUS—See Hexagon AB; *Int'l,* pg. 3369
OPENALPR SOFTWARE SOLUTIONS, LLC—See Rekor Systems, Inc.; *U.S. Public,* pg. 1778
OPENBET RETAIL LTD—See Silver Lake Group, LLC; *U.S. Private,* pg. 3654
OPENBET TECHNOLOGIES LTD.—See Silver Lake Group, LLC; *U.S. Private,* pg. 3654
OPENEDGE PAYMENTS LLC—See Global Payments Inc.; *U.S. Public,* pg. 944
OPENEDGE - PLEASANT GROVE—See Global Payments Inc.; *U.S. Public,* pg. 944
OPENET JAPAN—See Amdocs Limited; *Int'l,* pg. 420
OPENET TELECOM, INC.—See Amdocs Limited; *Int'l,* pg. 420
OPENET TELECOM MALAYSIA SDN BHD.—See Amdocs Limited; *Int'l,* pg. 420
OPENGOV, INC.—See Cox Enterprises, Inc.; *U.S. Private,* pg. 1078
OPEN OPTIONS L.P.—See ACRE, LLC; *U.S. Private,* pg. 65
OPENSPAN, INC.—See Pegasystems Inc.; *U.S. Public,* pg. 1660
OPEN SYSTEMS, INC.; *U.S. Private,* pg. 3029
OPENTABLE, INC.—See Booking Holdings, Inc.; *U.S. Public,* pg. 368
OPEN TECHNOLOGIES SRL—See FARO Technologies, Inc.; *U.S. Public,* pg. 823
OPERATIVE MEDIA, INC.—See Francisco Partners Management, LP; *U.S. Private,* pg. 1591
OPINIONLAB INC.—See Verint Systems Inc.; *U.S. Public,* pg. 2281
OPINIONMETER INC.—See PeriscopeIQ, Inc.; *U.S. Private,* pg. 3151
OPSCODE, INC.; *U.S. Private,* pg. 3033
OPSTECHNOLOGY, INC.—See Thoma Bravo, L.P.; *U.S. Private,* pg. 4153
OPSWAT, INC.; *U.S. Private,* pg. 3034
OPTAROS, INC.—See The Interpublic Group of Companies, Inc.; *U.S. Public,* pg. 2099
OPTICAL SOLUTIONS GROUP—See Synopsys, Inc.; *U.S. Public,* pg. 1970
OPTIFY, INC.; *U.S. Private,* pg. 3034
OPTILEAF, INC.; *U.S. Private,* pg. 3034
OPTIMA HEALTHCARE SOLUTIONS, LLC—See Level Equity Management, LLC; *U.S. Private,* pg. 2434
OPTIMA HEALTHCARE SOLUTIONS, LLC—See Silversmith Management, L.P.; *U.S. Private,* pg. 3664
OPTIMA HEALTHCARE SOLUTIONS, LLC—See The Carlyle Group Inc.; *U.S. Public,* pg. 2050
OPTIMAL IDM, LLC; *U.S. Private,* pg. 3034
OPTIMED SOFTWARE CORPORATION—See George Weston Limited; *Int'l,* pg. 2939
OPTIMUM SOLUTIONS INC.—See Hellman & Friedman LLC; *U.S. Private,* pg. 1911
OPTIONSCITY SOFTWARE, INC.—See Marlin Equity Partners, LLC; *U.S. Private,* pg. 2584
OPTIS NORTH AMERICA INC.—See ANSYS, Inc.; *U.S. Public,* pg. 139
OPTI-TIME -GEOCONCEPT GROUP—See GeoConcept SA; *Int'l,* pg. 2933
OPTUM360, LLC—See UnitedHealth Group Incorporated; *U.S. Public,* pg. 2247
ORACLE AUSTRIA GMBH—See Oracle Corporation; *U.S. Public,* pg. 1612
ORACLE CARIBBEAN, INC.—See Oracle Corporation; *U.S. Public,* pg. 1611
ORACLE CORPORATION; *U.S. Public,* pg. 1610
ORACLE FINANCIAL SERVICES SOFTWARE B.V.—See Oracle Corporation; *U.S. Public,* pg. 1613
ORACLE FINANCIAL SERVICES SOFTWARE B.V.—See Oracle Corporation; *U.S. Public,* pg. 1613
ORACLE FINANCIAL SERVICES SOFTWARE, INC-MINNEAPOLIS—See Oracle Corporation; *U.S. Public,* pg. 1613
ORACLE FINANCIAL SERVICES SOFTWARE, INC.—See Oracle Corporation; *U.S. Public,* pg. 1613
ORACLE FINANCIAL SERVICES SOFTWARE LIMITED—See Oracle Corporation; *U.S. Public,* pg. 1612
ORACLE FINANCIAL SERVICES SOFTWARE PTE. LTD.—See Oracle Corporation; *U.S. Public,* pg. 1612
ORACLE FINANCIAL SERVICES SOFTWARE S.A.—See Oracle Corporation; *U.S. Public,* pg. 1613
ORACLE HOSPITALITY—See Oracle Corporation; *U.S. Public,* pg. 1613
ORACLE (OFSS) BPO SERVICES INC.—See Oracle Corporation; *U.S. Public,* pg. 1612
ORACLE (OFSS) BPO SERVICES LIMITED—See Oracle Corporation; *U.S. Public,* pg. 1612
ORACLE SVENSKA AB—See Oracle Corporation; *U.S. Public,* pg. 1613
ORACLE TECHNOLOGY COMPANY—See Oracle Corporation; *U.S. Public,* pg. 1613
ORAD HI-TEC SYSTEMS POLAND SP. Z.O.O.—See Symphony Technology Group, LLC; *U.S. Private,* pg. 3901
ORBITA, INC.; *U.S. Private,* pg. 3038
ORBIT LOGIC, INC.—See Enlightenment Capital LLC; *U.S. Private,* pg. 1400
ORC AUSTRALIA PTY LTD.—See Broadridge Financial Solutions, Inc.; *U.S. Public,* pg. 392
ORC EDUCATION AB—See Broadridge Financial Solutions, Inc.; *U.S. Public,* pg. 392
ORC EXNET TRANSACTION SERVICES AB—See Broadridge Financial Solutions, Inc.; *U.S. Public,* pg. 392
ORC GROUP AB—See Broadridge Financial Solutions, Inc.; *U.S. Public,* pg. 392
ORC ITALY S.R.L.—See Broadridge Financial Solutions, Inc.; *U.S. Public,* pg. 392
ORC NETHERLANDS B.V.—See Broadridge Financial Solutions, Inc.; *U.S. Public,* pg. 392
ORC SOFTWARE GMBH—See Broadridge Financial Solutions, Inc.; *U.S. Public,* pg. 392
ORC SOFTWARE GMBH—See Broadridge Financial Solutions, Inc.; *U.S. Public,* pg. 392
ORC SOFTWARE HK LTD.—See Broadridge Financial Solutions, Inc.; *U.S. Public,* pg. 392
ORC SOFTWARE LTD.—See Broadridge Financial Solutions, Inc.; *U.S. Public,* pg. 392
ORC SOFTWARE STOCKHOLM AB—See Broadridge Financial Solutions, Inc.; *U.S. Public,* pg. 392
ORC USA INC.—See Broadridge Financial Solutions, Inc.; *U.S. Public,* pg. 392
ORCUS TECHNOLOGIES, INC; *U.S. Private,* pg. 3039
ORECX LLC—See CallMiner, Inc.; *U.S. Public,* pg. 722
ORIGINAL1 GMBH—See Giesecke & Devrient GmbH; *Int'l,* pg. 2970
ORIGIN DIGITAL, INC.—See Accenture plc; *Int'l,* pg. 86
OSISOFT, LLC; *U.S. Public,* pg. 3047
OTTR, INC.—See CareDx, Inc.; *U.S. Public,* pg. 435
OUTMATCH INC.—See Rubicon Technology Partners, LLC; *U.S. Private,* pg. 3499
OUTRIGHT, INC.—See KKR & Co. Inc.; *U.S. Public,* pg. 1252
OUTRIGHT, INC.—See Silver Lake Group, LLC; *U.S. Private,* pg. 3657
OUTRIGHT, INC.—See TCMI, Inc.; *U.S. Private,* pg. 3943
OUTSELL, LLC; *U.S. Private,* pg. 3051
OVERWATCH SYSTEMS, LTD.—See Textron Inc.; *U.S. Public,* pg. 2028
OWL COMPUTER SL—See CompuGroup Medical SE & Co. KGaA; *Int'l,* pg. 1757
OWNLOCAL, INC.; *U.S. Private,* pg. 3055
OXAGILE LLC; *U.S. Private,* pg. 3056
OXAGILE US—See Oxagile LLC; *U.S. Private,* pg. 3056
OXCYON, INC.; *U.S. Private,* pg. 3056

P2 ENERGY SOLUTIONS, INC. - LIVINGSTON—See Advent International Corporation; *U.S. Private,* pg. 105
P2 ENERGY SOLUTIONS, INC.—See Advent International Corporation; *U.S. Private,* pg. 105
P2 ENERGY SOLUTIONS PTY LTD—See Advent International Corporation; *U.S. Private,* pg. 105
PACIFIC DIGITAL USA CORPORATION, INC.; *U.S. Private,* pg. 3067
PACIOLAN, INC.—See Comcast Corporation; *U.S. Public,* pg. 537
PAGEFLEX INC.; *U.S. Private,* pg. 3075
PAGEPATH TECHNOLOGIES, INC.—See Print Reach, Inc.; *U.S. Private,* pg. 3265
PALO ALTO NETWORKS DENMARK APS—See Palo Alto Networks, Inc.; *U.S. Public,* pg. 1635
PALO ALTO NETWORKS (EU) B.V.—See Palo Alto Networks, Inc.; *U.S. Public,* pg. 1635
PALO ALTO NETWORKS, INC.; *U.S. Public,* pg. 1635
PALO ALTO NETWORKS (ISRAEL ANALYTICS) LTD.—See Palo Alto Networks, Inc.; *U.S. Public,* pg. 1635
PALO ALTO NETWORKS SAUDI ARABIAN LIMITED COMPANY—See Palo Alto Networks, Inc.; *U.S. Public,* pg. 1635
PANDA SECURITY, INC.—See Francisco Partners Management, LP; *U.S. Private,* pg. 1593
PANDA SECURITY S.L.—See Francisco Partners Management, LP; *U.S. Private,* pg. 1593
PANLAB S.L.—See Harvard Bioscience, Inc.; *U.S. Public,* pg. 987
PANOPTO, INC.—See K1 Investment Management, LLC; *U.S. Private,* pg. 2252
PANTERO CORPORATION—See Progress Software Corporation; *U.S. Public,* pg. 1725
PANTERRA NETWORKS INC.; *U.S. Private,* pg. 3087
PANZURA, INC.; *U.S. Private,* pg. 3087
PAPERLESS BUSINESS SYSTEMS, INC.; *U.S. Private,* pg. 3088
PARADIGM FZ-LLC—See Apax Partners LLP; *Int'l,* pg. 505
PARADIGM FZ-LLC—See JMI Services, Inc.; *U.S. Private,* pg. 2216
PARADIGM GEOPHYSICAL CANADA LIMITED—See Apax Partners LLP; *Int'l,* pg. 505
PARADIGM GEOPHYSICAL CANADA LIMITED—See JMI Services, Inc.; *U.S. Private,* pg. 2216
PARADIGM GEOPHYSICAL CORP.—See Apax Partners LLP; *Int'l,* pg. 505
PARADIGM GEOPHYSICAL CORP.—See JMI Services, Inc.; *U.S. Private,* pg. 2216
PARADIGM GEOPHYSICAL LLC—See Apax Partners LLP; *Int'l,* pg. 505
PARADIGM GEOPHYSICAL LLC—See JMI Services, Inc.; *U.S. Private,* pg. 2216
PARADIGM GEOPHYSICAL S.A.—See Apax Partners LLP; *Int'l,* pg. 505
PARADIGM GEOPHYSICAL S.A.—See JMI Services, Inc.; *U.S. Private,* pg. 2216
PARADIGM GEOPHYSICAL SDN BHD—See Apax Partners LLP; *Int'l,* pg. 505
PARADIGM GEOPHYSICAL SDN BHD—See JMI Services, Inc.; *U.S. Private,* pg. 2216
PARADIGM GEOPHYSICAL (UK) LIMITED—See Apax Partners LLP; *Int'l,* pg. 505
PARADIGM GEOPHYSICAL (UK) LIMITED—See JMI Services, Inc.; *U.S. Private,* pg. 2216
PARADIGM TECHNOLOGY (BEIJING) CO., LTD.—See Apax Partners LLP; *Int'l,* pg. 505
PARADIGM TECHNOLOGY (BEIJING) CO., LTD.—See JMI Services, Inc.; *U.S. Private,* pg. 2216
PARALLEL 6, INC.—See ICON plc; *Int'l,* pg. 3585
PARALLELS, INC.—See KKR & Co. Inc.; *U.S. Public,* pg. 1243
PARAMETRIC TECHNOLOGY ESPANA, S.A.—See PTC Inc.; *U.S. Public,* pg. 1735
PARAMETRIC TECHNOLOGY (INDIA) PRIVATE LTD.—See PTC Inc.; *U.S. Public,* pg. 1734
PARAMETRIC TECHNOLOGY ISRAEL LTD.—See PTC Inc.; *U.S. Public,* pg. 1735
PARAMETRIC TECHNOLOGY SINGAPORE PTE. LTD.—See PTC Inc.; *U.S. Public,* pg. 1735
PARAMOUNT TECHNOLOGIES, INC.—See PaperSave; *U.S. Private,* pg. 3088
PARASCRIPT LLC; *U.S. Private,* pg. 3093
PARCHMENT LLC—See KKR & Co. Inc.; *U.S. Public,* pg. 1253
PARDOT EMEA—See Salesforce, Inc.; *U.S. Public,* pg. 1837
PARDOT LLC—See Salesforce, Inc.; *U.S. Public,* pg. 1837
PARDOT NORDIC—See Salesforce, Inc.; *U.S. Public,* pg. 1837
PARETEUM CORPORATION; *U.S. Public,* pg. 1637
PARKING PANDA CORP.—See SpotHero, Inc.; *U.S. Private,* pg. 3761
PASSLOGIX, INC.—See Oracle Corporation; *U.S. Public,* pg. 1613
PASSUR AEROSPACE, INC.; *U.S. Public,* pg. 1651
PATHABLE, INC.—See Insight Venture Management, LLC; *U.S. Private,* pg. 2088
PATHLOCK, INC.; *U.S. Private,* pg. 3106

N.A.I.C.S. INDEX

513210 — SOFTWARE PUBLISHERS

PATIENTSLIKEME, LLC—See UnitedHealth Group Incorporated; *U.S. Public*, pg. 2249
PAYCOM SOFTWARE, INC.—See Welsh, Carson, Anderson & Stowe; *U.S. Private*, pg. 4480
PAYTRONIX SYSTEMS, INC.—See Access Technology Group Limited; *Int'l*, pg. 89
PCC TECHNOLOGY GROUP, LLC—See Government Contracting Resources, Inc.; *U.S. Private*, pg. 1746
PCI LLC; *U.S. Private*, pg. 3120
PDF SOLUTIONS KK—See PDF Solutions, Inc.; *U.S. Public*, pg. 1658
PEAK-CATALYST—See Sole Source Capital LLC; *U.S. Private*, pg. 3708
PEARCE RENEWABLES LLC—See Willcrest Partners; *U.S. Private*, pg. 4521
PEERFORM, INC.—See Versara Lending LLC; *U.S. Private*, pg. 4369
PEERLOGIX, INC.; *U.S. Private*, pg. 3129
PEGA JAPAN K.K.—See Pegasystems Inc.; *U.S. Public*, pg. 1660
PEGASUS IMAGING CORPORATION; *U.S. Private*, pg. 3129
PEGASYSTEMS AG—See Pegasystems Inc.; *U.S. Public*, pg. 1660
PEGASYSTEMS BILGI TEKNOLOJILERI ANONIM SIRKETI—See Pegasystems Inc.; *U.S. Public*, pg. 1661
PEGASYSTEMS B.V.—See Pegasystems Inc.; *U.S. Public*, pg. 1660
PEGASYSTEMS CANADA INC.—See Pegasystems Inc.; *U.S. Public*, pg. 1661
PEGASYSTEMS FRANCE, S.A.R.L.—See Pegasystems Inc.; *U.S. Public*, pg. 1661
PEGASYSTEMS GMBH—See Pegasystems Inc.; *U.S. Public*, pg. 1661
PEGASYSTEMS INC.; *U.S. Public*, pg. 1660
PEGASYSTEMS JAPAN K.K.—See Pegasystems Inc.; *U.S. Public*, pg. 1661
PEGASYSTEMS LIMITED—See Pegasystems Inc.; *U.S. Public*, pg. 1661
PEGASYSTEMS PRIVATE LIMITED—See Pegasystems Inc.; *U.S. Public*, pg. 1661
PEGASYSTEMS PROPRIETARY LIMITED—See Pegasystems Inc.; *U.S. Public*, pg. 1661
PEGASYSTEMS SPAIN, S.L.—See Pegasystems Inc.; *U.S. Public*, pg. 1661
PEGASYSTEMS SP. ZOO—See Pegasystems Inc.; *U.S. Public*, pg. 1661
PEGASYSTEMS THAILAND LIMITED—See Pegasystems Inc.; *U.S. Public*, pg. 1661
PEGASYSTEMS WORLDWIDE INC.—See Pegasystems Inc.; *U.S. Public*, pg. 1661
PEGASYSTEMS WORLDWIDE INDIA PRIVATE LIMITED—See Pegasystems Inc.; *U.S. Public*, pg. 1661
PELESYS LEARNING SYSTEMS INC.—See CAE Inc.; *Int'l*, pg. 1249
PENNEXX FOODS, INC.; *U.S. Public*, pg. 1663
PENTAFOUR SOLUTIONS, LLC; *U.S. Private*, pg. 3139
PENTAHO CORPORATION—See Hitachi, Ltd.; *Int'l*, pg. 3414
PENTAHO UK—See Hitachi, Ltd.; *Int'l*, pg. 3414
PEOPLEDOC, INCORPORATED—See Hellman & Friedman LLC; *U.S. Private*, pg. 1911
PERCEPTRONICS SOLUTIONS, INC.; *U.S. Private*, pg. 3146
PERCEPTRONICS SOLUTIONS, INC.—See Perceptronics Solutions, Inc.; *U.S. Private*, pg. 3146
PERCEPTRONICS SOLUTIONS, INC.—See Perceptronics Solutions, Inc.; *U.S. Private*, pg. 3146
PERCOLATE INDUSTRIES, INC.—See Seismic Software, Inc.; *U.S. Private*, pg. 3600
PERCUSSION SOFTWARE INC.; *U.S. Private*, pg. 3147
PERFICIENT, INC. - SAN FRANCISCO—See EQT AB; *Int'l*, pg. 2483
PERFORCE SOFTWARE, INC.-OHIO—See Clearlake Capital Group, L.P.; *U.S. Private*, pg. 936
PERFORCE SOFTWARE, INC.-OHIO—See Francisco Partners Management, LP; *U.S. Private*, pg. 1591
PERFORCE SOFTWARE, INC.—See Clearlake Capital Group, L.P.; *U.S. Private*, pg. 936
PERFORCE SOFTWARE, INC.—See Francisco Partners Management, LP; *U.S. Private*, pg. 1591
PERFORCE SOFTWARE PTY. LTD.—See Clearlake Capital Group, L.P.; *U.S. Private*, pg. 936
PERFORCE SOFTWARE PTY. LTD.—See Francisco Partners Management, LP; *U.S. Private*, pg. 1591
PERFORCE SOFTWARE UK LTD.—See Clearlake Capital Group, L.P.; *U.S. Private*, pg. 936
PERFORCE SOFTWARE UK LTD.—See Francisco Partners Management, LP; *U.S. Private*, pg. 1591
PERFORMANCE SOFTWARE CORPORATION; *U.S. Private*, pg. 3149
PERFORMLINE INC.; *U.S. Private*, pg. 3150
PERIGEE HOLDINGS INC.; *U.S. Private*, pg. 1676
PERIGEN INC.—See Halma plc; *Int'l*, pg. 3232
PERISCOPE HOLDINGS INC.—See KKR & Co. Inc.; *U.S. Public*, pg. 1267
PERISCOPEIQ, INC.; *U.S. Private*, pg. 3151

PERSEUS OPERATING GROUP—See Constellation Software Inc.; *Int'l*, pg. 1774
PERSIVIA, INC.; *U.S. Private*, pg. 3155
PERSONALITY SOFTWARE SYSTEMS, INC.; *U.S. Private*, pg. 3155
PERSONIFY INC.—See Pamlico Capital Management, L.P.; *U.S. Private*, pg. 3083
PHANTOM EFX, LLC—See Light & Wonder, Inc.; *U.S. Public*, pg. 1315
PHASE2 TECHNOLOGY, LLC; *U.S. Private*, pg. 3166
PHOENIX ENERGY TECHNOLOGIES; *U.S. Private*, pg. 3172
PHOENIX INTERACTIVE DESIGN INC.—See Diebold Nixdorf, Inc.; *U.S. Public*, pg. 661
PHOENIX MEDICAL SOFTWARE, INC.; *U.S. Private*, pg. 3173
PHOENIX TECHNOLOGIES LTD.—See Marlin Equity Partners, LLC; *U.S. Private*, pg. 2584
PHOTOREFLECT, LLC; *U.S. Private*, pg. 3174
PILGRIM QUALITY SOLUTIONS EMEA BV—See Riverside Partners, LLC; *U.S. Private*, pg. 3446
PILGRIM SOFTWARE INC.—See Riverside Partners, LLC; *U.S. Private*, pg. 3446
PINEBROOK IMAGING, INC.—See Applied Materials, Inc.; *U.S. Public*, pg. 172
PINGDOM AB—See Silver Lake Group, LLC; *U.S. Private*, pg. 3661
PINGDOM AB—See Thoma Bravo, L.P.; *U.S. Private*, pg. 4153
PING IDENTITY AUSTRALIA PTY. LTD.—See Vista Equity Partners, LLC; *U.S. Private*, pg. 4399
PING IDENTITY CORPORATION—See Vista Equity Partners, LLC; *U.S. Private*, pg. 4399
PING IDENTITY CORPORATION—See Vista Equity Partners, LLC; *U.S. Private*, pg. 4399
PINTEREST, INC.; *U.S. Public*, pg. 1692
PIPEDRIVE INC.; *U.S. Private*, pg. 3189
PIRACLE, INC.—See AvidXchange Holdings, Inc.; *U.S. Public*, pg. 246
PIRIFORM SOFTWARE LTD.—See Gen Digital Inc.; *U.S. Public*, pg. 910
PITNEY BOWES DEUTSCHLAND G.M.B.H.—See Pitney Bowes Inc.; *U.S. Public*, pg. 1694
PITNEY BOWES SOFTWARE GMBH—See Pitney Bowes Inc.; *U.S. Public*, pg. 1695
PITNEY BOWES SOFTWARE INC.—See Pitney Bowes Inc.; *U.S. Public*, pg. 1695
PITNEY BOWES SOFTWARE LIMITED—See Pitney Bowes Inc.; *U.S. Public*, pg. 1695
PITNEY BOWES UK LP—See Pitney Bowes Inc.; *U.S. Public*, pg. 1695
PIVOT3, INC.; *U.S. Private*, pg. 3192
PIVOT, INC.—See CME Group, Inc.; *U.S. Public*, pg. 518
PIVOTSHARE INC.—See Chicken Soup for the Soul Entertainment, Inc.; *U.S. Public*, pg. 488
PIXIA CORP.—See Elliott Management Corporation; *U.S. Private*, pg. 1368
PIXIA CORP.—See Veritas Capital Fund Management, LLC; *U.S. Private*, pg. 4362
PJLM SOFTWARE INC.—See Apax Partners LLP; *Int'l*, pg. 503
PLACESTER, INC.; *U.S. Private*, pg. 3194
PLANALYTICS, INC.; *U.S. Private*, pg. 3195
PLANET LABS PBC; *U.S. Public*, pg. 1697
PLANMILL LTD.—See CapMan PLC; *Int'l*, pg. 1315
PLANMILL LTD.—See Osprey Capital LLC; *U.S. Private*, pg. 3048
PLANSOURCE BENEFITS ADMINISTRATION, INC.—See Vista Equity Partners, LLC; *U.S. Private*, pg. 4399
PLANWELL, LLC—See ARC DOCUMENT SOLUTIONS, INC.; *U.S. Public*, pg. 179
PLARIUM GLOBAL LIMITED—See Aristocrat Leisure Limited; *Int'l*, pg. 566
THE PLATFORM GROUP AG—See Benner Holding GmbH; *Int'l*, pg. 974
PLAYCYBERGAMES COMPANY LIMITED—See Asphere Innovations Public Company Limited; *Int'l*, pg. 630
PLAYDOM, INC.—See The Walt Disney Company; *U.S. Public*, pg. 2139
PLAYFISH, INC.—See Electronic Arts Inc.; *U.S. Public*, pg. 724
PLAYNEXT, INC.; *U.S. Private*, pg. 3212
PLAYPHONE, INC.—See GungHo Online Entertainment, Inc.; *Int'l*, pg. 3183
PLUSGRADE PARENT L.P.—See General Atlantic Service Company, L.P.; *U.S. Private*, pg. 1663
POCKET GAMES, INC.; *U.S. Private*, pg. 3219
POCKET GEMS, INC.; *U.S. Private*, pg. 3219
POCKETMOBILE COMMUNICATIONS AB—See Trimble, Inc.; *U.S. Public*, pg. 2190
POCKETMOBILE NORGE AS—See Trimble, Inc.; *U.S. Public*, pg. 2190
POGO.COM—See Electronic Arts Inc.; *U.S. Public*, pg. 724
POINT4 DATA CORPORATION; *U.S. Private*, pg. 3222
POINTRIGHT, INC.—See Level Equity Management, LLC; *U.S. Private*, pg. 2434
POINTRIGHT, INC.—See Silversmith Management, L.P.; *U.S. Private*, pg. 3664

POINTRIGHT, INC.—See The Carlyle Group Inc.; *U.S. Public*, pg. 2050
POINTSEC MOBILE TECHNOLOGIES AB—See Check Point Software Technologies Ltd.; *Int'l*, pg. 1459
POKITDOK, INC.—See McKesson Corporation; *U.S. Public*, pg. 1407
POLARIS CONSULTING AND SERVICES JAPAN K.K.—See EQT AB; *Int'l*, pg. 2472
POLARIS CONSULTING & SERVICES B.V.—See EQT AB; *Int'l*, pg. 2472
POLARIS CONSULTING & SERVICES FZ LLC—See EQT AB; *Int'l*, pg. 2472
POLARIS CONSULTING & SERVICES INC.—See EQT AB; *Int'l*, pg. 2472
POLARIS CONSULTING & SERVICES LIMITED—See EQT AB; *Int'l*, pg. 2471
POLARIS CONSULTING & SERVICES PTE. LTD.—See EQT AB; *Int'l*, pg. 2472
POLARIS CONSULTING & SERVICES PTY LTD—See EQT AB; *Int'l*, pg. 2472
POLARIS SOFTWARE CONSULTING & SERVICES SDN BHD—See EQT AB; *Int'l*, pg. 2472
POLARIS SOFTWARE (SHANGHAI) COMPANY LIMITED—See EQT AB; *Int'l*, pg. 2472
POLICYSTAT, LLC—See TA Associates, Inc.; *U.S. Private*, pg. 3918
POLYBIA STUDIOS PTY, LTD—See Tautachrome Inc.; *U.S. Public*, pg. 1983
POLYMEDIA S.P.A.—See Piksel, Inc.; *U.S. Private*, pg. 3180
POLYRIGHT SA—See Adon Production AG; *Int'l*, pg. 152
POND5 INC.—See Shutterstock, Inc.; *U.S. Public*, pg. 1876
PONGO RESUME; *U.S. Private*, pg. 3227
PONTIFLEX INC.; *U.S. Private*, pg. 3227
POPCAP GAMES, LLC—See Electronic Arts Inc.; *U.S. Public*, pg. 724
PORTICO SYSTEMS, INC.—See McKesson Corporation; *U.S. Public*, pg. 1408
PORTUS HOLDINGS INC.; *U.S. Private*, pg. 3233
PORTWARE, LLC—See FactSet Research Systems Inc.; *U.S. Public*, pg. 820
POSITION LOGIC, LLC—See The Graham Group, Inc.; *U.S. Private*, pg. 4037
POS NATION—See Crimson Solutions, LLC; *U.S. Private*, pg. 1101
POS WORLD, INC.; *U.S. Private*, pg. 3233
POWER ANALYTICS CORPORATION—See WaveTech Global, Inc.; *U.S. Private*, pg. 4458
POWERCHORD, INC.; *U.S. Private*, pg. 3239
POWERDMS, INC.; *U.S. Private*, pg. 3239
POWERPLAN, INC.—See Roper Technologies, Inc.; *U.S. Public*, pg. 1812
PRECISELY, INC.—See Clearlake Capital Group, L.P.; *U.S. Private*, pg. 936
PRECISELY, INC.—See TA Associates, Inc.; *U.S. Private*, pg. 3917
PRECISION SOFTWARE LIMITED—See Thoma Bravo, L.P.; *U.S. Private*, pg. 4151
PREDICTIVEINTENT LTD.—See Altor Equity Partners AB; *Int'l*, pg. 395
PREEMPTIVE SOLUTIONS, LLC—See HGGC, LLC; *U.S. Private*, pg. 1929
PREFERRED COMMERCE, INC.; *U.S. Public*, pg. 1714
PREMIER COMPUTING, INC.; *U.S. Private*, pg. 3249
PREMIER LOGIC, LLC—See Alten S.A.; *Int'l*, pg. 389
PREMIER PURCHASING AND MARKETING ALLIANCE LLC—See ProBility Media Corporation; *U.S. Public*, pg. 1723
PRESAGIS—See CAE Inc.; *Int'l*, pg. 1249
PRESTO AUTOMATION, INC; *U.S. Public*, pg. 1716
PREVENTICE, INC; *U.S. Private*, pg. 3257
PREVISER CORPORATION—See Delta Dental Plan of New Hampshire, Inc.; *U.S. Private*, pg. 1199
PRICE SYSTEMS DEUTSCHLAND GMBH—See The Carlyle Group Inc.; *U.S. Public*, pg. 2056
PRIMARY PROVIDER MANAGEMENT COMPANY—See Clayton, Dubilier & Rice, LLC; *U.S. Private*, pg. 926
PRINCETON FINANCIAL SYSTEMS, LLC—See State Street Corporation; *U.S. Public*, pg. 1940
PRINT REACH, INC.; *U.S. Private*, pg. 3265
PRINTVISION, INC.; *U.S. Private*, pg. 3266
PRISM GROUP, INC.—See Sabre Corporation; *U.S. Public*, pg. 1833
PRISMRBS, LLC—See Collegiate Retail Alliance; *U.S. Private*, pg. 968
PRISMRBS, LLC—See Concise Capital Management LP; *U.S. Private*, pg. 1009
PRIZM LLC—See GIC Pte. Ltd.; *Int'l*, pg. 2964
PRIZM LLC—See Leonard Green & Partners, L.P.; *U.S. Private*, pg. 2425
PROACTIS HOLDINGS PLC—See DBAY Advisors Limited; *Int'l*, pg. 1987
PROALPHA FRANCE—See COFRA Holding AG; *Int'l*, pg. 1694
PROALPHA SOFTWARE CORPORATION—See COFRA Holding AG; *Int'l*, pg. 1694
PROCESS SOFTWARE, LLC—See Halo Technology Holdings, Inc.; *U.S. Private*, pg. 1845
PROCOMP INDUSTRIA ELETRONICA LTDA—See Diebold

4233

513210 — SOFTWARE PUBLISHERS

Nixdorf, Inc.; *U.S. Public*, pg. 660
PRODEA SYSTEMS, INC.; *U.S. Private*, pg. 3272
PRODUCTIVITY QUALITY SYSTEMS, INC.—See Advantive LLC; *U.S. Private*, pg. 95
PROFESSIONAL DATA SERVICES, INC.—See Audax Group, Limited Partnership; *U.S. Private*, pg. 390
PROFESSIONAL DATASOLUTIONS, INC.—See TA Associates, Inc.; *U.S. Private*, pg. 3917
PROFITKEY INTERNATIONAL, INC.—See Apax Partners LLP; *Int'l*, pg. 503
PROFITMASTER CANADA INC.—See Constellation Software Inc.; *Int'l*, pg. 1773
PROFITSTARS/ALOGENT—See Jack Henry & Associates, Inc.; *U.S. Public*, pg. 1182
PROFITSTARS - DATATRADE DIVISION—See Jack Henry & Associates, Inc.; *U.S. Public*, pg. 1182
PROFITSTARS—See Jack Henry & Associates, Inc.; *U.S. Public*, pg. 1182
PROFITSTARS—See Jack Henry & Associates, Inc.; *U.S. Public*, pg. 1182
PROGINET LLC—See Vista Equity Partners, LLC; *U.S. Private*, pg. 4402
PROGRESS JAPAN KK—See Progress Software Corporation; *U.S. Public*, pg. 1725
PROGRESS SECURITY CORPORATION—See Progress Software Corporation; *U.S. Public*, pg. 1725
PROGRESS SOFTWARE CORPORATION OF CANADA LTD.—See Progress Software Corporation; *U.S. Public*, pg. 1725
PROGRESS SOFTWARE CORPORATION; *U.S. Public*, pg. 1724
PROGRESS SOFTWARE DEVELOPMENT PRIVATE LIMITED—See Progress Software Corporation; *U.S. Public*, pg. 1726
PROGRESS SOFTWARE EAD—See Progress Software Corporation; *U.S. Public*, pg. 1725
PROGRESS SOFTWARE GMBH—See Progress Software Corporation; *U.S. Public*, pg. 1725
PROGRESS SOFTWARE—See Progress Software Corporation; *U.S. Public*, pg. 1725
PROGRESS SOLUTIONS INDIA PRIVATE LIMITED—See Progress Software Corporation; *U.S. Public*, pg. 1726
PROJEKT202 LLC—See Amdocs Limited; *Int'l*, pg. 420
PROLIM PLM; *U.S. Private*, pg. 3282
PROMETHEUS GROUP ENTERPRISES, LLC—See Genstar Capital, LLC; *U.S. Private*, pg. 1678
PROOFPOINT CANADA INC.—See Thoma Bravo, L.P.; *U.S. Private*, pg. 4151
PROOFPOINT EMAIL SOLUTIONS GMBH—See Thoma Bravo, L.P.; *U.S. Private*, pg. 4151
PROOFPOINT, INC.—See Thoma Bravo, L.P.; *U.S. Private*, pg. 4150
PROOFPOINT JAPAN KK—See Thoma Bravo, L.P.; *U.S. Private*, pg. 4151
PROOFPOINT LIMITED—See Thoma Bravo, L.P.; *U.S. Private*, pg. 4151
PROOFPOINT NI LTD.—See Thoma Bravo, L.P.; *U.S. Private*, pg. 4151
PROOFPOINT SINGAPORE PTE. LTD.—See Thoma Bravo, L.P.; *U.S. Private*, pg. 4151
PROPERTYINFO CORPORATION—See Stewart Information Services Corporation; *U.S. Public*, pg. 1948
PROPERTY SOLUTIONS INTERNATIONAL, INC.; *U.S. Private*, pg. 3285
PROPERTYWARE, INC.—See Thoma Bravo, L.P.; *U.S. Private*, pg. 4153
PROPHARM LTD.—See McKesson Corporation; *U.S. Public*, pg. 1408
PROPHESY TRANSPORTATION SOLUTIONS, INC.—See Accellos, Inc.; *U.S. Private*, pg. 50
PROPHOENIX INC.; *U.S. Private*, pg. 3286
PROS HOLDINGS, INC.; *U.S. Public*, pg. 1727
PROSPER BUSINESS DEVELOPMENT CORP.; *U.S. Private*, pg. 3288
PROTECTIVE BUSINESS & HEALTH SYSTEMS, INC.—See Marlin Equity Partners, LLC; *U.S. Private*, pg. 2585
PROTEXT MOBILITY, INC.; *U.S. Private*, pg. 3290
PROTEXX TECHNOLOGY CORPORATION—See WidePoint Corporation; *U.S. Public*, pg. 2370
PROVELOCITY LLC—See The Riverside Company; *U.S. Private*, pg. 4110
PROXIMIC, INC.—See comScore, Inc.; *U.S. Public*, pg. 561
PSI SYSTEMS, INC.—See Thoma Bravo, L.P.; *U.S. Private*, pg. 4154
PSYCHOLOGICAL SOFTWARE SOLUTIONS, INC.; *U.S. Private*, pg. 3298
PT. ASIASOFT—See Asphere Innovations Public Company Limited; *Int'l*, pg. 630
PTC EASTERN EUROPE LIMITED S.R.L.—See PTC Inc.; *U.S. Public*, pg. 1734
PTC INC. - FAIRFAX—See PTC Inc.; *U.S. Public*, pg. 1734
PTC INC.; *U.S. Public*, pg. 1734
PTC INTERNATIONAL LIMITED LIABILITY COMPANY—See PTC Inc.; *U.S. Public*, pg. 1734
PTC JAPAN KK—See PTC Inc.; *U.S. Public*, pg. 1734
PTC SOFTWARE (INDIA) PRIVATE LIMITED—See PTC Inc.; *U.S. Public*, pg. 1734

PT QAD ASIA INDONESIA—See Thoma Bravo, L.P.; *U.S. Private*, pg. 4151
PT. RED HAT INDONESIA—See International Business Machines Corporation; *U.S. Public*, pg. 1150
PUBLICSTUFF, LLC—See Accela Inc.; *U.S. Private*, pg. 49
PUBMATIC INC.; *U.S. Public*, pg. 1736
PULSE EVOLUTION CORPORATION; *U.S. Public*, pg. 1737
PULSEPOINT INC.; *U.S. Private*, pg. 3303
PULSEPOINT LTD.—See PulsePoint Inc.; *U.S. Private*, pg. 3303
PULSE SYSTEMS, INC.—See Constellation Software Inc.; *Int'l*, pg. 1773
PUPPET LABS INC.; *U.S. Private*, pg. 3304
PURECOMMERCE; *U.S. Private*, pg. 3306
PURE NETWORKS, INC.—See Hon Hai Precision Industry Co., Ltd.; *Int'l*, pg. 3456
PYMETRICS, INC.—See Rubicon Technology Partners, LLC; *U.S. Private*, pg. 3500
Q2 SOFTWARE, INC.—See Q2 Holdings, Inc.; *U.S. Public*, pg. 1741
QAD AUSTRALIA PTY LTD.—See Thoma Bravo, L.P.; *U.S. Private*, pg. 4151
QAD BRASIL LTDA.—See Thoma Bravo, L.P.; *U.S. Private*, pg. 4151
QAD BRAZIL LTDA.—See Thoma Bravo, L.P.; *U.S. Private*, pg. 4151
QAD CHINA, INC.—See Thoma Bravo, L.P.; *U.S. Private*, pg. 4151
QAD CHINA LTD.—See Thoma Bravo, L.P.; *U.S. Private*, pg. 4151
QAD EUROPE GMBH—See Thoma Bravo, L.P.; *U.S. Private*, pg. 4151
QAD EUROPE (IRELAND) LIMITED—See Thoma Bravo, L.P.; *U.S. Private*, pg. 4151
QAD EUROPE LIMITED—See Thoma Bravo, L.P.; *U.S. Private*, pg. 4151
QAD EUROPE N.V./S.A.—See Thoma Bravo, L.P.; *U.S. Private*, pg. 4151
QAD EUROPE S.A.S.—See Thoma Bravo, L.P.; *U.S. Private*, pg. 4152
QAD EUROPE S.L.—See Thoma Bravo, L.P.; *U.S. Private*, pg. 4152
QAD INC.—See Thoma Bravo, L.P.; *U.S. Private*, pg. 4151
QAD INDIA PRIVATE LIMITED—See Thoma Bravo, L.P.; *U.S. Private*, pg. 4152
QAD IRELAND LIMITED—See Thoma Bravo, L.P.; *U.S. Private*, pg. 4152
QAD ITALY S.R.L.—See Thoma Bravo, L.P.; *U.S. Private*, pg. 4152
QAD JAPAN INC.—See Thoma Bravo, L.P.; *U.S. Private*, pg. 4152
QAD JAPAN, INC.—See Thoma Bravo, L.P.; *U.S. Private*, pg. 4152
QAD NETHERLANDS B.V.—See Thoma Bravo, L.P.; *U.S. Private*, pg. 4152
QAD POLSKA SP. Z O.O.—See Thoma Bravo, L.P.; *U.S. Private*, pg. 4152
QAD SINGAPORE PTE LTD.—See Thoma Bravo, L.P.; *U.S. Private*, pg. 4152
QAD SISTEMAS INTEGRADOS SERVICIOS DE CONSULTORIA, S.A. DE C.V.—See Thoma Bravo, L.P.; *U.S. Private*, pg. 4152
QAD (THAILAND) LTD.—See Thoma Bravo, L.P.; *U.S. Private*, pg. 4151
QAD UNITED KINGDOM—See Thoma Bravo, L.P.; *U.S. Private*, pg. 4152
QCUE, INC.; *U.S. Private*, pg. 3312
QC VERIFY, LLC; *U.S. Private*, pg. 3312
QGIV, INC.—See Bloomerang, LLC; *U.S. Private*, pg. 584
QHR CORPORATION—See George Weston Limited; *Int'l*, pg. 2939
QILINSOFT, LLC—See Innovation Technology Group; *U.S. Private*, pg. 2081
QIMING INFORMATION TECHNOLOGY CO., LTD.—See China FAW Group Corporation; *Int'l*, pg. 1502
QL2 SOFTWARE, LLC—See DMEP Corporation; *U.S. Private*, pg. 1248
QLIKTECH INTERNATIONAL AB—See Thoma Bravo, L.P.; *U.S. Private*, pg. 4152
QLIK TECHNOLOGIES INC.—See Thoma Bravo, L.P.; *U.S. Private*, pg. 4152
QNARY LLC; *U.S. Private*, pg. 3313
QOMPLX, INC.; *U.S. Private*, pg. 3313
QS/1 GOVERNMENTAL SOLUTIONS—See J.M. Smith Corporation; *U.S. Private*, pg. 2169
QS/1—See J.M. Smith Corporation; *U.S. Private*, pg. 2169
QUADRANT SOFTWARE, INC.—See American Pacific Group, LLC; *U.S. Private*, pg. 242
QUADRIGA UK LTD.—See Exceptional Innovation BV; *Int'l*, pg. 2579
QUALCOMM CONNECTED EXPERIENCES SWITZERLAND AG—See PTC Inc.; *U.S. Public*, pg. 1735
QUALCOMM FIRETHORN HOLDINGS, LLC—See QUALCOMM Incorporated; *U.S. Public*, pg. 1747
QUALITA IN FARMACIA S.R.L.—See CompuGroup Medical SE & Co. KGaA; *Int'l*, pg. 1756
QUALITEST GROUP; *U.S. Private*, pg. 3317

QUALIZORG B.V.—See CompuGroup Medical SE & Co. KGaA; *Int'l*, pg. 1757
QUALMETRIX INC.; *U.S. Private*, pg. 3322
QUALTRICS INTERNATIONAL INC.—See Canada Pension Plan Investment Board; *Int'l*, pg. 1281
QUALTRICS INTERNATIONAL INC.—See Silver Lake Group, LLC; *U.S. Private*, pg. 3655
QUALYS, INC.; *U.S. Public*, pg. 1748
QUANTGATE SYSTEMS INC.; *U.S. Public*, pg. 1753
QUANTIFI, INC.; *U.S. Private*, pg. 3322
QUANT SYSTEMS, INC.; *U.S. Private*, pg. 3322
QUANTUM COMPLIANCE SYSTEMS, INC.—See Logic Solutions, Inc.; *U.S. Private*, pg. 2481
QUARK SOFTWARE, INC.—See Parallax Capital Partners, LLC; *U.S. Private*, pg. 3092
QUATRIS HEALTH LLC; *U.S. Private*, pg. 3324
QUBE GLOBAL SOFTWARE LTD.—See GI Manager L.P.; *U.S. Private*, pg. 1693
QUBOLE INC.—See HGGC, LLC; *U.S. Private*, pg. 1929
QUEST ANALYTICS LLC—See Vestar Capital Partners, LLC; *U.S. Private*, pg. 4372
QUEST INFORMATION SYSTEMS INC.—See Clearview Capital, LLC; *U.S. Private*, pg. 939
QUEST INTEGRITY GROUP, LLC—See Baker Hughes Company; *U.S. Public*, pg. 265
QUEST SOFTWARE INC.—See Francisco Partners Management, LP; *U.S. Private*, pg. 1591
QUICKOFFICE, INC.—See Alphabet Inc.; *U.S. Public*, pg. 84
QUMU, INC.—See Enghouse Systems Limited; *Int'l*, pg. 2427
QUORUM BUSINESS SOLUTIONS, INC. - DALLAS—See Thoma Bravo, L.P.; *U.S. Private*, pg. 4152
QUORUM BUSINESS SOLUTIONS, INC.—See Thoma Bravo, L.P.; *U.S. Private*, pg. 4152
QUOTE.COM—See Osceola Capital Management, LLC; *U.S. Private*, pg. 3047
QVIDIAN CORP.—See Upland Software, Inc.; *U.S. Public*, pg. 2264
QVIDIAN—See Upland Software, Inc.; *U.S. Public*, pg. 2264
QWIZDOM—See Boxlight Corporation; *U.S. Public*, pg. 377
R1SOFT—See BBS Technologies, Inc.; *U.S. Private*, pg. 498
R4, LLC—See Thoma Bravo, L.P.; *U.S. Private*, pg. 4148
RAADR, INC.; *U.S. Private*, pg. 3340
RACKWISE, INC.; *U.S. Private*, pg. 3342
RAD GAME TOOLS, INC.—See Epic Games Inc.; *U.S. Private*, pg. 1412
RADIANT LOGIC, INC.; *U.S. Private*, pg. 3343
RADIO COMPUTING SERVICES, INC.—See iHeartMedia, Inc.; *U.S. Public*, pg. 1096
RADIO COMPUTING SERVICES (INDIA) PVT. LTD.—See iHeartMedia, Inc.; *U.S. Public*, pg. 1095
RAILCAR MANAGEMENT, LLC—See General Electric Company; *U.S. Public*, pg. 920
RAMP HOLDINGS INC.—See VBrick Systems Inc.; *U.S. Private*, pg. 4348
RAM WARE, LLC—See Guggenheim Partners, LLC; *U.S. Private*, pg. 1812
RAPID7, INC.; *U.S. Public*, pg. 1763
RATEX BUSINESS SOLUTIONS, INC.—See Collegiate Retail Alliance; *U.S. Private*, pg. 968
RAWSOFT INC.; *U.S. Private*, pg. 3358
RAYMARK XPERT BUSINESS SYSTEMS INC.—See Mi9 Retail, Inc.; *U.S. Private*, pg. 2696
RAYTHEON INTELLIGENCE & SPACE—See RTX Corporation; *U.S. Public*, pg. 1825
RAYTHEON SOLIPSYS—See RTX Corporation; *U.S. Public*, pg. 1824
RAZORSIGHT INC.; *U.S. Private*, pg. 3360
RAZORSYNC, LLC—See Independence Capital Partners, LLC; *U.S. Private*, pg. 2056
REACH MESSAGING HOLDINGS, INC.; *U.S. Private*, pg. 3365
REACTION DESIGN, INC.—See ANSYS, Inc.; *U.S. Public*, pg. 139
READYTALK; *U.S. Private*, pg. 3367
REAL ASSET MANAGEMENT, INC.—See GI Manager L.P.; *U.S. Private*, pg. 1693
REAL ASSET MANAGEMENT LTD—See GI Manager L.P.; *U.S. Private*, pg. 1693
REAL DATA, INC.; *U.S. Private*, pg. 3367
REAL DIGITAL MEDIA LLC—See Stratacache Inc.; *U.S. Private*, pg. 3834
REALIA, INC.—See Broadcom Inc.; *U.S. Public*, pg. 390
REAL MAGNET, LLC—See Higher Logic, LLC; *U.S. Private*, pg. 1937
REALNET SOLUTIONS, INC.—See Zillow Group, Inc.; *U.S. Public*, pg. 2405
REALPAGE, INC.—See Thoma Bravo, L.P.; *U.S. Private*, pg. 4152
REAL TIME ENTERPRISES, INC.—See Elbit Systems Limited; *Int'l*, pg. 2344
REALTIME NORTH AMERICA, INC.; *U.S. Private*, pg. 3369
REALWINWIN, INC.; *U.S. Private*, pg. 3369
REAPIT LTD—See Accel Partners L.P.; *U.S. Private*, pg. 48
REAPIT LTD—See KKR & Co. Inc.; *U.S. Public*, pg. 1238
REBELMOUSE, INC.; *U.S. Private*, pg. 3370
RECAST SOFTWARE INC.; *U.S. Private*, pg. 3370
RECURLY, INC.; *U.S. Private*, pg. 3372

513210 — SOFTWARE PUBLISHERS

RED BEND SOFTWARE, INC.; *U.S. Private*, pg. 3373
REDCORE (INDIA) PRIVATE LIMITED—See Accenture plc; *Int'l*, pg. 87
RED HAT AB—See International Business Machines Corporation; *U.S. Public*, pg. 1150
RED HAT ASIA PACIFIC PTE LTD.—See International Business Machines Corporation; *U.S. Public*, pg. 1150
RED HAT ASIA PACIFIC PTY LTD—See International Business Machines Corporation; *U.S. Public*, pg. 1150
RED HAT BRASIL LIMITADA—See International Business Machines Corporation; *U.S. Public*, pg. 1150
RED HAT, BVBA—See International Business Machines Corporation; *U.S. Public*, pg. 1150
RED HAT BV—See International Business Machines Corporation; *U.S. Public*, pg. 1150
RED HAT CHILE LIMITADA—See International Business Machines Corporation; *U.S. Public*, pg. 1150
RED HAT COLOMBIA S.A.S—See International Business Machines Corporation; *U.S. Public*, pg. 1150
RED HAT CZECH, S.R.O.—See International Business Machines Corporation; *U.S. Public*, pg. 1150
RED HAT FRANCE SARL—See International Business Machines Corporation; *U.S. Public*, pg. 1150
RED HAT FZ LLC—See International Business Machines Corporation; *U.S. Public*, pg. 1150
RED HAT GMBH—See International Business Machines Corporation; *U.S. Public*, pg. 1150
RED HAT, INC.—See International Business Machines Corporation; *U.S. Public*, pg. 1149
RED HAT INDIA PVT. LTD.—See International Business Machines Corporation; *U.S. Public*, pg. 1150
RED HAT ISRAEL LTD.—See International Business Machines Corporation; *U.S. Public*, pg. 1150
RED HAT KK—See International Business Machines Corporation; *U.S. Public*, pg. 1150
RED HAT LIMITED—See International Business Machines Corporation; *U.S. Public*, pg. 1150
RED HAT MALAYSIA SDN. BHD.—See International Business Machines Corporation; *U.S. Public*, pg. 1150
RED HAT PHILIPPINES SOFTWARE SOLUTIONS CORP.—See International Business Machines Corporation; *U.S. Public*, pg. 1150
RED HAT POLAND SP.Z.O.O—See International Business Machines Corporation; *U.S. Public*, pg. 1150
RED HAT, S.L.—See International Business Machines Corporation; *U.S. Public*, pg. 1150
RED HAT SOUTH AFRICA (PTY) LTD—See International Business Machines Corporation; *U.S. Public*, pg. 1150
RED HAT S.R.L.—See International Business Machines Corporation; *U.S. Public*, pg. 1150
RED HAT UK LTD.—See International Business Machines Corporation; *U.S. Public*, pg. 1150
RED HAT YAZILIM SERVISLERI A.S.—See International Business Machines Corporation; *U.S. Public*, pg. 1150
REDI2 TECHNOLOGIES, INC.—See Bain Capital, LP; *U.S. Private*, pg. 439
REDIFY GROUP INC.; *U.S. Private*, pg. 3378
REDLOCK, INC.—See Palo Alto Networks, Inc.; *U.S. Public*, pg. 1635
REDPOINT GLOBAL INC.; *U.S. Private*, pg. 3379
RED RIVER SOFTWARE—See Constellation Software Inc.; *Int'l*, pg. 1775
REDWOOD SOFTWARE, INC.; *U.S. Private*, pg. 3381
REFLECT SYSTEMS, INC.—See Creative Realities, Inc.; *U.S. Public*, pg. 593
REFLEXION NETWORKS, INC.—See Apax Partners LLP; *Int'l*, pg. 506
REFLEX SYSTEMS, LLC; *U.S. Private*, pg. 3384
REGED, INC.—See Gryphon Investors, LLC; *U.S. Private*, pg. 1799
REGO PAYMENT ARCHITECTURES, INC.; *U.S. Public*, pg. 1777
RELAYHEALTH—See McKesson Corporation; *U.S. Public*, pg. 1408
RENAISSANCE LEARNING, INC.—See Francisco Partners Management, LP; *U.S. Private*, pg. 1591
RENAISSANCE LEARNING UK LIMITED—See Francisco Partners Management, LP; *U.S. Private*, pg. 1591
REPLICON INC.—See Roper Technologies, Inc.; *U.S. Public*, pg. 1811
REPOSITRAK INC; *U.S. Public*, pg. 1785
REPUTATION MANAGEMENT CONSULTANTS; *U.S. Private*, pg. 3403
RESEARCH SQUARE; *U.S. Private*, pg. 3404
RESMED MARIBO A/S—See ResMed Inc.; *U.S. Public*, pg. 1791
RESOLUTE SOLUTIONS CORPORATION; *U.S. Private*, pg. 3406
RESOLVE SYSTEMS, LLC—See Insight Venture Management, LLC; *U.S. Private*, pg. 2091
RESONATE, INC.; *U.S. Private*, pg. 3406
RESULTS SOFTWARE LLC—See Thomas H. Lee Partners, L.P.; *U.S. Private*, pg. 4155
RETAIL INFORMATION SYSTEMS, INC.; *U.S. Private*, pg. 3411
RETAIL SOLUTIONS, INC.—See Hellman & Friedman LLC; *U.S. Private*, pg. 1910

RETROSPECT, INC.—See StorCentric, Inc.; *U.S. Private*, pg. 3831
REVEAL DATA CORPORATION—See K1 Investment Management, LLC; *U.S. Private*, pg. 2252
REVEL SYSTEMS, INC.; *U.S. Private*, pg. 3413
REVELWOOD, INC.; *U.S. Private*, pg. 3413
REVIORA, LLC; *U.S. Private*, pg. 3416
REVITALISED LIMITED—See MAXIMUS, Inc.; *U.S. Public*, pg. 1402
REVSTREAM INC.; *U.S. Private*, pg. 3417
REWARD GATEWAY (UK) LTD—See Edenred S.A.; *Int'l*, pg. 2308
RFID GLOBAL SOLUTION INC.; *U.S. Private*, pg. 3420
RHEINKRAFT PRODUCTION GMBH—See Cliq Digital AG; *Int'l*, pg. 1660
RHOMOBILE, INC.; *U.S. Private*, pg. 3422
RIA IN A BOX LLC; *U.S. Private*, pg. 3424
RICHRELEVANCE FRANCE—See RichRelevance, Inc.; *U.S. Private*, pg. 3430
RICHRELEVANCE, INC.; *U.S. Private*, pg. 3430
RICHRELEVANCE UK—See RichRelevance, Inc.; *U.S. Private*, pg. 3430
RICS SOFTWARE; *U.S. Private*, pg. 3431
RIGHTANSWERS, INC.—See Upland Software, Inc.; *U.S. Public*, pg. 1979
RIGHT ON INTERACTIVE, LLC; *U.S. Private*, pg. 3436
RIGHTPOINT COMPANY—See Genpact Limited; *Int'l*, pg. 2926
RIGHTSCALE ASIA PACIFIC—See TA Associates, Inc.; *U.S. Private*, pg. 3915
RIGHTSCALE AUSTRALIA—See TA Associates, Inc.; *U.S. Private*, pg. 3915
RIGHTSCALE, INC.—See TA Associates, Inc.; *U.S. Private*, pg. 3915
RIGHTSCALE UK LTD—See TA Associates, Inc.; *U.S. Private*, pg. 3915
RIMES TECHNOLOGIES CORPORATION—See EQT AB; *Int'l*, pg. 2479
RINGCENTRAL AUSTRALIA PTY LTD—See RingCentral, Inc.; *U.S. Public*, pg. 1799
RINGCENTRAL, INC.; *U.S. Public*, pg. 1799
RINGCENTRAL IRELAND LTD—See RingCentral, Inc.; *U.S. Public*, pg. 1799
RINGCUBE SOFTWARE TECH PVT LTD—See Elliott Management Corporation; *U.S. Private*, pg. 1367
RINGCUBE SOFTWARE TECH PVT LTD.—See Vista Equity Partners, LLC; *U.S. Private*, pg. 4396
RINGLEAD, INC.—See ZoomInfo Technologies Inc.; *U.S. Public*, pg. 2411
RISIMA CONSULTING GMBH—See 3U Holding AG; *Int'l*, pg. 10
RISTKEN SOFTWARE SERVICES, L.P.; *U.S. Private*, pg. 3441
RIVERBED TECHNOLOGY B.V.—See Vector Capital Management, L.P.; *U.S. Private*, pg. 4352
RIVERBED TECHNOLOGY GMBH—See Vector Capital Management, L.P.; *U.S. Private*, pg. 4352
RIVERBED TECHNOLOGY K.K.—See Vector Capital Management, L.P.; *U.S. Private*, pg. 4352
RIVERBED TECHNOLOGY LIMITED—See Vector Capital Management, L.P.; *U.S. Private*, pg. 4352
RIVERBED TECHNOLOGY PTE LTD—See Vector Capital Management, L.P.; *U.S. Private*, pg. 4352
RIVERBED TECHNOLOGY SARL—See Vector Capital Management, L.P.; *U.S. Private*, pg. 4352
RIVERBED TECHNOLOGY S.R.L.—See Vector Capital Management, L.P.; *U.S. Private*, pg. 4352
RIVERBED TECNOLOGIA DE INFORMACAO LTDA—See Vector Capital Management, L.P.; *U.S. Private*, pg. 4352
RIVERDEEP, INC.—See Veritas Capital Fund Management, LLC; *U.S. Private*, pg. 4363
RIVERSAND TECHNOLOGIES, INC.—See The Jordan Company, L.P.; *U.S. Private*, pg. 4062
RIVEX TECHNOLOGY CORP.; *U.S. Public*, pg. 1801
RJMETRICS INC.; *U.S. Private*, pg. 3449
RKL ESOLUTIONS, LLC; *U.S. Private*, pg. 3450
RM INGENIERIE SAS—See Cegedim S.A.; *Int'l*, pg. 1390
ROADNET TECHNOLOGIES, INC.—See Vista Equity Partners, LLC; *U.S. Private*, pg. 4399
ROBBINS RESEARCH INTERNATIONAL; *U.S. Private*, pg. 3457
ROBERTSON GLOBAL HEALTH SOLUTIONS CORPORATION; *U.S. Private*, pg. 3460
ROBERTSON (UK) LIMITED—See CGG; *Int'l*, pg. 1432
ROBOCOM US, LLC; *U.S. Private*, pg. 3462
THE ROCKET SCIENCE GROUP LLC—See Intuit Inc.; *U.S. Public*, pg. 1160
ROCKET SOFTWARE, INC.—See Bain Capital, LP; *U.S. Private*, pg. 442
ROCKSAUCE STUDIOS, LLC—See Builder Homesite, Inc.; *U.S. Private*, pg. 681
ROCK SOLID UK LTD.; *U.S. Private*, pg. 3465
ROCKSTAR INTERNATIONAL LIMITED—See Take-Two Interactive Software, Inc.; *U.S. Public*, pg. 1979
ROCKSTAR LONDON, LTD.—See Take-Two Interactive Software, Inc.; *U.S. Public*, pg. 1979
ROCKSTAR NORTH LTD.—See Take-Two Interactive Software, Inc.; *U.S. Public*, pg. 1979

ROCKSTAR SAN DIEGO, INC.—See Take-Two Interactive Software, Inc.; *U.S. Public*, pg. 1979
ROGERS SOFTWARE DEVELOPMENT, INC.; *U.S. Private*, pg. 3472
ROGUE WAVE SOFTWARE JAPAN K.K.—See Clearlake Capital Group, L.P.; *U.S. Private*, pg. 936
ROGUE WAVE SOFTWARE JAPAN K.K.—See Francisco Partners Management, LP; *U.S. Private*, pg. 1591
ROI INSTITUTE, INC.; *U.S. Private*, pg. 3473
RO INNOVATION; *U.S. Private*, pg. 3453
ROKK3R INC.; *U.S. Private*, pg. 3473
ROLA SECURITY SOLUTIONS GMBH—See Deutsche Telekom AG; *Int'l*, pg. 2085
ROSETTA STONE INC.—See Veritas Capital Fund Management, LLC; *U.S. Private*, pg. 4361
ROSETTA STONE (UK) LTD.—See Veritas Capital Fund Management, LLC; *U.S. Private*, pg. 4361
ROSS SYSTEMS (UK) LIMITED—See TA Associates, Inc.; *U.S. Private*, pg. 3914
ROUTEMATCH SOFTWARE, INC.—See Constellation Software Inc.; *Int'l*, pg. 1775
ROVI CORPORATION—See Adeia Inc.; *U.S. Public*, pg. 41
ROVI EUROPE LIMITED—See Adeia Inc.; *U.S. Public*, pg. 41
ROVI KK—See Adeia Inc.; *U.S. Public*, pg. 41
THE ROWING TEAM, LLC—See Waud Capital Partners LLC; *U.S. Private*, pg. 4457
ROWL, INC.; *U.S. Private*, pg. 3490
ROXIO, INC.—See Vector Capital Management, L.P.; *U.S. Private*, pg. 4352
R.R. DONNELLEY—See Chatham Asset Management, LLC; *U.S. Private*, pg. 864
RSOFT, INC.—See Synopsys, Inc.; *U.S. Public*, pg. 1970
R SQUARE, INC.; *U.S. Private*, pg. 3331
R SYSTEMS EUROPE B.V.—See Blackstone Inc.; *U.S. Public*, pg. 357
THE RUBICON GROUP, LLC—See Amadeus IT Group, S.A.; *Int'l*, pg. 407
RUNTIME COLLECTIVE LIMITED—See Platinum Equity, LLC; *U.S. Private*, pg. 3202
RYCAN TECHNOLOGIES INC.—See TruBridge, Inc.; *U.S. Public*, pg. 2198
S3D INTERACTIVE, INC.—See Embracer Group AB; *Int'l*, pg. 2375
S3 MATCHING TECHNOLOGIES, LP; *U.S. Private*, pg. 3519
SAFEDOX, INC.; *U.S. Private*, pg. 3524
SAFETYCHAIN SOFTWARE, INC.; *U.S. Private*, pg. 3525
SAFRAN SOFTWARE SOLUTIONS AS—See Dovre Group Plc; *Int'l*, pg. 2182
SAGANTEC NORTH AMERICA; *U.S. Private*, pg. 3526
SAG EAST GMBH—See Silver Lake Group, LLC; *U.S. Private*, pg. 3658
SAILPOINT TECHNOLOGIES, INC.—See Thoma Bravo, L.P.; *U.S. Private*, pg. 4153
SAILTHRU, INC.; *U.S. Private*, pg. 3529
SALESFORCE.COM CANADA CORPORATION—See Salesforce, Inc.; *U.S. Public*, pg. 1837
SALESFORCE.COM FRANCE S.A.S.—See Salesforce, Inc.; *U.S. Public*, pg. 1837
SALESFORCE.COM GERMANY GMBH—See Salesforce, Inc.; *U.S. Public*, pg. 1837
SALESFORCE COMMERCE CLOUD—See Salesforce, Inc.; *U.S. Public*, pg. 1837
SALESFORCE.COM SARL—See Salesforce, Inc.; *U.S. Public*, pg. 1838
SALESFORCE.COM SINGAPORE PTE. LTD.—See Salesforce, Inc.; *U.S. Public*, pg. 1838
SALES SIMPLICITY SOFTWARE, INC.—See Berkshire Hathaway Inc.; *U.S. Public*, pg. 312
SALIENT PRODUCTS CORPORATION; *U.S. Private*, pg. 3532
SALSA LABS, INC.—See Insight Venture Management, LLC; *U.S. Private*, pg. 2090
SANBOLIC, INC.—See Elliott Management Corporation; *U.S. Private*, pg. 1367
SANBOLIC, INC.—See Vista Equity Partners, LLC; *U.S. Private*, pg. 4396
SANDERSON GROUP PLC—See TA Associates, Inc.; *U.S. Private*, pg. 3914
SANDERSON LIMITED—See TA Associates, Inc.; *U.S. Private*, pg. 3914
SANDERSON MULTI-CHANNEL SOLUTIONS LIMITED—See TA Associates, Inc.; *U.S. Private*, pg. 3914
SAN DIEGO CASH REGISTER COMPANY, INC.—See i3 Verticals, Inc.; *U.S. Public*, pg. 1081
SANYO EXTENDED SYSTEM SERVICES LIMITED—See Computer & Technologies Holdings Limited; *Int'l*, pg. 1758
SAS INSCHOOL—See SAS Institute Inc.; *U.S. Private*, pg. 3552
SAS INSTITUTE INC.; *U.S. Private*, pg. 3551
SATMETRIX SYSTEMS, INC.; *U.S. Private*, pg. 3553
SAVANTIS SOLUTIONS LLC - EXTON—See Savantis Solutions LLC; *U.S. Private*, pg. 3556
SAVANTIS SOLUTIONS LLC; *U.S. Private*, pg. 3556
SAVICOM, INC.; *U.S. Private*, pg. 3557

513210 — SOFTWARE PUBLISHERS

THE SAVO GROUP, LTD—See Seismic Software, Inc.; *U.S. Private*, pg. 3600
SAVVION, INC.—See Progress Software Corporation; *U.S. Public*, pg. 1726
SCC SOFT COMPUTER INC.; *U.S. Private*, pg. 3561
S.C. ELECTRONIC ARTS ROMANIA SRL—See Electronic Arts Inc.; *U.S. Public*, pg. 724
SCHAKRA, INC.; *U.S. Private*, pg. 3563
SCHAWK DIGITAL SOLUTIONS, INC.—See Matthews International Corporation; *U.S. Public*, pg. 1401
SCHEDULE STAR, LLC—See TEGNA Inc.; *U.S. Public*, pg. 1990
SCHOOLDUDE.COM; *U.S. Private*, pg. 3568
SCIENCELOGIC LLC; *U.S. Private*, pg. 3573
SCIENERGY, INC.; *U.S. Private*, pg. 3573
SCIENTIFIC GAMES DEUTSCHLAND GMBH—See Light & Wonder, Inc.; *U.S. Public*, pg. 1314
SCIENTIFIC GAMES LOTTERY SERVICES KFT—See Light & Wonder, Inc.; *U.S. Public*, pg. 1315
SCIENTIFIC GAMES SWEDEN AB—See Light & Wonder, Inc.; *U.S. Public*, pg. 1315
SCIQUEST, INC.—See Accel Partners L.P.; *U.S. Private*, pg. 48
SCIQUEST, INC.—See KKR & Co. Inc.; *U.S. Public*, pg. 1238
SCI SOLUTIONS INC.—See R1 RCM Inc.; *U.S. Public*, pg. 1758
SCISYS GROUP PLC—See CGI Inc.; *Int'l*, pg. 1434
SCISYS UK HOLDING LIMITED—See CGI Inc.; *Int'l*, pg. 1434
SCISYS UK LTD.—See CGI Inc.; *Int'l*, pg. 1434
SCONCE SOLUTIONS PTE. LTD.; *U.S. Private*, pg. 3575
SCORELOOP AG—See BlackBerry Limited; *Int'l*, pg. 1060
SCOUT RFP LLC—See Workday, Inc.; *U.S. Public*, pg. 2378
SCREENINGONE, INC.; *U.S. Private*, pg. 3579
SCROLLMOTION, INC.; *U.S. Private*, pg. 3580
SCRYPT CORPORATION; *U.S. Public*, pg. 1850
SCRYPT INC.—See Scrypt Corporation; *U.S. Public*, pg. 1850
SCWORX CORP.; *U.S. Public*, pg. 1850
SECUREBUY, LLC; *U.S. Private*, pg. 3594
SECUREWORKS, INC.—See Dell Technologies Inc.; *U.S. Public*, pg. 651
SECURIGENCE LLC—See Chenega Corporation; *U.S. Private*, pg. 872
SECURITY WEAVER; *U.S. Private*, pg. 3596
SEDONA GROUP; *U.S. Private*, pg. 3597
SEE PROGRESS, INC.—See Vista Equity Partners, LLC; *U.S. Private*, pg. 4401
SEI ARCHWAY TECHNOLOGY PARTNERS, LLC—See SEI Investments Company; *U.S. Public*, pg. 1856
SEISMIC SOFTWARE, INC.; *U.S. Private*, pg. 3599
SELERANT CORP.; *U.S. Private*, pg. 3602
SELERANT SRL—See Symphony Technology Group, LLC; *U.S. Private*, pg. 3902
SEMANTICSPACE TECHNOLOGIES; *U.S. Private*, pg. 3603
SEMATELL GMBH—See IMCap Partners AG; *Int'l*, pg. 3621
SENCHA, INC.—See HGGC, LLC; *U.S. Private*, pg. 1930
SENDGRID, INC.—See Twilio Inc.; *U.S. Public*, pg. 2206
SENDMAIL, INC.—See Thoma Bravo, L.P.; *U.S. Private*, pg. 4151
SENDOUTS LLC—See Insight Venture Management, LLC; *U.S. Private*, pg. 2087
SEOMOZ INC.—See Ziff Davis, Inc.; *U.S. Public*, pg. 2404
SEQUEST TECHNOLOGIES, INC.—See Genstar Capital, LLC; *U.S. Private*, pg. 1678
SERAPHIM SOFTWARE, LLC—See Blackbaud, Inc.; *U.S. Public*, pg. 341
SERRAVIEW AUSTRALIA PTY LTD—See Eptura, Inc.; *U.S. Private*, pg. 1414
SERVARUSRM; *U.S. Private*, pg. 3614
SERVICECHANNEL.COM, INC.—See Fortive Corporation; *U.S. Public*, pg. 871
SERVICECORE, LLC—See 1bg LLC; *U.S. Private*, pg. 3
SERVICECORE, LLC—See Mainsail Management Company, LLC; *U.S. Private*, pg. 2553
SERVICEMAX, INC.—See Silver Lake Group, LLC; *U.S. Private*, pg. 3658
SERVICEPOWER TECHNOLOGIES LTD—See Diversis Capital, LLC; *U.S. Private*, pg. 1244
SEVEN NETWORKS, INC.; *U.S. Private*, pg. 3618
SEVONE, INC.—See Turbonomic, Inc.; *U.S. Private*, pg. 4259
SEZMI CORPORATION—See Piksel, Inc.; *U.S. Private*, pg. 3180
SFDC AUSTRALIA PTY. LTD.—See Salesforce, Inc.; *U.S. Public*, pg. 1837
SFDC IRELAND LTD.—See Salesforce, Inc.; *U.S. Public*, pg. 1838
SFDC MEXICO S. DE R.L. DE C.V.—See Salesforce, Inc.; *U.S. Public*, pg. 1837
SFDC NETHERLANDS B.V.—See Salesforce, Inc.; *U.S. Public*, pg. 1837
SFDC SWEDEN AB (FINLAND)—See Salesforce, Inc.; *U.S. Public*, pg. 1837
SFDC SWEDEN AB—See Salesforce, Inc.; *U.S. Public*, pg. 1837
SFDC UK LTD. (LONDON)—See Salesforce, Inc.; *U.S. Public*, pg. 1837
SFDC UK LTD. (STAINES)—See Salesforce, Inc.; *U.S. Public*, pg. 1837
SFM SYSTEMS INC.—See State Fund Mutual Insurance Co.; *U.S. Private*, pg. 3792
SFM TECHNOLOGY, INC.—See Cadence Design Systems, Inc.; *U.S. Public*, pg. 419
SG GAMING UK LIMITED—See Light & Wonder, Inc.; *U.S. Public*, pg. 1314
SHANGHAI BAOSIGHT SOFTWARE CO., LTD.—See China Baowu Steel Group Corp., Ltd.; *Int'l*, pg. 1486
SHANGHAI EPAM SYSTEMS CO., LTD.—See EPAM Systems, Inc.; *U.S. Public*, pg. 783
SHANGHAI MENTOR MEDIA CO., LTD—See Carl Bennet AB; *Int'l*, pg. 1332
SHANGHAI MENTOR MEDIA PRINTING CO., LTD—See Carl Bennet AB; *Int'l*, pg. 1332
SHANGHAI WATERTEK INFORMATION TECHNOLOGY CO., LTD.—See Beijing Watertek Information Technology Co., Ltd.; *Int'l*, pg. 960
SHAREBUILDERS, INC.; *U.S. Private*, pg. 3626
SHARETHROUGH, INC.; *U.S. Private*, pg. 3626
SHARPLINK GAMING, INC.; *U.S. Private*, pg. 1873
SHARPLINK GAMING LTD.—See SharpLink Gaming, Inc.; *U.S. Public*, pg. 1873
SHARPSPRING, INC.; *U.S. Public*, pg. 1874
SHAZAM ENTERTAINMENT LTD.—See Apple Inc.; *U.S. Public*, pg. 169
SHENZHEN GEMVARY TECHNOLOGY CO., LTD.—See Guangdong Kinlong Hardware Prdcts Co., Ltd.; *Int'l*, pg. 3157
SHENZHEN WATERTEK INFORMATION TECHNOLOGY CO., LTD.—See Beijing Watertek Information Technology Co., Ltd.; *Int'l*, pg. 960
SHERPA SOFTWARE GROUP, LP; *U.S. Private*, pg. 3634
SHERWOOD MANUFACTURING CO., INC.—See Columbus A/S; *Int'l*, pg. 1706
SHI CANADA—See SHI International Corp.; *U.S. Private*, pg. 3635
SHI FRANCE—See SHI International Corp.; *U.S. Private*, pg. 3635
SHIFT PLUS INC.—See AltPlus Inc.; *Int'l*, pg. 397
SHI GERMANY—See SHI International Corp.; *U.S. Private*, pg. 3635
SHI HONG KONG—See SHI International Corp.; *U.S. Private*, pg. 3635
SHIPXPRESS, INC.—See General Electric Company; *U.S. Public*, pg. 920
SHI UK—See SHI International Corp.; *U.S. Private*, pg. 3635
SHI VANCOUVER—See SHI International Corp.; *U.S. Private*, pg. 3635
SHOPEYE, INC.; *U.S. Private*, pg. 3640
SHOPTECH SOFTWARE CORPORATION; *U.S. Private*, pg. 3640
SHORTCUTS SOFTWARE, INC.—See Constellation Software Inc.; *Int'l*, pg. 1773
SHOWCASE TECHNOLOGY, INC.—See Atlantic Street Capital Management LLC; *U.S. Private*, pg. 374
SIDECHANNEL, INC.; *U.S. Public*, pg. 1876
SIERRA ENTERTAINMENT, INC.—See Microsoft Corporation; *U.S. Public*, pg. 1439
SIGNALSCAPE, INC.; *U.S. Private*, pg. 3649
SIGN IN SOLUTIONS INC—See PSG Equity L.L.C.; *U.S. Private*, pg. 3297
SILKROAD TECHNOLOGY, INC.; *U.S. Private*, pg. 3652
SILVACO GROUP, INC.; *U.S. Public*, pg. 1880
SILVACO, INC.—See Silvaco Group, Inc.; *U.S. Public*, pg. 1880
SILVEREDGE GOVERNMENT SOLUTIONS—See Godspeed Capital Management LP; *U.S. Private*, pg. 1725
SILVERTECH MIDDLE EAST FZCO—See Rockwell Automation, Inc.; *U.S. Public*, pg. 1807
SIMIGON, INC.—See Maxify Solutions Inc.; *U.S. Private*, pg. 2618
SIMON & ARRINGTON INC.; *U.S. Private*, pg. 3666
SIMPLE ENERGY, INC.—See The AES Corporation; *U.S. Public*, pg. 2032
SIMPLEVIEW, INC.; *U.S. Private*, pg. 3667
SIMPLIFILE LC—See Intercontinental Exchange, Inc.; *U.S. Public*, pg. 1143
SIMPLITIUM LTD.—See Nasdaq, Inc.; *U.S. Public*, pg. 1492
SIMPLY MEASURED INC.—See Sprout Social, Inc.; *U.S. Public*, pg. 1920
SINCERELY INCORPORATED—See Qurate Retail, Inc.; *U.S. Public*, pg. 1758
SINNERSCHRADER PRAHA S.R.O.—See Accenture plc; *Int'l*, pg. 88
SINTECMEDIA, INC.—See Francisco Partners Management, LP; *U.S. Private*, pg. 1591
SINTECMEDIA WEM LTD—See Francisco Partners Management, LP; *U.S. Private*, pg. 1592
SIPX, INC.—See Cambridge Information Group, Inc.; *U.S. Private*, pg. 727
SIRIUSWARE, INC.—See accesso Technology Group Plc; *Int'l*, pg. 89
SISENCE INC.; *U.S. Private*, pg. 3675

CORPORATE AFFILIATIONS

SITE 9, INC.—See Astound Commerce Corp.; *U.S. Private*, pg. 361
SITECORE USA, INC.—See EQT AB; *Int'l*, pg. 2480
SITE ORGANIC, LLC; *U.S. Private*, pg. 3676
SITESCOUT INC.—See Centro Media, Inc.; *U.S. Private*, pg. 830
SITESPECT EUROPE—See SiteSpect, Inc.; *U.S. Private*, pg. 3676
SITESPECT GERMANY—See SiteSpect, Inc.; *U.S. Private*, pg. 3676
SITESPECT, INC.; *U.S. Private*, pg. 3676
SITESPECT UK—See SiteSpect, Inc.; *U.S. Private*, pg. 3676
SITEWIT CORP.; *U.S. Private*, pg. 3676
SITRION ONE—See NewsGator Technologies, Inc.; *U.S. Private*, pg. 2917
SIX88 SOLUTIONS, INC.; *U.S. Private*, pg. 3677
SKILLSNET, INC.; *U.S. Private*, pg. 3682
SKILLSOFT LIMITED—See Charterhouse Capital Partners LLP; *Int'l*, pg. 1456
SKIMBIT LTD.—See Symphony Technology Group, LLC; *U.S. Private*, pg. 3900
SKIMLINKS INC.—See Symphony Technology Group, LLC; *U.S. Private*, pg. 3900
SKINKERS LTD.—See Cisco Systems, Inc.; *U.S. Public*, pg. 499
SKYPE COMMUNICATIONS S.A.R.L.—See Microsoft Corporation; *U.S. Public*, pg. 1443
SKYTAP, INC.—See Kyndryl Holdings Inc.; *U.S. Public*, pg. 1278
SKYWAVE MOBILE COMMUNICATIONS (HK) LIMITED—See ORBCOMM, Inc.; *U.S. Public*, pg. 1614
SLEDGEHAMMER GAMES, INC—See Microsoft Corporation; *U.S. Public*, pg. 1439
SLEDGHAMMER GAMES, INC.—See Microsoft Corporation; *U.S. Public*, pg. 1439
SLIB S.A.—See Groupe BPCE; *Int'l*, pg. 3097
SLIDE, INC.—See Alphabet Inc.; *U.S. Public*, pg. 84
SLIGHTLY MAD STUDIOS LIMITED—See Electronic Arts Inc.; *U.S. Public*, pg. 723
SLI SYSTEMS, INC.; *U.S. Public*, pg. 3688
SLI SYSTEMS, INC.—See ESW Capital, LLC; *U.S. Private*, pg. 1430
SLI SYSTEMS, INC.—See SLI Systems, Inc.; *U.S. Public*, pg. 3688
SMARSH INC.—See K1 Investment Management, LLC; *U.S. Private*, pg. 2252
SMARTDATA ENTERPRISES INC.; *U.S. Private*, pg. 3691
SMARTDATA ENTERPRISES (INDIA) LTD.—See smartData Enterprises Inc.; *U.S. Private*, pg. 3692
SMARTDRAW.COM; *U.S. Private*, pg. 3692
SMARTERER, INC.—See Pluralsight, Inc.; *U.S. Public*, pg. 1699
SMARTFOCUS GERMANY GMBH—See Altor Equity Partners AB; *Int'l*, pg. 396
SMARTFOCUS HOLDINGS LTD.—See Altor Equity Partners AB; *Int'l*, pg. 395
SMARTFOCUS US INC.—See Altor Equity Partners AB; *Int'l*, pg. 396
SMARTRENT, INC.; *U.S. Public*, pg. 1895
SMARTRENT TECHNOLOGIES, INC.—See SmartRent, Inc.; *U.S. Public*, pg. 1896
SMARTSHEET AUSTRALIA PTY. LTD.—See Smartsheet Inc.; *U.S. Public*, pg. 1896
SMARTSHEET INC.; *U.S. Public*, pg. 1896
SMART SOFTWARE, INC.—See Clayton, Dubilier & Rice, LLC; *U.S. Private*, pg. 923
SMARTSTREAM TECHNOLOGIES LTD.—See DIFC Investments LLC; *Int'l*, pg. 2118
SMART TUITION; *U.S. Private*, pg. 3691
SMARTWARE GROUP; *U.S. Private*, pg. 3693
SMITH MICRO SOFTWARE, INC.—See Smith Micro Software, Inc.; *U.S. Public*, pg. 1896
SMITH MICRO SOFTWARE - WIRELESS & BROADBAND DIVISION—See Smith Micro Software, Inc.; *U.S. Public*, pg. 1896
SMITH SYSTEM PINION, LLC; *U.S. Private*, pg. 3695
SNAP INC.; *U.S. Public*, pg. 1897
SNAP-ON BUSINESS SOLUTIONS, INC.—See Snap-on Incorporated; *U.S. Public*, pg. 1898
SNAP-ON BUSINESS SOLUTIONS, SARL—See Snap-on Incorporated; *U.S. Public*, pg. 1898
S.N.P.S. ISRAEL LTD—See Synopsys, Inc.; *U.S. Public*, pg. 1971
SNUGG HOME LLC—See ABRY Partners, LLC; *U.S. Private*, pg. 41
SO CAL SOFT-PAK, INC.—See Dover Corporation; *U.S. Public*, pg. 682
SOCIAL INTEREST SOLUTIONS; *U.S. Private*, pg. 3703
SOCIAL POINT, S.L.—See Take-Two Interactive Software, Inc.; *U.S. Public*, pg. 1979
SOCIALTEXT, INC.; *U.S. Private*, pg. 3703
SOCIALWARE, INC.—See Thoma Bravo, L.P.; *U.S. Private*, pg. 4151
SOCIETY BRANDS, INC.; *U.S. Private*, pg. 3703
SOCIOUS, INC.—See Higher Logic, LLC; *U.S. Private*, pg. 1937
SOCIUS1 LLC—See Velosio, LLC; *U.S. Private*, pg. 4355

513210 — SOFTWARE PUBLISHERS

SOCRATA, INC.—See Tyler Technologies, Inc.; *U.S. Public,* pg. 2209
SOFTCHALK LLC—See Constellation Software Inc.; *Int'l,* pg. 1775
SOFTCOM GROUP INC.—See Hainan Traffic Administration Holding Co., Ltd.; *Int'l,* pg. 3215
SOFTECH, INC.; *U.S. Public,* pg. 1899
SOFTECH S.R.L.—See SofTech, Inc.; *U.S. Public,* pg. 1899
SOFTEL LTD.—See Belden, Inc.; *U.S. Public,* pg. 294
SOFTEON, INC.; *U.S. Private,* pg. 3705
SOFT-EX BV—See WidePoint Corporation; *U.S. Public,* pg. 2370
SOFT-EX COMMUNICATIONS LTD.—See WidePoint Corporation; *U.S. Public,* pg. 2370
SOFT-EX UK LIMITED—See WidePoint Corporation; *U.S. Public,* pg. 2370
SOFTGENETICS, LLC—See Insight Venture Management, LLC; *U.S. Private,* pg. 2090
SOFT TECH CONSULTING INC.; *U.S. Private,* pg. 3705
SOFTWARE AG (CANADA) INC.—See Silver Lake Group, LLC; *U.S. Private,* pg. 3659
SOFTWARE AG FINLAND OY—See Silver Lake Group, LLC; *U.S. Private,* pg. 3659
SOFTWARE AG FRANCE S.A.—See Silver Lake Group, LLC; *U.S. Private,* pg. 3659
SOFTWARE AG, INC.—See Silver Lake Group, LLC; *U.S. Private,* pg. 3660
SOFTWARE AG INDIA PVT LTD.—See Silver Lake Group, LLC; *U.S. Private,* pg. 3659
SOFTWARE AG NEDERLAND B.V.—See Silver Lake Group, LLC; *U.S. Private,* pg. 3660
SOFTWARE AG UK LTD.—See Silver Lake Group, LLC; *U.S. Private,* pg. 3660
SOFTWARE AG UK LTD.—See Silver Lake Group, LLC; *U.S. Private,* pg. 3660
THE SOFTWARE CONSTRUCTION CO. INC.; *U.S. Private,* pg. 4119
SOFTWARE CREDIT LP—See KKR & Co. Inc.; *U.S. Public,* pg. 1241
THE SOFTWARE DEVELOPMENT AND TESTING COMPANY, INC.; *U.S. Private,* pg. 4119
SOFTWARE DIVERSIFIED SERVICES; *U.S. Private,* pg. 3705
SOFTWARENOLOGY, LLC; *U.S. Private,* pg. 3706
SOFTWARE SECURE INC.—See Educational Testing Service Inc.; *U.S. Private,* pg. 1340
SOFTWEB SOLUTIONS INC.—See Avnet, Inc.; *U.S. Public,* pg. 254
SOFTWRITERS, INC.—See Roper Technologies, Inc.; *U.S. Public,* pg. 1812
SOLARWINDS MSP UK LTD.—See Silver Lake Group, LLC; *U.S. Private,* pg. 3661
SOLARWINDS MSP UK LTD.—See Thoma Bravo, L.P.; *U.S. Private,* pg. 4153
SOLERA ITALIA S.R.L.—See Vista Equity Partners, LLC; *U.S. Private,* pg. 4401
SOLERAN, INC.; *U.S. Private,* pg. 3709
SOLIUM OPTIONEASE, INC.—See Morgan Stanley; *U.S. Public,* pg. 1475
SOLUTIONS, INC.—See Constellation Software Inc.; *Int'l,* pg. 1774
SOMETRICS, INC.—See American Express Company; *U.S. Public,* pg. 102
SONANT SYSTEMS, INC.; *U.S. Private,* pg. 3712
SONIC SOLUTIONS LLC—See Adeia Inc.; *U.S. Public,* pg. 41
SOPHEON PLC—See Wellspring Worldwide, LLC; *U.S. Private,* pg. 4478
SOPHOS AB—See Apax Partners LLP; *Int'l,* pg. 506
SOPHOS ANTI-VIRUS ASIA PTE LTD.—See Apax Partners LLP; *Int'l,* pg. 506
SOPHOS B.V.—See Apax Partners LLP; *Int'l,* pg. 506
SOPHOS GMBH—See Apax Partners LLP; *Int'l,* pg. 506
SOPHOS INC.—See Apax Partners LLP; *Int'l,* pg. 506
SOPHOS ITALY S.R.L.—See Apax Partners LLP; *Int'l,* pg. 506
SOPHOS K.K.—See Apax Partners LLP; *Int'l,* pg. 506
SOPHOS LTD.—See Apax Partners LLP; *Int'l,* pg. 506
SOPHOS PTY LTD.—See Apax Partners LLP; *Int'l,* pg. 506
SOPHOS SARL—See Apax Partners LLP; *Int'l,* pg. 506
SORRISO TECHNOLOGIES, INC.; *U.S. Private,* pg. 3716
SOURCEBITS DIGITAL LLC—See Vora Ventures LLC; *U.S. Private,* pg. 4412
SOURCEPASS, INC.; *U.S. Private,* pg. 3718
SOUTH49 SOLUTIONS, INC.—See Movista Inc.; *U.S. Private,* pg. 2802
SOUTHEAST COMPUTER SOLUTIONS, INC.—See Net@Work, Inc.; *U.S. Private,* pg. 2887
SOUTHERN CROSS DISTRIBUTION SYSTEMS PTY LIMITED—See Elliott Management Corporation; *U.S. Private,* pg. 1373
SOUTHERN CROSS DISTRIBUTION SYSTEMS PTY LIMITED—See Siris Capital Group, LLC; *U.S. Private,* pg. 3674
SOUTHWARE INNOVATIONS, INC.—See Open Systems, Inc.; *U.S. Private,* pg. 3030
SPAMEXPERTS B.V.—See SolarWinds Corporation; *U.S. Public,* pg. 1900

SPARTA SYSTEMS, INC.—See New Mountain Capital, LLC; *U.S. Private,* pg. 2903
SPECIALIST DISTRIBUTION GROUP (SDG) LIMITED—See TD Synnex Corp; *U.S. Public,* pg. 1986
SPECTRUMDNA, INC.; *U.S. Private,* pg. 3753
SPELZON CORP.; *U.S. Private,* pg. 3754
SPIKES, INC.—See Aurionpro Solutions Limited; *Int'l,* pg. 711
SPILLMAN TECHNOLOGIES, INC.—See Motorola Solutions, Inc.; *U.S. Public,* pg. 1479
SPIN TECHNOLOGIES PVT. LTD.—See Cadence Design Systems, Inc.; *U.S. Public,* pg. 419
SPLUNK INC.—See Cisco Systems, Inc.; *U.S. Public,* pg. 500
SPLUNK TECHNOLOGY CONSULTING (BEIJING) CO., LTD.—See Cisco Systems, Inc.; *U.S. Public,* pg. 500
SPL WORLDGROUP, INC.—See Oracle Corporation; *U.S. Public,* pg. 1613
SPORTSENGINE, INC.—See Comcast Corporation; *U.S. Public,* pg. 540
SPORTSHUB GAMES NETWORK INC.—See SharpLink Gaming, Inc.; *U.S. Public,* pg. 1874
SPOT BUSINESS SYSTEMS, LLC.—See Clearent LLC; *U.S. Private,* pg. 932
SPOTHERO, INC.; *U.S. Private,* pg. 3761
SPOTZOT, INC.—See MacAndrews & Forbes Incorporated; *U.S. Private,* pg. 2532
SPRINGAHEAD; *U.S. Private,* pg. 3763
SPRINGER-MILLER INTERNATIONAL, LLC—See Constellation Software Inc.; *Int'l,* pg. 1773
SPRINGER-MILLER SYSTEMS - NEVADA—See Constellation Software Inc.; *Int'l,* pg. 1773
SPRINGER-MILLER SYSTEMS—See Constellation Software Inc.; *Int'l,* pg. 1773
SPRING METRICS, INC.; *U.S. Private,* pg. 3763
SPRYLOGIC TECHNOLOGIES LTD—See Aplab Limited; *Int'l,* pg. 515
SPSS INC. - ROCHESTER—See International Business Machines Corporation; *U.S. Public,* pg. 1148
SPSS INC.—See International Business Machines Corporation; *U.S. Public,* pg. 1148
SQL SENTRY, LLC—See SolarWinds Corporation; *U.S. Public,* pg. 1900
SQRRL DATA, INC.—See Amazon.com, Inc.; *U.S. Public,* pg. 90
SRAX, INC.; *U.S. Public,* pg. 1922
SRT SOLUTIONS INC.; *U.S. Private,* pg. 3768
SS&C TECHNOLOGIES HOLDINGS, INC. - HONG KONG—See SS&C Technologies Holdings, Inc.; *U.S. Public,* pg. 1924
SS&C TECHNOLOGIES HONG KONG LIMITED—See SS&C Technologies Holdings, Inc.; *U.S. Public,* pg. 1924
SS&C TECHNOLOGIES, INC.—See SS&C Technologies Holdings, Inc.; *U.S. Public,* pg. 1924
SS&C TECHNOLOGIES INDIA PRIVATE LIMITED—See SS&C Technologies Holdings, Inc.; *U.S. Public,* pg. 1924
SS&C TECHNOLOGIES (S) PTE LTD.—See SS&C Technologies Holdings, Inc.; *U.S. Public,* pg. 1924
STAFFPLAN LTD.—See Vista Equity Partners, LLC; *U.S. Private,* pg. 4394
STANDARDWARE INC.—See KKR & Co. Inc.; *U.S. Public,* pg. 1240
STAR-APIC SA—See 1Spatial Plc; *Int'l,* pg. 3
STAR-APIC SAS—See 1Spatial Plc; *Int'l,* pg. 3
STAR INFO TECH CO., LTD.—See Daido Steel Co., Ltd.; *Int'l,* pg. 1923
STARRETT BYTEWISE DEVELOPMENT, INC.—See MiddleGround Management, LP; *U.S. Private,* pg. 2713
STARTECH LABS, INC.; *U.S. Public,* pg. 1939
STATIT SOFTWARE, INC.—See Xerox Holdings Corporation; *U.S. Public,* pg. 2388
STATLINK SYSTEMS LLC; *U.S. Private,* pg. 3793
STATPRO ASIA LTD.—See TA Associates, Inc.; *U.S. Private,* pg. 3915
STATPRO (DEUTSCHLAND) GMBH—See TA Associates, Inc.; *U.S. Private,* pg. 3915
STATPRO FRANCE SARL—See TA Associates, Inc.; *U.S. Private,* pg. 3915
STATPRO GROUP LIMITED—See TA Associates, Inc.; *U.S. Private,* pg. 3915
STATPRO INC.—See TA Associates, Inc.; *U.S. Private,* pg. 3915
STATPRO ITALIA SRL—See TA Associates, Inc.; *U.S. Private,* pg. 3915
STATPRO S.A.—See TA Associates, Inc.; *U.S. Private,* pg. 3915
STATPRO SOUTH AFRICA PTY LTD.—See TA Associates, Inc.; *U.S. Private,* pg. 3915
STATSOFT, INC.—See Dell Technologies Inc.; *U.S. Public,* pg. 650
STATS PERFORM—See Vista Equity Partners, LLC; *U.S. Private,* pg. 4401
STEVIA CORP.; *U.S. Public,* pg. 1947
STIMULANT; *U.S. Private,* pg. 3812
STORAGECRAFT TECHNOLOGY CORPORATION—See Marlin Equity Partners, LLC; *U.S. Private,* pg. 2583
STORAGE TREASURES LLC—See OpenTech Alliance, Inc.; *U.S. Private,* pg. 3031

STORCENTRIC, INC.; *U.S. Private,* pg. 3831
STORD, INC.; *U.S. Private,* pg. 3831
STORMAN SOFTWARE, INC.—See Global Payments Inc.; *U.S. Public,* pg. 944
STORMAN SOFTWARE LIMITED—See Global Payments Inc.; *U.S. Public,* pg. 944
STORMAN SOFTWARE PTY LTD.—See Global Payments Inc.; *U.S. Public,* pg. 944
STORMSOURCE LLC—See Independence Capital Partners, LLC; *U.S. Private,* pg. 2056
STORMSOURCE LLC—See PCP Enterprise, L.P.; *U.S. Private,* pg. 3121
STRATA DECISION TECHNOLOGY, L.L.C.—See Roper Technologies, Inc.; *U.S. Public,* pg. 1813
STRATA MARKETING, INC.; *U.S. Private,* pg. 3833
STRATASOFT, INC.—See Vector Capital Management, L.P.; *U.S. Private,* pg. 4350
STRATATURE, INC.—See Microsoft Corporation; *U.S. Public,* pg. 1441
STREAMLINE DEVELOPMENT, LLC—See Siris Capital Group, LLC; *U.S. Private,* pg. 3673
STREAMWARE CORPORATION—See Crane NXT, Co.; *U.S. Public,* pg. 591
STREAMWEAVER, INC.—See KKR & Co. Inc.; *U.S. Public,* pg. 1241
STRIATA, INC.—See GI Manager L.P.; *U.S. Private,* pg. 1692
STRIPE, INC.; *U.S. Private,* pg. 3840
STRONGROOM SOLUTIONS, LLC—See AvidXchange Holdings, Inc.; *U.S. Public,* pg. 246
STUDIOFARMA S.R.L.—See CompuGroup Medical SE & Co. KGaA; *Int'l,* pg. 1756
SUBJEX CORPORATION; *U.S. Private,* pg. 3847
SUBSTANTIAL INC.; *U.S. Private,* pg. 3847
SUCCEED MANAGEMENT SOLUTIONS, LLC—See Providence Equity Partners L.L.C.; *U.S. Private,* pg. 3293
SUGARCRM DEUTSCHLAND GMBH—See Accel Partners L.P.; *U.S. Private,* pg. 49
SUGARCRM DEUTSCHLAND GMBH—See KKR & Co. Inc.; *U.S. Public,* pg. 1238
SUGARCRM, INC.—See Accel Partners L.P.; *U.S. Private,* pg. 48
SUGARCRM, INC.—See KKR & Co. Inc.; *U.S. Public,* pg. 1238
SUGARCRM SWEDEN—See Accel Partners L.P.; *U.S. Private,* pg. 49
SUGARCRM SWEDEN—See KKR & Co. Inc.; *U.S. Public,* pg. 1238
SUGARCRM UK—See Accel Partners L.P.; *U.S. Private,* pg. 49
SUGARCRM UK—See KKR & Co. Inc.; *U.S. Public,* pg. 1238
SUM EFFECT SOFTWARE, INC.; *U.S. Private,* pg. 3852
SUMMIT GROUP SOFTWARE; *U.S. Private,* pg. 3854
SUMOTEXT CORP.—See Cisco Systems, Inc.; *U.S. Public,* pg. 499
SUMTOTAL SYSTEMS LLC—See Clearlake Capital Group, L.P.; *U.S. Private,* pg. 934
SUMTOTAL SYSTEMS - PARSIPPANY—See Clearlake Capital Group, L.P.; *U.S. Private,* pg. 934
SUMTOTAL SYSTEMS - WEST DES MOINES—See Clearlake Capital Group, L.P.; *U.S. Private,* pg. 934
SUNCHIP TECHNOLOGY, INC.; *U.S. Private,* pg. 3865
SUNDAY GMBH—See Bertelsmann SE & Co. KGaA; *Int'l,* pg. 996
SUNDAYSKY INC.—See Clearhaven Partners LP; *U.S. Private,* pg. 933
SUNDAYSKY ISRAEL—See Clearhaven Partners LP; *U.S. Private,* pg. 933
SUNFLOWER SYSTEMS—See CGI Inc.; *Int'l,* pg. 1432
SUNFLOWER SYSTEMS—See CGI Inc.; *Int'l,* pg. 1432
SUNGARD AVAILABILITY SERVICES - SAN RAMON—See SunGard Availability Services Capital, Inc.; *U.S. Private,* pg. 3867
SUNGARD AVAILABILITY SERVICES (UK) LIMITED—See SunGard Availability Services Capital, Inc.; *U.S. Private,* pg. 3867
SUN MICROSYSTEMS KOREA, LTD.—See Oracle Corporation; *U.S. Public,* pg. 1611
SUNVIEW SOFTWARE INC.—See Serviceaide, Inc.; *U.S. Private,* pg. 3616
SUPERION PUBLIC SECTOR, LLC—See Vista Equity Partners, LLC; *U.S. Private,* pg. 4395
SUPERIOR MEDIA SOLUTIONS LLC; *U.S. Private,* pg. 3879
SUPPORT.COM, INC.—See RealDefense LLC; *U.S. Private,* pg. 3368
SUREHARVEST, INC.—See Where Food Comes From, Inc.; *U.S. Public,* pg. 2366
SURGE LLC; *U.S. Private,* pg. 3884
SURGICAL INFORMATION SYSTEMS, LLC—See Wells Fargo & Company; *U.S. Public,* pg. 2344
SURVEYCONNECT INC.—See Orcus Technologies, Inc; *U.S. Private,* pg. 3039
SURVEYMONKEY.COM LLC; *U.S. Private,* pg. 3885
SUYASH SOFTWARE PVT. LTD.—See Solventum Corporation; *U.S. Public,* pg. 1902
SVK SYSTEMS; *U.S. Private,* pg. 3889

513210 — SOFTWARE PUBLISHERS

SWIFTTRIP, LLC—See Altour International, Inc.; *U.S. Private*, pg. 210
SWK TECHNOLOGIES, INC.—See QXO, Inc.; *U.S. Public*, pg. 1758
SWRVE NEW MEDIA INC.—See Long Ridge Equity Partners, LLC; *U.S. Private*, pg. 2492
SYMANTEC CORPORATION - MIAMI—See Gen Digital Inc.; *U.S. Public*, pg. 911
SYMANTEC CORPORATION - OREM—See Gen Digital Inc.; *U.S. Public*, pg. 911
SYMANTEC CORPORATION - WALTHAM—See Gen Digital Inc.; *U.S. Public*, pg. 911
SYMANTEC INDIA PRIVATE LIMITED—See Gen Digital Inc.; *U.S. Public*, pg. 911
SYMANTEC (SWITZERLAND) SARL—See Gen Digital Inc.; *U.S. Public*, pg. 910
SYMANTEC TECHNOLOGIES (IRELAND) LIMITED—See Gen Digital Inc.; *U.S. Public*, pg. 911
SYMANTEC (UK) LTD. - READING—See Gen Digital Inc.; *U.S. Public*, pg. 911
SYMBILITY SOLUTIONS, INC.—See Insight Venture Management, LLC; *U.S. Public*, pg. 2089
SYMBILITY SOLUTIONS, INC.—See Stone Point Capital LLC; *U.S. Private*, pg. 3823
SYMBIOSYS, INC.; *U.S. Private*, pg. 3899
SYMBOLIC LOGIC, INC.—See CCUR Holdings Inc.; *U.S. Public*, pg. 461
SYMBRIO AB—See Carl Bennet AB; *Int'l*, pg. 1332
SYMBRIO AS—See Carl Bennet AB; *Int'l*, pg. 1332
SYMPHONYEYC D.O.O.—See Symphony Technology Group, LLC; *U.S. Private*, pg. 3902
SYMPHONYEYC FRANCE S.A.S.—See Symphony Technology Group, LLC; *U.S. Private*, pg. 3902
SYMPHONYEYC GMBH—See Symphony Technology Group, LLC; *U.S. Private*, pg. 3902
SYMPHONYEYC SOLUTION UK LTD.—See Symphony Technology Group, LLC; *U.S. Private*, pg. 3902
SYMPHONYEYC—See Symphony Technology Group, LLC; *U.S. Private*, pg. 3902
SYMPHONYEYC—See Symphony Technology Group, LLC; *U.S. Private*, pg. 3902
SYMPLICITY CORPORATION—See H.I.G. Capital, LLC; *U.S. Private*, pg. 1831
SYMPLIFIED INC.; *U.S. Private*, pg. 3902
SYMPRO, INC.—See Constellation Software Inc.; *Int'l*, pg. 1772
SYNAGEX, INC; *U.S. Private*, pg. 3902
SYNCPLICITY LLC—See Axway Software SA; *Int'l*, pg. 772
SYNERGY BUSINESS SOLUTIONS INC—See Velosio, LLC; *U.S. Private*, pg. 4355
SYNERZIP; *U.S. Private*, pg. 3904
SYNOPSYS DENMARK APS—See Synopsys, Inc.; *U.S. Public*, pg. 1971
SYNOPSYS EMULATION AND VERIFICATION S.A.S.—See Synopsys, Inc.; *U.S. Public*, pg. 1971
SYNOPSYS GMBH—See Synopsys, Inc.; *U.S. Public*, pg. 1971
SYNOPSYS INTERNATIONAL LIMITED—See Synopsys, Inc.; *U.S. Public*, pg. 1971
SYNOPSYS ITALIA S.R.L.—See Synopsys, Inc.; *U.S. Public*, pg. 1971
SYNOPSYS KOREA INC.—See Synopsys, Inc.; *U.S. Public*, pg. 1971
SYNOPSYS (NORTHERN EUROPE) LTD.—See Synopsys, Inc.; *U.S. Public*, pg. 1971
SYNOPSYS (SINGAPORE) PTE. LTD.—See Synopsys, Inc.; *U.S. Public*, pg. 1970
SYNOPSYS SWITZERLAND LLC—See Synopsys, Inc.; *U.S. Public*, pg. 1971
SYNOPSYS TAIWAN CO., LTD.—See Synopsys, Inc.; *U.S. Public*, pg. 1971
SYNOVIA SOLUTIONS LLC—See CalAmp Corp.; *U.S. Public*, pg. 422
SYSCON JUSTICE SYSTEMS, INC.—See Constellation Software Inc.; *Int'l*, pg. 1774
SYSMIND LLC; *U.S. Private*, pg. 3906
SYSOMOS INC.—See Meltwater News US Inc.; *U.S. Private*, pg. 2663
SYSOP TOOLS, INC.; *U.S. Private*, pg. 3906
SYSTAR SA—See Axway Software SA; *Int'l*, pg. 772
SYSTEM DEVELOPMENT.INTEGRATION LLC; *U.S. Private*, pg. 3906
SYSTEMS ALTERNATIVES INTERNATIONAL LLC—See Brady plc; *Int'l*, pg. 1135
SYSTRAN S.A.—See CHAPS Holding SAS; *Int'l*, pg. 1448
SYSTRAN SOFTWARE, INC.—See CHAPS Holding SAS; *Int'l*, pg. 1448
T2 SYSTEMS CANADA INC.—See Verra Mobility Corporation; *U.S. Public*, pg. 2287
T2 SYSTEMS, INC.—See Verra Mobility Corporation; *U.S. Public*, pg. 2287
TABBLER GMBH—See Bertelsmann SE & Co. KGaA; *Int'l*, pg. 996
TABLEAU SOFTWARE, INC.—See Salesforce, Inc.; *U.S. Public*, pg. 1838
TABLEAU SOFTWARE UK—See Salesforce, Inc; *U.S. Public*, pg. 1838
TABOOLA.COM LTD.; *U.S. Public*, pg. 1978

TACIT KNOWLEDGE LTD.—See Grid Dynamics Holdings, Inc.; *U.S. Public*, pg. 969
TACTICAL COMMUNICATIONS GROUP, LLC—See Curtiss-Wright Corporation; *U.S. Public*, pg. 612
TAG EMPLOYER SERVICES, LLC; *U.S. Private*, pg. 3922
TAGMAN, INC.—See Ensighten, Inc.; *U.S. Private*, pg. 1402
TAGMAN LIMITED—See Ensighten, Inc.; *U.S. Private*, pg. 1402
TAHZOO LLC; *U.S. Private*, pg. 3923
TAKE-TWO INTERACTIVE BENELUX B.V.—See Take-Two Interactive Software, Inc.; *U.S. Public*, pg. 1979
TAKE-TWO INTERACTIVE SOFTWARE EUROPE LIMITED—See Take-Two Interactive Software, Inc.; *U.S. Public*, pg. 1979
TALEND BEIJNG TECHNOLOGY CO., LTD.—See Thoma Bravo, L.P.; *U.S. Private*, pg. 4154
TALEND GMBH—See Thoma Bravo, L.P.; *U.S. Private*, pg. 4154
TALEND GMBH—See Thoma Bravo, L.P.; *U.S. Private*, pg. 4154
TALEND GMBH—See Thoma Bravo, L.P.; *U.S. Private*, pg. 4154
TALEND GMBH—See Thoma Bravo, L.P.; *U.S. Private*, pg. 4154
TALEND INC.—See Thoma Bravo, L.P.; *U.S. Private*, pg. 4154
TALEND KK—See Thoma Bravo, L.P.; *U.S. Private*, pg. 4154
TALEND LTD—See Thoma Bravo, L.P.; *U.S. Private*, pg. 4154
TALEND SA—See Thoma Bravo, L.P.; *U.S. Private*, pg. 4154
TALISMAN SYSTEMS GROUP, INC.—See Perspecta LLC; *U.S. Private*, pg. 3156
TALKPOINT EMEA—See Siris Capital Group, LLC; *U.S. Private*, pg. 3674
TALKPOINT HOLDINGS, L.L.C.—See Siris Capital Group, LLC; *U.S. Private*, pg. 3674
TALLEGA SOFTWARE, LLC—See InStream, LLC; *U.S. Private*, pg. 2094
TALYST, INC.; *U.S. Private*, pg. 3927
TANDBERG DATA GMBH—See Cyrus Capital Partners, L.P.; *U.S. Private*, pg. 1135
TANDBERG DATA (JAPAN) INC.—See Cyrus Capital Partners, L.P.; *U.S. Private*, pg. 1135
TANDBERG DATA NORGE AS—See Cyrus Capital Partners, L.P.; *U.S. Private*, pg. 1135
TANDBERG DATA—See Cyrus Capital Partners, L.P.; *U.S. Private*, pg. 1135
TANGOE (CHINA) CO., LTD.—See Marlin Equity Partners, LLC; *U.S. Private*, pg. 2583
TANGOE, INC.—See Marlin Equity Partners, LLC; *U.S. Private*, pg. 2583
TANGOE INDIA SOFTEK SERVICES PRIVATE LIMITED—See Marlin Equity Partners, LLC; *U.S. Private*, pg. 2584
TANGOME, INC.; *U.S. Private*, pg. 3931
TAPAD, INC.—See Experian plc; *Int'l*, pg. 2588
TAPESTRY SOLUTIONS, INC.—See The Boeing Company; *U.S. Public*, pg. 2040
TAPESTRY SOLUTIONS—See The Boeing Company; *U.S. Public*, pg. 2040
TAPINATOR, INC.; *U.S. Public*, pg. 1981
TAXACT, INC.—See Genstar Capital, LLC; *U.S. Private*, pg. 1676
TAX COMPLIANCE, INC.—See Corporation Service Company; *U.S. Private*, pg. 1058
TCN, INC.; *U.S. Private*, pg. 3943
TD AMERITRADE HONG KONG LIMITED—See The Charles Schwab Corporation; *U.S. Public*, pg. 2058
TD AMERITRADE SINGAPORE PTE. LTD.—See The Charles Schwab Corporation; *U.S. Public*, pg. 2058
TDC SYSTEMS INTEGRATION; *U.S. Private*, pg. 3944
TEAM SOLUTIONS GROUP, INC.; *U.S. Private*, pg. 3950
TEAMUNIFY, LLC—See Comcast Corporation; *U.S. Public*, pg. 540
TECHAPP SOLUTIONS, INC.; *U.S. Private*, pg. 3952
TECH CENTRAL INC.; *U.S. Public*, pg. 1988
TECH DATA LIMITED—See TD Synnex Corp; *U.S. Public*, pg. 1986
TECHINSIGHTS INC.—See CVC Capital Partners SICAV-FIS S.A.; *Int'l*, pg. 1888
TECHNICAL PERSPECTIVES, INC.—See Computer Automation Systems, Inc.; *U.S. Private*, pg. 1004
TECHNOLOGY CONCEPTS & DESIGN, INC.; *U.S. Private*, pg. 3955
TECHORBIT, INC.—See Brightcom Group Ltd.; *Int'l*, pg. 1162
TECHSMITH CORPORATION; *U.S. Private*, pg. 3956
TECHSQL4U, INC.; *U.S. Private*, pg. 3956
TECHTRACKER, INC.—See National Amusements, Inc.; *U.S. Private*, pg. 2840
TECHXTEND, INC.—See Climb Global Solutions, Inc.; *U.S. Public*, pg. 515
TEGRITY, INC.—See Platinum Equity, LLC; *U.S. Private*, pg. 3206
TEIKAMETRICS LLC; *U.S. Private*, pg. 3958
TELARIA BRAZIL PUBLICIDADE LTDA.—See Magnite, Inc.; *U.S. Public*, pg. 1354

CORPORATE AFFILIATIONS

TELARIX, INC.—See Vista Equity Partners, LLC; *U.S. Private*, pg. 4402
TELEDYNE CARIS, INC.—See Teledyne Technologies Incorporated; *U.S. Public*, pg. 1993
TELEPHARM, LLC—See Cardinal Health, Inc.; *U.S. Public*, pg. 434
TELERIK INDIA PRIVATE LIMITED—See Progress Software Corporation; *U.S. Public*, pg. 1726
TELERIK UK LTD.—See Progress Software Corporation; *U.S. Public*, pg. 1725
TELESOFT CORP.—See Sumeru Equity Partners LLC; *U.S. Private*, pg. 3852
TELESPHERE; *U.S. Private*, pg. 3961
TELESTREAM, LLC—See Genstar Capital, LLC; *U.S. Private*, pg. 1679
TELETRACKING TECHNOLOGIES, INC.; *U.S. Private*, pg. 3962
TELETRAC NAVMAN—See Vontier Corporation; *U.S. Public*, pg. 2309
TELLABS SANTA CLARA—See Marlin Equity Partners, LLC; *U.S. Private*, pg. 2585
TELLAGO INC.; *U.S. Private*, pg. 3962
TELMAR GROUP INC.—See Splashlight LLC; *U.S. Private*, pg. 3759
TELSTRAT, INC.—See Marlin Equity Partners, LLC; *U.S. Private*, pg. 2585
TEMPO SOFTWARE, INC.; *U.S. Private*, pg. 3964
TENDO SYSTEMS INC.; *U.S. Private*, pg. 3966
TENSTREET LLC—See Providence Equity Partners L.L.C.; *U.S. Private*, pg. 3293
TERACENT CORPORATION—See Alphabet Inc.; *U.S. Public*, pg. 84
TERADATA ASTER DATA—See Teradata Corporation; *U.S. Public*, pg. 2017
TERA TECHNOLOGIES, INC.; *U.S. Private*, pg. 3969
TERNA GMBH—See Allgeier SE; *Int'l*, pg. 337
TERNPRO INC.—See Smartsheet Inc.; *U.S. Public*, pg. 1896
TERRACOTTA, INC.—See Silver Lake Group, LLC; *U.S. Private*, pg. 3660
TESTPLANT UK LIMITED—See Keysight Technologies, Inc.; *U.S. Public*, pg. 1227
TEXAS INSTRUMENTS BROADBAND COMMUNICATIONS GROUP—See Texas Instruments Incorporated; *U.S. Public*, pg. 2026
TGA UTBILDNING AB—See AcadeMedia AB; *Int'l*, pg. 77
THINGWORX, INC.—See PTC Inc.; *U.S. Public*, pg. 1735
THINK BROWNSTONE INC.; *U.S. Private*, pg. 4144
THINSPACE TECHNOLOGY, INC.; *U.S. Public*, pg. 2155
THIRD FINANCIAL SOFTWARE LIMITED—See Grafton Capital Limited; *Int'l*, pg. 3050
THISMOMENT, INC.; *U.S. Private*, pg. 4145
THOMASTECH, LLC; *U.S. Private*, pg. 4158
THOMPSON TECHNOLOGIES, INC.; *U.S. Private*, pg. 4162
THOUSANDEYES, INC.—See Cisco Systems, Inc.; *U.S. Public*, pg. 500
THREAT STACK, INC.—See F5, Inc.; *U.S. Public*, pg. 819
THREATTRACK SECURITY, INC.; *U.S. Private*, pg. 4163
THREE RIVERS SYSTEMS, INC.—See Advent International Corporation; *U.S. Private*, pg. 107
THRIVEHIVE, INC.—See Gannett Co., Inc.; *U.S. Public*, pg. 906
THURSBY SOFTWARE SYSTEMS, INC.—See Identiv, Inc.; *U.S. Public*, pg. 1089
TIBCO EXTENDED RESULTS, INC.—See Vista Equity Partners, LLC; *U.S. Private*, pg. 4402
TIBCO LOGLOGIC LLC—See Vista Equity Partners, LLC; *U.S. Private*, pg. 4402
TIBCO SOFTWARE AB—See Vista Equity Partners, LLC; *U.S. Private*, pg. 4402
TIBCO SOFTWARE (BEIJING) CO., LTD.—See Vista Equity Partners, LLC; *U.S. Private*, pg. 4402
TIBCO SOFTWARE HONG KONG LIMITED—See Vista Equity Partners, LLC; *U.S. Private*, pg. 4402
TIBCO SOFTWARE INC. - PRINCETON—See Vista Equity Partners, LLC; *U.S. Private*, pg. 4402
TIBCO SOFTWARE INC.—See Vista Equity Partners, LLC; *U.S. Private*, pg. 4401
TIBCO SOFTWARE KOREA LTD.—See Vista Equity Partners, LLC; *U.S. Private*, pg. 4402
TIBCO SOFTWARE LIMITED—See Vista Equity Partners, LLC; *U.S. Private*, pg. 4402
TIBCO SOFTWARE N.V.—See Vista Equity Partners, LLC; *U.S. Private*, pg. 4402
TIBCO SOFTWARE PORTUGAL—See Vista Equity Partners, LLC; *U.S. Private*, pg. 4402
TIBCO SOFTWARE SA DE CV—See Vista Equity Partners, LLC; *U.S. Private*, pg. 4402
TIBCO SOFTWARE SINGAPORE PTE LTD.—See Vista Equity Partners, LLC; *U.S. Private*, pg. 4402
TIBCO YAZILIM SANAYI VE TICARET LIMITED SIRKETI—See Vista Equity Partners, LLC; *U.S. Private*, pg. 4402
TICKERPLANT LIMITED—See 63 moons technologies limited; *Int'l*, pg. 14
TICKET ALTERNATIVE, LLC; *U.S. Private*, pg. 4167
TICKETBISCUIT, LLC—See Intelli-Mark Technologies, Inc.; *U.S. Private*, pg. 2105

N.A.I.C.S. INDEX

513210 — SOFTWARE PUBLISHERS

TIEMPO DEVELOPMENT CENTER—See 3Pillar Global, Inc.; *U.S. Private*, pg. 14
TIEMPO DEVELOPMENT CENTER—See 3Pillar Global, Inc.; *U.S. Private*, pg. 14
TIEMPO DEVELOPMENT LLC—See 3Pillar Global, Inc.; *U.S. Private*, pg. 14
TIGERCONNECT, INC.; *U.S. Private*, pg. 4170
TIGERLOGIC CORPORATION; *U.S. Private*, pg. 4170
TIGERPAW SOFTWARE, INC.—See Rev.io, LLC; *U.S. Private*, pg. 3413
TIME LINK INTERNATIONAL CORP.—See Hellman & Friedman LLC; *U.S. Private*, pg. 1911
TIMETARGET PTY LTD—See Accel Partners L.P.; *U.S. Private*, pg. 49
TIMETARGET PTY LTD—See KKR & Co. Inc.; *U.S. Public*, pg. 1239
TINDER, INC.—See IAC Inc.; *U.S. Public*, pg. 1082
TITAN CLOUD SOFTWARE, LLC; *U.S. Private*, pg. 4177
TMW SYSTEMS, INC. - NASHVILLE—See Trimble, Inc.; *U.S. Public*, pg. 2191
TMW SYSTEMS, INC.—See Trimble, Inc.; *U.S. Public*, pg. 2191
TODAYTIX INC.—See Great Hill Partners, L.P.; *U.S. Private*, pg. 1763
TODD HSU CONSULTANTS, INC.—See Elliott Management Corporation; *U.S. Private*, pg. 1367
TODD HSU CONSULTANTS, INC.—See Vista Equity Partners, LLC; *U.S. Private*, pg. 4396
TOGETHERWORK HOLDINGS, LLC—See GI Manager L.P.; *U.S. Private*, pg. 1694
TOKUTEK, INC.—See Percona LLC.; *U.S. Private*, pg. 3147
TOO PLUS MICRO KAZAKHSTAN LP—See EPAM Systems, Inc.; *U.S. Public*, pg. 783
TOPAZ SYSTEMS, INC.; *U.S. Private*, pg. 4187
TOPICA, INC.; *U.S. Private*, pg. 4187
TOPLINGO DEVELOPMENT, INC.; *U.S. Private*, pg. 4187
TOP PRODUCER SYSTEMS COMPANY ULC—See Constellation Real Estate Group, Inc.; *U.S. Private*, pg. 1023
TORO DATA LABS, INC.; *U.S. Private*, pg. 4189
TOTAL SPECIFIC SOLUTIONS (TSS) B.V.—See Constellation Software Inc.; *Int'l*, pg. 1774
TOUCHNET INFORMATION SYSTEMS, INC.—See Global Payments Inc.; *U.S. Public*, pg. 944
TOUCHSUITE; *U.S. Private*, pg. 4193
TOUCHTOWN INC.—See Atlantic Street Capital Management LLC; *U.S. Private*, pg. 374
TOWERDATA, INC.; *U.S. Private*, pg. 4196
TPG SOFTWARE, INC.—See The Carlyle Group Inc.; *U.S. Public*, pg. 2045
TR3 SOLUTIONS, INC.—See Rock Solid UK Ltd.; *U.S. Private*, pg. 3465
TRACEGAINS, INC.—See Veralto Corporation; *U.S. Public*, pg. 2280
TRACE ONE SAS—See Symphony Technology Group, LLC; *U.S. Private*, pg. 3902
TRACK DATA CORPORATION; *U.S. Private*, pg. 4201
THE TRADE DESK, INC.; *U.S. Public*, pg. 2135
TRADESHIFT INC.; *U.S. Private*, pg. 4202
TRADING TECHNOLOGIES INTERNATIONAL, INC.; *U.S. Private*, pg. 4202
TRANSCORE HOLDINGS INC.—See Roper Technologies, Inc.; *U.S. Public*, pg. 1813
TRANSENGEN, INC.—See General Atlantic Service Company, L.P.; *U.S. Private*, pg. 1662
TRANSOFT GROUP LTD.—See HgCapital Trust plc; *Int'l*, pg. 3377
TRANZACT TECHNOLOGIES INC.; *U.S. Private*, pg. 4212
TRAVELCLICK, INC.—See Amadeus IT Group, S.A.; *Int'l*, pg. 407
TRAVEL TRIPPER, LLC; *U.S. Private*, pg. 4213
TRESENSA INC.—See Blackstone Inc.; *U.S. Public*, pg. 361
TREYARCH CORPORATION—See Microsoft Corporation; *U.S. Public*, pg. 1439
TRIBUTE INC.—See Constellation Software Inc.; *Int'l*, pg. 1776
TRICORE SOLUTIONS LLC—See Apollo Global Management, Inc.; *U.S. Public*, pg. 154
TRICYCLE, INC.—See Berkshire Hathaway Inc.; *U.S. Public*, pg. 316
TRILLIUM SOFTWARE, INC.—See Harte Hanks, Inc.; *U.S. Public*, pg. 986
TRIMBLE MEP—See Trimble, Inc.; *U.S. Public*, pg. 2192
TRINTECH TECHNOLOGIES LIMITED—See Summit Partners, L.P.; *U.S. Private*, pg. 3856
TRIPLE POINT TECHNOLOGY, INC.—See TA Associates, Inc.; *U.S. Private*, pg. 3918
TRIPLE POINT TECHNOLOGY PTY LTD.—See TA Associates, Inc.; *U.S. Private*, pg. 3919
TRIPLESEAT SOFTWARE, LLC—See Vista Equity Partners, LLC; *U.S. Private*, pg. 4402
TRIPSPARK TECHNOLOGIES—See Constellation Software Inc.; *Int'l*, pg. 1775
TRIPWIRE ASIA-PACIFIC—See HGGC, LLC; *U.S. Private*, pg. 1929
TRIPWIRE EMEA—See HGGC, LLC; *U.S. Private*, pg. 1929
TRIPWIRE, INC.—See HGGC, LLC; *U.S. Private*, pg. 1929
TRIPWIRE JAPAN KK—See HGGC, LLC; *U.S. Private*, pg. 1929

TRIRIGA INC.—See International Business Machines Corporation; *U.S. Public*, pg. 1150
TRITECH SOFTWARE SYSTEMS INC.—See Vista Equity Partners, LLC; *U.S. Private*, pg. 4395
TRITON DIGITAL INC.—See iHeartMedia, Inc.; *U.S. Public*, pg. 1097
TRIVANTIS CORPORATION—See Fundos Group LLC; *U.S. Private*, pg. 1623
TRIVANTIS CORPORATION—See Trinity Private Equity Group, LLC; *U.S. Private*, pg. 4235
TRUEABILITY INC.—See ALUMINUM.IO, INC.; *U.S. Private*, pg. 211
TRUECOMMERCE, INC.—See Welsh, Carson, Anderson & Stowe; *U.S. Private*, pg. 4480
TRUECONTEXT CORPORATION—See Battery Ventures, L.P.; *U.S. Private*, pg. 489
TRUE INFLUENCE, LLC; *U.S. Private*, pg. 4247
TSI HEALTHCARE, INC; *U.S. Private*, pg. 4253
T&T COMPUTERS, INC.; *U.S. Public*, pg. 3910
TTI TEAM TELECOM INTERNATIONAL LTD.—See TEOCO Corporation; *U.S. Private*, pg. 3969
TTI TELECOM—See TEOCO Corporation; *U.S. Private*, pg. 3969
TUBEMOGUL, INC.—See Adobe Inc.; *U.S. Public*, pg. 43
TUKATECH INC.; *U.S. Private*, pg. 4257
TUNECORE, INC.—See Believe SAS; *Int'l*, pg. 964
TUNGSTEN CORPORATION PLC—See Clearlake Capital Group, L.P.; *U.S. Private*, pg. 936
TUNGSTEN CORPORATION PLC—See TA Associates, Inc.; *U.S. Private*, pg. 3916
TURBOMED VERTRIEBS- UND SERVICE GMBH—See CompuGroup Medical SE & Co. KGaA; *Int'l*, pg. 1756
TURBONOMIC, INC.; *U.S. Private*, pg. 4259
TURNING TECHNOLOGIES, LLC—See Centre Lane Partners, LLC; *U.S. Private*, pg. 828
TURNTO NETWORKS, INC.—See Pixlee, Inc.; *U.S. Private*, pg. 3193
TVT VIDEO TECHNOLOGIES, INC.—See Vista Equity Partners, LLC; *U.S. Private*, pg. 4401
TWILIO BERLIN GMBH—See Twilio Inc.; *U.S. Public*, pg. 2206
TWILIO SWEDEN AB—See Twilio Inc.; *U.S. Public*, pg. 2206
TWISTBOX ENTERTAINMENT, INC.—See Digital Turbine, Inc.; *U.S. Public*, pg. 664
TWISTED TECHNOLOGIES, INC.—See TheIPGuys.Net LLC; *U.S. Private*, pg. 4141
TWO SIX TECHNOLOGIES, INC.—See The Carlyle Group Inc.; *U.S. Public*, pg. 2056
UBER AUSTRIA GMBH—See Uber Technologies, Inc.; *U.S. Public*, pg. 2217
UBER B.V.—See Uber Technologies, Inc.; *U.S. Public*, pg. 2217
UBER FRANCE SAS—See Uber Technologies, Inc.; *U.S. Public*, pg. 2217
UBER GERMANY GMBH—See Uber Technologies, Inc.; *U.S. Public*, pg. 2217
UBER INDIA SYSTEMS PRIVATE LIMITED—See Uber Technologies, Inc.; *U.S. Public*, pg. 2217
UBER JAPAN CO. LTD.—See Uber Technologies, Inc.; *U.S. Public*, pg. 2217
UBER LONDON LIMITED—See Uber Technologies, Inc.; *U.S. Public*, pg. 2217
UBER POLAND SP. Z O.O.—See Uber Technologies, Inc.; *U.S. Public*, pg. 2217
UBER SOUTH AFRICA TECHNOLOGY (PTY) LTD.—See Uber Technologies, Inc.; *U.S. Public*, pg. 2217
UBER TECHNOLOGIES, INC.; *U.S. Public*, pg. 2217
ULTRA ELECTRONICS ADVANCED TACTICAL SYSTEMS, INC.—See Advent International Corporation; *U.S. Private*, pg. 100
UNACAST, INC.; *U.S. Private*, pg. 4279
UNICOM GLOBAL IBERIA, S.A.—See UNICOM Global, Inc.; *U.S. Public*, pg. 4281
UNIDESK CORPORATION—See Elliott Management Corporation; *U.S. Private*, pg. 1367
UNIDESK CORPORATION—See Vista Equity Partners, LLC; *U.S. Private*, pg. 4396
UNIFIED DEVELOPMENT, INC.; *U.S. Private*, pg. 4282
UNISON SOFTWARE, INC.—See The Carlyle Group Inc.; *U.S. Public*, pg. 2056
UNISON SYSTEMS, INC.; *U.S. Private*, pg. 4286
UNIT4 NV—See Advent International Corporation; *U.S. Private*, pg. 107
UNIVA CORPORATION—See Altair Engineering, Inc.; *U.S. Public*, pg. 86
UNIVERSAL CONVERSION TECHNOLOGIES—See EquiSoft Inc.; *U.S. Private*, pg. 1416
UNIVERSE GROUP PLC—See TA Associates, Inc.; *U.S. Private*, pg. 3917
UPDATE CRM INC.—See ESW Capital, LLC; *U.S. Private*, pg. 1429
UPDATER INC.; *U.S. Private*, pg. 4311
UPFRONT HEALTHCARE SERVICES, INC.; *U.S. Private*, pg. 4311
UPLOGIX, INC.—See Lantronix, Inc.; *U.S. Public*, pg. 1293
UPP TECHNOLOGY, INC.; *U.S. Private*, pg. 4312
UPTAKE CANADA, INC.—See Uptake Technologies, LLC; *U.S. Private*, pg. 4313

UPTAKE TECHNOLOGIES, LLC; *U.S. Private*, pg. 4313
UPTOWN NETWORK, LLC; *U.S. Private*, pg. 4313
USERVOICE, INC.; *U.S. Private*, pg. 4323
U.S. HOSPITALITY PUBLISHERS, INC.—See Atlantic Street Capital Management LLC; *U.S. Private*, pg. 374
UTIMACO GMBH—See EQT AB; *Int'l*, pg. 2481
VALANT MEDICAL SOLUTIONS INC.—See Resurgens Technology Partners, LLC; *U.S. Private*, pg. 3411
VALIDAR INC.; *U.S. Private*, pg. 4332
VALIDITY, INC.—See Silversmith Management, L.P.; *U.S. Private*, pg. 3664
VALMIE RESOURCES, INC.; *U.S. Public*, pg. 2273
VALVE CORPORATION; *U.S. Private*, pg. 4338
VANGUARD SOFTWARE GROUP LLC—See Jack Henry & Associates, Inc.; *U.S. Public*, pg. 1183
VANTAGEPOINT AI, LLC; *U.S. Private*, pg. 4345
VANTEC RF SOLUTIONS CORPORATION—See KKR & Co. Inc.; *U.S. Public*, pg. 1259
VAROLII CORPORATION—See Microsoft Corporation; *U.S. Public*, pg. 1443
VARONIS SYSTEMS INC.; *U.S. Public*, pg. 2275
VASCO DATA SECURITY ASIA-PACIFIC PTE LTD—See OneSpan Inc.; *U.S. Public*, pg. 1604
VASCO DATA SECURITY AUSTRALIA PTY LTD—See OneSpan Inc.; *U.S. Public*, pg. 1603
VASCO DATA SECURITY B.V.—See OneSpan Inc.; *U.S. Public*, pg. 1604
VASCO DATA SECURITY EUROPE NV/SA—See OneSpan Inc.; *U.S. Public*, pg. 1604
VASCO DATA SECURITY PTY LTD—See OneSpan Inc.; *U.S. Public*, pg. 1604
VASONA NETWORKS, INC.—See ESW Capital, LLC; *U.S. Private*, pg. 1430
VAULTIVE, INC.—See CyberArk Software Ltd.; *Int'l*, pg. 1892
VAUTO, INC.—See Cox Enterprises, Inc.; *U.S. Private*, pg. 1076
VCREATIVE, INC.—See Banyan Software, Inc.; *U.S. Private*, pg. 470
VEEAM SOFTWARE GROUP GMBH—See Insight Venture Management, LLC; *U.S. Private*, pg. 2091
VEERAS INFOTEK PVT LTD.—See Gemini Communication Ltd.; *Int'l*, pg. 2916
VEEVA SYSTEMS, INC.; *U.S. Public*, pg. 2277
VEGA INFORMATICA E FARMACIA SRL—See CompuGroup Medical SE & Co. KGaA; *Int'l*, pg. 1756
VELOCITYEHS HOLDINGS, INC.—See CVC Capital Partners SICAV-FIS S.A.; *Int'l*, pg. 1885
VELOCITY TECHNOLOGY SOLUTIONS, INC.—See Accenture plc; *Int'l*, pg. 87
VELOSIO, LLC; *U.S. Private*, pg. 4355
VENAFI, INC.—See CyberArk Software Ltd.; *Int'l*, pg. 1892
VENDAVO, INC.—See Francisco Partners Management, LP; *U.S. Private*, pg. 1592
VENDIO SERVICES, INC.—See Alibaba Group Holding Limited; *Int'l*, pg. 326
VENTIV TECHNOLOGY INC.—See TA Associates, Inc.; *U.S. Private*, pg. 3918
VENTUREFORTH, INC.; *U.S. Private*, pg. 4358
VENTYX BARRANQUILLA—See ABB Ltd.; *Int'l*, pg. 52
VENTYX FRANCE—See ABB Ltd.; *Int'l*, pg. 52
VENTYX JOHANNESBURG—See ABB Ltd.; *Int'l*, pg. 52
VENTYX LIMA—See ABB Ltd.; *Int'l*, pg. 52
VENTYX POLAND—See ABB Ltd.; *Int'l*, pg. 52
VENTYX USA, INC.—See ABB Ltd.; *Int'l*, pg. 52
VERACORE, INC.—See Thoma Bravo, L.P.; *U.S. Private*, pg. 4154
VERACODE LTD—See Thoma Bravo, L.P.; *U.S. Private*, pg. 4154
VERA WHOLE HEALTH, INC.—See Clayton, Dubilier & Rice, LLC; *U.S. Private*, pg. 928
VERBALIZEIT, INC.—See Smartling, Inc.; *U.S. Private*, pg. 3692
VERBA TECHNOLOGIES ASIA PACIFIC PTE LTD.—See Verint Systems Inc.; *U.S. Public*, pg. 2281
VERBA TECHNOLOGIES LIMITED—See Verint Systems Inc.; *U.S. Public*, pg. 2281
VERGE SOLUTIONS, LLC—See TA Associates, Inc.; *U.S. Private*, pg. 3918
VERIAN TECHNOLOGIES, INC.—See Accel Partners L.P.; *U.S. Private*, pg. 48
VERIAN TECHNOLOGIES, INC.—See KKR & Co. Inc.; *U.S. Public*, pg. 1238
VERIAN TECHNOLOGIES, INC.—See Long Path Partners, LP; *U.S. Private*, pg. 2491
VERIFORCE, LLC—See Thoma Bravo, L.P.; *U.S. Private*, pg. 4150
VERINT SYSTEMS, INC. - ALPHARETTA—See Verint Systems Inc.; *U.S. Public*, pg. 2281
VERINT SYSTEMS INC.; *U.S. Public*, pg. 2280
VERIS GROUP, LLC—See Apax Partners LLP; *Int'l*, pg. 503
VERISMA SYSTEMS, INC.—See NewSpring Capital LLC; *U.S. Private*, pg. 2918
VERIZON CONNECT FLEET—See Verizon Communications Inc.; *U.S. Public*, pg. 2285
VERMILION SOFTWARE INC.—See FactSet Research Systems Inc.; *U.S. Public*, pg. 820

513210 — SOFTWARE PUBLISHERS

VERO SOFTWARE GMBH—See Hexagon AB; *Int'l*, pg. 3367
VERO SOFTWARE LTD.—See Hexagon AB; *Int'l*, pg. 3367
VERSATA SOFTWARE, INC.—See ESW Capital, LLC; *U.S. Private*, pg. 1430
VERSATERM INC.—See Banneker Partners, LLC; *U.S. Private*, pg. 469
VERSE INNOVATION PRIVATE LIMITED; *U.S. Private*, pg. 4369
VERTAFORE, INC.—See Roper Technologies, Inc.; *U.S. Public*, pg. 1814
VERTEX, INC.; *U.S. Public*, pg. 2287
VERTICAL COMPUTER SYSTEMS, INC.; *U.S. Private*, pg. 4370
VERTICALRESPONSE, INC.; *U.S. Private*, pg. 4370
VERTICAL SEARCH WORKS INC.; *U.S. Private*, pg. 4370
VERTICAL SYSTEMS, INC.—See Atlantic Street Capital Management LLC; *U.S. Private*, pg. 374
VERTIGLO; *U.S. Private*, pg. 4370
VERTIV S.A.—See Vertiv Holdings Co; *U.S. Public*, pg. 2289
VERTRO, INC.—See Inuvo, Inc.; *U.S. Public*, pg. 1161
VEVEO, INC.—See Xperi Inc.; *U.S. Public*, pg. 2392
VIASAT IRELAND LIMITED—See ViaSat, Inc.; *U.S. Public*, pg. 2292
VICIOUS CYCLE SOFTWARE, INC.—See Little Orbit LLC; *U.S. Private*, pg. 2469
VIDI EMI, INC.; *U.S. Private*, pg. 4381
VIDISTAR, LLC—See Hitachi, Ltd.; *Int'l*, pg. 3414
VIDYO ASIA PACIFIC—See Enghouse Systems Limited; *Int'l*, pg. 2428
VIDYO EMEA—See Enghouse Systems Limited; *Int'l*, pg. 2428
VIDYO, INC.—See Enghouse Systems Limited; *Int'l*, pg. 2428
VIDYO INDIA—See Enghouse Systems Limited; *Int'l*, pg. 2428
VIDYO ITALY—See Enghouse Systems Limited; *Int'l*, pg. 2428
VIDYO JAPAN—See Enghouse Systems Limited; *Int'l*, pg. 2428
VIDYO NETHERLANDS—See Enghouse Systems Limited; *Int'l*, pg. 2428
VIDYO NORDICS & BALTICS—See Enghouse Systems Limited; *Int'l*, pg. 2428
VIDYO UNITED KINGDOM—See Enghouse Systems Limited; *Int'l*, pg. 2428
VIEWLOCITY TECHNOLOGIES U.S. LLC—See Constellation Software Inc.; *Int'l*, pg. 1773
VIGILISTICS, INC.—See SafetyChain Software, Inc.; *U.S. Private*, pg. 3525
VIGILLO LLC—See ABRY Partners, LLC; *U.S. Private*, pg. 43
VIGLINK, INC.—See sovrn Holdings, Inc.; *U.S. Private*, pg. 3743
VINSOLUTIONS, INC.—See Cox Enterprises, Inc.; *U.S. Private*, pg. 1076
VIP LOYALTY CORP.; *U.S. Private*, pg. 4386
VIRTALIS INC.—See Alpina Capital Partners LLP; *Int'l*, pg. 371
VIRTUALPREMISE, INC.—See CoStar Group, Inc.; *U.S. Public*, pg. 586
VIRTUAL TECHNOLOGIES GROUP LLC—See Jacmel Growth Partners Management LLC; *U.S. Private*, pg. 2179
VIRTUSA INTERNATIONAL, B.V.—See EQT AB; *Int'l*, pg. 2472
VIRTUSA SINGAPORE PRIVATE LIMITED—See EQT AB; *Int'l*, pg. 2472
VISALLO, LLC—See S&P Global Inc.; *U.S. Public*, pg. 1832
VISIBLEGAINS, INC.; *U.S. Private*, pg. 4390
VISIBLE.NET, INC.; *U.S. Private*, pg. 4390
VISIBLE PATH CORP.—See Cannae Holdings, Inc.; *U.S. Public*, pg. 430
VISIBLE PATH CORP.—See CC Capital Partners, LLC; *U.S. Private*, pg. 798
VISIBLE PATH CORP.—See Intercontinental Exchange, Inc.; *U.S. Public*, pg. 1142
VISIBLE SYSTEMS CORPORATION; *U.S. Private*, pg. 4390
VISIBLE TECHNOLOGIES—See Platinum Equity, LLC; *U.S. Private*, pg. 3202
VISIBLETHREAD, LLC; *U.S. Private*, pg. 4390
VISION33 INC.; *U.S. Private*, pg. 4392
VISIONAEL CORP. - TULSA—See Upland Software, Inc.; *U.S. Public*, pg. 2264
VISIONONE, INC.—See accesso Technology Group Plc; *Int'l*, pg. 89
VISION PAYMENT SOLUTIONS, LLC—See Global Payments Inc.; *U.S. Public*, pg. 943
VISION SOLUTIONS, INC.—See Clearlake Capital Group, L.P.; *U.S. Private*, pg. 937
VISION SOLUTIONS, INC.—See TA Associates, Inc.; *U.S. Private*, pg. 3917
VISISTAT, INC.; *U.S. Private*, pg. 4392
VISMA AS—See Cinven Limited; *Int'l*, pg. 1616
VISMA AS—See HgCapital Trust plc; *Int'l*, pg. 3377
VISMA AS—See KKR & Co Inc.; *U.S. Public*, pg. 1266
VISMA MAMUT AS—See Cinven Limited; *Int'l*, pg. 1616

VISMA MAMUT AS—See HgCapital Trust plc; *Int'l*, pg. 3377
VISMA MAMUT AS—See KKR & Co. Inc.; *U.S. Public*, pg. 1266
VISTEON SOFTWARE TECHNOLOGIES SAS—See Visteon Corporation; *U.S. Public*, pg. 2306
VISUAL ACUMEN, INC.; *U.S. Private*, pg. 4403
VISUAL META GMBH—See Axel Springer SE; *Int'l*, pg. 767
VISUALSHARE, LLC—See GTCR LLC; *U.S. Private*, pg. 1807
VIWO LLC—See Gannett Co., Inc.; *U.S. Public*, pg. 906
VIYYA TECHNOLOGIES, INC.; *U.S. Private*, pg. 4406
VLINK INCORPORATED; *U.S. Private*, pg. 4408
VMWARE AUSTRALIA PTY LTD—See Broadcom Inc.; *U.S. Public*, pg. 390
VMWARE FRANCE SAS.—See Broadcom Inc.; *U.S. Public*, pg. 390
VMWARE GLOBAL, INC.—See Broadcom Inc.; *U.S. Public*, pg. 390
VMWARE GLOBAL, INC.—See Dell Technologies, Inc.; *U.S. Public*, pg. 651
VMWARE HONG KONG LIMITED—See Broadcom Inc.; *U.S. Public*, pg. 390
VMWARE INFORMATION TECHNOLOGY(CHINA) CO. LTD—See Broadcom Inc.; *U.S. Public*, pg. 390
VMWARE, K.K.—See Broadcom Inc.; *U.S. Public*, pg. 391
VMWARE MARKETING AUSTRIA GMBH—See Broadcom Inc.; *U.S. Public*, pg. 391
VMWARE NETHERLANDS B.V.—See Broadcom Inc.; *U.S. Public*, pg. 391
VMWARE RUS LLC—See Dell Technologies Inc.; *U.S. Public*, pg. 651
VMWARE SINGAPORE PTE. LTD.—See Broadcom Inc.; *U.S. Public*, pg. 391
VMWARE SOFTWARE INDIA PVT. LTD—See Broadcom Inc.; *U.S. Public*, pg. 391
VMWARE SPAIN, S.L.—See Broadcom Inc.; *U.S. Public*, pg. 391
VMWARE SWEDEN AB—See Broadcom Inc.; *U.S. Public*, pg. 391
VMWARE UK LIMITED—See Broadcom Inc.; *U.S. Public*, pg. 391
VOALTE, INC.—See Baxter International Inc.; *U.S. Public*, pg. 283
VOCUS EUROPE LIMITED—See Platinum Equity, LLC; *U.S. Private*, pg. 3202
VOCUS UK LIMITED—See Platinum Equity, LLC; *U.S. Private*, pg. 3202
VOICEPORT, LLC—See Enghouse Systems Limited; *Int'l*, pg. 2428
VOLUSION, INC.; *U.S. Private*, pg. 4411
VONTU, INC.—See Gen Digital Inc.; *U.S. Public*, pg. 911
VOTIGO SOFTWARE PRIVATE LIMITED—See Votigo, Inc.; *U.S. Private*, pg. 4413
VOVICI CORPORATION—See Verint Systems Inc.; *U.S. Public*, pg. 2281
VOXMOBILI S.A.—See Synchronoss Technologies, Inc.; *U.S. Public*, pg. 1970
VSEE LAB, INC.—See VSee Health, Inc.; *U.S. Public*, pg. 2313
VSOFT CORPORATION; *U.S. Private*, pg. 4415
VTLS, INC.—See HGGC, LLC; *U.S. Private*, pg. 1930
VTLS, INC.—See JMI Services, Inc.; *U.S. Private*, pg. 2216
VWORKER.COM—See Freelancer Ltd.; *Int'l*, pg. 2770
W2BI, INC.—See Advantest Corporation; *Int'l*, pg. 165
WAM SYSTEMS, INC.—See TA Associates, Inc.; *U.S. Private*, pg. 3919
WANDERFUL MEDIA—See OwnLocal, Inc.; *U.S. Private*, pg. 3055
WANDISCO INTERNATIONAL LIMITED—See Cirata PLC.; *Int'l*, pg. 1617
WASATCH SOFTWARE, INC.; *U.S. Private*, pg. 4445
WATCHDOX, INC.—See BlackBerry Limited; *Int'l*, pg. 1060
WATCHGUARD TECHNOLOGIES CANADA, INC.—See Francisco Partners Management, LP; *U.S. Private*, pg. 1593
WATCHGUARD TECHNOLOGIES, INC.—See Francisco Partners Management, LP; *U.S. Private*, pg. 1593
WATERTEK INTERNATIONAL (HONG KONG) LIMITED—See Beijing Watertek Information Technology Co., Ltd.; *Int'l*, pg. 960
WAVE TECHNOLOGY SOLUTIONS GROUP; *U.S. Private*, pg. 4458
WAZE LTD.—See Alphabet Inc.; *U.S. Public*, pg. 83
WEB4, INC.—See International Business Machines Corporation; *U.S. Public*, pg. 1149
WEBEX COMMUNICATIONS, INC.—See Cisco Systems, Inc.; *U.S. Public*, pg. 501
WEBGILITY INC.; *U.S. Private*, pg. 4465
WEBISTIX, INC.; *U.S. Private*, pg. 4466
WEBLINK INTERNATIONAL, INC.—See Pamlico Capital Management, L.P.; *U.S. Private*, pg. 3083
WEBPT, INC.—See Warburg Pincus LLC; *U.S. Private*, pg. 4440
WEBSPY US INC.—See Fastvue Inc.; *U.S. Private*, pg. 1483
WEBTRENDS AUSTRALASIA—See Webtrends Inc.; *U.S. Private*, pg. 4467
WEBTRENDS EMEA—See Webtrends Inc.; *U.S. Private*, pg. 4467

WEBTRENDS INC.; *U.S. Private*, pg. 4467
WEBTRENDS NORDIC—See Webtrends Inc.; *U.S. Private*, pg. 4467
WEB X.0 MEDIA—See Cyger Media; *U.S. Private*, pg. 1134
WEEBLY, INC.—See Block, Inc.; *U.S. Public*, pg. 362
WEGOWISE, INC.—See Measurabl, Inc.; *U.S. Private*, pg. 2648
WEIDENHAMMER SYSTEMS CORPORATION; *U.S. Private*, pg. 4470
WELLSKY CORPORATION—See Leonard Green & Partners, L.P.; *U.S. Private*, pg. 2430
WELLSKY CORPORATION—See TPG Capital, L.P.; *U.S. Private*, pg. 2177
THE WERCS, LTD.—See Underwriters Laboratories Inc.; *U.S. Private*, pg. 4280
WESTCON GROUP LIMITED—See TD Synnex Corp; *U.S. Public*, pg. 1987
WEWARDS, INC.; *U.S. Public*, pg. 2363
WHEELHOUSE ANALYTICS—See Bain Capital, LP; *U.S. Private*, pg. 439
WHI SOLUTIONS, INC.—See eBay Inc.; *U.S. Public*, pg. 709
WHITECANYON SOFTWARE, INC.—See Francisco Partners Management, LP; *U.S. Private*, pg. 1589
WHOSAY, INC.—See National Amusements, Inc.; *U.S. Private*, pg. 2844
WIDEORBIT INC.—See Constellation Software Inc.; *Int'l*, pg. 1773
WIDEPOINT SOLUTIONS CORP.—See WidePoint Corporation; *U.S. Public*, pg. 2370
WIDEVINE TECHNOLOGIES, INC.—See Alphabet Inc.; *U.S. Public*, pg. 84
WIDGIX, LLC; *U.S. Private*, pg. 4516
WILCOMP SOFTWARE, LLC—See Nelnet, Inc.; *U.S. Public*, pg. 1504
WILEY GLOBAL TECHNOLOGY (PRIVATE) LIMITED—See John Wiley & Sons, Inc.; *U.S. Public*, pg. 1193
WILLCO TECHNOLOGIES, INC.—See Metisentry LLC; *U.S. Private*, pg. 2684
WINDOW BOOK, INC.—See Platinum Equity, LLC; *U.S. Private*, pg. 3202
WIND RIVER AB—See TPG Capital, L.P.; *U.S. Public*, pg. 2177
WIND RIVER GMBH—See TPG Capital, L.P.; *U.S. Public*, pg. 2177
WIND RIVER K.K.—See TPG Capital, L.P.; *U.S. Public*, pg. 2177
WIND RIVER SYSTEMS, INC.—See TPG Capital, L.P.; *U.S. Public*, pg. 2177
WIND RIVER SYSTEMS INC.—See TPG Capital, L.P.; *U.S. Public*, pg. 2177
WIND RIVER SYSTEMS INTERNATIONAL, INC.—See TPG Capital, L.P.; *U.S. Public*, pg. 2177
WIND RIVER UK LTD.—See TPG Capital, L.P.; *U.S. Public*, pg. 2177
WINDSOR CIRCLE INC.—See Aquiline Capital Partners LLC; *U.S. Private*, pg. 305
WINSCRIBE EUROPE LTD.—See Microsoft Corporation; *U.S. Public*, pg. 1443
WINSCRIBE GMBH—See Microsoft Corporation; *U.S. Public*, pg. 1443
WINSCRIBE INC LTD.—See Microsoft Corporation; *U.S. Public*, pg. 1443
WINSHUTTLE LLC—See Symphony Technology Group, LLC; *U.S. Private*, pg. 3902
WINZIP COMPUTING LLC—See KKR & Co. Inc.; *U.S. Public*, pg. 1243
WIRELESS RONIN TECHNOLOGIES (CANADA), INC.—See Creative Realities, Inc.; *U.S. Public*, pg. 593
WISDOMFORCE TECHNOLOGIES, INC.—See Canada Pension Plan Investment Board; *Int'l*, pg. 1280
WISDOMTOOLS, LLC; *U.S. Private*, pg. 4549
WIZARD SOFTWARE SOLUTIONS INCORPORATED; *U.S. Private*, pg. 4551
WMODE INC.—See AppDirect Inc.; *U.S. Private*, pg. 296
WOLFRAM ALPHA LLC—See Wolfram Research Inc.; *U.S. Private*, pg. 4554
WOMBAT FINANCIAL SOFTWARE, INC.—See Insight Venture Management, LLC; *U.S. Private*, pg. 2091
WOMBAT SECURITY TECHNOLOGIES, INC.—See Thoma Bravo, L.P.; *U.S. Private*, pg. 4151
WONDER GROUP, INC.; *U.S. Private*, pg. 4556
WOODWARD ASSET CAPITAL LLC; *U.S. Private*, pg. 4561
WOODWING USA, INC.; *U.S. Private*, pg. 4561
WOOPRA INC.—See Appier Group, Inc.; *Int'l*, pg. 520
WORDS+, INC.—See Prentke Romich Company; *U.S. Private*, pg. 3252
WORDS OF WISDOM, LLC—See Perdoceo Education Corporation; *U.S. Public*, pg. 1673
WORKDAY, INC.; *U.S. Public*, pg. 2378
WORKDAY LIMITED—See Workday, Inc.; *U.S. Public*, pg. 2379
WORKDAY MALAYSIA SDN. BHD.—See Workday, Inc.; *U.S. Public*, pg. 2379
WORKDAY MEXICO, S. DE R.L. DE C.V.—See Workday, Inc.; *U.S. Public*, pg. 2379
WORKDAY SINGAPORE PTE. LTD.—See Workday, Inc.; *U.S. Public*, pg. 2379

N.A.I.C.S. INDEX

516110 — RADIO BROADCASTING ...

WORKDAY SWITZERLAND GMBH—See Workday, Inc.; *U.S. Public*, pg. 2379
WORKFORCE SOFTWARE, INC.—See Insight Venture Management, LLC; *U.S. Public*, pg. 2091
WORKFRONT, INC.—See Adobe Inc.; *U.S. Public*, pg. 43
WORKIVA FRANCE SAS—See Workiva Inc.; *U.S. Public*, pg. 2379
WORKIVA GERMANY GMBH—See Workiva Inc.; *U.S. Public*, pg. 2379
WORKIVA INC.; *U.S. Public*, pg. 2379
WORKPLACE SYSTEMS INTERNATIONAL LIMITED—See Insight Venture Management, LLC; *U.S. Private*, pg. 2091
WORKSCAPE INC.—See Automatic Data Processing, Inc.; *U.S. Public*, pg. 230
WORKSOFT, INC.—See Marlin Equity Partners, LLC; *U.S. Private*, pg. 2585
WORKWAVE LLC—See EQT AB; *Int'l*, pg. 2478
WORKWISE, LLC; *U.S. Private*, pg. 4564
WORLDDOC, INC.; *U.S. Private*, pg. 4568
WRIKE, INC.—See Elliott Management Corporation; *U.S. Private*, pg. 1367
WRIKE, INC.—See Vista Equity Partners, LLC; *U.S. Private*, pg. 4396
WYNNE SYSTEMS, INC.—See Constellation Software Inc.; *Int'l*, pg. 1776
XACTLY CORPORATION—See Vista Equity Partners, LLC; *U.S. Private*, pg. 4402
XAMARIN INC.—See Microsoft Corporation; *U.S. Public*, pg. 1443
XANDR INC.—See AT&T Inc.; *U.S. Public*, pg. 220
XCELMOBILITY INC.; *U.S. Public*, pg. 2385
X-FACTOR COMMUNICATIONS HOLDINGS, INC.; *U.S. Public*, pg. 2385
XIAM TECHNOLOGIES LIMITED—See QUALCOMM Incorporated; *U.S. Public*, pg. 1748
XI'AN XIGU MICROELECTRONICS CO., LTD.—See Beijing Watertek Information Technology Co., Ltd.; *Int'l*, pg. 960
XIFIN, INC.—See GTCR LLC; *U.S. Private*, pg. 1807
XIGNITE, INC.—See NewSpring Capital LLC; *U.S. Private*, pg. 2917
XIGO, LLC—See Asignet USA, Inc.; *U.S. Private*, pg. 351
XMPIE, LTD.—See Xerox Holdings Corporation; *U.S. Public*, pg. 2388
XPANSIV DATA SYSTEMS INC.; *U.S. Private*, pg. 4582
XPANXION, LLC—See UST Global Inc.; *U.S. Private*, pg. 4324
XPERIA SOLUTIONS APPAREL SOFTWARE; *U.S. Private*, pg. 4582
XTIME, INC.—See Cox Automotive LLC; *U.S. Private*, pg. 1074
XTIVA FINANCIAL SYSTEMS, INC.; *U.S. Private*, pg. 4583
XYBION CORPORATION; *U.S. Private*, pg. 4583
YAHOO! HUNGARY LABS KFT.—See Apollo Global Management, Inc.; *U.S. Public*, pg. 167
YARDI SYSTEMS, INC.; *U.S. Private*, pg. 4586
YAYOI CO., LTD.—See KKR & Co. Inc.; *U.S. Public*, pg. 1267
YESMAIL, INC.—See CCMP Capital Advisors, LP; *U.S. Private*, pg. 800
YEXT GMBH—See Yext, Inc.; *U.S. Public*, pg. 2399
YEXT, INC.; *U.S. Public*, pg. 2398
YINZCAM, INC.—See National Basketball Association; *U.S. Private*, pg. 2848
YIPPY, INC.; *U.S. Public*, pg. 2399
YODLEE CANADA, INC.—See Bain Capital, LP; *U.S. Private*, pg. 439
YODLEE GROUP AUSTRALIA PTY LTD.—See Bain Capital, LP; *U.S. Private*, pg. 439
YODLEE, INC.—See Bain Capital, LP; *U.S. Private*, pg. 439
YODLEE INFOTECH PRIVATE LIMITED—See Bain Capital, LP; *U.S. Private*, pg. 439
YOLA INC.; *U.S. Private*, pg. 4589
YOURCAUSE, LLC—See Blackbaud, Inc.; *U.S. Public*, pg. 341
YOURMEMBERSHIP.COM INC.—See Insight Venture Management, LLC; *U.S. Private*, pg. 2088
YOURPEOPLE, INC.—See General Atlantic Service Company, L.P.; *U.S. Private*, pg. 1663
YOUSENDIT, INC.; *U.S. Private*, pg. 4594
ZAPATA COMPUTING HOLDINGS INC.; *U.S. Public*, pg. 2401
ZEMAX, LLC—See EQT AB; *Int'l*, pg. 2482
ZENDESK APAC—See Hellman & Friedman LLC; *U.S. Private*, pg. 1911
ZENDESK EMEA—See Hellman & Friedman LLC; *U.S. Private*, pg. 1911
ZENDESK, INC.—See Hellman & Friedman LLC; *U.S. Private*, pg. 1911
ZENIMAX MEDIA, INC.—See Microsoft Corporation; *U.S. Public*, pg. 1443
ZENPAYROLL, INC.; *U.S. Private*, pg. 4601
ZENPRINT, LLC; *U.S. Private*, pg. 4601
ZERIFY, INC.; *U.S. Public*, pg. 2402
ZEROFOX, INC.—See Whanau Interests LLC; *U.S. Private*, pg. 4504

ZERTO LTD.—See Hewlett Packard Enterprise Company; *U.S. Public*, pg. 1032
ZETA GLOBAL LTD.—See Zeta Interactive Corporation; *U.S. Private*, pg. 4603
ZETTA, INC.—See Marlin Equity Partners, LLC; *U.S. Private*, pg. 2583
ZIMBRA SOFTWARE, LLC—See Centre Lane Partners, LLC; *U.S. Private*, pg. 827
ZIPPER BY ENFO AB—See Enfo Oyj; *Int'l*, pg. 2425
ZMAGS CORP.—See The Gores Group, LLC; *U.S. Private*, pg. 4035
ZOHO (BEIJING) TECHNOLOGY CO., LTD.—See Zoho Corporation; *U.S. Private*, pg. 4607
ZOHO CORPORATION PRIVATE LIMITED—See Zoho Corporation; *U.S. Private*, pg. 4607
ZOHO CORPORATION; *U.S. Private*, pg. 4607
ZOHO JAPAN CORPORATION—See Zoho Corporation; *U.S. Private*, pg. 4607
ZOOMDATA, INC.—See TA Associates, Inc.; *U.S. Private*, pg. 3915
ZUGARA INC.; *U.S. Private*, pg. 4610
ZUORA AUSTRALIA PTY. LTD.—See Zuora, Inc.; *U.S. Public*, pg. 2412
ZUORA GERMANY GMBH—See Zuora, Inc.; *U.S. Public*, pg. 2412
ZUORA, INC.; *U.S. Public*, pg. 2411
ZUORA INDIA PRIVATE LIMITED—See Zuora, Inc.; *U.S. Public*, pg. 2412
ZUORA JAPAN KK—See Zuora, Inc.; *U.S. Public*, pg. 2412
ZUORA UK LIMITED—See Zuora, Inc.; *U.S. Public*, pg. 2412
ZVENTS, INC.—See eBay Inc.; *U.S. Public*, pg. 709
ZYNGA INC.; *U.S. Public*, pg. 4611
ZYRION, INC.—See Insight Venture Management, LLC; *U.S. Private*, pg. 2091
ZYTO TECHNOLOGIES, INC.; *U.S. Private*, pg. 4611
ZYWAVE, INC.—See Clearlake Capital Group, L.P.; *U.S. Private*, pg. 938

516110 — RADIO BROADCASTING STATIONS

104.6 RTL—See Bertelsmann SE & Co. KGaA; *Int'l*, pg. 993
93.3 LA RAZA KRZZ FM—See Spanish Broadcasting System Inc.; *U.S. Public*, pg. 1914
94 COUNTRY WKKJ—See iHeartMedia, Inc.; *U.S. Public*, pg. 1096
98.7 WFGR—See Brookfield Corporation; *Int'l*, pg. 1183
ABC, INC.—See The Walt Disney Company; *U.S. Public*, pg. 2137
ABSOLUTE RADIO LTD.—See Heinrich Bauer Verlag KG; *Int'l*, pg. 3324
AFRICAN MEDIA ENTERTAINMENT LIMITED; *Int'l*, pg. 192
AIDARADIO GMBH—See Carnival Corporation; *U.S. Public*, pg. 437
ALASKA PUBLIC MEDIA, INC.; *U.S. Private*, pg. 151
AMERICAN URBAN RADIO NETWORKS -- CHICAGO SALES—See Sheridan Broadcasting Corporation; *U.S. Private*, pg. 3633
AMERICAN URBAN RADIO NETWORKS - NEW YORK SALES—See Sheridan Broadcasting Corporation; *U.S. Private*, pg. 3633
ANCHORAGE MEDIA GROUP—See Shivers Trading & Operating Company; *U.S. Private*, pg. 3638
ARSO RADIO CORPORATION; *U.S. Private*, pg. 339
AS STAR FM—See Providence Equity Partners L.L.C.; *U.S. Private*, pg. 3291
ASTRO RADIO SDN. BHD.—See Astro Malaysia Holdings Bhd; *Int'l*, pg. 662
ATLANTA RADIO, LLC—See Cumulus Media Inc.; *U.S. Public*, pg. 609
AUDIO.DIGITAL NRW GMBH—See Deutsche Post AG; *Int'l*, pg. 2083
BAS BROADCASTING, INC.; *U.S. Private*, pg. 484
BAS BROADCASTING - MOUNT VERNON—See BAS Broadcasting, Inc.; *U.S. Private*, pg. 484
BAS BROADCASTING - SANDUSKY—See BAS Broadcasting, Inc.; *U.S. Private*, pg. 484
BAUER MEDIA AB—See Heinrich Bauer Verlag KG; *Int'l*, pg. 3324
BAUER RADIO LTD.—See Heinrich Bauer Verlag KG; *Int'l*, pg. 3324
BEASLEY BROADCAST GROUP, INC. - BOSTON—See Beasley Broadcast Group, Inc.; *U.S. Public*, pg. 287
BEASLEY BROADCAST GROUP, INC. - GREENVILLE—See Beasley Broadcast Group, Inc.; *U.S. Public*, pg. 287
BELL MEDIA RADIO - CALGARY—See BCE Inc.; *Int'l*, pg. 927
BELL MEDIA RADIO—See BCE Inc.; *Int'l*, pg. 927
BERLINER RUNDFUNK—See Bertelsmann SE & Co. KGaA; *Int'l*, pg. 994
BIBLE BROADCASTING NETWORK; *U.S. Private*, pg. 550
BICOASTAL MEDIA - ALBANY—See Bicoastal Media, LLC; *U.S. Private*, pg. 550
BICOASTAL MEDIA - CENTRALIA—See Bicoastal Media, LLC; *U.S. Private*, pg. 550
BICOASTAL MEDIA - CRESCENT CITY—See Bicoastal Media, LLC; *U.S. Private*, pg. 550
BICOASTAL MEDIA - EUREKA—See Bicoastal Media, LLC; *U.S. Private*, pg. 551
BICOASTAL MEDIA - MEDFORD—See Bicoastal Media, LLC; *U.S. Private*, pg. 551
BICOASTAL MEDIA - UKIAH-LAKEPORT—See Bicoastal Media, LLC; *U.S. Private*, pg. 551
BLUE CHIP BROADCASTING, LTD.—See Urban One, Inc.; *U.S. Public*, pg. 2265
BONNEVILLE INTERNATIONAL CORPORATION—See Deseret Management Corporation; *U.S. Private*, pg. 1212
BONNEVILLE INTERNATIONAL CORP. - PHOENIX—See Deseret Management Corporation; *U.S. Private*, pg. 1212
BONNEVILLE INTERNATIONAL CORP. - SACRAMENTO—See Deseret Management Corporation; *U.S. Private*, pg. 1212
BONNEVILLE INTERNATIONAL CORP. - SAN FRANCISCO—See Deseret Management Corporation; *U.S. Private*, pg. 1212
BRISTOL BROADCASTING CO. INC.; *U.S. Private*, pg. 656
CAPITOL BROADCASTING COMPANY, INC. - SUNRISE BROADCASTING DIVISION—See Capitol Broadcasting Company, Inc.; *U.S. Private*, pg. 743
CAT COUNTRY 107 FM—See iHeartMedia, Inc.; *U.S. Public*, pg. 1096
CENTRAL MEDIA GROUP PROPRIETARY LIMITED—See African Media Entertainment Limited; *Int'l*, pg. 192
CFCO RADIO AM—See Blackburn Radio Inc; *Int'l*, pg. 1060
CFNY-FM RADIO—See Corus Entertainment Inc.; *Int'l*, pg. 1808
CHARLOTTE BROADCASTING, LLC—See Urban One, Inc.; *U.S. Public*, pg. 2265
CHICAGO RADIO, LLC—See Cumulus Media Inc.; *U.S. Public*, pg. 609
CHRYSALIS GROUP PLC—See Bertelsmann SE & Co. KGaA; *Int'l*, pg. 990
CLASSIC FM—See Global Radio Group Limited; *Int'l*, pg. 3000
CNN RADIO—See Warner Bros. Discovery, Inc.; *U.S. Public*, pg. 2328
COLUMBIA RIVER MEDIA GROUP—See Shivers Trading & Operating Company; *U.S. Private*, pg. 3638
COMMUNICORP GROUP LTD.; *Int'l*, pg. 1721
COOKEVILLE COMMUNICATIONS, LLC—See Great Plains Media, Inc.; *U.S. Private*, pg. 1767
CORK MEDIA ENTERPRISES LIMITED—See News Corporation; *U.S. Private*, pg. 1520
CORSICANA MEDIA, INC.—See GTCR LLC; *U.S. Private*, pg. 1805
COX RADIO, INC.—See Apollo Global Management, Inc.; *U.S. Public*, pg. 163
CRAWFORD BROADCASTING CO.; *U.S. Private*, pg. 1086
CROMWELL GROUP INC.; *U.S. Private*, pg. 1103
CUMULUS BROADCASTING INC. - INDIANAPOLIS, IN—See Cumulus Media Inc.; *U.S. Public*, pg. 609
CUMULUS BROADCASTING LLC - ABILENE, TX—See Cumulus Media Inc.; *U.S. Public*, pg. 609
CUMULUS BROADCASTING LLC - ALLENTOWN, PA—See Cumulus Media Inc.; *U.S. Public*, pg. 609
CUMULUS BROADCASTING LLC - ANN ARBOR, MI—See Cumulus Media Inc.; *U.S. Public*, pg. 609
CUMULUS BROADCASTING LLC - BATON ROUGE, LA—See Cumulus Media Inc.; *U.S. Public*, pg. 609
CUMULUS BROADCASTING LLC - BUFFALO, NY—See Cumulus Media Inc.; *U.S. Public*, pg. 609
CUMULUS BROADCASTING LLC - CINCINNATI, OH—See Cumulus Media Inc.; *U.S. Public*, pg. 609
CUMULUS BROADCASTING LLC - COLORADO SPRINGS, CO—See Cumulus Media Inc.; *U.S. Public*, pg. 609
CUMULUS BROADCASTING LLC - COLUMBIA, MO—See Cumulus Media Inc.; *U.S. Public*, pg. 609
CUMULUS BROADCASTING LLC - COLUMBIA, SC—See Cumulus Media Inc.; *U.S. Public*, pg. 609
CUMULUS BROADCASTING LLC - DALLAS, TX—See Cumulus Media Inc.; *U.S. Public*, pg. 609
CUMULUS BROADCASTING LLC - DUBUQUE, IA—See Cumulus Media Inc.; *U.S. Public*, pg. 609
CUMULUS BROADCASTING LLC - FAYETTEVILLE, NC—See Cumulus Media Inc.; *U.S. Public*, pg. 609
CUMULUS BROADCASTING LLC - HARRISBURG, PA—See Cumulus Media Inc.; *U.S. Public*, pg. 610
CUMULUS BROADCASTING LLC - HOUSTON, TX—See Cumulus Media Inc.; *U.S. Public*, pg. 610
CUMULUS BROADCASTING LLC - JEFFERSON CITY, MO—See Cumulus Media Inc.; *U.S. Public*, pg. 609
CUMULUS BROADCASTING LLC - KANSAS CITY, KS—See Cumulus Media Inc.; *U.S. Public*, pg. 610
CUMULUS BROADCASTING LLC - KOKOMO, IN—See Cumulus Media Inc.; *U.S. Public*, pg. 610
CUMULUS BROADCASTING LLC - LAFAYETTE, LA—See Cumulus Media Inc.; *U.S. Public*, pg. 610
CUMULUS BROADCASTING LLC - LITTLE ROCK, AR—See Cumulus Media Inc.; *U.S. Public*, pg. 610
CUMULUS BROADCASTING LLC -

N.A.I.C.S. Index
516110 — RADIO BROADCASTING ... CORPORATE AFFILIATIONS

MODESTO/STOCKTON, CA—See Cumulus Media Inc.; *U.S. Public*, pg. 610
CUMULUS BROADCASTING LLC - MUNCIE, IN—See Cumulus Media Inc.; *U.S. Public*, pg. 610
CUMULUS BROADCASTING LLC - NEW ORLEANS, LA—See Cumulus Media Inc.; *U.S. Public*, pg. 610
CUMULUS BROADCASTING LLC - OKLAHOMA CITY, OK—See Cumulus Media Inc.; *U.S. Public*, pg. 610
CUMULUS BROADCASTING LLC - SAGINAW, MI—See Cumulus Media Inc.; *U.S. Public*, pg. 610
CUMULUS BROADCASTING LLC - SALT LAKE CITY, UT—See Cumulus Media Inc.; *U.S. Public*, pg. 610
CUMULUS BROADCASTING LLC—See Cumulus Media Inc.; *U.S. Public*, pg. 609
CUMULUS BROADCASTING LLC - SYRACUSE, NY—See Cumulus Media Inc.; *U.S. Public*, pg. 610
CUMULUS BROADCASTING LLC - WICHITA FALLS, TX—See Cumulus Media Inc.; *U.S. Public*, pg. 610
CUMULUS BROADCASTING LLC - WORCESTER, MA—See Cumulus Media Inc.; *U.S. Public*, pg. 610
CUMULUS BROADCASTING LLC - YORK, PA—See Cumulus Media Inc.; *U.S. Public*, pg. 610
CURTIS MEDIA GROUP; *U.S. Private*, pg. 1126
DEBUT BROADCASTING CORPORATION, INC.; *U.S. Private*, pg. 1186
DETROIT RADIO, LLC—See Cumulus Media Inc.; *U.S. Public*, pg. 610
DIGITY COMPANIES, LLC; *U.S. Private*, pg. 1231
EAGLE COMMUNICATIONS INC.; *U.S. Private*, pg. 1308
EDUCATIONAL MEDIA FOUNDATION; *U.S. Private*, pg. 1339
EL DORADO BROADCASTERS; *U.S. Private*, pg. 1348
EL DORADO BROADCASTERS—See El Dorado Broadcasters; *U.S. Private*, pg. 1348
ELECTREON WIRELESS LTD.; *Int'l*, pg. 2348
EMMIS COMMUNICATIONS CORPORATION; *U.S. Public*, pg. 753
EMMIS INDIANA BROADCASTING, L.P.—See Emmis Communications Corporation; *U.S. Public*, pg. 753
EMMIS RADIO, L.L.C.—See Emmis Communications Corporation; *U.S. Public*, pg. 753
ENTERCOM BOSTON, LLC—See AUDACY, INC.; *U.S. Public*, pg. 226
ENTERCOM BUFFALO, LLC—See AUDACY, INC.; *U.S. Public*, pg. 226
ENTERCOM DENVER, LLC—See AUDACY, INC.; *U.S. Public*, pg. 226
ENTERCOM GAINESVILLE, LLC—See AUDACY, INC.; *U.S. Public*, pg. 226
ENTERCOM GREENSBORO, LLC—See AUDACY, INC.; *U.S. Public*, pg. 226
ENTERCOM GREENVILLE, LLC—See AUDACY, INC.; *U.S. Public*, pg. 226
ENTERCOM INDIANA, LLC—See AUDACY, INC.; *U.S. Public*, pg. 226
ENTERCOM KANSAS CITY, LLC—See AUDACY, INC.; *U.S. Public*, pg. 226
ENTERCOM MADISON, LLC—See AUDACY, INC.; *U.S. Public*, pg. 226
ENTERCOM MIAMI, LLC—See AUDACY, INC.; *U.S. Public*, pg. 226
ENTERCOM MILWAUKEE, LLC—See AUDACY, INC.; *U.S. Public*, pg. 226
ENTERCOM NEW ORLEANS, LLC—See AUDACY, INC.; *U.S. Public*, pg. 226
ENTERCOM NORFOLK, LLC—See AUDACY, INC.; *U.S. Public*, pg. 226
ENTERCOM ROCHESTER, LLC—See AUDACY, INC.; *U.S. Public*, pg. 226
ENTERCOM SAN DIEGO, LLC—See AUDACY, INC.; *U.S. Public*, pg. 226
ENTERCOM SEATTLE, LLC—See AUDACY, INC.; *U.S. Public*, pg. 226
ENTERCOM WICHITA, LLC—See AUDACY, INC.; *U.S. Public*, pg. 227
ENTERCOM WILKES-BARRE SCRANTON, LLC—See AUDACY, INC.; *U.S. Public*, pg. 227
ESSEX FM—See Global Radio Group Limited; *Int'l*, pg. 3000
EUROZET SP. Z.O.O.; *Int'l*, pg. 2559
EXPRES MEDIA S.R.O.—See Emmis Communications Corporation; *U.S. Public*, pg. 753
FALKLAND ISLANDS RADIO SERVICE; *Int'l*, pg. 2611
FAMILY STATIONS INC.; *U.S. Private*, pg. 1471
FAZ 93.6 BERLIN—See Frankfurter Allgemeine Zeitung GmbH; *Int'l*, pg. 2761
FIRST MEDIA SERVICES, LLC; *U.S. Private*, pg. 1521
FORCHT BROADCASTING, INC.—See Forcht Group of Kentucky, Inc.; *U.S. Private*, pg. 1564
FOREVER MEDIA, INC. - FRANKLIN—See Forever Media, Inc.; *U.S. Private*, pg. 1567
FOREVER MEDIA, INC.; *U.S. Private*, pg. 1567
FOX SPORTS RADIO 1350 AM—See iHeartMedia, Inc.; *U.S. Public*, pg. 1097
GALESBURG BROADCASTING CO.—See Pritchard Broadcasting Corp.; *U.S. Private*, pg. 3268
GOLD COAST BROADCASTING LLC—See Point Broadcasting Company; *U.S. Private*, pg. 3221
GOODRICH RADIO MARKETING INC.—See Goodrich Radio and Theaters Inc.; *U.S. Private*, pg. 1740
GREAT PLAINS MEDIA - LAWRENCE—See Great Plains Media, Inc.; *U.S. Private*, pg. 1767
GUANGXI RADIO & TV NETWORK CORPORATION; *Int'l*, pg. 3163
GUARANTY BROADCASTING COMPANY, LLC—See Guaranty Corporation; *U.S. Public*, pg. 973
HEART 102.4—See Global Radio Group Limited; *Int'l*, pg. 3000
HEART 103—See Global Radio Group Limited; *Int'l*, pg. 3000
HEART FM—See Global Radio Group Limited; *Int'l*, pg. 3000
HEART HOME COUNTIES—See Global Radio Group Limited; *Int'l*, pg. 3000
HEART THAMES VALLEY—See Global Radio Group Limited; *Int'l*, pg. 3000
HEART WALES—See Global Radio Group Limited; *Int'l*, pg. 3000
HIGH DESERT BROADCASTING LLC—See Point Broadcasting Company; *U.S. Private*, pg. 3221
HIT RADIO VERONICA—See Bertelsmann SE & Co. KGaA; *Int'l*, pg. 994
HUBBARD RADIO CINCINNATI, LLC—See Hubbard Broadcasting, Inc.; *U.S. Private*, pg. 2000
HUBBARD RADIO ST. LOUIS, LLC—See Hubbard Broadcasting, Inc.; *U.S. Private*, pg. 2000
HUNT BROADCASTING, LLC; *U.S. Private*, pg. 2008
IHEARTMEDIA + ENTERTAINMENT, INC. - ALBANY, GA—See iHeartMedia, Inc.; *U.S. Public*, pg. 1097
IHEARTMEDIA + ENTERTAINMENT, INC. - ALBANY, NY—See iHeartMedia, Inc.; *U.S. Public*, pg. 1097
IHEARTMEDIA + ENTERTAINMENT, INC. - ALBUQUERQUE, NM—See iHeartMedia, Inc.; *U.S. Public*, pg. 1097
IHEARTMEDIA + ENTERTAINMENT, INC. - AMES, IA—See iHeartMedia, Inc.; *U.S. Public*, pg. 1098
IHEARTMEDIA + ENTERTAINMENT, INC. - ANCHORAGE, AK—See iHeartMedia, Inc.; *U.S. Public*, pg. 1097
IHEARTMEDIA + ENTERTAINMENT, INC. - ASHLAND, OH—See iHeartMedia, Inc.; *U.S. Public*, pg. 1097
IHEARTMEDIA + ENTERTAINMENT, INC. - ATLANTA, GA—See iHeartMedia, Inc.; *U.S. Public*, pg. 1097
IHEARTMEDIA + ENTERTAINMENT, INC. - AUGUSTA, GA—See iHeartMedia, Inc.; *U.S. Public*, pg. 1097
IHEARTMEDIA + ENTERTAINMENT, INC. - BALTIMORE, MD—See iHeartMedia, Inc.; *U.S. Public*, pg. 1100
IHEARTMEDIA + ENTERTAINMENT, INC. - BATON ROUGE, LA—See iHeartMedia, Inc.; *U.S. Public*, pg. 1097
IHEARTMEDIA + ENTERTAINMENT, INC. - BEAUMONT, TX—See iHeartMedia, Inc.; *U.S. Public*, pg. 1097
IHEARTMEDIA + ENTERTAINMENT, INC. - BILOXI, MS—See iHeartMedia, Inc.; *U.S. Public*, pg. 1097
IHEARTMEDIA + ENTERTAINMENT, INC. - BINGHAMTON, NY—See iHeartMedia, Inc.; *U.S. Public*, pg. 1097
IHEARTMEDIA + ENTERTAINMENT, INC. - BIRMINGHAM, AL—See iHeartMedia, Inc.; *U.S. Public*, pg. 1097
IHEARTMEDIA + ENTERTAINMENT, INC. - BISMARCK, ND—See iHeartMedia, Inc.; *U.S. Public*, pg. 1097
IHEARTMEDIA + ENTERTAINMENT, INC. - BOSTON, MA—See iHeartMedia, Inc.; *U.S. Public*, pg. 1097
IHEARTMEDIA + ENTERTAINMENT, INC. - CEDAR RAPIDS, IA—See iHeartMedia, Inc.; *U.S. Public*, pg. 1097
IHEARTMEDIA + ENTERTAINMENT, INC. - CHARLESTON, SC—See iHeartMedia, Inc.; *U.S. Public*, pg. 1097
IHEARTMEDIA + ENTERTAINMENT, INC. - CHICAGO, IL—See iHeartMedia, Inc.; *U.S. Public*, pg. 1097
IHEARTMEDIA + ENTERTAINMENT, INC. - CHILLICOTHE, OH—See iHeartMedia, Inc.; *U.S. Public*, pg. 1097
IHEARTMEDIA + ENTERTAINMENT, INC. - CINCINNATI, OH—See iHeartMedia, Inc.; *U.S. Public*, pg. 1097
IHEARTMEDIA + ENTERTAINMENT, INC. - CLEVELAND, OH—See iHeartMedia, Inc.; *U.S. Public*, pg. 1097
IHEARTMEDIA + ENTERTAINMENT, INC. - COLUMBIA, SC—See iHeartMedia, Inc.; *U.S. Public*, pg. 1097
IHEARTMEDIA + ENTERTAINMENT, INC. - COLUMBUS, GA—See iHeartMedia, Inc.; *U.S. Public*, pg. 1097
IHEARTMEDIA + ENTERTAINMENT, INC. - COLUMBUS, OH—See iHeartMedia, Inc.; *U.S. Public*, pg. 1097
IHEARTMEDIA + ENTERTAINMENT, INC. - CORPUS CHRISTI, TX—See iHeartMedia, Inc.; *U.S. Public*, pg. 1098
IHEARTMEDIA + ENTERTAINMENT, INC. - DALLAS, TX—See iHeartMedia, Inc.; *U.S. Public*, pg. 1098
IHEARTMEDIA + ENTERTAINMENT, INC. - DAYTON, OH—See iHeartMedia, Inc.; *U.S. Public*, pg. 1098
IHEARTMEDIA + ENTERTAINMENT, INC. - DENVER, CO—See iHeartMedia, Inc.; *U.S. Public*, pg. 1098
IHEARTMEDIA + ENTERTAINMENT, INC. - DES MOINES, IA—See iHeartMedia, Inc.; *U.S. Public*, pg. 1098
IHEARTMEDIA + ENTERTAINMENT, INC. - DETROIT, MI—See iHeartMedia, Inc.; *U.S. Public*, pg. 1098
IHEARTMEDIA + ENTERTAINMENT, INC. - DICKINSON, ND—See iHeartMedia, Inc.; *U.S. Public*, pg. 1098
IHEARTMEDIA + ENTERTAINMENT, INC. - EL PASO, TX—See iHeartMedia, Inc.; *U.S. Public*, pg. 1098
IHEARTMEDIA + ENTERTAINMENT, INC. - FAIRBANKS, AK—See iHeartMedia, Inc.; *U.S. Public*, pg. 1098
IHEARTMEDIA + ENTERTAINMENT, INC. - FARMINGTON, NM—See iHeartMedia, Inc.; *U.S. Public*, pg. 1098
IHEARTMEDIA + ENTERTAINMENT, INC. - FAYETTEVILLE, AR—See iHeartMedia, Inc.; *U.S. Public*, pg. 1098
IHEARTMEDIA + ENTERTAINMENT, INC. - FLORIDA KEYS (KEY WEST), FL—See iHeartMedia, Inc.; *U.S. Public*, pg. 1098
IHEARTMEDIA + ENTERTAINMENT, INC. - FLORIDA KEYS (TAVERNIER), FL—See iHeartMedia, Inc.; *U.S. Public*, pg. 1098
IHEARTMEDIA + ENTERTAINMENT, INC. - FORT MYERS, FL—See iHeartMedia, Inc.; *U.S. Public*, pg. 1098
IHEARTMEDIA + ENTERTAINMENT, INC. - FORT SMITH, AR—See iHeartMedia, Inc.; *U.S. Public*, pg. 1098
IHEARTMEDIA + ENTERTAINMENT, INC. - GADSDEN, AL—See iHeartMedia, Inc.; *U.S. Public*, pg. 1098
IHEARTMEDIA + ENTERTAINMENT, INC. - GRAND FORKS, ND—See iHeartMedia, Inc.; *U.S. Public*, pg. 1098
IHEARTMEDIA + ENTERTAINMENT, INC. - GRAND RAPIDS, MI—See iHeartMedia, Inc.; *U.S. Public*, pg. 1098
IHEARTMEDIA + ENTERTAINMENT, INC. - GREENVILLE, SC—See iHeartMedia, Inc.; *U.S. Public*, pg. 1098
IHEARTMEDIA + ENTERTAINMENT, INC. - HARRISBURG, PA—See iHeartMedia, Inc.; *U.S. Public*, pg. 1098
IHEARTMEDIA + ENTERTAINMENT, INC. - HARTFORD, CT—See iHeartMedia, Inc.; *U.S. Public*, pg. 1098
IHEARTMEDIA + ENTERTAINMENT, INC. - HONOLULU, HI—See iHeartMedia, Inc.; *U.S. Public*, pg. 1098
IHEARTMEDIA + ENTERTAINMENT, INC. - HOUSTON, TX—See iHeartMedia, Inc.; *U.S. Public*, pg. 1098
IHEARTMEDIA + ENTERTAINMENT, INC. - HUNTSVILLE, AL—See iHeartMedia, Inc.; *U.S. Public*, pg. 1098
IHEARTMEDIA + ENTERTAINMENT, INC. - INDIANAPOLIS, IN—See iHeartMedia, Inc.; *U.S. Public*, pg. 1098
IHEARTMEDIA + ENTERTAINMENT, INC. - IOWA CITY, IA—See iHeartMedia, Inc.; *U.S. Public*, pg. 1098
IHEARTMEDIA + ENTERTAINMENT, INC. - JACKSON, MS—See iHeartMedia, Inc.; *U.S. Public*, pg. 1098
IHEARTMEDIA + ENTERTAINMENT, INC. - JACKSONVILLE, FL—See iHeartMedia, Inc.; *U.S. Public*, pg. 1098
IHEARTMEDIA + ENTERTAINMENT, INC. - LAGRANGE-NEWNAN, GA—See iHeartMedia, Inc.; *U.S. Public*, pg. 1097
IHEARTMEDIA + ENTERTAINMENT, INC. - LANCASTER/ANTELOPE, CA—See iHeartMedia, Inc.; *U.S. Public*, pg. 1098
IHEARTMEDIA + ENTERTAINMENT, INC. - LANCASTER, PA—See iHeartMedia, Inc.; *U.S. Public*, pg. 1098
IHEARTMEDIA + ENTERTAINMENT, INC. - LAS VEGAS, NV—See iHeartMedia, Inc.; *U.S. Public*, pg. 1098
IHEARTMEDIA + ENTERTAINMENT, INC. - LEXINGTON, KY—See iHeartMedia, Inc.; *U.S. Public*, pg. 1098
IHEARTMEDIA + ENTERTAINMENT, INC. - LIMA, OH—See iHeartMedia, Inc.; *U.S. Public*, pg. 1098
IHEARTMEDIA + ENTERTAINMENT, INC. - LITTLE ROCK, AR—See iHeartMedia, Inc.; *U.S. Public*, pg. 1099
IHEARTMEDIA + ENTERTAINMENT, INC. - LOS ANGELES, CA—See iHeartMedia, Inc.; *U.S. Public*, pg. 1099
IHEARTMEDIA + ENTERTAINMENT, INC. - LOUISVILLE, KY—See iHeartMedia, Inc.; *U.S. Public*, pg. 1099
IHEARTMEDIA + ENTERTAINMENT, INC. - MACON, GA—See iHeartMedia, Inc.; *U.S. Public*, pg. 1099
IHEARTMEDIA + ENTERTAINMENT, INC. - MADISON, WI—See iHeartMedia, Inc.; *U.S. Public*, pg. 1099
IHEARTMEDIA + ENTERTAINMENT, INC. - MANSFIELD, OH—See iHeartMedia, Inc.; *U.S. Public*, pg. 1097
IHEARTMEDIA + ENTERTAINMENT, INC. - MARION, OH—See iHeartMedia, Inc.; *U.S. Public*, pg. 1099
IHEARTMEDIA + ENTERTAINMENT, INC. - MEMPHIS, TN—See iHeartMedia, Inc.; *U.S. Public*, pg. 1099
IHEARTMEDIA + ENTERTAINMENT, INC. - MIAMI/FORT LAUDERDALE, FL—See iHeartMedia, Inc.; *U.S. Public*, pg. 1099
IHEARTMEDIA + ENTERTAINMENT, INC. - MILWAUKEE, WI—See iHeartMedia, Inc.; *U.S. Public*, pg. 1099
IHEARTMEDIA + ENTERTAINMENT, INC. - MINNEAPOLIS, MN—See iHeartMedia, Inc.; *U.S. Public*, pg. 1099
IHEARTMEDIA + ENTERTAINMENT, INC. - MINOT, ND—See iHeartMedia, Inc.; *U.S. Public*, pg. 1099
IHEARTMEDIA + ENTERTAINMENT, INC. - MOBILE, AL—See iHeartMedia, Inc.; *U.S. Public*, pg. 1099
IHEARTMEDIA + ENTERTAINMENT, INC. - MODESTO/STOCKTON, CA—See iHeartMedia, Inc.; *U.S. Public*, pg. 1099
IHEARTMEDIA + ENTERTAINMENT, INC. - MONTEREY, CA—See iHeartMedia, Inc.; *U.S. Public*, pg. 1099
IHEARTMEDIA + ENTERTAINMENT, INC. - MONTGOMERY, AL—See iHeartMedia, Inc.; *U.S. Public*, pg. 1099
IHEARTMEDIA + ENTERTAINMENT, INC. - NASHVILLE, TN—See iHeartMedia, Inc.; *U.S. Public*, pg. 1099
IHEARTMEDIA + ENTERTAINMENT, INC. - NASSAU/SUFFOLK, NY—See iHeartMedia, Inc.; *U.S. Public*, pg. 1099
IHEARTMEDIA + ENTERTAINMENT, INC. - NEW ORLEANS, LA—See iHeartMedia, Inc.; *U.S. Public*, pg. 1099
IHEARTMEDIA + ENTERTAINMENT, INC. - NEW YORK CITY, NY—See iHeartMedia, Inc.; *U.S. Public*, pg. 1099

N.A.I.C.S. INDEX

516110 — RADIO BROADCASTING ...

IHEARTMEDIA + ENTERTAINMENT, INC. - NORFOLK, VA—See iHeartMedia, Inc.; *U.S. Public*, pg. 1099
IHEARTMEDIA + ENTERTAINMENT, INC. - OMAHA, NE—See iHeartMedia, Inc.; *U.S. Public*, pg. 1099
IHEARTMEDIA + ENTERTAINMENT, INC. - ORLANDO, FL—See iHeartMedia, Inc.; *U.S. Public*, pg. 1099
IHEARTMEDIA + ENTERTAINMENT, INC. - PANAMA CITY, FL—See iHeartMedia, Inc.; *U.S. Public*, pg. 1099
IHEARTMEDIA + ENTERTAINMENT, INC. - PARKERSBURG, WV—See iHeartMedia, Inc.; *U.S. Public*, pg. 1099
IHEARTMEDIA + ENTERTAINMENT, INC. - PENSACOLA, FL—See iHeartMedia, Inc.; *U.S. Public*, pg. 1099
IHEARTMEDIA + ENTERTAINMENT, INC. - PHILADELPHIA, PA—See iHeartMedia, Inc.; *U.S. Public*, pg. 1099
IHEARTMEDIA + ENTERTAINMENT, INC. - PHOENIX, AZ—See iHeartMedia, Inc.; *U.S. Public*, pg. 1099
IHEARTMEDIA + ENTERTAINMENT, INC. - PITTSBURGH, PA—See iHeartMedia, Inc.; *U.S. Public*, pg. 1099
IHEARTMEDIA + ENTERTAINMENT, INC. - PORTLAND, OR—See iHeartMedia, Inc.; *U.S. Public*, pg. 1099
IHEARTMEDIA + ENTERTAINMENT, INC. - PORTSMOUTH, NH—See iHeartMedia, Inc.; *U.S. Public*, pg. 1099
IHEARTMEDIA + ENTERTAINMENT, INC. - PUNTA GORDA, FL—See iHeartMedia, Inc.; *U.S. Public*, pg. 1098
IHEARTMEDIA + ENTERTAINMENT, INC. - RALEIGH, NC—See iHeartMedia, Inc.; *U.S. Public*, pg. 1099
IHEARTMEDIA + ENTERTAINMENT, INC. - RICHMOND, VA—See iHeartMedia, Inc.; *U.S. Public*, pg. 1099
IHEARTMEDIA + ENTERTAINMENT, INC. - RIVERSIDE/SAN BERNARDINO, CA—See iHeartMedia, Inc.; *U.S. Public*, pg. 1099
IHEARTMEDIA + ENTERTAINMENT, INC. - ROCHESTER, MN—See iHeartMedia, Inc.; *U.S. Public*, pg. 1099
IHEARTMEDIA + ENTERTAINMENT, INC. - ROCHESTER, NY—See iHeartMedia, Inc.; *U.S. Public*, pg. 1100
IHEARTMEDIA + ENTERTAINMENT, INC. - SACRAMENTO, CA—See iHeartMedia, Inc.; *U.S. Public*, pg. 1100
IHEARTMEDIA + ENTERTAINMENT, INC. - SAINT LOUIS, MO—See iHeartMedia, Inc.; *U.S. Public*, pg. 1100
IHEARTMEDIA + ENTERTAINMENT, INC. - SALISBURY/OCEAN CITY, MD—See iHeartMedia, Inc.; *U.S. Public*, pg. 1100
IHEARTMEDIA + ENTERTAINMENT, INC. - SALT LAKE CITY, UT—See iHeartMedia, Inc.; *U.S. Public*, pg. 1100
IHEARTMEDIA + ENTERTAINMENT, INC. - SAN ANTONIO, TX—See iHeartMedia, Inc.; *U.S. Public*, pg. 1100
IHEARTMEDIA + ENTERTAINMENT, INC. - SAN DIEGO, CA—See iHeartMedia, Inc.; *U.S. Public*, pg. 1100
IHEARTMEDIA + ENTERTAINMENT, INC. - SAN FRANCISCO, CA—See iHeartMedia, Inc.; *U.S. Public*, pg. 1100
IHEARTMEDIA + ENTERTAINMENT, INC. - SAN JOSE, CA—See iHeartMedia, Inc.; *U.S. Public*, pg. 1100
IHEARTMEDIA + ENTERTAINMENT, INC. - SARASOTA, FL—See iHeartMedia, Inc.; *U.S. Public*, pg. 1100
IHEARTMEDIA + ENTERTAINMENT, INC. - SAVANNAH, GA—See iHeartMedia, Inc.; *U.S. Public*, pg. 1100
IHEARTMEDIA + ENTERTAINMENT, INC. - SEATTLE, WA—See iHeartMedia, Inc.; *U.S. Public*, pg. 1100
IHEARTMEDIA + ENTERTAINMENT, INC. - SPOKANE, WA—See iHeartMedia, Inc.; *U.S. Public*, pg. 1100
IHEARTMEDIA + ENTERTAINMENT, INC. - SPRINGFIELD, MA—See iHeartMedia, Inc.; *U.S. Public*, pg. 1100
IHEARTMEDIA + ENTERTAINMENT, INC. - SUSSEX, NJ—See iHeartMedia, Inc.; *U.S. Public*, pg. 1100
IHEARTMEDIA + ENTERTAINMENT, INC. - SYRACUSE, NY—See iHeartMedia, Inc.; *U.S. Public*, pg. 1100
IHEARTMEDIA + ENTERTAINMENT, INC. - TALLAHASSEE, FL—See iHeartMedia, Inc.; *U.S. Public*, pg. 1100
IHEARTMEDIA + ENTERTAINMENT, INC. - TAMPA, FL—See iHeartMedia, Inc.; *U.S. Public*, pg. 1100
IHEARTMEDIA + ENTERTAINMENT, INC. - TOLEDO, OH—See iHeartMedia, Inc.; *U.S. Public*, pg. 1100
IHEARTMEDIA + ENTERTAINMENT, INC. - TUCSON, AZ—See iHeartMedia, Inc.; *U.S. Public*, pg. 1100
IHEARTMEDIA + ENTERTAINMENT, INC. - TULSA, OK—See iHeartMedia, Inc.; *U.S. Public*, pg. 1100
IHEARTMEDIA + ENTERTAINMENT, INC. - TUPELO, MS—See iHeartMedia, Inc.; *U.S. Public*, pg. 1100
IHEARTMEDIA + ENTERTAINMENT, INC. - WACO, TX—See iHeartMedia, Inc.; *U.S. Public*, pg. 1100
IHEARTMEDIA + ENTERTAINMENT, INC. - WASHINGTON, DC—See iHeartMedia, Inc.; *U.S. Public*, pg. 1100
IHEARTMEDIA + ENTERTAINMENT, INC. - WEST PALM BEACH, FL—See iHeartMedia, Inc.; *U.S. Public*, pg. 1100
IHEARTMEDIA + ENTERTAINMENT, INC. - WICHITA, KS—See iHeartMedia, Inc.; *U.S. Public*, pg. 1100
IHEARTMEDIA + ENTERTAINMENT, INC. - WILLIAMSPORT, PA—See iHeartMedia, Inc.; *U.S. Public*, pg. 1100
IHEARTMEDIA + ENTERTAINMENT, INC. - WILMINGTON, DE—See iHeartMedia, Inc.; *U.S. Public*, pg. 1100
IHEARTMEDIA + ENTERTAINMENT, INC. - YOUNGSTOWN, OH—See iHeartMedia, Inc.; *U.S. Public*, pg. 1100
INADI S.A.—See Bertelsmann SE & Co. KGaA; *Int'l*, pg. 994
INFORADIO SP. Z O. O.—See Agora S.A.; *Int'l*, pg. 212
INTERACTIVE ONE, INC.—See Urban One, Inc.; *U.S. Public*, pg. 2265
JAM COMMUNICATIONS, INC.—See Federated Media Inc.; *U.S. Private*, pg. 1492
JERSEY SHORE BROADCASTING CORPORATION—See Beasley Broadcast Group, Inc.; *U.S. Public*, pg. 287
JVC BROADCASTING CORP.; *U.S. Private*, pg. 2246
KANSAS RADIO NETWORKS—See Shivers Trading & Operating Company; *U.S. Private*, pg. 3638
KBXX-FM—See Urban One, Inc.; *U.S. Public*, pg. 2265
KCKK-AM/FM—See Hunt Broadcasting, LLC; *U.S. Private*, pg. 2008
KDES-FM—See Alpha Media LLC; *U.S. Private*, pg. 198
KDON 102 5 FM—See iHeartMedia, Inc.; *U.S. Public*, pg. 1097
KEEZ-FM—See Alpha Media LLC; *U.S. Private*, pg. 198
KEY 103—See Heinrich Bauer Verlag KG; *Int'l*, pg. 3324
KEZR-FM—See Alpha Media LLC; *U.S. Private*, pg. 198
KFAX SAN FRANCISCO—See Salem Media Group, Inc.; *U.S. Public*, pg. 1836
KHTT—See Griffin Communications, LLC; *U.S. Private*, pg. 1787
KINK-FM—See Alpha Media LLC; *U.S. Private*, pg. 198
KIRO RADIO—See Deseret Management Corporation; *U.S. Private*, pg. 1212
KISS 100—See Heinrich Bauer Verlag KG; *Int'l*, pg. 3324
KKBQ-FM—See Apollo Global Management, Inc.; *U.S. Public*, pg. 163
KLASSIK RADIO GMBH & CO. KG—See Bertelsmann SE & Co. KGaA; *Int'l*, pg. 995
KLAX LICENSING, INC.—See Spanish Broadcasting System Inc.; *U.S. Public*, pg. 1914
KLOS RADIO, LLC—See Meruelo Group LLC; *U.S. Private*, pg. 2677
KMJQ-FM—See Urban One, Inc.; *U.S. Public*, pg. 2265
KNCI-FM—See Deseret Management Corporation; *U.S. Private*, pg. 1212
KOIT-FM—See Deseret Management Corporation; *U.S. Private*, pg. 1212
KPRZ 1210AM RADIO INC—See Salem Media Group, Inc.; *U.S. Public*, pg. 1836
KPWR-FM—See Meruelo Group LLC; *U.S. Private*, pg. 2677
KQKS-FM—See AUDACY, INC.; *U.S. Public*, pg. 226
KSCA-FM—See ForgeLight, LLC; *U.S. Private*, pg. 1568
KSCA-FM—See Searchlight Capital Partners, L.P.; *U.S. Private*, pg. 3590
KSHE-FM—See Hubbard Broadcasting, Inc.; *U.S. Private*, pg. 2000
KSTP-FM, LLC—See Hubbard Broadcasting, Inc.; *U.S. Private*, pg. 2000
KTGL-FM—See Digity Companies, LLC; *U.S. Private*, pg. 1231
KTNQ-AM—See ForgeLight, LLC; *U.S. Private*, pg. 1568
KTNQ-AM—See Searchlight Capital Partners, L.P.; *U.S. Private*, pg. 3590
KTSA-FM/AM—See Alpha Media LLC; *U.S. Private*, pg. 198
KXOJ INC.—See Stephens Media Group Management, LLC; *U.S. Private*, pg. 3803
KYGO-FM—See AUDACY, INC.; *U.S. Public*, pg. 226
LAKE COUNTRY RADIO—See Alden Global Capital LLC; *U.S. Private*, pg. 156
LA RADIO, LLC—See Cumulus Media Inc.; *U.S. Public*, pg. 610
LEGEND STUDIOS, INC.—See Bitcoin Brands Inc.; *U.S. Private*, pg. 567
LEIGHTON BROADCASTING - FERGUS FALLS—See Leighton Enterprises, Inc.; *U.S. Private*, pg. 2420
LEIGHTON BROADCASTING - WINONA—See Leighton Enterprises, Inc.; *U.S. Private*, pg. 2420
LEIGHTON ENTERPRISES, INC.; *U.S. Private*, pg. 2420
LIBERMAN BROADCASTING CORPORATION; *U.S. Private*, pg. 2442
LINCOLN FINANCIAL MEDIA COMPANY OF GEORGIA—See AUDACY, INC.; *U.S. Public*, pg. 227
LINCOLN FINANCIAL MEDIA COMPANY—See Lincoln National Corporation; *U.S. Public*, pg. 1319
LOTUS COMMUNICATIONS CORP.; *U.S. Private*, pg. 2497
THE MACDONALD BROADCASTING COMPANY; *U.S. Private*, pg. 4073
MAGIC 828 PROPRIETARY LIMITED—See African Equity Empowerment Investmts Limited; *Int'l*, pg. 191
MAPLETON COMMUNICATIONS, LLC - RADIO MERCED—See Mapleton Communications, LLC; *U.S. Private*, pg. 2568
MAPLETON COMMUNICATIONS, LLC - RADIO MONTEREY BAY—See Mapleton Communications, LLC; *U.S. Private*, pg. 2568
MAPLETON COMMUNICATIONS, LLC - RADIO SPOKANE—See Mapleton Communications, LLC; *U.S. Private*, pg. 2568
MARATHON MEDIA LLC; *U.S. Private*, pg. 2570
MARTZ COMMUNICATIONS GROUP INC.; *U.S. Private*, pg. 2597
M. BELMONT VER STANDIG, INC.—See Saga Communications, Inc.; *U.S. Public*, pg. 1835
METRO RADIO—See Heinrich Bauer Verlag KG; *Int'l*, pg. 3324
MIDCONTINENT MEDIA INC.—See Midcontinent Media Inc.; *U.S. Private*, pg. 2711
MID-WEST MANAGEMENT INC.; *U.S. Private*, pg. 2710
MINNESOTA PUBLIC RADIO INC.—See American Public Media Group; *U.S. Private*, pg. 244
NBCUNIVERSAL, LLC—See Comcast Corporation; *U.S. Public*, pg. 540
NEW INSPIRATION BROADCASTING CO. INC.—See Salem Media Group, Inc.; *U.S. Public*, pg. 1836
NEW JERSEY 101.5—See Brookfield Corporation; *Int'l*, pg. 1183
NEW YORK PUBLIC RADIO; *U.S. Private*, pg. 2911
NIELSEN MUSIC CONTROL NEDERLAND B.V.—See Brookfield Corporation; *Int'l*, pg. 1179
NIELSEN MUSIC CONTROL NEDERLAND B.V.—See Elliott Management Corporation; *U.S. Private*, pg. 1372
NORKRING BELGIE N.V.—See Cordiant Digital Infrastructure Limited; *Int'l*, pg. 1796
NRG MEDIA, LLC; *U.S. Private*, pg. 2969
OCALA BROADCASTING CORPORATION, LLC—See DIX 1898, Inc; *U.S. Private*, pg. 1244
ONE PLACE LLC—See Salem Media Group, Inc.; *U.S. Public*, pg. 1836
OY METRORADIO FINLAND AB—See Communicorp Group Ltd.; *Int'l*, pg. 1721
PAMAL BROADCASTING LTD.; *U.S. Private*, pg. 3082
PANDORA MEDIA, LLC—See Liberty Media Corporation; *U.S. Public*, pg. 1311
PEG BROADCASTING, LLC; *U.S. Private*, pg. 3129
PEG BROADCASTING - MCMINNVILLE/MANCHESTER—See PEG Broadcasting, LLC; *U.S. Private*, pg. 3129
PEG BROADCASTING - SPARTA—See PEG Broadcasting, LLC; *U.S. Private*, pg. 3129
PENNSYLVANIA MEDIA ASSOCIATES—See Salem Media Group, Inc.; *U.S. Public*, pg. 1836
POP RADIO, LP—See Cumulus Media Inc.; *U.S. Public*, pg. 610
POWELL GROUP INC.; *U.S. Private*, pg. 3237
PRITCHARD BROADCASTING CORP.; *U.S. Private*, pg. 3267
PUERTO RICO PUBLIC BROADCASTING CORP; *U.S. Private*, pg. 3302
QANTUM COMMUNICATIONS CORPORATION—See Nautic Partners, LLC; *U.S. Private*, pg. 2871
QMUSIC NEDERLAND B.V.—See DPG Media Group NV; *Int'l*, pg. 2188
RADIO 24 AG—See BT Holding AG; *Int'l*, pg. 1204
RADIO 32 AG—See BT Holding AG; *Int'l*, pg. 1204
RADIO 780 INC—See Salem Media Group, Inc.; *U.S. Public*, pg. 1836
RADIO 96FM PERTH PTY. LIMITED—See ARN Media Limited; *Int'l*, pg. 576
RADIO AIRE LTD—See Heinrich Bauer Verlag KG; *Int'l*, pg. 3324
RADIO CITY 93.7 FM—See Bertelsmann SE & Co. KGaA; *Int'l*, pg. 995
RADIO CITY LTD.—See Heinrich Bauer Verlag KG; *Int'l*, pg. 3324
RADIO CONTACT—See Bertelsmann SE & Co. KGaA; *Int'l*, pg. 995
RADIO HAMBURG GMBH & CO KG—See Bertelsmann SE & Co. KGaA; *Int'l*, pg. 995
RADIOHIO, INC.—See TEGNA Inc.; *U.S. Public*, pg. 1990
RADIO MUSIC RRM SRL—See Czech Media Invest as; *Int'l*, pg. 1898
RADIO NRW—See Bertelsmann SE & Co. KGaA; *Int'l*, pg. 995
RADIO ONE LICENSES, LLC—See Urban One, Inc.; *U.S. Public*, pg. 2265
RADIO ONE OF ATLANTA, LLC—See Urban One, Inc.; *U.S. Public*, pg. 2265
RADIO ONE OF CHARLOTTE, LLC—See Urban One, Inc.; *U.S. Public*, pg. 2265
RADIO ONE OF DETROIT, LLC—See Urban One, Inc.; *U.S. Public*, pg. 2265
RADIO ONE OF INDIANA, L.P.—See Urban One, Inc.; *U.S. Public*, pg. 2265
RADIO PLUS POLSKA SP. Z O.O.—See Czech Media Invest as; *Int'l*, pg. 1898
RADIOWE DORADZTWO REKLAMOWE SP. Z.O.O.—See Agora S.A.; *Int'l*, pg. 213
REACH SATELLITE NETWORK INC.—See Salem Media Group, Inc.; *U.S. Public*, pg. 1836
RFE/RL INC.; *U.S. Private*, pg. 3420
RINCON BROADCASTING LLC—See Point Broadcasting Company; *U.S. Private*, pg. 3221
ROCKKLASSIKER SVERIGE AB—See Warner Bros. Discovery, Inc.; *U.S. Public*, pg. 2326
RTL AUDIO VERMARKTUNG GMBH—See Bertelsmann SE & Co. KGaA; *Int'l*, pg. 993
RTL RADIO LETZEBUERG—See Bertelsmann SE & Co. KGaA; *Int'l*, pg. 995
RTL RADIO—See Bertelsmann SE & Co. KGaA; *Int'l*, pg. 995

516110 — RADIO BROADCASTING ...

RTL RADIO—See Bertelsmann SE & Co. KGaA; *Int'l*, pg. 995
SAGA COMMUNICATIONS, INC. - COLUMBUS RADIO GROUP—See Saga Communications, Inc.; *U.S. Public*, pg. 1835
SAGA RADIO NETWORKS, LLC—See Saga Communications, Inc.; *U.S. Public*, pg. 1835
SALEM COMMUNICATIONS TAMPA/SARASOTA—See Salem Media Group, Inc.; *U.S. Public*, pg. 1836
SALEM MEDIA GROUP, INC.; *U.S. Public*, pg. 1836
SALEM MEDIA OF COLORADO, INC.—See Salem Media Group, Inc.; *U.S. Public*, pg. 1836
SALEM MEDIA OF HAWAII, INC.—See Salem Media Group, Inc.; *U.S. Public*, pg. 1836
SALEM MEDIA OF MASSACHUSETTS, LLC—See Salem Media Group, Inc.; *U.S. Public*, pg. 1836
SALEM MEDIA OF OREGON—See Salem Media Group, Inc.; *U.S. Public*, pg. 1836
SALEM MEDIA OF PENNSYLVANIA—See Salem Media Group, Inc.; *U.S. Public*, pg. 1836
SALEM MEDIA OF TEXAS, INC.—See Salem Media Group, Inc.; *U.S. Public*, pg. 1836
SALEM MUSIC NETWORKS INC—See Salem Media Group, Inc.; *U.S. Public*, pg. 1836
SALEM RADIO REPRESENTATIVES—See Salem Media Group, Inc.; *U.S. Public*, pg. 1836
SBN NEWS—See Sheridan Broadcasting Corporation; *U.S. Private*, pg. 3633
SBS RADIO AB—See Warner Bros. Discovery, Inc.; *U.S. Public*, pg. 2326
SERVICE BROADCASTING LLC; *U.S. Private*, pg. 3614
SHERIDAN BROADCASTING CORPORATION; *U.S. Private*, pg. 3633
SIA STAR FM—See Providence Equity Partners L.L.C.; *U.S. Private*, pg. 3291
SIRIUS XM RADIO, INC.—See Liberty Media Corporation; *U.S. Public*, pg. 1311
SOUTH CENTRAL COMMUNICATIONS CORPORATION; *U.S. Private*, pg. 3720
SOUTHERN CALIFORNIA PUBLIC RADIO—See American Public Media Group; *U.S. Private*, pg. 245
SOUTHERN MEDIA COMMUNICATIONS INC.—See Creek Indian Enterprises; *U.S. Private*, pg. 1092
SOUTHERN WISCONSIN BROADCASTING LLC—See Adams Publishing Group, LLC; *U.S. Private*, pg. 74
SOUTH TEXAS BROADCASTING, INC.—See Salem Media Group, Inc.; *U.S. Public*, pg. 1836
SPANISH BROADCASTING SYSTEM OF CALIFORNIA INC.—See Spanish Broadcasting System Inc.; *U.S. Public*, pg. 1914
SPORTING NEWS RADIO—See Advance Publications, Inc.; *U.S. Private*, pg. 85
SRN NEWS—See Salem Media Group, Inc.; *U.S. Public*, pg. 1836
SSC CHILE S.A.—See GomSpace Group AB; *Int'l*, pg. 3037
STEPHENS MEDIA GROUP-WATERTOWN, LLC—See Stephens Media Group Management, LLC; *U.S. Private*, pg. 3803
SUN BROADCAST GROUP—See Gen Media Partners LLC; *U.S. Private*, pg. 1660
SUNRISE BROADCASTING OF NEW YORK, INC.; *U.S. Private*, pg. 3869
TALKING STICK COMMUNICATIONS, LLC—See Federated Media Inc.; *U.S. Private*, pg. 1492
TALK RADIO NETWORK; *U.S. Private*, pg. 3926
TELEVIMEX, S.A. DE C.V.—See Grupo Televisa, S.A.B.; *Int'l*, pg. 3136
TFM RADIO—See Heinrich Bauer Verlag KG; *Int'l*, pg. 3324
TIDEWATER COMMUNICATIONS, LLC—See Saga Communications, Inc.; *U.S. Public*, pg. 1835
TIMES-SHAMROCK, INC.; *U.S. Private*, pg. 4173
TITAN BROADCASTING, LLC—See Pritchard Broadcasting Corp.; *U.S. Private*, pg. 3268
TOWNSQUARE MEDIA ABILENE, LLC—See Brookfield Corporation; *Int'l*, pg. 1183
TOWNSQUARE MEDIA AMARILLO, LLC—See Brookfield Corporation; *Int'l*, pg. 1183
TOWNSQUARE MEDIA BILLINGS, LLC—See Brookfield Corporation; *Int'l*, pg. 1184
TOWNSQUARE MEDIA BINGHAMTON, LLC—See Brookfield Corporation; *Int'l*, pg. 1184
TOWNSQUARE MEDIA BROADCASTING, LLC—See Brookfield Corporation; *Int'l*, pg. 1183
TOWNSQUARE MEDIA CASPER, LLC—See Brookfield Corporation; *Int'l*, pg. 1184
TOWNSQUARE MEDIA FARIBAULT, LLC—See Brookfield Corporation; *Int'l*, pg. 1184
TOWNSQUARE MEDIA LANSING, LLC—See Brookfield Corporation; *Int'l*, pg. 1184
TOWNSQUARE MEDIA LAWTON, LLC—See Brookfield Corporation; *Int'l*, pg. 1183
TOWNSQUARE MEDIA LUBBOCK, LLC—See Brookfield Corporation; *Int'l*, pg. 1184
TOWNSQUARE MEDIA LUFKIN, LLC—See Brookfield Corporation; *Int'l*, pg. 1184
TOWNSQUARE MEDIA NEW BEDFORD, LLC—See Brookfield Corporation; *Int'l*, pg. 1184
TOWNSQUARE MEDIA ODESSA-MIDLAND II, LLC—See Brookfield Corporation; *Int'l*, pg. 1184
TOWNSQUARE MEDIA OF ALBANY, INC.—See Brookfield Corporation; *Int'l*, pg. 1184
TOWNSQUARE MEDIA OF BLOOMINGTON, INC.—See Brookfield Corporation; *Int'l*, pg. 1184
TOWNSQUARE MEDIA OF BUFFALO, INC.—See Brookfield Corporation; *Int'l*, pg. 1184
TOWNSQUARE MEDIA OF EL PASO, INC.—See Brookfield Corporation; *Int'l*, pg. 1184
TOWNSQUARE MEDIA OF EVANSVILLE/OWENSBORO, INC.—See Brookfield Corporation; *Int'l*, pg. 1184
TOWNSQUARE MEDIA OF FLINT, INC.—See Brookfield Corporation; *Int'l*, pg. 1184
TOWNSQUARE MEDIA OF FT. COLLINS, INC.—See Brookfield Corporation; *Int'l*, pg. 1184
TOWNSQUARE MEDIA OF GRAND RAPIDS, INC.—See Brookfield Corporation; *Int'l*, pg. 1184
TOWNSQUARE MEDIA OF KILLEEN-TEMPLE, INC.—See Brookfield Corporation; *Int'l*, pg. 1184
TOWNSQUARE MEDIA OF LAFAYETTE, INC.—See Brookfield Corporation; *Int'l*, pg. 1184
TOWNSQUARE MEDIA OF OWENSBORO—See Brookfield Corporation; *Int'l*, pg. 1184
TOWNSQUARE MEDIA OF ST. CLOUD, INC.—See Brookfield Corporation; *Int'l*, pg. 1184
TOWNSQUARE MEDIA OF UTICA/ROME, INC.—See Brookfield Corporation; *Int'l*, pg. 1184
TOWNSQUARE MEDIA PORTSMOUTH, LLC—See Brookfield Corporation; *Int'l*, pg. 1184
TOWNSQUARE MEDIA TEXARKANA, LLC—See Brookfield Corporation; *Int'l*, pg. 1184
TOWNSQUARE MEDIA TWIN FALLS, LLC—See Brookfield Corporation; *Int'l*, pg. 1184
TOWNSQUARE MEDIA TYLER, LLC—See Brookfield Corporation; *Int'l*, pg. 1184
TOWNSQUARE MEDIA VICTORIA, LLC—See Brookfield Corporation; *Int'l*, pg. 1184
TOWNSQUARE MEDIA WICHITA FALLS, LLC—See Brookfield Corporation; *Int'l*, pg. 1184
TRANS WORLD RADIO INC.; *U.S. Private*, pg. 4205
TREATY RADIO LIMITED—See News Corporation; *U.S. Public*, pg. 1520
UMOYA COMMUNICATIONS (PTY) LTD—See African Media Entertainment Limited; *Int'l*, pg. 192
UNITED STATIONS PROPRIETARY LIMITED—See African Media Entertainment Limited; *Int'l*, pg. 192
UNIVERSITY CORP.; *U.S. Private*, pg. 4307
UNIVISION RADIO—See ForgeLight, LLC; *U.S. Private*, pg. 1568
UNIVISION RADIO—See Searchlight Capital Partners, L.P.; *U.S. Private*, pg. 3590
VIKING RADIO LTD.—See Heinrich Bauer Verlag KG; *Int'l*, pg. 3324
VINYL AB—See Warner Bros. Discovery, Inc.; *U.S. Public*, pg. 2326
VIRGIN BEC-TERO RADIO (THAILAND) CO., LTD.—See BEC World Public Company Limited; *Int'l*, pg. 936
VOX COMMUNICATIONS - WESTERN MASSACHUSETTS—See Vox Communications Group LLC; *U.S. Private*, pg. 4414
WADO-AM—See ForgeLight, LLC; *U.S. Private*, pg. 1568
WADO-AM—See Searchlight Capital Partners, L.P.; *U.S. Private*, pg. 3590
WAMN-FM—See First Media Services, LLC; *U.S. Private*, pg. 1521
WAMO 100.1 FM—See Martz Communications Group Inc.; *U.S. Private*, pg. 2597
WARQ-FM—See YMF Media LLC; *U.S. Private*, pg. 4589
WAY MEDIA INC.; *U.S. Private*, pg. 4459
WBAL-AM—See The Hearst Corporation; *U.S. Private*, pg. 4048
WBBB-FM—See Curtis Media Group; *U.S. Private*, pg. 1126
WCHO RADIO—See iHeartMedia, Inc.; *U.S. Public*, pg. 1097
WCPR-FM—See Alpha Media LLC; *U.S. Private*, pg. 198
WDEF AM/FM—See Bahakel Communications, Ltd.; *U.S. Private*, pg. 425
WDHT—See Alpha Media LLC; *U.S. Private*, pg. 198
WDLA-FM—See iHeartMedia, Inc.; *U.S. Public*, pg. 1097
WE ARE ERA GMBH—See Bertelsmann SE & Co. KGaA; *Int'l*, pg. 996
WEPN-FM—See Emmis Communications Corporation; *U.S. Public*, pg. 753
WEST BEND BROADCASTING CO., INC.—See Adams Publishing Group, LLC; *U.S. Private*, pg. 74
WEST VIRGINIA RADIO CORPORATION; *U.S. Private*, pg. 4487
WGAU RADIO—See Apollo Global Management, Inc.; *U.S. Public*, pg. 164
WGBR-AM—See Curtis Media Group; *U.S. Private*, pg. 1126
WGCHAM 1490—See iHeartMedia, Inc.; *U.S. Public*, pg. 1097
WGN RADIO—See Nexstar Media Group, Inc.; *U.S. Public*, pg. 1525
WHAJ-FM—See First Media Services, LLC; *U.S. Private*, pg. 1521
WHKX-FM—See First Media Services, LLC; *U.S. Private*, pg. 1521

CORPORATE AFFILIATIONS

WHYY INC.; *U.S. Private*, pg. 4515
WIBC-FM—See Emmis Communications Corporation; *U.S. Public*, pg. 753
WIBW-AM—See Shivers Trading & Operating Company; *U.S. Private*, pg. 3638
WIBW-FM—See Shivers Trading & Operating Company; *U.S. Private*, pg. 3638
WILKS BROADCAST GROUP, LLC—See The Wicks Group of Companies, LLC; *U.S. Private*, pg. 4136
WISCONSIN EDUCATIONAL COMMUNICATIONS BOARD; *U.S. Private*, pg. 4548
WITHERS BROADCASTING COMPANY OF ILLINOIS, LLC—See Withers Broadcasting Company of West Virginia; *U.S. Private*, pg. 4550
WIYY-FM—See The Hearst Corporation; *U.S. Private*, pg. 4048
WJYY; *U.S. Private*, pg. 4551
WKQR-FM—See First Media Services, LLC; *U.S. Private*, pg. 1521
WKQX-FM—See Emmis Communications Corporation; *U.S. Public*, pg. 753
WKZO AM 590—See Midwest Communications, Inc.; *U.S. Private*, pg. 2720
WLDE OLDIES 101 7 FM—See iHeartMedia, Inc.; *U.S. Public*, pg. 1097
WLHK-FM—See Emmis Communications Corporation; *U.S. Public*, pg. 753
WLIF-FM—See AUDACY, INC.; *U.S. Public*, pg. 226
WMET 1160—See IDT Corporation; *U.S. Public*, pg. 1094
WMMB AM 1240—See iHeartMedia, Inc.; *U.S. Public*, pg. 1097
WNOU-FM—See Urban One, Inc.; *U.S. Public*, pg. 2265
WPCM-AM—See Curtis Media Group; *U.S. Private*, pg. 1126
WPNH—See Northeast Communications Inc.; *U.S. Private*, pg. 2949
WPRA, INC.—See Empresas Bechara, Inc.; *U.S. Private*, pg. 1388
WPTF-AM—See Curtis Media Group; *U.S. Private*, pg. 1126
WQDR-FM—See Curtis Media Group; *U.S. Private*, pg. 1126
WQHH 96 5 FM—See The Macdonald Broadcasting Company; *U.S. Private*, pg. 4073
WQHT-FM—See Emmis Communications Corporation; *U.S. Public*, pg. 753
WQSR-FM—See AUDACY, INC.; *U.S. Public*, pg. 226
WQXR FM—See New York Public Radio; *U.S. Private*, pg. 2911
WRAL-FM, INC.—See Capitol Broadcasting Company, Inc.; *U.S. Private*, pg. 743
WRIG, INC.—See Midwest Communications, Inc.; *U.S. Private*, pg. 2720
WRWD COUNTRY 1073—See iHeartMedia, Inc.; *U.S. Public*, pg. 1097
WSIG 96.9FM—See Vox Communications Group LLC; *U.S. Private*, pg. 4414
WSIP-FM—See Forcht Group of Kentucky, Inc.; *U.S. Private*, pg. 1564
WSM-AM—See Ryman Hospitality Properties, Inc.; *U.S. Public*, pg. 1829
WSRW 101.5—See iHeartMedia, Inc.; *U.S. Public*, pg. 1097
WTHI-FM—See Midwest Communications, Inc.; *U.S. Private*, pg. 2720
WTKS REAL RADIO 104 1 FM—See iHeartMedia, Inc.; *U.S. Public*, pg. 1097
WVEE-FM—See AUDACY, INC.; *U.S. Public*, pg. 226
WWDM-FM—See YMF Media LLC; *U.S. Private*, pg. 4589
WWNC AM—See iHeartMedia, Inc.; *U.S. Public*, pg. 1097
WWUS 104.1FM—See Vox Communications Group LLC; *U.S. Private*, pg. 4414
WXBB FM 105 3, INC.—See Brookfield Corporation; *Int'l*, pg. 1184
WXDJ LICENSING, INC.—See Spanish Broadcasting System Inc.; *U.S. Public*, pg. 1914
WXYT-FM—See AUDACY, INC.; *U.S. Public*, pg. 226
WZLX-FM—See AUDACY, INC.; *U.S. Public*, pg. 226
XM 1500 ECKINGTON LLC—See Liberty Media Corporation; *U.S. Public*, pg. 1311
Y95 RADIO STATION INC.—See Wehco Media, Inc.; *U.S. Private*, pg. 4470
YMF MEDIA MISSISSIPPI LLC—See YMF Media LLC; *U.S. Private*, pg. 4589
YMF MEDIA NEW YORK LLC—See YMF Media LLC; *U.S. Private*, pg. 4589
YMF MEDIA SOUTH CAROLINA LLC—See YMF Media LLC; *U.S. Private*, pg. 4589
ZIA BROADCASTING COMPANY—See Allsup Enterprises Inc.; *U.S. Private*, pg. 194

516120 — TELEVISION BROADCASTING STATIONS

11 FREUNDE VERLAG GMBH & CO. KG—See Bertelsmann SE & Co. KGaA; *Int'l*, pg. 993
24 KITCHEN MEDYA HIZMETLERI ANONIM SIRKETI—See The Walt Disney Company; *U.S. Public*, pg. 2140
24KITCHEN TELEVISION B.V.—See The Walt Disney Company; *U.S. Public*, pg. 2140
4FUN MEDIA S.A.; *Int'l*, pg. 12

N.A.I.C.S. INDEX

516120 — TELEVISION BROADCAS...

9&10 NEWS; *U.S. Private,* pg. 17
98.7 FM—See Window to the World Communications, Inc.; *U.S. Private,* pg. 4538
AB BROADCAST—See Groupe AB S.A.; *Int'l,* pg. 3091
ABC BROADCAST OPERATIONS & ENGINEERING—See The Walt Disney Company; *U.S. Public,* pg. 2137
ABC HORIZON PTE. LTD.—See Asahi Broadcasting Group Holdings Corporation; *Int'l,* pg. 592
ABC, INC.—See The Walt Disney Company; *U.S. Public,* pg. 2137
ABC NATIONAL TELEVISION SALES, INC.—See The Walt Disney Company; *U.S. Public,* pg. 2137
ABC OWNED TELEVISION STATIONS—See The Walt Disney Company; *U.S. Public,* pg. 2138
ABC TELEVISION NETWORK GROUP—See The Walt Disney Company; *U.S. Public,* pg. 2137
ABU DHABI MEDIA; *Int'l,* pg. 72
ACC LICENSEE, LLC—See Sinclair, Inc.; *U.S. Public,* pg. 1885
ACE METRIX, INC.—See ISpot.tv, Inc.; *U.S. Private,* pg. 2146
ADELMAN ENTERPRISES, INC.; *U.S. Private,* pg. 77
ADJACENT PRODUCTIONS, LLC—See British Broadcasting Corporation; *Int'l,* pg. 1168
ADVANCED DIGITAL BROADCAST HOLDINGS SA; *Int'l,* pg. 158
ADVENTURE LINE PRODUCTIONS S.A—See De Agostini S.p.A.; *Int'l,* pg. 1994
AGINCOURT PRODUCTIONS, INC.—See BCE Inc.; *Int'l,* pg. 927
ALABAMA PUBLIC TELEVISION; *U.S. Private,* pg. 148
ALBORAN S.P.A.—See Banca Mediolanum S.p.A.; *Int'l,* pg. 815
ALCHIMIE SA; *Int'l,* pg. 301
ALJAZEERA BALKANS D.O.O.—See Al-Jazeera Satellite Network; *Int'l,* pg. 286
AL JAZEERA MEDIA NETWORK.—See Al-Jazeera Satellite Network; *Int'l,* pg. 286
ALLEN MEDIA BROADCASTING EVANSVILLE, INC.—See Entertainment Studios, Inc.; *U.S. Private,* pg. 1405
ALLEN MEDIA BROADCASTING LAFAYETTE, INC.—See Entertainment Studios, Inc.; *U.S. Private,* pg. 1405
ALLEN MEDIA BROADCASTING LLC—See Entertainment Studios, Inc.; *U.S. Private,* pg. 1405
ALMA MEDIA INTERACTIVE OY—See Alma Media Corporation; *Int'l,* pg. 361
ALTA LOMA PRODUCTIONS, INC.—See PLBY Group, Inc.; *U.S. Public,* pg. 1698
AMARIN BOOK CENTER COMPANY LIMITED—See Amarin Printing & Publishing Public Company Limited; *Int'l,* pg. 412
AMARIN TELEVISION COMPANY LIMITED—See Amarin Printing & Publishing Public Company Limited; *Int'l,* pg. 412
AMERICAN PUBLIC TELEVISION; *U.S. Private,* pg. 245
ANIMAL PLANET EUROPE P/S—See Warner Bros. Discovery, Inc.; *U.S. Public,* pg. 2326
ANIPLUS INC.; *Int'l,* pg. 472
ANTENA 3 EVENTOS S.L.U.—See Atresmedia Corporacion de Medios de Comunicacion, S.A.; *Int'l,* pg. 693
ANTENNA TV S.A.—See Antenna Group; *Int'l,* pg. 482
ANTENNE NIEDERSACHSEN GMBH & CO. KG—See Bertelsmann SE & Co. KGaA; *Int'l,* pg. 993
ANYCOLOR INC.; *Int'l,* pg. 487
ARKANSAS HEARST ARGYLE TELEVISION, INC.—See The Hearst Corporation; *U.S. Private,* pg. 4048
ARTE RADIOTELEVISIVO ARGENTINO S.A.—See Grupo Clarin S.A.; *Int'l,* pg. 3124
ARVATO CRM NORDHORN GMBH—See Bertelsmann SE & Co. KGaA; *Int'l,* pg. 996
ARVATO CROSSMARKETING GMBH—See Bertelsmann SE & Co. KGaA; *Int'l,* pg. 996
ARVATO DIRECT SERVICES BRANDENBURG GMBH—See Bertelsmann SE & Co. KGaA; *Int'l,* pg. 997
ARVATO DIRECT SERVICES COTTBUS GMBH—See Bertelsmann SE & Co. KGaA; *Int'l,* pg. 997
ARVATO DIRECT SERVICES DORTMUND GMBH—See Bertelsmann SE & Co. KGaA; *Int'l,* pg. 997
ARVATO INFOSCORE GMBH—See Bertelsmann SE & Co. KGaA; *Int'l,* pg. 997
ARVATO MEDIA GMBH—See Bertelsmann SE & Co. KGaA; *Int'l,* pg. 997
ARVATO P.S. GMBH—See Bertelsmann SE & Co. KGaA; *Int'l,* pg. 997
ARVATO SCM IRELAND LIMITED—See Bertelsmann SE & Co. KGaA; *Int'l,* pg. 996
ARVATO SERVICES CHEMNITZ GMBH—See Bertelsmann SE & Co. KGaA; *Int'l,* pg. 997
ARVATO SERVICES DRESDEN GMBH—See Bertelsmann SE & Co. KGaA; *Int'l,* pg. 997
ARVATO SERVICES TECHNICAL INFORMATION GMBH—See Bertelsmann SE & Co. KGaA; *Int'l,* pg. 997
ARVATO TELCO SERVICES ERFURT GMBH—See Bertelsmann SE & Co. KGaA; *Int'l,* pg. 997
AS ALL MEDIA EESTI—See Providence Equity Partners L.L.C.; *U.S. Private,* pg. 3291
ASIA MEDIA CO., LTD.; *Int'l,* pg. 613
ASIANET STAR COMMUNICATIONS PRIVATE LIMITED—See The Walt Disney Company; *U.S. Public,* pg. 2137
ASIAN TELEVISION NETWORK INC.—See Asian Television Network International Ltd.; *Int'l,* pg. 619
ASIAN TELEVISION NETWORK INTERNATIONAL LTD.; *Int'l,* pg. 619
ASIA SPORTS VENTURES PTE LTD—See Bertelsmann SE & Co. KGaA; *Int'l,* pg. 993
ASIA TODAY LIMITED—See Essel Corporate Resources Pvt. Ltd.; *Int'l,* pg. 2510
ASIA TV LIMITED—See Essel Corporate Resources Pvt. Ltd.; *Int'l,* pg. 2509
A-SMART MEDIA PTE LTD—See A-Smart Holdings Ltd.; *Int'l,* pg. 20
ASTORY CO LTD.; *Int'l,* pg. 657
ATRESMEDIA CORPORACION DE MEDIOS DE COMUNICACION, S.A.; *Int'l,* pg. 693
ATV PRODUCTIONS LTD—See Best Medical International, Inc.; *U.S. Public,* pg. 543
AVANTI SPACE LIMITED—See Avanti Communications Group plc; *Int'l,* pg. 736
AVE GESELLSCHAFT FUR HORFUNKBETEILIGUNGEN MBH—See Bertelsmann SE & Co. KGaA; *Int'l,* pg. 993
BAHAKEL COMMUNICATIONS, LTD.; *U.S. Private,* pg. 425
BANGKOK BROADCASTING & TV CO., LTD.; *Int'l,* pg. 833
THE BANGKOK ENTERTAINMENT CO., LTD.—See BEC World Public Company Limited; *Int'l,* pg. 936
BARILOCHE TV S.A—See Grupo Clarin S.A.; *Int'l,* pg. 3124
BASIS LTD.—See Fuji Media Holdings, Inc.; *Int'l,* pg. 2813
BASTEI MEDIA GMBH—See Bastei Lubbe AG; *Int'l,* pg. 888
BAVARIA FILM- UND FERNSEHSTUDIOS GMBH—See Bavaria Film GmbH; *Int'l,* pg. 899
BAVARIA MEDIA TELEVISION GMBH—See Bavaria Film GmbH; *Int'l,* pg. 899
BBC GLOBAL NEWS LIMITED—See British Broadcasting Corporation; *Int'l,* pg. 1168
BBC STUDIOS AFRICA (PTY) LIMITED—See British Broadcasting Corporation; *Int'l,* pg. 1168
BBC STUDIOS AMERICAS INC.—See British Broadcasting Corporation; *Int'l,* pg. 1168
BBC STUDIOS AND POST PRODUCTION LIMITED—See British Broadcasting Corporation; *Int'l,* pg. 1168
BBC STUDIOS AUSTRALIA HOLDINGS PTY LIMITED—See British Broadcasting Corporation; *Int'l,* pg. 1168
BBC STUDIOS CANADA LIMITED—See British Broadcasting Corporation; *Int'l,* pg. 1168
BBC STUDIOS DISTRIBUTION LIMITED—See British Broadcasting Corporation; *Int'l,* pg. 1168
BBC STUDIOS FRANCE SARL—See British Broadcasting Corporation; *Int'l,* pg. 1168
BBC STUDIOS GERMANY GMBH—See British Broadcasting Corporation; *Int'l,* pg. 1168
BBC STUDIOS INDIA PRIVATE LIMITED—See British Broadcasting Corporation; *Int'l,* pg. 1168
BBC STUDIOS INTERMEDIADORA DE PROGRAMADORA ESTANGEIRA LIMITED—See British Broadcasting Corporation; *Int'l,* pg. 1168
BBC STUDIOS JAPAN LIMITED—See British Broadcasting Corporation; *Int'l,* pg. 1168
BBC STUDIOS POLSKA SP. Z O.O.—See British Broadcasting Corporation; *Int'l,* pg. 1168
BBC STUDIOS PRODUCTIONS LIMITED—See British Broadcasting Corporation; *Int'l,* pg. 1168
BBC STUDIOS SINGAPORE PTE. LIMITED—See British Broadcasting Corporation; *Int'l,* pg. 1168
BBC WORLDWIDE AUSTRALIA PTY LIMITED—See British Broadcasting Corporation; *Int'l,* pg. 1169
BEC NEWS BUREAU CO., LTD.—See BEC World Public Company Limited; *Int'l,* pg. 936
BEC-TERO RADIO CO., LTD.—See BEC World Public Company Limited; *Int'l,* pg. 936
BEC WORLD PUBLIC COMPANY LIMITED; *Int'l,* pg. 936
BEIJING GEHUA CATV NETWORK CO., LTD.; *Int'l,* pg. 950
BELGIUM TELEVISION SA—See Groupe AB S.A.; *Int'l,* pg. 3091
BERTELSMANN AVIATION GMBH—See Bertelsmann SE & Co. KGaA; *Int'l,* pg. 994
BFS HEALTH FINANCE GMBH—See Bertelsmann SE & Co. KGaA; *Int'l,* pg. 993
BIG TEN NETWORK, LLC—See Fox Corporation; *U.S. Public,* pg. 875
BINGO NATION, INC.; *U.S. Private,* pg. 561
BLACKHAWK BROADCASTING LLC - KSWT-DT—See Northwest Broadcasting, Inc.; *U.S. Private,* pg. 2959
BLACKHAWK BROADCASTING LLC - KYMA-DT—See Northwest Broadcasting, Inc.; *U.S. Private,* pg. 2959
BLACKHAWK BROADCASTING LLC—See Northwest Broadcasting, Inc.; *U.S. Private,* pg. 2959
BLU A/S—See Bertelsmann SE & Co. KGaA; *Int'l,* pg. 994
BLUE ANT MEDIA, INC.; *Int'l,* pg. 1067
BLUE ANT MEDIA NZ LIMITED; *Int'l,* pg. 1067
BLUE CIRCLE BV—See Bertelsmann SE & Co. KGaA; *Int'l,* pg. 994
BMG RIGHTS MANAGEMENT (EUROPE) GMBH—See Bertelsmann SE & Co. KGaA; *Int'l,* pg. 994
BRANDDELI C.V.—See Bertelsmann SE & Co. KGaA; *Int'l,* pg. 995
BREAKOUT KINGS PRODUCTIONS LLC—See The Walt Disney Company; *U.S. Public,* pg. 2140
BRIGHTSTAR FOX PRODUCTIONS LLC—See The Walt Disney Company; *U.S. Public,* pg. 2140
BROADBANDTV CORPORATION—See BBTV Holdings Inc.; *Int'l,* pg. 921
BROADCASTING CENTER EUROPE SA—See Bertelsmann SE & Co. KGaA; *Int'l,* pg. 994
BROADCASTING COMMUNICATIONS, LLC—See Northwest Broadcasting, Inc.; *U.S. Private,* pg. 2959
BROADCAST SPORTS INTERNATIONAL, LLC—See The Carlyle Group Inc.; *U.S. Public,* pg. 2049
BSN MEDIA HOLDINGS, INC.; *Int'l,* pg. 1202
BVS ENTERTAINMENT, INC.—See The Walt Disney Company; *U.S. Public,* pg. 2138
CABLENET, S.A.—See America Movil, S.A.B. de C.V.; *Int'l,* pg. 421
CABLE NEWS NETWORK, INC.—See Warner Bros. Discovery, Inc.; *U.S. Public,* pg. 2328
CABLE SISTEMA DE VICTORIA, S.A. DE C.V.—See Grupo Televisa, S.A.B.; *Int'l,* pg. 3136
CAIRO PUBBLICITA S.P.A—See Cairo Communication S.p.A.; *Int'l,* pg. 1253
CALIFORNIA BROADCAST CENTER, LLC—See AT&T Inc.; *U.S. Public,* pg. 220
CALIFORNIA OREGON BROADCASTING INC.; *U.S. Private,* pg. 720
CANAL RURAL SATELITAL S.A.—See Grupo Clarin S.A.; *Int'l,* pg. 3125
CAPITOL BROADCASTING COMPANY, INC.; *U.S. Private,* pg. 743
THE CARTOON NETWORK, INC.—See Warner Bros. Discovery, Inc.; *U.S. Public,* pg. 2328
CASCADE BROADCASTING GROUP LLC; *U.S. Private,* pg. 778
CBS BROADCASTING INC.—See National Amusements, Inc.; *U.S. Private,* pg. 2839
CBS ENTERTAINMENT DIVISION—See National Amusements, Inc.; *U.S. Private,* pg. 2839
CBS INTERNATIONAL SALES HOLDINGS B.V.—See National Amusements, Inc.; *U.S. Private,* pg. 2840
CBS NEWS—See National Amusements, Inc.; *U.S. Private,* pg. 2840
CBS OUTERNET INC.—See National Amusements, Inc.; *U.S. Private,* pg. 2840
CBS OVERSEAS INC.—See National Amusements, Inc.; *U.S. Private,* pg. 2840
CBS SPORTS DIVISION—See National Amusements, Inc.; *U.S. Private,* pg. 2840
CBS TELEVISION STATIONS INC.—See National Amusements, Inc.; *U.S. Private,* pg. 2840
CBS WORLDWIDE NETHERLANDS B.V.—See National Amusements, Inc.; *U.S. Private,* pg. 2841
CELADOR PRODUCTIONS LTD.; *Int'l,* pg. 1391
CENTURY SAGE SCIENTIFIC (TAIWAN) LIMITED—See Century Sage Scientific Holdings Limited; *Int'l,* pg. 1419
CHALLENGE TV—See Comcast Corporation; *U.S. Public,* pg. 541
CHANNEL 40, INC.—See Nexstar Media Group, Inc.; *U.S. Public,* pg. 1524
CHANNEL 5 BROADCASTING LTD.—See National Amusements, Inc.; *U.S. Private,* pg. 2841
CHANNEL FOUR TELEVISION CORPORATION; *Int'l,* pg. 1446
CHANNEL ONE LLC—See Veritas Capital Fund Management, LLC; *U.S. Private,* pg. 4363
CHARTER MEDIA COMPANY—See National Amusements, Inc.; *U.S. Private,* pg. 2841
CHEX-TV - DURHAM—See Corus Entertainment Inc.; *Int'l,* pg. 1808
CHEX-TV - PETERBOROUGH—See Corus Entertainment Inc.; *Int'l,* pg. 1808
CHINA BRIGHT CULTURE GROUP; *Int'l,* pg. 1487
CHINA NETWORKS INTERNATIONAL HOLDING LTD.; *Int'l,* pg. 1534
CHINA TELEVISION COMPANY; *Int'l,* pg. 1558
CHOICE N.V.; *Int'l,* pg. 1577
CINE LATINO, INC.—See Hemisphere Media Group, Inc.; *U.S. Private,* pg. 1913
CJ E&M CORPORATION—See CJ Corporation; *Int'l,* pg. 1632
CJ POWERCAST INC.—See CJ Corporation; *Int'l,* pg. 1633
CJ TELENIX CO., LTD.—See CJ Corporation; *Int'l,* pg. 1632
CKWS-TV—See Corus Entertainment Inc.; *Int'l,* pg. 1808
CNN HEADLINE NEWS—See Warner Bros. Discovery, Inc.; *U.S. Public,* pg. 2328
CNN NEWS SOURCE SALES INC.—See Warner Bros. Discovery, Inc.; *U.S. Public,* pg. 2328
COLORADO SATELLITE BROADCASTING, INC.—See L.F.P., Inc.; *U.S. Private,* pg. 2365
COMBINED COMMUNICATIONS CORPORATION OF OKLAHOMA, LLC—See TEGNA Inc.; *U.S. Public,* pg. 1990
COMMONWEALTH PUBLIC BROADCASTING CORP.; *U.S. Private,* pg. 987
COMMUNITY TELEVISION OF SOUTHERN CALIFORNIA; *U.S. Private,* pg. 997

516120 — TELEVISION BROADCAS...

CONNECTICUT PUBLIC BROADCASTING CORP.; *U.S. Private*, pg. 1016
CORAL RIDGE MINISTRIES MEDIA INC.; *U.S. Private*, pg. 1046
CORPORATION FOR PUBLIC BROADCASTING; *U.S. Private*, pg. 1056
CORPORATIVO TD SPORTS, S.A. DE C.V.—See Grupo Televisa, S.A.B.; *Int'l*, pg. 3136
CORPORATIVO VASCO DE QUIROGA, S.A. DE C.V.—See Grupo Televisa, S.A.B.; *Int'l*, pg. 3136
CORUS ENTERTAINMENT INC.; *Int'l*, pg. 1808
CORUS RADIO LTD.—See Corus Entertainment Inc.; *Int'l*, pg. 1808
COSE BELLE D'ITALIA S.P.A.—See Arrow Global Group PLC; *Int'l*, pg. 579
COSMOPOLITAN TV IBERIA S.L.—See The Hearst Corporation; *U.S. Private*, pg. 4044
COSMO SPACE OF AMERICA CO., LTD.—See Imagica Group Inc.; *Int'l*, pg. 3618
COUNTDOWN MEDIA GMBH—See Bertelsmann SE & Co. KGaA; *Int'l*, pg. 994
COUNTRY MUSIC TELEVISION LIMITED—See Corus Entertainment Inc.; *Int'l*, pg. 1808
CRCC MEDIA CO., LTD.—See Hisamitsu Pharmaceutical Co., Inc.; *Int'l*, pg. 3406
CSP MOBILE PRODUCTIONS, LLC; *U.S. Private*, pg. 1117
CTV ATLANTIC, HALIFAX—See BCE Inc.; *Int'l*, pg. 927
CTV ATLANTIC, MONCTON—See BCE Inc.; *Int'l*, pg. 927
CTV ATLANTIC, SAINT JOHN—See BCE Inc.; *Int'l*, pg. 927
CTV ATLANTIC, SYDNEY—See BCE Inc.; *Int'l*, pg. 927
CTV CALGARY—See BCE Inc.; *Int'l*, pg. 927
CTV EDMONTON—See BCE Inc.; *Int'l*, pg. 927
CTV LETHBRIDGE—See BCE Inc.; *Int'l*, pg. 927
CTV MONTREAL—See BCE Inc.; *Int'l*, pg. 927
CTV NORTHERN ONTARIO, NORTH BAY—See BCE Inc.; *Int'l*, pg. 927
CTV NORTHERN ONTARIO, SAULT SAINT MARIE—See BCE Inc.; *Int'l*, pg. 927
CTV NORTHERN ONTARIO, SUDBURY—See BCE Inc.; *Int'l*, pg. 927
CTV NORTHERN ONTARIO, TIMMINS—See BCE Inc.; *Int'l*, pg. 927
CTV OTTAWA—See BCE Inc.; *Int'l*, pg. 927
CTV PRINCE ALBERT—See BCE Inc.; *Int'l*, pg. 927
CTV REGINA—See BCE Inc.; *Int'l*, pg. 927
CTV SASKATOON—See BCE Inc.; *Int'l*, pg. 927
CTV VANCOUVER—See BCE Inc.; *Int'l*, pg. 927
CTV WINNIPEG—See BCE Inc.; *Int'l*, pg. 927
CTV YORKTON—See BCE Inc.; *Int'l*, pg. 927
THE CW TELEVISION NETWORK—See Nexstar Media Group, Inc.; *U.S. Public*, pg. 1524
DAFENG TV LTD.; *Int'l*, pg. 1912
DAYDREAM ENTERTAINMENT CO., LTD.; *Int'l*, pg. 1985
DB BROADCAST LTD.; *Int'l*, pg. 1986
DELTA ADVERTISING GMBH—See Bertelsmann SE & Co. KGaA; *Int'l*, pg. 994
DEMOCRACY NOW!; *U.S. Private*, pg. 1203
DENALI MEDIA ANCHORAGE, CORP.—See Liberty Broadband Corporation; *U.S. Public*, pg. 1310
DENALI MEDIA SOUTHEAST, CORP.—See Liberty Broadband Corporation; *U.S. Public*, pg. 1310
DIGIFY, INC.—See GMA Network, Inc.; *Int'l*, pg. 3012
DIKSATTRANSWORLD LIMITED; *Int'l*, pg. 2125
DINGLONG CULTURE CO., LTD.; *Int'l*, pg. 2127
DIRECTV COLOMBIA, LTDA.—See AT&T Inc.; *U.S. Public*, pg. 220
DIRECTV CUSTOMER SERVICES, INC.—See AT&T Inc.; *U.S. Public*, pg. 220
DIRECTV ENTERPRISES, LLC—See AT&T Inc.; *U.S. Public*, pg. 220
DIRECTV LATIN AMERICA, LLC—See AT&T Inc.; *U.S. Public*, pg. 220
DIRECTV PERU S.R.L.—See AT&T Inc.; *U.S. Public*, pg. 220
DIRECTV TRINIDAD LIMITED—See AT&T Inc.; *U.S. Public*, pg. 220
DISCOVERY ASIA SALES PRIVATE LIMITED—See Warner Bros. Discovery, Inc.; *U.S. Public*, pg. 2326
THE DISCOVERY CHANNEL—See BCE Inc.; *Int'l*, pg. 927
DISCOVERY COMMUNICATIONS BENELUX BV—See Warner Bros. Discovery, Inc.; *U.S. Public*, pg. 2326
DISCOVERY COMMUNICATIONS DEUTSCHLAND GMBH & CO. KG—See Warner Bros. Discovery, Inc.; *U.S. Public*, pg. 2326
DISCOVERY COMMUNICATIONS INDIA—See Warner Bros. Discovery, Inc.; *U.S. Public*, pg. 2326
DISCOVERY COMMUNICATIONS NORDIC APS—See Warner Bros. Discovery, Inc.; *U.S. Public*, pg. 2326
DISCOVERY CONTENT VERWALTUNGS GMBH—See Warner Bros. Discovery, Inc.; *U.S. Public*, pg. 2326
DISCOVERY EDUCATION, INC.—See Clearlake Capital Group, L.P.; *U.S. Private*, pg. 934
DISCOVERY LATIN AMERICA, L.L.C.—See Warner Bros. Discovery, Inc.; *U.S. Public*, pg. 2326
DISCOVERY NETWORKS DANMARK—See Warner Bros. Discovery, Inc.; *U.S. Public*, pg. 2326
DISCOVERY NETWORKS INTERNATIONAL HOLDINGS LTD.—See Warner Bros. Discovery, Inc.; *U.S. Public*, pg. 2326
DISCOVERY NZ LIMITED—See Warner Bros. Discovery, Inc.; *U.S. Public*, pg. 2326
DISCOVERY POLSKA SP Z.O.O.—See Warner Bros. Discovery, Inc.; *U.S. Public*, pg. 2326
DISCOVERY PRODUCTIONS, LLC—See Warner Bros. Discovery, Inc.; *U.S. Public*, pg. 2326
DISH TV INDIA LTD; *Int'l*, pg. 2135
DIVIMOVE GMBH—See Bertelsmann SE & Co. KGaA; *Int'l*, pg. 994
DOMINION VIDEO SATELLITE INC.; *U.S. Private*, pg. 1256
DORI MEDIA GROUP LTD.; *Int'l*, pg. 2176
DORI MEDIA INTERNATIONAL GMBH—See Dori Media Group Ltd.; *Int'l*, pg. 2176
DORI MEDIA SPIKE LTD.—See Dori Media Group Ltd.; *Int'l*, pg. 2176
DRAPER HOLDINGS BUSINESS TRUST; *U.S. Private*, pg. 1272
DRESDNER DRUCK- UND VERLAGSHAUS GMBH & CO. KG—See Bertelsmann SE & Co. KGaA; *Int'l*, pg. 994
DTV NETWORK SYSTEMS, INC.—See AT&T Inc.; *U.S. Public*, pg. 220
DW TELEVISION L.L.C.—See National Amusements, Inc.; *U.S. Private*, pg. 2842
EDGEWARE INC.—See Edgeware AB; *Int'l*, pg. 2309
EDUCATIONAL TELEVISION ASSOCIATION; *U.S. Private*, pg. 1339
EDUEXEL INFOTAINMENT LIMITED; *Int'l*, pg. 2316
ELEMENTAL TECHNOLOGIES, INC.; *U.S. Private*, pg. 1357
EMMIS OPERATING COMPANY—See Emmis Communications Corporation; *U.S. Public*, pg. 753
ENCOMPASS DIGITAL MEDIA, INC.—See Encompass Digital Media; *U.S. Private*, pg. 1390
ENCOMPASS DIGITAL MEDIA—See Encompass Digital Media; *U.S. Private*, pg. 1390
ENCOMPASS LONDON—See Encompass Digital Media; *U.S. Private*, pg. 1390
ENCOMPASS LOS ANGELES—See Encompass Digital Media; *U.S. Private*, pg. 1390
ENDEAVOR STREAMING, LLC—See William Morris Endeavor Entertainment, LLC; *U.S. Private*, pg. 4523
ENTRAVISION COMMUNICATIONS CORPORATION; *U.S. Public*, pg. 779
EPARTNERS LLC—See The Walt Disney Company; *U.S. Public*, pg. 2141
EREDIVISIE MEDIA & MARKETING C.V.—See The Walt Disney Company; *U.S. Public*, pg. 2140
E.SAT TV (PROPRIETARY) LIMITED—See Hosken Consolidated Investments Limited; *Int'l*, pg. 3485
ESTEEM BROADCASTING, LLC; *U.S. Private*, pg. 1429
ETC NETWORKS LTD.-BROADCASTING DIVISION—See Essel Corporate Resources Pvt. Ltd.; *Int'l*, pg. 2510
ETC NETWORKS LTD.-EDUCATION DIVISION—See Essel Corporate Resources Pvt. Ltd.; *Int'l*, pg. 2510
ETC NETWORKS LTD.—See Essel Corporate Resources Pvt. Ltd.; *Int'l*, pg. 2510
ETERNAL WORD TELEVISION NETWORK INC.; *U.S. Private*, pg. 1431
E.TV (PROPRIETARY) LIMITED—See Hosken Consolidated Investments Limited; *Int'l*, pg. 3485
EUROPEAN NEWS EXCHANGE—See Bertelsmann SE & Co. KGaA; *Int'l*, pg. 994
EUROSPORT DANMARK APS—See Warner Bros. Discovery, Inc.; *U.S. Public*, pg. 2326
EUROSPORT EVENTS LTD.—See Warner Bros. Discovery, Inc.; *U.S. Public*, pg. 2326
EUROSPORT FINLAND OY—See Warner Bros. Discovery, Inc.; *U.S. Public*, pg. 2327
EUROSPORT FRANCE SA—See Warner Bros. Discovery, Inc.; *U.S. Public*, pg. 2327
EUROSPORT ITALIA SPA—See Warner Bros. Discovery, Inc.; *U.S. Public*, pg. 2327
EUROSPORT MEDIA GMBH—See Warner Bros. Discovery, Inc.; *U.S. Public*, pg. 2327
EUROSPORT MEDIA—See Warner Bros. Discovery, Inc.; *U.S. Public*, pg. 2327
EUROSPORT NORGE AS—See Warner Bros. Discovery, Inc.; *U.S. Public*, pg. 2327
EUROSPORT POLSKA SP. Z O.O.—See Warner Bros. Discovery, Inc.; *U.S. Public*, pg. 2327
EUROSPORT TELEVISION AB—See Warner Bros. Discovery, Inc.; *U.S. Public*, pg. 2327
EUROSPORT TELEVISION BV—See Warner Bros. Discovery, Inc.; *U.S. Public*, pg. 2327
EUROSPORT TELEVISION SA—See Warner Bros. Discovery, Inc.; *U.S. Public*, pg. 2327
FASHION TV HOLDING LTD.; *Int'l*, pg. 2621
FENIX ENTERTAINMENT S.P.A.; *Int'l*, pg. 2634
FIJI TELEVISION LIMITED—See Fijian Holdings Limited; *Int'l*, pg. 2662
FIRST COAST NEWS—See TEGNA Inc.; *U.S. Public*, pg. 1990
FIRST ENTERTAINMENT GMBH—See Bavaria Film GmbH; *Int'l*, pg. 899
FL ENTERTAINMENT N.V.; *Int'l*, pg. 2697
FLOOD COMMUNICATIONS, LLC; *U.S. Private*, pg. 1546

CORPORATE AFFILIATIONS

FLORIDA WEST COAST PUBLIC BROADCASTING, INC.; *U.S. Private*, pg. 1551
FOX BROADCASTING COMPANY, LLC—See Fox Corporation; *U.S. Public*, pg. 875
FOX CABLE NETWORKS, INC.—See Fox Corporation; *U.S. Public*, pg. 875
FOX CRIME MEDYA HIZMETLERI ANONIM SIRKETI—See Fox Corporation; *U.S. Public*, pg. 876
FOX INTERNATIONAL CHANNELS ASIA PACIFIC LIMITED—See Fox Corporation; *U.S. Public*, pg. 876
FOX INTERNATIONAL CHANNELS CHILE LTDA.—See Fox Corporation; *U.S. Public*, pg. 876
FOX INTERNATIONAL CHANNELS SWEDEN AB—See Fox Corporation; *U.S. Public*, pg. 876
FOX LATIN AMERICAN CHANNELS (CHILE) LIMITADA—See Fox Corporation; *U.S. Public*, pg. 875
FOX NETWORKS GROUP ASIA PACIFIC LIMITED—See Fox Corporation; *U.S. Public*, pg. 876
FOX NETWORKS GROUP, LLC—See Fox Corporation; *U.S. Public*, pg. 876
FOX NETWORKS GROUP NORWAY AS—See Fox Corporation; *U.S. Public*, pg. 876
FOX NETWORKS GROUP POLAND SP.ZO.O.—See Fox Corporation; *U.S. Public*, pg. 876
FOX NEWS NETWORK, LLC—See Fox Corporation; *U.S. Public*, pg. 876
FOX SPORTS AUSTRALIA PTY LIMITED—See News Corporation; *U.S. Public*, pg. 1519
FOX SPORTS NET, LLC—See Sinclair, Inc.; *U.S. Public*, pg. 1885
FOX SPORTS NET OHIO, LLC—See Fox Corporation; *U.S. Public*, pg. 876
FOXTEL MANAGEMENT PTY. LTD.—See News Corporation; *U.S. Public*, pg. 1519
FREMANTLE INDIA TV PRODUCTIONS PVT LTD—See Bertelsmann SE & Co. KGaA; *Int'l*, pg. 994
FREMANTLE LICENSING GERMANY GMBH—See Bertelsmann SE & Co. KGaA; *Int'l*, pg. 994
FREMANTLEMEDIA ASIA PTE LTD—See Bertelsmann SE & Co. KGaA; *Int'l*, pg. 994
FREMANTLEMEDIA AUSTRALIA PTY LTD—See Bertelsmann SE & Co. KGaA; *Int'l*, pg. 994
FREMANTLEMEDIA BELGIUM NV—See Bertelsmann SE & Co. KGaA; *Int'l*, pg. 994
FREMANTLEMEDIA BRAZIL PRODUCAO DE TELEVISAO LTDA—See Bertelsmann SE & Co. KGaA; *Int'l*, pg. 994
FREMANTLEMEDIA FINLAND OY—See Bertelsmann SE & Co. KGaA; *Int'l*, pg. 994
FREMANTLEMEDIA FRANCE SAS—See Bertelsmann SE & Co. KGaA; *Int'l*, pg. 994
FREMANTLEMEDIA HRVATSKA D.O.O.—See Bertelsmann SE & Co. KGaA; *Int'l*, pg. 994
FREMANTLEMEDIA ITALIA SPA—See Bertelsmann SE & Co. KGaA; *Int'l*, pg. 994
FREMANTLEMEDIA LATIN AMERICA INC—See Bertelsmann SE & Co. KGaA; *Int'l*, pg. 994
FREMANTLEMEDIA MEXICO SA DE CV—See Bertelsmann SE & Co. KGaA; *Int'l*, pg. 994
FREMANTLEMEDIA NORGE AS—See Bertelsmann SE & Co. KGaA; *Int'l*, pg. 994
FREMANTLEMEDIA POLSKA SP.ZO.O.—See Bertelsmann SE & Co. KGaA; *Int'l*, pg. 994
FREMANTLEMEDIA PORTUGAL SA—See Bertelsmann SE & Co. KGaA; *Int'l*, pg. 994
FREMANTLEMEDIA SVERIGE AB—See Bertelsmann SE & Co. KGaA; *Int'l*, pg. 994
FREMANTLE PRODUCTIONS NORTH AMERICA INC—See Bertelsmann SE & Co. KGaA; *Int'l*, pg. 994
FREMANTLE PRODUCTIONS SA—See Bertelsmann SE & Co. KGaA; *Int'l*, pg. 994
FT. WAYNE TV, LLC—See Entertainment Studios, Inc.; *U.S. Private*, pg. 1405
FUJI CAREER DESIGN INC.—See Fuji Media Holdings, Inc.; *Int'l*, pg. 2813
FUJI MEDIA TECHNOLOGY, INC.—See Fuji Media Holdings, Inc.; *Int'l*, pg. 2813
FUJISANKEI COMMUNICATIONS INTERNATIONAL, INC. - LONDON OFFICE—See Fuji Media Holdings, Inc.; *Int'l*, pg. 2814
FUJISANKEI COMMUNICATIONS INTERNATIONAL, INC.—See Fuji Media Holdings, Inc.; *Int'l*, pg. 2814
FUJISANKEI PERSONNEL INC.—See Fuji Media Holdings, Inc.; *Int'l*, pg. 2814
FUJI SATELLITE BROADCASTING, INC.—See Fuji Media Holdings, Inc.; *Int'l*, pg. 2813
FUJI TELEVISION BANGKOK BUREAU—See Fuji Media Holdings, Inc.; *Int'l*, pg. 2813
FUJI TELEVISION BEIJING BUREAU—See Fuji Media Holdings, Inc.; *Int'l*, pg. 2814
FUJI TELEVISION MOSCOW BUREAU/ FNN MOSCOW BUREAU—See Fuji Media Holdings, Inc.; *Int'l*, pg. 2814
FUJI TELEVISION NETWORK, INC.—See Fuji Media Holdings, Inc.; *Int'l*, pg. 2814
FUNKHAUS HALLE GMBH & CO. KG—See Bertelsmann SE & Co. KGaA; *Int'l*, pg. 994
GAME ONE SAS—See National Amusements, Inc.; *U.S. Private*, pg. 2841
GEARHOUSE BROADCAST LLC—See Gravity Media

N.A.I.C.S. INDEX

516120 — TELEVISION BROADCAS...

Group Limited; *Int'l*, pg. 3062
GEARHOUSE BROADCAST PTY LIMITED—See Gravity Media Group Limited; *Int'l*, pg. 3062
GEORGIA TELEVISION COMPANY—See Apollo Global Management, Inc.; *U.S. Public*, pg. 164
GGP MEDIA GMBH—See Bertelsmann SE & Co. KGaA; *Int'l*, pg. 994
GMA NETWORK, INC.; *Int'l*, pg. 3012
GRACENOTE GMBH—See Brookfield Corporation; *Int'l*, pg. 1178
GRACENOTE GMBH—See Elliott Management Corporation; *U.S. Private*, pg. 1370
GRACENOTE KK—See Brookfield Corporation; *Int'l*, pg. 1178
GRACENOTE KK—See Elliott Management Corporation; *U.S. Private*, pg. 1370
GRACENOTE KOREA LTD.—See Brookfield Corporation; *Int'l*, pg. 1178
GRACENOTE KOREA LTD.—See Elliott Management Corporation; *U.S. Private*, pg. 1371
GRAHAM MEDIA GROUP, FLORIDA, INC.—See Graham Holdings Company; *U.S. Public*, pg. 955
GRAHAM MEDIA GROUP, HOUSTON, INC.—See Graham Holdings Company; *U.S. Public*, pg. 955
GRAHAM MEDIA GROUP, INC.—See Graham Holdings Company; *U.S. Public*, pg. 954
GRAHAM MEDIA GROUP, MICHIGAN, INC.—See Graham Holdings Company; *U.S. Public*, pg. 955
GRAHAM MEDIA GROUP, ORLANDO, INC.—See Graham Holdings Company; *U.S. Public*, pg. 955
GRAHAM MEDIA GROUP, SAN ANTONIO, INC.—See Graham Holdings Company; *U.S. Public*, pg. 955
GRAY MEDIA GROUP, INC.—See Gray Television, Inc.; *U.S. Public*, pg. 959
GRAY TELEVISION GROUP, INC.—See Gray Television, Inc.; *U.S. Public*, pg. 960
GREAT WALL MOVIE AND TELEVISION CO., LTD.; *Int'l*, pg. 3066
GRIFFIN TELEVISION, INC.; *U.S. Private*, pg. 1788
GRUPO TELESISTEMA, S.A. DE C.V.—See Grupo Televisa, S.A.B.; *Int'l*, pg. 3136
GRUPO TELEVISA, S.A.B.; *Int'l*, pg. 3136
GTV PRODUCTIONS—See De Agostini S.p.A.; *Int'l*, pg. 1995
GUARDIAN MEDIA LIMITED—See ANSA McAl Limited; *Int'l*, pg. 477
GUIZHOU BROADCASTING & TV INFORMATION NETWORK CO., LTD.; *Int'l*, pg. 3174
HAPPO TELEVISION, INC.—See Fuji Media Holdings, Inc.; *Int'l*, pg. 2814
HARPERCOLLINS CANADA LIMITED—See News Corporation; *U.S. Public*, pg. 1519
HBO ENTERTAINMENT—See Warner Bros. Discovery, Inc.; *U.S. Public*, pg. 2327
HENNEO MEDIA, SA; *Int'l*, pg. 3354
THE HERALD AND WEEKLY TIMES PTY. LIMITED—See News Corporation; *U.S. Public*, pg. 1520
HERITAGE BROADCASTING GROUP, INC.; *U.S. Private*, pg. 1922
HITRADIO RTL SACHSEN GMBH—See Bertelsmann SE & Co. KGaA; *Int'l*, pg. 994
HMTV, LLC—See Hemisphere Media Group, Inc.; *U.S. Private*, pg. 1913
HMTV TV DOMINICANA, LLC—See Hemisphere Media Group, Inc.; *U.S. Private*, pg. 1913
HONG KONG TECHNOLOGY VENTURE COMPANY LIMITED; *Int'l*, pg. 3467
HORIPRO INC.; *Int'l*, pg. 3478
HUBEI BROADCASTING & TELEVISION INFORMATION NETWORK CO., LTD.; *Int'l*, pg. 3517
HUB ONLINE GLOBAL PTY. LTD—See News Corporation; *U.S. Public*, pg. 1520
HUM NETWORK LIMITED; *Int'l*, pg. 3528
HUNAN TV & BROADCAST INTERMEDIARY CO., LTD.; *Int'l*, pg. 3534
HUNGAMA TV—See The Walt Disney Company; *U.S. Public*, pg. 2139
HYPERION S.A.; *Int'l*, pg. 3553
HYUNDAI FUTURENET CO., LTD—See Hyundai Department Store Co., Ltd.; *Int'l*, pg. 3556
I 2 I MUSIKPRODUKTIONS- UND MUSIKVERLAGSGESELLSCHAFT MBH—See Bertelsmann SE & Co. KGaA; *Int'l*, pg. 994
IAC INC.; *U.S. Public*, pg. 1081
IDAHO INDEPENDENT TELEVISION, INC.—See Block Communications, Inc.; *U.S. Private*, pg. 582
IMAGICA TV CORP.—See Imagica Group Inc.; *Int'l*, pg. 3618
IMBC CO., LTD.; *Int'l*, pg. 3620
INDEPENDENCE TELEVISION CO.—See Block Communications, Inc.; *U.S. Private*, pg. 582
INDEPENDENT TELEVISION NETWORK; *U.S. Private*, pg. 2061
INDUSIND MEDIA & COMMUNICATIONS LIMITED—See Hinduja Global Solutions Ltd.; *Int'l*, pg. 3398
INFOSTRADA CONCEPTS B.V.—See Nexstar Media Group, Inc.; *U.S. Public*, pg. 1524
INTERACT-TV, INCORPORATED; *U.S. Public*, pg. 1140
INTERMEDIA ESPANOL, INC.—See Hemisphere Media Group, Inc.; *U.S. Private*, pg. 1913
INTERNEWS NETWORK; *U.S. Private*, pg. 2122
ION MEDIA HITS, INC.—See The E.W. Scripps Company; *U.S. Public*, pg. 2067
ION MEDIA OF ALBANY, INC.—See The E.W. Scripps Company; *U.S. Public*, pg. 2067
ION MEDIA OF ATLANTA, INC.—See The E.W. Scripps Company; *U.S. Public*, pg. 2067
ION MEDIA OF BATTLE CREEK, INC.—See The E.W. Scripps Company; *U.S. Public*, pg. 2067
ION MEDIA OF BIRMINGHAM, INC.—See The E.W. Scripps Company; *U.S. Public*, pg. 2067
ION MEDIA OF BOSTON, INC.—See The E.W. Scripps Company; *U.S. Public*, pg. 2067
ION MEDIA OF BRUNSWICK, INC.—See The E.W. Scripps Company; *U.S. Public*, pg. 2067
ION MEDIA OF BUFFALO, INC.—See The E.W. Scripps Company; *U.S. Public*, pg. 2067
ION MEDIA OF CEDAR RAPIDS, INC.—See The E.W. Scripps Company; *U.S. Public*, pg. 2067
ION MEDIA OF CHICAGO, INC.—See The E.W. Scripps Company; *U.S. Public*, pg. 2067
ION MEDIA OF DALLAS, INC.—See The E.W. Scripps Company; *U.S. Public*, pg. 2067
ION MEDIA OF DENVER, INC.—See The E.W. Scripps Company; *U.S. Public*, pg. 2067
ION MEDIA OF DES MOINES, INC.—See The E.W. Scripps Company; *U.S. Public*, pg. 2067
ION MEDIA OF DETROIT, INC.—See The E.W. Scripps Company; *U.S. Public*, pg. 2067
ION MEDIA OF FAYETTEVILLE, INC.—See The E.W. Scripps Company; *U.S. Public*, pg. 2067
ION MEDIA OF GREENSBORO, INC.—See The E.W. Scripps Company; *U.S. Public*, pg. 2067
ION MEDIA OF GREENVILLE, INC.—See The E.W. Scripps Company; *U.S. Public*, pg. 2067
ION MEDIA OF HONOLULU, INC.—See The E.W. Scripps Company; *U.S. Public*, pg. 2067
ION MEDIA OF INDIANAPOLIS, INC.—See The E.W. Scripps Company; *U.S. Public*, pg. 2067
ION MEDIA OF KANSAS CITY, INC.—See The E.W. Scripps Company; *U.S. Public*, pg. 2067
ION MEDIA OF KNOXVILLE, INC.—See The E.W. Scripps Company; *U.S. Public*, pg. 2068
ION MEDIA OF LEXINGTON, INC.—See The E.W. Scripps Company; *U.S. Public*, pg. 2068
ION MEDIA OF LOS ANGELES, INC.—See The E.W. Scripps Company; *U.S. Public*, pg. 2068
ION MEDIA OF MEMPHIS, INC.—See The E.W. Scripps Company; *U.S. Public*, pg. 2068
ION MEDIA OF MILWAUKEE, INC.—See The E.W. Scripps Company; *U.S. Public*, pg. 2068
ION MEDIA OF MINNEAPOLIS, INC.—See The E.W. Scripps Company; *U.S. Public*, pg. 2068
ION MEDIA OF NASHVILLE, INC.—See The E.W. Scripps Company; *U.S. Public*, pg. 2068
ION MEDIA OF NEW ORLEANS, INC.—See The E.W. Scripps Company; *U.S. Public*, pg. 2068
ION MEDIA OF NEW YORK, INC.—See The E.W. Scripps Company; *U.S. Public*, pg. 2068
ION MEDIA OF NORFOLK, INC.—See The E.W. Scripps Company; *U.S. Public*, pg. 2068
ION MEDIA OF OKLAHOMA CITY, INC.—See The E.W. Scripps Company; *U.S. Public*, pg. 2068
ION MEDIA OF ORLANDO, INC.—See The E.W. Scripps Company; *U.S. Public*, pg. 2068
ION MEDIA OF PHILADELPHIA, INC.—See The E.W. Scripps Company; *U.S. Public*, pg. 2068
ION MEDIA OF PHOENIX, INC.—See The E.W. Scripps Company; *U.S. Public*, pg. 2068
ION MEDIA OF PORTLAND, INC.—See The E.W. Scripps Company; *U.S. Public*, pg. 2068
ION MEDIA OF PROVIDENCE, INC.—See The E.W. Scripps Company; *U.S. Public*, pg. 2068
ION MEDIA OF RALEIGH, INC.—See The E.W. Scripps Company; *U.S. Public*, pg. 2068
ION MEDIA OF ROANOKE, INC.—See The E.W. Scripps Company; *U.S. Public*, pg. 2068
ION MEDIA OF SACRAMENTO, INC.—See The E.W. Scripps Company; *U.S. Public*, pg. 2068
ION MEDIA OF SAN ANTONIO, INC.—See The E.W. Scripps Company; *U.S. Public*, pg. 2068
ION MEDIA OF SAN JOSE, INC.—See The E.W. Scripps Company; *U.S. Public*, pg. 2068
ION MEDIA OF SCRANTON, INC.—See The E.W. Scripps Company; *U.S. Public*, pg. 2068
ION MEDIA OF SEATTLE, INC.—See The E.W. Scripps Company; *U.S. Public*, pg. 2068
ION MEDIA OF SPOKANE, INC.—See The E.W. Scripps Company; *U.S. Public*, pg. 2068
ION MEDIA OF SYRACUSE, INC.—See The E.W. Scripps Company; *U.S. Public*, pg. 2068
ION MEDIA OF TULSA, INC.—See The E.W. Scripps Company; *U.S. Public*, pg. 2068
ION MEDIA OF WASHINGTON, INC.—See The E.W. Scripps Company; *U.S. Public*, pg. 2068
ION MEDIA OF WEST PALM BEACH, INC.—See The E.W. Scripps Company; *U.S. Public*, pg. 2068
JDG TELEVISION INC.—See Griffin Holdings Inc.; *U.S. Private*, pg. 1788
JOETV/KZJO-TV—See Nexstar Media Group, Inc.; *U.S. Public*, pg. 1524
JONES PROGRAMMING SERVICES, INC.—See Jones International University; *U.S. Private*, pg. 2233
JOYN GMBH—See Warner Bros. Discovery, Inc.; *U.S. Public*, pg. 2327
KAAL-TV LLC—See Hubbard Broadcasting, Inc.; *U.S. Private*, pg. 2000
KABB-TV—See Sinclair, Inc.; *U.S. Public*, pg. 1885
KABC-TV INC.—See The Walt Disney Company; *U.S. Public*, pg. 2138
KAINUUN SANOMAIN KIRJAPAINO OY—See Alma Media Corporation; *Int'l*, pg. 362
KAIT, LLC—See Gray Television, Inc.; *U.S. Public*, pg. 959
KAKE-TV—See Lockwood Broadcasting Inc.; *U.S. Private*, pg. 2478
KALB-TV NEWS CHANNEL 5—See Gray Television, Inc.; *U.S. Public*, pg. 960
KAMC-TV—See Mission Broadcasting, Inc.; *U.S. Private*, pg. 2747
KAME, LLC—See Sinclair, Inc.; *U.S. Public*, pg. 1885
KAMR-TV—See Nexstar Media Group, Inc.; *U.S. Public*, pg. 1522
KANSAI TELECASTING CORPORATION—See Fuji Media Holdings, Inc.; *Int'l*, pg. 2814
KARE-TV—See TEGNA Inc.; *U.S. Public*, pg. 1990
KASW-TV—See The E.W. Scripps Company; *U.S. Public*, pg. 2068
KASY-TV—See Tamer Media, LLC; *U.S. Private*, pg. 3928
KATC COMMUNICATIONS, INC.—See Evening Post Publishing Co.; *U.S. Private*, pg. 1436
KATV, LLC—See Sinclair, Inc.; *U.S. Public*, pg. 1886
KAUT-TV—See Nexstar Media Group, Inc.; *U.S. Public*, pg. 1524
KBJR, INC.—See Silver Point Capital, L.P.; *U.S. Private*, pg. 3661
KBMT OPERATING COMPANY, LLC—See TEGNA Inc.; *U.S. Public*, pg. 1990
KBSD-TV—See Gray Television, Inc.; *U.S. Public*, pg. 960
KBSH-TV—See Gray Television, Inc.; *U.S. Public*, pg. 960
KBSI LICENSEE L.P.—See Sinclair, Inc.; *U.S. Public*, pg. 1885
KBSI-TV—See Sinclair, Inc.; *U.S. Public*, pg. 1885
KBSL-TV—See Gray Television, Inc.; *U.S. Public*, pg. 960
KBTV-TV—See Sinclair, Inc.; *U.S. Public*, pg. 1885
KCAU-TV—See Nexstar Media Group, Inc.; *U.S. Public*, pg. 1522
KCBS-TV—See National Amusements, Inc.; *U.S. Private*, pg. 2840
KCBY-TV—See Sinclair, Inc.; *U.S. Public*, pg. 1886
KCCI-TV—See The Hearst Corporation; *U.S. Private*, pg. 4048
KCNC-TV—See National Amusements, Inc.; *U.S. Private*, pg. 2840
KCOP TELEVISION, LLC—See Fox Corporation; *U.S. Public*, pg. 876
KCOY-TV—See Cowles Company; *U.S. Private*, pg. 1073
KCPQ-TV—See Nexstar Media Group, Inc.; *U.S. Public*, pg. 1524
KCRA-TV—See The Hearst Corporation; *U.S. Private*, pg. 4048
KCRG-TV—See Gray Television, Inc.; *U.S. Public*, pg. 960
KCTS TELEVISION; *U.S. Private*, pg. 2270
KCTV-TV—See Meredith Corporation; *U.S. Public*, pg. 1423
KDAF, LLC—See Nexstar Media Group, Inc.; *U.S. Public*, pg. 1524
KDBC-TV—See Ellis, McQuary, Stanley & Associates LLC; *U.S. Private*, pg. 1374
KDFW-TV—See Fox Corporation; *U.S. Public*, pg. 876
KDNL-TV—See Sinclair, Inc.; *U.S. Public*, pg. 1885
KDRV-TV—See Entertainment Studios, Inc.; *U.S. Private*, pg. 1405
KDSM, LLC—See Sinclair, Inc.; *U.S. Public*, pg. 1885
KDVR-TV—See Nexstar Media Group, Inc.; *U.S. Public*, pg. 1524
KELO-TV—See Nexstar Media Group, Inc.; *U.S. Public*, pg. 1522
KENS-TV—See TEGNA Inc.; *U.S. Public*, pg. 1989
KEPR-TV—See Sinclair, Inc.; *U.S. Public*, pg. 1886
KERO-TV—See The E.W. Scripps Company; *U.S. Public*, pg. 2068
KETV HEARST-ARGYLE TELEVISION, INC.—See The Hearst Corporation; *U.S. Private*, pg. 4048
KEVN-TV—See Gray Television, Inc.; *U.S. Public*, pg. 960
KEYE-TV—See Sinclair, Inc.; *U.S. Public*, pg. 1885
KEZI-TV—See Entertainment Studios, Inc.; *U.S. Private*, pg. 1405
KFDM-TV—See Sinclair, Inc.; *U.S. Public*, pg. 1885
KFDX-TV—See Nexstar Media Group, Inc.; *U.S. Public*, pg. 1522
KFOR-TV—See Nexstar Media Group, Inc.; *U.S. Public*, pg. 1524
KFSM-TV—See Nexstar Media Group, Inc.; *U.S. Public*, pg. 1524
KFSN-TV INC.—See The Walt Disney Company; *U.S. Public*, pg. 2138

516120 — TELEVISION BROADCAS...

KFYR-TV—See Gray Television, Inc.; *U.S. Public*, pg. 960
KGAN LICENSEE, LLC—See Sinclair, Inc.; *U.S. Public*, pg. 1885
KGAN-TV—See Sinclair, Inc.; *U.S. Public*, pg. 1885
KGBT-TV—See Sinclair, Inc.; *U.S. Public*, pg. 1885
KGET-TV—See Nexstar Media Group, Inc.; *U.S. Public*, pg. 1522
KGO TELEVISION, INC.—See The Walt Disney Company; *U.S. Public*, pg. 2138
KGPE-TV—See Nexstar Media Group, Inc.; *U.S. Public*, pg. 1523
KGTV—See The E.W. Scripps Company; *U.S. Public*, pg. 2068
KGUN-TV—See The E.W. Scripps Company; *U.S. Public*, pg. 2068
KHOU HOLDINGS, INC.—See TEGNA Inc.; *U.S. Public*, pg. 1989
KHOU-TV, INC.—See TEGNA Inc.; *U.S. Public*, pg. 1990
KHQ, INCORPORATED—See Cowles Company; *U.S. Private*, pg. 1073
KIAH INC.—See Nexstar Media Group, Inc.; *U.S. Public*, pg. 1524
KICU-TV—See Apollo Global Management, Inc.; *U.S. Public*, pg. 164
KIDY/KXVA OPERATING COMPANY, LLC—See TEGNA Inc.; *U.S. Public*, pg. 1990
KITV-TV—See The Hearst Corporation; *U.S. Private*, pg. 4048
KIVI-TV—See The E.W. Scripps Company; *U.S. Public*, pg. 2068
KJRH—See The E.W. Scripps Company; *U.S. Public*, pg. 2068
KKTV-TV—See Gray Television, Inc.; *U.S. Public*, pg. 960
KLAS - TV—See Nexstar Media Group, Inc.; *U.S. Public*, pg. 1522
KLEW-TV—See Sinclair, Inc.; *U.S. Public*, pg. 1886
KLFY, LP—See Nexstar Media Group, Inc.; *U.S. Public*, pg. 1522
KLRT-TV—See Mission Broadcasting, Inc.; *U.S. Private*, pg. 2747
KMBC HEARST-ARGYLE TELEVISION, INC.—See The Hearst Corporation; *U.S. Private*, pg. 4048
KMEG-TV—See Ellis, McQuary, Stanley & Associates LLC; *U.S. Private*, pg. 1374
KMGH-TV—See The E.W. Scripps Company; *U.S. Public*, pg. 2068
KMOT-TV—See Gray Television, Inc.; *U.S. Public*, pg. 960
KMOV-TV, INC.—See Meredith Corporation; *U.S. Public*, pg. 1423
KMPH-TV—See Ellis, McQuary, Stanley & Associates LLC; *U.S. Private*, pg. 1374
KMSB-TV, INC.—See TEGNA Inc.; *U.S. Public*, pg. 1990
KMSP-TV—See Fox Corporation; *U.S. Public*, pg. 876
KMTR-TV—See Providence Equity Partners L.L.C.; *U.S. Private*, pg. 3293
KMTV-TV—See The E.W. Scripps Company; *U.S. Public*, pg. 2068
KMYS-TV—See Sinclair, Inc.; *U.S. Public*, pg. 1885
KMYT-TV—See Providence Equity Partners L.L.C.; *U.S. Private*, pg. 3293
KNBC-TV—See Comcast Corporation; *U.S. Public*, pg. 539
KNOE-TV—See Gray Television, Inc.; *U.S. Public*, pg. 960
KNOP-TV—See Gray Television, Inc.; *U.S. Public*, pg. 960
KNSD-TV—See Comcast Corporation; *U.S. Public*, pg. 539
KNTV-TV—See Comcast Corporation; *U.S. Public*, pg. 539
KNXV-TV—See The E.W. Scripps Company; *U.S. Public*, pg. 2068
KOAT HEARST-ARGYLE TELEVISION, INC.—See The Hearst Corporation; *U.S. Private*, pg. 4048
KOB-TV, INC.—See Hubbard Broadcasting, Inc.; *U.S. Private*, pg. 2000
KOCB, INC.—See Sinclair, Inc.; *U.S. Public*, pg. 1885
KOCB LICENSEE, LLC—See Sinclair, Inc.; *U.S. Public*, pg. 1885
KOCO-TV—See The Hearst Corporation; *U.S. Private*, pg. 4048
KODE-TV—See Mission Broadcasting, Inc.; *U.S. Private*, pg. 2747
KOFY, INC.—See Silver Point Capital, L.P.; *U.S. Private*, pg. 3661
KOKH-TV—See Sinclair, Inc.; *U.S. Public*, pg. 1886
KOKI-TV—See Providence Equity Partners L.L.C.; *U.S. Private*, pg. 3293
KOLD, LLC—See Gray Television, Inc.; *U.S. Public*, pg. 959
KOMO-TV—See Sinclair, Inc.; *U.S. Public*, pg. 1886
KONG-TV, INC.—See TEGNA Inc.; *U.S. Public*, pg. 1990
KOSA-TV CBS 7—See Gray Television, Inc.; *U.S. Public*, pg. 960
KOTV INC.—See Griffin Communications, LLC; *U.S. Private*, pg. 1787
KOVR-TV—See National Amusements, Inc.; *U.S. Private*, pg. 2840
KPDX-TV—See Meredith Corporation; *U.S. Public*, pg. 1423
KPHO-TV—See Meredith Corporation; *U.S. Public*, pg. 1423
KPIC-TV—See Sinclair, Inc.; *U.S. Public*, pg. 1886
KPIX-TV—See National Amusements, Inc.; *U.S. Private*, pg. 2840
KPLC, LLC—See Gray Television, Inc.; *U.S. Public*, pg. 959

KPLR, INC.—See Nexstar Media Group, Inc.; *U.S. Public*, pg. 1524
KPNX-TV—See TEGNA Inc.; *U.S. Public*, pg. 1990
KQED INC.; *U.S. Private*, pg. 2348
KRCW-TV—See Nexstar Media Group, Inc.; *U.S. Public*, pg. 1524
KREX-TV—See Nexstar Media Group, Inc.; *U.S. Public*, pg. 1522
KRIS COMMUNICATIONS INC.—See Evening Post Publishing Co.; *U.S. Private*, pg. 1436
KRIV-TV—See Fox Corporation; *U.S. Public*, pg. 876
KRON-TV—See Nexstar Media Group, Inc.; *U.S. Public*, pg. 1523
KRXI, LLC—See Sinclair, Inc.; *U.S. Public*, pg. 1885
KSAX-TV, INC.—See Hubbard Broadcasting, Inc.; *U.S. Private*, pg. 2000
KSBW-TV—See The Hearst Corporation; *U.S. Private*, pg. 4048
KSBY COMMUNICATIONS, INC.—See Evening Post Publishing Co.; *U.S. Private*, pg. 1436
KSDK-TV—See TEGNA Inc.; *U.S. Public*, pg. 1990
KSEE TELEVISION, INC.—See Nexstar Media Group, Inc.; *U.S. Public*, pg. 1523
KSFY-TV—See Gray Television, Inc.; *U.S. Public*, pg. 960
KSHB-TV—See The E.W. Scripps Company; *U.S. Public*, pg. 2068
KSKN TELEVISION, INC.—See TEGNA Inc.; *U.S. Public*, pg. 1990
KSLA, LLC—See Gray Television, Inc.; *U.S. Public*, pg. 959
KSL-TV—See Deseret Management Corporation; *U.S. Private*, pg. 1212
KSMO-TV—See Meredith Corporation; *U.S. Public*, pg. 1423
KSNF-TV—See Nexstar Media Group, Inc.; *U.S. Public*, pg. 1523
KSTC-TV, LLC—See Hubbard Broadcasting, Inc.; *U.S. Private*, pg. 2000
KSTP-TV, LLC—See Hubbard Broadcasting, Inc.; *U.S. Private*, pg. 2000
KSTU LICENSE, LLC—See Nexstar Media Group, Inc.; *U.S. Public*, pg. 1524
KSTU-TV—See Nexstar Media Group, Inc.; *U.S. Public*, pg. 1524
KSVI-TV—See Nexstar Media Group, Inc.; *U.S. Public*, pg. 1523
KSWB INC.—See Nexstar Media Group, Inc.; *U.S. Public*, pg. 1524
KTAB-TV—See Nexstar Media Group, Inc.; *U.S. Public*, pg. 1523
KTAL-TV—See Nexstar Media Group, Inc.; *U.S. Public*, pg. 1523
KTBC-TV—See Fox Corporation; *U.S. Public*, pg. 876
KTHV-TV—See TEGNA Inc.; *U.S. Public*, pg. 1990
KTIV-TV—See Gray Television, Inc.; *U.S. Public*, pg. 961
KTLA INC.—See Nexstar Media Group, Inc.; *U.S. Public*, pg. 1524
KTLN-TV—See OTA Broadcasting, LLC; *U.S. Private*, pg. 3048
KTNV-TV—See The E.W. Scripps Company; *U.S. Public*, pg. 2068
KTRK TELEVISION, INC.—See The Walt Disney Company; *U.S. Public*, pg. 2138
KTTC-TV—See Gray Television, Inc.; *U.S. Public*, pg. 961
KTTU-TV, INC.—See TEGNA Inc.; *U.S. Public*, pg. 1990
KTTV—See Fox Corporation; *U.S. Public*, pg. 876
KTUL, LLC—See Sinclair, Inc.; *U.S. Public*, pg. 1886
KTVA-TV—See Liberty Broadband Corporation; *U.S. Public*, pg. 1310
KTVE-TV—See Mission Broadcasting, Inc.; *U.S. Private*, pg. 2747
KTVI-TV—See Nexstar Media Group, Inc.; *U.S. Public*, pg. 1524
KTVK-3TV—See Meredith Corporation; *U.S. Public*, pg. 1423
KTVK, INC.—See Meredith Corporation; *U.S. Public*, pg. 1423
KTVL-TV—See Sinclair, Inc.; *U.S. Public*, pg. 1885
KTVT BROADCASTING COMPANY LP—See National Amusements, Inc.; *U.S. Private*, pg. 2840
KTVU, LLC—See Apollo Global Management, Inc.; *U.S. Public*, pg. 164
KTVX-TV—See Nexstar Media Group, Inc.; *U.S. Public*, pg. 1523
KTXD OPERATING COMPANY, LLC—See SunTx Capital Partners, L.P.; *U.S. Private*, pg. 3874
KUBE-TV—See Ellis, McQuary, Stanley & Associates LLC; *U.S. Private*, pg. 1374
KUMV-TV—See Gray Television, Inc.; *U.S. Public*, pg. 960
KUQI LICENSEE, LLC—See Sinclair, Inc.; *U.S. Public*, pg. 1885
KUSA-TV—See TEGNA Inc.; *U.S. Public*, pg. 1990
KUSTANNUS OY AAMULEHTI—See Alma Media Corporation; *Int'l*, pg. 362
KUTP-TV—See Fox Corporation; *U.S. Public*, pg. 876
KUTV-TV—See Sinclair, Inc.; *U.S. Public*, pg. 1885
KVAL-TV—See Sinclair, Inc.; *U.S. Public*, pg. 1886
KVCW, LLC—See Sinclair, Inc.; *U.S. Public*, pg. 1885
KVIE, INC.; *U.S. Private*, pg. 2359
KVLY-TV—See Gray Television, Inc.; *U.S. Public*, pg. 960

KVOA COMMUNICATIONS, INC.—See Gray Television, Inc.; *U.S. Public*, pg. 961
KVOS-TV—See OTA Broadcasting, LLC; *U.S. Private*, pg. 3048
KVUE TELEVISION, INC.—See TEGNA Inc.; *U.S. Public*, pg. 1990
KVUE-TV—See TEGNA Inc.; *U.S. Public*, pg. 1990
KVVU-TV—See Meredith Corporation; *U.S. Public*, pg. 1423
KWBQ-TV—See Tamer Media, LLC; *U.S. Private*, pg. 3928
KWCH-TV—See Gray Television, Inc.; *U.S. Public*, pg. 960
KWGN INC.—See Nexstar Media Group, Inc.; *U.S. Public*, pg. 1524
KWWL-TV—See Gray Television, Inc.; *U.S. Public*, pg. 961
KXAN LLC—See Nexstar Media Group, Inc.; *U.S. Public*, pg. 1523
KXAS-TV—See Comcast Corporation; *U.S. Public*, pg. 539
KXRM-TV—See Nexstar Media Group, Inc.; *U.S. Public*, pg. 1523
KXTV INC.—See TEGNA Inc.; *U.S. Public*, pg. 1990
KYODO EDIT, INC.—See Fuji Media Holdings, Inc.; *Int'l*, pg. 2814
KYODO TELEVISION, LTD.—See Fuji Media Holdings, Inc.; *Int'l*, pg. 2814
KYTX OPERATING COMPANY, LLC—See TEGNA Inc.; *U.S. Public*, pg. 1990
KYW-TV—See National Amusements, Inc.; *U.S. Private*, pg. 2840
LA CAPITAL CABLE S.A.—See Grupo Clarin S.A.; *Int'l*, pg. 3125
LAFAYETTE TV, LLC—See Entertainment Studios, Inc.; *U.S. Private*, pg. 1405
LAPIN KANSA OY—See Alma Media Corporation; *Int'l*, pg. 362
LAPTV LLC—See The Walt Disney Company; *U.S. Public*, pg. 2140
LA VOZ DEL INTERIOR S.A.—See Grupo Clarin S.A.; *Int'l*, pg. 3124
LEADER ASSOCIATED NEWSPAPERS PTY. LIMITED—See News Corporation; *U.S. Public*, pg. 1520
LEGACY BROADCASTING, LLC; *U.S. Private*, pg. 2416
LESEA BROADCASTING CORPORATION; *U.S. Private*, pg. 2432
LETSEB, S.A. DE C.V.—See Grupo Televisa, S.A.B.; *Int'l*, pg. 3136
LEVELING 8, INC.; *U.S. Private*, pg. 2434
LIMA COMMUNICATIONS CORP. WLIO TELEVISION—See Block Communications, Inc.; *U.S. Private*, pg. 582
LIN TELEVISION OF TEXAS, INC.—See Nexstar Media Group, Inc.; *U.S. Public*, pg. 1523
LIVE MEDIA GROUP, LLC; *U.S. Private*, pg. 2473
LOS ANGELES TELEVISION STATION KCAL LLC—See National Amusements, Inc.; *U.S. Private*, pg. 2840
LOUISIANA EDUCATIONAL TELEVISION AUTHORITY; *U.S. Private*, pg. 2499
LOUISIANA TELEVISION BROADCASTING CORPORATION; *U.S. Private*, pg. 2500
M2B WORLD PTE. LTD.—See AMARU, INC.; *Int'l*, pg. 412
MACROVISION SOLUTIONS NETWORKS—See Adeia Inc.; *U.S. Public*, pg. 41
MADISON SQUARE GARDEN NETWORK—See Sphere Entertainment Co.; *U.S. Public*, pg. 1918
MAGNOLIA ITALY—See De Agostini S.p.A.; *Int'l*, pg. 1994
MAGNOLIA SPAIN—See De Agostini S.p.A.; *Int'l*, pg. 1994
MARQUEE BROADCASTING, INC.; *U.S. Private*, pg. 2586
MASTIFF NORWAY—See De Agostini S.p.A.; *Int'l*, pg. 1995
MATCHING BROADCAST CO., LTD.—See Bangkok Broadcasting & TV Co., Ltd.; *Int'l*, pg. 833
MAXDOME GMBH—See Warner Bros. Discovery, Inc.; *U.S. Public*, pg. 2327
MAXXSOUTH BROADBAND—See Block Communications, Inc.; *U.S. Private*, pg. 582
MAZ & MORE TV-PRODUKTION GMBH—See Axel Springer SE; *Int'l*, pg. 766
MEDIA BROADCAST GMBH—See freenet AG; *Int'l*, pg. 2770
MEL WHEELER, INC.; *U.S. Private*, pg. 2661
MIAMI VALLEY BROADCASTING CORPORATION—See Apollo Global Management, Inc.; *U.S. Public*, pg. 164
MILANO DESIGN STUDIO S.R.L.—See National Amusements, Inc.; *U.S. Private*, pg. 2842
MISSISSIPPI TV, LLC—See Entertainment Studios, Inc.; *U.S. Private*, pg. 1405
MIX MEGAPOL.SE AB—See Warner Bros. Discovery, Inc.; *U.S. Public*, pg. 2326
MODERN MEDIA SYSTEMS—See Al Faisaliah Group; *Int'l*, pg. 277
MONA LISA PRODUCTION—See De Agostini S.p.A.; *Int'l*, pg. 1995
MORRIS NETWORK, INC.—See Morris Multimedia, Inc.; *U.S. Private*, pg. 2788
MOUNTAIN BROADCASTING, LLC—See Northwest Broadcasting, Inc.; *U.S. Private*, pg. 2959
MTV HONG KONG LIMITED—See National Amusements, Inc.; *U.S. Private*, pg. 2841
MTV NETWORKS AUSTRALIA PTY LTD—See National Amusements, Inc.; *U.S. Private*, pg. 2841
MTV NETWORKS BELGIUM BVBA—See National Amusements, Inc.; *U.S. Private*, pg. 2841

N.A.I.C.S. INDEX

516120 — TELEVISION BROADCAS...

MTV NETWORKS GERMANY GMBH—See National Amusements, Inc.; *U.S. Private*, pg. 2841
MTV NETWORKS JAPAN K.K.—See National Amusements, Inc.; *U.S. Private*, pg. 2841
MTV NETWORKS LATIN AMERICA INC.—See National Amusements, Inc.; *U.S. Private*, pg. 2841
MTV NETWORKS LTDA—See National Amusements, Inc.; *U.S. Private*, pg. 2841
MTV NETWORKS ON CAMPUS INC.—See National Amusements, Inc.; *U.S. Private*, pg. 2841
MTV NETWORKS POLSKA B.V.—See National Amusements, Inc.; *U.S. Private*, pg. 2841
MTV NETWORKS SCHWEIZ AG—See National Amusements, Inc.; *U.S. Private*, pg. 2842
MTV SISALLOT OY—See Bonnier AB; *Int'l*, pg. 1109
MULTIMEDIA KSDK, INC.—See TEGNA Inc.; *U.S. Public*, pg. 1990
MUSICA APARTE S.A.U.—See Atresmedia Corporacion de Medios de Comunicacion, S.A.; *Int'l*, pg. 693
MYNETWORKTV, INC.—See Fox Corporation; *U.S. Public*, pg. 876
N24 MEDIA GMBH—See Axel Springer SE; *Int'l*, pg. 766
NATIONAL GEOGRAPHIC CHANNEL ADVENTURE MEDYA HIZMETLERI A.S.—See The Walt Disney Company; *U.S. Public*, pg. 2141
NATIONAL GEOGRAPHIC PARTNERS, LLC—See The Walt Disney Company; *U.S. Public*, pg. 2140
NBC OLYMPICS LLC—See Comcast Corporation; *U.S. Public*, pg. 539
NBC PALM SPRINGS—See Entravision Communications Corporation; *U.S. Public*, pg. 779
NBC STATIONS MANAGEMENT II LLC—See Comcast Corporation; *U.S. Public*, pg. 539
NEP NEW ZEALAND HOLDINGS LTD.—See The Carlyle Group Inc.; *U.S. Public*, pg. 2050
NETRANGE MMH GMBH—See Access Co., Ltd.; *Int'l*, pg. 88
NETWORK CHICAGO—See Window to the World Communications, Inc.; *U.S. Private*, pg. 4538
NETWORK DIGITAL DISTRIBUTION SERVICES FZ-LLC—See National Amusements, Inc.; *U.S. Private*, pg. 2844
NETWORK TEN (ADELAIDE) PTY LIMITED—See National Amusements, Inc.; *U.S. Private*, pg. 2844
NETWORK TEN (BRISBANE) PTY LIMITED—See National Amusements, Inc.; *U.S. Private*, pg. 2844
NETWORK TEN (MELBOURNE) PTY LIMITED—See National Amusements, Inc.; *U.S. Private*, pg. 2844
NETWORK TEN (PERTH) PTY LIMITED—See National Amusements, Inc.; *U.S. Private*, pg. 2844
NETWORK TEN PTY. LIMITED—See National Amusements, Inc.; *U.S. Private*, pg. 2844
NEW MARKETS MEDIA & INTELLIGENCE LTD.—See APQ Global Limited; *Int'l*, pg. 522
NEW ORLEANS HEARST-ARGYLE TELEVISION, INC.—See The Hearst Corporation; *U.S. Private*, pg. 4048
NEWPORT TELEVISION LLC—See Providence Equity Partners L.L.C.; *U.S. Private*, pg. 3293
NEWS AMERICA MARKETING FSI L.L.C.—See Charlesbank Capital Partners, LLC; *U.S. Private*, pg. 854
NEWS AMERICA MARKETING PROPERTIES L.L.C.—See Charlesbank Capital Partners, LLC; *U.S. Private*, pg. 854
NEWSCHANNEL 5 NETWORK—See The E.W. Scripps Company; *U.S. Public*, pg. 2068
NEWS INTERNATIONAL NEWSPAPERS LIMITED—See News Corporation; *U.S. Public*, pg. 1521
NEW WORLD COMMUNICATIONS OF ATLANTA, INC.—See Fox Corporation; *U.S. Public*, pg. 876
NEW WORLD COMMUNICATIONS OF DETROIT, INC.—See Fox Corporation; *U.S. Public*, pg. 876
NEW WORLD COMMUNICATIONS OF TAMPA, INC.—See Fox Corporation; *U.S. Public*, pg. 876
NEW WORLD PRODUCTION CO, LTD.—See BEC World Public Company Limited; *Int'l*, pg. 936
NEW WORLD VIDEO—See The Walt Disney Company; *U.S. Public*, pg. 2140
NEW YORK TIMES TELEVISION—See The New York Times Company; *U.S. Public*, pg. 2117
NEXSTAR BROADCASTING, INC.—See Nexstar Media Group, Inc.; *U.S. Public*, pg. 1522
NEXTEP TV WORKSHOP CO., LTD.—See Fuji Media Holdings, Inc.; *Int'l*, pg. 2814
NGHT, LLC—See National Geographic Society; *U.S. Private*, pg. 2855
NICKELODEON GLOBAL NETWORK VENTURES INC.—See National Amusements, Inc.; *U.S. Private*, pg. 2842
NICKELODEON INTERNATIONAL LIMITED—See National Amusements, Inc.; *U.S. Private*, pg. 2842
NIELSEN TELEVISION AUDIENCE MEASUREMENT PTY. LTD.—See Brookfield Corporation; *Int'l*, pg. 1180
NIELSEN TELEVISION AUDIENCE MEASUREMENT PTY. LTD.—See Elliott Management Corporation; *U.S. Private*, pg. 1372
NIPPON BS BROADCASTING CORPORATION—See Bic Camera Inc.; *Int'l*, pg. 1018
NORDDEICH TV PRODUKTIONSGESELLSCHAFT MBH—See Bertelsmann SE & Co. KGaA; *Int'l*, pg. 995
NORTHSOUTH PRODUCTIONS—See The Hearst Corporation; *U.S. Private*, pg. 4049
NORTH TEXAS PUBLIC BROADCASTING; *U.S. Private*, pg. 2948
NPG OF OREGON, INC.—See News-Press & Gazette Company; *U.S. Private*, pg. 2917
NW COMMUNICATIONS OF AUSTIN, INC.—See Fox Corporation; *U.S. Public*, pg. 876
NW COMMUNICATIONS OF TEXAS, INC.—See Fox Corporation; *U.S. Public*, pg. 876
ONE MEDIA, LLC—See Sinclair, Inc.; *U.S. Public*, pg. 1885
ON GAME NETWORK INC.—See CJ Corporation; *Int'l*, pg. 1634
OPERBES, S.A. DE C.V.—See Grupo Televisa, S.A.B.; *Int'l*, pg. 3136
ORLANDO HEARST TELEVISION INC.—See The Hearst Corporation; *U.S. Private*, pg. 4048
OTA BROADCASTING, LLC; *U.S. Private*, pg. 3048
PACIFIC & SOUTHERN, LLC—See TEGNA Inc.; *U.S. Public*, pg. 1990
PARAMOUNT GLOBAL—See National Amusements, Inc.; *U.S. Private*, pg. 2839
PIKES PEAK TELEVISION, INC.—See News-Press & Gazette Company; *U.S. Private*, pg. 2917
PRESS COMMUNICATIONS, LLC; *U.S. Private*, pg. 3255
PRODUCT INFORMATION NETWORK—See Access Television Network; *U.S. Private*, pg. 53
PROGRAM PARTNERS, INC.; *U.S. Private*, pg. 3278
PUBLIC BROADCASTING SERVICE; *U.S. Private*, pg. 3298
PULSA MEDIA CONSULTING, S.L.—See The Walt Disney Company; *U.S. Public*, pg. 2140
PURE CAPITAL SOLUTIONS INC.; *U.S. Public*, pg. 1738
QUEEN CITY BROADCASTING OF NEW YORK, INC.—See The E.W. Scripps Company; *U.S. Public*, pg. 2068
QUINCY MEDIA, INC.—See Gray Television, Inc.; *U.S. Public*, pg. 961
RADFORD STUDIO CENTER INC.—See National Amusements, Inc.; *U.S. Private*, pg. 2843
RAW TV LTD.—See Warner Bros. Discovery, Inc.; *U.S. Public*, pg. 2326
RDF TELEVISION—See De Agostini S.p.A.; *Int'l*, pg. 1995
RDF TELEVISION WEST—See De Agostini S.p.A.; *Int'l*, pg. 1995
THE REAL HIP-HOP NETWORK, INC.; *U.S. Private*, pg. 4103
ROCHESTER TV, LLC—See Entertainment Studios, Inc.; *U.S. Private*, pg. 1405
ROCKY MOUNTAIN PUBLIC BROADCASTING NETWORK, INC.; *U.S. Private*, pg. 3469
ROVI NETHERLANDS BV—See Adeia Inc.; *U.S. Public*, pg. 41
RTL4 HOLDING SA—See Bertelsmann SE & Co. KGaA; *Int'l*, pg. 995
RTL ADCONNECT S.R.L.—See Bertelsmann SE & Co. KGaA; *Int'l*, pg. 993
RTL ADCONNECT UK LTD.—See Bertelsmann SE & Co. KGaA; *Int'l*, pg. 993
RTL DISNEY FERNSEHEN GMBH & CO. KG—See Bertelsmann SE & Co. KGaA; *Int'l*, pg. 995
RTL DISNEY FERNSEHEN GMBH & CO. KG—See The Walt Disney Company; *U.S. Public*, pg. 2139
RTL GROUP CABLE & SATELLITE GMBH—See Bertelsmann SE & Co. KGaA; *Int'l*, pg. 995
RTL HESSEN GMBH—See Bertelsmann SE & Co. KGaA; *Int'l*, pg. 995
RTL HESSEN PROGRAMMFENSTER GMBH—See Bertelsmann SE & Co. KGaA; *Int'l*, pg. 995
RTL KLUB—See Bertelsmann SE & Co. KGaA; *Int'l*, pg. 995
RTL NEDERLAND BV—See Bertelsmann SE & Co. KGaA; *Int'l*, pg. 995
RTL NEDERLAND INTERACTIEF BV—See Bertelsmann SE & Co. KGaA; *Int'l*, pg. 995
RTL NEDERLAND PRODUCTIONS BV—See Bertelsmann SE & Co. KGaA; *Int'l*, pg. 995
RTL NORD GMBH—See Bertelsmann SE & Co. KGaA; *Int'l*, pg. 995
RTL TELE LETZEBUERG—See Bertelsmann SE & Co. KGaA; *Int'l*, pg. 995
RTL TELEVISION GMBH—See Bertelsmann SE & Co. KGaA; *Int'l*, pg. 995
RTV MEDIA GROUP GMBH—See Bertelsmann SE & Co. KGaA; *Int'l*, pg. 996
RUNGSIROJVANIT CO., LTD.—See BEC World Public Company Limited; *Int'l*, pg. 936
SACRAMENTO TELEVISION STATIONS INC.—See National Amusements, Inc.; *U.S. Private*, pg. 2843
SAGA BROADCASTING CORPORATION—See Saga Communications, Inc.; *U.S. Public*, pg. 1835
SAGA CITY-VISION CO., LTD.—See Hisamitsu Pharmaceutical Co., Inc.; *Int'l*, pg. 3406
SAGA COMMUNICATIONS OF IOWA—See Saga Communications, Inc.; *U.S. Public*, pg. 1835
SANGRE DE CRISTO COMMUNICATIONS, INC.—See Evening Post Publishing Co.; *U.S. Private*, pg. 1436
SANOMA TELEVISION OY—See DPG Media Group NV; *Int'l*, pg. 2188
SARKES TARZIAN INC.; *U.S. Private*, pg. 3550
SATELLITE SERVICE CO., LTD.—See Fuji Media Holdings, Inc.; *Int'l*, pg. 2814
SELLWELL GMBH & CO. KG—See Bertelsmann SE & Co. KGaA; *Int'l*, pg. 995
SENDAI TELEVISION INC.—See Fuji Media Holdings, Inc.; *Int'l*, pg. 2814
SERVICIOS NOVASAT, S. DE R.L. DE C.V.—See Grupo Televisa, S.A.B.; *Int'l*, pg. 3136
SHIZUOKA TELECASTING CO., LTD—See Fuji Media Holdings, Inc.; *Int'l*, pg. 2814
SIA ALL MEDIA LATVIA—See Providence Equity Partners L.L.C.; *U.S. Private*, pg. 3291
SIERRA BROADCASTING COMPANY—See Intermountain West Communications Company; *U.S. Private*, pg. 2113
SINCLAIR BROADCAST GROUP, LLC—See Sinclair, Inc.; *U.S. Public*, pg. 1885
SINCLAIR MEDIA OF BOISE, LLC—See Sinclair, Inc.; *U.S. Public*, pg. 1886
SINCLAIR MEDIA OF IDAHO, LLC—See Sinclair, Inc.; *U.S. Public*, pg. 1886
SINCLAIR MEDIA SERVICES COMPANY—See Sinclair, Inc.; *U.S. Public*, pg. 1886
SINCLAIR TELEVISION MEDIA, INC.—See Sinclair, Inc.; *U.S. Public*, pg. 1886
SINCLAIR TELEVISION OF BAKERSFIELD, LLC—See Sinclair, Inc.; *U.S. Public*, pg. 1886
SINCLAIR TELEVISION OF OREGON, LLC—See Sinclair, Inc.; *U.S. Public*, pg. 1886
SINCLAIR TELEVISION OF PORTLAND, LLC—See Sinclair, Inc.; *U.S. Public*, pg. 1886
SINCLAIR TELEVISION OF WASHINGTON, LLC—See Sinclair, Inc.; *U.S. Public*, pg. 1886
SITI BHATIA NETWORK ENTERTAINMENT PRIVATE LIMITED—See Essel Corporate Resources Pvt. Ltd.; *Int'l*, pg. 2510
SITI CABLE TISAI SATELLITE LIMITED—See Essel Corporate Resources Pvt. Ltd.; *Int'l*, pg. 2510
SITI GUNTUR DIGITAL NETWORK PRIVATE LIMITED—See Essel Corporate Resources Pvt. Ltd.; *Int'l*, pg. 2510
SITI KRISHNA DIGITAL MEDIA PRIVATE LIMITED—See Essel Corporate Resources Pvt. Ltd.; *Int'l*, pg. 2510
SITI MAURYA CABLE NET PRIVATE LIMITED—See Essel Corporate Resources Pvt. Ltd.; *Int'l*, pg. 2509
SITI VISION DIGITAL MEDIA PRIVATE LIMITED—See Essel Corporate Resources Pvt. Ltd.; *Int'l*, pg. 2510
SIT-UP LTD.—See Aurelius Equity Opportunities SE & Co. KGaA; *Int'l*, pg. 710
SITV, INC.; *U.S. Private*, pg. 3677
SITV INC.; *U.S. Private*, pg. 3677
SKY BRASIL SERVICOS LTDA.—See AT&T Inc.; *U.S. Public*, pg. 220
SKY DEUTSCHLAND GMBH—See Comcast Corporation; *U.S. Public*, pg. 541
SKY ITALIA S.R.L.—See Comcast Corporation; *U.S. Public*, pg. 541
SKY LIVING—See Comcast Corporation; *U.S. Public*, pg. 541
SKYLOGIC MEDITERRANEO S.R.L—See Eutelsat Communications SA; *Int'l*, pg. 2560
SKY OSTERREICH FERNSEHEN GMBH—See Comcast Corporation; *U.S. Public*, pg. 541
SKY OSTERREICH GMBH—See Comcast Corporation; *U.S. Public*, pg. 541
SKY OSTERREICH VERWALTUNG GMBH—See Comcast Corporation; *U.S. Public*, pg. 541
SKY UK LIMITED—See Comcast Corporation; *U.S. Public*, pg. 541
SOL PRODUCTION PVT. LTD—See De Agostini S.p.A.; *Int'l*, pg. 1994
SOUTH FLORIDA PBS, INC.; *U.S. Private*, pg. 3722
SPECTRUM NEWS NY1—See Charter Communications, Inc.; *U.S. Public*, pg. 483
SPOKANE TELEVISION INC.; *U.S. Private*, pg. 3760
THE SPORTS NETWORK INC.—See BCE Inc.; *Int'l*, pg. 927
SPORTVISION, INC.—See Sportsmedia Technology Corp.; *U.S. Private*, pg. 3761
SPORTV MEDYA HIZMETLERI ANONIM SIRKETI—See Warner Bros. Discovery, Inc.; *U.S. Public*, pg. 2327
SPOTXCHANGE INC—See Bertelsmann SE & Co. KGaA; *Int'l*, pg. 995
SSB SOFTWARE SERVICE UND BERATUNG GMBH—See Bertelsmann SE & Co. KGaA; *Int'l*, pg. 995
STACK, INC.—See Genstar Capital, LLC; *U.S. Private*, pg. 1678
STAINLESS BROADCASTING, LLC—See Northwest Broadcasting, Inc.; *U.S. Private*, pg. 2959
STANDARD MEDIA GROUP LLC—See Standard General LP; *U.S. Private*, pg. 3778
STAR INDIA PRIVATE LIMITED—See National Amusements, Inc.; *U.S. Private*, pg. 2844
STAR MIDDLE EAST FZ-LLC—See National Amusements, Inc.; *U.S. Private*, pg. 2844
STARNETONE GMBH—See Hubert Burda Media Holding Kommanditgesellschaft; *Int'l*, pg. 3520

516120 — TELEVISION BROADCAS...

STAR SPORTS LNDIA PRIVATE LIMITED—See National Amusements, Inc.; *U.S. Private*, pg. 2844
STAR WEST SATELLITE—See Star West Satellite Inc.; *U.S. Private*, pg. 3785
ST. JOSEPH TV, LLC—See Heartland Media, LLC; *U.S. Private*, pg. 1900
STO-CPH PRODUKTION AB—See The Walt Disney Company; *U.S. Public*, pg. 2141
STYLE HAUL INC—See Bertelsmann SE & Co. KGaA; *Int'l*, pg. 995
SUNBEAM TELEVISION CORPORATION; *U.S. Private*, pg. 3864
THE SUNDAY TIMES LIMITED—See News Corporation; *U.S. Public*, pg. 1521
SUOMEN PAIKALLISSANOMAT OY—See Alma Media Corporation; *Int'l*, pg. 362
SUPERSTATION INC.—See Warner Bros. Discovery, Inc.; *U.S. Public*, pg. 2328
TAJ TELEVISION LTD.—See Essel Corporate Resources Pvt. Ltd.; *Int'l*, pg. 2510
TAJ TV LIMITED—See Essel Corporate Resources Pvt. Ltd.; *Int'l*, pg. 2509
TAJ TV LIMITED—See Essel Corporate Resources Pvt. Ltd.; *Int'l*, pg. 2510
TALKBACK THAMES—See Bertelsmann SE & Co. KGaA; *Int'l*, pg. 994
TCTFAMERICA, INC.—See The Walt Disney Company; *U.S. Public*, pg. 2141
TEGNA BROADCASTING GROUP—See TEGNA Inc.; *U.S. Public*, pg. 1990
TELEALLIANCE—See De Agostini S.p.A.; *Int'l*, pg. 1995
TELECENTER PANAMERICANA LTDA.—See AT&T Inc.; *U.S. Public*, pg. 220
TELEDIFUSORA BAHIENSE S.A.—See Grupo Clarin S.A.; *Int'l*, pg. 3125
TELELATINO NETWORK INC.—See Corus Entertainment Inc.; *Int'l*, pg. 1809
TELE M1 AG—See BT Holding AG; *Int'l*, pg. 1204
TELEMUNDO NETWORK LLC—See Comcast Corporation; *U.S. Public*, pg. 540
TELESIA S.P.A.—See Class Editori S.p.A.; *Int'l*, pg. 1652
TELEVICENTRO OF PUERTO RICO, LLC—See Hemisphere Media Group, Inc.; *U.S. Private*, pg. 1913
TELEVISA CORPORACION, S.A. DE C.V.—See Grupo Televisa, S.A.B.; *Int'l*, pg. 3137
TELEVISION SATELITAL CODIFICADA S.A.—See, AT&T Inc.; *U.S. Public*, pg. 220
TELEVISORA DE MEXICALI, S.A. DE C.V.—See Grupo Televisa, S.A.B.; *Int'l*, pg. 3137
TELEVISORA DE OCCIDENTE, S.A. DE C.V.—See Grupo Televisa, S.A.B.; *Int'l*, pg. 3137
TELEVISTA S.A.—See Warner Bros. Discovery, Inc.; *U.S. Public*, pg. 2327
TELEZURI AG—See BT Holding AG; *Int'l*, pg. 1204
TERRE HAUTE TV, LLC—See Entertainment Studios, Inc.; *U.S. Private*, pg. 1405
TEXAS CABLE NEWS—See TEGNA Inc.; *U.S. Public*, pg. 1991
THOROUGHBRED RACING PRODUCTIONS (VICTORIA) PTY LTD—See Australian Turf Club (ATC); *Int'l*, pg. 722
TITAN BROADCAST MANAGEMENT LLC—See Ellis, McQuary, Stanley & Associates LLC; *U.S. Private*, pg. 1374
TLD3 ENTERTAINMENT GROUP, INC.; *U.S. Public*, pg. 2161
TOKAI TELEVISION BROADCASTING CO., LTD.—See Fuji Media Holdings, Inc.; *Int'l*, pg. 2814
TOTAL LIVING NETWORK; *U.S. Private*, pg. 4191
TRANSFER NV—See The Walt Disney Company; *U.S. Public*, pg. 2140
TRES ARROYOS TELEVISORA COLOR S.A.—See Grupo Clarin S.A.; *Int'l*, pg. 3125
TRIBUNE BROADCASTING DENVER, LLC—See Nexstar Media Group, Inc.; *U.S. Public*, pg. 1525
TRIBUNE BROADCASTING HARTFORD, LLC—See Nexstar Media Group, Inc.; *U.S. Public*, pg. 1525
TRIBUNE BROADCASTING INDIANAPOLIS, LLC—See Nexstar Media Group, Inc.; *U.S. Public*, pg. 1525
TRIBUNE BROADCASTING OKLAHOMA CITY LICENSE, LLC—See Nexstar Media Group, Inc.; *U.S. Public*, pg. 1525
TRIBUNE CNLBC, LLC—See Nexstar Media Group, Inc.; *U.S. Public*, pg. 1525
TRIBUNE TELEVISION NEW ORLEANS, INC.—See Nexstar Media Group, Inc.; *U.S. Public*, pg. 1524
TRIBUNE TELEVISION NORTHWEST, INC.—See Nexstar Media Group, Inc.; *U.S. Public*, pg. 1524
TRI STATE CHRISTIAN TELEVISION—See TCT Ministries, Inc.; *U.S. Private*, pg. 3943
TRUE CORPORATION PUBLIC COMPANY LIMITED—See Charoen Pokphand Group Co., Ltd.; *Int'l*, pg. 1453
TSM SERVICES INC.—See National Amusements, Inc.; *U.S. Private*, pg. 2844
TUCSON COMMUNICATIONS LLC—See Cascade Broadcasting Group LLC; *U.S. Private*, pg. 778
TURNER BROADCASTING SALES, INC.—See Warner Bros. Discovery, Inc.; *U.S. Public*, pg. 2328
TURNER BROADCASTING SYSTEM ASIA PACIFIC INC.—See Warner Bros. Discovery, Inc.; *U.S. Public*, pg. 2328
TURNER BROADCASTING SYSTEM EUROPE LIMITED—See Warner Bros. Discovery, Inc.; *U.S. Public*, pg. 2328
TURNER BROADCASTING SYSTEM, INC.—See Warner Bros. Discovery, Inc.; *U.S. Public*, pg. 2328
TURNER ENTERTAINMENT NETWORKS INTERNATIONAL LIMITED—See Warner Bros. Discovery, Inc.; *U.S. Public*, pg. 2328
TURNER NETWORK TELEVISION, INC.—See Warner Bros. Discovery, Inc.; *U.S. Public*, pg. 2328
TV 2 AS—See Egmont Fonden; *Int'l*, pg. 2326
TV 2 TORGET AS—See Egmont Fonden; *Int'l*, pg. 2326
TV3 TELEVISION NETWORK—See Brookfield Corporation; *Int'l*, pg. 1181
TV AZTECA S.A.B DE C.V.—See Grupo Salinas, S.A. de C.V.; *Int'l*, pg. 3135
TVB 3 NETWORK CO., LTD.—See BEC World Public Company Limited; *Int'l*, pg. 936
TV.GUSTO GMBH—See Hubert Burda Media Holding Kommanditgesellschaft; *Int'l*, pg. 3520
TVI SA—See Bertelsmann SE & Co. KGaA; *Int'l*, pg. 995
TV NORGE AS—See Warner Bros. Discovery, Inc.; *U.S. Public*, pg. 2326
TV ONE, LLC—See Urban One, Inc.; *U.S. Public*, pg. 2265
TV SANTA FE, S.A. DE C.V.—See Grupo Televisa, S.A.B.; *Int'l*, pg. 3136
TWENTIETH CENTURY FOX FILM COMPANY LIMITED—See The Walt Disney Company; *U.S. Public*, pg. 2140
TWENTIETH CENTURY FOX OF GERMANY GMBH—See The Walt Disney Company; *U.S. Public*, pg. 2140
TWIN CITIES PUBLIC TELEVISION, INC.; *U.S. Private*, pg. 4264
TYC SPORTS—See Grupo Clarin S.A.; *Int'l*, pg. 3125
UAB ALL MEDIA LITHUANIA—See Providence Equity Partners L.L.C.; *U.S. Private*, pg. 3291
UBC CABLE NETWORK PUBLIC COMPANY LIMITED—See Charoen Pokphand Group Co., Ltd.; *Int'l*, pg. 1453
UBU HOLDINGS INC.; *U.S. Public*, pg. 2217
UFA CINEMA GMBH—See Bertelsmann SE & Co. KGaA; *Int'l*, pg. 995
UKTV INTERACTIVE LIMITED—See British Broadcasting Corporation; *Int'l*, pg. 1169
UKTV MEDIA LIMITED—See British Broadcasting Corporation; *Int'l*, pg. 1169
UNA VEZ MAS, LP; *U.S. Private*, pg. 4279
UNITED STATIONS RADIO NETWORKS INC.; *U.S. Private*, pg. 4300
UNIVERSAL CITY STUDIOS LLC—See Comcast Corporation; *U.S. Public*, pg. 540
UPC AUSTRIA SERVICES GMBH—See Deutsche Telekom AG; *Int'l*, pg. 2084
URBAN TELEVISION NETWORK CORP.; *U.S. Public*, pg. 2265
USTREAM, INC.—See International Business Machines Corporation; *U.S. Public*, pg. 1151
VAN EIGHT PRODUCTIONS, INC.—See Fuji Media Holdings, Inc.; *Int'l*, pg. 2814
VIACOM 18 MEDIA PVT. LTD.—See National Amusements, Inc.; *U.S. Private*, pg. 2844
VIACOM NETWORKS BRASIL PROGRAMACAO TELEVISIVA E PUBLICIDADE LTDA.—See National Amusements, Inc.; *U.S. Private*, pg. 2844
VIDEOLINK LLC—See Marlin Equity Partners, LLC; *U.S. Private*, pg. 2583
VIDEOPERSEL, LTD.—See Grupo Televisa, S.A.B.; *Int'l*, pg. 3137
VIENNA CINE & TV SERVICES GMBH—See Bavaria Film GmbH; *Int'l*, pg. 899
VIJAY TELEVISION PRIVATE LIMITED—See National Amusements, Inc.; *U.S. Private*, pg. 2844
VIMN BELGIUM BVBA—See National Amusements, Inc.; *U.S. Private*, pg. 2844
VIMN GERMANY GMBH—See National Amusements, Inc.; *U.S. Private*, pg. 2844
VIMN NETHERLANDS B.V.—See National Amusements, Inc.; *U.S. Private*, pg. 2844
VIMN NORDIC AB—See National Amusements, Inc.; *U.S. Private*, pg. 2844
VIMN POLAND SP. Z O.O.—See National Amusements, Inc.; *U.S. Private*, pg. 2844
VIMN POLSKA B.V.—See National Amusements, Inc.; *U.S. Private*, pg. 2844
VIMOND MEDIA SOLUTIONS INC.—See Egmont Fonden; *Int'l*, pg. 2326
VIMOND MEDIA SOLUTIONS—See Egmont Fonden; *Int'l*, pg. 2326
VOICE OF PROPHECY, INC.; *U.S. Private*, pg. 4409
VOX FILM & FERNSEH GMBH & CO. KG—See Bertelsmann SE & Co. KGaA; *Int'l*, pg. 996
WABC-TV INC.—See The Walt Disney Company; *U.S. Public*, pg. 2138
WABI-TV—See Gray Television, Inc.; *U.S. Public*, pg. 960
WALA-TV—See Meredith Corporation; *U.S. Public*, pg. 1423
WALB, LLC—See Gray Television, Inc.; *U.S. Public*, pg. 959
WAND TELEVISION, INC.—See Block Communications, Inc.; *U.S. Private*, pg. 582
WAPA AMERICA INC.—See Hemisphere Media Group, Inc.; *U.S. Private*, pg. 1913
WAPT HEARST-ARGYLE TELEVISION, INC.—See The Hearst Corporation; *U.S. Private*, pg. 4048
WARNER BROS. TELEVISION GROUP—See Warner Bros. Discovery, Inc.; *U.S. Public*, pg. 2329
WASHINGTON EDUCATIONAL TELECOMMUNICATIONS ASSOCIATION; *U.S. Private*, pg. 4447
WATERMAN BROADCASTING CORP.; *U.S. Private*, pg. 4454
WATL-TV—See TEGNA Inc.; *U.S. Public*, pg. 1990
WAVE HOLDINGS, LLC—See Gray Television, Inc.; *U.S. Public*, pg. 959
WAWS-TV—See Providence Equity Partners L.L.C.; *U.S. Private*, pg. 3293
WBAL HEARST-ARGYLE TELEVISION, INC.—See The Hearst Corporation; *U.S. Private*, pg. 4048
WBBM-TV—See National Amusements, Inc.; *U.S. Private*, pg. 2840
WBFF-TV—See Sinclair, Inc.; *U.S. Public*, pg. 1886
WBIR, INC.—See TEGNA Inc.; *U.S. Public*, pg. 1991
WBIR-TV, LLC—See TEGNA Inc.; *U.S. Public*, pg. 1991
WBNS TV, INC.—See TEGNA Inc.; *U.S. Public*, pg. 1991
WBOC INC.—See Draper Holdings Business Trust; *U.S. Private*, pg. 1272
WBRC, LLC—See Gray Television, Inc.; *U.S. Public*, pg. 959
WBRE-TV—See Nexstar Media Group, Inc.; *U.S. Public*, pg. 1523
WBTV, LLC—See Gray Television, Inc.; *U.S. Public*, pg. 959
WBTW-TV—See Nexstar Media Group, Inc.; *U.S. Public*, pg. 1523
WBZ-TV—See National Amusements, Inc.; *U.S. Private*, pg. 2840
WCAU-TV—See Comcast Corporation; *U.S. Public*, pg. 540
WCBD-TV—See Nexstar Media Group, Inc.; *U.S. Public*, pg. 1523
WCBS-TV—See National Amusements, Inc.; *U.S. Private*, pg. 2840
WCCO-TV—See National Amusements, Inc.; *U.S. Private*, pg. 2841
WCCT, INC.—See Nexstar Media Group, Inc.; *U.S. Public*, pg. 1524
WCGV, INC.—See Sinclair, Inc.; *U.S. Public*, pg. 1886
WCHS-TV—See Sinclair, Inc.; *U.S. Public*, pg. 1886
WCIV-TV—See Sinclair, Inc.; *U.S. Public*, pg. 1886
WCJB-TV—See Gray Television, Inc.; *U.S. Public*, pg. 960
WCNC-TV, INC.—See TEGNA Inc.; *U.S. Public*, pg. 1990
WCPO-TV—See The E.W. Scripps Company; *U.S. Public*, pg. 2069
WCSC, LLC—See Gray Television, Inc.; *U.S. Public*, pg. 959
WCSH-TV—See TEGNA Inc.; *U.S. Public*, pg. 1991
WCTV-TV—See Gray Television, Inc.; *U.S. Public*, pg. 960
WCVB HEARST-ARGYLE TELEVISION, INC.—See The Hearst Corporation; *U.S. Private*, pg. 4048
WCWJ-TV—See Graham Holdings Company; *U.S. Public*, pg. 955
WCWN LLC—See Sinclair, Inc.; *U.S. Public*, pg. 1886
WDAF TELEVISION, INC.—See Nexstar Media Group, Inc.; *U.S. Public*, pg. 1525
WDCW, LLC—See Nexstar Media Group, Inc.; *U.S. Public*, pg. 1524
WDEF-TV—See Morris Multimedia, Inc.; *U.S. Private*, pg. 2788
WDIO-TV, LLC—See Hubbard Broadcasting, Inc.; *U.S. Private*, pg. 2000
WDKY, INC.—See Sinclair, Inc.; *U.S. Public*, pg. 1886
WDTV-TV—See Gray Television, Inc.; *U.S. Public*, pg. 960
WEAR LICENSEE, LLC—See Sinclair, Inc.; *U.S. Public*, pg. 1886
WEAR-TV—See Sinclair, Inc.; *U.S. Public*, pg. 1886
WEEK-TV—See Silver Point Capital, L.P.; *U.S. Private*, pg. 3662
WEIGEL BROADCASTING CO.; *U.S. Private*, pg. 4471
WETM-TV—See Nexstar Media Group, Inc.; *U.S. Public*, pg. 1523
WEWS-TV—See The E.W. Scripps Company; *U.S. Public*, pg. 2069
WFAA-TV, INC.—See TEGNA Inc.; *U.S. Public*, pg. 1991
WFIE, LLC—See Gray Television, Inc.; *U.S. Public*, pg. 960
WFLA-TV—See Nexstar Media Group, Inc.; *U.S. Public*, pg. 1523
WFLD-TV—See Fox Corporation; *U.S. Public*, pg. 876
WFMY TELEVISION, LLC—See TEGNA Inc.; *U.S. Public*, pg. 1991
WFOR-TV—See National Amusements, Inc.; *U.S. Private*, pg. 2841
WFRV-TV—See Nexstar Media Group, Inc.; *U.S. Public*, pg. 1523
WFSB-TV—See Meredith Corporation; *U.S. Public*, pg. 1423
WFTS-TV—See The E.W. Scripps Company; *U.S. Public*, pg. 2069
WFTV, INC.—See Apollo Global Management, Inc.; *U.S. Public*, pg. 164
WFXG, LLC—See Lockwood Broadcasting Inc.; *U.S. Private*, pg. 2478

N.A.I.C.S. INDEX

516120 — TELEVISION BROADCAS...

WFXT-TV FOX25—See Apollo Global Management, Inc.; *U.S. Public*, pg. 164
WGAL HEARST-ARGYLE TELEVISION, INC.—See The Hearst Corporation; *U.S. Private*, pg. 4049
WGEM-TV—See Gray Television, Inc.; *U.S. Public*, pg. 961
WGHP, LLC—See Nexstar Media Group, Inc.; *U.S. Public*, pg. 1525
WGME, INC.—See Sinclair, Inc.; *U.S. Public*, pg. 1886
WGN CONTINENTAL BROADCASTING COMPANY—See Nexstar Media Group, Inc.; *U.S. Public*, pg. 1524
WGNO-TV—See Nexstar Media Group, Inc.; *U.S. Public*, pg. 1524
WGRZ-TV—See TEGNA Inc.; *U.S. Public*, pg. 1991
WHAG-TV—See Nexstar Media Group, Inc.; *U.S. Public*, pg. 1523
WHAM-TV—See Sinclair, Inc.; *U.S. Public*, pg. 1886
WHAT'S ON INDIA MEDIA PRIVATE LIMITED—See Nexstar Media Group, Inc.; *U.S. Public*, pg. 1525
WHBF-TV—See Nexstar Media Group, Inc.; *U.S. Public*, pg. 1523
WHDH TV INC.—See Sunbeam Television Corporation; *U.S. Private*, pg. 3864
WHISTLE SPORTS INC.; *U.S. Private*, pg. 4507
WHLT-TV—See Nexstar Media Group, Inc.; *U.S. Public*, pg. 1523
WHNT, LLC—See Nexstar Media Group, Inc.; *U.S. Public*, pg. 1525
WHO TELEVISION, LLC—See Nexstar Media Group, Inc.; *U.S. Public*, pg. 1525
WHO-TV—See Nexstar Media Group, Inc.; *U.S. Public*, pg. 1525
WHP-TV—See Sinclair, Inc.; *U.S. Public*, pg. 1886
WICD LICENSEE, LLC—See Sinclair, Inc.; *U.S. Public*, pg. 1887
WICD-TV—See Sinclair, Inc.; *U.S. Public*, pg. 1887
WICS-TV—See Sinclair, Inc.; *U.S. Public*, pg. 1887
WIFR-TV—See Gray Television, Inc.; *U.S. Public*, pg. 960
WINDOW TO THE WORLD COMMUNICATIONS, INC.; *U.S. Private*, pg. 4538
WIN SPORTS S.A.S.—See AT&T Inc.; *U.S. Public*, pg. 220
WISE-TV, INC.—See Silver Point Capital, L.P.; *U.S. Private*, pg. 3662
WIS, LLC—See Gray Television, Inc.; *U.S. Public*, pg. 960
WISN HEARST-ARGYLE TELEVISION, INC.—See The Hearst Corporation; *U.S. Private*, pg. 4049
WITI TELEVISION, LLC—See Nexstar Media Group, Inc.; *U.S. Public*, pg. 1525
WITI-TV—See Nexstar Media Group, Inc.; *U.S. Public*, pg. 1525
WITN-TV—See Gray Television, Inc.; *U.S. Public*, pg. 960
WJAC-TV—See Sinclair, Inc.; *U.S. Public*, pg. 1887
WJAR-TV—See Sinclair, Inc.; *U.S. Public*, pg. 1887
WJBF-TV—See Nexstar Media Group, Inc.; *U.S. Public*, pg. 1523
WJCL-TV—See The Hearst Corporation; *U.S. Private*, pg. 4049
WJHG-TV—See Gray Television, Inc.; *U.S. Public*, pg. 960
WJHL-TV—See Nexstar Media Group, Inc.; *U.S. Public*, pg. 1523
WJRT, INC.—See Entertainment Studios, Inc.; *U.S. Private*, pg. 1405
WJTV-TV—See Nexstar Media Group, Inc.; *U.S. Public*, pg. 1523
WJW TELEVISION, LLC—See Nexstar Media Group, Inc.; *U.S. Public*, pg. 1525
WJW-TV—See Nexstar Media Group, Inc.; *U.S. Public*, pg. 1525
WJZ-TV—See National Amusements, Inc.; *U.S. Private*, pg. 2841
WJZY-TV—See Capitol Broadcasting Company, Inc.; *U.S. Private*, pg. 743
WKOW-TV—See Gray Television, Inc.; *U.S. Public*, pg. 961
WKRC-TV—See Sinclair, Inc.; *U.S. Public*, pg. 1887
WKRG-TV—See Nexstar Media Group, Inc.; *U.S. Public*, pg. 1523
WKTV, LLC—See Heartland Media, LLC; *U.S. Private*, pg. 1900
WKYC-TV—See TEGNA Inc.; *U.S. Public*, pg. 1991
WKYT-TV—See Gray Television, Inc.; *U.S. Public*, pg. 960
WLAJ-TV—See Sinclair, Inc.; *U.S. Public*, pg. 1887
WLBT, LLC—See Gray Television, Inc.; *U.S. Public*, pg. 960
WLBZ-TV—See TEGNA Inc.; *U.S. Public*, pg. 1991
WLEX COMMUNICATIONS, LLC—See Evening Post Publishing Co.; *U.S. Private*, pg. 1436
WLFL, INC.—See Sinclair, Inc.; *U.S. Public*, pg. 1887
WLKY HEARST-ARGYLE TELEVISION, INC.—See The Hearst Corporation; *U.S. Private*, pg. 4049
WLNE-TV—See Standard General LP; *U.S. Private*, pg. 3778
WLOS-TV—See Sinclair, Inc.; *U.S. Public*, pg. 1887
WLOX, LLC—See Gray Television, Inc.; *U.S. Public*, pg. 960
WLS TELEVISION, INC.—See The Walt Disney Company; *U.S. Public*, pg. 2138
WLTX-TV—See TEGNA Inc.; *U.S. Public*, pg. 1991
WLUK-TV—See Sinclair, Inc.; *U.S. Public*, pg. 1887
WLVI-TV—See Sunbeam Television Corporation; *U.S. Private*, pg. 3864
WLWC-TV—See Nexstar Media Group, Inc.; *U.S. Public*, pg. 1523
WLWT-TV—See The Hearst Corporation; *U.S. Private*, pg. 4049
WMAQ-TV—See Comcast Corporation; *U.S. Public*, pg. 540
WMAR-TV—See The E.W. Scripps Company; *U.S. Public*, pg. 2069
WMAZ-TV—See TEGNA Inc.; *U.S. Public*, pg. 1991
WMBB-TV—See Nexstar Media Group, Inc.; *U.S. Public*, pg. 1523
WMBD-TV—See Nexstar Media Group, Inc.; *U.S. Public*, pg. 1523
WMDT-TV—See Marquee Broadcasting, Inc.; *U.S. Private*, pg. 2586
WMMP-TV—See Sinclair, Inc.; *U.S. Public*, pg. 1887
WMSN LICENSEE, LLC—See Sinclair, Inc.; *U.S. Public*, pg. 1887
WMSN-TV—See Sinclair, Inc.; *U.S. Public*, pg. 1887
WMTW-TV—See The Hearst Corporation; *U.S. Private*, pg. 4049
WMUR-TV—See The Hearst Corporation; *U.S. Private*, pg. 4049
WMYD-TV—See The E.W. Scripps Company; *U.S. Public*, pg. 2069
WMYV-TV—See Sinclair, Inc.; *U.S. Public*, pg. 1886
WNBC-TV—See Comcast Corporation; *U.S. Public*, pg. 540
WNCT-TV—See Nexstar Media Group, Inc.; *U.S. Public*, pg. 1523
WNEM-TV—See Meredith Corporation; *U.S. Public*, pg. 1423
WNEP, LLC—See Nexstar Media Group, Inc.; *U.S. Public*, pg. 1525
WNET; *U.S. Private*, pg. 4552
WNNE-TV—See The Hearst Corporation; *U.S. Private*, pg. 4049
WNOL-TV—See Nexstar Media Group, Inc.; *U.S. Public*, pg. 1524
WNYO, INC.—See Sinclair, Inc.; *U.S. Public*, pg. 1887
WNYT-TV—See Hubbard Broadcasting, Inc.; *U.S. Private*, pg. 2000
WNYW-TV—See Fox Corporation; *U.S. Public*, pg. 876
WOAI-TV—See Sinclair, Inc.; *U.S. Public*, pg. 1887
WOFL-TV—See Fox Corporation; *U.S. Public*, pg. 876
WOGX-TV—See Fox Corporation; *U.S. Public*, pg. 876
WOI-DT—See TEGNA Inc.; *U.S. Public*, pg. 1991
WOMENS NETWORK—See Corus Entertainment Inc.; *Int'l*, pg. 1809
WORD OF GOD FELLOWSHIP INC.; *U.S. Private*, pg. 4562
WORKJOY ARGENTINA S.A.—See AT&T Inc.; *U.S. Public*, pg. 220
WORLD WIDE ENTERTAINMENT PRODUCTION & SALES PTY. LTD.—See Ausmani Limited; *Int'l*, pg. 716
WORLDWIDE KNOWLEDGE (BEIJING) BUSINESS CONSULTING COMPANY LTD.—See British Broadcasting Corporation; *Int'l*, pg. 1169
WOWK-TV, LLC—See Nexstar Media Group, Inc.; *U.S. Public*, pg. 1523
WOWT-TV—See Gray Television, Inc.; *U.S. Public*, pg. 960
WPDE-TV—See Sinclair, Inc.; *U.S. Public*, pg. 1887
WPEC-TV—See Sinclair, Inc.; *U.S. Public*, pg. 1887
WPGX, LLC—See Lockwood Broadcasting Inc.; *U.S. Private*, pg. 2478
WPHL, LLC—See Nexstar Media Group, Inc.; *U.S. Public*, pg. 1525
WPIX, LLC—See Nexstar Media Group, Inc.; *U.S. Public*, pg. 1525
WPLG, INC.—See Berkshire Hathaway Inc.; *U.S. Public*, pg. 319
WPMI-TV—See Sinclair, Inc.; *U.S. Public*, pg. 1887
WPMT, LLC—See Nexstar Media Group, Inc.; *U.S. Public*, pg. 1525
WPSG-TV—See Nexstar Media Group, Inc.; *U.S. Public*, pg. 1524
WPTA-TV—See Gray Television, Inc.; *U.S. Public*, pg. 961
WPTV—See The E.W. Scripps Company; *U.S. Public*, pg. 2069
WPTZ-TV—See The Hearst Corporation; *U.S. Private*, pg. 4049
WPVI-TV INC.—See The Walt Disney Company; *U.S. Public*, pg. 2138
WPXI, INC.—See Apollo Global Management, Inc.; *U.S. Public*, pg. 164
WQAD, LLC—See Nexstar Media Group, Inc.; *U.S. Public*, pg. 1525
WQRF-TV—See Nexstar Media Group, Inc.; *U.S. Public*, pg. 1523
WRAL-TV—See Capitol Broadcasting Company, Inc.; *U.S. Private*, pg. 743
WRAZ-TV—See Capitol Broadcasting Company, Inc.; *U.S. Private*, pg. 743
WRBL-TV—See Nexstar Media Group, Inc.; *U.S. Public*, pg. 1523
WRC-TV—See Comcast Corporation; *U.S. Public*, pg. 540
WRDW-TV—See Gray Television, Inc.; *U.S. Public*, pg. 960
WREG, LLC—See Nexstar Media Group, Inc.; *U.S. Public*, pg. 1525
WRGB-TV—See Sinclair, Inc.; *U.S. Public*, pg. 1887
WRIC-TV—See Nexstar Media Group, Inc.; *U.S. Public*, pg. 1523
WRLH-TV—See Sinclair, Inc.; *U.S. Public*, pg. 1886
WROC-TV—See Nexstar Media Group, Inc.; *U.S. Public*, pg. 1523
WRTV—See The E.W. Scripps Company; *U.S. Public*, pg. 2069
WSAV-TV—See Nexstar Media Group, Inc.; *U.S. Public*, pg. 1523
WSAZ-TV—See Gray Television, Inc.; *U.S. Public*, pg. 960
WSET, INCORPORATED—See Sinclair, Inc.; *U.S. Public*, pg. 1886
WSFA, LLC—See Gray Television, Inc.; *U.S. Public*, pg. 960
WSFL, LLC—See Nexstar Media Group, Inc.; *U.S. Public*, pg. 1525
WSJV-TV—See Gray Television, Inc.; *U.S. Public*, pg. 961
WSLS-TV—See Graham Holdings Company; *U.S. Public*, pg. 955
WSMH, INC.—See Sinclair, Inc.; *U.S. Public*, pg. 1887
WSMV-TV—See Meredith Corporation; *U.S. Public*, pg. 1424
WSOC TELEVISION, INC.—See Apollo Global Management, Inc.; *U.S. Public*, pg. 164
WSPA-TV—See Nexstar Media Group, Inc.; *U.S. Public*, pg. 1523
WSVN-TV—See Sunbeam Television Corporation; *U.S. Private*, pg. 3864
WSYM-TV FOX 47—See The E.W. Scripps Company; *U.S. Public*, pg. 2069
WSYR-TV—See Nexstar Media Group, Inc.; *U.S. Public*, pg. 1523
WSYT-TV—See Sinclair, Inc.; *U.S. Public*, pg. 1887
WSYX LICENSEE, INC.—See Sinclair, Inc.; *U.S. Public*, pg. 1887
WSYX-TV—See Sinclair, Inc.; *U.S. Public*, pg. 1887
WTAE HEARST-ARGYLE TELEVISION, INC.—See The Hearst Corporation; *U.S. Private*, pg. 4049
WTCN-CA—See Sinclair, Inc.; *U.S. Public*, pg. 1887
WTEN-TV—See Nexstar Media Group, Inc.; *U.S. Public*, pg. 1523
WTHR-TV—See TEGNA Inc.; *U.S. Public*, pg. 1991
WTIC-TV—See Nexstar Media Group, Inc.; *U.S. Public*, pg. 1524
WTKR-TV—See Nexstar Media Group, Inc.; *U.S. Public*, pg. 1525
WTOC, LLC—See Gray Television, Inc.; *U.S. Public*, pg. 960
WTOL, LLC—See TEGNA Inc.; *U.S. Public*, pg. 1991
WTOV, INC.—See TEGNA Inc.; *U.S. Public*, pg. 1887
WTRF-TV, LLC—See Nexstar Media Group, Inc.; *U.S. Public*, pg. 1523
WTSP-TV—See TEGNA Inc.; *U.S. Public*, pg. 1991
WTTA-TV—See Nexstar Media Group, Inc.; *U.S. Public*, pg. 1523
WTTG-TV—See Fox Corporation; *U.S. Public*, pg. 876
WTTO, INC.—See Sinclair, Inc.; *U.S. Public*, pg. 1887
WTTO LICENSEE, LLC—See Sinclair, Inc.; *U.S. Public*, pg. 1887
WTTV-TV—See Nexstar Media Group, Inc.; *U.S. Public*, pg. 1525
WTVC-TV—See Sinclair, Inc.; *U.S. Public*, pg. 1887
WTVD-TV INC.—See The Walt Disney Company; *U.S. Public*, pg. 2138
WTVG, INC.—See SJL Broadcast Management Corp.; *U.S. Private*, pg. 3678
WTVH, LLC—See Silver Point Capital, L.P.; *U.S. Private*, pg. 3662
WTVJ-TV—See Comcast Corporation; *U.S. Public*, pg. 540
WTVO-TV—See Mission Broadcasting, Inc.; *U.S. Private*, pg. 2747
WTVQ-TV—See Morris Multimedia, Inc.; *U.S. Private*, pg. 2788
WTVR, LLC—See Nexstar Media Group, Inc.; *U.S. Public*, pg. 1525
WTVT-TV—See Fox Corporation; *U.S. Public*, pg. 876
WTVX-TV—See Sinclair, Inc.; *U.S. Public*, pg. 1887
WTVZ, INC.—See Sinclair, Inc.; *U.S. Public*, pg. 1887
WTWC-TV—See Sinclair, Inc.; *U.S. Public*, pg. 1887
WTXF-TV—See Fox Corporation; *U.S. Public*, pg. 876
WUCW-TV—See Sinclair, Inc.; *U.S. Public*, pg. 1887
WUHF-TV—See Sinclair, Inc.; *U.S. Public*, pg. 1887
WUTV-TV—See Sinclair, Inc.; *U.S. Public*, pg. 1886
WVEC-TELEVISION, INC.—See TEGNA Inc.; *U.S. Public*, pg. 1990
WVI FILMS B.V.—See National Amusements, Inc.; *U.S. Private*, pg. 2844
WVIT-TV—See Comcast Corporation; *U.S. Public*, pg. 540
WVLT-TV, INC.—See Gray Television, Inc.; *U.S. Public*, pg. 960
WVNS-TV, LLC—See Nexstar Media Group, Inc.; *U.S. Public*, pg. 1524
WVTM-TV—See The Hearst Corporation; *U.S. Private*, pg. 4049
WVTV-TV—See Sinclair, Inc.; *U.S. Public*, pg. 1887
WVVA-TV—See Gray Television, Inc.; *U.S. Public*, pg. 961
WWBT, LLC—See Gray Television, Inc.; *U.S. Public*, pg. 960
WWCI INC—See Window to the World Communications, Inc.; *U.S. Private*, pg. 4538
WWHB-CA—See Sinclair, Inc.; *U.S. Public*, pg. 1887

516120 — TELEVISION BROADCAS...

WWHO-TV—See Sinclair, Inc.; *U.S. Public*, pg. 1887
WWL-TV, INC.—See TEGNA Inc.; *U.S. Public*, pg. 1990
WWMT-TV—See Sinclair, Inc.; *U.S. Public*, pg. 1887
WWOR-TV—See Fox Corporation; *U.S. Public*, pg. 876
WWWB-TV—See Capitol Broadcasting Company, Inc.; *U.S. Private*, pg. 743
WXIA-TV—See TEGNA Inc.; *U.S. Public*, pg. 1991
WXII HEARST-ARGYLE TELEVISION, INC.—See The Hearst Corporation; *U.S. Private*, pg. 4049
WXIN-TV—See Nexstar Media Group, Inc.; *U.S. Public*, pg. 1525
WXLV-TV—See Sinclair, Inc.; *U.S. Public*, pg. 1886
WXMI, LLC—See Nexstar Media Group, Inc.; *U.S. Public*, pg. 1525
WXXA-TV; *U.S. Private*, pg. 4575
WXYZ-TV—See The E.W. Scripps Company; *U.S. Public*, pg. 2069
WYCW-TV—See Nexstar Media Group, Inc.; *U.S. Public*, pg. 1523
WYFF HEARST-ARGYLE TELEVISION, INC.—See The Hearst Corporation; *U.S. Private*, pg. 4049
WYMT-TV—See Gray Television, Inc.; *U.S. Public*, pg. 960
WYOU-TV—See Mission Broadcasting, Inc.; *U.S. Private*, pg. 2747
WYZZ, INC.—See Sinclair, Inc.; *U.S. Public*, pg. 1887
WZTV-TV—See Sinclair, Inc.; *U.S. Public*, pg. 1888
WZVN TV ABC 7—See Waterman Broadcasting Corp.; *U.S. Private*, pg. 4454
WZZM-TV—See TEGNA Inc.; *U.S. Public*, pg. 1991
YELLOW BIRD—See De Agostini S.p.A.; *Int'l*, pg. 1995
YOUKU TUDOU INC.—See Alibaba Group Holding Limited; *Int'l*, pg. 326
YOUNG BROADCASTING OF DAVENPORT, INC.—See Gray Television, Inc.; *U.S. Public*, pg. 960
YOUNG BROADCASTING OF GREEN BAY, INC.—See Gray Television, Inc.; *U.S. Public*, pg. 961
ZASER & LONGSTON INC.; *U.S. Private*, pg. 4598
ZEE ENTERTAINMENT ENTERPRISES LTD.—See Essel Corporate Resources Pvt. Ltd.; *Int'l*, pg. 2510
ZEE MEDIA CORPORATION LTD.—See Essel Corporate Resources Pvt. Ltd.; *Int'l*, pg. 2510
ZEE MULTIMEDIA (MAURICE) LIMITED—See Essel Corporate Resources Pvt. Ltd.; *Int'l*, pg. 2510
ZEE TELEFILMS MIDDLE EAST FZ-LLC—See Essel Corporate Resources Pvt. Ltd.; *Int'l*, pg. 2510
ZEE TURNER LIMITED—See Essel Corporate Resources Pvt. Ltd.; *Int'l*, pg. 2510
ZEE TURNER LIMITED—See Warner Bros. Discovery, Inc.; *U.S. Public*, pg. 2328
ZEE TV SOUTH AFRICA PTY. LTD.—See Essel Corporate Resources Pvt. Ltd.; *Int'l*, pg. 2510
ZODIAK ACTIVE S.P.A.—See De Agostini S.p.A.; *Int'l*, pg. 1994
ZODIAK AMERICAS—See De Agostini S.p.A.; *Int'l*, pg. 1994
ZODIAK BELGIUM—See De Agostini S.p.A.; *Int'l*, pg. 1994
ZODIAK FINLAND OY—See De Agostini S.p.A.; *Int'l*, pg. 1995
ZODIAK NEDERLAND—See De Agostini S.p.A.; *Int'l*, pg. 1994
ZODIAK NEW YORK—See De Agostini S.p.A.; *Int'l*, pg. 1994

516210 — MEDIA STREAMING DISTRIBUTION SERVICES, SOCIAL NETWORKS, AND OTHER MEDIA NETWORKS AND CONTENT PROVIDERS

010017 TELECOM GMBH—See 3U Holding AG; *Int'l*, pg. 10
102.4 WISH FM LIMITED—See News Corporation; *U.S. Public*, pg. 1520
17LIVE GROUP LIMITED; *Int'l*, pg. 3
33ACROSS INC.; *U.S. Private*, pg. 8
3U TELECOM GMBH—See 3U Holding AG; *Int'l*, pg. 10
6GWORLD, INC.—See InterDigital, Inc.; *U.S. Public*, pg. 1143
7DIGITAL GROUP PLC—See Songtradr, Inc.; *U.S. Private*, pg. 3713
ABC CABLE NETWORKS GROUP—See The Walt Disney Company; *U.S. Public*, pg. 2137
ABC FAMILY WORLDWIDE, INC.—See The Walt Disney Company; *U.S. Public*, pg. 2137
ABC MEDIA COMMUNICATIONS—See Asahi Broadcasting Group Holdings Corporation; *Int'l*, pg. 592
ABC NEWS, INC.—See The Walt Disney Company; *U.S. Public*, pg. 2137
ABC NEWS & SPORTS—See The Walt Disney Company; *U.S. Public*, pg. 2137
ABC SPORTS, INC.—See The Walt Disney Company; *U.S. Public*, pg. 2138
ABOUT, INC.—See IAC Inc.; *U.S. Public*, pg. 1081
ACCESS TELEVISION NETWORK; *U.S. Private*, pg. 53
ACCUWEATHER, INC.; *U.S. Private*, pg. 56
A&E NETWORK—See The Hearst Corporation; *U.S. Private*, pg. 4045
A&E NETWORK—See The Walt Disney Company; *U.S. Public*, pg. 2137
AGENCE FRANCE-PRESSE; *Int'l*, pg. 205

AGENCIA EFE, S.A.; *Int'l*, pg. 205
AGENCIA EFE, S.A.—See Agencia EFE, S.A.; *Int'l*, pg. 205
AGENCIA EFE, S.A.—See Agencia EFE, S.A.; *Int'l*, pg. 205
AGENCIA EFE, S.A.—See Agencia EFE, S.A.; *Int'l*, pg. 205
AGENCIA EFE, S.A.—See Agencia EFE, S.A.; *Int'l*, pg. 205
AGENCIA EFE, S.A.—See Agencia EFE, S.A.; *Int'l*, pg. 205
AGENCIA EFE, S.A.—See Agencia EFE, S.A.; *Int'l*, pg. 205
AGENCIA EFE, S.A.—See Agencia EFE, S.A.; *Int'l*, pg. 205
AGENCIE EFE—See Agencia EFE, S.A.; *Int'l*, pg. 205
AGENZIA GIORNALISTICA ITALIA SPA—See Eni S.p.A.; *Int'l*, pg. 2436
AIRCHECK INDIA PVT. LTD.—See iHeartMedia, Inc.; *U.S. Public*, pg. 1095
AIRE RADIO NETWORK LLC—See Spanish Broadcasting System Inc.; *U.S. Public*, pg. 1914
AKA GROUP LIMITED; *Int'l*, pg. 259
AL JAZEERA AMERICA, LLC—See Al-Jazeera Satellite Network; *Int'l*, pg. 286
AL JAZEERA ENGLISH—See Al-Jazeera Satellite Network; *Int'l*, pg. 286
ALPHA NETWORK ALLIANCE VENTURES INC.; *U.S. Public*, pg. 82
ALPHA TEL S.A.—See AT&T Inc.; *U.S. Public*, pg. 220
AMC NETWORKS CENTRAL EUROPE KFT—See AMC Networks Inc.; *U.S. Public*, pg. 92
AMC NETWORKS INC.; *U.S. Public*, pg. 92
AME INFO FZ LLC—See Apax Partners LLP; *Int'l*, pg. 507
AMERICAN MOVIE CLASSICS COMPANY LLC—See AMC Networks Inc.; *U.S. Public*, pg. 92
AMERICAN PUBLIC MEDIA—See American Public Media Group; *U.S. Private*, pg. 244
AMERICAN URBAN RADIO NETWORKS—See Sheridan Broadcasting Corporation; *U.S. Private*, pg. 3633
ANIMAL PLANET, LLC—See Warner Bros. Discovery, Inc.; *U.S. Public*, pg. 2326
ANP HOLDING B.V.; *Int'l*, pg. 474
ANTIETAM CABLE TELEVISION, INC.—See Schurz Communications, Inc.; *U.S. Private*, pg. 3571
ANTIGO DAILY JOURNAL—See Adams Publishing Group, LLC; *U.S. Private*, pg. 74
APA-AUSTRIA PRESSE AGENTUR EG; *Int'l*, pg. 500
APPBANK INC.; *Int'l*, pg. 519
APTICOM S.R.L.—See Hexatronic Group AB; *Int'l*, pg. 3370
ARIZONA NEWS SERVICE, LLC—See The Dolan Company; *U.S. Private*, pg. 4022
ARKANSAS DEMOCRAT-GAZETTE, INC.—See Wehco Media, Inc.; *U.S. Private*, pg. 4469
ARTEMIS CONSULTING, INC.—See Renovus Capital Partners; *U.S. Private*, pg. 3399
THE ASSOCIATED PRESS A/S—See The Associated Press; *U.S. Private*, pg. 3989
THE ASSOCIATED PRESS (BELGIUM) S.A.—See The Associated Press; *U.S. Private*, pg. 3989
THE ASSOCIATED PRESS DE VENEZUELA, S.A.—See The Associated Press; *U.S. Private*, pg. 3989
THE ASSOCIATED PRESS, LTD.—See The Associated Press; *U.S. Private*, pg. 3989
THE ASSOCIATED PRESS; *U.S. Private*, pg. 3989
THE ASSOCIATED PRESS—See The Associated Press; *U.S. Private*, pg. 3989
AUDDIA INC.; *U.S. Public*, pg. 227
AUDIBLE, INC.—See Amazon.com, Inc.; *U.S. Public*, pg. 90
AUSBILDUNG.DE GMBH—See Bertelsmann SE & Co. KGaA; *Int'l*, pg. 990
AUSMANI LIMITED; *Int'l*, pg. 716
AUSTRALIAN ASSOCIATED PRESS PTY LTD; *Int'l*, pg. 721
AUSTRALIAN NEWS CHANNEL PTY. LTD.—See News Corporation; *U.S. Public*, pg. 1519
AUSTRALIAN RADIO NETWORK PTY. LIMITED—See ARN Media Limited; *Int'l*, pg. 576
BAMBUSER AB; *Int'l*, pg. 813
BANDPAGE, INC.—See Alphabet Inc.; *U.S. Public*, pg. 84
BANGLADESH SUBMARINE CABLE CO., LTD.; *Int'l*, pg. 836
BANKS.COM, INC.—See Remark Holdings, Inc.; *U.S. Public*, pg. 1782
BAY COMMUNICATIONS INC.—See Hankyu Hanshin Holdings Inc.; *Int'l*, pg. 3254
BAY NEWS 9—See Charter Communications, Inc.; *U.S. Public*, pg. 483
BEASLEY MEDIA GROUP, INC.—See Beasley Broadcast Group, Inc.; *U.S. Public*, pg. 287
BEBO, INC.—See Amazon.com, Inc.; *U.S. Public*, pg. 91
BEND CABLE COMMUNICATIONS LLC—See Telephone & Data Systems, Inc.; *U.S. Public*, pg. 1997
BET INTERACTIVE, LLC—See National Amusements, Inc.; *U.S. Private*, pg. 2839
BHIMA RIDDHI INFOTAINMENT PRIVATE LIMITED—See Hinduja Global Solutions Ltd.; *Int'l*, pg. 3398
BILIBILI INC.; *Int'l*, pg. 1029
THE BIOGRAPHY CHANNEL—See The Hearst Corporation; *U.S. Private*, pg. 4045
THE BIOGRAPHY CHANNEL—See The Walt Disney Company; *U.S. Public*, pg. 2137
BLACK ENTERTAINMENT TELEVISION, LLC—See National Amusements, Inc.; *U.S. Private*, pg. 2839

BLOGHER INC.—See Great Hill Partners, L.P.; *U.S. Private*, pg. 1763
BLOOMBERG TELEVISION—See Bloomberg L.P.; *U.S. Private*, pg. 1102
BOLDYN NETWORKS GLOBAL LTD.; *Int'l*, pg. 1102
BOSTON HERALD INC.—See Alden Global Capital LLC; *U.S. Private*, pg. 155
BOTT RADIO NETWORK; *U.S. Private*, pg. 623
BOX TELEVISION LTD.—See Channel Four Television Corporation; *Int'l*, pg. 1446
BOX TELEVISION LTD.—See Heinrich Bauer Verlag KG; *Int'l*, pg. 3323
BPLATS, INC.; *Int'l*, pg. 1132
BRAVO MEDIA LLC—See Comcast Corporation; *U.S. Public*, pg. 539
BRIGHTCOVE INDIA PTE. LTD.—See Brightcove, Inc.; *U.S. Public*, pg. 383
BRITISH BROADCASTING CORPORATION; *Int'l*, pg. 1168
BROADCASTMED, INC.; *U.S. Private*, pg. 659
BUCKEYE CABLEVISION—See Block Communications, Inc.; *U.S. Private*, pg. 582
BURNED MEDIA LTD.; *U.S. Public*, pg. 412
BUSINESS WIRE, INC.—See Berkshire Hathaway Inc.; *U.S. Public*, pg. 303
BUZZFEED, INC.—See BuzzFeed, Inc.; *U.S. Public*, pg. 413
CABLEAMERICA CORPORATION; *U.S. Private*, pg. 711
THE CABLE CENTER; *U.S. Private*, pg. 4003
CABLECLIX USA, INC.; *U.S. Public*, pg. 416
CABLE ONE, INC.; *U.S. Public*, pg. 416
CABLEVISION OF MONMOUTH, INC.—See Altice USA, Inc.; *U.S. Public*, pg. 87
CABLEVISION SYSTEMS WESTCHESTER CORPORATION—See Altice USA, Inc.; *U.S. Public*, pg. 87
CALNEX AMERICAS CORPORATION—See Calnex Solutions Plc; *Int'l*, pg. 1265
CALOOSA BELLE—See Independent Newspapers, Inc.; *U.S. Private*, pg. 2060
CAM-TEL CO, INC.—See Wehco Media, Inc.; *U.S. Private*, pg. 4469
CAPITAL RADIO PRODUCTIONS LTD—See News Corporation; *U.S. Public*, pg. 1520
CAPTIONMAX, INC.—See Riverside Partners, LLC; *U.S. Private*, pg. 3445
CASTTV INC.—See Nexstar Media Group, Inc.; *U.S. Public*, pg. 1524
CBS INTERACTIVE INC.—See National Amusements, Inc.; *U.S. Private*, pg. 2840
CBS INTERACTIVE INC.—See National Amusements, Inc.; *U.S. Private*, pg. 2840
CBS INTERACTIVE JAPAN K.K.—See National Amusements, Inc.; *U.S. Private*, pg. 2840
CBS INTERACTIVE LIMITED—See National Amusements, Inc.; *U.S. Private*, pg. 2840
CBS INTERACTIVE PTE. LTD.—See National Amusements, Inc.; *U.S. Private*, pg. 2840
CBS SPORTSLINE.COM, INC.—See National Amusements, Inc.; *U.S. Private*, pg. 2840
CCR ESPANA - CONCESIONES Y PARTICIPACIONES S.L.—See CCR S.A.; *Int'l*, pg. 1369
CENTER FOR INVESTIGATIVE REPORTING, INC.; *U.S. Private*, pg. 810
CHARTER CABLE PARTNERS, L.L.C.—See Charter Communications, Inc.; *U.S. Public*, pg. 483
CHATCHING, INC.; *U.S. Private*, pg. 860
CHICKEN SOUP FOR THE SOUL ENTERTAINMENT, INC.; *U.S. Public*, pg. 488
CHINA DIGITAL CULTURE (GROUP) LIMITED; *Int'l*, pg. 1497
CHINA DIGITAL MEDIA CORPORATION; *Int'l*, pg. 1497
THE CHOSEN, INC.; *U.S. Private*, pg. 4009
CHRISTAL RADIO SALES, INC.—See iHeartMedia, Inc.; *U.S. Public*, pg. 1096
CHUBU CABLE NETWORK COMPANY, INCORPORATED—See Chubu Electric Power Co., Inc.; *Int'l*, pg. 1593
CIRCLE CITY BROADCASTING INC.; *U.S. Private*, pg. 899
CJ CGV AMERICA LA LLC—See CJ Corporation; *Int'l*, pg. 1632
CJ INTERNET INC.—See CJ Corporation; *Int'l*, pg. 1631
CLAIMPICKER AG; *Int'l*, pg. 1641
CLASSICAL SOUTH FLORIDA INC—See American Public Media Group; *U.S. Private*, pg. 244
CLEAR CHANNEL SPECTACOLOR, LLC—See Clear Channel Outdoor Holdings, Inc.; *U.S. Public*, pg. 512
CLICKER INC.; *U.S. Private*, pg. 942
CN8, THE COMCAST NETWORK—See Comcast Corporation; *U.S. Public*, pg. 537
CNBC LLC—See Comcast Corporation; *U.S. Public*, pg. 539
CNN AMERICA, INC.—See Warner Bros. Discovery, Inc.; *U.S. Public*, pg. 2328
CNN NEWSOURCE SALES, INC.—See Warner Bros. Discovery, Inc.; *U.S. Public*, pg. 2328
COGECO CABLE QUEBEC—See Gestion Audem, Inc.; *Int'l*, pg. 2946
COGECO COMMUNICATIONS INC.—See Gestion Audem, Inc.; *Int'l*, pg. 2946
COMCAST CABLE COMMUNICATIONS, LLC—See

N.A.I.C.S. INDEX

516210 — MEDIA STREAMING DIS...

Comcast Corporation; *U.S. Public,* pg. 537
COMCAST CABLEVISION INVESTMENT CORPORATION—See Comcast Corporation; *U.S. Public,* pg. 537
COMCAST CABLEVISION MD LP; *U.S. Private,* pg. 981
COMCAST CORPORATION; *U.S. Public,* pg. 536
COMCAST CORP.—See Comcast Corporation; *U.S. Public,* pg. 537
COMCAST CORP.—See Comcast Corporation; *U.S. Public,* pg. 537
COMCAST CORP.—See Comcast Corporation; *U.S. Public,* pg. 537
COMCAST CORP.—See Comcast Corporation; *U.S. Public,* pg. 537
COMCAST CORP.—See Comcast Corporation; *U.S. Public,* pg. 537
COMCAST INTERACTIVE CAPITAL, L.P.—See Comcast Corporation; *U.S. Public,* pg. 537
COMCAST MO OF DELAWARE, LLC—See Comcast Corporation; *U.S. Public,* pg. 537
COMCAST OF ARIZONA, INC.—See Comcast Corporation; *U.S. Public,* pg. 538
COMCAST OF COLORADO/PENNSYLVANIA/WEST VIRGINIA, LLC—See Comcast Corporation; *U.S. Public,* pg. 538
COMCAST OF DELMARVA, INC.—See Comcast Corporation; *U.S. Public,* pg. 538
COMCAST OF GARDEN STATE, L.P.—See Comcast Corporation; *U.S. Public,* pg. 538
COMCAST OF HARFORD COUNTY, LLC—See Comcast Corporation; *U.S. Public,* pg. 538
COMCAST OF ILLINOIS/INDIANA/OHIO, LLC—See Comcast Corporation; *U.S. Public,* pg. 538
COMCAST OF MAINE/NEW HAMPSHIRE, INC.—See Comcast Corporation; *U.S. Public,* pg. 538
COMCAST OF POTOMAC, LLC—See Comcast Corporation; *U.S. Public,* pg. 538
COMCAST SPORTS MANAGEMENT SERVICES, LLC—See Comcast Corporation; *U.S. Public,* pg. 539
COMCAST SPORTSNET MID-ATLANTIC, L.P.—See Comcast Corporation; *U.S. Public,* pg. 539
COMCAST SPORTSNET NEW ENGLAND, LLC—See Comcast Corporation; *U.S. Public,* pg. 539
COMCAST SPORTSNET PHILADELPHIA, L.P.—See Comcast Corporation; *U.S. Public,* pg. 539
COMEDY PARTNERS—See National Amusements, Inc.; *U.S. Private,* pg. 2841
COMMUNITY MEDIA GROUP; *U.S. Private,* pg. 995
COMTEX NEWS NETWORK, INC.; *U.S. Public,* pg. 563
CONNECT INTERACTIVE, INC.; *U.S. Private,* pg. 1014
CONSUMERSEARCH, INC.—See IAC Inc.; *U.S. Public,* pg. 1081
CONVERGENT MEDIA SYSTEMS, LLC—See Woodard Technology & Investments LLC; *U.S. Private,* pg. 4557
CORUS PREMIUM TELEVISION LTD.—See Corus Entertainment Inc.; *Int'l,* pg. 1808
COUNTRY MUSIC TELEVISION, INC.—See National Amusements, Inc.; *U.S. Private,* pg. 2841
COURTROOM TELEVISION NETWORK LLC—See Warner Bros. Discovery, Inc.; *U.S. Public,* pg. 2328
COX COMMUNICATIONS CLEVELAND AREA—See Cox Enterprises, Inc.; *U.S. Private,* pg. 1078
COX COMMUNICATIONS GAINESVILLE/OCALA—See Cox Enterprises, Inc.; *U.S. Private,* pg. 1078
COX COMMUNICATIONS GULF COAST, LLC—See Cox Enterprises, Inc.; *U.S. Private,* pg. 1078
COX COMMUNICATIONS, INC.—See Cox Enterprises, Inc.; *U.S. Private,* pg. 1078
COX COMMUNICATIONS KANSAS, LLC—See Cox Enterprises, Inc.; *U.S. Private,* pg. 1078
COX COMMUNICATIONS LAS VEGAS, INC.—See Cox Enterprises, Inc.; *U.S. Private,* pg. 1078
COX COMMUNICATIONS LOUISIANA, LLC—See Cox Enterprises, Inc.; *U.S. Private,* pg. 1078
COX COMMUNICATIONS - MIDDLE GEORGIA—See Cox Enterprises, Inc.; *U.S. Private,* pg. 1078
COX COMMUNICATIONS NORTHERN VIRGINIA—See Cox Enterprises, Inc.; *U.S. Private,* pg. 1078
COX COMMUNICATIONS OMAHA, LLC—See Cox Enterprises, Inc.; *U.S. Private,* pg. 1078
COX COMMUNICATIONS PHOENIX—See Cox Enterprises, Inc.; *U.S. Private,* pg. 1078
COX COMMUNICATIONS ROANOKE—See Cox Enterprises, Inc.; *U.S. Private,* pg. 1078
COX COMMUNICATIONS SANTA BARBARA—See Cox Enterprises, Inc.; *U.S. Private,* pg. 1078
CROWN MEDIA UNITED STATES LLC—See Hallmark Cards, Inc.; *U.S. Private,* pg. 1844
CRYSTAL VISION MEDIA PRIVATE LIMITED—See DEN Networks Limited; *Int'l,* pg. 2026
CSTV NETWORKS, INC.—See National Amusements, Inc.; *U.S. Private,* pg. 2840
CTC MEDIA, INC.; *Int'l,* pg. 1869
CTV NEWSNET—See BCE Inc.; *Int'l,* pg. 927
CUP INTERACTIVE SAS; *Int'l,* pg. 1878
CUSTOM CABLE SERVICES, INC.; *U.S. Private,* pg. 1128
CYFROWY POLSAT S.A.; *Int'l,* pg. 1895
D2C STORES INC.; *U.S. Private,* pg. 1143

THE DAILY BUZZ, LLC—See Mojo Brands Media, LLC; *U.S. Private,* pg. 2766
DANSK KABEL TV A/S - ESBJERG—See Arbejdsmarkedets Tillaegspension; *Int'l,* pg. 537
DAPD NACHRICHTENAGENTUR GMBH—See dapd Media Holding AG; *Int'l,* pg. 1970
DEAG DEUTSCHE ENTERTAINMENT AG; *Int'l,* pg. 1997
DEN ADN NETWORK PRIVATE LIMITED—See DEN Networks Limited; *Int'l,* pg. 2026
DEN AMBEY CABLE NETWORKS PRIVATE LIMITED—See DEN Networks Limited; *Int'l,* pg. 2026
DEN ENJOY CABLE NETWORKS PRIVATE LIMITED—See DEN Networks Limited; *Int'l,* pg. 2026
DESTINATION MEDIA, INC.—See RockBridge Growth Equity, LLC; *U.S. Private,* pg. 3465
DIAL COMMUNICATIONS GLOBAL MEDIA, LLC—See Cumulus Media Inc.; *U.S. Public,* pg. 610
DICK CLARK PRODUCTIONS, INC.—See Valence Media Group; *U.S. Private,* pg. 4331
DIGITAL ONE LTD.—See Canada Pension Plan Investment Board; *Int'l,* pg. 1278
DIGITALTOWN, INC.; *U.S. Public,* pg. 666
DIRECTV ARGENTINA, S.A.—See AT&T Inc.; *U.S. Public,* pg. 220
DIRECTV SPORTS NET PITTSBURGH, LLC—See AT&T Inc.; *U.S. Public,* pg. 220
DISCOUNT TELECOM S&V GMBH—See 3U Holding AG; *Int'l,* pg. 10
DISCOVERY EDUCATION EUROPE LTD.—See Clearlake Capital Group, L.P.; *U.S. Private,* pg. 934
DISCOVERY, INC. - NEW YORK OFFICE—See Warner Bros. Discovery, Inc.; *U.S. Public,* pg. 2326
DISCOVERY NETWORKS FINLAND OY—See Warner Bros. Discovery, Inc.; *U.S. Public,* pg. 2326
DISCOVERY NETWORKS, S.L.—See Warner Bros. Discovery, Inc.; *U.S. Public,* pg. 2326
DISCOVERY NETWORKS SWEDEN AB—See Warner Bros. Discovery, Inc.; *U.S. Public,* pg. 2326
DISNEY CANADA, INC.—See The Walt Disney Company; *U.S. Public,* pg. 2138
DISNEY INTERACTIVE MEDIA GROUP—See The Walt Disney Company; *U.S. Public,* pg. 2138
DKTV A/S—See Arbejdsmarkedets Tillaegspension; *Int'l,* pg. 537
D'LIVE CO., LTD.; *Int'l,* pg. 1899
EAST ARKANSAS VIDEO INC.—See Wehco Media, Inc.; *U.S. Private,* pg. 4469
EASTLINK—See Bragg Group of Companies; *Int'l,* pg. 1136
ECHOSTAR INTERNATIONAL CORPORATION—See EchoStar Corporation; *U.S. Public,* pg. 711
ECHOSTAR SATELLITE SERVICES LLC—See EchoStar Corporation; *U.S. Public,* pg. 711
ECHOSTAR TECHNOLOGIES LLC—See EchoStar Corporation; *U.S. Public,* pg. 711
ECRUSH.COM, INC.—See The Hearst Corporation; *U.S. Private,* pg. 4046
EDGE NETWORK SERVICES LIMITED—See Meta Platforms, Inc.; *U.S. Public,* pg. 1427
E! ENTERTAINMENT TELEVISION, LLC—See Comcast Corporation; *U.S. Public,* pg. 539
EFACTOR GROUP CORP.; *U.S. Private,* pg. 1343
EFE NEWS SERVICES (US) INC.—See Agencia EFE, S.A.; *Int'l,* pg. 205
EGYTEC CABLES COMPANY—See El Sewedy Electric Company; *Int'l,* pg. 2341
ELEMENT BLUE LLC—See Delta-v Capital, LLC; *U.S. Private,* pg. 1202
EMMIS AUSTIN RADIO BROADCASTING COMPANY, L.P.; *U.S. Public,* pg. 1383
EMPRESAS CABLEVISION, S.A.B. DE C.V.—See Grupo Televisa, S.A.B.; *Int'l,* pg. 3136
ENTERCOM COLORADO, LLC—See AUDACY, INC.; *U.S. Public,* pg. 226
ENTERCOM CONNECTICUT, LLC—See AUDACY, INC.; *U.S. Public,* pg. 226
ENTERCOM FLORIDA, LLC—See AUDACY, INC.; *U.S. Public,* pg. 226
ENTERCOM GEORGIA, LLC—See AUDACY, INC.; *U.S. Public,* pg. 226
ENTERCOM ILLINOIS, LLC—See AUDACY, INC.; *U.S. Public,* pg. 226
ENTERCOM LICENSE, LLC—See AUDACY, INC.; *U.S. Public,* pg. 226
ENTERCOM LOUISIANA, LLC—See AUDACY, INC.; *U.S. Public,* pg. 226
ENTERCOM MARYLAND, LLC—See AUDACY, INC.; *U.S. Public,* pg. 226
ENTERCOM MICHIGAN, LLC—See AUDACY, INC.; *U.S. Public,* pg. 226
ENTERCOM MINNESOTA, LLC—See AUDACY, INC.; *U.S. Public,* pg. 226
ENTERCOM NEVADA, LLC—See AUDACY, INC.; *U.S. Public,* pg. 226
ENTERCOM NORTH CAROLINA, LLC—See AUDACY, INC.; *U.S. Public,* pg. 226
ENTERCOM OHIO, LLC—See AUDACY, INC.; *U.S. Public,* pg. 226

ENTERCOM OREGON, LLC—See AUDACY, INC.; *U.S. Public,* pg. 226
ENTERCOM PENNSYLVANIA, LLC—See AUDACY, INC.; *U.S. Public,* pg. 226
ENTERCOM PORTLAND, LLC—See AUDACY, INC.; *U.S. Public,* pg. 226
ENTERCOM RADIO, LLC—See AUDACY, INC.; *U.S. Public,* pg. 226
ENTERCOM SOUTH CAROLINA, LLC—See AUDACY, INC.; *U.S. Public,* pg. 226
ENTERCOM TEXAS, LLC—See AUDACY, INC.; *U.S. Public,* pg. 226
ENTERCOM WASHINGTON DC, LLC—See AUDACY, INC.; *U.S. Public,* pg. 227
ENTERCOM WASHINGTON, LLC—See AUDACY, INC.; *U.S. Public,* pg. 227
ENTERCOM WISCONSIN, LLC—See AUDACY, INC.; *U.S. Public,* pg. 227
ENTERTAINMENT NETWORK (INDIA) LIMITED—See Bennett, Coleman & Co. Ltd.; *Int'l,* pg. 975
ENVIRONMENT & ENERGY PUBLISHING, LLC—See Sinclair, Inc.; *U.S. Public,* pg. 1885
ERIE COUNTY CABLEVISION—See Block Communications, Inc.; *U.S. Private,* pg. 582
ER MARKS, INC.—See Qurate Retail, Inc.; *U.S. Public,* pg. 1757
ESCAPE MEDIA GROUP, INC.; *U.S. Private,* pg. 1425
ESMG INC.—See Primco Management Inc.; *U.S. Private,* pg. 3261
ESPN SPORTS MEDIA LIMITED—See BT Group plc; *Int'l,* pg. 1203
ETVISION MULTIMEDIA LIMITED—See Hong Kong Economic Times Holdings Ltd; *Int'l,* pg. 3465
EUROSPORT INTERNATIONAL SA—See Warner Bros. Discovery, Inc.; *U.S. Public,* pg. 2326
EUROSPORT SAS—See Warner Bros. Discovery, Inc.; *U.S. Public,* pg. 2327
EUROSPORT TV LTD.—See Warner Bros. Discovery, Inc.; *U.S. Public,* pg. 2327
EVROPA 2, SPOL. S R.O.—See Czech Media Invest as; *Int'l,* pg. 1898
EXPRES NET A.S.—See Emmis Communications Corporation; *U.S. Public,* pg. 753
EYECOM INC.—See Telalaska Inc.; *U.S. Private,* pg. 3959
THE FAMILY CHANNEL, INC.—See DHX Media Ltd.; *Int'l,* pg. 2101
FENERBAHCE FUTBOL ANONIM SIRKETI; *Int'l,* pg. 2633
FIDELITY CABLE VISION INC.—See Cable One, Inc.; *U.S. Public,* pg. 416
FILMON.COM PLC; *Int'l,* pg. 2663
FIRST BANK OF HIGHLAND PARK; *U.S. Private,* pg. 1514
FON4U TELECOM GMBH—See 3U Holding AG; *Int'l,* pg. 10
FOTOLOG, INC.—See AdUX SA; *Int'l,* pg. 155
FOX CABLE NETWORK SERVICES, LLC—See Fox Corporation; *U.S. Public,* pg. 876
FOXTEL AUSTRALIA PTY LIMITED—See News Corporation; *U.S. Public,* pg. 1519
FOXTEL CABLE TELEVISION PTY. LIMITED—See News Corporation; *U.S. Public,* pg. 1519
FPT ONLINE SERVICES JOINT STOCK COMPANY—See FPT Corporation; *Int'l,* pg. 2757
FRANKLIN COMMUNICATIONS, INC.—See Saga Communications, Inc.; *U.S. Public,* pg. 1835
FUSE NETWORKS LLC—See SiTV, Inc.; *U.S. Private,* pg. 3677
FX NETWORKS, LLC—See The Walt Disney Company; *U.S. Public,* pg. 2140
G4 MEDIA, LLC—See Comcast Corporation; *U.S. Public,* pg. 539
GALAVISION, INC.—See ForgeLight, LLC; *U.S. Private,* pg. 1568
GALAVISION, INC.—See Searchlight Capital Partners, L.P.; *U.S. Private,* pg. 3590
GAWK, INCORPORATED; *U.S. Private,* pg. 1652
GCI CABLE, INC.—See Liberty Broadband Corporation; *U.S. Public,* pg. 1310
GEARHEART COMMUNICATIONS COMPANY, INC.; *U.S. Private,* pg. 1655
GIANT COMMUNICATIONS, INC.—See LICT Corporation; *U.S. Public,* pg. 1312
GLOBAL MOTION MEDIA, INC.—See TripAdvisor, Inc.; *U.S. Public,* pg. 2195
GLOBAL PERSONALS LTD.; *Int'l,* pg. 3000
GLOBAL RADIO GROUP LIMITED; *Int'l,* pg. 3000
GLOBENEWSWIRE, INC.—See Apollo Global Management, Inc.; *U.S. Public,* pg. 152
GMM MEDIA PLC—See GMM Grammy Public Company Limited; *Int'l,* pg. 3012
GOAL.COM NORTH AMERICA, INC.—See Vista Equity Partners, LLC; *U.S. Private,* pg. 4401
GODISH.COM; *U.S. Private,* pg. 1724
THE GOLF CHANNEL, LLC—See Comcast Corporation; *U.S. Public,* pg. 539
GOVLOOP, INC.—See Vista Equity Partners, LLC; *U.S. Private,* pg. 4398
GRANDPARENTS.COM, INC.; *U.S. Private,* pg. 1754
GRANT BROADCASTERS PTY. LTD.—See ARN Media Limited; *Int'l,* pg. 576

GREEN AIRPORTS INC.—See CCR S.A.; *Int'l*, pg. 1369
GROM SOCIAL ENTERPRISES, INC.; *U.S. Public*, pg. 970
GRUPO RADIO CENTRO, S.A. DE C.V.; *Int'l*, pg. 3134
GRUPO RADIO NOTICIAS S.R.L.; *Int'l*, pg. 3134
GS HOME SHOPPING, INC.—See GS Holdings Corp.; *Int'l*, pg. 3142
GUIDEWORKS, LLC—See Comcast Corporation; *U.S. Public*, pg. 538
HAMILTON TELECOMMUNICATIONS—See Nedelco Inc.; *U.S. Private*, pg. 2879
HARRON COMMUNICATIONS, L.P.; *U.S. Private*, pg. 1871
HATHWAY CABLE & DATACOM LTD.; *Int'l*, pg. 3284
HBO LATIN AMERICA MEDIA SERVICES, INC.—See Warner Bros. Discovery, Inc.; *U.S. Public*, pg. 2327
HBO SERVICES, INC.—See Warner Bros. Discovery, Inc.; *U.S. Public*, pg. 2327
HBO SPORTS—See Warner Bros. Discovery, Inc.; *U.S. Public*, pg. 2327
HEARST ENTERTAINMENT & SYNDICATION—See The Hearst Corporation; *U.S. Private*, pg. 4045
THE HISTORY CHANNEL—See The Hearst Corporation; *U.S. Private*, pg. 4045
THE HISTORY CHANNEL—See The Walt Disney Company; *U.S. Public*, pg. 2137
HOLLYWOOD CLASSICS NETWORK, INC.; *U.S. Private*, pg. 1966
HOMEADVISOR, INC.—See IAC Inc.; *U.S. Public*, pg. 1081
HOME BOX OFFICE, INC.—See Warner Bros. Discovery, Inc.; *U.S. Public*, pg. 2327
HOMETOWN CABLE COMPANY, INC.—See Schurz Communications, Inc.; *U.S. Private*, pg. 3571
HOPE COMMUNITY TV INC.—See Wehco Media, Inc.; *U.S. Private*, pg. 4469
HORNE CREATIVE GROUP, INC.—See The Hatcher Group; *U.S. Private*, pg. 4043
HSN, INC.—See Qurate Retail, Inc.; *U.S. Public*, pg. 1758
HSN, LLC—See IAC Inc.; *U.S. Public*, pg. 1082
HULU, LLC—See The Walt Disney Company; *U.S. Public*, pg. 2139
HUMOR RAINBOW, INC.—See IAC Inc.; *U.S. Public*, pg. 1082
HYPERLOCAL INDUSTRIES LLC—See SOCi, Inc.; *U.S. Private*, pg. 3702
IDEASTREAM; *U.S. Private*, pg. 2037
IHEARTCOMMUNICATIONS, INC.—See iHeartMedia, Inc.; *U.S. Public*, pg. 1096
IHEARTMEDIA + ENTERTAINMENT, INC.—See iHeartMedia, Inc.; *U.S. Public*, pg. 1096
IHLAS HABER AJANSI A.S—See Ihlas Holding A.S.; *Int'l*, pg. 3606
IMMEDIA BROADCAST LIMITED—See AVC Immedia Limited; *Int'l*, pg. 737
IN DEMAND L.L.C.—See Comcast Corporation; *U.S. Public*, pg. 538
THE INDEPENDENT—See Gannett Co., Inc.; *U.S. Public*, pg. 904
INFORMACION DE MEDIOS S.A.—See Brookfield Corporation; *Int'l*, pg. 1178
INFORMACION DE MEDIOS S.A.—See Elliott Management Corporation; *U.S. Private*, pg. 1371
INNEVATION, LLC—See DigitalBridge Group, Inc.; *U.S. Public*, pg. 665
IN PUBLISHING CO., LTD.—See GMM Grammy Public Company Limited; *Int'l*, pg. 3012
THE INSPIRATION NETWORKS; *U.S. Private*, pg. 4056
THE INSPIRATION NETWORKS—See The Inspiration Networks; *U.S. Private*, pg. 4056
INSTAGRAM, INC.—See Meta Platforms, Inc.; *U.S. Public*, pg. 1427
INTERACTIVE ONE, LLC—See Urban One, Inc.; *U.S. Public*, pg. 2265
INTER MOUNTAIN CABLE INC.—See Gearheart Communications Company, Inc.; *U.S. Private*, pg. 1655
INTERNATIONAL MEDIA DISTRIBUTION, LLC—See Comcast Corporation; *U.S. Public*, pg. 538
INTERNATIONAL NETWORKS, LLC—See Comcast Corporation; *U.S. Public*, pg. 538
INTERNETARRAY, INC.; *U.S. Public*, pg. 1158
INVESTOPEDIA LLC—See IAC Inc.; *U.S. Public*, pg. 1082
IQIYI, INC.—See Baidu, Inc.; *Int'l*, pg. 801
ISTREAMPLANET CO., LLC—See Warner Bros. Discovery, Inc.; *U.S. Public*, pg. 2328
IVOICEIDEAS, INC.; *U.S. Private*, pg. 2151
IXIT CORPORATION—See HS Holdings Co., Ltd.; *Int'l*, pg. 3503
IZUSHI CABLE, INC.—See Hi-Lex Corporation; *Int'l*, pg. 3381
JNJ MOBILE INC.; *U.S. Private*, pg. 2217
JONES KNOWLEDGE GROUP, INC.—See Jones International University; *U.S. Private*, pg. 2233
JONES SPACELINK, LTD.—See Jones International University; *U.S. Private*, pg. 2233
KANAL 24 NORGE AS—See Egmont Fonden; *Int'l*, pg. 2325
KANNET LIMITED—See Champion Technology Holdings Ltd; *Int'l*, pg. 1440
KATZ COMMUNICATIONS, INC.—See iHeartMedia, Inc.; *U.S. Public*, pg. 1096

KATZ MEDIA GROUP, INC.—See iHeartMedia, Inc.; *U.S. Public*, pg. 1096
KATZ MILLENNIUM SALES & MARKETING INC.—See iHeartMedia, Inc.; *U.S. Public*, pg. 1096
KING FEATURES SYNDICATE, INC.—See The Hearst Corporation; *U.S. Private*, pg. 4045
KITCHEN INC.—See TM Systems, LLC; *U.S. Private*, pg. 4179
KIWIBOX.COM, INC.; *U.S. Private*, pg. 2317
KNOLOGY OF HUNTSVILLE, INC.—See WideOpenWest, Inc.; *U.S. Public*, pg. 2370
KNOLOGY OF MONTGOMERY, INC.—See WideOpenWest, Inc.; *U.S. Public*, pg. 2370
KSI.INC—See Qurate Retail, Inc.; *U.S. Public*, pg. 1758
LAKEDALE COMMUNICATIONS LLC—See Windstream Holdings, Inc.; *U.S. Public*, pg. 2373
LAMONT DIGITAL SYSTEMS INC.; *U.S. Private*, pg. 2380
LEARFIELD COMMUNICATIONS, LLC—See Atairos Group, Inc.; *U.S. Private*, pg. 363
LEARFIELD NEWS—See Atairos Group, Inc.; *U.S. Private*, pg. 364
LEVEL 3 COMMUNICATIONS, LLC - PITTSBURGH—See Lumen Technologies, Inc.; *U.S. Public*, pg. 1347
LFP BROADCASTING, LLC—See L.F.P., Inc.; *U.S. Private*, pg. 2365
LIFETIME ENTERTAINMENT SERVICES, LLC—See The Hearst Corporation; *U.S. Private*, pg. 4045
LIFETIME ENTERTAINMENT SERVICES, LLC—See The Walt Disney Company; *U.S. Public*, pg. 2137
LIMELIGHT NETWORKS INC.—See EDGIO, INC.; *U.S. Public*, pg. 719
LIMELIGHT WEB TECHNOLOGIES (IL) LTD.—See EDGIO, INC.; *U.S. Public*, pg. 719
LINECALL TELECOM GMBH—See 3U Holding AG; *Int'l*, pg. 10
LINKEDIN CORPORATION—See Microsoft Corporation; *U.S. Public*, pg. 1441
LIQUIDUS MARKETING, INC.; *U.S. Private*, pg. 2466
LIVESTREAM LLC—See Vimeo, Inc.; *U.S. Public*, pg. 2298
LOCKWOOD BROADCASTING INC.; *U.S. Private*, pg. 2478
LOGO—See National Amusements, Inc.; *U.S. Private*, pg. 2841
LONGVIEW CABLE TELEVISION INC.—See Wehco Media, Inc.; *U.S. Private*, pg. 4469
LUDWIG ENTERPRISES, INC.; *U.S. Public*, pg. 1345
MANGALORE SPORTS DATA INDIA PRIVATE LIMITED—See Vista Equity Partners, LLC; *U.S. Private*, pg. 4401
MANGO.LV SIA—See AS Ekspress Grupp; *Int'l*, pg. 589
MANGOSPRING INC; *U.S. Private*, pg. 2563
MARKET NEWS INTERNATIONAL INC.—See DMEP Corporation; *U.S. Private*, pg. 1248
MARKETWIRED CHINA LTD.—See Apollo Global Management, Inc.; *U.S. Public*, pg. 152
MASSILLON CABLE TV, INC.; *U.S. Private*, pg. 2606
MASSIVE MEDIA MATCH NV—See IAC Inc.; *U.S. Public*, pg. 1082
MATCH.COM NORDIC AB—See IAC Inc.; *U.S. Public*, pg. 1082
MCCLATCHY-TRIBUNE INFORMATION SERVICES—See Chatham Asset Management, LLC; *U.S. Private*, pg. 867
MCCLATCHY-TRIBUNE INFORMATION SERVICES—See Tribune Publishing Company; *U.S. Public*, pg. 2946
MEDIACOM BROADBAND CORPORATION—See Mediacom Communications Corporation; *U.S. Private*, pg. 2653
MEDIACOM BROADBAND LLC—See Mediacom Communications Corporation; *U.S. Private*, pg. 2653
MEDIACOM COMMUNICATIONS CORPORATION; *U.S. Private*, pg. 2653
MEDIACOM IOWA LLC—See Mediacom Communications Corporation; *U.S. Private*, pg. 2653
MEDIACOM LLC—See Mediacom Communications Corporation; *U.S. Private*, pg. 2653
MEDIASPORTS DIGITAL GMBH—See Vista Equity Partners, LLC; *U.S. Private*, pg. 4401
MEET GROUP, INC.; *U.S. Public*, pg. 1414
MEEZ—See Donnerwood Media, Inc.; *U.S. Private*, pg. 1261
MELITA LTD.—See EQT AB; *Int'l*, pg. 2478
METROCAST COMMUNICATIONS—See Gestion Audem, Inc.; *Int'l*, pg. 2946
METRO NEWS SERVICE INC.; *U.S. Private*, pg. 2686
MGT SWEDEN AB—See MGT Capital Investments, Inc.; *U.S. Public*, pg. 1436
MIDCONTINENT BUSINESS SYSTEMS INC.—See Midcontinent Media Inc.; *U.S. Private*, pg. 2711
MIDCONTINENT CABLE CO. INC.—See Midcontinent Media Inc.; *U.S. Private*, pg. 2711
MIDCONTINENT MEDIA INC.; *U.S. Private*, pg. 2710
MILYONI, INC.—See Photobucket Corporation; *U.S. Private*, pg. 3174
MOBILINK S.A.—See Motorola Solutions, Inc.; *U.S. Public*, pg. 1478
MONTEZUMA MUTUAL TELEPHONE COMPANY—See Windstream Holdings, Inc.; *U.S. Public*, pg. 2373
THE MOVIE CHANNEL—See National Amusements, Inc.; *U.S. Private*, pg. 2843

MSAT CABLE JSC—See Holding Varna AD-Varna; *Int'l*, pg. 3450
MSNBC CABLE LLC—See Comcast Corporation; *U.S. Public*, pg. 539
MTV NETWORKS COMPANY—See National Amusements, Inc.; *U.S. Private*, pg. 2841
MTVN VIDEO HITS INC.—See National Amusements, Inc.; *U.S. Private*, pg. 2842
MULTICANAL S.A.—See Grupo Clarin S.A.; *Int'l*, pg. 3125
MULTIVISION S.A.—See Empresas Publicas de Medellin ESP; *Int'l*, pg. 2392
MUSIC CHOICE—See Charter Communications, Inc.; *U.S. Public*, pg. 483
MUSIC CHOICE—See Comcast Corporation; *U.S. Public*, pg. 537
MUSIC CHOICE—See Cox Enterprises, Inc.; *U.S. Private*, pg. 1078
MUSIC CHOICE—See Microsoft Corporation; *U.S. Public*, pg. 1441
MY JOB MATCHER, INC.; *U.S. Private*, pg. 2823
NAMESCO LTD—See HgCapital Trust plc; *Int'l*, pg. 3377
NATIONAL GEOGRAPHIC CHANNEL DENMARK APS—See The Walt Disney Company; *U.S. Public*, pg. 2141
NBA DIGITAL—See National Basketball Association; *U.S. Private*, pg. 2848
NBC NEWS BUREAUS LLC—See Comcast Corporation; *U.S. Public*, pg. 539
NBC NEWS DIGITAL LLC—See Comcast Corporation; *U.S. Public*, pg. 539
NBC SPORTS BAY AREA—See Comcast Corporation; *U.S. Public*, pg. 539
NBC SPORTS NETWORK, L.P.—See Comcast Corporation; *U.S. Public*, pg. 539
NC2 MEDIA, LLC; *U.S. Private*, pg. 2875
NETFLIX PTE. LTD.—See Netflix, Inc.; *U.S. Public*, pg. 1508
NET SERVICOS DE COMUNICACAO S.A.—See America Movil, S.A.B. de C.V.; *Int'l*, pg. 422
NEW ENGLAND CABLE NEWS—See Comcast Corporation; *U.S. Public*, pg. 540
NEWS 12 NEW JERSEY, INC.—See Altice USA, Inc.; *U.S. Public*, pg. 87
NEWS CORP UK & IRELAND LIMITED—See News Corporation; *U.S. Public*, pg. 1520
NEW VIDEO CHANNEL LLC—See British Broadcasting Corporation; *Int'l*, pg. 1169
NEW WORK SE—See Hubert Burda Media Holding Kommanditgesellschaft; *Int'l*, pg. 3520
THE NEW YORK TIMES NEWS SERVICE—See The New York Times Company; *U.S. Public*, pg. 2117
NGC NETWORK ASIA, LLC - SINGAPORE—See The Walt Disney Company; *U.S. Public*, pg. 2141
NGC NETWORK ASIA, LLC—See The Walt Disney Company; *U.S. Public*, pg. 2141
NGC NETWORK ASIA, LLC - TAIWAN—See The Walt Disney Company; *U.S. Public*, pg. 2141
NGC NETWORK (INDIA) PRIVATE LIMITED—See The Walt Disney Company; *U.S. Public*, pg. 2141
NGC NETWORK INTERNATIONAL, LLC—See The Walt Disney Company; *U.S. Public*, pg. 2140
NGC NETWORK US, LLC—See The Walt Disney Company; *U.S. Public*, pg. 2141
NICKELODEON AUSTRALIA—See National Amusements, Inc.; *U.S. Private*, pg. 2842
NICKELODEON DIRECT INC.—See National Amusements, Inc.; *U.S. Private*, pg. 2842
NINEMSN PTY. LTD.—See Microsoft Corporation; *U.S. Public*, pg. 1441
NING, INC.—See Glam Media, Inc.; *U.S. Private*, pg. 1706
NIPPON BROADCASTING PROJECT INC.—See Fuji Media Holdings, Inc.; *Int'l*, pg. 2814
NORTHLAND COMMUNICATIONS CORP.—See GTCR LLC; *U.S. Private*, pg. 1805
NSIGHT TELSERVICES—See Northeast Communications of Wisconsin Incorporated; *U.S. Private*, pg. 2949
NZME LIMITED—See ARN Media Limited; *Int'l*, pg. 576
OMAEZAKI CABLE TELEVISION—See Chubu Electric Power Co., Inc.; *Int'l*, pg. 1593
ON24, INC.; *U.S. Public*, pg. 1601
ON24 PTE LTD—See ON24, Inc.; *U.S. Public*, pg. 1601
ON24 UK—See ON24, Inc.; *U.S. Public*, pg. 1601
ONESCREEN, INC.; *U.S. Public*, pg. 1603
ONETEL TELECOMMUNICATION GMBH—See 3U Holding AG; *Int'l*, pg. 10
ONLINE DISRUPTIVE TECHNOLOGIES, INC.; *U.S. Public*, pg. 1605
THE OUTDOOR CHANNEL, INC.—See Kroenke Sports & Entertainment, LLC; *U.S. Private*, pg. 2352
OWN: OPRAH WINFREY NETWORK LLC—See Warner Bros. Discovery, Inc.; *U.S. Public*, pg. 2327
OXYGEN MEDIA LLC—See Comcast Corporation; *U.S. Public*, pg. 540
PACIFIC BUSINESS NEWS INC.—See Advance Publications, Inc.; *U.S. Private*, pg. 84
PARA. TV INC.—See Avex Inc.; *Int'l*, pg. 740
PATHEOS, INC.—See BN Media LLC; *U.S. Private*, pg. 601
PEER TO PEER NETWORK; *U.S. Private*, pg. 3128
PERFORM MEDIA ASIA PTE LTD—See Vista Equity Part-

N.A.I.C.S. INDEX

517111 — WIRED TELECOMMUNICA...

ners, LLC; *U.S. Private*, pg. 4401
PERFORM MEDIA DEUTSCHLAND GMBH—See Vista Equity Partners, LLC; *U.S. Private*, pg. 4401
PERFORM MEDIA INC—See Vista Equity Partners, LLC; *U.S. Private*, pg. 4401
PERFORM MEDIA JAPAN KK—See Vista Equity Partners, LLC; *U.S. Private*, pg. 4401
PERFORM MEDIA POLAND ZOO—See Vista Equity Partners, LLC; *U.S. Private*, pg. 4401
PERFORM MEDIA SERVICES SRL—See Vista Equity Partners, LLC; *U.S. Private*, pg. 4401
PESHTIGO TIMES PRINTERS & PUBLISHERS—See Multi Media Channels, LLC; *U.S. Private*, pg. 2812
PETES CONNECTION INC.; *U.S. Private*, pg. 3160
PHOENIX AMERICAN INCORPORATED; *U.S. Private*, pg. 3172
PHOTOBUCKET CORPORATION; *U.S. Private*, pg. 3174
PINE BLUFF CABLE TELEVISION INC.—See Wehco Media, Inc.; *U.S. Private*, pg. 4469
PLAYBOY ENTERTAINMENT GROUP, INC.—See PLBY Group, Inc.; *U.S. Public*, pg. 1698
PLAYERS NETWORK; *U.S. Public*, pg. 1698
PLAY SPORTS NETWORK LIMITED—See Warner Bros. Discovery, Inc.; *U.S. Public*, pg. 2327
POWERREVIEWS, INC.—See Battery Ventures, L.P.; *U.S. Private*, pg. 488
PRECISION VALLEY COMMUNICATIONS OF VERMONT, LLC—See Dycom Industries, Inc.; *U.S. Public*, pg. 699
PREMIERE NETWORKS, INC.—See iHeartMedia, Inc.; *U.S. Public*, pg. 1096
PR NEWSWIRE ASSOCIATION LLC—See Platinum Equity, LLC; *U.S. Private*, pg. 3202
PRONTO, LLC—See IAC Inc.; *U.S. Public*, pg. 1082
QUARTZ MEDIA, INC.—See Great Hill Partners, L.P.; *U.S. Private*, pg. 1763
QVC GRUNDSTUCKSVERWALTUNGS GMBH—See Qurate Retail, Inc.; *U.S. Public*, pg. 1758
RADIO COMPUTING SERVICES (AFRICA) PTY LTD.—See iHeartMedia, Inc.; *U.S. Public*, pg. 1095
RADIO COMPUTING SERVICES CANADA LTD.—See iHeartMedia, Inc.; *U.S. Public*, pg. 1096
RADIO COMPUTING SERVICES (SEA) PTE LTD.—See iHeartMedia, Inc.; *U.S. Public*, pg. 1095
RADIO COMPUTING SERVICES (UK) LTD.—See iHeartMedia, Inc.; *U.S. Public*, pg. 1096
RADIO COUNTY SOUND LIMITED—See News Corporation; *U.S. Public*, pg. 1520
RADIO MITRE S.A.—See Grupo Clarin S.A.; *Int'l*, pg. 3125
RADIO NETWORKS, LLC - DALLAS OFFICE—See Cumulus Media Inc.; *U.S. Public*, pg. 610
RADIO NETWORKS, LLC—See Cumulus Media Inc.; *U.S. Public*, pg. 610
RADIOWAVE (BLACKPOOL) LIMITED—See News Corporation; *U.S. Public*, pg. 1520
REACH MEDIA, INC.—See Urban One, Inc.; *U.S. Public*, pg. 2265
REAL CAPITAL ANALYTICS, INC.—See MSCI Inc.; *U.S. Public*, pg. 1483
REDDIT INC.—See Advance Publications, Inc.; *U.S. Private*, pg. 87
REFLECTOR ENTERTAINMENT LTD.—See BANDAI NAMCO Holdings Inc.; *Int'l*, pg. 829
RELIGION NEWS SERVICE—See Religion News LLC; *U.S. Private*, pg. 3395
REMARK ENTERTAINMENT (SHANGHAI) CO. LTD.—See Remark Holdings, Inc.; *U.S. Public*, pg. 1782
REPUBLICAN COMPANY INC.—See Advance Publications, Inc.; *U.S. Private*, pg. 87
RESORT TELEVISION CABLE COMPANY INCORPORATED—See Wehco Media, Inc.; *U.S. Private*, pg. 4469
REVISTAS DEPORTIVAS S.A.—See AT&T Inc.; *U.S. Public*, pg. 220
ROMANOFF TECHNOLOGIES OHIO LLC; *U.S. Private*, pg. 3476
R&R CABLE COMPANY INC.; *U.S. Private*, pg. 3333
RYAN SEACREST PRODUCTIONS, LLC—See Ryan Seacrest Enterprises, Inc.; *U.S. Private*, pg. 3510
SABRE RADIO NETWORKS SA (PTY) LTD—See The Carlyle Group Inc.; *U.S. Public*, pg. 2045
SAGA COMMUNICATIONS, INC.; *U.S. Public*, pg. 1835
SAGA COMMUNICATIONS OF SOUTH DAKOTA, LLC—See Saga Communications, Inc.; *U.S. Public*, pg. 1835
SALEM RADIO NETWORK INCORPORATED—See Salem Media Group, Inc.; *U.S. Public*, pg. 1836
SALON MEDIA GROUP, INC.; *U.S. Public*, pg. 1839
SANTEON GROUP, INC.; *U.S. Public*, pg. 1841
SCRIPPS MEDIA, INC.—See The E.W. Scripps Company; *U.S. Public*, pg. 2068
SERVICE ELECTRIC CABLE T.V. OF NEW JERSEY, INC.—See Altice USA, Inc.; *U.S. Public*, pg. 88
SEYALEMOYA COMMUNICATIONS (PTY) LTD—See African Media Entertainment Limited; *Int'l*, pg. 192
SHAL NETWORKS, LLC—See Windstream Holdings, Inc.; *U.S. Public*, pg. 2373
SHENANDOAH CABLE TELEVISION, LLC—See Shenandoah Telecommunications Co.; *U.S. Public*, pg. 1874

SHOPTOUCH, INC.—See IAC Inc.; *U.S. Public*, pg. 1082
SHOWTIME NETWORKS INC.—See National Amusements, Inc.; *U.S. Private*, pg. 2843
SHOWTIME NETWORKS INC. (UK)—See National Amusements, Inc.; *U.S. Private*, pg. 2843
SHOWTIME SATELLITE NETWORKS, INC.—See National Amusements, Inc.; *U.S. Private*, pg. 2843
SIGHTLINE MEDIA GROUP, LLC—See Regent, L.P.; *U.S. Private*, pg. 3388
SIGNAL RADIO LIMITED—See News Corporation; *U.S. Public*, pg. 1520
SIGNATURES—See Starcrest Products of California; *U.S. Private*, pg. 3786
SMR RESEARCH CORP.; *U.S. Private*, pg. 3698
THE SOUTHWEST TIMES—See HD Media Company, LLC; *U.S. Private*, pg. 1890
SPANISH BROADCASTING SYSTEM INC.; *U.S. Public*, pg. 1914
SPOON MEDIA, INC—See Her Campus Media, LLC; *U.S. Private*, pg. 1920
SPORTAL GMBH—See Vista Equity Partners, LLC; *U.S. Private*, pg. 4401
SPORTAL NEW ZEALAND PTY LTD—See Vista Equity Partners, LLC; *U.S. Private*, pg. 4401
SPORT-INFORMATIONS-DIENST GMBH UND CO. KG—See Agence France-Presse; *Int'l*, pg. 205
THE SPORTSMAN CHANNEL, INC.—See InterMedia Advisors, LLC; *U.S. Private*, pg. 2112
SPORTSNET NEW YORK, LLC—See Charter Communications, Inc.; *U.S. Public*, pg. 483
SPORTSNET NEW YORK, LLC—See Comcast Corporation; *U.S. Public*, pg. 539
SPORTSNET NEW YORK, LLC—See Sterling Equities, Inc.; *U.S. Public*, pg. 3805
SPREDFAST, INC.—See Vista Equity Partners, LLC; *U.S. Private*, pg. 4398
STAR ADVERTISING SALES LIMITED—See The Walt Disney Company; *U.S. Public*, pg. 2141
STARVISION, INC.—See Star Telephone Membership Corp.; *U.S. Private*, pg. 3785
STAR WEST SATELLITE—See Star West Satellite Inc.; *U.S. Private*, pg. 3785
ST. LOUIS TELECOMMUNICATIONS; *U.S. Private*, pg. 3772
STRATFOR ENTERPRISES, LLC—See Risk Assistance Network + Exchange Network, Inc.; *U.S. Private*, pg. 3440
STREETWISE REPORTS; *U.S. Private*, pg. 3839
STUMBLEUPON, INC.; *U.S. Private*, pg. 3844
SUREWEST KANSAS, INC.—See Consolidated Communications Holdings, Inc.; *U.S. Public*, pg. 570
SWITCHDIGITAL (LONDON) LIMITED—See News Corporation; *U.S. Public*, pg. 1520
SYFY LLC—See Comcast Corporation; *U.S. Public*, pg. 540
TAHLEQUAH CABLE TELEVISION INC.—See Wehco Media, Inc.; *U.S. Private*, pg. 4469
TALKSPORT LIMITED—See News Corporation; *U.S. Public*, pg. 1521
TCS COMMUNICATIONS, LLC—See Dycom Industries, Inc.; *U.S. Public*, pg. 699
TEKSTAR CABLEVISION INC.—See Arvig Enterprises, Inc.; *U.S. Private*, pg. 345
TELE COLUMBUS AG—See Morgan Stanley; *U.S. Public*, pg. 1472
TELE-MEDIA CORPORATION; *U.S. Private*, pg. 3959
TELETEXT LIMITED—See Daily Mail & General Trust plc; *Int'l*, pg. 1938
THE TENNIS CHANNEL, INC.—See Sinclair, Inc.; *U.S. Public*, pg. 1888
TETRON SICHERHEITSNETZ ERRICHTUNGS UND BETRIEBSGMBH—See Motorola Solutions, Inc.; *U.S. Public*, pg. 1479
TIME WARNER BUSINESS SERVICES LLC—See Warner Bros. Discovery, Inc.; *U.S. Public*, pg. 2328
TITANTV.COM—See Benedek Investment Group, LLC; *U.S. Public*, pg. 525
TORNEOS Y COMPETENCIAS S.A.—See AT&T Inc.; *U.S. Public*, pg. 220
TRIBUNE INTERACTIVE, INC.—See Nexstar Media Group, Inc.; *U.S. Public*, pg. 1525
TULALIP TRIBES; *U.S. Private*, pg. 4257
TULSAT-NEBRASKA—See ADDvantage Technologies Group, Inc.; *U.S. Public*, pg. 40
TUMBLR, INC.—See Apollo Global Management, Inc.; *U.S. Public*, pg. 167
TV8 MEDIA CENTER—See Vail Resorts, Inc.; *U.S. Public*, pg. 2271
TVWORKS, LLC—See Comcast Corporation; *U.S. Public*, pg. 541
U105 LIMITED—See News Corporation; *U.S. Public*, pg. 1520
UFA RADIO-PROGRAMMGESELLSCHAFT IN BAYERN MBH—See Bertelsmann SE & Co. KGaA; *Int'l*, pg. 995
UNITED PRESS INTERNATIONAL, INC.—See Family Federation for World Peace & Unification; *U.S. Private*, pg. 1469
UPC AUSTRIA GMBH—See Deutsche Telekom AG; *Int'l*, pg. 2084

UPDAY GMBH & CO. KG—See Axel Springer SE; *Int'l*, pg. 767
US CABLE OF COASTAL TEXAS LP—See US Cable Group; *U.S. Private*, pg. 4318
UUUM CO., LTD.—See FreakOut Holdings, Inc.; *Int'l*, pg. 2767
VEVO LLC—See Abu Dhabi Media; *Int'l*, pg. 72
VIACOM INTERNATIONAL SERVICES INC.—See National Amusements, Inc.; *U.S. Private*, pg. 2844
VIADEO SA—See Groupe Industriel Marcel Dassault S.A.; *Int'l*, pg. 3105
VICKSBURG VIDEO INC.—See Wehco Media, Inc.; *U.S. Private*, pg. 4469
VIDAROO CORPORATION; *U.S. Public*, pg. 4380
VIDEO, INC.—See Telephone Electronics Corporation; *U.S. Private*, pg. 3961
VIDGRID INC.—See Paylocity Holding Corporation; *U.S. Public*, pg. 1656
VUBIQUITY GROUP LIMITED—See Amdocs Limited; *Int'l*, pg. 420
VUBIQUITY, INC.—See Amdocs Limited; *Int'l*, pg. 420
VUBIQUITY MANAGEMENT LIMITED—See Amdocs Limited; *Int'l*, pg. 420
WALLY WORLD MEDIA, INC.; *U.S. Public*, pg. 2324
THE WALT DISNEY COMPANY (JAPAN) LTD.—See The Walt Disney Company; *U.S. Public*, pg. 2139
WANDERFLY, INC.—See TripAdvisor, Inc.; *U.S. Public*, pg. 2195
WARNER BROS. ENTERTAINMENT INC.—See Warner Bros. Discovery, Inc.; *U.S. Public*, pg. 2328
THE WASHINGTON POST NEWS SERVICE & SYNDICATE—See Nash Holdings LLC; *U.S. Private*, pg. 2836
THE WEATHER CHANNEL, LLC—See Entertainment Studios, Inc.; *U.S. Private*, pg. 1405
WEHCO VIDEO INC.—See Wehco Media, Inc.; *U.S. Private*, pg. 4469
WELLSTAR SPALDING REGIONAL HOSPITAL, INC.—See WellStar Health System, Inc.; *U.S. Private*, pg. 4478
WERKSPOT BV—See IAC Inc.; *U.S. Public*, pg. 1082
WESTWOOD ONE, INC.—See Cumulus Media Inc.; *U.S. Public*, pg. 610
WGN AMERICA—See Nexstar Media Group, Inc.; *U.S. Public*, pg. 1525
WHITE COUNTY VIDEO INC.—See Wehco Media, Inc.; *U.S. Private*, pg. 4469
WHITE COUNTY VIDEO INC.—See Wehco Media, Inc.; *U.S. Private*, pg. 4469
WORLD CHAMPIONSHIP SPORTS NETWORK, INC.—See Comcast Corporation; *U.S. Public*, pg. 539
WORLD CHAMPIONSHIP SPORTS NETWORK, INC.—See InterMedia Advisors, LLC; *U.S. Private*, pg. 2112
WRAL SPORTS FAN—See Capitol Broadcasting Company, Inc.; *U.S. Private*, pg. 743
X-L CABLE CORPORATION; *U.S. Private*, pg. 4579
XL DIGITAL SERVICES INC.—See Creative Vistas Inc.; *Int'l*, pg. 1834
Y28.COM LIMITED—See Champion Technology Holdings Ltd; *Int'l*, pg. 1440
YAHOO! ENTERTAINMENT—See Apollo Global Management, Inc.; *U.S. Public*, pg. 167
YAHOO! NEWS—See Apollo Global Management, Inc.; *U.S. Public*, pg. 167
YAHOO! SPORTS—See Apollo Global Management, Inc.; *U.S. Public*, pg. 168
YAMMER, INC.—See Microsoft Corporation; *U.S. Public*, pg. 1441
YANKEES ENTERTAINMENT & SPORTS NETWORK, LLC—See New York Yankees Partnership; *U.S. Private*, pg. 2912
YIRED (PROPRIETARY) LIMITED—See Hosken Consolidated Investments Limited; *Int'l*, pg. 3485
YOUSEE A/S—See Arbejdsmarkedets Tillaegspension; *Int'l*, pg. 537
ZANDICA, INC.—See Publishers Clearing House, Inc.; *U.S. Private*, pg. 3301
ZENCODER INC.—See Brightcove, Inc.; *U.S. Public*, pg. 383

517111 — WIRED TELECOMMUNICATIONS CARRIERS

AAPT LIMITED—See CK Hutchison Holdings Limited; *Int'l*, pg. 1638
ACACIA COMMUNICATIONS, INC.—See Cisco Systems, Inc.; *U.S. Public*, pg. 497
ACN, INC.; *U.S. Private*, pg. 62
ADAPT TELEPHONY SERVICES LLC—See TTEC Holdings, Inc.; *U.S. Public*, pg. 2203
ADVANCED CABLE COMMUNICATIONS, INC.—See Schurz Communications, Inc.; *U.S. Private*, pg. 3571
ADVANCED CALL CENTER TECHNOLOGIES, LLC.; *U.S. Private*, pg. 88
ADVENT SYSTEMS INC.—See Allied Universal Manager LLC; *U.S. Private*, pg. 191
ADVENTUS HOLDINGS LIMITED; *Int'l*, pg. 167
AFRIQUE TELECOM SA; *Int'l*, pg. 193

517111 — WIRED TELECOMMUNICA...

AIRLINK COMMUNICATIONS PVT. LTD.—See GTPL Hathway Ltd.; *Int'l*, pg. 3151
AIV GMBH + CO. KG; *Int'l*, pg. 254
ALGERIE TELECOM SPA; *Int'l*, pg. 318
ALLBRIDGE, LLC; *U.S. Private*, pg. 175
ALLSTREAM INC.—See DigitalBridge Group, Inc.; *U.S. Public*, pg. 665
ALLSTREAM INC.—See EQT AB; *Int'l*, pg. 2482
ALOG DATA CENTERS DO BRASIL S.A.—See Equinix, Inc.; *U.S. Public*, pg. 787
ALTICE LUXEMBOURG S.A.—See Altice Europe N.V.; *Int'l*, pg. 392
ALTRON LIMITED.; *Int'l*, pg. 398
AMALGAMATED TELECOM HOLDINGS KIRIBATI LIMITED—See Fiji National Provident Fund; *Int'l*, pg. 2661
AMALGAMATED TELECOM HOLDINGS LIMITED—See Fiji National Provident Fund; *Int'l*, pg. 2661
AN INTERNET GROUP; *U.S. Private*, pg. 271
ANIXTER DANMARK A.S.—See WESCO International, Inc.; *U.S. Public*, pg. 2350
ANIXTER DEUTSCHLAND GMBH—See WESCO International, Inc.; *U.S. Public*, pg. 2350
ANIXTER INDIA PRIVATE LIMITED—See WESCO International, Inc.; *U.S. Public*, pg. 2350
ANIXTER ITALIA S.R.L.—See WESCO International, Inc.; *U.S. Public*, pg. 2350
ANIXTER NEW ZEALAND LIMITED—See WESCO International, Inc.; *U.S. Public*, pg. 2350
ANIXTER NORGE A.N.S.—See WESCO International, Inc.; *U.S. Public*, pg. 2350
ANIXTER POLAND SP.Z.O.O.—See WESCO International, Inc.; *U.S. Public*, pg. 2350
ANIXTER PORTUGAL S.A.—See WESCO International, Inc.; *U.S. Public*, pg. 2350
ANIXTER SWITZERLAND SARL—See WESCO International, Inc.; *U.S. Public*, pg. 2350
ANNE ARUNDEL BROADBAND, LLC—See WideOpenWest, Inc.; *U.S. Public*, pg. 2369
ANTEC SERVICEPOOL GMBH—See Morgan Stanley; *U.S. Public*, pg. 1473
ANTENNA PLUS, LLC—See Airgain, Inc.; *U.S. Public*, pg. 68
A.R.C. NETWORKS, INC.—See Windstream Holdings, Inc.; *U.S. Public*, pg. 2373
ARKADIUM, INC.; *U.S. Private*, pg. 325
ARMSTRONG TELEPHONE COMPANY—See Armstrong Holdings, Inc.; *U.S. Private*, pg. 331
ARVATO DIRECT SERVICES EIWEILER GMBH—See Bertelsmann SE & Co. KGaA; *Int'l*, pg. 997
ARVATO DIRECT SERVICES FRANKFURT GMBH—See Bertelsmann SE & Co. KGaA; *Int'l*, pg. 997
ARVATO DIRECT SERVICES MUNSTER GMBH—See Bertelsmann SE & Co. KGaA; *Int'l*, pg. 997
ARVATO DIRECT SERVICES NECKARSULM GMBH—See Bertelsmann SE & Co. KGaA; *Int'l*, pg. 997
ARVATO DIRECT SERVICES NEUBRANDENBURG GMBH—See Bertelsmann SE & Co. KGaA; *Int'l*, pg. 997
ARVATO DIRECT SERVICES POTSDAM GMBH—See Bertelsmann SE & Co. KGaA; *Int'l*, pg. 997
ARVATO DIRECT SERVICES SCHWERIN GMBH—See Bertelsmann SE & Co. KGaA; *Int'l*, pg. 997
ARVATO DIRECT SERVICES STRALSUND GMBH—See Bertelsmann SE & Co. KGaA; *Int'l*, pg. 997
ARVATO DIRECT SERVICES WILHELMSHAVEN GMBH—See Bertelsmann SE & Co. KGaA; *Int'l*, pg. 997
ARVATO SERVICES DUISBURG GMBH—See Bertelsmann SE & Co. KGaA; *Int'l*, pg. 997
ARVATO SERVICES ESSEN GMBH—See Bertelsmann SE & Co. KGaA; *Int'l*, pg. 997
ARZNEIWERK AG VIDA; *Int'l*, pg. 589
ASCEND GMBH—See Alkem Laboratories Ltd.; *Int'l*, pg. 330
AST TELECOM, LLC—See Fiji National Provident Fund; *Int'l*, pg. 2661
ATC SEQUOIA LLC—See American Tower Corporation; *U.S. Public*, pg. 110
AT&T ARKANSAS—See AT&T Inc.; *U.S. Public*, pg. 219
AT&T COMMUNICATIONS CORP.—See AT&T Inc.; *U.S. Public*, pg. 219
AT&T KANSAS—See AT&T Inc.; *U.S. Public*, pg. 219
AT&T MESSAGING—See AT&T Inc.; *U.S. Public*, pg. 219
AT&T MISSOURI—See AT&T Inc.; *U.S. Public*, pg. 219
AT&T MOBILITY LLC—See AT&T Inc.; *U.S. Public*, pg. 219
AT&T OHIO—See AT&T Inc.; *U.S. Public*, pg. 219
AT&T OKLAHOMA—See AT&T Inc.; *U.S. Public*, pg. 219
AT&T SERVICES INC—See AT&T Inc.; *U.S. Public*, pg. 219
AT&T—See AT&T Inc.; *U.S. Public*, pg. 218
AT&T—See AT&T Inc.; *U.S. Public*, pg. 219
AT&T TEXAS—See AT&T Inc.; *U.S. Public*, pg. 219
AT&T WEST—See AT&T Inc.; *U.S. Public*, pg. 219
AVANT COMMUNICATIONS, INC.; *U.S. Private*, pg. 404
AVAYA DEUTSCHLAND GMBH—See Silver Lake Group, LLC; *U.S. Private*, pg. 3656
AVAYA DEUTSCHLAND GMBH—See TPG Capital, L.P.; *U.S. Public*, pg. 2169
AVAYA FRANCE S.A.—See Silver Lake Group, LLC; *U.S. Private*, pg. 3656
AVAYA FRANCE S.A.—See TPG Capital, L.P.; *U.S. Public*, pg. 2169
AVAYA ISRAEL—See Silver Lake Group, LLC; *U.S. Private*, pg. 3656
AVAYA ISRAEL—See TPG Capital, L.P.; *U.S. Public*, pg. 2169
AVID COMMUNICATIONS LLC—See Nelnet, Inc.; *U.S. Public*, pg. 1504
BAHRAIN TELECOMMUNICATIONS COMPANY BSC; *Int'l*, pg. 801
BAI COMMUNICATIONS PTY LTD; *Int'l*, pg. 801
BALTIC CABLE AB—See E.ON SE; *Int'l*, pg. 2252
BAYAN TELECOMMUNICATIONS, INC.—See Deutsche Telekom AG; *Int'l*, pg. 2083
BEL AIR INTERNET, LLC—See TAC Partners, Inc.; *U.S. Private*, pg. 3920
BELIZE TELECOMMUNICATIONS LIMITED; *Int'l*, pg. 965
BELL ALIANT—See BCE Inc.; *Int'l*, pg. 926
BELL CANADA—See BCE Inc.; *Int'l*, pg. 926
BELL ELECTRICAL CONTRACTORS, INC.—See MDU Resources Group, Inc.; *U.S. Public*, pg. 1410
BELLSOUTH, LLC—See AT&T Inc.; *U.S. Public*, pg. 219
BENIN TELECOMS SA; *Int'l*, pg. 974
BETTERWORLD TELECOM, LLC; *U.S. Private*, pg. 547
BIG BEND TELEPHONE COMPANY, INC.; *U.S. Private*, pg. 552
BLUESKY SAMOA LTD.—See Fiji National Provident Fund; *Int'l*, pg. 2661
BOOZT FASHION AB—See Boozt AB; *Int'l*, pg. 1111
BOOZT TECHNOLOGY BALTICS UAB—See Boozt AB; *Int'l*, pg. 1111
BREEDLINK BV—See Cellnex Telecom, S.A.; *Int'l*, pg. 1394
BRESNAN COMMUNICATIONS, INC.—See Charter Communications, Inc.; *U.S. Public*, pg. 483
BRIGHTSTAR PUERTO RICO, INC.—See Brightstar Capital Partners, L.P.; *U.S. Private*, pg. 653
BRITISH TELECOMMUNICATIONS PLC—See BT Group plc; *Int'l*, pg. 1203
BT AUSTRALASIA PTY LIMITED—See BT Group plc; *Int'l*, pg. 1203
BT ESPANA S.A.—See BT Group plc; *Int'l*, pg. 1203
BT HONG KONG LIMITED—See BT Group plc; *Int'l*, pg. 1203
BT ITALIA SPA—See BT Group plc; *Int'l*, pg. 1203
BT RETAIL—See BT Group plc; *Int'l*, pg. 1203
BT WHOLESALE—See BT Group plc; *Int'l*, pg. 1203
BUSINESS CONNEXION NAMIBIA (PTY) LIMITED—See Business Connexion Group Limited; *Int'l*, pg. 1228
CABLE BAHAMAS LTD.; *Int'l*, pg. 1246
CABLEVISION S.A.—See Cablevision Holding S.A.; *Int'l*, pg. 1246
CAMACC SYSTEMS INC.—See Stanley Black & Decker, Inc.; *U.S. Public*, pg. 1932
CAPE POINT HOLDINGS, INC.; *Int'l*, pg. 1303
CCM COMMUNICATION-CENTER MITTEL-DEUTSCHLAND GMBH—See Bertelsmann SE & Co. KGaA; *Int'l*, pg. 994
CCTV CAMERA PROS, LLC; *U.S. Private*, pg. 801
CDP CAPITAL TECHNOLOGIES—See Caisse de Depot et Placement du Quebec; *Int'l*, pg. 1253
CEATUS MEDIA GROUP LLC—See Advice Media LLC; *U.S. Private*, pg. 110
CECITY.COM, INC.—See Premier, Inc.; *U.S. Public*, pg. 1715
CEKAN/CDT A/S—See Belden, Inc.; *U.S. Public*, pg. 294
CELLNEX AUSTRIA GMBH—See Cellnex Telecom, S.A.; *Int'l*, pg. 1394
CELLNEX CONNECTIVITY SOLUTIONS LIMITED—See Cellnex Telecom, S.A.; *Int'l*, pg. 1394
CELLNEX DENMARK APS—See Cellnex Telecom, S.A.; *Int'l*, pg. 1394
CELLNEX ITALIA, S.R.L.—See Cellnex Telecom, S.A.; *Int'l*, pg. 1394
CELLNEX POLAND SP Z.O.O.—See Cellnex Telecom, S.A.; *Int'l*, pg. 1394
CENTRAL BOMBAY CABLE NETWORK LIMITED—See Essel Corporate Resources Pvt. Ltd.; *Int'l*, pg. 2509
CENTRICA TELECOMMUNICATIONS LTD.—See Centrica plc; *Int'l*, pg. 1413
CENTURYLINK LIMITED—See Lumen Technologies, Inc.; *U.S. Public*, pg. 1346
CENTURYLINK OF ADAMSVILLE, INC.—See Lumen Technologies, Inc.; *U.S. Public*, pg. 1346
CENTURYLINK OF MONROE COUNTY, LLC—See Lumen Technologies, Inc.; *U.S. Public*, pg. 1346
CENTURYLINK OF NORTH LOUISIANA, LLC—See Lumen Technologies, Inc.; *U.S. Public*, pg. 1346
CENTURYLINK OF THE SOUTHWEST, INC.—See Lumen Technologies, Inc.; *U.S. Public*, pg. 1346
CENTURYTEL HOLDINGS MISSOURI, INC.—See Lumen Technologies, Inc.; *U.S. Public*, pg. 1346
CENTURYTEL OF CENTRAL ARKANSAS, LLC—See Lumen Technologies, Inc.; *U.S. Public*, pg. 1346
CENTURYTEL OF CLAIBORNE, INC.—See Lumen Technologies, Inc.; *U.S. Public*, pg. 1346
CENTURYTEL OF LAKE DALLAS, INC.—See Lumen Technologies, Inc.; *U.S. Public*, pg. 1346
CENTURYTEL OF NORTHERN WISCONSIN, INC.—See Lumen Technologies, Inc.; *U.S. Public*, pg. 1346
CENTURYTEL OF THE NORTHWEST, INC.—See Lumen Technologies, Inc.; *U.S. Public*, pg. 1346
CEQUEL COMMUNICATIONS, LLC—See Altice USA, Inc.; *U.S. Public*, pg. 88
CHARTER COMMUNICATIONS, INC.; *U.S. Public*, pg. 482
CHIEF TELECOM INC.—See Chunghwa Telecom Co., Ltd.; *Int'l*, pg. 1598
CHINACACHE NETWORKS (HONG KONG) LIMITED—See ChinaCache International Holdings Ltd.; *Int'l*, pg. 1568
CHINACAST TECHNOLOGY (HK) LIMITED—See ChinaCast United Education Corporation; *Int'l*, pg. 1568
CHINA COMMUNICATIONS MULTIMEDIA GROUP CO., LTD.; *Int'l*, pg. 1491
CHINA NETCOM GROUP CORPORATION (HONG KONG) LIMITED—See China United Network Communications Group Company Limited; *Int'l*, pg. 1561
CHINA TELECOM AMERICAS—See China Telecommunications Corporation; *Int'l*, pg. 1558
CHINA UNICOM (EUROPE) OPERATIONS LIMITED—See China United Network Communications Group Company Limited; *Int'l*, pg. 1561
CHINA UNICOM (HONG KONG) LIMITED—See China United Network Communications Group Company Limited; *Int'l*, pg. 1561
CHINA UNICOM (JAPAN) OPERATIONS CORPORATION—See China United Network Communications Group Company Limited; *Int'l*, pg. 1561
CHORUS LIMITED; *Int'l*, pg. 1584
CISCO SYSTEMS ESTONIA OU—See Cisco Systems, Inc.; *U.S. Public*, pg. 498
CITIZENS TELEPHONE COMPANY—See Comporium Group; *U.S. Private*, pg. 1002
CITY ONLINE SERVICES LTD.; *Int'l*, pg. 1627
CLEARCOMM TECHNOLOGIES, LLC—See L3Harris Technologies, Inc.; *U.S. Public*, pg. 1284
CLOSINGCORP, INC.—See Insight Venture Management, LLC; *U.S. Private*, pg. 2088
COC RF TECHNOLOGY & INFORMATION PLC—See China GrenTech Corporation Limited; *Int'l*, pg. 1505
COGECO MEDIA INC.—See Gestion Audem, Inc.; *Int'l*, pg. 2946
COGENT COMMUNICATIONS DENMARK APS—See Cogent Communications Holdings, Inc.; *U.S. Public*, pg. 522
COGENT COMMUNICATIONS POLAND SP. Z O.O.—See Cogent Communications Holdings, Inc.; *U.S. Public*, pg. 522
COGENT COMMUNICATIONS SWEDEN AB—See Cogent Communications Holdings, Inc.; *U.S. Public*, pg. 522
COGENT LATVIA SIA—See Cogent Communications Holdings, Inc.; *U.S. Public*, pg. 522
COLT TECHNOLOGY SERVICES GMBH—See FMR LLC; *U.S. Private*, pg. 1554
COLT TECHNOLOGY SERVICES S.P.A.—See FMR LLC; *U.S. Private*, pg. 1554
COLT TELECOM AB—See FMR LLC; *U.S. Private*, pg. 1554
COLT TELECOM AG—See FMR LLC; *U.S. Private*, pg. 1554
COLT TELECOM A/S—See FMR LLC; *U.S. Private*, pg. 1554
COLT TELECOM AUSTRIA GMBH—See FMR LLC; *U.S. Private*, pg. 1554
COLT TELECOM B.V.—See FMR LLC; *U.S. Private*, pg. 1554
COLT TELECOM ESPANA SA—See FMR LLC; *U.S. Private*, pg. 1554
COLT TELECOM IRELAND LIMITED—See FMR LLC; *U.S. Private*, pg. 1554
COLT TELECOMMUNICATIONS FRANCE—See FMR LLC; *U.S. Private*, pg. 1554
COLT TELECOM NV/SA—See FMR LLC; *U.S. Private*, pg. 1554
COLT TELECOM PORTUGAL—See FMR LLC; *U.S. Private*, pg. 1554
COMANCHE COUNTY TELECOM—See First American Communications Enterprise Inc.; *U.S. Private*, pg. 1513
COMCAST PHONE OF D.C., LLC—See Comcast Corporation; *U.S. Public*, pg. 537
COMMCENTER S.A.; *Int'l*, pg. 1714
COMMNET BROADBAND, LLC—See ATN International, Inc.; *U.S. Public*, pg. 224
COMMSCON ITALIA, S.R.L.—See Cellnex Telecom, S.A.; *Int'l*, pg. 1394
COMNET COMMUNICATIONS LLC—See Comnet Communications LLC; *U.S. Private*, pg. 998
COMPANIA ANONIMA NACIONAL TELEFONOS DE VENEZUELA; *Int'l*, pg. 1748
COMTECH MOBILE DATACOM CORP.—See Comtech Telecommunications Corp.; *U.S. Public*, pg. 562
CONNESI S.P.A.—See DHH SpA; *Int'l*, pg. 2099
CONSOLIDATED COMMUNICATIONS, INC.—See Consolidated Communications Holdings, Inc.; *U.S. Public*, pg. 570
CONSOLIDATED COMMUNICATIONS OF TEXAS COMPANY—See Consolidated Communications Holdings, Inc.; *U.S. Public*, pg. 570
COUNTERPATH TECHNOLOGIES INC.—See Alianza Inc.; *U.S. Private*, pg. 167
CREATIVE VISTAS ACQUISITION CORP—See Creative Vistas Inc.; *Int'l*, pg. 1833
CTI COMPANIA DE TELEFONOS DEL INTERIOR

N.A.I.C.S. INDEX

517111 — WIRED TELECOMMUNICA...

S.A.—See America Movil, S.A.B. de C.V.; *Int'l*, pg. 421
CYBERA, INC.—See TA Associates, Inc.; *U.S. Private*, pg. 3917
CYBERLINK PACIFIC TELECOMMUNICATIONS LIMITED; *Int'l*, pg. 1893
DALRYMPLE BAY INFRASTRUCTURE MANAGEMENT PTY. LTD.—See Dalrymple Bay Infrastructure Limited; *Int'l*, pg. 1955
DASAN ZHONE SOLUTIONS, INC. - MIDDLE EAST, AFRICA & PAKISTAN—See DZS Inc.; *U.S. Public*, pg. 701
DATA TECHNOLOGY SOLUTIONS—See ViaSat, Inc.; *U.S. Public*, pg. 2292
DCN, LLC; *U.S. Private*, pg. 1180
DEFENTECT GROUP, INC.; *U.S. Public*, pg. 648
DELTA COUNTY TELE-COMM INC.—See Telephone & Data Systems, Inc.; *U.S. Public*, pg. 1998
DELTON CABLES LIMITED; *Int'l*, pg. 2022
DEN BROADBAND PRIVATE LIMITED—See DEN Networks Limited; *Int'l*, pg. 2026
DEN NETWORKS LIMITED; *Int'l*, pg. 2026
DENTSU HONG KONG LTD.—See Dentsu Group Inc.; *Int'l*, pg. 2037
DEPOSIT TELEPHONE CO. INC.—See Telephone & Data Systems, Inc.; *U.S. Public*, pg. 1998
DEUTSCHE TELEKOM AG; *Int'l*, pg. 2083
DHIVEHI RAAJJEYGE GULHUN PLC—See Bahrain Telecommunications Company BSC; *Int'l*, pg. 801
DICKEYVILLE TELEPHONE, LLC—See Telephone & Data Systems, Inc.; *U.S. Public*, pg. 1998
DISH NETWORK SERVICE, L.L.C.—See EchoStar Corporation; *U.S. Public*, pg. 711
DISTRIBUTEL COMMUNICATIONS LIMITED; *Int'l*, pg. 2136
DIVERSIFIED DATA COMMUNICATIONS; *U.S. Private*, pg. 1242
DOTCOM DISTRIBUTION—See Ryder System, Inc.; *U.S. Public*, pg. 1828
DYNAMIC QUEST, INC.—See Spire Capital Partners, LLC; *U.S. Private*, pg. 3757
EADS DEFENSE & SECURITY NETWORKS—See Airbus SE; *Int'l*, pg. 246
EARTHLINK, LLC.—See Trive Capital Inc.; *U.S. Private*, pg. 4239
ECHOSPHERE L.L.C.—See EchoStar Corporation; *U.S. Public*, pg. 711
ECI TELECOM GMBH—See Ribbon Communications Inc.; *U.S. Public*, pg. 1797
EDOTCO TOWERS (BANGLADESH) LIMITED—See Axiata Group Berhad; *Int'l*, pg. 768
EIRCOM LIMITED—See eircom Holdings (Ireland) Limited; *Int'l*, pg. 2334
EMBRATEL PARTICIPACOES S.A.—See America Movil, S.A.B. de C.V.; *Int'l*, pg. 422
EMURTEL, S.A.—See ACS, Actividades de Construccion y Servicios, S.A.; *Int'l*, pg. 112
ENABLE SERVICES LTD—See Christchurch City Holdings Ltd.; *Int'l*, pg. 1586
ENIRO 118 118 AB—See Eniro Group AB; *Int'l*, pg. 2439
EPIC LTD.—See Bahrain Telecommunications Company BSC; *Int'l*, pg. 801
EQUINIX (GERMANY) GMBH—See Equinix, Inc.; *U.S. Public*, pg. 787
EQUINIX GROUP LTD—See Equinix, Inc.; *U.S. Public*, pg. 787
EQUINIX (IBX SERVICES) GMBH—See Equinix, Inc.; *U.S. Public*, pg. 787
EQUINIX, INC.; *U.S. Public*, pg. 787
EQUINIX (SWITZERLAND) GMBH—See Equinix, Inc.; *U.S. Public*, pg. 787
ETIHAD ATHEEB TELECOM COMPANY—See Atheeb Group; *Int'l*, pg. 669
EUNETWORKS GROUP LIMITED—See Stonepeak Partners L.P.; *U.S. Private*, pg. 3830
EXEO ASIA CO., LTD.—See EXEO Group Inc.; *Int'l*, pg. 2583
F3 TECHNOLOGY PARTNERS LLC—See Fulcrum IT Partners; *Int'l*, pg. 2841
THE FARMERS & MERCHANTS MUTUAL TELEPHONE CO. OF WAYLAND, IOWA—See Kalona Cooperative Telephone Company; *U.S. Private*, pg. 2258
FE VELCOM—See America Movil, S.A.B. de C.V.; *Int'l*, pg. 421
FIDELITY SYSTEMS PLUS INC.—See Cable One, Inc.; *U.S. Public*, pg. 416
FIJI INTERNATIONAL TELECOMMUNICATIONS LIMITED—See Fiji National Provident Fund; *Int'l*, pg. 2661
FIRST AMERICAN COMMUNICATIONS ENTERPRISE INC.; *U.S. Private*, pg. 1513
FIRST COMMUNICATIONS LLC—See North Central Equity LLC; *U.S. Private*, pg. 2943
FLORIDA DIGITAL NETWORK INC.; *U.S. Private*, pg. 1548
FLUIDATA LTD.; *Int'l*, pg. 2713
FMHC CORP.—See Jacobs Engineering Group, Inc.; *U.S. Public*, pg. 1184
FORVAL TELECOM, INC.—See Forval Corporation; *Int'l*, pg. 2745
FRONTIER COMMUNICATIONS CORPORATE SERVICES INC.—See Frontier Communications Parent, Inc.; *U.S. Public*, pg. 887
FRONTIER COMMUNICATIONS CORPORATION—See Frontier Communications Parent, Inc.; *U.S. Public*, pg. 887
FRONTIER WEST VIRGINIA INC.—See Frontier Communications Parent, Inc.; *U.S. Public*, pg. 887
FSBM NET MEDIA SDN. BHD.—See FSBM Holdings Berhad; *Int'l*, pg. 2798
FUCHUAN CO., LTD.—See Hon Hai Precision Industry Co., Ltd.; *Int'l*, pg. 3457
GALTRONICS ELECTRONICS (WUXI) CO., LTD.—See Baylin Technologies Inc.; *Int'l*, pg. 914
GAMBIA TELECOMMUNICATIONS COMPANY LTD.; *Int'l*, pg. 2877
GAMMA COMMUNICATIONS BENELUX B.V.—See Gamma Communications PLC; *Int'l*, pg. 2878
GAMMA COMMUNICATIONS GERMANY GMBH—See Gamma Communications PLC; *Int'l*, pg. 2878
GARDEN VALLEY TELEPHONE COMPANY; *U.S. Private*, pg. 1643
GCI LIBERTY, INC.—See Liberty Broadband Corporation; *U.S. Public*, pg. 1310
GEONETRIC, INC.; *U.S. Private*, pg. 1681
GLOBE WIRELESS INC.—See ViaSat, Inc.; *U.S. Public*, pg. 2291
GOOGLE FIBER INC.—See Alphabet Inc.; *U.S. Public*, pg. 83
GRANITE TELECOMMUNICATIONS, LLC; *U.S. Private*, pg. 1756
GREEN PACKET BERHAD; *Int'l*, pg. 3072
GREENWAY GRID GLOBAL PTE. LTD.—See Chubu Electric Power Co., Inc.; *Int'l*, pg. 1593
GRENTECH RF COMMUNICATION NIGERIA LIMITED—See China GrenTech Corporation Limited; *Int'l*, pg. 1506
GRENTECH SA (PTY) LTD—See China GrenTech Corporation Limited; *Int'l*, pg. 1506
GTT COMMUNICATIONS HK LIMITED—See GTT Communications, Inc.; *U.S. Public*, pg. 1808
GTT COMMUNICATIONS, INC.; *U.S. Private*, pg. 1807
GULF COAST UTILITIES, INC.—See Keystone Group, L.P.; *U.S. Private*, pg. 2297
GULF COAST UTILITIES, INC.—See Pamlico Capital Management, L.P.; *U.S. Private*, pg. 3083
GUYANA TELEPHONE & TELEGRAPH CO (GT&T)—See ATN International, Inc.; *U.S. Public*, pg. 225
HANSOL TELECOM CO. LTD.—See Hansol Group; *Int'l*, pg. 3261
HARGRAY COMMUNICATIONS GROUP, INC.—See Cable One, Inc.; *U.S. Public*, pg. 416
HATHWAY BHAWANI CABLETEL & DATACOM LIMITED; *Int'l*, pg. 3284
HELLENIC TELECOMMUNICATIONS ORGANIZATION S.A.; *Int'l*, pg. 3333
HERE MEDIA INC.; *U.S. Private*, pg. 1921
HERNIS SCAN SYSTEMS - ASIA PTE LTD.—See Eaton Corporation plc; *Int'l*, pg. 2282
HERNIS SCAN SYSTEMS A/S—See Eaton Corporation plc; *Int'l*, pg. 2282
HEXATRONIC FIBEROPTIC AB—See Hexatronic Group AB; *Int'l*, pg. 3370
HFO TELECOM AG; *Int'l*, pg. 3375
HIGH CONNEXION SRL—See HighCo S.A.; *Int'l*, pg. 3386
HIGHCO SHOPPER SAS—See HighCo S.A.; *Int'l*, pg. 3387
HIGH WIRE NETWORKS, INC.; *U.S. Public*, pg. 1937
HILLSBORO TELEPHONE COMPANY, INC.—See Lumen Technologies, Inc.; *U.S. Public*, pg. 1346
HOFF COMPANIES, INC; *U.S. Private*, pg. 1959
HOKKAIDO TELECOMMUNICATION NETWORK—See Hokkaido Electric Power Co., Inc.; *Int'l*, pg. 3443
HOSTDIME.COM, INC.; *U.S. Private*, pg. 1988
HOSTED SOLUTIONS CHARLOTTE, LLC—See Windstream Holdings, Inc.; *U.S. Public*, pg. 2373
HOT TELECOMMUNICATION SYSTEMS LTD.; *Int'l*, pg. 3487
HQ REALTY, INC.—See Lumen Technologies, Inc.; *U.S. Public*, pg. 1347
HUNT TELECOMMUNICATIONS LLC—See Uniti Group Inc.; *U.S. Public*, pg. 2253
HUTCHISON TELECOMMUNICATIONS INTERNATIONAL LTD.—See CK Hutchison Holdings Limited; *Int'l*, pg. 1638
HYDRO ONE TELECOM INC.—See Hydro One Limited; *Int'l*, pg. 3546
ICSOLUTIONS, LLC.—See Centric Group LLC; *U.S. Private*, pg. 830
IDT CORPORATION DE ARGENTINA S.A.—See IDT Corporation; *U.S. Public*, pg. 1093
IDT EUROPE BVBA—See IDT Corporation; *U.S. Public*, pg. 1093
IDT FRANCE SARL—See IDT Corporation; *U.S. Public*, pg. 1093
IDT GLOBAL LIMITED—See IDT Corporation; *U.S. Public*, pg. 1093
IDT INTER DIRECT TEL SWEDEN AB—See IDT Corporation; *U.S. Public*, pg. 1093
IDT ITALIA S.R.L.—See IDT Corporation; *U.S. Public*, pg. 1093
IDT NETHERLANDS BV—See IDT Corporation; *U.S. Public*, pg. 1093
IDT SPAIN S.L.—See IDT Corporation; *U.S. Public*, pg. 1093
IENTRY, INC.; *U.S. Private*, pg. 2038
I-LAND INTERNET SERVICES LLC—See Keystone Group, L.P.; *U.S. Private*, pg. 2299
ILLINOIS CONSOLIDATED TELEPHONE COMPANY—See Consolidated Communications Holdings, Inc.; *U.S. Public*, pg. 570
ILLINOIS FIBER RESOURCES GROUP; *U.S. Private*, pg. 2042
IMAQLIQ SERVICE LTD.; *Int'l*, pg. 3619
IMARKET COMMUNICATIONS INC.—See Speakerbus, Inc.; *U.S. Private*, pg. 3747
INDIAN CABLE NET COMPANY LIMITED—See Essel Corporate Resources Pvt. Ltd.; *Int'l*, pg. 2509
INFRONTIER LTD.—See First Pacific Company Limited; *Int'l*, pg. 2686
INSEEGO AUSTRALIA PTY LTD.—See Inseego Corp.; *U.S. Public*, pg. 1129
INSEEGO NEW ZEALAND LTD.—See Inseego Corp.; *U.S. Public*, pg. 1129
INTEGRA TELECOM, INC.—See Warburg Pincus LLC; *U.S. Private*, pg. 4438
INTEGRA TELECOM OF NORTH DAKOTA, INC.—See Warburg Pincus LLC; *U.S. Private*, pg. 4438
INTELLIGENT INTEGRATION SYSTEMS, INC.; *U.S. Private*, pg. 2106
INTERACTIVATION HEALTH NETWORKS LLC - OPERATIONS OFFICE—See Interactivation Health Networks LLC; *U.S. Private*, pg. 2108
INTERACTIVATION HEALTH NETWORKS LLC; *U.S. Private*, pg. 2108
INTERACTIVE DIGITAL SOLUTIONS, INC.—See Berenson & Company, Inc.; *U.S. Private*, pg. 530
INTEREVCO, LTD.; *U.S. Private*, pg. 2110
INTERMEX WIRE TRANSFER, LLC—See International Money Express Inc.; *U.S. Public*, pg. 1154
INTERNET VIDEO ARCHIVE LLC—See Meta Data Software, Inc.; *U.S. Private*, pg. 2679
IT21 INC.—See HSMC Orizon LLC; *U.S. Private*, pg. 1999
ITALTEL S.P.A.—See Clayton, Dubilier & Rice, LLC; *U.S. Private*, pg. 925
JABRA—See GN Store Nord A/S; *Int'l*, pg. 3016
JAB WIRELESS, INC.; *U.S. Private*, pg. 2172
JIANGSU TELECOM COMPANY LIMITED—See China Telecommunications Corporation; *Int'l*, pg. 1558
JUMA TECHNOLOGY CORP.; *U.S. Public*, pg. 1210
KABELCOM RHEINHESSEN GMBH—See Morgan Stanley; *U.S. Public*, pg. 1473
KABELFERNSEHEN MUNCHEN SERVICENTER GMBH—See Morgan Stanley; *U.S. Public*, pg. 1473
KABELPLUS GMBH—See EVN AG; *Int'l*, pg. 2571
KING TELESERVICES LLC—See Skyview Capital, LLC; *U.S. Private*, pg. 3686
KKG KABELKOMMUNIKATION GUSTROW GMBH—See Morgan Stanley; *U.S. Public*, pg. 1473
KNURR ELECTRONICS GMBH—See Vertiv Holdings Co; *U.S. Public*, pg. 2289
KSP-KABELSERVICE PRENZLAU GMBH—See Morgan Stanley; *U.S. Public*, pg. 1473
LAIRD CONNECTIVITY, INC.—See Audax Group, Limited Partnership; *U.S. Private*, pg. 388
LAUNCHFAX.COM INC.; *U.S. Public*, pg. 2398
LEGACY LONG DISTANCE INTERNATIONAL, INC.; *U.S. Private*, pg. 2416
LEVEL 3 ARGENTINA, S.A.—See Lumen Technologies, Inc.; *U.S. Public*, pg. 1346
LEVEL 3 COMMUNICATIONS HONG KONG LIMITED—See Lumen Technologies, Inc.; *U.S. Public*, pg. 1347
LEVEL 3 COMMUNICATIONS LIMITED—See Lumen Technologies, Inc.; *U.S. Public*, pg. 1347
LEVEL 3 COMMUNICATIONS PEC IRELAND LIMITED—See Lumen Technologies, Inc.; *U.S. Public*, pg. 1347
LEVEL 3 MEXICO LANDING S. DE R.L.—See Lumen Technologies, Inc.; *U.S. Public*, pg. 1347
LICT CORPORATION; *U.S. Public*, pg. 1311
LIGADO NETWORKS; *U.S. Private*, pg. 2452
LIGHTEDGE SOLUTIONS, INC.—See GI Manager L.P.; *U.S. Private*, pg. 1692
LIMELIGHT NETWORKS GERMANY GMBH—See EDGIO, INC.; *U.S. Public*, pg. 718
LIMELIGHT NETWORKS INDIA PRIVATE LIMITED—See EDGIO, INC.; *U.S. Public*, pg. 719
LIMELIGHT NETWORKS NETHERLANDS B.V.—See EDGIO, INC.; *U.S. Public*, pg. 719
LIMELIGHT NETWORKS SINGAPORE PTE LTD.—See EDGIO, INC.; *U.S. Public*, pg. 719
LITESTREAM HOLDINGS, LLC; *U.S. Private*, pg. 2467
LUMEN TECHNOLOGIES GERMANY GMBH—See Lumen Technologies, Inc.; *U.S. Public*, pg. 1347
LUMEN TECHNOLOGIES, INC.; *U.S. Public*, pg. 1345
LUMEN TECHNOLOGIES UK LIMITED—See Lumen Technologies, Inc.; *U.S. Public*, pg. 1347

517111 — WIRED TELECOMMUNICA...

LUMOS LABS—See Warner Bros. Discovery, Inc.; *U.S. Public*, pg. 2327
LUMOS NETWORKS CORP.—See EQT AB; *Int'l*, pg. 2480
LUMOS NETWORKS INC.—See EQT AB; *Int'l*, pg. 2480
LUMOS NETWORKS OPERATING COMPANY—See EQT AB; *Int'l*, pg. 2480
MANX TELECOM PLC—See Colliers International Group Inc.; *Int'l*, pg. 1700
MASON GROUP LTD.—See Datatec Limited; *Int'l*, pg. 1980
MASTER CHANNEL COMMUNITY NETWORK PRIVATE LIMITED—See Essel Corporate Resources Pvt. Ltd.; *Int'l*, pg. 2509
MAXCOM TELECOMUNICACIONES, S.A.B. DE C.V.—See Transtelco Holding, Inc.; *U.S. Private*, pg. 4211
MDCC MAGDEBURG-CITY-COM GMBH—See Morgan Stanley; *U.S. Public*, pg. 1473
METROPOLITAN TELECOMMUNICATIONS, INC.; *U.S. Private*, pg. 2689
MG EXEO NETWORK INC.—See EXEO Group Inc.; *Int'l*, pg. 2583
MGM NETWORKS INC.—See Amazon.com, Inc.; *U.S. Public*, pg. 90
MICHIGAN BELL TELEPHONE COMPANY—See AT&T Inc.; *U.S. Public*, pg. 219
MICROCORP, LLC—See Cloud Service Partners, Inc.; *U.S. Private*, pg. 947
MICROSPACE COMMUNICATIONS CORPORATION—See Capitol Broadcasting Company, Inc.; *U.S. Private*, pg. 743
MOUNTAIN RURAL TELEPHONE COOPERATIVE CORPORATION, INC.; *U.S. Public*, pg. 2799
MOVIL@CCESS, S.A. DE C.V.—See Grupo Salinas, S.A. de C.V.; *Int'l*, pg. 3135
MULTINET PAKISTAN (PRIVATE) LIMITED—See Axiata Group Berhad; *Int'l*, pg. 768
MULTIPHONE—See FAYAT SAS; *Int'l*, pg. 2626
MVD COMMUNICATIONS, LLC; *U.S. Private*, pg. 2821
NAVITRANS S.R.L.—See Carnival Corporation; *U.S. Public*, pg. 438
NECOLICO LLC—See Chubu Electric Power Co., Inc.; *Int'l*, pg. 1593
NERA (MALAYSIA) SDN. BHD.—See Ennoconn Corporation; *Int'l*, pg. 2443
NERA PHILIPPINES, INC.—See Ennoconn Corporation; *Int'l*, pg. 2443
NERA TELECOMMUNICATIONS (INDIA) PVT LTD—See Ennoconn Corporation; *Int'l*, pg. 2443
NERA TELECOMMUNICATIONS LTD.—See Ennoconn Corporation; *Int'l*, pg. 2443
NERA TELECOMMUNICATIONS LTD.—See Ennoconn Corporation; *Int'l*, pg. 2443
NET2PHONE, INC.—See IDT Corporation; *U.S. Public*, pg. 1094
NETWORK SOLUTIONS PROVIDER (NSP); *U.S. Private*, pg. 2889
NEUTRONA NETWORKS INTERNATIONAL LLC—See Transtelco Holding, Inc.; *U.S. Private*, pg. 4211
NEW CASTLE TELEPHONE COMPANY—See Telephone & Data Systems, Inc.; *U.S. Public*, pg. 1998
THE NEW TELEPHONE COMPANY, INC—See Fortran Corporation; *U.S. Public*, pg. 872
NEXT DYNAMICS INC.; *U.S. Public*, pg. 1525
NORTHERNTEL LIMITED PARTNERSHIP—See BCE Inc.; *Int'l*, pg. 926
NORTHLAND TELEPHONE SYSTEMS, LTD.; *U.S. Private*, pg. 2955
NORTHWESTEL INC.—See BCE Inc.; *Int'l*, pg. 926
NOUR COMMUNICATION COMPANY—See Arab Supply & Trading Co.; *Int'l*, pg. 532
NUVERA COMMUNICATIONS, INC.; *U.S. Public*, pg. 1556
OCEANIC TIME WARNER CABLE LLC—See Charter Communications, Inc.; *U.S. Public*, pg. 483
ONDAS NETWORKS INC.—See Ondas Holdings, Inc.; *U.S. Public*, pg. 1602
ONEOTT INTERTAINMENT LIMITED—See Hinduja Global Solutions Ltd.; *Int'l*, pg. 3398
ONEVOICE COMMUNICATIONS, INC.; *U.S. Private*, pg. 3026
ONITELECOM - INFOCOMUNICACOES, S.A.—See The Riverside Company; *U.S. Private*, pg. 4109
ONTHENET—See Aware Super Pty Ltd; *Int'l*, pg. 752
OOO LEVEL 3 COMMUNICATIONS—See Lumen Technologies, Inc.; *U.S. Public*, pg. 1347
OPNET S.P.A.—See Jefferies Financial Group Inc.; *U.S. Public*, pg. 1189
OPTIMIZELY, INC.—See Insight Venture Management, LLC; *U.S. Private*, pg. 2090
ORANGE DOMINICANA SA—See Altice Europe N.V.; *Int'l*, pg. 392
P2P HOLDINGS LLC—See System One Holdings, LLC; *U.S. Private*, pg. 3907
PACKETFABRIC, INC; *U.S. Private*, pg. 3073
PAC-WEST TELECOMM, INC.; *U.S. Private*, pg. 3063
PALAU NATIONAL COMMUNICATIONS CORPORATION; *U.S. Private*, pg. 3076
PEG BANDWIDTH, LLC—See Uniti Group Inc.; *U.S. Public*, pg. 2253
PERVASIP CORP.; *U.S. Private*, pg. 3156

PFIZER LOGISTICS CENTER—See Pfizer Inc.; *U.S. Public*, pg. 1682
PINE ISLAND TELEPHONE COMPANY—See Arvig Enterprises, Inc.; *U.S. Private*, pg. 344
PINE ISLAND TELEPHONE COMPANY—See Blue Earth Valley Communications; *U.S. Private*, pg. 588
PINE ISLAND TELEPHONE COMPANY—See Nuvera Communications, Inc.; *U.S. Public*, pg. 1556
PLANTATION CORP.; *U.S. Private*, pg. 3197
PRECISION PHOTONICS CORPORATION—See IDEX Corp; *U.S. Public*, pg. 1091
P.T. KNET INDONESIA—See Hexatronic Group AB; *Int'l*, pg. 3371
PULASKI-WHITE RURAL TELEPHONE COOPERATIVE, INC.; *U.S. Private*, pg. 3303
QUALCOMM ATHEROS CANADA CORPORATION—See QUALCOMM Incorporated; *U.S. Public*, pg. 1747
QUALCOMM COMMUNICATION TECHNOLOGIES LTD.—See QUALCOMM Incorporated; *U.S. Public*, pg. 1747
QUALCOMM GLOBAL TRADING, INC.—See QUALCOMM Incorporated; *U.S. Public*, pg. 1747
QUALCOMM INDIA PRIVATE LIMITED—See QUALCOMM Incorporated; *U.S. Public*, pg. 1747
QUALCOMM (UK) LIMITED—See QUALCOMM Incorporated; *U.S. Public*, pg. 1747
QUANTUM NETWORKS, LLC—See Advantage Sales & Marketing, LLC; *U.S. Private*, pg. 95
QUICKLINE COMMUNICATIONS LIMITED—See Bigblu Broadband Group PLC; *Int'l*, pg. 1022
RCN TELECOM SERVICES, LLC—See Stonepeak Partners L.P.; *U.S. Private*, pg. 3829
REDTONE DIGITAL BERHAD—See Berjaya Corporation Berhad; *Int'l*, pg. 984
RETURN PATH AUSTRALIA—See Silversmith Management, L.P.; *U.S. Private*, pg. 3664
RETURN PATH BRAZIL—See Silversmith Management, L.P.; *U.S. Private*, pg. 3664
RETURN PATH FRANCE—See Silversmith Management, L.P.; *U.S. Private*, pg. 3664
RETURN PATH GERMANY—See Silversmith Management, L.P.; *U.S. Private*, pg. 3664
RETURN PATH, INC.—See Silversmith Management, L.P.; *U.S. Private*, pg. 3664
RETURN PATH UK—See Silversmith Management, L.P.; *U.S. Private*, pg. 3664
RFC RADIO-, FERNSEH- U. COMPUTERTECHNIK GMBH—See Morgan Stanley; *U.S. Public*, pg. 1473
ROBERTS COMMUNICATIONS NETWORK; *U.S. Private*, pg. 3459
ROCKWELL COLLINS CHINA—See RTX Corporation; *U.S. Public*, pg. 1823
ROVION, LLC—See TEGNA Inc.; *U.S. Public*, pg. 1990
RSL TELECOM PANAMA SA—See Enel S.p.A.; *Int'l*, pg. 2415
SC CONNET RO SRL—See Koch Industries, Inc.; *U.S. Private*, pg. 2333
SERVICIOS ANIXTER, S.A. DE C.V.—See WESCO International, Inc.; *U.S. Public*, pg. 2351
SHENANDOAH LONG DISTANCE CO. INC.—See Shenandoah Telecommunications Co.; *U.S. Public*, pg. 1874
SHENANDOAH TELECOMMUNICATIONS CO.; *U.S. Public*, pg. 1874
SHERE MASTEN B.V.—See Cellnex Telecom, S.A.; *Int'l*, pg. 1394
SHOREHAM TELEPHONE LLC—See Keystone Group, L.P.; *U.S. Private*, pg. 2299
SITICABLE BROADBAND SOUTH LIMITED—See Essel Corporate Resources Pvt. Ltd.; *Int'l*, pg. 2510
SITI NETWORKS LIMITED—See Essel Corporate Resources Pvt. Ltd.; *Int'l*, pg. 2509
SMARTRG, INC.—See ADTRAN Holdings, Inc.; *U.S. Public*, pg. 44
SOLUTIONZ, INC.—See Fernandez Holdings, Inc.; *U.S. Private*, pg. 1497
SONIFI SOLUTIONS, INC.; *U.S. Private*, pg. 3714
SOUTH CENTRAL UTAH TELEPHONE ASSOCIATION, INC.; *U.S. Private*, pg. 3721
SOUTHWESTERN BELL TELEPHONE L.P.—See AT&T Inc.; *U.S. Public*, pg. 219
STEADFAST INTERNATIONAL LIMITED—See Content Ventures Limited; *Int'l*, pg. 1779
STEADFAST TELEVISION LIMITED—See Content Ventures Limited; *Int'l*, pg. 1779
STRONG TOWER COMMUNICATIONS, LLC—See Squan Construction Services LLC; *U.S. Private*, pg. 3766
SUNFLOWER TELEPHONE CO.—See Consolidated Communications Holdings, Inc.; *U.S. Public*, pg. 570
SUREWEST LONG DISTANCE COMPANY—See Consolidated Communications Holdings, Inc.; *U.S. Public*, pg. 570
SUREWEST TELEPHONE—See Consolidated Communications Holdings, Inc.; *U.S. Public*, pg. 570
SUTTLE, INC.—See Pineapple Energy Inc.; *U.S. Public*, pg. 1691
T3 COMMUNICATIONS, INC.—See Digerati Technologies, Inc.; *U.S. Public*, pg. 661

TAMPEREEN TIETOVERKKO OY—See Elisa Corporation; *Int'l*, pg. 2361
TDC SOLUTIONS A/S—See Arbejdsmarkedets Tillaegspension; *Int'l*, pg. 537
TDS TELECOM—See Telephone & Data Systems, Inc.; *U.S. Public*, pg. 1997
TDS TELECOM—See Telephone & Data Systems, Inc.; *U.S. Public*, pg. 1997
TELE2 NETHERLANDS B.V.—See Deutsche Telekom AG; *Int'l*, pg. 2084
TELEBEC LIMITED PARTNERSHIP—See BCE Inc.; *Int'l*, pg. 926
TELECATS B.V.—See Concentrix Corporation; *U.S. Public*, pg. 565
TELECOM ARGENTINA S.A.—See Cablevision Holding S.A.; *Int'l*, pg. 1246
TELECOM COOK ISLANDS LIMITED—See Fiji National Provident Fund; *Int'l*, pg. 2661
TELECOM DECISION MAKERS, INC; *U.S. Private*, pg. 3960
TELECOM DEVELOPMENT COMPANY AFGHANISTAN LTD.—See Aga Khan Development Network; *Int'l*, pg. 199
TELEDYNAMIC COMMUNICATIONS INC.—See BCT Consulting, Inc.; *U.S. Private*, pg. 500
TELEKOM FINANZMANAGEMENT GMBH—See America Movil, S.A.B. de C.V.; *Int'l*, pg. 421
TELEMEDIA FREE ZONE LIMITED—See Belize Telecommunications Limited; *Int'l*, pg. 965
TELE-SYSTEM HARZ GMBH—See Morgan Stanley; *U.S. Public*, pg. 1473
TELE-TEC CONTRACTORS, INC.—See Frontier Communications Parent, Inc.; *U.S. Public*, pg. 887
TELKOM KENYA LIMITED—See Helios Investment Partners LLP; *Int'l*, pg. 3330
TELVISTA COMPANY; *U.S. Private*, pg. 3963
TENGOINTERNET; *U.S. Private*, pg. 3967
TESSELLIS S.P.A.—See Jefferies Financial Group Inc.; *U.S. Public*, pg. 1189
THING 5, LLC—See TZP Group LLC; *U.S. Private*, pg. 4269
TIMETRADE SYSTEMS, INC.—See Clearhaven Partners LP; *U.S. Private*, pg. 933
TOTAL ACCESS COMMUNICATION PUBLIC CO., LTD.—See Charoen Pokphand Group Co., Ltd.; *Int'l*, pg. 1453
TRI-COUNTY COMMUNICATIONS CORP.—See Telephone & Data Systems, Inc.; *U.S. Public*, pg. 1998
TRUCOM CORPORATION—See Windstream Holdings, Inc.; *U.S. Public*, pg. 2373
UAB ELTEL NETWORKS—See Eltel AB; *Int'l*, pg. 2371
UNICOM NEW CENTURY TELECOMMUNICATIONS CORPORATION LIMITED—See China United Network Communications Group Company Limited; *Int'l*, pg. 1561
UNIFIED COMMUNICATIONS PTE LTD—See Captii Limited; *Int'l*, pg. 1317
UNIFIEDONLINE, INC.; *U.S. Private*, pg. 4283
UNITED COMMUNICATION INDUSTRY PUBLIC COMPANY LIMITED—See Charoen Pokphand Group Co., Ltd.; *Int'l*, pg. 1453
UNITED UTILITIES, INC.—See Liberty Broadband Corporation; *U.S. Public*, pg. 1310
UNITELLER FINANCIAL SERVICES; *U.S. Private*, pg. 4302
UNITE PRIVATE NETWORKS, LLC—See Cox Enterprises, Inc.; *U.S. Private*, pg. 1078
UNIVERSAL NETWORK TELEVISION LLC—See Comcast Corporation; *U.S. Public*, pg. 540
UNIVERSAL TELESERVICES LLC; *U.S. Private*, pg. 4306
UPC TELEKABEL WIEN GMBH—See Deutsche Telekom AG; *Int'l*, pg. 2084
U.S. COLO, LLC—See American Tower Corporation; *U.S. Public*, pg. 111
UTAH BROADBAND, LLC—See Boston Omaha Corporation; *U.S. Public*, pg. 372
VALLEY NETWORK PARTNERSHIP—See Lumen Technologies, Inc.; *U.S. Public*, pg. 1348
VANTAGE SOFTWARE—See First Rate, Inc.; *U.S. Private*, pg. 1525
VERISSIMO GLOBAL, INC.; *U.S. Private*, pg. 4360
VERIZON COMMUNICATIONS INC.; *U.S. Public*, pg. 2283
VERIZON ENTERPRISE SOLUTIONS GROUP—See Verizon Communications Inc.; *U.S. Public*, pg. 2286
VERIZON PENNSYLVANIA INC.—See Verizon Communications Inc.; *U.S. Public*, pg. 2286
VERIZON WIRELESS - MIDWEST—See Verizon Communications Inc.; *U.S. Public*, pg. 2284
VIACOM GLOBAL SERVICES INC.—See National Amusements, Inc.; *U.S. Private*, pg. 2844
VIAG TELECOM BETEILGUNGS GMBH—See E.ON SE; *Int'l*, pg. 2260
VIASAT, INC.—See ViaSat, Inc.; *U.S. Public*, pg. 2292
VIATEL INFRASTRUCTURE (UK) LIMITED—See Digiweb Ltd.; *Int'l*, pg. 2124
VINSAT DIGITAL PRIVATE LIMITED—See Hinduja Global Solutions Ltd.; *Int'l*, pg. 3398
VIP COMMUNICATIONS, INC.; *U.S. Private*, pg. 4386
VIPER NETWORKS, INC.; *U.S. Public*, pg. 2298
VOIP-PAL.COM INC.; *U.S. Public*, pg. 2308
VOXITAS; *U.S. Private*, pg. 4414
VPLS INC.—See Evocative, Inc.; *U.S. Private*, pg. 1442

517112 — WIRELESS TELECOMMUN...

VR TELECOMMUNICATIONS GMBH & CO.—See E.ON SE; *Int'l*, pg. 2260
WATEEN TELECOM LIMITED—See Abu Dhabi Group; *Int'l*, pg. 71
WEBEX COMMUNICATIONS JAPAN, K.K.—See Cisco Systems, Inc.; *U.S. Public*, pg. 500
WEBEX COMMUNICATIONS UK, LTD.—See Cisco Systems, Inc.; *U.S. Public*, pg. 501
WHOLESALE CARRIER SERVICES, INC.; *U.S. Private*, pg. 4514
WIDEOPENWEST, INC.; *U.S. Public*, pg. 2369
WIDEOPENWEST NETWORKS, LLC—See WideOpenWest, Inc.; *U.S. Public*, pg. 2369
WINDSTREAM HOLDINGS, INC.; *U.S. Public*, pg. 2373
WINDSTREAM IOWA-COM, INC.—See Windstream Holdings, Inc.; *U.S. Public*, pg. 2373
WIRE AND WIRELESS TISAI SATELLITE LIMITED—See Essel Corporate Resources Pvt. Ltd.; *Int'l*, pg. 2510
THE WIRELESS EXPERIENCE GROUP—See Centre Partners Management LLC; *U.S. Private*, pg. 829
WTC WOHNEN & TELECOMMUNICATION GMBH & CO. KG—See Morgan Stanley; *U.S. Public*, pg. 1473
XPLORNET COMMUNICATIONS INC.—See Stonepeak Partners L.P.; *U.S. Private*, pg. 3829
ZIFF DAVIS, INC.; *U.S. Public*, pg. 2403

517112 — WIRELESS TELECOMMUNICATIONS CARRIERS (EXCEPT SATELLITE)

2ERGO AUSTRALIA PTY. LTD.—See Gomeeki Pty Ltd.; *Int'l*, pg. 3037
3D FUTURE VISION II, INC.; *U.S. Private*, pg. 9
3E TECHNOLOGIES INTERNATIONAL INC.—See Advent International Corporation; *U.S. Private*, pg. 100
5G NETWORKS HOLDINGS PTY. LTD.—See 5G Networks Limited; *Int'l*, pg. 13
727 COMMUNICATIONS, INC.; *U.S. Public*, pg. 9
A10 NETWORKS MALAYSIA SDN. BHD.—See A10 Networks, Inc.; *U.S. Public*, pg. 12
A1 BULGARIA EAD—See America Movil, S.A.B. de C.V.; *Int'l*, pg. 421
A1 HRVATSKA D.O.O.—See America Movil, S.A.B. de C.V.; *Int'l*, pg. 421
ACCENT TELECOM UK LIMITED—See CloudCoCo Group plc; *Int'l*, pg. 1662
ACCESS CO., LTD.; *Int'l*, pg. 88
ACCESSORY EXPORT, LLC; *U.S. Private*, pg. 53
ACCESS-POWER, INC.; *U.S. Private*, pg. 53
ACEAXIS LTD—See Ace Technologies Corp.; *Int'l*, pg. 95
ACHMEA INTERNE DIENSTEN N.V.—See Achmea B.V.; *Int'l*, pg. 103
ACSIP TECHNOLOGY CORP.; *Int'l*, pg. 117
ADDVALUE TECHNOLOGIES LTD.; *Int'l*, pg. 136
ADVANCED INFO SERVICE PLC; *Int'l*, pg. 159
ADVANCED WIRELESS NETWORK CO., LTD.—See Advanced Info Service Plc; *Int'l*, pg. 159
AEROFLEX LIMITED—See Viavi Solutions Inc.; *U.S. Public*, pg. 2295
AGENTEK, INC.; *U.S. Private*, pg. 127
AIRSPAN NETWORKS INC.—See Airspan Networks Holdings Inc.; *U.S. Public*, pg. 68
AIRSYS COMMUNICATIONS TECHNOLOGY LIMITED; *Int'l*, pg. 248
AIRTEL UGANDA LIMITED—See Bharti Enterprises Limited; *Int'l*, pg. 1013
AKA MEDIA INC; *U.S. Private*, pg. 144
ALASKA DIGITEL WIRELESS COMMUNICATIONS LLC; *U.S. Private*, pg. 150
ALGAR TELECOM S.A.; *Int'l*, pg. 317
ALLTEK TECHNOLOGY CORPORATION; *Int'l*, pg. 360
ALMA TELECOMMUNICATIONS KAZAKHSTAN JSC; *Int'l*, pg. 362
AMERICA MOVIL PERU, S.A.C.—See America Movil, S.A.B. de C.V.; *Int'l*, pg. 421
AMERICA MOVIL, S.A.B. DE C.V.; *Int'l*, pg. 421
AMERICAN TOWER INTERNATIONAL, INC.—See American Tower Corporation; *U.S. Public*, pg. 110
AMERICREW INC.; *U.S. Public*, pg. 113
AMOREG; *Int'l*, pg. 429
AMPER, S.A.; *Int'l*, pg. 433
AMX PARAGUAY, S.A.—See America Movil, S.A.B. de C.V.; *Int'l*, pg. 421
ANGEL TELECOM CORP.; *Int'l*, pg. 459
APIO (AFRICA) LTD; *Int'l*, pg. 515
APPFOG, INC.—See Lumen Technologies, Inc.; *U.S. Public*, pg. 1345
AP WIRELESS AUSTRALIA PTY LTD—See EQT AB; *Int'l*, pg. 2479
AP WIRELESS BELGIUM, BVBA—See EQT AB; *Int'l*, pg. 2479
AP WIRELESS CANADA, ULC—See EQT AB; *Int'l*, pg. 2479
ARDICOM DIGITAL COMMUNICATIONS INC.—See Arctic Co-Operatives Limited; *Int'l*, pg. 551
ARQIVA LIMITED—See Canada Pension Plan Investment Board; *Int'l*, pg. 1278
ARQIVA LIMITED—See Canada Pension Plan Investment Board; *Int'l*, pg. 1278

ARTERIA NETWORKS CORP.; *Int'l*, pg. 583
ARTIFICIAL LIFE ASIA LIMITED—See Artificial Life, Inc.; *Int'l*, pg. 584
ARTIFICIAL LIFE SOURCE HOLDING PLC—See Artificial Life, Inc.; *Int'l*, pg. 584
ARUBA NETWORKS, INC.—See HP Inc.; *U.S. Public*, pg. 1062
ARUBA NETWORKS INDIA PVT. LTD.—See HP Inc.; *U.S. Public*, pg. 1062
ASCOM (SWEDEN) AB—See Ascom Holding AG; *Int'l*, pg. 603
ASCOM TATECO AB—See Ascom Holding AG; *Int'l*, pg. 603
ASCOM UK GROUP LTD.—See Ascom Holding AG; *Int'l*, pg. 603
ASCOM (US) INC.—See Ascom Holding AG; *Int'l*, pg. 603
ASIACOM PHILIPPINES, INC.—See Deutsche Telekom AG; *Int'l*, pg. 2083
ASTEL JSC; *Int'l*, pg. 651
ATC FRANCE HOLDING S.A.S.—See American Tower Corporation; *U.S. Public*, pg. 110
ATC GERMANY SERVICES GMBH—See American Tower Corporation; *U.S. Public*, pg. 110
ATC MARKETING (UGANDA) LIMITED—See American Tower Corporation; *U.S. Public*, pg. 110
ATC PARAGUAY S.R.L.—See American Tower Corporation; *U.S. Public*, pg. 110
ATC SOUTH AFRICA SERVICES PTY LTD—See American Tower Corporation; *U.S. Public*, pg. 110
ATC TELECOM INFRASTRUCTURE PRIVATE LIMITED—See Brookfield Corporation; *Int'l*, pg. 1174
ATC TOWER (GHANA) LIMITED—See American Tower Corporation; *U.S. Public*, pg. 110
ATL TELECOM LIMITED; *Int'l*, pg. 673
ATN INTERNATIONAL, INC.; *U.S. Public*, pg. 224
AT&T COMUNICACIONES DIGITALES, S. DE R.L. DE C.V.—See AT&T Inc.; *U.S. Public*, pg. 219
AT&T MOBILITY LLC—See AT&T Inc.; *U.S. Public*, pg. 219
AT&T MOBILITY LLC—See AT&T Inc.; *U.S. Public*, pg. 219
AT&T MOBILITY LLC—See AT&T Inc.; *U.S. Public*, pg. 219
AT&T MOBILITY LLC—See AT&T Inc.; *U.S. Public*, pg. 219
AT&T MOBILITY LLC—See AT&T Inc.; *U.S. Public*, pg. 219
AT&T—See AT&T Inc.; *U.S. Public*, pg. 219
AURORA TELECOM CORPORATION—See Aurora Corporation; *Int'l*, pg. 713
AUTOCONT ONLINE A/S—See AutoCont Control Systems, s.r.o.; *Int'l*, pg. 726
AUTOMATED SYSTEMS DESIGN, INC.—See RAF Industries, Inc.; *U.S. Private*, pg. 3345
AVAYA UK - SCOTLAND OFFICE—See Silver Lake Group, LLC; *U.S. Private*, pg. 3656
AVAYA UK - SCOTLAND OFFICE—See TPG Capital, L.P.; *U.S. Private*, pg. 2169
AVIAT NETWORKS GHANA LIMITED—See Aviat Networks, Inc.; *U.S. Public*, pg. 245
AVIAT NETWORKS (INDIA) PRIVATE LIMITED—See Aviat Networks, Inc.; *U.S. Public*, pg. 245
AVIAT NETWORKS (S) PTE. LTD.—See Aviat Networks, Inc.; *U.S. Public*, pg. 245
AWI, INC.—See VIP Wireless, Inc.; *U.S. Private*, pg. 4387
AXIATA GROUP BERHAD; *Int'l*, pg. 768
AXICOM PTY LIMITED—See AustralianSuper Pty Ltd; *Int'l*, pg. 723
AXIS TEKNOLOGIES; *U.S. Private*, pg. 414
AZTEC NETWORKS, INC.; *U.S. Private*, pg. 416
BATELCO MIDDLE EAST COMPANY SPC—See Bahrain Telecommunications Company BSC; *Int'l*, pg. 801
BAYAN TELECOMMUNICATIONS HOLDINGS CORP.—See Deutsche Telekom AG; *Int'l*, pg. 2083
BDCOM ONLINE LIMITED; *Int'l*, pg. 929
BEARCOM INC. - CLEVELAND—See Bertram Capital Management, LLC; *U.S. Private*, pg. 540
BEC TECHNOLOGIES INC.—See Billion Electric Co., Ltd.; *Int'l*, pg. 1031
BELL ALIANT INC.—See BCE Inc.; *Int'l*, pg. 926
BELL EXPRESSVU, L.P.—See BCE Inc.; *Int'l*, pg. 926
BELL EXPRESSVU—See BCE Inc.; *Int'l*, pg. 926
BELL MOBILITY INC.—See BCE Inc.; *Int'l*, pg. 927
BELL MTS INC.—See BCE Inc.; *Int'l*, pg. 926
BERTRAM CORPORATION; *U.S. Private*, pg. 540
BETTWORK INDUSTRIES, INC.; *U.S. Public*, pg. 327
BHARTI AIRTEL LIMITED—See Bharti Enterprises Limited; *Int'l*, pg. 1012
BHATIA COMMUNICATION & RETAIL (INDIA) LIMITED; *Int'l*, pg. 1014
BINASAT COMMUNICATIONS BERHAD; *Int'l*, pg. 1033
BLACKBERRY AUSTRALIA PTY LIMITED—See BlackBerry Limited; *Int'l*, pg. 1060
BLACKBERRY AUSTRIA GMBH—See BlackBerry Limited; *Int'l*, pg. 1060
BLACKBERRY MOBILE SOUTH AFRICA (PROPRIETARY) LIMITED—See BlackBerry Limited; *Int'l*, pg. 1060
BLACKBERRY SINGAPORE PTE. LIMITED—See BlackBerry Limited; *Int'l*, pg. 1060
BLACK BOX NETWORK SERVICES—See Black Box Limited; *Int'l*, pg. 1057
BLACKWOOD COMMUNICATIONS—See Blackfoot Telephone Cooperative, Inc.; *U.S. Private*, pg. 573

BLUE EARTH VALLEY COMMUNICATIONS; *U.S. Private*, pg. 588
BLUESTREAM PROFESSIONAL SERVICES, LLC—See KGP Telecommunications, Inc.; *U.S. Private*, pg. 2301
BODYGUARDZ; *U.S. Private*, pg. 608
BOINGO LIMITED—See DigitalBridge Group, Inc.; *U.S. Public*, pg. 664
BOINGO WIRELESS, INC.—See DigitalBridge Group, Inc.; *U.S. Public*, pg. 664
BOOST MOBILE, LLC—See EchoStar Corporation; *U.S. Public*, pg. 711
BOUYGUES TELECOM SA—See Bouygues S.A.; *Int'l*, pg. 1122
BREDBAND2 I SKANDINAVIEN AB; *Int'l*, pg. 1144
BRIGHTSTAR 20:20 MOBILE—See Brightstar Capital Partners, L.P.; *U.S. Private*, pg. 653
BRIGHTSTAR ARGENTINA, S.A.—See Brightstar Capital Partners, L.P.; *U.S. Private*, pg. 653
BRIGHTSTAR COLOMBIA LTDA.—See Brightstar Capital Partners, L.P.; *U.S. Private*, pg. 653
BRIGHTSTAR MEXICO S.A. DE C.V.—See Brightstar Capital Partners, L.P.; *U.S. Private*, pg. 653
BRIGHTSTAR PARAGUAY S.R.L.—See Brightstar Capital Partners, L.P.; *U.S. Private*, pg. 653
BRIGHTSTAR PROCEEDOR DE SOLUCIONES TECNOLOGICAS S.A.—See Brightstar Capital Partners, L.P.; *U.S. Private*, pg. 653
BROADCASTER, INC.; *U.S. Private*, pg. 659
BROADPOINT, LLC—See MTPCS, LLC; *U.S. Private*, pg. 2809
BROAD SKY NETWORKS, LLC—See IntelliSite Corporation; *U.S. Private*, pg. 2106
BROOKSIDE ENTERPRISES, LLC; *U.S. Private*, pg. 665
BSG WIRELESS LIMITED—See GI Manager L.P.; *U.S. Private*, pg. 1694
BSM TECHNOLOGIES INC.—See Geotab, Inc.; *Int'l*, pg. 2941
BT REDCARE—See BT Group plc; *Int'l*, pg. 1203
BYBON GROUP COMPANY LIMITED; *Int'l*, pg. 1234
CABO VERDE TELECOM S.A.—See Altice Europe N.V.; *Int'l*, pg. 392
CALLMOBILE GMBH—See freenet AG; *Int'l*, pg. 2770
CANTV.NET—See Compania Anonima Nacional Telefonos de Venezuela; *Int'l*, pg. 1748
CAR TELEMATICS SA; *Int'l*, pg. 1319
CASCADE AUTOVON COMPANY—See Lumen Technologies, Inc.; *U.S. Public*, pg. 1345
CCATT LLC—See Crown Castle Inc.; *U.S. Public*, pg. 596
C.C.L.D. TECHNOLOGIES, INC.—See Crestview Partners, L.P.; *U.S. Private*, pg. 1098
CELCOMDIGI BERHAD; *Int'l*, pg. 1391
CELCOM (MALAYSIA) BERHAD—See Axiata Group Berhad; *Int'l*, pg. 768
THE CELERIS GROUP, LLC—See Microwave Transmission Systems, Inc.; *U.S. Private*, pg. 2704
CELL: CM LTD.—See EQT AB; *Int'l*, pg. 2479
CELLHIRE FRANCE SA—See Cellhire Plc; *Int'l*, pg. 1393
CELLHIRE (GERMANY) GMBH—See Cellhire Plc; *Int'l*, pg. 1393
CELLHIRE PLC; *Int'l*, pg. 1393
CELLHIRE USA LLC—See Cellhire Plc; *Int'l*, pg. 1393
CELLNET COMMUNICATIONS INC.; *U.S. Private*, pg. 807
CELLULAR ONE OF EAST CENTRAL ILLINOIS; *U.S. Private*, pg. 807
CELLULAR SALES OF KNOXVILLE, INC.; *U.S. Private*, pg. 808
CELLULAR SOUTH INC.—See Telapex Inc.; *U.S. Private*, pg. 3959
CELLULAR SOUTH—See Telapex Inc.; *U.S. Private*, pg. 3959
CENTURY CELLUNET INTERNATIONAL, INC.—See Lumen Technologies, Inc.; *U.S. Public*, pg. 1345
CENTURYLINK PUBLIC COMMUNICATIONS, INC.—See Lumen Technologies, Inc.; *U.S. Public*, pg. 1346
CENTURYTEL ACQUISITION LLC—See Lumen Technologies, Inc.; *U.S. Public*, pg. 1346
CENTURYTEL.COM, LLC—See Lumen Technologies, Inc.; *U.S. Public*, pg. 1348
CENTURYTEL INTERACTIVE COMPANY—See Lumen Technologies, Inc.; *U.S. Public*, pg. 1346
CENTURYTEL OF COLORADO, INC.—See Lumen Technologies, Inc.; *U.S. Public*, pg. 1346
CENTURYTEL OF INTER ISLAND, INC.—See Lumen Technologies, Inc.; *U.S. Public*, pg. 1346
CENTURYTEL OF NORTHWEST WISCONSIN, LLC—See Lumen Technologies, Inc.; *U.S. Public*, pg. 1346
CENTURYTEL OF OHIO, INC.—See Lumen Technologies, Inc.; *U.S. Public*, pg. 1346
CENTURYTEL OF OOLTEWAH-COLLEGEDALE, INC.—See Lumen Technologies, Inc.; *U.S. Public*, pg. 1346
CENTURYTEL SM TELECORP, INC.—See Lumen Technologies, Inc.; *U.S. Public*, pg. 1346
CENTURYTEL/TELEVIEW OF WISCONSIN, INC.—See Lumen Technologies, Inc.; *U.S. Public*, pg. 1346
CERAGON NETWORKS AS—See Ceragon Networks Ltd.; *Int'l*, pg. 1421
CFN SERVICES; *U.S. Private*, pg. 844

517112 — WIRELESS TELECOMMUN...   CORPORATE AFFILIATIONS

CHICKASAW PERSONAL COMMUNICATIONS, INC.—See Chickasaw Holding Company; *U.S. Private*, pg. 880
CHINA BESTER GROUP TELECOM CO., LTD.; *Int'l*, pg. 1486
CHINA GRENTECH CORPORATION LIMITED; *Int'l*, pg. 1505
CHINA MOBILE LIMITED—See China Mobile Communications Corporation; *Int'l*, pg. 1524
CHINA TOWER CORPORATION LIMITED; *Int'l*, pg. 1560
CHINA WI-MAX COMMUNICATIONS, INC.; *U.S. Private*, pg. 886
CHUNGHWA TELECOM CO., LTD.; *Int'l*, pg. 1598
CHUNGHWA TELECOM GLOBAL, INC.—See Chunghwa Telecom Co., Ltd.; *Int'l*, pg. 1598
CHUNGHWA TELECOM JAPAN CO., LTD—See Chunghwa Telecom Co., Ltd.; *Int'l*, pg. 1598
CHUNGHWA TELECOM SINGAPORE PTE LTD—See Chunghwa Telecom Co., Ltd.; *Int'l*, pg. 1598
CISCO SYSTEMS, INC.; *U.S. Public*, pg. 496
CLARION CANADA, INC.—See FORVIA SE; *Int'l*, pg. 2745
CLARO CHILE S.A.—See America Movil, S.A.B. de C.V.; *Int'l*, pg. 421
CLARO TELECOM PARTICIPACOES, S.A.—See America Movil, S.A.B. de C.V.; *Int'l*, pg. 421
CLOVER WIRELESS; *U.S. Private*, pg. 947
COASTAL COMMUNICATIONS, INC.—See Lumen Technologies, Inc.; *U.S. Public*, pg. 1346
COMBA TELECOM CO. LTD.—See Comba Telecom Systems Holdings Limited; *Int'l*, pg. 1708
THE COMEDY NETWORK—See BCE Inc.; *Int'l*, pg. 927
COMMDEX CONSULTING, LLC; *U.S. Private*, pg. 982
COMMNET WIRELESS, LLC—See ATN International, Inc.; *U.S. Public*, pg. 224
COMMUNICATIONS CORPORATION OF INDIANA—See Telephone & Data Systems, Inc.; *U.S. Public*, pg. 1997
COMMUNICATIONS INTERNATIONAL INC.; *U.S. Private*, pg. 988
COMMUNICATIONS NETWORK INC—See Kalona Cooperative Telephone Company; *U.S. Private*, pg. 2258
COMTECH KOREA CO., LTD.—See McWane, Inc.; *U.S. Private*, pg. 2645
COMUNICACION CELULAR S.A.—See America Movil, S.A.B. de C.V.; *Int'l*, pg. 421
COMWAVE NETWORKS, INC.; *Int'l*, pg. 1763
CONEXUS WORLD GLOBAL LLC—See Creative Realities, Inc.; *U.S. Public*, pg. 593
CONNECTED DEVELOPMENT; *U.S. Private*, pg. 1015
CONNECTIVITY WIRELESS, INC.—See TAC Partners, Inc.; *U.S. Private*, pg. 3920
CONNECT TECHNOLOGIES CORPORATION—See G Three Holdings Corp.; *Int'l*, pg. 2862
CONNEXION TECHNOLOGIES; *U.S. Private*, pg. 1018
CONSORCIO ECUATORIANO DE TELECOMUNICACIONES, S.A.—See America Movil, S.A.B. de C.V.; *Int'l*, pg. 421
CONSUMER CELLULAR, INC.—See GTCR LLC; *U.S. Private*, pg. 1804
CORE COMMUNICATION SERVICES LTD.; *Int'l*, pg. 1797
CORTEL BUSINESS SOLUTIONS, INC.—See Blueprint Technologies, Inc.; *U.S. Public*, pg. 366
COSMOTE MOBILE TELECOMMUNICATIONS SA—See Hellenic Telecommunications Organization S.A.; *Int'l*, pg. 3333
CRICKET WIRELESS LLC—See AT&T Inc.; *U.S. Public*, pg. 220
CROWN CASTLE INC.; *U.S. Public*, pg. 596
CROWN CASTLE NG WEST LLC—See Crown Castle Inc.; *U.S. Public*, pg. 596
CSE COMSOURCE PTY LTD—See CSE Global Ltd.; *Int'l*, pg. 1863
CTS ELECTRONIC COMPONENTS—See CTS Corporation; *U.S. Public*, pg. 603
CURRYS PLC; *Int'l*, pg. 1879
DANMAGI INDIA PVT. LTD—See Danmagi Group ApS; *Int'l*, pg. 1965
DANMAGI SERVICOS DE INFORMATICA LTDA.—See Danmagi Group ApS; *Int'l*, pg. 1965
DATAGARDENS, INC.—See Lumen Technologies, Inc.; *U.S. Public*, pg. 1346
DAVID MCDAVID AUTOMOTIVE GROUP—See Asbury Automotive Group, Inc.; *U.S. Public*, pg. 209
DAVID MCDAVID GMC—See David McDavid Automotive Group; *U.S. Private*, pg. 1170
DAVOLINK INC.; *Int'l*, pg. 1984
DCA SERVICES INC.—See Platinum Equity, LLC; *U.S. Private*, pg. 3202
DCS TOWER SUB, LLC—See American Tower Corporation; *U.S. Public*, pg. 111
DEBITEL AG—See freenet AG; *Int'l*, pg. 2770
DELTA COMMUNICATIONS, LLC—See Cable One, Inc.; *U.S. Public*, pg. 416
DELTEQ PTE. LTD.—See Digilife Technologies Limited; *Int'l*, pg. 2119
DEUTSCHE TELEKOM AG—See Deutsche Telekom AG; *Int'l*, pg. 2083
DEUTSCHE TELEKOM FRANCE—See Deutsche Telekom AG; *Int'l*, pg. 2083

DEUTSCHE TELEKOM SA/NV—See Deutsche Telekom AG; *Int'l*, pg. 2083
DEVELCON; *Int'l*, pg. 2086
DIALOG AXIATA PLC—See Axiata Group Berhad; *Int'l*, pg. 768
DIGICEL ARUBA—See Digicel Group Ltd.; *Int'l*, pg. 2119
DIGICEL (BARBADOS) LIMITED—See Digicel Group Ltd.; *Int'l*, pg. 2118
DIGICEL (BERMUDA) LIMITED—See Digicel Group Ltd.; *Int'l*, pg. 2118
DIGICEL BONAIRE—See Digicel Group Ltd.; *Int'l*, pg. 2119
DIGICEL (BVI) LIMITED—See Digicel Group Ltd.; *Int'l*, pg. 2118
DIGICEL CAYMAN LTD.—See Digicel Group Ltd.; *Int'l*, pg. 2119
DIGICEL CURACAO—See Digicel Group Ltd.; *Int'l*, pg. 2119
DIGICEL DOMINICA LTD.—See Digicel Group Ltd.; *Int'l*, pg. 2119
DIGICEL EL SALVADOR—See Digicel Group Ltd.; *Int'l*, pg. 2119
DIGICEL FIJI LTD—See Digicel Group Ltd.; *Int'l*, pg. 2119
DIGICEL GRENADA LTD.—See Digicel Group Ltd.; *Int'l*, pg. 2119
DIGICEL GROUP LTD.; *Int'l*, pg. 2118
DIGICEL GUYANA LTD.—See Digicel Group Ltd.; *Int'l*, pg. 2119
DIGICEL HAITI LTD.—See Digicel Group Ltd.; *Int'l*, pg. 2119
DIGICEL JAMAICA LTD.—See Digicel Group Ltd.; *Int'l*, pg. 2119
DIGICEL PANAMA LTD.—See Digicel Group Ltd.; *Int'l*, pg. 2119
DIGICEL (PNG) LIMITED—See Digicel Group Ltd.; *Int'l*, pg. 2118
DIGICEL SAMOA LIMITED—See Digicel Group Ltd.; *Int'l*, pg. 2119
DIGICEL (ST. LUCIA) LIMITED—See Digicel Group Ltd.; *Int'l*, pg. 2119
DIGICEL ST. VINCENT LIMITED—See Digicel Group Ltd.; *Int'l*, pg. 2119
DIGICEL (TONGA) LIMITED—See Digicel Group Ltd.; *Int'l*, pg. 2119
DIGICEL (TRINIDAD & TOBAGO) LIMITED—See Digicel Group Ltd.; *Int'l*, pg. 2119
DIGICEL TURKS & CAICOS LTD.—See Digicel Group Ltd.; *Int'l*, pg. 2119
DIGICEL VANUATU LTD.—See Digicel Group Ltd.; *Int'l*, pg. 2119
DIGI COMMUNICATIONS N.V; *Int'l*, pg. 2118
DIGILIFE TECHNOLOGIES LIMITED; *Int'l*, pg. 2119
DIGISPICE TECHNOLOGIES LTD.; *Int'l*, pg. 2120
DIGITAL DISPATCH INDIA PVT. LTD—See DDS Wireless International Inc.; *Int'l*, pg. 1994
DIGITAL DISPATCH (INTL) LTD—See DDS Wireless International Inc.; *Int'l*, pg. 1994
DIGITAL DISPATCH (ITL) PTE LTD—See DDS Wireless International Inc.; *Int'l*, pg. 1994
DIGITAL DISPATCH LTD—See DDS Wireless International Inc.; *Int'l*, pg. 1994
DIGITAL DISPATCH SCANDINAVIA AB—See DDS Wireless International Inc.; *Int'l*, pg. 1994
DIGITAL LEASH, LLC—See Tiptree Inc.; *U.S. Public*, pg. 2159
DIGITAL PHONE CO., LTD.—See Advanced Info Service Plc; *Int'l*, pg. 160
DIGITAL VIRGO ESPANA—See Digital Virgo Group SAS; *Int'l*, pg. 2123
DIRECTEL LLC; *U.S. Private*, pg. 1236
DIRECTEL HOLDINGS LIMITED; *Int'l*, pg. 2130
DOCOMO DIGITAL GERMANY GMBH—See Bango Plc; *Int'l*, pg. 836
DOCOMO DIGITAL LIMITED—See Bango Plc; *Int'l*, pg. 836
DOGUS TELEKOMUNIKASYON HIZMETLERI A.S.—See Dogus Holding AS; *Int'l*, pg. 2154
DONGHWA TELECOM CO. LTD—See Chunghwa Telecom Co., Ltd.; *Int'l*, pg. 1598
EADS SECURE NETWORKS—See Airbus SE; *Int'l*, pg. 246
EASSON HOLDINGS LIMITED; *Int'l*, pg. 2269
ECONET WIRELESS (PVT) LTD—See Econet Wireless Zimbabwe Limited; *Int'l*, pg. 2297
ECONET WIRELESS ZIMBABWE LIMITED; *Int'l*, pg. 2296
EE LIMITED—See BT Group plc; *Int'l*, pg. 1203
EIDEN COMMUNICATIONS CO., LTD.—See EDION Corporation; *Int'l*, pg. 2310
ELECTRONIC ENGINEERING CO.; *U.S. Private*, pg. 1355
ELISA CORPORATION; *Int'l*, pg. 2361
ELISA EESTI AS—See Elisa Corporation; *Int'l*, pg. 2361
ELTEL NETWORKS GMBH—See Eltel AB; *Int'l*, pg. 2371
EMBARQ COMMUNICATIONS, INC.—See Lumen Technologies, Inc.; *U.S. Public*, pg. 1346
EMBARQ MID-ATLANTIC MANAGEMENT SERVICES COMPANY—See Lumen Technologies, Inc.; *U.S. Public*, pg. 1346
EMBARQ MINNESOTA, INC.—See Lumen Technologies, Inc.; *U.S. Public*, pg. 1346
EMBLAZE MOBILE LTD.—See B.S.D. Crown Ltd.; *Int'l*, pg. 790
EMIRATES TELECOMMUNICATIONS GROUP COMPAPNY PJSC; *Int'l*, pg. 2382

EMKAT SOLUTIONS, INC.; *U.S. Private*, pg. 1383
EMMECOM S.R.L.—See Cassa Depositi e Prestiti S.p.A.; *Int'l*, pg. 1354
EMOZE LTD.—See B.S.D. Crown Ltd.; *Int'l*, pg. 790
EMPRESA DE TELECOMUNICACIONES DE BOGOTA SA; *Int'l*, pg. 2388
EMPRESAS Y CONTROLES EN COMUNICACIONES, S.A. DE C.V.—See America Movil, S.A.B. de C.V.; *Int'l*, pg. 421
ENTERPARTNERS CO., LTD; *Int'l*, pg. 2451
EPIC COMMUNICATIONS, INC.—See Microwave Transmission Systems, Inc.; *U.S. Private*, pg. 2704
E. RITTER COMMUNICATIONS, INC.—See E. Ritter & Company; *U.S. Private*, pg. 1304
E. RITTER COMMUNICATIONS, INC.—See Grain Management, LLC; *U.S. Private*, pg. 1751
ETIHAD ATHEEB TELECOMMUNICATION CO; *Int'l*, pg. 2523
EURONA WIRELESS TELECOM, S.A.; *Int'l*, pg. 2554
EUSKALTEL SA; *Int'l*, pg. 2559
EUTELSAT COMMUNICATIONS FINANCE S.A.S.—See Eutelsat Communications SA; *Int'l*, pg. 2559
EUTELSAT COMMUNICATIONS SA; *Int'l*, pg. 2559
EUTELSAT SERVICES UND BETEILIGUNGEN GMBH—See Eutelsat Communications SA; *Int'l*, pg. 2559
EUTELSAT VAS S.A.S.—See Eutelsat Communications SA; *Int'l*, pg. 2559
EXEO SANKO CORP.—See EXEO Group Inc.; *Int'l*, pg. 2583
EXERTIS (UK) LTD.—See DCC plc; *Int'l*, pg. 1990
EXFO ELECTRO-OPTICAL ENGINEERING INDIA PRIVATE LTD.—See EXFO Inc.; *Int'l*, pg. 2584
EXINDA INC.—See GFI Software S.A.; *Int'l*, pg. 2957
EXTERNET TELECOMMUNICATIONS SERVICE PROVIDER PUBLIC CO.; *Int'l*, pg. 2591
EXTREME NETWORKS SARL—See Extreme Networks, Inc.; *U.S. Public*, pg. 813
EXTREME NETWORKS SPAIN, SL—See Extreme Networks, Inc.; *U.S. Public*, pg. 813
EZETOP LTD.; *Int'l*, pg. 2594
FAITH WONDERWORKS, INC.—See Faith, Inc.; *Int'l*, pg. 2609
FATBEAM LLC—See SDC Capital Partners, LLC; *U.S. Private*, pg. 3581
FDLNET.CZ, S.R.O.—See CEZ, a.s.; *Int'l*, pg. 1427
FIBER ROADS, LLC—See EchoStar Corporation; *U.S. Public*, pg. 711
FJARSKIPTI HF.; *Int'l*, pg. 2697
FLUIDMESH NETWORKS LLC; *U.S. Private*, pg. 1552
FOCUS DIGITAL MEDIA LIMITED; *Int'l*, pg. 2719
FORENSIC TECHNOLOGY AEC THAILAND LIMITED—See Advent International Corporation; *U.S. Private*, pg. 100
FORENSIC TECHNOLOGY (EUROPE) LIMITED—See Advent International Corporation; *U.S. Private*, pg. 100
FULTON TECHNOLOGIES, INC.—See ADDvantage Technologies Group, Inc.; *U.S. Public*, pg. 40
FUNTALK CHINA HOLDINGS LIMITED; *Int'l*, pg. 2846
GAMMA COMMUNICATIONS PLC; *Int'l*, pg. 2878
GETWIRELESS, LLC; *U.S. Private*, pg. 1689
GINSMS INC.; *Int'l*, pg. 2977
GLOBAL ESCIENCE CORP.; *U.S. Private*, pg. 1714
GLOBALIVE COMMUNICATIONS INC.; *Int'l*, pg. 3004
GLOBALIVE TECHNOLOGY, INC.; *Int'l*, pg. 3004
GLOBAL SERVICE CENTER PUBLIC COMPANY LIMITED; *Int'l*, pg. 3000
GLOBALSTAR INC.; *U.S. Public*, pg. 946
GLOBAL TELESAT COMMUNICATIONS LIMITED—See NextPlat Corp.; *U.S. Public*, pg. 1526
GLOBAL TOWER, LLC—See American Tower Corporation; *U.S. Public*, pg. 111
GLOBAL VALLEY NETWORKS—See J.H. Evans Inc.; *U.S. Private*, pg. 2165
GLOBE TELECOM, INC.; *Int'l*, pg. 3006
GO2TEL.COM, INC.—See INNOVATE Corp.; *U.S. Public*, pg. 1126
GO INTERNET S.P.A.; *Int'l*, pg. 3017
GOLAN TELECOM LTD.—See IDB Development Corporation Ltd.; *Int'l*, pg. 3588
GOLDEN STATE CELLULAR, INC.—See Verizon Communications Inc.; *U.S. Public*, pg. 2284
GOLIVE! MOBILE, LLC; *U.S. Private*, pg. 1736
GOWIRELESS, INC.,; *U.S. Private*, pg. 1747
GOWIRELESS, INC.—See ABC Phones of North Carolina, Inc.; *U.S. Private*, pg. 36
GREATCALL, INC.—See Best Buy Co., Inc.; *U.S. Public*, pg. 326
GREEN PACKET NETWORKS (TAIWAN) PTE. LTD.—See Green Packet Berhad; *Int'l*, pg. 3072
GRENTECH INDIA PVT LTD—See China GrenTech Corporation Limited; *Int'l*, pg. 1505
GRENTECH PAKISTAN (PVT.) LTD—See China GrenTech Corporation Limited; *Int'l*, pg. 1505
GRENTECH RF COMMUNICATION NIGERIA LTD—See China GrenTech Corporation Limited; *Int'l*, pg. 1506
GTL INFRASTRUCTURE LIMITED; *Int'l*, pg. 3151
GTPL KCBPL BROADBAND PRIVATE LIMITED—See GTPL Hathway Ltd.; *Int'l*, pg. 3151

N.A.I.C.S. INDEX

517112 — WIRELESS TELECOMMUN...

GUEST-TEK INTERACTIVE ENTERTAINMENT LTD.; *Int'l*, pg. 3172
HANGZHOU EASTCOM CITY CO.LTD.—See Eastern communications Co., LTD.; *Int'l*, pg. 2272
HANGZHOU HUAXING CHUANGYE COMMUNICATION TECHNOLOGY STOCK CO., LTD.; *Int'l*, pg. 3248
HANSOL INTICUBE CO., LTD.; *Int'l*, pg. 3261
HAYAT COMMICATIONS COMPANY W.L.L.—See Hayat Communications Co. K.S.C.C.; *Int'l*, pg. 3290
HAYAT COMMICATIONS (MEA) FZCO—See Hayat Communications Co. K.S.C.C.; *Int'l*, pg. 3290
HELIO LLC—See EchoStar Corporation; *U.S. Public*, pg. 711
HELLENIC COMPANY FOR TELECOMMUNICATIONS & TELEMATIC APPLICATIONS S.A.; *Int'l*, pg. 3333
HIGH CONNEXION, S.A.S—See HighCo S.A.; *Int'l*, pg. 3387
HIKARI TSUSHIN, INC.; *Int'l*, pg. 3389
HITACHI KOKUSAI ELECTRIC EUROPE GMBH—See KKR & Co. Inc.; *U.S. Public*, pg. 1257
HITACHI KOKUSAI ELECTRIC, INC.—See KKR & Co. Inc.; *U.S. Public*, pg. 1257
HOLLEY COMMUNICATIONS CO. LTD.—See Holley Holding, Ltd.; *Int'l*, pg. 3451
HOMETOWN TELECOM; *U.S. Private*, pg. 1975
HOOAH LLC; *U.S. Private*, pg. 1977
HUAWEI TECHNOLOGIES INDIA PVT. LTD.—See Huawei Investment & Holding Co., Ltd.; *Int'l*, pg. 3515
HUAWEI TELECOMMUNICATIONS (INDIA) COMPANY PRIVATE LIMITED—See Huawei Investment & Holding Co., Ltd.; *Int'l*, pg. 3515
HUTCHISON 3G AUSTRIA GMBH—See CK Hutchison Holdings Limited; *Int'l*, pg. 1637
HUTCHISON ESSAR LIMITED—See CK Hutchison Holdings Limited; *Int'l*, pg. 1638
HUTCHISON ESSAR LIMITED—See Essar Global Limited; *Int'l*, pg. 2508
HUTCHISON TELECOMMUNICATIONS (AUSTRALIA) LIMITED—See CK Hutchison Holdings Limited; *Int'l*, pg. 1637
HUTCHISON TELECOMMUNICATIONS HONG KONG HOLDINGS LIMITED—See CK Hutchison Holdings Limited; *Int'l*, pg. 1638
HWACOM SYSTEMS, INC.; *Int'l*, pg. 3542
HYDEL INC.—See Equistone Partners Europe Limited; *Int'l*, pg. 2487
HYLA MOBILE, INC.—See Assurant, Inc.; *U.S. Public*, pg. 215
IBWAVE SOLUTIONS INC.—See Corning Incorporated; *U.S. Public*, pg. 579
ICANA B.V.—See Hon Hai Precision Industry Co., Ltd.; *Int'l*, pg. 3457
ICANA INC.—See Hon Hai Precision Industry Co., Ltd.; *Int'l*, pg. 3457
ICANA LTD.—See Hon Hai Precision Industry Co., Ltd.; *Int'l*, pg. 3457
IIVARI MONONEN OY; *Int'l*, pg. 3608
II-VI TAIWAN—See Coherent Corp.; *U.S. Public*, pg. 529
ILIAD S.A.; *Int'l*, pg. 3614
IMIMOBILE INTELLIGENT NETWORKS LIMITED—See Cisco Systems, Inc.; *U.S. Public*, pg. 499
INDUSTRIAL COMMUNICATIONS AND ELECTRONICS, INC.; *U.S. Private*, pg. 2065
INMARSAT SOLUTIONS (CANADA) INC. - MOUNT PEARL—See ViaSat, Inc.; *U.S. Public*, pg. 2292
INMARSAT SOLUTIONS (CANADA) INC.—See ViaSat, Inc.; *U.S. Public*, pg. 2292
INMARSAT SOLUTIONS GLOBAL LIMITED—See ViaSat, Inc.; *U.S. Public*, pg. 2292
INMARSAT SOLUTIONS GLOBAL LTD. - ABERDEEN—See ViaSat, Inc.; *U.S. Public*, pg. 2292
INNERWIRELESS, INC.—See Black Box Limited; *Int'l*, pg. 1058
INNOVATIVE COMMUNICATIONS; *U.S. Private*, pg. 2082
INPIXON CANADA, INC.—See XTI Aerospace, Inc.; *U.S. Public*, pg. 2393
INPIXON FEDERAL, INC.—See XTI Aerospace, Inc.; *U.S. Public*, pg. 2393
INSEEGO NORTH AMERICA, LLC—See Inseego Corp.; *U.S. Public*, pg. 1129
INTERDIGITAL CANADA LTEE.—See InterDigital, Inc.; *U.S. Public*, pg. 1144
INTERDIGITAL FACILITY COMPANY—See InterDigital, Inc.; *U.S. Public*, pg. 1144
INTERNATIONAL COMMUNICATION SERVICES LIMITED—See Belize Communications Limited; *Int'l*, pg. 965
INTEROP TECHNOLOGIES, LLC; *U.S. Private*, pg. 2122
INTEROUTE SLOVAKIA S.R.O.—See GTT Communications, Inc.; *U.S. Private*, pg. 1808
INTRADO EC INDIA PRIVATE LIMITED—See Apollo Global Management, Inc.; *U.S. Public*, pg. 152
INTRADO EC SINGAPORE PRIVATE LIMITED—See Apollo Global Management, Inc.; *U.S. Public*, pg. 152
INTRADO HONG KONG LIMITED—See Apollo Global Management, Inc.; *U.S. Public*, pg. 152
INTRADO JAPAN K.K—See Apollo Global Management, Inc.; *U.S. Public*, pg. 152

IRIDIUM WORLD COMMUNICATIONS LTD.; *U.S. Public*, pg. 1171
ISCO INTERNATIONAL LLC; *U.S. Private*, pg. 2143
ITOKK, INC.; *U.S. Public*, pg. 1175
I-WIRELESS INC.; *U.S. Private*, pg. 2026
IZON NETWORK, INC.; *U.S. Public*, pg. 1179
JAZZ WIRELESS DATA INC.—See KORE Wireless Group, Inc.; *U.S. Private*, pg. 2343
JET MULTIMEDIA TUNISIE SA—See Digital Virgo Group SAS; *Int'l*, pg. 2123
JOY! COMMUNICATIONS; *U.S. Private*, pg. 2238
KANAC CORP.—See EXEO Group Inc.; *Int'l*, pg. 2583
KANTONE HOLDINGS LTD—See Champion Technology Holdings Ltd; *Int'l*, pg. 1440
KODIAK NETWORKS, INC.—See Motorola Solutions, Inc.; *U.S. Public*, pg. 1478
L-3 COMMUNICATIONS GLOBAL NETWORK SOLUTIONS—See L3Harris Technologies, Inc.; *U.S. Public*, pg. 1282
L-3 POWER & CONTROL SYSTEMS GROUP—See L3Harris Technologies, Inc.; *U.S. Public*, pg. 1283
LENCO MOBILE INC.; *U.S. Private*, pg. 2421
LETSTALK.COM INC.—See Brightstar Capital Partners, L.P.; *U.S. Private*, pg. 653
LIGHTSQUARED COMPANY - CANADA—See Spectrum Brands Holdings, Inc.; *U.S. Public*, pg. 1915
LIVETV AIRFONE, LLC—See Gogo Inc.; *U.S. Public*, pg. 949
LOCUS TELECOMMUNICATIONS, INC.—See Telrite Holdings, Inc.; *U.S. Private*, pg. 3962
LOEA COMMUNICATIONS CORP.—See Trex Enterprises Corporation; *U.S. Private*, pg. 4219
LONG LINES, LLC—See Schurz Communications, Inc.; *U.S. Private*, pg. 3571
MACRO LYNX SDN. BHD.—See IGB Berhad; *Int'l*, pg. 3601
MADISON RIVER COMMUNICATIONS, LLC—See Lumen Technologies, Inc.; *U.S. Public*, pg. 1347
MAGICJACK VOCALTEC LTD.—See B. Riley Financial, Inc.; *U.S. Public*, pg. 262
MAGYAR TELEKOM TELECOMMUNICATIONS PLC—See Deutsche Telekom AG; *Int'l*, pg. 2083
MAJOR CUSTOM CABLE INC.—See VTG Corp.; *U.S. Private*, pg. 4415
MANAGE MOBILITY, LLC—See Sole Source Capital LLC; *U.S. Private*, pg. 3708
MASSIVE TELECOM—See I.T. Source; *U.S. Private*, pg. 2027
MASS RESPONSE DEUTSCHLAND GMBH—See America Movil, S.A.B. de C.V.; *Int'l*, pg. 421
MATRIX TELECOM, LLC—See Blue Casa Communications, Inc.; *U.S. Private*, pg. 586
MATRIX TELECOM, LLC—See Garrison Investment Group LP; *U.S. Private*, pg. 1646
MEBTEL, INC.—See Lumen Technologies, Inc.; *U.S. Public*, pg. 1347
MELLANOX TECHNOLOGIES JAPAN K.K.—See NVIDIA Corporation; *U.S. Public*, pg. 1558
MERU NETWORKS, INC.—See Fortinet, Inc.; *U.S. Public*, pg. 869
METALERT INC.; *U.S. Public*, pg. 1427
MICROSOFT MOBILE OY—See Microsoft Corporation; *U.S. Public*, pg. 1441
MIRON ENTERPRISES LLC; *U.S. Private*, pg. 2746
MIRS COMMUNICATIONS LIMITED—See Motorola Solutions, Inc.; *U.S. Public*, pg. 1478
MOBEX COMMUNICATIONS INC.; *U.S. Private*, pg. 2756
MOBILCOM COMMUNICATIONSTECHNIK GMBH—See freenet AG; *Int'l*, pg. 2770
MOBILEBITS HOLDINGS CORPORATION; *U.S. Private*, pg. 2757
MOBILE RADIO COMMUNICATIONS INC.; *U.S. Private*, pg. 2757
MOBILE SERVICE INTERNATIONAL CO. LTD.—See Digilife Technologies Limited; *Int'l*, pg. 2119
MOHAVE CELLULAR LTD. PARTNER; *U.S. Private*, pg. 2765
MONACO TELECOM SAM—See Bahrain Telecommunications Company BSC; *Int'l*, pg. 801
MORRIS COMMUNICATIONS, INC.; *U.S. Private*, pg. 2787
MOTION TM VERTRIEBS GMBH—See freenet AG; *Int'l*, pg. 2770
MOTOROLA AB—See Motorola Solutions, Inc.; *U.S. Public*, pg. 1478
MOTOROLA ASIA LIMITED—See Motorola Solutions, Inc.; *U.S. Public*, pg. 1478
MOTOROLA AUSTRALIA PTY. LTD.—See Motorola Solutions, Inc.; *U.S. Public*, pg. 1478
MOTOROLA B.V.—See Motorola Solutions, Inc.; *U.S. Public*, pg. 1478
MOTOROLA CHILE S.A.—See Motorola Solutions, Inc.; *U.S. Public*, pg. 1478
MOTOROLA DE COSTA RICA S.A.—See Motorola Solutions, Inc.; *U.S. Public*, pg. 1479
MOTOROLA GMBH—See Motorola Solutions, Inc.; *U.S. Public*, pg. 1478
MOTOROLA ISRAEL LIMITED—See Motorola Solutions, Inc.; *U.S. Public*, pg. 1478
MOTOROLA NEW ZEALAND LIMITED—See Motorola Solutions, Inc.; *U.S. Public*, pg. 1478

MOTOROLA SOLUTIONS CZ S.R.O.—See Motorola Solutions, Inc.; *U.S. Public*, pg. 1478
MOTOROLA SOLUTIONS ESPANA S.A.—See Motorola Solutions, Inc.; *U.S. Public*, pg. 1478
MOTOROLA VENEZUELA—See Motorola Solutions, Inc.; *U.S. Public*, pg. 1479
MOVILNET—See Compania Anonima Nacional Telefonos de Venezuela; *Int'l*, pg. 1748
MOVIUS INTERACTIVE CORPORATION; *U.S. Private*, pg. 2802
MTONE WIRELESS CORPORATION; *U.S. Private*, pg. 2809
MTONE WIRELESS TELECOMMUNICATIONS (SHANGHAI) CO., LTD.—See Mtone Wireless Corporation; *U.S. Private*, pg. 2809
MTSI, NORTHEAST DIVISION, INC.—See Microwave Transmission Systems, Inc.; *U.S. Private*, pg. 2704
NCELL PRIVATE LIMITED—See Axiata Group Berhad; *Int'l*, pg. 768
NEONWORX COMMUNICATIONS (THAILAND) CO., LTD.—See Communication and System Solution Public Company Limited; *Int'l*, pg. 1720
NETCOMM WIRELESS LIMITED—See Casa Systems, Inc.; *U.S. Public*, pg. 778
NETHAWK S.A.R.L—See EXFO Inc.; *Int'l*, pg. 2584
NETHAWK SOLUTIONS PVT. LTD.—See EXFO Inc.; *Int'l*, pg. 2584
NEW CELL, INC.—See Northeast Communications of Wisconsin Incorporated; *U.S. Private*, pg. 2949
NEW CINGULAR WIRELESS SERVICES, INC.—See AT&T Inc.; *U.S. Public*, pg. 220
NEXTEL COMMUNICATIONS ARGENTINA S.R.L.—See Cablevision Holding S.A.; *Int'l*, pg. 1246
NEXTEL TELECOMUNICACOES LTDA.—See America Movil, S.A.B. de C.V.; *Int'l*, pg. 421
NEXT GENERATION WIRELESS INC.; *U.S. Private*, pg. 2920
NEXT GLOBAL TECHNOLOGY SDN. BHD.—See Green Packet Berhad; *Int'l*, pg. 3072
NGT NETWORKS PTE. LTD.—See Green Packet Berhad; *Int'l*, pg. 3072
NII HOLDINGS, INC.; *U.S. Private*, pg. 2927
NOKIA MOBILE PHONES (KOREA) LTD.—See Microsoft Corporation; *U.S. Public*, pg. 1441
NOKIA MOBILE PHONES—See Microsoft Corporation; *U.S. Public*, pg. 1441
NOMAD DIGITAL LIMITED—See Alstom S.A.; *Int'l*, pg. 381
NORTHEAST COMMUNICATIONS OF WISCONSIN INCORPORATED; *U.S. Private*, pg. 2949
NOVATEL WIRELESS SOLUTIONS, INC.—See Inseego Corp.; *U.S. Public*, pg. 1129
NW TECH CAPITAL, INC.; *U.S. Public*, pg. 1558
OMNICOM MEDIA GROUP ASIA PACIFIC PTE LTD—See Omnicom Group Inc.; *U.S. Public*, pg. 1589
OMNITRACS, LLC—See Vista Equity Partners, LLC; *U.S. Private*, pg. 4399
ONE CRNA GORA DOO—See 4iG Nyrt.; *Int'l*, pg. 12
OPENWAVE MOBILITY, INC.—See Enea AB; *Int'l*, pg. 2410
ORANGE AUSTRIA TELECOMMUNICATION GMBH—See CK Hutchison Holdings Limited; *Int'l*, pg. 1637
ORASCOM TELECOM ALGERIE SPA—See Fonds National d'Investissement; *Int'l*, pg. 2725
PCTEL, INC.—See Amphenol Corporation; *U.S. Public*, pg. 132
PEAKNET, LLC—See Duke Energy Corporation; *U.S. Public*, pg. 691
PELEPHONE COMMUNICATIONS, LTD.—See Bezeq - The Israel Telecommunication Corp. Limited; *Int'l*, pg. 1006
PETROTEL SP. Z O.O—See Cyfrowy Polsat S.A.; *Int'l*, pg. 1895
PHONE.COM INC.; *U.S. Private*, pg. 3174
PHONES 4U LTD.—See BC Partners LLP; *Int'l*, pg. 925
PIONEER TELEPHONE; *U.S. Private*, pg. 3188
POINTRED TELECOM PVT. LTD.—See Gemini Communication Ltd.; *Int'l*, pg. 2916
POLKOMTEL S.A.—See Cyfrowy Polsat S.A.; *Int'l*, pg. 1895
POLYCOM DANMARK APS—See HP Inc.; *U.S. Public*, pg. 1064
PRIME COMMUNICATIONS LP; *U.S. Private*, pg. 3261
PRIMUS TELECOMMUNICATIONS (AUSTRALIA) PTY. LTD.—See Aware Super Pty Ltd; *Int'l*, pg. 752
PROJECTINA AG—See Advent International Corporation; *U.S. Private*, pg. 100
PTGI INTERNATIONAL CARRIER SERVICES LTD.—See INNOVATE Corp.; *U.S. Public*, pg. 1126
PT.GRENTECH INDONESIA—See China GrenTech Corporation Limited; *Int'l*, pg. 1506
PTI COMMUNICATIONS OF KETCHIKAN, INC.—See Lumen Technologies, Inc.; *U.S. Public*, pg. 1347
PT XL AXIATA TBK—See Axiata Group Berhad; *Int'l*, pg. 768
PURPLE COMMUNICATIONS, INC.—See Kinderhook Industries, LLC; *U.S. Private*, pg. 2306
QDI—See Arizona Wholesale Supply Company; *U.S. Private*, pg. 325
QINGDAO HAIER INTELLIGENT ELECTRONICS CO., LTD.—See Haier Smart Home Co., Ltd.; *Int'l*, pg. 3210
QUALCOMM CDMA TECHNOLOGIES (KOREA) Y.H.—See

517112 — WIRELESS TELECOMMUN...   CORPORATE AFFILIATIONS

QUALCOMM Incorporated; *U.S. Public*, pg. 1747
QUALCOMM GOVERNMENT TECHNOLOGIES—See QUALCOMM Incorporated; *U.S. Public*, pg. 1747
QUALCOMM INCORPORATED; *U.S. Public*, pg. 1747
QUALCOMM INTERNET SERVICES—See QUALCOMM Incorporated; *U.S. Public*, pg. 1747
QUALCOMM JAPAN—See QUALCOMM Incorporated; *U.S. Public*, pg. 1747
QUANZHOU LAKE COMMUNICATION CO., LTD.—See China GrenTech Corporation Limited; *Int'l*, pg. 1506
QUATRO RAIL TECH SOLUTIONS PVT. LTD.—See EMC Limited; *Int'l*, pg. 2376
QUICKPLAY MEDIA INC.—See Highview Capital, LLC; *U.S. Private*, pg. 1942
QUINTEL TECHNOLOGY LTD.—See Cirtek Holdings Philippines Corp.; *Int'l*, pg. 1618
QWEST BROADBAND SERVICES, INC.—See Lumen Technologies, Inc.; *U.S. Public*, pg. 1347
QWEST CORPORATION—See Lumen Technologies, Inc.; *U.S. Public*, pg. 1347
QX NETWORKING & DESIGN, INC.—See Trive Capital Inc.; *U.S. Private*, pg. 4239
RCS TELECOMMUNICATIONS PTY LTD—See CSE Global Ltd.; *Int'l*, pg. 1864
READY WIRELESS LLC; *U.S. Private*, pg. 3367
REALNETWORKS ASIA PACIFIC CO., LTD.—See RealNetworks, Inc.; *U.S. Private*, pg. 3369
REAL & VIRTUAL TECHNOLOGIES SDN BHD—See Digilife Technologies Limited; *Int'l*, pg. 2120
REDLINE COMMUNICATIONS GROUP INC.—See Aviat Networks, Inc.; *U.S. Public*, pg. 246
RENAISSANCE SCIENCES CORPORATION; *U.S. Private*, pg. 3397
RFIP INC.; *U.S. Private*, pg. 3420
ROBI AXIATA LIMITED—See Axiata Group Berhad; *Int'l*, pg. 768
RUSSELL CELLULAR, INC.; *U.S. Private*, pg. 3506
SAGEMCOM BROADBAND GERMANY GMBH—See Charterhouse Capital Partners LLP; *Int'l*, pg. 1456
SAGEMCOM BROADBAND SAS—See Charterhouse Capital Partners LLP; *Int'l*, pg. 1456
SAHA ADVANCE NETWORK CO., LTD.—See Advanced Info Service Plc; *Int'l*, pg. 160
SALEM COMMUNICATIONS HOLDING CORPORATION—See Salem Media Group, Inc.; *U.S. Public*, pg. 1836
SANJOLE INC.—See Keysight Technologies, Inc.; *U.S. Public*, pg. 1227
SASKATCHEWAN TELECOMMUNICATIONS HOLDINGS CORPORATION—See Crown Investments Corporation of Saskatchewan; *Int'l*, pg. 1857
SAUNALAHTI GROUP OYJ—See Elisa Corporation; *Int'l*, pg. 2361
SAVVIS COMMUNICATIONS K.K.—See Lumen Technologies, Inc.; *U.S. Public*, pg. 1347
SAVVIS FEDERAL SYSTEMS, INC.—See Lumen Technologies, Inc.; *U.S. Public*, pg. 1347
SAVVIS GERMANY GMBH—See Lumen Technologies, Inc.; *U.S. Public*, pg. 1347
SBA TELECOMMUNICATIONS, INC.—See SBA Communications Corporation; *U.S. Public*, pg. 1842
SCADATA SCIENTIFIC, LLC—See Wireless Ventures LLC; *U.S. Private*, pg. 4547
SEAL CONSULTING, INC.—See Lumen Technologies, Inc.; *U.S. Public*, pg. 1347
SENSEI, INC.—See Humana, Inc.; *U.S. Public*, pg. 1070
SERCOTEL, S.A. DE C.V.—See America Movil, S.A.B. de C.V.; *Int'l*, pg. 421
SG ENTERPRISES II, LLC; *U.S. Private*, pg. 3622
SHENANDOAH MOBILE CO. INC.—See Shenandoah Telecommunications Co.; *U.S. Public*, pg. 1874
SHENZHEN GRENTECH CO., LTD.—See China GrenTech Corporation Limited; *Int'l*, pg. 1506
SILICON IMAGE INDIA RESEARCH AND DEVELOPMENT PRIVATE LTD.—See Lattice Semiconductor Corporation; *U.S. Public*, pg. 1294
SINGTEL STRATEGIC INVESTMENTS PTE LTD.—See Advanced Info Service Plc; *Int'l*, pg. 160
SIOUX VALLEY WIRELESS—See Sioux Valley Energy; *U.S. Private*, pg. 3671
SITE COMMUNICATIONS, INC.—See Microwave Transmission Systems, Inc.; *U.S. Private*, pg. 2704
SMART AXIATA CO., LTD.—See Axiata Group Berhad; *Int'l*, pg. 768
SMART SYSTEMS LTDA.—See America Movil, S.A.B. de C.V.; *Int'l*, pg. 421
SOMA NETWORKS, INC.; *U.S. Private*, pg. 3711
SONAR RADIO CORP.; *U.S. Public*, pg. 1902
SOUTHERN COMMUNICATIONS SERVICES, INC.—See The Southern Company; *U.S. Public*, pg. 2131
SPECTRASITE COMMUNICATIONS, LLC—See American Tower Corporation; *U.S. Public*, pg. 111
SPIDERCLOUD WIRELESS, INC.—See Corning Incorporated; *U.S. Public*, pg. 579
SPIE COMMUNICATIONS SA—See Clayton, Dubilier & Rice, LLC; *U.S. Private*, pg. 926
SPLICE COMMUNICATIONS; *U.S. Private*, pg. 3759

SPRING COMMUNICATIONS—See Prime Communications LP; *U.S. Private*, pg. 3261
STANDARD TEL NETWORKS, INC.—See Blueprint Technologies, Inc.; *U.S. Private*, pg. 366
STARHOME MACH GMBH—See Vista Equity Partners, LLC; *U.S. Private*, pg. 4402
STARTRAK INFORMATION TECHNOLOGIES, LLC—See ORBCOMM, Inc.; *U.S. Public*, pg. 1614
STATMON TECHNOLOGIES CORP.; *U.S. Private*, pg. 3793
STRATAGEN SYSTEMS, INC.—See DDS Wireless International Inc.; *Int'l*, pg. 1994
STRATEGIC TELECOM SOLUTIONS; *U.S. Private*, pg. 3835
SUMMIT DIGITEL INFRASTRUCTURE PRIVATE LIMITED—See Data Infrastructure Trust; *Int'l*, pg. 1976
SUNSHINE ANSWERING SERVICE, INC.—See ECI Partners LLP; *Int'l*, pg. 2289
SUPER BROADBAND NETWORK CO., LTD.—See Advanced Info Service Plc; *Int'l*, pg. 160
SWEDTEL ARABIA LTD—See Al-Hejailan Group; *Int'l*, pg. 286
SWEDTEL INTERNATIONAL AB—See Al-Hejailan Group; *Int'l*, pg. 286
SWEDTEL INTERNATIONAL CO.—See Al-Hejailan Group; *Int'l*, pg. 286
SWEDTEL SEA SDN. BHD—See Al-Hejailan Group; *Int'l*, pg. 286
SYMBIO HOLDINGS LIMITED—See Aussie Broadband Ltd.; *Int'l*, pg. 716
SYNAPSE WIRELESS INC.—See McWane, Inc.; *U.S. Private*, pg. 2645
SYSOREX, INC.; *U.S. Public*, pg. 1977
TALKLINE GMBH—See freenet AG; *Int'l*, pg. 2770
TANGO TELECOM LIMITED—See CSG Systems International, Inc.; *U.S. Public*, pg. 601
T-CELLULAR, INC.; *U.S. Private*, pg. 3910
TECHFAITH INTELLIGENT HANDSET TECHNOLOGY LIMITED—See China TechFaith Wireless Communication Technology Limited; *Int'l*, pg. 1557
TECHFAITH (SHANGHAI)—See China TechFaith Wireless Communication Technology Limited; *Int'l*, pg. 1557
TECHFAITH (SHENZHEN)—See China TechFaith Wireless Communication Technology Limited; *Int'l*, pg. 1557
TECHNOLOGY RESOURCE CENTER OF AMERICA, LLC (TRCA); *U.S. Private*, pg. 3955
TELDATA; *U.S. Private*, pg. 3959
TELECO INC.; *U.S. Private*, pg. 3960
TELECOMMUNICATIONS MANAGEMENT, LLC—See Cable One, Inc.; *U.S. Public*, pg. 416
TELEFONOS DE MEXICO S.A.B. DE C.V.—See America Movil, S.A.B. de C.V.; *Int'l*, pg. 421
TELEKOM AUSTRIA TA AKTIENGESELLSCHAFT—See America Movil, S.A.B. de C.V.; *Int'l*, pg. 421
TELEKOM DEUTSCHLAND GMBH—See Deutsche Telekom AG; *Int'l*, pg. 2084
TELEKOM MALAYSIA INTERNATIONAL (CAMBODIA) CO. LTD.—See Axiata Group Berhad; *Int'l*, pg. 768
TELEPHONE USA OF WISCONSIN, LLC—See Lumen Technologies, Inc.; *U.S. Public*, pg. 1348
TELIA CARRIER AB—See Fjarde AP-fonden; *Int'l*, pg. 2697
TELIA CARRIER AB—See Forsta AP-fonden; *Int'l*, pg. 2737
TELMEX PERU, S.A.—See America Movil, S.A.B. de C.V.; *Int'l*, pg. 421
TELRAD CHILE S.A.—See EcoCash Holdings Zimbabwe Limited; *Int'l*, pg. 2295
TELRAD NETWORKS LTD.—See EcoCash Holdings Zimbabwe Limited; *Int'l*, pg. 2295
T.H.C. INTERNATIONAL CO., LTD.—See Digilife Technologies Limited; *Int'l*, pg. 2120
THREE IRELAND (HUTCHISON) LIMITED—See CK Hutchison Holdings Limited; *Int'l*, pg. 1638
THUMB CELLULAR LTD. PARTNERSHIP; *U.S. Private*, pg. 4165
TIANRONG INTERNET PRODUCTS & SERVICES, INC.; *U.S. Public*, pg. 2157
TIGO PVT LTD.—See Empresas Publicas de Medellin ESP; *Int'l*, pg. 2392
TING INC.—See EchoStar Corporation; *U.S. Public*, pg. 711
TING VIRGINIA, LLC—See EchoStar Corporation; *U.S. Public*, pg. 711
T-MOBILE AUSTRIA GMBH—See Deutsche Telekom AG; *Int'l*, pg. 2084
T-MOBILE CZECH REPUBLIC A.S.—See Deutsche Telekom AG; *Int'l*, pg. 2084
T-MOBILE INTERNATIONAL AG & CO. KG—See Deutsche Telekom AG; *Int'l*, pg. 2084
T-MOBILE NETHERLANDS BV—See Deutsche Telekom AG; *Int'l*, pg. 2084
T-MOBILE USA, INC.—See Deutsche Telekom AG; *Int'l*, pg. 2084
TOSYS NIIGATA CO., LTD.—See COMSYS Holdings Corporation; *Int'l*, pg. 1762
TOURTECH SUPPORT, INC.—See CES Power LLC; *U.S. Private*, pg. 842
TOWERCO; *U.S. Private*, pg. 4196
TOWERS DEVELOPMENT CORPORATION—See Crown Castle Inc.; *U.S. Public*, pg. 596

TPG TELECOM LIMITED—See CK Hutchison Holdings Limited; *Int'l*, pg. 1638
TRILOGY INTERNATIONAL PARTNERS LLC—See SG Enterprises II, LLC; *U.S. Private*, pg. 3622
TRIPLE S TOWERS, INC.—See Microwave Transmission Systems, Inc.; *U.S. Private*, pg. 2705
TRUE WIRELESS, INC; *U.S. Public*, pg. 4248
T-SYSTEMS BUSINESS SERVICES—See Deutsche Telekom AG; *Int'l*, pg. 2084
T-SYSTEMS INTERNATIONAL GMBH—See Deutsche Telekom AG; *Int'l*, pg. 2084
TURKCELL HOLDING AS—See Cukurova Holding A.S.; *Int'l*, pg. 1876
TVC COMMUNICATIONS, LLC—See WESCO International, Inc.; *U.S. Public*, pg. 2352
UBINETICS (VPT) LIMITED—See QUALCOMM Incorporated; *U.S. Public*, pg. 1748
ULTRA ELECTRONICS AUSTRALIA PTY LIMITED—See Advent International Corporation; *U.S. Private*, pg. 100
ULTRA ELECTRONICS FORENSIC TECHNOLOGY INC.—See Advent International Corporation; *U.S. Private*, pg. 100
UMNIAH MOBILE COMPANY PSC—See Bahrain Telecommunications Company BSC; *Int'l*, pg. 801
UNIFIED SIGNAL, INC.; *U.S. Private*, pg. 4283
UNILAVA CORPORATION; *U.S. Private*, pg. 4283
UNITED INFORMATION HIGHWAY CO., LTD.—See Charoen Pokphand Group Co., Ltd.; *Int'l*, pg. 1453
UNITED STATES CELLULAR CORPORATION—See Telephone & Data Systems, Inc.; *U.S. Public*, pg. 1998
UNITED TELEPHONE COMPANY OF PENNSYLVANIA LLC, THE—See Lumen Technologies, Inc.; *U.S. Public*, pg. 1348
UNITEK GLOBAL SERVICES, INC.—See Littlejohn & Co., LLC; *U.S. Private*, pg. 2472
UNITEK GLOBAL SERVICES, INC.—See New Mountain Capital, LLC; *U.S. Private*, pg. 2903
UNIVERSAL POWER SYSTEMS PRIVATE LIMITED—See Eros International Plc; *Int'l*, pg. 2497
UREACH TECHNOLOGIES, INC.—See Ribbon Communications Inc.; *U.S. Public*, pg. 1797
VERIZON BUSINESS GLOBAL LLC—See Verizon Communications Inc.; *U.S. Public*, pg. 2285
VERIZON WIRELESS - BARTLETT—See Verizon Communications Inc.; *U.S. Public*, pg. 2284
VERIZON WIRELESS - BEDMINSTER—See Verizon Communications Inc.; *U.S. Public*, pg. 2284
VERIZON WIRELESS - BELLEVUE—See Verizon Communications Inc.; *U.S. Public*, pg. 2285
VERIZON WIRELESS - BIRMINGHAM—See Verizon Communications Inc.; *U.S. Public*, pg. 2284
VERIZON WIRELESS - CHANDLER—See Verizon Communications Inc.; *U.S. Public*, pg. 2284
VERIZON WIRELESS - CLEVELAND—See Verizon Communications Inc.; *U.S. Public*, pg. 2284
VERIZON WIRELESS - COLUMBIA—See Verizon Communications Inc.; *U.S. Public*, pg. 2284
VERIZON WIRELESS - DOWNINGTOWN—See Verizon Communications Inc.; *U.S. Public*, pg. 2284
VERIZON WIRELESS - DUBLIN—See Verizon Communications Inc.; *U.S. Public*, pg. 2284
VERIZON WIRELESS - EL PASO—See Verizon Communications Inc.; *U.S. Public*, pg. 2284
VERIZON WIRELESS - ENGLEWOOD—See Verizon Communications Inc.; *U.S. Public*, pg. 2285
VERIZON WIRELESS - FAIRFIELD—See Verizon Communications Inc.; *U.S. Public*, pg. 2285
VERIZON WIRELESS - FLORENCE—See Verizon Communications Inc.; *U.S. Public*, pg. 2284
VERIZON WIRELESS FLORIDA—See Verizon Communications Inc.; *U.S. Public*, pg. 2285
VERIZON WIRELESS - FREDERICKSBURG—See Verizon Communications Inc.; *U.S. Public*, pg. 2284
VERIZON WIRELESS - FREDERICK—See Verizon Communications Inc.; *U.S. Public*, pg. 2284
VERIZON WIRELESS - GREENSBORO—See Verizon Communications Inc.; *U.S. Public*, pg. 2284
VERIZON WIRELESS - GREENVILLE—See Verizon Communications Inc.; *U.S. Public*, pg. 2284
VERIZON WIRELESS - GREENWOOD—See Verizon Communications Inc.; *U.S. Public*, pg. 2284
VERIZON WIRELESS - HENDERSONVILLE—See Verizon Communications Inc.; *U.S. Public*, pg. 2284
VERIZON WIRELESS - HOUSTON—See Verizon Communications Inc.; *U.S. Public*, pg. 2285
VERIZON WIRELESS - INDIANAPOLIS—See Verizon Communications Inc.; *U.S. Public*, pg. 2284
VERIZON WIRELESS - LANSING—See Verizon Communications Inc.; *U.S. Public*, pg. 2284
VERIZON WIRELESS - MINNEAPOLIS—See Verizon Communications Inc.; *U.S. Public*, pg. 2284
VERIZON WIRELESS - ORANGEBURG—See Verizon Communications Inc.; *U.S. Public*, pg. 2284
VERIZON WIRELESS - OVERLAND PARK—See Verizon Communications Inc.; *U.S. Public*, pg. 2284
VERIZON WIRELESS - OVIEDO—See Verizon Communications Inc.; *U.S. Public*, pg. 2285
VERIZON WIRELESS - SAINT LOUIS—See Verizon Com-

N.A.I.C.S. INDEX

517121 — TELECOMMUNICATIONS ...

munications Inc.; *U.S. Public*, pg. 2284
VERIZON WIRELESS - SOUTHFIELD—See Verizon Communications Inc.; *U.S. Public*, pg. 2284
VERIZON WIRELESS - SOUTH—See Verizon Communications Inc.; *U.S. Public*, pg. 2284
VERIZON WIRELESS - VANCOUVER—See Verizon Communications Inc.; *U.S. Public*, pg. 2285
VERIZON WIRELESS - WEST—See Verizon Communications Inc.; *U.S. Public*, pg. 2285
VERSATILE EUROPE LTD.—See Versatile Systems Inc.; *U.S. Private*, pg. 4369
VERSATILE SYSTEMS INC.; *U.S. Private*, pg. 4369
VHA CORP.; *U.S. Public*, pg. 4374
VIASAT - WIRELESS SERVICES DIVISION—See ViaSat, Inc.; *U.S. Public*, pg. 2292
VICTRA; *U.S. Public*, pg. 4379
VIDEO RIVER NETWORKS, INC.; *U.S. Public*, pg. 2297
VIP MOBILE D.O.O.—See America Movil, S.A.B. de C.V.; *Int'l*, pg. 421
VIP OPERATOR DOOEL—See America Movil, S.A.B. de C.V.; *Int'l*, pg. 421
VIP WIRELESS, INC.; *U.S. Private*, pg. 4387
VIRGIN MOBILE CANADA—See BCE Inc.; *Int'l*, pg. 927
VIRGIN MOBILE USA, INC.—See EchoStar Corporation; *U.S. Public*, pg. 711
VIRNETX, INC.—See VirnetX Holding Corp.; *U.S. Public*, pg. 2299
VISAGE MOBILE, INC.; *U.S. Private*, pg. 4389
VOCALTEC COMMUNICATIONS, LLC—See B. Riley Financial, Inc.; *U.S. Public*, pg. 262
VOCERA COMMUNICATIONS AUSTRALIA PTY LTD.—See Stryker Corporation; *U.S. Public*, pg. 1958
VOCERA COMMUNICATIONS UK LTD.—See Stryker Corporation; *U.S. Public*, pg. 1958
VODAFONE FIJI LTD.—See Fiji National Provident Fund; *Int'l*, pg. 2661
VODAFONE MALTA LTD.—See Bahrain Telecommunications Company BSC; *Int'l*, pg. 801
VODAFONE NEW ZEALAND LTD.—See Brookfield Corporation; *Int'l*, pg. 1189
VOICE 1 DIRECT LTD.; *U.S. Private*, pg. 4409
VOICENATION, LLC—See ECI Partners LLP; *Int'l*, pg. 2289
VOX NETWORK SOLUTIONS; *U.S. Private*, pg. 4414
VOZTELECOM OIGAA360, S.A.—See Gamma Communications PLC; *Int'l*, pg. 2878
WAFER SYSTEMS (HONG KONG) LIMITED—See GET Holdings Limited; *Int'l*, pg. 2946
WEST UC AUSTRALIA PTY LTD.—See Apollo Global Management, Inc.; *U.S. Public*, pg. 152
WEST UNIFIED COMMUNICATIONS SERVICES, INC.—See Apollo Global Management, Inc.; *U.S. Public*, pg. 152
WIGO—See Grupo Romero; *Int'l*, pg. 3135
WILKES COMMUNICATIONS; *U.S. Private*, pg. 4520
WINTHER WIRELESS AB—See DistIT AB; *Int'l*, pg. 2136
WIRECOMM SYSTEMS, INC.—See Littlejohn & Co., LLC; *U.S. Private*, pg. 2472
WIRECOMM SYSTEMS, INC.—See New Mountain Capital, LLC; *U.S. Public*, pg. 2903
WIRELESS COMMUNICATIONS INC.; *U.S. Private*, pg. 4546
WIRELESS PLUS, INC.—See Sentinel Capital Partners, L.L.C.; *U.S. Private*, pg. 3609
WIRELESS TECHNOLOGIES, INC.—See Cresco, Ltd.; *Int'l*, pg. 1840
WIRELESS TOYZ LLC; *U.S. Private*, pg. 4547
WIRELESS VENTURES LLC; *U.S. Private*, pg. 4547
WORLDCELL, INC.; *U.S. Private*, pg. 4568
WUHAN HONGXIN COMMUNICATION TECHNOLOGIES CO., LTD.—See FiberHome Technologies Group; *Int'l*, pg. 2652
WYND COMMUNICATIONS CORPORATION—See Kinderhook Industries, LLC; *U.S. Public*, pg. 2306
WYTEC INTERNATIONAL, INC.; *U.S. Public*, pg. 4579
X2NSAT, INC.; *U.S. Private*, pg. 4579
XIRGO TECHNOLOGIES, INC.—See Sensata Technologies Holding plc; *U.S. Public*, pg. 1866
XIRRUS, LLC—See Cambium Networks Corporation; *U.S. Public*, pg. 425
ZAKANG, INC.—See Cal-Comp Electronics (Thailand) pcl; *Int'l*, pg. 1261
ZAYO GROUP, LLC-LOUISEVILLE—See DigitalBridge Group, Inc.; *U.S. Public*, pg. 665
ZAYO GROUP, LLC-LOUISEVILLE—See EQT AB; *Int'l*, pg. 2482
ZHONGXIN CHUANGZHI (BEIJING) TECHNOLOGY LTD., CO.—See Addvalue Technologies Ltd.; *Int'l*, pg. 136

517121 — TELECOMMUNICATIONS RESELLERS

0800 REVERSE LIMITED—See BBG Communications, Inc.; *U.S. Private*, pg. 498
3 RIVERS TELEPHONE COOPERATIVE; *U.S. Private*, pg. 7
ACC BUSINESS—See AT&T Inc.; *U.S. Public*, pg. 218
ACCESSORYGEEKS.COM; *U.S. Private*, pg. 53

ACCESS POINT INC.—See GTT Communications, Inc.; *U.S. Private*, pg. 1808
ACE TELEPHONE ASSOCIATION; *U.S. Private*, pg. 57
ACS LONG DISTANCE LICENSE SUB, INC.—See ATN International, Inc.; *U.S. Public*, pg. 224
ACS LONG DISTANCE LICENSE SUB, INC.—See Freedom 3 Capital, LLC; *U.S. Private*, pg. 1603
ADVANCED TEL, INC.—See RTC Holdings, L.L.C.; *U.S. Private*, pg. 3498
ADVANTIX SOLUTIONS GROUP, INC.—See ScanSource, Inc.; *U.S. Public*, pg. 1843
AFFINITI LLC; *U.S. Private*, pg. 122
AFFINITY LLC - PENNSYLVANIA OFFICE—See Affiniti LLC; *U.S. Private*, pg. 122
AGGREGATO MOBILE PTY. LTD.—See Aggregato Global Pty. Ltd.; *Int'l*, pg. 209
AGGREGATO PREPAID PTY. LTD.—See Aggregato Global Pty. Ltd.; *Int'l*, pg. 209
AKL TELECOMMUNICATIONS GMBH—See TD Synnex Corp; *U.S. Public*, pg. 1985
ALASKA COMMUNICATIONS SYSTEMS GROUP, INC.—See ATN International, Inc.; *U.S. Public*, pg. 224
ALASKA COMMUNICATIONS SYSTEMS GROUP, INC.—See Freedom 3 Capital, LLC; *U.S. Private*, pg. 1603
ALASKA COMMUNICATIONS SYSTEMS HOLDINGS, INC.—See ATN International, Inc.; *U.S. Public*, pg. 224
ALASKA COMMUNICATIONS SYSTEMS HOLDINGS, INC.—See Freedom 3 Capital, LLC; *U.S. Private*, pg. 1603
ALASKA POWER & TELEPHONE—See Alaska Power & Telephone Company; *U.S. Public*, pg. 72
ALLCONNECT, INC.; *U.S. Public*, pg. 175
ALLIANCE GROUP SERVICES, INC.; *U.S. Private*, pg. 183
ALTEVA, INC.; *U.S. Private*, pg. 208
ALTURA COMMUNICATION SOLUTIONS, LLC—See Silver Oak Services Partners, LLC; *U.S. Private*, pg. 3661
AMA TECHTEL COMMUNICATIONS; *U.S. Private*, pg. 215
AMINO COMMUNICATIONS LIMITED—See Aferian plc; *Int'l*, pg. 185
ANGLIA TELECOM CENTRES LIMITED—See Daisy Group Limited; *Int'l*, pg. 1942
APPIA COMMUNICATIONS, INC.—See CallTower Inc.; *U.S. Private*, pg. 723
ARADIANT CORP.; *U.S. Private*, pg. 307
ARTEL, INC.; *U.S. Private*, pg. 340
ARVIG COMMUNICATIONS SYSTEMS—See Arvig Enterprises, Inc.; *U.S. Private*, pg. 344
ASIA ACCESS TELECOM, INC.; *U.S. Private*, pg. 351
AS TV PLAY BALTICS—See Providence Equity Partners L.L.C.; *U.S. Private*, pg. 3291
ATI TELECOM INTERNATIONAL COMPANY; *Int'l*, pg. 670
A&T SYSTEMS INC.; *U.S. Private*, pg. 21
AT&T EXTERNAL AFFAIRS—See Frontier Communications Parent, Inc.; *U.S. Public*, pg. 887
AT&T OF PUERTO RICO, INC.—See AT&T Inc.; *U.S. Public*, pg. 219
AT&T OPERATIONS, INC.—See AT&T Inc.; *U.S. Public*, pg. 219
AT&T—See AT&T Inc.; *U.S. Public*, pg. 218
AT&T—See AT&T Inc.; *U.S. Public*, pg. 218
AT&T—See AT&T Inc.; *U.S. Public*, pg. 218
AT&T—See AT&T Inc.; *U.S. Public*, pg. 219
AT&T—See AT&T Inc.; *U.S. Public*, pg. 219
AT&T SOUTHEAST—See AT&T Inc.; *U.S. Public*, pg. 219
ATX COMMUNICATIONS, INC.—See Windstream Holdings, Inc.; *U.S. Public*, pg. 2373
AUDIOCODES GMBH—See AudioCodes Ltd.; *Int'l*, pg. 701
AUDIOCODES INDIA PVT. LTD.—See AudioCodes Ltd.; *Int'l*, pg. 702
AUDIOCODES KOREA LTD.—See AudioCodes Ltd.; *Int'l*, pg. 702
AUDIOCODES LTD.—See AudioCodes Ltd.; *Int'l*, pg. 702
AUDIOCODES MEXICO—See AudioCodes Ltd.; *Int'l*, pg. 702
AUDIOCODES SINGAPORE—See AudioCodes Ltd.; *Int'l*, pg. 702
AUSSIE BROADBAND LTD.; *Int'l*, pg. 716
BAY SPRINGS TELEPHONE COMPANY, INC.—See Telephone Electronics Corporation; *U.S. Private*, pg. 3961
BBG COMMUNICATIONS, INC.; *U.S. Private*, pg. 498
BBG GLOBAL AG—See BBG Communications, Inc.; *U.S. Private*, pg. 498
BEN LOMAND RURAL TELEPHONE CO-OP, INC.; *U.S. Private*, pg. 523
BIG RIVER TELEPHONE COMPANY LLC; *U.S. Private*, pg. 554
BILENDI LIMITED—See Bilendi SA; *Int'l*, pg. 1023
BLACK BOX NETWORK SERVICES—See Black Box Limited; *Int'l*, pg. 1057
BLACKFOOT COMMUNICATIONS INC.—See Blackfoot Telephone Cooperative, Inc.; *U.S. Private*, pg. 573
BLACKFOOT TELEPHONE COOPERATIVE, INC.; *U.S. Private*, pg. 573
BLACKSTONE CALLING CARD, INC.; *U.S. Private*, pg. 576
BLEDSOE TELEPHONE COOPERATIVE CORPORATION; *U.S. Private*, pg. 580

BLUE CASA COMMUNICATIONS, INC.; *U.S. Private*, pg. 586
BLUE EARTH VALLEY COMMUNICATIONS—See Blue Earth Valley Communications; *U.S. Private*, pg. 588
BOB, LLC—See Windstream Holdings, Inc.; *U.S. Public*, pg. 2373
BRANDENBURG TELEPHONE COMPANY; *U.S. Private*, pg. 637
BRAZORIA TELEPHONE CO; *U.S. Private*, pg. 642
BRIGHTCOVE, INC.; *U.S. Public*, pg. 383
BROADVIEW NETWORKS HOLDINGS, INC.—See Windstream Holdings, Inc.; *U.S. Public*, pg. 2373
BULLSEYE TELECOM INC.—See Lingo Management, LLC; *U.S. Private*, pg. 2461
BUSINESS COMMUNICATIONS SYSTEMS, INC.—See Center For Computer Resources, LLC; *U.S. Private*, pg. 810
CALLONE; *U.S. Private*, pg. 722
CAMERON COMMUNICATION LLC—See Madison Dearborn Partners, LLC; *U.S. Private*, pg. 2540
CAMERON TELEPHONE COMPANY INC—See Madison Dearborn Partners, LLC; *U.S. Private*, pg. 2540
CANBY TELECOM; *U.S. Private*, pg. 733
CAPITAL TELECOMMUNICATIONS, INC.; *U.S. Private*, pg. 742
CAVALIER TELEPHONE, LLC—See Windstream Holdings, Inc.; *U.S. Public*, pg. 2373
CC COMMUNICATIONS; *U.S. Private*, pg. 799
CELLCOM ISRAEL LTD.—See IDB Development Corporation Ltd.; *Int'l*, pg. 3588
CENTRAL SCOTT TELEPHONE—See LICT Corporation; *U.S. Public*, pg. 1312
CENTRAL TEXAS TELEPHONE COOPERATIVE, INC.; *U.S. Private*, pg. 825
CENTRAL UTAH TELEPHONE, INC.—See LICT Corporation; *U.S. Public*, pg. 1312
CENTRIC TELECOM, INC.; *U.S. Private*, pg. 830
CENTURYLINK COMMUNICATIONS (IMPSAT) NEDERLAND B.V.—See Lumen Technologies, Inc.; *U.S. Public*, pg. 1345
CENTURYLINK COMMUNICATIONS ITALIA SRL—See Lumen Technologies, Inc.; *U.S. Public*, pg. 1345
CENTURYLINK COMUNICACOES DO BRASIL LTDA.—See Lumen Technologies, Inc.; *U.S. Public*, pg. 1345
CENTURYLINKECUADOR S.A.—See Lumen Technologies, Inc.; *U.S. Public*, pg. 1346
CENTURYLINK PANAMA—See Lumen Technologies, Inc.; *U.S. Public*, pg. 1346
CENTURYLINK PERU S.A.—See Lumen Technologies, Inc.; *U.S. Public*, pg. 1346
CENTURYTEL OF WISCONSIN, LLC—See Lumen Technologies, Inc.; *U.S. Public*, pg. 1346
CENTURYTEL OF WYOMING, INC.—See Lumen Technologies, Inc.; *U.S. Public*, pg. 1346
CERMATE TECHNOLOGIES INC.—See Advantech Co., Ltd.; *Int'l*, pg. 165
CERMATE TECHNOLOGIES (SHANGHAI) INC.—See Advantech Co., Ltd.; *Int'l*, pg. 165
THE CHAMPAIGN TELEPHONE COMPANY; *U.S. Private*, pg. 4007
CHARITON VALLEY TELEPHONE CORP.; *U.S. Private*, pg. 851
CHESTER TELEPHONE COMPANY; *U.S. Private*, pg. 875
CHICKAMAUGA TELEPHONE COMPANY—See Fail Telecommunications Corp.; *U.S. Private*, pg. 1461
CHICKASAW FINANCE COMPANY—See Chickasaw Holding Company; *U.S. Private*, pg. 880
CHICKASAW LONG DISTANCE COMPANY—See Chickasaw Holding Company; *U.S. Private*, pg. 880
CHICKASAW TELEPHONE COMPANY—See Chickasaw Holding Company; *U.S. Private*, pg. 880
CITIZENS TELECOMMUNICATIONS COMPANY OF MINNESOTA, LLC—See Frontier Communications Parent, Inc.; *U.S. Public*, pg. 887
CITIZENS TELECOMMUNICATIONS COMPANY OF NEBRASKA—See Frontier Communications Parent, Inc.; *U.S. Public*, pg. 887
CITY TELECOM INC.—See Hong Kong Technology Venture Company Limited; *Int'l*, pg. 3467
CJ INTERNET JAPAN CORP.—See CJ Corporation; *Int'l*, pg. 1632
CLARIN GLOBAL S.A.—See Grupo Clarin S.A.; *Int'l*, pg. 3125
CLI LAWYERS SA PTY. LTD.—See Archer Capital Pty. Ltd.; *Int'l*, pg. 547
COLUMBIA VENTURES BROADBAND, LLC—See Columbia Ventures Corporation; *U.S. Private*, pg. 978
COMBA TELECOM SYSTEMS LIMITED—See Comba Telecom Systems Holdings Limited; *Int'l*, pg. 1708
COMCAST CORP.—See Comcast Corporation; *U.S. Public*, pg. 537
COMMUNICATION SERVICES INC.; *U.S. Private*, pg. 988
COMMUNIGROUP OF K.C. INC.—See Telephone Electronics Corporation; *U.S. Private*, pg. 3961
COMPORIUM GROUP; *U.S. Private*, pg. 1002
COMPORIUM—See Comporium Group; *U.S. Private*, pg. 1002

517121 — TELECOMMUNICATIONS ...

CONNECTIONS ETC.—See Windstream Holdings, Inc.; *U.S. Public*, pg. 2373
CONNEX INTERNATIONAL INC.; *U.S. Private*, pg. 1018
CONSOLIDATED COMMUNICATIONS OF PENNSYLVANIA, LLC—See Consolidated Communications Holdings, Inc.; *U.S. Public*, pg. 570
CONVERGEONE UNIFIED TECHNOLOGY SOLUTIONS, INC.—See CVC Capital Partners SICAV-FIS S.A.; *Int'l*, pg. 1883
COOPERATIVE COMMUNICATIONS INC.—See Cooperative Holdings Inc.; *U.S. Private*, pg. 1042
COOPERATIVE HOLDINGS INC.; *U.S. Private*, pg. 1042
COPPER VALLEY TELE COOP INC.; *U.S. Private*, pg. 1045
CORNERSTONE TELEPHONE CO. LLC—See NewSpring Capital LLC; *U.S. Private*, pg. 2918
COUNTRYWIDE BROADBAND, LLC; *U.S. Private*, pg. 1067
CRAW-KAN TELEPHONE COOPERATIVE; *U.S. Private*, pg. 1086
CROCKETT TELEPHONE COMPANY, INC.—See Telephone Electronics Corporation; *U.S. Private*, pg. 3961
CSL TEXAS SYSTEM, LLC—See Windstream Holdings, Inc.; *U.S. Public*, pg. 2373
CTEK, INC.—See Digi International Inc.; *U.S. Public*, pg. 662
CTSI, LLC—See Frontier Communications Parent, Inc.; *U.S. Public*, pg. 887
CUBA CITY TELEPHONE EXCHANGE CO.—See LICT Corporation; *U.S. Public*, pg. 1312
DAISY COMMUNICATIONS LTD.—See Daisy Group Limited; *Int'l*, pg. 1942
DAISY CORPORATE SERVICES TRADING LIMITED—See Daisy Group Limited; *Int'l*, pg. 1943
DAISY WHOLESALE LIMITED—See Daisy Group Limited; *Int'l*, pg. 1942
DAISY WORLDWIDE LIMITED—See Daisy Group Limited; *Int'l*, pg. 1942
DB BROADBAND GMBH—See Deutsche Bahn AG; *Int'l*, pg. 2051
DEKALB TELEPHONE COOPERATIVE; *U.S. Private*, pg. 1192
DELTA TELEPHONE CO. INC.—See Telapex Inc.; *U.S. Private*, pg. 3959
DELTATHREE, LTD.—See deltathree, Inc.; *U.S. Private*, pg. 1202
DFT COMMUNICATIONS CORPORATION; *U.S. Private*, pg. 1220
DICE COMMUNICATIONS, INC.—See Waterfield Technologies, Inc.; *U.S. Private*, pg. 4453
DIGI COMMUNICATION SYSTEME GMBH—See Alpiq Holding AG; *Int'l*, pg. 372
DIGICORP, INC.—See Win, LLC; *U.S. Private*, pg. 4532
DIGITAL PLANET COMMUNICATIONS, INC.—See UPSTACK, Inc.; *U.S. Private*, pg. 4312
DIGI-TEL COMMUNICATIONS, LLC; *U.S. Private*, pg. 1229
DIRAD TECHNOLOGIES, INC.—See Telecloud, LLC; *U.S. Private*, pg. 3960
DOMINICAN COMMUNICATIONS CORP.; *U.S. Private*, pg. 1256
DOW MANAGEMENT COMPANY, INC.; *U.S. Private*, pg. 1268
DSCI, LLC—See Siris Capital Group, LLC; *U.S. Private*, pg. 3674
DUBOIS TELEPHONE EXCHANGE, INC.—See Range Telephone Cooperative, Inc.; *U.S. Private*, pg. 3354
DUN & BRADSTREET TECHNOLOGIES & DATA SERVICES PRIVATE LIMITED—See Cannae Holdings, Inc.; *U.S. Public*, pg. 429
DUN & BRADSTREET TECHNOLOGIES & DATA SERVICES PRIVATE LIMITED—See CC Capital Partners, LLC; *U.S. Private*, pg. 798
DUN & BRADSTREET TECHNOLOGIES & DATA SERVICES PRIVATE LIMITED—See Intercontinental Exchange, Inc.; *U.S. Public*, pg. 1142
DYNAMIC CONCEPTS INC.; *U.S. Private*, pg. 1297
EAGLE VALLEY TELEPHONE COMPANY—See Arvig Enterprises, Inc.; *U.S. Private*, pg. 344
EAGLE VALLEY TELEPHONE COMPANY—See Blue Earth Valley Communications; *U.S. Private*, pg. 588
EAGLE VALLEY TELEPHONE COMPANY—See Nuvera Communications, Inc.; *U.S. Public*, pg. 1556
EAST ASCENSION TELEPHONE COMPANY LLC—See RTC Holdings, L.L.C.; *U.S. Private*, pg. 3498
EASTEX TELEPHONE COOPERATIVE; *U.S. Private*, pg. 1321
EAST OTTER TAIL TELEPHONE COMPANY INC.—See Arvig Enterprises, Inc.; *U.S. Private*, pg. 345
EATEL CONSTRUCTION CO., INC.—See RTC Holdings, L.L.C.; *U.S. Private*, pg. 3498
EATELCORP INC.—See RTC Holdings, L.L.C.; *U.S. Private*, pg. 3498
ECHO 24, INC.; *U.S. Private*, pg. 1327
EDCO LLC; *U.S. Private*, pg. 1332
EDUCATION NETWORKS OF AMERICA, INC.—See ZelnickMedia Corp.; *U.S. Private*, pg. 4600
E&E ENTERPRISES GLOBAL, INC.; *U.S. Private*, pg. 1301
ELECTRONIC MEDIA SYSTEMS, INC.—See DigitalBridge Group, Inc.; *U.S. Public*, pg. 664
ELIZABETH TELEPHONE COMPANY—See Madison Dearborn Partners, LLC; *U.S. Private*, pg. 2540
ELLENSBURG TELEPHONE COMPANY—See Consolidated Communications Holdings, Inc.; *U.S. Public*, pg. 570
ENDEKA GROUP, INC.—See DigitalBridge Group, Inc.; *U.S. Public*, pg. 664
ENMR PLATEAU TELECOM; *U.S. Private*, pg. 1401
ENTANET INTERNATIONAL LTD.—See Antin Infrastructure Partners SAS; *Int'l*, pg. 483
EPOST—See Canada Post Corporation; *Int'l*, pg. 1282
EQS GROUP AG—See Thoma Bravo, L.P.; *U.S. Private*, pg. 4147
EQUINIX KOREA LLC—See Equinix, Inc.; *U.S. Public*, pg. 788
E. RITTER TELEPHONE COMPANY—See E. Ritter & Company; *U.S. Private*, pg. 1304
E. RITTER TELEPHONE COMPANY—See Grain Management, LLC; *U.S. Private*, pg. 1751
ETERNAL SPEECH, INC.; *Int'l*, pg. 2521
ETEX TELEPHONE COOPERATIVE; *U.S. Private*, pg. 1431
FAIL TELECOMMUNICATIONS CORP.; *U.S. Private*, pg. 1461
FARMERS TELECOMMUNICATIONS COOPERATIVE, INC.; *U.S. Private*, pg. 1479
FARMERS TELEPHONE CO. INC.; *U.S. Private*, pg. 1479
FARMERS TELEPHONE COOPERATIVE; *U.S. Private*, pg. 1479
FIDELITY COMMUNICATIONS CO.—See Cable One, Inc.; *U.S. Public*, pg. 416
FIRSTLIGHT FIBER, INC.—See Antin Infrastructure Partners SAS; *Int'l*, pg. 483
FIVE AREA TELEPHONE COOP INC.; *U.S. Private*, pg. 1537
FLASH NETWORKS INC.—See Constellation Software Inc.; *Int'l*, pg. 1775
FLASH NETWORKS SINGAPORE PTE LTD—See Constellation Software Inc.; *Int'l*, pg. 1775
FOLKERSON COMMUNICATIONS, LTD.—See Renaissance Systems, Inc.; *U.S. Private*, pg. 3397
FON WIRELESS LTD.; *Int'l*, pg. 2724
FORT RANDALL TELEPHONE COMPANY—See Hanson Communications Inc.; *U.S. Private*, pg. 1856
FRANKLIN TELEPHONE COMPANY INC.—See Telapex Inc.; *U.S. Private*, pg. 3959
FRONTIER COMMUNICATIONS OF BREEZEWOOD, LLC—See Frontier Communications Parent, Inc.; *U.S. Public*, pg. 887
FRONTIER COMMUNICATIONS OF MICHIGAN, INC.—See Frontier Communications Parent, Inc.; *U.S. Public*, pg. 887
FRONTIER COMMUNICATIONS OF MINNESOTA, INC.—See Frontier Communications Parent, Inc.; *U.S. Public*, pg. 887
FRONTIER COMMUNICATIONS OF MISSISSIPPI LLC—See Frontier Communications Parent, Inc.; *U.S. Public*, pg. 887
FRONTIER COMMUNICATIONS OF MT. PULASKI, INC.—See Frontier Communications Parent, Inc.; *U.S. Public*, pg. 887
FRONTIER COMMUNICATIONS OF NEW YORK, INC.—See Frontier Communications Parent, Inc.; *U.S. Public*, pg. 887
FRONTIER COMMUNICATIONS OF PENNSYLVANIA, LLC—See Frontier Communications Parent, Inc.; *U.S. Public*, pg. 887
FRONTIER COMMUNICATIONS OF WISCONSIN LLC—See Frontier Communications Parent, Inc.; *U.S. Public*, pg. 887
FRONTIER COMMUNICATIONS—See Frontier Communications Parent, Inc.; *U.S. Public*, pg. 887
FRONTIER NORTH INC.—See Frontier Communications Parent, Inc.; *U.S. Public*, pg. 887
FRONTIER WEST VIRGINIA INC.—See Frontier Communications Parent, Inc.; *U.S. Public*, pg. 887
FRONTIER WEST VIRGINIA INC.—See Frontier Communications Parent, Inc.; *U.S. Public*, pg. 887
FRONTIER WEST VIRGINIA INC.—See Frontier Communications Parent, Inc.; *U.S. Public*, pg. 887
FUSION CONNECT, INC.; *U.S. Private*, pg. 1625
GAMEWOOD TECHNOLOGY GROUP, INC.; *U.S. Private*, pg. 1640
G C PAN EUROPEAN CROSSING FRANCE; *Int'l*, pg. 2861
GLOBAL CONNECTION INC. OF AMERICA—See Milestone Partners Ltd.; *U.S. Private*, pg. 2728
GOLDEN WEST TELECOMMUNICATIONS; *U.S. Private*, pg. 1734
GRAND RIVER MUTUAL TELEPHONE CORPORATION; *U.S. Private*, pg. 1753
GST NET INC.; *U.S. Private*, pg. 1801
GUADALUPE VALLEY TELECOMMUNICATIONS COOPERATIVE—See GVTC Communications; *U.S. Private*, pg. 1821
GUEST-TEK INTERACTIVE ENTERTAINMENT INC—See Guest-Tek Interactive Entertainment Ltd.; *Int'l*, pg. 3172
GUEST-TEK INTERACTIVE ENTERTAINMENT SP. Z O.O.—See Guest-Tek Interactive Entertainment Ltd.; *Int'l*, pg. 3172
GUEST-TEK INTERNATIONAL GROUP LTD—See Guest-Tek Interactive Entertainment Ltd.; *Int'l*, pg. 3172
GVTC COMMUNICATIONS; *U.S. Private*, pg. 1821
HANSON COMMUNICATIONS INC.; *U.S. Private*, pg. 1856
HART TELEPHONE COMPANY INC.—See Lintel Inc.; *U.S. Private*, pg. 2463
HAVILAND TELEPHONE COMPANY, INC.—See LICT Corporation; *U.S. Public*, pg. 1312
HIGHLAND TELEPHONE COOPERATIVE, INC.; *U.S. Private*, pg. 1939
HOME TELEPHONE COMPANY INC.; *U.S. Private*, pg. 1972
HOP-ON, INC.; *U.S. Public*, pg. 1052
HORRY TELEPHONE LONG DISTANCE—See HTC Inc.; *U.S. Private*, pg. 1999
HTC HOLDING COMPANY; *U.S. Private*, pg. 1999
HTC INC.; *U.S. Private*, pg. 1999
HUTCHINSON TELEPHONE COMPANY—See Nuvera Communications, Inc.; *U.S. Public*, pg. 1556
IDEATEK TELECOM, LLC—See DigitalBridge Group, Inc.; *U.S. Public*, pg. 665
IDEATEK TELECOM, LLC—See EQT AB; *Int'l*, pg. 2482
IDT CARD SERVICES IRELAND LIMITED—See IDT Corporation; *U.S. Public*, pg. 1093
IDT CORPORATION; *U.S. Public*, pg. 1093
IDT RETAIL EUROPE LIMITED—See IDT Corporation; *U.S. Public*, pg. 1093
IDT TELECOM ASIA PACIFIC (AUSTRALIA) PTY. LTD.—See IDT Corporation; *U.S. Public*, pg. 1094
IKANO COMMUNICATIONS INC.—See Ikano Communications, Inc.; *U.S. Private*, pg. 2040
ILD CORP.; *U.S. Private*, pg. 2041
IMPACT TELECOM, INC.—See Blue Casa Communications, Inc.; *U.S. Private*, pg. 586
IMPACT TELECOM, INC.—See Garrison Investment Group LP; *U.S. Private*, pg. 1646
IM TELECOM, LLC—See KonaTel, Inc.; *U.S. Public*, pg. 1271
INLAND NETWORKS—See Western Elite Incorporated Services; *U.S. Private*, pg. 4492
INTELLA II, INC.—See Onstream Media Corporation; *U.S. Private*, pg. 3028
INTERACTIVE SERVICES NETWORK, INC.; *U.S. Private*, pg. 2108
INTER-COMMUNITY TELEPHONE COMPANY—See LICT Corporation; *U.S. Public*, pg. 1312
INTERCONNECT SERVICES GROUP; *U.S. Private*, pg. 2109
INTERDIRECT TEL LTD.—See IDT Corporation; *U.S. Public*, pg. 1093
INTERSTATE TELECOM COOPERATIVE, INC.; *U.S. Private*, pg. 2126
IOWA NETWORK SERVICES INC.; *U.S. Private*, pg. 2135
IQSTEL INC.; *U.S. Public*, pg. 1167
ITSBCHAIN, LLC—See IQSTEL Inc.; *U.S. Public*, pg. 1167
J.B.N. TELEPHONE CO.—See LICT Corporation; *U.S. Public*, pg. 1312
KONATEL INC.—See KonaTel, Inc.; *U.S. Public*, pg. 1271
LAKE LIVINGSTON TELEPHONE COMPANY; *U.S. Private*, pg. 2375
LCD COMMUNICATIONS LLC—See PulteGroup, Inc.; *U.S. Public*, pg. 1737
LEACO RURAL TELEPHONE COOP INC.; *U.S. Private*, pg. 2405
LEVEL 3 CHILE S.A.—See Lumen Technologies, Inc.; *U.S. Public*, pg. 1347
LEVEL 3 COLOMBIA S.A.—See Lumen Technologies, Inc.; *U.S. Public*, pg. 1347
LEVEL 3 COMMUNICATIONS (ASIA PACIFIC) LIMITED—See Lumen Technologies, Inc.; *U.S. Public*, pg. 1347
LEVEL 3 COMMUNICATIONS AUSTRIA GMBH—See Lumen Technologies, Inc.; *U.S. Public*, pg. 1347
LEVEL 3 COMMUNICATIONS JAPAN KK—See Lumen Technologies, Inc.; *U.S. Public*, pg. 1347
LEVEL 3 COMMUNICATIONS PEC LUXEMBOURG II S.A.R.L.—See Lumen Technologies, Inc.; *U.S. Public*, pg. 1347
LEVEL 3 COMMUNICATIONS SINGAPORE PTE. LTD.—See Lumen Technologies, Inc.; *U.S. Public*, pg. 1347
LEVEL 3 MEXICO II, S. DE R.L. DE C.V.—See Lumen Technologies, Inc.; *U.S. Public*, pg. 1347
LEVEL 3 TELECOM OF ARIZONA, LLC—See Lumen Technologies, Inc.; *U.S. Public*, pg. 1347
LEVEL 3 TELECOM OF GEORGIA, LP—See Lumen Technologies, Inc.; *U.S. Public*, pg. 1347
LEVEL 3 TELECOM OF OREGON, LLC—See Lumen Technologies, Inc.; *U.S. Public*, pg. 1347
LEVEL 3 TELECOM OF SOUTH CAROLINA, LLC—See Lumen Technologies, Inc.; *U.S. Public*, pg. 1347
LEVEL 3 TELECOM OF TEXAS, LLC—See Lumen Technologies, Inc.; *U.S. Public*, pg. 1347
LEVEL 3 TELEKOMUNIKACIJSKI STORITVE D.O.O.—See Lumen Technologies, Inc.; *U.S. Public*, pg. 1347
LIMELIGHT NETWORKS JAPAN—See EDGIO, INC.; *U.S. Public*, pg. 719
LIMELIGHT NETWORKS (UK) LIMITED—See EDGIO, INC.; *U.S. Public*, pg. 718

N.A.I.C.S. INDEX

517121 — TELECOMMUNICATIONS ...

LINCOLNVILLE TELEPHONE COMPANY; *U.S. Private*, pg. 2459

LINGO MANAGEMENT, LLC; *U.S. Private*, pg. 2461

LINTEL INC.; *U.S. Private*, pg. 2463

LOGIX COMMUNICATIONS, L.P.—See Astra Capital Management LLC; *U.S. Private*, pg. 361

LONG DISTANCE DIRECT HOLDINGS; *U.S. Private*, pg. 2490

LONG DISTANCE DIRECT INC.—See Long Distance Direct Holdings; *U.S. Private*, pg. 2490

LUMEN TECHNOLOGIES EUROPE LIMITED—See Lumen Technologies, Inc.; *U.S. Public*, pg. 1347

LUMEN TECHNOLOGIES POLAND SP. Z O.O.—See Lumen Technologies, Inc.; *U.S. Public*, pg. 1347

LUMEN TECHNOLOGIES SWITZERLAND AG—See Lumen Technologies, Inc.; *U.S. Public*, pg. 1347

LYNTEGAR ELECTRIC COOPERATIVE INC.; *U.S. Private*, pg. 2522

MACH USA INC.—See Great Universal Incorporated; *U.S. Private*, pg. 1768

MCCOM, LTD.—See Hexatronic Group AB; *Int'l*, pg. 3371

MCDANIEL CELLULAR TELEPHONE COMPANY—See Telephone & Data Systems, Inc.; *U.S. Public*, pg. 1998

MCI INTERNATIONAL, INC.—See Verizon Communications Inc.; *U.S. Public*, pg. 2285

MCI, LLC—See Verizon Communications Inc.; *U.S. Public*, pg. 2285

MCI WORLDCOM NETWORK SERVICES, INC.—See Verizon Communications Inc.; *U.S. Public*, pg. 2285

MCLEODUSA INFORMATION SERVICES LLC—See Windstream Holdings, Inc.; *U.S. Public*, pg. 2373

MIDAS S.A.—See Cyfrowy Polsat S.A.; *Int'l*, pg. 1895

MIDCONTINENT COMMUNICATIONS—See Comcast Corporation; *U.S. Public*, pg. 538

MIDCONTINENT COMMUNICATIONS—See Midcontinent Media Inc.; *U.S. Private*, pg. 2711

MID-RIVERS TELEPHONE COOPERATIVE; *U.S. Private*, pg. 2708

MILLENNIUM TELCOM, LLC—See Ubiquity Management, L.P.; *U.S. Private*, pg. 4273

MOBILEONE LLC; *U.S. Private*, pg. 2758

MOBILETEL INC.—See RTC Holdings, L.L.C.; *U.S. Private*, pg. 3498

MORA VALLEY WIRELESS, LP—See ATN International, Inc.; *U.S. Public*, pg. 225

MRV COMMUNICATIONS AMERICAS, INC.—See ADTRAN Holdings, Inc.; *U.S. Public*, pg. 44

MULTIBAND CORPORATION—See Goodman Networks, Inc.; *U.S. Private*, pg. 1739

NATIONAL TELEPHONE OF ALABAMA, INC.—See Telephone Electronics Corporation; *U.S. Private*, pg. 3961

NECC TELECOM, INC.; *U.S. Private*, pg. 2879

NEDELCO INC.; *U.S. Private*, pg. 2879

NELLYMOSER, INC.; *U.S. Private*, pg. 2882

NEMONT TELEPHONE CO-OPERATIVE; *U.S. Private*, pg. 2884

NEPTUNE MARKETING TECHNOLOGIES; *U.S. Private*, pg. 2884

NERIM SASU—See Bouygues S.A.; *Int'l*, pg. 1122

NET2PHONE CABLE TELEPHONY, LLC—See IDT Corporation; *U.S. Public*, pg. 1094

NET SYSTEMS; *U.S. Private*, pg. 2886

NETWORK ENHANCED TELECOM LLP; *U.S. Private*, pg. 2889

NEW YORK TELECOM PARTNERS, LLC—See DigitalBridge Group, Inc.; *U.S. Public*, pg. 664

NEXXTWORKS, INC.; *U.S. Private*, pg. 2922

NITCO HOLDING CORPORATION; *U.S. Private*, pg. 2929

NOBEL LIMITED COMPANY; *U.S. Private*, pg. 2932

NORTEX COMMUNICATIONS COMPANY; *U.S. Private*, pg. 2939

NORTH CENTRAL TELEPHONE COOPERATIVE; *U.S. Private*, pg. 2944

NORTHSTAR ACCESS—See Windstream Holdings, Inc.; *U.S. Public*, pg. 2373

NORTH STATE COMMUNICATIONS, LLC—See EQT AB; *Int'l*, pg. 2480

NORTHWEST FIBER LLC; *U.S. Private*, pg. 2960

NOS COMMUNICATIONS INC.; *U.S. Private*, pg. 2964

NOVOLINK COMMUNICATIONS, INC.; *U.S. Private*, pg. 2968

NOW COMMUNICATIONS; *U.S. Private*, pg. 2968

NUUDAY A/S—See Arbejdsmarkedets Tillaegspension; *Int'l*, pg. 537

OBJECTIF LUNE MALAYSIA SDN. BHD.—See Upland Software, Inc.; *U.S. Public*, pg. 2264

THE OHIO BELL TELEPHONE COMPANY—See AT&T Inc.; *U.S. Public*, pg. 219

ONTARIO TELEPHONE COMPANY, INC.—See Keystone Group, L.P.; *U.S. Private*, pg. 2299

OPTICAL & TELECOMMUNICATION SOLUTIONS, INC.—See Fujikura Ltd.; *Int'l*, pg. 2827

ORILLION CORPORATION; *U.S. Private*, pg. 3042

ORILLION USA INC.—See Orillion Corporation; *U.S. Private*, pg. 3042

OTELCO INC.—See Keystone Group, L.P.; *U.S. Private*, pg. 2299

OTELCO TELECOMMUNICATIONS LLC—See Keystone Group, L.P.; *U.S. Private*, pg. 2299

OTT COMMUNICATIONS—See Keystone Group, L.P.; *U.S. Private*, pg. 2299

OXYLION S.A.—See Cyber_Folks S.A.; *Int'l*, pg. 1892

PACIFIC BELL TELEPHONE COMPANY—See AT&T Inc.; *U.S. Public*, pg. 219

PANHANDLE TELEPHONE COOP; *U.S. Private*, pg. 3086

PAYPAL PTE. LTD.—See PayPal Holdings, Inc.; *U.S. Public*, pg. 1656

PDT COMMUNICATIONS, LTD.—See Waterfield Technologies, Inc.; *U.S. Private*, pg. 4453

PEOPLES TELEPHONE CO., INC.—See Telephone Electronics Corporation; *U.S. Private*, pg. 3961

PEOPLE'S TELEPHONE COOPERATIVE, INC.; *U.S. Private*, pg. 3141

PHONETIME NETWORKS, INC.—See Tellza Inc.; *U.S. Public*, pg. 1999

PIEDMONT RURAL TELEPHONE COOPERATIVE INC.; *U.S. Private*, pg. 3178

PINELAND TELEPHONE COOPERATIVE, INC.; *U.S. Private*, pg. 3183

PIONEER TELEPHONE ASSOCIATION INC.; *U.S. Private*, pg. 3188

PIONEER TELEPHONE COOPERATIVE INC.; *U.S. Private*, pg. 3188

PIONEER TELEPHONE COOPERATIVE; *U.S. Private*, pg. 3188

PLANETONE COMMUNICATIONS INC.—See Avant Communications, Inc.; *U.S. Private*, pg. 404

PLANT TELEPHONE COMPANY; *U.S. Private*, pg. 3197

PONDEROSA TELEPHONE CO; *U.S. Private*, pg. 3227

PRAESES, LLC; *U.S. Private*, pg. 3241

PRIMACOM BERLIN GMBH—See Morgan Stanley; *U.S. Public*, pg. 1473

PRIMUS TELECOMMUNICATIONS CANADA INC.—See Distributel Communications Limited; *Int'l*, pg. 2136

PROTEL COMMUNICATIONS, INC.; *U.S. Private*, pg. 3290

PUBLIC SERVICE TELEPHONE CO; *U.S. Private*, pg. 3300

QGLOBAL SMS, LLC—See IQSTEL Inc.; *U.S. Public*, pg. 1167

QUALSAT, LLC—See QualTek Services Inc.; *U.S. Public*, pg. 1748

RADIANT HOLDINGS INC.; *U.S. Private*, pg. 3343

RADIANT TELECOM INC.—See Radiant Holdings Inc.; *U.S. Private*, pg. 3343

RANGE TELEPHONE COOPERATIVE INC.; *U.S. Private*, pg. 3354

REVCHAIN SOLUTIONS, LLC—See Windstream Holdings, Inc.; *U.S. Public*, pg. 2373

RICHLAND TOWERS - ORLANDO, LLC—See American Tower Corporation; *U.S. Public*, pg. 111

RNK INC.; *U.S. Private*, pg. 3452

ROANOKE TELEPHONE COMPANY, INC.—See Telephone Electronics Corporation; *U.S. Private*, pg. 3961

RONCO COMMUNICATIONS & ELECTRONICS INC.; *U.S. Private*, pg. 3478

ROW 44, INC.—See PAR Capital Management, Inc.; *U.S. Private*, pg. 3089

RT COMMUNICATIONS INC.—See Range Telephone Cooperative Inc.; *U.S. Private*, pg. 3354

RURAL TELECOMMUNICATIONS OF AMERICA, INC.; *U.S. Private*, pg. 3504

RURAL TELEPHONE SERVICE CO; *U.S. Private*, pg. 3505

SACO RIVER TELEPHONE LLC—See Keystone Group, L.P.; *U.S. Private*, pg. 2299

SACRED WIND ENTERPRISES, INC.—See ATN International, Inc.; *U.S. Public*, pg. 224

SATELLITE COMM SYSTEMS; *U.S. Private*, pg. 3553

SCANSOURCE EUROPE BV—See ScanSource, Inc.; *U.S. Public*, pg. 1843

SCHLUMBERGER LIMITED—See Schlumberger Limited; *U.S. Public*, pg. 1845

SCHLUMBERGER OILFIELD SERVICES—See Schlumberger Limited; *U.S. Public*, pg. 1845

SCHLUMBERGER—See Schlumberger Limited; *U.S. Public*, pg. 1844

SCHWARTZ VENTURES INC.; *U.S. Private*, pg. 3572

SCT TELECOM S.A.S.—See Astorg Partners S.A.S.; *Int'l*, pg. 657

SELECT COMMUNICATIONS, INC.; *U.S. Private*, pg. 3600

SELECTRONICS CORP.; *U.S. Private*, pg. 3602

SERVERPLUS LLC; *U.S. Private*, pg. 3614

SHENANDOAH NETWORK COMPANY INC.—See Shenandoah Telecommunications Co.; *U.S. Public*, pg. 1874

SHENANDOAH TELEPHONE COMPANY INC.—See Shenandoah Telecommunications Co.; *U.S. Public*, pg. 1874

SHENZHEN CERMATE TECHNOLOGIES INC.—See Advantech Co., Ltd.; *Int'l*, pg. 165

SIERRA CELLULAR INC.—See Sierra Telecommunications Group; *U.S. Private*, pg. 3648

SIERRA TELECOMMUNICATIONS GROUP; *U.S. Private*, pg. 3647

SIERRA TELEPHONE CO. INC.—See Sierra Telecommunications Group; *U.S. Private*, pg. 3648

SIGECOM, LLC—See WideOpenWest, Inc.; *U.S. Public*, pg. 2370

SILVER STAR COMMUNICATIONS; *U.S. Private*, pg. 3662

SISKIYOU TELEPHONE CO.; *U.S. Private*, pg. 3675

SITESTAR.NET, INC.—See ENDI Corp.; *U.S. Public*, pg. 760

SJI LLC—See RTC Holdings, L.L.C.; *U.S. Private*, pg. 3498

SKYLINE TELEPHONE MEMBERSHIP CORPORATION; *U.S. Private*, pg. 3685

SKY TELECOM TPC; *U.S. Private*, pg. 3684

SLEEPY EYE TELEPHONE COMPANY—See Arvig Enterprises, Inc.; *U.S. Private*, pg. 344

SLEEPY EYE TELEPHONE COMPANY—See Blue Earth Valley Communications; *U.S. Public*, pg. 588

SLEEPY EYE TELEPHONE COMPANY—See Nuvera Communications, Inc.; *U.S. Public*, pg. 1556

SMARTBIZ TELECOM LLC—See IQSTEL Inc.; *U.S. Public*, pg. 1167

SMART CITY NETWORKS LP—See US Cable Group; *U.S. Private*, pg. 4318

SMART CITY TELECOMMUNICATIONS LLC—See US Cable Group; *U.S. Private*, pg. 4318

SMITHVILLE TELEPHONE COMPANY INCORPORATED; *U.S. Private*, pg. 3698

SOLARUS; *U.S. Private*, pg. 3708

SOS TARIFFE S.R.L.—See Gruppo MutuiOnline S.p.A; *Int'l*, pg. 3141

SOUL COMMUNICATIONS PTY. LIMITED—See CK Hutchison Holdings Limited; *Int'l*, pg. 1638

SOUTH CENTRAL RURAL TELEPHONE; *U.S. Private*, pg. 3721

THE SOUTHERN NEW ENGLAND TELEPHONE COMPANY—See Frontier Communications Parent, Inc.; *U.S. Public*, pg. 887

SPECTROTEL, INC.—See Grain Management, LLC; *U.S. Private*, pg. 1751

SPOK HOLDINGS, INC.; *U.S. Public*, pg. 1919

SPRING COMMUNICATIONS HOLDING, INC.—See Prime Communications LP; *U.S. Private*, pg. 3261

SRT COMMUNICATIONS INC.; *U.S. Private*, pg. 3768

STANDARD MOBILE, INC.; *U.S. Private*, pg. 3781

STARTEC GLOBAL COMMUNICATIONS CORPORATION—See Platinum Equity, LLC; *U.S. Private*, pg. 3208

STAR TELEPHONE MEMBERSHIP CORP.; *U.S. Private*, pg. 3785

SUMMIT BROADBAND INC.—See Cable Bahamas Ltd.; *Int'l*, pg. 1246

SUPREME TELECOM SYSTEMS INC.; *U.S. Private*, pg. 3883

SWIFTREACH NETWORKS, INC.—See Motorola Solutions, Inc.; *U.S. Public*, pg. 1479

SWISSLINK CARRIER AG—See IQSTEL Inc.; *U.S. Public*, pg. 1167

SWITCH, INC.—See DigitalBridge Group, Inc.; *U.S. Public*, pg. 665

TC3 TELECOM INC.; *U.S. Private*, pg. 3942

TDS TELECOMMUNICATIONS CORPORATION—See Telephone & Data Systems, Inc.; *U.S. Public*, pg. 1998

TDS TELECOM—See Telephone & Data Systems, Inc.; *U.S. Public*, pg. 1997

TDS TELECOM—See Telephone & Data Systems, Inc.; *U.S. Public*, pg. 1997

TDS TELECOM—See Telephone & Data Systems, Inc.; *U.S. Public*, pg. 1997

TDS TELECOM—See Telephone & Data Systems, Inc.; *U.S. Public*, pg. 1997

TDS TELECOM—See Telephone & Data Systems, Inc.; *U.S. Public*, pg. 1997

TDS TELECOM—See Telephone & Data Systems, Inc.; *U.S. Public*, pg. 1997

TDS TELECOM—See Telephone & Data Systems, Inc.; *U.S. Public*, pg. 1997

TDS TELECOM—See Telephone & Data Systems, Inc.; *U.S. Public*, pg. 1997

TDS TELECOM—See Telephone & Data Systems, Inc.; *U.S. Public*, pg. 1997

TDS TELECOM—See Telephone & Data Systems, Inc.; *U.S. Public*, pg. 1997

TDS TELECOM—See Telephone & Data Systems, Inc.; *U.S. Public*, pg. 1997

TDS TELECOM—See Telephone & Data Systems, Inc.; *U.S. Public*, pg. 1997

TDS TELECOM—See Telephone & Data Systems, Inc.; *U.S. Public*, pg. 1997

TDS TELECOM—See Telephone & Data Systems, Inc.; *U.S. Public*, pg. 1997

TDS TELECOM—See Telephone & Data Systems, Inc.; *U.S. Public*, pg. 1997

TDS TELECOM—See Telephone & Data Systems, Inc.; *U.S. Public*, pg. 1997

517121 — TELECOMMUNICATIONS ...

TDS TELECOM—See Telephone & Data Systems, Inc.; *U.S. Public*, pg. 1997
TDS TELECOM—See Telephone & Data Systems, Inc.; *U.S. Public*, pg. 1998
TEC OF JACKSON INC.—See Telephone Electronics Corporation; *U.S. Private*, pg. 3961
TE-COM TELEKOMMUNIKATIONS-TECHNIK GMBH—See Alpiq Holding AG; *Int'l*, pg. 372
TEC SERVICES, INC.—See Telephone Electronics Corporation; *U.S. Private*, pg. 3961
TELAPEX INC.; *U.S. Private*, pg. 3959
TELCOIQ, INC.; *U.S. Private*, pg. 3959
TELEPHONE & DATA SYSTEMS, INC.; *U.S. Public*, pg. 1996
TELEPHONE ELECTRONICS CORPORATION; *U.S. Private*, pg. 3961
TELEPHONE SERVICE CO.; *U.S. Private*, pg. 3961
TELESPHERE—See Telesphere; *U.S. Private*, pg. 3962
TELLZA INC.; *U.S. Public*, pg. 1999
TELSEON INCORPORATED; *U.S. Private*, pg. 3962
TELTRONIC S.A.U.—See Hytera Communications Corporation Limited; *Int'l*, pg. 3555
TOUCH-N-BUY, LLC—See IDT Corporation; *U.S. Public*, pg. 1094
TOWNES TELE-COMMUNICATIONS; *U.S. Private*, pg. 4198
TPG CORPORATION LIMITED—See CK Hutchison Holdings Limited; *Int'l*, pg. 1638
TRACFONE WIRELESS, INC.—See Verizon Communications Inc.; *U.S. Public*, pg. 2285
TRANSCOMMUNICATIONS INC.; *U.S. Private*, pg. 4207
TRIANGLE TELEPHONE COOP ASSOCIATION; *U.S. Private*, pg. 4226
TRUMANSBURG TELEPHONE COMPANY, INC.—See Keystone Group, L.P.; *U.S. Private*, pg. 2300
TWIN LAKES TELEPHONE COOP. CORP.; *U.S. Private*, pg. 4265
UNION TELECARD ARIZONA, LLC—See IDT Corporation; *U.S. Public*, pg. 1094
UNION TELECOM TEXAS LLC—See IDT Corporation; *U.S. Public*, pg. 1094
UNION TELEPHONE COMPANY INC.; *U.S. Private*, pg. 4285
UNITED COMMUNICATIONS, INC.—See Warburg Pincus LLC; *U.S. Private*, pg. 4438
UNITED COMMUNICATION SYSTEMS; *U.S. Private*, pg. 4289
U.S. TELEPACIFIC CORP.—See Siris Capital Group, LLC; *U.S. Private*, pg. 3674
VALLEY TELEPHONE COOPERATIVE INC; *U.S. Private*, pg. 4335
VARDATA LLC; *U.S. Private*, pg. 4346
VERIZON COMMUNICATIONS INC. - CLARKSBURG, WV—See Verizon Communications Inc.; *U.S. Public*, pg. 2285
VERIZON COMMUNICATIONS INC. - LIVERPOOL, NY—See Verizon Communications Inc.; *U.S. Public*, pg. 2285
VERIZON COMMUNICATIONS INC. - WATERTOWN, NY—See Verizon Communications Inc.; *U.S. Public*, pg. 2285
VERIZON COMMUNICATIONS INC. - WHITE PLAINS, NY—See Verizon Communications Inc.; *U.S. Public*, pg. 2285
VERIZON DELAWARE INC.—See Verizon Communications Inc.; *U.S. Public*, pg. 2286
VERIZON ENHANCED COMMUNITIES—See Verizon Communications Inc.; *U.S. Public*, pg. 2286
VERIZON ENTERPRISE SOLUTIONS GROUP—See Verizon Communications Inc.; *U.S. Public*, pg. 2286
VERIZON LICENSE ADMINISTRATION GROUP—See Verizon Communications Inc.; *U.S. Public*, pg. 2286
VERIZON NETWORK INTEGRATION CORPORATION—See Verizon Communications Inc.; *U.S. Public*, pg. 2286
VERIZON NEW JERSEY INC.—See Verizon Communications Inc.; *U.S. Public*, pg. 2286
VERIZON NEW YORK INC.—See Verizon Communications Inc.; *U.S. Public*, pg. 2286
VERIZON NORTHWEST INC.—See Verizon Communications Inc.; *U.S. Public*, pg. 2286
VERIZON VIRGINIA INC.—See Verizon Communications Inc.; *U.S. Public*, pg. 2286
VERIZON VIRGINIA INC.—See Verizon Communications Inc.; *U.S. Public*, pg. 2286
VERIZON WIRELESS - BERGENFIELD—See Verizon Communications Inc.; *U.S. Public*, pg. 2284
VERIZON WIRELESS - BOCA RATON—See Verizon Communications Inc.; *U.S. Public*, pg. 2284
VERIZON WIRELESS - CHANDLER—See Verizon Communications Inc.; *U.S. Public*, pg. 2285
VERIZON WIRELESS - FAIR LAWN—See Verizon Communications Inc.; *U.S. Public*, pg. 2284
VERIZON WIRELESS - LANCASTER—See Verizon Communications Inc.; *U.S. Public*, pg. 2284
VERIZON WIRELESS - NASHVILLE—See Verizon Communications Inc.; *U.S. Public*, pg. 2285
VERIZON WIRELESS - SANTA MONICA—See Verizon Communications Inc.; *U.S. Public*, pg. 2285
VERIZON WIRELESS - STROUDSBURG—See Verizon Communications Inc.; *U.S. Public*, pg. 2284
VERIZON WIRELESS - WILMINGTON—See Verizon Communications Inc.; *U.S. Public*, pg. 2284
VIRTUAL VOUCHER (PROPRIETARY) LIMITED—See Blue Label Telecoms Limited; *Int'l*, pg. 1068
VISION COMMUNICATIONS—See RTC Holdings, L.L.C.; *U.S. Private*, pg. 3498
VOLCANO COMMUNICATIONS CO.; *U.S. Private*, pg. 4410
WAVE 3 COMMUNICATIONS INC.; *U.S. Private*, pg. 4458
WEBPASS, INC.—See Alphabet Inc.; *U.S. Public*, pg. 84
WESTEL, INC.; *U.S. Private*, pg. 4490
WESTERN BROADBAND, LLC—See Evergreen Pacific Partners Management Co., Inc.; *U.S. Private*, pg. 1440
WEST RIVER TELECOM COOP; *U.S. Private*, pg. 4487
WEST TENNESSEE TELEPHONE CO., INC.—See Telephone Electronics Corporation; *U.S. Private*, pg. 3961
WHIDBEY TELECOM; *U.S. Private*, pg. 4506
WHITEFENCE, INC.—See Allconnect, Inc.; *U.S. Private*, pg. 175
WILSHIRE CONNECTION, LLC; *U.S. Private*, pg. 4529
WINDSTREAM ALABAMA—See Windstream Holdings, Inc.; *U.S. Public*, pg. 2373
WINDSTREAM COMMUNICATIONS—See Windstream Holdings, Inc.; *U.S. Public*, pg. 2373
WINDSTREAM CORPORATION—See Windstream Holdings, Inc.; *U.S. Public*, pg. 2373
WINDSTREAM FLORIDA, INC.—See Windstream Holdings, Inc.; *U.S. Public*, pg. 2373
WINDSTREAM LEXCOM COMMUNICATIONS, INC.—See Windstream Holdings, Inc.; *U.S. Public*, pg. 2373
WIRELESS WORLD; *U.S. Private*, pg. 4547
WNM COMMUNICATIONS—See LICT Corporation; *U.S. Public*, pg. 1312
WORLD TELECOM GROUP—See AppDirect Inc.; *U.S. Private*, pg. 296
W W T, INC.; *U.S. Private*, pg. 4417
XCHANGE TELECOM CORP.—See Nova Infrastructure Management, LLC; *U.S. Public*, pg. 2965
XO COLORADO, LLC—See XO Holdings, Inc.; *U.S. Private*, pg. 4582
XO UTAH INC.—See XO Holdings, Inc.; *U.S. Private*, pg. 4582
YANKEE TELECOM INC.; *U.S. Private*, pg. 4586
ZAYO GROUP, LLC—See DigitalBridge Group, Inc.; *U.S. Public*, pg. 665
ZAYO GROUP, LLC—See EQT AB; *Int'l*, pg. 2482
ZCORUM INC.; *U.S. Private*, pg. 4598

517122 — AGENTS FOR WIRELESS TELECOMMUNICATIONS SERVICES

LIQUID INTELLIGENT TECHNOLOGIES LTD.—See EcoCash Holdings Zimbabwe Limited; *Int'l*, pg. 2294
NAVITEK OY—See BHG Group AB; *Int'l*, pg. 1015
TERRITORY GMBH—See Bertelsmann SE & Co. KGaA; *Int'l*, pg. 996

517410 — SATELLITE TELECOMMUNICATIONS

ABILITY INC.; *Int'l*, pg. 61
ACC TOWER SUB, LLC—See American Tower Corporation; *U.S. Public*, pg. 110
AIRBUS DEFENCE AND SPACE SAS—See Airbus SE; *Int'l*, pg. 245
AIRTEL GHANA LIMITED—See Bharti Enterprises Limited; *Int'l*, pg. 1012
AIRTEL MALAWI LIMITED—See Bharti Enterprises Limited; *Int'l*, pg. 1012
AIRTEL M COMMERCE SERVICES LIMITED—See Bharti Enterprises Limited; *Int'l*, pg. 1012
AIRTEL MOBILE COMMERCE HOLDINGS B.V.—See Bharti Enterprises Limited; *Int'l*, pg. 1012
AIRTEL NETWORKS LIMITED—See Bharti Enterprises Limited; *Int'l*, pg. 1012
AIRTEL NETWORKS ZAMBIA PLC—See Bharti Enterprises Limited; *Int'l*, pg. 1012
AIRTEL RWANDA LIMITED—See Bharti Enterprises Limited; *Int'l*, pg. 1012
AIRTEL (SEYCHELLES) LIMITED—See Bharti Enterprises Limited; *Int'l*, pg. 1012
AIRTEL TANZANIA LIMITED—See Bharti Enterprises Limited; *Int'l*, pg. 1012
AIRTEL TCHAD S.A.—See Bharti Enterprises Limited; *Int'l*, pg. 1012
ALTAMIRA INFORMATION SL—See Collecte Localisation Satellites; *Int'l*, pg. 1699
AL YAH SATELLITE COMMUNICATIONS COMPANY PJSC—See Bayanat AI PLC; *Int'l*, pg. 901
ANRITSU CO. LTD.—See Anritsu Corporation; *Int'l*, pg. 475
APPLIED SATELLITE TECHNOLOGY AUSTRALIA PTY LTD—See HAL Trust N.V.; *Int'l*, pg. 3226
APPLIED SATELLITE TECHNOLOGY LTD—See HAL Trust N.V.; *Int'l*, pg. 3226
APPLIED SATELLITE TECHNOLOGY SYSTEMS LTD—See HAL Trust N.V.; *Int'l*, pg. 3226
APPLIED SATELLITE TECHNOLOGY SYSTEMS US LLC—See HAL Trust N.V.; *Int'l*, pg. 3226
APT SATELLITE HOLDINGS LIMITED—See APT Satellite International Company Limited; *Int'l*, pg. 523
ARAB SATELLITE COMMUNICATIONS ORGANIZATION; *Int'l*, pg. 531
ASC SIGNAL DIVISION, INC.—See Kratos Defense & Security Solutions, Inc.; *U.S. Public*, pg. 1275
ASIA SATELLITE TELECOMMUNICATIONS CO., LTD.—See CITIC Group Corporation; *Int'l*, pg. 1619
ASIA SATELLITE TELECOMMUNICATIONS CO., LTD.—See The Carlyle Group Inc.; *U.S. Public*, pg. 2045
ASIA SATELLITE TELECOMMUNICATIONS HOLDINGS LIMITED—See CITIC Group Corporation; *Int'l*, pg. 1619
ASIA SATELLITE TELECOMMUNICATIONS HOLDINGS LIMITED—See The Carlyle Group Inc.; *U.S. Public*, pg. 2045
AST DISTRIBUTION ASIA PTE LTD—See HAL Trust N.V.; *Int'l*, pg. 3226
AST MARINE SCIENCES LTD—See HAL Trust N.V.; *Int'l*, pg. 3226
ATC GERMANY OPERATING 1 GMBH—See American Tower Corporation; *U.S. Public*, pg. 110
AT&T ALASCOM—See Arlington Capital Partners LLC; *U.S. Private*, pg. 328
AVANTI COMMUNICATIONS LIMITED—See Avanti Communications Group plc; *Int'l*, pg. 736
AZERKOSMOS OJSC; *Int'l*, pg. 778
BANGKOK SATELLITES & TELECOMMUNICATION CO., LTD.—See BEC World Public Company Limited; *Int'l*, pg. 936
BEC BROADCASTING CENTER CO., LTD.—See BEC World Public Company Limited; *Int'l*, pg. 936
BEC-TERO ENTERTAINMENT PUBLIC COMPANY LIMITED—See BEC World Public Company Limited; *Int'l*, pg. 936
BHARTI AIRTEL LANKA (PRIVATE) LIMITED—See Bharti Enterprises Limited; *Int'l*, pg. 1013
BHARTI AIRTEL SERVICES LIMITED—See Bharti Enterprises Limited; *Int'l*, pg. 1013
BHARTI INTERNATIONAL (SINGAPORE) PTE. LTD—See Bharti Enterprises Limited; *Int'l*, pg. 1013
BIGBLU BROADBAND GROUP PLC; *Int'l*, pg. 1022
BLUE TREE SYSTEMS GMBH—See ORBCOMM, Inc.; *U.S. Public*, pg. 1614
BLUE TREE SYSTEMS INC.—See ORBCOMM, Inc.; *U.S. Public*, pg. 1614
BLUE TREE SYSTEMS LTD.—See ORBCOMM, Inc.; *U.S. Public*, pg. 1614
BLUE TREE SYSTEMS SARL—See ORBCOMM, Inc.; *U.S. Public*, pg. 1614
BOEING SATELLITE SYSTEMS INTERNATIONAL, INC.—See The Boeing Company; *U.S. Public*, pg. 2039
BSA LIMITED; *Int'l*, pg. 1201
CALNEX SOLUTIONS PLC; *Int'l*, pg. 1265
CASTELL SATCOM RADIO LTD—See HAL Trust N.V.; *Int'l*, pg. 3226
CELLNEX SWEDEN AB—See Cellnex Telecom, S.A.; *Int'l*, pg. 1394
CHARITY & TAYLOR (ELECTRONIC SERVICES) LTD—See HAL Trust N.V.; *Int'l*, pg. 3226
COBHAM SEMICONDUCTOR SOLUTIONS—See Advent International Corporation; *U.S. Private*, pg. 99
COLLECTE LOCALISATION SATELLITES PERU S.A.C.—See Collecte Localisation Satellites; *Int'l*, pg. 1699
COMTECH EF DATA CORP.—See Comtech Telecommunications Corp.; *U.S. Public*, pg. 562
COMTECH EF DATA CORP. - VIPERSAT NETWORKS GROUP—See Comtech Telecommunications Corp.; *U.S. Public*, pg. 562
DATAPATH, INC.—See Gilat Satellite Networks Ltd.; *Int'l*, pg. 2973
DBSD NORTH AMERICA, INC.—See EchoStar Corporation; *U.S. Public*, pg. 711
DELTA BRIDGE, INC.—See Amentum Services, Inc.; *U.S. Private*, pg. 219
DIGITAL FACTORY CO., LTD.—See BEC World Public Company Limited; *Int'l*, pg. 936
DIRECTV, LLC—See AT&T Inc.; *U.S. Public*, pg. 220
DISH NETWORK L.L.C.—See EchoStar Corporation; *U.S. Public*, pg. 711
DISHONE SATELLITE; *U.S. Private*, pg. 1238
DISITRON INDUSTRIES, INC.; *U.S. Private*, pg. 1238
EADS MULTICOMS—See Airbus SE; *Int'l*, pg. 246
ECAPS AB—See GomSpace Group AB; *Int'l*, pg. 3037
ECHOSTAR BROADCASTING CORPORATION—See EchoStar Corporation; *U.S. Public*, pg. 711
ECHOSTAR MOBILE LIMITED—See EchoStar Corporation; *U.S. Public*, pg. 711
ECHOSTAR SATELLITE OPERATING CORPORATION—See EchoStar Corporation; *U.S. Public*, pg. 711
EION INC.; *Int'l*, pg. 2334
EMIRATE INTEGRATED TELECOMMUNICATIONS COMPANY PJSC; *Int'l*, pg. 2381

N.A.I.C.S. INDEX

517810 — ALL OTHER TELECOMMU...

EPRCOMUNICAZIONE S.P.A.; *Int'l*, pg. 2465
EUROPEAN SATELLITE LINK GMBH; *Int'l*, pg. 2557
EUTELSAT AMERICA CORP.—See Eutelsat Communications SA; *Int'l*, pg. 2559
EUTELSAT DO BRASIL SA—See Eutelsat Communications SA; *Int'l*, pg. 2559
EUTELSAT GMBH—See Eutelsat Communications SA; *Int'l*, pg. 2559
EUTELSAT POLSKA S.P.Z.O.—See Eutelsat Communications SA; *Int'l*, pg. 2559
EUTELSAT UK LTD.—See Eutelsat Communications SA; *Int'l*, pg. 2559
FLEET MANAGEMENT SOLUTIONS, INC.—See Vector Capital Management, L.P.; *U.S. Private*, pg. 4353
FORGE SERVICES, INC.—See Forge Global Holdings, Inc.; *U.S. Public*, pg. 867
GENERAL DYNAMICS MISSION SYSTEMS, LLC—See General Dynamics Corporation; *U.S. Public*, pg. 915
GHT CO., LTD.; *Int'l*, pg. 2960
GILAT COLOMBIA S.A. E.S.P—See Gilat Satellite Networks Ltd.; *Int'l*, pg. 2973
GILAT DO BRAZIL LTDA.—See Gilat Satellite Networks Ltd.; *Int'l*, pg. 2973
GILAT SATELLITE NETWORK MDC—See Gilat Satellite Networks Ltd.; *Int'l*, pg. 2973
GILAT SATELLITE NETWORKS B.V.—See Gilat Satellite Networks Ltd.; *Int'l*, pg. 2973
GILAT SATELLITE NETWORKS INDIA PRIVATE LTD.—See Gilat Satellite Networks Ltd.; *Int'l*, pg. 2973
GILAT SATELLITE NETWORKS LTD.—See Gilat Satellite Networks Ltd.; *Int'l*, pg. 2973
GILAT SATELLITE NETWORKS (MEXICO) S.A. DE C.V.—See Gilat Satellite Networks Ltd.; *Int'l*, pg. 2973
GILAT SATELLITE NETWORKS (THAILAND) LTD.—See Gilat Satellite Networks Ltd.; *Int'l*, pg. 2973
GILAT TO HOME PERU S.A—See Gilat Satellite Networks Ltd.; *Int'l*, pg. 2973
GLOBAL POSITIONING AUGMENTATION SERVICE CORPORATION—See Hitachi Zosen Corporation; *Int'l*, pg. 3410
GLOBALSTAR CANADA SATELLITE CO.—See Globalstar, Inc.; *U.S. Public*, pg. 946
GLOBAL TOWER SERVICES, LLC—See American Tower Corporation; *U.S. Public*, pg. 111
GLOBAL TOWER SITES I, LLC—See American Tower Corporation; *U.S. Public*, pg. 111
GMO DIGIROCK, INC.—See GMO Internet Group, Inc.; *Int'l*, pg. 3013
GTP SOUTH ACQUISITIONS II, LLC—See American Tower Corporation; *U.S. Public*, pg. 111
HARRIS NORGE AS—See L3Harris Technologies, Inc.; *U.S. Public*, pg. 1280
HELLAS SAT CONSORTIUM LIMITED—See Arab Satellite Communications Organization; *Int'l*, pg. 531
HELLAS SAT S.A.—See Arab Satellite Communications Organization; *Int'l*, pg. 531
HNS AMERICAS COMMUNICACOES, LTDA.—See EchoStar Corporation; *U.S. Public*, pg. 711
HNS DE MEXICO S.A. DE C.V.—See EchoStar Corporation; *U.S. Public*, pg. 711
HORIZON GLOBEX GMBH—See Touchpoint Group Holdings, Inc.; *U.S. Public*, pg. 2165
HUGHES COMMUNICATIONS, INC.—See EchoStar Corporation; *U.S. Public*, pg. 711
HUGHES NETWORK SYSTEMS EUROPE, LTD.—See EchoStar Corporation; *U.S. Public*, pg. 711
HUGHES NETWORK SYSTEMS INDIA, LTD.—See EchoStar Corporation; *U.S. Public*, pg. 711
HUGHES NETWORK SYSTEMS, LLC—See EchoStar Corporation; *U.S. Public*, pg. 711
HUGHES SATELLITE SYSTEMS CORPORATION—See EchoStar Corporation; *U.S. Public*, pg. 711
ICONECTIV, LLC; *U.S. Private*, pg. 2032
INFOTERRA LIMITED—See Airbus SE; *Int'l*, pg. 245
INMARSAT GLOBAL LIMITED—See ViaSat, Inc.; *U.S. Public*, pg. 2291
INMARSAT INC.—See ViaSat, Inc.; *U.S. Public*, pg. 2291
INMARSAT INC.—See ViaSat, Inc.; *U.S. Public*, pg. 2292
INMARSAT SOLUTIONS B.V.—See ViaSat, Inc.; *U.S. Public*, pg. 2292
INMARSAT SOLUTIONS PTE. LTD.—See ViaSat, Inc.; *U.S. Public*, pg. 2292
INMARSAT SOLUTIONS (US) INC.—See ViaSat, Inc.; *U.S. Public*, pg. 2292
INTEGRAL SYSTEMS EUROPE LTD.—See Kratos Defense & Security Solutions, Inc.; *U.S. Public*, pg. 1276
INTELSAT S.A.—See BC Partners LLP; *Int'l*, pg. 924
INTELSAT S.A.—See Silver Lake Group, LLC; *U.S. Private*, pg. 3658
INTERNEXA S.A.—See Ecopetrol S.A; *Int'l*, pg. 2299
IRIDIUM COMMUNICATIONS INC.; *U.S. Public*, pg. 1171
IRIDIUM GOVERNMENT SERVICES LLC—See Iridium Communications Inc.; *U.S. Public*, pg. 1171
IRIS GATEWAY SATELLITE SERVICES LIMITED—See Cyprus Telecommunications Authority; *Int'l*, pg. 1897
ITC GLOBAL AUSTRALIA—See Apax Partners LLP; *Int'l*, pg. 504
ITC GLOBAL GUINEA—See Apax Partners LLP; *Int'l*, pg. 504
ITC GLOBAL INC.—See Apax Partners LLP; *Int'l*, pg. 504
ITC GLOBAL UK—See Apax Partners LLP; *Int'l*, pg. 505
JERSEY AIRTEL LIMITED—See Bharti Enterprises Limited; *Int'l*, pg. 1013
KBRWYLE TECHNOLOGY SOLUTIONS, LLC—See KBR, Inc.; *U.S. Public*, pg. 1216
KRATOS COMMUNICATIONS LTD.—See Kratos Defense & Security Solutions, Inc.; *U.S. Public*, pg. 1276
KRATOS INTEGRAL SYSTEMS EUROPE S.A.S.—See Kratos Defense & Security Solutions, Inc.; *U.S. Public*, pg. 1276
KRATOS INTEGRAL SYSTEMS INTERNATIONAL, INC.—See Kratos Defense & Security Solutions, Inc.; *U.S. Public*, pg. 1276
KRATOS NORWAY AS—See Kratos Defense & Security Solutions, Inc.; *U.S. Public*, pg. 1276
KVH EUROPE A/S—See KVH Industries Inc; *U.S. Public*, pg. 1278
KVH INDUSTRIES A/S—See KVH Industries Inc; *U.S. Public*, pg. 1278
KVH INDUSTRIES JAPAN CO. LTD.—See KVH Industries Inc; *U.S. Public*, pg. 1278
KVH INDUSTRIES NORWAY A/S—See KVH Industries Inc; *U.S. Public*, pg. 1278
KVH MEDIA GROUP LTD.—See KVH Industries Inc; *U.S. Public*, pg. 1278
KVH MEDIA GROUP LTD.—See KVH Industries Inc; *U.S. Public*, pg. 1278
KYORITSU RADIO SERVICE CO., LTD.—See Furuno Electric Co., Ltd.; *Int'l*, pg. 2848
L-3 COMMUNICATIONS DATRON—See L3Harris Technologies, Inc.; *U.S. Public*, pg. 1282
LEPTON GLOBAL SOLUTIONS LLC—See Kymeta Corporation; *U.S. Private*, pg. 2360
LIGHTSQUARED COMPANY—See Spectrum Brands Holdings, Inc.; *U.S. Public*, pg. 1915
LOCKHEED MARTIN COMMERCIAL SPACE SYSTEMS—See Lockheed Martin Corporation; *U.S. Public*, pg. 1338
LSE SPACE ENGINEERING & OPERATIONS AG—See GomSpace Group AB; *Int'l*, pg. 3037
LYDIS B.V.—See Econocom Group SA; *Int'l*, pg. 2298
MAJOREL BERLIN GMBH—See Bertelsmann SE & Co. KGaA; *Int'l*, pg. 993
MAJOREL DORTMUND GMBH—See Bertelsmann SE & Co. KGaA; *Int'l*, pg. 993
MAJOREL NEUBRANDENBURG GMBH—See Bertelsmann SE & Co. KGaA; *Int'l*, pg. 993
MAJOREL ROSTOCK I GMBH—See Bertelsmann SE & Co. KGaA; *Int'l*, pg. 993
MARLINK AS—See Apax Partners LLP; *Int'l*, pg. 504
MARLINK COMMUNICATIONS S.A.—See Apax Partners LLP; *Int'l*, pg. 504
MARLINK, INC.—See Airbus SE; *Int'l*, pg. 245
MARLINK K.K.—See Apax Partners LLP; *Int'l*, pg. 504
MARLINK LTD.—See Apax Partners LLP; *Int'l*, pg. 504
MARLINK PTE. LTD.—See Apax Partners LLP; *Int'l*, pg. 504
MARLINK S.A.—See Apax Partners LLP; *Int'l*, pg. 504
MARLINK SAS—See Apax Partners LLP; *Int'l*, pg. 504
MATC INFRAESTRUCTURA, S. DE R.L. DE C.V.—See American Tower Corporation; *U.S. Public*, pg. 111
MDA SYSTEMS INC.—See Advent International Corporation; *U.S. Private*, pg. 103
MOBILE MEDIANET INC.—See Denso Corporation; *Int'l*, pg. 2032
MOBI (THAI) CO., LTD.—See BEC World Public Company Limited; *Int'l*, pg. 936
ND SATCOM GMBH—See Airbus SE; *Int'l*, pg. 245
NEW TOWERS LLC—See American Tower Corporation; *U.S. Public*, pg. 111
NEXTPLAT CORP.; *U.S. Public*, pg. 1526
NOVACOM SERVICES SA—See Collecte Localisation Satellites; *Int'l*, pg. 1699
NSSLGLOBAL APS.—See Arendals Fossekompani ASA; *Int'l*, pg. 559
NSSLGLOBAL LLC—See Arendals Fossekompani ASA; *Int'l*, pg. 559
NSSL GLOBAL LTD—See Arendals Fossekompani ASA; *Int'l*, pg. 559
NSSLGLOBAL POLSKA SP. Z.O.O.—See Arendals Fossekompani ASA; *Int'l*, pg. 559
NSSLGLOBAL PTE LTD.—See Arendals Fossekompani ASA; *Int'l*, pg. 559
NSSLGLOBAL TECHNOLOGIES AS—See Arendals Fossekompani ASA; *Int'l*, pg. 559
OHB ITALIA S.P.A.—See Hiscox Ltd.; *Int'l*, pg. 3407
ONE HORIZON GROUP PLC—See Touchpoint Group Holdings, Inc.; *U.S. Public*, pg. 2165
ORBCOMM EUROPE, B.V.—See ORBCOMM, Inc.; *U.S. Public*, pg. 1614
ORBCOMM EUROPE GMBH—See ORBCOMM, Inc.; *U.S. Public*, pg. 1614
ORBCOMM, INC.; *U.S. Public*, pg. 1614
ORBCOMM IRELAND LTD.—See ORBCOMM, Inc.; *U.S. Public*, pg. 1614
ORBITAL MEDIA NETWORKS, INC.—See Satellite Holdings, Inc.; *U.S. Private*, pg. 3553
PARADIGM SERVICES LTD.—See Airbus SE; *Int'l*, pg. 245
PENINSULA FIBER NETWORK, LLC; *U.S. Private*, pg. 3133
PERATON GOVERNMENT COMMUNICATIONS, INC.; *U.S. Private*, pg. 3146
PRIMETIME 24 JOINT VENTURE—See Great Universal Incorporated; *U.S. Public*, pg. 1768
PROOCEANO—See Collecte Localisation Satellites; *Int'l*, pg. 1699
PT CLS ARGOS INDONESIA—See Collecte Localisation Satellites; *Int'l*, pg. 1699
PT SATELIT PALAPA INDONESIA SATELINDO—See Deutsche Telekom AG; *Int'l*, pg. 2084
RADLINK PTY. LTD.—See Epiroc AB; *Int'l*, pg. 2463
REVCOM INC.; *U.S. Private*, pg. 3413
RINGCENTRAL GERMANY GMBH—See RingCentral, Inc.; *U.S. Public*, pg. 1799
SAMUELSON COMMUNICATIONS LIMITED—See Viad Corp.; *U.S. Public*, pg. 2291
SATCOM RESOURCES; *U.S. Private*, pg. 3553
SATELITES MEXICANOS S.A DE C.V.—See Eutelsat Communications SA; *Int'l*, pg. 2559
SATELLITE COMMUNICATION LTD.—See Brithol Michcoma Mozambique Limited; *Int'l*, pg. 1165
SDN GLOBAL, INC.—See Synergy Core LLC; *U.S. Private*, pg. 3904
SEGOVIA, INC—See ViaSat, Inc.; *U.S. Public*, pg. 2292
SKYLOGIC S.P.A.—See Eutelsat Communications SA; *Int'l*, pg. 2560
SMARTSAT, INC.; *U.S. Private*, pg. 3692
SOLARIS MOBILE LTD.—See EchoStar Corporation; *U.S. Public*, pg. 711
SSC SPACE AUSTRALIA PTY LTD.—See GomSpace Group AB; *Int'l*, pg. 3037
STAR WEST SATELLITE INC.; *U.S. Private*, pg. 3785
STRATOS OFFSHORE SERVICES COMPANY—See ViaSat, Inc.; *U.S. Public*, pg. 2292
SURREY SATELLITE TECHNOLOGY LTD.—See Airbus SE; *Int'l*, pg. 245
SWEDISH SPACE CORPORATION—See GomSpace Group AB; *Int'l*, pg. 3037
TERRESTAR CORPORATION; *U.S. Private*, pg. 3972
THRANE & THRANE A/S—See Advent International Corporation; *U.S. Private*, pg. 100
T.R.E. S.R.L.—See Collecte Localisation Satellites; *Int'l*, pg. 1699
TRICOM S.A.—See Altice Europe N.V.; *Int'l*, pg. 393
UGANDA TOWERS LIMITED—See Bharti Enterprises Limited; *Int'l*, pg. 1013
VECTOR SPACE SYSTEMS; *U.S. Private*, pg. 4353
VIASAT EUROPE LIMITED—See ViaSat, Inc.; *U.S. Public*, pg. 2292
VIASAT SINGAPORE HOLDINGS PTE. LTD.—See ViaSat, Inc.; *U.S. Public*, pg. 2292
VIZADA AS—See Airbus SE; *Int'l*, pg. 245
VIZADA RO HONG KONG—See Airbus SE; *Int'l*, pg. 245
VIZADA RO SINGAPORE—See Airbus SE; *Int'l*, pg. 245
VIZADA SAS—See Airbus SE; *Int'l*, pg. 245
WHEC-TV LLC—See Hubbard Broadcasting, Inc.; *U.S. Private*, pg. 2000

517810 — ALL OTHER TELECOMMUNICATIONS

0014 PTY. LTD.—See Aware Super Pty Ltd; *Int'l*, pg. 752
01024 TELEFONDIENSTE GMBH—See freenet AG; *Int'l*, pg. 2770
01050.COM GMBH—See freenet AG; *Int'l*, pg. 2770
123-REG LIMITED—See KKR & Co. Inc.; *U.S. Public*, pg. 1252
123-REG LIMITED—See Silver Lake Group, LLC; *U.S. Private*, pg. 3657
123-REG LIMITED—See TCMI, Inc.; *U.S. Private*, pg. 3943
3GNS SP. Z O.O.—See Iliad S.A.; *Int'l*, pg. 3614
3S NETWORK INC.; *U.S. Private*, pg. 14
5G NETWORK OPERATIONS PTY., LTD.—See 5G Networks Limited; *Int'l*, pg. 13
5LINX ENTERPRISES, INC.; *U.S. Private*, pg. 16
8990 HOLDINGS, INC.; *Int'l*, pg. 15
A1 TELEKOM AUSTRIA AG—See America Movil, S.A.B. de C.V.; *Int'l*, pg. 421
A2A SMART CITY S.P.A.—See A2A S.p.A.; *Int'l*, pg. 29
A3 ALLMANNA IT-OCH TELEKOMAKTI; *Int'l*, pg. 30
A3 PRIVATE AB; *Int'l*, pg. 30
AA ALARMS, INC.—See Stanley Black & Decker, Inc.; *U.S. Public*, pg. 1931
AAVOIP (EXPRESS)—See Odyssey Telecommunications, Inc.; *U.S. Private*, pg. 2996
ACACIA COMMUNICATIONS (CANADA) LIMITED—See Cisco Systems, Inc.; *U.S. Public*, pg. 497
ACCELA INC.—See Berkshire Partners LLC; *U.S. Private*, pg. 534
ACCELERATED CONNECTIONS INC.—See GTT Communications, Inc.; *U.S. Private*, pg. 1807
ACCEL SOLUTIONS LTD.; *Int'l*, pg. 79
ACCENTIV' SERVICOS TECNOLOGICA DA INFORMACAO

517810 — ALL OTHER TELECOMMU... CORPORATE AFFILIATIONS

S/A—See Edenred S.A.; *Int'l*, pg. 2307
ACCESS (BEIJING) CO., LTD.—See Access Co., Ltd.; *Int'l*, pg. 88
ACCORD SYNERGY LTD.; *Int'l*, pg. 93
ACER INTERNET SERVICES INC.—See Acer Incorporated; *Int'l*, pg. 99
ACLIVITI LLC; *U.S. Private*, pg. 60
ACS INTERNET, INC.—See ATN International, Inc.; *U.S. Public*, pg. 224
ACS INTERNET, INC.—See Freedom 3 Capital, LLC; *U.S. Private*, pg. 1603
ACS TELEFONIA MOVIL, S.L.—See ACS, Actividades de Construccion y Servicios, S.A.; *Int'l*, pg. 109
ACTEL KFT.—See Cyprus Telecommunications Authority; *Int'l*, pg. 1897
ACTIVISION BLIZZARD DEUTSCHLAND GMBH—See Microsoft Corporation; *U.S. Public*, pg. 1438
ACUATIVE - RESEARCH & DEVELOPMENT—See Acuative Corp.; *U.S. Private*, pg. 71
ADB BROADBAND S.P.A.—See Advanced Digital Broadcast Holdings SA; *Int'l*, pg. 158
ADDVALUE INNOVATION PTE LTD—See Addvalue Technologies Ltd.; *Int'l*, pg. 136
ADESTA LLC—See Allied Universal Manager LLC; *U.S. Private*, pg. 188
ADEX CORPORATION—See High Wire Networks Inc.; *U.S. Public*, pg. 1035
ADP SCREENING & SELECTION SERVICES—See Automatic Data Processing, Inc.; *U.S. Public*, pg. 230
ADR TEL S.P.A.—See Edizione S.r.l.; *Int'l*, pg. 2312
ADVANCED COMMUNICATIONS TECHNOLOGY, INC.—See Range Telephone Cooperative Inc.; *U.S. Private*, pg. 3354
ADVANCED DIGITAL BROADCAST SPAIN S.L.U.—See Advanced Digital Broadcast Holdings SA; *Int'l*, pg. 158
ADVANCED INTERNET TECHNOLOGIES INC.; *U.S. Private*, pg. 90
ADVANTAGE COMMUNICATIONS GROUP, LLC; *U.S. Private*, pg. 94
ADVA OPTICAL NETWORKING NORTH AMERICA, INC.—See ADTRAN Holdings, Inc.; *U.S. Public*, pg. 44
ADVA OPTICAL NETWORKING NORTH AMERICA, INC.—See ADTRAN Holdings, Inc.; *U.S. Public*, pg. 44
ADVA OPTICAL NETWORKING NORTH AMERICA, INC.—See ADTRAN Holdings, Inc.; *U.S. Public*, pg. 44
ADVISEN LTD.—See Clearlake Capital Group, L.P.; *U.S. Private*, pg. 938
ADVIZEX TECHNOLOGIES LLC; *U.S. Private*, pg. 110
ADYA INC.; *Int'l*, pg. 169
AEROSOLUTIONS, LLC; *U.S. Private*, pg. 119
AFFLUENCE CORP.; *U.S. Public*, pg. 57
AFONE PARTICIPATIONS SA; *Int'l*, pg. 189
AGILE TELECOM SPA—See Growens S.p.A.; *Int'l*, pg. 3112
AGILTRON, INC.; *U.S. Private*, pg. 128
AGNI SYSTEMS LIMITED; *Int'l*, pg. 211
AICHI NDS CO., LTD.—See COMSYS Holdings Corporation; *Int'l*, pg. 1761
AIN GLOBALCOMM CO., LTD.—See Advanced Info Service Plc; *Int'l*, pg. 159
AIRCELL BUSINESS AVIATION SERVICES LLC—See Gogo Inc.; *U.S. Public*, pg. 949
AIRCOM INTERNATIONAL LTD.—See TEOCO Corporation; *U.S. Private*, pg. 3969
AIRCOM PACIFIC INC.—See Aerkomm Inc.; *U.S. Public*, pg. 52
AIR LYNX SAS—See Atos SE; *Int'l*, pg. 690
AIRTEL AFRICA PLC; *Int'l*, pg. 249
AIRTEL NETWORKS KENYA LIMITED—See Bharti Enterprises Limited; *Int'l*, pg. 1011
AKAMAI TECHNOLOGIES ISRAEL LIMITED—See Akamai Technologies, Inc.; *U.S. Public*, pg. 68
ALABAMA INTERACTIVE, LLC—See Tyler Technologies, Inc.; *U.S. Public*, pg. 2208
ALLIANCE CONNECT, LLC—See Iowa Network Services Inc.; *U.S. Private*, pg. 2135
ALLIED TELESIS CAPITAL CORP.—See ALLIED TELESIS HOLDINGS K.K.; *Int'l*, pg. 358
ALLTEK TECHNOLOGY (SINGAPORE) PTE. LTD.—See Alltek Technology Corporation; *Int'l*, pg. 360
ALLTERCO JSCO; *Int'l*, pg. 360
ALPHEUS COMMUNICATIONS LP—See Astra Capital Management LLC; *U.S. Private*, pg. 361
ALPINE, INC.—See Headspace Inc.; *U.S. Private*, pg. 1891
ALSATEL—See Eiffage S.A.; *Int'l*, pg. 2329
ALTEN SIR AND TELECOM—See Alten S.A.; *Int'l*, pg. 389
ALTEVA OF SYRACUSE, INC.—See Alteva, Inc.; *U.S. Private*, pg. 208
AMDOCS INC. - SAN JOSE—See Amdocs Limited; *Int'l*, pg. 419
AMERICAN BROADBAND HOLDING COMPANY—See Madison Dearborn Partners, LLC; *U.S. Private*, pg. 2540
AMERICAS CALL CENTER, LLC—See Porch Group, Inc.; *U.S. Public*, pg. 1702
AMERICATEL CORPORATION—See Blue Casa Communications, Inc.; *U.S. Private*, pg. 586
AMERICATEL CORPORATION—See Garrison Investment Group LP; *Int'l*, pg. 1646

AMNET BROADBAND PTY. LTD.—See Aware Super Pty Ltd; *Int'l*, pg. 752
AMPLOGIX TECHNOLOGY SDN. BHD.—See Cabnet Holding Berhad; *Int'l*, pg. 1246
AM WIRELESS URUGUAY, S.A.—See America Movil, S.A.B. de C.V.; *Int'l*, pg. 421
ANRITSU SOLUTIONS S.R.L.—See Anritsu Corporation; *Int'l*, pg. 476
ANSWERNET EDUCATION SERVICES, INC.; *U.S. Private*, pg. 286
ANX E-BUSINESS CORP.; *U.S. Private*, pg. 289
ANYTHINGWEATHER COMMUNICATIONS, INC.; *U.S. Private*, pg. 289
ANYWIRE CORPORATION; *Int'l*, pg. 487
APC WIRELESS; *U.S. Private*, pg. 290
APIGATE SDN BHD—See Axiata Group Berhad; *Int'l*, pg. 768
APPLIED VOICE & SPEECH TECHNOLOGIES, INC.—See StoneCalibre, LLC; *U.S. Private*, pg. 3827
AP WIRELESS IRELAND INVESTMENTS LTD—See EQT AB; *Int'l*, pg. 2479
AP WIRELESS (UK) LIMITED—See EQT AB; *Int'l*, pg. 2479
APWPT II INVESTIMENTOS, S.A.—See EQT AB; *Int'l*, pg. 2479
AQUASOL MORELIA S.A. DE C.V.—See Empresas Publicas de Medellin ESP; *Int'l*, pg. 2391
ARGENT ASSOCIATES INC.; *U.S. Private*, pg. 319
ARMOR CONNECTIC SAS—See Eiffage S.A.; *Int'l*, pg. 2329
ARMSTRONG UTILITIES, INC.—See Armstrong Holdings, Inc.; *U.S. Private*, pg. 331
ARROW ENTERPRISE COMPUTING SOLUTIONS S3—See Arrow Electronics, Inc.; *U.S. Public*, pg. 198
ARROW ENTERPRISE COMPUTING SOLUTIONS S3—See Arrow Electronics, Inc.; *U.S. Public*, pg. 198
ARROW TECHNOLOGIES, LLC; *U.S. Private*, pg. 336
ARVIXE, LLC; *U.S. Private*, pg. 345
ARYA OMNITALK WIRELESS SOLUTIONS PRIVATE LIMITED—See Arvind Fashions Ltd.; *Int'l*, pg. 587
ASAVIE TECHNOLOGIES LIMITED—See Akamai Technologies, Inc.; *U.S. Public*, pg. 69
ASAVIE UK LIMITED—See Akamai Technologies, Inc.; *U.S. Public*, pg. 69
ASCOM (NEDERLAND) BV—See Ascom Holding AG; *Int'l*, pg. 603
ASIA GLOBAL CROSSING LTD.; *Int'l*, pg. 612
ASIALINK TECHNOLOGY DEVELOPMENT LIMITED—See FSBM Holdings Berhad; *Int'l*, pg. 2798
ASIA PACIFIC TELECOM CO., LTD.; *Int'l*, pg. 614
ASK APPLICATIONS, INC.—See IAC Inc.; *U.S. Public*, pg. 1082
AT CONFERENCE, INC.; *U.S. Private*, pg. 363
ATH CALL CENTRE LIMITED—See Fiji National Provident Fund; *Int'l*, pg. 2661
ATLANTIC BROADBAND GROUP LLC—See Gestion Audem, Inc.; *Int'l*, pg. 2946
ATLANTIC METRO COMMUNICATIONS, INC.—See Stonecourt Capital LP; *U.S. Private*, pg. 3828
ATLAS COPCO ASAP N.V.—See Atlas Copco AB; *Int'l*, pg. 678
ATRADA TRADING NETWORK AG—See Deutsche Telekom AG; *Int'l*, pg. 2083
AT&T ADVANCED SOLUTIONS, INC.—See AT&T Inc.; *U.S. Public*, pg. 219
AT&T—See AT&T Inc.; *U.S. Public*, pg. 219
AT&T—See AT&T Inc.; *U.S. Public*, pg. 219
AT&T TELEHOLDINGS, INC—See AT&T Inc.; *U.S. Public*, pg. 219
AUDIOCODES ARGENTINA S.A.—See AudioCodes Ltd.; *Int'l*, pg. 701
AUDIOCODES BRASIL EQUIPAMENTOS DE VOZ SOBRE IP LTDA.—See AudioCodes Ltd.; *Int'l*, pg. 701
AUDIOCODES, INC.—See AudioCodes Ltd.; *Int'l*, pg. 702
AUSTIN TELE-SERVICES PARTNERS, L.P.—See Genesis Networks Enterprises, LLC; *U.S. Private*, pg. 1669
AUTHEN-TECH COMMUNICATIONS CANADA INC.; *Int'l*, pg. 724
AVAILO AB—See EQT AB; *Int'l*, pg. 2475
AVAILO NETWORKS AB—See EQT AB; *Int'l*, pg. 2475
AVANCE TECHNOLOGIES LTD.; *Int'l*, pg. 734
AVANTI BROADBAND LIMITED—See Avanti Communications Group plc; *Int'l*, pg. 736
AVAYA, LLC—See Silver Lake Group, LLC; *U.S. Private*, pg. 3656
AVAYA, LLC—See TPG Capital, L.P.; *U.S. Public*, pg. 2169
AVERY HOLDINGS, INC.—See Billing Services Group, LLC; *U.S. Private*, pg. 559
AWECOMM TECHNOLOGIES, LLC—See Audax Group, Limited Partnership; *U.S. Private*, pg. 387
AXS PTE LTD—See DBS Group Holdings Ltd.; *Int'l*, pg. 1988
AZAVEA INCORPORATED; *U.S. Private*, pg. 415
BAIDU (CHINA) CO., LTD.—See Baidu, Inc.; *Int'l*, pg. 801
BAIDU ONLINE NETWORK TECHNOLOGY (BEIJING) CO. LTD.—See Baidu, Inc.; *Int'l*, pg. 801
BALTIC TELEKOM AS; *Int'l*, pg. 812
BANDAI NAMCO ONLINE INC.—See BANDAI NAMCO Holdings Inc.; *Int'l*, pg. 829
BANDWIDTH INC.; *U.S. Public*, pg. 269

BANG & OLUFSEN TELECOM A/S—See Bang & Olufsen a/s; *Int'l*, pg. 831
BANKINTER CONSULTORIA, ASESORAMIENTO Y ATENCION TELEFONICA, S.A.—See Bankinter, S.A.; *Int'l*, pg. 850
BATM FRANCE—See BATM Advanced Communications Ltd.; *Int'l*, pg. 890
BAYCOM, INC.—See OwnersEdge Inc.; *U.S. Private*, pg. 3055
BAYLIN TECHNOLOGIES DO BRAZIL PRODUTOS DE TELECOMMUNICACOES LTDA.—See Baylin Technologies Inc.; *Int'l*, pg. 914
BBNED NV—See Deutsche Telekom AG; *Int'l*, pg. 2084
BBTV HOLDINGS INC.—See BBTV Holdings Inc.; *Int'l*, pg. 921
BD MULTIMEDIA SA; *Int'l*, pg. 929
BEANFIELD TECHNOLOGIES, INC.—See DigitalBridge Group, Inc.; *U.S. Public*, pg. 664
BEIJING BEWINNER COMMUNICATIONS CO., LTD.; *Int'l*, pg. 946
BEIJING ENTERPRISES ENVIRONMENT GROUP LIMITED—See Beijing Enterprises Holdings Limited; *Int'l*, pg. 949
BEIJING NET-INFINITY TECHNOLOGY DEVELOPMENT CO. LTD.—See CK Hutchison Holdings Limited; *Int'l*, pg. 1636
BEIJING SINNET TECHNOLOGY COMPANY LIMITED; *Int'l*, pg. 957
BENDIGO TELCO LIMITED; *Int'l*, pg. 971
BENEFIT JAPAN CO., LTD.; *Int'l*, pg. 972
THE BERMUDA TELEPHONE COMPANY LIMITED—See Digicel Group Ltd.; *Int'l*, pg. 2119
BESTPHONE, S.A. DE C.V.—See Grupo Televisa, S.A.B.; *Int'l*, pg. 3136
BESTWEB CORPORATION—See Antin Infrastructure Partners SAS; *Int'l*, pg. 483
BHARAT TELECOM LTD.; *Int'l*, pg. 1011
BHARTI AIRTEL (FRANCE) SAS—See Bharti Enterprises Limited; *Int'l*, pg. 1013
BHARTI AIRTEL INTERNATIONAL (NETHERLANDS) B.V.—See Bharti Enterprises Limited; *Int'l*, pg. 1013
BHARTI AIRTEL (UK) LIMITED—See Bharti Enterprises Limited; *Int'l*, pg. 1013
BH TELECOM D.D.; *Int'l*, pg. 1009
BIG PLANET, INC.—See Nu Skin Enterprises, Inc.; *U.S. Public*, pg. 1551
BIRCH COMMUNICATIONS, INC.—See Fusion Connect, Inc.; *U.S. Private*, pg. 1625
BITTIUM GERMANY GMBH—See Bittium Oyj; *Int'l*, pg. 1050
BITTIUM MEXICO S.A. DE C.V—See Bittium Oyj; *Int'l*, pg. 1050
BITTIUM SAFEMOVE OY—See Bittium Oyj; *Int'l*, pg. 1050
BITTIUM SINGAPORE PTE. LTD.—See Bittium Oyj; *Int'l*, pg. 1050
BITTIUM USA, INC.—See Bittium Oyj; *Int'l*, pg. 1050
BITTIUM WIRELESS OY—See Bittium Oyj; *Int'l*, pg. 1050
BLACKBERRY CORPORATION—See BlackBerry Limited; *Int'l*, pg. 1060
BLACK BOX CANADA CORP.—See Black Box Limited; *Int'l*, pg. 1058
BLACK BOX LIMITED; *Int'l*, pg. 1056
BLACK BOX NETWORK SERVICES—See Black Box Limited; *Int'l*, pg. 1057
BLACK BOX NETWORK SERVICES—See Black Box Limited; *Int'l*, pg. 1057
BLACK BOX NETWORK SERVICES—See Black Box Limited; *Int'l*, pg. 1057
BLACK BOX NETWORK SERVICES—See Black Box Limited; *Int'l*, pg. 1057
BLACK BOX NETWORK SERVICES—See Black Box Limited; *Int'l*, pg. 1058
BLACK BOX NETWORK SERVICES-VOICE SERVICES CANADA—See Black Box Limited; *Int'l*, pg. 1058
BLACK EARTH TELEPHONE CO.—See Telephone & Data Systems, Inc.; *U.S. Public*, pg. 1998
BLUEFACE LTD.—See Comcast Corporation; *U.S. Public*, pg. 537
BLUE RIDGE TELEPHONE CO.—See Telephone & Data Systems, Inc.; *U.S. Public*, pg. 1998
BORTEK, LLC—See Liberty Broadband Corporation; *U.S. Public*, pg. 1310
BOUYGUES ENERGIES & SERVICES SAS—See Bouygues S.A.; *Int'l*, pg. 1122
BRAZIL PLANTRONICS TELECOMMUNICACOES LTDA.—See HP Inc.; *U.S. Public*, pg. 1064
BRIGHTNET OKLAHOMA—See Chickasaw Holding Company; *U.S. Private*, pg. 880
BROADNET TELESERVICES; *U.S. Private*, pg. 659
BROADPLEX LLC—See Court Square Capital Partners, L.P.; *U.S. Private*, pg. 1068
BROADRIVER COMMUNICATIONS CORPORATION—See Integracore, Inc.; *U.S. Private*, pg. 2098
BROADVIEW NETWORKS, INC.—See Windstream Holdings, Inc.; *U.S. Public*, pg. 2373
BROADWING COMMUNICATIONS, INC.; *U.S. Private*, pg. 660
BRODOS AG; *Int'l*, pg. 1173
BRS MEDIA INC.; *U.S. Private*, pg. 670

N.A.I.C.S. INDEX

517810 — ALL OTHER TELECOMMU...

BRYN RESOURCES, INC.; *U.S. Public*, pg. 408
BT BILISIM HIZMETLERI ANONIM SIRKETI—See BT Group plc; *Int'l*, pg. 1202
BT COMMUNICATIONS DO BRASIL LIMITADA—See BT Group plc; *Int'l*, pg. 1203
BT COMMUNICATIONS IRELAND LIMITED—See BT Group plc; *Int'l*, pg. 1203
BT CONVERGENT SOLUTIONS LIMITED—See BT Group plc; *Int'l*, pg. 1203
BT ENIA TELECOMUNICAZIONI S.P.A.—See BT Group plc; *Int'l*, pg. 1203
BT GLOBAL COMMUNICATIONS INDIA PRIVATE LIMITED—See BT Group plc; *Int'l*, pg. 1203
BT GLOBAL SERVICES—See BT Group plc; *Int'l*, pg. 1203
BT INFONET—See BT Group plc; *Int'l*, pg. 1203
BT SINGAPORE PTE LTD—See BT Group plc; *Int'l*, pg. 1203
BT SWITZERLAND AG—See BT Group plc; *Int'l*, pg. 1203
BT TELEKOM HIZMETLERI ANONIM SIRKETI—See BT Group plc; *Int'l*, pg. 1203
BUCKEYE TELESYSTEM, INC.—See Block Communications, Inc.; *U.S. Public*, pg. 582
BUDDYTV; *U.S. Private*, pg. 679
BUILDPOINT CORPORATION; *U.S. Private*, pg. 683
BULGARIAN TELECOMMUNICATIONS COMPANY EAD—See BC Partners LLP; *Int'l*, pg. 923
BUS COMMUNICATIONS PTY LTD—See CSE Global Ltd.; *Int'l*, pg. 1863
BUSINESS CONNEXION COMMUNICATIONS (PTY) LIMITED—See Business Connexion Group Limited; *Int'l*, pg. 1228
BYTES TECHNOLOGY GROUP (PROPRIETARY) LIMITED—See Altron Limited; *Int'l*, pg. 399
CABLEMAS, S.A. DE C.V.—See Grupo Televisa, S.A.B.; *Int'l*, pg. 3136
CABLE RUNNER AUSTRIA GMBH & CO. KG—See America Movil, S.A.B. de C.V.; *Int'l*, pg. 421
CABLE RUNNER IBERICA S.L.—See America Movil, S.A.B. de C.V.; *Int'l*, pg. 421
CABLE SYSTEMS, INC.—See Altice USA, Inc.; *U.S. Public*, pg. 87
CABLE & WIRELESS (SEYCHELLES) LTD.; *Int'l*, pg. 1246
CADSYS TECHNOLOGIES LLC—See Cadsys (India) Ltd.; *Int'l*, pg. 1248
CALIAN LTD. - SED SYSTEMS DIVISION—See Calian Group Ltd.; *Int'l*, pg. 1264
CALIFORNIA TELESERVICES INC.; *U.S. Private*, pg. 721
CALLFIRE; *U.S. Private*, pg. 722
CALLTEC PTY. LTD.—See Azure Healthcare Limited; *Int'l*, pg. 782
CALLTOWER INC.; *U.S. Private*, pg. 723
CALPOP.COM, INC.; *U.S. Private*, pg. 723
CAMDEN TELEPHONE & TELEGRAPH COMPANY, INC.—See Telephone & Data Systems, Inc.; *U.S. Public*, pg. 1998
CANAR TELECOMMUNICATIONS CO. LTD.—See Bank of Khartoum; *Int'l*, pg. 845
CAPELLA TELECOMMUNICATIONS INC.; *Int'l*, pg. 1303
CAPITA WEST GMBH—See Capita plc; *Int'l*, pg. 1308
CARDINALCOMMERCE CORP.—See Visa, Inc.; *U.S. Public*, pg. 2301
CARDINAL COMMUNICATIONS, INC.; *U.S. Private*, pg. 750
CAREER ENGINE SOLUTIONS—See Classified Solutions Group, Inc.; *U.S. Private*, pg. 917
CARNIVAL MARITIME GMBH—See Carnival Corporation; *U.S. Public*, pg. 438
CAROUSEL INDUSTRIES OF NORTH AMERICA, INC.—See American Securities LLC; *U.S. Private*, pg. 250
CARRIER SRL—See Carrier Global Corporation; *U.S. Public*, pg. 443
C.C.D. COGENT COMMUNICATIONS DEUTSCHLAND GMBH—See Cogent Communications Holdings, Inc.; *U.S. Public*, pg. 522
C-CHANNEL AG—See Constellation Software Inc.; *Int'l*, pg. 1772
CCMI—See United Communications Group; *U.S. Private*, pg. 4289
CED DIGITAL & SERVIZI SRL—See Caltagirone Editore S.p.A.; *Int'l*, pg. 1265
CELCOM AXIATA BERHAD—See CelcomDigi Berhad; *Int'l*, pg. 1391
CELCOM TRANSMISSION (M) SDN BHD—See CelcomDigi Berhad; *Int'l*, pg. 1391
CELLFIND (PROPRIETARY) LIMITED—See Blue Label Telecoms Limited; *Int'l*, pg. 1068
CELLUFUN INC.; *U.S. Private*, pg. 807
CEMIG TELECOMUNICACOES S.A.—See Companhia Energetica de Minas Gerais - CEMIG; *Int'l*, pg. 1747
CENTRLNYI TELEGRAF; *Int'l*, pg. 1413
CENTURYLINK CANADA, INC.—See Lumen Technologies, Inc.; *U.S. Public*, pg. 1345
CENTURYLINK CHILE S.A.—See Lumen Technologies, Inc.; *U.S. Public*, pg. 1345
CENTURYLINK COMMUNICATIONS BELGIUM SA—See Lumen Technologies, Inc.; *U.S. Public*, pg. 1345
CENTURYLINK COMMUNICATIONS, LLC—See Lumen Technologies, Inc.; *U.S. Public*, pg. 1347
CENTURYTEL ARKANSAS HOLDINGS, INC.—See Lumen Technologies, Inc.; *U.S. Public*, pg. 1346
CENTURYTEL BROADBAND WIRELESS, LLC—See Lumen Technologies, Inc.; *U.S. Public*, pg. 1346
CENTURYTEL OF CENTRAL INDIANA, INC.—See Lumen Technologies, Inc.; *U.S. Public*, pg. 1346
CENTURYTEL OF NORTHWEST LOUISIANA, INC.—See Lumen Technologies, Inc.; *U.S. Public*, pg. 1346
CENTURYTEL TELEVIDEO, INC.—See Lumen Technologies, Inc.; *U.S. Public*, pg. 1346
CERAGON COLOMBIA—See Ceragon Networks Ltd.; *Int'l*, pg. 1421
CERAGON NETWORKS APAC (S) PTE LTD—See Ceragon Networks Ltd.; *Int'l*, pg. 1421
CERAGON NETWORKS AUSTRALIA PTY LTD—See Ceragon Networks Ltd.; *Int'l*, pg. 1421
CERAGON NETWORKS DO BRASIL LTDA—See Ceragon Networks Ltd.; *Int'l*, pg. 1421
CERAGON NETWORKS HELLAS S.A.—See Ceragon Networks Ltd.; *Int'l*, pg. 1421
CERAGON NETWORKS (HK) LTD.—See Ceragon Networks Ltd.; *Int'l*, pg. 1421
CERAGON NETWORKS (NIGERIA) LIMITED—See Ceragon Networks Ltd.; *Int'l*, pg. 1421
CERAGON NETWORKS SARL—See Ceragon Networks Ltd.; *Int'l*, pg. 1421
CERAGON THAILAND—See Ceragon Networks Ltd.; *Int'l*, pg. 1421
CERAGON USA—See Ceragon Networks Ltd.; *Int'l*, pg. 1421
CERILLION PLC; *Int'l*, pg. 1422
CEZNET, A.S.—See CEZ, a.s.; *Int'l*, pg. 1427
CEZTEL, A.S.—See CEZ, a.s.; *Int'l*, pg. 1427
CHACHA SEARCH, INC.; *U.S. Private*, pg. 845
CHARIOT LIMITED—See CK Hutchison Holdings Limited; *Int'l*, pg. 1638
CHARITY DYNAMICS; *U.S. Private*, pg. 851
CHICKASAW TELECOMMUNICATIONS SERVICES, INC.—See Chickasaw Holding Company; *U.S. Private*, pg. 880
CHINA COMMUNICATIONS SERVICES CORPORATION LIMITED—See China Telecommunications Corporation; *Int'l*, pg. 1557
CHINA FINANCE ONLINE—See China Finance Online Co. Limited; *Int'l*, pg. 1502
CHINA MOBILE IOT COMPANY LIMITED; *Int'l*, pg. 1524
CHINA MOTION TELECOM (HK) LIMITED—See VelaTel Global Communications, Inc.; *U.S. Private*, pg. 4354
CHINA NETCOM (USA) OPERATIONS LIMITED—See China United Network Communications Group Company Limited; *Int'l*, pg. 1561
CHINA SATELLITE COMMUNICATIONS CO., LTD.—See China Aerospace Science and Technology Corporation; *Int'l*, pg. 1481
CHINA TELECOM (AUSTRALIA) PTY LTD—See China Telecommunications Corporation; *Int'l*, pg. 1557
CHINA TELECOM (CANADA) ULC—See China Telecommunications Corporation; *Int'l*, pg. 1558
CHINA TELECOM (DEUTSCHLAND) GMBH—See China Telecommunications Corporation; *Int'l*, pg. 1558
CHINA TELECOM DO BRASIL LTDA.—See China Telecommunications Corporation; *Int'l*, pg. 1558
CHINA TELECOM (EUROPE) LIMITED—See China Telecommunications Corporation; *Int'l*, pg. 1558
CHINA TELECOM (FRANCE) LTD.—See China Telecommunications Corporation; *Int'l*, pg. 1558
CHINA TELECOM GLOBAL LTD—See China Telecommunications Corporation; *Int'l*, pg. 1558
CHINA TELECOM (INDIA) PRIVATE LIMITED—See China Telecommunications Corporation; *Int'l*, pg. 1558
CHINA TELECOM INFORMATION TECHNOLOGY (VIETNAM) CO., LTD.—See China Telecommunications Corporation; *Int'l*, pg. 1558
CHINA TELECOM (KAZAKHSTAN) LIMITED LIABILITY PARTNERSHIP—See China Telecommunications Corporation; *Int'l*, pg. 1558
CHINA TELECOM KOREA LIMITED—See China Telecommunications Corporation; *Int'l*, pg. 1558
CHINA TELECOM (MALAYSIA) SDN. BHD.—See China Telecommunications Corporation; *Int'l*, pg. 1558
CHINA TELECOM MIDDLE EAST—See China Telecommunications Corporation; *Int'l*, pg. 1558
CHINA TELECOM (SINGAPORE) PTE. LTD.—See China Telecommunications Corporation; *Int'l*, pg. 1558
CHINA TELECOM SOUTH AFRICA (PTY) LTD—See China Telecommunications Corporation; *Int'l*, pg. 1558
CHINA UNICOM USA CORPORATION—See China United Network Communications Group Company Limited; *Int'l*, pg. 1561
CHINA UNITED NETWORK COMMUNICATIONS LIMITED—See China United Network Communications Group Company Limited; *Int'l*, pg. 1561
CHORUS CALL AUSTRALIA PTY LTD—See Chorus Call, Inc.; *U.S. Private*, pg. 889
CHORUS CALL CANADA CORP.—See Chorus Call, Inc.; *U.S. Private*, pg. 889
CHORUS CALL CONFERENCING SERVICES INDIA PRIVATE LTD.—See Chorus Call, Inc.; *U.S. Private*, pg. 889
CHORUS CALL CONFERENCING SERVICES INDIA PRIVATE LTD.—See Chorus Call, Inc.; *U.S. Private*, pg. 889
CHORUS CALL GERMANY GMBH—See Chorus Call, Inc.; *U.S. Private*, pg. 889
CHORUS CALL HELLAS A.E.—See Chorus Call, Inc.; *U.S. Private*, pg. 889
CHORUS CALL, INC.; *U.S. Private*, pg. 888
CHORUS CALL ITALIA S.R.L.—See Chorus Call, Inc.; *U.S. Private*, pg. 889
CHORUS CALL (PTY) LTD.—See Chorus Call, Inc.; *U.S. Private*, pg. 888
CHORUS CALL SA—See Chorus Call, Inc.; *U.S. Private*, pg. 889
CHUNGHWA TELECOM (THAILAND) CO., LTD.—See Chunghwa Telecom Co., Ltd.; *Int'l*, pg. 1598
CIBL, INC.; *U.S. Public*, pg. 494
CIENA CORPORATION - SPOKANE VALLEY MAIN OFFICE & TRAINING CENTER—See Ciena Corporation; *U.S. Public*, pg. 494
C I HOST; *U.S. Private*, pg. 701
CIK POWER DISTRIBUTORS, LLC.; *U.S. Private*, pg. 897
CILAS SA—See Airbus SE; *Int'l*, pg. 246
CITIC TELECOM INTERNATIONAL HOLDINGS LIMITED—See CITIC Group Corporation; *Int'l*, pg. 1620
CITIZENS TELEPHONE COOPERATIVE; *U.S. Private*, pg. 904
CITRIX ONLINE LLC—See Elliott Management Corporation; *U.S. Private*, pg. 1366
CITRIX ONLINE LLC—See Vista Equity Partners, LLC; *U.S. Private*, pg. 4395
CITYSEARCH—See IAC Inc.; *U.S. Public*, pg. 1082
CJSC KAZTELEPORT—See Halyk Bank of Kazakhstan JSC; *Int'l*, pg. 3234
CLARANET SOHO—See Claranet Limited; *Int'l*, pg. 1642
CLEARFLY COMMUNICATIONS; *U.S. Private*, pg. 932
CLEARWAVE TELECOMMUNICATIONS, INC.; *U.S. Public*, pg. 513
THE CLOUD NETWORKS LIMITED—See Comcast Corporation; *U.S. Public*, pg. 541
CM.COM N.V.; *Int'l*, pg. 1666
CM TELECOM BV; *Int'l*, pg. 1666
COGECO CABLE ONTARIO—See Gestion Audem, Inc.; *Int'l*, pg. 2946
COGENT CANADA, INC.—See Cogent Communications Holdings, Inc.; *U.S. Public*, pg. 522
COGENT COMMUNICATIONS ESPANA SA—See Cogent Communications Holdings, Inc.; *U.S. Public*, pg. 522
COGENT COMMUNICATIONS FRANCE SAS—See Cogent Communications Holdings, Inc.; *U.S. Public*, pg. 522
COGENT COMMUNICATIONS, INC.—See Cogent Communications Holdings, Inc.; *U.S. Public*, pg. 522
COGENT COMMUNICATIONS NETHERLANDS B.V.—See Cogent Communications Holdings, Inc.; *U.S. Public*, pg. 522
COGENT COMMUNICATIONS NORDICS—See Cogent Communications Holdings, Inc.; *U.S. Public*, pg. 522
COGENT COMMUNICATIONS UK LTD.—See Cogent Communications Holdings, Inc.; *U.S. Public*, pg. 522
COLO ATL, LLC—See American Tower Corporation; *U.S. Public*, pg. 111
COLOGIX, INC.—See Stonepeak Partners L.P.; *U.S. Private*, pg. 3829
COLOMBIA MOVIL S.A E.S.P.—See Empresas Publicas de Medellin ESP; *Int'l*, pg. 2392
COLSPACE CORPORATION—See Vista Equity Partners, LLC; *U.S. Private*, pg. 4398
COMCAST PHONE OF COLORADO, LLC—See Comcast Corporation; *U.S. Public*, pg. 537
COMETZ SARL—See Bertelsmann SE & Co. KGaA; *Int'l*, pg. 992
COMLINK SOUTHWEST, LLC—See Comlink Contractors Inc.; *U.S. Private*, pg. 982
COMMUNICATION CONCEPT GESELLSCHAFT FUR KOMMUNIKATIONSTECHNIK MBH—See Deutsche Wohnen SE; *Int'l*, pg. 2085
COMMUNICATIONS FIJI LTD.; *Int'l*, pg. 1720
COMMUNICATION TECHNOLOGIES, INC.; *U.S. Private*, pg. 988
COMMUNITY LONG DISTANCE, INC.—See Comporium Group; *U.S. Private*, pg. 1002
COMM-WORKS, LLC; *U.S. Private*, pg. 982
COM-NET SERVICES, LLC—See The Newtron Group Inc.; *U.S. Private*, pg. 4084
COMPANIA DE TELECOMUNICACIONES DE EL SALVADOR (CTE), S.A. DE C.V.—See America Movil, S.A.B. de C.V.; *Int'l*, pg. 421
COMPANIA NACIONAL DE TELEFONOS TELEFONICA DEL SUR S.A.; *Int'l*, pg. 1749
COMSOURCE, INC.—See Sentinel Capital Partners, L.L.C.; *U.S. Private*, pg. 3609
CONCENTRIX SERVICE HUNGARY KFT.—See TD Synnex Corp; *U.S. Public*, pg. 1984
CONFERENCE CALL DO BRASIL—See Chorus Call, Inc.; *U.S. Private*, pg. 889
CONFERENCECALL SERVICES INDIA PRIVATE LIMITED—See Apollo Global Management, Inc.; *U.S. Public*, pg. 152

517810 — ALL OTHER TELECOMMU...

CONNECT MANAGED SERVICES (UK) LIMITED—See G3 Comms Ltd.; *Int'l*, pg. 2866
CONNECTWISE, INC.—See Thoma Bravo, L.P.; *U.S. Private*, pg. 4146
CONNEXIS LLC—See Ygomi LLC; *U.S. Private*, pg. 4589
CONSOLIDATED TELECOMMUNICATIONS COMPANY; *U.S. Private*, pg. 1022
CONSULTEDGE, INC.; *U.S. Private*, pg. 1025
CONVERGED COMMUNICATION SYSTEMS, LLC; *U.S. Private*, pg. 1035
CONVERGENZE S.P.A.; *Int'l*, pg. 1787
COOP MINERALOEL AG—See Coop-Gruppe Genossenschaft; *Int'l*, pg. 1790
COORDINATED BUSINESS SYSTEMS, LTD.; *U.S. Private*, pg. 1043
COPASAT, LLC; *U.S. Private*, pg. 1044
COPEL TELECOMUNICACOES S.A.; *Int'l*, pg. 1793
COPERNIC INC.—See Constellation Software Inc.; *Int'l*, pg. 1774
COPPER STATE COMMUNICATIONS, INC.—See BlackPoint IT Services, Inc.; *U.S. Private*, pg. 576
COPPER VALLEY TELEPHONE COOPERATIVE, INC.; *U.S. Private*, pg. 1045
CORPORACION DE PERSONAL ADMINISTRATIVO S. A. DE C. V.—See Empresas Publicas de Medellin ESP; *Int'l*, pg. 2391
CORR WIRELESS INC.; *U.S. Private*, pg. 1058
COSI MEDICAL IT GMBH—See CompuGroup Medical SE & Co. KGaA; *Int'l*, pg. 1755
COSMOTE E-VALUE S.A.—See Hellenic Telecommunications Organization S.A.; *Int'l*, pg. 3333
CPI ESSCO INC.—See Odyssey Investment Partners, LLC; *U.S. Private*, pg. 2994
CQG, INC.; *U.S. Private*, pg. 1081
CREALOGIX AG—See Constellation Software Inc.; *Int'l*, pg. 1772
CREALOGIX (DEUTSCHLAND) AG—See Constellation Software Inc.; *Int'l*, pg. 1772
CRF INC.; *U.S. Private*, pg. 1099
CROIX CONNECT; *U.S. Private*, pg. 1103
CSDVRS, LLC—See Kinderhook Industries, LLC; *U.S. Private*, pg. 2306
CSE CROSSCOM PTY LTD—See CSE Global Ltd.; *Int'l*, pg. 1863
CSE-ITS PTE LTD—See CSE Global Ltd.; *Int'l*, pg. 1863
CSG INTERACTIVE MESSAGING, INC.—See CSG Systems International, Inc.; *U.S. Public*, pg. 601
CS LOXINFO PUBLIC COMPANY LIMITED—See Advanced Info Service Plc; *Int'l*, pg. 160
CTDI - AUSTRALIA PTY LIMITED—See Communications Test Design Inc.; *U.S. Private*, pg. 989
CTDI DO BRAZIL LTDA—See Communications Test Design Inc.; *U.S. Private*, pg. 989
CTDI EUROPE GMBH—See Communications Test Design Inc.; *U.S. Private*, pg. 989
CTDI HONG KONG LIMITED—See Communications Test Design Inc.; *U.S. Private*, pg. 989
CTDI NETHOUSE SERVICES KFT.—See Communications Test Design Inc.; *U.S. Private*, pg. 989
CTDI NETHOUSE SERVICES LTD—See Communications Test Design Inc.; *U.S. Private*, pg. 989
CTDI S.R.L.—See Communications Test Design Inc.; *U.S. Private*, pg. 989
CTRACK FINANCE LIMITED—See Inseego Corp.; *U.S. Public*, pg. 1129
CTRACK (SA) (PTY) LIMITED—See Inseego Corp.; *U.S. Public*, pg. 1129
CUBO BRAND COMMUNICATIONS LIMITED—See Cubo Communications Group Plc; *Int'l*, pg. 1875
CYBER INTERNET SERVICES (PRIVATE) LIMITED—See COLGATE-PALMOLIVE (PAKISTAN) LTD; *Int'l*, pg. 1698
CYBERPLEX INC.-BOSTON—See EQ Inc.; *Int'l*, pg. 2466
CYBERTAN CORPORATION—See CyberTAN Technology, Inc.; *Int'l*, pg. 1894
CYBERZ INC.—See CyberAgent, Inc.; *Int'l*, pg. 1892
CYCOS AG; *Int'l*, pg. 1895
CYNERGY PROFESSIONAL SYSTEMS, LLC; *U.S. Private*, pg. 1134
CYTACOM SOLUTIONS LIMITED—See Cyprus Telecommunications Authority; *Int'l*, pg. 1897
CYTAGLOBAL—See Cyprus Telecommunications Authority; *Int'l*, pg. 1897
CYTA (UK) LTD—See Hellenic Television Ltd; *Int'l*, pg. 3334
DACIA ANTENA, S.R.L.—See EQT AB; *Int'l*, pg. 2479
DAISY WHOLESALE LIMITED; *Int'l*, pg. 1943
DASCOM SYSTEMS GROUP LLC—See Strength Capital Partners, LLC; *U.S. Private*, pg. 3839
DATA FOUNDRY, INC.—See DigitalBridge Group, Inc.; *U.S. Public*, pg. 665
DATA HORIZON CORPORATION; *Int'l*, pg. 1976
DATATEC LIMITED; *Int'l*, pg. 1980
DBA TELECOMMUNICATION (ASIA) HOLDINGS LIMITED; *Int'l*, pg. 1986
DB ELETTRONICA TELECOMUNICAZIONI SPA; *Int'l*, pg. 1986
DEAN ONE B.V.—See Gamma Communications PLC; *Int'l*, pg. 2878

DEBITEL KONZERNFINANZIERUNGS GMBH—See freenet AG; *Int'l*, pg. 2770
DEEP SPACE MEDIA GROUP AG; *Int'l*, pg. 2002
DELAWARE.NET, INC.; *U.S. Private*, pg. 1196
DELAWARE THIRTEEN LTD.; *Int'l*, pg. 2010
DENALI MEDIA JUNEAU, CORP.—See Liberty Broadband Corporation; *U.S. Public*, pg. 1310
DENTSU AEGIS NETWORK IBERIA S.L—See Dentsu Group Inc.; *Int'l*, pg. 2036
DENTSU DIGITAL HOLDINGS INC.—See Dentsu Group Inc.; *Int'l*, pg. 2034
DENTSU UTAMA SDN. BHD.—See Dentsu Group Inc.; *Int'l*, pg. 2037
DESPEGAR.COM USA, INC.—See Despegar.com, Corp.; *Int'l*, pg. 2046
DIAL800; *U.S. Private*, pg. 1222
DIALOG BROADBAND NETWORKS (PRIVATE) LIMITED—See Axiata Group Berhad; *Int'l*, pg. 768
DIGITAL FOREST, INC.—See Halyard Capital Management, LLC; *U.S. Private*, pg. 1847
DIGITAL UNITED, INC.; *Int'l*, pg. 2123
DIGI TELECOMMUNICATIONS SDN BHD—See Celcom-Digi Berhad; *Int'l*, pg. 1391
DIGIWEB LTD.; *Int'l*, pg. 2124
DISTINCT INFRASTRUCTURE GROUP INC.; *Int'l*, pg. 2135
DIVERSIFIED COMMUNICATIONS INDIA—See Diversified Communications; *U.S. Private*, pg. 1241
DIVERSIFIED EVENTS HONG KONG—See Diversified Communications; *U.S. Private*, pg. 1241
DMG INFORMATION US INC.—See Daily Mail & General Trust plc; *Int'l*, pg. 1937
DMN LTD.—See The Gores Group, LLC; *U.S. Private*, pg. 4034
DOWNER EDI ENGINEERING - CONTRACTING / POWER SYSTEMS—See Downer EDI Limited; *Int'l*, pg. 2185
DSLEXTREME.COM INC.—See Broadvoice, Inc.; *U.S. Private*, pg. 660
DTAC NETWORK CO., LTD.—See Charoen Pokphand Group Co., Ltd.; *Int'l*, pg. 1453
DXSTORM.COM INC.; *Int'l*, pg. 2237
DYNAMIC SYSTEMS TECHNOLOGY, INC.; *U.S. Private*, pg. 1299
DYNIS LLC.; *U.S. Private*, pg. 1300
EARTHLINK BUSINESS, LLC—See Windstream Holdings, Inc.; *U.S. Public*, pg. 2373
EASTCOM NETWORK CO., LTD.—See Eastern communications Co., LTD.; *Int'l*, pg. 2272
EASTLINK CABLE SYSTEMS—See Bragg Group of Companies; *Int'l*, pg. 1136
EAST TEXAS FIBER LINE, INC.—See Consolidated Communications Holdings, Inc.; *U.S. Public*, pg. 570
EASYBELL GMBH—See ecotel communication ag; *Int'l*, pg. 2300
EASYSEAT, LLC; *U.S. Private*, pg. 1323
ECI TELECOM—See Ribbon Communications Inc.; *U.S. Public*, pg. 1797
ECI TELECOM UKRAINE LLC—See Ribbon Communications Inc.; *U.S. Public*, pg. 1797
ECKOH UK LIMITED—See Eckoh plc; *Int'l*, pg. 2291
ECONOCOM TELECOM SERVICES SAS—See Econocom Group SA; *Int'l*, pg. 2298
ECOTEL PRIVATE GMBH—See ecotel communication ag; *Int'l*, pg. 2300
EDI HEALTH GROUP; *U.S. Private*, pg. 1336
E.DISCOM TELEKOMMUNIKATION GMBH—See E.ON SE; *Int'l*, pg. 2300
EDOTCO BANGLADESH CO. LTD.—See Axiata Group Berhad; *Int'l*, pg. 768
EDOTCO GROUP SDN BHD—See Axiata Group Berhad; *Int'l*, pg. 768
EFASHIONS SOLUTIONS, LLC; *U.S. Private*, pg. 1343
EFTEL PTY LIMITED—See Aware Super Pty Ltd; *Int'l*, pg. 752
EKAHAU OY—See Ziff Davis, Inc.; *U.S. Public*, pg. 2403
EKINOPS BELGIUM NV—See Ekinops S.A.; *Int'l*, pg. 2338
EKINOPS CORPORATION—See Ekinops S.A.; *Int'l*, pg. 2338
EKINOPS ESPANA SRL.—See Ekinops S.A.; *Int'l*, pg. 2338
EKINOPS FRANCE SA—See Ekinops S.A.; *Int'l*, pg. 2338
EKINOPS INDIA PVT. LTD.—See Ekinops S.A.; *Int'l*, pg. 2338
EKINOPS ITALIA SRL.—See Ekinops S.A.; *Int'l*, pg. 2338
EKITAN & CO., LTD.; *Int'l*, pg. 2338
ELGIA, INC.; *U.S. Private*, pg. 1359
ELITETELE.COM HOLDINGS PLC; *Int'l*, pg. 2363
ELLIPSIZ COMMUNICATIONS LTD.; *Int'l*, pg. 2366
EMIRATES TELECOMMUNICATIONS & MARINE SERVICES FZE—See Emirates Telecommunications Group Compapny PJSC; *Int'l*, pg. 2368
EMPRESA NACIONAL DE TELECOMUNICACIONES S.A.—See Almendral S.A.; *Int'l*, pg. 364
EMPRESAS PUBLICAS DE ORIENTE ANTIOQUENO S.A.—See Empresas Publicas de Medellin ESP; *Int'l*, pg. 2392
EMS WIRING SYSTEMS PTE LTD; *Int'l*, pg. 2393
ENBW PERSPEKTIVEN GMBH—See EnBW Energie Baden-Wurttemberg AG; *Int'l*, pg. 2398

ENDEVIS, LLC—See My Job Matcher, Inc.; *U.S. Private*, pg. 2823
ENERGY CENTRAL; *U.S. Private*, pg. 1394
ENGHOUSE NETWORKS (GERMANY) GMBH—See Enghouse Systems Limited; *Int'l*, pg. 2427
ENGIN LIMITED—See Aware Super Pty Ltd; *Int'l*, pg. 752
ENGRO ENFRASHARE (PRIVATE) LIMITED—See Engro Corporation Limited; *Int'l*, pg. 2435
ENROLLCOM, INC.—See American Fidelity Corporation; *U.S. Private*, pg. 234
ENSOURCE, INC.—See Black Box Limited; *Int'l*, pg. 1058
EN-TEL COMMUNICATIONS LLC—See Windstream Holdings, Inc.; *U.S. Public*, pg. 2373
ENTERTAINMENT GATEWAY GROUP CORP—See Globe Telecom, Inc.; *Int'l*, pg. 3006
EPM CAPITAL MEXICO S.A. DE C.V—See Empresas Publicas de Medellin ESP; *Int'l*, pg. 2391
EPSILON TELECOMMUNICATIONS GMBH—See Gamma Communications PLC; *Int'l*, pg. 2878
EQS GROUP AG—See Thoma Bravo, L.P.; *U.S. Private*, pg. 4147
EQS GROUP INC.—See Thoma Bravo, L.P.; *U.S. Private*, pg. 4147
EQS GROUP LTD.—See Thoma Bravo, L.P.; *U.S. Private*, pg. 4147
EQS GROUP SAS—See Thoma Bravo, L.P.; *U.S. Private*, pg. 4147
EQS WEB TECHNOLOGIES PVT. LTD.—See Thoma Bravo, L.P.; *U.S. Private*, pg. 4147
EQUILAR; *U.S. Private*, pg. 1415
EQUINIX ASIA PACIFIC PTE. LTD.—See Equinix, Inc.; *U.S. Public*, pg. 787
EQUINIX AUSTRALIA PTY. LIMITED—See Equinix, Inc.; *U.S. Public*, pg. 787
EQUINIX (BULGARIA) DATA CENTERS EAD—See Equinix, Inc.; *U.S. Public*, pg. 787
EQUINIX CANADA LTD.—See Equinix, Inc.; *U.S. Public*, pg. 787
EQUINIX EUROPE, INC.—See Equinix, Inc.; *U.S. Public*, pg. 787
EQUINIX (GERMANY) ENTERPRISES GMBH—See Equinix, Inc.; *U.S. Public*, pg. 787
EQUINIX (HONG KONG) ENTERPRISES LIMITED—See Equinix, Inc.; *U.S. Public*, pg. 787
EQUINIX HONG KONG LIMITED—See Equinix, Inc.; *U.S. Public*, pg. 787
EQUINIX (ITALY) ENTERPRISES S.R.L.—See Equinix, Inc.; *U.S. Public*, pg. 787
EQUINIX JAPAN K.K.—See Equinix, Inc.; *U.S. Public*, pg. 787
EQUINIX (LD10) LIMITED—See Equinix, Inc.; *U.S. Public*, pg. 787
EQUINIX OPERATING CO., LLC—See Equinix, Inc.; *U.S. Public*, pg. 788
EQUINIX SINGAPORE PTE. LTD.—See Equinix, Inc.; *U.S. Public*, pg. 787
EQUINIX (SWEDEN) AB—See Equinix, Inc.; *U.S. Public*, pg. 787
EQUINIX (SWITZERLAND) ENTERPRISES GMBH—See Equinix, Inc.; *U.S. Public*, pg. 787
EQUINIX UK LIMITED—See Equinix, Inc.; *U.S. Public*, pg. 787
EQUITYSTORY RS, LLC—See Thoma Bravo, L.P.; *U.S. Private*, pg. 4147
ERGON ENERGY TELECOMMUNICATIONS PTY LTD—See Ergon Energy Corporation Limited; *Int'l*, pg. 2491
ESENDEX—See HgCapital Trust plc; *Int'l*, pg. 3376
ESSAR TELEHOLDING LTD.—See Essar Global Limited; *Int'l*, pg. 2508
ESTORE CORPORATION; *Int'l*, pg. 2518
EUNETWORKS B.V.—See Stonepeak Partners L.P.; *U.S. Private*, pg. 3830
EUNETWORKS FIBER UK LIMITED—See Stonepeak Partners L.P.; *U.S. Private*, pg. 3830
EUNETWORKS GMBH—See Stonepeak Partners L.P.; *U.S. Private*, pg. 3830
EUNETWORKS IRELAND - PRIVATE FIBER LIMITED—See Stonepeak Partners L.P.; *U.S. Private*, pg. 3830
EUROTEL S.A.; *Int'l*, pg. 2558
EUTELSAT ASIA PTE. LTD.—See Eutelsat Communications SA; *Int'l*, pg. 2559
EUTELSAT DO BRASIL PARTICIPATOES LTDA.—See Eutelsat Communications SA; *Int'l*, pg. 2560
EUTELSAT LATIN AMERICA S.A.—See Eutelsat Communications SA; *Int'l*, pg. 2559
EUTELSAT MADEIRA LDA.—See Eutelsat Communications SA; *Int'l*, pg. 2559
EUTELSAT NETWORKS LLC—See Eutelsat Communications SA; *Int'l*, pg. 2559
EUTELSAT S.A.—See Eutelsat Communications SA; *Int'l*, pg. 2559
EVERBRIDGE EUROPE LIMITED—See Thoma Bravo, L.P.; *U.S. Private*, pg. 4147
EVERBRIDGE, INC.—See Thoma Bravo, L.P.; *U.S. Private*, pg. 4147

N.A.I.C.S. INDEX 517810 — ALL OTHER TELECOMMU...

EVOLVING SYSTEMS NC, INC.—See CCUR Holdings Inc.; *U.S. Public*, pg. 461
EWE TEL GMBH—See EWE Aktiengesellschaft; *Int'l*, pg. 2575
EXCEL TELECOMMUNICATIONS—See Blue Casa Communications, Inc.; *U.S. Private*, pg. 586
EXCEL TELECOMMUNICATIONS—See Garrison Investment Group LP; *U.S. Private*, pg. 1646
EXPERIAN IRELAND LTD.—See Experian plc; *Int'l*, pg. 2587
EXPERT WIRELESS SOLUTIONS, INC.; *U.S. Private*, pg. 1450
EXPERT WIRELESS SOLUTIONS, INC.—See eXpert Wireless Solutions, Inc.; *U.S. Private*, pg. 1450
EXPRIMM IT—See Bouygues S.A.; *Int'l*, pg. 1123
EXXE GROUP, INC.; *U.S. Public*, pg. 813
EZENTIS CHILE, S.A.—See Grupo Ezentis S.A.; *Int'l*, pg. 3129
FABLAB S.R.L.—See CompuGroup Medical SE & Co. KGaA; *Int'l*, pg. 1756
FAIRPOINT CARRIER SERVICES, INC.—See Consolidated Communications Holdings, Inc.; *U.S. Public*, pg. 570
FAR REACH TECHNOLOGIES CORPORATION; *U.S. Private*, pg. 1473
FASTWIRE PTE. LTD.; *Int'l*, pg. 2622
FIBERKOM APS—See Bravida Holding AB; *Int'l*, pg. 1142
FIBERPIPE, INC.—See Tonaquint Data Centers, Inc.; *U.S. Private*, pg. 4184
THE FIBERSMITH COMPANY; *U.S. Private*, pg. 4028
FIBER TECHNOLOGIES, INC.—See Dycom Industries, Inc.; *U.S. Public*, pg. 699
FIEBIG+TEAM GMBH; *Int'l*, pg. 2655
FINTECH SELECT LTD.; *Int'l*, pg. 2677
FLEXIROAM LIMITED; *Int'l*, pg. 2705
FLOWROUTE, LLC—See Thompson Street Capital Manager LLC; *U.S. Private*, pg. 4160
FLUENTSTREAM TECHNOLOGIES, LLC; *U.S. Private*, pg. 1552
FOCUS 4U LTD.; *Int'l*, pg. 2718
FOLIOFN, INC.; *U.S. Private*, pg. 1559
FONALITY, INC.; *U.S. Private*, pg. 1559
FONEX DATA SYSTEMS INC; *Int'l*, pg. 2726
FONIAL GMBH—See EnBW Energie Baden-Wurttemberg AG; *Int'l*, pg. 2401
FOOTHILLS RURAL TELEPHONE COOPERATIVE CORPORATION INC.; *U.S. Private*, pg. 1562
FORESHORE LIMITED—See Bahrain Telecommunications Company BSC; *Int'l*, pg. 801
FORMULA ONE ADMINISTRATION LIMITED—See Liberty Media Corporation; *U.S. Public*, pg. 1311
FORMULA TELECOM LIMITED—See Formula Telecom Solutions Limited; *Int'l*, pg. 2737
FORT MILL TELEPHONE COMPANY—See Comporium Group; *U.S. Private*, pg. 1002
FORVAL CORPORATION; *Int'l*, pg. 2745
FPT TELECOM JOINT STOCK COMPANY—See FPT Corporation; *Int'l*, pg. 2758
FREEBIT CO., LTD.; *Int'l*, pg. 2769
FREENET DATENKOMMUNIKATIONS GMBH—See freenet AG; *Int'l*, pg. 2770
FREENET DIREKT GMBH—See freenet AG; *Int'l*, pg. 2770
FREE SAS—See Iliad S.A.; *Int'l*, pg. 3614
FRONTIER COMMUNICATIONS OF DELAWARE, INC.—See Frontier Communications Parent, Inc.; *U.S. Public*, pg. 887
FRONTIER COMMUNICATIONS OF THORNTOWN LLC—See Frontier Communications Parent, Inc.; *U.S. Public*, pg. 887
FRONTIER COMMUNICATIONS—See Frontier Communications Parent, Inc.; *U.S. Public*, pg. 887
FRTEK JAPAN INC.—See FRTEK Co., Ltd.; *Int'l*, pg. 2797
F.T.S- FORMULA TELECOM SOLUTIONS BULGARIA—See Formula Telecom Solutions Limited; *Int'l*, pg. 2737
F.T.S. GLOBAL LIMITED—See Formula Telecom Solutions Limited; *Int'l*, pg. 2737
FUJITSU RESEARCH AND DEVELOPMENT CENTER CO., LTD.—See Fujitsu Limited; *Int'l*, pg. 2835
FUJITSU TECHNOLOGY & BUSINESS OF AMERICA, INC.—See Fujitsu Limited; *Int'l*, pg. 2836
FUJITSU TELECOMUNICACOES PORTUGAL, S.A.—See Fujitsu Limited; *Int'l*, pg. 2837
FUJI XEROX (HONG KONG) LIMITED—See FUJIFILM Holdings Corporation; *Int'l*, pg. 2825
FUJI XEROX PHILIPPINES INC.—See FUJIFILM Holdings Corporation; *Int'l*, pg. 2825
FULLERTON TECHNOLOGY CO., LTD.; *Int'l*, pg. 2842
FULLNET COMMUNICATIONS, INC; *U.S. Public*, pg. 892
FUNA GMBH NACHRICHTENTECHNIK—See L3Harris Technologies, Inc.; *U.S. Public*, pg. 1281
FUSION INTERACTIVE CORP.; *U.S. Private*, pg. 893
FUTURE COMMUNICATIONS CO. GLOBAL K.S.C.C.; *Int'l*, pg. 2853
FYBERCOM, LLC; *U.S. Private*, pg. 1628
G3 COMMS LTD.; *Int'l*, pg. 2866
GABON TELECOM SA—See Emirates Telecommunications Group Compapny PJSC; *Int'l*, pg. 2382
GAMEBASE, INC.; *U.S. Private*, pg. 1640

GAMMA BUSINESS COMMUNICATIONS LIMITED—See Gamma Communications PLC; *Int'l*, pg. 2878
GAMMA COMMUNICATIONS GMBH—See Gamma Communications PLC; *Int'l*, pg. 2878
GAMMA NETWORK SOLUTIONS LIMITED—See Gamma Communications PLC; *Int'l*, pg. 2878
GAMMA TELECOM LIMITED—See Gamma Communications PLC; *Int'l*, pg. 2878
GARRETTCOM EUROPE LTD.—See Belden, Inc.; *U.S. Public*, pg. 294
GARTNER AUSTRALASIA PTY. LTD.—See Gartner, Inc.; *U.S. Public*, pg. 906
GATR TECHNOLOGIES INC.—See Elliott Management Corporation; *U.S. Private*, pg. 1368
GATR TECHNOLOGIES INC.—See Veritas Capital Fund Management, LLC; *U.S. Private*, pg. 4362
GBS SOLUTIONS NA LLC—See BULPROS Consulting AD; *Int'l*, pg. 1214
GCI COMMUNICATION CORP.—See Liberty Broadband Corporation; *U.S. Public*, pg. 1310
GCI, LLC—See Liberty Broadband Corporation; *U.S. Public*, pg. 1310
GDKN CORPORATION; *U.S. Private*, pg. 1654
GENASYS II SPAIN, S.A.U.—See Genasys, Inc.; *U.S. Public*, pg. 911
GENBAND US LLC—See Ribbon Communications Inc.; *U.S. Public*, pg. 1797
GENERAL DYNAMICS MISSION SYSTEMS - ITALY S.R.L.—See General Dynamics Corporation; *U.S. Public*, pg. 915
GENIE GATEWAY; *U.S. Private*, pg. 1671
GEOPLAN NAMTECH INC.—See FinTech Global Incorporated; *Int'l*, pg. 2677
GERMANOS S.A.—See Hellenic Telecommunications Organization S.A.; *Int'l*, pg. 3333
GERMANOS TELECOM ROMANIA S.A.—See Hellenic Telecommunications Organization S.A.; *Int'l*, pg. 3333
GERMANOS TELECOM S.A.—See Hellenic Telecommunications Organization S.A.; *Int'l*, pg. 3333
GETRONICS COLUMBIA LTDA—See OpenGate Capital Management, LLC; *U.S. Private*, pg. 3030
GIGASET AG; *Int'l*, pg. 2972
GIGASET ILETISIM CIHAZLARI A.S.—See Gigaset AG; *Int'l*, pg. 2972
GILAT TELECOM LTD.; *Int'l*, pg. 2973
GIST COMMUNICATIONS, INC.; *U.S. Private*, pg. 1702
GLOBAL COMMUNICATION PLANNING CO., LTD.; *Int'l*, pg. 2994
GLOBAL CONNECT, LLC—See TCN, Inc.; *U.S. Private*, pg. 3943
GLOBAL DOMAINS INTERNATIONAL, INC.; *U.S. Private*, pg. 1713
GLOBALPOPS, INC.—See Ad-Base Group, Inc.; *U.S. Private*, pg. 72
GLOBAL TELECOM & TECHNOLOGY AMERICAS, INC.—See GTT Communications, Inc.; *U.S. Private*, pg. 1808
GLOBAL TEL LINK CORPORATION - VALIDATION STATION—See American Securities LLC; *U.S. Private*, pg. 249
GMO AD MARKETING INC.—See GMO Internet Group, Inc.; *Int'l*, pg. 3013
GMO BRIGHTS CONSULTING INC.—See GMO Internet Group, Inc.; *Int'l*, pg. 3013
GMO CARS K.K.—See GMO Internet Group, Inc.; *Int'l*, pg. 3013
GMO COMMERCE, INC.—See GMO Internet Group, Inc.; *Int'l*, pg. 3013
GMO E-LAB MARKETING RESEARCH (SHANGHAI) CO, LTD.—See GMO Internet Group, Inc.; *Int'l*, pg. 3013
GMO GLOBALSIGN PHILIPPINES CORP.—See GMO Internet Group, Inc.; *Int'l*, pg. 3013
GMO INSIGHT INC.—See GMO Internet Group, Inc.; *Int'l*, pg. 3013
GMO INTERNET GROUP, INC.; *Int'l*, pg. 3013
GMO KUMAPON INC.—See GMO Internet Group, Inc.; *Int'l*, pg. 3014
GMO RESEARCH PTE. LTD.—See GMO Internet Group, Inc.; *Int'l*, pg. 3014
GMO RESEARCH PVT. LTD.—See GMO Internet Group, Inc.; *Int'l*, pg. 3014
GMO RESEARCH SDN. BHD.—See GMO Internet Group, Inc.; *Int'l*, pg. 3014
GMO-Z.COM ACE CO., LTD.—See GMO Internet Group, Inc.; *Int'l*, pg. 3014
GMO-Z.COM BRIGHTS VIETNAM CO., LTD.—See GMO Internet Group, Inc.; *Int'l*, pg. 3014
GMO-Z.COM NETDESIGN HOLDINGS CO., LTD.—See GMO Internet Group, Inc.; *Int'l*, pg. 3014
GMO-Z.COM RUNSYSTEM JSC—See GMO Internet Group, Inc.; *Int'l*, pg. 3014
GMO-Z.COM VIETNAM LAB CENTER CO., LTD.—See GMO Internet Group, Inc.; *Int'l*, pg. 3014
GM VOICES, INC.—See GetBlend Inc.; *U.S. Private*, pg. 1688
GODSINLOSEN NORDIC AB; *Int'l*, pg. 3021
GOODMAN NETWORKS, INC.; *U.S. Private*, pg. 1739
GOTTHARDT INFORMATIONSSYSTEME GMBH—See CompuGroup Medical SE & Co. KGaA; *Int'l*, pg. 1756
GRANDE COMMUNICATIONS NETWORKS LLC—See Stonepeak Partners L.P.; *U.S. Private*, pg. 3829
GRASSHOPPER GROUP, LLC—See Elliott Management Corporation; *U.S. Private*, pg. 1367
GRASSHOPPER GROUP, LLC—See Vista Equity Partners, LLC; *U.S. Private*, pg. 4396
GREAT WORKS INTERNET; *U.S. Private*, pg. 1768
GREENWICH VILLAGE GAZETTE—See Gilford Graphics International; *U.S. Private*, pg. 1699
GRIFFIN INFORMATION SYSTEMS LTD.; *Int'l*, pg. 3083
GROUP SJR; *U.S. Private*, pg. 1794
GRUPO EZENTIS S.A.; *Int'l*, pg. 3129
GTG VENTURES, INC.; *Int'l*, pg. 3151
GTS HUNGARY TELECOMMUNICATION KFT.—See Deutsche Telekom AG; *Int'l*, pg. 2083
GTS TELECOM ROMANIA—See Deutsche Telekom AG; *Int'l*, pg. 2083
GTT-EMEA, LTD.—See GTT Communications, Inc.; *U.S. Private*, pg. 1808
GTT GMBH—See GTT Communications, Inc.; *U.S. Private*, pg. 1808
THE GUITAMMER COMPANY; *U.S. Private*, pg. 4040
GULFTEL COMMUNICATIONS—See Lumen Technologies, Inc.; *U.S. Public*, pg. 1346
GUOMAI TECHNOLOGIES, INC.; *Int'l*, pg. 3186
GWI, INC.; *U.S. Private*, pg. 1821
HAMILTON TELECOMMUNICATIONS—See Nedelco Inc.; *U.S. Private*, pg. 2879
HANGZHOU AMPHENOL PHOENIX TELECOM PARTS CO. LTD.—See Amphenol Corporation; *U.S. Public*, pg. 130
HANGZHOU ANYSOFT INFORMATION TECH CO LTD; *Int'l*, pg. 3246
HANGZHOU FREELY COMMUNICATION CO., LTD.; *Int'l*, pg. 3247
HAWE S.A.; *Int'l*, pg. 3288
HEALTHCOMMUNITIES.COM, INC.; *U.S. Private*, pg. 1895
HELIOS TOWERS PLC; *Int'l*, pg. 3330
HELLASCOM S.A.—See Hellenic Telecommunications Organization S.A.; *Int'l*, pg. 3333
HER CAMPUS MEDIA, LLC; *U.S. Private*, pg. 1920
HEXATRONIC AUSTRALIA PTY. LTD.—See Hexatronic Group AB; *Int'l*, pg. 3370
HFR INC.; *Int'l*, pg. 3375
HIBERNIA ATLANTIC CABLE SYSTEM LIMITED—See GTT Communications, Inc.; *U.S. Private*, pg. 1808
HIGHROAD SOLUTION; *U.S. Private*, pg. 1941
HIGHTEL TOWERS SPA; *Int'l*, pg. 3388
HILL ASSOCIATES INC.; *U.S. Private*, pg. 1944
HKBN LTD.—See Hong Kong Technology Venture Company Limited; *Int'l*, pg. 3467
HL KOMM TELEKOMMUNIKATIONS GMBH—See Morgan Stanley; *U.S. Public*, pg. 1473
HOLLY CONNECTS, INC.—See Apollo Global Management, Inc.; *U.S. Public*, pg. 152
HOLOSFIND S.A.; *Int'l*, pg. 3453
HOSHIN GIGAMEDIA CENTER INC.—See GigaMedia Limited; *Int'l*, pg. 2971
HOSPEDIA LIMITED—See Marlin Equity Partners, LLC; *U.S. Private*, pg. 2584
HOST EUROPE GROUP LIMITED—See KKR & Co. Inc.; *U.S. Public*, pg. 1252
HOST EUROPE GROUP LIMITED—See Silver Lake Group, LLC; *U.S. Private*, pg. 3657
HOST EUROPE GROUP LIMITED—See TCMI, Inc.; *U.S. Private*, pg. 3943
HOTSPOT INTERNATIONAL, S DE R.L. DE C.V.; *Int'l*, pg. 3489
HRVATSKI TELEKOM D.D.—See Deutsche Telekom AG; *Int'l*, pg. 2083
HTG MANAGED SERVICES LIMITED—See Helios Towers PLC; *Int'l*, pg. 3330
HUBIFY LIMITED; *Int'l*, pg. 3520
HUB TELECOM—See Aeroports de Paris S.A.; *Int'l*, pg. 181
HUDSON FIBER NETWORK—See Stonepeak Partners L.P.; *U.S. Private*, pg. 3829
HUGE CONNECT PROPRIETARY LIMITED—See Huge Group Limited; *Int'l*, pg. 3524
HUGE NETWORKS PROPRIETARY LIMITED—See Huge Group Limited; *Int'l*, pg. 3524
HUGE TELECOM PROPRIETARY LIMITED—See Huge Group Limited; *Int'l*, pg. 3524
HUGHES COMMUNICATIONS INDIA PRIVATE LTD.—See EchoStar Corporation; *U.S. Public*, pg. 711
HUMAN TECHNOLOGY CO., LTD.; *Int'l*, pg. 3529
IAB HOLDINGS LIMITED; *Int'l*, pg. 3568
ICE GROUP ASA—See Access Industries, Inc.; *U.S. Private*, pg. 51
ICON COMMUNICATIONS CJSC; *Int'l*, pg. 3583
I-CUBE GMBH—See ecotel communication ag; *Int'l*, pg. 2300
IDC ASIA & PACIFIC—See China Oceanwide Holdings Group Co., Ltd.; *Int'l*, pg. 1536
IDC ASIA & PACIFIC—See IDG Capital; *Int'l*, pg. 3593
IDC CENTRAL EUROPE GMBH—See China Oceanwide Holdings Group Co., Ltd.; *Int'l*, pg. 1537
IDC CENTRAL EUROPE GMBH—See IDG Capital; *Int'l*, pg. 3593

517810 — ALL OTHER TELECOMMU...

IDC COLUMBIA—See China Oceanwide Holdings Group Co., Ltd.; *Int'l*, pg. 1537
IDC COLUMBIA—See IDG Capital; *Int'l*, pg. 3593
IDC GLOBAL, INC.—See GTT Communications, Inc.; *U.S. Private*, pg. 1808
IDC ITALY—See China Oceanwide Holdings Group Co., Ltd.; *Int'l*, pg. 1537
IDC ITALY—See IDG Capital; *Int'l*, pg. 3593
IDC JAPAN CO., LTD.—See China Oceanwide Holdings Group Co., Ltd.; *Int'l*, pg. 1537
IDC JAPAN CO., LTD.—See IDG Capital; *Int'l*, pg. 3593
IDC LATIN AMERICA—See China Oceanwide Holdings Group Co., Ltd.; *Int'l*, pg. 1537
IDC LATIN AMERICA—See IDG Capital; *Int'l*, pg. 3593
IDC MEXICO—See China Oceanwide Holdings Group Co., Ltd.; *Int'l*, pg. 1537
IDC MEXICO—See IDG Capital; *Int'l*, pg. 3593
IDC RUSSIA—See China Oceanwide Holdings Group Co., Ltd.; *Int'l*, pg. 1537
IDC RUSSIA—See IDG Capital; *Int'l*, pg. 3594
IDG COMMUNICATIONS ITALIA SRL—See China Oceanwide Holdings Group Co., Ltd.; *Int'l*, pg. 1537
IDG COMMUNICATIONS ITALIA SRL—See IDG Capital; *Int'l*, pg. 3594
IDG DENMARK A/S—See China Oceanwide Holdings Group Co., Ltd.; *Int'l*, pg. 1537
IDG DENMARK A/S—See IDG Capital; *Int'l*, pg. 3594
IFBYPHONE; *U.S. Private*, pg. 2038
IFILM CORP.—See National Amusements, Inc.; *U.S. Private*, pg. 2842
IFNET INC.—See FTGroup Co Ltd.; *Int'l*, pg. 2800
IFX NETWORKS ARGENTINA SRL—See Enel S.p.A.; *Int'l*, pg. 2414
IFX NETWORKS CHILE SA—See Enel S.p.A.; *Int'l*, pg. 2414
IFX NETWORKS LLC—See Enel S.p.A.; *Int'l*, pg. 2415
IHLAS NET A.S—See Ihlas Holding A.S.; *Int'l*, pg. 3606
IINET LIMITED—See CK Hutchison Holdings Limited; *Int'l*, pg. 1638
IMAGE PROCESSING SYSTEMS, INC.—See Edenred S.A.; *Int'l*, pg. 2307
IMVU INC.; *U.S. Private*, pg. 2051
INCOMM SOLUTIONS, INC.—See Chorus Call, Inc.; *U.S. Private*, pg. 889
INFINITE CONFERENCING, INC.—See Onstream Media Corporation; *U.S. Private*, pg. 3028
INFINITE NETWORKS CORPORATION; *U.S. Private*, pg. 2071
INFINITY INTERNET, INC.—See Atmosera, Inc.; *U.S. Private*, pg. 381
INFO2CELL.COM—See Altruist Technologies Pvt. Ltd.; *Int'l*, pg. 399
INFODESK, INC.—See Cuadrilla Capital LLC; *U.S. Private*, pg. 1119
INFORMATIVE, INC.—See Satmetrix Systems, Inc.; *U.S. Private*, pg. 3553
INGENIO, LLC—See Thryv Holdings, Inc.; *U.S. Public*, pg. 2157
INGRAM MICRO MOBILITY—See Hainan Traffic Administration Holding Co., Ltd.; *Int'l*, pg. 3215
INGRAM MICRO SOUTHERN AFRICA (PROPRIETARY) LIMITED—See Hainan Traffic Administration Holding Co., Ltd.; *Int'l*, pg. 3215
INMARSAT AUSTRALIA PTY LIMITED—See ViaSat, Inc.; *U.S. Public*, pg. 2291
INMARSAT HONG KONG LIMITED—See ViaSat, Inc.; *U.S. Public*, pg. 2292
INMARSAT KK—See ViaSat, Inc.; *U.S. Public*, pg. 2292
INMARSAT PLC—See ViaSat, Inc.; *U.S. Public*, pg. 2291
INMARSAT SA—See ViaSat, Inc.; *U.S. Public*, pg. 2292
INMARSAT SOLUTIONS AS—See ViaSat, Inc.; *U.S. Public*, pg. 2292
INMARSAT SOLUTIONS SA PTY LIMITED—See ViaSat, Inc.; *U.S. Public*, pg. 2292
INMARSAT SOLUTIONS SHANGHAI CO. LIMITED—See ViaSat, Inc.; *U.S. Public*, pg. 2292
INMARSAT SPAIN S.A—See ViaSat, Inc.; *U.S. Public*, pg. 2292
INNERFAX INC.; *U.S. Private*, pg. 2080
INNOVATIVE COLLABORATION, INC.; *U.S. Private*, pg. 2082
INSITE WIRELESS GROUP, LLC—See American Tower Corporation; *U.S. Public*, pg. 111
INSTAMED COMMUNICATIONS, LLC—See JPMorgan Chase & Co.; *U.S. Public*, pg. 1207
INTDEV INTERNET TECHNOLOGIES PROPRIETARY LIMITED—See Alviva Holdings Limited; *Int'l*, pg. 402
INTEG GROUP PTY. LTD.—See DXC Technology Company; *U.S. Public*, pg. 696
INTEGRA TELECOM HOLDINGS, INC.—See Warburg Pincus LLC; *U.S. Private*, pg. 4438
INTEGRITY COMMUNICATIONS; *U.S. Private*, pg. 2102
INTELECOM UK LTD.—See Herkules Capital AS; *Int'l*, pg. 3362
INTELEPEER, INC.; *U.S. Private*, pg. 2104
INTELLIGENT MOBILE SOLUTIONS, INC.; *U.S. Private*, pg. 2106
INTERACTIVE SOLUTIONS, INC.; *U.S. Private*, pg. 2108
INTERCALL DE MEXICO, S. DE R.L. DE C.V.—See Apollo Global Management, Inc.; *U.S. Public*, pg. 152
INTERCALL DE MEXICO S DE RL DE CV—See Apollo Global Management, Inc.; *U.S. Public*, pg. 152
INTERIOR TELEPHONE COMPANY—See Telalaska, Inc.; *U.S. Private*, pg. 3959
INTERMETRO COMMUNICATIONS, INC.; *U.S. Private*, pg. 2112
INTERNAP JAPAN CO., LTD.—See Internap Holding LLC; *U.S. Private*, pg. 2113
INTERNAP NETWORK SERVICES UK LTD.—See Internap Holding LLC; *U.S. Private*, pg. 2113
INTERNET AUTOPARTS, INC.—See Clayton, Dubilier & Rice, LLC; *U.S. Private*, pg. 923
INTERNET CENTRAL LTD.—See Goodwin PLC; *Int'l*, pg. 3042
INTERNET SERVICES FIJI LIMITED—See Fiji National Provident Fund; *Int'l*, pg. 2661
INTEROUTE AUSTRIA GMBH—See GTT Communications, Inc.; *U.S. Private*, pg. 1808
INTEROUTE BULGARIA JSCO—See GTT Communications, Inc.; *U.S. Private*, pg. 1808
INTEROUTE COMMUNICATIONS LIMITED—See GTT Communications, Inc.; *U.S. Private*, pg. 1808
INTEROUTE CZECH S.R.O—See GTT Communications, Inc.; *U.S. Private*, pg. 1808
INTEROUTE FINLAND OY—See GTT Communications, Inc.; *U.S. Private*, pg. 1808
INTEROUTE FRANCE SAS—See GTT Communications, Inc.; *U.S. Private*, pg. 1808
INTEROUTE IBERIA S.A.U—See GTT Communications, Inc.; *U.S. Private*, pg. 1808
INTEROUTE MAGYARORSZAG TAVKOZLESI KFT—See GTT Communications, Inc.; *U.S. Private*, pg. 1808
INTEROUTE MANAGED SERVICES DENMARK A/S—See GTT Communications, Inc.; *U.S. Private*, pg. 1808
INTEROUTE MANAGED SERVICES SWEDEN AB—See GTT Communications, Inc.; *U.S. Private*, pg. 1808
INTEROUTE S.R.L—See GTT Communications, Inc.; *U.S. Private*, pg. 1808
INTEROUTE USA INC.—See GTT Communications, Inc.; *U.S. Private*, pg. 1808
INTERSTAR COMMUNICATIONS, INC.—See Star Telephone Membership Corp.; *U.S. Private*, pg. 3785
INTLX SOLUTIONS, LLC; *U.S. Private*, pg. 2129
INTRADO BELGIUM—See Apollo Global Management, Inc.; *U.S. Public*, pg. 152
INTRADO CORPORATION—See Apollo Global Management, Inc.; *U.S. Public*, pg. 152
INTRADO EC SERVICES SPAIN SA—See Apollo Global Management, Inc.; *U.S. Public*, pg. 152
INTRADO ITALY S.R.L.—See Apollo Global Management, Inc.; *U.S. Public*, pg. 152
INTRALINKS INC.—See SS&C Technologies Holdings, Inc.; *U.S. Public*, pg. 1923
INVITECH ICT SERVICES KFT. LTD.—See 4iG Nyrt.; *Int'l*, pg. 12
INVOCO COMMUNICATION CENTER GMBH—See Conduent Incorporated; *U.S. Public*, pg. 566
INVOCO CUSTOMER SERVICE GMBH—See Conduent Incorporated; *U.S. Public*, pg. 566
INVOICE INC.—See Fuyo General Lease Co., Ltd.; *Int'l*, pg. 2859
IPANEMA SOLUTIONS LLC—See Allbridge, LLC; *U.S. Private*, pg. 175
IP COMMUNICATIONS LLC; *U.S. Private*, pg. 2136
IRIDIUM SATELLITE LLC—See Iridium Communications Inc.; *U.S. Public*, pg. 1171
ITCONIC PORTUGAL, S.A.—See Equinix, Inc.; *U.S. Public*, pg. 788
IT FREEDOM, LLC—See Court Square Capital Partners, L.P.; *U.S. Private*, pg. 1070
ITT CORP. - SUMTER—See ITT Inc.; *U.S. Public*, pg. 1178
IVER AB—See EQT AB; *Int'l*, pg. 2478
J2 GLOBAL CANADA, INC.—See Ziff Davis, Inc.; *U.S. Public*, pg. 2404
J2 GLOBAL IRELAND LIMITED—See Ziff Davis, Inc.; *U.S. Public*, pg. 2404
JACKSON ASSOCIATES, INC.; *U.S. Private*, pg. 2175
JAPAN NETWORK ENGINEERING CO., LTD.—See Electric Power Development Co., Ltd.; *Int'l*, pg. 2349
JAYBIRD, LLC—See Logitech International S.A.; *U.S. Public*, pg. 1341
JEFFERSON PUBLIC RADIO; *U.S. Private*, pg. 2198
JENZABAR, INC.; *U.S. Private*, pg. 2201
J.I.L. COMMUNICATIONS, INC.—See Bluewave Technology Group, LLC; *U.S. Private*, pg. 599
JIVE COMMUNICATIONS MEXICO, S. DE R.L. DE C.V.—See Elliott Management Corporation; *U.S. Private*, pg. 1368
JIVE COMMUNICATIONS MEXICO, S. DE R.L. DE C.V.—See Francisco Partners Management, LP; *U.S. Private*, pg. 1590
JIVE TELECOMUNICACOES DO BRASIL, LTDA.—See Elliott Management Corporation; *U.S. Private*, pg. 1368
JIVE TELECOMUNICACOES DO BRASIL, LTDA.—See Francisco Partners Management, LP; *U.S. Private*, pg. 1590
JOHN STAURULAKIS, LLC; *U.S. Private*, pg. 2224
JTOWER, INC.—See DigitalBridge Group, Inc.; *U.S. Public*, pg. 665
JUNCTION NETWORKS INC.—See Ooma, Inc.; *U.S. Public*, pg. 1605
JUVO TECHNOLOGIES, LLC; *U.S. Private*, pg. 2246
KALAHARI LIMITED—See BGC Group, Inc.; *U.S. Public*, pg. 329
KALONA COOPERATIVE TELEPHONE COMPANY; *U.S. Private*, pg. 2258
KANE INFRASTRUCTURE SERVICES HOLDINGS, LLC—See Aterian Investment Management, L.P.; *U.S. Private*, pg. 366
KEARNEY O'DOHERTY PUBLIC AFFAIRS, LLC; *U.S. Private*, pg. 2271
KEARSARGE TELEPHONE CO.—See Telephone & Data Systems, Inc.; *U.S. Public*, pg. 1998
KGB USA, INC.; *U.S. Private*, pg. 2301
KNOLOGY OF FLORIDA, LLC—See WideOpenWest, Inc.; *U.S. Public*, pg. 2370
KNOLOGY TOTAL COMMUNICATIONS, INC.—See WideOpenWest, Inc.; *U.S. Public*, pg. 2370
KOCO CONNECTOR GMBH—See CompuGroup Medical SE & Co. KGaA; *Int'l*, pg. 1757
KOOEE COMMUNICATIONS PTY LTD—See CK Hutchison Holdings Limited; *Int'l*, pg. 1638
KOOEE PTY LTD—See CK Hutchison Holdings Limited; *Int'l*, pg. 1638
KOPLAR COMMUNICATIONS INTERNATIONAL, INC.; *U.S. Private*, pg. 2343
KPN EURORINGS B.V.—See GTT Communications, Inc.; *U.S. Private*, pg. 1808
KPN INTERNATIONAL—See GTT Communications, Inc.; *U.S. Private*, pg. 1808
KPN INTERNATIONAL—See GTT Communications, Inc.; *U.S. Private*, pg. 1808
KPN INTERNATIONAL—See GTT Communications, Inc.; *U.S. Private*, pg. 1808
KRA CORPORATION; *U.S. Private*, pg. 2348
L-3 WOLF COACH—See L3Harris Technologies, Inc.; *U.S. Public*, pg. 1284
LANCASTER TELEPHONE COMPANY—See Comporium Group; *U.S. Private*, pg. 1002
LATTICE INC.; *U.S. Public*, pg. 1294
LAW.COM—See Apax Partners LLP; *Int'l*, pg. 504
LEMCON NETWORKS MEXICO S. DE R.L. DE C.V.—See Lemcon USA Corporation; *U.S. Private*, pg. 2421
LEMCON USA CORPORATION; *U.S. Private*, pg. 2421
LEVEL 3 COMMUNICATIONS, LLC—See Lumen Technologies, Inc.; *U.S. Public*, pg. 1347
LEVEL 4 TELCOM; *U.S. Private*, pg. 2434
LEWISPORT TELEPHONE COMPANY INC.—See Telephone & Data Systems, Inc.; *U.S. Public*, pg. 1998
LIBERTY BROADBAND CORPORATION; *U.S. Public*, pg. 1310
LIGHTRIVER TECHNOLOGIES, INC.—See Grain Management, LLC; *U.S. Private*, pg. 1751
LIMITED LIABILITY COMPANY CHINA TELECOM—See China Telecommunications Corporation; *Int'l*, pg. 1558
LINE SYSTEMS, INC.; *U.S. Private*, pg. 2460
LINEWIZE SERVICES LIMITED—See Family Zone Cyber Safety Limited; *Int'l*, pg. 2612
LINK AMERICA INC.; *U.S. Private*, pg. 2461
LINKLINE COMMUNICATIONS INC.; *U.S. Private*, pg. 2462
LINODE, LLC—See Akamai Technologies, Inc.; *U.S. Public*, pg. 69
LIQUID WEB, INC.; *U.S. Private*, pg. 2466
LMC S.R.O.—See Alma Media Corporation; *Int'l*, pg. 362
LNS KOMMUNIKATION AB—See Elisa Corporation; *Int'l*, pg. 2361
LOCALNET CORP.; *U.S. Private*, pg. 2477
LODGENET STAYONLINE INC.—See SONIFI Solutions, Inc.; *U.S. Private*, pg. 3714
LOJACK DE MEXICO, S. DE R.L. DE CV—See CalAmp Corp.; *U.S. Public*, pg. 422
LONG WAVE INCORPORATED; *U.S. Private*, pg. 2492
MACRO BLOB SDN. BHD.—See GMO Internet Group, Inc.; *Int'l*, pg. 3014
MACRO KIOSK (MYANMAR) CO. LTD.—See GMO Internet Group, Inc.; *Int'l*, pg. 3014
MACRO KIOSK (TAIWAN) TECHNOLOGY LIMITED—See GMO Internet Group, Inc.; *Int'l*, pg. 3014
MAGNET NETWORKS LTD.—See AMP Limited; *Int'l*, pg. 432
MAINLINE DIGITAL COMMUNICATIONS LIMITED—See BT Group plc; *Int'l*, pg. 1203
MAINONE CABLE COMPANY GHANA LTD.—See Equinix, Inc.; *U.S. Public*, pg. 788
MAINONE CABLE COMPANY LTD.—See Equinix, Inc.; *U.S. Public*, pg. 788
MAINONE CABLE COMPANY NIGERIA LIMITED—See Equinix, Inc.; *U.S. Public*, pg. 788
MAINONE CABLE COMPANY PORTUGAL, S.A.—See Equinix, Inc.; *U.S. Public*, pg. 788
MARATHON STRATEGIES, LLC; *U.S. Private*, pg. 2570
MAROC TELECOM S.A.—See Emirates Telecommunications Group Compapny PJSC; *Int'l*, pg. 2382
MASCO SERVICES, INC.—See Masco Corporation; *U.S. Public*, pg. 1391

N.A.I.C.S. INDEX

517810 — ALL OTHER TELECOMMU...

MASERGY COMMUNICATIONS UK LIMITED—See Berkshire Partners LLC; *U.S. Private*, pg. 535
MATCH.COM CANADA LTD.—See IAC Inc.; *U.S. Public*, pg. 1082
MAURITEL SA—See Emirates Telecommunications Group Compapny PJSC; *Int'l*, pg. 2382
MAVERICK NETWORKS, INC.; *U.S. Private*, pg. 2616
MCG MARLINK COMM GMBH—See Airbus SE; *Int'l*, pg. 242
MCGRAW COMMUNICATIONS, INC.; *U.S. Private*, pg. 2635
MCMINN, INC.—See CRH plc; *Int'l*, pg. 1847
MDG CONNECTED SOLUTIONS, INC.; *U.S. Private*, pg. 2646
MDI ACCESS; *U.S. Private*, pg. 2646
MEDEM, INC.; *U.S. Private*, pg. 2651
MED-TEL.COM INC; *U.S. Private*, pg. 2650
MEETUP, INC.—See Bending Spoons S.p.A.; *Int'l*, pg. 971
MEMOTEC INC.—See Comtech Telecommunications Corp.; *U.S. Public*, pg. 562
MERRIMACK COUNTY TELEPHONE COMPANY, INC.—See Telephone & Data Systems, Inc.; *U.S. Public*, pg. 1998
MFG.COM CHINA—See MFG.com, Inc.; *U.S. Private*, pg. 2693
MHT ELEKTRONIK TASARIM VE TICARET A.S.—See Exceptional Innovation BV; *Int'l*, pg. 2579
MICROSOFT MOBILE DEUTSCHLAND GMBH DUSSELDORF—See Microsoft Corporation; *U.S. Public*, pg. 1441
MID-STATE TELEPHONE CO.—See Telephone & Data Systems, Inc.; *U.S. Public*, pg. 1998
MIETHO & BAR KABELKOM KABELKOMMUNIKATIONS-BETRIEBS GMBH—See Morgan Stanley; *U.S. Public*, pg. 1473
MILAR, S.A. DE C.V.—See Grupo Televisa, S.A.B.; *Int'l*, pg. 3136
MITCHELL COMMUNICATIONS GROUP; *U.S. Private*, pg. 2750
MITCHELL INTERNATIONAL, INC.—See Stone Point Capital LLC; *U.S. Private*, pg. 3823
MITEL COMMUNICATIONS AB—See Searchlight Capital Partners, L.P.; *U.S. Private*, pg. 3588
MITEL COMMUNICATIONS INC.—See Searchlight Capital Partners, L.P.; *U.S. Private*, pg. 3589
MITEL INCORPORATED MEXICO S.A. DE C.V.—See Searchlight Capital Partners, L.P.; *U.S. Private*, pg. 3589
MITEL MOBILITY INC.—See Searchlight Capital Partners, L.P.; *U.S. Private*, pg. 3589
MITEL NETSOLUTIONS, INC.—See Searchlight Capital Partners, L.P.; *U.S. Private*, pg. 3589
MITEL NETWORKS SOLUTIONS INC—See Searchlight Capital Partners, L.P.; *U.S. Private*, pg. 3589
MITEL SOUTH PACIFIC PTY. LIMITED—See Searchlight Capital Partners, L.P.; *U.S. Private*, pg. 3589
MITEL SPAIN, S.L.—See Searchlight Capital Partners, L.P.; *U.S. Private*, pg. 3589
MITEL SWEDEN AB—See Searchlight Capital Partners, L.P.; *U.S. Private*, pg. 3589
MOBILCOM-DEBITEL GMBH—See freenet AG; *Int'l*, pg. 2770
THE MOBILESTORE LTD.—See Essar Global Limited; *Int'l*, pg. 2508
MOBILITIE, LLC—See BAI Communications Pty Ltd; *Int'l*, pg. 801
MOBITV, INC.; *U.S. Private*, pg. 2758
MOBOMO; *U.S. Private*, pg. 2758
MODAMEDIA COMMUNICATIONS, INC.—See Dovetail Solutions Inc.; *U.S. Private*, pg. 1268
MODELLBAU SCHONHEIDE GMBH—See ALFA, S.A.B. de C.V.; *Int'l*, pg. 313
MONEY.NET, INC.; *U.S. Private*, pg. 2770
MONTANA INTERACTIVE, LLC—See Tyler Technologies, Inc.; *U.S. Public*, pg. 2208
MOXX B.V.—See Diebold Nixdorf, Inc.; *U.S. Public*, pg. 661
MUKLUK TELEPHONE COMPANY INC—See Telalaska Inc.; *U.S. Private*, pg. 3959
MULTELINK SERVICES PTY LIMITED—See Aware Super Pty Ltd; *Int'l*, pg. 752
MYERS POWER PRODUCTS—See Myers Power Products, Inc.; *U.S. Private*, pg. 2824
MY NET FONE AUSTRALIA PTY LIMITED—See Aussie Broadband Ltd.; *Int'l*, pg. 716
NACT EUROPE LTD.—See Kinderhook Industries, LLC; *U.S. Private*, pg. 2307
NACT TELECOMMUNICATIONS, INC.—See Kinderhook Industries, LLC; *U.S. Private*, pg. 2307
NATEC USA LLC—See Hochland SE; *Int'l*, pg. 3437
NATIONAL RURAL TELECOMMUNICATIONS COOPERATIVE; *U.S. Private*, pg. 2862
NATIONAL TELEPHONE SERVICES CO. LLC—See Al Yousef Group; *Int'l*, pg. 283
NAUTILUS HYOSUNG, LTD.—See Hyosung Corporation; *Int'l*, pg. 3552
ND SATCOM PRODUCTS GMBH—See Airbus SE; *Int'l*, pg. 245
NECKARCOM TELEKOMMUNIKATION GMBH—See EnBW Energie Baden-Wurttemberg AG; *Int'l*, pg. 2399

NEGOCIOS Y TELEFONIA NEDETEL SA—See Enel S.p.A.; *Int'l*, pg. 2414
NEOMEDIA TECHNOLOGIES, INC.; *U.S. Public*, pg. 1506
NEONOVA NETWORK SERVICES INC.—See National Rural Telecommunications Cooperative; *U.S. Private*, pg. 2862
NEOTEL 2000 S.L.U.—See Gamma Communications PLC; *Int'l*, pg. 2878
NERA (THAILAND) LTD—See Ennoconn Corporation; *Int'l*, pg. 2443
NETCOM BW GMBH—See EnBW Energie Baden-Wurttemberg AG; *Int'l*, pg. 2399
NETCOM BW GMBH—See EnBW Energie Baden-Wurttemberg AG; *Int'l*, pg. 2399
NETIA SA—See Cyfrowy Polsat S.A.; *Int'l*, pg. 1895
NETRIVER INCORPORATED—See Lincoln Property Company; *U.S. Private*, pg. 2458
NET STAR TELECOMMUNICATIONS, INC.—See Astra Capital Management LLC; *U.S. Private*, pg. 361
NETWORK BILLING SYSTEMS, LLC—See Fusion Connect, Inc.; *U.S. Private*, pg. 1625
NEW HORIZON COMMUNICATIONS GROUP; *U.S. Private*, pg. 2897
THE NEW KNOXVILLE TELEPHONE COMPANY—See Schurz Communications, Inc.; *U.S. Private*, pg. 3571
NEXTA LTD.—See CHL S.p.A.; *Int'l*, pg. 1576
NEXT ID GMBH—See freenet AG; *Int'l*, pg. 2770
NEXTLEVEL INTERNET, INC.—See Digerati Technologies, Inc.; *U.S. Public*, pg. 661
NEXTNET AS—See Hafslund ASA; *Int'l*, pg. 3206
NEXT TELECOMMUNICATIONS SDN. BHD.—See Green Packet Berhad; *Int'l*, pg. 3072
NEXT TELECOM PTY. LTD.—See Comms Group Ltd; *Int'l*, pg. 1720
NIMBELINK CORP.—See Airgain, Inc.; *U.S. Public*, pg. 68
NIPPON COMSYS CORPORATION—See COMSYS Holdings Corporation; *Int'l*, pg. 1762
NITEL, INC.; *U.S. Private*, pg. 2929
NKTELCO, INC.—See Schurz Communications, Inc.; *U.S. Private*, pg. 3571
NLAYER COMMUNICATIONS, INC.—See GTT Communications, Inc.; *U.S. Private*, pg. 1808
NLETS, INC.; *U.S. Private*, pg. 2931
NORMACTION SA—See Bouygues S.A.; *Int'l*, pg. 1122
NORTHFIELD TELEPHONE COMPANY—See Telephone & Data Systems, Inc.; *U.S. Public*, pg. 1998
NORTHPOINT COMMUNICATIONS GROUP, INC.; *U.S. Private*, pg. 2956
NORTH STATE TELECOMMUNICATIONS CORPORATION—See EQT AB; *Int'l*, pg. 2480
NORWAY TELEPHONE CO. INC.—See Telephone & Data Systems, Inc.; *U.S. Public*, pg. 1998
NSIGHT TELESERVICES—See Northeast Communications of Wisconsin Incorporated; *U.S. Private*, pg. 2949
NSIGHT TELSERVICES—See Northeast Communications of Wisconsin Incorporated; *U.S. Private*, pg. 2949
NT NETWORK SERVICES, LLC—See GTT Communications, Inc.; *U.S. Private*, pg. 1808
NTS COMMUNICATIONS, INC.—See Keystone Group, L.P.; *U.S. Private*, pg. 2297
NTS COMMUNICATIONS, INC.—See Pamlico Capital Management, L.P.; *U.S. Private*, pg. 3083
O1 COMMUNICATIONS, INC.—See Siris Capital Group, LLC; *U.S. Private*, pg. 3675
OAKMAN TELEPHONE COMPANY, INC.—See Telephone & Data Systems, Inc.; *U.S. Public*, pg. 1998
OATH JAPAN KK—See Apollo Global Management, Inc.; *U.S. Public*, pg. 167
O-BIT TELECOM LIMITED—See Daisy Group Limited; *Int'l*, pg. 1943
OBLONG, INC.; *U.S. Public*, pg. 1560
OCEUS NETWORKS INC.—See Battle Investment Group LLC; *U.S. Private*, pg. 489
OCLC ASIA PACIFIC—See Online Computer Library Center, Inc.; *U.S. Private*, pg. 3026
OCLC CANADA—See Online Computer Library Center, Inc.; *U.S. Private*, pg. 3026
OCLC FOREST PRESS—See Online Computer Library Center, Inc.; *U.S. Private*, pg. 3027
OCLC LATIN AMERICA AND THE CARIBBEAN—See Online Computer Library Center, Inc.; *U.S. Private*, pg. 3027
OCLC PICA—See Online Computer Library Center, Inc.; *U.S. Private*, pg. 3027
ODYSSEY TELECOMMUNICATIONS, INC.; *U.S. Private*, pg. 2996
OIL-LAW RECORDS CORP.—See Hellman & Friedman LLC; *U.S. Private*, pg. 1908
OLM, LLC; *U.S. Private*, pg. 3011
ONATEL SA—See Emirates Telecommunications Group Compapny PJSC; *Int'l*, pg. 2382
ONDAS MEDIA, S.A.—See Aptiv PLC; *Int'l*, pg. 525
ONE CALL CONCEPTS INCORPORATED; *U.S. Private*, pg. 3020
ONSOLVE, LLC—See BC Partners LLP; *Int'l*, pg. 924
ONYX INFOSOFT; *U.S. Private*, pg. 3028
OPENFIBER KENTUCKY CO. LLC; *U.S. Private*, pg. 3030
OPENONLINE, LLC—See Sackett National Holdings, Inc.; *U.S. Private*, pg. 3522

OPTELIAN ACCESS NETWORKS, INC.—See DZS Inc.; *U.S. Public*, pg. 701
ORBITEL COMMUNICATIONS, LLC—See Schurz Communications, Inc.; *U.S. Private*, pg. 3571
ORISKANY FALLS TELEPHONE CORP, INC.—See Telephone & Data Systems, Inc.; *U.S. Public*, pg. 1998
ORLANDO SANFORD DOMESTIC INC—See ACS, Actividades de Construccion y Servicios, S.A.; *Int'l*, pg. 112
OTE ACADEMY S.A.—See Hellenic Telecommunications Organization S.A.; *Int'l*, pg. 3333
OTE INTERNATIONAL SOLUTIONS S.A.—See Hellenic Telecommunications Organization S.A.; *Int'l*, pg. 3334
OUTSOURCE CONSULTANTS, LLC; *U.S. Private*, pg. 3052
P4 SP. Z O.O.—See Iliad S.A.; *Int'l*, pg. 3614
PACKET ONE NETWORKS (MALAYSIA) SDN. BHD.—See Green Packet Berhad; *Int'l*, pg. 3072
PACKET ONE SDN. BHD.—See Green Packet Berhad; *Int'l*, pg. 3072
PAGINAS AMARELAS S.A.—See Apax Partners LLP; *Int'l*, pg. 507
PAGINAS AMARELAS S.A.—See Cinven Limited; *Int'l*, pg. 1615
PALMETTO RURAL TELEPHONE COOPERATIVE, INC.; *U.S. Private*, pg. 3081
PAMPLIN COMMUNICATIONS CORPORATION—See R.B. Pamplin Corporation; *U.S. Private*, pg. 3334
PANNON ANTENNA, KFT—See EQT AB; *Int'l*, pg. 2479
PANSMART PROPRIETARY LIMITED—See Huge Group Limited; *Int'l*, pg. 3524
PAUL BUNYAN COMMUNICATIONS; *U.S. Private*, pg. 3112
PEER 1 NETWORK ENTERPRISES, INC.—See DigitalBridge Group, Inc.; *U.S. Public*, pg. 664
PEER 1 NETWORK (USA), INC.—See DigitalBridge Group, Inc.; *U.S. Public*, pg. 664
PEPCOM GMBH—See Morgan Stanley; *U.S. Public*, pg. 1473
PGH CONNECT, INC.—See Ad-Base Group, Inc.; *U.S. Private*, pg. 72
PHOENIX TOWER INTERNATIONAL LLC—See Blackstone Inc.; *U.S. Public*, pg. 356
PHONE POWER, LLC; *U.S. Private*, pg. 3174
PINELAND COGENTES, INC.—See Pineland Telephone Cooperative, Inc.; *U.S. Private*, pg. 3183
PIPE TRANSMISSION PTY LTD—See CK Hutchison Holdings Limited; *Int'l*, pg. 1638
PIQUNIQ MANAGEMENT CORP.—See Arctic Slope Regional Corporation; *U.S. Private*, pg. 316
PLANTRONICS ACOUSTICS ITALIA, S.R.L.—See HP Inc.; *U.S. Public*, pg. 1064
PLANTRONICS B.V.—See HP Inc.; *U.S. Public*, pg. 1064
PLANTRONICS CANADA LIMITED—See HP Inc.; *U.S. Public*, pg. 1064
PLANTRONICS GMBH—See HP Inc.; *U.S. Public*, pg. 1064
PLANTRONICS INTERNATIONAL DO BRASIL, LTDA.—See HP Inc.; *U.S. Public*, pg. 1064
PLANTRONICS JAPAN LTD.—See HP Inc.; *U.S. Public*, pg. 1064
PLANTRONICS SINGAPORE PTE. LTD.—See HP Inc.; *U.S. Public*, pg. 1064
PLUSNET INFRASTRUKTUR GMBH & CO. KG—See EnBW Energie Baden-Wurttemberg AG; *Int'l*, pg. 2399
PLUSNET PLC—See BT Group plc; *Int'l*, pg. 1203
POCKETINET COMMUNICATIONS INC.—See Columbia Ventures Corporation; *U.S. Private*, pg. 978
POINTSEC MOBILE TECHNOLOGIES LIMITED—See Check Point Software Technologies Ltd.; *Int'l*, pg. 1459
POINT TO POINT COMMUNICATIONS, INC.—See Dycom Industries, Inc.; *U.S. Public*, pg. 699
POLOCO USA, INC.—See Ralph Lauren Corporation; *U.S. Public*, pg. 1761
P-OSS SOLUTIONS S.L.U.—See Elisa Corporation; *Int'l*, pg. 2361
POWER INTERNET LIMITED—See Horizon Capital LLP; *Int'l*, pg. 3479
POWERNET GLOBAL COMMUNICATIONS; *U.S. Private*, pg. 3239
POWER & TELEPHONE SUPPLY OF CANADA—See Power & Telephone Supply Company; *U.S. Private*, pg. 3237
PREMIERE GLOBAL SERVICES, INC.-KANSAS—See Siris Capital Group, LLC; *U.S. Private*, pg. 3674
PRENETCOM A.S.—See EnBW Energie Baden-Wurttemberg AG; *Int'l*, pg. 2399
PRESERVISNF S.R.O.—See EnBW Energie Baden-Wurttemberg AG; *Int'l*, pg. 2399
PRESTIGE WHOLESALE INC.; *U.S. Private*, pg. 3256
PRIMA COMMUNICATIONS, INC.; *U.S. Private*, pg. 3260
PRIMERA RED INTERACTIVA DE MEDIOS ARGENTINOS (PRIMA) S.A.—See Grupo Clarin S.A.; *Int'l*, pg. 3125
PRINCE TELECOM LLC—See Dycom Industries, Inc.; *U.S. Public*, pg. 699
PRODUCTIONHUB INC.; *U.S. Private*, pg. 3273
PROYECTOS DE INGENIERIA CORPORATIVA, S.A. DE C.V.—See Empresas Publicas de Medellin ESP; *Int'l*, pg. 2392
PSION TEKLOGIX, S.A. DE C.V.—See Zebra Technologies Corporation; *U.S. Public*, pg. 2401
PT CHINA TELECOM INDONESIA—See China Telecommu...

517810 — ALL OTHER TELECOMMU...

nications Corporation; *Int'l*, pg. 1558
P.T. COMMUNICATIONS & SECURITY—See CSE Global Ltd.; *Int'l*, pg. 1864
PT CONTACT - TELEMARKETING E SERVICOS DE INFORMACAO, S.A.—See Altice Europe N.V.; *Int'l*, pg. 392
PT INOVACAO - ALTICE LABS—See Altice Europe N.V.; *Int'l*, pg. 392
PT TRANSTEL ENGINEERING—See CSE Global Ltd.; *Int'l*, pg. 1864
PUBLIC COMMUNICATIONS SERVICES, INC.; *U.S. Private*, pg. 3298
PULSE TELESERVICE INC.—See Enghouse Systems Limited; *Int'l*, pg. 2427
PURCELL SYSTEMS INTERNATIONAL AB—See EnerSys; *U.S. Public*, pg. 767
PWR, LLC; *U.S. Private*, pg. 3308
Q-DSL HOME GMBH—See EnBW Energie Baden-Wurttemberg AG; *Int'l*, pg. 2399
QUADGEN WIRELESS SOLUTIONS INC.; *U.S. Private*, pg. 3315
QUALTEK, LLC—See QualTek Services Inc.; *U.S. Public*, pg. 1748
QUMU LTD.—See Enghouse Systems Limited; *Int'l*, pg. 2427
QWEST SERVICES CORPORATION—See Lumen Technologies, Inc.; *U.S. Public*, pg. 1347
RACINGONE MULTIMEDIA, LLC—See National Association for Stock Car Auto Racing, Inc.; *U.S. Private*, pg. 2846
RADIANCE TECHNOLOGIES, INC.; *U.S. Private*, pg. 3343
RADIANT COMMUNICATIONS CORP.—See Comwave Networks, Inc.; *Int'l*, pg. 1763
RAILWORKS SIGNALS & COMMUNICATIONS, INC.—See Wind Point Advisors LLC; *U.S. Private*, pg. 4535
RAYTHEON INTEGRATED COMMUNICATIONS SYSTEMS—See RTX Corporation; *U.S. Public*, pg. 1824
R & B TELEPHONE LLC—See EQT AB; *Int'l*, pg. 2480
RCS & RDS S.A.—See Digi Communications N.V; *Int'l*, pg. 2118
REALCOM SOLUTIONS—See Charlesbank Capital Partners, LLC; *U.S. Private*, pg. 854
REALNETWORKS, INC. - RESTON—See RealNetworks, Inc.; *U.S. Private*, pg. 3369
RED HAT ASIA PACIFIC PTY. LTD.—See International Business Machines Corporation; *U.S. Public*, pg. 1150
REDSTONE COMMUNICATIONS LTD—See GI Manager L.P.; *U.S. Private*, pg. 1693
REDWOOD TELECOMMUNICATIONS LIMITED—See Horizon Capital LLP; *Int'l*, pg. 3479
REGISTER S.P.A—See HgCapital Trust plc; *Int'l*, pg. 3377
REMITDATA, INC.; *U.S. Private*, pg. 3396
REMOTE IT.COM, INC.—See Hergo Ergonomic Support Systems, Inc.; *U.S. Private*, pg. 1921
REPEATER COMMUNICATIONS GROUP, LLC—See American Tower Corporation; *U.S. Public*, pg. 111
RHINO COMMUNICATION RENTALS, LLC—See OwnersEdge Inc.; *U.S. Private*, pg. 3055
RIBBON COMMUNICATIONS DO BRASIL LTDA—See Ribbon Communications Inc.; *U.S. Public*, pg. 1797
RIBBON COMMUNICATIONS ISRAEL LIMITED—See Ribbon Communications Inc.; *U.S. Public*, pg. 1797
RIBBON COMMUNICATIONS K.K.—See Ribbon Communications Inc.; *U.S. Public*, pg. 1797
RIBBON COMMUNICATIONS RUS LIMITED LIABILITY COMPANY—See Ribbon Communications Inc.; *U.S. Public*, pg. 1797
RIBBON COMMUNICATIONS SINGAPORE PTE. LTD.—See Ribbon Communications Inc.; *U.S. Public*, pg. 1797
RIBBON NETWORKS LTD. CO.—See Ribbon Communications Inc.; *U.S. Public*, pg. 1797
RIDGELINK, LLC—See Blue Ridge Electric Membership Corporation; *U.S. Private*, pg. 591
RIGHTWAY GATE, INC.; *U.S. Private*, pg. 3436
RIGNET AS—See ViaSat, Inc.; *U.S. Public*, pg. 2292
RIGNET AUSTRALIA PTY LTD—See ViaSat, Inc.; *U.S. Public*, pg. 2292
RIGNET, INC.—See ViaSat, Inc.; *U.S. Public*, pg. 2292
RIGNET PTE LTD—See ViaSat, Inc.; *U.S. Public*, pg. 2292
RIGNET QATAR W.L.L.—See ViaSat, Inc.; *U.S. Public*, pg. 2292
RIGNET SERVICOS DE TELECOMUNICACOES BRASIL LTDA.—See ViaSat, Inc.; *U.S. Public*, pg. 2292
RINGCENTRAL CH GMBH—See RingCentral, Inc.; *U.S. Public*, pg. 1799
RINGGOLD TELEPHONE CO. INC.; *U.S. Private*, pg. 3438
RIPARIUS COMMUNICATION SERVICES—See Riparius Corporation; *U.S. Private*, pg. 3439
RJE TELECOM, LLC—See Dycom Industries, Inc.; *U.S. Public*, pg. 699
ROGUE STATION COMPANIES, INC.; *U.S. Public*, pg. 1808
RTC HOLDINGS, L.L.C.; *U.S. Private*, pg. 3498
SAGO NETWORKS, LLC; *U.S. Private*, pg. 3528
SANDBOX.COM, INC.—See Gamebase, Inc.; *U.S. Private*, pg. 1640
SANDLER PARTNERS; *U.S. Private*, pg. 3544
SAVOO LTD.—See Platinum Equity, LLC; *U.S. Private*, pg. 3201

SCANDINAVIA ONLINE AS—See Aller Holding A/S; *Int'l*, pg. 336
SCANSOURCE COMMUNICATIONS, INC.—See ScanSource, Inc.; *U.S. Public*, pg. 1843
SC COSMOTE ROMANIAN MOBILE TELECOMMUNICATIONS S.A.—See Hellenic Telecommunications Organization S.A.; *Int'l*, pg. 3333
SCHIPHOL CONNECT B.V.—See Gamma Communications PLC; *Int'l*, pg. 2878
SCHLESINGER GROUP; *U.S. Private*, pg. 3565
SCHLUMBERGER NETWORK SOLUTIONS—See Schlumberger Limited; *U.S. Public*, pg. 1845
SEA LION CORPORATION; *U.S. Private*, pg. 3582
SEGRA—See EQT AB; *Int'l*, pg. 2480
SELENE SPA—See A2A S.p.A.; *Int'l*, pg. 29
SENDMAIL, LTD.—See Thoma Bravo, L.P.; *U.S. Private*, pg. 4151
SENDMAIL S.A.R.L—See Thoma Bravo, L.P.; *U.S. Private*, pg. 4151
SERIOUS CIGARS—See British American Tobacco plc; *Int'l*, pg. 1168
SERVIABERTIS, S.L.—See ACS, Actividades de Construccion y Servicios, S.A.; *Int'l*, pg. 112
SERVICEMAGIC LIMITED—See IAC Inc.; *U.S. Public*, pg. 1082
SERVICIOS OPERBES, S.A. DE C.V.—See Grupo Televisa, S.A.B.; *Int'l*, pg. 3136
SHAREDPHONE INTERNATIONAL (PROPRIETARY) LIMITED—See Blue Label Telecoms Limited; *Int'l*, pg. 1068
SHIAWASSEE TELEPHONE CO. INC.—See Telephone & Data Systems, Inc.; *U.S. Public*, pg. 1998
SHORETEL UK LTD.—See Searchlight Capital Partners, L.P.; *U.S. Private*, pg. 3589
SICAP SCHWEIZ AG—See Constellation Software Inc.; *Int'l*, pg. 1775
SIGMABROADBAND CO.; *U.S. Public*, pg. 1877
SIGOS GMBH—See H.I.G. Capital, LLC; *U.S. Private*, pg. 1833
SILVERLINK COMMUNICATIONS, LLC—See Welltok, Inc.; *U.S. Private*, pg. 4478
SILVER PEAK SYSTEMS, INC.—See Hewlett Packard Enterprise Company; *U.S. Public*, pg. 1032
SIMPLESIGNAL, INC.; *U.S. Private*, pg. 3667
SINCLAIR TECHNOLOGIES INC.—See Hytera Communications Corporation Limited; *Int'l*, pg. 3555
SINGLE DIGITS, INC.—See GI Manager L.P.; *U.S. Private*, pg. 1694
SITA LABORATORIES, INC.—See Marchex, Inc.; *U.S. Public*, pg. 1365
SITICOM GMBH—See Datatec Limited; *Int'l*, pg. 1980
SKY HOME COMMUNICATIONS LIMITED—See Comcast Corporation; *U.S. Public*, pg. 541
SKYMESH PTY. LTD.—See Bigblu Broadband Group PLC; *Int'l*, pg. 1022
SKYRIVER COMMUNICATIONS, INC.—See Trive Capital Inc.; *U.S. Private*, pg. 4239
SLOVAK TELEKOM A.S.—See Deutsche Telekom AG; *Int'l*, pg. 2084
SNC-LAVALIN TELECOM INC.—See AtkinsRealis Group Inc.; *Int'l*, pg. 673
S&N COMMUNICATIONS, INC.—See Sun Capital Partners, Inc.; *U.S. Private*, pg. 3860
SOCIAL MEDIA INDIA LIMITED—See Equippp Social Impact Technologies Ltd; *Int'l*, pg. 2485
SOCIEDADE DE ACTIVITIES EM MULTIMIDIA LTDA.—See CCR S.A.; *Int'l*, pg. 1369
SOCKET HOLDINGS CORP.; *U.S. Private*, pg. 3704
SOLEO COMMUNICATIONS, INC.; *U.S. Private*, pg. 3709
SONAE.COM—See Efanor Investimentos, SGPS, SA; *Int'l*, pg. 2319
SONUS NETWORKS (INDIA) PRIVATE LIMITED—See Ribbon Communications Inc.; *U.S. Public*, pg. 1797
SOTELMA SA—See Emirates Telecommunications Group Compapny PJSC; *Int'l*, pg. 2382
SOTEL SYSTEMS, LLC; *U.S. Private*, pg. 3716
SOUL PATTINSON TELECOMMUNICATIONS PTY LTD—See CK Hutchison Holdings Limited; *Int'l*, pg. 1638
SOUNDCONNECT, LLC; *U.S. Private*, pg. 3717
SOUTHERN PHONE COMPANY LIMITED—See AGL Energy Limited; *Int'l*, pg. 211
SOUTHWESTERN TELEPHONE COMPANY—See Telephone & Data Systems, Inc.; *U.S. Public*, pg. 1998
SPARCALL GMBH—See ecotel communication ag; *Int'l*, pg. 2300
SPARKPLUG, INC.—See GTT Communications, Inc.; *U.S. Private*, pg. 1808
SPECTRUM COMMUNICATIONS CABLING SERVICES, INC.; *U.S. Private*, pg. 3752
SPEEDNET, LLC—See TPT Global Tech, Inc.; *U.S. Public*, pg. 2178
SPRINT COMMUNICATIONS, INC.—See Deutsche Telekom AG; *Int'l*, pg. 2084
SPT TELECOMMUNICATIONS PTY LTD—See CK Hutchison Holdings Limited; *Int'l*, pg. 1638
SS8 NETWORKS, INC.—See HighBar Management, LLC; *U.S. Private*, pg. 1937
STAGE 2 NETWORKS; *U.S. Private*, pg. 3775

STALWART SYSTEMS, LLC—See EQT AB; *Int'l*, pg. 2480
STARGATE INDUSTRIES LLC; *U.S. Private*, pg. 3786
STARPOWER COMMUNICATIONS, LLC—See Stonepeak Partners L.P.; *U.S. Private*, pg. 3829
STELKOM D.O.O.—See Elektro Slovenia d.o.o.; *Int'l*, pg. 2357
STERICYCLE COMMUNICATION SOLUTIONS, INC.—See Infomedia Group Inc; *U.S. Private*, pg. 2072
STRATEGIC DATA SYSTEMS; *U.S. Private*, pg. 3834
STREAMING MEDIA, INC.—See Information Today Inc.; *U.S. Private*, pg. 2073
SUBSIDIUM TECHNOLOGIES INC.—See UPSTACK, Inc.; *U.S. Private*, pg. 4313
SUPERB INTERNET CORP—See CherryRoad Technologies Inc.; *U.S. Private*, pg. 874
SUPPORT LOGISTIC SERVICES S.R.L.—See Cassa Depositi e Prestiti S.p.A.; *Int'l*, pg. 1355
SURE (GUERNSEY) LIMITED—See Bahrain Telecommunications Company BSC; *Int'l*, pg. 801
SURGEPAYS INC.; *U.S. Public*, pg. 1967
SURREY SATELLITE SERVICES LTD.—See Airbus SE; *Int'l*, pg. 245
SVO ACCESS GMBH—See E.ON SE; *Int'l*, pg. 2259
SWN COMMUNICATIONS, INC.—See BC Partners LLP; *Int'l*, pg. 924
SYKES KOZEP-EUROPA KFT—See Creadev SAS; *Int'l*, pg. 1831
SYMPATICO—See BCE Inc.; *Int'l*, pg. 927
SYNERGYPLUS GMBH—See ecotel communication ag; *Int'l*, pg. 2300
SYNERGY TELECOM, INC.—See Digerati Technologies, Inc.; *U.S. Public*, pg. 661
SYNIVERSE TECHNOLOGIES LIMITED—See The Carlyle Group Inc.; *U.S. Public*, pg. 2054
SYNIVERSE TECHNOLOGIES, LLC—See The Carlyle Group Inc.; *U.S. Public*, pg. 2054
SYNVIA MEDIA GMBH—See Deutsche Wohnen SE; *Int'l*, pg. 2085
SYSCOM EMIRATES LLC—See Dubai Investments PJSC; *Int'l*, pg. 2219
TAGGED, INC.; *U.S. Private*, pg. 3922
TALECH, INC.—See U.S. Bancorp; *U.S. Public*, pg. 2212
TAQUA LLC—See Ribbon Communications Inc.; *U.S. Public*, pg. 1797
TDF S.A.S.—See Arcus Infrastructure Partners LLP; *Int'l*, pg. 553
TDF S.A.S.—See Brookfield Infrastructure Partners L.P.; *Int'l*, pg. 1190
TDS BAJA BROADBAND LLC—See Telephone & Data Systems, Inc.; *U.S. Public*, pg. 1997
TDS METRO-COM—See Telephone & Data Systems, Inc.; *U.S. Public*, pg. 1997
TDS TELECOM—See Telephone & Data Systems, Inc.; *U.S. Public*, pg. 1997
TDS TELECOM—See Telephone & Data Systems, Inc.; *U.S. Public*, pg. 1997
TDS TELECOM—See Telephone & Data Systems, Inc.; *U.S. Public*, pg. 1997
TDS TELECOM—See Telephone & Data Systems, Inc.; *U.S. Public*, pg. 1997
TEAM DES MOINES PARTNERS, LLC—See Telephone & Data Systems, Inc.; *U.S. Public*, pg. 1998
TECHBARN.COM, INC.; *U.S. Private*, pg. 3952
TECHNICAL COMMUNITIES, INC.; *U.S. Private*, pg. 3953
TECHNICAL SOLUTIONS, LLC.; *U.S. Private*, pg. 3954
TECHNOLOGY ASSOCIATES EC INC.; *U.S. Private*, pg. 3955
TECHNOPARK IMMOBILIEN AG—See AXA S.A.; *Int'l*, pg. 758
TEKCOM RESOURCES, INC.; *U.S. Private*, pg. 3958
TEKEGLDMPIRE, INC.; *U.S. Public*, pg. 1991
TEKSELL, INC.; *U.S. Public*, pg. 3959
TELALASKA INC.; *U.S. Private*, pg. 3959
TELCO CUBA, INC.; *U.S. Public*, pg. 1992
TELCO PRO SERVICES, A. S.—See CEZ, a.s.; *Int'l*, pg. 1428
TELE AG—See Deutsche Wohnen SE; *Int'l*, pg. 2085
TELECARD NETWORK, L.L.C.—See IDT Corporation; *U.S. Public*, pg. 1094
TELE-CENTRE SERVICES PTE. LTD.—See Hai Leck Holdings Limited; *Int'l*, pg. 3208
TELECO GMBH COTTBUS TELEKOMMUNIKATION—See Morgan Stanley; *U.S. Public*, pg. 1473
TELECOM FIJI LTD.—See Fiji National Provident Fund; *Int'l*, pg. 2661
TELECOM IBERICA DE INVERSIONES, S.L.—See EQT AB; *Int'l*, pg. 2479
TELECOM SERVICE CO., LTD.—See Hikari Tsushin, Inc.; *Int'l*, pg. 3390
TELECOM VANUATU LIMITED—See Fiji National Provident Fund; *Int'l*, pg. 2661
TELECOM VASTGOED, B.V.—See EQT AB; *Int'l*, pg. 2479
TELECOR, S.A.—See El Corte Ingles, S.A.; *Int'l*, pg. 2340
TELEDESIC LLC; *U.S. Private*, pg. 3960
TELEFONIA DIALOG S.A.—See Cyfrowy Polsat S.A.; *Int'l*, pg. 1895
TELEFONICA MOVILES GUATEMALA, S.A.—See America Movil, S.A.B. de C.V.; *Int'l*, pg. 421

N.A.I.C.S. INDEX

517810 — ALL OTHER TELECOMMU...

TELEFON-SERVICEGESELLSCHAFT DER DEUTSCHEN BANK MBH—See Deutsche Bank Aktiengesellschaft; *Int'l*, pg. 2062
TELEGUAM HOLDINGS, LLC—See Huntsman Family Investments, LLC; *U.S. Private*, pg. 2011
TELEKOM AUSTRIA AG—See America Movil, S.A.B. de C.V.; *Int'l*, pg. 421
TELEPAK NETWORKS, INC.—See Telapex Inc.; *U.S. Private*, pg. 3959
TELEPORT COMMUNICATIONS AMERICA, LLC—See AT&T Inc.; *U.S. Public*, pg. 220
TELEQUALITY COMMUNICATIONS LLC—See ZelnickMedia Corp.; *U.S. Private*, pg. 4600
TELEQUERY.NET, INC.; *U.S. Private*, pg. 3961
TELESOURCE, INC.; *U.S. Private*, pg. 3961
TELESPAN NETWORK SERVICES, LLC—See Byers Engineering Company; *U.S. Private*, pg. 700
TELETRANS SA—See CNTEE TRANSELECTRICA SA; *Int'l*, pg. 1679
TELEVISAT, S.A. DE C.V.—See Grupo Televisa, S.A.B.; *Int'l*, pg. 3137
TELKONET, INC.; *U.S. Public*, pg. 1999
TELMEX COLOMBIA, S.A.—See America Movil, S.A.B. de C.V.; *Int'l*, pg. 422
TELTECH SYSTEMS, INC.—See IAC Inc.; *U.S. Public*, pg. 1083
TENNEY TELEPHONE COMPANY—See Telephone & Data Systems, Inc.; *U.S. Public*, pg. 1998
TERREMARK WORLDWIDE, INC.-MIAMI—See Verizon Communications Inc.; *U.S. Public*, pg. 2285
TERRITORY EMBRACE GMBH—See Bertelsmann SE & Co. KGaA; *Int'l*, pg. 996
TESAT-SPACECOM GMBH & CO. KG—See Airbus SE; *Int'l*, pg. 243
TEW PLUS LIMITED—See L.B. Foster Company; *U.S. Public*, pg. 1279
THINKTEL COMMUNICATIONS LTD.—See Distributel Communications Limited; *Int'l*, pg. 2136
THOMAS TECHNOLOGY SOLUTIONS (UK) LTD.—See Thomas Publishing Company LLC; *U.S. Private*, pg. 4157
TIE TECHNOLOGIES, INC.; *U.S. Public*, pg. 2158
TIGERTMS LIMITED—See Searchlight Capital Partners, L.P.; *U.S. Private*, pg. 3589
TIMICO LIMITED—See Horizon Capital LLP; *Int'l*, pg. 3479
TIMICO PARTNER SERVICES LIMITED—See Horizon Capital LLP; *Int'l*, pg. 3479
TNCI OPERATING COMPANY, LLC—See Blue Casa Communications, Inc.; *U.S. Private*, pg. 586
TNCI OPERATING COMPANY, LLC—See Garrison Investment Group LP; *U.S. Private*, pg. 1646
TNCI—See Blue Casa Communications, Inc.; *U.S. Private*, pg. 586
TNCI—See Garrison Investment Group LP; *U.S. Private*, pg. 1646
TOWEL TRACKER, LLC; *U.S. Private*, pg. 4193
TOWNGAS TELECOMMUNICATIONS FIXED NETWORK LIMITED—See Henderson Land Development Co. Ltd.; *Int'l*, pg. 3344
TPG INTERNET PTY. LTD.—See CK Hutchison Holdings Limited; *Int'l*, pg. 1638
TPT GLOBAL TECH, INC.; *U.S. Public*, pg. 2178
TRADE ONLY DESIGN LIBRARY; *U.S. Private*, pg. 4201
TRADE SERVICE CO. LLC—See Trimble, Inc.; *U.S. Public*, pg. 2191
TRADE VISION, LTD.—See BIPROGY Inc.; *Int'l*, pg. 1045
TRANSACTTOOLS, INC.; *U.S. Private*, pg. 4206
TRANSBEAM, INC.—See GTT Communications, Inc.; *U.S. Private*, pg. 1808
TRANSMODE SYSTEMS, INC.—See Infinera Corporation; *U.S. Public*, pg. 1117
TRANS NATIONAL GROUP SERVICES; *U.S. Private*, pg. 4205
TRANSTELCO HOLDING, INC.; *U.S. Private*, pg. 4211
TRANSTEL ENGINEERING PNG LTD—See CSE Global Ltd.; *Int'l*, pg. 1864
TRANSTEL ENGINEERING (THAILAND) CO LIMITED—See CSE Global Ltd.; *Int'l*, pg. 1864
TRANSTEL LIMITED—See Fiji National Provident Fund; *Int'l*, pg. 2661
TRANSTRON AMERICA, INC.—See Fujitsu Limited; *Int'l*, pg. 2838
TRELLISWARE TECHNOLOGIES, INC.—See ViaSat, Inc.; *U.S. Public*, pg. 2292
TRI-COUNTY COMMUNICATIONS COOPERATIVE, INC.; *U.S. Private*, pg. 4222
TRIPLE T BROADBAND PUBLIC COMPANY LIMITED—See Advanced Info Service Plc; *Int'l*, pg. 160
TRIPLE T INTERNET CO., LTD.—See Advanced Info Service Plc; *Int'l*, pg. 160
TROIKA MEDIA GROUP, INC.; *U.S. Public*, pg. 2197
TRUEPATH.COM—See Etica Entertainment Inc.; *U.S. Private*, pg. 1432
TSC ACQUISITION CORP.; *U.S. Private*, pg. 4252
TSUNAGU NETWORK COMMUNICATIONS, INC.—See Arteria Networks Corp.; *Int'l*, pg. 583
T-SYSTEMS AUSTRIA GES.M.B.H—See Deutsche Telekom AG; *Int'l*, pg. 2084

T-SYSTEMS BELGIUM S.A.—See Deutsche Telekom AG; *Int'l*, pg. 2084
T-SYSTEMS CHINA LTD.—See Deutsche Telekom AG; *Int'l*, pg. 2084
T-SYSTEMS DANMARK AS—See Deutsche Telekom AG; *Int'l*, pg. 2084
T-SYSTEMS DO BRASIL LTDA.—See Deutsche Telekom AG; *Int'l*, pg. 2085
T-SYSTEMS HUNGARY KFT.—See Deutsche Telekom AG; *Int'l*, pg. 2084
T-SYSTEMS ITALIA S.P.A.—See Deutsche Telekom AG; *Int'l*, pg. 2084
T-SYSTEMS JAPAN K.K.—See Deutsche Telekom AG; *Int'l*, pg. 2084
T-SYSTEMS LTD.—See Deutsche Telekom AG; *Int'l*, pg. 2084
T-SYSTEMS LUXEMBURG S.A.—See Deutsche Telekom AG; *Int'l*, pg. 2084
T-SYSTEMS NEDERLAND B.V.—See Deutsche Telekom AG; *Int'l*, pg. 2085
T-SYSTEMS NORTH AMERICA INC.—See Deutsche Telekom AG; *Int'l*, pg. 2085
T-SYSTEMS POLSKA SP. Z O.O.—See Deutsche Telekom AG; *Int'l*, pg. 2085
T-SYSTEMS SINGAPORE PTE. LTD.—See Deutsche Telekom AG; *Int'l*, pg. 2085
T-SYSTEMS SOUTH AFRICA (PTY) LTD.—See Deutsche Telekom AG; *Int'l*, pg. 2085
T-SYSTEMS SWITZERLAND LTD.—See Deutsche Telekom AG; *Int'l*, pg. 2085
TWISTBOX GAMES LTD. & CO KG—See Digital Turbine, Inc.; *U.S. Public*, pg. 664
TWISTED PAIR SOLUTIONS, INC.—See Motorola Solutions, Inc.; *U.S. Public*, pg. 1479
TWO DEGREES MOBILE LIMITED—See SG Enterprises II, LLC; *U.S. Private*, pg. 3622
UAB ACTA IUVENTUS—See City Service SE; *Int'l*, pg. 1628
UFINET ARGENTINA SA—See Enel S.p.A.; *Int'l*, pg. 2415
UFINET BRASIL SA—See Enel S.p.A.; *Int'l*, pg. 2415
UFINET CHILE SA—See Enel S.p.A.; *Int'l*, pg. 2415
UFINET COLOMBIA SA—See Enel S.p.A.; *Int'l*, pg. 2415
UFINET COSTA RICA SA—See Enel S.p.A.; *Int'l*, pg. 2415
UFINET ECUADOR UFIEC SA—See Enel S.p.A.; *Int'l*, pg. 2415
UFINET EL SALVADOR SA DE CV—See Enel S.p.A.; *Int'l*, pg. 2415
UFINET FTTH GUATEMALA LTDA.—See Enel S.p.A.; *Int'l*, pg. 2415
UFINET GUATEMALA SA—See Enel S.p.A.; *Int'l*, pg. 2415
UFINET HONDURAS SA—See Enel S.p.A.; *Int'l*, pg. 2415
UFINET LATAM SLU—See Enel S.p.A.; *Int'l*, pg. 2415
UFINET MEXICO S DE RL DE CV—See Enel S.p.A.; *Int'l*, pg. 2415
UFINET NICARAGUA SA—See Enel S.p.A.; *Int'l*, pg. 2415
UFINET PANAMA SA—See Enel S.p.A.; *Int'l*, pg. 2415
UFINET PARAGUAY SA—See Enel S.p.A.; *Int'l*, pg. 2415
UFINET PERU SAC—See Enel S.p.A.; *Int'l*, pg. 2415
UNE EPM TELECOMUNICACIONES SA—See Empresas Publicas de Medellin ESP; *Int'l*, pg. 2392
UNIFY GMBH & CO. KG—See Searchlight Capital Partners, L.P.; *U.S. Private*, pg. 3590
UNIFY SOFTWARE & SOLUTIONS GMBH & CO. KG—See Searchlight Capital Partners, L.P.; *U.S. Private*, pg. 3589
UNIGATE TELECOM INC.—See Chunghwa Telecom Co., Ltd.; *Int'l*, pg. 1598
UNION TELECARD ALLIANCE, LLC—See IDT Corporation; *U.S. Public*, pg. 1094
UNION TELEPHONE COMPANY—See Telephone & Data Systems, Inc.; *U.S. Public*, pg. 1998
UNITED-KUC, INC.—See Liberty Broadband Corporation; *U.S. Public*, pg. 1311
UNITED TELEPHONE SOUTHEAST LLC—See Lumen Technologies, Inc.; *U.S. Public*, pg. 1348
UNOS SDN. BHD.—See FSBM Holdings Berhad; *Int'l*, pg. 2798
UPCO SYSTEMS INC.—See Adamant Holding Inc.; *Int'l*, pg. 123
UPC TELEKABEL-FERNSEHNETZ WIENER NEUSTADT/NEUNKIRCHEN BETRIEBSGESELLSCHAFT MBH—See Deutsche Telekom AG; *Int'l*, pg. 2084
UPC TELEKABEL KLAGENFURT GMBH—See Deutsche Telekom AG; *Int'l*, pg. 2084
UPDATA INFRASTRUCTURE UK LTD.—See Capita plc; *Int'l*, pg. 1309
URBAN COMMUNICATIONS INC.—See DigitalBridge Group, Inc.; *U.S. Public*, pg. 664
USABLENET, INC.; *U.S. Private*, pg. 4322
USABLENET UK LTD.—See Usablenet, Inc.; *U.S. Private*, pg. 4322
USA.NET, INC.; *U.S. Private*, pg. 4321
USBID, INC.; *U.S. Private*, pg. 4322
USHIP, INC.; *U.S. Private*, pg. 4323
US INTERNET CORPORATION; *U.S. Private*, pg. 4319
U.S. SATELLITE CORPORATION—See United Natural Foods, Inc.; *U.S. Public*, pg. 2232
VELOCITEL INC.—See Willis Stein & Partners, LLC; *U.S. Private*, pg. 4528

V-EMPOWER, INC.; *U.S. Private*, pg. 4327
VERACITY NETWORKS; *U.S. Private*, pg. 4359
VERIZON BUSINESS NETWORK SERVICES INC.—See Verizon Communications Inc.; *U.S. Public*, pg. 2285
VERSATURE CORP.—See IDT Corporation; *U.S. Public*, pg. 1094
VERTICAL BRIDGE, LLC—See DigitalBridge Group, Inc.; *U.S. Public*, pg. 665
VIATEL INFRASTRUCTURE FRANCE SA—See Digiweb Ltd.; *Int'l*, pg. 2124
VIATEL INFRASTRUCTURE NEDERLAND B.V.—See Digiweb Ltd.; *Int'l*, pg. 2124
VIATEL INFRASTRUCTURE SWITZERLAND AG—See Digiweb Ltd.; *Int'l*, pg. 2124
VIAVI SOLUTIONS UK LIMITED—See Viavi Solutions Inc.; *U.S. Public*, pg. 2295
VIDEO MONITORING SERVICES OF AMERICA, LP; *U.S. Private*, pg. 4380
VIPNET USLUGE D.O.O.—See America Movil, S.A.B. de C.V.; *Int'l*, pg. 421
VIRAL STYLE LLC; *U.S. Private*, pg. 4387
VIRGIN MOBILE POLSKA SP. Z O.O—See Iliad S.A.; *Int'l*, pg. 3614
VIZADA B.V.—See Airbus SE; *Int'l*, pg. 245
VIZADA GMBH—See Airbus SE; *Int'l*, pg. 245
VIZADA NETWORKS LTD.—See Airbus SE; *Int'l*, pg. 245
VOCUS FIBRE PTY LIMITED—See Aware Super Pty Ltd; *Int'l*, pg. 752
VOCUS GROUP LIMITED—See Aware Super Pty Ltd; *Int'l*, pg. 752
VOCUS GROUP LTD.—See Aware Super Pty Ltd; *Int'l*, pg. 752
VOCUS PTY LIMITED—See Aware Super Pty Ltd; *Int'l*, pg. 752
VOICENET SOLUTIONS LIMITED—See 8x8, Inc.; *U.S. Public*, pg. 10
VOIP GORILLA—See Odyssey Telecommunications, Inc.; *U.S. Private*, pg. 2996
VOLT TELECOM GROUP—See American CyberSystems, Inc.; *U.S. Private*, pg. 230
VOLT TELECOMMUNICATIONS GROUP, INC.—See American CyberSystems, Inc.; *U.S. Private*, pg. 230
VOTACALL, INC.; *U.S. Private*, pg. 4413
VOXEL DOT NET, INC.—See Internap Holding LLC; *U.S. Private*, pg. 2114
VOXTEL RNIS TELECOMMUNICATIONS INC.—See ATW Tech Inc.; *Int'l*, pg. 697
VYYO LTD.—See Gilo Ventures, LLC; *U.S. Private*, pg. 1701
WAAT MEDIA CORP.—See Digital Turbine, Inc.; *U.S. Public*, pg. 664
WAVSYS LLC; *U.S. Private*, pg. 4458
WBS CONNECT, LLC—See GTT Communications, Inc.; *U.S. Private*, pg. 1808
WEBAXXS.COM—See OLM, LLC; *U.S. Private*, pg. 3011
WESTCON CONVERGENCE UK—See TD Synnex Corp; *U.S. Public*, pg. 1987
WESTELL, INC.—See Westell Technologies, Inc.; *U.S. Public*, pg. 2354
WESTNET LTD—See CK Hutchison Holdings Limited; *Int'l*, pg. 1638
WEST NOTIFICATION, INC.—See Apollo Global Management, Inc.; *U.S. Public*, pg. 152
WEST SAFETY SERVICES, INC.—See Apollo Global Management, Inc.; *U.S. Public*, pg. 152
WEST UC GERMANY GMBH—See Apollo Global Management, Inc.; *U.S. Public*, pg. 152
WEST UC SWEDEN AB—See Apollo Global Management, Inc.; *U.S. Public*, pg. 152
WEST UNIFIED COMMUNICATIONS SERVICES CANADA, INC.—See Apollo Global Management, Inc.; *U.S. Public*, pg. 152
WIALAN TECHNOLOGIES, INC.; *U.S. Public*, pg. 2369
WINDSTREAM KDL, INC.—See Windstream Holdings, Inc.; *U.S. Public*, pg. 2373
WINDSTREAM MISSOURI, INC.—See Windstream Holdings, Inc.; *U.S. Public*, pg. 2373
WINDSTREAM NEBRASKA, INC.—See Windstream Holdings, Inc.; *U.S. Public*, pg. 2373
WINDSTREAM NEW YORK, INC.—See Windstream Holdings, Inc.; *U.S. Public*, pg. 2373
WINDSTREAM SUGAR LAND, INC.—See Windstream Holdings, Inc.; *U.S. Public*, pg. 2373
WIREDTREE; *U.S. Private*, pg. 4546
WORD SYSTEMS, INC.; *U.S. Private*, pg. 4562
WTT HK LIMITED—See TPG Capital, L.P.; *U.S. Public*, pg. 2177
WYANDOTTE NETTEL—See Wyandotte Tribal Corporation; *U.S. Private*, pg. 4575
X5 SOLUTIONS—See NewSpring Capital LLC; *U.S. Private*, pg. 2918
XCEED PASIFIKA LIMITED—See Fiji National Provident Fund; *Int'l*, pg. 2661
XCONNECT AMERICAS, INC.—See Somos, Inc.; *U.S. Private*, pg. 3712
XCONNECT GLOBAL NETWORKS (ISRAEL) LTD—See Somos, Inc.; *U.S. Private*, pg. 3712
XCONNECT GLOBAL NETWORKS LTD.—See Somos, Inc.; *U.S. Private*, pg. 3712

517810 — ALL OTHER TELECOMMU...

XFONE USA, INC.—See Keystone Group, L.P.; *U.S. Private*, pg. 2297
XFONE USA, INC.—See Pamlico Capital Management, L.P.; *U.S. Private*, pg. 3083
XO COMMUNICATIONS, LLC—See XO Holdings, Inc.; *U.S. Private*, pg. 4582
XTELESIS CORP.—See Protel Communications, Inc.; *U.S. Private*, pg. 3290
XWELL, INC.; *U.S. Public*, pg. 2393
YAHOO! CONNECTED LIFE—See Apollo Global Management, Inc.; *U.S. Public*, pg. 167
YAHOO, INC.—See Apollo Global Management, Inc.; *U.S. Public*, pg. 167
ZAKLAD USLUG TELEINFORMATYCZNYCH ZZE S.A. IT-SERWIS SP. Z O.O.—See ENEA S.A.; *Int'l*, pg. 2410
ZAPTEL CORPORATION; *U.S. Public*, pg. 4598
ZAYO GROUP UK LIMITED—See DigitalBridge Group, Inc.; *U.S. Public*, pg. 665
ZAYO GROUP UK LIMITED—See EQT AB; *Int'l*, pg. 2482
ZEPHYRTEL, INC.—See ESW Capital, LLC; *U.S. Private*, pg. 1430
ZERIGO, INC.—See 8x8, Inc.; *U.S. Public*, pg. 10
ZILLIANT, INC.; *U.S. Private*, pg. 4604
ZIMMERMAN ASSOCIATES INC.; *U.S. Private*, pg. 4605
ZINTEL COMMUNICATIONS LTD.—See Ziff Davis, Inc.; *U.S. Public*, pg. 2404
ZINTEL COMMUNICATIONS PTY. LIMITED—See Ziff Davis, Inc.; *U.S. Public*, pg. 2404
ZONE LIMITED—See Great Wall Terroir Holdings Limited; *Int'l*, pg. 3066
ZONE TELECOM PTE LTD—See Great Wall Terroir Holdings Limited; *Int'l*, pg. 3066
ZULIE VENTURE INC.; *U.S. Private*, pg. 4610

518210 — DATA PROCESSING, HOSTING, AND RELATED SERVICES

1SPATIAL FRANCE SAS—See 1Spatial Plc; *Int'l*, pg. 3
1SPATIAL GROUP LIMITED—See 1Spatial Plc; *Int'l*, pg. 3
THE 20 MSP GROUP LLC; *U.S. Private*, pg. 3980
360SCIENCE LTD.—See Bridge Growth Partners, LLC; *U.S. Private*, pg. 648
365 SERVICES LLC—See Stonecourt Capital LP; *U.S. Private*, pg. 3828
3 C DEUTSCHLAND GMBH—See Bertelsmann SE & Co. KGaA; *Int'l*, pg. 989
3D LABS INC., LTD.—See Creative Technology Ltd.; *Int'l*, pg. 1833
4SL CONSULTING LIMITED—See Databarracks Limited; *Int'l*, pg. 1977
ABACUS GROUP, LLC—See WestView Capital Partners, L.P.; *U.S. Private*, pg. 4501
ABBOTT RAPID DIAGNOSTICS INFORMATICS, INC.—See Abbott Laboratories; *U.S. Public*, pg. 18
ABSOLUTE SOFTWARE CORPORATION—See Crosspoint Capital Partners LP; *U.S. Private*, pg. 1107
ACCESS DIRECT SYSTEMS, INC.; *U.S. Private*, pg. 50
ACCOUNTABILIT, LLC—See WestView Capital Partners, L.P.; *U.S. Private*, pg. 4501
ACER AI CLOUD INC.—See Acer Incorporated; *Int'l*, pg. 98
ACER CYBER CENTER SERVICES LTD—See Acer Incorporated; *Int'l*, pg. 99
ACOM SOLUTIONS INC.; *U.S. Private*, pg. 62
ACTIVE HEALTH MANAGEMENT, INC.—See CVS Health Corporation; *U.S. Public*, pg. 614
ACTIVEPATH SOLUTIONS, INC.—See Broadridge Financial Solutions, Inc.; *U.S. Public*, pg. 391
ACTIVEPATH SOLUTIONS LTD.—See Broadridge Financial Solutions, Inc.; *U.S. Public*, pg. 391
ACXIOM DEUTSCHLAND GMBH—See The Interpublic Group of Companies, Inc.; *U.S. Public*, pg. 2090
ACXIOM GLOBAL SERVICE CENTER POLSKA SP.Z.O.O.—See The Interpublic Group of Companies, Inc.; *U.S. Public*, pg. 2090
ACXIOM LLC—See The Interpublic Group of Companies, Inc.; *U.S. Public*, pg. 2090
ACYCLICA INC.—See Teledyne Technologies Incorporated; *U.S. Public*, pg. 1993
ADAPT GROUP LIMITED—See Apollo Global Management, Inc.; *U.S. Public*, pg. 154
A.D. COMPUTER CORPORATION—See NCR Voyix Corporation.; *U.S. Public*, pg. 1502
ADDONS, INC.—See COSOL Ltd.; *Int'l*, pg. 1814
ADDTECH BUSINESS SUPPORT AB—See Addtech AB; *Int'l*, pg. 131
ADESSO ORANGE AUSTRIA GMBH—See adesso SE; *Int'l*, pg. 144
ADFERENCE GMBH—See ABOUT YOU Holding SE; *Int'l*, pg. 67
ADP EMPLOYER SERVICES GMBH—See Automatic Data Processing, Inc.; *U.S. Public*, pg. 229
ADP, INC. - ALPHARETTA (WINDWARD) OFFICE—See Automatic Data Processing, Inc.; *U.S. Public*, pg. 230
ADP, INC. - CAMARILLO OFFICE—See Automatic Data Processing, Inc.; *U.S. Public*, pg. 230
ADP, INC.—See Automatic Data Processing, Inc.; *U.S. Public*, pg. 230

ADPLAY S.R.L.—See Azerion Group N.V.; *Int'l*, pg. 778
ADP NEDERLAND B.V.—See Automatic Data Processing, Inc.; *U.S. Public*, pg. 230
ADS ALLIANCE DATA SYSTEMS, INC.—See Bread Financial Holdings Inc.; *U.S. Public*, pg. 380
ADVANCED CYBER SECURITY SYSTEMS, LLC—See NEWTEKONE, INC.; *U.S. Public*, pg. 1521
ADVANTAGECOM NETWORKS, INC.—See Cloud Equity Group, LLC; *U.S. Private*, pg. 946
ADVENTECH, INC.; *U.S. Private*, pg. 108
ADVENT SOFTWARE (MIDDLE EAST) LIMITED—See SS&C Technologies Holdings, Inc.; *U.S. Public*, pg. 1922
AENEAS COMMUNICATIONS, LLC; *U.S. Private*, pg. 117
AEROHIVE NETWORKS, INC.—See Extreme Networks, Inc.; *U.S. Public*, pg. 813
AEROPUERTO DE GUADALAJARA, S.A. DE C.V.—See Grupo Aeroportuario del Pacifico, S.A.B. de C.V.; *Int'l*, pg. 3118
AEROPUERTO DE MANZANILLO, S.A. DE C.V.—See Grupo Aeroportuario del Pacifico, S.A.B. de C.V.; *Int'l*, pg. 3118
AEROPUERTO DE SAN JOSE DEL CABO, S.A. DE C.V.—See Grupo Aeroportuario del Pacifico, S.A.B. de C.V.; *Int'l*, pg. 3118
AFFILIATED COMPUTER SERVICES GMBH—See Conduent Incorporated; *U.S. Public*, pg. 566
AFFINISCAPE, INC.—See Insight Venture Management, LLC; *U.S. Private*, pg. 2088
AFFINITY SPORTS, LLC—See Genstar Capital, LLC; *U.S. Private*, pg. 1678
AFILIAS, INC.—See Ethos Capital, LLC; *U.S. Private*, pg. 1432
AFREECATV CO., LTD.; *Int'l*, pg. 189
AGARIK SAS—See Atos SE; *Int'l*, pg. 691
AGGREGATE INTELLIGENCE, INC.; *U.S. Private*, pg. 127
AIADVERTISING, INC.; *U.S. Public*, pg. 63
AII DATA PROCESSING LTD.; *Int'l*, pg. 232
AI-MEDIA TECHNOLOGIES LIMITED; *Int'l*, pg. 227
AIR INTERNET SERVICE CO., LTD.—See Aeria Inc.; *Int'l*, pg. 179
AIRNET GROUP, INC.; *U.S. Private*, pg. 141
AJIS MALAYSIA SDN BHD.—See AJIS Co., Ltd.; *Int'l*, pg. 258
AKAMAI TECHNOLOGIES GMBH—See Akamai Technologies, Inc.; *U.S. Public*, pg. 68
AKAMAI TECHNOLOGIES INDIA PRIVATE LTD.—See Akamai Technologies, Inc.; *U.S. Public*, pg. 68
AKAMAI TECHNOLOGIES LTD.—See Akamai Technologies, Inc.; *U.S. Public*, pg. 69
AKAMAI TECHNOLOGIES SARL—See Akamai Technologies, Inc.; *U.S. Public*, pg. 69
ALBERT INC.—See Accenture plc; *Int'l*, pg. 83
THE ALESCO GROUP, LLC; *U.S. Private*, pg. 3983
ALIGHT, INC.; *U.S. Public*, pg. 75
ALLANT GROUP, LLC—See Vencap Technologies, LLC; *U.S. Private*, pg. 4356
ALLEGIANT NETWORKS, LLC—See Crexendo, Inc.; *U.S. Public*, pg. 594
ALLIANCE TECHNOLOGIES; *U.S. Private*, pg. 184
ALLIED MARKETING GROUP, INC.; *U.S. Private*, pg. 186
ALLTERRA DEUTSCHLAND GMBH—See Trimble, Inc.; *U.S. Public*, pg. 2190
ALMAWAVE DO BRASIL LTDA.—See Almawave S.p.A.; *Int'l*, pg. 363
ALPHABET FRANCE S.A.S.—See Bayerische Motoren Werke Aktiengesellschaft; *Int'l*, pg. 910
ALTERNET SYSTEMS, INC.; *U.S. Private*, pg. 208
ALVEO LLC—See Stagwell, Inc.; *U.S. Public*, pg. 1925
AMADEUS ASIA LIMITED—See Amadeus IT Group, S.A.; *Int'l*, pg. 405
AMADEUS FRANCE S.A.—See Amadeus IT Group, S.A.; *Int'l*, pg. 405
AMADEUS IT GROUP S.A.—See Amadeus IT Group, S.A.; *Int'l*, pg. 405
AMA XPERTEYE GMBH—See AMA Corporation Plc; *Int'l*, pg. 403
AMERICAN TELEMEDICINE, INC.—See MEDNAX, Inc.; *U.S. Public*, pg. 1414
AMPHENOL INTERCON SYSTEMS, INC.—See Amphenol Corporation; *U.S. Public*, pg. 128
ANCHOR COMPUTER INC.; *U.S. Private*, pg. 272
ANCHOR COMPUTER INC.—See Anchor Computer Inc.; *U.S. Private*, pg. 272
ANCHOR SYSTEMS PTY LTD—See Deluxe Corporation; *U.S. Public*, pg. 652
ANCOR INFORMATION MANAGEMENT LLC—See GI Manager L.P.; *U.S. Private*, pg. 1692
ANDOVER NATIONAL CORPORATION; *U.S. Private*, pg. 279
ANDRITZ FABRICS AND ROLLS LIMITED—See ANDRITZ AG; *Int'l*, pg. 453
ANDRITZ FABRICS AND ROLLS OY—See ANDRITZ AG; *Int'l*, pg. 453
ANTWORKS PTE. LTD.; *Int'l*, pg. 485
ANZ NEW ZEALAND SECURITIES LIMITED—See Australia & New Zealand Banking Group Limited; *Int'l*, pg. 720
APH INC.; *U.S. Private*, pg. 293
APPCAST, INC.—See Axel Springer SE; *Int'l*, pg. 766

APPEN LIMITED; *Int'l*, pg. 519
APPLIED INSIGHT, LLC—See CACI International Inc.; *U.S. Public*, pg. 417
APPLIED TECH SOLUTIONS INC—See PLATTE RIVER NETWORKS INC.; *U.S. Private*, pg. 3211
APPLIED UNDERWRITERS CAPTIVE RISK ASSURANCE COMPANY, INC.—See Quadrant Management, Inc.; *U.S. Private*, pg. 3316
APPRISS HOLDINGS, INC.; *U.S. Private*, pg. 300
ARBOR ITALIA S.R.L.—See Arbor Technology Corp.; *Int'l*, pg. 538
ARCBEST TECHNOLOGIES, INC.—See ArcBest Corporation; *U.S. Public*, pg. 180
ARCHTIS LIMITED; *Int'l*, pg. 549
ARCONTECH LTD.—See Arcontech Group PLC; *Int'l*, pg. 550
ARC TECHNOLOGIES, INC.—See Hexcel Corporation; *U.S. Public*, pg. 1032
ARG, INC.; *U.S. Private*, pg. 319
ARGOT PARTNERS, LLC—See Avesi Partners, LLC; *U.S. Private*, pg. 405
ARROW ECS D.O.O.—See Arrow Electronics, Inc.; *U.S. Public*, pg. 196
ARROW ECS FINLAND OY—See Arrow Electronics, Inc.; *U.S. Public*, pg. 196
ARROW ECS INTERNET SECURITY AG—See Arrow Electronics, Inc.; *U.S. Public*, pg. 196
ARROW ECS NORDIC A/S—See Arrow Electronics, Inc.; *U.S. Public*, pg. 196
ARROW ECS NORWAY AS—See Arrow Electronics, Inc.; *U.S. Public*, pg. 196
ARROW ECS SA NV—See Arrow Electronics, Inc.; *U.S. Public*, pg. 196
ARROW ECS, SAS—See Arrow Electronics, Inc.; *U.S. Public*, pg. 195
ARROW ECS SERVICES SP.Z.O.O.—See Arrow Electronics, Inc.; *U.S. Public*, pg. 196
ARROW ECS SP.Z.O.O.—See Arrow Electronics, Inc.; *U.S. Public*, pg. 196
ARROW ECS SWEDEN AB—See Arrow Electronics, Inc.; *U.S. Public*, pg. 196
ARROW ENTERPRISE COMPUTING SOLUTIONS LTD.—See Arrow Electronics, Inc.; *U.S. Public*, pg. 198
ARSALON TECHNOLOGIES, LLC; *U.S. Private*, pg. 337
ARTEC AQUA AS—See Endur ASA; *Int'l*, pg. 2409
ARVATO DIGITAL SERVICES LIMITED—See Bertelsmann SE & Co. KGaA; *Int'l*, pg. 990
AS ARCHIVU SERVISS—See Iron Mountain Incorporated; *U.S. Public*, pg. 1172
ASB SECURITIES LIMITED—See Commonwealth Bank of Australia; *Int'l*, pg. 1719
ASCENTEK, INC.—See Synagex, Inc; *U.S. Private*, pg. 3902
ASCENTY DATA CENTERS E TELECOMUNICOES S.A—See Digital Realty Trust, Inc.; *U.S. Public*, pg. 663
ASCIO GMBH—See HgCapital Trust plc; *Int'l*, pg. 3377
ASFD, INC.—See eBay Inc.; *U.S. Public*, pg. 709
ASH CREEK ENTERPRISES, INC.; *U.S. Private*, pg. 349
ASJ INC.; *Int'l*, pg. 621
ASK JEEVES UK PARTNERSHIP—See IAC Inc.; *U.S. Public*, pg. 1082
ASL AUTOMATED (THAILAND) LTD.—See Beijing Teamsun Technology Co., Ltd.; *Int'l*, pg. 958
ASPERMONT LIMITED; *Int'l*, pg. 629
ASSUREVAULT LLC—See The HF Group LLC; *U.S. Private*, pg. 4052
ASTOUND BROADBAND, LLC—See Stonepeak Partners L.P.; *U.S. Private*, pg. 3829
ASTRALIS NEXUS APS—See Astralis A/S; *Int'l*, pg. 658
ATISHAY LIMITED; *Int'l*, pg. 670
ATMOSERA, INC.; *U.S. Private*, pg. 381
AT-NET SERVICES, INC.; *U.S. Private*, pg. 363
ATOS INTERNATIONAL GERMANY GMBH—See Atos SE; *Int'l*, pg. 691
ATOS LUXEMBOURG SF S.A.—See Atos SE; *Int'l*, pg. 691
ATTAINIA, INC.—See TA Associates, Inc.; *U.S. Private*, pg. 3918
AURORA KENDRICK JAMES LIMITED—See Daisy Group Limited; pg. 1943
AURORA MOBILE LIMITED; *Int'l*, pg. 714
AURUM SOFTWARES AND SOLUTIONS PRIVATE LIMITED—See Aurum PropTech Ltd.; *Int'l*, pg. 715
AUTOMATED SYSTEMS HOLDINGS LIMITED—See Beijing Teamsun Technology Co., Ltd.; *Int'l*, pg. 958
AUTOMOTIVE DATA SERVICES PTY. LTD.—See carsales.com Limited; *Int'l*, pg. 1346
AUTOSCOUT24 GMBH—See Hellman & Friedman LLC; *U.S. Private*, pg. 1907
AVANTAX, INC.—See Genstar Capital, LLC; *U.S. Private*, pg. 1676
AVENGA; *Int'l*, pg. 738
AXA TECHNOLOGY SERVICES SAS.—See AXA S.A.; *Int'l*, pg. 758
AXEL SPRINGER NORWAY AS—See Axel Springer SE; *Int'l*, pg. 766
AXOS DIGITAL ASSETS LLC—See Axos Financial, Inc.; *U.S. Public*, pg. 256
AZBIL INFORMATION TECHNOLOGY CENTER (DALIAN)

N.A.I.C.S. INDEX

518210 — DATA PROCESSING, HO...

CO., LTD.—See Azbil Corporation; *Int'l*, pg. 777
AZUL SYSTEMS, INC.; *U.S. Private*, pg. 416
AZUL SYSTEMS UNITED KINGDOM LIMITED—See Azul Systems, Inc.; *U.S. Private*, pg. 416
BACKBLAZE, INC.; *U.S. Public*, pg. 263
BACKUPIFY, INC.—See Insight Venture Management, LLC; *U.S. Private*, pg. 2090
BACKUP MY INFO!, INC.; *U.S. Private*, pg. 423
BAE SYSTEMS—See BAE Systems plc; *Int'l*, pg. 797
BA MERCHANT SERVICES, LLC—See Bank of America Corporation; *U.S. Public*, pg. 271
BANCTEC, INC.—See Gainline Capital Partners LP; *U.S. Private*, pg. 1635
BANCTEC LTD.—See Gainline Capital Partners LP; *U.S. Private*, pg. 1635
BANERPORTEN AB—See AcadeMedia AB; *Int'l*, pg. 75
BARCO CO., LTD.—See Barco N.V.; *Int'l*, pg. 863
BARCO CONTROL ROOMS—See Barco N.V.; *Int'l*, pg. 863
BARCODING, INC.—See The Graham Group, Inc.; *U.S. Private*, pg. 4036
BARCO ELECTRONIC SYSTEMS LTD.—See Barco N.V.; *Int'l*, pg. 863
BARCO ELECTRONIC SYSTEMS S.A.—See Barco N.V.; *Int'l*, pg. 863
BARCO GMBH—See Barco N.V.; *Int'l*, pg. 863
BARCO LTDA.—See Barco N.V.; *Int'l*, pg. 863
BARCO LTD.—See Barco N.V.; *Int'l*, pg. 863
BARCO LTD.—See Barco N.V.; *Int'l*, pg. 863
BARCO LTD.—See Barco N.V.; *Int'l*, pg. 863
BARCO LTD.—See Barco N.V.; *Int'l*, pg. 863
BARCO PTE. LTD.—See Barco N.V.; *Int'l*, pg. 863
BARCO S.A.—See Barco N.V.; *Int'l*, pg. 863
BARCO SDN BHD—See Barco N.V.; *Int'l*, pg. 863
BARCO SILEX N.V.—See Barco N.V.; *Int'l*, pg. 863
BARCO SP. Z O.O.—See Barco N.V.; *Int'l*, pg. 863
BARCO S.R.L.—See Barco N.V.; *Int'l*, pg. 863
BARCO SYSTEMS PTY LTD.—See Barco N.V.; *Int'l*, pg. 863
BARCO TRADING (SHANGHAI) CO., LTD.—See Barco N.V.; *Int'l*, pg. 863
BARCOVIEW AVIONICS—See Barco N.V.; *Int'l*, pg. 864
BARKAWI MANAGEMENT CONSULTANTS GMBH & CO. KG—See Genpact Limited; *Int'l*, pg. 2926
BAT BLUE CORPORATION—See Fortinet, Inc.; *U.S. Public*, pg. 869
BCW GROUP HOLDING, INC.; *U.S. Public*, pg. 929
BEEKS FINANCIAL CLOUD GROUP PLC; *Int'l*, pg. 939
BEIJING VASTDATA TECHNOLOGY CO., LTD.; *Int'l*, pg. 959
BEIJING ZHIDEMAI TECHNOLOGY CO., LTD.; *Int'l*, pg. 961
BENDING SPOONS S.P.A.; *Int'l*, pg. 971
BENEFITFOCUS.COM, INC.—See Voya Financial, Inc.; *U.S. Public*, pg. 2311
BERINGER ASSOCIATES, INC.; *U.S. Private*, pg. 532
BERTELSMANN DATA SERVICES GMBH—See Bertelsmann SE & Co. KGaA; *Int'l*, pg. 990
BF CO., LTD.—See Hokuetsu Corporation; *Int'l*, pg. 3443
BHPA, INC.; *U.S. Public*, pg. 330
BICK GROUP, INC.; *U.S. Private*, pg. 550
BILLIONTON SYSTEMS INC.; *Int'l*, pg. 1031
BILLMATRIX CORPORATION—See Fiserv, Inc.; *U.S. Public*, pg. 850
BIMOBJECT AB; *Int'l*, pg. 1032
BIODISCOVERY, INC.—See Bionano Genomics, Inc.; *U.S. Public*, pg. 338
BIRST, INC.—See Koch Industries, Inc.; *U.S. Private*, pg. 2330
BITFUFU INC.; *Int'l*, pg. 1050
BITGLASS, INC.—See Francisco Partners Management, LP; *U.S. Private*, pg. 1588
BIZ-CORE—See Data Core Systems Inc.; *U.S. Private*, pg. 1162
BIZMATICS INC.—See Constellation Software Inc.; *Int'l*, pg. 1773
BLACK DIAMOND PERFORMANCE REPORTING, LLC—See SS&C Technologies Holdings, Inc.; *U.S. Public*, pg. 1922
BLOOMINGDALES.COM—See Macy's, Inc.; *U.S. Public*, pg. 1353
BLUE FOUNTAIN MEDIA INC.—See China Electronics Corporation; *Int'l*, pg. 1499
BLUE HILL DATA SERVICES, INC.; *U.S. Private*, pg. 589
BLUEHOST INC.—See Clearlake Capital Group, L.P.; *U.S. Private*, pg. 934
BLUEHOST INC.—See Siris Capital Group, LLC; *U.S. Private*, pg. 3673
BLUE KAI, INC.—See Oracle Corporation; *U.S. Public*, pg. 1610
BLUE KEY TECHNOLOGY LLC—See GadellNet Consulting Services, LLC; *U.S. Private*, pg. 1633
BLUEPOINT DATA, INC.; *U.S. Private*, pg. 597
BLUE SKY HOSTING LTD; *Int'l*, pg. 1069
BNK SYSTEM CO., LTD.—See BNK Financial Group Inc.; *Int'l*, pg. 1079
BODIS, LLC; *U.S. Private*, pg. 608
BONDED SERVICES INTERNATIONAL LIMITED—See Iron Mountain Incorporated; *U.S. Public*, pg. 1172

BONDED SERVICES LIMITED—See Iron Mountain Incorporated; *U.S. Public*, pg. 1172
BOOKER SOFTWARE, INC.—See Vista Equity Partners, LLC; *U.S. Private*, pg. 4398
BOOMI INTERNATIONAL OY; *Int'l*, pg. 1110
BORDERFREE, INC.—See Global-E Online Ltd.; *Int'l*, pg. 3003
BOTA BIO CO., LTD.; *Int'l*, pg. 1118
BRAINPAD INC.; *Int'l*, pg. 1137
BRAINTREE, INC.—See PayPal Holdings, Inc.; *U.S. Public*, pg. 1656
BRAINWARE, INC.; *U.S. Private*, pg. 634
BRANNEN BANK SERVICES INC.—See Brannen Banks of Florida, Inc.; *U.S. Private*, pg. 640
BRIAN UNLIMITED DISTRIBUTION COMPANY, INC.; *U.S. Private*, pg. 647
BRIDGESTONE/FIRESTONE INFORMATION SERVICES COMPANY—See Bridgestone Corporation; *Int'l*, pg. 1157
BRIGHTCOVE FZ-LLC—See Brightcove, Inc.; *U.S. Public*, pg. 383
BRIGHTCOVE KOREA—See Brightcove, Inc.; *U.S. Public*, pg. 383
BRIGHTCOVE SINGAPORE PTE. LTD.—See Brightcove, Inc.; *U.S. Public*, pg. 383
BRIGHTCOVE UK LTD—See Brightcove, Inc.; *U.S. Public*, pg. 383
BRINKSTER COMMUNICATIONS CORPORATION—See Trapp Technology, Inc.; *U.S. Private*, pg. 4212
BRIVO SYSTEMS, LLC; *U.S. Private*, pg. 657
BROADCAST INTERACTIVE MEDIA, LLC—See Benedek Investment Group, LLC; *U.S. Private*, pg. 524
THE BROADLEAF GROUP, LLC; *U.S. Private*, pg. 4000
BROADMEDIA CORPORATION; *Int'l*, pg. 1172
BROADRIDGE (JAPAN) LTD.—See Broadridge Financial Solutions, Inc.; *U.S. Public*, pg. 391
BROADRIDGE (SINGAPORE) PRIVATE LIMITED—See Broadridge Financial Solutions, Inc.; *U.S. Public*, pg. 391
BROADSMART GLOBAL, INC.—See Ooma, Inc.; *U.S. Public*, pg. 1605
BROADVOICE, INC.; *U.S. Private*, pg. 660
BROWSERSOFT INC.—See Lightbeam Health Solutions LLC; *U.S. Private*, pg. 2452
BT AMERICAS INC.—See BT Group plc; *Int'l*, pg. 1203
BT LATAM BRASIL LTDA—See BT Group plc; *Int'l*, pg. 1203
BUILDFAX, INC.—See Verisk Analytics, Inc.; *U.S. Public*, pg. 2282
BUSINESS INTELLIGENCE ASSOCIATES, INC.—See Quad-C Management, Inc.; *U.S. Private*, pg. 3315
BUSINESS KEEPER GMBH—See Thoma Bravo, L.P.; *U.S. Private*, pg. 4147
BUYERS EDGE PLATFORM LLC; *U.S. Private*, pg. 699
BYERS ENGINEERING COMPANY; *U.S. Private*, pg. 700
BYTEGRID HOLDINGS LLC—See Lincoln Property Company; *U.S. Private*, pg. 2458
BYTEK S.R.L.—See Datrix S.p.A.; *Int'l*, pg. 1982
CAC MARUHA NICHIRO SYSTEMS LTD.—See CAC Corporation; *Int'l*, pg. 1247
CAFEPRESS, INC.—See Claranova SA; *Int'l*, pg. 1642
CAL.NET, INC.; *U.S. Private*, pg. 715
CAMBEY & WEST, INC.; *U.S. Private*, pg. 725
CAMPAIGN MAIL & DATA, INC.; *U.S. Private*, pg. 730
CAMS BLUEWIRE TECHNOLOGY, LLC; *U.S. Private*, pg. 732
CANAL VENTURES, LTD.—See BIPROGY Inc.; *Int'l*, pg. 1045
CAPGEMINI FRANCE - RENNES—See Capgemini SE; *Int'l*, pg. 1305
CAPGEMINI SCHWEIZ AG—See Capgemini SE; *Int'l*, pg. 1306
CAP GEMINI TELECOM MEDIA & NETWORKS DEUTSCHLAND GMBH—See Capgemini SE; *Int'l*, pg. 1304
CAPGEMINI UNIVERSITE—See Capgemini SE; *Int'l*, pg. 1306
CAPILLARY TECHNOLOGIES INTERNATIONAL PTE LTD.; *Int'l*, pg. 1307
CAPITAL NOVUS; *U.S. Private*, pg. 741
CAPSTONE INFORMATION TECHNOLOGIES INCORPORATED—See Frontenac Company LLC; *U.S. Private*, pg. 1613
CARASENT NORGE AS—See Carasent ASA; *Int'l*, pg. 1319
CARESYNTAX, INC.; *U.S. Private*, pg. 754
CARETECH SOLUTIONS INC.; *U.S. Private*, pg. 754
CARRIER FIRE & SECURITY LTD.—See Carrier Global Corporation; *U.S. Public*, pg. 442
CARROLLPUB, INC.—See TechnoMile LLC; *U.S. Private*, pg. 3956
CARS.COM, LLC—See Cars.com Inc.; *U.S. Public*, pg. 444
CASHDASH UK LTD.; *Int'l*, pg. 1352
CASH TECHNOLOGIES, INC.; *U.S. Private*, pg. 782
CASS INTERNATIONAL LLC—See Cass Information Systems, Inc.; *U.S. Public*, pg. 447
CASTUP ISRAEL LLC—See Cisco Systems, Inc.; *U.S. Public*, pg. 497
CDK GLOBAL (CANADA) LIMITED—See Brookfield Corporation; *Int'l*, pg. 1175

CDS GLOBAL, INC.—See The Hearst Corporation; *U.S. Private*, pg. 4046
CDSNET, INC.; *U.S. Private*, pg. 803
CEGEKA HEALTH CARE NV—See Cegeka Groep NV; *Int'l*, pg. 1390
CENTARE HOLDINGS INC.—See Hadley Capital LLC; *U.S. Private*, pg. 1839
CENTAURI HEALTH SOLUTIONS, INC.—See ABRY Partners, LLC; *U.S. Private*, pg. 41
CENTRETEK SOLUTIONS, LLC—See Amulet Capital Partners, L.P.; *U.S. Private*, pg. 269
CENTRICA CONNECTED HOME LIMITED—See Centrica plc; *Int'l*, pg. 1413
CENTURYLINK COLOMBIA S.A.—See Lumen Technologies, Inc.; *U.S. Public*, pg. 1345
CENTURYLINK CORPORATION JAPAN—See Lumen Technologies, Inc.; *U.S. Public*, pg. 1345
CENTURYLINK COSTA RICA, S.R.L.—See Lumen Technologies, Inc.; *U.S. Public*, pg. 1345
CENTURYLINK GERMANY GMBH—See Lumen Technologies, Inc.; *U.S. Public*, pg. 1345
CENTURYLINK TECHNOLOGY AUSTRALIA PTY. LIMITED—See Lumen Technologies, Inc.; *U.S. Public*, pg. 1346
CENTURYLINK TECHNOLOGY SINGAPORE PTE LTD.—See Lumen Technologies, Inc.; *U.S. Public*, pg. 1346
CENTURYLINK TELECOMUNICACIONES S.A.—See Lumen Technologies, Inc.; *U.S. Public*, pg. 1346
CERDANT, INC.; *U.S. Private*, pg. 840
CERTICA SOLUTIONS, INC.—See New Harbor Capital Management LLC; *U.S. Private*, pg. 2896
CES LIMITED; *Int'l*, pg. 1423
CGG CANADA—See CGG; *Int'l*, pg. 1431
CGG JAKARTA—See CGG; *Int'l*, pg. 1431
CGG SEISMIC IMAGING (AUSTRALIA) PTY. LTD.—See CGG; *Int'l*, pg. 1431
CGG SEISMIC IMAGING (NORWAY) AS—See CGG; *Int'l*, pg. 1431
CGG SEISMIC IMAGING (UK) LIMITED—See CGG; *Int'l*, pg. 1431
CHANGE HEALTHCARE HOLDINGS, INC.—See McKesson Corporation; *U.S. Public*, pg. 1407
CHARTWORLD AMERICAS MARITIME SERVICES LTD.—See Teledyne Technologies Incorporated; *U.S. Public*, pg. 1992
CHARTWORLD ASIA PACIFIC PTE. LTD.—See Teledyne Technologies Incorporated; *U.S. Public*, pg. 1992
CHARTWORLD GMBH—See Teledyne Technologies Incorporated; *U.S. Public*, pg. 1992
CHARTWORLD INTERNATIONAL LIMITED—See Teledyne Technologies Incorporated; *U.S. Public*, pg. 1992
CHATSWORTH PRODUCTS INC.; *U.S. Public*, pg. 868
CHEDDAR INC.—See Altice USA, Inc.; *U.S. Public*, pg. 88
CHENMING ELECTRONIC TECH. CORP.; *Int'l*, pg. 1470
CHESAPEAKE NETCRAFTSMEN, LLC—See Source Capital, LLC; *U.S. Private*, pg. 3718
CHINA ELITE INFORMATION CO., LTD.—See Goldstream Investment Limited; *Int'l*, pg. 3034
CHINANETCENTER CO., LTD.; *Int'l*, pg. 1568
CHUNGHWA TELECOM VIETNAM CO., LTD.—See Chunghwa Telecom Co., Ltd.; *Int'l*, pg. 1598
CIOX HEALTH, LLC - GREEN BAY—See New Mountain Capital, LLC; *U.S. Private*, pg. 2901
CLARANET BENELUX BV—See Claranet Limited; *Int'l*, pg. 1642
CLARANET GMBH—See Claranet Limited; *Int'l*, pg. 1642
CLARANET PORTUGAL—See Claranet Limited; *Int'l*, pg. 1642
CLARANET SAS—See Claranet Limited; *Int'l*, pg. 1642
CLARANET S.A.U.—See Claranet Limited; *Int'l*, pg. 1642
CLARAVIEW, INC.—See Teradata Corporation; *U.S. Public*, pg. 2017
CLEARONE LTD.—See ClearOne, Inc.; *U.S. Public*, pg. 512
CLEARPATH SOLUTIONS GROUP; *U.S. Private*, pg. 938
CLEARSTREAM OPERATIONS PRAGUE S.R.O—See Deutsche Borse AG; *Int'l*, pg. 2063
CLINICAL OUTCOMES RESOURCE APPLICATION CORPORATION—See Cencora, Inc.; *U.S. Public*, pg. 467
CLOUD 8 SIXTEEN, INC.; *U.S. Private*, pg. 946
CLOUDICAL DEUTSCHLAND GMBH—See Allgeier SE; *Int'l*, pg. 337
CLOUD JUMPER LLC—See NetApp, Inc.; *U.S. Public*, pg. 1507
CLOUD MUSIC INC.; *Int'l*, pg. 1662
THE CLOUD NETWORKS GERMANY GMBH—See freenet AG; *Int'l*, pg. 2770
CLOUDSCALE365, INC.; *U.S. Private*, pg. 947
CLOUDWERX DATA SOLUTIONS INC.—See George Weston Limited; *Int'l*, pg. 2939
CMD GROUP, LLC—See Roper Technologies, Inc.; *U.S. Public*, pg. 1814
CM TELECOM FRANCE S.A.S.—See CM.com N.V.; *Int'l*, pg. 1666
COBRA TECHNOLOGIA S.A.—See Banco do Brasil S.A.; *Int'l*, pg. 822
COCC, INC.; *U.S. Private*, pg. 959

4277

518210 — DATA PROCESSING, HO...

COGECO PEER 1—See DigitalBridge Group, Inc.; *U.S. Public*, pg. 664
COGNITAS GMBH—See Etteplan Oyj; *Int'l*, pg. 2524
COGNITIVE CONSULTING SDN. BHD.—See Censof Holdings Berhad; *Int'l*, pg. 1401
COINSILIUM GROUP LTD.; *Int'l*, pg. 1696
COLLABRALINK TECHNOLOGIES; *U.S. Private*, pg. 968
COLLABRX—See Rennova Health, Inc.; *U.S. Public*, pg. 1783
COLLAGES.NET INC.; *U.S. Private*, pg. 968
COLO4; *U.S. Public*, pg. 970
COMBELL NV; *Int'l*, pg. 1708
COMFORTHOST.NET—See Cloud Equity Group, LLC; *U.S. Private*, pg. 946
COMMNET FOUR CORNERS, LLC—See ATN International, Inc.; *U.S. Public*, pg. 224
THE COMMUNITY BROADCASTING COMPANY OF SAN DIEGO, INCORPORATED—See Entravision Communications Corporation; *U.S. Public*, pg. 779
COMMUNITY FIRST DATA SERVICES—See The Sturm Financial Group, Inc.; *U.S. Private*, pg. 4124
COMPACT INFORMATION SYSTEMS, INC.; *U.S. Private*, pg. 998
COMPASS DATACENTERS, LLC—See RedBird Capital Partners L.P.; *U.S. Private*, pg. 3377
COMPASS SOLUTIONS, LLC.; *U.S. Private*, pg. 999
COMPLIT AS—See Crayon Group Holding ASA; *Int'l*, pg. 1829
COMPORIUM DATA SERVICES—See Comporium Group; *U.S. Private*, pg. 1002
COMPUFIX LIMITED—See Computacenter plc; *Int'l*, pg. 1758
COMPUNET CONSULTING GROUP, INC.; *U.S. Private*, pg. 1004
COMPUTACENTER AG—See Computacenter plc; *Int'l*, pg. 1758
COMPUTACENTER BV—See Computacenter plc; *Int'l*, pg. 1758
COMPUTACENTER MEXICO S.A. DE C.V.—See Computacenter plc; *Int'l*, pg. 1758
COMPUTACENTER SERVICES KFT—See Computacenter plc; *Int'l*, pg. 1758
COMPUTACENTER SERVICES (MALAYSIA) SDN BHD—See Computacenter plc; *Int'l*, pg. 1758
COMPUTACENTER SERVICES & SOLUTIONS (PTY) LIMITED—See Computacenter plc; *Int'l*, pg. 1758
COMPUTACENTER (U.S.) INC.—See Computacenter plc; *Int'l*, pg. 1758
COMPUTER CONSULTANTS OF AMERICA; *U.S. Private*, pg. 1004
COMPUTER SERVICES, INC.; *U.S. Public*, pg. 561
COMPUTER TECHNOLOGY RESOURCES, INC.—See Applications Software Technology LLC; *U.S. Private*, pg. 298
CONCERTO CLOUD SERVICES, LLC—See DXC Technology Company; *U.S. Public*, pg. 696
CONNECTSOLUTIONS, INC.; *U.S. Private*, pg. 1017
CONSCIA ENTERPRISE SYSTEMS LIMITED—See McKesson Corporation; *U.S. Public*, pg. 1407
CONSTRUCTION MARKET DATA GROUP LLC—See Roper Technologies, Inc.; *U.S. Public*, pg. 1811
CONTACT AT ONCE!, LLC—See LivePerson, Inc.; *U.S. Public*, pg. 1332
CONVENTION DATA SERVICES; *U.S. Private*, pg. 1035
CONVERGE TECHNOLOGY SOLUTIONS CORP.; *Int'l*, pg. 1787
CONVERGYS FRANCE SAS—See Concentrix Corporation; *U.S. Public*, pg. 565
CONVERGYS PHILIPPINES SERVICES CORPORATION—See Concentrix Corporation; *U.S. Public*, pg. 565
COREDIAL, LLC—See Thompson Street Capital Manager LLC; *U.S. Private*, pg. 4160
CORESITE DENVER, L.L.C.—See American Tower Corporation; *U.S. Public*, pg. 111
COSNET, INC.—See Madison Dearborn Partners, LLC; *U.S. Private*, pg. 2541
COVERMYMEDS LLC—See McKesson Corporation; *U.S. Public*, pg. 1407
CRAYON POLAND SP. Z O.O.—See Crayon Group Holding ASA; *Int'l*, pg. 1829
CRAZY DOMAINS FZ-LLC—See Dreamscape Networks Limited; *Int'l*, pg. 2203
CREATIVE BREAKTHROUGHS, INC.—See Converge Technology Solutions Corp.; *Int'l*, pg. 1787
CREDEMTEL SPA—See Credito Emiliano S.p.A.; *Int'l*, pg. 1836
CRESAN, S.A.—See Lone Star Funds; *U.S. Private*, pg. 2485
CRESCENT PROCESSING COMPANY, LP; *U.S. Private*, pg. 1094
CRESCO COMMUNICATIONS INC.—See Cresco, Ltd.; *Int'l*, pg. 1840
CRIMSONLOGIC PTE LTD; *Int'l*, pg. 1850
CRIMSON TIDE MPRO LIMITED—See Crimson Tide plc; *Int'l*, pg. 1850
CRISTIE SOFTWARE LIMITED; *Int'l*, pg. 1850

CRUCIAL PARADIGM PTY LTD—See Deluxe Corporation; *U.S. Public*, pg. 652
CRYPTOLOGIC INC.—See Light & Wonder, Inc.; *U.S. Public*, pg. 1314
CRYPTOSTAR CORP.; *Int'l*, pg. 1860
CSH GROUP (PTY) LTD—See Experian plc; *Int'l*, pg. 2586
CU*ANSWERS; *U.S. Private*, pg. 1119
CUSTOMERSAT, INC.—See EQT AB; *Int'l*, pg. 2475
CUSTOM STORAGE, INC.—See Frontier Technology LLC; *U.S. Private*, pg. 1616
CUSTOM STORAGE, INC.—See Frontier Technology LLC; *U.S. Private*, pg. 1616
CVENT, INC.—See Blackstone Inc.; *U.S. Public*, pg. 353
CWG PLC; *Int'l*, pg. 1890
CXAPP INC.; *U.S. Public*, pg. 616
CX COMPANY GMBH—See CM.com N.V.; *Int'l*, pg. 1666
CYBERSITE SERVICES PTE LIMITED—See Great Wall Terroir Holdings Limited; *Int'l*, pg. 3066
CYBERSOURCE CORPORATION—See Visa, Inc.; *U.S. Public*, pg. 2301
CYBERSOURCE K.K.—See Visa, Inc.; *U.S. Public*, pg. 2301
CYBERSOURCE LTD.—See Visa, Inc.; *U.S. Public*, pg. 2302
CYBERVERSE, INC.—See Evocative, Inc.; *U.S. Private*, pg. 1442
CYXTERA TECHNOLOGIES, INC.—See Cyxtera Technologies, Inc.; *U.S. Public*, pg. 618
DANMAR LINES AG—See Deutsche Post AG; *Int'l*, pg. 2072
DAPAT VISTA (M) SDN. BHD.—See HeiTech Padu Berhad; *Int'l*, pg. 3326
DARTPOINTS LLC—See Astra Capital Management LLC; *U.S. Private*, pg. 361
DATA#3 BUSINESS SYSTEMS PTY. LTD.—See Data#3 Limited; *Int'l*, pg. 1977
DATABANK, LTD.; *U.S. Private*, pg. 1164
DATABARRACKS LIMITED; *Int'l*, pg. 1977
DATA CENTER INC.; *U.S. Private*, pg. 1162
DATACENTRE DYNAMICS INDIA PVT. LTD—See Data Center Dynamics Ltd; *Int'l*, pg. 1976
DATA CENTRE DYNAMICS MEXICO S. DE RL DE CV—See Data Center Dynamics Ltd; *Int'l*, pg. 1976
DATA CLEAN CORP.—See Angeles Equity Partners, LLC; *U.S. Private*, pg. 282
DATA COMMUNICATIONS MANAGEMENT CORP.; *Int'l*, pg. 1976
DATA DIMENSIONS CORP.; *U.S. Private*, pg. 1162
THE DATA ENTRY COMPANY; *U.S. Private*, pg. 4018
DATA FUSION TECHNOLOGIES INC.—See Levine Leichtman Capital Partners, LLC; *U.S. Private*, pg. 2435
DATAGROUP FINANCIAL IT SERVICES GMBH—See DATAGROUP SE; *Int'l*, pg. 1977
DATALAB USA; *U.S. Private*, pg. 1165
DATALINE SYSTEMS, LLC—See CardWorks, Inc.; *U.S. Private*, pg. 751
DATA LOGIC SERVICES CORP—See Berkshire Partners LLC; *U.S. Private*, pg. 534
DATA-MAIL, INC.—See Incline MGMT Corp.; *U.S. Private*, pg. 2054
DATAMARK INC.; *U.S. Private*, pg. 1166
DATAMINR INC.; *U.S. Private*, pg. 1166
DATA OUTSOURCING CENTRE DOO—See Iron Mountain Incorporated; *U.S. Public*, pg. 1172
DATAPIPE, INC.—See Apollo Global Management, Inc.; *U.S. Public*, pg. 154
DATA RECOGNITION CORPORATION; *U.S. Private*, pg. 1163
DATAROBOT, INC.—See Right Side Capital Management, LLC; *U.S. Private*, pg. 3436
DATA SEARCH NY INC.; *U.S. Private*, pg. 1163
DATASECTION INC.; *Int'l*, pg. 1979
DATASHIELD LLC—See Apollo Global Management, Inc.; *U.S. Public*, pg. 146
DATASIFT INC.; *U.S. Private*, pg. 1166
DATASIFT LTD.—See DataSift Inc.; *U.S. Private*, pg. 1166
DATA STORE 365 LIMITED—See Bechtle AG; *Int'l*, pg. 938
DATASTREAM CONTENT SOLUTIONS, LLC—See The Dolan Company; *U.S. Private*, pg. 4022
DATA SYSTEMS CONSULTING CO., LTD.; *Int'l*, pg. 1976
DATATRAK DEUTSCHLAND, GMBH—See DATATRAK International, Inc.; *U.S. Public*, pg. 635
DATAWARE, LLC—See Midcontinent Media Inc.; *U.S. Private*, pg. 2711
DDC FREIGHT PROCESS OUTSOURCING LLC—See The DDC Group; *U.S. Private*, pg. 4019
DDP DIRECT GMBH—See Fred, Olsen & Co.; *Int'l*, pg. 2768
DECIPHER, INC.; *U.S. Private*, pg. 1187
DEFINITIVEDATA, INC.—See L.I.S.T. Inc.; *U.S. Private*, pg. 2366
DELCAN TECHNOLOGIES, INC.—See Parsons Corporation; *U.S. Public*, pg. 1651
DEMOS-INTERNET—See Demos LLC; *Int'l*, pg. 2025
DENSAN CO., LTD.; *Int'l*, pg. 2028
DESIGN INTERACTIVE, INC.; *U.S. Private*, pg. 1213
DESIGN IS DEAD BVBA—See Emakina Group S.A.; *Int'l*, pg. 2373
THE DESIGN PEOPLE, INC.; *U.S. Private*, pg. 4020
DESIGN STRATEGY CORPORATION; *U.S. Private*, pg. 1214

DETICA-STREAMSHIELD—See BAE Systems plc; *Int'l*, pg. 798
DIAGNOS INC.; *Int'l*, pg. 2103
DICE INC.—See DHI Group, Inc.; *U.S. Public*, pg. 658
DIGILITI MONEY GROUP, INC.; *U.S. Private*, pg. 1229
DIGIMAX GLOBAL INC.; *Int'l*, pg. 2120
DIGIOP TECHNOLOGIES, LTD.—See GTCR LLC; *U.S. Private*, pg. 1802
DIGITAL MAP PRODUCTS, INC.—See Battery Ventures, L.P.; *U.S. Private*, pg. 489
DIGITAL MAP PRODUCTS, INC.—See Silver Lake Group, LLC; *U.S. Private*, pg. 3658
DIGITAL PACIFIC PTY LTD—See Deluxe Corporation; *U.S. Public*, pg. 653
DIGITALPROJEKT 1 GMBH—See EWE Aktiengesellschaft; *Int'l*, pg. 2575
DIGITAL WORKFORCE SP. Z O.O.—See Digital Workforce Services Plc; *Int'l*, pg. 2123
DIRECT ANALYTICS GMBH—See Bertelsmann SE & Co. KGaA; *Int'l*, pg. 992
DIRECTI GROUP; *Int'l*, pg. 2130
DIRECT MAIL COMPANY AG—See Die Schweizerische Post AG; *Int'l*, pg. 2112
DISASTER RECOVERY SERVICES LIMITED—See Iron Mountain Incorporated; *U.S. Public*, pg. 1172
DISCOVERREADY, LLC—See GI Manager L.P.; *U.S. Private*, pg. 1692
DISCOVERY FLEET CORPORATION—See Discovery World Corporation; *Int'l*, pg. 2134
D MASONS SOFTWARE, LLC—See SPS Commerce, Inc.; *U.S. Public*, pg. 1920
DMCS/SOURCELINK INC.; *U.S. Private*, pg. 1248
DNI CORP.; *U.S. Private*, pg. 1249
DOCMAGIC, INC.; *U.S. Private*, pg. 1251
DOCON TECHNOLOGIES PRIVATE LIMITED; *Int'l*, pg. 2153
DOC-TECH, INC.—See DocMagic, Inc.; *U.S. Private*, pg. 1251
DOMAINZ LTD—See 5G Networks Limited; *Int'l*, pg. 13
DOMINION SYSTEMS, INC.—See Anderson Anderson & Brown LLP; *U.S. Private*, pg. 450
THE DONKEY BARN, LLC—See Godspeed Capital Management LP; *U.S. Private*, pg. 1725
DOTMAILER LIMITED—See dotdigital Group PLC; *Int'l*, pg. 2180
DOTSTER, INC.; *U.S. Private*, pg. 1265
DP SERVICE LLC—See Dynaxys LLC; *U.S. Private*, pg. 1300
DRP CONSULTING, INC.—See Twining Inc.; *U.S. Private*, pg. 4266
DTS WEST CORPORATION—See DTS Corporation; *Int'l*, pg. 2217
DUN & BRADSTREET ESTONIA AS—See Dun & Bradstreet Holdings, Inc.; *U.S. Public*, pg. 691
DUN & BRADSTREET SLOVAKIA, S.R.O.—See Dun & Bradstreet Holdings, Inc.; *U.S. Public*, pg. 691
DUOS TECHNOLOGIES GROUP, INC.; *U.S. Public*, pg. 692
DXC TECHNOLOGY BALTIC UAB—See DXC Technology Company; *U.S. Public*, pg. 696
DXN LIMITED; *Int'l*, pg. 2237
DYNAMIC COMPUTING TECHNOLOGY CO., LTD.—See Hon Hai Precision Industry Co., Ltd.; *Int'l*, pg. 3456
DYNASIS INTEGRATED SYSTEMS CORP.—See Perpetual Capital, LLC; *U.S. Private*, pg. 3153
DYN; *U.S. Private*, pg. 1296
EARTH SIGNAL PROCESSING LTD.; *Int'l*, pg. 2268
EASIPROCESS PRIVATE LTD.—See J.C. Flowers & Co., LLC; *U.S. Private*, pg. 2160
EBAY CORPORATE SERVICES GMBH—See eBay Inc.; *U.S. Public*, pg. 709
EBAY GMARKET CO., LTD.—See eBay Inc.; *U.S. Public*, pg. 709
EBECS BUSINESS SOLUTIONS (IRELAND) LIMITED—See DXC Technology Company; *U.S. Public*, pg. 697
EBECS COMPANY LIMITED—See DXC Technology Company; *U.S. Public*, pg. 697
EBS DEALING RESOURCES INTERNATIONAL LIMITED—See CME Group, Inc.; *U.S. Public*, pg. 516
EBUREAU LLC—See TransUnion; *U.S. Public*, pg. 2185
ECLERX SERVICES LTD; *Int'l*, pg. 2291
ECLIPSE SOFTWARE SYSTEMS LLC—See Bestpass, Inc.; *U.S. Private*, pg. 544
ECOBUILT HOLDINGS BERHAD; *Int'l*, pg. 2294
E-COMETRUE INC.; *Int'l*, pg. 2247
ECS BIZTECH LIMITED; *Int'l*, pg. 2301
EDGAR ONLINE—See Donnelley Financial Solutions, Inc.; *U.S. Public*, pg. 677
EDGE HOSTING, LLC—See DataBank, Ltd.; *U.S. Private*, pg. 1164
EDIFIXIO S.A.S.—See Atos SE; *Int'l*, pg. 692
EFFYIS, INC.—See Hotto Link Inc.; *Int'l*, pg. 3490
EIS HOLDINGS, LLC—See Sun Capital Partners, Inc.; *U.S. Private*, pg. 3859
ELATERAL, INC.—See Elateral Ltd.; *Int'l*, pg. 2343
ELECTRONIC INK—See LiquidHub, Inc.; *U.S. Private*, pg. 2466
ELEMENT DATA, INC.; *U.S. Private*, pg. 1357

ELEMENT PAYMENT SERVICES, INC.; *U.S. Private*, pg. 1357
ELIANCE (PTY) LIMITED; *Int'l*, pg. 2360
ELLEN PHILIP ASSOCIATES, INC.—See Integrated Software Solutions, Inc.; *U.S. Private*, pg. 2101
ELM COMPUTER TECHNOLOGIES LIMITED—See Beijing Teamsun Technology Co., Ltd.; *Int'l*, pg. 958
ELM LLC; *U.S. Private*, pg. 1376
EMAG SOLUTIONS LLC—See Patriarch Partners, LLC; *U.S. Private*, pg. 3109
EMAILDIRECT; *U.S. Private*, pg. 1378
EMAKINA BV—See Emakina Group S.A.; *Int'l*, pg. 2373
EMAKINA.CH SA.—See Emakina Group S.A.; *Int'l*, pg. 2373
EMAKINA.FR SA.—See Emakina Group S.A.; *Int'l*, pg. 2373
EMAKINA GROUP S.A.; *Int'l*, pg. 2373
EMAKINA.NL BV—See Emakina Group S.A.; *Int'l*, pg. 2373
EMC DEL PERU S.A.—See Dell Technologies Inc.; *U.S. Public*, pg. 651
EMC NEW ZEALAND CORPORATION LIMITED—See Dell Technologies Inc.; *U.S. Public*, pg. 650
EMDEON BUSINESS SERVICES—See McKesson Corporation; *U.S. Public*, pg. 1407
EMDEON BUSINESS SERVICES—See McKesson Corporation; *U.S. Public*, pg. 1407
EMERGING MARKETS PAYMENTS—See Emirates NBD PJSC; *Int'l*, pg. 2382
EMERSON PROCESS MANAGEMENT—See Emerson Electric Co.; *U.S. Public*, pg. 746
EMMAUS LIFE SCIENCES, INC.; *U.S. Public*, pg. 752
ENCORE RECEIVABLE MANAGEMENT, INC.—See Concentrix Corporation; *U.S. Public*, pg. 565
ENECHANGE CO., LTD.—See EPCO Co., Ltd.; *Int'l*, pg. 2459
ENERGY SERVICES GROUP, LLC; *U.S. Private*, pg. 1396
ENETICA PTY LTD—See Dreamscape Networks Limited; *Int'l*, pg. 2203
ENSONO GMBH—See KKR & Co. Inc.; *U.S. Public*, pg. 1244
ENSONO LIMITED—See KKR & Co. Inc.; *U.S. Public*, pg. 1244
ENVISIONAL LIMITED—See HgCapital Trust plc; *Int'l*, pg. 3377
ENVISION PHARMACEUTICAL SERVICES, LLC—See New Rite Aid, LLC; *U.S. Private*, pg. 2905
EOH HOLDINGS LIMITED; *Int'l*, pg. 2457
EOSCENE CORPORATION; *U.S. Private*, pg. 1411
EPID RESEARCH OY—See IQVIA Holdings Inc.; *U.S. Public*, pg. 1168
EPISERVER AUSTRALIA PTY. LTD.—See Insight Venture Management, LLC; *U.S. Private*, pg. 2090
EPISERVER INC.—See Insight Venture Management, LLC; *U.S. Private*, pg. 2090
EQS GROUP GMBH—See Thoma Bravo, L.P.; *U.S. Private*, pg. 4147
EQS GROUP S.R.L.—See Thoma Bravo, L.P.; *U.S. Private*, pg. 4147
EQUIFAX PARAGUAY S.A.—See Equifax Inc.; *U.S. Public*, pg. 786
EQUIFAX WORKFORCE SOLUTIONS—See Equifax Inc.; *U.S. Public*, pg. 786
EQUINIX (OTTAWA) GOVERNMENT LTD.—See Equinix, Inc.; *U.S. Public*, pg. 787
EQUITYMETRIX; *U.S. Private*, pg. 1416
ERECRUITMENT SOLUTIONS SP. Z O.O.—See Grupa Pracuj S.A.; *Int'l*, pg. 3117
ESCENIC AS—See CCI Europe A/S; *Int'l*, pg. 1366
E-SEIKATSU CO., LTD.; *Int'l*, pg. 2249
ESP COMPUTER SERVICES, INC.; *U.S. Private*, pg. 1426
ESPIRA ABOL AS—See AcadeMedia AB; *Int'l*, pg. 75
ESPIRA ARHAUG AS—See AcadeMedia AB; *Int'l*, pg. 75
ESPIRA GASERUD AS—See AcadeMedia AB; *Int'l*, pg. 75
ESPIRA HOYTORP FORT AS—See AcadeMedia AB; *Int'l*, pg. 75
ESPIRA LOVESTAD AS—See AcadeMedia AB; *Int'l*, pg. 76
ESPIRA OSTREM AS—See AcadeMedia AB; *Int'l*, pg. 76
ESPIRA STONGAFJELLET AS—See AcadeMedia AB; *Int'l*, pg. 76
ESPIRA UND JOKI KINDERBETREUUNG GMBH—See AcadeMedia AB; *Int'l*, pg. 76
ESPIRA VARBAK ARCEN AS—See AcadeMedia AB; *Int'l*, pg. 76
ESROC, LLC—See Great Hill Partners, L.P.; *U.S. Private*, pg. 1763
ESSENTIAL DATA CORPORATION; *U.S. Private*, pg. 1427
EUCLYDE DC2—See I Squared Capital Advisors (US) LLC; *U.S. Private*, pg. 2025
EUROFINS INFORMATION SYSTEMS GMBH—See Eurofins Scientific S.E.; *Int'l*, pg. 2548
EURO-PRO GESELLSCHAFT FUR DATA PROCESSING MBH—See Allianz SE; *Int'l*, pg. 352
EVERBRIGHT SECURITIES DIGITAL FINANCE (HK) LIMITED—See Allied Group Limited; *Int'l*, pg. 357
EVEREST CONSULTANTS INC.; *U.S. Private*, pg. 1437
EVERTEC GROUP, LLC—See EVERTEC, Inc.; *U.S. Private*, pg. 802
EVIDERA, INC.—See Thermo Fisher Scientific Inc.; *U.S. Public*, pg. 2150

EXACTEARTH LTD.—See Spire Global, Inc.; *U.S. Public*, pg. 1918
EXASOL SCHWEIZ AG—See Exasol AG; *Int'l*, pg. 2577
EXASOL UK LTD.—See Exasol AG; *Int'l*, pg. 2577
EXATEL S.A.; *Int'l*, pg. 2577
EXCENTUM TECHNOLOGY SERVICES, INC.—See The Chickasaw Nation; *U.S. Private*, pg. 4008
EXELA TECHNOLOGIES, INC.; *U.S. Public*, pg. 806
EXELA TECHNOLOGIES S.A.—See Exela Technologies, Inc.; *U.S. Public*, pg. 806
EXELATE, INC.—See Brookfield Corporation; *Int'l*, pg. 1181
EXELATE, INC.—See Elliott Management Corporation; *U.S. Private*, pg. 1373
EXPEDIEN, INC.; *U.S. Private*, pg. 1449
EXPERIAN AUSTRALIA CREDIT SERVICES PTY LTD—See Experian plc; *Int'l*, pg. 2586
EXPERIAN DECISION ANALYTICS—See Experian plc; *Int'l*, pg. 2586
EXPERIAN GMBH—See Experian plc; *Int'l*, pg. 2587
EXPERIAN SERVICES COSTA RICA, S.A.—See Experian plc; *Int'l*, pg. 2587
EXPERIENCED OFFICE SOLUTIONS LLC—See Alpine Investors; *U.S. Private*, pg. 201
EXPLORE INFORMATION SERVICES, LLC—See Vista Equity Partners, LLC; *U.S. Private*, pg. 4400
EXXCOM LIMITED—See Enghouse Systems Limited; *Int'l*, pg. 2427
EXXONMOBIL CORPORATION—See Exxon Mobil Corporation; *U.S. Public*, pg. 815
F24 AG—See HgCapital Trust plc; *Int'l*, pg. 3376
FACTSET BENELUX B.V.—See FactSet Research Systems Inc.; *U.S. Public*, pg. 819
FACTSET DATA SYSTEMS, INC.—See FactSet Research Systems Inc.; *U.S. Public*, pg. 819
FACTSET EUROPE LIMITED—See FactSet Research Systems Inc.; *U.S. Public*, pg. 819
FACTSET GMBH—See FactSet Research Systems Inc.; *U.S. Public*, pg. 819
FACTSET ITALIA S.R.L.—See FactSet Research Systems Inc.; *U.S. Public*, pg. 819
FACTSET JCF S.A.S.—See FactSet Research Systems Inc.; *U.S. Public*, pg. 819
FACTSET PACIFIC, INC.—See FactSet Research Systems Inc.; *U.S. Public*, pg. 819
FACTSET RESEARCH SYSTEMS INC.; *U.S. Public*, pg. 819
FAIR ISAAC DEUTSCHLAND GMBH—See Fair Isaac Corporation; *U.S. Public*, pg. 820
FALCON CONSULTING GROUP, LLC—See Avaap Inc.; *U.S. Private*, pg. 403
FANDUEL INC.—See Flutter Entertainment plc; *Int'l*, pg. 2715
FANSIDE INC.—See FreeBit Co., Ltd.; *Int'l*, pg. 2769
FASHINVEST, LTD.—See Penske Media Corporation; *U.S. Private*, pg. 3139
FASTDOMAIN INC.—See Clearlake Capital Group, L.P.; *U.S. Private*, pg. 934
FASTDOMAIN INC.—See Siris Capital Group, LLC; *U.S. Private*, pg. 3673
FASTMETRICS LLC—See Paxio Inc.; *U.S. Private*, pg. 3115
FEITIAN TECHNOLOGIES US,INC.—See Feitian Technologies Co., Ltd.; *Int'l*, pg. 2632
FIBERNET CORP; *U.S. Private*, pg. 1502
FIDELITY NATIONAL INFORMATION SERVICES, INC. - NORCROSS—See Fidelity National Infor; *U.S. Public*, pg. 832
FILMON NETWORKS USA—See FilmOn.com Plc; *Int'l*, pg. 2663
FILM PAYROLL SERVICES INC.—See Oberman Tivoli Miller Pickert; *U.S. Private*, pg. 2987
FINALI CORPORATION—See Concentrix Corporation; *U.S. Public*, pg. 565
FINANCIAL PROCESSING SYSTEMS CORPORATION—See Orange Coast Title Company Inc.; *U.S. Private*, pg. 3037
FINPROM S.R.L.—See Gruppo MutuiOnline S.p.A; *Int'l*, pg. 3141
FINSCIENCE S.R.L.—See Datrix S.p.A.; *Int'l*, pg. 1982
FIRECLICK, INC.—See Siris Capital Group, LLC; *U.S. Private*, pg. 3672
FIRSTBANK DATA CORPORATION—See Firstbank Holding Company of Colorado, Inc.; *U.S. Private*, pg. 1531
FIRST DATA RESOURCES INC.—See Fiserv, Inc.; *U.S. Public*, pg. 851
FIRSTRAIN, INC.—See ESW Capital, LLC; *U.S. Private*, pg. 1430
FIS DATA SYSTEMS INC.—See Fidelity National Infor; *U.S. Public*, pg. 832
FISERV AUTOMOTIVE SOLUTIONS, INC.—See Fiserv, Inc.; *U.S. Public*, pg. 851
FISERV, INC.; *U.S. Public*, pg. 850
FISERV POLSKA SP. Z.O.O.—See Fiserv, Inc.; *U.S. Public*, pg. 851
FLASHBANC, LLC—See Independence Capital Partners, LLC; *U.S. Private*, pg. 2056
FLEXENTIAL COLORADO CORP.—See GI Manager L.P.; *U.S. Private*, pg. 1693
FLIGHT DATA SERVICES LIMITED—See L3Harris Technologies, Inc.; *U.S. Public*, pg. 1279
FLIGHTLINE DATA SERVICES, INC.—See Sabre Corporation; *U.S. Public*, pg. 1833
FLIPSIDE, INC.; *U.S. Private*, pg. 1546
FLS GLOBAL FINANCE A/S—See FLSmidth & Co. A/S; *Int'l*, pg. 2710
FORIAN INC.; *U.S. Public*, pg. 868
FORTINET MALAYSIA SDN. BHD.—See Fortinet, Inc.; *U.S. Public*, pg. 869
FORTUNE VALLEY TREASURES, INC.; *Int'l*, pg. 2744
FOTONATION CORPORATION—See Adeia Inc.; *U.S. Public*, pg. 41
FOTV MEDIA NETWORKS INC.; *U.S. Private*, pg. 1579
FRACTAL ANALYTICS INC.; *U.S. Private*, pg. 1586
FREDERATOR NETWORKS INC.—See Kartoon Studios, Inc.; *U.S. Public*, pg. 1214
FREEDOM SOLUTIONS GROUP INC.—See ARG, Inc.; *U.S. Private*, pg. 319
FRIENDFINDER NETWORKS INC.; *U.S. Private*, pg. 1611
FRONTEO, INC.; *Int'l*, pg. 2794
FTD.COM INC.—See Tenth Avenue Holdings LLC; *U.S. Private*, pg. 3968
FUGRO CERTIFICATION SERVICES LTD.—See Fugro N.V.; *Int'l*, pg. 2805
FUGRO MULTI CLIENT SERVICES PTY LTD.—See Fugro N.V.; *Int'l*, pg. 2806
FUGRO ROADWARE, INC.—See Fugro N.V.; *Int'l*, pg. 2805
FUJIMIC, INC.—See Fuji Media Holdings, Inc.; *Int'l*, pg. 2814
FUJI XEROX SYSTEM SERVICE CO., LTD.—See FUJIFILM Holdings Corporation; *Int'l*, pg. 2825
FULCO, INC.; *U.S. Private*, pg. 1620
FUNAI SOKEN DIGITAL INC.—See Funai Soken Holdings Incorporated; *Int'l*, pg. 2845
FUNDASSIST LIMITED—See Broadridge Financial Solutions, Inc.; *U.S. Public*, pg. 391
FUSION CONSULTING INC; *U.S. Private*, pg. 1625
FUSION DATA CO., LTD.; *Int'l*, pg. 2849
FUTRIX LIMITED—See CVS Health Corporation; *U.S. Public*, pg. 614
GABIA INC.; *Int'l*, pg. 2867
GAD EG; *Int'l*, pg. 2868
GAMEWITH, INC.; *Int'l*, pg. 2878
GAZDUIRE WEB S.R.L—See Cyber_Folks S.A.; *Int'l*, pg. 1892
GCC SERVICING SYSTEMS, INC.—See Constellation Software Inc.; *Int'l*, pg. 1774
GD RESEARCH CENTRE PRIVATE LIMITED—See GlobalData Plc; *Int'l*, pg. 3003
GE ENERGY—See General Electric Company; *U.S. Public*, pg. 917
GENERALI INFORMATIQUE S.A.—See Assicurazioni Generali S.p.A.; *Int'l*, pg. 645
GENICAD, S.R.O.—See Xometry, Inc.; *U.S. Public*, pg. 2391
GEOMNI, INC.—See Verisk Analytics, Inc.; *U.S. Public*, pg. 2283
GEORGIA PUBLIC WEB—See OpenFiber Kentucky Co. LLC; *U.S. Private*, pg. 3030
GERMAN EDGE CLOUD GMBH & CO.KG—See Friedhelm Loh Stiftung & Co. KG; *Int'l*, pg. 2791
GET IMAGING, INC.—See MIDCON Data Services LLC; *U.S. Private*, pg. 2710
GIGAFLOPS JAPAN INC.—See CYBIRD Holdings Co., Ltd.; *Int'l*, pg. 1894
GIGAS HOSTING S.A; *Int'l*, pg. 2972
GITHUB, INC.—See Microsoft Corporation; *U.S. Public*, pg. 1439
GLACIER SERVICES, INC.—See Koniag Inc.; *U.S. Private*, pg. 2342
GLOBAL COMMERCE & INFORMATION, INC.; *U.S. Private*, pg. 1712
GLOBAL COMMUNICATION NETWORKS INC.; *U.S. Private*, pg. 1712
GLOBALDATA AUSTRALIA PTY LIMITED—See GlobalData Plc; *Int'l*, pg. 3003
GLOBAL FORMAT GMBH & CO. KG—See BayernLB Holding AG; *Int'l*, pg. 914
GLOBAL GEOPHYSICAL SERVICES, INC.; *U.S. Private*, pg. 1714
GLOBAL NETWATCH, INC.—See The Strawhecker Group, LLC; *U.S. Private*, pg. 4123
GLOBALSIGN K.K.—See GMO Internet Group, Inc.; *Int'l*, pg. 3014
GLOBALWAY, INC.; *Int'l*, pg. 3005
GMO BRAND SECURITY INC.—See GMO Internet Group, Inc.; *Int'l*, pg. 3013
GMO CREATORS NETWORK, INC.—See GMO Internet Group, Inc.; *Int'l*, pg. 3013
GMO OSHIETE AI, INC.—See GMO Internet Group, Inc.; *Int'l*, pg. 3014
GMO-Z.COM BRAND SECURITY VIETNAM CO., LTD.—See GMO Internet Group, Inc.; *Int'l*, pg. 3014
GMO-Z.COM RESEARCH PTE. LTD.—See GMO Internet Group, Inc.; *Int'l*, pg. 3014
GMO-Z.COM RESEARCH PVT. LTD.—See GMO Internet Group, Inc.; *Int'l*, pg. 3014
GMO Z COM RESEARCH SDN. BHD.—See GMO Internet Group, Inc.; *Int'l*, pg. 3014

518210 — DATA PROCESSING, HO...

GMO-Z.COM USA INC.—See GMO Internet Group, Inc.; *Int'l*, pg. 3014
GOCONNECT LIMITED; *Int'l*, pg. 3018
GODADDY.COM, LLC—See KKR & Co. Inc.; *U.S. Public*, pg. 1252
GODADDY.COM, LLC—See Silver Lake Group, LLC; *U.S. Private*, pg. 3657
GODADDY.COM, LLC—See TCMI, Inc.; *U.S. Private*, pg. 3943
GOOD GAMING, INC.—See CMG Holdings Group, Inc.; *U.S. Public*, pg. 518
GOOGLE-ATLANTA—See Alphabet Inc.; *U.S. Public*, pg. 83
GOOGLE AUSTRALIA PTY. LTD.—See Alphabet Inc.; *U.S. Public*, pg. 83
GOOGLE-BOSTON—See Alphabet Inc.; *U.S. Public*, pg. 83
GOOGLE-CANADA—See Alphabet Inc.; *U.S. Public*, pg. 83
GOOGLE-CHICAGO—See Alphabet Inc.; *U.S. Public*, pg. 83
GOOGLE-DETROIT—See Alphabet Inc.; *U.S. Public*, pg. 83
GOOGLE FRANCE SARL—See Alphabet Inc.; *U.S. Public*, pg. 83
GOOGLE GERMANY GMBH—See Alphabet Inc.; *U.S. Public*, pg. 83
GOOGLE-GREATER CHINA—See Alphabet Inc.; *U.S. Public*, pg. 83
GOOGLE INDIA PVT LTD—See Alphabet Inc.; *U.S. Public*, pg. 83
GOOGLE IRELAND LIMITED—See Alphabet Inc.; *U.S. Public*, pg. 83
GOOGLE ITALY S.R.L.—See Alphabet Inc.; *U.S. Public*, pg. 83
GOOGLE JAPAN INC.—See Alphabet Inc.; *U.S. Public*, pg. 83
GOOGLE NETHERLANDS B.V.—See Alphabet Inc.; *U.S. Public*, pg. 83
GOOGLE-NEW YORK—See Alphabet Inc.; *U.S. Public*, pg. 83
GOOGLE-SEATTLE—See Alphabet Inc.; *U.S. Public*, pg. 83
GOOGLE SPAIN, S.L.—See Alphabet Inc.; *U.S. Public*, pg. 83
GOOGLE UK LIMITED—See Alphabet Inc.; *U.S. Public*, pg. 83
GORILLA TECHNOLOGY GROUP INC.; *Int'l*, pg. 3043
GOSECURE INC.; *U.S. Private*, pg. 1744
GRAPHNET INC.; *U.S. Private*, pg. 1758
GREATER THAN AB; *Int'l*, pg. 3067
GREENGEEKS, LLC; *U.S. Private*, pg. 1778
GREETEAT CORPORATION; *U.S. Public*, pg. 965
GRESHAM COMPUTER SERVICES LIMITED—See Symphony Technology Group, LLC; *U.S. Private*, pg. 3900
GROUP Z, INC.; *U.S. Private*, pg. 1794
GSPANN TECHNOLOGIES, INC.; *U.S. Private*, pg. 1801
GUANGZHOU AUTOMATED SYSTEMS LIMITED—See Beijing Teamsun Technology Co., Ltd.; *Int'l*, pg. 958
GUANGZHOU DIGITAL RISE CO., LTD.—See Guangdong Rising Assets Management Co., Ltd.; *Int'l*, pg. 3159
GUARDIUM, INC.—See International Business Machines Corporation; *U.S. Public*, pg. 1145
GYANSYS INC.; *U.S. Private*, pg. 1821
H2O SYSTEM CO., LTD.—See H2O Retailing Corp.; *Int'l*, pg. 3200
HAIVISION NETWORK VIDEO GMBH—See HaiVision Systems, Inc.; *Int'l*, pg. 3218
HALLMARK DATA SYSTEMS, INC.—See Omeda Communications, Inc.; *U.S. Private*, pg. 3015
HAMILTON DATA SERVICES EOOD—See Iron Mountain Incorporated; *U.S. Public*, pg. 1172
HANDSHAKE NETWORKING CO., LTD.—See Guardforce AI Co., Limited; *Int'l*, pg. 3169
HANKYU BUSINESS ASSOCIATE CO., LTD.—See Hankyu Hanshin Holdings Inc.; *Int'l*, pg. 3255
HANSEN CORPORATION INVESTMENTS PTY LIMITED—See Hansen Technologies Limited; *Int'l*, pg. 3260
HANSEN TECHNOLOGIES CANADA, INC.—See Hansen Technologies Limited; *Int'l*, pg. 3260
HANSEN TECHNOLOGIES DENMARK A/S—See Hansen Technologies Limited; *Int'l*, pg. 3260
HANSEN TECHNOLOGIES NORWAY AS—See Hansen Technologies Limited; *Int'l*, pg. 3260
HANSEN TECHNOLOGIES SWEDEN AB—See Hansen Technologies Limited; *Int'l*, pg. 3260
HANSEN TECHNOLOGIES VIETNAM LLC—See Hansen Technologies Limited; *Int'l*, pg. 3260
HARMONIC FRANCE SAS—See Harmonic, Inc.; *U.S. Public*, pg. 985
HARTE-HANKS DATA TECHNOLOGIES, INC.—See Harte Hanks, Inc.; *U.S. Public*, pg. 986
HATCH INSIGHT KK—See Aflac Incorporated; *U.S. Public*, pg. 57
HATHWAY INC.—See Bounteous, Inc.; *U.S. Private*, pg. 624
HAWAII INFORMATION CONSORTIUM, LLC—See Tyler Technologies, Inc.; *U.S. Public*, pg. 2208
HAWKEYE SYSTEMS, INC.; *U.S. Public*, pg. 989
HAYSTAX TECHNOLOGY, INC.—See Edgewater Services, LLC; *U.S. Private*, pg. 1335
HBIS DIGITAL TECHNOLOGY CO., LTD.—See HBIS Group Co., Ltd.; *Int'l*, pg. 3296
HBIS GROUP FINANCIAL MANAGEMENT CLOUD TECHNOLOGY CO., LTD.—See HBIS Group Co., Ltd.; *Int'l*, pg. 3296
HDC DATA CENTRE LIMITED—See Henderson Land Development Co. Ltd.; *Int'l*, pg. 3344
H-D INTERNATIONAL HOLDINGS GROUP COMPANY; *U.S. Public*, pg. 976
HDI SOLUTIONS, INC.; *U.S. Private*, pg. 1890
HEALTH 2.0, LLC—See Healthcare Information & Management Systems Society; *U.S. Private*, pg. 1895
HEALTHAXIS GROUP, LLC; *U.S. Private*, pg. 1895
HEALTHCARE BILLING SYSTEMS LLC—See Varsity Management Company, LP; *U.S. Private*, pg. 4347
HEALTH INFORMATION DESIGNS, INC.—See HDI Solutions, Inc.; *U.S. Private*, pg. 1890
HEALTHJUMP, INC.; *U.S. Private*, pg. 1897
HEALTHLYNKED CORP.; *U.S. Public*, pg. 1016
HEALTH MANAGEMENT SYSTEMS, INC.—See Veritas Capital Fund Management, LLC; *U.S. Private*, pg. 4362
HEALTHPAC COMPUTER SYSTEMS, INC.; *U.S. Private*, pg. 1897
HEWLETT-PACKARD SERVICIOS ESPANA S.L—See Hewlett Packard Enterprise Company; *U.S. Public*, pg. 1032
HIGH STANDARDS TECHNOLOGY, INC.—See Vector Choice Technology Solutions, Corp.; *U.S. Private*, pg. 4353
HITACHI DATA SYSTEMS AS—See Hitachi, Ltd.; *Int'l*, pg. 3413
HITS, INC; *U.S. Private*, pg. 1953
HIVELOCITY VENTURES CORP.; *U.S. Private*, pg. 1953
HMVOD LTD.; *Int'l*, pg. 3433
HOKUDEN INFORMATION TECHNOLOGY—See Hokkaido Electric Power Co., Inc.; *Int'l*, pg. 3443
HOMEVALET, INC.; *U.S. Private*, pg. 1975
HOPIN LTD.—See Bending Spoons S.p.A.; *Int'l*, pg. 971
HOST EUROPE GMBH—See KKR & Co. Inc.; *U.S. Public*, pg. 1252
HOST EUROPE GMBH—See Silver Lake Group, LLC; *U.S. Private*, pg. 3657
HOST EUROPE GMBH—See TCMI, Inc.; *U.S. Private*, pg. 3943
HOSTGATOR.COM LLC—See Clearlake Capital Group, L.P.; *U.S. Private*, pg. 934
HOSTGATOR.COM LLC—See Siris Capital Group, LLC; *U.S. Private*, pg. 3673
HOSTING.COM, INC.; *U.S. Private*, pg. 1988
HOSTMYSITE.COM; *U.S. Private*, pg. 1988
HOSTOPIA.COM INC.—See Deluxe Corporation; *U.S. Public*, pg. 653
HOSTPAPA, INC.; *Int'l*, pg. 3487
HOSTWAY SERVICES, INC.—See Hosting.com, Inc.; *U.S. Private*, pg. 1988
HOTTO LINK INC.; *Int'l*, pg. 3489
HOYA SERVICE CORPORATION—See Hoya Corporation; *Int'l*, pg. 3494
HPI LIMITED—See Vista Equity Partners, LLC; *U.S. Private*, pg. 4400
HSBC BOOKING SECURITIES ASIA LTD.—See HSBC Holdings plc; *Int'l*, pg. 3506
HSBC ELECTRONIC DATA PROCESSING INDIA PRIVATE LIMITED—See HSBC Holdings plc; *Int'l*, pg. 3505
HSK PARTNERS; *Int'l*, pg. 3507
THE HUMAN GEO GROUP LLC—See Advent International Corporation; *U.S. Private*, pg. 104
HUMEDICA, INC.—See UnitedHealth Group Incorporated; *U.S. Public*, pg. 2241
HWT, INC.—See UnitedHealth Group Incorporated; *U.S. Public*, pg. 2248
I4DM; *U.S. Private*, pg. 2027
ICF CONSULTING GROUP, INC.—See ICF International, Inc.; *U.S. Public*, pg. 1086
ICOLO LIMITED—See Digital Realty Trust, Inc.; *U.S. Public*, pg. 663
ICOLO MOZAMBIQUE, LIMITADA—See Digital Realty Trust, Inc.; *U.S. Public*, pg. 663
ICONTROL NETWORKS, INC.; *U.S. Private*, pg. 2033
ID BUSINESS SOLUTIONS LTD.; *Int'l*, pg. 3587
IDENTITII LIMITED; *Int'l*, pg. 3592
IDENTIV GMBH—See Identiv, Inc.; *U.S. Public*, pg. 1089
IDENTIV KK—See Identiv, Inc.; *U.S. Public*, pg. 1089
IDOLOGY INC.—See GB Group plc; *Int'l*, pg. 2892
IFACTOR CONSULTING, INC.—See The Hearst Corporation; *U.S. Private*, pg. 4049
IGENII, INC.; *U.S. Private*, pg. 2039
IGN ENTERTAINMENT, INC.—See Ziff Davis, Inc.; *U.S. Private*, pg. 2404
IKANO COMMUNICATIONS, INC.; *U.S. Private*, pg. 2040
ILEARNINGENGINES HOLDINGS, INC.—See iLearningEngines, Inc.; *U.S. Private*, pg. 1101
ILLUMIS, INC.; *U.S. Private*, pg. 2043
IMAGE API INC.; *U.S. Private*, pg. 2044
IMAGE INTERGRATION SYSTEMS, INC.—See Clearlake Capital Group, L.P.; *U.S. Private*, pg. 936
IMAGE INTEGRATION SYSTEMS, INC.—See TA Associates, Inc.; *U.S. Private*, pg. 3916
IMAGENET, LLC; *U.S. Private*, pg. 2045
IMAGE SCAN HOLDINGS PLC; *Int'l*, pg. 3617
IMMOBILE PVT. LTD.—See Cisco Systems, Inc.; *U.S. Public*, pg. 499
IMPACT DATA SOLUTIONS LIMITED—See Hexatronic Group AB; *Int'l*, pg. 3371
IMPRESSU PRINT GROUP PTY. LTD.—See Domino's Pizza Enterprises Ltd.; *Int'l*, pg. 2162
IMPRIMA (DEUTSCHLAND) GMBH—See HAL Trust N.V.; *Int'l*, pg. 3224
IMPRIMA (FRANCE) SARL—See HAL Trust N.V.; *Int'l*, pg. 3224
IMPRIMA IROOMS LIMITED—See HAL Trust N.V.; *Int'l*, pg. 3224
IMPRIMA (NEDERLAND) B.V.—See HAL Trust N.V.; *Int'l*, pg. 3224
IM TAPE STORAGE OY—See Iron Mountain Incorporated; *U.S. Public*, pg. 1172
INC RESEARCH—See Elliott Management Corporation; *U.S. Private*, pg. 1365
INC RESEARCH—See Patient Square Capital, L.P.; *U.S. Private*, pg. 3108
INC RESEARCH—See Veritas Capital Fund Management, LLC; *U.S. Private*, pg. 4364
INDECON INC.; *U.S. Private*, pg. 2055
INFINITII AI—See Carl Data Solutions, Inc.; *Int'l*, pg. 1332
INFOFORT BAHRAIN CO.WLL—See Iron Mountain Incorporated; *U.S. Public*, pg. 1172
INFOFORT EGYPT S.A.E.—See Iron Mountain Incorporated; *U.S. Public*, pg. 1172
INFOFORT MUSCAT SPC—See Iron Mountain Incorporated; *U.S. Public*, pg. 1172
INFOMEDIA INC; *U.S. Private*, pg. 2072
INFORMATICA IRELAND LIMITED—See Canada Pension Plan Investment Board; *Int'l*, pg. 1280
INFORMATICA SOFTWARE LTD.—See Canada Pension Plan Investment Board; *Int'l*, pg. 1280
THE INFORMATION MANAGEMENT GROUP (NZ) LIMITED—See Freightways Group Limited; *Int'l*, pg. 2772
THE INFORMATION MANAGEMENT GROUP PTY LIMITED—See Freightways Group Limited; *Int'l*, pg. 2772
INFORMATION TRANSPORT SOLUTIONS, INC—See Uniti Group Inc.; *U.S. Public*, pg. 2253
INFURN (USA) LLC—See GI Ventures; *Int'l*, pg. 2960
INFUTOR DATA SOLUTIONS, INC.; *U.S. Private*, pg. 2075
INGRAM MICRO INDIA PRIVATE LIMITED—See Hainan Traffic Administration Holding Co., Ltd.; *Int'l*, pg. 3214
INITIATE SYSTEMS, INC.—See International Business Machines Corporation; *U.S. Public*, pg. 1148
INNODATA, INC.; *U.S. Public*, pg. 1125
INNOVATIVE INTEGRATION, INC.; *U.S. Private*, pg. 2082
INNOVE COMMUNICATIONS INC—See Globe Telecom, Inc.; *Int'l*, pg. 3006
INOC LLC—See GenNx360 Capital Partners, L.P.; *U.S. Private*, pg. 1672
INSIGHT HEALTH GMBH—See CompuGroup Medical SE & Co. KGaA; *Int'l*, pg. 1757
INSIGNIS, INC.—See Resurgens Technology Partners, LLC; *U.S. Private*, pg. 3411
INSPIRAFS, INC.—See ABRY Partners, LLC; *U.S. Private*, pg. 42
INSTEM INFORMATION SYSTEMS (SHANGHAI) LIMITED—See ArchiMed SAS; *Int'l*, pg. 548
INTEGRA BUSINESS CENTER INC.; *U.S. Private*, pg. 2097
INTELIUS, INC.; *U.S. Private*, pg. 2104
INTELLIDYN CORPORATION; *U.S. Private*, pg. 2105
INTELLISTANCE, LLC—See Verisk Analytics, Inc.; *U.S. Public*, pg. 2283
INTERGRID GROUP PTY. LTD.—See 5G Networks Limited; *Int'l*, pg. 13
INTERMEDIA.NET, INC.—See Madison Dearborn Partners, LLC; *U.S. Private*, pg. 2541
INTERNAP CONNECTIVITY LLC—See Internap Holding LLC; *U.S. Private*, pg. 2113
INTERNAP NETWORK SERVICES (AUSTRALIA) LTD.—See Internap Holding LLC; *U.S. Private*, pg. 2113
INTERNATIONAL BANK OF COMMERCE—See International Bancshares Corporation; *U.S. Public*, pg. 1145
INTERNATIONAL COLLEGE OF CAPOEIRA PTY. LIMITED—See Academies Australasia Group Limited; *Int'l*, pg. 77
INTERNET DISCLOSURE CO., LTD.—See Avant Corporation; *Int'l*, pg. 735
INTERNET NUMBER CORPORATION—See GMO Internet Group, Inc.; *Int'l*, pg. 3014
INTERPHASE SYSTEMS, INC.—See NewSpring Capital LLC; *U.S. Private*, pg. 2918
INTERSECTIONS INC.—See General Catalyst Partners; *U.S. Private*, pg. 1664
INTERSECTIONS INC.—See iSubscribed Inc.; *U.S. Private*, pg. 2147
INTERSECTIONS INC.—See WndrCo Holdings, LLC; *U.S. Private*, pg. 4552
INTERXION BELGIUM N.V.—See Digital Realty Trust, Inc.; *U.S. Public*, pg. 663
INTERXION DANMARK APS—See Digital Realty Trust, Inc.; *U.S. Public*, pg. 663
INTERXION DEUTSCHLAND GMBH—See Digital Realty Trust, Inc.; *U.S. Public*, pg. 663

N.A.I.C.S. INDEX — 518210 — DATA PROCESSING, HO...

INTERXION ESPANA SA—See Digital Realty Trust, Inc.; *U.S. Public*, pg. 663
INTERXION EUROPE LTD.—See Digital Realty Trust, Inc.; *U.S. Public*, pg. 663
INTERXION FRANCE SAS—See Digital Realty Trust, Inc.; *U.S. Public*, pg. 663
INTERXION IRELAND LTD.—See Digital Realty Trust, Inc.; *U.S. Public*, pg. 663
INTERXION N.V.—See Digital Realty Trust, Inc.; *U.S. Public*, pg. 663
INTERXION OSTERREICH GMBH—See Digital Realty Trust, Inc.; *U.S. Public*, pg. 663
INTERXION (SCHWEIZ) AG—See Digital Realty Trust, Inc.; *U.S. Public*, pg. 663
INTERXION SVERIGE AB—See Digital Realty Trust, Inc.; *U.S. Public*, pg. 663
INTRADO COMMUNICATIONS LLC—See Apollo Global Management, Inc.; *U.S. Public*, pg. 152
INTRALINKS ASIA PACIFIC PTE. LTD.—See SS&C Technologies Holdings, Inc.; *U.S. Public*, pg. 1923
INTRALINKS PTY LIMITED—See SS&C Technologies Holdings, Inc.; *U.S. Public*, pg. 1923
INTRALINKS SERVICOS DE INFORMATICA LTDA.—See SS&C Technologies Holdings, Inc.; *U.S. Public*, pg. 1923
INTRICITY, LLC—See KKR & Co. Inc.; *U.S. Public*, pg. 1261
INTRIDEA INC.; *U.S. Private*, pg. 2129
THE INTRUST GROUP, INC.; *U.S. Private*, pg. 4057
I-ON DIGITAL CORP.; *Int'l*, pg. 3563
ION INTERACTIVE, INC.; *U.S. Private*, pg. 2133
IPACESETTERS INDIA—See iPacesetters, LLC; *U.S. Private*, pg. 2136
IPACESETTERS, LLC; *U.S. Private*, pg. 2136
IPASS ASIA PTE LTD.—See Pareteum Corporation; *U.S. Public*, pg. 1637
IPASS DEUTSCHLAND GMBH—See Pareteum Corporation; *U.S. Public*, pg. 1637
IPASS, INC.—See Pareteum Corporation; *U.S. Public*, pg. 1637
IPASS INDIA PRIVATE LIMITED—See Pareteum Corporation; *U.S. Public*, pg. 1637
IPASS JAPAN K.K.—See Pareteum Corporation; *U.S. Public*, pg. 1637
IPASS UK LTD—See Pareteum Corporation; *U.S. Public*, pg. 1637
IPESA DE GUATEMALA—See Hewlett Packard Enterprise Company; *U.S. Public*, pg. 1032
IP-ONLY TELECOMMUNICATION AB—See EQT AB; *Int'l*, pg. 2475
IPOWERWEB INC.; *U.S. Private*, pg. 2137
IP PATHWAYS, LLC; *U.S. Private*, pg. 2136
IQVIA SOLUTIONS TAIWAN LTD.—See IQVIA Holdings Inc.; *U.S. Public*, pg. 1168
IRHYTHM TECHNOLOGIES, INC.; *U.S. Public*, pg. 1171
IRON MOUNTAIN BULGARIA—See Iron Mountain Incorporated; *U.S. Public*, pg. 1172
IRON MOUNTAIN CYPRUS LIMITED—See Iron Mountain Incorporated; *U.S. Public*, pg. 1172
IRON MOUNTAIN DATA MANAGEMENT (BEIJING) CO., LTD.—See Iron Mountain Incorporated; *U.S. Public*, pg. 1172
IRON MOUNTAIN FZ-LLC—See Iron Mountain Incorporated; *U.S. Public*, pg. 1173
IRON MOUNTAIN (IRELAND) SERVICES LIMITED—See Iron Mountain Incorporated; *U.S. Public*, pg. 1172
IRON MOUNTAIN PHILIPPINES INC.—See Iron Mountain Incorporated; *U.S. Public*, pg. 1173
IRON MOUNTAIN TAIWAN INC.—See Iron Mountain Incorporated; *U.S. Public*, pg. 1173
IRONNET, INC.; *U.S. Public*, pg. 1174
THE IRONSIDE GROUP, INC.; *U.S. Private*, pg. 4057
IRONSOURCE LTD.—See Unity Software Inc.; *U.S. Public*, pg. 2254
IS COSTA RICA, S.A.—See Hewlett Packard Enterprise Company; *U.S. Public*, pg. 1032
I SOLUTIONS INC.—See Emerson Electric Co.; *U.S. Public*, pg. 744
ISP (POLSKA) SP.Z O.O.—See Ashland Inc.; *U.S. Public*, pg. 212
ITELAGEN INC; *U.S. Private*, pg. 2149
IT-ERNITY INTERNET SERVICES BV—See Combell NV; *Int'l*, pg. 1708
IT-HANTVERKARNA SVERIGE AB—See Dustin Group AB; *Int'l*, pg. 2235
ITIVITI LIMITED—See Broadridge Financial Solutions, Inc.; *U.S. Public*, pg. 391
IT-NOVUM SCHWEIZ GMBH—See Allgeier SE; *Int'l*, pg. 337
IT WORKS INTERNET PTE. LTD.—See Dreamscape Networks Limited; *Int'l*, pg. 2203
IVILLAGE LLC—See Comcast Corporation; *U.S. Public*, pg. 540
IVISION SCALE, LLC; *U.S. Private*, pg. 2151
IWEB GROUP INC.—See Internap Holding LLC; *U.S. Private*, pg. 2114
IWEB TECHNOLOGIES INC.—See Internap Holding LLC; *U.S. Private*, pg. 2114
JACKRABBIT TECHNOLOGIES, INC.; *U.S. Private*, pg. 2175
J.A. THOMAS & ASSOCIATES, INC.—See Microsoft Corporation; *U.S. Public*, pg. 1442
JEPPESEN GMBH—See The Boeing Company; *U.S. Public*, pg. 2039
JOBON CORPORATION—See Corporate Press Inc.; *U.S. Private*, pg. 1055
JONES INTERACTIVE, INC.—See Jones International University; *U.S. Private*, pg. 2233
JS COMPUTEK LLC—See The 20 Msp Group LLC; *U.S. Private*, pg. 3980
JUNGLE DISK LLC—See Apollo Global Management, Inc.; *U.S. Public*, pg. 154
JUPITER EVENTS—See Mecklermedia Corporation; *U.S. Private*, pg. 2649
K2SHARE, LLC.; *U.S. Private*, pg. 2253
KEEN HEALTHCARE COMPANY; *U.S. Private*, pg. 2272
KEI.PL SP. Z O.O.—See Cyber_Folks S.A.; *Int'l*, pg. 1892
KELLEY CONNECT CO.; *U.S. Private*, pg. 2275
KEY PERFORMANCE IDEAS INC.—See Century Park Capital Partners, LLC; *U.S. Private*, pg. 833
KEYSTROKES TRANSCRIPTION SERVICE, INC.; *U.S. Private*, pg. 2300
KLIENTEC INTERNATIONAL SDN. BHD.—See Esthetics International Group Berhad; *Int'l*, pg. 2518
KLIK TECHNOLOGIES CORP.—See Checkalt, LLC; *U.S. Private*, pg. 869
KNOWLEDGE LINK INC.—See Axiologic Solutions, LLC; *U.S. Private*, pg. 413
KNOWNHOST LLC; *U.S. Private*, pg. 2324
KPHO BROADCASTING CORPORATION—See Meredith Corporation; *U.S. Public*, pg. 1423
KPS CONSULTING—See Bridgepoint Group Plc; *Int'l*, pg. 1154
KROLL ONTRACK, LLC—See Pivotal Acquisition Corp.; *U.S. Private*, pg. 3192
KROLL ONTRACK SARL—See Pivotal Acquisition Corp.; *U.S. Private*, pg. 3192
KRUEGER ASSOCIATES INC.; *U.S. Private*, pg. 2353
KX SYSTEMS, INC.—See FD Technologies PLC; *Int'l*, pg. 2628
L-3 COMMUNICATIONS TARGA SYSTEMS—See L3Harris Technologies, Inc.; *U.S. Public*, pg. 1283
LABELLE STRATEGIC RESOURCES, INC.—See Knowledge Anywhere, Inc.; *U.S. Private*, pg. 2323
LABYRINTH SOLUTIONS INC.—See BGF Group PLC; *Int'l*, pg. 1007
LAPEYRE SERVICES (LGS)—See Compagnie de Saint-Gobain SA; *Int'l*, pg. 1724
LATISYS-ASHBURN, LLC—See DigitalBridge Group, Inc.; *U.S. Public*, pg. 665
LATISYS-ASHBURN, LLC—See EQT AB; *Int'l*, pg. 2481
LATISYS-CHICAGO, LLC—See DigitalBridge Group, Inc.; *U.S. Public*, pg. 665
LATISYS-CHICAGO, LLC—See EQT AB; *Int'l*, pg. 2481
LB MEDIA GROUP, LLC—See Leafbuyer Technologies, Inc.; *U.S. Public*, pg. 1296
LCG, LLC—See Entravision Communications Corporation; *U.S. Public*, pg. 779
LEADSPACE, INC.; *U.S. Private*, pg. 2407
LEANNETWORKING KFT.—See adesso SE; *Int'l*, pg. 144
LEAPFORCE, INC.—See Appen Limited; *Int'l*, pg. 519
LENORD, BAUER & CO. GMBH—See Fukuda Corporation; *Int'l*, pg. 2839
LEVEL ONE LLC—See GI Manager L.P.; *U.S. Private*, pg. 1692
LEWTAN TECHNOLOGIES INC.—See Moody's Corporation; *U.S. Public*, pg. 1468
LIAONING BRINGSPRING FINANCIAL SERVICE CO., LTD—See Bringspring Science & Technology Co., Ltd.; *Int'l*, pg. 1164
LIBERATED SYNDICATION INC.; *U.S. Public*, pg. 1310
LIFFEY THAMES GROUP LLC—See Lightyear Capital LLC; *U.S. Private*, pg. 2454
LIGHTBEAM HEALTH SOLUTIONS LLC; *U.S. Private*, pg. 2452
LIGHTHOUSE TECHNOLOGIES HOLDINGS CORP.—See Lightyear Capital LLC; *U.S. Private*, pg. 2454
LIGHTSPEED TECHNOLOGIES, INC.—See Integra Business Center Inc.; *U.S. Private*, pg. 2098
LIVE CURRENT MEDIA INC.; *U.S. Public*, pg. 1327
LIVEDRIVE INTERNET LIMITED—See Ziff Davis, Inc.; *U.S. Public*, pg. 2403
LIVERAMP HOLDINGS, INC.; *U.S. Public*, pg. 1333
LIVEVOL, LLC—See Cboe Global Markets, Inc.; *U.S. Public*, pg. 459
LOGITECH ITALIA SRL—See Logitech International S.A.; *U.S. Public*, pg. 1341
LOKION INC.; *U.S. Private*, pg. 2482
LOOKSMART CANADA LTD—See LookSmart Group, Inc.; *U.S. Public*, pg. 1342
LOOM INC.—See Atlassian Corporation; *Int'l*, pg. 686
LUFTHANSA AIRPLUS SERVICEKARTEN GMBH—See Deutsche Lufthansa AG; *Int'l*, pg. 2068
LUFTHANSA SYSTEMS BERLIN GMBH—See Deutsche Lufthansa AG; *Int'l*, pg. 2069
LUNARLINE, INC.; *U.S. Private*, pg. 2515
LUNARPAGES INTERNET SOLUTIONS; *U.S. Private*, pg. 2515
M2B WORLD ASIA PACIFIC PTE. LTD.—See AMARU, INC.; *Int'l*, pg. 412
MAILING LIST SYSTEMS CORP.; *U.S. Private*, pg. 2551
MANAGEDSTORAGE INTERNATIONAL, INC.; *U.S. Private*, pg. 2559
MANAGEMENT APPLIED PROGRAMMING INC.; *U.S. Private*, pg. 2560
MARKER SEVEN, INC.; *U.S. Private*, pg. 2578
MARKETAXESS POST-TRADE B.V.—See MarketAxess Holdings Inc.; *U.S. Public*, pg. 1369
MARKETAXESS POST-TRADE LIMITED—See MarketAxess Holdings Inc.; *U.S. Public*, pg. 1369
MARS GLOBAL SERVICES—See Mars, Incorporated; *U.S. Private*, pg. 2589
MATRIX TRUST COMPANY—See Broadridge Financial Solutions, Inc.; *U.S. Public*, pg. 392
MBO PARTNERS; *U.S. Private*, pg. 2624
MDA HUB LIMITED—See Advent International Corporation; *U.S. Private*, pg. 103
MEDIANEWS GROUP INTERACTIVE, INC.—See Alden Global Capital LLC; *U.S. Private*, pg. 156
MEDIA RECOVERY, INC.—See Capital Southwest Corporation; *U.S. Public*, pg. 432
MEDIARING.COM (SHANGHAI) LIMITED—See Digilife Technologies Limited; *Int'l*, pg. 2119
MEDIASITE KK—See Enghouse Systems Limited; *Int'l*, pg. 2427
MEDIA TEMPLE, INC.—See KKR & Co. Inc.; *U.S. Public*, pg. 1252
MEDIA TEMPLE, INC.—See Silver Lake Group, LLC; *U.S. Private*, pg. 3657
MEDIA TEMPLE, INC.—See TCMI, Inc.; *U.S. Private*, pg. 3943
MEDICAL MARKETING SERVICE INC.; *U.S. Private*, pg. 2655
MEDICITY, INC.—See Health Catalyst, Inc.; *U.S. Public*, pg. 1014
MEDIQUANT, INC.; *U.S. Private*, pg. 2657
MEDPRICER.COM, INC.—See Premier, Inc.; *U.S. Public*, pg. 1715
MEED MEDIA FZ LLC—See GlobalData Plc; *Int'l*, pg. 3003
MENTORA GROUP, INC.—See CDW Corporation; *U.S. Public*, pg. 463
MERCK SHARP & DOHME (EUROPE) INC.—See Merck & Co., Inc.; *U.S. Public*, pg. 1419
MERRITT RESEARCH SERVICES LLC—See Investortools Inc.; *U.S. Private*, pg. 2132
MICROAD, INC.—See CyberAgent, Inc.; *Int'l*, pg. 1892
MICROSTRATEGY BENELUX B.V.—See MicroStrategy, Inc.; *U.S. Public*, pg. 1443
MICROSTRATEGY CANADA INC.—See MicroStrategy, Inc.; *U.S. Public*, pg. 1443
MICROSTRATEGY DEUTSCHLAND GMBH—See MicroStrategy, Inc.; *U.S. Public*, pg. 1443
MICROSTRATEGY FRANCE SARL—See MicroStrategy, Inc.; *U.S. Public*, pg. 1443
MICROSTRATEGY ITALY S.R.L.—See MicroStrategy, Inc.; *U.S. Public*, pg. 1443
MICROSTRATEGY KOREA CO., LTD.—See MicroStrategy, Inc.; *U.S. Public*, pg. 1443
MICROSTRATEGY PORTUGAL, LDA.—See MicroStrategy, Inc.; *U.S. Public*, pg. 1444
MICROSTRATEGY PTY. LTD.—See MicroStrategy, Inc.; *U.S. Public*, pg. 1444
MICROSTRATEGY SCHWEIZ AG—See MicroStrategy, Inc.; *U.S. Public*, pg. 1444
MICROSTRATEGY SINGAPORE PTE. LTD.—See MicroStrategy, Inc.; *U.S. Public*, pg. 1444
MICROSTRATEGY UK LIMITED—See MicroStrategy, Inc.; *U.S. Public*, pg. 1444
MID AMERICA COMPUTER CORP.—See Constellation Software Inc.; *Int'l*, pg. 1774
MIDCON DATA SERVICES LLC; *U.S. Private*, pg. 2710
MILLBROOK, INC.—See Guidewire Software, Inc.; *U.S. Public*, pg. 974
MINDBREEZE CORPORATION—See Fabasoft AG; *Int'l*, pg. 2598
MINDBREEZE GMBH—See Fabasoft AG; *Int'l*, pg. 2598
MISSION TUITION, INC.—See Cardiff Lexington Corporation; *U.S. Public*, pg. 433
MJ FREEWAY LLC—See Gryphon Digital Mining, Inc.; *U.S. Public*, pg. 973
MKS INSTRUMENTS AB—See MKS Instruments, Inc.; *U.S. Public*, pg. 1452
MLS DATA MANAGEMENT SOLUTIONS INC.—See Mailing List Systems Corp.; *U.S. Private*, pg. 2551
MOBILETRAC LLC—See OPENLANE, INC.; *U.S. Public*, pg. 1607
MODULAR TECHNOLOGY LLC—See Frontenac Company LLC; *U.S. Private*, pg. 1614
MOZILLA CORPORATION—See Mozilla Foundation; *U.S. Private*, pg. 2803
MUSE CORPORATION COMPANY LIMITED—See CMO Public Company Limited; *Int'l*, pg. 1671
MYHOME, A WILLISTON FINANCIAL GROUP COMPANY, LLC—See Williston Financial Group, LLC; *U.S. Private*, pg. 4528

518210 — DATA PROCESSING, HO...

MYSPACE, LLC—See Specific Media Inc.; *U.S. Private*, pg. 3751
NAMEJET, LLC—See Siris Capital Group, LLC; *U.S. Private*, pg. 3675
NATIONAL BUSINESS SYSTEMS, INC.—See Aquiline Capital Partners LLC; *U.S. Private*, pg. 305
NATIONAL INFORMATION SOLUTIONS COOPERATIVE (NISC); *U.S. Private*, pg. 2856
NAVBHARAT ARCHIVE XPRESS PRIVATE LIMITED—See Iron Mountain Incorporated; *U.S. Public*, pg. 1174
NAVINET, INC.—See NantWorks, LLC; *U.S. Private*, pg. 2834
NAVISITE EUROPE LIMITED—See Accenture plc; *Int'l*, pg. 87
NAVISITE INDIA PRIVATE LIMITED—See Accenture plc; *Int'l*, pg. 87
NAVISITE LLC—See Accenture plc; *Int'l*, pg. 87
NAVIS; *U.S. Private*, pg. 2873
NCR JAPAN, LTD.—See NCR Voyix Corporation.; *U.S. Public*, pg. 1503
NEOCLYDE SAS—See I Squared Capital Advisors (US) LLC; *U.S. Private*, pg. 2025
NETCLOUD (HONG KONG) TECHNOLOGY LIMITED—See Forgame Holdings Limited; *Int'l*, pg. 2733
NETFORTIS, INC.; *U.S. Private*, pg. 2887
NETGAIN TECHNOLOGIES INC.—See Alpine Investors; *U.S. Private*, pg. 201
NET LOGISTICS PTY LTD.—See Dreamscape Networks Limited; *Int'l*, pg. 2203
NETNAMES A/S—See HgCapital Trust plc; *Int'l*, pg. 3377
NETNAMES AS—See HgCapital Trust plc; *Int'l*, pg. 3377
NETNAMES INC.—See HgCapital Trust plc; *Int'l*, pg. 3377
NETSCOUT SYSTEMS (HK) LIMITED—See NetScout Systems, Inc.; *U.S. Public*, pg. 1509
NETSCOUT SYSTEMS INDIA PTE LTD—See NetScout Systems, Inc.; *U.S. Public*, pg. 1509
NETSCOUT SYSTEMS SINGAPORE PTE LTD.—See NetScout Systems, Inc.; *U.S. Public*, pg. 1509
NETSCOUT SYSTEMS (UK) LIMITED—See NetScout Systems, Inc.; *U.S. Public*, pg. 1509
NETSKOPE, INC.; *U.S. Private*, pg. 2888
NETWORK AND SIMULATION TECHNOLOGIES INCORPORATED—See Saalex Corp.; *U.S. Private*, pg. 3520
NETWORK SUPPORT COMPANY, LLC—See The Riverside Company; *U.S. Private*, pg. 4109
NEURO-ID, INC.—See Experian plc; *Int'l*, pg. 2588
NEW CHARTER TECHNOLOGIES, LLC—See Oval Partners; *U.S. Private*, pg. 3052
NEW CONTEXT SERVICES, INC.; *U.S. Private*, pg. 2893
NEWFOLD DIGITAL INC.—See Clearlake Capital Group, L.P.; *U.S. Public*, pg. 934
NEWFOLD DIGITAL INC.—See Siris Capital Group, LLC; *U.S. Private*, pg. 3673
NEW HOME TECHNOLOGIES, LLC—See Builder Homesite, Inc.; *U.S. Private*, pg. 681
NEW SIGNATURE CANADA INC.—See Cognizant Technology Solutions Corporation; *U.S. Public*, pg. 525
NEW SIGNATURE UK LIMITED—See Cognizant Technology Solutions Corporation; *U.S. Public*, pg. 525
NEXCESS.NET LLC; *U.S. Private*, pg. 2919
NEXTERA COMMUNICATIONS LLC—See Trive Capital Inc.; *U.S. Private*, pg. 4239
NEXTRIO, INC.; *U.S. Private*, pg. 2921
NGENX CORPORATION—See Windstream Holdings, Inc.; *U.S. Public*, pg. 2373
NIC SERVICES, LLC—See Tyler Technologies, Inc.; *U.S. Public*, pg. 2208
NIC SOLUTIONS, LLC—See Tyler Technologies, Inc.; *U.S. Public*, pg. 2208
NIELSEN SPORTS AMERICA, LLC.—See Brookfield Corporation; *Int'l*, pg. 1179
NIELSEN SPORTS AMERICA, LLC.—See Elliott Management Corporation; *U.S. Private*, pg. 1372
NIELSEN SPORTS DEUTSCHLAND GMBH—See Brookfield Corporation; *Int'l*, pg. 1179
NIELSEN SPORTS DEUTSCHLAND GMBH—See Elliott Management Corporation; *U.S. Private*, pg. 1372
NIELSEN SPORTS PTY. LTD.—See Brookfield Corporation; *Int'l*, pg. 1180
NIELSEN SPORTS PTY. LTD.—See Elliott Management Corporation; *U.S. Private*, pg. 1372
NIIT TECHNOLOGIES LIMITED—See Coforge Ltd.; *Int'l*, pg. 1693
NIMBIT, INC.—See PreSonus Audio Electronics, Inc.; *U.S. Private*, pg. 3255
NOBLE COMPUTER SERVICES (PVT) LIMITED—See House of Habib; *Int'l*, pg. 3491
NOMINALIA INTERNET S.L.—See HgCapital Trust plc; *Int'l*, pg. 3377
NOVACES, LLC; *U.S. Private*, pg. 2966
NOWSPOTS, INC.—See Marin Software Inc.; *U.S. Public*, pg. 1366
NOZONE, INC.; *U.S. Private*, pg. 2969
NTIVA, INC.—See Southfield Capital Advisors, LLC; *U.S. Private*, pg. 3736
NUCIVIC, INC.—See Actua Corporation; *U.S. Private*, pg. 71
NUNATAC S.R.L—See Alkemy SpA; *Int'l*, pg. 331

NUSPIRE CORP; *U.S. Private*, pg. 2974
NUTANIX, INC.; *U.S. Public*, pg. 1555
NUTANIX NETHERLANDS B. V.—See Nutanix, Inc.; *U.S. Public*, pg. 1555
NUTRINO HEALTH LTD.—See Brookfield Corporation; *Int'l*, pg. 1180
NUTRINO HEALTH LTD.—See Elliott Management Corporation; *U.S. Private*, pg. 1372
NXTKEY CORPORATION; *U.S. Private*, pg. 2976
OBJECTSTREAM, INC.; *U.S. Private*, pg. 2987
OFFICE REMEDIES, INC.; *U.S. Private*, pg. 3001
OJO LABS, INC.—See The Northwestern Mutual Life Insurance Company; *U.S. Private*, pg. 4085
OMNIPOTECH, LTD.; *U.S. Private*, pg. 3017
ON DEMAND ICARS, INC.; *U.S. Private*, pg. 3018
ONE COMMUNICATIONS, LLC—See ATN International, Inc.; *U.S. Public*, pg. 225
ONEDEV LLC—See The O'Neil Group Company, LLC; *U.S. Private*, pg. 4087
ONEPOINTCITY, LLC—See Fidelity National Financial, Inc.; *U.S. Public*, pg. 831
ONPLATINUM ICT PTY. LTD.—See Comms Group Ltd; *Int'l*, pg. 1720
ONRAMP ACCESS, LLC—See GI Manager L.P.; *U.S. Private*, pg. 1692
OOMBA, INC.; *U.S. Private*, pg. 3028
OPENDNS, INC.—See Cisco Systems, Inc.; *U.S. Public*, pg. 499
OPENPAY COLOMBIA SAS—See Banco Bilbao Vizcaya Argentaria, S.A.; *Int'l*, pg. 818
OPENPAY S.A. DE C.V.—See Banco Bilbao Vizcaya Argentaria, S.A.; *Int'l*, pg. 818
OPENWAY SAS—See Arrow Electronics, Inc.; *U.S. Public*, pg. 294
OPSCOMPASS, LLC; *U.S. Private*, pg. 3033
OPTICONX, INC.—See Belden, Inc.; *U.S. Public*, pg. 294
OPTIMAL BLUE, LLC—See Constellation Software Inc.; *Int'l*, pg. 1774
OPTISCAN, INC.; *U.S. Private*, pg. 3035
ORBIT BUSINESS TECHNOLOGIES—See Circle Computer Resources, Inc.; *U.S. Private*, pg. 899
ORBIT MEDIA STUDIOS, INC.; *U.S. Private*, pg. 3038
ORBOGRAPH LTD.—See KLA Corporation; *U.S. Public*, pg. 1268
ORCHESTRA SERVICE GMBH—See Avnet, Inc.; *U.S. Public*, pg. 253
OSG RECORDS MANAGEMENT CRYPTQ LLC—See Iron Mountain Incorporated; *U.S. Public*, pg. 1174
OSG RECORDS MANAGEMENT LLC—See Iron Mountain Incorporated; *U.S. Public*, pg. 1174
OSG RECORDS MANAGEMENT LLC—See Iron Mountain Incorporated; *U.S. Public*, pg. 1174
OSG RECORDS MANAGEMENT LLC—See Iron Mountain Incorporated; *U.S. Public*, pg. 1174
OSG RECORDS MANAGEMENT LLP—See Iron Mountain Incorporated; *U.S. Public*, pg. 1174
OSI, INC.; *U.S. Private*, pg. 3047
OVERLAND STORAGE GMBH—See Overland Storage, Inc.; *U.S. Private*, pg. 3053
OXYA CONSULTING BENELUX NV—See Hitachi, Ltd.; *Int'l*, pg. 3423
OXYA CORPORATION—See Hitachi, Ltd.; *Int'l*, pg. 3423
OXYA UK LIMITED—See Hitachi, Ltd.; *Int'l*, pg. 3423
OY IBM FINLAND AB—See International Business Machines Corporation; *U.S. Public*, pg. 1149
PAIR NETWORKS, INC.—See Liberated Syndication Inc.; *U.S. Public*, pg. 1310
PALM COAST DATA, LLC—See Irish Studio, LLC; *U.S. Private*, pg. 2138
PANW (PORTUGAL) UNIPESSOAL, LDA—See Palo Alto Networks, Inc.; *U.S. Public*, pg. 1635
PAPERLESS OFFICE SOLUTIONS, INC.—See New York Community Bancorp, Inc.; *U.S. Public*, pg. 1513
PAPERLESS TRANSACTION CORPORATION; *U.S. Private*, pg. 3088
PARAGON DEVELOPMENT SYSTEMS, INC.—See Converge Technology Solutions Corp.; *Int'l*, pg. 1787
PARAGON INTERNATIONAL, INC.; *U.S. Private*, pg. 3091
PAX8, INC.—See Arrow Electronics, Inc.; *U.S. Public*, pg. 199
PAXATA, INC.—See Right Side Capital Management, LLC; *U.S. Private*, pg. 3436
PAXIO INC.; *U.S. Private*, pg. 3115
PAYCE, INC.—See Deluxe Corporation; *U.S. Public*, pg. 653
PAYPAL, INC.—See PayPal Holdings, Inc.; *U.S. Public*, pg. 1656
PEAK 10, INC.—See GI Manager L.P.; *U.S. Private*, pg. 1692
PEAK METHODS, INC.; *U.S. Private*, pg. 3123
PEER 1 NETWORK (TORONTO) INC.—See DigitalBridge Group, Inc.; *U.S. Public*, pg. 664
PEGASUS SOLUTIONS COMPANIES—See Travel Tripper, LLC; *U.S. Private*, pg. 4213
PENNCOMP LLC; *U.S. Private*, pg. 3135
PERCEPTIVE INSTRUMENTS LIMITED—See ArchiMed SAS; *Int'l*, pg. 548
PERFORMANCE ENHANCEMENTS INC.—See Trinity Hunt Management, L.P.; *U.S. Private*, pg. 4234

PERSPECTA LLC; *U.S. Private*, pg. 3156
PHUNWARE, INC.; *U.S. Public*, pg. 1689
PHYTEL, INC.—See International Business Machines Corporation; *U.S. Public*, pg. 1148
PICSCOUT LTD.—See CC Capital Partners, LLC; *U.S. Private*, pg. 797
PIN BUSINESS NETWORK; *U.S. Private*, pg. 3181
PIPAL RESEARCH CORPORATION—See S&P Global Inc.; *U.S. Public*, pg. 1831
PIRELLI SISTEMI INFORMATIVI S.R.L.—See China National Chemical Corporation; *Int'l*, pg. 1528
PITNEY BOWES SOFTWARE K. K.—See Pitney Bowes Inc.; *U.S. Public*, pg. 1695
PIXELED BUSINESS SYSTEMS; *U.S. Private*, pg. 3192
PLANET DATA SOLUTIONS, INC.—See Veristar LLC; *U.S. Private*, pg. 4360
PLANETRISK, INC.; *U.S. Private*, pg. 3196
PLOTWATT, INC.—See American Efficient LLC; *U.S. Private*, pg. 231
PLURALSIGHT, LLC—See Pluralsight, Inc.; *U.S. Public*, pg. 1699
PODCASTONE, INC.—See LiveOne, Inc.; *U.S. Public*, pg. 1332
POLYCOM, INC. - BOSTON—See HP Inc.; *U.S. Public*, pg. 1065
POLYSYSTEMS INC.; *U.S. Private*, pg. 3226
POMCO, INC.—See UnitedHealth Group Incorporated; *U.S. Public*, pg. 2249
POSTMAIL AG—See Die Schweizerische Post AG; *Int'l*, pg. 2113
POWERTEK CORPORATION; *U.S. Private*, pg. 3240
PREDILYTICS, INC.—See Welltok, Inc.; *U.S. Private*, pg. 4478
PRICEGRABBER.COM INC.—See Symphony Technology Group, LLC; *U.S. Private*, pg. 3900
PRISM INTEGRATED SDN. BHD.—See Iron Mountain Incorporated; *U.S. Public*, pg. 1174
PROEMION HOLDING GMBH—See Battery Ventures, L.P.; *U.S. Private*, pg. 489
PROFESSIONAL DATA DIMENSIONS; *U.S. Private*, pg. 3275
PROGRESSIVE COMPUTER SYSTEMS, INC.—See Alpine Investors; *U.S. Private*, pg. 201
PROHEALTH CARE, INC.; *U.S. Private*, pg. 3280
PT. TDATA INDONESIA—See Teradata Corporation; *U.S. Public*, pg. 2016
PUBCO REPORTING SERVICES, INC.—See ProBility Media Corporation; *U.S. Public*, pg. 1723
PUBLICATION FULFILLMENT SERVICES, INC.; *U.S. Private*, pg. 3300
PULSANT (SCOTLAND) LIMITED—See Keystone Group, L.P.; *U.S. Private*, pg. 2299
PUNKTUM DK A/S—See Arbejdsmarkedets Tillaegspension; *Int'l*, pg. 537
PURITY IT AS—See Dustin Group AB; *Int'l*, pg. 2235
QLIKTECH INTERNATIONAL LTD.—See Hilan Ltd.; *Int'l*, pg. 3390
QNTM GROUP AB—See Altor Equity Partners AB; *Int'l*, pg. 395
QQ SOLUTIONS, INC.—See Roper Technologies, Inc.; *U.S. Public*, pg. 1814
QUALITEST GROUP UK LTD.—See Bridgepoint Group Plc; *Int'l*, pg. 1154
QUALITY EXPERIENCE DESIGN CO., LTD.—See Arisawa Manufacturing Co., Ltd.; *Int'l*, pg. 566
QVINE LLC—See Godspeed Capital Management LP; *U.S. Private*, pg. 1725
RACKSPACE HOSTING, INC.—See Apollo Global Management, Inc.; *U.S. Public*, pg. 154
RACKSPACE LTD.—See Apollo Global Management, Inc.; *U.S. Public*, pg. 154
RACO INDUSTRIES, INC.; *U.S. Private*, pg. 3342
RADIANT MISSION SOLUTIONS INC.—See Advent International Corporation; *U.S. Private*, pg. 103
RALLY POINT MANAGEMENT, LLC; *U.S. Private*, pg. 3350
RAPIDLD; *U.S. Private*, pg. 3356
RAPID SYSTEMS LTD.—See Arjun Infrastructure Partners Limited; *Int'l*, pg. 568
REALVIEW TV, LLC—See ITC Holding Company, LLC; *U.S. Private*, pg. 2149
RED BOOK AUTOMOTIVE DATA SERVICES (BEIJING) LIMITED—See carsales.com Limited; *Int'l*, pg. 1347
RED BOOK AUTOMOTIVE SERVICES (M) SDN. BHD.—See carsales.com Limited; *Int'l*, pg. 1347
RED CLAY INTERACTIVE; *U.S. Private*, pg. 3373
RED RIVER TECHNOLOGY LLC—See Cerberus Capital Management, L.P.; *U.S. Private*, pg. 839
REDTAIL SOLUTIONS INC—See Accellos, Inc.; *U.S. Private*, pg. 50
REIMBURSEMENT SERVICES GROUP, INC.—See Veritas Capital Fund Management, LLC; *U.S. Private*, pg. 4362
RENEW DATA CORP.; *U.S. Private*, pg. 3398
REQUISIGHT, LLC—See Morningstar, Inc.; *U.S. Public*, pg. 1477
RESOURCIS INFORMATION SERVICES, INC.; *U.S. Private*, pg. 3407
RETAIL DATA, LLC—See Markel Group Inc.; *U.S. Public*, pg. 1369

518210 — DATA PROCESSING, HO...

THE RETAIL EQUATION INC.—See Appriss Holdings, Inc.; *U.S. Private*, pg. 300
RETAIL MEETUP, LLC—See Providence Equity Partners L.L.C.; *U.S. Private*, pg. 3293
RETAIL MEETUP, LLC—See Searchlight Capital Partners, L.P.; *U.S. Private*, pg. 3588
RETRONIX GLOBAL INC.—See Jabil Inc.; *U.S. Public*, pg. 1182
RETRONIX LTD.—See Jabil Inc.; *U.S. Public*, pg. 1182
THE REYNOLDS & REYNOLDS COMPANY; *U.S. Private*, pg. 4106
RHIPE MALAYSIA SDN. BHD.—See Crayon Group Holding ASA; *Int'l*, pg. 1830
RHIPE NEW ZEALAND LTD.—See Crayon Group Holding ASA; *Int'l*, pg. 1830
RHIPE PHILIPPINES, INC.—See Crayon Group Holding ASA; *Int'l*, pg. 1830
RHIPE SINGAPORE PTE. LTD.—See Crayon Group Holding ASA; *Int'l*, pg. 1830
RIGHTSIDE GROUP, LTD.—See Ethos Capital, LLC; *U.S. Private*, pg. 1432
RIO SEO, INC.—See Ares Management Corporation; *U.S. Public*, pg. 190
RIO SEO, INC.—See Leonard Green & Partners, L.P.; *U.S. Private*, pg. 2427
RISER ID SERVICES GMBH—See Deutsche Post AG; *Int'l*, pg. 2082
RISING MEDICAL SOLUTIONS, LLC; *U.S. Private*, pg. 3440
RISKONNECT, INC.—See TA Associates, Inc.; *U.S. Private*, pg. 3918
RIVERBED TECHNOLOGY AB—See Vector Capital Management, L.P.; *U.S. Private*, pg. 4352
RIVERBED TECHNOLOGY AG—See Vector Capital Management, L.P.; *U.S. Private*, pg. 4352
RIVERBED TECHNOLOGY (BEIJING) LIMITED—See Vector Capital Management, L.P.; *U.S. Private*, pg. 4352
RIVERBED TECHNOLOGY INDIA PRIVATE LIMITED—See Vector Capital Management, L.P.; *U.S. Private*, pg. 4352
RIVERBED TECHNOLOGY KOREA, INC.—See Vector Capital Management, L.P.; *U.S. Private*, pg. 4352
RIVERBED TECHNOLOGY LIMITED—See Vector Capital Management, L.P.; *U.S. Private*, pg. 4352
RIVERBED TECHNOLOGY LTD.—See Vector Capital Management, L.P.; *U.S. Private*, pg. 4352
RIVERBED TECHNOLOGY PHILIPPINES—See Vector Capital Management, L.P.; *U.S. Private*, pg. 4352
RIVERBED TECHNOLOGY PTY LTD.—See Vector Capital Management, L.P.; *U.S. Private*, pg. 4352
RIVERBED TECHNOLOGY SDN. BHD.—See Vector Capital Management, L.P.; *U.S. Private*, pg. 4352
RIVERBED TECHNOLOGY SHANGHAI—See Vector Capital Management, L.P.; *U.S. Private*, pg. 4352
RIVERBED TECHNOLOGY SL—See Vector Capital Management, L.P.; *U.S. Private*, pg. 4352
RIVERBED TECHNOLOGY SOUTH AFRICA (PROPRIETARY) LIMITED—See Vector Capital Management, L.P.; *U.S. Private*, pg. 4352
RIVERBED TECHNOLOGY TAIWAN—See Vector Capital Management, L.P.; *U.S. Private*, pg. 4352
RJM SYSTEMS INC.—See Jenzabar, Inc.; *U.S. Private*, pg. 2201
RUBICON PROFESSIONAL SERVICES; *U.S. Private*, pg. 3499
RUBICON TECHNOLOGIES HOLDINGS, LLC—See Rubicon Technologies, Inc.; *U.S. Public*, pg. 1825
RUBICON TECHNOLOGIES, INC.; *U.S. Public*, pg. 1825
RUBIXIS INC.—See TransUnion; *U.S. Public*, pg. 2184
RURAL SOURCING, INC.—See Bain Capital, LP; *U.S. Private*, pg. 431
RURBANC DATA SERVICES, INC.—See SB Financial Group, Inc.; *U.S. Public*, pg. 1842
RVM INC.; *U.S. Private*, pg. 3508
SABLE37 DMCC—See DXC Technology Company; *U.S. Public*, pg. 696
SAFE SYSTEMS, INC.; *U.S. Private*, pg. 3524
SALARY.COM, LLC—See Accel Partners L.P.; *U.S. Private*, pg. 48
SALARY.COM, LLC—See KKR & Co. Inc.; *U.S. Public*, pg. 1238
SALESFORCE.ORG EMEA LIMITED—See Salesforce, Inc.; *U.S. Public*, pg. 1838
SALESFORCE TECHNOLOGIES MOROCCO—See Salesforce, Inc.; *U.S. Public*, pg. 1837
SALESFORCE UK LIMITED—See Salesforce, Inc.; *U.S. Public*, pg. 1837
SALESGENIE.COM, INC.—See CCMP Capital Advisors, LP; *U.S. Private*, pg. 800
SANDATA TECHNOLOGIES, LLC.—See Sandata Holdings, Inc.; *U.S. Private*, pg. 3543
SAN DIEGO DATA PROCESSING CORPORATION; *U.S. Private*, pg. 3539
SANWIRE CORP.; *U.S. Private*, pg. 3548
SATURN CORPORATION; *U.S. Private*, pg. 3553
SAVEDAILY.COM, INC.—See SaveDaily, Inc.; *U.S. Private*, pg. 3556
SAWTST, LLC; *U.S. Private*, pg. 3558

SCAN-OPTICS, LTD.—See Patriarch Partners, LLC; *U.S. Private*, pg. 3109
SCORE MEDIA AND GAMING INC.—See PENN Entertainment, Inc.; *U.S. Public*, pg. 1662
SEARCH TECHNOLOGIES, LLC—See Accenture plc; *Int'l*, pg. 88
SECURE DESIGNS, INC.; *U.S. Private*, pg. 3593
SELL POINTS INC.—See Summit Partners, L.P.; *U.S. Private*, pg. 3856
SELL POINTS INC.—See The Jordan Company, L.P.; *U.S. Private*, pg. 4062
SEMAFOR, INC.; *U.S. Private*, pg. 3603
SENAO NETWORKS, INC.—See Chunghwa Telecom Co., Ltd.; *Int'l*, pg. 1598
SENET INTERNATIONAL CORPORATION—See Gaming Laboratories International LLC; *U.S. Private*, pg. 1640
SERENOVA, LLC—See Marlin Equity Partners, LLC; *U.S. Private*, pg. 2585
SERMO, INC.—See WorldOne, Inc.; *U.S. Private*, pg. 4569
SERVERBEACH—See DigitalBridge Group, Inc.; *U.S. Public*, pg. 664
SERVICEMAX GLOBAL LTD.—See PTC Inc.; *U.S. Public*, pg. 1735
SERVICEMAX TECHNOLOGIES (INDIA) PRIVATE LIMITED—See PTC Inc.; *U.S. Public*, pg. 1735
SGT SOLUTIONS PROPRIETARY LIMITED—See AYO Technology Solutions Ltd.; *Int'l*, pg. 775
SGT SOLUTIONS PROPRIETARY LIMITED—See AYO Technology Solutions Ltd.; *Int'l*, pg. 775
SGT SOLUTIONS PROPRIETARY LIMITED—See AYO Technology Solutions Ltd.; *Int'l*, pg. 775
SGT SOLUTIONS PROPRIETARY LIMITED—See AYO Technology Solutions Ltd.; *Int'l*, pg. 775
SHAREDLABS, INC.; *U.S. Private*, pg. 3626
SHARE INVESTING LIMITED—See Australia & New Zealand Banking Group Limited; *Int'l*, pg. 720
SHAZAM, INC.; *U.S. Private*, pg. 3628
SHOW MEDIA; *U.S. Private*, pg. 3643
SIMCORP NORGE AS—See Deutsche Borse AG; *Int'l*, pg. 2064
SIMEIO SOLUTIONS, LLC—See ZelnickMedia Corp.; *U.S. Private*, pg. 4600
SIX DEGREES TECHNOLOGY GROUP LTD.—See Charlesbank Capital Partners, LLC; *U.S. Private*, pg. 856
SKC GROUP LIMITED—See ANTA Sports Products Limited; *Int'l*, pg. 481
SKIENCE LLC—See Berenson & Company, Inc.; *U.S. Private*, pg. 530
SKIENCE LLC—See Sagewind Capital LLC; *U.S. Private*, pg. 3528
SKYERA, INC.—See Western Digital Corporation; *U.S. Public*, pg. 2355
SLACKER, INC.—See LiveOne, Inc.; *U.S. Public*, pg. 1332
SMARTPROCURE, INC.—See Endicott Group Equity Partners, L.P.; *U.S. Private*, pg. 1391
SMARTPROCURE, INC.—See Thompson Street Capital Manager LLC; *U.S. Private*, pg. 4161
S M RESOURCES CORPORATION; *U.S. Private*, pg. 3512
SOAPBOXSAMPLE—See Interviewing Service of America; *U.S. Private*, pg. 2128
SOCIALPLAY USA, INC.; *U.S. Public*, pg. 1899
SOFTLAYER TECHNOLOGIES ASIA—See International Business Machines Corporation; *U.S. Public*, pg. 1150
SOFTLAYER TECHNOLOGIES EUROPE—See International Business Machines Corporation; *U.S. Public*, pg. 1150
SOFTLAYER TECHNOLOGIES, INC.—See International Business Machines Corporation; *U.S. Public*, pg. 1150
SOGETI USA LLC—See Capgemini SE; *Int'l*, pg. 1307
SOGETI USA LLC—See Capgemini SE; *Int'l*, pg. 1307
SOMOS, INC.; *U.S. Private*, pg. 3712
SONIC FOUNDRY INTERNATIONAL B.V.—See Enghouse Systems Limited; *Int'l*, pg. 2427
SOURCEFIRE, INC.—See Cisco Systems, Inc.; *U.S. Public*, pg. 500
SOUTHDATA, INC.; *U.S. Private*, pg. 3724
SOUTHRIDGE TECHNOLOGY GRP, LLC.; *U.S. Private*, pg. 3737
SPADE TECHNOLOGY INC.—See IT Solutions Consulting LLC; *U.S. Private*, pg. 2148
SPATIALAGE SOLUTIONS DIVISION—See Byers Engineering Company; *U.S. Private*, pg. 700
SPATIAL NETWORKS, INC.; *U.S. Private*, pg. 3747
SPC ITALIA SRL—See BT Group plc; *Int'l*, pg. 1203
SP DATASERVE, LTD.—See Iberdrola, S.A.; *Int'l*, pg. 3573
S&P GLOBAL MARKET INTELLIGENCE INC.—See S&P Global Inc.; *U.S. Public*, pg. 1831
SPIN SYSTEMS INC.—See Dine Development Corporation; *U.S. Private*, pg. 1233
SPIREMEDIA, INC.—See BC Partners LLP; *Int'l*, pg. 925
SPRINGPATH LLC—See Cisco Systems, Inc.; *U.S. Public*, pg. 500
STACKMOB, LLC—See eBay Inc.; *U.S. Public*, pg. 709
STARHOME MACH—See Vista Equity Partners, LLC; *U.S. Private*, pg. 4402
STARK SERVICES; *U.S. Private*, pg. 3787
STARTEL CORPORATION; *U.S. Private*, pg. 3788

STATES TITLE, INC.—See Doma Holdings, Inc.; *U.S. Public*, pg. 673
ST. CROIX SOLUTIONS, INC.—See Pinnacle Business Systems, Inc.; *U.S. Private*, pg. 3184
STEPSTONE DEUTSCHLAND GMBH—See Axel Springer SE; *Int'l*, pg. 767
STEPSTONE NV—See Axel Springer SE; *Int'l*, pg. 767
STORE FINANCIAL SERVICES, LLC—See EML Payments Limited; *Int'l*, pg. 2384
STRATEGIC DATA MANAGEMENT PTY LTD—See DWS Limited; *Int'l*, pg. 2236
STRATEGIC INTERNET MARKETING PARTNERS, INC.—See Reputation.com, Inc.; *U.S. Private*, pg. 3403
STREETINSIDER.COM, INC.—See Fusion Media Ltd.; *Int'l*, pg. 2849
SUNGARD AVAILABILITY SERVICES MISSISSAUGA—See SunGard Availability Services Capital, Inc.; *U.S. Private*, pg. 3867
SUPERIOR STORAGE LIMITED—See Iron Mountain Incorporated; *U.S. Public*, pg. 1174
SUPPORT.COM INDIA PVT LTD—See RealDefense LLC; *U.S. Private*, pg. 3368
SWIFTEL COMMUNICATIONS INC.; *U.S. Private*, pg. 3893
SWIFTSTACK, INC.—See NVIDIA Corporation; *U.S. Public*, pg. 1558
SWIFT SYSTEMS, INC.—See Tonka Bay Equity Partners LLC; *U.S. Private*, pg. 4185
SWISS POST INTERNATIONAL MANAGEMENT AG—See Die Schweizerische Post AG; *Int'l*, pg. 2113
SWISS POST SOLUTIONS AG—See Die Schweizerische Post AG; *Int'l*, pg. 2113
SWISS POST SOLUTIONS GMBH, PRIEN—See Die Schweizerische Post AG; *Int'l*, pg. 2113
SWISS POST SOLUTIONS GMBH, PULSNITZ—See Die Schweizerische Post AG; *Int'l*, pg. 2113
SWISS POST SOLUTIONS GMBH—See Die Schweizerische Post AG; *Int'l*, pg. 2113
SWISS POST SOLUTIONS GMBH—See Die Schweizerische Post AG; *Int'l*, pg. 2113
SWISS POST SOLUTIONS INC.—See Die Schweizerische Post AG; *Int'l*, pg. 2113
SWISS POST SOLUTIONS LTD—See Die Schweizerische Post AG; *Int'l*, pg. 2113
SWISS POST SOLUTIONS SAS—See Die Schweizerische Post AG; *Int'l*, pg. 2113
SWISS POST SOLUTIONS SINGAPORE—See Die Schweizerische Post AG; *Int'l*, pg. 2113
SWISS POST SOLUTIONS S.P.A.—See Die Schweizerische Post AG; *Int'l*, pg. 2113
SWISS POST SOLUTIONS S.R.O—See Die Schweizerische Post AG; *Int'l*, pg. 2113
SYLINT GROUP INC.; *U.S. Private*, pg. 3898
SYMPHONY PERFORMANCE HEALTH, INC.—See Ares Management Corporation; *U.S. Public*, pg. 190
SYMPHONY PERFORMANCE HEALTH, INC.—See Leonard Green & Partners, L.P.; *U.S. Private*, pg. 2427
SYNCHRONOSS TECHNOLOGIES, INC.; *U.S. Public*, pg. 1969
SYNTEL DEUTSCHLAND GMBH—See Atos SE; *Int'l*, pg. 692
SYSTEM1, INC.; *U.S. Public*, pg. 1977
SYSTEM BEE D.O.O—See DHH SpA; *Int'l*, pg. 2099
SYSTEMS AND METHODS INC.; *U.S. Private*, pg. 3907
TAG ONE, INC.—See AE Industrial Partners, LP; *U.S. Private*, pg. 111
TAIWAN AUTOMATED SYSTEMS LTD.—See Beijing Teamsun Technology Co., Ltd.; *Int'l*, pg. 958
TANXIA SYSTEM, INC.; *U.S. Public*, pg. 1981
TASQ TECHNOLOGY, INC.—See Fiserv, Inc.; *U.S. Public*, pg. 851
TATS - TRAVEL AGENCY TECHNOLOGIES & SERVICES GMBH—See Deutsche Lufthansa AG; *Int'l*, pg. 2070
TCOOMBS & ASSOCIATES LLC; *U.S. Private*, pg. 3943
TDATA CORPORATION (MALAYSIA) SDN. BHD.—See Teradata Corporation; *U.S. Public*, pg. 2016
TDC COLOMBIA LIMITADA—See Teradata Corporation; *U.S. Public*, pg. 2016
TEAM COMPANIES; *U.S. Private*, pg. 3949
TEAMULTRA LIMITED—See Computacenter plc; *Int'l*, pg. 1758
TECHLINK, INC.—See Great Mill Rock LLC; *U.S. Private*, pg. 1766
TECHNATOMY CORPORATION; *U.S. Private*, pg. 3953
TECHNO5, INC.—See ManpowerGroup Inc.; *U.S. Public*, pg. 1362
TECHNOLOGUE—See The Hearst Corporation; *U.S. Private*, pg. 4045
TECHTARGET LIMITED—See TechTarget, Inc.; *U.S. Public*, pg. 1989
TELEBEEP WIRELESS—See JAB Wireless, Inc.; *U.S. Private*, pg. 2274
TELESTO GROUP LLC; *U.S. Private*, pg. 3962
TELLUS, LLC—See TA Associates, Inc.; *U.S. Private*, pg. 3917
TERADATA AUSTRALIA PTY. LTD.—See Teradata Corporation; *U.S. Public*, pg. 2016
TERADATA AUSTRIA GMBH—See Teradata Corporation; *U.S. Public*, pg. 2017

518210 — DATA PROCESSING, HO...

TERADATA BELGIUM SNC—See Teradata Corporation; *U.S. Public*, pg. 2017
TERADATA BILISIM SISTEMLERI LTD. STI.—See Teradata Corporation; *U.S. Public*, pg. 2017
TERADATA CANADA ULC—See Teradata Corporation; *U.S. Public*, pg. 2017
TERADATA CHILE TECNOLOGIAS DE INFORMACION LIMITADA—See Teradata Corporation; *U.S. Public*, pg. 2017
TERADATA CZECH REPUBLIC, SPOL. S R.O.—See Teradata Corporation; *U.S. Public*, pg. 2017
TERADATA DANMARK APS—See Teradata Corporation; *U.S. Public*, pg. 2017
TERADATA DE ARGENTINA S.R.L.—See Teradata Corporation; *U.S. Public*, pg. 2017
TERADATA DE MEXICO, S. DE R.L. DE C.V.—See Teradata Corporation; *U.S. Public*, pg. 2017
TERADATA FINLAND OY—See Teradata Corporation; *U.S. Public*, pg. 2017
TERADATA FRANCE SAS—See Teradata Corporation; *U.S. Public*, pg. 2017
TERADATA GMBH—See Teradata Corporation; *U.S. Public*, pg. 2017
TERADATA IBERIA SLU—See Teradata Corporation; *U.S. Public*, pg. 2017
TERADATA INDIA PRIVATE LIMITED—See Teradata Corporation; *U.S. Public*, pg. 2017
TERADATA INFORMATION SYSTEMS (BEIJING) LIMITED—See Teradata Corporation; *U.S. Public*, pg. 2017
TERADATA IRELAND LIMITED—See Teradata Corporation; *U.S. Public*, pg. 2017
TERADATA ITALIA S.R.L.—See Teradata Corporation; *U.S. Public*, pg. 2017
TERADATA JAPAN LTD.—See Teradata Corporation; *U.S. Public*, pg. 2017
TERADATA MAGYARORSZAG KFT—See Teradata Corporation; *U.S. Public*, pg. 2017
TERADATA NETHERLANDS B.V.—See Teradata Corporation; *U.S. Public*, pg. 2017
TERADATA NORGE AS—See Teradata Corporation; *U.S. Public*, pg. 2017
TERADATA (NZ) CORPORATION—See Teradata Corporation; *U.S. Public*, pg. 2016
TERADATA PAKISTAN LIMITED—See Teradata Corporation; *U.S. Public*, pg. 2017
TERADATA PHILIPPINES LLC, MANILA BRANCH—See Teradata Corporation; *U.S. Public*, pg. 2017
TERADATA POLSKA SP. Z O.O—See Teradata Corporation; *U.S. Public*, pg. 2017
TERADATA SCHWEIZ GMBH—See Teradata Corporation; *U.S. Public*, pg. 2017
TERADATA (SINGAPORE) PTE. LTD.—See Teradata Corporation; *U.S. Public*, pg. 2016
TERADATA SWEDEN AB—See Teradata Corporation; *U.S. Public*, pg. 2017
TERADATA (THAILAND) CO LTD—See Teradata Corporation; *U.S. Public*, pg. 2016
TERADATA UK LIMITED—See Teradata Corporation; *U.S. Public*, pg. 2017
TERAWAREHOUSE KOREA CO., LTD.—See Teradata Corporation; *U.S. Public*, pg. 2016
TIERPOINT, LLC—See Cequel III, LLC; *U.S. Private*, pg. 835
TIERPOINT, LLC—See Charterhouse Group, Inc.; *U.S. Private*, pg. 859
TIERPOINT, LLC—See Thompson Street Capital Manager LLC; *U.S. Private*, pg. 4160
TOSHO COMPUTER SYSTEMS CO., LTD.—See FUJISOFT INCORPORATED; *Int'l*, pg. 2830
TOTALJOBS GROUP LIMITED—See Axel Springer SE; *Int'l*, pg. 767
TOTAL SPORTS MEDIA, INC.; *U.S. Private*, pg. 4191
TOTAL SYSTEM SERVICES HOLDING EUROPE LP—See Global Payments Inc.; *U.S. Public*, pg. 944
TOTAL SYSTEM SERVICES PROCESSING EUROPE LIMITED—See Global Payments Inc.; *U.S. Public*, pg. 945
TOTAL SYSTEM SERVICES SALES EUROPE LIMITED—See Global Payments Inc.; *U.S. Public*, pg. 945
TOUCHCORP LIMITED—See Block, Inc.; *U.S. Public*, pg. 361
TOUCH NETWORKS PTY. LTD.—See Block, Inc.; *U.S. Public*, pg. 362
TQUILA AUTOMATION, INC.—See Delta-v Capital, LLC; *U.S. Private*, pg. 1202
TRADE ME GROUP LIMITED—See Apax Partners LLP; *Int'l*, pg. 507
TRADEMOTION, LLC—See The Reynolds & Reynolds Company; *U.S. Private*, pg. 4106
TRAITAL S.R.L.—See BKW AG; *Int'l*, pg. 1056
TRANGLO SDN. BHD.—See Currenc Group Inc.; *U.S. Public*, pg. 611
TRANSCENDENT ONE, INC.—See AppTech; *U.S. Private*, pg. 300
TRANSCENTRA, INC.—See Gainline Capital Partners LP; *U.S. Private*, pg. 1635
TRANSIP GROUP BV—See Combell NV; *Int'l*, pg. 1708

TRANSPO SERVICE LTD. INC.—See Centre Limited Inc.; *U.S. Private*, pg. 828
TRDT BRASIL TECNOLOGIA LTDA.—See Teradata Corporation; *U.S. Public*, pg. 2016
TRIFACTA, INC.—See Clearlake Capital Group, L.P.; *U.S. Private*, pg. 933
TRIFACTA, INC.—See Insight Venture Management, LLC; *U.S. Private*, pg. 2087
TRIMBLE FORESTRY GMBH—See Trimble, Inc.; *U.S. Public*, pg. 2192
TRIMBLE TRANSPORTATION ENTERPRISE SOLUTIONS INC.—See Trimble, Inc.; *U.S. Public*, pg. 2193
TRIZETTO CORPORATION—See Cognizant Technology Solutions Corporation; *U.S. Public*, pg. 525
TRIZETTO PROVIDER SOLUTIONS, LLC - NHXS—See Cognizant Technology Solutions Corporation; *U.S. Public*, pg. 525
TRIZETTO PROVIDER SOLUTIONS, LLC—See Cognizant Technology Solutions Corporation; *U.S. Public*, pg. 525
TSYS CARD TECH LIMITED—See Global Payments Inc.; *U.S. Public*, pg. 944
TSYS INTERNATIONAL MANAGEMENT LIMITED—See Global Payments Inc.; *U.S. Public*, pg. 944
TULSARR INDUSTRIAL RESEARCH B.V.—See Barco N.V.; *Int'l*, pg. 864
TXOL INTERNET, INC.—See Rural Telecommunications of America, Inc.; *U.S. Private*, pg. 3504
TYLITE HOLDINGS, INC.—See Northwest Fiber LLC; *U.S. Private*, pg. 2960
UBERSMITH, INC.—See Internap Holding LLC; *U.S. Private*, pg. 2114
ULLINK INC.—See Broadridge Financial Solutions, Inc.; *U.S. Public*, pg. 392
ULLINK LIMITED—See Broadridge Financial Solutions, Inc.; *U.S. Public*, pg. 392
U-MIND CLUB, INC.—See PHMC, Inc.; *U.S. Private*, pg. 3172
UNCO DATA SYSTEMS, INC.—See Culligan Soft Water Service Co.; *U.S. Private*, pg. 1121
UNIBAND ENTERPRISES—See Turtle Mountain Band of Chippewa Indians Inc.; *U.S. Private*, pg. 4262
UNICOM SOLUTIONS GROUP INC.—See Hill, Barth & King LLC; *U.S. Private*, pg. 1945
UNIFOCUS, LP.; *U.S. Private*, pg. 4283
UNITED FINANCIAL SERVICES, INC.—See Nicolet Bankshares, Inc.; *U.S. Public*, pg. 1528
UNITEDLAYER, INC.—See Accelon Capital LLC; *U.S. Private*, pg. 50
UNITED STATES STEEL CORP.—See United States Steel Corporation; *U.S. Public*, pg. 2237
U.S. DATA MINING GROUP, INC.—See Hut 8 Corp.; *U.S. Public*, pg. 1076
US SEARCH.COM INC.—See Intelius, Inc.; *U.S. Private*, pg. 2105
VALIDIC, INC.; *U.S. Private*, pg. 4332
VALORE INC.—See Follett Corporation; *U.S. Private*, pg. 1559
VALTIX LLC—See Cisco Systems, Inc.; *U.S. Public*, pg. 500
VALUE LINE DISTRIBUTION CENTER, INC.—See Arnold Bernhard & Co.; *U.S. Private*, pg. 333
VARIOUS, INC.—See FriendFinder Networks Inc.; *U.S. Private*, pg. 1611
VELOCITY TECHNOLOGY SOLUTIONS III, INC.—See Accenture plc; *Int'l*, pg. 87
VENYU SOLUTIONS INC.—See Astra Capital Management LLC; *U.S. Private*, pg. 361
VERDICT MEDIA LIMITED—See GlobalData Plc; *Int'l*, pg. 3003
VERISIGN COLOMBIA SAS—See VeriSign, Inc.; *U.S. Public*, pg. 2282
VERISIGN INFORMATION SERVICES, INC.—See VeriSign, Inc.; *U.S. Public*, pg. 2282
VERISIGN SERVICES INDIA PRIVATE LIMITED—See VeriSign, Inc.; *U.S. Public*, pg. 2282
VERITAS DGC (MALAYSIA) SDN. BHD.—See CGG; *Int'l*, pg. 1432
VERITAS TECHNOLOGIES LLC—See The Carlyle Group Inc.; *U.S. Public*, pg. 2056
VERIZON DATA SERVICES—See Verizon Communications Inc.; *U.S. Public*, pg. 2286
VERIZON DATA SERVICES—See Verizon Communications Inc.; *U.S. Public*, pg. 2286
VERMONT INFORMATION CONSORTIUM, LLC—See Tyler Technologies, Inc.; *U.S. Public*, pg. 2209
VF SERVICES, LLC—See V. F. Corporation; *U.S. Public*, pg. 2269
VIECORE FEDERAL SYSTEMS DIVISION, INC.—See Microsoft Corporation; *U.S. Public*, pg. 1443
VIMEO.COM, INC.—See Vimeo, Inc.; *U.S. Public*, pg. 2298
VISIONAEL CORPORATION—See Upland Software, Inc.; *U.S. Public*, pg. 2264
VISP.NET; *U.S. Private*, pg. 4393
VITESSE, LLC—See Meta Platforms, Inc.; *U.S. Public*, pg. 1427
VIZIYA CORPORATION—See Genstar Capital, LLC; *U.S. Private*, pg. 1678
VODIEN INTERNET SOLUTIONS PTE LTD—See Dreamscape Networks Limited; *Int'l*, pg. 2203

CORPORATE AFFILIATIONS

VYKIN CORPORATION—See SOS International LLC; *U.S. Private*, pg. 3716
WAL-MART LABS—See Walmart Inc.; *U.S. Public*, pg. 2325
WANDISCO, PTY LTD—See Cirata PLC.; *Int'l*, pg. 1617
WANDISCO SOFTWARE (CHENGDU) LTD.—See Cirata PLC.; *Int'l*, pg. 1617
WARNER BROS. DIGITAL NETWORKS LABS INC.—See Warner Bros. Discovery, Inc.; *U.S. Public*, pg. 2328
WAUKESHA HEALTH CARE, INC.—See ProHealth Care, Inc.; *U.S. Private*, pg. 3280
WAYIN, INC.—See Vector Capital Management, L.P.; *U.S. Private*, pg. 4350
WEBAFFAIRS INC—See EQ Inc.; *Int'l*, pg. 2466
WEB BENEFITS DESIGN CORPORATION—See CNO Financial Group, Inc.; *U.S. Public*, pg. 520
WEBCENTRAL GROUP PTY LTD—See 5G Networks Limited; *Int'l*, pg. 13
WEB.COM, INC.—See Siris Capital Group, LLC; *U.S. Private*, pg. 3675
WEB FX INC.; *U.S. Private*, pg. 4463
WEBTASY D.O.O.—See DHH SpA; *Int'l*, pg. 2099
WEBTPA, INC.—See AmWINS Group, Inc.; *U.S. Private*, pg. 270
WELLTODESK INC.—See COSYN Limited; *Int'l*, pg. 1815
WESTERN NEW YORK CLINICAL INFORMATION EXCHANGE, INC.; *U.S. Private*, pg. 4494
WEST VIRGINIA INTERACTIVE, LLC—See Tyler Technologies, Inc.; *U.S. Public*, pg. 2209
WHIPPLEHILL COMMUNICATIONS, INC.—See Blackbaud, Inc.; *U.S. Public*, pg. 341
WHOIS PRIVACY SERVICES PTY LIMITED—See Enero Group Limited; *Int'l*, pg. 2424
WINGED MEDIA LLC; *U.S. Private*, pg. 4541
WINTERS BROADBAND LLC—See Cal.net, Inc.; *U.S. Private*, pg. 715
WIRED REAL ESTATE GROUP INC.; *U.S. Private*, pg. 4546
WIRELESSTUDIOS INC.—See Cameron Thomson Group Ltd.; *Int'l*, pg. 1272
WOOZWORLD INC.—See Azerion Group N.V.; *Int'l*, pg. 778
WORKPLACE INTEGRA INC.—See Demant A/S; *Int'l*, pg. 2025
WORKS COMPUTING LLC—See Converge Technology Solutions Corp.; *Int'l*, pg. 1787
WORLD MARKET INTELLIGENCE LIMITED—See GlobalData Plc; *Int'l*, pg. 3003
WORLDS INC.; *U.S. Public*, pg. 2382
WPENGINE, INC.; *U.S. Private*, pg. 4571
XANTRION, INC.; *U.S. Private*, pg. 4580
XCELLENCE, INC.—See JLL Partners, LLC; *U.S. Private*, pg. 2213
XENETIC OY—See Elisa Corporation; *Int'l*, pg. 2362
XING INC.—See Brother Industries, Ltd.; *Int'l*, pg. 1198
XS INTERNATIONAL, INC.; *U.S. Private*, pg. 4582
YAHOO! 350 SAS—See Apollo Global Management, Inc.; *U.S. Public*, pg. 167
YAHOO SOFTWARE DEVELOPMENT INDIA PRIVATE LIMITED—See Apollo Global Management, Inc.; *U.S. Public*, pg. 167
YAHOO! TECHNOLOGIES NORWAY AS—See Apollo Global Management, Inc.; *U.S. Public*, pg. 168
YOUTUBE, LLC—See Alphabet Inc.; *U.S. Public*, pg. 84
ZAKURA INC.—See Future Corporation; *Int'l*, pg. 2853
ZAPLABS LLC—See Anywhere Real Estate Inc.; *U.S. Public*, pg. 142
ZEDX, INC.—See BASF SE; *Int'l*, pg. 876
ZEKIAH TECHNOLOGIES, INC.; *U.S. Private*, pg. 4600
ZERODESKTOP, INC.; *U.S. Private*, pg. 4602
ZERTO, INC.—See Hewlett Packard Enterprise Company; *U.S. Public*, pg. 1032
ZETTICS, INC.—See DRW Holdings, LLC; *U.S. Private*, pg. 1280
ZETTICS, INC.—See Emergence Capital Partners; *U.S. Private*, pg. 1380
ZETTICS, INC.—See North Bridge Venture Management Company, Inc.; *U.S. Private*, pg. 2942
ZETTICS, INC.—See Voyager Capital, LLC; *U.S. Private*, pg. 4414
ZIFF DAVIS B2B FOCUS, INC.—See Ziff Davis, Inc.; *U.S. Public*, pg. 2404
ZILLOW, INC.—See Zillow Group, Inc.; *U.S. Public*, pg. 2405
ZONIAC INC.—See CEIPAL Corp.; *U.S. Private*, pg. 806
ZSCALER SOFTECH INDIA PRIVATE LIMITED—See Zscaler, Inc.; *U.S. Public*, pg. 2411
ZYCRON INC.—See BGSF, Inc.; *U.S. Public*, pg. 330

519210 — LIBRARIES AND ARCHIVES

ALLEGHENY COUNTY LIBRARY ASSOCIATION; *U.S. Private*, pg. 175
AMIGOS LIBRARY SERVICES; *U.S. Private*, pg. 263
BRODART CO. - BOOKS & LIBRARY SERVICES DIVISION—See Brodart Co.; *U.S. Private*, pg. 661
BUCKS COUNTY FREE LIBRARY; *U.S. Private*, pg. 678
CASA DOS LIVROS EDITORA LTDA.—See Charlesbank Capital Partners, LLC; *U.S. Private*, pg. 854
EDUCURIOUS PARTNERS; *U.S. Private*, pg. 1340
EISEN-BIBLIOTHEK STIFTUNG DER GEORG FISCHER

519290 — WEB SEARCH PORTALS ...

AG—See Georg Fischer AG; *Int'l*, pg. 2935
ENOCH PRATT FREE LIBRARY; *U.S. Private*, pg. 1401
GFT INBOXX GMBH.—See GFT Technologies SE; *Int'l*, pg. 2957
HUIJSMANS EN KUIJPERS AUTOMATISERING BV—See Online Computer Library Center, Inc.; *U.S. Private*, pg. 3026
THE HUNTINGTON LIBRARY, ART COLLECTIONS, AND BOTANICAL GARDENS; *U.S. Private*, pg. 4054
JONES E-GLOBAL LIBRARY, INC.—See Jones International University; *U.S. Private*, pg. 2233
LA CROSSE PUBLIC LIBRARY; *U.S. Private*, pg. 2368
LOS ANGELES PUBLIC LIBRARY DOCENTS; *U.S. Private*, pg. 2497
MARTIN LIBRARY ASSOCIATION; *U.S. Private*, pg. 2595
NATIONWIDE ARCHIVE SYSTEMS—See Nucor Corporation; *U.S. Public*, pg. 1553
NETLIBRARY, INC.—See Online Computer Library Center, Inc.; *U.S. Private*, pg. 3027
THE NEWBERRY; *U.S. Private*, pg. 4083
THE NEW YORK PUBLIC LIBRARY; *U.S. Private*, pg. 4083
OCLC B.V.—See Online Computer Library Center, Inc.; *U.S. Private*, pg. 3026
OCLC GMBH—See Online Computer Library Center, Inc.; *U.S. Private*, pg. 3027
ONLINE COMPUTER LIBRARY CENTER, INC.; *U.S. Private*, pg. 3026
ORBIS CASCADE ALLIANCE; *U.S. Private*, pg. 3038
PENNSYLVANIA LIBRARY ASSOCIATION.; *U.S. Private*, pg. 3136
PIKES PEAK LIBRARY DISTRICT; *U.S. Private*, pg. 3180
PRINCE GEORGE'S COUNTY MEMORIAL LIBRARY SYSTEM; *U.S. Private*, pg. 3264
PRO-TEK VAULTS—See LAC Group; *U.S. Private*, pg. 2371
RICHLAND LIBRARY; *U.S. Private*, pg. 3430
ROCHESTER PUBLIC LIBRARY; *U.S. Private*, pg. 3464
SAN DIEGO PUBLIC LIBRARY FOUNDATION; *U.S. Private*, pg. 3539
SIA RIA TECH—See Iron Mountain Incorporated; *U.S. Public*, pg. 1174
SISIS INFORMATIONSSYSTEME GMBH—See Online Computer Library Center, Inc.; *U.S. Private*, pg. 3026
THE SMITHTOWN LIBRARY; *U.S. Private*, pg. 4119
WESTCHESTER ACADEMIC LIBRARY DIRECTORS ORGANIZATION; *U.S. Private*, pg. 4489

519290 — WEB SEARCH PORTALS AND ALL OTHER INFORMATION SERVICES

180S, LLC; *U.S. Private*, pg. 3
1880 NUMMEROPPLYSNING AS—See Eniro Group AB; *Int'l*, pg. 2439
2-20 RECORDS MANAGEMENT, LLC—See Windjammer Capital Investors, LLC; *U.S. Private*, pg. 4538
3FORCES INC.; *U.S. Private*, pg. 9
3I PEOPLE, INC.; *U.S. Private*, pg. 13
ABACUS SOLUTIONS GROUP LLC (ASG); *U.S. Private*, pg. 34
ABBOTT INFORMATICS ASIA PACIFIC LIMITED—See Abbott Laboratories; *U.S. Public*, pg. 15
ABBOTT INFORMATICS AUSTRALIA PTY LIMITED—See Abbott Laboratories; *U.S. Public*, pg. 15
ABBOTT INFORMATICS CORPORATION—See Abbott Laboratories; *U.S. Public*, pg. 15
ABBOTT INFORMATICS GERMANY GMBH—See Abbott Laboratories; *U.S. Public*, pg. 15
ABBOTT INFORMATICS NETHERLANDS B.V.—See Abbott Laboratories; *U.S. Public*, pg. 15
ABBOTT INFORMATICS SINGAPORE PTE. LIMITED—See Abbott Laboratories; *U.S. Public*, pg. 15
ABBOTT INFORMATICS TECHNOLOGIES LTD—See Abbott Laboratories; *U.S. Public*, pg. 15
ABIS GMBH—See Deutsche Post AG; *Int'l*, pg. 2071
ABLE INFORMATION TECHNOLOGIES, INC.; *U.S. Private*, pg. 39
ABLE INFORMATION TECHNOLOGIES, INC.—See Able Information Technologies, Inc.; *U.S. Private*, pg. 39
ACCELYA HOLDING WORLD SL—See Vista Equity Partners, LLC; *U.S. Private*, pg. 4394
ACCESS SYSTEMS, INC.; *U.S. Private*, pg. 52
ACCUDATA HOLDINGS, INC.—See Compact Information Systems, Inc.; *U.S. Private*, pg. 998
ACMOS INC.; *Int'l*, pg. 107
ACTIONET, INC.; *U.S. Private*, pg. 68
ACTIV FINANCIAL SYSTEMS, INC—See ABRY Partners, LLC; *U.S. Private*, pg. 43
ADESSO SE; *Int'l*, pg. 144
ADP BRASIL LTDA—See Automatic Data Processing, Inc.; *U.S. Public*, pg. 229
AD-SOL NISSIN CORPORATION; *Int'l*, pg. 123
ADVANCED HEALTH MEDIA, LLC—See Arlington Capital Partners LLC; *U.S. Private*, pg. 327
ADVANTAGE COMMUNICATIONS, INC.; *Int'l*, pg. 164
AFFECTO DENMARK A/S—See CGI Inc.; *Int'l*, pg. 1433
A.F.P. CAPITAL S.A.—See Grupo de Inversiones Suramericana S.A.; *Int'l*, pg. 3125
AGCAREERS.COM—See Farms.com Ltd.; *Int'l*, pg. 2620

AGILE GLOBAL SOLUTIONS INC.; *U.S. Private*, pg. 127
AGINGCARE, LLC; *U.S. Private*, pg. 128
AI FINANCIAL INFORMATION UK LIMITED—See Genstar Capital, LLC; *U.S. Private*, pg. 1675
AIM CONSULTING GROUP, LLC; *U.S. Private*, pg. 132
ALPIQ INTEC ROMANDIE SA—See Bouygues S.A.; *Int'l*, pg. 1123
AMADA AILINK SERVICE CO., LTD.—See Amada Holdings Co., Ltd.; *Int'l*, pg. 403
AMBER ROAD CHINA, LTD.—See Insight Venture Management, LLC; *U.S. Public*, pg. 2087
AMBER ROAD SOFTWARE PRIVATE, LTD.—See Insight Venture Management, LLC; *U.S. Public*, pg. 2087
AMERICAN BUSINESS SOLUTIONS, INC.; *U.S. Private*, pg. 226
AMERICAN DRIVING RECORDS, INC.—See ABRY Partners, LLC; *U.S. Private*, pg. 43
ANALYTIX ON DEMAND, INC.; *U.S. Private*, pg. 271
ANGIE'S LIST, INC.—See IAC Inc.; *U.S. Public*, pg. 1081
ANSEARCH.COM.AU PTY LTD—See Adslot Ltd.; *Int'l*, pg. 154
ANSWERS CORPORATION—See Apax Partners LLP; *Int'l*, pg. 501
AOL DEUTSCHLAND MEDIEN GMBH—See Apollo Global Management, Inc.; *U.S. Public*, pg. 167
ARCHIVAGES ET SERVICES—See Iron Mountain Incorporated; *U.S. Public*, pg. 1172
ARDENTEC CORPORATION; *Int'l*, pg. 554
ARGUS MEDIA LIMITED—See General Atlantic Service Company, L.P.; *U.S. Private*, pg. 1662
ARGUS MEDIA LIMITED—See HgCapital Trust plc; *Int'l*, pg. 3376
ARGUS MEDIA LTD. - JAPAN—See General Atlantic Service Company, L.P.; *U.S. Private*, pg. 1662
ARGUS MEDIA LTD. - JAPAN—See HgCapital Trust plc; *Int'l*, pg. 3376
ARGUS MEDIA LTD. - RUSSIA—See General Atlantic Service Company, L.P.; *U.S. Private*, pg. 1662
ARGUS MEDIA LTD. - RUSSIA—See HgCapital Trust plc; *Int'l*, pg. 3376
ARIA SOLUTIONS INC.—See TTEC Holdings, Inc.; *U.S. Public*, pg. 2203
ARKPHIRE GROUP LTD.—See BC Partners LLP; pg. 925
ARTECH CHINA LIMITED—See Artech Information Systems LLC; *U.S. Private*, pg. 340
ARTECH CHINA LIMITED—See Artech Information Systems LLC; *U.S. Private*, pg. 340
ARTECH CHINA-SHANGHAI—See Artech Information Systems LLC; *U.S. Private*, pg. 340
ARTECH INFOSYSTEMS PRIVATE LIMITED—See Artech Information Systems LLC; *U.S. Private*, pg. 340
ARTECH INFOSYSTEMS PRIVATE LIMITED—See Artech Information Systems LLC; *U.S. Private*, pg. 340
ART RESOURCE, INC.; *U.S. Private*, pg. 340
ASAHI INTELLIGENCE SERVICE CO.,LTD.; *Int'l*, pg. 594
ASCEND TECHNOLOGIES, LLC—See TAC Partners, Inc.; *U.S. Private*, pg. 3920
AS KINNISVARAPORTAAL—See Alma Media Corporation; *Int'l*, pg. 361
A-SMART TECHNOLOGIES PTE LTD—See A-Smart Holdings Ltd.; *Int'l*, pg. 20
ASM RESEARCH LLC—See Accenture plc; *Int'l*, pg. 85
ASSCENT INFOSERVE PVT. LTD.—See Accentia Technologies Limited; *Int'l*, pg. 82
ASSET INTERNATIONAL AUSTRALIA PTY LTD—See Genstar Capital, LLC; *U.S. Private*, pg. 1675
ASSET INTERNATIONAL HONG KONG LTD.—See Genstar Capital, LLC; *U.S. Private*, pg. 1675
ASSET INTERNATIONAL INC.—See Genstar Capital, LLC; *U.S. Private*, pg. 1675
ASSOCIATED PRESS TELEVISION NEWS—See The Associated Press; *U.S. Private*, pg. 3989
ASTOR & SANDERS CORPORATION; *U.S. Private*, pg. 360
THE AUSTRALIAN TRAFFIC NETWORK PTY. LIMITED—See GTCR LLC; *U.S. Private*, pg. 1805
AUTOVIN CANADA INC.—See OPENLANE, Inc.; *U.S. Public*, pg. 1607
AVAILITY, LLC—See GuideWell Mutual Holding Corporation; *U.S. Private*, pg. 1813
AVAILITY, LLC—See Humana, Inc.; *U.S. Public*, pg. 1069
AVNET PARTNER SOLUTIONS, S. DE R.L. DE C.V.—See Avnet, Inc.; *U.S. Public*, pg. 252
AXEL SPRINGER IDEAS ENGINEERING GMBH—See Axel Springer SE; *Int'l*, pg. 766
AXIELL GROUP AB; *Int'l*, pg. 768
BAIDU.COM TIMES TECHNOLOGY (BEIJING) CO., LTD.—See Baidu, Inc.; *Int'l*, pg. 801
BANDWAVE SYSTEMS, LLC—See Lingo Management, LLC; *U.S. Private*, pg. 2461
BAUVERLAG BV GMBH—See Apax Partners LLP; *Int'l*, pg. 502
BAUVERLAG BV GMBH—See TowerBrook Capital Partners, L.P.; *U.S. Private*, pg. 4195
BEATPORT, LLC—See LiveStyle, Inc.; *U.S. Private*, pg. 2473

BEDROCK TECHNOLOGY PARTNERS; *U.S. Private*, pg. 512
BEIJING ULTRAPOWER SOFTWARE CO., LTD.; *Int'l*, pg. 959
BENTEK ENERGY LLC—See S&P Global Inc.; *U.S. Public*, pg. 1830
BERG FASHION LIBRARY LIMITED—See Bloomsbury Publishing Plc; *Int'l*, pg. 1065
BIDSTACK GROUP PLC; *Int'l*, pg. 1019
BIG FRESH MEDIA, INC.; *U.S. Private*, pg. 553
BIGSUPERSEARCH.COM, INC.; *U.S. Public*, pg. 331
BISNOW LLC—See The Wicks Group of Companies, LLC; *U.S. Private*, pg. 4135
BLUEALLY TECHNOLOGY SOLUTIONS, LLC—See Source Capital, LLC; *U.S. Private*, pg. 3717
BOATRACS LLC; *U.S. Private*, pg. 603
BOUNDLESS IMMIGRATION INC.; *U.S. Private*, pg. 623
BOVISION AB—See Alma Media Corporation; *Int'l*, pg. 362
B RESOURCE, INC.; *U.S. Private*, pg. 417
BRIDGEPOINTE TECHNOLOGIES, INC—See Charlesbank Capital Partners, LLC; *U.S. Private*, pg. 854
BRIDGEVINE, INC.; *U.S. Private*, pg. 649
BRMI; *U.S. Private*, pg. 658
BURELLESLUCE—See Burrelle's Information Services LLC; *U.S. Private*, pg. 691
BURGEL ERFURT GMBH & CO. KG—See Allianz SE; *Int'l*, pg. 351
C2 SOLUTIONS GROUP, INC.; *U.S. Private*, pg. 709
CAD S.R.L.—See CAD IT S.p.A.; *Int'l*, pg. 1247
CAICA DIGITAL INC.; *Int'l*, pg. 1252
CAMBRIDGE HEALTHTECH INSTITUTE; *U.S. Private*, pg. 727
CAMEO SOLUTIONS—See New Era Technology, Inc.; *U.S. Private*, pg. 2896
CANADIAN TRAFFIC NETWORK—See GTCR LLC; *U.S. Private*, pg. 1805
CAPITAL CONCEPT LIMITED AD; *Int'l*, pg. 1310
CDW LOGISTICS, INC.—See CDW Corporation; *U.S. Public*, pg. 462
CENTERAC TECHNOLOGIES LTD.; *Int'l*, pg. 1403
CENTRICSIT, LLC; *U.S. Private*, pg. 830
CEREBRA INTEGRATED TECHNOLOGIES LTD.; *Int'l*, pg. 1422
CERTIPOST SA/NV—See bpost NV/SA; *Int'l*, pg. 1133
CHAMELEON INTEGRATED SERVICES; *U.S. Private*, pg. 846
CHETU, INC.; *U.S. Private*, pg. 876
CHINESEINVESTORS.COM, INC.; *U.S. Private*, pg. 886
CHINESEWORLDNET.COM INC.; *Int'l*, pg. 1569
CITIC TELECOM INTERNATIONAL CPC LIMITED—See CITIC Group Corporation; *Int'l*, pg. 1620
CLEANTECH GROUP, INC.; *U.S. Private*, pg. 931
CLEARAVENUE, LLC; *U.S. Private*, pg. 932
CLICKSQUARED LTD.—See Zeta Interactive Corporation; *U.S. Private*, pg. 4603
COGENT DATA SOLUTIONS, LLC; *U.S. Private*, pg. 962
COLLABERA INC.; *U.S. Private*, pg. 968
COMMUNICATION TECHNOLOGIES, INC.—See Consolidated Communications Holdings, Inc.; *U.S. Public*, pg. 569
COMPASS, INC.; *U.S. Public*, pg. 561
COMPLUS TECHNOLOGIES SE; *Int'l*, pg. 1753
THE COMPUTER COMPANY, INC.; *U.S. Private*, pg. 4013
CONCENTRIX CORPORATION; *U.S. Public*, pg. 564
CONDUENT HEALTHCARE INFORMATION SERVICES, INC.—See Conduent Incorporated; *U.S. Public*, pg. 566
CONIGENT; *U.S. Private*, pg. 1014
CONTENT RULES INC.; *U.S. Private*, pg. 1027
COOCON CORP.; *Int'l*, pg. 1788
COOPERATIVE AGRONOMY SERVICES—See CHS INC.; *U.S. Public*, pg. 492
COR365 INFORMATION SOLUTIONS; *U.S. Private*, pg. 1046
CORE DIGITAL MEDIA, INC.—See RockBridge Growth Equity, LLC; *U.S. Private*, pg. 3465
CORELOGIC, INC.—See Insight Venture Management, LLC; *U.S. Private*, pg. 2088
CORELOGIC, INC.—See Stone Point Capital LLC; *U.S. Private*, pg. 3822
CORELOGIC TRANSPORTATION SERVICES—See Insight Venture Management, LLC; *U.S. Private*, pg. 2089
CORELOGIC TRANSPORTATION SERVICES—See Stone Point Capital LLC; *U.S. Private*, pg. 3822
CORETECH CONSULTING GROUP LLC—See Asseco Poland S.A.; *Int'l*, pg. 642
CRAZY INFOTECH LTD.; *Int'l*, pg. 1830
CREDITRISKMONITOR.COM, INC.; *U.S. Public*, pg. 593
CRITICAL MENTION, INC.; *U.S. Private*, pg. 1101
CRUSOE ENERGY SYSTEMS LLC; *U.S. Private*, pg. 1114
CSIT BOTSWANA (PTY) LTD—See Experian plc; *Int'l*, pg. 2586
CW FACHVERLAG GMBH—See China Oceanwide Holdings Group Co., Ltd.; *Int'l*, pg. 1536
CW FACHVERLAG GMBH—See IDG Capital; *Int'l*, pg. 3593
DAIKIN INFORMATION SYSTEMS CO., LTD.—See Daikin Industries, Ltd.; *Int'l*, pg. 1934
DARELLE MEDIA INC.—See Darelle Online Solutions Inc.; *Int'l*, pg. 1972

519290 — WEB SEARCH PORTALS ...

DASSAULT DATA SERVICES—See Dassault Systemes S.A.; *Int'l*, pg. 1974
DATA CALL TECHNOLOGIES, INC.; *U.S. Public*, pg. 635
DATA CENTER DYNAMICS ASIA LIMITED—See Data Center Dynamics Ltd; *Int'l*, pg. 1976
DATA CENTER DYNAMICS INC.—See Data Center Dynamics Ltd; *Int'l*, pg. 1976
DATA CENTER DYNAMICS LTD; *Int'l*, pg. 1975
DATA CENTER DYNAMICS MEA FZ-LLC—See Data Center Dynamics Ltd; *Int'l*, pg. 1976
DATA CENTER DYNAMICS SARL—See Data Center Dynamics Ltd; *Int'l*, pg. 1976
DATA CENTER DYNAMICS SHANGHAI CO. LTD.—See Data Center Dynamics Ltd; *Int'l*, pg. 1976
DATA CENTER DYNAMICS (HOLLAND) BV—See Data Center Dynamics Ltd; *Int'l*, pg. 1976
DATA CENTRE DYNAMICS SPAIN S.L.U.—See Data Center Dynamics Ltd; *Int'l*, pg. 1976
DATA COMMUNICATIONS LTD—See Argus Group Holdings Limited; *Int'l*, pg. 563
DATALAND B.V.—See BNG Bank N.V.; *Int'l*, pg. 1079
DATAQUICK INFORMATION SYSTEMS, INC.—See Insight Venture Management, LLC; *U.S. Private*, pg. 2089
DATAQUICK INFORMATION SYSTEMS, INC.—See Stone Point Capital LLC; *U.S. Private*, pg. 3822
DATASTREAM MARKET INTELLIGENCE, INC.; *U.S. Private*, pg. 1166
DATA SYSTEMS ANALYSTS INC. (DSA); *U.S. Private*, pg. 1163
DATA TRACE INFORMATION SERVICES LLC—See First American Financial Corporation; *U.S. Public*, pg. 835
DCI DATABASE FOR COMMERCE AND INDUSTRY AG; *Int'l*, pg. 1991
DEALIX CORPORATION—See One Planet Group LLC; *U.S. Private*, pg. 3020
DECISION ECONOMICS, INC.; *U.S. Private*, pg. 1187
DEFIANCE VENTURES LLC; *U.S. Private*, pg. 1191
DELIVERY HERO SE; *Int'l*, pg. 2013
DEVCARE SOLUTIONS; *U.S. Private*, pg. 1217
DEV INFORMATION TECHNOLOGY PVT. LTD.; *Int'l*, pg. 2086
DIALOG, LLC—See Clarivate PLC; *Int'l*, pg. 1649
DIGITAL CHOSUN INC.; *Int'l*, pg. 2121
DISCOVERY HEALTH RECORD SOLUTIONS, LLC—See Silverhawk Capital Partners, LLC; *U.S. Private*, pg. 3663
DNA RESPONSE, INC.—See Bluewater Media LLC; *U.S. Private*, pg. 598
DOCPLANNER GROUP; *Int'l*, pg. 2153
DOEXTRA CRM SOLUTIONS, LLC—See TAC Partners, Inc.; *U.S. Private*, pg. 3920
DOUSHEN BEIJING EDUCATION & TECHNOLOGY INC.; *Int'l*, pg. 2182
DOW JONES CANADA, INC.—See News Corporation; *U.S. Public*, pg. 1518
DOW JONES ENTERPRISE MEDIA—See News Corporation; *U.S. Public*, pg. 1518
DOW JONES INTERNATIONAL LTD.—See News Corporation; *U.S. Public*, pg. 1518
DOW JONES NEDERLAND BV—See News Corporation; *U.S. Public*, pg. 1518
DOW JONES NEWS GMBH—See News Corporation; *U.S. Public*, pg. 1518
DOW JONES NEWSWIRES—See News Corporation; *U.S. Public*, pg. 1518
DRIVESAVERS DATA RECOVERY, INC.; *U.S. Private*, pg. 1278
DSA TECHNOLOGIES INC.—See Executech Utah, LLC; *U.S. Private*, pg. 1447
DUCKER WORLDWIDE LLC—See Ducker FSG Holdings LLC; *U.S. Private*, pg. 1284
DUN & BRADSTREET BELGIUM N.V.—See Cannae Holdings, Inc.; *U.S. Public*, pg. 429
DUN & BRADSTREET BELGIUM N.V.—See CC Capital Partners, LLC; *U.S. Private*, pg. 798
DUN & BRADSTREET BELGIUM N.V.—See Intercontinental Exchange, Inc.; *U.S. Public*, pg. 1142
DUN & BRADSTREET B.V.—See Cannae Holdings, Inc.; *U.S. Public*, pg. 429
DUN & BRADSTREET B.V.—See CC Capital Partners, LLC; *U.S. Private*, pg. 798
DUN & BRADSTREET B.V.—See Intercontinental Exchange, Inc.; *U.S. Public*, pg. 1142
DUN & BRADSTREET CANADA LTD.—See Cannae Holdings, Inc.; *U.S. Public*, pg. 429
DUN & BRADSTREET CANADA LTD.—See CC Capital Partners, LLC; *U.S. Private*, pg. 798
DUN & BRADSTREET CANADA LTD.—See Intercontinental Exchange, Inc.; *U.S. Public*, pg. 1142
THE DUN & BRADSTREET CORPORATION—See Cannae Holdings, Inc.; *U.S. Public*, pg. 429
THE DUN & BRADSTREET CORPORATION—See CC Capital Partners, LLC; *U.S. Private*, pg. 798
THE DUN & BRADSTREET CORPORATION—See Intercontinental Exchange, Inc.; *U.S. Public*, pg. 1141
DUN & BRADSTREET FRANCE SA—See Base D'Informations Legales Holding S.A.S.; *Int'l*, pg. 871
DUN & BRADSTREET INFORMATION SERVICES INDIA PVT LTD.—See Cannae Holdings, Inc.; *U.S. Public*, pg. 429
DUN & BRADSTREET INFORMATION SERVICES INDIA PVT LTD.—See CC Capital Partners, LLC; *U.S. Private*, pg. 798
DUN & BRADSTREET INFORMATION SERVICES INDIA PVT LTD.—See Intercontinental Exchange, Inc.; *U.S. Public*, pg. 1142
DUN & BRADSTREET LTD.—See Cannae Holdings, Inc.; *U.S. Public*, pg. 429
DUN & BRADSTREET LTD.—See CC Capital Partners, LLC; *U.S. Private*, pg. 798
DUN & BRADSTREET LTD.—See Intercontinental Exchange, Inc.; *U.S. Public*, pg. 1142
DUN & BRADSTREET (SINGAPORE) PTE. LTD.—See Cannae Holdings, Inc.; *U.S. Public*, pg. 429
DUN & BRADSTREET (SINGAPORE) PTE. LTD.—See CC Capital Partners, LLC; *U.S. Private*, pg. 798
DUN & BRADSTREET (SINGAPORE) PTE. LTD.—See Intercontinental Exchange, Inc.; *U.S. Public*, pg. 1142
ECONET GLOBAL LTD.—See Econet Wireless Zimbabwe Limited; *Int'l*, pg. 2297
EDULENCE CORPORATION—See Fundos Group LLC; *U.S. Private*, pg. 1623
EDULENCE CORPORATION—See Trinity Private Equity Group, LLC; *U.S. Private*, pg. 4235
EF HUTTON AMERICA, INC.; *U.S. Public*, pg. 721
E-GUARDIAN, INC.; *Int'l*, pg. 2247
EISYS, INC.—See GEO Holdings Corporation; *Int'l*, pg. 2932
E.KUNDENSERVICE NETZ GMBH—See E.ON SE; *Int'l*, pg. 2260
E-MEDIAT AG—See CSL Limited; *Int'l*, pg. 1867
EMERGENT, LLC; *U.S. Private*, pg. 1381
EMERGN LIMITED; *Int'l*, pg. 2379
EMERGN LIMITED—See Emergn Limited; *Int'l*, pg. 2379
EMERGN LIMITED—See Emergn Limited; *Int'l*, pg. 2379
EMERGTECH BUSINESS SOLUTIONS, INC.; *U.S. Private*, pg. 1381
ENDURANCE IT SERVICES; *U.S. Private*, pg. 1392
ENERGY ACUITY LLC—See Hellman & Friedman LLC; *U.S. Private*, pg. 1908
ENTERPRISE ONSITE SERVICES CO.; *U.S. Private*, pg. 1404
EPELICAN.COM, INC.; *U.S. Private*, pg. 1412
EQUIPMENTWATCH—See Aurora Capital Group, LLC; *U.S. Private*, pg. 394
ERIMAX, INC.; *U.S. Private*, pg. 1421
ESRI MALAYSIA SDN BHD—See Boustead Singapore Limited; *Int'l*, pg. 1120
EVERYDAY HEALTH, INC.—See Ziff Davis, Inc.; *U.S. Public*, pg. 2404
EVN GEOINFO GMBH—See EVN AG; *Int'l*, pg. 2571
EXCET, INC.; *U.S. Private*, pg. 1446
EXERTIS (UK) LIMITED—See DCC plc; *Int'l*, pg. 1990
EXPERIAN ASIA-PACIFIC HOLDINGS PTE. LTD.—See Experian plc; *Int'l*, pg. 2586
EXPERIAN BACKGROUND DATA, INC.—See Experian plc; *Int'l*, pg. 2586
EXPERIAN BILGI HIZMETLERI LIMITED SIRKETI—See Experian plc; *Int'l*, pg. 2586
EXPERIAN BULGARIA EAD—See Experian plc; *Int'l*, pg. 2586
EXPERIAN BUREAU DE CREDITO, S.A.—See Experian plc; *Int'l*, pg. 2586
EXPERIAN CREDIT INFORMATION COMPANY OF INDIA PRIVATE LIMITED—See Experian plc; *Int'l*, pg. 2586
EXPERIAN CREDIT SERVICE (BEIJING) COMPANY LIMITED—See Experian plc; *Int'l*, pg. 2586
EXPERIAN DATA QUALITY UK—See Experian plc; *Int'l*, pg. 2586
EXPERIAN INFORMATION SERVICES (MALAYSIA) SDN. BHD.—See Experian plc; *Int'l*, pg. 2587
EXPERIAN ITALIA S.P.A.—See Experian plc; *Int'l*, pg. 2587
EXPERIAN JAPAN CO., LTD.—See Experian plc; *Int'l*, pg. 2587
EXPERIAN (MALAYSIA) SDN. BHD.—See Experian plc; *Int'l*, pg. 2586
EXPERIAN MICRO ANALYTICS SAM—See Experian plc; *Int'l*, pg. 2587
EXPERIAN NEW ZEALAND LIMITED—See Experian plc; *Int'l*, pg. 2587
EXPERIAN OSTERREICH GMBH—See Experian plc; *Int'l*, pg. 2587
EXPERIAN PERU S.A.C—See Experian plc; *Int'l*, pg. 2587
EXPERIAN POLSKA SPOLKA Z OGRANICZONA ODPOWIEDZIALNOSCIA—See Experian plc; *Int'l*, pg. 2587
EXPERIAN SERVICES CHILE S.A.—See Experian plc; *Int'l*, pg. 2587
EXPERIAN SERVICES INDIA PRIVATE LIMITED—See Experian plc; *Int'l*, pg. 2588
EXPERIAN STRATEGIC SOLUTIONS SA—See Experian plc; *Int'l*, pg. 2588
EXPERIAN TECNOLOGIA BRASIL LTDA—See Experian plc; *Int'l*, pg. 2588
EXPERIAN (THAILAND) CO., LTD.—See Experian plc; *Int'l*, pg. 2586

CORPORATE AFFILIATIONS

EXPERTEAM S.A./N.V.—See DXC Technology Company; *U.S. Public*, pg. 695
EXPLORANCE, INC.; *Int'l*, pg. 2588
FANDANGO, LLC—See Comcast Corporation; *U.S. Public*, pg. 540
FANSFRENZY CORP.; *U.S. Public*, pg. 821
FARMS.COM RISK MANAGEMENT INC.—See Farms.com Ltd.; *Int'l*, pg. 2620
FEARLESS MEDIA, LLC—See Infinite Realty; *U.S. Private*, pg. 2071
FERATEL ESPANA SL—See Feratel Media Technologies AG; *Int'l*, pg. 2635
FERATEL MEDIA TECHNOLOGIES AG; *Int'l*, pg. 2635
FERATEL MEDIA TECHNOLOGIES B.V.—See Feratel Media Technologies AG; *Int'l*, pg. 2635
FERATEL MEDIA TECHNOLOGIES GMBH—See Feratel Media Technologies AG; *Int'l*, pg. 2635
FERATEL SCHWEIZ AG—See Feratel Media Technologies AG; *Int'l*, pg. 2635
FIBRESOURCES CORP.; *Int'l*, pg. 2653
FIC GLOBAL, INC; *Int'l*, pg. 2653
FINANTEC CO., LTD.; *Int'l*, pg. 2669
FIREFLY E-VENTURES LIMITED—See HT Media Limited; *Int'l*, pg. 3508
FIRST ADVANTAGE AUSTRALASIA PTY. LTD.—See Silver Lake Group, LLC; *U.S. Private*, pg. 3654
FIRST ADVANTAGE PTE. LTD.—See Silver Lake Group, LLC; *U.S. Private*, pg. 3654
FIRST ADVANTAGE PVT. LTD.—See Silver Lake Group, LLC; *U.S. Private*, pg. 3654
FIRST AMERICAN DATA TREE LLC—See First American Financial Corporation; *U.S. Public*, pg. 836
FIRST AMERICAN (INDIA) PRIVATE LIMITED—See First American Financial Corporation; *U.S. Public*, pg. 836
FIRSTSOURCE LABORATORY SOLUTIONS, INC.—See Laboratory Corporation of America Holdings; *U.S. Public*, pg. 1287
FNGUIDE INC.; *Int'l*, pg. 2718
FONFUN CORPORATION; *Int'l*, pg. 2726
FONTIS INTERNATIONAL, INC.—See Iron Mountain Incorporated; *U.S. Public*, pg. 1172
FORBES.COM LLC—See Forbes Media LLC; *U.S. Private*, pg. 1563
FORWARD HEALTH; *U.S. Private*, pg. 1578
FREEDOM LEAF, INC.; *U.S. Public*, pg. 884
FRONTIER STRATEGY GROUP LLC—See Ducker FSG Holdings LLC; *U.S. Private*, pg. 1284
FSBM MES ELITE SDN. BHD.—See FSBM Holdings Berhad; *Int'l*, pg. 2798
FUJITSU FIP CORPORATION—See Fujitsu Limited; *Int'l*, pg. 2834
G1440 INC.—See Constellation Software Inc.; *Int'l*, pg. 1772
GALAXIA MONEYTREE CO., LTD.; *Int'l*, pg. 2871
GARTNER AUSTRALIA - BRISBANE—See Gartner, Inc.; *U.S. Public*, pg. 906
GARTNER AUSTRALIA - CANBERRA—See Gartner, Inc.; *U.S. Public*, pg. 907
GARTNER AUSTRALIA - MELBOURNE—See Gartner, Inc.; *U.S. Public*, pg. 907
GAS STRATEGIES CONSULTING LTD.—See S&P Global Inc.; *U.S. Public*, pg. 1831
GENERATION ZERO GROUP, INC.; *U.S. Private*, pg. 1668
GENSCAPE, INC.—See Verisk Analytics, Inc.; *U.S. Public*, pg. 2282
GERSON LEHRMAN GROUP, INC.; *U.S. Public*, pg. 934
GETRONICS GLOBAL SERVICES BV—See Aurelius Equity Opportunities SE & Co. KGaA; *Int'l*, pg. 708
GLANTUS LTD.; *Int'l*, pg. 2988
GLOBAL DIRECTMAIL B.V.—See Global Industrial Company; *U.S. Public*, pg. 942
GLOBAL INDUSTRIAL SERVICES INC.—See Global Industrial Company; *U.S. Public*, pg. 942
GLOBAL RELIEF TECHNOLOGIES, LLC—See Persephone Capital Partners LLC; *U.S. Private*, pg. 3155
GLOBAL TRAFFIC NETWORK (UK) LIMITED—See GTCR LLC; *U.S. Private*, pg. 1805
GOVDOCS, INC.; *U.S. Private*, pg. 1746
GREENLEAF GENETICS LLC—See China National Chemical Corporation; *Int'l*, pg. 1529
GREENWICH ASSOCIATES CANADA, ULC—See S&P Global Inc.; *U.S. Public*, pg. 1830
GREENWICH ASSOCIATES JAPAN K.K.—See S&P Global Inc.; *U.S. Public*, pg. 1830
GREENWICH ASSOCIATES SINGAPORE PTE. LTD.—See S&P Global Inc.; *U.S. Public*, pg. 1830
GREENWICH ASSOCIATES UK LIMITED—See S&P Global Inc.; *U.S. Public*, pg. 1830
GROUPON SPAIN, SLU—See Groupon Inc.; *U.S. Public*, pg. 972
G-SEARCH LTD.—See Fujitsu Limited; *Int'l*, pg. 2834
GTPL HATHWAY LTD.; *Int'l*, pg. 3151
GURUNAVI, INC.; *Int'l*, pg. 3188
HAREL MALLAC TECHNOLOGIES LTD—See Harel Mallac & Co. Ltd.; *Int'l*, pg. 3274
HASEKO SYSTEMS INC.—See Haseko Corporation; *Int'l*, pg. 3283
HAWAII PACIFIC TELEPORT, LP—See Calian Group Ltd.; *Int'l*, pg. 1264

N.A.I.C.S. INDEX

519290 — WEB SEARCH PORTALS ...

HC GROUP, INC.; *Int'l*, pg. 3297
THE HEALTHCENTRAL NETWORK, INC.—See Topspin Partners, L.P.; *U.S. Private*, pg. 4188
HEALTHLINE NETWORKS, INC.; *U.S. Private*, pg. 1897
HEARTLAND INFORMATION SERVICES, INC.—See Microsoft Corporation; *U.S. Public*, pg. 1443
HEREN HEALTH CO., LTD.; *Int'l*, pg. 3361
HIGHER POWER INC.—See Qurate Retail, Inc.; *U.S. Public*, pg. 1757
HITHINK ROYALFLUSH INFORMATION NETWORK CO., LTD.; *Int'l*, pg. 3426
HOME FRONT COMMUNICATIONS, LLC; *U.S. Private*, pg. 1971
HOMEGURU PTY LTD.—See News Corporation; *U.S. Public*, pg. 1520
HOTSCHEDULES; *U.S. Private*, pg. 1989
HPC SOLUTIONS; *U.S. Private*, pg. 1996
HUB DEALS CORP.; *U.S. Public*, pg. 1065
HUMANTOUCH, LLC; *U.S. Private*, pg. 2006
IAC SEARCH & MEDIA, INC.—See IAC Inc.; *U.S. Public*, pg. 1082
IBASE TECHNOLOGY PTE. LTD.; *Int'l*, pg. 3569
IBM ARGENTINA SOCIEDAD DE RESPONSABILIDAD LIMITADA—See International Business Machines Corporation; *U.S. Public*, pg. 1145
IBM BURKINA FASO SARL—See International Business Machines Corporation; *U.S. Public*, pg. 1146
ICARIO, INC.—See CVC Capital Partners SICAV-FIS S.A.; *Int'l*, pg. 1888
ICHIYOSHI RESEARCH INSTITUTE INC—See Ichiyoshi Securities Co., Ltd.; *Int'l*, pg. 3581
ICONIC IT, LLC—See Frontenac Company LLC; *U.S. Private*, pg. 1613
ICORECONNECT INC.—See iCoreConnect Inc.; *U.S. Public*, pg. 1086
IDC AUSTRALIA—See China Oceanwide Holdings Group Co., Ltd.; *Int'l*, pg. 1536
IDC AUSTRALIA—See IDG Capital; *Int'l*, pg. 3593
IDC PORTUGAL—See China Oceanwide Holdings Group Co., Ltd.; *Int'l*, pg. 1537
IDC PORTUGAL—See IDG Capital; *Int'l*, pg. 3594
IDENTIFIX, INC.—See Vista Equity Partners, LLC; *U.S. Private*, pg. 4400
IDOXSOLUTIONS, INC.—See Bart & Associates Inc.; *U.S. Private*, pg. 482
IFIRMA S.A.; *Int'l*, pg. 3599
IMAGE INFORMATION INC.; *Int'l*, pg. 3617
INCENTIVE TECHNOLOGY GROUP, LLC—See ICF International, Inc.; *U.S. Public*, pg. 1086
INDEPENDER.NL N.V.—See DPG Media Group NV; *Int'l*, pg. 2188
INDEXIUM AG—See Deutsche Borse AG; *Int'l*, pg. 2064
INDUSTRY DATA EXCHANGE ASSOCIATION, INC.; *U.S. Private*, pg. 2069
INFORM INFORMATION SYSTEMS LIMITED—See TA Associates, Inc.; *U.S. Private*, pg. 3917
INFOSMART SYSTEMS, INC.; *U.S. Private*, pg. 2074
INRIX, INC.; *U.S. Private*, pg. 2085
INSIGHT INVESTMENTS LLC; *U.S. Private*, pg. 2086
INSIGNIA TECHNOLOGY SERVICES, LLC; *U.S. Private*, pg. 2091
INSURANCE SERVICES OFFICE, INC.—See Verisk Analytics, Inc.; *U.S. Public*, pg. 2282
INTEGBUSINESS SERVICES, INC.—See Berkshire Partners LLC; *U.S. Private*, pg. 534
INTEGRATED SECURE, LLC; *U.S. Private*, pg. 2101
INTEGRATION PARTNERS - NY CORPORATION—See InterCloud Systems, Inc.; *U.S. Public*, pg. 1141
INTEGRITEK LLC; *U.S. Private*, pg. 2102
INTELLIGENT SOLUTIONS, INC.; *U.S. Private*, pg. 2106
INTERNATIONAL CENTER FOR POSTGRADUATE MEDICAL EDUCATION, LLC—See The Wicks Group of Companies, LLC; *U.S. Private*, pg. 4135
INTERPACE BIOPHARMA, LLC—See Flagship Biosciences, Inc.; *U.S. Private*, pg. 1539
INTERREL CONSULTING PARTNERS; *U.S. Private*, pg. 2123
INTRINSIQ, LLC—See Cencora, Inc.; *U.S. Public*, pg. 467
INVESTVIEW, INC.; *U.S. Public*, pg. 1165
INVOLTA, LLC; *U.S. Private*, pg. 2133
IREVNA LIMITED—See S&P Global Inc.; *U.S. Public*, pg. 1830
IRON MOUNTAIN ARSIVLEME HIZMETLERI AS—See Iron Mountain Incorporated; *U.S. Public*, pg. 1173
IRON MOUNTAIN A/S.—See Iron Mountain Incorporated; *U.S. Public*, pg. 1173
IRON MOUNTAIN AUSTRALIA GROUP PTY. LTD.—See Iron Mountain Incorporated; *U.S. Public*, pg. 1173
IRON MOUNTAIN AUSTRALIA SERVICES PTY LTD—See Iron Mountain Incorporated; *U.S. Public*, pg. 1172
IRON MOUNTAIN COLOMBIA, S.A.S.—See Iron Mountain Incorporated; *U.S. Public*, pg. 1172
IRON MOUNTAIN INFORMATION MANAGEMENT, LLC—See Iron Mountain Incorporated; *U.S. Public*, pg. 1173
IRON MOUNTAIN (NEDERLAND) SERVICES BV—See Iron Mountain Incorporated; *U.S. Public*, pg. 1173
IRON MOUNTAIN RECORDS MANAGEMENT (SHANGHAI) CO LIMITED—See Iron Mountain Incorporated; *U.S. Public*, pg. 1173
IRON VINE SECURITY, LLC—See ASGN Incorporated; *U.S. Public*, pg. 210
ISHPI INFORMATION TECHNOLOGIES, INC.; *U.S. Private*, pg. 2143
ISI (CHINA) CO., LTD.—See DXC Technology Company; *U.S. Public*, pg. 695
ISI-DENTSU OF HONG KONG, LTD.—See Dentsu Group Inc.; *Int'l*, pg. 2038
ISUBSCRIBED INC.; *U.S. Private*, pg. 2147
IT DIRECT, LLC—See CompassMSP LLC; *U.S. Private*, pg. 999
ITELIOS S.A.S.—See Capgemini SE; *Int'l*, pg. 1307
ITSAVVY LLC—See GenNx360 Capital Partners, L.P.; *U.S. Private*, pg. 1672
ITT CONTROL TECHNOLOGIES GMBH—See ITT Inc.; *U.S. Public*, pg. 1178
IZENDA, INC.—See TA Associates, Inc.; *U.S. Private*, pg. 3915
JDA FRONTLINE, INC.—See Blue Engine Message & Media, LLC; *U.S. Private*, pg. 588
JEEVES INFORMATION SYSTEMS AB—See Battery Ventures, L.P.; *U.S. Private*, pg. 489
JELLYFISH.COM, INC.—See Microsoft Corporation; *U.S. Public*, pg. 1441
JEPPESEN ASIA/PACIFIC PTE. LTD.—See The Boeing Company; *U.S. Public*, pg. 2039
JONES KNOWLEDGE, INC.—See Jones International University; *U.S. Private*, pg. 2233
JR EAST JAPAN INFORMATION SYSTEMS COMPANY—See East Japan Railway Company; *Int'l*, pg. 2270
JR EAST NET STATION CO., LTD.—See East Japan Railway Company; *Int'l*, pg. 2270
KINETIC PUBLISHING SERVICES, LLC—See Westchester Publishing Services, LLC; *U.S. Private*, pg. 4489
KN INFORMATION SYSTEMS CORPORATION—See Core Corporation; *Int'l*, pg. 1797
KONINKLIJKE DIRKZWAGER B.V.—See Electricite de France S.A.; *Int'l*, pg. 2351
KORE TELEMATICS—See KORE Wireless Group, Inc.; *U.S. Private*, pg. 2343
KRILLION, INC.—See Local Corporation; *U.S. Public*, pg. 1337
LA.COM—See Alden Global Capital LLC; *U.S. Public*, pg. 156
LANMARK TECHNOLOGY INC.; *U.S. Private*, pg. 2390
LANTRONIX JAPAN K.K.—See Lantronix, Inc.; *U.S. Public*, pg. 1293
LANTRONIX NETHERLANDS B.V.—See Lantronix, Inc.; *U.S. Public*, pg. 1293
LASHBACK, LLC—See PerformLine Inc.; *U.S. Private*, pg. 3150
LCS TECHNOLOGIES, INC.; *U.S. Private*, pg. 2404
LEANDOG; *U.S. Private*, pg. 2407
LEARNVEST INC.—See The Northwestern Mutual Life Insurance Company; *U.S. Private*, pg. 4085
LEGISLATIVE INFORMATION SERVICES OF AMERICA, LLC—See The Dolan Company; *U.S. Private*, pg. 4022
LIGHT MEDIA HOLDINGS, INC.; *U.S. Public*, pg. 1315
LINK SOLUTIONS, INC.; *U.S. Private*, pg. 2461
LISTEN360, INC.; *U.S. Private*, pg. 2466
LOCALLOOP, INC.—See InterCloud Systems, Inc.; *U.S. Public*, pg. 1141
LOGICAL TECHNICAL SERVICES, CORP. (LTS)—See Sentrillion Corporation; *U.S. Private*, pg. 3610
LOWERMYBILLS, INC.—See RockBridge Growth Equity, LLC; *U.S. Private*, pg. 3465
LUFTHANSA GLOBAL TELE SALES GMBH—See Deutsche Lufthansa AG; *Int'l*, pg. 2069
LUMANITY, INC.—See Arsenal Capital Management LP; *U.S. Private*, pg. 338
MACY'S SYSTEMS AND TECHNOLOGY, INC.—See Macy's, Inc.; *U.S. Public*, pg. 1353
MAG DS CORP.; *U.S. Private*, pg. 2545
MAPQUEST, INC.—See Apollo Global Management, Inc.; *U.S. Public*, pg. 167
MARATHON TS, INC.; *U.S. Private*, pg. 2570
MARITZ HOLDINGS INC.; *U.S. Private*, pg. 2577
MARKETRESEARCH.COM; *U.S. Private*, pg. 2581
MARLABS, INC.; *U.S. Private*, pg. 2582
MECKLERMEDIA CORPORATION; *U.S. Private*, pg. 2649
MEDERGY HEALTHGROUP INC.—See Arsenal Capital Management LP; *U.S. Private*, pg. 338
MEDIA MATTERS FOR AMERICA; *U.S. Private*, pg. 2652
MEDICINENET, INC.—See KKR & Co. Inc.; *U.S. Public*, pg. 1254
MEDI-COPY SERVICES INC.—See PCP Enterprise, L.P.; *U.S. Private*, pg. 3121
MEDSCAPE, LLC—See KKR & Co. Inc.; *U.S. Public*, pg. 1254
MEINESTADT.DE GMBH—See Axel Springer SE; *Int'l*, pg. 767
MENSENLINQ BV—See DPG Media Group NV; *Int'l*, pg. 2189
MEQASA LIMITED—See Frontier Digital Ventures Limited; *Int'l*, pg. 2795
MERCARIS COMPANY—See General Atlantic Service Company, L.P.; *U.S. Private*, pg. 1662
MERCARIS COMPANY—See HgCapital Trust plc; *Int'l*, pg. 3376
MEYERS RESEARCH, LLC—See MidOcean Partners, LLP; *U.S. Private*, pg. 2717
MICRO STRATEGIES INC.—See Micro Strategies Inc.; *U.S. Private*, pg. 2702
MISCO SOLUTIONS B.V.—See Computacenter plc; *Int'l*, pg. 1758
MMC SYSTEMS INC.; *U.S. Private*, pg. 2754
MOTOR RACING NETWORK, INC.—See National Association for Stock Car Auto Racing, Inc.; *U.S. Private*, pg. 2846
MOTORSPORT NETWORK, LLC—See GMF Capital LLC; *U.S. Private*, pg. 1721
MYCLIKS INC.; *U.S. Private*, pg. 2823
NETCALLIDUS LIMITED—See dotdigital Group PLC; *Int'l*, pg. 2180
NETEZZA CORPORATION LTD.—See International Business Machines Corporation; *U.S. Public*, pg. 1149
NETROADSHOW, INC.; *U.S. Private*, pg. 2888
NETWORK INFRASTRUCTURE TECHNOLOGIES, INC.—See Asseco Poland S.A.; *Int'l*, pg. 642
NEUSTAR, INC.—See TransUnion; *U.S. Public*, pg. 2184
NEUSTAR INFORMATION SERVICES, INC.—See TransUnion; *U.S. Public*, pg. 2184
NEW ERA TECHNOLOGY, INC.; *U.S. Private*, pg. 2896
NEWLIFE BIKES, INC.; *U.S. Private*, pg. 2915
NEW SIA GREECE S.A.—See Cassa Depositi e Prestiti S.p.A.; *Int'l*, pg. 1355
NEWS LIMITED—See News Corporation; *U.S. Public*, pg. 1519
NEXTERA MEDIA, LLC; *U.S. Private*, pg. 2920
NOVELSTEM INTERNATIONAL CORP.; *U.S. Public*, pg. 1549
OATH (CANADA) CORP.—See Apollo Global Management, Inc.; *U.S. Public*, pg. 167
OATH (UK) LIMITED—See Apollo Global Management, Inc.; *U.S. Public*, pg. 167
OCCHEALTH SYSTEMS, LLC—See MCMC LLC; *U.S. Private*, pg. 2642
ONEMARKETDATA, LLC; *U.S. Private*, pg. 3025
ONTARGETJOBS CANADA, INC.—See Ziff Davis, Inc.; *U.S. Public*, pg. 2404
ONTELLUS—See Aquiline Capital Partners LLC; *U.S. Private*, pg. 304
OOZLE MEDIA, INC.—See Association Member Benefits Advisors, LLC; *U.S. Private*, pg. 358
OPERATIONAL SERVICES GMBH & CO. KG—See Fraport AG; *Int'l*, pg. 2764
OR-LIVE, INC.—See BroadcastMed, Inc.; *U.S. Private*, pg. 659
OUTREACH TECHNOLOGY LLC; *U.S. Private*, pg. 3051
PANJIVA, INC.—See S&P Global Inc.; *U.S. Public*, pg. 1831
PARALLON TECHNOLOGY SOLUTIONS, LLC—See HCA Healthcare, Inc.; *U.S. Public*, pg. 1006
PATIENTPOINT NETWORK SOLUTIONS, LLC—See Catterton Management Company, LLC; *U.S. Private*, pg. 793
PEAK HEALTH SOLUTIONS, INC.—See AMN Healthcare Services, Inc.; *U.S. Public*, pg. 125
PIERCE EISLEN, INC.—See Yardi Systems, Inc.; *U.S. Private*, pg. 4586
PLANETOUT, INC.—See Here Media Inc.; *U.S. Private*, pg. 1921
PLEXENT; *U.S. Private*, pg. 3214
POMAROM S.R.L.—See Floridienne SA; *Int'l*, pg. 2708
PPOONE, INC.—See UnitedHealth Group Incorporated; *U.S. Public*, pg. 2253
PRAETORIAN DIGITAL, INC.; *U.S. Private*, pg. 3241
PRESCRYPTIVE HEALTH, INC.; *U.S. Private*, pg. 3254
PRISMADE LABS GMBH—See Edding AG; *Int'l*, pg. 2304
PRO COMPUTER SERVICE, LLC; *U.S. Private*, pg. 3269
THE PROFILE GROUP (UK) LIMITED—See Centaur Media plc; *Int'l*, pg. 1402
PT ESRI INDONESIA—See Boustead Singapore Limited; *Int'l*, pg. 1121
PT. EXPERIAN DECISION ANALYTICS INDONESIA—See Experian plc; *Int'l*, pg. 2588
QGENDA, LLC; *U.S. Private*, pg. 3313
QUISITIVE TECHNOLOGY SOLUTIONS, INC.; *U.S. Private*, pg. 3329
R2 UNIFIED TECHNOLOGIES; *U.S. Private*, pg. 3340
RAKUTEN INTELLIGENCE, INC.—See Advent International Corporation; *U.S. Public*, pg. 105
RBID.COM, INC.; *U.S. Public*, pg. 1767
REALSELF INC.; *U.S. Private*, pg. 3369
REALTIME LOGIC, INC.—See Kratos Defense & Security Solutions, Inc.; *U.S. Public*, pg. 1276
REBBIZ CO LTD—See Frontier Digital Ventures Limited; *Int'l*, pg. 2795
REBOOT NETWORKS LLC—See Trinity Hunt Management, L.P.; *U.S. Private*, pg. 4234
REFINERY 29, INC.—See Monroe Capital LLC; *U.S. Private*, pg. 2773

519290 — WEB SEARCH PORTALS ...

REFINERY 29, INC.—See Soros Fund Management LLC; *U.S. Private*, pg. 3716
REMEDY HEALTH MEDIA, LLC—See Topspin Partners, L.P.; *U.S. Private*, pg. 4188
RESPOND.COM—See TEOCO Corporation; *U.S. Private*, pg. 3969
RETAILNEXT, INC.; *U.S. Private*, pg. 3411
REVALIZE, INC.—See TA Associates, Inc.; *U.S. Private*, pg. 3918
REVENEER, INC.; *U.S. Private*, pg. 3413
RISI, INC—See Astorg Partners S.A.S.; *Int'l*, pg. 656
RISI, INC—See Epiris Managers LLP; *Int'l*, pg. 2461
RPX FREEDOM CORPORATION—See HGGC, LLC; *U.S. Private*, pg. 1930
RYUGIN SOUGO KENKYUSHO., LTD.—See Bank of The Ryukyus, Ltd.; *Int'l*, pg. 849
SAFEWAY PHILTECH INC.—See Cerberus Capital Management, L.P.; *U.S. Private*, pg. 836
SAHAS TECHNOLOGIES LLC; *U.S. Private*, pg. 3528
SAI GLOBAL CZECH S.R.O—See EQT AB; *Int'l*, pg. 2471
SAI GLOBAL GMBH—See EQT AB; *Int'l*, pg. 2471
SAI GLOBAL INC—See EQT AB; *Int'l*, pg. 2471
SAI GLOBAL INDIA—See EQT AB; *Int'l*, pg. 2471
SAI GLOBAL PTY. LIMITED—See EQT AB; *Int'l*, pg. 2471
SAINERGY; *U.S. Private*, pg. 3529
SEARCHFLOW LIMITED—See Daily Mail & General Trust plc; *Int'l*, pg. 1937
SECURE TECHNOLOGY INTEGRATION GROUP LTD.; *U.S. Private*, pg. 3594
SEEKING ALPHA LTD.; *U.S. Private*, pg. 3598
SERVICESOURCE INTERNATIONAL JAPAN G.K.—See Concentrix Corporation; *U.S. Public*, pg. 564
SHARECARE, INC.—See Altaris Capital Partners, LLC; *U.S. Private*, pg. 206
SIGMA TECHNOLOGY SOLUTIONS, INC.—See Pivot Technology Solutions, Inc.; *U.S. Public*, pg. 1695
SIMPLIFY COMPLIANCE HOLDINGS LLC—See Leeds Equity Partners, LLC; *U.S. Private*, pg. 2415
SIX3 SYSTEMS, INC.—See CACI International Inc.; *U.S. Public*, pg. 418
SNAP-ON BUSINESS SOLUTIONS GMBH—See Snap-on Incorporated; *U.S. Public*, pg. 1898
SNAP-ON BUSINESS SOLUTIONS LIMITED—See Snap-on Incorporated; *U.S. Public*, pg. 1898
SNAP-ON BUSINESS SOLUTIONS, S.A.—See Snap-on Incorporated; *U.S. Public*, pg. 1898
SNAP-ON BUSINESS SOLUTIONS, SRL—See Snap-on Incorporated; *U.S. Public*, pg. 1898
SNOOGOO CORP.; *U.S. Private*, pg. 3700
SOFTEC SOLUTIONS, INC.; *U.S. Private*, pg. 3705
SOURCE MEDIA LLC—See Observer Capital LLC; *U.S. Private*, pg. 2988
SPDJ HOLDINGS, LLC—See Medicus Solutions, LLC; *U.S. Private*, pg. 2656
S&P GLOBAL MARKET INTELLIGENCE INFORMATION MANAGEMENT CONSULTING (BEIJING) CO., LTD.—See S&P Global Inc.; *U.S. Private*, pg. 1831
S&P GLOBAL PLATTS—See S&P Global Inc.; *U.S. Public*, pg. 1831
SPICEWORKS, INC.—See Ziff Davis, Inc.; *U.S. Public*, pg. 2404
SPOT IMAGE S.A.S.—See Airbus SE; *Int'l*, pg. 246
S R LABS, LLC—See Insight Venture Management, LLC; *U.S. Private*, pg. 2091
STATRAD; *U.S. Private*, pg. 3794
STATS LLC—See Vista Equity Partners, LLC; *U.S. Private*, pg. 4401
STEPSTONE OSTERREICH GMBH—See Axel Springer SE; *Int'l*, pg. 767
STEPSTONE PL SP. Z O.O.—See Axel Springer SE; *Int'l*, pg. 767
STONEEAGLE, INC.—See StoneEagle F&I, Inc; *U.S. Private*, pg. 3828
STOXX LTD.—See Deutsche Borse AG; *Int'l*, pg. 2064
STRATEGIC COMMUNICATIONS, LLC.; *U.S. Private*, pg. 3834
STROLL; *U.S. Private*, pg. 3840
SUMMIT BUSINESS MEDIA, LLC; *U.S. Private*, pg. 3853
SUMMIT HOSTING LLC; *U.S. Private*, pg. 3854
SUNCOAST RHIO, INC.; *U.S. Private*, pg. 3866
SUPER DERIVATIVES INC.—See Intercontinental Exchange, Inc.; *U.S. Public*, pg. 1143
SWETS INFORMATION SERVICES B.V.—See Gilde Buy Out Partners B.V.; *Int'l*, pg. 2975
SWETS INFORMATION SERVICES, INC—See Gilde Buy Out Partners B.V.; *Int'l*, pg. 2975
THE SWIFT GROUP, LLC; *U.S. Private*, pg. 4126
SWISSSIGN GROUP AG—See Die Schweizerische Post AG; *Int'l*, pg. 2114
SYMPHONY HEALTH SOLUTIONS CORPORATION—See ICON plc; *Int'l*, pg. 3585
SYMPOZ, LLC—See Apple Leisure Group; *U.S. Private*, pg. 297
SYNDIGO LLC—See Summit Partners, L.P.; *U.S. Private*, pg. 3856
SYNDIGO LLC—See The Jordan Company, L.P.; *U.S. Private*, pg. 4062
SYNECHRON IT TOWERS—See Synechron Inc.; *U.S. Private*, pg. 3903
SYNECHRON LIMITED—See Synechron Inc.; *U.S. Private*, pg. 3903
SYNECHRON—See Synechron Inc.; *U.S. Private*, pg. 3903
SYNTERACTIVE; *U.S. Private*, pg. 3905
SYSTEMAX BUSINESS SERVICES K.F.T.—See Global Industrial Company; *U.S. Public*, pg. 942
TECHNOLOGY TRANSFER INSTITUTE/VANGUARD; *U.S. Private*, pg. 3956
TELAID INDUSTRIES, INC.; *U.S. Private*, pg. 3959
TELEQUOTE DATA INTERNATIONAL LIMITED—See Frontier Services Group Limited; *Int'l*, pg. 2796
TELMAR COMMUNICATIONS LIMITED—See Splashlight LLC; *U.S. Private*, pg. 3759
TELMAR-HET MEDIA INSTITUUT BV—See Splashlight LLC; *U.S. Private*, pg. 3759
TELMAR HMS LTD.—See Splashlight LLC; *U.S. Private*, pg. 3759
TELMAR INFORMATION SERVICES CORP.—See Splashlight LLC; *U.S. Private*, pg. 3759
TELMAR MEDIA SYSTEMS (PTY) LIMITED—See Splashlight LLC; *U.S. Private*, pg. 3759
TELMAR PEAKTIME S.A.S.—See Splashlight LLC; *U.S. Private*, pg. 3759
TELMAR POLSKA SP ZOO—See Splashlight LLC; *U.S. Private*, pg. 3759
THEWEBDIGEST CORP, *U.S. Private*, pg. 4143
THIS LIFE, INC.; *U.S. Private*, pg. 4145
THOMAS PUBLISHING COMPANY LLC MADE2SPEC—See Thomas Publishing Company LLC; *U.S. Private*, pg. 4157
THRIVE OPERATIONS, LLC—See Court Square Capital Partners, L.P.; *U.S. Private*, pg. 1070
TICK DATA, INC.; *U.S. Private*, pg. 4167
TICOM GEOMATICS, INC.—See CACI International Inc.; *U.S. Public*, pg. 418
TOTAL SITE SOLUTIONS—See TSS, Inc.; *U.S. Public*, pg. 2202
TRADERPLANET.COM, LLC; *U.S. Private*, pg. 4202
TRANSFORMATION ADVISORS GROUP, LLC; *U.S. Private*, pg. 4208
TRAPP TECHNOLOGY, INC.; *U.S. Private*, pg. 4212
TRIPADVISOR LLC—See TripAdvisor, Inc.; *U.S. Public*, pg. 2195
TRUE PROCESS, INC.—See Baxter International Inc.; *U.S. Public*, pg. 284
TSM CORP.—See Parsons Corporation; *U.S. Public*, pg. 1651
UAB CITY24—See Alma Media Corporation; *Int'l*, pg. 362
UNITAS GLOBAL LLC; *U.S. Private*, pg. 4287
UNITED DATA TECHNOLOGIES, INC.; *U.S. Private*, pg. 4291
UNITED ONLINE, INC.—See B. Riley Financial, Inc.; *U.S. Private*, pg. 262
UNITED STATES TRAFFIC NETWORK, LLC; *U.S. Private*, pg. 4300
UNITED TECHNOLOGY GROUP, LLC—See Wells Fargo & Company; *U.S. Public*, pg. 2344
VERINT SYSTEMS (AUSTRALIA) PTY LTD.—See Verint Systems Inc.; *U.S. Public*, pg. 2281
VERISTA INC.—See Lightview Capital LLC; *U.S. Private*, pg. 2454
VERIZON PRIVACY GROUP—See Verizon Communications Inc.; *U.S. Public*, pg. 2286
VIAPRINTO GMBH & CO. KG—See CEWE Stiftung & Co. KGaA; *Int'l*, pg. 1425
VIGILANT TECHNOLOGY, LLC; *U.S. Private*, pg. 4382
VIRTUALARMOUR INTERNATIONAL, INC.; *U.S. Public*, pg. 2300
VIRTUAL GRAFFITI, INC.—See Source Capital, LLC; *U.S. Private*, pg. 3718
VIRTUAL MEDICAL INTERNATIONAL, INC.; *U.S. Public*, pg. 2300
VIVO, INC.; *U.S. Private*, pg. 4406
VRC COMPANIES, LLC—See Windjammer Capital Investors, LLC; *U.S. Private*, pg. 4538
VWD NETSOLUTIONS GMBH—See Borsenmedien AG; *Int'l*, pg. 1115
WAND, INC.; *U.S. Private*, pg. 4435
WEBFIRM SEARCH PTY LTD—See Adslot Ltd.; *Int'l*, pg. 154
WEBMD GLOBAL LLC—See KKR & Co. Inc.; *U.S. Public*, pg. 1254
WEBMD, LLC—See KKR & Co. Inc.; *U.S. Public*, pg. 1254
WEB TEKS, INC.—See DroneUp LLC; *U.S. Private*, pg. 1279
WELKIN ASSOCIATES, LTD—See The Carlyle Group Inc.; *U.S. Public*, pg. 2049
WER LIEFERT WAS GMBH—See Capvis AG; *Int'l*, pg. 1318
WEST WORLD MEDIA LLC—See Fimalac S.A.; *Int'l*, pg. 2664
WINCOR NIXDORF LTD.—See Diebold Nixdorf, Inc.; *U.S. Public*, pg. 660
WINGSWEPT; *U.S. Private*, pg. 4541
WOOD MACKENZIE LTD.—See Veritas Capital Fund Management, LLC; *U.S. Private*, pg. 4366
WORKSMART; *U.S. Private*, pg. 4564
WORLDLINK, INC.; *U.S. Private*, pg. 4568
WORLD TARIFF, LIMITED—See FedEx Corporation; *U.S. Public*, pg. 828
WORLD WIDE WEB FOUNDATION; *U.S. Public*, pg. 4568
XCEL SOLUTIONS, CORP.; *U.S. Private*, pg. 4580
XYLO TECHNOLOGIES, INC.; *U.S. Private*, pg. 4583
YAHOO! (CHINA) LIMITED—See Alibaba Group Holding Limited; *Int'l*, pg. 326
YAHOO! COMMUNICATIONS & COMMUNITIES—See Apollo Global Management, Inc.; *U.S. Public*, pg. 167
YAHOO! FINANCE—See Apollo Global Management, Inc.; *U.S. Public*, pg. 167
YAHOO! FRANCE S.A.S.—See Apollo Global Management, Inc.; *U.S. Public*, pg. 167
YAHOO! GROUPS—See Apollo Global Management, Inc.; *U.S. Public*, pg. 167
YAHOO! LOCAL—See Apollo Global Management, Inc.; *U.S. Public*, pg. 168
YAHOO! MAIL—See Apollo Global Management, Inc.; *U.S. Public*, pg. 167
YAHOO! MEDIA—See Apollo Global Management, Inc.; *U.S. Public*, pg. 167
YAHOO! NETWORK—See Apollo Global Management, Inc.; *U.S. Public*, pg. 167
YAHOO! SEARCH—See Apollo Global Management, Inc.; *U.S. Public*, pg. 168
ZEELANDNET B.V.—See EQT AB; *Int'l*, pg. 2482
ZIPLINK, INC.; *U.S. Public*, pg. 2408
ZPG LIMITED—See Silver Lake Group, LLC; *U.S. Private*, pg. 3661

521110 — MONETARY AUTHORITIES-CENTRAL BANK

BANCA CENTRALE DELLA REPUBBLICA DI SAN MARINO; *Int'l*, pg. 814
BANCA COMERCIALA CARPATICA SA; *Int'l*, pg. 814
BANCA NATIONALA A MOLDOVEI; *Int'l*, pg. 815
BANCO CENTRAL DE CHILE; *Int'l*, pg. 819
BANCO CENTRAL DE CUBA; *Int'l*, pg. 819
BANCO CENTRAL DE HONDURAS; *Int'l*, pg. 820
BANCO CENTRAL DE LA REPUBLICA ARGENTINA; *Int'l*, pg. 820
BANCO CENTRAL DE LA REPUBLICA DOMINICA; *Int'l*, pg. 820
BANCO CENTRAL DEL ECUADOR; *Int'l*, pg. 820
BANCO CENTRAL DEL PARAGUAY; *Int'l*, pg. 820
BANCO CENTRAL DEL URUGUAY; *Int'l*, pg. 820
BANCO CENTRAL DE RESERVA DE EL SALVADOR; *Int'l*, pg. 820
BANCO CENTRAL DE RESERVA DEL PERU; *Int'l*, pg. 820
BANCO CENTRAL DE VENEZUELA; *Int'l*, pg. 820
BANCO CENTRAL DO BRASIL; *Int'l*, pg. 820
BANCO DE ESPANA; *Int'l*, pg. 820
BANCO DE GUATEMALA; *Int'l*, pg. 820
BANCO DE LA REPUBLICA COLOMBIA; *Int'l*, pg. 821
BANCO DE MOCAMBIQUE; *Int'l*, pg. 821
BANCO DE PORTUGAL; *Int'l*, pg. 821
BANGKO SENTRAL NG PILIPINAS; *Int'l*, pg. 832
BANGLADESH BANK; *Int'l*, pg. 835
BANK AL-MAGHRIB; *Int'l*, pg. 836
BANKA SLOVENIJE; *Int'l*, pg. 850
BANK CENTRALI TA' MALTA; *Int'l*, pg. 837
BANK INDONESIA; *Int'l*, pg. 838
BANK NEGARA MALAYSIA; *Int'l*, pg. 839
BANK OF ALBANIA; *Int'l*, pg. 840
BANK OF BOTSWANA; *Int'l*, pg. 840
BANK OF ENGLAND; *Int'l*, pg. 842
BANK OF GUYANA; *Int'l*, pg. 843
BANK OF JAMAICA; *Int'l*, pg. 845
BANK OF MAURITIUS; *Int'l*, pg. 845
BANK OF PAPUA NEW GUINEA; *Int'l*, pg. 847
BANK OF SIERRA LEONE; *Int'l*, pg. 848
BANK OF THAILAND; *Int'l*, pg. 848
BANK OF ZAMBIA; *Int'l*, pg. 849
BANK VAN DE NEDERLANDSE ANTILLEN; *Int'l*, pg. 850
BANQUE CENTRALE DES ETATS DE L'AFRIQUE DE L'OUEST; *Int'l*, pg. 853
BANQUE CENTRALE DU LUXEMBOURG; *Int'l*, pg. 853
BANQUE D'ALGERIE; *Int'l*, pg. 853
BANQUE DE PATRIMOINES PRIVES, SA—See Credit Andorra, S.A.; *Int'l*, pg. 1834
BANQUE DU LIBAN; *Int'l*, pg. 853
BANQUE NATIONALE DU RWANDA; *Int'l*, pg. 854
BERMUDA MONETARY AUTHORITY; *Int'l*, pg. 986
CAISSE DES DEPOTS ET CONSIGNATIONS - BANKING SERVICES—See Caisse des Depots et Consignations; *Int'l*, pg. 1257
CAYMAN ISLANDS MONETARY AUTHORITY; *Int'l*, pg. 1364
CENTRAL BANK & FINANCIAL SERVICES AUTHORITY OF IRELAND; *Int'l*, pg. 1404
CENTRAL BANK OF BAHRAIN; *Int'l*, pg. 1404
CENTRAL BANK OF BARBADOS; *Int'l*, pg. 1404
CENTRAL BANK OF BELIZE; *Int'l*, pg. 1404
CENTRAL BANK OF EGYPT; *Int'l*, pg. 1404
CENTRAL BANK OF IRAQ; *Int'l*, pg. 1404

N.A.I.C.S. INDEX

522110 — COMMERCIAL BANKING

CENTRAL BANK OF KENYA; *Int'l*, pg. 1404
CENTRAL BANK OF KUWAIT; *Int'l*, pg. 1404
CENTRAL BANK OF LESOTHO; *Int'l*, pg. 1404
CENTRAL BANK OF LIBYA; *Int'l*, pg. 1404
CENTRAL BANK OF NIGERIA; *Int'l*, pg. 1405
CENTRAL BANK OF OMAN; *Int'l*, pg. 1405
CENTRAL BANK OF SAMOA; *Int'l*, pg. 1405
CENTRAL BANK OF SEYCHELLES; *Int'l*, pg. 1405
CENTRAL BANK OF SOLOMON ISLANDS; *Int'l*, pg. 1405
CENTRAL BANK OF SRI LANKA; *Int'l*, pg. 1405
CENTRAL BANK OF SWAZILAND; *Int'l*, pg. 1405
CENTRAL BANK OF THE RUSSIAN FEDERATION; *Int'l*, pg. 1405
CENTRAL BANK OF THE UNITED ARAB EMIRATES; *Int'l*, pg. 1405
CENTRAL BANK OF THE UNITED REPUBLIC OF TANZANIA; *Int'l*, pg. 1405
CENTRAL BANK OF TRINIDAD & TOBAGO; *Int'l*, pg. 1405
CENTRALE BANK VAN ARUBA; *Int'l*, pg. 1410
CENTRALE BANK VAN SURINAME; *Int'l*, pg. 1410
CENTRAL RESERVE BANK OF ATLANTA—See Federal Reserve Bank of Atlanta; *U.S. Private*, pg. 1490
CREDIT ANDORRA PRIVATE BANKERS—See Credit Andorra, S.A.; *Int'l*, pg. 1834
DANMARKS NATIONALBANK; *Int'l*, pg. 1965
DE NEDERLANDSCHE BANK N.V.; *Int'l*, pg. 1996
DUBAI FINANCIAL SERVICES AUTHORITY; *Int'l*, pg. 2218
EUROPEAN BANK FOR RECONSTRUCTION & DEVELOPMENT; *Int'l*, pg. 2555
EUROPEAN CENTRAL BANK; *Int'l*, pg. 2555
FEDERAL RESERVE BANK KANSAS CITY; *U.S. Private*, pg. 1489
FEDERAL RESERVE BANK OF ATLANTA; *U.S. Private*, pg. 1489
FEDERAL RESERVE BANK OF CHICAGO; *U.S. Private*, pg. 1490
FEDERAL RESERVE BANK OF DALLAS; *U.S. Private*, pg. 1490
FEDERAL RESERVE BANK OF ST. LOUIS; *U.S. Private*, pg. 1491
FIRST FINANCIAL BANK—See FirstFed Bancorp, Inc.; *U.S. Private*, pg. 1532
FIRST INVESTMENT BANK ALBANIA SH.A—See First Investment Bank AD; *Int'l*, pg. 2685
FIS BROKERAGE & SECURITIES SERVICES LLC—See Fidelity National Infor; *U.S. Public*, pg. 832
FIS ENERGY SOLUTIONS LIMITED—See Fidelity National Infor; *U.S. Public*, pg. 832
FIS FINANCIAL SYSTEMS (FRANCE) SAS—See Fidelity National Infor; *U.S. Public*, pg. 832
FIS GLOBAL TRADING (IBERICA) S.L. UNIPERSONAL—See Fidelity National Infor; *U.S. Public*, pg. 832
FIS INVESTMENT SYSTEMS LLC—See Fidelity National Infor; *U.S. Public*, pg. 832
FIS PAYMENTS (UK) LIMITED—See Fidelity National Infor; *U.S. Public*, pg. 832
FIS SYSTEME GMBH—See Fidelity National Infor; *U.S. Public*, pg. 832
FIS WORKFLOW SOLUTIONS LLC—See Fidelity National Infor; *U.S. Public*, pg. 832
GTBANK UK LTD.—See Guaranty Trust Holding Company PLC; *Int'l*, pg. 3169
HONG KONG MONETARY AUTHORITY; *Int'l*, pg. 3467
HRVATSKA NORADNA BANKA; *Int'l*, pg. 3502
KS BANK, INC.—See KS Bancorp Inc.; *U.S. Public*, pg. 1277
PAYPAL U.K. LTD.—See PayPal Holdings, Inc.; *U.S. Public*, pg. 1656
PT BANK PERMATA TBK—See Bangkok Bank Public Company Limited; *Int'l*, pg. 833
SLMC FINANCE CORPORATION—See Select Medical Holdings Corporation; *U.S. Public*, pg. 1859

522110 — COMMERCIAL BANKING

1880 BANK—See Delmarva Bancshares, Inc.; *U.S. Private*, pg. 1197
1ST BANK—See Glacier Bancorp, Inc.; *U.S. Public*, pg. 938
1ST CAPITAL BANK; *U.S. Private*, pg. 3
1ST CENTURY BANK—See Midland Financial Co.; *U.S. Private*, pg. 2715
1ST COLONIAL COMMUNITY BANK; *U.S. Public*, pg. 2
1ST CONSTITUTION BANK—See Provident Financial Services, Inc.; *U.S. Public*, pg. 1730
1ST FINANCIAL BANK USA; *U.S. Private*, pg. 4
1ST SECURITY BANK OF WASHINGTON—See FS Bancorp, Inc.; *U.S. Public*, pg. 888
1ST SOURCE BANK—See 1st Source Corporation; *U.S. Public*, pg. 2
1ST SOURCE CAPITAL CORPORATION—See 1st Source Corporation; *U.S. Public*, pg. 3
1ST SUMMIT BANK—See 1st Summit Bancorp Johnstown, Inc.; *U.S. Public*, pg. 3
4FRONT CREDIT UNION; *U.S. Private*, pg. 15
AAREAL BANK AG—See Advent International Corporation; *U.S. Private*, pg. 96
AAREAL BANK AG—See Centerbridge Partners, L.P.; *U.S. Private*, pg. 812
AASEN SPAREBANK; *Int'l*, pg. 38
ABAXBANK SPA—See Credito Emiliano S.p.A.; *Int'l*, pg. 1836
AB BANK LIMITED; *Int'l*, pg. 39
ABBEY MORTGAGE BANK PLC.; *Int'l*, pg. 56
ABC ANSAI RURAL BANK LIMITED LIABILITY COMPANY—See Agricultural Bank of China Limited; *Int'l*, pg. 216
ABC FINANCIAL LEASING CO., LTD.—See Agricultural Bank of China Limited; *Int'l*, pg. 216
ABC HUBEI HANCHUAN RURAL BANK LIMITED LIABILITY COMPANY—See Agricultural Bank of China Limited; *Int'l*, pg. 217
ABC INTERNATIONAL HOLDINGS LIMITED—See Agricultural Bank of China Limited; *Int'l*, pg. 217
ABC S.A.—See Arab Banking Corporation B.S.C.; *Int'l*, pg. 529
ABERDEEN GLOBAL STATE STREET BANK LUXEMBOURG S.A—See abrdn PLC; *Int'l*, pg. 68
ABN AMRO BANK BRUSSELS—See ABN AMRO Group N.V.; *Int'l*, pg. 64
ABN AMRO BANK N.V.—See ABN AMRO Group N.V.; *Int'l*, pg. 63
ABN AMRO CLEARING SYDNEY NOMINEES PTY. LTD.—See ABN AMRO Group N.V.; *Int'l*, pg. 65
ABN AMRO GROENBANK B.V.—See ABN AMRO Group N.V.; *Int'l*, pg. 64
AB PAREX BANKAS—See AS Reverta; *Int'l*, pg. 591
AB "CITADELE" BANKAS—See Ripplewood Holdings LLC; *U.S. Private*, pg. 3439
ABSA BANK LIMITED—See Absa Group Limited; *Int'l*, pg. 69
ABSA BANK MOZAMBIQUE, SA—See Absa Group Limited; *Int'l*, pg. 69
ABSOLUT BANK OAO; *Int'l*, pg. 70
ABU DHABI COMMERCIAL BANK PJSC; *Int'l*, pg. 70
ABU DHABI COMMERCIAL BANK—See Abu Dhabi Commercial Bank PJSC; *Int'l*, pg. 71
ABU DHABI ISLAMIC BANK PJSC; *Int'l*, pg. 72
ABU DHABI NATIONAL ISLAMIC FINANCE PVT. JSC—See First Abu Dhabi Bank P.J.S.C.; *Int'l*, pg. 2681
ACCEPTANCE LOAN CO. INC.—See First US Bancshares, Inc.; *U.S. Public*, pg. 848
ACCESS BANK (D.R. CONGO) SARL—See Access Corporation; *Int'l*, pg. 88
ACCESS BANK (GAMBIA) LIMITED—See Access Corporation; *Int'l*, pg. 88
ACCESS BANK (GHANA) LIMITED—See Access Corporation; *Int'l*, pg. 88
ACCESS BANK (RWANDA) LIMITED—See Access Corporation; *Int'l*, pg. 88
ACCESS BANK (SIERRA LEONE) LIMITED—See Access Corporation; *Int'l*, pg. 88
ACCESS BANK—See 3MV Bancorp, Inc.; *U.S. Private*, pg. 13
ACCESS BANK (UK) LIMITED—See Access Corporation; *Int'l*, pg. 88
ACCESS BANK (ZAMBIA) LIMITED—See Access Corporation; *Int'l*, pg. 88
ACCESS CORPORATION; *Int'l*, pg. 88
ACCORD FINANCE S.A.—See Auchan Holding S.A.; *Int'l*, pg. 699
ACHMEA BANK N.V.—See Achmea B.V.; *Int'l*, pg. 103
ACHMEA PENSIOEN - EN LEVENSVERZEKERINGEN N.V.—See Achmea B.V.; *Int'l*, pg. 103
ACKLEY STATE BANK; *U.S. Private*, pg. 60
ACNB BANK—See ACNB Corporation; *U.S. Public*, pg. 35
ADAMS BANK & TRUST, CORPORATE OFFICE—See Adbanc, Inc.; *U.S. Private*, pg. 76
ADBANC, INC.; *U.S. Private*, pg. 76
ADCB SECURITIES LLC—See Abu Dhabi Commercial Bank PJSC; *Int'l*, pg. 71
ADDIKO BANK AG; *Int'l*, pg. 129
ADIRONDACK BANK—See Adirondack Bankcorp, Inc.; *U.S. Private*, pg. 79
THE ADIRONDACK TRUST COMPANY; *U.S. Public*, pg. 2030
ADVISORENGINE INC.—See Franklin Resources, Inc.; *U.S. Public*, pg. 879
ADYEN IBERIA SLU—See Adyen N.V.; *Int'l*, pg. 169
ADYEN MEXICO, S.A. DE C.V.—See Adyen N.V.; *Int'l*, pg. 170
ADYEN NORDIC AB—See Adyen N.V.; *Int'l*, pg. 170
AFFILIATED BANK, N.A; *U.S. Public*, pg. 53
AFRICAN BANKING CORPORATION ZAMBIA LIMITED—See Atlas Mara Limited; *Int'l*, pg. 686
AFRILAND FIRST BANK; *Int'l*, pg. 192
AGRICULTURAL BANK OF CHINA - HONG KONG—See Agricultural Bank of China Limited; *Int'l*, pg. 217
AGRICULTURAL BANK OF CHINA LIMITED; *Int'l*, pg. 216
AGRICULTURAL BANK OF CHINA (MOSCOW) LIMITED; *Int'l*, pg. 216
AGRICULTURAL BANK OF CHINA - SINGAPORE—See Agricultural Bank of China Limited; *Int'l*, pg. 217
AGRICULTURAL BANK OF CHINA - TOKYO—See Agricultural Bank of China Limited; *Int'l*, pg. 217
AGRICULTURAL BANK OF CHINA - UK—See Agricultural Bank of China Limited; *Int'l*, pg. 217
AGRICULTURAL DEVELOPMENT BANK LIMITED; *Int'l*, pg. 217
AGRIPHAR DE COSTA RICA SA—See Element Solutions Inc.; *U.S. Public*, pg. 725
AGROPROMCREDIT JSCB; *Int'l*, pg. 220
AHLI BANK QPSC; *Int'l*, pg. 223
AHLI BANK S.A.O.G.; *Int'l*, pg. 223
AIB CORPORATE BANKING LIMITED—See AIB Group plc; *Int'l*, pg. 228
THE AICHI BANK, LTD.—See Aichi Financial Group Co., Ltd.; *Int'l*, pg. 229
AION SA/NV—See Warburg Pincus LLC; *U.S. Private*, pg. 4436
AIRAN LIMITED; *Int'l*, pg. 241
AJMAN BANK PJSC; *Int'l*, pg. 258
AKBANK AG—See Akbank T.A.S.; *Int'l*, pg. 261
AKBANK (DUBAI) LIMITED—See Akbank T.A.S.; *Int'l*, pg. 261
AKBANK T.A.S.; *Int'l*, pg. 260
AKB AVANGARD OAO; *Int'l*, pg. 260
A.K. CAPITAL SERVICES LTD.; *Int'l*, pg. 25
AKIBANK PJSC; *Int'l*, pg. 263
AKTIA BANK PLC; *Int'l*, pg. 265
AKTIF YATIRIM BANKASI A.S.; *Int'l*, pg. 267
ALANDSBANKEN ABP; *Int'l*, pg. 290
ALANDSBANKEN ASSET MANAGEMENT AB—See Alandsbanken Abp; *Int'l*, pg. 290
ALANDSBANKEN EQUITIES RESEARCH AB—See Alandsbanken Abp; *Int'l*, pg. 290
ALANDSBANKEN FONDBOLAG AB—See Alandsbanken Abp; *Int'l*, pg. 290
ALANDSBANKEN SVERIGE AB—See Alandsbanken Abp; *Int'l*, pg. 290
AL ARABI INVESTMENT GROUP CO.—See Arab Bank plc; *Int'l*, pg. 529
AL-ARAFAH ISLAMI BANK PLC; *Int'l*, pg. 284
ALBANY BANK & TRUST COMPANY, N.A.; *U.S. Private*, pg. 151
AL BARAKA BANK EGYPT—See Al Baraka Banking Group B.S.C.; *Int'l*, pg. 276
AL BARAKA BANKING GROUP B.S.C.; *Int'l*, pg. 275
AL BARAKA BANK LEBANON SAL—See Al Baraka Banking Group B.S.C.; *Int'l*, pg. 276
AL BARAKA BANK LTD.—See Al Baraka Banking Group B.S.C.; *Int'l*, pg. 276
AL BARAKA BANK (PAKISTAN) LIMITED—See Al Baraka Banking Group B.S.C.; *Int'l*, pg. 276
AL BARAKA BANK SUDAN—See Al Baraka Banking Group B.S.C.; *Int'l*, pg. 276
AL BARAKA BANK SYRIA—See Al Baraka Banking Group B.S.C.; *Int'l*, pg. 276
AL BARAKA BANK TUNISIA—See Al Baraka Banking Group B.S.C.; *Int'l*, pg. 276
AL BARAKA ISLAMIC BANK E.C.—See Al Baraka Banking Group B.S.C.; *Int'l*, pg. 276
ALBARAKA TURKISH FINANCE HOUSE—See Al Baraka Banking Group B.S.C.; *Int'l*, pg. 276
ALBARAKA TURK KATILIM BANKASI A.S.; *Int'l*, pg. 293
ALCENTRA NY LLC—See Franklin Resources, Inc.; *U.S. Public*, pg. 879
ALDEN STATE BANK; *U.S. Private*, pg. 159
ALDERMORE BANK PLC—See AnaCap Financial Partners LLP; *Int'l*, pg. 445
ALEF-BANK CJSC JSCB; *Int'l*, pg. 306
ALEXANDRIA BANCORP LTD—See Guardian Capital Group Limited; *Int'l*, pg. 3169
ALFA-BANK JSC—See ABH Holdings S.A.; *Int'l*, pg. 60
ALFA CAPITAL LLC—See Alfa Group; *Int'l*, pg. 308
ALFRED HERRHAUSEN GESELLSCHAFT - DAS INTERNATIONALE FORUM DER DEUTSCHEN BANK - MBH—See Deutsche Bank Aktiengesellschaft; *Int'l*, pg. 2055
ALINMA BANK; *Int'l*, pg. 329
ALIOR BANK S.A.; *Int'l*, pg. 329
ALIZZ ISLAMIC BANK SAOG—See Arab Bank plc; *Int'l*, pg. 529
AL JAZEERA SUDANESE JORDANIAN BANK; *Int'l*, pg. 280
ALLEGIANCE BANK—See Stellar Bancorp, Inc.; *U.S. Public*, pg. 1944
ALLIANCE BANK INC.; *U.S. Private*, pg. 181
ALLIANCE BANK; *U.S. Private*, pg. 181
ALLIANCE BANK—See Alliance Bancorp; *U.S. Private*, pg. 181
ALLIANCE FINANCIAL GROUP BERHAD; *Int'l*, pg. 338
ALLIANZ BANK FINANCIAL ADVISORS S.P.A.—See Allianz SE; *Int'l*, pg. 344
ALLIED BANK LIMITED—See Ibrahim Fibres Limited; *Int'l*, pg. 3576
ALLIED FIRST BANK—See Allied First Bancorp, Inc.; *U.S. Private*, pg. 186
ALLY BANK—See Ally Financial Inc.; *U.S. Public*, pg. 81
ALMA EXCHANGE BANK & TRUST—See South Banking Company; *U.S. Private*, pg. 3719
ALM. BRAND A/S; *Int'l*, pg. 361
ALPHA BANK CYPRUS LIMITED—See Alpha Services and Holdings S.A.; *Int'l*, pg. 369

522110 — COMMERCIAL BANKING

ALPHA BANK LONDON LTD—See Alpha Services and Holdings S.A.; *Int'l*, pg. 369
ALPHA GROUP JERSEY LTD—See Alpha Services and Holdings S.A.; *Int'l*, pg. 369
ALPHA SERVICES AND HOLDINGS S.A.; *Int'l*, pg. 369
ALPINE BANK—See Alpine Banks of Colorado; *U.S. Public*, pg. 85
AL RAJHI BANK - JORDAN LTD.—See Al Rajhi Bank; *Int'l*, pg. 282
AL RAJHI BANK - MALAYSIA SDN. BHD.—See Al Rajhi Bank; *Int'l*, pg. 282
AL RAJHI BANK; *Int'l*, pg. 282
AL SALAM BANK-BAHRAIN B.S.C.; *Int'l*, pg. 282
AL SALAM BANK - SUDAN; *Int'l*, pg. 282
ALTA BANKA A.D.; *Int'l*, pg. 383
ALTABANK—See Glacier Bancorp, Inc.; *U.S. Public*, pg. 938
AL TANMYAH SERVICES L.L.C.—See Dubai Islamic Bank PSJ; *Int'l*, pg. 2219
ALTERNATIF YATIRIM A.S.—See AG Anadolu Grubu Holding A.S.; *Int'l*, pg. 197
ALTERRA BANK—See First Business Financial Services, Inc.; *U.S. Public*, pg. 840
ALVA STATE BANK & TRUST COMPANY—See Grace Investment Company, Inc.; *U.S. Private*, pg. 1749
AMALGAMATED BANK OF CHICAGO—See Amalgamated Investments Co.; *U.S. Private*, pg. 215
AMALGAMATED BANK—See Amalgamated Financial Corp.; *U.S. Public*, pg. 89
AMALGA TRUST INC.—See Amalgamated Investments Co.; *U.S. Private*, pg. 215
AM ARA REIT MANAGERS SDN BHD—See AMMB Holdings Berhad; *Int'l*, pg. 429
AMARILLO NATIONAL BANK—See Amarillo National Bancorp, Inc.; *U.S. Private*, pg. 216
AMBANK (M) BERHAD—See AMMB Holdings Berhad; *Int'l*, pg. 429
AMBOY BANK; *U.S. Private*, pg. 218
AMC TREASURY SERVICES LTD—See Amalgamated Metal Corporation PLC; *Int'l*, pg. 408
AMEGY BANK—See Zions Bancorporation, National Association; *U.S. Public*, pg. 2408
AMERANT BANK, N.A.—See Amerant Bancorp Inc.; *U.S. Public*, pg. 94
AMERASIA BANK; *U.S. Private*, pg. 219
AMERICAN BANCORP OF OKLAHOMA; *U.S. Private*, pg. 223
AMERICAN BANK—See American Bank Incorporated; *U.S. Public*, pg. 97
AMERICAN BANK—See Guaranty Development Company; *U.S. Private*, pg. 1809
AMERICAN BANK & TRUST COMPANY; *U.S. Private*, pg. 223
AMERICAN BANK & TRUST COMPANY—See American Bank Holding Inc.; *U.S. Private*, pg. 224
AMERICAN BANK & TRUST—See American Bancorp, Inc.; *U.S. Public*, pg. 97
AMERICAN BANK & TRUST—See Leackco Bank Holding Company, Inc.; *U.S. Public*, pg. 2405
AMERICAN BUSINESS BANK; *U.S. Public*, pg. 98
AMERICAN CAPITAL TRUST I—See American Bank Incorporated; *U.S. Public*, pg. 97
AMERICAN COMMUNITY BANK OF INDIANA—See AMB Financial Corp.; *U.S. Public*, pg. 91
AMERICAN CONTINENTAL BANK—See American Continental Bancorp; *U.S. Private*, pg. 228
AMERICAN EXPRESS CARTE FRANCE SA—See American Express Company; *U.S. Public*, pg. 101
AMERICAN EXPRESS CHANGE SAS—See American Express Company; *U.S. Public*, pg. 101
AMERICAN EXPRESS NATIONAL BANK—See American Express Company; *U.S. Public*, pg. 101
AMERICAN FIRST NATIONAL BANK NA; *U.S. Private*, pg. 234
AMERICAN HERITAGE BANK; *U.S. Private*, pg. 236
AMERICAN HERITAGE NATIONAL BANK; *U.S. Private*, pg. 236
AMERICAN MOMENTUM BANK—See The Adam Corporation/Group; *U.S. Private*, pg. 3981
AMERICAN NATIONAL BANK INC.—See American National Corporation; *U.S. Private*, pg. 241
AMERICAN NATIONAL BANK OF MINNESOTA—See American Bancorporation of Minnesota, Inc.; *U.S. Private*, pg. 223
AMERICAN NATIONAL BANK & TRUST—See AmeriBancShares, Inc.; *U.S. Private*, pg. 220
AMERICAN RIVIERA BANK; *U.S. Public*, pg. 109
AMERICAN STATE BANK—See Steele Holdings, Inc.; *U.S. Private*, pg. 3796
AMERICAN STATE BANK & TRUST COMPANY OF WILLISTON—See American State Bank Holding Company, Inc.; *U.S. Private*, pg. 255
AMERICAN STATE BANK & TRUST COMPANY—See American State Bancshares, Inc.; *U.S. Private*, pg. 255
AMERIS BANK—See Ameris Bancorp; *U.S. Public*, pg. 114
AMERISERV FINANCIAL BANK—See Ameriserv Financial, Inc.; *U.S. Public*, pg. 115
AMEX CANADA INC.—See American Express Company; *U.S. Public*, pg. 101

AMINTERNATIONAL (L) LTD—See AMMB Holdings Berhad; *Int'l*, pg. 429
AMISLAMIC BANK BERHAD—See AMMB Holdings Berhad; *Int'l*, pg. 429
AML RIGHTSOURCE LLC; *U.S. Private*, pg. 263
AMMB HOLDINGS BERHAD; *Int'l*, pg. 429
AM NOMINEES (TEMPATAN) SDN BHD—See AMMB Holdings Berhad; *Int'l*, pg. 429
AMP BANK LIMITED—See AMP Limited; *Int'l*, pg. 431
AMTEX BANCSHARES INC.; *U.S. Private*, pg. 268
ANB BANK—See The Sturm Financial Group, Inc.; *U.S. Private*, pg. 4124
ANCHOR BANK; *U.S. Private*, pg. 272
ANDOVER BANK—See Andover Bancorp, Inc.; *U.S. Public*, pg. 136
ANOD BANK; *Int'l*, pg. 474
ANSA MERCHANT BANK LIMITED—See ANSA McAL Limited; *Int'l*, pg. 476
ANSTAFF BANK—See First National Bancorp, Inc.; *U.S. Public*, pg. 1521
ANZ ASIA LIMITED—See Australia & New Zealand Banking Group Limited; *Int'l*, pg. 720
ANZ BANK (EUROPE) LIMITED—See Australia & New Zealand Banking Group Limited; *Int'l*, pg. 720
ANZ BANK (KIRIBATI) LIMITED—See Australia & New Zealand Banking Group Limited; *Int'l*, pg. 720
ANZ BANK (SAMOA) LIMITED—See Australia & New Zealand Banking Group Limited; *Int'l*, pg. 719
ANZ BANK SOLOMON ISLANDS—See Australia & New Zealand Banking Group Limited; *Int'l*, pg. 719
ANZ BANK (VANUATU) LIMITED—See Australia & New Zealand Banking Group Limited; *Int'l*, pg. 719
ANZ COOK ISLANDS—See Australia & New Zealand Banking Group Limited; *Int'l*, pg. 719
ANZ FIJI—See Australia & New Zealand Banking Group Limited; *Int'l*, pg. 719
ANZ GERMANY—See Australia & New Zealand Banking Group Limited; *Int'l*, pg. 720
ANZ GUAM INC.—See Australia & New Zealand Banking Group Limited; *Int'l*, pg. 720
ANZ INSTITUTIONAL DIVISION—See Australia & New Zealand Banking Group Limited; *Int'l*, pg. 720
ANZ JAPAN—See Australia & New Zealand Banking Group Limited; *Int'l*, pg. 719
ANZ KOREA—See Australia & New Zealand Banking Group Limited; *Int'l*, pg. 719
ANZ MALAYSIA—See Australia & New Zealand Banking Group Limited; *Int'l*, pg. 719
ANZ PHILIPPINES—See Australia & New Zealand Banking Group Limited; *Int'l*, pg. 719
ANZ SECURITIES INC.—See Australia & New Zealand Banking Group Limited; *Int'l*, pg. 719
ANZ SHANGHAI—See Australia & New Zealand Banking Group Limited; *Int'l*, pg. 719
ANZ TAIWAN—See Australia & New Zealand Banking Group Limited; *Int'l*, pg. 719
ANZ TONGA—See Australia & New Zealand Banking Group Limited; *Int'l*, pg. 720
ANZ UK—See Australia & New Zealand Banking Group Limited; *Int'l*, pg. 720
AOZORA BANK, LTD.—See Cerberus Capital Management, L.P.; *U.S. Private*, pg. 836
AP ANLAGE & PRIVATBANK AG—See Ripplewood Holdings LLC; *U.S. Private*, pg. 3439
APE COMMERCIAL PROPERTY A.E.—See Alpha Services and Holdings S.A.; *Int'l*, pg. 369
APEX BANK—See Clayton HC, Inc.; *U.S. Private*, pg. 918
APOLLO BANK—See Seacoast Banking Corporation of Florida; *U.S. Public*, pg. 1851
APOLLO TRUST COMPANY—See Apollo Bancorp, Inc.; *U.S. Public*, pg. 145
THE APPLE CREEK BANKING COMPANY—See Apple Creek Banc Corp.; *U.S. Private*, pg. 296
A PROMOTORA, SOCIEDADE DE CAPITAL DE RISCO, S.A.R.L.—See Caixa Geral de Depositos S.A.; *Int'l*, pg. 1260
AQUESTA BANK—See United Community Banks, Inc.; *U.S. Public*, pg. 2230
ARAB AFRICAN INTERNATIONAL BANK; *Int'l*, pg. 529
ARAB BANK AUSTRALIA LTD—See Arab Bank plc; *Int'l*, pg. 529
ARAB BANKING CORPORATION B.S.C.; *Int'l*, pg. 529
ARAB BANK PLC; *Int'l*, pg. 529
ARAB BANK (SWITZERLAND) LTD.—See Arab Bank plc; *Int'l*, pg. 529
ARAB BANK-SYRIA—See Arab Bank plc; *Int'l*, pg. 529
ARAB INVESTMENT BANK S.A.L.—See Arab Bank plc; *Int'l*, pg. 529
ARAB ISLAMIC BANK; *Int'l*, pg. 530
ARAB JORDAN INVESTMENT BANK; *Int'l*, pg. 530
ARAB NATIONAL BANK; *Int'l*, pg. 531
ARAB SUDANESE BANK LIMITED—See Arab Bank plc; *Int'l*, pg. 529
ARAB TUNISIAN BANK—See Arab Bank plc; *Int'l*, pg. 529
ARARATBANK OJSC; *Int'l*, pg. 536
ARBEJDERNES LANDSBANK A/S; *Int'l*, pg. 537
ARBUTHNOT BANKING GROUP PLC; *Int'l*, pg. 539
ARDSHINBANK CJSC; *Int'l*, pg. 557

ARION BANK HF.; *Int'l*, pg. 565
ARION BANKI HF; *Int'l*, pg. 565
ARIZONA BANK & TRUST—See Heartland Financial USA, Inc.; *U.S. Public*, pg. 1018
ARKANSAS VALLEY STATE BANK; *U.S. Private*, pg. 326
ARMBUSINESSBANK CJSC; *Int'l*, pg. 574
ARMECONOMBANK OJSC; *Int'l*, pg. 574
ARMED FORCES BANK, N.A.—See Dickinson Financial Corporation; *U.S. Private*, pg. 1227
ARTHUR STATE BANK; *U.S. Private*, pg. 342
ARTIGIANCASSA SPA—See BNP Paribas SA; *Int'l*, pg. 1079
ARVEST BANK—See Arvest Bank Group, Inc.; *U.S. Private*, pg. 344
ASA BANKA D.D. SARAJEVO; *Int'l*, pg. 591
ASA BANKA D.D.; *Int'l*, pg. 591
ASA INTERNATIONAL INDIA MICROFINANCE LIMITED—See ASA International Group plc; *Int'l*, pg. 591
ASA MICROFINANCE (TANZANIA) LTD.—See ASA International Group plc; *Int'l*, pg. 591
ASA PAKISTAN LIMITED—See ASA International Group plc; *Int'l*, pg. 592
AS CITADELE BANKA EESTI FILIAAL—See Ripplewood Holdings LLC; *U.S. Private*, pg. 3439
AS CITADELE BANKA—See Ripplewood Holdings LLC; *U.S. Private*, pg. 3439
ASHARI AGENCIES LTD.; *Int'l*, pg. 606
ASHTON STATE BANK—See Ashton Bancshares, Inc.; *U.S. Private*, pg. 350
ASIA COMMERCIAL BANK; *Int'l*, pg. 611
ASIACREDIT BANK JSC; *Int'l*, pg. 616
ASIA UNITED BANK CORPORATION; *Int'l*, pg. 616
ASKARI BANK LTD.—See Fauji Foundation; *Int'l*, pg. 2623
AS REVERTA; *Int'l*, pg. 591
ASSOCIATED BANK, NA—See Associated Banc-Corp; *U.S. Public*, pg. 214
ATAG ASSET MANAGEMENT AG—See Basellandschaftliche Kantonalbank; *Int'l*, pg. 871
ATASCOSA NATIONAL BANK; *U.S. Private*, pg. 365
ATG TRUST COMPANY—See Midland States Bancorp, Inc.; *U.S. Public*, pg. 1445
ATHOL SAVINGS BANK INC.; *U.S. Private*, pg. 368
ATLANTIC COMMUNITY BANKERS BANK; *U.S. Private*, pg. 372
ATLANTIC STEWARDSHIP BANK—See Columbia Financial, Inc.; *U.S. Public*, pg. 534
ATLANTIC UNION BANK—See Atlantic Union Bankshares Corporation; *U.S. Public*, pg. 223
ATL LEASING; *Int'l*, pg. 673
ATTICA BANK S.A.; *Int'l*, pg. 696
ATTIJARIWAFA BANK—See Banco Santander, S.A.; *Int'l*, pg. 825
AUBURNBANK—See Auburn National Bancorporation, Inc.; *U.S. Public*, pg. 225
AUBURN SAVINGS BANK—See Auburn Bancorp, Inc.; *U.S. Public*, pg. 225
AURSKOG SPAREBANK; *Int'l*, pg. 714
AUSTIN BANK CORP., INC.; *U.S. Private*, pg. 395
AUSTIN BANK, TEXAS N.A.—See Austin Bank Corp., Inc.; *U.S. Private*, pg. 395
AUSTIN CAPITAL BANK; *U.S. Private*, pg. 395
AUSWIDE BANK LTD.; *Int'l*, pg. 724
AVIDBANK—See Avidbank Holdings, Inc.; *U.S. Public*, pg. 246
AXA BANK AG.—See AXA S.A.; *Int'l*, pg. 757
AXA BANK BELGIUM SABELGIUM SA—See AXA S.A.; *Int'l*, pg. 756
AXA BANK EUROPE CZECH REPUBLIC—See AXA S.A.; *Int'l*, pg. 755
AXA BANK EUROPE SLOVAKIA—See AXA S.A.; *Int'l*, pg. 755
AXIS BANK LIMITED; *Int'l*, pg. 769
B1BANK—See Business First Bancshares, Inc.; *U.S. Public*, pg. 413
BAADER HELVEA AG—See Baader Bank AG; *Int'l*, pg. 791
BAADER HELVEA INC.—See Baader Bank AG; *Int'l*, pg. 791
BAADER HELVEA LTD.—See Baader Bank AG; *Int'l*, pg. 791
BAANX GROUP LTD.; *Int'l*, pg. 792
BABYLON BANK S.A.; *Int'l*, pg. 793
BAC FLORIDA BANK—See Banco Bradesco S.A.; *Int'l*, pg. 819
BA FINANS AS—See Auchan Holding S.A.; *Int'l*, pg. 699
BAHRAIN ISLAMIC BANK; *Int'l*, pg. 800
BAIKALINVESTBANK JSC; *Int'l*, pg. 802
BAKER-BOYER NATIONAL BANK INC.—See Baker Boyer Bancorp; *U.S. Public*, pg. 264
BAL GLOBAL FINANCE (DEUTSCHLAND) GMBH—See Bank of America Corporation; *U.S. Public*, pg. 270
BALLSTON SPA BANCORP INC.; *U.S. Public*, pg. 268
BALOISE BANK SOBA—See Baloise Holding AG; *Int'l*, pg. 811
BANAMEX USA BANCORP—See Citigroup Inc.; *U.S. Public*, pg. 501
BANCA CARIGE S.P.A.; *Int'l*, pg. 814
BANCA CATTOLICA S.P.A.—See Credito Valtellinese Societa Cooperativa; *Int'l*, pg. 1837
BANCA COMERCIALA ROMANA CHISINAU S.A.—See B.C. Victoriabank S.A.; *Int'l*, pg. 789

522110 — COMMERCIAL BANKING

BANCA COMERCIALA ROMANA S.A.—See Erste Group Bank AG; *Int'l*, pg. 2497
BANCA DE ECONOMII S.A.; *Int'l*, pg. 814
BANCA DELLA CAMPANIA S.P.A.—See BPER BANCA S.p.A; *Int'l*, pg. 1132
BANCA DELLA NUOVA TERRA—See BPER BANCA S.p.A; *Int'l*, pg. 1132
BANCA DI CIVIDALE S.P.A.; *Int'l*, pg. 814
BANCA DI SASSARI S.P.A.—See BPER BANCA S.p.A; *Int'l*, pg. 1132
BANCADVICE, LLC; *U.S. Private*, pg. 464
BANCA EUROMOBILIARE SPA—See Credito Emiliano S.p.A.; *Int'l*, pg. 1836
BANCA INTESA JSC; *Int'l*, pg. 815
BANCA MARCH-LONDON—See Alba Grupo March; *Int'l*, pg. 292
BANCA MARCH S.A.—See Alba Grupo March; *Int'l*, pg. 292
BANCA MONTE DEI PASCHI DI SIENA S.P.A.; *Int'l*, pg. 815
BANCA NAZIONALE DEL LAVORO S.P.A.—See BNP Paribas SA; *Int'l*, pg. 1089
BANCA PER LO SVILUPPO DELLA COOPERAZIONE DI CREDITO S.P.A.—See Iccrea Holding S.p.A.; *Int'l*, pg. 3578
BANCAPERTA S.P.A.—See Credito Valtellinese Societa Cooperativa; *Int'l*, pg. 1837
BANCA POPOLARE DELL'ETRURIA E DEL LAZIO S.C.; *Int'l*, pg. 815
BANCA POPOLARE DI CROTONE S.P.A.—See BPER BANCA S.p.A; *Int'l*, pg. 1132
BANCA POPOLARE DI LANCIANO E SULMONA S.P.A.—See BPER BANCA S.p.A; *Int'l*, pg. 1132
BANCA POPOLARE DI NOVARA S.P.A.—See Banco BPM S.p.A; *Int'l*, pg. 819
BANCA POPOLARE DI RAVENNA S.P.A.—See BPER BANCA S.p.A; *Int'l*, pg. 1132
BANCA POPOLARE DI SONDRIO S.P.A.; *Int'l*, pg. 815
BANCA POPOLARE DI SPOLETO S.P.A.; *Int'l*, pg. 816
BANCA POPOLARE DI VERONA - S. GEMINIANO E S. PROSPERO S.P.A.—See Banco BPM S.p.A.; *Int'l*, pg. 819
BANCA PRIVATA D'ANDORRA, SA; *Int'l*, pg. 816
BANCA PROGETTO S.P.A.—See Brookfield Corporation; *Int'l*, pg. 1181
BANCA SERFIN, S.A.—See Banco Santander, S.A.; *Int'l*, pg. 826
BANCA SISTEMA S.P.A.; *Int'l*, pg. 816
BANCFIRST—See BancFirst Corporation; *U.S. Public*, pg. 269
BANCO ALFA DE INVESTIMENTO SA; *Int'l*, pg. 816
BANCO ALIADO, S.A.—See Grupo Aliado S.A.; *Int'l*, pg. 3119
BANCO AZTECA SA—See Grupo Salinas, S.A. de C.V.; *Int'l*, pg. 3135
BANCO BAC DE PANAMA, S.A.; *Int'l*, pg. 816
BANCO BARCLAYS S.A.—See Barclays PLC; *Int'l*, pg. 859
BANCO BBVA ARGENTINA S.A.—See Banco Bilbao Vizcaya Argentaria, S.A.; *Int'l*, pg. 817
BANCO BILBAO VIZCAYA ARGENTARIA (PORTUGAL), S.A.—See Banco Bilbao Vizcaya Argentaria, S.A.; pg. 817
BANCO BILBAO VIZCAYA ARGENTARIA, S.A.; *Int'l*, pg. 816
BANCO BMG S.A.; *Int'l*, pg. 818
BANCO BOAVISTA S.A.—See Banco Bradesco S.A.; *Int'l*, pg. 819
BANCO BPI, S.A.—See Lone Star Funds; *U.S. Private*, pg. 2484
BANCO BPM SPA; *Int'l*, pg. 819
BANCO BRADESCO EUROPA S.A.—See Banco Bradesco S.A.; *Int'l*, pg. 819
BANCO BRADESCO FINANCIAMENTOS S.A.—See Banco Bradesco S.A.; *Int'l*, pg. 819
BANCO BRADESCO S.A.; *Int'l*, pg. 819
BANCO CAIXA GERAL BRASIL, S.A.—See ABANCA CORPORACION BANCARIA, SA; *Int'l*, pg. 48
BANCO CITIBANK S.A.—See Citigroup Inc.; *U.S. Public*, pg. 501
BANCO COMAFI S.A.; *Int'l*, pg. 820
BANCO COMERCIAL DE MACAU, S.A.—See Dah Sing Financial Holdings Limited; *Int'l*, pg. 1913
BANCO COMERCIAL DO ATLANTICO, S.A.R.L.—See Caixa Geral de Depositos S.A.; *Int'l*, pg. 1260
BANCO COMERCIAL PORTUGUES, S.A.; *Int'l*, pg. 820
BANCO COMPARTAMOS, S.A., INSTITUCION DE BANCA MULTIPLE—See Gentera, S.A.B. de C.V.; *Int'l*, pg. 2928
BANCO CRUZEIRO DO SUL SA; *Int'l*, pg. 820
BANCO DA AMAZONIA S/A; *Int'l*, pg. 820
BANCO DA CHINA BRASIL S.A.—See Bank of China, Ltd.; *Int'l*, pg. 841
BANCO DAVIVIENDA (COSTA RICA) S.A.—See Grupo Bolivar S.A.; *Int'l*, pg. 3123
BANCO DAVIVIENDA HONDURAS S.A.—See Grupo Bolivar S.A.; *Int'l*, pg. 3123
BANCO DAVIVIENDA S.A.—See Grupo Bolivar S.A.; *Int'l*, pg. 3123
BANCO DAYCOVAL S.A.; *Int'l*, pg. 820
BANCO DE BOGOTA SA; *Int'l*, pg. 820
BANCO DE COMERCIO S.A.; *Int'l*, pg. 820

BANCO DE CREDITO DEL PERU SA—See Credicorp Ltd.; *Int'l*, pg. 1834
BANCO DE CREDITO E INVERSIONES S.A.—See Empresas Juan Yarur S.A.C.; *Int'l*, pg. 2391
BANCO DE HONDURAS S.A.—See Citigroup Inc.; *U.S. Public*, pg. 501
BANCO DE LA NACION ARGENTINA; *Int'l*, pg. 820
BANCO DEL BAJIO, S.A.; *Int'l*, pg. 822
BANCO DEL CARIBE, C.A. BANCO UNIVERSAL; *Int'l*, pg. 822
BANCO DELTA S.A.; *Int'l*, pg. 822
BANCO DE OCCIDENTE S.A.—See Grupo Aval Acciones y Valores S.A.; *Int'l*, pg. 3121
BANCO DE OCCIDENTE; *Int'l*, pg. 821
BANCO DE ORO SAVINGS BANK INC.—See BDO Unibank, Inc.; *Int'l*, pg. 930
BANCO DEPOSITARIO BBVA, S.A.—See Banco Bilbao Vizcaya Argentaria, S.A.; *Int'l*, pg. 817
BANCO DESIO LAZIO S P A—See Banco Di Desio e Della Brianza S.p.A.; *Int'l*, pg. 822
BANCO DE VENEZUELA, S.A.—See Banco Santander, S.A.; *Int'l*, pg. 825
BANCO DI CARIBE (ARUBA) N.V.—See Banco di Caribe N.V.; *Int'l*, pg. 822
BANCO DI DESIO E DELLA BRIANZA S.P.A.; *Int'l*, pg. 822
BANCO DI SARDEGNA S.P.A.—See BPER BANCA S.p.A; *Int'l*, pg. 1132
BANCO DO BRASIL S.A. - NEW YORK—See Banco do Brasil S.A.; *Int'l*, pg. 822
BANCO DO BRASIL S.A.; *Int'l*, pg. 822
BANCO DO ESTADO DO RIO GRANDE DO SUL SA; *Int'l*, pg. 822
BANCO GENERAL (COSTA RICA), S.A.—See Banco General, S.A.; *Int'l*, pg. 822
BANCO GENERAL, S.A.; *Int'l*, pg. 822
BANCO GMAC S.A.—See General Motors Company; *U.S. Public*, pg. 925
BANCO GNB COLOMBIA S.A.—See Banco GNB Sudameris S.A.; *Int'l*, pg. 823
BANCO GNB PARAGUAY S.A.—See Banco GNB Sudameris S.A.; *Int'l*, pg. 823
BANCO GNB PERU S.A.—See Banco GNB Sudameris S.A.; *Int'l*, pg. 823
BANCO GNB SUDAMERIS S.A.; *Int'l*, pg. 822
BANCO GUAYAQUIL SA; *Int'l*, pg. 823
BANCO GUIPUZCOANO S.A.—See Banco de Sabadell, S.A.; *Int'l*, pg. 821
BANCO HSBC SALVADORENO, S.A.—See HSBC Holdings plc; *Int'l*, pg. 3503
BANCO INBURSA S.A.—See Grupo Financiero Inbursa, S.A. de C.V.; *Int'l*, pg. 3129
BANCO INDUSVAL MULTISTOCK - PORTO ALEGRE UNIT—See Banco Master S.A.; *Int'l*, pg. 823
BANCO INDUSVAL MULTISTOCK - RECIFE UNIT—See Banco Master S.A.; *Int'l*, pg. 823
BANCO INDUSVAL MULTISTOCK - RIO DE JANEIRO UNIT—See Banco Master S.A.; *Int'l*, pg. 823
BANCO INDUSVAL MULTISTOCK—See Banco Master S.A.; *Int'l*, pg. 823
BANCO INTERATLANTICO, S.A.R.L.—See Caixa Geral de Depositos S.A.; *Int'l*, pg. 1260
BANCO INTERNACIONAL DE COSTA RICA, S.A.; *Int'l*, pg. 823
BANCO INTERNACIONAL; *Int'l*, pg. 823
BANCO INTER S.A.; *Int'l*, pg. 823
BANCO KEB DO BRASIL S.A.—See Hana Financial Group, Inc.; *Int'l*, pg. 3240
BANCO KEB HANA DO BRASIL S.A.—See Hana Financial Group, Inc.; *Int'l*, pg. 3240
BANCOLOMBIA PUERTO RICO INTERNACIONAL INC—See Bancolombia S.A.; *Int'l*, pg. 828
BANCO MACRO S.A.; *Int'l*, pg. 823
BANCO MASTER S.A.; *Int'l*, pg. 823
BANCO MEDIOLANUM, S.A.—See Banca Mediolanum S.p.A.; *Int'l*, pg. 815
BANCO MULTIVA, S.A.—See Grupo Empresarial Angeles, S.A. de C.V.; *Int'l*, pg. 3126
BANCO NACIONAL DE MEXICO, S.A.—See Citigroup Inc.; *U.S. Public*, pg. 504
BANCO NACIONAL DE PANAMA; *Int'l*, pg. 823
BANCO PAN S.A.—See BTG Pactual Holding S.A.; *Int'l*, pg. 1204
BANCO PATAGONIA SUDAMERIS S.A.—See Banco do Brasil S.A.; *Int'l*, pg. 822
BANCO PICHINCHA MIAMI AGENCY; *U.S. Private*, pg. 464
BANCO PINE S.A.; *Int'l*, pg. 824
BANCO POPULAR DE PUERTO RICO—See Popular, Inc.; *U.S. Public*, pg. 1702
BANCO PROCREDIT COLUMBIA S.A.—See Creditos y Ahorro Credifinanciera S.A., Compania de Financiamiento; *Int'l*, pg. 1837
BANCO PROVINCIAL OVERSEAS N.V.—See Banco Bilbao Vizcaya Argentaria, S.A.; *Int'l*, pg. 817
BANCO RABOBANK INTERNACIONAL BRASIL S.A.—See Cooperatieve Centrale Raiffeisen-Boerenleenbank B.A.; *Int'l*, pg. 1791
BANCO RIO DE LA PLATA S.A.—See Banco Santander, S.A.; *Int'l*, pg. 825

THE BANCORP BANK—See The Bancorp, Inc.; *U.S. Public*, pg. 2036
BANCO SAFRA S.A.; *Int'l*, pg. 824
BANCO SANTANDER (BRASIL) S.A.—See Banco Santander, S.A.; *Int'l*, pg. 826
BANCO SANTANDER CENTRAL HISPANO (GUERNSEY), LTD.—See Banco Santander, S.A.; *Int'l*, pg. 825
BANCO SANTANDER DE NEGOCIOS PORTUGAL, S.A.—See Banco Santander, S.A.; *Int'l*, pg. 825
BANCO SANTANDER INTERNATIONAL—See First BanCorp; *U.S. Public*, pg. 839
BANCO SANTANDER (PANAMA), S.A.—See Banco Santander, S.A.; *Int'l*, pg. 825
BANCO SANTANDER PERU S.A.—See Banco Santander, S.A.; *Int'l*, pg. 825
BANCO SANTANDER PORTUGAL, S.A.—See Banco Santander, S.A.; *Int'l*, pg. 825
BANCO SANTANDER RIO S.A.—See Banco Santander, S.A.; *Int'l*, pg. 825
BANCO SANTANDER (SUISSE), S.A.—See Banco Santander, S.A.; *Int'l*, pg. 825
BANCO SANTANDER TOTTA, S.A.—See Banco Santander, S.A.; *Int'l*, pg. 825
BANCO SOFISA S.A.; *Int'l*, pg. 828
BANCO URQUIJO S.A.—See Banco de Sabadell, S.A.; *Int'l*, pg. 821
BANCPOST—See Eurobank Ergasias Services and Holdings S.A.; *Int'l*, pg. 2532
BANCSABADELL D'ANDORRA, S.A.—See Banco de Sabadell, S.A.; *Int'l*, pg. 821
BANCWEST INVESTMENT SERVICES, INC.—See BNP Paribas SA; *Int'l*, pg. 1087
BANDHAN BANK LIMITED—See Bandhan Financial Services Ltd.; *Int'l*, pg. 830
BANESCO BANCO UNIVERSAL C.A.; *Int'l*, pg. 831
BANESCO S.A.; *Int'l*, pg. 831
BANESCO USA; *U.S. Private*, pg. 465
BANESTES S.A. BANCO DO ESTADO DO ESPIRITO SANTO; *Int'l*, pg. 831
BANGKOK BANK BERHAD—See Bangkok Bank Public Company Limited; *Int'l*, pg. 833
BANGKOK BANK (CHINA) CO., LTD.—See Bangkok Bank Public Company Limited; *Int'l*, pg. 833
BANGKOK BANK PUBLIC COMPANY LIMITED; *Int'l*, pg. 832
BANIF-BANCO INTERNACIONAL DO FUNCHAL (BRASIL), SA—See Banco Santander, S.A.; *Int'l*, pg. 825
BANIF BANCO INTERNACIONAL DO FUNCHAL SA—See Banco Santander, S.A.; *Int'l*, pg. 825
BANISTMO S.A.—See Bancolombia S.A.; *Int'l*, pg. 828
BANK AGROROS JSC; *Int'l*, pg. 836
BANK ALEXANDROVSKY PJSC; *Int'l*, pg. 836
BANK ALFALAH LIMITED—See Abu Dhabi Group; *Int'l*, pg. 71
BANK AL-HABIB LIMITED—See Habib Group of Companies; *Int'l*, pg. 3203
BANK ALJAZIRA; *Int'l*, pg. 836
BANK AL-SHARQ S.A.S; *Int'l*, pg. 836
BANK AM BELLEVUE AG—See Bellevue Group AG; *Int'l*, pg. 967
BANK AUDI FRANCE S.A.—See Bank Audi sal; *Int'l*, pg. 837
BANK AUDI LLC—See Bank Audi sal; *Int'l*, pg. 837
BANK AUDI SAL - JORDAN BRANCHES—See Bank Audi sal; *Int'l*, pg. 837
BANK AUDI SAL; *Int'l*, pg. 837
BANK AUDI SYRIA SA—See Bank Audi sal; *Int'l*, pg. 837
BANK AUSTRALIA LIMITED; *Int'l*, pg. 837
BANK BPH SPOBKA AKCYJNA—See General Electric Company; *U.S. Public*, pg. 916
BANK BTB OJSC; *Int'l*, pg. 837
BANK CENTERCREDIT JSC; *Int'l*, pg. 837
BANK CLER AG—See Basler Kantonalbank AG; *Int'l*, pg. 887
BANK DELEN N.V.—See Ackermans & van Haaren NV; *Int'l*, pg. 104
BANK DHOFAR SAOG; *Int'l*, pg. 837
BANKDIRECT—See Texas Capital Bancshares, Inc.; *U.S. Public*, pg. 2025
BANKENSERVICE GMBH—See Deutscher Sparkassen- und Giroverband e.V.; *Int'l*, pg. 2085
BANKERS' BANK—See Bankers' Bancorporation, Inc.; *U.S. Private*, pg. 468
THE BANKERS BANK—See Bankers Bancorp of Oklahoma, Inc.; *U.S. Private*, pg. 467
BANKERS FINANCIAL CORPORATION—See Bankers International Financial Corporation; *U.S. Private*, pg. 467
BANKERS INTERNATIONAL CORPORATION (BRASIL) LTDA.—See Deutsche Bank Aktiengesellschaft; *Int'l*, pg. 2055
BANKERS TRUST COMPANY—See BTC Financial Corporation; *U.S. Private*, pg. 675
BANKFIRST FINANCIAL SERVICES—See BankFirst Capital Corporation; *U.S. Public*, pg. 274
BANK FUR TIROL UND VORARLBERG AG; *Int'l*, pg. 838
BANK GPB INTERNATIONAL S.A.—See Gazprombank JSC; *Int'l*, pg. 2892
BANKGUAM HOLDING COMPANY; *U.S. Public*, pg. 274

522110 — COMMERCIAL BANKING

BANK HANDLOWY W WARSZAWIE S.A.—See Citigroup Inc.; *U.S. Public*, pg. 502
BANKHAUS AUGUST LENZ & CO. AG—See Banca Mediolanum S.p.A.; *Int'l*, pg. 815
BANKHAUS ERBE JSC; *Int'l*, pg. 850
BANKHAUS LAMPE KG—See Dr. August Oetker KG; *Int'l*, pg. 2190
BANKHAUS W. FORTMANN & SOHNE KG—See Allianz SE; *Int'l*, pg. 351
BANKHAUS WOLBERN AG & CO. KG; *Int'l*, pg. 850
BANKIA, S.A.—See Lone Star Funds; *U.S. Private*, pg. 2484
BANK INDEPENDENT—See BancIndependent Inc.; *U.S. Private*, pg. 464
BANKINTER CONSUMER FINANCE, EFC, S.A.—See Bankinter, S.A.; *Int'l*, pg. 850
BANKINTER EMISIONES, S.A.—See Bankinter, S.A.; *Int'l*, pg. 850
BANKINTER GESTAO DE ATIVOS, S.A.—See Bankinter, S.A.; *Int'l*, pg. 850
BANKINTER LUXEMBOURG, S.A.—See Bankinter, S.A.; *Int'l*, pg. 850
BANKINTER, S.A.; *Int'l*, pg. 850
BANKINTER, S.A. - SUCURSAL EM PORTUGAL—See Bankinter, S.A.; *Int'l*, pg. 850
BANK IOWA—See Bank Iowa Corporation; *U.S. Private*, pg. 466
BANKISLAMI PAKISTAN LIMITED; *Int'l*, pg. 850
BANK J. VAN BREDA & CO. N.V.—See Ackermans & van Haaren NV; *Int'l*, pg. 104
BANK KERJASAMA RAKYAT MALAYSIA BERHAD; *Int'l*, pg. 838
BANK KUZNECKIY; *Int'l*, pg. 838
BANK LEUMI (JERSEY) LTD.—See Bank Leumi Le-Israel B.M.; *Int'l*, pg. 838
BANK LEUMI LE-ISRAEL B.M.; *Int'l*, pg. 838
BANK LEUMI USA—See Bank Leumi Le-Israel B.M.; *Int'l*, pg. 839
BANK LEUMI USA—See Bank Leumi Le-Israel B.M.; *Int'l*, pg. 839
BANK LEVOBEREZHNY PJSC; *Int'l*, pg. 839
BANK LINTH LLB AG; *Int'l*, pg. 839
BANK MAKRAMAH LIMITED—See Arif Habib Corporation Limited; *Int'l*, pg. 564
BANK MASSAD LTD.—See FIBI Holdings Ltd.; *Int'l*, pg. 2652
BANK MELLAT; *Int'l*, pg. 839
BANK MIDWEST; *U.S. Private*, pg. 466
BANK MIDWEST—See National Bank Holdings Corporation; *U.S. Public*, pg. 1493
BANK MILLENNIUM S.A.—See Banco Comercial Portugues, S.A.; *Int'l*, pg. 820
BANK MUAMALAT MALAYSIA BERHAD—See DRB-HICOM Berhad; *Int'l*, pg. 2201
BANK MUSCAT SAOG; *Int'l*, pg. 839
BANK NAGELMACKERS NV—See Anbang Insurance Group Co., Ltd.; *Int'l*, pg. 447
THE BANK, NATIONAL ASSOCIATION—See N.B.M. Corporation; *U.S. Private*, pg. 2827
BANK NIZWA SAOG; *Int'l*, pg. 839
BANK NORTHWEST—See Caldwell County Bancshares, Inc.; *U.S. Private*, pg. 716
BANK OF AFRICA - BENIN—See BOA Group S.A.; *Int'l*, pg. 1094
BANK OF AFRICA - BURKINA FASO—See BOA Group S.A.; *Int'l*, pg. 1094
BANK OF AFRICA - COTE D'IVOIRE—See BOA Group S.A.; *Int'l*, pg. 1094
BANK OF AFRICA - KENYA LTD.—See BOA Group S.A.; *Int'l*, pg. 1094
BANK OF AFRICA - MADAGASCAR—See BOA Group S.A.; *Int'l*, pg. 1094
BANK OF AFRICA - MALI—See BOA Group S.A.; *Int'l*, pg. 1094
BANK OF AFRICA; *Int'l*, pg. 839
BANK OF AFRICA - TANZANIA LIMITED—See BOA Group S.A.; *Int'l*, pg. 1094
BANK OF AFRICA - UGANDA LTD.—See BOA Group S.A.; *Int'l*, pg. 1094
BANK OF AGRICULTURE & COMMERCE; *U.S. Private*, pg. 466
BANK OF ALMA; *U.S. Private*, pg. 466
BANK OF AMERICA CUSTODIAL SERVICES (IRELAND) LIMITED—See Bank of America Corporation; *U.S. Public*, pg. 270
BANK OF AMERICA GLOBAL CONSUMER & SMALL BUSINESS BANKING—See Bank of America Corporation; *U.S. Public*, pg. 270
BANK OF AMERICA GLOBAL CORPORATE & INVESTMENT BANKING—See Bank of America Corporation; *U.S. Public*, pg. 271
BANK OF AMERICA MERRILL LYNCH BANCO MULTIPLO S.A.—See Bank of America Corporation; *U.S. Public*, pg. 270
BANK OF AMERICA MERRILL LYNCH—See Bank of America Corporation; *U.S. Public*, pg. 270
BANK OF AMERICA MEXICO, S.A. INSTITUCION DE BANCA MULTIPLE—See Bank of America Corporation; *U.S. Public*, pg. 270

BANK OF AMERICA MORTGAGE—See Bank of America Corporation; *U.S. Public*, pg. 271
BANK OF AMERICA, N.A. - CANADA—See Bank of America Corporation; *U.S. Public*, pg. 271
BANK OF AMERICA, N.A.—See Bank of America Corporation; *U.S. Public*, pg. 270
BANK OF AMERICAN FORK—See Glacier Bancorp, Inc.; *U.S. Public*, pg. 938
BANK OF AMERICA SINGAPORE LIMITED—See Bank of America Corporation; *U.S. Public*, pg. 271
BANK OF ANN ARBOR—See Arbor Bancorp, Inc.; *U.S. Private*, pg. 308
BANK OF ASTANA JSC—See Astana Finance, JSC; *Int'l*, pg. 651
BANK OF AUGUSTA—See Pigeon Falls State Bank; *U.S. Private*, pg. 3179
BANK OF BAKU OJSC; *Int'l*, pg. 840
BANK OF BARODA (BOTSWANA) LTD.—See Bank of Baroda; *Int'l*, pg. 840
BANK OF BARODA (GHANA) LTD.—See Bank of Baroda; *Int'l*, pg. 840
BANK OF BARODA (GUYANA) INC.—See Bank of Baroda; *Int'l*, pg. 840
BANK OF BARODA (KENYA) LTD.—See Bank of Baroda; *Int'l*, pg. 840
BANK OF BARODA (NEW ZEALAND) LTD.—See Bank of Baroda; *Int'l*, pg. 840
BANK OF BARODA; *Int'l*, pg. 840
BANK OF BARODA (TANZANIA) LTD.—See Bank of Baroda; *Int'l*, pg. 840
BANK OF BARODA (TRINIDAD & TOBAGO) LTD.—See Bank of Baroda; *Int'l*, pg. 840
BANK OF BARODA (UGANDA) LTD.—See Bank of Baroda; *Int'l*, pg. 840
BANK OF BARODA (UK) LIMITED—See Bank of Baroda; *Int'l*, pg. 840
BANK OF BEIJING CO., LTD.; *Int'l*, pg. 840
BANK OF BEIRUT S.A.L.; *Int'l*, pg. 840
BANK OF BEIRUT (UK) LTD—See Bank of Beirut S.A.L.; *Int'l*, pg. 840
BANK OF BERMUDA (CAYMAN) LTD.—See HSBC Holdings plc; *Int'l*, pg. 3504
BANK OF BILLINGS—See First Miami Bancshares, Inc.; *U.S. Private*, pg. 1521
BANK OF BLUE VALLEY—See Heartland Financial USA, Inc.; *U.S. Public*, pg. 1018
BANK OF BOTETOURT INC.; *U.S. Public*, pg. 272
THE BANK OF CASTILE—See Tompkins Financial Corporation; *U.S. Public*, pg. 2162
BANK OF CENTRAL FLORIDA; *U.S. Private*, pg. 466
BANK OF CEYLON; *Int'l*, pg. 840
BANK OF CEYLON (UK) LIMITED—See Bank of Ceylon; *Int'l*, pg. 840
BANK OF CHANGSHA CO., LTD.; *Int'l*, pg. 841
BANK OF CHENGDU CO., LTD.; *Int'l*, pg. 841
BANK OF CHINA (CENTRAL & EASTERN EUROPE) LIMITED—See Bank of China, Ltd.; *Int'l*, pg. 841
BANK OF CHINA (EUROPE) S.A.—See Bank of China, Ltd.; *Int'l*, pg. 841
BANK OF CHINA (HONG KONG) LIMITED—See Bank of China, Ltd.; *Int'l*, pg. 841
BANK OF CHINA, LTD.; *Int'l*, pg. 841
BANK OF CHINA (LUXEMBOURG) S.A.—See Bank of China, Ltd.; *Int'l*, pg. 841
BANK OF CHINA (MACAU) LIMITED—See Bank of China, Ltd.; *Int'l*, pg. 841
BANK OF CHINA (MALAYSIA) BERHAD—See Bank of China, Ltd.; *Int'l*, pg. 841
BANK OF CHINA (MAURITIUS) LIMITED—See Bank of China, Ltd.; *Int'l*, pg. 841
BANK OF CHINA MEXICO, S.A.—See Bank of China, Ltd.; *Int'l*, pg. 841
BANK OF CHINA (NEW ZEALAND) LIMITED—See Bank of China, Ltd.; *Int'l*, pg. 841
BANK OF CHINA (PERU) S.A.—See Bank of China, Ltd.; *Int'l*, pg. 841
BANK OF CHINA SRBIJA A.D.—See Bank of China, Ltd.; *Int'l*, pg. 841
BANK OF CHINA (THAI) PUBLIC COMPANY LIMITED—See Bank of China, Ltd.; *Int'l*, pg. 841
BANK OF CHINA TURKEY A.S.—See Bank of China, Ltd.; *Int'l*, pg. 841
BANK OF CHINA (ZAMBIA) LIMITED—See Bank of China, Ltd.; *Int'l*, pg. 841
BANK OF CHONGQING CO., LTD.; *Int'l*, pg. 842
BANK OF CLARENDON; *U.S. Private*, pg. 466
BANK OF CLARKSON—See First Breckenridge Bancshares; *U.S. Private*, pg. 1514
BANK OF COLORADO—See Pinnacle Bancorp, Inc.; *U.S. Private*, pg. 3184
BANK OF COMMERCE INC.; *U.S. Private*, pg. 466
BANK OF COMMERCE—See Southeast Bancshares, Inc.; *U.S. Private*, pg. 3725
BANK OF COMMERCE & TRUST CO.; *U.S. Private*, pg. 466
BANK OF COMMUNICATIONS CO., LTD.; *Int'l*, pg. 842
BANK OF CROCKETT—See Security BanCorp of Tennessee, Inc.; *U.S. Private*, pg. 3595

BANK OF CYPRUS AUSTRALIA PTY LTD—See Bendigo & Adelaide Bank Ltd.; *Int'l*, pg. 970
BANK OF CYPRUS (CHANNEL ISLANDS) LTD—See Bank of Cyprus Holdings Public Limited Company; *Int'l*, pg. 842
BANK OF CYPRUS HOLDINGS PUBLIC LIMITED COMPANY; *Int'l*, pg. 842
BANK OF CYPRUS ROMANIA LTD—See Bank of Cyprus Holdings Public Limited Company; *Int'l*, pg. 842
THE BANK OF DENVER—See Denver Bankshares, Inc.; *U.S. Public*, pg. 656
BANK OF EASTERN OREGON—See BEO Bancorp; *U.S. Public*, pg. 297
THE BANK OF EDWARDSVILLE INC.; *U.S. Private*, pg. 3991
THE BANK OF ELK RIVER; *U.S. Private*, pg. 3991
BANK OF FARMINGTON—See Farmington Bancorp, Inc.; *U.S. Private*, pg. 1480
THE BANK OF FINCASTLE—See First National Corporation; *U.S. Public*, pg. 846
THE BANK OF FUKUOKA, LTD.—See Fukuoka Financial Group, Inc.; *Int'l*, pg. 2840
BANK OF GANSU CO., LTD.; *Int'l*, pg. 842
BANK OF GHANA; *Int'l*, pg. 843
THE BANK OF GLEN BURNIE—See Glen Burnie Bancorp; *U.S. Public*, pg. 940
BANK OF GREECE S.A.; *Int'l*, pg. 843
BANK OF GREELEYVILLE—See Southeastern Bancorp, Inc.; *U.S. Private*, pg. 3727
THE BANK OF GREENE COUNTY—See Greene County Bancorp, Inc.; *U.S. Public*, pg. 964
BANK OF GUAM—See BankGuam Holding Company; *U.S. Public*, pg. 274
BANK OF GUIYANG CO., LTD.; *Int'l*, pg. 843
BANK OF GUIZHOU CO., LTD.; *Int'l*, pg. 843
BANK OF HALLS—See Security BanCorp of Tennessee, Inc.; *U.S. Private*, pg. 3595
BANK OF HAWAII—See Bank of Hawaii Corporation; *U.S. Public*, pg. 273
BANK OF HAZLEHURST—See Hazlehurst Investors, Inc.; *U.S. Private*, pg. 1886
BANK OF HEMET; *U.S. Private*, pg. 466
BANK OF HOLLAND—See Holland Bancorp, Inc.; *U.S. Private*, pg. 1964
BANK OF HOPE—See Hope Bancorp, Inc.; *U.S. Public*, pg. 1052
BANK OF INDIA (NEW ZEALAND) LTD.—See Bank of India; *Int'l*, pg. 843
BANK OF INDIA; *Int'l*, pg. 843
BANK OF INDIA (TANZANIA) LTD.—See Bank of India; *Int'l*, pg. 843
BANK OF INDIA (UGANDA) LTD.—See Bank of India; *Int'l*, pg. 843
BANK OF IRELAND BUSINESS BANKING UK - BELFAST—See Bank of Ireland Group plc; *Int'l*, pg. 844
BANK OF IRELAND BUSINESS BANKING UK - LONDON—See Bank of Ireland Group plc; *Int'l*, pg. 844
BANK OF IRELAND - BUSINESS ON LINE—See Bank of Ireland Group plc; *Int'l*, pg. 844
BANK OF IRELAND CORPORATE BANKING - BELFAST—See Bank of Ireland Group plc; *Int'l*, pg. 844
BANK OF IRELAND CORPORATE BANKING - FRANKFURT—See Bank of Ireland Group plc; *Int'l*, pg. 844
BANK OF IRELAND CORPORATE BANKING - LONDON—See Bank of Ireland Group plc; *Int'l*, pg. 844
BANK OF IRELAND CORPORATE BANKING—See Bank of Ireland Group plc; *Int'l*, pg. 844
BANK OF IRELAND FINANCE LTD.—See Bank of Ireland Group plc; *Int'l*, pg. 844
BANK OF IRELAND GLOBAL MARKETS - STAMFORD—See Bank of Ireland Group plc; *Int'l*, pg. 845
BANK OF IRELAND INSURANCE SERVICES LTD—See Bank of Ireland Group plc; *Int'l*, pg. 844
BANK OF IRELAND INTERNATIONAL FINANCE LTD.—See Bank of Ireland Group plc; *Int'l*, pg. 844
BANK OF IRELAND (I.O.M.) LIMITED—See Bank of Ireland Group plc; *Int'l*, pg. 844
BANK OF IRELAND PRIVATE BANKING LIMITED—See Bank of Ireland Group plc; *Int'l*, pg. 844
BANK OF IRELAND UK FINANCIAL SERVICES—See Bank of Ireland Group plc; *Int'l*, pg. 844
BANK OF IRELAND (UK) PLC—See Bank of Ireland Group plc; *Int'l*, pg. 844
BANK OF JACKSON HOLE INC.; *U.S. Private*, pg. 466
THE BANK OF JACKSON—See Security BanCorp of Tennessee, Inc.; *U.S. Private*, pg. 3595
BANK OF JAPAN; *Int'l*, pg. 845
BANK OF JERUSALEM, LTD.; *Int'l*, pg. 845
BANK OF JIANGSU COMPANY LIMITED; *Int'l*, pg. 845
BANK OF JINZHOU CO., LTD.; *Int'l*, pg. 845
BANK OF JIUJIANG CO., LTD.; *Int'l*, pg. 845
BANK OF JORDAN PLC; *Int'l*, pg. 845
BANK OF JORDAN SYRIA—See Bank of Jordan PLC; *Int'l*, pg. 845
BANK OF KATHMANDU LIMITED; *Int'l*, pg. 845
BANK OF KATHMANDU LUMBINI LTD.—See Bank of Kath-

N.A.I.C.S. INDEX

522110 — COMMERCIAL BANKING

mandu Limited; *Int'l*, pg. 845
BANK OF KHARTOUM; *Int'l*, pg. 845
BANK OF LANZHOU CO., LTD.; *Int'l*, pg. 845
BANK OF LUXEMBURG; *U.S. Private*, pg. 466
BANK OF MALDIVES PLC; *Int'l*, pg. 845
BANK OF MARIN—See Bank of Marin Bancorp; *U.S. Public*, pg. 273
THE BANK OF MAUSTON; *U.S. Private*, pg. 3991
THE BANK OF MISSOURI; *U.S. Private*, pg. 3991
BANK OF MONTGOMERY—See Grant Bancshares, Inc.; *U.S. Private*, pg. 1756
BANK OF MONTREAL ASSESSORIA E SERVICOS LTDA.—See Bank of Montreal; *Int'l*, pg. 846
BANK OF MONTREAL (CHINA) CO. LTD.—See Bank of Montreal; *Int'l*, pg. 846
BANK OF MONTREAL FINANCE LTD.—See Bank of Montreal; *Int'l*, pg. 846
BANK OF MONTREAL IRELAND PLC—See Bank of Montreal; *Int'l*, pg. 846
BANK OF MONTREAL; *Int'l*, pg. 845
BANK OF MOUNT HOPE; *U.S. Private*, pg. 466
BANK OF NAMIBIA; *Int'l*, pg. 847
BANK OF NANJING CO., LTD.; *Int'l*, pg. 847
BANK OF NEVADA—See Western Alliance Bancorporation; *U.S. Public*, pg. 2354
BANK OF NEW ALBANY; *U.S. Private*, pg. 466
THE BANK OF NEW YORK MELLON SA/NV—See The Bank of New York Mellon Corporation; *U.S. Public*, pg. 2038
THE BANK OF NEW YORK—See The Bank of New York Mellon Corporation; *U.S. Public*, pg. 2038
THE BANK OF NEW YORK—See The Bank of New York Mellon Corporation; *U.S. Public*, pg. 2038
THE BANK OF NEW YORK—See The Bank of New York Mellon Corporation; *U.S. Public*, pg. 2038
BANK OF NINGBO CO., LTD.; *Int'l*, pg. 847
BANK OF NORTH DAKOTA; *U.S. Private*, pg. 466
BANK OF OAK RIDGE—See Oak Ridge Financial Services, Inc.; *U.S. Public*, pg. 1560
BANK OF PONTIAC—See Pontiac Bancorp, Inc.; *U.S. Public*, pg. 1701
BANK OF PUTNAM COUNTY; *U.S. Private*, pg. 466
BANK OF QINGDAO CO., LTD.; *Int'l*, pg. 847
THE BANK OF ROMNEY; *U.S. Private*, pg. 3991
BANK OF RUSTON—See Century Next Financial Corporation; *U.S. Public*, pg. 475
BANK OF SAN FRANCISCO; *U.S. Public*, pg. 273
BANK OF SANTA CLARITA—See California BanCorp; *U.S. Public*, pg. 423
BANK OF SHANGHAI CO., LTD; *Int'l*, pg. 848
BANK OF SHANGHAI (HONG KONG) LIMITED—See Bank of Shanghai Co., Ltd; *Int'l*, pg. 848
BANK OF SHARJAH P.S.C.; *Int'l*, pg. 848
THE BANK OF SOUTH CAROLINA—See Bank of South Carolina Corporation; *U.S. Public*, pg. 273
BANK OF SOUTHSIDE VIRGINIA; *U.S. Private*, pg. 466
BANK OF SPRINGFIELD—See Spring Bancorp, Inc.; *U.S. Private*, pg. 3763
BANK OF STOCKTON—See 1867 Western Financial Corporation; *U.S. Public*, pg. 2
BANK OF ST. VINCENT & THE GRENADINES; *Int'l*, pg. 848
BANK OF SUN PRAIRIE—See BOSP BANCSHARES, INC.; *U.S. Private*, pg. 620
BANK OF SUZHOU CO., LTD.; *Int'l*, pg. 848
BANK OF SYRIA & OVERSEAS S.A.; *Int'l*, pg. 848
THE BANK OF TAMPA—See Tampa Banking Co.; *U.S. Private*, pg. 3928
BANK OF THE FLINT HILLS—See Wamego Bancshares, Inc.; *U.S. Private*, pg. 4435
BANK OF THE JAMES—See Bank of the James Financial Group, Inc.; *U.S. Public*, pg. 273
BANK OF THE LAKES NA; *U.S. Private*, pg. 466
BANK OF THE ORIENT; *U.S. Private*, pg. 467
BANK OF THE OZARKS—See Bank OZK; *U.S. Public*, pg. 274
THE BANK OF THE PACIFIC—See PACIFIC FINANCIAL CORPORATION; *U.S. Public*, pg. 1631
BANK OF THE PHILIPPINE ISLANDS (EUROPE) PLC—See Bank of the Philippine Islands; *Int'l*, pg. 849
BANK OF THE RYUKYUS, LTD.; *Int'l*, pg. 849
BANK OF THE SAN JUANS—See Glacier Bancorp, Inc.; *U.S. Public*, pg. 938
BANK OF THE SIERRA—See Sierra Bancorp; *U.S. Public*, pg. 1877
BANK OF THE WEST—See BNP Paribas SA; *Int'l*, pg. 1087
BANK OF TIANJIN CO., LTD.; *Int'l*, pg. 849
THE BANK OF TIOGA—See Treynor Bancshares, Inc.; *U.S. Private*, pg. 4219
BANK OF TOYAMA LTD.; *Int'l*, pg. 849
BANK OF TRAVELERS REST INC.; *U.S. Private*, pg. 467
BANK OF UGANDA; *Int'l*, pg. 849
BANK OF UTAH—See BOU Bancorp, Inc.; *U.S. Private*, pg. 623
BANK OF UTICA; *U.S. Public*, pg. 273
BANK OF VALLETTA P.L.C.; *Int'l*, pg. 849
BANK OF WASHINGTON INC.; *U.S. Private*, pg. 467
BANK OF WEDOWEE; *U.S. Private*, pg. 467

BANK OF WESTERN AUSTRALIA LTD.—See Commonwealth Bank of Australia; *Int'l*, pg. 1719
BANK OF WISCONSIN DELLS; *U.S. Private*, pg. 467
BANK OF WOLCOTT—See Wolcott Bancorp; *U.S. Private*, pg. 4553
BANK OF XIAN CO., LTD .—See Bank of Beijing Co., Ltd.; *Int'l*, pg. 840
THE BANK OF YOKOHAMA, LTD.—See Concordia Financial Group, Ltd.; *Int'l*, pg. 1765
BANK OF YORK; *U.S. Private*, pg. 467
BANK OF ZHENGZHOU CO., LTD.; *Int'l*, pg. 849
BANK OTSAR HA-HAYAL LTD.—See FIBI Holdings Ltd.; *Int'l*, pg. 2652
BANK OTSAR HAHAYAL LTD.—See FIBI Holdings Ltd.; *Int'l*, pg. 2652
BANK PASARGAD; *Int'l*, pg. 849
BANKPLUS—See BankPlus Corporation; *U.S. Private*, pg. 468
BANK POALEY AGUDAT ISRAEL LTD.—See FIBI Holdings Ltd.; *Int'l*, pg. 2652
BANK POLSKA KASA OPIEKI SPOLKA AKCYJNA; *Int'l*, pg. 849
BANK RBK JSC; *Int'l*, pg. 850
BANK RHODE ISLAND—See Brookline Bancorp, Inc.; *U.S. Public*, pg. 395
BANK SADERAT OF IRAN; *Int'l*, pg. 850
BANK SADERAT PLC; *Int'l*, pg. 850
BANK SIAB PJSC; *Int'l*, pg. 850
BANK TEJARAT; *Int'l*, pg. 850
BANKUNITED, N.A.—See BankUnited, Inc.; *U.S. Public*, pg. 274
BANKVISTA—See Abdo Investments, Inc.; *U.S. Private*, pg. 37
BANK VON ERNST (LIECHTENSTEIN) AG—See EFG International AG; *Int'l*, pg. 2319
BANKWELL BANK—See Bankwell Financial Group, Inc.; *U.S. Public*, pg. 275
BANKWEST, INC.—See South Dakota Bancshares, Inc.; *U.S. Private*, pg. 3722
BANK ZARECHYE JSC; *Int'l*, pg. 850
BANNER BANK—See Banner Corporation; *U.S. Public*, pg. 275
BANNER CAPITAL BANK—See Banner County Ban Corporation; *U.S. Private*, pg. 469
BANQUE AIG S.A.—See American International Group, Inc.; *U.S. Public*, pg. 104
BANQUE AL BARAKA D'ALGERIE—See Al Baraka Banking Group B.S.C.; *Int'l*, pg. 276
BANQUE BANORIENT FRANCE—See BLOM Bank, S.A.L.; *Int'l*, pg. 1064
BANQUE BANORIENT (SWITZERLAND) SA—See BLOM Bank, S.A.L.; *Int'l*, pg. 1064
BANQUE BCP S.A.S.—See Groupe BPCE; *Int'l*, pg. 3097
BANQUE BEMO S.A.L.; *Int'l*, pg. 852
BANQUE BEMO SAUDI FRANSI S.A.; *Int'l*, pg. 852
BANQUE CANTONALE DE GENEVE (FRANCE) SA—See Banque Cantonale de Geneve S.A.; *Int'l*, pg. 852
BANQUE CANTONALE DU JURA S.A.; *Int'l*, pg. 853
BANQUE CANTONALE VAUDOISE; *Int'l*, pg. 853
BANQUE CENTRALE DES COMORES; *Int'l*, pg. 853
BANQUE CENTRALE POPULAIRE S.A.; *Int'l*, pg. 853
BANQUE COMMERCIALE DU CONGO S.A.R.L.; *Int'l*, pg. 853
BANQUE DE CHINE (DJIBOUTI) S.A.—See Bank of China, Ltd.; *Int'l*, pg. 842
BANQUE DEGROOF LUXEMBOURG S.A.—See Banque Degroof S.A.; *Int'l*, pg. 853
BANQUE DE KIGALI S.A.; *Int'l*, pg. 853
BANQUE DE LA REUNION SA—See Groupe BPCE; *Int'l*, pg. 3097
BANQUE DE NEUFLIZE—See ABN AMRO Group N.V.; *Int'l*, pg. 65
BANQUE DE NOUVELLE-CALEDONIE SA—See Groupe BPCE; *Int'l*, pg. 3092
BANQUE DE TUNISIE ET DES EMIRATS; *Int'l*, pg. 853
BANQUE DE WALLIS ET FUTUNA—See BNP Paribas SA; *Int'l*, pg. 1089
BANQUE DU CAIRE; *Int'l*, pg. 853
BANQUE ET CAISSE D'EPARGNE DE L'ETAT; *Int'l*, pg. 853
BANQUE FRANCO LAO LTD.—See Groupe BPCE; *Int'l*, pg. 3092
BANQUE HAVILLAND S.A.—See Blackfish Capital Management Ltd.; *Int'l*, pg. 1060
BANQUE INTERNATIONALE POUR LAFRIQUE AU TOGO SA; *Int'l*, pg. 854
BANQUE INTERNATIONALE POUR LE COMMERCE ET L'INDUSTRIE DE LA COTE D'IVOIRE, S.A.—See BNP Paribas SA; *Int'l*, pg. 1089
BANQUE INTERNATIONALE POUR LE COMMERCE ET L'INDUSTRIE DU GABON—See BNP Paribas SA; *Int'l*, pg. 1089
BANQUE INTERNATIONALE POUR LE COMMERCE ET L'INDUSTRIE DU MALI SA—See BNP Paribas SA; *Int'l*, pg. 1089
BANQUE INTERNATIONALE POUR LE COMMERCE ET L'INDUSTRIE DU SENEGAL SA—See BNP Paribas SA; *Int'l*, pg. 1089

BANQUE LBLUX S.A.—See Helaba Landesbank Hessen-Thuringen; *Int'l*, pg. 3327
BANQUE MALGACHE DE L'OCEAN INDIEN—See Banque Centrale Populaire S.A.; *Int'l*, pg. 853
BANQUE MAROCAINE DU COMMERCE ET DE L'INDUSTRIE OFFSHORE—See BNP Paribas SA; *Int'l*, pg. 1089
BANQUE MAROCAINE POUR LE COMMERCE ET L'INDUSTRIE S.A.—See BNP Paribas SA; *Int'l*, pg. 1089
BANQUE MAURITANIENNE POUR LE COMMERCE INTERNATIONAL; *Int'l*, pg. 854
BANQUE MISR; *Int'l*, pg. 854
BANQUE NATIONALE DE BELGIQUE S.A.; *Int'l*, pg. 854
BANQUE PALATINE S.A.—See Groupe BPCE; *Int'l*, pg. 3094
BANQUE POPULAIRE ALSACE LORRAINE CHAMPAGNE—See Groupe BPCE; *Int'l*, pg. 3097
BANQUE POPULAIRE AQUITAINE CENTRE ATLANTIQUE SCCV—See Groupe BPCE; *Int'l*, pg. 3092
BANQUE POPULAIRE ATLANTIQUE—See Groupe BPCE; *Int'l*, pg. 3097
BANQUE POPULAIRE AUVERGNE RHONE ALPES SCM—See Groupe BPCE; *Int'l*, pg. 3092
BANQUE POPULAIRE BOURGOGNE FRANCHE-COMTE—See Groupe BPCE; *Int'l*, pg. 3097
BANQUE POPULAIRE CENTRE ATLANTIQUE—See Groupe BPCE; *Int'l*, pg. 3097
BANQUE POPULAIRE COTE D'AZUR—See Groupe BPCE; *Int'l*, pg. 3097
BANQUE POPULAIRE DE L'OUEST—See Groupe BPCE; *Int'l*, pg. 3097
BANQUE POPULAIRE DES ALPES—See Groupe BPCE; *Int'l*, pg. 3097
BANQUE POPULAIRE DU MASSIF CENTRAL—See Groupe BPCE; *Int'l*, pg. 3097
BANQUE POPULAIRE DU NORD—See Groupe BPCE; *Int'l*, pg. 3097
BANQUE POPULAIRE DU SUD-OUEST—See Groupe BPCE; *Int'l*, pg. 3097
BANQUE POPULAIRE DU SUD SCCV—See Groupe BPCE; *Int'l*, pg. 3092
BANQUE POPULAIRE DU SUD—See Groupe BPCE; *Int'l*, pg. 3097
BANQUE POPULAIRE GRAND OUEST SCA—See Groupe BPCE; *Int'l*, pg. 3092
BANQUE POPULAIRE LOIRE ET LYONNAIS—See Groupe BPCE; *Int'l*, pg. 3097
BANQUE POPULAIRE LORRAINE CHAMPAGNE—See Groupe BPCE; *Int'l*, pg. 3097
BANQUE POPULAIRE OCCITANE—See Groupe BPCE; *Int'l*, pg. 3097
BANQUE POPULAIRE PROVENCALE ET CORSE—See Groupe BPCE; *Int'l*, pg. 3097
BANQUE POPULAIRE RIVES DE PARIS—See Groupe BPCE; *Int'l*, pg. 3097
BANQUE POPULAIRE VAL DE FRANCE—See Groupe BPCE; *Int'l*, pg. 3097
BANQUE PROFIL DE GESTION SA; *Int'l*, pg. 854
BANQUE TRANSATLANTIQUE—See Confederation Nationale du Credit Mutuel; *Int'l*, pg. 1767
BANQUE TUNISO KOWEITIENNE SA—See Groupe BPCE; *Int'l*, pg. 3092
BANSABADELL FACTURA, S.L.—See Banco de Sabadell, S.A.; *Int'l*, pg. 821
BANSABADELL FINANZIARIA SPA.—See Banco de Sabadell, S.A.; *Int'l*, pg. 821
BANTERRA BANK—See Banterra Corp.; *U.S. Private*, pg. 470
BAO VIET COMMERCIAL JOINT STOCK BANK—See Bao Viet Holdings; *Int'l*, pg. 855
BAPRO MANDATOS Y NEGOCIOS S.A.—See Banco de la Provincia de Buenos Aires; *Int'l*, pg. 821
THE BARABOO NATIONAL BANK—See Baraboo Bancorporation, Inc.; *U.S. Public*, pg. 275
BARCLAYS ASIA LIMITED—See Barclays PLC; *Int'l*, pg. 859
BARCLAYS BANK MEXICO, S.A.—See Barclays PLC; *Int'l*, pg. 860
BARCLAYS BANK OF BOTSWANA LTD.—See Barclays PLC; *Int'l*, pg. 860
BARCLAYS BANK OF GHANA LTD.—See Barclays PLC; *Int'l*, pg. 860
BARCLAYS BANK OF KENYA LTD.—See Barclays PLC; *Int'l*, pg. 860
BARCLAYS BANK PLC—See Barclays PLC; *Int'l*, pg. 859
BARCLAYS BANK—See Barclays PLC; *Int'l*, pg. 859
BARCLAYS BANK—See Barclays PLC; *Int'l*, pg. 859
BARCLAYS BANK (SOUTH EAST ASIA) NOMINEES PRIVATE LIMITED—See Barclays PLC; *Int'l*, pg. 859
BARCLAYS CAPITAL CANADA INC—See Barclays PLC; *Int'l*, pg. 860
BARCLAYS PRIVATE BANKING SERVICES LIMITED—See Barclays PLC; *Int'l*, pg. 861
BARCLAYS PRIVATE BANK LTD—See Barclays PLC; *Int'l*, pg. 861
BARCLAYS PRIVATE BANK & TRUST (ISLE OF MAN) LIMITED—See Barclays PLC; *Int'l*, pg. 861
BARCLAYS PRIVATE BANK & TRUST LTD.—See Barclays PLC; *Int'l*, pg. 860

522110 — COMMERCIAL BANKING

BARCLAYTRUST (SUISSE) SA—See Barclays PLC; *Int'l*, pg. 862
BAR HARBOR BANK & TRUST—See Bar Harbor Bankshares; *U.S. Public*, pg. 275
BARODA GLOBAL SHARED SERVICES LTD.—See Bank of Baroda; *Int'l*, pg. 840
BASELLANDSCHAFTLICHE KANTONALBANK; *Int'l*, pg. 871
BASLER KANTONALBANK AG; *Int'l*, pg. 887
BAWAG P.S.K. DATENDIENST GESELLSCHAFT M.B.H.—See BAWAG Group AG; *Int'l*, pg. 900
BAYCOAST BANK—See Narragansett Financial Corp.; *U.S. Private*, pg. 2835
BAYER POLYURETHANES B.V.—See Bayer Aktiengesellschaft; *Int'l*, pg. 905
BAYFIRST NATIONAL BANK—See BayFirst Financial Corp.; *U.S. Public*, pg. 284
BAY STATE SAVINGS BANK; *U.S. Private*, pg. 494
BAZHONG CDB VILLAGE BANK CO., LTD.—See China Development Bank Corporation; *Int'l*, pg. 1497
BBK B.S.C.; *Int'l*, pg. 920
BBR BANK AO; *Int'l*, pg. 921
BBVA BANCOMER AFORE—See Banco Bilbao Vizcaya Argentaria, S.A.; *Int'l*, pg. 818
BBVA BANCO PROVINCIAL, S.A.—See Banco Bilbao Vizcaya Argentaria, S.A.; *Int'l*, pg. 817
BBVA COLOMBIA S.A.—See Banco Bilbao Vizcaya Argentaria, S.A.; *Int'l*, pg. 817
BCB COMMUNITY BANK—See BCB Bancorp, Inc.; *U.S. Public*, pg. 285
BC COMERTBANK SA; *Int'l*, pg. 921
BCI MER ROUGE—See BNP Paribas SA; *Int'l*, pg. 1080
BC MOLDINDCONBANK S.A.; *Int'l*, pg. 921
BC MOLDOVA AGROINDBANK S.A.; *Int'l*, pg. 922
BCP BANK (MAURITIUS) LTD—See Banque Centrale Populaire S.A.; *Int'l*, pg. 853
BCT BANK INTERNATIONAL S.A.; *Int'l*, pg. 929
B.C. VICTORIABANK S.A.; *Int'l*, pg. 789
BDO ELITE SAVINGS BANK, INC.—See BDO Unibank, Inc.; *Int'l*, pg. 930
BDO PRIVATE BANK, INC.—See BDO Unibank, Inc.; *Int'l*, pg. 930
BDO UNIBANK, INC.; *Int'l*, pg. 930
BEACH COMMUNITY BANK—See Beach Community Bancshares, Inc.; *U.S. Public*, pg. 285
BEAL BANK USA—See Beal Financial Corporation; *U.S. Private*, pg. 505
BEILUN CDB VILLAGE BANK CO., LTD.—See China Development Bank Corporation; *Int'l*, pg. 1497
BELAGROPROMBANK JSC; *Int'l*, pg. 963
BELFIUS BANK SA/NV; *Int'l*, pg. 963
BELGAZPROMBANK OJSC—See Gazprombank JSC; *Int'l*, pg. 2892
BELGOLAISE SA—See BNP Paribas SA; *Int'l*, pg. 1089
THE BELIZE BANK LIMITED—See Caribbean Investment Holdings Limited; *Int'l*, pg. 1330
BELLARINE PENINSULA COMMUNITY BRANCH LIMITED—See Bendigo & Adelaide Bank Ltd.; *Int'l*, pg. 970
BELL STATE BANK & TRUST—See State Bankshares, Inc.; *U.S. Private*, pg. 3791
BENDIGO & ADELAIDE BANK LTD.; *Int'l*, pg. 970
BENDURA BANK AG—See Citychamp Watch & Jewellery Group Limited; *Int'l*, pg. 1628
BENEFICIAL STATE BANK—See Beneficial State Foundation; *U.S. Private*, pg. 525
THE BENNINGTON STATE BANK; *U.S. Private*, pg. 3993
BEOBANK NV/SA—See Confederation Nationale du Credit Mutuel; *Int'l*, pg. 1767
BERGOS AG; *Int'l*, pg. 980
THE BERKSHIRE BANK—See Berkshire Bancorp Inc.; *U.S. Private*, pg. 533
BERKSHIRE BANK—See Berkshire Hills Bancorp, Inc.; *U.S. Public*, pg. 320
BERLINER BANK AG & CO. KG—See Deutsche Bank Aktiengesellschaft; *Int'l*, pg. 2055
BERLINER VOLKSBANK EG; *Int'l*, pg. 986
BERMUDA COMMERCIAL BANK LTD.—See ICM Limited; *Int'l*, pg. 3582
BERNER KANTONALBANK AG; *Int'l*, pg. 988
BESSEMER TRUST CO. - ATLANTA—See The Bessemer Group, Incorporated; *U.S. Private*, pg. 3994
BESSEMER TRUST CO. - CHICAGO—See The Bessemer Group, Incorporated; *U.S. Private*, pg. 3994
BEVERLY BANK & TRUST COMPANY, N.A. - OAK LAWN BANK & TRUST—See Wintrust Financial Corporation; *U.S. Public*, pg. 2374
B&F CAPITAL MARKETS, INC.—See Stifel Financial Corp.; *U.S. Public*, pg. 1949
BGL BNP PARIBAS S.A.—See BNP Paribas SA; *Int'l*, pg. 1084
BGZ BNPP FAKTORING SPOLKA Z O.O.—See BNP Paribas SA; *Int'l*, pg. 1080
BHARGAV BIKASH BANK LIMITED; *Int'l*, pg. 1011
BHUTAN NATIONAL BANK LIMITED; *Int'l*, pg. 1016
BIAO-COTE D'IVOIRE; *Int'l*, pg. 1017
BIA TOGO—See BIA Overseas S.A.; *Int'l*, pg. 1017
BIC BRED (SUISSE) SA—See Groupe BPCE; *Int'l*, pg. 3092

BICECORP SA; *Int'l*, pg. 1018
BIG BANC SPLIT CORP.; *Int'l*, pg. 1021
BIG DATA HEALTHCARE LLC—See Fifth Third Bancorp; *U.S. Public*, pg. 833
BIG SKY WESTERN BANK—See Glacier Bancorp, Inc.; *U.S. Public*, pg. 938
BJCC, INC.—See Bank of America Corporation; *U.S. Public*, pg. 270
BKS BANK AG—See Bank fur Tirol und Vorarlberg Ag; *Int'l*, pg. 838
BLACKHAWK STATE BANK—See First Mid Bancshares, Inc.; *U.S. Public*, pg. 846
BLACKSTAR ENTERPRISE GROUP, INC; *U.S. Public*, pg. 347
BLADEX REPRESENTACAO LTDA.—See Banco Latinoamericano de Comercio Exterior, S.A.; *Int'l*, pg. 823
BLC BANK SAL; *Int'l*, pg. 1063
BLC COMMUNITY BANK—See Independent Bancorp., Limited; *U.S. Private*, pg. 2058
BLI CAPITAL LIMITED—See Bay Leasing & Investment Limited; *Int'l*, pg. 901
BLOM BANK EGYPT S.A.E.—See BLOM Bank, S.A.L.; *Int'l*, pg. 1064
BLOM BANK, S.A.L.; *Int'l*, pg. 1064
BLOMINVEST BANK SAL—See BLOM Bank, S.A.L.; *Int'l*, pg. 1064
BLUEHARBOR BANK; *U.S. Public*, pg. 365
BLUE NILE MAHSREG BANK; *Int'l*, pg. 1069
BLUE RIDGE BANK AND TRUST CO.—See Blue Ridge Bancshares Inc.; *U.S. Private*, pg. 591
BLUE RIDGE BANK—See Blue Ridge Bankshares, Inc.; *U.S. Public*, pg. 365
BMCE INTERNATIONAL, S.A.U.—See Bank of Africa; *Int'l*, pg. 839
BMI BANK BSC—See Al Salam Bank-Bahrain B.S.C.; *Int'l*, pg. 282
BMO CAPITAL MARKETS EQUITY GROUP (U.S.), INC.—See Bank of Montreal; *Int'l*, pg. 846
BMO FINANCE COMPANY I, S.A R.L.—See Bank of Montreal; *Int'l*, pg. 846
BMO HARRIS BANK N.A.—See Bank of Montreal; *Int'l*, pg. 846
BMO HARRIS FINANCING, INC.—See Bank of Montreal; *Int'l*, pg. 846
BNA INSURANCE & INVESTMENTS, INC.—See Bank of New Albany; *U.S. Private*, pg. 466
BNB BANK—See Financial Services Corp.; *U.S. Private*, pg. 1508
BNC NATIONAL BANK—See BNCCORP, Inc.; *U.S. Public*, pg. 366
BNK BANKING CORPORATION LIMITED; *Int'l*, pg. 1079
BNP PACIFIC (AUSTRALIA) LTD.—See BNP Paribas SA; *Int'l*, pg. 1081
BNP PARIBAS ABU DHABI—See BNP Paribas SA; *Int'l*, pg. 1081
BNP PARIBAS ANTILLES GUYANE SA—See BNP Paribas SA; *Int'l*, pg. 1081
BNP PARIBAS BANGKOK—See BNP Paribas SA; *Int'l*, pg. 1081
BNP PARIBAS BANK POLSKA SA—See BNP Paribas SA; *Int'l*, pg. 1082
BNP PARIBAS CAPITAL (SINGAPORE) LTD.—See BNP Paribas SA; *Int'l*, pg. 1083
BNP PARIBAS-CHICAGO—See BNP Paribas SA; *Int'l*, pg. 1087
BNP PARIBAS (CHINA) LTD.—See BNP Paribas SA; *Int'l*, pg. 1081
BNP PARIBAS DUBAI—See BNP Paribas SA; *Int'l*, pg. 1083
BNP PARIBAS EL DJAZAIR S.P.A.—See BNP Paribas SA; *Int'l*, pg. 1083
BNP PARIBAS FORTIS FUNDING SA—See BNP Paribas SA; *Int'l*, pg. 1084
BNP PARIBAS FORTIS MERCHANT BANKING—See BNP Paribas SA; *Int'l*, pg. 1084
BNP PARIBAS FORTIS SA/NV—See BNP Paribas SA; *Int'l*, pg. 1084
BNP PARIBAS INVESTMENT PARTNERS (AUSTRALIA) LTD—See BNP Paribas SA; *Int'l*, pg. 1085
BNP PARIBAS (JAPAN) LIMITED—See BNP Paribas SA; *Int'l*, pg. 1081
BNP PARIBAS LEASE GROUP BELGIUM SA—See BNP Paribas SA; *Int'l*, pg. 1085
BNP PARIBAS LE CAIRE—See BNP Paribas SA; *Int'l*, pg. 1085
BNP PARIBAS MACAU—See BNP Paribas SA; *Int'l*, pg. 1081
BNP PARIBAS - MEXICO REPRESENTATIVE OFFICE—See BNP Paribas SA; *Int'l*, pg. 1081
BNP PARIBAS PORTUGAL—See BNP Paribas SA; *Int'l*, pg. 1086
BNP PARIBAS RCC, INC.—See BNP Paribas SA; *Int'l*, pg. 1087
BNP PARIBAS REUNION—See BNP Paribas SA; *Int'l*, pg. 1086
BNP PARIBAS SAE—See BNP Paribas SA; *Int'l*, pg. 1087
BNP PARIBAS-SAN FRANCISCO—See BNP Paribas SA; *Int'l*, pg. 1087

BNP PARIBAS TAIWAN—See BNP Paribas SA; *Int'l*, pg. 1081
BNP PARIBAS ZAO—See BNP Paribas SA; *Int'l*, pg. 1088
BNPP ASSET MANAGEMENT USA INC.—See BNP Paribas SA; *Int'l*, pg. 1087
BNPP CARDIF POJISTOVNA AS—See BNP Paribas SA; *Int'l*, pg. 1088
BNPP FINANSAL KIRALAMA AS—See BNP Paribas SA; *Int'l*, pg. 1088
BNPP MALAYSIA BERHAD—See BNP Paribas SA; *Int'l*, pg. 1088
BNPP SECURITIES INDIA PRIVATE LTD.—See BNP Paribas SA; *Int'l*, pg. 1088
BNY FUND SERVICES (IRELAND) LTD.—See The Bank of New York Mellon Corporation; *U.S. Public*, pg. 2036
BNY MELLON ARX INVESTIMENTOS LTDA.—See The Bank of New York Mellon Corporation; *U.S. Public*, pg. 2036
BNY MELLON ASSET MANAGEMENT JAPAN LIMITED—See The Bank of New York Mellon Corporation; *U.S. Public*, pg. 2036
BNY MELLON-HONG KONG—See The Bank of New York Mellon Corporation; *U.S. Public*, pg. 2037
BNY MELLON (POLAND) SP. Z O.O.—See The Bank of New York Mellon Corporation; *U.S. Public*, pg. 2036
BNY MELLON SINGAPORE—See The Bank of New York Mellon Corporation; *U.S. Public*, pg. 2037
BNY MELLON TRUST OF DELAWARE—See The Bank of New York Mellon Corporation; *U.S. Public*, pg. 2037
BOFA CANADA BANK—See Bank of America Corporation; *U.S. Public*, pg. 271
BOILING SPRINGS SAVINGS BANK INC.; *U.S. Private*, pg. 609
BOKF, N.A. - BANK OF ALBUQUERQUE—See BOK Financial Corporation; *U.S. Public*, pg. 367
BOKF, N.A. - BANK OF ARIZONA—See BOK Financial Corporation; *U.S. Public*, pg. 367
BOKF, N.A. - BANK OF ARKANSAS—See BOK Financial Corporation; *U.S. Public*, pg. 367
BOKF, N.A. - BANK OF TEXAS, HOUSTON REGIONAL OFFICE—See BOK Financial Corporation; *U.S. Public*, pg. 367
BOKF, N.A. - BANK OF TEXAS—See BOK Financial Corporation; *U.S. Public*, pg. 367
BOKF, N.A. - COLORADO STATE BANK & TRUST—See BOK Financial Corporation; *U.S. Public*, pg. 367
BOKF, N.A. - MOBANK—See BOK Financial Corporation; *U.S. Public*, pg. 367
BOONE BANK AND TRUST CO.—See Ames National Corporation; *U.S. Public*, pg. 115
THE BOONE COUNTY NATIONAL BANK OF COLUMBIA—See Central Bancompany, Inc.; *U.S. Public*, pg. 473
BOSC AGENCY, INC.—See BOK Financial Corporation; *U.S. Public*, pg. 367
BOSTON PRIVATE BANK & TRUST COMPANY—See Boston Private Financial Holdings, Inc.; *U.S. Public*, pg. 372
BOSTON PRIVATE BANK & TRUST CO. - SAN FRANCISCO BAY AREA DIVISION—See Boston Private Financial Holdings, Inc.; *U.S. Public*, pg. 372
BOSTON PRIVATE BANK & TRUST CO. - SOUTHERN CALIFORNIA DIVISION—See Boston Private Financial Holdings, Inc.; *U.S. Public*, pg. 372
BOUNDARY WATERS BANK—See Highland Bankshares Inc.; *U.S. Private*, pg. 1938
BPI COMPUTER SYSTEMS CORP—See Bank of the Philippine Islands; *Int'l*, pg. 848
BPI DIRECT BANKO INC.—See Bank of the Philippine Islands; *Int'l*, pg. 848
BPI EXPRESS REMITTANCE CORP.—See Bank of the Philippine Islands; *Int'l*, pg. 848
BPI EXPRESS REMITTANCE SPAIN S.A—See Bank of the Philippine Islands; *Int'l*, pg. 848
BPI WEALTH HONG KONG LIMITED—See Bank of the Philippine Islands; *Int'l*, pg. 848
BPS-SBERBANK OJSC; *Int'l*, pg. 1133
BRADESCO CORRETORA T.V.M.—See Banco Bradesco S.A.; *Int'l*, pg. 819
BRADFORD BANCORP, INC.; *U.S. Private*, pg. 631
THE BRADFORD NATIONAL BANK OF GREENVILLE—See Bradford Bancorp, Inc.; *U.S. Private*, pg. 631
BRAMER CORPORATION LIMITED—See British American Investment Co. (Mtius) Ltd.; *Int'l*, pg. 1165
BRAND BANKING COMPANY; *U.S. Private*, pg. 635
BRANNEN BANKS OF FLORIDA, INC.; *U.S. Private*, pg. 640
BRANNEN BANK—See Brannen Banks of Florida, Inc.; *U.S. Private*, pg. 640
BRAVERA BANK—See American Bancor, Ltd.; *U.S. Private*, pg. 223
BRED BANK CAMBODIA PLC—See Groupe BPCE; *Int'l*, pg. 3092
BRED BANK FIJI LTD.—See Groupe BPCE; *Int'l*, pg. 3092
BRED BANQUE POPULAIRE—See Groupe BPCE; *Int'l*, pg. 3097
BRED I.T. THAILAND LTD.—See Groupe BPCE; *Int'l*, pg. 3092

N.A.I.C.S. INDEX
522110 — COMMERCIAL BANKING

BRED VANUATU LTD.—See Groupe BPCE; *Int'l*, pg. 3092
BREMER KREDITBANK AG—See Apollo Global Management, Inc.; *U.S. Public*, pg. 148
BREMER KREDITBANK AG—See Grovepoint Capital LLP; *Int'l*, pg. 3112
BREMER KREDITBANK AG—See Teacher Retirement System of Texas; *U.S. Private*, pg. 3944
THE BRENHAM NATIONAL BANK—See Brenham Bancshares, Inc.; *U.S. Private*, pg. 645
BRIANFID-LUX S A—See Banco Di Desio e Della Brianza S.p.A.; *Int'l*, pg. 822
BRICKYARD BANCORP; *U.S. Private*, pg. 648
BRICKYARD BANK—See Brickyard Bancorp; *U.S. Private*, pg. 648
BRIDGE CITY STATE BANK—See AmTex Bancshares Inc.; *U.S. Private*, pg. 268
BRIDGEVIEW BANK GROUP—See Old National Bancorp; *U.S. Public*, pg. 1567
BRIDGEWATER BANK—See Bridgewater Bancshares, Inc.; *U.S. Public*, pg. 382
BRIGHTON BANK; *U.S. Private*, pg. 652
B. RILEY FBR, INC.—See B. Riley Financial, Inc.; *U.S. Public*, pg. 260
BRITISH ARAB COMMERCIAL BANK LIMITED; *Int'l*, pg. 1168
BROADWAY NATIONAL BANK—See Broadway Bancshares, Inc.; *U.S. Private*, pg. 660
BROTHERHOOD BANK & TRUST CO—See Brotherhood Bancshares Inc.; *U.S. Public*, pg. 396
THE BRYN MAWR TRUST COMPANY—See Bryn Mawr Bank Corporation; *U.S. Public*, pg. 408
BSP FINANCIAL GROUP LIMITED; *Int'l*, pg. 1202
BS SAVINGS BANK CO., LTD.—See BNK Financial Group Inc.; *Int'l*, pg. 1079
BTA BANK JSC; *Int'l*, pg. 1204
BTG PACTUAL NY CORPORATION—See BCO BTG PACTUAL S.A.; *Int'l*, pg. 928
BTI BANK COMPANY—See Al Baraka Banking Group B.S.C.; *Int'l*, pg. 276
BTP BANQUE SA—See Groupe BPCE; *Int'l*, pg. 3092
BTP CAPITAL CONSEIL SAS—See Groupe BPCE; *Int'l*, pg. 3092
BTV LEASING GMBH—See Bank fur Tirol und Vorarlberg Ag; *Int'l*, pg. 838
BUCKEYE STATE BANK—See Buckeye State Bancshares, Inc.; *U.S. Private*, pg. 677
BUFFALO FEDERAL SAVINGS BANK—See Crazy Woman Creek Bancorp, Inc.; *U.S. Public*, pg. 593
BULGARIAN NATIONAL BANK; *Int'l*, pg. 1213
BURKE & HERBERT BANK & TRUST COMPANY; *U.S. Private*, pg. 687
BURTON STATE BANK—See Burton Bancshares, Inc.; *U.S. Private*, pg. 693
BUSAN BANK, LTD.—See BNK Financial Group Inc.; *Int'l*, pg. 1079
BUSEY BANK—See First Busey Corporation; *U.S. Public*, pg. 840
BUSEY WEALTH MANAGEMENT, INC.—See First Busey Corporation; *U.S. Public*, pg. 840
BUSINESS DEVELOPMENT BANK OF CANADA; *Int'l*, pg. 1228
BYBLOS BANK AFRICA LTD.—See Byblos Bank S.A.L.; *Int'l*, pg. 1233
BYBLOS BANK ARMENIA CJSC—See Byblos Bank S.A.L.; *Int'l*, pg. 1233
BYBLOS BANK EUROPE S.A.—See Byblos Bank S.A.L.; *Int'l*, pg. 1233
BYBLOS BANK INVEST S.A.L—See Byblos Bank S.A.L.; *Int'l*, pg. 1233
BYBLOS BANK S.A.L.; *Int'l*, pg. 1233
BYBLOS BANK SYRIA S.A.—See Byblos Bank S.A.L.; *Int'l*, pg. 1233
BYLINE BANK—See Byline Bancorp, Inc.; *U.S. Public*, pg. 414
BYSTROBANK PJSC; *Int'l*, pg. 1235
BZ BANK AKTIENGESELLSCHAFT; *Int'l*, pg. 1237
CABO VERDE, S.A.R.L.—See Caixa Geral de Depositos S.A.; *Int'l*, pg. 1260
CACHE VALLEY BANK—See Cache Valley Banking Company; *U.S. Private*, pg. 712
CAIRO AMMAN BANK; *Int'l*, pg. 1253
CAISSE D'EPARGNE AQUITAINE POITOU-CHARENTES SCA—See Groupe BPCE; *Int'l*, pg. 3093
CAISSE D'EPARGNE BRETAGNE PAYS DE LOIRE SCA—See Groupe BPCE; *Int'l*, pg. 3093
CAISSE D'EPARGNE COTE D'AZUR S.A—See Groupe BPCE; *Int'l*, pg. 3093
CAISSE D'EPARGNE D'AUVERGNE ET DU LIMOUSIN SCA—See Groupe BPCE; *Int'l*, pg. 3093
CAISSE D'EPARGNE DE BOURGOGNE FRANCHE-COMTE SAS—See Groupe BPCE; *Int'l*, pg. 3093
CAISSE D'EPARGNE DE MIDI-PYRENEES S.A—See Groupe BPCE; *Int'l*, pg. 3093
CAISSE D'EPARGNE ET DE PREVOYANCE DE RHONE ALPES—See Groupe BPCE; *Int'l*, pg. 3097
CAISSE D'EPARGNE ET DE PREVOYANCE ILE-DE-FRANCE—See Groupe BPCE; *Int'l*, pg. 3097
CAISSE D'EPARGNE ET DE PREVOYANCE PROVENCE-ALPES-CORSE—See Groupe BPCE; *Int'l*, pg. 3097
CAISSE D'EPARGNE GRAND EST EUROPE SCA—See Groupe BPCE; *Int'l*, pg. 3093
CAISSE D'EPARGNE HAUTS DE FRANCE SAS—See Groupe BPCE; *Int'l*, pg. 3093
CAISSE D'EPARGNE LANGUEDOC-ROUSSILLON SCA—See Groupe BPCE; *Int'l*, pg. 3093
CAISSE D'EPARGNE LOIRE-CENTRE SCA—See Groupe BPCE; *Int'l*, pg. 3093
CAISSE D'EPARGNE LOIRE DROME ARDECHE SCA—See Groupe BPCE; *Int'l*, pg. 3093
CAISSE D'EPARGNE NORMANDIE SAS—See Groupe BPCE; *Int'l*, pg. 3093
CAISSE D'EPARGNE RHONE ALPES SCA—See Groupe BPCE; *Int'l*, pg. 3093
CAISSE REGIONALE DE CREDIT AGRICOLE MUTUEL ATLANTIQUE VENDEE SC; *Int'l*, pg. 1259
CAISSE REGIONALE DE CREDIT AGRICOLE MUTUEL BRIE PICARDIE SCA; *Int'l*, pg. 1259
CAISSE REGIONALE DE CREDIT AGRICOLE MUTUEL DE NORD DE FRANCE SC; *Int'l*, pg. 1259
CAISSE REGIONALE DE CREDIT AGRICOLE MUTUEL D'ILLE-ET-VILLAINE SC; *Int'l*, pg. 1259
CAISSE REGIONALE DE CREDIT AGRICOLE MUTUEL SUD RHONE ALPES; *Int'l*, pg. 1259
CAIXA - BANCO DE INVESTIMENTO, S.A.—See Caixa Geral de Depositos S.A.; *Int'l*, pg. 1260
CAIXA ECONOMICA FEDERAL; *Int'l*, pg. 1259
CAIXA ECONOMICA MONTEPIO GERAL; *Int'l*, pg. 1259
CALBANK PLC; *Int'l*, pg. 1261
CALIFORNIA BANK & TRUST—See Zions Bancorporation, National Association; *U.S. Public*, pg. 2408
CALIFORNIA BUSINESS BANK; *U.S. Public*, pg. 423
CALIFORNIA INTERNATIONAL BANK; *U.S. Public*, pg. 423
CALPRIVATE BANK—See Private Bancorp of America, Inc.; *U.S. Public*, pg. 1722
CALVIN B. TAYLOR BANKSHARES, INC.; *U.S. Public*, pg. 425
CAMBRIDGE TRUST COMPANY OF NEW HAMPSHIRE, INC.—See Cambridge Bancorp; *U.S. Public*, pg. 426
CAMBRIDGE TRUST COMPANY—See Cambridge Bancorp; *U.S. Public*, pg. 425
CAM CAPITAL, S.A.U.—See Banco de Sabadell, S.A.; *Int'l*, pg. 821
THE CAMDEN NATIONAL BANK—See Camden National Corporation; *U.S. Public*, pg. 426
CAMPBELL & FETTER BANK; *U.S. Private*, pg. 730
CANADIAN IMPERIAL BANK OF COMMERCE; *Int'l*, pg. 1283
CANADIAN TIRE BANK—See Canadian Tire Corporation Limited; *Int'l*, pg. 1286
CANADIAN WESTERN BANK; *Int'l*, pg. 1286
CANAL BANK, S.A.; *Int'l*, pg. 1287
THE CANANDAIGUA NATIONAL BANK & TRUST COMPANY—See Canandaigua National Corporation; *U.S. Public*, pg. 428
CANARA BANK SECURITIES LTD.—See Canara Bank; *Int'l*, pg. 1287
CANARA BANK; *Int'l*, pg. 1287
CANARA BANK (TANZANIA) LTD.—See Canara Bank; pg. 1287
CAPITA FUNDING DE MEXICO, SOCIEDAD ANONIMA DE CAPITAL VARIABLE SOFOM ENR—See First Citizens BancShares, Inc.; *U.S. Public*, pg. 841
CAPITAL APPRECIATION LTD.; *Int'l*, pg. 1309
CAPITAL BANK - GRAWE GRUPPE AG; *Int'l*, pg. 1310
CAPITAL BANK KAZAKHSTAN JSC; *Int'l*, pg. 1310
CAPITAL BANK; *Int'l*, pg. 1310
CAPITAL BANK—See Capital Bank - GRAWE Gruppe AG; *Int'l*, pg. 1310
CAPITAL CITY BANK—See Capital City Bank Group, Inc.; *U.S. Public*, pg. 431
CAPITAL FIN S.P.A.—See Banca IFIS S.p.A.; *Int'l*, pg. 815
CAPITAL MERCHANT BANKING AND FINANCE LIMITED; *Int'l*, pg. 1311
CAPITAL ONE, N.A.—See Capital One Financial Corporation; *U.S. Public*, pg. 431
CAPITEC BANK LIMITED—See Capitec Bank Holdings Limited; *Int'l*, pg. 1314
CAPITOL NATIONAL BANK; *U.S. Private*, pg. 744
CAPSTAR BANK—See Old National Bancorp; *U.S. Public*, pg. 1567
CARES - COMPANHIA DE SEGUROS, S.A.—See Fosun International Limited; *Int'l*, pg. 2750
CARES MULTIASSISTANCE, S.A.—See Caixa Geral de Depositos S.A.; *Int'l*, pg. 1260
CARES RH - COMPANHIA DE ASSISTENCIA E REPRESENTACAO DE SEGUROS, S.A.—See Caixa Geral de Depositos S.A.; *Int'l*, pg. 1260
CARGILLS BANK LIMITED; *Int'l*, pg. 1325
CARIBBEAN DEVELOPMENT BANK; *Int'l*, pg. 1330
CAROLINA ALLIANCE BANK—See Park National Corporation; *U.S. Public*, pg. 1638
CAROLINA BANK AND TRUST CO.; *U.S. Private*, pg. 767
CARROLLTON BANK; *U.S. Private*, pg. 774
CARSON COMMUNITY BANK—See Carson Financial Holding Company, Inc.; *U.S. Private*, pg. 774
CARTER BANK & TRUST—See Carter Bankshares, Inc.; *U.S. Public*, pg. 445
CARTU BANK JSC—See Cartu Group JSC; *Int'l*, pg. 1348
CASDEN BANQUE POPULAIRE—See Groupe BPCE; *Int'l*, pg. 3097
CASHMERE VALLEY BANK; *U.S. Public*, pg. 446
CASSA DI RISPARMIO DI ASTI S.P.A.; *Int'l*, pg. 1355
CASSA DI RISPARMIO DI BIELLA E VERCELLI S.P.A.—See Cassa di Risparmio di Asti S.p.A.; *Int'l*, pg. 1355
CASSA DI RISPARMIO DI FANO S.P.A.—See Credito Valtellinese Societa Cooperativa; *Int'l*, pg. 1837
CASSA RURALE ED ARTIGIANA DI BINASCO CREDITO COOPERATIVO; *Int'l*, pg. 1355
CASTLE BANK N.A.—See First National of Nebraska, Inc.; *U.S. Private*, pg. 1523
CATER ALLEN LIMITED—See Banco Santander, S.A.; *Int'l*, pg. 827
CATHAY BANK—See Cathay General Bancorp; *U.S. Public*, pg. 454
CATHAY NEW ASIA COMMUNITY DEVELOPMENT CORPORATION—See Cathay General Bancorp; *U.S. Public*, pg. 454
CATSKILL HUDSON BANK—See Catskill Hudson Bancorp, Inc.; *U.S. Public*, pg. 454
CAVITE UNITED RURAL BANK CORPORATION—See Asia United Bank Corporation; *Int'l*, pg. 616
CBC FINANCE LIMITED—See Commercial Bank of Ceylon PLC; *Int'l*, pg. 1715
CBC MYANMAR MICROFINANCE COMPANY LIMITED—See Commercial Bank of Ceylon PLC; *Int'l*, pg. 1715
CBC TECH SOLUTIONS LIMITED—See Commercial Bank of Ceylon PLC; *Int'l*, pg. 1715
CB ENERGOTRANSBANK JSC; *Int'l*, pg. 1364
CB KUBAN CREDIT LIMITED LIABILITY COMPANY; *Int'l*, pg. 1364
CB LOCKO-BANK JSC; *Int'l*, pg. 1364
CB&S BANK, INC.—See CB&S Bank, Inc.; *U.S. Private*, pg. 796
CBZ BANK LIMITED—See CBZ Holdings Limited; *Int'l*, pg. 1366
CCEI BANK GE—See Afriland First Bank; *Int'l*, pg. 192
CCP AUSTRIA ABWICKLUNGSSTELLE FUR BORSENGESCHAFTE GMBH—See CEESEG AG; *Int'l*, pg. 1389
CDB LEASING CO., LTD.—See China Development Bank Corporation; *Int'l*, pg. 1497
CECIL BANK—See Cecil Bancorp, Inc.; *U.S. Public*, pg. 463
THE CECILIAN BANK—See First Cecilian Bancorp, Inc.; *U.S. Private*, pg. 1515
CEDAR RAPIDS BANK & TRUST COMPANY—See QCR Holdings, Inc.; *U.S. Public*, pg. 1742
CEMBRA MONEY BANK AG; *Int'l*, pg. 1396
CENTENNIAL BANK—See Home BancShares, Inc.; *U.S. Public*, pg. 1045
CENTER-INVEST BANK PJSC; *Int'l*, pg. 1403
CENTIER BANK INC.—See First Bancshares Inc.; *U.S. Private*, pg. 1513
CENTINEL BANK OF TAOS; *U.S. Private*, pg. 817
CENTRAL BANCSHARES, INC.; *U.S. Private*, pg. 819
CENTRAL BANK CORPORATION; *U.S. Private*, pg. 819
CENTRAL BANK OF ARMENIA; *Int'l*, pg. 1404
CENTRAL BANK OF AUDRAIN COUNTY—See Central Bancompany, Inc.; *U.S. Public*, pg. 472
CENTRAL BANK OF INDIA LIMITED; *Int'l*, pg. 1404
CENTRAL BANK OF JORDAN; *Int'l*, pg. 1404
CENTRAL BANK OF LAKE OF THE OZARKS—See Central Bancompany, Inc.; *U.S. Public*, pg. 472
CENTRAL BANK OF OKLAHOMA—See Central Bancompany, Inc.; *U.S. Public*, pg. 472
CENTRAL BANK OF ST. LOUIS—See Central Bancompany, Inc.; *U.S. Public*, pg. 472
CENTRAL BANK; *U.S. Private*, pg. 819
CENTRAL BANK—See Central Bank Corporation; *U.S. Private*, pg. 819
CENTRAL BANK—See Central Financial Holdings, Inc.; *U.S. Private*, pg. 820
CENTRAL BANK—See Commercial Financial Corp.; *U.S. Private*, pg. 983
CENTRAL BANK & TRUST CO.; *U.S. Private*, pg. 819
CENTRAL COOPERATIVE BANK PLC—See Chimimport AD; *Int'l*, pg. 1479
CENTRALNA KOOPERATIVNA BANKA AD—See Chimimport AD; *Int'l*, pg. 1479
CENTRAL NATIONAL BANK OF ENID; *U.S. Private*, pg. 823
CENTRAL NATIONAL BANK; *U.S. Private*, pg. 823
CENTRAL NATIONAL BANK; *U.S. Private*, pg. 823
CENTRAL NATIONAL BANK—See Centrabanc Corporation; *U.S. Private*, pg. 818
CENTRAL PACIFIC BANK—See Central Pacific Financial Corporation; *U.S. Public*, pg. 473
CENTRAL SAVINGS BANK; *U.S. Private*, pg. 824
CENTRAL STATE BANK—See AJJ Bancorp, Inc.; *U.S. Private*, pg. 144
CENTRAL STATE BANK—See State Center Financial, Inc.; *U.S. Private*, pg. 3791

522110 — COMMERCIAL BANKING

THE CENTRAL TRUST BANK—See Central Bancompany, Inc.; *U.S. Public*, pg. 473
CENTRAL VALLEY COMMUNITY BANK—See Community West Bancshares; *U.S. Public*, pg. 558
CENTRIC BANK—See First Commonwealth Financial Corporation; *U.S. Public*, pg. 842
CENTROCREDIT BANK; *Int'l*, pg. 1414
CENTURION FUNDING, INC.—See Wells Fargo & Company; *U.S. Public*, pg. 2343
CENTURY BANK OF FLORIDA—See Century Bancshares of Florida, Inc.; *U.S. Private*, pg. 831
CENTURY BANK OF KENTUCKY, INC.—See Century Bancshares, Inc.; *U.S. Private*, pg. 832
CENTURY BANK OF THE OZARKS; *U.S. Private*, pg. 832
CENTURY BANK; *U.S. Private*, pg. 832
CENTURY BANK & TRUST; *U.S. Private*, pg. 832
CENTURY NATIONAL BANK—See Park National Corporation; *U.S. Public*, pg. 1638
CESKA SPORITELNA A.S.—See Erste Group Bank AG; *Int'l*, pg. 2498
CETRA - CENTRO TECNICO DE REPARACAO AUTO-MOVEL, S.A.—See Caixa Geral de Depositos S.A.; *Int'l*, pg. 1260
CFG COMMUNITY BANK—See Capital Funding Group, Inc.; *U.S. Private*, pg. 740
CGD INVESTIMENTOS CVC—See Caixa Geral de Depositos S.A.; *Int'l*, pg. 1260
CGD NORTH AMERICA FINANCE LLC—See Caixa Geral de Depositos S.A.; *Int'l*, pg. 1260
CHAM BANK; *Int'l*, pg. 1439
CHAMBERS BANK—See Chambers Bancshares Inc.; *U.S. Private*, pg. 846
CHAMPLAIN NATIONAL BANK—See Champlain Bank Corporation; *U.S. Private*, pg. 847
CHANGE FINANCIAL LIMITED; *Int'l*, pg. 1443
CHANG HWA BANK (TAICHUNG)—See Chang Hwa Commercial Bank Ltd.; *Int'l*, pg. 1441
CHANG HWA BANK (TAIPEI)—See Chang Hwa Commercial Bank Ltd.; *Int'l*, pg. 1441
CHANG HWA COMMERCIAL BANK LTD.; *Int'l*, pg. 1441
CHANG HWA COMMERCIAL BANK - NEW YORK BRANCH—See Chang Hwa Commercial Bank Ltd.; *Int'l*, pg. 1441
CHANG HWA INTERNATIONAL BANKING—See Chang Hwa Commercial Bank Ltd.; *Int'l*, pg. 1441
CHARLES SCHWAB BANK—See The Charles Schwab Corporation; *U.S. Public*, pg. 2058
CHARLOTTE STATE BANK & TRUST—See Crews Banking Corporation; *U.S. Private*, pg. 1099
CHAYO GROUP PUBLIC COMPANY LIMITED; *Int'l*, pg. 1458
THE CHECKLEY AGENCY, INC.—See First Mid Bancshares, Inc.; *U.S. Public*, pg. 846
CHELSEA SAVINGS BANK—See Chebelle Corporation; *U.S. Private*, pg. 868
CHELSEA STATE BANK; *U.S. Private*, pg. 870
CHELYABINVESTBANK PJSC; *Int'l*, pg. 1460
CHEMUNG CANAL TRUST COMPANY—See Chemung Financial Corporation; *U.S. Public*, pg. 484
CHENGDU RURAL COMMERCIAL BANK CO., LTD.—See Anbang Insurance Group Co., Ltd.; *Int'l*, pg. 447
CHESAPEAKE BANK—See Chesapeake Financial Shares, Inc.; *U.S. Public*, pg. 485
CHINA BANKING CORPORATION; *Int'l*, pg. 1484
CHINABANK SAVINGS, INC.—See China Banking Corporation; *Int'l*, pg. 1484
CHINA BOHAI BANK CO., LTD.; *Int'l*, pg. 1487
CHINA CITIC BANK CORPORATION LIMITED—See CITIC Group Corporation; *Int'l*, pg. 1620
CHINA CITIC BANK INTERNATIONAL LIMITED—See CITIC Group Corporation; *Int'l*, pg. 1620
CHINA CITIC BANK INTERNATIONAL LTD. - LOS ANGELES BRANCH—See CITIC Group Corporation; *Int'l*, pg. 1620
CHINA CITIC BANK INTERNATIONAL LTD. - NEW YORK BRANCH—See CITIC Group Corporation; *Int'l*, pg. 1620
CHINA CONSTRUCTION BANK (ASIA) CORPORATION LIMITED—See China Construction Bank Corporation; *Int'l*, pg. 1491
CHINA CONSTRUCTION BANK (BRASIL) BANCO MULTIPLO S/A—See China Construction Bank Corporation; *Int'l*, pg. 1491
CHINA CONSTRUCTION BANK CORPORATION; *Int'l*, pg. 1491
CHINA CONSTRUCTION BANK (RUSSIA) LIMITED; *Int'l*, pg. 1491
CHINA DEVELOPMENT BANK CAPITAL CO., LTD.—See China Development Bank Corporation; *Int'l*, pg. 1497
CHINA DEVELOPMENT BANK SECURITIES CO., LTD.—See China Development Bank Corporation; *Int'l*, pg. 1497
CHINA EVERBRIGHT BANK CO., LTD.—See China Everbright Group Limited; *Int'l*, pg. 1501
CHINA GUANGFA BANK CO., LTD.; *Int'l*, pg. 1506
CHINA MERCHANTS BANK CO LTD; *Int'l*, pg. 1520
CHINA MERCHANTS BANK CO., LTD.—See China Merchants Group Limited; *Int'l*, pg. 1520

CHINA MINSHENG BANKING CORPORATION LTD.; *Int'l*, pg. 1524
CHINATRUST (PHILIPPINES) COMMERCIAL BANK CORPORATION—See CTBC Financial Holding Co., Ltd.; *Int'l*, pg. 1869
CHINA ZHESHANG BANK CO., LTD.; *Int'l*, pg. 1567
CHINO COMMERCIAL BANK—See Chino Commercial Bancorp; *U.S. Public*, pg. 489
CHIPPEWA VALLEY BANK; *U.S. Private*, pg. 886
CHOICE FINANCIAL GROUP—See Northlane Capital Partners, LLC; *U.S. Private*, pg. 2956
CHOICEONE BANK—See ChoiceOne Financial Services, Inc.; *U.S. Public*, pg. 490
CHONGQING RURAL COMMERCIAL BANK CO., LTD.; *Int'l*, pg. 1580
THE CHUGOKU BANK, LIMITED—See Chugin Financial Group, Inc.; *Int'l*, pg. 1594
THE CHUKYO BANK, LTD.—See Aichi Financial Group Co., Ltd.; *Int'l*, pg. 229
CIBC BANK USA—See Canadian Imperial Bank of Commerce; *Int'l*, pg. 1283
CIBM BANK—See CIB Marine Bancshares, Inc.; *U.S. Public*, pg. 494
CIC IBERBANCO—See Confederation Nationale du Credit Mutuel; *Int'l*, pg. 1767
CIMB BANK (CAMBODIA) PLC—See CIMB Group Holdings Berhad; *Int'l*, pg. 1607
CIMB PRIVATE EQUITY SDN BHD—See CIMB Group Holdings Berhad; *Int'l*, pg. 1607
CIMB SECURITIES (HK) LTD—See CIMB Group Holdings Berhad; *Int'l*, pg. 1608
CIMB SECURITIES INTERNATIONAL PTE LTD—See CIMB Group Holdings Berhad; *Int'l*, pg. 1607
CIMB THAI BANK PUBLIC COMPANY LIMITED—See CIMB Group Holdings Berhad; *Int'l*, pg. 1608
CIT CAPITAL FINANCE (UK) LIMITED—See First Citizens BancShares, Inc.; *U.S. Public*, pg. 841
CIT (FRANCE) SA—See First Citizens BancShares, Inc.; *U.S. Public*, pg. 841
THE CIT GROUP/COMMERCIAL SERVICES, INC. (VA.)—See First Citizens BancShares, Inc.; *U.S. Public*, pg. 842
CITIBANK BERHAD—See Citigroup Inc.; *U.S. Public*, pg. 502
CITIBANK CANADA—See Citigroup Inc.; *U.S. Public*, pg. 502
CITIBANK (CHINA) CO., LTD.—See Citigroup Inc.; *U.S. Public*, pg. 501
CITIBANK-COLOMBIA S.A.—See Citigroup Inc.; *U.S. Public*, pg. 503
CITIBANK (COSTA RICA) S.A.—See Citigroup Inc.; *U.S. Public*, pg. 502
CITIBANK-DISTRIBUIDORA DE TITULOS E VALORES MOBILIARIOS S.A.—See Citigroup Inc.; *U.S. Public*, pg. 501
CITIBANK EUROPE PLC, ORGANIZACNI SLOZKA—See Citigroup Inc.; *U.S. Public*, pg. 502
CITIBANK EUROPE PLC—See Citigroup Inc.; *U.S. Public*, pg. 502
CITIBANK (HONG KONG) LIMITED—See Citigroup, Inc.; *U.S. Public*, pg. 502
CITIBANK JAPAN LTD.—See Citigroup Inc.; *U.S. Public*, pg. 503
CITIBANK LEASING S.A.-ARRENDAMENTO MERCANTIL—See Citigroup Inc.; *U.S. Public*, pg. 501
CITIBANK MAGHREB—See Citigroup Inc.; *U.S. Public*, pg. 501
CITIBANK, N.A.—See Citigroup Inc.; *U.S. Public*, pg. 501
CITIBANK, N.A.—See Citigroup Inc.; *U.S. Public*, pg. 502
CITIBANK, N.A.—See Citigroup Inc.; *U.S. Public*, pg. 502
CITIBANK NIGERIA LIMITED—See Citigroup Inc.; *U.S. Public*, pg. 502
CITIBANK OVERSEAS INVESTMENT CORPORATION—See Citigroup Inc.; *U.S. Public*, pg. 502
CITIBANK SINGAPORE LTD.—See Citigroup Inc.; *U.S. Public*, pg. 503
CITIBANK TAIWAN LIMITED—See Citigroup Inc.; *U.S. Public*, pg. 503
CITIBANK UNITED ARAB EMIRATES—See Citigroup Inc.; *U.S. Public*, pg. 503
CITI CONSUMER BANKING—See Citigroup Inc.; *U.S. Public*, pg. 501
CITICORP DATA SYSTEMS INCORPORATED—See Citigroup Inc.; *U.S. Public*, pg. 503
CITICORP FINANCE (INDIA) LIMITED—See Citigroup Inc.; *U.S. Public*, pg. 502
CITIGROUP ACQUISITION LLC—See Citigroup Inc.; *U.S. Public*, pg. 503
CITIGROUP GLOBAL MARKETS AUSTRALIA PTY LIMITED—See Citigroup Inc.; *U.S. Public*, pg. 503
CITIGROUP PTY LIMITED—See Citigroup Inc.; *U.S. Public*, pg. 504
CITIZENS 1ST BANK; *U.S. Private*, pg. 902
CITIZENS BANCORP OF VIRGINIA, INC.; *U.S. Public*, pg. 504
CITIZENS BANK AND TRUST CO.; *U.S. Private*, pg. 903
CITIZENS BANK MINNESOTA—See Citizens Bancorporation of New Ulm, Inc.; *U.S. Private*, pg. 902

CORPORATE AFFILIATIONS

CITIZENS BANK OF CAPE VINCENT, INC.—See Cambray Mutual Holding Company; *U.S. Private*, pg. 726
THE CITIZENS BANK OF COCHRAN—See Putnam-Greene Financial Corporation; *U.S. Public*, pg. 3307
THE CITIZENS BANK OF EDMOND—See Citizens Bancshares, Inc.; *U.S. Private*, pg. 903
CITIZENS BANK OF LAFAYETTE—See Citizens Bancorp Investment, Inc.; *U.S. Private*, pg. 504
CITIZENS BANK OF LOGAN—See The Merchants National Bank; *U.S. Private*, pg. 4078
CITIZENS BANK OF MASSACHUSETTS—See Citizens Financial Group, Inc.; *U.S. Public*, pg. 505
CITIZENS BANK OF PENNSYLVANIA—See Citizens Financial Group, Inc.; *U.S. Public*, pg. 505
THE CITIZENS BANK OF PHILADELPHIA, MISSISSIPPI—See Citizens Holding Company; *U.S. Public*, pg. 506
CITIZENS BANK; *U.S. Private*, pg. 903
CITIZENS BANK; *U.S. Private*, pg. 903
CITIZENS BANK; *U.S. Private*, pg. 903
CITIZENS BANK; *U.S. Private*, pg. 903
CITIZENS BANK; *U.S. Public*, pg. 504
CITIZENS BANK—See Citba Financial Corp.; *U.S. Public*, pg. 501
CITIZENS BANK—See Citco Community Bancshares, Inc.; *U.S. Private*, pg. 901
THE CITIZENS BANK—See Citizens Bancshares Corporation; *U.S. Private*, pg. 902
THE CITIZENS BANK—See Citizens Bancshares of Batesville, Inc.; *U.S. Private*, pg. 902
CITIZENS BANK—See Citizens Bankshares Inc.; *U.S. Private*, pg. 903
CITIZENS BANK—See Citizens Corporation; *U.S. Private*, pg. 903
CITIZENS BANK—See East Texas Financial Corporation; *U.S. Private*, pg. 1318
CITIZENS BANK & TRUST COMPANY; *U.S. Private*, pg. 903
CITIZENS BANK & TRUST COMPANY—See Southern Missouri Bancorp, Inc.; *U.S. Public*, pg. 1912
CITIZENS BANK & TRUST CO. OF JACKSON—See John R. Turner Holding Company; *U.S. Private*, pg. 2224
CITIZENS BANK & TRUST CO.—See Citizens Bancshares of Hutchinson, Inc.; *U.S. Private*, pg. 902
CITIZENS BANK & TRUST—See Citizens B & T Holdings, Inc.; *U.S. Private*, pg. 902
CITIZEN'S BANK & TRUST—See Latt Maxcy Corporation; *U.S. Private*, pg. 2397
CITIZENS BUSINESS BANK—See CVB Financial Corp.; *U.S. Public*, pg. 613
CITIZENS COMMUNITY BANK—See Glacier Bancorp, Inc.; *U.S. Public*, pg. 938
CITIZENS DEPOSIT BANK & TRUST COMPANY—See Premier Financial Bancorp, Inc.; *U.S. Public*, pg. 1715
CITIZENS & FARMERS BANK—See C&F Financial Corporation; *U.S. Public*, pg. 414
CITIZENS FINANCE OF ILLINOIS CO.—See Heartland Financial USA, Inc.; *U.S. Public*, pg. 1018
CITIZENS NATIONAL BANK INC.; *U.S. Private*, pg. 903
THE CITIZENS NATIONAL BANK OF BLUFFTON—See Citizens Bancshares, Inc.; *U.S. Private*, pg. 902
CITIZENS NATIONAL BANK OF CHEBOYGAN—See CNB Corporation; *U.S. Public*, pg. 519
CITIZENS NATIONAL BANK OF GREATER ST LOUIS—See Cardinal Bancorp Inc.; *U.S. Private*, pg. 749
CITIZENS NATIONAL BANK OF MERIDIAN; *U.S. Private*, pg. 904
CITIZENS NATIONAL BANK OF PAINTSVILLE—See Citizens National Corporation; *U.S. Public*, pg. 506
CITIZENS & NORTHERN BANK—See Citizens & Northern Corporation; *U.S. Public*, pg. 504
CITIZENS STATE BANK; *U.S. Private*, pg. 904
CITIZENS STATE BANK—See C.S.B. BANCSHARES, INC.; *U.S. Private*, pg. 709
CITIZENS STATE BANK—See Herky Hawk Financial Corp.; *U.S. Private*, pg. 1925
CITIZENS TRUST BANK—See Citizens Bancshares Corporation; *U.S. Public*, pg. 504
C.I.T. LEASING CORPORATION—See First Citizens BancShares, Inc.; *U.S. Public*, pg. 841
CIT LEASING DE ARGENTINA S.R.L.—See First Citizens BancShares, Inc.; *U.S. Public*, pg. 841
CITY BANK—See South Plains Financial, Inc.; *U.S. Public*, pg. 1911
CITY BANK & TRUST COMPANY OF MOBERLY—See Central Bancompany, Inc.; *U.S. Public*, pg. 472
CITY BANK & TRUST CO.—See TCM Company; *U.S. Private*, pg. 3942
CITY NATIONAL BANK OF FLORIDA—See Empresas Juan Yarur S.A.C.; *Int'l*, pg. 2391
CITY NATIONAL BANK OF WEST VIRGINIA—See City Holding Company; *U.S. Public*, pg. 506
CITYSTATE SAVINGS BANK, INC.; *Int'l*, pg. 1630
CITY UNION BANK LTD - INTERNATIONAL BANKING DIVISION—See City Union Bank Ltd; *Int'l*, pg. 1628
CITY UNION BANK LTD; *Int'l*, pg. 1628
CITYWIDE BANKS—See Heartland Financial USA, Inc.; *U.S. Public*, pg. 1018

N.A.I.C.S. INDEX

522110 — COMMERCIAL BANKING

CIVIL BANK LIMITED; *Int'l*, pg. 1630
CIVISTA BANK—See Civista Bancshares, Inc.; *U.S. Public*, pg. 507
CLARION COUNTY COMMUNITY BANK; *U.S. Public*, pg. 507
CLARIS LEASING SPA—See Cassa Centrale Banca-Credito Cooperativo del Nord Est SpA; *Int'l*, pg. 1354
CLARK COUNTY BANCORPORATION; *U.S. Public*, pg. 507
CLASSIC BANK; *U.S. Private*, pg. 916
CLATSOP COMMUNITY BANK—See Lewis & Clark Bank; *U.S. Public*, pg. 1309
CLAY COUNTY SAVINGS BANK—See CCSB Financial Corp.; *U.S. Public*, pg. 461
CLEARFIELD BANK & TRUST CO.; *U.S. Private*, pg. 932
CLIFROY LIMITED—See Bendigo & Adelaide Bank Ltd.; *Int'l*, pg. 970
CLINTON SAVINGS BANK; *U.S. Private*, pg. 945
CNB BANK—See CNB Financial Corporation; *U.S. Public*, pg. 519
COASTAL CAROLINA NATIONAL BANK—See Coastal Carolina Bancshares, Inc.; *U.S. Public*, pg. 520
COASTAL COMMUNITY BANK; *U.S. Private*, pg. 955
COCONUT GROVE BANK; *U.S. Private*, pg. 959
COFACE EGYPT—See Coface S.A.; *Int'l*, pg. 1690
COLLECTOR AB; *Int'l*, pg. 1699
COLOMBO FORT INVESTMENTS PLC; *Int'l*, pg. 1702
COLONY BANK—See Colony Bankcorp, Inc.; *U.S. Public*, pg. 533
COMERICA BANK MEXICO, S.A.—See Comerica Incorporated; *U.S. Public*, pg. 542
COMERICA BANK—See Comerica Incorporated; *U.S. Public*, pg. 542
COMERICA BANK & TRUST, NATIONAL ASSOCIATION—See Comerica Incorporated; *U.S. Public*, pg. 542
COMERICA HOLDINGS INCORPORATED—See Comerica Incorporated; *U.S. Public*, pg. 542
COMMBANK EUROPE LIMITED—See Commonwealth Bank of Australia; *Int'l*, pg. 1720
COMMENCEMENT BANK; *U.S. Private*, pg. 982
COMMERCE BANK, N.A.—See Commerce Bancshares, Inc.; *U.S. Public*, pg. 544
THE COMMERCE BANK OF OREGON—See Zions Bancorporation, National Association; *U.S. Public*, pg. 2408
THE COMMERCE BANK OF WASHINGTON—See Zions Bancorporation, National Association; *U.S. Public*, pg. 2408
THE COMMERCE BANK—See Indiana Members Credit Union; *U.S. Private*, pg. 2062
COMMERCE BROKERAGE SERVICES, INC.—See Commerce Bancshares, Inc.; *U.S. Public*, pg. 544
COMMERCEWEST BANK; *U.S. Public*, pg. 545
THE COMMERCIAL AND SAVINGS BANK OF MILLERSBURG, OHIO—See CSB Bancorp, Inc.; *U.S. Public*, pg. 601
COMMERCIAL BANK ALLIANZ BULGARIA AD—See Allianz SE; *Int'l*, pg. 344
COMMERCIAL BANK INTERNATIONAL P.S.C.; *Int'l*, pg. 1714
COMMERCIAL BANK MOSKOMMERTSBANK LLC—See Halyk Bank of Kazakhstan JSC; *Int'l*, pg. 3234
COMMERCIAL BANK OF AFRICA LIMITED; *Int'l*, pg. 1714
COMMERCIAL BANK OF CALIFORNIA—See CBC Bancorp; *U.S. Private*, pg. 796
COMMERCIAL BANK OF CEYLON PLC; *Int'l*, pg. 1714
COMMERCIAL BANK OF DUBAI PSC; *Int'l*, pg. 1715
COMMERCIAL BANK OF KUWAIT S.A.K.; *Int'l*, pg. 1715
COMMERCIAL BANK OF MALDIVES PRIVATE LIMITED—See Commercial Bank of Ceylon PLC; *Int'l*, pg. 1715
COMMERCIAL BANK—See Commercial Bancgroup, Inc.; *U.S. Private*, pg. 983
COMMERCIAL BANK & TRUST COMPANY—See Synovus Financial Corp.; *U.S. Public*, pg. 1971
COMMERCIAL BANK & TRUST COMPANY—See Synovus Financial Corp.; *U.S. Public*, pg. 1972
COMMERCIAL BANK & TRUST OF PENNSYLVANIA—See Commercial National Financial Corporation; *U.S. Public*, pg. 547
COMMERCIAL INTERNATIONAL BANK (EGYPT) S.A.E.; *Int'l*, pg. 1715
COMMERCIAL STATE BANK—See Palmer Bancshares, Inc.; *U.S. Private*, pg. 3080
COMMERZBANK BRASIL S.A. - BANCO MULTIPLO—See Commerzbank AG; *Int'l*, pg. 1717
COMMERZBANK DUISBURG—See Commerzbank AG; *Int'l*, pg. 1717
COMMERZBANK FINANCE & COVERED BOND S.A.—See Commerzbank AG; *Int'l*, pg. 1717
COMMERZBANK IMMOBILIEN- UND VERMOGENSVERWALTUNGSGESELLSCHAFT MBH—See Commerzbank AG; *Int'l*, pg. 1717
COMMERZBANK ZRT.—See Erste Group Bank AG; *Int'l*, pg. 2498
COMMERZ FINANZ GMBH—See BNP Paribas SA; *Int'l*, pg. 1090
COMMERZ REAL DIGITALE VERTRIEBS- UND SERVICE GMBH—See Commerzbank AG; *Int'l*, pg. 1716
COMMERZ REAL FRANCE & SOUTH EURL—See Commerzbank AG; *Int'l*, pg. 1716
COMMERZ REAL FUND MANAGEMENT S.A R.L.—See Commerzbank AG; *Int'l*, pg. 1716
COMMERZ REAL KAPITALVERWALTUNGSGESELLSCHAFT MBH—See Commerzbank AG; *Int'l*, pg. 1716
COMMERZ REAL NORTH LTD.—See Commerzbank AG; *Int'l*, pg. 1716
COMMERZ REAL WEST BV—See Commerzbank AG; *Int'l*, pg. 1716
COMMERZ SERVICES HOLDING GMBH—See Commerzbank AG; *Int'l*, pg. 1716
COMMONWEALTH BANK OF AUSTRALIA - U.S.A.—See Commonwealth Bank of Australia; *Int'l*, pg. 1720
COMMONWEALTH BANK & TRUST COMPANY—See Stock Yards Bancorp, Inc.; *U.S. Public*, pg. 1950
COMMONWEALTH BUSINESS BANK—See CBB Bancorp, Inc.; *U.S. Public*, pg. 455
COMMUNITY BANK NORTH MISSISSIPPI—See Community Bancshares of Mississippi, Inc.; *U.S. Private*, pg. 989
COMMUNITY BANK OF PLEASANT HILL—See Lolyn Financial Corporation; *U.S. Private*, pg. 2483
COMMUNITY BANK OF RAYMORE—See Lolyn Financial Corporation; *U.S. Private*, pg. 2483
COMMUNITY BANK OF SANTA MARIA; *U.S. Public*, pg. 549
COMMUNITY BANK OF THE BAY; *U.S. Private*, pg. 990
COMMUNITY BANK OF THE CHESAPEAKE—See Shore Bancshares, Inc.; *U.S. Public*, pg. 1875
COMMUNITY BANK OF THE MIDWEST—See Peoples Bank and Trust; *U.S. Private*, pg. 3141
COMMUNITY BANKS OF COLORADO—See National Bank Holdings Corporation; *U.S. Public*, pg. 1493
THE COMMUNITY BANK—See Campello Bancorp, Inc.; *U.S. Private*, pg. 731
COMMUNITY BANK—See CB Financial Services, Inc.; *U.S. Public*, pg. 455
COMMUNITY BANK—See Nebraska Bankshares, Inc.; *U.S. Private*, pg. 2878
COMMUNITY BANK—See Sooner Southwest Bankshares, Inc.; *U.S. Public*, pg. 3715
COMMUNITY BANK & TRUST - ALABAMA—See Community Bankshares, Inc.; *U.S. Private*, pg. 990
COMMUNITY BANK & TRUST INC.; *U.S. Private*, pg. 990
COMMUNITY BANK & TRUST—See QCR Holdings, Inc.; *U.S. Public*, pg. 1742
COMMUNITY BANK & TRUST - WEST GEORGIA—See Community Bankshares, Inc.; *U.S. Private*, pg. 990
COMMUNITY DEVELOPMENT BANK, FSB—See Midwest Minnesota Community Development Corporation; *U.S. Private*, pg. 2722
COMMUNITY FINANCIAL GROUP, INC.—See Glacier Bancorp, Inc.; *U.S. Public*, pg. 938
COMMUNITY FINANCIAL SERVICES; *U.S. Private*, pg. 991
COMMUNITY FIRST BANK OF INDIANA; *U.S. Private*, pg. 991
COMMUNITY FIRST BANK—See Community First Bancshares, Inc.; *U.S. Public*, pg. 991
COMMUNITY FIRST BANK—See First Bancshares, Inc.; *U.S. Private*, pg. 1513
COMMUNITY NATIONAL BANK—See Community Bancorp, Inc.; *U.S. Public*, pg. 549
COMMUNITY NATIONAL BANK & TRUST OF TEXAS—See Community Bank Holdings of Texas, Inc.; *U.S. Private*, pg. 990
COMMUNITY SAVINGS BANK—See Community Financial Corp; *U.S. Private*, pg. 991
COMMUNITY SPIRIT BANK—See Independent Bancshares, Inc.; *U.S. Private*, pg. 2058
COMMUNITY STATE BANK; *U.S. Private*, pg. 997
COMMUNITY STATE BANK—See QCR Holdings, Inc.; *U.S. Public*, pg. 1742
COMMUNITY TITLE AGENCY, INC.—See Consumers Bancorp, Inc.; *U.S. Public*, pg. 573
COMMUNITY TRUST BANK, INC.—See Community Trust Bancorp Inc; *U.S. Public*, pg. 558
COMPAGNIE INTERNATIONALE ARABE DE RECOUVREMENT—See Banque Internationale Arabe de Tunisie; *Int'l*, pg. 854
COMPAGNIE MONEGASQUE DE BANQUE; *Int'l*, pg. 1746
COMPANHIA GERAL DE CREDITO PREDIAL PORTUGUES, S.A.—See Banco Santander, S.A.; *Int'l*, pg. 825
COMPANHIA PORTUGUESA DE RESSEGUROS, S.A.—See Caixa Geral de Depósitos S.A.; *Int'l*, pg. 1260
COMPASS BANK—See The PNC Financial Services Group, Inc.; *U.S. Public*, pg. 2119
COMTS FINANCE GMBH—See Commerzbank AG; *Int'l*, pg. 1715
COMTS GMBH—See Commerzbank AG; *Int'l*, pg. 1715
COMTS LOGISTICS GMBH—See Commerzbank AG; *Int'l*, pg. 1716
COMTS MITTE GMBH—See Commerzbank AG; *Int'l*, pg. 1716
COMTS NORD GMBH—See Commerzbank AG; *Int'l*, pg. 1716
COMTS OST GMBH—See Commerzbank AG; *Int'l*, pg. 1716
COMTS RHEIN-RUHR GMBH—See Commerzbank AG; *Int'l*, pg. 1716
COMTS WEST GMBH—See Commerzbank AG; *Int'l*, pg. 1716
CONCENTRIX SERVICES (NETHERLANDS) B.V—See TD Synnex Corp; *U.S. Public*, pg. 1984
CONGRESSIONAL BANK—See Congressional Bancshares, Inc.; *U.S. Public*, pg. 1014
CONNECTONE BANK—See ConnectOne Bancorp, Inc.; *U.S. Public*, pg. 568
CONTINENTAL NATIONAL BANK OF MIAMI—See First American Bank Corporation; *U.S. Private*, pg. 1512
THE CONWAY NATIONAL BANK INC.—See CNB Corporation; *U.S. Public*, pg. 519
THE CO-OPERATIVE BANK P.L.C.—See Co-operative Group Limited; *Int'l*, pg. 1679
COOPERATIVE CENTRAL BANK LTD.; *Int'l*, pg. 1792
COOPERLEASING SPA—See BNP Paribas SA; *Int'l*, pg. 1090
COREFIRST BANK & TRUST; *U.S. Private*, pg. 1049
CORNERSTONE BANK—See First York Ban Corp.; *U.S. Private*, pg. 1531
CORNERSTONE BANK—See Princeton Bancorp, Inc.; *U.S. Public*, pg. 1719
CORPORACION ANDINA DE FOMENTO; *Int'l*, pg. 1803
CORPORACION FINANCIERA COLOMBIANA S.A.; *Int'l*, pg. 1803
CORPORACION FINANCIERA DE DESARROLLO SA; *Int'l*, pg. 1803
CORPORATE DEVELOPMENT BANK LIMITED; *Int'l*, pg. 1805
CORPORATION FOR REVITALIZING EARTHQUAKE-AFFECTED BUSINESS—See Deposit Insurance Corporation of Japan; *Int'l*, pg. 2041
CORTLAND SAVINGS & BANKING CO.—See Farmers National Banc Corp.; *U.S. Public*, pg. 822
CORYDON STATE BANK—See Dentel Bancorporation; *U.S. Private*, pg. 1206
COUNCIL OAK PARTNERS, LLC—See BancFirst Corporation; *U.S. Public*, pg. 269
COUNTRY BANK—See OceanFirst Financial Corp.; *U.S. Public*, pg. 1563
COUNTY BANK; *U.S. Private*, pg. 1068
COUNTY NATIONAL BANK—See CNB Community Bancorp, Inc.; *U.S. Public*, pg. 519
COVENANT BANK; *U.S. Private*, pg. 1071
CRDB BANK PLC; *Int'l*, pg. 1830
CREALOGIX BAAS GMBH & CO. KG—See Constellation Software Inc.; *Int'l*, pg. 1772
CREALOGIX MBA LTD.—See Constellation Software Inc.; *Int'l*, pg. 1772
CREALOGIX PTE. LTD.—See Constellation Software Inc.; *Int'l*, pg. 1772
CREDICORP BANK; *Int'l*, pg. 1834
CREDIRAMA SPA—See BNP Paribas SA; *Int'l*, pg. 1090
CREDIT ANDORRA, S.A.; *Int'l*, pg. 1834
CREDIT BANK OF MOSCOW OJSC; *Int'l*, pg. 1835
CREDIT COOPERATIF—See Groupe BPCE; *Int'l*, pg. 3097
CREDITCORP OF TENNESSEE INC.—See Check Into Cash Inc.; *U.S. Public*, pg. 869
CREDIT EUROPE BANK (DUBAI) LTD.—See Fiba Holding A.S.; *Int'l*, pg. 2651
CREDIT EUROPE BANK LTD.—See Fiba Holding A.S.; *Int'l*, pg. 2651
CREDIT EUROPE BANK N.V.—See Fiba Holding A.S.; *Int'l*, pg. 2651
CREDIT EUROPE BANK (ROMANIA) S.A.—See Fiba Holding A.S.; *Int'l*, pg. 2651
CREDIT EUROPE BANK (SUISSE) S.A.—See Fiba Holding A.S.; *Int'l*, pg. 2651
CREDIT FIRST NATIONAL ASSOCIATION—See Bridgestone Corporation; *Int'l*, pg. 1157
CREDIT IMMOBILIER ET HOTELIER SA; *Int'l*, pg. 1835
CREDIT INDUSTRIEL ET COMMERCIAL SA—See Confederation Nationale du Credit Mutuel; *Int'l*, pg. 1767
CREDIT MUTUEL NORD EUROPE BELGIUM NV—See Confederation Nationale du Credit Mutuel; *Int'l*, pg. 1767
CREDITO BERGAMASCO S.P.A.—See Banco BPM S.p.A.; *Int'l*, pg. 819
CREDITO EMILIANO SPA—See Credito Emiliano S.p.A.; *Int'l*, pg. 1836
CREDIT ONE BANK N.A.—See Sherman Financial Group LLC; *U.S. Private*, pg. 3634
CREDITO PIEMONTESE S.P.A.—See Credito Valtellinese Societa Cooperativa; *Int'l*, pg. 1837
CREDIT UNION OF DENVER; *U.S. Private*, pg. 1091
CREDIT URAL BANK JSC—See Gazprombank JSC; *Int'l*, pg. 2892
CRELAN SA/NV—See CrelanCo CVBA; *Int'l*, pg. 1838
CRESCENT BANK & TRUST—See CB&T Holding Corporation; *U.S. Private*, pg. 796
CRESCO BANK & TRUST COMPANY—See Security Agency, Inc.; *U.S. Private*, pg. 3594
THE CROGHAN COLONIAL BANK—See Croghan Bancshares, Inc.; *U.S. Public*, pg. 595
CROSS COUNTY FEDERAL SAVINGS BANK; *U.S. Private*, pg. 1104

522110 — COMMERCIAL BANKING

CROSSKEY BANKING SOLUTIONS AB LTD.—See Alandsbanken Abp; *Int'l*, pg. 290
CROSS KEYS BANK—See BSJ Bancshares, Inc.; *U.S. Private*, pg. 675
CROSSROADS BANK—See FFW Corporation; *U.S. Public*, pg. 830
CSA COMMERZ SOUTH AFRICA (PROPRIETARY) LIMITED—See Commerzbank AG; *Int'l*, pg. 1715
CSI ENTREPRISES INC.—See Edenred S.A.; *Int'l*, pg. 2307
CTBC BANK CORP. (USA)—See CTBC Financial Holding Co., Ltd.; *Int'l*, pg. 1869
CUB OJSC—See Gazprombank JSC; *Int'l*, pg. 2892
CULLMAN SAVINGS BANK—See Cullman Bancorp, Inc.; *U.S. Public*, pg. 604
CUSCAL LTD.; *Int'l*, pg. 1880
CUSTOMERS BANK—See Customers Bancorp, Inc.; *U.S. Public*, pg. 612
CYNERGY BANK LTD.—See Cynergy Capital Ltd.; *Int'l*, pg. 1896
C-ZONE S.P.A.—See Bank of America Corporation; *U.S. Public*, pg. 271
DACOTAH BANK—See Dacotah Banks, Inc.; *U.S. Public*, pg. 620
THE DAEGU BANK, LTD.—See DGB Financial Group Co., Ltd.; *Int'l*, pg. 2096
DAEGU CREDIT INFORMATION CO., LTD.—See DGB Financial Group Co., Ltd.; *Int'l*, pg. 2096
DAH SING BANKING GROUP LIMITED—See Dah Sing Financial Holdings Limited; *Int'l*, pg. 1913
THE DAISHI BANK, LTD.—See Daishi Hokuetsu Financial Group, Inc.; *Int'l*, pg. 1941
THE DAISHI HOKUETSU BANK, LTD.—See Daishi Hokuetsu Financial Group, Inc.; *Int'l*, pg. 1941
DAIWA NEXT BANK, LTD.—See Daiwa Securities Group Inc.; *Int'l*, pg. 1948
DAIWA SECURITIES TRUST COMPANY—See Daiwa Securities Group Inc.; *Int'l*, pg. 1948
DAKOTA COMMUNITY BANK & TRUST, N.A.—See Dakota Community Banshares, Inc.; *U.S. Private*, pg. 1147
DALATE CDB VILLAGE BANK CO., LTD.—See China Development Bank Corporation; *Int'l*, pg. 1497
DANSKE ANDELSKASSERS BANK A/S; *Int'l*, pg. 1969
DANSKE BANK A/S; *Int'l*, pg. 1969
DANSKE BANK INTERNATIONAL S.A.—See Danske Bank A/S; *Int'l*, pg. 1969
DANSKE LEASING A/S—See Danske Bank A/S; *Int'l*, pg. 1969
DAR AL-MAAL AL-ISLAMI TRUST; *Int'l*, pg. 1971
DAR ES SALAM INVESTMENT BANK; *Int'l*, pg. 1972
DARIEN ROWAYTON BANK; *U.S. Public*, pg. 633
DART BANK; *U.S. Private*, pg. 1159
DATONG CDB VILLAGE BANK CO., LTD.—See China Development Bank Corporation; *Int'l*, pg. 1497
DAYE CDB VILLAGE BANK CO., LTD.—See China Development Bank Corporation; *Int'l*, pg. 1497
DB AKELA, S.A R.L.—See Deutsche Bank Aktiengesellschaft; *Int'l*, pg. 2056
DB BLUEBELL INVESTMENTS (CAYMAN) PARTNERSHIP—See Deutsche Bank Aktiengesellschaft; *Int'l*, pg. 2056
DBC CONTINUANCE INC.—See Deutsche Bank Aktiengesellschaft; *Int'l*, pg. 2057
DB DEPOSITOR INC.—See Deutsche Bank Aktiengesellschaft; *Int'l*, pg. 2056
DB EQUITY S.A R.L.—See Deutsche Bank Aktiengesellschaft; *Int'l*, pg. 2056
DB GLOBAL TECHNOLOGY, INC.—See Deutsche Bank Aktiengesellschaft; *Int'l*, pg. 2056
DB GROUP SERVICES (UK) LIMITED—See Deutsche Bank Aktiengesellschaft; *Int'l*, pg. 2056
DB INTERNATIONAL (ASIA) LIMITED—See Deutsche Bank Aktiengesellschaft; *Int'l*, pg. 2056
DBJ EUROPE LIMITED—See Development Bank of Japan, Inc.; *Int'l*, pg. 2087
DBJ SINGAPORE LIMITED—See Development Bank of Japan, Inc.; *Int'l*, pg. 2087
DB PARTNERSHIP MANAGEMENT LTD.—See Deutsche Bank Aktiengesellschaft; *Int'l*, pg. 2056
DBS BANK (HONG KONG) LIMITED—See DBS Group Holdings Ltd.; *Int'l*, pg. 1988
DBS BANK INDIA LIMITED—See DBS Group Holdings Ltd.; *Int'l*, pg. 1988
DBS BANK (TAIWAN) LIMITED—See DBS Group Holdings Ltd.; *Int'l*, pg. 1988
DB SERVICIOS MEXICO, S.A. DE C.V.—See Deutsche Bank Aktiengesellschaft; *Int'l*, pg. 2059
DBSN SERVICES PTE. LTD.—See DBS Group Holdings Ltd.; *Int'l*, pg. 1988
DB STRATEGIC ADVISORS, INC.—See Deutsche Bank Aktiengesellschaft; *Int'l*, pg. 2056
DB UK BANK LIMITED—See Deutsche Bank Aktiengesellschaft; *Int'l*, pg. 2057
DCB BANK LIMITED; *Int'l*, pg. 1989
DEBITUM INVEST REIT; *Int'l*, pg. 1998
DECORAH BANK & TRUST COMPANY—See Security Agency, Inc.; *U.S. Private*, pg. 3594
DEERWOOD BANK—See Deerwood Bancshares, Inc.; *U.S. Private*, pg. 1190

DELAWARE PLACE BANK—See Security Chicago Corporation; *U.S. Private*, pg. 3595
DELHI BANK CORP.; *U.S. Public*, pg. 648
DELTA BANK JSC; *Int'l*, pg. 2015
DENIZBANK AG—See Emirates NBD PJSC; *Int'l*, pg. 2381
DENIZBANK A.S.—See Emirates NBD PJSC; *Int'l*, pg. 2381
DEN JYSKE SPAREKASSE AS—See Arbejdernes Landsbank A/S; *Int'l*, pg. 537
DEPFA ACS BANK PLC—See FMS Wertmanagement Aor; *Int'l*, pg. 2717
DEPFA BANK PLC—See FMS Wertmanagement Aor; *Int'l*, pg. 2717
DEPFA FINANCE N.V.—See FMS Wertmanagement Aor; *Int'l*, pg. 2717
DESERT COMMUNITY BANK—See New York Community Bancorp, Inc.; *U.S. Public*, pg. 1512
DE SURINAAMSCHE BANK N.V.—See Assuria N.V.; *Int'l*, pg. 650
DEUTSCHE APOTHEKER- UND ARZTEBANK EG; *Int'l*, pg. 2049
DEUTSCHE AUSTRALIA LIMITED—See Deutsche Bank Aktiengesellschaft; *Int'l*, pg. 2058
DEUTSCHE BAHN FINANCE B. V.—See Deutsche Bahn AG; *Int'l*, pg. 2051
DEUTSCHE BANK AG (NEW YORK)—See Deutsche Bank Aktiengesellschaft; *Int'l*, pg. 2058
DEUTSCHE BANK AKTIENGESELLSCHAFT; *Int'l*, pg. 2055
DEUTSCHE BANK A.S.—See Deutsche Bank Aktiengesellschaft; *Int'l*, pg. 2057
DEUTSCHE BANK EUROPE GMBH—See Deutsche Bank Aktiengesellschaft; *Int'l*, pg. 2058
DEUTSCHE BANK GROUP SERVICES LTD.—See Deutsche Bank Aktiengesellschaft; *Int'l*, pg. 2059
DEUTSCHE BANK INTERNATIONAL LIMITED—See Deutsche Bank Aktiengesellschaft; *Int'l*, pg. 2059
DEUTSCHE BANK (MALTA) LTD—See Deutsche Bank Aktiengesellschaft; *Int'l*, pg. 2058
DEUTSCHE BANK (MAURITIUS) LIMITED—See Deutsche Bank Aktiengesellschaft; *Int'l*, pg. 2058
DEUTSCHE BANK NEDERLAND N.V.—See Deutsche Bank Aktiengesellschaft; *Int'l*, pg. 2059
DEUTSCHE BANK NOMINEES (JERSEY) LIMITED—See Deutsche Bank Aktiengesellschaft; *Int'l*, pg. 2059
DEUTSCHE BANK OSTERREICH AG—See Deutsche Bank Aktiengesellschaft; *Int'l*, pg. 2062
DEUTSCHE BANK (PERU) S.A.—See Deutsche Bank Aktiengesellschaft; *Int'l*, pg. 2058
DEUTSCHE BANK PRIVAT UND GESCHAFTSKUNDEN AG—See Deutsche Bank Aktiengesellschaft; *Int'l*, pg. 2060
DEUTSCHE BANK REPRESENTATIVE OFFICE NIGERIA LIMITED—See Deutsche Bank Aktiengesellschaft; *Int'l*, pg. 2060
DEUTSCHE BANK SERVICES (JERSEY) LIMITED—See Deutsche Bank Aktiengesellschaft; *Int'l*, pg. 2060
DEUTSCHE BANK—See Deutsche Bank Aktiengesellschaft; *Int'l*, pg. 2058
DEUTSCHE BANK S.P.A.—See Deutsche Bank Aktiengesellschaft; *Int'l*, pg. 2060
DEUTSCHE BANK TRUST COMPANY DELAWARE—See Deutsche Bank Aktiengesellschaft; *Int'l*, pg. 2060
DEUTSCHE BANK TRUSTEE SERVICES (GUERNSEY) LIMITED—See Deutsche Bank Aktiengesellschaft; *Int'l*, pg. 2060
DEUTSCHE BUNDESBANK HAUPTVERWALTUNG BERLIN—See Deutsche Bundesbank; *Int'l*, pg. 2065
DEUTSCHE BUNDESBANK HAUPTVERWALTUNG DUSSELDORF—See Deutsche Bundesbank; *Int'l*, pg. 2065
DEUTSCHE BUNDESBANK HAUPTVERWALTUNG FRANKFURT—See Deutsche Bundesbank; *Int'l*, pg. 2065
DEUTSCHE BUNDESBANK HAUPTVERWALTUNG HAMBURG—See Deutsche Bundesbank; *Int'l*, pg. 2065
DEUTSCHE BUNDESBANK HAUPTVERWALTUNG HANNOVER—See Deutsche Bundesbank; *Int'l*, pg. 2065
DEUTSCHE BUNDESBANK HAUPTVERWALTUNG LEIPZIG—See Deutsche Bundesbank; *Int'l*, pg. 2065
DEUTSCHE BUNDESBANK HAUPTVERWALTUNG MAINZ—See Deutsche Bundesbank; *Int'l*, pg. 2065
DEUTSCHE BUNDESBANK; *Int'l*, pg. 2065
DEUTSCHE CUSTODY N.V.—See Deutsche Bank Aktiengesellschaft; *Int'l*, pg. 2060
DEUTSCHE NEW ZEALAND LIMITED—See Deutsche Bank Aktiengesellschaft; *Int'l*, pg. 2060
DEUTSCHE NOMINEES LIMITED—See Deutsche Bank Aktiengesellschaft; *Int'l*, pg. 2060
DEUTSCHE PFANDBRIEFBANK - CENTRAL & EASTERN EUROPE—See Hypo Real Estate Holding AG; *Int'l*, pg. 3553
DEUTSCHE PFANDBRIEFBANK - LONDON—See Hypo Real Estate Holding AG; *Int'l*, pg. 3553
DEUTSCHE PFANDBRIEFBANK - MADRID—See Hypo Real Estate Holding AG; *Int'l*, pg. 3553

DEUTSCHE PFANDBRIEFBANK - MILAN—See Hypo Real Estate Holding AG; *Int'l*, pg. 3553
DEUTSCHE PFANDBRIEFBANK - PARIS—See Hypo Real Estate Holding AG; *Int'l*, pg. 3553
DEUTSCHE POSTBANK AG—See Deutsche Post AG; *Int'l*, pg. 2080
DEUTSCHER RING BAUSPARKASSE AKTIENGESELLSCHAFT—See BAWAG Group AG; *Int'l*, pg. 900
DEUTSCHE SECURITIES MENKUL DEGERLER A.S.—See Deutsche Bank Aktiengesellschaft; *Int'l*, pg. 2061
THE DEVELOPMENT BANK OF SINGAPORE, LTD.—See DBS Group Holdings Ltd.; *Int'l*, pg. 1988
DEVELOPMENT CAPITAL BANK JSC; *Int'l*, pg. 2088
DEVELOPMENT FINANCE COMPANY OF UGANDA LTD.; *Int'l*, pg. 2088
DEVON BANK; *U.S. Private*, pg. 1219
DEXIA BANK DENMARK A/S—See Dexia SA; *Int'l*, pg. 2092
DEXIA CLF BANQUE S.A—See Dexia SA; *Int'l*, pg. 2092
DEXIA CREDIOP S.P.A.—See Dexia SA; *Int'l*, pg. 2092
DEXIA KOMMUNALKREDIT BANK AG—See Dexia SA; *Int'l*, pg. 2092
DF CAPITAL BANK LIMITED—See Distribution Finance Capital Holdings plc; *Int'l*, pg. 2136
DFCC VARDHANA BANK LIMITED—See DFCC Bank PLC; *Int'l*, pg. 2094
DFCU BANK LIMITED—See Development Finance Company of Uganda Ltd.; *Int'l*, pg. 2088
DFZ TUSSENHOLDING N.V.—See Achmea B.V.; *Int'l*, pg. 103
DHANLAXMI BANK LTD.; *Int'l*, pg. 2098
DHOFAR INTERNATIONAL DEVELOPMENT & INVESTMENT HOLDING COMPANY S.A.O.G; *Int'l*, pg. 2099
DIAMOND TRUST BANK BURUNDI S.A.—See Diamond Trust Bank Kenya Limited; *Int'l*, pg. 2106
DIAMOND TRUST BANK TANZANIA LTD—See Aga Khan Development Network; *Int'l*, pg. 199
DIAMOND TRUST BANK UGANDA LIMITED—See Diamond Trust Bank Kenya Limited; *Int'l*, pg. 2106
DIAMOND TRUST BANK UGANDA LTD—See Aga Khan Development Network; *Int'l*, pg. 199
DIB BANK KENYA LTD.—See Dubai Islamic Bank PSJ; *Int'l*, pg. 2219
DIEBOLD NIXDORF TECHNOLOGIES LLC—See Diebold Nixdorf, Inc.; *U.S. Public*, pg. 660
DIME ABSTRACT LLC—See Dime Community Bancshares, Inc.; *U.S. Public*, pg. 666
THE DIME BANK—See Dimeco Inc.; *U.S. Public*, pg. 666
DIME COMMUNITY BANK—See Dime Community Bancshares, Inc.; *U.S. Public*, pg. 666
DIREKTNA BANKA A.D.; *Int'l*, pg. 2130
DISCOVER BANK—See Discover Financial Services; *U.S. Public*, pg. 668
DJURSLANDS BANK A/S; *Int'l*, pg. 2138
DKB SERVICE GMBH—See BayernLB Holding AG; *Int'l*, pg. 913
DKC DEKA KOMMUNAL CONSULT GMBH—See DekaBank; *Int'l*, pg. 2005
D.L. EVANS BANK—See D.L. Evans Bancorp; *U.S. Private*, pg. 1142
DNB ASIA LTD.—See DNB Bank ASA; *Int'l*, pg. 2147
DNB BANK ASA; *Int'l*, pg. 2147
DNB BANK POLSKA S.A.—See DNB Bank ASA; *Int'l*, pg. 2147
DNB BOLIGKREDITT AS—See DNB Bank ASA; *Int'l*, pg. 2147
DNB EIENDOM AS—See DNB Bank ASA; *Int'l*, pg. 2148
DNB LUXEMBOURG S.A.—See DNB Bank ASA; *Int'l*, pg. 2148
DNB NAERINGSMEGLING AS—See DNB Bank ASA; *Int'l*, pg. 2148
DOBANK SPA; *Int'l*, pg. 2152
DOGWOOD STATE BANK; *U.S. Public*, pg. 672
DOHA BANK Q.S.C.; *Int'l*, pg. 2155
DONEGAL FINANCIAL SERVICES CORPORATION—See Northwest Bancshares, Inc.; *U.S. Public*, pg. 1541
DONGBU SAVINGS BANK CO., LTD.—See Dongbu Group; *Int'l*, pg. 2166
DONGGUAN RURAL COMMERCIAL BANK CO., LTD.; *Int'l*, pg. 2167
DORNBIRNER SPARKASSE BANK AG; *Int'l*, pg. 2179
DRESDNER BANK AG—See Commerzbank AG; *Int'l*, pg. 1717
DRESDNER KLEINWORT PFANDBRIEFE INVESTMENTS, INC.—See Bank of America Corporation; *U.S. Public*, pg. 272
DRUMMOND COMMUNITY BANK—See Drummond Banking Company; *U.S. Private*, pg. 1280
DUBAI FINANCIAL GROUP—See Dubai Holding LLC; *Int'l*, pg. 2218
DUBAI ISLAMIC BANK PSJ; *Int'l*, pg. 2219
DUBAI ISLAMIC FINANCIAL SERVICES L.L.C.—See Dubai Islamic Bank PSJ; *Int'l*, pg. 2220
DUBUQUE BANK & TRUST COMPANY—See Heartland Financial USA, Inc.; *U.S. Public*, pg. 1018
DUNDEE BANK—See Mackey Banco, Inc.; *U.S. Private*, pg. 2537

N.A.I.C.S. INDEX

522110 — COMMERCIAL BANKING

DUO BANK OF CANADA—See Centerbridge Partners, L.P.; *U.S. Private*, pg. 814
DUTCH-BANGLA BANK PLC; *Int'l*, pg. 2235
DVB BANK AMERICA N.V.—See DZ BANK AG Deutsche Zentral-Genossenschaftsbank; *Int'l*, pg. 2243
DWS FAR EASTERN INVESTMENTS LIMITED—See Deutsche Bank Aktiengesellschaft; *Int'l*, pg. 2057
DYER BANK & TRUST—See Wintrust Financial Corporation; *U.S. Public*, pg. 2375
DZ PRIVATBANK S.A.—See DZ BANK AG Deutsche Zentral-Genossenschaftsbank; *Int'l*, pg. 2244
EAGLEBANK—See Eagle Bancorp, Inc.; *U.S. Public*, pg. 701
E.A.P.S. - EMPRESA DE ANALISE, PREVENCAO E SEGURANCA, S.A.—See Caixa Geral de Depositos S.A.; *Int'l*, pg. 1260
EARLHAM SAVINGS BANK; *U.S. Private*, pg. 1313
EAST BOSTON SAVINGS BANK—See Meridian Bancorp, Inc.; *U.S. Public*, pg. 1424
EAST CAMBRIDGE SAVINGS BANK INC.; *U.S. Private*, pg. 1315
EASTERN BANK PLC; *Int'l*, pg. 2271
EASTERN BANK—See Eastern Bankshares, Inc.; *U.S. Public*, pg. 704
EASTERN CARIBBEAN AMALGAMATED BANK; *Int'l*, pg. 2272
EASTERN CARIBBEAN CENTRAL BANK; *Int'l*, pg. 2272
THE EASTERN COLORADO BANK—See Weed Investment Group, Inc.; *U.S. Private*, pg. 4469
EASTERN MICHIGAN BANK—See Eastern Michigan Financial Corp; *U.S. Public*, pg. 704
EASTERN MICHIGAN FINANCIAL CORP; *U.S. Public*, pg. 704
EASTERN NATIONAL BANK INC.; *U.S. Private*, pg. 1320
EAST GOSFORD & DISTRICTS FINANCIAL SERVICES LTD.—See Bendigo & Adelaide Bank Ltd.; *Int'l*, pg. 971
EAST SIDE FINANCIAL, INC.; *U.S. Public*, pg. 703
EAST WEST BANK (CHINA) LIMITED—See East West Bancorp, Inc.; *U.S. Public*, pg. 703
EAST WEST BANKING CORPORATION—See Filinvest Development Corporation; *Int'l*, pg. 2663
EAST WEST BANK—See East West Bancorp, Inc.; *U.S. Public*, pg. 703
EASYBANK AG—See BAWAG Group AG; *Int'l*, pg. 900
EBI SA—See Ecobank Transnational Incorporated; *Int'l*, pg. 2293
ECOBANK CENTRAFRIQUE—See Ecobank Transnational Incorporated; *Int'l*, pg. 2293
ECOBANK CHAD LTD.—See Ecobank Transnational Incorporated; *Int'l*, pg. 2293
ECOBANK CONGO BRAZZAVILLE LIMITED—See Ecobank Transnational Incorporated; *Int'l*, pg. 2294
ECOBANK CONGO RDC LIMITED—See Ecobank Transnational Incorporated; *Int'l*, pg. 2294
ECOBANK COTE D'IVOIRE S.A.—See Ecobank Transnational Incorporated; *Int'l*, pg. 2294
ECOBANK GHANA LIMITED—See Ecobank Transnational Incorporated; *Int'l*, pg. 2294
ECOBANK GUINEA EQUATORIALE LTD.—See Ecobank Transnational Incorporated; *Int'l*, pg. 2294
ECOBANK KENYA LIMITED—See Ecobank Transnational Incorporated; *Int'l*, pg. 2294
ECOBANK MALAWI LIMITED—See Ecobank Transnational Incorporated; *Int'l*, pg. 2294
ECOBANK NIGERIA PLC—See Ecobank Transnational Incorporated; *Int'l*, pg. 2294
ECOBANK RWANDA PLC—See Ecobank Transnational Incorporated; *Int'l*, pg. 2294
ECOBANK SIERRA LEONE LIMITED—See Ecobank Transnational Incorporated; *Int'l*, pg. 2294
ECOBANK TANZANIA LIMITED—See Ecobank Transnational Incorporated; *Int'l*, pg. 2294
ECOBANK TCHAD S.A.—See Ecobank Transnational Incorporated; *Int'l*, pg. 2294
ECOBANK TOGO S.A.—See Ecobank Transnational Incorporated; *Int'l*, pg. 2294
ECOBANK ZAMBIA LIMITED—See Ecobank Transnational Incorporated; *Int'l*, pg. 2294
ECOBANK ZIMBABWE LIMITED—See Ecobank Transnational Incorporated; *Int'l*, pg. 2294
ECOFI INVESTISSEMENT SA—See Groupe BPCE; *Int'l*, pg. 3094
THE ECONOMY BANK N V—See BNP Paribas SA; *Int'l*, pg. 1093
EDISON NATIONAL BANK—See Edison Bancshares, Inc.; *U.S. Private*, pg. 1336
EDMOND DE ROTHSCHILD (BAHAMAS) LTD.—See Edmond de Rothschild Holding S.A.; *Int'l*, pg. 2312
EDMOND DE ROTHSCHILD (EUROPE) SA/NV—See Edmond de Rothschild Holding S.A.; *Int'l*, pg. 2312
EDMOND DE ROTHSCHILD (ISRAEL) LTD.—See Edmond de Rothschild Holding S.A.; *Int'l*, pg. 2313
EDMOND DE ROTHSCHILD (LUGANO) S.A.—See Edmond de Rothschild Holding S.A.; *Int'l*, pg. 2313
EDMOND DE ROTHSCHILD (MONACO) LTD.—See Edmond de Rothschild Holding S.A.; *Int'l*, pg. 2313
EDMOND DE ROTHSCHILD PRIVATE EQUITY PARTNERS (ISRAEL) LTD.—See Edmond de Rothschild Holding S.A.; *Int'l*, pg. 2313
EDMOND DE ROTHSCHILD (UK) LIMITED—See Edmond de Rothschild Holding S.A.; *Int'l*, pg. 2313
EDMONTON BANCSHARES INC.; *U.S. Private*, pg. 1337
EDMONTON STATE BANK—See Edmonton Bancshares Inc.; *U.S. Private*, pg. 1337
EDWARDS DEVELOPMENT CORPORATION; *U.S. Private*, pg. 1342
EFG BANK AB—See EFG International AG; *Int'l*, pg. 2320
EFG BANK AG—See EFG International AG; *Int'l*, pg. 2320
EFG BANK (GIBRALTAR) LTD—See EFG International AG; *Int'l*, pg. 2320
EFG BANK (LUXEMBOURG) SA—See EFG International AG; *Int'l*, pg. 2320
EFG BANK (MONACO)—See EFG International AG; *Int'l*, pg. 2320
EFG-HERMES LEASING COMPANY—See EFG Holding; *Int'l*, pg. 2319
EFG PRIVATE BANK (CHANNEL ISLANDS) LIMITED—See EFG International AG; *Int'l*, pg. 2320
EFG PRIVATE BANK LIMITED—See EFG International AG; *Int'l*, pg. 2320
EGG AND CITI UK CONSUMER—See Citigroup Inc.; *U.S. Public*, pg. 503
EGHTESAD NOVIN BANK; *Int'l*, pg. 2324
EGYPTIAN GULF BANK; *Int'l*, pg. 2327
EGYPTIAN SAUDI FINANCE BANK—See Al Baraka Banking Group B.S.C.; *Int'l*, pg. 276
THE EIGHTEENTH BANK, LIMITED—See Fukuoka Financial Group, Inc.; *Int'l*, pg. 2840
EIK BANK P/F; *Int'l*, pg. 2332
EKSPRES BANK AS—See BNP Paribas SA; *Int'l*, pg. 1090
ELAF ISLAMIC BANK; *Int'l*, pg. 2342
ELKEM METALS CANADA INC.-HAMILTON—See China National Chemical Corporation; *Int'l*, pg. 1527
ELLIOTT WILSON INSURANCE, LLC—See Shore Bancshares, Inc.; *U.S. Public*, pg. 1875
ELMIRA SAVINGS BANK—See Community Bank System, Inc.; *U.S. Public*, pg. 550
EMBASSY BANCORP, INC.; *U.S. Public*, pg. 735
EMBASSY BANK—See Embassy Bancorp, Inc.; *U.S. Public*, pg. 736
EMIRATES INVESTMENT BANK P.J.S.C.—See Al-Futtaim Private Company LLC; *Int'l*, pg. 285
EMIRATES ISLAMIC BANK PJSC; *Int'l*, pg. 2381
EMIRATES LEBANON BANK S.A.L.—See Bank of Sharjah P.S.C.; *Int'l*, pg. 848
EMIRATES NBD BANK PJSC—See Emirates NBD PJSC; *Int'l*, pg. 2382
EMIRATES NBD PJSC; *Int'l*, pg. 2381
EMPIRE NATIONAL BANK—See Flushing Financial Corporation; *U.S. Public*, pg. 860
EMPRISE BANK—See Emprise Financial Corporation; *U.S. Private*, pg. 1388
EMPRISE FINANCIAL CORPORATION; *U.S. Private*, pg. 1388
EM.RO. POPOLARE S.P.A.—See BPER BANCA S.p.A; *Int'l*, pg. 1132
ENCORE BANK, NATIONAL ASSOCIATION—See Ovation Holdings, Inc.; *U.S. Private*, pg. 3052
ENERGOMASHBANK, PLC; *Int'l*, pg. 2421
ENGLEWOOD BANK & TRUST—See Crews Banking Corporation; *U.S. Private*, pg. 1099
ENNOWYSE CORPORATION—See Ennoconn Corporation; *Int'l*, pg. 2443
ENTEGRA BANK—See First Citizens BancShares, Inc.; *U.S. Public*, pg. 842
ENTERPRISE BANK AND TRUST COMPANY—See Enterprise Bancorp, Inc.; *U.S. Public*, pg. 778
ENTERPRISE BANK—See Enterprise Financial Services Group, Inc.; *U.S. Public*, pg. 778
ENTERPRISE BANK & TRUST—See Enterprise Financial Services Corp; *U.S. Public*, pg. 778
ENTERPRISE FINANCIAL SERVICES CORP; *U.S. Public*, pg. 778
ENTIE COMMERCIAL BANK, LTD.; *Int'l*, pg. 2452
ENTRUST SECURITIES PLC; *Int'l*, pg. 2453
EPHRATA NATIONAL BANK—See ENB Financial Corp.; *U.S. Public*, pg. 754
EQUA BANK A.S.—See AnaCap Financial Partners LLP; *Int'l*, pg. 445
EQUITABLE BANK—See Equitable Financial Corp.; *U.S. Public*, pg. 788
EQUITAS SMALL FINANCE BANK LIMITED—See Equitas Holdings Limited; *Int'l*, pg. 2488
EQUITY BANK—See Equity Bancshares, Inc.; *U.S. Public*, pg. 790
EQUITY GROUP HOLDINGS PLC; *Int'l*, pg. 2488
EQUITY INSURANCE AGENCY, INC.—See Wells Fargo & Company; *U.S. Public*, pg. 2343
ERIEBANK, A DIVISION OF CNB BANK—See CNB Financial Corporation; *U.S. Public*, pg. 519
ERSTE BANK AD NOVI SAD—See Erste Group Bank AG; *Int'l*, pg. 2498
ERSTE BANK AD PODGORICA—See Erste Group Bank AG; *Int'l*, pg. 2498
ERSTE BANK D.D.—See Erste Group Bank AG; *Int'l*, pg. 2498
ERSTE BANK DER OESTERREICHISCHEN SPARKASSEN AG—See Erste Group Bank AG; *Int'l*, pg. 2498
ERSTE BANK HUNGARY NYRT.—See Erste Group Bank AG; *Int'l*, pg. 2498
ERSTE BANK (MALTA) LIMITED—See Erste Group Bank AG; *Int'l*, pg. 2498
ERSTE CORPORATE FINANCE, A.S.—See Erste Group Bank AG; *Int'l*, pg. 2498
ERSTE DMD D.O.O.—See Erste Group Bank AG; *Int'l*, pg. 2498
ERSTE & STEIERMARKISCHE BANK D.D.—See Erste Group Bank AG; *Int'l*, pg. 2498
ESCORTS CAPITAL LIMITED—See Escorts Investment Bank Limited; *Int'l*, pg. 2502
ESCORTS INVESTMENT BANK LIMITED; *Int'l*, pg. 2502
ESQUIRE BANK, NATIONAL ASSOCIATION—See Esquire Financial Holdings, Inc.; *U.S. Public*, pg. 794
ESSA BANK & TRUST—See ESSA Bancorp, Inc.; *U.S. Public*, pg. 795
ESSEX BANK—See United Bankshares, Inc.; *U.S. Public*, pg. 2229
E.SUN BANK (CHINA), LTD.—See E. Sun Financial Holding Co., Ltd.; *Int'l*, pg. 2250
E.SUN COMMERCIAL BANK, LTD.—See E. Sun Financial Holding Co., Ltd.; *Int'l*, pg. 2250
EULER HERMES COLLECTIONS SP. Z O.O.—See Allianz SE; *Int'l*, pg. 352
EURASIAN BANK JSC; *Int'l*, pg. 2527
EURASIAN BANK PJSC—See Eurasian Bank JSC; *Int'l*, pg. 2527
EURASIAN DEVELOPMENT BANK; *Int'l*, pg. 2527
EUROBANK BULGARIA AD—See Eurobank Ergasias Services and Holdings S.A.; *Int'l*, pg. 2532
EUROBANK CYPRUS LTD.—See Eurobank Ergasias Services and Holdings S.A.; *Int'l*, pg. 2532
EUROBANK EFG A.D. BELGRADE—See Eurobank Ergasias Services and Holdings S.A.; *Int'l*, pg. 2532
EUROBANK EFG CYPRUS LTD.—See Eurobank Ergasias Services and Holdings S.A.; *Int'l*, pg. 2532
EUROBANK PRIVATE BANK LUXEMBOURG SA—See Eurobank Ergasias Services and Holdings S.A.; *Int'l*, pg. 2532
EURO BANK SPOLKA AKCYJNA—See Banco Comercial Portugues, S.A.; *Int'l*, pg. 820
EURO MENKUL KIYMET YATIRIM ORTAKLIGI AS; *Int'l*, pg. 2531
EUROPEAN DEPOSITARY BANK SA—See Apex Fund Services Holdings Ltd.; *Int'l*, pg. 510
EUROPE ARAB BANK PLC—See Arab Bank plc; *Int'l*, pg. 529
EUROSTANDARD BANKA AD; *Int'l*, pg. 2558
THE EVANGELINE BANK & TRUST CO.; *U.S. Private*, pg. 4027
EVANS NATIONAL HOLDING CORP.—See Evans Bancorp, Inc.; *U.S. Public*, pg. 799
EVLI PANKKI OYJ; *Int'l*, pg. 2570
EVO BANCO S.A.—See Bankinter, S.A.; *Int'l*, pg. 850
EVOLVE BANK & TRUST; *U.S. Private*, pg. 1443
EVO PAYMENTS INTERNATIONAL CORP.—See Global Payments Inc.; *U.S. Public*, pg. 943
EVROFINANCE MOSNARBANK OJSC; *Int'l*, pg. 2574
EXCEL DEVELOPMENT BANK LTD.; *Int'l*, pg. 2577
EXCHANGE BANK OF MISSOURI—See Northern Missouri Bancshares, Inc.; *U.S. Private*, pg. 2953
EXCHANGE BANK OF NORTHEAST MISSOURI—See Lincoln County Bancorp., Inc.; *U.S. Private*, pg. 2457
EXCHANGE BANKSHARES, INC.; *U.S. Private*, pg. 1446
EXCHANGE BANK & TRUST; *U.S. Private*, pg. 1446
EXECUTIVE NATIONAL BANK; *U.S. Private*, pg. 1448
EXIMBANK KAZAKHSTAN JSC; *Int'l*, pg. 2585
EXIM FINANCE (HONG KONG) LIMITED—See Export Import Bank of Bangladesh Limited; *Int'l*, pg. 2590
EXIM ISLAMI INVESTMENT LTD.—See Export Import Bank of Bangladesh Limited; *Int'l*, pg. 2590
EXPOBANK CZ A.S.—See Expobank LLC; *Int'l*, pg. 2589
EXPOBANK LLC; *Int'l*, pg. 2589
EXPORT DEVELOPMENT BANK OF EGYPT; *Int'l*, pg. 2590
EXPORT DEVELOPMENT BANK; *Int'l*, pg. 2590
EXPORT IMPORT BANK OF BANGLADESH LIMITED; *Int'l*, pg. 2590
EXPRESSBANK OJSC; *Int'l*, pg. 2590
EXTRACO BANKS—See Extraco Corporation; *U.S. Private*, pg. 1452
FAB PRIVATE BANK (SUISSE) SA—See First Abu Dhabi Bank P.J.S.C.; *Int'l*, pg. 2681
FAHEY BANKING COMPANY; *U.S. Public*, pg. 820
FAIRFIELD NATIONAL BANK—See Park National Corporation; *U.S. Public*, pg. 1638
FAISAL ISLAMIC BANK OF EGYPT; *Int'l*, pg. 2609
FALCON INTERNATIONAL BANK; *U.S. Private*, pg. 1466
FALCON NATIONAL BANK; *U.S. Private*, pg. 1466
FARMERS AND MERCHANTS BANK—See Country Bank Shares, Inc.; *U.S. Private*, pg. 1066
FARMERS AND MERCHANTS BANK—See Farmers and Merchants Bancshares, Inc.; *U.S. Public*, pg. 822
FARMERS BANK AND TRUST; *U.S. Private*, pg. 1476

522110 — COMMERCIAL BANKING

THE FARMERS BANK OF APPOMATTOX; *U.S. Public*, pg. 2073
FARMERS BANK OF NORTHERN MISSOURI—See Northern Missouri Bancshares, Inc.; *U.S. Private*, pg. 2953
FARMERS BANK—See Farmers Bancorporation, Inc.; *U.S. Private*, pg. 1476
THE FARMERS BANK—See First Farmers Bancshares Inc.; *U.S. Private*, pg. 1517
FARMERS BANK—See Park National Corporation; *U.S. Public*, pg. 1638
THE FARMERS BANK—See Putnam-Greene Financial Corporation; *U.S. Private*, pg. 3307
FARMERS BANK—See Towne Bank; *U.S. Public*, pg. 2166
FARMERS BANK & TRUST COMPANY—See Magnolia Banking Corporation; *U.S. Private*, pg. 2548
FARMERS BANK & TRUST; *U.S. Private*, pg. 1476
FARMERS COMMERCIAL BANK; *Int'l*, pg. 2619
FARMERS DEPOSIT BANK OF MIDDLEBURG, INC.—See John R. Turner Holding Company; *U.S. Private*, pg. 2224
FARMERS MERCHANTS BANK LONG BEACH; *U.S. Public*, pg. 822
FARMERS & MERCHANTS BANK OF CENTRAL CALIFORNIA—See Farmers & Merchants Bancorp; *U.S. Public*, pg. 821
FARMERS-MERCHANTS BANK OF ILLINOIS—See Merchants Bancorp; *U.S. Public*, pg. 1415
FARMERS & MERCHANTS BANK OF SOUTH CAROLINA—See FMB of S.C. Bancshares, Incorporated; *U.S. Private*, pg. 378
FARMERS & MERCHANTS BANK; *U.S. Private*, pg. 1475
FARMERS & MERCHANTS BANK—See F&M Bank Corp.; *U.S. Public*, pg. 818
FARMERS & MERCHANTS BANK—See Putnam-Greene Financial Corporation; *U.S. Private*, pg. 3307
FARMERS & MERCHANTS STATE BANK—See Farmers & Merchants Bancorp, Inc.; *U.S. Public*, pg. 822
FARMERS & MERCHANTS TRUST CHAMBERSBURG—See Franklin Financial Services Corporation; *U.S. Public*, pg. 879
THE FARMERS NATIONAL BANK OF CANFIELD—See Farmers National Banc Corp.; *U.S. Public*, pg. 822
THE FARMERS NATIONAL BANK OF DANVILLE—See Boyle Bancorp Inc.; *U.S. Public*, pg. 1
THE FARMERS NATIONAL BANK OF EMLENTON—See Farmers National Banc Corp.; *U.S. Public*, pg. 822
FARMERS NATIONAL INSURANCE LLC—See Farmers National Banc Corp.; *U.S. Public*, pg. 822
FARMERS SAVINGS BANK INC.; *U.S. Private*, pg. 1479
FARMERS STATE BANK OF BRUSH—See First Pioneer Bank Corp.; *U.S. Private*, pg. 1524
FARMERS STATE BANK OF WATKINS—See Neisen Bancshares, Inc.; *U.S. Private*, pg. 2882
FARMERS STATE BANK; *U.S. Private*, pg. 1479
FARMERS STATE BANK—See F.S. Bancorp; *U.S. Private*, pg. 1457
FARMERS STATE BANK—See FSC Bancshares, Inc.; *U.S. Private*, pg. 1618
FARMERS STATE BANK—See Groesbeck Bancshares, Inc.; *U.S. Private*, pg. 1791
FARMERS STATE BANK—See Neighbor Insurance Services; *U.S. Private*, pg. 2881
FARMERS TRUST & SAVINGS BANK—See FTS Financial, Inc.; *U.S. Private*, pg. 1619
FARMERS TRUST & SAVINGS BANK—See Koss-Winn Bancshares, Inc.; *U.S. Private*, pg. 2344
FAYSAL BANK LIMITED—See Dar Al-Maal Al-Islami Trust; *Int'l*, pg. 1971
FBC BANK LIMITED—See FBC Holdings Limited; *Int'l*, pg. 2627
FBN BANK (UK) LTD—See FBN Holdings PLC; *Int'l*, pg. 2627
FCBANK, A DIVISION OF CNB BANK—See CNB Financial Corporation; *U.S. Public*, pg. 519
FCMB BANK (UK) LIMITED—See FCMB Group Plc; *Int'l*, pg. 2628
FCN BANK; *U.S. Private*, pg. 1486
FDS BANK—See Macy's, Inc.; *U.S. Public*, pg. 1353
FEDERAL RESERVE BANK OF CLEVELAND; *U.S. Private*, pg. 1490
FEDERAL RESERVE BANK OF DALLAS, HOUSTON BRANCH—See Federal Reserve Bank of Dallas; *U.S. Private*, pg. 1490
FEDERAL RESERVE BANK OF PHILADELPHIA; *U.S. Private*, pg. 1491
FEDERAL RESERVE—See Federal Reserve Bank of Dallas; *U.S. Private*, pg. 1490
FELICIANA BANK & TRUST COMPANY; *U.S. Public*, pg. 829
FELLOW FINANCE PLC—See Evli Pankki Oyj; *Int'l*, pg. 2570
FFBW, INC.; *U.S. Public*, pg. 829
FHB LIFE ANNUITY LTD.—See FHB Mortgage Bank Public Limited Company; *Int'l*, pg. 2650
FHB SERVICES LTD—See FHB Mortgage Bank Public Limited Company; *Int'l*, pg. 2650
FIBABANKA A.S.; *Int'l*, pg. 2651
FIBANC PENSIONES S.G.F.P. S.A.—See Banca Mediolanum S.p.A.; *Int'l*, pg. 815

FIBANC SA—See Banca Mediolanum S.p.A.; *Int'l*, pg. 815
FIDEICOMISO DE CREDITO BANCO GENERAL COSTA RICA; *Int'l*, pg. 2654
THE FIDELITY BANK INC.; *U.S. Public*, pg. 4028
FIDELITY BANK OF FLORIDA, N.A.; *U.S. Private*, pg. 1502
FIDELITY BANK PLC.; *Int'l*, pg. 2654
FIDELITY BANK—See Fidelity Financial Corporation; *U.S. Private*, pg. 1503
THE FIDELITY DEPOSIT & DISCOUNT BANK—See Fidelity D & D Bancorp, Inc.; *U.S. Public*, pg. 830
FIDOR BANK AG—See Groupe BPCE; *Int'l*, pg. 3097
FIDUCIARY COMPANY INCORPORATED; *U.S. Private*, pg. 1503
FIDUCIARY TRUST CO. INC.—See Fiduciary Company Incorporated; *U.S. Private*, pg. 1503
FIDUCIARY TRUST COMPANY INTERNATIONAL—See Franklin Resources, Inc.; *U.S. Public*, pg. 880
FIELDPOINT PRIVATE BANK & TRUST; *U.S. Private*, pg. 1504
FIH ERHVERVSBANK A/S; *Int'l*, pg. 2661
FIMBANK P.L.C.; *Int'l*, pg. 2664
FINANCE ACCOUNTANCY MOHASSABA SA—See Arab Bank plc; *Int'l*, pg. 529
FINANCIAL FEDERAL BANK—See Financial FedCorp, Inc.; *U.S. Private*, pg. 1507
FINANCIAL SERVICES CORP.; *U.S. Private*, pg. 1508
FINANCIERA EFECTIVA SA; *Int'l*, pg. 2665
FINBANK SA—See Access Corporation; *Int'l*, pg. 89
FINEMARK NATIONAL BANK & TRUST—See FineMark Holdings, Inc.; *U.S. Public*, pg. 834
FINEX KREDIT OJSC; *Int'l*, pg. 2674
FINO PAYMENTS BANK LIMITED; *Int'l*, pg. 2676
FIRESIDE BANK—See Kemper Corporation; *U.S. Public*, pg. 1220
FIRST ABU DHABI BANK MISR S.A.E—See First Abu Dhabi Bank P.J.S.C.; *Int'l*, pg. 2681
FIRST ABU DHABI BANK P.J.S.C.; *Int'l*, pg. 2681
FIRST ABU DHABI BANK USA N.V.—See First Abu Dhabi Bank P.J.S.C.; *Int'l*, pg. 2681
FIRST ADVANTAGE BANK—See United Community Banks, Inc.; *U.S. Public*, pg. 2230
FIRST AMERICA BANK—See Stark Bank Group Ltd.; *U.S. Private*, pg. 3786
FIRST AMERICAN BANK—See First American Bank Corporation; *U.S. Private*, pg. 1513
FIRST AMERICAN BANK—See First Artesia Bancshares, Inc.; *U.S. Private*, pg. 1513
FIRST AMERICAN BANK & TRUST CO.; *U.S. Private*, pg. 1512
FIRST AMERICAN BANK & TRUST—See One American Corp.; *U.S. Private*, pg. 3020
FIRST AMERICAN NATIONAL BANK—See First American Bancshares, Inc.; *U.S. Private*, pg. 1512
FIRST ARKANSAS BANK & TRUST—See First Arkansas Bancshares, Inc.; *U.S. Private*, pg. 1513
FIRST BANCSHARES INC OF COLD SPRING—See Granite Bank; *U.S. Private*, pg. 1755
FIRST BANCSHARES, INC.; *U.S. Private*, pg. 1513
FIRST BANK AND TRUST—See First BankCorp Inc.; *U.S. Private*, pg. 1514
FIRST BANKCORP INC.; *U.S. Private*, pg. 1514
FIRST BANK CORP.; *U.S. Private*, pg. 1514
FIRST BANK ELK RIVER—See First National Financial Services, Inc.; *U.S. Private*, pg. 1523
FIRST BANKERS TRUST COMPANY—See First Bankers Trustshares Inc.; *U.S. Public*, pg. 840
FIRST BANK FINANCIAL CENTRE—See Oconomowoc Bancshares, Inc.; *U.S. Private*, pg. 1563
FIRSTBANK FLORIDA—See First BanCorp; *U.S. Public*, pg. 839
FIRSTBANK, HAMPDEN & YOSEMITE—See Firstbank Holding Company of Colorado, Inc.; *U.S. Private*, pg. 1531
FIRST BANK OF ALABAMA—See FirstBanc of Alabama, Inc.; *U.S. Private*, pg. 1531
FIRSTBANK OF AVON, INC.—See Firstbank Holding Company of Colorado, Inc.; *U.S. Private*, pg. 1531
FIRST BANK OF CHANDLER—See BancFirst Corporation; *U.S. Public*, pg. 269
FIRST BANK OF COASTAL GEORGIA—See Putnam-Greene Financial Corporation; *U.S. Private*, pg. 3307
FIRSTBANK OF COLORADO, INC.—See Firstbank Holding Company of Colorado, Inc.; *U.S. Private*, pg. 1531
FIRSTBANK OF ERIE, INC.—See Firstbank Holding Company of Colorado, Inc.; *U.S. Private*, pg. 1531
FIRST BANK OF JASPER—See Synovus Financial Corp.; *U.S. Public*, pg. 1971
FIRST BANK OF JASPER—See Synovus Financial Corp.; *U.S. Public*, pg. 1972
FIRST BANK OF LINDEN—See First Linden Bancshares, Inc.; *U.S. Private*, pg. 1520
FIRST BANK OF MONTANA—See Glacier Bancorp, Inc.; *U.S. Public*, pg. 938
FIRST BANK OF OHIO; *U.S. Public*, pg. 840
FIRST BANK OF OWASSO; *U.S. Private*, pg. 1514
FIRSTBANK OF SOUTH JEFFCO, INC.—See Firstbank Holding Company of Colorado, Inc.; *U.S. Private*, pg. 1531

CORPORATE AFFILIATIONS

FIRSTBANK OF VAIL, INC.—See Firstbank Holding Company of Colorado, Inc.; *U.S. Private*, pg. 1531
FIRSTBANK OVERSEAS CORP.—See First BanCorp; *U.S. Public*, pg. 839
FIRSTBANK PUERTO RICO—See First BanCorp; *U.S. Public*, pg. 839
FIRST BANK RICHMOND—See First Mutual of Richmond, Inc.; *U.S. Private*, pg. 1521
FIRST BANK; *U.S. Public*, pg. 839
FIRSTBANK—See First Antlers Bancorporation, Inc.; *U.S. Private*, pg. 1513
FIRST BANK—See First National Corporation; *U.S. Public*, pg. 846
FIRST BANK—See First Southwest Corporation; *U.S. Private*, pg. 1528
FIRST BANK—See Peoples Independent Bancshares, Inc.; *U.S. Private*, pg. 3142
FIRST BANK—See Pioneer Bankcorp, Inc.; *U.S. Public*, pg. 1692
FIRSTBANK SOUTHWEST—See FirstPerryton Bancorp, Inc.; *U.S. Private*, pg. 1532
FIRST BANK & TRUST COMPANY OF ILLINOIS INC.—See Northwest Bancorporation of Illinois, Inc.; *U.S. Private*, pg. 2959
FIRST BANK & TRUST COMPANY—See BancFirst Corporation; *U.S. Public*, pg. 269
FIRST BANK & TRUST COMPANY—See FNBT Bancshares, Perry, OK, Inc.; *U.S. Private*, pg. 1555
FIRST BANK & TRUST COMPANY—See Midwest Banco Corporation; *U.S. Private*, pg. 2720
FIRST BANK & TRUST CO.; *U.S. Private*, pg. 1513
FIRST BANK & TRUST EAST TEXAS; *U.S. Private*, pg. 1513
FIRST BANK & TRUST—See Firstrust Corporation; *U.S. Private*, pg. 1532
FIRST BANK & TRUST—See Heartland Financial USA, Inc.; *U.S. Public*, pg. 1018
FIRST BANK, UPPER MICHIGAN—See First Bancshares Corporation; *U.S. Private*, pg. 1513
FIRST BRECKENRIDGE BANCSHARES; *U.S. Private*, pg. 1514
FIRST BUSINESS BANK-MILWAUKEE—See First Business Financial Services, Inc.; *U.S. Public*, pg. 840
FIRST BUSINESS BANK—See First Business Financial Services, Inc.; *U.S. Public*, pg. 840
FIRST CAPITAL BANK LIMITED—See FMBcapital Holdings plc; *Int'l*, pg. 2717
FIRST CAPITAL BANK PLC—See FMBcapital Holdings plc; *Int'l*, pg. 2717
FIRST CAROLINA STATE BANK—See First Carolina Financial Services, Inc.; *U.S. Private*, pg. 1515
FIRST CENTRAL BANK—See Central Bancompany, Inc.; *U.S. Public*, pg. 472
FIRST CENTURY BANK, NATIONAL ASSOCIATION—See First Century Bancorp; *U.S. Private*, pg. 1515
FIRST CENTURY BANK; *U.S. Private*, pg. 1515
FIRST CHATHAM BANK—See FCB Financial Corp.; *U.S. Private*, pg. 1485
FIRST CHOICE BANK—See Enterprise Financial Services Corp; *U.S. Public*, pg. 778
FIRST CITIZENS BANK—See First Citizens Financial Corp.; *U.S. Private*, pg. 1515
FIRST-CITIZENS BANK & TRUST COMPANY—See First Citizens BancShares, Inc.; *U.S. Public*, pg. 842
FIRST CITIZENS CAPITAL LLC—See Civista Bancshares, Inc.; *U.S. Public*, pg. 507
FIRST CITIZENS COMMUNITY BANK—See Citizens Financial Services, Inc.; *U.S. Public*, pg. 506
THE FIRST CITIZENS NATIONAL BANK; *U.S. Private*, pg. 4029
FIRST-CITIZENS NATIONAL BANK—See First Citizens Bancshares, Inc.; *U.S. Public*, pg. 841
FIRST CITRUS BANK—See First Citrus Bancorporation, Inc.; *U.S. Private*, pg. 1515
FIRST COLLINSVILLE BANK INC.; *U.S. Private*, pg. 1516
FIRST COMMERCE BANK; *U.S. Public*, pg. 842
FIRST COMMERCIAL BANK LTD.—See First Financial Holding Co., Ltd.; *Int'l*, pg. 2683
FIRST COMMERCIAL BANK (U.S.A.)—See First Financial Holding Co., Ltd.; *Int'l*, pg. 2683
FIRST COMMONWEALTH BANK—See First Commonwealth Financial Corporation; *U.S. Public*, pg. 842
FIRST COMMUNITY BANCORP, INC.—See Eagle Bancorp Montana, Inc.; *U.S. Public*, pg. 701
FIRST COMMUNITY BANK—See First Community Bancshares, Inc.; *U.S. Public*, pg. 1516
FIRST COMMUNITY BANK—See First Community Bankshares, Inc.; *U.S. Public*, pg. 842
FIRST COMMUNITY BANK—See First Community Corporation; *U.S. Public*, pg. 843
FIRST COMMUNITY WEALTH MANAGEMENT, INC.—See First Community Bankshares, Inc.; *U.S. Public*, pg. 842
FIRST CONVENIENCE BANK—See First Community Bancshares, Inc.; *U.S. Private*, pg. 1516
FIRST CREDIT BANK; *U.S. Private*, pg. 1516
FIRST DAKOTA FINANCIAL CORP.; *U.S. Private*, pg. 1516
FIRST DAKOTA NATIONAL BANK—See First Dakota Financial Corp.; *U.S. Private*, pg. 1517

522110 — COMMERCIAL BANKING

FIRST DATA CANADA LTD.—See Fiserv, Inc.; *U.S. Public*, pg. 850
FIRST ENTERPRISE BANK INC.; *U.S. Private*, pg. 1517
FIRST EQUITY CARD CORPORATION—See Vervent Inc.; *U.S. Private*, pg. 4371
FIRST FARMERS BANCSHARES INC.; *U.S. Private*, pg. 1517
THE FIRST & FARMERS BANK—See Full Service Insurance Agency, Inc.; *U.S. Private*, pg. 1621
FIRST FARMERS BANK & TRUST COMPANY—See First Farmers Financial Corporation; *U.S. Private*, pg. 1517
FIRST FARMERS & MERCHANTS BANK—See First Farmers and Merchants Corporation; *U.S. Public*, pg. 843
FIRST FARMERS & MERCHANTS NATIONAL BANK—See 215 Holding Co.; *U.S. Private*, pg. 5
FIRST FARMERS & MERCHANTS NATIONAL BANK—See 215 Holding Co.; *U.S. Private*, pg. 5
FIRST FARMERS & MERCHANTS NATIONAL BANK—See 215 Holding Co.; *U.S. Private*, pg. 5
FIRST FARMERS & MERCHANTS STATE BANK OF GRAND MEADOW—See 215 Holding Co.; *U.S. Private*, pg. 5
FIRST FARMERS & MERCHANTS STATE BANK—See 215 Holding Co.; *U.S. Private*, pg. 5
FIRST & FARMERS NATIONAL BANK, INC.—See Albany Bancorp, Inc.; *U.S. Private*, pg. 151
FIRST FEDERAL COMMUNITY BANK, N.A.—See FFD Financial Corporation; *U.S. Public*, pg. 830
FIRST FIDELITY BANK—See First Fidelity Bancorp, Inc.; *U.S. Private*, pg. 1519
FIRST FINANCIAL NORTHWEST BANK—See First Financial Northwest, Inc.; *U.S. Public*, pg. 844
FIRST FOUNDATION BANK—See First Foundation Inc.; *U.S. Public*, pg. 844
FIRST GENERAL BANK; *U.S. Public*, pg. 844
FIRST GLOBAL BANK LTD—See GraceKennedy Limited; *Int'l*, pg. 3048
FIRST GUARANTY BANK—See First Guaranty Bancshares, Inc.; *U.S. Public*, pg. 844
FIRST HAWAIIAN BANK—See BNP Paribas SA; *Int'l*, pg. 1088
FIRST HAWAIIAN, INC.—See BNP Paribas SA; *Int'l*, pg. 1087
FIRST HEARTLAND JUSAN BANK JSC—See First Heartland Capital JSC; *Int'l*, pg. 2684
FIRST HOME BANK—See First Bancshares, Inc.; *U.S. Public*, pg. 839
FIRST IC BANK; *U.S. Public*, pg. 845
FIRST ILLINOIS BANK—See First Illinois Bancorp, Inc.; *U.S. Private*, pg. 1520
FIRST INDEPENDENCE BANK—See First Independence Corporation; *U.S. Private*, pg. 1520
FIRST INDEPENDENT BANK—See Finlayson Bancshares, Inc.; *U.S. Private*, pg. 1510
FIRST INDEPENDENT BANK—See Western Alliance Bancorporation; *U.S. Public*, pg. 2354
FIRST INTERNATIONAL BANK OF ISRAEL LTD.—See FIBI Holdings Ltd.; *Int'l*, pg. 2652
THE FIRST INTERNATIONAL & CO.-UNDERWRITING AND INVESTMENT LTD.—See FIBI Holdings Ltd.; *Int'l*, pg. 2652
FIRST INTERNET BANK OF INDIANA—See First Internet Bancorp; *U.S. Public*, pg. 845
FIRST INTERSTATE BANK—See First Interstate BancSystem, Inc.; *U.S. Public*, pg. 845
FIRST INVESTMENT BANK AD; *Int'l*, pg. 2684
FIRST IPSWICH BANK—See Brookline Bancorp, Inc.; *U.S. Public*, pg. 396
FIRST KENTUCKY BANK, INC.; *U.S. Private*, pg. 1520
FIRST KEYSTONE COMMUNITY BANK—See FIRST KEYSTONE CORPORATION; *U.S. Public*, pg. 845
FIRST-KNOX NATIONAL BANK—See Park National Corporation; *U.S. Public*, pg. 1638
FIRST MADISON BANK & TRUST—See United Community Banks, Inc.; *U.S. Public*, pg. 2230
FIRST MERCHANTS BANK—See First Merchants Corporation; *U.S. Public*, pg. 845
FIRSTMERIT MORTGAGE CORPORATION—See Huntington Bancshares Incorporated; *U.S. Public*, pg. 1071
FIRST MICROFINANCE LAGHUBITTA BITTIYA SANSTHA LTD.; *Int'l*, pg. 2685
FIRST MID INSURANCE GROUP, INC.—See First Mid Bancshares, Inc.; *U.S. Public*, pg. 846
FIRST MIDWEST BANK OF POPLAR BLUFF; *U.S. Private*, pg. 1521
FIRST MIDWEST BANK—See Old National Bancorp; *U.S. Public*, pg. 1567
FIRST MINNESOTA BANK—See McLeod Bancshares, Inc.; *U.S. Private*, pg. 2641
THE FIRST, N.A.—See The First Bancorp, Inc.; *U.S. Public*, pg. 2073
FIRST NATIONAL BANK ALASKA; *U.S. Public*, pg. 846
FIRST NATIONAL BANK, ALBANY/BRECKENRIDGE; *U.S. Public*, pg. 1523
FIRST NATIONAL BANK, AMES, IOWA—See Ames National Corporation; *U.S. Public*, pg. 115
FIRST NATIONAL BANK & CO.; *U.S. Private*, pg. 1522
FIRST NATIONAL BANK FREMONT—See First National of Nebraska, Inc.; *U.S. Private*, pg. 1523

FIRST NATIONAL BANK IN ALAMOGORDO; *U.S. Private*, pg. 1522
FIRST NATIONAL BANK IN FAIRFIELD—See MidWestOne Financial Group, Inc.; *U.S. Public*, pg. 1446
FIRST NATIONAL BANK IN HOWELL—See FNBH Bancorp, Inc.; *U.S. Private*, pg. 1555
FIRST NATIONAL BANK IN NEW BREMEN; *U.S. Private*, pg. 1522
FIRST NATIONAL BANK IN OKEENE—See Grace Investment Company, Inc.; *U.S. Private*, pg. 1749
FIRST NATIONAL BANK IN OLNEY; *U.S. Private*, pg. 1522
THE FIRST NATIONAL BANK IN TREMONT; *U.S. Private*, pg. 4029
FIRST NATIONAL BANK MUSCATINE—See MidWestOne Financial Group, Inc.; *U.S. Public*, pg. 1446
FIRST NATIONAL BANK OF ABSECON—See Absecon Bancorp; *U.S. Public*, pg. 27
FIRST NATIONAL BANK OF ALTAVISTA—See Pinnacle Bankshares Corp.; *U.S. Public*, pg. 1691
FIRST NATIONAL BANK OF AMERICA INC.; *U.S. Private*, pg. 1522
FIRST NATIONAL BANK OF ARENZVILLE; *U.S. Private*, pg. 1522
FIRST NATIONAL BANK OF BASTROP; *U.S. Private*, pg. 1522
THE FIRST NATIONAL BANK OF BELLS/SAVOY—See First Bells Bankshares, Inc.; *U.S. Private*, pg. 1514
FIRST NATIONAL BANK OF BOTSWANA—See FirstRand Limited; *Int'l*, pg. 2690
THE FIRST NATIONAL BANK OF CENTRAL TEXAS; *U.S. Private*, pg. 4029
FIRST NATIONAL BANK OF DECATUR COUNTY—See Bainbridge Bancshares, Inc.; *U.S. Private*, pg. 453
FIRST NATIONAL BANK OF DRYDEN; *U.S. Private*, pg. 1522
FIRST NATIONAL BANK OF ELMER—See Elmer Bancorp, Inc.; *U.S. Public*, pg. 735
THE FIRST NATIONAL BANK OF EMORY—See Emory Bancshares, Inc.; *U.S. Public*, pg. 1383
THE FIRST NATIONAL BANK OF FORT SMITH—See First Bank Corp.; *U.S. Private*, pg. 1514
FIRST NATIONAL BANK OF GILMER—See First Gilmer Bankshares, Inc.; *U.S. Private*, pg. 1519
FIRST NATIONAL BANK OF GRANBURY; *U.S. Private*, pg. 1522
FIRST NATIONAL BANK OF GROTON; *U.S. Public*, pg. 846
FIRST NATIONAL BANK OF HOLCOMB—See American State Bancshares, Inc.; *U.S. Private*, pg. 255
THE FIRST NATIONAL BANK OF HOOKER—See Hooker National Bancshares, Inc.; *U.S. Private*, pg. 1978
FIRST NATIONAL BANK OF HUNTSVILLE; *U.S. Private*, pg. 1522
FIRST NATIONAL BANK OF ILLINOIS—See Wintrust Financial Corporation; *U.S. Public*, pg. 2375
THE FIRST NATIONAL BANK OF KEMP—See FNBK Holdings, Inc.; *U.S. Private*, pg. 1555
FIRST NATIONAL BANK OF LAYTON—See Glacier Bancorp, Inc.; *U.S. Public*, pg. 938
THE FIRST NATIONAL BANK OF LONG ISLAND—See The First of Long Island Corporation; *U.S. Public*, pg. 2074
FIRST NATIONAL BANK OF LOUISIANA—See Financial Corporation of Louisiana; *U.S. Private*, pg. 1506
FIRST NATIONAL BANK OF MIFFLINTOWN—See First Community Financial Corporation; *U.S. Public*, pg. 843
FIRST NATIONAL BANK OF MONTEREY; *U.S. Private*, pg. 1522
FIRST NATIONAL BANK OF OMAHA—See First National of Nebraska, Inc.; *U.S. Private*, pg. 1523
FIRST NATIONAL BANK OF ONEIDA; *U.S. Private*, pg. 1522
FIRST NATIONAL BANK OF OXFORD; *U.S. Private*, pg. 1522
FIRST NATIONAL BANK OF PALMERTON; *U.S. Private*, pg. 1523
FIRST NATIONAL BANK OF PASCO—See Florida Bancshares, Inc.; *U.S. Private*, pg. 1547
FIRST NATIONAL BANK OF PENNSYLVANIA—See F.N.B. Corporation; *U.S. Public*, pg. 818
FIRST NATIONAL BANK OF PONTOTOC; *U.S. Private*, pg. 1523
FIRST NATIONAL BANK OF PULASKI—See First Pulaski National Corporation; *U.S. Public*, pg. 1524
FIRST NATIONAL BANK OF RIVER FALLS; *U.S. Private*, pg. 1523
FIRST NATIONAL BANK OF ROGERS—See First Bank Corp.; *U.S. Private*, pg. 1514
FIRST NATIONAL BANK OF SCOTIA; *U.S. Private*, pg. 1523
FIRST NATIONAL BANK OF SHARP COUNTY; *U.S. Private*, pg. 1523
THE FIRST NATIONAL BANK OF SONORA—See First Sonora; *U.S. Private*, pg. 1528
THE FIRST NATIONAL BANK OF SOUTH MIAMI—See United Community Banks, Inc.; *U.S. Public*, pg. 2230
THE FIRST NATIONAL BANK OF TAHOKA—See Tahoka First Bancorp Inc.; *U.S. Private*, pg. 3923

THE FIRST NATIONAL BANK OF TRENTON—See Captex Bancshares, Inc.; *U.S. Private*, pg. 746
THE FIRST NATIONAL BANK OF WYNNE—See First National Corporation of Wynne; *U.S. Private*, pg. 1523
FIRST NATIONAL BANK OF ZAMBIA LIMITED—See FirstRand Limited; *Int'l*, pg. 2690
FIRST NATIONAL BANK; *U.S. Private*, pg. 1521
FIRST NATIONAL BANK; *U.S. Private*, pg. 1522
FIRST NATIONAL BANK; *U.S. Private*, pg. 1522
FIRST NATIONAL BANK; *U.S. Private*, pg. 1522
FIRST NATIONAL BANK—See First Bancshares, Inc.; *U.S. Public*, pg. 839
FIRST NATIONAL BANK—See First Groesbeck Holding Company; *U.S. Private*, pg. 1519
FIRST NATIONAL BANK—See First Paragould Bankshares, Inc.; *U.S. Private*, pg. 1524
FIRST NATIONAL BANK—See FirstRand Limited; *Int'l*, pg. 2690
THE FIRST NATIONAL BANK—See MGB Bancshares, Inc.; *U.S. Private*, pg. 2694
FIRST NATIONAL BANK—See Sooner Southwest Bankshares, Inc.; *U.S. Private*, pg. 3715
FIRST NATIONAL BANK SOUTH DAKOTA—See First National of Nebraska, Inc.; *U.S. Private*, pg. 1523
FIRST NATIONAL BANK TEXAS—See First Community Bancshares, Inc.; *U.S. Public*, pg. 1516
FIRST NATIONAL BANK & TRUST COMPANY OF ARDMORE—See First National Corporation of Ardmore, Inc.; *U.S. Private*, pg. 1523
THE FIRST NATIONAL BANK & TRUST COMPANY OF IRON MOUNTAIN—See FNB Bancshares, Inc.; *U.S. Private*, pg. 1555
FIRST NATIONAL BANK & TRUST COMPANY OF MCALESTER—See First National Bank & Co.; *U.S. Private*, pg. 1522
THE FIRST NATIONAL BANK & TRUST COMPANY OF MIAMI—See First Miami Bancshares, Inc.; *U.S. Private*, pg. 1521
THE FIRST NATIONAL BANK & TRUST COMPANY OF OKMULGEE—See First Okmulgee Corporation; *U.S. Private*, pg. 1524
THE FIRST NATIONAL BANK & TRUST COMPANY—See Centre 1 Bancorp, Inc.; *U.S. Public*, pg. 827
FIRST NATIONAL BANK & TRUST CO OF NEWTOWN—See FNB Bancorp, Inc.; *U.S. Private*, pg. 1555
FIRST NATIONAL BANK & TRUST CO.; *U.S. Private*, pg. 1522
FIRST NATIONAL BANK WATERLOO—See First Waterloo Bancshares, Inc.; *U.S. Private*, pg. 1530
FIRST NATIONAL INSURANCE AGENCY, LLC—See F.N.B. Corporation; *U.S. Public*, pg. 818
FIRST NATIONS BANK OF CANADA; *Int'l*, pg. 2686
FIRST NEBRASKA BANK; *U.S. Private*, pg. 1524
FIRST NEODESHA BANK—See Southeast Bancshares, Inc.; *U.S. Private*, pg. 3725
FIRST NORTHERN BANK OF DIXON—See First Northern Community Bancorp; *U.S. Public*, pg. 846
FIRST OPTION BANK—See The Osawatomie Agency Inc.; *U.S. Private*, pg. 4089
FIRST PARAMOUNT MODARABA; *Int'l*, pg. 2686
FIRST PEOPLES BANK—See First Peoples Bankshares, Inc.; *U.S. Private*, pg. 1524
FIRST & PEOPLES BANK & TRUST CO.; *U.S. Private*, pg. 1512
FIRST PIONEER NATIONAL BANK—See First Pioneer Bank Corp.; *U.S. Private*, pg. 1524
FIRST PREMIER BANK—See United National Corporation; *U.S. Public*, pg. 4295
FIRST RELIANCE BANK—See First Reliance BancShares, Inc.; *U.S. Public*, pg. 847
FIRST REPUBLIC BANK—See JPMorgan Chase & Co.; *U.S. Public*, pg. 1206
FIRST RESOURCE BANK; *U.S. Private*, pg. 1527
FIRST RESOURCE BANK—See Ameri Financial Group, Inc.; *U.S. Private*, pg. 220
FIRST ROBINSON SAVINGS BANK N.A.—See First Robinson Financial Corporation; *U.S. Public*, pg. 847
FIRSTRUST CORPORATION; *U.S. Private*, pg. 1532
FIRST SAVINGS BANK FSB—See First Savings Bank; *U.S. Private*, pg. 1527
FIRST SAVINGS BANK—See First Savings Financial Group, Inc.; *U.S. Public*, pg. 847
FIRST SECURITY BANK - CANBY—See First Sleepy Eye Bancorporation, Inc.; *U.S. Private*, pg. 1527
FIRST SECURITY BANK OF HELENA—See Ascent Bancorp; *U.S. Private*, pg. 348
FIRST SECURITY BANK OF MISSOULA—See Glacier Bancorp, Inc.; *U.S. Public*, pg. 938
FIRST SECURITY BANK - SLEEPY EYE—See First Sleepy Eye Bancorporation, Inc.; *U.S. Private*, pg. 1527
FIRST SECURITY BANK—See First Security Bancorp; *U.S. Private*, pg. 1527
FIRST SECURITY BANK—See Glacier Bancorp, Inc.; *U.S. Public*, pg. 938
FIRST SECURITY ISLAMI BANK LIMITED; *Int'l*, pg. 2687
FIRST SECURITY ISLAMI CAPITAL & INVESTMENT

522110 — COMMERCIAL BANKING

LIMITED—See First Security Islami Bank Limited; *Int'l*, pg. 2687
FIRST SECURITY TRUST & SAVINGS BANK—See Wirtz Corporation; *U.S. Private*, pg. 4547
FIRST SOUND BANK; *U.S. Public*, pg. 847
FIRST SOUTHERN BANK—See Midwest Community Bancshares, Inc.; *U.S. Private*, pg. 2720
FIRST SOUTHERN NATIONAL BANK—See First Southern Bancorp, Inc.; *U.S. Private*, pg. 1528
FIRST STATE BANK AND TRUST CO.—See Synovus Financial Corp.; *U.S. Public*, pg. 1971
FIRST STATE BANK AND TRUST CO.—See Synovus Financial Corp.; *U.S. Public*, pg. 1972
FIRST STATE BANK INC.; *U.S. Private*, pg. 1528
THE FIRST STATE BANK, KIOWA, KANSAS—See Grace Investment Company, Inc.; *U.S. Private*, pg. 1749
FIRST STATE BANK NEBRASKA—See First State Holding Co.; *U.S. Private*, pg. 1529
FIRST STATE BANK OF BLOOMINGTON - HEYWORTH—See First State Bank of Bloomington; *U.S. Private*, pg. 1528
FIRST STATE BANK OF EAST DETROIT INC.—See First State Financial Corp.; *U.S. Private*, pg. 1529
FIRST STATE BANK OF LIVINGSTON—See East Texas Bancshares, Inc.; *U.S. Private*, pg. 1318
THE FIRST STATE BANK OF SHELBY—See Prairie Bancshares Corporation; *U.S. Private*, pg. 3242
FIRST STATE BANK OF THE FLORIDA KEYS; *U.S. Private*, pg. 1528
FIRST STATE BANK OF UVALDE; *U.S. Private*, pg. 1528
FIRST STATE BANK OF WARREN—See Bradley Bancshares, Inc.; *U.S. Private*, pg. 632
FIRST STATE BANK—See First State Bancshares Inc.; *U.S. Private*, pg. 1528
FIRST STATE BANK—See First State Bancshares, Inc.; *U.S. Private*, pg. 1528
FIRST STATE BANK—See Full Service Insurance Agency, Inc.; *U.S. Private*, pg. 1621
FIRST STATE BANK—See Glacier Bancorp, Inc.; *U.S. Public*, pg. 939
FIRST STATE BANK—See Nebraska Bankshares, Inc.; *U.S. Private*, pg. 2878
FIRST STATE BANK—See Nebraska Bankshares, Inc.; *U.S. Private*, pg. 2878
FIRST STATE BANK—See Tri-County Financial Group, Inc.; *U.S. Public*, pg. 2189
FIRST STATE BANK—See Van Diest Family, LLC; *U.S. Private*, pg. 4339
FIRST STATE BANK SOUTHWEST—See First Rushmore Bancorporation, Inc.; *U.S. Private*, pg. 1527
FIRST STATE BANK & TRUST COMPANY, INC.—See First State Bancorp, Inc.; *U.S. Private*, pg. 1528
FIRST STATE COMMUNITY BANK—See First State Bancshares Inc.; *U.S. Private*, pg. 1528
FIRST STATE CORP.; *U.S. Private*, pg. 1529
FIRST STATE FINANCIAL CORP.; *U.S. Private*, pg. 1529
FIRST TENNESSEE BANK, N.A.—See First Horizon Corporation; *U.S. Public*, pg. 844
FIRST TEXAS BANK—See First Texas Bancorp, Inc.; *U.S. Private*, pg. 1530
FIRST UNION CAPITAL II—See Wells Fargo & Company; *U.S. Public*, pg. 2343
FIRST UNION FINANCIAL CORP.; *U.S. Private*, pg. 1530
FIRST UNITED BANK & TRUST COMPANY—See Durant Bancorp, Inc.; *U.S. Private*, pg. 1292
FIRST UNITED BANK & TRUST—See First United Corporation; *U.S. Public*, pg. 848
FIRST US BANK—See First US Bancshares, Inc.; *U.S. Public*, pg. 848
FIRST WESTERN BANCSHARES INC.; *U.S. Private*, pg. 1530
FIRST WESTERN BANK & TRUST; *U.S. Private*, pg. 1530
FIVE STAR BANK—See Financial Institutions, Inc.; *U.S. Public*, pg. 834
FLAGLER BANK—See Dort Financial Credit Union; *U.S. Private*, pg. 1264
FLAGSHIP BANK MINNESOTA—See Flagship Financial Group, Inc.; *U.S. Private*, pg. 1539
FLAGSHIP BANK—See West Florida Bank Corporation; *U.S. Private*, pg. 4485
FLAGSTAR COMMERCIAL CORPORATION—See New York Community Bancorp, Inc.; *U.S. Public*, pg. 1513
FLATEX BANK AG—See flatexDEGIRO AG; *Int'l*, pg. 2698
FLEETWOOD BANK; *U.S. Public*, pg. 852
FLEXIGROUP (NEW ZEALAND) LIMITED—See Humm Group Limited; *Int'l*, pg. 3531
FLORIDA CITIZENS BANK; *U.S. Private*, pg. 1547
F&M BANK; *U.S. Public*, pg. 1455
F&M BANK—See F&M Financial Corporation; *U.S. Private*, pg. 1455
F&M BANK-SOUTH SIOUX CITY—See F&M Bank; *U.S. Private*, pg. 1455
F&M BANK & TRUST COMPANY; *U.S. Private*, pg. 1455
F&M FINANCIAL CORP.; *U.S. Private*, pg. 1455
FNB BANCORP, INC.; *U.S. Private*, pg. 1555
FNBC BANK & TRUST—See F.N.B.C. of La Grange, Inc.; *U.S. Private*, pg. 1457
FNB COMMUNITY BANK—See First Midwest Acquisition Corp.; *U.S. Private*, pg. 1521
THE FNB COMMUNITY BANK—See First Vandalia Corp.; *U.S. Private*, pg. 1530
FNB LESOTHO LIMITED—See FirstRand Limited; *Int'l*, pg. 2689
FNB OF CENTRAL ALABAMA—See BankFirst Capital Corporation; *U.S. Public*, pg. 274
FNBT BANK—See Southern National Banks, Inc.; *U.S. Private*, pg. 3734
FNB ZAMBIA LIMITED—See FirstRand Limited; *Int'l*, pg. 2689
FOKUS BANK ASA—See Danske Bank A/S; *Int'l*, pg. 1969
THE FOOTHILLS BANK—See Glacier Bancorp, Inc.; *U.S. Public*, pg. 939
FORT DAVIS STATE BANK; *U.S. Private*, pg. 1574
FORTEBANK JSC; *Int'l*, pg. 2737
FORT HOOD NATIONAL BANK—See First Community Bancshares, Inc.; *U.S. Private*, pg. 1516
FORTIS BANK POLSKA S.A.—See BNP Paribas SA; *Int'l*, pg. 1084
FORTIS BANQUE S.A.—See BNP Paribas SA; *Int'l*, pg. 1084
FOUR CORNERS COMMUNITY BANK; *U.S. Private*, pg. 1581
FRANDSEN BANK & TRUST—See Frandsen Corporation; *U.S. Private*, pg. 1593
FRANKFURTER SPARKASSE; *Int'l*, pg. 2761
FRANKLIN BANK & TRUST COMPANY—See Franklin Bancorp Inc.; *U.S. Private*, pg. 1596
FRANKLIN SYNERGY BANK—See FB Financial Corporation; *U.S. Public*, pg. 824
FRANSABANK EL DJAZAIR SPA—See Fransabank SAL; *Int'l*, pg. 2762
FRANSABANK (FRANCE) SA—See Fransabank SAL; *Int'l*, pg. 2762
FRANSABANK OJSC—See Fransabank SAL; *Int'l*, pg. 2762
FRANSABANK SAL; *Int'l*, pg. 2762
FRANSABANK SAL—See Fransabank SAL; *Int'l*, pg. 2762
FRANSABANK SYRIA SA—See Fransabank SAL; *Int'l*, pg. 2762
FREEDOM BANK OF AMERICA; *U.S. Private*, pg. 1603
THE FREEDOM BANK OF VIRGINIA; *U.S. Public*, pg. 2074
FREEDOM NATIONAL BANK—See Bristol County Savings Bank; *U.S. Private*, pg. 656
FREMANTLE COMMUNITY FINANCIAL SERVICES LIMITED—See Bendigo & Adelaide Bank Ltd.; *Int'l*, pg. 971
FREMONT BANK—See Fremont Bancorporation; *U.S. Private*, pg. 1608
FRENCH AMERICAN BANKING CORP.—See BNP Paribas SA; *Int'l*, pg. 1088
FRESNO FIRST BANK—See Communities First Financial Corporation; *U.S. Public*, pg. 549
FRIEND BANK—See SNB Holdings, Inc.; *U.S. Private*, pg. 3700
FRIENDLY HILLS BANK; *U.S. Public*, pg. 886
FRIENDS BANK—See FAIRWINDS Credit Union; *U.S. Private*, pg. 1465
FRIENDSHIP STATE BANK; *U.S. Private*, pg. 1612
FRONTIER BANK—See Whitcorp Financial Company; *U.S. Private*, pg. 4507
FROST BANK—See Cullen/Frost Bankers, Inc.; *U.S. Public*, pg. 604
FSC CORP.—See Bank of America Corporation; *U.S. Public*, pg. 272
FUBON BANK (HONG KONG) LIMITED—See Fubon Financial Holding Co. Ltd.; *Int'l*, pg. 2801
FUJIAN FU'AN CQRC VILLAGE & TOWNSHIP BANK CO., LTD.—See Chongqing Rural Commercial Bank Co., Ltd.; *Int'l*, pg. 1580
FUJIAN PINGTAN CQRC VILLAGE & TOWNSHIP BANK CO., LTD.—See Chongqing Rural Commercial Bank Co., Ltd.; *Int'l*, pg. 1580
FUJIAN SHAXIAN CQRC VILLAGE & TOWNSHIP BANK CO., LTD.—See Chongqing Rural Commercial Bank Co., Ltd.; *Int'l*, pg. 1581
FUJIAN SHISHI CQRC VILLAGE & TOWNSHIP BANK CO., LTD.—See Chongqing Rural Commercial Bank Co., Ltd.; *Int'l*, pg. 1581
FUKUOKA CHUO BANK LTD.; *Int'l*, pg. 2840
FULTON BANK OF NEW JERSEY—See Fulton Financial Corporation; *U.S. Public*, pg. 892
FUTURUM BANK AG—See Bitcoin Group SE; *Int'l*, pg. 1049
FUYO GENERAL LEASE CO., LTD.; *Int'l*, pg. 2858
FVCBANK—See FVCBankcorp, Inc.; *U.S. Public*, pg. 893
FYNSKE BANK A/S; *Int'l*, pg. 2860
GAB INVESTMENT COMPANY, INC.—See German American Bancorp, Inc.; *U.S. Public*, pg. 934
GANDAKI BIKASH BANK LIMITED; *Int'l*, pg. 2880
GARANT-INVEST COMMERCIAL BANK JSC; *Int'l*, pg. 2883
GARIMA BIKAS BANK LIMITED; *Int'l*, pg. 2884
GATES BANKING & TRUST COMPANY—See Security BanCorp of Tennessee, Inc.; *U.S. Private*, pg. 3595
GATEWAY BANK, F.S.B.—See RBB Bancorp; *U.S. Public*, pg. 1766
GAZPROMBANK - ASSET MANAGEMENT CJSC—See Gazprombank JSC; *Int'l*, pg. 2892

GAZPROMBANK JSC; *Int'l*, pg. 2891
GAZPROMBANK (SWITZERLAND) LTD.—See Gazprombank JSC; *Int'l*, pg. 2892
GCB BANK LIMITED; *Int'l*, pg. 2894
GENERAL BANK OF GREECE S.A.; *Int'l*, pg. 2917
GENEVA CAPITAL LIMITED—See Geneva Finance Limited; *Int'l*, pg. 2922
GEORGIA BANKING COMPANY—See FJ Capital Management; *U.S. Private*, pg. 1538
GEORGIA BANKING COMPANY—See Independence Capital Partners, LLC; *U.S. Private*, pg. 2056
GEP - GESTAO DE PERITAGENS AUTOMOVEIS, S.A.—See Caixa Geral de Depositos S.A.; *Int'l*, pg. 1260
GERMAN AMERICAN BANK—See German American Bancorp, Inc.; *U.S. Public*, pg. 934
GERMAN AMERICAN INSURANCE, INC.—See ABRY Partners, LLC; *U.S. Private*, pg. 43
GES FIBANC S.G.I.I.C. S.A.—See Banca Mediolanum S.p.A.; *Int'l*, pg. 815
GHANA INTERBANK PAYMENT AND SETTLEMENT SYSTEMS LTD—See Bank of Ghana; *Int'l*, pg. 843
GHANA INTERNATIONAL BANK PLC—See Bank of Ghana; *Int'l*, pg. 843
GIBRALTAR MORTGAGE SERVICES, LLC—See Blackstone Inc.; *U.S. Public*, pg. 359
GLACIER BANK—See Glacier Bancorp, Inc.; *U.S. Public*, pg. 938
GLARNER KANTONALBANK; *Int'l*, pg. 2988
GLENS FALLS NATIONAL BANK & TRUST COMPANY—See Arrow Financial Corporation; *U.S. Public*, pg. 200
GLENVIEW STATE BANK—See Crane NXT, Co.; *U.S. Public*, pg. 591
GLENVILLE BANK HOLDING CO., INC.; *U.S. Public*, pg. 940
GLOBAL BANK CORPORATION; *Int'l*, pg. 2993
GLOBAL IME BANK LIMITED; *Int'l*, pg. 2997
GLOBAL IME CAPITAL LTD.—See Global IME Bank Limited; *Int'l*, pg. 2997
GLOBAL IME LAGHUBITTA BITTIYA SANSTHA LTD.—See Global IME Bank Limited; *Int'l*, pg. 2997
GLOBOKAS PERU SA; *Int'l*, pg. 3008
GMAC UK PLC—See General Motors Company; *U.S. Public*, pg. 925
GNB BANCORPORATION; *U.S. Private*, pg. 1723
GNB - COMPANHIA DE SEGUROS DE VIDA, S.A.—See Apax Partners LLP; *Int'l*, pg. 504
GOENKA BUSINESS & FINANCE LTD.; *Int'l*, pg. 3021
GOGEBIC RANGE BANK—See West End Financial Corp.; *U.S. Private*, pg. 4485
GOLDEN PACIFIC BANK, N.A.—See Golden Pacific Bancorp, Inc.; *U.S. Public*, pg. 950
GOLDEN VALLEY BANK; *U.S. Public*, pg. 951
GOLDMAN SACHS BANK (EUROPE) PLC—See The Goldman Sachs Group, Inc.; *U.S. Public*, pg. 2081
GOLDMAN SACHS BANK USA—See The Goldman Sachs Group, Inc.; *U.S. Public*, pg. 2081
GOLDMAN SACHS MITSUI MARINE DERIVATIVE PRODUCTS, LP—See The Goldman Sachs Group, Inc.; *U.S. Public*, pg. 2081
GOPPERT FINANCIAL BANK—See Goppert Financial Corp.; *U.S. Private*, pg. 1741
GOPPERT STATE SERVICE BANK—See Goppert Financial Corp.; *U.S. Private*, pg. 1741
GORHAM SAVINGS BANK—See Gorham Bancorp, MHC; *U.S. Private*, pg. 1743
THE GOVERNOR AND COMPANY OF THE BANK OF IRELAND—See Bank of Ireland Group plc; *Int'l*, pg. 844
GPB INTERNATIONAL S.A—See Gazprombank JSC; *Int'l*, pg. 2892
GRAND RAPIDS STATE BANK—See Wilcox Bancshares, Inc.; *U.S. Private*, pg. 4518
GRAND SAVINGS BANK—See Grand Bancorp, Inc.; *U.S. Private*, pg. 1752
GRANDSOUTH BANK—See First Bancorp; *U.S. Public*, pg. 839
GRANTIKA CESKE SPORITELNY, A.S.—See Erste Group Bank AG; *Int'l*, pg. 2499
GRAUBUENDNER KANTONALBANK; *Int'l*, pg. 3061
GREAT AMERICAN BANK; *U.S. Private*, pg. 1762
GREAT SOUTHERN BANK—See Great Southern Capital Corp.; *U.S. Private*, pg. 1768
GREAT WESTERN BANK—See Great Western Bancorp, Inc.; *U.S. Public*, pg. 962
GREENFIELD BANKING COMPANY—See Greenfield Bancshares Inc.; *U.S. Private*, pg. 1777
GREENVILLE NATIONAL BANK; *U.S. Public*, pg. 1780
THE GREENWOOD'S STATE BANK—See Greenwoods Financial Group, Inc.; *U.S. Private*, pg. 1782
GRINNELL STATE BANK—See Grinnell Bancshares, Inc.; *U.S. Private*, pg. 1790
GRONG SPAREBANK; *Int'l*, pg. 3088
GRONLANDSBANKEN A/S; *Int'l*, pg. 3088
GRUNDY NATIONAL BANK; *U.S. Private*, pg. 1797
GRUPO BANCO PROVINCIA S.A.—See Banco de la Provincia de Buenos Aires; *Int'l*, pg. 821
GRUPO ELEKTRA S.A.B. DE C.V.—See Grupo Salinas, S.A. de C.V.; *Int'l*, pg. 3135

N.A.I.C.S. INDEX
522110 — COMMERCIAL BANKING

GRUPO FINANCIERO BBVA-BANCOMER, S.A.—See Banco Bilbao Vizcaya Argentaria, S.A.; *Int'l*, pg. 818
GRUPO FINANCIERO INTERACCIONES, S.A. DE C.V.—See Grupo Financiero Banorte, S.A.B. de C.V.; *Int'l*, pg. 3129
GTB LIBERIA LIMITED—See Guaranty Trust Bank plc; *Int'l*, pg. 3169
GTB REGISTRARS LIMITED—See Guaranty Trust Bank plc; *Int'l*, pg. 3169
GUANGXI LUZHAI CQRC VILLAGE & TOWNSHIP BANK CO., LTD.—See Chongqing Rural Commercial Bank Co., Ltd.; *Int'l*, pg. 1581
GUANGZHOU RURAL COMMERCIAL BANK CO., LTD.; *Int'l*, pg. 3167
GUARANTY BANK AND TRUST COMPANY—See Guaranty Capital Corp; *U.S. Private*, pg. 1809
GUARANTY BANK—See QCR Holdings, Inc.; *U.S. Public*, pg. 1742
GUARANTY BANK & TRUST COMPANY—See Independent Bank Group, Inc.; *U.S. Public*, pg. 1116
GUARANTY REALTY, INC.—See QCR Holdings, Inc.; *U.S. Public*, pg. 1742
GUARANTY TRUST BANK (GAMBIA) LIMITED—See Guaranty Trust Bank plc; *Int'l*, pg. 3169
GUARANTY TRUST BANK PLC; *Int'l*, pg. 3169
GUARANTY TRUST BANK (UK) LIMITED—See Guaranty Trust Bank plc; *Int'l*, pg. 3169
GUHESWORI MERCHANT BANKING & FINANCE LIMITED; *Int'l*, pg. 3173
GUILFORD SAVINGS BANK; *U.S. Private*, pg. 1814
GUIPUZCOANO CORREDURIA DE SEGUROS DEL GRUPO BANCO GUIPUZCOANO, S.A.—See Banco de Sabadell, S.A.; *Int'l*, pg. 821
GULF BANK K.S.C.P.; *Int'l*, pg. 3179
GULF COAST BANK; *U.S. Private*, pg. 1815
GULF COAST BANK & TRUST COMPANY; *U.S. Private*, pg. 1815
GULF COMMERCIAL BANK; *Int'l*, pg. 3180
GULF INTERNATIONAL BANK B.S.C.; *Int'l*, pg. 3181
GULF INTERNATIONAL BANK (UK) LTD.—See Gulf International Bank B.S.C.; *Int'l*, pg. 3181
GUNAY BANK OJSC; *Int'l*, pg. 3183
GUTA-BANK JSC; *Int'l*, pg. 3188
GUYANA BANK FOR TRADE & INDUSTRY LTD.—See Edward B. Beharry & Co. Ltd.; *Int'l*, pg. 2316
HABIB AMERICAN BANK; *U.S. Private*, pg. 1837
HABIB BANK AG ZURICH; *Int'l*, pg. 3202
HABIB BANK LIMITED; *Int'l*, pg. 3202
HABIB METROPOLITAN BANK LIMITED—See Habib Bank AG Zurich; *Int'l*, pg. 3202
HABIBSONS BANK LIMITED—See Habib Group of Companies; *Int'l*, pg. 3203
HALYK BANK OF KAZAKHSTAN JSC; *Int'l*, pg. 3234
HALYK FINANCE JSC—See Halyk Bank of Kazakhstan JSC; *Int'l*, pg. 3234
HAMBURG COMMERCIAL BANK AG—See Cerberus Capital Management, L.P.; *U.S. Private*, pg. 838
HAMBURG COMMERCIAL BANK AG—See GoldenTree Asset Management LP; *U.S. Private*, pg. 1734
HAMBURG COMMERCIAL BANK AG—See J.C. Flowers & Co. LLC; *U.S. Private*, pg. 2159
HAMBURGER SPARKASSE AG; *Int'l*, pg. 3237
HAMLIN BANK & TRUST COMPANY; *U.S. Public*, pg. 982
HAMPDEN INVESTMENT CORPORATION II—See Berkshire Hills Bancorp, Inc.; *U.S. Public*, pg. 320
HAMRO BIKAS BANK LIMITED; *Int'l*, pg. 3240
HANA BANK (CHINA) CO., LTD.—See Hana Financial Group, Inc.; *Int'l*, pg. 3240
HANA SAVINGS BANK CO., LTD.—See Hana Financial Group, Inc.; *Int'l*, pg. 3240
HANCOCK WHITNEY BANK—See Hancock Whitney Corporation; *U.S. Public*, pg. 982
HANG SENG BANK (CHINA) LIMITED—See HSBC Holdings plc; *Int'l*, pg. 3506
HANMI BANK—See Hanmi Financial Corporation; *U.S. Public*, pg. 983
HANOVER COMMUNITY BANK—See Hanover Bancorp Inc.; *U.S. Public*, pg. 984
HANWHA BANK HUNGARY LTD.—See Hanwha Group; *Int'l*, pg. 3266
HANWHA SAVINGS BANK—See Hanwha Group; *Int'l*, pg. 3266
HANYANG SECURITIES CO., LTD.; *Int'l*, pg. 3267
HAP SENG CREDIT SDN. BHD.—See Hap Seng Consolidated Berhad; *Int'l*, pg. 3268
HARBIN BANK CO., LTD.; *Int'l*, pg. 3270
HARBORONE BANK—See HarborOne Bancorp, Inc.; *U.S. Public*, pg. 984
HARDIN COUNTY SAVINGS BANK—See Hardin County Bancorporation; *U.S. Private*, pg. 1863
HARFORD BANK; *U.S. Public*, pg. 984
HARLEYSVILLE SAVINGS BANK—See Harleysville Financial Corporation; *U.S. Public*, pg. 985
HARRIS EXPLORATION, INC.; *U.S. Public*, pg. 986
HAUCK & AUFHAUSER FUND PLATFORMS S.A.—See Fosun International Limited; *Int'l*, pg. 2751
THE HAVANA NATIONAL BANK—See Community Investment Group, Ltd.; *U.S. Public*, pg. 995

HAVEN SAVINGS BANK—See Haven Bancorp, MHC; *U.S. Private*, pg. 1880
HAWTHORN BANK—See Hawthorn Bancshares, Inc.; *U.S. Public*, pg. 989
HDFC BANK LIMITED—See Housing Development Finance Corporation Limited; *Int'l*, pg. 3491
HEARTLAND BANK LIMITED; *Int'l*, pg. 3304
HEARTLAND BANK—See Heartland BancCorp; *U.S. Public*, pg. 1017
HEARTLAND BANK & TRUST COMPANY—See HBT Financial, Inc.; *U.S. Public*, pg. 990
HEARTLAND BUSINESS CREDIT CORPORATION—See Midland States Bancorp, Inc.; *U.S. Public*, pg. 1445
HEBRON SAVINGS BANK; *U.S. Private*, pg. 1903
HEIDELBERG DISTRICT COMMUNITY ENTERPRISE LIMITED—See Bendigo & Adelaide Bank Ltd.; *Int'l*, pg. 971
HELABA LANDESBANK HESSEN-THURINGEN; *Int'l*, pg. 3327
HELGELAND SPAREBANK; *Int'l*, pg. 3329
HELLENIC ALICO LIFE INSURANCE COMPANY LTD—See Hellenic Bank Public Company Ltd.; *Int'l*, pg. 3333
HELLENIC BANK PUBLIC COMPANY LTD.; *Int'l*, pg. 3333
HELM BANK USA; *U.S. Private*, pg. 1911
HENRY COUNTY BANK—See Civista Bancshares, Inc.; *U.S. Public*, pg. 507
HERALD NATIONAL BANK—See BankUnited, Inc.; *U.S. Public*, pg. 274
HERITAGE BANK INC.; *U.S. Private*, pg. 1922
HERITAGE BANK LIMITED; *Int'l*, pg. 3361
HERITAGE BANK OF COMMERCE—See Heritage Commerce Corp; *U.S. Public*, pg. 1028
HERITAGE BANK OF ST. TAMMANY—See Heritage NOLA Bancorp, Inc.; *U.S. Public*, pg. 1028
THE HERITAGE BANK; *U.S. Public*, pg. 4051
HERITAGE BANK—See Heritage Financial Corporation; *U.S. Public*, pg. 1028
HERITAGE BANK—See Heritage Group, Inc.; *U.S. Public*, pg. 1923
HERITAGE GROUP, INC.; *U.S. Public*, pg. 1923
HIAWATHA NATIONAL BANK; *U.S. Private*, pg. 1932
HICKORY POINT BANK & TRUST FSB; *U.S. Private*, pg. 1933
THE HIGASHI-NIPPON BANK, LTD.—See Concordia Financial Group, Ltd.; *Int'l*, pg. 1765
HIGHLAND BANK—See Highland Bankshares Inc.; *U.S. Private*, pg. 1938
HIGHLANDS STATE BANK—See Provident Financial Services, Inc.; *U.S. Public*, pg. 1730
HIGH PLAINS BANK—See First Keyes Bancshares, Inc.; *U.S. Private*, pg. 1520
HILLCREST BANK—See National Bank Holdings Corporation; *U.S. Public*, pg. 1493
HILLS BANK & TRUST COMPANY—See Hills Bancorporation; *U.S. Public*, pg. 1038
HILLSBORO BANK; *U.S. Private*, pg. 1947
HINSDALE BANK & TRUST COMPANY, N.A.—See Wintrust Financial Corporation; *U.S. Public*, pg. 2375
HNB NATIONAL BANK; *U.S. Private*, pg. 1955
HOCKING VALLEY BANK—See Hocking Valley Bancshares, Inc.; *U.S. Public*, pg. 1044
HOKKAIDO BANK, LTD.—See Hokuhoku Financial Group, Inc.; *Int'l*, pg. 3444
THE HOKKAIDO BANK, LTD.—See Hokuhoku Financial Group, Inc.; *Int'l*, pg. 3444
THE HOKUETSU BANK, LTD.—See Daishi Hokuetsu Financial Group, Inc.; *Int'l*, pg. 1941
THE HOKURIKU BANK, LTD.—See Hokuhoku Financial Group, Inc.; *Int'l*, pg. 3444
THE HOKURIKU BANK, LTD.—See Hokuhoku Financial Group, Inc.; *Int'l*, pg. 3444
THE HOKUTO BANK, LTD.—See FIDEA Holdings Co. Ltd.; *Int'l*, pg. 2653
HOLAND OG SETSKOG SPAREBANK; *Int'l*, pg. 3445
HOME FEDERAL BANK CORPORATION—See HFB Financial Corporation; *U.S. Public*, pg. 1034
HOME FEDERAL BANK OF HOLLYWOOD—See Home BancGroup, Inc.; *U.S. Private*, pg. 1970
HOME FEDERAL BANK—See Home Federal Bancorp, Inc. of Louisiana; *U.S. Public*, pg. 1046
HOME FEDERAL SAVINGS AND LOAN ASSOCIATION OF NILES—See First Niles Financial, Inc.; *U.S. Public*, pg. 846
HOME FINANCE COMPANY LIMITED—See Fiji National Provident Fund; *Int'l*, pg. 2661
THE HOME LOAN SAVINGS BANK—See Home Loan Financial Corporation; *U.S. Public*, pg. 1046
HOME SAVINGS BANK—See Home Bancorp Wisconsin, Inc.; *U.S. Public*, pg. 1045
HOMESERVICES LENDING, LLC—See Wells Fargo & Company; *U.S. Public*, pg. 2343
HOMESTREET BANK—See HomeStreet, Inc.; *U.S. Public*, pg. 1046
HOMESTREET CAPITAL CORPORATION—See HomeStreet, Inc.; *U.S. Public*, pg. 1046
HOMETOWN BANK, NATIONAL ASSOCIATION; *U.S. Private*, pg. 1975
HOMETOWN BANK—See Atlantic Union Bankshares Corporation; *U.S. Public*, pg. 223
HOMETOWN NATIONAL BANK—See LaSalle Bancorp, Inc.; *U.S. Private*, pg. 2394
HOMETRUST BANK—See HomeTrust Bancshares, Inc.; *U.S. Public*, pg. 1046
THE HONESDALE NATIONAL BANK—See Honat Bancorp Inc.; *U.S. Public*, pg. 1046
HONG LEONG BANK BERHAD—See Hong Leong Investment Holdings Pte. Ltd.; *Int'l*, pg. 3468
HONOR STATE BANK; *U.S. Private*, pg. 1977
HORICON STATE BANK; *U.S. Private*, pg. 1980
HORIZON BANK—See Horizon Bancorp, Inc.; *U.S. Public*, pg. 1053
HOTELS COLOMBO (1963) LIMITED—See Bank of Ceylon; *Int'l*, pg. 841
HOUSING & DEVELOPMENT BANK SAE; *Int'l*, pg. 3491
HOUSING DEVELOPMENT FINANCE CORPORATION LIMITED; *Int'l*, pg. 3491
HOWARD BANK—See F.N.B. Corporation; *U.S. Public*, pg. 818
HPCKAL, LLC—See Huntington Bancshares Incorporated; *U.S. Public*, pg. 1071
HRVATSKA BANKA ZA OBNOVU I RAZVITAK; *Int'l*, pg. 3502
HSBC ALGERIA—See HSBC Holdings plc; *Int'l*, pg. 3503
HSBC AMANAH MALAYSIA BERHAD—See HSBC Holdings plc; *Int'l*, pg. 3506
HSBC ASSET FINANCE (UK) LIMITED—See HSBC Holdings plc; *Int'l*, pg. 3503
HSBC BANK ARGENTINA SA—See HSBC Holdings plc; *Int'l*, pg. 3503
HSBC BANK AUSTRALIA LIMITED—See HSBC Holdings plc; *Int'l*, pg. 3506
HSBC BANK (BAHAMAS) LTD.—See HSBC Holdings plc; *Int'l*, pg. 3503
HSBC BANK (CHINA) COMPANY LIMITED—See HSBC Holdings plc; *Int'l*, pg. 3506
HSBC BANK EGYPT (SAE)—See HSBC Holdings plc; *Int'l*, pg. 3503
HSBC BANK MALAYSIA BERHAD—See HSBC Holdings plc; *Int'l*, pg. 3506
HSBC BANK MIDDLE EAST LIMITED—See HSBC Holdings plc; *Int'l*, pg. 3503
HSBC BANK PLC, LUXEMBOURG BRANCH—See HSBC Holdings plc; *Int'l*, pg. 3503
HSBC BANK PLC—See HSBC Holdings plc; *Int'l*, pg. 3503
HSBC BANK POLSKA S.A.—See HSBC Holdings plc; *Int'l*, pg. 3503
HSBC BANK (URUGUAY) S.A.—See HSBC Holdings plc; *Int'l*, pg. 3503
HSBC CORPORATE BANKING SWITZERLAND—See HSBC Holdings plc; *Int'l*, pg. 3505
HSBC CORPORATION (ISLE OF MAN) LIMITED—See HSBC Holdings plc; *Int'l*, pg. 3504
HSBC EXPAT—See HSBC Holdings plc; *Int'l*, pg. 3504
HSBC GLOBAL SERVICES (UK) LIMITED—See HSBC Holdings plc; *Int'l*, pg. 3505
HSBC INTERNATIONAL FINANCE CORPORATION LIMITED—See HSBC Holdings plc; *Int'l*, pg. 3504
HSBC INTERNATIONAL TRUSTEE (BVI) LIMITED—See HSBC Holdings plc; *Int'l*, pg. 3505
HSBC INVESTMENT BANK PLC—See HSBC Holdings plc; *Int'l*, pg. 3504
HSBC MEXICO S.A.—See HSBC Holdings plc; *Int'l*, pg. 3503
HSBC PRIVATE BANK (C.I.) LIMITED—See HSBC Holdings plc; *Int'l*, pg. 3505
HSBC PRIVATE BANK INTERNATIONAL—See HSBC Holdings plc; *Int'l*, pg. 3505
THE HSBC SAVINGS BANK—See HSBC Holdings plc; *Int'l*, pg. 3506
HSBC SECURITIES, INC.—See HSBC Holdings plc; *Int'l*, pg. 3505
HSBC TRINKAUS & BURKHARDT (INTERNATIONAL) S.A.—See HSBC Holdings plc; *Int'l*, pg. 3504
HSH NORDBANK AG (LUXEMBOURG)—See Cerberus Capital Management, L.P.; *U.S. Private*, pg. 838
HSH NORDBANK AG (LUXEMBOURG)—See GoldenTree Asset Management LP; *U.S. Private*, pg. 1734
HSH NORDBANK AG (LUXEMBOURG)—See J.C. Flowers & Co. LLC; *U.S. Private*, pg. 2159
HUA NAN COMMERCIAL BANK, LTD. - OFFSHORE BANKING—See Hua Nan Financial Holdings Co., Ltd.; *Int'l*, pg. 3509
HUA NAN COMMERCIAL BANK, LTD. - SINGAPORE—See Hua Nan Financial Holdings Co., Ltd.; *Int'l*, pg. 3509
HUA NAN COMMERCIAL BANK, LTD.—See Hua Nan Financial Holdings Co., Ltd.; *Int'l*, pg. 3509
HUA NAN COMMERCIAL BANK, LTD.—See Hua Nan Financial Holdings Co., Ltd.; *Int'l*, pg. 3509
HUARONG XIANGJIANG BANK CO., LTD.—See China CITIC Financial Asset Management Co., Ltd.; *Int'l*, pg. 1489
HUA XIA BANK CO., LIMITED; *Int'l*, pg. 3510
HUISHANG BANK CORPORATION LIMITED; *Int'l*, pg. 3527
HULETT BANCORP; *U.S. Private*, pg. 2005
HUNTINGTON INSURANCE, INC.—See Huntington

Bancshares Incorporated; *U.S. Public*, pg. 1071
THE HUNTINGTON NATIONAL BANK—See Huntington Bancshares Incorporated; *U.S. Public*, pg. 1071
HUNTINGTON PUBLIC CAPITAL CORPORATION—See Huntington Bancshares Incorporated; *U.S. Public*, pg. 1071
HUNTINGTON TECHNOLOGY FINANCE, INC.—See Huntington Bancshares Incorporated; *U.S. Public*, pg. 1071
HVIDBJERG BANK A/S; *Int'l*, pg. 3541
HYDROMELIORACIE AS; *Int'l*, pg. 3548
HYPO REAL ESTATE CAPITAL HONG KONG CORPORATION LIMITED—See Hypo Real Estate Holding AG; *Int'l*, pg. 3553
HYPO REAL ESTATE CAPITAL INDIA CORPORATION PRIVATE LIMITED—See Hypo Real Estate Holding AG; *Int'l*, pg. 3553
HYPO REAL ESTATE CAPITAL JAPAN CORPORATION—See Hypo Real Estate Holding AG; *Int'l*, pg. 3554
HYPO REAL ESTATE CAPITAL SINGAPORE CORPORATION PRIVATE LIMITED—See Hypo Real Estate Holding AG; *Int'l*, pg. 3554
HYPOTHEKARBANK LENZBURG AG; *Int'l*, pg. 3554
IA AUTO FINANCE INC.—See iA Financial Corporation Inc.; *Int'l*, pg. 3568
IBERIABANK—See First Horizon Corporation; *U.S. Public*, pg. 845
IBI PROMOTORA DE VENDAS LTDA—See Banco Bradesco S.A.; *Int'l*, pg. 819
IBSP PLC; *Int'l*, pg. 3577
IB WEALTH MANAGEMENT, INC.—See Independent Bank Corporation; *U.S. Public*, pg. 1116
ICAP-AP (THAILAND) CO. LTD.—See CME Group, Inc.; *U.S. Public*, pg. 517
ICAP SECURITIES COLOMBIA S.A.—See CME Group, Inc.; *U.S. Public*, pg. 517
ICBC TURKEY BANK A.S.; *Int'l*, pg. 3578
ICB FINANCIAL GROUP HOLDINGS AG; *Int'l*, pg. 3578
ICB ISLAMIC BANK LIMITED—See ICB Financial Group Holdings AG; *Int'l*, pg. 3578
ICCREA BANCA S.P.A.—See Iccrea Holding S.p.A.; *Int'l*, pg. 3578
ICICI BANK CANADA LTD.—See ICICI Bank Limited; *Int'l*, pg. 3581
ICICI BANK LIMITED; *Int'l*, pg. 3581
ICICI BANK UK PLC—See ICICI Bank Limited; *Int'l*, pg. 3581
IDAHO FIRST BANK; *U.S. Private*, pg. 2034
IDEA BANK S.A.—See Getin Holding S.A.; *Int'l*, pg. 2947
IDEA BANK S.A.—See Getin Holding S.A.; *Int'l*, pg. 2947
IDFC FIRST BANK LIMITED; *Int'l*, pg. 3592
IFIC MONEY TRANSFER (UK) LIMITED—See IFIC Bank PLC; *Int'l*, pg. 3599
IFIS RENTAL SERVICES S.R.L.—See Banca IFIS S.p.A.; *Int'l*, pg. 815
ILLINOIS BANK & TRUST—See Heartland Financial USA, Inc.; *U.S. Public*, pg. 1018
IMMORENT BETA, LEASING DRUZBA, D.O.O.—See Erste Group Bank AG; *Int'l*, pg. 2499
IMOCAIXA - GESTAO IMOBILIARIA, S.A.—See Caixa Geral de Depositos S.A.; *Int'l*, pg. 1260
INCAPITAL HOLDINGS, LLC—See Bank of America Corporation; *U.S. Public*, pg. 272
INDEPENDENCE BANK; *U.S. Private*, pg. 2055
INDEPENDENT BANK; *U.S. Private*, pg. 2058
INDEPENDENT BANK—See Independent Bank Corporation; *U.S. Public*, pg. 1116
INDEPENDENT BANK—See Independent Bank Group, Inc.; *U.S. Public*, pg. 1116
INDIA INFRADEBT LTD.—See Bank of Baroda; *Int'l*, pg. 840
INDO ZAMBIA BANK LTD.—See Bank of Baroda; *Int'l*, pg. 840
INDO ZAMBIA BANK LTD.—See Bank of India; *Int'l*, pg. 843
INDO ZAMBIA BANK LTD.—See Central Bank of India Limited; *Int'l*, pg. 1404
INDUSTRIAL ALLIANCE PACIFIC GENERAL INSURANCE CORPORATION—See iA Financial Corporation Inc.; *Int'l*, pg. 3567
INDUSTRIAL ALLIANCE TRUST INC.—See iA Financial Corporation Inc.; *Int'l*, pg. 3567
INDUSTRIAL BANK—See IBW Financial Corporation; *U.S. Public*, pg. 1083
INFINITY BANK; *U.S. Public*, pg. 1117
INFORMATIONS TECHNOLOGIE AUSTRIA SK SPOL. S R.O.—See Erste Group Bank AG; *Int'l*, pg. 2499
INLAND BANK & TRUST—See Byline Bancorp, Inc.; *U.S. Public*, pg. 414
INNOFIS ESGM S.L.—See Constellation Software Inc.; *Int'l*, pg. 1772
INSBANK—See InsCorp, Inc.; *U.S. Public*, pg. 1129
INSHA GMBH—See Albaraka Turk Katilim Bankasi A.S.; *Int'l*, pg. 293
INSIGHT INVESTMENT MANAGEMENT (GLOBAL) LIMITED—See The Bank of New York Mellon Corporation; *U.S. Public*, pg. 2037
INSOUTH BANK—See Independent Southern Bancshares, Inc.; *U.S. Private*, pg. 2061
INSPUR FINANCIAL INFORMATION SYSTEM CO., LTD.—See Diebold Nixdorf, Inc.; *U.S. Public*, pg. 661

INSTITUTION FOR SAVINGS IN NEWBURYPORT & ITS VICINITY; *U.S. Private*, pg. 2094
INTEGRATED LOGISTICS, LLC—See U.S. Bancorp; *U.S. Public*, pg. 2212
INTELLIGENT PROCESSING SOLUTIONS LIMITED—See Unisys Corporation; *U.S. Public*, pg. 2228
INTERACTIVE BROKERS CENTRAL EUROPE ZRT.—See Interactive Brokers Group, Inc.; *U.S. Public*, pg. 1140
INTERBANK—See Olney Bancshares of Texas, Inc.; *U.S. Private*, pg. 3011
INTERCREDIT BANK, N.A.; *U.S. Private*, pg. 2110
INTERNATIONAL BANK OF COMMERCE, BROWNSVILLE—See International Bancshares Corporation; *U.S. Public*, pg. 1145
INTERNATIONAL BANK OF COMMERCE, ZAPATA—See International Bancshares Corporation; *U.S. Public*, pg. 1145
INTERNATIONAL COMMERCIAL BANK LAO LTD—See ICB Financial Group Holdings AG; *Int'l*, pg. 3578
INTERNATIONAL COMMERCIAL BANK LIMITED—See FBN Holdings PLC; *Int'l*, pg. 2627
INTERNATIONAL COMMERCIAL BANK LIMITED—See ICB Financial Group Holdings AG; *Int'l*, pg. 3578
INTERNATIONAL COMMERCIAL BANK (MOZAMBIQUE), S.A.—See ICB Financial Group Holdings AG; *Int'l*, pg. 3578
INTERNATIONAL COMMERCIAL BANK SH.A.—See ICB Financial Group Holdings AG; *Int'l*, pg. 3578
INTERNATIONAL COMMERCIAL BANK ZAMBIA LTD—See ICB Financial Group Holdings AG; *Int'l*, pg. 3578
INTER-PACIFIC EQUITY NOMINEES (ASING) SDN BHD—See Berjaya Corporation Berhad; *Int'l*, pg. 984
INTRUST BANK, N.A.—See Intrust Financial Corporation; *U.S. Private*, pg. 2130
INVERLOCH & DISTRICT FINANCIAL ENTERPRISES LIMITED—See Bendigo & Adelaide Bank Ltd.; *Int'l*, pg. 971
INVESTBANK AD—See Festa Holding Plc; *Int'l*, pg. 2646
INVESTORS COMMUNITY BANK—See Nicolet Bankshares, Inc.; *U.S. Public*, pg. 1528
INWOOD NATIONAL BANK INC.—See Inwood Bancshares Inc.; *U.S. Private*, pg. 2133
ION BANK—See Ion Financial, MHC; *U.S. Private*, pg. 2133
IOWA STATE BANK; *U.S. Private*, pg. 2135
IOWA STATE SAVINGS BANK—See Ames National Corporation; *U.S. Public*, pg. 115
IOWA TRUST AND SAVINGS BANK—See Bradley Bancorp, Inc.; *U.S. Private*, pg. 632
IOWA TRUST & SAVINGS BANK—See Emmetsburg Bank Shares, Inc.; *U.S. Private*, pg. 1383
ISABELLA BANK—See Isabella Bank Corporation; *U.S. Public*, pg. 1174
ISB CANARIAS SA—See Barclays PLC; *Int'l*, pg. 862
ISLAMIC INTERNATIONAL ARAB BANK PLC—See Arab Bank plc; *Int'l*, pg. 529
ISLANDERS BANK—See Banner Corporation; *U.S. Public*, pg. 275
ISRAEL DISCOUNT BANK LTD.—See IDB Development Corporation Ltd.; *Int'l*, pg. 3588
ISRAEL DISCOUNT BANK OF NEW YORK—See IDB Development Corporation Ltd.; *Int'l*, pg. 3588
ITASCA BANK & TRUST CO.—See Itasca Bancorp Inc.; *U.S. Private*, pg. 2149
JACKSON COUNTY BANK—See Bancorp of Southern Indiana; *U.S. Public*, pg. 269
JANATA CAPITAL LTD.—See Global IME Bank Limited; *Int'l*, pg. 2997
JAPAN ECONOMIC RESEARCH INSTITUTE INC.—See Development Bank of Japan, Inc.; *Int'l*, pg. 2088
JCCA, INC.—See Bank of America Corporation; *U.S. Public*, pg. 272
JEFF BANK—See Jeffersonville Bancorp; *U.S. Public*, pg. 1189
JEFFERSON BANK OF FLORIDA; *U.S. Private*, pg. 2197
JEFFERSON BANK OF MISSOURI—See Central Bancompany, Inc.; *U.S. Public*, pg. 472
JEFFERSON SECURITY BANK; *U.S. Private*, pg. 2198
JERSEY SHORE STATE BANK—See Penns Woods Bancorp, Inc.; *U.S. Public*, pg. 1663
JIANGSU ZHANGJIAGANG CQRC VILLAGE & TOWNSHIP BANK CO., LTD.—See Chongqing Rural Commercial Bank Co., Ltd.; *Int'l*, pg. 1581
JIM THORPE NEIGHBORHOOD BANK—See JTNB Bancorp, Inc.; *U.S. Public*, pg. 1210
JOHNSON COUNTY BANK—See SKYLINE BANKSHARES, INC.; *U.S. Public*, pg. 1892
JORDAN ISLAMIC BANK—See Al Baraka Banking Group B.S.C.; *Int'l*, pg. 276
JOURNEY BANK—See Muncy Columbia Financial Corporation; *U.S. Public*, pg. 1486
JPMORGAN CHASE BANK, N.A. - LOUISVILLE—See JPMorgan Chase & Co.; *U.S. Public*, pg. 1209
JPMORGAN CHASE - SOUTHERN REGIONAL OFFICE—See JPMorgan Chase & Co.; *U.S. Public*, pg. 1209
J.P.MORGAN SERVICES INDIA PRIVATE LIMITED—See JPMorgan Chase & Co.; *U.S. Public*, pg. 1208
JPMORGAN TRUST COMPANY (BAHAMAS) LIMITED—See JPMorgan Chase & Co.; *U.S. Public*, pg. 1210
JSB GPB-MORTGAGE OJSC—See Gazprombank JSC; *Int'l*, pg. 2892
JSC CITIBANK KAZAKHSTAN—See Citigroup Inc.; *U.S. Public*, pg. 504
JSC RUSSIAN STANDARD BANK—See CJSC Russian Standard Corporation; *Int'l*, pg. 1634
THE JUHACHI-SHINWA BANK, LTD.—See Fukuoka Financial Group, Inc.; *Int'l*, pg. 2840
THE JUNIATA VALLEY BANK—See Juniata Valley Financial Corp.; *U.S. Public*, pg. 1210
KAFUE HOUSE LIMITED—See Barclays PLC; *Int'l*, pg. 862
KASPI BANK JSC—See Baring Vostok Capital Partners; *Int'l*, pg. 865
KATAHDIN TRUST COMPANY—See Katahdin Bankshares Corp.; *U.S. Public*, pg. 1215
KAZKOMMERTSBANK JSC—See Halyk Bank of Kazakhstan JSC; *Int'l*, pg. 3234
K BANK—See K Capital Corporation; *U.S. Private*, pg. 2249
KEB ASIA FINANCE LIMITED—See Hana Financial Group, Inc.; *Int'l*, pg. 3240
KEB AUSTRALIA LTD.—See Hana Financial Group, Inc.; *Int'l*, pg. 3240
KEB LA FINANCIAL CORP.—See Hana Financial Group, Inc.; *Int'l*, pg. 3240
KEB NY FINANCIAL CORP.—See Hana Financial Group, Inc.; *Int'l*, pg. 3240
KEB USA INTERNATIONAL CORP.—See Hana Financial Group, Inc.; *Int'l*, pg. 3240
KENNEBEC SAVINGS BANK—See Kennebec Savings Bank, MHC; *U.S. Private*, pg. 2284
KENTUCKY BANK—See Stock Yards Bancorp, Inc.; *U.S. Public*, pg. 1951
KENTUCKY FARMERS BANK CORPORATION; *U.S. Private*, pg. 2288
KERMIA LTD—See Bank of Cyprus Holdings Public Limited Company; *Int'l*, pg. 842
KEYBANK N.A. - KEY COMMUNITY BANK DIVISION—See KeyCorp; *U.S. Public*, pg. 1225
KEYSTONE BANK, NATIONAL ASSOCIATION—See Keystone Bancshares, Inc.; *U.S. Private*, pg. 2295
KEYSTONE COMMUNITY BANK—See Mercantile Bank Corporation; *U.S. Public*, pg. 1414
KEYTRADE BANK S.A.—See Confederation Nationale du Credit Mutuel; *Int'l*, pg. 1767
KHALEEJI BANK B.S.C.—See GFH Financial Group B.S.C.; *Int'l*, pg. 2956
THE KILLBUCK SAVINGS BANK COMPANY—See Killbuck Bancshares, Inc.; *U.S. Public*, pg. 1228
KIRKPATRICK BANK—See American BanCorp of Oklahoma; *U.S. Private*, pg. 223
KIRKWOOD BANK OF NEVADA—See JBNV Holding Corp.; *U.S. Private*, pg. 2194
KIRKWOOD BANK & TRUST CO.—See Kirkwood Bancorporation Co.; *U.S. Private*, pg. 2315
KIS-BANK INC.—See Hyosung Corporation; *Int'l*, pg. 3552
KISH BANK—See Kish Bancorp, Inc.; *U.S. Public*, pg. 1236
KISLAK NATIONAL BANK—See J.I. Kislak Inc.; *U.S. Private*, pg. 2167
KITSAP BANK—See Olympic Bancorp; *U.S. Private*, pg. 3012
KLEBERG BANK, N.A.—See Kleberg & Company Bankers, Inc.; *U.S. Private*, pg. 2318
KONSUL INKASSO GMBH—See Deutsche Bank Aktiengesellschaft; *Int'l*, pg. 2061
KOREA EXCHANGE BANK (DEUTSCHLAND) AG—See Hana Financial Group, Inc.; *Int'l*, pg. 3241
KOREA EXCHANGE BANK OF CANADA—See Hana Financial Group, Inc.; *Int'l*, pg. 3241
THE KUMAMOTO BANK, LTD.—See Fukuoka Financial Group, Inc.; *Int'l*, pg. 2840
KYONGNAM BANK CO., LTD.—See BNK Financial Group Inc.; *Int'l*, pg. 1079
KYRGYZ INVESTMENT AND CREDIT BANK LTD—See Aga Khan Development Network; *Int'l*, pg. 199
KYRGYZKOMMERTSBANK OJSC—See Halyk Bank of Kazakhstan JSC; *Int'l*, pg. 3234
LAFAYETTE AMBASSADOR BANK—See Fulton Financial Corporation; *U.S. Public*, pg. 892
LAKE CITY BANK INVESTMENTS LIMITED—See Lakeland Financial Corporation; *U.S. Public*, pg. 1288
LAKE CITY BANK—See Lakeland Financial Corporation; *U.S. Public*, pg. 1288
LAKE ELMO BANK; *U.S. Private*, pg. 2375
LAKE FOREST BANK & TRUST COMPANY, N.A.—See Wintrust Financial Corporation; *U.S. Public*, pg. 2375
LAKELAND BANK—See Provident Financial Services, Inc.; *U.S. Public*, pg. 1730
LAKE SHORE SAVINGS BANK—See Lake Shore Bancorp, Inc.; *U.S. Public*, pg. 1288
LAKESIDE BANK; *U.S. Private*, pg. 2377
LAKESIDE BANK—See Lakeside Bancshares, Inc.; *U.S. Public*, pg. 1289
LAKESIDE BANK—See PFBS Holdings, Inc.; *U.S. Private*, pg. 3164
LANDESBANK BERLIN AG—See Deutscher Sparkassen- und Giroverband e.V.; *Int'l*, pg. 2085

N.A.I.C.S. INDEX 522110 — COMMERCIAL BANKING

LANDMARK BANK—See Clinton Bancshares, Inc.; *U.S. Private*, pg. 944
LANDMARK NATIONAL BANK—See Landmark Bancorp, Inc.; *U.S. Public*, pg. 1292
LAURITZEN CORPORATION; *U.S. Private*, pg. 2400
LAVORO BANK AG—See BNP Paribas SA; *Int'l*, pg. 1089
LCNB NATIONAL BANK—See LCNB Corp.; *U.S. Public*, pg. 1296
LEADER BANK, N.A.; *U.S. Private*, pg. 2405
THE LEADERS BANK—See Providence Financial Corporation; *U.S. Private*, pg. 3294
LEE BANK—See Berkshire Financial Services, Inc.; *U.S. Private*, pg. 533
LEGACY BANK OF FLORIDA—See Seacoast Banking Corporation of Florida; *U.S. Public*, pg. 1851
LEGACY BANK OF TEXAS—See Legacy Texas Group, Inc.; *U.S. Private*, pg. 2417
LEGACY BANK—See InBankshares Corp.; *U.S. Public*, pg. 1114
LEGACY BANK—See Midstate Bancorp, Inc.; *U.S. Private*, pg. 2717
LEGACY BANK & TRUST COMPANY—See Century Bancshares, Inc.; *U.S. Private*, pg. 832
LEGACY TEXAS GROUP, INC.; *U.S. Private*, pg. 2417
LEGACYTEXAS INSURANCE SERVICES, INC.—See Prosperity Bancshares, Inc.; *U.S. Public*, pg. 1728
LENDR, LLC; *U.S. Private*, pg. 2421
LEVELFIELD FINANCIAL, INC.; *U.S. Private*, pg. 2434
LEWIS & CLARK BANK; *U.S. Public*, pg. 1309
LEWISTON STATE BANK—See Glacier Bancorp, Inc.; *U.S. Public*, pg. 938
LIBERTY BANK, N.A.—See DMG Bancshares, Inc.; *U.S. Private*, pg. 1248
LIBERTY BANK; *U.S. Private*, pg. 2443
LIBERTY BANK; *U.S. Private*, pg. 2443
LIBERTY BANK & TRUST COMPANY—See Liberty Financial Services, Inc.; *U.S. Private*, pg. 2444
LIBERTY FINANCIAL—See Evansville Teachers Federal Credit Union; *U.S. Private*, pg. 1435
LIBERTY NATIONAL BANK; *U.S. Private*, pg. 2446
LIBERTYVILLE BANK & TRUST COMPANY, N.A.—See Wintrust Financial Corporation; *U.S. Public*, pg. 2375
LIGHTHOUSE BANK; *U.S. Private*, pg. 2452
THE LINCOLN NATIONAL BANK OF HODGENVILLE—See First Cecilian Bancorp, Inc.; *U.S. Public*, pg. 1515
LINCOLN PARK BANCORP—See Ion Financial, MHC; *U.S. Private*, pg. 2133
LINCOLN SAVINGS BANK; *U.S. Private*, pg. 2458
LINCOLN WAY COMMUNITY BANK—See LWCBancorp, Inc.; *U.S. Private*, pg. 2518
LINKBANK—See LINKBANCORP, Inc.; *U.S. Public*, pg. 1320
LIVE OAK BANKING COMPANY—See Live Oak Bancshares, Inc.; *U.S. Public*, pg. 1331
LOCKWOOD ADVISORS, INC.—See The Bank of New York Mellon Corporation; *U.S. Public*, pg. 2037
LOGAN COMMUNITY FINANCIAL SERVICES LIMITED—See Bendigo & Adelaide Bank Ltd.; *Int'l*, pg. 971
LONE STAR CAPITAL BANK, N.A.; *U.S. Private*, pg. 2484
LONE STAR STATE BANK OF WEST TEXAS—See Prosperity Bancshares, Inc.; *U.S. Public*, pg. 1728
LONGKOU NANSHAN CDB VILLAGE BANK CO., LTD.—See China Development Bank Corporation; *Int'l*, pg. 1497
LOS ALAMOS NATIONAL BANK—See Enterprise Financial Services Corp; *U.S. Public*, pg. 778
LUMBEE GUARANTY BANK; *U.S. Public*, pg. 1345
LURI 4, S.A.—See Banco Santander, S.A.; *Int'l*, pg. 826
LUXEMBOURG FAMILY OFFICE S.A.—See Deutsche Bank Aktiengesellschaft; *Int'l*, pg. 2061
THE LUZERNE BANK—See Penns Woods Bancorp, Inc.; *U.S. Public*, pg. 1663
THE LYONS NATIONAL BANK—See Lyons Bancorp, Inc.; *U.S. Public*, pg. 1350
MABREY BANK—See Mabrey Bancorporation Inc.; *U.S. Private*, pg. 2531
MACATAWA BANK—See Wintrust Financial Corporation; *U.S. Public*, pg. 2375
MACRO SECURITIES S.A.—See Banco Macro S.A.; *Int'l*, pg. 823
MADISON BANK OF MARYLAND—See Bay-Vanguard, M.H.C.; *U.S. Private*, pg. 495
MADISON VALLEY BANK—See Jackass Creek Land & Livestock Company; *U.S. Private*, pg. 2175
MAHOPAC BANK—See Tompkins Financial Corporation; *U.S. Public*, pg. 2162
MAIN INCUBATOR GMBH—See Commerzbank AG; *Int'l*, pg. 1719
MAIN STREET BANK CORP.—See Main Street Financial Services Corp.; *U.S. Public*, pg. 1355
MAINSTREET BANK—See MainStreet Bancshares, Inc.; *U.S. Public*, pg. 1355
MALVERN BANK, NATIONAL ASSOCIATION—See First Bank; *U.S. Public*, pg. 840
MALVERN INSURANCE ASSOCIATES, LLC—See First Bank; *U.S. Public*, pg. 840

THE MALVERN NATIONAL BANK—See MNB Bancshares, Inc.; *U.S. Private*, pg. 2755
MANNINGHAM COMMUNITY ENTERPRISES LIMITED—See Bendigo & Adelaide Bank Ltd.; *Int'l*, pg. 971
MANOR NATIONAL BANK; *U.S. Public*, pg. 1357
MANUFACTURERS & TRADERS TRUST COMPANY—See M&T Bank Corporation; *U.S. Public*, pg. 1350
MARBLEHEAD BANK; *U.S. Private*, pg. 2570
MARCH - UNIPSA CORREDURIA DE SEGUROS, S.A.U—See Alba Grupo March; *Int'l*, pg. 292
MARINE BANK—See Marine Bancorp, Inc.; *U.S. Private*, pg. 2575
MARINE BANK & TRUST COMPANY—See Marine Bancorp of Florida, Inc.; *U.S. Public*, pg. 1366
MARLIN BUSINESS BANK—See HPS Investment Partners, LLC; *U.S. Private*, pg. 1997
MARQUIS BANK—See Marquis Bancorp, Inc.; *U.S. Private*, pg. 2587
MARS BANK—See NexTier, Inc.; *U.S. Private*, pg. 2921
MARTHA'S VINEYARD SAVINGS BANK; *U.S. Private*, pg. 2594
MASON BANK—See Mason Bancshares, Inc.; *U.S. Private*, pg. 2601
MAUCH CHUNK TRUST COMPANY; *U.S. Private*, pg. 2614
MAXWELL STATE BANK—See Dentel Bancorporation; *U.S. Private*, pg. 1206
MBANK HIPOTECZNY S.A.—See Commerzbank AG; *Int'l*, pg. 1719
MBANK S.A.—See Commerzbank AG; *Int'l*, pg. 1719
MBANK—See Mackinac Financial Corporation; *U.S. Public*, pg. 1352
MB BUSINESS CAPITAL CANADA INC.—See Fifth Third Bancorp; *U.S. Public*, pg. 833
MBSL SAVINGS BANK LIMITED—See Bank of Ceylon; *Int'l*, pg. 841
M C BANK & TRUST COMPANY—See M C Bancshares, Inc.; *U.S. Private*, pg. 2523
MCHENRY BANK & TRUST—See Wintrust Financial Corporation; *U.S. Public*, pg. 2374
MCM ASIA LIMITED—See ChinLink International Holdings Limited; *Int'l*, pg. 1570
MCNB BANK AND TRUST CO.—See MCNB Banks, Inc.; *U.S. Public*, pg. 1409
MECHANICS BANK—See Ford Financial Fund II, L.P.; *U.S. Private*, pg. 1564
MECHANICS BANK—See Mechanics Banc Holding Company; *U.S. Private*, pg. 2649
MEDALLION BANK—See Medallion Financial Corp.; *U.S. Public*, pg. 1411
MEDICAPITAL BANK PLC—See Bank of Africa; *Int'l*, pg. 840
MEDIOLANUM DISTRIBUZIONE FINANZIARIA S.P.A.—See Banca Mediolanum S.p.A.; *Int'l*, pg. 815
MEDITERRANEAN BANK PLC—See AnaCap Financial Partners LLP; *Int'l*, pg. 445
MEDITERRANEAN CORPORATE BANK LIMITED—See AnaCap Financial Partners LLP; *Int'l*, pg. 445
MELLON BANK, N.A—See The Bank of New York Mellon Corporation; *U.S. Public*, pg. 2037
MELLON FUNDING CORPORATION—See The Bank of New York Mellon Corporation; *U.S. Public*, pg. 2037
MELROSE COOPERATIVE BANK—See Melrose Bancorp, Inc.; *U.S. Private*, pg. 2663
MERCANTILE BANK OF MICHIGAN—See Mercantile Bank Corporation; *U.S. Public*, pg. 1414
MERCANTILE BANK—See United Community Bancorp, Inc.; *U.S. Private*, pg. 4289
MERCANTILE DISCOUNT BANK LTD—See IDB Development Corporation Ltd.; *Int'l*, pg. 3588
MERCANTILE SOUTHERN MARYLAND BANK—See The PNC Financial Services Group, Inc.; *U.S. Public*, pg. 2119
MERCHANTS BANK OF COMMERCE—See Bank of Commerce Holdings; *U.S. Public*, pg. 272
MERCHANTS BANK; *U.S. Private*, pg. 2669
MERCHANTS & FARMERS BANK—See M&F Bancorp, Inc.; *U.S. Private*, pg. 2524
MERCHANTS & MARINE BANK—See Merchants & Marine Bancorp, Inc.; *U.S. Public*, pg. 1415
THE MERCHANTS NATIONAL BANK; *U.S. Private*, pg. 4078
MERIDIAN BANK—See Meridian Corporation; *U.S. Public*, pg. 1424
METAIRIE BANK & TRUST CO.; *U.S. Public*, pg. 1427
METRO CITY BANK—See MetroCity Bankshares, Inc.; *U.S. Public*, pg. 1431
METRO PHOENIX BANK; *U.S. Public*, pg. 1431
METROPOLITAN BANK HOLDING CORP.; *U.S. Public*, pg. 1431
METUCHEN SAVINGS BANK; *U.S. Private*, pg. 2691
MEVAS BANK LIMITED—See Dah Sing Financial Holdings Limited; *Int'l*, pg. 1913
M&F BANK—See M&F Bancorp, Inc.; *U.S. Public*, pg. 1350
MFINANCE FRANCE S.A.—See Commerzbank AG; *Int'l*, pg. 1719
MICROSTART SCRL—See BNP Paribas SA; *Int'l*, pg. 1092
MIDAMERICA NATIONAL BANK—See MidAmerica National Bancshares, Inc.; *U.S. Private*, pg. 2710

THE MIDDLEFIELD BANKING COMPANY—See Middlefield Banc Corp.; *U.S. Public*, pg. 1445
MIDDLETOWN VALLEY BANK—See Community Heritage Financial, Inc.; *U.S. Public*, pg. 558
MIDLAND FEDERAL SAVINGS AND LOAN ASSOCIATION—See Midland Capital Holdings Corp.; *U.S. Private*, pg. 2714
MIDLAND STATES BANK—See Midland States Bancorp, Inc.; *U.S. Public*, pg. 1445
MID PENN BANK—See Mid Penn Bancorp, Inc.; *U.S. Public*, pg. 1444
MIDWEST BANKCENTRE—See Stupp Bros., Inc.; *U.S. Private*, pg. 3844
MIDWEST BANK NATIONAL ASSOCIATION; *U.S. Private*, pg. 2720
MIDWEST BANK—See Western Illinois Bancshares, Inc.; *U.S. Private*, pg. 4493
MIDWEST COMMUNITY BANK; *U.S. Private*, pg. 2720
MIDWESTONE BANK—See MidWestOne Financial Group, Inc.; *U.S. Public*, pg. 1446
MIFFLINBURG BANK & TRUST CO.—See Mifflinburg Bancorp, Inc.; *U.S. Private*, pg. 2724
MILLBURY NATIONAL BANK; *U.S. Private*, pg. 2731
MILLINGTON BANK—See Kearny Financial Corp.; *U.S. Public*, pg. 1217
MILUO CDB VILLAGE BANK CO., LTD.—See China Development Bank Corporation; *Int'l*, pg. 1497
MINNESOTA BANK & TRUST—See Heartland Financial USA, Inc.; *U.S. Public*, pg. 1018
MINNESOTA LAKES BANK—See Wilcox Bancshares, Inc.; *U.S. Private*, pg. 4518
MINNWEST BANK—See Minnwest Corporation; *U.S. Private*, pg. 2744
MINSTER BANK; *U.S. Private*, pg. 2744
MISSION BANK—See Mission Bancorp; *U.S. Public*, pg. 1450
MISSISSIPPI RIVER BANK—See Merchants & Marine Bancorp, Inc.; *U.S. Public*, pg. 1415
MODERN BANK; *U.S. Private*, pg. 2759
MOLDINDCONBANK S.A.—See Doverie United Holding AD; *Int'l*, pg. 2182
MONONA STATE BANK—See Monona Bankshares, Inc.; *U.S. Private*, pg. 2772
MONROE RECRUITMENT CONSULTING GROUP CO LIMITED—See Empresaria Group Plc; *Int'l*, pg. 2389
MONTECITO BANCORP; *U.S. Private*, pg. 2775
MONTECITO BANK & TRUST—See Montecito Bancorp; *U.S. Private*, pg. 2775
MONTEREY COUNTY BANK—See PCB Financial, Inc; *U.S. Private*, pg. 3119
MONTGOMERY BANCORPORATION INC.; *U.S. Private*, pg. 2776
MONTGOMERY BANK—See Montgomery Bancorporation Inc.; *U.S. Private*, pg. 2776
MOODY NATIONAL BANK—See Moody Bancshares, Inc.; *U.S. Private*, pg. 2778
MOOROOLBARK & DISTRICT FINANCIAL SERVICES LIMITED—See Bendigo & Adelaide Bank Ltd.; *Int'l*, pg. 971
MORGAN STANLEY BANK ASIA LIMITED—See Morgan Stanley; *U.S. Public*, pg. 1472
MORGAN STANLEY (SWITZERLAND) AG—See Morgan Stanley; *U.S. Public*, pg. 1472
MORGAN STANLEY TAIWAN LIMITED—See Morgan Stanley; *U.S. Public*, pg. 1475
MORGAN STANLEY TRADING BETEILIGUNGSGMBH—See Morgan Stanley; *U.S. Public*, pg. 1475
THE MORRILL & JANES BANK & TRUST COMPANY—See Heartland Financial USA, Inc.; *U.S. Public*, pg. 1018
MORRIS BANK—See Morris State Bancshares, Inc.; *U.S. Public*, pg. 1477
MORRIS COUPLING COMPANY; *U.S. Private*, pg. 2787
MORTON COMMUNITY BANK—See Hometown Community Bancorp, Inc.; *U.S. Private*, pg. 1975
MOSCOW INDUSTRIAL BANK PC JSCB—See Central Bank of the Russian Federation; *Int'l*, pg. 1405
MOUNTAIN COMMERCE BANK—See Mountain Commerce Bancorp, Inc.; *U.S. Public*, pg. 1479
MOUNTAINONE BANK—See Mountain One Financial Partners; *U.S. Private*, pg. 2799
MOUNTAIN VALLEY COMMUNITY BANK—See Piedmont Bancorp, Inc.; *U.S. Private*, pg. 3177
MOUNTAIN WEST BANK—See Glacier Bancorp, Inc.; *U.S. Public*, pg. 939
MUFG UNION BANK, N.A.—See U.S. Bancorp; *U.S. Public*, pg. 2212
MULTICARE - SEGUROS DE SAUDE, S.A.—See Fosun International Limited; *Int'l*, pg. 2752
MUNICIPAL BANK LTD.—See Dexia SA; *Int'l*, pg. 2092
MUTUAL FEDERAL, A DIVISION OF FIRST BANK RICHMOND—See First Mutual of Richmond, Inc.; *U.S. Private*, pg. 1521
MUTUAL FEDERAL BANK; *U.S. Public*, pg. 1487
MUTUALONE BANK; *U.S. Private*, pg. 2820
MVB BANK, INC.—See MVB Financial Corp.; *U.S. Public*, pg. 1487
MY MONEY BANK S.A.—See Cerberus Capital Management, L.P.; *U.S. Private*, pg. 839

522110 — COMMERCIAL BANKING

NACION SERVICIOS S.A.—See Banco de la Nacion Argentina; *Int'l*, pg. 820
NADIA S.P.A.—See BPER BANCA S.p.A; *Int'l*, pg. 1132
THE NAINITAL BANK LTD.—See Bank of Baroda; *Int'l*, pg. 840
NANYANG COMMERCIAL BANK LIMITED—See China Cinda Asset Management Co., Ltd.; *Int'l*, pg. 1488
NATIONAL BANK OF ARIZONA—See Zions Bancorporation, National Association; *U.S. Public*, pg. 2408
THE NATIONAL BANK OF BLACKSBURG—See National Bankshares, Inc.; *U.S. Public*, pg. 1493
NATIONAL BANK OF COMMERCE LIMITED—See Absa Group Limited; *Int'l*, pg. 69
NATIONAL BANK OF COMMERCE—See NATCOM Bancshares, Inc.; *U.S. Private*, pg. 2838
NATIONAL BANK OF COXSACKIE; *U.S. Public*, pg. 1493
NATIONAL BANK OF DUBAI PJSC—See Emirates NBD PJSC; *Int'l*, pg. 2382
THE NATIONAL BANK OF INDIANAPOLIS—See The National Bank of Indianapolis Corporation; *U.S. Private*, pg. 4082
NATIONAL BANK OF MIDDLEBURY—See Middlebury National Corp.; *U.S. Public*, pg. 1445
NATIONAL BANK OF NEW YORK CITY—See NEWTEKONE, INC.; *U.S. Public*, pg. 1521
THE NATIONAL BANK OF NEW ZEALAND LTD.—See Australia & New Zealand Banking Group Limited; *Int'l*, pg. 720
NATIONAL BANK OF SALLISAW—See First Bank Corp.; *U.S. Private*, pg. 1514
NATIONAL BANK OF SUDAN—See Bank Audi sal; *Int'l*, pg. 837
NATIONAL BANK TRUST CO. OF SYCAMORE; *U.S. Private*, pg. 2848
NATIONAL CAPITAL BANK OF WASHINGTON; *U.S. Private*, pg. 2849
NATIONAL COMMERCIAL BANK LTD.—See British American Investment Co. (Mtius) Ltd.; *Int'l*, pg. 1165
NATIONAL EXCHANGE BANK & TRUST—See NEB Corporation; *U.S. Public*, pg. 2878
THE NATIONAL GRAND BANK OF MARBLEHEAD—See Grand Bank Corporation; *U.S. Public*, pg. 956
NATIONAL IRISH BANK LIMITED—See Danske Bank A/S; *Int'l*, pg. 1969
NATIXIS ALGERIE SP.A.—See Groupe BPCE; *Int'l*, pg. 3096
NATIXIS - BOGOTA—See Groupe BPCE; *Int'l*, pg. 3094
NATIXIS - BUENOS AIRES—See Groupe BPCE; *Int'l*, pg. 3094
NATIXIS - HANOI—See Groupe BPCE; *Int'l*, pg. 3094
NATIXIS - HO CHI MINH—See Groupe BPCE; *Int'l*, pg. 3094
NATIXIS - HONG KONG—See Groupe BPCE; *Int'l*, pg. 3094
NATIXIS - KUALA LUMPUR—See Groupe BPCE; *Int'l*, pg. 3094
NATIXIS - LABUAN—See Groupe BPCE; *Int'l*, pg. 3094
NATIXIS - LONDON—See Groupe BPCE; *Int'l*, pg. 3094
NATIXIS - SINGAPORE—See Groupe BPCE; *Int'l*, pg. 3094
NATIXIS WEALTH MANAGEMENT SA—See Groupe BPCE; *Int'l*, pg. 3098
NB BANCORP, INC.; *U.S. Public*, pg. 1500
NBC OKLAHOMA—See NBC Corp. of Oklahoma; *U.S. Private*, pg. 2874
NBH BANK—See National Bank Holdings Corporation; *U.S. Public*, pg. 1493
NBT BANK, N.A.—See NBT Bancorp Inc.; *U.S. Public*, pg. 1500
NBT BANK, N.A.—See NBT Bancorp Inc.; *U.S. Public*, pg. 1500
NBT BANK, N.A.—See NBT Bancorp Inc.; *U.S. Public*, pg. 1500
NBT BANK, N.A.—See NBT Bancorp Inc.; *U.S. Public*, pg. 1500
NCINO OPCO, INC.—See nCino, Inc.; *U.S. Public*, pg. 1501
NCR ATLEOS CORPORATION; *U.S. Public*, pg. 1501
NEEDHAM COOPERATIVE BANK INC.; *U.S. Private*, pg. 2880
THE NEFFS NATIONAL BANK—See Neffs Bancorp, Inc.; *U.S. Public*, pg. 1504
NEIGHBORHOOD NATIONAL BANK—See Peoples Bankshares, Inc.; *U.S. Private*, pg. 3141
NETWORK INTERNATIONAL LLC—See Emirates NBD PJSC; *Int'l*, pg. 2382
NEVADA STATE BANK—See Zions Bancorporation, National Association; *U.S. Public*, pg. 2408
NEW ENGLAND COMMERCIAL PROPERTIES LLC—See NORTHEAST COMMUNITY BANCORP, INC.; *U.S. Public*, pg. 1537
NEWFIELD NATIONAL BANK—See Newfield Bancorp Inc.; *U.S. Private*, pg. 2914
NEW HORIZON BANK, N.A.—See CSBH LLC; *U.S. Private*, pg. 1116
NEW MEXICO BANK & TRUST—See Heartland Financial USA, Inc.; *U.S. Public*, pg. 1018
NEW MILLENNIUM BANK; *U.S. Public*, pg. 1512
NEW OMNI BANK, N.A.; *U.S. Private*, pg. 2904
NEW PEOPLES BANK—See New Peoples Bankshares, Inc.; *U.S. Public*, pg. 1512
NEWPORT FEDERAL BANK—See United Tennessee Bankshares, Inc.; *U.S. Public*, pg. 2237

NEW PRESTITEMPO S.P.A.—See Deutsche Bank Aktiengesellschaft; *Int'l*, pg. 2061
NEW RESOURCE BANK; *U.S. Public*, pg. 1512
NEWREZ LLC—See Rithm Capital Corp.; *U.S. Public*, pg. 1800
NEW TRIPOLI BANK—See New Tripoli Bancorp, Inc.; *U.S. Public*, pg. 1512
NEW WASHINGTON STATE BANK INC.; *U.S. Private*, pg. 2907
NEW YORK COMMERCIAL BANK—See New York Community Bancorp, Inc.; *U.S. Public*, pg. 1513
NIBC BANK N.V. - BRUSSELS OFFICE—See Blackstone Inc.; *U.S. Public*, pg. 356
NIBC BANK N.V. - LONDON OFFICE—See Blackstone Inc.; *U.S. Public*, pg. 356
NIBC BANK N.V.—See Blackstone Inc.; *U.S. Public*, pg. 356
NICOLET ADVISORY SERVICES, LLC—See Nicolet Bankshares, Inc.; *U.S. Public*, pg. 1528
NIIB GROUP LIMITED—See Bank of Ireland Group plc; *Int'l*, pg. 844
NIXON STATE BANK; *U.S. Private*, pg. 2930
NJM BANK FSB—See New Jersey Manufacturers Insurance Company; *U.S. Private*, pg. 2898
NODAWAY VALLEY BANK; *U.S. Private*, pg. 2933
NOOR ISLAMIC BANK PJSC—See Dubai Islamic Bank PSJ; *Int'l*, pg. 2220
NORDNET AB—See E. Ohman J:or AB; *Int'l*, pg. 2250
NORLEASE, INC.—See Northern Trust Corporation; *U.S. Public*, pg. 1539
NORTHBROOK BANK & TRUST COMPANY, N.A.—See Wintrust Financial Corporation; *U.S. Public*, pg. 2375
NORTH CASCADES BANK—See Glacier Bancorp, Inc.; *U.S. Public*, pg. 939
NORTH DALLAS BANK & TRUST CO.; *U.S. Public*, pg. 1536
NORTHEAST GEORGIA BANK—See First Security Bankshares Inc.; *U.S. Public*, pg. 1527
NORTHEAST SECURITY BANK—See Independence Bancshares, Inc.; *U.S. Private*, pg. 2055
NORTHERN BANK LIMITED—See Danske Bank A/S; *Int'l*, pg. 1969
NORTHERN BANK & TRUST COMPANY; *U.S. Private*, pg. 2952
NORTHERN CALIFORNIA NATIONAL BANK; *U.S. Public*, pg. 1537
NORTHERN OPERATING SERVICES PRIVATE LIMITED—See Northern Trust Corporation; *U.S. Public*, pg. 1539
NORTHERN TRUST CAYMAN INTERNATIONAL, LTD.—See Northern Trust Corporation; *U.S. Public*, pg. 1538
NORTHERN TRUST COMPANY OF CALIFORNIA—See Northern Trust Corporation; *U.S. Public*, pg. 1539
NORTHERN TRUST FUND MANAGERS (IRELAND) LIMITED—See Northern Trust Corporation; *U.S. Public*, pg. 1539
NORTHERN TRUST INTERNATIONAL FUND ADMINISTRATION SERVICES (GUERNSEY) LIMITED—See Northern Trust Corporation; *U.S. Public*, pg. 1538
NORTHFIELD SAVINGS BANK INC.; *U.S. Private*, pg. 2955
NORTHMARK BANK—See Cambridge Bancorp; *U.S. Public*, pg. 426
NORTHRIM BANK—See Northrim BanCorp, Inc.; *U.S. Public*, pg. 1539
NORTH RYDE COMMUNITY FINANCE LIMITED—See Bendigo & Adelaide Bank Ltd.; *Int'l*, pg. 971
NORTH SHORE BANK OF COMMERCE—See North Shore Financial Corporation; *U.S. Private*, pg. 2946
NORTH SHORE COMMUNITY BANK & TRUST—See Wintrust Financial Corporation; *U.S. Public*, pg. 2376
NORTH SIDE BANK & TRUST CO.; *U.S. Private*, pg. 2947
THE NORTHUMBERLAND NATIONAL BANK—See Northumberland Bancorp; *U.S. Public*, pg. 1541
NORTHVIEW BANK—See Finlayson Bancshares, Inc.; *U.S. Private*, pg. 1510
NORTHWAY BANK—See Northway Financial, Inc.; *U.S. Public*, pg. 1541
NORTHWEST BANCORPORATION OF ILLINOIS, INC.; *U.S. Private*, pg. 2959
NORTHWEST BANK OF ROCKFORD—See Foresight Financial Group Inc.; *U.S. Public*, pg. 867
NORTHWEST BANK—See Northwest Bancshares, Inc.; *U.S. Public*, pg. 1542
NORTHWEST BANK—See Northwest Financial Corp.; *U.S. Private*, pg. 2960
NORTHWEST BANK—See Western Capital Corporation; *U.S. Private*, pg. 4491
NORTHWEST COMMERCIAL CREDIT CORP.—See Northwest Financial Corp.; *U.S. Private*, pg. 2960
NORTHWESTERN BANK; *U.S. Private*, pg. 2962
NORTHWEST GEORGIA BANK—See NW Services Corporation; *U.S. Private*, pg. 2975
NORWOOD CO-OPERATIVE BANK; *U.S. Private*, pg. 2964
NOVA FINANCIAL HOLDINGS, INC.; *U.S. Private*, pg. 2965
NUEVO BANCO SUQUIA S.A.—See Banco Macro S.A.; *Int'l*, pg. 823
OAKSTAR BANK—See Oakstar Bancshares, Inc.; *U.S. Private*, pg. 2985

OAK VALLEY COMMUNITY BANK—See Oak Valley Bancorp; *U.S. Public*, pg. 1560
OAK VIEW NATIONAL BANK; *U.S. Private*, pg. 2984
OBERBANK AG—See Bank fur Tirol und Vorarlberg Ag; *Int'l*, pg. 838
OBERBANK GESCHAFTSBEREICH TSCHECHIEN SPOL S.R.O.—See Bank fur Tirol und Vorarlberg Ag; *Int'l*, pg. 838
OBERBANK LEASING SPOL S.R.O.—See Bank fur Tirol und Vorarlberg Ag; *Int'l*, pg. 838
OBERBANK LEASING S.R.O.—See Bank fur Tirol und Vorarlberg Ag; *Int'l*, pg. 838
OCEAN BANK—See Ocean Bankshares, Inc.; *U.S. Private*, pg. 2988
OCONEE STATE BANK; *U.S. Private*, pg. 2992
OFB GKH GESELLSCHAFT FUR KOMMUNALBAU IN HESSEN MBH—See Helaba Landesbank Hessen-Thuringen; *Int'l*, pg. 3328
OHANA PACIFIC BANK; *U.S. Public*, pg. 1564
THE OHIO VALLEY BANK COMPANY—See Ohio Valley Banc Corp.; *U.S. Public*, pg. 1565
OHIO VALLEY FINANCIAL GROUP, INC.—See Ohio Valley Bancorp, Inc.; *U.S. Private*, pg. 3005
OHRIDSKA BANKA A.D.—See Erste Group Bank AG; *Int'l*, pg. 2499
OJSC ROSGOSSTRAKH BANK—See Central Bank of the Russian Federation; *Int'l*, pg. 1405
OKLAHOMA FIDELITY BANK—See Fidelity Financial Corporation; *U.S. Private*, pg. 1503
OLD MISSION BANK—See 4Front Credit Union; *U.S. Private*, pg. 15
OLD MISSOURI BANK—See Jamesmark Bancshares, Inc.; *U.S. Private*, pg. 2185
THE OLD POINT NATIONAL BANK OF PHOEBUS—See Old Point Financial Corporation; *U.S. Public*, pg. 1567
OLD SECOND BANCORP, INC.; *U.S. Public*, pg. 1569
OLD SECOND NATIONAL BANK—See Old Second Bancorp, Inc.; *U.S. Public*, pg. 1569
OMAHA STATE BANK INC.; *U.S. Private*, pg. 3014
OMAN ARAB BANK S.A.O.C.—See Arab Bank plc; *Int'l*, pg. 529
ONE AMERICAN CORP.; *U.S. Private*, pg. 3020
ONE BRYANT PARK LLC—See Bank of America Corporation; *U.S. Public*, pg. 272
ONE UNITED BANK; *U.S. Private*, pg. 3024
ONEUNITED BANK—See One United Bank; *U.S. Private*, pg. 3024
ONEY BANK SA—See Groupe BPCE; *Int'l*, pg. 3099
ONEY MAGYARORSZAG ZRT.—See Auchan Holding S.A.; *Int'l*, pg. 699
OOO HSBC BANK (RR)—See HSBC Holdings plc; *Int'l*, pg. 3506
OOO MERRILL LYNCH SECURITIES—See Bank of America Corporation; *U.S. Public*, pg. 272
OPEN BANK, S.A.—See Banco Santander, S.A.; *Int'l*, pg. 826
OPPORTUNITY BANK OF MONTANA—See Eagle Bancorp Montana, Inc.; *U.S. Public*, pg. 701
OPTIMUMBANK—See OptimumBank Holdings Inc.; *U.S. Public*, pg. 1609
OPTUM BANK, INC.—See UnitedHealth Group Incorporated; *U.S. Public*, pg. 2248
ORANGE BANK & TRUST COMPANY—See Orange County Bancorp, Inc.; *U.S. Public*, pg. 1614
ORBISONIA COMMUNITY BANCORP INC.; *U.S. Private*, pg. 3038
OREGON TRAIL BANK—See Banner County Ban Corporation; *U.S. Private*, pg. 469
ORIENTAL BANK—See OFG Bancorp; *U.S. Public*, pg. 1564
ORIENTAL BANK - US VIRGIN ISLANDS—See OFG Bancorp; *U.S. Public*, pg. 1564
ORIGIN BANK—See Origin Bancorp, Inc.; *U.S. Public*, pg. 1617
ORRSTOWN BANK—See Orrstown Financial Services, Inc.; *U.S. Public*, pg. 1618
OSAGE FEDERAL BANK—See American Heritage Bank; *U.S. Private*, pg. 236
OTP BANK ROMANIA S.A.—See Banca Transilvania S.A.; *Int'l*, pg. 816
OWEN COUNTY STATE BANK—See Owen Financial Corporation; *U.S. Private*, pg. 3054
OXFORD BANK AND TRUST; *U.S. Private*, pg. 3056
OXFORD BANK—See Oxford Bank Corporation; *U.S. Public*, pg. 1628
OZARK MOUNTAIN BANK—See Central Bancompany, Inc.; *U.S. Public*, pg. 473
PACIFIC ALLIANCE BANK; *U.S. Public*, pg. 1631
PACIFIC CITY BANK—See PCB Bancorp; *U.S. Public*, pg. 1658
PACIFIC ENTERPRISE BANK—See Pacific Enterprise Bancorp; *U.S. Public*, pg. 1631
PACIFIC MERCANTILE BANK—See Banc of California, Inc.; *U.S. Public*, pg. 269
PACIFIC VALLEY BANK; *U.S. Public*, pg. 1632
PACIFIC WEST BANK; *U.S. Public*, pg. 1632
PACIFIC WESTERN BANK—See Banc of California, Inc.; *U.S. Public*, pg. 269
PADUCAH BANK & TRUST CO., INC.—See Paducah Bank

N.A.I.C.S. INDEX
522110 — COMMERCIAL BANKING

Shares, Inc.; *U.S. Private*, pg. 3074
PALMETTO STATE BANK—See Palmetto State Bankshares, Inc.; *U.S. Private*, pg. 3082
PALO ALTO PARTNERS, LLC—See Wells Fargo & Company; *U.S. Public*, pg. 2345
PANARMENIAN BANK OJSC—See Central Bank of Armenia; *Int'l*, pg. 1404
PANCYPRIAN INSURANCE COMPANY LTD—See Hellenic Bank Public Company Ltd.; *Int'l*, pg. 3333
PARAMOUNT THEATER SCP L.P.—See Wells Fargo & Company; *U.S. Public*, pg. 2345
PAREX BANK SWEIGNIEDERLASSUNG BERLIN—See AS Reverta; *Int'l*, pg. 591
PARK BANK—See Old National Bancorp; *U.S. Public*, pg. 1567
PARKE BANK—See Parke Bancorp, Inc.; *U.S. Public*, pg. 1640
PARKLAND SENIOR HOUSING, LP—See Wells Fargo & Company; *U.S. Public*, pg. 2345
PARK STATE BANK, INC.—See Park Financial Group, Inc.; *U.S. Private*, pg. 3096
PARKWAY BANK & TRUST COMPANY—See Parkway Bancorp, Inc.; *U.S. Private*, pg. 3098
PARTHOLON CDO 1 PLC—See Bank of Ireland Group plc; *Int'l*, pg. 845
PARTNERS BANK OF CALIFORNIA; *U.S. Public*, pg. 1651
PARTNERS BANK OF WISCONSIN—See Stratford Bancshares, Inc.; *U.S. Private*, pg. 3837
PARTNERS UNITED FINANCIAL, LLC—See Rithm Capital Corp.; *U.S. Public*, pg. 1800
PATAGON BANK, S.A.—See Banco Santander, S.A.; *Int'l*, pg. 826
PATHFINDER BANK—See Pathfinder Bancorp, Inc.; *U.S. Public*, pg. 1651
PATHWARD, N.A.—See Pathward Financial, Inc.; *U.S. Public*, pg. 1652
PATRIOT BANK MORTGAGE, INC.—See Veritex Holdings, Inc.; *U.S. Public*, pg. 2283
PATRIOT BANK—See Security BanCorp of Tennessee, Inc.; *U.S. Private*, pg. 3595
PAVILLION BANK—See AmTex Bancshares Inc.; *U.S. Private*, pg. 268
PBI BANK—See Peoples Bancorp Inc.; *U.S. Public*, pg. 1667
PBT BANCSHARES, INC.; *U.S. Private*, pg. 3119
PCB FINANCLAL, INC; *U.S. Private*, pg. 3119
PCSB BANK—See Brookline Bancorp, Inc.; *U.S. Public*, pg. 396
PEAPACK-GLADSTONE BANK—See Peapack-Gladstone Financial Corporation; *U.S. Public*, pg. 1659
PEDESTAL BANK—See Business First Bancshares, Inc.; *U.S. Public*, pg. 413
PEGASUS BANK—See BancFirst Corporation; *U.S. Public*, pg. 269
PEKAO BANK HIPOTECZNY S.A.—See Bank Polska Kasa Opieki Spolka Akcyjna; *Int'l*, pg. 849
PELLEGRINI S.A.—See Banco de la Nacion Argentina; *Int'l*, pg. 820
PENN BANCSHARES, INC.; *U.S. Public*, pg. 1661
PENN COMMUNITY BANK—See Penn Community Financial Corporation; *U.S. Private*, pg. 3134
PEOPLES BANCORP OF NORTH CAROLINA, INC.; *U.S. Public*, pg. 1667
PEOPLES BANCORP WASH; *U.S. Public*, pg. 1667
PEOPLESBANK, A CODORUS VALLEY COMPANY—See Orrstown Financial Services, Inc.; *U.S. Public*, pg. 1619
PEOPLES BANK AND TRUST; *U.S. Private*, pg. 3141
THE PEOPLES BANK CO. INC; *U.S. Private*, pg. 4093
PEOPLES BANK OF ALABAMA—See Altrust Financial Services, Inc.; *U.S. Public*, pg. 89
PEOPLES BANK OF COMMERCE; *U.S. Private*, pg. 3141
PEOPLES BANK OF NORTH ALABAMA; *U.S. Private*, pg. 3141
THE PEOPLE'S BANK; *U.S. Private*, pg. 4093
PEOPLES BANK—See Peoples Bancorp of North Carolina, Inc.; *U.S. Public*, pg. 1667
PEOPLES BANK—See Peoples Bancorp; *U.S. Private*, pg. 3141
THE PEOPLES BANK—See Peoples Financial Corporation; *U.S. Public*, pg. 1667
PEOPLES BANK—See Texas Peoples National Bancshares, Inc.; *U.S. Private*, pg. 3976
PEOPLES BANK & TRUST COMPANY OF MADISON COUNTY—See Whitaker Bank Corporation of Kentucky; *U.S. Private*, pg. 4507
PEOPLES BANK & TRUST CO.—See Lincoln County Bancorp., Inc.; *U.S. Private*, pg. 2457
PEOPLES BANK & TRUST—See People First Bancshares, Inc.; *U.S. Privato*, pg. 3140
PEOPLE'S COMMUNITY BANK; *U.S. Private*, pg. 3140
PEOPLES EXCHANGE BANK OF MONROE COUNTY—See Peoples Exchange Bancshares, Inc.; *U.S. Private*, pg. 3142
PEOPLES EXCHANGE BANK—See American State Bancshares, Inc.; *U.S. Private*, pg. 255
PEOPLES INDEPENDENT BANK—See Peoples Independent Bancshares, Inc.; *U.S. Private*, pg. 3142
THE PEOPLES NATIONAL BANK OF MOUNT PLEASANT—See Consumers Bancorp, Inc.; *U.S. Public*, pg. 573
PEOPLES SECURITY BANK AND TRUST COMPANY—See Peoples Financial Services Corp.; *U.S. Public*, pg. 1667
PEOPLESSOUTH BANK—See PeoplesSouth Bancshares, Inc.; *U.S. Private*, pg. 3142
PEOPLES STATE BANK OF PLAINVIEW—See WRZ Bankshares, Inc.; *U.S. Public*, pg. 4574
THE PEOPLES STATE BANK; *U.S. Private*, pg. 4093
PEOPLES STATE BANK—See AmTex Bancshares Inc.; *U.S. Private*, pg. 268
PEOPLES TRUST COMPANY OF ST. ALBANS; *U.S. Public*, pg. 1667
PEOPLE'S UNITED BANK, N.A.—See M&T Bank Corporation; *U.S. Public*, pg. 1351
PEREGRIN TECHNOLOGIES INC; *U.S. Public*, pg. 3147
PERSIA INTERNATIONAL BANK PLC LONDON—See Bank Mellat; *Int'l*, pg. 839
PHOENIX LEASING BANK SERVICES—See Phoenix American Incorporated; *U.S. Public*, pg. 3172
PI COUNTY CDB VILLAGE BANK CO., LTD.—See China Development Bank Corporation; *Int'l*, pg. 1497
THE PIEDMONT BANK—See Piedmont Bancorp, Inc.; *U.S. Private*, pg. 3177
PIGEON FALLS STATE BANK; *U.S. Private*, pg. 3179
PILOT BANK—See Lake Michigan Credit Union; *U.S. Private*, pg. 2375
PILOT GROVE SAVINGS BANK; *U.S. Private*, pg. 3181
PINGLIANG JINGCHUAN HUITONG VILLAGE BANK CO., LTD.—See China Development Bank Corporation; *Int'l*, pg. 1497
PINNACLE BANK OF OREGON; *U.S. Public*, pg. 1691
PINNACLE BANK SIOUX CITY—See Pinnacle Bancorp, Inc.; *U.S. Private*, pg. 3184
PINNACLE BANK; *U.S. Public*, pg. 1691
PINNACLE BANK—See Iowa River Bancorp, Inc.; *U.S. Private*, pg. 2135
PINNACLE BANK—See Pinnacle Bancorp, Inc.; *U.S. Private*, pg. 3184
PINNACLE BANK—See Pinnacle Bancorp, Inc.; *U.S. Private*, pg. 3184
PINNACLE BANK—See Pinnacle Bancshares, Inc.; *U.S. Public*, pg. 1691
PINNACLE BANK—See Pinnacle Financial Corporation; *U.S. Private*, pg. 3185
PINNACLE BANK—See Pinnacle Financial Partners, Inc.; *U.S. Public*, pg. 1692
PINNACLE BANK - WYOMING—See Pinnacle Bancorp, Inc.; *U.S. Private*, pg. 3184
PIONEER BANK—See Pioneer Bankshares, Inc.; *U.S. Public*, pg. 1692
PIONEER COMMERCIAL BANK—See Pioneer Savings Bank; *U.S. Private*, pg. 3188
PIONEER STATE BANK—See NBE Bancshares, Inc.; *U.S. Private*, pg. 2875
PIONEER TRUST BANK NA INC—See Planet Trust Bank Corporation; *U.S. Private*, pg. 3196
PIRAEUS BANK BULGARIA AD—See Eurobank Ergasias Services and Holdings S.A.; *Int'l*, pg. 2532
PITTSFIELD CO-OPERATIVE BANK; *U.S. Private*, pg. 3192
PJSC CREDIT EUROPE BANK—See Fiba Holding A.S.; *Int'l*, pg. 2651
PJSC UKRSOTSBANK—See Alfa Group; *Int'l*, pg. 308
PLAINSCAPITAL BANK—See Hilltop Holdings Inc.; *U.S. Public*, pg. 1039
PLANET TRUST BANK CORPORATION; *U.S. Private*, pg. 3196
PLANTERS BANK, INC.—See Planters Financial Group, Inc.; *U.S. Private*, pg. 3197
PLANTERS BANK & TRUST COMPANY—See Planters Holding Company Inc.; *U.S. Private*, pg. 3197
PLATINUM BANK; *U.S. Public*, pg. 3200
PLATTE VALLEY BANK NEBRASKA—See Platte Valley Financial Service Companies Inc.; *U.S. Private*, pg. 3211
PLATTE VALLEY BANK—See Platte Valley Financial Service Companies Inc.; *U.S. Private*, pg. 3211
PLATTE VALLEY BANK WYOMING—See Platte Valley Financial Service Companies Inc.; *U.S. Private*, pg. 3211
THE PLEASANT HILL BANK—See Goppert Financial Corp.; *U.S. Private*, pg. 1741
PNC BANK, CENTRAL PENNSYLVANIA—See The PNC Financial Services Group, Inc.; *U.S. Public*, pg. 2119
PNC BANK, GREATER MARYLAND—See The PNC Financial Services Group, Inc.; *U.S. Public*, pg. 2119
PNC BANK, GREATER WASHINGTON, D.C. AREA—See The PNC Financial Services Group, Inc.; *U.S. Public*, pg. 2119
PNC BANK, KENTUCKY & INDIANA—See The PNC Financial Services Group, Inc.; *U.S. Public*, pg. 2119
PNC BANK, NORTHEAST PENNSYLVANIA—See The PNC Financial Services Group, Inc.; *U.S. Public*, pg. 2119
PNC BANK, NORTHWEST PENNSYLVANIA—See The PNC Financial Services Group, Inc.; *U.S. Public*, pg. 2119
PNC BANK, OHIO & NORTHERN KENTUCKY—See The PNC Financial Services Group, Inc.; *U.S. Public*, pg. 2119
PNC BANK, PHILADELPHIA & SOUTHERN NEW JERSEY—See The PNC Financial Services Group, Inc.; *U.S. Public*, pg. 2119
PNC BANK—See The PNC Financial Services Group, Inc.; *U.S. Public*, pg. 2119
PNC LEASING LLC—See The PNC Financial Services Group, Inc.; *U.S. Public*, pg. 2120
PNC LIFE INSURANCE COMPANY—See The PNC Financial Services Group, Inc.; *U.S. Public*, pg. 2120
POCAHONTAS STATE BANK—See Dentel Bancorporation; *U.S. Private*, pg. 1206
THE POCA VALLEY BANKSHARES; *U.S. Private*, pg. 4097
POINT BANCORP INC.; *U.S. Private*, pg. 3221
PONY EXPRESS COMMUNITY BANK—See Pony Express Bancorp, Inc.; *U.S. Public*, pg. 3227
POPULAR BANK—See Popular, Inc.; *U.S. Public*, pg. 1702
POTOMAC BANCSHARES INC.; *U.S. Public*, pg. 1705
PRAIRIE STATE BANK AND TRUST; *U.S. Private*, pg. 3243
PREFERRED BANK; *U.S. Public*, pg. 1714
PREMIER BANK, INC.—See Premier Financial Bancorp, Inc.; *U.S. Public*, pg. 1715
PREMIER BANK; *U.S. Private*, pg. 3249
PREMIER VALLEY BANK—See Heartland Financial USA, Inc.; *U.S. Public*, pg. 1018
PRIMARY BANK; *U.S. Public*, pg. 1716
PRIME MERIDIAN BANK—See Prime Meridian Holding Company; *U.S. Public*, pg. 1717
PRIMESOUTH BANCSHARES, INC.—See CB&S Bank, Inc.; *U.S. Private*, pg. 796
PRIMESOUTH BANK—See PrimeSouth Bancshares, Inc.; *U.S. Private*, pg. 3263
PRIMIS BANK—See Primis Financial Corp.; *U.S. Public*, pg. 1717
PRINCETON BANCORP, INC.; *U.S. Public*, pg. 1719
PRINEVILLE BANCORPORATION; *U.S. Public*, pg. 1722
PRIORITYONE BANK—See PriorityOne Capital Corporation; *U.S. Private*, pg. 3267
PRIORITY PROPERTY HOLDINGS, LLC—See First Busey Corporation; *U.S. Public*, pg. 840
PROFESSIONAL BANK—See Professional Holding Corp.; *U.S. Public*, pg. 1724
PROGRESS BANK & TRUST—See Oportun, Inc.; *U.S. Private*, pg. 3032
PROMONTORY INTERFINANCIAL NETWORK, LLC—See The Bank of New York Mellon Corporation; *U.S. Public*, pg. 2038
PROSPECT BANK; *U.S. Private*, pg. 3287
PROSPERITY BANK—See Prosperity Bancshares, Inc.; *U.S. Public*, pg. 1728
PROVIDENCE BANK—See PB Financial Corporation; *U.S. Public*, pg. 1657
PROVIDENCE BANK—See PB Financial Corporation; *U.S. Public*, pg. 1657
PROVIDENCE BANK—See PB Financial Corporation; *U.S. Public*, pg. 1657
PROVIDENCE BANK—See PB Financial Corporation; *U.S. Public*, pg. 1657
PROVIDENCE BANK & TRUST—See Providence Financial Corporation; *U.S. Private*, pg. 3294
THE PROVIDENT BANK—See BankProv; *U.S. Public*, pg. 274
THE PROVIDENT BANK—See Provident Financial Services, Inc.; *U.S. Public*, pg. 1730
PROVIDENT FINANCIAL CORP—See Provident Financial Holdings, Inc.; *U.S. Public*, pg. 1730
PROVINCIA BURSATIL S.A.—See Banco de la Provincia de Buenos Aires; *Int'l*, pg. 821
PROVINCIA MICROEMPRESAS S.A.—See Banco de la Provincia de Buenos Aires; *Int'l*, pg. 821
PROVINCIA SEGUROS S.A.—See Banco de la Provincia de Buenos Aires; *Int'l*, pg. 821
PRUDENTIAL BANK & TRUST, FSB—See Prudential Financial, Inc.; *U.S. Public*, pg. 1732
PRYSM GENERAL INSURANCE INC.—See iA Financial Corporation Inc.; *Int'l*, pg. 3567
PSA BANK DEUTSCHLAND GMBH—See Banco Santander, S.A.; *Int'l*, pg. 826
PSA BANQUE FRANCE SA—See Banco Santander, S.A.; *Int'l*, pg. 826
PT BANK BNP PARIBAS INDONESIA—See BNP Paribas SA; *Int'l*, pg. 1081
PT BANK CIMB NIAGA TBK—See CIMB Group Holdings Berhad; *Int'l*, pg. 1608
PT BANK DBS INDONESIA—See DBS Group Holdings Ltd.; *Int'l*, pg. 1989
PT BANK KEB HANA INDONESIA—See Hana Financial Group, Inc.; *Int'l*, pg. 3241
PT. BANK KEB HANA—See Hana Financial Group, Inc.; *Int'l*, pg. 3241
PT BANK OF INDIA INDONESIA, TBK.—See Bank of India; *Int'l*, pg. 843
PT. BANK RABOBANK INTERNATIONAL INDONESIA—See Cooperatieve Centrale Raiffeisen-Boerenleenbank B.A.; *Int'l*, pg. 1791
PT BANK SWADESI TBK—See Bank of India; *Int'l*, pg. 843
PT CIMB SECURITIES INDONESIA—See CIMB Group Holdings Berhad; *Int'l*, pg. 1608

522110 — COMMERCIAL BANKING

PT ICAP INDONESIA—See CME Group, Inc.; *U.S. Public*, pg. 517
PT PRINCIPAL ASSET MANAGEMENT—See CIMB Group Holdings Berhad; *Int'l*, pg. 1608
PT PRINCIPAL ASSET MANAGEMENT—See Principal Financial Group, Inc.; *U.S. Public*, pg. 1720
PT SAHABAT FINANSIAL KELUARGA—See Bangkok Bank Public Company Limited; *Int'l*, pg. 833
PUBLIC COMPANY ERSTE BANK—See Erste Group Bank AG; *Int'l*, pg. 2499
PUBLIC JOINT-STOCK COMPANY BANK OTKRITIE FINANCIAL CORPORATION—See Central Bank of the Russian Federation; *Int'l*, pg. 1405
PUBLIC JOINT STOCK COMPANY DEUTSCHE BANK DBU—See Deutsche Bank Aktiengesellschaft; *Int'l*, pg. 2061
PUEBLO BANK & TRUST CO. INC.—See Pueblo Bancorporation; *U.S. Private*, pg. 3301
PUTNAM BANK—See Centreville Bank; *U.S. Private*, pg. 829
PUTNAM COUNTY BANK INC.; *U.S. Private*, pg. 3307
PUTNAM COUNTY NATIONAL BANK; *U.S. Public*, pg. 1739
PYRAMAX BANK—See 1895 Bancorp of Wisconsin, Inc.; *U.S. Public*, pg. 2
QNB BANK—See QNB Corp.; *U.S. Public*, pg. 1743
QNB—See QNB Corp.; *U.S. Public*, pg. 1743
QUAD CITY BANK & TRUST COMPANY—See QCR Holdings, Inc.; *U.S. Public*, pg. 1742
QUAIL CREEK BANCSHARES INC.; *U.S. Private*, pg. 3316
QUAINT OAK BANK—See QUAINT OAK BANCORP, INC.; *U.S. Public*, pg. 1745
QUALIFIED INVESTORS FUND III, LLC—See SVB Financial Group; *U.S. Public*, pg. 1968
QUEENSTOWN BANK OF MARYLAND; *U.S. Private*, pg. 3325
RABOBANK AUSTRALIA LIMITED—See Cooperatieve Centrale Raiffeisen-Boerenleenbank B.A.; *Int'l*, pg. 1792
RABOBANK CHILE S.A.—See Cooperatieve Centrale Raiffeisen-Boerenleenbank B.A.; *Int'l*, pg. 1792
RABOBANK IRELAND PLC—See Cooperatieve Centrale Raiffeisen-Boerenleenbank B.A.; *Int'l*, pg. 1792
RABOBANK NEW ZEALAND LIMITED—See Cooperatieve Centrale Raiffeisen-Boerenleenbank B.A.; *Int'l*, pg. 1792
RABO INDIA FINANCE PVT LTD—See Cooperatieve Centrale Raiffeisen-Boerenleenbank B.A.; *Int'l*, pg. 1791
RAMSEY NATIONAL BANK—See Ramsey Financial Corporation; *U.S. Private*, pg. 3352
RAND MERCHANT BANK—See FirstRand Limited; *Int'l*, pg. 2690
RAYNE STATE BANK & TRUST COMPANY—See Financial Corporation of Louisiana; *U.S. Private*, pg. 1506
R BANK—See R Corp Financial; *U.S. Private*, pg. 3331
RCB BANK—See RCB Holding Company, Inc.; *U.S. Private*, pg. 3361
REDDING BANK OF COMMERCE—See Bank of Commerce Holdings; *U.S. Public*, pg. 272
RED RIVER BANK—See Red River Bancshares, Inc.; *U.S. Public*, pg. 1769
REDUS CHARLOTTE HOUSING, LLC—See Wells Fargo & Company; *U.S. Public*, pg. 2345
REDWOOD CAPITAL BANK; *U.S. Public*, pg. 1771
REGAL BANK; *U.S. Private*, pg. 3385
REGENT BANK NA—See Regent Capital Corporation; *U.S. Private*, pg. 3387
REGIONAL MISSOURI BANK—See RMB Bancshares, Inc.; *U.S. Private*, pg. 3451
REGIONS BANK—See Regions Financial Corporation; *U.S. Public*, pg. 1776
RELIANCE BANK—See Simmons First National Corporation; *U.S. Public*, pg. 1881
RELIANCE SAVINGS BANK—See Reliance Bancorp, Inc.; *U.S. Private*, pg. 3394
RELIANCE STATE BANK—See Ames National Corporation; *U.S. Public*, pg. 115
RELIANT BANK—See United Community Banks, Inc.; *U.S. Public*, pg. 2230
RELYANCE BANK, N.A.; *U.S. Private*, pg. 3395
RENASANT BANK—See Renasant Corporation; *U.S. Public*, pg. 1783
REPUBLIC BANK OF ARIZONA—See RBAZ BANCORP, INC.; *U.S. Public*, pg. 1765
REPUBLIC BANK OF CHICAGO—See Republic Bancorp Co.; *U.S. Private*, pg. 3401
REPUBLIC BANK & TRUST COMPANY—See Republic Bancorp, Inc.; *U.S. Public*, pg. 1785
REPUBLIC FINANCIAL CORPORATION; *U.S. Private*, pg. 3402
REPUBLIC FIRST BANK—See Republic First Bancorp, Inc.; *U.S. Public*, pg. 1785
RESOURCE BANK NATIONAL ASSOCIATION—See Resource Bank; *U.S. Private*, pg. 3406
REUSCHEL & CO. KOMMANDITGESELLSCHAFT—See Commerzbank AG; *Int'l*, pg. 1718
RHINEBECK BANK; *U.S. Private*, pg. 3421
RICHLAND BANK—See Park National Corporation; *U.S. Public*, pg. 1638
THE RICHWOOD BANKING COMPANY—See Richwood Bancshares, Inc.; *U.S. Private*, pg. 3431
RIVER BANK HOLDING CO.; *U.S. Private*, pg. 3443
RIVER BANK—See River Bank Holding Co.; *U.S. Private*, pg. 3443
RIVER CITY BANK INC.; *U.S. Public*, pg. 1800
RIVER VALLEY COMMUNITY BANK; *U.S. Public*, pg. 1801
RIVERVIEW BANK—See Mid Penn Bancorp, Inc.; *U.S. Public*, pg. 1444
RIVERVIEW COMMUNITY BANK—See Riverview Bancorp, Inc.; *U.S. Public*, pg. 1801
RIVERWOOD BANK—See Great River Holding Company; *U.S. Private*, pg. 1767
ROBERTSON BANKING COMPANY—See RBC, Inc.; *U.S. Private*, pg. 3360
ROCKLAND TRUST COMPANY—See Independent Bank Corp.; *U.S. Public*, pg. 1116
ROCKWOOD BANCSHARES, INC.; *U.S. Private*, pg. 3467
ROCKWOOD BANK—See Rockwood Bancshares, Inc.; *U.S. Private*, pg. 3467
ROLLING HILLS BANK & TRUST; *U.S. Private*, pg. 3475
THE ROSCOE STATE BANK—See Cornerstone Mortgage Co.; *U.S. Private*, pg. 1052
ROSE HILL BANK—See American State Bancshares, Inc.; *U.S. Private*, pg. 255
ROUNDBANK; *U.S. Private*, pg. 3488
ROYAL BANKS OF MISSOURI—See Royal Bancshares, Inc.; *U.S. Private*, pg. 3491
ROYAL BANK—See Royal Bancshares, Inc.; *U.S. Private*, pg. 3491
ROYAL BUSINESS BANK—See RBB Bancorp; *U.S. Public*, pg. 1766
RSNB BANK—See RSNB Bancorp; *U.S. Private*, pg. 3497
RURAL BANK LIMITED—See Bendigo & Adelaide Bank Ltd.; *Int'l*, pg. 971
RURAL BANK OF ANGELES, INC.—See Asia United Bank Corporation; *Int'l*, pg. 616
RYE & DISTRICT COMMUNITY FINANCIAL SERVICES LIMITED—See Bendigo & Adelaide Bank Ltd.; *Int'l*, pg. 971
SABADELLCAM—See Banco de Sabadell, S.A.; *Int'l*, pg. 821
SABAL PALM BANK; *U.S. Private*, pg. 3520
SABINE BANK OPERATION CENTER INC.—See Sabine Bancshares Inc.; *U.S. Private*, pg. 3521
SABINE STATE BANK & TRUST COMPANY—See Sabine Bancshares Inc.; *U.S. Private*, pg. 3521
SAFRA NATIONAL BANK OF NEW YORK; *U.S. Private*, pg. 3525
SAFWA ISLAMIC BANK—See Dubai Islamic Bank PSJ; *Int'l*, pg. 2220
SAGICOR BANK JAMAICA LIMITED—See Alignvest Management Corporation; *Int'l*, pg. 327
SALAFIN SA—See Bank of Africa; *Int'l*, pg. 840
SALUSANSVAR AB—See Folksam omsesidig sakforsakring; *Int'l*, pg. 2721
SANABLE ALKHAIR FOR FINANCIAL INVESTMENT—See Al Baraka Banking Group B.S.C.; *Int'l*, pg. 276
SANDRINGHAM COMMUNITY FINANCIAL SERVICES LIMITED—See Bendigo & Adelaide Bank Ltd.; *Int'l*, pg. 971
SANDY SPRING BANK—See Sandy Spring Bancorp, Inc.; *U.S. Public*, pg. 1840
SANIBEL CAPTIVA COMMUNITY BANK; *U.S. Private*, pg. 3546
SAN REMO DISTRICT FINANCIAL SERVICES LTD—See Bendigo & Adelaide Bank Ltd.; *Int'l*, pg. 971
SANTA ANA BUSINESS BANK; *U.S. Private*, pg. 3546
SANTA CRUZ COUNTY BANK—See West Coast Community Bancorp; *U.S. Public*, pg. 2352
SANTANDER BENELUX SA/NV—See Banco Santander, S.A.; *Int'l*, pg. 826
SANTANDER CONSUMER BANK AS—See Banco Santander, S.A.; *Int'l*, pg. 826
SANTANDER CONSUMER BANK S.A.—See Banco Santander, S.A.; *Int'l*, pg. 826
SANTANDER CONSUMER BANQUE S.A.—See Banco Santander, S.A.; *Int'l*, pg. 827
SANTANDER CONSUMER FINANCE, S.A.—See Banco Santander, S.A.; *Int'l*, pg. 827
SANTANDER INVESTMENT SECURITIES INC.—See Banco Santander, S.A.; *Int'l*, pg. 827
SANTANDER UK PLC - ISLE OF MAN BRANCH—See Banco Santander, S.A.; *Int'l*, pg. 827
SARATOGA NATIONAL BANK & TRUST COMPANY—See Arrow Financial Corporation; *U.S. Public*, pg. 200
SARINA & DISTRICT COMMUNITY FINANCIAL SERVICES LIMITED—See Bendigo & Adelaide Bank Ltd.; *Int'l*, pg. 971
SAUDI CREALOGIX SINGLE-PARTNER LLC—See Constellation Software Inc.; *Int'l*, pg. 1772
SAVERS COOPERATIVE BANK; *U.S. Private*, pg. 3556
SAVINGS BANK MENDOCINO COUNTY; *U.S. Private*, pg. 3557
THE SAVINGS BANK; *U.S. Private*, pg. 4114
SBANKEN ASA—See DNB Bank ASA; *Int'l*, pg. 2148
SCHRETLEN & CO N.V.—See Cooperatieve Centrale Raiffeisen-Boerenleenbank B.A.; *Int'l*, pg. 1792
SEACOAST COMMERCE BANK; *U.S. Private*, pg. 3583

SEACOAST NATIONAL BANK—See Seacoast Banking Corporation of Florida; *U.S. Public*, pg. 1851
SEASIDE NATIONAL BANK & TRUST—See United Community Banks, Inc.; *U.S. Public*, pg. 2230
SECURITY BANK OF KANSAS CITY—See Valley View Bancshares, Inc.; *U.S. Private*, pg. 4336
SECURITY BANK; *U.S. Public*, pg. 3595
SECURITY BANK—See Security BanCorp of Tennessee, Inc.; *U.S. Private*, pg. 3595
SECURITY BANK & TRUST COMPANY; *U.S. Private*, pg. 3595
SECURITY FINANCIAL BANK—See Security Financial Services Corporation; *U.S. Private*, pg. 3595
SECURITY FIRST BANK—See First State Bancshares, Inc.; *U.S. Private*, pg. 1528
SECURITY FIRST BANK—See Stockmens Financial Corporation; *U.S. Private*, pg. 3815
SECURITY FIRST NATIONAL BANK OF HUGO—See Sooner Southwest Bankshares, Inc.; *U.S. Private*, pg. 3715
SECURITY NATIONAL BANK; *U.S. Private*, pg. 3596
SECURITY NATIONAL BANK—See Park National Corporation; *U.S. Public*, pg. 1638
SECURITY NATIONAL CORPORATION; *U.S. Private*, pg. 3596
SECURITY STATE BANK—See Mackey Banco, Inc.; *U.S. Private*, pg. 2537
SECURITY STATE BANK—See Old O'Brien Banc Shares, Inc.; *U.S. Private*, pg. 3009
SECURITY STATE BANK—See Security State Corporation; *U.S. Private*, pg. 3596
SECURITY STATE BANK & TRUST; *U.S. Private*, pg. 3596
SELAN HOLDING GMBH—See Baader Bank AG; *Int'l*, pg. 791
SELECT BANK & TRUST COMPANY—See First Bancorp; *U.S. Public*, pg. 839
SENECA SAVINGS—See Seneca Financial Corp.; *U.S. Public*, pg. 1864
SENTENIAL S.A.R.L.—See EML Payments Limited; *Int'l*, pg. 2384
SERVIBANCA S.A.—See Banco GNB Sudameris S.A.; *Int'l*, pg. 823
SERVISFIRST BANK—See ServisFirst Bancshares, Inc.; *U.S. Public*, pg. 1872
SEVERN BANCORP, INC.—See Shore Bancshares, Inc.; *U.S. Public*, pg. 1875
SEVIER COUNTY BANK—See Sevier County Bancshares, Inc.; *U.S. Public*, pg. 1873
SGG SUISSE S.A.—See Astorg Partners S.A.S.; *Int'l*, pg. 657
SHAMIL BANK OF BAHRAIN B.S.C.—See Dar Al-Maal Al-Islami Trust; *Int'l*, pg. 1971
SHAMROCK BANK OF FLORIDA; *U.S. Private*, pg. 3624
SHELBY COUNTY STATE BANK; *U.S. Public*, pg. 3630
SHINHAN BNP PARIBAS ASSET MANAGEMENT CO., LTD.—See BNP Paribas SA; *Int'l*, pg. 1082
THE SHINWA BANK, LTD.—See Fukuoka Financial Group, Inc.; *Int'l*, pg. 2840
THE SHONAI BANK, LTD.—See FIDEA Holdings Co. Ltd.; *Int'l*, pg. 2654
SHORE UNITED BANK—See Shore Bancshares, Inc.; *U.S. Public*, pg. 1875
SHRIJANA FINANCE (FINANCIAL INSTITUTION) LTD.—See Citizens Bank International Limited; *Int'l*, pg. 1626
SICHUAN DAZHU CQRC VILLAGE & TOWNSHIP BANK CO., LTD.—See Chongqing Rural Commercial Bank Co. Ltd.; *Int'l*, pg. 1581
SIGNATURE BANK OF ARKANSAS; *U.S. Private*, pg. 3649
SIGNATURE BANK OF GEORGIA; *U.S. Public*, pg. 1878
SILICON VALLEY BANK—See Federal Deposit Insurance Corporation; *U.S. Private*, pg. 1487
SIMMONS BANK—See Simmons First National Corporation; *U.S. Public*, pg. 1881
SISTEMA DE AHORRO PARA EL RETIRO—See Banco Bilbao Vizcaya Argentaria, S.A.; *Int'l*, pg. 818
SISTEMI PARABANCARI S.R.L.—See BPER BANCA S.p.A; *Int'l*, pg. 1132
SKOWHEGAN SAVINGS BANK; *U.S. Private*, pg. 3683
SKYLINE NATIONAL BANK—See SKYLINE BANKSHARES, INC.; *U.S. Public*, pg. 1892
SLOVENSKA SPORITELNA, A.S.—See Erste Group Bank AG; *Int'l*, pg. 2499
SMARTBANK—See SmartFinancial, Inc.; *U.S. Public*, pg. 1895
SMARTYPIG, L.L.C.—See Q2 Holdings, Inc.; *U.S. Public*, pg. 1741
SOCIETE DE BANQUE FRANCAISE ET INTERNATIONALE—See Groupe BPCE; *Int'l*, pg. 3097
SOCIETE DE POLE DE COMPETITIVITE DE MONASTIR - EL FEJJA—See Banque Internationale Arabe de Tunisie; *Int'l*, pg. 854
SOLERA NATIONAL BANK—See Solera National Bancorp, Inc.; *U.S. Public*, pg. 1900
SOMERSET TRUST CO.; *U.S. Private*, pg. 3712
SOMERVILLE BANK—See Somerville Bancorp; *U.S. Private*, pg. 3712
THE SOMERVILLE BANK & TRUST COMPANY—See

N.A.I.C.S. INDEX 522110 — COMMERCIAL BANKING

Trustmark Corporation; *U.S. Public*, pg. 2202
SONABANK—See Primis Financial Corp.; *U.S. Public*, pg. 1717
SOUND BANK—See Capital Bancorp, Inc.; *U.S. Public*, pg. 431
SOUND COMMUNITY BANK—See Sound Financial Bancorp, Inc.; *U.S. Public*, pg. 1910
THE SOUTH AFRICAN BANK OF ATHENS LTD—See AFGRI Limited; *Int'l*, pg. 189
SOUTH ATLANTIC BANK—See South Atlantic Bancshares, Inc.; *U.S. Public*, pg. 1911
SOUTH BANKING COMPANY; *U.S. Private*, pg. 3719
SOUTH BURNETT COMMUNITY ENTERPRISES LIMITED—See Bendigo & Adelaide Bank Ltd.; *Int'l*, pg. 971
SOUTH CENTRAL BANK, N.A.—See Verve, a Credit Union; *U.S. Private*, pg. 4371
SOUTHEASTERN BANK INC.—See Southeastern Banking Corp.; *U.S. Public*, pg. 1911
SOUTHEASTERN BANKING CORP.; *U.S. Public*, pg. 1911
SOUTHERN BANCORP BANK—See Southern Bancorp, Inc.; *U.S. Private*, pg. 3729
THE SOUTHERN BANK COMPANY—See The Southern Banc Company, Inc.; *U.S. Public*, pg. 2130
SOUTHERN BANK—See Southern Missouri Bancorp, Inc.; *U.S. Public*, pg. 1912
SOUTHERN BANK & TRUST CO.—See Southern BancShares (N.C.), Inc.; *U.S. Public*, pg. 1911
SOUTHERN FIRST BANK—See Southern First Bancshares, Inc.; *U.S. Public*, pg. 1911
SOUTHERN HERITAGE BANK; *U.S. Private*, pg. 3732
SOUTHERN MICHIGAN BANK & TRUST—See Southern Michigan Bancorp Inc.; *U.S. Public*, pg. 1911
SOUTHERN STATES BANK—See Southern States Bancshares, Inc.; *U.S. Public*, pg. 1912
SOUTHLAND ASSOCIATES, INC.—See Truist Financial Corporation; *U.S. Public*, pg. 2199
SOUTH OTTUMWA SAVINGS BANK; *U.S. Private*, pg. 3723
SOUTHSIDE BANK IS A STATE BANK—See Southside Bancshares, Inc.; *U.S. Public*, pg. 1912
SOUTHSIDE BANK—See Southside Bancshares, Inc.; *U.S. Public*, pg. 1912
SOUTHWEST MISSOURI BANK; *U.S. Private*, pg. 3740
SOUTHWEST NATIONAL BANK—See Republic Financial Corporation; *U.S. Private*, pg. 3402
SOUTHWEST REINSURE, INC.—See iA Financial Corporation Inc.; *Int'l*, pg. 3568
SPARKASSE MUHLVIERTEL WEST BANK AKTIENGESELLSCHAFT—See Erste Group Bank AG; *Int'l*, pg. 2499
SPEED INTERNATIONAL, INC—See Bank of the Philippine Islands; *Int'l*, pg. 849
SPRINGFIELD FIRST COMMUNITY BANK—See QCR Holdings, Inc.; *U.S. Public*, pg. 1742
SPRINGS VALLEY BANK & TRUST CO.—See SVB&T Corporation; *U.S. Private*, pg. 3888
SSB BANK—See SSB Bancorp, Inc.; *U.S. Public*, pg. 1924
STAALBANKIERS N.V.—See Achmea B.V.; *Int'l*, pg. 103
STANDARD BANK JSC—See Abu Dhabi Group; *Int'l*, pg. 71
STANDARD LIFE BANK LIMITED—See Barclays PLC; *Int'l*, pg. 860
STANDING STONE BANK; *U.S. Public*, pg. 1931
STAR BANK—See Midwest Bancorporation, Inc.; *U.S. Private*, pg. 2720
STAR FINANCIAL BANK—See STAR Financial Group Inc.; *U.S. Public*, pg. 1937
THE STATE BANK AND TRUST COMPANY—See SB Financial Group, Inc.; *U.S. Public*, pg. 1842
STATE BANK FINANCIAL—See First Bancorporation Inc.; *U.S. Private*, pg. 1513
STATE BANK OF ARCADIA, INC.—See Treynor Bancshares, Inc.; *U.S. Private*, pg. 4219
STATE BANK OF CHILTON—See Calumet Bancorporation, Inc.; *U.S. Private*, pg. 724
STATE BANK OF COUNTRYSIDE INC.; *U.S. Private*, pg. 3791
STATE BANK OF CROSS PLAINS—See S.B.C.P. Bancorp, Inc.; *U.S. Public*, pg. 1832
STATE BANK OF LINCOLN CORP.; *U.S. Private*, pg. 3791
STATE BANK OF LISMORE—See First Western Bank & Trust; *U.S. Private*, pg. 1530
STATE BANK OF LIZTON—See Lizton Financial Corporation; *U.S. Private*, pg. 2474
STATE BANK OF SOUTHERN UTAH; *U.S. Private*, pg. 3791
STATE BANK OF TEXAS—See SBT Bancshares, Inc.; *U.S. Private*, pg. 3560
STATE BANK OF THE LAKES, N.A.—See Wintrust Financial Corporation; *U.S. Public*, pg. 2375
THE STATE BANK—See Fentura Financial, Inc.; *U.S. Public*, pg. 829
STATE BANK—See Wonder Bancorp, Inc.; *U.S. Private*, pg. 4556
STATE BANK & TRUST COMPANY; *U.S. Private*, pg. 3791
STATE BANK & TRUST CO.—See Ames National Corporation; *U.S. Public*, pg. 116
STATE CENTRAL BANK; *U.S. Private*, pg. 3791

STATE FARM BANK, F.S.B.—See State Farm Mutual Automobile Insurance Company; *U.S. Private*, pg. 3792
STATE GUARANTY BANK—See First Keyes Bancshares, Inc.; *U.S. Private*, pg. 1520
STATE STREET BANK GMBH - BRUSSELS BRANCH—See State Street Corporation; *U.S. Public*, pg. 1940
STATE STREET BANK GMBH—See State Street Corporation; *U.S. Public*, pg. 1940
S&T BANK—See S&T Bancorp, Inc.; *U.S. Public*, pg. 1832
ST. CHARLES BANK & TRUST COMPANY—See Wintrust Financial Corporation; *U.S. Public*, pg. 2375
STEIERMARKISCHE BANK UND SPARKASSEN AG—See Erste Group Bank AG; *Int'l*, pg. 2499
STEPHENSON NATIONAL BANK & TRUST; *U.S. Private*, pg. 3803
STERLING BANCORP, INC.; *U.S. Public*, pg. 1946
STERLING BANK—See Sterling Bancshares, Inc.; *U.S. Private*, pg. 3804
STERLING NATIONAL BANK—See Sterling Bancorp; *U.S. Public*, pg. 1946
THE ST. HENRY BANK; *U.S. Private*, pg. 4120
STIFEL BANK—See Stifel Financial Corp.; *U.S. Public*, pg. 1950
STIFEL BANK & TRUST—See Stifel Financial Corp.; *U.S. Public*, pg. 1950
STIFEL EUROPE BANK AG—See Stifel Financial Corp.; *U.S. Public*, pg. 1950
STILLMAN BANCCORP N.A.; *U.S. Private*, pg. 3812
STILLMAN BANK—See Stillman BancCorp N.A.; *U.S. Private*, pg. 3812
ST. LANDRY HOMESTEAD FEDERAL SAVINGS BANK; *U.S. Private*, pg. 3772
STOCKMAN BANK OF MONTANA—See Stockman Financial Corp.; *U.S. Private*, pg. 3815
STOCKMAN FINANCIAL CORP.; *U.S. Private*, pg. 3815
STOCKMAN INSURANCE INC.—See Stockman Financial Corp.; *U.S. Private*, pg. 3815
STOCKMANS BANK; *U.S. Private*, pg. 3815
STOCK YARDS BANK & TRUST COMPANY—See Stock Yards Bancorp, Inc.; *U.S. Public*, pg. 1951
STRATEGIC INVESTORS FUND V-B, L.P.—See SVB Financial Group; *U.S. Public*, pg. 1968
STRATEGIC INVESTORS FUND VII, L.P.—See SVB Financial Group; *U.S. Public*, pg. 1968
STUPA HEIZWERK FRANKFURT (ODER) NORD BETEILIGUNGSGESELLSCHAFT MBH—See Deutsche Bank Aktiengesellschaft; *Int'l*, pg. 2062
STURGIS BANK & TRUST COMPANY—See Sturgis Bancorp, Inc.; *U.S. Public*, pg. 1958
SULLIVAN BANK—See Mid-Missouri Holding Company, Inc.; *U.S. Private*, pg. 2708
SUMMIT BANK; *U.S. Private*, pg. 3853
SUMMIT COMMUNITY BANK, INC.—See Summit Financial Group, Inc.; *U.S. Public*, pg. 1959
SUMMIT NATIONAL BANK—See Hulett Bancorp; *U.S. Private*, pg. 2005
SUMMIT STATE BANK—See Summit State Bank; *U.S. Public*, pg. 1961
SUMNER BANK & TRUST—See Edmonton Bancshares Inc.; *U.S. Private*, pg. 1337
SUNRISE BANK—See Sunrise Bancshares, Inc.; *U.S. Private*, pg. 3869
SUNSHINE COAST COMMUNITY FINANCIAL SERVICES LIMITED—See Bendigo & Adelaide Bank Ltd.; *Int'l*, pg. 971
SUNSOUTH BANK—See SunSouth Bancshares, Inc.; *U.S. Private*, pg. 3872
SUNTRUST BANK—See Truist Financial Corporation; *U.S. Public*, pg. 2200
SUNTRUST DELAWARE TRUST COMPANY—See Truist Financial Corporation; *U.S. Public*, pg. 2200
SUNWEST BANK—See Sunwest Bancorp, Inc.; *U.S. Private*, pg. 3874
SUPERIOR NATIONAL BANK & TRUST COMPANY; *U.S. Private*, pg. 3879
SVB WEALTH ADVISORY, INC.—See SVB Financial Group; *U.S. Public*, pg. 1968
S WOHNBAUBANK AG—See Erste Group Bank AG; *Int'l*, pg. 2499
SYNDBANK SERVICES LIMITED—See Canara Bank; *Int'l*, pg. 1287
SYNDICATE BANK LTD.—See Canara Bank; *Int'l*, pg. 1287
SYNERGY BANK—See Synergy Bancshares Inc.; *U.S. Private*, pg. 3904
SYNOVUS BANK—See Synovus Financial Corp.; *U.S. Public*, pg. 1971
SYNOVUS BANK—See Synovus Financial Corp.; *U.S. Public*, pg. 1971
SYNOVUS BANK—See Synovus Financial Corp.; *U.S. Public*, pg. 1971
SYNOVUS BANK—See Synovus Financial Corp.; *U.S. Public*, pg. 1971
TAGUS - SOCIEDADE DE TITULARIZACAO DE CREDITOS, S.A.—See Deutsche Bank Aktiengesellschaft; *Int'l*, pg. 2062
TAIPEI FUBON COMMERCIAL BANK CO., LTD.—See Fubon Financial Holding Co. Ltd.; *Int'l*, pg. 2802

TALLAHASSEE STATE BANK—See Synovus Financial Corp.; *U.S. Public*, pg. 1971
TALLAHASSEE STATE BANK—See Synovus Financial Corp.; *U.S. Public*, pg. 1972
TANFEETH LLC—See Emirates NBD PJSC; *Int'l*, pg. 2382
TARGOBANK AG & CO. KGAA—See Confederation Nationale du Credit Mutuel; *Int'l*, pg. 1767
TASMANIAN BANKING SERVICES LIMITED—See Bendigo & Adelaide Bank Ltd.; *Int'l*, pg. 971
TATINVESTBANK ZAO—See Chimimport AD; *Int'l*, pg. 1479
T BANK, N.A.—See Tectonic Financial, Inc.; *U.S. Public*, pg. 1989
TEAMBANK AG—See DZ BANK AG Deutsche Zentral-Genossenschaftsbank; *Int'l*, pg. 2245
TEMPO BANK—See Scott Credit Union; *U.S. Private*, pg. 3576
TENNESSEE STATE BANK; *U.S. Private*, pg. 3968
TERRABANK NA; *U.S. Private*, pg. 3970
TEXAS BANK HOLDING COMPANY—See Doss, Ltd.; *U.S. Private*, pg. 1264
TEXAS BANK—See Doss, Ltd.; *U.S. Private*, pg. 1264
TEXAS BANK & TRUST COMPANY—See Overton Financial Corporation; *U.S. Private*, pg. 3054
TEXAS CAPITAL BANK, N.A.—See Texas Capital Bancshares, Inc.; *U.S. Public*, pg. 2025
TEXAS FIRST NATIONAL BANK; *U.S. Private*, pg. 3975
TEXAS HERITAGE BANK—See Southwestern Bancorp, Inc.; *U.S. Private*, pg. 3741
TEXAS HERITAGE NATIONAL BANK—See Daingerfield Holding Company; *U.S. Private*, pg. 1145
TEXAS PARTNERS BANK—See Southwest Bancshares, Inc.; *U.S. Private*, pg. 3738
TEXAS REGIONAL BANK—See Texas State Bankshares, Inc.; *U.S. Private*, pg. 3977
TEXAS REPUBLIC BANK, N.A.—See TXRB Holdings, Inc.; *U.S. Private*, pg. 4267
TEXAS STAR BANK; *U.S. Private*, pg. 3977
THAI SMART CARD CO., LTD.—See C.P. All Public Company Limited; *Int'l*, pg. 1244
THIRD CENTURY BANCORP; *U.S. Public*, pg. 2155
THIRD COAST BANK, SSB—See Third Coast Bancshares, Inc.; *U.S. Public*, pg. 2155
THE THIRD NATIONAL BANK OF SEDALIA—See Central Bancompany, Inc.; *U.S. Public*, pg. 473
TIMBERLAND SERVICE CORPORATION—See Timberland Bancorp, Inc.; *U.S. Public*, pg. 2159
TINAU MISSION DEVELOPMENT BANK LIMITED—See Citizens Bank International Limited; *Int'l*, pg. 1626
TIOGA STATE BANK—See TSB Services Inc.; *U.S. Private*, pg. 4252
T-MELMAX SDN. BHD.—See Censof Holdings Berhad; *Int'l*, pg. 1402
TODAY'S BANK—See Mathias Bancshares, Inc.; *U.S. Private*, pg. 2611
THE TOKYO STAR BANK, LIMITED—See CTBC Financial Holding Co., Ltd.; *Int'l*, pg. 1869
TOKYO STAR BUSINESS FINANCE, LTD.—See CTBC Financial Holding Co., Ltd.; *Int'l*, pg. 1869
TOMPKINS TRUST COMPANY—See Tompkins Financial Corporation; *U.S. Public*, pg. 2162
TOMPKINS VIST BANK—See Tompkins Financial Corporation; *U.S. Public*, pg. 2162
TONGALA & DISTRICT FINANCIAL SERVICES LIMITED—See Bendigo & Adelaide Bank Ltd.; *Int'l*, pg. 971
TONGZHOU CDB VILLAGE BANK CO., LTD.—See China Development Bank Corporation; *Int'l*, pg. 1497
TORREY PINES BANK—See Western Alliance Bancorporation; *U.S. Public*, pg. 2354
TOUCHSTONE BANK; *U.S. Public*, pg. 2165
TOUR EL GHAZAL-BNPI—See BNP Paribas SA; *Int'l*, pg. 1093
TOWN BANK—See Wintrust Financial Corporation; *U.S. Public*, pg. 2375
TOWN CENTER BANK; *U.S. Public*, pg. 2165
TOWN & COUNTRY BANCORP INC.; *U.S. Private*, pg. 4196
TOWN & COUNTRY BANCORP, INC.; *U.S. Private*, pg. 4196
TOWN & COUNTRY BANK SPRINGFIELD—See Town & Country Bancorp Inc.; *U.S. Private*, pg. 4196
TOWN & COUNTRY BANK & TRUST COMPANY; *U.S. Private*, pg. 4196
TOWN-COUNTRY NATIONAL BANK—See United Bancorporation of Alabama, Inc.; *U.S. Public*, pg. 2229
TOWNE BANK; *U.S. Public*, pg. 2165
TRADERS & FARMERS BANK; *U.S. Private*, pg. 4202
TRADITIONAL BANCORPORATION; *U.S. Private*, pg. 4203
TRADITIONAL BANK, INC.—See Traditional Bancorporation; *U.S. Private*, pg. 4203
TRANS PACIFIC NATIONAL BANK—See Trans Pacific Bancorp; *U.S. Private*, pg. 4205
TRANSUNION LIMITED—See American Express Company; *U.S. Public*, pg. 101
TREYNOR STATE BANK—See Treynor Bancshares, Inc.; *U.S. Private*, pg. 4219

522110 — COMMERCIAL BANKING

TRI CITY BANKSHARES CORPORATION; *U.S. Public*, pg. 2188
TRICITY NATIONAL BANK INC—See Tri City Bankshares Corporation; *U.S. Public*, pg. 2188
TRI COUNTIES BANK—See TriCo Bancshares; *U.S. Public*, pg. 2189
TRINITY BANK N.A; *U.S. Public*, pg. 2193
TRI-STATE BANK OF MEMPHIS; *U.S. Private*, pg. 4223
TRISTATE CAPITAL BANK—See Raymond James Financial, Inc.; *U.S. Public*, pg. 1765
TROY BANK & TRUST COMPANY—See Henderson Bancshares, Inc.; *U.S. Private*, pg. 1913
TRUIST BANK—See Truist Financial Corporation; *U.S. Public*, pg. 2200
TRUIST INVESTMENT SERVICES, INC.—See Truist Financial Corporation; *U.S. Public*, pg. 2201
TRUSTCO BANK TRUST DEPT—See TrustCo Bank Corp NY; *U.S. Public*, pg. 2202
TSB BANK PLC—See Banco de Sabadell, S.A.; *Int'l*, pg. 821
TURBOTVILLE NATIONAL BANK; *U.S. Public*, pg. 2205
TURK EKONOMI BANKASI A.S.—See BNP Paribas SA; *Int'l*, pg. 1093
TW GROUP, INC.—See World Insurance Associates LLC; *U.S. Private*, pg. 4566
TWIN BRIDGE CAPITAL CORPORATION—See ConnectOne Bancorp, Inc.; *U.S. Public*, pg. 568
TWIN CITIES FINANCIAL SERVICES; *U.S. Private*, pg. 4264
TWIN LAKES COMMUNITY BANK—See First National Bancorp, Inc.; *U.S. Private*, pg. 1521
TWIN RIVER NATIONAL BANK; *U.S. Public*, pg. 4265
TWO RIVER COMMUNITY BANK—See OceanFirst Financial Corp.; *U.S. Public*, pg. 1563
UBANK LTD.—See FIBI Holdings Ltd.; *Int'l*, pg. 2652
UBANK—See Huntington Bancshares Inc.; *U.S. Private*, pg. 2010
UBANK TRUST COMPANY LTD.—See FIBI Holdings Ltd.; *Int'l*, pg. 2652
UBI BANCA INTERNATIONAL S.A.—See EFG International AG; *Int'l*, pg. 2321
UBL BANK (TANZANIA) LIMITED—See Bestway (Holdings) Limited; *Int'l*, pg. 1001
UKRSIBBANK—See BNP Paribas SA; *Int'l*, pg. 1093
UMB BANC LEASING CORP.—See UMB Financial Corporation; *U.S. Public*, pg. 2224
UMB FINANCIAL SERVICES, INC.—See UMB Financial Corporation; *U.S. Public*, pg. 2224
UMPQUA BANK—See Columbia Banking System, Inc.; *U.S. Public*, pg. 534
UMPQUA BANK—See Columbia Banking System, Inc.; *U.S. Public*, pg. 534
UMPQUA BANK—See Columbia Banking System, Inc.; *U.S. Public*, pg. 534
UMPQUA BANK—See Columbia Banking System, Inc.; *U.S. Public*, pg. 534
UNIAO PARTICIPACOES LTDA—See Banco Bradesco S.A.; *Int'l*, pg. 819
UNIBANK—See U & I Financial Corp.; *U.S. Public*, pg. 2211
UNICO BANK - PARAGOULD, KINGSHIGHWAY—See Washco Bancshares, Inc.; *U.S. Private*, pg. 4445
UNICO BANK—See Washco Bancshares, Inc.; *U.S. Private*, pg. 4445
UNIFIED BANK—See United Bancorp, Inc.; *U.S. Public*, pg. 2229
THE UNION BANK COMPANY—See United Bancshares, Inc.; *U.S. Public*, pg. 2229
UNION BANK—See Union Bankshares, Inc.; *U.S. Public*, pg. 2226
UNION BANK & TRUST COMPANY—See Farmers & Merchants Investment Inc.; *U.S. Private*, pg. 1475
UNION BANK & TRUST COMPANY—See First Union Financial Corp.; *U.S. Private*, pg. 1530
UNION COMMERCIAL BANK PLC—See E. Sun Financial Holding Co., Ltd.; *Int'l*, pg. 2250
UNION COMMERCIAL BANK PUBLIC LIMITED CORPORATION—See E. Sun Financial Holding Co., Ltd.; *Int'l*, pg. 2250
UNION COMMUNITY BANK FSB—See Northwest Bancshares, Inc.; *U.S. Public*, pg. 1541
UNION COMMUNITY BANK FSB—See Northwest Bancshares, Inc.; *U.S. Public*, pg. 1541
UNION NATIONAL BANK PJSC—See Abu Dhabi Commercial Bank PJSC; *Int'l*, pg. 71
UNION STATE BANK; *U.S. Public*, pg. 4285
THE UNION STATE BANK—See Docking Bancshares, Inc.; *U.S. Private*, pg. 1251
UNION STATE BANK—See Greenfield Bancorporation Ltd.; *U.S. Private*, pg. 1777
UNION STATE BANK—See Union State Bancshares, Inc.; *U.S. Private*, pg. 4285
UNIPOL BANCA S.P.A.—See BPER BANCA S.p.A; *Int'l*, pg. 1132
UNIPOL MERCHANT S.P.A.—See BPER BANCA S.p.A; *Int'l*, pg. 1132
UNITED BANK AG—See Bestway (Holdings) Limited; *Int'l*, pg. 1001
UNITED BANK LIMITED—See Bestway (Holdings) Limited; *Int'l*, pg. 1001

UNITED BANK OF IOWA—See Ida Grove Bancshares, Inc.; *U.S. Private*, pg. 2034
UNITED BANK OF MICHIGAN INC—See United Community Financial; *U.S. Private*, pg. 4290
UNITED BANK OF PHILADELPHIA—See United Bancshares, Inc.; *U.S. Private*, pg. 4288
UNITED BANK—See United Bancorporation of Alabama, Inc.; *U.S. Private*, pg. 2229
UNITED BANK—See United Bank Corporation; *U.S. Private*, pg. 4288
UNITED BANK—See United Bankshares, Inc.; *U.S. Public*, pg. 2229
UNITED BANK & TRUST COMPANY; *U.S. Private*, pg. 4288
UNITED BUSINESS BANK—See BayCom Corp; *U.S. Public*, pg. 284
UNITED COMMUNITY BANK OF NORTH DAKOTA—See American Bancor, Ltd.; *U.S. Private*, pg. 223
UNITED COMMUNITY BANK OF WEST KENTUCKY, INC.; *U.S. Private*, pg. 4290
UNITED COMMUNITY BANK—See Community Bancorp of Louisiana, Inc.; *U.S. Private*, pg. 989
UNITED COMMUNITY BANK—See United Community Banks, Inc.; *U.S. Public*, pg. 2230
UNITED COMMUNITY FINANCIAL; *U.S. Private*, pg. 4290
UNITED EUROPEAN BANK & TRUST (NASSAU) LTD.—See BNP Paribas SA; *Int'l*, pg. 1093
UNITED NATIONAL BANK LIMITED—See Bestway (Holdings) Limited; *Int'l*, pg. 1001
UNITED NATIONAL BANK; *U.S. Public*, pg. 2231
UNITED SECURITY BANK—See United Security Bancshares; *U.S. Public*, pg. 2235
UNITED SOUTHERN BANK; *U.S. Private*, pg. 4298
UNITED VALLEY BANK; *U.S. Private*, pg. 4301
UNITY BANK—See Unity Bancorp, Inc.; *U.S. Public*, pg. 2253
UNITY NJ REIT, INC.—See Unity Bancorp, Inc.; *U.S. Public*, pg. 2253
UNIVERSITY BANK—See University Bancorp, Inc.; *U.S. Public*, pg. 2262
THE UNIVERSITY NATIONAL BANK OF LAWRENCE—See Lawrence Financial Corporation; *U.S. Private*, pg. 2401
UNIVEST BANK & TRUST CO.—See Univest Financial Corporation; *U.S. Public*, pg. 2262
UNIZAN CAPITAL, LLC—See Huntington Bancshares Incorporated; *U.S. Public*, pg. 1071
UPS CAPITAL BUSINESS CREDIT—See United Parcel Service, Inc.; *U.S. Public*, pg. 2233
USAA SAVINGS BANK—See United Services Automobile Association; *U.S. Private*, pg. 4297
USA BANK; *U.S. Private*, pg. 4321
U.S. BANK HOME MORTGAGE—See U.S. Bancorp; *U.S. Public*, pg. 2213
U.S. BANK NATIONAL ASSOCIATION ND—See U.S. Bancorp; *U.S. Public*, pg. 2213
U.S. BANK NATIONAL ASSOCIATION—See U.S. Bancorp; *U.S. Public*, pg. 2213
U.S. BANK TRUST NATIONAL ASSOCIATION SD—See U.S. Bancorp; *U.S. Public*, pg. 2213
USB BANK PLC—See BLC Bank SAL; *Int'l*, pg. 1063
USNY BANK; *U.S. Private*, pg. 4323
UWHARRIE BANK—See Uwharrie Capital Corp.; *U.S. Public*, pg. 2268
VALLEY BANK OF HELENA—See Glacier Bancorp, Inc.; *U.S. Public*, pg. 939
VALLEY BANK & TRUST; *U.S. Private*, pg. 4332
VALLEY REPUBLIC BANK; *U.S. Private*, pg. 4335
THE VALLEY STATE BANK—See Morley Bancshares Corporation; *U.S. Private*, pg. 2785
VALUEBANK TEXAS; *U.S. Private*, pg. 4338
VANTAGE BANK TEXAS—See VBT Financial Corporation; *U.S. Private*, pg. 4348
VAUBAN INFRASTRUCTURE PARTNERS SCA—See Groupe BPCE; *Int'l*, pg. 3099
VECTRA BANK COLORADO—See Zions Bancorporation, National Association; *U.S. Public*, pg. 2408
VERABANK, N.A.—See VeraBank, Inc.; *U.S. Private*, pg. 4359
VERITEX COMMUNITY BANK—See Veritex Holdings, Inc.; *U.S. Public*, pg. 2283
VERMILION BANK & TRUST COMPANY—See Vermilion Bancshares Corporation; *U.S. Private*, pg. 4367
VERUS BANK OF COMMERCE; *U.S. Private*, pg. 4370
VESTJYSK BANK A/S—See Arbejdernes Landsbank A/S; *Int'l*, pg. 537
THE VICTORY BANK—See The Victory Bancorp, Inc.; *U.S. Public*, pg. 2137
VICTORY STATE BANK—See Northfield Bancorp, Inc.; *U.S. Public*, pg. 1539
VIKING BANK, N.A.—See Viking Financial Corporation; *U.S. Private*, pg. 4382
VILLAGE BANK—See Village Bancshares, Inc.; *U.S. Private*, pg. 4383
VILLAGE BANK—See Village Bank & Trust Financial Corp.; *U.S. Public*, pg. 2297
VILLAGE BANK & TRUST—See Wintrust Financial Corporation; *U.S. Public*, pg. 2375
VILLAGES URBAN INVESTMENTS, LLC—See Bank of America Corporation; *U.S. Public*, pg. 272

THE VINTON COUNTY NATIONAL BANK—See Community Bancshares, Inc.; *U.S. Public*, pg. 549
VIRGINIA BANK & TRUST CO.—See Virginia Bank Bankshares, Inc.; *U.S. Public*, pg. 4387
VIRGINIA COMMONWEALTH BANK—See Blue Ridge Bankshares, Inc.; *U.S. Public*, pg. 365
VIRGINIA COMMUNITY BANK—See Blue Ridge Bankshares, Inc.; *U.S. Public*, pg. 365
VIRGINIA NATIONAL BANK—See Virginia National Bankshares Corporation; *U.S. Public*, pg. 2299
VISTA BANK; *U.S. Public*, pg. 4393
VOB-ZVD PROCESSING GMBH—See Deutsche Bank Aktiengesellschaft; *Int'l*, pg. 2062
VOLVO AUTO BANK DEUTSCHLAND GMBH—See Ford Motor Company; *U.S. Public*, pg. 867
VON ESSEN GMBH & CO. KG BANKGESELLSCHAFT—See BNP Paribas SA; *Int'l*, pg. 1084
VSB BANCORP, INC.—See Northfield Bancorp, Inc.; *U.S. Public*, pg. 1539
WAKE FOREST FEDERAL SAVINGS AND LOAN ASSOCIATION—See Wake Forest Bancshares, Inc.; *U.S. Public*, pg. 2321
WALLIS STATE BANK INC.; *U.S. Private*, pg. 4431
WASHINGTON BUSINESS BANK; *U.S. Public*, pg. 2329
WASHINGTON MILL LOFTS LLC—See Bank of America Corporation; *U.S. Public*, pg. 272
WASHINGTON TRUST BANK—See W.T.B. Financial Corporation; *U.S. Public*, pg. 2319
THE WASHINGTON TRUST COMPANY, OF WESTERLY—See Washington Trust Bancorp, Inc.; *U.S. Public*, pg. 2329
WATERSTONE BANK, SSB—See Waterstone Financial, Inc.; *U.S. Public*, pg. 2336
WATERTOWN SAVINGS BANK; *U.S. Private*, pg. 4454
WATONGA BANCSHARES, INC.—See Bank7 Corp.; *U.S. Public*, pg. 274
WAUKESHA STATE BANK; *U.S. Private*, pg. 4457
WAYNE BANK—See Norwood Financial Corp.; *U.S. Public*, pg. 1543
WAYNE SAVINGS COMMUNITY BANK—See Main Street Financial Services Corp.; *U.S. Public*, pg. 1355
WCF FINANCIAL BANK—See WCF Bancorp, Inc.; *U.S. Public*, pg. 2338
WEALTHCRAFT CAPITAL, INC.; *U.S. Public*, pg. 2339
WEDBUSH BANK—See Wedbush Capital Partners; *U.S. Private*, pg. 4468
WELLINGTON STATE BANK; *U.S. Private*, pg. 4475
WELLS FARGO AUDIT SERVICES—See Wells Fargo & Company; *U.S. Public*, pg. 2346
WELLS FARGO BANK INTERNATIONAL—See Wells Fargo & Company; *U.S. Public*, pg. 2345
WELLS FARGO BANK NORTHWEST, NATIONAL ASSOCIATION—See Wells Fargo & Company; *U.S. Public*, pg. 2345
WELLS FARGO BANK; *U.S. Private*, pg. 4476
WELLS FARGO FINANCIAL CARDS—See Wells Fargo & Company; *U.S. Public*, pg. 2346
WELLS FARGO FINANCIAL WASHINGTON, INC.—See Wells Fargo & Company; *U.S. Public*, pg. 2346
WELLS FARGO SPECIAL RISKS, INC.—See Wells Fargo & Company; *U.S. Public*, pg. 2347
WESBANCO BANK, INC.—See WesBanco, Inc.; *U.S. Public*, pg. 2349
WESBANCO BANK, INC. - WESTERN PENNSYLVANIA REGIONAL OFFICE—See WesBanco, Inc.; *U.S. Public*, pg. 2350
WESBANCO TITLE AGENCY, LLC—See WesBanco, Inc.; *U.S. Public*, pg. 2350
WEST ALABAMA BANK & TRUST; *U.S. Private*, pg. 4483
WESTAMERICA BANK—See Westamerica Bancorporation; *U.S. Public*, pg. 2354
WEST BANK—See West Bancorporation Inc.; *U.S. Public*, pg. 2352
WESTBURY BANK—See Westbury Bancorp, Inc.; *U.S. Public*, pg. 2354
WESTERN BANK OF CLOVIS—See Western Bancshares of Clovis, Inc.; *U.S. Private*, pg. 4491
WESTERN COMMERCE BANK; *U.S. Private*, pg. 4491
WESTERN HERITAGE BANK—See Nusenda Credit Union; *U.S. Private*, pg. 2973
WESTERN NATIONAL BANK—See Western Bancorporation, Inc.; *U.S. Private*, pg. 4491
WESTERN NATIONAL BANK—See Western Bancorporation, Inc.; *U.S. Private*, pg. 4491
WESTERN SECURITY BANK—See Glacier Bancorp, Inc.; *U.S. Public*, pg. 939
THE WESTERN STATE BANK; *U.S. Private*, pg. 4134
WESTERN STATE BANK—See Western State Agency, Inc.; *U.S. Private*, pg. 4497
WESTERN STATES BANK—See Western States BanCorporation; *U.S. Private*, pg. 4497
WESTFIELD BANK, FSB—See Ohio Farmers Insurance Company; *U.S. Private*, pg. 3004
WEST MILTON STATE BANK; *U.S. Private*, pg. 4486
WEST POINT BANK—See First Breckenridge Bancshares; *U.S. Private*, pg. 1514

N.A.I.C.S. INDEX

WEST SHORE BANK—See West Shore Bank Corporation; *U.S. Public*, pg. 2353

WESTSIDE BANK—See Piedmont Bancorp, Inc.; *U.S. Private*, pg. 3177

WESTSTAR BANK—See Weststar Bank Holding Company, Inc.; *U.S. Private*, pg. 4501

WEST SUBURBAN BANK—See Old Second Bancorp, Inc.; *U.S. Public*, pg. 1569

WEST TOWN BANK & TRUST—See Capital Bancorp, Inc.; *U.S. Public*, pg. 431

WEX BANK—See WEX, Inc.; *U.S. Public*, pg. 2365

WHEATLAND BANK—See Glacier Bancorp, Inc.; *U.S. Public*, pg. 938

WHEATON BANK & TRUST, N.A.—See Wintrust Financial Corporation; *U.S. Public*, pg. 2375

WHIDBEY ISLAND BANK—See Heritage Financial Corporation; *U.S. Public*, pg. 1028

WHITAKER BANK, INC.—See Whitaker Bank Corporation of Kentucky; *U.S. Public*, pg. 4507

WHITE RIVER BANCSHARES COMPANY; *U.S. Public*, pg. 2369

WHITE ROCK BANK—See 215 Holding Co.; *U.S. Private*, pg. 5

WIDE BAY AUSTRALIA—See Auswide Bank Ltd.; *Int'l*, pg. 724

WIENER PRIVATBANK IMMOBILIENMAKLER GMBH—See Arca Capital Slovakia, A.S.; *Int'l*, pg. 540

WILLAMETTE COMMUNITY BANK—See Peoples Bank of Commerce; *U.S. Private*, pg. 3141

WILLAMETTE VALLEY BANK—See Oregon Bancorp, Inc.; *U.S. Public*, pg. 1615

WILSON BANK & TRUST—See Wilson Bank Holding Company; *U.S. Public*, pg. 2372

WILSON & MUIR BANCORP INC; *U.S. Private*, pg. 4530

WILSON & MUIR BANK & TRUST COMPANY—See Wilson & Muir Bancorp Inc; *U.S. Private*, pg. 4530

WILSON & MUIR BANK & TRUST CO—See Wilson & Muir Bancorp Inc; *U.S. Private*, pg. 4530

WING LUNG BANK LIMITED—See China Merchants Group Limited; *Int'l*, pg. 1520

WINTRUST BANK, N.A.—See Wintrust Financial Corporation; *U.S. Public*, pg. 2376

WISCONSIN BANK & TRUST—See Heartland Financial USA, Inc.; *U.S. Public*, pg. 1018

WOLF RIVER COMMUNITY BANK—See Wolf River Bancorp, Inc.; *U.S. Private*, pg. 4553

WOOD AND HUSTON BANCORPORATION; *U.S. Private*, pg. 4556

WOOD AND HUSTON BANK—See Wood and Huston Bancorporation; *U.S. Private*, pg. 4556

WOODFOREST FINANCIAL GROUP, INC.; *U.S. Private*, pg. 4558

WOODFOREST NATIONAL BANK—See Woodforest Financial Group, Inc.; *U.S. Private*, pg. 4558

WOODLANDS BANK—See Woodlands Financial Services Company; *U.S. Public*, pg. 2377

WOODLANDS NATIONAL BANK—See Mille Lacs Bancorporation, Inc.; *U.S. Private*, pg. 2731

WOODSBORO BANK; *U.S. Private*, pg. 4560

WOODTRUST BANK, N.A.—See WoodTrust Financial Corporation; *U.S. Private*, pg. 4561

WOODTRUST FINANCIAL CORPORATION; *U.S. Private*, pg. 4561

WORTHINGTON NATIONAL BANK—See BancFirst Corporation; *U.S. Public*, pg. 269

WPS COMMUNITY BANK—See Wisconsin Physicians Service Insurance Corporation; *U.S. Private*, pg. 4549

WYOMING BANK & TRUST; *U.S. Private*, pg. 4578

XIQING CDB VILLAGE BANK CO., LTD.—See China Development Bank Corporation; *Int'l*, pg. 1497

YICHENG CDB VILLAGE BANK CO., LTD.—See China Development Bank Corporation; *Int'l*, pg. 1497

YNB REAL ESTATE LLC—See HomeStreet, Inc.; *U.S. Public*, pg. 1046

YNB—See International Bancshares of Oklahoma, Inc.; *U.S. Private*, pg. 2114

YORK STATE BANK—See York Holdings, Inc.; *U.S. Private*, pg. 4590

YORKTOWN BANK—See Yorktown Financial Holdings, Inc.; *U.S. Private*, pg. 4591

YORK TRADITIONS BANK; *U.S. Public*, pg. 2399

YUNNAN DALI CQRC VILLAGE & TOWNSHIP BANK CO., LTD.—See Chongqing Rural Commercial Bank Co., Ltd.; *Int'l*, pg. 1581

YUNNAN HEQING CQRC VILLAGE & TOWNSHIP BANK CO., LTD.—See Chongqing Rural Commercial Bank Co., Ltd.; *Int'l*, pg. 1581

YUNNAN SHANGRI-LA CQRC VILLAGE & TOWNSHIP BANK CO., LTD.—See Chongqing Rural Commercial Bank Co., Ltd.; *Int'l*, pg. 1581

YUNNAN XISHAN CQRC VILLAGE & TOWNSHIP BANK CO., LTD.—See Chongqing Rural Commercial Bank Co., Ltd.; *Int'l*, pg. 1581

YUNNUN XIANGYUN CQRC VILLAGE & TOWNSHIP BANK CO., LTD.—See Chongqing Rural Commercial Bank Co., Ltd.; *Int'l*, pg. 1581

ZAO CITIBANK—See Citigroup Inc.; *U.S. Public*, pg. 504

ZAO DANSKE BANK—See Danske Bank A/S; *Int'l*, pg. 1969

ZHENLAI CDB VILLAGE BANK CO., LTD.—See China Development Bank Corporation; *Int'l*, pg. 1497

ZIONS BANK—See Zions Bancorporation, National Association; *U.S. Public*, pg. 2408

522130 — CREDIT UNIONS

121 FINANCIAL CREDIT UNION—See VyStar Credit Union; *U.S. Private*, pg. 4417

1ST MIDAMERICA CREDIT UNION; *U.S. Private*, pg. 4

1ST NORTHERN CALIFORNIA CREDIT UNION; *U.S. Private*, pg. 4

1ST RESOURCE CREDIT UNION—See Legacy Community Federal Credit Union; *U.S. Private*, pg. 2416

ABBOTT LABORATORIES EMPLOYEES CREDIT UNION; *U.S. Private*, pg. 35

ACE CASH EXPRESS, INC.—See JLL Partners, LLC; *U.S. Private*, pg. 2212

ACHIEVA CREDIT UNION; *U.S. Private*, pg. 58

ADVANCIAL FEDERAL CREDIT UNION; *U.S. Private*, pg. 93

ADVANTIS CREDIT UNION; *U.S. Private*, pg. 95

ADVENTURE CREDIT UNION; *U.S. Private*, pg. 109

ADVIA CREDIT UNION; *U.S. Private*, pg. 110

AFFINITY FEDERAL CREDIT UNION; *U.S. Private*, pg. 122

ALABAMA CREDIT UNION; *U.S. Private*, pg. 148

ALABAMA ONE CREDIT UNION; *U.S. Private*, pg. 148

ALIGN CREDIT UNION; *U.S. Private*, pg. 168

ALLEGIANCE CREDIT UNION; *U.S. Private*, pg. 176

ALLIANCE CREDIT UNION; *U.S. Private*, pg. 181

ALLIANT CREDIT UNION; *U.S. Private*, pg. 184

ALTURA CREDIT UNION; *U.S. Private*, pg. 210

AMERICAN FIRST CREDIT UNION; *U.S. Private*, pg. 234

AMERICA'S CHRISTIAN CREDIT UNION; *U.S. Private*, pg. 221

ANOKA HENNEPIN SCHOOL DISTRICT CREDIT UNION, INC.; *U.S. Private*, pg. 285

APCO EMPLOYEES CREDIT UNION; *U.S. Private*, pg. 290

ARIZONA CENTRAL CREDIT UNION; *U.S. Private*, pg. 324

ARIZONA STATE CREDIT UNION; *U.S. Private*, pg. 324

ARROWHEAD CREDIT UNION; *U.S. Private*, pg. 336

ASSOCIATED CREDIT UNION OF TEXAS; *U.S. Private*, pg. 355

ATLANTA POSTAL CREDIT UNION; *U.S. Private*, pg. 371

ATOMIC CREDIT UNION, INC.; *U.S. Private*, pg. 381

AUSTRALIAN CENTRAL CREDIT UNION LTD; *Int'l*, pg. 721

AVADIAN CREDIT UNION; *U.S. Private*, pg. 403

BEACON CREDIT UNION; *U.S. Private*, pg. 504

BELCO COMMUNITY CREDIT UNION; *U.S. Private*, pg. 517

BELLWETHER COMMUNITY CREDIT UNION; *U.S. Private*, pg. 520

BOULDER DAM CREDIT UNION; *U.S. Private*, pg. 623

BRIDGESTONE/FIRESTONE CREDIT CARD DIVISION—See Bridgestone Corporation; *Int'l*, pg. 1157

CALIFORNIA COAST CREDIT UNION; *U.S. Private*, pg. 718

CALIFORNIA CREDIT UNION; *U.S. Private*, pg. 718

CAMPUS USA CREDIT UNION; *U.S. Private*, pg. 732

CAPITAL CREDIT UNION; *U.S. Private*, pg. 739

CHAMPION CREDIT UNION; *U.S. Private*, pg. 846

CHRISTIAN COMMUNITY CREDIT UNION; *U.S. Private*, pg. 890

CITIZENS EQUITY FIRST CREDIT UNION; *U.S. Private*, pg. 903

CITY COUNTY CREDIT UNION; *U.S. Private*, pg. 905

CLARINDA CO-OP; *U.S. Private*, pg. 911

CLARKCOUNTY CREDIT UNION; *U.S. Private*, pg. 914

COASTAL COMMUNITY AND TEACHERS CREDIT UNION; *U.S. Private*, pg. 955

COAST CENTRAL CREDIT UNION; *U.S. Private*, pg. 954

COMMONWEALTH CENTRAL CREDIT UNION; *U.S. Private*, pg. 986

COMMUNITYAMERICA CREDIT UNION; *U.S. Private*, pg. 997

COMMUNITY RESOURCE CREDIT UNION; *U.S. Private*, pg. 996

CONNECTICUT STATE EMPLOYEES CREDIT UNION, INC.; *U.S. Private*, pg. 1016

CONNEX CREDIT UNION; *U.S. Private*, pg. 1018

CONNEXUS CREDIT UNION; *U.S. Private*, pg. 1018

CONSUMERS CREDIT UNION; *U.S. Private*, pg. 1026

COOPERATIVA DE AHORRO Y CEDITO DE BARRANQUITAS; *U.S. Private*, pg. 1042

COOPERATIVA DE AHORRO Y CREDITO DE CAMUY; *U.S. Private*, pg. 1042

COOPERATIVA DE AHORRO Y CREDITO DE ISABELA; *U.S. Private*, pg. 1042

COOPERATIVE DE AHORRO Y CREDITO SAN RAFAEL; *U.S. Private*, pg. 1042

CORNERSTONE FINANCIAL CREDIT UNION; *U.S. Private*, pg. 1052

CORPORATE AMERICA FAMILY CREDIT UNION; *U.S. Private*, pg. 1054

CORPORATE CENTRAL CREDIT UNION; *U.S. Private*, pg. 1054

522130 — CREDIT UNIONS

CREDIT UNION 1; *U.S. Private*, pg. 1091

CREDIT UNION OF AMERICA; *U.S. Private*, pg. 1091

CREDIT UNION OF GEORGIA; *U.S. Private*, pg. 1091

CREDIT UNION OF SOUTHERN CALIFORNIA; *U.S. Private*, pg. 1091

CREDIT UNION ONE, INC.; *U.S. Private*, pg. 1091

CREDIT UNION WEST; *U.S. Private*, pg. 1091

CRESCENT CREDIT UNION; *U.S. Private*, pg. 1093

DANAHER CONTROLS CORP.—See Danaher Corporation; *U.S. Public*, pg. 626

DATCU CREDIT UNION; *U.S. Private*, pg. 1167

DAY AIR CREDIT UNION, INC.; *U.S. Private*, pg. 1176

DEL NORTE CREDIT UNION; *U.S. Private*, pg. 1193

DESERET FIRST CREDIT UNION INC.; *U.S. Private*, pg. 1212

DHCU COMMUNITY CREDIT UNION; *U.S. Private*, pg. 1221

DIVERSIFIED MEMBERS CREDIT UNION; *U.S. Private*, pg. 1243

DOCO CREDIT UNION; *U.S. Private*, pg. 1251

DORT FINANCIAL CREDIT UNION; *U.S. Private*, pg. 1264

DUPAGE CREDIT UNION; *U.S. Private*, pg. 1291

DUPONT COMMUNITY CREDIT UNION; *U.S. Private*, pg. 1291

DUTCH POINT CREDIT UNION; *U.S. Private*, pg. 1294

DUTRAC COMMUNITY CREDIT UNION; *U.S. Private*, pg. 1295

EARTHMOVER CREDIT UNION; *U.S. Private*, pg. 1314

EAST IDAHO CREDIT UNION; *U.S. Private*, pg. 1316

EASTMAN CREDIT UNION; *U.S. Private*, pg. 1322

EAST TEXAS PROFESSIONAL CREDIT UNION; *U.S. Private*, pg. 1318

ECOLAB CREDIT UNION—See Ecolab Inc.; *U.S. Public*, pg. 713

EDUCATIONAL COMMUNITY CREDIT UNION; *U.S. Private*, pg. 1339

EDUCATIONAL EMPLOYEES CREDIT UNION; *U.S. Private*, pg. 1339

ELEVATIONS CREDIT UNION; *U.S. Private*, pg. 1358

ELGA CREDIT UNION; *U.S. Private*, pg. 1359

EMORY ALLIANCE CREDIT UNION—See Credit Union 1; *U.S. Private*, pg. 1091

EMPEOPLE CREDIT UNION; *U.S. Private*, pg. 1384

ENVISION CREDIT UNION; *U.S. Private*, pg. 1410

ESL FEDERAL CREDIT UNION—See Eastman Kodak Company; *U.S. Public*, pg. 706

EVANSVILLE TEACHERS FEDERAL CREDIT UNION; *U.S. Private*, pg. 1435

EVERGREEN CREDIT UNION; *U.S. Private*, pg. 1439

FAA CREDIT UNION; *U.S. Private*, pg. 1458

FAIRWINDS CREDIT UNION; *U.S. Private*, pg. 1465

FAMILY SAVINGS CREDIT UNION; *U.S. Private*, pg. 1471

FARM CREDIT SERVICES MISSOURI; *U.S. Private*, pg. 1475

FIBRE FEDERAL CREDIT UNION; *U.S. Private*, pg. 1502

FINANCIAL CENTER CREDIT UNION; *U.S. Private*, pg. 1506

FINANCIAL ONE CREDIT UNION—See Magnifi Financial Credit Union; *U.S. Private*, pg. 2548

FINANCIAL PARTNERS CREDIT UNION; *U.S. Private*, pg. 1508

FIRST CREDIT UNION; *U.S. Private*, pg. 1516

FIRST FINANCIAL CREDIT UNION; *U.S. Private*, pg. 1519

FIRST FINANCIAL CREDIT UNION; *U.S. Private*, pg. 1519

FIRST FLORIDA CREDIT UNION; *U.S. Private*, pg. 1519

FIRST HERITAGE CREDIT LLC—See CURO Group Holdings Corp.; *U.S. Public*, pg. 611

FIRSTMARK CREDIT UNION; *U.S. Private*, pg. 1532

FIRST NORTHERN CREDIT UNION; *U.S. Private*, pg. 1524

FIRST SERVICE CREDIT UNION; *U.S. Private*, pg. 1527

FIVE COUNTY CREDIT UNION; *U.S. Private*, pg. 1537

FIVE STAR CREDIT UNION; *U.S. Private*, pg. 1537

FLORIDA CREDIT UNION; *U.S. Private*, pg. 1547

FLORIDA HOSPITAL CREDIT UNION—See Adventist Health System Sunbelt Healthcare Corporation; *U.S. Private*, pg. 109

FORT SILL FEDERAL CREDIT UNION; *U.S. Private*, pg. 1575

FORT WORTH COMMUNITY CREDIT UNION; *U.S. Private*, pg. 1575

FREEDOM CREDIT UNION; *U.S. Private*, pg. 1603

FREUDENBERG NOK—See Freudenberg SE; *Int'l*, pg. 2788

GARDNER ABRASIVES—See FIVES, Societe Anonyme; *Int'l*, pg. 2696

GENERAL ELECTRIC CREDIT UNION; *U.S. Private*, pg. 1664

GENERAL MILLS—See General Mills, Inc.; *U.S. Public*, pg. 922

GENISYS CREDIT UNION; *U.S. Private*, pg. 1671

GEORGIA'S OWN CREDIT UNION; *U.S. Private*, pg. 1685

GEORGIA UNITED CREDIT UNION; *U.S. Private*, pg. 1685

GESA CREDIT UNION; *U.S. Private*, pg. 1688

GLOBAL CREDIT UNION; *U.S. Private*, pg. 1713

GOLDEN 1 CREDIT UNION; *U.S. Private*, pg. 1730

GREATER NEVADA CREDIT UNION; *U.S. Private*, pg. 1770

GREAT LAKES CREDIT UNION; *U.S. Private*, pg. 1764

522130 — CREDIT UNIONS

GREENWOOD CREDIT UNION; *U.S. Private*, pg. 1781
GROW FINANCIAL FEDERAL CREDIT UNION; *U.S. Private*, pg. 1795
GTE FINANCIAL; *U.S. Private*, pg. 1807
GULF CREDIT UNION; *U.S. Private*, pg. 1816
HAPO COMMUNITY CREDIT UNION; *U.S. Private*, pg. 1857
HARBOR CREDIT UNION—See Southland Credit Union; *U.S. Private*, pg. 3736
HARBORSTONE CREDIT UNION; *U.S. Private*, pg. 1859
HARSCO INDUSTRIAL PATTERSON-KELLEY—See Enviri Corporation; *U.S. Public*, pg. 780
HEARTLAND CREDIT UNION; *U.S. Private*, pg. 1899
HERITAGE SOUTH COMMUNITY CREDIT UNION; *U.S. Private*, pg. 1924
HOMELAND CREDIT UNION, INC.; *U.S. Private*, pg. 1973
HONOR CREDIT UNION; *U.S. Private*, pg. 1977
HOOSIER HILLS CREDIT UNION; *U.S. Private*, pg. 1978
HORIZON CREDIT UNION; *U.S. Private*, pg. 1980
HUDSON VALLEY CREDIT UNION; *U.S. Private*, pg. 2002
ICON CREDIT UNION; *U.S. Private*, pg. 2032
IDAHO CENTRAL CREDIT UNION; *U.S. Private*, pg. 2034
IH MISSISSIPPI VALLEY CREDIT UNION; *U.S. Private*, pg. 2040
ILWU CREDIT UNION; *U.S. Private*, pg. 2043
INDIANA MEMBERS CREDIT UNION; *U.S. Private*, pg. 2062
INSPIRUS CREDIT UNION; *U.S. Private*, pg. 2092
INTERRA CREDIT UNION; *U.S. Private*, pg. 2123
INTOUCH CREDIT UNION; *U.S. Private*, pg. 2129
IQ CREDIT UNION; *U.S. Private*, pg. 2137
JEFFERSON FINANCIAL CREDIT UNION; *U.S. Private*, pg. 2197
KEMBA CREDIT UNION, INC.; *U.S. Private*, pg. 2281
KEMBA FINANCIAL CREDIT UNION; *U.S. Private*, pg. 2281
LAKE MICHIGAN CREDIT UNION; *U.S. Private*, pg. 2375
LAND OF LINCOLN CREDIT UNION; *U.S. Private*, pg. 2383
LBS FINANCIAL CREDIT UNION; *U.S. Private*, pg. 2403
LEADERS CREDIT UNION; *U.S. Private*, pg. 2406
LEOMINSTER CREDIT UNION; *U.S. Private*, pg. 2422
LGE COMMUNITY CREDIT UNION; *U.S. Private*, pg. 2441
LIBERTY BAY CREDIT UNION; *U.S. Private*, pg. 2443
LIMONEIRA INTERNATIONAL DIVISION, LLC—See Limoneira Company; *U.S. Public*, pg. 1316
LINN AREA CREDIT UNION; *U.S. Private*, pg. 2462
LISTERHILL CREDIT UNION INC.; *U.S. Private*, pg. 2467
LOS ANGELES FIREMENS CREDIT UNION; *U.S. Private*, pg. 2496
MAGNIFI FINANCIAL CREDIT UNION; *U.S. Private*, pg. 2548
MAINE STATE CREDIT UNION; *U.S. Private*, pg. 2552
MAINSTREET CREDIT UNION; *U.S. Private*, pg. 2554
MAPS CREDIT UNION; *U.S. Private*, pg. 2569
MAX CREDIT UNION; *U.S. Private*, pg. 2617
MCT CREDIT UNION; *U.S. Private*, pg. 2644
MEMBERS 1ST CREDIT UNION; *U.S. Private*, pg. 2663
MEMBERS COOPERATIVE CREDIT UNION; *U.S. Private*, pg. 2663
MEMPHIS CITY EMPLOYEES CREDIT UNION; *U.S. Private*, pg. 2664
MERITRUST CREDIT UNION; *U.S. Private*, pg. 2675
METRO CREDIT UNION; *U.S. Private*, pg. 2685
MICHIGAN STATE UNIVERSITY FEDERAL CREDIT UNION; *U.S. Private*, pg. 2701
MIDFLORIDA CREDIT UNION; *U.S. Private*, pg. 2714
MILEPOST CREDIT UNION—See Sound Credit Union; *U.S. Private*, pg. 3717
MISSION FEDERAL CREDIT UNION; *U.S. Private*, pg. 2747
MUNA FEDERAL CREDIT UNION; *U.S. Private*, pg. 2813
MUTUAL SAVINGS CREDIT UNION INC.; *U.S. Private*, pg. 2820
MUTUAL SECURITY CREDIT UNION, INC.; *U.S. Private*, pg. 2820
NATIONAL ASSOCIATION OF FEDERAL CREDIT UNIONS; *U.S. Private*, pg. 2846
NAVIGANT CREDIT UNION; *U.S. Private*, pg. 2873
NAVIGATOR CREDIT UNION; *U.S. Private*, pg. 2873
NAVY ARMY COMMUNITY CREDIT UNION; *U.S. Private*, pg. 2873
NAVY FEDERAL CREDIT UNION; *U.S. Private*, pg. 2873
NEIGHBORHOOD CREDIT UNION; *U.S. Private*, pg. 2881
NEW HORIZONS CREDIT UNION; *U.S. Private*, pg. 2897
NORTH ISLAND CREDIT UNION—See California Credit Union; *U.S. Private*, pg. 718
NOTRE DAME FEDERAL CREDIT UNION; *U.S. Private*, pg. 2965
NUMARK CREDIT UNION; *U.S. Private*, pg. 2973
NUMERICA CREDIT UNION; *U.S. Private*, pg. 2973
OKLAHOMA CENTRAL CREDIT UNION; *U.S. Private*, pg. 3007
OKLAHOMA'S CREDIT UNION; *U.S. Private*, pg. 3007
ONPOINT COMMUNITY CREDIT UNION; *U.S. Private*, pg. 3027
ORANGE COUNTY'S CREDIT UNION; *U.S. Private*, pg. 3037

OREGON COMMUNITY CREDIT UNION; *U.S. Private*, pg. 3040
ORION FUNDING CREDIT UNION; *U.S. Private*, pg. 3043
PACIFIC MARINE CREDIT UNION; *U.S. Private*, pg. 3068
PACIFIC SERVICE CREDIT UNION; *U.S. Private*, pg. 3070
PACIFIC TRANSPORTATION FEDERAL CREDIT UNION—See Credit Union of Southern California; *U.S. Private*, pg. 1091
PATHWAYS FINANCIAL CREDIT UNION, INC.; *U.S. Private*, pg. 3106
PAWTUCKET CREDIT UNION; *U.S. Private*, pg. 3115
PEACH STATE FEDERAL CREDIT UNION; *U.S. Private*, pg. 3123
PELICAN STATE CREDIT UNION; *U.S. Private*, pg. 3130
PENNSYLVANIA STATE EMPLOYEES CREDIT UNION; *U.S. Private*, pg. 3137
PENTAGON FEDERAL CREDIT UNION; *U.S. Private*, pg. 3139
POINT BREEZE CREDIT UNION; *U.S. Private*, pg. 3221
POINT LOMA CREDIT UNION; *U.S. Private*, pg. 3222
POLISH NATIONAL CREDIT UNION; *U.S. Private*, pg. 3224
PREMIER AMERICA CREDIT UNION; *U.S. Private*, pg. 3249
QUALSTAR CREDIT UNION; *U.S. Private*, pg. 3322
QUEST CREDIT UNION; *U.S. Private*, pg. 3325
REALPAGE PAYMENTS SERVICES LLC—See Thoma Bravo, L.P.; *U.S. Private*, pg. 4153
RED CANOE CREDIT UNION; *U.S. Private*, pg. 3373
REDWOOD CREDIT UNION; *U.S. Private*, pg. 3381
RESOURCE ONE CREDIT UNION; *U.S. Private*, pg. 3407
RHODE ISLAND CREDIT UNION; *U.S. Private*, pg. 3422
ROYAL CREDIT UNION; *U.S. Private*, pg. 3492
SAFE 1 CREDIT UNION; *U.S. Private*, pg. 3523
SAFEAMERICA CREDIT UNION; *U.S. Private*, pg. 3524
SALAL CREDIT UNION; *U.S. Private*, pg. 3530
SAN DIEGO COUNTY CREDIT UNION; *U.S. Private*, pg. 3539
SAN MATEO CREDIT UNION; *U.S. Private*, pg. 3542
SCHOOLS FINANCIAL CREDIT UNION; *U.S. Private*, pg. 3568
SCOTT CREDIT UNION; *U.S. Private*, pg. 3576
SELF-HELP CREDIT UNION; *U.S. Private*, pg. 3602
SERVICE CREDIT UNION; *U.S. Private*, pg. 3615
SEVEN SEVENTEEN CREDIT UNION, INC.; *U.S. Private*, pg. 3619
SF FIRE CREDIT UNION; *U.S. Private*, pg. 3621
SF POLICE CREDIT UNION; *U.S. Private*, pg. 3621
SHARON CREDIT UNION; *U.S. Private*, pg. 3626
SIERRA CENTRAL CREDIT UNION; *U.S. Private*, pg. 3646
SILVER STATE SCHOOLS CREDIT UNION; *U.S. Private*, pg. 3662
SIU CREDIT UNION; *U.S. Private*, pg. 3677
SMART FINANCIAL CREDIT UNION; *U.S. Private*, pg. 3691
SOLARITY CREDIT UNION; *U.S. Private*, pg. 3708
SOO LINE RAILROAD COMPANY—See Canadian Pacific Kansas City Limited; *Int'l*, pg. 1285
SOUND CREDIT UNION; *U.S. Private*, pg. 3717
SOUTHEAST FINANCIAL CREDIT UNION; *U.S. Private*, pg. 3725
SOUTHLAND CREDIT UNION; *U.S. Private*, pg. 3736
SPOKANE TEACHERS CREDIT UNION; *U.S. Private*, pg. 3760
ST. ANNE'S CREDIT UNION; *U.S. Private*, pg. 3770
STAR ONE CREDIT UNION; *U.S. Private*, pg. 3785
STATE EMPLOYEES CREDIT UNION OF MARYLAND, INC.; *U.S. Private*, pg. 3791
STATE EMPLOYEES' CREDIT UNION; *U.S. Private*, pg. 3791
STATE EMPLOYEES CREDIT UNION; *U.S. Private*, pg. 3791
ST. MARY'S BANK; *U.S. Private*, pg. 3773
ST. MARY'S CREDIT UNION; *U.S. Private*, pg. 3773
SUNCOAST CREDIT UNION; *U.S. Private*, pg. 3865
SUPERIOR CHOICE CREDIT UNION; *U.S. Private*, pg. 3876
TEACHERS CREDIT UNION; *U.S. Private*, pg. 3944
THE TENNESSEE CREDIT UNION; *U.S. Private*, pg. 4126
TEXANS CREDIT UNION; *U.S. Private*, pg. 3974
TEXAS BAY AREA CREDIT UNION; *U.S. Private*, pg. 3974
TEXAS DOW EMPLOYEES CREDIT UNION; *U.S. Private*, pg. 3975
TEXAS TRUST CREDIT UNION; *U.S. Private*, pg. 3978
TEXELL CREDIT UNION; *U.S. Private*, pg. 3978
TINKER FEDERAL CREDIT UNION; *U.S. Private*, pg. 4175
TOPLINE FINANCIAL CREDIT UNION; *U.S. Private*, pg. 4187
TOWN & COUNTRY CREDIT UNION; *U.S. Private*, pg. 4196
TRAVIS CREDIT UNION; *U.S. Private*, pg. 4214
TRELLANCE, INC.; *U.S. Private*, pg. 4217
TRUMARK FINANCIAL CREDIT UNION; *U.S. Private*, pg. 4250
TRUWEST CREDIT UNION; *U.S. Private*, pg. 4251
TTCU THE CREDIT UNION; *U.S. Private*, pg. 4254
TVA COMMUNITY CREDIT UNION; *U.S. Private*, pg. 4263
TWINSTAR CREDIT UNION; *U.S. Private*, pg. 4266
TYNDALL FEDERAL CREDIT UNION INC.; *U.S. Private*, pg. 4268

UNITED FEDERAL CREDIT UNION; *U.S. Private*, pg. 4292
UNITED HERITAGE CREDIT UNION; *U.S. Private*, pg. 4293
UNITUS COMMUNITY CREDIT UNION; *U.S. Private*, pg. 4302
UNIVERSAL 1 CREDIT UNION, INC.; *U.S. Private*, pg. 4303
USC CREDIT UNION; *U.S. Private*, pg. 4322
USE CREDIT UNION; *U.S. Private*, pg. 4322
USF FEDERAL CREDIT UNION; *U.S. Private*, pg. 4323
VALLEY FIRST CREDIT UNION; *U.S. Private*, pg. 4333
VALLEY STRONG CREDIT UNION; *U.S. Private*, pg. 4335
VECTORPLY CORPORATION—See MSouth Equity Partners, LLC; *U.S. Private*, pg. 2808
VELOCITY CREDIT UNION; *U.S. Private*, pg. 4354
VENTURA COUNTY CREDIT UNION; *U.S. Private*, pg. 4357
VERIDIAN CREDIT UNION; *U.S. Private*, pg. 4360
VERITY CREDIT UNION; *U.S. Private*, pg. 4366
VERMONT STATE EMPLOYEES CREDIT UNION; *U.S. Private*, pg. 4367
VERVE, A CREDIT UNION; *U.S. Private*, pg. 4370
VIA CREDIT UNION; *U.S. Private*, pg. 4375
VIASAT CREDIT CORP—See ViaSat, Inc.; *U.S. Public*, pg. 2292
VIBE CREDIT UNION; *U.S. Private*, pg. 4376
VOLUNTEER CORPORATE CREDIT UNION; *U.S. Private*, pg. 4411
VYSTAR CREDIT UNION; *U.S. Private*, pg. 4417
WATER & POWER COMMUNITY CREDIT UNION; *U.S. Private*, pg. 4451
WESCOM CREDIT UNION; *U.S. Private*, pg. 4482
WESTBY CO-OP CREDIT UNION; *U.S. Private*, pg. 4489
WESTCONSIN CREDIT UNION; *U.S. Private*, pg. 4489
WESTERN COOPERATIVE CREDIT UNION; *U.S. Private*, pg. 4492
WHATCOM EDUCATIONAL CREDIT UNION; *U.S. Private*, pg. 4504
WHITEFISH CREDIT UNION; *U.S. Private*, pg. 4511
WINGS FINANCIAL ADVISORS, LLC; *U.S. Private*, pg. 4541
WINSOUTH CREDIT UNION; *U.S. Private*, pg. 4543
WORKERS' CREDIT UNION; *U.S. Private*, pg. 4563
WORLD COUNCIL OF CREDIT UNIONS, INC.; *U.S. Private*, pg. 4565
ZAIS GROUP (UK) LIMITED—See ZAIS Group Holdings, Inc.; *U.S. Private*, pg. 4597
ZEAL CREDIT UNION; *U.S. Private*, pg. 4598

522180 — SAVINGS INSTITUTIONS AND OTHER DEPOSITORY CREDIT INTERMEDIATION

1822 CORPUS IMMOBILIEN-VERMITTLUNG GMBH—See Frankfurter Sparkasse; *Int'l*, pg. 2761
1822 DIREKT—See Frankfurter Sparkasse; *Int'l*, pg. 2761
1ST FEDERAL SAVINGS BANK OF SC, INC.; *U.S. Private*, pg. 4
ABINGTON BANK—See Hometown Financial Group, Inc.; *U.S. Private*, pg. 1975
AB&T NATIONAL BANK—See Community Capital Bancshares, Inc.; *U.S. Public*, pg. 550
ACADEMY BANK, N.A.—See Dickinson Financial Corporation; *U.S. Private*, pg. 1227
AFFINITY BANK, NATIONAL ASSOCIATION—See Affinity Bancshares, Inc.; *U.S. Public*, pg. 56
AFRICAN EXPORT-IMPORT BANK LIMITED; *Int'l*, pg. 191
ALERUS FINANCIAL, NATIONAL ASSOCIATION—See Alerus Financial Corporation; *U.S. Public*, pg. 74
AMBLER SAVINGS BANK; *U.S. Private*, pg. 218
AMERICAN SAVINGS BANK, F.S.B.—See Hawaiian Electric Industries, Inc.; *U.S. Public*, pg. 989
ANDROSCOGGIN SAVINGS BANK; *U.S. Private*, pg. 280
APPLE BANK FOR SAVINGS; *U.S. Private*, pg. 296
ARTISANS' BANK; *U.S. Private*, pg. 343
ATLANTIC CAPITAL BANK, N.A.—See SouthState Corporation; *U.S. Public*, pg. 1912
ATTICA WEALTH MANAGEMENT S.A.—See ATTICA BANK S.A.; *Int'l*, pg. 696
AUTO CLUB TRUST, FSB—See The Auto Club Group; *U.S. Private*, pg. 3990
AVIDIA BANK—See Assabet Valley Bancorp; *U.S. Private*, pg. 353
AXIOM BANK, N.A.; *U.S. Private*, pg. 413
AXOS BANK—See Axos Financial, Inc.; *U.S. Public*, pg. 256
BANCA POPOLARE DI APRILIA S.P.A.—See BPER BANCA S.p.A; *Int'l*, pg. 1132
BANC OF CALIFORNIA, N.A.—See Banc of California, Inc.; *U.S. Public*, pg. 268
BANCO POPULAR DE PUERTO RICO - TRUST DIVISION—See Popular, Inc.; *U.S. Public*, pg. 1702
BANGOR SAVINGS BANK; *U.S. Private*, pg. 466
BANK 34—See Bancorp 34, Inc.; *U.S. Public*, pg. 269
BANK ASIA LIMITED; *Int'l*, pg. 837
BANKFINANCIAL, F.S.B.—See BankFinancial Corporation; *U.S. Public*, pg. 274
BANK FIRST, N.A.—See Bank First Corporation; *U.S. Public*, pg. 270
BANKNEWPORT; *U.S. Private*, pg. 468

N.A.I.C.S. INDEX

522180 — SAVINGS INSTITUTION...

BANK OCHRONY SRODOWISKA S.A.; *Int'l*, pg. 839
BANK OF CLARKE COUNTY—See Eagle Financial Services, Inc.; *U.S. Public*, pg. 702
BANK OF COMMERCE—See Commerce Bancshares, Inc.; *U.S. Private*, pg. 982
THE BANK OF FAYETTE COUNTY—See Moscow Bancshares, Inc.; *U.S. Private*, pg. 2792
BANK OF NEW HAMPSHIRE—See BNH Financial; *U.S. Private*, pg. 601
BANKUNITED, INC.; *U.S. Public*, pg. 274
BANQUE DE LA POSTE S.A./BANK VAN DE POST N.V.—See BNP Paribas SA; *Int'l*, pg. 1084
BANQUE DE LA POSTE S.A./BANK VAN DE POST N.V.—See bpost NV/SA; *Int'l*, pg. 1133
BARRINGTON BANK & TRUST COMPANY, N.A.—See Wintrust Financial Corporation; *U.S. Public*, pg. 2374
BATH SAVINGS INSTITUTION; *U.S. Private*, pg. 487
BAY-VANGUARD FEDERAL SAVINGS BANK—See Bay-Vanguard, M.H.C.; *U.S. Private*, pg. 495
BEAL BANK INC.—See Beal Financial Corporation; *U.S. Private*, pg. 505
BEAL FINANCIAL CORPORATION; *U.S. Private*, pg. 505
BENEFICIAL SOUTH CAROLINA INC.—See HSBC Holdings plc; *Int'l*, pg. 3505
BEVERLY BANK & TRUST COMPANY, N.A.—See Wintrust Financial Corporation; *U.S. Public*, pg. 2374
BHW BAUSPARKASSE AG—See Deutsche Post AG; *Int'l*, pg. 2079
BNP PARIBAS ASIA PRIVATE BANKING—See BNP Paribas SA; *Int'l*, pg. 1081
BNP PARIBAS-BRUSSELS BRANCH—See BNP Paribas SA; *Int'l*, pg. 1088
BNP PARIBAS COLUMBIA—See BNP Paribas SA; *Int'l*, pg. 1083
BNP PARIBAS ISTANBUL—See BNP Paribas SA; *Int'l*, pg. 1085
BNP PARIBAS LEASE GROUP IFN S.A.—See BNP Paribas SA; *Int'l*, pg. 1085
BNP PARIBAS LEASING SOLUTIONS (BELGIUM) S.A.—See BNP Paribas SA; *Int'l*, pg. 1085
BNP PARIBAS LEASING SOLUTIONS N.V.—See BNP Paribas SA; *Int'l*, pg. 1085
BNP PARIBAS LEASING SOLUTIONS SP. Z O.O.—See BNP Paribas SA; *Int'l*, pg. 1085
BNP PARIBAS PRIVATE BANK PLC—See BNP Paribas SA; *Int'l*, pg. 1086
BNP PARIBAS TEL-AVIV—See BNP Paribas SA; *Int'l*, pg. 1087
BOGOTA SAVINGS BANK; *U.S. Private*, pg. 609
BOKF, NATIONAL ASSOCIATION—See BOK Financial Corporation; *U.S. Public*, pg. 367
BPI DIRECT SAVINGS BANK—See Bank of the Philippine Islands; *Int'l*, pg. 848
BPI FAMILY SAVINGS BANK, INC.—See Bank of the Philippine Islands; *Int'l*, pg. 848
BREMER BANK, N.A.—See Bremer Financial Corporation; *U.S. Private*, pg. 645
BRENTWOOD BANK; *U.S. Private*, pg. 646
BRIDGEWATER SAVINGS BANK; *U.S. Private*, pg. 650
BRISTOL COUNTY SAVINGS BANK; *U.S. Private*, pg. 656
BROADWAY FEDERAL BANK, F.S.B.—See Broadway Financial Corporation; *U.S. Public*, pg. 392
BROADWAY FINANCIAL CORPORATION; *U.S. Public*, pg. 392
BROOKLINE BANK—See Brookline Bancorp, Inc.; *U.S. Public*, pg. 396
BUSINESS CAROLINA, INC.—See United Community Banks, Inc.; *U.S. Public*, pg. 2230
C3BANK, NATIONAL ASSOCIATION—See C3 Bancorp; *U.S. Private*, pg. 710
CALIFORNIA BANK OF COMMERCE, N.A.—See California BanCorp; *U.S. Public*, pg. 423
CAMBRIDGE SAVINGS BANK—See Cambridge Financial Group, Inc.; *U.S. Private*, pg. 726
CAPE ANN SAVINGS BANK; *U.S. Private*, pg. 737
CAPE COD FIVE CENTS SAVINGS BANK—See Mutual Bancorp; *U.S. Private*, pg. 2819
CAPITOL FEDERAL SAVINGS BANK—See Capitol Federal Financial, Inc.; *U.S. Public*, pg. 432
CARVER BANCORP INC.; *U.S. Public*, pg. 445
CARVER FEDERAL SAVINGS BANK—See Carver Bancorp Inc.; *U.S. Public*, pg. 445
CASSA DI RISPARMIO DELLA PROVINCIA DELL AQUILA S.P.A.—See BPER BANCA S.p.A; *Int'l*, pg. 1132
CASS COMMERCIAL BANK—See Cass Information Systems, Inc.; *U.S. Public*, pg. 447
CATALUNYA BANC, S.A.—See Banco Bilbao Vizcaya Argentaria, S.A.; *Int'l*, pg. 817
CENLAR CAPITAL CORPORATION; *U.S. Private*, pg. 809
CENTRAL BANK OF THE MIDWEST—See Central Bancompany, Inc.; *U.S. Private*, pg. 472
CENTRAL BANK; *U.S. Private*, pg. 819
CENTRAL DEPOSITORY SERVICES (INDIA) LIMITED—See Bombay Stock Exchange Limited; *Int'l*, pg. 1104
CENTRAL FEDERAL SAVINGS & LOAN ASSOCIATION; *U.S. Private*, pg. 820
CENTREVILLE BANK; *U.S. Private*, pg. 829

CENTURY BANK FSB—See Century Financial Services Corp.; *U.S. Private*, pg. 833
CENTURY FINANCIAL SERVICES CORP.; *U.S. Private*, pg. 833
CENTURY SAVINGS BANK; *U.S. Private*, pg. 834
CERTUSBANK, N.A.—See CertusHoldings, Inc.; *U.S. Private*, pg. 842
CFBANK, NATIONAL ASSOCIATION—See CF Bankshares Inc.; *U.S. Public*, pg. 476
CFM INDOSUEZ WEALTH SA; *Int'l*, pg. 1430
CHARLEROI FEDERAL SAVINGS BANK; *U.S. Private*, pg. 851
CHELSEA GROTON SAVINGS BANK INC.; *U.S. Private*, pg. 870
CHESAPEAKE BANK OF MARYLAND; *U.S. Private*, pg. 874
CINCINNATI FEDERAL SAVINGS & LOAN ASSOCIATION; *U.S. Private*, pg. 897
CIT BANK, N.A.—See First Citizens BancShares, Inc.; *U.S. Public*, pg. 841
CITIZENS COMMUNITY FEDERAL N.A.—See Citizens Community Bancorp, Inc.; *U.S. Public*, pg. 505
CITIZENS SAVINGS BANK; *U.S. Private*, pg. 904
CLAREMONT SAVINGS BANK; *U.S. Private*, pg. 910
THE CLINTON NATIONAL BANK; *U.S. Private*, pg. 4010
CNB BANK & TRUST, N.A.—See CNB Bank Shares, Inc.; *U.S. Public*, pg. 519
COASTAL FEDERAL BANK—See Coastal Financial Corp.; *U.S. Private*, pg. 956
COATESVILLE SAVINGS BANK; *U.S. Private*, pg. 957
COLONIAL SAVINGS, F.A.; *U.S. Private*, pg. 971
COLORADO FEDERAL SAVINGS BANK; *U.S. Private*, pg. 973
COLUMBIA BANK—See Columbia Financial, Inc.; *U.S. Public*, pg. 534
COMMUNITY BANK, N.A.—See Community Bank System, Inc.; *U.S. Public*, pg. 549
COMMUNITYBANK OF TEXAS, N.A.—See Stellar Bancorp, Inc.; *U.S. Public*, pg. 1944
CONNECTICUT COMMUNITY BANK, N.A.—See Associated Community Bancorp, Inc.; *U.S. Private*, pg. 355
CONSUMERS NATIONAL BANK—See Consumers Bancorp, Inc.; *U.S. Public*, pg. 573
CORTAL CONSORS—See BNP Paribas SA; *Int'l*, pg. 1090
CORTRUST BANK N.A.—See Hopkins Financial Corporation; *U.S. Private*, pg. 1979
COUNTRY BANK FOR SAVINGS; *U.S. Private*, pg. 1066
CRESCO UNION SAVINGS BANK INC.; *U.S. Private*, pg. 1094
CRYSTAL LAKE BANK & TRUST COMPANY, N.A.—See Wintrust Financial Corporation; *U.S. Public*, pg. 2374
CUMBERLAND VALLEY NATIONAL BANK & TRUST COMPANY—See Cumberland Valley Financial Corporation; *U.S. Private*, pg. 1123
CWM, LLC; *U.S. Private*, pg. 1132
DEARBORN FEDERAL SAVINGS BANK; *U.S. Private*, pg. 1185
DEARBORN SAVINGS BANK—See DSA Financial Corp.; *U.S. Public*, pg. 689
DEDHAM INSTITUTION FOR SAVINGS INC.; *U.S. Private*, pg. 1188
DEVA BIKAS BANK LIMITED; *Int'l*, pg. 2086
DIME BANK; *U.S. Private*, pg. 1232
DOLLAR BANK, FEDERAL SAVINGS BANK—See Dollar Mutual Bancorp; *U.S. Private*, pg. 1254
DOLLAR BANK LEASING CORP.—See Dollar Mutual Bancorp; *U.S. Private*, pg. 1254
DSRM NATIONAL BANK—See Valero Energy Corporation; *U.S. Public*, pg. 2272
EAGLE BANK; *U.S. Private*, pg. 1308
EASTERN SAVINGS BANK, FSB; *U.S. Private*, pg. 1321
EASTHAMPTON SAVINGS BANK—See Hometown Financial Group, Inc.; *U.S. Private*, pg. 1975
EATON FEDERAL SAVINGS BANK; *U.S. Private*, pg. 1323
EDGEWATER BANK—See United Federal Credit Union; *U.S. Private*, pg. 4292
EL DORADO SAVINGS BANK, F.S.B.; *U.S. Private*, pg. 1349
ELECTRONIC DATA PAYMENT SYSTEMS; *U.S. Private*, pg. 1355
EMIGRANT BANK—See New York Private Bank & Trust Corporation; *U.S. Private*, pg. 2911
EMPIRE STATE BANK—See ES Bancshares, Inc.; *U.S. Public*, pg. 793
THE EQUITABLE BANK—See The Equitable Bank SSB; *U.S. Private*, pg. 4026
THE EQUITABLE BANK SSB; *U.S. Private*, pg. 4026
EQUITABLE SAVINGS & LOAN ASSOCIATION; *U.S. Private*, pg. 1416
ERSTE BANK AG—See Erste Group Bank AG; *Int'l*, pg. 2498
ESSEX BANK OF MARYLAND—See United Bankshares, Inc.; *U.S. Public*, pg. 2229
E*TRADE BANK—See E*TRADE Financial Corporation; *U.S. Public*, pg. 1302
EUREKA SAVINGS BANK; *U.S. Private*, pg. 1433
EVANS BANK, N.A.—See Evans Bancorp, Inc.; *U.S. Public*, pg. 799

EVERGREEN FEDERAL SAVINGS & LOAN ASSOCIATION; *U.S. Private*, pg. 1439
EXCHANGE BANK; *U.S. Public*, pg. 805
FAIRFIELD COUNTY BANK—See Fairfield County Bank, MHC; *U.S. Private*, pg. 1463
FAIRFIELD FEDERAL SAVINGS & LOAN ASSOCIATION; *U.S. Private*, pg. 1463
FALL RIVER FIVE CENTS SAVINGS BANK; *U.S. Private*, pg. 1467
FANNIN BANK; *U.S. Private*, pg. 1472
FARM BUREAU BANK FSB—See FB Bancorp; *U.S. Private*, pg. 1484
THE FARMERS & MERCHANTS BANK—See The Farmers & Merchants Bankshares, Inc.; *U.S. Private*, pg. 4027
FARMERS TRUST & SAVINGS BANK—See Easter Enterprises, Inc.; *U.S. Private*, pg. 1319
FARMERS TRUST & SAVINGS BANK—See J. Carl H. Bancorporation; *U.S. Private*, pg. 2155
FB BANCORP; *U.S. Private*, pg. 1484
FEDERAL RESERVE BANK OF BOSTON; *U.S. Private*, pg. 1490
FEDERAL RESERVE BANK OF MINNEAPOLIS; *U.S. Private*, pg. 1490
FEDERAL RESERVE BANK OF NEW YORK; *U.S. Private*, pg. 1490
FIDELITY CO-OPERATIVE BANK—See Mutual Bancorp; *U.S. Private*, pg. 2819
FIDELITY HOMESTEAD SAVINGS BANK; *U.S. Private*, pg. 1503
FIDELITY PERSONAL TRUST COMPANY, FSB—See FMR LLC; *U.S. Private*, pg. 1555
FIFTH DISTRICT SAVINGS BANK; *U.S. Private*, pg. 1505
FIFTH THIRD BANK, NATIONAL ASSOCIATION—See Fifth Third Bancorp; *U.S. Public*, pg. 833
THE FIRST, A NATIONAL BANKING ASSOCIATION—See The First Bancshares, Inc.; *U.S. Public*, pg. 2073
FIRSTBANK AT WADSWORTH/COLE MINE, INC.—See Firstbank Holding Company of Colorado, Inc.; *U.S. Private*, pg. 1531
FIRSTBANK HOLDING COMPANY OF COLORADO, INC.; *U.S. Private*, pg. 1531
FIRSTBANK NORTH—See Firstbank Holding Company of Colorado, Inc.; *U.S. Private*, pg. 1531
FIRST BANK OF ARAPAHOE COUNTY—See Firstbank Holding Company of Colorado, Inc.; *U.S. Private*, pg. 1531
FIRSTBANK OF ARVADA, INC.—See Firstbank Holding Company of Colorado, Inc.; *U.S. Private*, pg. 1531
FIRSTBANK OF AURORA, INC.—See Firstbank Holding Company of Colorado, Inc.; *U.S. Private*, pg. 1531
FIRST BANK OF BERNE—See First Berne Financial Corporation; *U.S. Private*, pg. 1514
FIRSTBANK OF BOULDER, INC.—See Firstbank Holding Company of Colorado, Inc.; *U.S. Private*, pg. 1531
FIRST BANK OF CHERRY CREEK—See Firstbank Holding Company of Colorado, Inc.; *U.S. Private*, pg. 1531
FIRSTBANK OF DOUGLAS COUNTY—See Firstbank Holding Company of Colorado, Inc.; *U.S. Private*, pg. 1531
FIRSTBANK OF LAKEWOOD, INC.—See Firstbank Holding Company of Colorado, Inc.; *U.S. Private*, pg. 1531
FIRST BANK OF LITTLETON, INC.—See Firstbank Holding Company of Colorado, Inc.; *U.S. Private*, pg. 1531
FIRSTBANK OF LONGMONT, INC.—See Firstbank Holding Company of Colorado, Inc.; *U.S. Private*, pg. 1531
FIRSTBANK OF NORTHERN COLORADO, INC.—See Firstbank Holding Company of Colorado, Inc.; *U.S. Private*, pg. 1531
FIRSTBANK OF SUMMIT COUNTY—See Firstbank Holding Company of Colorado, Inc.; *U.S. Private*, pg. 1531
FIRSTBANK OF TECH CENTER, INC.—See Firstbank Holding Company of Colorado, Inc.; *U.S. Private*, pg. 1531
FIRSTBANK OF WHEAT RIDGE, INC.—See Firstbank Holding Company of Colorado, Inc.; *U.S. Private*, pg. 1531
FIRST BANK OF WYOMING—See Glacier Bancorp, Inc.; *U.S. Public*, pg. 938
FIRSTBANK, REPUBLIC PLAZA BRANCH—See Firstbank Holding Company of Colorado, Inc.; *U.S. Private*, pg. 1531
FIRST BANK—See First Bancorp; *U.S. Public*, pg. 839
FIRST BANK—See First Banks, Inc.; *U.S. Private*, pg. 1514
FIRST COUNTY BANK; *U.S. Private*, pg. 1516
FIRST FEDERAL BANK, A FSB—See Southeastern Financial Inc.; *U.S. Private*, pg. 3728
FIRST FEDERAL BANK OF KANSAS CITY; *U.S. Private*, pg. 1517
FIRST FEDERAL BANK OF LOUISIANA; *U.S. Private*, pg. 1518
FIRST FEDERAL BANK OF OHIO; *U.S. Private*, pg. 1518
FIRST FEDERAL BANK—See First Federal Bancorp, Inc.; *U.S. Private*, pg. 1517
FIRST FEDERAL BANK—See Southeastern Bancorp, Inc.; *U.S. Private*, pg. 3727
FIRST FEDERAL COMMUNITY BANK OF BUCYRUS—See Community Investors Bancorp, Inc.; *U.S. Public*, pg. 558
FIRST FEDERAL COMMUNITY BANK; *U.S. Private*, pg. 1518
FIRST FEDERAL SAVINGS BANK OF CHAMPAIGN-

522180 — SAVINGS INSTITUTION...

URBANA—See Great American Bancorp, Inc.; *U.S. Public*, pg. 961
FIRST FEDERAL SAVINGS BANK OF FRANKFORT—See First Federal MHC; *U.S. Private*, pg. 1518
FIRST FEDERAL SAVINGS BANK; *U.S. Private*, pg. 1518
FIRST FEDERAL SAVINGS BANK; *U.S. Private*, pg. 1518
FIRST FEDERAL SAVINGS BANK; *U.S. Private*, pg. 1518
FIRST FEDERAL SAVINGS BANK—See First Bancorp of Indiana, Inc.; *U.S. Public*, pg. 839
FIRST FEDERAL SAVINGS BANK—See Northeast Indiana Bancorp, Inc.; *U.S. Public*, pg. 1537
FIRST FEDERAL SAVINGS BANK TWIN FALLS; *U.S. Private*, pg. 1518
FIRST FEDERAL SAVINGS & LOAN ASSOCIATION OF GREENE COUNTY; *U.S. Private*, pg. 1518
FIRST FEDERAL SAVINGS & LOAN ASSOCIATION OF LAKEWOOD; *U.S. Private*, pg. 1518
FIRST FEDERAL SAVINGS & LOAN ASSOCIATION OF LORAIN; *U.S. Private*, pg. 1518
FIRST FEDERAL SAVINGS & LOAN ASSOCIATION OF PASCAGOULA-MOSS POINT; *U.S. Private*, pg. 1518
FIRST FEDERAL SAVINGS & LOAN ASSOCIATION OF PORT ANGELES—See First Northwest Bancorp; *U.S. Public*, pg. 846
FIRST FEDERAL SAVINGS & LOAN ASSOCIATION—See First Federal MHC; *U.S. Private*, pg. 1518
FIRST FEDERAL SAVINGS & LOAN; *U.S. Private*, pg. 1518
FIRST FINANCIAL BANC CORPORATION; *U.S. Private*, pg. 1519
FIRST FINANCIAL BANCORP SERVICE CORPORATION—See First Financial Bancorp.; *U.S. Public*, pg. 843
FIRST FINANCIAL BANK, N.A.—See First Financial Bankshares, Inc.; *U.S. Public*, pg. 843
FIRST FINANCIAL BANK, N.A.—See First Financial Corporation; *U.S. Public*, pg. 843
FIRST FINANCIAL BANK—See First Financial Banc Corporation; *U.S. Private*, pg. 1519
FIRST HARRISON BANK—See First Capital, Inc.; *U.S. Public*, pg. 841
FIRST MID BANK & TRUST, N.A.—See First Mid Bancshares, Inc.; *U.S. Public*, pg. 846
FIRST NATIONAL BANKER'S BANK—See First National Bankers Bankshares, Inc.; *U.S. Private*, pg. 1523
THE FIRST NATIONAL BANK IN CRESTON—See Northwest Financial Corp.; *U.S. Private*, pg. 2960
FIRST NATIONAL BANK IN STAUNTON; *U.S. Private*, pg. 1522
THE FIRST NATIONAL BANK OF HUGO—See First Liberty Capital Corporation; *U.S. Private*, pg. 1520
THE FIRST NATIONAL BANK OF HUTCHINSON—See First Kansas Bancshares, Inc.; *U.S. Private*, pg. 1520
FIRST NATIONAL BANK OF JASPER—See East Texas Bancshares, Inc.; *U.S. Private*, pg. 1318
FIRST NATIONAL BANK OF THE GULF COAST—See TGR Financial Inc.; *U.S. Private*, pg. 3979
FIRST NATIONAL BANK—See Spearman Bancshares, Inc.; *U.S. Private*, pg. 3748
FIRST PIEDMONT FEDERAL SAVINGS & LOAN ASSOCIATION OF GAFFNEY; *U.S. Private*, pg. 1524
FIRSTRUST BANK; *U.S. Private*, pg. 1532
FIRST SAVINGS BANK OF HEGEWISCH; *U.S. Private*, pg. 1527
FIRST SAVINGS BANK PERKASIE; *U.S. Private*, pg. 1527
FIRST SAVINGS BANK; *U.S. Private*, pg. 1527
FIRST SEACOAST BANK—See First Seacoast Bancorp, Inc.; *U.S. Public*, pg. 847
FIRST SHORE FEDERAL SAVINGS & LOAN ASSOCIATION; *U.S. Private*, pg. 1527
FIRST STATE BANK OF BLOOMINGTON; *U.S. Private*, pg. 1528
FITZGIBBONS AGENCY LLC—See Pathfinder Bancorp, Inc.; *U.S. Public*, pg. 1651
FLAGSTAR BANK, FSB—See New York Community Bancorp, Inc.; *U.S. Public*, pg. 1512
FLORENCE SAVINGS BANK INC.; *U.S. Private*, pg. 1547
FLUSHING SAVINGS BANK INC.—See Flushing Financial Corporation; *U.S. Public*, pg. 860
FNB BANK, N.A.—See Fulton Financial Corporation; *U.S. Public*, pg. 892
FORCHT BANK, N.A.—See Forcht Group of Kentucky, Inc.; *U.S. Private*, pg. 1564
FORTRESS BANK—See First State Bancorporation, Inc.; *U.S. Private*, pg. 1528
FRANKFURTER BANKGESELLSCHAFT—See Frankfurter Sparkasse; *Int'l*, pg. 2761
FRANKLIN SAVINGS BANK; *U.S. Private*, pg. 1597
FRANKLIN SAVINGS BANK; *U.S. Private*, pg. 1598
FREEHOLD SAVINGS BANK; *U.S. Private*, pg. 1604
FULTON BANK, N.A.—See Fulton Financial Corporation; *U.S. Public*, pg. 892
FULTON SAVINGS BANK INC.; *U.S. Private*, pg. 1622
GATE CITY BANK; *U.S. Private*, pg. 1649
GEAUGA SAVINGS BANK INC.; *U.S. Private*, pg. 1655
GENERATIONS BANK—See Generations Bancorp NY, Inc.; *U.S. Public*, pg. 930
GLEN ROCK SAVINGS BANK; *U.S. Private*, pg. 1709
GOUVERNEUR SAVINGS & LOAN ASSOCIATION—See Cambray Mutual Holding Company; *U.S. Private*, pg. 726
GREAT MIDWEST BANK, S.S.B.; *U.S. Private*, pg. 1765
GREAT SOUTHERN BANK—See Great Southern Bancorp, Inc.; *U.S. Public*, pg. 962
GREEN BANK, N.A.—See Veritex Holdings, Inc.; *U.S. Public*, pg. 2283
GREENFIELD SAVINGS BANK; *U.S. Private*, pg. 1778
GREENVILLE FEDERAL—See Greenville Federal Financial Corporation; *U.S. Public*, pg. 965
GUARANTY BANK & TRUST, N.A.—See Guaranty Bancshares, Inc.; *U.S. Public*, pg. 973
GUARDIAN SAVINGS BANK FSB; *U.S. Private*, pg. 1810
HABIB FINANCE INTERNATIONAL LIMITED—See Habib Bank Limited; *Int'l*, pg. 3203
HADDON SAVINGS BANK; *U.S. Private*, pg. 1839
HANCOCK COUNTY SAVINGS BANK, F.S.B.; *U.S. Private*, pg. 1852
HANSARD GLOBAL PLC; *Int'l*, pg. 3259
HAWAII NATIONAL BANK—See Hawaii National Bancshares, Inc.; *U.S. Private*, pg. 1881
HERITAGE BANK N.A.—See Heritage Bancshares Group, Inc.; *U.S. Private*, pg. 1922
HERITAGE STATE BANK—See HBancorporation Inc.; *U.S. Public*, pg. 990
HERRING BANK—See Herring Bancorp, Inc.; *U.S. Private*, pg. 1926
HIGH COUNTRY BANK—See High Country Bancorp, Inc.; *U.S. Public*, pg. 1035
HINGHAM INSTITUTION FOR SAVINGS; *U.S. Public*, pg. 1042
HITACHI CAPITAL AMERICA CORP.—See Hitachi, Ltd.; *Int'l*, pg. 3413
HITACHI CAPITAL AMERICA VENDOR SERVICES—See Hitachi, Ltd.; *Int'l*, pg. 3413
HOME, NATIONAL ASSOCIATION—See Home Bancorp, Inc.; *U.S. Public*, pg. 1045
HOME BANK SB; *U.S. Private*, pg. 1970
HOME FEDERAL BANK OF TENNESSEE FSB; *U.S. Private*, pg. 1970
HOME FEDERAL SAVINGS BANK—See Alerus Financial Corporation; *U.S. Public*, pg. 75
HOME LOAN & INVESTMENT BANK FSB INC.—See Home Loan & Investment Bank; *U.S. Private*, pg. 1971
HOME LOAN & INVESTMENT BANK; *U.S. Private*, pg. 1971
HOME STATE BANK, N.A.—See Home State Bancorp, Inc.; *U.S. Private*, pg. 1972
HOMETOWN BANK; *U.S. Private*, pg. 1975
HOMETOWN BANK—See Hometown Financial Group, Inc.; *U.S. Private*, pg. 1975
HOUSING DEVELOPMENT FINANCE CORPORATION BANK OF SRI LANKA; *Int'l*, pg. 3491
HOYNE SAVINGS BANK—See Hoyne Financial Corporation; *U.S. Private*, pg. 1996
HSBC INVESTMENT BANK ASIA LIMITED—See HSBC Holdings plc; *Int'l*, pg. 3506
HSBC PRIVATE BANK (JERSEY) LIMITED—See HSBC Holdings plc; *Int'l*, pg. 3504
HSBC TRINKAUS & BURKHARDT AG—See HSBC Holdings plc; *Int'l*, pg. 3505
HUNTINGTON FEDERAL SAVINGS BANK; *U.S. Private*, pg. 2010
IA PRIVATE WEALTH INC.—See iA Financial Corporation Inc.; *Int'l*, pg. 3568
IA PRIVATE WEALTH (USA) INC.—See iA Financial Corporation Inc.; *Int'l*, pg. 3568
IDAHO TRUST BANK—See Idaho Trust Bancorp; *U.S. Private*, pg. 2035
IFIC BANK PLC; *Int'l*, pg. 3599
INDIANA FIRST SAVINGS BANK; *U.S. Private*, pg. 2062
INTERAMERICAN BANK FSB; *U.S. Private*, pg. 2109
INVESTAR BANK, N.A.—See Investar Holding Corporation; *U.S. Public*, pg. 1164
INVESTORS BANK—See Citizens Financial Group, Inc.; *U.S. Public*, pg. 505
IOWA STATE SAVINGS BANK—See Duclarkee, Inc.; *U.S. Private*, pg. 1284
IROQUOIS FEDERAL SAVINGS & LOAN ASSOCIATION—See IF Bancorp, Inc.; *U.S. Public*, pg. 1095
JEFF DAVIS BANK & TRUST COMPANY—See Jeff Davis Bancshares, Inc.; *U.S. Private*, pg. 2196
JEFFERSON BANK & TRUST COMPANY—See First Mid Bancshares, Inc.; *U.S. Public*, pg. 846
JEWETT CITY SAVINGS BANK; *U.S. Private*, pg. 2205
JOHNSON BANK—See S.C. Johnson & Son, Inc.; *U.S. Private*, pg. 3516
JONESTOWN BANK & TRUST COMPANY; *U.S. Private*, pg. 2234
JW BOND CONSULTANTS, INC.—See Kelso & Company, L.P.; *U.S. Private*, pg. 2280
KEARNY BANK—See Kearny Financial Corp.; *U.S. Public*, pg. 1217
KENNEBUNK SAVINGS BANK; *U.S. Private*, pg. 2284
KEYBANK NATIONAL ASSOCIATION—See KeyCorp; *U.S. Public*, pg. 1225
LANDMARK BANK, N.A.—See Landrum Company; *U.S. Private*, pg. 2386

CORPORATE AFFILIATIONS

LEE BANK; *U.S. Private*, pg. 2411
LIBERTY BANK FOR SAVINGS INC.; *U.S. Private*, pg. 2443
LIBERTY CAPITAL INC.; *U.S. Private*, pg. 2443
LIBERTY SAVINGS BANK, F.S.B.—See Liberty Capital Inc.; *U.S. Private*, pg. 2443
LINCOLN FEDERAL SAVINGS BANK OF NEBRASKA; *U.S. Private*, pg. 2457
LINDELL BANK & TRUST COMPANY—See First Illinois Bancorp, Inc.; *U.S. Private*, pg. 1520
LOGANSPORT SAVINGS BANK—See Logansport Financial Corp.; *U.S. Public*, pg. 1340
LOOMIS FEDERAL SAVINGS & LOAN ASSOCIATION—See Hoyne Financial Corporation; *U.S. Private*, pg. 1996
LOWELL FIVE CENT SAVINGS BANK; *U.S. Private*, pg. 2505
LUTHER BURBANK SAVINGS—See WaFd, Inc.; *U.S. Public*, pg. 2321
MACHIAS SAVINGS BANK; *U.S. Private*, pg. 2535
MADISON COUNTY BANK—See Madison County Financial, Inc.; *U.S. Public*, pg. 1353
MAGYAR BANK—See Magyar Bancorp, MHC; *U.S. Private*, pg. 2550
MALAGA BANK FSB—See Malaga Financial Corp.; *U.S. Public*, pg. 1355
MANASQUAN SAVINGS BANK—See MSB Mutual Holding Company; *U.S. Private*, pg. 2806
MANGROVE EQUITY PARTNERS, LP; *U.S. Private*, pg. 2563
MANSFIELD COOPERATIVE BANK; *U.S. Private*, pg. 2566
MAPLE CITY SAVINGS BANK, FSB—See Maple City Savings, MHC; *U.S. Private*, pg. 2568
MARLBOROUGH SAVINGS BANK; *U.S. Private*, pg. 2583
MARQUETTE BANK—See Marquette National Corporation; *U.S. Public*, pg. 1370
MARQUETTE SAVINGS BANK; *U.S. Private*, pg. 2587
MASCOMA SAVINGS BANK—See Mascoma Mutual Financial Services Corporation; *U.S. Private*, pg. 2601
MASPETH FEDERAL SAVINGS & LOAN ASSOCIATION; *U.S. Private*, pg. 2603
THE MASSMUTUAL TRUST COMPANY, FSB—See Massachusetts Mutual Life Insurance Company; *U.S. Private*, pg. 2606
MB FINANCIAL BANK, N.A.—See Fifth Third Bancorp; *U.S. Public*, pg. 833
MCHENRY SAVINGS BANK—See McHenry Bancorp, Inc.; *U.S. Public*, pg. 1407
MECHANICS SAVINGS BANK NA; *U.S. Private*, pg. 2649
MEREDITH VILLAGE SAVINGS BANK; *U.S. Private*, pg. 2672
METABANK, N.A.—See Pathward Financial, Inc.; *U.S. Public*, pg. 1652
MIDCOUNTRY BANK—See MidCountry Acquisition Corp.; *U.S. Private*, pg. 2711
MIDDLESEX FEDERAL SAVINGS F.A.; *U.S. Private*, pg. 2714
MIDDLESEX SAVINGS BANK—See Middlesex Bancorp, MHC; *U.S. Private*, pg. 2714
MIDFIRST BANK—See Midland Financial Co.; *U.S. Private*, pg. 2715
MID-SOUTHERN SAVINGS BANK, FSB—See Mid-Southern Bancorp, Inc.; *U.S. Public*, pg. 1445
MIDWEST HERITAGE BANK—See Hy-Vee, Inc.; *U.S. Private*, pg. 2016
MILFORD BANK; *U.S. Private*, pg. 2729
MILFORD FEDERAL SAVINGS & LOAN ASSOCIATION; *U.S. Private*, pg. 2729
MINEOLA COMMUNITY BANK SSB—See Texas Community Bancshares, Inc.; *U.S. Public*, pg. 2025
MOUNTAIN VALLEY BANK, N.A.—See Mountain-Valley Bancshares, Inc.; *U.S. Public*, pg. 2801
MUNICIPAL TRUST & SAVINGS BANK; *U.S. Private*, pg. 2814
MUTUAL SAVINGS BANK—See Oconee Federal Financial Corp.; *U.S. Public*, pg. 1563
NATIXIS FACTOR S.A.—See Groupe BPCE; *Int'l*, pg. 3096
NEWBURYPORT FIVE CENTS SAVINGS BANK; *U.S. Private*, pg. 2914
NEWTOWN SAVINGS BANK; *U.S. Private*, pg. 2918
NEW YORK COMMUNITY BANK—See New York Community Bancorp, Inc.; *U.S. Public*, pg. 1513
NEXBANK, SSB—See NexBank Capital, Inc.; *U.S. Private*, pg. 2919
NEXTIER BANK, N.A.—See NexTier, Inc.; *U.S. Private*, pg. 2921
NICOLET NATIONAL BANK—See Nicolet Bankshares, Inc.; *U.S. Public*, pg. 1528
NORTH AMERICAN SAVINGS BANK, F.S.B.—See NASB Financial, Inc.; *U.S. Public*, pg. 1491
NORTHEAST BANK; *U.S. Public*, pg. 1537
NORTHEAST COMMUNITY BANK—See NORTHEAST COMMUNITY BANCORP, INC.; *U.S. Public*, pg. 1537
NORTH EASTON SAVINGS BANK—See 1864 Bancorp, Inc; *U.S. Private*, pg. 3
THE NORTHERN TRUST COMPANY—See Northern Trust Corporation; *U.S. Public*, pg. 1539

N.A.I.C.S. INDEX

NORTHFIELD BANK—See Northfield Bancorp, Inc.; *U.S. Public*, pg. 1539
NORTH MIDDLESEX SAVINGS BANK; *U.S. Private*, pg. 2946
NORTH MILL CAPITAL LLC—See SLR Investment Corp.; *U.S. Public*, pg. 1895
NORTH SHORE BANK, A CO-OPERATIVE BANK—See Hometown Financial Group, Inc.; *U.S. Private*, pg. 1975
NORTH SHORE BANK, FSB; *U.S. Private*, pg. 2946
NORTH SHORE TRUST AND SAVINGS; *U.S. Private*, pg. 2947
NORTHWEST COMMUNITY BANK; *U.S. Private*, pg. 2959
NORTHWESTERN BANK, N.A.—See Northwestern Bancshares, Inc.; *U.S. Private*, pg. 2962
NORWAY SAVINGS BANK—See Norway Bancorp, Inc.; *U.S. Private*, pg. 2964
NOVA SAVINGS BANK—See NOVA Financial Holdings, Inc.; *U.S. Private*, pg. 2965
NVE BANK; *U.S. Private*, pg. 2975
OCEANFIRST BANK, NATIONAL ASSOCIATION—See OceanFirst Financial Corp.; *U.S. Public*, pg. 1563
OCONEE FEDERAL SAVINGS & LOAN ASSOCIATON, INC.—See Oconee Federal Financial Corp.; *U.S. Public*, pg. 1563
OLD NATIONAL BANK—See Old National Bancorp; *U.S. Public*, pg. 1567
OLD PLANK TRAIL COMMUNITY BANK, N.A.—See Wintrust Financial Corporation; *U.S. Public*, pg. 2375
OUR COMMUNITY BANK—See Crane Credit Union; *U.S. Private*, pg. 1085
OZARKS FEDERAL SAVINGS & LOAN ASSOCIATION; *U.S. Private*, pg. 3058
PACIFIC CREST SAVINGS BANK—See Pacific Crest Bancorp, Inc.; *U.S. Private*, pg. 3067
PACIFIC PREMIER BANK—See Pacific Premier Bancorp, Inc.; *U.S. Public*, pg. 1632
THE PARK BANK; *U.S. Private*, pg. 4091
THE PARK NATIONAL BANK—See Park National Corporation; *U.S. Public*, pg. 1638
PASSUMPSIC SAVINGS BANK—See Passumpsic Bancorp Inc.; *U.S. Private*, pg. 3104
PATRIOT BANK, N.A.—See Patriot National Bancorp, Inc.; *U.S. Public*, pg. 1653
PATRIOT WEALTH MANAGEMENT, INC.—See Mariner Wealth Advisors, LLC; *U.S. Private*, pg. 2576
PENTUCKET BANK; *U.S. Private*, pg. 3140
PEOPLESBANK; *U.S. Private*, pg. 3142
PEOPLES BANK—See NorthWest Indiana Bancorp; *U.S. Public*, pg. 1542
PEOPLES BANK—See Peoples Bancorp Inc.; *U.S. Public*, pg. 1667
PEOPLES BANK & TRUST COMPANY; *U.S. Private*, pg. 3141
PEOPLES FIRST PROPERTIES INC.; *U.S. Private*, pg. 3142
PEOPLES STATE BANK—See PSB Holdings, Inc.; *U.S. Public*, pg. 1734
PERPETUAL FEDERAL SAVINGS BANK, INC.—See Farmers & Merchants Bancorp, Inc.; *U.S. Public*, pg. 822
PHOENIXVILLE FEDERAL BANK & TRUST; *U.S. Private*, pg. 3174
PHYSICIAN BILLING PARTNERS LLC—See Medstreaming, LLC; *U.S. Private*, pg. 2659
PIEDMONT FEDERAL SAVINGS BANK—See Piedmont Financial Holding Company; *U.S. Private*, pg. 3177
PIONEER BANK; *U.S. Private*, pg. 3186
PIONEER SAVINGS BANK; *U.S. Private*, pg. 3188
PNC BANK, NATIONAL ASSOCIATION—See The PNC Financial Services Group, Inc.; *U.S. Public*, pg. 2119
PREFERRED BANK—See Preferred Bancshares, Inc.; *U.S. Private*, pg. 3247
PRESIDENTIAL BANK, FSB; *U.S. Private*, pg. 3254
PRINCIPAL BANK—See Principal Financial Group, Inc.; *U.S. Public*, pg. 1720
PROGRESSIVE SAVINGS BANK; *U.S. Private*, pg. 3279
PROVIDENT SAVINGS BANK, F.S.B.—See Provident Financial Holdings, Inc.; *U.S. Public*, pg. 1730
PRUDENTIAL BANK—See Fulton Financial Corporation; *U.S. Public*, pg. 892
PUTNAM COUNTY SAVINGS BANK; *U.S. Private*, pg. 3307
QUARRY CITY SAVINGS AND LOAN ASSOCIATION INC.—See Community National Bank & Trust; *U.S. Private*, pg. 996
RADIUS BANK—See LendingClub Corporation; *U.S. Public*, pg. 1305
THE RAHWAY SAVINGS INSTITUTION; *U.S. Private*, pg. 4102
RANDOLPH SAVINGS BANK—See Hometown Financial Group, Inc.; *U.S. Private*, pg. 1975
RAYMOND JAMES BANK, NATIONAL ASSOCIATION—See Raymond James Financial, Inc.; *U.S. Public*, pg. 1764
REGISTRO DE PRESTACIONES INFORMATICAS, S.A.—See Lone Star Funds; *U.S. Private*, pg. 2485
RIDGEWOOD SAVINGS BANK; *U.S. Private*, pg. 3434
RIVERMARK COMMUNITY CREDIT UNION; *U.S. Private*, pg. 3444
RIVER VALLEY BANK—See River Valley Bancorporation, Inc.; *U.S. Private*, pg. 3444

ROANOKE RAPIDS SAVINGS BANK, SSB; *U.S. Private*, pg. 3453
ROLLSTONE BANK & TRUST; *U.S. Private*, pg. 3475
ROSEDALE FEDERAL SAVINGS & LOAN ASSOCIATION; *U.S. Private*, pg. 3482
ROSELLE SAVINGS BANK; *U.S. Private*, pg. 3483
ROYAL SAVINGS BANK—See Royal Financial, Inc.; *U.S. Public*, pg. 1815
SACO & BIDDEFORD SAVINGS INSTITUTION; *U.S. Private*, pg. 3522
SALEM FIVE CENTS SAVINGS BANK—See Salem Five Bancorp; *U.S. Private*, pg. 3531
SALZBURGER SPARKASSE BANK AG—See Erste Group Bank AG; *Int'l*, pg. 2498
SANFORD INSTITUTION FOR SAVINGS; *U.S. Private*, pg. 3545
SANTANDER BANK, N.A.—See Banco Santander, S.A.; *Int'l*, pg. 827
SAVINGS BANK OF DANBURY; *U.S. Private*, pg. 3557
SAVINGS BANK OF WALPOLE; *U.S. Private*, pg. 3557
SCHAUMBURG BANK & TRUST COMPANY, N.A.—See Wintrust Financial Corporation; *U.S. Public*, pg. 2375
SECOND NATIONAL BANK—See Park National Corporation; *U.S. Public*, pg. 1638
SECURITY FEDERAL BANK—See Security Federal Corporation; *U.S. Public*, pg. 1856
SECURITY FEDERAL SAVINGS BANK OF MCMINNVILLE—See Security Bancorp, Inc.; *U.S. Public*, pg. 1855
SECURITY FEDERAL SAVINGS BANK; *U.S. Private*, pg. 3595
SENECA FEDERAL SAVINGS & LOAN ASSOCIATION; *U.S. Private*, pg. 3606
SEVERN SAVINGS BANK, FSB—See Shore Bancshares, Inc.; *U.S. Public*, pg. 1875
SHAMROCK BANK, N.A.—See Shamrock Bancshares, Inc.; *U.S. Private*, pg. 3624
SOMERSET SAVINGS BANK, SLA; *U.S. Private*, pg. 3712
SOUTHBRIDGE SAVINGS BANK—See SSB Community Bancorp MHC; *U.S. Private*, pg. 3768
SOUTH COASTAL BANK; *U.S. Private*, pg. 3721
SOUTHCREST BANK, N.A.—See Colony Bankcorp, Inc.; *U.S. Public*, pg. 533
SOUTHFIRST BANK—See FirstBanc of Alabama, Inc.; *U.S. Private*, pg. 1531
SOUTH SHORE SAVINGS BANK; *U.S. Private*, pg. 3724
SOUTH STATE BANK, N.A.—See SouthState Corporation; *U.S. Public*, pg. 1913
SOUTHTRUST BANK, N.A.—See Live Oak Bancshares Corporation; *U.S. Private*, pg. 2473
SPAARBELEG KAS N.V.—See Aegon N.V.; *Int'l*, pg. 175
SPARKASSE HAINBURG-BRUCK-NEUSIEDL AG—See Erste Group Bank AG; *Int'l*, pg. 2498
SPENCER SAVINGS BANK, SLA; *U.S. Private*, pg. 3755
SPENCER SAVINGS BANK—See SSB Community Bancorp MHC; *U.S. Private*, pg. 3768
STANDARD BANK, PASB—See Dollar Mutual Bancorp; *U.S. Private*, pg. 1254
STATE BANK OF FOX LAKE—See Farmers State Bank; *U.S. Private*, pg. 1479
STEARNS BANK HOLDINGFORD N.A.—See Stearns Financial Services, Inc.; *U.S. Private*, pg. 3795
STEARNS BANK N.A.—See Stearns Financial Services, Inc.; *U.S. Private*, pg. 3795
STEARNS BANK UPSALA N.A.—See Stearns Financial Services, Inc.; *U.S. Private*, pg. 3795
STERLING BANK & TRUST, FSB—See Sterling Bancorp, Inc.; *U.S. Public*, pg. 1946
STERLING FEDERAL BANK FSB; *U.S. Private*, pg. 3805
STONEHAM BANK; *U.S. Private*, pg. 3828
STURDY SAVINGS BANK; *U.S. Private*, pg. 3844
SUGAR RIVER SAVINGS BANK; *U.S. Private*, pg. 3849
SUMMIT STATE BANK; *U.S. Public*, pg. 1960
SUNFLOWER BANK, NATIONAL ASSOCIATION—See FirstSun Capital Bancorp; *U.S. Public*, pg. 850
SUNNYSIDE FEDERAL SAVINGS & LOAN ASSOCIATION OF IRVINGTON—See Vecta Inc.; *U.S. Private*, pg. 4349
SYNCHRONY BANK—See Synchrony Financial; *U.S. Public*, pg. 1970
TBK BANK, SSB—See Triumph Financial, Inc.; *U.S. Public*, pg. 2196
TECNISEGUROS, SOCIEDAD DE AGENCIA DE SEGUROS, S.A.—See Grupo Catalana Occidente, S.A.; *Int'l*, pg. 3124
TERRITORIAL SAVINGS BANK—See Territorial Bancorp Inc.; *U.S. Public*, pg. 2021
TEXAS CITIZENS BANK, N.A.—See Business First Bancshares, Inc.; *U.S. Public*, pg. 413
TEXAS FIRST BANK—See Preferred Bancshares, Inc.; *U.S. Private*, pg. 3247
THIRD FEDERAL SAVINGS & LOAN ASSOCIATION OF CLEVELAND—See TFS Financial Corporation; *U.S. Public*, pg. 2029
THOMASTON SAVINGS BANK; *U.S. Private*, pg. 4158
THUMB BANK & TRUST—See Thumb Bancorp, Inc.; *U.S. Private*, pg. 4165
TIAA, FSB—See Teachers Insurance Association - College Retirement Fund; *U.S. Private*, pg. 3948

522210 — CREDIT CARD ISSUING

TIB THE INDEPENDENT BANKERSBANK, NATIONAL ASSOCIATION—See Independent Bankers Financial Corporation; *U.S. Private*, pg. 2058
TIMBERLAND BANK—See Timberland Bancorp, Inc.; *U.S. Public*, pg. 2159
TIROLER SPARKASSE BANK AG—See Erste Group Bank AG; *Int'l*, pg. 2498
THE TORRINGTON SAVINGS BANK INC.; *U.S. Private*, pg. 4127
TRUSTCO BANK—See TrustCo Bank Corp NY; *U.S. Public*, pg. 2201
TRUSTMARK NATIONAL BANK—See Trustmark Corporation; *U.S. Public*, pg. 2202
TRUSTTEXAS BANK; *U.S. Private*, pg. 4251
TSB BANK; *U.S. Private*, pg. 4252
TWO RIVERS BANK & TRUST—See Two Rivers Financial Group, Inc.; *U.S. Public*, pg. 2207
UEB (SWITZERLAND)—See BNP Paribas SA; *Int'l*, pg. 1093
ULSTER SAVINGS BANK; *U.S. Private*, pg. 4277
UMB BANK, N.A.—See UMB Financial Corporation; *U.S. Public*, pg. 2224
UNIBANK FOR SAVINGS—See UFS Bancorp; *U.S. Private*, pg. 4274
UNION BANK; *U.S. Private*, pg. 4284
UNION COUNTY SAVINGS BANK; *U.S. Private*, pg. 4284
UNION SAVINGS BANK; *U.S. Private*, pg. 4285
UNION SAVINGS & LOAN ASSOCIATION; *U.S. Private*, pg. 4285
UNITED BANK—See Park National Corporation; *U.S. Public*, pg. 1638
UNITED BANK & TRUST NA—See Ames National Corporation; *U.S. Public*, pg. 116
UNITED COMMUNITY BANK—See United Community Bancorp, Inc.; *U.S. Private*, pg. 4289
UNITED FIDELITY BANK, FSB—See Fidelity Federal Bancorp; *U.S. Public*, pg. 830
UNITED MIDWEST SAVINGS BANK, N.A.; *U.S. Private*, pg. 4294
UNITED SAVINGS BANK; *U.S. Private*, pg. 4297
UNIVERSAL BANK; *U.S. Private*, pg. 4303
USAA FEDERAL SAVINGS BANK—See United Services Automobile Association; *U.S. Private*, pg. 4297
VALLEY NATIONAL BANK—See Valley National Bancorp; *U.S. Public*, pg. 2273
VERSICHERUNGSSERVICE DER FRANKFURTER SPARKASSE GMBH—See Frankfurter Sparkasse; *Int'l*, pg. 2761
VISION BANK, N.A.—See Vision Bancshares, Inc.; *U.S. Private*, pg. 4390
VOLUNTEER FEDERAL SAVINGS BANK; *U.S. Private*, pg. 4411
WALDEN SAVINGS BANKS; *U.S. Private*, pg. 4428
WALLKILL VALLEY FEDERAL SAVINGS & LOAN ASSOCIATION—See Wallkill Valley Bancorp Inc.; *U.S. Private*, pg. 4431
WALPOLE COOPERATIVE BANK; *U.S. Private*, pg. 4432
WASHINGTON FEDERAL, NATIONAL ASSOCIATION—See WaFd, Inc.; *U.S. Public*, pg. 2321
WATERTOWN SAVINGS BANK INC.; *U.S. Private*, pg. 4454
WEBSTER BANK, N.A.—See Webster Financial Corporation; *U.S. Public*, pg. 2341
WEBSTER FIVE CENTS SAVINGS BANK; *U.S. Private*, pg. 4467
WEST END BANK, S.B.—See 3Rivers Federal Credit Union; *U.S. Private*, pg. 14
WESTERN ALLIANCE BANK—See Western Alliance Bancorporation; *U.S. Public*, pg. 2354
WESTFIELD BANK—See Western New England Bancorp, Inc.; *U.S. Public*, pg. 2356
WEST VIEW SAVINGS BANK—See WVS Financial Corp.; *U.S. Public*, pg. 2384
WILLIAM PENN BANK—See William Penn Bancorporation; *U.S. Public*, pg. 2371
WILMINGTON SAVINGS FUND SOCIETY, FEDERAL SAVINGS BANK—See WSFS Financial Corporation; *U.S. Public*, pg. 2384
WINCHESTER SAVINGS BANK; *U.S. Private*, pg. 4533
WINTER HILL BANK; *U.S. Private*, pg. 4545
WOODSVILLE GUARANTY SAVINGS BANK; *U.S. Private*, pg. 4561
YAKIMA FEDERAL SAVINGS & LOAN ASSOCIATION; *U.S. Private*, pg. 4584
ZIONS BANCORPORATION, NATIONAL ASSOCIATION; *U.S. Public*, pg. 2408

522210 — CREDIT CARD ISSUING

ABU DHABI ISLAMIC BANK-EGYPT; *Int'l*, pg. 72
ADDIKO BANK A.D.—See Addiko Bank AG; *Int'l*, pg. 129
ADDIKO BANK A.D.—See Addiko Bank AG; *Int'l*, pg. 129
ADDIKO BANK A.D.—See Addiko Bank AG; *Int'l*, pg. 129
ADDIKO BANK D.D.—See Addiko Bank AG; *Int'l*, pg. 129
ADDIKO BANK D.D.—See Addiko Bank AG; *Int'l*, pg. 129
ADDIKO BANK D.D.—See Addiko Bank AG; *Int'l*, pg. 129
ADUNO HOLDING AG; *Int'l*, pg. 154

522210 — CREDIT CARD ISSUING

ADVANCED MAGIC CARD CO., LTD.—See Advanced Info Service Plc; *Int'l*, pg. 159
ADYEN HONG KONG LIMITED—See Adyen N.V.; *Int'l*, pg. 169
ADYEN SINGAPORE PTE. LTD.—See Adyen N.V.; *Int'l*, pg. 170
ADYEN UK LIMITED—See Adyen N.V.; *Int'l*, pg. 170
AIGIN DC CARD CO., LTD.—See Aichi Financial Group Co., Ltd.; *Int'l*, pg. 229
AIRLINK TECHNOLOGY CO., LTD.—See Apollo Global Management, Inc.; *U.S. Public*, pg. 151
ALGEMENE ZEEUWSE VERZEKERING MAATSCHAPPIJ N.V.—See De Goudse N.V.; *Int'l*, pg. 1995
ALPHA CARD SCRL—See American Express Company; *U.S. Public*, pg. 101
AMC FS, INC.—See CU Cooperative Systems, Inc.; *U.S. Private*, pg. 1119
AMERICAN EXPRESS AUSTRIA BANK GMBH—See American Express Company; *U.S. Public*, pg. 100
AMERICAN EXPRESS BRASIL ASSESSORIA EMPRESARIAL LTDA.—See American Express Company; *U.S. Public*, pg. 100
AMERICAN EXPRESS COMPANY AS—See American Express Company; *U.S. Public*, pg. 101
AMERICAN EXPRESS CREDIT CORPORATION—See American Express Company; *U.S. Public*, pg. 101
AMERICAN EXPRESS FRANCE SAS—See American Express Company; *U.S. Public*, pg. 100
AMERICAN EXPRESS GLOBAL COMMERCIAL CARD GROUP—See American Express Company; *U.S. Public*, pg. 100
AMERICAN EXPRESS INTERNATIONAL (TAIWAN), INC.—See American Express Company; *U.S. Public*, pg. 101
AMERICAN EXPRESS (MALAYSIA) SDN. BHD.—See American Express Company; *U.S. Public*, pg. 100
AMERICAN EXPRESS OVERSEAS CREDIT CORPORATION LIMITED—See American Express Company; *U.S. Public*, pg. 101
AMEX BANK OF CANADA—See American Express Company; *U.S. Public*, pg. 101
AMEX CARD SERVICES COMPANY—See American Express Company; *U.S. Public*, pg. 101
ASSET ACCEPTANCE CAPITAL CORP.—See Encore Capital Group, Inc.; *U.S. Public*, pg. 759
ASSET EXCHANGE, INC.—See Fidelity National Infor; *U.S. Public*, pg. 832
BALBOA FINANCE S.A.—See Alba Grupo March; *Int'l*, pg. 292
BAMCARD D.D.; *Int'l*, pg. 813
BANCO FIBRA S.A.; *Int'l*, pg. 822
BANCO HIPOTECARIO SA; *Int'l*, pg. 823
BANCO SMARTBANK S.A.—See Banco Master S.A.; *Int'l*, pg. 823
BAYERN CARD-SERVICES GMBH—See BayernLB Holding AG; *Int'l*, pg. 913
BELFIUS LEASE SERVICES SA/NV—See Belfius Bank SA/NV; *Int'l*, pg. 963
BESSEMER GROUP UK LTD.—See The Bessemer Group, Incorporated; *U.S. Private*, pg. 3994
BESSEMER TRUST COMPANY (CAYMAN) LIMITED—See The Bessemer Group, Incorporated; *U.S. Private*, pg. 3994
BIOSMART CO. LTD.; *Int'l*, pg. 1042
BOB FINANCIAL SOLUTIONS LIMITED—See Bank of Baroda; *Int'l*, pg. 840
BOQ EQUIPMENT FINANCE LIMITED—See Bank of Queensland Limited; *Int'l*, pg. 848
BORGUN HF; *Int'l*, pg. 1114
BPI CARD CORPORATION—See Bank of the Philippine Islands; *Int'l*, pg. 848
BRADESPAR S.A.; *Int'l*, pg. 1134
BRIGHTWELL PAYMENTS, INC.—See Navigation Capital Partners, Inc.; *U.S. Private*, pg. 2873
CABELA'S CREDIT CARD MASTER NOTE TRUST; *U.S. Private*, pg. 710
CABELA'S MASTER CREDIT CARD TRUST; *U.S. Private*, pg. 710
CANADIAN WESTERN TRUST—See Canadian Western Bank; *Int'l*, pg. 1286
CAPITAL ONE BANK (USA), NATIONAL ASSOCIATION—See Capital One Financial Corporation; *U.S. Public*, pg. 431
CAPITAL ONE (EUROPE) PLC—See Capital One Financial Corporation; *U.S. Public*, pg. 431
CARDCASH LLC; *U.S. Private*, pg. 749
CARECREDIT LLC—See Synchrony Financial; *U.S. Public*, pg. 1970
CARECREDIT LLC—See Synchrony Financial; *U.S. Public*, pg. 1970
CARECREDIT LLC—See Synchrony Financial; *U.S. Public*, pg. 1970
CARECREDIT LLC—See Synchrony Financial; *U.S. Public*, pg. 1970
CATERPILLAR FINANCIAL SERVICES CORPORATION—See Caterpillar, Inc.; *U.S. Public*, pg. 450
CCS CESKA SPOLECNOST PRO PLATEBNI KARTY SRO—See Corpay, Inc.; *U.S. Public*, pg. 579
CENCOSUD ADMINISTRADORA DE TARJETAS S.A.—See Cencosud S.A.; *Int'l*, pg. 1400
CHASE CARD SERVICES, INC.—See JPMorgan Chase & Co.; *U.S. Public*, pg. 1206
CHEAHA BANK—See Investar Holding Corporation; *U.S. Public*, pg. 1164
CHEMUNG FINANCIAL CORPORATION; *U.S. Public*, pg. 484
CITIBANK CREDIT CARD ISSUANCE TRUST; *U.S. Private*, pg. 901
CITIBANK (SOUTH DAKOTA), N.A.—See Citigroup Inc.; *U.S. Public*, pg. 502
CITI CARDS CANADA INC.—See Citigroup Inc.; *U.S. Public*, pg. 501
CITI GLOBAL CARDS—See Citigroup Inc.; *U.S. Public*, pg. 502
CITIZENS ONE CARD SERVICES—See Citizens Financial Group, Inc.; *U.S. Public*, pg. 505
COFINOGA S.A.—See BNP Paribas SA; *Int'l*, pg. 1091
COFINOGA S.A.—See Galeries Lafayette SA; *Int'l*, pg. 2872
COLIN BUCHANAN & PARTNERS LTD.—See Belfius Bank SA/NV; *Int'l*, pg. 963
COMPERIA.PL SA; *Int'l*, pg. 1753
CREDIMAX B.S.C.—See BBK B.S.C.; *Int'l*, pg. 920
CREDIT ACCEPTANCE CORPORATION; *U.S. Public*, pg. 593
CREDITCARDS.COM, INC.; *U.S. Private*, pg. 1092
CREDIT SAISON CO., LTD.; *Int'l*, pg. 1835
CROGHAN BANCSHARES, INC.; *U.S. Public*, pg. 595
THE DAISHI DC CARD CO., LTD.—See Daishi Hokuetsu Financial Group, Inc.; *Int'l*, pg. 1941
THE DAISHI JCB CARD CO., LTD.—See Daishi Hokuetsu Financial Group, Inc.; *Int'l*, pg. 1941
DAIWA HOUSE FINANCIAL CO., LTD.—See Daiwa House Industry Co., Ltd.; *Int'l*, pg. 1945
DBS BANK LTD.—See DBS Group Holdings Ltd.; *Int'l*, pg. 1988
DBS CARD CENTRE PTE. LTD.—See DBS Group Holdings Ltd.; *Int'l*, pg. 1988
DENT-A-MED INC.—See Harbert Management Corporation; *U.S. Private*, pg. 1858
DINERS CLUB UAE LLC—See Emirates NBD PJSC; *Int'l*, pg. 2381
DISCOVER CARD—See Discover Financial Services; *U.S. Public*, pg. 668
DISCOVER FINANCIAL SERVICES; *U.S. Public*, pg. 668
ECARD S.A.; *Int'l*, pg. 2287
EFG RETAIL SERVICES IFN S.A.—See Eurobank Ergasias Services and Holdings S.A.; *Int'l*, pg. 2532
EFT-USLUGE D.O.O—See Euronet Worldwide, Inc.; *U.S. Public*, pg. 797
THE EIGHTEENTH CARD CO., LTD.—See Fukuoka Financial Group, Inc.; *Int'l*, pg. 2840
ELECTRONIC CHECK SERVICES INC; *U.S. Private*, pg. 1355
EML PAYMENTS LIMITED; *Int'l*, pg. 2383
ERSTE CARD CLUB D.D.—See Erste Group Bank AG; *Int'l*, pg. 2498
EURCO LTD.—See Belfius Bank SA/NV; *Int'l*, pg. 963
EURONET SERVICES GMBH—See Euronet Worldwide, Inc.; *U.S. Public*, pg. 798
EURONET SERVICES, SPOL. S.R.O.—See Euronet Worldwide, Inc.; *U.S. Public*, pg. 798
EURONET SERVICES SRL—See Euronet Worldwide, Inc.; *U.S. Public*, pg. 798
EURONET WORLDWIDE GREECE—See Euronet Worldwide, Inc.; *U.S. Public*, pg. 798
FCE BANK PLC—See Ford Motor Company; *U.S. Public*, pg. 865
FIRST BUSINESS FINANCIAL SERVICES, INC.; *U.S. Public*, pg. 840
FIRST CITIZENS INVESTOR SERVICES, INC.—See First Citizens BancShares, Inc.; *U.S. Public*, pg. 842
FIS CARD PROCESSING SERVICES (CHILE) S.A.—See Fidelity National Infor; *U.S. Public*, pg. 832
FORD CREDIT A/S—See Ford Motor Company; *U.S. Public*, pg. 865
FORD CREDIT CANADA COMPANY—See Ford Motor Company; *U.S. Public*, pg. 866
FORTE PAYMENT SYSTEMS, INC.—See CSG Systems International, Inc.; *U.S. Public*, pg. 601
FRANCIS DAVID CORPORATION—See BharCap Partners, LLC; *U.S. Private*, pg. 549
GARANTI ODEME SISTEMLERI AS—See Banco Bilbao Vizcaya Argentaria, S.A.; *Int'l*, pg. 818
GE CREDITLINE—See General Electric Company; *U.S. Public*, pg. 920
GEO PAYMENT SERVICE CORPORATION—See GEO Holdings Corporation; *Int'l*, pg. 2932
GLOBAL PAYMENT SERVICES W.L.L.—See BBK B.S.C.; *Int'l*, pg. 920
GOGO ENERGY SINGAPORE PTE. LTD.—See GOGOX Holdings Limited; *Int'l*, pg. 3022
GREEN DOT BANK—See Green Dot Corporation; *U.S. Public*, pg. 963
GREEN DOT CORPORATION; *U.S. Public*, pg. 963
HACHIJUNI DC CARD CO., LTD.; *Int'l*, pg. 3203
HANA SK CARD—See Hana Financial Group, Inc.; *Int'l*, pg. 3240
HANG SENG BANK LIMITED—See HSBC Holdings plc; *Int'l*, pg. 3507
HOKKOKU GENERAL LEASING CO., LTD.—See Hokkoku Financial Holdings, Inc.; *Int'l*, pg. 3443
THE HOKUETSU CARD CO., LTD.—See Daishi Hokuetsu Financial Group, Inc.; *Int'l*, pg. 1941
HOUSE PAYMENT CO., LTD.—See Daito Trust Construction Co., Ltd.; *Int'l*, pg. 1943
HYWEB TECHNOLOGY CO., LTD.; *Int'l*, pg. 3561
IDEMITSU CREDIT CO., LTD.—See Credit Saison Co., Ltd.; *Int'l*, pg. 1836
INTERNATIONAL CARD SERVICES B.V.—See ABN AMRO Group N.V.; *Int'l*, pg. 65
JCC PAYMENT SYSTEMS LTD—See Bank of Cyprus Holdings Public Limited Company; *Int'l*, pg. 842
JOHN DEERE CAPITAL CORPORATION—See Deere & Company; *U.S. Public*, pg. 646
KEB HANA CARD CO., LTD.—See Hana Financial Group, Inc.; *Int'l*, pg. 3241
LAFAYETTE SERVICES LASER—See BNP Paribas SA; *Int'l*, pg. 1091
LAFAYETTE SERVICES LASER—See Galeries Lafayette SA; *Int'l*, pg. 2872
LASER POLSKA—See BNP Paribas SA; *Int'l*, pg. 1091
LASER POLSKA—See Galeries Lafayette SA; *Int'l*, pg. 2872
LEGEND CREDIT, INC.—See Bitcoin Brands Inc.; *U.S. Private*, pg. 567
LONE STAR AG CREDIT; *U.S. Private*, pg. 2484
MAINE COMMUNITY BANK—See Maine Community Bancorp, MHC; *U.S. Private*, pg. 2552
MANNATEC, INC.—See Corpay, Inc.; *U.S. Public*, pg. 580
MASTERCARD CANADA, INC.—See Mastercard Incorporated; *U.S. Public*, pg. 1394
MASTERCARD EUROPE SA—See Mastercard Incorporated; *U.S. Public*, pg. 1394
MASTERCARD INTERNATIONAL INCORPORATED - IRELAND—See Mastercard Incorporated; *U.S. Public*, pg. 1394
MBF CARDS (MSIA) SDN. BHD.—See AMMB Holdings Berhad; *Int'l*, pg. 429
MBNA LIMITED—See Bank of America Corporation; *U.S. Public*, pg. 271
MERCHANT SERVICES DIRECT LLC; *U.S. Private*, pg. 2669
MOGO FINANCE TECHNOLOGY, INC.—See Difference Capital Financial Inc.; *Int'l*, pg. 2118
NETSPEND CORPORATION—See Rev Worldwide, Inc.; *U.S. Private*, pg. 3412
NETSPEND CORPORATION—See Searchlight Capital Partners, L.P.; *U.S. Private*, pg. 3590
NFINANSE INC.—See AccountNow, Inc.; *U.S. Private*, pg. 54
OBERTHUR CARD SYSTEMS KART SISTEMLERI SANAYI VE TICARET LIMITED SIRKETI—See Advent International Corporation; *U.S. Private*, pg. 102
OBERTHUR CARD SYSTEMS OOO—See Advent International Corporation; *U.S. Private*, pg. 102
OBERTHUR CARD SYSTEMS PVT. LTD.—See Advent International Corporation; *U.S. Private*, pg. 102
OBERTHUR CARD SYSTEMS SCIENCE & TECHNOLOGY (SHENZHEN) CO. LTD—See Advent International Corporation; *U.S. Private*, pg. 102
OBERTHUR TECHNOLOGIES IBERICA—See Advent International Corporation; *U.S. Private*, pg. 102
OBERTHUR TECHNOLOGIES THE NETHERLANDS BV—See Advent International Corporation; *U.S. Private*, pg. 103
OBERTHUR TECHNOLOGIES UK LTD.—See Advent International Corporation; *U.S. Private*, pg. 103
PACIFIC PRIDE SERVICES, LLC—See WEX, Inc.; *U.S. Public*, pg. 2364
PIONEER FINANCIAL SERVICES, INC.—See MidCountry Financial Corp.; *U.S. Private*, pg. 2711
PLUMAS BANK—See Plumas Bancorp; *U.S. Public*, pg. 1699
PREMIER BANKCARD, LLC—See United National Corporation; *U.S. Private*, pg. 4295
PREPAYD, INC.; *U.S. Private*, pg. 3252
PULSE NETWORK LLC—See Discover Financial Services; *U.S. Public*, pg. 668
RABOBANK CURACAO NV—See Cooperatieve Centrale Raiffeisen-Boerenleenbank B.A.; *Int'l*, pg. 1792
RABOBANK FRANCE—See Cooperatieve Centrale Raiffeisen-Boerenleenbank B.A.; *Int'l*, pg. 1792
RABOBANK SINGAPORE—See Cooperatieve Centrale Raiffeisen-Boerenleenbank B.A.; *Int'l*, pg. 1792
READY FINANCIAL GROUP, INC.—See Green Dot Corporation; *U.S. Public*, pg. 963
REAGRA SA—See Belfius Bank SA/NV; *Int'l*, pg. 963
REPUBLIC BANK INC.—See Republic Bancshares, Inc.; *U.S. Private*, pg. 3401
RYUGIN DC CO., LTD.—See Bank of The Ryukyus, Ltd.; *Int'l*, pg. 849
SANTANDER CARDS UK LTD.—See Banco Santander, S.A.; *Int'l*, pg. 827

522220 — SALES FINANCING

SECURENTA CONSEIL—See Belfius Bank SA/NV; *Int'l*, pg. 963
SECURIFUND NV—See Belfius Bank SA/NV; *Int'l*, pg. 963
SECURUS PAYMENTS; *U.S. Private*, pg. 3597
SERVE VIRTUAL ENTERPRISES, INC.—See American Express Company; *U.S. Public*, pg. 102
SKYLIGHT FINANCIAL, INC.—See Rev Worldwide, Inc.; *U.S. Private*, pg. 3413
SKYLIGHT FINANCIAL, INC.—See Searchlight Capital Partners, L.P.; *U.S. Private*, pg. 3590
SWIFT PREPAID SOLUTIONS, INC.—See Bain Capital, LP; *U.S. Private*, pg. 436
SWIFT PREPAID SOLUTIONS, INC.—See Silversmith Management, L.P.; *U.S. Private*, pg. 3664
SWISSCARD AECS AG—See American Express Company; *U.S. Public*, pg. 101
SWISSCARD AECS GMBH—See American Express Company; *U.S. Public*, pg. 102
SYNCHRONY FINANCIAL CANADA—See Synchrony Financial; *U.S. Public*, pg. 1970
SYNERGY CARDS SDN. BHD.—See Advance Synergy Berhad; *Int'l*, pg. 157
TAKASHIMAYA CREDIT CO. LTD.—See Credit Saison Co., Ltd.; *Int'l*, pg. 1836
T CARD & MARKETING CO., LTD.—See Culture Convenience Club Co., Ltd.; *Int'l*, pg. 1877
TEXTRON FINANCIAL INVESTMENT CORPORATION—See Textron Inc.; *U.S. Public*, pg. 2029
TRAVELCARD, B.V.—See Corpay, Inc.; *U.S. Public*, pg. 580
UNITED CONSUMER FINANCIAL SERVICES COMPANY—See Berkshire Hathaway Inc.; *U.S. Public*, pg. 300
VALUEDESIGN SINGAPORE PTE. LTD.—See Arara, Inc.; *Int'l*, pg. 536
VANITYSTYLE SP. Z O.O.—See Benefit Systems SA; *Int'l*, pg. 972
VELOCITY PORTFOLIO GROUP, INC.; *U.S. Private*, pg. 4354
VISA EUROPE LIMITED—See Visa, Inc.; *U.S. Public*, pg. 2301
VISA U.S.A., INC.—See Visa, Inc.; *U.S. Public*, pg. 2301
WELLS FARGO FINANCIAL, INC.—See Wells Fargo & Company; *U.S. Public*, pg. 2346
WELLS FARGO FINANCIAL—See Wells Fargo & Company; *U.S. Public*, pg. 2346

522220 — SALES FINANCING

1ST SOURCE LEASING, INC.—See 1st Source Corporation; *U.S. Public*, pg. 3
360 FINANCE PTY LTD—See Eagers Automotive Limited; *Int'l*, pg. 2263
3 STEP IT AS—See 3 Step It Group Oy; *Int'l*, pg. 6
3 STEP IT OY—See 3 Step It Group Oy; *Int'l*, pg. 6
ABIRAMI FINANCIAL SERVICES INDIA LTD.; *Int'l*, pg. 62
ABU DHABI NATIONAL LEASING LLC—See First Abu Dhabi Bank P.J.S.C.; *Int'l*, pg. 2681
ACCIONA CONCESIONES, S.L.—See Acciona, S.A.; *Int'l*, pg. 90
ACCORD CAPX LLC—See Accord Financial Corp.; *Int'l*, pg. 92
ACCORD FINANCIAL GROUP INC.; *U.S. Private*, pg. 53
ACCORD FINANCIAL INC.—See Accord Financial Corp.; *Int'l*, pg. 92
ACCORD SMALL BUSINESS FINANCE CORP—See Accord Financial Corp.; *Int'l*, pg. 92
ADVANTAGE FUNDING MANAGEMENT CO., INC.—See Sterling Bancorp; *U.S. Public*, pg. 1946
ADVANTEST PRE-OWNED SOLUTIONS CO., LTD.—See Advantest Corporation; *Int'l*, pg. 166
AFS ACCEPTANCE LLC—See Credito Real S.A.B. de C.V.; *Int'l*, pg. 1837
ALBIS LEASING AG; *Int'l*, pg. 299
ALIOR LEASING SP. Z O.O.—See Alior Bank S.A.; *Int'l*, pg. 329
ALL IN ONE VERMIETUNG GMBH—See BNP Paribas SA; *Int'l*, pg. 1079
AL MANAR FINANCING & LEASING CO.; *Int'l*, pg. 281
AMERICAN INDUSTRIAL LEASING COMPANY INC.—See Elkin Co.; *U.S. Private*, pg. 1363
AMW CAPITAL LEASING & FINANCE PLC; *Int'l*, pg. 443
ARAB LEASING COMPANY PSC—See Arab Palestinian Investment Company; *Int'l*, pg. 531
ARETE ACQUISITIONS, LLC; *U.S. Private*, pg. 318
ARVAL DEUTSCHLAND GMBH—See BNP Paribas SA; *Int'l*, pg. 1080
ARVAL MAROC—See BNP Paribas SA; *Int'l*, pg. 1080
ASB LEASING LLC—See Belarusbank; *Int'l*, pg. 963
ASHOK LEYLAND FINANCE LTD.—See Hinduja Group Ltd.; *Int'l*, pg. 3398
ASSOCIATED MOTOR FINANCE COMPANY PLC; *Int'l*, pg. 649
ASTA FUNDING, INC.; *U.S. Private*, pg. 360
ATEL FINANCIAL SERVICES—See ATEL Capital Group; *U.S. Private*, pg. 366
AUTOBANK AG; *Int'l*, pg. 726

AUTOCAPITAL CANADA INC.; *Int'l*, pg. 726
AUTO CREDIT OF FLORIDA INC.—See Scott-McRae Automotive Group Inc.; *U.S. Private*, pg. 3578
AUTO CREDIT OF GEORGIA INC.—See Scott-McRae Automotive Group Inc.; *U.S. Private*, pg. 3578
AUTOMOTIVE PRODUCT CONSULTANTS, INC.; *U.S. Private*, pg. 400
AUTO TRADING LEASING IFN S.A.—See Banco BPM S.p.A.; *Int'l*, pg. 818
AUXIMIO AG—See IGP Advantag AG; *Int'l*, pg. 3603
AVANGARD CAPITAL GROUP, INC.; *U.S. Private*, pg. 404
BAIYING HOLDINGS GROUP LIMITED; *Int'l*, pg. 803
BALBOA CAPITAL CORPORATION; *U.S. Private*, pg. 458
BALLYVESEY FINANCE LTD—See Ballyvesey Holdings Limited; *Int'l*, pg. 809
BALTIC LEASING LLC—See Central Bank of the Russian Federation; *Int'l*, pg. 1405
BANC OF AMERICA LEASING & CAPITAL, LLC—See Bank of America Corporation; *U.S. Public*, pg. 270
BARCLAY LEASING LIMITED—See Barclays PLC; *Int'l*, pg. 859
BARCLAYS LEASING (NO.9) LIMITED—See Barclays PLC; *Int'l*, pg. 861
BBAM LLC; *U.S. Private*, pg. 497
BBVA LEASING MEXICO SA DE CV—See Banco Bilbao Vizcaya Argentaria, S.A.; *Int'l*, pg. 817
BCC LEASE SPA—See Iccrea Holding S.p.A.; *Int'l*, pg. 3578
BMW BANK GMBH—See Bayerische Motoren Werke Aktiengesellschaft; *Int'l*, pg. 911
BMW FINANCIAL SERVICES NA, LLC—See Bayerische Motoren Werke Aktiengesellschaft; *Int'l*, pg. 912
BMW LEASING GMBH—See Bayerische Motoren Werke Aktiengesellschaft; *Int'l*, pg. 912
BNP PARIBAS LEASING SOLUTIONS ZRT—See BNP Paribas SA; *Int'l*, pg. 1086
BOEING INTERNATIONAL B.V. & CO. HOLDING KGAA—See The Boeing Company; *U.S. Public*, pg. 2040
BOMBARDIER CAPITAL INCORPORATED—See Bombardier Inc.; *Int'l*, pg. 1104
BOSTON SERVICE COMPANY, INC.—See Truist Financial Corporation; *U.S. Public*, pg. 2199
BPCE LEASE SA—See Groupe BPCE; *Int'l*, pg. 3092
BPI LEASING CORPORATION—See Bank of the Philippine Islands; *Int'l*, pg. 848
BRILLIANCE-BEA AUTO FINANCE CO., LTD.—See Brilliance China Automotive Holdings Limited; *Int'l*, pg. 1163
BROLI FINANCE PTY. LTD.—See Australia Finance Group Ltd; *Int'l*, pg. 720
BYRIDER FINANCE, LLC—See Altamont Capital Partners; *U.S. Private*, pg. 205
BYRIDER SALES OF INDIANA, LLC—See Altamont Capital Partners; *U.S. Private*, pg. 205
CARFINCO INC.—See Banco Santander, S.A.; *Int'l*, pg. 825
CCAP AUTO LEASE LTD.—See Banco Santander, S.A.; *Int'l*, pg. 825
CELTIC LEASING CORP.—See Fifth Third Bancorp; *U.S. Public*, pg. 834
CENTERONE FINANCIAL SERVICES, LLC—See JM Family Enterprises Inc.; *U.S. Private*, pg. 2214
CESSNA FINANCE CORPORATION—See Textron Inc.; *U.S. Public*, pg. 2029
C&F FINANCE COMPANY—See C&F Financial Corporation; *U.S. Public*, pg. 414
CHAILEASE INTERNATIONAL FINANCE CORPORATION—See Chailease Holding Company Limited; *Int'l*, pg. 1437
C. H. BROWN CO., LLC—See Platte Valley Financial Service Companies Inc.; *U.S. Private*, pg. 3211
CHINA ART FINANCIAL HOLDINGS LIMITED; *Int'l*, pg. 1483
CIT AEROSPACE LLC—See First Citizens BancShares, Inc.; *U.S. Public*, pg. 841
CIT FINANCE & LEASING CORPORATION—See First Citizens BancShares, Inc.; *U.S. Public*, pg. 841
CIT FINANCE LLC—See First Citizens BancShares, Inc.; *U.S. Public*, pg. 841
THE CIT GROUP/COMMERCIAL SERVICES (ASIA), LIMITED—See First Citizens BancShares, Inc.; *U.S. Public*, pg. 842
CIT GROUP (FRANCE) SA—See First Citizens BancShares, Inc.; *U.S. Public*, pg. 841
CIT GROUP (FRANCE) SAS—See First Citizens BancShares, Inc.; *U.S. Public*, pg. 841
CITIZENS BANK, N.A.—See Citizens Financial Group, Inc.; *U.S. Public*, pg. 505
CLEAN POWER FINANCE INC.; *U.S. Private*, pg. 931
CNH INDUSTRIAL CAPITAL LLC—See CNH Industrial N.V.; *Int'l*, pg. 1674
COCA-COLA FINANCIAL CORPORATION—See The Coca-Cola Company; *U.S. Public*, pg. 2063
COMMERCIAL CREDIT GROUP INC.—See BDT Capital Partners, LLC; *U.S. Private*, pg. 502
COMMERZBANK LEASING LIMITED—See Commerzbank AG; *Int'l*, pg. 1717
CONSUMER AUTOMOTIVE FINANCE, INC.; *U.S. Public*, pg. 572

CONSUMER CREDIT, LLC—See Encore Capital Group, Inc.; *U.S. Public*, pg. 759
CQRC FINANCIAL LEASING CO., LTD.—See Chongqing Rural Commercial Bank Co., Ltd.; *Int'l*, pg. 1580
CRESTMARK—See Pathward Financial, Inc.; *U.S. Public*, pg. 1652
DBS ASIA LTD.—See DBS Group Holdings Ltd.; *Int'l*, pg. 1988
DEA LEASING IFN S.A.—See Banca Transilvania S.A.; *Int'l*, pg. 816
DEMETER-SOUTH BELOIT DIVISION—See Demeter LP; *U.S. Private*, pg. 1203
DEUTSCHE FORFAIT GMBH—See DF Deutsche Forfait AG; *Int'l*, pg. 2094
DEUTSCHE SCHIFFSBANK AG—See Commerzbank AG; *Int'l*, pg. 1717
DEXTER FINANCIAL SERVICES, INC.—See Dexter Apache Holdings, Inc.; *U.S. Private*, pg. 1220
DIRECT CAPITAL CORPORATION—See First Citizens BancShares, Inc.; *U.S. Public*, pg. 841
DNB SWEDEN AB—See DNB Bank ASA; *Int'l*, pg. 2148
DOMINION HOLDINGS, INC.—See BDO Unibank, Inc.; *Int'l*, pg. 930
DOOSAN CHINA FINANCIAL LEASING CORP.—See Doosan Corporation; *Int'l*, pg. 2173
DRIVEWAY FINANCE CORPORATION—See Lithia Motors, Inc.; *U.S. Public*, pg. 1322
EASYHOME U.S. LTD.—See goeasy Ltd.; *Int'l*, pg. 3021
EASYLEASING GMBH—See BAWAG Group AG; *Int'l*, pg. 900
EBV - LEASING GESELLSCHAFT M.B.H. & CO. KG.—See Erste Group Bank AG; *Int'l*, pg. 2498
EDGE FINANCIAL, INC.; *U.S. Private*, pg. 1334
EFG LEASING A.D. BELGRADE—See Eurobank Ergasias Services and Holdings S.A.; *Int'l*, pg. 2532
EFG LEASING IFN S.A.—See Eurobank Ergasias Services and Holdings S.A.; *Int'l*, pg. 2532
EFG LEASING POLAND SP. Z O.O—See Eurobank Ergasias Services and Holdings S.A.; *Int'l*, pg. 2532
EKAM LEASING & FINANCE CO. LTD.; *Int'l*, pg. 2338
EKSPORTFINANS ASA; *Int'l*, pg. 2340
ELCO LEASING LIMITED—See Commerzbank AG; *Int'l*, pg. 1718
ELKIN CO.; *U.S. Private*, pg. 1363
EMIL-RO LEASING S.P.A.—See BPER BANCA S.p.A.; *Int'l*, pg. 1132
EMKAY, INC.; *U.S. Private*, pg. 1383
ENKA FINANSAL KIRALAMA A.S.—See Enka Insaat ve Sanayi A.S.; *Int'l*, pg. 2440
ENNOBLE FINANCE, LLC—See CURO Group Holdings Corp.; *U.S. Public*, pg. 611
ERVIN LEASING COMPANY—See Ervin Industries, Inc.; *U.S. Private*, pg. 1424
ESTES LEASING LLC—See Aim Leasing Co.; *U.S. Private*, pg. 132
EXETER FINANCE LLC—See Blackstone Inc.; *U.S. Public*, pg. 353
FCB INTERNATIONAL LEASING CO., LTD.—See First Financial Holding Co., Ltd.; *Int'l*, pg. 2683
FCB LEASING CO., LTD—See First Financial Holding Co., Ltd.; *Int'l*, pg. 2683
FCE BANK PLC - SPAIN—See Ford Motor Company; *U.S. Public*, pg. 865
FERRARI FINANCIAL SERVICES S.P.A.—See Ferrari N.V.; *Int'l*, pg. 2639
FEXCO ASSET FINANCE—See FEXCO Holdings; *Int'l*, pg. 2649
FINALYSIS CREDIT & GUARANTEE CO. LTD.; *Int'l*, pg. 2664
FINANZIA AUTORENTING, S.A.—See Banco Bilbao Vizcaya Argentaria, S.A.; *Int'l*, pg. 817
FIRESTONE FINANCIAL, LLC—See Berkshire Hills Bancorp, Inc.; *U.S. Public*, pg. 320
FIRST FINANCIAL LEASING (CHENGDU) LTD.—See First Financial Holding Co., Ltd.; *Int'l*, pg. 2683
FIRST HAWAIIAN LEASING, INC.—See BNP Paribas SA; *Int'l*, pg. 1088
FIRST MIDWEST EQUIPMENT FINANCE CO.—See Old National Bancorp; *U.S. Public*, pg. 1567
FIRST SOUTHWEST LEASING COMPANY—See Hilltop Holdings Inc.; *U.S. Public*, pg. 1038
FIVE POINT CAPITAL, INC.; *U.S. Private*, pg. 1537
FLAGSHIP CREDIT ACCEPTANCE LLC—See Flagship Credit Corporation; *U.S. Private*, pg. 1539
FLEET NETWORK PTY LIMITED—See Consolidated Operations Group Limited; *Int'l*, pg. 1771
FLEXIRENT CAPITAL (NEW ZEALAND) LTD.—See Humm Group Limited; *Int'l*, pg. 3531
FLEXIRENT CAPITAL PTY. LTD.—See Humm Group Limited; *Int'l*, pg. 3531
FLEXIRENT SPV NO 4 PTY LIMITED—See Humm Group Limited; *Int'l*, pg. 3531
FORD CREDIT CP AUTO RECEIVABLES LLC—See Ford Motor Company; *U.S. Public*, pg. 866
FORTELEASING JSC—See ForteBank JSC; *Int'l*, pg. 2737
F&S FINANCE AND SERVICE LEASING GMBH—See Erste Group Bank AG; *Int'l*, pg. 2498
FUQIN FINTECH LIMITED; *Int'l*, pg. 2846

522220 — SALES FINANCING

FY FINANCIAL (SHENZHEN) CO., LTD.; *Int'l*, pg. 2859
GADDIS CAPITAL CORPORATION; *U.S. Private*, pg. 1633
GARANTI BBVA LEASING AS—See Banco Bilbao Vizcaya Argentaria, S.A.; *Int'l*, pg. 818
GAZPROMBANK LEASING JSC—See Gazprombank JSC; *Int'l*, pg. 2892
GENERAL MOTORS FINANCIAL SUISSE SA—See General Motors Company; *U.S. Public*, pg. 925
GLESBY-MARKS LTD; *U.S. Private*, pg. 1711
GLOBAL DEVELOPMENTS, INC.; *U.S. Public*, pg. 941
GLOCKNER QUALITY LEASING—See Glockner Chevrolet Co. Inc.; *U.S. Private*, pg. 1720
GMAC BANQUE S.A.—See General Motors Company; *U.S. Public*, pg. 925
GMAC ESPANA DE FINANCIACION, S.A. UNIPERSONAL—See General Motors Company; *U.S. Public*, pg. 925
GMAC - INSTITUICAO FINANCEIRA DE CREDITO, S.A.—See General Motors Company; *U.S. Public*, pg. 925
GMAC ITALIA SPA—See General Motors Company; *U.S. Public*, pg. 925
GMAC NEDERLAND N.V.—See General Motors Company; *U.S. Public*, pg. 925
GM FINANCIAL AB—See General Motors Company; *U.S. Public*, pg. 925
GM FINANCIAL GMBH—See General Motors Company; *U.S. Public*, pg. 925
GO-AHEAD LEASING LIMITED—See GLOBALVIA Inversiones, S.A.U.; *Int'l*, pg. 3005
GOWRA LEASING & FINANCE LIMITED; *Int'l*, pg. 3045
GRAYBAR FINANCIAL SERVICES, INC.—See Graybar Electric Company, Inc.; *U.S. Private*, pg. 1760
GREATAMERICA LEASING CORPORATION; *U.S. Private*, pg. 1768
HACHIJUNI LEASE CO., LTD; *Int'l*, pg. 3203
HAITONG UNITRUST INTERNATIONAL FINANCIAL LEASING CO., LTD.—See Haitong Securities Co., Ltd.; *Int'l*, pg. 3218
HBIS FINANCIAL LEASING CO., LTD.—See HBIS Group Co., Ltd.; *Int'l*, pg. 3296
HB LEASING & FINANCE COMPANY LIMITED; *Int'l*, pg. 3295
HERITAGE INSURANCE INC—See Covenant Logistics Group, Inc.; *U.S. Public*, pg. 588
HOEHN MOTORS; *U.S. Private*, pg. 1959
HOKUHOKU TOKAI TOKYO SECURITIES CO., LTD.—See Hokuhoku Financial Group, Inc.; *Int'l*, pg. 3444
HONDA FINANCE EUROPE PLC—See Honda Motor Co., Ltd.; *Int'l*, pg. 3462
HORIZON KEYSTONE FINANCIAL LLC—See HPS Investment Partners, LLC; *U.S. Private*, pg. 1997
HSBC AUTO FINANCE—See HSBC Holdings plc; *Int'l*, pg. 3505
H.W. KAUFMAN FINANCIAL GROUP, INC.; *U.S. Private*, pg. 1836
HYUNDAI CAPITAL AMERICA, INC.—See Hyundai Motor Company; *Int'l*, pg. 3559
HYUNDAI CAPITAL SERVICES, INC.—See Hyundai Motor Company; *Int'l*, pg. 3559
IBM GLOBAL FINANCING—See International Business Machines Corporation; *U.S. Public*, pg. 1146
IMOLEASING-SOCCIEDADE DE LOCACAO FINANCIERA IMOBILIARIA SA—See Caixa Geral de Depositos S.A.; *Int'l*, pg. 1260
IPDC FINANCE LIMITED—See Aga Khan Development Network; *Int'l*, pg. 199
IVECO FINANCE AG—See Barclays PLC; *Int'l*, pg. 862
J.D. BYRIDER SYSTEMS, LLC—See Altamont Capital Partners; *U.S. Private*, pg. 205
JINSHANG INTERNATIONAL FINANCIAL LEASING CO., LTD.—See Arta TechFin Corporation Limited; *Int'l*, pg. 581
JOHN DEERE FINANCIAL, F.S.B.—See Deere & Company; *U.S. Public*, pg. 646
KEMPTHORN MOTORS INC.; *U.S. Private*, pg. 2282
KEY EQUIPMENT FINANCE INTERNATIONAL INC.—See KeyCorp; *U.S. Public*, pg. 1225
KOREA LEASE FINANCING CO., LTD.—See DGB Financial Group Co., Ltd.; *Int'l*, pg. 2096
LEAF COMMERCIAL CAPITAL, INC.—See M&T Bank Corporation; *U.S. Public*, pg. 1351
LEASING ASSOCIATES INC.; *U.S. Private*, pg. 2408
LEASING TECHNOLOGIES INTERNATIONAL INC.; *U.S. Private*, pg. 2408
LOCAPOR - COMPANHIA PORTUGUESA LOCACAO FINANCERIA MOBILIARIA, S.A.—See Caixa Geral de Depositos S.A.; *Int'l*, pg. 1260
LSQ FUNDING GROUP, L.C.; *U.S. Private*, pg. 2509
LUFTHANSA TECHNIK AIRMOTIVE IRELAND LEASING LTD—See Deutsche Lufthansa AG; *Int'l*, pg. 2070
M2 EQUIPMENT FINANCE, LLC—See QCR Holdings, Inc.; *U.S. Public*, pg. 1742
MACROLEASE CORPORATION—See Brookline Bancorp, Inc.; *U.S. Public*, pg. 396
MAG CAPITAL, LLC—See Mid Western Automotive LLC; *U.S. Private*, pg. 2706

MERCANTILE CREDIT COMPANY LIMITED—See Barclays PLC; *Int'l*, pg. 862
MERCANTILE INDUSTRIAL LEASING LIMITED—See Barclays PLC; *Int'l*, pg. 862
MERCURY EQUIPMENT FINANCE GROUP; *U.S. Private*, pg. 2670
MORGAN STANLEY INDIA COMPANY PRIVATE LIMITED—See Morgan Stanley; *U.S. Public*, pg. 1472
MOUNT PLEASANT CAPITAL CORP.; *U.S. Private*, pg. 2798
NORDIC AVIATION CAPITAL INC.; *U.S. Private*, pg. 2936
NUTANA AVIATION CAPITAL IFSC PRIVATE LIMITED—See Easy Trip Planners Limited; *Int'l*, pg. 2276
OOO AFIN LEASING VOSTOK LLC—See CNH Industrial N.V.; *Int'l*, pg. 1676
OPEL LEASING AUSTRIA GMBH—See General Motors Company; *U.S. Public*, pg. 927
PACCAR FINANCIAL FRANCE S.A.S.—See PACCAR Inc.; *U.S. Public*, pg. 1630
PACCAR FINANCIAL PTY. LTD.—See PACCAR Inc.; *U.S. Public*, pg. 1631
PACCAR FINANCIAL SERVICES CORP.—See PACCAR Inc.; *U.S. Public*, pg. 1631
PDS GAMING CORPORATION—See Northlight Financial LLC; *U.S. Private*, pg. 2956
PENTECH FINANCIAL SERVICES; *U.S. Private*, pg. 3140
PEOPLE'S UNITED EQUIPMENT FINANCE CORP.—See M&T Bank Corporation; *U.S. Public*, pg. 1351
PIONEER SERVICES SALES FINANCE, INC.—See Mid-Country Acquisition Corp.; *U.S. Public*, pg. 2711
POLARIS ACCEPTANCE INC.—See Polaris, Inc.; *U.S. Public*, pg. 1700
PRIME CREDIT LEASING BERHAD—See Berjaya Corporation Berhad; *Int'l*, pg. 984
PT CHAILEASE INDONESIA FINANCE—See Chailease Holding Company Limited; *Int'l*, pg. 1437
RAILMARK HOLDINGS INC.; *U.S. Private*, pg. 3346
RELATIONAL LLC—See Relational LLC; *U.S. Private*, pg. 3392
REPUBLIC FINANCIAL CORPORATION; *U.S. Private*, pg. 3402
S AUTOLEASING A.S.—See Erste Group Bank AG; *Int'l*, pg. 2499
S AUTOLEASING GMBH—See Erste Group Bank AG; *Int'l*, pg. 2499
SCHNEIDER FINANCE, INC.—See Schneider National, Inc.; *U.S. Public*, pg. 1846
SCOTCHMAN CREDIT CORP.—See Krofam Inc.; *U.S. Private*, pg. 2353
SCOTTISH PACIFIC BUSINESS FINANCE PTY. LIMITED—See Balmain Corp.; *Int'l*, pg. 810
SECURITY LEASING & FINANCE INC.—See Carriage Corporation; *U.S. Private*, pg. 772
SECURITY NATIONAL AUTOMOTIVE ACCEPTANCE COMPANY, LLC; *U.S. Private*, pg. 3596
SHELTER FINANCIAL SERVICES, INC.—See Shelter Mutual Insurance Company; *U.S. Private*, pg. 3631
S MORAVA LEASING, A.S.—See Erste Group Bank AG; *Int'l*, pg. 2499
SOUTHEAST TOYOTA FINANCE—See JM Family Enterprises Inc.; *U.S. Private*, pg. 2214
STEELCASE FINANCIAL SERVICES, INC.—See Steelcase Inc.; *U.S. Public*, pg. 1944
SUMMIT FUNDING GROUP INC.; *U.S. Private*, pg. 3854
SYTNER FINANCE LIMITED—See Penske Automotive Group, Inc.; *U.S. Public*, pg. 1666
TANDEM FINANCE INC.—See Chesswood Group Limited; *Int'l*, pg. 1472
TARGO COMMERCIAL FINANCE AG—See Confederation Nationale du Credit Mutuel; *Int'l*, pg. 1767
TARGO LEASING GMBH—See Confederation Nationale du Credit Mutuel; *Int'l*, pg. 1767
TBI LEASING IFN S.A.—See 4finance Holding S.A.; *Int'l*, pg. 12
THORN EQUIPMENT FINANCE PTY LTD—See ICM Limited; *Int'l*, pg. 3582
TOHO SHINYO HOSHO COMPANY—See Prudential Financial, Inc.; *U.S. Public*, pg. 1733
TORO CREDIT COMPANY—See The Toro Company; *U.S. Public*, pg. 2135
TRINITY CAPITAL CORP.; *U.S. Private*, pg. 4233
TRUCK PARTS AND EQUIPMENT CO.; *U.S. Private*, pg. 4246
UKRAINIAN LEASING COMPANY—See BNP Paribas SA; *Int'l*, pg. 1093
UNION LEASING, INC.—See Sasser Family Holdings, Inc.; *U.S. Private*, pg. 3552
UNIPOL LEASING S.P.A.—See BPER BANCA S.p.A; *Int'l*, pg. 1132
UNIVEST CAPITAL, INC.—See Univest Financial Corporation; *U.S. Public*, pg. 2263
U.S. BANK ASSET MANAGEMENT—See U.S. Bancorp; *U.S. Public*, pg. 2213
US PREMIUM FINANCE, INC.—See Ameris Bancorp; *U.S. Public*, pg. 115
VAB LEASING—See 4finance Holding S.A.; *Int'l*, pg. 12
VERIZON COMMUNICATIONS INC. - BUFFALO, WV—See Verizon Communications Inc.; *U.S. Public*, pg. 2285
VFS FINANCIAL SERVICES (UK) LTD—See AB Volvo; *Int'l*, pg. 44
VFS NORDIC AB—See AB Volvo; *Int'l*, pg. 44
VOLVO FINANCE PERU S.A.—See AB Volvo; *Int'l*, pg. 43
WAY CHONG FINANCE LIMITED—See HSBC Holdings plc; *Int'l*, pg. 3506
WEBBANK—See Steel Partners Holdings L.P.; *U.S. Public*, pg. 1943
WELLS FARGO DEALER SERVICES, INC.—See Wells Fargo & Company; *U.S. Public*, pg. 2346
WELLS FARGO EQUIPMENT FINANCE, INC.—See Wells Fargo & Company; *U.S. Public*, pg. 2346
WELLS FARGO EQUIPMENT FINANCE—See Wells Fargo & Company; *U.S. Public*, pg. 2346
WESTERN FINANCIAL, INC.—See Western State Agency, Inc.; *U.S. Private*, pg. 4497
WILLIS LEASE FINANCE CORPORATION; *U.S. Public*, pg. 2371
WIRTH BUSINESS CREDIT, INC.—See Winmark Corporation; *U.S. Public*, pg. 2374
WORLD OMNI FINANCIAL CORP.—See JM Family Enterprises Inc.; *U.S. Private*, pg. 2214
YANKEE ENERGY FINANCIAL SERVICES COMPANY—See Eversource Energy; *U.S. Public*, pg. 802
ZIONS CREDIT CORPORATION—See Zions Bancorporation, National Association; *U.S. Public*, pg. 2408

522291 — CONSUMER LENDING

1ST FRANKLIN FINANCIAL CORPORATION; *U.S. Private*, pg. 4
1ST MERCHANT FUNDING, LLC; *U.S. Private*, pg. 4
44 BUSINESS CAPITAL—See Berkshire Hills Bancorp, Inc.; *U.S. Public*, pg. 320
ACCEPTANCE LOAN COMPANY, INC.—See First US Bancshares, Inc.; *U.S. Public*, pg. 848
ACCESS GROUP INC.; *U.S. Private*, pg. 51
ACCUTRAC CAPITAL SOLUTIONS, INC.—See Global Merchant Fund Corp.; *U.S. Private*, pg. 1716
ADVANCE AMERICA, CASH ADVANCE CENTERS, INC.—See Grupo Salinas, S.A. de C.V.; *Int'l*, pg. 3135
ADYEN N.V.—See Adyen N.V.; *Int'l*, pg. 169
AEON CREDIT SERVICE (ASIA) COMPANY LIMITED—See AEON Financial Service Co., Ltd; *Int'l*, pg. 178
AEON CREDIT SERVICE (M) BERHAD—See AEON Co., Ltd.; *Int'l*, pg. 176
AEON FINANCIAL SERVICE CO., LTD; *Int'l*, pg. 178
AEON (THAILAND) CO., LTD—See AEON Co., Ltd.; *Int'l*, pg. 176
AG CAPITAL LIMITED—See Allied Group Limited; *Int'l*, pg. 357
AGENCY HOLDING COMPANY OF MARYLAND INC.; *U.S. Private*, pg. 126
AGENCY SERVICES, INC.—See Agency Holding Company of Maryland Inc.; *U.S. Private*, pg. 126
AGENCY SERVICES INC.—See Agency Holding Company of Maryland Inc.; *U.S. Private*, pg. 126
AGRILEASE BV—See BNP Paribas SA; *Int'l*, pg. 1079
AG TWIN BROOK BDC, INC.; *U.S. Private*, pg. 125
AIFUL PARTNERS CORPORATION—See AIFUL Corporation; *Int'l*, pg. 231
AIRA SECURITIES PUBLIC COMPANY LIMITED—See AIRA Capital Public Company Limited; *Int'l*, pg. 241
AKSO HEALTH GROUP; *Int'l*, pg. 265
ALFA FINANCIAL CORPORATION—See Alfa Corporation; *U.S. Private*, pg. 164
ALLIED AFFILIATED FUNDING, LP—See Axiom Bank, N.A.; *U.S. Private*, pg. 413
ALL MEDIA CAPITAL, INC.—See Providence Capital Funding, Inc.; *U.S. Private*, pg. 3291
ALLO COMMUNICATIONS, LLC—See Nelnet, Inc.; *U.S. Public*, pg. 1504
AMERICAN EXPRESS COMPANY; *U.S. Public*, pg. 100
AMERICAN HONDA FINANCE CORP.—See Honda Motor Co., Ltd.; *Int'l*, pg. 3459
AMIGO LOANS INTERNATIONAL LIMITED; *Int'l*, pg. 427
AMIGO LOANS IRELAND LIMITED—See Amigo Loans International Limited; *Int'l*, pg. 427
AMIGO LOANS LIMITED—See Amigo Holdings PLC; *Int'l*, pg. 427
APTUS VALUE HOUSING FINANCE INDIA LIMITED; *Int'l*, pg. 526
AQUA FINANCE, INC.—See Blackstone Inc.; *U.S. Public*, pg. 348
ARC FINANCE LIMITED; *Int'l*, pg. 539
ARTISTE HOLDING LIMITED—See EZCORP, Inc.; *U.S. Public*, pg. 817
ASA INTERNATIONAL GROUP PLC; *Int'l*, pg. 591
ASA MICROFINANCE (UGANDA) LIMITED—See ASA International Group plc; *Int'l*, pg. 592
ASPIAL LIFESTYLE LIMITED; *Int'l*, pg. 630
AU SMALL FINANCE BANK LIMITED; *Int'l*, pg. 697
AUTO CREDIT EXPRESS, INC.—See KKR & Co. Inc.; *U.S. Public*, pg. 1253

522291 — CONSUMER LENDING

AVIO CREDIT, INC.—See CURO Group Holdings Corp.; *U.S. Public*, pg. 611
AXIS CAPITAL USA LLC—See Axis Bank Limited; *Int'l*, pg. 769
AXSESSTODAY LIMITED—See Cerberus Capital Management, L.P.; *U.S. Private*, pg. 837
BAD HOMBURGER INKASSO GMBH—See DXC Technology Company; *U.S. Public*, pg. 695
BANDHAN FINANCIAL SERVICES LTD.; *Int'l*, pg. 830
BANGLADESH FINANCE LIMITED; *Int'l*, pg. 835
BANGLADESH INDUSTRIAL FINANCE COMPANY LIMITED; *Int'l*, pg. 836
THE BANK OF CANTON; *U.S. Private*, pg. 3991
BANK OF IRELAND CONSUMER LENDING—See Bank of Ireland Group plc; *Int'l*, pg. 844
BAZEL INTERNATIONAL LIMITED; *Int'l*, pg. 920
BENEFICIAL FINANCES—See HSBC Holdings plc; *Int'l*, pg. 3505
BENEFICIAL MANAGEMENT INC.—See HSBC Holdings plc; *Int'l*, pg. 3505
BENEFICIAL NEW MEXICO INC.—See HSBC Holdings plc; *Int'l*, pg. 3505
BENEFICIAL WASHINGTON INC.—See HSBC Holdings plc; *Int'l*, pg. 3505
BENEFITED, LLC—See Nelnet, Inc.; *U.S. Public*, pg. 1504
B&F FINANCE CORP.; *U.S. Private*, pg. 418
BIT DIGITAL, INC.; *U.S. Public*, pg. 339
BLACKSTONE CAPITAL PARTNERS—See Blackstone Inc.; *U.S. Public*, pg. 349
BLB LTD; *Int'l*, pg. 1063
BLUE OWL CAPITAL CORPORATION—See Blue Owl Capital Inc.; *U.S. Public*, pg. 364
BREAL CAPITAL LTD.; *Int'l*, pg. 1144
BREMER BUSINESS FINANCE CORPORATION—See Bremer Financial Corporation; *U.S. Private*, pg. 645
BRIDGEVIEW CAPITAL SOLUTIONS, LLC—See Old National Bancorp; *U.S. Public*, pg. 1567
BT LEASING MD SRL—See Banca Transilvania S.A.; *Int'l*, pg. 816
BUDGET LOANS LTD—See Cynotech Holdings Limited; *Int'l*, pg. 1896
BUDGET NATIONAL FINANCE CO.; *U.S. Private*, pg. 679
BUSINESS DEVELOPMENT CORPORATION OF SOUTH CAROLINA—See Wells Fargo & Company; *U.S. Public*, pg. 2343
CALIBER HOME LOANS, INC.—See Rithm Capital Corp.; *U.S. Public*, pg. 1799
CANADIAN DIRECT FINANCIAL—See Canadian Western Bank; *Int'l*, pg. 1286
CAPE FEAR FARM CREDIT, ACA; *U.S. Private*, pg. 737
CARFINANCE CAPITAL LLC—See Flagship Credit Corporation; *U.S. Private*, pg. 1539
CASH AMERICA EAST, INC.—See FirstCash Holdings, Inc.; *U.S. Public*, pg. 849
CASH AMERICA, INC. OF ALASKA—See FirstCash Holdings, Inc.; *U.S. Public*, pg. 849
CASH AMERICA, INC. OF ILLINOIS—See FirstCash Holdings, Inc.; *U.S. Public*, pg. 849
CASH AMERICA, INC. OF NORTH CAROLINA—See FirstCash Holdings, Inc.; *U.S. Public*, pg. 849
CASH AMERICA, INC. OF OKLAHOMA—See FirstCash Holdings, Inc.; *U.S. Public*, pg. 849
CASH AMERICA OF MISSOURI, INC.—See FirstCash Holdings, Inc.; *U.S. Public*, pg. 849
CASH AMERICA PAWN L.P.—See FirstCash Holdings, Inc.; *U.S. Public*, pg. 849
CASHCALL, INC.; *U.S. Private*, pg. 783
CBD LIFE SCIENCES, INC.; *U.S. Public*, pg. 455
CETELEM ALGERIE SPA—See BNP Paribas SA; *Int'l*, pg. 1090
CETELEM IFN SA—See BNP Paribas SA; *Int'l*, pg. 1090
CETELEM SFAC—See BNP Paribas SA; *Int'l*, pg. 1089
CETELEM SLOVENSKO A.S.—See BNP Paribas SA; *Int'l*, pg. 1090
CETELEM TAIWAN—See BNP Paribas SA; *Int'l*, pg. 1090
CHASE EDUCATION FINANCE—See JPMorgan Chase & Co.; *U.S. Public*, pg. 1206
CITIFINANCIAL CREDIT COMPANY—See Citigroup Inc.; *U.S. Public*, pg. 501
CITIZENS BUSINESS CAPITAL—See Citizens Financial Group, Inc.; *U.S. Public*, pg. 505
CITIZENS FINANCE CO.—See Heartland Financial USA, Inc.; *U.S. Public*, pg. 1018
CITY FINANCE; *U.S. Private*, pg. 905
CLAL FINANCING CONSUMER CREDIT LTD.—See IDB Development Corporation Ltd.; *Int'l*, pg. 3588
CNH CAPITAL EUROPE BV—See BNP Paribas SA; *Int'l*, pg. 1089
COAST 2 COAST LENDERS, LLC—See Coast 2 Coast Financial Group, LLC; *U.S. Private*, pg. 954
COASTAL FINANCIAL CORP.; *U.S. Private*, pg. 956
COCHLEAR EUROPE FINANCE GMBH—See Cochlear Limited; *Int'l*, pg. 1687
COLONIAL AUTO FINANCE, INC.—See America's Car-Mart, Inc.; *U.S. Public*, pg. 95
COMFORT INTECH LIMITED; *Int'l*, pg. 1711
COMMERCIAL ACCEPTANCES LIMITED—See Close Brothers Group plc; *Int'l*, pg. 1661

CONSUMER PORTFOLIO SERVICES, INC.; *U.S. Public*, pg. 572
CONSUMER PORTFOLIO SERVICES, INC.—See Consumer Portfolio Services, Inc.; *U.S. Public*, pg. 572
CONTINENTAL FINANCE; *U.S. Private*, pg. 1029
CONTINENTAL SECURITIES LIMITED; *Int'l*, pg. 1784
COOPACA; *U.S. Private*, pg. 1040
COTTONWOOD FINANCIAL LTD; *U.S. Private*, pg. 1064
CRE ALLIANCE, INC.—See CRE, Inc.; *Int'l*, pg. 1830
CREDENTIAL LEASING CORP.—See Freeman Spogli & Co. Incorporated; *U.S. Private*, pg. 1606
CREDIBLE LABS, INC.—See Fox Corporation; *U.S. Public*, pg. 875
CREDITO REAL S.A.B. DE C.V.; *Int'l*, pg. 1836
CSI FINANCIAL SERVICES, LLC—See TPG Capital, L.P.; *U.S. Public*, pg. 2168
CU DIRECT CORPORATION; *U.S. Private*, pg. 1119
CUSTOM FINANCIAL SOLUTIONS—See Virtual Sourcing, LLC; *U.S. Private*, pg. 4389
DARIC CORPORATION; *U.S. Private*, pg. 1159
DBJ AMERICAS INC.—See Development Bank of Japan, Inc.; *Int'l*, pg. 2087
DBJ INVESTMENT CONSULTING (BEIJING) CO., LTD.—See Development Bank of Japan, Inc.; *Int'l*, pg. 2087
DEFAM B.V.—See ABN AMRO Group N.V.; *Int'l*, pg. 65
DELL FUNDING L.L.C.—See Dell Technologies Inc.; *U.S. Public*, pg. 649
DEUTSCHE BANK CAPITAL CORPORATION—See Deutsche Bank Aktiengesellschaft; *Int'l*, pg. 2059
DEVILLE INVESTMENT, INC.; *U.S. Private*, pg. 1218
DFL INFRASTRUCTURE FINANCE LIMITED; *Int'l*, pg. 2095
DHANI SERVICES LTD.; *Int'l*, pg. 2098
DIAC SALAF S.A.; *Int'l*, pg. 2101
DIAMOND TRUST BANK KENYA LIMITED; *Int'l*, pg. 2105
DIEBOLD GLOBAL FINANCE CORP—See Diebold Nixdorf, Inc.; *U.S. Public*, pg. 659
DINERS CLUB PTY LIMITED—See Citigroup Inc.; *U.S. Public*, pg. 502
DIRECT WONEN N V; *Int'l*, pg. 2130
DISCOVER STUDENT LOANS—See Discover Financial Services; *U.S. Public*, pg. 668
EASYFINANCIAL SERVICES INC.—See goeasy Ltd.; *Int'l*, pg. 3021
EDSON FINANCIAL INC.—See Krystal Infinity LLC; *U.S. Private*, pg. 2354
EDUCATIONAL FUNDING OF THE SOUTH; *U.S. Private*, pg. 1339
ELEVATE CREDIT INTERNATIONAL LIMITED—See Park Cities Asset Management LLC; *U.S. Private*, pg. 3095
ENGLISH LEASING LIMITED; *Int'l*, pg. 2435
EQ CORP.—See Equilease Holding Corp.; *U.S. Private*, pg. 1415
EQUILEASE FINANCIAL SERVICES—See Equilease Holding Corp.; *U.S. Private*, pg. 1415
EQUITY BANK LIMITED; *Int'l*, pg. 2488
ERNST RUSS AG; *Int'l*, pg. 2495
EXPRESS CHECK ADVANCE LLC; *U.S. Private*, pg. 1451
EXPRESS CHECK ADVANCE OF SOUTH CAROLINA, LLC—See QC Holdings, Inc.; *U.S. Public*, pg. 1742
EXXON INTERNATIONAL FINANCE COMPANY—See Exxon Mobil Corporation; *U.S. Public*, pg. 814
FARBANCA S.P.A.; *Int'l*, pg. 2618
FARM CREDIT OF FLORIDA; *U.S. Private*, pg. 1474
FARM CREDIT OF NORTHWEST FLORIDA ACA; *U.S. Private*, pg. 1475
FCFS SC, INC.—See FirstCash Holdings, Inc.; *U.S. Public*, pg. 849
FINANCE OF AMERICA COMPANIES INC.; *U.S. Public*, pg. 834
FINANCIA CREDIT, S.A.; *Int'l*, pg. 2664
FINANCIERA FAMILIAR, S.A.; *Int'l*, pg. 2665
FIRST INVESTORS FINANCIAL SERVICES GROUP, INC.—See Gallatin Point Capital LLC; *U.S. Private*, pg. 1639
FIRST PENINSULA CREDIT SDN BHD—See Chin Hin Group Berhad; *Int'l*, pg. 1480
FOCUS INDUSTRIAL RESOURCES LIMITED; *Int'l*, pg. 2719
FORD MOTOR CREDIT COMPANY LLC—See Ford Motor Company; *U.S. Public*, pg. 865
FORMATION SPORTS CAPITAL LIMITED—See Formation Group PLC; *Int'l*, pg. 2734
FRANKLIN LEASING & FINANCE LIMITED; *Int'l*, pg. 2762
FUKUGIN GUARANTEE CO., LTD.—See Fukuoka Financial Group, Inc.; *Int'l*, pg. 2840
FUNDERA INC.; *U.S. Private*, pg. 1623
GENERAL MOTORS FINANCIAL COMPANY, INC.—See General Motors Company; *U.S. Public*, pg. 924
GENEVA FINANCE LIMITED; *Int'l*, pg. 2922
GENTRY FINANCE CORPORATION; *U.S. Private*, pg. 1679
GEORGIA CASH AMERICA, INC.—See FirstCash Holdings, Inc.; *U.S. Public*, pg. 849
GOVERNMENT CAPITAL CORPORATION-SOUTHEASTERN REGION—See Government Capital Corporation; *U.S. Private*, pg. 1746
GREEN TREE SERVICING LLC—See Ditech Holding Corporation; *U.S. Private*, pg. 1240
GRENKELEASING D.O.O.—See Grenke AG; *Int'l*, pg. 3081
HARREN EQUITY PARTNERS; *U.S. Private*, pg. 1868
HARRISON, VICKERS & WATERMAN, INC.—See Attitude Drinks Incorporated; *U.S. Public*, pg. 383
HDFC CREDILA FINANCIAL SERVICES LTD.—See Housing Development Finance Corporation Limited; *Int'l*, pg. 3492
HEIGHTS FINANCE CORPORATION—See CURO Group Holdings Corp.; *U.S. Public*, pg. 611
HIGHLAND LEASE CORPORATION—See M&T Bank Corporation; *U.S. Public*, pg. 1350
HOME POINT CAPITAL INC.—See Mr. Cooper Group Inc.; *U.S. Public*, pg. 1480
HONDA CANADA FINANCE, INC.—See Honda Motor Co., Ltd.; *Int'l*, pg. 3461
HSBC FINANCE CORPORATION—See HSBC Holdings plc; *Int'l*, pg. 3505
HUMM GROUP LIMITED—See Humm Group Limited; *Int'l*, pg. 3531
ICS FUNDING PTE. LTD.—See Credit Intelligence Limited; *Int'l*, pg. 1835
IDLC FINANCE PLC.; *Int'l*, pg. 3595
IFS VENTURES PRIVATE LIMITED—See IFS Capital Limited; *Int'l*, pg. 3600
IKON FINANCIAL GROUP; *U.S. Private*, pg. 2041
INDEPENDENT FINANCIAL AGENTS; *U.S. Private*, pg. 2059
INDUSTRIAL FINANCE CO., INC.—See The Pape Group, Inc.; *U.S. Private*, pg. 4090
INFOVISA INC.—See Farmers & Merchants Investment Inc.; *U.S. Private*, pg. 1476
IRRITROL SYSTEMS—See The Toro Company; *U.S. Public*, pg. 2135
ISLAND FINANCE, INC.—See First BanCorp; *U.S. Public*, pg. 839
J.P. MORGAN PARTNERS, LLC—See JPMorgan Chase & Co.; *U.S. Public*, pg. 1208
KIPLINGERS PERSONAL FINANCE—See Future plc; *Int'l*, pg. 2857
LANDMARK FINANCIAL ADVISORS, LLC—See TA Associates, Inc.; *U.S. Private*, pg. 3919
LENDBUZZ, INC.; *U.S. Private*, pg. 2421
LENDDIRECT CORP.—See CURO Group Holdings Corp.; *U.S. Public*, pg. 611
LENDINGPOT PRIVATE LIMITED—See IFS Capital Limited; *Int'l*, pg. 3600
LIBERTY PREMIUM FINANCE, INC.—See Fosun International Limited; *Int'l*, pg. 2752
LIFCO, LLC—See J.C. Flowers & Co. LLC; *U.S. Private*, pg. 2159
LOANDEPOT.COM, LLC; *U.S. Public*, pg. 2477
MAGELLAN S.A.—See Banca Farmafactoring S.p.A.; *Int'l*, pg. 814
MAGYAR CETELEM BANK ZRT.—See BNP Paribas SA; *Int'l*, pg. 1090
MARINER FINANCE, LLC—See Warburg Pincus LLC; *U.S. Private*, pg. 4439
MASTER RISK, INC.—See Marshall & Sterling Enterprises, Inc.; *U.S. Private*, pg. 2592
MERCANTIL DO BRASIL FINANCEIRA S.A.—See Banco Mercantil do Brasil S.A.; *Int'l*, pg. 823
MINTAKA FINANCIAL, LLC; *U.S. Private*, pg. 2745
MOUNTAINEER CAPITAL, LP—See Alpha Natural Resources, Inc.; *U.S. Private*, pg. 199
M&T CREDIT CORPORATION—See M&T Bank Corporation; *U.S. Public*, pg. 1350
MUTUAL BENEFIT ASSOCIATION HAWAII; *U.S. Private*, pg. 2819
NAGASAKI GUARANTEE SERVICE CO., LTD.—See Fukuoka Financial Group, Inc.; *Int'l*, pg. 2840
NATION FUNDING GROUP INC—See US Buildings LLC; *U.S. Private*, pg. 4318
NATIONWIDE ACCEPTANCE CORPORATION—See Nationwide Group; *U.S. Private*, pg. 2866
NATIONWIDE GROUP; *U.S. Private*, pg. 2866
NAVIENT CREDIT FUNDING, LLC—See Navient Corporation; *U.S. Public*, pg. 1500
NAVIENT SOLUTIONS, INC.—See Navient Corporation; *U.S. Public*, pg. 1500
NEIGHBORHOOD HOUSING SERVICES OF CHICAGO INC.; *U.S. Private*, pg. 2881
NELNET, INC.; *U.S. Public*, pg. 1504
NEW CREDIT AMERICA, LLC; *U.S. Private*, pg. 2893
NICHOLAS FINANCIAL, INC.; *U.S. Public*, pg. 1527
NISHI-KYUSHU CREDIT GUARANTEE CO., LTD.—See Fukuoka Financial Group, Inc.; *Int'l*, pg. 2840
NOBLE FINANCE CORPORATION—See Gentry Finance Corporation; *U.S. Private*, pg. 1680
NORWEST CENTER, INC.—See Wells Fargo & Company; *U.S. Public*, pg. 2344
OPEN 24 S.A.—See Eurobank Ergasias Services and Holdings S.A.; *Int'l*, pg. 2533
ORIGENCE LENDING SERVICES—See CU Direct Corporation; *U.S. Private*, pg. 1119
PACCAR FINANCIAL MEXICO, S.A. DE C.V., SOFOM, E.N.R.—See PACCAR Inc.; *U.S. Public*, pg. 1631
PAGASA PHILIPPINES FINANCE CORPORATION,

522291 — CONSUMER LENDING

INC.—See ASA International Group plc; *Int'l*, pg. 592
PASSFORT LIMITED—See Moody's Corporation; *U.S. Public*, pg. 1469
PAYBRIGHT INC.—See Affirm Holdings, Inc.; *U.S. Public*, pg. 57
PEMBERTON MARKETING INTERNATIONAL LIMITED—See Clayton, Dubilier & Rice, LLC; *U.S. Private*, pg. 928
PEPPER GROUP LIMITED—See KKR & Co. Inc.; *U.S. Public*, pg. 1262
PERSONAL FINANCE COMPANY, LLC—See Warburg Pincus LLC; *U.S. Private*, pg. 4439
PIONEER CREDIT COMPANY INC.; *U.S. Private*, pg. 3186
PLATTE VALLEY AG CREDIT CO.—See Platte Valley Financial Service Companies Inc.; *U.S. Private*, pg. 3211
PREFERRED AUTO CREDIT INC.—See Preferred Auto Inc.; *U.S. Private*, pg. 3247
PREMIUM FINANCE CO. OF THE VIRGIN ISLANDS—See Lockhart Companies Inc.; *U.S. Private*, pg. 2478
PROFESSIONAL BANKERS CORP—See Continental Holding Company; *U.S. Private*, pg. 1029
QC HOLDINGS, INC.; *U.S. Public*, pg. 1741
QUICK BRIDGE FUNDING, LLC—See National Funding Inc.; *U.S. Private*, pg. 2855
RABO AGRIFINANCE, INC.—See Cooperatieve Centrale Raiffeisen-Boerenleenbank B.A.; *Int'l*, pg. 1791
REGIONAL ACCEPTANCE CORPORATION—See Truist Financial Corporation; *U.S. Public*, pg. 2199
REGIONAL FINANCE CORPORATION OF SOUTH CAROLINA—See Regional Management Corp.; *U.S. Public*, pg. 1776
REGIONAL MANAGEMENT CORP.; *U.S. Public*, pg. 1776
REPUBLIC BUSINESS CREDIT, LLC; *U.S. Private*, pg. 3401
RISE CREDIT SERVICE OF TEXAS, LLC—See Park Cities Asset Management LLC; *U.S. Private*, pg. 3095
ROYAL FINANCE CORP—See Gentry Finance Corporation; *U.S. Private*, pg. 1680
RUNWAY GROWTH FINANCE CORP.; *U.S. Public*, pg. 1826
SAAB FINANCIAL SERVICES CORP.—See General Motors Company; *U.S. Public*, pg. 925
SABER ACCEPTANCE COMPANY INC.; *U.S. Private*, pg. 3520
SAFROCK FINANCE CORPORATION (QLD) PTY LTD—See Cash Converters International Limited; *Int'l*, pg. 1352
SALT BLOCKCHAIN INC.; *U.S. Private*, pg. 3533
SANTANDER CONSUMER USA INC.—See Banco Santander, S.A.; *Int'l*, pg. 827
SECURITY FINANCE CORPORATION—See Continental Holding Company; *U.S. Private*, pg. 1029
SECURITY FINANCE CORP. SPARTANBURG—See Continental Holding Company; *U.S. Private*, pg. 1029
SECURITY PREMIUM FINANCE CO.—See Steel Partners Holdings L.P.; *U.S. Public*, pg. 1943
SHAMROCK HOME LOANS, INC.—See Lendbuzz, Inc.; *U.S. Private*, pg. 2421
SHK FINANCE LIMITED—See Allied Group Limited; *Int'l*, pg. 357
SIMMONS FIRST FINANCE COMPANY—See Simmons First National Corporation; *U.S. Public*, pg. 1881
STERLING FINANCE COMPANY—See Mathes Management Enterprises; *U.S. Private*, pg. 2610
SUNBELT CREDIT INC.—See Continental Holding Company; *U.S. Private*, pg. 1030
SUN FINANCE COMPANY, LLC; *U.S. Private*, pg. 3863
SWIFT FINANCIAL, LLC—See PayPal Holdings, Inc.; *U.S. Public*, pg. 1657
T0.COM, INC.—See Beyond, Inc.; *U.S. Public*, pg. 327
TEB CETELEM TUKETICI FINANSMANI A.S.—See BNP Paribas SA; *Int'l*, pg. 1093
TELEFLEX FUNDING CORPORATION—See Teleflex Incorporated; *U.S. Public*, pg. 1995
THINKME FINANCE PTY. LTD.—See Collection House Limited; *Int'l*, pg. 1699
TOLEDO FINANCE CORP.; *U.S. Private*, pg. 4181
TOUCAN INTERACTIVE CORP.; *U.S. Public*, pg. 2165
TOWER LOAN OF MISSISSIPPI, INC.—See Prospect Capital Corporation; *U.S. Public*, pg. 1728
TUITION MANAGEMENT SYSTEMS, LLC—See Nelnet, Inc.; *U.S. Public*, pg. 1504
TV PROFILE, LLC—See Finbond Group Limited; *Int'l*, pg. 2670
UNITED AUTO CREDIT CORPORATION—See Pine Brook Partners, LLC; *U.S. Private*, pg. 3182
UNITED FINANCE CO.; *U.S. Private*, pg. 4292
UNITED PROPERTY FINANCE LIMITED—See Global Token Limited; *Int'l*, pg. 3001
UPSTART NETWORK, INC.—See Upstart Holdings, Inc.; *U.S. Public*, pg. 2264
VERSARA LENDING LLC; *U.S. Private*, pg. 4369
VERVENT INC.; *U.S. Private*, pg. 4371
VISTA FINANCE INC.—See Gentry Finance Corporation; *U.S. Private*, pg. 1680
WAC DE MEXICO SA DE CV, SOFOM, ENR—See World Acceptance Corporation; *U.S. Public*, pg. 2379
WELLS FARGO FINANCIAL ARIZONA, INC.—See Wells Fargo & Company; *U.S. Public*, pg. 2346
WELLS FARGO FINANCIAL CORPORATION CANADA—See Wells Fargo & Company; *U.S. Public*, pg. 2346
WELLS FARGO FINANCIAL FLORIDA, INC.—See Wells Fargo & Company; *U.S. Public*, pg. 2346
WELLS FARGO FINANCIAL LEASING, INC—See Wells Fargo & Company; *U.S. Public*, pg. 2346
WEST ENGINE FUNDING LLC—See Willis Lease Finance Corporation; *U.S. Public*, pg. 2371
WESTERN FINANCE & LEASE, INC.1990—See Western State Agency, Inc.; *U.S. Private*, pg. 4496
WESTERN FUNDING INC.; *U.S. Private*, pg. 4493
WESTERN SHAMROCK CORPORATION; *U.S. Private*, pg. 4496
WORLD ACCEPTANCE CORPORATION OF ALABAMA—See World Acceptance Corporation; *U.S. Public*, pg. 2379
WORLD ACCEPTANCE CORPORATION OF MISSOURI—See World Acceptance Corporation; *U.S. Public*, pg. 2379
WORLD ACCEPTANCE CORPORATION OF OKLAHOMA, INC.—See World Acceptance Corporation; *U.S. Public*, pg. 2379
WORLD ACCEPTANCE CORPORATION; *U.S. Public*, pg. 2379
WORLD FINANCE COMPANY OF KENTUCKY, LLC—See World Acceptance Corporation; *U.S. Public*, pg. 2379
WORLD FINANCE CORP.—See World Acceptance Corporation; *U.S. Public*, pg. 2379
WORLD FINANCE INC.—See World Acceptance Corporation; *U.S. Public*, pg. 2379
WORLD FINANCE INC.—See World Acceptance Corporation; *U.S. Public*, pg. 2379
WORLD FINANCE INC.—See World Acceptance Corporation; *U.S. Public*, pg. 2379
YOUR CREDIT INC.—See Gentry Finance Corporation; *U.S. Private*, pg. 1680

522292 — REAL ESTATE CREDIT

360 MORTGAGE GROUP, LLC; *U.S. Private*, pg. 8
AAREAL BANK AG—See Advent International Corporation; *U.S. Private*, pg. 96
AAREAL BANK AG—See Centerbridge Partners, L.P.; *U.S. Private*, pg. 812
AAREAL BANK ASIA LIMITED—See Advent International Corporation; *U.S. Private*, pg. 96
AAREAL BANK ASIA LIMITED—See Centerbridge Partners, L.P.; *U.S. Private*, pg. 812
AAREAL CAPITAL CORPORATION—See Advent International Corporation; *U.S. Private*, pg. 96
AAREAL CAPITAL CORPORATION—See Centerbridge Partners, L.P.; *U.S. Private*, pg. 812
ABL EXCHANGE LLC—See Alexander & Baldwin, Inc.; *U.S. Public*, pg. 75
A&B WAIANAE LLC—See Alexander & Baldwin, Inc.; *U.S. Public*, pg. 75
ACADEMY MORTGAGE CORPORATION; *U.S. Private*, pg. 46
AGGEORGIA FARM CREDIT, ACA; *U.S. Private*, pg. 127
AIRBUS BANK GMBH—See Airbus SE; *Int'l*, pg. 242
ALASKA HOUSING FINANCE CORPORATION; *U.S. Private*, pg. 150
ALL AMERICAN LENDING GROUP, LLC; *U.S. Private*, pg. 169
AMCAP MORTGAGE LTD.—See Crosscountry Mortgage, LLC; *U.S. Private*, pg. 1106
AMERICAN HOME MORTGAGES; *U.S. Private*, pg. 236
AMERICAN MORTGAGE SERVICE COMPANY—See Thrive Mortgage LLC; *U.S. Private*, pg. 4165
AMERIFIRST FINANCIAL CORPORATION—See Union Home Mortgage Corp.; *U.S. Private*, pg. 4284
APEX HOME LOANS, INC.; *U.S. Private*, pg. 292
APWIRELESS INFRASTRUCTURE PARTNERS, LLC—See EQT AB; *Int'l*, pg. 2479
ARVEST MORTGAGE COMPANY—See Arvest Bank Group, Inc.; *U.S. Private*, pg. 344
ASAX CO., LTD.; *Int'l*, pg. 599
ASIAN - PACIFIC BANK PJSC—See Central Bank of the Russian Federation; *Int'l*, pg. 1405
AVENUE MORTGAGE CORPORATION—See CIB Marine Bancshares, Inc.; *U.S. Public*, pg. 494
BALTIC INVESTMENT BANK PJSC; *Int'l*, pg. 812
BANK BPH S.A.—See General Electric Company; *U.S. Public*, pg. 920
BANK DOM.RF JSC; *Int'l*, pg. 837
BANK ZENIT PJSC; *Int'l*, pg. 850
BELL MORTGAGE—See State Bankshares, Inc.; *U.S. Private*, pg. 3791
BETTER MORTGAGE CORPORATION—See Better Home & Finance Holding Company; *U.S. Public*, pg. 327
BLAIR SERVICES OF AMERICA INC.; *U.S. Private*, pg. 578
BLUE SKY GROUP HOLDINGS, INC.; *U.S. Private*, pg. 593
BORROWMONEY.COM, INC.; *U.S. Public*, pg. 371
BTV LEASING SCHWEIZ AG—See Bank fur Tirol und Vorarlberg Ag; *Int'l*, pg. 838
BUILD KING HOLDINGS LIMITED; *Int'l*, pg. 1212
CAPITAL CITY HOME LOANS, LLC—See Capital City Bank Group, Inc.; *U.S. Public*, pg. 431
CAPITAL FINANCE, LLC—See Capital Funding Group, Inc.; *U.S. Private*, pg. 740
CAPITALSOURCE—See Banc of California, Inc.; *U.S. Public*, pg. 269
CAREY, KRAMER, PETTIT, PANICHELLI & ASSOCIATES, INC.—See M&T Bank Corporation; *U.S. Public*, pg. 1350
CB KHLYNOV JSC; *Int'l*, pg. 1364
CBRE CAPITAL MARKETS, INC.—See CBRE Group, Inc.; *U.S. Public*, pg. 460
CB SOLIDARNOST JSC; *Int'l*, pg. 1364
CENT BANK HOME FINANCE LIMITED—See Central Bank of India Limited; *Int'l*, pg. 1404
CENTRAL PACIFIC HOMELOANS, INC.—See Central Pacific Financial Corporation; *U.S. Public*, pg. 473
C&F MORTGAGE CORPORATION—See C&F Financial Corporation; *U.S. Public*, pg. 414
CHAMPION MORTGAGE CO., INC.—See Mr. Cooper Group Inc.; *U.S. Public*, pg. 1480
CHASE MANHATTAN MORTGAGE CORP.—See JPMorgan Chase & Co.; *U.S. Public*, pg. 1206
CHESAPEAKE MORTGAGE COMPANY—See Chesapeake Financial Shares, Inc.; *U.S. Public*, pg. 485
CHONG KUNDANG INDUSTRIAL CO., LTD.—See Chong Kun Dang Holdings Corp.; *Int'l*, pg. 1578
CITIZENS MORTGAGE CORPORATION—See Citizens Financial Group, Inc.; *U.S. Public*, pg. 505
CITY INVEST BANK AO; *Int'l*, pg. 1626
CLAL MORTGAGES—See IDB Development Corporation Ltd.; *Int'l*, pg. 3588
CLINTON COUNTY LANDFILL PARTNERSHIP—See Republic Services, Inc.; *U.S. Public*, pg. 1786
CMB WEALTH MANAGEMENT LTD—See Compagnie Monegasque de Banque; *Int'l*, pg. 1746
COMMERCE MORTGAGE; *U.S. Private*, pg. 982
COMMUNITY BANC MORTGAGE CORPORATION—See United Community Bancorp, Inc.; *U.S. Public*, pg. 4289
THE COMMUNITY PRESERVATION CORPORATION; *U.S. Private*, pg. 4012
CONTINENTAL MORTGAGE BANKERS; *U.S. Private*, pg. 1030
COUNTRYPLACE MORTGAGE, LTD.—See Cavco Industries, Inc.; *U.S. Public*, pg. 455
COUSINS HOME LENDING, INC.; *U.S. Private*, pg. 1071
CRCC FINANCE COMPANY LIMITED—See China Railway Construction Corporation Limited; *Int'l*, pg. 1542
CREDIT FONCIER DE FRANCE—See Groupe BPCE; *Int'l*, pg. 3094
CREDITMAX LLC; *U.S. Private*, pg. 1092
CRESCENT MORTGAGE COMPANY—See United Bankshares, Inc.; *U.S. Public*, pg. 2229
CROSSROADS PLAZA DEVELOPMENT PARTNERS, LLC—See Alexander & Baldwin, Inc.; *U.S. Public*, pg. 75
CUNA MUTUAL MORTGAGE—See Onity Group Inc.; *U.S. Public*, pg. 1604
DEUTSCHE PFANDBRIEFBANK AG—See Hypo Real Estate Holding AG; *Int'l*, pg. 3553
DOVENMUEHLE INSURANCE AGENCY INC.—See Dovenmuehle Mortgage Inc.; *U.S. Private*, pg. 1268
DOVENMUEHLE MORTGAGE INC.; *U.S. Private*, pg. 1268
DS CAPITAL, LLC; *U.S. Private*, pg. 1281
DUKE REALTY CORPORATION—See Prologis, Inc.; *U.S. Public*, pg. 1726
DZ HYP AG—See DZ BANK AG Deutsche Zentral-Genossenschaftsbank; *Int'l*, pg. 2244
EAGLE HOME MORTGAGE LLC—See Lennar Corporation; *U.S. Public*, pg. 1306
EATON MORTGAGE, LLC—See Wells Fargo & Company; *U.S. Public*, pg. 2343
ELITE FINANCING GROUP, LLC—See Fathom Holdings Inc.; *U.S. Public*, pg. 824
EMIGRANT MORTGAGE COMPANY, INC.—See New York Private Bank & Trust Corporation; *U.S. Private*, pg. 2911
ESSEGIBI PROMOZIONI IMMOBILIARI S.R.L.—See Banco BPM S.p.A.; *Int'l*, pg. 818
EUSTIS MORTGAGE CORP.; *U.S. Private*, pg. 1434
EVERLEND MORTGAGE COMPANY—See Security National Financial Corporation; *U.S. Public*, pg. 1856
FAIRWAY INDEPENDENT MORTGAGE CORPORATION; *U.S. Private*, pg. 1465
FAMC CORPORATION; *U.S. Private*, pg. 1468
FAMILY MORTGAGE INC.; *U.S. Private*, pg. 1471
FBN MORTGAGES LTD.—See FBN Holdings PLC; *Int'l*, pg. 2627
FEDERAL HOME LOAN BANK OF DES MOINES; *U.S. Private*, pg. 1488
FEDERAL HOME LOAN BANK OF PITTSBURGH; *U.S. Private*, pg. 1488
FGH BANK N.V.—See Cooperatieve Centrale Raiffeisen-Boerenleenbank B.A.; *Int'l*, pg. 1791
FHB MORTGAGE BANK PUBLIC LIMITED COMPANY; *Int'l*, pg. 2650
FHB REAL ESTATE LTD.—See FHB Mortgage Bank Public Limited Company; *Int'l*, pg. 2650
FIN-WEST GROUP; *U.S. Private*, pg. 1506

FLORIDA HOUSING FINANCE CORPORATION; *U.S. Private*, pg. 1549
FOREST CITY CAPITAL CORPORATION—See Brookfield Corporation; *Int'l*, pg. 1187
FRANKLIN AMERICAN MORTGAGE CO.—See Citizens Financial Group, Inc.; *U.S. Public*, pg. 505
FRANKLIN STREET PROPERTIES CORP.; *U.S. Public*, pg. 883
FREEDMONT MORTGAGE CORP.—See radius financial group, inc.; *U.S. Private*, pg. 3344
FREEDOM MORTGAGE CORPORATION; *U.S. Private*, pg. 1604
FREIGHT MANAGEMENT PLUS—See The Jordan Company, L.P.; *U.S. Private*, pg. 4061
GAIA SECURITIZADORA S.A.; *Int'l*, pg. 2869
GENTRY HOMELOANS, LLC—See Central Pacific Financial Corporation; *U.S. Public*, pg. 473
GEORGE MASON MORTGAGE, LLC—See United Bankshares, Inc.; *U.S. Public*, pg. 2229
GERSHMAN MORTGAGE CORPORATION; *U.S. Private*, pg. 1688
GLOBAL FINANCIAL & CREDIT, LLC—See Lovell Minnick Partners LLC; *U.S. Private*, pg. 2503
GLOBE MORTGAGE AMERICA, LLC; *U.S. Private*, pg. 1720
GO MORTGAGE GROUP, LLC; *U.S. Private*, pg. 1723
GO MORTGAGE, LLC—See Go Companies, LLC; *U.S. Private*, pg. 1723
GRANT-HATCH & ASSOCIATES INC.—See Leavitt Group Enterprises, Inc.; *U.S. Private*, pg. 2409
GREENTREE MORTGAGE COMPANY L P; *U.S. Private*, pg. 1780
GUARDIAN MORTGAGE—See FirstSun Capital Bancorp; *U.S. Public*, pg. 850
GUILD MORTGAGE COMPANY, LLC—See McCarthy Group, LLC; *U.S. Private*, pg. 2626
HALL STRUCTURED FINANCE—See Hall Financial Group, Ltd.; *U.S. Private*, pg. 1843
HARBORONE MORTGAGE, LLC—See HarborOne Bancorp, Inc.; *U.S. Public*, pg. 984
HASEKO HOMELOANS, LLC—See Central Pacific Financial Corporation; *U.S. Public*, pg. 473
HATFIELD SPAIN, S.L.—See Starwood Property Trust, Inc.; *U.S. Public*, pg. 1939
HF GROUP PLC; *Int'l*, pg. 3374
HOLMGREN & ASSOCIATES; *U.S. Private*, pg. 1968
HOME POINT FINANCIAL CORPORATION—See Mr. Cooper Group Inc.; *U.S. Public*, pg. 1480
HORSETOOTH FINANCIAL LLC—See SageView Advisory Group LLC; *U.S. Private*, pg. 3527
HSBC MORTGAGE SERVICES—See HSBC Holdings plc; *Int'l*, pg. 3505
THE HUNTINGTON MORTGAGE GROUP—See Huntington Bancshares Incorporated; *U.S. Public*, pg. 1071
IBERIABANK MORTGAGE COMPANY—See First Horizon Corporation; *U.S. Public*, pg. 845
IFREEDOM DIRECT CORPORATION—See Wintrust Financial Corporation; *U.S. Public*, pg. 2374
ILLIMITY BANK S.P.A.; *Int'l*, pg. 3615
IMO PROPERTY INVESTMENTS A.D.—See Eurobank Ergasias Services and Holdings S.A.; *Int'l*, pg. 2533
IMPERIAL HOMES MORTGAGE BANK LIMITED—See Guaranty Trust Bank plc; *Int'l*, pg. 3169
INGLET BLAIR LLC—See QC Ally, LLC; *U.S. Private*, pg. 3312
INLAND MORTGAGE CAPITAL, LLC—See The Inland Real Estate Group of Companies, Inc.; *U.S. Private*, pg. 4056
INTERCOASTAL MORTGAGE, LLC; *U.S. Private*, pg. 2109
INTERSTATE HOME LOAN CENTER; *U.S. Private*, pg. 2125
ISLAND PACIFIC HOMELOANS, LLC—See Central Pacific Financial Corporation; *U.S. Public*, pg. 473
JAMES B. NUTTER & COMPANY; *U.S. Private*, pg. 2183
JAMES MONROE CAPITAL CORPORATION; *U.S. Public*, pg. 1187
JEFFERIES MORTGAGE FINANCE, LLC—See Jefferies Financial Group Inc.; *U.S. Public*, pg. 1189
J.I. KISLAK, INC.; *U.S. Private*, pg. 2167
JOHNSON MORTGAGE COMPANY, LLC—See LINKBANCORP, Inc.; *U.S. Public*, pg. 1320
KBA MORTGAGE, LLC—See Bank of America Corporation; *U.S. Public*, pg. 272
KENSINGTON MORTGAGES LIMITED—See Barclays PLC; *Int'l*, pg. 860
KEYCORP REAL ESTATE CAPITAL MARKETS, INC.—See KeyCorp; *U.S. Public*, pg. 1226
KEYSTONE FUNDING, INC.; *U.S. Private*, pg. 2296
KINGHORN DRIVER HOUGH & CO.—See Pohlad Companies; *U.S. Private*, pg. 3220
KORTH DIRECT MORTGAGE INC.; *U.S. Private*, pg. 2344
KUKUI'ULA VILLAGE LLC—See Alexander & Baldwin, Inc.; *U.S. Public*, pg. 75
LEADER ONE FINANCIAL CORP.; *U.S. Private*, pg. 2406
LENNAR FINANCIAL SERVICES, INC.—See Lennar Corporation; *U.S. Public*, pg. 1306
LIBERTY HOME MORTGAGE CORPORATION; *U.S. Private*, pg. 2444

LMI CAPITAL, INC.—See Marcus & Millichap, Inc.; *U.S. Public*, pg. 1365
LOAN CENTRAL, INC.—See Ohio Valley Banc Corp.; *U.S. Public*, pg. 1565
LOVE FUNDING CORPORATION—See Dwight Capital LLC; *U.S. Private*, pg. 1295
LPS FIELD SERVICES, INC.—See Fidelity National Financial, Inc.; *U.S. Public*, pg. 831
LSF LOAN SOLUTIONS FRANKFURT GMBH—See Commerzbank AG; *Int'l*, pg. 1718
LUXURY MORTGAGE CORP.—See Tiptree Inc.; *U.S. Public*, pg. 2159
MANHATTAN BRIDGE CAPITAL, INC.; *U.S. Public*, pg. 1356
MANNING FINANCIAL GROUP, INC.; *U.S. Private*, pg. 2565
MARCUS & MILLICHAP CAPITAL CORPORATION—See Marcus & Millichap, Inc.; *U.S. Public*, pg. 1365
MARCUS & MILLICHAP REAL ESTATE INVESTMENT BROKERAGE COMPANY—See Marcus & Millichap, Inc.; *U.S. Public*, pg. 1365
MEL FOSTER CO. INC.; *U.S. Private*, pg. 2661
MERCANTILE BANK - MORTGAGE CENTER—See United Community Bancorp, Inc.; *U.S. Private*, pg. 4289
MERCHANT CREDIT OF SRI LANKA LTD—See Bank of Ceylon; *Int'l*, pg. 841
MERCHANTS MORTGAGE & TRUST CORPORATION, LLC—See KKR & Co. Inc.; *U.S. Public*, pg. 1261
MERIDIAN HOME MORTGAGE CORP.; *U.S. Private*, pg. 2673
M/I FINANCIAL CORP.—See M/I Homes, Inc.; *U.S. Public*, pg. 1351
MORTGAGE ACCESS CORP.—See Weichert Co.; *U.S. Private*, pg. 4470
MORTGAGE CADENCE LLC—See Accenture plc; *Int'l*, pg. 86
MORTGAGE INVESTORS CORPORATION; *U.S. Private*, pg. 2791
MORTGAGE INVESTORS GROUP, INC.; *U.S. Private*, pg. 2791
MORTGAGE LENDER SERVICES, INC.—See Total Lender Solutions, Inc.; *U.S. Private*, pg. 4191
MORTGAGES PLC—See Bank of America Corporation; *U.S. Public*, pg. 272
MORTGAGE WORLD BANKERS, INC.—See PDL Community Bancorp; *U.S. Public*, pg. 1658
M&T MORTGAGE CORP.—See M&T Bank Corporation; *U.S. Public*, pg. 1350
M&T REALTY CAPITAL CORPORATION—See M&T Bank Corporation; *U.S. Public*, pg. 1350
MULTI CAPITAL GROUP I, LLC; *U.S. Private*, pg. 2812
NATIONWIDE MORTGAGE BANKERS, INC.; *U.S. Private*, pg. 2866
NAVITAS CREDIT CORP.—See United Community Banks, Inc.; *U.S. Public*, pg. 2230
NEBRASKA INVESTMENT FINANCE AUTHORITY INC.; *U.S. Private*, pg. 2878
NJ LENDERS CORP.; *U.S. Private*, pg. 2930
NORTHMARQ CAPITAL, LLC—See Pohlad Companies; *U.S. Private*, pg. 3220
NVR FUNDING II, INC.—See NVR Incorporated; *U.S. Public*, pg. 1558
NVR MORTGAGE FINANCE, INC.—See NVR Incorporated; *U.S. Public*, pg. 1558
OCEANS FUNDING COMPANY INC.; *U.S. Private*, pg. 2990
OPEN MORTGAGE, LLC; *U.S. Private*, pg. 3029
OTERA CAPITAL, INC.—See Caisse de Depot et Placement du Quebec; *Int'l*, pg. 1254
PARAMOUNT RESIDENTIAL MORTGAGE GROUP, INC.; *U.S. Private*, pg. 3093
PASQUINELLI CONSTRUCTION CO., INC.; *U.S. Private*, pg. 3104
PCN NETWORK; *U.S. Private*, pg. 3120
PETALUMA HOME LOANS—See American Pacific Mortgage; *U.S. Private*, pg. 242
PLATINUM HOME MORTGAGE CORPORATION—See Planet Financial Group, LLC; *U.S. Private*, pg. 3196
PRESIDENTIAL BANK FSB - MORTGAGE DIVISION—See Presidential Bank, FSB; *U.S. Private*, pg. 3254
PRIMEWEST MORTGAGE CORPORATION—See Heartland Financial USA, Inc.; *U.S. Public*, pg. 1018
PRIVATE MORTGAGE ADVISORS, LLC—See Wells Fargo & Company; *U.S. Public*, pg. 2345
PROVIDENT FUNDING; *U.S. Private*, pg. 3295
PRUDENTIAL FINANCIAL—See Prudential Financial, Inc.; *U.S. Public*, pg. 1732
PRUDENTIAL HUNTOON PAIGE ASSOCIATES, LTD.—See Prudential Financial, Inc.; *U.S. Public*, pg. 1732
PUBLIC SERVICE MORTGAGE, INC.; *U.S. Private*, pg. 3300
QUALITY MORTGAGE SERVICES LLC; *U.S. Private*, pg. 3320
QUEST COMMERCIAL CAPITAL CORP.—See Pohlad Companies; *U.S. Private*, pg. 3220
RAYMOND JAMES MORTGAGE COMPANY, INC.—See Raymond James Financial, Inc.; *U.S. Public*, pg. 1764
REALTY HOME MORTGAGE CO. LLC—See Presidential Bank, FSB; *U.S. Public*, pg. 3254

REGIONS MORTGAGE, INC.—See Regions Financial Corporation; *U.S. Public*, pg. 1776
REICO INVESTICNI SPOLECNOST CESKE SPORITELNY, A.S.—See Erste Group Bank AG; *Int'l*, pg. 2499
REPUBLIC MORTGAGE HOME LOAN LLC; *U.S. Private*, pg. 3402
RESIDENTIAL MORTGAGE SERVICES, INC.—See American National Corporation; *U.S. Public*, pg. 241
RESOURCE LENDERS INC.; *U.S. Private*, pg. 3407
RUOFF MORTGAGE COMPANY, INC.; *U.S. Private*, pg. 3504
SARATOGA CAPITAL INC.—See Pacific Properties III; *U.S. Private*, pg. 3070
SAUL CENTERS, INC.; *U.S. Public*, pg. 1842
SIGNATURE MORTGAGE CORPORATION—See Eustis Mortgage Corp.; *U.S. Private*, pg. 1434
SOUTHERN TRUST MORTGAGE, LLC; *U.S. Private*, pg. 3735
STANDARD MORTGAGE CORPORATION; *U.S. Private*, pg. 3781
STATE OF NEW YORK MORTGAGE AGENCY; *U.S. Private*, pg. 3792
STERLING NATIONAL MORTGAGE COMPANY, INC.—See Sterling Bancorp; *U.S. Public*, pg. 1946
STORE MASTER FUNDING I, LLC—See Blue Owl Capital Inc.; *U.S. Public*, pg. 364
STORE MASTER FUNDING I, LLC—See GIC Pte. Ltd.; *Int'l*, pg. 2964
SUBURBAN MORTGAGE INC.; *U.S. Private*, pg. 3848
SUMMIT HOME MORTGAGE, LLC—See Rithm Capital Corp.; *U.S. Public*, pg. 1800
SUNTRUST MORTGAGE INC.—See Truist Financial Corporation; *U.S. Public*, pg. 2200
TAMWEEL PJSC—See Dubai Islamic Bank PSJ; *Int'l*, pg. 2220
TOWNEBANK MORTGAGE—See Towne Bank; *U.S. Public*, pg. 2166
TREPP, LLC—See Daily Mail & General Trust plc; *Int'l*, pg. 1938
TREPP UK LTD.—See Daily Mail & General Trust plc; *Int'l*, pg. 1938
TUTHILL FINANCE; *U.S. Private*, pg. 4263
UCI UNION DE CREDITOS IMOBILIARIOS—See BNP Paribas SA; *Int'l*, pg. 1093
UNION CAPITAL MORTGAGE CORPORATION—See First Niles Financial, Inc.; *U.S. Public*, pg. 846
UNION MORTGAGE GROUP, INC.—See Atlantic Union Bankshares Corporation; *U.S. Public*, pg. 223
UNITY MORTGAGE CORP.; *U.S. Private*, pg. 4303
UNIVERSAL AMERICAN MORTGAGE COMPANY-LENNAR—See Lennar Corporation; *U.S. Public*, pg. 1307
UNIVERSAL AMERICAN MORTGAGE COMPANY—See Lennar Corporation; *U.S. Public*, pg. 1307
UNIVERSAL LENDING CORPORATION; *U.S. Private*, pg. 4305
VANDERBILT MORTGAGE & FINANCE, INC.—See Berkshire Hathaway Inc.; *U.S. Public*, pg. 304
VISTA CAPITAL LLC; *U.S. Private*, pg. 4393
WALKER & DUNLOP, LLC—See Walker & Dunlop, Inc.; *U.S. Public*, pg. 2324
WATSON GROUP FINANCIAL CORPORATION; *U.S. Private*, pg. 4455
WESTDEUTSCHE IMMOBILIEN SERVICING AG—See Advent International Corporation; *U.S. Public*, pg. 97
WESTDEUTSCHE IMMOBILIEN SERVICING AG—See Centerbridge Partners, L.P.; *U.S. Private*, pg. 813
WESTERN FINANCIAL CAPITAL CORPORATION—See Creative Media & Community Trust Corporation; *U.S. Public*, pg. 593
W.J. BRADLEY MORTGAGE CAPITAL, LLC; *U.S. Private*, pg. 4420

522299 — INTERNATIONAL, SECONDARY MARKET, AND ALL OTHER NONDEPOSITORY CREDIT INTERMEDIATION

1ST FARM CREDIT SERVICES, ACA; *U.S. Private*, pg. 4
AAJ CAPITAL 2 CORP.; *Int'l*, pg. 31
AARAMBHA MICROFINANCE BITTIYA SANSTHA LIMITED; *Int'l*, pg. 37
ABC INTERNATIONAL BANK PLC—See Arab Banking Corporation B.S.C.; *Int'l*, pg. 529
ABM AMRO COMMERCIAL FINANCE N.V.—See ABN AMRO Group N.V.; *Int'l*, pg. 63
ABN AMRO BANK (LUXEMBOURG) S.A.—See BNP Paribas SA; *Int'l*, pg. 1084
ABO GRUNDSTUCKSVERWALTUNGSGESELLSCHAFT MBH—See DZ BANK AG Deutsche Zentral-Genossenschaftsbank; *Int'l*, pg. 2243
ABSON INDUSTRIES LIMITED; *Int'l*, pg. 70
AB SVENSK EXPORTKREDIT; *Int'l*, pg. 41
ACCESS CAPITAL, INC.; *U.S. Private*, pg. 50
ACCORD FINANCIAL, INC.—See Accord Financial Corp.; *Int'l*, pg. 92
ADVANCE ACCEPTANCE CORPORATION—See First Western Bank & Trust; *U.S. Private*, pg. 1530

ADVANCE BUSINESS CAPITAL LLC—See Triumph Financial, Inc.; *U.S. Public*, pg. 2196
ADVANTAGE FUNDING CORPORATION; *U.S. Private*, pg. 94
AEP TEXAS CENTRAL TRANSITION FUNDING III LLC—See American Electric Power Company, Inc.; *U.S. Public*, pg. 99
AEP TEXAS CENTRAL TRANSITION FUNDING II LLC—See American Electric Power Company, Inc.; *U.S. Public*, pg. 99
AEP TEXAS CENTRAL TRANSITION FUNDING LLC—See American Electric Power Company, Inc.; *U.S. Public*, pg. 99
AETNA REALTY FINANCIAL CORP.—See United States Realty & Investment Company; *U.S. Private*, pg. 4299
AF1 CAPITAL CORP.; *Int'l*, pg. 184
AFFILIATED FINANCE INC.—See Affiliated Foods, Inc.; *U.S. Private*, pg. 122
AFRICAN DAWN CAPITAL LIMITED; *Int'l*, pg. 191
AFS/IBEX FINANCIAL SERVICES INC. OF CALIFORNIA—See Pathward Financial, Inc.; *U.S. Public*, pg. 1652
AFS/IBEX—See Pathward Financial, Inc.; *U.S. Public*, pg. 1652
AGCAROLINA FINANCIAL; *U.S. Private*, pg. 126
AGCHOICE FARM CREDIT; *U.S. Private*, pg. 126
AGCOUNTRY FARM CREDIT SERVICES, ACA; *U.S. Private*, pg. 126
AG CREDIT, ACA; *U.S. Private*, pg. 124
AGFIRST FARM CREDIT BANK—See Federal Farm Credit Banks Funding Corporation; *U.S. Private*, pg. 1487
AG NEW MEXICO, FARM CREDIT SERVICES, PCA—See Lone Star AG Credit; *U.S. Private*, pg. 2484
AGRIBANK, FCB—See Federal Farm Credit Banks Funding Corporation; *U.S. Private*, pg. 1487
AGRI BUSINESS FINANCE, INC.—See Kova Fertilizer Inc.; *U.S. Private*, pg. 2345
AGRI-MAX FINANCIAL SERVICES, L.P.—See Dairy Farmers of America, Inc.; *U.S. Private*, pg. 1145
AIB CAPITAL MARKETS PLC—See AIB Group plc; *Int'l*, pg. 228
AIB CORPORATE FINANCE LTD.—See AIB Group plc; *Int'l*, pg. 228
AKG EXIM LTD.; *Int'l*, pg. 263
A-L FINANCIAL CORPORATION; *U.S. Private*, pg. 22
ALLIANZ GLOBAL INVESTORS (LUXEMBOURG) S.A.—See Allianz SE; *Int'l*, pg. 346
ALLIANZ INVEST KAPITALANLAGEGESELLSCHAFT MBH—See Allianz SE; *Int'l*, pg. 348
ALLY COMMERCIAL FINANCE LLC—See Ally Financial Inc.; *U.S. Public*, pg. 81
ALPHANCO VENTURE CORP.; *Int'l*, pg. 370
ALTINA CAPITAL CORP.; *Int'l*, pg. 393
ALTINUM GVG MBH & CO. SONNENHOF—See Commerzbank AG; *Int'l*, pg. 1717
AMERICAN PAWN & JEWELRY, INC.; *U.S. Private*, pg. 243
AMERICAN PAYDAY LOANS INC.; *U.S. Private*, pg. 243
AMERICAN STUDENT ASSISTANCE; *U.S. Private*, pg. 256
AMMERCHANT BANK BERHAD—See AMMB Holdings Berhad; *Int'l*, pg. 429
AMP SERVICES HOLDINGS LIMITED—See AMP Limited; *Int'l*, pg. 432
AMSTERDAM TRADE BANK N.V.—See ABH Holdings S.A.; *Int'l*, pg. 60
ANC CAPITAL VENTURES, INC.; *Int'l*, pg. 447
ANDEAN PRECIOUS METALS CORP.; *Int'l*, pg. 449
ANTALIS VENTURES CORP.; *Int'l*, pg. 481
ANZ AUSTRALIAN CAPITAL TERRITORY—See Australia & New Zealand Banking Group Limited; *Int'l*, pg. 720
ANZ NORTHERN TERRITORY—See Australia & New Zealand Banking Group Limited; *Int'l*, pg. 720
ANZ PRIVATE BANK—See Australia & New Zealand Banking Group Limited; *Int'l*, pg. 720
ANZ SINGAPORE LIMITED—See Australia & New Zealand Banking Group Limited; *Int'l*, pg. 719
ANZ THAILAND—See Australia & New Zealand Banking Group Limited; *Int'l*, pg. 719
APEX CREDIT MANAGEMENT LIMITED—See Encore Capital Group, Inc.; *U.S. Public*, pg. 759
APOGEE MINERALS LTD.; *Int'l*, pg. 517
APPALACHIAN CONSUMER RATE RELIEF FUNDING LLC—See American Electric Power Company, Inc.; *U.S. Public*, pg. 99
ARAB FINANCIAL SERVICES B.S.C.; *Int'l*, pg. 530
ARISTA CAPITAL LTD.—See Arista Financial Corp.; *U.S. Private*, pg. 323
ARMSTRONG CORK FINANCE LLC—See Armstrong World Industries, Inc.; *U.S. Public*, pg. 194
ASAHI KASEI MORTGAGE CORPORATION—See Asahi Kasei Corporation; *Int'l*, pg. 596
ASB BANK LIMITED—See Commonwealth Bank of Australia; *Int'l*, pg. 1719
ASSET RESOLUTION LIMITED; *Int'l*, pg. 642
ASSIMOCO VITA S.P.A.—See DZ BANK AG Deutsche Zentral-Genossenschaftsbank; *Int'l*, pg. 2243
ASTANA FINANCE, JSC; *Int'l*, pg. 651
ATLANTIC FORFAITIERUNGS AG—See Dr. August Oetker KG; *Int'l*, pg. 2190

ATRADIUS N.V.—See Grupo Catalana Occidente, S.A.; *Int'l*, pg. 3124
ATTIJARIWAFA BANK EGYPT S.A.E—See Banco Santander, S.A.; *Int'l*, pg. 825
AUTOMOTIVE FINANCE CORPORATION—See OPENLANE, Inc.; *U.S. Public*, pg. 1607
AVIC INTERNATIONAL BEIJING COMPANY LIMITED—See AVIC International Holdings Limited; *Int'l*, pg. 742
AVIS FINANCE COMPANY PLC—See Avis Budget Group, Inc.; *U.S. Public*, pg. 248
AXIS FINANCE LTD.—See Axis Bank Limited; *Int'l*, pg. 769
AXXON WERTPAPIERHANDELSBANK AG; *Int'l*, pg. 773
AYONDO LTD.; *Int'l*, pg. 775
BALCHEM CORPORATION; *U.S. Public*, pg. 265
BALTIC I ACQUISITION CORP.; *Int'l*, pg. 812
BANCA FARMAFACTORING S.P.A.; *Int'l*, pg. 814
BANCA HIPOTECARIA—See Banco Bilbao Vizcaya Argentaria, S.A.; *Int'l*, pg. 818
BANCO ABC BRASIL S.A.—See Arab Banking Corporation B.S.C.; *Int'l*, pg. 529
BANCO BNP PARIBAS BRASIL—See BNP Paribas SA; *Int'l*, pg. 1089
BANCO BRADESCO ARGENTINA S.A.—See Banco Bradesco S.A.; *Int'l*, pg. 819
BANCO BRADESCO NEW YORK—See Banco Bradesco S.A.; *Int'l*, pg. 819
BANCO CAIXA GERAL, S.A.—See Caixa Geral de Depositos S.A.; *Int'l*, pg. 1260
BANCO CETELEM S.A.—See BNP Paribas SA; *Int'l*, pg. 1089
BANCO DE LA NACION ARGENTINA - NEW YORK—See Banco de la Nacion Argentina; *Int'l*, pg. 820
BANCO DE LA NACION ARGENTINA—See Banco de la Nacion Argentina; *Int'l*, pg. 820
BANCO DE LA PROVINCIA DE BUENOS AIRES; *Int'l*, pg. 821
BANCO DO BRASIL AG AUSTRIA—See Banco do Brasil S.A.; *Int'l*, pg. 822
BANCO ITAU ARGENTINA S.A.—See Banco Macro S.A.; *Int'l*, pg. 823
BANCO LATINOAMERICANO DE COMERCIO EXTERIOR, S.A.; *Int'l*, pg. 823
BANCO POPULAR S.A.—See Popular, Inc.; *U.S. Public*, pg. 1702
BANCO PRIMUS S.A—See Groupe BPCE; *Int'l*, pg. 3092
BANCO PRIMUS SPAIN S.A—See Groupe BPCE; *Int'l*, pg. 3092
BANGKOK LAND (CAYMAN ISLANDS) LIMITED—See Bangkok Land Public Company Limited; *Int'l*, pg. 834
BANK AL-SHARQ S.A.S.—See Banque Libano-Francaise S.A.L.; *Int'l*, pg. 854
BANK BNP LIPPO UTAMA LEASING—See BNP Paribas SA; *Int'l*, pg. 1081
BANK BNP PARIBAS LUXEMBOURG—See BNP Paribas SA; *Int'l*, pg. 1089
BANKERS HEALTHCARE GROUP, LLC - FINANCIAL HEADQUARTERS—See Bankers Healthcare Group, LLC; *U.S. Private*, pg. 467
BANKERS HEALTHCARE GROUP, LLC; *U.S. Private*, pg. 467
BANK LEUMI (LUXEMBOURG) S.A.—See Bank Leumi Le-Israel B.M.; *Int'l*, pg. 838
BANK LEUMI (UK) PLC—See Bank Leumi Le-Israel B.M.; *Int'l*, pg. 838
BANK OF AMERICA BUSINESS CAPITAL—See Bank of America Corporation; *U.S. Public*, pg. 270
BANK OF AMERICA BUSINESS CREDIT—See Bank of America Corporation; *U.S. Public*, pg. 270
BANK OF AMERICA (FRANCE)—See Bank of America Corporation; *U.S. Public*, pg. 270
BANK OF AMERICA LEASING CANADA—See Bank of America Corporation; *U.S. Public*, pg. 270
BANK OF AMERICA LEASING—See Bank of America Corporation; *U.S. Public*, pg. 270
BANK OF CHINA LIMITED (SINGAPORE)—See Bank of China, Ltd.; *Int'l*, pg. 841
BANK OF CHINA-NEW YORK—See Bank of China, Ltd.; *Int'l*, pg. 841
BANK OF IDAHO—See Bank of Idaho Holding Company; *U.S. Public*, pg. 273
BANK OF IRELAND CREDIT CARD SERVICES—See Bank of Ireland Group plc; *Int'l*, pg. 844
BANK OF IRELAND HOME MORTGAGES LIMITED—See Bank of Ireland Group plc; *Int'l*, pg. 844
BANK OF IRELAND TRASURY LIMITED—See Bank of Ireland Group plc; *Int'l*, pg. 845
BANK OF IRELAND TREASURY & INTERNATIONAL BANKING LIMITED—See Bank of Ireland Group plc; *Int'l*, pg. 844
BANQUE DE TAHITI S.A.—See Bank of Hawaii Corporation; *U.S. Public*, pg. 273
BANQUE SAUDI FRANSI; *Int'l*, pg. 854
BANSABADELL INVERSION, S.A., S.G.I.I.C.—See Banco de Sabadell, S.A.; *Int'l*, pg. 821
BARCLAYS ASSET FINANCE—See Barclays PLC; *Int'l*, pg. 859
BARCLAYS BANK IRELAND PLC—See Barclays PLC; *Int'l*, pg. 859

BARCLAYS BANK - MAURITIUS—See Barclays PLC; *Int'l*, pg. 859
BARCLAYS BANK OF UGANDA LTD.—See Barclays PLC; *Int'l*, pg. 860
BARCLAYS BANK OF ZAMBIA LTD.—See Barclays PLC; *Int'l*, pg. 860
BARCLAYS BANK (SEYCHELLES) LTD.—See Barclays PLC; *Int'l*, pg. 859
BARCLAYS BANK—See Barclays PLC; *Int'l*, pg. 859
BARCLAYS BANK—See Barclays PLC; *Int'l*, pg. 859
BARCLAYS BANK—See Barclays PLC; *Int'l*, pg. 859
BARCLAYS BANK—See Barclays PLC; *Int'l*, pg. 859
BARCLAYS BANK—See Barclays PLC; *Int'l*, pg. 859
BARCLAYS BANK—See Barclays PLC; *Int'l*, pg. 859
BARCLAYS BANK TANZANIA LTD.—See Barclays PLC; *Int'l*, pg. 860
BARCLAYS CAPITAL JAPAN LIMITED—See Barclays PLC; *Int'l*, pg. 860
BAR NONE, INC.; *U.S. Private*, pg. 471
BAYERISCHE LANDESBANK GIROZENTRALE—See BayernLB Holding AG; *Int'l*, pg. 913
BAYERISCHE LANDESBANK INTERNATIONAL S.A.—See BayernLB Holding AG; *Int'l*, pg. 913
BAYERISCHE LANDESBODENKREDITANSTALT—See BayernLB Holding AG; *Int'l*, pg. 913
BB ADMINISTRADORA DE CARTOES DE CREDITO S.A.—See Banco do Brasil S.A.; *Int'l*, pg. 822
BB LEASING-ARRANDEMENTO MERCANTIL—See Banco do Brasil S.A.; *Int'l*, pg. 822
BBVA (SUIZA) S.A.—See Banco Bilbao Vizcaya Argentaria, S.A.; *Int'l*, pg. 817
BCV ITALIA SRL—See Banque Cantonale Vaudoise; *Int'l*, pg. 853
BCW GROUP (GOTHIA) LIMITED—See Bertelsmann SE & Co. KGaA; *Int'l*, pg. 996
BELFIUS COMMERCIAL FINANCE—See Belfius Bank SA/NV; *Int'l*, pg. 963
BELFIUS LEASE—See Belfius Bank SA/NV; *Int'l*, pg. 963
BERLIN HYP AG—See Deutscher Sparkassen- und Giroverband e.V.; *Int'l*, pg. 2085
BERLIN HYP AG - WARSAW OFFICE—See Deutscher Sparkassen- und Giroverband e.V.; *Int'l*, pg. 2085
BHARTIA BACHAT LIMITED; *Int'l*, pg. 1013
BIG-IMMOBILIEN GESELLSCHAFT MIT BESCHRANKTER HAFTUNG—See DZ BANK AG Deutsche Zentral-Genossenschaftsbank; *Int'l*, pg. 2243
BKS-IMMOBILIENLEASING GESELLSCHAFT MBH—See Bank fur Tirol und Vorarlberg Ag; *Int'l*, pg. 838
BKS-LEASING GESELLSCHAFT MBH—See Bank fur Tirol und Vorarlberg Ag; *Int'l*, pg. 838
BLACKARCH PARTNERS LP.—See Regions Financial Corporation; *U.S. Public*, pg. 1776
BLACKROCK (CHANNEL ISLANDS) LIMITED—See BlackRock, Inc.; *U.S. Public*, pg. 344
BLUEBONNET PROPERTIES, LLC—See Security National Financial Corporation; *U.S. Public*, pg. 1856
BLUEWATER ACQUISITION CORP.; *Int'l*, pg. 1075
BMGB CAPITAL CORP.; *Int'l*, pg. 1076
BMW BANK OF NORTH AMERICA INC.—See Bayerische Motoren Werke Aktiengesellschaft; *Int'l*, pg. 912
BMW LEASE (MALAYSIA) SDN. BHD.—See Bayerische Motoren Werke Aktiengesellschaft; *Int'l*, pg. 911
BNP FACTOR - PORTUGAL—See BNP Paribas SA; *Int'l*, pg. 1080
BNP PARIBAS ATHENS BRANCH—See BNP Paribas SA; *Int'l*, pg. 1082
BNP PARIBAS BANK JSC—See BNP Paribas SA; *Int'l*, pg. 1082
BNP PARIBAS BANK N.V.—See BNP Paribas SA; *Int'l*, pg. 1086
BNP PARIBAS BULGARIA EAD—See BNP Paribas SA; *Int'l*, pg. 1082
BNP PARIBAS (CANADA) INC.—See BNP Paribas SA; *Int'l*, pg. 1081
BNP PARIBAS CANADA—See BNP Paribas SA; *Int'l*, pg. 1082
BNP PARIBAS COMMERCIAL FINANCE LTD.—See BNP Paribas SA; *Int'l*, pg. 1084
BNP PARIBAS DUBLIN—See BNP Paribas SA; *Int'l*, pg. 1083
BNP PARIBAS FACTOR ASIA LTD.—See BNP Paribas SA; *Int'l*, pg. 1084
BNP PARIBAS FACTOR A/S—See BNP Paribas SA; *Int'l*, pg. 1084
BNP PARIBAS FACTOR GMBH—See BNP Paribas SA; *Int'l*, pg. 1084
BNP PARIBAS FACTOR, SA SUCURSAL EN ESPANA—See BNP Paribas SA; *Int'l*, pg. 1084
BNP PARIBAS FACTOR—See BNP Paribas SA; *Int'l*, pg. 1083
BNP PARIBAS FORTIS FACTOR NV/SA—See BNP Paribas SA; *Int'l*, pg. 1084
BNP PARIBAS FRANKFURT BRANCH—See BNP Paribas SA; *Int'l*, pg. 1084
BNP PARIBAS GUANGZHOU—See BNP Paribas SA; *Int'l*, pg. 1081
BNP PARIBAS-HOUSTON—See BNP Paribas SA; *Int'l*, pg. 1087

N.A.I.C.S. INDEX

BNP PARIBAS HUNGARIA BANK RT—See BNP Paribas SA; *Int'l*, pg. 1085
BNP PARIBAS-MANAMA BRANCH—See BNP Paribas SA; *Int'l*, pg. 1088
BNP PARIBAS-MANILA OFFSHORE BRANCH—See BNP Paribas SA; *Int'l*, pg. 1081
BNP PARIBAS MUMBAI BRANCH—See BNP Paribas SA; *Int'l*, pg. 1086
BNP PARIBAS NEW DELHI BRANCH—See BNP Paribas SA; *Int'l*, pg. 1086
BNP PARIBAS NOUVELLE CALEDONIE—See BNP Paribas SA; *Int'l*, pg. 1086
BNP PARIBAS QATAR—See BNP Paribas SA; *Int'l*, pg. 1086
BNP PARIBAS SHANGHAI—See BNP Paribas SA; *Int'l*, pg. 1081
BNP PARIBAS SUCCURSALE ITALIA—See BNP Paribas SA; *Int'l*, pg. 1087
BNP PARIBAS SUISSE S.A.—See BNP Paribas SA; *Int'l*, pg. 1081
BNP PARIBAS URUGUAY S.A.—See BNP Paribas SA; *Int'l*, pg. 1088
BNY INTERNATIONAL FINANCING CORPORATION—See The Bank of New York Mellon Corporation; *U.S. Public*, pg. 2036
BONAIRE SOFTWARE SOLUTIONS, LLC—See Broadridge Financial Solutions, Inc.; *U.S. Public*, pg. 391
BONANZA MINING CORPORATION; *Int'l*, pg. 1105
BPIFRANCE FINANCEMENT—See Caisse des Depots et Consignations; *Int'l*, pg. 1258
BPIFRANCE FINANCEMENT—See EPIC Bpifrance; *Int'l*, pg. 2460
BRASILIAN AMERICAN MERCHANT BANK—See Banco do Brasil S.A.; *Int'l*, pg. 822
BRAZOS HIGHER EDUCATION SERVICE CORPORATION; *U.S. Private*, pg. 642
BRE FAKTORING S.A.—See Commerzbank AG; *Int'l*, pg. 1719
BRE LEASING SP. Z O.O.—See Commerzbank AG; *Int'l*, pg. 1717
BROADRIDGE BUSINESS PROCESS OUTSOURCING, LLC—See Broadridge Financial Solutions, Inc.; *U.S. Public*, pg. 391
BROOKRIDGE FUNDING CORP.; *U.S. Private*, pg. 664
BROTHER FINANCE (JAPAN), LTD.—See Brother Industries, Ltd.; *Int'l*, pg. 1196
BROTHER FINANCE (U.K.) PLC—See Brother Industries, Ltd.; *Int'l*, pg. 1196
BTV REAL-LEASING III NACHFOLGE GMBH AND CO KG—See Bank fur Tirol und Vorarlberg Ag; *Int'l*, pg. 838
BURGO FACTOR SPA—See Burgo Group S.p.A.; *Int'l*, pg. 1223
BUSAN CREDIT & INFORMATION CO., LTD.—See BNK Financial Group Inc.; *Int'l*, pg. 1079
BUZBUZ CAPITAL CORP.; *Int'l*, pg. 1230
CABOT FINANCIAL (EUROPE) LIMITED—See Encore Capital Group, Inc.; *U.S. Public*, pg. 759
CAISSE SOLIDAIRE SCCV—See Groupe BPCE; *Int'l*, pg. 3093
CAIXA GERAL DE DEPOSITOS (FRANCE)—See Caixa Geral de Depositos S.A.; *Int'l*, pg. 1260
CAIXA LEASING & FACTORING, IFIC, SA—See Caixa Geral de Depositos S.A.; *Int'l*, pg. 1260
CALIFORNIA FACTORS & FINANCE LP; *U.S. Private*, pg. 719
CALYPSO GMBH—See DZ BANK AG Deutsche Zentral-Genossenschaftsbank; *Int'l*, pg. 2243
CAMPUS DOOR HOLDINGS INC.—See Incenter, LLC; *U.S. Private*, pg. 2053
CAN CAPITAL, INC.; *U.S. Private*, pg. 732
CAN FIN HOMES LIMITED—See Canara Bank; *Int'l*, pg. 1287
CANNA 8 INVESTMENT TRUST; *Int'l*, pg. 1291
CANN-IS CAPITAL CORP.; *Int'l*, pg. 1291
CAPITAL FARM CREDIT, ACA; *U.S. Private*, pg. 740
CAPITOL FINANCIAL STRATEGIES, LLC; *U.S. Private*, pg. 743
CAPX PARTNERS—See Accord Financial Corp.; *Int'l*, pg. 92
CARD SERVICES FOR CREDIT UNIONS, INC.; *U.S. Private*, pg. 749
CAROLINA FARM CREDIT, ACA; *U.S. Private*, pg. 768
CASA DE CAMBIO BANCOMER—See Banco Bilbao Vizcaya Argentaria, S.A.; *Int'l*, pg. 818
CASH CONVERTERS PTY LTD—See Cash Converters International Limited; *Int'l*, pg. 1352
CASH CONVERTERS (STORES) PTY LTD—See Cash Converters International Limited; *Int'l*, pg. 1352
CASH CONVERTERS UK HOLDINGS PLC—See Cash Converters International Limited; *Int'l*, pg. 1352
CASH-N-PAWN INTERNATIONAL, LTD.—See EZCORP, Inc.; *U.S. Public*, pg. 817
CASH-N-PAWN OF MINNESOTA, LTD.—See EZCORP, Inc.; *U.S. Public*, pg. 817
CASTLEBAR CAPITAL CORP.; *Int'l*, pg. 1357
CASTLECAP CAPITAL, INC.; *Int'l*, pg. 1357
CBFC LIMITED—See Commonwealth Bank of Australia; *Int'l*, pg. 1719
CC-BANK AKTIENGESELLSCHAFT—See Banco Santander, S.A.; *Int'l*, pg. 825
CCF REPRESENTACAO E ASSESSORIA S/C LTDA.—See HSBC Holdings plc; *Int'l*, pg. 3505
CE BRANDS, INC.; *Int'l*, pg. 1372
CELTIC CAPITAL CORPORATION—See Banc of California, Inc.; *U.S. Public*, pg. 269
CERRADO GOLD INC.; *Int'l*, pg. 1422
CETELEM BELGIUM—See BNP Paribas SA; *Int'l*, pg. 1089
CETELEM—See BNP Paribas SA; *Int'l*, pg. 1089
CF GLOBAL TRADING, LLC—See State Street Corporation; *U.S. Public*, pg. 1940
CGI MBH—See Commerzbank AG; *Int'l*, pg. 1715
CHAILEASE FINANCE CO., LTD.—See Chailease Holding Company Limited; *Int'l*, pg. 1436
CHINA HI-TECH GROUP CO., LTD.; *Int'l*, pg. 1507
CHS CAPITAL, LLC—See CHS INC.; *U.S. Public*, pg. 491
CHURCHILL RESOURCES INC.; *Int'l*, pg. 1600
THE CIT GROUP/BUSINESS CREDIT, INC.—See First Citizens BancShares, Inc.; *U.S. Public*, pg. 842
THE CIT GROUP/CAPITAL FINANCE, INC.—See First Citizens BancShares, Inc.; *U.S. Public*, pg. 842
THE CIT GROUP/COMMERCIAL SERVICES, INC.—See First Citizens BancShares, Inc.; *U.S. Public*, pg. 842
THE CIT GROUP/SALES FINANCING, INC.—See First Citizens BancShares, Inc.; *U.S. Public*, pg. 842
CITIBANK EUROPE PLC - FINLAND REPRESENTATIVE OFFICE—See Citigroup Inc.; *U.S. Public*, pg. 502
CITIBANK EUROPE PLC - FRANCE REPRESENTATIVE OFFICE—See Citigroup Inc.; *U.S. Public*, pg. 502
CITIBANK KOREA INC.—See Citigroup Inc.; *U.S. Public*, pg. 503
CITIBANK, N.A.—See Citigroup Inc.; *U.S. Public*, pg. 502
CITICORP SECURITIES INTERNATIONAL, INC.—See Citigroup Inc.; *U.S. Public*, pg. 503
CITIGROUP GLOBAL MARKETS (PROPRIETARY) LIMITED—See Citigroup Inc.; *U.S. Public*, pg. 503
CITIZENS BUSINESS BANK - DAIRY & LIVESTOCK INDUSTRIES GROUP—See CVB Financial Corp.; *U.S. Public*, pg. 613
CJSC HALYK LEASING—See Halyk Bank of Kazakhstan JSC; *Int'l*, pg. 3234
CLAL CREDIT & FINANCING LTD.—See IDB Development Corporation Ltd.; *Int'l*, pg. 3588
CLAL FACTORING LTD.—See IDB Development Corporation Ltd.; *Int'l*, pg. 3588
CLOUD DX, INC.; *Int'l*, pg. 1661
C-N-P NORTHWEST, LTD.—See EZCORP, Inc.; *U.S. Public*, pg. 817
COASTAL CREDIT, LLC—See PCP Enterprise, L.P.; *U.S. Private*, pg. 3121
COBANK, ACB; *U.S. Public*, pg. 520
COFACE AUSTRIA GMBH—See Groupe BPCE; *Int'l*, pg. 3093
COFACE AUSTRIA KREDITVERSICHERUNG AG—See Coface S.A.; *Int'l*, pg. 1691
COFACE CENTRAL EUROPE HOLDING AG—See Coface S.A.; *Int'l*, pg. 1691
COFACE CREDIT MANAGEMENT NORTH AMERICA, INC.—See Coface S.A.; *Int'l*, pg. 1691
COFACE DANMARK—See Coface S.A.; *Int'l*, pg. 1691
COFACE NORTH AMERICA, INC.—See Coface S.A.; *Int'l*, pg. 1691
COFACE S.A.; *Int'l*, pg. 1690
COFACE UK SERVICES LIMITED—See Coface S.A.; *Int'l*, pg. 1691
COLLEGIUM GLASHUTTEN ZENTRUM FUR KOMMUNIKATION GMBH—See Commerzbank AG; *Int'l*, pg. 1715
COLLINGWOOD RESOURCES CORP.; *Int'l*, pg. 1702
COLONIAL FARM CREDIT A.C.A.; *U.S. Public*, pg. 970
COLSON CAPITAL CORP.; *Int'l*, pg. 1705
COMDIRECT BANK AG—See Commerzbank AG; *Int'l*, pg. 1717
COMMERZBANK BELGIUM S.A.N.V.—See Commerzbank AG; *Int'l*, pg. 1717
COMMERZBANK (BUDAPEST) RT—See Commerzbank AG; *Int'l*, pg. 1717
COMMERZBANK CAPITAL MARKETS CORPORATION—See Commerzbank AG; *Int'l*, pg. 1717
COMMERZBANK (EURASIJA) SAO—See Commerzbank AG; *Int'l*, pg. 1717
COMMERZBANK (NEDERLAND) N.V.—See Commerzbank AG; *Int'l*, pg. 1717
COMMERZ (EAST ASIA) LTD.—See Commerzbank AG; *Int'l*, pg. 1716
COMMERZLEASING UND IMMOBILIEN GMBH—See Commerzbank AG; *Int'l*, pg. 1717
COMMONWEALTH BANK OF AUSTRALIA - BEIJING—See Commonwealth Bank of Australia; *Int'l*, pg. 1720
COMMONWEALTH BANK OF AUSTRALIA - GRAND CAYMAN—See Commonwealth Bank of Australia; *Int'l*, pg. 1720
COMMONWEALTH BANK OF AUSTRALIA - HONG KONG—See Commonwealth Bank of Australia; *Int'l*, pg. 1720
COMMONWEALTH BANK OF AUSTRALIA - JAPAN—See Commonwealth Bank of Australia; *Int'l*, pg. 1720
COMMONWEALTH BANK OF AUSTRALIA - SHANGHAI—See Commonwealth Bank of Australia; *Int'l*, pg. 1720
COMMONWEALTH BANK OF AUSTRALIA - UK—See Commonwealth Bank of Australia; *Int'l*, pg. 1720
COMPEER FINANCIAL, ACA; *U.S. Private*, pg. 1000
COMPREHENSIVE HEALTHCARE SYSTEMS INC.; *Int'l*, pg. 1754
CONTINENTAL BUSINESS CREDIT, INC.—See Republic Business Credit, LLC; *U.S. Private*, pg. 3401
CORPORATE BILLING, LLC—See SouthState Corporation; *U.S. Public*, pg. 1913
CORTUS METALS, INC.; *Int'l*, pg. 1808
CREDEM INTERNATIONAL (LUX) S.A.—See Credito Emiliano S.p.A.; *Int'l*, pg. 1836
CREDIFY INFORMATIONSDIENSTLEISTUNGEN GMBH—See Bertelsmann SE & Co. KGaA; *Int'l*, pg. 992
CREDIT DIRECT LIMITED—See FCMB Group Plc; *Int'l*, pg. 2628
CREDIT MOBILIER DE MONACO S.A.; *Int'l*, pg. 1835
CREDIT ORGANIZATION OF SMALL & MEDIUM-SIZED ENTERPRISES CO., LTD.; *Int'l*, pg. 1835
CREDITWEST FAKTORING A.S.; *Int'l*, pg. 1837
CSNK WORKING CAPITAL FINANCE CORP.—See Heritage Commerce Corp; *U.S. Public*, pg. 1028
CTC—See Concurrent Technologies Corporation; *U.S. Private*, pg. 1011
DAH SING BANK LIMITED—See Dah Sing Financial Holdings Limited; *Int'l*, pg. 1913
DAH SING FINANCE LIMITED—See Dah Sing Financial Holdings Limited; *Int'l*, pg. 1913
THE DAISHI GUARANTY CO., LTD.—See Daishi Hokuetsu Financial Group, Inc.; *Int'l*, pg. 1941
DANONE FINANCIAL CENTER B.V.—See Danone; *Int'l*, pg. 1966
DAURA CAPITAL CORP.; *Int'l*, pg. 1983
DAVENHAM TRADE FINANCE LIMITED—See Davenham Group Plc; *Int'l*, pg. 1983
DB SERVICE CENTRE LIMITED—See Deutsche Bank Aktiengesellschaft; *Int'l*, pg. 2056
DEGUSSA BANK AG—See Apollo Global Management, Inc.; *U.S. Public*, pg. 148
DEGUSSA BANK AG—See Grovepoint Capital LLP; *Int'l*, pg. 3112
DEGUSSA BANK AG—See Teacher Retirement System of Texas; *U.S. Private*, pg. 3944
DEKA INTERNATIONAL (IRELAND) LTD.—See DekaBank; *Int'l*, pg. 2005
DEL TORO LOAN SERVICING, INC.; *U.S. Private*, pg. 1193
DEUTSCHE BANK AG-AMSTERDAM—See Deutsche Bank Aktiengesellschaft; *Int'l*, pg. 2058
DEUTSCHE BANK AG (BOMBAY)—See Deutsche Bank Aktiengesellschaft; *Int'l*, pg. 2058
DEUTSCHE BANK AG JOHANNESBURG—See Deutsche Bank Aktiengesellschaft; *Int'l*, pg. 2058
DEUTSCHE BANK AG-LONDON—See Deutsche Bank Aktiengesellschaft; *Int'l*, pg. 2059
DEUTSCHE BANK AG (MACAU)—See Deutsche Bank Aktiengesellschaft; *Int'l*, pg. 2058
DEUTSCHE BANK AG (MANILA)—See Deutsche Bank Aktiengesellschaft; *Int'l*, pg. 2058
DEUTSCHE BANK AG (NEW DELHI)—See Deutsche Bank Aktiengesellschaft; *Int'l*, pg. 2058
DEUTSCHE BANK AG (PRAGUE)—See Deutsche Bank Aktiengesellschaft; *Int'l*, pg. 2058
DEUTSCHE BANK AG (SEOUL)—See Deutsche Bank Aktiengesellschaft; *Int'l*, pg. 2058
DEUTSCHE BANK AG—See Deutsche Bank Aktiengesellschaft; *Int'l*, pg. 2058
DEUTSCHE BANK AG (TAIPEI)—See Deutsche Bank Aktiengesellschaft; *Int'l*, pg. 2058
DEUTSCHE BANK AG (TEHRAN)—See Deutsche Bank Aktiengesellschaft; *Int'l*, pg. 2058
DEUTSCHE BANK AG (TOKYO)—See Deutsche Bank Aktiengesellschaft; *Int'l*, pg. 2058
DEUTSCHE BANK FACTORING S.P.A.—See Deutsche Bank Aktiengesellschaft; *Int'l*, pg. 2059
DEUTSCHE BANK FINANCE N.V.—See Deutsche Bank Aktiengesellschaft; *Int'l*, pg. 2059
DEUTSCHE BANK INTERNATIONAL—See Deutsche Bank Aktiengesellschaft; *Int'l*, pg. 2059
DEUTSCHE BANK LTD.—See Deutsche Bank Aktiengesellschaft; *Int'l*, pg. 2059
DEUTSCHE BANK (MALAYSIA) BERHAD—See Deutsche Bank Aktiengesellschaft; *Int'l*, pg. 2058
DEUTSCHE BANK MEXICO S.A. DE C.V.—See Deutsche Bank Aktiengesellschaft; *Int'l*, pg. 2059
DEUTSCHE BANK RT—See Deutsche Bank Aktiengesellschaft; *Int'l*, pg. 2060
DEUTSCHE BANK S.A.-BANCO ALEMAO—See Deutsche Bank Aktiengesellschaft; *Int'l*, pg. 2060
DEUTSCHE BANK S.A.E.—See Deutsche Bank Aktiengesellschaft; *Int'l*, pg. 2060
DEUTSCHE BANK SAO PAULO—See Deutsche Bank Aktiengesellschaft; *Int'l*, pg. 2060
DEUTSCHE BANK (SCHWEIZ) AG—See Deutsche Bank Aktiengesellschaft; *Int'l*, pg. 2058
DEUTSCHE BANK (SUISSE) S.A.—See Deutsche Bank Aktiengesellschaft; *Int'l*, pg. 2058

522299 — INTERNATIONAL, SECO...

DEUTSCHE BANK (SVIZZERA) S.A.—See Deutsche Bank Aktiengesellschaft; *Int'l*, pg. 2058
DEUTSCHE BANK (URUGUAY) S.A.I.F.E.—See Deutsche Bank Aktiengesellschaft; *Int'l*, pg. 2058
DEUTSCHE INTERNATIONAL TRUST CORPORATION (CI) LIMITED—See Deutsche Bank Aktiengesellschaft; *Int'l*, pg. 2060
DEVELOPMENT BANK OF JAPAN, INC.; *Int'l*, pg. 2087
DEXIA BANK NEDERLAND N.V.—See Dexia SA; *Int'l*, pg. 2092
DEXIA CREDIT LOCAL SA—See Dexia SA; *Int'l*, pg. 2092
DEXIA CREDIT LOCAL—See Dexia SA; *Int'l*, pg. 2092
DEXIA CREDIT LOCAL—See Dexia SA; *Int'l*, pg. 2092
DEXIA CREDIT; *U.S. Private*, pg. 1220
DEXIA SOCIETE DE CREDIT SA—See Dexia SA; *Int'l*, pg. 2092
DF DEUTSCHE FORFAIT AG PAKISTAN (PVT.) LTD.—See DF Deutsche Forfait AG; *Int'l*, pg. 2094
DF DEUTSCHE FORFAIT AMERICAS INC—See DF Deutsche Forfait AG; *Int'l*, pg. 2094
DF DEUTSCHE FORFAIT S.R.O—See DF Deutsche Forfait AG; *Int'l*, pg. 2094
DGN SERVICE GMBH—See Deutsche Apotheker- und Arztebank eG; *Int'l*, pg. 2049
DILLARD INVESTMENT CO., INC.—See Dillard's Inc.; *U.S. Public*, pg. 666
DINERS CLUB ISRAEL LTD.—See IDB Development Corporation Ltd.; *Int'l*, pg. 3588
DIRECT LENDING PARTNER—See Don Wenner Home Selling, Inc.; *U.S. Public*, pg. 1259
DIREXXIS LLC—See Broadridge Financial Solutions, Inc.; *U.S. Public*, pg. 391
DNEX DRILLING TECH & OILFIELD SERVICES SDN. BHD.—See Dagang NeXchange Berhad; *Int'l*, pg. 1912
DNEX TECHNOLOGY SDN. BHD.—See Dagang NeXchange Berhad; *Int'l*, pg. 1912
DVB INVESTMENT MANAGEMENT N.V.—See DZ BANK AG Deutsche Zentral-Genossenschaftsbank; *Int'l*, pg. 2243
DZ BANK IRELAND PLC—See DZ BANK AG Deutsche Zentral-Genossenschaftsbank; *Int'l*, pg. 2243
DZ BANK POLSKA—See DZ BANK AG Deutsche Zentral-Genossenschaftsbank; *Int'l*, pg. 2243
DZ BANK SAO PAULO REPRESENTACAO LTDA.—See DZ BANK AG Deutsche Zentral-Genossenschaftsbank; *Int'l*, pg. 2243
DZ PRIVATBANK (SCHWEIZ) AG—See DZ BANK AG Deutsche Zentral-Genossenschaftsbank; *Int'l*, pg. 2244
EARLYBIRDCAPITAL INC.; *U.S. Private*, pg. 1313
EAST LOS ANGELES COMMUNITY UNION; *U.S. Private*, pg. 1316
EBS DEALING RESOURCES INC—See CME Group, Inc.; *U.S. Public*, pg. 516
ECOMMISSION FINANCIAL SERVICES, INC.—See Lightyear Capital LLC; *U.S. Private*, pg. 2454
EDGE TOTAL INTELLIGENCE INC.; *Int'l*, pg. 2309
EDUCATIONAL CREDIT MANAGEMENT CO.; *U.S. Private*, pg. 1339
ELBROOK CASH & CARRY LTD.; *Int'l*, pg. 2345
ELECTRIC ROYALTIES LTD.; *Int'l*, pg. 2349
ELK ASSOCIATES FUNDING CORPORATION—See Ameritrans Capital Corporation; *U.S. Public*, pg. 115
ELK CAPITAL CORPORATION—See Ameritrans Capital Corporation; *U.S. Public*, pg. 115
ELK-DESA RESOURCES BHD; *Int'l*, pg. 2363
EMILIA ROMAGNA FACTOR S.P.A.—See BPER BANCA S.p.A; *Int'l*, pg. 1132
ENDEAVOUR FINANCIAL LTD.; *Int'l*, pg. 2402
ENERGIZER TRADING LIMITED—See Energizer Holdings, Inc.; *U.S. Public*, pg. 761
EQUIPMENT FINANCE LIMITED—See Haier Smart Home Co., Ltd.; *Int'l*, pg. 3210
ESSEGIBI FINANZIARIA S.P.A.—See Banco BPM S.p.A.; *Int'l*, pg. 818
ESSEX CREDIT CORPORATION—See BNP Paribas SA; *Int'l*, pg. 1087
EULER HERMES DEUTSCHLAND AG—See Allianz SE; *Int'l*, pg. 352
EULER HERMES RATING GMBH—See Allianz SE; *Int'l*, pg. 353
EUROBANK EFG FACTORS S.A.—See Eurobank Ergasias Services and Holdings S.A.; *Int'l*, pg. 2532
EUROHYPO EUROPAISCHE HYPOTHEKENBANK S.A. DUBLIN BRANCH—See Commerzbank AG; *Int'l*, pg. 1718
EXELERATE CAPITAL CORP.; *Int'l*, pg. 2583
EXPERIAN A/S—See Experian plc; *Int'l*, pg. 2587
EXPORT-IMPORT BANK OF THE UNITED STATES; *U.S. Private*, pg. 1450
EXWORKS CAPITAL, LLC—See Capitol Financial Strategies, LLC; *U.S. Private*, pg. 743
EXWORKS CAPITAL, LLC—See RedRidge Finance Group, LLC; *U.S. Private*, pg. 3379
EXWORKS CAPITAL, LLC - WASHINGTON, D.C. OFFICE—See Capitol Financial Strategies, LLC; *U.S. Private*, pg. 744
EXWORKS CAPITAL, LLC - WASHINGTON, D.C. OFFICE—See RedRidge Finance Group, LLC; *U.S. Private*, pg. 3379
EZ ONLINE OKLAHOMA, LLC—See EZCORP, Inc.; *U.S. Public*, pg. 817
EZPAWN MANAGEMENT MEXICO, SRL DE CV (LTD., INC.)—See EZCORP, Inc.; *U.S. Public*, pg. 817
FABA VERMIETUNGSGESELLSCHAFT MBH—See Commerzbank AG; *Int'l*, pg. 1717
FACTORAJE BANCOMER—See Banco Bilbao Vizcaya Argentaria, S.A.; *Int'l*, pg. 818
FACTORING CESKE SPORITELNY A.S.—See Erste Group Bank AG; *Int'l*, pg. 2498
FACTORIT S.P.A.—See Banca Popolare di Sondrio S.p.A.; *Int'l*, pg. 816
FACTORS SOUTHWEST, LLC—See Oxford Bank Corporation; *U.S. Public*, pg. 1628
FALCON LEASING, LLC—See Falcon National Bank; *U.S. Private*, pg. 1466
FARM CREDIT BANK OF TEXAS—See Federal Farm Credit Banks Funding Corporation; *U.S. Private*, pg. 1487
FARM CREDIT OF CENTRAL FLORIDA ACA; *U.S. Private*, pg. 1474
FARM CREDIT OF NORTH FLORIDA ACA; *U.S. Private*, pg. 1474
FARM CREDIT OF WESTERN NEW YORK ACA INC.; *U.S. Private*, pg. 1475
FARM CREDIT SERVICE OF CENTRAL ARKANSAS INC.; *U.S. Private*, pg. 1475
FARM CREDIT SERVICES MANDAN; *U.S. Private*, pg. 1475
FARM CREDIT SERVICES OF AMERICA PCA/FLCA; *U.S. Private*, pg. 1475
FARM CREDIT SERVICES SOUTHWEST; *U.S. Private*, pg. 1475
FARMER MAC II LLC—See Federal Agricultural Mortgage Corporation; *U.S. Public*, pg. 825
FAST A/R FUNDING—See Republic Business Credit, LLC; *U.S. Private*, pg. 3401
FAST FINANCE S.A.; *Int'l*, pg. 2621
FBC FINANCE CO.—See Farmer Brothers Co.; *U.S. Public*, pg. 821
FCFS MO, INC.—See FirstCash Holdings, Inc.; *U.S. Public*, pg. 849
FCS FINANCIAL; *U.S. Private*, pg. 1486
FDCTECH, INC.; *U.S. Public*, pg. 825
FEDERAL HOME LOAN BANK OF DALLAS; *U.S. Private*, pg. 1488
FEDERAL LAND BANK ASSOCIATION YOSEMITE; *U.S. Private*, pg. 1489
FH CENTER, INC.—See BNP Paribas SA; *Int'l*, pg. 1088
FINACITY CORPORATION—See White Oak Global Advisors, LLC; *U.S. Private*, pg. 4509
FINANCE FACTORS, LIMITED1952; *U.S. Private*, pg. 1506
FINANSA CREDIT LTD.—See FNS HOLDINGS PUBLIC COMPANY LIMITED; *Int'l*, pg. 2718
FIRST AMERICAN FINANCE CORPORATION—See The Marcus Corporation; *U.S. Public*, pg. 2112
FIRST EAGLE PRIVATE CREDIT, LLC—See Blackstone Inc.; *U.S. Public*, pg. 353
FIRST EAGLE PRIVATE CREDIT, LLC—See Corsair Capital, LLC; *U.S. Private*, pg. 1059
FIRST SOUTH FARM CREDIT; *U.S. Private*, pg. 1528
FIRST VOLUNTEER BANK—See First Volunteer Corporation; *U.S. Private*, pg. 1530
FISHER & PAYKEL FINANCIAL SERVICES LIMITED—See Haier Smart Home Co., Ltd.; *Int'l*, pg. 3210
FLOWSERVE LIMITORQUE DIV.—See Flowserve Corporation; *U.S. Public*, pg. 856
FLOW TRADERS NV; *Int'l*, pg. 2709
FNP, INC.; *U.S. Private*, pg. 1556
FOCUS BUSINESS SOLUTIONS, INC.; *U.S. Private*, pg. 1556
FONDO ACH, S.A. DE C.V. SOFOM, E.N.R—See EZCORP, Inc.; *U.S. Public*, pg. 818
THE FOODFELLAS LTD.—See Charoen Pokphand Foods Public Company Limited; *Int'l*, pg. 1453
FORD INTERNATIONAL CAPITAL CORPORATION—See Ford Motor Company; *U.S. Public*, pg. 865
FOREX CAPITAL MARKETS LLC—See Global Brokerage, Inc.; *U.S. Public*, pg. 940
FORTIS COMMERCIAL FINANCE S.A.S.—See BNP Paribas SA; *Int'l*, pg. 1084
FORTIS COMMERCIAL FINANCE S.P.A.—See BNP Paribas SA; *Int'l*, pg. 1084
FORTIS COMMERCIAL FINANCE SP. Z O.O.—See BNP Paribas SA; *Int'l*, pg. 1084
FORTIS FAKTORING A.S.—See BNP Paribas SA; *Int'l*, pg. 1093
FORWARD ENERGY GENERATION LTD.—See Dagang NeXchange Berhad; *Int'l*, pg. 1912
FRASER & COMPANY LIMITED; *Int'l*, pg. 2765
FRESHLOCAL SOLUTIONS INC.; *Int'l*, pg. 2781
FRESNO-MADERA FARM CREDIT ASSOCIATION; *U.S. Private*, pg. 1610
FRIONA AGRICULTURE CREDIT CORP.—See Friona Industries, LP; *U.S. Public*, pg. 1612
FUJIAN FYNEX GARMENT CO., LTD.—See Fujian Fynex Textile Science & Technology Co., Ltd.; *Int'l*, pg. 2818
FULLCAST FINANCE CO., LTD.—See Fullcast Holdings Co., Ltd.; *Int'l*, pg. 2842
FUNDAMENTA-LAKASKASSZA LAKASTAKAREKPENZTAR ZRT.—See DZ BANK AG Deutsche Zentral-Genossenschaftsbank; *Int'l*, pg. 2244
FWU PROVISIONS-FACTORING GMBH—See FWU AG; *Int'l*, pg. 2859
FXCM BULLION LIMITED—See Global Brokerage, Inc.; *U.S. Public*, pg. 940
GAIN CAPITAL JAPAN CO., LTD.—See StoneX Group Inc.; *U.S. Public*, pg. 1952
GATX CORPORATION—See GATX Corporation; *U.S. Public*, pg. 907
G.E.I.E. A.I.G.L.E—See Groupe Limagrain Holding SA; *Int'l*, pg. 3107
GENESIS ACQUISITION CORP.; *Int'l*, pg. 2921
GENIUS TERMINAL CO., LTD.—See Gem Terminal Ind. Co., Ltd.; *Int'l*, pg. 2915
GENIUS TERMINAL (HK) LTD.—See Gem Terminal Ind. Co., Ltd.; *Int'l*, pg. 2915
GERBER TRADE FINANCE, INC.; *U.S. Private*, pg. 1686
GHP NOETIC SCIENCE-PSYCHEDELIC PHARMA, INC.; *Int'l*, pg. 2960
GILLCO FINANCE COMPANY—See Gillman Companies; *U.S. Private*, pg. 1700
GLACIER ENTERPRISES (PTY) LTD—See Cullinan Holdings Limited; *Int'l*, pg. 1877
GLOBAL ECOMMERCE LIMITED—See Dagang NeXchange Berhad; *Int'l*, pg. 1912
GLOBAL INVESTMENTS CAPITAL CORP.; *Int'l*, pg. 2998
GOLD MOUNTAIN MINING CORP.; *Int'l*, pg. 3025
GOOD2GO CORP.; *Int'l*, pg. 3039
GOODMAN FACTORS, INC.—See Independent Bank; *U.S. Private*, pg. 2058
GOTHIA A/S—See Bertelsmann SE & Co. KGaA; *Int'l*, pg. 996
GOTHIA AS—See Bertelsmann SE & Co. KGaA; *Int'l*, pg. 996
GOTHIA DEUTSCHLAND GMBH—See Bertelsmann SE & Co. KGaA; *Int'l*, pg. 996
GOTHIA OY—See Bertelsmann SE & Co. KGaA; *Int'l*, pg. 996
GOVERNMENT CAPITAL CORPORATION; *U.S. Private*, pg. 1746
GOVERNMENT CAPITAL CORPORATION-SOUTH TEXAS—See Government Capital Corporation; *U.S. Private*, pg. 1746
GREENCORE FINANCE LIMITED—See Greencore Group plc; *Int'l*, pg. 3074
GREEN PANDA CAPITAL CORP.; *Int'l*, pg. 3072
GREENSTONE FARM CREDIT SERVICES; *U.S. Private*, pg. 1780
GRENKEFACTORING GMBH—See Grenke AG; *Int'l*, pg. 3081
GROVE CAPITAL MANAGEMENT LIMITED—See Encore Capital Group, Inc.; *U.S. Public*, pg. 759
GRUPO SUPERVIELLE S.A.; *Int'l*, pg. 3135
GSD DIS TICARET A.S.—See GSD Holding A.S.; *Int'l*, pg. 3144
GUARANTY TRUST BANK (SIERRA LEONE) LIMITED—See Guaranty Trust Bank plc; *Int'l*, pg. 3169
GURU ORGANIC ENERGY CORP.; *Int'l*, pg. 3188
HADRIAN'S WALL SECURED INVESTMENTS LTD.; *Int'l*, pg. 3205
HAKKEN CAPITAL CORP.; *Int'l*, pg. 3219
HANSCO CAPITAL CORP.; *Int'l*, pg. 3259
HANSEATICA SECHZEHNTE GRUNDBESITZ INVESTITIONSGESELLSCHAFT MBH & CO. KG—See DZ BANK AG Deutsche Zentral-Genossenschaftsbank; *Int'l*, pg. 2244
HENRY S. MILLER FUNDING CORPORATION—See Henry S. Miller Management Corp.; *U.S. Private*, pg. 1919
HGI IMMOBILIEN GMBH & CO. GB I KG—See DZ BANK AG Deutsche Zentral-Genossenschaftsbank; *Int'l*, pg. 2244
HIGHLAND HOMELOANS, LLC—See Hilltop Holdings Inc.; *U.S. Public*, pg. 1038
HIGHMARK INTERACTIVE INC.; *Int'l*, pg. 3388
HOIST HELLAS S.A—See Hoist Finance AB; *Int'l*, pg. 3442
HOKURIKU CARD CO., LTD.—See Hokuhoku Financial Group, Inc.; *Int'l*, pg. 3444
HOME MORTGAGE BANK; *Int'l*, pg. 3455
THE HONG KONG & SHANGHAI BANKING CORPORATION LTD.-TAIWAN—See HSBC Holdings plc; *Int'l*, pg. 3507
HSBC BANK UK PLC—See HSBC Holdings plc; *Int'l*, pg. 3503
HSBC BANK USA, N.A.—See HSBC Holdings plc; *Int'l*, pg. 3505
HSBC BANK (VIETNAM) LTD.—See HSBC Holdings plc; *Int'l*, pg. 3506
HSBC FRANCE—See HSBC Holdings plc; *Int'l*, pg. 3505
HSBC SECURITIES ASIA LTD.—See HSBC Holdings plc; *Int'l*, pg. 3506
HSBC USA, INC.—See HSBC Holdings plc; *Int'l*, pg. 3505
HT USA INC.—See Hidria d.o.o.; *Int'l*, pg. 3384
HUNT MORTGAGE GROUP, LLC—See Hunt Companies, Inc.; *U.S. Private*, pg. 2008

HYOSUNG CAPITAL CO., LTD.; *Int'l*, pg. 3550
ICAP AUSTRALIA PTY LIMITED—See CME Group, Inc.; *U.S. Public*, pg. 516
ICAP FOREIGN EXCHANGE BROKERAGE LIMITED—See CME Group, Inc.; *U.S. Public*, pg. 516
ICF KURSMAKLER AG; *Int'l*, pg. 3579
IDAHO AGRICULTURAL CREDIT ASSOCIATION; *U.S. Private*, pg. 2034
IDEA MONEY S.A.—See Getin Holding S.A.; *Int'l*, pg. 2947
IFCI FACTORS LTD—See IFCI Limited; *Int'l*, pg. 3599
IFIS FINANCE SP. Z O.O.—See Banca IFIS S.p.A.; *Int'l*, pg. 815
IKB DEUTSCHE INDUSTRIEBANK AG—See Lone Star Global Acquisitions, LLC; *U.S. Private*, pg. 2488
IKB EQUITY FINANCE GMBH—See Lone Star Global Acquisitions, LLC; *U.S. Private*, pg. 2488
IKB LEASING GMBH—See Lone Star Global Acquisitions, LLC; *U.S. Private*, pg. 2489
IKB PRIVATE EQUITY GMBH—See Lone Star Global Acquisitions, LLC; *U.S. Private*, pg. 2489
IMPERIAL LIFE SETTLEMENTS, LLC—See Emergent Capital, Inc.; *U.S. Private*, pg. 1381
IMPERIAL PREMIUM FINANCE, LLC—See Emergent Capital, Inc.; *U.S. Private*, pg. 1381
INFOSCORE AG—See Bertelsmann SE & Co. KGaA; *Int'l*, pg. 997
INSTITUTIONAL TRADING, MONEY MANAGEMENT OFFICE—See The Ziegler Companies, Inc.; *U.S. Private*, pg. 4140
INTEGRATED HEALTHCARE COMMUNICATIONS, INC.—See Stagwell, Inc.; *U.S. Public*, pg. 1927
INTER-AMERICAN DEVELOPMENT BANK; *U.S. Private*, pg. 2107
INTERBANK—See ABN AMRO Group N.V.; *Int'l*, pg. 65
IPFS CORPORATION; *U.S. Private*, pg. 2136
ISRAEL CREDIT CARDS LTD.—See IDB Development Corporation Ltd.; *Int'l*, pg. 3588
ITALEASE NETWORK S.P.A.—See Banco BPM S.p.A.; *Int'l*, pg. 819
JET HOMELOANS, LLC—See Hilltop Holdings Inc.; *U.S. Public*, pg. 1039
JOHN DEERE CREDIT COMPANY—See Deere & Company; *U.S. Public*, pg. 646
J.P. MORGAN (SUISSE) S.A.—See JPMorgan Chase & Co.; *U.S. Public*, pg. 1209
JSC ALTYN BANK—See Halyk Bank of Kazakhstan JSC; *Int'l*, pg. 3234
KEY HEALTH GROUP INC.—See Oasis Legal Finance LLC; *U.S. Private*, pg. 2986
KGAL GMBH & CO. KG—See Commerzbank AG; *Int'l*, pg. 1718
KING PAWN II, INC.—See FirstCash Holdings, Inc.; *U.S. Public*, pg. 849
KING PAWN, INC.—See FirstCash Holdings, Inc.; *U.S. Public*, pg. 849
LATIN AMERICAN AGRIBUSINESS DEVELOPMENT CORPORATION; *U.S. Private*, pg. 2397
LBS BAYERISCHE LANDESBAUSPARKASSE—See BayernLB Holding AG; *Int'l*, pg. 913
LEDGE WEALTH MANAGEMENT, INC.—See Dakota Wealth Management LLC; *U.S. Private*, pg. 1148
LEGAL & GENERAL INSURANCE LTD.—See Allianz SE; *Int'l*, pg. 353
LENDINGPOINT LLC; *U.S. Private*, pg. 2421
LEUMI & CO. INVESTMENT HOUSE LTD.—See Bank Leumi Le-Israel B.M.; *Int'l*, pg. 839
LEUMI FINANCE CO., LTD.—See Bank Leumi Le-Israel B.M.; *Int'l*, pg. 839
LEUMI INDUSTRIAL DEVELOPMENT LTD.—See Bank Leumi Le-Israel B.M.; *Int'l*, pg. 839
LEUMI (LATIN AMERICA)—See Bank Leumi Le-Israel B.M.; *Int'l*, pg. 839
LEUMI LEASING LTD.—See Bank Leumi Le-Israel B.M.; *Int'l*, pg. 839
LEUMI L.P. LTD.—See Bank Leumi Le-Israel B.M.; *Int'l*, pg. 839
LEUMI MORTGAGE BANK LTD.—See Bank Leumi Le-Israel B.M.; *Int'l*, pg. 839
LEUMI (SCHWEIZ) AG—See Bank Leumi Le-Israel B.M.; *Int'l*, pg. 839
LIBANO-FRANCAISE FINANCE S.A.L.—See Banque Libano-Francaise S.A.L.; *Int'l*, pg. 854
LIQUID CAPITAL CORP.—See Garrington Group of Companies Inc.; *U.S. Private*, pg. 2886
LIQUIDX, INC.—See Broadridge Financial Solutions, Inc.; *U.S. Public*, pg. 392
LONDON FORFAITING AMERICAS INC.—See FIMBank p.l.c.; *Int'l*, pg. 2664
LONDON FORFAITING COMPANY LTD—See FIMBank p.l.c.; *Int'l*, pg. 2664
LONDON FORFAITING DO BRASIL LTDA—See FIMBank p.l.c.; *Int'l*, pg. 2664
LUMINA FOUNDATION FOR EDUCATION; *U.S. Private*, pg. 2514
MAROC FACTORING—See Bank of Africa; *Int'l*, pg. 840
MARQUETTE BUSINESS CREDIT, LLC—See UMB Financial Corporation; *U.S. Public*, pg. 2224

MARS CAPITAL FINANCE LIMITED—See Arrow Global Group PLC; *Int'l*, pg. 579
MATHES MANAGEMENT ENTERPRISES; *U.S. Private*, pg. 2610
MAXI-CASH (CLEMENTI) PTE. LTD.—See Aspial Lifestyle Limited; *Int'l*, pg. 630
MCM CAPITAL GROUP INCORPORATED; *U.S. Private*, pg. 2641
MCT TRADING, INC; *U.S. Private*, pg. 2645
MEDALLION BUSINESS CREDIT, LLC—See Medallion Financial Corp.; *U.S. Public*, pg. 1411
MERCANTILE BANK HOLDINGS LIMITED—See Capitec Bank Holdings Limited; *Int'l*, pg. 1314
MERCHANT FACTORS CORP.; *U.S. Private*, pg. 2669
MERCHANT ONE; *U.S. Private*, pg. 2669
MERCURY TRADE FINANCE SOLUTIONS, S.L.—See Banco Santander, S.A.; *Int'l*, pg. 826
METROPOLITAN CAPITAL ADVISORS, LTD.—See Marcus & Millichap, Inc.; *U.S. Public*, pg. 1365
MILBERG FACTORS, INC.; *U.S. Private*, pg. 2727
MUNSTERLANDISCHE BANK THIE & CO. KG—See Allianz SE; *Int'l*, pg. 354
NATIOBAIL 2 S.A.—See BNP Paribas SA; *Int'l*, pg. 1092
NATIXIS FINANCE—See Groupe BPCE; *Int'l*, pg. 3094
NATIXIS LEASE—See Groupe BPCE; *Int'l*, pg. 3094
NBAD AMERICAS N.V.—See First Abu Dhabi Bank P.J.S.C.; *Int'l*, pg. 2681
NEW YORK LIFE INSURANCE LTD.—See New York Life Insurance Company; *U.S. Private*, pg. 2910
NORDSTROM CREDIT, INC.—See Nordstrom, Inc.; *U.S. Public*, pg. 1535
NORISBANK GMBH—See Deutsche Bank Aktiengesellschaft; *Int'l*, pg. 2061
THE NORTHERN TRUST COMPANY CANADA—See Northern Trust Corporation; *U.S. Public*, pg. 1539
NORTHERN TRUST CORPORATION - UNITED KINGDOM—See Northern Trust Corporation; *U.S. Public*, pg. 1538
THE NORTHERN TRUST INTERNATIONAL BANKING CORPORATION—See Northern Trust Corporation; *U.S. Public*, pg. 1539
NORTHSTAR RESEARCH PARTNERS INC.—See Stagwell, Inc.; *U.S. Public*, pg. 1927
NORTHWEST FARM CREDIT SERVICES ACA; *U.S. Private*, pg. 2960
NOVOMATRIX INTERNATIONAL TRADING (SHANGHAI) CO. LTD.—See Eastman Chemical Company; *U.S. Public*, pg. 705
NSFX LTD.—See FDCTECH, INC.; *U.S. Public*, pg. 825
NTS REALTY CAPITAL, INC.—See NTS Corporation; *U.S. Private*, pg. 2971
OAK STREET FUNDING LLC—See First Financial Bancorp.; *U.S. Public*, pg. 843
OASIS LEGAL FINANCE LLC; *U.S. Private*, pg. 2986
OCWEN LOAN SERVICING, LLC—See Onity Group Inc.; *U.S. Public*, pg. 1604
OEWA WASSER UND ABWASSER GMBH—See E.ON SE; *Int'l*, pg. 2253
OFFICE VAUDOIS DE CAUTIONNEMENT AGRICOLE SA—See Banque Cantonale Vaudoise; *Int'l*, pg. 853
OHIO PHASE-IN-RECOVERY FUNDING LLC—See American Electric Power Company, Inc.; *U.S. Public*, pg. 100
OLDENBURGISCHE LANDESBANK AG—See Apollo Global Management, Inc.; *U.S. Public*, pg. 148
OLDENBURGISCHE LANDESBANK AG—See Grovepoint Capital LLP; *Int'l*, pg. 3112
OLDENBURGISCHE LANDESBANK AG—See Teacher Retirement System of Texas; *U.S. Private*, pg. 3944
OMI REFRACTORIES, LLC—See Osceola Capital Management, LLC; *U.S. Private*, pg. 3047
ONBRAND—See Stagwell, Inc.; *U.S. Public*, pg. 1927
OPEN LENDING, LLC—See Open Lending Corporation; *U.S. Public*, pg. 1606
ORANGE COMMERICAL CREDIT, INC.; *U.S. Private*, pg. 3037
PAUL ERNST VERSICHERUNGSVERMITTLUNGS MBH—See DZ BANK AG Deutsche Zentral-Genossenschaftsbank; *Int'l*, pg. 2244
PAULSEN FOOD GMBH—See Charoen Pokphand Foods Public Company Limited; *Int'l*, pg. 1453
PAYNET, INC.—See Equifax Inc.; *U.S. Public*, pg. 786
PEKAO FAKTORING SP. ZOO—See Bank Polska Kasa Opieki Spolka Akcyjna; *Int'l*, pg. 849
PINNAFRICA INSURANCE—See BNP Paribas SA; *Int'l*, pg. 1092
PIRIE STREET CUSTODIAN LTD.—See Bendigo & Adelaide Bank Ltd.; *Int'l*, pg. 970
PLAYMAKER CAPITAL INC.—See Better Collective A/S; *Int'l*, pg. 1003
PLC ENTERPRISES INC.; *U.S. Private*, pg. 3213
PNC COMMERCIAL CORPORATION—See The PNC Financial Services Group, Inc.; *U.S. Public*, pg. 2120
PORTER CAPITAL CORPORATION; *U.S. Private*, pg. 3231
PRESIDENTIAL FINANCIAL CORPORATION—See Midland Financial Co.; *U.S. Private*, pg. 2715
PRESTIGE CAPITAL CORP.—See Forest Investments, Inc.; *U.S. Private*, pg. 1567

PRIVATE CAPITAL INCORPORATED; *U.S. Private*, pg. 3268
PRODUCERS CREDIT CORPORATION—See United Producers, Inc.; *U.S. Private*, pg. 4296
PROPEL FINANCIAL SERVICES, LLC—See Encore Capital Group, Inc.; *U.S. Public*, pg. 760
PRUDENTIAL AGRICULTURAL INVESTMENTS, INC.—See Prudential Financial, Inc.; *U.S. Public*, pg. 1732
PRUDENTIAL MORTGAGE CAPITAL COMPANY, LLC—See Prudential Financial, Inc.; *U.S. Public*, pg. 1733
PSEG ENERGY RESOURCES & TRADE LLC—See Public Service Enterprise Group Incorporated; *U.S. Public*, pg. 1736
P.T. ANZ PANIN BANK—See Australia & New Zealand Banking Group Limited; *Int'l*, pg. 720
PT DAGANG NET INDONESIA—See Dagang NeXchange Berhad; *Int'l*, pg. 1912
PUERTO RICO FARM CREDIT A C A; *U.S. Private*, pg. 3302
QUALITY PROPERTIES ASSET MANAGEMENT COMPANY—See Bank of America Corporation; *U.S. Public*, pg. 272
RAINMAKER CAPITAL, LLC; *U.S. Private*, pg. 3348
R&B RECEIVABLES MANAGEMENT; *U.S. Private*, pg. 3331
RC II S.A.R.L.—See DZ BANK AG Deutsche Zentral-Genossenschaftsbank; *Int'l*, pg. 2244
REDRIDGE FINANCE GROUP, LLC; *U.S. Public*, pg. 3379
REFINANCIA S.A.—See Encore Capital Group, Inc.; *U.S. Public*, pg. 760
RENEW FINANCIAL CORP. II—See Renewable Funding Group, Inc.; *U.S. Private*, pg. 3398
RENEW FINANCIAL II LLC—See Renewable Funding Group, Inc.; *U.S. Private*, pg. 3398
RENOVA PARTNERS, LLC—See Allstar Financial Group Inc.; *U.S. Private*, pg. 193
RESURGENT CAPITAL SERVICES, LP—See Sherman Financial Group LLC; *U.S. Private*, pg. 3634
RF ENCORE S.A.S—See Encore Capital Group, Inc.; *U.S. Public*, pg. 760
RIVER VALLEY AG CREDIT; *U.S. Private*, pg. 3444
RIVIERA FINANCE LLC; *U.S. Private*, pg. 3448
RK CAPITAL PARTNERS, LLC; *U.S. Private*, pg. 3450
ROSENTHAL & ROSENTHAL, INC.; *U.S. Private*, pg. 3484
ROSEVIEW CAPITAL PARTNERS LLC—See Madison Marquette Development Corporation; *U.S. Private*, pg. 2544
SACE S.P.A.—See Cassa Depositi e Prestiti S.p.A.; *Int'l*, pg. 1355
SANFORD C. BERNSTEIN (CREST NOMINEES) LIMITED—See Equitable Holdings, Inc.; *U.S. Public*, pg. 789
SANTANDER BANK AND TRUST (BAHAMAS), LTD.—See Banco Santander, S.A.; *Int'l*, pg. 826
SANTANDER CONSUMER CREDIT SERVICES LIMITED—See Banco Santander, S.A.; *Int'l*, pg. 827
SBIGEO MARKETING CO., LTD.—See GEO Holdings Corporation; *Int'l*, pg. 2932
SENECA PARTNERS INC.; *U.S. Private*, pg. 3606
SHERMAN FINANCIAL GROUP LLC; *U.S. Private*, pg. 3634
SIXPOINT PARTNERS, LLC—See The PNC Financial Services Group, Inc.; *U.S. Public*, pg. 2119
SKY CAC LIMITED—See Alpha Services and Holdings S.A.; *Int'l*, pg. 369
SLM FINANCIAL CORP.—See SLM Corporation; *U.S. Public*, pg. 1894
SMITH HAYES FINANCIAL SERVICES CORPORATION—See D.A. Davidson Companies; *U.S. Private*, pg. 1140
SNAP-ON CREDIT LLC—See Snap-on Incorporated; *U.S. Public*, pg. 1898
SOCIETE LIBANAISE DE FACTORING SAL—See Bank Audi sal; *Int'l*, pg. 837
SOUTHWEST STUDENT SERVICES CORP.—See SLM Corporation; *U.S. Public*, pg. 1894
SPEEDWAY FUNDING, LLC—See Sonic Financial Corporation; *U.S. Private*, pg. 3713
STANDARD MANAGEMENT COMPANY; *U.S. Private*, pg. 3780
STAPLE COTTON DISCOUNT CORPORATION—See Staple Cotton Cooperative Association; *U.S. Private*, pg. 3783
STATE BANK—See Everly Bancorporation; *U.S. Private*, pg. 1440
STATIM FINANCE LIMITED—See McKesson Corporation; *U.S. Public*, pg. 1408
STEELHEAD FINANCE, LLC—See Peoples Bank of Commerce; *U.S. Private*, pg. 3141
STERLING ACCEPTANCE CORP.; *U.S. Private*, pg. 3804
SUTTONS AND ROBERTSONS LIMITED—See Lone Star Global Acquisitions, LLC; *U.S. Private*, pg. 2487
SYNCORA GUARANTEE INC.—See GoldenTree Asset Management LP; *U.S. Private*, pg. 1734
T BANK S.A.—See Eurobank Ergasias Services and Holdings S.A.; *Int'l*, pg. 2533

522299 — INTERNATIONAL, SECO...

TBC FINANCIAL SERVICES, INC.—See Flowers Foods, Inc.; *U.S. Public*, pg. 854
TEB FAKTORING INC.—See BNP Paribas SA; *Int'l*, pg. 1093
TEKSTIL FAKTORING A.S.—See GSD Holding A.S.; *Int'l*, pg. 3144
T.M. SUTTON LIMITED—See Lone Star Global Acquisitions, LLC; *U.S. Private*, pg. 2487
TREMONT REALTY ADVISORS LLC—See The RMR Group Inc.; *U.S. Public*, pg. 2126
UCB LOCABAIL IMMOBILIER 2—See BNP Paribas SA; *Int'l*, pg. 1093
UIR VERWALTUNGSGESELLSCHAFT MBH—See DZ BANK AG Deutsche Zentral-Genossenschaftsbank; *Int'l*, pg. 2245
UNION ACCEPTANCE COMPANY LLC—See PCP Enterprise, L.P.; *U.S. Private*, pg. 3121
UNITED CAPITAL FUNDING CORP.; *U.S. Private*, pg. 4288
UNITED CREDIT CORP.; *U.S. Public*, pg. 4290
UNITED FINANCIAL OF ILLINOIS INC.; *U.S. Private*, pg. 4292
UNLIMITED MERCHANT SERVICES—See I.T. Source; *U.S. Private*, pg. 2027
UPS CAPITAL CORPORATION—See United Parcel Service, Inc.; *U.S. Public*, pg. 2233
USA PAWN & JEWELRY CO IV, LLC—See EZCORP, Inc.; *U.S. Public*, pg. 818
V3 MARKETS, LLC—See Global Brokerage, Inc.; *U.S. Public*, pg. 940
VALUE FINANCIAL SERVICES, INC.—See EZCORP, Inc.; *U.S. Public*, pg. 818
VERITAS COMMUNICATIONS, INC.—See Stagwell, Inc.; *U.S. Public*, pg. 1928
VIRGINIA CREDIT & FINANCE, INC.—See Encore Capital Group, Inc.; *U.S. Public*, pg. 760
VISA ARGENTINA S.A.—See Banco Macro S.A.; *Int'l*, pg. 823
VISECA CARD SERVICES SA—See Aduno Holding AG; *Int'l*, pg. 154
VISION FINANCIAL GROUP, INC.—See Civista Bancshares, Inc.; *U.S. Public*, pg. 507
VOLVO FINANCE AUSTRALIA PTY LTD.—See AB Volvo; *Int'l*, pg. 43
VOLVO FINANCE NORTH AMERICA INC.; *U.S. Private*, pg. 4411
VSTITLE, LLC—See F&M Bank Corp.; *U.S. Public*, pg. 818
WBS WOHNWIRTSCHAFTLICHE BAUBETREUUNGS- UND SERVICEGESELLSCHAFT MBH—See DZ BANK AG Deutsche Zentral-Genossenschaftsbank; *Int'l*, pg. 2245
WELLS FARGO BANK, N.A. - HONG KONG BRANCH—See Wells Fargo & Company; *U.S. Public*, pg. 2346
WELLS FARGO BUSINESS CREDIT—See Wells Fargo & Company; *U.S. Public*, pg. 2346
WELLS FARGO CAPITAL FINANCE, LLC—See Wells Fargo & Company; *U.S. Public*, pg. 2346
WELLS FARGO REAL ESTATE GROUP—See Wells Fargo & Company; *U.S. Public*, pg. 2347
WESTERN AGCREDIT; *U.S. Private*, pg. 4490
WESTMINSTER CAPITAL INC.; *U.S. Private*, pg. 4499
WYNSTON HILL CAPITAL LLC—See ALT5 Sigma Corporation; *U.S. Public*, pg. 85
XEROX CANADA FINANCE INC.—See Xerox Holdings Corporation; *U.S. Public*, pg. 2390

522310 — MORTGAGE AND NONMORTGAGE LOAN BROKERS

1300 HOME LOAN HOLDINGS PTY LTD—See BNK Banking Corporation Limited; *Int'l*, pg. 1079
21ST MORTGAGE CORPORATION; *U.S. Private*, pg. 5
84 FINANCIAL L.P.—See 84 Lumber Company; *U.S. Private*, pg. 17
ABN AMRO HYPOTHEKEN GROEP B.V.—See ABN AMRO Group N.V.; *Int'l*, pg. 64
ACAP (MALAYSIA) SDN. BHD.—See Asia Capital Public Company Limited; *Int'l*, pg. 610
ACCEPTANCE CAPITAL MORTGAGE CORPORATION—See Complete Financial Solutions, Inc.; *U.S. Public*, pg. 561
ACCORD LEASING LLC—See Accord Financial Group Inc.; *U.S. Private*, pg. 53
ACENDEN LIMITED—See Barclays PLC; *Int'l*, pg. 860
A.C.N. 603 303 126 PTY LTD—See Cerberus Capital Management, L.P.; *U.S. Private*, pg. 837
ADVISORS MORTGAGE GROUP, LLC; *U.S. Private*, pg. 110
AEA FEDERAL CREDIT UNION; *U.S. Private*, pg. 112
AFG HOME LOANS PTY LTD—See Australia Finance Group Ltd; *Int'l*, pg. 720
AGAMERICA LENDING LLC—See Land South Holdings, LLC; *U.S. Private*, pg. 2384
AGATE BAY RESIDENTIAL MORTGAGE SECURITIES LLC—See Two Harbors Investment Corp.; *U.S. Public*, pg. 2207
AIB MORTGAGE BANK UNLIMITED COMPANY—See AIB Group plc; *Int'l*, pg. 228
AIFUL CORPORATION; *Int'l*, pg. 231
AILERON CAPITAL MANAGEMENT, LLC; *U.S. Private*, pg. 132
ALASKA GROWTH CAPITAL BIDCO, INC.—See Arctic Slope Regional Corporation; *U.S. Private*, pg. 316
ALCOVA MORTGAGE; *U.S. Private*, pg. 154
ALEXANDER MORTGAGE CORP.; *U.S. Private*, pg. 163
ALFAM HOLDING N.V.—See ABN AMRO Group N.V.; *Int'l*, pg. 65
ALLIED MORTGAGE & FINANCIAL CORP.; *U.S. Private*, pg. 187
ALLSTATE MORTGAGE CORP.; *U.S. Private*, pg. 193
AMERICAN AGCREDIT; *U.S. Private*, pg. 221
AMERICAN BUSINESS LENDING, INC.—See Varde Partners, Inc.; *U.S. Private*, pg. 4346
AMERICAN EAGLE MORTGAGE CO., LLC; *U.S. Private*, pg. 231
AMERICAN EQUITY MORTGAGE INC.; *U.S. Private*, pg. 232
AMERICAN FINANCIAL RESOURCES, INC.—See Proprietary Capital LLC; *U.S. Private*, pg. 3286
AMERICAN HOME PARTNERS, INC.; *U.S. Private*, pg. 236
AMERICAN MORTGAGE SERVICES; *U.S. Private*, pg. 241
AMERICAN PACIFIC MORTGAGE; *U.S. Private*, pg. 242
AMERICAN RESIDENTIAL MORTGAGE LP; *U.S. Private*, pg. 246
AMERICA'S MORTGAGE PROFESSIONALS; *U.S. Private*, pg. 221
AMERICA'S SUPER PAWN, INC.; *U.S. Private*, pg. 221
AMERIQUEST CAPITAL CORPORATION; *U.S. Private*, pg. 260
AMERITRUST MORTGAGE CORPORATION; *U.S. Private*, pg. 261
A + MORTGAGE SERVICES, INC.; *U.S. Private*, pg. 18
AMRAPALI FINCAP LIMITED; *Int'l*, pg. 437
ANGAS SECURITIES LIMITED; *Int'l*, pg. 459
ANZ LENDERS MORTGAGE INSURANCE PTY. LIMITED—See Australia & New Zealand Banking Group Limited; *Int'l*, pg. 720
AOZORA LOAN SERVICES CO., LTD.—See Cerberus Capital Management, L.P.; *U.S. Private*, pg. 836
ARIVA MORTGAGE SERVICES, LLC—See Hilltop Holdings Inc.; *U.S. Public*, pg. 1038
ASCENTIUM CAPITAL LLC—See Regions Financial Corporation; *U.S. Public*, pg. 1776
ASFG, INC.; *U.S. Private*, pg. 348
ASO SAVINGS & LOANS PLC; *Int'l*, pg. 628
ASPEN MORTGAGE CORP.; *U.S. Private*, pg. 352
ASSURANT INTERMEDIARY LTD.—See Assurant, Inc.; *U.S. Public*, pg. 215
ATLANTIC BAY MORTGAGE GROUP LLC; *U.S. Private*, pg. 371
ATLANTIC INVESTMENT COMPANY—See Norfolk Southern Corporation; *U.S. Public*, pg. 1535
ATRIUM MORTGAGE INVESTMENT CORPORATION; *Int'l*, pg. 694
AURORA FINANCIAL GROUP INC.—See Cherry Hill Mortgage Investment Corporation; *U.S. Public*, pg. 485
AUSTBROKERS LIFE PTY LTD—See AUB Group Limited; *Int'l*, pg. 698
AUSTRALIA FINANCE GROUP LTD; *Int'l*, pg. 720
AVANT CREDIT CORP.; *U.S. Private*, pg. 404
AVIVA EQUITY RELEASE UK LIMITED—See Aviva plc; *Int'l*, pg. 745
BALMAIN CORP.; *Int'l*, pg. 810
BANCOKLAHOMA MORTGAGE CORPORATION—See BOK Financial Corporation; *U.S. Public*, pg. 367
BANK OF AMERICA HOME LOANS—See Bank of America Corporation; *U.S. Public*, pg. 271
BANK OF IRELAND CONSUMER BANKING UK—See Bank of Ireland Group plc; *Int'l*, pg. 844
BANK OF IRELAND MORTGAGE BANK PLC—See Bank of Ireland Group plc; *Int'l*, pg. 844
BANK OF THE OZARKS - MORTGAGE DIVISION—See Bank OZK; *U.S. Public*, pg. 274
BARCLAYS COMMERCIAL MORTGAGE SECURITIES LLC—See Barclays PLC; *Int'l*, pg. 860
BATH BUILDING SOCIETY; *Int'l*, pg. 889
BAY CAPITAL MORTGAGE CORPORATION; *U.S. Private*, pg. 492
BAYPORT MORTGAGE - LAS VEGAS—See The Warmington Group; *U.S. Private*, pg. 4133
BEAZER MORTGAGE CORPORATION—See Beazer Homes USA, Inc.; *U.S. Public*, pg. 288
BEECHUM FINANCIAL CORP.; *U.S. Private*, pg. 513
BELLWETHER ENTERPRISE - CHARLOTTE—See Enterprise Community Partners, Inc.; *U.S. Private*, pg. 1403
BERKADIA COMMERCIAL MORTGAGE LLC; *U.S. Private*, pg. 532
BERRETT MORTGAGE SERVICES—See Xcel Financial LLC; *U.S. Private*, pg. 4580
BETTER CHOICE HOME LOANS PTY LTD—See BNK Banking Corporation Limited; *Int'l*, pg. 1079
BEVERLEY BUILDING SOCIETY; *Int'l*, pg. 1004
BILLGUARD, INC.—See Prosper Marketplace, Inc.; *U.S. Private*, pg. 3288
BLUEHONE SECURED ASSETS LIMITED; *Int'l*, pg. 1071
BNP PARIBAS HOME LOAN SFH—See BNP Paribas SA; *Int'l*, pg. 1085
BNP PARIBAS MORTGAGE CORPORATION—See BNP Paribas SA; *Int'l*, pg. 1087
BNP PARIBAS PERSONAL FINANCE BV—See BNP Paribas SA; *Int'l*, pg. 1086
BOEFLY, INC.—See ConnectOne Bancorp, Inc.; *U.S. Public*, pg. 567
BOEING CAPITAL LOAN CORPORATION—See The Boeing Company; *U.S. Public*, pg. 2039
BORDERFREE LIMITED—See Pitney Bowes Inc.; *U.S. Public*, pg. 1694
BRIDGE PRIVATE LENDING, LP; *U.S. Public*, pg. 649
BROADMARK PRIVATE REIT MANAGEMENT, LLC—See Waterfall Asset Management LLC; *U.S. Private*, pg. 4453
BROADMARK REALTY CAPITAL INC.—See Waterfall Asset Management LLC; *U.S. Private*, pg. 4453
BROKER SOLUTIONS, INC.; *U.S. Private*, pg. 661
BS CAPITAL CO., LTD.—See BNK Financial Group Inc.; *Int'l*, pg. 1079
BUCKINGHAMSHIRE BUILDING SOCIETY; *Int'l*, pg. 1210
BUSINESS LENDERS, LLC—See Bank of America Corporation; *U.S. Public*, pg. 272
CAFG AUSTRALEASE PTY. LTD.; *Int'l*, pg. 1250
CALLIDUS CAPITAL CORPORATION; *Int'l*, pg. 1265
CAMBRIDGE BUILDING SOCIETY; *Int'l*, pg. 1269
CAMPUS PARTNERS; *U.S. Private*, pg. 732
CANADA MORTGAGE & HOUSING CORPORATION; *Int'l*, pg. 1278
CAPITAL ONE MULTIFAMILY FINANCE—See Capital One Financial Corporation; *U.S. Public*, pg. 431
CAPSTEAD, INC.—See Franklin Resources, Inc.; *U.S. Public*, pg. 879
CARDINAL FINANCE LLC—See Wells Fargo & Company; *U.S. Public*, pg. 2343
CARMAX AUTO FINANCE—See CarMax, Inc.; *U.S. Public*, pg. 437
CARNEGIE MORTGAGE PARTNERS, LLC—See Rithm Capital Corp.; *U.S. Public*, pg. 1800
CAROLINA ONE MORTGAGE, LLC—See Rithm Capital Corp.; *U.S. Public*, pg. 1800
CASH COLORADO, LLC—See CURO Group Holdings Corp.; *U.S. Public*, pg. 611
CASHFIRST PTY LTD—See Credit Corp Group Limited; *Int'l*, pg. 1835
CAZLEY INC.; *U.S. Private*, pg. 796
CCV VIRGINIA, INC.—See EZCORP, Inc.; *U.S. Public*, pg. 817
CDPQ MORTGAGE CORPORATION—See Caisse de Depot et Placement du Quebec; *Int'l*, pg. 1253
CENTURY LEGEND FINANCE LIMITED—See Century Legend Holdings Ltd; *Int'l*, pg. 1418
CHARCOL LIMITED; *Int'l*, pg. 1448
CHERRY CREEK MORTGAGE CO. INC.; *U.S. Private*, pg. 874
CHINA SUCCESS FINANCE GROUP HOLDINGS LIMITED; *Int'l*, pg. 1556
CHONG SING HOLDINGS FINTECH GROUP LIMITED; *Int'l*, pg. 1578
CIS FINANCIAL SERVICES, INC.—See ECN Capital Corp.; *U.S. Public*, pg. 2292
THE CIT GROUP/CONSUMER FINANCE, INC.—See First Citizens BancShares, Inc.; *U.S. Public*, pg. 842
CITIFINANCIAL CANADA EAST CORP.—See Citigroup Inc.; *U.S. Public*, pg. 502
CITIMORTGAGE, INC.—See Citigroup Inc.; *U.S. Public*, pg. 501
CITIZENS FINANCIAL SERVICES CORPORATION—See Citizens Financial Group, Inc.; *U.S. Public*, pg. 505
CITIZENS NATIONAL BANK; *U.S. Public*, pg. 903
CIVIC FINANCIAL SERVICES, LLC—See Banc of California, Inc.; *U.S. Public*, pg. 268
CLASSIC FINANCE PTY. LTD.—See Earlypay Ltd.; *Int'l*, pg. 2267
CMG MORTGAGE, INC.—See CMG Financial Services Inc.; *U.S. Private*, pg. 951
COASTAL HOME MORTGAGE, LLC—See Towne Bank; *U.S. Public*, pg. 2165
COAST ONE MORTGAGE LLC—See Rithm Capital Corp.; *U.S. Public*, pg. 1800
COHEN FINANCIAL, LLC—See Truist Financial Corporation; *U.S. Public*, pg. 2199
COLONIAL NATIONAL MORTGAGE—See Colonial Savings, F.A.; *U.S. Private*, pg. 972
COLORADO INCOME HOLDINGS INC.; *U.S. Private*, pg. 974
COMMERCE MORTGAGE CORP.—See Commerce Bancshares, Inc.; *U.S. Public*, pg. 545
COMMERCIAL FACILITIES COMPANY S.A.K.C.; *Int'l*, pg. 1715
COMMONWEALTH BANCORP; *U.S. Private*, pg. 986
COMMUNITY FINANCIAL CORPORATION—See Banner Corporation; *U.S. Public*, pg. 275
COMMUNITY MORTGAGE CORPORATION; *U.S. Private*, pg. 996
COMMUNITY WEST BANK—See Community West Bancshares; *U.S. Public*, pg. 558
CONSOLIDATED FINANCE GROUP PTY LIMITED—See

N.A.I.C.S. INDEX
522310 — MORTGAGE AND NONMOR...

Consolidated Operations Group Limited; *Int'l*, pg. 1771
CORAL INDIA FINANCE & HOUSING LIMITED; *Int'l*, pg. 1794
COREALCREDIT BANK AG—See Advent International Corporation; *U.S. Private*, pg. 96
COREALCREDIT BANK AG—See Centerbridge Partners, L.P.; *U.S. Private*, pg. 812
CORNERSTONE HOME MORTGAGE—See Mercedes Homes Inc.; *U.S. Private*, pg. 2668
CORNERSTONE MORTGAGE CO.; *U.S. Private*, pg. 1052
COUNTRYWIDE FINANCIAL CORPORATION—See Bank of America Corporation; *U.S. Public*, pg. 271
CPC RESOURCES INC.—See The Community Preservation Corporation; *U.S. Private*, pg. 4012
CREDIT ASSOCIATION ORDA CREDIT LLP; *Int'l*, pg. 1835
CREDIVANCE N.V.—See ABN AMRO Group N.V.; *Int'l*, pg. 65
CRESTLINE FUNDING CORP.; *U.S. Private*, pg. 1096
CROSSCOUNTRY MORTGAGE, LLC; *U.S. Private*, pg. 1106
CSB MORTGAGE COMPANY, INC.—See Farmers National Banc Corp.; *U.S. Public*, pg. 822
CUMBERLAND BUILDING SOCIETY; *Int'l*, pg. 1877
DARLINGTON BUILDING SOCIETY; *Int'l*, pg. 1973
DAS ACQUISITION COMPANY, LLC; *U.S. Private*, pg. 1160
DBH FINANCE PLC; *Int'l*, pg. 1988
DB PRIVATE WEALTH MORTGAGE LTD.—See Deutsche Bank Aktiengesellschaft; *Int'l*, pg. 2056
DELMAR FINANCIAL COMPANY; *U.S. Private*, pg. 1197
DELTA FUNDING CORPORATION; *U.S. Private*, pg. 1200
DEPOSITORS INSURANCE FUND; *U.S. Private*, pg. 1209
DEUTSCHE HYPOTHEKENBANK (ACTIEN-GESELLSCHAFT); *Int'l*, pg. 2065
DHANI LOANS & SERVICES LIMITED—See Dhani Services Ltd.; *Int'l*, pg. 2098
DHANVARSHA FINVEST LIMITED; *Int'l*, pg. 2098
DHI MORTGAGE COMPANY LTD.—See D.R. Horton, Inc.; *U.S. Public*, pg. 619
DHI TITLE—See D.R. Horton, Inc.; *U.S. Public*, pg. 619
DIGITAL RISK, LLC—See Blackstone Inc.; *U.S. Public*, pg. 356
DIRECT CREDIT ATLANTIC INC.—See QC Holdings, Inc.; *U.S. Private*, pg. 1742
DIREKTBANK N.V.—See ABN AMRO Group N.V.; *Int'l*, pg. 65
DISCOVER HOME LOANS, INC.—See Discover Financial Services; *U.S. Public*, pg. 668
DITECH FINANCIAL LLC—See Rithm Capital Corp.; *U.S. Public*, pg. 1800
DIVERSIFIED MORTGAGE, INC.; *U.S. Private*, pg. 1243
DOM.RF JSC; *Int'l*, pg. 2159
DOVENMUEHLE FUNDING INC.—See Dovenmuehle Mortgage Inc.; *U.S. Private*, pg. 1268
DUDLEY BUILDING SOCIETY; *Int'l*, pg. 2223
DUXFORD FINANCIAL, INC.—See Brookfield Corporation; *Int'l*, pg. 1183
EARL SHILTON BUILDING SOCIETY; *Int'l*, pg. 2267
EBP MONEY PTY. LTD.—See FSA Group Limited; *Int'l*, pg. 2798
ECOLOGY BUILDING SOCIETY; *Int'l*, pg. 2295
EDISON FINANCIAL ULC—See Rocket Companies, Inc.; *U.S. Public*, pg. 1804
EF CMO LLC—See Ellington Management Group, L.L.C.; *U.S. Private*, pg. 1364
EF MORTGAGE LLC—See Ellington Management Group, L.L.C.; *U.S. Private*, pg. 1364
ELLINGTON FINANCIAL OPERATING PARTNERSHIP LLC—See Ellington Management Group, L.L.C.; *U.S. Private*, pg. 1364
ELLINGTON MANAGEMENT GROUP, L.L.C.; *U.S. Private*, pg. 1364
E-LOAN, INC.—See Popular, Inc.; *U.S. Public*, pg. 1702
EMBRACE HOME LOANS, INC.; *U.S. Private*, pg. 1378
EMC MORTGAGE CORP.—See JPMorgan Chase & Co.; *U.S. Public*, pg. 1206
ENCOMPASS LENDING GROUP, LP—See Fathom Holdings Inc.; *U.S. Public*, pg. 824
ENERBANK USA—See Regions Financial Corporation; *U.S. Public*, pg. 1776
ENHANCED RETAIL FUNDING, LLC—See Gordon Brothers Group, LLC; *U.S. Private*, pg. 1742
ENTERPRISE HOME LOANS—See Enterprise Financial Services Corp; *U.S. Private*, pg. 778
EQB INC.; *Int'l*, pg. 2466
EQUITY LOANS LLC; *U.S. Private*, pg. 1416
EUROHYPO EUROPAISCHE HYPOTHEKENBANK S.A.—See Commerzbank AG; *Int'l*, pg. 1718
EVERETT FINANCIAL, INC.; *U.S. Private*, pg. 1438
EVERGREEN MONEYSOURCE MORTGAGE CO.; *U.S. Private*, pg. 1439
EVERGREEN PACIFIC MORTGAGE; *U.S. Private*, pg. 1440
EXTRACO MORTGAGE CORP.—See Extraco Corporation; *U.S. Private*, pg. 1452
EZMONEY ALABAMA, INC.—See EZCORP, Inc.; *U.S. Public*, pg. 817
EZMONEY IDAHO, INC.—See EZCORP, Inc.; *U.S. Public*, pg. 817

EZMONEY SOUTH DAKOTA, INC.—See EZCORP, Inc.; *U.S. Public*, pg. 817
EZPAWN HOLDINGS, INC.—See EZCORP, Inc.; *U.S. Public*, pg. 817
EZPAWN INDIANA, INC.—See EZCORP, Inc.; *U.S. Public*, pg. 817
EZPAWN NEVADA, INC.—See EZCORP, Inc.; *U.S. Public*, pg. 817
FAF INTERNATIONAL SIGORTA ARACILIK HIZMETIERI ANONIM SIRKETI—See First American Financial Corporation; *U.S. Public*, pg. 835
FAIRSTONE FINANCIAL INC.—See Centerbridge Partners, L.P.; *U.S. Private*, pg. 814
FANTINI & GORGA LLC; *U.S. Private*, pg. 1473
FBC BUILDING SOCIETY—See FBC Holdings Limited; *Int'l*, pg. 2627
FBC MORTGAGE, LLC; *U.S. Private*, pg. 1485
FEDERAL AGRICULTURAL MORTGAGE CORPORATION; *U.S. Public*, pg. 825
FEDERAL HOME LOAN BANK OF ATLANTA; *U.S. Private*, pg. 1488
FEDERAL HOME LOAN BANK OF BOSTON; *U.S. Private*, pg. 1488
FEDERAL HOME LOAN BANK OF CHICAGO; *U.S. Private*, pg. 1488
FEDERAL HOME LOAN BANK OF CINCINNATI; *U.S. Private*, pg. 1488
FEDERAL HOME LOAN BANK OF INDIANAPOLIS; *U.S. Private*, pg. 1488
FEDERAL HOME LOAN BANK OF NEW YORK; *U.S. Private*, pg. 1488
FEDERAL HOME LOAN BANK OF SAN FRANCISCO; *U.S. Private*, pg. 1488
FEDERAL HOME LOAN BANK OF TOPEKA; *U.S. Private*, pg. 1488
FEDERAL HOME LOAN MORTGAGE CORPORATION; *U.S. Public*, pg. 825
FEDERAL NATIONAL MORTGAGE ASSOCIATION; *U.S. Public*, pg. 825
FINANCIAL FREEDOM ACQUISITION LLC—See First Citizens BancShares, Inc.; *U.S. Public*, pg. 841
FINANCIAL MORTGAGE GROUP LTD.; *U.S. Private*, pg. 1508
FINANCIAL PARTNERS GROUP CO., LTD.; *Int'l*, pg. 2665
FIRST AMERICAN TITLE INSURANCE COMPANY LENDERS ADVANTAGE—See First American Financial Corporation; *U.S. Public*, pg. 837
FIRST ARKANSAS MORTGAGE CO.—See First Arkansas Bancshares, Inc.; *U.S. Private*, pg. 1513
FIRST BUSINESS CAPITAL CORP.—See First Business Financial Services, Inc.; *U.S. Public*, pg. 840
FIRST CENTENNIAL MORTGAGE CORPORATION—See McCarthy Group, LLC; *U.S. Private*, pg. 2626
FIRST EQUITY MORTGAGE BANKERS, INC.; *U.S. Private*, pg. 1517
FIRST FINANCIAL HOLDINGS INC.; *U.S. Private*, pg. 1519
FIRST FINANCIAL OF TENNESSEE; *U.S. Private*, pg. 1519
FIRST GUARANTY MORTGAGE CORP.; *U.S. Private*, pg. 1519
FIRST HOUSING DEVELOPMENT CORPORATION OF FLORIDA; *U.S. Private*, pg. 1520
FIRST LENDERS MORTGAGE CORP.; *U.S. Private*, pg. 1520
FIRSTMERIT EQUIPMENT FINANCE, INC.—See Huntington Bancshares Incorporated; *U.S. Public*, pg. 1071
FIRST NATIONAL FINANCIAL CORPORATION; *Int'l*, pg. 2686
FIRST OHIO HOME FINANCE, INC; *U.S. Private*, pg. 1524
FIRST RESIDENTIAL MORTGAGE SERVICES CORP.; *U.S. Private*, pg. 1527
FIRST SAVINGS MORTGAGE CORP.; *U.S. Private*, pg. 1527
FLAT BRANCH HOME LOANS; *U.S. Private*, pg. 1541
FLORIDA BUSINESS DEVELOPMENT CORPORATION; *U.S. Private*, pg. 1547
FLORIDA FIRST CAPITAL FINANCE CORPORATION; *U.S. Private*, pg. 1548
FORTUNE FINANCIAL INC.; *U.S. Private*, pg. 1577
FRANKLIN AMERICAN MORTGAGE COMPANY (FAMC)—See FAMC Corporation; *U.S. Public*, pg. 1468
FRANKLIN AMERICAN MORTGAGE COMPANY (FAMC)—See FAMC Corporation; *U.S. Public*, pg. 1468
FRANKLIN CREDIT MANAGEMENT CORPORATION; *U.S. Public*, pg. 878
FREDDIE MAC INC; *U.S. Private*, pg. 1601
FURNESS BUILDING SOCIETY; *Int'l*, pg. 2846
GATEWAY MORTGAGE GROUP LLC; *U.S. Private*, pg. 1650
GE CAPITAL FINANCE AUSTRALASIA PTY. LTD.—See General Electric Company; *U.S. Public*, pg. 920
GENEQUITY MORTGAGE, INC.—See Paragon Global Resources, Inc.; *U.S. Private*, pg. 3091
GENESIS FINANCIAL, INC.—See FDCTECH, INC.; *U.S. Public*, pg. 825
GLOBAL INTERNATIONAL CREDIT GROUP LIMITED; *Int'l*, pg. 2997
GMFS LLC—See Waterfall Asset Management LLC; *U.S. Private*, pg. 4453

GM PREFERRED FINANCE CO. HOLDINGS LLC—See General Motors Company; *U.S. Public*, pg. 924
GOAL FINANCIAL, LLC; *U.S. Private*, pg. 1724
GODIVA MORTGAGES LIMITED—See Coventry Building Society; *Int'l*, pg. 1821
GOLD STAR MORTGAGE FINANCIAL GROUP CORP.; *U.S. Private*, pg. 1728
GOODMORTGAGE.COM—See First Guaranty Mortgage Corp.; *U.S. Private*, pg. 1519
GRANDBRIDGE REAL ESTATE CAPITAL LLC—See Truist Financial Corporation; *U.S. Public*, pg. 2200
GRAND HOME LOANS, LLC—See Hilltop Holdings Inc.; *U.S. Public*, pg. 1038
GRANITE MANAGEMENT CORP.—See Ford Motor Company; *U.S. Public*, pg. 866
GREEN BRICK MORTGAGE, LLC—See Hilltop Holdings Inc.; *U.S. Public*, pg. 1038
GROUP9, INC.; *U.S. Private*, pg. 1794
GUARANTEED HOME MORTGAGE, INC.; *U.S. Private*, pg. 1809
GUARANTEED RATE, INC.; *U.S. Private*, pg. 1809
GUILD MORTGAGE—See McCarthy Group, LLC; *U.S. Private*, pg. 2627
HANLEY ECONOMIC BUILDING SOCIETY; *Int'l*, pg. 3256
HARPENDEN BUILDING SOCIETY; *Int'l*, pg. 3278
HAVEN MORTGAGES LTD.—See AIB Group plc; *Int'l*, pg. 228
HEALTH CARE CAPITAL CONSOLIDATED; *U.S. Private*, pg. 1892
HEALTHCARE REVENUE RECOVERY GROUP, LLC—See Blackstone Inc.; *U.S. Public*, pg. 359
HELIA GROUP LIMITED; *Int'l*, pg. 3329
HINCKLEY AND RUGBY BUILDING SOCIETY; *Int'l*, pg. 3397
HIPOTECARIA SECURITY PRINCIPAL, S.A.—See Principal Financial Group, Inc.; *U.S. Public*, pg. 1720
HOMEBRIDGE FINANCIAL SERVICES, INC. - SHERMAN OAKS—See HomeBridge Financial Services, Inc.; *U.S. Private*, pg. 1973
HOMEBRIDGE FINANCIAL SERVICES, INC.; *U.S. Private*, pg. 1973
HOMEBRIDGE FINANCIAL SERVICES, INC.—See HomeBridge Financial Services, Inc.; *U.S. Private*, pg. 1973
HOME FIRST FINANCE COMPANY INDIA LIMITED; *Int'l*, pg. 3454
HOMELOAN MANAGEMENT LIMITED—See Computershare Limited; *Int'l*, pg. 1760
HOMEQ CORPORATION—See Birch Hill Equity Partners Management Inc.; *Int'l*, pg. 1046
HOMESALE LENDING, LLC—See Wells Fargo & Company; *U.S. Public*, pg. 2343
HOMESIDE FINANCIAL, LLC; *U.S. Private*, pg. 1974
HOME TOWN FUNDING, INC.—See Canandaigua National Corporation; *U.S. Public*, pg. 428
HOME TOWN MORTGAGE INC.; *U.S. Private*, pg. 1972
HONG KONG FINANCE GROUP LIMITED; *Int'l*, pg. 3466
HORIZON MORTGAGE CORPORATION; *U.S. Private*, pg. 1982
HOUSTON CAPITAL MORTGAGE—See Paragon Global Resources, Inc.; *U.S. Private*, pg. 3091
HSBC FINANCE (BRUNEI) BERHAD—See HSBC Holdings plc; *Int'l*, pg. 3505
HSBC HIRE PURCHASE & LEASING LTD.—See HSBC Holdings plc; *Int'l*, pg. 3506
ICICI HOME FINANCE COMPANY LIMITED—See ICICI Bank Limited; *Int'l*, pg. 3581
IKF FINANCE LIMITED; *Int'l*, pg. 3610
I LOAN INC.; *U.S. Private*, pg. 2020
IMH FINANCIAL CORPORATION; *U.S. Private*, pg. 2047
IMH HOLDINGS, LLC—See IMH Financial Corporation; *U.S. Private*, pg. 2047
IMORTGAGE SERVICES, LLC; *U.S. Private*, pg. 2048
IMPAC FUNDING CORPORATION—See Impac Mortgage Holdings, Inc.; *U.S. Public*, pg. 1113
IMPACT FINANCIAL SYSTEMS—See Roper Technologies, Inc.; *U.S. Public*, pg. 1812
INTEGRATED ASSET SERVICES, LLC; *U.S. Private*, pg. 2098
INTEGRIS SECURITISATION SERVICES PTY LIMITED—See Cuscal Ltd.; *Int'l*, pg. 1880
INTEGRITY FIRST FINANCIAL GROUP INC.; *U.S. Private*, pg. 2102
INTERCONTINENTAL HOMES SAVINGS & LOANS LIMITED—See Access Corporation; *Int'l*, pg. 89
INTERVEST MORTGAGE INVESTMENT COMPANY—See Columbia Banking System, Inc.; *U.S. Public*, pg. 534
INTERVEST MORTGAGE INVESTMENT COMPANY—See Columbia Banking System, Inc.; *U.S. Public*, pg. 534
IOU CENTRAL INC.—See Neuberger Berman Group LLC; *U.S. Private*, pg. 2890
IOU FINANCIAL INC.—See Neuberger Berman Group LLC; *U.S. Private*, pg. 2890
IP MORTGAGE BORROWER LLC—See Vornado Realty Trust; *U.S. Public*, pg. 2310
JAPAN MORTGAGE CO., LTD.—See Fuyo General Lease Co., Ltd.; *Int'l*, pg. 2859
JERSEY HOME LOANS LIMITED—See J.C. Flowers & Co. LLC; *U.S. Private*, pg. 2160

522310 — MORTGAGE AND NONMOR...

J.G. WENTWORTH HOME LENDING, LLC—See Freedom Mortgage Corporation; *U.S. Private*, pg. 1604
JSE, INC.; *U.S. Private*, pg. 2241
KALIN FINANCIAL DIVISION—See Kalin Enterprises, Inc.; *U.S. Private*, pg. 2257
K. HOVNANIAN AMERICAN MORTGAGE LLC—See Hovnanian Enterprises, Inc.; *U.S. Public*, pg. 1056
KOENIG & STREY GMAC REAL ESTATE—See Berkshire Hathaway Inc.; *U.S. Public*, pg. 306
KRAUS-ANDERSON MORTGAGE COMPANY—See Kraus-Anderson Incorporated; *U.S. Private*, pg. 2350
LADDER CAPITAL CORP.; *U.S. Public*, pg. 1287
LAKE OSWEGO HOLDINGS INC.—See St. John Holdings Inc.; *U.S. Private*, pg. 3772
LANDED HOME LOANS LLC—See Rithm Capital Corp.; *U.S. Public*, pg. 1800
LANDMARK HOME WARRANTY, LLC—See frontdoor, inc.; *U.S. Public*, pg. 887
LAUBERGE NEWCO, LLC—See IMH Financial Corporation; *U.S. Private*, pg. 2047
LC MORTGAGE CORPORATION; *U.S. Private*, pg. 2403
LEADERONE FINANCIAL; *U.S. Private*, pg. 2406
LEGACY COMMUNITY FEDERAL CREDIT UNION; *U.S. Private*, pg. 2416
LENDINGCLUB CORPORATION; *U.S. Public*, pg. 1305
LENDINGTREE, INC.; *U.S. Public*, pg. 1305
LENDINGTREE, LLC—See LendingTree, Inc.; *U.S. Public*, pg. 1305
LENDI PTY. LTD.—See Bailador Technology Investments Limited; *Int'l*, pg. 802
LENDMARK FINANCIAL SERVICES, INC.—See Lightyear Capital LLC; *U.S. Private*, pg. 2454
LIBERTY MORTGAGE CO. INC.; *U.S. Private*, pg. 2445
LOANBRIGHT.COM; *U.S. Public*, pg. 2477
LOAN RESOLUTION CORPORATION; *U.S. Private*, pg. 2476
LOANS4LESS.COM, INC.; *U.S. Public*, pg. 1337
M3 CAPITAL PARTNERS LLC; *U.S. Private*, pg. 2530
THE MARDENT GROUP PTY LIMITED—See Consolidated Operations Group Limited; *Int'l*, pg. 1771
MASON-McDUFFIE MORTGAGE CORP.; *U.S. Private*, pg. 2602
MEILLEURTAUX SA—See Equistone Partners Europe Limited; *Int'l*, pg. 2486
MERCANTILE CAPITAL CORPORATION—See First Horizon Corporation; *U.S. Public*, pg. 845
MERIDIAN CAPITAL GROUP, LLC—See Banco Santander, S.A.; *Int'l*, pg. 826
M FINANCIAL GROUP; *U.S. Private*, pg. 2523
MID AMERICA MORTGAGE, INC.; *U.S. Private*, pg. 2705
MIDLAND MORTGAGE CO.—See Midland Financial Co.; *U.S. Private*, pg. 2715
MILDURA FINANCE PTY LIMITED—See Consolidated Operations Group Limited; *Int'l*, pg. 1771
MILEND, INC.; *U.S. Private*, pg. 2727
MILESTONE HOME LENDING, LLC—See Rithm Capital Corp.; *U.S. Public*, pg. 1800
MILITARY FAMILY HOME LOANS, LLC—See Wells Fargo & Company; *U.S. Public*, pg. 2344
MINMETALS INTERNATIONAL TENDERING CO., LTD.—See China Rare Earth Resources And Technology Co., Ltd.; *Int'l*, pg. 1546
MMA REALTY CAPITAL, INC.—See Fundamental Advisors LP; *U.S. Private*, pg. 1622
MONEYOU B.V.—See ABN AMRO Group N.V.; *Int'l*, pg. 65
MORSERV, INC.—See JPMorgan Chase & Co.; *U.S. Public*, pg. 1210
MORTGAGEBOT LLC—See Spectrum Equity Investors, L.P.; *U.S. Private*, pg. 3752
MORTGAGE CAPITAL ASSOCIATES, INC.; *U.S. Private*, pg. 2791
MORTGAGE CHOICE LIMITED—See News Corporation; *U.S. Public*, pg. 1521
MORTGAGE CONNECT, LP; *U.S. Private*, pg. 2791
MORTGAGE LENDERS OF AMERICA, LLC; *U.S. Private*, pg. 2791
MORTGAGE OUTLET INC.; *U.S. Private*, pg. 2791
MORTGAGE SERVICE NETWORK, INC.—See Movement Mortgage, LLC; *U.S. Public*, pg. 2802
MORTGAGE SUCCESS SOURCE, LLC; *U.S. Private*, pg. 2791
MORTGAGE WAREHOUSE, LLC; *U.S. Private*, pg. 2791
MOVEMENT MORTGAGE, LLC; *U.S. Public*, pg. 2802
MR. AMAZING LOANS CORPORATION; *U.S. Private*, pg. 2804
MSC MORTGAGE—See Wells Fargo & Company; *U.S. Public*, pg. 2344
NATIONAL CITY MORTGAGE CO.—See The PNC Financial Services Group, Inc.; *U.S. Public*, pg. 2119
NATIONAL DIRECT FINANCE (AUSTRALIA) PTY LIMITED—See Consolidated Operations Group Limited; *Int'l*, pg. 1771
NATIONAL EDUCATION LOAN NETWORK, INC.—See Nelnet, Inc.; *U.S. Public*, pg. 1504
NATIONAL MORTGAGE MARKET CORPORATION PTY LTD—See Bendigo & Adelaide Bank Ltd.; *Int'l*, pg. 971
NATIONS RELIABLE LENDING, LLC; *U.S. Private*, pg. 2865

NATIONSTAR MORTGAGE HOLDINGS INC.—See Mr. Cooper Group Inc.; *U.S. Public*, pg. 1480
NATIONSTAR MORTGAGE LLC—See Mr. Cooper Group Inc.; *U.S. Public*, pg. 1480
NATIONWIDE TITLE CLEARING, LLC—See Covius Holdings, Inc.; *U.S. Private*, pg. 1073
NATIXIS REAL ESTATE CAPITAL INC.—See Groupe BPCE; *Int'l*, pg. 3095
NAVIENT CORPORATION; *U.S. Public*, pg. 1500
NEIGHBORHOOD LOANS; *U.S. Private*, pg. 2881
NELLIE MAE CORPORATION—See SLM Corporation; *U.S. Public*, pg. 1894
NETWORK CAPITAL FUNDING CORP.; *U.S. Private*, pg. 2889
NEWREZ LLC—See Rithm Capital Corp.; *U.S. Public*, pg. 1800
NEW SOUTH FEDERAL SAVINGS BANK—See New South Bancshares Inc.; *U.S. Private*, pg. 2906
NEWTEK SMALL BUSINESS FINANCE, INC.—See NEWTEKONE, INC.; *U.S. Public*, pg. 1521
NORTH SHORE MORTGAGE INCORPORATED; *U.S. Private*, pg. 2946
NOTE WORLD—See Credit-Based Asset Servicing & Securitization LLC; *U.S. Private*, pg. 1092
NVR SERVICES, INC.—See NVR Incorporated; *U.S. Public*, pg. 1558
OAK MORTGAGE COMPANY, LLC—See Republic First Bancorp, Inc.; *U.S. Public*, pg. 1785
OAK STREET SERVICING, LLC—See First Financial Bancorp.; *U.S. Public*, pg. 843
OBVION N.V.—See Cooperatieve Centrale Raiffeisen-Boerenleenbank B.A.; *Int'l*, pg. 1791
OMEGA COMMERCIAL FINANCE CORPORATION; *U.S. Public*, pg. 1571
ON DECK CAPITAL INC.—See Enova International, Inc.; *U.S. Public*, pg. 769
ONEWEST RESOURCES LLC—See First Citizens BancShares, Inc.; *U.S. Public*, pg. 841
OPTIMUM MORTGAGE—See Canadian Western Bank; *Int'l*, pg. 1287
PACIFIC COAST CAPITAL PARTNERS, LLC; *U.S. Private*, pg. 3066
PARAMOUNT EQUITY MORTGAGE, LLC; *U.S. Private*, pg. 3093
PENNYMAC FINANCIAL SERVICES, INC.; *U.S. Public*, pg. 1664
PENNYMAC MORTGAGE INVESTMENT TRUST; *U.S. Public*, pg. 1664
PEOPLES MORTGAGE COMPANY; *U.S. Private*, pg. 3142
PHH CORPORATION—See Onity Group Inc.; *U.S. Public*, pg. 1604
PHH HOME LOANS, LLC—See Onity Group Inc.; *U.S. Public*, pg. 1605
PHH MORTGAGE CAPITAL LLC—See Onity Group Inc.; *U.S. Public*, pg. 1605
PHH MORTGAGE CORPORATION—See Onity Group Inc.; *U.S. Public*, pg. 1605
PHOENIX LEASING PORTFOLIO SERVICES, INC.—See Phoenix American Incorporated; *U.S. Private*, pg. 3172
PINNACLE PUBLIC FINANCE, INC.—See BankUnited, Inc.; *U.S. Public*, pg. 274
PIONEER SERVICES CORP.—See MidCountry Acquisition Corp.; *U.S. Private*, pg. 2711
PIT-STOP CREDIT (SG) PTE. LTD.—See Aspial Lifestyle Limited; *Int'l*, pg. 630
PLATFORM CONSOLIDATED GROUP PTY LIMITED—See Consolidated Operations Group Limited; *Int'l*, pg. 1771
PLATFORM FUNDING LIMITED—See Co-operative Group Limited; *Int'l*, pg. 1679
PLATFORM HOME LOANS LIMITED—See Co-operative Group Limited; *Int'l*, pg. 1679
PLEDGED PROPERTY LLC—See Credit-Based Asset Servicing & Securitization LLC; *U.S. Private*, pg. 1092
PLUS RELOCATION MORTGAGE, LLC—See Rithm Capital Corp.; *U.S. Public*, pg. 1800
PREFERRED LENDING SERVICES, LLC—See Rithm Capital Corp.; *U.S. Public*, pg. 1800
PREMIUM MORTGAGE CORPORATION; *U.S. Private*, pg. 3252
PRIMARY RESIDENTIAL MORTGAGE, INC.; *U.S. Private*, pg. 3261
PRIMELENDING, A PLAINSCAPITAL COMPANY—See Hilltop Holdings Inc.; *U.S. Public*, pg. 1039
PRIME MORTGAGE USA INC.; *U.S. Private*, pg. 3262
PRINCIPAL CREDITOS HIPOTECARIOS, S.A.—See Compania de Seguros de Vida Cruz del Sur S.A; *Int'l*, pg. 1749
PRIORITY ONE FINANCIAL SERVICES INC.; *U.S. Private*, pg. 3266
PROFESSIONAL NATIONAL TITLE NETWORK, INC.; *U.S. Private*, pg. 3275
PROSPER MARKETPLACE, INC.; *U.S. Private*, pg. 3288
PRUDENTIAL ASSET RESOURCES, INC.—See Prudential Financial, Inc.; *U.S. Public*, pg. 1732
PRUDENTIAL INVESTMENT MANAGEMENT, INC.—See Prudential Financial, Inc.; *U.S. Public*, pg. 1732
PTS-TEXAS TITLE, INC.—See Altisource Portfolio Solutions S.A.; *Int'l*, pg. 393

PULTE MORTGAGE LLC—See PulteGroup, Inc.; *U.S. Public*, pg. 1737
PV MORTGAGE COMPANY—See Platte Valley Financial Service Companies Inc.; *U.S. Private*, pg. 3211
RADIUS FINANCIAL GROUP, INC.; *U.S. Private*, pg. 3344
RAM FUNDING SERVICES CORP.; *U.S. Private*, pg. 3351
RCC BUSINESS MORTGAGE BROKERS LTD.—See Christie Group plc; *Int'l*, pg. 1587
REALKREDIT DANMARK A/S—See Danske Bank A/S; *Int'l*, pg. 1969
REDWOOD MORTGAGE INVESTORS IX, LLC; *U.S. Private*, pg. 3381
REGIONAL FINANCE COMPANY OF NEW MEXICO, LLC—See Regional Management Corp.; *U.S. Public*, pg. 1776
REGIONAL FINANCE COMPANY OF OKLAHOMA, LLC—See Regional Management Corp.; *U.S. Public*, pg. 1776
REGIONAL FINANCE CORPORATION OF ALABAMA—See Regional Management Corp.; *U.S. Public*, pg. 1776
REGIONAL FINANCE CORPORATION OF GEORGIA—See Regional Management Corp.; *U.S. Public*, pg. 1776
REGIONAL FINANCE CORPORATION OF NORTH CAROLINA—See Regional Management Corp.; *U.S. Public*, pg. 1776
REGIONAL FINANCE CORPORATION OF TENNESSEE—See Regional Management Corp.; *U.S. Public*, pg. 1776
REGIONAL FINANCE CORPORATION OF TEXAS—See Regional Management Corp.; *U.S. Public*, pg. 1776
RELIANCE INC.; *U.S. Private*, pg. 3394
RELIANCE PROPERTY LOANS LIMITED—See J.C. Flowers & Co. LLC; *U.S. Private*, pg. 2160
RENAISSANCE MORTGAGE GROUP INC.; *U.S. Private*, pg. 3397
REPUBLIC STATE MORTGAGE CO.; *U.S. Private*, pg. 3402
RESIDENTIAL MORTGAGE, LLC; *U.S. Private*, pg. 3405
REVERSE MORTGAGE SOLUTIONS, INC.—See Onity Group Inc.; *U.S. Public*, pg. 1605
RJ FINANCE CORP. ONE—See Bombardier Inc.; *Int'l*, pg. 1104
RMC VANGUARD MORTGAGE CORPORATION; *U.S. Private*, pg. 3451
ROOST 2007 LIMITED—See AMP Limited; *Int'l*, pg. 433
ROSOLITE MORTGAGES LIMITED—See Computershare Limited; *Int'l*, pg. 1760
ROSS MORTGAGE CORPORATION; *U.S. Private*, pg. 3485
RP FUNDING, INC.; *U.S. Private*, pg. 3494
RPM MORTGAGE, INC.; *U.S. Private*, pg. 3495
SAGEN MI CANADA INC.—See Brookfield Corporation; *Int'l*, pg. 1181
SANCTUARY HOME MORTGAGE LLC—See Rithm Capital Corp.; *U.S. Public*, pg. 1800
SAXON MORTGAGE, INC.—See Morgan Stanley; *U.S. Public*, pg. 1475
SCOTT ACCEPTANCE CORPORATION—See The Randall Group Inc.; *U.S. Private*, pg. 4102
SECURITY LOAN INC.—See C.S. Wo & Sons Ltd.; *U.S. Private*, pg. 709
SECURITY NATIONAL CAPITAL, INC.—See Security National Financial Corporation; *U.S. Public*, pg. 1856
SECURITYNATIONAL MORTGAGE COMPANY—See Security National Financial Corporation; *U.S. Public*, pg. 1856
SEMINOLE FINANCIAL SERVICES, LLC—See Seminole Holdings Group, LLC; *U.S. Private*, pg. 3604
SEMPER HOME LOANS; *U.S. Private*, pg. 3605
SENTE MORTGAGE, INC.; *U.S. Private*, pg. 3608
SHANNON FUNDING LLC—See Annaly Capital Management, Inc.; *U.S. Public*, pg. 138
SHELTER HOME MORTGAGE, LLC—See Rithm Capital Corp.; *U.S. Public*, pg. 1800
SHELTER MORTGAGE COMPANY, LLC—See Rithm Capital Corp.; *U.S. Public*, pg. 1800
SHELTER MORTGAGE TJV LLC—See Rithm Capital Corp.; *U.S. Public*, pg. 1800
SHEPHERD'S FINANCE, LLC; *U.S. Private*, pg. 3632
SIBERITE MORTGAGES LIMITED—See Computershare Limited; *Int'l*, pg. 1760
SILVERTON MORTGAGE SPECIALISTS, INC.; *U.S. Private*, pg. 3664
SIRVA MORTGAGE, INC.—See Madison Dearborn Partners, LLC; *U.S. Private*, pg. 2542
SIXTH STREET SPECIALTY LENDING, INC.; *U.S. Public*, pg. 1890
SLM CORPORATION; *U.S. Public*, pg. 1894
SMARTER MORTGAGES; *U.S. Private*, pg. 3692
SMART LEASING INC.; *U.S. Private*, pg. 3691
SOUTHERN FIDELITY MORTGAGE; *U.S. Private*, pg. 3731
SOUTHERN MANAGEMENT CORPORATION—See Milestone Partners LLC; *U.S. Private*, pg. 2729
SOUTHFIRST MORTGAGE, INC.—See FirstBanc of Alabama, Inc.; *U.S. Private*, pg. 1531
SOUTHLAND FINANCE, INC.—See Old National Bancorp; *U.S. Public*, pg. 1567
SOUTHWEST FUNDING L.P.; *U.S. Private*, pg. 3739

N.A.I.C.S. INDEX

522320 — FINANCIAL TRANSACTI...

SOVEREIGN LENDING GROUP, INC.; *U.S. Private*, pg. 3743
SOVEREIGN REVERSIONS LIMITED—See Grainger plc; *Int'l*, pg. 3052
SPECIALIZED LOAN SERVICING LLC—See Computershare Limited; *Int'l*, pg. 1760
SPRING EQUITY, LLC—See Rithm Capital Corp.; *U.S. Public*, pg. 1800
SS VENTURES II INC.; *U.S. Private*, pg. 3768
START MORTGAGES LIMITED—See Lone Star Global Acquisitions, LLC; *U.S. Private*, pg. 2489
STATEWIDE MORTGAGE, LLC; *U.S. Private*, pg. 3793
STEARNS HOLDINGS, LLC—See Blackstone Inc.; *U.S. Public*, pg. 358
STEARNS LENDING, LLC—See Blackstone Inc.; *U.S. Public*, pg. 358
STOCK FINANCIAL—See Stock Development, LLC; *U.S. Private*, pg. 3814
SUMMIT MORTGAGE CORPORATION; *U.S. Private*, pg. 3855
SUMMIT MORTGAGE; *U.S. Private*, pg. 3855
SUN HUNG KAI CREDIT LIMITED—See Allied Group Limited; *Int'l*, pg. 357
SYNERGY DIRECT MORTGAGE, INC.; *U.S. Private*, pg. 3904
SYNERGY HOME MORTGAGE, LLC—See Rithm Capital Corp.; *U.S. Public*, pg. 1800
TARBELL FINANCIAL CORPORATION; *U.S. Private*, pg. 3933
TCF COMMERCIAL FINANCE CANADA, INC.—See Huntington Bancshares Incorporated; *U.S. Public*, pg. 1071
TEAM LENDING CONCEPTS LLC; *U.S. Private*, pg. 3949
THOMAS D. WOOD AND COMPANY - SARASOTA—See Thomas D. Wood and Company; *U.S. Private*, pg. 4155
THOMAS D. WOOD AND COMPANY; *U.S. Private*, pg. 4155
THOMAS D. WOOD AND COMPANY—See Thomas D. Wood and Company; *U.S. Private*, pg. 4155
THOMAS D. WOOD AND COMPANY—See Thomas D. Wood and Company; *U.S. Private*, pg. 4155
THOROUGHBRED MORTGAGE, LLC—See Wells Fargo & Company; *U.S. Public*, pg. 2345
THRIVE MORTGAGE LLC; *U.S. Private*, pg. 4165
TOLL BROTHERS MORTGAGE COMPANY—See Toll Brothers, Inc.; *U.S. Public*, pg. 2162
TOP FLITE FINANCIAL, INC., *U.S. Private*, pg. 4186
TOTAL MORTGAGE SERVICES, LLC; *U.S. Private*, pg. 4191
TOWN & COUNTRY CREDIT CORP.—See Ameriquest Capital Corporation; *U.S. Private*, pg. 260
TOWNEBANK COMMERCIAL MORTGAGE, LLC—See Towne Bank; *U.S. Public*, pg. 2166
TRIAD FINANCIAL SERVICES, INC.—See ECN Capital Corp.; *Int'l*, pg. 2292
UCB INGATLANHITEL RT—See BNP Paribas SA; *Int'l*, pg. 1093
UCI—See BNP Paribas SA; *Int'l*, pg. 1093
UNION HOME MORTGAGE CORP.; *U.S. Private*, pg. 4284
UNION SAVINGS BANK; *U.S. Private*, pg. 4285
UNITED ASIA FINANCE LIMITED—See Allied Group Limited; *Int'l*, pg. 357
UNITED PACIFIC MORTGAGE CO., INC.; *U.S. Private*, pg. 4295
UNITY FINANCIAL SERVICES, INC.—See Unity Bancorp, Inc.; *U.S. Public*, pg. 2253
UPSTATE MORTGAGE INC.; *U.S. Private*, pg. 4313
URBAN LENDING SOLUTIONS LLC; *U.S. Private*, pg. 4314
VA MORTGAGE CENTER.COM; *U.S. Private*, pg. 4328
VELOCITY COMMERCIAL CAPITAL, LLC; *U.S. Private*, pg. 4354
VIP MORTGAGE, INC.; *U.S. Private*, pg. 4386
VISTA HYPOTHEKEN B.V.—See Cooperatieve Centrale Raiffeisen-Boerenleenbank B.A.; *Int'l*, pg. 1792
VOLT VIEWTECH, INC.—See American CyberSystems, Inc.; *U.S. Private*, pg. 230
VSI NEARSHORE OUTSOURCING; *U.S. Private*, pg. 4415
WALLICK AND VOLK INC.; *U.S. Private*, pg. 4431
WATERSTONE MORTGAGE CORP.; *U.S. Private*, pg. 4454
WATSON MORTGAGE CORP.; *U.S. Private*, pg. 4455
WCS LENDING, LLC; *U.S. Private*, pg. 4462
WEBSTER BUSINESS CREDIT CORPORATION—See Webster Financial Corporation; *U.S. Public*, pg. 2341
WELLS FARGO MORTGAGE LOAN TRUST II, LLC—See Wells Fargo & Company; *U.S. Public*, pg. 2346
WELLS FARGO MULTIFAMILY CAPITAL—See Wells Fargo & Company; *U.S. Public*, pg. 2346
WENDOVER FINANCIAL SERVICES CORPORATION—See Veritas Capital Fund Management, LLC; *U.S. Private*, pg. 4364
WESTERN CAPITAL RESOURCES, INC.—See Blackstreet Capital Management, LLC; *U.S. Private*, pg. 577
WESTERN MORTGAGE SERVICES LIMITED—See Capita plc; *Int'l*, pg. 1308
WILLOW BEND MORTGAGE COMPANY; *U.S. Private*, pg. 4528
WINTRUST MORTGAGE CORP.—See Wintrust Financial Corporation; *U.S. Public*, pg. 2374

W.R. STARKEY MORTGAGE LLP; *U.S. Private*, pg. 4422
WYNDHAM CAPITAL MORTGAGE, INC.—See SoFi Technologies, Inc.; *U.S. Public*, pg. 1899
YOUR HOME FINANCIAL LLC—See Rithm Capital Corp.; *U.S. Public*, pg. 1800

522320 — FINANCIAL TRANSACTIONS PROCESSING, RESERVE, AND CLEARINGHOUSE ACTIVITIES

777 PARTNERS LLC; *U.S. Private*, pg. 17
A1 BANK AG—See America Movil, S.A.B. de C.V.; *Int'l*, pg. 421
ABN AMRO CLEARING CHICAGO LLC—See ABN AMRO Group N.V.; *Int'l*, pg. 64
ACCOUNTNOW, INC.; *U.S. Private*, pg. 54
ACCRETIVE CO., LTD.—See Fuyo General Lease Co., Ltd.; *Int'l*, pg. 2859
ACCURO SOLUTIONS, LLC; *U.S. Private*, pg. 55
A-CHECK AMERICA INC.—See Sterling Check Corp.; *U.S. Public*, pg. 1946
ACHIEVERS CORP.—See P2 Capital Partners, LLC; *U.S. Private*, pg. 3061
ACHIEVERS CORP.—See Silver Lake Group, LLC; *U.S. Private*, pg. 3656
ACHIEVERS LLC—See P2 Capital Partners, LLC; *U.S. Private*, pg. 3061
ACHIEVERS LLC—See Silver Lake Group, LLC; *U.S. Private*, pg. 3656
ACI MERCHANT SYSTEMS, LLC—See NCR Voyix Corporation.; *U.S. Public*, pg. 1502
ACI WORLDWIDE CORP. - CHANTILLY OFFICE—See ACI Worldwide, Inc.; *U.S. Public*, pg. 34
ACI WORLDWIDE CORP. - COLUMBUS OFFICE—See ACI Worldwide, Inc.; *U.S. Public*, pg. 34
ACI WORLDWIDE CORP. - PRINCETON OFFICE—See ACI Worldwide, Inc.; *U.S. Public*, pg. 34
ACI WORLDWIDE (HELLAS) EPE—See ACI Worldwide, Inc.; *U.S. Public*, pg. 34
ACORNS GROW INCORPORATED; *U.S. Private*, pg. 64
ACTIVI DEPLOYMENT SERVICES (PROPRIETARY) LIMITED—See Blue Label Telecoms Limited; *Int'l*, pg. 1068
ADACOM S.A.—See Ideal Group S.A.; *Int'l*, pg. 3589
ADELAIDE BANK LIMITED—See Bendigo & Adelaide Bank Ltd.; *Int'l*, pg. 970
ADEPTRA PTY. LTD.—See Fair Isaac Corporation; *U.S. Public*, pg. 820
ADMINISTER OY; *Int'l*, pg. 151
ADUNO FINANCE AG—See Aduno Holding AG; *Int'l*, pg. 154
ADUNOKAUTION PLC—See Aduno Holding AG; *Int'l*, pg. 154
ADVANTIS CREDIT LIMITED—See Bain Capital, LP; *U.S. Private*, pg. 433
ADYEN DO BRAZIL LTDA.—See Adyen N.V.; *Int'l*, pg. 170
ADYEN INDIA TECH HUB PVT. LTD.—See Adyen N.V.; *Int'l*, pg. 169
ADYEN N.V.; *Int'l*, pg. 169
AEON BANK, LTD.—See AEON Co., Ltd.; *Int'l*, pg. 176
AFFINIPAY, LLC; *U.S. Private*, pg. 122
AFORE BANAMEX, S.A. DE C.V.—See Citigroup Inc.; *U.S. Public*, pg. 501
AFTERPAY HOLDINGS LIMITED—See Block, Inc.; *U.S. Public*, pg. 361
AG MEDICAL CORPORATION—See AIFUL Corporation; *Int'l*, pg. 231
AGM GROUP HOLDINGS INC.; *Int'l*, pg. 211
AIQ LIMITED; *Int'l*, pg. 236
AIRPLUS INTERNATIONAL, INC.—See Deutsche Lufthansa AG; *Int'l*, pg. 2068
AIRPLUS INTERNATIONAL LIMITED—See Deutsche Lufthansa AG; *Int'l*, pg. 2068
AKIN FAKTORING HIZMETLERI A.S.; *Int'l*, pg. 263
AKODE ELEKTRONIK PARA VE ODEME HIZMETLERI A.S.—See Akbank T.A.S.; *Int'l*, pg. 261
ALESCO RISK MANAGEMENT SERVICES LIMITED—See Arthur J. Gallagher & Co.; *U.S. Public*, pg. 202
AL-ZAMIN INVESTBANK; *Int'l*, pg. 289
AMERICAN CONSUMER FINANCIAL NETWORK; *U.S. Private*, pg. 228
AMERICAN CREDIT CARD PROCESSING CORP.—See Priority Payment Systems, LLC; *U.S. Private*, pg. 3267
AMERICAN EXPRESS ARGENTINA S.A.—See American Express Company; *U.S. Public*, pg. 100
AMERICAN EXPRESS ITALIA S.R.L.—See American Express Company; *U.S. Public*, pg. 100
AMERICAN EXPRESS SERVICIOS PROFESIONALES, S. DE R.L. DE C.V.—See American Express Company; *U.S. Public*, pg. 101
AMERICAN EXPRESS (THAI) COMPANY LIMITED—See American Express Company; *U.S. Public*, pg. 101
AMERICAN EXPRESS TLS HK LIMITED—See American Express Company; *U.S. Public*, pg. 100
AMEX AL OMANIA LLC—See American Express Company; *U.S. Public*, pg. 101
AMEX EGYPT COMPANY LIMITED LIABILITY COMPANY—See American Express Company; *U.S. Public*, pg. 102
AMEX (MIDDLE EAST) QFC LLC—See American Express Company; *U.S. Public*, pg. 100
AMP SERVICES (NZ) LIMITED—See AMP Limited; *Int'l*, pg. 432
ANDERSON ZAKS LIMITED—See Global Payments Inc.; *U.S. Public*, pg. 943
APEX CLEARING CORPORATION—See Apex Fintech Solutions LLC; *U.S. Private*, pg. 292
APEX FINTECH SOLUTIONS LLC; *U.S. Private*, pg. 292
APEX-POWER GREEN TECHNOLOGY CO., LTD.—See Apex International Financial Engineering Research & Technology Co., Limited; *Int'l*, pg. 511
APOFINANZ GMBH—See Deutsche Apotheker- und Arztebank eG; *Int'l*, pg. 2049
APPLIED CARD HOLDINGS INC.; *U.S. Private*, pg. 298
APPLIED CARD SYSTEMS INC.; *U.S. Private*, pg. 298
APPTECH PAYMENTS CORP.; *U.S. Public*, pg. 174
ARGUS KREDITT AS—See TowerBrook Capital Partners, L.P.; *U.S. Private*, pg. 4194
ARI FINANCIAL SERVICES, INC.—See Holman Automotive Group, Inc.; *U.S. Private*, pg. 1967
ARMED FORCES FINANCIAL NETWORK, LLC—See Fidelity National Infor; *U.S. Public*, pg. 832
ARMENIAN CARD CJSC—See Central Bank of Armenia; *Int'l*, pg. 1404
ARRENDADORA JOHN DEERE S.A. DE C.V.—See Deere & Company; *U.S. Public*, pg. 646
ASESORIAS E INVERSIONES AMERICAN EXPRESS CHILE LIMITADA—See American Express Company; *U.S. Public*, pg. 102
ASX CLEARING CORPORATION LIMITED—See ASX Limited; *Int'l*, pg. 664
ASX SETTLEMENT CORPORATION LIMITED—See ASX Limited; *Int'l*, pg. 664
ATLANTO AG—See Helvetia Holding AG; *Int'l*, pg. 3339
ATM NATIONAL, LLC—See NCR Voyix Corporation.; *U.S. Public*, pg. 1501
AUSTRALIAN BOND EXCHANGE PTY LTD.—See Australian Bond Exchange Holdings Limited; *Int'l*, pg. 721
AUSTRALIAN FACTORING COMPANY PTY. LTD.—See Butn Limited; *Int'l*, pg. 1229
AUTHORIZE.NET HOLDINGS, INC.—See Visa, Inc.; *U.S. Public*, pg. 2301
AVANTHA BUSINESS SOLUTIONS LIMITED—See Avantha Group; *Int'l*, pg. 735
AVANTHA BUSINESS SOLUTIONS USA, INC.—See Avantha Group; *Int'l*, pg. 735
AXA BANQUE—See AXA S.A.; *Int'l*, pg. 755
AXIATA DIGITAL CAPITAL SDN BHD—See Axiata Group Berhad; *Int'l*, pg. 768
AXIATA DIGITAL ECODE SDN BHD—See Axiata Group Berhad; *Int'l*, pg. 768
AYCASH GMBH—See Fiserv, Inc.; *U.S. Public*, pg. 851
BABS PAYLINK AB—See British Columbia Investment Management Corp.; *Int'l*, pg. 1170
BABS PAYLINK AB—See Francisco Partners Management, LP; *U.S. Private*, pg. 1592
BA EXCHANGE COMPANY (UK) LIMITED—See Bank Asia Limited; *Int'l*, pg. 837
BA EXPRESS USA INC.—See Bank Asia Limited; *Int'l*, pg. 837
BAMBORA AB—See Apollo Global Management, Inc.; *U.S. Public*, pg. 151
BAMBORA INC.—See Apollo Global Management, Inc.; *U.S. Public*, pg. 151
BANCA POPOLARE DELL'EMILIA ROMAGNA (EUROPE) INTERNATIONAL S.A.—See BPER BANCA S.p.A; *Int'l*, pg. 1132
BANCA UCB S.P.A.—See BNP Paribas SA; *Int'l*, pg. 1087
BANCO B3 S.A.—See B3 S.A.; *Int'l*, pg. 791
BANCO BILBAO VIZCAYA ARGENTARIA URUGUAY S.A.—See Banco Bilbao Vizcaya Argentaria, S.A.; *Int'l*, pg. 817
BANCO CETELEM ARGENTINA SA—See BNP Paribas SA; *Int'l*, pg. 1089
BANCO DE GALICIA Y BUENOS AIRES S.A.—See Grupo Financiero Galicia S.A.; *Int'l*, pg. 3129
BANCOMER TRANSFER SERVICES, INC.—See Banco Bilbao Vizcaya Argentaria, S.A.; *Int'l*, pg. 818
BANCO OCCIDENTAL SA—See Banco Bilbao Vizcaya Argentaria, S.A.; *Int'l*, pg. 817
BANCO SANTANDER-CHILE—See Banco Santander, S.A.; *Int'l*, pg. 825
BANGKOK PAYMENT SOLUTIONS CO., LTD.—See BTS Group Holdings Public Company Limited; *Int'l*, pg. 1205
BANGKOK SMARTCARD SYSTEM CO., LTD.—See BTS Group Holdings Public Company Limited; *Int'l*, pg. 1205
BANGO.NET LIMITED—See Bango Plc; *Int'l*, pg. 836
BANK FOR INTERNATIONAL SETTLEMENTS; *Int'l*, pg. 837
BANK HANDLOWY W WARSZAWIE S.A.—See Citigroup Inc.; *U.S. Public*, pg. 501
BANK OF IRELAND 365—See Bank of Ireland Group plc; *Int'l*, pg. 844
BANK OF KAOHSIUNG CO., LTD.; *Int'l*, pg. 845
BANK OF QUEENSLAND LIMITED; *Int'l*, pg. 847

522320 — FINANCIAL TRANSACTI... CORPORATE AFFILIATIONS

BANK POLICY INSTITUTE; *U.S. Private*, pg. 467
BANQUE AL BARAKA D'ALGERIE S.P.A.—See Al Baraka Banking Group B.S.C.; *Int'l*, pg. 276
BANQUE DE BRETAGNE—See BNP Paribas SA; *Int'l*, pg. 1089
BANQUE INTERNATIONALE POUR LE COMMERCE ET L'INDUSTRIE AU MALI—See BNP Paribas SA; *Int'l*, pg. 1089
BANQUE INTERNATIONALE POUR LE COMMERCE ET L'INDUSTRIE DE LA GUINEE—See BNP Paribas SA; *Int'l*, pg. 1089
BANQUE INTERNATIONALE POUR LE COMMERCE, L'INDUSTRIE ET L'AGRICULTURE DU BURKINA—See BNP Paribas SA; *Int'l*, pg. 1089
BANSAMEX, S.A.—See American Express Company; *U.S. Public*, pg. 102
BASSILICHI CEE D.O.O.; *Int'l*, pg. 888
BAVARIA CARBON HOLDINGS GMBH—See Graphite India Ltd; *Int'l*, pg. 3061
BBVA BRASIL BANCO DE INVESTIMENTO SA—See Banco Bilbao Vizcaya Argentaria, S.A.; *Int'l*, pg. 817
BBVA PROVINCIAL OVERSEAS NV—See Banco Bilbao Vizcaya Argentaria, S.A.; *Int'l*, pg. 817
BBVA SOCIEDAD TITULIZADORA S.A—See Banco Bilbao Vizcaya Argentaria, S.A.; *Int'l*, pg. 817
BBVA TRANSFER SERVICES INC.—See Banco Bilbao Vizcaya Argentaria, S.A.; *Int'l*, pg. 817
BCR SOCIAL FINANCE IFN S.A.—See Erste Group Bank AG; *Int'l*, pg. 2497
BDO REMITTANCE (USA) INC.—See BDO Unibank, Inc.; *Int'l*, pg. 930
BEAUTIFUL CHINA HOLDINGS COMPANY LIMITED; *Int'l*, pg. 934
BEST EFFORTS BANK PJSC; *Int'l*, pg. 999
BETTERMENT LLC; *U.S. Private*, pg. 547
BETTER MERCHANT RATES INC.; *U.S. Private*, pg. 547
BGC ENVIRONMENTAL BROKERAGE SERVICES, L.P.—See BGC Group, Inc.; *U.S. Public*, pg. 328
BGC MARKET DATA, L.P.—See BGC Group, Inc.; *U.S. Public*, pg. 328
BGC USA, L.P.—See BGC Group, Inc.; *U.S. Public*, pg. 328
BILLINGORCHARD—See Payscape Advisors; *U.S. Private*, pg. 3117
BILLING SYSTEM CORP.; *Int'l*, pg. 1031
BIRLESIK ODEME HIZMETLERI A.S.—See Fibabanka A.S.; *Int'l*, pg. 2651
BLACKHAWK NETWORK (AUSTRALIA) PTY LTD.—See P2 Capital Partners, LLC; *U.S. Private*, pg. 3061
BLACKHAWK NETWORK (AUSTRALIA) PTY LTD.—See Silver Lake Group, LLC; *U.S. Private*, pg. 3656
BLACKHAWK NETWORK CALIFORNIA, INC.—See P2 Capital Partners, LLC; *U.S. Private*, pg. 3061
BLACKHAWK NETWORK CALIFORNIA, INC.—See Silver Lake Group, LLC; *U.S. Private*, pg. 3656
BLOCK, INC.; *U.S. Public*, pg. 361
BLUE DOG BUSINESS SERVICES, LLC—See Fortis Payment Systems LLC; *U.S. Private*, pg. 1576
BLUE LABEL MEXICO S.A. DE C.V—See Grupo Bimbo, S.A.B. de C.V.; *Int'l*, pg. 3123
BLUE LABEL TELECOMS LIMITED; *Int'l*, pg. 1068
BLUEPAY CANADA, ULC—See Fiserv, Inc.; *U.S. Public*, pg. 850
BLUESQUARE RESOLUTIONS, LLC.; *U.S. Private*, pg. 597
BMW FINANCIAL SERVICES GMBH—See Bayerische Motoren Werke Aktiengesellschaft; *Int'l*, pg. 911
BNG BANK N.V.; *Int'l*, pg. 1078
BNK CAPITAL CO., LTD.—See BNK Financial Group Inc.; *Int'l*, pg. 1079
BNL FINANCE SPA—See BNP Paribas SA; *Int'l*, pg. 1080
BNP PARIBAS ANDES—See BNP Paribas SA; *Int'l*, pg. 1081
BNP PARIBAS ARGENTINA—See BNP Paribas SA; *Int'l*, pg. 1081
BNP PARIBAS ASSET MANAGEMENT S.A.S.—See BNP Paribas SA; *Int'l*, pg. 1082
BNP PARIBAS BEIJING—See BNP Paribas SA; *Int'l*, pg. 1081
BNP PARIBAS CANADA-QUEBEC—See BNP Paribas SA; *Int'l*, pg. 1082
BNP PARIBAS (CANADA)—See BNP Paribas SA; *Int'l*, pg. 1081
BNP PARIBAS CANADA-TORONTO—See BNP Paribas SA; *Int'l*, pg. 1082
BNP PARIBAS CHINA GROUP—See BNP Paribas SA; *Int'l*, pg. 1081
BNP PARIBAS GUYANE—See BNP Paribas SA; *Int'l*, pg. 1085
BNP PARIBAS HONG KONG—See BNP Paribas SA; *Int'l*, pg. 1081
BNP PARIBAS LEASING SOLUTIONS LIMITED—See BNP Paribas SA; *Int'l*, pg. 1085
BNP PARIBAS MARTINIQUE—See BNP Paribas SA; *Int'l*, pg. 1086
BNP PARIBAS NETHERLANDS—See BNP Paribas SA; *Int'l*, pg. 1086
BNP PARIBAS PANAMA—See BNP Paribas SA; *Int'l*, pg. 1086

BNP PARIBAS PRIVATE BANK SWITZERLAND S.A.—See BNP Paribas SA; *Int'l*, pg. 1086
BNP PARIBAS (SINGAPORE) PTE. LTD.—See BNP Paribas SA; *Int'l*, pg. 1081
BNP PARIBAS - SOUTH EAST ASIA—See BNP Paribas SA; *Int'l*, pg. 1081
BNP PARIBAS SOUTH KOREA—See BNP Paribas SA; *Int'l*, pg. 1081
BNP PARIBAS-SUCCURSALE ITALIA—See BNP Paribas SA; *Int'l*, pg. 1087
BNP PARIBAS SYDNEY—See BNP Paribas SA; *Int'l*, pg. 1081
BNPP ASSET MANAGEMENT BRASIL LTDA—See BNP Paribas SA; *Int'l*, pg. 1088
BNPP CARDIF COMPANIA DE SEGUROS Y REASEGUROS SA—See BNP Paribas SA; *Int'l*, pg. 1088
BNPP COLOMBIA CORPORACION FINANCIERA SA—See BNP Paribas SA; *Int'l*, pg. 1088
BNPP FACTOR NV—See BNP Paribas SA; *Int'l*, pg. 1088
BNPP PERSONAL FINANCE SA—See BNP Paribas SA; *Int'l*, pg. 1088
BNY MELLON ASSET SERVICING B.V.—See The Bank of New York Mellon Corporation; *U.S. Public*, pg. 2037
BNY MELLON INTERNATIONAL ASSET MANAGEMENT GROUP LIMITED—See The Bank of New York Mellon Corporation; *U.S. Public*, pg. 2037
BNY MELLON INVESTMENT SERVICING (US) INC.—See The Bank of New York Mellon Corporation; *U.S. Public*, pg. 2037
BOFA SECURITIES INDIA LIMITED—See Bank of America Corporation; *U.S. Public*, pg. 271
BOKU, INC.; *U.S. Private*, pg. 610
BOOST PAYMENT SOLUTIONS, INC.; *U.S. Private*, pg. 616
BRAINTREE PAYMENT SOLUTIONS, LLC—See PayPal Holdings, Inc.; *U.S. Public*, pg. 1656
BRASPAG TECNO. EM PAGTO. LTDA.—See Cielo S.A.; *Int'l*, pg. 1605
BRIEFING.COM, INC.; *U.S. Private*, pg. 650
BRIGHTFLOW.AI, INC.; *U.S. Private*, pg. 652
B. RILEY CAPITAL MANAGEMENT, LLC—See B. Riley Financial, Inc.; *U.S. Public*, pg. 260
BRITE:BILL EMPLOYMENT COMPANY LIMITED—See Amdocs Limited; *Int'l*, pg. 420
BRITE:BILL GROUP LIMITED—See Amdocs Limited; *Int'l*, pg. 420
BRITE:BILL LIMITED—See Amdocs Limited; *Int'l*, pg. 420
BRODOS ROMANIA SRL—See Euronet Worldwide, Inc.; *U.S. Public*, pg. 797
BROWN BROTHERS HARRIMAN FUND ADMINISTRATION SERVICES (IRELAND) LIMITED—See Brown Brothers Harriman & Co.; *U.S. Private*, pg. 667
BULGARIAN AMERICAN CREDIT BANK AD; *Int'l*, pg. 1213
CAMBRIDGE MERCANTILE (AUSTRALIA) PTY. LTD.—See Corpay, Inc.; *U.S. Public*, pg. 579
CAMBRIDGE MERCANTILE CORP.—See Corpay, Inc.; *U.S. Public*, pg. 579
CAMBRIDGE MERCANTILE CORP. (U.K.) LTD.—See Corpay, Inc.; *U.S. Public*, pg. 579
CAMBRIDGE MERCANTILE CORP. (U.S.A.)—See Corpay, Inc.; *U.S. Public*, pg. 579
CANTALOUPE, INC.; *U.S. Public*, pg. 430
CAPCO CONSULTING SINGAPORE PTE. LTD.—See Fidelity National Infor; *U.S. Public*, pg. 832
CAPITA INTERNATIONAL FINANCIAL SERVICES LTD.—See Capita plc; *Int'l*, pg. 1308
CAPITAL IQ INFORMATION SYSTEMS (INDIA) PVT. LTD.—See S&P Global Inc.; *U.S. Public*, pg. 1831
CARACONSULT GMBH—See Thor Industries, Inc.; *U.S. Public*, pg. 2156
CARDHERO PTY. LTD.—See 8common Limited; *Int'l*, pg. 16
CARD PAYMENT SERVICES INC.—See Global Payments Inc.; *U.S. Public*, pg. 944
CARD PAY SDN. BHD.—See General Atlantic Service Company, L.P.; *U.S. Private*, pg. 1661
CARDSERVICE INTERNATIONAL, INC.—See Fiserv, Inc.; *U.S. Public*, pg. 850
CARDS OFF SA; *Int'l*, pg. 1323
CARDTRONICS CANADA ATM PROCESSING PARTNERSHIP—See NCR Voyix Corporation.; *U.S. Public*, pg. 1501
CARDTRONICS DE MEXICO S.A. DE C.V.—See NCR Voyix Corporation.; *U.S. Public*, pg. 1502
CARDTRONICS PTY. LTD.—See NCR Voyix Corporation.; *U.S. Public*, pg. 1501
CARDTRONICS UK LIMITED—See NCR Voyix Corporation.; *U.S. Public*, pg. 1501
CARDTRONICS USA, INC.—See NCR Voyix Corporation.; *U.S. Public*, pg. 1502
CARMAX BUSINESS SERVICES, LLC—See CarMax, Inc.; *U.S. Public*, pg. 437
CASTLES TECHNOLOGY UK & IRELAND LTD.—See Castles Technology Co., Ltd; *Int'l*, pg. 1357
CATTLES LIMITED; *Int'l*, pg. 1361
CAYAN LLC—See Global Payments Inc.; *U.S. Public*, pg. 944
CELERO COMMERCE LLC—See Independence Capital Partners, LLC; *U.S. Private*, pg. 2056

CENTRABAIL SA—See Dexia SA; *Int'l*, pg. 2092
CENTRAL PAYMENT; *U.S. Private*, pg. 824
CENTRUM ELEKTRONICZNYCH USLUG PLATNICZYCH ESERVICE SP. Z O.O.—See Global Payments Inc.; *U.S. Public*, pg. 943
CENTURY PAYMENTS, INC.—See Advent International Corporation; *U.S. Private*, pg. 108
CENTURY PAYMENTS, INC.—See Bain Capital, LP; *U.S. Private*, pg. 452
CERTEGY EZI-PAY PTY LTD—See Humm Group Limited; *Int'l*, pg. 3531
CFJ G.K.—See Citigroup Inc.; *U.S. Public*, pg. 501
CHASE PAYMENTECH EUROPE LIMITED—See JPMorgan Chase & Co.; *U.S. Public*, pg. 1209
CHASE PAYMENTECH SOLUTIONS, LLC—See JPMorgan Chase & Co.; *U.S. Public*, pg. 1206
CHASE PAYMENTECH SOLUTIONS, LLC—See JPMorgan Chase & Co.; *U.S. Public*, pg. 1209
CHASE PAYMENTECH SOLUTIONS—See JPMorgan Chase & Co.; *U.S. Public*, pg. 1206
CHECKALT, LLC; *U.S. Private*, pg. 869
CHECK-N-GO FINANCIAL CORP.; *U.S. Private*, pg. 869
CHEVYPLAN S.A. SOCIEDAD ADMINISTRADORA DE PLANES DE AUTOFINANCIAMIENTO COMERCIAL—See General Motors Company; *U.S. Public*, pg. 923
CHINA PNR CO., LTD.—See Huifu Payment Limited; *Int'l*, pg. 3526
CHINA YOUZAN LIMITED; *Int'l*, pg. 1565
THE CHUGIN OPERATION CENTER, CO., LIMITED—See Chugin Financial Group, Inc.; *Int'l*, pg. 1595
CIMB BANK BHD.—See CIMB Group Holdings Berhad; *Int'l*, pg. 1607
CISCO SYSTEMS CAPITAL K.K.—See Cisco Systems, Inc.; *U.S. Public*, pg. 498
CISCO SYSTEMS CAPITAL (KOREA) LIMITED—See Cisco Systems, Inc.; *U.S. Public*, pg. 498
CITIBANAMEX SEGUROS, S.A. DE C.V.—See Citigroup Inc.; *U.S. Public*, pg. 502
CITIBANK DEL PERU S.A.—See Citigroup Inc.; *U.S. Public*, pg. 503
CITIBANK TANZANIA LIMITED—See Citigroup Inc.; *U.S. Public*, pg. 503
CITIGROUP GLOBAL MARKETS INDIA PRIVATE LIMITED—See Citigroup Inc.; *U.S. Public*, pg. 503
CITIGROUP OVERSEAS HOLDINGS GK—See Citigroup Inc.; *U.S. Public*, pg. 504
CITISHARE CORPORATION—See Citigroup Inc.; *U.S. Public*, pg. 504
CLARION GRAMERCY (UK) LIMITED—See Franklin Resources, Inc.; *U.S. Public*, pg. 881
CLAYTON SERVICES, LLC—See Covius Holdings, Inc.; *U.S. Private*, pg. 1073
CLEAR2PAY AMERICAS, INC.—See Fidelity National Infor; *U.S. Public*, pg. 832
CLEARCASH LIMITED—See ClearDebt Group Plc; *Int'l*, pg. 1656
CLEARENT LLC; *U.S. Private*, pg. 932
CLEAR ONE, S.L.—See Global Payments Inc.; *U.S. Public*, pg. 943
CLEARSTREAM AUSTRALIA LIMITED—See Deutsche Borse AG; *Int'l*, pg. 2063
CLEARSTREAM FUND CENTRE AG—See Deutsche Borse AG; *Int'l*, pg. 2063
CLINTRAX GLOBAL, INC.—See Leonard Green & Partners, L.P.; *U.S. Private*, pg. 2430
CMS PROCESSING LLC—See Alvarez & Marsal, Inc.; *U.S. Private*, pg. 212
CNL CAPITAL E.K.E.S. AIFM; *Int'l*, pg. 1677
COIN CITADEL INC.; *U.S. Public*, pg. 530
COLUMBIA CAPITAL MANAGEMENT; *U.S. Private*, pg. 976
COLUMBUS DATA SERVICES LLC—See NCR Voyix Corporation.; *U.S. Public*, pg. 1502
COMDATA CORPORATION—See Corpay, Inc.; *U.S. Public*, pg. 579
COMMERZ TRANSACTION SERVICES MITTE GMBH—See Commerzbank AG; *Int'l*, pg. 1716
COMMERZ TRANSACTION SERVICES NORD GMBH—See Commerzbank AG; *Int'l*, pg. 1716
COMMERZ TRANSACTION SERVICES WEST GMBH—See Commerzbank AG; *Int'l*, pg. 1716
COMPAGNIE FINANCIERE DE LA COTE D'IVOIRE—See BNP Paribas SA; *Int'l*, pg. 1090
COMPANHIA BRASILEIRA DE SOLUCOES E SERVICOS S.A.—See Banco Bradesco S.A.; *Int'l*, pg. 819
COMPARTAMOS FINANCIERA; *Int'l*, pg. 1749
COMPUTER AGE MANAGEMENT SERVICES LIMITED; *Int'l*, pg. 1758
CONCARDIS GMBH—See Concardis Payment Group GmbH; *Int'l*, pg. 1763
CONCARDIS PAYMENT GROUP GMBH; *Int'l*, pg. 1763
CONNECTYOURCARE LLC—See ABS Capital Partners, L.P.; *U.S. Private*, pg. 44
CONSENSUS ASSET MANAGEMENT AB; *Int'l*, pg. 1770
CONSENSYS DIGITAL SECURITIES, LLC—See ConsenSys, Inc.; *U.S. Private*, pg. 1019
CONSOLIDATED INFORMATION SERVICES SOLUTIONS,

N.A.I.C.S. INDEX

522320 — FINANCIAL TRANSACTI...

LLC—See Lovell Minnick Partners LLC; *U.S. Private*, pg. 2502
CONTINENTAL EXCHANGE SOLUTIONS, INC.—See Euronet Worldwide, Inc.; *U.S. Public*, pg. 797
CORCENTRIC, INC.; *U.S. Private*, pg. 1047
CORPAY, INC.; *U.S. Public*, pg. 579
COSTAS, INC., *U.S. Public*, pg. 586
CRAFT3; *U.S. Private*, pg. 1082
CRANE NXT PRIVATE LIMITED—See Crane NXT, Co.; *U.S. Public*, pg. 591
CRANE PAYMENT INNOVATIONS AG—See Crane NXT, Co.; *U.S. Public*, pg. 591
CREATION CONSUMER FINANCE LTD.—See BNP Paribas SA; *Int'l*, pg. 1090
CREATION FINANCIAL SERVICES LTD.—See BNP Paribas SA; *Int'l*, pg. 1090
CREDIT AGRICOLE DU MORBIHAN; *Int'l*, pg. 1834
CREDITEX GROUP, INC.—See Intercontinental Exchange, Inc.; *U.S. Public*, pg. 1143
CREDITRON CANADA, INC.—See Huntington Bancshares Incorporated; *U.S. Public*, pg. 1071
CREDOMATIC OF FLORIDA INC.—See Banco Bradesco S.A.; *Int'l*, pg. 819
CRITERION TEC LIMITED—See Aviva plc; *Int'l*, pg. 746
CSU CARDSYSTEM S.A.; *Int'l*, pg. 1868
CUMMINS-ALLISON ULC—See Crane NXT, Co.; *U.S. Public*, pg. 591
CURRENCY EXCHANGE INTERNATIONAL, CORP.; *U.S. Public*, pg. 611
CYTORI CELL RESEARCH INSTITUTE INC.—See ACA Partners Pte Ltd.; *Int'l*, pg. 74
THE DAISHI CASH BUSINESS CO., LTD.—See Daishi Hokuetsu Financial Group, Inc.; *Int'l*, pg. 1941
DALENYS PAYMENT SAS—See Groupe BPCE; *Int'l*, pg. 3093
DANAL CO., LTD; *Int'l*, pg. 1958
DASH FINANCIAL SERVICES 2, LLC—See Israel A. Englander & Co., LLC; *U.S. Private*, pg. 2147
DAVE INC.; *U.S. Public*, pg. 635
DAVENHAM GROUP PLC; *Int'l*, pg. 1983
DE LA RUE NORTH AMERICA INC.—See De La Rue plc; *Int'l*, pg. 1996
DELTA EURONET GMBH—See Euronet Worldwide, Inc.; *U.S. Public*, pg. 797
DENIZBANK MOSCOW JSC; *Int'l*, pg. 2027
DG FINANCIAL TECHNOLOGY, INC.—See Digital Garage, Inc.; *Int'l*, pg. 2122
DIALCOM24 SP. Z O.O.; *Int'l*, pg. 2104
DIEBOLD NIXDORF OY—See Diebold Nixdorf, Inc.; *U.S. Public*, pg. 661
DINERS CLUB (SINGAPORE) PTE. LTD.—See Ezy Net Pte Ltd.; *Int'l*, pg. 2594
DINERS CLUB SPAIN, S.A.—See Banco Santander, S.A.; *Int'l*, pg. 825
DIRECT CONNECT LLC; *U.S. Private*, pg. 1235
DIXIELINE BUILDERS FUND CONTROL, INC.—See Builders FirstSource, Inc.; *U.S. Public*, pg. 410
DMCARD CARTOES DE CREDITO S.A.; *Int'l*, pg. 2142
DOLEX DOLLAR EXPRESS, INC.—See Palladium Equity Partners, LLC; *U.S. Private*, pg. 3077
DOLEX ENVIOS, S.A. DE C.V.—See Palladium Equity Partners, LLC; *U.S. Private*, pg. 3077
DRESDNER BANK ZAO—See Commerzbank AG; *Int'l*, pg. 1718
DUNSNET, LLC—See Cannae Holdings, Inc.; *U.S. Public*, pg. 429
DUNSNET, LLC—See CC Capital Partners, LLC; *U.S. Private*, pg. 798
DUNSNET, LLC—See Intercontinental Exchange, Inc.; *U.S. Public*, pg. 1142
DUPACO COMMUNITY CREDIT UNION; *U.S. Private*, pg. 1291
DVB TRANSPORT (US) LLC—See DZ BANK AG Deutsche Zentral-Genossenschaftsbank; *Int'l*, pg. 2243
DWIGHT CAPITAL LLC; *U.S. Private*, pg. 1295
DYNASTY TECHNOLOGY GROUP S.A.—See Diebold Nixdorf, Inc.; *U.S. Public*, pg. 660
EARTHPORTFX LIMITED—See Foreign Currency Direct PLC; *Int'l*, pg. 2731
ECOBANK BENIN LIMITED—See Ecobank Transnational Incorporated; *Int'l*, pg. 2293
ECOBANK BURKINA FASO S.A.—See Ecobank Transnational Incorporated; *Int'l*, pg. 2293
ECOBANK BURUNDI S.A.—See Ecobank Transnational Incorporated; *Int'l*, pg. 2293
ECOBANK CAMEROON S.A.—See Ecobank Transnational Incorporated; *Int'l*, pg. 2293
ECOBANK CAPE VERDE LTD.—See Ecobank Transnational Incorporated; *Int'l*, pg. 2293
ECOBANK GABON S.A.—See Ecobank Transnational Incorporated; *Int'l*, pg. 2294
ECOBANK GAMBIA LIMITED—See Ecobank Transnational Incorporated; *Int'l*, pg. 2294
ECOBANK GUINEA BISSAU S.A.—See Ecobank Transnational Incorporated; *Int'l*, pg. 2294
ECOBANK GUINEA LTD.—See Ecobank Transnational Incorporated; *Int'l*, pg. 2294

ECOBANK LIBERIA LIMITED—See Ecobank Transnational Incorporated; *Int'l*, pg. 2294
ECOBANK MICRO FINANCE SIERRA LEONE S.L.—See Ecobank Transnational Incorporated; *Int'l*, pg. 2294
ECOBANK MOZAMBIQUE S.A.—See Ecobank Transnational Incorporated; *Int'l*, pg. 2294
ECOBANK SAO TOME S.A.—See Ecobank Transnational Incorporated; *Int'l*, pg. 2294
ECOBANK SENEGAL LTD.—See Ecobank Transnational Incorporated; *Int'l*, pg. 2294
ECOBANK UGANDA LIMITED—See Ecobank Transnational Incorporated; *Int'l*, pg. 2294
E-COMMERCE EXCHANGE INC.; *U.S. Private*, pg. 1302
E-COMPLISH LLC; *U.S. Private*, pg. 1302
EDARAN TRADE NETWORK SDN. BHD.—See Edran Berhad; *Int'l*, pg. 2315
EDCC BANK LTD.—See Ecobank Transnational Incorporated; *Int'l*, pg. 2293
EFT CANADA INC.; *Int'l*, pg. 2321
EFTPOS NEW ZEALAND LIMITED—See British Columbia Investment Management Corp.; *Int'l*, pg. 1170
EFTPOS NEW ZEALAND LIMITED—See Francisco Partners Management, LP; *U.S. Private*, pg. 1592
EFT SOLUTIONS HOLDINGS LIMITED; *Int'l*, pg. 2321
EGYPTIAN SMART CARDS COMPANY—See Brookfield Corporation; *Int'l*, pg. 1189
ELAVON CANADA COMPANY—See U.S. Bancorp; *U.S. Public*, pg. 2212
ELAVON FINANCIAL SERVICES DAC—See U.S. Bancorp; *U.S. Public*, pg. 2212
ELAVON, INC.—See U.S. Bancorp; *U.S. Public*, pg. 2212
ELAYAWAY, INC.; *U.S. Private*, pg. 1350
ELECTRONIC CASH SYSTEMS, INC.; *U.S. Private*, pg. 1355
ELECTRONIC CLEARING HOUSE, INC.—See Intuit Inc.; *U.S. Public*, pg. 1160
ELECTRONIC FUNDS SOURCE LLC - CHANHASSEN—See WEX, Inc.; *U.S. Public*, pg. 2364
ELECTRONIC FUNDS SOURCE LLC—See WEX, Inc.; *U.S. Public*, pg. 2364
ELECTRONIC PAYMENT PROVIDERS, INC.—See Repay Holdings Corporation; *U.S. Public*, pg. 1784
ELECTRONIC PAYMENTS, INC.; *U.S. Private*, pg. 1355
ELECTRONIC PAYMENT SYSTEMS GLOBAL—See The Celler Organization; *U.S. Private*, pg. 4006
ELECTRONIC PAYMENT SYSTEMS, LLC; *U.S. Private*, pg. 1355
ELECTRONIC TRANSFER, INC.; *U.S. Private*, pg. 1356
EMDEON BUSINESS SERVICES LLC—See McKesson Corporation; *U.S. Public*, pg. 1407
EMONECO, INC.; *U.S. Private*, pg. 1383
ENETT INTERNATIONAL (SINGAPORE) PTE. LTD.—See WEX, Inc.; *U.S. Public*, pg. 2365
ENJAZ PAYMENT SERVICES COMPANY LTD.—See BANK ALBILAD; *Int'l*, pg. 836
ENSO FINANCIAL MANAGEMENT, LLP—See Bendigo Partners, LLC; *U.S. Private*, pg. 524
ENTIERA, INC.—See Fair Isaac Corporation; *U.S. Public*, pg. 820
ENTIERA SOLUTIONS COMPANY LIMITED—See Fair Isaac Corporation; *U.S. Public*, pg. 820
ENVIOS DE VALORES LA NACIONAL CORP.—See International Money Express Inc.; *U.S. Public*, pg. 1154
ENVOY SERVICES LIMITED—See Mastercard Incorporated; *U.S. Public*, pg. 1394
E-ONLINEDATA, LLC—See Global Payments Inc.; *U.S. Public*, pg. 943
E-PAY ASIA PTY. LTD.—See General Atlantic Service Company, L.P.; *U.S. Private*, pg. 1661
E-PAY AUSTRALIA PTY LTD.—See Euronet Worldwide, Inc.; *U.S. Public*, pg. 799
EPAY AUSTRALIA PTY LTD—See Euronet Worldwide, Inc.; *U.S. Public*, pg. 799
E-PAY (M) SDN. BHD.—See General Atlantic Service Company, L.P.; *U.S. Private*, pg. 1661
EPAY NETHERLANDS B.V.—See Euronet Worldwide, Inc.; *U.S. Public*, pg. 799
EQUALS MONEY PLC—See Equals Group Plc; *Int'l*, pg. 2483
EURONET BANKTECHNIKAI SZOLGALTATO KFT.—See Euronet Worldwide, Inc.; *U.S. Public*, pg. 797
EURONET CARD SERVICES, S.A.—See Euronet Worldwide, Inc.; *U.S. Public*, pg. 797
EURONET MIDDLE EAST W.L.L.—See Euronet Worldwide, Inc.; *U.S. Public*, pg. 797
EURONET POLSKA SPOLKA Z O.O.—See Euronet Worldwide, Inc.; *U.S. Public*, pg. 798
EURONET POLSKA SP. Z.O.O.—See Euronet Worldwide, Inc.; *U.S. Public*, pg. 798
EURONET SERVICES D.O.O.—See Euronet Worldwide, Inc.; *U.S. Public*, pg. 798
EURONET SERVICES KFT.—See Euronet Worldwide, Inc.; *U.S. Public*, pg. 798
EURONET SERVICES SAS—See Euronet Worldwide, Inc.; *U.S. Public*, pg. 798
EURONET TELERECARGA, S.L.—See Euronet Worldwide, Inc.; *U.S. Public*, pg. 798

EURONET UKRAINE LLC—See Euronet Worldwide, Inc.; *U.S. Public*, pg. 798
EURONET WORLDWIDE, INC.; *U.S. Public*, pg. 797
EURO PAYMENT GROUP GMBH—See Gauselmann AG; *Int'l*, pg. 2890
EUROPEAN CENTRAL COUNTERPARTY N.V.—See Cboe Global Markets, Inc.; *U.S. Public*, pg. 459
EUROPEAN MERCHANT SERVICES B.V.—See Fiserv, Inc.; *U.S. Public*, pg. 850
EU TAXFREE DEUTSCHLAND GMBH—See Eurazeo SE; *Int'l*, pg. 2528
EVERPIA KOREA JSC—See Everpia Joint Stock Company; *Int'l*, pg. 2568
EVERTEC BRASIL SOLUTIONS INFORMATICA LTDA.—See EVERTEC, Inc.; *U.S. Public*, pg. 802
EVERTEC CHILE SPA—See EVERTEC, Inc.; *U.S. Public*, pg. 802
EVERTEC COLOMBIA, SAS—See EVERTEC, Inc.; *U.S. Public*, pg. 802
EVO MERCHANT SERVICES CANADA CO.—See Global Payments Inc.; *U.S. Public*, pg. 943
EVO PAYMENTS, INC.—See Global Payments Inc.; *U.S. Public*, pg. 943
EVO PAYMENTS INTERNATIONAL GMBH—See EVO Payments International, LLC; *U.S. Private*, pg. 1442
EVO PAYMENTS INTERNATIONAL, LLC - CANADA—See EVO Payments International, LLC; *U.S. Private*, pg. 1442
EVO PAYMENTS INTERNATIONAL, LLC; *U.S. Private*, pg. 1442
EVO PAYMENTS INTERNATIONAL, LLC - USA—See EVO Payments International, LLC; *U.S. Private*, pg. 1442
EVO PAYMENTS INTERNATIONAL SP. Z O.O.—See Global Payments Inc.; *U.S. Public*, pg. 943
EVO PAYMENTS UK LTD.—See Global Payments Inc.; *U.S. Public*, pg. 943
EXETER TRUST COMPANY—See Callodine Acquisition Corporation; *U.S. Public*, pg. 424
EXPORT INSPECTION COUNCIL PRIVATE LIMITED—See Ecobank Transnational Incorporated; *Int'l*, pg. 2294
EZY NET PTE LTD.; *Int'l*, pg. 2594
FACTSET FRANCE S.A.R.L.—See FactSet Research Systems Inc.; *U.S. Public*, pg. 819
FAIR ISAAC ASIA PACIFIC CORP.—See Fair Isaac Corporation; *U.S. Public*, pg. 820
FAIR, ISAAC DO BRASIL LTDA.—See Fair Isaac Corporation; *U.S. Public*, pg. 820
FAIR ISAAC INTERNATIONAL LIMITED—See Fair Isaac Corporation; *U.S. Public*, pg. 820
FAIR ISAAC SERVICES LIMITED—See Fair Isaac Corporation; *U.S. Public*, pg. 820
FAIR ISAAC UK INTERNATIONAL HOLDINGS LTD.—See Fair Isaac Corporation; *U.S. Public*, pg. 820
FAITH DIRECT INC.; *U.S. Private*, pg. 1465
FASTCRED ADMINISTRACAO E SERVICOS LTDA.—See WEX, Inc.; *U.S. Public*, pg. 2364
FEDERATED PAYMENT CANADA CORPORATION—See Global Payments Inc.; *U.S. Public*, pg. 943
FFG CARD CO., LTD.—See Fukuoka Financial Group, Inc.; *Int'l*, pg. 2840
FIDELITY BROKERAGE SERVICES LLC—See FMR LLC; *U.S. Private*, pg. 1555
FIDELITY PROCESSADORA S.A.—See Fidelity National Infor; *U.S. Public*, pg. 833
FINANCIAL INFORMATION TECHNOLOGIES, INC.; *U.S. Private*, pg. 1507
FINANCIERA CONFIANZA S.A.A; *Int'l*, pg. 2665
FINDOMESTIC BANCA S.P.A—See BNP Paribas SA; *Int'l*, pg. 1090
FINVOLUTION GROUP; *Int'l*, pg. 2677
FIRST DATA AUSTRIA GMBH—See Fiserv, Inc.; *U.S. Public*, pg. 850
FIRST DATA COMMERCIAL SERVICES HOLDINGS, INC.—See Fiserv, Inc.; *U.S. Public*, pg. 850
FIRST DATA CORPORATION AUSTRALIA (HOLDINGS) PTY LIMITED—See Fiserv, Inc.; *U.S. Public*, pg. 850
FIRST DATA CORPORATION—See Fiserv, Inc.; *U.S. Public*, pg. 850
FIRST DATA DEUTSCHLAND GMBH—See Fiserv, Inc.; *U.S. Public*, pg. 850
FIRST DATA EUROPE LIMITED—See Fiserv, Inc.; *U.S. Public*, pg. 850
FIRST DATA GOVERNMENT SOLUTIONS, INC.—See Fiserv, Inc.; *U.S. Public*, pg. 850
FIRST DATA MAGYARORSZAG KFT.—See Fiserv, Inc.; *U.S. Public*, pg. 851
FIRST DATA MERCHANT SERVICES CORPORATION—See Fiserv, Inc.; *U.S. Public*, pg. 850
FIRST DATA MERCHANT SERVICES CORPORATION—See Fiserv, Inc.; *U.S. Public*, pg. 850
FIRST DATA MERCHANT SOLUTIONS AUSTRALIA PTY. LTD.—See Fiserv, Inc.; *U.S. Public*, pg. 850
FIRST DATA POLSKA S.A.—See Fiserv, Inc.; *U.S. Public*, pg. 851
FIRST DATA RESOURCES AUSTRALIA LIMITED—See Fiserv, Inc.; *U.S. Public*, pg. 850
FIRST DATA RESOURCES—See Fiserv, Inc.; *U.S. Public*, pg. 851

522320 — FINANCIAL TRANSACTI...

FIRSTECH, INC.—See First Busey Corporation; *U.S. Public,* pg. 840
FIRST GLOBAL DATA LIMITED; *Int'l,* pg. 2684
FIRST SOUTH FINANCIAL CREDIT UNION; *U.S. Private,* pg. 1528
FLEETCOR EUROPE LIMITED—See Corpay, Inc.; *U.S. Public,* pg. 579
FLEX-E-CARD LIMITED—See EML Payments Limited; *Int'l,* pg. 2383
FLOW TRADERS ASIA PTE. LTD.—See Flow Traders NV; *Int'l,* pg. 2709
FLOW TRADERS TECHNOLOGIES SRL—See Flow Traders NV; *Int'l,* pg. 2709
FLOW TRADERS U.S. LLC—See Flow Traders NV; *Int'l,* pg. 2709
FNDS3000 CORP.; *U.S. Public,* pg. 862
FORESIGHT GROUP CI LIMITED—See Foresight VCT Plc; *Int'l,* pg. 2732
FORESIGHT GROUP IBERIA SL—See Foresight VCT Plc; *Int'l,* pg. 2732
FORTIS LUX FINANCIAL, INC.—See Massachusetts Mutual Life Insurance Company; *U.S. Public,* pg. 2605
FORTIS PAYMENT SYSTEMS LLC; *U.S. Private,* pg. 1576
FOURTH POINT WEALTH; *U.S. Private,* pg. 1583
FPT OPERATING COMPANY, LLC—See Alvarez & Marsal, Inc.; *U.S. Private,* pg. 212
FRANX B.V.—See ABN AMRO Group N.V.; *Int'l,* pg. 65
FSMC, INC.—See Madison Dearborn Partners, LLC; *U.S. Private,* pg. 2542
FSV PAYMENT SYSTEMS, INC.—See U.S. Bancorp; *U.S. Public,* pg. 2213
FUJIAN LANDI COMMERCIAL EQUIPMENT CO., LTD.—See Apollo Global Management, Inc.; *U.S. Public,* pg. 151
FUNDSXPRESS FINANCIAL NETWORK, INC.—See Fiserv, Inc.; *U.S. Public,* pg. 851
GAB EZEE ATM LP—See Morgan Stanley; *U.S. Public,* pg. 1474
GALAXIA MONEYTREE CO. LTD.—See Hyosung ITX CO., LTD.; *Int'l,* pg. 3552
GARANTIBANK BBVA INTERNATIONAL N.V.—See Banco Bilbao Vizcaya Argentaria, S.A.; *Int'l,* pg. 818
GARDA CL ATLANTIC, INC.—See BC Partners LLP; *Int'l,* pg. 924
GARDA CL GREAT LAKES, INC.—See BC Partners LLP; *Int'l,* pg. 924
GARDA CL WEST, INC.—See BC Partners LLP; *Int'l,* pg. 924
GCC CONSUMO ESTABLECIMIENTO FINANCIERO DE CREDITO SA—See BNP Paribas SA; *Int'l,* pg. 1091
GEOJIT FINANCIAL DISTRIBUTION PRIVATE LIMITED—See Geojit Financial Services Limited; *Int'l,* pg. 2933
GESCORO INC.—See Euronet Worldwide, Inc.; *U.S. Public,* pg. 798
GFT GLOBAL MARKETS ASIA PTE, LTD.—See StoneX Group Inc.; *U.S. Public,* pg. 1952
GHLSYS PHILIPPINES INC.—See General Atlantic Service Company, L.P.; *U.S. Private,* pg. 1661
GHL SYSTEMS BERHAD—See General Atlantic Service Company, L.P.; *U.S. Private,* pg. 1661
GIBMEDIA S.A.R.L.; *Int'l,* pg. 2963
GLOBAL BIFS ACADEMY PVT. LTD.—See Global Education Limited; *Int'l,* pg. 2995
GLOBAL BLUE S.A.—See Silver Lake Group, LLC; *U.S. Private,* pg. 3657
GLOBAL BLUE (UK) LIMITED—See Silver Lake Group, LLC; *U.S. Private,* pg. 3657
GLOBAL CARD SYSTEM, INC.—See GMO Internet Group, Inc.; *Int'l,* pg. 3014
GLOBAL COLLECT SERVICES USA, INC.—See Apollo Global Management, Inc.; *U.S. Public,* pg. 151
GLOBAL FUTURES & FOREX, LTD.—See StoneX Group Inc.; *U.S. Public,* pg. 1952
GLOBAL PAYMENTS ASIA-PACIFIC LANKA (PRIVATE) LIMITED—See Global Payments Inc.; *U.S. Public,* pg. 943
GLOBAL PAYMENTS ASIA PACIFIC LIMITED—See Global Payments Inc.; *U.S. Public,* pg. 943
GLOBAL PAYMENTS ASIA-PACIFIC PHILIPPINES INCORPORATED—See Global Payments Inc.; *U.S. Public,* pg. 943
GLOBAL PAYMENTS ASIA-PACIFIC (SINGAPORE) PRIVATE LIMITED—See Global Payments Inc.; *U.S. Public,* pg. 943
GLOBAL PAYMENTS CANADA INC.—See Global Payments Inc.; *U.S. Public,* pg. 943
GLOBAL PAYMENTS DIRECT, INC.—See Global Payments Inc.; *U.S. Public,* pg. 944
GLOBAL PAYMENTS EUROPE, S.R.O.—See Global Payments Inc.; *U.S. Public,* pg. 944
GLOBAL PAYMENTS GAMING SERVICES, INC.—See Global Payments Inc.; *U.S. Public,* pg. 944
GLOBAL PAYMENTS INC.; *U.S. Public,* pg. 943
GLOBAL PAYMENTS LIMITED—See Global Payments Inc.; *U.S. Public,* pg. 944
GLOBAL PAYMENT SYSTEMS ASIA-PACIFIC (MALAYSIA) SDN. BHD.—See Global Payments Inc.; *U.S. Public,* pg. 943

GLOBALPAYNET HOLDINGS INC.; *U.S. Private,* pg. 1719
GLOBEOP FINANCIAL SERVICES (INDIA) PRIVATE LIMITED—See SS&C Technologies Holdings, Inc.; *U.S. Public,* pg. 1923
GLOBEOP FINANCIAL SERVICES TECHNOLOGIES (INDIA) PRIVATE LIMITED—See SS&C Technologies Holdings, Inc.; *U.S. Public,* pg. 1924
GMO DATA, INC.—See GMO Internet Group, Inc.; *Int'l,* pg. 3013
GMO FINANCIAL GATE, INC.—See GMO Internet Group, Inc.; *Int'l,* pg. 3013
GMO PAYMENT GATEWAY INC.—See GMO Internet Group, Inc.; *Int'l,* pg. 3014
GOCARDLESS LTD.; *Int'l,* pg. 3018
GOGO ENERGY LIMITED—See GOGOX Holdings Limited; *Int'l,* pg. 3022
GOOD.BEE SERVICE RO SRL—See Erste Group Bank AG; *Int'l,* pg. 2499
GP FINANCE, INC.—See Global Payments Inc.; *U.S. Public,* pg. 943
GRACEKENNEDY MONEY SERVICES (UK) LIMITED—See GraceKennedy Limited; *Int'l,* pg. 3049
GRAVITY PAYMENTS; *U.S. Private,* pg. 1759
GREAT AMERICAN CAPITAL PARTNERS, LLC—See B. Riley Financial, Inc.; *U.S. Public,* pg. 261
GREENHAWK RESOURCES INC.; *Int'l,* pg. 3074
GREENPHIRE, INC.—See Thoma Bravo, L.P.; *U.S. Private,* pg. 4148
GRINDROD BANK LIMITED—See Grindrod Limited; *Int'l,* pg. 3086
GULF COAST BILLING—See CareCloud, Inc.; *U.S. Public,* pg. 435
GUOTAI JUNAN CAPITAL LIMITED—See Guotai Junan Securities Co., Ltd.; *Int'l,* pg. 3187
GUOTAI JUNAN INNOVATION INVESTMENT CO., LTD.—See Guotai Junan Securities Co., Ltd.; *Int'l,* pg. 3187
GUOTAI JUNAN ZHENGYU INVESTMENT CO., LTD.—See Guotai Junan Securities Co., Ltd.; *Int'l,* pg. 3187
H2O COMMUNICATION NEXT CORPORATION—See H2O Retailing Corp.; *Int'l,* pg. 3200
HEARTLAND PAYMENT SYSTEMS, LLC—See Global Payments Inc.; *U.S. Public,* pg. 944
HELABA DUBLIN LANDESBANK HESSEN-THURINGEN INTERNATIONAL—See Helaba Landesbank Hessen-Thuringen; *Int'l,* pg. 3328
HELLO DIGIT, LLC—See Oportun Financial Corporation; *U.S. Public,* pg. 1608
HIGHTECH PAYMENT SYSTEMS S A; *Int'l,* pg. 3388
HIPAY SAS—See GibMedia S.a.r.l.; *Int'l,* pg. 2963
HITACHI DIGITAL PAYMENT SOLUTIONS LIMITED—See Hitachi, Ltd.; *Int'l,* pg. 3416
HITACHI DIGITAL PAYMENT SOLUTIONS PHILIPPINES, INC.—See Hitachi, Ltd.; *Int'l,* pg. 3416
HITACHI PAYMENT SERVICES PRIVATE LIMITED—See Hitachi, Ltd.; *Int'l,* pg. 3420
HOME & CAPITAL ADVISERS LIMITED—See Grainger plc; *Int'l,* pg. 3052
HOME & CAPITAL TRUSTEE COMPANY LIMITED—See Grainger plc; *Int'l,* pg. 3052
THE HOME & CAPITAL TRUST GROUP LIMITED—See Grainger plc; *Int'l,* pg. 3052
HOPETECH SDN. BHD.; *Int'l,* pg. 3473
HORIZON REMIT SDN. BHD.—See The Western Union Company; *U.S. Public,* pg. 2141
HOWDEN RISK MANAGEMENT CONSULTANTS SDN. BHD.—See Howden Group Holdings Limited; *Int'l,* pg. 3494
HSBC (SINGAPORE) LTD.—See HSBC Holdings plc; *Int'l,* pg. 3506
HSH NORDBANK SECURITIES S.A.—See Cerberus Capital Management, L.P.; *U.S. Private,* pg. 838
HSH NORDBANK SECURITIES S.A.—See GoldenTree Asset Management LP; *U.S. Private,* pg. 1734
HSH NORDBANK SECURITIES S.A.—See J.C. Flowers & Co. LLC; *U.S. Private,* pg. 2159
HUATAI PURPLE GOLD INVESTMENT CO., LTD.—See Huatai Securities Co., Ltd.; *Int'l,* pg. 3514
HUIFU PAYMENT LIMITED; *Int'l,* pg. 3526
HUOBI GLOBAL LTD.; *Int'l,* pg. 3537
HYPERCOM CORPORATION—See British Columbia Investment Management Corp.; *Int'l,* pg. 1170
HYPERCOM CORPORATION—See Francisco Partners Management, LP; *U.S. Private,* pg. 1592
HYUNDAI CARD CO., LTD.—See Hyundai Motor Company; *Int'l,* pg. 3559
ICE CLEAR CANADA, INC.—See Intercontinental Exchange, Inc.; *U.S. Public,* pg. 1143
ICE CLEAR CREDIT LLC—See Intercontinental Exchange, Inc.; *U.S. Public,* pg. 1143
ICE CLEAR U.S., INC.—See Intercontinental Exchange, Inc.; *U.S. Public,* pg. 1143
IDEAL CREDIT UNION; *U.S. Public,* pg. 2035
IGORIA TRADE SA; *Int'l,* pg. 3603
IHS MARKIT LTD.—See S&P Global Inc.; *U.S. Public,* pg. 1830
IKB IMMOBILIEN MANAGEMENT GMBH—See Lone Star Global Acquisitions, LLC; *U.S. Private,* pg. 2489

IMC TRADING B.V.—See IMC International Marketmakers Combination B.V.; *Int'l,* pg. 3620
INGENICO BUSINESS SUPPORT SAS—See Apollo Global Management, Inc.; *U.S. Public,* pg. 151
INGENICO CANADA LTD.—See Apollo Global Management, Inc.; *U.S. Public,* pg. 151
INGENICO CZ S.R.O.—See Apollo Global Management, Inc.; *U.S. Public,* pg. 151
INGENICO DO BRASIL LTDA.—See Apollo Global Management, Inc.; *U.S. Public,* pg. 152
INGENICO E-COMMERCE SOLUTIONS BVBA—See Apollo Global Management, Inc.; *U.S. Public,* pg. 152
INGENICO E-COMMERCE SOLUTIONS BV—See Apollo Global Management, Inc.; *U.S. Public,* pg. 152
INGENICO E-COMMERCE SOLUTIONS LTD.—See Apollo Global Management, Inc.; *U.S. Public,* pg. 152
INGENICO E-COMMERCE SOLUTIONS SAS—See Apollo Global Management, Inc.; *U.S. Public,* pg. 152
INGENICO FINANCIAL SOLUTIONS SA—See Apollo Global Management, Inc.; *U.S. Public,* pg. 151
INGENICO FRANCE SAS—See Apollo Global Management, Inc.; *U.S. Public,* pg. 151
INGENICO GROUP S.A.—See Apollo Global Management, Inc.; *U.S. Public,* pg. 151
INGENICO HEALTHCARE GMBH—See Apollo Global Management, Inc.; *U.S. Public,* pg. 152
INGENICO HUNGARY KFT.—See Apollo Global Management, Inc.; *U.S. Public,* pg. 151
INGENICO INTERNATIONAL (PACIFIC) PTY. LTD.—See Apollo Global Management, Inc.; *U.S. Public,* pg. 151
INGENICO INTERNATIONAL (SINGAPORE) PTE. LTD.—See Apollo Global Management, Inc.; *U.S. Public,* pg. 151
INGENICO LLC—See Apollo Global Management, Inc.; *U.S. Public,* pg. 151
INGENICO MEXICO S.A. DE C.V.—See Apollo Global Management, Inc.; *U.S. Public,* pg. 151
INGENICO ODEME SISTEM COZUMLERI A.S.—See Apollo Global Management, Inc.; *U.S. Public,* pg. 152
INGENICO POLSKA SP. Z O.O.—See Apollo Global Management, Inc.; *U.S. Public,* pg. 152
INGENICO SOLUTIONS (MALAYSIA) SDN. BHD.—See Apollo Global Management, Inc.; *U.S. Public,* pg. 152
INGENICO SWITZERLAND SA—See Apollo Global Management, Inc.; *U.S. Public,* pg. 152
INGENICO TERMINALS SAS—See Apollo Global Management, Inc.; *U.S. Public,* pg. 152
INGENICO (THAILAND) CO., LTD.—See Apollo Global Management, Inc.; *U.S. Public,* pg. 151
INGENICO VIETNAM CO., LTD.—See Apollo Global Management, Inc.; *U.S. Public,* pg. 152
INNOVATIVE PAYMENT SOLUTIONS, INC.; *U.S. Public,* pg. 1127
INOVANT, LLC—See Visa, Inc.; *U.S. Public,* pg. 2302
INSTAMED HOLDINGS, INC.—See JPMorgan Chase & Co.; *U.S. Public,* pg. 1207
INTELLIGENT PAYMENTS GROUP LIMITED—See Global Payments Inc.; *U.S. Public,* pg. 943
INTERCEPT CORPORATION; *U.S. Private,* pg. 2109
INTERNATIONAL FACTORS ITALIA SPA—See BNP Paribas SA; *Int'l,* pg. 1091
INTL CUSTODY & CLEARING SOLUTIONS INC.—See StoneX Group Inc.; *U.S. Public,* pg. 1952
INTRIA ITEMS INC.—See Canadian Imperial Bank of Commerce; *Int'l,* pg. 1283
INVOICE2GO, LLC—See BILL HOLDINGS, INC.; *U.S. Public,* pg. 331
IPAY TECHNOLOGIES, LLC—See Jack Henry & Associates, Inc.; *U.S. Public,* pg. 1183
IREMIT EUROPE REMITTANCE CONSULTING AG—See I-Remit, Inc.; *Int'l,* pg. 3564
I-REMIT, INC.; *Int'l,* pg. 3564
ISEND LLC—See ezetop Ltd.; *Int'l,* pg. 2594
ITG HONG KONG LIMITED—See Virtu Financial, Inc.; *U.S. Public,* pg. 2300
IZUMIYA CARD CO., LTD.—See H2O Retailing Corp.; *Int'l,* pg. 3200
JEFFERIES EXECUTION SERVICES, INC.—See Jefferies Financial Group Inc.; *U.S. Public,* pg. 1188
JETPAY CORPORATION—See NCR Voyix Corporation.; *U.S. Public,* pg. 1502
JET PAY, LLC—See NCR Voyix Corporation.; *U.S. Public,* pg. 1502
JIANGXI TAO-TAOGU E-COMMERCE CO., LIMITED—See FinTech Chain Limited; *Int'l,* pg. 2677
JOHN DEERE FINANCIAL LIMITED—See Deere & Company; *U.S. Public,* pg. 646
JOHN DEERE FINANCIAL MEXICO, S.A. DE C.V. SOFOM, E.N.R.—See Deere & Company; *U.S. Public,* pg. 646
J.P. MORGAN CLEARING CORP.—See JPMorgan Chase & Co.; *U.S. Public,* pg. 1208
JPN COLLECTION SERVICE CO., LTD.—See Credit Saison Co., Ltd; *Int'l,* pg. 1836
KEY BS JLT W.L.L.—See Arabi Holding Group Company K.S.C.C.; *Int'l,* pg. 532
KIPLEPAY SDN. BHD.—See Green Packet Berhad; *Int'l,* pg. 3072
KP CREDIT GAIN FINANCE COMPANY LIMITED—See

N.A.I.C.S. INDEX 522320 — FINANCIAL TRANSACTI...

China Financial Services Holdings Limited; *Int'l*, pg. 1503
LADBROKES GROUP FINANCE PLC—See Entain PLC; *Int'l*, pg. 2450
LEAGUESAFE, LLC—See SharpLink Gaming, Inc.; *U.S. Public*, pg. 1874
LEASEDIMENSIONS, INC.—See Genpact Limited; *Int'l*, pg. 2927
LERCARI MOTOR S.R.L.—See Gruppo MutuiOnline S.p.A; *Int'l*, pg. 3141
LETTERLOGIC, LLC—See GTCR LLC; *U.S. Private*, pg. 1806
LEXCEL SOLUTIONS, INC.—See Fidelity National Infor; *U.S. Public*, pg. 833
LOCATION SERVICES, LLC; *U.S. Private*, pg. 2477
LON OPERATIONS LLC—See Bread Financial Holdings Inc.; *U.S. Public*, pg. 381
LOYALTY PARTNER GMBH—See American Express Company; *U.S. Public*, pg. 102
LRS LUFTHANSA REVENUE SERVICES GMBH—See Deutsche Lufthansa AG; *Int'l*, pg. 2069
LUCKY STAR MANAGEMENT LIMITED—See I-Remit, Inc.; *Int'l*, pg. 3564
MACY'S, INC. - FINANCIAL, ADMINISTRATIVE & CREDIT SERVICES GROUP—See Macy's, Inc.; *U.S. Public*, pg. 1353
MARAC FINANCE & LENDING—See Heartland Bank Limited; *Int'l*, pg. 3304
MARKETAXESS CORPORATION—See MarketAxess Holdings Inc.; *U.S. Public*, pg. 1369
MARKETAXESS EUROPE LTD—See MarketAxess Holdings Inc.; *U.S. Public*, pg. 1369
MASTERCARD INTERNATIONAL INCORPORATED—See Mastercard Incorporated; *U.S. Public*, pg. 1394
MASTERCARD PAYMENT GATEWAY SERVICES LTD.—See Mastercard Incorporated; *U.S. Public*, pg. 1394
MB GLOBAL ADVISERS, LLC; *U.S. Private*, pg. 2623
MEDICAL PAYMENT CORP.—See Fuyo General Lease Co., Ltd.; *Int'l*, pg. 2859
MERCHANT EQUIPMENT STORE; *U.S. Private*, pg. 2669
MERCHANT FINANCE PTE LIMITED—See Fijian Holdings Limited; *Int'l*, pg. 2662
MERCHANT INDUSTRY LLC; *U.S. Private*, pg. 2669
MERCHANT PROCESSING SERVICES, INC.; *U.S. Private*, pg. 2669
MERCHANT SERVICES LTD.; *U.S. Private*, pg. 2669
MERCURY PAYMENT SERVICES S.P.A.—See Advent International Corporation; *U.S. Private*, pg. 105
MERCURY PAYMENT SERVICES S.P.A.—See Bain Capital, LP; *U.S. Private*, pg. 442
MERCURY PAYMENT SYSTEMS, LLC—See GTCR LLC; *U.S. Private*, pg. 1806
MERCURY PROCESSING SERVICES INTERNATIONAL LLC—See Advent International Corporation; *U.S. Private*, pg. 105
MERCURY PROCESSING SERVICES INTERNATIONAL LLC—See Bain Capital, LP; *U.S. Private*, pg. 442
MERCURY PROCESSING SERVICES INTERNATIONAL PAYMENT CARD PROCESSING & DEVELOPMENT LTD.—See Advent International Corporation; *U.S. Private*, pg. 105
MERCURY PROCESSING SERVICES INTERNATIONAL PAYMENT CARD PROCESSING & DEVELOPMENT LTD.—See Bain Capital, LP; *U.S. Private*, pg. 442
MERRICK BANK CORPORATION—See CardWorks, Inc.; *U.S. Private*, pg. 751
MERRILL LYNCH PROFESSIONAL CLEARING CORP.—See Bank of America Corporation; *U.S. Public*, pg. 272
MERRILL LYNCH YATIRIM BANK A.S.—See Bank of America Corporation; *U.S. Public*, pg. 272
MICAMP SOLUTIONS, LLC; *U.S. Private*, pg. 2697
MONDELEZ INTERNATIONAL FINANCE AG—See Mondelez International, Inc.; *U.S. Public*, pg. 1463
MONERIS SOLUTIONS CORPORATION—See Bank of Montreal; *Int'l*, pg. 847
MONEYGRAM FOUNDATION, INC.—See Madison Dearborn Partners, LLC; *U.S. Private*, pg. 2541
MONEYGRAM INTERNATIONAL LTD.—See Madison Dearborn Partners, LLC; *U.S. Private*, pg. 2541
MONEYGRAM OVERSEAS (PTY) LIMITED SOUTH AFRICA—See Madison Dearborn Partners, LLC; *U.S. Private*, pg. 2541
MONEYGRAM PAYMENT SYSTEMS BELGIUM N.V.—See Madison Dearborn Partners, LLC; *U.S. Private*, pg. 2541
MONEYGRAM PAYMENT SYSTEMS, INC.—See Madison Dearborn Partners, LLC; *U.S. Private*, pg. 2541
MONEYGRAM PAYMENT SYSTEMS ITALY, S.R.L.—See Madison Dearborn Partners, LLC; *U.S. Private*, pg. 2541
MONEYGRAM PAYMENT SYSTEMS SPAIN, S.A.—See Madison Dearborn Partners, LLC; *U.S. Private*, pg. 2541
MONEYGRAM PAYMENT SYSTEMS WORLDWIDE, INC.—See Madison Dearborn Partners, LLC; *U.S. Private*, pg. 2541
MOR ASSOCIATES, LP—See Raymond James Financial, Inc.; *U.S. Public*, pg. 1764
MORGAN STANLEY BANK INTERNATIONAL LIMITED—See Morgan Stanley; *U.S. Public*, pg. 1472

MSC MONERIS SERVICES CORP.—See Bank of Montreal; *Int'l*, pg. 847
MSCW CO., LTD.—See AKS Corporation Public Company Limited; *Int'l*, pg. 264
MUNICIPAY, LLC—See Stella Point Capital, LP; *U.S. Private*, pg. 3799
MYECHECK, INC.; *U.S. Private*, pg. 2824
MYFIN EAD—See First Investment Bank AD; *Int'l*, pg. 2685
NASSAU FINANCIAL GROUP, LP—See Golden Gate Capital Management II, LLC; *U.S. Private*, pg. 1731
NATIONAL BANKCARD SYSTEMS, INC.; *U.S. Private*, pg. 2848
NATIONAL PROCESSING COMPANY—See GTCR LLC; *U.S. Private*, pg. 1806
NATIONAL SECURITIES CLEARING CORPORATION—See The Depository Trust & Clearing Corporation; *U.S. Private*, pg. 4020
NCR (NIGERIA) PLC—See NCR Voyix Corporation.; *U.S. Public*, pg. 1502
NELITO SYSTEMS PRIVATE LIMITED—See DTS Corporation; *Int'l*, pg. 2217
NES FINANCIAL; *U.S. Private*, pg. 2885
NETS DENMARK A/S—See Advent International Corporation; *U.S. Private*, pg. 105
NETS DENMARK A/S—See Bain Capital, LP; *U.S. Private*, pg. 442
NETS DENMARK A/S—See GIC Pte. Ltd.; *Int'l*, pg. 2965
NETS DENMARK A/S—See Hellman & Friedman LLC; *U.S. Private*, pg. 1910
NETS NORWAY AS—See Advent International Corporation; *U.S. Private*, pg. 105
NETS NORWAY AS—See Bain Capital, LP; *U.S. Private*, pg. 442
NETS NORWAY AS—See GIC Pte. Ltd.; *Int'l*, pg. 2965
NETS NORWAY AS—See Hellman & Friedman LLC; *U.S. Private*, pg. 1910
NETS SWEDEN AB—See Advent International Corporation; *U.S. Private*, pg. 105
NETS SWEDEN AB—See Bain Capital, LP; *U.S. Private*, pg. 442
NETS SWEDEN AB—See GIC Pte. Ltd.; *Int'l*, pg. 2965
NETS SWEDEN AB—See Hellman & Friedman LLC; *U.S. Private*, pg. 1910
NETWORK INTERNATIONAL HOLDINGS PLC—See Brookfield Corporation; *Int'l*, pg. 1189
NETWORK INTERNATIONAL PAYMENT SERVICES PROPRIETARY LIMITED—See Brookfield Corporation; *Int'l*, pg. 1189
NETWORK INTERNATIONAL PAYMENTS SERVICES NIGERIA LIMITED—See Brookfield Corporation; *Int'l*, pg. 1189
NETWORK INTERNATIONAL SERVICES LIMITED—See Brookfield Corporation; *Int'l*, pg. 1189
NETWORK MERCHANTS, LLC—See Francisco Partners Management, LP; *U.S. Private*, pg. 1590
NEW YORK CLEARING HOUSE ASSOCIATION LLC—See Bank Policy Institute; *U.S. Private*, pg. 467
NEXXAR GROUP INC.; *U.S. Private*, pg. 2922
N KOLAY ODEME KURULU U A.S.—See Aktif Yatirim Bankasi A.S.; *Int'l*, pg. 267
NORTH AMERICAN BANCARD, LLC; *U.S. Private*, pg. 2940
NOVENTIS INC.—See WEX, Inc.; *U.S. Public*, pg. 2364
NPC GROUP, INC.—See GTCR LLC; *U.S. Private*, pg. 1806
NVOICEPAY, INC.—See Corpay, Inc.; *U.S. Public*, pg. 580
NWP SERVICES CORPORATION—See Thoma Bravo, L.P.; *U.S. Private*, pg. 4153
NXGEN PAYMENT SERVICES; *U.S. Private*, pg. 2975
NYCE PAYMENTS NETWORK, LLC—See Fidelity National Infor; *U.S. Public*, pg. 833
NZ FACTORING COMPANY LTD.—See Butn Limited; *Int'l*, pg. 1229
OAKBRIDGE ADVISORS, INC.—See Kelso & Company, L.P.; *U.S. Private*, pg. 2280
OBERTHUR CARD SYSTEMS KK—See Advent International Corporation; *U.S. Private*, pg. 102
OCCIDENTAL TOWER CORPORATION—See Occidental Petroleum Corporation; *U.S. Public*, pg. 1561
OKI BERING MIDDLE EAST, FZE—See Sycamore Partners Management, LP; *U.S. Private*, pg. 3896
OMEGA PROCESSING SOLUTIONS, LLC—See Independence Capital Partners, LLC; *U.S. Private*, pg. 2056
OMNICARD, LLC—See P2 Capital Partners, LLC; *U.S. Private*, pg. 3061
OMNICARD, LLC—See Silver Lake Group, LLC; *U.S. Private*, pg. 3656
OMNISURE GROUP, LLC—See Milestone Partners Ltd.; *U.S. Private*, pg. 2729
OPENPAY ARGENTINA, S.A.—See Banco Bilbao Vizcaya Argentaria, S.A.; *Int'l*, pg. 818
OPENPAY PERU, S.A.—See Banco Bilbao Vizcaya Argentaria, S.A.; *Int'l*, pg. 818
OPTAL LIMITED—See WEX, Inc.; *U.S. Public*, pg. 2364
ORIENTAL CITY GROUP (THAILAND) COMPANY LIMITED—See China Smartpay Group Holdings Limited; *Int'l*, pg. 1552
ORIENTAL PAYMENT GROUP HOLDINGS LTD.—See China Smartpay Group Holdings Limited; *Int'l*, pg. 1552

ORIGO SERVICES LIMITED—See Aviva plc; *Int'l*, pg. 746
ORION DIVERSIFIED HOLDINGS CO. INC.; *U.S. Public*, pg. 1617
OUTPUT SERVICES GROUP, INC.—See Aquiline Capital Partners LLC; *U.S. Private*, pg. 304
OV LOOP, INC.; *U.S. Private*, pg. 3052
PACCAR FINANCIAL PTY. LTD.—See PACCAR Inc.; *U.S. Public*, pg. 1631
PAKISTAN OPPORTUNITIES LIMITED—See Aisha Steel Mills Limited; *Int'l*, pg. 251
PAN-AFRICAN SAVINGS & LOANS GHANA LIMITED—See Ecobank Transnational Incorporated; *Int'l*, pg. 2294
PARFIPAR SA—See Belfius Bank SA/NV; *Int'l*, pg. 963
PARK CITIES ASSET MANAGEMENT LLC; *U.S. Private*, pg. 3095
PAVO TEKNIK SERVIS ELEKTRIK ELEKTRONIK SANAYI VE TICARET A.S.—See Aktif Yatirim Bankasi A.S.; *Int'l*, pg. 267
PAYACCSYS SERVICES (PTY) LTD—See Adcorp Holdings Limited; *Int'l*, pg. 127
PAYCORP PAYMENT SOLUTIONS PTY LTD—See General Atlantic Service Company, L.P.; *U.S. Private*, pg. 1661
PAYDEE SDN. BHD.—See Advance Synergy Berhad; *Int'l*, pg. 157
PAYGENT CO., LTD.—See DeNA Co., Ltd.; *Int'l*, pg. 2026
PAYLEASE LLC—See Global Payments Inc.; *U.S. Public*, pg. 944
PAYLINK PAYMENT PLANS, LLC—See Milestone Partners Ltd.; *U.S. Private*, pg. 2729
PAYMENT ALLIANCE INTERNATIONAL, INC.—See Further Global Capital Management, L.P.; *U.S. Private*, pg. 1625
PAYMENTCLOUD INC.—See BharCap Partners, LLC; *U.S. Private*, pg. 549
PAYMENTMAX PROCESSING INC.; *U.S. Private*, pg. 3117
PAYMENTUS CORPORATION; *U.S. Private*, pg. 3117
PAYMETRIC INC.—See GTCR LLC; *U.S. Private*, pg. 1806
PAYONEER, INC.—See Payoneer Global Inc.; *U.S. Public*, pg. 1656
PAYPAL CANADA CO.—See PayPal Holdings, Inc.; *U.S. Public*, pg. 1656
PAYPLUG SAS—See Groupe BPCE; *Int'l*, pg. 3099
PAYPOP CO., LTD.—See Energy Absolute Public Company Limited; *Int'l*, pg. 2422
PAYSIGN, INC.; *U.S. Public*, pg. 1657
PAYSPOT, LLC—See Euronet Worldwide, Inc.; *U.S. Public*, pg. 798
PAYZER, LLC—See WEX, Inc.; *U.S. Public*, pg. 2364
PAYZONE IRELAND LIMITED—See AIB Group plc; *Int'l*, pg. 228
PAYZONE IRELAND LIMITED—See First Data Corporation; *U.S. Private*, pg. 1517
PAYZONE UK LIMITED—See Grovepoint Capital LLP; *Int'l*, pg. 3112
PAZIEN, INC.—See GTCR LLC; *U.S. Private*, pg. 1806
PEPSICO FINANCE (ANTILLES B) N.V.—See PepsiCo, Inc.; *U.S. Public*, pg. 1671
PERSHING LIMITED—See The Bank of New York Mellon Corporation; *U.S. Public*, pg. 2038
PERSHING LLC—See The Bank of New York Mellon Corporation; *U.S. Public*, pg. 2038
PETROS PACE FINANCE, LLC—See Apollo Global Management, Inc.; *U.S. Public*, pg. 147
PINEAPPLE PAYMENTS, LLC—See Global Payments Inc.; *U.S. Public*, pg. 943
PIVOTAL CAPITAL CORP.—See Axis Auto Finance Inc.; *Int'l*, pg. 769
PLAINS COMMERCE BANK; *U.S. Private*, pg. 3195
PLANET PAYMENT AUSTRIA GMBH—See Eurazeo SE; *Int'l*, pg. 2529
PLANET PAYMENT BELGIUM SA—See Eurazeo SE; *Int'l*, pg. 2529
PLANET PAYMENT DENMARK APS—See Eurazeo SE; *Int'l*, pg. 2529
PLANET PAYMENT FINLAND OY—See Eurazeo SE; *Int'l*, pg. 2529
PLANET PAYMENT FRANCE SAS—See Eurazeo SE; *Int'l*, pg. 2529
PLANET PAYMENT GERMANY GMBH—See Eurazeo SE; *Int'l*, pg. 2529
PLANET PAYMENT (GREECE) TAX SERVICES SINGLE PARTNER LIMITED—See Eurazeo SE; *Int'l*, pg. 2529
PLANET PAYMENT ICELAND EHF.—See Eurazeo SE; *Int'l*, pg. 2529
PLANET PAYMENT IRELAND LIMITED—See Eurazeo SE; *Int'l*, pg. 2529
PLANET PAYMENT ITALY S.R.L.—See Eurazeo SE; *Int'l*, pg. 2529
PLANET PAYMENT LUXEMBOURG SARL—See Eurazeo SE; *Int'l*, pg. 2529
PLANET PAYMENT MALTA LIMITED—See Eurazeo SE; *Int'l*, pg. 2529
PLANET PAYMENT NETHERLANDS B.V.—See Eurazeo SE; *Int'l*, pg. 2529
PLANET PAYMENT NORWAY A/S—See Eurazeo SE; *Int'l*, pg. 2529
PLANET PAYMENT POLAND SP. Z O.O.—See Eurazeo SE; *Int'l*, pg. 2529

522320 — FINANCIAL TRANSACTI...

PLANET PAYMENT PORTUGAL UNIPESSOAL LDA.—See Eurazeo SE; *Int'l*, pg. 2529
PLANET PAYMENT SWEDEN AB—See Eurazeo SE; *Int'l*, pg. 2529
PLANET PAYMENT SWITZERLAND GMBH—See Eurazeo SE; *Int'l*, pg. 2529
PLANET PAYMENT UK LIMITED—See Eurazeo SE; *Int'l*, pg. 2529
PLASTYC INC.; *U.S. Private*, pg. 3200
PLATFORM SECURITIES LLP—See Fidelity National Infor; *U.S. Public*, pg. 833
PLAYSPAN, INC.—See Visa, Inc.; *U.S. Public*, pg. 2302
POINT INTERNATIONAL AS—See British Columbia Investment Management Corp.; *Int'l*, pg. 1170
POINT INTERNATIONAL AS—See Francisco Partners Management, LP; *U.S. Private*, pg. 1592
POINT & PAY LLC; *U.S. Private*, pg. 3221
POISTOVNA CARDIF SLOVAKIA AS—See BNP Paribas SA; *Int'l*, pg. 1092
POSTFINANCE AG—See Die Schweizerische Post AG; *Int'l*, pg. 2113
POSTPAY SDN. BHD.—See Advance Synergy Berhad; *Int'l*, pg. 157
POWERPAY; *U.S. Private*, pg. 3239
PRECASH INC.; *U.S. Private*, pg. 3243
PRIMEREVENUE, INC; *U.S. Private*, pg. 3263
PRIORITY ONE FINANCIAL SERVICES LIMITED—See AMP Limited; *Int'l*, pg. 433
PRIORITY PAYMENT SYSTEMS CALIFORNIA—See Priority Payment Systems, LLC; *U.S. Private*, pg. 3267
PRIORITY PAYMENT SYSTEMS, LLC; *U.S. Private*, pg. 3267
PRIORITY PAYMENT SYSTEMS RSM—See Priority Payment Systems, LLC; *U.S. Private*, pg. 3267
PRIORITY PAYMENT SYSTEMS WEST—See Priority Payment Systems, LLC; *U.S. Private*, pg. 3267
PROCESSA, S.A.S—See EVERTEC, Inc.; *U.S. Public*, pg. 802
PROCESS PINK, LLC—See Mullen Automotive, Inc.; *U.S. Public*, pg. 1486
PROVANA LLC; *U.S. Private*, pg. 3291
PSCU FINANCIAL SERVICES, INC.; *U.S. Private*, pg. 3297
PULSE EFT ASSOCIATION—See Discover Financial Services; *U.S. Public*, pg. 668
PULSE MARKETS PTY. LTD.—See BIR Financial Limited; *Int'l*, pg. 1046
PURE COMMERCE KOREA YH—See Euronet Worldwide, Inc.; *U.S. Public*, pg. 798
PURE COMMERCE PTY LIMITED—See Euronet Worldwide, Inc.; *U.S. Public*, pg. 798
PURE COMMERCE (S) PTE. LTD.—See Euronet Worldwide, Inc.; *U.S. Public*, pg. 798
PUSH PAY, INC.—See OV Loop, Inc.; *U.S. Private*, pg. 3052
QC ALLY, LLC; *U.S. Private*, pg. 3312
QUICKPARTS.COM, INC.—See Trilantic Capital Management L.P.; *U.S. Private*, pg. 4231
RABBIT INTERNET CO., LTD.—See BTS Group Holdings Public Company Limited; *Int'l*, pg. 1205
RAPID FINANCIAL SOLUTIONS, LLC—See Tyler Technologies, Inc.; *U.S. Public*, pg. 2209
RATEPAY GMBH—See Advent International Corporation; *U.S. Private*, pg. 105
RATEPAY GMBH—See Bain Capital, LP; *U.S. Private*, pg. 442
RDM CORPORATION—See Deluxe Corporation; *U.S. Public*, pg. 653
REDFIN NETWORK, INC.; *U.S. Private*, pg. 3378
REGAL TECHNOLOGIES LLC—See e-Complish LLC; *U.S. Private*, pg. 1302
REICH & TANG DEPOSIT NETWORKS, LLC—See Reich & Tang, Inc.; *U.S. Private*, pg. 3390
RELIANCE INTEGRATED SOLUTIONS LLC—See Fidelity National Infor; *U.S. Public*, pg. 832
RELIANCE STAR PAYMENT SERVICES INC.; *U.S. Private*, pg. 3394
REMESAS QUISQUEYANA INC.—See Palladium Equity Partners, LLC; *U.S. Private*, pg. 3078
RENAISSANCE ASSOCIATES INC.—See Rev19, LLC; *U.S. Private*, pg. 3413
REPAY HOLDINGS LLC—See Repay Holdings Corporation; *U.S. Public*, pg. 1784
RETRIEVER MEDICAL/DENTAL PAYMENTS, LLC; *U.S. Private*, pg. 3412
REV19, LLC; *U.S. Private*, pg. 3413
REVCO SOLUTIONS, INC.—See Longshore Capital Partners; *U.S. Private*, pg. 2493
REVOLUTION MONEY INC.—See American Express Company; *U.S. Public*, pg. 102
REVOLUTION RETAIL SYSTEMS, LLC—See GLORY Ltd.; *Int'l*, pg. 3010
REVSPRING, INC. - OAKS—See GTCR LLC; *U.S. Private*, pg. 1806
REVSPRING, INC. - PHOENIX—See GTCR LLC; *U.S. Private*, pg. 1806
REV WORLDWIDE, INC.; *U.S. Private*, pg. 3412
REXPORT, INC.—See American Express Company; *U.S. Public*, pg. 102
RIA DE CENTROAMERICA, S.A. DE C.V.—See Euronet Worldwide, Inc.; *U.S. Public*, pg. 798
RIA DEUTSCHLAND GMBH—See Euronet Worldwide, Inc.; *U.S. Public*, pg. 798
RIA ENVIA, INC.—See Euronet Worldwide, Inc.; *U.S. Public*, pg. 798
RIA FINANCIAL SERVICES NORWAY AS—See Euronet Worldwide, Inc.; *U.S. Public*, pg. 798
RIA FINANCIAL SERVICES SWEDEN AB—See Euronet Worldwide, Inc.; *U.S. Public*, pg. 798
RIA PAYMENT INSTITUTION EP, S.A.—See Euronet Worldwide, Inc.; *U.S. Public*, pg. 798
RIA TELECOMMUNICATIONS OF NEW YORK, INC.—See Euronet Worldwide, Inc.; *U.S. Public*, pg. 798
RIVERSIDE PAYMENTS, INC.; *U.S. Private*, pg. 3446
R.J. O'BRIEN LIMITED—See R.J. O'Brien & Associates, LLC; *U.S. Private*, pg. 3337
ROYAL GATE INC.—See Daiwa House Industry Co., Ltd.; *Int'l*, pg. 2198
RUNDLE & CO., LIMITED—See Bain Capital, LP; *U.S. Private*, pg. 435
RUSSELL IMPLEMENTATION SERVICES, INC.—See The Northwestern Mutual Life Insurance Company; *U.S. Private*, pg. 4085
SANTANDER FINANCIAL SERVICES PLC—See Banco Santander, S.A.; *Int'l*, pg. 827
S-BETEILIGUNGSGESELLSCHAFT HESSEN-THURINGEN MBH—See Helaba Landesbank Hessen-Thuringen; *Int'l*, pg. 3328
SECURCASH NEDERLAND B.V.—See Diebold Nixdorf, Inc.; *U.S. Public*, pg. 660
SECURE PAYMENT SOLUTIONS PTY LTD.—See Global Payments Inc.; *U.S. Public*, pg. 944
SECUREPOST AG—See Die Schweizerische Post AG; *Int'l*, pg. 2113
SECUREVISION, W.S GAUCI LTD.—See Hi Sharp Electronics Co., Ltd.; *Int'l*, pg. 3379
SECURITY CARD SERVICES LLC; *U.S. Private*, pg. 3595
SEI INVESTMENTS COMPANY; *U.S. Public*, pg. 1856
SENTENIA B.V.B.A.—See EML Payments Limited; *Int'l*, pg. 2383
SENTENIAL LIMITED—See EML Payments Limited; *Int'l*, pg. 2384
SERVICIOS VISA INTERNATIONAL LIMITADA—See Visa, Inc.; *U.S. Public*, pg. 2301
SERVICIO UNITELLER INC—See Uniteller Financial Services; *U.S. Private*, pg. 4302
SESAME BANKHALL VALUATION SERVICES LIMITED—See Aviva plc; *Int'l*, pg. 746
SEZZLE INC.; *U.S. Public*, pg. 1873
SHANGHAI GUOTAI JUNAN SECURITIES ASSET MANAGEMENT CO., LTD.—See Guotai Junan Securities Co., Ltd.; *Int'l*, pg. 3187
SHF, LLC—See SHF Holdings, Inc.; *U.S. Public*, pg. 1874
SHIFT4 PAYMENTS, LLC—See Shift4 Payments, Inc.; *U.S. Public*, pg. 1874
SIA RIGAS KARTE—See Conduent Incorporated; *U.S. Public*, pg. 566
SIGNAPAY; *U.S. Private*, pg. 3649
SIGNATURE AGENCY, INC.—See The Allstate Corporation; *U.S. Public*, pg. 2034
SILVEREDGE, LLC; *U.S. Private*, pg. 3663
SLG PARTNERS, LP II—See Raymond James Financial, Inc.; *U.S. Public*, pg. 1765
SNIDER ADVISORS; *U.S. Private*, pg. 3700
SOCIETA INTERBANCARIA PER L'AUTOMAZIONE-CEDBORSA S.P.A.—See Cassa Depositi e Prestiti S.p.A.; *Int'l*, pg. 1354
SOLTRX TRANSACTION SERVICES GMBH—See Commerzbank AG; *Int'l*, pg. 1719
SORRENTO CAPITAL, INC.; *U.S. Private*, pg. 3716
SOUTHERN COMMUNITY CAPITAL, LLC—See Trustmark Corporation; *U.S. Public*, pg. 2202
SPARK ATM SYSTEMS PROPRIETARY LIMITED—See NCR Voyix Corporation.; *U.S. Public*, pg. 1502
SPIRE PAYMENTS ESPANA—See KleinPartners Capital Corp.; *U.S. Private*, pg. 2319
SQUARE 1 ASSET MANAGEMENT, INC.—See Banc of California, Inc.; *U.S. Public*, pg. 269
SQUARE CANADA, INC.—See Block, Inc.; *U.S. Public*, pg. 362
SS&C TECHNOLOGIES CANADA CORP.—See SS&C Technologies Holdings, Inc.; *U.S. Public*, pg. 1924
STANDARD & POOR'S (DUBAI) LIMITED—See S&P Global Inc.; *U.S. Public*, pg. 1831
STANDARD & POOR'S MAALOT LTD.—See S&P Global Inc.; *U.S. Public*, pg. 1831
STAR NETWORKS, INC.—See Fiserv, Inc.; *U.S. Public*, pg. 851
STASH FINANCIAL, INC.; *U.S. Private*, pg. 3790
STATE STREET CALIFORNIA, INC.—See State Street Corporation; *U.S. Public*, pg. 1940
STEDDI PAYMENTS AS—See Elmera Group ASA; *Int'l*, pg. 2367
STEEL SPORTS INC.—See Steel Partners Holdings L.P.; *U.S. Public*, pg. 1943
STERLING PAYMENT TECHNOLOGIES, INC.—See EVO Payments International, LLC; *U.S. Private*, pg. 1442

CORPORATE AFFILIATIONS

STONEX COLOMBIA S.A.—See StoneX Group Inc.; *U.S. Public*, pg. 1953
SULLIVAN, BRUYETTE, SPEROS & BLAYNEY, LLC—See Creative Planning, LLC; *U.S. Private*, pg. 1090
SVB GLOBAL FINANCIAL, INC.—See SVB Financial Group; *U.S. Public*, pg. 1968
SWISSBILLING AG—See Cembra Money Bank AG; *Int'l*, pg. 1396
SYNCADA EUROPE BVBA—See U.S. Bancorp; *U.S. Public*, pg. 2212
SYNTER RESOURCE GROUP, LLC; *U.S. Private*, pg. 3905
TANDEM INNOVATIVE PAYMENT SOLUTIONS LLC—See Independence Capital Partners, LLC; *U.S. Private*, pg. 2056
TEB LEASING INC—See BNP Paribas SA; *Int'l*, pg. 1093
TEB YATIRIM MENKUL DEGERLER AS—See BNP Paribas SA; *Int'l*, pg. 1093
TEKKIS SDN. BHD.—See HeiTech Padu Berhad; *Int'l*, pg. 3326
TELECHECK SERVICES CANADA INC.—See Fiserv, Inc.; *U.S. Public*, pg. 851
TELECHECK SERVICES, INC.—See Fiserv, Inc.; *U.S. Public*, pg. 851
TEXAS NICUSA, LLC—See Tyler Technologies, Inc.; *U.S. Public*, pg. 2209
TIPTREE OPERATING COMPANY, LLC—See Tiptree Inc.; *U.S. Public*, pg. 2159
TNS, INC.—See Koch Industries, Inc.; *U.S. Private*, pg. 2333
TORA WALLET SINGLE MEMBER S.A.—See Greek Organisation of Football Prognostics S.A.; *Int'l*, pg. 3069
TOTAL SYSTEM SERVICES, INC.—See Global Payments Inc.; *U.S. Public*, pg. 944
TOT NEW EDGE, LLC—See Mullen Automotive, Inc.; *U.S. Public*, pg. 1486
TOUCH 'N GO SDN. BHD.—See CIMB Group Holdings Berhad; *Int'l*, pg. 1608
TRADE SETTLEMENT, INC.—See Virtus Partners LLC; *U.S. Private*, pg. 4389
TRAIANA, INC.—See CME Group, Inc.; *U.S. Public*, pg. 517
TRANSACT ELEKTRONISCHE ZAHLUNGSSYSTEME GMBH—See Euronet Worldwide, Inc.; *U.S. Public*, pg. 798
TRANSACTION JUNCTION (PROPRIETARY) LIMITED—See Blue Label Telecoms Limited; *Int'l*, pg. 1068
TRANSACTION NETWORK SERVICES, INC.—See Koch Industries, Inc.; *U.S. Private*, pg. 2333
TRANSACTION SOLUTIONS INTERNATIONAL (INDIA) PRIVATE LIMITED—See CX Advisors LLP; *Int'l*, pg. 1891
TRANSACTIS, INC.—See Mastercard Incorporated; *U.S. Public*, pg. 1394
TRANS FAST REMITTANCE, INC.—See Mastercard Incorporated; *U.S. Public*, pg. 1394
TRANSFIRST, LLC—See Global Payments Inc.; *U.S. Public*, pg. 944
TRANSPLATINUM SERVICE, LLC—See WEX, Inc.; *U.S. Public*, pg. 2364
TRANSPORTATION ALLIANCE BANK—See FJ Management, Inc.; *U.S. Private*, pg. 1538
TRAVELEX GLOBAL BUSINESS PAYMENTS, INC.—See The Western Union Company; *U.S. Public*, pg. 2141
TRAXYS AFRICA PTY. LTD.—See The Carlyle Group Inc.; *U.S. Private*, pg. 2056
TREND HEALTH PARTNERS LLC; *U.S. Private*, pg. 4218
TRIONIS SCRL—See Fiserv, Inc.; *U.S. Public*, pg. 851
TRISOURCE SOLUTIONS, LLC—See Repay Holdings Corporation; *U.S. Public*, pg. 1784
TRITON GLOBAL SERVICES INC.—See NeoMedia Technologies, Inc.; *U.S. Public*, pg. 1506
TRM EQUITY LLC; *U.S. Private*, pg. 4241
TRYCERA FINANCIAL, INC.; *U.S. Private*, pg. 4251
TSYS ACQUIRING SOLUTIONS LLC—See Global Payments Inc.; *U.S. Public*, pg. 944
TSYS CARD TECH SERVICES LIMITED—See Global Payments Inc.; *U.S. Public*, pg. 944
TSYS MANAGED SERVICES CANADA, INC.—See Global Payments Inc.; *U.S. Public*, pg. 944
TSYS MANAGED SERVICES EMEA LIMITED—See Global Payments Inc.; *U.S. Public*, pg. 944
TSYS MANAGED SERVICES EMEA (NETHERLANDS) B.V.—See Global Payments Inc.; *U.S. Public*, pg. 944
TSYS MERCHANT SOLUTIONS - ATLANTA—See Global Payments Inc.; *U.S. Public*, pg. 944
TWINSPIRES—See Churchill Downs, Inc.; *U.S. Public*, pg. 494
UNIFIED PAYMENTS, LLC—See Mullen Automotive, Inc.; *U.S. Public*, pg. 1486
UNITED COMMUNITY MORTGAGE SERVICES, INC.—See United Community Banks, Inc.; *U.S. Public*, pg. 2230
UNITED EUROPHIL, S.A.—See Palladium Equity Partners, LLC; *U.S. Private*, pg. 3077
UNITED MERCHANT SERVICES INC.; *U.S. Private*, pg. 4294
UNITED PAYMENT SERVICES, INC.—See Direct Connect LLC; *U.S. Private*, pg. 1235
UNIVERSALPAY, ENTIDAD DE PAGO, S.L.—See Global Payments Inc.; *U.S. Public*, pg. 943

N.A.I.C.S. INDEX

522390 — OTHER ACTIVITIES RE...

UPT ODEME HIZMETLERI A.S.—See Aktif Yatirim Bankasi A.S.; *Int'l*, pg. 267
USAEPAY, INC.—See Francisco Partners Management, LP; *U.S. Private*, pg. 1590
U.S. BANK TRUSTEES LIMITED—See U.S. Bancorp; *U.S. Public*, pg. 2213
USB CAPITAL IX—See U.S. Bancorp; *U.S. Public*, pg. 2213
USIO INC.; *U.S. Public*, pg. 2267
VALITOR HOLDING HF.—See Arion Bank hf.; *Int'l*, pg. 565
VALUEDESIGN, INC.—See Arara, Inc.; *Int'l*, pg. 536
VALUED MERCHANT SERVICES; *U.S. Private*, pg. 4338
VALUE EXCHANGE CORPORATION; *U.S. Private*, pg. 4337
VALUE PAYMENT SYSTEMS, LLC.; *U.S. Private*, pg. 4337
VANTIV, LLC—See GTCR LLC; *U.S. Private*, pg. 1806
VELOCITY MERCHANT SERVICES; *U.S. Private*, pg. 4354
VERIFONE GMBH—See British Columbia Investment Management Corp.; *Int'l*, pg. 1170
VERIFONE GMBH—See Francisco Partners Management, LP; *U.S. Private*, pg. 1592
VERIFONE NORWAY AS—See British Columbia Investment Management Corp.; *Int'l*, pg. 1170
VERIFONE NORWAY AS—See Francisco Partners Management, LP; *U.S. Private*, pg. 1592
VERIFONE SERVICES UK & IRELAND LTD.—See British Columbia Investment Management Corp.; *Int'l*, pg. 1170
VERIFONE SERVICES UK & IRELAND LTD.—See Francisco Partners Management, LP; *U.S. Private*, pg. 1592
VERIFONE SWEDEN AB—See British Columbia Investment Management Corp.; *Int'l*, pg. 1170
VERIFONE SWEDEN AB—See Francisco Partners Management, LP; *U.S. Private*, pg. 1592
VERISEC APAC PTY. LTD.—See Freja eID Group AB; *Int'l*, pg. 2772
VERISEC LATAM S.A. DE C.V.—See Freja eID Group AB; *Int'l*, pg. 2772
VERISEC TECHNOLOGY D.O.O.—See Freja eID Group AB; *Int'l*, pg. 2772
VERSE PAYMENTS LITHUANIA UAB—See Block, Inc.; *U.S. Public*, pg. 362
VIBBEK AG—See Aduno Holding AG; *Int'l*, pg. 154
VIBBEK GMBH—See Aduno Holding AG; *Int'l*, pg. 154
VIPPS AS—See DNB Bank ASA; *Int'l*, pg. 2148
VIRTU AMERICAS LLC—See Virtu Financial, Inc.; *U.S. Public*, pg. 2300
VIRTUS PARTNERS LLC; *U.S. Private*, pg. 4389
VISA AP (AUSTRALIA) PTY LIMITED—See Visa, Inc.; *U.S. Public*, pg. 2301
VISA CANADA CORPORATION—See Visa, Inc.; *U.S. Public*, pg. 2301
VISA CEMEA (UK) LIMITED—See Visa, Inc.; *U.S. Public*, pg. 2301
VISA INTERNATIONAL SERVICE ASSOCIATION—See Visa, Inc.; *U.S. Public*, pg. 2301
VISA WORLDWIDE PTE. LIMITED—See Visa, Inc.; *U.S. Public*, pg. 2302
VITANA-X, INC.; *U.S. Public*, pg. 2306
VR PAYMENT GMBH—See DZ BANK AG Deutsche Zentral-Genossenschaftsbank; *Int'l*, pg. 2245
THE WALT DISNEY COMPANY IBERIA S.L.—See The Walt Disney Company; *U.S. Public*, pg. 2139
WASHINGTON MEDICAL BILLING—See CareCloud, Inc.; *U.S. Public*, pg. 435
WEALTHFRONT CORPORATION; *U.S. Private*, pg. 4462
WEIZMANN FOREX LIMITED—See Ebix Inc.; *U.S. Public*, pg. 710
THE WELFARE DWELLINGS TRUST LIMITED—See Grainger plc; *Int'l*, pg. 3052
WEPAY, INC.—See JPMorgan Chase & Co.; *U.S. Public*, pg. 1206
WESTERN UNION BUSINESS SOLUTIONS (AUSTRALIA) PTY LIMITED—See The Western Union Company; *U.S. Public*, pg. 2141
WESTERN UNION BUSINESS SOLUTIONS JAPAN KK—See The Western Union Company; *U.S. Public*, pg. 2142
WESTERN UNION BUSINESS SOLUTIONS (MALTA) LIMITED—See The Western Union Company; *U.S. Public*, pg. 2141
WESTERN UNION BUSINESS SOLUTIONS (NEW ZEALAND)—See The Western Union Company; *U.S. Public*, pg. 2141
WESTERN UNION BUSINESS SOLUTIONS (SINGAPORE) PTE LIMITED—See The Western Union Company; *U.S. Public*, pg. 2141
WESTERN UNION BUSINESS SOLUTIONS (UK) LIMITED—See The Western Union Company; *U.S. Public*, pg. 2142
WESTERN UNION BUSINESS SOLUTIONS (USA) LLC—See The Western Union Company; *U.S. Public*, pg. 2142
THE WESTERN UNION COMPANY; *U.S. Public*, pg. 2141
WESTERN UNION CONSULTING SERVICES (BEIJING), CO., LTD.—See The Western Union Company; *U.S. Public*, pg. 2142
WESTERN UNION FINANCIAL SERVICES, INC.—See The Western Union Company; *U.S. Public*, pg. 2142
WESTERN UNION GLOBAL NETWORK PTE. LTD.—See The Western Union Company; *U.S. Public*, pg. 2142
WESTERN UNION INTERNATIONAL BANK GMBH—See The Western Union Company; *U.S. Public*, pg. 2142
WESTERN UNION MT EAST LTD.—See The Western Union Company; *U.S. Public*, pg. 2142
WESTERN UNION PROCESSING LITHUANIA, UAB—See The Western Union Company; *U.S. Public*, pg. 2142
WESTERN UNION RETAIL SERVICES BELGIUM—See The Western Union Company; *U.S. Public*, pg. 2142
WEX ASIA PTE—See WEX, Inc.; *U.S. Public*, pg. 2364
WEX EUROPE SERVICES BVBA—See WEX, Inc.; *U.S. Public*, pg. 2365
WEX EUROPE SERVICES SRL—See WEX, Inc.; *U.S. Public*, pg. 2365
WEX NEW ZEALAND—See WEX, Inc.; *U.S. Public*, pg. 2365
WIRECARD CENTRAL EASTERN EUROPE GMBH—See Aurin Investment Group GmbH; *Int'l*, pg. 711
WIRECARD PAYMENT SOLUTIONS MALAYSIA SDN. BHD.—See Finch Capital Partners B.V.; *Int'l*, pg. 2672
WOMPI S.A.S.—See Bancolombia S.A.; *Int'l*, pg. 828
WORKCOMPEDI, INC.; *U.S. Private*, pg. 4563
WORLD FINANCIAL NETWORK CREDIT CARD MASTER TRUST; *U.S. Private*, pg. 4565
WORLDPAY COMPANY, LLC—See GTCR LLC; *U.S. Private*, pg. 1806
WORLDPAY, INC.—See GTCR LLC; *U.S. Private*, pg. 1806
WORLDPAY LTD.—See Advent International Corporation; *U.S. Private*, pg. 108
WORLDPAY LTD.—See Bain Capital, LP; *U.S. Private*, pg. 452
WORLDPAY US, INC.—See Advent International Corporation; *U.S. Private*, pg. 108
WORLDPAY US, INC.—See Bain Capital, LP; *U.S. Private*, pg. 452
WRIGHT EXPRESS AUSTRALIA HOLDINGS - PTY LTD—See WEX, Inc.; *U.S. Public*, pg. 2365
WRIGHT EXPRESS PREPAID CARDS AUSTRALIA PTY LTD—See WEX, Inc.; *U.S. Public*, pg. 2365
WUBS PAYMENTS LTD.—See The Western Union Company; *U.S. Public*, pg. 2141
YAPSTONE INC.—See Liturgical Publications, Inc.; *U.S. Private*, pg. 2472
YOUTRANSACTOR SAS—See Jabil Inc.; *U.S. Public*, pg. 1182
YOUYING (SHANGHAI) INFORMATION TECH. CO., LTD.—See Apex International Financial Engineering Research & Technology Co., Limited; *Int'l*, pg. 511
ZENTITH INFORMATION SYSTEMS, INC.—See Axos Financial, Inc.; *U.S. Public*, pg. 256
ZIPZAP PROCESSING INCORPORATED—See BGH Capital Pty Ltd; *Int'l*, pg. 1008
ZIPZAP PROCESSING INCORPORATED—See Sixth Street Partners LLC; *U.S. Private*, pg. 3678
ZPREPAY INC.—See Zulie Venture Inc.; *U.S. Private*, pg. 4610

522390 — OTHER ACTIVITIES RELATED TO CREDIT INTERMEDIATION

ABANCA CORPORACION BANCARIA, SA; *Int'l*, pg. 48
ACC LOAN MANAGEMENT DAC—See Capita plc; *Int'l*, pg. 1308
ACE FIANZAS MONTERREY, S.A.—See Chubb Limited; *Int'l*, pg. 1590
ACROFAX INC.—See Equifax Inc.; *U.S. Public*, pg. 786
AFFIRMATIVE FINANCE LIMITED; *Int'l*, pg. 188
AGCO FINANCE LLC—See AGCO Corporation; *U.S. Public*, pg. 58
ALPHA CREDIT SA/NV—See BNP Paribas SA; *Int'l*, pg. 1084
ALPHA FX EUROPE LIMITED—See Alpha Group International plc; *Int'l*, pg. 368
ALPINE PAYMENT SYSTEMS; *U.S. Private*, pg. 201
AMAL ASSET MANAGEMENT LIMITED—See Balmain Corp.; *Int'l*, pg. 810
AMAL NEW ZEALAND LIMITED—See Balmain Corp.; *Int'l*, pg. 810
AMERICAN EXPRESS SPOL. S.R.O.—See American Express Company; *U.S. Public*, pg. 101
AMEX ASESORES DE SEGUROS, S.A. (SOCIEDAD UNIPERSONAL)—See American Express Company; *U.S. Public*, pg. 101
APERTURE DEBT SOLUTIONS LLP; *Int'l*, pg. 508
ARVATO FINANCIAL SOLUTIONS LIMITED—See Bertelsmann SE & Co. KGaA; *Int'l*, pg. 996
ASA SAVINGS & LOANS LIMITED—See ASA International Group plc; *Int'l*, pg. 592
ASESORES Y GESTORES FINANCIEROS SA—See Banque Cantonale Vaudoise; *Int'l*, pg. 853
AXACTOR SE; *Int'l*, pg. 761
BARCLAYS FAMILY S.P.A—See Barclays PLC; *Int'l*, pg. 861
BAUSPARKASSE SCHWABISCH HALL AKTIENGESELLSCHAFT - BAUSPARKASSE DER VOLKSBANKEN UND RAIFFEISENBANKEN—See DZ BANK AG Deutsche Zentral-Genossenschaftsbank; *Int'l*, pg. 2243
BCC CORPORATE NV/SA—See American Express Company; *U.S. Public*, pg. 101
BEST CAPITAL ITALY S.R.L.—See BEST S.A.; *Int'l*, pg. 999
BEST ITALIA S.R.L.—See BEST S.A.; *Int'l*, pg. 999
BMW CREDIT (MALAYSIA) SDN BHD—See Bayerische Motoren Werke Aktiengesellschaft; *Int'l*, pg. 911
BTV ANLAGENLEASING 2 GMBH—See Bank fur Tirol und Vorarlberg Ag; *Int'l*, pg. 838
BTV ANLAGENLEASING 3 GMBH—See Bank fur Tirol und Vorarlberg Ag; *Int'l*, pg. 838
BTV MOBILIEN LEASING GMBH—See Bank fur Tirol und Vorarlberg Ag; *Int'l*, pg. 838
BUCKEYE CHECK CASHING INC.; *U.S. Private*, pg. 677
CABOT FINANCIAL GROUP LIMITED—See AnaCap Financial Partners LLP; *Int'l*, pg. 445
CABOT FINANCIAL (IRELAND) LIMITED—See AnaCap Financial Partners LLP; *Int'l*, pg. 445
CALLCREDIT LIMITED—See GTCR LLC; *U.S. Private*, pg. 1804
CANBANK FACTORS LIMITED—See Canara Bank; *Int'l*, pg. 1287
CANBANK FINANCIAL SERVICES LIMITED—See Canara Bank; *Int'l*, pg. 1287
CAPITAL AUTO RECEIVABLES LLC; *U.S. Private*, pg. 738
CAPITAL MARKETS COOPERATIVE, LLC—See Computershare Limited; *Int'l*, pg. 1760
CARDCONNECT LLC—See Fiserv, Inc.; *U.S. Public*, pg. 850
CASHLAND FINANCIAL SERVICES, INC.—See FirstCash Holdings, Inc.; *U.S. Public*, pg. 849
CASH MONEY CHEQUE CASHING, INC.—See CURO Group Holdings Corp.; *U.S. Public*, pg. 611
CATENO GESTAO DE CONTAS DE PAGTO S.A.—See Cielo S.A.; *Int'l*, pg. 1605
CBRE LOAN SERVICES, INC.—See CBRE Group, Inc.; *U.S. Public*, pg. 460
CERTEGY FRANCE—See Fidelity National Infor; *U.S. Public*, pg. 832
CHAPTER TWO HOLDINGS PTY. LTD.—See Credit Intelligence Limited; *Int'l*, pg. 1835
THE CHECK CASHING PLACE, INC.; *U.S. Private*, pg. 4007
CHECK INTO CASH INC.; *U.S. Private*, pg. 869
CHECK INTO CASH OF INDIANA LLC—See Check Into Cash Inc.; *U.S. Private*, pg. 869
CHECK INTO CASH OF KENTUCKY LLC—See Check Into Cash Inc.; *U.S. Private*, pg. 869
CHECK INTO CASH OF WISCONSIN LLC—See Check Into Cash Inc.; *U.S. Private*, pg. 869
CHECK MART OF LOUISIANA, INC.—See Lone Star Global Acquisitions, LLC; *U.S. Private*, pg. 2487
CHECK MART OF NEW MEXICO, INC.—See Lone Star Global Acquisitions, LLC; *U.S. Private*, pg. 2487
CHERRY CREEK MORTGAGE LLC—See McCarthy Group, LLC; *U.S. Private*, pg. 2626
CHINA ASSURANCE FINANCE GROUP LIMITED—See China Assurance Finance Group Limited; *Int'l*, pg. 1483
CHINA ASSURANCE FINANCE GROUP LIMITED—See China Assurance Finance Group Limited; *Int'l*, pg. 1483
CITIZENS BUSINESS BANK - BANKCARD SERVICES—See CVB Financial Corp.; *U.S. Public*, pg. 613
CLAYTON FIXED INCOME SERVICES, INC.—See Radian Group, Inc.; *U.S. Public*, pg. 1759
CLEARONE ADVANTAGE, LLC; *U.S. Private*, pg. 938
CMC FUNDING, INC.—See Computershare Limited; *Int'l*, pg. 1760
COFACE AUSTRIA BANK AG—See Coface S.A.; *Int'l*, pg. 1691
COFACE RECEIVABLES FINANCE LIMITED—See Coface S.A.; *Int'l*, pg. 1691
COFACE SERVICES—See Coface S.A.; *Int'l*, pg. 1691
CONSUMER CREDIT COUNSELING SERVICE OF GREATER ATLANTA, INC.—See Money Management International; *U.S. Private*, pg. 2770
CONTINENTAL CURRENCY SERVICES INC.; *U.S. Private*, pg. 1028
CONTINENTAL EXPRESS MONEY ORDER COMPANY INC.—See Continental Currency Services Inc.; *U.S. Private*, pg. 1028
CO-OP NETWORK—See CU Cooperative Systems, Inc.; *U.S. Private*, pg. 1119
CP2 (UK) LIMITED—See CP2 Group Limited; *Int'l*, pg. 1823
CREDEMFACTOR SPA—See Credito Emiliano S.p.A.; *Int'l*, pg. 1836
CREDEMLEASING S.P.A.—See Credito Emiliano S.p.A.; *Int'l*, pg. 1836
CREDEX CORPORATION—See The Cannabis Depot Holding Corp.; *U.S. Private*, pg. 4004
CREDIT MODERNE ANTILLES GUYANE SA—See BNP Paribas SA; *Int'l*, pg. 1090
CREDIT MODERNE OCEAN INDIEN SA—See BNP Paribas SA; *Int'l*, pg. 1090
CSI ENTERPRISES, INC.—See Edenred S.A.; *U.S. Private*, pg. 2307
CYAN PARTNERS, LP; *U.S. Private*, pg. 1133
CYCLE30, INC.—See Liberty Broadband Corporation; *U.S. Public*, pg. 1310

522390 — OTHER ACTIVITIES RE...

DEALERS' FINANCIAL SERVICES, LLC—See Lone Star Global Acquisitions, LLC; *U.S. Private*, pg. 2487
DFS SERVICES LLC—See Discover Financial Services; *U.S. Public*, pg. 668
DHI MORTGAGE COMPANY GP, INC.—See D.R. Horton, Inc.; *U.S. Public*, pg. 619
DIGITAL CURRENCY SERVICES INC.; *U.S. Private*, pg. 1230
DIGITAL FINANCIAL GROUP; *U.S. Private*, pg. 1230
DOLLAR FINANCIAL CZECH REPUBLIC S.R.O.—See Lone Star Global Acquisitions, LLC; *U.S. Private*, pg. 2487
DOLLAR FINANCIAL U.S., INC.—See Lone Star Global Acquisitions, LLC; *U.S. Private*, pg. 2487
DONGBU CAPITAL CO., LTD.—See Dongbu Group; *Int'l*, pg. 2166
DUN & BRADSTREET CREDIBILITY CORP.—See Cannae Holdings, Inc.; *U.S. Public*, pg. 429
DUN & BRADSTREET CREDIBILITY CORP.—See CC Capital Partners, LLC; *U.S. Private*, pg. 798
DUN & BRADSTREET CREDIBILITY CORP.—See Intercontinental Exchange, Inc.; *U.S. Public*, pg. 1142
DUN & BRADSTREET, INC. - CREDIT SERVICES—See Cannae Holdings, Inc.; *U.S. Public*, pg. 429
DUN & BRADSTREET, INC. - CREDIT SERVICES—See CC Capital Partners, LLC; *U.S. Private*, pg. 798
DUN & BRADSTREET, INC. - CREDIT SERVICES—See Intercontinental Exchange, Inc.; *U.S. Public*, pg. 1142
ECUSTA CREDIT UNION—See Champion Credit Union; *U.S. Private*, pg. 846
EGUARANTEE, INC.; *Int'l*, pg. 2327
ELAINE SECURITIES PLC; *Int'l*, pg. 2342
ELEVATE CREDIT, INC.—See Park Cities Asset Management LLC; *U.S. Private*, pg. 3095
ELITE MERCHANT SOLUTIONS; *U.S. Private*, pg. 1361
ENCORE CAPITAL GROUP, INC.; *U.S. Public*, pg. 759
EQUALS GROUP PLC; *Int'l*, pg. 2483
EQUIFAX WORKFORCE SOLUTIONS—See Equifax Inc.; *U.S. Public*, pg. 786
EXIM EXCHANGE COMPANY (UK) LIMITED—See Export Import Bank of Bangladesh Limited; *Int'l*, pg. 2590
FAIR ISAAC INFORMATION TECHNOLOGY (BEIJING) CO., LTD.—See Fair Isaac Corporation; *U.S. Public*, pg. 820
FAITH, INC.; *Int'l*, pg. 2609
FARM CREDIT EAST; *U.S. Private*, pg. 1474
FEDERAL FARM CREDIT BANKS FUNDING CORPORATION; *U.S. Private*, pg. 1487
FIRST AMERICAN PAYMENT SYSTEMS, L.P.—See Deluxe Corporation; *U.S. Public*, pg. 653
FIRST CHOICE LOAN SERVICES INC.—See Crosscountry Mortgage, LLC; *U.S. Private*, pg. 1106
FITCH GROUP, INC.—See The Hearst Corporation; *U.S. Private*, pg. 4044
FLEETONE FACTORING, LLC—See WEX, Inc.; *U.S. Public*, pg. 2364
FLEETONE, LLC—See WEX, Inc.; *U.S. Public*, pg. 2364
FORD AUTOMOTIVE FINANCE (CHINA) LIMITED—See Ford Motor Company; *U.S. Public*, pg. 865
FORTH SMART CAPITAL CO., LTD.—See Forth Smart Service Public Company Limited; *Int'l*, pg. 2738
FREEMAN MANAGEMENT CORP.—See Founders Equity, Inc.; *U.S. Private*, pg. 1581
FRIENDLY CHECK CASHING CORP.; *U.S. Private*, pg. 1611
FUJI ELECTRIC FINANCE & ACCOUNTING SUPPORT CO., LTD.—See Fuji Electric Co., Ltd.; *Int'l*, pg. 2811
FUNDING CIRCLE DEUTSCHLAND GMBH—See Funding Circle Holdings PLC; *Int'l*, pg. 2845
FUNDING CIRCLE ESPANA S.L.—See Funding Circle Holdings PLC; *Int'l*, pg. 2845
FUNDING CIRCLE NEDERLAND B.V.—See Funding Circle Holdings PLC; *Int'l*, pg. 2845
GIROMEX INC.—See Nexxar Group Inc.; *U.S. Private*, pg. 2922
GOLDEN STATE FARM CREDIT; *U.S. Private*, pg. 1733
HARLEY-DAVIDSON FINANCIAL SERVICES INTERNATIONAL, INC.—See Harley-Davidson, Inc.; *U.S. Public*, pg. 985
HAVERTYS CREDIT SERVICES, INC.—See Haverty Furniture Companies, Inc.; *U.S. Public*, pg. 988
HELSINGIN HUUTOKAUPPAKAMARI OY—See Lone Star Global Acquisitions, LLC; *U.S. Private*, pg. 2487
HIFM LIMITED—See Euronet Worldwide, Inc.; *U.S. Public*, pg. 798
HILTON HONORS WORLDWIDE LLC—See Hilton Worldwide Holdings Inc.; *U.S. Public*, pg. 1040
HITACHI INTERNATIONAL TREASURY (MALAYSIA) SDN. BHD.—See Hitachi, Ltd.; *Int'l*, pg. 3419
HONG LEONG FINANCE LIMITED—See Hong Leong Investment Holdings Pte. Ltd.; *Int'l*, pg. 3469
HTS-LOAN SERVICING, INC.—See Hyatt Hotels Corporation; *U.S. Public*, pg. 1077
HUP HOE CREDIT PTE. LTD.—See Credit Intelligence Limited; *Int'l*, pg. 1835
ICAP MANAGEMENT SERVICES LIMITED—See CME Group, Inc.; *U.S. Public*, pg. 516

IFIS NPL INVESTING S.P.A.—See Banca IFIS S.p.A.; *Int'l*, pg. 815
IFIS NPL SERVICING S.P.A.—See Banca IFIS S.p.A.; *Int'l*, pg. 815
IM MORTGAGE SOLUTIONS, LLC—See Iron Mountain Incorporated; *U.S. Public*, pg. 1172
INVERSIONES EQUIFAX DE CHILE LTDA.—See Equifax Inc.; *U.S. Public*, pg. 786
IREMIT GLOBAL REMITTANCE LIMITED—See I-Remit, Inc.; *Int'l*, pg. 3564
I-REMIT NEW ZEALAND LIMITED—See I-Remit, Inc.; *Int'l*, pg. 3564
JAFARI CREDIT LIMITED—See Centum Investment Company Limited; *Int'l*, pg. 1416
LENDERLIVE NETWORK, LLC—See Computershare Limited; *Int'l*, pg. 1760
LIBERIS—See Lone Star Global Acquisitions, LLC; *U.S. Private*, pg. 2487
LIBERTY CASH-A-CHECK, INC.—See Liberty Bank; *U.S. Private*, pg. 2443
LOAN MART OF OKLAHOMA, INC.—See Lone Star Global Acquisitions, LLC; *U.S. Private*, pg. 2487
MACY'S CREDIT AND CUSTOMER SERVICES, INC.—See Macy's, Inc.; *U.S. Public*, pg. 1353
MARQUETTE COMMERCIAL FINANCE—See UMB Financial Corporation; *U.S. Public*, pg. 2224
MARQUETTE TRANSPORTATION FINANCE, LLC—See UMB Financial Corporation; *U.S. Public*, pg. 2224
MEM CONSUMER FINANCE LIMITED—See Lone Star Global Acquisitions, LLC; *U.S. Private*, pg. 2487
MERCHANTS BANK OF INDIANA—See Merchants Bancorp; *U.S. Public*, pg. 1415
MIDLAND CREDIT MANAGEMENT, INC.—See Encore Capital Group, Inc.; *U.S. Public*, pg. 759
MOBILE MONEY INC.—See Continental Currency Services Inc.; *U.S. Private*, pg. 1028
MONETIVA, INC.; *U.S. Private*, pg. 2769
MONEY MART CANADA INC.—See Lone Star Global Acquisitions, LLC; *U.S. Private*, pg. 2487
MONEY STORE LP; *U.S. Private*, pg. 2770
MONEYTREE, INC.; *U.S. Private*, pg. 2770
MOODY'S AMERICA LATINA LTDA.—See Moody's Corporation; *U.S. Public*, pg. 1468
MOODY'S ANALYTICS, INC.—See Moody's Corporation; *U.S. Public*, pg. 1468
MOODY'S CANADA, INC.—See Moody's Corporation; *U.S. Public*, pg. 1468
MOODY'S DEUTSCHLAND GMBH—See Moody's Corporation; *U.S. Public*, pg. 1468
MOODY'S FRANCE S.A.S.—See Moody's Corporation; *U.S. Public*, pg. 1468
MOODY'S JAPAN KK—See Moody's Corporation; *U.S. Public*, pg. 1469
MOODY'S SINGAPORE PTE. LTD.—See Moody's Corporation; *U.S. Public*, pg. 1468
MORTIMER CLARKE SOLICITORS LIMITED—See Encore Capital Group, Inc.; *U.S. Public*, pg. 760
MSI CREDIT SOLUTIONS; *U.S. Private*, pg. 2807
NATIXIS - RECEIVABLES MANAGEMENT—See Groupe BPCE; *Int'l*, pg. 3096
OBERTHUR CASH PROTECTION UK LIMITED—See Advent International Corporation; *U.S. Private*, pg. 102
OKINAWA CREDIT SERVICE CO., LTD.—See Bank of The Ryukyus, Ltd.; *Int'l*, pg. 849
OK MONEY POLAND SP. Z.O.O.—See Lone Star Global Acquisitions, LLC; *U.S. Private*, pg. 2487
PAYABILITY, LLC; *U.S. Private*, pg. 3116
PAY-O-MATIC CHECK CASHING CORP.—See Founders Equity, Inc.; *U.S. Private*, pg. 1581
THE PAY-O-MATIC CORP.—See Founders Equity, Inc.; *U.S. Private*, pg. 1581
THE PAY-O-MATIC CORP.—See Founders Equity, Inc.; *U.S. Private*, pg. 1581
PAYSCAPE ADVISORS; *U.S. Private*, pg. 3117
PRA GROUP CANADA INC.—See PRA Group, Inc.; *U.S. Public*, pg. 1712
PRA GROUP DEUTSCHLAND GMBH—See PRA Group, Inc.; *U.S. Public*, pg. 1712
PRA GROUP EUROPE AS—See PRA Group, Inc.; *U.S. Public*, pg. 1712
PRA GROUP OSTERREICH INKASSO GMBH—See PRA Group, Inc.; *U.S. Public*, pg. 1712
PRESIDENTIAL MORTGAGE CORP—See Presidential Bank, FSB; *U.S. Private*, pg. 3254
PROPAY INC.—See Global Payments Inc.; *U.S. Public*, pg. 944
PT. HITACHI TERMINAL SOLUTIONS INDONESIA—See Hitachi, Ltd.; *Int'l*, pg. 3424
Q.C.& G. FINANCIAL, INC.—See JLL Partners, LLC; *U.S. Private*, pg. 2212
QUANTUM SERVICING CORPORATION—See Covius Holdings, Inc.; *U.S. Private*, pg. 1073
RESCUE ONE FINANCIAL; *U.S. Private*, pg. 3403
REVALEA S.P.A.—See Banca IFIS S.p.A.; *Int'l*, pg. 815
ROBERT BIGGAR (ESTD. 1830) LIMITED—See Lone Star Global Acquisitions, LLC; *U.S. Private*, pg. 2487
ROCKLOANS MARKETPLACE LLC—See Rocket Companies, Inc.; *U.S. Public*, pg. 1804

SELECT PORTFOLIO SERVICING, INC.; *U.S. Private*, pg. 3600
SERFACTORING S.P.A.—See Eni S.p.A.; *Int'l*, pg. 2438
SERVICIOS INTEGRALES DE INFORMACION S.A.—See Equifax Inc.; *U.S. Public*, pg. 787
SIGNATURE HOME MORTGAGE, LLC—See Wells Fargo & Company; *U.S. Public*, pg. 2345
STERLING FACTORS CORPORATION—See Sterling Bancorp; *U.S. Public*, pg. 1946
STERLING RESOURCE FUNDING CORP.—See Sterling Bancorp; *U.S. Public*, pg. 1946
SUMMIT MORTGAGE, INC.—See Northwest Bancshares, Inc.; *U.S. Public*, pg. 1541
TOTTA & ACORES INC.—See Banco Santander, S.A.; *Int'l*, pg. 828
TRI POINTE CONNECT, L.L.C.—See Tri Pointe Homes, Inc.; *U.S. Public*, pg. 2188
TYR EQUITY, INC.; *U.S. Private*, pg. 4269
VERSAPAY CORPORATION—See Great Hill Partners, L.P.; *U.S. Private*, pg. 1763
VILLAGE BANK MORTGAGE CORPORATION—See Village Bank & Trust Financial Corp.; *U.S. Public*, pg. 2297
VNB NEW YORK, LLC—See Valley National Bancorp; *U.S. Public*, pg. 2273
WELLS FARGO PREFERRED CAPITAL, INC.—See Wells Fargo & Company; *U.S. Public*, pg. 2347
WESCOT TOPCO LIMITED—See Encore Capital Group, Inc.; *U.S. Public*, pg. 760
WEST SUBURBAN CURRENCY EXCHANGES; *U.S. Private*, pg. 4487
WORLDWIDE EXCHANGE PTY. LTD.—See I-Remit, Inc.; *Int'l*, pg. 3564
WSFX GLOBAL PAY LIMITED—See DiGiSPICE Technologies Ltd.; *Int'l*, pg. 2120
XCEL FINANCIAL LLC; *U.S. Private*, pg. 4580
ZOHARI CREDIT LIMITED—See Centum Investment Company Limited; *Int'l*, pg. 1416

523150 — INVESTMENT BANKING AND SECURITIES INTERMEDIATION

360T ASIA PACIFIC PTE. LTD.—See Deutsche Borse AG; *Int'l*, pg. 2063
360 TRADING NETWORKS INC—See Deutsche Borse AG; *Int'l*, pg. 2063
360 TRADING NETWORKS LLC—See Deutsche Borse AG; *Int'l*, pg. 2063
360 TREASURY SYSTEMS AG—See Deutsche Borse AG; *Int'l*, pg. 2063
4IP MANAGEMENT AG; *Int'l*, pg. 12
AAGAM CAPITAL LIMITED; *Int'l*, pg. 31
AAREAL BANK CAPITAL FUNDING TRUST—See Advent International Corporation; *U.S. Private*, pg. 96
AAREAL BANK CAPITAL FUNDING TRUST—See Centerbridge Partners, L.P.; *U.S. Private*, pg. 812
AAREON DEUTSCHLAND GMBH—See Advent International Corporation; *U.S. Private*, pg. 96
AAREON DEUTSCHLAND GMBH—See Centerbridge Partners, L.P.; *U.S. Private*, pg. 812
ABANS ENTERPRISES LIMITED; *Int'l*, pg. 48
ABC ISLAMIC BANK EC—See Arab Banking Corporation B.S.C.; *Int'l*, pg. 529
ABERDEEN STANDARD INVESTMENTS INC.—See abrdn PLC; *Int'l*, pg. 68
ABG SUNDAL COLLIER AB—See ABG Sundal Collier Holding ASA; *Int'l*, pg. 60
ABG SUNDAL COLLIER FORVALTNING AS—See ABG Sundal Collier Holding ASA; *Int'l*, pg. 60
ABG SUNDAL COLLIER HOLDING ASA; *Int'l*, pg. 60
ABG SUNDAL COLLIER INC.—See ABG Sundal Collier Holding ASA; *Int'l*, pg. 60
ABG SUNDAL COLLIER LTD.—See ABG Sundal Collier Holding ASA; *Int'l*, pg. 60
ABG SUNDAL COLLIER NORGE ASA—See ABG Sundal Collier Holding ASA; *Int'l*, pg. 60
ABN AMRO CLEARING HONG KONG LTD.—See ABN AMRO Group N.V.; *Int'l*, pg. 64
ABN AMRO CLEARING SINGAPORE PTE LTD—See ABN AMRO Group N.V.; *Int'l*, pg. 64
ABN AMRO CLEARING SYDNEY PTY—See ABN AMRO Group N.V.; *Int'l*, pg. 64
ABN AMRO CLEARING TOKYO LTD—See ABN AMRO Group N.V.; *Int'l*, pg. 64
ABN AMRO COMMERCIAL FINANCE GMBH—See ABN AMRO Group N.V.; *Int'l*, pg. 64
ABN AMRO COMMERCIAL FINANCE S.A.—See ABN AMRO Group N.V.; *Int'l*, pg. 64
ABN AMRO COMMERCIAL FINANCE (UK) LTD—See ABN AMRO Group N.V.; *Int'l*, pg. 64
ABN AMRO (GUERNSEY) LIMITED—See ABN AMRO Group N.V.; *Int'l*, pg. 64
ABN AMRO MEESPIERSON—See ABN AMRO Group N.V.; *Int'l*, pg. 64
AB SECURITIES LIMITED—See AB Bank Limited; *Int'l*, pg. 39
ABSOLUT CAPITAL MANAGEMENT HOLDING LTD; *Int'l*, pg. 70

523150 — INVESTMENT BANKING ...

ACACIA CAPITAL PARTNERS LIMITED; *Int'l*, pg. 74
ACCIONES Y VALORES BANAMEX, S.A. DE C.V.—See Citigroup Inc.; *U.S. Public*, pg. 504
ACE LEASING BV—See BNP Paribas SA; *Int'l*, pg. 1079
ACORNS SECURITIES, LLC—See Acorns Grow Incorporated; *U.S. Private*, pg. 64
ACTINVER S.A. DE C.V.; *Int'l*, pg. 118
ADENZA SINGAPORE PTE. LTD.—See Nasdaq, Inc.; *U.S. Public*; pg. 1491
ADEX SECURITIES, INC.; *Int'l*, pg. 145
ADJUTORIS CONSEIL S.A.—See Edmond de Rothschild Holding S.A.; *Int'l*, pg. 2312
THE ADVEST GROUP, INC.—See Equitable Holdings, Inc.; *U.S. Public*, pg. 790
AEC SECURITIES PUBLIC COMPANY LIMITED; *Int'l*, pg. 171
AEGON COMPANIES OF FLORIDA—See Aegon N.V.; *Int'l*, pg. 174
AFCO ACCEPTANCE CORPORATION—See Truist Financial Corporation; *U.S. Public*, pg. 2201
AFFIN HOLDINGS BERHAD; *Int'l*, pg. 186
AFFIN HWANG FUTURES SDN. BHD.—See AFFIN Holdings Berhad; *Int'l*, pg. 186
AFFIN HWANG INVESTMENT BANK BERHAD—See AFFIN Holdings Berhad; *Int'l*, pg. 186
AFORGE DEGROOF FINANCE SA—See Banque Degroof S.A.; *Int'l*, pg. 853
AFRICAN BANKING CORPORATION BOTSWANA LIMITED—See Atlas Mara Limited; *Int'l*, pg. 686
AFRICAN BANKING CORPORATION MOZAMBIQUE LIMITED—See Atlas Mara Limited; *Int'l*, pg. 686
AFRICAN BANKING CORPORATION TANZANIA LIMITED—See Atlas Mara Limited; *Int'l*, pg. 686
A&G BANCA PRIVADA S.A.U.—See EFG International AG; *Int'l*, pg. 2319
AGF SECURITIES (CANADA) LTD.—See AGF Management Limited; *Int'l*, pg. 206
AGNC INVESTMENT CORP.; *U.S. Public*, pg. 62
AGORA CORRETORA DE TITULOS E VALORES MOBILIARIOS S.A.—See Banco Bradesco S.A.; *Int'l*, pg. 819
AGRIBANK SECURITIES JOINT STOCK CORPORATION; *Int'l*, pg. 216
AGRO FINANCE REIT; *Int'l*, pg. 218
AGW CAPITAL ADVISORS; *U.S. Private*, pg. 130
AIG INTERNATIONAL INC.—See American International Group, Inc.; *U.S. Public*, pg. 104
AIMS FINANCIAL GROUP; *Int'l*, pg. 234
AJ BELL SECURITIES LIMITED—See AJ Bell Plc.; *Int'l*, pg. 255
AKBANK INTERNATIONAL N.V.—See Akbank T.A.S.; *Int'l*, pg. 261
AKD SECURITIES LIMITED—See AKD Capital Limited; *Int'l*, pg. 261
AK SECURITIES—See Akbank T.A.S.; *Int'l*, pg. 261
AKTIA WEALTH MANAGEMENT LTD.—See Aktia Bank PLC; *Int'l*, pg. 265
ALACRITY SECURITIES LIMITED; *Int'l*, pg. 289
AL-AMAL FINANCIAL INVESTMENT COMPANY; *Int'l*, pg. 284
ALHAMRANI UNIVERSAL COMPANY LTD—See Alhamrani Group; *Int'l*, pg. 319
ALIGHT FINANCIAL SOLUTIONS, LLC—See Alight, Inc.; *U.S. Public*, pg. 76
ALLEN C. EWING & CO.; *U.S. Private*, pg. 178
ALLEN & COMPANY INCORPORATED—See Allen Holding Inc.; *U.S. Private*, pg. 179
ALLEN & COMPANY OF FLORIDA, INC.—See LPL Financial Holdings Inc.; *U.S. Public*, pg. 1343
ALLFUNDS BANK, S.A.—See GIC Pte. Ltd.; *Int'l*, pg. 2964
ALLFUNDS BANK, S.A.—See Hellman & Friedman LLC; *U.S. Private*, pg. 1907
ALLIANCE BANK MALAYSIA BHD—See Alliance Financial Group Berhad; *Int'l*, pg. 338
ALLIANCE ENTREPRENDRE SAS—See Groupe BPCE; *Int'l*, pg. 3092
ALLIANCE INVESTMENT BANK BHD—See Alliance Financial Group Berhad; *Int'l*, pg. 339
ALLIANZ COMPAGNIA ITALIANA FINANZIAMENTI S.P.A.—See Allianz SE; *Int'l*, pg. 344
ALLIANZ GLOBAL INVESTORS DISTRIBUTORS LLC—See Allianz SE; *Int'l*, pg. 346
ALLIED BUSINESS GROUP, INC.—See Mariner Wealth Advisors, LLC; *U.S. Private*, pg. 2575
ALLIED PROPERTIES REAL ESTATE INVESTMENT TRUST; *Int'l*, pg. 358
AL MADAR INVESTMENT CO K.S.C.P; *Int'l*, pg. 281
AL-MAL SECURITIES & SERVICES LIMITED; *Int'l*, pg. 286
ALMONDZ CAPITAL MARKETS PVT. LTD.—See Almondz Global Scourities Limited; *Int'l*, pg. 364
ALMONDZ GLOBAL SECURITIES LIMITED; *Int'l*, pg 364
ALPHA RHEINTAL BANK AG; *Int'l*, pg. 369
ALPINE ASSOCIATES, L.P.; *U.S. Private*, pg. 200
ALPINVEST PARTNERS INC.—See The Carlyle Group Inc.; *U.S. Public*, pg. 2054
ALPIQ SWISSTRADE LTD.—See Alpiq Holding AG; *Int'l*, pg. 373
AL RAJHI CAPITAL COMPANY—See Al Rajhi Bank; *Int'l*, pg. 282

AL RAMZ CAPITAL LLC; *Int'l*, pg. 282
AL-SAFAT INVESTMENT COMPANY K.S.C.C.; *Int'l*, pg. 288
AL-SANABEL INTERNATIONAL FOR ISLAMIC INVESTMENT (HOLDING) PLC; *Int'l*, pg. 288
ALTA SKUPINA D.D.; *Int'l*, pg. 384
AMERGERIS WEALTH MANAGEMENT AG—See Amergeris Wealth Management Group GmbH; *Int'l*, pg. 420
AMERICAN CHEMICALS, LLC—See Morgan Stanley; *U.S. Public*, pg. 1471
AMERICAN REPUBLIC INVESTMENT CO.—See AMREP Corporation; *U.S. Public*, pg. 133
AMERICAN SKANDIA MARKETING, INCORPORATED—See Prudential Financial, Inc.; *U.S. Public*, pg. 1732
AMERITAS INVESTMENT CORP.—See Ameritas Mutual Holding Company; *U.S. Private*, pg. 261
AMHEARST GLEN, INC.; *U.S. Private*, pg. 262
AMHERST SECURITIES GROUP LP; *U.S. Private*, pg. 263
AMRAPALI CAPITAL AND FINANCE SERVICES LIMITED; *Int'l*, pg. 437
AMRAPALI INDUSTRIES LIMITED; *Int'l*, pg. 437
ANAND RATHI WEALTH LIMITED; *Int'l*, pg. 446
ANB INVEST—See Arab National Bank; *Int'l*, pg. 531
ANGEL ONE LIMITED; *Int'l*, pg. 459
ANGO WORLD HOLDINGS, INC.; *U.S. Public*, pg. 137
ANKUSH FINSTOCK LIMITED; *Int'l*, pg. 473
ANNALY CAPITAL MANAGEMENT, INC.; *U.S. Public*, pg. 137
AN TEXTILE MILLS LIMITED; *Int'l*, pg. 443
ANTHEM SECURITIES, INC—See Atlas Energy Group, LLC; *U.S. Public*, pg. 223
ANZ SECURITIES LIMITED—See Australia & New Zealand Banking Group Limited; *Int'l*, pg. 720
AOZORA SECURITIES CO., LTD.—See Cerberus Capital Management, L.P.; *U.S. Private*, pg. 836
APEX CAPITAL & FINANCE LIMITED; *Int'l*, pg. 509
APG SECURITIES JOINT STOCK COMPANY; *Int'l*, pg. 512
AQUA SECURITIES, L.P.—See BGC Group, Inc.; *U.S. Public*, pg. 328
ARAB BANKING CORPORATION ALGERIA SPA—See Arab Banking Corporation B.S.C.; *Int'l*, pg. 529
ARAB BANKING CORPORATION - EGYPT S.A.E.—See Arab Banking Corporation B.S.C.; *Int'l*, pg. 529
ARAB BANKING CORPORATION (JORDAN)—See Arab Banking Corporation B.S.C.; *Int'l*, pg. 529
ARAB BANKING CORPORATION TUNISIA, S.A.—See Arab Banking Corporation B.S.C.; *Int'l*, pg. 529
ARBOR INVESTMENT GROUP; *U.S. Private*, pg. 308
ARCAPITA BANK B.S.C. (C)—See Arcapita Group Holdings Limited; *Int'l*, pg. 542
ARCHELON LLC; *U.S. Private*, pg. 310
ARCHON GROUP EUROPE GMBH—See The Goldman Sachs Group, Inc.; *U.S. Public*, pg. 2076
ARGO GROUP LIMITED; *Int'l*, pg. 562
ARGO UNDERWRITING AGENCY, LTD.—See Brookfield Reinsurance Ltd.; *Int'l*, pg. 1194
ARIHANT CAPITAL (IFSC) LIMITED—See Arihant Capital Markets Ltd.; *Int'l*, pg. 564
ARIX BIOSCIENCE PLC; *Int'l*, pg. 567
ARLINGTON ASSET INVESTMENT CORP.—See Ellington Management Group, L.L.C.; *U.S. Private*, pg. 1364
ARS WEALTH ADVISORS, LLC; *U.S. Private*, pg. 337
ARTISAN PARTNERS ASSET MANAGEMENT INC.; *U.S. Public*, pg. 208
ARUNIS ABODE LTD.; *Int'l*, pg. 586
ARVIN INTERNATIONAL HOLLAND B.V.—See Cummins Inc.; *U.S. Public*, pg. 608
ARYAMAN CAPITAL MARKETS LTD—See ARYAMAN FINANCIAL SERVICES LTD; *Int'l*, pg. 588
ARYAMAN FINANCIAL SERVICES LTD; *Int'l*, pg. 588
ASGARD FINANCIAL SERVICES LTD—See Arnotts Ltd.; *Int'l*, pg. 577
ASHIKA CAPITAL LIMITED; *Int'l*, pg. 607
ASHIRWAD CAPITAL LIMITED; *Int'l*, pg. 607
ASHUR INTERNATIONAL BANK FOR INVESTMENT; *Int'l*, pg. 609
ASIA CAPITAL PLC; *Int'l*, pg. 610
ASIA CAPITAL PUBLIC COMPANY LIMITED; *Int'l*, pg. 610
ASIA-PACIFIC SECURITIES JOINT STOCK COMPANY; *Int'l*, pg. 616
ASIA PLUS GROUP HOLDINGS PUBLIC COMPANY LIMITED; *Int'l*, pg. 614
ASR VERMOGENSBEHEER N.V.—See ASR Nederland N.V.; *Int'l*, pg. 632
ASSAM ENTRADE LIMITED; *Int'l*, pg. 641
ASSET ALLIANCE ADVISORS INC—See Asset Alliance Corporation; *U.S. Private*, pg. 354
ASSET ALLIANCE CORPORATION; *U.S. Private*, pg. 353
ASSET ALLIANCE HOLDING GROUP—See Asset Alliance Corporation; *U.S. Private*, pg. 354
ASSOCIATED INVESTMENT SERVICES, INC.—See Associated Banc-Corp; *U.S. Public*, pg. 214
ASSOCIATED TRUST COMPANY, NA—See Associated Banc-Corp; *U.S. Public*, pg. 214
ASTAIRE GROUP PLC; *Int'l*, pg. 651
ASTANA INVESTMENT HOUSE JSC—See Central-Asian Power Energy Company JSC; *Int'l*, pg. 1410
ASTERON ADVISORY SERVICES LIMITED—See Dai-ichi Life Holdings, Inc.; *Int'l*, pg. 1918
ASTRAZENECA CORPORATE IS—See AstraZeneca PLC; *Int'l*, pg. 659
ASTRUM CAPITAL MANAGEMENT LIMITED—See Astrum Financial Holdings Limited; *Int'l*, pg. 662
ASTRUM FINANCIAL HOLDINGS LIMITED; *Int'l*, pg. 662
ATB CAPITAL MARKETS INC.—See Alberta Treasury Branches; *Int'l*, pg. 298
ATEL SECURITIES CORPORATION—See ATEL Capital Group; *U.S. Private*, pg. 366
ATLAS FUTURES FUND, LIMITED PARTNERSHIP; *U.S. Private*, pg. 376
ATN INTERNATIONAL LIMITED; *Int'l*, pg. 687
ATREYU CAPITAL MARKETS LTD.; *Int'l*, pg. 693
ATTICABANK PROPERTIES S.A—See ATTICA BANK S.A.; *Int'l*, pg. 696
ATTRAX S.A.—See DZ BANK AG Deutsche Zentral-Genossenschaftsbank; *Int'l*, pg. 2245
AUDI CAPITAL (KSA) CJSC—See Bank Audi sal; *Int'l*, pg. 837
AUDI CAPITAL (SYRIA) LLC—See Bank Audi sal; *Int'l*, pg. 837
AUDI SARADAR INVESTMENT BANK SAL—See Bank Audi sal; *Int'l*, pg. 837
AURORA LOAN SERVICES LLC—See Lehman Brothers Holdings Inc. Plan Trust; *U.S. Private*, pg. 2419
AUSBIL INVESTMENT MANAGEMENT—See Dexia SA; *Int'l*, pg. 2092
AUSTBROKERS PROFESSIONAL SERVICES PTY. LTD.—See AUB Group Limited; *Int'l*, pg. 698
AUSTBROKERS SYDNEY PTY. LTD.—See AUB Group Limited; *Int'l*, pg. 698
AU VIET SECURITIES CORPORATION; *Int'l*, pg. 697
AUXLY CANNABIS GROUP INC.; *Int'l*, pg. 733
THE AVEON GROUP L.P.; *U.S. Public*, pg. 3990
AVM ASSOCIATES LLC; *U.S. Private*, pg. 409
AVONDALE PARTNERS, LLC; *U.S. Private*, pg. 410
AVONDALE SECURITIES S.A.—See Bank of Ireland Group plc; *Int'l*, pg. 844
AXA ADVISORS, LLC—See Equitable Holdings, Inc.; *U.S. Public*, pg. 788
AXIS ASSET MANAGEMENT COMPANY LTD.—See Axis Bank Limited; *Int'l*, pg. 769
AXIS BANK UK LTD.—See Axis Bank Limited; *Int'l*, pg. 769
AXIS MUTUAL FUND TRUSTEE LTD.—See Axis Bank Limited; *Int'l*, pg. 769
AXIS SECURITIES LTD.—See Axis Bank Limited; *Int'l*, pg. 769
AXON SECURITIES S.A.—See AXON Holdings S.A.; *Int'l*, pg. 770
BAHRAIN MIDDLE EAST BANK BSC; *Int'l*, pg. 800
BAIN & COMPANY (HONG KONG)—See Bain & Company, Inc.; *U.S. Private*, pg. 427
BAIN & COMPANY, INC. - UNITED KINGDOM—See Bain & Company, Inc.; *U.S. Private*, pg. 428
BAIN & COMPANY JAPAN, INC.—See Bain & Company, Inc.; *U.S. Private*, pg. 427
BAIRD, PATRICK & CO., INC.; *U.S. Private*, pg. 454
BALGOPAL COMMERCIAL LIMITED; *Int'l*, pg. 808
BANAS FINANCE LIMITED; *Int'l*, pg. 814
BANCA ALETTI & C. S.P.A.—See Banco BPM S.p.A.; *Int'l*, pg. 818
BANCA GENERALI S.P.A.—See Assicurazioni Generali S.p.A.; *Int'l*, pg. 643
BANCA INTERMOBILIARE DI INVESTIMENTI E GESTIONI S.P.A.; *Int'l*, pg. 815
BANCA POPOLARE DI CREMONA S.P.A.—See Banco BPM S.p.A.; *Int'l*, pg. 819
BANCA POPOLARE DI LODI S.P.A.—See Banco BPM S.p.A.; *Int'l*, pg. 819
BANCA POPOLARE DI SONDRIO (SUISSE) S.A.—See Banca Popolare di Sondrio S.p.A.; *Int'l*, pg. 816
BANCA PROFILO S.P.A.; *Int'l*, pg. 816
BANCA TRANSILVANIA S.A.; *Int'l*, pg. 816
BANCO BIC PORTUGUES S.A.; *Int'l*, pg. 816
BANCO BTG PACTUAL S.A.—See BTG Pactual Holding S.A.; *Int'l*, pg. 1204
BANCO DE MADRID, S.A.—See Banca Privada D'Andorra, SA; *Int'l*, pg. 816
BANCO HSBC S.A.—See HSBC Holdings plc; *Int'l*, pg. 3503
BANCO INTERAMERICANO DE FINANZAS SA; *Int'l*, pg. 823
BANCOLOMBIA CAPITAL LLC—See Bancolombia S.A.; *Int'l*, pg. 828
BANCOLOMBIA PANAMA S.A.—See Bancolombia S.A.; *Int'l*, pg. 828
BANCO MERCANTIL DO BRASIL S.A.; *Int'l*, pg. 823
BANCORP WEALTH MANAGEMENT NEW ZEALAND LTD.; *Int'l*, pg. 828
BANCO VOITER S.A.—See Banco Master S.A.; *Int'l*, pg. 823
BANGLADESH FINANCE CAPITAL LIMITED—See Bangladesh Finance Limited; *Int'l*, pg. 835
BANK ALBILAD; *Int'l*, pg. 836
BANKA POSTANSKA STEDIONICA A.D.; *Int'l*, pg. 850
BANK ASIA SECURITIES LIMITED—See Bank Asia Limited; *Int'l*, pg. 837

523150 — INVESTMENT BANKING ... **CORPORATE AFFILIATIONS**

BANK ESKHATA OJSC; *Int'l*, pg. 837
BANKHAUS JUNGHOLZ AG—See Alpha RHEINTAL Bank AG; *Int'l*, pg. 369
BANK J. SAFRA SARASIN AG—See Banco Safra S.A.; *Int'l*, pg. 825
BANK J. SAFRA SARASIN (GIBRALTAR) LTD.—See Banco Safra S.A.; *Int'l*, pg. 825
BANK OF CHINA CONSUMER FINANCE CO., LTD.—See Bank of China, Ltd.; *Int'l*, pg. 841
BANK OF CHINA INVESTMENT MANAGEMENT CO., LTD.—See Bank of China, Ltd.; *Int'l*, pg. 841
BANK OF HANGZHOU CO., LTD.; *Int'l*, pg. 843
BANK OF IRELAND RETAIL (IRELAND & UK) DIVISION—See Bank of Ireland Group plc; *Int'l*, pg. 844
THE BANK OF NEW YORK MELLON TRUST COMPANY, N.A.—See The Bank of New York Mellon Corporation; *U.S. Public*, pg. 2038
THE BANK STREET GROUP LLC; *U.S. Private*, pg. 3991
BANQUE AUDI (SUISSE) SA—See Bank Audi sal; *Int'l*, pg. 837
BANQUE DES TERRITOIRES—See Caisse des Depots et Consignations; *Int'l*, pg. 1257
BANQUE ESPIRITO SANTO ET DE LA VENETIE S.A.—See Cerberus Capital Management, L.P.; *U.S. Private*, pg. 839
BANQUE HERITAGE (SUISSE) S.A.; *Int'l*, pg. 853
BANQUE HERITAGE (URUGUAY) S.A.—See Banque Heritage (Suisse) S.A.; *Int'l*, pg. 854
BANQUE INTERNATIONALE ARABE DE TUNISIE; *Int'l*, pg. 854
BANQUE J. SAFRA SARASIN (MONACO) SA—See Banco Safra S.A.; *Int'l*, pg. 825
BANQUE LIBANO-FRANCAISE S.A.L.; *Int'l*, pg. 854
BANQUE PIGUET GALLAND & CIE SA—See Banque Cantonale Vaudoise; *Int'l*, pg. 853
BANQUE SYZ SA—See Financiere SYZ & CO SA; *Int'l*, pg. 2669
BAOCHENG FUTURES CO., LTD.—See China Huaneng Group Co., Ltd.; *Int'l*, pg. 1509
BAO VIET SECURITIES JOINT STOCK COMPANY—See Bao Viet Holdings; *Int'l*, pg. 855
BARCLAYS CAPITAL INC.—See Barclays PLC; *Int'l*, pg. 860
BARCLAYS CAPITAL SECURITIES LIMITED—See Barclays PLC; *Int'l*, pg. 860
BARCLAYS CAPITAL SERVICES LIMITED—See Barclays PLC; *Int'l*, pg. 861
BARCLAYS CAPITAL—See Barclays PLC; *Int'l*, pg. 860
BARCLAYS CAPITAL—See Barclays PLC; *Int'l*, pg. 860
BARCLAYS FRANCE SA—See Barclays PLC; *Int'l*, pg. 861
BARCLAYS PRIVATE BANK & TRUST COMPANY—See Barclays PLC; *Int'l*, pg. 860
BARCLAYS SECURITIES (INDIA) PRIVATE LIMITED—See Barclays PLC; *Int'l*, pg. 860
BARCLAYS (SECURITY REALISATION) LIMITED—See Barclays PLC; *Int'l*, pg. 859
BARCLAYS SHAREDEALING LIMITED—See Barclays PLC; *Int'l*, pg. 861
BARING ASSET MANAGEMENT GMBH—See Massachusetts Mutual Life Insurance Company; *U.S. Private*, pg. 2604
BARING FRANCE SAS—See Massachusetts Mutual Life Insurance Company; *U.S. Private*, pg. 2604
BARINGTON CAPITAL GROUP, L.P.; *U.S. Private*, pg. 475
BARKSDALE FEDERAL CREDIT UNION; *U.S. Private*, pg. 475
BARON CAPITAL GROUP, INC.; *U.S. Private*, pg. 478
BARRAMUNDI LIMITED; *Int'l*, pg. 867
BARR BROTHERS & CO., INC.; *U.S. Private*, pg. 479
BATS TRADING LIMITED—See Cboe Global Markets, Inc.; *U.S. Public*, pg. 459
BATTEA - CLASS ACTION SERVICES, LLC—See SS&C Technologies Holdings, Inc.; *U.S. Public*, pg. 1922
BAYAN INVESTMENT HOLDING COMPANY K.S.C.C.; *Int'l*, pg. 901
BAYER CAPITAL CORPORATION B.V.—See Bayer Aktiengesellschaft; *Int'l*, pg. 902
BAYERISCHE LANDESBANK IMMOBILIEN-BETEILIGUNGS-GESELLSCHAFT MBH & CO. KG—See BayernLB Holding AG; *Int'l*, pg. 913
BAY MUTUAL FINANCIAL, LLC; *U.S. Private*, pg. 494
BAYVIEW FINANCIAL, L.P.; *U.S. Private*, pg. 497
BAYVIEW FINANCIAL SMALL BUSINESS FUNDING LLC—See Bayview Financial, L.P.; *U.S. Private*, pg. 497
BB BANCO DE INVESTIMENTO S.A.—See Banco do Brasil S.A.; *Int'l*, pg. 822
BB&T INVESTMENT SERVICES, INC.—See Truist Financial Corporation; *U.S. Public*, pg. 2200
BB&T REAL ESTATE FUNDING LLC—See Truist Financial Corporation; *U.S. Public*, pg. 2200
BBVA PARAGUAY SA—See Banco Bilbao Vizcaya Argentaria, S.A.; *Int'l*, pg. 817
BBVA SEGUROS COLOMBIA SA—See Banco Bilbao Vizcaya Argentaria, S.A.; *Int'l*, pg. 817
BBV BILBAO—See Banco Bilbao Vizcaya Argentaria, S.A.; *Int'l*, pg. 817
BBV INTERACTIVOS—See Banco Bilbao Vizcaya Argentaria, S.A.; *Int'l*, pg. 817

BBV MADRID—See Banco Bilbao Vizcaya Argentaria, S.A.; *Int'l*, pg. 817
BBV PRIVANZA—See Banco Bilbao Vizcaya Argentaria, S.A.; *Int'l*, pg. 817
B*CAPITAL—See BNP Paribas SA; *Int'l*, pg. 1080
BCC INVEST JSC—See Bank CenterCredit JSC; *Int'l*, pg. 837
BCG HOLDINGS INC—See Barington Capital Group, L.P.; *U.S. Private*, pg. 475
BCO BTG PACTUAL S.A.; *Int'l*, pg. 928
BEAZLEY GROUP LIMITED—See Beazley plc; *Int'l*, pg. 935
BEHRINGER SECURITIES LP—See Behringer Harvard Holdings, LLC; *U.S. Private*, pg. 515
BELARUSBANK; *Int'l*, pg. 963
BELLEVUE GROUP AG; *Int'l*, pg. 967
BELTONE INVESTMENT BANKING—See Chimera Investments LLC; *Int'l*, pg. 1479
BELTONE SECURITIES BROKERAGE—See Chimera Investments LLC; *Int'l*, pg. 1479
BENTLEY CAPITAL LTD.; *Int'l*, pg. 977
BERENSON & COMPANY, LLC—See Berenson & Company, Inc.; *U.S. Private*, pg. 530
BERKERY, NOYES & CO., LLC; *U.S. Private*, pg. 533
BERTHEL FISHER & CO. FINANCIAL SERVICES—See Berthel Fisher & Company Inc.; *U.S. Private*, pg. 539
BERTHEL FISHER & COMPANY INC.; *U.S. Private*, pg. 539
BERTHEL FISHER INVESTMENTS INC—See Berthel Fisher & Company Inc.; *U.S. Private*, pg. 539
BETHMANN BANK AG—See ABN AMRO Group N.V.; *Int'l*, pg. 65
BGC BROKERS L.P.—See BGC Group, Inc.; *U.S. Public*, pg. 328
BGC FINANCIAL GROUP, INC.—See BGC Group, Inc.; *U.S. Public*, pg. 328
BGC GROUP, INC.; *U.S. Public*, pg. 327
BGC INTERNATIONAL—See BGC Group, Inc.; *U.S. Public*, pg. 328
BGC PARTNERS CIS LLC—See BGC Group, Inc.; *U.S. Public*, pg. 328
BGC PARTNERS MENKUL DEGERLER A.S.—See BGC Group, Inc.; *U.S. Public*, pg. 328
BGC PARTNERS (SINGAPORE) LIMITED—See BGC Group, Inc.; *U.S. Public*, pg. 328
BGC SECURITIES SARL—See BGC Group, Inc.; *U.S. Public*, pg. 328
BHM CAPITAL FINANCIAL SERVICES PSC; *Int'l*, pg. 1015
BIBANCA S.P.A.—See BPER BANCA S.p.A; *Int'l*, pg. 1132
BIEN SPAREBANK A.S.A.; *Int'l*, pg. 1020
BIOMIND LABS INC.; *Int'l*, pg. 1040
BIPL SECURITIES LTD.; *Int'l*, pg. 1045
BIRDHI CHAND PANNALAL AGENCIES LIMITED; *Int'l*, pg. 1047
BISHOP ROSEN & CO. INC.; *U.S. Private*, pg. 565
BISON BANK, S.A; *Int'l*, pg. 1049
BK SECURITIES LIMITED—See Banque de Kigali S.A.; *Int'l*, pg. 853
BLAYLOCK ROBERT VAN LLC; *U.S. Private*, pg. 580
BLAYLOCK ROBERT VAN LLC—See Blaylock Robert Van LLC; *U.S. Private*, pg. 580
BLEVINS FRANKS FINANCIAL MANAGEMENT LIMITED; *Int'l*, pg. 1063
BLOOMBERG TRADEBOOK LLC—See Bloomberg L.P.; *U.S. Private*, pg. 583
BLUEBLOOD VENTURES LIMITED; *Int'l*, pg. 1070
BLUE CREEK INVESTMENT PARTNERS; *U.S. Private*, pg. 586
BLUE SKY ALTERNATIVE INVESTMENTS LIMITED; *Int'l*, pg. 1069
BMCE CAPITAL BOURSE—See Bank of Africa; *Int'l*, pg. 839
BMCE CAPITAL—See Bank of Africa; *Int'l*, pg. 839
BMO CAPITAL MARKETS CORP.—See Bank of Montreal; *Int'l*, pg. 846
BMO CAPITAL MARKETS LIMITED—See Bank of Montreal; *Int'l*, pg. 846
BMO CAPITAL MARKETS—See Bank of Montreal; *Int'l*, pg. 846
BMO INVESTORLINE, INC.—See Bank of Montreal; *Int'l*, pg. 846
BNK ADVISORY GROUP, INC.—See Asplundh Tree Expert Co.; *U.S. Private*, pg. 353
BNK ASSET MANAGEMENT CO., LTD.—See BNK Financial Group Inc.; *Int'l*, pg. 1079
BNK CREDIT INFORMATION CO., LTD.—See BNK Financial Group Inc.; *Int'l*, pg. 1079
BNK SAVINGS BANK CO., LTD.—See BNK Financial Group Inc.; *Int'l*, pg. 1079
BNK VENTURE CAPITAL CO., LTD.—See BNK Financial Group Inc.; *Int'l*, pg. 1079
BNP COOPER-NEFF GROUP—See BNP Paribas SA; *Int'l*, pg. 1087
BNP PARIBAS BROKERAGE SERVICES, INC—See BNP Paribas SA; *Int'l*, pg. 1087
BNP PARIBAS EQUITY STRATEGIES S.N.C.—See BNP Paribas SA; *Int'l*, pg. 1083
BNP PARIBAS ESPANA S.A.—See BNP Paribas SA; *Int'l*, pg. 1083
BNP PARIBAS INDIA SOLUTIONS PRIVATE LTD.—See BNP Paribas SA; *Int'l*, pg. 1085

BNP PARIBAS-NEW YORK—See BNP Paribas SA; *Int'l*, pg. 1087
BNP PARIBAS PEREGRINE THAILAND—See BNP Paribas SA; *Int'l*, pg. 1081
BNP PARIBAS PERSONAL INVESTORS—See BNP Paribas SA; *Int'l*, pg. 1090
BNP PARIBAS PRIME BROKERAGE INC.—See BNP Paribas SA; *Int'l*, pg. 1087
BNP PARIBAS SECURITIES (ASIA) LTD.—See BNP Paribas SA; *Int'l*, pg. 1087
BNP PARIBAS SECURITIES CORP.—See BNP Paribas SA; *Int'l*, pg. 1087
BNP PARIBAS SECURITIES (JAPAN) LIMITED—See BNP Paribas SA; *Int'l*, pg. 1081
BNP PARIBAS SECURITIES KOREA COMPANY LTD.—See BNP Paribas SA; *Int'l*, pg. 1087
BNP PARIBAS SECURITIES (SINGAPORE) PTE LTD.—See BNP Paribas SA; *Int'l*, pg. 1087
BNP PARIBAS SECURITIES (TAIWAN) CO LTD.—See BNP Paribas SA; *Int'l*, pg. 1087
BNP PARIBAS (SUISSE) SA—See BNP Paribas SA; *Int'l*, pg. 1081
B N RATHI SECURITIES LTD.; *Int'l*, pg. 783
BNY MELLON CAPITAL MARKETS, LLC—See The Bank of New York Mellon Corporation; *U.S. Public*, pg. 2037
BNY MELLON SECURITIES SERVICES (IRELAND) LIMITED—See The Bank of New York Mellon Corporation; *U.S. Public*, pg. 2037
BOB CAPITAL MARKETS LTD.—See Bank of Baroda; *Int'l*, pg. 840
BOC INTERNATIONAL CHINA CO., LTD.; *Int'l*, pg. 1096
BOC INTERNATIONAL HOLDINGS LIMITED—See Bank of China, Ltd.; *Int'l*, pg. 841
BOCOM INTERNATIONAL HOLDINGS CO., LTD.—See Bank of Communications Co., Ltd.; *Int'l*, pg. 842
BOENNING & SCATTERGOOD, INC.; *U.S. Private*, pg. 608
BOFA SECURITIES JAPAN CO., LTD.—See Bank of America Corporation; *U.S. Public*, pg. 271
BOG'ART BUILDING MANAGEMENT SRL—See Bog'Art S.R.L.; *Int'l*, pg. 1100
BOI MERCHANT BANKERS LTD.—See Bank of India; *Int'l*, pg. 843
BOK FINANCIAL SECURITIES, INC.—See BOK Financial Corporation; *U.S. Public*, pg. 367
BONDPARTNERS SA; *Int'l*, pg. 1106
BOOKOOK SECURITIES CO., LTD.; *Int'l*, pg. 1110
BOSC AGENCY, INC.—See BOK Financial Corporation; *U.S. Public*, pg. 367
BOSTON MANAGEMENT AND RESEARCH—See Morgan Stanley; *U.S. Public*, pg. 1472
BOURSE DIRECT ET BOURSE DISCOUNT SA; *Int'l*, pg. 1120
BOUSTEAD WAVEFRONT INC.; *Int'l*, pg. 1121
BPER BANK LUXEMBOURG S.A.—See BPER BANCA S.p.A; *Int'l*, pg. 1132
BPI CAPITAL CORPORATION—See Bank of the Philippine Islands; *Int'l*, pg. 848
BPI SECURITIES CORPORATION—See Bank of the Philippine Islands; *Int'l*, pg. 848
BRAC BANK LIMITED—See BRAC; *Int'l*, pg. 1134
BRADESCO SECURITIES, INC.—See Banco Bradesco S.A.; *Int'l*, pg. 819
BRASIL PLURAL S.A. BANCO MULTIPLO; *Int'l*, pg. 1140
BREWIN DOLPHIN HOLDINGS PLC; *Int'l*, pg. 1150
BREWIN DOLPHIN SECURITIES—See Brewin Dolphin Holdings PLC; *Int'l*, pg. 1150
BREWIN NOMINEES LIMITED—See Brewin Dolphin Holdings PLC; *Int'l*, pg. 1150
BRICKELL BANK; *U.S. Private*, pg. 648
BRIDGE SECURITIES LIMITED; *Int'l*, pg. 1152
BRIGHT SMART SECURITIES & COMMODITIES GROUP LIMITED; *Int'l*, pg. 1162
B. RILEY & CO., LLC—See B. Riley Financial, Inc.; *U.S. Public*, pg. 260
B. RILEY FBR, INC.—See B. Riley Financial, Inc.; *U.S. Public*, pg. 260
BROKERTEC—See CME Group, Inc.; *U.S. Public*, pg. 517
BROMPTON OIL SPLIT CORP.; *Int'l*, pg. 1174
BROWN BROTHERS HARRIMAN & CO.; *U.S. Private*, pg. 666
BROWN BROTHERS HARRIMAN TRUST CO., LLC—See Brown Brothers Harriman & Co.; *U.S. Private*, pg. 667
BROWN, GIBBONS, LANG & COMPANY, LLC; *U.S. Private*, pg. 669
THE BRYN MAWR TRUST COMPANY OF DELAWARE—See Bryn Mawr Bank Corporation; *U.S. Public*, pg. 408
BS SECURITIES CO., LTD.—See BNK Financial Group Inc.; *Int'l*, pg. 1079
BT CAPITAL PARTNERS S.A.—See Banca Transilvania S.A.; *Int'l*, pg. 816
BTG PACTUAL ARGENTINA S.A.—See BCO BTG PACTUAL S.A.; *Int'l*, pg. 928
BTG PACTUAL ASIA LIMITED—See BCO BTG PACTUAL S.A.; *Int'l*, pg. 928
BTG PACTUAL CASA DE BOLSA, S.A. DE C.V.—See BCO BTG PACTUAL S.A.; *Int'l*, pg. 928

BTG PACTUAL EUROPE LLP—See BCO BTG PACTUAL S.A.; *Int'l*, pg. 928
BTV LEASING DEUTSCHLAND GMBH—See Bank fur Tirol und Vorarlberg Ag; *Int'l*, pg. 838
BUALUANG SECURITIES PUBLIC COMPANY LIMITED—See Bangkok Bank Public Company Limited; *Int'l*, pg. 833
BURLINGTON BAY RESIDENTIAL MORTGAGE SECURITIES LLC—See Two Harbors Investment Corp.; *U.S. Public*, pg. 2207
BURLINGTON CAPITAL LLC; *U.S. Private*, pg. 689
CABOT LODGE SECURITIES, LLC; *U.S. Private*, pg. 711
CADARET, GRANT & CO., INC—See Lee Equity Partners LLC; *U.S. Private*, pg. 2412
CAIDAO CAPITAL LIMITED; *Int'l*, pg. 1252
CAIDA SECURITIES CO., LTD.; *Int'l*, pg. 1252
CAIN BROTHERS & COMPANY, LLC—See KeyCorp; *U.S. Public*, pg. 1226
CAIXA GERAL DE DEPOSITOS S.A.; *Int'l*, pg. 1259
CALAMOS INVESTMENTS LLP—See Calamos Asset Management, Inc.; *U.S. Private*, pg. 716
CALTON & ASSOCIATES, INC.; *U.S. Private*, pg. 723
CAMBRIDGE INVESTMENT RESEARCH, INC.—See Cambridge Investment Group, Inc.; *U.S. Private*, pg. 727
CANACCORD GENUITY ASIA (BEIJING) LIMITED—See Canaccord Genuity Group Inc.; *Int'l*, pg. 1277
CANACCORD GENUITY CORP.—See Canaccord Genuity Group Inc.; *Int'l*, pg. 1277
CANACCORD GENUITY (DUBAI) LTD.—See Canaccord Genuity Group Inc.; *Int'l*, pg. 1277
CANACCORD GENUITY (HONG KONG) LIMITED—See Canaccord Genuity Group Inc.; *Int'l*, pg. 1277
CANACCORD GENUITY INC.—See Canaccord Genuity Group Inc.; *Int'l*, pg. 1277
CANACCORD GENUITY LIMITED—See Canaccord Genuity Group Inc.; *Int'l*, pg. 1277
CANACCORD GENUITY MANAGEMENT COMPANY LIMITED—See Canaccord Genuity Group Inc.; *Int'l*, pg. 1277
CANACCORD GENUITY SAS—See Canaccord Genuity Group Inc.; *Int'l*, pg. 1277
CANACCORD GENUITY SG PTE. LTD.—See Canaccord Genuity Group Inc.; *Int'l*, pg. 1277
CANACCORD GENUITY WEALTH (INTERNATIONAL) LIMITED—See Canaccord Genuity Group Inc.; *Int'l*, pg. 1277
CANDRIAM INVESTORS GROUP-FRANCE—See New York Life Insurance Company; *U.S. Private*, pg. 2911
CANON MEDICAL FINANCE CO., LTD.—See Canon Inc.; *Int'l*, pg. 1296
CANTERBURY CONSULTING INCORPORATED; *U.S. Private*, pg. 735
CANTOR FITZGERALD & CO.—See Cantor Fitzgerald, L.P.; *U.S. Private*, pg. 736
CANTOR FITZGERALD, L.P.; *U.S. Private*, pg. 736
CAPFIN INDIA LIMITED; *Int'l*, pg. 1303
CAPITA LIFE & PENSIONS SERVICES LIMITED—See Capita plc; *Int'l*, pg. 1308
CAPITAL INTERNATIONAL CDPQ—See Caisse de Depot et Placement du Quebec; *Int'l*, pg. 1254
CAPITAL INTERNATIONAL LIMITED—See Capital International Group Limited; *Int'l*, pg. 1311
CAPITAL MARKETS COMPLIANCE LLC—See Genstar Capital, LLC; *U.S. Private*, pg. 1677
CAPITAL SECURITIES CO., LTD.—See Beijing Capital Group Co., Ltd.; *Int'l*, pg. 947
CAPITAL SECURITIES CORPORATION; *Int'l*, pg. 1312
CAPITAL SECURITIES (HONG KONG) LTD.—See Capital Securities Corporation; *Int'l*, pg. 1312
CAPRI GLOBAL CAPITAL LIMITED; *Int'l*, pg. 1315
CARI CAPITAL COMPANY, LLC—See Cari Investment Company; *U.S. Private*, pg. 760
CARI INVESTMENT COMPANY; *U.S. Private*, pg. 760
CARL KLIEM S.A.—See StoneX Group Inc.; *U.S. Public*, pg. 1951
CARL MARKS & CO., INC.; *U.S. Private*, pg. 762
CARLYLE SECURED LENDING, INC.; *U.S. Public*, pg. 437
CARNEGIE INC.—See Altor Equity Partners AB; *Int'l*, pg. 394
CARNEGIE INVESTMENT BANK AB—See Altor Equity Partners AB; *Int'l*, pg. 394
CASA DE BOLSA BBVA MEXICO, S.A. DE C.V.—See Banco Bilbao Vizcaya Argentaria, S.A.; *Int'l*, pg. 817
CASH FINANCIAL SERVICES GROUP LIMITED; *Int'l*, pg. 1352
CASH WEALTH MANAGEMENT LIMITED—See CASH Financial Services Group Limited; *Int'l*, pg. 1352
CASSEL SALPETER & CO., LLC; *U.S. Private*, pg. 783
CAVENDISH FINANCIAL PLC; *Int'l*, pg. 1362
CAVENDISH SECURITIES PLC—See Cavendish Financial plc; *Int'l*, pg. 1362
CBH COMPAGNIE BANCAIRE HELVETIQUE SA; *Int'l*, pg. 1365
CBIZ FINANCIAL SOLUTIONS, INC.—See CBIZ, Inc.; *U.S. Public*, pg. 456
CCT TELECOM SECURITIES LIMITED—See CCT Fortis Holdings Limited; *Int'l*, pg. 1370
CENTBANK FINANCIAL SERVICES LIMITED—See Central Bank of India Limited; *Int'l*, pg. 1404
CENTRAL CHINA EQUITY EXCHANGE CO., LTD.—See Central China Securities Co., Ltd.; *Int'l*, pg. 1405
CENTRAL CHINA SECURITIES CO., LTD.; *Int'l*, pg. 1405
CENTRALNY DOM MAKLERSKI PEKAO S.A.—See Bank Polska Kasa Opieki Spolka Akcyjna; *Int'l*, pg. 849
CENTRAL TANSHI CO., LTD.; *Int'l*, pg. 1410
CENTRAL TANSHI FX CO., LTD.—See Central Tanshi Co., Ltd.; *Int'l*, pg. 1410
CENTRUM CAPITAL LTD.; *Int'l*, pg. 1415
CENTURION COUNSEL, INC.; *U.S. Private*, pg. 831
CENTURY SECURITIES ASSOCIATES, INCORPORATED—See Stifel Financial Corp.; *U.S. Public*, pg. 1949
CERES MANAGED FUTURES LLC—See Morgan Stanley; *U.S. Public*, pg. 1471
C&F WEALTH MANAGEMENT CORPORATION—See C&F Financial Corporation; *U.S. Public*, pg. 414
CG&B INVESTMENT SERVICES, INC.—See Arthur J. Gallagher & Co.; *U.S. Public*, pg. 204
CGS-CIMB SECURITIES (SINGAPORE) PTE. LTD—See CIMB Group Holdings Berhad; *Int'l*, pg. 1608
CHANGJIANG SECURITIES COMPANY LIMITED; *Int'l*, pg. 1443
CHARLES SCHWAB & COMPANY, INC.—See The Charles Schwab Corporation; *U.S. Public*, pg. 2058
THE CHARLES SCHWAB CORPORATION - AUSTIN—See The Charles Schwab Corporation; *U.S. Public*, pg. 2058
CHASE STUDENT LOANS, INC.—See JPMorgan Chase & Co.; *U.S. Public*, pg. 1206
CHINA BANK SECURITIES CORPORATION—See China Banking Corporation; *Int'l*, pg. 1484
CHINA DING YI FENG HOLDINGS LIMITED; *Int'l*, pg. 1498
CHINA GALAXY INTERNATIONAL FINANCIAL HOLDINGS COMPANY LIMITED—See China Galaxy Securities Company Limited; *Int'l*, pg. 1503
CHINA INDUSTRIAL SECURITIES INTERNATIONAL CAPITAL LIMITED—See China Industrial Securities Financial Group; *Int'l*, pg. 1509
CHINA INTERNATIONAL CAPITAL CORPORATION (UK) LIMITED—See China International Capital Corporation Limited; *Int'l*, pg. 1510
CHINA INVESTMENT SECURITIES COMPANY LIMITED—See China International Capital Corporation Limited; *Int'l*, pg. 1510
CHINALIN SECURITIES CO., LTD.; *Int'l*, pg. 1568
CHINA MERCHANTS SECURITIES CO., LTD.—See China Merchants Group Limited; *Int'l*, pg. 1521
CHINA RENAISSANCE SECURITIES (US) INC.—See China Renaissance Holdings Ltd.; *Int'l*, pg. 1547
CHINA SECURITIES (INTERNATIONAL) FINANCE HOLDING COMPANY LIMITED—See CSC Financial Co., Ltd; *Int'l*, pg. 1862
CHINATRUST SECURITIES CO., INC.—See CTBC Financial Holding Co., Ltd.; *Int'l*, pg. 1869
CHINATRUST SECURITIES CO., LTD.—See CTBC Financial Holding Co., Ltd.; *Int'l*, pg. 1869
CHITTAGONG CAPITAL LIMITED; *Int'l*, pg. 1574
CHITTAGONG STOCK EXCHANGE LTD.; *Int'l*, pg. 1574
CHOICE EQUITY BROKING PRIVATE LIMITED—See Choice International Limited; *Int'l*, pg. 1577
CHOICE INTERNATIONAL LIMITED; *Int'l*, pg. 1577
CHUGIN SECURITIES CO., LTD.—See Chugin Financial Group, Inc.; *Int'l*, pg. 1595
CIBC INC.—See Canadian Imperial Bank of Commerce; *Int'l*, pg. 1283
CIBC WOOD GUNDY—See Canadian Imperial Bank of Commerce; *Int'l*, pg. 1284
CIBC WOOD GUNDY—See Canadian Imperial Bank of Commerce; *Int'l*, pg. 1284
CIBC WORLD MARKETS CORP.—See Canadian Imperial Bank of Commerce; *Int'l*, pg. 1284
CIBC WORLD MARKETS INC.—See Canadian Imperial Bank of Commerce; *Int'l*, pg. 1284
CICC US SECURITIES, INC.—See China International Capital Corporation Limited; *Int'l*, pg. 1510
CIMARRON INVESTMENTS LLC—See Morgan Stanley; *U.S. Public*, pg. 1471
CIMB BANK (L) LTD.—See CIMB Group Holdings Berhad; *Int'l*, pg. 1607
CIMB BANK (VIETNAM) LIMITED—See CIMB Group Holdings Berhad; *Int'l*, pg. 1607
CINDA INTERNATIONAL HOLDINGS LIMITED; *Int'l*, pg. 1610
CINDA SECURITIES CO., LTD.—See China Cinda Asset Management Co., Ltd.; *Int'l*, pg. 1488
CITIBANK, N.A. PUERTO RICO—See Citigroup Inc.; *U.S. Public*, pg. 502
CITIBANK (SWITZERLAND) AG—See Citigroup Inc.; *U.S. Public*, pg. 502
CITICORP INTERNATIONAL LIMITED—See Citigroup Inc.; *U.S. Public*, pg. 502
CITIC SECURITIES INTERNATIONAL CO., LTD.—See CITIC Securities Co., Ltd.; *Int'l*, pg. 1622
CITIC SECURITIES (ZHEJIANG) CO., LTD.—See CITIC Securities Co., Ltd.; *Int'l*, pg. 1622
CITIC WANTONG SECURITIES CO., LTD.—See CITIC Securities Co., Ltd.; *Int'l*, pg. 1622
CITIGROUP CAPITAL STRATEGIES INC.—See Citigroup Inc.; *U.S. Public*, pg. 503
CITIGROUP CORPORATE & INVESTMENT BANKING—See Citigroup Inc.; *U.S. Public*, pg. 503
CITIGROUP GLOBAL MARKETS DEUTSCHLAND AG—See Citigroup Inc.; *U.S. Public*, pg. 502
CITIGROUP GLOBAL MARKETS EUROPE LIMITED—See Citigroup Inc.; *U.S. Public*, pg. 503
CITIGROUP GLOBAL MARKETS INC.—See Citigroup Inc.; *U.S. Public*, pg. 503
CITIGROUP GLOBAL MARKETS JAPAN INC.—See Citigroup Inc.; *U.S. Public*, pg. 504
CITIGROUP GLOBAL MARKETS KOREA SECURITIES LIMITED—See Citigroup Inc.; *U.S. Public*, pg. 503
CITIGROUP GLOBAL MARKETS LIMITED—See Citigroup Inc.; *U.S. Public*, pg. 503
CITIGROUP GLOBAL MARKETS MAURITIUS PRIVATE LIMITED—See Citigroup Inc.; *U.S. Public*, pg. 503
CITIGROUP GLOBAL MARKETS U.K. EQUITY LIMITED—See Citigroup Inc.; *U.S. Public*, pg. 503
CITI INSTITUTIONAL CLIENTS GROUP—See Citigroup Inc.; *U.S. Public*, pg. 502
CITI ISLAMIC INVESTMENT BANK EC—See Citigroup Inc.; *U.S. Public*, pg. 502
CITY OF LONDON US INVESTMENTS LIMITED—See City of London Investment Group PLC; *Int'l*, pg. 1627
CLAIRVEST GROUP INC.; *Int'l*, pg. 1641
CLAL FINANCE LTD.—See IDB Development Corporation Ltd.; *Int'l*, pg. 3588
CLARKSON SECURITIES LIMITED—See Clarkson PLC; *Int'l*, pg. 1651
CLARKSONS PLATOU SECURITIES AS—See Clarkson PLC; *Int'l*, pg. 1650
CLEARLEND—See Wells Fargo & Company; *U.S. Public*, pg. 2343
CLEARLEND - WEST COAST—See Wells Fargo & Company; *U.S. Public*, pg. 2343
CLEARSTREAM BANKING AG—See Deutsche Borse AG; *Int'l*, pg. 2063
CLEARSTREAM BANKING S.A.—See Deutsche Borse AG; *Int'l*, pg. 2063
CL GROUP (HOLDINGS) LIMITED; *Int'l*, pg. 1640
CLIMATEROCK; *Int'l*, pg. 1659
CLSA AUSTRALIA HOLDINGS PTY .LTD.—See CITIC Securities Co., Ltd.; *Int'l*, pg. 1622
CLSA B.V.—See CITIC Securities Co., Ltd.; *Int'l*, pg. 1622
CLSA LIMITED—See CITIC Securities Co., Ltd.; *Int'l*, pg. 1622
CMBC CAPITAL HOLDINGS LIMITED; *Int'l*, pg. 1668
CMB INTERNATIONAL CAPITAL CORPORATION LIMITED—See China Merchants Group Limited; *Int'l*, pg. 1520
CME GROUP ASIA HOLDINGS PTE. LTD—See CME Group, Inc.; *U.S. Public*, pg. 516
CME INFORMATION SERVICES (BEIJING) CO., LTD.—See S&P Global Inc.; *U.S. Public*, pg. 1830
CM SECURITIES (HONGKONG) COMPANY LIMITED—See China Vered Financial Holding Corporation Limited; *Int'l*, pg. 1562
CNL SECURITIES CORP.—See CNL Financial Group, Inc.; *U.S. Private*, pg. 952
COASTAL SECURITIES, INC.—See First Horizon Corporation; *U.S. Public*, pg. 844
C.O. CAPITAL AGENCIA DE VALORES, S.A.—See Grupo Catalana Occidente, S.A.; *Int'l*, pg. 3124
COHEN & STEERS ASIA LIMITED—See Cohen & Steers, Inc.; *U.S. Public*, pg. 526
COL FINANCIAL GROUP, INC.; *Int'l*, pg. 1697
COLONIAL FIRST STATE INVESTMENTS LIMITED—See KKR & Co. Inc.; *U.S. Public*, pg. 1243
COLUMBIA WANGER ASSET MANAGEMENT, LLC—See Ameriprise Financial, Inc.; *U.S. Public*, pg. 114
COMERICA SECURITIES, INC.—See Comerica Incorporated; *U.S. Public*, pg. 542
COMMERZBANK AG - NEW YORK BRANCH—See Commerzbank AG; *Int'l*, pg. 1717
COMMERZBANK SECURITIES LTD.—See Commerzbank AG; *Int'l*, pg. 1717
COMMERZBANK SECURITIES NOMINEES LIMITED—See Commerzbank AG; *Int'l*, pg. 1717
COMMERZ MARKETS LLC—See Commerzbank AG; *Int'l*, pg. 1716
COMMERZ (NEDERLAND) N.V.—See Commerzbank AG; *Int'l*, pg. 1716
COMMERZ SECURITIES HONG KONG LIMITED—See Commerzbank AG; *Int'l*, pg. 1716
COMMONWEALTH CAPITAL SECURITIES CORP.—See Commonwealth Capital Corp.; *U.S. Private*, pg. 986
COMMONWEALTH EQUITY SERVICES LLP; *U.S. Private*, pg. 986
COMMONWEALTH SECURITIES LIMITED—See Commonwealth Bank of Australia; *Int'l*, pg. 1720
CONCERN GENERAL INVEST LLC; *Int'l*, pg. 1764
CONCORD FINANCIAL INTERMEDIARY GMBH—See Concord Investmentbank AG; *Int'l*, pg. 1765
CONCORD INTERNATIONAL SECURITIES CO., LTD.; *Int'l*, pg. 1765
CONCORD INVESTMENTBANK AG; *Int'l*, pg. 1765

523150 — INVESTMENT BANKING ...

CONDUIT CAPITAL LIMITED; *Int'l*, pg. 1766
CONNECT CO. LTD.—See Daiwa Securities Group Inc.; *Int'l*, pg. 1947
COPENHAGEN CAPITAL A/S; *Int'l*, pg. 1793
COR CLEARING LLC—See Axos Financial, Inc.; *U.S. Public*, pg. 256
CORNERSTONE SECURITIES LIMITED—See Cornerstone Financial Holdings Limited; *Int'l*, pg. 1801
CORPORACION ACTINVER SAB DE CV; *Int'l*, pg. 1803
COSTANOA VENTURE CAPITAL MANAGEMENT LLC; *U.S. Private*, pg. 1063
CREDICORP SECURITIES INC.—See Credicorp Ltd.; *Int'l*, pg. 1834
CREDIT AGRICOLE CIB AO; *Int'l*, pg. 1834
CREDIT ANDORRA PANAMA SECURITIES SA.—See Credit Andorra, S.A.; *Int'l*, pg. 1834
CREDITO ARTIGIANO S.P.A.—See Credito Valtellinese Societa Cooperativa; *Int'l*, pg. 1837
CREDIT SUISSE (DEUTSCHLAND) AG—See ABN AMRO Group N.V.; *Int'l*, pg. 65
CREWS & ASSOCIATES INCORPORATED—See First Security Bancorp; *U.S. Private*, pg. 1527
CRONTO LIMITED—See OneSpan Inc.; *U.S. Public*, pg. 1603
CROSBY ROCK LLC; *U.S. Private*, pg. 1104
CROSS KEYS CAPITAL LLC; *U.S. Private*, pg. 1105
CROWELL, WEEDON & CO.—See D.A. Davidson Companies; *U.S. Private*, pg. 1140
CRUTTENDEN PARTNERS, LLC; *U.S. Private*, pg. 1114
CS WEALTH SECURITIES LIMITED—See CSC Holdings Limited; *Int'l*, pg. 1862
CTBC ASSET MANAGEMENT CO., LTD.—See CTBC Financial Holding Co., Ltd.; *Int'l*, pg. 1869
CTBC BANK CORP.—See CTBC Financial Holding Co., Ltd.; *Int'l*, pg. 1869
CTBC BANK (PHILIPPINES) CORP.—See CTBC Financial Holding Co., Ltd.; *Int'l*, pg. 1869
CTBC INVESTMENTS CO., LTD.—See CTBC Financial Holding Co., Ltd.; *Int'l*, pg. 1869
CTBC SECURITY CO., LTD.—See CTBC Financial Holding Co., Ltd.; *Int'l*, pg. 1869
CTBC VENTURE CAPITAL CO., LTD.—See CTBC Financial Holding Co., Ltd.; *Int'l*, pg. 1869
CTS GLOBAL EQUITY GROUP, INC.; *Int'l*, pg. 1874
CUENTAS INC.; *U.S. Public*, pg. 604
CUKIERMAN & CO. S.A.—See Cukierman & Co. Investment House Ltd.; *Int'l*, pg. 1876
CUNA BROKERAGE SERVICES, INC.—See CMFG Life Insurance Company; *U.S. Private*, pg. 950
CURRENEX, INC.—See State Street Corporation; *U.S. Public*, pg. 1940
CYPRESS CAPITAL MANAGEMENT LTD.—See AGF Management Limited; *Int'l*, pg. 206
DAB BANK AG—See BNP Paribas SA; *Int'l*, pg. 1090
D.A. DAVIDSON & CO. - EQUITY CAPITAL MARKETS—See D.A. Davidson Companies; *U.S. Private*, pg. 1140
D.A. DAVIDSON & CO. - FIXED INCOME CAPITAL MARKETS—See D.A. Davidson Companies; *U.S. Private*, pg. 1140
D.A. DAVIDSON & CO.—See D.A. Davidson Companies; *U.S. Private*, pg. 1140
DAILY GROWTH SECURITIES LIMITED—See China Finance Online Co. Limited; *Int'l*, pg. 1502
DAIWA CAPITAL MARKETS AMERICA INC.—See Daiwa Securities Group Inc.; *Int'l*, pg. 1948
DAIWA CAPITAL MARKETS AUSTRALIA LIMITED—See Daiwa Securities Group Inc.; *Int'l*, pg. 1948
DAIWA CAPITAL MARKETS DEUTSCHLAND GMBH—See Daiwa Securities Group Inc.; *Int'l*, pg. 1947
DAIWA CAPITAL MARKETS EUROPE LIMITED—See Daiwa Securities Group Inc.; *Int'l*, pg. 1948
DAIWA CAPITAL MARKETS HONG KONG LIMITED—See Daiwa Securities Group Inc.; *Int'l*, pg. 1948
DAIWA CAPITAL MARKETS SINGAPORE LIMITED—See Daiwa Securities Group Inc.; *Int'l*, pg. 1948
DAIWA-CATHAY CAPITAL MARKETS CO., LTD.—See Daiwa Securities Group Inc.; *Int'l*, pg. 1948
DAIWA FACILITIES CO., LTD.—See Daiwa Securities Group Inc.; *Int'l*, pg. 1948
DAIWA INTERENATIONAL HOLDINGS LTD.—See Daiwa Securities Group Inc.; *Int'l*, pg. 1948
DAIWA INTERNATIONAL HOLDINGS INC.—See Daiwa Securities Group Inc.; *Int'l*, pg. 1948
DAIWA INVESTMENT MANAGEMENT INC.—See Daiwa Securities Group Inc.; *Int'l*, pg. 1948
DAIWA SECURITIES CO., LTD.—See Daiwa Securities Group Inc.; *Int'l*, pg. 1948
DALAL STREET INVESTMENTS LIMITED; *Int'l*, pg. 1950
DALE K. EHRHART, INC.; *U.S. Private*, pg. 1148
DANIELS TANSEY LLP—See Creative Planning, LLC; *U.S. Private*, pg. 1090
DANIEL STEWART & COMPANY PLC—See Daniel Stewart Securities plc; *Int'l*, pg. 1962
DANIEL STEWART SECURITIES PLC; *Int'l*, pg. 1962
DANSKE MARKETS INC.—See Danske Bank A/S; *Int'l*, pg. 1969
DANSKE MORTGAGE BANK PLC—See Danske Bank A/S; *Int'l*, pg. 1969
DANSKE PRIVATE EQUITY—See Danske Bank A/S; *Int'l*, pg. 1969
DAO HENG SECURITIES LIMITED—See Hong Leong Investment Holdings Pte. Ltd.; *Int'l*, pg. 3468
DATA ANALYSIS, INC.; *U.S. Private*, pg. 1162
DAUGHERTY & COMPANY LLC; *U.S. Private*, pg. 1167
DAULAT SECURITIES LIMITED; *Int'l*, pg. 1982
DAVENPORT & COMPANY LLC; *U.S. Private*, pg. 1169
DAVID A. NOYES & COMPANY; *U.S. Private*, pg. 1169
DAVID LERNER ASSOCIATES INC.; *U.S. Private*, pg. 1170
DAWOOD EQUITIES LIMITED; *Int'l*, pg. 1984
DB CAPITAL MARKETS (DEUTSCHLAND) GMBH—See Deutsche Bank Aktiengesellschaft; *Int'l*, pg. 2056
DB GLOBAL TECHNOLOGY SRL—See Deutsche Bank Aktiengesellschaft; *Int'l*, pg. 2056
DB IO LP—See Deutsche Bank Aktiengesellschaft; *Int'l*, pg. 2056
DB IROC LEASING CORP.—See Deutsche Bank Aktiengesellschaft; *Int'l*, pg. 2056
DB MANAGEMENT PARTNERS, L.P.—See Deutsche Bank Aktiengesellschaft; *Int'l*, pg. 2056
DBP-DAIWA CAPITAL MARKETS PHILIPPINES, INC.—See Daiwa Securities Group Inc.; *Int'l*, pg. 1948
DBS ASIA CAPITAL LIMITED—See DBS Group Holdings Ltd.; *Int'l*, pg. 1988
DBS VICKERS (HONG KONG) LIMITED—See DBS Group Holdings Ltd.; *Int'l*, pg. 1988
DBS VICKERS RESEARCH (SINGAPORE) PTE LTD—See DBS Group Holdings Ltd.; *Int'l*, pg. 1988
DBS VICKERS SECURITIES HOLDINGS PTE LTD—See DBS Group Holdings Ltd.; *Int'l*, pg. 1988
DBS VICKERS SECURITIES (HONG KONG) LIMITED—See DBS Group Holdings Ltd.; *Int'l*, pg. 1988
DBS VICKERS SECURITIES NOMINEES (SINGAPORE) PTE LTD—See DBS Group Holdings Ltd.; *Int'l*, pg. 1988
DBS VICKERS SECURITIES ONLINE HOLDINGS PTE LTD—See DBS Group Holdings Ltd.; *Int'l*, pg. 1988
DBS VICKERS SECURITIES (THAILAND) CO. LTD.—See DBS Group Holdings Ltd.; *Int'l*, pg. 1988
DBS VICKERS SECURITIES (UK) LTD—See DBS Group Holdings Ltd.; *Int'l*, pg. 1988
DCS ADVISORY LLC—See Daiwa Securities Group Inc.; *Int'l*, pg. 1947
DEALERWEB INC.—See Tradeweb Markets Inc.; *U.S. Public*, pg. 2178
DEGROOF PETERCAM CORPORATE FINANCE SA/NV—See Banque Degroof S.A.; *Int'l*, pg. 853
DEKABANK; *Int'l*, pg. 2005
DEKA INVESTMENT GMBH—See DekaBank; *Int'l*, pg. 2005
DELTA AMERICA LTD.—See Delta Electronics, Inc.; *Int'l*, pg. 2016
DELTAONE CAPITAL PARTNERS CORP.—See iA Financial Corporation Inc.; *Int'l*, pg. 3567
DEMETRA HOLDINGS PLC; *Int'l*, pg. 2025
DENALI CAPITAL ACQUISITION CORP.; *U.S. Public*, pg. 653
THE DEPOSITORY TRUST & CLEARING CORPORATION; *U.S. Private*, pg. 4020
DERMAVEST, INC.—See Bausch Health Companies Inc.; *Int'l*, pg. 898
DERZHAVA PJSCB; *Int'l*, pg. 2043
DESILVA+PHILLIPS LLC; *U.S. Private*, pg. 1215
DEUTSCHE ASSET MANAGEMENT (ASIA) LIMITED—See Deutsche Bank Aktiengesellschaft; *Int'l*, pg. 2057
DEUTSCHE ASSET MANAGEMENT GMBH—See Deutsche Bank Aktiengesellschaft; *Int'l*, pg. 2058
DEUTSCHE ASSET MANAGEMENT (JAPAN) LIMITED—See Deutsche Bank Aktiengesellschaft; *Int'l*, pg. 2058
DEUTSCHE BANK AG-BANGKOK—See Deutsche Bank Aktiengesellschaft; *Int'l*, pg. 2058
DEUTSCHE BANK AG-BERLIN—See Deutsche Bank Aktiengesellschaft; *Int'l*, pg. 2059
DEUTSCHE BANK AG-CAIRO—See Deutsche Bank Aktiengesellschaft; *Int'l*, pg. 2059
DEUTSCHE BANK AG CANADA—See Deutsche Bank Aktiengesellschaft; *Int'l*, pg. 2058
DEUTSCHE BANK AG-COLOMBO—See Deutsche Bank Aktiengesellschaft; *Int'l*, pg. 2059
DEUTSCHE BANK AG (ISTANBUL)—See Deutsche Bank Aktiengesellschaft; *Int'l*, pg. 2058
DEUTSCHE BANK AG-JAKARTA—See Deutsche Bank Aktiengesellschaft; *Int'l*, pg. 2059
DEUTSCHE BANK AG-KARACHI—See Deutsche Bank Aktiengesellschaft; *Int'l*, pg. 2059
DEUTSCHE BANK AG-LAHORE—See Deutsche Bank Aktiengesellschaft; *Int'l*, pg. 2059
DEUTSCHE BANK AG-MANAMA—See Deutsche Bank Aktiengesellschaft; *Int'l*, pg. 2059
DEUTSCHE BANK AG-MELBOURNE—See Deutsche Bank Aktiengesellschaft; *Int'l*, pg. 2059
DEUTSCHE BANK AG-PARIS—See Deutsche Bank Aktiengesellschaft; *Int'l*, pg. 2059
DEUTSCHE BANK AG-SINGAPORE—See Deutsche Bank Aktiengesellschaft; *Int'l*, pg. 2057
DEUTSCHE BANK AG-SURABAYA—See Deutsche Bank Aktiengesellschaft; *Int'l*, pg. 2059
DEUTSCHE BANK AG-VIENNA—See Deutsche Bank Aktiengesellschaft; *Int'l*, pg. 2059
DEUTSCHE BANK AUSTRALIA—See Deutsche Bank Aktiengesellschaft; *Int'l*, pg. 2059
DEUTSCHE BANK (CHILE) S.A.—See Deutsche Bank Aktiengesellschaft; *Int'l*, pg. 2058
DEUTSCHE BANK (CHINA) CO., LTD.—See Deutsche Bank Aktiengesellschaft; *Int'l*, pg. 2058
DEUTSCHE BANK CORRETORA DE VALORES S.A.—See Deutsche Bank Aktiengesellschaft; *Int'l*, pg. 2059
DEUTSCHE BANK GOVERNMENT SECURITIES, INC.—See Deutsche Bank Aktiengesellschaft; *Int'l*, pg. 2059
DEUTSCHE BANK INVESTMENTS (GUERNSEY) LIMITED—See Deutsche Bank Aktiengesellschaft; *Int'l*, pg. 2059
DEUTSCHE BANK LUXEMBOURG S.A.—See Deutsche Bank Aktiengesellschaft; *Int'l*, pg. 2059
DEUTSCHE BANK POLSKA S.A.—See Deutsche Bank Aktiengesellschaft; *Int'l*, pg. 2059
DEUTSCHE BANK SAAR AG—See Deutsche Bank Aktiengesellschaft; *Int'l*, pg. 2060
DEUTSCHE BANK, S.A.E.—See Deutsche Bank Aktiengesellschaft; *Int'l*, pg. 2060
DEUTSCHE BANK SECURITIES LIMITED—See Deutsche Bank Aktiengesellschaft; *Int'l*, pg. 2060
DEUTSCHE CAPITAL MARKETS AUSTRALIA LIMITED—See Deutsche Bank Aktiengesellschaft; *Int'l*, pg. 2060
DEUTSCHE INTERNATIONAL CORPORATE SERVICES (IRELAND) LTD.—See Deutsche Bank Aktiengesellschaft; *Int'l*, pg. 2060
DEUTSCHE KREDITBANK AG—See BayernLB Holding AG; *Int'l*, pg. 913
DEUTSCHE SECURITIES ASIA LIMITED—See Deutsche Bank Aktiengesellschaft; *Int'l*, pg. 2061
DEUTSCHE SECURITIES CORREDORES DE BOLSA LTDA.—See Deutsche Bank Aktiengesellschaft; *Int'l*, pg. 2061
DEUTSCHE SECURITIES INC.—See Deutsche Bank Aktiengesellschaft; *Int'l*, pg. 2061
DEUTSCHE SECURITIES (INDIA) PRIVATE LIMITED—See Deutsche Bank Aktiengesellschaft; *Int'l*, pg. 2060
DEUTSCHE SECURITIES ISRAEL LTD.—See Deutsche Bank Aktiengesellschaft; *Int'l*, pg. 2061
DEUTSCHE SECURITIES KOREA CO—See Deutsche Bank Aktiengesellschaft; *Int'l*, pg. 2061
DEUTSCHE SECURITIES (PROPRIETARY) LIMITED—See Deutsche Bank Aktiengesellschaft; *Int'l*, pg. 2061
DEUTSCHE SECURITIES, S.A. DE C.V.—See Deutsche Bank Aktiengesellschaft; *Int'l*, pg. 2059
DEVELOPMENT CORPORATION FOR ISRAEL; *U.S. Private*, pg. 1217
DFCC BANK PLC; *Int'l*, pg. 2094
DFC RESIDUAL CORP.—See Deutsche Bank Aktiengesellschaft; *Int'l*, pg. 2057
DHAKA BANK PLC; *Int'l*, pg. 2097
DHENU BUILDCON INFRA LIMITED; *Int'l*, pg. 2099
DIB CAPITAL LIMITED—See Dubai Islamic Bank PSJ; *Int'l*, pg. 2220
DISCOUNT CAPITAL LTD.—See ImageSat International (ISI) Ltd.; *Int'l*, pg. 3618
DISCOVERY-THE FINANCIAL INFORMATION GROUP, INC.; *U.S. Private*, pg. 1238
DISHA RESOURCES LIMITED; *Int'l*, pg. 2135
DIXON, HUBARD, FEINOUR & BROWN, INC.—See Atlantic Union Bankshares Corporation; *U.S. Public*, pg. 223
DLALA ISLAMIC BROKERAGE COMPANY (W.L.L.)—See Dlala Brokerage and Investments Holding Company Q.S.C; *Int'l*, pg. 2140
DLC ASIA LTD.; *Int'l*, pg. 2140
DNB AUTO FINANCE OY—See DNB Bank ASA; *Int'l*, pg. 2147
DNB MARKETS, INC.—See DNB Bank ASA; *Int'l*, pg. 2148
DNH MEDICAL MANAGEMENT, INC.—See DaVita Inc.; *U.S. Public*, pg. 637
DOLAT INVESTMENTS LTD.; *Int'l*, pg. 2156
DOMINICK & DOMINICK—See B. Riley Financial, Inc.; *U.S. Public*, pg. 260
DOMINO DEUTSCHLAND GMBH—See Brother Industries, Ltd.; *Int'l*, pg. 1197
DOM MAKLERSKI BZ WBK S.A.—See Banco Santander, S.A.; *Int'l*, pg. 826
DONGXING SECURITIES CO., LTD.; *Int'l*, pg. 2171
DOUGHERTY FINANCIAL GROUP LLC; *U.S. Private*, pg. 1266
DRESDNER BANK MEXICO S.A.—See Commerzbank AG; *Int'l*, pg. 1718
DRESDNER KLEINWORT DEUTSCHLAND GMBH—See Commerzbank AG; *Int'l*, pg. 1717
DRESDNER KLEINWORT FRANCE SA—See Commerzbank AG; *Int'l*, pg. 1717
DRESDNER KLEINWORT LIMITED—See Commerzbank AG; *Int'l*, pg. 1717
DRESDNER KLEINWORT SHANGHAI—See Commerzbank AG; *Int'l*, pg. 1718

N.A.I.C.S. INDEX 523150 — INVESTMENT BANKING ...
N.A.I.C.S. Index

DRESDNER KLEINWORT—See Commerzbank AG; *Int'l*, pg. 1717
DRW HOLDINGS, LLC; *U.S. Private*, pg. 1280
DRW INVESTMENTS (UK) LTD.—See DRW Holdings, LLC; *U.S. Private*, pg. 1280
DT CAPITAL LIMITED; *Int'l*, pg. 2216
DUBAI INVESTMENTS PJSC; *Int'l*, pg. 2219
DUBILIER & COMPANY, INC.; *U.S. Private*, pg. 1283
DUNCAN-WILLIAMS, INC.; *U.S. Private*, pg. 1288
DWITIYA TRADING LIMITED; *Int'l*, pg. 2236
DWS (AUSTRIA) INVESTMENTGESELLSCHAFT MBH—See Deutsche Bank Aktiengesellschaft; *Int'l*, pg. 2057
DWS INVESTMENT GMBH—See Deutsche Bank Aktiengesellschaft; *Int'l*, pg. 2057
DWS INVESTMENTS DISTRIBUTORS, INC.—See Deutsche Bank Aktiengesellschaft; *Int'l*, pg. 2057
DWS INVESTMENTS S.G.I.I.C.—See Deutsche Bank Aktiengesellschaft; *Int'l*, pg. 2057
DWS POLSKA TFI S.A.—See Deutsche Bank Aktiengesellschaft; *Int'l*, pg. 2057
DZ BANK NEW YORK BRANCH—See DZ BANK AG Deutsche Zentral-Genossenschaftsbank; *Int'l*, pg. 2243
DZ FINANCIAL MARKETS LLC—See DZ BANK AG Deutsche Zentral-Genossenschaftsbank; *Int'l*, pg. 2243
D&Z LIMITED—See Morgan Stanley; *U.S. Public*, pg. 1471
DZ PRIVATBANK SINGAPORE LTD.—See DZ BANK AG Deutsche Zentral-Genossenschaftsbank; *Int'l*, pg. 2244
EAGLE INVESTMENT SERVICES INC.—See Eagle Financial Services, Inc.; *U.S. Public*, pg. 702
EAI PARTNERSHIP LP; *U.S. Private*, pg. 1312
ECOBANK DEVELOPMENT CORPORATION—See Ecobank Transnational Incorporated; *Int'l*, pg. 2294
ECP EMERGING GROWTH LIMITED; *Int'l*, pg. 2300
EDC INVESTMENT CORPORATION—See Ecobank Transnational Incorporated; *Int'l*, pg. 2294
EDC STOCKBROKERS LIMITED—See Ecobank Transnational Incorporated; *Int'l*, pg. 2294
EDELWEISS BROKING LIMITED—See Edelweiss Financial Services Ltd.; *Int'l*, pg. 2306
EDELWEISS SECURITIES LIMITED—See Edelweiss Financial Services Ltd.; *Int'l*, pg. 2306
EDGEVIEW PARTNERS L.P.—See Piper Sandler Companies; *U.S. Public*, pg. 1694
EFG AG—See EFG International AG; *Int'l*, pg. 2319
EFG ASESORIAS FINANCIERAS SPA—See EFG International AG; *Int'l*, pg. 2320
EFG ASSET MANAGEMENT (AMERICAS) CORP.—See EFG International AG; *Int'l*, pg. 2320
EFG ASSET MANAGEMENT (HONG KONG) LTD.—See EFG International AG; *Int'l*, pg. 2320
EFG ASSET MANAGEMENT (SINGAPORE) PTE. LTD.—See EFG International AG; *Int'l*, pg. 2320
EFG ASSET MANAGEMENT (UK) LTD.—See EFG International AG; *Int'l*, pg. 2320
EFG ASSET MANAGERS SAM—See EFG International AG; *Int'l*, pg. 2320
EFG BANK LTD.—See EFG International AG; *Int'l*, pg. 2320
EFG BANK & TRUST (BAHAMAS) LTD.—See EFG International AG; *Int'l*, pg. 2320
EFG BANK VON ERNST AG—See EFG International AG; *Int'l*, pg. 2320
EFG CAPITAL ASESORES FINANCIEROS S.A.C.—See EFG International AG; *Int'l*, pg. 2320
EFG CAPITAL INTERNATIONAL CORP.—See EFG International AG; *Int'l*, pg. 2320
EFG HARRIS ALLDAY—See EFG International AG; *Int'l*, pg. 2320
EFG HERMES UAE LTD—See EFG Holding; *Int'l*, pg. 2319
EFG HOLDING; *Int'l*, pg. 2319
EFG INDEPENDENT FINANCIAL ADVISERS—See EFG International AG; *Int'l*, pg. 2320
EFG INTERNATIONAL AG; *Int'l*, pg. 2319
EFG INVESTMENT BANK—See EFG International AG; *Int'l*, pg. 2320
EFG OFFSHORE LIMITED—See EFG International AG; *Int'l*, pg. 2320
EFG OFICINA DE REPRESENTACION URUGUAY SA—See EFG International AG; *Int'l*, pg. 2320
EFG (PANAMA) S.A.—See EFG International AG; *Int'l*, pg. 2319
EFG PLATTS FIELLO LIMITED—See EFG International AG; *Int'l*, pg. 2320
EFG SA—See EFG International AG; *Int'l*, pg. 2320
EFG SECURITIES BULGARIA E.A.D.—See Eurobank Ergasias Services and Holdings S.A.; *Int'l*, pg. 2532
EFG WEALTH MANAGEMENT (BERMUDA) LTD.—See EFG International AG; *Int'l*, pg. 2320
EFG WEALTH MANAGEMENT (CAYMAN) LTD.—See EFG International AG; *Int'l*, pg. 2321
EFG WEALTH SOLUTIONS (SINGAPORE) LTD.—See EFG International AG; *Int'l*, pg. 2321
EGYPTIAN ARABIAN CMAR SECURITIES BROKERAGE; *Int'l*, pg. 2327
EIENDOMSSELSKAPET DRONNING MAUDS GATE 15 AS—See Eksportfinans ASA; *Int'l*, pg. 2340
EIGHT CAPITAL—See Dundee Corporation; *Int'l*, pg. 2226
EIKO LIFESCIENCES LIMITED; *Int'l*, pg. 2332
E-KENT GECIS SISTEMLERI VE BILETLEME TEKNOLOJILERI A.S.—See Aktif Yatirim Bankasi A.S.; *Int'l*, pg. 267
E.K. RILEY INVESTMENTS, LLC—See LPL Financial Holdings Inc.; *U.S. Public*, pg. 1343
ELIXIR CAPITAL LTD.; *Int'l*, pg. 2363
ELIXIR EQUITIES PRIVATE LIMITED—See Elixir Capital Ltd.; *Int'l*, pg. 2363
EMIRATES INVESTMENT SERVICES LTD—See Emirates NBD PJSC; *Int'l*, pg. 2382
EMIRATES NBD CAPITAL KSA LLC—See Emirates NBD PJSC; *Int'l*, pg. 2382
EMIRATES NBD CAPITAL LTD.—See Emirates NBD PJSC; *Int'l*, pg. 2382
EMIRATES NBD SECURITIES LLC—See Emirates NBD PJSC; *Int'l*, pg. 2382
EMIRATES NBD TRUST COMPANY (JERSEY) LIMITED—See Emirates NBD PJSC; *Int'l*, pg. 2382
EMKAY GLOBAL FINANCIAL SERVICES LIMITED; *Int'l*, pg. 2383
EMMERSON PLC; *Int'l*, pg. 2384
EMPRENDIMIENTOS DE VALOR S.A—See Banco Bilbao Vizcaya Argentaria, S.A.; *Int'l*, pg. 817
ENCAVIS PORTFOLIO MANAGEMENT GMBH—See Encavis AG; *Int'l*, pg. 2401
ENHANCED SECURITIES LIMITED—See G-Resources Group Limited; *Int'l*, pg. 2862
ENVISION CAPITAL GROUP LLC; *U.S. Private*, pg. 1410
EQUITA GROUP S.P.A.; *Int'l*, pg. 2487
EQUITY LOAN BROKING PTY LTD.—See Count Limited; *Int'l*, pg. 1817
EQUITY SERVICES, INC.—See National Life Insurance Company; *U.S. Private*, pg. 2858
EQUITY TRUST COMPANY; *U.S. Private*, pg. 1416
ERSTE ALAPKEZELO ZRT.—See Erste Group Bank AG; *Int'l*, pg. 2498
ERSTE PRIVATE EQUITY LIMITED—See Erste Group Bank AG; *Int'l*, pg. 2498
ERSTE SECURITIES POLSKA S.A.—See Erste Group Bank AG; *Int'l*, pg. 2498
ESECLENDING (EUROPE) LIMITED—See PCP Enterprise, L.P.; *U.S. Private*, pg. 3121
ESECLENDING LLC—See PCP Enterprise, L.P.; *U.S. Private*, pg. 3121
ESKMUIR SECURITIES LTD—See Eskmuir Properties Ltd; *Int'l*, pg. 2503
ESTRADA HINOJOSA & CO., INC.—See Texas State Bankshares, Inc.; *U.S. Private*, pg. 3977
E.SUN SECURITIES CO., LTD.—See E. Sun Financial Holding Co., Ltd.; *Int'l*, pg. 2250
E.SUN SECURITIES INVESTMENT TRUST CO., LTD.—See E. Sun Financial Holding Co., Ltd.; *Int'l*, pg. 2250
E.T.F.S. LLC—See Emirates NBD PJSC; *Int'l*, pg. 2381
ETICO PARTNERS, LLC—See Quaestus Holdings, LLC; *U.S. Private*, pg. 3316
E*TRADE SECURITIES LLC—See E*TRADE Financial Corporation; *U.S. Private*, pg. 1302
EUGENE INVESTMENT & FUTURES CO., LTD.—See Eugene Investment & Securities Co., Ltd.; *Int'l*, pg. 2526
EUGENE INVESTMENT & SECURITIES CO., LTD.; *Int'l*, pg. 2526
EUROFINANCE INVESTMENT COMPANY JSC; *Int'l*, pg. 2535
EUROHAUS LLC; *Int'l*, pg. 2552
EURO PACIFIC CAPITAL, INC.; *U.S. Private*, pg. 1433
EUROPEAN FINANCE ASSOCIATES S.A.—See ELLAKTOR S.A.; *Int'l*, pg. 2365
EUROPEAN INVESTMENT BANK; *Int'l*, pg. 2556
EUROPEAN WHOLESALE SECURITIES MARKET LIMITED—See Euronext N.V.; *Int'l*, pg. 2554
EUWAX AG; *Int'l*, pg. 2560
EVERBRIGHT SECURITIES CO., LTD.—See China Everbright Group Limited; *Int'l*, pg. 1501
EVERCORE, INC.; *U.S. Public*, pg. 799
EVERCORE PARTNERS LIMITED—See Evercore, Inc.; *U.S. Public*, pg. 800
EVERCORE PARTNERS MEXICO, S. DE R.L.—See Evercore, Inc.; *U.S. Public*, pg. 800
EVEREST BANK LIMITED; *Int'l*, pg. 2563
EXCALIBUR FUTURES LIMITED—See GoFintech Innovation Limited; *Int'l*, pg. 3021
EXCALIBUR SECURITIES LIMITED—See GoFintech Innovation Limited; *Int'l*, pg. 3021
EXCEL FOR FINANCIAL INVESTMENT COMPANY LTD.—See Bank of Jordan PLC; *Int'l*, pg. 845
EXCELSIA INVESTMENT ADVISORS—See Bennett Thrasher; *U.S. Private*, pg. 527
EXPLICIT FINANCE LIMITED; *Int'l*, pg. 2588
EYE SURGEONS; *U.S. Private*, pg. 1453
FAIRFIELD GROUP—See Franklin Resources, Inc.; *U.S. Public*, pg. 882
FAR EASTERN BANK OJSC; *Int'l*, pg. 2617
FAREAST ISLAMI SECURITIES LIMITED—See Fareast Islami Life Insurance Co. Ltd.; *Int'l*, pg. 2618
FARLIE, TURNER & CO., LLC; *U.S. Private*, pg. 1474
FASTATOR AB; *Int'l*, pg. 2622
FBN CAPITAL LTD.—See FBN Holdings PLC; *Int'l*, pg. 2627
FBN (MERCHANT BANKERS) LIMITED—See FBN Holdings PLC; *Int'l*, pg. 2627
FC INVESTMENT ADVISERS CO., LTD.—See Fund Creation Group Co., Ltd.; *Int'l*, pg. 2845
FEDERATED SECURITIES CORP.—See Federated Hermes, Inc.; *U.S. Public*, pg. 827
FIFTH THIRD SECURITIES, INC.—See Fifth Third Bancorp; *U.S. Public*, pg. 833
FIG PARTNERS LLC—See The Penn Mutual Life Insurance Company; *U.S. Private*, pg. 4092
FINANCE 500, INC.—See Stifel Financial Corp.; *U.S. Public*, pg. 1949
FINANCIAL WEST INVESTMENT GROUP INC.; *U.S. Private*, pg. 1508
FINANSIA SYRUS SECURITIES PUBLIC COMPANY LIMITED; *Int'l*, pg. 2669
FINNAT INVESTMENTS SPA—See Banca Finnat Euramerica S.p.A.; *Int'l*, pg. 814
FINTECH GLOBAL INCORPORATED; *Int'l*, pg. 2677
FINXACT LLC—See Fiserv, Inc.; *U.S. Public*, pg. 850
FIRST ALLIED SECURITIES, INC.—See RCAP Holdings, LLC; *U.S. Private*, pg. 3361
FIRST BROKERS SECURITIES LLC—See CME Group, Inc.; *U.S. Public*, pg. 517
FIRST CAPITAL EQUITIES LIMITED—See First Capital Securities Corporation Limited; *Int'l*, pg. 2682
FIRST CAPITAL SECURITIES CO., LTD.; *Int'l*, pg. 2682
FIRST CAPITAL SECURITIES LIMITED—See China First Capital Group Limited; *Int'l*, pg. 1503
FIRST CITIZENS INVESTMENTS, INC.—See Civista Bancshares, Inc.; *U.S. Public*, pg. 507
FIRST CITY MONUMENT BANK LIMITED—See FCMB Group Plc; *Int'l*, pg. 2628
FIRST DAWOOD PROPERTIES LIMITED; *Int'l*, pg. 2683
FIRST EMPIRE SECURITIES INC.; *U.S. Private*, pg. 1517
FIRST EQUITY DEVELOPMENT INCORPORATED—See First Equity Group, Inc.; *U.S. Private*, pg. 1517
FIRST FINANCIAL BANK—See First Financial Bancorp.; *U.S. Public*, pg. 843
FIRST MANHATTAN CO.; *U.S. Private*, pg. 1521
FIRST METRO INVESTMENT CORPORATION; *Int'l*, pg. 2685
FIRST NATIONAL EQUITIES LIMITED; *Int'l*, pg. 2686
FIRST NATIONAL INVESTMENT BANKING—See First National of Nebraska, Inc.; *U.S. Private*, pg. 1524
FIRST NEW YORK SECURITIES LLC; *U.S. Private*, pg. 1524
FIRST NZ CAPITAL LIMITED; *Int'l*, pg. 2686
FIRSTRADE SECURITIES, INC.; *U.S. Private*, pg. 1532
FIRST REPUBLIC SECURITIES COMPANY, LLC—See JPMorgan Chase & Co.; *U.S. Public*, pg. 1207
FIRST SECURITIES INC.—See First Financial Holding Co., Ltd.; *Int'l*, pg. 2683
FIRST SHANGHAI FINANCE LIMITED—See First Shanghai Investments Limited; *Int'l*, pg. 2687
FIRST SHANGHAI FINANCIAL HOLDING LIMITED—See First Shanghai Investments Limited; *Int'l*, pg. 2687
FIRST SHANGHAI SECURITIES LIMITED—See First Shanghai Investments Limited; *Int'l*, pg. 2687
FIRST TAISEC SECURITIES INC.—See First Financial Holding Co., Ltd.; *Int'l*, pg. 2683
FIRST WESTERN TRUST BANK—See First Western Financial, Inc.; *U.S. Public*, pg. 848
FIRST WORLDSEC SECURITIES LIMITED—See First Financial Holding Co., Ltd.; *Int'l*, pg. 2683
FISERV CLEARING, INC.—See Fiserv, Inc.; *U.S. Public*, pg. 851
FISHER ENTERPRISES, LLC; *U.S. Private*, pg. 1534
FIVE BROKERS CAPITAL JSC; *Int'l*, pg. 2696
FLASHFUNDERS, INC.; *U.S. Private*, pg. 1540
FLATEXDEGIRO AG; *Int'l*, pg. 2698
FLOMIC GLOBAL LOGISTICS LTD.; *Int'l*, pg. 2707
FMSBONDS, INC.; *U.S. Private*, pg. 1555
FNS HOLDINGS PUBLIC COMPANY LIMITED; *Int'l*, pg. 2718
FOLGER NOLAN FLEMING DOUGLAS INCORPORATED; *U.S. Private*, pg. 1558
FORESTERS FINANCIAL SERVICES, INC.—See Golden Gate Capital Management II, LLC; *U.S. Private*, pg. 1731
FOREX CAPITAL MARKETS LIMITED—See Global Brokerage, Inc.; *U.S. Public*, pg. 940
FOREX TRADING LLC—See Global Brokerage, Inc.; *U.S. Public*, pg. 940
FORTIS CAPITAL CORP.—See BNP Paribas SA; *Int'l*, pg. 1084
FORTIS PRIVATE EQUITY BELGIUM NV—See BNP Paribas SA; *Int'l*, pg. 1084
FORTUNE (HK) SECURITIES LIMITED—See GoFintech Innovation Limited; *Int'l*, pg. 3021
FORTUNE INTERNATIONAL LIMITED; *Int'l*, pg. 2743
FORTUNE SECURITIES CORPORATION; *Int'l*, pg. 2744
FOUNDATION SECURITIES (PVT) LIMITED—See Fauji Foundation; *Int'l*, pg. 2623
FOUNDER SECURITIES CO., LTD.; *Int'l*, pg. 2753
FOUNDRY GROUP LLC; *U.S. Private*, pg. 1581
FOUNTAIN ASSET CORP.; *Int'l*, pg. 2754
FRANKFURTER BANKGESELLSCHAFT (SCHWEIZ)

523150 — INVESTMENT BANKING ...

AG—See Helaba Landesbank Hessen-Thuringen; *Int'l*, pg. 3327
FRANKFURT FAMILY OFFICE GMBH—See Deutsche Bank Aktiengesellschaft; *Int'l*, pg. 2062
FREEDOM INTERNATIONAL BROKERAGE COMPANY—See BGC Group, Inc.; *U.S. Public*, pg. 328
FREEDOM INVESTMENTS, INC.—See Oppenheimer Holdings Inc.; *U.S. Public*, pg. 1608
THE FRIEDKIN GROUP, INC.; *U.S. Private*, pg. 4031
FRONTPOINT MANAGEMENT INC.—See Morgan Stanley; *U.S. Public*, pg. 1472
FROST BROKERAGE SERVICES, INC.—See Cullen/Frost Bankers, Inc.; *U.S. Public*, pg. 604
FROST SECURITIES, INC.—See Cullen/Frost Bankers, Inc.; *U.S. Public*, pg. 604
FRUITION VENTURES LIMITED; *Int'l*, pg. 2797
FUBON ASSET MANAGEMENT CO., LTD.—See Fubon Financial Holding Co. Ltd.; *Int'l*, pg. 2801
FUBON SECURITIES CO., LTD.—See Fubon Financial Holding Co. Ltd.; *Int'l*, pg. 2802
FUBON SECURITIES USA LLC—See Fubon Financial Holding Co. Ltd.; *Int'l*, pg. 2802
FUND CREATION GROUP CO., LTD.; *Int'l*, pg. 2845
FUTURISTIC SECURITIES LIMITED; *Int'l*, pg. 2858
FUTU SECURITIES INTERNATIONAL (HONG KONG) LIMITED—See Futu Holdings Limited; *Int'l*, pg. 2852
FX PRIME BY GMO CORPORATION—See GMO Internet Group, Inc.; *Int'l*, pg. 3013
GABELLI VALUE FOR ITALY SPA; *Int'l*, pg. 2867
GAIN CAPITAL-FOREX.COM U.K., LTD.—See StoneX Group Inc.; *U.S. Public*, pg. 1952
GAIN CAPITAL HOLDINGS, INC.—See StoneX Group Inc.; *U.S. Public*, pg. 1952
GALILEO GLOBAL SECURITIES, LLC—See Galileo Global Advisors, LLC; *U.S. Private*, pg. 1637
GANGES SECURITIES LIMITED; *Int'l*, pg. 2880
GARANTI BANK SA—See Banco Bilbao Vizcaya Argentaria, S.A.; *Int'l*, pg. 818
GARANTI BBVA AS—See Banco Bilbao Vizcaya Argentaria, S.A.; *Int'l*, pg. 817
GARANTI BBVA YATIRIM AS—See Banco Bilbao Vizcaya Argentaria, S.A.; *Int'l*, pg. 818
GARDEN STATE SECURITIES INC.; *U.S. Private*, pg. 1643
GCM SECURITIES LIMITED—See Global Capital Markets Limited; *Int'l*, pg. 2994
GEDIK YATIRIM MENKUL DEGERLER A.S.; *Int'l*, pg. 2910
GEMSTONE INVESTMENTS LIMITED; *Int'l*, pg. 2916
GENERAL AMERICAN INVESTORS, INC.; *U.S. Public*, pg. 913
GENERALI ALAPKEZELO ZARTKORUEN MUKODO RESZVENYTARSASAG—See Assicurazioni Generali S.p.A.; *Int'l*, pg. 644
GENERAL SECURITIES CORP.—See Assicurazioni Generali S.p.A.; *Int'l*, pg. 644
GENESIS INVESTMENT BANK LIMITED—See Genesis Financial Holdings Limited; *Int'l*, pg. 2921
GENO BROKER GMBH—See DZ BANK AG Deutsche Zentral-Genossenschaftsbank; *Int'l*, pg. 2244
GEN RE SECURITIES HOLDINGS LLC—See Berkshire Hathaway Inc.; *U.S. Public*, pg. 301
GEORGE K. BAUM & COMPANY—See Stifel Financial Corp.; *U.S. Public*, pg. 1949
GESD CAPITAL PARTNERS; *U.S. Private*, pg. 1688
GETIN HOLDING S.A.; *Int'l*, pg. 2947
GETIN NOBLE BANK S.A.; *Int'l*, pg. 2947
GF FUND MANAGEMENT CO., LTD.—See GF Securities Co., Ltd.; *Int'l*, pg. 2955
GF FUTURES CO., LTD.—See GF Securities Co., Ltd.; *Int'l*, pg. 2955
GF FUTURES CO., LTD.—See GF Securities Co., Ltd.; *Int'l*, pg. 2955
GFH FINANCIAL GROUP B.S.C.; *Int'l*, pg. 2956
GFI GROUP INC.—See BGC Group, Inc.; *U.S. Public*, pg. 328
GFI GROUP PTE. LTD.—See BGC Group, Inc.; *U.S. Public*, pg. 329
GFI GROUP SERVICES LUX LTD—See BGC Group, Inc.; *U.S. Public*, pg. 329
GFI SECURITIES LTD.—See BGC Group, Inc.; *U.S. Public*, pg. 329
GF SECURITIES (CANADA) CO., LTD.—See GF Securities Co., Ltd.; *Int'l*, pg. 2955
GIANT OAK CORPORATION; *U.S. Private*, pg. 1695
GIB CAPITAL LLC—See Gulf International Bank B.S.C.; *Int'l*, pg. 3181
GILFORD SECURITIES INC.; *U.S. Private*, pg. 1700
GINALFI FINANCE—See BGC Group, Inc.; *U.S. Public*, pg. 329
GIRARD SECURITIES, INC.—See RCAP Holdings, LLC; *U.S. Private*, pg. 3361
G. K. GOH HOLDINGS LIMITED; *Int'l*, pg. 2864
THE GLADSTONE COMPANIES, INC.; *U.S. Private*, pg. 4033
GLOBAL EQUITY HIGH YIELD FUND B.V.—See Morgan Stanley; *U.S. Public*, pg. 1472
GLOBAL FINANCIAL SERVICES LLC—See Lee Equity Partners LLC; *U.S. Private*, pg. 2412
GLOBAL VALUE FUND LIMITED; *Int'l*, pg. 3002

GLOBESCAN CAPITAL INC.—See Brasada Capital Management LP; *U.S. Private*, pg. 640
GMO CLICK SECURITIES, INC.—See GMO Internet Group, Inc.; *Int'l*, pg. 3013
GMP SECURITIES, LLC—See StoneX Group Inc.; *U.S. Public*, pg. 1952
GMT CAPITAL CORP.; *U.S. Private*, pg. 1723
GOLDEN BRIDGE VIETNAM SECURITIES JOINT STOCK COMPANY; *Int'l*, pg. 3028
GOLDEN RICH SECURITIES LIMITED—See China Finance Investment Holdings Limited; *Int'l*, pg. 1502
GOLDMAN SACHS (ASIA) LLC—See The Goldman Sachs Group, Inc.; *U.S. Public*, pg. 2081
GOLDMAN SACHS AUSTRALIA PTY LTD—See The Goldman Sachs Group, Inc.; *U.S. Public*, pg. 2081
GOLDMAN SACHS BANK EUROPE SE—See The Goldman Sachs Group, Inc.; *U.S. Public*, pg. 2081
GOLDMAN SACHS CANADA INC.—See The Goldman Sachs Group, Inc.; *U.S. Public*, pg. 2076
GOLDMAN SACHS & CO. LLC—See The Goldman Sachs Group, Inc.; *U.S. Public*, pg. 2076
GOLDMAN, SACHS & CO.—See The Goldman Sachs Group, Inc.; *U.S. Public*, pg. 2081
GOLDMAN SACHS FOREIGN EXCHANGE (SINGAPORE) PTE—See The Goldman Sachs Group, Inc.; *U.S. Public*, pg. 2081
GOLDMAN SACHS GLOBAL COMMODITIES (CANADA) CORPORATION—See The Goldman Sachs Group, Inc.; *U.S. Public*, pg. 2081
GOLDMAN SACHS INTERNATIONAL BANK—See The Goldman Sachs Group, Inc.; *U.S. Public*, pg. 2081
GOLDMAN SACHS INTERNATIONAL—See The Goldman Sachs Group, Inc.; *U.S. Public*, pg. 2081
GOLDMAN SACHS JAPAN CO., LTD.—See The Goldman Sachs Group, Inc.; *U.S. Public*, pg. 2081
GOLDMAN SACHS PARIS INC. ET CIE—See The Goldman Sachs Group, Inc.; *U.S. Public*, pg. 2081
GOLDMAN SACHS REALTY JAPAN LTD.—See The Goldman Sachs Group, Inc.; *U.S. Public*, pg. 2081
GOLDMAN SACHS REALTY MANAGEMENT EUROPE GMBH—See The Goldman Sachs Group, Inc.; *U.S. Public*, pg. 2081
GOLDMAN SACHS (SINGAPORE) PTE.—See The Goldman Sachs Group, Inc.; *U.S. Public*, pg. 2081
GOOD FINANCE SECURITIES CO LTD; *Int'l*, pg. 3038
GPB FINANCIAL SERVICES LIMITED—See Gazprombank JSC; *Int'l*, pg. 2892
GRACE BROTHERS LTD.; *U.S. Private*, pg. 1748
GRAND PACIFIC FINANCIAL CORP.—See Chailease Holding Company Limited; *Int'l*, pg. 1437
GREAT POINT INVESTORS, LLC—See Washington Capital Management, LLC; *U.S. Private*, pg. 4446
GREENCREST FINANCIAL SERVICES LIMITED; *Int'l*, pg. 3074
GREENE HOLCOMB & FISHER, LLC—See Bank of Montreal; *Int'l*, pg. 847
GREEN SECURITIES LIMITED—See Green International Holdings Limited; *Int'l*, pg. 3071
GREENWAY PARTNERS, LP; *U.S. Private*, pg. 1781
THE GREENWICH GROUP INTERNATIONAL LLC; *U.S. Private*, pg. 4039
GRENKE AG; *Int'l*, pg. 3080
GRENKE BANK AG—See Grenke AG; *Int'l*, pg. 3081
GRETEX CORPORATE SERVICES LTD; *Int'l*, pg. 3082
GREYSTONE & CO., INC.; *U.S. Private*, pg. 1785
GRIFFIN CAPITAL SECURITIES, INC.—See Griffin Capital Corporation; *U.S. Private*, pg. 1787
GRIFFIN KBIK STEPHENS & THOMPSON; *U.S. Private*, pg. 1788
GROUPE PRIMONIAL SAS; *Int'l*, pg. 3110
GROUP ONE TRADING, L.P. - SAN FRANCISCO—See Group One Trading, L.P.; *U.S. Private*, pg. 1794
GROUP ONE TRADING, L.P.; *U.S. Private*, pg. 1794
GRUPO BURSATIL MEXICANO SA DE CV CASA DE BOLSA; *Int'l*, pg. 3123
GRUPO FINANCIERO BARCLAYS MEXICO, S.A. DE C.V.—See Barclays PLC; *Int'l*, pg. 862
GRUPO PRIVAL S.A.; *Int'l*, pg. 3134
GSD YATIRIM BANKASI A.S.—See GSD Holding A.S.; *Int'l*, pg. 3144
GSTM LLC—See The Goldman Sachs Group, Inc.; *U.S. Public*, pg. 2076
GT CAPITAL LIMITED—See GT Group Holdings Limited; *Int'l*, pg. 3151
GUILFORD SPECIALTY GROUP, INC.—See IFG Companies; *U.S. Private*, pg. 2038
GUIPUZCOANO CAPITAL, S.A.—See Banco de Sabadell, S.A.; *Int'l*, pg. 821
GUOLIAN SECURITIES CO., LTD; *Int'l*, pg. 3186
GUOSEN SECURITIES CO. LTD.; *Int'l*, pg. 3187
GUOTAI JUNAN INTERNATIONAL HOLDINGS LIMITED—See Guotai Junan Securities Co., Ltd.; *Int'l*, pg. 3187
GUOTAI JUNAN SECURITIES (VIETNAM) CORP.; *Int'l*, pg. 3187
GUYANA AMERICAS MERCHANT BANK INC.—See Edward B. Beharry & Co. Ltd.; *Int'l*, pg. 2316

HABIBSONS BANK LIMITED—See Habib Bank Limited; *Int'l*, pg. 3203
HAITONG BANCO DE INVESTIMENTO DO BRASIL S.A.—See Haitong Securities Co., Ltd.; *Int'l*, pg. 3218
HAITONG BANK, S.A.—See Haitong Securities Co., Ltd.; *Int'l*, pg. 3218
HAITONG BANK, S.A. - SPAIN BRANCH—See Haitong Securities Co., Ltd.; *Int'l*, pg. 3218
HAITONG BANK, S.A. - WARSAW BRANCH—See Haitong Securities Co., Ltd.; *Int'l*, pg. 3218
HAITONG INNOVATION SECURITIES INVESTMENT CO., LTD.—See Haitong Securities Co., Ltd.; *Int'l*, pg. 3218
HAITONG INVESTMENT IRELAND PLC—See Haitong Securities Co., Ltd.; *Int'l*, pg. 3218
HAITONG SECURITIES CO., LTD.; *Int'l*, pg. 3218
HAITONG SECURITIES (UK) LIMITED—See Haitong Securities Co., Ltd.; *Int'l*, pg. 3218
HAMAGIN TOKAI TOKYO SECURITIES CO., LTD.—See Concordia Financial Group, Ltd.; *Int'l*, pg. 1765
HANA DAETOO SECURITIES CO., LTD.—See Hana Financial Group, Inc.; *Int'l*, pg. 3240
HANCOCK WHITNEY INVESTMENT SERVICES, INC.—See Hancock Whitney Corporation; *U.S. Public*, pg. 982
HANSBERGER GROWTH INVESTORS, LP—See Groupe BPCE; *Int'l*, pg. 3096
HANWHA SECURITIES CO., LTD.—See Hanwha Group; *Int'l*, pg. 3266
HARBORLIGHT CAPITAL GROUP, LLC; *U.S. Private*, pg. 1859
HARGREAVES LANSDOWN STOCKBROKERS LTD—See Hargreaves Lansdown PLC; *Int'l*, pg. 3275
HARRIS ASSOCIATES, L.P.—See Groupe BPCE; *Int'l*, pg. 3096
HARRODS BANK LTD—See Harrods Ltd.; *Int'l*, pg. 3279
HARTFIELD, TITUS & DONNELLY LLC—See CME Group, Inc.; *U.S. Public*, pg. 517
HARTTERGRUPPE GMBH—See Axxiome AG; *Int'l*, pg. 773
HAUCK & AUFHAUSER ASSET MANAGEMENT SERVICES S.A R.L.—See Deutsche Bank Aktiengesellschaft; *Int'l*, pg. 2062
HAUCK AUFHAUSER LAMPE PRIVATBANK AG—See Fosun International Limited; *Int'l*, pg. 2751
H. BECK, INC.—See Warburg Pincus LLC; *U.S. Private*, pg. 4439
HBL ASSET MANAGEMENT LIMITED—See Habib Bank Limited; *Int'l*, pg. 3202
HB PORTFOLIO LTD.; *Int'l*, pg. 3295
HCI INVEST 3 HOLDCO PROPRIETARY LIMITED—See E Media Holdings Limited; *Int'l*, pg. 2246
H.C. WAINWRIGHT & CO., LLC; *U.S. Private*, pg. 1825
HDFC SECURITIES LIMITED—See Housing Development Finance Corporation Limited; *Int'l*, pg. 3492
H.D. VEST, INC.—See Genstar Capital, LLC; *U.S. Private*, pg. 1676
HEAD ASSET MANAGEMENT OY—See Head Invest Oy; *Int'l*, pg. 3300
HEADWATERS MB LLC—See Huntington Bancshares Incorporated; *U.S. Public*, pg. 1071
HEALTHCARE GROWTH PARTNERS; *U.S. Private*, pg. 1895
HECTO FINANCIAL CO., LTD.; *Int'l*, pg. 3307
HEFREN-TILLOTSON, INC.; *U.S. Private*, pg. 1904
HELABA LANDESBANK HESSEN-THURINGEN GIROZENTRALE—See Helaba Landesbank Hessen-Thuringen; *Int'l*, pg. 3328
HELLENIC BANK (INVESTMENTS) LTD—See Hellenic Bank Public Company Ltd.; *Int'l*, pg. 3333
HENGTAI CHANGCAI SECURITIES CO., LTD.—See HengTai Securities Co., Ltd.; *Int'l*, pg. 3347
HENGTAI SECURITIES CO., LTD; *Int'l*, pg. 3347
HENRY S. MILLER INVESTMENT SERVICES, LLC—See Henry S. Miller Management Corp.; *U.S. Private*, pg. 1919
HERITAGE CAPITAL GROUP, INC.; *U.S. Private*, pg. 1922
HERMES SECURITIES BROKERAGE—See EFG Holding; *Int'l*, pg. 2319
HILLTOP SECURITIES INC.—See Hilltop Holdings Inc.; *U.S. Public*, pg. 1038
HILLTOP SECURITIES INDEPENDENT NETWORK INC.—See Hilltop Holdings Inc.; *U.S. Public*, pg. 1039
HIMALAYAN BANK LIMITED; *Int'l*, pg. 3396
HINES SECURITIES, INC.; *U.S. Private*, pg. 1949
HING LEE SECURITIES LIMITED—See Global Token Limited; *Int'l*, pg. 3001
HNA CAPITAL GROUP CO., LTD.—See Hainan Traffic Administration Holding Co., Ltd.; *Int'l*, pg. 3213
HOA BINH SECURITIES JOINT STOCK COMPANY; *Int'l*, pg. 3435
HO CHI MINH CITY SECURITIES CORPORATION; *Int'l*, pg. 3434
HOLD BROTHERS INC.; *U.S. Private*, pg. 1962
HOLDING SVETA SOFIA AD; *Int'l*, pg. 3450
HOLLY FUTURES CO., LTD.; *Int'l*, pg. 3451
HOME FEDERAL PRIVATE BANKING—See Alerus Financial Corporation; *U.S. Public*, pg. 75
HONGKONG BAY SECURITIES LIMITED—See Bay Area Gold Group Limited; *Int'l*, pg. 900

N.A.I.C.S. INDEX

523150 — INVESTMENT BANKING ...

THE HONG KONG & SHANGHAI BANKING CORPORATION LTD.-THAILAND—See HSBC Holdings plc; *Int'l*, pg. 3507
HONG LEONG CAPITAL BERHAD—See Hong Leong Investment Holdings Pte. Ltd.; *Int'l*, pg. 3468
HONGTA SECURITIES CO., LTD.; *Int'l*, pg. 3471
HORNOR, TOWNSEND & KENT, INC.—See The Penn Mutual Life Insurance Company; *U.S. Private*, pg. 4092
HOUSTON ASSET MANAGEMENT, INC.—See Lightyear Capital LLC; *U.S. Private*, pg. 2454
HOVDE GROUP, LLC; *U.S. Private*, pg. 1994
HOWE BARNES INVESTMENTS, INC.; *U.S. Private*, pg. 1995
HPB STAMBENA STEDIONICA D.D.—See Hrvatska Postanska banka d.d.; *Int'l*, pg. 3502
HQ AB; *Int'l*, pg. 3501
HRVATSKA POSTANSKA BANKA D.D.; *Int'l*, pg. 3502
HSBC BANK INTERNATIONAL LIMITED—See HSBC Holdings plc; *Int'l*, pg. 3503
HSBC BROKING SERVICES ASIA LTD—See HSBC Holdings plc; *Int'l*, pg. 3506
HSBC CAPITAL MARKETS CORPORATION—See HSBC Holdings plc; *Int'l*, pg. 3505
HSBC EQUATOR BANK PLC—See HSBC Holdings plc; *Int'l*, pg. 3504
HSBC GERMANY HOLDINGS GMBH—See HSBC Holdings plc; *Int'l*, pg. 3505
HSBC PRIVATE BANK (SUISSE) S.A.—See HSBC Holdings plc; *Int'l*, pg. 3504
HSBC SECURITIES AND CAPITAL MARKETS (INDIA) PRIVATE LIMITED—See HSBC Holdings plc; *Int'l*, pg. 3506
HSBC SECURITIES JAPAN LIMITED—See HSBC Holdings plc; *Int'l*, pg. 3506
HSBC SECURITIES SERVICES (IRELAND) LIMITED—See HSBC Holdings plc; *Int'l*, pg. 3506
HSBC SECURITIES SERVICES (MALTA) LTD—See HSBC Holdings plc; *Int'l*, pg. 3506
HSBC SECURITIES (SOUTH AFRICA) (PTY) LIMITED—See HSBC Holdings plc; *Int'l*, pg. 3505
HUAAN SECURITIES CO. LTD.; *Int'l*, pg. 3510
HUAJIN FINANCIAL (INTERNATIONAL) HOLDINGS LIMITED—See Huafa Property Services Group Company Limited; *Int'l*, pg. 3511
HUA NAN SECURITIES CO., LTD.—See Hua Nan Financial Holdings Co., Ltd.; *Int'l*, pg. 3510
HUARONG FINANCIAL (SHENZHEN) EQUITY INVESTMENT FUND MANAGEMENT CO., LTD.—See China CITIC Financial Asset Management Co., Ltd.; *Int'l*, pg. 1489
HUARONG INTERNATIONAL ASSET MANAGEMENT LIMITED—See China CITIC Financial Asset Management Co., Ltd.; *Int'l*, pg. 1489
HUARONG INTERNATIONAL SECURITIES LIMITED—See China CITIC Financial Asset Management Co., Ltd.; *Int'l*, pg. 1489
HUARONG SECURITIES CO., LTD.—See China CITIC Financial Asset Management Co., Ltd.; *Int'l*, pg. 1489
HUARONG TIANHAI (SHANGHAI) INVESTMENT MANAGEMENT COMPANY LIMITED—See China CITIC Financial Asset Management Co., Ltd.; *Int'l*, pg. 1489
HUATAI UNITED SECURITIES CO., LTD.—See Huatai Securities Co., Ltd.; *Int'l*, pg. 3514
HUAXI SECURITIES CO., LTD.; *Int'l*, pg. 3515
HUA YING SECURITIES CO., LTD.—See Guolian Securities Co., Ltd; *Int'l*, pg. 3186
THE HUNTINGTON INVESTMENT COMPANY—See Huntington Bancshares Incorporated; *U.S. Public*, pg. 1071
HUNTLEIGH SECURITIES CORP.; *U.S. Private*, pg. 2010
HUTCHINSON SHOCKEY ERLEY & CO.; *U.S. Private*, pg. 2014
HWASEUNG SAVINGS BANK—See DHSteel; *Int'l*, pg. 2100
HYPOTHEEKFONDS VOOR OVERHEIDSPERSONEEL B.V.—See BNG Bank N.V.; *Int'l*, pg. 1079
HYUNDAI CAPITAL BANK EUROPE GMBH—See Banco Santander, S.A.; *Int'l*, pg. 826
HYUNDAI CAPITAL BANK EUROPE GMBH—See Hyundai Motor Company; *Int'l*, pg. 3559
I-BANKERS SECURITIES, INC.; *U.S. Private*, pg. 2026
IBANK MARKETING CO., LTD.—See Fukuoka Financial Group, Inc.; *Int'l*, pg. 2840
IBF FINANCIAL HOLDINGS CO., LTD.; *Int'l*, pg. 3574
IBG LLC—See Interactive Brokers Group, Inc.; *U.S. Public*, pg. 1140
IB SECURITIES JOINT STOCK COMPANY; *Int'l*, pg. 3569
ICAP AP (SINGAPORE) PTE LIMITED—See CME Group, Inc.; *U.S. Public*, pg. 516
ICAP BROKERS PTY LIMITED—See CME Group, Inc.; *U.S. Public*, pg. 516
ICAP CAPITAL MARKETS LLC—See CME Group, Inc.; *U.S. Public*, pg. 517
ICAP CORPORATES LLC—See CME Group, Inc.; *U.S. Public*, pg. 517
ICAP CURRENCY OPTIONS PTE LIMITED—See CME Group, Inc.; *U.S. Public*, pg. 516
ICAP DEL ECUADOR S.A.—See CME Group, Inc.; *U.S. Public*, pg. 517
ICAP DEUTSCHLAND GMBH—See CME Group, Inc.; *U.S. Public*, pg. 516

ICAP ELECTRONIC BROKING LIMITED—See CME Group, Inc.; *U.S. Public*, pg. 516
ICAP ELECTRONIC BROKING LLC—See CME Group, Inc.; *U.S. Public*, pg. 516
ICAP ENERGY PTE LIMITED—See CME Group, Inc.; *U.S. Public*, pg. 516
ICAP FUTURES (AUSTRALIA) PTY LTD—See CME Group, Inc.; *U.S. Public*, pg. 516
ICAP FUTURES LLC—See CME Group, Inc.; *U.S. Public*, pg. 517
ICAP (HONG KONG) LIMITED—See CME Group, Inc.; *U.S. Public*, pg. 516
ICAP INDIA PRIVATE LIMITED—See CME Group, Inc.; *U.S. Public*, pg. 516
ICAP NEW ZEALAND LIMITED—See CME Group, Inc.; *U.S. Public*, pg. 516
ICAP NORTH AMERICA, INC.—See CME Group, Inc.; *U.S. Public*, pg. 517
ICAP SCANDINAVIA A/S—See CME Group, Inc.; *U.S. Public*, pg. 517
ICAP SECURITIES ARGENTINA S.A.—See CME Group, Inc.; *U.S. Public*, pg. 517
ICAP SECURITIES LIMITED—See CME Group, Inc.; *U.S. Public*, pg. 517
ICAP SERVICES NORTH AMERICA LLC—See CME Group, Inc.; *U.S. Public*, pg. 517
ICAP TOTAN SECURITIES CO., LTD.; *Int'l*, pg. 3578
ICAP UNITED INC—See CME Group, Inc.; *U.S. Public*, pg. 517
ICAP WCLK LIMITED—See CME Group, Inc.; *U.S. Public*, pg. 517
ICDS LIMITED; *Int'l*, pg. 3579
ICE DATA INDICES, LLC—See Intercontinental Exchange, Inc.; *U.S. Public*, pg. 1142
ICE MARKETS LIMITED—See Intercontinental Exchange, Inc.; *U.S. Public*, pg. 1143
ICHIYOSHI SECURITIES CO., LTD.; *Int'l*, pg. 3581
ICICI SECURITIES INC.—See ICICI Bank Limited; *Int'l*, pg. 3581
ICIMB (MALAYSIA) SDN. BHD.—See CIMB Group Holdings Berhad; *Int'l*, pg. 1607
ICIM SERVICES INC.—See ICI Mutual Insurance Company; *U.S. Private*, pg. 2031
IDC BRAZIL—See China Oceanwide Holdings Group Co., Ltd.; *Int'l*, pg. 1536
IDC BRAZIL—See IDG Capital; *Int'l*, pg. 3593
IDC SPAIN—See China Oceanwide Holdings Group Co., Ltd.; *Int'l*, pg. 1537
IDC SPAIN—See IDG Capital; *Int'l*, pg. 3594
IDEA BANK SA—See Getin Holding S.A.; *Int'l*, pg. 2947
IDFC AMC TRUSTEE COMPANY LIMITED—See IDFC Limited; *Int'l*, pg. 3593
IDFC CAPITAL LIMITED—See IDFC Limited; *Int'l*, pg. 3593
IDG ENTERTAINMENT VERLAG GMBH—See China Oceanwide Holdings Group Co., Ltd.; *Int'l*, pg. 1537
IDG ENTERTAINMENT VERLAG GMBH—See IDG Capital; *Int'l*, pg. 3594
IDG GLOBAL SOLUTIONS APAC—See China Oceanwide Holdings Group Co., Ltd.; *Int'l*, pg. 1537
IDG GLOBAL SOLUTIONS APAC—See IDG Capital; *Int'l*, pg. 3594
IDG GLOBAL SOLUTIONS—See China Oceanwide Holdings Group Co., Ltd.; *Int'l*, pg. 1537
IDG GLOBAL SOLUTIONS—See IDG Capital; *Int'l*, pg. 3594
IDLC SECURITIES LIMITED—See IDLC Finance PLC.; *Int'l*, pg. 3595
IFCI FINANCIAL SERVICES LTD—See IFCI Limited; *Int'l*, pg. 3599
IFC SOLID CJSC; *Int'l*, pg. 3598
IFS FINANCIAL SERVICES, INC.—See Western & Southern Financial Group, Inc.; *U.S. Private*, pg. 4490
IIFL ASSET MANAGEMENT LTD.—See 360 ONE WAM Limited; *Int'l*, pg. 6
IMPERIAL CAPITAL GROUP, INC.; *U.S. Private*, pg. 2049
INCAPITAL LLC; *U.S. Private*, pg. 2052
INDEPENDENCE CAPITAL COMPANY; *U.S. Private*, pg. 2055
INDUSTRIAL ALLIANCE SECURITIES INC.—See iA Financial Corporation Inc.; *Int'l*, pg. 3567
INFAST BROKERAGE LIMITED—See FDG Electric Vehicles Limited; *Int'l*, pg. 2629
INFINEX INVESTMENTS, INC.—See Infinex Financial Holdings, Inc.; *U.S. Private*, pg. 2070
INLAND SECURITIES CORPORATION—See The Inland Real Estate Group of Companies, Inc.; *U.S. Private*, pg. 4056
INTERACTIVE BROKERS CANADA, INC.—See Interactive Brokers Group, Inc.; *U.S. Public*, pg. 1140
INTERACTIVE BROKERS HONG KONG LIMITED—See Interactive Brokers Group, Inc.; *U.S. Public*, pg. 1140
INTERACTIVE BROKERS (INDIA) PRIVATE LIMITED—See Interactive Brokers Group, Inc.; *U.S. Public*, pg. 1140
INTERACTIVE BROKERS, LLC—See Interactive Brokers Group, Inc.; *U.S. Public*, pg. 1140
INTERACTIVE BROKERS (UK) LIMITED—See Interactive Brokers Group, Inc.; *U.S. Public*, pg. 1140
INTERACTIVE FINANCIAL CORPORATION; *U.S. Private*, pg. 2108

INTERACTIVE INVESTOR SERVICES LIMITED—See abrdn PLC; *Int'l*, pg. 69
INTERBOLSA S.A.—See Euronext N.V.; *Int'l*, pg. 2554
INTERDIN, S.A.—See Banca Privada D'Andorra, SA; *Int'l*, pg. 816
INTERMAT TRADING CORP.; *U.S. Private*, pg. 2112
INTERPACIFIC INVESTORS SERVICES, INC.; *U.S. Private*, pg. 2122
INTER-PACIFIC SECURITIES SDN BHD—See Berjaya Corporation Berhad; *Int'l*, pg. 982
INTL FCSTONE FINANCIAL INC.—See StoneX Group Inc.; *U.S. Public*, pg. 1952
INVERSORA BURSATIL S.A. DE C.V.—See Grupo Financiero Inbursa, S.A. de C.V.; *Int'l*, pg. 3129
INVESCO GREAT WALL FUND MANAGEMENT COMPANY LIMITED—See Invesco Ltd.; *U.S. Public*, pg. 1162
INVESTACORP, INC.—See Reverence Capital Partners LLC; *U.S. Private*, pg. 3414
INVESTMENT PROFESSIONALS, INC.—See Ameriprise Financial, Inc.; *U.S. Public*, pg. 114
INVESTORS CAPITAL HOLDINGS, LTD.—See RCAP Holdings, LLC; *U.S. Private*, pg. 3361
INVESTRUST, N.A.—See American Fidelity Corporation; *U.S. Private*, pg. 234
IOWA SECURITIES INVESTMENT CORPORATION—See LLJ Inc.; *U.S. Private*, pg. 2475
IQ PHYSICAL DIAMOND TRUST; *U.S. Private*, pg. 2137
IRONRIDGE GLOBAL PARTNERS, LLC; *U.S. Private*, pg. 2140
ISRAEL A. ENGLANDER & CO., LLC; *U.S. Private*, pg. 2146
ITG AUSTRALIA LIMITED—See Virtu Financial, Inc.; *U.S. Public*, pg. 2300
ITG CANADA CORP.—See Virtu Financial, Inc.; *U.S. Public*, pg. 2300
ITG PLATFORMS SPAIN, S.L.—See Virtu Financial, Inc.; *U.S. Public*, pg. 2300
ITHRAA CAPITAL LLC—See Atheeb Group; *Int'l*, pg. 669
ITI CAPITAL LIMITED—See Da Vinci Capital LLC; *Int'l*, pg. 1902
ITI SECURITIES LIMITED—See Crest Ventures Limited; *Int'l*, pg. 1841
ITQAN CAPITAL—See Al Baraka Banking Group B.S.C.; *Int'l*, pg. 276
JACOBSON PARTNERS; *U.S. Private*, pg. 2180
JAFFE TILCHIN INVESTMENT PARTNERS, LLC; *U.S. Private*, pg. 2181
JANNEY MONTGOMERY SCOTT LLC—See The Penn Mutual Life Insurance Company; *U.S. Public*, pg. 4092
JDV LIMITED—See Commonwealth Bank of Australia; *Int'l*, pg. 1720
JEFFERIES BACHE LIMITED—See Jefferies Financial Group Inc.; *U.S. Public*, pg. 1188
JEFFERIES BROADVIEW—See Jefferies Financial Group Inc.; *U.S. Public*, pg. 1189
JEFFERIES HONG KONG LIMITED—See Jefferies Financial Group Inc.; *U.S. Public*, pg. 1189
JEFFERIES INDIA PRIVATE LTD.—See Jefferies Financial Group Inc.; *U.S. Public*, pg. 1189
JEFFERIES INTERNATIONAL LIMITED—See Jefferies Financial Group Inc.; *U.S. Public*, pg. 1188
JEFFERIES (JAPAN) LIMITED—See Jefferies Financial Group Inc.; *U.S. Public*, pg. 1188
JEFFERIES LLC - LOS ANGELES—See Jefferies Financial Group Inc.; *U.S. Public*, pg. 1189
JEFFERIES LLC—See Jefferies Financial Group Inc.; *U.S. Public*, pg. 1188
JEFFERIES (SWITZERLAND) LTD.—See Jefferies Financial Group Inc.; *U.S. Public*, pg. 1188
JF APEX SECURITIES BERHAD—See Apex Equity Holdings Berhad; *Int'l*, pg. 509
J.J.B. HILLIARD, W.L. LYONS, LLC—See Houchens Industries, Inc.; *U.S. Private*, pg. 1990
J.L. BAINBRIDGE AND COMPANY, INC.; *U.S. Private*, pg. 2167
JMP SECURITIES LLC - NEW YORK—See Citizens Financial Group, Inc.; *U.S. Public*, pg. 506
JMP SECURITIES LLC—See Citizens Financial Group, Inc.; *U.S. Public*, pg. 505
JOHNSTON, LEMON & CO. INC.; *U.S. Private*, pg. 2230
JOHN & WONG SECURITIES COMPANY LIMITED—See Imagi International Holdings Ltd.; *Int'l*, pg. 3618
JONESTRADING INSTITUTIONAL SERVICES LLC; *U.S. Private*, pg. 2234
JORDAN CREEK FINANCIAL SOLUTIONS—See Cambridge Investment Group, Inc.; *U.S. Private*, pg. 727
THE JORDAN, EDMISTON GROUP, INC.; *U.S. Private*, pg. 4063
JPMORGAN ASSET MANAGEMENT (JAPAN) LIMITED—See JPMorgan Chase & Co.; *U.S. Public*, pg. 1209
J.P. MORGAN BANK CANADA—See JPMorgan Chase & Co.; *U.S. Public*, pg. 1208
J.P. MORGAN BROKING (HONG KONG) LIMITED—See JPMorgan Chase & Co.; *U.S. Public*, pg. 1208
JPMORGAN CAZENOVE LTD.—See JPMorgan Chase & Co.; *U.S. Public*, pg. 1209
JPMORGAN CHASE - WESTERN REGIONAL

523150 — INVESTMENT BANKING ...

OFFICE—See JPMorgan Chase & Co.; *U.S. Public*, pg. 1209
J.P. MORGAN SECURITIES (ASIA PACIFIC) LIMITED—See JPMorgan Chase & Co.; *U.S. Public*, pg. 1208
J.P. MORGAN SECURITIES ASIA PTE. LTD.—See JPMorgan Chase & Co.; *U.S. Public*, pg. 1208
J.P. MORGAN SECURITIES PLC—See JPMorgan Chase & Co.; *U.S. Public*, pg. 1208
J.P. TURNER & COMPANY, LLC—See RCAP Holdings, LLC; *U.S. Private*, pg. 3361
JSCB TENGE BANK—See Halyk Bank of Kazakhstan JSC; *Int'l*, pg. 3234
JTI SECURITIES LIMITED—See Heng Xin China Holdings Limited; *Int'l*, pg. 3345
J.W. COLE FINANCIAL, INC.; *U.S. Private*, pg. 2172
KAMEN & CO.; *U.S. Private*, pg. 2258
KEEFE, BRUYETTE & WOODS INC. -SAN FRANCISCO—See Stifel Financial Corp.; *U.S. Public*, pg. 1950
KEEFE, BRUYETTE & WOODS INC.—See Stifel Financial Corp.; *U.S. Public*, pg. 1949
KEEFE, BRUYETTE & WOODS LIMITED—See Stifel Financial Corp.; *U.S. Public*, pg. 1950
KENANGA CAPITAL ISLAMIC SDN BHD—See Bay Group Holdings Sdn Bhd; *Int'l*, pg. 901
KENMAR SECURITIES INC.—See Ambroisie Capital Holding S.A.S.; *Int'l*, pg. 415
KESTRA INVESTMENT SERVICES, LLC—See Warburg Pincus LLC; *U.S. Private*, pg. 4439
KEYBANC CAPITAL MARKETS INC.—See KeyCorp; *U.S. Public*, pg. 1225
KINGFISHER CAPITAL, LLC—See Genstar Capital, LLC; *U.S. Private*, pg. 1677
KINGFISHER CAPITAL, LLC—See Keystone Group, L.P.; *U.S. Private*, pg. 2298
KINGSVIEW LLC; *U.S. Private*, pg. 2312
KIS PRICING—See Moody's Corporation; *U.S. Public*, pg. 1467
KKR CAPITAL MARKETS LLC—See KKR & Co. Inc.; *U.S. Public*, pg. 1256
KNIGHTSWOOD HOLDINGS LTD.—See Auxly Cannabis Group Inc.; *Int'l*, pg. 733
KOHLBERG KRAVIS ROBERTS GMBH—See KKR & Co. Inc.; *U.S. Public*, pg. 1257
KPMG CORPORATE FINANCE, LLC—See KPMG LLP; *U.S. Private*, pg. 2346
KYPROU SECURITIES SA—See Bank of Cyprus Holdings Public Limited Company; *Int'l*, pg. 841
KYTE BROKING LIMITED—See R.J. O'Brien & Associates, LLC; *U.S. Private*, pg. 3337
LADDER CAPITAL SECURITIES LLC—See Ladder Capital Corp.; *U.S. Public*, pg. 1288
LADY ALICE MINES PTY LTD.—See Cobra Resources plc; *Int'l*, pg. 1683
LAIDLAW GLOBAL CORPORATION; *U.S. Private*, pg. 2373
LAKE PACIFIC PARTNERS, LLC; *U.S. Private*, pg. 2375
LANKA SECURITIES PVT. LTD.—See Bank of Ceylon; *Int'l*, pg. 841
LANKA SECURITIES PVT. LTD.—See First Capital Securities Corporation Limited; *Int'l*, pg. 2682
LARSON FINANCIAL SECURITIES, LLC—See Larson Financial Holdings, LLC; *U.S. Private*, pg. 2394
LASALLE INTERNATIONAL PARTNER; *U.S. Private*, pg. 2394
LA SALLE STREET SECURITIES; *U.S. Private*, pg. 2369
LEGG MASON CAPITAL MANAGEMENT INC.—See Franklin Resources, Inc.; *U.S. Public*, pg. 882
LEGG MASON, INC.—See Franklin Resources, Inc.; *U.S. Public*, pg. 881
LEHMAN BROTHERS INC.—See Lehman Brothers Holdings Inc. Plan Trust; *U.S. Private*, pg. 2419
LEHMAN COMMERCIAL PAPER INC—See Lehman Brothers Holdings Inc. Plan Trust; *U.S. Private*, pg. 2419
LIBREMAX CAPITAL, LLC; *U.S. Private*, pg. 2447
LIFEMARK SECURITIES CORP.; *U.S. Private*, pg. 2450
LIME BROKERAGE, LLC—See Wedbush Capital Partners; *U.S. Private*, pg. 4468
LIMITED LIABILITY COMPANY BARCLAYS CAPITAL—See Barclays PLC; *Int'l*, pg. 862
LINCOLN FINANCIAL SECURITIES CORPORATION—See Lincoln National Corporation; *U.S. Public*, pg. 1319
THE LINK ASSET AND SECURITIES COMPANY LIMITED—See CME Group, Inc.; *U.S. Public*, pg. 518
LINK SECURITIES HONG KONG LIMITED—See CME Group, Inc.; *U.S. Public*, pg. 517
LIONTREE ADVISORS LLC—See LionTree LLC; *U.S. Private*, pg. 2464
LIONTREE LLC; *U.S. Private*, pg. 2464
LLOYD GEORGE MANAGEMENT (HONG KONG) LIMITED—See Bank of Montreal; *Int'l*, pg. 847
LOEB HOLDING CORPORATION; *U.S. Private*, pg. 2479
LOEB PARTNERS CORPORATION—See Loeb Holding Corporation; *U.S. Private*, pg. 2479
LOOMIS, SAYLES & COMPANY, L.P.—See Groupe BPCE; *Int'l*, pg. 3096
LOOP CAPITAL MARKETS; *U.S. Private*, pg. 2494

LPL FINANCIAL LLC—See LPL Financial Holdings Inc.; *U.S. Public*, pg. 1343
LPL INSURANCE ASSOCIATES, INC.—See LPL Financial Holdings Inc.; *U.S. Public*, pg. 1343
LRI INVEST S.A.—See Augur Capital AG; *Int'l*, pg. 703
MACROMARKETS LLC; *U.S. Private*, pg. 2538
MADURA MICRO FINANCE LIMITED—See CreditAccess Grameen Limited; *Int'l*, pg. 1836
MAINE SECURITIES CORPORATION; *U.S. Private*, pg. 2552
MAINFIRST BANK AG—See Stifel Financial Corp.; *U.S. Public*, pg. 1950
MANNING & NAPIER, INC.—See Callodine Acquisition Corporation; *U.S. Public*, pg. 424
MARSHBERRY CAPITAL, INC.—See Marsh, Berry & Company, Inc.; *U.S. Private*, pg. 2592
MASSENA PARTNERS S.A—See Groupe BPCE; *Int'l*, pg. 3098
MASSENA PARTNERS SA—See Groupe BPCE; *Int'l*, pg. 3098
MCGHEE RISK CAPITAL LLC; *U.S. Private*, pg. 2634
MCM CAPITAL PARTNERS, LP—See *U.S. Private*, pg. 2641
MCORPORATE FINANCE S.A—See Commerzbank AG; *Int'l*, pg. 1719
MEDVESEK PUSNIK BORZNO POSREDNISKA HISA D.D. LJUBLJANA—See ALTA Skupina d.d.; *Int'l*, pg. 384
MEESPIERSON (CURACAO) N.V.—See ABN AMRO Group N.V.; *Int'l*, pg. 64
MELIORFACTOR SPA—See BPER BANCA S.p.A; *Int'l*, pg. 1132
MERCER EMPLOYEE BENEFITS LIMITED—See Marsh & McLennan Companies, Inc.; *U.S. Public*, pg. 1385
MERCHANT BANK OF SRI LANKA LTD—See Bank of Ceylon; *Int'l*, pg. 841
MERIDIAN CAPITAL, LLC; *U.S. Private*, pg. 2672
MERRILL LYNCH CANADA INC.—See Bank of America Corporation; *U.S. Public*, pg. 272
MERRILL LYNCH DERIVATIVE PRODUCTS AG—See Bank of America Corporation; *U.S. Public*, pg. 272
MERRILL LYNCH JAPAN SECURITIES CO., LTD.—See Bank of America Corporation; *U.S. Public*, pg. 272
MERRILL LYNCH MEXICO, S.A. DE C.V., CASA DE BOLSA—See Bank of America Corporation; *U.S. Public*, pg. 272
MERRILL LYNCH S.A. CORRETORA DE TITULOS E VALORES MOBILIARIOS—See Bank of America Corporation; *U.S. Public*, pg. 272
MERRIMAN CAPITAL, INC.—See Merriman Holdings, Inc.; *U.S. Private*, pg. 2676
MESIROW FINANCIAL, INC. - DETROIT—See Mesirow Financial Holdings, Inc.; *U.S. Private*, pg. 2678
MESIROW FINANCIAL, INC. - HIGHLAND PARK—See Mesirow Financial Holdings, Inc.; *U.S. Private*, pg. 2679
MESIROW FINANCIAL, INC. - TAMPA—See Mesirow Financial Holdings, Inc.; *U.S. Private*, pg. 2679
MGI SECURITIES INC.—See iA Financial Corporation Inc.; *Int'l*, pg. 3567
MHR FUND MANAGEMENT LLC; *U.S. Private*, pg. 2695
MIDDLEBURG TRUST COMPANY—See Atlantic Union Bankshares Corporation; *U.S. Public*, pg. 223
MIDDLEBURG TRUST COMPANY—See Atlantic Union Bankshares Corporation; *U.S. Public*, pg. 223
MIDDLEBURG TRUST COMPANY—See Atlantic Union Bankshares Corporation; *U.S. Public*, pg. 223
MIDTOWN PARTNERS & CO., LLC; *U.S. Private*, pg. 2718
MIGDAL STOCK EXCHANGE SERVICES (N.E.) LTD.—See Assicurazioni Generali S.p.A.; *Int'l*, pg. 647
MILLBURN RIDGEFIELD CORPORATION; *U.S. Private*, pg. 2730
MINMETALS SECURITIES BROKERAGE CO. LTD.—See China Rare Earth Resources And Technology Co., Ltd.; *Int'l*, pg. 1546
MITSUBISHI UFJ MORGAN STANLEY SECURITIES CO., LTD.—See Morgan Stanley; *U.S. Public*, pg. 1473
MML DISTRIBUTORS, LLC—See Massachusetts Mutual Life Insurance Company; *U.S. Private*, pg. 2605
MML INVESTORS SERVICES, INC.—See Massachusetts Mutual Life Insurance Company; *U.S. Private*, pg. 2605
MOELIS & COMPANY GERMANY GMBH—See Moelis & Company; *U.S. Public*, pg. 1456
MOELIS & COMPANY NETHERLANDS BV—See Moelis & Company; *U.S. Public*, pg. 1456
MOOMOO INC.—See Futu Holdings Limited; *Int'l*, pg. 2852
MOORS & CABOT INC.; *U.S. Private*, pg. 2781
MORAN EDWARDS ASSET MANAGEMENT GROUP; *U.S. Private*, pg. 2781
MORGAN FINANCE LTD.—See First Steamship Co., Ltd.; *Int'l*, pg. 2688
MORGAN JOSEPH TRIARTISAN LLC—See Morgan Joseph TriArtisan Group Inc.; *U.S. Private*, pg. 2784
MORGAN STANLEY AB—See Morgan Stanley; *U.S. Public*, pg. 1473
MORGAN STANLEY ASIA LTD.—See Morgan Stanley; *U.S. Public*, pg. 1473
MORGAN STANLEY ASIA (SINGAPORE) SECURITIES PTE LTD.—See Morgan Stanley; *U.S. Public*, pg. 1472
MORGAN STANLEY AUSTRALIA LIMITED—See Morgan Stanley; *U.S. Public*, pg. 1472

MORGAN STANLEY BANK AG—See Morgan Stanley; *U.S. Public*, pg. 1473
MORGAN STANLEY B.V.—See Morgan Stanley; *U.S. Public*, pg. 1472
MORGAN STANLEY (CHINA) PRIVATE EQUITY INVESTMENT MANAGEMENT CO., LTD.—See Morgan Stanley; *U.S. Public*, pg. 1472
MORGAN STANLEY & CO. INTERNATIONAL PLC—See Morgan Stanley; *U.S. Public*, pg. 1472
MORGAN STANLEY & CO. LLC - BROOKLYN—See Morgan Stanley; *U.S. Public*, pg. 1472
MORGAN STANLEY & CO. LLC—See Morgan Stanley; *U.S. Public*, pg. 1472
MORGAN STANLEY & CO. LLC—See Morgan Stanley; *U.S. Public*, pg. 1472
MORGAN STANLEY CORRETORA DE TITULOS E VALORES MOBILIARIOS S.A.—See Morgan Stanley; *U.S. Public*, pg. 1473
MORGAN STANLEY DEAN WITTER (THAILAND) LTD.—See Morgan Stanley; *U.S. Public*, pg. 1473
MORGAN STANLEY (FRANCE) SAS—See Morgan Stanley; *U.S. Public*, pg. 1472
MORGAN STANLEY FUND SERVICES (IRELAND) LIMITED—See Morgan Stanley; *U.S. Public*, pg. 1472
MORGAN STANLEY HONG KONG LIMITED—See Morgan Stanley; *U.S. Public*, pg. 1472
MORGAN STANLEY INVESTMENT MANAGEMENT (AUSTRALIA) PTY LIMITED—See Morgan Stanley; *U.S. Public*, pg. 1473
MORGAN STANLEY (ISRAEL) LTD.—See Morgan Stanley; *U.S. Public*, pg. 1472
MORGAN STANLEY JAPAN GROUP CO., LTD.—See Morgan Stanley; *U.S. Public*, pg. 1475
MORGAN STANLEY JAPAN HOLDINGS CO., LTD.—See Morgan Stanley; *U.S. Public*, pg. 1475
MORGAN STANLEY MUFG SECURITIES CO., LTD.—See Morgan Stanley; *U.S. Public*, pg. 1475
MORGAN STANLEY SAUDI ARABIA—See Morgan Stanley; *U.S. Public*, pg. 1475
MORGAN STANLEY SERVICES CANADA CORP.—See Morgan Stanley; *U.S. Public*, pg. 1475
MORGAN STANLEY SERVICES PTY LIMITED—See Morgan Stanley; *U.S. Public*, pg. 1475
MORGAN STANLEY SINGAPORE PTE. LTD.—See Morgan Stanley; *U.S. Public*, pg. 1475
MORGAN STANLEY SOLUTIONS INDIA PRIVATE LIMITED—See Morgan Stanley; *U.S. Public*, pg. 1475
MORGAN STANLEY, S.V.,S.A.U—See Morgan Stanley; *U.S. Public*, pg. 1473
MORGAN STANLEY (THAILAND) LIMITED—See Morgan Stanley; *U.S. Public*, pg. 1472
MORGAN STANLEY UK LIMITED—See Morgan Stanley; *U.S. Public*, pg. 1475
MORGAN STANLEY WEALTH MANAGEMENT AUSTRALIA PTY LTD.—See Morgan Stanley; *U.S. Public*, pg. 1473
MORGAN STANLEY WEALTH MANAGEMENT AUSTRALIA PTY LTD.—See Morgan Stanley; *U.S. Public*, pg. 1475
MOSS ADAMS CAPITAL LLC—See Meridian Capital, LLC; *U.S. Private*, pg. 2672
MS SOLAR INVESTMENTS LLC—See Morgan Stanley; *U.S. Public*, pg. 1472
M&T SECURITIES, INC.—See M&T Bank Corporation; *U.S. Public*, pg. 1351
MULTI-BANK SERVICES LTD.; *U.S. Private*, pg. 2812
MURPHY & DURIEU; *U.S. Private*, pg. 2815
MUSCAT SECURITY HOUSE LLC—See Bank Muscat SAOG; *Int'l*, pg. 839
MUZINICH & CO., INC.; *U.S. Private*, pg. 2821
MYANMAR SECURITIES EXCHANGE CENTRE CO., LTD.—See Daiwa Securities Group Inc.; *Int'l*, pg. 1949
MYSTOCKFUND SECURITIES, INC—See Remark Holdings, Inc.; *U.S. Public*, pg. 1782
NACION BURSATIL S.A—See Banco de la Nacion Argentina; *Int'l*, pg. 820
NAGASAKI HOSHO SERVICE CO., LTD.—See Fukuoka Financial Group, Inc.; *Int'l*, pg. 2840
NATHAN & LEWIS SECURITIES INC; *U.S. Private*, pg. 2838
NATIONAL FINANCIAL SERVICES LLC—See FMR LLC; *U.S. Private*, pg. 1555
NATIONAL INTEGRITY LIFE INSURANCE COMPANY—See Western & Southern Financial Group, Inc.; *U.S. Public*, pg. 4490
NATIONAL SECURITIES CORPORATION—See B. Riley Financial, Inc.; *U.S. Public*, pg. 261
NATIXIS BLEICHROEDER INC.—See Groupe BPCE; *Int'l*, pg. 3094
NATIXIS CAPITAL MARKETS INC.—See Groupe BPCE; *Int'l*, pg. 3094
NATIXIS - CORPORATE & INVESTMENT BANKING—See Groupe BPCE; *Int'l*, pg. 3094
NATIXIS IM MEXICO, S. DE R.L. DE C.V.—See Groupe BPCE; *Int'l*, pg. 3098
NATIXIS INVESTMENT MANAGERS HONG KONG LIMITED—See Groupe BPCE; *Int'l*, pg. 3098
NATIXIS INVESTMENT MANAGERS, NORDICS FILIAL AB—See Groupe BPCE; *Int'l*, pg. 3098

N.A.I.C.S. INDEX

523150 — INVESTMENT BANKING ...

NATIXIS INVESTMENT MANAGERS S.A—See Groupe BPCE; *Int'l*, pg. 3098
NATIXIS INVESTMENT MANAGERS SECURITIES INVESTMENT CONSULTING CO., LTD.—See Groupe BPCE; *Int'l*, pg. 3098
NATIXIS INVESTMENT MANAGERS SWITZERLAND SARL—See Groupe BPCE; *Int'l*, pg. 3098
NATIXIS INVESTMENT MANAGERS UK LTD.—See Groupe BPCE; *Int'l*, pg. 3098
NATIXIS INVESTMENT MANAGERS URUGUAY S.A.—See Groupe BPCE; *Int'l*, pg. 3098
NATIXIS JAPAN SECURITIES CO., LTD.—See Groupe BPCE; *Int'l*, pg. 3098
NATIXIS MILAN S.A—See Groupe BPCE; *Int'l*, pg. 3098
NATIXIS SECURITIES NORTH AMERICA INC.—See Groupe BPCE; *Int'l*, pg. 3095
NATIXIS TAIWAN LIMITED—See Groupe BPCE; *Int'l*, pg. 3098
NAVEGAR LP—See A. Soriano Corporation; *Int'l*, pg. 22
NBAD PRIVATE BANK (SUISSE) SA—See First Abu Dhabi Bank P.J.S.C.; *Int'l*, pg. 2681
NBAD SECURITIES LLC—See First Abu Dhabi Bank P.J.S.C.; *Int'l*, pg. 2681
NCW GROUP INC.—See Financial Gravity Companies, Inc.; *U.S. Public*, pg. 834
NEEDHAM & COMPANY INC.; *U.S. Private*, pg. 2879
NEIDIGER TUCKER BRUNER INC.; *U.S. Private*, pg. 2880
NEWMARK OF LONG ISLAND LLC—See BGC Group, Inc.; *U.S. Public*, pg. 329
NEWMARK OF WASHINGTON D.C. LLC—See BGC Group, Inc.; *U.S. Public*, pg. 329
NEX GROUP LIMITED—See CME Group, Inc.; *U.S. Public*, pg. 516
NIBC MARKETS N.V.—See Blackstone Inc.; *U.S. Public*, pg. 356
NOBLE CAPITAL MARKETS; *U.S. Private*, pg. 2932
NOBLE SECURITIES S.A—See Getin Noble Bank S.A.; *Int'l*, pg. 2947
NORTHEAST CAPITAL & ADVISORY INC; *U.S. Private*, pg. 2949
NORTHEAST SECURITIES INC.; *U.S. Private*, pg. 2951
NORTH SEA PARTNERS LLC; *U.S. Private*, pg. 2946
NORTHWEST FINANCIAL SERVICES, INC.—See Northwest Bancshares, Inc.; *U.S. Public*, pg. 1542
NOVAMEDI S.A—See Abbott Laboratories; *U.S. Public*, pg. 20
NPM SECURITIES, LLC—See Nasdaq, Inc.; *U.S. Public*, pg. 1492
NUMIS CORPORATION LIMITED—See Deutsche Bank Aktiengesellschaft; *Int'l*, pg. 2061
NUMIS SECURITIES INC—See Deutsche Bank Aktiengesellschaft; *Int'l*, pg. 2061
NUVEEN SELECT TAX-FREE INCOME PORTFOLIO—See Teachers Insurance Association - College Retirement Fund; *U.S. Public*, pg. 3947
OAK HILL ADVISORS (AUSTRALIA) PTY. LTD.—See T. Rowe Price Group Inc.; *U.S. Public*, pg. 1978
OAK HILL ADVISORS (HONG KONG) LIMITED—See T. Rowe Price Group Inc.; *U.S. Public*, pg. 1978
OANDA CORP.—See CVC Capital Partners SICAV-FIS S.A.; *Int'l*, pg. 1885
OBERON SECURITIES, LLC; *U.S. Private*, pg. 2987
OCTAVUS GROUP LLC; *U.S. Private*, pg. 2992
OFSCAP LLC; *U.S. Private*, pg. 3003
OHIO NATIONAL EQUITIES, INC.—See Caisse de Depot et Placement du Quebec; *Int'l*, pg. 1254
OIDC—See China Steel Corporation; *Int'l*, pg. 1556
OKOBOJI FINANCIAL SERVICES, INC.; *U.S. Private*, pg. 3008
OLD HILL PARTNERS INC—See Spouting Rock Financial Partners LLC; *U.S. Private*, pg. 3762
OLIVER WYMAN FZ-LLC—See Marsh & McLennan Companies, Inc.; *U.S. Public*, pg. 1387
OLIVER WYMAN LTD.—See Marsh & McLennan Companies, Inc.; *U.S. Public*, pg. 1387
OLIVER WYMAN SNC—See Marsh & McLennan Companies, Inc.; *U.S. Public*, pg. 1387
OMEGA CAPITAL EUROPE PLC—See BNP Paribas SA; *Int'l*, pg. 1092
OMEGA CAPITAL INVESTMENTS PLC—See BNP Paribas SA; *Int'l*, pg. 1092
ONB INVESTMENT SERVICES—See Old National Bancorp; *U.S. Public*, pg. 1567
O'NEIL SECURITIES, INCORPORATED—See William O'Neil & Co., Inc.; *U.S. Private*, pg. 4524
ONP OWNER LLC—See Ladder Capital Corp.; *U.S. Public*, pg. 1288
OOO GOLDMAN SACHS BANK—See The Goldman Sachs Group, Inc.; *U.S. Public*, pg. 2082
OPPENHEIMER HOLDINGS INC.; *U.S. Public*, pg. 1608
OPPENHEIM LANDERT FAMILY OFFICE AG—See Deutsche Bank Aktiengesellschaft; *Int'l*, pg. 2062
OPTIONSXPRESS HOLDINGS, INC.—See The Charles Schwab Corporation; *U.S. Public*, pg. 2058
OPTIONSXPRESS SINGAPORE PTE LTD.—See The Charles Schwab Corporation; *U.S. Public*, pg. 2058
ORIENTAL FINANCIAL SERVICES LLC—See OFG Bancorp; *U.S. Public*, pg. 1564

ORYX INTERNATIONAL GROWTH FUND LIMITED—See Harwood Capital LLP; *Int'l*, pg. 3282
OSCAR GRUSS & SON INCORPORATED; *U.S. Private*, pg. 3046
OTR GLOBAL LLC—See Infinedi Partners LP; *U.S. Private*, pg. 2070
PACIFIC CREST SECURITIES LLC—See KeyCorp; *U.S. Public*, pg. 1226
PACIFIC STRATEGIC INVESTMENTS PTY LIMITED—See BKI Investment Company Limited; *Int'l*, pg. 1054
PANMURE GORDON (BROKING) LIMITED—See Atlas Merchant Capital LLC; *U.S. Private*, pg. 379
PANMURE GORDON (UK) LIMITED—See Atlas Merchant Capital LLC; *U.S. Private*, pg. 379
PANTELAKIS SECURITIES S.A.—See HSBC Holdings plc; *Int'l*, pg. 3506
PAREX BROKERAGE SYSTEM—See AS Reverta; *Int'l*, pg. 591
PARIBAS ASIA EQUITY LTD.—See BNP Paribas SA; *Int'l*, pg. 1092
THE PARK CIRCLE MOTOR CO.; *U.S. Private*, pg. 4091
PASKEWITZ ASSET MANAGEMENT LLC; *U.S. Private*, pg. 3104
PATERSON SECURITIES PVT LTD—See Hinduja Group Ltd.; *Int'l*, pg. 3399
PAULSON INVESTMENT COMPANY, LLC; *U.S. Private*, pg. 3114
PAYCHEX SECURITIES CORPORATION—See Paychex, Inc.; *U.S. Public*, pg. 1656
PCIB SECURITIES, INC.—See BDO Unibank, Inc.; *Int'l*, pg. 930
PENSERRA SECURITIES LLC; *U.S. Private*, pg. 3138
PERSHING GROUP LLC—See The Bank of New York Mellon Corporation; *U.S. Public*, pg. 2038
PERVEZ AHMED SECURITIES LIMITED—See D.S. Industries Limited; *Int'l*, pg. 1901
PGS INTERNATIONAL N.V.—See Bayer Aktiengesellschaft; *Int'l*, pg. 910
PHEDINA HYPOTHEKEN 2010 BV—See BNP Paribas SA; *Int'l*, pg. 1092
PIGUET GALLAND & CIE SA—See Banque Cantonale Vaudoise; *Int'l*, pg. 853
PINNACLE ACQUISITIONS LLC—See ModivCare, Inc.; *U.S. Public*, pg. 1456
PIPER JAFFRAY COMPANIES-SEATTLE—See Piper Sandler Companies; *U.S. Public*, pg. 1694
PIPER JAFFRAY LTD.—See Piper Sandler Companies; *U.S. Public*, pg. 1694
PJT PARTNERS (FRANCE) SAS—See PJT Partners Inc.; *U.S. Public*, pg. 1696
PJT PARTNERS JAPAN K.K.—See PJT Partners Inc.; *U.S. Public*, pg. 1696
PKB PRIVATBANK SA—See Compagnie de l'Occident pour la Finance et l'Industrie S.A.; *Int'l*, pg. 1722
PKF O'CONNOR DAVIES CAPITAL, LLC—See PKF O'Connor Davies, LLP; *U.S. Private*, pg. 3193
PNC CAPITAL MARKETS LLC—See The PNC Financial Services Group, Inc.; *U.S. Public*, pg. 2120
POLEN CAPITAL MANAGEMENT, INC.; *U.S. Private*, pg. 3223
PORTZAMPARC SOCIETE DE BOURSE S.A.—See BNP Paribas SA; *Int'l*, pg. 1080
POYRY CAPITAL LIMITED—See AFRY AB; *Int'l*, pg. 195
PRAGER & CO., LLC; *U.S. Private*, pg. 3241
PRECEPT ADVISORY GROUP LLC—See Truist Financial Corporation; *U.S. Public*, pg. 2199
PREMIS CAPITAL PARTNERS, INC.—See Groupe BPCE; *Int'l*, pg. 3096
PRIVATBANK DEGROOF, S.A.U.—See Banque Degroof S.A.; *Int'l*, pg. 853
PROCHOICE CHRIMATISTIRIAKI LTD—See A.L. Prochoice Group Public Ltd.; *Int'l*, pg. 25
PROEQUITIES, INC.; *U.S. Public*, pg. 3274
PROFESSIONAL TRADING SOLUTIONS, INC.; *U.S. Private*, pg. 3276
PROGRESSIVE CAPITAL MANAGEMENT CORP.—See The Progressive Corporation; *U.S. Public*, pg. 2125
PRO SECURITIES, LLC—See Beyond, Inc.; *U.S. Public*, pg. 327
PROSPERA FINANCIAL SERVICES; *U.S. Private*, pg. 3288
PRUDENTIAL CAPITAL GROUP, L.P.—See Prudential Financial, Inc.; *U.S. Public*, pg. 1732
PRUDENTIAL FINANCIAL—See Prudential Financial, Inc.; *U.S. Public*, pg. 1732
PRUDENTIAL GLOBAL FUNDING, LLC—See Prudential Financial, Inc.; *U.S. Public*, pg. 1732
PSAGOT OFEK INVESTMENT HOUSE LTD.—See Apax Partners LLP; *Int'l*, pg. 505
PT ATTACHMENT SOLUTIONS, LLC—See Duke Energy Corporation; *U.S. Public*, pg. 691
PT BANK CIMB NIAGA TBK—See CIMB Group Holdings Berhad; *Int'l*, pg. 1608
PT BANK CTBC INDONESIA—See CTBC Financial Holding Co., Ltd.; *Int'l*, pg. 1869
PT BANK HSBC INDONESIA—See HSBC Holdings plc; *Int'l*, pg. 3507
PT BNP PARIBAS SECURITIES INDONESIA—See BNP Paribas SA; *Int'l*, pg. 1092

PT DEUTSCHE SECURITIES INDONESIA—See Deutsche Bank Aktiengesellschaft; *Int'l*, pg. 2061
PT. KIWOOM SECURITIES INDONESIA—See Daou Data Corp.; *Int'l*, pg. 1970
PULSE TRADING, INC.—See State Street Corporation; *U.S. Public*, pg. 1940
PUNJAB CAPITAL SECURITIES (PRIVATE) LIMITED—See First Punjab Modaraba; *Int'l*, pg. 2687
QUAKER SECURITIES—See ACG Advisors (UK) LLP; *Int'l*, pg. 102
QUESTAR CAPITAL CORPORATION—See Allianz SE; *Int'l*, pg. 347
RABO AUSTRALIA LIMITED—See Cooperatieve Centrale Raiffeisen-Boerenleenbank B.A.; *Int'l*, pg. 1792
RABO CAPITAL SERVICES, INC.—See Cooperatieve Centrale Raiffeisen-Boerenleenbank B.A.; *Int'l*, pg. 1791
RAFFERTY CAPITAL MARKETS, LLC—See Tradeweb Markets Inc.; *U.S. Public*, pg. 2178
RAND WEALTH, LLC—See Stifel Financial Corp.; *U.S. Public*, pg. 1949
RAYMOND JAMES AFFORDABLE HOUSING INVESTMENTS—See Raymond James Financial, Inc.; *U.S. Public*, pg. 1764
RAYMOND JAMES & ASSOCIATES, INC.—See Raymond James Financial, Inc.; *U.S. Public*, pg. 1764
RAYMOND JAMES LTD.—See Raymond James Financial, Inc.; *U.S. Public*, pg. 1764
REALTY MANAGEMENT SERVICE INC.—See Morgan Stanley; *U.S. Public*, pg. 1475
REGULATORY CONSULTANTS, INC.—See DEKRA e.V.; *Int'l*, pg. 2010
RELIANT FINANCIAL SERVICES INC.; *U.S. Private*, pg. 3395
RENAISSANCE TECHNOLOGIES, LLC; *U.S. Private*, pg. 3397
RETELA CREA SECURITIES CO., LTD.—See Daiwa Securities Group Inc.; *Int'l*, pg. 1949
RIAZZI RHYNE & SWAIM INVESTMENT GROUP OF WELLS FARGO ADVISORS—See Wells Fargo & Company; *U.S. Public*, pg. 2345
RJ EQUITIES, INC.—See Raymond James Financial, Inc.; *U.S. Public*, pg. 1764
RJL HOLDING LLC; *U.S. Public*, pg. 3449
R.J. O'BRIEN (UK) LIMITED—See R.J. O'Brien & Associates, LLC; *U.S. Private*, pg. 3337
RMB AUSTRALIA LTD.—See FirstRand Limited; *Int'l*, pg. 2690
R.M. STARK & CO. INC.; *U.S. Private*, pg. 3339
ROBERT W. BAIRD & CO., INCORPORATED—See Baird Financial Group, Inc.; *U.S. Private*, pg. 453
ROCHDALE CORPORATION; *U.S. Private*, pg. 3463
ROCHDALE SECURITIES LLC; *U.S. Private*, pg. 3463
ROCK (NOMINEES) LIMITED—See Raymond James Financial, Inc.; *U.S. Public*, pg. 1764
ROCKY MOUNTAIN BANK—See Heartland Financial USA, Inc.; *U.S. Public*, pg. 1018
ROGGE GLOBAL PARTNERS LTD.—See Allianz SE; *Int'l*, pg. 346
ROOSEVELT & CROSS INC.; *U.S. Private*, pg. 3479
ROTH CAPITAL PARTNERS LLC; *U.S. Private*, pg. 3486
ROUND HILL SECURITIES; *U.S. Private*, pg. 3488
ROYAL ALLIANCE ASSOCIATES, INC.—See Reverence Capital Partners LLC; *U.S. Private*, pg. 3415
ROYAL SEAL INVESTMENTS INC—See Royal Seal Construction Inc.; *U.S. Public*, pg. 3493
RRB BERATUNGSGESELLSCHAFT FUR ALTERSVERSORGUNG MBH—See Marsh & McLennan Companies, Inc.; *U.S. Public*, pg. 1388
R.W. PRESSPRICH & CO., INCORPORATED; *U.S. Private*, pg. 3340
RYVYL INC.; *U.S. Public*, pg. 1829
SABADELL CORPORATE FINANCE, S.L.—See Banco de Sabadell, S.A.; *Int'l*, pg. 821
SAGEPOINT FINANCIAL, INC.—See Reverence Capital Partners LLC; *U.S. Private*, pg. 3415
SAGICOR FINANCE INC.—See Alignvest Management Corporation; *Int'l*, pg. 327
SAGICOR INVESTMENTS JAMAICA LIMITED—See Alignvest Management Corporation; *Int'l*, pg. 327
SAL. OPPENHEIM JR. & CIE. AG & CO. KGAA—See Deutsche Bank Aktiengesellschaft; *Int'l*, pg. 2062
SAL. OPPENHEIM JR. & CIE. (SWITZERLAND) LTD.—See Deutsche Bank Aktiengesellschaft; *Int'l*, pg. 2062
SAMMONS SECURITIES COMPANY, LLC—See Sammons Enterprises, Inc.; *U.S. Private*, pg. 3537
SAMPO BANK PLC—See Danske Bank A/S; *Int'l*, pg. 1969
SAMUEL A. RAMIREZ & CO. INC.; *U.S. Private*, pg. 3538
SANDERS MORRIS HARRIS INC.—See Lee Equity Partners LLC; *U.S. Private*, pg. 2412
SANDLER, O'NEILL & PARTNERS, L.P.—See Piper Sandler Companies; *U.S. Public*, pg. 1694
SANDS BROTHERS & CO. LTD.—See Sands Brothers Asset Management LLC; *U.S. Private*, pg. 3545
SANTANDER BANK & TRUST, LTD.—See Banco Santander, S.A.; *Int'l*, pg. 826
SANTANDER SECURITIES CORPORATION—See First BanCorp; *U.S. Public*, pg. 839
SA STONE WEALTH MANAGEMENT INC.—See StoneX

523150 — INVESTMENT BANKING ...

Group Inc.; *U.S. Public*, pg. 1953
SBC PROPERTIES, INC.—See First Metro Investment Corporation; *Int'l*, pg. 2685
S BROKER AG & CO. KG—See DekaBank; *Int'l*, pg. 2005
SCHONFELD SECURITIES, LLC—See Schonfeld Group Holdings, LLC; *U.S. Private*, pg. 3568
SCOTT & STRINGFELLOW, LLC—See Truist Financial Corporation; *U.S. Public*, pg. 2201
SCP PRIVATE EQUITY PARTNERS—See Safeguard Scientifics, Inc.; *U.S. Public*, pg. 1834
SECOND STREET SECURITIES, INC.—See SS&C Technologies Holdings, Inc.; *U.S. Public*, pg. 1922
SEMGIMENENEA S.P.A.—See Assicurazioni Generali S.p.A.; *Int'l*, pg. 643
SERAFINI FINANCIAL SERVICE INC.—See TA Associates, Inc.; *U.S. Private*, pg. 3919
SERVICIOS DE PRODUCCION SALTILLO, S.A. DE C.V.—See Grupo Industrial Saltillo S.A. de C.V.; *Int'l*, pg. 3130
SHAREHOLDER SERVICES GROUP—See Altruist Corp; *U.S. Private*, pg. 210
SHAREKHAN LTD.—See BNP Paribas SA; *Int'l*, pg. 1092
SHARE PLC—See abrdn PLC; *Int'l*, pg. 69
SHAYKIN & COMPANY; *U.S. Private*, pg. 3628
SHENG-RAAMCO MANAGEMENT INC.—See Raamco International Incorporated; *U.S. Private*, pg. 3341
SHINWA VENTURE CAPITAL CO., LTD.—See Fukuoka Financial Group, Inc.; *Int'l*, pg. 2840
SHIRAZI INVESTMENTS (PRIVATE) LIMITED—See Atlas Group of Companies; *Int'l*, pg. 685
SIF SWISS INVESTMENT FUNDS S.A.—See EFG International AG; *Int'l*, pg. 2321
SIGULER GUFF & COMPANY, LP; *U.S. Private*, pg. 3651
SIMMONS & COMPANY INTERNATIONAL LIMITED—See Piper Sandler Companies; *U.S. Public*, pg. 1694
SIMMONS & COMPANY INTERNATIONAL—See Piper Sandler Companies; *U.S. Public*, pg. 1694
SIMMONS FIRST INVESTMENT GROUP, INC.—See Simmons First National Corporation; *U.S. Public*, pg. 1881
SIMMONS PRIVATE EQUITY II, L.P.—See Piper Sandler Companies; *U.S. Public*, pg. 1694
SINO WEALTH SECURITIES LIMITED—See Heng Tai Consumables Group Limited; *Int'l*, pg. 3345
SMILE—See Co-operative Group Limited; *Int'l*, pg. 1679
SOLICOUR INC.—See iA Financial Corporation Inc.; *Int'l*, pg. 3568
SONAE CAPITAL, SGPS, SA—See Efanor Investimentos, SGPS, SA; *Int'l*, pg. 2318
SOVEREIGN SECURITIES CORPORATION, LLC—See Banco Santander, S.A.; *Int'l*, pg. 827
SPARKASSE BANK D.D.—See Erste Group Bank AG; *Int'l*, pg. 2499
SPENCER TRASK & CO.; *U.S. Private*, pg. 3755
SPENCER TRASK VENTURES, INC.—See Spencer Trask & Co.; *U.S. Private*, pg. 3755
SPV68, S.R.O.—See HTC holding a.s.; *Int'l*, pg. 3508
STAMFORD PARTNERS LLP—See Piper Sandler Companies; *U.S. Public*, pg. 1694
STANDARD SECURITY INVESTORS CORPORATION—See Geneve Holdings Corp.; *U.S. Private*, pg. 1671
STEPHENS, INC.—See SF Holding Corp.; *U.S. Private*, pg. 3621
STERLING CAPITAL MANAGEMENT LLC—See Guardian Capital Group Limited; *Int'l*, pg. 3170
STEWARD PARTNERS INVESTMENT SOLUTIONS, LLC—See Steward Partners Global Advisory, LLC; *U.S. Private*, pg. 3811
STIFEL EUROPE ADVISORY GMBH—See Stifel Financial Corp.; *U.S. Public*, pg. 1950
STIFEL, NICOLAUS & COMPANY, INCORPORATED—See Stifel Financial Corp.; *U.S. Public*, pg. 1950
STIGMA PARTICIPACOES S.A.—See BTG Pactual Holding S.A.; *Int'l*, pg. 1204
ST. JOHN HOLDINGS INC.; *U.S. Private*, pg. 3771
STONE & YOUNGBERG LLC—See Stifel Financial Corp.; *U.S. Public*, pg. 1950
STRYKER JAPAN HOLDING KK—See Stryker Corporation; *U.S. Public*, pg. 1957
SUMMIT BROKERAGE SERVICES, INC.—See RCAP Holdings, LLC; *U.S. Private*, pg. 3361
SUNAMERICA ASSET MANAGEMENT, LLC—See American International Group, Inc.; *U.S. Public*, pg. 105
SUNAMERICA CAPITAL SERVICES, INC.—See American International Group, Inc.; *U.S. Public*, pg. 105
SUN HUNG KAI INVESTMENT SERVICES LIMITED - MACAU BRANCH—See Allied Group Limited; *Int'l*, pg. 357
SUN HUNG KAI INVESTMENT SERVICES LIMITED - SHENZHEN BRANCH—See Allied Group Limited; *Int'l*, pg. 357
SUN LIFE INSURANCE & ANNUITY COMPANY OF NEW YORK—See Guggenheim Partners, LLC; *U.S. Private*, pg. 1813
SUNTRON INVESTMENTS LIMITED—See CJ Corporation; *Int'l*, pg. 1634
SUNVIEW NIRMAN PRIVATE LIMITED—See Gretex Corporate Services Ltd; *Int'l*, pg. 3082

SUSQUEHANNA INTERNATIONAL GROUP, LLP; *U.S. Private*, pg. 3885
SUSQUEHANNA INTERNATIONAL SECURITIES, LTD.—See Susquehanna International Group, LLP; *U.S. Private*, pg. 3885
SUTTER SECURITIES, INC.—See Flashfunders, Inc.; *U.S. Private*, pg. 1540
SYNOVUS SECURITIES, INC.—See Synovus Financial Corp.; *U.S. Public*, pg. 1972
TAGLICH BROTHERS, INC.; *U.S. Private*, pg. 3922
TAGLICH BROTHERS, INC.—See Taglich Brothers, Inc.; *U.S. Private*, pg. 3922
TAIWAN LIFE INSURANCE CO., LTD.—See CTBC Financial Holding Co., Ltd.; *Int'l*, pg. 1869
TAIWAN LOTTERY CORPORATION—See CTBC Financial Holding Co., Ltd.; *Int'l*, pg. 1869
TCW FUNDS MANAGEMENT, INC.—See The Carlyle Group Inc.; *U.S. Public*, pg. 2056
TD AMERITRADE ASIA PTE. LTD.—See The Charles Schwab Corporation; *U.S. Public*, pg. 2058
TD AMERITRADE CLEARING, INC.—See The Charles Schwab Corporation; *U.S. Public*, pg. 2058
TD AMERITRADE, INC.—See The Charles Schwab Corporation; *U.S. Public*, pg. 2058
TEB INVESTMENT SECURITIES, INC—See BNP Paribas SA; *Int'l*, pg. 1093
TEGRIS LLC—See LionTree LLC; *U.S. Private*, pg. 2464
TEMPLE-INLAND RESOURCE COMPANY—See International Paper Company; *U.S. Public*, pg. 1158
TENEX CAPITAL MANAGEMENT, L.P.; *U.S. Private*, pg. 3966
TETON TRUST COMPANY—See Truist Financial Corporation; *U.S. Public*, pg. 2199
TFI BNP PARIBAS POLSKA SA—See BNP Paribas SA; *Int'l*, pg. 1084
TFS-ICAP LIMITED—See CME Group, Inc.; *U.S. Public*, pg. 517
TFS-ICAP LLC—See CME Group, Inc.; *U.S. Public*, pg. 518
THB INTERNATIONAL INC—See AmWINS Group, Inc.; *U.S. Private*, pg. 270
THINKTECH, INC.—See The Charles Schwab Corporation; *U.S. Public*, pg. 2058
THIRD PARTY PLATFORM PTY LTD—See Bell Financial Group Limited; *Int'l*, pg. 966
THOMAS WEISEL PARTNERS LLC—See Stifel Financial Corp.; *U.S. Public*, pg. 1950
THORNHILL SECURITIES, INC.; *U.S. Private*, pg. 4163
THREESIXTY TRADING NETWORKS (INDIA) PVT LTD—See Deutsche Borse AG; *Int'l*, pg. 2063
THRIVENT FINANCIAL INVESTOR SERVICES INC.—See Thrivent Financial for Lutherans Foundation; *U.S. Private*, pg. 4165
THRIVENT INVESTMENT MANAGEMENT INC.—See Thrivent Financial for Lutherans Foundation; *U.S. Private*, pg. 4165
THROGMORTON STREET CAPITAL LTD.—See ADVFN PLC; *Int'l*, pg. 168
THUNDERBIRD INVESTMENTS PLC—See BNP Paribas SA; *Int'l*, pg. 1093
TIMBER HILL EUROPE AG—See Interactive Brokers Group, Inc.; *U.S. Public*, pg. 1140
TKO MILLER, LLC; *U.S. Private*, pg. 4178
TMC BONDS, LLC—See Intercontinental Exchange, Inc.; *U.S. Public*, pg. 1143
TORREYA PARTNERS LLC—See Stifel Financial Corp.; *U.S. Public*, pg. 1950
TRADEGO S.A./N.V.—See Euroclear S.A./N.V.; *Int'l*, pg. 2534
TRADESTAR INVESTMENTS, INC.—See Fiserv, Inc.; *U.S. Public*, pg. 851
TRADE THE MARKETS; *U.S. Public*, pg. 4202
TRANSAMERICA FINANCIAL ADVISORS, INC.—See Aegon N.V.; *Int'l*, pg. 174
TRIACT CANADA MARKETPLACE LP—See Cboe Global Markets, Inc.; *U.S. Public*, pg. 459
TRUIST SECURITIES, INC.—See Truist Financial Corporation; *U.S. Public*, pg. 2200
T.R. WINSTON & COMPANY, LLC; *U.S. Private*, pg. 3912
TWO SIGMA INVESTMENTS, LP; *U.S. Private*, pg. 4267
UAB PAREX INVESTICIJU VALDYMAS—See AS Reverta; *Int'l*, pg. 591
UMB CAPITAL CORPORATION—See UMB Financial Corporation; *U.S. Public*, pg. 2224
UNIFIED FINANCIAL SECURITIES, LLC—See GTCR LLC; *U.S. Private*, pg. 1806
UNION SQUARE VENTURES LLC; *U.S. Private*, pg. 4285
UNITED BROKERAGE SERVICES, INC.—See United Bankshares, Inc.; *U.S. Public*, pg. 2229
UNITED HERITAGE MUTUAL LIFE INSURANCE COMPANY INC.; *U.S. Private*, pg. 4293
UNITED PLANNERS' FINANCIAL SERVICES OF AMERICA—See Pacific Mutual Holding Company; *U.S. Private*, pg. 3069
UNIVEST INVESTMENTS, INC.—See Univest Financial Corporation; *U.S. Public*, pg. 2263
USAA INVESTMENT MANAGEMENT CO.—See The Charles Schwab Corporation; *U.S. Public*, pg. 2058

U.S. BANCORP INVESTMENTS, INC.—See U.S. Bancorp; *U.S. Public*, pg. 2213
UTAH HOUSING CORPORATION; *U.S. Private*, pg. 4324
UWHARRIE INVESTMENT ADVISORS INC.—See Uwharrie Capital Corp.; *U.S. Public*, pg. 2268
VAKUFSKA BANKA D.D. SARAJEVO—See CID Adriatic Investments GmbH; *Int'l*, pg. 1603
VALORES BANCOLOMBIA S.A.—See Bancolombia S.A.; *Int'l*, pg. 828
VALUE PARTNERS, LTD.; *U.S. Private*, pg. 4337
VANDHAM SECURITIES CORP.—See Wall Street Access Corp.; *U.S. Private*, pg. 4430
VANGUARD BROKERAGE SERVICES—See The Vanguard Group, Inc.; *U.S. Private*, pg. 4130
VANGUARD CAPITAL; *U.S. Private*, pg. 4343
VANGUARD INVESTMENTS AUSTRALIA LTD.—See The Vanguard Group, Inc.; *U.S. Private*, pg. 4130
VARIANT CAPITAL ADVISORS LLC—See Conway MacKenzie, Inc.; *U.S. Private*, pg. 1036
VCS QUALITY SERVICES PVT. LTD—See I Squared Capital Advisors (US) LLC; *U.S. Private*, pg. 2023
VELOSI QUALITY MANAGEMENT INTERNATIONAL L.L.C.—See I Squared Capital Advisors (US) LLC; *U.S. Private*, pg. 2024
VERDBREFASKRANING ISLANDS HF.—See Nasdaq, Inc.; *U.S. Public*, pg. 1492
VERMILION PARTNERS LIMITED—See Groupe BPCE; *Int'l*, pg. 3099
VERMILION PARTNERS (UK) LIMITED—See Groupe BPCE; *Int'l*, pg. 3099
VERTRIEBSGESELLSCHAFT MBH DER DEUTSCHEN BANK PRIVAT- UND GESCHAFTSKUNDEN—See Deutsche Bank Aktiengesellschaft; *Int'l*, pg. 2062
VFINANCE, INC.—See B. Riley Financial, Inc.; *U.S. Public*, pg. 261
VFINANCE INVESTMENTS, INC.—See B. Riley Financial, Inc.; *U.S. Public*, pg. 261
VICTOR SECURITIES; *U.S. Private*, pg. 4377
VIEWTRADE SECURITIES INC.; *U.S. Private*, pg. 4381
VINING-SPARKS IBG LP; *U.S. Private*, pg. 4385
VIRTU FINANCIAL, INC.; *U.S. Public*, pg. 2299
VIRTU ITG HOLDINGS LLC—See Virtu Financial, Inc.; *U.S. Public*, pg. 2300
VIRTU KNIGHT CAPITAL GROUP, LLC—See Virtu Financial, Inc.; *U.S. Public*, pg. 2300
VISION FINANCIAL MARKETS LLC; *U.S. Private*, pg. 4390
VISION INVESTMENT SERVICES CO. (S.A.O.C)—See EFG Holding; *Int'l*, pg. 2319
VITAE INVESTMENT CO., INC.—See Neville Chemical Company; *U.S. Private*, pg. 2891
VOYA FINANCIAL ADVISORS, INC.—See Genstar Capital, LLC; *U.S. Private*, pg. 1676
VOYA INVESTMENT MANAGEMENT LLC—See Voya Financial, Inc.; *U.S. Public*, pg. 2311
VOYA INVESTMENT MANAGEMENT—See Voya Financial, Inc.; *U.S. Public*, pg. 2311
VOYA INVESTMENT MANAGEMENT—See Voya Financial, Inc.; *U.S. Public*, pg. 2311
VSR FINANCIAL SERVICES, INC.—See RCAP Holdings, LLC; *U.S. Private*, pg. 3361
WALL STREET ACCESS CORP.; *U.S. Private*, pg. 4430
WAUWATOSA INVESTMENTS, INC.—See Waterstone Financial, Inc.; *U.S. Public*, pg. 2336
WBK NIERUCHOMOSCI S.A.—See Banco Santander, S.A.; *Int'l*, pg. 826
WCM BETEILIGUNGS- UND GRUNDBESITZ-AKTIENGESELLSCHAFT—See Aroundtown SA; *Int'l*, pg. 578
WEDBUSH CAPITAL PARTNERS; *U.S. Private*, pg. 4468
WEDBUSH SECURITIES, INC.—See Wedbush Capital Partners; *U.S. Private*, pg. 4468
WEEDEN & CO., LP—See Piper Sandler Companies; *U.S. Public*, pg. 1694
WEEDEN PRIME SERVICES, LLC—See Siebert Financial Corp.; *U.S. Public*, pg. 1876
WELLINGTON SHIELDS & CO., LLC; *U.S. Private*, pg. 4475
WELLS FARGO ADVISORS FINANCIAL NETWORK, LLC—See Wells Fargo & Company; *U.S. Public*, pg. 2345
WELLS FARGO ADVISORS, LLC—See Wells Fargo & Company; *U.S. Public*, pg. 2345
WELLS FARGO FUNDS DISTRIBUTOR, LLC—See Wells Fargo & Company; *U.S. Public*, pg. 2345
WELLS FARGO PRIME SERVICES, LLC - NEW YORK—See Wells Fargo & Company; *U.S. Public*, pg. 2347
WELLS FARGO PRIME SERVICES, LLC—See Wells Fargo & Company; *U.S. Public*, pg. 2347
WELLS FARGO SECURITIES, LLC—See Wells Fargo & Company; *U.S. Public*, pg. 2347
WERTZ YORK CAPITAL MANAGEMENT GROUP LLC; *U.S. Private*, pg. 4482
WESBANCO SECURITIES, INC.—See WesBanco, Inc.; *U.S. Public*, pg. 2350
WESTERN INTERNATIONAL SECURITIES, INC.—See Lee Equity Partners LLC; *U.S. Private*, pg. 2412
THE WESTERN & SOUTHERN LIFE INSURANCE

N.A.I.C.S. INDEX

COMPANY—See Western & Southern Financial Group, Inc.; *U.S. Private*, pg. 4490
WESTHOUSE SECURITIES LIMITED—See ICM Limited; *Int'l*, pg. 3582
W FINANCE GROUPE PRIMONIAL—See Groupe Primonial SAS; *Int'l*, pg. 3110
WHITNEY & CO., LLC; *U.S. Private*, pg. 4513
WILLIAM O'NEIL & CO., INC.; *U.S. Private*, pg. 4524
WILSON-DAVIS & COMPANY; *U.S. Private*, pg. 4531
WINCHESTER CAPITAL INVESTMENT MANAGEMENT CORPORATION; *U.S. Private*, pg. 4533
WING LUNG SECURITIES LTD.—See China Merchants Group Limited; *Int'l*, pg. 1520
WINTERFLOOD SECURITIES LIMITED—See Close Brothers Group plc; *Int'l*, pg. 1661
WOODBURY FINANCIAL SERVICES, INC.—See Reverence Capital Partners LLC; *U.S. Private*, pg. 3415
WOODSTOCK HOLDINGS, INC.; *U.S. Public*, pg. 2377
WORLD EQUITY GROUP, INC.—See Wentworth Management Services LLC; *U.S. Private*, pg. 4481
WORLDSOURCE SECURITIES INC.—See Guardian Capital Group Limited; *Int'l*, pg. 3170
WORLDSOURCE WEALTH MANAGEMENT INC.—See Guardian Capital Group Limited; *Int'l*, pg. 3170
W.P. STEWART & CO., LTD.—See Equitable Holdings, Inc.; *U.S. Public*, pg. 789
WR HAMBRECHT & CO. LLC; *U.S. Private*, pg. 4571
WRIGHTSON ICAP LLC—See CME Group, Inc.; *U.S. Public*, pg. 517
WSFS INVESTMENT GROUP, INC.—See WSFS Financial Corporation; *U.S. Public*, pg. 2384
ZAO DEUTSCHE SECURITIES—See Deutsche Bank Aktiengesellschaft; *Int'l*, pg. 2062
THE ZIEGLER COMPANIES, INC.; *U.S. Private*, pg. 4140
ZXY MEQQE CORPORATION—See Cresco, Ltd.; *Int'l*, pg. 1840

523160 — COMMODITY CONTRACTS INTERMEDIATION

141 CAPITAL, INC.; *U.S. Public*, pg. 2
3I HONG KONG—See 3i Group plc; *Int'l*, pg. 8
3I SWEDEN—See 3i Group plc; *Int'l*, pg. 8
3I SWITZERLAND LIMITED—See 3i Group plc; *Int'l*, pg. 8
ABDULLA FOUAD HOLDING CO.; *Int'l*, pg. 58
ADHIRAJ DISTRIBUTORS LTD.; *Int'l*, pg. 145
ADM BENSON INC.—See Archer-Daniels-Midland Company; *U.S. Public*, pg. 181
ADM INVESTOR SERVICES INC.—See Archer-Daniels-Midland Company; *U.S. Public*, pg. 182
ADM INVESTOR SERVICES INTERNATIONAL LIMITED—See Archer-Daniels-Midland Company; *U.S. Public*, pg. 182
ADVANCE TRADING INC.; *U.S. Private*, pg. 87
AFFIN MONEYBROKERS SDN. BHD.—See AFFIN Holdings Berhad; *Int'l*, pg. 186
AKTIF BANK SUKUK VARLIK KIRALAMA A.S.; *Int'l*, pg. 267
ALANKIT CORPORATE SERVICES LIMITED; *Int'l*, pg. 290
AL JABER TRADING LLC—See Al Jaber Group; *Int'l*, pg. 279
ALLIANCE RECOVERY CORP.; *U.S. Public*, pg. 79
ALMONDZ COMMODITIES PVT. LTD.—See Almondz Global Securities Limited; *Int'l*, pg. 364
ALPHA GROUP INTERNATIONAL PLC; *Int'l*, pg. 368
AMALGAMATED METAL TRADING LTD—See Amalgamated Metal Corporation PLC; *Int'l*, pg. 408
AMBRIAN METALS LIMITED—See Ambrian plc; *Int'l*, pg. 415
AMC PHYSICAL TRADING LTD—See Amalgamated Metal Corporation PLC; *Int'l*, pg. 408
AMERICAN NATIONAL TRADING CORP.—See Peregrine Financial Group, Inc.; *U.S. Private*, pg. 3147
AMFUTURES SDN BHD—See AMMB Holdings Berhad; *Int'l*, pg. 429
AMRAWORLD AGRICO LTD.; *Int'l*, pg. 437
AMT FUTURES LIMITED—See Amalgamated Metal Corporation PLC; *Int'l*, pg. 408
ARCHER FINANCIAL SERVICES, INC. (AFS)—See Archer-Daniels-Midland Company; *U.S. Public*, pg. 182
ARGENTEX GROUP PLC; *Int'l*, pg. 561
ARIF HABIB DMCC—See Arif Habib Corporation Limited; *Int'l*, pg. 564
ASAMA; *Int'l*, pg. 599
ASTRA GRAIN TRADE DIVISION—See Arab Supply & Trading Co.; *Int'l*, pg. 532
THE AURORA FUNDS INC.; *U.S. Private*, pg. 3990
AUTOMATED POWER EXCHANGE INC.; *U.S. Private*, pg. 399
BAKKT MARKETPLACE, LLC—See Intercontinental Exchange, Inc.; *U.S. Public*, pg. 1141
BANGLADESH FINANCE SECURITIES LIMITED—See Bangladesh Finance Limited; *Int'l*, pg. 835
BASF METAL FORWARDS LIMITED—See BASF SE; *Int'l*, pg. 880
BAYERISCHE STADTE- UND WOHNUNGSBAU GMBH & CO. KG; *Int'l*, pg. 913

BEEKAY NIRYAT LTD.; *Int'l*, pg. 939
BEIRA GRAIN TERMINAL, S.A.—See Seaboard Corporation; *U.S. Public*, pg. 1850
BENCHMARK SERVICES, INC.; *U.S. Private*, pg. 524
BENSON-QUINN COMMODITIES INC.—See Archer-Daniels-Midland Company; *U.S. Public*, pg. 181
BERJAYA HOLDINGS (HK) LIMITED—See Berjaya Corporation Berhad; *Int'l*, pg. 984
BGC CAPITAL MARKETS & FOREIGN EXCHANGE BROKER (KOREA) LTD.—See BGC Group, Inc.; *U.S. Public*, pg. 328
BGC LIQUIDEZ DISTRIBUIDORA DE TITULOS E VALORES MOBILIARIOS LTDA.—See BGC Group, Inc.; *U.S. Public*, pg. 328
BLUE CHIP VENTURE COMPANY, LTD; *U.S. Private*, pg. 586
BNP COMMODITY FUTURES INC.—See BNP Paribas SA; *Int'l*, pg. 1087
BOOK & CLAIM LTD.—See AAK AB; *Int'l*, pg. 32
BROKERSCLUB AG; *Int'l*, pg. 1173
BT BROKERAGE, INC.—See BT Trucking, Inc.; *U.S. Private*, pg. 675
CAMAU TRADING JOINT STOCK COMPANY; *Int'l*, pg. 1268
CANADA SQUARE OPERATIONS LIMITED—See Citigroup Inc.; *U.S. Public*, pg. 502
CARGILL MIDDLE EAST DMCC—See Cargill, Inc.; *U.S. Private*, pg. 758
CASA DE BOLSA SANTANDER SERFIN, S.A. DE C.V.—See Banco Santander, S.A.; *Int'l*, pg. 826
CASPIY COMMODITY EXCHANGE JSC; *Int'l*, pg. 1354
CASTILE VENTURES; *U.S. Private*, pg. 784
CAXTON ASSOCIATES LLC; *U.S. Private*, pg. 795
CEDAR PETROCHEMICALS, INC.; *U.S. Private*, pg. 805
CENTANA GROWTH PARTNERS, LLC—See Deutsche Borse AG; *Int'l*, pg. 2063
CHARMS INDUSTRIES LTD.; *Int'l*, pg. 1451
CHINA FUTURES CO., LTD.—See CSC Financial Co., Ltd; *Int'l*, pg. 1862
CHORI CO. (HONG KONG) LTD.—See Chori Co., Ltd.; *Int'l*, pg. 1583
CHORI FASHION NETWORK CO., LTD.—See Chori Co., Ltd.; *Int'l*, pg. 1583
CHS SINGAPORE TRADING COMPANY PTE. LTD.—See CHS INC.; *U.S. Public*, pg. 491
CHS TRADING COMPANY AUSTRALIA PTY. LTD.—See CHS INC.; *U.S. Public*, pg. 492
CI COM SA; *Int'l*, pg. 1600
CITICS FUTURES CO., LTD.—See CITIC Securities Co., Ltd.; *Int'l*, pg. 1622
CITYON SYSTEMS (INDIA) LTD.; *Int'l*, pg. 1630
CMC MARKETS UK PLC; *Int'l*, pg. 1669
CME EUROPE LIMITED—See CME Group, Inc.; *U.S. Public*, pg. 516
COMFORT COMMOTRADE LIMITED; *Int'l*, pg. 1711
COMMERZBANK FUTURES LLC—See Commerzbank AG; *Int'l*, pg. 1717
CONFIDENCE FINANCE AND TRADING LIMITED; *Int'l*, pg. 1767
CORTAL CONSORS S.A.—See BNP Paribas SA; *Int'l*, pg. 1090
CRYPTO FINANCE AG—See Deutsche Borse AG; *Int'l*, pg. 2063
CRYPTO FINANCE (ASSET MANAGEMENT) AG—See Deutsche Borse AG; *Int'l*, pg. 2063
DANSKE COMMODITIES DEUTSCHLAND GMBH—See Equinor ASA; *Int'l*, pg. 2484
DANSKE COMMODITIES TURKEY ENERJI TICARET A.S.—See Equinor ASA; *Int'l*, pg. 2484
DBS VICKERS SECURITIES (SINGAPORE) PTE LTD—See DBS Group Holdings Ltd.; *Int'l*, pg. 1988
DEV HARI EXPORTS INDIA LTD.; *Int'l*, pg. 2086
DIERREVI SPA—See CVC Capital Partners SICAV-FIS S.A.; *Int'l*, pg. 1882
DISCOVERY CAPITAL CORPORATION; *Int'l*, pg. 2134
DIVA TRADE A.D.; *Int'l*, pg. 2137
DR. HABEEBULLAH LIFE SCIENCES LIMITED; *Int'l*, pg. 2191
DUNE MERCANTILE LIMITED; *Int'l*, pg. 2226
EDWARD THOMAS TRADING COMPANY; *U.S. Private*, pg. 1341
EEX ASIA PTE. LIMITED—See Deutsche Borse AG; *Int'l*, pg. 2064
ENERGIEFINANZ GMBH—See EnBW Energie Baden-Wurttemberg AG; *Int'l*, pg. 2398
ENTREX CARBON MARKET LLC—See Entrex Carbon Market, LLC; *U.S. Public*, pg. 779
EP COMMODITIES, A.S.—See Energeticky a Prumyslovy Holding, a.s.; *Int'l*, pg. 2419
EURAFRIQUE—See Seaboard Corporation; *U.S. Public*, pg. 1850
EUREX GLOBAL DERIVATIVES AG—See Deutsche Borse AG; *Int'l*, pg. 2063
EUROPEAN COMMODITY CLEARING AG—See Deutsche Borse AG; *Int'l*, pg. 2064
EUROPEAN COMMODITY CLEARING LUXEMBOURG S.A R.L—See Deutsche Borse AG; *Int'l*, pg. 2064

523160 — COMMODITY CONTRACTS...

EUROPEAN ENERGY EXCHANGE AG—See Deutsche Borse AG; *Int'l*, pg. 2064
EVOLUTION MARKETS, LLC—See Xpansiv Data Systems Inc.; *U.S. Private*, pg. 4582
EXIM EXCHANGE COMPANY (CANADA) LTD.—See Export Import Bank of Bangladesh Limited; *Int'l*, pg. 2590
EZFOREX.COM, INC.—See Currency Exchange International, Corp.; *U.S. Public*, pg. 611
EZ-NERGY SAS—See Energy One Limited; *Int'l*, pg. 2423
FAIRVIEW CAPITAL PARTNERS, INC.; *U.S. Private*, pg. 1464
FALLEK CHEMICAL JAPAN KK—See ICC Industries, Inc.; *U.S. Private*, pg. 2029
FCSTONE CANADA ULC—See StoneX Group Inc.; *U.S. Public*, pg. 1952
FCSTONE MERCHANT SERVICES, LLC—See StoneX Group Inc.; *U.S. Public*, pg. 1952
FIRST RATE ENTERPRISES LIMITED—See Bank of Ireland Group plc; *Int'l*, pg. 844
FIRST RATE EXCHANGE SERVICES LIMITED—See Bank of Ireland Group plc; *Int'l*, pg. 844
FIRST SHANGHAI FUTURES LIMITED—See First Shanghai Investments Limited; *Int'l*, pg. 2687
FOGELMAN PROPERTIES, LLC; *U.S. Private*, pg. 1557
FREEPOINT COMMODITIES LLC—See Stone Point Capital LLC; *U.S. Private*, pg. 3824
FXPRO FINANCIAL SERVICES LTD; *Int'l*, pg. 2859
GAIL GLOBAL SINGAPORE PTE. LTD.—See GAIL (India) Limited; *Int'l*, pg. 2869
GAIN CAPITAL GROUP LLC—See StoneX Group Inc.; *U.S. Public*, pg. 1952
GAVITA AS—See The Scotts Miracle-Gro Company; *U.S. Public*, pg. 2126
GCM COMMODITY & DERIVATIVES LTD.; *Int'l*, pg. 2895
GELBER GROUP LLC; *U.S. Private*, pg. 1656
GENCO FUTURES INC.—See Coffee America (USA) Corporation; *U.S. Private*, pg. 961
GEN RE INTERMEDIARIES CORPORATION—See Berkshire Hathaway Inc.; *U.S. Public*, pg. 301
GERALD FINANCIAL GROUP INC.—See Gerald Metals Inc.; *U.S. Private*, pg. 1686
GIRDHARILAL SUGAR & ALLIED INDUSTRIES LIMITED; *Int'l*, pg. 2979
GLOBE COMMERCIALS LIMITED; *Int'l*, pg. 3006
GOGIA CAPITAL SERVICES LIMITED; *Int'l*, pg. 3022
GOKUL SOLUTIONS LIMITED; *Int'l*, pg. 3023
GOLD PRICE GROUP, INC.—See A-Mark Precious Metals, Inc.; *U.S. Public*, pg. 10
HAITONG FUTURES CO., LTD.—See Haitong Securities Co., Ltd.; *Int'l*, pg. 3218
HANSEN-MUELLER CO. INC.; *U.S. Private*, pg. 1856
HAVEN COMMODITIES LLC—See Mid-Kansas Co-op Association; *U.S. Private*, pg. 2708
HDP TRADING B.V.—See The Scotts Miracle-Gro Company; *U.S. Public*, pg. 2126
HENGTAI FUTURES CO., LTD.—See HengTai Securities CO., LTD; *Int'l*, pg. 3347
HIFX EUROPE LIMITED—See Euronet Worldwide, Inc.; *U.S. Public*, pg. 798
HINRICHS TRADING LLC—See Cargill, Inc.; *U.S. Private*, pg. 754
HINRICHS TRADING LLC—See CHS INC.; *U.S. Public*, pg. 491
HINRICHS TRADING LLC—See Conagra Brands, Inc.; *U.S. Public*, pg. 563
HIROSE TUSYO, INC.; *Int'l*, pg. 3405
HLH GLOBAL TRADING PTE LTD—See Hong Lai Huat Group Limited; *Int'l*, pg. 3467
HOLLY SU FUTURES (HONGKONG) CO., LTD.—See Holly Futures Co., Ltd.; *Int'l*, pg. 3451
HUATAI FINANCIAL HOLDINGS (HONG KONG) LIMITED—See Huatai Securities Co., Ltd.; *Int'l*, pg. 3514
HUATAI FINANCIAL USA INC—See Huatai Securities Co., Ltd.; *Int'l*, pg. 3514
ICAP ENERGY LLC—See CME Group, Inc.; *U.S. Public*, pg. 517
ICAP PHILIPPINES INC—See CME Group, Inc.; *U.S. Public*, pg. 517
ICAP SHIPPING TANKER DERIVATIVES LIMITED—See CME Group, Inc.; *U.S. Public*, pg. 517
ICC CHEMICAL (UK) LIMITED—See ICC Industries, Inc.; *U.S. Private*, pg. 2029
ICC IBERICA S.A.—See ICC Industries, Inc.; *U.S. Private*, pg. 2030
ICC ITALIA S.R.L.—See ICC Industries, Inc.; *U.S. Private*, pg. 2030
ICC TRADING, INC.—See ICC Industries, Inc.; *U.S. Private*, pg. 2030
ICC TRADING (TAIWAN) LTD.—See ICC Industries, Inc.; *U.S. Private*, pg. 2030
ICE CLEAR SINGAPORE PTE. LTD.—See Intercontinental Exchange, Inc.; *U.S. Public*, pg. 1142
ICE FUTURES SINGAPORE PTE. LTD.—See Intercontinental Exchange, Inc.; *U.S. Public*, pg. 1142
INDIAN BULLION MARKET ASSOCIATION LIMITED—See 63 moons technologies limited; *Int'l*, pg. 14
INTERNATIONAL REMITTANCE (CANADA) LTD.—See I-Remit, Inc.; *Int'l*, pg. 3564

523160 — COMMODITY CONTRACTS...

INTER-PACIFIC TRADING SDN BHD—See Berjaya Corporation Berhad; *Int'l*, pg. 982
INTL ASIA PTE. LTD—See StoneX Group Inc.; *U.S. Public*, pg. 1952
INTL CIBSA S.A.—See StoneX Group Inc.; *U.S. Public*, pg. 1952
INTL FCSTONE BANCO DE CAMBIO S.A.—See StoneX Group Inc.; *U.S. Public*, pg. 1952
INTL FCSTONE COMMODITIES DMCC—See StoneX Group Inc.; *U.S. Public*, pg. 1952
INTL FCSTONE DE MEXICO, S. DE R.L. DE C.V.—See StoneX Group Inc.; *U.S. Public*, pg. 1952
INTL FCSTONE DTVM LTDA.—See StoneX Group Inc.; *U.S. Public*, pg. 1952
INTL FCSTONE FINANCIAL (CANADA) INC.—See StoneX Group Inc.; *U.S. Public*, pg. 1952
INTL FCSTONE (HK) LTD.—See StoneX Group Inc.; *U.S. Public*, pg. 1952
INTL FCSTONE PTE. LTD.—See StoneX Group Inc.; *U.S. Public*, pg. 1952
INTL FCSTONE (SHANGHAI) TRADING CO., LTD—See StoneX Group Inc.; *U.S. Public*, pg. 1952
INTL NETHERLANDS B.V.—See StoneX Group Inc.; *U.S. Public*, pg. 1952
J. ARON & CO.—See The Goldman Sachs Group, Inc.; *U.S. Public*, pg. 2082
JEFFERIES FINANCIAL SERVICES, INC.—See Jefferies Financial Group Inc.; *U.S. Public*, pg. 1188
J.P. MORGAN ASSET MANAGEMENT—See JPMorgan Chase & Co.; *U.S. Public*, pg. 1208
J.P. MORGAN FUTURES INC.—See JPMorgan Chase & Co.; *U.S. Public*, pg. 1208
K3 CAPITAL GROUP LTD—See Sun Capital Partners, Inc.; *U.S. Private*, pg. 3861
KING INTERNATIONAL BULLION LIMITED—See Aceso Life Science Group Limited; *Int'l*, pg. 102
KOCH METALS TRADING LIMITED—See Koch Industries, Inc.; *U.S. Private*, pg. 2333
LANSING ETHANOL SERVICES, LLC—See The Andersons Incorporated; *U.S. Public*, pg. 2034
LANSING LOUISIANA, LLC—See The Andersons Incorporated; *U.S. Public*, pg. 2034
LANSING TRADE GROUP LLC—See The Andersons Incorporated; *U.S. Public*, pg. 2034
LEMARCO S.A.—See Gellert Global Group; *U.S. Private*, pg. 1657
LOGISTICS PLANNING SERVICES, INC.; *U.S. Private*, pg. 2482
LONGFIN CORP.; *U.S. Public*, pg. 1342
M. A. CARGILL TRADING LTD.—See Cargill, Inc.; *U.S. Private*, pg. 759
MESIROW FINANCIAL, INC. - NEW YORK CITY—See Mesirow Financial Holdings, Inc.; *U.S. Private*, pg. 2679
MID-CO COMMODITIES, INC.—See Growmark, Inc.; *U.S. Private*, pg. 1795
MISSOURI AGRICULTURAL MARKETING ASSOCIATION—See Missouri Farm Bureau; *U.S. Private*, pg. 2749
MULTI-CURRENCY FX CORP.—See First Metro Investment Corporation; *Int'l*, pg. 2685
NATIONAL BULK HANDLING CORPORATION—See 63 moons technologies limited; *Int'l*, pg. 14
NATIONAL TRADING & SERVICES CO. LTD.—See Bank of Khartoum; *Int'l*, pg. 845
NESTOR PARTNERS; *U.S. Private*, pg. 2886
NEWBRIDGE FINANCIAL, INC.; *U.S. Private*, pg. 2913
NITTAN CAPITAL GROUP CO., LTD.—See Central Tanshi Co., Ltd.; *Int'l*, pg. 1410
PACIFIC INTER-LINK SDN BHD—See Hayel Saeed Anam Group of Companies; *Int'l*, pg. 3291
PAN ASIAN CURRENCY EXCHANGE CORP.; *U.S. Private*, pg. 3084
PANCOSMA SA—See Archer-Daniels-Midland Company; *U.S. Public*, pg. 185
PEPPERSTONE GROUP LIMITED—See CHAMP Private Equity Pty. Ltd.; *Int'l*, pg. 1439
PEREGRINE FINANCIAL GROUP, INC. - CHICAGO—See Peregrine Financial Group, Inc.; *U.S. Private*, pg. 3147
PEREGRINE FINANCIAL GROUP, INC.; *U.S. Private*, pg. 3147
PHIBRO LLC; *U.S. Private*, pg. 3168
PREMIER FINANCIAL SERVICES (PVT) LIMITED—See Crescent Fibres Limited; *Int'l*, pg. 1839
PRINCIPAL GLOBAL INVESTORS (SINGAPORE), LTD—See Principal Financial Group, Inc.; *U.S. Public*, pg. 1721
PRINCIPAL TRUST COMPANY (ASIA) LIMITED—See Principal Financial Group, Inc.; *U.S. Public*, pg. 1721
PS INTERNATIONAL, LLC—See Seaboard Corporation; *U.S. Public*, pg. 1850
PT BANK CHINA CONSTRUCTION BANK INDONESIA TBK—See China Construction Bank Corporation; *Int'l*, pg. 1491
RAYDIUS GMBH—See IG Group Holdings plc; *Int'l*, pg. 3601
RHODIUM ENTERPRISES, INC.; *U.S. Private*, pg. 3422
RIVER/GULF GRAIN COMPANY—See Alter Companies; *U.S. Private*, pg. 206
R.J. O'BRIEN & ASSOCIATES CANADA INC.—See R.J. O'Brien & Associates, LLC; *U.S. Private*, pg. 3337
R.J. O'BRIEN & ASSOCIATES, LLC; *U.S. Private*, pg. 3337
RMB CIS MANCO (PROPRIETARY) LIMITED—See Ashburton; *Int'l*, pg. 606
S.C. CHS AGRITRADE ROMANIA SRL—See CHS INC.; *U.S. Public*, pg. 492
SCIENTIFIC ADVANCES, INC.—See Battelle Memorial Institute; *U.S. Private*, pg. 487
SEABOARD FOODS OF IOWA, LLC—See Seaboard Corporation; *U.S. Public*, pg. 1851
SEABOARD OVERSEAS LTD.—See Seaboard Corporation; *U.S. Public*, pg. 1851
SEABOARD TRADING & SHIPPING LTD. INC.—See Seaboard Corporation; *U.S. Public*, pg. 1851
SECURE CASH NETWORK, INC.; *U.S. Private*, pg. 3593
SHARPS PIXLEY BROKERS INCORPORATED—See Deutsche Bank Aktiengesellschaft; *Int'l*, pg. 2058
SPLIT ROCK PARTNERS, LLC—See The Travelers Companies, Inc.; *U.S. Public*, pg. 2136
STONE CAPITAL GROUP INC.; *U.S. Private*, pg. 3818
STONEHENGE CAPITAL CORP.; *U.S. Private*, pg. 3828
STX SERVICES B.V.—See Ekwienox Limited; *Int'l*, pg. 2340
STX SERVICES—See Ekwienox Limited; *Int'l*, pg. 2340
SUNRISE BROKERS, LLC—See BGC Group, Inc.; *U.S. Public*, pg. 330
SUPAMA FOREX PRIVATE LIMITED—See Arvog; *Int'l*, pg. 588
THINKORSWIM—See The Charles Schwab Corporation; *U.S. Public*, pg. 2058
TJX AUSTRALIA PTY. LTD.—See The TJX Companies, Inc.; *U.S. Public*, pg. 2134
TRADERFOX GMBH—See Axel Springer SE; *Int'l*, pg. 767
TRANSFERMARKT GMBH & CO. KG—See Axel Springer SE; *Int'l*, pg. 767
TRANSMARKET GROUP INC.; *U.S. Private*, pg. 4209
TRIOPTIMA ASIA PACIFIC PTE LIMITED—See CME Group, Inc.; *U.S. Public*, pg. 518
T. ROWE PRICE AUSTRALIA, LTD.—See T. Rowe Price Group Inc.; *U.S. Public*, pg. 1978
T. ROWE PRICE GROUP INC.; *U.S. Public*, pg. 1978
T. ROWE PRICE JAPAN, INC.—See T. Rowe Price Group Inc.; *U.S. Public*, pg. 1978
UNITED STATES OIL FUND, LP; *U.S. Public*, pg. 2236
VIRTU FINANCIAL GLOBAL MARKETS LLC—See Virtu Financial, Inc.; *U.S. Public*, pg. 2300
WALL STREET EXCHANGE CENTRE L.L.C—See Emirates Post; *Int'l*, pg. 2382
WALL STREET FOREX LONDON LTD—See Emirates Post; *Int'l*, pg. 2382
W CAPITAL MANAGEMENT LLC; *U.S. Private*, pg. 4417
WING LUNG FUTURES LIMITED—See China Merchants Group Limited; *Int'l*, pg. 1520
W.Y. CAMPBELL & COMPANY—See Comerica Incorporated; *U.S. Public*, pg. 542
XE.COM INC.—See Daseke, Inc.; *U.S. Private*, pg. 1162

523210 — SECURITIES AND COMMODITY EXCHANGES

AB NASDAQ OMX VILNIUS—See Nasdaq, Inc.; *U.S. Public*, pg. 1491
ABU DHABI SECURITIES EXCHANGE; *Int'l*, pg. 73
ADENZA FRANCE SARL—See Nasdaq, Inc.; *U.S. Public*, pg. 1491
ADENZA HONG KONG CO., LTD.—See Nasdaq, Inc.; *U.S. Public*, pg. 1491
ADENZA LTD.—See Nasdaq, Inc.; *U.S. Public*, pg. 1491
ALBILAD INVESTMENT COMPANY—See BANK ALBILAD; *Int'l*, pg. 836
AMMAN STOCK EXCHANGE; *Int'l*, pg. 429
AMSEC NOMINEES (ASING) SDN BHD—See AMMB Holdings Berhad; *Int'l*, pg. 429
AMSEC NOMINEES (TEMPATAN) SDN BHD—See AMMB Holdings Berhad; *Int'l*, pg. 429
ANCHOR CAPITAL PROPRIETARY LIMITED—See Anchor Group Limited; *Int'l*, pg. 448
ANCHOR SECURITIES PRIVATE CLIENTS PROPRIETARY LIMITED—See Anchor Group Limited; *Int'l*, pg. 448
AQUIS STOCK EXCHANGE LIMITED—See CME Group, Inc.; *U.S. Public*, pg. 516
ARMENIA SECURITIES EXCHANGE—See Nasdaq, Inc.; *U.S. Public*, pg. 1491
AS LATVIJAS CENTRALAIS DEPOZITARIJS—See Nasdaq, Inc.; *U.S. Public*, pg. 1491
ASTANA INTERNATIONAL EXCHANGE LIMITED; *Int'l*, pg. 651
ATHENS EXCHANGE S.A.—See Hellenic Exchanges-Athens Stock Exchange S.A.; *Int'l*, pg. 3333
AUSTRALIAN SECURITIES EXCHANGE LIMITED—See ASX Limited; *Int'l*, pg. 664
AUTOBACS FINANCIAL SERVICE CO., LTD.—See Autobacs Seven Co., Ltd.; *Int'l*, pg. 725
AXIOMA ARGENTINA S.A.U—See Deutsche Borse AG; *Int'l*, pg. 2063
AXIOMA (CH) GMBH—See Deutsche Borse AG; *Int'l*, pg. 2063
AXIOMA GERMANY GMBH—See Deutsche Borse AG; *Int'l*, pg. 2063
AXIOMA JAPAN G.K.—See Deutsche Borse AG; *Int'l*, pg. 2063
AXIOMA S.A.S.U—See Deutsche Borse AG; *Int'l*, pg. 2063
AXIOMSL HOLDINGS BV—See Nasdaq, Inc.; *U.S. Public*, pg. 1491
B3 S.A.; *Int'l*, pg. 791
BAHAMAS INTERNATIONAL SECURITIES EXCHANGE; *Int'l*, pg. 799
BAHRAIN BOURSE; *Int'l*, pg. 800
BAKU STOCK EXCHANGE; *Int'l*, pg. 806
BANGALORE STOCK EXCHANGE LIMITED; *Int'l*, pg. 832
BARBADOS STOCK EXCHANGE INC.; *Int'l*, pg. 858
BATS GLOBAL MARKETS HOLDINGS, INC.—See Cboe Global Markets, Inc.; *U.S. Public*, pg. 459
BAYERISCHE BORSE AG; *Int'l*, pg. 910
BERMUDA STOCK EXCHANGE—See Miami International Holdings, Inc.; *U.S. Private*, pg. 2697
BNK SECURITIES CO., LTD.—See BNK Financial Group Inc.; *Int'l*, pg. 1079
B N RATHI COMTRADE PRIVATE LIMITED—See B N Rathi Securities Ltd.; *Int'l*, pg. 783
THE BOARD OF TRADE OF KANSAS CITY, MISSOURI, INC.—See CME Group, Inc.; *U.S. Public*, pg. 518
BOERSE BERLIN AG—See Deutsche Borse AG; *Int'l*, pg. 2065
BOLSA DE COMERCIO DE BUENOS AIRES; *Int'l*, pg. 1103
BOLSA DE COMERCIO DE SANTIAGO, BOLSA DE VALORES; *Int'l*, pg. 1103
BOLSA DE VALORES DE CARACAS; *Int'l*, pg. 1103
BOLSA DE VALORES DE LIMA S.A.; *Int'l*, pg. 1103
BOLSA DE VALORES DE PANAMA S.A.; *Int'l*, pg. 1103
BOLSA MEXICANA DE VALORES, S.A.B. DE C.V.; *Int'l*, pg. 1103
BOLSA NACIONAL DE VALORES, S.A.; *Int'l*, pg. 1103
BOLSAS Y MERCADOS ARGENTINOS S.A. (BYMA)—See Bolsa de Comercio de Buenos Aires; *Int'l*, pg. 1103
BOMBAY STOCK EXCHANGE LIMITED; *Int'l*, pg. 1104
BORSA DE BARCELONA; *Int'l*, pg. 1115
BORSA INSTANBUL A.S.; *Int'l*, pg. 1115
BORZA TA' MALTA; *Int'l*, pg. 1115
BORZEN, D.O.O.—See Elektro Slovenia d.o.o.; *Int'l*, pg. 2357
BOTSWANA STOCK EXCHANGE; *Int'l*, pg. 1118
BOURSE REGIONALE DES VALEURS MOBILIERS; *Int'l*, pg. 1120
BULGARIAN STOCK EXCHANGE - SOFIA AD; *Int'l*, pg. 1213
BURSA DE VALORI BUCURESTI; *Int'l*, pg. 1227
BURSA MALAYSIA BERHAD; *Int'l*, pg. 1227
BURSEI DE VALORI A MOLDOVEI; *Int'l*, pg. 1227
BURZA CENNYCH PAPIEROV V BRATISLAVE, A.S.; *Int'l*, pg. 1227
BURZA CENNYCH PAPIRU PRAHA, A.S.—See CEESEG AG; *Int'l*, pg. 1389
BWISE GERMANY GMBH—See EQT AB; *Int'l*, pg. 2471
BZ FUND MANAGEMENT AKTIENGESELLSCHAFT—See BZ Bank Aktiengesellschaft; *Int'l*, pg. 1237
CAIRO & ALEXANDRIA STOCK EXCHANGES; *Int'l*, pg. 1253
CALCUTTA STOCK EXCHANGE ASSOCIATION LTD.; *Int'l*, pg. 1262
CANTOR FUTURES EXCHANGE, L.P.—See Cantor Fitzgerald, L.P.; *U.S. Private*, pg. 736
CAYMAN ISLANDS STOCK EXCHANGE LIMITED; *Int'l*, pg. 1364
CBOE EUROPE LIMITED—See Cboe Global Markets, Inc.; *U.S. Public*, pg. 459
CEESEG AG; *Int'l*, pg. 1389
CELESTIAL SECURITIES LIMITED—See CASH Financial Services Group Limited; *Int'l*, pg. 1352
CENTRAL DEPOSITORY OF ARMENIA OPEN JOINT STOCK COMPANY—See Nasdaq, Inc.; *U.S. Public*, pg. 1491
CHANNEL ISLANDS STOCK EXCHANGE; *Int'l*, pg. 1446
CHICAGO BOARD OPTIONS EXCHANGE, INCORPORATED—See Cboe Global Markets, Inc.; *U.S. Public*, pg. 459
CHICAGO CLIMATE EXCHANGE, INC.—See Intercontinental Exchange, Inc.; *U.S. Public*, pg. 1143
CLEARSTREAM INTERNATIONAL S.A.—See Deutsche Borse AG; *Int'l*, pg. 2063
CLIMATE EXCHANGE PLC—See Intercontinental Exchange; *U.S. Public*, pg. 1143
CME CLEARING EUROPE LIMITED—See CME Group, Inc.; *U.S. Public*, pg. 516
CNSX MARKETS INC.; *Int'l*, pg. 1678
COLOMBO STOCK EXCHANGE; *Int'l*, pg. 1702
CR&T VENTURES AB—See Bure Equity AB; *Int'l*, pg. 1221
CYPRUS STOCK EXCHANGE; *Int'l*, pg. 1897
DBS SECURITIES (JAPAN) CO., LTD.—See DBS Group Holdings Ltd.; *Int'l*, pg. 1988
THE DEPOSITORY TRUST COMPANY—See The Depository Trust & Clearing Corporation; *U.S. Private*, pg. 4020
DEUTSCHE BOERSE MARKET DATA + SERVICES SINGAPORE PTE. LTD.—See Deutsche Borse AG; *Int'l*, pg. 2063

N.A.I.C.S. INDEX

523910 — MISCELLANEOUS INTER...

DEUTSCHE BOERSE SYSTEMS INC.—See Deutsche Borse AG; *Int'l*, pg. 2063
DHAKA STOCK EXCHANGE LTD.; *Int'l*, pg. 2097
DOM INWESTYCYJNY BRE BANKU SA—See Commerzbank AG; *Int'l*, pg. 1719
DUBAI MERCANTILE EXCHANGE LIMITED—See CME Group, Inc.; *U.S. Public*, pg. 516
DUBAI MERCANTILE EXCHANGE LIMITED—See Dubai Holding LLC; *Int'l*, pg. 2218
EASTERN CARIBBEAN SECURITIES EXCHANGE; *Int'l*, pg. 2272
ECCO TANNERY HOLDING (SINGAPORE) PTE. LTD.—See Ecco Sko A/S; *Int'l*, pg. 2288
ECSPONENT SOUTH AFRICA (PTY) LTD—See Afristrat Investment Holdings Limited; *Int'l*, pg. 193
EIC SECURITIES LTD.—See Eastern Insurance Company Limited; *Int'l*, pg. 2273
EUREX FRANKFURT AG—See Deutsche Borse AG; *Int'l*, pg. 2063
EUREX ZURICH AG—See Deutsche Borse AG; *Int'l*, pg. 2063
EUROCLEAR FINLAND OY—See Euroclear S.A./N.V.; *Int'l*, pg. 2534
EUROCLEAR S.A./N.V.; *Int'l*, pg. 2534
EUROCLEAR SWEDEN AB—See Euroclear S.A./N.V.; *Int'l*, pg. 2534
EUROCLEAR UK & IRELAND—See Euroclear S.A./N.V.; *Int'l*, pg. 2534
EURONEXT AMSTERDAM N.V.—See Euronext N.V.; *Int'l*, pg. 2554
EURONEXT BRUSSELS N.V./S.A.—See Euronext N.V.; *Int'l*, pg. 2554
EURONEXT LISBON - SOCIEDAD GESTORA DE MERCADOS REGULAMENTADOS, S.A.—See Euronext N.V.; *Int'l*, pg. 2554
EURONEXT LONDON LIMITED—See Euronext N.V.; *Int'l*, pg. 2554
EURONEXT PARIS S.A.—See Euronext N.V.; *Int'l*, pg. 2554
EVESTMENT ALLIANCE AUSTRALIA PTY LTD—See Nasdaq, Inc.; *U.S. Public*, pg. 1492
FAMILY FIRST HOSPICE INC.—See Dorilton Capital Advisors LLC; *U.S. Private*, pg. 1263
F&C MANAGEMENT LIMITED—See Bank of Montreal; *Int'l*, pg. 847
FENICS MARKETS XCHANGE, LLC—See BGC Group, Inc.; *U.S. Public*, pg. 328
FINANCIAL INDUSTRY REGULATORY AUTHORITY, INC.; *U.S. Private*, pg. 1507
FINRA REGULATION—See Financial Industry Regulatory Authority, Inc.; *U.S. Private*, pg. 1507
FOREIGN CURRENCY DIRECT PLC; *Int'l*, pg. 2731
FORWARDLY, INC.; *U.S. Public*, pg. 874
FXONLINE JAPAN CO., LTD.—See IG Group Holdings plc; *Int'l*, pg. 3601
GEORGIAN STOCK EXCHANGE; *Int'l*, pg. 2939
GF FINANCIAL MARKETS (U.K.) LTD.—See GF Securities Co., Ltd.; *Int'l*, pg. 2955
GFX CORPORATION—See CME Group, Inc.; *U.S. Public*, pg. 516
GHANA STOCK EXCHANGE; *Int'l*, pg. 2958
GIELDA PAPIEROW WARTOSCIOWYCH W WARSZAWIE S.A.; *Int'l*, pg. 2968
GRAFF CAPITAL MANAGEMENT AG—See Basellandschaftliche Kantonalbank; *Int'l*, pg. 871
HAIPHONG SECURITIES JOINT STOCK COMPANY; *Int'l*, pg. 3216
HERITAGE RESOURCES LTD.—See Ascendis Health Limited; *Int'l*, pg. 601
HKFE CLEARING CORPORATION LIMITED—See Hong Kong Exchanges & Clearing Limited; *Int'l*, pg. 3466
HKSCC NOMINEES LIMITED—See Hong Kong Exchanges & Clearing Limited; *Int'l*, pg. 3466
HONG KONG EXCHANGES & CLEARING LIMITED; *Int'l*, pg. 3466
HONG KONG FUTURES EXCHANGE LTD.—See Hong Kong Exchanges & Clearing Limited; *Int'l*, pg. 3466
HONG KONG SECURITIES CLEARING COMPANY LIMITED—See Hong Kong Exchanges & Clearing Limited; *Int'l*, pg. 3466
HWANGDBS VICKERS RESEARCH SDN. BHD.—See Alliance Financial Group Berhad; *Int'l*, pg. 339
HYDERABAD STOCK EXCHANGE LIMITED; *Int'l*, pg. 3546
ICAP ENERGY LIMITED—See CME Group, Inc.; *U.S. Public*, pg. 516
ICAP EUROPE LIMITED—See CME Group, Inc.; *U.S. Public*, pg. 516
ICE DATA SERVICES, INC.—See Intercontinental Exchange, Inc.; *U.S. Public*, pg. 1143
ICE ENDEX MARKETS B.V.—See Intercontinental Exchange, Inc.; *U.S. Public*, pg. 1142
ICE FUTURES CANADA, INC.—See Intercontinental Exchange, Inc.; *U.S. Public*, pg. 1143
ICE FUTURES EUROPE—See Intercontinental Exchange, Inc.; *U.S. Public*, pg. 1143
ICE FUTURES U.S., INC.—See Intercontinental Exchange, Inc.; *U.S. Public*, pg. 1143
ICE NGX CANADA, INC.—See Intercontinental Exchange, Inc.; *U.S. Public*, pg. 1143

ICE TRADE VAULT EUROPE LIMITED—See Intercontinental Exchange, Inc.; *U.S. Public*, pg. 1143
ICE UK LP, LLC—See Intercontinental Exchange, Inc.; *U.S. Public*, pg. 1143
ICX PLATFORM (PTY) LTD.—See 63 moons technologies limited; *Int'l*, pg. 14
IMAREX ASA; *Int'l*, pg. 3619
IMAREX, INC.—See IMAREX ASA; *Int'l*, pg. 3619
INTERNATIONAL SECURITIES EXCHANGE HOLDINGS, INC.—See Nasdaq, Inc.; *U.S. Public*, pg. 1491
INTERNATIONAL SECURITIES EXCHANGE LLC—See Nasdaq, Inc.; *U.S. Public*, pg. 1491
INTERNATIONAL STANDARD RESOURCES SECURITIES LIMITED—See Golden Century International Holdings Group Limited; *Int'l*, pg. 3028
INVESTORS' EXCHANGE LLC—See IEX Group, Inc.; *U.S. Private*, pg. 2038
THE IRISH STOCK EXCHANGE PLC—See Euronext N.V.; *Int'l*, pg. 2554
LITHUANIAN CENTRAL SECURITIES DEPOSITARY—See Nasdaq, Inc.; *U.S. Public*, pg. 1491
MARKET VECTORS COMMODITY TRUST—See Van Eck Associates Corp.; *U.S. Private*, pg. 4340
MERCARI PTY. LTD.—See Financial & Energy Exchange Limited; *Int'l*, pg. 2665
MINNEAPOLIS GRAIN EXCHANGE, INC.—See Miami International Holdings, Inc.; *U.S. Private*, pg. 2697
NADEX, INC.—See IG Group Holdings plc; *Int'l*, pg. 3601
NASDAQ AB—See Nasdaq, Inc.; *U.S. Public*, pg. 1492
NASDAQ HELSINKI LTD—See Nasdaq, Inc.; *U.S. Public*, pg. 1492
NASDAQ OMX CLEARING AB—See Nasdaq, Inc.; *U.S. Public*, pg. 1492
NASDAQ OMX COPENHAGEN A/S—See Nasdaq, Inc.; *U.S. Public*, pg. 1492
NASDAQ OMX HELSINKI OY—See Nasdaq, Inc.; *U.S. Public*, pg. 1492
NASDAQ OMX ICELAND HF.—See Nasdaq, Inc.; *U.S. Public*, pg. 1492
NASDAQ OMX PHLX, INC.—See Nasdaq, Inc.; *U.S. Public*, pg. 1492
NASDAQ OMX STOCKHOLM AB—See Nasdaq, Inc.; *U.S. Public*, pg. 1492
NASDAQ OMX TALLINN AS—See Nasdaq, Inc.; *U.S. Public*, pg. 1492
NASDAQ OPTIONS SERVICES, LLC—See Nasdaq, Inc.; *U.S. Public*, pg. 1492
NASDAQ OSLO ASA—See Nasdaq, Inc.; *U.S. Public*, pg. 1492
THE NASDAQ STOCK MARKET LLC—See Nasdaq, Inc.; *U.S. Public*, pg. 1492
NEW YORK MERCANTILE EXCHANGE, INC.—See CME Group, Inc.; *U.S. Public*, pg. 518
NEW YORK STOCK EXCHANGE LLC—See Intercontinental Exchange, Inc.; *U.S. Public*, pg. 1143
NEX SERVICES PTE. LTD.—See CME Group, Inc.; *U.S. Public*, pg. 518
NODAL EXCHANGE HOLDINGS, LLC—See Deutsche Borse AG; *Int'l*, pg. 2064
NORDURAL HF—See Century Aluminum Company; *U.S. Public*, pg. 474
NYSE AMERICAN LLC—See Intercontinental Exchange, Inc.; *U.S. Public*, pg. 1143
NYSE ARCA, INC.—See Intercontinental Exchange, Inc.; *U.S. Public*, pg. 1143
NYSE CHICAGO, INC.—See Intercontinental Exchange, Inc.; *U.S. Public*, pg. 1143
NYSE LIFFE US LLC—See Intercontinental Exchange, Inc.; *U.S. Public*, pg. 1143
NYSE MARKET (DE), INC.—See Intercontinental Exchange, Inc.; *U.S. Public*, pg. 1143
NYSE NATIONAL, INC.—See Intercontinental Exchange, Inc.; *U.S. Public*, pg. 1143
OSLO BORS ASA—See Euronext N.V.; *Int'l*, pg. 2554
OTC COMMODITY MARKETS, LLC—See Intercontinental Exchange, Inc.; *U.S. Public*, pg. 1143
OTC MARKETS GROUP INC.; *U.S. Public*, pg. 1622
THE PALESTINE SECURITIES EXCHANGE, LTD.—See Arab Supply & Trading Co.; *Int'l*, pg. 532
PORTFOLIO BUREAU PROPRIETARY LIMITED—See Anchor Group Limited; *Int'l*, pg. 448
THE PROXY ADVISORY GROUP, LLC—See Alliance Advisors LLC; *U.S. Private*, pg. 181
REDCHIP CHINA—See RedChip Companies, Inc.; *U.S. Private*, pg. 3377
ROBERT COWEN INVESTMENT PROPRIETARY LIMITED—See Anchor Group Limited; *Int'l*, pg. 448
SANABEL SECURITY CO.—See Bank of Khartoum; *Int'l*, pg. 845
SAUDI FRANSI CAPITAL LLC—See Banque Saudi Fransi; *Int'l*, pg. 854
SECURITY FIRST INTERNATIONAL HOLDINGS, INC.; *U.S. Public*, pg. 1856
THE SEHK OPTIONS CLEARING HOUSE LIMITED—See Hong Kong Exchanges & Clearing Limited; *Int'l*, pg. 3466
SHANGHAI ORIENTAL FUTURES CO., LTD.—See China Rare Earth Resources And Technology Co., Ltd.; *Int'l*, pg. 1546

SIF ICAP S.A. DE C.V.—See Bolsa Mexicana de Valores, S.A.B. de C.V.; *Int'l*, pg. 1103
SIF ICAP S.A. DE C.V.—See CME Group, Inc.; *U.S. Public*, pg. 517
SMARTPOOL TRADING LIMITED—See Euronext N.V.; *Int'l*, pg. 2554
THE STOCK EXCHANGE OF HONG KONG LIMITED—See Hong Kong Exchanges & Clearing Limited; *Int'l*, pg. 3466
TOWAROWA GIELDA ENERGII SA—See Gielda Papierow Wartosciowych w Warszawie S.A.; *Int'l*, pg. 2969
TRADEGATE EXCHANGE GMBH—See Deutsche Borse AG; *Int'l*, pg. 2064
TRIOPTIMA JAPAN K.K.—See CME Group, Inc.; *U.S. Public*, pg. 518
WIENER BOERSE AG—See CEESEG AG; *Int'l*, pg. 1389

523910 — MISCELLANEOUS INTERMEDIATION

3I ASIA PACIFIC LTD—See 3i Group plc; *Int'l*, pg. 8
3I BENELUX B.V.—See 3i Group plc; *Int'l*, pg. 7
3I EUROPE PLC, BENELUX—See 3i Group plc; *Int'l*, pg. 8
3I EUROPE PLC—See 3i Group plc; *Int'l*, pg. 8
3I PLC—See 3i Group plc; *Int'l*, pg. 8
3I SGR—See 3i Group plc; *Int'l*, pg. 8
ABBVIE BIOTECH VENTURES INC.—See AbbVie Inc.; *U.S. Public*, pg. 21
ACCESS MEDIQUIP, LLC—See Water Street Healthcare Partners, LLC; *U.S. Private*, pg. 4452
AGOGE GLOBAL USA, INC.—See SPARTA COMMERCIAL SERVICES, INC.; *U.S. Public*, pg. 1914
AIB FINANCE & LEASING LTD.—See AIB Group plc; *Int'l*, pg. 228
ALPHA LEASING A.E.—See Alpha Services and Holdings S.A.; *Int'l*, pg. 369
AMERICAN BAILEY CORPORATION; *U.S. Private*, pg. 223
AN/MNI ACQUISITION CORP.—See AutoNation, Inc.; *U.S. Public*, pg. 232
APACHE OFFSHORE INVESTMENT PARTNERSHIP—See APA Corporation; *U.S. Public*, pg. 143
ARCH VENTURE PARTNERS; *U.S. Private*, pg. 310
ASSET PRESERVATION, INC.—See Stewart Information Services Corporation; *U.S. Public*, pg. 1947
ATTICA VENTURES S.A.—See ATTICA BANK S.A.; *Int'l*, pg. 696
BARCLAYS STOCKBROKERS LTD.—See Barclays PLC; *Int'l*, pg. 860
BASF VENTURE CAPITAL GMBH—See BASF SE; *Int'l*, pg. 882
BERVIN INVESTMENT & LEASING LIMITED; *Int'l*, pg. 998
BITCOIN GROUP SE; *Int'l*, pg. 1049
BNP PARIBAS CAPITAL (ASIA PACIFIC) LTD.—See BNP Paribas SA; *Int'l*, pg. 1083
BNP PARIBAS CAPITAL INVESTMENTS LTD.—See BNP Paribas SA; *Int'l*, pg. 1083
BNP PARIBAS CAPSTAR PARTNERS INC.—See BNP Paribas SA; *Int'l*, pg. 1087
BNP PARIBAS PEREGRINE—See BNP Paribas SA; *Int'l*, pg. 1081
BROWN BROTHERS HARRIMAN SERVICES AG—See Brown Brothers Harriman & Co.; *U.S. Private*, pg. 667
BTOMORROW VENTURES LIMITED—See British American Tobacco plc; *Int'l*, pg. 1165
THE CADLE COMPANY INC.; *U.S. Private*, pg. 4003
CANTOR VENTURES—See Cantor Fitzgerald, L.P.; *U.S. Private*, pg. 736
CAPEVIN INVESTMENTS LIMITED; *Int'l*, pg. 1303
CAPITAL RESOURCES OF VIRGINIA, INC.—See Alex Lee, Inc.; *U.S. Private*, pg. 163
CAPMAN PUBLIC MARKET MANAGER S.A.—See CapMan PLC; *Int'l*, pg. 1315
THE CATHOLIC SCHOOLS FOUNDATION INC; *U.S. Private*, pg. 4006
CBG COMMERZ BETEILIGUNGSGESELLSCHAFT HOLDING MBH—See Commerzbank AG; *Int'l*, pg. 1715
CBG COMMERZ—See Commerzbank AG; *Int'l*, pg. 1715
CDI GROUP INC.; *U.S. Private*, pg. 802
THE CIBC WOOD GUNDY CORPORATION—See Canadian Imperial Bank of Commerce; *Int'l*, pg. 1284
CIBC WORLD MARKETS PLC—See Canadian Imperial Bank of Commerce; *Int'l*, pg. 1284
CKD VENTURE CAPITAL CORP.—See Chong Kun Dang Holdings Corp.; *Int'l*, pg. 1578
CLARKSON AUSTRALIA HOLDINGS PTY LTD—See Clarkson PLC; *Int'l*, pg. 1650
CLEARBRIDGE WEALTH MANAGEMENT, INC.—See Merit Financial Group, LLC; *U.S. Private*, pg. 2674
COLEMAN RESEARCH GROUP, INC. (CRG); *U.S. Private*, pg. 967
COLEMAN RESEARCH GROUP, INC.—See Coleman Research Group, Inc. (CRG); *U.S. Private*, pg. 967
COMMERZBANK ONLINE VENTURES LIMITED—See Commerzbank AG; *Int'l*, pg. 1717
COMPANY K PARTNERS LIMITED; *Int'l*, pg. 1749
COMPUTER ENTERPRISES, INC.—See Computer Enterprises Inc.; *U.S. Private*, pg. 1004
CONGRESS ASSET MANAGEMENT CO.; *U.S. Private*, pg. 1013

523910 — MISCELLANEOUS INTER...

CONSOLIDATED ASSET RECOVERY SYSTEMS, INC.—See Kinderhook Industries, LLC; *U.S. Private*, pg. 2307
THE CONVEX GROUP, INC.; *U.S. Private*, pg. 4014
CORNWELL CORP.; *U.S. Private*, pg. 1053
COVESTOR LIMITED—See Interactive Brokers Group, Inc.; *U.S. Public*, pg. 1140
CROSS TIMBERS ROYALTY TRUST; *U.S. Public*, pg. 595
CUKIERMAN & CO. LIFE SCIENCES—See Cukierman & Co. Investment House Ltd.; *Int'l*, pg. 1876
CVC ASIA PACIFIC (BEIJING) LIMITED—See CVC Capital Partners SICAV-FIS S.A.; *Int'l*, pg. 1885
CVC ASIA PACIFIC (SHANGHAI) LIMITED—See CVC Capital Partners SICAV-FIS S.A.; *Int'l*, pg. 1885
CVC ASIA PACIFIC (SINGAPORE) PTE LTD—See CVC Capital Partners SICAV-FIS S.A.; *Int'l*, pg. 1885
CVC CAPITAL PARTNERS DENMARK A/S—See CVC Capital Partners SICAV-FIS S.A.; *Int'l*, pg. 1888
CVC CAPITAL PARTNERS JERSEY LIMITED—See CVC Capital Partners SICAV-FIS S.A.; *Int'l*, pg. 1888
CVC CAPITAL PARTNERS SRL—See CVC Capital Partners SICAV-FIS S.A.; *Int'l*, pg. 1888
CVC CAPITAL PARTNERS SVENSKA AB—See CVC Capital Partners SICAV-FIS S.A.; *Int'l*, pg. 1888
CVC CAPITAL PARTNERS SWITZERLAND GMBH—See CVC Capital Partners SICAV-FIS S.A.; *Int'l*, pg. 1888
CYBERAGENT VENTURES INC.—See CyberAgent, Inc.; *Int'l*, pg. 1892
DC THOMSON VENTURES—See D.C. Thomson & Co. Ltd.; *Int'l*, pg. 1900
DEUTSCHE BANK (PORTUGAL) SA—See ABANCA CORPORACION BANCARIA, SA; *Int'l*, pg. 48
DEXIA REAL ESTATE CAPITAL MARKETS—See Dexia SA; *Int'l*, pg. 2092
DIGITAL ASSET MONETARY NETWORK, INC.; *U.S. Public*, pg. 662
DIZON COPPER-SILVER MINES, INC.; *Int'l*, pg. 2138
DOMAIN ASSOCIATES LLC; *U.S. Private*, pg. 1255
DORIC NIMROD AIR THREE LIMITED; *Int'l*, pg. 2177
THE DREYFUS CORPORATION—See The Bank of New York Mellon Corporation; *U.S. Public*, pg. 2038
DSC INVESTMENT INC.; *Int'l*, pg. 2209
DWS INVESTMENT S.A. LUXEMBOURG—See Deutsche Bank Aktiengesellschaft; *Int'l*, pg. 2057
EDWARD HEALTH VENTURES—See Edward Hospital & Health Services; *U.S. Private*, pg. 1341
EL DORADO INVESTMENT COMPANY—See Pinnacle West Capital Corporation; *U.S. Public*, pg. 1692
ENTHEOS CAPITAL CORP.; *Int'l*, pg. 2452
ESSO TOWER—See Exxon Mobil Corporation; *U.S. Public*, pg. 816
EUROFINS EASTERN VENTURES BV—See Eurofins Scientific S.E.; *Int'l*, pg. 2540
EVOLUTION CAPITAL (UK) LIMITED; *Int'l*, pg. 2572
FATFISH GROUP LTD.; *Int'l*, pg. 2623
FIRST EFINANCE LIMITED—See First Shanghai Investments Limited; *Int'l*, pg. 2687
FIRST FUNDS LTD.—See FBN Holdings PLC; *Int'l*, pg. 2627
FREMONT INVESTMENT ADVISORS—See Fremont Group, LLC; *U.S. Private*, pg. 1608
FRITZ NOLS AG; *Int'l*, pg. 2794
FTV MANAGEMENT COMPANY LP; *U.S. Private*, pg. 1619
GENERAL CATALYST PARTNERS; *U.S. Private*, pg. 1664
GET NICE HOLDINGS LIMITED; *Int'l*, pg. 2946
GLENCORE CAPITAL LLC; *U.S. Private*, pg. 1709
GLOBAL GAMING SOLUTIONS, LLC; *U.S. Private*, pg. 1714
GLOBAL IOT TECHNOLOGY VENTURES, INC.—See BROADBAND TOWER, INC.; *Int'l*, pg. 1172
HARBOURVEST PARTNERS (U.K.) LIMITED—See HarbourVest Partners, LLC; *U.S. Private*, pg. 1861
HAWAII DIVERSIFIED INNOVATION FUND, LLC—See Bank of Hawaii Corporation; *U.S. Private*, pg. 273
H.B. FULLER PENSION TRUSTEES LIMITED—See H.B. Fuller Company; *U.S. Public*, pg. 978
HDF INVESTMENTS LIMITED—See Cabot Corporation; *U.S. Public*, pg. 417
HNP CAPITAL, LLC—See Financial Institutions, Inc.; *U.S. Public*, pg. 834
HOTEL EQUITIES, INC.; *U.S. Private*, pg. 1989
HSBC (KUALA LUMPUR) NOMINEES SDN BHD—See HSBC Holdings plc; *Int'l*, pg. 3506
HSBC PRIVATE BANK NOMINEES LTD—See HSBC Holdings plc; *Int'l*, pg. 3504
HSBC PRIVATE BANK (UK) LTD—See HSBC Holdings plc; *Int'l*, pg. 3504
ICICI SECURITIES LIMITED—See ICICI Bank Limited; *Int'l*, pg. 3581
IHLAS GIRISIM SERMAYESI YATIRIM ORTAKLIGI A.S.—See Ihlas Holding A.S.; *Int'l*, pg. 3606
IN-Q-TEL, INC.; *U.S. Private*, pg. 2052
INTERACTIVE BROKERS AUSTRALIA NOMINEES PTY LIMITED—See Interactive Brokers Group, Inc.; *U.S. Public*, pg. 1140
INTERACTIVE BROKERS GROUP, INC.; *U.S. Public*, pg. 1140
ITRONIX UK—See General Dynamics Corporation; *U.S. Public*, pg. 916

JAMS, THE RESOLUTION EXPERTS; *U.S. Private*, pg. 2186
JPMORGAN ASSET MANAGEMENT (UK) LIMITED—See JPMorgan Chase & Co.; *U.S. Public*, pg. 1209
J.P. MORGAN BANK INTERNATIONAL (LLC)—See JPMorgan Chase & Co.; *U.S. Public*, pg. 1209
JPMORGAN CHASE - MIDWEST REGIONAL OFFICE—See JPMorgan Chase & Co.; *U.S. Public*, pg. 1209
J.P. MORGAN (SUISSE) SA—See JPMorgan Chase & Co.; *U.S. Public*, pg. 1208
JUGGERNAUT MANAGEMENT, LLC; *U.S. Private*, pg. 2242
KIMBERLY-CLARK PENSION TRUSTS LTD.—See Kimberly-Clark Corporation; *U.S. Public*, pg. 1231
KKR & CO. L.P. - MENLO PARK—See KKR & Co. Inc.; *U.S. Public*, pg. 1255
LANDMARK PARTNERS, LLC—See Ares Management Corporation; *U.S. Public*, pg. 189
LOCKWOOD FINANCIAL GROUP, INC.—See The Bank of New York Mellon Corporation; *U.S. Public*, pg. 2038
LONDON FORFAITING A PARIS SA—See FIMBank p.l.c.; *Int'l*, pg. 2664
LONDON FORFAITING DEUTSCHLAND GMBH—See FIMBank p.l.c.; *Int'l*, pg. 2664
LONDON FORFAITING POLSKA SP. Z.O.O—See FIMBank p.l.c.; *Int'l*, pg. 2664
MAKILALA MINING COMPANY, INC.—See Celsius Resources Limited; *Int'l*, pg. 1395
MANUFACTURERS CAPITAL—See BDT Capital Partners, LLC; *U.S. Private*, pg. 502
MARSH USA INC. - WASHINGTON, D.C.—See Marsh & McLennan Companies, Inc.; *U.S. Public*, pg. 1382
MASTRAPASQUA ASSET MANAGEMENT, INC.—See Sequoia Financial Group, LLC; *U.S. Private*, pg. 3612
MILLS & PARTNERS—See Kainos Capital, LLC; *U.S. Private*, pg. 2255
NHS MANAGEMENT, LLC.; *U.S. Private*, pg. 2924
NORTHCURRENT PARTNERS, LLC; *U.S. Private*, pg. 2949
NORTHERN OAK WEALTH MANAGEMENT INC.—See Old National Bancorp; *U.S. Public*, pg. 1567
OAK HC/FT LDI BLOCKER CORP.—See UnitedHealth Group Incorporated; *U.S. Public*, pg. 2247
ODYSSEY VENTURES, INC.—See Thermo Fisher Scientific Inc.; *U.S. Public*, pg. 2149
ONSET VENTURES; *U.S. Private*, pg. 3028
PACCAR FINANCIAL BELUX BVBA—See PACCAR Inc.; *U.S. Public*, pg. 1630
PACCAR FINANCIAL ESPANA S.R.L.—See PACCAR Inc.; *U.S. Public*, pg. 1630
PACCAR FINANCIAL ITALIA SRL—See PACCAR Inc.; *U.S. Public*, pg. 1630
PACCAR FINANCIAL LTD.—See PACCAR Inc.; *U.S. Public*, pg. 1630
PACCAR FINANCIAL PLC—See PACCAR Inc.; *U.S. Public*, pg. 1631
PATRIOT MORTGAGE CORPORATION; *U.S. Private*, pg. 3110
PENNANTPARK SBIC GP, LLC—See PennantPark Investment Corporation; *U.S. Public*, pg. 1663
PEOPLE'S CREDIT UNION; *U.S. Private*, pg. 3140
PERMIAN BASIN ROYALTY TRUST; *U.S. Public*, pg. 1538
PERMROCK ROYALTY TRUST; *U.S. Public*, pg. 1677
PM EQUITY PARTNER SARL—See Philip Morris International Inc.; *U.S. Public*, pg. 1685
PROPELLER, INC.; *U.S. Private*, pg. 3285
RADIAN INVESTOR SURETY INC.—See Radian Group, Inc.; *U.S. Public*, pg. 1759
REGIS MANAGEMENT COMPANY LLC—See Genstar Capital, LLC; *U.S. Private*, pg. 1677
REGIS MANAGEMENT COMPANY LLC—See Keystone Group, L.P.; *U.S. Private*, pg. 2299
RENTWORKS AFRICA (PTY) LTD—See FirstRand Limited; *Int'l*, pg. 2690
RI/RMP ACQUISITION CORP.—See AutoNation, Inc.; *U.S. Public*, pg. 237
RISQUE ET SERENITE S.A.—See Assicurazioni Generali S.p.A.; *Int'l*, pg. 645
RIV CAPITAL INC—See Cansortium, Inc.; *U.S. Public*, pg. 430
ROOSEVELT MANAGEMENT COMPANY, LLC—See Mr. Cooper Group Inc.; *U.S. Public*, pg. 1480
ROYALTY FLOW INC.; *U.S. Private*, pg. 3494
SABINE ROYALTY TRUST; *U.S. Public*, pg. 1833
SADIM INVERSIONES S.A.—See Hulleras del Norte, S.A.; *Int'l*, pg. 3528
SIEBERT FINANCIAL CORP.; *U.S. Public*, pg. 1876
SIERRA INCOME CORPORATION—See Barings BDC, Inc.; *U.S. Public*, pg. 276
SOCIEDAD DE PARTICIPACION Y PROMOCION EMPRESARIAL CAJA DE MADRID—See Lone Star Funds; *U.S. Private*, pg. 2485
SOLUTIONPOINT INTERNATIONAL INC.; *U.S. Private*, pg. 3711
SPIRIT SPE PORTFOLIO 2012-1, LLC—See Spirit Realty Capital, Inc.; *U.S. Public*, pg. 1919
STATE STREET MASSACHUSETTS SECURITIES CORPORATION—See State Street Corporation; *U.S. Public*, pg. 1941
STRATFORD CONSULTING LLC—See Creative Planning, LLC; *U.S. Private*, pg. 1538
TATRO CAPITAL LLC—See Warburg Pincus LLC; *U.S. Private*, pg. 4439
TRANSITIONS WEALTH MANAGEMENT LLC—See Genstar Capital, LLC; *U.S. Private*, pg. 1677
TRANSITIONS WEALTH MANAGEMENT LLC—See Keystone Group, L.P.; *U.S. Private*, pg. 2298
TRIUMPH CAPITAL, L.P.; *U.S. Public*, pg. 4239
UNITED SHAREHOLDER SERVICES, INC.—See U.S. Global Investors, Inc.; *U.S. Public*, pg. 2213
UNITED STATES COAST GUARD; *U.S. Private*, pg. 4298
@VENTURES—See Steel Connect, Inc.; *U.S. Public*, pg. 1941
VERITAS TITLE PARTNERS LLC—See Old Republic International Corporation; *U.S. Public*, pg. 1569
WATERLAND VENTURE CAPITAL CO., LTD.—See IBF Financial Holdings Co., Ltd.; *Int'l*, pg. 3574
WHITEHORSE FINANCE WAREHOUSE, LLC—See WhiteHorse Finance, Inc.; *U.S. Public*, pg. 2369
WISDOMTREE ASSET MANAGEMENT CANADA, INC.—See CI Financial Corporation; *Int'l*, pg. 1601
WSFS CAPITAL MANAGEMENT, LLC—See WSFS Financial Corporation; *U.S. Public*, pg. 2383
ZIEGLER CAPITAL MARKETS GROUP—See The Ziegler Companies, Inc.; *U.S. Private*, pg. 4140
ZIEGLER & CO.—See The Ziegler Companies, Inc.; *U.S. Private*, pg. 4140
ZIMMER INVESTMENTS, LLC—See Zimmer Biomet Holdings, Inc.; *U.S. Public*, pg. 2407

523940 — PORTFOLIO MANAGEMENT AND INVESTMENT ADVICE

10-15 ASSOCIATES, INC.—See TA Associates, Inc.; *U.S. Private*, pg. 3919
1201 LOUISIANA CO. L.P.—See Brookfield Corporation; *Int'l*, pg. 1186
1323785 ALBERTA LTD.—See First Canadian Management Corporation; *Int'l*, pg. 2682
1600 SMITH CO. LLC—See Brookfield Corporation; *Int'l*, pg. 1186
1897 SERVICES CORPORATION—See BNP Paribas SA; *U.S. Public*, pg. 1087
1901 PARTNERS MANAGEMENT, LP; *U.S. Private*, pg. 3
1919 INVESTMENT COUNSEL, LLC—See Stifel Financial Corp.; *U.S. Public*, pg. 1949
1ST C.O.R.P. SERVICES; *U.S. Private*, pg. 3
1ST SOURCE CORPORATION INVESTMENT ADVISORS, INC.—See 1st Source Corporation; *U.S. Public*, pg. 3
2100 XENON GROUP LLC—See Callodine Acquisition Corporation; *U.S. Public*, pg. 424
33 SOUTH 6TH STREET LLC—See Brookfield Corporation; *Int'l*, pg. 1186
360 CAPITAL INVESTMENT MANAGEMENT LIMITED—See Centuria Capital Limited; *Int'l*, pg. 1416
360 ONE WAM LIMITED; *Int'l*, pg. 6
3I ASIA PACIFIC PLC—See 3i Group plc; *Int'l*, pg. 8
3I CORPORATION—See 3i Group plc; *Int'l*, pg. 8
3I DEUTSCHLAND GESELLSCHAFT FUR INDUSTRIE-BETEILIGUNGEN MBH—See 3i Group plc; *Int'l*, pg. 8
3I EUROPE PLC—See 3i Group plc; *Int'l*, pg. 8
3I FRANCE SAS—See 3i Group plc; *Int'l*, pg. 8
3I GESTION S.A.—See 3i Group plc; *Int'l*, pg. 8
3I INDIA PRIVATE LIMITED—See 3i Group plc; *Int'l*, pg. 8
3I INFRASTRUCTURE PLC—See 3i Group plc; *Int'l*, pg. 8
3I INVESTMENTS PLC—See 3i Group plc; *Int'l*, pg. 8
3I NETHERLANDS B.V.—See 3i Group plc; *Int'l*, pg. 8
3I NORDIC PLC—See 3i Group plc; *Int'l*, pg. 8
40/86 ADVISORS, INC.—See CNO Financial Group, Inc.; *U.S. Public*, pg. 519
4AIM SICAF SPA; *Int'l*, pg. 11
50 SOUTH CAPITAL ADVISORS, LLC—See Northern Trust Corporation; *U.S. Public*, pg. 1538
5.11 ACQUISITION CORP.—See Compass Diversified Holdings; *U.S. Public*, pg. 559
524 PARTICIPACOES S.A.; *Int'l*, pg. 12
5PAISA CAPITAL LTD.; *Int'l*, pg. 13
65PLUS S.R.L.—See Gruppo MutuiOnline S.p.A.; *Int'l*, pg. 3140
8TELECOM INTERNATIONAL HOLDINGS CO. LTD.; *Int'l*, pg. 16
8VIC MALAYSIA SDN. BHD.—See 8VI Holdings Limited; *Int'l*, pg. 16
A1 CAPITAL YATIRIM MENKUL DEGERLER A.S.; *Int'l*, pg. 28
ABACUS FUNDS MANAGEMENT LIMITED—See Abacus Group, LLC; *Int'l*, pg. 47
ABACUS WEALTH PARTNERS, LLC; *U.S. Private*, pg. 34
ABAX INVESTMENTS PROPRIETARY LIMITED—See Affiliated Managers Group, Inc.; *U.S. Public*, pg. 53
AB BERNSTEIN ISRAEL LTD.—See Equitable Holdings, Inc.; *U.S. Public*, pg. 788
ABBEY CAPITAL LIMITED; *Int'l*, pg. 56

N.A.I.C.S. INDEX

523940 — PORTFOLIO MANAGEMEN...

ABBEY CAPITAL (US) LLC—See Abbey Capital Limited; *Int'l*, pg. 56
ABBEY INVESTMENTS LIMITED—See Gallagher Holdings Ltd.; *Int'l*, pg. 2873
ABBOTT INVESTMENTS LIMITED—See Abbott Laboratories; *U.S. Public*, pg. 16
ABBOTT (UK) FINANCE LIMITED—See Abbott Laboratories; *U.S. Public*, pg. 16
ABBVIE INVESTMENT KFT.—See AbbVie Inc.; *U.S. Public*, pg. 21
AB CARVAL INVESTORS, L.P.—See Equitable Holdings, Inc.; *U.S. Public*, pg. 788
ABC-CA FUND MANAGEMENT CO., LTD.—See Agricultural Bank of China Limited; *Int'l*, pg. 217
ABERDEEN ASSET MANAGEMENT COMPANY LIMITED—See abrdn PLC; *Int'l*, pg. 68
ABERDEEN ASSET MANAGEMENT PLC—See abrdn PLC; *Int'l*, pg. 68
ABERDEEN ASSET MANAGERS LTD.—See abrdn PLC; *Int'l*, pg. 68
ABERDEEN CAPITAL MANAGEMENT LLC—See abrdn PLC; *Int'l*, pg. 68
ABERDEEN EMERGING MARKETS INVESTMENT CO., LTD.; *Int'l*, pg. 60
ABERDEEN FUND MANAGEMENT LIMITED—See Giordano International Limited; *Int'l*, pg. 2977
ABERDEEN STANDARD INVESTMENTS SWEDEN AB—See abrdn PLC; *Int'l*, pg. 68
ABERFORTH SPLIT LEVEL INCOME TRUST PLC; *Int'l*, pg. 60
ABHISHEK FINLEASE LIMITED; *Int'l*, pg. 61
AB INTERNATIONAL FINANCE LTD—See AB Bank Limited; *Int'l*, pg. 39
ABN AMRO PARTICIPATIES—See ABN AMRO Group N.V.; *Int'l*, pg. 64
AB PRIVATE CREDIT INVESTORS CORPORATION; *U.S. Private*, pg. 33
ABRAMS CAPITAL MANAGEMENT, LLC—See Abrams Capital, LLC; *U.S. Private*, pg. 40
ABRDN LIFE SCIENCES INVESTORS; *U.S. Public*, pg. 26
ABRDN NATIONAL MUNICIPAL INCOME FUND; *U.S. Public*, pg. 27
ABSA PORTFOLIO MANAGERS PROPRIETARY LIMITED—See Absa Group Limited; *Int'l*, pg. 69
ABSOLUTE CAPITAL MANAGEMENT LLC; *U.S. Private*, pg. 44
ABSOLUTE RETURN CAPITAL, LLC—See Bain Capital, LP; *U.S. Private*, pg. 428
ACACIA FINANCIAL GROUP, INC.; *U.S. Private*, pg. 46
ACACIA WEALTH ADVISORS, LLC—See HighTower Holding LLC; *U.S. Private*, pg. 1941
ACADIAN ASSET MANAGEMENT LLC—See BrightSphere Investment Group Inc.; *U.S. Public*, pg. 383
ACB CAPITAL MANAGEMENT COMPANY LIMITED—See Asia Commercial Bank; *Int'l*, pg. 611
ACCESS COMMERCIAL INVESTORS 4 PLC; *Int'l*, pg. 88
ACCOUNTFULLY LLC; *U.S. Private*, pg. 54
ACCURACY SAS—See Aon plc; *Int'l*, pg. 488
ACCURACY SRL—See Aon plc; *Int'l*, pg. 488
ACEHILL INVESTMENTS PTY. LTD.—See Elders Limited; *Int'l*, pg. 2346
ACG ADVISORS (UK) LLP; *Int'l*, pg. 102
ACM BERNSTEIN GMBH—See Equitable Holdings, Inc.; *U.S. Public*, pg. 789
ACORNS ADVISERS, LLC—See Acorns Grow Incorporated; *U.S. Private*, pg. 64
ACP VERMOGENSVERWALTUNG GMBH & CO. KG NR. 4A—See Allianz SE; *Int'l*, pg. 341
ACP VERMOGENSVERWALTUNG GMBH & CO. KG NR. 4C—See Allianz SE; *Int'l*, pg. 341
ACROUD AB; *Int'l*, pg. 109
ACSION LIMITED; *Int'l*, pg. 117
ACTCELERATE INTERNATIONAL GROUP LIMITED; *Int'l*, pg. 117
ACTIVIA PROPERTIES INC.; *Int'l*, pg. 120
ADAM FINANCIAL ASSOCIATES INC.—See Genstar Capital, LLC; *U.S. Private*, pg. 1677
ADAM FINANCIAL ASSOCIATES INC.—See Keystone Group, L.P.; *U.S. Private*, pg. 2298
ADBODMER AG—See Bellevue Group AG; *Int'l*, pg. 967
ADCOCK FINANCIAL GROUP; *U.S. Private*, pg. 76
ADCORP MANAGEMENT SERVICES (PTY) LIMITED—See Adcorp Holdings Limited; *Int'l*, pg. 127
ADENIA PARTNERS LTD; *Int'l*, pg. 142
ADIG FONDSVERTRIEB GMBH—See Allianz SE; *Int'l*, pg. 341
ADIRONDACK ROCK CREEK EMERGING MARKETS FUND, LP—See Wells Fargo & Company; *U.S. Public*, pg. 2343
ADITYA BIRLA SUN LIFE AMC LTD.; *Int'l*, pg. 149
ADMINISTRADORA DE FONDOS DE CESANTIA S.A.—See Grupo de Inversiones Suramericana S.A.; *Int'l*, pg. 3125
ADMINISTRADORA EVERCORE, S.C.—See Evercore, Inc.; *U.S. Public*, pg. 800
ADMIRAL FINANCIAL CORP.; *U.S. Private*, pg. 81
ADVANCEDADVT LIMITED; *Int'l*, pg. 163
ADVANCE EQUITY HOLDING; *Int'l*, pg. 156

ADVANCE FINANCIAL; *U.S. Private*, pg. 83
ADVENT CONVERTIBLE & INCOME FUND; *U.S. Public*, pg. 49
ADVENT DO BRASIL CONSULTORIA E PARTICIPACOES LTDA.—See Advent International Corporation; *U.S. Private*, pg. 97
ADVENT INDIA PE ADVISORS PVT. LTD.—See Advent International Corporation; *U.S. Private*, pg. 97
ADVENT INTERNATIONAL ADVISORY S.L.—See Advent International Corporation; *U.S. Private*, pg. 97
ADVENT INTERNATIONAL COLOMBIA S.A.S.—See Advent International Corporation; *U.S. Private*, pg. 97
ADVENT INTERNATIONAL GMBH—See Advent International Corporation; *U.S. Private*, pg. 97
ADVENT INTERNATIONAL PE ADVISORS S.C.—See Advent International Corporation; *U.S. Private*, pg. 97
ADVENT INTERNATIONAL PLC—See Advent International Corporation; *U.S. Private*, pg. 97
ADVENT INTERNATIONAL ROMANIA S.R.L.—See Advent International Corporation; *U.S. Private*, pg. 97
ADVENT INTERNATIONAL SAS—See Advent International Corporation; *U.S. Private*, pg. 97
ADVENT INTERNATIONAL (SHANGHAI) CO LTD.—See Advent International Corporation; *U.S. Private*, pg. 97
ADVENT INTERNATIONAL SP. Z.O.O. SP.K—See Advent International Corporation; *U.S. Private*, pg. 97
ADVENT INTERNATIONAL S.R.O—See Advent International Corporation; *U.S. Private*, pg. 97
ADVISER INVESTMENT MANAGEMENT INC; *U.S. Private*, pg. 110
ADVISERS CAPITAL MANAGEMENT INC.; *U.S. Private*, pg. 110
ADVISORSTREAM LTD.—See Broadridge Financial Solutions, Inc.; *U.S. Public*, pg. 391
ADVISORY RESEARCH, INC.; *U.S. Private*, pg. 110
ADVIUM CORPORATE FINANCE OY—See eQ Oyj; *Int'l*, pg. 2466
ADYTON RESOURCES CORPORATION; *Int'l*, pg. 170
AEGIS HEDGING SOLUTIONS, LLC; *U.S. Private*, pg. 116
AEGON MAGYARORSZAG BEFEKTETESI ALAPKEZELO ZARTKORUEN MUKODO RESZVENYTARSASAG—See Aegon N.V.; *Int'l*, pg. 175
AEGON USA-INDIVIDUAL DIVISION—See Aegon N.V.; *Int'l*, pg. 174
AETNA MULTI-STRATEGY 1099 FUND—See CVS Health Corporation; *U.S. Public*, pg. 615
AEW CENTRAL EUROPE SP. Z O.O—See Groupe BPCE; *Int'l*, pg. 3092
AEW CILOGER—See Groupe BPCE; *Int'l*, pg. 3096
AFC CAPITAL LTD.—See Active Fine Chemicals Limited; *Int'l*, pg. 120
AFFILIATED MANAGERS GROUP, INC.; *U.S. Public*, pg. 53
AFFILIATED MANAGERS GROUP (SWITZERLAND) AG—See Affiliated Managers Group, Inc.; *U.S. Public*, pg. 53
AFFINITY EQUITY PARTNERS BEIJING LIMITED LIABILITY COMPANY—See Affinity Equity Partners (HK) Ltd.; *Int'l*, pg. 186
AFFINITY EQUITY PARTNERS (S) PTE LTD—See Affinity Equity Partners (HK) Ltd.; *Int'l*, pg. 186
AFORE SURA S.A. DE C.V.—See Grupo de Inversiones Suramericana S.A.; *Int'l*, pg. 3125
AFP INTEGRA S.A,.—See Grupo de Inversiones Suramericana S.A.; *Int'l*, pg. 3125
AFRICA ISRAEL (FINANCE) 1985 LTD.—See Africa Israel Investments Ltd.; *Int'l*, pg. 190
AFRICA ISRAEL INVESTMENTS LTD.; *Int'l*, pg. 189
AFRICAN & OVERSEAS ENTERPRISES LIMITED; *Int'l*, pg. 191
AFRICAN RAINBOW CAPITAL INVESTMENTS; *Int'l*, pg. 192
AFRICINVEST; *Int'l*, pg. 192
AFRISTRAT INVESTMENT HOLDINGS LIMITED; *Int'l*, pg. 193
AFROCENTRIC INVESTMENT CORPORATION LIMITED; *Int'l*, pg. 193
AGC (CHINA) HOLDINGS CO., LTD.—See AGC Inc.; *Int'l*, pg. 200
AGELLAN CAPITAL PARTNERS INC.; *Int'l*, pg. 205
AGF INTERNATIONAL ADVISORS COMPANY LTD.—See AGF Management Limited; *Int'l*, pg. 206
AGF INTERNATIONAL COMPANY LTD.—See AGF Management Limited; *Int'l*, pg. 206
AGM INDIA ADVISORS PRIVATE LIMITED—See Apollo Global Management, Inc.; *U.S. Public*, pg. 146
AGMO CORPORATION—See MFA Incorporated; *U.S. Private*, pg. 2693
AGRICULTURAL LAND MANAGEMENT LIMITED—See Elders Limited; *Int'l*, pg. 2346
AGRICULTURAL LAND TRUST; *Int'l*, pg. 217
A.H. ALGOSAIBI & BROS.; *Int'l*, pg. 24
AHC ADVISORS, INC.—See Mission Wealth Management, LLC; *U.S. Private*, pg. 2748
AHTNA NETIYE', INC.—See Ahtna Incorporated; *U.S. Private*, pg. 131
A.I. HOLDINGS (USA) CORP.—See Africa Israel Investments Ltd.; *Int'l*, pg. 189

AIICO CAPITAL LIMITED—See AIICO Insurance PLC; *Int'l*, pg. 232
AIICO INSURANCE PLC; *Int'l*, pg. 232
AI INTERNATIONAL CORP.; *U.S. Private*, pg. 131
AIM3 VENTURES, INC.; *Int'l*, pg. 232
AIMS APAC REIT; *Int'l*, pg. 234
AIM TRIMARK INVESTMENTS—See Invesco Ltd.; *U.S. Public*, pg. 1161
AJ BELL MEDIA LIMITED—See AJ Bell Plc.; *Int'l*, pg. 255
AJCON GLOBAL SERVICES LTD.; *Int'l*, pg. 255
AJU IB INVESTMENT CO., LTD.; *Int'l*, pg. 258
AK ASSET MANAGEMENT—See Akbank T.A.S.; *Int'l*, pg. 260
AKCIONARSKO DRUSTVO ZA UPRAVLJANJE DOBROVOLJNIM PENZIJSKIM FONDOM GENERALI—See Assicurazioni Generali S.p.A.; *Int'l*, pg. 643
AKD CAPITAL LIMITED; *Int'l*, pg. 261
AKER ASA; *Int'l*, pg. 262
AKER HORIZONS ASA—See Aker ASA; *Int'l*, pg. 262
AKKO INVEST NYRT.; *Int'l*, pg. 263
AK PORTFOY YONETIMI A.S.—See Akbank T.A.S.; *Int'l*, pg. 261
AKTIA FUND MANAGEMENT COMPANY LTD.—See Aktia Bank PLC; *Int'l*, pg. 265
AKTIA LIFE INSURANCE LTD.—See Aktia Bank PLC; *Int'l*, pg. 265
AK YATIRIM MENKUL DEGERLER A.S.—See Akbank T.A.S.; *Int'l*, pg. 261
AK YATIRIM ORTAKLIGI A.S.—See Akbank T.A.S.; *Int'l*, pg. 261
AKZO NOBEL (C) HOLDINGS B.V.—See Akzo Nobel N.V.; *Int'l*, pg. 268
AKZO NOBEL HOLDING DUITSLAND B.V.—See Akzo Nobel N.V.; *Int'l*, pg. 271
AKZO NOBEL HOLDING OSTERREICH GMBH—See Akzo Nobel N.V.; *Int'l*, pg. 271
AKZO NOBEL MANAGEMENT B.V.—See Akzo Nobel N.V.; *Int'l*, pg. 272
A-LABS CAPITAL II CORP.; *Int'l*, pg. 19
AL AHLI TAKAFUL COMPANY—See Arabian Shield Cooperative Insurance Company; *Int'l*, pg. 533
ALARKO HOLDING A.S.; *Int'l*, pg. 291
ALBANY INVESTMENTS LIMITED—See CK Asset Holdings Limited; *Int'l*, pg. 1635
ALBARAKA PORTFOY YONETIMI A.S.—See Albaraka Turk Katilim Bankasi A.S.; *Int'l*, pg. 293
AL BILAD SECURITIES & INVESTMENT CO.; *Int'l*, pg. 276
ALBION CROWN VCT PLC; *Int'l*, pg. 299
ALBION DEVELOPMENT VCT PLC; *Int'l*, pg. 299
ALBION INVESTORS, LLC; *U.S. Private*, pg. 153
ALBOURNE PARTNERS LIMITED; *Int'l*, pg. 299
ALBRIGHT CAPITAL MANAGEMENT LLC; *U.S. Private*, pg. 153
ALBURY ASSET RENTALS LTD.—See BNP Paribas SA; *Int'l*, pg. 1079
ALCENTRA LIMITED—See The Bank of New York Mellon Corporation; *U.S. Public*, pg. 2036
ALCHEMY PARTNERS LLP; *Int'l*, pg. 300
ALCUIN CAPITAL PARTNERS LLP; *Int'l*, pg. 303
ALFA FINANCE HOLDING AD; *Int'l*, pg. 307
ALFALAH GHP INVESTMENT MANAGEMENT LIMITED—See Abu Dhabi Group; *Int'l*, pg. 71
ALFA LAVAL HOLDING AB—See Alfa Laval AB; *Int'l*, pg. 308
ALFA LAVAL HOLDING BV—See Alfa Laval AB; *Int'l*, pg. 309
ALFA LAVAL HOLDINGS LTD—See Alfa Laval AB; *Int'l*, pg. 310
ALFRED BERG ASSET MANAGEMENT AB—See BNP Paribas SA; *Int'l*, pg. 1082
ALFRED BERG FONDER AB—See BNP Paribas SA; *Int'l*, pg. 1082
ALFRED BERG FORVALTNING AS—See BNP Paribas SA; *Int'l*, pg. 1082
ALFRED BERG KAPITALFORVALTNING AS—See BNP Paribas SA; *Int'l*, pg. 1082
ALFRED BERG KAPITALFORVALTNING FINLAND AB—See BNP Paribas SA; *Int'l*, pg. 1082
ALIBABA HEALTH INFORMATION TECHNOLOGY LIMITED; *Int'l*, pg. 326
ALICORN LIMITED; *Int'l*, pg. 327
ALIOR TFI SA—See Alior Bank S.A.; *Int'l*, pg. 329
ALIXPARTNERS ARGENTINA SRL—See Caisse de Depot et Placement du Quebec; *Int'l*, pg. 1253
ALIXPARTNERS UK LLP—See Caisse de Depot et Placement du Quebec; *Int'l*, pg. 1253
AL KHALEEJ INVESTMENT P.J.S.C.; *Int'l*, pg. 280
ALLCAP ASSET MANAGEMENT LTD; *Int'l*, pg. 333
ALLERTHAL-WERKE AG; *Int'l*, pg. 336
ALLEYCORP; *U.S. Private*, pg. 181
ALLIANCEBERNSTEIN (CHILE) SPA—See Equitable Holdings, Inc.; *U.S. Public*, pg. 788
ALLIANCEBERNSTEIN GLOBAL DERIVATIVES CORPORATION—See Equitable Holdings, Inc.; *U.S. Public*, pg. 789
ALLIANCEBERNSTEIN HOLDINGS LIMITED—See Equitable Holdings, Inc.; *U.S. Public*, pg. 789
ALLIANCEBERNSTEIN INVESTMENTS, INC.—See Equitable Holdings, Inc.; *U.S. Public*, pg. 789
ALLIANCEBERNSTEIN INVESTOR SERVICES, INC.—See

523940 — PORTFOLIO MANAGEMEN...   CORPORATE AFFILIATIONS

Equitable Holdings, Inc.; *U.S. Public*, pg. 789
ALLIANCEBERNSTEIN SERVICES LIMITED—See Equitable Holdings, Inc.; *U.S. Public*, pg. 789
ALLIANCE TRUST INVESTMENTS LIMITED—See Alliance Trust PLC; *Int'l*, pg. 341
ALLIANCE TRUST SAVINGS LIMITED—See abrdn PLC; *Int'l*, pg. 68
ALLIANZ ACTIO FRANCE—See Allianz SE; *Int'l*, pg. 343
ALLIANZ ACTIONS AEQUITAS—See Allianz SE; *Int'l*, pg. 343
ALLIANZ ACTIONS EURO VALUE—See Allianz SE; *Int'l*, pg. 343
ALLIANZ ACTIONS FRANCE MIDCAP—See Allianz SE; *Int'l*, pg. 343
ALLIANZ ACTIONS FRANCE—See Allianz SE; *Int'l*, pg. 343
ALLIANZ ACTIONS JAPON—See Allianz SE; *Int'l*, pg. 343
ALLIANZ ASSET MANAGEMENT OF AMERICA L.P.—See Allianz SE; *Int'l*, pg. 343
ALLIANZ AVI 1 FONDS—See Allianz SE; *Int'l*, pg. 343
ALLIANZ AVM B FONDS—See Allianz SE; *Int'l*, pg. 343
ALLIANZ BULGARIA PENSION COMPANY AD—See Allianz SE; *Int'l*, pg. 344
ALLIANZ DGD FONDS—See Allianz SE; *Int'l*, pg. 344
ALLIANZGI CAPITAL LLC—See Allianz SE; *Int'l*, pg. 346
ALLIANZ GLOBAL INVESTORS GMBH—See Allianz SE; *Int'l*, pg. 346
ALLIANZ GLOBAL INVESTORS ITALIA S.P.A—See Allianz SE; *Int'l*, pg. 347
ALLIANZ GLOBAL INVESTORS JAPAN CO., LTD.—See Allianz SE; *Int'l*, pg. 347
ALLIANZ GLOBAL INVESTORS KAPITALANLAGEGESELLSCHAFT MBH—See Allianz SE; *Int'l*, pg. 346
ALLIANZ GLOBAL INVESTORS MANAGED ACCOUNTS LLC—See Allianz SE; *Int'l*, pg. 347
ALLIANZ GLOBAL INVESTORS—See Allianz SE; *Int'l*, pg. 346
ALLIANZ GLOBAL INVESTORS—See Allianz SE; *Int'l*, pg. 346
ALLIANZ INSURANCE COMPANY OF KENYA LIMITED—See Allianz SE; *Int'l*, pg. 348
ALLIANZ INVESTMENT MANAGEMENT LLC—See Allianz SE; *Int'l*, pg. 348
ALLIANZ LAD FONDS—See Allianz SE; *Int'l*, pg. 348
ALLIANZ LEBENCO FONDS—See Allianz SE; *Int'l*, pg. 348
ALLIANZ MAROC S.A.—See Allianz SE; *Int'l*, pg. 349
ALLIANZ PENSION CONSULT GMBH—See Allianz SE; *Int'l*, pg. 349
ALLIANZ PRIVATE EQUITY PARTNERS VERWALTUNGS GMBH—See Allianz SE; *Int'l*, pg. 349
ALLIANZ ROSNO ASSET MANAGEMENT—See Allianz SE; *Int'l*, pg. 354
ALLIANZ SOA FONDS—See Allianz SE; *Int'l*, pg. 350
ALLIANZ SOUTH AMERICA HOLDING B.V.—See Allianz SE; *Int'l*, pg. 350
ALLIED TECHNOLOGY TRUST PLC; *Int'l*, pg. 356
ALLIED PROPERTIES (H.K.) LIMITED—See Allied Group Limited; *Int'l*, pg. 357
ALL INVEST SECURITIES LTD.; *Int'l*, pg. 332
ALLSTATE INVESTMENTS, LLC—See The Allstate Corporation; *U.S. Public*, pg. 2032
ALLSTATE SOLUTIONS PRIVATE LIMITED—See The Allstate Corporation; *U.S. Public*, pg. 2033
ALPHA ADVISORS, INC.—See The Doctors Company; *U.S. Private*, pg. 4021
ALPHA FINANCIAL MARKETS CONSULTING PLC—See Bridgepoint Group Plc; *Int'l*, pg. 1153
ALPHA TRUST; *Int'l*, pg. 370
ALPHA VENTURES A.E.—See Alpha Services and Holdings S.A.; *Int'l*, pg. 369
ALPINA CAPITAL PARTNERS LLP; *Int'l*, pg. 371
ALPINE SELECT AG; *Int'l*, pg. 371
ALPINVEST PARTNERS LIMITED—See The Carlyle Group Inc.; *U.S. Public*, pg. 2044
AL-SALAM REAL ESTATE INVESTMENT TRUST; *Int'l*, pg. 288
ALSONS CONSOLIDATED RESOURCES, INC.—See Alcantara Group; *Int'l*, pg. 300
ALTA CAPITAL MANAGEMENT, LLC—See Guardian Capital Group Limited; *Int'l*, pg. 3169
AL TAIF INVESTMENT COMPANY LLC—See Dubai Investments PJSC; *Int'l*, pg. 2219
ALTA S.A.; *Int'l*, pg. 384
ALTEGRIS ADVISORS, LLC—See Aquiline Capital Partners LLC; *U.S. Private*, pg. 303
ALTEGRIS ADVISORS, LLC—See Genstar Capital, LLC; *U.S. Private*, pg. 1675
ALTEGRIS INVESTMENTS, INC.—See Aquiline Capital Partners LLC; *U.S. Private*, pg. 303
ALTEGRIS INVESTMENTS, INC.—See Genstar Capital, LLC; *U.S. Private*, pg. 1675
ALTEGRIS PORTFOLIO MANAGEMENT, INC.—See Aquiline Capital Partners LLC; *U.S. Private*, pg. 303
ALTEGRIS PORTFOLIO MANAGEMENT, INC.—See Genstar Capital, LLC; *U.S. Private*, pg. 1675
ALTERNATIVE CREDIT INVESTMENTS PLC; *Int'l*, pg. 391
ALTERNATIVE INVESTMENT TRUST; *Int'l*, pg. 392
ALTERNATIVE STRATEGIES GROUP, INC.—See Wells Fargo & Company; *U.S. Public*, pg. 2343

ALTICOR CORPORATE ENTERPRISES—See Alticor Inc.; *U.S. Private*, pg. 208
ALTIMA PARTNERS LLP; *Int'l*, pg. 393
ALTISOURCE PORTFOLIO SOLUTIONS S.A.; *Int'l*, pg. 393
ALTISOURCE SOLUTIONS, INC.—See Altisource Portfolio Solutions S.A.; *Int'l*, pg. 393
ALTRI, PARTICIPACIONES Y TRADING, S.L.—See Altri, SGPS, S.A.; *Int'l*, pg. 398
ALTRON FINANCE (PTY) LIMITED—See Altron Limited.; *Int'l*, pg. 399
ALTUS HOLDINGS LIMITED; *Int'l*, pg. 399
ALTUS POWER, INC.; *U.S. Public*, pg. 89
ALTUS S.A.; *Int'l*, pg. 399
ALTUS TOWARZYSTWO FUNDUSZY INWESTYCYJNYCH S.A.; *Int'l*, pg. 399
AMANAHRAYA REAL ESTATE INVESTMENT TRUST; *Int'l*, pg. 409
AMANAT HOLDINGS PJSC; *Int'l*, pg. 409
AMANO EUROPE HOLDINGS N.V.—See Amano Corporation; *Int'l*, pg. 410
AMASSE CAPITAL HOLDINGS LTD.; *Int'l*, pg. 412
AMBAC ASSURANCE CORPORATION—See Ambac Financial Group, Inc.; *U.S. Public*, pg. 92
AMBAC ASSURANCE CORP—See Ambac Financial Group, Inc.; *U.S. Public*, pg. 92
AMBAC CAPITAL CORPORATION—See Ambac Financial Group, Inc.; *U.S. Public*, pg. 92
AMBA RESEARCH COSTA RICA SA—See Moody's Corporation; *U.S. Public*, pg. 1466
AMBA RESEARCH (INDIA) PRIVATE LIMITED—See Moody's Corporation; *U.S. Public*, pg. 1466
AMBA RESEARCH LANKA (PRIVATE) LIMITED—See Moody's Corporation; *U.S. Public*, pg. 1466
AMBA RESEARCH SINGAPORE PTE. LTD.—See Moody's Corporation; *U.S. Public*, pg. 1466
AMBA RESEARCH UK LIMITED—See Moody's Corporation; *U.S. Public*, pg. 1466
AMBA RESEARCH USA INC.—See Moody's Corporation; *U.S. Public*, pg. 1466
AMBER CAPITAL, LP—See Amber Capital UK LLP; *Int'l*, pg. 414
AMBROMOBILIARE S.P.A.; *Int'l*, pg. 416
AMEI TECHNOLOGIES, INC.—See Orthofix Medical Inc.; *U.S. Public*, pg. 1619
AMERGERIS WEALTH MANAGEMENT GROUP GMBH; *Int'l*, pg. 420
AMERICAN BEACON ADVISORS—See Pharos Capital Group, LLC; *U.S. Private*, pg. 3166
AMERICAN BEACON ADVISORS—See TPG Capital, L.P.; *U.S. Public*, pg. 2175
AMERICAN CAPITAL SENIOR FLOATING, LTD.; *U.S. Private*, pg. 226
AMERICAN CENTURY BROKERAGE, INC.—See American Century Companies, Inc.; *U.S. Private*, pg. 226
AMERICAN CENTURY COMPANIES, INC.; *U.S. Private*, pg. 226
AMERICAN CONSUMER NEWS, LLC; *U.S. Private*, pg. 228
AMERICAN EXPRESS CENTURION BANK—See American Express Company; *U.S. Public*, pg. 101
AMERICAN FUNDS DISTRIBUTORS, INC.—See The Capital Group Companies, Inc.; *U.S. Private*, pg. 4004
AMERICAN HEALTHCARE INVESTORS LLC; *U.S. Private*, pg. 235
AMERICAN MONEY MANAGEMENT CORPORATION—See American Financial Group, Inc.; *U.S. Public*, pg. 102
AMERICAN NATIONAL REGISTERED INVESTMENT ADVISOR, INC.—See Brookfield Corporation; *Int'l*, pg. 1174
AMERICAN NATIONAL TRUST & INVESTMENT MANAGEMENT CORP.—See Old National Bancorp; *U.S. Public*, pg. 1567
AMERICAN REALTY ADVISORS; *U.S. Private*, pg. 245
AMERIPRISE ADVISOR SERVICES, INC.—See Ameriprise Financial, Inc.; *U.S. Public*, pg. 114
AMERIPRISE FINANCIAL, INC.; *U.S. Public*, pg. 113
AMERITAS INVESTMENT PARTNERS, INC.—See Ameritas Mutual Holding Company; *U.S. Private*, pg. 261
AMES WATSON HOLDING LLC; *U.S. Private*, pg. 262
AMETHYST GROUP LIMITED—See Cathay Investments Limited; *Int'l*, pg. 1360
AMEY ROADSTONE INTERNATIONAL LIMITED—See Heidelberg Materials AG; *Int'l*, pg. 3308
AMFIRST REAL ESTATE INVESTMENT TRUST; *Int'l*, pg. 424
AMG CANADA CORP.—See Affiliated Managers Group, Inc.; *U.S. Public*, pg. 53
AMG FUNDS LLC—See Affiliated Managers Group, Inc.; *U.S. Public*, pg. 53
AMINCOR, INC.; *U.S. Public*, pg. 124
AMINVESTMENT SERVICES BERHAD—See AMMB Holdings Berhad; *Int'l*, pg. 429
AMIT SECURITIES LIMITED; *Int'l*, pg. 428
AMP CAPITAL INVESTMENTS LIMITED—See AMP Limited; *Int'l*, pg. 431
AMP CAPITAL INVESTORS LIMITED—See AMP Limited; *Int'l*, pg. 431
AMP CAPITAL INVESTORS (NEW ZEALAND) LIMITED—See AMP Limited; *Int'l*, pg. 431
AMP FINANCIAL PLANNING PTY LIMITED—See AMP Limited; *Int'l*, pg. 432
AMP GROUP FINANCE SERVICES LIMITED—See AMP Limited; *Int'l*, pg. 432
AMP GROUP SERVICES LIMITED—See AMP Limited; *Int'l*, pg. 432
AMPHION INNOVATIONS PLC; *Int'l*, pg. 433
AMPHION INNOVATIONS US, INC.—See Amphion Innovations plc; *Int'l*, pg. 433
AMTD IDEA GROUP—See AMTD Group Company Limited; *Int'l*, pg. 441
AMURCON CORPORATION OF VIRGINIA—See Amurcon Corporation; *U.S. Private*, pg. 269
AMX USA HOLDING, S.A. DE C.V.—See America Movil, S.A.B. de C.V.; *Int'l*, pg. 421
ANALOG DEVICES INTERNATIONAL FINANCIAL SERVICES LIMITED—See Analog Devices, Inc.; *U.S. Public*, pg. 134
ANALYTIC INVESTORS, LLC—See Wells Fargo & Company; *U.S. Public*, pg. 2343
ANAWON TRUST—See Bristol County Savings Bank; *U.S. Private*, pg. 656
ANCHIN CAPITAL ADVISORS LLC—See Anchin, Block & Anchin LLP; *U.S. Private*, pg. 272
ANCHOR CAPITAL ADVISORS LLC; *U.S. Private*, pg. 272
ANDCO CONSULTING, LLC; *U.S. Private*, pg. 275
ANDLINGER & COMPANY GMBH—See Andlinger & Company, Inc.; *U.S. Private*, pg. 278
ANDULELA INVESTMENT HOLDINGS LIMITED; *Int'l*, pg. 457
ANIMA ALTERNATIVE SGR S.P.A.—See ANIMA Holding S.p.A.; *Int'l*, pg. 471
ANIMA SGR S.P.A.—See ANIMA Holding S.p.A.; *Int'l*, pg. 471
ANNADEL CAPITAL INC.—See Defined Financial Planning, LLC; *U.S. Private*, pg. 1191
ANQUIRO VENTURES LTD.; *Int'l*, pg. 475
ANTENNA DEXTERRA ASIA PACIFIC PTY LTD.—See Pegasystems Inc.; *U.S. Public*, pg. 1660
ANTIPODES GLOBAL INVESTMENT COMPANY LIMITED; *Int'l*, pg. 483
ANTONETTI CAPITAL MANAGEMENT, LLC; *U.S. Private*, pg. 288
ANXIN TRUST CO., LTD.; *Int'l*, pg. 486
AON ADVISORS, INC.—See Aon plc; *Int'l*, pg. 489
AON SECURITIES INC.—See Aon plc; *Int'l*, pg. 494
AOSP INVESTMENTS, LLC—See Pyxus International, Inc.; *U.S. Public*, pg. 1740
APACHE DELAWARE INVESTMENT LLC—See APA Corporation; *U.S. Public*, pg. 143
APAC RESOURCES LIMITED; *Int'l*, pg. 500
AP CITY LIMITED—See Hang Lung Group Limited; *Int'l*, pg. 3244
APEF MANAGEMENT COMPANY 5 LIMITED—See Alpha Associes Conseil SAS; *Int'l*, pg. 366
APELLA CAPITAL LLC; *U.S. Private*, pg. 291
APERIO GROUP LLC—See BlackRock, Inc.; *U.S. Public*, pg. 344
APEX CORPORATE SERVICES (NETHERLANDS) B.V.—See Apex Fund Services Holdings Ltd.; *Int'l*, pg. 509
APEX FINANCIAL SERVICES, INC.—See Apex Fund Services Holdings Ltd.; *Int'l*, pg. 510
APEX FLEET INC.—See Deutsche Bank Aktiengesellschaft; *Int'l*, pg. 2055
APEX FUND & CORPORATE SERVICES (GUERNSEY) LIMITED—See Apex Fund Services Holdings Ltd.; *Int'l*, pg. 510
APEX FUND & CORPORATE SERVICES (JERSEY) LIMITED—See Apex Fund Services Holdings Ltd.; *Int'l*, pg. 510
APEX FUND & CORPORATE SERVICES (UK) LIMITED—See Apex Fund Services Holdings Ltd.; *Int'l*, pg. 510
APEX FUND SERVICES (ABU DHABI) LTD.—See Apex Fund Services Holdings Ltd.; *Int'l*, pg. 510
APEX FUND SERVICES BAHRAIN WLL—See Apex Fund Services Holdings Ltd.; *Int'l*, pg. 510
APEX FUND SERVICES (BULGARIA) EOOD—See Apex Fund Services Holdings Ltd.; *Int'l*, pg. 510
APEX FUND SERVICES (CANADA) LTD.—See Apex Fund Services Holdings Ltd.; *Int'l*, pg. 510
APEX FUND SERVICES (CHARLOTTE) LLC—See Apex Fund Services Holdings Ltd.; *Int'l*, pg. 510
APEX FUND SERVICES (CHICAGO) LLC—See Apex Fund Services Holdings Ltd.; *Int'l*, pg. 510
APEX FUND SERVICES (HK) LIMITED—See Apex Fund Services Holdings Ltd.; *Int'l*, pg. 510
APEX FUND SERVICES (IOM) LTD.—See Apex Fund Services Holdings Ltd.; *Int'l*, pg. 510
APEX FUND SERVICES (IRELAND) LTD.—See Apex Fund Services Holdings Ltd.; *Int'l*, pg. 510
APEX FUND SERVICES LIMITED—See Apex Fund Services Holdings Ltd.; *Int'l*, pg. 510
APEX FUND SERVICES LLP—See Apex Fund Services Holdings Ltd.; *Int'l*, pg. 510

N.A.I.C.S. INDEX 523940 — PORTFOLIO MANAGEMEN...

APEX FUND SERVICES LTD.—See Apex Fund Services Holdings Ltd.; *Int'l*, pg. 510
APEX FUND SERVICES (MALTA) LTD.—See Apex Fund Services Holdings Ltd.; *Int'l*, pg. 510
APEX FUND SERVICES (MAURITIUS) LTD.—See Apex Fund Services Holdings Ltd.; *Int'l*, pg. 510
APEX FUND SERVICES (SINGAPORE) PTE. LTD.—See Apex Fund Services Holdings Ltd.; *Int'l*, pg. 510
APEX FUND SERVICES (SYDNEY) PTY LIMITED—See Apex Fund Services Holdings Ltd.; *Int'l*, pg. 510
APEX FUND SERVICES (UK) LTD.—See Apex Fund Services Holdings Ltd.; *Int'l*, pg. 510
APEX FUND SERVICES (URUGUAY) S.A.—See Apex Fund Services Holdings Ltd.; *Int'l*, pg. 510
APEX FUND SERVICES US INC.—See Apex Fund Services Holdings Ltd.; *Int'l*, pg. 510
APEX GROUP LTD.—See Apex Fund Services Holdings Ltd.; *Int'l*, pg. 510
APEX INVESTMENT CONSULTING (SHANGHAI) CO., LTD.—See Apex Fund Services Holdings Ltd.; *Int'l*, pg. 510
APEX INVESTMENT SERVICES BERHAD; *Int'l*, pg. 511
APICORP PETROLEUM SHIPPING FUND LIMITED—See Arab Petroleum Investments Corporation; *Int'l*, pg. 531
AP INSTITUTIONAL ADVISORS LLC.—See Actua Corporation; *U.S. Private*, pg. 71
APJ ASSET PROTECTION JERSEY LIMITED—See Apollo Global Management, Inc.; *U.S. Public*, pg. 147
APOLLO AF LOAN TRUST—See Aflac Incorporated; *U.S. Public*, pg. 57
APOLLO INVESTMENT MANAGEMENT, L.P.—See Apollo Global Management, Inc.; *U.S. Public*, pg. 146
APOLLO MANAGEMENT INTERNATIONAL LLP—See Apollo Global Management, Inc.; *U.S. Public*, pg. 146
APOLLO ST DEBT ADVISORS LLC—See Apollo Global Management, Inc.; *U.S. Public*, pg. 146
APOTHECARY HOLDCO, LLC—See Wells Fargo & Company; *U.S. Public*, pg. 2344
APPIAN CAPITAL ADVISORY LLP; *Int'l*, pg. 520
APPLIED MATERIALS DEUTSCHLAND HOLDING GMBH—See Applied Materials, Inc.; *U.S. Public*, pg. 172
APPLIED TOYS LIMITED—See Applied Development Holdings Limited; *Int'l*, pg. 521
APRIO WEALTH MANAGEMENT, LLC—See Aprio, LLP; *U.S. Private*, pg. 301
AP SUCCESS LIMITED—See Hang Lung Group Limited; *Int'l*, pg. 3244
AP UNIVERSAL LIMITED—See Hang Lung Group Limited; *Int'l*, pg. 3244
AQR CAPITAL MANAGEMENT, LLC; *U.S. Private*, pg. 302
AQUA CAPITAL; *Int'l*, pg. 527
AQUA CORPORATION PUBLIC COMPANY LIMITED; *Int'l*, pg. 527
AQUEDUCT CAPITAL S.A R.L.—See Deutsche Bank Aktiengesellschaft; *Int'l*, pg. 2055
ARA ASSET MANAGEMENT LIMITED—See ESR Group Limited; *Int'l*, pg. 2507
ARA ASSET MANAGEMENT (PROSPERITY) LIMITED—See ESR Group Limited; *Int'l*, pg. 2507
ARAB AFRICAN INVESTMENT MANAGEMENT—See Arab African International Bank; *Int'l*, pg. 529
ARABIAN GULF INVESTMENTS (FAR EAST) LIMITED—See HSBC Holdings plc; *Int'l*, pg. 3503
ARABIA S.A.L. HOLDING COMPANY—See Arabia Insurance Co.; *Int'l*, pg. 533
ARA KOREA LIMITED—See ESR Group Limited; *Int'l*, pg. 2508
ARA LOGOS LOGISTICS TRUST; *Int'l*, pg. 528
ARA PARTNERS GROUP, LLC—See Affiliated Managers Group, Inc.; *U.S. Public*, pg. 53
ARA PARTNERS GROUP; *U.S. Private*, pg. 306
ARA TRUST MANAGEMENT (SUNTEC) LIMITED—See ESR Group Limited; *Int'l*, pg. 2508
ARBONA AB; *Int'l*, pg. 537
ARBORINVEST, S.A.U.—See The Procter & Gamble Company; *U.S. Public*, pg. 2120
ARBOUR CLO LIMITED—See Brookfield Corporation; *Int'l*, pg. 1181
ARCA CAPITAL BOHEMIA, A.S.—See Arca Capital Slovakia, A.S.; *Int'l*, pg. 539
ARCA CAPITAL FINANCE GROUP, A.S.—See Arca Capital Slovakia, A.S.; *Int'l*, pg. 540
ARCA CAPITAL SLOVAKIA, A.S.; *Int'l*, pg. 539
ARCAPITA GROUP HOLDINGS LIMITED; *Int'l*, pg. 542
ARCAPITA INVESTMENT ADVISORS UK LIMITED—See Arcapita Group Holdings Limited; *Int'l*, pg. 542
ARCAPITA INVESTMENT MANAGEMENT SINGAPORE PTE. LTD.—See Arcapita Group Holdings Limited; *Int'l*, pg. 542
AR CAPITAL, LLC—See AR Global Investments, LLC; *U.S. Private*, pg. 306
ARC FINANCIAL CORP.; *Int'l*, pg. 539
ARCHER CAPITAL PTY. LTD.; *Int'l*, pg. 547
ARCHER WEALTH MANAGEMENT LLC—See HighTower Holding LLC; *U.S. Private*, pg. 1941
ARCHWAY FINANCE & OPERATIONS, INC.—See SEI Investments Company; *U.S. Public*, pg. 1856
ARCIS EQUITY PARTNERS LLC; *U.S. Private*, pg. 312

ARC SLIMLINE LIMITED—See Heidelberg Materials AG; *Int'l*, pg. 3308
ARDSLEY PARTNERS; *U.S. Private*, pg. 317
AREM PACIFIC CORP.; *Int'l*, pg. 558
ARENA HOSPITALITY GROUP D.D.; *Int'l*, pg. 558
ARENA INVESTMENT MANAGEMENT LIMITED; *Int'l*, pg. 558
ARE - QRS CORP.—See Alexandria Real Estate Equities, Inc.; *U.S. Public*, pg. 75
ARES ADMINISTRATIVE SERVICES (DIFC) LIMITED—See Ares Management Corporation; *U.S. Public*, pg. 187
ARES ASIA MANAGEMENT (HK), LIMITED—See Ares Management Corporation; *U.S. Public*, pg. 187
ARES CAPITAL MANAGEMENT LLC—See Ares Management Corporation; *U.S. Public*, pg. 187
ARES MANAGEMENT CORPORATION; *U.S. Public*, pg. 187
ARES MANAGEMENT LIMITED—See Ares Management Corporation; *U.S. Public*, pg. 188
ARES MANAGEMENT UK LIMITED—See Ares Management Corporation; *U.S. Public*, pg. 188
ARE - TECH SQUARE, LLC—See Alexandria Real Estate Equities, Inc.; *U.S. Public*, pg. 75
ARGENT ADVISORS, INC.—See Argent Financial Group, Inc.; *U.S. Private*, pg. 320
ARGENT CAPITAL MANAGEMENT, LLC; *U.S. Private*, pg. 319
ARGENT GROUP EUROPE LIMITED; *Int'l*, pg. 560
ARGENTINA CLEARING S.A.—See Banco Macro S.A.; *Int'l*, pg. 823
ARGI FINANCIAL GROUP; *U.S. Private*, pg. 320
ARGILETUM MERCHANT S.P.A.; *Int'l*, pg. 561
ARGO INVESTMENTS LIMITED; *Int'l*, pg. 562
ARGO REAL ESTATE OPPORTUNITIES FUND—See Argo Group Limited; *Int'l*, pg. 562
ARGOSY CAPITAL GROUP, LLC; *U.S. Private*, pg. 321
ARGOSY PROPERTY LIMITED; *Int'l*, pg. 563
ARGUS INVESTORS' COUNSEL, INC.—See The Argus Research Group, Inc.; *U.S. Private*, pg. 3988
ARIEL CAPITAL MANAGEMENT LLC; *U.S. Private*, pg. 322
ARIF HABIB CONSULTANCY (PVT.) LIMITED—See Aisha Steel Mills Limited; *Int'l*, pg. 251
ARIMA INSURANCE SOFTWARE W.L.L.—See Arab Insurance Group B.S.C.; *Int'l*, pg. 530
ARISTOTLE CAPITAL MANAGEMENT, LLC; *U.S. Private*, pg. 323
ARISTOTLE PACIFIC CAPITAL, LLC—See Aristotle Capital Management, LLC; *U.S. Private*, pg. 323
ARJUN INFRASTRUCTURE PARTNERS LIMITED; *Int'l*, pg. 567
ARLINGTON INVESTMENT COMPANY—See Credit Acceptance Corporation; *U.S. Public*, pg. 593
ARMCO METALS (SHANGHAI) HOLDINGS, LTD.—See Armco Metals Holdings, Inc.; *U.S. Public*, pg. 330
ARMSTRONG GLOBAL HOLDINGS, INC.—See Armstrong International, Inc.; *U.S. Private*, pg. 331
ARPADIS GROUP; *Int'l*, pg. 578
ARRIVE WEALTH MANAGEMENT LIMITED—See AMP Limited; *Int'l*, pg. 432
ARROW ACQUISITION LLC—See Affiliated Managers Group, Inc.; *U.S. Public*, pg. 53
ARROW CAPITAL MANAGEMENT, INC.; *Int'l*, pg. 579
ARROWPOINT ASSET MANAGEMENT LLC; *U.S. Private*, pg. 336
A.R. SCHMEIDLER & CO., INC.—See Pine Street Alternative Asset Management LP; *U.S. Private*, pg. 3183
ARTAL LUXEMBOURG S.A.—See Artal Group S.A.; *Int'l*, pg. 581
A.R.T. DIGITAL HOLDINGS CORP.; *U.S. Public*, pg. 12
ARTEMIS ALPHA TRUST PLC; *Int'l*, pg. 581
ARTEMIS INVESTMENT MANAGEMENT LIMITED; *Int'l*, pg. 582
ARTEMIS INVESTMENT MANAGEMENT LLP—See Affiliated Managers Group, Inc.; *U.S. Public*, pg. 53
ARTEMIS VCT PLC; *Int'l*, pg. 583
ARTI YATIRIM HOLDING A.S.; *Int'l*, pg. 584
ARUNDEL AG; *Int'l*, pg. 586
ARVEST ASSET MANAGEMENT—See Arvest Bank Group, Inc.; *U.S. Private*, pg. 344
ARYAN SHARES & STOCK BROKERS LTD.; *Int'l*, pg. 588
ASAS CAPITAL LTD; *Int'l*, pg. 599
ASB CAPITAL MANAGEMENT, LLC; *U.S. Private*, pg. 345
ASCALON CAPITAL MANAGERS LIMITED—See Generation Development Group; *Int'l*, pg. 2920
ASCENT INVESTMENT PARTNERS, LLC—See Mariner Wealth Advisors, LLC; *U.S. Private*, pg. 2575
ASHBURTON; *Int'l*, pg. 606
ASHFIELD CAPITAL PARTNERS, LLC; *U.S. Private*, pg. 349
ASHOKA INDIA EQUITY INVESTMENT TRUST PLC; *Int'l*, pg. 608
ASIA ASSET FINANCE PLC—See Asia Capital PLC; *Int'l*, pg. 610
ASIA CAPITAL GROUP PUBLIC COMPANY LIMITED; *Int'l*, pg. 610
ASIA CONTINENT INVESTMENT HOLDINGS PTE. LTD.—See Asia Cement Corporation; *Int'l*, pg. 611

ASIAN CAPITAL RESOURCES (HOLDINGS) LIMITED; *Int'l*, pg. 617
ASIA OPTICAL INTERNATIONAL LTD.—See Asia Optical Co., Inc.; *Int'l*, pg. 613
ASIA-PAC FINANCIAL INVESTMENT COMPANY LIMITED; *Int'l*, pg. 616
ASIA PLUS ADVISORY COMPANY LIMITED—See Asia Plus Group Holdings Public Company Limited; *Int'l*, pg. 614
ASIA STRATEGIC HOLDINGS LIMITED; *Int'l*, pg. 615
ASKARI INVESTMENT MANAGEMENT LIMITED—See Fauji Foundation; *Int'l*, pg. 2623
A-SMART COMMERCE PTE LTD—See A-Smart Holdings Ltd.; *Int'l*, pg. 20
ASML VENTURES 1 INC.—See ASML Holding N.V.; *Int'l*, pg. 627
A. SORIANO CORPORATION; *Int'l*, pg. 22
ASPEN CAPITAL ADVISORS INC.—See Apollo Global Management, Inc.; *U.S. Public*, pg. 147
ASPEN FUNDS MANAGEMENT LTD.—See Aspen Group Limited; *Int'l*, pg. 629
ASPEN PROPERTY TRUST—See Aspen Group Limited; *Int'l*, pg. 629
ASSA ABLOY ASIA HOLDING AB—See ASSA ABLOY AB; *Int'l*, pg. 633
ASSA ABLOY HOLDINGS (SA) LTD—See ASSA ABLOY AB; *Int'l*, pg. 635
ASSANTE WEALTH MANAGEMENT (CANADA) LTD.—See CI Financial Corporation; *Int'l*, pg. 1600
ASSETANDO REAL ESTATE GMBH—See Ernst Russ AG; *Int'l*, pg. 2495
ASSET MANAGEMENT ONE CO., LTD.—See Dai-ichi Life Holdings, Inc.; *Int'l*, pg. 1917
ASSET MANAGEMENT ONE HONG KONG LIMITED—See Dai-ichi Life Holdings, Inc.; *Int'l*, pg. 1917
ASSET MANAGEMENT ONE SINGAPORE PTE. LTD.—See Dai-ichi Life Holdings, Inc.; *Int'l*, pg. 1917
ASSET MANAGEMENT SLOVENSKEJ SPORITELNE SPRAV SPOL A S.—See Erste Group Bank AG; *Int'l*, pg. 2498
ASSETMARK, INC.—See Huatai Securities Co., Ltd.; *Int'l*, pg. 3514
ASSET PLUS LIMITED; *Int'l*, pg. 642
ASSOCIATED CAPITAL GROUP, INC.; *U.S. Public*, pg. 214
ASSURA INVESTMENTS LIMITED—See Assura plc; *Int'l*, pg. 649
ASSURED GUARANTY MUNICIPAL HOLDINGS INC.—See Assured Guaranty Ltd.; *Int'l*, pg. 650
ASTELLAS VENTURE MANAGEMENT LLC—See Astellas Pharma Inc.; *Int'l*, pg. 653
ASTMAX INVESTMENTS MANAGEMENT, INC.—See ASTMAX Trading, Inc.; *Int'l*, pg. 655
ASUKA ASSET MANAGEMENT CO., LTD.—See Aizawa Securities Group Co., Ltd.; *Int'l*, pg. 255
ASUTOSH ENTERPRISES LIMITED; *Int'l*, pg. 664
ATALANTA SOSNOFF CAPITAL, LLC; *U.S. Private*, pg. 364
ATALAYA CAPITAL MANAGEMENT LP—See Blue Owl Capital Inc.; *U.S. Public*, pg. 364
ATEL EQUIPMENT CORPORATION—See ATEL Capital Group; *U.S. Private*, pg. 366
ATEL INVESTOR SERVICES—See ATEL Capital Group; *U.S. Private*, pg. 366
ATHEEB (UK) LTD.—See Atheeb Group; *Int'l*, pg. 669
ATHENA CAPITAL ADVISORS LLC—See Franklin Resources, Inc.; *U.S. Public*, pg. 880
ATHENE ASSET MANAGEMENT, L.P.—See Apollo Global Management, Inc.; *U.S. Public*, pg. 147
AT INVESTMENT ADVISERS, INC.—See Canadian Imperial Bank of Commerce; *Int'l*, pg. 1283
ATLANCE SA/NV—See Econocom Group SA; *Int'l*, pg. 2297
ATLANCE SAS—See Econocom Group SA; *Int'l*, pg. 2297
ATLANTA CAPITAL MANAGEMENT COMPANY, LLC—See Morgan Stanley; *U.S. Public*, pg. 1471
ATLANTA FINANCIAL ASSOCIATES INC.—See Genstar Capital, LLC; *U.S. Public*, pg. 1677
ATLANTA FINANCIAL ASSOCIATES INC.—See Keystone Group, L.P.; *U.S. Private*, pg. 2298
ATLANTIC TRUST GROUP, LLC - BALTIMORE—See Canadian Imperial Bank of Commerce; *Int'l*, pg. 1283
ATLANTIC TRUST GROUP, LLC - BOSTON—See Canadian Imperial Bank of Commerce; *Int'l*, pg. 1283
ATLANTIC TRUST GROUP, LLC—See Canadian Imperial Bank of Commerce; *Int'l*, pg. 1283
ATLAS ASSET MANAGEMENT LIMITED—See Atlas Group of Companies; *Int'l*, pg. 685
ATLAS MENKUL KIYMETLER YATIRIM ORTAKLIGI A.S.; *Int'l*, pg. 686
ATLAS RESOURCE PARTNERS GP, LLC—See Atlas Energy Group, LLC; *U.S. Public*, pg. 223
ATLE AB—See 3i Group plc; *Int'l*, pg. 8
ATTESTOR LIMITED; *Int'l*, pg. 696
ATTICA CONSULTING S.A.—See ATTICA BANK S.A.; *Int'l*, pg. 696
AUB GROUP LIMITED; *Int'l*, pg. 697
AUGMENTUM FINTECH PLC; *Int'l*, pg. 703
AUGUR CAPITAL AG; *Int'l*, pg. 703
AURA FINANCIAL CORPORATION; *U.S. Private*, pg. 393

523940 — PORTFOLIO MANAGEMEN...

AURATOR ASSET MANAGEMENT LTD.—See Evli Pankki Oyj; *Int'l*, pg. 2570
AURELIUS FINANCE COMPANY LTD.—See Aurelius Equity Opportunities SE & Co. KGaA; *Int'l*, pg. 707
AURELIUS NEDERLAND B.V.—See Aurelius Equity Opportunities SE & Co. KGaA; *Int'l*, pg. 707
AURELIUS NORDICS AB—See Aurelius Equity Opportunities SE & Co. KGaA; *Int'l*, pg. 707
AURELIUS TRANSAKTIONSBERATUNGS AG—See Aurelius Equity Opportunities SE & Co. KGaA; *Int'l*, pg. 707
AURORA ABSOLUTE RETURN FUND; *Int'l*, pg. 713
AURORA FUNDS MANAGEMENT LIMITED; *Int'l*, pg. 713
AURORA GLOBAL INCOME TRUST; *Int'l*, pg. 713
AURORA INVESTMENT TRUST PLC; *Int'l*, pg. 713
AUSTRALIA CHINA HOLDINGS LIMITED; *Int'l*, pg. 720
AUSTRALIA & INTERNATIONAL HOLDINGS LIMITED; *Int'l*, pg. 719
AUSTRALIAN ETHICAL INVESTMENT LIMITED; *Int'l*, pg. 721
AUSTRALIAN ETHICAL SUPERANNUATION PTY LIMITED—See Australian Ethical Investment Limited; *Int'l*, pg. 721
AUSTRALIAN FOUNDATION INVESTMENT COMPANY LIMITED; *Int'l*, pg. 721
AUSTRALIAN UNITED INVESTMENT COMPANY LTD; *Int'l*, pg. 722
AUSTRALIAN UNITY CARE SERVICES PTY LTD—See Australian Unity Limited; *Int'l*, pg. 722
AUTO PORTFOLIO SERVICES, LLC—See OPENLANE, Inc.; *U.S. Public*, pg. 1607
AUTOWALLIS PUBLIC LIMITED COMPANY; *Int'l*, pg. 732
AVALON ACTON, INC.—See AvalonBay Communities, Inc.; *U.S. Public*, pg. 240
AVALONBAY SHREWSBURY, INC.—See AvalonBay Communities, Inc.; *U.S. Public*, pg. 240
AVALONBAY TRAVILLE, LLC—See AvalonBay Communities, Inc.; *U.S. Public*, pg. 240
AVALON DEL REY APARTMENTS, LLC—See AvalonBay Communities, Inc.; *U.S. Public*, pg. 240
AVALON NEWPORT, L.P.—See AvalonBay Communities, Inc.; *U.S. Public*, pg. 240
AVALON NORTH BERGEN, LLC—See AvalonBay Communities, Inc.; *U.S. Public*, pg. 240
AVALON OAKS, INC.—See AvalonBay Communities, Inc.; *U.S. Public*, pg. 240
AVALON PARK CREST, LLC—See AvalonBay Communities, Inc.; *U.S. Public*, pg. 240
AVALON SHARON, INC.—See AvalonBay Communities, Inc.; *U.S. Public*, pg. 240
AVALON TINTON FALLS, LLC—See AvalonBay Communities, Inc.; *U.S. Public*, pg. 240
AVALON TOWERS BELLEVUE, LLC—See AvalonBay Communities, Inc.; *U.S. Public*, pg. 240
AVALON UNION CITY, L.P.—See AvalonBay Communities, Inc.; *U.S. Public*, pg. 240
AVANTAX PLANNING PARTNERS, INC.—See Genstar Capital, LLC; *U.S. Private*, pg. 1676
AVANTI CAPITAL PLC; *Int'l*, pg. 736
AVEM PARTNERS, LLC; *U.S. Private*, pg. 405
AVENIR FINANCE PARTENAIRES—See Advenis; *Int'l*, pg. 167
AVENUE CAPITAL MANAGEMENT II, L.P.—See Avenue Capital Group, LLC; *U.S. Private*, pg. 405
AVI FINANCIAL SERVICES (PTY) LIMITED—See AVI Limited; *Int'l*, pg. 740
AVIVA INVESTORS CANADA INC.—See Aviva plc; *Int'l*, pg. 745
AVIVA INVESTORS FRANCE SA—See Aviva plc; *Int'l*, pg. 745
AVIVA INVESTORS NORTH AMERICA, INC.—See Aviva plc; *Int'l*, pg. 745
AVIVA INVESTORS REAL ESTATE FRANCE S.A.—See Aviva plc; *Int'l*, pg. 746
AVIVA INVESTORS SCHWEIZ GMBH—See Aviva plc; *Int'l*, pg. 746
AVONDALE ADVISORS, LLC—See Avondale Partners, LLC; *U.S. Private*, pg. 410
AVONDALE CONSULTING; *U.S. Private*, pg. 410
AVONDALE STRATEGIC PARTNERS; *U.S. Private*, pg. 410
AVP MANAGEMENT SERVICES, INC.—See Austin Ventures, LP; *U.S. Private*, pg. 396
AVRASYA GAYRIMENKUL YATIRIM ORTAKLIGI A.S.; *Int'l*, pg. 750
AXA-ARAG PROTECTION JURIDIQUE SA—See AXA S.A.; *Int'l*, pg. 759
AXA CHINA REGION INSURANCE COMPANY LIMITED—See AXA S.A.; *Int'l*, pg. 755
AXA FRAMLINGTON—See AXA S.A.; *Int'l*, pg. 756
AXA HOLDING MAROC S.A.—See AXA S.A.; *Int'l*, pg. 756
AXA INVESTMENT MANAGERS ASIA LIMITED—See AXA S.A.; *Int'l*, pg. 756
AXA INVESTMENT MANAGERS ASIA (SINGAPORE) LTD.—See AXA S.A.; *Int'l*, pg. 756
AXA INVESTMENT MANAGERS BENELUX SA/NV—NETHERLANDS—See AXA S.A.; *Int'l*, pg. 756
AXA INVESTMENT MANAGERS BENELUX SA/NV—See AXA S.A.; *Int'l*, pg. 756

AXA INVESTMENT MANAGERS DEUTSCHLAND GMBH—See AXA S.A.; *Int'l*, pg. 756
AXA INVESTMENT MANAGERS GS LTD., SUCURSAL EN ESPANA—See AXA S.A.; *Int'l*, pg. 756
AXA INVESTMENT MANAGERS, INC.—See AXA S.A.; *Int'l*, pg. 756
AXA INVESTMENT MANAGERS ITALIA S.P.A.—See AXA S.A.; *Int'l*, pg. 756
AXA INVESTMENT MANAGERS JAPAN LTD.—See AXA S.A.; *Int'l*, pg. 756
AXA INVESTMENT MANAGERS PARIS S.A.—See AXA S.A.; *Int'l*, pg. 756
AXA INVESTMENT MANAGERS SCHWEIZ AG—See AXA S.A.; *Int'l*, pg. 756
AXA LIABILITIES MANAGERS SAS—See AXA S.A.; *Int'l*, pg. 757
AXA MULTI MANAGER—See Equitable Holdings, Inc.; *U.S. Public*, pg. 788
AXA POLSKA S.A.—See AXA S.A.; *Int'l*, pg. 758
AXAR CAPITAL MANAGEMENT L.P.; *U.S. Private*, pg. 411
AXA TOWARZYSTWO FUNDUSZY INWESTYCYJNYCH S.A.—See Equitable Holdings, Inc.; *U.S. Public*, pg. 789
AXA TURKEY HOLDING A.S.—See AXA S.A.; *Int'l*, pg. 758
AXCEL MANAGEMENT A/S; *Int'l*, pg. 761
AXEL SPRINGER DIGITAL VENTURES GMBH—See Axel Springer SE; *Int'l*, pg. 766
AX INVESTMENTS PLC; *Int'l*, pg. 754
AXIO GROUP MANAGEMENT LTD.—See Epiris Managers LLP; *Int'l*, pg. 2461
AXIOM PROPERTIES LIMITED; *Int'l*, pg. 769
AXION GLOBAL DIGITS TECHNOLOGY (HONG KONG) LIMITED—See Edvance International Holdings Limited; *Int'l*, pg. 2316
AXIUM INFRASTRUCTURE INC.; *U.S. Public*, pg. 414
AXXSYS DANMARK APS—See Bridgepoint Group Plc; *Int'l*, pg. 1153
THE AYCO COMPANY, L.P.—See The Goldman Sachs Group, Inc.; *U.S. Public*, pg. 2082
AZ-ARGES VERMOGENSVERWALTUNGSGESELLSCHAFT MBH—See Allianz SE; *Int'l*, pg. 343
AZ-ARGOS 50 VERMOGENSVERWALTUNGSGESELLSCHAFT MBH & CO. KG—See Allianz SE; *Int'l*, pg. 343
AZ-ARGOS 51 VERMOGENSVERWALTUNGSGESELLSCHAFT MBH & CO. KG—See Allianz SE; *Int'l*, pg. 343
AZ-ARGOS 56 VERMOGENSVERWALTUNGSGESELLSCHAFT MBH—See Allianz SE; *Int'l*, pg. 343
AZIMUT CONSULENZA SIM SPA—See Azimut Holding SpA; *Int'l*, pg. 779
AZIMUT HOLDING SPA; *Int'l*, pg. 779
AZIMUT INVESTMENTS S.A.—See Azimut Holding SpA; *Int'l*, pg. 779
AZ INVESTMENT MANAGEMENT—See Azimut Holding SpA; *Int'l*, pg. 779
AZ LIFE LTD—See Azimut Holding SpA; *Int'l*, pg. 779
AZOLVER SVENSKA AS—See Francotyp-Postalia Holding AG; *Int'l*, pg. 2761
AZ SWISS S.A.—See Azimut Holding SpA; *Int'l*, pg. 779
BABCOCK CANADA INC.—See Babcock International Group PLC; *Int'l*, pg. 792
BABELON INVESTMENTS CO. P.L.C.; *Int'l*, pg. 793
BAE SYSTEMS (OVERSEAS HOLDINGS) LIMITED—See BAE Systems plc; *Int'l*, pg. 796
BAHMAN INVESTMENT COMPANY; *Int'l*, pg. 800
BAILLIE GIFFORD CHINA GROWTH TRUST PLC; *Int'l*, pg. 803
BAILLIE GIFFORD INTERNATIONAL LLC—See Baillie Gifford & Co.; *Int'l*, pg. 803
BAILLIE GIFFORD JAPAN TRUST PLC; *Int'l*, pg. 803
BAIN CAPITAL ADVISORS (CHINA) LTD.—See Bain Capital, LP; *U.S. Private*, pg. 431
BAIN CAPITAL ADVISORS (INDIA) PRIVATE LIMITED—See Bain Capital, LP; *U.S. Private*, pg. 431
BAIN CAPITAL ASIA, LLC—See Bain Capital, LP; *U.S. Private*, pg. 431
BAIN CAPITAL BETEILIGUNGSBERATUNG GMBH—See Bain Capital, LP; *U.S. Private*, pg. 431
BAIN CAPITAL LUXEMBOURG S.A.R.L.—See Bain Capital, LP; *U.S. Private*, pg. 431
BAIN CAPITAL PRIVATE EQUITY, LP—See Bain Capital, LP; *U.S. Private*, pg. 431
BAIN CAPITAL SPECIALTY FINANCE, INC.; *U.S. Public*, pg. 264
BAIN & COMPANY ARGENTINA S.R.L.—See Bain & Company, Inc.; *U.S. Private*, pg. 427
BAIN & COMPANY BRAZIL, INC.—See Bain & Company, Inc.; *U.S. Private*, pg. 427
BAIRD ADVISORS—See Baird Financial Group, Inc.; *U.S. Private*, pg. 454
BAIRD CAPITAL PARTNERS EUROPE LIMITED—See Baird Financial Group, Inc.; *U.S. Private*, pg. 453
BAIRD FINANCIAL CORPORATION—See Baird Financial Group, Inc.; *U.S. Private*, pg. 454
BAKER STEEL RESOURCES TRUST LIMITED; *Int'l*, pg. 805
BAKER STREET ADVISORS, LLC—See Affiliated Managers Group, Inc.; *U.S. Public*, pg. 53
BAKER TILLY INVESTMENT SOLUTIONS LIMITED—See Baker Tilly UK Holdings Limited; *Int'l*, pg. 805

BALANCED EQUITY MANAGEMENT PTY. LIMITED—See Franklin Resources, Inc.; *U.S. Public*, pg. 879
BALFOUR BEATTY CAPITAL GROUP INC—See Balfour Beatty plc; *Int'l*, pg. 807
BALFOUR BEATTY INVESTMENTS INC.—See Balfour Beatty plc; *Int'l*, pg. 808
BALLOU PLUM WEALTH ADVISORS, LLC—See EP Wealth Advisors, LLC; *U.S. Private*, pg. 1411
BALLYVESEY HOLDINGS LIMITED; *Int'l*, pg. 809
BALOISE ASSET MANAGEMENT INTERNATIONAL AG—See Baloise Holding AG; *Int'l*, pg. 810
BALOISE ASSET MANAGEMENT SCHWEIZ AG—See Baloise Holding AG; *Int'l*, pg. 811
BALTIMORE FINANCIAL BROKERAGE, INC.—See Baltimore Life Insurance Company Inc.; *U.S. Private*, pg. 462
BAMBU AG; *Int'l*, pg. 813
BANCA CONSULIA S.P.A.—See Banca Intermobiliare di Investimenti e Gestioni S.p.A.; *Int'l*, pg. 815
BANCA MEDIOLANUM S.P.A.; *Int'l*, pg. 815
BANCA PRIVADA D'ANDORRA (PANAMA), S.A.—See Banca Privada D'Andorra, SA; *Int'l*, pg. 816
BANCO ALCALA, SA—See Credit Andorra, S.A.; *Int'l*, pg. 1834
BANC OF AMERICA PREFERRED FUNDING CORPORATION—See Bank of America Corporation; *U.S. Public*, pg. 270
BANCO OPPORTUNITY S/A; *Int'l*, pg. 823
BANKERS INTERNATIONAL CORPORATION—See Deutsche Bank Aktiengesellschaft; *Int'l*, pg. 2055
BANKERS & INVESTORS CO.—See Valley View Bancshares, Inc.; *U.S. Private*, pg. 4336
BANK LEUMI LE-ISRAEL TRUST CO. LTD.—See Bank Leumi Le-Israel B.M.; *Int'l*, pg. 838
BANKNOTE CAPITAL CORP.; *U.S. Private*, pg. 468
BANK OF AMERICA GLOBAL WEALTH & INVESTMENT MANAGEMENT—See Bank of America Corporation; *U.S. Public*, pg. 271
BANK OF CHINA GROUP INVESTMENT LIMITED—See Bank of China, Ltd.; *Int'l*, pg. 841
BANK OF IRELAND COMMERCIAL FINANCE LTD.—See Bank of Ireland Group plc; *Int'l*, pg. 844
THE BANK OF NEW YORK CAPITAL MARKETS, LIMITED—See The Bank of New York Mellon Corporation; *U.S. Public*, pg. 2038
BANKOH INVESTMENT SERVICES, INC.—See Bank of Hawaii Corporation; *U.S. Public*, pg. 273
BANNOCKBURN GLOBAL FOREX, LLC—See First Financial Bancorp.; *U.S. Public*, pg. 843
BANQUE PRIVEE SAINT DOMINIQUE—See Groupe BPCE; *Int'l*, pg. 3095
BANQUE REGIONALE DE L'AIN—See Confederation Nationale du Credit Mutuel; *Int'l*, pg. 1767
BANQUE SCALBERT DUPONT—See Confederation Nationale du Credit Mutuel; *Int'l*, pg. 1767
BANYAN MEZZANINE FUND, L.P.; *U.S. Private*, pg. 470
BARCLAYCARD FUNDING PLC—See Barclays PLC; *Int'l*, pg. 859
BARCLAYS ALMA MATER GENERAL PARTNER LIMITED—See Barclays PLC; *Int'l*, pg. 859
BARCLAYS BANK PLC - WEALTH & INVESTMENT MANAGEMENT DIVISION—See Barclays PLC; *Int'l*, pg. 860
BARCLAYS CAPITAL LUXEMBOURG S.A R.L.—See Barclays PLC; *Int'l*, pg. 861
BARCLAYS CCP FUNDING LLP—See Barclays PLC; *Int'l*, pg. 860
BARCLAYS COVERED BOND FUNDING LLP—See Barclays PLC; *Int'l*, pg. 861
BARCLAYS COVERED BONDS LIMITED LIABILITY PARTNERSHIP—See Barclays PLC; *Int'l*, pg. 861
BARCLAYS GBP FUNDING LIMITED—See Barclays PLC; *Int'l*, pg. 861
BARCLAYS INFRASTRUCTURE FUNDS MANAGEMENT LIMITED—See 3i Group plc; *Int'l*, pg. 8
BARCLAYS INTERNATIONAL FUND MANAGERS LIMITED—See Barclays PLC; *Int'l*, pg. 861
BARCLAYS PATRIMOINE S.C.S.—See Barclays PLC; *Int'l*, pg. 861
BARCLAYS PRIVATE TRUST LIMITED—See Barclays PLC; *Int'l*, pg. 861
BARCLAYS SECURED FUNDING (LM) LIMITED—See Barclays PLC; *Int'l*, pg. 861
BARCLAYS WEALTH ASSET MANAGEMENT (MONACO) S.A.M.—See Barclays PLC; *Int'l*, pg. 861
BARCLAYS WEALTH MANAGERS FRANCE SA—See Barclays PLC; *Int'l*, pg. 861
BARCLAYS WEALTH NOMINEES LIMITED—See Barclays PLC; *Int'l*, pg. 861
BARCLAYS WEALTH TRUSTEES (GUERNSEY) LIMITED—See Barclays PLC; *Int'l*, pg. 861
BARCLAYS WEALTH TRUSTEES (HONG KONG) LIMITED—See Barclays PLC; *Int'l*, pg. 861
BARCLAYS WEALTH TRUSTEES (INDIA) PRIVATE LIMITED—See Barclays PLC; *Int'l*, pg. 862
BARD & COMPANY, INC.; *U.S. Private*, pg. 473
BARING ASSET MANAGEMENT (ASIA) LIMITED—See Massachusetts Mutual Life Insurance Company; *U.S. Private*, pg. 2604
BARING ASSET MANAGEMENT (JAPAN) LIMITED—See

N.A.I.C.S. INDEX

523940 — PORTFOLIO MANAGEMEN...

Massachusetts Mutual Life Insurance Company; *U.S. Private*, pg. 2604
BARING ASSET MANAGEMENT KOREA LIMITED—See Massachusetts Mutual Life Insurance Company; *U.S. Private*, pg. 2604
BARING NORTH AMERICA LLC - SAN FRANCISCO OFFICE—See Massachusetts Mutual Life Insurance Company; *U.S. Private*, pg. 2605
BARING NORTH AMERICA LLC—See Massachusetts Mutual Life Insurance Company; *U.S. Private*, pg. 2605
BARING PRIVATE EQUITY ASIA K.K.—See Affiliated Managers Group, Inc.; *U.S. Public*, pg. 54
BARING PRIVATE EQUITY ASIA PTE LIMITED—See Affiliated Managers Group, Inc.; *U.S. Public*, pg. 54
BARINGS CAPITAL INVESTMENT CORPORATION; *U.S. Private*, pg. 475
BARING SICE (TAIWAN) LTD—See Massachusetts Mutual Life Insurance Company; *U.S. Private*, pg. 2604
BARINGS LLC—See Massachusetts Mutual Life Insurance Company; *U.S. Private*, pg. 2604
BARITA INVESTMENTS LIMITED; *Int'l*, pg. 865
BARKLY INVESTMENTS LTD.—See Deutsche Bank Aktiengesellschaft; *Int'l*, pg. 2055
BARODA ASSET MANAGEMENT INDIA LTD—See Bank of Baroda; *Int'l*, pg. 840
BARON GLOBAL FINANCIAL CANADA LTD.—See Hatcher Group Ltd.; *Int'l*, pg. 3284
BARONSMEAD VENTURE TRUST PLC; *Int'l*, pg. 867
BARRETT ASSET MANAGEMENT, LLC—See CI Financial Corporation; *Int'l*, pg. 1600
BARTLETT & CO. LLC; *U.S. Private*, pg. 483
BASALT INFRASTRUCTURE PARTNERS LLP—See Colliers International Group Inc.; *Int'l*, pg. 1700
BASF LIZENZ GMBH—See BASF SE; *Int'l*, pg. 880
BASIC DIVERSIFIED INDUSTRIAL HOLDINGS, INC—See Basic Energy Corporation; *Int'l*, pg. 886
BATES FINANCIAL ADVISORS, INC.—See QCR Holdings, Inc.; *U.S. Public*, pg. 1742
BATH AND PORTLAND STONE (HOLDINGS) LIMITED—See Heidelberg Materials AG; *Int'l*, pg. 3308
BATTERY MINERAL RESOURCES CORP.; *Int'l*, pg. 890
BAUBECON ASSETS GMBH—See Barclays PLC; *Int'l*, pg. 862
BAYER BETEILIGUNGSVERWALTUNG GOSLAR GMBH—See Bayer Aktiengesellschaft; *Int'l*, pg. 902
BBFS ALPHA VERWALTUNGS GMBH—See Bilfinger SE; *Int'l*, pg. 1024
BBGI GLOBAL INFRASTRUCTURE S.A; *Int'l*, pg. 920
BB GRUNDBESITZ GMBH—See Bilfinger SE; *Int'l*, pg. 1024
BB&T INSTITUTIONAL INVESTMENT ADVISERS, INC.—See Truist Financial Corporation; *U.S. Public*, pg. 2200
BCAP LLC—See Barclays PLC; *Int'l*, pg. 860
BCC FACTORING SPA—See Iccrea Holding S.p.A.; *Int'l*, pg. 3578
BCCM ADVISORS, LLC—See Air T, Inc.; *U.S. Public*, pg. 67
BDO CAPITAL ADVISORS, LLC—See BDO USA, LLP; *U.S. Private*, pg. 501
BEACON CAPITAL MANAGEMENT, INC.—See Sammons Enterprises, Inc.; *U.S. Private*, pg. 3537
BEACON POINTE ADVISORS, LLC—See Beacon Pointe Holdings, LLC; *U.S. Private*, pg. 505
BEACON POINTE WEALTH ADVISORS, LLC—See Beacon Pointe Holdings, LLC; *U.S. Private*, pg. 505
BEACON TRUST COMPANY—See Provident Financial Services, Inc.; *U.S. Public*, pg. 1730
BEAUFORT INVESTMENTS COMPANY—See EFG Holding; *Int'l*, pg. 2319
BEAU SEVRAN INVEST SCI—See BNP Paribas SA; *Int'l*, pg. 1089
BECHTEL FINANCING SERVICES, INC.—See Bechtel Group, Inc.; *U.S. Private*, pg. 510
BECHTLE COMSOFT SAS—See Bechtle AG; *Int'l*, pg. 937
BEEDIE CAPITAL PARTNERS; *Int'l*, pg. 939
BEHSHAHR INDUSTRIAL DEVELOPMENT CORP.; *Int'l*, pg. 942
BEIJING COSCO SHIPPING INVESTMENT CO., LTD.—See China COSCO Shipping Corporation Limited; *Int'l*, pg. 1492
BEIJING GAINFULL WEALTH INVESTMENT MANAGEMENT CO., LTD.—See Fortune Fountain (Beijing) Holding Group Co., Ltd.; *Int'l*, pg. 2743
BEIJING HENGTAI HENGZHONG INFORMATION SERVICE CO., LTD.—See HengTai Securities CO., LTD; *Int'l*, pg. 3347
BEIJING HENGTAI HONGZE INVESTMENT CO., LTD.—See HengTai Securities CO., LTD; *Int'l*, pg. 3347
BEIJING NORTH STAR COMPANY LIMITED; *Int'l*, pg. 954
BEIJING PROPERTIES (HOLDINGS) LIMITED; *Int'l*, pg. 955
BEL AIR INVESTMENT ADVISORS LLC—See Fiera Capital Corporation; *Int'l*, pg. 2659
BELFIUS IRELAND—See Belfius Bank SA/NV; *Int'l*, pg. 963
BELHASA REAL ESTATE—See Belhasa Group of Companies; *Int'l*, pg. 964
BELICO HOLDING AB—See AAK AB; *Int'l*, pg. 32
BELL ALIANT PREFERRED EQUITY INC.—See BCE Inc.; *U.S. Private*, pg. 926

BELLECAPITAL AG; *Int'l*, pg. 966
BELL FINANCIAL GROUP LIMITED; *Int'l*, pg. 966
BELL POTTER CAPITAL LIMITED—See Bell Financial Group Limited; *Int'l*, pg. 966
BELL ROCK CAPITAL, LLC—See WSFS Financial Corporation; *U.S. Public*, pg. 2383
BELL WEALTH MANAGEMENT INC.—See Genstar Capital, LLC; *U.S. Private*, pg. 1677
BELL WEALTH MANAGEMENT INC.—See Keystone Group, L.P.; *U.S. Private*, pg. 2298
BELMONT GROUP INC.; *U.S. Private*, pg. 520
BELTONE ASSET MANAGEMENT—See Chimera Investments LLC; *Int'l*, pg. 1479
BELUGA NV; *Int'l*, pg. 968
BENDIGO INVESTMENT SERVICES LIMITED—See Bendigo & Adelaide Bank Ltd.; *Int'l*, pg. 970
BENEFICIENT—See GWG Holdings, Inc.; *U.S. Public*, pg. 975
BENEFITS OF MISSOURI INC.—See Aquiline Capital Partners LLC; *U.S. Private*, pg. 303
BENEFITS OF MISSOURI INC.—See Genstar Capital, LLC; *U.S. Private*, pg. 1675
THE BENEFITS SOLUTION GROUP INC.—See Aon plc; *Int'l*, pg. 497
BENEFIT STREET PARTNERS LLC—See Franklin Resources, Inc.; *U.S. Public*, pg. 879
BENEFIT TRUST GMBH—See Deutsche Bank Aktiengesellschaft; *Int'l*, pg. 2055
BENTLEY REID & COMPANY LIMITED—See Bentley Reid (Holdings) Limited; *Int'l*, pg. 977
BERG & BERG ENTERPRISES, LLC—See Berg & Berg Enterprises, Inc.; *U.S. Private*, pg. 530
BERGEN ENERGI AB—See World Kinect Corporation; *U.S. Public*, pg. 2380
BERGEN ENERGI AS—See World Kinect Corporation; *U.S. Public*, pg. 2380
BERKLEY CAPITAL, LLC—See W.R. Berkley Corporation; *U.S. Public*, pg. 2316
BERKLEY DEAN & COMPANY, INC.—See W.R. Berkley Corporation; *U.S. Public*, pg. 2316
BERLINER EFFEKTENGESELLSCHAFT AG; *Int'l*, pg. 986
BERMUDA INTERNATIONAL INVESTMENT MANAGEMENT LTD.—See HSBC Holdings plc; *Int'l*, pg. 3504
BERNARD R. WOLFE & ASSOCIATES INC.—See Aon plc; *Int'l*, pg. 495
BERNSTEIN AUTONOMOUS LLP—See Equitable Holdings, Inc.; *U.S. Public*, pg. 789
BERYL SECURITIES LIMITED; *Int'l*, pg. 998
BESSEMER GROUP TRUST COMPANY OF FLORIDA—See The Bessemer Group, Incorporated; *U.S. Private*, pg. 3994
BESSEMER INVESTMENT PARTNERS LLC; *U.S. Private*, pg. 541
BESSEMER INVESTORS LLC—See Bessemer Investment Partners LLC; *U.S. Private*, pg. 541
BESSEMER TRUST COMPANY OF CALIFORNIA - LOS ANGELES—See The Bessemer Group, Incorporated; *U.S. Private*, pg. 3994
BESTIGE HOLDINGS LLC; *U.S. Private*, pg. 544
BESTINVER, S.A.—See Acciona, S.A.; *Int'l*, pg. 90
BETA CAPITAL MANAGEMENT LP—See Credit Andorra, S.A.; *Int'l*, pg. 1834
BETA DB LINDSELL LIMITED S.C.S.—See Deutsche Bank Aktiengesellschaft; *Int'l*, pg. 2055
BETTER CAPITAL PCC LIMITED; *Int'l*, pg. 1003
BEUTEL, GOODMAN & COMPANY LTD.—See Affiliated Managers Group, Inc.; *U.S. Public*, pg. 54
BFP BETEILIGUNGSGESELLSCHAFT FUR PROJEKTE MBH—See Bilfinger SE; *Int'l*, pg. 1024
BFSG, LLC—See Clayton, Dubilier & Rice, LLC; *U.S. Private*, pg. 923
BFSG, LLC—See Stone Point Capital LLC; *U.S. Private*, pg. 3824
BG FIDUCIARIA SIM S.P.A.—See Assicurazioni Generali S.p.A.; *Int'l*, pg. 643
BG INVESTMENT SERVICES, INC.—See BankGuam Holding Company; *U.S. Public*, pg. 274
BHI HOLDINGS INC.; *Int'l*, pg. 1015
BH MACRO LTD.; *Int'l*, pg. 1009
BHW - GESELLSCHAFT FUR WOHNUNGSWIRTSCHAFT MBH & CO. IMMOBILIENVERWALTUNGS KG—See Deutsche Bank Aktiengesellschaft; *Int'l*, pg. 2055
BHW - GESELLSCHAFT FUR WOHNUNGSWIRTSCHAFT MBH—See Deutsche Bank Aktiengesellschaft; *Int'l*, pg. 2055
BIBBY FACTOR FRANCE S.A.—See Bibby Line Group Limited; *Int'l*, pg. 1017
BIBBY FINANCIAL SERVICES AB—See Bibby Line Group Limited; *Int'l*, pg. 1018
BIBBY FINANCIAL SERVICES (CA), INC—See Bibby Line Group Limited; *Int'l*, pg. 1018
BIBBY FINANCIAL SERVICES (HOLDINGS) INC—See Global Merchant Fund Corp.; *U.S. Private*, pg. 1716
BICKLEYLAKE LIMITED—See Heidelberg Materials AG; *Int'l*, pg. 3309
BIG SHOULDERS CAPITAL LLC; *U.S. Private*, pg. 554
BILFINGER BERGER A1 MOBIL GMBH—See Bilfinger SE; *Int'l*, pg. 1024

BILTMORE CAPITAL ADVISORS LLC—See Merit Financial Group, LLC; *U.S. Private*, pg. 2674
BIOMASS HOLDINGS S.A R.L.—See Deutsche Bank Aktiengesellschaft; *Int'l*, pg. 2055
BIP INVESTMENT PARTNERS S.A.; *Int'l*, pg. 1045
BISON CAPITAL ASSET MANAGEMENT, LLC; *U.S. Private*, pg. 566
BKD WEALTH ADVISORS, LLC—See BKD, LLP; *U.S. Private*, pg. 568
BLACKFIN CAPITAL PARTNERS SAS; *Int'l*, pg. 1060
BLACK MOUNTAIN SYSTEMS, LLC—See Vista Equity Partners, LLC; *U.S. Private*, pg. 4395
THE BLACK PHOENIX GROUP; *U.S. Private*, pg. 3995
BLACK RIVER ASSET MANAGEMENT LLC—See Cargill, Inc.; *U.S. Private*, pg. 754
BLACKROCK ASSET MANAGEMENT NORTH ASIA LIMITED—See BlackRock, Inc.; *U.S. Public*, pg. 344
BLACKROCK ASSET MANAGEMENT (SCHWEIZ) AG—See BlackRock, Inc.; *U.S. Public*, pg. 344
BLACKROCK CAPITAL INVESTMENT CORPORATION; *U.S. Public*, pg. 342
BLACKROCK COLOMBIA INFRAESTRUCTURA S.A.S.—See BlackRock, Inc.; *U.S. Public*, pg. 345
BLACKROCK COLOMBIA SAS—See BlackRock, Inc.; *U.S. Public*, pg. 345
BLACKROCK FINANCIAL MANAGEMENT, INC.—See BlackRock, Inc.; *U.S. Public*, pg. 345
BLACKROCK GREATER EUROPE INVESTMENT TRUST PLC; *Int'l*, pg. 1061
BLACKROCK HUNGARY KFT—See BlackRock, Inc.; *U.S. Public*, pg. 345
BLACKROCK INCOME & GROWTH INVESTMENT TRUST PLC; *Int'l*, pg. 1062
BLACKROCK INCOME TRUST, INC.; *U.S. Public*, pg. 342
BLACKROCK INTERNATIONAL LIMITED—See BlackRock, Inc.; *U.S. Public*, pg. 345
BLACKROCK INVESTMENT MANAGEMENT (AUSTRALIA) LIMITED—See BlackRock, Inc.; *U.S. Public*, pg. 345
BLACKROCK INVESTMENT MANAGEMENT (TAIWAN) LIMITED—See BlackRock, Inc.; *U.S. Public*, pg. 345
BLACKROCK INVESTMENT MANAGEMENT (UK) LIMITED—See BlackRock, Inc.; *U.S. Public*, pg. 345
BLACKROCK LATIN AMERICAN INVESTMENT TRUST PLC; *Int'l*, pg. 1062
BLACKROCK LIMITED DURATION INCOME TRUST; *U.S. Public*, pg. 342
BLACKROCK (LUXEMBOURG) S.A.—See BlackRock, Inc.; *U.S. Public*, pg. 344
BLACKROCK PERU ASESORIAS S.A.—See BlackRock, Inc.; *U.S. Public*, pg. 345
BLACKROCK SAUDI ARABIA—See BlackRock, Inc.; *U.S. Public*, pg. 345
BLACKROCK (SHANGHAI) CO., LTD.—See BlackRock, Inc.; *U.S. Public*, pg. 344
BLACKROCK (SINGAPORE) LIMITED—See BlackRock, Inc.; *U.S. Public*, pg. 344
BLACKROCK SMALLER COMPANIES TRUST PLC; *Int'l*, pg. 1062
BLACKROCK SUSTAINABLE AMERICAN INCOME TRUST PLC; *Int'l*, pg. 1062
BLACKROCK THROGMORTON TRUST PLC; *Int'l*, pg. 1062
BLACKROCK UK HOLDCO LIMITED—See BlackRock, Inc.; *U.S. Public*, pg. 345
BLACKROCK WORLD MINING TRUST PLC; *Int'l*, pg. 1062
BLACKSTONE ADVISORS INDIA PRIVATE LIMITED—See Blackstone Inc.; *U.S. Public*, pg. 360
BLACKSTONE ADVISORY PARTNERS L.P.—See Blackstone Inc.; *U.S. Public*, pg. 348
BLACKSTONE ALTERNATIVE ASSET MANAGEMENT L.P.—See Blackstone Inc.; *U.S. Public*, pg. 348
BLACKSTONE ALTERNATIVE CREDIT ADVISORS LP—See Blackstone Inc.; *U.S. Public*, pg. 348
BLACKSTONE DEBT ADVISORS L.P.—See Blackstone Inc.; *U.S. Public*, pg. 349
THE BLACKSTONE GROUP GERMANY GMBH—See Blackstone Inc.; *U.S. Public*, pg. 361
THE BLACKSTONE GROUP (HK) LIMITED—See Blackstone Inc.; *U.S. Public*, pg. 360
THE BLACKSTONE GROUP INTERNATIONAL PARTNERS LLP—See Blackstone Inc.; *U.S. Public*, pg. 361
THE BLACKSTONE GROUP JAPAN K.K.—See Blackstone Inc.; *U.S. Public*, pg. 361
BLACKSTONE PROPERTY MANAGEMENT LIMITED—See Blackstone Inc.; *U.S. Public*, pg. 360
BLACKSTONE SENFINA ADVISORS LLC—See Blackstone Inc.; *U.S. Public*, pg. 352
BLACKWALL LIMITED; *Int'l*, pg. 1062
BLAZE PORTFOLIO SYSTEMS LLC—See LPL Financial Holdings Inc.; *U.S. Public*, pg. 1343
BLD ASSET MANAGEMENT EAD—See AG Capital; *Int'l*, pg. 197
BLOOM INVESTMENT COUNSEL, INC.; *Int'l*, pg. 1065
BLUE CHIP INDIA LTD.; *Int'l*, pg. 1067
BLUE CIRCLE SERVICES LIMITED; *Int'l*, pg. 1067
BLUE DELTA CAPITAL PARTNERS LLC; *U.S. Private*, pg. 588
BLUEFIELD SOLAR INCOME FUND; *Int'l*, pg. 1071

BLUE FINANCIAL COMMUNICATION S.P.A.; *Int'l*, pg. 1068
BLUEGEM CAPITAL PARTNERS LLP; *Int'l*, pg. 1071
BLUEMOUNTAIN CAPITAL MANAGEMENT, LLC—See Affiliated Managers Group, Inc.; *U.S. Public*, pg. 54
BLUEMOUNTAIN CAPITAL PARTNERS (LONDON) LLP—See Affiliated Managers Group, Inc.; *U.S. Public*, pg. 54
BLUEMOUNTAIN CLO MANAGEMENT, LLC—See Assured Guaranty Ltd.; *Int'l*, pg. 650
BLUE OWL CREDIT INCOME CORP.; *U.S. Private*, pg. 589
BLUE OWL TECHNOLOGY FINANCE CORP.; *U.S. Private*, pg. 589
BLUE PLANET INVESTMENT TRUST PLC; *Int'l*, pg. 1069
BLUEPRINT FINANCIAL LLC—See Lightyear Capital LLC; *U.S. Private*, pg. 2454
BLUE ROAD MANAGEMENT, L.P.; *U.S. Private*, pg. 592
BLUESPHERE ADVISORS LLC; *U.S. Private*, pg. 597
BLUE TORCH CAPITAL, LP; *U.S. Private*, pg. 594
BLUE WOLF CAPITAL MANAGEMENT LLC—See Blue Wolf Capital Partners LLC; *U.S. Private*, pg. 594
BMCE CAPITAL CONSEIL—See Bank of Africa; *Int'l*, pg. 839
BMCE CAPITAL GESTION—See Bank of Africa; *Int'l*, pg. 839
B. METZLER SEEL. SOHN & CO. HOLDING AG; *Int'l*, pg. 788
BMI BENEFITS, L.L.C.—See Aon plc; *Int'l*, pg. 495
BML LIFE SCIENCE HOLDINGS, INC.—See BML, Inc.; *Int'l*, pg. 1076
BMO ASSET MANAGEMENT CORP.—See Bank of Montreal; *Int'l*, pg. 846
BMO HARRIS FINANCIAL ADVISORS, INC.—See Bank of Montreal; *Int'l*, pg. 846
BMO NESBITT BURNS INC.—See Bank of Montreal; *Int'l*, pg. 846
BMTC GROUP INC.; *Int'l*, pg. 1078
BNG VASTGOEDONTWIKKELING B.V.—See BNG Bank N.V.; *Int'l*, pg. 1079
BNP PARIBAS ASSET MANAGEMENT HOLDING SA—See BNP Paribas SA; *Int'l*, pg. 1081
BNP PARIBAS ASSET MANAGEMENT INC.—See BNP Paribas SA; *Int'l*, pg. 1082
BNP PARIBAS ASSET MANAGEMENT INDIA PRIVATE LTD—See BNP Paribas SA; *Int'l*, pg. 1082
BNP PARIBAS ASSET MANAGEMENT LUXEMBOURG S.A.—See BNP Paribas SA; *Int'l*, pg. 1082
BNP PARIBAS ASSET MANAGEMENT SINGAPORE LIMITED—See BNP Paribas SA; *Int'l*, pg. 1082
BNP PARIBAS ASSET MANAGEMENT—See BNP Paribas SA; *Int'l*, pg. 1082
BNP PARIBAS BDDI PARTICIPATIONS—See BNP Paribas SA; *Int'l*, pg. 1082
BNP PARIBAS COMMODITY FUTURES LTD.—See BNP Paribas SA; *Int'l*, pg. 1083
BNP PARIBAS E & B LTD.—See BNP Paribas SA; *Int'l*, pg. 1083
BNP PARIBAS FIN AMS—See BNP Paribas SA; *Int'l*, pg. 1084
BNP PARIBAS FINANCE (HONG-KONG) LTD.—See BNP Paribas SA; *Int'l*, pg. 1084
BNP PARIBAS FLEET HOLDINGS LTD.—See BNP Paribas SA; *Int'l*, pg. 1084
BNP PARIBAS FUND SERVICES AUSTRALASIA LTD.—See BNP Paribas SA; *Int'l*, pg. 1084
BNP PARIBAS FUND SERVICES DUBLIN LTD.—See BNP Paribas SA; *Int'l*, pg. 1085
BNP PARIBAS INVESTMENT PARTNERS ASIA LIMITED—See BNP Paribas SA; *Int'l*, pg. 1082
BNP PARIBAS INVESTMENT PARTNERS ASIA LTD—See BNP Paribas SA; *Int'l*, pg. 1085
BNP PARIBAS INVESTMENT PARTNERS - BOSTON—See BNP Paribas SA; *Int'l*, pg. 1082
BNP PARIBAS INVESTMENT PARTNERS BSC—See BNP Paribas SA; *Int'l*, pg. 1085
BNP PARIBAS INVESTMENT PARTNERS (HONG KONG) LIMITED—See BNP Paribas SA; *Int'l*, pg. 1082
BNP PARIBAS INVESTMENT PARTNERS JAPAN LTD.—See BNP Paribas SA; *Int'l*, pg. 1082
BNP PARIBAS INVESTMENT PARTNERS LUXEMBOURG SA—See BNP Paribas SA; *Int'l*, pg. 1085
BNP PARIBAS INVESTMENT PARTNERS NETHERLANDS NV—See BNP Paribas SA; *Int'l*, pg. 1085
BNP PARIBAS INVESTMENT PARTNERS NL HOLDING NV—See BNP Paribas SA; *Int'l*, pg. 1085
BNP PARIBAS INVESTMENT PARTNERS SINGAPORE LIMITED—See BNP Paribas SA; *Int'l*, pg. 1085
BNP PARIBAS LEASE GROUP LIZING RT—See BNP Paribas SA; *Int'l*, pg. 1085
BNP PARIBAS LEASE GROUP (RENTALS) LTD.—See BNP Paribas SA; *Int'l*, pg. 1085
BNP PARIBAS LEASE GROUP SA EFC—See BNP Paribas SA; *Int'l*, pg. 1085
BNP PARIBAS PEREGRINE—See BNP Paribas SA; *Int'l*, pg. 1081
BNP PARIBAS SERVICES (HONG KONG) LTD.—See BNP Paribas SA; *Int'l*, pg. 1087
BNP PARIBAS TRUST COMPANY (GUERNESEY) LTD.—See BNP Paribas SA; *Int'l*, pg. 1087
BNP PARIBAS WEALTH MANAGEMENT MONACO—See BNP Paribas SA; *Int'l*, pg. 1088
BNP PARIBAS WEALTH MANAGEMENT—See BNP Paribas SA; *Int'l*, pg. 1088
BNPP ASSET MANAGEMENT ASIA LTD.—See BNP Paribas SA; *Int'l*, pg. 1088
BNPP ASSET MANAGEMENT JAPAN LTD.—See BNP Paribas SA; *Int'l*, pg. 1088
BNPP ASSET MANAGEMENT NEDERLAND NV—See BNP Paribas SA; *Int'l*, pg. 1088
BNP PRIME PEREGRINE (SECURITIES) PTE LTD.—See BNP Paribas SA; *Int'l*, pg. 1081
BNS SPLIT CORP II; *Int'l*, pg. 1093
BNY MELLON FUND MANAGERS LIMITED—See The Bank of New York Mellon Corporation; *U.S. Public*, pg. 2037
BNY MELLON HIGH YIELD STRATEGIES FUND; *U.S. Public*, pg. 366
BNY MELLON INTERNATIONAL OPERATIONS (INDIA) PRIVATE LIMITED—See The Bank of New York Mellon Corporation; *U.S. Public*, pg. 2037
BNY MELLON MUNICIPAL INCOME, INC.; *U.S. Public*, pg. 366
BNY MELLON, NATIONAL ASSOCIATION—See The Bank of New York Mellon Corporation; *U.S. Public*, pg. 2037
BNY MELLON STRATEGIC MUNICIPAL BOND FUND, INC.; *U.S. Public*, pg. 366
BNY MELLON WEALTH MANAGEMENT - MENLO PARK—See The Bank of New York Mellon Corporation; *U.S. Public*, pg. 2037
BNY MELLON WEALTH MANAGEMENT—See The Bank of New York Mellon Corporation; *U.S. Public*, pg. 2037
BOC ASSET MANAGEMENT LTD.—See Bank of Cyprus Holdings Public Limited Company; *Int'l*, pg. 842
BOC FINANCIAL ASSET INVESTMENT COMPANY LIMITED—See Bank of China, Ltd.; *Int'l*, pg. 841
BOEHRINGER INGELHEIM VENTURE FUND GMBH—See C.H. Boehringer Sohn AG & Co. KG; *Int'l*, pg. 1242
BOGAZICI VARLIK YONETIM A.S.; *Int'l*, pg. 1100
BOI SHAREHOLDING LIMITED—See Bank of India; *Int'l*, pg. 843
BOK FINANCIAL PRIVATE WEALTH, INC.—See BOK Financial Corporation; *U.S. Public*, pg. 367
BOLTHOUSE INVESTMENT COMPANY—See Campbell Soup Company; *U.S. Public*, pg. 426
BOMBARDIER TRANSPORTATION HOLDINGS (THAILAND) LTD.—See Alstom S.A.; *Int'l*, pg. 382
BONDED SERVICES GROUP LIMITED—See The Wicks Group of Companies, LLC; *U.S. Private*, pg. 4135
BONEFISH HOLDINGS, LLC—See Bloomin' Brands, Inc.; *U.S. Public*, pg. 362
BONNASSE LYONNAISE DE BANQUE—See Confederation Nationale du Credit Mutuel; *Int'l*, pg. 1767
BONSAI INVESTMENT AG—See Deutsche Bank Aktiengesellschaft; *Int'l*, pg. 2055
BOREA ASSET MANAGEMENT AS—See Borea AS; *Int'l*, pg. 1113
BOREA AS; *Int'l*, pg. 1113
BOREINVEST AB—See Bore Tech AB; *Int'l*, pg. 1113
BORTEX GROUP FINANCE PLC; *Int'l*, pg. 1115
BOSC INTERNATIONAL COMPANY LIMITED—See Bank of Shanghai Co., Ltd; *Int'l*, pg. 848
BOSKALIS MARITIME INVESTMENTS B.V.—See HAL Trust N.V.; *Int'l*, pg. 3225
BOSTON ADVISORS LLC—See Equitable Holdings, Inc.; *U.S. Public*, pg. 790
BOSTON FINANCIAL MANAGEMENT, INC.; *U.S. Private*, pg. 621
BOTJ INVESTMENT GROUP, INC.—See Bank of the James Financial Group, Inc.; *U.S. Public*, pg. 273
BOUWFONDS INVESTMENT MANAGEMENT B.V.; *Int'l*, pg. 1121
BOWLING PORTFOLIO MANAGEMENT LLC—See CI Financial Corporation; *Int'l*, pg. 1600
BOWMARK CAPITAL LLP; *Int'l*, pg. 1124
BOW STREET, LLC; *U.S. Private*, pg. 625
BOYD WATTERSON ASSET MANAGEMENT, LLC—See TAMCO Holdings, LLC; *U.S. Private*, pg. 3928
BPA IPWM (SUISSE), S.A.—See Banca Privada D'Andorra, SA; *Int'l*, pg. 816
BP (CHINA) HOLDINGS LIMITED—See BP plc; *Int'l*, pg. 1126
BPI ASSET MANAGEMENT—See Bank of the Philippine Islands; *Int'l*, pg. 848
BPIFRANCE INVESTISSEMENT SAS—See Caisse des Depots et Consignations; *Int'l*, pg. 1258
BPIFRANCE INVESTISSEMENT SAS—See EPIC Bpifrance; *Int'l*, pg. 2460
BPI (SUISSE) S.A.—See Lone Star Funds; *U.S. Private*, pg. 2484
BP PRUDHOE BAY ROYALTY TRUST; *U.S. Public*, pg. 378
BRAEMONT CAPITAL MANAGEMENT LLC; *U.S. Private*, pg. 633
BRAIN CAPITAL GMBH—See BRAIN Biotech AG; *Int'l*, pg. 1137
BRANDYWINE GLOBAL INVESTMENT MANAGEMENT (EUROPE) LIMITED—See Franklin Resources, Inc.; *U.S. Public*, pg. 881
BRANDYWINE GLOBAL INVESTMENT MANAGEMENT, LLC—See Franklin Resources, Inc.; *U.S. Public*, pg. 881
BRASILPREV PREVIDENCIA PRIVADA S.A.—See Principal Financial Group, Inc.; *U.S. Public*, pg. 1719
BRASILPREV SEGUROS E PREVIDENCIA S.A.—See Banco do Brasil S.A.; *Int'l*, pg. 822
BRAVE ASSET MANAGEMENT INC.; *U.S. Private*, pg. 641
BRAVEHEART INVESTMENT GROUP PLC; *Int'l*, pg. 1141
BRE HOLDING SP. Z O.O.—See Commerzbank AG; *Int'l*, pg. 1719
BREMER FINANCIAL SERVICES, INC.—See Bremer Financial Corporation; *U.S. Private*, pg. 645
BRE WEALTH MANAGEMENT S.A.—See Commerzbank AG; *Int'l*, pg. 1719
BREWIN DOLPHIN CAPITAL & INVESTMENTS (IRELAND) LIMITED—See Brewin Dolphin Holdings PLC; *Int'l*, pg. 1150
BRICKELL GLOBAL MARKETS, INC.—See Brickell Bank; *U.S. Private*, pg. 648
BRIDGE GROWTH PARTNERS, LLC; *U.S. Private*, pg. 648
BRIDGEPOINT INVESTMENT CONSULTANTS (SHANGHAI) CO., LTD.—See Bridgepoint Group Plc; *Int'l*, pg. 1155
BRIDGEPOINT NETHERLANDS B.V.—See Bridgepoint Group Plc; *Int'l*, pg. 1155
BRIDGEWATER WEALTH & FINANCIAL MANAGEMENT LLC—See Clayton, Dubilier & Rice, LLC; *U.S. Private*, pg. 923
BRIDGEWATER WEALTH & FINANCIAL MANAGEMENT LLC—See Stone Point Capital LLC; *U.S. Private*, pg. 3824
BRIGHTON PARK CAPITAL MANAGEMENT, L.P.; *U.S. Private*, pg. 652
BRIGHTSIDE GROUP PLC—See AnaCap Financial Partners LLP; *Int'l*, pg. 445
B. RILEY ALTERNATIVES GP, LLC—See B. Riley Financial, Inc.; *U.S. Public*, pg. 260
B. RILEY WEALTH MANAGEMENT, INC.—See B. Riley Financial, Inc.; *U.S. Public*, pg. 260
BRINKER CAPITAL HOLDINGS INC; *U.S. Private*, pg. 654
BRINKLEY FINANCIAL GROUP; *U.S. Private*, pg. 655
BRINK'S BETEILIGUNGSGESELLSCHAFT MBH—See The Brink's Company; *U.S. Public*, pg. 2042
BRISTLECONE ADVISORS; *U.S. Private*, pg. 655
BRITISH & AMERICAN INVESTMENT TRUST PLC; *Int'l*, pg. 1165
BRITISH & MALAYAN TRUSTEES LIMITED; *Int'l*, pg. 1165
BRITISH SMALLER COMPANIES VCT PLC; *Int'l*, pg. 1171
BRK FINANCIAL GROUP S.A.; *Int'l*, pg. 1171
BROADRIDGE CORPORATE ISSUER SOLUTIONS, INC.—See Broadridge Financial Solutions, Inc.; *U.S. Public*, pg. 391
BROADVIEW GROUP HOLDINGS, LLC; *U.S. Private*, pg. 660
BROADWAY ASSET MANAGEMENT, INC.—See Synovus Financial Corp.; *U.S. Public*, pg. 1971
BROMPTON FUNDS LIMITED; *Int'l*, pg. 1173
BROMPTON LIFECO SPLIT CORP.; *Int'l*, pg. 1174
BROOKDALE REALTY SERVICE, LLC—See The Brookdale Group LLC; *U.S. Private*, pg. 4001
BROOKFIELD INFRASTRUCTURE L.P.—See Brookfield Infrastructure Partners L.P.; *Int'l*, pg. 1190
BROOKFIELD INVESTMENT MANAGEMENT INC.—See Brookfield Corporation; *Int'l*, pg. 1181
BROOKFIELD INVESTMENT PARTNERS, LLC—See Nicolet Bankshares, Inc.; *U.S. Public*, pg. 1528
BROOKFIELD RENEWABLE POWER PREFERRED EQUITY INC.—See Brookfield Corporation; *Int'l*, pg. 1186
BROOKSIDE CAPITAL, INC.; *U.S. Private*, pg. 665
BROOKSIDE CAPITAL PARTNERS FUND, L.P.—See Bain Capital, LP; *U.S. Private*, pg. 437
BROOKS MACDONALD FUNDS LIMITED—See Brooks Macdonald Group plc; *Int'l*, pg. 1194
BROOKS MACDONALD GROUP PLC; *Int'l*, pg. 1194
BROWALLIA AB—See Bronsstadet AB; *Int'l*, pg. 1174
BROWN ADVISORY US SMALLER COMPANIES PLC; *Int'l*, pg. 1198
BROWN BROTHERS HARRIMAN (HONG KONG) LTD.—See Brown Brothers Harriman & Co.; *U.S. Private*, pg. 666
BROWN BROTHERS HARRIMAN INVESTORS SERVICES INCORPORATED—See Brown Brothers Harriman & Co.; *U.S. Private*, pg. 667
BROWN BROTHERS HARRIMAN (POLAND) SP. Z O.O.—See Brown Brothers Harriman & Co.; *U.S. Private*, pg. 667
BROWN BROTHERS HARRIMAN SECURITIES (JAPAN) INC.—See Brown Brothers Harriman & Co.; *U.S. Private*, pg. 667
B.R.R. GUARDIAN MODARABA; *Int'l*, pg. 790
BRUNNER INVESTMENT TRUST PLC; *Int'l*, pg. 1200
BRYN MAWR CAPITAL MANAGEMENT, INC.—See WSFS Financial Corporation; *U.S. Public*, pg. 2383
BSF ENTERPRISE PLC; *Int'l*, pg. 1202
BSI TRUST CORPORATION (MALTA) LIMITED—See EFG International AG; *Int'l*, pg. 2320
BSL LEASING CO., LTD.—See Bangkok Bank Public Company Limited; *Int'l*, pg. 833
BTG PACTUAL; *Int'l*, pg. 1204

N.A.I.C.S. INDEX 523940 — PORTFOLIO MANAGEMEN...

N.A.I.C.S. Index

B.T.I. INVESTMENTS INC.—See Deutsche Bank Aktiengesellschaft; *Int'l*, pg. 2055
BT INVESTMENTS S.R.L.—See Banca Transilvania S.A.; *Int'l*, pg. 816
BTR CAPITAL MANAGEMENT INC.—See TA Associates, Inc.; *U.S. Private*, pg. 3919
BT SABLE, L.L.C.—See Deutsche Bank Aktiengesellschaft; *Int'l*, pg. 2055
BT SECURITIES S.A.—See Banca Transilvania S.A.; *Int'l*, pg. 816
B.T. VORDERTAUNUS (LUXEMBOURG), S.A R.L.—See Deutsche Bank Aktiengesellschaft; *Int'l*, pg. 2055
BUCK CONSULTANTS (ADMINISTRATION & INVESTMENT) LIMITED—See Arthur J. Gallagher & Co.; *U.S. Public*, pg. 204
BUCKINGHAM ASSET MANAGEMENT, LLC—See Clayton, Dubilier & Rice, LLC; *U.S. Private*, pg. 923
BUCKINGHAM ASSET MANAGEMENT, LLC—See Stone Point Capital LLC; *U.S. Private*, pg. 3824
BUCKINGHAM CAPITAL MANAGEMENT, INC.—See Buckingham & Company; *U.S. Private*, pg. 677
BUCKINGHAM STRATEGIC PARTNERS, LLC—See Clayton, Dubilier & Rice, LLC; *U.S. Private*, pg. 923
BUCKINGHAM STRATEGIC PARTNERS, LLC—See Stone Point Capital LLC; *U.S. Private*, pg. 3824
BULVARIA HOLDING EAD—See Eurohold Bulgaria AD; *Int'l*, pg. 2553
BULVESTA HOLDING AD; *Int'l*, pg. 1215
BUSEY CAPITAL MANAGEMENT, INC.—See First Busey Corporation; *U.S. Public*, pg. 840
BUSH O'DONNELL INVESTMENT ADVISORS, INC.—See Bush O'Donnell & Co., Inc.; *U.S. Private*, pg. 694
BUSINESS GROWTH FUND LIMITED—See BGF Group PLC; *Int'l*, pg. 1007
BUZZ CAPITAL 2, INC.; *Int'l*, pg. 1230
BUZZ CAPITAL, INC.; *Int'l*, pg. 1230
BVB BETEILIGUNGS-GMBH—See Borussia Dortmund GmbH & Co. KGaA; *Int'l*, pg. 1115
BVB STADION HOLDING GMBH—See Borussia Dortmund GmbH & Co. KGaA; *Int'l*, pg. 1115
B.V. CTH GROEP—See Darling Ingredients Inc.; *U.S. Public*, pg. 633
BWXT TECHNICAL SERVICES GROUP, INC.—See BWX Technologies, Inc.; *U.S. Public*, pg. 413
BXR PARTNERS KFT—See BXR Group B.V.; *Int'l*, pg. 1233
BXR PARTNERS LLP—See BXR Group B.V.; *Int'l*, pg. 1233
BXR PARTNERS PTE. LTD.—See BXR Group B.V.; *Int'l*, pg. 1233
BZ WBK ASSET MANAGEMENT S.A.—See Banco Santander, S.A.; *Int'l*, pg. 826
C2 OPTIONS EXCHANGE, INCORPORATED—See Cboe Global Markets, Inc.; *U.S. Public*, pg. 459
C5 WEALTH MANAGEMENT, LLC; *U.S. Private*, pg. 710
THE CABANA GROUP, LLC; *U.S. Private*, pg. 4003
CACHEMATRIX HOLDINGS, LLC—See BlackRock, Inc.; *U.S. Public*, pg. 345
CAC LLC—See Berkshire Hathaway Inc.; *U.S. Public*, pg. 298
CACONDE PARTICIPACOES S.A.; *Int'l*, pg. 1247
CADOGAN MANAGEMENT, LLC; *U.S. Private*, pg. 713
CAIAC FUND MANAGEMENT AG; *Int'l*, pg. 1252
CA IMMO CZECH REPUBLIC—See Starwood Capital Group Global I, LLC; *U.S. Private*, pg. 3789
CAISSE DE DEPOT ET PLACEMENT DU QUEBEC; *Int'l*, pg. 1253
CAISSE FRANCAISE DE FINANCEMENT LOCAL; *Int'l*, pg. 1259
CAISSE REGIONALE DE CREDIT AGRICOLE MUTUEL DE LA TOURAINE ET DU POITOU SCACV; *Int'l*, pg. 1259
CAISSE REGIONALE DE CREDIT AGRICOLE MUTUEL DE PARIS ET D'ILE DE FRANCE SC; *Int'l*, pg. 1259
CAISSE REGIONALE DE CREDIT AGRICOLE TOULOUSE 31; *Int'l*, pg. 1259
CAIXA GESTAO DE ATIVOS, SGOIC, SA—See Caixa Geral de Depositos S.A.; *Int'l*, pg. 1260
CALAMOS ASSET MANAGEMENT, INC.; *U.S. Private*, pg. 716
CALAMOS INVESTMENTS LLC—See Calamos Asset Management, Inc.; *U.S. Private*, pg. 716
CALAR BELGIUM S.A./N.V.—See Euroclear S.A./N.V.; *Int'l*, pg. 2534
CALATRAVA CAPITAL S.A.; *Int'l*, pg. 1261
CALCULUS VCT PLC; *Int'l*, pg. 1262
CALIFORNIA HEALTHCARE MEDICAL BILLING, LLC—See Veradigm Inc.; *U.S. Public*, pg. 2280
CALIMMUNE INC.—See CSL Limited; *Int'l*, pg. 1865
CALLAHAN FINANCIAL PLANNING COMPANY; *U.S. Private*, pg. 722
CALVERT ASSET MANAGEMENT COMPANY, INC.—See Ameritas Mutual Holding Company; *U.S. Private*, pg. 261
CAMBIAR INVESTORS LLC; *U.S. Private*, pg. 726
CAMBRIA AFRICA PLC; *Int'l*, pg. 1269
CAMBRIDGE ASSOCIATES LLC; *U.S. Private*, pg. 726
CAMBRIDGE INVESTMENT GROUP, INC.; *U.S. Private*, pg. 727
CAMGESTION—See BNP Paribas SA; *Int'l*, pg. 1089
CAMPER & NICHOLSONS MARINA INVST. LTD.; *Int'l*, pg. 1274
CANACCORD GENUITY (AUSTRALIA) LIMITED—See Canaccord Genuity Group Inc.; *Int'l*, pg. 1277
CANACCORD GENUITY FINANCIAL LIMITED—See Canaccord Genuity Group Inc.; *Int'l*, pg. 1277
CANACCORD GENUITY HAWKPOINT LIMITED—See Canaccord Genuity Group Inc.; *Int'l*, pg. 1277
CANADIAN PREFERRED SHARE TRUST; *Int'l*, pg. 1285
CANARA ROBECCO ASSET MANAGEMENT COMPANY LTD.—See Canara Bank; *Int'l*, pg. 1287
CANDRIAM INVESTORS GROUP-GERMANY—See New York Life Insurance Company; *U.S. Private*, pg. 2911
CANDRIAM INVESTORS GROUP-ITALY—See New York Life Insurance Company; *U.S. Private*, pg. 2911
CANDRIAM INVESTORS GROUP-SPAIN—See New York Life Insurance Company; *U.S. Private*, pg. 2911
CANDRIAM INVESTORS GROUP-SWITZERLAND—See New York Life Insurance Company; *U.S. Private*, pg. 2911
CANDRIAM INVESTORS GROUP-THE NETHERLANDS—See New York Life Insurance Company; *U.S. Private*, pg. 2911
CANNAMED ENTERPRISES, INC.; *U.S. Private*, pg. 734
CANOE FINANCIAL LP; *Int'l*, pg. 1292
CANON MJ IT GROUP HOLDINGS INC.—See Canon Inc.; *Int'l*, pg. 1296
CANTOR FITZGERALD INVESTMENT ADVISORS, L.P.—See Cantor Fitzgerald, L.P.; *U.S. Private*, pg. 736
CAPEVIEW CAPITAL LLP—See Affiliated Managers Group, Inc.; *U.S. Public*, pg. 54
CAPEVIN HOLDINGS LIMITED; *Int'l*, pg. 1303
CAPFINANCIAL PARTNERS, LLC—See The CapFinancial Group, LLC; *U.S. Private*, pg. 4004
CAPGEN CAPITAL ADVISERS LLC—See CapGen Financial Group LP; *U.S. Private*, pg. 738
CAPITAL ADVISORS PARTNERS ASIA PTE. LTD.—See TRG Management LP; *U.S. Private*, pg. 4219
CAPITAL ADVISORS PARTNERS ASIA SDN. BHD.—See TRG Management LP; *U.S. Private*, pg. 4219
CAPITAL ANALYSTS, INC.—See Lincoln Investment Planning Inc.; *U.S. Private*, pg. 2458
CAPITALAND FUND MANAGEMENT LIMITED—See CapitaLand Investment Limited; *Int'l*, pg. 1313
CAPITAL DIRECTIONS, INC.; *U.S. Public*, pg. 431
CAPITAL DYNAMICS, INC.—See Capital Dynamics Ltd.; *Int'l*, pg. 1310
CAPITAL DYNAMICS LTD.; *Int'l*, pg. 1310
CAPITAL ESTATE LIMITED; *Int'l*, pg. 1310
CAPITAL FINANCIAL GROUP, INC.—See Arrow Financial Corporation; *U.S. Public*, pg. 200
CAPITAL FINANCIAL MARKETS LIMITED—See Capital International Group Limited; *Int'l*, pg. 1311
CAPITAL FINANCIAL PRESS LIMITED; *Int'l*, pg. 1311
CAPITAL FINANCIAL SERVICES, INC.—See Capital Financial Holdings, Inc.; *U.S. Public*, pg. 431
CAPITAL FIRST LTD.—See IDFC First Bank Limited; *Int'l*, pg. 3592
CAPITAL FIRST SECURITIES LIMITED—See IDFC First Bank Limited; *Int'l*, pg. 3593
CAPITAL FUNDING, LLC—See Capital Funding Group, Inc.; *U.S. Private*, pg. 740
THE CAPITAL GROUP COMPANIES, INC.; *U.S. Private*, pg. 4004
CAPITAL GROUP INTERNATIONAL, INC.—See The Capital Group Companies, Inc.; *U.S. Private*, pg. 4004
CAPITAL GUARDIAN LLC; *U.S. Private*, pg. 740
CAPITAL GUARDIAN TRUST COMPANY—See The Capital Group Companies, Inc.; *U.S. Private*, pg. 4004
CAPITAL INTERNATIONAL ASSET MANAGEMENT (CANADA), INC.—See The Capital Group Companies, Inc.; *U.S. Private*, pg. 4004
CAPITAL INVESTMENT ADVISORS, INC.; *U.S. Private*, pg. 741
CAPITAL PARTNERS LLC; *U.S. Private*, pg. 741
CAPITAL PARTNERS S.A.; *Int'l*, pg. 1312
CAPITAL PROFESSIONAL LIMITED; *Int'l*, pg. 1312
CAPITAL REALM FINANCIAL HOLDINGS GROUP LIMITED; *Int'l*, pg. 1312
THE CAPITAL RESEARCH & MANAGEMENT CO.—See The Capital Group Companies, Inc.; *U.S. Private*, pg. 4004
CAPITALSOUTH CORP.; *U.S. Private*, pg. 742
CAPITAL STREET DELAWARE LP—See Banco Santander, S.A.; *Int'l*, pg. 827
CAPITAL TRANSMISSION S.A.—See Banque Cantonale de Geneve S.A.; *Int'l*, pg. 852
CAPITAL TREASURY SERVICES LIMITED—See Capital International Group Limited; *Int'l*, pg. 1311
CAPITAL VC LIMITED; *Int'l*, pg. 1313
CAPITANIA SECURITIES II FII FUND; *Int'l*, pg. 1314
CAPITOL MERIDIAN PARTNERS; *U.S. Private*, pg. 744
CAPMAN SWEDEN AB—See CapMan PLC; *Int'l*, pg. 1315
CAPMONT GMBH; *Int'l*, pg. 1315
CAPRICORN INVESTMENT PARTNERS LIMITED; *Int'l*, pg. 1316
CAPSENSIXX AG; *Int'l*, pg. 1317
CAPSTAN FINANCIAL CONSULTING GROUP LLC; *U.S. Private*, pg. 746
CAPSTONE PARTNERS LLC—See Huntington Bancshares Incorporated; *U.S. Public*, pg. 1071
CAPTRUST ADVISORS, LLC; *U.S. Private*, pg. 747
CAPULA INVESTMENT JAPAN LIMITED—See Affiliated Managers Group, Inc.; *U.S. Public*, pg. 54
CAPULA INVESTMENT MANAGEMENT ASIA LIMITED—See Affiliated Managers Group, Inc.; *U.S. Public*, pg. 54
CAPULA INVESTMENT MANAGEMENT LLP—See Affiliated Managers Group, Inc.; *U.S. Public*, pg. 54
CAPULA INVESTMENT US LP—See Affiliated Managers Group, Inc.; *U.S. Public*, pg. 54
CAPVIS AG; *Int'l*, pg. 1318
CARDNO HOLDINGS PTY. LTD.—See Cardno Limited; *Int'l*, pg. 1322
CARDON GROUP INC.; *Int'l*, pg. 1323
CARESPAN HEALTH, INC.; *Int'l*, pg. 1325
CARGOJET HOLDINGS LTD.—See Cargojet Inc.; *Int'l*, pg. 1325
CARILLON FUND DISTRIBUTORS, INC.—See Raymond James Financial, Inc.; *U.S. Public*, pg. 1764
CARILLON TOWER ADVISERS, INC.—See Raymond James Financial, Inc.; *U.S. Public*, pg. 1763
CARLSON CAPITAL, L.P. - NEW YORK OFFICE—See Carlson Capital, L.P.; *U.S. Private*, pg. 764
CARLSON CAPITAL, L.P.; *U.S. Private*, pg. 764
CARLTON INVESTMENTS LIMITED; *Int'l*, pg. 1341
CARLYLE ASIA INVESTMENT ADVISORS LIMITED—See The Carlyle Group Inc.; *U.S. Public*, pg. 2045
CARLYLE AVIATION SECURITIES PARTNERS, LLC—See The Carlyle Group Inc.; *U.S. Public*, pg. 2045
THE CARLYLE GROUP (LUXEMBOURG) S.A.R.L.—See The Carlyle Group Inc.; *U.S. Public*, pg. 2055
CARLYLE SINGAPORE INVESTMENT ADVISORS PTE LTD—See The Carlyle Group Inc.; *U.S. Public*, pg. 2045
CARMELINA CAPITAL PARTNERS; *U.S. Private*, pg. 766
CARMILA SA; *Int'l*, pg. 1342
CARNEGIE INVESTMENT COUNSEL; *U.S. Private*, pg. 766
CAROUSEL CAPITAL PARTNERS; *U.S. Private*, pg. 769
CARPATHIA CAPITAL SA; *Int'l*, pg. 1343
CARPENTER FUND MANAGEMENT COMPANY, LLC—See CCFW, Inc.; *U.S. Private*, pg. 799
THE CARTA GROUP, INC.—See Community Bank System, Inc.; *U.S. Public*, pg. 550
CASA DE BOLSA FINAMEX, S.A.B. DE C.V.; *Int'l*, pg. 1349
CASH ASSET MANAGEMENT LIMITED—See CASH Financial Services Group Limited; *Int'l*, pg. 1352
CASPAR ASSET MANAGEMENT SA; *Int'l*, pg. 1354
CASPIAN CORPORATE SERVICES LIMITED; *Int'l*, pg. 1354
CASSIDY & COMPANY, LLC—See Galiot Insurance Services, Inc.; *U.S. Private*, pg. 1638
CASTIK CAPITAL PARTNERS GMBH—See Castik Capital S.a.r.l.; *Int'l*, pg. 1356
CATELLA AB; *Int'l*, pg. 1359
CATERPILLAR (LUXEMBOURG) INVESTMENT CO. S.A.R.L.—See Caterpillar, Inc.; *U.S. Public*, pg. 449
CAUSEWAY CAPITAL MANAGEMENT LLC; *U.S. Private*, pg. 794
CAVENDISH CORPORATE FINANCE LLP—See Cavendish Financial plc; *Int'l*, pg. 1362
CAVEO FUND SOLUTIONS PROPRIETARY LIMITED—See Alexander Forbes Group Holdings Limited; *Int'l*, pg. 307
CBA ASSET MG OR; *Int'l*, pg. 1364
CBG CAPITAL LIMITED—See Clime Capital Limited; *Int'l*, pg. 1659
CBR ASSET MANAGEMENT BELGIUM S.A.—See Heidelberg Materials AG; *Int'l*, pg. 3309
CBRE CLARION SECURITIES LLC—See CBRE Group, Inc.; *U.S. Public*, pg. 460
CBZ HOLDINGS LIMITED; *Int'l*, pg. 1366
CCB FUTURES CO., LTD.—See China Construction Bank Corporation; *Int'l*, pg. 1491
CC CAPITAL PARTNERS, LLC; *U.S. Private*, pg. 797
CCCC INTERNATIONAL HOLDING LIMITED—See China Communications Construction Company Limited; *Int'l*, pg. 1490
CCIAM FUTURE ENERGY LIMITED; *Int'l*, pg. 1366
CCI GROUP, LLC—See Bristol Bay Native Corporation; *U.S. Private*, pg. 656
CCO CAPITAL, LLC—See CIM Group, LLC; *U.S. Private*, pg. 897
CCO INVESTMENT SERVICES CORP.—See Citizens Financial Group, Inc.; *U.S. Public*, pg. 505
CCSL LIMITED; *Int'l*, pg. 1369
C & C TOURS, INC.; *U.S. Private*, pg. 701
CDH CHINA MANAGEMENT COMPANY LIMITED; *Int'l*, pg. 1370
CDL HOSPITALITY TRUSTS; *Int'l*, pg. 1371
CDL INVESTMENTS NEW ZEALAND LIMITED; *Int'l*, pg. 1371
CDP CAPITAL US INC.—See Caisse de Depot et Placement du Quebec; *Int'l*, pg. 1253
CDP FINANCIAL, INC.—See Caisse de Depot et Placement du Quebec; *Int'l*, pg. 1253
CDP IMMOBILIARE SGR S.P.A.—See Cassa Depositi e

Prestiti S.p.A.; *Int'l*, pg. 1354
CDPQ CHINA—See Caisse de Depot et Placement du Quebec; *Int'l*, pg. 1253
CD&R LLP—See Clayton, Dubilier & Rice, LLC; *U.S. Private*, pg. 920
CECOVILLE SAS—See BNP Paribas SA; *Int'l*, pg. 1089
CECP INVESTMENT ADVISORS FRANCE S.A.R.L.—See The Carlyle Group Inc.; *U.S. Public*, pg. 2045
CEDAR BROOK FINANCIAL PARTNERS, LLC; *U.S. Private*, pg. 804
CEDAR HOLDINGS GROUP CO., LTD.; *Int'l*, pg. 1388
CEETRUS ITALY SPA—See Auchan Holding S.A.; *Int'l*, pg. 699
CELADON PHARMACEUTICALS PLC; *Int'l*, pg. 1391
CELEBRITY NATIONAL FINANCIAL SERVICE SAOG; *Int'l*, pg. 1392
CELERITAS MANAGEMENT, INC.—See Palladium Equity Partners, LLC; *U.S. Private*, pg. 3077
CEMEX HOLDINGS (ISRAEL) LIMITED—See CEMEX, S.A.B. de C.V.; *Int'l*, pg. 1398
THE CENTENNIAL GROUP LLC; *U.S. Private*, pg. 4006
CENTERGATE CAPITAL, LP; *U.S. Private*, pg. 816
CENTERSQUARE INVESTMENT MANAGEMENT, INC.—See Lovell Minnick Partners LLC; *U.S. Private*, pg. 2501
CENTERVIEW PARTNERS LLC; *U.S. Private*, pg. 817
CENTRIC WEALTH GROUP—See CHAMP Private Equity Pty. Ltd.; *Int'l*, pg. 1439
CENTRO SUR, S.A. DE C.V.—See Empresas ICA S.A.B. de C.V.; *Int'l*, pg. 2390
CENTRUM WEALTH LIMITED—See Centrum Capital Ltd.; *Int'l*, pg. 1415
CENTURY CAPITAL MANAGEMENT LLC—See Congress Asset Management Co.; *U.S. Private*, pg. 1013
CENTURY GROUP LLC—See Century Communities, Inc.; *U.S. Public*, pg. 475
CEPHEUS INTERNATIONAL CO., LTD.—See Catcher Technology Co., Ltd.; *Int'l*, pg. 1359
CEQUEL III, LLC; *U.S. Private*, pg. 835
CERBERUS BEIJING ADVISORS LTD—See Cerberus Capital Management, L.P.; *U.S. Private*, pg. 837
CERBERUS CALIFORNIA, LLC—See Cerberus Capital Management, L.P.; *U.S. Private*, pg. 837
CERBERUS CAPITAL CHICAGO, LLC—See Cerberus Capital Management, L.P.; *U.S. Private*, pg. 837
CERBERUS EUROPEAN CAPITAL ADVISORS, LLP—See Cerberus Capital Management, L.P.; *U.S. Private*, pg. 837
CERBERUS JAPAN K.K.—See Cerberus Capital Management, L.P.; *U.S. Private*, pg. 837
CERBERUS OPERATIONS AND ADVISORY COMPANY, LLC—See Cerberus Capital Management, L.P.; *U.S. Private*, pg. 837
CEREDEX VALUE ADVISORS LLC—See Virtus Investment Partners, Inc.; *U.S. Public*, pg. 2300
CERES CLASSIC L.P.; *U.S. Private*, pg. 840
CERES GLOBAL AG CORP.; *U.S. Public*, pg. 475
CERES VENTURES, INC.; *U.S. Public*, pg. 475
CERIDIAN EUROPE LIMITED—See Dayforce, Inc.; *U.S. Public*, pg. 645
CERIDIAN (MAURITIUS) LTD.—See Dayforce, Inc.; *U.S. Public*, pg. 645
CERITY PARTNERS LLC—See Genstar Capital, LLC; *U.S. Private*, pg. 1676
CESKOMORAVSKY BETON, A.S.—See Heidelberg Materials AG; *Int'l*, pg. 3309
CETERA ADVISOR NETWORKS LLC—See Genstar Capital, LLC; *U.S. Private*, pg. 1676
CETERA ADVISORS LLC—See Genstar Capital, LLC; *U.S. Private*, pg. 1676
CETERA ADVISORS LLC—See TA Associates, Inc.; *U.S. Private*, pg. 3919
CETERA FINANCIAL GROUP, INC.—See Genstar Capital, LLC; *U.S. Private*, pg. 1676
CETERA INVESTMENT SERVICES LLC—See Genstar Capital, LLC; *U.S. Private*, pg. 1676
CEYLON GUARDIAN INVESTMENT TRUST PLC—See Carson Cumberbatch PLC; *Int'l*, pg. 1347
CEYLON INVESTMENT PLC—See Carson Cumberbatch PLC; *Int'l*, pg. 1347
CFS GROUP, INC.—See Chemung Financial Corporation; *U.S. Public*, pg. 484
CHALLENGER ACQUISITIONS LIMITED; *Int'l*, pg. 1438
CHANDRIMA MERCANTILES LIMITED; *Int'l*, pg. 1441
CHARGER INVESTMENT PARTNERS LP; *U.S. Private*, pg. 850
CHARLEMAGNE CAPITAL (IOM) LIMITED—See Fiera Capital Corporation; *Int'l*, pg. 2659
CHARLES RIVER SYSTEMS, INC.—See State Street Corporation; *U.S. Public*, pg. 1940
CHARLES SCHWAB INVESTMENT MANAGEMENT, INC.—See The Charles Schwab Corporation; *U.S. Public*, pg. 2058
CHARLES STANLEY & CO. LTD.—See Raymond James Financial, Inc.; *U.S. Public*, pg. 1764
CHARLES STANLEY GROUP PLC—See Raymond James Financial, Inc.; *U.S. Public*, pg. 1764

CHARTER ATLANTIC CORPORATION; *U.S. Private*, pg. 858
CHARTER PACIFIC CORPORATION LIMITED; *Int'l*, pg. 1454
CHARTWELL GROUP LIMITED—See Close Brothers Group plc; *Int'l*, pg. 1661
CHARTWELL INVESTMENT PARTNERS, L.P.—See Raymond James Financial, Inc.; *U.S. Public*, pg. 1765
CHATHAM ASSET MANAGEMENT, LLC; *U.S. Private*, pg. 860
CHAZAK VALUE CORP.; *U.S. Private*, pg. 868
CHB P H R LIMITED—See Heidelberg Materials AG; *Int'l*, pg. 3309
CHECKMATE ADVISORS, LLC; *U.S. Private*, pg. 869
CHE INTERNATIONAL GROUP, LLC; *U.S. Private*, pg. 868
CHEMTROS CO., LTD.; *Int'l*, pg. 1464
CHENGDA TECHNOLOGY CO., LTD.; *Int'l*, pg. 1467
CHEPRI HOLDING B.V.; *Int'l*, pg. 1471
CHEQUEFECTIVO, S.A.; *Int'l*, pg. 1471
CHEQUERS SA; *Int'l*, pg. 1471
CHEVRON CANADA FINANCE LTD.—See Chevron Corporation; *U.S. Public*, pg. 486
CHICAGO DEFERRED EXCHANGE COMPANY, LLC—See Wintrust Financial Corporation; *U.S. Public*, pg. 2374
CHICAGO EQUITY PARTNERS, LLC—See Affiliated Managers Group, Inc.; *U.S. Public*, pg. 54
CHILDREN'S HOSPITAL COLORADO HEALTH SYSTEM; *U.S. Private*, pg. 884
CHIMERA INVESTMENTS LLC; *Int'l*, pg. 1479
CHINA ASSET MANAGEMENT CO., LTD; *Int'l*, pg. 1483
CHINA ASSET MANAGEMENT (HONG KONG) LIMITED—See China Asset Management Co., Ltd.; *Int'l*, pg. 1483
CHINA BANK CAPITAL CORPORATION—See China Banking Corporation; *Int'l*, pg. 1484
CHINA CAPITAL MANAGEMENT CO., LTD.—See CSC Financial Co., Ltd; *Int'l*, pg. 1862
CHINA CASTON 81 FINANCE COMPANY LIMITED"; *Int'l*, pg. 1488
CHINA CINDA (HK) HOLDINGS CO., LTD.—See China Cinda Asset Management Co., Ltd.; *Int'l*, pg. 1488
CHINA CINDA (MACAU) ASSET MANAGEMENT CO., LTD.—See China Cinda Asset Management Co., Ltd.; *Int'l*, pg. 1488
CHINA DAYE NON-FERROUS METALS MINING LIMITED; *Int'l*, pg. 1497
CHINA ECO-FARMING LIMITED; *Int'l*, pg. 1498
CHINA FUND MANAGEMENT CO., LTD.—See CSC Financial Co., Ltd; *Int'l*, pg. 1862
CHINA GREAT WALL ASSET MANAGEMENT CORPORATION; *Int'l*, pg. 1505
CHINA INDUSTRIAL SECURITIES INTERNATIONAL ASSET MANAGEMENT LIMITED—See China Industrial Securities Financial Group; *Int'l*, pg. 1509
CHINA INDUSTRIAL SECURITIES INTERNATIONAL WEALTH MANAGEMENT LIMITED—See China Industrial Securities Financial Group; *Int'l*, pg. 1510
CHINA INFRASTRUCTURE INVESTMENT LIMITED; *Int'l*, pg. 1510
CHINA INNOVATION INVESTMENT LIMITED; *Int'l*, pg. 1510
CHINA INTERNATIONAL CAPITAL CORPORATION (HONG KONG) LIMITED—See China International Capital Corporation Limited; *Int'l*, pg. 1510
CHINA INTERNATIONAL CAPITAL CORPORATION (SINGAPORE) PTE. LIMITED—See China International Capital Corporation Limited; *Int'l*, pg. 1510
CHINA INVESTMENT AND FINANCE GROUP LIMITED; *Int'l*, pg. 1513
CHINA INVESTMENT CORPORATION; *Int'l*, pg. 1513
CHINA JINGU INTERNATIONAL TRUST CO., LTD.—See China Cinda Asset Management Co., Ltd.; *Int'l*, pg. 1488
CHINA LIFE AMP ASSET MANAGEMENT COMPANY—See China Life Insurance Company Limited; *Int'l*, pg. 1515
CHINA LIFE ASSET MANAGEMENT COMPANY LIMITED—See China Life Insurance Company Limited; *Int'l*, pg. 1515
CHINA LIFE WEALTH MANAGEMENT COMPANY LIMITED—See China Life Insurance Company Limited; *Int'l*, pg. 1515
CHINA MERCHANTS CAPITAL INVESTMENT CO., LTD.—See China Merchants Group Limited; *Int'l*, pg. 1520
CHINA MERCHANTS FUND MANAGEMENT CO., LTD.—See China Merchants Group Limited; *Int'l*, pg. 1520
CHINA NATIONAL MACHINERY INDUSTRY CORPORATION; *Int'l*, pg. 1531
CHINA PROPERTIES INVESTMENT HOLDINGS LIMITED; *Int'l*, pg. 1542
CHINA RENAISSANCE HOLDINGS LTD.; *Int'l*, pg. 1547
CHINA RUYI HOLDINGS LIMITED; *Int'l*, pg. 1549
CHINA SOUTHERN ASSET MANAGEMENT CO., LTD.—See Huatai Securities Co., Ltd.; *Int'l*, pg. 3514
CHINLINK FINANCE LEASE COMPANY LIMITED—See ChinLink International Holdings Limited; *Int'l*, pg. 1570
CHINLINK SUPPLY CHAIN SERVICES (SHAANXI) COM-

PANY LIMITED—See ChinLink International Holdings Limited; *Int'l*, pg. 1570
CHINLINK TIAN HUI COMPANY LIMITED—See ChinLink International Holdings Limited; *Int'l*, pg. 1570
CHOICE CAPITAL ADVISORS PRIVATE LIMITED—See Choice International Limited; *Int'l*, pg. 1577
CHORI SHANGHAI LTD.—See Chori Co., Ltd.; *Int'l*, pg. 1583
CHOU ASSOCIATES MANAGEMENT INC.; *Int'l*, pg. 1584
CHUANG'S CONSORTIUM INTERNATIONAL LIMITED; *Int'l*, pg. 1590
CHUBB GROUP SECURITY LIMITED—See Carrier Global Corporation; *U.S. Public*, pg. 441
CIBC AUSTRALIA LTD.—See Canadian Imperial Bank of Commerce; *Int'l*, pg. 1283
CIBC GLOBAL ASSET MANAGEMENT INC.—See Canadian Imperial Bank of Commerce; *Int'l*, pg. 1283
CIBC INVESTOR SERVICES INC.—See Canadian Imperial Bank of Commerce; *Int'l*, pg. 1283
CIBRASEC-COMPANHIA BRASILEIRA DE SECURITIZACAO; *Int'l*, pg. 1602
CICC ALPHA (BEIJING) INVESTMENT FUND MANAGEMENT CO., LTD—See China International Capital Corporation Limited; *Int'l*, pg. 1510
CICC ZHIDE CAPITAL CORPORATION LIMITED—See China International Capital Corporation Limited; *Int'l*, pg. 1510
CIFC ASSET MANAGEMENT LLC—See Centricus Partners LP; *Int'l*, pg. 1413
CIGNA BENEFITS FINANCING, INC.—See The Cigna Group; *U.S. Public*, pg. 2060
CI INVESTMENTS INC.—See CI Financial Corporation; *Int'l*, pg. 1600
CILSA INVESTMENTS (PTY) LTD.—See Capital International Group Limited; *Int'l*, pg. 1311
CIMARRON HEALTHCARE CAPITAL LLC; *U.S. Private*, pg. 897
CIMB-PRINCIPAL ASSET MANAGEMENT BERHAD—See CIMB Group Holdings Berhad; *Int'l*, pg. 1608
CIMB-PRINCIPAL ASSET MANAGEMENT BERHAD—See Principal Financial Group, Inc.; *U.S. Public*, pg. 1720
CIMB-PRINCIPAL ASSET MANAGEMENT (SINGAPORE) PTE LTD—See CIMB Group Holdings Berhad; *Int'l*, pg. 1608
CIMB-PRINCIPAL ASSET MANAGEMENT (SINGAPORE) PTE LTD—See Principal Financial Group, Inc.; *U.S. Public*, pg. 1720
CINDA CAPITAL MANAGEMENT CO., LTD.—See China Cinda Asset Management Co., Ltd.; *Int'l*, pg. 1488
CINDA FINANCIAL LEASING CO., LTD.—See China Cinda Asset Management Co., Ltd.; *Int'l*, pg. 1488
CINDA FUTURES CO., LTD.—See China Cinda Asset Management Co., Ltd.; *Int'l*, pg. 1488
CINDA INNOVATION INVESTMENT CO., LTD.—See China Cinda Asset Management Co., Ltd.; *Int'l*, pg. 1488
CINDA INVESTMENT CO., LTD.—See China Cinda Asset Management Co., Ltd.; *Int'l*, pg. 1488
CINVEN CAPITAL MANAGEMENT (V) GENERAL PARTNER LIMITED—See Cinven Limited; *Int'l*, pg. 1611
CINVEN GMBH—See Cinven Limited; *Int'l*, pg. 1611
CINVEN HK LIMITED—See Cinven Limited; *Int'l*, pg. 1611
CINVEN LUXEMBOURG S.A R.L—See Cinven Limited; *Int'l*, pg. 1611
CINVEN PARTNERS LLP—See Cinven Limited; *Int'l*, pg. 1611
CINVEN S.R.L.—See Cinven Limited; *Int'l*, pg. 1611
CION INVESTMENT CORPORATION; *U.S. Public*, pg. 496
CIPIO PARTNERS GMBH; *Int'l*, pg. 1616
CIP MERCHANT CAPITAL LIMITED; *Int'l*, pg. 1616
CIRCLE PEAK CAPITAL LLC; *U.S. Private*, pg. 900
CIS CO., LTD.; *Int'l*, pg. 1618
CITIC ASSETS MANAGEMENT CORPORATION LTD.—See CITIC Group Corporation; *Int'l*, pg. 1619
CITIC SECURITIES INVESTMENT LIMITED—See CITIC Securities Co., Ltd.; *Int'l*, pg. 1622
CITIFINANCIAL EUROPE PLC—See Citigroup Inc.; *U.S. Public*, pg. 502
CITI GLOBAL WEALTH MANAGEMENT—See Citigroup Inc.; *U.S. Public*, pg. 502
CITIGROUP FIRST INVESTMENT MANAGEMENT AMERICAS LLC—See Citigroup Inc.; *U.S. Public*, pg. 503
CITIZENS BANK NEW HAMPSHIRE—See Citizens Financial Group, Inc.; *U.S. Public*, pg. 505
CITIZENS BUSINESS BANK - WEALTH MANAGEMENT GROUP—See CVB Financial Corp.; *U.S. Public*, pg. 613
CITY OF LONDON HELIPORT LIMITED—See Heidelberg Materials AG; *Int'l*, pg. 3310
CITY OF LONDON INVESTMENT MANAGEMENT COMPANY LIMITED—See City of London Investment Group PLC; *Int'l*, pg. 1627
CITY OF LONDON INVESTMENT MANAGEMENT (SINGAPORE) PTE. LTD.—See City of London Investment Group PLC; *Int'l*, pg. 1627
CITY REFRIGERATION HOLDINGS (UK) LIMITED; *Int'l*, pg. 1627
CITY SERVICE SE; *Int'l*, pg. 1627
CIVIL AND MARINE (HOLDINGS) LIMITED—See Heidelberg Materials AG; *Int'l*, pg. 3310

N.A.I.C.S. INDEX

523940 — PORTFOLIO MANAGEMEN...

CJM SOLUTIONS INC.—See Arthur J. Gallagher & Co.; *U.S. Public*, pg. 204
CLAAS FINANCIAL SERVICES INC.—See BNP Paribas SA; *Int'l*, pg. 1087
CLAL ELECTRONIC INDUSTRIES LTD.—See Access Industries, Inc.; *U.S. Private*, pg. 51
CLAREN ROAD ASSET MANAGEMENT LLC—See The Carlyle Group Inc.; *U.S. Public*, pg. 2045
CLARFELD FINANCIAL ADVISORS, LLC—See Citizens Financial Group, Inc.; *U.S. Public*, pg. 505
CLARK CAPITAL MANAGEMENT GROUP, INC.; *U.S. Private*, pg. 912
CLAYTON EURO RISK, LTD.—See Radian Group, Inc.; *U.S. Public*, pg. 1759
CLEARARC CAPITAL, INC.—See Fifth Third Bancorp; *U.S. Public*, pg. 833
CLEARBRIDGE ASSET MANAGEMENT INC.—See Franklin Resources, Inc.; *U.S. Public*, pg. 881
CLEARBRIDGE INVESTMENTS LIMITED—See Franklin Resources, Inc.; *U.S. Public*, pg. 881
CLEARBRIDGE INVESTMENTS, LLC—See Franklin Resources, Inc.; *U.S. Public*, pg. 881
CLEARBRIDGE, LLC—See Franklin Resources, Inc.; *U.S. Public*, pg. 882
CLEARLOGIC FINANCIAL, INC.; *U.S. Private*, pg. 938
CLEARROCK CAPITAL, LLC—See Genstar Capital, LLC; *U.S. Private*, pg. 1677
CLEARROCK CAPITAL, LLC—See Keystone Group, L.P.; *U.S. Private*, pg. 2298
CLEARVIEW FINANCIAL ADVICE PTY LIMITED—See ClearView Wealth Limited; *Int'l*, pg. 1657
CLEARY GULL INC.—See Canadian Imperial Bank of Commerce; *Int'l*, pg. 1283
CLIENT 1ST ADVISORS, INC.; *U.S. Private*, pg. 943
CLIFFWATER INVESTMENTS, LLC—See Virtus Investment Partners, Inc.; *U.S. Public*, pg. 2300
THE CLIFTON GROUP INVESTMENT MANAGEMENT COMPANY—See Morgan Stanley; *U.S. Public*, pg. 1472
CLIFTON WEALTH LTD—See Clifton Asset Management Plc; *Int'l*, pg. 1659
CLIME ASSET MANAGEMENT PTY. LTD.—See Clime Investment Management Limited; *Int'l*, pg. 1659
CLIPPINGER FINANCIAL GROUP, L.L.C.—See Aon plc; *Int'l*, pg. 495
CLOUD LENDING, INC.—See Q2 Holdings, Inc.; *U.S. Public*, pg. 1741
CMA VENTURES, INC.—See Central Iowa Power Cooperative; *U.S. Private*, pg. 822
CMGE TECHNOLOGY GROUP LIMITED; *Int'l*, pg. 1670
CNL STRATEGIC CAPITAL, LLC—See CNL Strategic Capital Management LLC; *U.S. Private*, pg. 952
CNMC (SHENYANG) MINING INVESTMENT CO., LTD.—See China Nonferrous Metal Mining (Group) Co., Ltd.; *Int'l*, pg. 1535
COBEMA SA—See BNP Paribas SA; *Int'l*, pg. 1090
COBRA FINANCIAL SERVICES LIMITED—See Apax Partners LLP; *Int'l*, pg. 505
COBRA RESOURCES PLC; *Int'l*, pg. 1683
COE FINANCIAL SERVICES INC.—See Creative Planning, LLC; *U.S. Private*, pg. 1089
COFIPARC SNC—See BNP Paribas SA; *Int'l*, pg. 1090
COGENTRIX ENERGY POWER MANAGEMENT, LLC—See The Carlyle Group Inc.; *U.S. Public*, pg. 2045
COGNITION HOLDINGS LIMITED—See Caxton and CTP Publishers and Printers Ltd.; *Int'l*, pg. 1363
COHEN & COMPAGNIE, SAS—See Cohen & Company Inc.; *U.S. Public*, pg. 526
COHEN & STEERS EUROPE S.A.—See Cohen & Steers, Inc.; *U.S. Public*, pg. 526
COHEN & STEERS, INC.; *U.S. Public*, pg. 526
COHEN & STEERS JAPAN, LLC—See Cohen & Steers, Inc.; *U.S. Public*, pg. 526
COHEN & STEERS UK LIMITED—See Cohen & Steers, Inc.; *U.S. Public*, pg. 526
COLDSTREAM CAPITAL MANAGEMENT, INC.—See Hersman Serles Almond PLLC; *U.S. Private*, pg. 1927
COLDSTREAM CAPITAL MANAGEMENT, INC.—See Seidman Insurance Consultants LLC; *U.S. Private*, pg. 3599
COLLECTIVE MINING LTD.; *Int'l*, pg. 1699
THE COLONY GROUP, LLC—See Clayton, Dubilier & Rice, LLC; *U.S. Private*, pg. 923
THE COLONY GROUP, LLC—See Stone Point Capital LLC; *U.S. Private*, pg. 3824
COLONY PARK FINANCIAL SERVICES LLC—See Sandlapper Securities, LLC; *U.S. Private*, pg. 3544
THE COLUMBIA BANK—See Fulton Financial Corporation; *U.S. Public*, pg. 892
COLUMBIA RIDGE CAPITAL MANAGEMENT, INC.—See NBT Bancorp Inc.; *U.S. Public*, pg. 1500
COLUMBIA THREADNEEDLE AM (HOLDINGS) PLC—See Bank of Montreal; *Int'l*, pg. 846
COLUMBIA THREADNEEDLE INVESTMENTS (ME) LIMITED—See Ameriprise Financial, Inc.; *U.S. Public*, pg. 114
COLUMBUS HOLDINGS—See Banco Bradesco S.A.; *Int'l*, pg. 819

COMINVEST INVESTMENT LUXEMBOURG S.A.—See Allianz SE; *Int'l*, pg. 347
COMMCISE SOFTWARE LTD.—See Euronext N.V.; *Int'l*, pg. 2554
COMMERZBANK AUSLANDSBANKEN HOLDING AG—See Commerzbank AG; *Int'l*, pg. 1717
COMMERZBANK AUSLANDSBANKEN HOLDING NOVA GMBH—See Commerzbank AG; *Int'l*, pg. 1717
COMMERZBANK CAPITAL INVESTMENT COMPANY LIMITED—See Commerzbank AG; *Int'l*, pg. 1717
COMMERZBANK INLANDSBANKEN HOLDING GMBH—See Commerzbank AG; *Int'l*, pg. 1717
COMMERZBANK INVESTMENTS (UK) LIMITED—See Commerzbank AG; *Int'l*, pg. 1717
COMMERZBANK REPRESENTATIVE OFFICE NIGERIA LIMITED—See Commerzbank AG; *Int'l*, pg. 1717
COMMERZBANK SAO PAULO SERVICOS LTDA.—See Commerzbank AG; *Int'l*, pg. 1717
COMMERZ FINANZ-MANAGEMENT GMBH—See Commerzbank AG; *Int'l*, pg. 1716
COMMERZ GRUNDBESITZ INVESTMENTGESELLSCHAFT MBH—See Commerzbank AG; *Int'l*, pg. 1716
COMMERZLEASING GMBH—See Commerzbank AG; *Int'l*, pg. 1717
COMMERZ REAL ASSET STRUCTURING GMBH—See Commerzbank AG; *Int'l*, pg. 1716
COMMUNITY BANK FUNDING COMPANY—See Republic Financial Corporation; *U.S. Private*, pg. 3402
COMMUNITY INVESTMENT SERVICES, INC.—See Community Bank System, Inc.; *U.S. Public*, pg. 549
COMMUNITY TRUST AND INVESTMENT COMPANY—See Community Trust Bancorp Inc; *U.S. Public*, pg. 558
COMMUNITY VENTURES PARTNERSHIPS LIMITED—See Galliford Try Holdings plc; *Int'l*, pg. 2874
COMPAGNIE DE GESTION PRIVEE MONEGASQUE SAM—See Azimut Holding SpA; *Int'l*, pg. 779
COMPAGNIE D INVESTISSEMENTS DE PARIS C.I.P—See BNP Paribas SA; *Int'l*, pg. 1090
COMPAGNIE FINANCIERE OTTOMANE SA—See BNP Paribas SA; *Int'l*, pg. 1090
COMPANHIA CELG DE PARTICIPACOES - CELGPAR; *Int'l*, pg. 1746
COMPANHIA DE PARTICIPACOES ALIANCA DA BAHIA; *Int'l*, pg. 1747
COMPANHIA ENERGETICA DE BRASILIA - CEB; *Int'l*, pg. 1747
COMPANHIA MELHORAMENTOS DE SAO PAULO; *Int'l*, pg. 1747
COMPASS ADVISERS LIMITED—See Compass Advisers Group LLC; *U.S. Private*, pg. 998
COMPASS CAPITAL MANAGEMENT, LLC—See Aon plc; *Int'l*, pg. 495
COMPASS FINANCIAL PARTNERS, LLC—See Marsh & McLennan Companies, Inc.; *U.S. Public*, pg. 1380
COMPASS GROUP MANAGEMENT LLC; *U.S. Private*, pg. 999
COMPASS PARTNERS ADVISORS, LLP—See Compass Advisers Group LLC; *U.S. Private*, pg. 998
COMPASS POINT RETIREMENT PLANNING, INC.—See Arthur J. Gallagher & Co.; *U.S. Public*, pg. 204
COMPASS WORKING CAPITAL; *U.S. Private*, pg. 999
CONCENTRATED LEADERS FUND LIMITED; *Int'l*, pg. 1763
CONCHA PLC; *Int'l*, pg. 1764
CONCORD NEW ENERGY GROUP LIMITED; *Int'l*, pg. 1765
CONFINVEST F.L. S.P.A.; *Int'l*, pg. 1768
THE CONNABLE OFFICE, INC.—See Cresset Asset Management, LLC; *U.S. Private*, pg. 1095
CONSERVATIVE CONCEPT PORTFOLIO MANAGEMENT AG—See Baader Bank AG; *Int'l*, pg. 791
CONSOLIDATED FIRSTFUND CAPITAL CORPORATION; *Int'l*, pg. 1770
CONSOLIDATED OPERATIONS GROUP LIMITED; *Int'l*, pg. 1771
CONSOLIDATED PLANNING INC.; *U.S. Private*, pg. 1021
CONSORCIO ALFA DE ADMINISTRACAO S.A.; *Int'l*, pg. 1771
CONSTANCE CAPITAL LIMITED—See Easyknit International Holdings Ltd.; *Int'l*, pg. 2276
CONSUS ASSET MANAGEMENT CO., LTD.; *Int'l*, pg. 1778
CONTANGO FUNDS MANAGEMENT LIMITED—See Associate Global Partners Limited; *Int'l*, pg. 648
CONTANGO HOLDINGS PLC; *Int'l*, pg. 1779
CONTIASIA—See Continental Grain Company; *U.S. Private*, pg. 1029
CONTIL INDIA LIMITED; *Int'l*, pg. 1780
CONTROLADORA DE OPERACIONES DE INFRAESTRUCTURA, S. A. DE C. V.—See Empresas ICA S.A.B. de C.V.; *Int'l*, pg. 2390
CONVERGENCE INVESTMENT PARTNERS, LLC—See Mariner Wealth Advisors, LLC; *U.S. Private*, pg. 2575
CONVERGENCE PARTNERS (PTY) LIMITED; *Int'l*, pg. 1787
CONVERGEONE, INC.—See CVC Capital Partners SICAV-FIS S.A.; *Int'l*, pg. 1883
CONVERTO AS; *Int'l*, pg. 1787
COOKE & BIELER, LP; *U.S. Private*, pg. 1039
COPE PRIVATE EQUITY SDN. BHD.—See Cahya Mata Sarawak Berhad; *Int'l*, pg. 1251
COPERNICO SIM SPA; *Int'l*, pg. 1793
CORNELL CAPITAL MANAGEMENT LLC; *U.S. Private*, pg. 1051
CORNERSTONE ADVISORS, INC.; *U.S. Private*, pg. 1051
CORNERSTONE CAPITAL MANAGEMENT HOLDINGS LLC—See New York Life Insurance Company; *U.S. Private*, pg. 2910
CORNERSTONE MANAGEMENT, INC.; *Int'l*, pg. 1801
CORNERSTONE RETIREMENT GROUP, INC.—See Prime Capital Investment Advisors, LLC; *U.S. Private*, pg. 3261
CORNERSTONE WEALTH MANAGEMENT, LLC—See Vivaldi Capital Management, LLC; *U.S. Private*, pg. 4406
CORONATION GLOBAL FUND MANAGERS (IRELAND) LTD—See Coronation Fund Managers Limited; *Int'l*, pg. 1802
CORPORATE ASSET BACKED CORPORATION; *U.S. Private*, pg. 1054
CORPORATE ASSET SOLUTIONS LIMITED—See Close Brothers Group plc; *Int'l*, pg. 1661
CORPORATE MERCHANT BANKERS LIMITED; *Int'l*, pg. 1805
CORSTONE ASIA CO., LTD.—See Corstone Corporation; *U.S. Private*, pg. 1060
CORSTONE CORPORATION; *U.S. Private*, pg. 1060
CORTAL CONSORS BELGIUM—See BNP Paribas SA; *Int'l*, pg. 1090
COTTAGE STREET INVESTMENTS LLC—See Prudential Financial, Inc.; *U.S. Public*, pg. 1731
COUGAR GLOBAL INVESTMENTS LIMITED—See Raymond James Financial, Inc.; *U.S. Public*, pg. 1764
COUNTRY CAPITAL MANAGEMENT COMPANY—See COUNTRY Financial; *U.S. Private*, pg. 1066
COURBET SA; *Int'l*, pg. 1819
COURIER CAPITAL CORPORATION - JAMESTOWN OFFICE—See Financial Institutions, Inc.; *U.S. Public*, pg. 834
COURIER CAPITAL, LLC—See Financial Institutions, Inc.; *U.S. Public*, pg. 834
COURTEVILLE LOSS ADJUSTERS LTD.—See Courteville Business Solutions Plc.; *Int'l*, pg. 1819
COVEA FINANCE SAS—See Covea Groupe S.A.S.; *Int'l*, pg. 1820
CPCM, LLC; *U.S. Private*, pg. 1080
CPH CAPITAL FONDSMAEGLERSELSKAB A/S—See Equitable Holdings, Inc.; *U.S. Public*, pg. 789
CRAMER ROSENTHAL MCGLYNN LLC; *U.S. Private*, pg. 1084
CRANE ASSET MANAGEMENT LLC—See Carnegie Investment Counsel; *U.S. Private*, pg. 766
CREADOR ADVISORS INDIA PRIVATE LIMITED—See Creador Sdn. Bhd.; *Int'l*, pg. 1831
CREA GERMANY GMBH—See The Carlyle Group Inc.; *U.S. Public*, pg. 2045
CREDIINVEST SA—See Credit Andorra, S.A.; *Int'l*, pg. 1834
CREDIMO NV; *Int'l*, pg. 1834
CREDIT INDUSTRIEL D'ALSACE ET DE LORRAINE—See Confederation Nationale du Credit Mutuel; *Int'l*, pg. 1767
CREDIT INDUSTRIEL DE NORMANDIE—See Confederation Nationale du Credit Mutuel; *Int'l*, pg. 1767
CREDIT VALUE PARTNERS, LP—See New York Life Insurance Company; *U.S. Private*, pg. 2910
CRESTA INVESTMENT PTE LTD—See Chuan Hup Holdings Limited; *Int'l*, pg. 1589
CREST FINSERV LIMITED—See Crest Ventures Limited; *Int'l*, pg. 1841
CRESTONE WEALTH MANAGEMENT LIMITED - MELBOURNE—See Crestone Wealth Management Limited; *Int'l*, pg. 1841
CRESTONE WEALTH MANAGEMENT LIMITED; *Int'l*, pg. 1841
CRESTWOOD ADVISORS GROUP, LLC—See Clayton, Dubilier & Rice, LLC; *U.S. Private*, pg. 923
CRESTWOOD ADVISORS GROUP, LLC—See Stone Point Capital LLC; *U.S. Private*, pg. 3824
CRESTWOOD ADVISORS LLC—See Clayton, Dubilier & Rice, LLC; *U.S. Private*, pg. 923
CRESTWOOD ADVISORS LLC—See Stone Point Capital LLC; *U.S. Private*, pg. 3824
CRESTWOOD PARTNERS LLC—See Crestwood Equity Partners LP; *U.S. Public*, pg. 594
CRM STUDENTS LTD.—See CORESTATE Capital Holding SA; *Int'l*, pg. 1799
CROMWELL EUROPEAN REAL ESTATE INVESTMENT TRUST; *Int'l*, pg. 1853
CROMWELL PROPERTY GROUP CZECH REPUBLIC S.R.O.—See Cromwell Property Group; *Int'l*, pg. 1854
CROSSCOUNTRY CONSULTING LLC; *U.S. Private*, pg. 1106
CROSSROADS CAPITAL, INC.; *U.S. Private*, pg. 1108
CROWDCUBE LIMITED; *Int'l*, pg. 1857
CROWE HORWATH (NZ) LTD—See Financial Index Australia Pty Ltd.; *Int'l*, pg. 2665
CROWN BAUS CAPITAL CORP.; *U.S. Private*, pg. 1110
CROWN CAPITAL INVESTMENTS LLC; *U.S. Private*, pg. 1110
CROWN CAPITAL PARTNERS, INC.; *Int'l*, pg. 1857
CROWN CAPITAL SECURITIES LP—See LPL Financial

4359

Holdings Inc.; *U.S. Public*, pg. 1343
CROWN INTERNATIONAL CORPORATION LIMITED; *Int'l*, pg. 1857
CRYSTAL AMBER ASSET MANAGEMENT (GUERNSEY) LLP; *Int'l*, pg. 1860
CRYSTAL FINANCIAL LLC—See SLR Investment Corp.; *U.S. Public*, pg. 1894
CSB INVESTMENT SERVICES, LLC—See CSB Bancorp, Inc.; *U.S. Public*, pg. 601
CSC FINANCIAL CO., LTD; *Int'l*, pg. 1862
CSENGE ADVISORY GROUP, LLC; *U.S. Private*, pg. 1116
CSENGE ADVISORY GROUP, LLC—See Csenge Advisory Group, LLC; *U.S. Private*, pg. 1116
C.S. MCKEE LP—See Estancia Capital Management, LLC; *U.S. Private*, pg. 1428
CTC CONSULTING LLC—See Bank of Montreal; *Int'l*, pg. 846
CT GLOBAL MANAGED PORTFOLIO TRUST PLC; *Int'l*, pg. 1868
CTOS HOLDING SDN BHD—See Creador Sdn. Bhd.; *Int'l*, pg. 1831
CT PRIVATE EQUITY TRUST PLC; *Int'l*, pg. 1868
CT UK CAPITAL AND INCOME INVESTMENT TRUST PLC; *Int'l*, pg. 1868
CUCINA ACQUISITION (UK) LIMITED—See Sysco Corporation; *U.S. Public*, pg. 1973
CUMBERLAND PLACE FINANCIAL MANAGEMENT LIMITED—See abrdn PLC; *Int'l*, pg. 68
CUMMINGS ACQUISITION, INC.—See Gannett Co., Inc.; *U.S. Public*, pg. 896
CUSHING ASSET MANAGEMENT, LP—See Swank Capital, LLC; *U.S. Private*, pg. 3890
CUSPIS CAPITAL LTD.; *Int'l*, pg. 1880
CUTTER & COMPANY BROKERAGE, INC.; *U.S. Private*, pg. 1131
CUTWATER ASSET MANAGEMENT CORP.—See The Bank of New York Mellon Corporation; *U.S. Public*, pg. 2037
CVC CAPITAL PARTNERS ADVISORY (U.S.), INC.—See CVC Capital Partners SICAV-FIS S.A.; *Int'l*, pg. 1885
CVC CREDIT PARTNERS LIMITED—See CVC Capital Partners SICAV-FIS S.A.; *Int'l*, pg. 1888
CVC CREDIT PARTNERS, LLC—See CVC Capital Partners SICAV-FIS S.A.; *Int'l*, pg. 1888
CVC INCOME & GROWTH LIMITED; *Int'l*, pg. 1889
CVC MANAGERS PTY. LIMITED—See CVC Limited; *Int'l*, pg. 1889
CW TECH PTE. LTD.—See CW Group Holdings Limited; *Int'l*, pg. 1890
CX ADVISORS LLP; *Int'l*, pg. 1891
CX CAPITAL MANAGEMENT LIMITED—See CX Advisors LLP; *Int'l*, pg. 1891
CYNOTECH HOLDINGS LIMITED; *Int'l*, pg. 1896
CYPRESS CAPITAL MANAGEMENT, LLC—See WSFS Financial Corporation; *U.S. Public*, pg. 2383
CYPRESS WEALTH ADVISORS, LLC—See Cresset Asset Management, LLC; *U.S. Private*, pg. 1095
DAE CAPITAL ADVISORS LLC—See Dubai Aerospace Enterprise Ltd; *Int'l*, pg. 2218
DAEWOO SPECIAL PURPOSE ACQUISITION 2 CO., LTD.; *Int'l*, pg. 1910
DAEWOO SPECIAL PURPOSE ACQUISITION 3 CO., LTD.; *Int'l*, pg. 1911
DAICEL FINANCE LTD.—See Daicel Corporation; *Int'l*, pg. 1918
DAI-ICHI LIFE REALTY ASSET MANAGEMENT CO., LTD.—See Dai-ichi Life Holdings, Inc.; *Int'l*, pg. 1917
DAIWA CORPORATE ADVISORY GMBH—See Daiwa Securities Group Inc.; *Int'l*, pg. 1948
DAIWA CORPORATE ADVISORY LIMITED—See Daiwa Securities Group Inc.; *Int'l*, pg. 1948
DAIWA CORPORATE ADVISORY SAS—See Daiwa Securities Group Inc.; *Int'l*, pg. 1948
DAIWA CORPORATE ADVISORY SLU—See Daiwa Securities Group Inc.; *Int'l*, pg. 1948
DAIWA CORPORATE ADVISORY S.R.L.—See Daiwa Securities Group Inc.; *Int'l*, pg. 1948
DAIWA ENERGY & INFRASTRUCTURE CO. LTD.—See Daiwa Securities Group Inc.; *Int'l*, pg. 1948
DAIWA FUND CONSULTING CO. LTD.—See Daiwa Securities Group Inc.; *Int'l*, pg. 1948
DAIWA HOUSE ASSET MANAGEMENT CO., LTD.—See Daiwa House Industry Co., Ltd.; *Int'l*, pg. 1945
DAIWA HOUSE MORIMOTO ASSET MANAGEMENT CO., LTD.—See Daiwa House Industry Co., Ltd.; *Int'l*, pg. 1945
DAIWA INSTITUTE OF RESEARCH AMERICA INC.—See Daiwa Securities Group Inc.; *Int'l*, pg. 1948
DAIWA SECURITIES CAPITAL MARKETS KOREA CO., LTD.—See Daiwa Securities Group Inc.; *Int'l*, pg. 1948
DAIWA (SHANGHAI) CORPORATE STRATEGIC ADVISORY CO. LTD.—See Daiwa Securities Group Inc.; *Int'l*, pg. 1947
DAKOTA WEALTH MANAGEMENT LLC; *U.S. Private*, pg. 1148
DALETH PARTICIPACOES S.A.; *Int'l*, pg. 1951
DALMORE CAPITAL LIMITED; *Int'l*, pg. 1954
DALTON, GREINER, HARTMAN & MAHER & CO. LLC—See Boston Private Financial Holdings, Inc.; *U.S. Public*, pg. 372
DANCAP PRIVATE EQUITY INC.; *Int'l*, pg. 1958
DANICA LIFE LTD.—See Danske Bank A/S; *Int'l*, pg. 1969
DANZAS HOLDING AG—See Deutsche Post AG; *Int'l*, pg. 2079
DANZHOU HNA INVESTMENT AND DEVELOPMENT CO., LTD.—See Hainan Traffic Administration Holding Co., Ltd.; *Int'l*, pg. 3213
DARBY ASIA INVESTORS (INDIA) PRIVATE LIMITED—See Franklin Resources, Inc.; *U.S. Public*, pg. 879
DATASCAN HOLDINGS LLC—See JM Family Enterprises Inc.; *U.S. Private*, pg. 2214
DAUPHINE MAURITIUS INVESTMENT LIMITED—See JPMorgan Chase & Co.; *U.S. Public*, pg. 1206
DAVIDSON FIXED INCOME MANAGEMENT, INC.—See D.A. Davidson Companies; *U.S. Private*, pg. 1140
DAVIDSON INVESTMENT ADVISORS, INC.—See D.A. Davidson Companies; *U.S. Private*, pg. 1140
DAVIDSON KEMPNER CAPITAL MANAGEMENT LP; *U.S. Private*, pg. 1172
DAVIS SELECTED ADVISORS, L.P.; *U.S. Private*, pg. 1174
DAY & ENNIS LLC—See Genstar Capital, LLC; *U.S. Private*, pg. 1677
DAY & ENNIS LLC—See Keystone Group, L.P.; *U.S. Private*, pg. 2298
DB ADVISORS SICAV—See Deutsche Bank Aktiengesellschaft; *Int'l*, pg. 2056
DBAH CAPITAL, LLC—See Deutsche Bank Aktiengesellschaft; *Int'l*, pg. 2057
DB ALEX. BROWN HOLDINGS INCORPORATED—See Deutsche Bank Aktiengesellschaft; *Int'l*, pg. 2056
DB AOTEAROA INVESTMENTS LIMITED—See Deutsche Bank Aktiengesellschaft; *Int'l*, pg. 2056
DBAY ADVISORS LIMITED; *Int'l*, pg. 1986
DB CAPITAL MARKETS ASSET MANAGEMENT HOLDING GMBH—See Deutsche Bank Aktiengesellschaft; *Int'l*, pg. 2056
DB CHESTNUT HOLDINGS LIMITED—See Deutsche Bank Aktiengesellschaft; *Int'l*, pg. 2056
DB CONCERTO LIMITED—See Deutsche Bank Aktiengesellschaft; *Int'l*, pg. 2056
DB DELAWARE HOLDINGS (EUROPE) LIMITED—See Deutsche Bank Aktiengesellschaft; *Int'l*, pg. 2056
DBG VERMOGENSVERWALTUNGSGESELLSCHAFT MBH—See Deutsche Bank Aktiengesellschaft; *Int'l*, pg. 2057
DB HOLDINGS (NEW YORK), INC.—See Deutsche Bank Aktiengesellschaft; *Int'l*, pg. 2056
DB HOME LENDING HOLDINGS LLC—See Deutsche Bank Aktiengesellschaft; *Int'l*, pg. 2062
DB INDUSTRIAL HOLDINGS BETEILIGUNGS GMBH & CO. KG—See Deutsche Bank Aktiengesellschaft; *Int'l*, pg. 2056
DB INDUSTRIAL HOLDINGS GMBH—See Deutsche Bank Aktiengesellschaft; *Int'l*, pg. 2056
DB INVESTMENT RESOURCES (US) CORPORATION—See Deutsche Bank Aktiengesellschaft; *Int'l*, pg. 2056
DBO PARTNERS HOLDING LLC—See Piper Sandler Companies; *U.S. Public*, pg. 1693
DB OVERSEAS HOLDINGS LIMITED—See Deutsche Bank Aktiengesellschaft; *Int'l*, pg. 2056
DB PLATINUM ADVISORS S.A.—See Deutsche Bank Aktiengesellschaft; *Int'l*, pg. 2056
DB VERSICHERUNGSMANAGER GMBH—See Deutsche Bank Aktiengesellschaft; *Int'l*, pg. 2057
DDJ CAPITAL MANAGEMENT, LLC—See Polen Capital Management, Inc.; *U.S. Private*, pg. 3224
DDM INVEST VII D.O.O.—See DDM Holding AG; *Int'l*, pg. 1993
DEANS KNIGHT CAPITAL MANAGEMENT LTD.—See Affiliated Managers Group, Inc.; *U.S. Public*, pg. 54
DEAP CAPITAL MANAGEMENT & TRUST PLC; *Int'l*, pg. 1998
DECA INVESTMENTS AIFM; *Int'l*, pg. 1999
DECISIONPOINT INTERNATIONAL; *U.S. Private*, pg. 1187
DEFINED FINANCIAL PLANNING, LLC; *U.S. Private*, pg. 1191
DEKABANK DEUTSCHE GIROZENTRALE LUXEMBOURG S.A.—See DekaBank; *Int'l*, pg. 2005
DEKA INTERNATIONAL S.A.—See DekaBank; *Int'l*, pg. 2005
DEKA VERMOGENSVERWALTUNGS GMBH—See DekaBank; *Int'l*, pg. 2005
DELAWARE INVESTMENTS MINNESOTA MUNICIPAL INCOME FUND II, INC.; *U.S. Public*, pg. 648
DELEN PRIVATE BANK NV—See Ackermans & van Haaren NV; *Int'l*, pg. 105
DELPHI HOLDING GMBH—See Aptiv PLC; *Int'l*, pg. 525
DELPHX CAPITAL MARKETS, INC.; *Int'l*, pg. 2015
DELPHX CORPORATION—See Delphx Capital Markets, Inc.; *Int'l*, pg. 2015
DELTA ENERGY SYSTEMS (SINGAPORE) PTE. LTD.—See Delta Electronics, Inc.; *Int'l*, pg. 2018
DELTA PILOTS MUTUAL AID; *U.S. Private*, pg. 1201
DELTON TECHNOLOGY SE—See Delton AG; *Int'l*, pg. 2021
DEMOSS CAPITAL INC.—See Blue Creek Investment Partners; *U.S. Private*, pg. 586
DENTSU INNOVATION PARTNERS INC.—See Dentsu Group Inc.; *Int'l*, pg. 2035
DESAI CAPITAL MANAGEMENT INCORPORATED; *U.S. Private*, pg. 1210
DESCO CAPITAL—See Desco Corporation; *U.S. Private*, pg. 1211
DESENVOLVIMENTO TURISTICO E HOTELEIRO, SA—See Estoril Sol, SGPS, S.A.; *Int'l*, pg. 2518
DEUKONA VERSICHERUNGS-VERMITTLUNGS-GMBH—See Deutsche Bank Aktiengesellschaft; *Int'l*, pg. 2057
DEUTSCHE ACCESS INVESTMENTS LIMITED—See Deutsche Bank Aktiengesellschaft; *Int'l*, pg. 2057
DEUTSCHE ASSET MANAGEMENT CANADA LIMITED—See Deutsche Bank Aktiengesellschaft; *Int'l*, pg. 2058
DEUTSCHE ASSET MANAGEMENT (KOREA) COMPANY LIMITED—See Deutsche Bank Aktiengesellschaft; *Int'l*, pg. 2058
DEUTSCHE BAHN IBERICA HOLDING, S.L.—See Deutsche Bahn AG; *Int'l*, pg. 2051
DEUTSCHE BAHN STIFTUNG GGMBH—See Deutsche Bahn AG; *Int'l*, pg. 2051
DEUTSCHE BALATON AG; *Int'l*, pg. 2055
DEUTSCHE BANK AG—See Deutsche Bank Aktiengesellschaft; *Int'l*, pg. 2058
DEUTSCHE BANK CAPITAL MARKETS S.R.L.—See Deutsche Bank Aktiengesellschaft; *Int'l*, pg. 2059
DEUTSCHE BANK HOLDINGS, INC.—See Deutsche Bank Aktiengesellschaft; *Int'l*, pg. 2059
DEUTSCHE BANK MUTUI S.P.A.—See Deutsche Bank Aktiengesellschaft; *Int'l*, pg. 2059
DEUTSCHE BETEILIGUNGSGESELLSCHAFT MBH—See Deutsche Beteiligungs AG; *Int'l*, pg. 2062
DEUTSCHE CLIMATE CHANGE FIXED INCOME QP TRUST—See Deutsche Bank Aktiengesellschaft; *Int'l*, pg. 2060
DEUTSCHE COLOMBIA S.A.—See Deutsche Bank Aktiengesellschaft; *Int'l*, pg. 2060
DEUTSCHE EFFECTEN- UND WECHSEL-BETEILIGUNGSGESELLSCHAFT AG.; *Int'l*, pg. 2065
DEUTSCHE EQUITIES INDIA PRIVATE LIMITED—See Deutsche Bank Aktiengesellschaft; *Int'l*, pg. 2060
DEUTSCHE FUTURES SINGAPORE PTE LTD—See Deutsche Bank Aktiengesellschaft; *Int'l*, pg. 2060
DEUTSCHE GRUNDBESITZ-ANLAGEGESELLSCHAFT MIT BESCHRANKTER HAFTUNG—See Deutsche Bank Aktiengesellschaft; *Int'l*, pg. 2060
DEUTSCHE GRUNDBESITZ BETEILIGUNGSGESELL-SCHAFT MBH—See Deutsche Bank Aktiengesellschaft; *Int'l*, pg. 2060
DEUTSCHE INVERSIONES LIMITADA—See Deutsche Bank Aktiengesellschaft; *Int'l*, pg. 2060
DEUTSCHE INVESTMENTS INDIA PRIVATE LIMITED—See Deutsche Bank Aktiengesellschaft; *Int'l*, pg. 2060
DEUTSCHE INVESTOR SERVICES PRIVATE LIMITED—See Deutsche Bank Aktiengesellschaft; *Int'l*, pg. 2060
DEUTSCHE MANAGED INVESTMENTS LIMITED—See Deutsche Bank Aktiengesellschaft; *Int'l*, pg. 2060
DEUTSCHE NEDERLAND N.V.—See Deutsche Bank Aktiengesellschaft; *Int'l*, pg. 2060
DEUTSCHE OPPENHEIM FAMILY OFFICE AG—See Deutsche Bank Aktiengesellschaft; *Int'l*, pg. 2060
DEUTSCHE POST BETEILIGUNGEN HOLDING GMBH—See Deutsche Post AG; *Int'l*, pg. 2079
DEVELICA DEUTSCHLAND LIMITED; *Int'l*, pg. 2087
DEXUS ASSET MANAGEMENT LIMITED—See DEXUS; *Int'l*, pg. 2093
DFA AUSTRALIA LIMITED—See Dimensional Fund Advisors LP; *U.S. Private*, pg. 1233
DGA S.A.; *Int'l*, pg. 2096
DGB ASSET MANAGEMENT CO., LTD.—See DGB Financial Group Co., Ltd.; *Int'l*, pg. 2096
DG INNOVATE PLC; *Int'l*, pg. 2096
DH CAPITAL, LLC—See Citizens Financial Group, Inc.; *U.S. Public*, pg. 505
DHFL PRAMERICA ASSET MANAGERS PRIVATE LIMITED—See Prudential Financial, Inc.; *U.S. Public*, pg. 1732
DHL GLOBAL MAIL UK—See Deutsche Post AG; *Int'l*, pg. 2072
DHL HOLDING (FRANCE) SAS—See Deutsche Post AG; *Int'l*, pg. 2076
DIAMOND HILL CAPITAL MANAGEMENT, INC.—See Diamond Hill Investment Group, Inc.; *U.S. Public*, pg. 658
DIAMOND HILL INVESTMENT GROUP, INC.; *U.S. Public*, pg. 658
DIAMOND STATE VENTURES, LLC; *U.S. Private*, pg. 1224
DICON INVESTMENT LLC—See Alpha Dhabi Holding PJSC; *Int'l*, pg. 367
DIDIM E&F; *Int'l*, pg. 2112
DIEVINI HOPP BIOTECH HOLDING GMBH & CO. KG; *Int'l*, pg. 2117

N.A.I.C.S. INDEX 523940 — PORTFOLIO MANAGEMEN...

DIF MANAGEMENT B.V.—See DIF Management Holding B.V.; *Int'l*, pg. 2117
DIMAH CAPITAL INVESTMENT COMPANY-K.S.C.—See Al Imtiaz Investment Group Company- K.S.C.; *Int'l*, pg. 279
DIMENSIONAL FUND ADVISORS CANADA INC.—See Dimensional Fund Advisors LP; *U.S. Private*, pg. 1233
DIMENSIONAL FUND ADVISORS LTD.—See Dimensional Fund Advisors LP; *U.S. Private*, pg. 1233
DIMEO SCHNEIDER & ASSOCIATES LLC—See Aon plc; *Int'l*, pg. 495
DINERS CLUB ITALIA S.R.L.—See Discover Financial Services; *U.S. Public*, pg. 668
DINIT D.O.O.—See Discover Financial Services; *U.S. Public*, pg. 668
DINOCRATES GROUP LLC; *U.S. Private*, pg. 1233
DISCA BETEILIGUNGSGESELLSCHAFT MBH—See Deutsche Bank Aktiengesellschaft; *Int'l*, pg. 2057
DISCOVERY DATA HOLDINGS INC.—See Deutsche Borse AG; *Int'l*, pg. 2063
DISCOVERY ONE INVESTMENT CORP.; *Int'l*, pg. 2134
DJERRIWARRH INVESTMENTS LIMITED; *Int'l*, pg. 2138
DKB WOHNEN GMBH—See BayernLB Holding AG; *Int'l*, pg. 913
DK WILD & COMPANY LIMITED—See Epiris Managers LLP; *Int'l*, pg. 2461
DLT ASA; *Int'l*, pg. 2142
DMI ADMINISTRATIVE SERVICES S.A.—See Dar Al-Maal Al-Islami Trust; *Int'l*, pg. 1971
DOHOD INVESTMENT COMPANY JSC; *Int'l*, pg. 2156
DOMINION RESOURCES BLACK WARRIOR TRUST; *U.S. Public*, pg. 674
DOMINO HOLDINGS FRANCE SARL—See Philip Morris International Inc.; *U.S. Public*, pg. 1687
DOM INWESTYCYJNY XELION SP. Z O.O.—See Bank Polska Kasa Opieki Spolka Akcyjna; *Int'l*, pg. 849
DONAU KIES VERWALTUNGS GMBH—See Heidelberg Materials AG; *Int'l*, pg. 3310
THE DONERAIL GROUP LP; *U.S. Private*, pg. 4022
DONGWU CEMENT INTERNATIONAL LIMITED; *Int'l*, pg. 2171
DORCHESTER CAPITAL PARTNERS ASP FUND, A SERIES OF ALTERNATIVE STRATEGIES PLATFORM, LLC—See Wells Fargo & Company; *U.S. Public*, pg. 2343
DORSEY, WRIGHT & ASSOCIATES, LLC—See Nasdaq, Inc.; *U.S. Public*, pg. 1491
DOUBLELINE CAPITAL LP; *U.S. Private*, pg. 1266
DOUBLELINE GROUP LP—See DoubleLine Capital LP; *U.S. Private*, pg. 1266
DOUGLAS C LANE & ASSOCIATES, INC.—See Clayton, Dubilier & Rice, LLC; *U.S. Private*, pg. 923
DOUGLAS C LANE & ASSOCIATES, INC.—See Stone Point Capital LLC; *U.S. Private*, pg. 3824
DOVERIE UNITED HOLDING AD; *Int'l*, pg. 2182
DOWLING & YAHNKE, LLC—See CI Financial Corporation; *Int'l*, pg. 1601
DOWNING STRATEGIC MICRO-CAP INVESTMENT TRUST PLC; *Int'l*, pg. 2186
DOWNING TWO VCT PLC; *Int'l*, pg. 2187
DOYLE WEALTH MANAGEMENT, INC.; *U.S. Private*, pg. 1270
DREAM IMPACT TRUST; *Int'l*, pg. 2202
DREAM UNLIMITED CORP.; *Int'l*, pg. 2203
DREIECK FIDUCIARIA SA—See EFG International AG; *Int'l*, pg. 2320
DSS INTERNATIONAL INC.—See DSS, Inc.; *U.S. Public*, pg. 689
DUET INVESTMENT HOLDINGS LIMITED—See CK Hutchison Holdings Limited; *Int'l*, pg. 1636
DUFF & PHELPS INVESTMENT MANAGEMENT CO—See Virtus Investment Partners, Inc.; *U.S. Public*, pg. 2300
DUKE ROYALTY LIMITED; *Int'l*, pg. 2224
DUMAC INC.; *U.S. Private*, pg. 1286
DUNHAM & ASSOCIATES INVESTMENT COUNCIL, INC.; *U.S. Private*, pg. 1289
DUNS INVESTING CORPORATION—See Cannae Holdings, Inc.; *U.S. Public*, pg. 429
DUNS INVESTING CORPORATION—See CC Capital Partners, LLC; *U.S. Public*, pg. 798
DUNS INVESTING CORPORATION—See Intercontinental Exchange, Inc.; *U.S. Public*, pg. 1142
DURATIONAL CAPITAL MANAGEMENT, LP; *U.S. Private*, pg. 1293
DUTA PLANTATIONS SDN. BHD.—See DutaLand Berhad; *Int'l*, pg. 2235
DUXTON WATER LIMITED; *Int'l*, pg. 2236
DWS ALTERNATIVES GLOBAL LIMITED—See Deutsche Bank Aktiengesellschaft; *Int'l*, pg. 2057
DWS ASSET MANAGEMENT (KOREA) COMPANY LIMITED—See Deutsche Bank Aktiengesellschaft; *Int'l*, pg. 2057
DWS CH AG—See Deutsche Bank Aktiengesellschaft; *Int'l*, pg. 2057
DWS DISTRIBUTORS, INC.—See Deutsche Bank Aktiengesellschaft; *Int'l*, pg. 2057
DWS GRUNDBESITZ GMBH—See Deutsche Bank Aktiengesellschaft; *Int'l*, pg. 2057
DWS HOLDING & SERVICE GMBH—See Deutsche Bank Aktiengesellschaft; *Int'l*, pg. 2057
DWS INVESTMENT S.A.—See Deutsche Bank Aktiengesellschaft; *Int'l*, pg. 2057
DWS INVESTMENTS AUSTRALIA LIMITED—See Deutsche Bank Aktiengesellschaft; *Int'l*, pg. 2057
DWS INVESTMENTS HONG KONG LIMITED—See Deutsche Bank Aktiengesellschaft; *Int'l*, pg. 2057
DWS INVESTMENTS SERVICE COMPANY—See Deutsche Bank Aktiengesellschaft; *Int'l*, pg. 2057
DWS INVESTMENTS SINGAPORE LIMITED—See DWS Group GmbH & Co. KGAA; *Int'l*, pg. 2236
DYNAMIC ASSETS MANAGEMENT COMPANY (LUXEMBOURG) SA—See Banque Profil de Gestion SA; *Int'l*, pg. 854
DYNEX ENERGY SA; *Int'l*, pg. 2242
EAB GROUP OYJ; *Int'l*, pg. 2261
EACM ADVISORS LLC—See The Bank of New York Mellon Corporation; *U.S. Public*, pg. 2037
EAGLE ASSET MANAGEMENT, INC.—See Raymond James Financial, Inc.; *U.S. Public*, pg. 1763
EAGLE FUND SERVICES, INC.—See Raymond James Financial, Inc.; *U.S. Public*, pg. 1764
EAGLE LIFE INSURANCE COMPANY—See Brookfield Reinsurance Ltd.; *Int'l*, pg. 1193
EA, INC.—See Cresset Asset Management, LLC; *U.S. Private*, pg. 1095
EAM NELSON HOLDING, LLC—See Entergy Corporation; *U.S. Public*, pg. 777
EAST CONTINENTAL SUPPLIES LLC—See Bain Capital, LP; *U.S. Private*, pg. 440
EASUN CAPITAL MARKETS LIMITED; *Int'l*, pg. 2275
EATON PARTNERS, LLC - SAN DIEGO—See Stifel Financial Corp.; *U.S. Public*, pg. 1949
EATON PARTNERS, LLC—See Stifel Financial Corp.; *U.S. Public*, pg. 1949
EATON PARTNERS (UK) LLP—See Stifel Financial Corp.; *U.S. Public*, pg. 1949
EATON VANCE ACQUISITIONS—See Morgan Stanley; *U.S. Public*, pg. 1471
EATON VANCE CORP.—See Morgan Stanley; *U.S. Public*, pg. 1471
EATON VANCE DISTRIBUTORS, INC.—See Morgan Stanley; *U.S. Public*, pg. 1471
EATON VANCE INVESTMENT COUNSEL—See Morgan Stanley; *U.S. Public*, pg. 1471
EATON VANCE MANAGEMENT (INTERNATIONAL) LIMITED—See Morgan Stanley; *U.S. Public*, pg. 1472
EATON VANCE MANAGEMENT—See Morgan Stanley; *U.S. Public*, pg. 1472
EATON VANCE TAX-MANAGED GLOBAL DIVERSIFIED EQUITY INCOME FUND; *U.S. Public*, pg. 709
EATON VANCE WATEROAK ADVISORS—See Morgan Stanley; *U.S. Public*, pg. 1472
EBEST SPECIAL PURPOSE ACQUISITION 3 COMPANY; *Int'l*, pg. 2285
ECF GROUP B.V.—See Chepri Holding B.V.; *Int'l*, pg. 1471
ECHMI S.A.; *Int'l*, pg. 2289
ECOFIN GLOBAL UTILITIES & INFRASTRUCTURE TRUST PLC; *Int'l*, pg. 2295
ECOLUMBER S.A.; *Int'l*, pg. 2295
ECONO TRADE (INDIA) LIMITED; *Int'l*, pg. 2297
ECO SECURITIZADORA DE DIREITOS CREDITORIOS DO AGRONEGOCIO S.A.; *Int'l*, pg. 2292
ECT HOLDINGS CORP.—See Deutsche Bank Aktiengesellschaft; *Int'l*, pg. 2061
EC WORLD REIT; *Int'l*, pg. 2287
ECZACIBASI ASSET MANAGEMENT CO.—See Eczacibasi Holding A.S.; *Int'l*, pg. 2301
EDELMAN FINANCIAL ENGINES, LLC—See Hellman & Friedman LLC; *U.S. Public*, pg. 1908
EDELMAN FINANCIAL SERVICES, LLC—See Hellman & Friedman LLC; *U.S. Public*, pg. 1907
EDELWEISS FINANCIAL SERVICES LTD.; *Int'l*, pg. 2306
EDELWEISS MULTI STRATEGY FUND ADVISORS LLP—See Edelweiss Financial Services Ltd.; *Int'l*, pg. 2306
EDENTREE INVESTMENT MANAGEMENT LIMITED—See Ecclesiastical Insurance Office plc; *Int'l*, pg. 2288
EDGE INVESTMENT MANAGEMENT LIMITED—See Edge Group Limited; *Int'l*, pg. 2309
EDGESTONE CAPITAL PARTNERS INC.; *Int'l*, pg. 2309
EDUCATORS PREFERRED CORPORATION—See Aon plc; *Int'l*, pg. 496
EDWARD BILLINGTON & SON LTD.; *Int'l*, pg. 2316
EFG BANK AG—See EFG International AG; *Int'l*, pg. 2320
EFG BANK (LUXEMBOURG) S.A.—See EFG International AG; *Int'l*, pg. 2320
EFG EUROBANK FINANCE S.A.—See Eurobank Ergasias Services and Holdings S.A.; *Int'l*, pg. 2532
EFG-HERMES INVESTMENT BANKING—See EFG Holding; *Int'l*, pg. 2319
EFG HERMES PAKISTAN LIMITED—See EFG Holding; *Int'l*, pg. 2319
EFG INDEPENDENT FINANCIAL ADVISORS LTD—See EFG International AG; *Int'l*, pg. 2320
EFG WEALTH MANAGEMENT (CANADA) LIMITED—See EFG International AG; *Int'l*, pg. 2321
EGELI & CO ENERJI YATIRIMLARI A.S.; *Int'l*, pg. 2322
EGELI & CO TARIM GIRISIM SERMAYESI YATIRIM ORTAKLIGI AS; *Int'l*, pg. 2322
EIG GLOBAL ENERGY (ASIA) LTD.—See Affiliated Managers Group, Inc.; *U.S. Public*, pg. 54
EIG GLOBAL ENERGY (AUSTRALIA) PTY. LTD.—See Affiliated Managers Group, Inc.; *U.S. Public*, pg. 54
EIG GLOBAL ENERGY (BRASIL) REPRESENTACOES LTDA.—See Affiliated Managers Group, Inc.; *U.S. Public*, pg. 54
EIG GLOBAL ENERGY (EUROPE) LTD.—See Affiliated Managers Group, Inc.; *U.S. Public*, pg. 54
EIG GLOBAL ENERGY KOREA, LTD.—See Affiliated Managers Group, Inc.; *U.S. Public*, pg. 54
EIGHT CAPITAL PARTNERS PLC; *Int'l*, pg. 2331
EIGHTEEN SEVENTY CORPORATION; *U.S. Private*, pg. 1347
EIGNABJARG EHF.—See Arion Bank hf.; *Int'l*, pg. 565
EIH PLC; *Int'l*, pg. 2332
EILERS FINANCIAL SERVICES, INC.—See Aon plc; *Int'l*, pg. 496
E.I. SIGNATURE INVESTMENTS LIMITED; *Int'l*, pg. 2251
EJF CAPITAL LLC; *U.S. Private*, pg. 1348
EJF INVESTMENTS LTD.; *Int'l*, pg. 2337
EKUITI NASIONAL BERHAD; *Int'l*, pg. 2340
ELBRIDGE INVESTMENTS (CYPRUS) LTD.; *Int'l*, pg. 2345
ELCOT CAPITAL MANAGEMENT LIMITED; *Int'l*, pg. 2346
ELDERSTREET INVESTMENTS LTD.; *Int'l*, pg. 2346
ELEPHANT CAPITAL PLC; *Int'l*, pg. 2359
ELEPHANT HILL CAPITAL, INC.; *Int'l*, pg. 2359
ELIA ASSET SA—See Elia Group SA; *Int'l*, pg. 2360
ELI LILLY FINANCE, S.A.—See Eli Lilly & Company; *U.S. Public*, pg. 732
ELIZABETHAN HOLDINGS LIMITED—See Deutsche Bank Aktiengesellschaft; *Int'l*, pg. 2061
ELLERSTON ASIAN INVESTMENTS LIMITED; *Int'l*, pg. 2365
ELLIOTT MANAGEMENT CORPORATION; *U.S. Private*, pg. 1364
ELOPAK AS - MARKET UNIT—See Ferd AS; *Int'l*, pg. 2636
ELOPAK D.O.O.—See Ferd AS; *Int'l*, pg. 2636
ELOPAK EQS GMBH—See Ferd AS; *Int'l*, pg. 2636
ELOPAK ISRAEL AS—See Ferd AS; *Int'l*, pg. 2636
ELOPAK PRODUCTION SERVICES GMBH & CO KG—See Ferd AS; *Int'l*, pg. 2636
ELOPAK SOUTH AFRICA (PTY) LTD.—See Ferd AS; *Int'l*, pg. 2636
ELRON OY—See Elomatic Oy; *Int'l*, pg. 2368
ELYSIUM CAPITAL MANAGEMENT, LLC; *U.S. Private*, pg. 1377
ELYSIUM FUND MANAGEMENT LIMITED; *Int'l*, pg. 2372
EMBER INFRASTRUCTURE MANAGEMENT, LP; *U.S. Private*, pg. 1378
EMERALD FINANCIAL SERVICES, LLC—See H&R Block, Inc.; *U.S. Public*, pg. 976
EMERGING INVESTMENT PARTNERS; *Int'l*, pg. 2379
EMERGING SOVEREIGN GROUP LLC; *U.S. Private*, pg. 1381
EMERSON MEXICO FINANCE, S.A. DE C.V., SOFOM, ENR—See Emerson Electric Co.; *U.S. Public*, pg. 745
EMERY HOWARD PORTFOLIO MANAGEMENT, INC.—See Creative Planning, LLC; *U.S. Private*, pg. 1090
EMF CAPITAL PARTNERS LIMITED; *Int'l*, pg. 2380
EMIRATES INTERNATIONAL TELECOMMUNICATIONS LLC—See Dubai Holding LLC; *Int'l*, pg. 2218
EMPIRE LIFE INVESTMENTS INC.—See E-L Financial Corporation Limited; *Int'l*, pg. 2248
EMPIRIC STUDENT PROPERTY PLC; *Int'l*, pg. 2387
EMP MANAGEMENT, LLC; *U.S. Private*, pg. 1384
EMPOWERING FINANCIAL SOLUTIONS, INC.—See Bluesphere Advisors LLC; *U.S. Private*, pg. 597
EMPRESA NACIONAL DE COMERCIO REDITO E PARTICIPACOES, S.A.-ENCORPAR; *Int'l*, pg. 2388
ENBD REIT CEIC PLC; *Int'l*, pg. 2396
ENBEE TRADE & FINANCE LIMITED; *Int'l*, pg. 2396
ENCAP FLATROCK MIDSTREAM—See EnCap Investments L.P.; *U.S. Private*, pg. 1389
ENDICOTT GROUP EQUITY PARTNERS, L.P.; *U.S. Private*, pg. 1391
ENDO FINANCE PLC; *Int'l*, pg. 2403
ENERGY INTERNATIONAL INVESTMENTS HOLDINGS LIMITED; *Int'l*, pg. 2422
ENERGYO SOLUTIONS INVEST AB; *Int'l*, pg. 2423
ENERTECH CAPITAL PARTNERS—See Safeguard Scientifics, Inc.; *U.S. Public*, pg. 1834
ENEX INFRASTRUCTURE INVESTMENT CORP.; *Int'l*, pg. 2425
ENFINITY WF SOLAR TRUST I—See Wells Fargo & Company; *U.S. Public*, pg. 2343
ENR ASSET MANAGEMENT INC.; *Int'l*, pg. 2445
ENRC LEASING BV—See Eurasian Natural Resources Corporation Limited; *Int'l*, pg. 2527
ENR RUSSIA INVEST SA; *Int'l*, pg. 2445
ENSO WZHI PTE LIMITED—See Enso Group; *Int'l*, pg. 2448
ENSTAR (US) INC.—See Enstar Group Limited; *Int'l*, pg. 2448
ENTERPRISE WEALTH SERVICES LLC—See Enterprise Bancorp, Inc.; *U.S. Public*, pg. 778

ENTRE PRENEUR CO., LTD.—See FTGroup Co Ltd.; *Int'l*, pg. 2800
THE ENTRUST GROUP, INC.; *U.S. Private*, pg. 4026
ENVESTNET PORTFOLIO SOLUTIONS, INC.—See Bain Capital, LP; *U.S. Private*, pg. 439
ENVIT CAPITAL GROUP, INC.; *U.S. Public*, pg. 781
ENZUMO CORPORATION PTY LTD—See Centrepoint Alliance Limited; *Int'l*, pg. 1412
E.ON ENGINEERING GMBH—See E.ON SE; *Int'l*, pg. 2253
E.ON FIRST FUTURE ENERGY HOLDING B.V.—See E.ON SE; *Int'l*, pg. 2254
E.ON IBERIA HOLDING GMBH—See E.ON SE; *Int'l*, pg. 2254
E.ON PORTFOLIO SOLUTION GMBH—See E.ON SE; *Int'l*, pg. 2253
E.ON RUHRGAS DUTCH HOLDING B.V.—See E.ON SE; *Int'l*, pg. 2255
E&P FINANCIAL GROUP LIMITED; *Int'l*, pg. 2247
EPIRIS MANAGERS LLP; *Int'l*, pg. 2460
EP WEALTH ADVISORS, LLC; *U.S. Private*, pg. 1411
EQT SCANDINAVIAN PARTNERS LTD.—See EQT AB; *Int'l*, pg. 2475
EQUATERRA BV; *Int'l*, pg. 2483
EQUINOX CONSULTING SAS—See Cognizant Technology Solutions Corporation; *U.S. Public*, pg. 524
EQUISTONE PARTNERS EUROPE (SCHWEIZ) AG—See Equistone Partners Europe Limited; *Int'l*, pg. 2486
EQUISTONE PARTNERS GMBH—See Equistone Partners Europe Limited; *Int'l*, pg. 2486
EQUITABLE ADVISORS, LLC—See Equitable Holdings, Inc.; *U.S. Public*, pg. 789
EQUITABLE FINANCIAL LIFE INSURANCE COMPANY; *U.S. Private*, pg. 1416
EQUI-TRAX ASSET SOLUTIONS LP.—See Southwest Business Corporation; *U.S. Private*, pg. 3738
EQUITRUST GMBH—See E.R. CAPITAL HOLDING GmbH & Cie. KG; *Int'l*, pg. 2260
EQUITY & ADVISORY LTD.—See E&A Limited; *Int'l*, pg. 2247
EQUITY OFFICE MANAGEMENT, LLC—See Blackstone Inc.; *U.S. Public*, pg. 350
EQUIUS PARTNERS, INC.—See TA Associates, Inc.; *U.S. Private*, pg. 3919
ERISA FIDUCIARY ADVISORS, INC.—See Aon plc; *Int'l*, pg. 496
ERSTE ASSET MANAGEMENT GMBH—See Erste Group Bank AG; *Int'l*, pg. 2498
ERSTE EUROPAISCHE PFANDBRIEF- UND KOMMUNALKREDITBANK AKTIENGESELLSCHAFT—See Commerzbank AG; *Int'l*, pg. 1718
ERSTE K·W·A BETEILIGUNGSGESELLSCHAFT MBH—See Bayer Aktiengesellschaft; *Int'l*, pg. 907
ESCORP ASSET MANAGEMENT LIMITED; *Int'l*, pg. 2502
ESFIN GESTION SA—See Groupe BPCE; *Int'l*, pg. 3094
ESGTI AG; *Int'l*, pg. 2503
ESON EUROPE S.R.O.—See Eson Precision Ind. Co., Ltd.; *Int'l*, pg. 2504
E SPLIT CORP.; *Int'l*, pg. 2246
ESR INVESTMENT MANAGEMENT (S) PTE. LTD.; *Int'l*, pg. 2508
ESSA ADVISORY SERVICES, LLC—See ESSA Bancorp, Inc.; *U.S. Public*, pg. 795
ESSEX EQUITY MANAGEMENT, LLC; *U.S. Private*, pg. 1428
ESSEX INVESTMENT MANAGEMENT COMPANY, LLC; *U.S. Private*, pg. 1428
ESSEX, LLC; *U.S. Private*, pg. 1428
E SUB LIMITED—See Heidelberg Materials AG; *Int'l*, pg. 3310
ETHOS CAPITAL PARTNERS LIMITED; *Int'l*, pg. 2523
ET NET LIMITED—See Hong Kong Economic Times Holdings Ltd; *Int'l*, pg. 3465
ET NET NEWS AGENCY LIMITED—See Hong Kong Economic Times Holdings Ltd; *Int'l*, pg. 3465
E*TRADE CAPITAL MANAGEMENT, LLC—See E*TRADE Financial Corporation; *U.S. Private*, pg. 1302
EUCLID ADVISORS LLC—See Virtus Investment Partners, Inc.; *U.S. Public*, pg. 2301
EUGENE SPECIAL PURPOSE ACQUISITION 3 CO., LTD; *Int'l*, pg. 2526
EULER SFAC ASSET MANAGEMENT—See Allianz SE; *Int'l*, pg. 353
EURASIA FONCIERE INVESTISSEMENTS SA; *Int'l*, pg. 2527
EUREKA EQUITY PARTNERS, L.P.; *U.S. Private*, pg. 1433
EUROFINS ENVIRONMENT TESTING LUX HOLDING SARL—See Eurofins Scientific S.E.; *Int'l*, pg. 2544
EUROFINS ENVIRONMENT TESTING NETHERLANDS HOLDING BV—See Eurofins Scientific S.E.; *Int'l*, pg. 2544
EUROFINS FOOD US HOLDINGS I BV—See Eurofins Scientific S.E.; *Int'l*, pg. 2542
EUROFINS INTERNATIONAL HOLDINGS LUX SARL—See Eurofins Scientific S.E.; *Int'l*, pg. 2544
EUROFINS PHARMA US HOLDINGS BV—See Eurofins Scientific S.E.; *Int'l*, pg. 2547
EUROGRID GMBH—See Elia Group SA; *Int'l*, pg. 2360
EUROLAND CORPORATE SA; *Int'l*, pg. 2553

EUROLAND FINANCE SA; *Int'l*, pg. 2553
EUROPEA DE TITULIZACION, S.A. S.G.F.T.—See Banco Bilbao Vizcaya Argentaria, S.A.; *Int'l*, pg. 817
EUROPEAN BANK FOR FINANCIAL SERVICES GMBH—See Caisse de Depot et Placement du Quebec; *Int'l*, pg. 1254
EUROPEAN BANK FOR FINANCIAL SERVICES GMBH—See Generation Investment Management LLP; *Int'l*, pg. 2920
THE EUROPEAN EQUITY FUND, INC.; *U.S. Public*, pg. 2073
EURO TREND YATIRIM ORTAKLIGI AS; *Int'l*, pg. 2531
EUROZ HARTLEYS GROUP LIMITED; *Int'l*, pg. 2559
EVERBANK WEALTH MANAGEMENT, INC.—See Teachers Insurance Association - College Retirement Fund; *U.S. Private*, pg. 3948
EVERBERG CAPITAL, LLC; *U.S. Private*, pg. 1437
EVERBRIGHT PGIM FUND MANAGEMENT CO., LTD.—See Prudential Financial, Inc.; *U.S. Public*, pg. 1731
EVERCORE ADVISORS L.L.C.—See Evercore, Inc.; *U.S. Public*, pg. 800
EVERCORE ADVISORY (MIDDLE EAST) LIMITED—See Evercore, Inc.; *U.S. Public*, pg. 800
EVERCORE ASIA LIMITED—See Evercore, Inc.; *U.S. Public*, pg. 800
EVERCORE ASIA (SINGAPORE) PTE. LTD.—See Evercore, Inc.; *U.S. Public*, pg. 800
EVERCORE CASA DE BOLSA, S.A. DE C.V.—See Evercore, Inc.; *U.S. Public*, pg. 800
EVERCORE CONSULTING (BEIJING) CO. LTD.—See Evercore, Inc.; *U.S. Public*, pg. 800
EVERCORE GMBH—See Evercore, Inc.; *U.S. Public*, pg. 800
EVERCORE GROUP SERVICES LIMITED—See Evercore, Inc.; *U.S. Public*, pg. 800
EVERCORE ISI INTERNATIONAL LIMITED—See Evercore, Inc.; *U.S. Public*, pg. 800
EVERCORE (JAPAN) LTD.—See Evercore, Inc.; *U.S. Public*, pg. 800
EVERCORE PARTNERS CANADA LTD.—See Evercore, Inc.; *U.S. Public*, pg. 800
EVERCORE PARTNERS INTERNATIONAL L.L.P.—See Evercore, Inc.; *U.S. Public*, pg. 800
EVERCORE PARTNERS SERVICES EAST L.L.C.—See Evercore, Inc.; *U.S. Public*, pg. 800
EVERCORE TRUST COMPANY, N.A.—See Evercore, Inc.; *U.S. Public*, pg. 800
EVERCORE TRUST COMPANY OF DELAWARE—See Evercore, Inc.; *U.S. Public*, pg. 800
EVERCORE WEALTH MANAGEMENT L.L.C.—See Evercore, Inc.; *U.S. Public*, pg. 800
EVEREST FINANCIAL GROUP LIMITED; *Int'l*, pg. 2563
EVERGENT INVESTMENTS SA; *Int'l*, pg. 2565
EVERGREEN ADVISORS, LLC; *U.S. Private*, pg. 1438
EVERGREEN CAPITAL L.P.; *U.S. Private*, pg. 1438
EVERSHORE FINANCIAL GROUP, INC.; *U.S. Private*, pg. 1440
EVERSHORE FINANCIAL GROUP, INC—See Evershore Financial Group, Inc.; *U.S. Private*, pg. 1440
EVLI AWARDS MANAGEMENT OY—See Evli Pankki Oyj; *Int'l*, pg. 2570
EVOLEM S.A.; *Int'l*, pg. 2572
EVOLUTION CAPITAL MANAGEMENT LLC; *U.S. Private*, pg. 1442
EXENCIAL WEALTH ADVISORS, LLC; *U.S. Private*, pg. 1448
EXFIN AG—See DekaBank; *Int'l*, pg. 2005
EXHIBIT SYSTEMS, INC.; *U.S. Private*, pg. 1448
EXIDE HOLDING NETHERLANDS B.V.—See Exide Technologies, LLC; *U.S. Private*, pg. 1448
EXPANSION CAPITAL GROUP, LLC; *U.S. Private*, pg. 1449
EXPERIAN FINANCE HOLDINGS LIMITED—See Experian plc; *Int'l*, pg. 2587
EXPERIAN HOLDINGS IRELAND LIMITED—See Experian plc; *Int'l*, pg. 2587
EXPLORNATION MANAGEMENT LLC—See ExplorNation Energy, Inc.; *U.S. Private*, pg. 1450
EXPONENTIAL INVESTMENTS CO., LTD.—See ESTsoft Corp; *Int'l*, pg. 2519
EXPONENT PRIVATE EQUITY LLP; *Int'l*, pg. 2589
EXPORT DEVELOPMENT CANADA; *Int'l*, pg. 2590
EXPORT DEVELOPMENT CORPORATION—See Export Development Canada; *Int'l*, pg. 2590
EXSULAR FINANCIAL GROUP INC.; *Int'l*, pg. 2591
FACTSET FRANCE SAS—See FactSet Research Systems Inc.; *U.S. Public*, pg. 819
FACT UNTERNEHMENSBERATUNG GMBH—See Silver Lake Group, LLC; *U.S. Private*, pg. 3658
FALCON PRIVATE WEALTH LTD.—See Dolfin Group Ltd.; *Int'l*, pg. 2158
FAMOUS PLAYERS INVESTMENTS B.V.—See National Amusements, Inc.; *U.S. Private*, pg. 2841
FAR EAST HOTELS AND ENTERTAINMENT LIMITED; *Int'l*, pg. 2616
FARMERS TRUST COMPANY—See Farmers National Banc Corp.; *U.S. Public*, pg. 822
FARSTARCAP INVESTMENT CORP.; *Int'l*, pg. 2620

FARUQUE (PVT) LTD—See Cherat Cement Company Limited; *Int'l*, pg. 1471
FAUCHIER PARTNERS CORPORATION—See BNP Paribas SA; *Int'l*, pg. 1087
FAVORIT HOLD AD; *Int'l*, pg. 2623
FAYEZ SAROFIM & CO.; *U.S. Private*, pg. 1484
FBR FUND ADVISERS, LLC—See B. Riley Financial, Inc.; *U.S. Public*, pg. 260
F&C ASSET MANAGERS LIMITED—See Bank of Montreal; *Int'l*, pg. 847
FCB-HARLOW BUTLER PTY LIMITED—See CME Group, Inc.; *U.S. Public*, pg. 516
FCL VENTURES LTD.—See Federated Co-operatives Limited; *Int'l*, pg. 2630
FCMB ASSET MANAGEMENT LIMITED—See FCMB Group Plc; *Int'l*, pg. 2628
F&C NETHERLANDS B.V.—See Bank of Montreal; *Int'l*, pg. 847
FDG KINETIC LIMITED—See FDG Electric Vehicles Limited; *Int'l*, pg. 2629
FDX ADVISORS INC.—See Actua Corporation; *U.S. Private*, pg. 71
FEDERAL STREET ADVISORS, INC.—See Lovell Minnick Partners LLC; *U.S. Private*, pg. 2503
FEDERATED EQUITY MANAGEMENT COMPANY OF PENNSYLVANIA—See Federated Hermes, Inc.; *U.S. Public*, pg. 827
FEDERATED HERMES, INC.; *U.S. Public*, pg. 827
FEDERATED HERMES LIMITED—See Federated Hermes, Inc.; *U.S. Public*, pg. 827
FEDERATED MDTA LLC—See Federated Hermes, Inc.; *U.S. Public*, pg. 827
FEDON FAR EAST LIMITED—See EssilorLuxottica SA; *Int'l*, pg. 2515
FERD EIENDOM—See Ferd AS; *Int'l*, pg. 2636
FERD INVESTMENT GROUP—See Ferd AS; *Int'l*, pg. 2636
FERD INVEST—See Ferd AS; *Int'l*, pg. 2636
FERD PRIVATE EQUITY—See Ferd AS; *Int'l*, pg. 2636
FFC MANAGEMENT, INC.—See Fulton Financial Corporation; *U.S. Public*, pg. 892
FFP SA; *Int'l*, pg. 2649
FHN FINANCIAL MAIN STREET ADVISORS, LLC—See First Horizon Corporation; *U.S. Public*, pg. 844
FIBA FAKTORING A.S.—See Fiba Holding A.S.; *Int'l*, pg. 2651
FIBON CAPITAL SDN. BHD.—See Fibon Berhad; *Int'l*, pg. 2652
FIDELITY INVESTMENTS JAPAN LIMITED—See FMR LLC; *U.S. Private*, pg. 1555
FIDELITY INVESTMENTS MANAGEMENT (H.K.) LIMITED—See FMR LLC; *U.S. Private*, pg. 1555
FIDELIUM GMBH; *Int'l*, pg. 2654
FIDUCIAN PORTFOLIO SERVICES LIMITED—See Fiducian Group Limited; *Int'l*, pg. 2655
FIDUCIARY EXCHANGE, LLC—See Bain Capital, LP; *U.S. Private*, pg. 439
FIDUCIARY FINANCIAL SERVICES WEALTH MANAGEMENT—See B. Riley Financial, Inc.; *U.S. Public*, pg. 260
FIDUCIARY INVESTMENT ADVISORS LLC—See Aon plc; *Int'l*, pg. 495
FIDUCIARY MANAGEMENT ASSOCIATES, LLC; *U.S. Private*, pg. 1503
FIDUCIARY TRUST (INTERNATIONAL) SARL—See Franklin Resources, Inc.; *U.S. Public*, pg. 880
FIELD ASSET SERVICES, INC—See Assurant, Inc.; *U.S. Public*, pg. 215
FIERA CAPITAL (ASIA) HONG KONG LIMITED—See Fiera Capital Corporation; *Int'l*, pg. 2659
FIERA CAPITAL (GERMANY) GMBH—See Fiera Capital Corporation; *Int'l*, pg. 2659
FIERA CAPITAL INC.—See Fiera Capital Corporation; *Int'l*, pg. 2659
FIERA CAPITAL (IOM) LIMITED—See Fiera Capital Corporation; *Int'l*, pg. 2659
FIERA CAPITAL (UK) LIMITED—See Fiera Capital Corporation; *Int'l*, pg. 2659
FIERA INFRASTRUCTURE INC.—See Fiera Capital Corporation; *Int'l*, pg. 2659
FIFTH STREET MANAGEMENT LLC—See Fifth Street Capital LLC; *U.S. Private*, pg. 1505
FIL LIMITED—See FMR LLC; *U.S. Private*, pg. 1555
FIL (LUXEMBOURG) S.A. SVERIGE FILIAL—See FMR LLC; *U.S. Private*, pg. 1555
FIM BUSINESS SOLUTIONS LIMITED—See FIMBank p.l.c.; *Int'l*, pg. 2664
FIMESTIC EXPANSION SA—See BNP Paribas SA; *Int'l*, pg. 1091
FINALP ZRT.—See DDM Holding AG; *Int'l*, pg. 1993
FINAM INVESTMENT COMPANY JSC; *Int'l*, pg. 2664
FINANCIAL ADVANTAGE INC.; *U.S. Private*, pg. 1506
FINANCIAL ASSURANCE JAPAN, INC.—See Prudential Financial, Inc.; *U.S. Public*, pg. 1731
FINANCIAL BROKERAGE GROUP—See EFG Holding; *Int'l*, pg. 2319
FINANCIAL CONSULTANTS OF AMERICA, INC.—See Arthur J. Gallagher & Co.; *U.S. Public*, pg. 204
FINANCIAL GROUP FUTURE PJSC; *Int'l*, pg. 2665

N.A.I.C.S. INDEX
523940 — PORTFOLIO MANAGEMEN...

FINANCIAL GUARD, LLC—See Franklin Resources, Inc.; *U.S. Public*, pg. 882
FINANCIAL INDEX AUSTRALIA PTY LTD.; *Int'l*, pg. 2665
FINANCIAL INVESTMENTS CORPORATION; *U.S. Private*, pg. 1507
FINANCIAL INVESTMENTS INC; *U.S. Private*, pg. 1508
FINANCIAL RECOVERY TECHNOLOGIES LLC—See The Cross Country Group, LLC; *U.S. Private*, pg. 4017
FINANCIAL WISDOM LIMITED—See Commonwealth Bank of Australia; *Int'l*, pg. 1720
FINANCIERA INDEPENDENCIA, S.A.B. DE C.V., SOFOM, E.N.R.; *Int'l*, pg. 2665
FINANCIERE BNP PARIBAS SAS—See BNP Paribas SA; *Int'l*, pg. 1091
FINANCIERE DE TUBIZE SA; *Int'l*, pg. 2668
FINANCIERE HOCHE BAINS-LES-BAINS SA; *Int'l*, pg. 2668
FINANCIERE PARIS HAUSSMANN—See BNP Paribas SA; *Int'l*, pg. 1091
FINANCO LIMITED—See Raymond James Financial, Inc.; *U.S. Public*, pg. 1764
FINANSA SECURITIES LTD.—See FNS HOLDINGS PUBLIC COMPANY LIMITED; *Int'l*, pg. 2718
FINCHOICE PTY LIMITED—See News Corporation; *U.S. Public*, pg. 1521
FINCRAFT CAPITAL JSC; *Int'l*, pg. 2672
FINCRAFT GROUP LLP; *Int'l*, pg. 2672
FINCRAFT INVESTMENT HOUSE JSC; *Int'l*, pg. 2672
FINET GROUP LIMITED; *Int'l*, pg. 2674
FINET HOLDINGS LIMITED—See Finet Group Limited; *Int'l*, pg. 2674
FINET SECURITIES LIMITED—See Finet Group Limited; *Int'l*, pg. 2674
FINEX SICAV SIF S.A. - PRIVATE EQUITY VII—See Elemental Holding S.A.; *Int'l*, pg. 2358
FINISTERRE CAPITAL LLP—See Principal Financial Group, Inc.; *U.S. Public*, pg. 1720
FINRA DISPUTE RESOLUTION, INC.—See Financial Industry Regulatory Authority, Inc.; *U.S. Private*, pg. 1507
FINTAN PARTNERS, LLC—See BGC Group, Inc.; *U.S. Public*, pg. 328
FIRST ALLIED ADVISORY SERVICES, INC.—See RCAP Holdings, LLC; *U.S. Private*, pg. 3361
FIRST AMERICAN EXCHANGE COMPANY, LLC—See First American Financial Corporation; *U.S. Public*, pg. 836
FIRST ASSET INVESTMENT MANAGEMENT INC.; *Int'l*, pg. 2682
FIRST AU LIMITED; *Int'l*, pg. 2682
FIRST BROTHERS ASSET MANAGEMENT CO., LTD.—See First Brothers Co., Ltd.; *Int'l*, pg. 2682
FIRST CAPITAL HOLDINGS PLC; *Int'l*, pg. 2682
FIRST CAPITAL INTERNATIONAL FINANCE LIMITED—See China First Capital Group Limited; *Int'l*, pg. 1503
FIRST CAPITAL MANAGEMENT INC.—See First Financial Holding Co., Ltd.; *Int'l*, pg. 2683
FIRST EAGLE INVESTMENT MANAGEMENT, LLC—See Blackstone Inc.; *U.S. Public*, pg. 353
FIRST EAGLE INVESTMENT MANAGEMENT, LLC—See Corsair Capital, LLC; *U.S. Private*, pg. 1059
FIRST FEDERAL BANK OF THE MIDWEST—See Premier Financial Corp.; *U.S. Public*, pg. 1715
FIRST FIDELITY LEASING MODARABA; *Int'l*, pg. 2683
FIRST FINANCIAL RESOURCES LTD.—See Aon plc; *Int'l*, pg. 496
FIRST FOUNDATION ADVISORS—See First Foundation Inc.; *U.S. Public*, pg. 844
FIRSTHAND CAPITAL MANAGEMENT, INC.; *U.S. Private*, pg. 1532
FIRST HEARTLAND JUSAN INVEST JSC; *Int'l*, pg. 2684
FIRST HELP FINANCIAL, LLC; *U.S. Private*, pg. 1519
FIRST INTERNATIONAL COMPUTER, INC—See FIC Global, INC; *Int'l*, pg. 2653
THE FIRST MERCANTILE TRUST COMPANY—See Mid Atlantic Capital Group, Inc.; *U.S. Private*, pg. 2705
FIRST METRO ASSET MANAGEMENT, INC.—See First Metro Investment Corporation; *Int'l*, pg. 2685
FIRST MUTUAL HOLDINGS LIMITED; *Int'l*, pg. 2685
FIRST PACIFIC ADVISORS, LLC; *U.S. Private*, pg. 1524
FIRST QUADRANT, L.P.—See Affiliated Managers Group, Inc.; *U.S. Public*, pg. 54
FIRST REPUBLIC INVESTMENT MANAGEMENT, INC.—See JPMorgan Chase & Co.; *U.S. Public*, pg. 1207
FIRST REPUBLIC TRUST COMPANY—See JPMorgan Chase & Co.; *U.S. Public*, pg. 1207
FIRST REPUBLIC WEALTH ADVISORS, LLC—See JPMorgan Chase & Co.; *U.S. Public*, pg. 1207
FIRST SAVINGS INVESTMENTS, INC.—See First Savings Financial Group, Inc.; *U.S. Public*, pg. 847
FIRST SECURITIES INVESTMENT TRUST CO., LTD—See First Financial Holding Co., Ltd.; *Int'l*, pg. 2683
FIRST SENTIER INVESTORS (UK) FUNDS LIMITED—See KKR & Co. Inc.; *U.S. Public*, pg. 1243
FIRST SHANGHAI CAPITAL LIMITED—See First Shanghai Investments Limited; *Int'l*, pg. 2687
FIRST SHANGHAI DIRECT INVESTMENTS LIMITED—See First Shanghai Investments Limited; *Int'l*, pg. 2687

FIRST SHANGHAI INVESTMENTS LIMITED; *Int'l*, pg. 2687
FIRST STATE CINDA FUND MANAGEMENT CO., LTD.—See China Cinda Asset Management Co., Ltd.; *Int'l*, pg. 1488
FIRST TRUST ADVISORS L.P.—See First Trust Portfolios L.P.; *U.S. Private*, pg. 1530
FIRST TRUST ENERGY INCOME & GROWTH FUND; *U.S. Public*, pg. 848
FIRST TRUST HIGH INCOME LONG/SHORT FUND; *U.S. Public*, pg. 848
FIRST TRUST NEW OPPORTUNITIES MLP & ENERGY FUND; *U.S. Public*, pg. 848
FIRST TRUST PORTFOLIOS L.P.; *U.S. Private*, pg. 1530
FIRST TRUST SENIOR FLOATING RATE INCOME FUND II; *U.S. Public*, pg. 848
FISCHER, FRANCIS, TREES & WATTS, INC.—See BNP Paribas SA; *Int'l*, pg. 1082
FISHER GRAHAM LIMITED; *Int'l*, pg. 2693
FIS WEALTH MANAGEMENT SERVICES, INC.—See Fidelity National Infor; *U.S. Public*, pg. 832
FJ CAPITAL MANAGEMENT; *U.S. Private*, pg. 1538
F & J PRINCE HOLDINGS CORPORATION; *Int'l*, pg. 2594
FLAGSTAR INVESTMENT GROUP, INC.—See New York Community Bancorp, Inc.; *U.S. Public*, pg. 1513
FLAT ROCK CAPITAL CORP.; *U.S. Public*, pg. 1541
FLEXDEAL SIMFE S.A.; *Int'l*, pg. 2704
FLEXIBLE PLAN INVESTMENTS LTD.; *U.S. Private*, pg. 1544
FLEXSTONE PARTNERS LLC—See Groupe BPCE; *Int'l*, pg. 3098
FLEXSTONE PARTNERS SAS—See Groupe BPCE; *Int'l*, pg. 3098
FLEXTRONICS GERMANY HOLDING GMBH—See Flex Ltd.; *Int'l*, pg. 2702
FLINTBROOK LIMITED—See Platinum Equity, LLC; *U.S. Private*, pg. 3210
FLIPPIN, BRUCE & PORTER, INC.—See Cantor Fitzgerald, L.P.; *U.S. Private*, pg. 736
FLOW CAPITAL CORP.; *Int'l*, pg. 2709
FLYING FINANCIAL SERVICE HOLDINGS LIMITED; *Int'l*, pg. 2716
FNBJ HOLDING CORP.—See Jeffersonville Bancorp; *U.S. Public*, pg. 1189
FNZ GROUP LTD.; *Int'l*, pg. 2718
FNZ HOLDINGS LTD—See Caisse de Depot et Placement du Quebec; *Int'l*, pg. 1254
FNZ HOLDINGS LTD—See Generation Investment Management LLP; *Int'l*, pg. 2920
FOCUS FINANCIAL PARTNERS, LLC—See Clayton, Dubilier & Rice, LLC; *U.S. Private*, pg. 923
FOCUS FINANCIAL PARTNERS, LLC—See Stone Point Capital LLC; *U.S. Private*, pg. 3824
FOLGER NOLAN FLEMING DOUGLAS CAPITAL MANAGEMENT, INC.—See Folger Nolan Fleming Douglas Incorporated; *U.S. Private*, pg. 1558
FOLIENCE, INC.; *U.S. Private*, pg. 1559
FOLIO DYNAMICS INC.—See Bain Capital, LP; *U.S. Private*, pg. 439
FONDINVEST CAPITAL; *Int'l*, pg. 2725
FONDSMANAGEMENT BERLIN GMBH—See Bilfinger SE; *Int'l*, pg. 1028
FOOTHILLS ASSET MANAGEMENT LTD.—See Capital Insight Partners, LLC; *U.S. Private*, pg. 740
FORBION CAPITAL PARTNERS GERMANY GMBH—See Forbion Capital Partners Management Holding BV; *Int'l*, pg. 2729
FOREBRIGHT CAPITAL MANAGEMENT LTD.; *Int'l*, pg. 2731
FORESIGHT ENTERPRISE VCT PLC; *Int'l*, pg. 2731
FORESIGHT SOLAR & TECHNOLOGY VCT PLC; *Int'l*, pg. 2732
FORESTERS INVESTMENT MANAGEMENT COMPANY, INC.—See Golden Gate Capital Management II, LLC; *U.S. Private*, pg. 1731
FORIS AG; *Int'l*, pg. 2733
FORISE INTERNATIONAL LTD.; *Int'l*, pg. 2733
FORMATION WEALTH SOLUTIONS LIMITED—See Formation Group PLC; *Int'l*, pg. 2734
FORMICA CAPITAL HOLDING AB; *Int'l*, pg. 2734
FORTIGENT, LLC—See LPL Financial Holdings Inc.; *U.S. Public*, pg. 1343
FORTIS FINANCE BELGIUM S.C.R.L.—See BNP Paribas SA; *Int'l*, pg. 1084
FORTIS HAITONG INVESTMENT MANAGEMENT CO., LTD.—See BNP Paribas SA; *Int'l*, pg. 1082
FORTIS INVESTMENT MANAGEMENT CHILE SA—See BNP Paribas SA; *Int'l*, pg. 1084
FORT PITT CAPITAL GROUP, INC.—See Clayton, Dubilier & Rice, LLC; *U.S. Private*, pg. 923
FORT PITT CAPITAL GROUP, INC.—See Stone Point Capital LLC; *U.S. Private*, pg. 3824
FORTRESS PARTNERS CAPITAL MANAGEMENT, LTD.; *U.S. Private*, pg. 1576
FORTRESS PARTNERS STRATEGIC CAPITAL ADVISORS—See Fortress Partners Capital Management, Ltd.; *U.S. Private*, pg. 1576
FORTSTONE INTERNATIONAL (HONG KONG) LIMITED—See China Biotech Services Holdings Limited; *Int'l*, pg. 1487
FORTUNE WEALTH MANAGEMENT LIMITED—See GoFintech Innovation Limited; *Int'l*, pg. 3022
FORT WASHINGTON INVESTMENT ADVISORS, INC.—See Western & Southern Financial Group, Inc.; *U.S. Private*, pg. 4490
FORUM CAPITAL MARKETS, LLC—See Wells Fargo & Company; *U.S. Public*, pg. 2343
FORUM STEGLITZ 2 GMBH—See Hammerson plc; *Int'l*, pg. 3238
FOSSIL (ASIA) HOLDINGS LTD. - TAIWAN OFFICE—See Fossil Group, Inc.; *U.S. Public*, pg. 874
FOSTER DENOVO LIMITED; *Int'l*, pg. 2749
FOTEX HOLDING SE; *Int'l*, pg. 2752
FOUNDERS BAY HOLDINGS; *U.S. Public*, pg. 875
FOUNTAIN SET (HOLDINGS) LIMITED; *Int'l*, pg. 2754
FOX ASSET MANAGEMENT LLC—See Morgan Stanley; *U.S. Public*, pg. 1471
FOYSTON GORDON & PAYNE INC.—See Affiliated Managers Group, Inc.; *U.S. Public*, pg. 54
FOYSTON, GORDON & PAYNE INC.—See Affiliated Managers Group, Inc.; *U.S. Public*, pg. 55
FP FINANCE B.V.—See Francotyp-Postalia Holding AG; *Int'l*, pg. 2761
FPR PARTNERS LLC—See Fremont Group, LLC; *U.S. Private*, pg. 1608
FRAGRANT PROSPERITY HOLDINGS LIMITED; *Int'l*, pg. 2758
FRANKLIN ALTERNATIVE STRATEGIES ADVISERS, LLC—See Franklin Resources, Inc.; *U.S. Public*, pg. 880
FRANKLIN BSP CAPITAL CORPORATION; *U.S. Private*, pg. 1596
FRANKLIN BSP LENDING CORPORATION; *U.S. Public*, pg. 877
FRANKLIN CAPITAL CORPORATION—See Franklin Resources, Inc.; *U.S. Public*, pg. 880
FRANKLIN-JEFFERSON STRATEGIES, LLC; *U.S. Private*, pg. 1598
FRANKLIN MUTUAL ADVISERS, LLC—See Franklin Resources, Inc.; *U.S. Public*, pg. 880
FRANKLIN PARK ASSOCIATES, LLC; *U.S. Private*, pg. 1597
FRANKLIN TEMPLETON ASSET MANAGEMENT (INDIA) PRIVATE LIMITED—See Franklin Resources, Inc.; *U.S. Public*, pg. 880
FRANKLIN TEMPLETON ASSET MANAGEMENT MEXICO, S.A. DE C.V.—See Franklin Resources, Inc.; *U.S. Public*, pg. 880
FRANKLIN TEMPLETON COMPANIES, LLC—See Franklin Resources, Inc.; *U.S. Public*, pg. 880
FRANKLIN/TEMPLETON DISTRIBUTORS, INC.—See Franklin Resources, Inc.; *U.S. Public*, pg. 881
FRANKLIN TEMPLETON FRANCE S.A.—See Franklin Resources, Inc.; *U.S. Public*, pg. 880
FRANKLIN TEMPLETON FUND MANAGEMENT LIMITED—See Franklin Resources, Inc.; *U.S. Public*, pg. 880
FRANKLIN TEMPLETON INVESTMENTS AUSTRALIA LIMITED—See Franklin Resources, Inc.; *U.S. Public*, pg. 880
FRANKLIN TEMPLETON INVESTMENTS (ME) LIMITED—See Franklin Resources, Inc.; *U.S. Public*, pg. 880
FRANKLIN TEMPLETON INVESTMENTS POLAND SP. Z O.O.—See Franklin Resources, Inc.; *U.S. Public*, pg. 881
FRANKLIN TEMPLETON INVESTMENTS SOUTH AFRICA (PTY) LTD—See Franklin Resources, Inc.; *U.S. Public*, pg. 881
FRANKLIN TEMPLETON INVESTMENT TRUST MANAGEMENT CO., LTD.—See Franklin Resources, Inc.; *U.S. Public*, pg. 880
FRANKLIN TEMPLETON ITALIA SIM S.P.A.—See Franklin Resources, Inc.; *U.S. Public*, pg. 881
FRANKLIN/TEMPLETON TRAVEL, INC.—See Franklin Resources, Inc.; *U.S. Public*, pg. 881
FRASERS LOGISTICS & INDUSTRIAL TRUST—See Frasers Property Limited; *Int'l*, pg. 2766
FRAZIER MANAGEMENT, LLC; *U.S. Private*, pg. 1600
FRED ALGER & COMPANY INCORPORATED—See Alger Associates, Inc.; *U.S. Private*, pg. 166
FRED ALGER MANAGEMENT, INC.—See Alger Associates, Inc.; *U.S. Private*, pg. 166
FREEDOM FINANCE JSC; *Int'l*, pg. 2769
FREEDOM INTERNET GROUP, INC.; *U.S. Private*, pg. 1603
FREEMAN SPOGLI MANAGEMENT CO., LLC—See Freeman Spogli & Co. Incorporated; *U.S. Private*, pg. 1606
FREIGHT TECHNOLOGIES, INC.; *U.S. Public*, pg. 885
FREMMAN CAPITAL LIMITED; *Int'l*, pg. 2772
FREMONT REALTY CAPITAL—See Fremont Group, LLC; *U.S. Private*, pg. 1608
FRENKEL TOPPING LIMITED—See Frenkel Topping Group plc; *Int'l*, pg. 2773
FREY & ASSOCIATES, LLC; *U.S. Public*, pg. 1610
FRIEDLAND PARTICIPATION ET GESTION S.A.—See BNP Paribas SA; *Int'l*, pg. 1091
FRIENDS FIRST HOLDINGS LTD.—See Achmea B.V.; *Int'l*, pg. 103

523940 — PORTFOLIO MANAGEMEN...   CORPORATE AFFILIATIONS

FRIGATE AS; *Int'l*, pg. 2792
FRIGATE LUXEMBOURG S.A.—See Frigate AS; *Int'l*, pg. 2792
FRIGATE PAY UAB—See Frigate AS; *Int'l*, pg. 2792
FRIGATE SA—See Frigate AS; *Int'l*, pg. 2792
FRIMEX INVESTMENT LLC—See Hayel Saeed Anam Group of Companies; *Int'l*, pg. 3290
FRONT BARNETT ASSOCIATES LLC—See Mesirow Financial Holdings, Inc.; *U.S. Private*, pg. 2678
FRONTIER CAPITAL MANAGEMENT COMPANY, LLC—See Affiliated Managers Group, Inc.; *U.S. Public*, pg. 55
FRONTIER DIGITAL VENTURES LIMITED; *Int'l*, pg. 2795
FRONTIER WEALTH MANAGEMENT, LLC—See The Cap Financial Group, LLC; *U.S. Private*, pg. 4004
FRONTLINE SECURITIES LTD.; *Int'l*, pg. 2796
FRONTPOINT PARTNERS LLC; *U.S. Private*, pg. 1616
FROU FROU INVESTMENTS LTD—See Alkis H. Hadjikyriacos (Frou Frou Biscuits) Public Ltd.; *Int'l*, pg. 331
FRP TRANSIT BUSINESS PARK—See FRP Holdings, Inc.; *U.S. Public*, pg. 888
FSA GROUP LIMITED; *Int'l*, pg. 2798
F S CAPITAL GROUP—See Franklin Resources, Inc.; *U.S. Public*, pg. 879
FSC SECURITIES CORPORATION—See Reverence Capital Partners LLC; *U.S. Private*, pg. 3414
FSN CAPITAL PARTNERS AS; *Int'l*, pg. 2798
FTB ADVISORS, INC.—See First Horizon Corporation; *U.S. Public*, pg. 844
FTC INVESTOR SERVICES INC.—See Franklin Resources, Inc.; *U.S. Public*, pg. 879
FTN FINANCIAL CORPORATION—See First Horizon Corporation; *U.S. Public*, pg. 844
FTN FINANCIAL MAIN STREET ADVISORS, LLC—See First Horizon Corporation; *U.S. Public*, pg. 844
FTN FINANCIAL SECURITIES CORP.—See First Horizon Corporation; *U.S. Public*, pg. 844
FUJIFILM HOLDINGS NZ LIMITED—See FUJIFILM Holdings Corporation; *Int'l*, pg. 2824
FUJIFILM SERICOL OVERSEAS HOLDINGS LIMITED—See FUJIFILM Holdings Corporation; *Int'l*, pg. 2823
FUJITSU (CHINA) HOLDINGS CO., LTD.—See Fujitsu Limited; *Int'l*, pg. 2833
FUJITSU TECHNOLOGY SOLUTIONS (HOLDING) B.V.—See Fujitsu Limited; *Int'l*, pg. 2836
FULCRUM UTILITY SERVICES LIMITED; *Int'l*, pg. 2841
FULL CIRCLE FIBER PARTNERS, INC.—See Guggenheim Partners, LLC; *U.S. Private*, pg. 1812
FULL FORTUNE HOLDINGS PTE LTD—See China Food Company Plc; *Int'l*, pg. 1503
FULL IN PARTNERS MANAGEMENT, LLC; *U.S. Private*, pg. 1620
FULTON FINANCIAL ADVISORS—See Fulton Financial Corporation; *U.S. Public*, pg. 892
FUNDAMENTUM ASSET MANAGEMENT S.A.—See BNP Paribas SA; *Int'l*, pg. 1091
FUND EVALUATION GROUP, LLC; *U.S. Private*, pg. 1622
FUNDQUEST ADVISOR SASU—See BNP Paribas SA; *Int'l*, pg. 1091
FUNDQUEST MM LTD.—See BNP Paribas SA; *Int'l*, pg. 1091
FUNDQUEST UK LTD.—See BNP Paribas SA; *Int'l*, pg. 1091
FURE FINANCIAL CORP.—See Genstar Capital, LLC; *U.S. Private*, pg. 1677
FURE FINANCIAL CORP.—See Keystone Group, L.P.; *U.S. Private*, pg. 2298
FUTUREADVISOR, INC.—See BlackRock, Inc.; *U.S. Public*, pg. 345
FUTURE FINANCIAL STRATEGY CORP.—See Future Corporation; *Int'l*, pg. 2853
FUTURE FUND INVESTMENT INC.; *U.S. Private*, pg. 1627
FUTURE GENERATION AUSTRALIA LIMITED; *Int'l*, pg. 2856
FUTURE GENERATION GLOBAL LIMITED; *Int'l*, pg. 2856
FUTURESTREAM NETWORKS CO., LTD.; *Int'l*, pg. 2858
FVLCRUM PARTNERS LLC; *U.S. Private*, pg. 1627
FXCM AUSTRALIA LIMITED—See Global Brokerage, Inc.; *U.S. Public*, pg. 940
FXCM PRO LLC—See Global Brokerage, Inc.; *U.S. Public*, pg. 940
FX CONNECT, LLC—See State Street Corporation; *U.S. Public*, pg. 1940
GABELLI & COMPANY INVESTMENT ADVISERS, INC.—See GAMCO Investors, Inc.; *U.S. Public*, pg. 895
GABELLI FUNDS, LLC—See GAMCO Investors, Inc.; *U.S. Public*, pg. 895
GAINS INVESTMENT CORPORATION—See China Steel Corporation; *Int'l*, pg. 1555
GAINVEST URUGUAY ASSET MANAGEMENT S.A.—See StoneX Group Inc.; *U.S. Public*, pg. 1952
GALA CAPITAL PARTNERS, LLC; *U.S. Private*, pg. 1635
GALACTICO CORPORATE SERVICES LIMITED; *Int'l*, pg. 2870
GALAXY ENTERTAINMENT GROUP LIMITED; *Int'l*, pg. 2871
GALICIA ADMINISTRADORA DE FONDOS S.A.—See Grupo Financiero Galicia S.A.; *Int'l*, pg. 3129
GALILEO GLOBAL ADVISORS, LLC; *U.S. Private*, pg. 1637
GALLE FACE CAPITAL PARTNERS PLC—See Carson Cumberbatch PLC; *Int'l*, pg. 1347
GALVAN RESEARCH & TRADING, LTD.—See StoneX Group Inc.; *U.S. Public*, pg. 1952
GAMBIT FINANCIAL SOLUTIONS SA—See BNP Paribas SA; *Int'l*, pg. 1091
GAMCO ASSET MANAGEMENT INC.—See GAMCO Investors, Inc.; *U.S. Public*, pg. 895
GAMCO ASSET MANAGEMENT (UK) LIMITED—See GAMCO Investors, Inc.; *U.S. Public*, pg. 895
GAM (DEUTSCHLAND) AG—See GAM Holding AG; *Int'l*, pg. 2876
GAM DUBAI LTD.—See GAM Holding AG; *Int'l*, pg. 2876
GAM FUND MANAGEMENT LTD—See GAM Holding AG; *Int'l*, pg. 2876
GAM HONG KONG LTD.—See GAM Holding AG; *Int'l*, pg. 2876
GAM INVESTMENT MANAGEMENT (SWITZERLAND) AG—See GAM Holding AG; *Int'l*, pg. 2876
GAM (ITALIA) SGR S.P.A.—See GAM Holding AG; *Int'l*, pg. 2876
GAM JAPAN LIMITED—See GAM Holding AG; *Int'l*, pg. 2876
GAM LIMITED—See GAM Holding AG; *Int'l*, pg. 2876
GAM LONDON LTD.—See GAM Holding AG; *Int'l*, pg. 2876
GAM (LUXEMBOURG) S.A. - MADRID BRANCH—See GAM Holding AG; *Int'l*, pg. 2876
GAM (LUXEMBOURG) S.A.—See GAM Holding AG; *Int'l*, pg. 2876
GAM USA INC.—See GAM Holding AG; *Int'l*, pg. 2876
GANON PRODUCTS LIMITED; *Int'l*, pg. 2881
GARANTI BBVA FACTORING AS—See Banco Bilbao Vizcaya Argentaria, S.A.; *Int'l*, pg. 818
GARANTI BBVA PORTFOY AS—See Banco Bilbao Vizcaya Argentaria, S.A.; *Int'l*, pg. 818
GARDA CAPITAL GROUP; *Int'l*, pg. 2883
GARDA CAPITAL PARTNERS LP—See Affiliated Managers Group, Inc.; *U.S. Public*, pg. 55
GARDEN CITY TOWNHOMES, LLC—See AvalonBay Communities, Inc.; *U.S. Public*, pg. 240
GARDLINE SHIPPING LIMITED—See HAL Trust N.V.; *Int'l*, pg. 3226
GARDNER STANDARD LLC; *U.S. Private*, pg. 1644
GARMIN DEUTSCHLAND BETEILIGUNGS GMBH & CO, KG—See Garmin Ltd.; *Int'l*, pg. 2885
GARNET INTERNATIONAL LIMITED; *Int'l*, pg. 2885
GARY A. DOSSICK & ASSOCIATES, INC.—See Callahan Financial Planning Company; *U.S. Private*, pg. 722
GATES FINANCING, LLC—See AvalonBay Communities, Inc.; *U.S. Public*, pg. 240
GATEWAY INSTITUTIONAL TAX CREDIT FUND II, LTD—See Raymond James Financial, Inc.; *U.S. Public*, pg. 1764
GAW CAPITAL ADVISORS LIMITED; *Int'l*, pg. 2891
GAW CAPITAL ADVISORS (SHANGHAI) CO., LTD.—See Gaw Capital Advisors Limited; *Int'l*, pg. 2891
GAW CAPITAL PARTNERS (USA), LLC—See Gaw Capital Advisors Limited; *Int'l*, pg. 2891
GBST HOLDINGS LIMITED - GBST FINANCIAL SERVICES DIVISION—See GBST Holdings Limited; *Int'l*, pg. 2893
GCA SAVIAN HOLDINGS CORPORATION—See Houlihan Lokey, Inc.; *U.S. Public*, pg. 1055
GCM GROSVENOR HOLDINGS (CANADA) ULC—See GCM Grosvenor Inc.; *U.S. Public*, pg. 908
GCM INVESTMENTS HONG KONG LIMITED—See GCM Grosvenor Inc.; *U.S. Public*, pg. 908
GCM INVESTMENTS JAPAN K.K.—See GCM Grosvenor Inc.; *U.S. Public*, pg. 908
GCM INVESTMENTS UK LLP—See GCM Grosvenor Inc.; *U.S. Public*, pg. 908
GCP INFRASTRUCTURE INVESTMENTS LIMITED; *Int'l*, pg. 2895
GC SBIC V, L.P.—See Golub Capital, Inc.; *U.S. Private*, pg. 1736
GDL FUND; *U.S. Public*, pg. 908
GDM ADVISORY GROUP LTD.—See TA Associates, Inc.; *U.S. Private*, pg. 3919
GE CAPITAL GLOBAL HOLDINGS, LLC—See General Electric Company; *U.S. Public*, pg. 916
GELCO CORPORATION—See Element Fleet Management Corporation; *Int'l*, pg. 2358
GENERALI BANK AG—See Assicurazioni Generali S.p.A.; *Int'l*, pg. 645
GENERALI IMMOBILIARE ITALIA SGR S.P.A.—See Assicurazioni Generali S.p.A.; *Int'l*, pg. 646
GENERALI INVESTMENTS ASIA LIMITED—See Assicurazioni Generali S.p.A.; *Int'l*, pg. 646
GENERALI INVESTMENTS CEE, INVESTICNI SPOLECNOST, A.S.—See Assicurazioni Generali S.p.A.; *Int'l*, pg. 646
GENERALI INVESTMENTS, DRUZBA ZA UPRAVLJANJE, D.O.O.—See Assicurazioni Generali S.p.A.; *Int'l*, pg. 646
GENERALI INVESTMENTS PARTNERS S.P.A. SOCIETA DI GESTIONE RISPARMIO—See Assicurazioni Generali S.p.A.; *Int'l*, pg. 646
GENERAL NUTRITION INVESTMENT COMPANY—See Ares Management Corporation; *U.S. Public*, pg. 189
GENERATION GROWTH CAPITAL, INC; *U.S. Private*, pg. 1668
GENERATION INVESTMENT MANAGEMENT LLP; *Int'l*, pg. 2920
GENERFID S.P.A.—See Assicurazioni Generali S.p.A.; *Int'l*, pg. 643
GENESIS INVESTMENT MANAGEMENT, LLP—See Affiliated Managers Group, Inc.; *U.S. Public*, pg. 55
GENEVE CREDIT & LEASING SA—See BNP Paribas SA; *Int'l*, pg. 1091
GENII CAPITAL SA—See Genii Capital SA; *Int'l*, pg. 2923
GENII CAPITAL UK LTD.—See Genii Capital SA; *Int'l*, pg. 2923
GENOST CONSULTING GMBH—See CORESTATE Capital Holding SA; *Int'l*, pg. 1800
GENWORTH FINANCIAL ADVISERS CORPORATION—See Genworth Financial, Inc.; *U.S. Public*, pg. 933
GENWORTH FINANCIAL TRUST COMPANY—See Genworth Financial, Inc.; *U.S. Public*, pg. 934
GEORG FISCHER HOLDING SRL—See Georg Fischer AG; *Int'l*, pg. 2936
GEORGIA CAPITAL PLC; *Int'l*, pg. 2939
GEORGIAN INTERNATIONAL LIMITED; *Int'l*, pg. 2939
GERIFONDS S.A.—See Banque Cantonale Vaudoise; *Int'l*, pg. 853
GERMAN AMERICAN FINANCIAL ADVISORS & TRUST COMPANY—See German American Bancorp, Inc.; *U.S. Public*, pg. 934
GERMAN STARTUPS GROUP GMBH & CO. KGAA; *Int'l*, pg. 2943
GERSTEIN, FISHER & ASSOCIATES, INC.—See M&T Bank Corporation; *U.S. Public*, pg. 1351
GESTION ET LOCATION HOLDING S.A.S.—See BNP Paribas SA; *Int'l*, pg. 1091
GET NICE FINANCIAL GROUP LIMITED—See Get Nice Holdings Limited; *Int'l*, pg. 2946
GF HOLDINGS (HONG KONG) CORPORATION LIMITED—See GF Securities Co., Ltd.; *Int'l*, pg. 2955
GFH PARTNERS LTD—See GFH Financial Group B.S.C.; *Int'l*, pg. 2956
GF INTERNATIONAL INVESTMENT MANAGEMENT LIMITED—See GF Securities Co., Ltd.; *Int'l*, pg. 2955
GF XINDE INVESTMENT MANAGEMENT CO., LTD.—See GF Securities Co., Ltd.; *Int'l*, pg. 2955
GIC ASSET MANAGEMENT PTE. LTD.—See GIC Pte. Ltd.; *Int'l*, pg. 2964
GILDE BUY OUT PARTNERS AG—See Gilde Buy Out Partners B.V.; *Int'l*, pg. 2974
GILDE BUY OUT PARTNERS BVBA—See Gilde Buy Out Partners B.V.; *Int'l*, pg. 2974
GILDE INVESTMENT MANAGEMENT B.V.; *Int'l*, pg. 2975
GILMAN CIOCIA, INC.—See B. Riley Financial, Inc.; *U.S. Public*, pg. 261
GIMV GERMANY HOLDING GMBH—See Gimv NV; *Int'l*, pg. 2976
GIRARD PARTNERS LTD.—See Univest Financial Corporation; *U.S. Public*, pg. 2263
GLADSTONE MANAGEMENT CORPORATION; *U.S. Private*, pg. 1705
GLANCE FINANCE LIMITED; *Int'l*, pg. 2988
GLASSBRIDGE ASSET MANAGEMENT, LLC—See GlassBridge Enterprises, Inc.; *U.S. Public*, pg. 939
GLAXO WELLCOME INVESTMENTS B.V.—See GSK plc; *Int'l*, pg. 3145
GLENHILL CAPITAL ADVISORS, LLC—See Glenhill Advisors, LLC; *U.S. Private*, pg. 1710
GLENHILL CAPITAL MANAGEMENT, LLC—See Glenhill Advisors, LLC; *U.S. Private*, pg. 1710
THE GLENMEDE TRUST COMPANY; *U.S. Private*, pg. 4033
GLINTT ANGOLA, LDA.—See Glintt - Global Intelligent Technologies, S.A.; *Int'l*, pg. 2992
GLINTT BRASIL, LTDA.—See Glintt - Global Intelligent Technologies, S.A.; *Int'l*, pg. 2992
GLINTT ESPANA, S.L.—See Glintt - Global Intelligent Technologies, S.A.; *Int'l*, pg. 2992
GLINTT - GLOBAL INTELLIGENT TECHNOLOGIES, S.A.; *Int'l*, pg. 2992
GLINTT POLSKA, SP. Z O.O.—See Glintt - Global Intelligent Technologies, S.A.; *Int'l*, pg. 2992
GLOBAL ASSET MANAGEMENT LIMITED; *Int'l*, pg. 2993
GLOBAL CURRENTS INVESTMENT MANAGEMENT, LLC—See Franklin Resources, Inc.; *U.S. Public*, pg. 881
GLOBAL FRANCHISE GROUP, LLC—See Fog Cutter Capital Group Inc.; *U.S. Private*, pg. 1557
GLOBAL INVESTMENT SERVICES SA; *Int'l*, pg. 2998
GLOBAL INVESTMENTS LIMITED; *Int'l*, pg. 2998
GLOBAL LEISURE PARTNERS LLC—See Global Leisure Partners LLP; *Int'l*, pg. 2998
GLOBAL LEISURE PARTNERS LLP; *Int'l*, pg. 2998
GLOBAL RETIREMENT PARTNERS, LLC; *U.S. Private*, pg. 1717
GLOBAL TAX FREE CO., LTD.; *Int'l*, pg. 3001
GLOBAL TESTING CORPORATION LIMITED; *Int'l*, pg. 3001

N.A.I.C.S. INDEX

523940 — PORTFOLIO MANAGEMEN...

GLOBALWORTH REAL ESTATE INVESTMENTS LIMITED; *Int'l*, pg. 3005
GLOBE CAPITAL LIMITED; *Int'l*, pg. 3006
GLOBEOP FINANCIAL SERVICES LIMITED—See SS&C Technologies Holdings, Inc.; *U.S. Public*, pg. 1923
GLOBERER INC—See Enso Group; *Int'l*, pg. 2448
GL PHARM TECH CORP; *Int'l*, pg. 2986
GLP JAPAN ADVISORS INC.—See Global Logistic Properties Limited; *Int'l*, pg. 2999
GLP J-REIT; *Int'l*, pg. 3011
GMA HOLDINGS, INC.; *Int'l*, pg. 3012
GM FINANCE CO. HOLDINGS LLC—See General Motors Company; *U.S. Public*, pg. 924
GMO VENTURE PARTNERS, INC.—See GMO Internet Group, Inc.; *Int'l*, pg. 3014
GMP PROPERTY SOCIMI SA; *Int'l*, pg. 3014
GOFEN & GLOSSBERG, LLC; *U.S. Private*, pg. 1726
GOLDENBRIDGE NO.2 SPECIAL PURPOSE ACQUISITION CO., LTD; *Int'l*, pg. 3032
GOLDEN CAPITAL MANAGEMENT, LLC—See Wells Fargo & Company; *U.S. Public*, pg. 2343
GOLDEN RESERVE, LLC; *U.S. Private*, pg. 1732
GOLDEN ROCK GLOBAL PLC; *Int'l*, pg. 3031
GOLDENTREE ASSET MANAGEMENT LLC—See GoldenTree Asset Management LP; *U.S. Private*, pg. 1734
GOLDENTREE ASSET MANAGEMENT SINGAPORE PTE. LTD.—See GoldenTree Asset Management LP; *U.S. Private*, pg. 1734
GOLDENTREE ASSET MANAGEMENT UK LLP—See GoldenTree Asset Management LP; *U.S. Private*, pg. 1734
GOLDIN FINANCIAL HOLDINGS LIMITED; *Int'l*, pg. 3033
GOLD LINE INTERNATIONAL FINVEST LIMITED; *Int'l*, pg. 3024
GOLDMAN SACHS ASSET MANAGEMENT INTERNATIONAL—See The Goldman Sachs Group, Inc.; *U.S. Public*, pg. 2081
GOLDMAN SACHS ASSET MANAGEMENT, L.P.—See The Goldman Sachs Group, Inc.; *U.S. Public*, pg. 2081
GOLDMAN SACHS MIDDLE MARKET LENDING CORP.—See The Goldman Sachs Group, Inc.; *U.S. Public*, pg. 2081
GOLDMAN SACHS PRIVATE MIDDLE MARKET CREDIT LLC—See The Goldman Sachs Group, Inc.; *U.S. Public*, pg. 2081
GOLDPOINT PARTNERS LLC—See New York Life Insurance Company; *U.S. Private*, pg. 2910
GOLDSTEIN MUNGER & ASSOCIATES—See Genstar Capital, LLC; *U.S. Private*, pg. 1677
GOLDSTEIN MUNGER & ASSOCIATES—See Keystone Group, L.P.; *U.S. Private*, pg. 2298
GOLDSTONE INVESTMENT GROUP LIMITED; *Int'l*, pg. 3034
GOLD-ZACK AG; *Int'l*, pg. 3026
GOODE PARTNERS, LLC; *U.S. Private*, pg. 1739
GOOD LIFE COMPANIES LLC; *U.S. Private*, pg. 1738
GOODMAN PLUS TRUST; *Int'l*, pg. 3041
GOOD SPIRITS HOSPITALITY LIMITED; *Int'l*, pg. 3039
GOURMET INVESTMENTS PVT LTD—See Bharti Enterprises Limited; *Int'l*, pg. 1013
GOWER HOUSE LIMITED—See Brown & Brown, Inc.; *U.S. Public*, pg. 400
GRANDBRIDGE LIMITED; *Int'l*, pg. 3057
GRAND LIBERTY CO., LTD.—See Eson Precision Ind. Co., Ltd.; *Int'l*, pg. 2504
GRAND TREASURERS LIMITED—See Consolidated Hallmark Insurance Plc.; *Int'l*, pg. 1770
GRANGE CAPITAL PTY LTD—See Grange Resources Limited; *Int'l*, pg. 3058
GRANTHAM, MAYO, VAN OTTERLOO & CO. LLC - SAN FRANCISCO—See Grantham, Mayo, Van Otterloo & Co. LLC; *U.S. Private*, pg. 1757
GRANTHAM, MAYO, VAN OTTERLOO & CO. LLC; *U.S. Private*, pg. 1757
GREAT ELM CAPITAL CORP.—See Forest Investments, Inc.; *U.S. Private*, pg. 1567
GREATER CHINA ASSET SERVICES LIMITED—See Asia-Pac Financial Investment Company Limited; *Int'l*, pg. 616
GREATER CHINA CORPORATE CONSULTANCY & SERVICES LIMITED—See Asia-Pac Financial Investment Company Limited; *Int'l*, pg. 616
GREAT LAKES ADVISORS HOLDINGS, LLC—See Wintrust Financial Corporation; *U.S. Public*, pg. 2375
GREAT WALL (HOLDING) COMPANY LIMITED—See Cosmos Machinery Enterprises Limited; *Int'l*, pg. 1813
GREENBACKER RENEWABLE ENERGY COMPANY LLC; *U.S. Private*, pg. 1774
GREENCOAT RENEWABLES PLC; *Int'l*, pg. 3073
GREENCOAT UK WIND PLC; *Int'l*, pg. 3073
GREEN DELTA CAPITAL LTD—See Green Delta Insurance Company Limited; *Int'l*, pg. 3070
GREENLEAF-TNX SIKH SOLAR, LLC; *U.S. Private*, pg. 1778
GREENLIGHT ACQUISITION CORPORATION—See Verra Mobility Corporation; *U.S. Public*, pg. 2286
GREENLIGHT CAPITAL, INC.; *U.S. Private*, pg. 1778
GREENLINK FINANCIAL, LLC; *U.S. Private*, pg. 1779

GREEN, PLAGGE & SHAW, LTD.—See Savant Capital, LLC; *U.S. Private*, pg. 3556
GREENSPRING ASSOCIATES LIMITED PARTNERSHIP—See StepStone Group Inc.; *U.S. Public*, pg. 1945
GREEN STREET ADVISORS INC.—See Welsh, Carson, Anderson & Stowe; *U.S. Private*, pg. 4480
GREENWOOD INVESTMENT MANAGEMENT INC.—See Curi Holdings, Inc.; *U.S. Private*, pg. 1125
G.RESEARCH, LLC—See Morgan Group Holding Co.; *U.S. Public*, pg. 1471
GRESHAM INVESTMENT MANAGEMENT LLC—See Teachers Insurance Association - College Retirement Fund; *U.S. Private*, pg. 3947
G-RESOURCES GROUP LIMITED; *Int'l*, pg. 2862
GREYSTONE AFFORDABLE HOUSING INITIATIVES, LLC—See Greystone & Co., Inc.; *U.S. Private*, pg. 1785
GREYSTONE SERVICING CORPORATION, INC.—See Greystone & Co., Inc.; *U.S. Private*, pg. 1786
GR FINANCIAL LLC—See Radian Group, Inc.; *U.S. Public*, pg. 1759
GRIFFIN CAPITAL CORPORATION; *U.S. Private*, pg. 1787
GRINDSTONE PARTNERS, LLC; *U.S. Private*, pg. 1790
GROEIVERMOGEN N.V.—See ABN AMRO Group N.V.; *Int'l*, pg. 65
GROUPE CIOA SA; *Int'l*, pg. 3101
GROUPE IRD SA; *Int'l*, pg. 3105
GROWTH PARTNERS, L.P.—See SVB Financial Group; *U.S. Public*, pg. 1968
GROWTHPOINT BUILDING MANAGERS (PTY) LIMITED—See Growthpoint Properties Limited; *Int'l*, pg. 3113
GROWTHPOINT MANAGEMENT SERVICES (PTY) LIMITED—See Growthpoint Properties Limited; *Int'l*, pg. 3113
GRUPA ZASTAVA VOZILA U RESTRUKTURIRANJU A.D.; *Int'l*, pg. 3117
GRUPO SECURITY S.A.; *Int'l*, pg. 3135
GRUPPO MUTUIONLINE S.P.A; *Int'l*, pg. 3140
GRYPHON CAPITAL INCOME TRUST; *Int'l*, pg. 3141
GSFM PTY LIMITED—See CI Financial Corporation; *Int'l*, pg. 1601
GSG FINANCIAL—See Material Handling Services, LLC; *U.S. Private*, pg. 2609
GSO CAPITAL PARTNERS INTERNATIONAL LLP—See Blackstone Inc.; *U.S. Public*, pg. 360
GSO CAPITAL PARTNERS (TEXAS) LP—See Blackstone Inc.; *U.S. Public*, pg. 349
GSO EUROPEAN SENIOR DEBT ASSOCIATES LLC—See Blackstone Inc.; *U.S. Public*, pg. 349
GSP INVESTMENTS LIMITED—See GSP Finance Company (Bangladesh) Limited; *Int'l*, pg. 3150
GSTECHNOLOGIES LTD.; *Int'l*, pg. 3150
GUANGDONG GDC CULTURAL PARK LIMITED—See Global Digital Creations Holdings Limited; *Int'l*, pg. 2994
GUANGDONG JOIN-SHARE FINANCING GUARANTEE INVESTMENT CO., LTD.; *Int'l*, pg. 3157
GUANGDONG YUEKE FINANCE GROUP CO., LTD.—See Guangdong Hongtu Technology (Holdings) Co., Ltd.; *Int'l*, pg. 3156
GUANGXI INVESTMENT GROUP CO., LTD.; *Int'l*, pg. 3163
GUARDIAN CAPITAL ADVISORS LP—See Guardian Capital Group Limited; *Int'l*, pg. 3169
GUARDIAN CAPITAL ENTERPRISES LIMITED—See Guardian Capital Group Limited; *Int'l*, pg. 3169
GUGGENHEIM FUNDS DISTRIBUTORS, LLC—See Guggenheim Partners, LLC; *U.S. Public*, pg. 1812
GUGGENHEIM STRATEGIC OPPORTUNITIES FUND; *U.S. Public*, pg. 974
GUIDANT FINANCIAL GROUP, INC.; *U.S. Private*, pg. 1813
GUIPUZCOANO ENTIDAD GESTORA DE FONDOS DE PENSIONES, S.A.—See Banco de Sabadell, S.A.; *Int'l*, pg. 821
GULF CAPITAL PJSC; *Int'l*, pg. 3179
GULF WARRANTIES W.L.L.—See Arab Insurance Group B.S.C.; *Int'l*, pg. 530
GUOLIAN CAPITAL CO., LTD.—See Guolian Securities Co., Ltd; *Int'l*, pg. 3186
GUTHRIE OVERSEAS INVESTMENTS PTE LTD—See Guthrie GTS Limited; *Int'l*, pg. 3189
GW&K INVESTMENT MANAGEMENT, LLC—See Affiliated Managers Group, Inc.; *U.S. Public*, pg. 55
GXP GERMAN PROPERTIES AG; *Int'l*, pg. 3190
H2O AM ASIA PTE LTD.—See Groupe BPCE; *Int'l*, pg. 3098
H 47 VERWALTUNGSGESELLSCHAFT MBH—See Commerzbank AG; *Int'l*, pg. 1718
HADLEY CAPITAL LLC; *U.S. Private*, pg. 1839
HAHN INVESTMENT STEWARDS & COMPANY INC.—See iA Financial Corporation Inc.; *Int'l*, pg. 3567
HA HOWARD SERVICES LLC—See Hannon Armstrong Sustainable Infrastructure Capital, Inc.; *U.S. Public*, pg. 983
HAINAN GOLDEN GULF INVESTMENT & DEVELOPMENT CO., LTD.—See Hainan Traffic Administration Holding Co., Ltd.; *Int'l*, pg. 3215
HAITONG CAPITAL INVESTMENT CO., LTD.—See Haitong Securities Co., Ltd.; *Int'l*, pg. 3218
HAITONG-FORTIS PRIVATE EQUITY FUND MANAGE-

MENT CO., LTD.—See Haitong Securities Co., Ltd.; *Int'l*, pg. 3218
HAITONG INTERNATIONAL SECURITIES KK—See Haitong Securities Co., Ltd.; *Int'l*, pg. 3218
HAITONG INTERNATIONAL SECURITIES (UK) LIMITED—See Haitong Securities Co., Ltd.; *Int'l*, pg. 3218
HALITRON, INC.; *U.S. Public*, pg. 979
HALL CAPITAL PARTNERS LLC—See Lovell Minnick Partners LLC; *U.S. Private*, pg. 2503
HALO COMPANIES, INC.; *U.S. Public*, pg. 981
HALO PORTFOLIO ADVISORS, LLC—See Halo Companies, Inc.; *U.S. Public*, pg. 981
HALSEY ASSOCIATES, INC.—See Washington Trust Bancorp, Inc.; *U.S. Public*, pg. 2329
HAMBLIN WATSA INVESTMENT COUNSEL LTD.—See Fairfax Financial Holdings Limited; *Int'l*, pg. 2607
HAMILTON LANE ADVISORS, LLC; *U.S. Private*, pg. 1848
HAMILTON LANE ALLIANCE HOLDINGS I, INC.—See Hamilton Lane Incorporated; *U.S. Public*, pg. 982
HAMILTON LANE (AUSTRALIA) PTY LIMITED—See Hamilton Lane Incorporated; *U.S. Public*, pg. 982
HAMILTON LANE DO BRASIL LTDA.—See Hamilton Lane Advisors, LLC; *U.S. Private*, pg. 1848
HAMILTON LANE (HONG KONG) LIMITED—See Hamilton Lane Advisors, LLC; *U.S. Private*, pg. 1848
HAMILTON LANE INCORPORATED; *U.S. Public*, pg. 981
HAMILTON LANE INVESTIMENTOS LTDA.—See Hamilton Lane Incorporated; *U.S. Public*, pg. 982
HAMILTON LANE ISRAEL LTD.—See Hamilton Lane Advisors, LLC; *U.S. Private*, pg. 1848
HAMILTON LANE (JAPAN) CO., LTD.—See Hamilton Lane Advisors, LLC; *U.S. Private*, pg. 1848
HAMILTON LANE (UK) LIMITED—See Hamilton Lane Advisors, LLC; *U.S. Private*, pg. 1848
HAMMOND HANLON CAMP LLC—See Fifth Third Bancorp; *U.S. Public*, pg. 833
HANA ALTERNATIVE ASSET MANAGEMENT CO., LTD.—See Hana Financial Group, Inc.; *Int'l*, pg. 3240
HANJIN HEAVY INDUSTRIES & CONSTRUCTION CO., LTD.; *Int'l*, pg. 3252
HANLEIGH MANAGEMENT INC.—See Truist Financial Corporation; *U.S. Public*, pg. 2200
HANNOVER LEASING INVESTMENT GMBH—See COR-ESTATE Capital Holding SA; *Int'l*, pg. 1800
HANOVER ACCEPTANCES LIMITED; *Int'l*, pg. 3258
HANSEATISCHE IMMOBILIEN MANAGEMENT NIEDERLANDE GMBH—See Ernst Russ AG; *Int'l*, pg. 2496
HANSON AGGREGATES HOLDING NEDERLAND B.V.—See Heidelberg Materials AG; *Int'l*, pg. 3311
HANSON AUSTRALIA INVESTMENTS PTY LIMITED—See Heidelberg Materials AG; *Int'l*, pg. 3311
HANSON BATTERIES LIMITED—See Heidelberg Materials AG; *Int'l*, pg. 3311
HANSONGNEOTECH CO., LTD.; *Int'l*, pg. 3261
HANSON INDUSTRIAL (ENGINEERING HOLDINGS) LIMITED—See Heidelberg Materials AG; *Int'l*, pg. 3312
HANSON INDUSTRIAL LIMITED—See Heidelberg Materials AG; *Int'l*, pg. 3312
HANSON INTERNATIONAL HOLDINGS LIMITED—See Heidelberg Materials AG; *Int'l*, pg. 3312
HANSON LHA LIMITED—See Heidelberg Materials AG; *Int'l*, pg. 3312
HANSON QUARRY PRODUCTS VENTURES LIMITED—See Heidelberg Materials AG; *Int'l*, pg. 3313
HANSON RBS TRUSTEES LIMITED—See Heidelberg Materials AG; *Int'l*, pg. 3313
HANSON TIS HOLDINGS LIMITED—See Heidelberg Materials AG; *Int'l*, pg. 3313
HANSTEEN HOLDINGS PLC—See Blackstone Inc.; *U.S. Public*, pg. 350
HANTZ FINANCIAL SERVICES, INC.—See Hantz Group, Inc.; *U.S. Private*, pg. 1857
HANWHA ACE SPECIAL PURPOSE ACQUISITION 2ND CO., LTD.; *Int'l*, pg. 3264
HANWHA LIFE INVESTMENT (AMERICA) LTD.—See Hanwha Group; *Int'l*, pg. 3266
HAOHUA HITONE INVESTMENT MANAGEMENT CO., LTD.—See China National Chemical Corporation; *Int'l*, pg. 1527
HAPPY LIFE INSURANCE CO., LTD.—See China Cinda Asset Management Co., Ltd.; *Int'l*, pg. 1488
HARBORLIGHT CAPITAL MANAGEMENT, LLC—See HarborLight Capital Group, LLC; *U.S. Private*, pg. 1859
HARBOURVEST HORIZON—See HarbourVest Partners, LLC; *U.S. Private*, pg. 1861
HARBOURVEST PARTNERS (ASIA) LIMITED—See HarbourVest Partners, LLC; *U.S. Private*, pg. 1861
HARBOURVEST PARTNERS (JAPAN) LIMITED—See HarbourVest Partners, LLC; *U.S. Private*, pg. 1861
HARBOURVEST PARTNERS, LLC; *U.S. Private*, pg. 1861
HARBOURVEST PARTNERS, LLC—See HarbourVest Partners, LLC; *U.S. Private*, pg. 1861
HAREL FINANCE OPERATING SERVICES LTD.—See Harel Insurance Investments & Financial Services Ltd.; *Int'l*, pg. 3274
HAREL MUTUAL FUNDS LTD.—See Harel Insurance Investments & Financial Services Ltd.; *Int'l*, pg. 3274

523940 — PORTFOLIO MANAGEMEN...

HAREWOOD ASSET MANAGEMENT (US) INC.—See BNP Paribas SA; *Int'l*, pg. 1088
HARGREAVE HALE AIM VCT PLC; *Int'l*, pg. 3274
HARGREAVES LANSDOWN PLC; *Int'l*, pg. 3274
HARO FINANCIAL CORPORATION—See Crown Investments Corporation of Saskatchewan; *Int'l*, pg. 1857
HARRIS MYCFO, INC.—See Bank of Montreal; *Int'l*, pg. 846
HARTFIELD LOUISVILLE, LLC—See Aon plc; *Int'l*, pg. 496
HARTFORD INVESTMENT MANAGEMENT COMPANY—See The Hartford Financial Services Group, Inc.; *U.S. Public*, pg. 2088
HARVEST FUND ADVISORS, LLC—See Blackstone Inc.; *U.S. Public*, pg. 354
HARVEST GROUP FINANCIAL SERVICES, CORP.—See The Goldman Sachs Group, Inc.; *U.S. Public*, pg. 2082
HARVEST PORTFOLIOS GROUP INC.; *Int'l*, pg. 3281
HASBRO INTERNATIONAL HOLDINGS, B.V.—See Hasbro, Inc.; *U.S. Public*, pg. 988
HATCHER GROUP LTD.; *Int'l*, pg. 3284
HATFIELD PHILIPS DEUTSCHLAND GMBH—See Starwood Property Trust, Inc.; *U.S. Public*, pg. 1939
HAZELTREE FUND SERVICES INC—See Bendigo Partners, LLC; *U.S. Private*, pg. 524
H.B. FULLER DEUTSCHLAND PRODUKTIONS GMBH—See H.B. Fuller Company; *U.S. Public*, pg. 978
HBIS CARBON ASSETS MANAGEMENT CO., LTD.—See HBIS Group Co., Ltd.; *Int'l*, pg. 3295
HBIS COMMERCIAL FACTORING CO., LTD.—See HBIS Group Co., Ltd.; *Int'l*, pg. 3296
HBIS GROUP FINANCE CO., LTD.—See HBIS Group Co., Ltd.; *Int'l*, pg. 3296
HBIS GROUP INVESTMENT HOLDING CO., LTD.—See HBIS Group Co., Ltd.; *Int'l*, pg. 3296
HBP ENERGY CORP.; *Int'l*, pg. 3297
HC ASIA HOLDING GMBH—See Heidelberg Materials AG; *Int'l*, pg. 3310
HC FINANCIAL ADVISORS INC.—See The Mather Group, LLC; *U.S. Private*, pg. 4075
HCI ASSET GMBH—See Ernst Russ AG; *Int'l*, pg. 2495
HCI HANSEATISCHE CAPITALBERATUNGSGESELLSCHAFT FUR BETEILIGUNGSKAPITAL MBH—See Ernst Russ AG; *Int'l*, pg. 2495
HCI INSTITUTIONAL FUNDS GMBH—See Ernst Russ AG; *Int'l*, pg. 2495
HCI TREUHAND GMBH—See Ernst Russ AG; *Int'l*, pg. 2496
HDFC CAPITAL ADVISORS LTD.—See Housing Development Finance Corporation Limited; *Int'l*, pg. 3492
HEADLAND CAPITAL PARTNERS (INDIA) PRIVATE LIMITED—See Headland Capital Partners Limited; *Int'l*, pg. 3301
HEADLAND CAPITAL PARTNERS (SHANGHAI) LIMITED—See Headland Capital Partners Limited; *Int'l*, pg. 3301
HEADLAND INVESTMENT CONSULTING (SHANGHAI) CORPORATION LIMITED—See Headland Capital Partners Limited; *Int'l*, pg. 3301
HEADQUARTERS ADVISORY GROUP, LLC—See Genstar Capital, LLC; *U.S. Private*, pg. 1676
HEDEF GIRISIM SERMAYESI YATI ORTAK; *Int'l*, pg. 3307
HEDGEYE RISK MANAGEMENT LLC; *U.S. Private*, pg. 1903
HEIDELBERGCEMENT CENTRAL EUROPE EAST HOLDING B.V.—See Heidelberg Materials AG; *Int'l*, pg. 3314
HEIDELBERGCEMENT NETHERLANDS HOLDING B.V.—See Heidelberg Materials AG; *Int'l*, pg. 3315
HEIDELBERGCEMENT UK HOLDING II LIMITED—See Heidelberg Materials AG; *Int'l*, pg. 3315
HEIDELBERGER BETEILIGUNGSHOLDING AG; *Int'l*, pg. 3321
HEIDELBERGER KS BETEILIGUNGEN DEUTSCHLAND VERWALTUNGSGESELLSCHAFT MBH—See Heidelberg Materials AG; *Int'l*, pg. 3316
HELABA INVEST KAPITALANLAGEGESELLSCHAFT MBH—See Helaba Landesbank Hessen-Thuringen; *Int'l*, pg. 3328
HELABA LANDESBANK HESSEN THURINGEN—See Helaba Landesbank Hessen-Thuringen; *Int'l*, pg. 3328
HELIAD AG; *Int'l*, pg. 3329
HELIX FINANCIAL SYSTEMS, L.P.—See Cantor Fitzgerald, L.P.; *U.S. Private*, pg. 736
HELLOWALLET, LLC—See KeyCorp; *U.S. Public*, pg. 1225
HENDERSON DIVERSIFIED INCOME TRUST PLC; *Int'l*, pg. 3344
HENDERSON FAR EAST INCOME LIMITED; *Int'l*, pg. 3344
HENDERSON HIGH INCOME TRUST PLC; *Int'l*, pg. 3344
HENGTAI PIONEER INVESTMENTS CO., LTD.—See HengTai Securities CO., LTD; *Int'l*, pg. 3347
HENGTAI YINGWO ASSET MANAGEMENT CO., LTD.—See HengTai Securities CO., LTD; *Int'l*, pg. 3347
HENNESSY ADVISORS, INC.; *U.S. Public*, pg. 1025
HERALD INVESTMENT MANAGEMENT LIMITED; *Int'l*, pg. 3358
HERCULES SILVER CORP.; *Int'l*, pg. 3361
HERIOT REIT LTD.; *Int'l*, pg. 3361
HERITAGE FINANCIAL SYSTEMS—See ConsenSys, Inc.; *U.S. Private*, pg. 1019
HERITAGE WAY ADVISORS, LLC—See Creative Planning, LLC; *U.S. Private*, pg. 1090

HERMES EQUITY OWNERSHIP SERVICES LIMITED—See Federated Hermes, Inc.; *U.S. Public*, pg. 827
HERMES FINANCIAL MANAGEMENT EGYPT, LTD.—See EFG Holding; *Int'l*, pg. 2319
HERMES GPE LLP—See Federated Hermes, Inc.; *U.S. Public*, pg. 827
HERMES GPE (SINGAPORE) PTE. LIMITED—See Federated Hermes, Inc.; *U.S. Public*, pg. 827
HERMES GPE (USA) INC.—See Federated Hermes, Inc.; *U.S. Public*, pg. 827
HERMES INVESTMENT MANAGEMENT LTD.—See Federated Hermes, Inc.; *U.S. Public*, pg. 827
HFB FINANCIAL PLANNING LTD.; *Int'l*, pg. 3374
HFS HELVETIC FINANCIAL SERVICES AG—See CORESTATE Capital Holding SA; *Int'l*, pg. 1800
HFT INVESTMENT MANAGEMENT CO., LTD.—See Haitong Securities Co., Ltd.; *Int'l*, pg. 3218
HFX HOLDING CORP.; *Int'l*, pg. 3375
HI AI 1ST SPECIAL PURPOSE ACQUISITION CO; *Int'l*, pg. 3379
HIDDEN CHAMPIONS CAPITAL MANAGEMENT PTE. LTD.—See 8I Holdings Limited; *Int'l*, pg. 16
HIDDEN HARBOR CAPITAL PARTNERS; *U.S. Private*, pg. 1934
H.I.G. BIOVENTURES, LLC—See H.I.G. Capital, LLC; *U.S. Private*, pg. 1827
H.I.G. BRAZIL INVESTMENT ADVISORY LTDA.—See H.I.G. Capital, LLC; *U.S. Private*, pg. 1828
H.I.G. CAPITAL, LLC - BOSTON OFFICE—See H.I.G. Capital, LLC; *U.S. Private*, pg. 1828
H.I.G. EUROPEAN CAPITAL PARTNERS LLP—See H.I.G. Capital, LLC; *U.S. Private*, pg. 1828
H.I.G. EUROPEAN CAPITAL PARTNERS SPAIN, S.L.U.—See H.I.G. Capital, LLC; *U.S. Private*, pg. 1828
HIGHBAR MANAGEMENT, LLC; *U.S. Private*, pg. 1937
HIGHBRIDGE CAPITAL MANAGEMENT, LLC—See JPMorgan Chase & Co.; *U.S. Public*, pg. 1207
HIGHBRIDGE CAPITAL MANAGEMENT (UK), LTD.—See JPMorgan Chase & Co.; *U.S. Public*, pg. 1207
HIGHLAND CAPITAL MANAGEMENT, LLC—See Argent Financial Group, Inc.; *U.S. Private*, pg. 320
HIGHLAND CAPITAL MANAGEMENT, L.P.; *U.S. Private*, pg. 1938
HILBROY ADVISORY INC.; *Int'l*, pg. 3391
HILLROSS FINANCIAL SERVICES LIMITED—See AMP Limited; *Int'l*, pg. 432
HILTON CAPITAL MANAGEMENT, LLC—See Rafferty Holdings, LLC; *U.S. Private*, pg. 3345
HIRTLE CALLAGHAN & CO.; *U.S. Private*, pg. 1951
HISPANA DOS S.A.—See FAES Farma, S.A.; *Int'l*, pg. 2601
HISPANIC EXPRESS, INC.; *U.S. Public*, pg. 1042
HI SPECIAL PURPOSE ACQUISITION COMPANY; *Int'l*, pg. 3379
HITACHI INVESTMENT MANAGEMENT, LTD.—See Hitachi, Ltd.; *Int'l*, pg. 3420
HI-TECH CARE, INC.—See Amedisys, Inc.; *U.S. Public*, pg. 94
HIVEST CAPITAL PARTNERS SAS; *Int'l*, pg. 3427
HK FINANCIAL—See Pure Financial Advisors, Inc.; *U.S. Private*, pg. 3305
HK HOLDINGS (NO.1) LIMITED—See Heidelberg Materials AG; *Int'l*, pg. 3311
HLB INTERNATIONAL LIMITED; *Int'l*, pg. 3430
HL CAPITAL CORP.—See Zurn Elkay Water Solutions Corporation; *U.S. Public*, pg. 2413
HLM MANAGEMENT CO., INC.; *U.S. Private*, pg. 1954
HLM MANAGEMENT CO., LLC—See HLM Management Co., Inc.; *U.S. Private*, pg. 1954
HNA DAJI INVESTMENT & DEVELOPMENT CO., LTD.—See Hainan Traffic Administration Holding Co., Ltd.; *Int'l*, pg. 3213
HNA INVESTMENT GROUP CO., LTD.; *Int'l*, pg. 3433
HNA TOPWIN FUTURES CO., LTD.—See Hainan Traffic Administration Holding Co., Ltd.; *Int'l*, pg. 3215
HOBART REVENUE MANAGEMENT LIMITED; *Int'l*, pg. 3437
THE HOFFMANN FAMILY OF COMPANIES; *U.S. Private*, pg. 4053
HOLDING NOV VEK AD; *Int'l*, pg. 3450
HOLLEWAY CAPITAL PARTNERS LLC; *U.S. Private*, pg. 1964
HOLLISWEALTH ADVISORY SERVICES INC.—See iA Financial Corporation Inc.; *Int'l*, pg. 3567
HOLY STONE HOLDINGS CO., LTD.—See Holy Stone Enterprise Co., Ltd.; *Int'l*, pg. 3454
HOMETOWN INVESTMENT SERVICES, INC.—See Great Western Bancorp, Inc.; *U.S. Public*, pg. 962
HOPENING SA; *Int'l*, pg. 3473
HOPSON DEVELOPMENT HOLDINGS LIMITED; *Int'l*, pg. 3474
HORAN CAPITAL MANAGEMENT, LLC; *U.S. Private*, pg. 1980
HORIZON CAPITAL LLP; *Int'l*, pg. 3479
HOULIHAN LOKEY (CHINA) LIMITED—See Houlihan Lokey, Inc.; *U.S. Public*, pg. 1055
HOULIHAN LOKEY EMEA, LLP—See Houlihan Lokey, Inc.; *U.S. Public*, pg. 1055

HOULIHAN LOKEY (ESPANA) S.A.—See Houlihan Lokey, Inc.; *U.S. Public*, pg. 1055
HOULIHAN LOKEY (EUROPE) LIMITED—See Houlihan Lokey, Inc.; *U.S. Public*, pg. 1055
HOULIHAN LOKEY GMBH—See Houlihan Lokey, Inc.; *U.S. Public*, pg. 1055
HOULIHAN LOKEY, INC.; *U.S. Public*, pg. 1055
HOULIHAN LOKEY (NETHERLANDS) B.V.—See Houlihan Lokey, Inc.; *U.S. Public*, pg. 1055
HOUSEHOLDER GROUP INC.; *U.S. Private*, pg. 1992
HOUSERATE LIMITED—See Heidelberg Materials AG; *Int'l*, pg. 3316
HOWE BARNES CAPITAL MANAGEMENT, INC.—See Raymond James Financial, Inc.; *U.S. Public*, pg. 1764
HPB INVEST D.O.O.—See Hrvatska Postanska banka d.d.; *Int'l*, pg. 3502
HPL ESTATES LIMITED—See Heidelberg Materials AG; *Int'l*, pg. 3311
HPS INVESTMENT PARTNERS, LLC; *U.S. Private*, pg. 1997
HPS INVESTMENT PARTNERS (UK) LLP—See HPS Investment Partners, LLC; *U.S. Private*, pg. 1997
HSBC ARGENTINA HOLDINGS S.A.—See HSBC Holdings plc; *Int'l*, pg. 3503
HSBC ASSET MANAGEMENT (INDIA) PRIVATE LIMITED—See HSBC Holdings plc; *Int'l*, pg. 3503
HSBC GLOBAL ASSET MANAGEMENT (DEUTSCHLAND) GMBH—See HSBC Holdings plc; *Int'l*, pg. 3504
HSBC GLOBAL ASSET MANAGEMENT (HONG KONG) LIMITED—See HSBC Holdings plc; *Int'l*, pg. 3506
HSBC GLOBAL ASSET MANAGEMENT (JAPAN) K.K.—See HSBC Holdings plc; *Int'l*, pg. 3504
HSBC GLOBAL ASSET MANAGEMENT (MALTA) LTD—See HSBC Holdings plc; *Int'l*, pg. 3504
HSBC GLOBAL ASSET MANAGEMENT (SINGAPORE) LTD—See HSBC Holdings plc; *Int'l*, pg. 3506
HSBC INVESTMENT TRUST (JAPAN) K.K.—See HSBC Holdings plc; *Int'l*, pg. 3506
HSBC IRELAND—See HSBC Holdings plc; *Int'l*, pg. 3504
HSBC TRINKAUS CAPITAL MANAGEMENT GMBH—See HSBC Holdings plc; *Int'l*, pg. 3504
HSBC UNIT TRUST MANAGEMENT LIMITED—See HSBC Holdings plc; *Int'l*, pg. 3504
HUABANG CORPORATE FINANCE LIMITED—See Huabang Technology Holdings Limited; *Int'l*, pg. 3510
HUA CAPITAL MANAGEMENT CO., LTD.; *Int'l*, pg. 3509
HUA NAN ASSETS MANAGEMENT CO., LTD.—See Hua Nan Financial Holdings Co., Ltd.; *Int'l*, pg. 3509
HUANENG INVESCO WLR INVESTMENT CONSULTING CO., LTD.—See China Huaneng Group Co., Ltd.; *Int'l*, pg. 1509
HUARONG FUTURES CO., LTD.—See China CITIC Financial Asset Management Co., Ltd.; *Int'l*, pg. 1489
HUB24 LIMITED; *Int'l*, pg. 3516
HUB GIRISIM SERMAYESI YATIRIM ORTAKLIGI A.S.; *Int'l*, pg. 3516
HUCENTECH CO., LTD.; *Int'l*, pg. 3521
HUDSON ADVISORS LLC; *U.S. Private*, pg. 2001
HUGE GROUP LIMITED; *Int'l*, pg. 3523
HUIXINJIA CAPITAL GROUP, INC.; *U.S. Private*, pg. 2004
HULIC REIT MANAGEMENT CO., LTD.—See Hulic Co., Ltd.; *Int'l*, pg. 3528
HULL STREET ENERGY, LLC; *U.S. Private*, pg. 2005
HUME BROPHY COMMUNICATIONS; *U.S. Private*, pg. 2007
HUNAN PUBLISHING INVESTMENT HOLDING GROUP FINANCIAL CO., LTD.—See China South Publishing & Media Group Co., Ltd.; *Int'l*, pg. 1553
HUNTER GROUP ASA; *Int'l*, pg. 3536
HURON TRANSACTION ADVISORY LLC—See Huron Consulting Group Inc.; *U.S. Public*, pg. 1076
HYDE PARK FACILITIES, INC.—See Wintrust Financial Corporation; *U.S. Public*, pg. 2375
HYPERION ASSET MANAGEMENT LIMITED; *Int'l*, pg. 3553
HYPOPORT SE; *Int'l*, pg. 3554
HYSAN DEVELOPMENT COMPANY LIMITED; *Int'l*, pg. 3554
HYUNDAI ABLE 1ST SPECIAL PURPOSE ACQUISITION COMPANY; *Int'l*, pg. 3555
HYUNDAI INVESTMENT (AMERICA) LTD.—See Hyundai Marine & Fire Insurance Co., Ltd.; *Int'l*, pg. 3558
IARGENTO HI TECH ASSETS LP; *Int'l*, pg. 3569
IBERIA FINANCIAL SERVICES, LLC—See First Horizon Corporation; *U.S. Public*, pg. 845
IBI CORPORATE FINANCE LIMITED—See Daiwa Securities Group Inc.; *Int'l*, pg. 1948
ICAHN CAPITAL MANAGEMENT LP—See Icahn Enterprises L.P.; *U.S. Public*, pg. 1084
ICAHN PARTNERS MASTER FUND LP—See Icahn Enterprises L.P.; *U.S. Public*, pg. 1084
ICAP COLOMBIA INVESTMENT CORPORATION—See CME Group, Inc.; *U.S. Public*, pg. 516
ICAP EQUITIES ASIA LIMITED—See CME Group, Inc.; *U.S. Public*, pg. 516
ICC FINANCIAL LIMITED—See CSI Properties Limited; *Int'l*, pg. 1865

N.A.I.C.S. INDEX　　　　　　　　　　523940 — PORTFOLIO MANAGEMEN...

IC FONDS GMBH—See IC Immobilien Holding AG; *Int'l*, pg. 3577
ICG-LONGBOW SENIOR SECURED UK PROP DEBT INV LTD.; *Int'l*, pg. 3579
ICHIGO ASSET MANAGEMENT, LTD.; *Int'l*, pg. 3580
ICHIYOSHI ASSET MANAGEMENT CO., LTD.—See Ichiyoshi Securities Co., Ltd.; *Int'l*, pg. 3581
ICICI VENTURE FUNDS MANAGEMENT COMPANY LIMITED—See ICICI Bank Limited; *Int'l*, pg. 3581
ICI HOLDINGS (AUSTRALIA) PTY LTD—See Akzo Nobel N.V.; *Int'l*, pg. 274
ICI SOUTH PACIFIC HOLDINGS PTY LTD—See Akzo Nobel N.V.; *Int'l*, pg. 274
ICM CAPITAL RESEARCH LIMITED—See ICM Limited; *Int'l*, pg. 3581
ICM CORPORATE SERVICES (PTY) LTD—See ICM Limited; *Int'l*, pg. 3581
ICM INVESTMENT MANAGEMENT LIMITED—See ICM Limited; *Int'l*, pg. 3581
ICM INVESTMENT RESEARCH LIMITED—See ICM Limited; *Int'l*, pg. 3581
ICM NZ LIMITED—See ICM Limited; *Int'l*, pg. 3581
ICM RESEARCH PTE LTD—See ICM Limited; *Int'l*, pg. 3581
ICON CLINICAL INVESTMENTS, LLC—See ICON plc; *Int'l*, pg. 3584
ICRA GLOBAL CAPITAL, INC.—See Moody's Corporation; *U.S. Public*, pg. 1467
ICRA ONLINE LIMITED—See Moody's Corporation; *U.S. Public*, pg. 1467
ICRA SAPPHIRE INC.—See Moody's Corporation; *U.S. Public*, pg. 1467
IC ZERICH CAPITAL MANAGEMENT JSC; *Int'l*, pg. 3577
IDBI HOMEFINANCE LTD.; *Int'l*, pg. 3588
ID CONSEIL—See Jones Lang LaSalle Incorporated; *U.S. Public*, pg. 1202
IDEA CAPITAL FUNDS SGR—See De Agostini S.p.A.; *Int'l*, pg. 1995
IDI ASSET MANAGEMENT SA—See IDI SCA; *Int'l*, pg. 3595
IDLC FINANCE LIMITED - MERCHANT BANKING DIVISION—See IDLC Finance PLC.; *Int'l*, pg. 3595
IDM S.A.; *Int'l*, pg. 3595
IDS GMBH-ANALYSIS AND REPORTING SERVICES—See Allianz SE; *Int'l*, pg. 353
IEX GROUP N.V.; *Int'l*, pg. 3598
IFAST CAPITAL SDN. BHD.—See iFAST Corporation Limited; *Int'l*, pg. 3598
IFAST FINANCIAL (HK) LIMITED—See iFAST Corporation Limited; *Int'l*, pg. 3598
IFAST FINANCIAL LIMITED—See iFAST Corporation Limited; *Int'l*, pg. 3598
IFAST FINANCIAL PTE. LTD.—See iFAST Corporation Limited; *Int'l*, pg. 3598
IFAST PLATFORM SERVICES (HK) LIMITED—See iFAST Corporation Limited; *Int'l*, pg. 3598
IFC ASSET MANAGEMENT COMPANY—See The World Bank Group; *U.S. Private*, pg. 4139
IFCI LIMITED; *Int'l*, pg. 3599
IFCI VENTURE CAPITAL FUNDS LTD—See IFCI Limited; *Int'l*, pg. 3599
IFG GROUP PLC—See Epiris Managers LLP; *Int'l*, pg. 2461
IFG QUIGLEY LIMITED—See Epiris Managers LLP; *Int'l*, pg. 2461
IGB REAL ESTATE INVESTMENT TRUST; *Int'l*, pg. 3602
IK PARTNERS; *Int'l*, pg. 3610
ILSHIN INVESTMENT CO., LTD.—See Ilshin Spinning Co., Ltd.; *Int'l*, pg. 3616
I&M BURBIDGE CAPITAL LIMITED—See I&M Group Plc; *Int'l*, pg. 3562
IMC ASSET MANAGEMENT B.V.—See IMC International Marketmakers Combination B.V.; *Int'l*, pg. 3620
IMC HOLDINGS GMBH—See Berkshire Hathaway Inc.; *U.S. Public*, pg. 307
IMMOBILIENVERWALTUNGSGESELLSCHAFT SCHLACHTHOF OFFENBACH MBH—See Commerzbank AG; *Int'l*, pg. 1718
IMMOPARIBAS ROYALE-NEUVE SA—See BNP Paribas SA; *Int'l*, pg. 1091
IMMOVALOR GESTION S.A.—See Allianz SE; *Int'l*, pg. 353
INDEPENDENCE COMMUNITY COMMERCIAL REINVESTMENT CORP.—See Banco Santander, S.A.; *Int'l*, pg. 827
INDEPENDENT CAPITAL MANAGEMENT; *U.S. Private*, pg. 2058
INDEPENDENT FINANCIAL GROUP, LLC; *U.S. Private*, pg. 2059
INDEPENDENT FINANCIAL PARTNERS; *U.S. Private*, pg. 2059
INDEPENDENT TRUST COMPANY OF AMERICA, LLC; *U.S. Private*, pg. 2061
INDUSTRIAL AND FINANCIAL SYSTEMS, IFS UK LTD—See EQT AB; *Int'l*, pg. 2478
INDUSTRIAL PROMOTION SERVICES LTD—See Aga Khan Development Network; *Int'l*, pg. 199
INDUSTRIAL VALUE PARTNERS, LLC; *U.S. Private*, pg. 2069
IND-X ADVISORS LIMITED—See Haitong Securities Co., Ltd.; *Int'l*, pg. 3218
INFORMATION SERVICES GROUP EUROPE LIMITED—See Information Services Group, Inc.; *U.S. Public*, pg. 1118
ING COMPANIA DE INVERSIONES Y SERVICIOS LTDA—See Grupo de Inversiones Suramericana S.A.; *Int'l*, pg. 3125
INGERSOLL-RAND EUROPEAN HOLDING COMPANY B.V.—See Ingersoll Rand Inc.; *U.S. Public*, pg. 1121
ING INVESTMENT MANAGEMENT—See Grupo de Inversiones Suramericana S.A.; *Int'l*, pg. 3125
INLAND REAL ESTATE INVESTMENT CORPORATION—See The Inland Real Estate Group of Companies, Inc.; *U.S. Private*, pg. 4056
INNO-BAG LIMITED—See China Eco-Farming Limited; *Int'l*, pg. 1498
INSIGHT INVESTMENT MANAGEMENT (EUROPE) LIMITED—See The Bank of New York Mellon Corporation; *U.S. Public*, pg. 2037
INSINGER DE BEAUFORT ASSET MANAGEMENT NV—See BNP Paribas SA; *Int'l*, pg. 1091
INSINGER DE BEAUFORT ASSOCIATES BV—See BNP Paribas SA; *Int'l*, pg. 1091
INSINGER DE BEAUFORT BV—See BNP Paribas SA; *Int'l*, pg. 1091
INSTARAGF ASSET MANAGEMENT INC.—See AGF Management Limited; *Int'l*, pg. 206
INSTITUTIONAL CAPITAL NETWORK, INC.; *U.S. Private*, pg. 2094
INSTITUTIONAL CASH DISTRIBUTORS LLC—See PCP Enterprise, L.P.; *U.S. Private*, pg. 3121
INSTITUTIONAL LIFE SERVICES, LLC—See Aon plc; *Int'l*, pg. 496
INSTITUTIONAL SHAREHOLDER SERVICES GERMANY AG—See Deutsche Borse AG; *Int'l*, pg. 2064
INSTITUTIONAL SHAREHOLDER SERVICES INC.—See Deutsche Borse AG; *Int'l*, pg. 2064
INSTITUTIONAL SHAREHOLDER SERVICES UK LIMITED—See Deutsche Borse AG; *Int'l*, pg. 2064
INTANDEM CAPITAL PARTNERS, LLC; *U.S. Private*, pg. 2097
INTEGRATED FINANCIAL PARTNERS, INC.—See Integrated Wealth Concepts, LLC; *U.S. Private*, pg. 2101
INTEGRATED WEALTH CONCEPTS, LLC; *U.S. Private*, pg. 2101
INTERACTIVE INVESTOR LIMITED—See abrdn PLC; *Int'l*, pg. 68
INTER CAPITAL REALTY CORPORATION—See Old Republic International Corporation; *U.S. Public*, pg. 1567
INTERFACE AMERICAS HOLDINGS, LLC—See Interface, Inc.; *U.S. Public*, pg. 1144
INTERLAKEN CAPITAL, INC.; *U.S. Private*, pg. 2111
INTERNATIONAL FUND SERVICES (N.A.), L.L.C.—See State Street Corporation; *U.S. Public*, pg. 1940
INTERNATIONAL POWER CONSOLIDATED HOLDINGS LIMITED—See ENGIE SA; *Int'l*, pg. 2434
INTERNATIONAL STRATEGY & INVESTMENT GROUP L.L.C.—See Evercore, Inc.; *U.S. Public*, pg. 800
INTER-PACIFIC ASSET MANAGEMENT SDN BHD—See Berjaya Corporation Berhad; *Int'l*, pg. 982
INTERWELL AS—See Ferd AS; *Int'l*, pg. 2636
INTERWELL AUSTRALIA PTY LTD—See Ferd AS; *Int'l*, pg. 2636
INTERWELL LLC—See Ferd AS; *Int'l*, pg. 2636
INTERWELL QATAR PETROLEUM TECHNOLOGY CO. W.L.L.—See Ferd AS; *Int'l*, pg. 2636
INTERWELL SAUDI ARABIA GAS & OIL TECHNOLOGIES L.L.C—See Ferd AS; *Int'l*, pg. 2636
INTERWELL UK LTD—See Ferd AS; *Int'l*, pg. 2636
INTERWELL US LLC—See Ferd AS; *Int'l*, pg. 2636
INTL ADVISORY CONSULTANTS INC.—See StoneX Group Inc.; *U.S. Public*, pg. 1952
INTL GAINVEST S.A.—See StoneX Group Inc.; *U.S. Public*, pg. 1952
INTL KOREA LIMITED—See StoneX Group Inc.; *U.S. Public*, pg. 1952
INTREPID CAPITAL MANAGEMENT, INC.; *U.S. Private*, pg. 2129
INTUITIVE SURGICAL HOLDINGS, INC.—See Intuitive Surgical, Inc.; *U.S. Public*, pg. 1160
INVESCO ADVISERS, INC.—See Invesco Ltd.; *U.S. Public*, pg. 1161
INVESCO ASIA TRUST PLC—See Invesco Ltd.; *U.S. Public*, pg. 1164
INVESCO ASSET MANAGEMENT ASIA LIMITED—See Invesco Ltd.; *U.S. Public*, pg. 1162
INVESCO ASSET MANAGEMENT (INDIA) PVT. LTD.—See Invesco Ltd.; *U.S. Public*, pg. 1162
INVESCO ASSET MANAGEMENT (SCHWEIZ) AG—See Invesco Ltd.; *U.S. Public*, pg. 1161
INVESCO CANADA LTD.—See Invesco Ltd.; *U.S. Public*, pg. 1162
INVESCO CAPITAL MARKETS, INC.—See Invesco Ltd.; *U.S. Public*, pg. 1162
INVESCO FAR EAST LIMITED—See Invesco Ltd.; *U.S. Public*, pg. 1162
INVESCO FUND MANAGERS LIMITED—See Invesco Ltd.; *U.S. Public*, pg. 1163
INVESCO GLOBAL ADVISORS, INC.—See Invesco Ltd.; *U.S. Public*, pg. 1163
INVESCO GLOBAL REAL ESTATE ASIA PACIFIC INC.M—See Invesco Ltd.; *U.S. Public*, pg. 1162
INVESCO INSTITUTIONAL (N.A.) INC.—See Invesco Ltd.; *U.S. Public*, pg. 1162
INVESCO INSTITUTIONAL—See Invesco Ltd.; *U.S. Public*, pg. 1162
INVESCO INVESTMENT ADVISERS LLC—See Invesco Ltd.; *U.S. Public*, pg. 1162
INVESCO INVESTMENT MANAGEMENT (SHANGHAI) LIMITED—See Invesco Ltd.; *U.S. Public*, pg. 1162
INVESCO IP HOLDINGS (CANADA) LTD.—See Invesco Ltd.; *U.S. Public*, pg. 1162
INVESCO MANAGED ACCOUNTS, LLC—See Invesco Ltd.; *U.S. Public*, pg. 1163
INVESCO NORTH AMERICA—See Invesco Ltd.; *U.S. Public*, pg. 1163
INVESCO (NY) INC.—See Invesco Ltd.; *U.S. Public*, pg. 1161
INVESCO PERPETUAL (NOMINEES) LIMITED—See Invesco Ltd.; *U.S. Public*, pg. 1163
INVESCO POWERSHARES CAPITAL MANAGEMENT LLC—See Invesco Ltd.; *U.S. Public*, pg. 1163
INVESCO REAL ESTATE ADVISORS (SHANGHAI) LIMITED—See Invesco Ltd.; *U.S. Public*, pg. 1163
INVESCO REAL ESTATE KOREA—See Invesco Ltd.; *U.S. Public*, pg. 1163
INVESCO SELECT TRUST PLC—See Invesco Ltd.; *U.S. Public*, pg. 1163
INVESCO TRIMARK LTD.—See Invesco Ltd.; *U.S. Public*, pg. 1163
INVESTACORP ADVISORY SERVICES INC.—See Reverence Capital Partners LLC; *U.S. Private*, pg. 3414
INVESTMENT COUNSELORS OF MARYLAND, LLC—See William Blair Investment Management LLC; *U.S. Private*, pg. 4522
INVESTMENT PARTNERS ASSET MANAGEMENT, INC.—See Investment Partners Group, Inc.; *U.S. Private*, pg. 2132
INVESTMENT SECURITY GROUP INC.—See HighTower Holding LLC; *U.S. Private*, pg. 1941
INVESTMENT TRUST COMPANY; *U.S. Private*, pg. 2132
INVESTOR FINANCIAL SOLUTIONS, LLC—See Lee Equity Partners LLC; *U.S. Private*, pg. 2412
INVESTORS CAPITAL CORPORATION—See RCAP Holdings, LLC; *U.S. Private*, pg. 3361
INVESTORS CAPITAL MANAGEMENT COMPANY—See Investors Title Company; *U.S. Public*, pg. 1165
INVESTORS MUTUAL LIMITED—See Groupe BPCE; *Int'l*, pg. 3098
INVESTOR SOLUTIONS INC.; *U.S. Private*, pg. 2132
INVITALIA PARTECIPAZIONI S.P.A.—See Agenzia Nazionale per l'Attrazione degli Investimenti e lo Sviluppo d'Impresa SpA; *Int'l*, pg. 206
INVUS FINANCIAL ADVISORS, LLC—See The Invus Group, LLC; *U.S. Private*, pg. 4057
IPM INFORMED PORTFOLIO MANAGEMENT AB—See Catella AB; *Int'l*, pg. 1359
IR DEUTSCHE HOLDING GMBH—See Ingersoll Rand Inc.; *U.S. Public*, pg. 1121
IRON PATH CAPITAL, L.P.; *U.S. Private*, pg. 2139
IRONWOOD CAPITAL MANAGEMENT LLC; *U.S. Private*, pg. 2140
ISG INFORMATION SERVICES GROUP AMERICAS, INC.—See Information Services Group, Inc.; *U.S. Public*, pg. 1118
ISLAMIC INVESTMENT COMPANY OF THE GULF (BAHAMAS) LIMITED—See Dar Al-Maal Al-Islami Trust; *Int'l*, pg. 1971
I SQUARED CAPITAL ADVISORS (US) LLC; *U.S. Private*, pg. 2020
ISS CORPORATE SERVICES, INC.—See Deutsche Borse AG; *Int'l*, pg. 2064
ITALFONDIARIO S.P.A.—See doBank SpA; *Int'l*, pg. 2152
ITA SERVICES PTY LTD.—See Microsoft Corporation; *U.S. Public*, pg. 1442
ITC INVESTMENT PARTNERS CORPORATION—See ASTMAX Trading, Inc.; *Int'l*, pg. 655
ITG PLATFORMS INC.—See Virtu Financial, Inc.; *U.S. Public*, pg. 2300
ITG SOLUTIONS NETWORK, INC.—See Virtu Financial, Inc.; *U.S. Public*, pg. 2300
IVORY CAPITAL GROUP, LLC—See Affiliated Managers Group, Inc.; *U.S. Public*, pg. 55
IVZ BAHAMAS PRIVATE LIMITED—See Invesco Ltd.; *U.S. Public*, pg. 1161
JACKSON FINANCIAL MANAGEMENT, INC.—See Genstar Capital, LLC; *U.S. Private*, pg. 1677
JACKSON FINANCIAL MANAGEMENT, INC.—See Keystone Group, L.P.; *U.S. Private*, pg. 2298
JACKSON NATIONAL ASSET MANAGEMENT LLC—See Jackson Financial Inc.; *U.S. Public*, pg. 1183
JACKSON SQUARE PARTNERS, LLC—See Affiliated Managers Group, Inc.; *U.S. Public*, pg. 55
JACMEL GROWTH PARTNERS MANAGEMENT LLC; *U.S. Private*, pg. 2179
JACOBS MATASIS (PTY) LTD.—See Jacobs Engineering Group, Inc.; *U.S. Public*, pg. 1185
JACSTEN HOLDINGS, LLC; *U.S. Private*, pg. 2180

523940 — PORTFOLIO MANAGEMEN...

JAPAN OFFICE ADVISORS, INC.—See Ichigo Asset Management, Ltd.; *Int'l*, pg. 3580
JCPE INVESTMENTS; *U.S. Private*, pg. 2195
JEFFERIES ENERGY GROUP—See Jefferies Financial Group Inc.; *U.S. Public*, pg. 1188
JEFFERIES HIGH YIELD HOLDINGS, LLC—See Jefferies Financial Group Inc.; *U.S. Public*, pg. 1188
JEFFERIES INVESTMENT ADVISERS, LLC—See Jefferies Financial Group Inc.; *U.S. Public*, pg. 1189
JELF GROUP PLC—See Marsh & McLennan Companies, Inc.; *U.S. Public*, pg. 1377
JEMSTEP, INC.—See Invesco Ltd.; *U.S. Public*, pg. 1163
JENNISON ASSOCIATES LLC—See Prudential Financial, Inc.; *U.S. Public*, pg. 1731
J.H. BAXTER & COMPANY; *U.S. Private*, pg. 2165
JKMILNE ASSET MANAGEMENT; *U.S. Private*, pg. 2211
JLL MACAU LIMITED—See Jones Lang LaSalle Incorporated; *U.S. Public*, pg. 1202
J.M. HARTWELL L.P.—See Keystone Group, L.P.; *U.S. Private*, pg. 2297
JMP ASSET MANAGEMENT LLC—See Citizens Financial Group, Inc.; *U.S. Public*, pg. 505
JOHN DEERE CREDIT OY—See Deere & Company; *U.S. Public*, pg. 646
JOHNSON & JOHNSON FINANCIAL SERVICES GMBH—See Johnson & Johnson; *U.S. Public*, pg. 1198
JOHNSON SCANNELL & ASSOCIATES; *U.S. Private*, pg. 2229
JOHN W. HENRY & COMPANY, INC.; *U.S. Private*, pg. 2225
JONES BARCLAY BOSTON—See Clayton, Dubilier & Rice, LLC; *U.S. Private*, pg. 923
JONES BARCLAY BOSTON—See Stone Point Capital LLC; *U.S. Private*, pg. 3824
JONES LANG LASALLE CORPORATE FINANCE LIMITED—See Jones Lang LaSalle Incorporated; *U.S. Public*, pg. 1203
JONES LANG LASALLE GLOBAL FINANCE LUXEMBOURG SARL—See Jones Lang LaSalle Incorporated; *U.S. Public*, pg. 1203
JONES LANG LASALLE HOTELS (NSW) PTY LIMITED—See Jones Lang LaSalle Incorporated; *U.S. Public*, pg. 1203
JONES LANG LASALLE LIMITED LIABILITY COMPANY—See Jones Lang LaSalle Incorporated; *U.S. Public*, pg. 1204
JONES LANG LASALLE LIMITED—See Jones Lang LaSalle Incorporated; *U.S. Public*, pg. 1204
JONES LANG LASALLE LTD.—See Jones Lang LaSalle Incorporated; *U.S. Public*, pg. 1204
JONES LANG LASALLE SARL—See Jones Lang LaSalle Incorporated; *U.S. Public*, pg. 1204
JONES LANG LASALLE SE—See Jones Lang LaSalle Incorporated; *U.S. Public*, pg. 1204
JORDAN CAPITAL AM, LLC—See The Jordan Company; *U.S. Private*, pg. 4059
JORDAN/ZALAZNICK ADVISERS, INC.; *U.S. Private*, pg. 2235
JOSEPH WONES (HOLDINGS) LIMITED—See Heidelberg Materials AG; *Int'l*, pg. 3317
JOTA-VERMOGENSVERWALTUNGSGESELLSCHAFT MBH—See Allianz SE; *Int'l*, pg. 353
JOVIAN ASSET MANAGEMENT INC.—See iA Financial Corporation Inc.; *Int'l*, pg. 3567
JPMORGAN ASSET MANAGEMENT (CANADA) INC.—See JPMorgan Chase & Co.; *U.S. Public*, pg. 1209
JPMORGAN ASSET MANAGEMENT (EUROPE) S.A.R.L—See JPMorgan Chase & Co.; *U.S. Public*, pg. 1209
J.P. MORGAN (CHINA) VENTURE CAPITAL INVESTMENT COMPANY LIMITED—See JPMorgan Chase & Co.; *U.S. Public*, pg. 1208
J.P. MORGAN RESEARCH TOTAL RETURN FUND LLC—See JPMorgan Chase & Co.; *U.S. Public*, pg. 1208
J-POWER HOLDINGS (THAILAND) CO., LTD.—See Electric Power Development Co., Ltd.; *Int'l*, pg. 2349
JSC UKRSIB ASSET MANAGEMENT—See BNP Paribas SA; *Int'l*, pg. 1093
JTH FINANCIAL, LLC—See B. Riley Financial, Inc.; *U.S. Public*, pg. 261
JTH FINANCIAL, LLC—See Irradiant Partners, LP; *U.S. Private*, pg. 2140
JVB FINANCIAL GROUP LLC—See Cohen & Company Inc.; *U.S. Public*, pg. 526
JZ ASSET MANAGEMENT UK LLP—See Jordan/Zalaznick Advisers, Inc.; *U.S. Private*, pg. 2235
JZ INTERNATIONAL LTD.—See Jordan/Zalaznick Advisers, Inc.; *U.S. Private*, pg. 2235
K2 ADVISORS LIMITED—See Franklin Resources, Inc.; *U.S. Public*, pg. 881
K2 ADVISORS L.L.C.—See Franklin Resources, Inc.; *U.S. Public*, pg. 881
KA FUND ADVISORS LLC—See Kayne Anderson Capital Advisors, L.P.; *U.S. Private*, pg. 2267
KAIROS PARTNERS SGR, S.P.A.—See ANIMA Holding S.p.A.; *Int'l*, pg. 471
KAISER HEALTH PLAN ASSET MANAGEMENT, INC.—See Kaiser Permanente; *U.S. Private*, pg. 2256
KAISER HOSPITAL ASSET MANAGEMENT, INC.—See Kaiser Permanente; *U.S. Private*, pg. 2256
KAKIVIK ASSET MANAGEMENT, LLC—See Bristol Bay Native Corporation; *U.S. Private*, pg. 656
KANCHANMANIK SECURITIES PRIVATE LIMITED—See Ajcon Global Services Ltd.; *Int'l*, pg. 255
KARIS CAPITAL PARTNERS, LLC—See Morgan Joseph TriArtisan Group LLC; *U.S. Private*, pg. 2784
KARR BARTH ASSOCIATES INC.; *U.S. Private*, pg. 2263
KASA COMPANIES INC.; *U.S. Private*, pg. 2263
KATARSIS CAPITAL ADVISORS SA—See Azimut Holding SpA; *Int'l*, pg. 779
KATONAH DEBT ADVISORS, L.L.C.—See LibreMax Capital, LLC; *U.S. Private*, pg. 2448
KAYNE ANDERSON BDC, INC.; *U.S. Private*, pg. 2267
KAYNE ANDERSON RUDNICK INVESTMENT MANAGEMENT, LLC—See Virtus Investment Partners, Inc.; *U.S. Public*, pg. 2301
KAZAKHSTAN CEMENT HOLDING B.V.—See Heidelberg Materials AG; *Int'l*, pg. 3317
KDI CAPITAL PARTNERS, LLC—See Investors Management Corporation; *U.S. Private*, pg. 2132
KEBA GESELLSCHAFT FUR INTERNE SERVICES MBH—See Deutsche Bank Aktiengesellschaft; *Int'l*, pg. 2061
KEELEY-TETON ADVISORS, LLC—See Teton Advisors, Inc.; *U.S. Public*, pg. 2021
KENMAR GLOBAL INVESTMENT MANAGEMENT LLC—See Ambroisie Capital Holding S.A.S.; *Int'l*, pg. 415
KENNEDY CAPITAL MANAGEMENT, INC.; *U.S. Private*, pg. 2284
KENNEDY & COE WEALTH MANAGEMENT, LLC—See KCoe Isom, LLP; *U.S. Private*, pg. 2270
KERKERING BARBERIO FINANCIAL SERVICES, INC.—See Kerkering, Barberio & Co.; *U.S. Private*, pg. 2290
KIEWIT ROYALTY TRUST—See Peter Kiewit Sons', Inc.; *U.S. Private*, pg. 3158
KINETIC VENTURES, L.L.C.—See ITC Holding Company, LLC; *U.S. Private*, pg. 2149
KINGFISHER CANADA HOLDINGS LLC—See Deutsche Bank Aktiengesellschaft; *Int'l*, pg. 2061
KISSINGER FINANCIAL—See Lee Equity Partners LLC; *U.S. Private*, pg. 2412
KIU KWONG INVESTMENT CO. LTD.—See Bank of China, Ltd.; *Int'l*, pg. 842
KIWOOM INVESTMENT CO., LTD.—See Daou Data Corp.; *Int'l*, pg. 1970
KKR ALTERNATIVE INVESTMENT MANAGEMENT—See KKR & Co. Inc.; *U.S. Public*, pg. 1255
KKR AUSTRALIA INVESTMENT MANAGEMENT PTY. LIMITED—See KKR & Co. Inc.; *U.S. Public*, pg. 1256
KKR AUSTRALIA PTY LIMITED—See KKR & Co. Inc.; *U.S. Public*, pg. 1255
KKR CANADA ULC—See KKR & Co. Inc.; *U.S. Public*, pg. 1256
KKR CAPITAL MARKETS INDIA PRIVATE LIMITED—See KKR & Co. Inc.; *U.S. Public*, pg. 1256
KKR CAPITAL MARKETS JAPAN LIMITED—See KKR & Co. Inc.; *U.S. Public*, pg. 1256
KKR CREDIT ADVISORS (IRELAND)—See KKR & Co. Inc.; *U.S. Public*, pg. 1256
KKR CREDIT ADVISORS (US) LLC—See KKR & Co. Inc.; *U.S. Public*, pg. 1256
KKR CREDIT ADVISORY (UK) LLP—See KKR & Co. Inc.; *U.S. Public*, pg. 1256
KKR INDIA ADVISORS PRIVATE LIMITED—See KKR & Co. Inc.; *U.S. Public*, pg. 1256
KKR JAPAN LIMITED—See KKR & Co. Inc.; *U.S. Public*, pg. 1256
KLEIN FINANCIAL ADVISORS INC.—See EP Wealth Advisors, LLC; *U.S. Private*, pg. 1411
KLOCKNER INDUSTRIEBETEILIGUNGSGESELLSCHAFT MBH—See Deutsche Bank Aktiengesellschaft; *Int'l*, pg. 2061
KLS PROFESSIONAL ADVISORS GROUP, LLC—See Boston Private Financial Holdings, Inc.; *U.S. Public*, pg. 372
KNOLL OVERSEAS, INC.—See MillerKnoll, Inc.; *U.S. Public*, pg. 1447
KOCH MINERALS S.A.—See Koch Industries, Inc.; *U.S. Private*, pg. 2333
KOHLBERG KRAVIS ROBERTS (ESPANA) ASESORES SL—See KKR & Co. Inc.; *U.S. Public*, pg. 1257
KOVITZ INVESTMENT GROUP, LLC—See Clayton, Dubilier & Rice, LLC; *U.S. Private*, pg. 923
KOVITZ INVESTMENT GROUP, LLC—See Stone Point Capital LLC; *U.S. Private*, pg. 3824
KR CAPITAL ADVISORS INC.; *U.S. Private*, pg. 2348
K-TRON INVESTMENT CO.—See Hillenbrand, Inc.; *U.S. Public*, pg. 1037
KUSSKE FINANCIAL ASSET MANAGEMENT, INC.—See Arthur J. Gallagher & Co.; *U.S. Public*, pg. 206
KVB KUNLUN NEW ZEALAND LIMITED—See CITIC Securities Co., Ltd.; *Int'l*, pg. 1622
KVB KUNLUN PTY LIMITED—See CITIC Securities Co., Ltd.; *Int'l*, pg. 1622
KW INVESTMENT MANAGEMENT LTD.—See Kennedy Wilson Holdings, Inc.; *U.S. Public*, pg. 1223
KYNEX INC—See Genstar Capital, LLC; *U.S. Private*, pg. 1678
LADDER CAPITAL ADVISER LLC—See Ladder Capital Corp.; *U.S. Public*, pg. 1288
LAIKI FINANCIAL SERVICES LTD—See Bank of Cyprus Holdings Public Limited Company; *Int'l*, pg. 842
LAIRD NORTON TYEE—See Laird Norton Company, LLC; *U.S. Private*, pg. 2374
LAKE CAPITAL MANAGEMENT LLC; *U.S. Private*, pg. 2374
LAKE COUNTRY CAPITAL LLC; *U.S. Private*, pg. 2374
LAKEVIEW HOTEL INVESTMENT CORP.—See First Canadian Management Corporation; *Int'l*, pg. 2682
LAND & BUILDINGS INVESTMENT MANAGEMENT, LLC; *U.S. Private*, pg. 2382
LANDMARK FAS LTD.—See Daily Mail & General Trust plc; *Int'l*, pg. 1938
LANDMARK GROWTH CAPITAL PARTNERS, LP; *U.S. Private*, pg. 2385
LANDPARK ADVISORS, LLC; *U.S. Private*, pg. 2386
LANDSBERG BENNETT PRIVATE WEALTH MANAGEMENT; *U.S. Private*, pg. 2387
LARSON FINANCIAL GROUP, LLC—See Larson Financial Holdings, LLC; *U.S. Private*, pg. 2394
LARSON FINANCIAL SERVICES, INC.; *U.S. Private*, pg. 2394
LARSON WEALTH PARTNERS, LLC—See Larson Financial Holdings, LLC; *U.S. Private*, pg. 2394
LASALLE GMBH—See Jones Lang LaSalle Incorporated; *U.S. Public*, pg. 1205
LASALLE INVESTMENT (LUXEMBOURG) SARL—See Jones Lang LaSalle Incorporated; *U.S. Public*, pg. 1204
LASALLE INVESTMENT MANAGEMENT ASIA PTE LTD—See Jones Lang LaSalle Incorporated; *U.S. Public*, pg. 1203
LASALLE INVESTMENT MANAGEMENT BV—See Jones Lang LaSalle Incorporated; *U.S. Public*, pg. 1203
LASALLE INVESTMENT MANAGEMENT ESPANA, S.L.U.—See Jones Lang LaSalle Incorporated; *U.S. Public*, pg. 1203
LAU ASSOCIATES LLC—See Bryn Mawr Bank Corporation; *U.S. Public*, pg. 408
LAUREL HILL CAPITAL PARTNERS LLC; *U.S. Private*, pg. 2398
LAUREL WEALTH ADVISORS, INC.—See Integrated Wealth Concepts, LLC; *U.S. Private*, pg. 2101
LAURUS CAPITAL MANAGEMENT, LLC; *U.S. Private*, pg. 2400
LAVISTA LICENSEE SOLUTIONS PTY LIMITED—See ClearView Wealth Limited; *Int'l*, pg. 1657
LAZARD GLOBAL TOTAL RETURN & INCOME FUND, INC.; *U.S. Public*, pg. 2402
LCD (VIETNAM) PTE LTD—See Aspial Corporation Limited; *Int'l*, pg. 630
LCD (VIETNAM) PTE LTD—See Fragrance Group Limited; *Int'l*, pg. 2758
LECA (GREAT BRITAIN) LIMITED—See Heidelberg Materials AG; *Int'l*, pg. 3318
LEERINK PARTNERS LLC—See Bain Capital, LP; *U.S. Private*, pg. 432
LEGACY FINANCIAL PLANNING LLC—See TA Associates, Inc.; *U.S. Private*, pg. 3919
LEGEND ADVISORY LLC—See Lincoln Investment Planning Inc.; *U.S. Private*, pg. 2458
LEGEND FINANCIAL ADVISORS, INC; *U.S. Private*, pg. 2418
THE LEGEND GROUP—See Lincoln Investment Planning Inc.; *U.S. Private*, pg. 2458
LEGG MASON ASSET MANAGEMENT (SINGAPORE) PTE LTD.—See Franklin Resources, Inc.; *U.S. Public*, pg. 882
LEGG MASON INVESTMENTS (LUXEMBOURG) S.A.—See Franklin Resources, Inc.; *U.S. Public*, pg. 882
LEGG MASON INVESTOR SERVICES, LLC—See Franklin Resources, Inc.; *U.S. Public*, pg. 882
LEGOSYS SOLUTIONS, LLC—See Central Iowa Power Cooperative; *U.S. Private*, pg. 822
LEHIGH NORTHWEST MARINE, LLC—See Heidelberg Materials AG; *Int'l*, pg. 3318
LEISURE CAPITAL CORPORATION—See Hilton Grand Vacations Inc.; *U.S. Public*, pg. 1040
LENOX WEALTH MANAGEMENT, INC.—See Creative Planning, LLC; *U.S. Private*, pg. 1090
LEONARDO & CO. S.P.A.—See Houlihan Lokey, Inc.; *U.S. Public*, pg. 1055
LEONETTI & ASSOCIATES, LLC—See Lee Equity Partners LLC; *U.S. Private*, pg. 2412
LEON FRAZER & ASSOCIATES INC.—See iA Financial Corporation Inc.; *Int'l*, pg. 3567
LEUCADIA ASSET MANAGEMENT LLC—See Jefferies Financial Group Inc.; *U.S. Public*, pg. 1189
LEVERAGED EQUITIES LIMITED—See Bendigo & Adelaide Bank Ltd.; *Int'l*, pg. 970
LEXINGTON PARTNERS INC.—See Franklin Resources, Inc.; *U.S. Public*, pg. 883
LEXINGTON WEALTH MANAGEMENT; *U.S. Private*, pg. 2440
LGT FUND MANAGERS (IRELAND) LTD.—See Castle Private Equity AG; *Int'l*, pg. 1357

N.A.I.C.S. INDEX

523940 — PORTFOLIO MANAGEMEN...

LIBERTY 77 CAPITAL, L.P.; *U.S. Private*, pg. 2443
LIBERTY TAX SERVICE INC.—See B. Riley Financial, Inc.; *U.S. Public*, pg. 261
LIBERTY TAX SERVICE INC.—See Irradiant Partners, LP; *U.S. Private*, pg. 2140
LIFE PARTNERS IRA HOLDER PARTNERSHIP, LLC; *U.S. Private*, pg. 2449
LIFE PARTNERS POSITION HOLDER TRUST; *U.S. Private*, pg. 2449
LIGHTHOUSE FINANCE LLC—See Greenbacker Renewable Energy Company LLC; *U.S. Private*, pg. 1774
LIGHTSTONE VALUE PLUS REIT LLC—See The Lightstone Group, LLC; *U.S. Private*, pg. 4070
LILIUM GROUP LLC; *U.S. Private*, pg. 2455
LILLY VENTURES FUND I LLC—See Eli Lilly & Company; *U.S. Public*, pg. 733
LIME ROCK NEW ENERGY GP LP—See Lime Rock Partners, LLC; *U.S. Private*, pg. 2456
LINCOLN FINANCIAL DISTRIBUTORS, INC.—See Lincoln National Corporation; *U.S. Public*, pg. 1319
LINCOLN VARIABLE INSURANCE PRODUCTS TRUST—See Lincoln National Corporation; *U.S. Public*, pg. 1319
LINDUSTRIES LIMITED—See Heidelberg Materials AG; *Int'l*, pg. 3318
LIONGATE CAPITAL MANAGEMENT INC.—See Principal Financial Group, Inc.; *U.S. Public*, pg. 1720
LIONGATE CAPITAL MANAGEMENT LLP—See Principal Financial Group, Inc.; *U.S. Public*, pg. 1720
LIONSTONE PARTNERS, LLC—See Ameriprise Financial, Inc.; *U.S. Public*, pg. 114
LION STREET INC.—See Integrity Marketing Group LLC; *U.S. Private*, pg. 2103
LITTELFUSE GMBH—See Littelfuse, Inc.; *U.S. Public*, pg. 1327
LIVE OAK PRIVATE WEALTH, LLC—See Live Oak Bancshares, Inc.; *U.S. Public*, pg. 1331
LLOYD GEORGE MANAGEMENT (EUROPE) LIMITED—See Bank of Montreal; *Int'l*, pg. 847
LLOYD GEORGE MANAGEMENT (SINGAPORE) PTE LTD.—See Bank of Montreal; *Int'l*, pg. 847
LMP CAPITAL & INCOME FUND, INC.; *U.S. Public*, pg. 1337
LODESTAR INVESTMENT COUNSEL, LLC—See Canadian Imperial Bank of Commerce; *Int'l*, pg. 1283
LOFRA VERWALTUNGS-GESELLSCHAFT MBH—See Commerzbank AG; *Int'l*, pg. 1718
LONE STAR FUNDS; *U.S. Private*, pg. 2484
LONETREE CAPITAL LLC; *U.S. Private*, pg. 2490
LONG RIDGE EQUITY PARTNERS, LLC; *U.S. Private*, pg. 2492
LONGSHORE CAPITAL PARTNERS; *U.S. Private*, pg. 2493
LORD ABBETT & CO.; *U.S. Private*, pg. 2495
LORD GERMANY GMBH—See Parker Hannifin Corporation; *U.S. Public*, pg. 1641
LORIENT CAPITAL MANAGEMENT LLC; *U.S. Private*, pg. 2495
LOUISBOURG INVESTMENTS INC.—See Assumption Mutual Life Insurance Company; *Int'l*, pg. 649
LOURD CAPITAL LLC; *U.S. Private*, pg. 2500
LOVELESS WEALTH MANAGEMENT LLC—See Dakota Wealth Management LLC; *U.S. Private*, pg. 1148
LOVETT MILLER & CO.; *U.S. Private*, pg. 2504
LOYAL FINANCE AG—See Banque Cantonale de Geneve S.A.; *Int'l*, pg. 852
LP FIRST CAPITAL; *U.S. Private*, pg. 2507
LRG INVESTOR LLC—See KKR & Co. Inc.; *U.S. Public*, pg. 1259
LSCG MANAGEMENT, INC.; *U.S. Private*, pg. 2508
LS POWER EQUITY ADVISORS, LLC—See LS Power Development, LLC; *U.S. Private*, pg. 2508
L SQUARED CAPITAL MANAGEMENT LP; *U.S. Private*, pg. 2361
LTI PORTFOLIO MANAGEMENT CORP.—See Leasing Technologies International Inc.; *U.S. Private*, pg. 2409
LUTHER BURBANK CORPORATION—See WaFd, Inc.; *U.S. Public*, pg. 2321
LUTHER KING CAPITAL MANAGEMENT CORPORATION; *U.S. Private*, pg. 2517
MACHINERY FINANCE RESOURCES, LLC—See Morris Group, Inc.; *U.S. Private*, pg. 2787
MACKAY SHIELDS LLC—See New York Life Insurance Company; *U.S. Private*, pg. 2911
MADISON FINANCIAL ADVISORS, LTD.—See Keystone Group, L.P.; *U.S. Private*, pg. 2297
MADISON INVESTMENT ADVISORS, INC.; *U.S. Private*, pg. 2544
MADISON LIQUIDITY INVESTORS LLC; *U.S. Private*, pg. 2544
MAINSTREET INVESTMENT ADVISORS, LLC—See Fifth Third Bancorp; *U.S. Public*, pg. 834
MANITOU FINANCE LTD.—See BNP Paribas SA; *Int'l*, pg. 1091
MANNING & NAPIER ADVISORS, LLC—See Callodine Acquisition Corporation; *U.S. Public*, pg. 424
MARCH PATRIMONIOS S.A.—See Alba Grupo March; *Int'l*, pg. 292

MARGARET INC.—See BNP Paribas SA; *Int'l*, pg. 1088
MARIGNAN GESTION S.A.—See Cerberus Capital Management, L.P.; *U.S. Private*, pg. 839
MARINER INVESTMENT GROUP LLC; *U.S. Private*, pg. 2575
MARKEL CATCO INVESTMENT MANAGEMENT LTD.—See Markel Group Inc.; *U.S. Public*, pg. 1368
MARKETAXESS NL B.V.—See MarketAxess Holdings Inc.; *U.S. Public*, pg. 1369
MARPLES RIDGWAY LIMITED—See Heidelberg Materials AG; *Int'l*, pg. 3318
MARQUETTE ASSET MANAGEMENT, LLC—See UMB Financial Corporation; *U.S. Public*, pg. 2224
MARQUIS ASSOCIATES, INC.; *U.S. Private*, pg. 2586
MARQUIS HEALTH SERVICES—See Tryko Partners, LLC; *U.S. Private*, pg. 4252
MARQUIS WEALTH MANAGEMENT GROUP; *U.S. Private*, pg. 2587
MARRET ASSET MANAGEMENT INC.—See CI Financial Corporation; *Int'l*, pg. 1601
MARSHALL STREET CAPITAL, INC.; *U.S. Private*, pg. 2593
MARTHA'S VINEYARD FINANCIAL GROUP—See Martha's Vineyard Savings Bank; *U.S. Private*, pg. 2594
MARTIN & COMPANY, INC.—See First Horizon Corporation; *U.S. Public*, pg. 845
MARTIN CURRIE, INC.—See Franklin Resources, Inc.; *U.S. Public*, pg. 882
MARTIN CURRIE INVESTMENT MANAGEMENT LIMITED—See Franklin Resources, Inc.; *U.S. Public*, pg. 882
MASCHINO HUDELSON & ASSOCIATES LLC—See Aon plc; *Int'l*, pg. 496
MATRA HOLDING GMBH—See Airbus SE; *Int'l*, pg. 242
MATRIX PLANNING SOLUTIONS LIMITED—See ClearView Wealth Limited; *Int'l*, pg. 1657
MATTHEWS INTERNATIONAL CAPITAL MANAGEMENT, LLC; *U.S. Private*, pg. 2613
MATTRESS HOLDINGS INTERNATIONAL B.V.—See Tempur Sealy International, Inc.; *U.S. Public*, pg. 1999
MBIA—See MBIA Inc.; *U.S. Public*, pg. 1403
MBM ADVISORS, INC.—See BOK Financial Corporation; *U.S. Public*, pg. 367
MCCARTHY CAPITAL CORPORATION—See McCarthy Group, LLC; *U.S. Private*, pg. 2627
MCCARTHY GROUP, LLC; *U.S. Private*, pg. 2626
MCCOMBS PARTNERS—See McCombs Enterprises; *U.S. Private*, pg. 2629
MCDANIEL KNUTSON FINANICIAL, INC.—See Lightyear Capital LLC; *U.S. Private*, pg. 2454
MCKINLEY CAPITAL MANAGEMENT; *U.S. Private*, pg. 2638
MCLEAN & PARTNERS WEALTH MANAGEMENT LTD.—See Canadian Western Bank; *Int'l*, pg. 1287
MCM ADVISERS, LP—See Mackenzie Capital Management, LP; *U.S. Private*, pg. 2537
MDH INVESTMENT MANAGEMENT, INC.—See Farmers National Banc Corp.; *U.S. Public*, pg. 822
M.D. SASS ASSOCIATES, INC.—See M.D. Sass Holdings, Inc.; *U.S. Private*, pg. 2528
M.D. SASS INVESTORS SERVICES, INC.—See M.D. Sass Holdings, Inc.; *U.S. Private*, pg. 2528
MEDIOCREDITO EUROPEO SPA—See Argiletum Merchant S.p.A.; *Int'l*, pg. 561
MEDIOLANUM ASSET MANAGEMENT LTD—See Banca Mediolanum S.p.A.; *Int'l*, pg. 815
MEKETA INVESTMENT GROUP, INC.; *U.S. Private*, pg. 2661
MELLON INVESTMENTS CORPORATION—See The Bank of New York Mellon Corporation; *U.S. Public*, pg. 2037
MENAFACTORS LIMITED—See FIMBank p.l.c.; *Int'l*, pg. 2664
MERCER ADVISORS INC.—See Genstar Capital, LLC; *U.S. Private*, pg. 1677
MERCER ADVISORS INC.—See Keystone Group, L.P.; *U.S. Private*, pg. 2298
MERCER FINANCIAL ADVICE (AUSTRALIA) PTY LTD—See Marsh & McLennan Companies, Inc.; *U.S. Public*, pg. 1385
MERCER GLOBAL ADVISORS INC.—See Genstar Capital, LLC; *U.S. Private*, pg. 1677
MERCER GLOBAL ADVISORS INC.—See Keystone Group, L.P.; *U.S. Private*, pg. 2298
MERCER INVESTMENT CONSULTING, INC.—See Marsh & McLennan Companies, Inc.; *U.S. Public*, pg. 1385
MERCER INVESTMENT MANAGEMENT, INC.—See Marsh & McLennan Companies, Inc.; *U.S. Public*, pg. 1385
MERCER INVESTMENTS (KOREA) CO., LTD.—See Marsh & McLennan Companies, Inc.; *U.S. Public*, pg. 1386
MERCER LESTISHARAT ALAMAL LP—See Marsh & McLennan Companies, Inc.; *U.S. Public*, pg. 1386
MERCER SUPERANNUATION (AUSTRALIA) LIMITED—See Marsh & McLennan Companies, Inc.; *U.S. Public*, pg. 1386
MERCHANT CAPITAL SOLUTIONS LLC—See KKR & Co. Inc.; *U.S. Public*, pg. 1261
MERCK LUMIRA BIOSCIENCES FUND L.P.—See Merck & Co., Inc.; *U.S. Public*, pg. 1419

MERGANSER CAPITAL MANAGEMENT, INC.—See Annaly Capital Management, Inc.; *U.S. Public*, pg. 138
MERIDIAN WEALTH PARTNERS, LLC—See Meridian Corporation; *U.S. Public*, pg. 1424
MERIT CAPITAL ADVANCE, LLC—See Island Capital Group LLC; *U.S. Private*, pg. 2144
MERIT FINANCIAL GROUP, LLC; *U.S. Private*, pg. 2674
MERRILL LYNCH, KINGDOM OF SAUDI ARABIA COMPANY—See Bank of America Corporation; *U.S. Public*, pg. 272
MESAR BERATUNG—See BVE Holding SE; *Int'l*, pg. 1231
MESIROW FINANCIAL COMMODITIES MANAGEMENT, LLC—See Mesirow Financial Holdings, Inc.; *U.S. Private*, pg. 2678
MESIROW FINANCIAL HONG KONG, LIMITED—See Mesirow Financial Holdings, Inc.; *U.S. Private*, pg. 2678
MESIROW FINANCIAL, INC. - FORT LAUDERDALE—See Mesirow Financial Holdings, Inc.; *U.S. Private*, pg. 2678
MESIROW FINANCIAL PRIVATE EQUITY ADVISORS, INC.—See Mesirow Financial Holdings, Inc.; *U.S. Private*, pg. 2678
MESIROW FINANCIAL PRIVATE EQUITY, INC.—See Mesirow Financial Holdings, Inc.; *U.S. Private*, pg. 2678
MESIROW FINANCIAL SERVICES, INC.—See Mesirow Financial Holdings, Inc.; *U.S. Private*, pg. 2678
MESTERGRUPPEN AS—See Ferd AS; *Int'l*, pg. 2636
METALMARK MANAGEMENT LLC—See Metalmark Capital Holdings LLC; *U.S. Private*, pg. 2681
METLIFE INVESTMENT MANAGEMENT, LLC—See MetLife, Inc.; *U.S. Public*, pg. 1430
METTLER-TOLEDO INTERNATIONAL FINANCE, INC.—See Mettler-Toledo International, Inc.; *U.S. Public*, pg. 1432
MEZZANINE CORPORATION—See Houlihan Lokey, Inc.; *U.S. Public*, pg. 1055
MFS SERVICE CENTER INC.—See Guggenheim Partners, LLC; *U.S. Private*, pg. 1812
MG CAPITAL GMBH—See GEA Group Aktiengesellschaft; *Int'l*, pg. 2904
M. GRIFFITH INVESTMENT SERVICES, INC.—See Baird Financial Group, Inc.; *U.S. Private*, pg. 454
MGT OF AMERICA CONSULTING LLC—See The Vistria Group, LP; *U.S. Private*, pg. 4132
MICHAEL G. RUDELSON AND COMPANY—See Aon plc; *Int'l*, pg. 496
MIDAS MANAGEMENT CORPORATION—See Winmill & Co., Incorporated; *U.S. Public*, pg. 2374
MID ATLANTIC CAPITAL CORPORATION—See Mid Atlantic Capital Group, Inc.; *U.S. Private*, pg. 2705
MID ATLANTIC STATES INVESTMENT COMPANY—See Old Republic International Corporation; *U.S. Public*, pg. 1568
MIDDLEGROUND MANAGEMENT, LP; *U.S. Private*, pg. 2711
MIDLAND FINANCIAL ADVISORS, INC.—See Midland States Bancorp, Inc.; *U.S. Public*, pg. 1445
MIDLAND TRUST COMPANY—See Midland States Bancorp, Inc.; *U.S. Public*, pg. 1445
MIDLAND WEALTH ADVISORS LLP—See Midland States Bancorp, Inc.; *U.S. Public*, pg. 1445
MIG II REALTY ADVISORS INC.—See Brookfield Corporation; *Int'l*, pg. 1175
MILES CAPITAL, INC.—See PMA Financial Network, LLC; *U.S. Private*, pg. 3217
MILLBURN MULTI-MARKETS FUND L.P.—See Millburn Ridgefield Corporation; *U.S. Private*, pg. 2731
MILLENNIUM MANAGEMENT LLC; *U.S. Private*, pg. 2732
MILLENNIUM TRUST COMPANY, LLC—See ABRY Partners, LLC; *U.S. Private*, pg. 42
MILLER-GREEN FINANCIAL SERVICES, INC.—See Lee Equity Partners LLC; *U.S. Private*, pg. 2412
MILLER INVESTMENT MANAGEMENT, LLC; *U.S. Private*, pg. 2734
MILLER/RUSSELL & ASSOCIATES LLC; *U.S. Private*, pg. 2736
MILLS MUSIC TRUST; *U.S. Public*, pg. 1448
MILTON STREET CAPITAL, LLC; *U.S. Private*, pg. 2739
MIRACLE MILE ADVISORS, LLC; *U.S. Private*, pg. 2745
MIRA GMBH & CO. KG—See Deutsche Bank Aktiengesellschaft; *Int'l*, pg. 2061
MIROVA US LLC—See Groupe BPCE; *Int'l*, pg. 3098
MISSION CAPITAL ADVISORS, LLC—See Marcus & Millichap, Inc.; *U.S. Public*, pg. 1365
MITCHELL & MORONESO INSURANCE SERVICES INC.—See Aon plc; *Int'l*, pg. 496
MITEL NETWORKS HOLDINGS LIMITED—See Searchlight Capital Partners, L.P.; *U.S. Private*, pg. 3589
M.J. SMITH & ASSOCIATES, INC.—See Genstar Capital, LLC; *U.S. Private*, pg. 1677
M.J. SMITH & ASSOCIATES, INC.—See Keystone Group, L.P.; *U.S. Private*, pg. 2298
MKM PARTNERS, LLC—See Roth Capital Partners LLC; *U.S. Private*, pg. 3487
MMA SECURITIES LLC—See Marsh & McLennan Companies, Inc.; *U.S. Public*, pg. 1377
MMC SECURITIES CORP.—See Marsh & McLennan Companies, Inc.; *U.S. Public*, pg. 1377
MOBILE MINI UK HOLDINGS LIMITED—See WillScot Mo-

bile Mini Holdings Corp.; *U.S. Public*, pg. 2372
MODALTON LIMITED—See Hang Lung Group Limited; *Int'l*, pg. 3245
MODERA WEALTH MANAGEMENT, LLC; *U.S. Private*, pg. 2759
MODERN WEALTH MANAGEMENT, LLC—See Crestview Partners, L.P.; *U.S. Private*, pg. 1098
MODUS SELECTIVE INVESTMENT MANAGEMENT & ADVICE LTD.—See FIBI Holdings Ltd.; *Int'l*, pg. 2652
MOELIS & COMPANY ASIA LIMITED—See Moelis & Company; *U.S. Public*, pg. 1456
MOELIS & COMPANY CONSULTING (BEIJING) COMPANY LIMITED—See Moelis & Company; *U.S. Public*, pg. 1456
MOELIS & COMPANY EUROPE LIMITED—See Moelis & Company; *U.S. Public*, pg. 1456
MOELIS & COMPANY FRANCE SAS—See Moelis & Company; *U.S. Public*, pg. 1456
MOELIS & COMPANY INDIA PRIVATE LIMITED—See Moelis & Company; *U.S. Public*, pg. 1456
MOELIS & COMPANY LLC—See Moelis Asset Management LP; *U.S. Private*, pg. 2764
MOELIS & COMPANY UK LLP—See Moelis & Company; *U.S. Public*, pg. 1456
MOELIS & COMPANY UK LLP—See Moelis & Company; *U.S. Public*, pg. 1456
MOELIS & COMPANY UK LLP—See Moelis & Company; *U.S. Public*, pg. 1456
MOELIS & COMPANY UK LLP—See Moelis & Company; *U.S. Public*, pg. 1456
MOELIS & COMPANY UK LLP—See Moelis Asset Management LP; *U.S. Private*, pg. 2764
MOELIS UK LLP—See Moelis & Company; *U.S. Public*, pg. 1456
MONETA GROUP, LLC.; *U.S. Private*, pg. 2769
MONEYAM LIMITED—See AJ Bell Plc.; *Int'l*, pg. 255
MONEY SERVICES INC.—See Aegon N.V.; *Int'l*, pg. 174
MONROE CAPITAL INCOME PLUS CORPORATION; *U.S. Private*, pg. 2772
MONROE STREET PARTNERS LLC; *U.S. Private*, pg. 2773
MOODY'S INVESTORS SERVICE INDIA PRIVATE LIMITED—See Moody's Corporation; *U.S. Public*, pg. 1468
MOODY'S INVESTORS SERVICE MIDDLE EAST LIMITED—See Moody's Corporation; *U.S. Public*, pg. 1468
MOODY'S INVESTORS SERVICE PTY LIMITED—See Moody's Corporation; *U.S. Public*, pg. 1468
MOODY'S LATIN AMERICA AGENTE DE CALIFICACION DE RIESGO SA—See Moody's Corporation; *U.S. Public*, pg. 1469
MOORELAND PARTNERS LLC—See Stifel Financial Corp.; *U.S. Public*, pg. 1950
MOREHEAD CAPITAL MANAGEMENT LLC—See Investors Management Corporation; *U.S. Private*, pg. 2132
MORGAN STANLEY AIP GP LP—See Morgan Stanley; *U.S. Public*, pg. 1472
MORGAN STANLEY CANADA LTD.—See Morgan Stanley; *U.S. Public*, pg. 1473
MORGAN STANLEY & CO. COMMODITIES—See Morgan Stanley; *U.S. Public*, pg. 1472
MORGAN STANLEY ELZ GMBH—See Morgan Stanley; *U.S. Public*, pg. 1472
MORGAN STANLEY INVESTMENT MANAGEMENT, INC. - PHILADELPHIA—See Morgan Stanley; *U.S. Public*, pg. 1474
MORGAN STANLEY INVESTMENT MANAGEMENT, INC. - SAN FRANCISCO—See Morgan Stanley; *U.S. Public*, pg. 1475
MORGAN STANLEY INVESTMENT MANAGEMENT, INC.—See Morgan Stanley; *U.S. Public*, pg. 1474
MORGAN STANLEY INVESTMENT MANAGEMENT (JAPAN) CO., LTD.—See Morgan Stanley; *U.S. Public*, pg. 1473
MORGAN STANLEY INVESTMENT MANAGEMENT LIMITED—See Morgan Stanley; *U.S. Public*, pg. 1474
MORGAN STANLEY SMITH BARNEY LLC—See Citigroup Inc.; *U.S. Public*, pg. 503
MORGAN STANLEY SMITH BARNEY LLC—See Morgan Stanley; *U.S. Public*, pg. 1475
MORGENTHALER MANAGEMENT CORPORATION; *U.S. Private*, pg. 2785
MORLEY FINANCIAL SERVICES—See Principal Financial Group, Inc.; *U.S. Public*, pg. 1720
MORNINGSTAR ASSOCIATES KOREA CO., LTD.—See Morningstar, Inc.; *U.S. Public*, pg. 1476
MORNINGSTAR CANADA GROUP, INC.—See Morningstar, Inc.; *U.S. Public*, pg. 1476
MORNINGSTAR DANMARK A/S—See Morningstar, Inc.; *U.S. Public*, pg. 1476
MORNINGSTAR DEUTSCHLAND GMBH—See Morningstar, Inc.; *U.S. Public*, pg. 1476
MORNINGSTAR EUROPE, B.V.—See Morningstar, Inc.; *U.S. Public*, pg. 1476
MORNINGSTAR FRANCE FUND INFORMATION SARL—See Morningstar, Inc.; *U.S. Public*, pg. 1476
MORNINGSTAR GROUP AUSTRALIA PTY LIMITED—See Morningstar, Inc.; *U.S. Public*, pg. 1476
MORNINGSTAR, INC.; *U.S. Public*, pg. 1476

MORNINGSTAR INVESTMENT MANAGEMENT EUROPE LIMITED—See Morningstar, Inc.; *U.S. Public*, pg. 1476
MORNINGSTAR INVESTMENT MANAGEMENT SOUTH AFRICA (PTY) LIMITED—See Morningstar, Inc.; *U.S. Public*, pg. 1476
MORNINGSTAR ITALY, S.R.L.—See Morningstar, Inc.; *U.S. Public*, pg. 1476
MORNINGSTAR RESEARCH LIMITED—See Morningstar, Inc.; *U.S. Public*, pg. 1476
MORNINGSTAR RESEARCH THAILAND LIMITED—See Morningstar, Inc.; *U.S. Public*, pg. 1476
MORNINGSTAR SWEDEN AB—See Morningstar, Inc.; *U.S. Public*, pg. 1476
MORNINGSTAR SWITZERLAND GMBH—See Morningstar, Inc.; *U.S. Public*, pg. 1476
MORRIS CAPITAL MANAGEMENT, LLC; *U.S. Private*, pg. 2786
MORRIS (S.P.) HOLDINGS LIMITED—See Commerzbank AG; *Int'l*, pg. 1719
THE MORTGAGE PARTNERSHIP OF AMERICA, L.L.C.—See Altisource Portfolio Solutions S.A.; *Int'l*, pg. 393
MORTON CAPITAL MANAGEMENT—See U.S. Bancorp; *U.S. Public*, pg. 2212
MOSAIC CAPITAL PARTNERS; *U.S. Private*, pg. 2792
MOSAIC ESTERHAZY HOLDINGS ULC—See The Mosaic Company; *U.S. Public*, pg. 2116
MOSS ADAMS WEALTH ADVISORS LLC—See Moss Adams LLP; *U.S. Private*, pg. 2794
MPP BETEILIGUNGSGESELLSCHAFT MBH—See Deutsche Bank Aktiengesellschaft; *Int'l*, pg. 2061
MSCI BARRA SA—See MSCI Inc.; *U.S. Public*, pg. 1483
MSCI S. DE R.L. DE C.V.—See MSCI Inc.; *U.S. Public*, pg. 1483
MSCP III, LLC—See Morgan Stanley; *U.S. Public*, pg. 1472
MSD PARTNERS, L.P.—See MSD Capital, L.P.; *U.S. Private*, pg. 2806
MSOUTH EQUITY PARTNERS, LLC; *U.S. Private*, pg. 2808
MTS HEALTH PARTNERS, L.P.; *U.S. Private*, pg. 2809
MUAMALAT INVEST SDN. BHD.—See DRB-HICOM Berhad; *Int'l*, pg. 2202
MUDRICK CAPITAL MANAGEMENT L.P.; *U.S. Private*, pg. 2810
MUELLER MIDDLE EAST B.S.C.—See Mueller Industries, Inc.; *U.S. Public*, pg. 1485
MUELLER SERVICE CO., LLC—See Mueller Water Products, Inc.; *U.S. Public*, pg. 1486
MUKAFAT PORTFOY YONETIMI A.S.—See Aktif Yatirim Bankasi A.S.; *Int'l*, pg. 267
MULTILATERAL INVESTMENT GUARANTEE AGENCY—See The World Bank Group; *U.S. Private*, pg. 4139
MUNDER CAPITAL MANAGEMENT INC.—See Crestview Partners, L.P.; *U.S. Private*, pg. 1098
MURPHY CAPITAL MANAGEMENT INC.—See Peapack-Gladstone Financial Corporation; *U.S. Public*, pg. 1659
MUTUAL FEDERAL HOUSING COMPANY—See Northwest Bancshares, Inc.; *U.S. Public*, pg. 1541
MUTUAL OF AMERICA CAPITAL MANAGEMENT CORPORATION—See Mutual of America Life Insurance Company; *U.S. Private*, pg. 2820
MVP DISTRIBUTION PARTNERS—See Wells Fargo & Company; *U.S. Public*, pg. 2344
MWAGIA, INC.—See Modern Woodmen of America; *U.S. Private*, pg. 2763
MWM INVESTMENT CONSULTING, LLC—See Keystone Group, L.P.; *U.S. Private*, pg. 2297
MYCIO WEALTH PARTNERS, LLC—See Affiliated Managers Group, Inc.; *U.S. Public*, pg. 55
NABO CAPITAL LIMITED—See Centum Investment Company Limited; *Int'l*, pg. 1416
NAH FINANCIAL SERVICES, INC.—See Hoganas AB; *Int'l*, pg. 3441
NASDAQ COPENHAGEN A/S—See Nasdaq, Inc.; *U.S. Public*, pg. 1492
NASDAQ CSD ICELAND HF—See Nasdaq, Inc.; *U.S. Public*, pg. 1492
NASDAQ ICELAND HF—See Nasdaq, Inc.; *U.S. Public*, pg. 1492
NASDAQ RIGA, AS—See Nasdaq, Inc.; *U.S. Public*, pg. 1492
NASHVILLE CAPITAL CORP.—See Renasant Corporation; *U.S. Public*, pg. 1783
NATIOCREDIBAIL SA—See BNP Paribas SA; *Int'l*, pg. 1092
NATIONAL ASSET MANAGEMENT, INC.—See B. Riley Financial, Inc.; *U.S. Public*, pg. 261
NATIONAL BANKSHARES FINANCIAL SERVICES, INC.—See National Bankshares, Inc.; *U.S. Public*, pg. 1493
NATIONAL INVESTMENT SERVICES, INC.; *U.S. Private*, pg. 2858
NATIONAL STAR LIMITED—See Heidelberg Materials AG; *Int'l*, pg. 3318
NATIXIS ASSET MANAGEMENT ADVISORS, L.P.—See Groupe BPCE; *Int'l*, pg. 3096
NATIXIS ASSET MANAGEMENT S.A.—See Groupe BPCE; *Int'l*, pg. 3096

NATIXIS AUSTRALIA PTY LTD.—See Groupe BPCE; *Int'l*, pg. 3098
NATIXIS DISTRIBUTION, LP—See Groupe BPCE; *Int'l*, pg. 3098
NATIXIS DUBAI LIMITED—See Groupe BPCE; *Int'l*, pg. 3098
NATIXIS GLOBAL ASSOCIATES INTERNATIONAL—See Groupe BPCE; *Int'l*, pg. 3096
NATIXIS INVESTMENT MANAGERS AUSTRALIA PTY LIMITED—See Groupe BPCE; *Int'l*, pg. 3098
NATIXIS INVESTMENT MANAGERS KOREA LIMITED—See Groupe BPCE; *Int'l*, pg. 3098
NATIXIS INVESTMENT MANAGERS, LP—See Groupe BPCE; *Int'l*, pg. 3098
NATIXIS INVESTMENT MANAGERS MIDDLE EAST LLC—See Groupe BPCE; *Int'l*, pg. 3098
NATIXIS INVESTMENT MANAGERS S.A,ZWEIGNIERDERLAASUNG DEUTSCHLAND—See Groupe BPCE; *Int'l*, pg. 3098
NATIXIS INVESTMENT MANAGERS, SUCURSAL EN ESPANA SL—See Groupe BPCE; *Int'l*, pg. 3098
NATIXIS PARTNERS—See Groupe BPCE; *Int'l*, pg. 3097
NATIXIS SECURITIES AMERICAS LLC—See Groupe BPCE; *Int'l*, pg. 3098
NAVIGANT CAPITAL ADVISORS, LLC—See Bain Capital, LP; *U.S. Private*, pg. 432
NAVIGATOR ACQUISITION CORP.; *U.S. Public*, pg. 1500
NAVIGATOR INVESTMENT SERVICES LIMITED—See Aviva plc; *Int'l*, pg. 746
NB ALTERNATIVES ADVISERS LLC—See Neuberger Berman Group LLC; *U.S. Private*, pg. 2890
NBT CAPITAL CORP.—See NBT Bancorp Inc.; *U.S. Public*, pg. 1500
NBT CAPITAL CORP.—See NBT Bancorp Inc.; *U.S. Public*, pg. 1501
NELSON CAPITAL MANAGEMENT, LLC—See Wells Fargo & Company; *U.S. Public*, pg. 2344
NEPSIS INC.; *U.S. Private*, pg. 2885
NEUBERGER BERMAN LLC—See Neuberger Berman Group LLC; *U.S. Private*, pg. 2890
NEVTAH CAPITAL MANAGEMENT CORP.; *U.S. Public*, pg. 1511
NEW CHINA FUND MANAGEMENT CO., LTD.—See HengTai Securities CO., LTD; *Int'l*, pg. 3347
NEW ENGLAND INVESTMENT & RETIREMENT GROUP, INC.; *U.S. Private*, pg. 2894
NEWFLEET ASSET MANAGEMENT LLC—See Virtus Investment Partners, Inc.; *U.S. Public*, pg. 2301
NEWFUNDS PROPRIETARY LIMITED—See Barclays PLC; *Int'l*, pg. 862
NEW HORIZONS ASSET MANAGEMENT GROUP, LLC—See Rhinebeck Bank; *U.S. Private*, pg. 3421
NEW SUNWARD HOLDING B.V.—See CEMEX, S.A.B. de C.V.; *Int'l*, pg. 1399
NEW SUNWARD HOLDING FINANCIAL VENTURES B.V.—See CEMEX, S.A.B. de C.V.; *Int'l*, pg. 1399
NEW YORK CITY HOUSING DEVELOPMENT CORP—See New York City Housing Development Corporation; *U.S. Private*, pg. 2909
NEW YORK LIFE INSURANCE COMPANY—See New York Life Insurance Company; *U.S. Private*, pg. 2910
NEXPOINT ADVISORS, L.P.—See Highland Capital Management, L.P.; *U.S. Private*, pg. 1938
NEXTCARE HOLDING WLL—See Allianz SE; *Int'l*, pg. 354
NEXT FINANCIAL GROUP, INC.—See Lee Equity Partners LLC; *U.S. Private*, pg. 2412
NEXTMART, INC.; *U.S. Public*, pg. 1526
NFJ INVESTMENT GROUP LP—See Allianz SE; *Int'l*, pg. 346
NFP FDR FINANCIAL GROUP, INC.—See Aon plc; *Int'l*, pg. 496
NGAM CANADA LP—See Groupe BPCE; *Int'l*, pg. 3096
NIPPONEX HOLDINGS LLC—See Bayer Aktiengesellschaft; *Int'l*, pg. 902
NMS CAPITAL SERVICES, LLC; *U.S. Private*, pg. 2931
NOBEL INDUSTRIES HOLDING B.V.—See Akzo Nobel N.V.; *Int'l*, pg. 274
NOCA HOLDING AS—See Guardian Capital Group Limited; *Int'l*, pg. 3170
NORRSKEN FINANCE SA—See BNP Paribas SA; *Int'l*, pg. 1092
NORSE CROWN CO. (M) SDN BHD—See Ferd AS; *Int'l*, pg. 2636
NORTH AMERICAN HOGANAS HOLDINGS, INC.—See Hoganas AB; *Int'l*, pg. 3441
NORTH-EAST HNA INVESTMENT GROUP CO., LTD—See Hainan Traffic Administration Holding Co., Ltd.; *Int'l*, pg. 3215
NORTHERN CAPITAL MANAGEMENT, LLC—See Clayton, Dubilier & Rice, LLC; *U.S. Private*, pg. 923
NORTHERN CAPITAL MANAGEMENT, LLC—See Stone Point Capital LLC; *U.S. Private*, pg. 3824
NORTHERN TIER ENERGY GP LLC—See Marathon Petroleum Corporation; *U.S. Public*, pg. 1363
THE NORTHERN TRUST COMPANY—See Northern Trust Corporation; *U.S. Public*, pg. 1538
NORTHERN TRUST GLOBAL FUND SERVICES CAYMAN

LIMITED—See Northern Trust Corporation; *U.S. Public*, pg. 1539
NORTHERN TRUST (GUERNSEY) LIMITED—See Northern Trust Corporation; *U.S. Public*, pg. 1538
NORTHERN TRUST INTERNATIONAL FUND ADMINISTRATION SERVICES (IRELAND) LIMITED—See Northern Trust Corporation; *U.S. Public*, pg. 1538
NORTHERN TRUST MANAGEMENT SERVICES LIMITED—See Northern Trust Corporation; *U.S. Public*, pg. 1539
NORTHLIGHT FINANCIAL LLC; *U.S. Private*, pg. 2956
NORTH POINT HOLDINGS LTD—See Gamma-Civic Ltd; *Int'l*, pg. 2878
NORTHSTAR FINANCIAL SERVICES GROUP LLC—See TA Associates, Inc.; *U.S. Private*, pg. 3917
NORTHWEST ADVISORS, INC.—See Northwest Bancshares, Inc.; *U.S. Public*, pg. 1542
NORTHWEST CONSUMER DISCOUNT COMPANY—See Northwest Bancshares, Inc.; *U.S. Public*, pg. 1542
NORTHWEST WEALTH MANAGEMENT, LLC—See Northwest Financial Corp.; *U.S. Private*, pg. 2960
NOTTINGHAM ADVISORS, INC.—See Community Bank System, Inc.; *U.S. Public*, pg. 550
NOVETHIC—See Caisse des Depots et Consignations; *Int'l*, pg. 1258
NOWINFINITY PTY. LTD.—See HUB24 Limited; *Int'l*, pg. 3517
NTX HEALTHCARE PROPERTIES, LLC—See Universal Health Realty Income Trust; *U.S. Public*, pg. 2255
NUCLEUS FINANCIAL GROUP PLC—See HPS Investment Partners, LLC; *U.S. Private*, pg. 1997
NUMERIX LLC—See Genstar Capital, LLC; *U.S. Private*, pg. 1677
NUVEEN ASSET MANAGEMENT, LLC—See Teachers Insurance Association - College Retirement Fund; *U.S. Private*, pg. 3945
NUVEEN CHURCHILL DIRECT LENDING CORP.—See Teachers Insurance Association - College Retirement Fund; *U.S. Private*, pg. 3945
NUVEEN EMERGING MARKETS DEBT 2022 TARGET TERM FUND—See Teachers Insurance Association - College Retirement Fund; *U.S. Private*, pg. 3946
NUVEEN SECURITIES, LLC—See Teachers Insurance Association - College Retirement Fund; *U.S. Private*, pg. 3947
NWQ INVESTMENT MANAGEMENT COMPANY, LLC—See Teachers Insurance Association - College Retirement Fund; *U.S. Private*, pg. 3947
NYLIFE DISTRIBUTORS LLC—See New York Life Insurance Company; *U.S. Private*, pg. 2910
OAK HILL ADVISORS (EUROPE), LLP—See T. Rowe Price Group Inc.; *U.S. Public*, pg. 1978
OAK HILL ADVISORS, L.P.; *U.S. Private*, pg. 2983
OAK RIDGE CAPITAL GROUP, INC.; *U.S. Private*, pg. 2984
OAKTREE CAPITAL (AUSTRALIA) PTY. LIMITED—See Brookfield Corporation; *Int'l*, pg. 1182
OAKTREE CAPITAL MANAGEMENT (DUBAI) LIMITED—See Brookfield Corporation; *Int'l*, pg. 1182
OAKTREE CAPITAL MANAGEMENT FUND—See Brookfield Corporation; *Int'l*, pg. 1182
OAKTREE CAPITAL MANAGEMENT (UK) LLP—See Brookfield Corporation; *Int'l*, pg. 1182
OAKTREE CAPITAL (SHANGHAI) LTD.—See Brookfield Corporation; *Int'l*, pg. 1182
OAKTREE FUND ADVISORS, LLC—See Brookfield Corporation; *Int'l*, pg. 1182
OAKTREE STRATEGIC INCOME CORPORATION—See Brookfield Corporation; *Int'l*, pg. 1182
OBS FINANCIAL SERVICES, INC.—See Huatai Securities Co., Ltd.; *Int'l*, pg. 3514
OCEANICA AG—See BMT Group Limited; *Int'l*, pg. 1077
OCEANIC CAPITAL MANAGEMENT LLC—See Ecobank Transnational Incorporated; *Int'l*, pg. 2294
OCH-ZIFF CAPITAL MANAGEMENT HONG KONG LIMITED—See Rithm Capital Corp.; *U.S. Public*, pg. 1800
OCH-ZIFF MANAGEMENT EUROPE LIMITED—See Rithm Capital Corp.; *U.S. Public*, pg. 1800
OCM INVESTMENTS, LLC—See Brookfield Corporation; *Int'l*, pg. 1181
OEP CAPITAL ADVISORS, L.P.; *U.S. Private*, pg. 2997
OGH ACQUISITION CORPORATION—See Waste Management, Inc.; *U.S. Public*, pg. 2331
OHIO INDEMNITY COMPANY - OIC LENDER SERVICES DIVISION—See BancInsurance Corporation; *U.S. Private*, pg. 464
OHIO NATIONAL INVESTMENTS, INC.—See Caisse de Depot et Placement du Quebec; *Int'l*, pg. 1254
OKLAHOMA FINANCIAL CENTER, INC.—See Aon plc; *Int'l*, pg. 497
OLD DOMINION CAPITAL MANAGEMENT, INC.—See Atlantic Union Bankshares Corporation; *U.S. Public*, pg. 223
OLD POINT TRUST & FINANCIAL SERVICES, N.A.—See Old Point Financial Corporation; *U.S. Public*, pg. 1567
OLD REPUBLIC SURETY COMPANY—See Old Republic International Corporation; *U.S. Public*, pg. 1568
OLSON MOBECK INVESTMENT ADVISORS INC.—See M&T Bank Corporation; *U.S. Public*, pg. 1351
OLTIS SOFTWARE, LLC—See Bain Capital, LP; *U.S. Private*, pg. 439
OLYMPIA CAPITAL MANAGEMENT INC.—See Ambroisie Capital Holding S.A.S.; *Int'l*, pg. 416
OLYMPIA CAPITAL MANAGEMENT S.A.—See Ambroisie Capital Holding S.A.S.; *Int'l*, pg. 415
OMEGA ADVISORS, INC.; *U.S. Private*, pg. 3015
OMNI WEALTH ADVISORS, LLC—See Affiliated Managers Group, Inc.; *U.S. Public*, pg. 56
OMNI WEALTH ADVISORS, LLC—See HGGC, LLC; *U.S. Private*, pg. 1930
ONCURE HOLDINGS, INC.—See Vestar Capital Partners, LLC; *U.S. Private*, pg. 4371
ONEDIGITAL INVESTMENT ADVISORS LLC—See New Mountain Capital, LLC; *U.S. Private*, pg. 2901
ONE EQUITY PARTNERS EUROPE GMBH—See OEP Capital Advisors, L.P.; *U.S. Private*, pg. 2999
ONEPOWER SYSTEMS LTD.; *U.S. Private*, pg. 3025
THE O.N. EQUITY SALES COMPANY—See Caisse de Depot et Placement du Quebec; *Int'l*, pg. 1254
ONEY - INSTITUICAO FINANCEIRA DE CREDITO, S.A.—See Auchan Holding S.A.; *Int'l*, pg. 699
ON Q FINANCIAL, INC.; *U.S. Private*, pg. 3018
OPPENHEIM ASSET MANAGEMENT GMBH—See Deutsche Bank Aktiengesellschaft; *Int'l*, pg. 2062
OPPENHEIM CAPITAL ADVISORY GMBH—See Deutsche Bank Aktiengesellschaft; *Int'l*, pg. 2062
OPPENHEIMER ASSET MANAGEMENT INC.—See Oppenheimer Holdings Inc.; *U.S. Public*, pg. 1608
OPPENHEIMER & CO. INC. - TROY—See Oppenheimer Holdings Inc.; *U.S. Public*, pg. 1608
OPPENHEIMERFUNDS DISTRIBUTOR, INC.—See Invesco Ltd.; *U.S. Public*, pg. 1163
OPTIMA SGR S.P.A.—See BPER BANCA S.p.A; *Int'l*, pg. 1132
ORASCOM FINANCIAL HOLDING SAE—See B Investments Holding SAE; *Int'l*, pg. 783
ORIGIN ASSET MANAGEMENT LLP—See Principal Financial Group, Inc.; *U.S. Public*, pg. 1720
ORION ADVISOR SOLUTIONS, LLC; *U.S. Private*, pg. 3042
ORION RESOURCE PARTNERS (USA) LP; *U.S. Private*, pg. 3043
ORM TIMBER FUND II, INC.—See Rayonier Inc.; *U.S. Public*, pg. 1765
ORO DE ALTAR, S.A. DE C.V.—See Alamos Gold Inc.; *Int'l*, pg. 290
ORO FINANCECORP PLC.—See CREED Corporation; *Int'l*, pg. 1837
OSP GROUP MANAGEMENT SERVICES, L.P.—See Charlesbank Capital Partners, LLC; *U.S. Private*, pg. 855
OSP GROUP MANAGEMENT SERVICES, L.P.—See Webster Equity Partners, LLC; *U.S. Private*, pg. 4467
OSPRAIE MANAGEMENT, LLC; *U.S. Private*, pg. 3048
O.S.T.C LIMITED—See BGC Group, Inc.; *U.S. Public*, pg. 330
OTIS INVESTMENTS LIMITED—See Otis Worldwide Corporation; *U.S. Public*, pg. 1623
OUDART PATRIMOINE—See EFG International AG; *Int'l*, pg. 2320
OUDART SA—See EFG International AG; *Int'l*, pg. 2320
OUEST CROISSANCE SCR SAS—See Groupe BPCE; *Int'l*, pg. 3099
OUSA-F LLP—See ForteBank JSC; *Int'l*, pg. 2737
OVER FIFTY SENIORS EQUITY RELEASE PTY LTD—See Centuria Capital Limited; *Int'l*, pg. 1416
OXFORD SQUARE CAPITAL CORP.; *U.S. Public*, pg. 1629
OXOID INVESTMENTS GMBH—See Thermo Fisher Scientific Inc.; *U.S. Public*, pg. 2154
OZ MANAGEMENT II LP—See Rithm Capital Corp.; *U.S. Public*, pg. 1800
P10, INC.; *U.S. Public*, pg. 1630
P&A CAPITAL ADVISORS, INC.—See Aon plc; *Int'l*, pg. 497
PACIFIC INCOME ADVISERS INC.; *U.S. Private*, pg. 3067
PACIFIC INVESTMENT MANAGEMENT COMPANY LLC—See Allianz SE; *Int'l*, pg. 346
PACIFIC LIFE FUND ADVISORS LLC—See Pacific Mutual Holding Company; *U.S. Private*, pg. 3069
PACIFIC PREMIER TRUST—See Pacific Premier Bancorp, Inc.; *U.S. Public*, pg. 1632
PACIFIC VALLEY INVESTORS INC.; *U.S. Private*, pg. 3071
PACWEST FINANCIAL MANAGEMENT, INC.—See Clayton, Dubilier & Rice, LLC; *U.S. Private*, pg. 923
PACWEST FINANCIAL MANAGEMENT, INC.—See Stone Point Capital LLC; *U.S. Private*, pg. 3824
PALADIN HEALTHCARE MANAGEMENT, LLC—See Paladin Healthcare Capital, LLC; *U.S. Private*, pg. 3076
PALATINE ASSET MANAGEMENT SA—See Groupe BPCE; *Int'l*, pg. 3099
PALEX LIMITED—See Hang Lung Group Limited; *Int'l*, pg. 3245
THE PALISADES GROUP LLC; *U.S. Private*, pg. 4090
PALLINGHURST ADVISORS (PTY) LIMITED—See Gemfields Group Limited; *Int'l*, pg. 2916
PALMER SQUARE CAPITAL BDC INC.; *U.S. Public*, pg. 1634
PALUEL-MARMONT CAPITAL SA—See Compagnie Lebon SA; *Int'l*, pg. 1745
PAMLICO CAPITAL MANAGEMENT, L.P.; *U.S. Private*, pg. 3083
PANORAMA CAPITAL CORP.; *U.S. Public*, pg. 1636
PANTHEON CAPITAL (ASIA) LIMITED—See Affiliated Managers Group, Inc.; *U.S. Public*, pg. 55
PANTHEON HOLDINGS LIMITED—See Affiliated Managers Group, Inc.; *U.S. Public*, pg. 55
PANTHEON KOREA INC.—See Affiliated Managers Group, Inc.; *U.S. Public*, pg. 55
PANTHEON SECURITIES LLC—See Affiliated Managers Group, Inc.; *U.S. Public*, pg. 55
PANTHEON (US) LLC—See Affiliated Managers Group, Inc.; *U.S. Public*, pg. 55
PANTHEON VENTURES (HK) LLP—See Affiliated Managers Group, Inc.; *U.S. Public*, pg. 55
PANTHEON VENTURES (UK) LLP—See Affiliated Managers Group, Inc.; *U.S. Public*, pg. 55
PARADY FINANCIAL GROUP, INC.—See Kelso & Company, L.P.; *U.S. Private*, pg. 2280
PARAGEM PTY LTD—See HUB24 Limited; *Int'l*, pg. 3517
PARETO INVESTMENT MANAGEMENT LIMITED—See The Bank of New York Mellon Corporation; *U.S. Public*, pg. 2038
PARIC HOLDINGS, INC.; *U.S. Private*, pg. 3094
PARKERGALE, LLC; *U.S. Private*, pg. 3098
PARK HILL REAL ESTATE GROUP L.L.C.—See Blackstone Inc.; *U.S. Public*, pg. 350
PARKWAY FINANCIAL GROUP, LLC—See Century Communities, Inc.; *U.S. Public*, pg. 475
PARSEC FINANCIAL MANAGEMENT, INC.—See Modera Wealth Management, LLC; *U.S. Private*, pg. 2759
PARTNERRE ASSET MANAGEMENT CORPORATION—See Covea Groupe S.A.S.; *Int'l*, pg. 1820
PARTNERRE HOLDINGS SWITZERLAND GMBH—See Covea Groupe S.A.S.; *Int'l*, pg. 1820
PARTNERSHIP CAPITAL GROWTH LLC; *U.S. Private*, pg. 3103
PATHSTONE FAMILY OFFICE, LLC—See Lovell Minnick Partners LLC; *U.S. Private*, pg. 2503
PATRIMONY 1873 SA—See EFG International AG; *Int'l*, pg. 2321
PATRIOT MEDIA CONSULTING LLC; *U.S. Private*, pg. 3110
PATTEN AND PATTEN, INC.; *U.S. Private*, pg. 3111
THE PATTERSON CAPITAL CORPORATION—See Estancia Capital Management, LLC; *U.S. Private*, pg. 1428
PAULSON & CO. INC.; *U.S. Private*, pg. 3114
PAX WORLD FUNDS; *U.S. Private*, pg. 3115
PAYDEN & RYGEL GLOBAL LIMITED—See Payden & Rygel; *U.S. Private*, pg. 3117
PAYDEN & RYGEL; *U.S. Private*, pg. 3116
PAYPAL ASSET MANAGEMENT, INC.—See PayPal Holdings, Inc.; *U.S. Public*, pg. 1656
PBE COMPANIES, LLC—See Banco Santander, S.A.; *Int'l*, pg. 827
PBNA, LLC—See Peoples Bancorp Inc.; *U.S. Public*, pg. 1667
PCM PROPERTIES LLC—See Invesco Ltd.; *U.S. Public*, pg. 1163
PEARSON JONES PLC—See abrdn PLC; *Int'l*, pg. 69
PEIRCE PARK GROUP, INC.—See Marquette Associates, Inc.; *U.S. Private*, pg. 2587
PEKAO INVESTMENT BANKING S.A.—See Bank Polska Kasa Opieki Spolka Akcyjna; *Int'l*, pg. 850
PEKAO TFI S.A.—See Bank Polska Kasa Opieki Spolka Akcyjna; *Int'l*, pg. 850
PELAGOS CAPITAL MANAGEMENT, LLC—See Franklin Resources, Inc.; *U.S. Public*, pg. 883
PELICAN ENERGY PARTNERS LP; *U.S. Private*, pg. 3130
PEMBA CAPITAL PARTNERS PTY. LTD.—See FirstRand Limited; *Int'l*, pg. 2690
PENCRETE LIMITED—See Heidelberg Materials AG; *Int'l*, pg. 3318
PENNSYLVANIA TRUST CO.—See Fiduciary Company Incorporated; *U.S. Private*, pg. 1503
PENNYMAC CORP.—See PennyMac Mortgage Investment Trust; *U.S. Public*, pg. 1664
PENSIONMARK RETIREMENT GROUP LLC—See World Insurance Associates LLC; *U.S. Private*, pg. 4566
THE PENTAD GROUP PTY. LTD.—See Capricorn Investment Partners Limited; *Int'l*, pg. 1316
PENTEGRA RETIREMENT SERVICES; *U.S. Private*, pg. 3140
PEOPLE'S UNITED ADVISORS, INC.—See M&T Bank Corporation; *U.S. Public*, pg. 1351
PEQUOT CAPITAL MANAGEMENT INC.; *U.S. Private*, pg. 3146
PERCHERON INVESTMENT MANAGEMENT LP; *U.S. Private*, pg. 3146
PEREGRINE CAPITAL MANAGEMENT, INC.—See Wells Fargo & Company; *U.S. Public*, pg. 2345
PERFECT TIMING, INC.—See Sun Capital Partners, Inc.; *U.S. Private*, pg. 3860
PERFORMANCE EQUITY MANAGEMENT, LLC; *U.S. Private*, pg. 3149
PERIGON PARTNERS LLC; *U.S. Private*, pg. 3150
PERSHING SQUARE CAPITAL MANAGEMENT, L.P.; *U.S. Private*, pg. 3155

523940 — PORTFOLIO MANAGEMEN...

PERSIMMON CAPITAL MANAGEMENT, LP—See Dakota Wealth Management LLC; *U.S. Private*, pg. 1148
PETROVIC FINANCIAL SOLUTIONS LLC; *U.S. Private*, pg. 3163
PEX HOLDING INC.; *U.S. Private*, pg. 3164
PGB TRUST AND INVESTMENTS OF DELAWARE—See Peapack-Gladstone Financial Corporation; *U.S. Public*, pg. 1659
PGIM GLOBAL HIGH YIELD FUND, INC.; *U.S. Public*, pg. 1684
PHH INVESTMENTS, LTD.; *U.S. Private*, pg. 3167
PHILADELPHIA INDUSTRIES, INC.—See IG Design Group Plc; *Int'l*, pg. 3600
PHILIP MORRIS CAPITAL CORP.—See Altria Group, Inc.; *U.S. Public*, pg. 89
PHOENIX ASSET MANAGEMENT, LLC; *U.S. Private*, pg. 3172
PIEDMONT INVESTMENT ADVISORS, LLC; *U.S. Private*, pg. 3177
PIEDMONT LITHIUM INC.; *U.S. Public*, pg. 1690
PIKE STREET CAPITAL, LP; *U.S. Private*, pg. 3179
PILLAR CAPITAL MANAGEMENT LIMITED—See Marsh & McLennan Companies, Inc.; *U.S. Public*, pg. 1388
PIMCO ADVISORY—See Allianz SE; *Int'l*, pg. 346
PIMCO EUROPE GMBH—See Allianz SE; *Int'l*, pg. 355
PIMCO GLOBAL ADVISORS LLC—See Allianz SE; *Int'l*, pg. 347
PIMCO (SCHWEIZ) GMBH—See Allianz SE; *Int'l*, pg. 355
PIM FINANCIAL SERVICES INC.—See Centurion Counsel, Inc.; *U.S. Private*, pg. 831
PINE BROOK ROAD PARTNERS, LLC; *U.S. Private*, pg. 3182
PINENO LEVIN & FORD ASSET MANAGEMENT, INC.—See Dakota Wealth Management LLC; *U.S. Private*, pg. 1148
PINEWELL CAPITAL LLC; *U.S. Private*, pg. 3184
PINNACLE ADVISORY GROUP; *U.S. Private*, pg. 3184
PINNACLEART INTERNATIONAL, LLC; *U.S. Private*, pg. 3186
PINNACLE ASSET MANAGEMENT, L.P.; *U.S. Private*, pg. 3184
PINNACLE ASSOCIATES, LTD., *U.S. Private*, pg. 3184
PIONEER INTERNATIONAL INVESTMENTS LIMITED—See Heidelberg Materials AG; *Int'l*, pg. 3318
PIONEER PEKAO INVESTMENT MANAGEMENT S.A.—See Bank Polska Kasa Opieki Spolka Akcyjna; *Int'l*, pg. 850
PIPER SANDLER & CO.—See Piper Sandler Companies; *U.S. Public*, pg. 1694
PITCAIRN FINANCIAL GROUP; *U.S. Private*, pg. 3190
PITCHBOOK DATA, INC.—See Morningstar, Inc.; *U.S. Public*, pg. 1476
PITNEY BOWES INTERNATIONAL HOLDINGS, INC.—See Pitney Bowes Inc.; *U.S. Public*, pg. 1695
PITTSTON COAL MANAGEMENT COMPANY—See The Brink's Company; *U.S. Public*, pg. 2043
PJT PARTNERS INC.; *U.S. Public*, pg. 1696
PJT PARTNERS (UK) LIMITED—See PJT Partners Inc.; *U.S. Public*, pg. 1696
PK AIR FINANCE FRANCE SAS—See Apollo Global Management, Inc.; *U.S. Public*, pg. 154
PK AIRFINANCE JAPAN G.K.—See Apollo Global Management, Inc.; *U.S. Public*, pg. 154
PKDW EQUITY PARTNERS, LLC; *U.S. Private*, pg. 3193
PLANCONNECT, LLC—See Equitable Holdings, Inc.; *U.S. Public*, pg. 790
PLANVIEW, INC.—See TA Associates, Inc.; *U.S. Private*, pg. 3917
PLANVIEW, INC.—See TPG Capital, L.P.; *U.S. Public*, pg. 2175
PLATINUM EQUITY ADVISORS, LLC—See Platinum Equity, LLC; *U.S. Private*, pg. 3207
PLATINUM WEALTH PARTNERS, INC.; *U.S. Private*, pg. 3210
PLATTE VALLEY INVESTMENT CENTER INC.—See Platte Valley Financial Service Companies Inc.; *U.S. Private*, pg. 3212
PMC FINANCIAL SERVICE GROUP LLC—See PMC Capital Partners, LLC; *U.S. Private*, pg. 3217
PNC CAPITAL ADVISORS, LLC—See The PNC Financial Services Group, Inc.; *U.S. Public*, pg. 2119
PNC DELAWARE TRUST COMPANY—See The PNC Financial Services Group, Inc.; *U.S. Public*, pg. 2119
POINT72 ASSET MANAGEMENT, L.P.; *U.S. Private*, pg. 3222
POINT BREAK HOLDINGS LLC—See INSPIRATO INCORPORATED; *U.S. Public*, pg. 1131
POLARIS GROWTH MANAGEMENT, LLC; *U.S. Private*, pg. 3223
POMONA CAPITAL; *U.S. Private*, pg. 3226
POP CAPITAL LLC; *U.S. Private*, pg. 3228
PORTELL FINANCIAL SERVICES, INC.—See Aon plc; *Int'l*, pg. 497
PORTFOLIO MANAGEMENT CONSULTANTS, INC.—See Bain Capital, LP; *U.S. Private*, pg. 439
POSADA HOLDING B.V.—See Envipco Holding N.V.; *Int'l*, pg. 2453
POST ADVISORY GROUP, LLC—See Principal Financial Group, Inc.; *U.S. Public*, pg. 1721
POWERGEN US HOLDINGS LIMITED—See E.ON SE; *Int'l*, pg. 2258
POWERGEN US INVESTMENTS—See E.ON SE; *Int'l*, pg. 2258
POWERGEN US SECURITIES LIMITED—See E.ON SE; *Int'l*, pg. 2258
PPL UK INVESTMENTS LIMITED—See PPL Corporation; *U.S. Public*, pg. 1712
PPM AMERICA, INC.—See Jackson Financial Inc.; *U.S. Public*, pg. 1183
PRAGATI DEVELOPMENT CONSULTING SERVICES LTD.—See Moody's Corporation; *U.S. Public*, pg. 1469
PRAMERICA SGR S.P.A—See Prudential Financial, Inc.; *U.S. Public*, pg. 1732
PRATT & WHITNEY CANADA HOLDINGS CORP.—See RTX Corporation; *U.S. Public*, pg. 1823
PRAZSKA PLYNARENSKA SPRAVA MAJETKU, S.R.O.—See E.ON SE; *Int'l*, pg. 2259
PREMIER BEVERAGE GROUP CORP.; *U.S. Private*, pg. 3249
PREMIER SOLUTION CO., LTD.—See Chow Steel Industries Public Company Limited; *Int'l*, pg. 1584
PRESCOTT SECURITIES LIMITED—See Financial Index Australia Pty Ltd.; *Int'l*, pg. 2665
PRESIDENT'S CHOICE BANK—See George Weston Limited; *Int'l*, pg. 2938
PRICE & ASSOCIATES CPAS, LLC; *U.S. Private*, pg. 3258
PRIME AE GROUP, INC.—See NewHold Enterprises LLC; *U.S. Private*, pg. 2915
PRINCIPAL ASSET MANAGEMENT COMPANY ASIA, LTD.—See Principal Financial Group, Inc.; *U.S. Public*, pg. 1721
PRINCIPAL COMMERCIAL FUNDING, LLC—See Principal Financial Group, Inc.; *U.S. Public*, pg. 1720
PRINCIPAL DEVELOPMENT INVESTORS, LLC—See Principal Financial Group, Inc.; *U.S. Public*, pg. 1720
PRINCIPAL ENTERPRISE CAPITAL, LLC—See Principal Financial Group, Inc.; *U.S. Public*, pg. 1720
PRINCIPAL FINANCIAL ADVISORS, INC.—See Principal Financial Group, Inc.; *U.S. Public*, pg. 1720
PRINCIPAL GLOBAL COLUMBUS CIRCLE, LLC—See Principal Financial Group, Inc.; *U.S. Public*, pg. 1721
PRINCIPAL GLOBAL INVESTORS (ASIA) LIMITED—See Principal Financial Group, Inc.; *U.S. Public*, pg. 1721
PRINCIPAL GLOBAL INVESTORS (AUSTRALIA) LIMITED—See Principal Financial Group, Inc.; *U.S. Public*, pg. 1721
PRINCIPAL GLOBAL INVESTORS (AUSTRALIA) SERVICE COMPANY PTY LIMITED—See Principal Financial Group, Inc.; *U.S. Public*, pg. 1721
PRINCIPAL GLOBAL INVESTORS (EUROPE) LIMITED—See Principal Financial Group, Inc.; *U.S. Public*, pg. 1721
PRINCIPAL INVESTMENT & RETIREMENT SERVICES LIMITED—See Principal Financial Group, Inc.; *U.S. Public*, pg. 1721
PRINCIPAL ISLAMIC ASSET MANAGEMENT SDN. BHD.—See CIMB Group Holdings Berhad; *Int'l*, pg. 1608
PRINCIPAL ISLAMIC ASSET MANAGEMENT SDN. BHD.—See Principal Financial Group, Inc.; *U.S. Public*, pg. 1721
PRINCIPAL REAL ESTATE B.V.—See Principal Financial Group, Inc.; *U.S. Public*, pg. 1722
PRINCIPAL REAL ESTATE EUROPE LIMITED—See Principal Financial Group, Inc.; *U.S. Public*, pg. 1722
PRINCIPAL REAL ESTATE GMBH—See Principal Financial Group, Inc.; *U.S. Public*, pg. 1722
PRINCIPAL REAL ESTATE KAPITALVERWALTUNGSGESELLSCHAFT MBH—See Principal Financial Group, Inc.; *U.S. Public*, pg. 1722
PRINCIPAL REAL ESTATE S.A.R.L.—See Principal Financial Group, Inc.; *U.S. Public*, pg. 1722
PRINCIPAL REAL ESTATE SAS—See Principal Financial Group, Inc.; *U.S. Public*, pg. 1722
PRINCIPAL REAL ESTATE S.L.—See Principal Financial Group, Inc.; *U.S. Public*, pg. 1722
PRISMA CAPITAL MANAGEMENT INTERNATIONAL LLP—See PAAMCO Prisma Holdings, LLC; *U.S. Private*, pg. 3062
PRISMA CAPITAL PARTNERS LP—See PAAMCO Prisma Holdings, LLC; *U.S. Private*, pg. 3062
PRIVATE ASSET MANAGEMENT, INC.—See Genstar Capital, LLC; *U.S. Private*, pg. 1677
PRIVATE ASSET MANAGEMENT, INC.—See Keystone Group, L.P.; *U.S. Private*, pg. 2298
PRIVATE CAPITAL MANAGEMENT, INC.—See Independent Bank Group, Inc.; *U.S. Public*, pg. 1116
PRIVATE CAPITAL MANAGEMENT, LLC; *U.S. Private*, pg. 3268
PRIVATE MARKET CONNECT LLC—See S&P Global Inc.; *U.S. Public*, pg. 1831
PRIVATE OCEAN LLC—See Aon plc; *Int'l*, pg. 498
PROACTIVE CAPITAL GROUP, LLC; *U.S. Private*, pg. 3271
PROCLICK VENTURES, INC.; *U.S. Private*, pg. 3272
PROCTER & GAMBLE BUSINESS SERVICES CANADA COMPANY—See The Procter & Gamble Company; *U.S. Public*, pg. 2121
PROFESSIONAL INVESTMENT ADVISORY SERVICES PTE. LTD.—See Aviva plc; *Int'l*, pg. 746
PROGRESSIVE INVESTMENT COMPANY, INC.—See The Progressive Corporation; *U.S. Public*, pg. 2125
PROLOGIS UK HOLDINGS S.A.—See Prologis, Inc.; *U.S. Public*, pg. 1727
PROLOGIS UK LIMITED—See Prologis, Inc.; *U.S. Public*, pg. 1727
PROMOTORA E INVERSORA ADISA, S.A. DE C.V.—See Empresas ICA S.A.B. de C.V.; *Int'l*, pg. 2391
PROMUS CAPITAL, LLC—See Promus Holdings, LLC; *U.S. Private*, pg. 3283
PROPRIETARY CAPITAL LLC; *U.S. Private*, pg. 3286
PROSHARES TRUST II; *U.S. Private*, pg. 3287
PROVISE MANAGEMENT GROUP, LLC—See Aon plc; *Int'l*, pg. 497
PRUCO SECURITIES, LLC—See Prudential Financial, Inc.; *U.S. Public*, pg. 1732
PRUDENTIAL CAPITAL & INVESTMENT SERVICES, LLC—See Prudential Financial, Inc.; *U.S. Public*, pg. 1732
PRUDENTIAL INVESTMENTS LLC—See Prudential Financial, Inc.; *U.S. Public*, pg. 1733
PRUDENTIAL MUTUAL FUND SERVICES LLC—See Prudential Financial, Inc.; *U.S. Public*, pg. 1733
PRUDENTIAL PRIVATE PLACEMENT INVESTORS L.P.—See Prudential Financial, Inc.; *U.S. Public*, pg. 1733
PRUDENTIAL TRUST COMPANY—See Prudential Financial, Inc.; *U.S. Public*, pg. 1733
PRUDEO PARTNERS L.L.C.—See Perigon Wealth Management LLC; *U.S. Private*, pg. 3150
P.S.A. FINANCIAL ADVISORS, INC.—See PSA Holdings, Inc.; *U.S. Private*, pg. 3296
P.S.A. FINANCIAL, INC.—See PSA Holdings, Inc.; *U.S. Private*, pg. 3296
PSC FINANCIAL, LLC—See Emergent Capital, Inc.; *U.S. Private*, pg. 1381
PT ABN AMRO MANAJEMEN INVESTASI—See BNP Paribas SA; *Int'l*, pg. 1082
PT AFFINITY EQUITY PARTNERS INDONESIA—See Affinity Equity Partners (HK) Ltd.; *Int'l*, pg. 186
PT BNP PARIBAS INVESTMENT PARTNERS—See BNP Paribas SA; *Int'l*, pg. 1082
PT CREADOR INDONESIA—See Creador Sdn. Bhd.; *Int'l*, pg. 1831
PUBLIC FINANCIAL MANAGEMENT, INC.; *U.S. Private*, pg. 3299
PURE FINANCIAL ADVISORS, INC.; *U.S. Private*, pg. 3305
PURPLE SQUARE MANAGEMENT PARTNERS BV—See Ctac N.V.; *Int'l*, pg. 1869
PYRFORD INTERNATIONAL LIMITED—See Bank of Montreal; *Int'l*, pg. 846
PYROTEX SARL—See BNP Paribas SA; *Int'l*, pg. 1092
PZENA INVESTMENT MANAGEMENT, INC.; *U.S. Public*, pg. 1741
PZENA INVESTMENT MANAGEMENT, LTD—See Pzena Investment Management, Inc.; *U.S. Public*, pg. 1741
PZENA INVESTMENT MANAGEMENT PTY LTD—See Pzena Investment Management, Inc.; *U.S. Public*, pg. 1741
QC FINANCIAL SERVICES, INC.—See QC Holdings, Inc.; *U.S. Public*, pg. 1742
QC FINANCIAL SERVICES OF TEXAS, INC.—See QC Holdings, Inc.; *U.S. Public*, pg. 1742
Q-FREE (BRISTOL) UK LTD.—See Guardian Capital Group Limited; *Int'l*, pg. 3170
QIANLONG ASSET MANAGEMENT LIMITED—See China Financial Services Holdings Limited; *Int'l*, pg. 1503
QIAN LONG ASSETS MANAGEMENT COMPANY LIMITED—See China Financial Services Holdings Limited; *Int'l*, pg. 1503
QMA WADHWANI LLP—See Prudential Financial, Inc.; *U.S. Public*, pg. 1733
QS INVESTORS, LLC—See Franklin Resources, Inc.; *U.S. Public*, pg. 882
QUANTITATIVE MANAGEMENT ASSOCIATES LLC—See Prudential Financial, Inc.; *U.S. Public*, pg. 1733
QUANTUM CAPITAL GROUP LLC; *U.S. Private*, pg. 3322
QUANTUM ENERGY PARTNERS, LLC; *U.S. Private*, pg. 3323
QUBED DERIVATIVES LLP—See BGC Group, Inc.; *U.S. Public*, pg. 330
QUEEN CITY INVESTMENTS, INC.; *U.S. Public*, pg. 1754
QUEENSLAND URBAN PROJECTS PTY LTD—See Finasucre S.A.; *Int'l*, pg. 2670
QUEST CAPITAL MANAGEMENT INC—See Genstar Capital, LLC; *U.S. Private*, pg. 1677
QUEST CAPITAL MANAGEMENT INC—See Keystone Group, L.P.; *U.S. Private*, pg. 2298
QUEST INTEGRITY MIDDLE EAST FZ-LLC—See Team, Inc.; *U.S. Public*, pg. 1988
QUEST PATENT RESEARCH CORPORATION; *U.S. Public*, pg. 1756
QUINTILLION SERVICES LIMITED—See U.S. Bancorp; *U.S. Public*, pg. 2212
QVT FINANCIAL, LP; *U.S. Private*, pg. 3331
RACE ROCK GP, L.L.C; *U.S. Private*, pg. 3341

523940 — PORTFOLIO MANAGEMEN...

RADIAL EQUITY PARTNERS LP; *U.S. Private*, pg. 3342
RAGE FRAMEWORKS, INC.—See Genpact Limited; *Int'l*, pg. 2927
RAGE FRAMEWORKS INDIA PVT. LTD..—See Genpact Limited; *Int'l*, pg. 2927
RAGINGBULL.COM, LLC; *U.S. Private*, pg. 3345
RAINIER INVESTMENT MANAGEMENT, INC.—See Callodine Acquisition Corporation; *U.S. Public*, pg. 424
RAIT PARTNERSHIP, L.P.—See RAIT Financial Trust; *U.S. Private*, pg. 3349
RALCORP RECEIVABLES, LLC—See Conagra Brands, Inc.; *U.S. Public*, pg. 564
RANCH CREEK PARTNERS, LLC; *U.S. Private*, pg. 3352
RAYMOND JAMES ARGENTINA SOCIEDAD DE BOLSA, S.A.—See Raymond James Financial, Inc.; *U.S. Public*, pg. 1765
RAYMOND JAMES CORPORATE FINANCE GMBH—See Raymond James Financial, Inc.; *U.S. Public*, pg. 1764
RAYMOND JAMES FINANCIAL INTERNATIONAL, LTD. (U.K.)—See Raymond James Financial, Inc.; *U.S. Public*, pg. 1764
RAYMOND JAMES FINANCIAL PLANNING LTD.—See Raymond James Financial, Inc.; *U.S. Public*, pg. 1764
RAYMOND JAMES FINANCIAL SERVICES ADVISORS, INC.—See Raymond James Financial, Inc.; *U.S. Public*, pg. 1764
RAYMOND JAMES GENEVA S.A.—See Raymond James Financial, Inc.; *U.S. Public*, pg. 1764
RAYMOND JAMES INVESTMENT COUNSEL LTD.—See Raymond James Financial, Inc.; *U.S. Public*, pg. 1765
RAYMOND JAMES INVESTMENT SERVICES LIMITED—See Raymond James Financial, Inc.; *U.S. Public*, pg. 1764
RAYMOND JAMES LATIN ADVISORS LIMITED—See Raymond James Financial, Inc.; *U.S. Public*, pg. 1764
RAYMOND JAMES URUGUAY, S.A.—See Raymond James Financial, Inc.; *U.S. Public*, pg. 1765
RD TRADING LIMITED—See Computacenter plc; *Int'l*, pg. 1758
REALTY PARTNERS LLC; *U.S. Private*, pg. 3369
RECONFIGURATION BV—See BNP Paribas SA; *Int'l*, pg. 1092
REDBLACK SOFTWARE, LLC—See Invesco Ltd.; *U.S. Public*, pg. 1163
REDCHIP COMPANIES, INC.; *U.S. Private*, pg. 3377
REDCHIP KOREA—See RedChip Companies, Inc.; *U.S. Private*, pg. 3377
REDPOINT VENTURES—See Brentwood Venture Management, LLC; *U.S. Private*, pg. 646
REDPOINT VENTURES—See Brentwood Venture Management, LLC; *U.S. Private*, pg. 646
RED ROCK WEALTH MANAGEMENT—See Lightyear Capital LLC; *U.S. Private*, pg. 2454
REDSTONE COMPANIES HOSPITALITY, LLC—See The Redstone Companies, L.P.; *U.S. Private*, pg. 4103
REED MANAGEMENT LLC—See NACCO Industries, Inc.; *U.S. Public*, pg. 1489
REGAL ASSETS, LLC; *U.S. Private*, pg. 3385
REGIONAL ECONOMY VITALIZATION CORPORATION OF JAPAN—See Deposit Insurance Corporation of Japan; *Int'l*, pg. 2041
REGIONS BUSINESS CAPITAL CORPORATION—See Regions Financial Corporation; *U.S. Public*, pg. 1776
REGIONS INVESTMENT MANAGEMENT, INC.—See Regions Financial Corporation; *U.S. Public*, pg. 1776
REGISTRAR & TRANSFER COMPANY; *U.S. Private*, pg. 3389
RELATED FUND MANAGEMENT LLC—See The Related Companies, L.P.; *U.S. Private*, pg. 4103
RELIANCE CAPITAL MARKETS II, LLC - RCM ALTERNATIVES DIVISION—See Reliance Capital Markets II, LLC; *U.S. Private*, pg. 3394
RELIANCE CAPITAL MARKETS II, LLC; *U.S. Private*, pg. 3394
REMATE LINCE, S.A.P.I. DE C.V.—See BGC Group, Inc.; *U.S. Public*, pg. 330
REMATE USA INC.—See BGC Group, Inc.; *U.S. Public*, pg. 330
RENAISSANCE BENEFIT ADVISORS, INC.—See Aon plc; *Int'l*, pg. 497
THE RENAISSANCE GROUP LLC—See Affiliated Managers Group, Inc.; *U.S. Public*, pg. 55
RENEWAY A/S—See 7C Solarparken AG; *Int'l*, pg. 15
REPUBLIC FIRST BANCORP, INC.; *U.S. Public*, pg. 1785
RESERVOIR OPERATIONS, L.P.—See Reservoir Capital Group, L.L.C.; *U.S. Private*, pg. 3405
RESOLUTE INVESTMENT MANAGERS, INC.—See Kelso & Company, L.P.; *U.S. Private*, pg. 2280
RESOURCE ADVISORY SERVICES INC.—See The Mather Group, LLC; *U.S. Private*, pg. 4075
RESOURCE PLANNING GROUP LTD.—See Genstar Capital, LLC; *U.S. Private*, pg. 1677
RESOURCE PLANNING GROUP LTD.—See Keystone Group, L.P.; *U.S. Private*, pg. 2298
RESURGENS SPECIALTY UNDERWRITING, INC.—See Berkshire Hathaway Inc.; *U.S. Public*, pg. 299
RETIREMENT ADVISORY GROUP—See TA Associates, Inc.; *U.S. Private*, pg. 3919

RETIREMENT INVESTMENT ADVISORS, INC.—See Aon plc; *Int'l*, pg. 497
RET PARTICIPACOES S.A.—See Citigroup Inc.; *U.S. Public*, pg. 504
REVOLENT CAPITAL SOLUTIONS; *U.S. Private*, pg. 3416
REVOLUTION PARTNERS, LLC—See Regions Financial Corporation; *U.S. Public*, pg. 1776
R.E. WACKER ASSOCIATES, INC.—See U.S. Bancorp; *U.S. Public*, pg. 2212
RGT WEALTH ADVISORS, LLC—See CI Financial Corporation; *Int'l*, pg. 1601
RHONE GROUP ADVISORS LLC—See Rhone Group, LLC; *U.S. Private*, pg. 3424
RHP INVESTMENTS, INC.—See Ryman Hospitality Properties, Inc.; *U.S. Public*, pg. 1829
RH WEALTH ADVISORS, INC.—See Larry Mathis Financial Planning, LLC; *U.S. Private*, pg. 2393
RIALTO MANAGEMENT GROUP, LLC—See Lennar Corporation; *U.S. Public*, pg. 1307
RICE, HALL, JAMES & ASSOCIATES; *U.S. Private*, pg. 3425
RICHARD C. YOUNG & CO., LTD.; *U.S. Private*, pg. 3428
RICHMOND HILL INVESTMENTS, LLC—See Essex Equity Management, LLC; *U.S. Private*, pg. 1428
RINGTURM KAPITALANLAGEGESELLSCHAFT M.B.H.—See Erste Group Bank AG; *Int'l*, pg. 2499
RIO GRANDE MANAGEMENT COMPANY, LLC—See ModivCare, Inc.; *U.S. Public*, pg. 1456
RISING INVESTMENT CO., LTD.—See Guangdong Rising Assets Management Co., Ltd.; *Int'l*, pg. 3159
RISKLAB GMBH—See Allianz SE; *Int'l*, pg. 347
RISK MANAGEMENT SERVICES, LLC—See Hilton Grand Vacations Inc.; *U.S. Public*, pg. 1040
RISKMETRICS (SINGAPORE) PTE. LTD.—See MSCI Inc.; *U.S. Public*, pg. 1483
RISKMETRICS SOLUTIONS, LLC—See MSCI Inc.; *U.S. Public*, pg. 1483
RITTENHOUSE VENTURES, LLC; *U.S. Private*, pg. 3442
RIVERPOINT CAPITAL MANAGEMENT, INC.—See Mariner Wealth Advisors, LLC; *U.S. Private*, pg. 2575
RIVER ROAD ASSET MANAGEMENT LLC—See Affiliated Managers Group, Inc.; *U.S. Public*, pg. 55
RIVERSTONE HOLDINGS LLC - LONDON OFFICE—See Riverstone Holdings LLC; *U.S. Private*, pg. 3447
RIVERVIEW ASSET MANAGEMENT CORP.—See Riverview Bancorp, Inc.; *U.S. Public*, pg. 1801
RJ DELTA CAPITAL S.A.—See Raymond James Financial, Inc.; *U.S. Public*, pg. 1765
RJ DELTA FUND MANAGEMENT S.A.—See Raymond James Financial, Inc.; *U.S. Public*, pg. 1765
RMB CAPITAL MANAGEMENT, LLC—See Curi Holdings, Inc.; *U.S. Private*, pg. 1125
RMR ADVISORS LLC—See The RMR Group Inc.; *U.S. Public*, pg. 2126
THE RMR GROUP LLC—See The RMR Group Inc.; *U.S. Public*, pg. 2126
ROBASCIOTTI & ASSOCIATES, INC.—See Abacus Wealth Partners, LLC; *U.S. Private*, pg. 34
ROCK CREEK AUSTIN FUND, L.P.—See Wells Fargo & Company; *U.S. Public*, pg. 2345
THE ROCK CREEK GROUP, LP; *U.S. Private*, pg. 4111
ROCKMONT CAPITAL PARTNERS LTD.; *U.S. Private*, pg. 3467
ROGAN & ASSOCIATES, INC.; *U.S. Private*, pg. 3471
ROGERS CAPITAL LTD.—See ENL Limited; *Int'l*, pg. 2442
ROGERSCASEY, INC.—See The Segal Group, Inc.; *U.S. Private*, pg. 4116
RONDELLI ADVISERS S.R.L.—See Compass Advisers Group LLC; *U.S. Private*, pg. 999
THE ROOSEVELT INVESTMENT GROUP, INC.—See CI Financial Corporation; *Int'l*, pg. 1601
ROOTS EQUITY GROUP LLC; *U.S. Private*, pg. 3480
ROSE RYAN INC.—See RFE Investment Partners; *U.S. Private*, pg. 3420
ROSEWOOD ACQUISITION CORPORATION—See The Rosewood Corporation; *U.S. Private*, pg. 4112
ROUNDWOOD ASSET MANAGEMENT LLC—See Berkshire Hathaway Inc.; *U.S. Public*, pg. 299
ROUTE 2 CAPITAL PARTNERS; *U.S. Private*, pg. 3490
ROYAL PALM CAPITAL, LLC—See Bimini Capital Management, Inc.; *U.S. Public*, pg. 332
ROYCE & ASSOCIATES, LLC—See Franklin Resources, Inc.; *U.S. Public*, pg. 882
ROYCE & ASSOCIATES, LP—See Franklin Resources, Inc.; *U.S. Public*, pg. 882
RPH FINANCIAL SERVICES INC.—See The Mather Group, LLC; *U.S. Private*, pg. 4075
RREEF CHINA REIT MANAGEMENT LIMITED—See Deutsche Bank Aktiengesellschaft; *Int'l*, pg. 2057
RREEF INVESTMENT GMBH—See Deutsche Bank Aktiengesellschaft; *Int'l*, pg. 2061
RREEF NORTH AMERICAN INFRASTRUCTURE ONSHORE FUND A, L.P.—See Deutsche Bank Aktiengesellschaft; *Int'l*, pg. 2058
RSUI INDEMNITY COMPANY—See Berkshire Hathaway Inc.; *U.S. Public*, pg. 299
RUSAGRO-INVEST—See Gruppa Kompaniy Rusagro OOO; *Int'l*, pg. 3140

RUSSELL INVESTMENT GROUP LTD—See The Northwestern Mutual Life Insurance Company; *U.S. Private*, pg. 4085
RUSSELL INVESTMENT GROUP PRIVATE LIMITED—See The Northwestern Mutual Life Insurance Company; *U.S. Private*, pg. 4085
RUSSELL INVESTMENT GROUP PTY LIMITED—See The Northwestern Mutual Life Insurance Company; *U.S. Private*, pg. 4085
RUSSELL INVESTMENT MANAGEMENT LTD—See The Northwestern Mutual Life Insurance Company; *U.S. Private*, pg. 4085
RUSSELL INVESTMENTS CANADA LIMITED—See The Northwestern Mutual Life Insurance Company; *U.S. Private*, pg. 4085
RUSSELL INVESTMENTS GROUP, LLC.—See Reverence Capital Partners LLC; *U.S. Private*, pg. 3415
RUSSELL INVESTMENTS GROUP, LLC—See TA Associates, Inc.; *U.S. Private*, pg. 3918
RUSSELL INVESTMENTS KOREA LIMITED—See The Northwestern Mutual Life Insurance Company; *U.S. Private*, pg. 4085
RUSSELL INVESTMENTS LIMITED—See The Northwestern Mutual Life Insurance Company; *U.S. Private*, pg. 4085
SADOFF INVESTMENT MANAGEMENT—See TA Associates, Inc.; *U.S. Private*, pg. 3919
SAGEVIEW ADVISORY GROUP LLC; *U.S. Private*, pg. 3527
SAGEWOOD ASSET MANAGEMENT LLC—See Stifel Financial Corp.; *U.S. Public*, pg. 1950
SAGICOR FUNDS INCORPORATED—See Alignvest Management Corporation; *Int'l*, pg. 327
SAIB BNP PARIBAS ASSET MANAGEMENT CO., LTD.—See BNP Paribas SA; *Int'l*, pg. 1082
S.A.I. BROKER S.A.—See BRK Financial Group S.A.; *Int'l*, pg. 1171
SAI ERSTE ASSET MANAGEMENT S.A.—See Erste Group Bank AG; *Int'l*, pg. 2499
SAISON ASSET MANAGEMENT CO., LTD.—See Credit Saison Co., Ltd.; *Int'l*, pg. 1836
SAKANA HOLISTIC HOUSING SOLUTIONS B.S.C.—See Dar Al-Maal Al-Islami Trust; *Int'l*, pg. 1971
SALEM ERODE INVESTMENTS LIMITED—See ICL Fincorp Limited; *Int'l*, pg. 3581
SALIENT PARTNERS, L.P.; *U.S. Private*, pg. 3532
SAL OPPENHEIM FRANCE—See Deutsche Bank Aktiengesellschaft; *Int'l*, pg. 2062
SAM SUSTAINABLE ASSET MANAGEMENT AG—See S&P Global Inc.; *U.S. Public*, pg. 1831
SAMUEL WILKINSON & SONS LIMITED—See Heidelberg Materials AG; *Int'l*, pg. 3319
SANDLER CAPITAL MANAGEMENT; *U.S. Private*, pg. 3544
SANDS BROTHERS ASSET MANAGEMENT LLC; *U.S. Private*, pg. 3544
SANFORD C. BERNSTEIN & CO., LLP—See Equitable Holdings, Inc.; *U.S. Public*, pg. 789
SANFORD C. BERNSTEIN (INDIA) PRIVATE LIMITED—See Equitable Holdings, Inc.; *U.S. Public*, pg. 790
SANFORD C. BERNSTEIN (SCHWIEZ) GMBH—See Equitable Holdings, Inc.; *U.S. Public*, pg. 790
SAN JUAN BASIN ROYALTY TRUST; *U.S. Public*, pg. 1839
SANKATY ADVISORS (AUSTRALIA), PTY. LTD—See Bain Capital, LP; *U.S. Private*, pg. 444
SANKATY ADVISORS ILLINOIS, LLC—See Bain Capital, LP; *U.S. Private*, pg. 444
SANKATY ADVISORS, LLC—See Bain Capital, LP; *U.S. Private*, pg. 444
SANKATY ADVISORS LTD.—See Bain Capital, LP; *U.S. Private*, pg. 444
SANKATY ADVISORS (NY), LLC—See Bain Capital, LP; *U.S. Private*, pg. 444
SANKATY EUROPEAN INVESTMENTS, S.A.R.L.—See Bain Capital, LP; *U.S. Private*, pg. 444
SANKEI BUILDING ASSET MANAGEMENT CO., LTD.—See Fuji Media Holdings, Inc.; *Int'l*, pg. 2814
SANTANDER ASSET MANAGEMENT CHILE S.A.—See Banco Santander, S.A.; *Int'l*, pg. 826
SANTANDER ASSET MANAGEMENT, S.A., S.G.I.I.C.—See Banco Santander, S.A.; *Int'l*, pg. 826
SANTANDER ASSET MANAGEMENT S.A.—See Banco Santander, S.A.; *Int'l*, pg. 826
SANTANDER ASSET MANAGEMENT UK LIMITED—See Banco Santander, S.A.; *Int'l*, pg. 826
SANTANDER TOWARZYSTWO FUNDUSZY INWESTYCYJNYCH S.A.—See Banco Santander, S.A.; *Int'l*, pg. 827
SARGENT BICKHAM LAGUDIS LLC—See Colorado Financial Management, Inc.; *U.S. Private*, pg. 974
SASU BFC CROISSANCE—See Groupe BPCE; *Int'l*, pg. 3099
SATURNA CAPITAL CORPORATION; *U.S. Private*, pg. 3553
SAVANO DIRECT CAPITAL PARTNERS LLC; *U.S. Private*, pg. 3556
SAVANT CAPITAL, LLC; *U.S. Private*, pg. 3556

523940 — PORTFOLIO MANAGEMEN...

SAWGRASS ASSET MANAGEMENT LLC; *U.S. Private*, pg. 3557
SAW MILL CAPITAL LLC; *U.S. Private*, pg. 3557
SCANCEM CENTRAL AFRICA HOLDING 1 AB—See Heidelberg Materials AG; *Int'l*, pg. 3319
SCHARF INVESTMENTS, LLC; *U.S. Private*, pg. 3563
SCHMIDT FINANCIAL GROUP, INC.—See Aon plc; *Int'l*, pg. 497
SCI CHAMPVERNIER—See BNP Paribas SA; *Int'l*, pg. 1092
SCIENTIFIC GAMES HOLDINGS (CANADA) ULC—See Light & Wonder, Inc.; *U.S. Public*, pg. 1314
SCOTTO & MELCHIORRE GROUP LLC; *U.S. Private*, pg. 3578
SCOUT INVESTMENTS, INC.—See Raymond James Financial, Inc.; *U.S. Public*, pg. 1764
SCULLY CAPITAL SERVICES, INC.—See Value Recovery Group, Inc.; *U.S. Private*, pg. 4337
SCULPTOR CAPITAL MANAGEMENT HONG KONG LIMITED—See Rithm Capital Corp.; *U.S. Public*, pg. 1800
SCULPTOR CAPITAL MANAGEMENT, INC.—See Rithm Capital Corp.; *U.S. Public*, pg. 1800
SCURA PARTNERS SECURITIES LLC; *U.S. Private*, pg. 3581
SDC CAPITAL PARTNERS, LLC; *U.S. Private*, pg. 3581
SEAM GROUP LLC—See ABB Ltd.; *Int'l*, pg. 56
SEAPORT GLOBAL HOLDINGS LLC; *U.S. Private*, pg. 3586
SEAPORT GLOBAL SECURITIES LLC—See Seaport Global Holdings LLC; *U.S. Private*, pg. 3586
SEATTLE CAPITAL MANAGEMENT COMPANY—See D.A. Davidson Companies; *U.S. Private*, pg. 1140
SECOND CITY PROPERTIES LIMITED—See Heidelberg Materials AG; *Int'l*, pg. 3319
SECURITIES AMERICA, INC.—See Reverence Capital Partners LLC; *U.S. Private*, pg. 3415
SECURITIES MANAGEMENT & RESEARCH, INC.—See Brookfield Corporation; *Int'l*, pg. 1174
SECURITIES SERVICE NETWORK INC.—See Reverence Capital Partners LLC; *U.S. Private*, pg. 3415
SECURITISATION ADVISORY SERVICES PTY LIMITED—See Commonwealth Bank of Australia; *Int'l*, pg. 1720
SECURITY BENEFIT CORPORATION—See Guggenheim Partners, LLC; *U.S. Private*, pg. 1812
SECURITY INVESTORS, LLC—See Guggenheim Partners, LLC; *U.S. Private*, pg. 1812
SEDGWICK NOBLE LOWNDES GROUP LIMITED—See Marsh & McLennan Companies, Inc.; *U.S. Public*, pg. 1388
SEGAL ADVISORS, INC.—See The Segal Group, Inc.; *U.S. Private*, pg. 4115
SEIDMAN INSURANCE CONSULTANTS LLC; *U.S. Private*, pg. 3599
SEI INSTITUTIONAL TRANSFER AGENT, INC.—See SEI Investments Company; *U.S. Public*, pg. 1857
SEI INVESTMENTS (ASIA), LIMITED—See SEI Investments Company; *U.S. Public*, pg. 1857
SEI INVESTMENTS CANADA COMPANY—See SEI Investments Company; *U.S. Public*, pg. 1857
SEI INVESTMENTS GLOBAL FUNDS SERVICES—See SEI Investments Company; *U.S. Public*, pg. 1857
SEI INVESTMENTS - GUERNSEY LIMITED—See SEI Investments Company; *U.S. Public*, pg. 1857
SEI INVESTMENTS (SOUTH AFRICA) LIMITED—See SEI Investments Company; *U.S. Public*, pg. 1857
SEI INVESTMENTS TRUSTEE & CUSTODIAL SERVICES (IRELAND) LIMITED—See SEI Investments Company; *U.S. Public*, pg. 1857
SEI TRUST COMPANY—See SEI Investments Company; *U.S. Public*, pg. 1857
SEIX INVESTMENT ADVISORS LLC—See Virtus Investment Partners, Inc.; *U.S. Public*, pg. 2301
SEKURA INDIA MANAGEMENT LIMITED—See Edelweiss Financial Services Ltd.; *Int'l*, pg. 2306
SELECTA HOLDING GMBH—See Allianz SE; *Int'l*, pg. 355
SEMINOLE ADVISORY SERVICES, LLC—See Seminole Holdings Group, LLC; *U.S. Private*, pg. 3604
SENTINEL ADVISORS CO.—See National Life Insurance Company; *U.S. Private*, pg. 2858
SENTINEL BROKERS CO., INC.; *U.S. Private*, pg. 3608
SEQUOIA FINANCIAL GROUP, LLC; *U.S. Private*, pg. 3612
SER CAPITAL PARTNERS LLC; *U.S. Private*, pg. 3612
SERVI CYLINDERSERVICE AS—See Ferd AS; *Int'l*, pg. 2636
SERVI HYDRANOR AS—See Ferd AS; *Int'l*, pg. 2636
SERVI ULSTEINVIK AS—See Ferd AS; *Int'l*, pg. 2636
THE SETTLEMENT ALLIANCE, LLC—See Sage Settlement Consulting, LLC; *U.S. Private*, pg. 3527
SF INVESTMENTS, INC.; *U.S. Private*, pg. 3621
SGGH, LLC—See Elah Holdings, Inc.; *U.S. Public*, pg. 722
SG TECH HOLDINGS LIMITED—See CW Group Holdings Limited; *Int'l*, pg. 1890
SHAANXI CHINLINK FINANCIAL GUARANTEE LIMITED—See ChinLink International Holdings Limited; *Int'l*, pg. 1570
SHAH CAPITAL PARTNERS, LP; *U.S. Private*, pg. 3623
SHANGHAI FUJIN INVESTMENT MANAGEMENT CO., LTD.—See Fortune Fountain (Beijing) Holding Group Co., Ltd.; *Int'l*, pg. 2743
SHANGHAI HAITONG SECURITIES ASSET MANAGEMENT COMPANY LIMITED—See Haitong Securities Co., Ltd.; *Int'l*, pg. 3218
SHANGHAI HONGDIAN INVESTMENT MANAGEMENT CO., LTD.—See HengTai Securities CO., LTD; *Int'l*, pg. 3347
SHANGHAI YINGWO INVESTMENT MANAGEMENT CO., LTD.—See HengTai Securities CO., LTD; *Int'l*, pg. 3347
SHAPEDIRECT LIMITED—See Heidelberg Materials AG; *Int'l*, pg. 3319
SHERIDAN CAPITAL PARTNERS LLC; *U.S. Private*, pg. 3633
SHI HOLDINGS PTY LIMITED—See Gowing Brothers Limited; *Int'l*, pg. 3044
SHOEMAKER FINANCIAL—See Securian Financial Group, Inc.; *U.S. Private*, pg. 3594
SHORELINE FINANCIAL ADVISORS, LLC—See Exencial Wealth Advisors, LLC; *U.S. Private*, pg. 1448
SIEBERT ADVISORNXT, INC.—See Siebert Financial Corp.; *U.S. Public*, pg. 1876
SIEMPRETAX LLC—See B. Riley Financial, Inc.; *U.S. Public*, pg. 261
SIEMPRETAX LLC—See Irradiant Partners, LP; *U.S. Private*, pg. 2141
SIG ASIA INVESTMENTS, LLLP—See Susquehanna International Group, LLP; *U.S. Private*, pg. 3885
SIGNATURE ESTATE & INVESTMENT ADVISORS, LLC—See Reverence Capital Partners LLC; *U.S. Private*, pg. 3415
THE SIGNATURE GROUP, LLC—See North Carolina Mutual Life Insurance Company; *U.S. Private*, pg. 2943
SILVANT CAPITAL MANAGEMENT, LLC—See Virtus Investment Partners, Inc.; *U.S. Public*, pg. 2301
SILVERCREST ASSET MANAGEMENT GROUP INC.; *U.S. Public*, pg. 1880
SILVERCREST ASSET MANAGEMENT GROUP LLC—See Silvercrest Asset Management Group Inc.; *U.S. Public*, pg. 1880
SILVERCREST L.P.—See Silvercrest Asset Management Group Inc.; *U.S. Public*, pg. 1880
SIMCORP A/S—See Deutsche Borse AG; *Int'l*, pg. 2064
SIMCORP LUXEMBOURG S.A.—See Deutsche Borse AG; *Int'l*, pg. 2064
SINGER & XENOS, INC.—See Mariner Wealth Advisors, LLC; *U.S. Private*, pg. 2576
SITIA BETEILIGUNGS- UND VERWALTUNGS GMBH—See Allianz SE; *Int'l*, pg. 355
SIT INVESTMENT ASSOCIATES, INC; *U.S. Private*, pg. 3676
SITUS INTERNATIONAL LIMITED—See Stone Point Capital LLC; *U.S. Private*, pg. 3825
SIXTH STREET ADVISERS, LLC—See Sixth Street Specialty Lending, Inc.; *U.S. Public*, pg. 1891
SKAJAQUODA GROUP INC.; *U.S. Private*, pg. 3681
SKYWAY ADVISORS, LLC—See Skyway Capital Partners, LLC; *U.S. Private*, pg. 3686
S.L. DE GESTION MOBILIARIA—See Lone Star Funds; *U.S. Private*, pg. 2485
SL GREEN FUNDING LLC—See SL Green Realty Corp.; *U.S. Public*, pg. 1894
SL INVESTMENT CORP.—See North Haven Private Income Fund LLC; *U.S. Private*, pg. 2945
SMART EXPO LIMITED—See News Corporation; *U.S. Public*, pg. 1520
SMARTSTOP ASSET MANAGEMENT, LLC—See Strategic Capital Holdings, LLC; *U.S. Private*, pg. 3834
SMH CAPITAL ADVISORS, INC.—See Lee Equity Partners LLC; *U.S. Private*, pg. 2412
SMITH, GRAHAM & COMPANY INVESTMENT ADVISORS, LP.; *U.S. Private*, pg. 3696
SMP ASSET MANAGEMENT, LLC; *U.S. Private*, pg. 3698
SOCIETE FRANCAISE DE GESTION ET DINVESTISSEMENT SOFRAGI SA—See Aema Groupe; *Int'l*, pg. 175
SOCIETE ORBAISIENNE DE PARTICIPATIONS—See BNP Paribas SA; *Int'l*, pg. 1092
SONTAG ADVISORY, LLC—See Aon plc; *Int'l*, pg. 497
SORTIS HOLDINGS, INC.; *U.S. Public*, pg. 1909
SOUND POINT CAPITAL MANAGEMENT, LP; *U.S. Private*, pg. 3717
SOUTHEASTERN ASSET MANAGEMENT, INC.; *U.S. Private*, pg. 3727
SOUTHEASTERN ASSET MANAGEMENT INTERNATIONAL (UK) LTD.—See Southeastern Asset Management, Inc.; *U.S. Private*, pg. 3727
SOUTHERNSUN ASSET MANAGEMENT, LLC—See Affiliated Managers Group, Inc.; *U.S. Public*, pg. 55
SOUTHERN WEALTH MANAGEMENT LLP—See The Cap Financial Group, LLC; *U.S. Private*, pg. 4004
SOUTHLAND MANAGEMENT LLC—See The Ensign Group, Inc.; *U.S. Public*, pg. 2072
SOVEREIGN DELAWARE INVESTMENT CORPORATION—See Banco Santander, S.A.; *Int'l*, pg. 827
SPARKASSE KREMSTAL PYHRN AKTIENGESELLSCHAFT—See Erste Group Bank AG; *Int'l*, pg. 2499

CORPORATE AFFILIATIONS

SPARROWS OFFSHORE GROUP LIMITED—See Altrad Investment Authority SAS; *Int'l*, pg. 398
SP CAPITAL AB—See E*TRADE Financial Corporation; *U.S. Private*, pg. 1302
SPC MANAGEMENT CO., INC. - BEDMINSTER OFFICE—See Swander Pace Capital, LLC; *U.S. Private*, pg. 3890
SPC MANAGEMENT CO., INC.—See Swander Pace Capital, LLC; *U.S. Private*, pg. 3890
S&P DJ INDICES UK LTD—See S&P Global Inc.; *U.S. Public*, pg. 1831
S&P DOW JONES INDICES LLC—See S&P Global Inc.; *U.S. Public*, pg. 1831
SPECPRO TECHNICAL SERVICES, LLC—See Bristol Bay Native Corporation; *U.S. Private*, pg. 656
SPECTRUM ASSET MANAGEMENT, INC.—See Principal Financial Group, Inc.; *U.S. Public*, pg. 1722
SPECTRUM AUTOMOTIVE HOLDINGS LLC—See Cornell Capital LLC; *U.S. Private*, pg. 1051
SPEND MANAGEMENT EXPERTS, LLC—See Gryphon Investors, LLC; *U.S. Private*, pg. 1800
SPINDLETOP CAPITAL MANAGEMENT LLC; *U.S. Private*, pg. 3757
SPIRE INVESTMENT PARTNERS LLC; *U.S. Private*, pg. 3757
SPRL FERME DE WISEMPIERRE—See Heidelberg Materials AG; *Int'l*, pg. 3319
SPRUCE PRIVATE INVESTORS LLC; *U.S. Private*, pg. 3765
SSARIS ADVISORS, LLC; *U.S. Private*, pg. 3768
SSB INVESTMENTS, INC.—See State Street Corporation; *U.S. Public*, pg. 1940
SS&C HEDGE FUND SERVICES NORTH AMERICA, INC.—See SS&C Technologies Holdings, Inc.; *U.S. Public*, pg. 1924
SS&C PRIVATE EQUITY SERVICES, INC.—See SS&C Technologies Holdings, Inc.; *U.S. Public*, pg. 1924
SSGM INTERNATIONAL UK—See State Street Corporation; *U.S. Public*, pg. 1941
SSI INVESTMENT MANAGEMENT, INC.—See Kelso & Company, L.P.; *U.S. Private*, pg. 2280
STACKLA PTY. LTD.—See Bailador Technology Investments Limited; *Int'l*, pg. 802
STADION MONEY MANAGEMENT, LLC—See TA Associates, Inc.; *U.S. Private*, pg. 3918
STAGE 1 VENTURES, LLC; *U.S. Private*, pg. 3775
THE STAGWELL GROUP LLC—See Stagwell, Inc.; *U.S. Public*, pg. 1928
STANDARD & POOR'S COMPUSTAT SERVICES, INC.—See S&P Global Inc.; *U.S. Public*, pg. 1831
STANDISH MELLON ASSET MANAGEMENT COMPANY LLC—See The Bank of New York Mellon Corporation; *U.S. Public*, pg. 2038
STARBOARD VALUE LP; *U.S. Private*, pg. 3786
STARCAPITAL AG—See Bellevue Group AG; *Int'l*, pg. 967
STARK CAPITAL MANAGEMENT LLC—See Atlantic Capital Group, Inc.; *U.S. Private*, pg. 372
STARWOOD CAPITAL EUROPE ADVISERS, LLP—See Starwood Capital Group Global I, LLC; *U.S. Private*, pg. 3789
STARWOOD CAPITAL GROUP EUROPEAN SARL—See Starwood Capital Group Global I, LLC; *U.S. Private*, pg. 3789
STARWOOD REAL ESTATE SECURITIES, LLC—See Starwood Capital Group Global I, LLC; *U.S. Private*, pg. 3789
STATE FARM INVESTMENT MANAGEMENT CORP.—See State Farm Mutual Automobile Insurance Company; *U.S. Private*, pg. 3792
STATE STREET AUSTRALIA LTD.—See State Street Corporation; *U.S. Public*, pg. 1940
STATE STREET BANK GMBH - ZURICH BRANCH—See State Street Corporation; *U.S. Public*, pg. 1940
STATE STREET BANK S.P.A.—See State Street Corporation; *U.S. Public*, pg. 1940
STATE STREET BANK & TRUST COMPANY - SEOUL—See State Street Corporation; *U.S. Public*, pg. 1940
STATE STREET BANK & TRUST COMPANY - SINGAPORE—See State Street Corporation; *U.S. Public*, pg. 1940
STATE STREET BANK & TRUST COMPANY—See State Street Corporation; *U.S. Public*, pg. 1940
STATE STREET BANK & TRUST COMPANY - TAIPEI—See State Street Corporation; *U.S. Public*, pg. 1940
STATE STREET EUROPE LIMITED—See State Street Corporation; *U.S. Public*, pg. 1941
STATE STREET FUND SERVICES IRELAND LTD—See State Street Corporation; *U.S. Public*, pg. 1941
STATE STREET FUND SERVICES TORONTO, INC.—See State Street Corporation; *U.S. Public*, pg. 1941
STATE STREET GLOBAL ADVISORS AG—See State Street Corporation; *U.S. Public*, pg. 1941
STATE STREET GLOBAL ADVISORS ASIA LIMITED—See State Street Corporation; *U.S. Public*, pg. 1941
STATE STREET GLOBAL ADVISORS AUSTRALIA LTD.—See State Street Corporation; *U.S. Public*, pg. 1941
STATE STREET GLOBAL ADVISORS GMBH—See State

N.A.I.C.S. INDEX
523940 — PORTFOLIO MANAGEMEN...

Street Corporation; *U.S. Public*, pg. 1941
STATE STREET GLOBAL ADVISORS, INC.—See State Street Corporation; *U.S. Public*, pg. 1941
STATE STREET GLOBAL ADVISORS SA/NV—See State Street Corporation; *U.S. Public*, pg. 1941
STATE STREET GLOBAL ADVISORS SINGAPORE LIMITED—See State Street Corporation; *U.S. Public*, pg. 1941
STATE STREET GLOBAL ADVISORS—See State Street Corporation; *U.S. Public*, pg. 1941
STATE STREET GLOBAL MARKETS, LLC—See State Street Corporation; *U.S. Public*, pg. 1941
STATE STREET INTERNATIONAL IRELAND LIMITED—See State Street Corporation; *U.S. Public*, pg. 1941
STATE STREET TRUST COMPANY CANADA—See State Street Corporation; *U.S. Public*, pg. 1941
STEELE CREEK CAPITAL CORPORATION; *U.S. Private*, pg. 3796
STEELRIVER INFRASTRUCTURE PARTNERS LP; *U.S. Private*, pg. 3797
STEEN & STROM HOLDING AB—See BNP Paribas SA; *Int'l*, pg. 1092
STELLUS CAPITAL MANAGEMENT, LLC; *U.S. Private*, pg. 3801
STEPSTONE GESTAO DE RECURSOS LTDA.—See StepStone Group Inc.; *U.S. Public*, pg. 1945
STEPSTONE GROUP (CHINA) LIMITED—See StepStone Group Inc.; *U.S. Public*, pg. 1945
STEPSTONE GROUP EUROPE ALTERNATIVE INVESTMENTS LIMITED—See StepStone Group Inc.; *U.S. Public*, pg. 1945
STEPSTONE GROUP (HK) LIMITED—See StepStone Group Inc.; *U.S. Public*, pg. 1945
STEPSTONE GROUP INC.; *U.S. Public*, pg. 1945
THE STERLING GROUP, L.P.; *U.S. Private*, pg. 4121
STERLING TRADE CAPITAL—See Sterling Bancorp; *U.S. Public*, pg. 1946
STEWART CAPITAL ADVISORS, LLC—See S&T Bancorp, Inc.; *U.S. Public*, pg. 1832
STEWART FINANCIAL SERVICES, INC.—See Stewart Information Services Corporation; *U.S. Public*, pg. 1948
STICHTING DELTA ZEELAND FONDS—See Delta N.V.; *Int'l*, pg. 2019
STIFEL TRUST COMPANY, NATIONAL ASSOCIATION—See Stifel Financial Corp.; *U.S. Public*, pg. 1950
STILLWATER INVESTMENT MANAGEMENT, LLC—See Dakota Wealth Management LLC; *U.S. Private*, pg. 1148
STOCKCROSS FINANCIAL SERVICES, INC; *U.S. Private*, pg. 3814
STOCKMAN ASSET MANAGEMENT, INC.—See Stockman Financial Corp.; *U.S. Private*, pg. 3815
STOKER OSTLER WEALTH ADVISORS, INC.—See Bank of Montreal; *Int'l*, pg. 846
STONE ASSET MANAGEMENT, INC.—See Avidian Wealth Solutions, LLC; *U.S. Private*, pg. 407
STONE POINT CREDIT CORPORATION; *U.S. Private*, pg. 3826
STORM HOLDING NORWAY AS—See BNP Paribas SA; *Int'l*, pg. 1092
STOUT RISIUS ROSS, INC.; *U.S. Private*, pg. 3832
STRAIGHT PATH COMMUNICATIONS INC.—See Verizon Communications Inc.; *U.S. Public*, pg. 2285
STRATEGAS RESEARCH PARTNERS, LLC; *U.S. Private*, pg. 3834
STRATEGIC ADVISORY GROUP INC.—See Jones Lang LaSalle Incorporated; *U.S. Public*, pg. 1206
STRATEGIC ASSET MANAGEMENT GROUP ADVISORS, INC.; *U.S. Private*, pg. 3834
STRATEGIC FINANCIAL SOLUTIONS, LLC—See Nasdaq, Inc.; *U.S. Public*, pg. 1492
STRATEGIC WEALTH ADVISORY LLC—See Informed Family Financial Services, Inc.; *U.S. Private*, pg. 2073
THE STRATFORD-CAMBRIDGE GROUP CO.; *U.S. Private*, pg. 4123
STRONG WAY INVESTMENT LIMITED—See Dynamic Holdings Limited; *Int'l*, pg. 2240
STRUCTURED ASSET MANAGEMENT INC.—See Apella Capital LLC; *U.S. Private*, pg. 291
STRUCTURED PRODUCTS CORP.—See Citigroup Inc.; *U.S. Public*, pg. 503
SUMITOMO MITSUI DS ASSET MANAGEMENT COMPANY, LIMITED—See Daiwa Securities Group Inc.; *Int'l*, pg. 1949
SUMMIT EQUITY GROUP, LLC; *U.S. Private*, pg. 3854
SUMMIT PARTNERS LIMITED—See Summit Partners, L.P.; *U.S. Private*, pg. 3856
SUMMIT STRATEGIES INC.; *U.S. Private*, pg. 3857
SUMMIT SYSTEMS AND DESIGN, LLC—See NEWTEKONE, INC.; *U.S. Public*, pg. 1521
SUNRISE ADVISORS, INC.—See Creative Planning, LLC; *U.S. Public*, pg. 1090
SUNSET FINANCIAL SERVICES, INC.—See Reverence Capital Partners LLC; *U.S. Private*, pg. 3415
SUNTRUST INVESTMENT SERVICES, INC.—See Truist Financial Corporation; *U.S. Public*, pg. 2200
SUN VALLEY GOLD LLC; *U.S. Private*, pg. 3864

SUPERIOR FINANCIAL SERVICES, INC.—See First Horizon Corporation; *U.S. Public*, pg. 844
SUSQUEHANNA GROWTH EQUITY, LLC—See Susquehanna International Group, LLP; *U.S. Private*, pg. 3885
SUSTAINABLE GROWTH ADVISERS, LP—See Virtus Investment Partners, Inc.; *U.S. Public*, pg. 2301
SUSTAINALYTICS JAPAN INC.—See Morningstar, Inc.; *U.S. Public*, pg. 1477
SUSTAINALYTICS UK LIMITED—See Morningstar, Inc.; *U.S. Public*, pg. 1477
SUSTAINALYTICS U.S. INC.—See Morningstar, Inc.; *U.S. Public*, pg. 1477
SUZHOU DONGWU CEMENT CO., LTD.—See Dongwu Cement International Limited; *Int'l*, pg. 2171
SVB ASSET MANAGEMENT—See Federal Deposit Insurance Corporation; *U.S. Private*, pg. 1487
SVB BUSINESS PARTNERS (BEIJING) CO. LTD.—See SVB Financial Group; *U.S. Public*, pg. 1968
SVB ISRAEL ADVISORS, LTD.—See SVB Financial Group; *U.S. Public*, pg. 1968
SVERICA INTERNATIONAL (SAN FRANCISCO) LLC—See Sverica Capital Management LP; *U.S. Private*, pg. 3888
SVM ASSET MANAGEMENT LIMITED—See AssetCo plc; *Int'l*, pg. 643
SWAP FINANCIAL GROUP LLC—See GoldenTree Asset Management LP; *U.S. Private*, pg. 1734
SWIFTSURE CAPITAL LLC; *U.S. Private*, pg. 3893
SWINEFORD NATIONAL BANK—See Fulton Financial Corporation; *U.S. Public*, pg. 892
SYCOMORE ASSET MANAGEMENT S.A.—See Assicurazioni Generali S.p.A.; *Int'l*, pg. 648
SYMPHONY ASSET MANAGEMENT, LLC—See Teachers Insurance Association - College Retirement Fund; *U.S. Private*, pg. 3947
SYNOVUS MORTGAGE CORP.—See Synovus Financial Corp.; *U.S. Public*, pg. 1971
SYNOVUS MORTGAGE CORP.—See Synovus Financial Corp.; *U.S. Public*, pg. 1972
SYNTRUS ACHMEA PENSIOENBEHEER N.V.—See Achmea B.V.; *Int'l*, pg. 104
SYNTRUS ACHMEA REAL ESTATE & FINANCE B.V.—See Achmea B.V.; *Int'l*, pg. 104
SYSTEMATICA INVESTMENTS LIMITED—See Affiliated Managers Group, Inc.; *U.S. Public*, pg. 56
SYSTEMATICA INVESTMENTS US LLC—See Affiliated Managers Group, Inc.; *U.S. Public*, pg. 56
SYSTEMATIC FINANCIAL MANAGEMENT, L.P.—See Affiliated Managers Group, Inc.; *U.S. Public*, pg. 56
SYZ ASSET MANAGEMENT (SUISSE) SA—See Financiere SYZ & CO SA; *Int'l*, pg. 2669
T2 PARTNERS MANAGEMENT, LP—See T2 Partners Group, LLC; *U.S. Private*, pg. 3913
T3 LIVE LLC; *U.S. Private*, pg. 3913
TA ASSOCIATES MANAGEMENT, L.P.—See TA Associates, Inc.; *U.S. Private*, pg. 3918
TA ASSOCIATES (UK), LLP—See TA Associates, Inc.; *U.S. Private*, pg. 3918
TAC PROPERTY CO., LTD.—See Charoen Pokphand Group Co., Ltd.; *Int'l*, pg. 1453
TAG RESOURCES LLC—See Aegon N.V.; *Int'l*, pg. 174
TAG WORLDWIDE HOLDINGS LIMITED—See Dentsu Group Inc.; *Int'l*, pg. 2039
TAILWIND MANAGEMENT LP—See Tailwind Capital Group, LLC; *U.S. Private*, pg. 3924
TAIPING FUND MANAGEMENT COMPANY LIMITED—See China Taiping Insurance Holdings Company Limited; *Int'l*, pg. 1557
TAITBOUT PARTICIPATION 3 SNC—See BNP Paribas SA; *Int'l*, pg. 1093
TAKAFUL RE LIMITED—See Arab Insurance Group B.S.C.; *Int'l*, pg. 530
TALIS ADVISORY SERVICES LLC—See Generational Equity Group, Inc.; *U.S. Private*, pg. 1668
TARGA PIPELINE PARTNERS GP LLC—See Targa Resources Corp.; *U.S. Public*, pg. 1982
TARSADIA INVESTMENTS, LLC; *U.S. Private*, pg. 3934
TAYLOR RAFFERTY ASSOCIATES, INC.; *U.S. Private*, pg. 3940
TCW ASSET MANAGEMENT CO., INC.—See The Carlyle Group Inc.; *U.S. Public*, pg. 2056
TCW DIRECT LENDING LLC; *U.S. Private*, pg. 3943
TD AMERITRADE SERVICES COMPANY, INC.—See The Charles Schwab Corporation; *U.S. Public*, pg. 2058
TECTONIC ADVISORS, LLC—See Tectonic Financial, Inc.; *U.S. Public*, pg. 1989
TEGRATON LIMITED—See Hang Lung Group Limited; *Int'l*, pg. 3245
T.E. INVESTMENT COUNSEL INC.—See iA Financial Corporation Inc.; *Int'l*, pg. 3567
TELECOMPUTING SWEDEN AB—See IK Investment Partners Limited; *Int'l*, pg. 3610
TELEMUS CAPITAL PARTNERS, LLC—See Clayton, Dubilier & Rice, LLC; *U.S. Private*, pg. 923
TELEMUS CAPITAL PARTNERS, LLC—See Stone Point Capital LLC; *U.S. Private*, pg. 3824
TEMPLAR ESSEX INC.—See International Paper Company; *U.S. Public*, pg. 1158

TEMPLETON DO BRASIL LTDA.—See Franklin Resources, Inc.; *U.S. Public*, pg. 883
TEMPLETON GLOBAL ADVISORS LIMITED—See Franklin Resources, Inc.; *U.S. Public*, pg. 883
TEMPLETON INTERNATIONAL, INC.—See Franklin Resources, Inc.; *U.S. Public*, pg. 883
TEMPLETON INVESTMENT COUNSEL, LLC—See Franklin Resources, Inc.; *U.S. Public*, pg. 883
TEMPLETON WORLDWIDE, INC.—See Franklin Resources, Inc.; *U.S. Public*, pg. 883
TENASKA CAPITAL MANAGEMENT, LLC—See Tenaska, Inc.; *U.S. Private*, pg. 3965
TERMINUS CAPITAL PARTNERS, LLC; *U.S. Private*, pg. 3969
TEUCRIUM TRADING, LLC—See BGC Group, Inc.; *U.S. Public*, pg. 330
TEXTRON GERMANY HOLDING GMBH—See Textron Inc.; *U.S. Public*, pg. 2028
TFI ALLIANZ POLSKA S.A.—See Allianz SE; *Int'l*, pg. 356
TGP INVESTMENTS, LLC; *U.S. Private*, pg. 3979
THAI ASSET ENFORCEMENT AND RECOVERY ASSET MANAGEMENT COMPANY LIMITED—See Deutsche Bank Aktiengesellschaft; *Int'l*, pg. 2062
THALIA SA—See EFG International AG; *Int'l*, pg. 2320
THIRD AVENUE MANAGEMENT LLC—See Quaestus Holdings, LLC; *U.S. Private*, pg. 3316
THIRD POINT LLC; *U.S. Private*, pg. 4145
THE THIRTY-EIGHT HUNDRED FUND, LLC—See Wells Fargo & Company; *U.S. Public*, pg. 2345
THOMAS WEISEL CAPITAL MANAGEMENT LLC—See Stifel Financial Corp.; *U.S. Public*, pg. 1950
THOMSON, HORSTMANN & BRYANT, INC.—See Victory Capital Holdings, Inc.; *U.S. Public*, pg. 2296
THREADNEEDLE PORTFOLIO SERVICES HONG KONG LTD.—See Ameriprise Financial, Inc.; *U.S. Public*, pg. 114
THREADNEEDLE PROPERTY INVESTMENTS LTD.—See Ameriprise Financial, Inc.; *U.S. Public*, pg. 114
THREESIXTY SERVICES LLP—See Fintel plc; *Int'l*, pg. 2677
THROGMORTON UK LTD.—See Apex Fund Services Holdings Ltd.; *Int'l*, pg. 510
TH TRS CORP.—See Two Harbors Investment Corp.; *U.S. Public*, pg. 2207
TIEDEMANN WEALTH MANAGEMENT, LLC—See AlTi Global, Inc.; *U.S. Public*, pg. 87
TIGER INFRASTRUCTURE PARTNERS LP; *U.S. Private*, pg. 4170
TILLOTSON COMMERCIAL MOTORS LIMITED—See Heidelberg Materials AG; *Int'l*, pg. 3320
TIMIOS DEFAULT SERVICES, INC.—See Ideanomics, Inc.; *U.S. Public*, pg. 1088
TIROLINVEST KAPITALANLAGEGESELLSCHAFT MBH.—See Erste Group Bank AG; *Int'l*, pg. 2499
TKB BNP PARIBAS INVESTMENT PARTNERS JSC—See BNP Paribas SA; *Int'l*, pg. 1082
TMI HOLDINGS, INC.—See Tuesday Morning Corporation; *U.S. Public*, pg. 2204
THE TOKARZ GROUP ADVISERS, LLC; *U.S. Private*, pg. 4127
TOM JOHNSON INVESTMENT MANAGEMENT, LLC (TJIM); *U.S. Private*, pg. 4182
TORTOISE CAPITAL ADVISORS, LLC—See Lovell Minnick Partners LLC; *U.S. Private*, pg. 2503
TORTOISE CREDIT STRATEGIES, LLC—See Lovell Minnick Partners LLC; *U.S. Private*, pg. 2503
TOWARZYSTWO FUNDUSZY INWESTYCYJNYCH CAPITAL PARTNERS SA—See Capital Partners S.A.; *Int'l*, pg. 1312
TOWER THREE PARTNERS, LLC; *U.S. Private*, pg. 4194
TOWNSEND GROUP ASIA LIMITED—See Aon plc; *Int'l*, pg. 495
TPG CAPITAL LLP—See TPG Capital, L.P.; *U.S. Public*, pg. 2175
TQI EXCHANGE, LLC—See Deutsche Bank Aktiengesellschaft; *Int'l*, pg. 2062
TRADEWISE ADVISORS, INC.—See The Charles Schwab Corporation; *U.S. Public*, pg. 2058
TRAFALGAR MANAGED INVESTMENTS LIMITED—See Centuria Capital Limited; *Int'l*, pg. 1416
TRANSAMERICA FINANCIAL ADVISORS, INC.—See Aegon N.V.; *Int'l*, pg. 174
TRANSAMERICA INVESTMENT MANAGEMENT—See Aegon N.V.; *Int'l*, pg. 174
TRANSAMERICA RETIREMENT SOLUTIONS, LLC—See Aegon N.V.; *Int'l*, pg. 174
TRAVERSE POINTE PARTNERS LLC; *U.S. Private*, pg. 4214
TREUINVEST SERVICE GMBH—See Deutsche Bank Aktiengesellschaft; *Int'l*, pg. 2062
TRG MANAGEMENT LP; *U.S. Private*, pg. 4219
TRIAD ADVISORS, INC.—See Reverence Capital Partners LLC; *U.S. Private*, pg. 3415
TRIAD FINANCIAL ADVISORS INC.—See New Mountain Capital, LLC; *U.S. Private*, pg. 2901
TRI FUND MANAGEMENT, L.P.; *U.S. Private*, pg. 4226
TRI-ARTISAN PARTNERS ADVISORS EUROPE LLP—See

523940 — PORTFOLIO MANAGEMEN...

Morgan Joseph TriArtisan Group Inc.; *U.S. Private*, pg. 2784
TRILANTIC CAPITAL MANAGEMENT L.P.; *U.S. Private*, pg. 4231
TRILOGY CAPITAL GROUP, LLC; *U.S. Private*, pg. 4232
TRILOGY GLOBAL ADVISORS INTERNATIONAL LLP—See Affiliated Managers Group, Inc.; *U.S. Public*, pg. 56
TRILOGY GLOBAL ADVISORS, LP—See Affiliated Managers Group, Inc.; *U.S. Public*, pg. 56
TRIOPTIMA AB—See CME Group, Inc.; *U.S. Public*, pg. 518
TRIPLEPOINT PRIVATE VENTURE CREDIT INC.; *U.S. Private*, pg. 4237
TRIVE CAPITAL MANAGEMENT LLC—See Trive Capital Inc.; *U.S. Private*, pg. 4240
TROON MANAGEMENT CORPORATION—See Old Republic International Corporation; *U.S. Public*, pg. 1569
T. ROWE PRICE ADVISORY SERVICES, INC.—See T. Rowe Price Group Inc.; *U.S. Public*, pg. 1978
T. ROWE PRICE FUNDS SICAV—See T. Rowe Price Group Inc.; *U.S. Public*, pg. 1978
T. ROWE PRICE INTERNATIONAL, INC.—See T. Rowe Price Group Inc.; *U.S. Public*, pg. 1978
T. ROWE PRICE INTERNATIONAL LTD—See T. Rowe Price Group Inc.; *U.S. Public*, pg. 1978
T. ROWE PRICE INVESTMENT SERVICES INC.—See T. Rowe Price Group Inc.; *U.S. Public*, pg. 1978
T. ROWE PRICE RETIREMENT PLAN SERVICES, INC.—See T. Rowe Price Group Inc.; *U.S. Public*, pg. 1978
T. ROWE PRICE (SWITZERLAND) GMBH—See T. Rowe Price Group Inc.; *U.S. Public*, pg. 1978
TRUENORTH, INC.—See IMA Financial Group, Inc.; *U.S. Private*, pg. 2044
TRUEPOINT INC.; *U.S. Private*, pg. 4249
TRYKO PARTNERS, LLC; *U.S. Private*, pg. 4251
TTCP MANAGEMENT SERVICES, LLC.; *U.S. Private*, pg. 4254
TUDOR CAPITAL AUSTRALIA PTY. LTD.—See Tudor Investment Corporation; *U.S. Private*, pg. 4257
TUDOR INVESTMENT CORPORATION; *U.S. Private*, pg. 4257
TURNER INVESTMENTS, INC.—See Veracen Funds LP; *U.S. Private*, pg. 4359
TWEEDY, BROWNE COMPANY LLC—See Affiliated Managers Group, Inc.; *U.S. Public*, pg. 56
TYNDALE ADVISORS, LLC; *U.S. Private*, pg. 4268
UBI MANAGEMENT COMPANY SA—See EFG International AG; *Int'l*, pg. 2321
UBL FUND MANAGERS LIMITED—See Bestway (Holdings) Limited; *Int'l*, pg. 1001
UCB ASSET MANAGEMENT, INC.—See UCBH Holdings, Inc.; *U.S. Private*, pg. 4273
UDELL ASSOCIATES, INC.—See Aon plc; *Int'l*, pg. 497
UDS (NO 3) LIMITED—See Heidelberg Materials AG; *Int'l*, pg. 3320
ULLICO INVESTMENT ADVISORS, INC.—See Ullico Inc.; *U.S. Private*, pg. 4276
ULLICO INVESTMENT COMPANY, INC.—See Ullico Inc.; *U.S. Private*, pg. 4276
ULTIMUS ASSET SERVICES, LLC—See GTCR LLC; *U.S. Private*, pg. 1806
ULTIMUS FUND SOLUTIONS, LLC—See GTCR LLC; *U.S. Private*, pg. 1806
UNION FINANCIERE DE FRANCE BANQUE SA—See Aema Groupe; *Int'l*, pg. 175
UNION INVESTMENT AUSTRIA GMBH—See DZ BANK AG Deutsche Zentral-Genossenschaftsbank; *Int'l*, pg. 2245
UNION INVESTMENT FINANCIAL SERVICES S.A.—See DZ BANK AG Deutsche Zentral-Genossenschaftsbank; *Int'l*, pg. 2245
UNION INVESTMENT INSTITUTIONAL GMBH—See DZ BANK AG Deutsche Zentral-Genossenschaftsbank; *Int'l*, pg. 2245
UNION INVESTMENT INSTITUTIONAL PROPERTY GMBH—See DZ BANK AG Deutsche Zentral-Genossenschaftsbank; *Int'l*, pg. 2245
UNION INVESTMENT REAL ESTATE ASIA PACIFIC PTE. LTD.—See DZ BANK AG Deutsche Zentral-Genossenschaftsbank; *Int'l*, pg. 2245
UNION INVESTMENT REAL ESTATE AUSTRIA AG—See DZ BANK AG Deutsche Zentral-Genossenschaftsbank; *Int'l*, pg. 2245
UNION INVESTMENT REAL ESTATE FRANCE S.A.S.—See DZ BANK AG Deutsche Zentral-Genossenschaftsbank; *Int'l*, pg. 2245
UNITED CAPITAL FINANCIAL ADVISERS, LLC - SILICON VALLEY—See The Goldman Sachs Group, Inc.; *U.S. Public*, pg. 2082
UNITED CAPITAL FINANCIAL ADVISERS, LLC—See The Goldman Sachs Group, Inc.; *U.S. Public*, pg. 2082
UNITY DELAWARE INVESTMENT 2, INC.—See Unity Bancorp, Inc.; *U.S. Public*, pg. 2253
UNITY NATIONAL BANK—See Park National Corporation; *U.S. Public*, pg. 1638
URB INVESTMENTS LIMITED—See Centuria Capital Limited; *Int'l*, pg. 1416

U.S. BANCORP ADVISORS, LLC—See U.S. Bancorp; *U.S. Public*, pg. 2212
U.S. BANCORP EQUIPMENT FINANCE, INC.—See U.S. Bancorp; *U.S. Public*, pg. 2212
U.S. FINANCIAL SERVICES, LLC; *U.S. Private*, pg. 4270
U.S. GLOBAL INVESTORS, INC.; *U.S. Public*, pg. 2213
U.S. TRUST COMPANY, N.A.—See Bank of America Corporation; *U.S. Public*, pg. 271
U.S. TRUST COMPANY—See Bank of America Corporation; *U.S. Public*, pg. 271
U.S. TRUST COMPANY—See Bank of America Corporation; *U.S. Public*, pg. 271
U.S. TRUST COMPANY—See Bank of America Corporation; *U.S. Public*, pg. 271
U.S. TRUST COMPANY—See Bank of America Corporation; *U.S. Public*, pg. 271
U.S. TRUST COMPANY—See Bank of America Corporation; *U.S. Public*, pg. 271
U.S. TRUST COMPANY—See Bank of America Corporation; *U.S. Public*, pg. 271
U.S. TRUST COMPANY—See Bank of America Corporation; *U.S. Public*, pg. 271
U.S. TRUST COMPANY—See Bank of America Corporation; *U.S. Public*, pg. 271
U.S. TRUST COMPANY—See Bank of America Corporation; *U.S. Public*, pg. 271
U.S. TRUST COMPANY—See Bank of America Corporation; *U.S. Public*, pg. 271
U.S. TRUST COMPANY—See Bank of America Corporation; *U.S. Public*, pg. 271
U.S. TRUST COMPANY—See Bank of America Corporation; *U.S. Public*, pg. 271
U.S. TRUST COMPANY—See Bank of America Corporation; *U.S. Public*, pg. 271
U.S. TRUST COMPANY—See Bank of America Corporation; *U.S. Public*, pg. 271
U.S. TRUST COMPANY—See Bank of America Corporation; *U.S. Public*, pg. 271
U.S. TRUST COMPANY—See Bank of America Corporation; *U.S. Public*, pg. 271
U.S. TRUST COMPANY—See Bank of America Corporation; *U.S. Public*, pg. 271
U.S. TRUST COMPANY—See Bank of America Corporation; *U.S. Public*, pg. 271
U.S. TRUST COMPANY—See Bank of America Corporation; *U.S. Public*, pg. 271
U.S. TRUST COMPANY—See Bank of America Corporation; *U.S. Public*, pg. 271
U.S. TRUST COMPANY—See Bank of America Corporation; *U.S. Public*, pg. 271
VACO SAN ANTONIO—See Olympus Partners; *U.S. Private*, pg. 3014
VAIL ASSOCIATES INVESTMENTS, INC.—See Vail Resorts, Inc.; *U.S. Public*, pg. 2271
VALEANT CANADA HOLDINGS LIMITED—See Bausch Health Companies Inc.; *Int'l*, pg. 898
VALIRA ASSET MANAGEMENT SL—See Credit Andorra, S.A.; *Int'l*, pg. 1835
VALORA HOLDING FINANCE LTD.—See Fomento Economico Mexicano, S.A.B. de C.V.; *Int'l*, pg. 2724
VALSTONE ASSET MANAGEMENT—See ValStone Partners, LLC; *U.S. Private*, pg. 4337
VAN BORTEL FINANCE CORPORATION—See Van Bortel Aircraft Inc.; *U.S. Private*, pg. 4339
VAN ECK ASSOCIATES CORP.; *U.S. Private*, pg. 4339
VAN ECK SWITZERLAND AG—See Van Eck Associates Corp.; *U.S. Private*, pg. 4340
VAN KAMPEN GELD B.V.—See ASR Nederland N.V.; *Int'l*, pg. 632
VAN KAMPEN GROEP HOLDING B.V.—See ASR Nederland N.V.; *Int'l*, pg. 632
VARAGON CAPITAL PARTNERS, L.P.—See Aflac Incorporated; *U.S. Public*, pg. 57
VAUGHAN NELSON INVESTMENT MANAGEMENT, L.P.—See Groupe BPCE; *Int'l*, pg. 3096
VBG CONSULTING (BEIJING) CO., LTD.—See Hatcher Group Ltd.; *Int'l*, pg. 3284
VCB FINANCIAL GROUP, INC.—See Blue Ridge Bankshares, Inc.; *U.S. Public*, pg. 365
VECTOR WEALTH MANAGEMENT—See Warburg Pincus LLC; *U.S. Private*, pg. 4439
VEGA INVESTMENT MANAGERS—See Groupe BPCE; *Int'l*, pg. 3096
VELTEX CORPORATION; *U.S. Public*, pg. 2277
VENTURE CAPITAL BANK BSC—See Esterad Investment Company BSC; *Int'l*, pg. 2518
VERITABLE, LP—See Affiliated Managers Group, Inc.; *U.S. Public*, pg. 56
VERITAS ASSET MANAGEMENT LLP—See Affiliated Managers Group, Inc.; *U.S. Public*, pg. 56
VERONIS SUHLER STEVENSON PARTNERS LLC; *U.S. Private*, pg. 4368
VESEY STREET CAPITAL PARTNERS, L.L.C; *U.S. Private*, pg. 4371
VETCO ENTERPRISE GMBH—See NOV, Inc.; *U.S. Public*, pg. 1547
VICTORY CAPITAL HOLDINGS, INC.; *U.S. Public*, pg. 2296
VICTORY CAPITAL MANAGEMENT, INC.—See Crestview Partners, L.P.; *U.S. Private*, pg. 1098

CORPORATE AFFILIATIONS

VICTORY PARK CAPITAL ADVISORS, LLC; *U.S. Private*, pg. 4379
VIKING INVESTMENTS GROUP, LLC—See Camber Energy, Inc.; *U.S. Public*, pg. 425
VILLA WORLD LIMITED—See AVID Property Group; *Int'l*, pg. 743
VIRTUAL LEASE SERVICES LIMITED—See NetSol Technologies, Inc.; *U.S. Public*, pg. 1509
VIRTUE CAPITAL MANAGEMENT LLC; *U.S. Private*, pg. 4389
VIRTUS ETF SOLUTIONS LLC—See Virtus Investment Partners, Inc.; *U.S. Public*, pg. 2301
VIRTUS INVESTMENT ADVISERS, INC.—See Virtus Investment Partners, Inc.; *U.S. Public*, pg. 2301
VIRTUS INVESTMENT PARTNERS, INC.; *U.S. Public*, pg. 2300
VISIONREFINE LIMITED—See Heidelberg Materials AG; *Int'l*, pg. 3320
VISTA EQUITY PARTNERS MANAGEMENT, LLC—See Vista Equity Partners, LLC; *U.S. Private*, pg. 4402
VISTANA PORTFOLIO SERVICES, INC.—See Marriott International, Inc.; *U.S. Public*, pg. 1372
VITURA—See Northwood Investors, LLC; *U.S. Private*, pg. 2963
VIVALDI CAPITAL MANAGEMENT, LLC; *U.S. Private*, pg. 4406
VNA HOLDING INC.—See AB Volvo; *Int'l*, pg. 42
VOLKSFURSORGE FIXED ASSET GMBH—See Cinven Limited; *Int'l*, pg. 1616
VOLVO HOLDING SVERIGE AB—See AB Volvo; *Int'l*, pg. 44
VOLVO TREASURY AB—See AB Volvo; *Int'l*, pg. 45
VOYAGER DIGITAL LTD; *U.S. Public*, pg. 2312
VR CONSULTINGPARTNER GMBH—See DZ BANK AG Deutsche Zentral-Genossenschaftsbank; *Int'l*, pg. 2245
VR FACTOREM GMBH—See DZ BANK AG Deutsche Zentral-Genossenschaftsbank; *Int'l*, pg. 2245
VS&A COMMUNICATIONS PARTNERS III—See Veronis Suhler Stevenson Partners LLC; *U.S. Private*, pg. 4368
WADLEY-DONOVAN GROWTHTECH LLC—See Wadley-Donovan Group; *U.S. Private*, pg. 4425
WAFRA, INC.; *U.S. Private*, pg. 4425
WAFRA INVESTMENT ADVISORY GROUP, INC.; *U.S. Private*, pg. 4425
WAFRA PARTNERS LLC—See Wafra Investment Advisory Group, Inc.; *U.S. Private*, pg. 4425
WAGNER RESOURCE GROUP, INC.—See Integrated Wealth Concepts, LLC; *U.S. Private*, pg. 2101
WALDEN CAPITAL ADVISORS, LLC—See Beacon Pointe Holdings, LLC; *U.S. Private*, pg. 505
WALL STREET FINANCIAL GROUP—See Reverence Capital Partners LLC; *U.S. Private*, pg. 3415
WANNING HNA DAKANGLE INVESTMENT AND DEVELOPMENT CO., LTD.—See Hainan Traffic Administration Holding Co., Ltd.; *Int'l*, pg. 3216
WASHINGTON CAPITAL MANAGEMENT, INC.; *U.S. Private*, pg. 4446
WASHINGTON FINANCIAL GROUP—See Hellman & Friedman LLC; *U.S. Private*, pg. 1909
WASHINGTON STREET INVESTMENTS LLC—See Prudential Financial, Inc.; *U.S. Public*, pg. 1734
WASMER, SCHROEDER & COMPANY, LLC—See The Charles Schwab Corporation; *U.S. Public*, pg. 2058
WATERFALL ASSET MANAGEMENT LLC; *U.S. Private*, pg. 4452
WATERSHED INVESTMENT CONSULTANTS, INC.—See J.H. Ellwood & Associates; *U.S. Private*, pg. 2165
WAUKESHA STATE BANK WEALTH MANAGEMENT—See Waukesha State Bank; *U.S. Private*, pg. 4457
WAVERLY ADVISORS, LLC—See Affiliated Managers Group, Inc.; *U.S. Public*, pg. 56
WAVERLY ADVISORS, LLC—See HGGC, LLC; *U.S. Private*, pg. 1930
WAVERTON INVESTMENT MANAGEMENT LIMITED—See ICM Limited; *Int'l*, pg. 3582
WAYPOINT ADVISORS LLC—See Cary Street Partners Financial LLC; *U.S. Private*, pg. 777
WC SACD ONE, INC.—See General Catalyst Partners; *U.S. Private*, pg. 1664
WC SACD ONE, INC.—See iSubscribed Inc.; *U.S. Private*, pg. 2147
WC SACD ONE, INC.—See WndrCo Holdings, LLC; *U.S. Private*, pg. 4552
WDM AUTORYZOWANY DORADCA SP. Z.O.O—See Graviton Capital S.A.; *Int'l*, pg. 3062
WEALTH DESIGN, LLC—See Beacon Pointe Holdings, LLC; *U.S. Private*, pg. 505
WEALTH ENHANCEMENT BROKERAGE SERVICES, LLC—See TA Associates, Inc.; *U.S. Private*, pg. 3919
WEALTH ENHANCEMENT GROUP, LLC—See TA Associates, Inc.; *U.S. Private*, pg. 3919
WEALTH PARTNERS CAPITAL GROUP, LLC—See Affiliated Managers Group, Inc.; *U.S. Public*, pg. 56
WEALTHPARTNERS, LLP—See Warburg Pincus LLC; *U.S. Private*, pg. 4439
WEALTHSPIRE ADVISORS, L.P.—See Aon plc; *Int'l*, pg. 498
WEALTH STRATEGIES GROUP INC.—See MAS Advisors, LLC; *U.S. Private*, pg. 2600

N.A.I.C.S. INDEX

WEATHERFORD CAPITAL MANAGEMENT SERVICES LIMITED LIABILITY—See Weatherford International plc; *U.S. Public*, pg. 2340
WEBSTER WEALTH ADVISORS, INC.—See Webster Financial Corporation; *U.S. Public*, pg. 2341
WEDBUSH CAPITAL PARTNERS, L.P.—See Wedbush Capital Partners; *U.S. Private*, pg. 4468
W.E. DONOGHUE & CO., INC.—See Minella Capital Management LLC; *U.S. Private*, pg. 2741
W.E. FAMILY OFFICES, LLC—See Truist Financial Corporation; *U.S. Public*, pg. 2199
WELBECSON GROUP LIMITED—See Heidelberg Materials AG; *Int'l*, pg. 3320
WELCH & FORBES LLC—See Affiliated Managers Group, Inc.; *U.S. Public*, pg. 56
WELLESLEY INVESTMENT PARTNERS, LLC—See Cambridge Bancorp; *U.S. Public*, pg. 426
WELLINGTON GLOBAL INVESTMENT MANAGEMENT LTD—See Wellington Management Company, LLP; *U.S. Private*, pg. 4475
WELLINGTON INTERNATIONAL MANAGEMENT COMPANY PTE LTD—See Wellington Management Company, LLP; *U.S. Private*, pg. 4475
WELLINGTON MANAGEMENT COMPANY, LLP; *U.S. Private*, pg. 4475
WELLINGTON MANAGEMENT INTERNATIONAL LTD—See Wellington Management Company, LLP; *U.S. Private*, pg. 4475
WELLS CAPITAL MANAGEMENT INCORPORATED—See Wells Fargo & Company; *U.S. Public*, pg. 2345
WELLS CAPITAL MANAGEMENT INCORPORATED—See Wells Fargo & Company; *U.S. Public*, pg. 2346
WELLS FARGO ADVANTAGE FUNDS—See Wells Fargo & Company; *U.S. Public*, pg. 2345
WELLS FARGO FUNDS MANAGEMENT, LLC—See Wells Fargo & Company; *U.S. Public*, pg. 2345
WELLS NELSON & ASSOCIATES, LLC—See D.A. Davidson Companies; *U.S. Private*, pg. 1140
WELTY CAPITAL MANAGEMENT, LLC—See Warburg Pincus LLC; *U.S. Private*, pg. 4439
WENTO SP. Z O.O.—See Equinor ASA; *Int'l*, pg. 2485
WESCOTT FINANCIAL ADVISORY GROUP LLC; *U.S. Private*, pg. 4482
WEST CAPITAL MANAGEMENT—See WSFS Financial Corporation; *U.S. Public*, pg. 2384
WESTERN ASSET GLOBAL HIGH INCOME FUND, INC.—See Franklin Resources, Inc.; *U.S. Public*, pg. 882
WESTERN ASSET HIGH INCOME OPPORTUNITY FUND, INC.—See Franklin Resources, Inc.; *U.S. Public*, pg. 882
WESTERN ASSET MANAGED MUNICIPALS FUND, INC.—See Franklin Resources, Inc.; *U.S. Public*, pg. 882
WESTERN ASSET MANAGEMENT COMPANY DISTRIBUIDORA DE TITULOS E VALORES MOBILIARIOS LIMITADA—See Franklin Resources, Inc.; *U.S. Public*, pg. 883
WESTERN ASSET MANAGEMENT COMPANY LTD—See Franklin Resources, Inc.; *U.S. Public*, pg. 882
WESTERN ASSET MANAGEMENT COMPANY PTE LTD.—See Franklin Resources, Inc.; *U.S. Public*, pg. 882
WESTERN ASSET MANAGEMENT COMPANY PTY LTD—See Franklin Resources, Inc.; *U.S. Public*, pg. 882
WESTERN ASSET MUNICIPAL DEFINED OPPORTUNITY TRUST, INC.—See Franklin Resources, Inc.; *U.S. Public*, pg. 883
WESTERN ASSET VARIABLE RATE STRATEGIC FUND, INC.—See Franklin Resources, Inc.; *U.S. Public*, pg. 883
WEST FINANCIAL SERVICES, INC.—See Sandy Spring Bancorp, Inc.; *U.S. Public*, pg. 1840
WESTINVEST GESELLSCHAFT FUR INVESTMENTFONDS MBH—See DekaBank; *Int'l*, pg. 2005
WESTWOOD HOLDINGS GROUP, INC.; *U.S. Public*, pg. 2363
WESTWOOD MANAGEMENT CORPORATION—See Westwood Holdings Group, Inc.; *U.S. Public*, pg. 2363
WESTWOOD TRUST - HOUSTON—See Westwood Holdings Group, Inc.; *U.S. Public*, pg. 2363
WHEATLAND ADVISORS, INC—See Orrstown Financial Services, Inc.; *U.S. Public*, pg. 1619
WHITEBOX ADVISORS, LLC; *U.S. Private*, pg. 4511
WHITE MOUNTAINS ADVISORS LLC—See White Mountains Insurance Group, Ltd.; *U.S. Public*, pg. 2369
THE WHITE OAK GROUP, INC.; *U.S. Private*, pg. 4135
WHITETAIL ROCK CAPITAL MANAGEMENT, LLC—See Nelnet, Inc.; *U.S. Private*, pg. 1504
WHITNELL & CO.—See Rockefeller Capital Management; *U.S. Private*, pg. 3466
THE WHITTIER TRUST COMPANY OF NEVADA, INC.—See Whittier Trust Company; *U.S. Private*, pg. 4514
WHITTIER TRUST COMPANY; *U.S. Private*, pg. 4513
WHP GLOBAL; *U.S. Private*, pg. 4515
WIEGERS CAPITAL PARTNERS; *U.S. Private*, pg. 4516
WIJKERTUNNEL BEHEER III B.V.—See Commerzbank AG; *Int'l*, pg. 1719
WILBANKS, SMITH & THOMAS ASSET MANAGEMENT, LLC—See Edwards Capital, LLC; *U.S. Private*, pg. 1341
WILKINSON O'GRADY & CO., INC.—See Fiera Capital Corporation; *Int'l*, pg. 2660

WILLIAM BLAIR INVESTMENT MANAGEMENT LLC; *U.S. Private*, pg. 4522
WILLIAM HARRIS INVESTORS, INC.; *U.S. Private*, pg. 4523
WILLIAMS FINANCIAL GROUP, INC.; *U.S. Private*, pg. 4525
WILLIAMS WEALTH MANAGEMENT GROUP, INC.; *U.S. Private*, pg. 4527
WILSHIRE HOLDINGS I, INC.—See NEWTEKONE, INC.; *U.S. Public*, pg. 1521
WILSON FINANCIAL GROUP, INC.—See Service Corporation International; *U.S. Public*, pg. 1871
WILSON, KEMP & ASSOCIATES, INC.—See Comerica Incorporated; *U.S. Public*, pg. 542
WINDSAIL CAPITAL GROUP, LLC; *U.S. Private*, pg. 4539
WINMILL & CO., INCORPORATED; *U.S. Public*, pg. 2374
WINSLOW CAPITAL MANAGEMENT, LLC—See Teachers Insurance Association - College Retirement Fund; *U.S. Private*, pg. 3948
WINTHROP RESOURCES CORPORATION—See Huntington Bancshares Incorporated; *U.S. Public*, pg. 1071
WINTON CAPITAL ASIA LIMITED—See Affiliated Managers Group, Inc.; *U.S. Public*, pg. 56
WINTON CAPITAL US LLC—See Affiliated Managers Group, Inc.; *U.S. Public*, pg. 56
WINTON GROUP LIMITED—See Affiliated Managers Group, Inc.; *U.S. Public*, pg. 56
WISDOMTREE EUROPE LTD.—See WisdomTree, Inc.; *U.S. Public*, pg. 2376
WOOD CREEK CAPITAL MANAGEMENT, LLC—See Massachusetts Mutual Life Insurance Company; *U.S. Private*, pg. 2605
WOODSON EQUITY LLC; *U.S. Private*, pg. 4560
WORLD GOLD TRUST; *U.S. Public*, pg. 2379
WORLDQUANT, LLC; *U.S. Private*, pg. 4569
WORLD REALTY & DEVELOPMENT, LTD.; *U.S. Private*, pg. 4567
WORLDSOURCE FINANCIAL MANAGEMENT INC.—See Guardian Capital Group Limited; *Int'l*, pg. 3170
WORLD TRADE CAPITAL GROUP LIMITED—See First Shanghai Investments Limited; *Int'l*, pg. 2687
WORLD TRADING (DELAWARE) INC.—See Deutsche Bank Aktiengesellschaft; *Int'l*, pg. 2062
WORLDVEST EQUITY, INC.; *U.S. Public*, pg. 2382
W. P. CAREY & CO. B.V.—See W.P. Carey Inc.; *U.S. Public*, pg. 2316
WP GROUP, LLC—See Affiliated Managers Group, Inc.; *U.S. Public*, pg. 56
W.P. STEWART ASSET MANAGEMENT (CURACAO) N.V.—See Equitable Holdings, Inc.; *U.S. Public*, pg. 789
W.P. STEWART ASSET MANAGEMENT LTD.—See Equitable Holdings, Inc.; *U.S. Public*, pg. 789
W.P. STEWART ASSET MANAGEMENT (NA), INC.—See Equitable Holdings, Inc.; *U.S. Public*, pg. 789
W.R. HUFF ASSET MANAGEMENT CO., INC.; *U.S. Private*, pg. 4422
WVF-PARAMOUNT 745 INVESTOR, L.P.—See Paramount Group Inc.; *U.S. Public*, pg. 1637
XENIA HOTELS & RESORTS, INC.; *U.S. Public*, pg. 2386
XINFENG INVESTMENT MANAGEMENT CO., LTD.—See China Cinda Asset Management Co., Ltd.; *Int'l*, pg. 1488
XML FINANCIAL GROUP; *U.S. Private*, pg. 4581
XOOM ENERGY CANADA, ULC—See NRG Energy, Inc.; *U.S. Public*, pg. 1551
XOOM ENERGY NEW JERSEY, LLC—See NRG Energy, Inc.; *U.S. Public*, pg. 1551
XOOM ENERGY TEXAS, LLC—See NRG Energy, Inc.; *U.S. Public*, pg. 1551
XSEEDWEALTH PTY LTD—See Centrepoint Alliance Limited; *Int'l*, pg. 1412
YACKTMAN ASSET MANAGEMENT LP—See Affiliated Managers Group, Inc.; *U.S. Public*, pg. 56
YOKOHAMA CAPITAL CO., LTD.—See Concordia Financial Group, Ltd.; *Int'l*, pg. 1765
YORK CAPITAL MANAGEMENT GLOBAL ADVISORS, LLC; *U.S. Private*, pg. 4590
YORKVILLE ADVISORS, LLC; *U.S. Private*, pg. 4591
ZACKS INVESTMENT RESEARCH INC.; *U.S. Private*, pg. 4597
ZAIS GROUP, LLC—See ZAIS Group Holdings, Inc.; *U.S. Private*, pg. 4597
ZAO UFG INVEST—See Deutsche Bank Aktiengesellschaft; *Int'l*, pg. 2062
ZEMENICK & WALKER, INC.; *U.S. Private*, pg. 4601
ZENITH CAPITAL CORPORATION; *U.S. Public*, pg. 2402
ZHONGRUN ECONOMIC DEVELOPMENT CO., LTD.—See China Cinda Asset Management Co., Ltd.; *Int'l*, pg. 1488
ZIONS DIRECT, INC.—See Zions Bancorporation, National Association; *U.S. Public*, pg. 2408
ZOLFO COOPER BRITISH VIRGIN ISLANDS—See Zolfo Cooper, LLC; *U.S. Private*, pg. 4607
ZOLFO COOPER CAYMAN ISLANDS—See Zolfo Cooper, LLC; *U.S. Private*, pg. 4607
ZWEIG ADVISERS LLC—See Virtus Investment Partners, Inc.; *U.S. Public*, pg. 2301

523991 — TRUST, FIDUCIARY, AND CUSTODY ACTIVITIES

ABRDN GOLD ETF TRUST; *U.S. Public*, pg. 26
ACADIA TRUST, N.A.—See Camden National Corporation; *U.S. Public*, pg. 426
AEW UK REIT PLC; *Int'l*, pg. 183
AIB SECURITIES SERVICES LTD.—See AIB Group plc; *Int'l*, pg. 228
AIM INDUSTRIAL GROWTH FREEHOLD & LEASEHOLD REIT; *Int'l*, pg. 232
ALLIANCE TRUST PLC; *Int'l*, pg. 341
ALLIANZ NEDERLAND—See Allianz SE; *Int'l*, pg. 349
AMATA SUMMIT GROWTH FREEHOLD & LEASEHOLD REAL ESTATE INVESTMENT TRUST; *Int'l*, pg. 413
AMG NATIONAL TRUST BANK; *U.S. Private*, pg. 262
AMICORP NETHERLANDS B.V.—See Amicorp Group AG; *Int'l*, pg. 427
AMICORP SWITZERLAND AG—See Amicorp Group AG; *Int'l*, pg. 427
AOZORA TRUST BANK, LTD.—See Cerberus Capital Management, L.P.; *U.S. Private*, pg. 837
ARC PA-QRS TRUST—See Realty Income Corporation; *U.S. Public*, pg. 1768
ARDEN TRUST COMPANY—See Warburg Pincus LLC; *U.S. Private*, pg. 4439
ASKARI DEVELOPMENT HOLDINGS PVT LTD—See Army Welfare Trust LLC; *Int'l*, pg. 575
AUDI SARADAR PRIVATE BANK SAL—See Bank Audi sal; *Int'l*, pg. 837
AXACTOR GERMANY HOLDING GMBH—See Axactor SE; *Int'l*, pg. 761
THE BANK OF BERMUDA LTD.—See HSBC Holdings plc; *Int'l*, pg. 3504
BANK OF IRELAND—See Bank of Ireland Group plc; *Int'l*, pg. 844
BARCLAYS FIDUCIARY SERVICES (UK) LIMITED—See Barclays PLC; *Int'l*, pg. 861
BARCLAYS FUNDS LTD.—See Barclays PLC; *Int'l*, pg. 860
BAR HARBOR TRUST SERVICES—See Bar Harbor Bankshares; *U.S. Public*, pg. 275
BEDELL CRISTIN; *Int'l*, pg. 938
BELLEVUE HEALTHCARE TRUST PLC; *Int'l*, pg. 967
BENTLEY TRUST (MALTA) LIMITED—See Bentley Reid (Holdings) Limited; *Int'l*, pg. 977
BERMUDA TRUST (HONG KONG) LTD.—See HSBC Holdings plc; *Int'l*, pg. 3504
BESSEMER GROUP TRUST COMPANY OF FLORIDA - MIAMI—See The Bessemer Group, Incorporated; *U.S. Private*, pg. 3994
BESSEMER GROUP TRUST COMPANY OF FLORIDA - NAPLES—See The Bessemer Group, Incorporated; *U.S. Private*, pg. 3994
BESSEMER TRUST COMPANY, N.A.—See The Bessemer Group, Incorporated; *U.S. Private*, pg. 3994
BESSEMER TRUST COMPANY—See The Bessemer Group, Incorporated; *U.S. Private*, pg. 3994
BGL LUXEMBOURG—See BNP Paribas SA; *Int'l*, pg. 1084
BITCOIN SERVICES, INC.; *U.S. Public*, pg. 339
BMO CAPITAL TRUST—See Bank of Montreal; *Int'l*, pg. 846
BMO TRUST COMPANY—See Bank of Montreal; *Int'l*, pg. 846
BNP JERSEY TRUST CORP. LIMITED—See BNP Paribas SA; *Int'l*, pg. 1081
BNY MELLON INVESTMENT SERVICING (INTERNATIONAL) LIMITED—See The Bank of New York Mellon Corporation; *U.S. Public*, pg. 2037
BNY MELLON TRUST COMPANY OF ILLINOIS—See The Bank of New York Mellon Corporation; *U.S. Public*, pg. 2037
BRL TRUST SERVICOS FIDUCIARIOS E PARTICIPACOES LTDA.—See Apex Fund Services Holdings Ltd.; *Int'l*, pg. 510
BROWN BROTHERS HARRIMAN TRUST CO. (CAYMAN) LTD.—See Brown Brothers Harriman & Co.; *U.S. Private*, pg. 667
BROWN BROTHERS HARRIMAN TRUSTEE SERVICES (IRELAND) LIMITED—See Brown Brothers Harriman & Co.; *U.S. Private*, pg. 667
BUCKINGHAM FINANCIAL GROUP, INC.—See Buckingham & Company; *U.S. Private*, pg. 677
CAPITAL CITY TRUST COMPANY—See Capital City Bank Group, Inc.; *U.S. Public*, pg. 431
CARDIF-ASSURANCES RISQUES DIVERS S.A.—See BNP Paribas SA; *Int'l*, pg. 1083
CBANK—See Republic Bancorp, Inc.; *U.S. Public*, pg. 1785
CENTRAL TRUST & INVESTMENT COMPANY—See Central Bancompany, Inc.; *U.S. Public*, pg. 472
CHARTER TRUST COMPANY—See Bar Harbor Bankshares; *U.S. Public*, pg. 275
CHAUTAUQUA CAPITAL MANAGEMENT LLC—See Baird Financial Group, Inc.; *U.S. Private*, pg. 454
THE CHICAGO TRUST COMPANY, N.A.—See Wintrust Financial Corporation; *U.S. Public*, pg. 2375
CHRISTIANA TRUST COMPANY OF DELAWARE - LAS VEGAS OFFICE—See WSFS Financial Corporation; *U.S. Public*, pg. 2383

523991 — TRUST, FIDUCIARY, A...

CHRISTIANA TRUST COMPANY OF DELAWARE—See WSFS Financial Corporation; *U.S. Public*, pg. 2383
CHUBB NEDERLAND B.V.—See Carrier Global Corporation; *U.S. Public*, pg. 441
CIBC FIRST CARIBBEAN INTERNATIONAL BANK LIMITED—See Canadian Imperial Bank of Commerce; *Int'l*, pg. 1283
CIBC MELLON—See Canadian Imperial Bank of Commerce; *Int'l*, pg. 1283
CIBC MELLON—See The Bank of New York Mellon Corporation; *U.S. Public*, pg. 2037
CICF L.L.C.—See The Carlyle Group Inc.; *U.S. Public*, pg. 2045
CLAYMORE SILVER BULLION TRUST; *Int'l*, pg. 1653
COLUMBIA TRUST COMPANY—See Columbia Banking System, Inc.; *U.S. Public*, pg. 534
COLUMBIA TRUST COMPANY—See Columbia Banking System, Inc.; *U.S. Public*, pg. 534
COMINVEST ASSET MANAGEMENT GMBH—See Allianz SE; *Int'l*, pg. 347
COMMONWEALTH MANAGED INVESTMENTS LIMITED—See Commonwealth Bank of Australia; *Int'l*, pg. 1720
COMPUTERSHARE CORPORATE TRUST—See Computershare Limited; *Int'l*, pg. 1760
THE CORAL GABLES TRUST COMPANY; *U.S. Private*, pg. 4014
CPN RETAIL GROWTH LEASEHOLD REIT; *Int'l*, pg. 1826
CREDIT UNION DISPUTE RESOLUTION CENTRE PTY LIMITED—See Cuscal Ltd.; *Int'l*, pg. 1880
CREDIT UNION FOUNDATION AUSTRALIA PTY LIMITED—See Cuscal Ltd.; *Int'l*, pg. 1880
CUSCAL MANAGEMENT PTY LIMITED—See Cuscal Ltd.; *Int'l*, pg. 1880
CUSTODIAL TRUST COMPANY—See JPMorgan Chase & Co.; *U.S. Public*, pg. 1206
THE DAISHI BUSINESS SERVICE CO., LTD.—See Daishi Hokuetsu Financial Group, Inc.; *Int'l*, pg. 1941
DAVIDSON TRUST CO.—See D.A. Davidson Companies; *U.S. Private*, pg. 1140
DBS TRUSTEE LTD.—See DBS Group Holdings Ltd.; *Int'l*, pg. 1988
DB TRUST COMPANY LIMITED JAPAN—See Deutsche Bank Aktiengesellschaft; *Int'l*, pg. 2056
DB TRUSTEE SERVICES LIMITED—See Deutsche Bank Aktiengesellschaft; *Int'l*, pg. 2056
DB TRUSTEES (HONG KONG) LIMITED—See Deutsche Bank Aktiengesellschaft; *Int'l*, pg. 2057
DEUTSCHE BANK INTERNATIONAL TRUST CO. (CAYMAN) LIMITED—See Deutsche Bank Aktiengesellschaft; *Int'l*, pg. 2059
DEUTSCHE BANK INTERNATIONAL TRUST CO. (JERSEY) LIMITED—See Deutsche Bank Aktiengesellschaft; *Int'l*, pg. 2059
DEUTSCHE BANK INTERNATIONAL TRUST CO. LIMITED—See Deutsche Bank Aktiengesellschaft; *Int'l*, pg. 2059
DEUTSCHE BANK TRUST COMPANY, NATIONAL ASSOCIATION—See Deutsche Bank Aktiengesellschaft; *Int'l*, pg. 2060
DEUTSCHE BANK TRUST COMPANY NEW JERSEY LTD.—See Deutsche Bank Aktiengesellschaft; *Int'l*, pg. 2060
DEUTSCHE BANK TRUST CORPORATION—See Deutsche Bank Aktiengesellschaft; *Int'l*, pg. 2060
DEUTSCHE FIDUCIARY SERVICES (SUISSE) SA—See Deutsche Bank Aktiengesellschaft; *Int'l*, pg. 2060
DEUTSCHE STIFTUNGSTRUST GMBH—See Deutsche Bank Aktiengesellschaft; *Int'l*, pg. 2061
DEUTSCHE TRUSTEE COMPANY LIMITED—See Deutsche Bank Aktiengesellschaft; *Int'l*, pg. 2061
DEUTSCHE TRUSTEE SERVICES (INDIA) PRIVATE LIMITED—See Deutsche Bank Aktiengesellschaft; *Int'l*, pg. 2061
DIGITAL RFQ LTD.—See Nukkleus Inc.; *U.S. Public*, pg. 1555
DUXTON FARMS LIMITED; *Int'l*, pg. 2236
EDR MANAGEMENT INC.—See Greystar Real Estate Partners, LLC; *U.S. Private*, pg. 1785
ENTERPRISE TRUST COMPANY—See Enterprise Financial Services Corp; *U.S. Public*, pg. 778
EQUINOX-COGNIZANT SARL—See Cognizant Technology Solutions Corporation; *U.S. Public*, pg. 524
EQUITY TRUSTEES LIMITED; *Int'l*, pg. 2488
ESCROW OPTIONS GROUP INC.; *U.S. Private*, pg. 1425
EUROPEAN RESIDENTIAL REIT; *Int'l*, pg. 2557
FINANCIAL DESIGNS LTD.; *U.S. Private*, pg. 1507
FINNAT FIDUCIARIA SPA—See Banca Finnat Euramerica S.p.A.; *Int'l*, pg. 814
FIRST ADVISORY GROUP LIMITED; *Int'l*, pg. 2681
FIRST AMERICAN TRUSTEE SERVICING SOLUTIONS, LLC—See First American Financial Corporation; *U.S. Public*, pg. 838
FIRST AMERICAN TRUST, F.S.B.—See First American Financial Corporation; *U.S. Public*, pg. 837
FIRST CHAIR HOUSING TRUSTEE LLC—See Vail Resorts, Inc.; *U.S. Public*, pg. 2271

FIRST NATIONAL TRUST COMPANY—See F.N.B. Corporation; *U.S. Public*, pg. 818
FIRST TRUST OF MIDAMERICA—See Lolyn Financial Corporation; *U.S. Private*, pg. 2483
FONDSENBEHEER NEDERLAND B.V.—See Cooperatieve Centrale Raiffeisen-Boerenleenbank B.A.; *Int'l*, pg. 1791
FORTIS PRIVATE BANKING - BRUSSELS—See BNP Paribas SA; *Int'l*, pg. 1084
FORTIS PRIVATE INVESTMENT MANAGEMENT LIMITED—See BNP Paribas SA; *Int'l*, pg. 1084
FRANKLIN TEMPLETON BANK & TRUST, F.S.B.—See Franklin Resources, Inc.; *U.S. Public*, pg. 880
FRASERS PROPERTY THAILAND INDUSTRIAL FREEHOLD & LEASEHOLD REIT; *Int'l*, pg. 2766
FREEDOM TRUST SERVICES LIMITED—See Marsh & McLennan Companies, Inc.; *U.S. Public*, pg. 1375
GENWORTH MORTGAGE SERVICES, LLC—See Genworth Financial, Inc.; *U.S. Public*, pg. 934
GLOBAL TRUST COMPANY, INC.—See Community Bank System, Inc.; *U.S. Public*, pg. 550
GRAYSCALE BITCOIN TRUST; *U.S. Public*, pg. 961
HARIYANA METALS INDUSTRIES LIMITED; *Int'l*, pg. 3277
HARLEY-DAVIDSON MOTORCYCLE TRUST 2013-1—See Harley-Davidson, Inc.; *U.S. Public*, pg. 985
HAWKSFORD INTERNATIONAL; *Int'l*, pg. 3289
HOIST HELLAS S.L.D.S.A.—See Hoist Finance AB; *Int'l*, pg. 3442
HSBC FINANCIAL SERVICES (CAYMAN) LIMITED—See HSBC Holdings plc; *Int'l*, pg. 3505
HSBC GUYERZELLER TRUST COMPANY SA—See HSBC Holdings plc; *Int'l*, pg. 3505
HSBC INSTITUTIONAL TRUST SERVICES (IRELAND) LIMITED—See HSBC Holdings plc; *Int'l*, pg. 3505
HSBC INSTITUTIONAL TRUST SERVICES SINGAPORE LIMITED—See HSBC Holdings plc; *Int'l*, pg. 3504
HSBC INTERNATIONAL TRUSTEE LIMITED—See HSBC Holdings plc; *Int'l*, pg. 3504
HSBC INTERNATIONAL TRUSTEE (SINGAPORE) LIMITED—See HSBC Holdings plc; *Int'l*, pg. 3506
HSBC SECURITY SERVICES (MAURITIUS) LIMITED—See HSBC Holdings plc; *Int'l*, pg. 3506
HSBC TRUSTEE (C.I.) LIMITED—See HSBC Holdings plc; *Int'l*, pg. 3504
HSBC TRUSTEE (HONG KONG) LIMITED—See HSBC Holdings plc; *Int'l*, pg. 3507
HSBC TRUSTEE (JERSEY) LIMITED—See HSBC Holdings plc; *Int'l*, pg. 3504
HSBC TRUSTEE (SINGAPORE) LIMITED—See HSBC Holdings plc; *Int'l*, pg. 3506
HSBK EUROPE B.V.—See Halyk Bank of Kazakhstan JSC; *Int'l*, pg. 3234
HUGOTON ROYALTY TRUST; *U.S. Public*, pg. 1068
HUNTINGTON MUNICIPAL SECURITIES, INC.—See Huntington Bancshares Incorporated; *U.S. Public*, pg. 1071
INTERTRUST (BELGIUM) NV/SA—See Corporation Service Company; *U.S. Private*, pg. 1057
INTERTRUST CAYMAN ISLANDS—See Corporation Service Company; *U.S. Private*, pg. 1057
INTERTRUST CHINA - GUANGZHOU OFFICE—See Corporation Service Company; *U.S. Private*, pg. 1058
INTERTRUST (CURACAO) BV—See Corporation Service Company; *U.S. Private*, pg. 1057
INTERTRUST DANISMANLIK AS—See Corporation Service Company; *U.S. Private*, pg. 1057
INTERTRUST (DENMARK) A/S—See Corporation Service Company; *U.S. Private*, pg. 1057
INTERTRUST (DUBAI) LIMITED—See Corporation Service Company; *U.S. Private*, pg. 1057
INTERTRUST FIDUCIARY SERVICES (JERSEY) LIMITED—See Corporation Service Company; *U.S. Private*, pg. 1057
INTERTRUST (GUERNSEY) LIMITED—See Corporation Service Company; *U.S. Private*, pg. 1057
INTERTRUST HOLDINGS (UK) LIMITED—See Corporation Service Company; *U.S. Private*, pg. 1057
INTERTRUST HONG KONG LIMITED—See Corporation Service Company; *U.S. Private*, pg. 1057
INTERTRUST (LUXEMBOURG) S.A.R.L.—See Corporation Service Company; *U.S. Private*, pg. 1057
INTERTRUST MANAGEMENT IRELAND LIMITED—See Corporation Service Company; *U.S. Private*, pg. 1057
INTERTRUST (NETHERLANDS) B.V.—See Corporation Service Company; *U.S. Private*, pg. 1057
INTERTRUST SERVICES (SCHWEIZ) AG—See Corporation Service Company; *U.S. Private*, pg. 1057
INTERTRUST (SHANGHAI) CONSULTANTS LIMITED—See Corporation Service Company; *U.S. Private*, pg. 1058
INTERTRUST (SINGAPORE) LTD.—See Corporation Service Company; *U.S. Private*, pg. 1058
INTERTRUST (SPAIN) S.L.—See Corporation Service Company; *U.S. Private*, pg. 1057
INTERTRUST (SWEDEN) AB—See Corporation Service Company; *U.S. Private*, pg. 1057
KCA SUPER PTY LIMITED—See Kimberly-Clark Corporation; *U.S. Public*, pg. 1229
KKR 2006 FUND (GDG) L.P.—See KKR & Co. Inc.; *U.S. Public*, pg. 1255

LEUMI OVERSEAS TRUST CORPORATION LTD—See Bank Leumi Le-Israel B.M.; *Int'l*, pg. 839
LION INTERNATIONAL MANAGEMENT LIMITED—See HSBC Holdings plc; *Int'l*, pg. 3504
LUXCSD S.A.—See Deutsche Borse AG; *Int'l*, pg. 2064
MAL PAKISTAN LTD.—See Army Welfare Trust LLC; *Int'l*, pg. 576
MELIOR TRUST SPA—See BPER BANCA S.p.A; *Int'l*, pg. 1132
MIDDLEBURG TRUST COMPANY—See Atlantic Union Bankshares Corporation; *U.S. Public*, pg. 223
MIDFIRST TRUST CO.—See Midland Financial Co.; *U.S. Private*, pg. 2715
MISSION MANAGEMENT & TRUST, CO.—See Notre Dame Federal Credit Union; *U.S. Private*, pg. 2965
MONTANA TITLE AND ESCROW COMPANY—See First American Financial Corporation; *U.S. Public*, pg. 838
THE NEW ZEALAND GUARDIAN TRUST COMPANY LIMITED—See Bath Street Capital Limited; *Int'l*, pg. 889
NORTHEAST RETIREMENT SERVICES, LLC—See Community Bank System, Inc.; *U.S. Public*, pg. 550
NORTHERN TRUST FIDUCIARY SERVICES (GUERNSEY) LIMITED—See Northern Trust Corporation; *U.S. Public*, pg. 1538
NORTHERN TRUST SECURITIES LLP—See Northern Trust Corporation; *U.S. Public*, pg. 1539
NORTHERN TRUST SWITZERLAND AG—See Northern Trust Corporation; *U.S. Public*, pg. 1538
OKLAHOMA STATE UNIVERSITY MEDICAL CENTER TRUST; *U.S. Private*, pg. 3007
PACCAR FINANCIAL SERVICES LTD.—See PACCAR Inc.; *U.S. Public*, pg. 1631
PERPETUAL TRUST LIMITED—See Bath Street Capital Limited; *Int'l*, pg. 889
PREMIER TRUST, INC.—See Reverence Capital Partners LLC; *U.S. Public*, pg. 3414
PROVIDENT TRUST GROUP, LLC—See Aquiline Capital Partners LLC; *U.S. Private*, pg. 304
PROVIDENT TRUST GROUP, LLC—See Genstar Capital, LLC; *U.S. Private*, pg. 1675
RELIANCE OPERATIONS SERVICES LLC—See Fidelity National Infor; *U.S. Public*, pg. 832
RELIANCE TRUST COMPANY—See Fidelity National Infor; *U.S. Public*, pg. 832
SALEM TRUST CO.—See Tuesday Morning Corporation; *U.S. Public*, pg. 2204
SECURITY NATIONAL TRUST CO., INC. LANCASTER—See Security National Trust Co., Inc.; *U.S. Private*, pg. 3596
SECURITY NATIONAL TRUST CO., INC.; *U.S. Private*, pg. 3596
STAR WEALTH MANAGEMENT INC—See STAR Financial Group Inc.; *U.S. Public*, pg. 1937
STATE STREET BANK LUXEMBOURG S.A.—See State Street Corporation; *U.S. Public*, pg. 1940
STATE STREET BANK & TRUST COMPANY - HONG KONG—See State Street Corporation; *U.S. Public*, pg. 1940
STATE STREET BANK & TRUST COMPANY - LONDON—See State Street Corporation; *U.S. Public*, pg. 1940
STATE STREET BANK & TRUST COMPANY - TOKYO—See State Street Corporation; *U.S. Public*, pg. 1940
STATE STREET GLOBAL ADVISORS LIMITED—See State Street Corporation; *U.S. Public*, pg. 1941
TD AMERITRADE TRUST COMPANY—See The Charles Schwab Corporation; *U.S. Public*, pg. 2058
TEMIS CONSEIL & FORMATION—See The Brink's Company; *U.S. Public*, pg. 2043
THL CREDIT ADVISORS LLC—See Blackstone Inc.; *U.S. Public*, pg. 353
THL CREDIT ADVISORS LLC—See Corsair Capital, LLC; *U.S. Private*, pg. 1059
THRIVENT TRUST COMPANY—See Thrivent Financial for Lutherans Foundation; *U.S. Private*, pg. 4165
UMB DISTRIBUTION SERVICES, LLC—See UMB Financial Corporation; *U.S. Public*, pg. 2224
UMB FUND SERVICES, INC.—See UMB Financial Corporation; *U.S. Public*, pg. 2224
UNIFIED TRUST COMPANY, N.A.—See Unified Financial Services, Inc.; *U.S. Private*, pg. 4282
U.S. TRUST COMPANY—See Bank of America Corporation; *U.S. Public*, pg. 271
VALLEY VIEW FINANCIAL GROUP TRUST COMPANY—See Valley View Bancshares, Inc.; *U.S. Private*, pg. 4336
VAUGHAN NELSON TRUST COMPANY—See Groupe BPCE; *Int'l*, pg. 3097
VAULTED GOLD BULLION TRUST; *U.S. Private*, pg. 4348
VISTRA MANAGEMENT SERVICES (NETHERLANDS) B.V.—See EQT AB; *Int'l*, pg. 2472
THE WESTWOOD FUNDS—See Westwood Holdings Group, Inc.; *U.S. Public*, pg. 2363
WESTWOOD TRUST—See Westwood Holdings Group, Inc.; *U.S. Public*, pg. 2363
WILSON-MCSHANE CORP.; *U.S. Private*, pg. 4531

N.A.I.C.S. INDEX

523999 — MISCELLANEOUS FINANCIAL INVESTMENT ACTIVITIES

10X CAPITAL VENTURE ACQUISITION CORP.; *U.S. Public*, pg. 1
1.12 ACQUISITION CORP.; *U.S. Public*, pg. 1
1315 CAPITAL LLC; *U.S. Private*, pg. 3
15384150 CANADA INC.—See BBTV Holdings Inc.; *Int'l*, pg. 921
180 DEGREE CAPITAL CORP.; *U.S. Public*, pg. 2
180 LIFE SCIENCES CORP.; *U.S. Public*, pg. 2
1834 INVESTMENT ADVISORS CO.—See Old National Bancorp; *U.S. Public*, pg. 1566
1855 CAPITAL PARTNERS, LLC; *U.S. Private*, pg. 3
1933 INDUSTRIES INC.; *Int'l*, pg. 3
1SHARPE ACQUISITION CORP.; *U.S. Private*, pg. 3
21 CENTRALE PARTNERS SA—See 21 Investimenti Societa' di Gestione del Risparmio S.p.A.; *Int'l*, pg. 4
21 PARTNERS S.P.A.—See 21 Investimenti Societa' di Gestione del Risparmio S.p.A.; *Int'l*, pg. 4
24HOLDINGS INC.; *U.S. Private*, pg. 6
26 CAPITAL ACQUISITION CORP.; *U.S. Public*, pg. 3
26NORTH BDC, INC.; *U.S. Private*, pg. 6
361 CAPITAL LLC—See Hamilton Lane Incorporated; *U.S. Public*, pg. 982
37 BAKING HOLDINGS, LLC; *U.S. Private*, pg. 8
39 NORTH CAPITAL LLC—See Eastbridge Group; *Int'l*, pg. 2271
3AC CO., LTD.; *Int'l*, pg. 7
3DX INDUSTRIES, INC.; *U.S. Public*, pg. 4
3G CAPITAL INC.; *U.S. Private*, pg. 9
3G CAPITAL MANAGEMENT LLC; *U.S. Private*, pg. 11
3G CAPITAL PARTNERS L.P.; *U.S. Private*, pg. 11
3MV ENERGY CORP.; *Int'l*, pg. 9
3 RIVERS CAPITAL, LLC; *U.S. Private*, pg. 7
3RIVERS FEDERAL CREDIT UNION; *U.S. Private*, pg. 14
412688 B.C. LTD.—See Esstra Industries Inc.; *Int'l*, pg. 2517
424 CAPITAL, LLC; *U.S. Private*, pg. 15
4K INVEST INTERNATIONAL; *Int'l*, pg. 12
5:01 ACQUISITION CORP.; *U.S. Public*, pg. 9
51 CREDIT CARD INC.; *Int'l*, pg. 12
54 LOMBARD STREET INVESTMENTS LIMITED—See Barclays PLC; *Int'l*, pg. 859
5AM VENTURE MANAGEMENT, LLC; *U.S. Private*, pg. 16
5D MARKETING LLC—See Plains GP Holdings, L.P.; *U.S. Public*, pg. 1697
5G EDGE ACQUISITION CORP.; *U.S. Public*, pg. 9
5V INC.; *Int'l*, pg. 14
6TH & K LTD. PARTNERSHIP; *U.S. Private*, pg. 16
7 ACQUISITION CORPORATION; *U.S. Public*, pg. 9
7GC & CO. HOLDINGS INC.; *U.S. Private*, pg. 9
8I ENTERPRISES ACQUISITION CORP; *Int'l*, pg. 16
99 ACQUISITION GROUP INC.; *U.S. Public*, pg. 10
A1 GROUP, INC.; *U.S. Private*, pg. 29
A1 INVESTMENTS & RESOURCES LTD.; *Int'l*, pg. 29
A2E VENTURE CATALYSTS LIMITED; *Int'l*, pg. 37
AAA INVESTMENT CO.—See The American Automobile Association, Inc.; *U.S. Private*, pg. 3985
AAC CAPITAL BENELUX—See AAC Capital Partners Holding B.V.; *Int'l*, pg. 30
AAC NORDIC ADVISORY AB—See AAC Capital Partners Holding B.V.; *Int'l*, pg. 30
A AGENCIA BRASILEIRA DE PROMOCAO DE EXPORTACOES E INVESTIMENTOS; *Int'l*, pg. 17
AAR COMMERCIAL COMPANY LTD.; *Int'l*, pg. 37
AAREAL IT BETEILIGUNGEN GMBH—See Advent International Corporation; *U.S. Private*, pg. 96
AAREAL IT BETEILIGUNGEN GMBH—See Centerbridge Partners, L.P.; *U.S. Private*, pg. 812
AARHUSKARLSHAMN BALTIC HOLDING AB—See AAK AB; *Int'l*, pg. 32
AARNAV FASHIONS LIMITED; *Int'l*, pg. 37
AAR SHYAM INDIA INVESTMENT COMPANY LIMITED; *Int'l*, pg. 37
AASTAMANGALAM FINANCE LIMITED; *Int'l*, pg. 38
AAVIN, LLC; *U.S. Private*, pg. 33
A'AYAN LEASING AND INVESTMENT COMPANY KSCC; *Int'l*, pg. 19
ABANS FINANCE PLC; *Int'l*, pg. 48
ABB BETEILIGUNGS- UND VERWALTUNGSGES. MBH—See ABB Ltd.; *Int'l*, pg. 50
ABB GROUP INVESTMENT MANAGEMENT PTY. LTD.—See ABB Ltd.; *Int'l*, pg. 50
ABB HOLDINGS BV—See ABB Ltd.; *Int'l*, pg. 50
ABB HOLDINGS LIMITED—See ABB Ltd.; *Int'l*, pg. 53
ABB INTERNATIONAL FINANCE LIMITED—See ABB Ltd.; *Int'l*, pg. 52
ABB NORDEN HOLDING AB—See ABB Ltd.; *Int'l*, pg. 53
ABB TURBO SYSTEMS HOLDING LTD.—See ABB Ltd.; *Int'l*, pg. 54
ABB VERWALTUNGS AG—See ABB Ltd.; *Int'l*, pg. 55
ABC FACTORS A.E.—See Alpha Services and Holdings S.A.; *Int'l*, pg. 369
AB EFFECTENBETEILIGUNGEN AG; *Int'l*, pg. 39
ABENEX CAPITAL S.A.; *Int'l*, pg. 59
ABERCROSS HOLDINGS LTD.; *Int'l*, pg. 60
ABERDEEN GLOBAL SERVICES S.A.—See abrdn PLC; *Int'l*, pg. 68
ABERDEEN INVESTMENT MANAGEMENT K.K.—See abrdn PLC; *Int'l*, pg. 68
ABERFORTH PARTNERS LLP; *Int'l*, pg. 60
AB FORTUM VARME HOLDING SAMAGT MED STOCKHOLMS STAD—See Fortum Oyj; *Int'l*, pg. 2741
ABHIJIT TRADING COMPANY LTD.; *Int'l*, pg. 60
ABHINAV CAPITAL SERVICES LIMITED; *Int'l*, pg. 60
ABHINAV LEASING & FINANCE LIMITED; *Int'l*, pg. 60
ABINGWORTH LLP; *Int'l*, pg. 61
ABITS GROUP INC.; *U.S. Private*, pg. 62
ABLE BRANDS CO.; *U.S. Public*, pg. 25
ABLECO FINANCE, LLC—See Cerberus Capital Management, L.P.; *U.S. Private*, pg. 835
ABN AMRO CLEARING LONDON LTD.—See ABN AMRO Group N.V.; *Int'l*, pg. 65
ABOITIZ EQUITY VENTURES, INC.; *Int'l*, pg. 66
ABRDN ASIA FOCUS PLC; *Int'l*, pg. 68
ABRDN INCOME CREDIT STRATEGIES FUND; *U.S. Public*, pg. 26
ABRDN WORLD HEALTHCARE FUND; *U.S. Public*, pg. 27
ABRI CREDIT UNION; *U.S. Private*, pg. 40
ABRIS CAPITAL PARTNERS SP. Z O.O.; *Int'l*, pg. 69
ABRY PARTNERS, LLC; *U.S. Private*, pg. 40
ABSA FINANCIAL SERVICES AFRICA HOLDINGS PROPRIETARY LIMITED—See Absa Group Limited; *Int'l*, pg. 69
ABSA FINANCIAL SERVICES LIMITED—See Absa Group Limited; *Int'l*, pg. 69
ABSA TRUST LIMITED—See Absa Group Limited; *Int'l*, pg. 69
ABSA WEALTH & INVESTMENT MANAGEMENT—See Absa Group Limited; *Int'l*, pg. 69
ABS CAPITAL PARTNERS, L.P.; *U.S. Private*, pg. 43
ABU DHABI INVESTMENT COMPANY; *Int'l*, pg. 72
ACACIA CAPITAL NL LLC; *U.S. Private*, pg. 46
ACACIA INVERSION S.G.I.I.C., S.A.U.; *Int'l*, pg. 75
ACACIA PARTNERS LLC; *U.S. Private*, pg. 46
A.C. ADVISORY, INC.—See Public Financial Management, Inc.; *U.S. Private*, pg. 3299
ACA PARTNERS PTE LTD.; *Int'l*, pg. 74
ACCELER8 VENTURES PLC; *Int'l*, pg. 79
ACCELERATE ACQUISITION CORP.; *U.S. Public*, pg. 32
ACCELERO CAPITAL HOLDINGS SARL; *Int'l*, pg. 80
ACCEL-KKR COMPANY LLC—See Accel Partners L.P.; *U.S. Private*, pg. 47
ACCEL-KKR COMPANY LLC—See KKR & Co. Inc.; *U.S. Public*, pg. 1237
ACCELON CAPITAL LLC; *U.S. Private*, pg. 50
ACCEL PARTNERS L.P.; *U.S. Private*, pg. 47
ACCELSTAR PACIFIC LIMITED—See China Oil & Gas Group Limited; *Int'l*, pg. 1538
ACCENT EQUITY PARTNERS AB; *Int'l*, pg. 81
ACCENTURE BRANCH HOLDINGS B.V.—See Accenture plc; *Int'l*, pg. 82
ACCENTURE CAPITAL INC.—See Accenture plc; *Int'l*, pg. 85
ACCENTURE DENMARK HOLDINGS A/S—See Accenture plc; *Int'l*, pg. 83
ACCENTURE FINANCIAL CORPORATION—See Accenture plc; *Int'l*, pg. 85
ACCENTURE HOLDING GMBH & CO. KG—See Accenture plc; *Int'l*, pg. 83
ACCENTURE HOLDINGS B.V.—See Accenture plc; *Int'l*, pg. 83
ACCENTURE HOLDINGS (IBERIA) S.L.—See Accenture plc; *Int'l*, pg. 83
ACCENTURE HUMAN CAPITAL MGMT. SOL. S.L.—See Accenture plc; *Int'l*, pg. 83
ACCENTURE INTERNATIONAL CAPITAL SCA—See Accenture plc; *Int'l*, pg. 83
ACCESS CAPITAL PARTNERS SA; *Int'l*, pg. 88
ACCESS VALUE INVESTORS LLC; *U.S. Private*, pg. 53
ACCLIME; *Int'l*, pg. 90
ACCOR ACQUISITION COMPANY S.A.; *Int'l*, pg. 90
ACCORDION PARTNERS LLC; *U.S. Private*, pg. 53
ACCRELIST CROWDFUNDING PTE. LTD.—See Accrelist Ltd.; *Int'l*, pg. 93
ACCRETION ACQUISITION CORP.; *U.S. Public*, pg. 33
ACCURSIA CAPITAL GMBH; *Int'l*, pg. 94
ACE GLOBAL BUSINESS ACQUISITION LIMITED; *Int'l*, pg. 94
ACE MEN ENGG WORKS LIMITED; *Int'l*, pg. 94
ACE NEVADA CORP.—See Icahn Enterprises L.P.; *U.S. Public*, pg. 1083
ACER AMERICAN HOLDING CORP.—See Acer Incorporated; *Int'l*, pg. 98
ACER CAPITAL CORPORATION—See Acer Incorporated; *Int'l*, pg. 98
ACETO (HOLDING) B.V.—See Aceto Corporation; *U.S. Private*, pg. 58
ACF INVESTMENT CORP.—See General Motors Company; *U.S. Public*, pg. 924
ACHAL INVESTMENTS LIMITED; *Int'l*, pg. 102
ACHERON PORTFOLIO CORP (LUXEMBOURG) SA; *Int'l*, pg. 103
ACHIEVE PARTNERS MANAGEMENT, LLC; *U.S. Private*, pg. 59
ACI CAPITAL CO. LLC; *U.S. Private*, pg. 59
ACI (SINGAPORE) PTE. LTD.—See ACI Worldwide, Inc.; *U.S. Public*, pg. 34
ACKLEY BEVERAGE GROUP, LLC; *U.S. Private*, pg. 60
ACMBERNSTEIN GMBH—See Equitable Holdings, Inc.; *U.S. Public*, pg. 789
ACOMO INVESTMENTS B.V.—See ACOMO N.V.; *Int'l*, pg. 108
ACON INVESTMENTS, LLC; *U.S. Private*, pg. 62
ACORDY INVEST S.A.; *Int'l*, pg. 108
ACORN CAPITAL LIMITED; *Int'l*, pg. 108
ACORN INCOME CORP.; *Int'l*, pg. 108
ACP ENERGY PLC; *Int'l*, pg. 108
ACP GMBH & CO. BETEILIGUNGEN KG—See Allianz SE; *Int'l*, pg. 341
ACRI CAPITAL ACQUISITION CORPORATION; *U.S. Public*, pg. 36
ACRO ENERGY TECHNOLOGIES CORP.; *U.S. Private*, pg. 65
ACROPOLIS INFRASTRUCTURE ACQUISITION CORP.; *U.S. Public*, pg. 36
A.C. SIMMONDS & SONS, INC.; *Int'l*, pg. 23
ACTAVIA LIFE SCIENCES, INC.; *U.S. Public*, pg. 36
ACTELION US HOLDING CO.—See Johnson & Johnson; *U.S. Public*, pg. 1194
ACTERA GROUP STRATEJIK YONETIM HIZMETLERI A.S.; *Int'l*, pg. 117
ACTION FINANCIAL SERVICES (INDIA) LTD.; *Int'l*, pg. 119
ACTIS LLP - BEIJING OFFICE—See General Atlantic Service Company, L.P.; *U.S. Private*, pg. 1661
ACTIS LLP - MUMBAI OFFICE—See General Atlantic Service Company, L.P.; *U.S. Private*, pg. 1661
ACTIS LLP - SAO PAULO OFFICE—See General Atlantic Service Company, L.P.; *U.S. Private*, pg. 1661
ACTIS LLP—See General Atlantic Service Company, L.P.; *U.S. Private*, pg. 1660
ACTIVA CAPITAL S.A.S.; *Int'l*, pg. 119
ACTIVATE PERMANENT CAPITAL CORP.; *U.S. Private*, pg. 68
ACTIVE CAPITAL COMPANY HOLDING BV; *Int'l*, pg. 120
ACTIVE PRIVATE EQUITY ADVISORY LLP; *Int'l*, pg. 120
ACUITY FUNDS LTD—See AGF Management Limited; *Int'l*, pg. 206
ACUITY INVESTMENT MANAGEMENT INC—See AGF Management Limited; *Int'l*, pg. 206
ACUREN CORPORATION; *Int'l*, pg. 121
ACWA HOLDING CO.; *Int'l*, pg. 121
ADAMANTEM CAPITAL MANAGEMENT PTY LIMITED; *Int'l*, pg. 123
ADAMS DIVERSIFIED EQUITY FUND, INC.; *U.S. Public*, pg. 38
ADAPTHEALTH CORP.; *U.S. Public*, pg. 38
ADARSH MERCANTILE LIMITED; *Int'l*, pg. 125
ADC ACQUISITION CORP. PJSC; *Int'l*, pg. 126
ADC AFRICAN DEVELOPMENT CORPORATION AG—See Atlas Mara Limited; *Int'l*, pg. 686
ADCON CAPITAL SERVICES LTD.; *Int'l*, pg. 127
ADDISON CAPITAL PARTNERS; *U.S. Private*, pg. 77
ADECCO HOLDING FRANCE SASU—See Adecco Group AG; *Int'l*, pg. 137
ADECCO INTERNATIONAL FINANCIAL SERVICES BV.—See Adecco Group AG; *Int'l*, pg. 137
ADEEM INVESTMENT & WEALTH MANAGEMENT CO., K.S.C.C.—See Efad Real Estate Company; *Int'l*, pg. 2318
ADELIS EQUITY PARTNERS AB; *Int'l*, pg. 142
ADEM ALLGEMEINE DIENSTLEISTUNGEN FUR ENGINEERING UND MANAGEMENT GMBH—See BayernLB Holding AG; *Int'l*, pg. 913
ADEPTIO LLC; *Int'l*, pg. 143
ADERANS FRANCE SAS—See Aderans Co., Ltd.; *Int'l*, pg. 143
ADHARSHILA CAPITAL SERVICES LTD.; *Int'l*, pg. 145
ADIDAS BETEILIGUNGSGESELLSCHAFT MBH—See adidas AG; *Int'l*, pg. 146
ADIDAS CDC IMMOBILIENINVEST GMBH—See adidas AG; *Int'l*, pg. 146
ADIDAS FINANCE SPAIN S.A.—See adidas AG; *Int'l*, pg. 147
ADIDAS INTERNATIONAL FINANCE B.V.—See adidas AG; *Int'l*, pg. 147
ADINATH EXIM RESOURCES LTD.; *Int'l*, pg. 148
ADIT EDTECH ACQUISITION CORP.—See GRIID Infrastructure Inc.; *U.S. Public*, pg. 969
ADITYA BIRLA CAPITAL LTD.; *Int'l*, pg. 149
ADIUVA CAPITAL GMBH; *Int'l*, pg. 149
ADM ENERGY PLC; *Int'l*, pg. 151
ADMINISTRADORA DE FONDOS DE PENSIONES Y CESANTIA PROTECCION SA; *Int'l*, pg. 151
ADMIRAL GROUP PLC; *Int'l*, pg. 151
ADMIRALTY PARTNERS, INC.; *U.S. Private*, pg. 81
ADMY TECHNOLOGY GROUP, INC.; *U.S. Private*, pg. 81
A.D.O. GROUP LTD.—See ADLER Group SA; *Int'l*, pg. 150
ADRIATIC MEDIA INVESTORS LLC; *U.S. Private*, pg. 82
ADTHEORENT HOLDING COMPANY, INC.; *U.S. Public*, pg. 43

523999 — MISCELLANEOUS FINAN...

ADULARIA INVERSIONES 2010 S.L.—See Crown Holdings, Inc.; *U.S. Public*, pg. 597
ADVANCE AMERICA, CASH ADVANCE CENTERS OF TENNESSEE, INC.—See Grupo Salinas, S.A. de C.V.; *Int'l*, pg. 3135
ADVANCE AMERICA, CASH ADVANCE CENTERS OF VIRGINIA, INC.—See Grupo Salinas, S.A. de C.V.; *Int'l*, pg. 3135
ADVANCED FINANCIAL INC.—See The Advanced Group of Companies; *U.S. Private*, pg. 3982
ADVANCED MARKETING GROUP, INC.; *U.S. Private*, pg. 91
ADVANCED MERGER PARTNERS, INC.; *U.S. Public*, pg. 48
ADVANTAGE CAPITAL CORPORATION; *U.S. Private*, pg. 94
ADVANTAGE CAPITAL FUNDS LLC; *U.S. Private*, pg. 94
ADVANTAGE PARTNERS LLP; *Int'l*, pg. 164
ADVANTUS CAPITAL MANAGEMENT, INC.—See Securian Financial Group, Inc.; *U.S. Private*, pg. 3594
ADVENIS; *Int'l*, pg. 166
ADVENT INTERNATIONAL CORPORATION; *U.S. Private*, pg. 95
ADVERITAS LIMITED; *Int'l*, pg. 167
ADVFINANCE SP. Z O.O.—See Grupa SMT S.A.; *Int'l*, pg. 3117
ADVIK CAPITAL LTD; *Int'l*, pg. 168
AEA-BRIDGES IMPACT CORP.; *Int'l*, pg. 170
AEA INVESTORS (ASIA) LIMITED—See AEA Investors LP; *U.S. Private*, pg. 113
AEA INVESTORS (GERMANY) GMBH—See AEA Investors LP; *U.S. Private*, pg. 113
AEA INVESTORS LP; *U.S. Private*, pg. 112
AEA INVESTORS (UK) LIMITED—See AEA Investors LP; *U.S. Private*, pg. 113
AEDAN FINANCIAL CORP.; *U.S. Private*, pg. 116
AEGA ASA; *Int'l*, pg. 173
AEGON BANK N.V.—See BAWAG Group AG; *Int'l*, pg. 900
AEGON USA INVESTMENT MANAGEMENT LLC—See Aegon N.V.; *Int'l*, pg. 174
AE INDUSTRIAL PARTNERS, LP; *U.S. Private*, pg. 111
AELUMA, INC.; *U.S. Public*, pg. 52
AEON ACQUISITION CORP.; *U.S. Public*, pg. 117
AEQUI ACQUISITION CORP.; *U.S. Public*, pg. 52
AEQUITA SE & CO. KGAA; *Int'l*, pg. 179
AEQUITAS GMBH ALLIANZ EQUITY - ALTERNATIVE STRATEGIES—See Allianz SE; *Int'l*, pg. 343
AEROEQUITY PARTNERS, LLC; *U.S. Private*, pg. 118
AEROMED GROUP LLC—See Copley Equity Partners,LLC; *U.S. Private*, pg. 1045
AETHER GLOBAL INNOVATIONS CORP.; *Int'l*, pg. 183
AETHERIUM ACQUISITION CORP.; *U.S. Public*, pg. 53
AETHON MINERALS CORP.—See AbraSilver Resource Corp.; *Int'l*, pg. 67
AEVIS EUROPA, S.L.—See Banco Santander, S.A.; *Int'l*, pg. 825
AEVIS VICTORIA SA; *Int'l*, pg. 183
AF ACQUISITION CORP.; *U.S. Public*, pg. 53
AFAQ FOR ENERGY CO. PLC; *Int'l*, pg. 185
AFAQ HOLDING FOR INVESTMENT & REAL ESTATE DEVELOPMENT CO P.L.C.; *Int'l*, pg. 185
A.F. ENTERPRISES LIMITED; *Int'l*, pg. 23
AFFILIATED MANAGERS GROUP LIMITED—See Affiliated Managers Group, Inc.; *U.S. Public*, pg. 53
AFFIN HWANG ASSET MANAGEMENT BERHAD—See AFFIN Holdings Berhad; *Int'l*, pg. 186
AFFINITY EQUITY PARTNERS (AUSTRALIA) PTY. LTD.—See Affinity Equity Partners (HK) Ltd.; *Int'l*, pg. 186
AFFINITY EQUITY PARTNERS (HK) LTD.; *Int'l*, pg. 186
AFFINITY EQUITY PARTNERS KOREA LLC—See Affinity Equity Partners (HK) Ltd.; *Int'l*, pg. 186
AFFIRMA CAPITAL MANAGERS (SINGAPORE) PTE. LTD.—See Affirma Capital Limited; *Int'l*, pg. 187
AFGRI FINANCIAL AND LOGISTICS SERVICES—See AFGRI Limited; *Int'l*, pg. 188
AFI EUROPE FINANCING B.V.—See Africa Israel Investments Ltd.; *Int'l*, pg. 190
AFI GERMANY INVESTMENT GMBH—See Africa Israel Investments Ltd.; *Int'l*, pg. 190
AFINE INVESTMENTS LIMITED; *Int'l*, pg. 189
AFINUM MANAGEMENT GMBH; *Int'l*, pg. 189
AFI PARTNERS LLC; *U.S. Private*, pg. 123
AFM CAPITAL PARTNERS, INC.; *U.S. Private*, pg. 123
AFRICA CAPITALWORKS HOLDINGS; *Int'l*, pg. 189
AFRICA ISRAEL INTERNATIONAL HOLDINGS LTD.—See Africa Israel Investments Ltd.; *Int'l*, pg. 190
AFRICAN GOLD ACQUISITION CORPORATION; *U.S. Public*, pg. 57
AFRICAN INFRASTRUCTURE INVESTMENT MANAGERS; *Int'l*, pg. 191
AFRICAN MINERALS EXPLORATION & DEVELOPMENT SICAR SCA; *Int'l*, pg. 192
AFS SENSUB CORP.—See General Motors Company; *U.S. Public*, pg. 925
AFTERNEXT HEALTHTECH ACQUISITION CORP.; *U.S. Public*, pg. 57
AG ACQUISITION GROUP, INC.; *U.S. Private*, pg. 124
AGAMYA CAPITAL LLC; *U.S. Private*, pg. 125

AGBA GROUP HOLDING LIMITED; *Int'l*, pg. 200
AG CAPITAL; *Int'l*, pg. 197
AGC CAPITAL, INC.—See AGC Inc.; *Int'l*, pg. 200
AGC FINANCE CO., LTD.—See AGC Inc.; *Int'l*, pg. 202
AG CROWDFUNDING CO.,LTD.—See AIFUL Corporation; *Int'l*, pg. 231
AGC SINGAPORE SERVICES PTE. LTD.—See AGC Inc.; *Int'l*, pg. 203
AGENZIA NAZIONALE PER L'ATTRAZIONE DEGLI INVESTIMENTI E LO SVILLUPO D'IMPRESA SPA; *Int'l*, pg. 206
AGFA FINANCE INC.—See Agfa-Gevaert N.V.; *Int'l*, pg. 207
AGFA FINANCE NV—See Agfa-Gevaert N.V.; *Int'l*, pg. 207
AGFA-GEVAERT INVESTMENT FUND NV—See Agfa-Gevaert N.V.; *Int'l*, pg. 208
AGF CAPITAL INVESTISSEMENT 2—See Allianz SE; *Int'l*, pg. 342
AGFIA LIMITED—See AGF Management Limited; *Int'l*, pg. 206
AGF INVESTMENTS INC.—See AGF Management Limited; *Int'l*, pg. 206
AGF MANAGEMENT LIMITED; *Int'l*, pg. 206
AG HILL PARTNERS LLC; *U.S. Private*, pg. 124
AGILE CAPITAL; *Int'l*, pg. 209
AGILE GROWTH CORP.; *U.S. Public*, pg. 60
AGILIS HOLDING COMPANY LLC; *U.S. Private*, pg. 128
AGILITAS PRIVATE EQUITY LLP; *Int'l*, pg. 209
AGRARINVEST AG; *Int'l*, pg. 214
AGRICO ACQUISITION CORP.—See Kalera Public Limited Company; *U.S. Public*, pg. 1213
AGRICULTURE & NATURAL SOLUTIONS ACQUISITION CORPORATION; *U.S. Public*, pg. 63
AGRO CAPITAL MANAGEMENT CORP.; *U.S. Public*, pg. 63
AGROENERGY INVEST REIT; *Int'l*, pg. 218
AGRONOMICS LTD.; *Int'l*, pg. 220
AG SMILE LEASEBACK CORPORATION—See AIFUL Corporation; *Int'l*, pg. 231
AHC DIGITAL LLC—See Arthur J. Gallagher & Co.; *U.S. Public*, pg. 205
AHEIM CAPITAL GMBH; *Int'l*, pg. 223
AHLSTROM ASIA HOLDINGS PTE LTD—See Ahlstrom Capital Oy; *Int'l*, pg. 223
AHLSTROM ASIA HOLDINGS PTE LTD—See Bain Capital, LP; *U.S. Private*, pg. 429
AHLSTROM CAPITAL OY; *Int'l*, pg. 223
AHREN ACQUISITION CORP.; *Int'l*, pg. 225
AIAS INVESTMENT PUBLIC LTD.; *Int'l*, pg. 227
AIB HOLDINGS (NI) LIMITED—See AIB Group plc; *Int'l*, pg. 228
AIB INTERNATIONAL FINANCE—See AIB Group plc; *Int'l*, pg. 228
AIFINYO AG; *Int'l*, pg. 231
AIFUL BUSINESS FINANCE CORPORATION—See AIFUL Corporation; *Int'l*, pg. 231
AIGLON CAPITAL MANAGEMENT LLC; *U.S. Private*, pg. 132
AIKIDO PHARMA INC.; *U.S. Public*, pg. 63
AIMEI HEALTH TECHNOLOGY CO., LTD.; *U.S. Public*, pg. 63
AIP, LLC - SAN FRANCISCO—See AIP, LLC; *U.S. Private*, pg. 133
AIP, LLC; *U.S. Private*, pg. 133
AIRA ADVISORY CO., LTD.—See AIRA Factoring Public Company Limited; *Int'l*, pg. 241
AIRA & AIFUL PUBLIC COMPANY LIMITED—See AIFUL Corporation; *Int'l*, pg. 231
AIRA FACTORING PUBLIC COMPANY LIMITED; *Int'l*, pg. 241
AIRA LEASING PLC—See AIRA Factoring Public Company Limited; *Int'l*, pg. 241
AIRBORNE WIRELESS NETWORK; *U.S. Private*, pg. 140
AIRPLUS HOLDING GMBH—See Deutsche Lufthansa AG; *Int'l*, pg. 2068
AIRSPAN NETWORKS HOLDINGS INC.; *U.S. Public*, pg. 68
AISLING CAPITAL LLC; *U.S. Private*, pg. 142
AIVE BST SPA—See Capgemini SE; *Int'l*, pg. 1303
AJAX RESOURCES PLC; *Int'l*, pg. 255
AKIS GAYRIMENKUL YATIRIM ORTAKLIGI A.S.; *Int'l*, pg. 263
AKMERKEZ GAYRIMENKUL YATIRIM ORTAKLIGI A.S.; *Int'l*, pg. 264
AKOUSTIS, INC.—See Akoustis Technologies, Inc.; *U.S. Public*, pg. 69
AKOUSTIS TECHNOLOGIES, INC.; *U.S. Public*, pg. 69
AKOYA CAPITAL LLC; *U.S. Private*, pg. 146
AKTIEBOLAGET NORRKOPING SILVRET 1—See Eurocommercial Properties N.V.; *Int'l*, pg. 2534
AKZO NOBLE FINANCE UNITED STATES INC—See Akzo Nobel N.V.; *Int'l*, pg. 273
AL AHLY FOR DEVELOPMENT & INVESTMENT; *Int'l*, pg. 275
AL-AMAN INVESTMENT COMPANY K.S.C.C.; *Int'l*, pg. 284
AL AMEEN REAL ESTATE INVESTMENT CO.; *Int'l*, pg. 275
AL AMIN FOR INVESTMENT P.L.C.; *Int'l*, pg. 275
ALANTRA PARTNERS, SA; *Int'l*, pg. 291
ALA SPA; *Int'l*, pg. 289

AL BATEK FINANCIAL INVESTMENT CO.; *Int'l*, pg. 276
ALBERTON ACQUISITION CORPORATION; *Int'l*, pg. 298
ALBION CAPITAL; *Int'l*, pg. 299
ALBION TECHNOLOGY & GENERAL VCT PLC; *Int'l*, pg. 299
ALBION VENTURE CAPITAL TRUST PLC; *Int'l*, pg. 299
ALCEON GROUP PTY LTD.; *Int'l*, pg. 300
ALDAMAN FOR INVESTMENTS PLC; *Int'l*, pg. 304
AL-DEERA HOLDING CO. K.S.C.C.; *Int'l*, pg. 285
ALDEN GLOBAL CAPITAL LLC; *U.S. Private*, pg. 155
ALDER FUND I AB; *Int'l*, pg. 304
ALDER II AB—See Alder Fund I AB; *Int'l*, pg. 304
ALDERMORE INVOICE FINANCE LIMITED—See AnaCap Financial Partners LLP; *Int'l*, pg. 445
ALDINE CAPITAL PARTNERS, INC.; *U.S. Private*, pg. 159
ALDRICH CAPITAL PARTNERS, LLC; *U.S. Private*, pg. 160
ALEF S.A.; *Int'l*, pg. 306
ALERION CAPITAL GROUP, LLC; *U.S. Private*, pg. 160
THE ALEUT CORPORATION; *U.S. Private*, pg. 3983
ALEXANDER FORBES CHANNEL ISLANDS LIMITED—See Alexander Forbes Group Holdings Limited; *Int'l*, pg. 306
ALEXANDER FORBES COMMUNITY TRUST—See Alexander Forbes Group Holdings Limited; *Int'l*, pg. 306
ALEXANDER FORBES CONSULTING ACTUARIES NIGERIA LIMITED—See Alexander Forbes Group Holdings Limited; *Int'l*, pg. 306
ALEXANDER FORBES GROUP HOLDINGS LIMITED; *Int'l*, pg. 306
ALEXANDER FORBES LIMITED—See Alexander Forbes Group Holdings Limited; *Int'l*, pg. 306
ALEXANDER TECH CORP.; *Int'l*, pg. 307
ALEXANDRIA AGTECH/CLIMATE INNOVATION ACQUISITION CORP.; *U.S. Private*, pg. 164
ALEXANDRIA GLOBAL INVESTMENT MANAGEMENT LTD.—See Guardian Capital Group Limited; *Int'l*, pg. 3169
ALEXANDRIA GROUP OYJ; *Int'l*, pg. 307
ALEXANDRIA NATIONAL COMPANY FOR FINANCIAL INVESTMENT; *Int'l*, pg. 307
ALFA GROUP; *Int'l*, pg. 308
ALFALAH SECURITIES (PVT.) LTD.—See Abu Dhabi Group; *Int'l*, pg. 71
ALFA LAVAL FINANCE CO LTD—See Alfa Laval AB; *Int'l*, pg. 310
ALFA LAVAL NEDERLAND BV—See Alfa Laval AB; *Int'l*, pg. 310
ALFA LAVAL TREASURY INTERNATIONAL AB—See Alfa Laval AB; *Int'l*, pg. 311
ALFRED BERG KAPITALFORVALTNING AB—See BNP Paribas SA; *Int'l*, pg. 1082
AL GASSIM INVESTMENT HOLDING CO.; *Int'l*, pg. 277
ALGER ASSOCIATES, INC.; *U.S. Private*, pg. 166
ALGER GROUP HOLDINGS, LLC.—See Alger Associates, Inc.; *U.S. Private*, pg. 166
ALIADO FACTORING, S.A.—See Grupo Aliado S.A.; *Int'l*, pg. 3119
ALIADO LEASING, S.A.—See Grupo Aliado S.A.; *Int'l*, pg. 3119
ALIGN CAPITAL PARTNERS, LLC; *U.S. Private*, pg. 167
ALIGNVEST AQUISITION II CORP.—See Alignvest Management Corporation; *Int'l*, pg. 327
ALIGNVEST MANAGEMENT CORPORATION; *Int'l*, pg. 327
ALIGN WEALTH MANAGEMENT, LLC—See Hellman & Friedman LLC; *U.S. Private*, pg. 1908
AL IMTIAZ INVESTMENT GROUP COMPANY- K.S.C.; *Int'l*, pg. 279
ALINDA INVESTMENTS LLC—See Astatine Investment Partners LLC; *U.S. Private*, pg. 360
ALINMA INVESTMENT COMPANY—See Alinma Bank; *Int'l*, pg. 329
ALITER CAPITAL LLP; *Int'l*, pg. 329
AL JAMIL FOR INVESTMENT COMPANY; *Int'l*, pg. 280
AL JAZIRA OIL & GAS SERVICES COMPANY EC—See Dabbagh Group Holding Company Ltd.; *Int'l*, pg. 1902
ALJ FINANSMAN A.S.; *Int'l*, pg. 329
ALKA SECURITIES LIMITED; *Int'l*, pg. 330
ALKEMY CAPITAL INVESTMENTS PLC; *Int'l*, pg. 331
AL KHAZER FOR CONSTRUCTION MATERIALS, REAL ESTATE INVESTMENTS & GENERAL CONTRACTING; *Int'l*, pg. 280
ALKURI GLOBAL ACQUISITION CORP.; *U.S. Public*, pg. 78
ALL ACTIVE ASSET CAPITAL LTD.; *Int'l*, pg. 331
ALL AMERICAN HOLDINGS LLC; *U.S. Private*, pg. 169
ALLARD NAZARIAN GROUP INC.; *U.S. Private*, pg. 174
ALLEGHANY CAPITAL CORPORATION—See Berkshire Hathaway Inc.; *U.S. Public*, pg. 298
ALLEGRO FUNDS PTY. LTD.; *Int'l*, pg. 336
ALLEGRO MERGER CORP.; *U.S. Private*, pg. 178
ALLFUNDS GROUP PLC; *Int'l*, pg. 336
ALLGREENTECH INTERNATIONAL PLC; *Int'l*, pg. 338
ALLIANCEBERNSTEIN (ARGENTINA) S.R.L—See Equitable Holdings, Inc.; *U.S. Public*, pg. 789
ALLIANCEBERNSTEIN ASSET MANAGEMENT (KOREA) LTD.—See Equitable Holdings, Inc.; *U.S. Public*, pg. 789
ALLIANCEBERNSTEIN AUSTRALIA LIMITED—See Equi-

523999 — MISCELLANEOUS FINAN...

table Holdings, Inc.; *U.S. Public*, pg. 789
ALLIANCEBERNSTEIN CANADA, INC—See Equitable Holdings, Inc.; *U.S. Public*, pg. 789
ALLIANCEBERNSTEIN (FRANCE) S.A.S.—See Equitable Holdings, Inc.; *U.S. Public*, pg. 789
ALLIANCEBERNSTEIN GLOBAL WEALTH MANAGEMENT—See Equitable Holdings, Inc.; *U.S. Public*, pg. 789
ALLIANCEBERNSTEIN HONG KONG LIMITED—See Equitable Holdings, Inc.; *U.S. Public*, pg. 789
ALLIANCEBERNSTEIN INSTITUTIONAL INVESTMENTS—See Equitable Holdings, Inc.; *U.S. Public*, pg. 789
ALLIANCEBERNSTEIN INVESTMENT MANAGEMENT AUSTRALIA LIMITED—See Equitable Holdings, Inc.; *U.S. Public*, pg. 789
ALLIANCEBERNSTEIN INVESTMENTS TAIWAN LIMITED—See Equitable Holdings, Inc.; *U.S. Public*, pg. 789
ALLIANCEBERNSTEIN JAPAN LTD—See Equitable Holdings, Inc.; *U.S. Public*, pg. 789
ALLIANCEBERNSTEIN LIMITED—See Equitable Holdings, Inc.; *U.S. Public*, pg. 789
ALLIANCEBERNSTEIN LIMITED—See Equitable Holdings, Inc.; *U.S. Public*, pg. 789
ALLIANCEBERNSTEIN L.P.—See Equitable Holdings, Inc.; *U.S. Public*, pg. 789
ALLIANCEBERNSTEIN (LUXEMBOURG) S.A.—See Equitable Holdings, Inc.; *U.S. Public*, pg. 789
ALLIANCEBERNSTEIN (SINGAPORE) LIMITED—See Equitable Holdings, Inc.; *U.S. Public*, pg. 789
ALLIANCEBERNSTEIN TAIWAN LIMITED—See Equitable Holdings, Inc.; *U.S. Public*, pg. 789
ALLIANCE DEVELOPMENT GROUP; *U.S. Private*, pg. 182
ALLIANCE ENTERTAINMENT HOLDING CORPORATION; *U.S. Public*, pg. 79
ALLIANCE FINANCIAL SERVICES, INC.—See Lennar Corporation; *U.S. Public*, pg. 1305
ALLIANCE PHYSICAL THERAPY PARTNERS, LLC—See GPB Capital Holdings, LLC; *U.S. Private*, pg. 1748
ALLIANZ ALTERNATIVE ASSETS HOLDING GMBH—See Allianz SE; *Int'l*, pg. 343
ALLIANZ AUSTRALIA SERVICES PTY LIMITED—See Allianz SE; *Int'l*, pg. 343
ALLIANZ AZL VERMOGENSVERWALTUNG GMBH—See Allianz SE; *Int'l*, pg. 343
ALLIANZ BIZNES SP. Z O.O.—See Allianz SE; *Int'l*, pg. 344
ALLIANZ BUSINESS SERVICES S.R.O.—See Allianz SE; *Int'l*, pg. 351
ALLIANZ EQUITY INVESTMENTS LTD.—See Allianz SE; *Int'l*, pg. 345
ALLIANZ FINANCE III B.V.—See Allianz SE; *Int'l*, pg. 345
ALLIANZ FINANCE PTY LTD.—See Allianz SE; *Int'l*, pg. 345
ALLIANZ FRANCE INFRASTRUCTURE 1—See Allianz SE; *Int'l*, pg. 345
ALLIANZGI DIVERSIFIED INCOME & CONVERTIBLE FUND; *U.S. Private*, pg. 185
ALLIANZ GLOBAL INVESTORS AG—See Allianz SE; *Int'l*, pg. 346
ALLIANZ GLOBAL INVESTORS ASIA PACIFIC GMBH—See Allianz SE; *Int'l*, pg. 347
ALLIANZ GLOBAL INVESTORS ASIA PACIFIC LIMITED—See Allianz SE; *Int'l*, pg. 347
ALLIANZ GLOBAL INVESTORS CAPITAL LLC—See Allianz SE; *Int'l*, pg. 347
ALLIANZ GLOBAL INVESTORS FUND MANAGEMENT LLC—See Allianz SE; *Int'l*, pg. 347
ALLIANZ GLOBAL INVESTORS HONG KONG LIMITED—See Allianz SE; *Int'l*, pg. 346
ALLIANZ GLOBAL INVESTORS IRELAND LTD.—See Allianz SE; *Int'l*, pg. 347
ALLIANZ GLOBAL INVESTORS LUXEMBOURG S.A.; *Int'l*, pg. 341
ALLIANZ GLOBAL INVESTORS NOMINEES (UK) LTD.—See Allianz SE; *Int'l*, pg. 347
ALLIANZ GLOBAL INVESTORS (SCHWEIZ) AG—See Allianz SE; *Int'l*, pg. 346
ALLIANZ GLOBAL INVESTORS SECURITIES INVESTMENT CONSULTING CO. LTD.—See Allianz SE; *Int'l*, pg. 346
ALLIANZ GLOBAL INVESTORS SINGAPORE LTD.—See Allianz SE; *Int'l*, pg. 346
ALLIANZ GLOBAL INVESTORS SOLUTIONS LLC—See Allianz SE; *Int'l*, pg. 347
ALLIANZ GLOBAL INVESTORS TAIWAN LTD.—See Allianz SE; *Int'l*, pg. 346
ALLIANZ GLOBAL INVESTORS (UK) LTD.—See Allianz SE; *Int'l*, pg. 346
ALLIANZ HOLDING EINS GMBH—See Allianz SE; *Int'l*, pg. 348
ALLIANZ HOLDING FRANCE SAS—See Allianz SE; *Int'l*, pg. 348
ALLIANZ HOLDINGS PLC—See Allianz SE; *Int'l*, pg. 348
ALLIANZ INVERSIONES S.A.—See Allianz SE; *Int'l*, pg. 348
ALLIANZ INVESTMENTBANK AG—See Allianz SE; *Int'l*, pg. 348
ALLIANZ INVESTMENT COMPANY LLC—See Allianz SE; *Int'l*, pg. 348

ALLIANZ NEW EUROPE HOLDING GMBH—See Allianz SE; *Int'l*, pg. 349
ALLIANZ PRIVATE EQUITY PARTNERS GMBH—See Allianz SE; *Int'l*, pg. 344
ALLIANZ SUISSE IMMOBILIEN AG—See Allianz SE; *Int'l*, pg. 350
ALLIED GAMING & ENTERTAINMENT, INC.; *U.S. Public*, pg. 80
ALLIED IRISH BANKS (HOLDINGS & INVESTMENTS) LIMITED—See AIB Group plc; *Int'l*, pg. 228
ALLIED IRISH FINANCE LIMITED—See AIB Group plc; *Int'l*, pg. 228
ALLIES LIMITED; *U.S. Private*, pg. 191
ALLY AUTO ASSETS LLC; *U.S. Private*, pg. 194
ALLY WHOLESALE ENTERPRISES LLC; *U.S. Private*, pg. 194
AL-MADINA FOR FINANCE & INVESTMENT COMPANY KSCC; *Int'l*, pg. 286
AL-MAL INVESTMENT COMPANY KSCC; *Int'l*, pg. 286
ALMANIA INVESTMENTS (PROPRIETARY) LIMITED—See Hosken Consolidated Investments Limited; *Int'l*, pg. 3485
ALOE PRIVATE EQUITY SAS; *Int'l*, pg. 365
AL OMANIYA FINANCIAL SERVICES (SAOG); *Int'l*, pg. 281
ALON NATURAL GAS EXPLORATION LTD.—See Alon Israel Oil Company Ltd.; *Int'l*, pg. 365
ALP ASSOCIATES; *U.S. Private*, pg. 196
ALPHA ASSOCIES CONSEIL SAS; *Int'l*, pg. 366
ALPHA BULGARIA JSC; *Int'l*, pg. 367
ALPHA CAPITAL ACQUISITION COMPANY; *U.S. Public*, pg. 82
ALPHA CAPITAL PARTNERS, LTD.; *U.S. Private*, pg. 197
ALPHACORE CAPITAL LLC; *U.S. Private*, pg. 200
ALPHA CREDIT NEDERLAND B.V.—See ABN AMRO Group N.V.; *Int'l*, pg. 65
ALPHA FINANCE A.E.P.E.Y.—See Alpha Services and Holdings S.A.; *Int'l*, pg. 369
ALPHA FINANCE ROMANIA S.A.—See Alpha Services and Holdings S.A.; *Int'l*, pg. 369
ALPHAKINETIC LTD.—See Fidelity National Infor; *U.S. Public*, pg. 832
ALPHA LEASING ROMANIA IFN S.A.—See Alpha Services and Holdings S.A.; *Int'l*, pg. 369
ALPHA PEAK LEISURE INC.; *Int'l*, pg. 369
ALPHA REAL ESTATE MANAGEMENT & INVESTMENTS S.A.—See Alpha Services and Holdings S.A.; *Int'l*, pg. 369
ALPHA STAR ACQUISITION CORPORATION; *U.S. Public*, pg. 82
ALPHATIME ACQUISITION CORP.; *U.S. Public*, pg. 84
ALPHA TRUST CORPORATION—See Roper Technologies, Inc.; *U.S. Public*, pg. 1810
ALPHA UNIVERSAL MANAGEMENT PLC; *Int'l*, pg. 370
ALPHAVEST ACQUISITION CORP.; *U.S. Public*, pg. 85
ALPINE ACQUISITION CORP.; *U.S. Public*, pg. 85
ALPINE GROVE (NETHERLANDS) B.V.—See Alpine Grove Partners LLP; *U.S. Private*, pg. 201
ALPINE GROVE PARTNERS LLP; *U.S. Private*, pg. 201
ALPINE GROVE PARTNERS (US) LLC—See Alpine Grove Partners LLP; *U.S. Private*, pg. 201
ALPINE INVESTORS; *U.S. Private*, pg. 201
ALPINVEST PARTNERS B.V.—See The Carlyle Group Inc.; *U.S. Public*, pg. 2054
ALPIQ FINANZBETEILIGUNGEN LTD.—See Alpiq Holding AG; *Int'l*, pg. 373
AL RAJHI BANKING & INVESTMENT CORPORATION BHD—See Al Rajhi Bank; *Int'l*, pg. 282
AL RAJHI BANK - KUWAIT WLL—See Al Rajhi Bank; *Int'l*, pg. 282
ALSAIF STORES FOR DEVELOPMENT & INVESTMENT COMPANY; *Int'l*, pg. 379
AL SALAM ASIA-PACIFIC PTE LTD.—See Al Salam Bank-Bahrain B.S.C.; *Int'l*, pg. 282
AL SALAM BANK SEYCHELLES LIMITED—See Al Salam Bank-Bahrain B.S.C.; *Int'l*, pg. 282
AL SALAM GROUP HOLDING COMPANY KSCC; *Int'l*, pg. 282
ALSTON CAPITAL PARTNERS LLC; *U.S. Private*, pg. 203
ALTA EQUIPMENT GROUP INC.; *U.S. Public*, pg. 85
AL TAJAMOUAT FOR TOURISTIC PROJECTS CO. PLC; *Int'l*, pg. 283
ALTAMIR S.C.A.; *Int'l*, pg. 385
ALTAMONT CAPITAL PARTNERS; *U.S. Private*, pg. 204
ALTAMONT PHARMA ACQUISITION CORP.; *U.S. Private*, pg. 205
ALTAN RIO MINERALS LIMITED; *Int'l*, pg. 385
ALTARIS CAPITAL PARTNERS, LLC; *U.S. Private*, pg. 205
ALTAS PARTNERS LP; *Int'l*, pg. 386
ALTC ACQUISITION CORP.; *U.S. Public*, pg. 87
ALTENERGY ACQUISITION CORP.; *U.S. Public*, pg. 87
ALTERATION EARTH PLC; *Int'l*, pg. 391
ALTERI PARTNERS LLP; *Int'l*, pg. 391
ALTERNA CAPITAL PARTNERS LLC; *U.S. Private*, pg. 207
ALTERNATIVE INVESTMENT CORPORATION; *U.S. Private*, pg. 207
ALTERNATIVE RE LIMITED—See Arch Capital Group Ltd.; *Int'l*, pg. 546
ALTERNATIVE UNDERWRITING SERVICES, LTD.—See Arch Capital Group Ltd.; *Int'l*, pg. 546
AL-TIJARI FINANCIAL BROKERAGE COMPANY K.S.C.—See Commercial Bank of Kuwait S.A.K.; *Int'l*, pg. 1715
ALTIMETER GROWTH CORP.; *U.S. Public*, pg. 88
ALTITUDE ACQUISITION CORP.; *U.S. Public*, pg. 88
ALTOR EQUITY PARTNERS AB; *Int'l*, pg. 394
ALTOR EQUITY PARTNERS A/S—See Altor Equity Partners AB; *Int'l*, pg. 394
ALTOR EQUITY PARTNERS OY—See Altor Equity Partners AB; *Int'l*, pg. 394
ALTRAN DEUTSCHLAND HOLDING GMBH—See Capgemini SE; *Int'l*, pg. 1304
ALTRAN LUXEMBOURG S.A.N.V.—See Capgemini SE; *Int'l*, pg. 1304
ALTRAN USA HOLDINGS INC.—See Capgemini SE; *Int'l*, pg. 1305
ALTRUIST CORP; *U.S. Private*, pg. 210
ALTUS CAPITAL PARTNERS, INC.; *U.S. Private*, pg. 211
ALTUS RESOURCE CAPITAL LIMITED; *Int'l*, pg. 399
ALUMINA LIMITED—See Alcoa Corporation; *U.S. Public*, pg. 74
ALUMINUM.IO, INC.; *U.S. Private*, pg. 211
ALUSSA ENERGY ACQUISITION CORP.; *Int'l*, pg. 401
AL WIAAM FOR FINANCIAL INVESTMENT CO.; *Int'l*, pg. 283
AL ZAWRAA FINANCIAL INVESTMENT PLC; *Int'l*, pg. 283
AL ZAYANI INVESTMENTS WLL; *Int'l*, pg. 283
AMADEUS CAPITAL PARTNERS LTD.; *Int'l*, pg. 404
AMANAH LEASING PUBLIC COMPANY LIMITED; *Int'l*, pg. 409
AMARA HOLDINGS LTD.; *Int'l*, pg. 411
AMAR FINANCE & LEASING COMPANY (K.S.C.C.); *Int'l*, pg. 411
AMARNATH SECURITIES LIMITED; *Int'l*, pg. 412
AMAS-INVESTMENT AND PROJECT SERVICES LTD.—See Hinduja Group Ltd.; *Int'l*, pg. 3399
AMBASSADOR SUPPLY, LLC—See Ambassador Enterprises, LLC; *U.S. Private*, pg. 217
AMBER HILL FINANCIAL HOLDINGS LTD.; *Int'l*, pg. 414
AMBIENTA SGR S.P.A.; *Int'l*, pg. 414
AMBRIAN PLC; *Int'l*, pg. 415
A&M CAPITAL ADVISORS EUROPE, LLP—See Alvarez & Marsal, Inc.; *U.S. Private*, pg. 212
A&M CAPITAL ADVISORS, LLC—See Alvarez & Marsal, Inc.; *U.S. Private*, pg. 212
AMCIL LIMITED; *Int'l*, pg. 416
AMDOCS HOLDINGS ULC—See Amdocs Limited; *Int'l*, pg. 419
AMDOCS INVESTMENTS SWITZERLAND LIMITED—See Amdocs Limited; *Int'l*, pg. 419
AMEDEO AIR FOUR PLUS LIMITED; *Int'l*, pg. 420
AMEDEO RESOURCES PLC; *Int'l*, pg. 420
AMEREDEV II, LLC; *U.S. Private*, pg. 219
AMERICAN ACQUISITION OPPORTUNITY, INC.; *U.S. Public*, pg. 95
AMERICAN AGCREDIT FLCA—See American AgCredit; *U.S. Private*, pg. 221
AMERICAN AGCREDIT PCA—See American AgCredit; *U.S. Private*, pg. 222
THE AMERICAN BAR ASSOCIATION MEMBERS/NORTHERN TRUST COLLECTIVE TRUST; *U.S. Private*, pg. 3985
AMERICAN BLOCKCHAINBIOCHAR CORPORATION; *U.S. Private*, pg. 224
AMERICAN CENTURY INVESTMENTS—See American Century Companies, Inc.; *U.S. Private*, pg. 226
AMERICAN CHURCH MORTGAGE COMPANY; *U.S. Public*, pg. 98
AMERICAN ENTERPRISE INVESTMENT SERVICES, INC.—See Ameriprise Financial, Inc.; *U.S. Public*, pg. 114
AMERICAN FAMILY FINANCIAL SERVICES, INC.—See American Family Mutual Insurance Company; *U.S. Private*, pg. 233
AMERICAN FINANCIAL ENTERPRISES, INC.—See American Financial Group, Inc.; *U.S. Public*, pg. 102
AMERICAN GENE ENGINEER CORP.; *U.S. Private*, pg. 235
AMERICAN INTERNATIONAL VENTURES, INC.; *U.S. Public*, pg. 108
AMERICAN PACIFIC GROUP, LLC; *U.S. Private*, pg. 242
AMERICAN PRUDENTIAL CAPITAL, INC.—See Stellar Bancorp, Inc.; *U.S. Public*, pg. 1944
AMERICAN RESTAURANTS, LLC—See American Restaurant Holdings, Inc.; *U.S. Private*, pg. 246
AMERICAN RIVER VENTURES, LLC; *U.S. Private*, pg. 246
AMERICAN SECURITIES LLC; *U.S. Private*, pg. 247
AMERICAN SOFTWARE CAPITAL INC—See ASC Global Inc.; *U.S. Private*, pg. 345
AMERICAN VIRTUAL CLOUD TECHNOLOGIES, INC.; *U.S. Public*, pg. 112
AMERICA'S FINANCIAL CHOICE, LLC—See Finbond Group Limited; *Int'l*, pg. 2670
AMERICAS PRODUCTS & DISTRIBUTION, INC.—See CRH plc; *Int'l*, pg. 1842
AMERICAS TECHNOLOGY ACQUISITION CORP.; *U.S. Public*, pg. 113

523999 — MISCELLANEOUS FINAN...   CORPORATE AFFILIATIONS

N.A.I.C.S. Index

AMERIPRISE CERTIFICATE COMPANY—See Ameriprise Financial, Inc.; *U.S. Public*, pg. 114
AMERIPRISE FINANCIAL SERVICES, INC.—See Ameriprise Financial, Inc.; *U.S. Public*, pg. 114
AMERITRANS CAPITAL CORPORATION; *U.S. Public*, pg. 115
AMERRA CAPITAL MANAGEMENT LLC; *Int'l*, pg. 424
AMER SPORTS FINANCE OY—See ANTA Sports Products Limited; *Int'l*, pg. 480
AMER SPORTS HOLDING GMBH—See ANTA Sports Products Limited; *Int'l*, pg. 480
AMER SPORTS HOLDING S.A.S.—See ANTA Sports Products Limited; *Int'l*, pg. 480
AMERY CAPITAL LIMITED; *Int'l*, pg. 424
AMFIL TECHNOLOGIES INC.; *Int'l*, pg. 424
AMG ADVANCED METALLURGICAL GROUP INVESTMENT BV—See AMG Critical Materials N.V.; *Int'l*, pg. 425
AMG BRAZILIAN HOLDING BV—See AMG Critical Materials N.V.; *Int'l*, pg. 425
AMG EURO HOLDINGS CV—See AMG Critical Materials N.V.; *Int'l*, pg. 425
AMLAK FINANCE PJSC—See Emaar Properties PJSC; *Int'l*, pg. 2372
AMP CAPITAL INVESTORS (LUXEMBOURG) S.A R.L.—See AMP Limited; *Int'l*, pg. 431
AMP CAPITAL INVESTORS (US) LIMITED—See AMP Limited; *Int'l*, pg. 431
AMP CAPITAL OFFICE AND INDUSTRIAL PTY LIMITED—See AMP Limited; *Int'l*, pg. 432
AMP CUSTODIAN SERVICES (NZ) LIMITED—See AMP Limited; *Int'l*, pg. 432
AMPERSAND MANAGEMENT LLC; *U.S. Private*, pg. 265
AMP LIMITED; *Int'l*, pg. 431
AMP SUPERANNUATION LIMITED—See AMP Limited; *Int'l*, pg. 432
AMULET CAPITAL PARTNERS, L.P.; *U.S. Private*, pg. 268
AMWAL INVEST PLC; *Int'l*, pg. 443
AMZAK CAPITAL MANAGEMENT, LLC; *U.S. Private*, pg. 270
ANACACIA CAPITAL PTY LTD; *Int'l*, pg. 445
ANACAP FINANCIAL PARTNERS LLP; *Int'l*, pg. 445
ANADOLU GIRISIM SERMAYESI YATIRIM ORTAKLIGI A.S.; *Int'l*, pg. 445
ANALOGUE HOLDINGS LIMITED; *Int'l*, pg. 446
ANALYST IMS INVESTMENT MANAGEMENT SERVICES LTD.; *Int'l*, pg. 446
ANCHORAGE CAPITAL GROUP, L.L.C.; *U.S. Private*, pg. 273
ANCHORAGE CAPITAL PARTNERS PTY. LIMITED; *Int'l*, pg. 448
ANCHOR GROUP LIMITED; *Int'l*, pg. 448
ANCOR HOLDINGS, L.P.; *U.S. Private*, pg. 274
ANDERA PARTNERS SCA; *Int'l*, pg. 449
ANDERCO INVESTMENT PTE LTD; *Int'l*, pg. 450
THE ANDERSON GROUP, LLC; *U.S. Private*, pg. 3986
ANDES 7, INC.; *U.S. Private*, pg. 278
ANDLINGER & COMPANY, INC.; *U.S. Private*, pg. 278
ANDOVER CAPITAL CORPORATION; *Int'l*, pg. 451
ANDREESSEN HOROWITZ; *U.S. Private*, pg. 279
ANDREW W. BYRD & CO., LLC; *U.S. Private*, pg. 280
ANERI FINCAP LIMITED; *Int'l*, pg. 458
ANFIMA NV—See Ackermans & van Haaren NV; *Int'l*, pg. 104
ANGELES EQUITY PARTNERS, LLC; *U.S. Private*, pg. 281
ANGEL FINCAP PRIVATE LIMITED—See Angel One Limited; *Int'l*, pg. 459
ANGEL ISLAND CAPITAL MANAGEMENT, LLC—See Golden Gate Capital Management II, LLC; *U.S. Private*, pg. 1731
ANGELO, GORDON & CO., L.P.—See TPG Capital, L.P.; *U.S. Public*, pg. 2166
ANGEL POND HOLDINGS CORPORATION; *U.S. Public*, pg. 136
ANGERMAYER, BRUMM & LANGE UNTERNEHMENSGRUPPE GMBH; *Int'l*, pg. 460
ANGLO AMERICAN METALLURGICAL COAL HOLDINGS LIMITED—See Anglo American PLC; *Int'l*, pg. 461
ANGLO SCOTTISH ASSET FINANCE LIMITED; *Int'l*, pg. 463
ANGUS RESOURCES INC.; *Int'l*, pg. 463
ANHUI XINLI FINANCE CO., LTD.; *Int'l*, pg. 470
ANJANI FINANCE LIMITED; *Int'l*, pg. 472
ANKAM INC.; *U.S. Public*, pg. 137
ANLI FINANCIAL COMMUNICATIONS LIMITED—See China Success Finance Group Holdings Limited; *Int'l*, pg. 1556
ANNALY COMMERCIAL REAL ESTATE GROUP, INC.—See Annaly Capital Management, Inc.; *U.S. Public*, pg. 137
ANNEX CAPITAL MANAGEMENT LLC; *U.S. Private*, pg. 285
ANNIDIS CORPORATION; *Int'l*, pg. 474
ANPULO FOOD DEVELOPMENT, INC.; *Int'l*, pg. 475
ANSA SECURITIES LIMITED—See ANSA McAl Limited; *Int'l*, pg. 476
ANSON ADVISORS INC; *Int'l*, pg. 479
ANTARCHILE S.A.; *Int'l*, pg. 481
ANTARCTICA CAPITAL, LLC; *U.S. Private*, pg. 286

ANTARES CAPITAL CORPORATION; *U.S. Private*, pg. 287
ANTARES CAPITAL LP—See Canada Pension Plan Investment Board; *Int'l*, pg. 1278
ANTHROPOS CAPITAL CORP.; *U.S. Public*, pg. 140
ANTIAGING QUANTUM LIVING INC.; *U.S. Public*, pg. 140
ANTIQUITAS VERWALTUNGSGESELLSCHAFT MBH—See DMG MORI Co., Ltd.; *Int'l*, pg. 2144
ANUPAM FINSERV LTD.; *Int'l*, pg. 485
ANUTRA CORP; *U.S. Private*, pg. 289
ANZ BANK (THAI) PUBLIC COMPANY LIMITED—See Australia & New Zealand Banking Group Limited; *Int'l*, pg. 720
ANZ INVESTMENT SERVICES (NEW ZEALAND) LIMITED—See Australia & New Zealand Banking Group Limited; *Int'l*, pg. 720
ANZ NEW ZEALAND INVESTMENTS LIMITED—See Australia & New Zealand Banking Group Limited; *Int'l*, pg. 720
ANZU PARTNERS, LLC; *U.S. Private*, pg. 289
AORERE RESOURCES LIMITED; *Int'l*, pg. 498
AOTECAR NEW ENERGY TECHNOLOGY CO., LTD.; *Int'l*, pg. 498
AOZORA INVESTMENT CO., LTD.—See Cerberus Capital Management, L.P.; *U.S. Private*, pg. 836
AP ACQUISITION CORP.; *Int'l*, pg. 499
APAX GLOBAL ALPHA LTD.; *Int'l*, pg. 501
APAX INVESTMENT (SHANGHAI) COMPANY LTD—See Apax Partners LLP; *Int'l*, pg. 501
APAX PARTNERS BETEILIGUNGSBERATUNG GMBH—See Apax Partners LLP; *Int'l*, pg. 501
APAX PARTNERS BRAZIL CONSULTORIA LTDA.—See Apax Partners LLP; *Int'l*, pg. 501
APAX PARTNERS ESPANA, S.L.—See Apax Partners LLP; *Int'l*, pg. 501
APAX PARTNERS HONG KONG LTD—See Apax Partners LLP; *Int'l*, pg. 501
APAX PARTNERS INDIA ADVISERS PRIVATE LIMITED—See Apax Partners LLP; *Int'l*, pg. 501
APAX PARTNERS (ISRAEL) LTD.—See Apax Partners LLP; *Int'l*, pg. 501
APAX PARTNERS LLP; *Int'l*, pg. 501
APAX PARTNERS, L.P.—See Apax Partners LLP; *Int'l*, pg. 502
APAX PARTNERS SAS—See Apax Partners LLP; *Int'l*, pg. 501
APAX PARTNERS (UK) LTD—See Apax Partners LLP; *Int'l*, pg. 501
AP CAPITAL INVESTMENT, LP; *U.S. Private*, pg. 290
APEIRON CAPITAL INVESTMENT CORP.; *U.S. Public*, pg. 144
APERION MANAGEMENT GROUP LLC; *U.S. Private*, pg. 291
APERION MANAGEMENT; *U.S. Private*, pg. 291
APERTURE ACQUISITION CORP.; *U.S. Public*, pg. 144
APEX 2, INC.; *U.S. Private*, pg. 291
APEX PARTNERS PTY LTD; *Int'l*, pg. 512
APG ASSET MANAGEMENT NV; *Int'l*, pg. 512
APIARY CAPITAL LLP; *Int'l*, pg. 515
APIS PARTNERS, LLP; *Int'l*, pg. 515
APKV US PRIVATE REIT GP LLC—See Allianz SE; *Int'l*, pg. 342
APKV US PRIVATE REIT LP—See Allianz SE; *Int'l*, pg. 343
APLICA SOLUCIONES TECNOLOGICAS CHILE LIMITADA—See Banco Bilbao Vizcaya Argentaria, S.A.; *Int'l*, pg. 817
APLITT S.A.; *Int'l*, pg. 515
APLJ CAPITAL MANAGEMENT LLC; *U.S. Private*, pg. 294
APNA MICROFINANCE BANK LIMITED; *Int'l*, pg. 516
APOLLO ACQUISITION CORPORATION; *U.S. Private*, pg. 294
APOLLO ASSET MANAGEMENT, INC.—See Apollo Global Management, Inc.; *U.S. Public*, pg. 145
APOLLO DEBT SOLUTIONS BDC; *U.S. Private*, pg. 294
APOLLO FINVEST (INDIA) LIMITED; *Int'l*, pg. 517
APOLLO PARTNERS LLC; *U.S. Private*, pg. 295
APOLLO REALTY INCOME SOLUTIONS, INC.; *U.S. Private*, pg. 295
APOLLO SENIOR FLOATING RATE FUND INC.—See Apollo Global Management, Inc.; *U.S. Public*, pg. 146
APOORVA LEASING FINANCE & INVESTMENT COMPANY LTD.; *Int'l*, pg. 519
APPLEPIE CAPITAL, INC.; *U.S. Private*, pg. 297
APPLIANCESMART HOLDINGS, LLC—See Live Ventures Incorporated; *U.S. Public*, pg. 1332
APPLIED INVESTMENT (ASIA) LIMITED—See Applied Development Holdings Limited; *Int'l*, pg. 521
APPLIED VALUE LLC; *U.S. Private*, pg. 300
APPLY ADVANCED MOBILE TECHNOLOGIES LTD.; *Int'l*, pg. 521
APPOSITE CAPITAL LLP; *Int'l*, pg. 522
APPRISE MEDIA, LLC; *U.S. Private*, pg. 300
APQ GLOBAL LIMITED; *Int'l*, pg. 522
APRIORI CAPITAL PARTNERS L.P.; *U.S. Private*, pg. 301
APSE CAPITAL LTD.; *Int'l*, pg. 523
APSONIC SDN. BHD.—See Engtex Group Berhad; *Int'l*, pg. 2436
APTUS FINANCE INDIA PRIVATE LIMITED—See Aptus Value Housing Finance India Limited; *Int'l*, pg. 526

AQUARON ACQUISITION CORP.; *U.S. Public*, pg. 175
AQUASIUM TECHNOLOGY LIMITED; *Int'l*, pg. 528
AQUILA ACQUISITION CORPORATION; *Int'l*, pg. 528
AQUILINE CAPITAL PARTNERS LLC; *U.S. Public*, pg. 303
AQUILINI INVESTMENT GROUP; *Int'l*, pg. 528
AQUIS EXCHANGE PLC; *Int'l*, pg. 528
ARAB FINANCIAL SERVICES COMPANY B.S.C.—See Arab Banking Corporation B.S.C.; *Int'l*, pg. 529
ARABLE CAPITAL PARTNERS LLC; *U.S. Private*, pg. 307
ARAB MOLTAQA INVESTMENTS COMPANY; *Int'l*, pg. 531
ARAB NATIONAL LEASING COMPANY LTD—See Arab Bank plc; *Int'l*, pg. 529
ARAB PETROLEUM INVESTMENTS CORPORATION; *Int'l*, pg. 531
ARAB REAL ESTATE DEVELOPMENT COMPANY PSC; *Int'l*, pg. 531
ARAG SE; *Int'l*, pg. 534
ARAVALI SECURITIES & FINANCE LIMITED; *Int'l*, pg. 536
ARAWATA ASSETS LIMITED—See Australia & New Zealand Banking Group Limited; *Int'l*, pg. 720
ARBOR PRIVATE INVESTMENT COMPANY, LLC; *U.S. Private*, pg. 309
ARBUTHNOT LATHAM & CO. LIMITED—See Arbuthnot Banking Group plc; *Int'l*, pg. 539
ARCADE CHINA ACQUISITION CORP.; *U.S. Private*, pg. 309
ARCADIS BELGIUM HOLDING NV—See ARCADIS N.V.; *Int'l*, pg. 540
ARCADIS HOLDING FRANCE S.A.S.—See ARCADIS N.V.; *Int'l*, pg. 540
ARCA IMPRESA GESTIONI SGR S.P.A.; *Int'l*, pg. 540
ARCA INVESTMENTS, A.S.; *Int'l*, pg. 540
ARCAPITA, INC.—See Arcapita Group Holdings Limited; *Int'l*, pg. 542
ARCAPITA INVESTMENT MANAGEMENT B.S.C.(C)—See Arcapita Group Holdings Limited; *Int'l*, pg. 543
ARC FUNDS LIMITED; *Int'l*, pg. 539
ARCHAEA ENERGY INC.—See BP plc; *Int'l*, pg. 1126
ARCHBROOK CAPITAL MANAGEMENT LLC; *U.S. Private*, pg. 310
ARCH CAPITAL GROUP LTD.; *Int'l*, pg. 546
ARCH EQUITY PARTNERS, LLC; *U.S. Private*, pg. 310
ARCHIMED SAS; *Int'l*, pg. 548
ARCLIGHT CAPITAL PARTNERS, LLC—See ArcLight Capital Holdings, LLC; *U.S. Private*, pg. 312
ARCLINE INVESTMENT MANAGEMENT LP; *U.S. Private*, pg. 312
ARCTOS NORTHSTAR ACQUISITION CORP.; *U.S. Public*, pg. 186
ARCUS INFRASTRUCTURE PARTNERS LLP; *Int'l*, pg. 552
ARCWEST EXPLORATION INC.; *Int'l*, pg. 553
ARDIAN GERMANY GMBH—See Ardian SAS; *Int'l*, pg. 554
ARDIAN INVESTMENT SINGAPORE PTE. LTD.—See Ardian SAS; *Int'l*, pg. 554
ARDIAN INVESTMENT SWITZERLAND AG—See Ardian SAS; *Int'l*, pg. 554
ARDIAN INVESTMENT UK LIMITED—See Ardian SAS; *Int'l*, pg. 554
ARDIAN ITALY S.R.L.—See Ardian SAS; *Int'l*, pg. 554
ARDIAN SAS; *Int'l*, pg. 554
ARDIAN US LLC—See Ardian SAS; *Int'l*, pg. 554
ARDI INVESTMENTS & TRADING COMPANY LIMITED; *Int'l*, pg. 554
ARENA FORTIFY ACQUISITION CORP.; *U.S. Public*, pg. 187
THE ARENA GROUP HOLDINGS, INC; *U.S. Public*, pg. 2035
ARENA INVESTORS, LP; *U.S. Private*, pg. 318
ARES ACQUISITION CORPORATION; *U.S. Public*, pg. 187
ARES CAPITAL CORPORATION—See Ares Management Corporation; *U.S. Public*, pg. 187
ARES CAPITAL EUROPE LIMITED—See Ares Management Corporation; *U.S. Public*, pg. 188
ARES EIF MANAGEMENT, LLC—See Ares Management Corporation; *U.S. Public*, pg. 188
ARES MANAGEMENT LLC-CAPITAL MARKETS GROUP—See Ares Management Corporation; *U.S. Public*, pg. 188
ARES MANAGEMENT LLC-PRIVATE DEBT GROUP—See Ares Management Corporation; *U.S. Public*, pg. 188
ARES MANAGEMENT LLC-PRIVATE EQUITY GROUP—See Ares Management Corporation; *U.S. Public*, pg. 188
ARES MANAGEMENT LLC-REAL ESTATE GROUP—See Ares Management Corporation; *U.S. Public*, pg. 188
ARES MANAGEMENT LLC—See Ares Management Corporation; *U.S. Public*, pg. 187
ARES REAL ESTATE INCOME TRUST INC.—See Black Creek Group, LLC; *U.S. Private*, pg. 570
ARES STRATEGIC MINING INC.; *Int'l*, pg. 559
ARGAND PARTNERS, LP; *U.S. Private*, pg. 319
ARGENTIL CAPITAL PARTNERS LIMITED; *Int'l*, pg. 561
THE ARGENTUM GROUP; *U.S. Private*, pg. 3987
ARGO GLOBAL LISTED INFRASTRUCTURE LIMITED; *Int'l*, pg. 562
ARGO INFRASTRUCTURE PARTNERS LLC; *U.S. Private*, pg. 320
ARGONAUT PRIVATE EQUITY, LLC; *U.S. Private*, pg. 321

523999 — MISCELLANEOUS FINAN...

ARGONNE CAPITAL GROUP, LLC; *U.S. Private*, pg. 321
ARGOS WITYU FRANCE SAS—See Argos Wityu S.A.; *Int'l*, pg. 563
ARGOS WITYU ITALIA S.P.A.—See Argos Wityu S.A.; *Int'l*, pg. 563
ARGOS WITYU S.A.; *Int'l*, pg. 563
ARGOSY HEALTHCARE PARTNERS—See Argosy Capital Group, LLC; *U.S. Private*, pg. 321
ARGUS CAPITAL CORP.; *U.S. Public*, pg. 191
ARGYLE STREET MANAGEMENT LIMITED; *Int'l*, pg. 563
ARGYLL PARTNERS LTD.; *Int'l*, pg. 563
ARHT MEDIA INC.; *Int'l*, pg. 563
ARIADNE AUSTRALIA LIMITED; *Int'l*, pg. 563
ARI FLEET SERVICES OF CANADA, INC.—See ITE Management L.P.; *U.S. Private*, pg. 2149
ARIHANT CAPITAL MARKETS LTD.; *Int'l*, pg. 564
ARIHANT'S SECURITIES LIMITED; *Int'l*, pg. 565
ARISZ ACQUISITION CORP.; *U.S. Public*, pg. 192
ARIZONA SILVER EXPLORATION INC.; *Int'l*, pg. 567
ARKANSAS FEDERAL CREDIT UNION; *U.S. Private*, pg. 326
ARKEMA CHINA INVESTMENT CO. LTD—See Arkema S.A.; *Int'l*, pg. 568
ARLINGTON CAPITAL PARTNERS LLC; *U.S. Private*, pg. 326
ARLON GROUP LLC—See Continental Grain Company; *U.S. Private*, pg. 1029
ARMADA ENTERPRISES, LP; *U.S. Private*, pg. 329
ARMADA HOFFLER PROPERTIES, INC.; *U.S. Public*, pg. 193
ARMADA INVESTMENT HOLDING LTD—See CIMB Group Holdings Berhad; *Int'l*, pg. 1607
ARMADALE CAPITALL PLC; *Int'l*, pg. 574
ARMADA MERCANTILE LTD.; *U.S. Public*, pg. 193
ARMADILLO RESOURCES LTD.; *Int'l*, pg. 574
ARMAN FINANCIAL SERVICES LTD.; *Int'l*, pg. 574
ARMSTRONG SECURITIES, INC.—See BDO Unibank, Inc.; *Int'l*, pg. 930
ARMY EMERGENCY RELIEF; *U.S. Private*, pg. 332
AROCA DEL PINAR SOCIMI, S.A.; *Int'l*, pg. 577
AROGO CAPITAL ACQUISITION CORP.; *U.S. Public*, pg. 194
AROMA ENTERPRISES (INDIA) LIMITED; *Int'l*, pg. 577
AROWANA INC.; *Int'l*, pg. 578
ARPAK INTERNATIONAL INVESTMENTS LTD.; *Int'l*, pg. 578
ARROW COMPANIES, LLC; *U.S. Private*, pg. 335
ARROW EC INCOME ADVANTAGE ALTERNATIVE FUND; *Int'l*, pg. 579
ARROWMARK FINANCIAL CORP.; *U.S. Public*, pg. 201
ARSENAL CAPITAL MANAGEMENT LP; *U.S. Private*, pg. 337
ARSENAL GROUP, LLC; *U.S. Private*, pg. 339
ARTA CAPITAL SGEIC SA; *Int'l*, pg. 580
ARTA TECHFIN CORPORATION LIMITED; *Int'l*, pg. 580
ARTEMIS ACQUISITION CORP.; *U.S. Public*, pg. 201
ARTEMIS STRATEGIC INVESTMENT CORPORATION; *U.S. Public*, pg. 201
ARTEMIS THERAPEUTICS, INC.; *U.S. Public*, pg. 201
ARTISAN ACQUISITION CORP.; *Int'l*, pg. 584
ARTISAN ENERGY CORPORATION; *Int'l*, pg. 584
ARTIS REAL ESTATE INVESTMENT TRUST; *Int'l*, pg. 584
ARUNDEL GROUP LIMITED—See Arundel AG; *Int'l*, pg. 586
ARUNDEL (MAURITIUS) LIMITED—See Arundel AG; *Int'l*, pg. 586
ARUNJYOTI BIO VENTURES LIMITED; *Int'l*, pg. 586
ARVANA INC.; *U.S. Public*, pg. 208
ARVOG; *Int'l*, pg. 588
ARX EQUITY PARTNERS S.R.O.; *Int'l*, pg. 588
ARYA SCIENCES ACQUISITION CORP.; *U.S. Private*, pg. 345
ARYZTA HOLDINGS ASIA PACIFIC BV—See ARYZTA AG; *Int'l*, pg. 588
ARZAN FINANCIAL GROUP FOR FINANCING & INVESTMENT K.S.P.C.; *Int'l*, pg. 589
ARZAN SECURITIES BROKERAGE CO. SAE—See Arzan Financial Group for Financing & Investment K.S.P.C.; *Int'l*, pg. 589
ARZAN WEALTH (DIFC) CO. LIMITED—See Arzan Financial Group for Financing & Investment K.S.P.C.; *Int'l*, pg. 589
ASA GOLD & PRECIOUS METALS LTD.; *U.S. Public*, pg. 209
ASAHI BEER (CHINA) INVESTMENT CO., LTD.—See Asahi Group Holdings Ltd.; *Int'l*, pg. 593
ASB GROUP INVESTMENTS LIMITED—See Commonwealth Bank of Australia; *Int'l*, pg. 1719
ASCENCIA INVESTMENT MANAGEMENT LIMITED—See Frenkel Topping Group plc; *Int'l*, pg. 2773
ASCENDENT CAPITAL PARTNERS (ASIA) LIMITED; *Int'l*, pg. 601
ASCENDIO CO., LTD.; *Int'l*, pg. 601
ASCEND VENTURE GROUP, LLC; *U.S. Private*, pg. 346
THE ASCENT GROUP LLC; *U.S. Private*, pg. 3988
ASGARD PARTNERS & CO., LLC; *U.S. Private*, pg. 348
A' SHARQIYA INVESTMENT HOLDING CO. SAOG; *Int'l*, pg. 19

ASHMORE EMERGING MARKETS INCOME FUND; *Int'l*, pg. 607
ASHMORE GROUP PLC; *Int'l*, pg. 607
ASHMORE INVESTMENT MANAGEMENT LIMITED—See Ashmore Group plc; *Int'l*, pg. 608
ASIA CAPITAL LTD.; *Int'l*, pg. 610
ASIA COAL LIMITED; *Int'l*, pg. 611
ASIA DEVELOPMENT CAPITAL CO., LTD.; *Int'l*, pg. 611
ASIA ENVIRONMENTAL PARTNERS, L.P.—See Olympus Capital Holdings Asia; *U.S. Private*, pg. 3012
ASIA EQUITY EXCHANGE GROUP INC.; *Int'l*, pg. 612
ASIA INTERACTIVE MEDIA INC.; *Int'l*, pg. 613
ASIAN DEVELOPMENT BANK; *Int'l*, pg. 617
ASIAN PAY TELEVISION TRUST; *Int'l*, pg. 619
THE ASIA PACIFIC FUND, INC.; *U.S. Private*, pg. 3989
ASIA PLUS SECURITIES COMPANY LIMITED—See Asia Plus Group Holdings Public Company Limited; *Int'l*, pg. 614
A-SMART HOLDINGS LTD.; *Int'l*, pg. 20
ASM IP HOLDING B.V.—See ASM INTERNATIONAL N.V.; *Int'l*, pg. 626
ASML CAPITAL US, INC.—See ASML Holding N.V.; *Int'l*, pg. 627
ASM PACIFIC HOLDING B.V.—See ASM INTERNATIONAL N.V.; *Int'l*, pg. 626
ASPEN EQUITY INVESTMENTS PTY. LIMITED—See Aspen Group Limited; *Int'l*, pg. 628
ASP FIBERMARK HOLDINGS LLC.; *U.S. Private*, pg. 351
ASPIAL LIFESTYLE LIMITED—See Aspial Corporation Limited; *Int'l*, pg. 630
ASPIRANT GROUP, INC.; *Int'l*, pg. 630
ASPIRIANT HOLDINGS, LLC; *U.S. Private*, pg. 352
ASPIS INTERNATIONAL AEDAK—See Eurobank Ergasias Services and Holdings S.A.; *Int'l*, pg. 2533
ASRR CAPITAL LTD.; *Int'l*, pg. 632
ASSA ABLOY HOLDING ITALIA S.P.A.—See ASSA ABLOY AB; *Int'l*, pg. 635
THE ASSET ADVISORY GROUP, INC.—See Genstar Capital, LLC; *U.S. Private*, pg. 1677
THE ASSET ADVISORY GROUP, INC.—See Keystone Group, L.P.; *U.S. Private*, pg. 2298
ASSET MANAGEMENT COMPANY, LLC; *U.S. Private*, pg. 354
ASSETMARK FINANCIAL HOLDINGS, INC.—See GTCR LLC; *U.S. Private*, pg. 1802
ASSETOWL LIMITED; *Int'l*, pg. 643
ASSIETTA PRIVATE EQUITY SGR S.P.A.; *Int'l*, pg. 648
ASSOCIATED FINANCIAL CORP.; *U.S. Private*, pg. 355
ASSOCIATED FINANCIAL GROUP, LLC - WAUKESHA OFFICE—See Caisse de Depot et Placement du Quebec; *Int'l*, pg. 1256
ASSOCIATED FINANCIAL GROUP, LLC - WAUKESHA OFFICE—See KKR & Co. Inc.; *U.S. Public*, pg. 1265
ASSOCIATED PARTNERS, LP; *U.S. Private*, pg. 356
ASSOCIATE GLOBAL PARTNERS LIMITED; *Int'l*, pg. 648
ASSURED GUARANTY (EUROPE) SA—See Assured Guaranty Ltd.; *Int'l*, pg. 649
ASSURED INVESTMENT MANAGEMENT LLC—See Sound Point Capital Management, LP; *U.S. Private*, pg. 3717
ASSURED INVESTMENT MANAGEMENT (LONDON) LLP—See Assured Guaranty Ltd.; *Int'l*, pg. 650
ASSURE HOLDINGS, LLC; *U.S. Private*, pg. 359
ASSURIA BELEGGINGSMAATSCHAPPIJ N.V.—See Assuria N.V.; *Int'l*, pg. 650
ASTATINE CAPITAL PARTNERS LLC—See Astatine Investment Partners LLC; *U.S. Private*, pg. 360
ASTATINE INVESTMENT PARTNERS LLC; *U.S. Private*, pg. 360
ASTERION INDUSTRIAL PARTNERS SGEIC SA; *Int'l*, pg. 654
ASTERON LIMITED—See Dai-ichi Life Holdings, Inc.; *Int'l*, pg. 1918
ASTORG PARTNERS S.A.S.; *Int'l*, pg. 655
ASTORG PARTNERS UK—See Astorg Partners S.A.S.; *Int'l*, pg. 655
ASTRA CAPITAL MANAGEMENT LLC; *U.S. Private*, pg. 361
ASTRAZENECA HOLDING GMBH—See AstraZeneca PLC; *Int'l*, pg. 660
ASTRAZENECA TREASURY LIMITED—See AstraZeneca PLC; *Int'l*, pg. 661
ASTREA ACQUISITION CORP.; *U.S. Public*, pg. 217
AS TRIGON CAPITAL GROUP; *Int'l*, pg. 591
AST SPACEMOBILE, INC.; *U.S. Public*, pg. 216
ATAG ASSET MANAGEMENT (LUXEMBOURG) S.A.—See Basellandschaftliche Kantonalbank; *Int'l*, pg. 871
ATAIROS GROUP, INC.; *U.S. Private*, pg. 363
ATAKULE GAYRIMENKUL YATIRIM ORTAKLIGI AS; *Int'l*, pg. 665
ATAR CAPITAL, LLC; *U.S. Private*, pg. 364
ATB SECURITIES INC.—See Alberta Treasury Branches; *Int'l*, pg. 298
AT CAPITAL PTE LIMITED; *Int'l*, pg. 664
ATEL 14, LLC—See ATEL Capital Group; *U.S. Private*, pg. 366
ATEL 15, LLC—See ATEL Capital Group; *U.S. Private*, pg. 366

ATEL GROWTH CAPITAL FUND 8, LLC—See ATEL Capital Group; *U.S. Private*, pg. 366
ATEL VENTURES, INC.—See ATEL Capital Group; *U.S. Private*, pg. 366
ATERIAN INVESTMENT MANAGEMENT, L.P.; *U.S. Private*, pg. 366
AT GLOBAL MARKETS (UK) LIMITED; *Int'l*, pg. 664
ATHELNEY TRUST PLC; *Int'l*, pg. 669
ATHENA CONSUMER ACQUISITION CORP.; *U.S. Public*, pg. 221
ATHENIAN VENTURE PARTNERS LP; *U.S. Private*, pg. 367
ATHLON ACQUISITION CORP.; *U.S. Public*, pg. 221
ATHOS SERVICE GMBH; *Int'l*, pg. 670
ATHRIS HOLDING AG; *Int'l*, pg. 670
ATINUM INVESTMENT CO., LTD; *Int'l*, pg. 670
ATLANTICA, INC.; *U.S. Public*, pg. 223
ATLANTIC ALLIANCE PARTNERSHIP CORP.; *U.S. Public*, pg. 222
ATLANTIC AMERICAN PARTNERS, LLC; *U.S. Private*, pg. 371
ATLANTIC AVENUE ACQUISITION CORP; *U.S. Public*, pg. 222
ATLANTIC BRIDGE VENTURES; *Int'l*, pg. 674
ATLANTIC MERCHANT CAPITAL INVESTORS, LLC; *U.S. Private*, pg. 373
ATLANTIC SECURITIES LTD.—See Atlantic Insurance Company Public Ltd; *Int'l*, pg. 675
ATLANTIC STREET CAPITAL MANAGEMENT LLC; *U.S. Private*, pg. 374
ATLAS COPCO CUSTOMER FINANCE AB—See Atlas Copco AB; *Int'l*, pg. 678
ATLAS COPCO CUSTOMER FINANCE AUSTRALIA PTY LTD—See Atlas Copco AB; *Int'l*, pg. 678
ATLAS COPCO CUSTOMER FINANCE CHILE LTDA—See Atlas Copco AB; *Int'l*, pg. 678
ATLAS COPCO HOLDING GMBH—See Atlas Copco AB; *Int'l*, pg. 679
ATLAS COPCO HOLDINGS SOUTH AFRICA (PTY) LTD—See Atlas Copco AB; *Int'l*, pg. 679
ATLAS ESTATES LIMITED; *Int'l*, pg. 685
ATLAS GROWTH ACQUISITION LTD.; *Int'l*, pg. 685
ATLAS HITEC (PVT). LIMITED—See Atlas Group of Companies; *Int'l*, pg. 685
ATLASINVEST; *Int'l*, pg. 686
ATLAS MERCHANT CAPITAL LLC; *U.S. Private*, pg. 379
ATLAS MERCHANT CAPITAL UK LLP—See Atlas Merchant Capital LLC; *U.S. Private*, pg. 379
ATLAS REAL ESTATE PARTNERS; *U.S. Private*, pg. 379
ATLAS TECHNICAL CONSULTANTS, INC.—See GI Manager L.P.; *U.S. Private*, pg. 1691
ATL PARTNERS, LLC; *U.S. Private*, pg. 369
ATON LLC; *Int'l*, pg. 689
ATORKA GROUP HF; *Int'l*, pg. 690
ATP PRIVATE EQUITY ADVISORS APS—See Arbejdsmarkedets Tillaegspension; *Int'l*, pg. 537
ATRATO ONSITE ENERGY PLC; *Int'l*, pg. 693
ATTILAN GROUP LIMITED; *Int'l*, pg. 696
AUA BETEILIGUNGEN GESELLSCHAFT M.B.H.—See Deutsche Lufthansa AG; *Int'l*, pg. 2066
AUA PRIVATE EQUITY PARTNERS LLC; *U.S. Private*, pg. 384
AUCTUS CAPITAL PARTNERS AG; *Int'l*, pg. 700
AUDANT INVESTMENTS PTY. LTD.; *Int'l*, pg. 700
AUDAX CREDIT BDC INC.; *U.S. Private*, pg. 385
AUDAX MANAGEMENT COMPANY, LLC—See Audax Group, Limited Partnership; *U.S. Private*, pg. 385
AUDAX MEZZANINE—See Audax Group, Limited Partnership; *U.S. Private*, pg. 390
AUDLEY CAPITAL ADVISORS LLP; *Int'l*, pg. 702
AUGUST CAPITAL; *U.S. Private*, pg. 392
AUGUST EQUITY LLP; *Int'l*, pg. 703
AULT DISRUPTIVE TECHNOLOGIES CORPORATION; *U.S. Public*, pg. 227
AURA INVESTMENTS LTD.; *Int'l*, pg. 706
AURA RENEWABLE ACQUISITIONS PLC; *Int'l*, pg. 706
AURELIUS ACTIVE MANAGEMENT HOLDING GMBH—See Aurelius Equity Opportunities SE & Co. KGaA; *Int'l*, pg. 707
AURELIUS ALPHA LIMITED—See Aurelius Equity Opportunities SE & Co. KGaA; *Int'l*, pg. 707
AURELIUS EQUITY OPPORTUNITIES SE & CO. KGAA; *Int'l*, pg. 707
AUREX ENERGY CORP.; *Int'l*, pg. 710
AURIN INVESTMENT GROUP GMBH; *Int'l*, pg. 711
AURORA CAPITAL GROUP, LLC; *U.S. Private*, pg. 393
AURORA RESURGENCE MANAGEMENT PARTNERS LLC—See Aurora Capital Group, LLC; *U.S. Private*, pg. 393
AURVANDIL ACQUISITION CORP.; *U.S. Public*, pg. 228
AUSTASIA GROUP LTD.; *Int'l*, pg. 715
AUSTERLITZ ACQUISITION CORP I; *U.S. Private*, pg. 395
AUSTIN RESOURCES LTD.; *Int'l*, pg. 718
AUSTIN VENTURES, LP; *U.S. Private*, pg. 396
AUSTON CAPITAL CORP.; *Int'l*, pg. 719
AUSTRALIAN ASSET AGGREGATION PTY LTD—See BNK Banking Corporation Limited; *Int'l*, pg. 1079
AUSTRALIAN CAPITAL HOME LOANS PTY LTD—See BNK

Banking Corporation Limited; *Int'l*, pg. 1079
AUSTRALIAN INVESTMENT COMPANY SERVICES LIMITED—See Australian Foundation Investment Company Limited; *Int'l*, pg. 721
AUSTRALIAN MEAT INDUSTRY SUPERANNUATION TRUST PTY LTD.; *Int'l*, pg. 721
AUSTRALIAN UNITY BOWRAL DEVELOPMENT PTY LTD—See Australian Unity Limited; *Int'l*, pg. 722
AUSTRALIAN UNITY FUNDS MANAGEMENT LIMITED—See Australian Unity Limited; *Int'l*, pg. 723
AUSTRALIAN UNITY GROUP SERVICES PROPRIETARY LIMITED—See Australian Unity Limited; *Int'l*, pg. 723
AUSTRALIAN UNITY HEALTH CARE LIMITED—See Australian Unity Limited; *Int'l*, pg. 723
AUSTRALIAN UNITY INVESTMENT BONDS LIMITED—See Australian Unity Limited; *Int'l*, pg. 723
AUSTRALIAN UNITY PROPERTY LIMITED—See Australian Unity Limited; *Int'l*, pg. 723
AUSTRALIAN UNITY RETIREMENT LIVING SERVICES LIMITED—See Australian Unity Limited; *Int'l*, pg. 723
AUTHENTIC EQUITY ACQUISITION CORP.; *U.S. Public*, pg. 228
AUTHUM INVESTMENT INFRASTRUCTURE LTD.; *Int'l*, pg. 724
AUTOMOTIVE FINCO CORP.; *Int'l*, pg. 730
AUXO INVESTMENT PARTNERS, LLC; *U.S. Private*, pg. 402
AVAC, LTD.; *Int'l*, pg. 733
AVAILABLE FINANCE LIMITED; *Int'l*, pg. 734
AVALANCHE INTERNATIONAL CORP.; *U.S. Public*, pg. 239
AVALON ACQUISITION INC.—See GWG Holdings, Inc.; *U.S. Public*, pg. 975
AVALT, LLC; *U.S. Private*, pg. 403
AVANCE INVESTMENT MANAGEMENT, LLC; *U.S. Private*, pg. 403
AVANEA ENERGY ACQUISITION CORP.; *U.S. Public*, pg. 241
AVANT BRANDS INC.; *Int'l*, pg. 734
AVANTE CAPITAL PARTNERS; *U.S. Private*, pg. 404
AVANTE MEZZANINE PARTNERS, INC.; *U.S. Private*, pg. 404
AVANTEOS INVESTMENTS LIMITED—See Commonwealth Bank of Australia; *Int'l*, pg. 1719
AVANT-GARDE ADVISORS LLC; *U.S. Private*, pg. 404
AVANTI ACQUISITION CORP.; *Int'l*, pg. 736
AVANZA BANK HOLDING AB; *Int'l*, pg. 736
AVASARA FINANCE LIMITED; *Int'l*, pg. 737
AV CAPITAL HOLDINGS MANAGEMENT, LLC; *U.S. Private*, pg. 402
AVENIR WELLNESS SOLUTIONS, INC.; *U.S. Public*, pg. 242
AVENUE CAPITAL GROUP, LLC; *U.S. Private*, pg. 405
AVIC INDUSTRY-FINANCE HOLDINGS CO., LTD.—See Aviation Industry Corporation of China; *Int'l*, pg. 741
AVIDIAN WEALTH SOLUTIONS, LLC; *U.S. Private*, pg. 407
AVI JAPAN OPPORTUNITY TRUST PLC; *Int'l*, pg. 740
AVI LION HOLDINGS LLC—See Access Value Investors LLC; *U.S. Private*, pg. 53
AVI LION HOLDINGS LLC—See Lion Equity Partners, LLC; *U.S. Private*, pg. 2463
AVI PARTNERS, LLC; *U.S. Private*, pg. 406
AVISTA CAPITAL PARTNERS, L.P.; *U.S. Private*, pg. 408
AVIVA GROUP HOLDINGS LIMITED—See Aviva plc; *Int'l*, pg. 745
AVIVA INVESTORS GLOBAL SERVICES LIMITED—See Aviva plc; *Int'l*, pg. 745
AVIVA INVESTORS HOLDINGS LIMITED—See Aviva plc; *Int'l*, pg. 745
AVIVA INVESTORS UK FUND SERVICES LIMITED—See Aviva plc; *Int'l*, pg. 745
AVIVA POWSZECHNE TOWARZYSTWO EMERYTALNE AVIVA BZ WBK S.A.—See Aviva plc; *Int'l*, pg. 746
AVON MERCANTILE LIMITED; *Int'l*, pg. 749
AVONMORE CAPITAL & MANAGEMENT SERVICES LTD.; *Int'l*, pg. 750
AVRASYA PETROL VE TURISTIK TESISLER YATIRIMLAR AS; *Int'l*, pg. 750
AVRIO VENTURES LTD.; *Int'l*, pg. 750
AVTIL ENTERPRISE LIMITED; *Int'l*, pg. 751
AWN HOLDINGS LIMITED; *Int'l*, pg. 753
AW PROPERTY CO.; *U.S. Public*, pg. 410
AXA ADVISORS, LLC—See Equitable Holdings, Inc.; *U.S. Public*, pg. 788
AXA AUSTRALIA—See AMP Limited; *Int'l*, pg. 432
AXA FRAMLINGTON—See AXA S.A.; *Int'l*, pg. 756
AXA INVESTICNI SPOLECNOST A.S.—See AXA S.A.; *Int'l*, pg. 759
AXA INVESTICNI SPOLECNOST A.S.—See AXA S.A.; *Int'l*, pg. 759
AXA INVESTMENT MANAGERS LLC—See AXA S.A.; *Int'l*, pg. 756
AXA MANSARD INVESTMENTS LIMITED—See AXA S.A.; *Int'l*, pg. 757
AXA ROSENBERG CANADA CO.—See AXA S.A.; *Int'l*, pg. 758
AXA ROSENBERG INVESTMENT MANAGEMENT ASIA PACIFIC LTD.—See AXA S.A.; *Int'l*, pg. 758

AXA ROSENBERG INVESTMENT MANAGEMENT LIMITED—See AXA S.A.; *Int'l*, pg. 758
AXA ROSENBERG INVESTMENT MANAGEMENT LLC—See Equitable Holdings, Inc.; *U.S. Public*, pg. 788
AXA SPDB INVESTMENT MANAGERS CO., LTD—See AXA S.A.; *Int'l*, pg. 758
AXA WEALTH MANAGEMENT (HK) LIMITED—See AXA S.A.; *Int'l*, pg. 755
AXCAP VENTURES INC.; *Int'l*, pg. 761
AXEL JOHNSON INC.—See Axel Johnson Gruppen AB; *Int'l*, pg. 765
AXEL LINDGREN AB; *Int'l*, pg. 765
AXION VENTURES INC.; *Int'l*, pg. 769
AXIOS SUSTAINABLE GROWTH ACQUISITION CORPORATION; *U.S. Public*, pg. 255
AXIS AUTO FINANCE INC.; *Int'l*, pg. 769
AXIS PRIVATE EQUITY LIMITED—See Axis Bank Limited; *Int'l*, pg. 769
AXIS SPECIALTY UK HOLDINGS LIMITED—See AXIS Capital Holdings Limited; *Int'l*, pg. 770
AXONPRIME INFRASTRUCTURE ACQUISITION CORP.; *U.S. Public*, pg. 256
AXXESS CAPITAL; *Int'l*, pg. 772
AXXION ASSET MANAGEMENT SAC; *Int'l*, pg. 773
THE AXXON GROUP SERVICOS DE CONSULTORIA E ASSESSORIA LTDA—See Groupe BPCE; *Int'l*, pg. 3096
AYTU BIOPHARMA, INC.; *U.S. Public*, pg. 256
AZALEA CAPITAL, LLC; *U.S. Private*, pg. 415
AZARBAIJAN INVESTMENT DEVELOPMENT COMPANY; *Int'l*, pg. 776
AZAR INTERNATIONAL CORP.; *Int'l*, pg. 776
AZ JUPITER 4 B.V.—See Allianz SE; *Int'l*, pg. 343
AZ JUPITER 8 B.V.—See Allianz SE; *Int'l*, pg. 343
AZ JUPITER 9 B.V.—See Allianz SE; *Int'l*, pg. 343
AZ-SGD PRIVATE EQUITY FONDS GMBH—See Allianz SE; *Int'l*, pg. 343
AZTAR INDIANA GAMING COMPANY, LLC—See Caesars Entertainment, Inc.; *U.S. Public*, pg. 420
AZTAR RIVERBOAT HOLDING COMPANY, LLC—See Caesars Entertainment, Inc.; *U.S. Public*, pg. 420
AZURE CAPITAL PARTNERS, LP; *U.S. Private*, pg. 416
AZURE HOLDING GROUP CORP.; *U.S. Private*, pg. 416
AZ VERS US PRIVATE REIT GP LLC—See Allianz SE; *Int'l*, pg. 343
AZ VERS US PRIVATE REIT LP—See Allianz SE; *Int'l*, pg. 343
AZZURRO SOLUTIONS CORP.; *Int'l*, pg. 783
B2HOLDING AS; *Int'l*, pg. 790
B2 KAPITAL D.O.O.—See B2Holding AS; *Int'l*, pg. 790
B90 HOLDINGS PLC; *Int'l*, pg. 791
BAADER BANK AG; *Int'l*, pg. 791
BAADER & HEINS CAPITAL MANAGEMENT AG—See Baader Bank AG; *Int'l*, pg. 791
BAADER HEINS & SEITZ CAPITAL MANAGEMENT AG—See Baader Bank AG; *Int'l*, pg. 791
BABCOCK INTERNATIONAL HOLDINGS BV—See Babcock International Group PLC; *Int'l*, pg. 792
BADARO NO.19 SHIP INVESTMENT COMPANY; *Int'l*, pg. 795
BAD LEONFELDEN HOTELBETRIEBS GESELLSCHAFT MBH—See Erste Group Bank AG; *Int'l*, pg. 2497
BAE SYSTEMS SURFACE SHIPS (HOLDINGS) LIMITED—See BAE Systems plc; *Int'l*, pg. 796
BAHRAIN COMMERCIAL FACILITIES COMPANY BSC; *Int'l*, pg. 800
BAID FINSERV LIMITED; *Int'l*, pg. 801
BAILADOR TECHNOLOGY INVESTMENTS LIMITED; *Int'l*, pg. 802
BAILLIE GIFFORD SHIN NIPPON PLC; *Int'l*, pg. 803
BAIN ALNAHRAIN INVESTMENT COMPANY; *Int'l*, pg. 803
BAIN CAPITAL DOUBLE IMPACT, LP—See Bain Capital, LP; *U.S. Private*, pg. 431
BAIN CAPITAL, LP; *U.S. Private*, pg. 428
BAIN CAPITAL LTD.—See Bain Capital, LP; *U.S. Private*, pg. 431
BAIN CAPITAL NY, LLC—See Bain Capital, LP; *U.S. Private*, pg. 431
BAIN CAPITAL TECH OPPORTUNITIES, LP—See Bain Capital, LP; *U.S. Private*, pg. 436
BAIN CAPITAL VENTURES, LLC—See Bain Capital, LP; *U.S. Private*, pg. 436
BAIRD CAPITAL PARTNERS—See Baird Financial Group, Inc.; *U.S. Private*, pg. 453
BAJAJ FINSERV LIMITED—See Bajaj Auto Ltd.; *Int'l*, pg. 804
BAJAJ GLOBAL LIMITED; *Int'l*, pg. 804
BAKER CAPITAL PARTNERS, LLC; *U.S. Private*, pg. 455
BAKKT HOLDINGS, INC.; *U.S. Public*, pg. 265
BALANCE POINT CAPITAL ADVISORS, LLC; *U.S. Private*, pg. 457
BALANCE RESORT AG—See Erste Group Bank AG; *Int'l*, pg. 2497
BALDERTON AVIATION HOLDINGS LIMITED—See BlackRock, Inc.; *U.S. Public*, pg. 346
BALDERTON AVIATION HOLDINGS LIMITED—See Blackstone Inc.; *U.S. Public*, pg. 358
BALDERTON AVIATION HOLDINGS LIMITED—See Cascade Investment LLC; *U.S. Private*, pg. 780

BALDERTON CAPITAL; *Int'l*, pg. 807
BALDOR HOLDINGS INC—See ABB Ltd.; *Int'l*, pg. 51
BALFOUR BEATTY INVESTMENT HOLDINGS LTD—See Balfour Beatty plc; *Int'l*, pg. 808
BALFOUR BEATTY INVESTMENTS LIMITED—See Balfour Beatty plc; *Int'l*, pg. 808
BALLAST POINT VENTURES LP; *U.S. Private*, pg. 461
BALMER LAWRIE INVESTMENTS LTD.; *Int'l*, pg. 810
BALMORAL FUNDS LLC; *U.S. Private*, pg. 461
BALOISE DELTA HOLDING S.A.R.L.—See Baloise Holding AG; *Int'l*, pg. 811
BALOISE FUND INVEST ADVICO—See Baloise Holding AG; *Int'l*, pg. 811
BALOISE FUND INVEST—See Baloise Holding AG; *Int'l*, pg. 811
BALOISE (LUXEMBOURG) HOLDING S.A.—See Baloise Holding AG; *Int'l*, pg. 810
BAL SERVICING CORPORATION—See Deutsche Bank Aktiengesellschaft; *Int'l*, pg. 2055
BALTCAP AS; *Int'l*, pg. 812
BAMPSL SECURITIES LIMITED; *Int'l*, pg. 813
BANCA IFIS S.P.A.; *Int'l*, pg. 815
THE BANC FUNDS COMPANY LLC; *U.S. Private*, pg. 3991
BANCO BNP PARIBAS PERSONAL FINANCE SA—See BNP Paribas SA; *Int'l*, pg. 1089
BANCO CNH CAPITAL S.A.—See CNH Industrial N.V.; *Int'l*, pg. 1674
BANCO DE SABADELL, S.A.; *Int'l*, pg. 821
BANCO DI CARIBE N.V.; *Int'l*, pg. 822
BANCOLOMBIA S.A.; *Int'l*, pg. 828
BANCO MADESANT - SOCIEDADE UNIPESSOAL, S.A.—See Banco Santander, S.A.; *Int'l*, pg. 825
BANCO MERCANTIL DE INVESTIMENTOS S.A.—See Banco Mercantil do Brasil S.A.; *Int'l*, pg. 823
BANCO PARIS S.A.—See Cencosud S.A.; *Int'l*, pg. 1400
BANCO SANTANDER DE NEGOCIOS COLOMBIA S.A.—See Banco Santander, S.A.; *Int'l*, pg. 825
BANCO VOLVO (BRASIL) SA—See AB Volvo; *Int'l*, pg. 45
BANEXI VENTURES PARTNERS—See BNP Paribas SA; *Int'l*, pg. 1089
BANGKOK COMMERCIAL ASSET MANAGEMENT PUBLIC COMPANY LIMITED; *Int'l*, pg. 833
BANK AUDI S.A.M.—See Bank Audi sal; *Int'l*, pg. 837
THE BANKERS CLUB, INC.—See BNP Paribas SA; *Int'l*, pg. 1088
BANKFIL LIMITED—See Barclays PLC; *Int'l*, pg. 859
BANKHALL SUPPORT SERVICES LIMITED—See Aviva plc; *Int'l*, pg. 746
BANK INSINGER DE BEAUFORT SAFE CUSTODY NV—See BNP Paribas SA; *Int'l*, pg. 1089
BANK OF IRELAND GLOBAL MARKETS - LONDON—See Bank of Ireland Group plc; *Int'l*, pg. 845
BANK OF MONTREAL CAPITAL MARKETS (HOLDINGS) LIMITED—See Bank of Montreal; *Int'l*, pg. 846
BANNEKER PARTNERS, LLC; *U.S. Private*, pg. 468
BANNER ACQUISITION CORP.; *U.S. Public*, pg. 275
BANNIX ACQUISITION CORP.; *U.S. Public*, pg. 275
BANQUE CANTONALE DE GENEVE SA; *Int'l*, pg. 852
BANQUE PRIVEE EDMOND DE ROTHSCHILD EUROPE—See Edmond de Rothschild Holding S.A.; *Int'l*, pg. 2312
BANQUE PRIVEE EDMOND DE ROTHSCHILD S.A.—See Edmond de Rothschild Holding S.A.; *Int'l*, pg. 2312
BANQUE SBA S.A.—See Banque Libano-Francaise S.A.L.; *Int'l*, pg. 854
BANSABADELL FINCOM, E.F.C., S.A.—See Banco de Sabadell, S.A.; *Int'l*, pg. 821
BANSABADELL HOLDING, S.L.—See Banco de Sabadell, S.A.; *Int'l*, pg. 821
BANSK GROUP LLC; *U.S. Private*, pg. 469
BANTRY BAY VENTURES-ASIA, LLC; *U.S. Private*, pg. 470
BANYAN CAPITAL PARTNERS—See Connor, Clark & Lunn Financial Group; *Int'l*, pg. 1769
BANYAN INVESTMENT GROUP; *U.S. Private*, pg. 470
BANYAN TECHNOLOGIES GROUP, LLC; *U.S. Private*, pg. 470
BAO VIET FUND MANAGEMENT COMPANY—See Bao Viet Holdings; *Int'l*, pg. 855
BAO VIET HOLDINGS; *Int'l*, pg. 855
BARAFOR LIMITED—See Barclays PLC; *Int'l*, pg. 859
BARCLAYS ALDERSGATE INVESTMENTS LIMITED—See Barclays PLC; *Int'l*, pg. 859
BARCLAYS CAPITAL ASIA LIMITED—See Barclays PLC; *Int'l*, pg. 860
BARCLAYS CAPITAL ENERGY INC.—See Barclays PLC; *Int'l*, pg. 860
BARCLAYS CAPITAL FINANCE LIMITED—See Barclays PLC; *Int'l*, pg. 860
BARCLAYS CAPITAL GLOBAL SERVICES SINGAPORE PTE. LIMITED—See Barclays PLC; *Int'l*, pg. 861
BARCLAYS CAPITAL MARGIN FINANCING LIMITED—See Barclays PLC; *Int'l*, pg. 861
BARCLAYS CAPITAL MARKETS MALAYSIA SDN BHD.—See Barclays PLC; *Int'l*, pg. 861
BARCLAYS CAPITAL PRINCIPAL INVESTMENTS LIMITED—See Barclays PLC; *Int'l*, pg. 861
BARCLAYS CAPITAL STRATEGIC ADVISERS

LIMITED—See Barclays PLC; *Int'l*, pg. 861
BARCLAYS CONVERTED INVESTMENTS (NO.2) LIMITED—See Barclays PLC; *Int'l*, pg. 861
BARCLAYS DARNAY EURO INVESTMENTS LIMITED—See Barclays PLC; *Int'l*, pg. 861
BARCLAYS DIRECTORS LIMITED—See Barclays PLC; *Int'l*, pg. 861
BARCLAYS DIVERSIFICATION SA.—See Barclays PLC; *Int'l*, pg. 861
BARCLAYS DRYROCK ISSUANCE TRUST; *U.S. Private*, pg. 473
BARCLAYS FINANCE EUROPE LIMITED—See Barclays PLC; *Int'l*, pg. 861
BARCLAYS FINANCIAL PLANNING LTD—See Barclays PLC; *Int'l*, pg. 861
BARCLAYS FINANCIAL SERVICES ITALIA S.P.A.—See Barclays PLC; *Int'l*, pg. 861
BARCLAYS FINANCIAL SERVICES LIMITED—See Barclays PLC; *Int'l*, pg. 861
BARCLAYS FUNDS INVESTMENTS LIMITED—See Barclays PLC; *Int'l*, pg. 861
BARCLAYS GLOBAL INVESTORS LIMITED—See Barclays PLC; *Int'l*, pg. 860
BARCLAYS GROUP HOLDINGS LIMITED—See Barclays PLC; *Int'l*, pg. 861
BARCLAYSHARE NOMINEES LIMITED—See Barclays PLC; *Int'l*, pg. 862
BARCLAYS HOLDINGS (ISLE OF MAN) LIMITED—See Barclays PLC; *Int'l*, pg. 861
BARCLAYS INVESTMENTS & LOANS (INDIA) LIMITED—See Barclays PLC; *Int'l*, pg. 860
BARCLAYS LONG ISLAND LIMITED—See Barclays PLC; *Int'l*, pg. 861
BARCLAYS MARLIST LIMITED—See Barclays PLC; *Int'l*, pg. 861
BARCLAYS MERCANTILE BUSINESS FINANCE LIMITED—See Barclays PLC; *Int'l*, pg. 861
BARCLAYS MERCANTILE LIMITED—See Barclays PLC; *Int'l*, pg. 861
BARCLAYS METALS LIMITED—See Barclays PLC; *Int'l*, pg. 861
BARCLAYS PHYSICAL TRADING LIMITED—See Barclays PLC; *Int'l*, pg. 861
BARCLAYS SECURED NOTES FINANCE LLP—See Barclays PLC; *Int'l*, pg. 861
BARCLAYS SERVICES LLC—See Barclays PLC; *Int'l*, pg. 860
BARCLAYS UNQUOTED INVESTMENTS LIMITED—See Barclays PLC; *Int'l*, pg. 861
BARCLAYS VENTURE NOMINEES LIMITED—See Barclays PLC; *Int'l*, pg. 860
BARCLAYS WEALTH CORPORATE SERVICES (GUERNSEY) LIMITED—See Barclays PLC; *Int'l*, pg. 861
BARCLAYS WEALTH NOMINEES (JERSEY) LIMITED—See Barclays PLC; *Int'l*, pg. 861
BARCLAYS ZIMBABWE NOMINEES (PVT) LIMITED—See Barclays PLC; *Int'l*, pg. 862
BARCLAYTRUST CHANNEL ISLANDS LIMITED—See Barclays PLC; *Int'l*, pg. 862
BARCLAYTRUST INTERNATIONAL (JERSEY) LIMITED—See Barclays PLC; *Int'l*, pg. 862
BARD CAPITAL GROUP, LLC—See Bard & Company, Inc.; *U.S. Private*, pg. 473
BAREKET CAPITAL LTD.; *Int'l*, pg. 864
BARING ASSET MANAGEMENT LTD.—See Massachusetts Mutual Life Insurance Company; *U.S. Private*, pg. 2604
BARINGS PRIVATE CREDIT CORPORATION; *U.S. Private*, pg. 475
BARINGTON/HILCO ACQUISITION CORP.; *U.S. Private*, pg. 475
BARING VOSTOK CAPITAL PARTNERS; *Int'l*, pg. 865
BARK, INC.; *U.S. Public*, pg. 276
BARON PARTNERS LIMITED; *Int'l*, pg. 867
BARRA & ASSOCIATES LLC—See Reliance Global Group, Inc.; *U.S. Public*, pg. 1778
BARRICK GOLD FINANCE COMPANY—See Barrick Gold Corporation; *Int'l*, pg. 869
THE BARTHOLOMEW COMPANY, INC.; *U.S. Private*, pg. 3992
BASALT INFRASTRUCTURE PARTNERS LLC—See Colliers International Group Inc.; *U.S. Private*, pg. 1700
BASE INTELLIGENCE, INC; *U.S. Private*, pg. 484
BASF BATTERY TECHNOLOGY INVESTMENT GMBH & CO. KG—See BASF SE; *Int'l*, pg. 872
BASF CATALYSTS ASIA B.V.—See BASF SE; *Int'l*, pg. 875
BASF CATALYSTS HOLDING ASIA B.V.—See BASF SE; *Int'l*, pg. 875
BASF CATALYSTS HOLDING CHINA LLC—See BASF SE; *Int'l*, pg. 875
BASF CATALYSTS NL FINANCE C.V.—See BASF SE; *Int'l*, pg. 875
BASF CATALYSTS UK HOLDINGS LIMITED—See BASF SE; *Int'l*, pg. 875
BASF CONSTRUCTION CANADA HOLDINGS INC.—See BASF SE; *Int'l*, pg. 874
BASF FINANCE MALTA GMBH—See BASF SE; *Int'l*, pg. 878

BASF HOLDINGS SOUTH AFRICA (PTY.) LTD.—See BASF SE; *Int'l*, pg. 879
BASF IT SERVICES HOLDING GMBH—See BASF SE; *Int'l*, pg. 879
BASF IT SERVICES HOLDING LTD.—See BASF SE; *Int'l*, pg. 879
BASF NEW BUSINESS GMBH—See BASF SE; *Int'l*, pg. 880
BASF VC BETEILIGUNGS- UND MANAGEMENTGESELLSCHAFT—See BASF SE; *Int'l*, pg. 882
BASF VENTURE CAPITAL AMERICA INC.—See BASF SE; *Int'l*, pg. 876
BASIC CAPITAL MANAGEMENT CO., LTD.; *Int'l*, pg. 886
BASIC ELEMENT COMPANY; *Int'l*, pg. 886
BASINGHALL FINANCE PLC—See Erste Abwicklungsanstalt AoR; *Int'l*, pg. 2497
BASIN WELL LOGGING WIRELINE SERVICES, INC.,—See Steel Partners Holdings L.P.; *U.S. Public*, pg. 1943
BASSET CREEK CAPITAL, INC.; *U.S. Private*, pg. 486
BATH STREET CAPITAL LIMITED; *Int'l*, pg. 889
BATIC INVESTMENTS & LOGISTICS CO; *Int'l*, pg. 889
B.A.T. INTERNATIONAL FINANCE P.L.C.—See British American Tobacco plc; *Int'l*, pg. 1165
BAT INVESTMENTS, INC.; *U.S. Private*, pg. 486
BATTERY FUTURE ACQUISITION CORP.; *U.S. Public*, pg. 279
BATTERY VENTURES, L.P. - MENLO PARK—See Battery Ventures, L.P.; *U.S. Private*, pg. 488
BATTERY VENTURES, L.P.; *U.S. Private*, pg. 488
BATTLE INVESTMENT GROUP LLC; *U.S. Private*, pg. 489
BAUBECON HOLDING 1 GMBH—See Barclays PLC; *Int'l*, pg. 862
BAUM CAPITAL PARTNERS MANAGEMENT LLC; *U.S. Private*, pg. 490
THE BAUPOST GROUP LLC; *U.S. Private*, pg. 3992
BAVARIA INDUSTRIES GROUP AG; *Int'l*, pg. 899
BAWAG ALLIANZ MITARBEITERVORSORGEKASSE AG—See Allianz SE; *Int'l*, pg. 351
BAY CAPITAL PLC; *Int'l*, pg. 900
BAY EQUITY, LLC.; *U.S. Private*, pg. 492
BAYER CANADIAN HOLDINGS INC.—See Bayer Aktiengesellschaft; *Int'l*, pg. 902
BAYER CROPSCIENCE HOLDING SA—See Bayer Aktiengesellschaft; *Int'l*, pg. 903
BAYER CROPSCIENCE HOLDINGS PTY LTD.—See Bayer Aktiengesellschaft; *Int'l*, pg. 903
BAYER FINANCE LTDA.—See Bayer Aktiengesellschaft; *Int'l*, pg. 904
BAYER GLOBAL INVESTMENTS B.V.—See Bayer Aktiengesellschaft; *Int'l*, pg. 904
BAYER HOLDING LTD.—See Bayer Aktiengesellschaft; *Int'l*, pg. 905
BAYERNLB HOLDING AG; *Int'l*, pg. 913
BAYERNLB—See BayernLB Holding AG; *Int'l*, pg. 913
BAY GROVE CAPITAL LLC; *U.S. Private*, pg. 492
BAY LEASING & INVESTMENT LIMITED; *Int'l*, pg. 901
BAYMARK PARTNERS; *U.S. Private*, pg. 496
BAYNON INTERNATIONAL CORPORATION—See Henry Schein, Inc.; *U.S. Public*, pg. 1025
BAYPORT FIMSA S.A.S—See Bayport Management Limited; *Int'l*, pg. 915
BAYPORT FINANCIAL SERVICES 2010 (PROPRIETARY) LIMITED—See Bayport Management Limited; *Int'l*, pg. 915
BAYPORT FINANCIAL SERVICES GHANA LIMITED—See Bayport Management Limited; *Int'l*, pg. 915
BAYPORT FINANCIAL SERVICES LIMITED—See Bayport Management Limited; *Int'l*, pg. 915
BAYPORT FINANCIAL SERVICES MOZAMBIQUE (MCB), SA—See Bayport Management Limited; *Int'l*, pg. 915
BAYPORT FINANCIAL SERVICES (T) LIMITED—See Bayport Management Limited; *Int'l*, pg. 915
BAYPORT FINANCIAL SERVICES UGANDA LIMITED—See Bayport Management Limited; *Int'l*, pg. 915
BAYPORT MANAGEMENT LIMITED; *Int'l*, pg. 914
BAYSIDE CAPITAL, INC.—See H.I.G. Capital, LLC; *U.S. Private*, pg. 1827
BAYSWATER FALLING WATERS LLC—See Icahn Enterprises L.P.; *U.S. Public*, pg. 1084
BAY TREE PRIVATE EQUITY LLP; *Int'l*, pg. 901
BB BIOTECH AG—See Bellevue Group AG; *Int'l*, pg. 967
BB GAMMA PPP-PROJEKTGESELLSCHAFT MBH—See Bilfinger SE; *Int'l*, pg. 1024
BBGR GMBH—See EssilorLuxottica SA; *Int'l*, pg. 2512
B&B INVESTMENT PARTNERS LLP; *Int'l*, pg. 783
BBSA SERVICOS E PARTICIPACOES LIMITADA—See Barclays PLC; *Int'l*, pg. 859
BB SECURITIES LTD.—See Banco do Brasil S.A.; *Int'l*, pg. 822
BB&T CAPITAL PARTNERS, LLC—See Truist Financial Corporation; *U.S. Public*, pg. 2200
BBVA INSTITUICAO FINANCEIRA DE CREDITO, S.A.—See Banco Bilbao Vizcaya Argentaria, S.A.; *Int'l*, pg. 817
BBVA IRELAND PLC—See Banco Bilbao Vizcaya Argentaria, S.A.; *Int'l*, pg. 817

BBVA LUXINVEST, S.A.—See Banco Bilbao Vizcaya Argentaria, S.A.; *Int'l*, pg. 817
BBVA WEALTH SOLUTIONS, INC.—See Banco Bilbao Vizcaya Argentaria, S.A.; *Int'l*, pg. 817
BBX CAPITAL, INC.; *U.S. Public*, pg. 284
B CAPITAL TECHNOLOGY OPPORTUNITIES CORP.; *U.S. Private*, pg. 417
BCC INVESTMENT CORP.; *U.S. Private*, pg. 499
BCL ENTERPRISES LTD.; *Int'l*, pg. 928
BCLS ACQUISITION CORP.; *U.S. Public*, pg. 285
BCO BRASIL S.A.; *Int'l*, pg. 928
BCO ESTADO DO PARA S.A.; *Int'l*, pg. 928
BCO NORDESTE DO BRASIL S.A.; *Int'l*, pg. 928
BC PARTNERS, INC.—See BC Partners LLP; *Int'l*, pg. 923
BC PARTNERS LENDING CORPORATION; *U.S. Private*, pg. 498
BC PARTNERS LLP; *Int'l*, pg. 922
BCR PROCESARE SRL—See Erste Group Bank AG; *Int'l*, pg. 2497
B D & B INVESTMENTS LIMITED—See Barclays PLC; *Int'l*, pg. 859
BD-CAPITAL PARTNERS LIMITED; *Int'l*, pg. 929
BD FINANCE CAPITAL HOLDINGS LIMITED—See Bangladesh Finance Limited; *Int'l*, pg. 835
BD FINANCE SECURITIES LIMITED—See Bangladesh Finance Limited; *Int'l*, pg. 835
BDO CAPITAL & INVESTMENT CORPORATION—See BDO Unibank, Inc.; *Int'l*, pg. 930
BDO SECURITIES CORPORATION—See BDO Unibank, Inc.; *Int'l*, pg. 930
BDT CAPITAL PARTNERS, LLC; *U.S. Private*, pg. 502
BD VENTURES LLC—See Becton, Dickinson & Company; *U.S. Public*, pg. 288
THE BEACHBODY COMPANY, INC.; *U.S. Public*, pg. 2038
BEACON ACQUISITION PARTNERS INC.; *U.S. Private*, pg. 503
BEARBULL INTERNATIONAL LTD—See Banque Degroof S.A.; *Int'l*, pg. 853
BEARD ENERGY TRANSITION ACQUISITION CORP.; *U.S. Public*, pg. 287
BEAUFORT CAPITAL GMBH; *Int'l*, pg. 934
BEAUMONT CAPITAL LLP; *Int'l*, pg. 934
BEAUMONT DEVELOPMENT CENTRE HOLDING LTD.—See Accenture plc; *Int'l*, pg. 86
BEAUMONT SELECT CORPORATIONS INC.; *Int'l*, pg. 934
BEAZLEY INVESTMENTS LIMITED—See Beazley plc; *Int'l*, pg. 935
BECI CORPORATION CO., LTD.—See BEC World Public Company Limited; *Int'l*, pg. 936
BEC MULTIMEDIA CO., LTD.—See BEC World Public Company Limited; *Int'l*, pg. 936
BECTON DICKINSON FINANCE B.V.—See Becton, Dickinson & Company; *U.S. Public*, pg. 289
BECTON DICKINSON INFUSION THERAPY HOLDINGS AB—See Becton, Dickinson & Company; *U.S. Public*, pg. 289
BEDFORD CAPITAL LTD.; *Int'l*, pg. 938
BEDFORD EDUCATION PARTNERSHIP LIMITED—See Bilfinger SE; *Int'l*, pg. 1024
BEDFORD FUNDING; *U.S. Private*, pg. 512
BEECKEN PETTY O'KEEFE & COMPANY, LLC; *U.S. Private*, pg. 514
THE BEEKMAN GROUP, LLC; *U.S. Private*, pg. 3992
BEHRMAN BROTHERS MANAGEMENT CORP.; *U.S. Private*, pg. 515
BEIF MANAGEMENT LIMITED—See Barclays PLC; *Int'l*, pg. 859
BEIJING CENTURY GSR VENTURES MANAGEMENT CO., LTD.; *Int'l*, pg. 947
BEIJING ELECTRONIC ZONE HIGH-TECH GROUP CO., LTD.; *Int'l*, pg. 949
BEIJING E-TOWN INTERNATIONAL INVESTMENT & DEVELOPMENT CO., LTD.; *Int'l*, pg. 949
BEIJING HEALTH (HOLDINGS) LIMITED; *Int'l*, pg. 951
BEIJING SPORTS & ENTERTAINMENT INDUSTRY GROUP LIMITED; *Int'l*, pg. 957
BEIJING ZHONGKE TONGRONG PRIVATE EQUITY INVESTMENT FUND CO., LTD; *Int'l*, pg. 961
BELET ACQUISITIONS, INC.—See The Belet Group, Inc.; *U.S. Private*, pg. 3993
BELHEALTH INVESTMENT PARTNERS LLC; *U.S. Private*, pg. 517
BELLAIR VENTURES INC.; *Int'l*, pg. 966
BELL IXL INVESTMENTS PTY. LTD.; *Int'l*, pg. 966
BELL POTTER SECURITIES (HK) LIMITED—See Bell Financial Group Limited; *Int'l*, pg. 966
BELL POTTER (US) HOLDINGS INC.—See Bell Financial Group Limited; *Int'l*, pg. 966
BELLWETHER FINANCIAL GROUP, INC.; *U.S. Private*, pg. 520
BELONG ACQUISITION CORP.; *U.S. Public*, pg. 295
BELTONE PRIVATE EQUITY—See Chimera Investments LLC; *Int'l*, pg. 1479
BELTWAY CAPITAL PARTNERS, LLC; *U.S. Private*, pg. 521
BELTZ IANNI & ASSOCIATES—See Crestview Partners, L.P.; *U.S. Private*, pg. 1098

523999 — MISCELLANEOUS FINAN...   CORPORATE AFFILIATIONS

BEL VENTURES INC.—See Bel Fuse Inc.; *U.S. Public*, pg. 293
BELVERON REAL ESTATE PARTNERS, LLC; *U.S. Private*, pg. 521
BEMETALS CORP.; *Int'l*, pg. 969
BENCHMARK CAPITAL; *U.S. Private*, pg. 523
BENCHMARK CAPITAL—See Benchmark Capital; *U.S. Private*, pg. 523
BENCIS CAPITAL PARTNERS B.V.; *Int'l*, pg. 970
BEND FINANCIAL, INC.—See Webster Financial Corporation; *U.S. Public*, pg. 2341
BENDIGO FINANCIAL PLANNING LIMITED—See Bendigo & Adelaide Bank Ltd.; *Int'l*, pg. 970
BENDIGO PARTNERS, LLC; *U.S. Private*, pg. 524
BENEDEK INVESTMENT GROUP, LLC; *U.S. Private*, pg. 524
BENEFICIAL ADVISORS, LLC—See WSFS Financial Corporation; *U.S. Public*, pg. 2384
BENESSERE CAPITAL ACQUISITION CORP.; *U.S. Public*, pg. 296
BENFORD CAPITAL PARTNERS, LLC; *U.S. Private*, pg. 525
BENGAL & ASSAM COMPANY LTD.; *Int'l*, pg. 973
BENNETT CAPITAL PARTNERS, LLC; *U.S. Private*, pg. 527
BENTLEY COMMERCIAL ENTERPRISES LIMITED; *Int'l*, pg. 977
BENTLEY FORBES GROUP, LLC; *U.S. Private*, pg. 528
BENZ MINING CORP.; *Int'l*, pg. 977
BEOWULF ENERGY LLC; *U.S. Private*, pg. 529
BERAFINA AG.—See Hinduja Group Ltd.; *Int'l*, pg. 3399
BERENSON & COMPANY, INC.; *U.S. Private*, pg. 529
BERETTA VENTURES LTD.; *Int'l*, pg. 979
BERGGRUEN HOLDINGS, INC.; *U.S. Private*, pg. 531
BERGGRUEN HOLDINGS, LTD.—See Berggruen Holdings, Inc.; *U.S. Private*, pg. 531
BERGMAN & BEVING INVEST AB—See Bergman & Beving AB; *Int'l*, pg. 980
BERINGER CAPITAL; *Int'l*, pg. 981
BERKSHIRE ASSET MANAGEMENT, LLC; *U.S. Private*, pg. 533
BERKSHIRE PARTNERS LLC; *U.S. Private*, pg. 534
BERNARD KRIEF CONSULTANTS SA; *Int'l*, pg. 986
BERNHARD CAPITAL PARTNERS MANAGEMENT, LP; *U.S. Private*, pg. 536
BERTRAM CAPITAL MANAGEMENT, LLC; *U.S. Private*, pg. 539
BERWIND CORPORATION; *U.S. Private*, pg. 540
BESPOKE CAPITAL PARTNERS, LLC—See Global Leisure Partners LLP; *Int'l*, pg. 2998
BESPOKE EXTRACTS, INC.; *U.S. Public*, pg. 326
BESSEMER VENTURE PARTNERS; *U.S. Private*, pg. 541
BEST AGROLIFE LTD.; *Int'l*, pg. 998
BEST FINANCE COMPANY LIMITED; *Int'l*, pg. 999
BESTON GLOBAL FOOD COMPANY LIMITED; *Int'l*, pg. 1000
BESTSUN ENERGY CO., LTD.; *Int'l*, pg. 1000
BETAPART PARTICIPACOES S/A; *Int'l*, pg. 1002
BETA SECURITIZADORA S.A.; *Int'l*, pg. 1002
BETLAN DOS S.A.; *Int'l*, pg. 1002
BETTER CAPITAL LLP—See Heritage Group Ltd.; *Int'l*, pg. 3361
BETTER HOME & FINANCE HOLDING COMPANY; *U.S. Public*, pg. 326
BEVERLY CAPITAL LLC; *U.S. Private*, pg. 547
BFI-BETEILIGUNGSGESELLSCHAFT FUR INDUSTRIEWERTE MBH—See Deutsche Bank Aktiengesellschaft; *Int'l*, pg. 2055
BF INVESTMENT LIMITED; *Int'l*, pg. 1006
BFL ASSET FINVEST LIMITED; *Int'l*, pg. 1006
BFL LEASING GMBH—See BAWAG Group AG; *Int'l*, pg. 900
B.F. MODARABA; *Int'l*, pg. 789
BGC SA FINANCIAL BROKERS (PTY) LIMITED—See BGC Group, Inc.; *U.S. Public*, pg. 328
BGF GROUP PLC; *Int'l*, pg. 1007
BGH CAPITAL PTY LTD; *Int'l*, pg. 1007
BGS ACQUISITION CORP.; *Int'l*, pg. 1009
BHARAT BHUSHAN FINANCE & COMMODITY BROKERS LTD.; *Int'l*, pg. 1010
BHARAT HIGHWAYS INVIT.; *Int'l*, pg. 1011
BHARCAP ACQUISITION CORP.; *U.S. Private*, pg. 549
BHARCAP PARTNERS, LLC; *U.S. Private*, pg. 549
BHMS INVESTMENTS LP; *U.S. Private*, pg. 549
BI ACQUISITION CORP.; *U.S. Private*, pg. 549
BIDV SECURITIES JOINT STOCK COMPANY; *Int'l*, pg. 1019
BIG 8 SPLIT, INC.; *Int'l*, pg. 1020
BIG SKY GROWTH PARTNERS, INC.; *U.S. Public*, pg. 554
BI-INVEST ADVISORS S.A.; *Int'l*, pg. 1016
BILANDER ACQUISITION CORP.; *U.S. Public*, pg. 331
BIL AUSTRALIA PTY LIMITED—See Hong Leong Investment Holdings Pte. Ltd.; *Int'l*, pg. 3468
BILFINGER BERGER PI INTERNATIONAL HOLDING GMBH—See Bilfinger SE; *Int'l*, pg. 1026
BINDAR TRADING & INVESTMENT CO. PLC; *Int'l*, pg. 1033
B INVESTMENTS HOLDING SAE; *Int'l*, pg. 783
BIOETHICS, LTD.; *U.S. Public*, pg. 335

BIOGASPARK NV; *Int'l*, pg. 1038
BIOMX INC.; *Int'l*, pg. 1040
BIOPLUS ACQUISITION CORP.; *U.S. Public*, pg. 338
BIOTECH ACQUISITION COMPANY; *U.S. Public*, pg. 339
BIOTECH GROUP ACQUISITION CORPORATION; *U.S. Public*, pg. 339
BIOTECH INVESTMENT GROUP LLC; *U.S. Private*, pg. 563
BIP OPPORTUNITIES FUND, LP; *U.S. Private*, pg. 563
BIP VENTURES EVERGREEN BDC; *U.S. Private*, pg. 563
BIRCH HILL EQUITY PARTNERS MANAGEMENT INC.; *Int'l*, pg. 1046
BIRCH SWING CAPITAL LLC; *U.S. Private*, pg. 564
BIRCHTREE INVESTMENTS LTD.; *Int'l*, pg. 1046
BIRDIE WIN CORPORATION; *Int'l*, pg. 1047
BIRLA SUN LIFE INSURANCE COMPANY LIMITED; *Int'l*, pg. 1047
BIS BETEILIGUNGSVERWALTUNGS GMBH—See Bilfinger SE; *Int'l*, pg. 1025
BISHOP STREET CAPITAL MANAGEMENT CORPORATION—See BNP Paribas SA; *Int'l*, pg. 1088
BISON INVESTMENTS INC.; *U.S. Private*, pg. 566
BITCOIN BRANDS INC.; *U.S. Private*, pg. 567
BITCOIN DEPOT INC.; *U.S. Public*, pg. 339
BITE ACQUISITION CORP.—See Above Food Ingredients Inc.; *Int'l*, pg. 67
BITRUSH CORP.; *Int'l*, pg. 1050
BITWISE BITCOIN ETP TRUST; *U.S. Private*, pg. 567
BIZZOOM INC.; *U.S. Private*, pg. 568
BKCV SDN BHD—See Chin Hin Group Berhad; *Int'l*, pg. 1480
BKF CAPITAL GROUP, INC.; *U.S. Public*, pg. 340
BKGM INDUSTRIES SDN BHD—See Chin Hin Group Berhad; *Int'l*, pg. 1480
BKI INVESTMENT COMPANY LIMITED; *Int'l*, pg. 1054
BLACKBERN PARTNERS LLC; *U.S. Private*, pg. 573
BLACK CANYON CAPITAL LLC; *U.S. Private*, pg. 569
BLACK DIAMOND CAPITAL MANAGEMENT LIMITED—See Black Diamond Capital Holdings, LLC; *U.S. Private*, pg. 570
BLACK DIAMOND CAPITAL MANAGEMENT, LLC - GREENWICH OFFICE—See Black Diamond Capital Holdings, LLC; *U.S. Private*, pg. 570
BLACK DIAMOND CAPITAL MANAGEMENT, LLC—See Black Diamond Capital Holdings, LLC; *U.S. Private*, pg. 570
BLACK DIAMOND FINANCIAL GROUP, LLC; *U.S. Private*, pg. 571
BLACK DRAGON CAPITAL LLC; *U.S. Private*, pg. 571
BLACKEAGLE PARTNERS, LLC; *U.S. Private*, pg. 573
BLACKFINCH SPRING VCT PLC; *Int'l*, pg. 1060
BLACKFISH CAPITAL MANAGEMENT LTD.; *Int'l*, pg. 1060
BLACKFORD CAPITAL LLC; *U.S. Private*, pg. 574
BLACK HAWK ACQUISITION CORPORATION; *U.S. Public*, pg. 340
BLACKHAWK CAPITAL LLP; *Int'l*, pg. 1061
BLACK LAKE CAPITAL, LLC; *U.S. Private*, pg. 572
BLACK MOUNTAIN ACQUISITION CORP.; *U.S. Public*, pg. 341
BLACK PEARL S.A.; *Int'l*, pg. 1059
BLACKROCK CAPITAL MANAGEMENT, INC.—See BlackRock, Inc.; *U.S. Public*, pg. 345
BLACKROCK CORE BOND TRUST; *U.S. Public*, pg. 342
BLACKROCK FINANCE EUROPE LIMITED—See BlackRock, Inc.; *U.S. Public*, pg. 345
BLACKROCK, INC.; *U.S. Public*, pg. 344
BLACKROCK JAPAN CO., LTD.—See BlackRock, Inc.; *U.S. Public*, pg. 345
BLACKROCK MUNICIPAL 2030 TARGET TERM TRUST; *U.S. Public*, pg. 343
BLACKROCK TCP CAPITAL CORP.; *U.S. Public*, pg. 344
BLACK SPADE ACQUISITION CO.; *Int'l*, pg. 1060
BLACKSTONE ASSESSORIA EM INVESTIMENTOS LTDA—See Blackstone Inc.; *U.S. Public*, pg. 349
THE BLACKSTONE GROUP DENMARK APS—See Blackstone Inc.; *U.S. Public*, pg. 359
THE BLACKSTONE GROUP INTERNATIONAL LIMITED—See Blackstone Inc.; *U.S. Public*, pg. 359
BLACKSTONE INC.; *U.S. Public*, pg. 347
BLACKSTONE RESOURCES AG; *Int'l*, pg. 1062
BLACKSTREET CAPITAL MANAGEMENT, LLC; *U.S. Private*, pg. 577
BLACKTHORNE PARTNERS LTD.; *U.S. Private*, pg. 577
BLACKWELL CAPITAL GROUP LLC; *U.S. Private*, pg. 577
BLEECKER SA; *Int'l*, pg. 1063
BLENDER FINANCIAL TECHNOLOGIES LTD.; *Int'l*, pg. 1063
BLEUACACIA LTD.; *U.S. Public*, pg. 361
BLIXT GROUP LIMITED; *Int'l*, pg. 1064
BLOCKCHAIN MOON ACQUISITION CORP.; *U.S. Public*, pg. 362
BLOCKCHAIN SOLUTIONS INC.; *U.S. Private*, pg. 583
BLOCKCHAIN VENTURE CAPITAL INC.; *Int'l*, pg. 1064
BLOM ASSET MANAGEMENT COMPANY S.A.L.—See BLOM Bank, S.A.L.; *Int'l*, pg. 1064
BLOM BANK QATAR LLC—See BLOM Bank, S.A.L.; *Int'l*, pg. 1064

BLOM DEVELOPMENT BANK S.A.L.—See BLOM Bank, S.A.L.; *Int'l*, pg. 1064
BLOM EGYPT INVESTMENT S.A.E.—See BLOM Bank, S.A.L.; *Int'l*, pg. 1065
BLOM EGYPT SECURITIES S.A.E.—See BLOM Bank, S.A.L.; *Int'l*, pg. 1065
BLOMINVEST BANK SAUDI ARABIA COMPANY—See BLOM Bank, S.A.L.; *Int'l*, pg. 1065
BLOOM EQUITY PARTNERS MANAGEMENT, LLC; *U.S. Private*, pg. 583
BLUE CAP AG; *Int'l*, pg. 1067
BLUE CHIP CAPITAL GROUP, INC.; *U.S. Private*, pg. 586
BLUECREST CAPITAL FINANCE CORP.; *U.S. Private*, pg. 596
BLUE EQUITY, LLC; *U.S. Private*, pg. 588
BLUE HARBOUR GROUP, L.P.; *U.S. Private*, pg. 589
BLUE HORIZON SOFTWARE HOLDINGS LLC; *U.S. Private*, pg. 589
BLUE HUB VENTURES B.V.—See Anadolu Efes Biracilik ve Malt Sanayii A.S.; *Int'l*, pg. 445
BLUELINE PARTNERS, LLC; *U.S. Private*, pg. 597
BLUE OCEAN ACQUISITION CORP.; *U.S. Public*, pg. 364
BLUE OWL CAPITAL INC.; *U.S. Public*, pg. 364
BLUE PLANET WORLDWIDE FINANCIALS INVESTMENT TRUST PLC; *Int'l*, pg. 1069
BLUE POINT CAPITAL PARTNERS, LLC; *U.S. Private*, pg. 590
BLUEPRINT HEALTH MERGER CORP.; *U.S. Private*, pg. 597
BLUEPRINT VENTURES, LLC; *U.S. Private*, pg. 597
BLUE RIDGE CAPITAL, LLC; *U.S. Private*, pg. 591
BLUERIVER ACQUISITION CORP.; *U.S. Public*, pg. 366
BLUEROCK VENTURES CORP.; *Int'l*, pg. 1072
BLUERUN VENTURES; *U.S. Private*, pg. 597
BLUE SAFARI GROUP ACQUISITION CORP.; *Int'l*, pg. 1069
BLUE SAGE CAPITAL, L.P.; *U.S. Private*, pg. 592
BLUESCAPE OPPORTUNITIES ACQUISITION CORP.; *U.S. Public*, pg. 366
BLUE SEA CAPITAL MANAGEMENT LLC; *U.S. Private*, pg. 592
BLUESKY DIGITAL ASSETS CORP.; *Int'l*, pg. 1074
BLUESPRING WEALTH PARTNERS LLC—See Warburg Pincus LLC; *U.S. Private*, pg. 4439
BLUE STAR CAPITAL PLC; *Int'l*, pg. 1069
BLUESTEM EQUITY, LTD.; *U.S. Private*, pg. 598
BLUESTONE INVESTMENT PARTNERS, LLC; *U.S. Private*, pg. 598
BLUE TORCH FINANCE LLC—See Blue Torch Capital, LP; *U.S. Private*, pg. 594
THE BLUE VENTURE FUND; *U.S. Private*, pg. 3995
BLUEWATER CREEK MANAGEMENT CO.—See Deutsche Bank Aktiengesellschaft; *Int'l*, pg. 2055
BLUE WATER ENERGY LLP; *Int'l*, pg. 1070
BLUE WOLF CAPITAL PARTNERS LLC; *U.S. Private*, pg. 594
BLUE WORLD ACQUISITION CORPORATION; *U.S. Public*, pg. 365
BLUFF POINT ASSOCIATES CORP.; *U.S. Private*, pg. 599
BLUM CAPITAL PARTNERS, L.P.; *U.S. Private*, pg. 599
BLUO SICAV-SIF; *Int'l*, pg. 1075
B. METZLER SEEL. SOHN & CO. KGAA—See B. Metzler seel. Sohn & Co. Holding AG; *Int'l*, pg. 788
BM&F USA INC.—See B3 S.A.; *Int'l*, pg. 791
BM H BETEILIGUNGS MANAGEMENTGESELLSCHAFT HESSEN MBH—See Helaba Landesbank Hessen-Thuringen; *Int'l*, pg. 3327
BMO GLOBAL ASSET MANAGEMENT (EMEA)—See Bank of Montreal; *Int'l*, pg. 846
BMO PRIVATE EQUITY (CANADA) INC.—See Bank of Montreal; *Int'l*, pg. 846
BMP BETEILIGUNGSMANAGEMENT AG; *Int'l*, pg. 1076
BM TECHNOLOGIES, INC.; *U.S. Public*, pg. 366
BMW FINANCIAL SERVICES (GB) LTD—See Bayerische Motoren Werke Aktiengesellschaft; *Int'l*, pg. 911
BMW FINANZ VERWALTUNGS GMBH—See Bayerische Motoren Werke Aktiengesellschaft; *Int'l*, pg. 911
BMW OVERSEAS ENTERPRISES N. V.—See Bayerische Motoren Werke Aktiengesellschaft; *Int'l*, pg. 912
BMW (UK) CAPITAL PLC—See Bayerische Motoren Werke Aktiengesellschaft; *Int'l*, pg. 911
BMW US CAPITAL, LLC—See Bayerische Motoren Werke Aktiengesellschaft; *Int'l*, pg. 912
BNC REAL ESTATE; *U.S. Private*, pg. 601
BNDES PARTICIPACOES SA; *Int'l*, pg. 1078
BNG CAPITAL MANAGEMENT B.V.—See BNG Bank N.V.; *Int'l*, pg. 1078
BNG GEBIEDSONTWIKKELING BV—See BNG Bank N.V.; *Int'l*, pg. 1078
BNG MANAGEMENT SERVICES B.V.—See BNG Bank N.V.; *Int'l*, pg. 1079
BNG VERMOGENSBEHEER BV—See BNG Bank N.V.; *Int'l*, pg. 1079
BNP PARIBAS ARBITRAGE—See BNP Paribas SA; *Int'l*, pg. 1081
BNP PARIBAS CARDIF EMEKLILIK ANONIM SIRKETI—See BNP Paribas SA; *Int'l*, pg. 1083

N.A.I.C.S. INDEX

523999 — MISCELLANEOUS FINAN...

BNP PARIBAS CMG LTD.—See BNP Paribas SA; *Int'l*, pg. 1082
BNP PARIBAS DEVELOPPEMENT SA—See BNP Paribas SA; *Int'l*, pg. 1083
BNP PARIBAS FINANCE PLC—See BNP Paribas SA; *Int'l*, pg. 1084
BNP PARIBAS FINANCIAL SERVICES LLC—See BNP Paribas SA; *Int'l*, pg. 1087
BNP PARIBAS INVESTMENT PARTNERS BELGIUM SA—See BNP Paribas SA; *Int'l*, pg. 1085
BNP PARIBAS INVESTMENT PARTNERS UK LTD—See BNP Paribas SA; *Int'l*, pg. 1085
BNP PARIBAS ISLAMIC ISSUANCE BV—See BNP Paribas SA; *Int'l*, pg. 1085
BNP PARIBAS ISSUANCE B.V.—See BNP Paribas SA; *Int'l*, pg. 1085
BNP PARIBAS LEASE GROUP LUXEMBOURG SA—See BNP Paribas SA; *Int'l*, pg. 1085
BNP PARIBAS LEASING SOLUTIONS NV—See BNP Paribas SA; *Int'l*, pg. 1086
BNP PARIBAS PERSONAL FINANCE EAD—See Eurobank Ergasias Services and Holdings S.A.; *Int'l*, pg. 2532
BNP PARIBAS PERSONAL FINANCE SPA—See BNP Paribas SA; *Int'l*, pg. 1086
BNP PARIBAS PRINCIPAL INVESTMENTS JAPAN LTD.—See BNP Paribas SA; *Int'l*, pg. 1086
BNP PARIBAS PRIVATE EQUITY—See BNP Paribas SA; *Int'l*, pg. 1082
BNP PARIBAS SECURITIES SERVICES (HOLDINGS) LTD.—See BNP Paribas SA; *Int'l*, pg. 1087
BNP PARIBAS SECURITIES SERVICES—See BNP Paribas SA; *Int'l*, pg. 1087
BNP PARIBAS UK TREASURY LTD.—See BNP Paribas SA; *Int'l*, pg. 1087
BNPP GLOBAL SECURITIES OPERATIONS PRIVATE LTD.—See BNP Paribas SA; *Int'l*, pg. 1088
BNY MELLON-ALCENTRA MEZZANINE PARTNERS—See Franklin Resources, Inc.; *U.S. Public*, pg. 879
BNY MELLON FUND MANAGEMENT (LUXEMBOURG) SA—See The Bank of New York Mellon Corporation; *U.S. Public*, pg. 2037
BNY MELLON INVESTMENT MANAGEMENT EMEA LIMITED—See The Bank of New York Mellon Corporation; *U.S. Public*, pg. 2037
BNY MELLON STRATEGIC MUNICIPALS, INC.; *U.S. Public*, pg. 366
BOARDWALKTECH SOFTWARE CORP.; *U.S. Public*, pg. 366
BOATHOUSE CAPITAL MANAGEMENT, LLC; *U.S. Private*, pg. 603
BOBST UK HOLDINGS LTD—See Bobst Group S.A.; *Int'l*, pg. 1096
BOC FINANCIAL LEASING CO., LTD.—See Bank of China, Ltd.; *Int'l*, pg. 841
BOC FINANCIAL TECHNOLOGY CO., LTD.—See Bank of China, Ltd.; *Int'l*, pg. 841
BOC FULLERTON COMMUNITY BANK CO., LTD.—See Bank of China, Ltd.; *Int'l*, pg. 841
BOHAI INDUSTRIAL INVESTMENT FUND MANAGEMENT COMPANY LTD.; *Int'l*, pg. 1100
BOHEMIA FAKTORING, A.S.; *Int'l*, pg. 1100
BOLD INVESTMENT CO., LTD.; *Int'l*, pg. 1102
BOLD STROKE VENTURES INC.; *Int'l*, pg. 1102
BOLSENA HOLDING GMBH & CO. KG—See Deutsche Bank Aktiengesellschaft; *Int'l*, pg. 2055
BOMBARDIER TRANSPORTATION (SHARED SERVICES) PHILIPPINES INC.—See Alstom S.A.; *Int'l*, pg. 382
BONACCORD CAPITAL PARTNERS LLC—See P10, Inc.; *U.S. Public*, pg. 1630
BONATLA PROPERTY HOLDINGS LIMITED; *Int'l*, pg. 1105
BONAVENTURE CAPITAL LLC; *U.S. Private*, pg. 613
BONDEXCEL (PTY) LTD—See Finbond Group Limited; *Int'l*, pg. 2670
BOQ FINANCE (AUST) LIMITED—See Bank of Queensland Limited; *Int'l*, pg. 848
BOREA OPPORTUNITY MANAGEMENT AS—See Borea AS; *Int'l*, pg. 1113
BORE TECH AB; *Int'l*, pg. 1113
BORGMAN CAPITAL LLC; *U.S. Private*, pg. 618
BORQS TECHNOLOGIES, INC.; *Int'l*, pg. 1114
BOS GLOBAL HOLDINGS LIMITED; *Int'l*, pg. 1115
BOSTON LEASING & FINANCE LTD.; *Int'l*, pg. 1118
BOULEVARD ACQUISITION CORP. II; *U.S. Public*, pg. 375
BOUSSARD & GAVAUDAN ASSET MANAGEMENT, LP—See Boussard & Gavaudan Holding Limited; *Int'l*, pg. 1120
BOUSSARD & GAVAUDAN HOLDING LIMITED; *Int'l*, pg. 1120
BOUTIQUE COLLECTIVE INVESTMENTS (RF) (PTY) LTD—See Apex Fund Services Holdings Ltd.; *Int'l*, pg. 510
BOWEN ACQUISITION CORP.; *U.S. Public*, pg. 376
BOW RIVER ASSET MANAGEMENT CORP.; *U.S. Private*, pg. 625
BOWX ACQUISITION CORP.; *U.S. Public*, pg. 377
BOXED, INC.—See MSG Distributors, Inc.; *U.S. Private*, pg. 2807
BOXWOOD PARTNERS LLC; *U.S. Private*, pg. 627

BOYNE CAPITAL MANAGEMENT, LLC; *U.S. Private*, pg. 628
BPA GESTIO, SA—See Banca Privada D'Andorra, SA; *Int'l*, pg. 816
BPB HOLDINGS S.A.—See Barclays PLC; *Int'l*, pg. 859
B. P. CAPITAL LIMITED; *Int'l*, pg. 788
BP CAPITAL MARKETS PLC—See BP plc; *Int'l*, pg. 1128
BPCE FACTOR SA—See Groupe BPCE; *Int'l*, pg. 3092
BPCE LEASE MADRID SE—See Groupe BPCE; *Int'l*, pg. 3092
BPEA EQT LIMITED—See EQT AB; *Int'l*, pg. 2469
BP ENERGY PARTNERS, LLC; *U.S. Private*, pg. 629
BPER EUROPE ISRAEL—See Edmond de Rothschild Holding S.A.; *Int'l*, pg. 2312
BPE UNTERNEHMENS BETEILIGUNGEN GMBH; *Int'l*, pg. 1131
BP GLOBAL INVESTMENTS LTD.—See BP plc; *Int'l*, pg. 1129
BPIFRANCE PARTICIPATIONS—See Caisse des Depots et Consignations; *Int'l*, pg. 1258
BPIFRANCE PARTICIPATIONS—See EPIC Bpifrance; *Int'l*, pg. 2460
BRADESCO LEASING S.A. ARRENDAMENTO MERCANTIL—See Banco Bradesco S.A.; *Int'l*, pg. 819
BRAEMAR NAVES CORPORATE FINANCE LIMITED—See Braemar PLC; *Int'l*, pg. 1135
BRAGANZA AS; *Int'l*, pg. 1136
BRAHMSQ OBJEKT GMBH & CO. KG—See Allianz SE; *Int'l*, pg. 351
BRAILLE ENERGY SYSTEMS INC.; *Int'l*, pg. 1136
BRAINCHIP HOLDINGS LTD.; *Int'l*, pg. 1137
BRAIT INTERNATIONAL LTD—See Brait S.E.; *Int'l*, pg. 1137
BRAIT MAURITIUS LIMITED—See Brait S.E.; *Int'l*, pg. 1137
BRAIT S.E.; *Int'l*, pg. 1137
BRAIT SOUTH AFRICA LIMITED—See Brait S.E.; *Int'l*, pg. 1137
BRANDENBURG ENERGY CORP.; *Int'l*, pg. 1139
BRANDENBURG PROPERTIES; *U.S. Private*, pg. 637
BRANDON CAPITAL PARTNERS PTY LTD.; *Int'l*, pg. 1140
BRAND VELOCITY ACQUISITION CORP.; *U.S. Private*, pg. 637
BRAND VELOCITY PARTNERS; *U.S. Private*, pg. 637
BRANDYWINEGLOBAL - GLOBAL INCOME OPPORTUNITIES FUND INC.; *U.S. Public*, pg. 380
BRANFORD CASTLE PARTNERS, L.P.—See Branford Castle, Inc.; *U.S. Private*, pg. 639
BRASIL DE IMOVEIS E PARTICIPACOES LTDA.—See Allianz SE; *Int'l*, pg. 351
BRASS RING CAPITAL INC.; *U.S. Private*, pg. 640
BRAVIA CAPITAL HONG KONG LIMITED; *Int'l*, pg. 1141
BRAVIA CAPITAL PARTNERS, INC.—See Bravia Capital Hong Kong Limited; *Int'l*, pg. 1141
BRAVIA CAPITAL SERVICES INDIA PVT. LTD.—See Bravia Capital Hong Kong Limited; *Int'l*, pg. 1141
BRB BCO DE BRASILIA S.A.; *Int'l*, pg. 1143
BRB - DISTRIBUIDORA DE TITULOS E VALORES MOBILIARIOS S.A.—See BRB BCO DE BRASILIA S.A.; *Int'l*, pg. 1143
BREEZE HOLDINGS ACQUISITION CORP.; *U.S. Public*, pg. 381
BREGAL CAPITAL LLP—See COFRA Holding AG; *Int'l*, pg. 1693
BREGAL FRESHSTREAM LLP—See COFRA Holding AG; *Int'l*, pg. 1693
BREGAL INVESTMENTS, INC.—See COFRA Holding AG; *Int'l*, pg. 1694
BREGAL INVESTMENTS LLP—See COFRA Holding AG; *Int'l*, pg. 1693
BREGAL PARTNERS, L.P.—See COFRA Holding AG; *Int'l*, pg. 1694
BREGAL SAGEMOUNT—See COFRA Holding AG; *Int'l*, pg. 1694
BREL-COM SP. Z O. O.—See Commerzbank AG; *Int'l*, pg. 1717
BRENNTAG AUSTRIA HOLDING GMBH—See BRENNTAG SE; *Int'l*, pg. 1146
BRENNTAG FOREIGN HOLDING GMBH—See BRENNTAG SE; *Int'l*, pg. 1147
BRENNTAG FRANCE HOLDING SAS—See BRENNTAG SE; *Int'l*, pg. 1147
BRENNTAG GERMANY HOLDING GMBH—See BRENNTAG SE; *Int'l*, pg. 1147
BRENNTAG (HOLDING) B.V.—See BRENNTAG SE; *Int'l*, pg. 1146
BRENNTAG HOLDING S.P.A.—See BRENNTAG SE; *Int'l*, pg. 1146
BRENTWOOD ASSOCIATES; *U.S. Private*, pg. 645
BRENTWOOD VENTURE MANAGEMENT, LLC; *U.S. Private*, pg. 646
B.R. HOLDINGS SIA—See Africa Israel Investments Ltd.; *Int'l*, pg. 190
BRIACELL THERAPEUTICS CORP.; *Int'l*, pg. 1151
BRICKFIELD PROPERTIES LIMITED—See Centremanor Ltd.; *Int'l*, pg. 1411
BRIDGEGATE PICTURES CORPORATION; *U.S. Public*, pg. 382
BRIDGEPOINT AB—See Bridgepoint Group Plc; *Int'l*, pg. 1153

BRIDGEPOINT ADVISERS LIMITED—See Bridgepoint Group Plc; *Int'l*, pg. 1153
BRIDGEPOINT ADVISERS UK LIMITED—See Bridgepoint Group Plc; *Int'l*, pg. 1153
BRIDGEPOINT DEVELOPMENT CAPITAL LIMITED—See Bridgepoint Group Plc; *Int'l*, pg. 1153
BRIDGEPOINT GMBH—See Bridgepoint Group Plc; *Int'l*, pg. 1154
BRIDGEPOINT LTD. STI.—See Bridgepoint Group Plc; *Int'l*, pg. 1154
BRIDGEPOINT S.A.—See Bridgepoint Group Plc; *Int'l*, pg. 1154
BRIDGEPOINT S.A.S.—See Bridgepoint Group Plc; *Int'l*, pg. 1154
BRIDGEPOINT S.P.A.—See Bridgepoint Group Plc; *Int'l*, pg. 1155
BRIDGEPOINT SP. Z O.O.—See Bridgepoint Group Plc; *Int'l*, pg. 1155
BRIDGEPORT CAPITAL MANAGEMENT PTY LTD; *Int'l*, pg. 1155
BRIDGEPORT PARTNERS LP; *U.S. Private*, pg. 649
BRIDGESTONE FINANCE CORPORATION—See Bridgestone Corporation; *Int'l*, pg. 1159
BRIDGES VENTURES LLP; *Int'l*, pg. 1155
BRIDGETOWN HOLDINGS LIMITED; *Int'l*, pg. 1160
BRIDGEWEST GROUP, INC.; *U.S. Private*, pg. 650
BRIERLEY HOLDINGS LIMITED—See Hong Leong Investment Holdings Pte. Ltd.; *Int'l*, pg. 3468
BRIGANTINE ACQUISITION CORP.; *U.S. Private*, pg. 650
BRIGHT LIGHTS ACQUISITION CORP.; *U.S. Public*, pg. 382
BRIGHTON PARTNERS, LLC; *U.S. Private*, pg. 652
BRIGHTSPARK CAPITOL CORP.; *U.S. Public*, pg. 383
BRIGHTSPHERE INTERNATIONAL, LTD.—See BrightSphere Investment Group Inc.; *U.S. Public*, pg. 383
BRIGHTSPHERE INVESTMENT GROUP INC.; *U.S. Public*, pg. 383
BRIGHTSTAR CAPITAL PARTNERS, L.P.; *U.S. Private*, pg. 652
BRIGHTWOOD CAPITAL ADVISORS, LLC; *U.S. Private*, pg. 653
BRIJLAXMI LEASING & FINANCE LIMITED; *Int'l*, pg. 1163
BRILLIANT ACQUISITION CORPORATION—See Nukkleus Inc.; *U.S. Public*, pg. 1555
BRILLIANT PORTFOLIOS LIMITED; *Int'l*, pg. 1163
BRIMCO, S. DE R.L. DE C.V.—See Deutsche Bank Aktiengesellschaft; *Int'l*, pg. 2059
BRIMSTONE ACQUISITION HOLDINGS CORP.; *U.S. Private*, pg. 654
BRINKMERE CAPITAL PARTNERS LLC; *U.S. Private*, pg. 655
BRINVEST NV—See Ackermans & van Haaren NV; *Int'l*, pg. 104
BRISTOL INVESTMENTS, LTD.; *U.S. Private*, pg. 656
BRITAM HOLDINGS PLC; *Int'l*, pg. 1164
BRITANNIA LIMITED—See Deutsche Bank Aktiengesellschaft; *Int'l*, pg. 2055
BRITISH-AMERICAN TOBACCO (HOLDINGS) LTD.—See British American Tobacco plc; *Int'l*, pg. 1167
BRITISH AMERICAN TOBACCO HOLDINGS SOUTH AFRICA (PTY) LTD.—See British American Tobacco plc; *Int'l*, pg. 1166
BRITISH AMERICAN TOBACCO HOLDINGS (THE NETHERLANDS) B.V.—See British American Tobacco plc; *Int'l*, pg. 1166
BRITISH AMERICAN TOBACCO (INVESTMENTS) LTD.—See British American Tobacco plc; *Int'l*, pg. 1166
BRITISH COLUMBIA INVESTMENT MANAGEMENT CORP.; *Int'l*, pg. 1169
BRIXEY & MEYER CAPITAL LLC—See Brixey & Meyer, Inc.; *U.S. Private*, pg. 658
BRIXMOR PROPERTY GROUP INC.—See Blackstone Inc.; *U.S. Public*, pg. 352
BRK, INC.; *U.S. Private*, pg. 658
BROAD CAPITAL ACQUISITION CORP.; *U.S. Public*, pg. 388
BROADSCALE ACQUISITION CORP.; *U.S. Public*, pg. 392
BROADSTONE ACQUISITION CORP.; *Int'l*, pg. 1172
BROAD STREET REALTY, INC.—See Broad Street Realty, LLC; *U.S. Private*, pg. 658
BROADTREE PARTNERS, LLC; *U.S. Private*, pg. 659
BROADVIEW HOLDING B.V.—See HAL Trust N.V.; *Int'l*, pg. 3223
BROADVIEW INDUSTRIES AG—See HAL Trust N.V.; *Int'l*, pg. 3223
BROCKHAUS PRIVATE EQUITY GMBH; *Int'l*, pg. 1172
BROCKWAY MORAN & PARTNERS, INC.; *U.S. Private*, pg. 661
BROMWELL FINANCIAL FUND, LIMITED PARTNERSHIP; *U.S. Private*, pg. 662
BROODSTOCK CAPITAL AS; *Int'l*, pg. 1174
THE BROOKDALE GROUP LLC; *U.S. Private*, pg. 4001
BROOKE PRIVATE EQUITY ASSOCIATES MANAGEMENT LLC; *U.S. Private*, pg. 663
BROOKFIELD BRIDGE LENDING FUND INC—See Brookfield Corporation; *Int'l*, pg. 1175
BROOKSIDE CAPITAL, LLC—See Bain Capital, LP; *U.S. Private*, pg. 437

BROOKSIDE EQUITY PARTNERS LLC—See Brookside International Incorporated; *U.S. Private*, pg. 665
BROOKSIDE INTERNATIONAL INCORPORATED; *U.S. Private*, pg. 665
BROOKS MACDONALD ASSET MANAGEMENT LIMITED—See Brooks Macdonald Group plc; *Int'l*, pg. 1194
BROOKS MACDONALD ASSET MANAGEMENT (TUNBRIDGE WELLS) LIMITED—See Brooks Macdonald Group plc; *Int'l*, pg. 1194
BROWN BROTHERS HARRIMAN TRUST COMPANY, N.A.—See Brown Brothers Harriman & Co.; *U.S. Private*, pg. 667
BROWN BROTHERS HARRIMAN TRUST COMPANY, OF DELAWARE, N. A.—See Brown Brothers Harriman & Co.; *U.S. Private*, pg. 667
BRUCKMANN, ROSSER, SHERRILL & CO., LLC; *U.S. Private*, pg. 671
BRUIN CAPITAL HOLDINGS, LLC; *U.S. Private*, pg. 671
BRUINS SPORTS CAPITAL, LLC; *U.S. Private*, pg. 671
BRUKER BIOSPIN INTERNATIONAL AG—See Bruker Corporation; *U.S. Public*, pg. 404
THE BRYDON GROUP LLC; *U.S. Private*, pg. 4001
THE BRYNAVON GROUP, INC.; *U.S. Private*, pg. 4001
BRYNWOOD PARTNERS MANAGEMENT LLC; *U.S. Private*, pg. 674
BRZ INVESTIMENTOS S.A.; *Int'l*, pg. 1201
B.S.D. CROWN LTD.; *Int'l*, pg. 790
BSEC S.A.—See Banque BEMO S.A.L.; *Int'l*, pg. 852
BSI GROUP LIMITED—See Capita plc; *Int'l*, pg. 1308
BSI (PANAMA) S.A.—See EFG International AG; *Int'l*, pg. 2320
BSP ACQUISITION CORP.; *U.S. Private*, pg. 675
BSP CAPITAL LIMITED—See BSP Financial Group Limited; *Int'l*, pg. 1202
BSP CONVERTIBLE NOTES LIMITED—See BSP Financial Group Limited; *Int'l*, pg. 1202
BSP LIFE (FIJI) LIMITED—See BSP Financial Group Limited; *Int'l*, pg. 1202
BSP LIFE (PNG) LIMITED—See BSP Financial Group Limited; *Int'l*, pg. 1202
BT ASSET MANAGEMENT SAI S.A.—See Banca Transilvania S.A.; *Int'l*, pg. 816
BTC HEALTH LIMITED; *Int'l*, pg. 1204
BT DIRECT IFN S.A.—See Banca Transilvania S.A.; *Int'l*, pg. 816
BTG GLOBAL ADVISORY LIMITED—See Begbies Traynor Group plc; *Int'l*, pg. 940
BTG INTELLIGENCE LIMITED—See Begbies Traynor Group plc; *Int'l*, pg. 940
BT GLOBENET NOMINEES LIMITED—See Deutsche Bank Aktiengesellschaft; *Int'l*, pg. 2055
BTHC X, INC.; *Int'l*, pg. 1204
BT MURITZ GMBH—See Deutsche Bank Aktiengesellschaft; *Int'l*, pg. 2055
BTRS HOLDINGS INC.—See EQT AB; *Int'l*, pg. 2472
BTU METALS CORP.; *Int'l*, pg. 1206
BUALI INVESTMENT COMPANY; *Int'l*, pg. 1206
BUALUANG VENTURES LTD.—See Bangkok Bank Public Company Limited; *Int'l*, pg. 833
BUCHANAN STREET PARTNERS, INC.; *U.S. Private*, pg. 676
BUCHER BETEILIGUNGEN GMBH—See Bucher Industries AG; *Int'l*, pg. 1207
BUCKINGHAM CAPITAL, LLC; *U.S. Private*, pg. 677
BUCKTHORN PARTNERS LLP; *Int'l*, pg. 1210
BUILD ACQUISITION CORP.; *U.S. Public*, pg. 409
BUILDERS CAPITAL MORTGAGE CORP.; *Int'l*, pg. 1212
BUILDEX VENTURE CAPITAL CORPORATION; *Int'l*, pg. 1212
BUILDING INDUSTRY PARTNERS LLC; *U.S. Private*, pg. 682
BUILD INVESTMENTS GROUP JSC; *Int'l*, pg. 1212
BUKIT SEMBAWANG RUBBER COMPANY LIMITED—See Bukit Sembawang Estates Ltd; *Int'l*, pg. 1213
BULBROKERS AD—See Alfa Finance Holding AD; *Int'l*, pg. 307
BULLMAN MINERALS INC.; *Int'l*, pg. 1214
BULLPEN PARLAY ACQUISITION COMPANY; *U.S. Public*, pg. 410
BULL TRADING AND INVESTMENTS LTD.; *Int'l*, pg. 1214
BULL WEALTH MANAGEMENT GROUP INC.—See EFG International AG; *Int'l*, pg. 2319
BULVARIA VARNA EOOD—See Eurohold Bulgaria AD; *Int'l*, pg. 2553
BUMRUNGRAD MONGOLIA LLC—See Bumrungrad Hospital Public Company Limited; *Int'l*, pg. 1215
BUNKER HILL CAPITAL LP; *U.S. Private*, pg. 685
BUNZL HOLDING GMBH—See Bunzl plc; *Int'l*, pg. 1217
BURFORD CAPITAL LIMITED; *Int'l*, pg. 1223
BURFORD CAPITAL LLC; *U.S. Private*, pg. 686
BURGEL BETEILIGUNGS GMBH—See Allianz SE; *Int'l*, pg. 351
BURGEL ERFURT BETEILIGUNGSGESELLSCHAFT MBH—See Allianz SE; *Int'l*, pg. 351
BURGERFI INTERNATIONAL, INC.; *U.S. Public*, pg. 412
BURGESS STEEL PRODUCTS CORP; *U.S. Private*, pg. 687

BURGUNDY TECHNOLOGY ACQUISITION CORPORATION; *Int'l*, pg. 1224
BURLINGTON CAPITAL PARTNERS, LLC; *U.S. Private*, pg. 689
BURRUS INVESTMENT GROUP INC.; *U.S. Private*, pg. 692
BURSA MALAYSIA DERIVATIVES BERHAD—See Bursa Malaysia Berhad; *Int'l*, pg. 1227
BURSA MALAYSIA INFORMATION SDN BHD—See Bursa Malaysia Berhad; *Int'l*, pg. 1227
BURSA MALAYSIA IT SDN BHD—See Bursa Malaysia Berhad; *Int'l*, pg. 1227
BURSA MALAYSIA PROPERTY SDN BHD—See Bursa Malaysia Berhad; *Int'l*, pg. 1227
BURTECH ACQUISITION CORP.; *U.S. Public*, pg. 412
BUSCAR CO.; *U.S. Public*, pg. 413
THE BUSINESS BACKER, LLC—See Enova International, Inc.; *U.S. Public*, pg. 770
BUSINESS GROWTH FUND PLC - MIDLANDS—See BGF Group PLC; *Int'l*, pg. 1007
BUSINESS GROWTH FUND PLC - NORTH, NORTHEAST & IRELAND—See BGF Group PLC; *Int'l*, pg. 1007
BUSINESS GROWTH FUND PLC - SCOTLAND—See BGF Group PLC; *Int'l*, pg. 1007
BUTCHER VENTURE CAPITAL COMPANY; *U.S. Private*, pg. 696
BUTLER CAPITAL PARTNERS SA; *Int'l*, pg. 1229
BUTN LIMITED; *Int'l*, pg. 1229
BUTTERFLY EQUITY LP; *U.S. Private*, pg. 698
BUZZFEED, INC.; *U.S. Public*, pg. 413
BUZZ TECHNOLOGIES, INC.; *Int'l*, pg. 1230
BV HOLDING AG; *Int'l*, pg. 1231
BV INVESTMENT PARTNERS, LLC; *U.S. Private*, pg. 699
BWA GROUP PLC; *Int'l*, pg. 1232
BWB PARTNERS P/S; *Int'l*, pg. 1232
BWK GMBH UNTERNEHMENS BETEILIGUNGSGESELLSCHAFT; *Int'l*, pg. 1232
BWT MALTA HOLDINGS LTD.—See BWT Aktiengesellschaft; *Int'l*, pg. 1232
BXR GROUP B.V.; *Int'l*, pg. 1233
BYNORDIC ACQUISITION CORPORATION; *Int'l*, pg. 1235
C3 CAPITAL PARTNERS, LP; *U.S. Private*, pg. 710
C5 ACQUISITION CORPORATION; *U.S. Public*, pg. 416
CABINDA PARTICIPACOES S.A.; *Int'l*, pg. 1245
CABLE CAR CAPITAL LLC; *U.S. Private*, pg. 711
CABOT FINANCIAL (MARLIN) LIMITED—See Encore Capital Group, Inc.; *U.S. Public*, pg. 759
CABOT PROPERTIES, INC.; *U.S. Private*, pg. 711
CABOT SQUARE CAPITAL LLP; *Int'l*, pg. 1246
CACHE CREEK INDUSTRIES, LLC; *U.S. Private*, pg. 711
CADENCE CAPITAL MANAGEMENT LLC—See Pacific Mutual Holding Company; *U.S. Private*, pg. 3069
CADENCE MINERALS PLC; *Int'l*, pg. 1247
CADENT ENERGY PARTNERS, LLC; *U.S. Private*, pg. 713
CADILLAC VENTURES HOLDINGS INC.—See Cadillac Ventures Inc.; *Int'l*, pg. 1248
CA GLOBAL PROPERTY INTERNATIONALE IMMOBILIEN AG—See Assicurazioni Generali S.p.A.; *Int'l*, pg. 645
CA HEALTHCARE ACQUISITION CORP; *U.S. Public*, pg. 416
CAHYA MATA SARAWAK BERHAD; *Int'l*, pg. 1251
CAHYA SURIA ENERGY SDN. BHD.—See Annica Holdings Limited; *Int'l*, pg. 474
CAI CAPITAL MANAGEMENT INC.—See CAI Private Equity; *Int'l*, pg. 1252
CAI CAPITAL MANAGEMENT INC.—See CAI Private Equity; *Int'l*, pg. 1252
CAIN ACQUISITION CORPORATION; *U.S. Private*, pg. 714
CAIN INTERNATIONAL LIMITED; *Int'l*, pg. 1252
CAI PRIVATE EQUITY; *Int'l*, pg. 1252
CAIRO DEVELOPMENT & INVESTMENT, (S.A.E.); *Int'l*, pg. 1253
CAIRO RESOURCES INC.; *Int'l*, pg. 1253
CAIXABANK, S.A.—See Lone Star Funds; *U.S. Private*, pg. 2484
CALAMOS CONVERTIBLE OPPRTNTY & INCOME; *U.S. Public*, pg. 421
CALAMOS DYNAMIC CONVERTIBLE AND INCOME FUND; *U.S. Public*, pg. 421
CALAMOS FINANCIAL SERVICES LLC—See Calamos Asset Management, Inc.; *U.S. Private*, pg. 716
CALASTONE LIMITED; *Int'l*, pg. 1261
CALEDONIA GROUP SERVICES LTD—See Caledonia Investments plc; *Int'l*, pg. 1262
CALEDONIAN PROPERTY INVESTMENTS LIMITED—See Derwent London plc; *Int'l*, pg. 2043
CALEDONIA (PRIVATE) INVESTMENTS PTY. LTD.; *Int'l*, pg. 1262
CALEDONIA TREASURY LTD—See Caledonia Investments plc; *Int'l*, pg. 1262
CALERA CAPITAL MANAGEMENT, INC.; *U.S. Private*, pg. 717
CALIBERCOS, INC.; *U.S. Public*, pg. 423
CALIFORNIA FINANCIAL PARTNERS, INC.; *U.S. Private*, pg. 719
CALKAIN COMPANIES INC.; *U.S. Private*, pg. 721
CALLAWAY CAPITAL MANAGEMENT, LLC; *U.S. Private*, pg. 722

CALLAWAY TEMECULA LIMITED PARTNERSHIP; *U.S. Private*, pg. 722
CALLISTA PRIVATE EQUITY GMBH & CO. KG; *Int'l*, pg. 1265
CALLODINE ACQUISITION CORPORATION; *U.S. Public*, pg. 424
CALLODINE GROUP, LLC—See Callodine Acquisition Corporation; *U.S. Public*, pg. 424
CALTIUS CAPITAL MANAGEMENT, L.P.; *U.S. Private*, pg. 723
CALTIUS MEZZANINE PARTNERS—See Caltius Capital Management, L.P.; *U.S. Private*, pg. 723
CALTIUS PRIVATE EQUITY PARTNERS I, L.P.—See Caltius Capital Management, L.P.; *U.S. Private*, pg. 723
CALVERT STREET CAPITAL PARTNERS; *U.S. Private*, pg. 724
CALVETON UK LTD; *Int'l*, pg. 1266
CAM ALTERNATIVES GMBH; *Int'l*, pg. 1266
CAMARICO INVESTMENT GROUP LTD.; *Int'l*, pg. 1268
CAMBIUM GLOBAL TIMBERLAND LIMITED; *Int'l*, pg. 1269
CAMBRIDGE CAPITAL ACQUISITION CORPORATION; *U.S. Private*, pg. 726
CAMBUHY INVESTIMENTOS LTDA.; *Int'l*, pg. 1270
CAMDEN PARTNERS HOLDINGS, LLC; *U.S. Private*, pg. 728
CAMERIT AG; *Int'l*, pg. 1271
CAMERON HOLDINGS CORPORATION; *U.S. Private*, pg. 728
CAMERON HOLDINGS CORPORATION - ST. LOUIS OFFICE—See Cameron Holdings Corporation; *U.S. Private*, pg. 728
CAMPBELL ALTERNATIVE ASSET TRUST—See Reverence Capital Partners LLC; *U.S. Private*, pg. 3415
CAMPBELL & COMPANY, INC.—See Reverence Capital Partners LLC; *U.S. Private*, pg. 3415
CANAAN PARTNERS; *U.S. Private*, pg. 732
CANACCORD GENUITY GROUP INC.; *Int'l*, pg. 1277
CANADA COMPUTATIONAL UNLIMITED CORP.; *Int'l*, pg. 1277
CANADIAN RESOURCES INCOME TRUST; *Int'l*, pg. 1285
CANAF-CLAL FINANCE MANAGEMENT LTD.—See IDB Development Corporation Ltd.; *Int'l*, pg. 3588
CANAL PARTNERS, LLC; *U.S. Private*, pg. 733
CAN CAPITAL, INC.—See CAN Capital, Inc.; *U.S. Private*, pg. 732
CANCER CAPITAL CORP.; *U.S. Public*, pg. 428
CANDELARIA MINING CORP.; *Int'l*, pg. 1289
CANDESCENT PARTNERS, LLC; *U.S. Private*, pg. 733
CANDOVER SERVICES LIMITED—See Candover Investments plc; *Int'l*, pg. 1289
CANEM HOLDINGS LTD.—See Bird Construction Inc.; *Int'l*, pg. 1047
CANNA-GLOBAL ACQUISITION CORP.; *U.S. Public*, pg. 428
CANNAMATRIX, INC.; *U.S. Private*, pg. 734
CANNAWORLD VENTURES INC.; *Int'l*, pg. 1292
CANO HEALTH, INC.; *U.S. Public*, pg. 430
CANOPY FINANCE LIMITED; *Int'l*, pg. 1298
CANTECH HOLDING, INC.; *U.S. Private*, pg. 735
CANYON BRIDGE CAPITAL PARTNERS, INC.; *Int'l*, pg. 1300
CANYON CAPITAL ADVISORS LLC; *U.S. Private*, pg. 736
CAP10 PARTNERS LLP; *Int'l*, pg. 1301
CAPCELLENCE MITTELSTANDSPARTNER GMBH; *Int'l*, pg. 1302
CAPE ACQUISITION CORP.—See Deutsche Bank Aktiengesellschaft; *Int'l*, pg. 2055
CAPE-NATIXIS S.G.R. S.P.A.—See Cimino & Associati Private Equity S.p.A.; *Int'l*, pg. 1609
CAPE-NATIXIS S.G.R. S.P.A.—See Groupe BPCE; *Int'l*, pg. 3095
CAPGEMINI BUSINESS SERVICES CHILE LTDA.—See Capgemini SE; *Int'l*, pg. 1304
CAPGEMINI FINANCIAL SERVICES AUSTRALIA PTY LTD.—See Capgemini SE; *Int'l*, pg. 1304
CAPGEMINI FINANCIAL SERVICES USA INC.—See Capgemini SE; *Int'l*, pg. 1305
CAPGEN FINANCIAL GROUP LP; *U.S. Private*, pg. 738
CAPITA INTERNATIONAL DEVELOPMENT—See Capita plc; *Int'l*, pg. 1308
CAPITAL ALIGNMENT PARTNERS, INC.; *U.S. Private*, pg. 738
CAPITALAND INDIA TRUST; *Int'l*, pg. 1313
CAPITAL CITY BANC INVESTMENTS, INC.—See Capital City Bank Group, Inc.; *U.S. Public*, pg. 431
CAPITAL DGMC INC.; *Int'l*, pg. 1310
CAPITAL DYNAMICS AG—See Capital Dynamics Ltd.; *Int'l*, pg. 1310
CAPITAL FOR BUSINESS, INC.—See Commerce Bancshares, Inc.; *U.S. Public*, pg. 544
CAPITAL FOR COLLEAGUES PLC; *Int'l*, pg. 1311
CAPITAL FUNDING GMBH & CO. KG—See Advent International Corporation; *U.S. Private*, pg. 96
CAPITAL FUNDING GMBH & CO. KG—See Centerbridge Partners, L.P.; *U.S. Private*, pg. 812
CAPITALG MANAGEMENT COMPANY LLC—See Alphabet Inc.; *U.S. Public*, pg. 82

N.A.I.C.S. INDEX

523999 — MISCELLANEOUS FINAN...

CAPITAL GROUP HOLDINGS, INC.; *U.S. Public,* pg. 431
CAPITALGROUP LIMITED; *Int'l,* pg. 1314
CAPITAL INSIGHT PARTNERS, LLC; *U.S. Private,* pg. 740
CAPITAL INTERNATIONAL PRIVATE EQUITY FUNDS—See The Capital Group Companies, Inc.; *U.S. Private,* pg. 4004
CAPITAL INVESTMENT & BROKERAGE COMPANY LIMITED—See Capital Bank; *Int'l,* pg. 1310
CAPITAL INVESTMENT COMPANY—See Capital Bank; *Int'l,* pg. 1310
CAPITAL INVESTMENT MANAGEMENT CORP.—See Capital Securities Corporation; *Int'l,* pg. 1312
CAPITAL ONE AUTO RECEIVABLES LLC; *U.S. Private,* pg. 741
CAPITALPART PARTICIPACOES S.A.; *Int'l,* pg. 1314
CAPITAL PEOPLE S.A.; *Int'l,* pg. 1312
CAPITAL POINT LTD.; *Int'l,* pg. 1312
CAPITAL PROPERTIES, LLC—See Sage Partners, LLC; *U.S. Private,* pg. 3526
CAPITAL & REGIONAL PLC; *Int'l,* pg. 1309
CAPITAL RESOURCE PARTNERS, L.P.; *U.S. Private,* pg. 741
CAPITAL RESOURCES, INC.—See Alex Lee, Inc.; *U.S. Private,* pg. 163
CAPITAL SENIOR LIVING CORPORATION—See Sonida Senior Living, Inc.; *U.S. Public,* pg. 1903
CAPITAL SOUTHWEST CORPORATION; *U.S. Public,* pg. 432
CAPITAL SOUTHWEST VENTURE CORPORATION—See Capital Southwest Corporation; *U.S. Public,* pg. 432
CAPITALSPRING LLC; *U.S. Private,* pg. 742
CAPITAL SQUARE PARTNERS PTE LTD.; *Int'l,* pg. 1312
CAPITAL TRADE LINKS LIMITED; *Int'l,* pg. 1312
CAPITAL TRUST LIMITED; *Int'l,* pg. 1313
CAPITALVIEW INVESTMENT PARTNERS, LLC; *U.S. Private,* pg. 742
CAPITALWORKS EMERGING MARKETS ACQUISITION CORPORATION; *U.S. Public,* pg. 432
CAPITALWORKS INVESTMENT PARTNERS (PTY) LTD; *Int'l,* pg. 1314
CAPITALWORKS, LLC; *U.S. Private,* pg. 742
CAPITAL Z PARTNERS MANAGEMENT, LLC—See Paine Schwartz Partners, LLC; *U.S. Private,* pg. 3075
CAPITA TRUST COMPANY LIMITED—See Capita plc; *Int'l,* pg. 1308
CAPITOLE FINANCE SAS—See Groupe BPCE; *Int'l,* pg. 3093
CAPITOL PARTNERS LLC; *U.S. Private,* pg. 744
CAPITON AG; *Int'l,* pg. 1314
CAPMAN CAPITAL MANAGEMENT OY—See CapMan PLC; *Int'l,* pg. 1315
CAPMAN FINANCIALS LIMITED; *Int'l,* pg. 1315
CAPMAN FUND INVESTMENT SICAV-SIF—See CapMan PLC; *Int'l,* pg. 1315
CAPMAN GROWTH EQUITY OY—See CapMan PLC; *Int'l,* pg. 1315
CAPMAN PRIVATE EQUITY ADVISORS LIMITED—See CapMan PLC; *Int'l,* pg. 1315
CAPSTONE FINANCIAL GROUP, INC.; *U.S. Private,* pg. 746
CAPSTONE HEADWATERS LLC—See Huntington Bancshares Incorporated; *U.S. Public,* pg. 1071
THE CAPSTREET GROUP LLC; *U.S. Private,* pg. 4004
CAPTAIN CASH HOLDING COMPANY LIMITED—See Chow Steel Industries Public Company Limited; *Int'l,* pg. 1584
CAPTOR CAPITAL CORP.; *Int'l,* pg. 1317
CAPVEST LIMITED; *Int'l,* pg. 1318
CAPVEST PARTNERS LLP—See CapVest Limited; *Int'l,* pg. 1318
CARAT NORDIC AB—See Dentsu Group Inc.; *Int'l,* pg. 2035
CARCADE OOO—See Gazprombank JSC; *Int'l,* pg. 2892
CARDANO RISK MANAGEMENT LTD—See Marsh & McLennan Companies, Inc.; *U.S. Public,* pg. 1384
CARDIAC IMAGING SOLUTIONS, LLC; *U.S. Private,* pg. 749
CARDINAL EQUITY PARTNERS, LLC; *U.S. Private,* pg. 750
CARDINAL HEALTH CAPITAL CORPORATION—See Cardinal Health, Inc.; *U.S. Public,* pg. 433
CARDINAL POINT MANAGEMENT, LLC; *U.S. Private,* pg. 750
CAREMAX, INC.; *U.S. Public,* pg. 435
CARE RATINGS (AFRICA) PRIVATE LIMITED—See CARE Ratings Limited; *Int'l,* pg. 1323
CARE RISK SOLUTIONS PRIVATE LIMITED—See CARE Ratings Limited; *Int'l,* pg. 1323
CARETRUST REIT, INC.; *U.S. Public,* pg. 435
CAREY WATERMARK INVESTORS INCORPORATED—See W.P. Carey Inc.; *U.S. Public,* pg. 2316
CARGOTEC HOLDING NETHERLANDS B.V.—See Cargotec Corporation; *Int'l,* pg. 1327
CARGOTEC HOLDING SWEDEN AB—See Cargotec Corporation; *Int'l,* pg. 1327
CAR HOUSE HOLDING CO., LTD.; *Int'l,* pg. 1319
CARIBBEAN DIVERSIFIED INVESTMENTS INC.; *Int'l,* pg. 1330

CARILLION (ASPIRE CONSTRUCTION) HOLDINGS NO 2 LTD—See Carillion plc; *Int'l,* pg. 1330
CARILLION PRIVATE FINANCE LTD—See Carillion plc; *Int'l,* pg. 1330
CARLING CAPITAL PARTNERS PTY LTD.; *Int'l,* pg. 1338
CARLIN O'BRIEN INC.; *U.S. Private,* pg. 763
CAR LOAN PAL HOLDINGS LLC—See Digital Media Solutions, Inc.; *U.S. Public,* pg. 663
CARLSBERG INVEST A/S—See Carlsberg A/S; *Int'l,* pg. 1340
CARLTON RESOURCES PLC; *Int'l,* pg. 1341
CARLYLE CREDIT SOLUTIONS, INC.; *U.S. Private,* pg. 765
CARLYLE JAPAN ASSET MANAGEMENT YK—See The Carlyle Group Inc.; *U.S. Public,* pg. 2054
CARNEGIE CLEAN ENERGY LIMITED; *Int'l,* pg. 1342
CARNIVAL GROUP INTERNATIONAL HOLDINGS LIMITED; *Int'l,* pg. 1342
CARO HOLDINGS, INC.; *Int'l,* pg. 1342
CARPATCEMENT HOLDING S.A.—See Heidelberg Materials AG; *Int'l,* pg. 3309
CARPATERRA CAPITAL PARTNERS SRO; *Int'l,* pg. 1343
CARREFOUR FINANCE SA—See Carrefour SA; *Int'l,* pg. 1344
CARROLL CAPITAL LLC; *U.S. Private,* pg. 773
CARSON PRIVATE CAPITAL INCORPORATED; *U.S. Private,* pg. 774
CARSONS MANAGEMENT SERVICES (PRIVATE) LIMITED—See Carson Cumberbatch PLC; *Int'l,* pg. 1347
CARTESIAN CAPITAL GROUP, LLC; *U.S. Private,* pg. 776
CARTICA ACQUISITION CORP.; *U.S. Public,* pg. 445
CARY STREET PARTNERS INVESTMENT ADVISORY LLC—See Luxon Financial LLC; *U.S. Private,* pg. 2518
CASA MINERALS INC.; *Int'l,* pg. 1349
CASCADE ACQUISITION CORP.; *U.S. Public,* pg. 445
CASCADE INVESTMENT LLC; *U.S. Private,* pg. 779
CASCADIA ACQUISITION CORP.; *U.S. Public,* pg. 445
CASE GROUP AB; *Int'l,* pg. 1351
CASE UNITED KINGDOM LIMITED—See CNH Industrial N.V.; *Int'l,* pg. 1674
CASH FLOW SPOLKA AKCYJNA; *Int'l,* pg. 1352
CASINO PROPERTIES, INC.—See Archon Corporation; *U.S. Public,* pg. 185
CASSIUS VENTURES LTD.; *Int'l,* pg. 1355
CASTANEA PARTNERS, INC.; *U.S. Private,* pg. 784
CASTELNAU GROUP LIMITED; *Int'l,* pg. 1356
CASTIK CAPITAL S.A.R.L.; *Int'l,* pg. 1356
CASTLE HARLAN, INC.; *U.S. Private,* pg. 784
CASTLE ISLAND PARTNERS LLC; *U.S. Private,* pg. 785
CASTLE PRIVATE EQUITY AG; *Int'l,* pg. 1357
CAT9 GROUP INC.; *Int'l,* pg. 1358
CATACAP MANAGEMENT AS; *Int'l,* pg. 1358
CATALYST INVESTMENT MANAGERS PTY. LIMITED; *Int'l,* pg. 1358
CATALYST INVESTMENTS, L.P.—See Cukierman & Co. Investment House Ltd.; *Int'l,* pg. 1876
CATALYST INVESTORS, LLC; *U.S. Private,* pg. 786
CATALYST PARTNERS ACQUISITION CORP.; *U.S. Private,* pg. 786
CATAPULT ACQUISITIONS CORP.; *U.S. Public,* pg. 787
CATAPULT ENERGY SERVICES GROUP, LLC; *U.S. Private,* pg. 787
CATCHA INVESTMENT CORP.; *Int'l,* pg. 1359
CATCHMARK TIMBER TRUST, INC.—See PotlatchDeltic Corporation; *U.S. Public,* pg. 1704
CAT DESENVOLUPAMENT DE CONCESSIONS CATALANES, S.L—See ACS, Actividades de Construccion y Servicios, S.A.; *U.S. Public,* pg. 110
CATERPILLAR FINANCIAL SERVICES NETHERLANDS B.V.—See Caterpillar, Inc.; *U.S. Public,* pg. 450
CATERPILLAR FINANCIAL SERVICES PHILIPPINES INC.—See Caterpillar, Inc.; *U.S. Public,* pg. 450
CATERPILLAR FINANCIAL SERVICES (U.K.) LIMITED—See Caterpillar, Inc.; *U.S. Public,* pg. 450
CATFISH QUEEN PARTNERSHIP IN COMMENDAM—See Caesars Entertainment, Inc.; *U.S. Public,* pg. 420
CATHAY INVESTMENTS LIMITED; *Int'l,* pg. 1360
CATHEDRA BITCOIN INC.; *Int'l,* pg. 1360
CATTERTON MANAGEMENT COMPANY, LLC; *U.S. Private,* pg. 792
CATTLES INVOICE FINANCE (OXFORD) LIMITED—See Cattles Limited; *Int'l,* pg. 1361
CAVE SHEPHERD CARD (BARBADOS) INC.—See Cave Shepherd & Co., Ltd.; *Int'l,* pg. 1362
CAVOTEC US HOLDINGS INC—See Cavotec SA; *Int'l,* pg. 1363
CAVU TECHNOLOGY ACQUISITION CORP.; *U.S. Public,* pg. 455
CBAL S.A.—See Erste Abwicklungsanstalt AoR; *Int'l,* pg. 2497
CBD FINANCIAL SERVICES LLC—See Commercial Bank of Dubai PSC; *Int'l,* pg. 1715
CBG COMMERZ BETEILIGUNGSKAPITAL GMBH & CO. KG—See Commerzbank AG; *Int'l,* pg. 1715
CBIZ VALUATION GROUP, LLC—See CBIZ, Inc.; *U.S. Public,* pg. 457
CBOE CLEAR EUROPE N.V.—See Cboe Global Markets, Inc.; *U.S. Public,* pg. 459

CBPE CAPITAL LLP; *Int'l,* pg. 1366
CBRE ACQUISITION HOLDINGS, INC.; *U.S. Public,* pg. 459
CBR MANAGEMENT GMBH; *Int'l,* pg. 1366
CBZ ASSET MANAGEMENT COMPANY (PRIVATE) LIMITED—See CBZ Holdings Limited; *Int'l,* pg. 1366
CBZ INSURANCE (PRIVATE) LIMITED—See CBZ Holdings Limited; *Int'l,* pg. 1366
CCB INTERNATIONAL (HOLDINGS) LIMITED—See China Construction Bank Corporation; *Int'l,* pg. 1491
CCB TRUST CO., LTD.—See China Construction Bank Corporation; *Int'l,* pg. 1491
CCC CAYMAN, LTD.—See KBR, Inc.; *U.S. Public,* pg. 1215
CCCC INVESTMENT CO., LTD.—See China Communications Construction Company Limited; *Int'l,* pg. 1490
CCC INTELLIGENT SOLUTIONS HOLDINGS INC.; *U.S. Public,* pg. 461
CC FINANCIAL, LLC—See Park Cities Asset Management LLC; *U.S. Private,* pg. 3095
CC LAND HOLDINGS LIMITED; *Int'l,* pg. 1366
CCM ACQUISITION CORP.; *U.S. Private,* pg. 799
CCMC VENTURES, INC.—See Connecticut Children's Medical Center Corporation, Inc.; *U.S. Private,* pg. 1015
CCMP CAPITAL ADVISORS, LLC - HOUSTON OFFICE—See CCMP Capital Advisors, LP; *U.S. Private,* pg. 800
CCMP CAPITAL ADVISORS, LP; *U.S. Private,* pg. 800
CCMP CAPITAL ADVISORS (UK), LLP—See CCMP Capital Advisors, LP; *U.S. Private,* pg. 800
CCMP GROWTH ADVISORS, LP—See CCMP Capital Advisors, LP; *U.S. Private,* pg. 800
CC NEUBERGER PRINCIPAL HOLDINGS II—See CC Capital Partners, LLC; *U.S. Private,* pg. 797
CCP FUND III MANAGEMENT LLC; *U.S. Private,* pg. 801
CCR SPECIALTY CHEMICALS LLC—See Palo Duro Capital, LLC; *U.S. Private,* pg. 3082
CD CAPITAL ASSET MANAGEMENT LTD; *Int'l,* pg. 1370
CDC GROUP PLC; *Int'l,* pg. 1370
CDH INVESTMENTS MANAGEMENT (HONG KONG) LIMITED—See CDH China Management Company Limited; *Int'l,* pg. 1370
CD INVESTISSEMENTS SARL—See Christian Dior S.A.; *Int'l,* pg. 1586
CE CAPITAL PARTNER GMBH; *Int'l,* pg. 1372
CEDAR CREEK PARTNERS LLC; *U.S. Private,* pg. 804
CEDARLAKE ACQUISITION CORP.; *Int'l,* pg. 1388
CEDAR SPRING CAPITAL LLC; *U.S. Private,* pg. 805
CEDULAS COLON DE CAPITALIZACION COLSEGUROS S.A.—See Allianz SE; *Int'l,* pg. 351
CEEJAY FINANCE LIMITED; *Int'l,* pg. 1388
CEE PROPERTIES REIT; *Int'l,* pg. 1388
CEEREF S.A.; *Int'l,* pg. 1389
CEFC GLOBAL STRATEGIC HOLDINGS, INC.; *Int'l,* pg. 1389
CEIBA INVESTMENTS LIMITED; *Int'l,* pg. 1391
CELEO CONCESIONES E INVERSIONES, S.L.U.—See Elecnor, S.A.; *Int'l,* pg. 2347
CELEO REDES BRASIL, S.A.—See Elecnor, S.A.; *Int'l,* pg. 2347
CELEO REDES CHILE LTDA.—See Elecnor, S.A.; *Int'l,* pg. 2347
CELESTIAL ASIA SECURITIES HOLDINGS LIMITED; *Int'l,* pg. 1392
CEMEX ASIAN SOUTHEAST CORPORATION—See CEMEX, S.A.B. de C.V.; *Int'l,* pg. 1398
CENPOS, LLC—See U.S. Bancorp; *U.S. Public,* pg. 2212
CENTENNIAL AS—See Groupe Centennial Holding SAH; *Int'l,* pg. 3101
CENTERBRIDGE PARTNERS, L.P.; *U.S. Private,* pg. 811
CENTERFIELD CAPITAL PARTNERS, LLC; *U.S. Private,* pg. 816
CENTEROAK PARTNERS LLC; *U.S. Private,* pg. 816
CENTER ROCK CAPITAL PARTNERS, LP; *U.S. Private,* pg. 811
CENTERVIEW CAPITAL, L.P.—See Centerview Partners LLC; *U.S. Private,* pg. 817
CENTERVIEW PARTNERS MANAGEMENT LLC—See Centerview Partners LLC; *U.S. Private,* pg. 817
CENTRAFIN PROPRIETARY LIMITED—See Alviva Holdings Limited; *Int'l,* pg. 402
CENTRAL ASIAN MINERALS & RESOURCES PLC; *Int'l,* pg. 1404
CENTRAL FINANCE LIMITED; *Int'l,* pg. 1406
CENTRAL-FUND KOCKAZATI TOKEALAP-KEZELO ZRT—See Central Group; *Int'l,* pg. 1407
CENTRAL GROUP; *Int'l,* pg. 1407
CENTRAL HUIJIN INVESTMENT LTD.—See China Investment Corporation; *Int'l,* pg. 1513
CENTRAL SECURITIES CORPORATION; *U.S. Public,* pg. 474
CENTRAL WEALTH SECURITIES INVESTMENT LIMITED—See Central Wealth Group Holdings Limited; *Int'l,* pg. 1410
CENTRAL WISCONSIN DEVELOPMENT CORPORATION—See MGE Energy, Inc.; *U.S. Public,* pg. 1434
CENTRAS SECURITIES JSC; *Int'l,* pg. 1411

523999 — MISCELLANEOUS FINAN...

CENTRE JAUDE CLERMONT SAS—See BNP Paribas SA; *Int'l*, pg. 1089
CENTRE LANE PARTNERS, LLC; *U.S. Private*, pg. 827
CENTRE PARTNERS MANAGEMENT LLC; *U.S. Private*, pg. 828
CENTRIPETAL CAPITAL PARTNERS, LLC; *U.S. Private*, pg. 830
CENTRUM FINANCIAL SERVICES LIMITED—See Centrum Capital Ltd.; *Int'l*, pg. 1415
CENTRUM MICROCREDIT LIMITED—See Centrum Capital Ltd.; *Int'l*, pg. 1415
CENTUM INVESTMENT COMPANY LIMITED; *Int'l*, pg. 1416
CENTURIA CAPITAL LIMITED; *Int'l*, pg. 1416
CENTURION FINANCE SA; *Int'l*, pg. 1417
CENTURY EQUITY PARTNERS LLC; *U.S. Private*, pg. 832
CENTURY GLOBAL COMMODITIES CORPORATION; *Int'l*, pg. 1418
CENTURY INVESTMENT GROUP P.L.C.; *Int'l*, pg. 1418
CENTURY PARK CAPITAL PARTNERS, LLC; *U.S. Private*, pg. 833
CERBERUS CAPITAL MANAGEMENT, L.P.; *U.S. Private*, pg. 835
CERBERUS GLOBAL INVESTMENT ADVISORS, LLC—See Cerberus Capital Management, L.P.; *U.S. Private*, pg. 837
CERBERUS TELECOM ACQUISITION CORP.—See Cerberus Capital Management, L.P.; *U.S. Private*, pg. 837
CERIUM TECHNOLOGY LLC; *U.S. Private*, pg. 841
CEROS FINANCIAL SERVICES, INC.—See Ceros Holding AG; *Int'l*, pg. 1422
CEROS VERMOGENSVERWALTUNG AG—See Ceros Holding AG; *Int'l*, pg. 1422
CERTEGY SNC—See Fidelity National Infor; *U.S. Public*, pg. 832
CETUS CAPITAL ACQUISITION CORP.; *Int'l*, pg. 1424
CEZ FINANCE B.V.—See CEZ, a.s.; *Int'l*, pg. 1426
CF FINANCE ACQUISITION CORP.—See GCM Grosvenor Inc.; *U.S. Public*, pg. 908
CG CAPITAL AND INVESTMENTS LIMITED—See Avantha Group; *Int'l*, pg. 735
CGF CAPITAL B.V.—See Heidelberg Materials AG; *Int'l*, pg. 3309
CGG CANADA GRUNDBESITZ GMBH—See Commerzbank AG; *Int'l*, pg. 1715
CGG HOLDING (U.S.) INC.—See CGG; *Int'l*, pg. 1431
CGN NUCLEAR TECHNOLOGY DEVELOPMENT CO., LTD.; *Int'l*, pg. 1435
CGROWTH CAPITAL INC.; *U.S. Public*, pg. 477
CGS-CIMB SECURITIES (UK) LIMITED—See CIMB Group Holdings Berhad; *Int'l*, pg. 1608
CGS MANAGEMENT AG; *Int'l*, pg. 1435
CH2 CONTORHAUS HANSESTADT HAMBURG AG—See Aves One AG; *Int'l*, pg. 739
CH2 LOGISTICA PORTFOLIOVERWALTUNG GMBH & CO. KG—See Aves One AG; *Int'l*, pg. 739
CHAGALA INTERNATIONAL HOLDING B.V.—See Chagala Group Limited; *Int'l*, pg. 1436
CHAILEASE CONSUMER FINANCE CO., LTD.—See Chailease Holding Company Limited; *Int'l*, pg. 1436
CHALLANGE EIGHTEEN SP. Z O.O.—See CPD S.A.; *Int'l*, pg. 1824
CHALLANI CAPITAL LIMITED; *Int'l*, pg. 1438
CHALLENGER GROUP HOLDINGS LIMITED—See Challenger Limited; *Int'l*, pg. 1438
CHALLENGER MANAGED INVESTMENTS LTD—See Challenger Limited; *Int'l*, pg. 1438
CHAMPLAIN CAPITAL MANAGEMENT LLC; *U.S. Private*, pg. 847
CHAMPLAIN FINANCIAL CORPORATION; *Int'l*, pg. 1440
CHAMP PRIVATE EQUITY PTE. LTD.—See CHAMP Private Equity Pty. Ltd.; *Int'l*, pg. 1439
CHAMP PRIVATE EQUITY PTY. LTD.; *Int'l*, pg. 1439
CHANGE CAPITAL PARTNERS LLP; *Int'l*, pg. 1443
CHANNEL PARTNERS LLC; *U.S. Private*, pg. 848
CHANT WEST HOLDINGS LIMITED; *Int'l*, pg. 1446
CHAPELCREST INVESTMENTS LIMITED—See Barclays PLC; *Int'l*, pg. 862
CHAPMANS LIMITED; *Int'l*, pg. 1448
CHARDAN METROPOL ACQUISITION CORP.; *Int'l*, pg. 1448
CHARDAN NEXTECH ACQUISITION CORP.; *U.S. Public*, pg. 478
CHARGEPOINT HOLDINGS, INC.; *U.S. Public*, pg. 479
CHARLEMAGNE CAPITAL LIMITED—See Fiera Capital Corporation; *Int'l*, pg. 2659
CHARLESBANK CAPITAL PARTNERS, LLC - NEW YORK OFFICE—See Charlesbank Capital Partners, LLC; *U.S. Private*, pg. 855
CHARLESBANK CAPITAL PARTNERS, LLC; *U.S. Private*, pg. 854
CHARLES RIVER VENTURES; *U.S. Private*, pg. 853
CHARLES TAYLOR INVESTMENT MANAGEMENT COMPANY LIMITED—See Lovell Minnick Partners LLC; *U.S. Private*, pg. 2502
CHARLOTTE CAPITAL CORP.; *U.S. Private*, pg. 857
CHAR TECHNOLOGIES LTD.; *Int'l*, pg. 1448

CHARTERED CAPITAL & INVESTMENT LTD.; *Int'l*, pg. 1454
CHARTERHOUSE CAPITAL PARTNERS LLP; *Int'l*, pg. 1454
CHARTERHOUSE GROUP, INC.; *U.S. Private*, pg. 859
CHARTER OAK EQUITY, L.P.; *U.S. Private*, pg. 858
CHARTER OAK INTERNATIONAL PARTNERS, LLC—See Charter Oak Equity, L.P.; *U.S. Private*, pg. 858
CHARTWELL INVESTMENTS; *U.S. Private*, pg. 859
CHARTWELL RETIREMENT RESIDENCES; *Int'l*, pg. 1456
CHASE ASIA PUBLIC COMPANY LIMITED; *Int'l*, pg. 1456
CHASE HOME FINANCE LLC—See JPMorgan Chase & Co.; *U.S. Public*, pg. 1206
THE CHATTERJEE GROUP; *U.S. Private*, pg. 4007
CHECK POINT HOLDING AB—See Check Point Software Technologies Ltd.; *Int'l*, pg. 1458
CHEER HOLDING, INC.; *Int'l*, pg. 1459
CHEETAH HOLDING CORPORATION; *U.S. Private*, pg. 869
CHEMTRADE PULP CHEMICALS TRUST—See Chemtrade Logistics Income Fund; *Int'l*, pg. 1464
CHENGHE ACQUISITION CO.; *Int'l*, pg. 1470
CHENGHE ACQUISITION I CO.; *U.S. Public*, pg. 484
CHERRY STREET CAPITAL; *U.S. Public*, pg. 485
CHESAPEAKE SERVICE COMPANY—See Chesapeake Utilities Corporation; *U.S. Public*, pg. 485
CHESSWOOD GP LIMITED—See Chesswood Group Limited; *Int'l*, pg. 1472
CHESSWOOD GROUP LIMITED; *Int'l*, pg. 1472
CHEVRILLON & ASSOCIES SCA; *Int'l*, pg. 1474
CHEWDEF GP GMBH—See Barclays PLC; *Int'l*, pg. 862
CHICAGO CITY CAPITOL GROUP; *U.S. Private*, pg. 877
CHICAGO GROWTH PARTNERS, LLC; *U.S. Private*, pg. 877
CHICAGO PACIFIC FOUNDERS; *U.S. Private*, pg. 878
CHIC HOLDINGS, INC.—See Hikari Tsushin, Inc.; *Int'l*, pg. 3389
CHILTERN CAPITAL LLP; *Int'l*, pg. 1479
CHINA AGRICULTURAL FINANCE CO., LTD.—See Agricultural Bank of China Limited; *Int'l*, pg. 217
CHINA-ASEAN CAPITAL ADVISORY COMPANY; *Int'l*, pg. 1567
CHINA ASSETS (HOLDINGS) LIMITED; *Int'l*, pg. 1483
CHINA BILLS FINANCE CORPORATION; *Int'l*, pg. 1486
CHINA BRIGHT STONE INVESTMENT MANAGEMENT GROUP; *Int'l*, pg. 1487
CHINA CINDA ASSET MANAGEMENT CO., LTD.; *Int'l*, pg. 1488
CHINA CITIC FINANCIAL ASSET MANAGEMENT CO., LTD.; *Int'l*, pg. 1489
CHINA CONSTRUCTION BANK (EUROPE) S.A.—See China Construction Bank Corporation; *Int'l*, pg. 1491
CHINA CONSTRUCTION BANK (LONDON) LIMITED—See China Construction Bank Corporation; *Int'l*, pg. 1491
CHINA CONSTRUCTION BANK (MALAYSIA) BERHAD—See China Construction Bank Corporation; *Int'l*, pg. 1491
CHINA CONSTRUCTION BANK (NEW ZEALAND) LIMITED—See China Construction Bank Corporation; *Int'l*, pg. 1491
CHINA CULTURE INDUSTRIAL INVESTMENT FUND MANAGEMENT CO., LTD.; *Int'l*, pg. 1496
CHINA DEMETER FINANCIAL INVESTMENTS LIMITED; *Int'l*, pg. 1497
CHINA DEVELOPMENT BANK INTERNATIONAL INVESTMENT LIMITED—See China Development Bank Corporation; *Int'l*, pg. 1497
CHINA ECAPITAL CORPORATION; *Int'l*, pg. 1498
CHINA EVER GRAND FINANCIAL LEASING GROUP CO., LTD.; *Int'l*, pg. 1500
CHINA EVERGREEN ACQUISITION CORPORATION; *Int'l*, pg. 1501
CHINA FINANCE ONLINE (BEIJING) CO., LTD.—See China Finance Online Co. Limited; *Int'l*, pg. 1502
CHINA FINANCE ONLINE CO. LIMITED; *Int'l*, pg. 1502
CHINA FIRST CAPITAL GROUP LIMITED; *Int'l*, pg. 1503
CHINA FORTUNE GROUP STRATEGIC INVESTMENT COMPANY LIMITED—See GoFintech Innovation Limited; *Int'l*, pg. 3021
CHINA GALAXY SECURITIES COMPANY LIMITED; *Int'l*, pg. 1503
CHINA GREAT WALL SECURITIES CO., LTD.; *Int'l*, pg. 1505
CHINA HUANENG FINANCE CO., LTD.—See China Huaneng Group Co., Ltd.; *Int'l*, pg. 1509
CHINA INDUSTRIAL SECURITIES FINANCIAL GROUP; *Int'l*, pg. 1509
CHINA INDUSTRIAL SECURITIES INTERNATIONAL BROKERAGE LIMITED—See China Industrial Securities Financial Group; *Int'l*, pg. 1509
CHINA INDUSTRIAL SECURITIES INTERNATIONAL FUTURES LIMITED—See China Industrial Securities Financial Group; *Int'l*, pg. 1509
CHINA INTERNATIONAL CAPITAL CORPORATION HONG KONG ASSET MANAGEMENT LIMITED—See China International Capital Corporation Limited; *Int'l*, pg. 1510
CHINA INTERNATIONAL CAPITAL CORPORATION LIMITED; *Int'l*, pg. 1510

CHINA JIANYIN INVESTMENT LIMITED—See China Investment Corporation; *Int'l*, pg. 1513
CHINA LIFE INSURANCE COMPANY LIMITED; *Int'l*, pg. 1515
CHINA MERCHANTS LAND LIMITED—See China Merchants Group Limited; *Int'l*, pg. 1521
CHINA MINMET INVESTMENT LIMITED—See China Rare Earth Resources And Technology Co., Ltd.; *Int'l*, pg. 1545
CHINA MINSHENG JIAYE INVESTMENT CO., LTD.—See China Minsheng Investment Group Corp., Ltd.; *Int'l*, pg. 1524
CHINA POST LIFE INSURANCE CO., LTD.—See China Post Group Corporation Limited; *Int'l*, pg. 1541
CHINA RAILWAY CONSTRUCTION INVESTMENT GROUP CO., LTD.—See China Railway Construction Corporation Limited; *Int'l*, pg. 1543
CHINA REINSURANCE (GROUP) CORPORATION; *Int'l*, pg. 1547
CHINA RESOURCES & CONSULTING, INC.; *U.S. Private*, pg. 886
CHINA RESOURCES DEVELOPMENT INC.; *Int'l*, pg. 1549
CHINA SMARTER ENERGY GROUP HOLDINGS LTD.; *Int'l*, pg. 1552
CHINA YIBAI UNITED GUARANTEE INTERNATIONAL HOLDING, INC.; *Int'l*, pg. 1564
CHIRISA CAPITAL MANAGEMENT LTD.; *Int'l*, pg. 1574
CHL MEDICAL PARTNERS; *U.S. Private*, pg. 887
CHP MERGER CORP.; *U.S. Public*, pg. 490
CHRONIC DISEASE FUND, INC.; *U.S. Private*, pg. 893
CHRYSALIS INVESTMENTS LIMITED; *Int'l*, pg. 1588
CHRYSALIS VENTURES; *U.S. Private*, pg. 893
CHRYSCAPITAL INVESTMENT ADVISORS (INDIA) PRIVATE LIMITED; *Int'l*, pg. 1588
CHRYSCAPITAL MANAGEMENT CO.; *Int'l*, pg. 1588
CHUBB FINANCIAL SOLUTIONS, INC.—See Chubb Limited; *Int'l*, pg. 1591
CHURCHILL CAPITAL CORP. VII; *U.S. Public*, pg. 493
CHURCHILL CAPITAL, LLC—See Churchill Equity, Inc.; *U.S. Private*, pg. 894
CHURCHILL EQUITY, INC.; *U.S. Private*, pg. 894
CHURCHILL FINANCIAL LLC—See The Carlyle Group Inc.; *U.S. Public*, pg. 2045
CIAN PLC; *Int'l*, pg. 1602
CIBC SECURITIES, INC.—See Canadian Imperial Bank of Commerce; *Int'l*, pg. 1283
CIBC TRUST CORPORATION—See Canadian Imperial Bank of Commerce; *Int'l*, pg. 1283
CIBC WOOD GUNDY FINANCIAL SERVICES INC.—See Canadian Imperial Bank of Commerce; *Int'l*, pg. 1284
CIBC WORLD MARKETS (JAPAN) INC.—See Canadian Imperial Bank of Commerce; *Int'l*, pg. 1284
CI CAPITAL PARTNERS LLC; *U.S. Private*, pg. 895
CICC EUROPE—See China International Capital Corporation Limited; *Int'l*, pg. 1510
CICLAD SA; *Int'l*, pg. 1602
CIC MANAGEMENT—See Chelsea Investments Corporation; *U.S. Private*, pg. 870
CIC PARTNERS, L.P.; *U.S. Private*, pg. 896
CID ADRIATIC INVESTMENTS GMBH; *Int'l*, pg. 1603
CID CAPITAL II, INC.; *U.S. Private*, pg. 896
CID GROUP; *Int'l*, pg. 1603
CIGALAH TRADING ESTABLISHMENT; *Int'l*, pg. 1607
CIIG MERGER CORP.; *U.S. Public*, pg. 494
CII INFRASTRUCTURE SERVICES CO., LTD.—See Ho Chi Minh City Infrastructure Investment Joint Stock Company; *Int'l*, pg. 3434
CI INVESTMENT SERVICES INC.—See CI Financial Corporation; *Int'l*, pg. 1600
CIMB-PRINCIPAL ASSET MANAGEMENT COMPANY LIMITED—See CIMB Group Holdings Berhad; *Int'l*, pg. 1608
CIMB PRINCIPAL ASSET MANAGEMENT COMPANY LIMITED—See CIMB Group Holdings Berhad; *Int'l*, pg. 1608
CIMB-PRINCIPAL ASSET MANAGEMENT COMPANY LIMITED—See Principal Financial Group, Inc.; *U.S. Public*, pg. 1720
CIMB WEALTH ADVISORS BERHAD—See CIMB Group Holdings Berhad; *Int'l*, pg. 1608
CIMB WEALTH ADVISORS BERHAD—See Principal Financial Group, Inc.; *U.S. Public*, pg. 1720
CIMC ENRIC HOLDINGS LIMITED—See China International Marine Containers (Group) Co., Ltd.; *Int'l*, pg. 1511
CIMC HOLDINGS AUSTRALIA PTY LTD—See China International Marine Containers (Group) Co., Ltd.; *Int'l*, pg. 1511
CIM FINANCIAL SERVICES LIMITED; *Int'l*, pg. 1607
CIMINO & ASSOCIATI PRIVATE EQUITY S.P.A.; *Int'l*, pg. 1609
CIMS S.A.; *Int'l*, pg. 1609
CINDRELLA FINANCIAL SERVICES LIMITED; *Int'l*, pg. 1610
CINVEN LIMITED; *Int'l*, pg. 1611
CIPHER MINING INC.; *U.S. Public*, pg. 496
CI PRIVATE COUNSEL LP—See CI Financial Corporation; *Int'l*, pg. 1601
CI PRIVATE WEALTH—See CI Financial Corporation; *Int'l*, pg. 1601

N.A.I.C.S. INDEX

523999 — MISCELLANEOUS FINAN...

CIRCLE INTERNET FINANCIAL, LLC; *U.S. Private*, pg. 900
CIS COMPANY SECRETARIES (PTY) LTD—See Computershare Limited; *Int'l*, pg. 1760
CITADEL CAPITAL S.A.E.; *Int'l*, pg. 1619
CITADEL ENTERPRISE AMERICAS LLC; *U.S. Private*, pg. 901
CITAGLOBAL CAPITAL SDN. BHD.—See Citaglobal Berhad; *Int'l*, pg. 1619
CITG CAPITAL PARTNERS, LLC; *U.S. Private*, pg. 901
THE CIT GROUP/EQUIPMENT FINANCING, INC.—See First Citizens BancShares, Inc.; *U.S. Public*, pg. 842
CITIC AUSTRALIA PTY. LTD.—See CITIC Group Corporation; *Int'l*, pg. 1620
CITIC CAPITAL HOLDINGS LIMITED—See CITIC Group Corporation; *Int'l*, pg. 1619
CITIC CAPITAL PARTNERS LLC—See CITIC Group Corporation; *Int'l*, pg. 1619
CITIC DEVELOPMENT CO., LTD.—See CITIC Group Corporation; *Int'l*, pg. 1620
CITIC GUOAN INFORMATION INDUSTRY CO., LTD.—See CITIC Group Corporation; *Int'l*, pg. 1620
CITICORP TRUST SOUTH DAKOTA; *U.S. Private*, pg. 901
CITIC PRIVATE EQUITY FUNDS MANAGEMENT CO., LTD.—See CITIC Group Corporation; *Int'l*, pg. 1621
CITIC SECURITIES BROKERAGE (HK) LIMITED—See CITIC Securities Co., Ltd.; *Int'l*, pg. 1622
CITIGROUP CAPITAL PARTNERS JAPAN—See Citigroup Inc.; *U.S. Public*, pg. 503
CITIGROUP CAPITAL UK LIMITED—See Citigroup Inc.; *U.S. Public*, pg. 504
CITIGROUP JAPAN HOLDINGS CORP.—See Citigroup Inc.; *U.S. Public*, pg. 503
CITIGROUP PRIVATE BANK—See Citigroup Inc.; *U.S. Public*, pg. 502
CITIPORT FINANCIAL SERVICES LIMITED; *Int'l*, pg. 1622
CITIUS ONCOLOGY, INC.—See Citius Pharmaceuticals, Inc.; *U.S. Public*, pg. 504
CITIUS PHARMACEUTICALS, INC.; *U.S. Public*, pg. 504
CITIUS RESOURCES PLC; *Int'l*, pg. 1623
CITIZEN FINANCIAL SERVICE CO., LTD.—See Citizen Watch Co., Ltd.; *Int'l*, pg. 1623
CITIZENS BANK INTERNATIONAL LIMITED; *Int'l*, pg. 1625
CITRINE GLOBAL CORP.; *Int'l*, pg. 1626
CIT STRATEGIC FINANCE, INC.—See First Citizens BancShares, Inc.; *U.S. Public*, pg. 841
CITY CAPITAL ADVISORS, LLC; *U.S. Private*, pg. 905
CITY CAPITAL VENTURES, LLC—See City Capital Advisors, LLC; *U.S. Private*, pg. 905
CITY DEVELOPMENTS LIMITED—See Hong Leong Investment Holdings Pte. Ltd.; *Int'l*, pg. 3468
CITY LEASING (DONSIDE) LIMITED—See Deutsche Bank Aktiengesellschaft; *Int'l*, pg. 2056
CITY LEASING LIMITED—See Deutsche Bank Aktiengesellschaft; *Int'l*, pg. 2056
CITY LEASING (WEARSIDE) LIMITED—See Deutsche Bank Aktiengesellschaft; *Int'l*, pg. 2056
CITY OFFICE REIT, INC.; *Int'l*, pg. 1627
CITY OF LONDON FINANCIAL SERVICES LIMITED—See City of London Group PLC; *Int'l*, pg. 1627
CITY OF LONDON GROUP PLC; *Int'l*, pg. 1627
CITY OF LONDON INVESTMENT GROUP PLC; *Int'l*, pg. 1627
CIVC PARTNERS LLC; *U.S. Private*, pg. 907
CIVIL MERCHANT BITTIYA SANSTHA LIMITED; *Int'l*, pg. 1630
CIWEN MEDIA CO., LTD.; *Int'l*, pg. 1630
CJK GROUP, INC.; *U.S. Private*, pg. 909
CJSC SBERBANK CIB; *Int'l*, pg. 1634
CLACKMANNANSHIRE SCHOOLS EDUCATION PARTNERSHIP (HOLDINGS) LTD.—See Bilfinger SE; *Int'l*, pg. 1028
CLAL BIOTECHNOLOGY INDUSTRIES LTD.—See Access Industries, Inc.; *U.S. Private*, pg. 51
CLARIANT FINANCE (LUXEMBOURG) S.A.—See Clariant AG; *Int'l*, pg. 1647
CLARIM ACQUISITION CORP.; *U.S. Public*, pg. 507
CLARION CAPITAL PARTNERS, LLC; *U.S. Private*, pg. 911
CLARITY PARTNERS, L.P.; *U.S. Private*, pg. 911
CLARITY SERVICES, INC.—See Experian plc; *Int'l*, pg. 2586
CLARIVEST ASSET MANAGEMENT, LLC—See Raymond James Financial, Inc.; *U.S. Public*, pg. 1764
CLARK ORIENT (BVI) LTD.; *Int'l*, pg. 1650
CLARUS THERAPEUTICS HOLDINGS, INC.; *U.S. Public*, pg. 508
CLARUS VENTURES LLC—See Blackstone Inc.; *U.S. Public*, pg. 352
CLARUS VENTURES LLC—See Blackstone Inc.; *U.S. Public*, pg. 352
CLASS ACCELERATION CORP.; *U.S. Public*, pg. 508
CLASSIC ELECTRICALS LIMITED; *Int'l*, pg. 1652
CLASSIC GLOBAL FINANCE & CAPITAL LTD.; *Int'l*, pg. 1652
CLAYTON, DUBILIER & RICE, LLC; *U.S. Private*, pg. 918
CLEAN ENERGY SPECIAL SITUATIONS CORP.; *U.S. Public*, pg. 508
CLEAN SEED CAPITAL GROUP LTD.; *Int'l*, pg. 1654
CLEANSPARK, INC.; *U.S. Public*, pg. 510

CLEARDEBT LIMITED—See ClearDebt Group Plc; *Int'l*, pg. 1657
CLEARHAVEN PARTNERS LP; *U.S. Private*, pg. 933
CLEARINGHOUSE COMMUNITY DEVELOPMENT FINANCIAL INSTITUTION; *U.S. Public*, pg. 933
CLEARLAKE CAPITAL GROUP, L.P.; *U.S. Private*, pg. 933
CLEARSIGHT ADVISORS INC.—See Regions Financial Corporation; *U.S. Public*, pg. 1776
CLEARSPRING CAPITAL PARTNERS; *Int'l*, pg. 1657
CLEARSTEAD ADVISORS, LLC—See Edwards Capital, LLC; *U.S. Private*, pg. 1341
CLEARSTONE VENTURE PARTNERS; *U.S. Private*, pg. 938
CLEARSTREAM BANKING JAPAN, LTD.—See Deutsche Borse AG; *Int'l*, pg. 2063
CLEARSTREAM GLOBAL SECURITIES SERVICES LIMITED—See Deutsche Borse AG; *Int'l*, pg. 2063
CLEARSTREAM HOLDING AG—See Deutsche Borse AG; *Int'l*, pg. 2063
CLEARVIEW CAPITAL, LLC; *U.S. Private*, pg. 938
CLEARVIEW WEALTH LIMITED; *Int'l*, pg. 1657
CLEARWATER CAPITAL PARTNERS LLC—See Fiera Capital Corporation; *Int'l*, pg. 2659
CLEARWATER TECHNOLOGIES LTD—See Clariant AG; *Int'l*, pg. 1648
CLEGHORN MINERALS LTD.; *Int'l*, pg. 1657
CLIC TECHNOLOGY, INC.; *U.S. Private*, pg. 942
CLIFFSIDE LTD.; *Int'l*, pg. 1659
CLIME CAPITAL LIMITED; *Int'l*, pg. 1659
CLIO INFOTECH LTD.; *Int'l*, pg. 1660
CLOSED LOOP PARTNERS LLC; *U.S. Private*, pg. 946
CLOSE FINANCE (CI) LIMITED—See Close Brothers Group plc; *Int'l*, pg. 1661
CLOUD EQUITY GROUP, LLC; *U.S. Private*, pg. 946
CLOUDWEB, INC.; *U.S. Public*, pg. 515
CLOVER CREEK PARTNERS, LLC; *U.S. Private*, pg. 947
CLOVER LEAF CAPITAL CORP.; *U.S. Public*, pg. 515
CLP BUSINESS MANAGEMENT (BEIJING) COMPANY LIMITED—See CLP Holdings Limited; *Int'l*, pg. 1663
CLSA CAPITAL PARTNERS (HK) LIMITED—See CITIC Securities Co., Ltd.; *Int'l*, pg. 1622
CLSA EUROPE B.V.—See CITIC Securities Co., Ltd.; *Int'l*, pg. 1622
CLSA PREMIUM LTD—See CITIC Securities Co., Ltd.; *Int'l*, pg. 1622
CLUBCOM HOLDING COMPANY, INC.—See ANTA Sports Products Limited; *Int'l*, pg. 480
CLUNE TECHNOLOGY GROUP; *Int'l*, pg. 1664
CLUNY CAPITAL CORP.; *Int'l*, pg. 1664
CLYDE BLOWERS LTD.—See Clyde Blowers Capital IM LLP; *Int'l*, pg. 1664
CM EQUITY PARTNERS, L.P.—See Carl Marks & Co., Inc.; *U.S. Private*, pg. 762
CMH CAPITAL, INC.—See Berkshire Hathaway Inc.; *U.S. Public*, pg. 303
CMK FINANCE CORPORATION—See CMK Corporation; *Int'l*, pg. 1671
CML GLOBAL CAPITAL LTD.; *Int'l*, pg. 1671
CMP CAPITAL MANAGEMENT-PARTNERS GMBH; *Int'l*, pg. 1671
CMP HOLDINGS B.V.—See McDermott International, Inc.; *U.S. Public*, pg. 1405
CMR GMBH; *Int'l*, pg. 1672
CMS INFO SYSTEMS LIMITED; *Int'l*, pg. 1672
CMV MEDIFORCE S.A.—See BNP Paribas SA; *Int'l*, pg. 1089
CMXL INC.; *U.S. Private*, pg. 952
CNC HOLDINGS LIMITED; *Int'l*, pg. 1673
CNH CAPITAL EUROPE S.A.S.—See BNP Paribas SA; *Int'l*, pg. 1089
CNH INDUSTRIAL CAPITAL AUSTRALIA PTY LIMITED—See CNH Industrial N.V.; *Int'l*, pg. 1674
CNH INDUSTRIAL CAPITAL (INDIA) PRIVATE LIMITED—See CNH Industrial N.V.; *Int'l*, pg. 1674
CNH INDUSTRIAL CAPITAL LIMITED—See CNH Industrial N.V.; *Int'l*, pg. 1674
CNL PRIVATE EQUITY CORP.—See CNL Financial Group, Inc.; *U.S. Private*, pg. 952
CNL STRATEGIC CAPITAL MANAGEMENT LLC; *U.S. Private*, pg. 952
CNPC CAPITAL COMPANY LIMITED—See China National Petroleum Corporation; *Int'l*, pg. 1533
COASTAL QSR, LLC—See Prometheus Partners, L.P.; *U.S. Private*, pg. 3283
COAST INVESTMENT & DEVELOPMENT COMPANY K.S.C.C.; *Int'l*, pg. 1681
COBALT INVESTMENTS LIMITED—See Barclays PLC; *Int'l*, pg. 862
COBE CAPITAL LLC; *U.S. Private*, pg. 957
COBEPA S.A.; *Int'l*, pg. 1682
COBRA CONCESIONES BRASIL, S.L.—See ACS, Actividades de Construccion y Servicios, S.A.; *Int'l*, pg. 110
COCA-COLA SOUTH ASIA HOLDINGS, INC.—See The Coca-Cola Company; *U.S. Public*, pg. 2065
COCOON HOLDINGS LIMITED; *Int'l*, pg. 1687
CODEX ACQUISITIONS PLC; *Int'l*, pg. 1688
COELI AB; *Int'l*, pg. 1689

COFACE CZECH INSURANCE S.R.O—See Groupe BPCE; *Int'l*, pg. 3093
COFACE NEDERLAND BV—See Groupe BPCE; *Int'l*, pg. 3093
COFACE PKZ D.D—See Groupe BPCE; *Int'l*, pg. 3093
COFACE POLAND FACTORING SP. Z O.O.—See Groupe BPCE; *Int'l*, pg. 3093
COFACE PORTUGAL, SA—See Groupe BPCE; *Int'l*, pg. 3093
COFACE ROMANIA CMS S.R.L—See Groupe BPCE; *Int'l*, pg. 3093
COFACE ROMANIA INSURANCE SRL—See Groupe BPCE; *Int'l*, pg. 3093
COFACE RUS INSURANCE COMPANY ZAO—See Groupe BPCE; *Int'l*, pg. 3093
COFACE (SINGAPORE) PTE LTD.—See Groupe BPCE; *Int'l*, pg. 3092
COFACE SLOVAKIA INSURANCE SA—See Groupe BPCE; *Int'l*, pg. 3093
COFACE SVERIGE AB—See Groupe BPCE; *Int'l*, pg. 3093
COFFEYVILLE FINANCE INC.—See Icahn Enterprises L.P.; *U.S. Public*, pg. 1084
COFFEYVILLE NITROGEN FERTILIZERS, INC.—See Icahn Enterprises L.P.; *U.S. Public*, pg. 1084
COFFEYVILLE RESOURCES CRUDE TRANSPORTATION, LLC—See Icahn Enterprises L.P.; *U.S. Public*, pg. 1084
COFFEYVILLE RESOURCES NITROGEN FERTILIZERS, LLC—See Icahn Enterprises L.P.; *U.S. Public*, pg. 1084
COFFEYVILLE RESOURCES REFINING & MARKETING, LLC—See Icahn Enterprises L.P.; *U.S. Public*, pg. 1084
COFFEYVILLE RESOURCES TERMINAL, LLC—See Icahn Enterprises L.P.; *U.S. Public*, pg. 1084
COFIX GROUP LTD.; *Int'l*, pg. 1692
COG FINANCIAL SERVICES LIMITED; *Int'l*, pg. 1694
COHEN & COMPANY INC.; *U.S. Public*, pg. 525
COHEN PRIVATE VENTURES, LLC; *U.S. Private*, pg. 963
COHEN & STEERS CLOSED-END OPP FD, INC.; *U.S. Public*, pg. 526
COHEN & STEERS SINGAPORE PRIVATE LIMITED—See Cohen & Steers, Inc.; *U.S. Public*, pg. 526
COHESIVE CAPITAL PARTNERS; *U.S. Private*, pg. 963
COHN ROBBINS HOLDINGS CORP.; *U.S. Public*, pg. 529
COINBASE ASSET MANAGEMENT, LLC—See Coinbase Global, Inc.; *U.S. Public*, pg. 530
COINBASE GLOBAL, INC.; *U.S. Public*, pg. 530
COINSHARES CAPITAL, LLC—See CoinShares International Limited; *Int'l*, pg. 1696
COINSHARES INTERNATIONAL LIMITED; *Int'l*, pg. 1696
COLD SPRING CAPITAL INC.; *U.S. Private*, pg. 965
COLICITY INC.; *U.S. Public*, pg. 533
COLINA FINANCIAL ADVISORS LTD.—See Colina Holdings Bahamas Limited; *Int'l*, pg. 1698
COLISEUM ACQUISITION CORP.; *U.S. Public*, pg. 533
COLISEUM CAPITAL MANAGEMENT LLC; *U.S. Private*, pg. 967
COLLER CAPITAL, INC—See Coller Capital Ltd.; *Int'l*, pg. 1699
COLLER CAPITAL LIMITED—See Coller Capital Ltd.; *Int'l*, pg. 1699
COLLER CAPITAL LTD.; *Int'l*, pg. 1699
COLONIAL COAL INTERNATIONAL CORPORATION; *Int'l*, pg. 1702
COLONIAL HOLDING COMPANY LIMITED—See Commonwealth Bank of Australia; *Int'l*, pg. 1719
COLOPLAST SHARED SERVICES SP. Z.O.O—See Coloplast A/S; *Int'l*, pg. 1704
COLORADO FINANCIAL MANAGEMENT, INC.; *U.S. Private*, pg. 974
COLTERRA CAPITAL CORPORATION; *Int'l*, pg. 1706
COLUMBIA CAPITAL, LLC; *U.S. Private*, pg. 976
COLUMBIA MANAGEMENT INVESTMENT ADVISORS, LLC; *U.S. Private*, pg. 977
COLUMBIA PROPERTIES TAHOE, LLC—See Caesars Entertainment, Inc.; *U.S. Public*, pg. 421
COLUMBIA THREADNEEDLE INVESTMENT SERVICES LIMITED—See Bank of Montreal; *Int'l*, pg. 847
COLUMBIA VENTURES CORPORATION; *U.S. Private*, pg. 978
COLUMBUS FACTORING SOLUTIONS S.A.—See Fast Finance S.A.; *Int'l*, pg. 2621
COLVILLE CAPITAL LLC; *U.S. Private*, pg. 979
COMERGENCE COMPLIANCE MONITORING, LLC—See Constellation Software Inc.; *Int'l*, pg. 1774
COMFORT FINCAP LIMITED; *Int'l*, pg. 1711
COMFORT SECURITIES LIMITED—See Comfort Commotrade Limited; *Int'l*, pg. 1711
COMMERCEBYUS, INC.; *U.S. Private*, pg. 982
COMMERZBANK FINANCE BV—See Commerzbank AG; *Int'l*, pg. 1717
COMMERZBANK HOLDINGS FRANCE SAS—See Commerzbank AG; *Int'l*, pg. 1717
COMMERZBANK REPRESENTATIVE OFFICE PANAMA, S.A.—See Commerzbank AG; *Int'l*, pg. 1717
COMMERZBANK U.S. FINANCE, INC.—See Commerzbank AG; *Int'l*, pg. 1717
COMMERZFACTORING GMBH—See Commerzbank AG; *Int'l*, pg. 1716
COMMERZ GRUNDBESITZ GESTAO DE CENTROS COM-

523999 — MISCELLANEOUS FINAN...

MERCIAIS, SOCIEDADE UNIPESSOAL, LDA.—See Commerzbank AG; *Int'l*, pg. 1716
COMMERZ REAL IT-LEASING GMBH—See Commerzbank AG; *Int'l*, pg. 1716
COMMITTED CAPITAL ACQUISITION CORPORATION II; *U.S. Private*, pg. 985
COMMONWEALTH BANK OF AUSTRALIA; *Int'l*, pg. 1719
COMMONWEALTH INCOME & GROWTH FUND 8, LP; *U.S. Private*, pg. 987
COMMUNICATIONS INVESTMENT PARTNERS LIMITED; *Int'l*, pg. 1721
COMMUNITY ENERGY AUSTRALIA PTY LTD—See Bendigo & Adelaide Bank Ltd.; *Int'l*, pg. 971
COMPAGNIE FINANCIERE MICHELIN SCMA—See Compagnie Generale des Etablissements Michelin SCA; *Int'l*, pg. 1742
COMPAGNIE POUR LE FINANCEMENT DES LOISIRS - COFI LOISIRS—See BNP Paribas SA; *Int'l*, pg. 1090
COMPANHIA DE SEGUROS ASOREANA, SA—See Banco Santander, S.A.; *Int'l*, pg. 825
COMPASS DIGITAL ACQUISITION CORP.; *U.S. Public*, pg. 559
COMPASS EQUITY PARTNERS, LLC; *U.S. Private*, pg. 999
COMPASS EXCHANGE ADVISORS LLC—See Independent Bank Corp.; *U.S. Public*, pg. 1116
COMPASS GROUP FRANCE HOLDINGS SAS—See Compass Group PLC; *Int'l*, pg. 1750
COMPASS GROUP, LLC; *U.S. Private*, pg. 999
COMPASS PARTNERS ASSET MANAGEMENT LLC—See Compass Advisers Group LLC; *U.S. Private*, pg. 998
COMPASS PARTNERS CAPITAL LLC—See Compass Advisers Group LLC; *U.S. Private*, pg. 998
COMPASS PARTNERS INTERNATIONAL LLP—See Compass Advisers Group LLC; *U.S. Private*, pg. 998
COMPATRIOT CAPITAL, INC.—See Sammons Enterprises, Inc.; *U.S. Private*, pg. 3537
COMPOSECURE, INC.; *U.S. Public*, pg. 561
COMPOSITE ALLIANCE GROUP INC.; *Int'l*, pg. 1754
COMPUTERSHARE COMMUNICATION SERVICES GMBH—See Computershare Limited; *Int'l*, pg. 1760
COMPUTERSHARE ITALY S.R.L.—See Computershare Limited; *Int'l*, pg. 1760
COMPUTERSHARE NETHERLANDS B.V.—See Computershare Limited; *Int'l*, pg. 1760
COMPUTERSHARE SOUTH AFRICA (PTY) LTD—See Computershare Limited; *Int'l*, pg. 1760
COMSTOCK PARTNERS LC; *U.S. Private*, pg. 1006
COMTEC SOLAR SYSTEMS GROUP LIMITED; *Int'l*, pg. 1762
COMVEST GROUP HOLDINGS LLC - NEW YORK OFFICE—See Comvest Group Holdings LLC; *U.S. Private*, pg. 1007
COMVEST GROUP HOLDINGS LLC; *U.S. Private*, pg. 1006
CONCENTRIC EQUITY PARTNERS—See Financial Investments Corporation; *U.S. Private*, pg. 1507
CONCIERGE BUILDING SERVICES, LLC; *U.S. Private*, pg. 1009
CONCORD ACQUISITION CORP.; *U.S. Public*, pg. 565
CONCORDIS GROUP, INC.; *U.S. Public*, pg. 565
CONCRETE INFRA & MEDIA LIMITED; *Int'l*, pg. 1766
CONCRETE PUMPING HOLDINGS, INC.; *U.S. Public*, pg. 566
CONDIRE MANAGEMENT LP; *U.S. Private*, pg. 1011
CONDUIT PHARMACEUTICALS INC.; *U.S. Public*, pg. 566
CONEXUS CATTLE CORP.; *U.S. Private*, pg. 1012
CONGRUENT INVESTMENT PARTNERS, LLC; *U.S. Private*, pg. 1014
CONLON & DART LLC—See EP Wealth Advisors, LLC; *U.S. Private*, pg. 1411
CONNECTED MINERALS LIMITED; *Int'l*, pg. 1769
CONNECTM TECHNOLOGY SOLUTIONS, INC.; *U.S. Public*, pg. 567
CONNECTOR CAPITAL CORPORATION; *U.S. Private*, pg. 1016
CONNECTUS GROUP LLC—See Clayton, Dubilier & Rice, LLC; *U.S. Private*, pg. 923
CONNECTUS GROUP LLC—See Stone Point Capital LLC; *U.S. Private*, pg. 3824
CONNOR, CLARK & LUNN FINANCIAL GROUP; *Int'l*, pg. 1769
CONNOR, CLARK & LUNN INFRASTRUCTURE—See Connor, Clark & Lunn Financial Group; *Int'l*, pg. 1769
CONSECUTIVE INVESTMENT & TRADING COMPANY LTD.; *Int'l*, pg. 1769
CONSELLO CAPITAL LLC—See Consello Management LP; *U.S. Private*, pg. 1019
CONSELLO MANAGEMENT LP; *U.S. Private*, pg. 1019
CONSERVATIVE BROADCAST MEDIA & JOURNALISM INC.; *U.S. Public*, pg. 569
CONSILIUM SGR P.A.; *Int'l*, pg. 1770
CONSILIUM SGR SPA; *Int'l*, pg. 1770
CONSOL FINANCIAL INC.—See CONSOL Energy Inc.; *U.S. Public*, pg. 569
CONSOLIDATED FINANCE COMPANY LIMITED—See ANSA McAL Limited; *Int'l*, pg. 476
CONSOLIDATED INVESTMENT GROUP, LLC; *U.S. Private*, pg. 1021

CONSONANCE CAPITAL PARTNERS LLC; *U.S. Private*, pg. 1022
CONSORCIO CEMENTERO DEL SUR SA; *Int'l*, pg. 1771
CONSTELLATION REAL ESTATE GROUP, INC.; *U.S. Private*, pg. 1023
CONSUMER FINANCE COMPANY LIMITED—See Bayport Management Limited; *Int'l*, pg. 915
CONSUMER GROWTH PARTNERS LLC; *U.S. Private*, pg. 1025
CONTENT PARTNERS LLC; *U.S. Private*, pg. 1027
CONTENTREEJOONGANG CORP.; *Int'l*, pg. 1779
CONTINENTAL ALLOY WHEEL CORPORATION; *U.S. Private*, pg. 1028
CONTINENTAL HOLDINGS LIMITED; *Int'l*, pg. 1784
CONTINENTAL JEWELRY (U.S.A.) INC.—See Continental Holdings Limited; *Int'l*, pg. 1784
CONTINUUM SOCS S.A.S.—See DXC Technology Company; *U.S. Public*, pg. 695
CONVERGENT CAPITAL PARTNERS LLC; *U.S. Private*, pg. 1035
CONVERGENT FINANCE LLP; *Int'l*, pg. 1787
CONVERGE TOWERS, LLC—See BGC Group, Inc.; *U.S. Public*, pg. 328
CONVERSION CAPITAL PARTNERS LTD.; *Int'l*, pg. 1787
CONX CORP.; *U.S. Public*, pg. 573
COOPERATIVA DE AHORRO Y CREDITO AGUADA; *U.S. Private*, pg. 1042
COOPERS PARK INVESTMENT HOLDINGS LIMITED—See Coopers Park Corporation; *Int'l*, pg. 1792
COPILOT CAPITAL LIMITED; *Int'l*, pg. 1793
COPLEY EQUITY PARTNERS,LLC; *U.S. Private*, pg. 1045
COPPERMINE CAPITAL, LLC; *U.S. Private*, pg. 1045
COPPER STANDARD RESOURCES INC.; *Int'l*, pg. 1794
COPROMED S.A. DE C.V.—See Banco Bilbao Vizcaya Argentaria, S.A.; *Int'l*, pg. 817
CORAZON CAPITAL V838 MONOCEROS CORP.; *U.S. Private*, pg. 1046
CORBEL MANAGEMENT LLC; *U.S. Private*, pg. 1047
COR BUSINESS DEVELOPMENT COMPANY LLC; *U.S. Private*, pg. 1046
CORDET CAPITAL PARTNERS LLP; *Int'l*, pg. 1796
CORDIANT DIGITAL INFRASTRUCTURE LIMITED; *Int'l*, pg. 1796
CORDOVA, SMART & WILLIAMS, LLC—See The Williams Capital Group, L.P.; *U.S. Private*, pg. 4136
CORE CANADIAN DIVIDEND TRUST; *Int'l*, pg. 1797
CORE CAPITAL PARTNERS; *U.S. Private*, pg. 1048
CORE EQUITY HOLDINGS SA; *Int'l*, pg. 1798
CORE INDUSTRIAL PARTNERS, LLC; *U.S. Private*, pg. 1048
CORENERGY INFRASTRUCTURE TRUST, INC.; *U.S. Public*, pg. 577
CORE RESOURCE MANAGEMENT, INC.; *U.S. Public*, pg. 576
CORESTATES CAPITAL ADVISORS, LLC; *U.S. Private*, pg. 1049
CORINTHIAN CAPITAL GROUP, LLC; *U.S. Private*, pg. 1050
CORNELL CAPITAL LLC; *U.S. Private*, pg. 1051
CORNER GROWTH ACQUISITION CORP.; *U.S. Public*, pg. 577
CORNERSTONE EQUITY INVESTORS, LLC; *U.S. Private*, pg. 1052
CORNERSTONE INVESTMENT CAPITAL HOLDINGS CO.; *U.S. Private*, pg. 1052
CORN INVESTMENT LTD.—See Allianz SE; *Int'l*, pg. 352
CORONATION FUND MANAGERS LIMITED; *Int'l*, pg. 1802
CORPACQ LTD.—See CorpAcq Holdings Limited; *Int'l*, pg. 1802
CORPFIN CAPITAL SA; *Int'l*, pg. 1802
CORPORACION DE FINANZAS DEL PAIS; *Int'l*, pg. 1803
CORPORATE PARTNERS LLC; *U.S. Private*, pg. 1055
CORPORATE PROPERTY ASSOCIATES 18 - GLOBAL INCORPORATED—See W.P. Carey Inc.; *U.S. Public*, pg. 2315
CORPORATE UNIVERSE, INC.; *U.S. Public*, pg. 580
CORRIDOR CAPITAL, LLC; *U.S. Private*, pg. 1058
CORSAIR CAPITAL, LLC; *U.S. Private*, pg. 1059
CORSAIR CAPITAL LLP—See Corsair Capital, LLC; *U.S. Private*, pg. 1059
CORSAIR PARTNERING CORPORATION; *U.S. Public*, pg. 580
CORTEC GROUP MANAGEMENT SERVICES, LLC; *U.S. Private*, pg. 1060
CORTINA CAPITAL CORP.; *Int'l*, pg. 1808
CORTRONIX BIOMEDICAL ADVANCEMENT TECHNOLOGIES INC.; *U.S. Private*, pg. 1061
CORVUS CAPITAL LTD.; *Int'l*, pg. 1809
COSAN CAYMAN FINANCE LIMITED—See Cosan S.A.; *Int'l*, pg. 1809
COSCO FINANCE CO., LTD.—See China COSCO Shipping Corporation Limited; *Int'l*, pg. 1491
COTTON CREEK CAPITAL MANAGEMENT LLC; *U.S. Private*, pg. 1063
COTTONWOOD ACQUISITIONS LLC; *U.S. Private*, pg. 1064
COUNCIL CAPITAL; *U.S. Private*, pg. 1065
COUNSEL WEALTH MANAGEMENT, INC.—See Larson

Financial Holdings, LLC; *U.S. Private*, pg. 2394
COUNTERPOINT CAPITAL PARTNERS, LLC; *U.S. Private*, pg. 1066
COUNTER PRESS ACQUISITION CORPORATION; *U.S. Public*, pg. 587
COUNTRY GROUP SECURITIES PUBLIC COMPANY LIMITED; *Int'l*, pg. 1818
COUNTRYSIDE FOODS, LLC—See Ramex, Inc.; *U.S. Private*, pg. 3351
COUNTRY TRUST BANK—See COUNTRY Financial; *U.S. Private*, pg. 1067
COUNTRYWIDE ASSURED PLC—See Chesnara Plc; *Int'l*, pg. 1472
THE COURTNEY GROUP, INCORPORATED; *U.S. Private*, pg. 4015
COURT SQUARE CAPITAL PARTNERS, L.P.; *U.S. Private*, pg. 1068
COVALIS CAPITAL (AMERICA) LLC—See Covalis Capital LP; *Int'l*, pg. 1819
COVALIS CAPITAL LLP—See Covalis Capital LP; *Int'l*, pg. 1820
COVALIS CAPITAL LP; *Int'l*, pg. 1819
COVANTAGE CREDIT UNION; *U.S. Private*, pg. 1071
COVE HILL PARTENRS, L.P.; *U.S. Private*, pg. 1071
COVENANT CAPITAL GROUP, LLC; *U.S. Private*, pg. 1071
COVENTRY EDUCATION PARTNERSHIP HOLDINGS LIMITED—See Bilfinger SE; *Int'l*, pg. 1028
COVENTRY FIRST LLC; *U.S. Private*, pg. 1072
COVINGTON CAPITAL CORPORATION; *Int'l*, pg. 1821
CP2 LIMITED—See CP2 Group Limited; *Int'l*, pg. 1823
CPA17 MERGER SUB LLC—See W.P. Carey Inc.; *U.S. Public*, pg. 2315
CPG INVESTMENTS PTE LTD.—See China Architecture Design & Research Group; *Int'l*, pg. 1483
CPP GLOBAL ASSISTANCE BANGLADESH LIMITED—See CPPGroup Plc; *Int'l*, pg. 1826
CPS CAPITAL; *Int'l*, pg. 1826
CPS GROUP INVESTMENTS PTY. LTD.; *Int'l*, pg. 1826
CPS PAYMENT SERVICES, LLC—See Repay Holdings Corporation; *U.S. Public*, pg. 1784
CQS NATURAL RESOURCES GROWTH & INCOME PLC; *Int'l*, pg. 1826
CRAFTPORT CANNABIS CORP.; *Int'l*, pg. 1827
CRAFTSMAN CAPITAL PARTNERS, LLC; *U.S. Private*, pg. 1082
CRAVEN HOUSE CAPITAL PLC; *Int'l*, pg. 1828
CRB SHARE CUSTODIAN SERVICES LTD.; *Int'l*, pg. 1830
CREADES AB; *Int'l*, pg. 1830
CREADEV SAS; *Int'l*, pg. 1830
CREADOR SDN. BHD.; *Int'l*, pg. 1831
CREAT GROUP CORPORATION; *Int'l*, pg. 1831
CREATIVE PLANNING, LLC; *U.S. Private*, pg. 1089
CREAT RESOURCES HOLDINGS LIMITED; *Int'l*, pg. 1831
CREDENT CAPITAL CORP.; *Int'l*, pg. 1834
CREDENT GLOBAL FINANCE LIMITED; *Int'l*, pg. 1834
CREDICORP CAPITAL PERU S.A.A.; *Int'l*, pg. 1834
CREDICORP CAPITAL USA INC.—See Credicorp Ltd.; *Int'l*, pg. 1834
CREDIFARMA S.P.A.—See Banca IFIS S.p.A.; *Int'l*, pg. 815
CREDIOP OVERSEAS BANK LTD.—See Dexia SA; *Int'l*, pg. 2092
CREDITACCESS GRAMEEN LIMITED; *Int'l*, pg. 1836
CREDIT AGRICOLE PRIVATE EQUITY S.A.—See Coller Capital Ltd.; *Int'l*, pg. 1699
CREDIT-BASED ASSET SERVICING & SECURITIZATION LLC; *U.S. Private*, pg. 1092
CREDIT BUREAU ASIA LIMITED; *Int'l*, pg. 1835
CREDITCHECK PARTNERS PRIVATE LIMITED; *Int'l*, pg. 1836
CREDIT CLEAR LIMITED; *Int'l*, pg. 1835
CREDIT CORP GROUP LIMITED; *Int'l*, pg. 1835
CREDIT CORPORATION (PNG) LIMITED; *Int'l*, pg. 1835
CREDIT CORP SOLUTIONS INC.—See Credit Corp Group Limited; *Int'l*, pg. 1835
CREDIT INFORMATION SYSTEMS COMPANY LIMITED—See TransUnion; *U.S. Public*, pg. 2184
CREDIT PLAN B PTY LIMITED—See Credit Corp Group Limited; *Int'l*, pg. 1835
CREDIT POUR HABITATIONS SOCIALES—See BNP Paribas SA; *Int'l*, pg. 1090
CRESCENDO CORPORATION BERHAD; *Int'l*, pg. 1839
CRESCENDO INVESTMENT HOLDINGS LIMITED—See Barclays PLC; *Int'l*, pg. 862
CRESCENDO VENTURE MANAGEMENT, LLC; *U.S. Private*, pg. 1093
CRESCENT CAPITAL BDC, INC.; *U.S. Public*, pg. 593
CRESCENT CAPITAL FINANCE GROUP, INC.; *U.S. Private*, pg. 1093
CRESCENT CAPITAL PARTNERS LTD.; *Int'l*, pg. 1839
CRESCENT HILL CAPITAL CORPORATION; *U.S. Private*, pg. 1093
CRESCENT LEASING LTD.; *Int'l*, pg. 1839
CRESCENT PRIVATE CREDIT INCOME CORP.; *U.S. Private*, pg. 1094
CRESCERA CAPITAL ACQUISITION CORP.; *Int'l*, pg. 1839
CRESSET ASSET MANAGEMENT, LLC; *U.S. Private*, pg. 1094
CRESSEY & COMPANY, LP; *U.S. Private*, pg. 1095

CRESTLINE INVESTORS, INC.; *U.S. Private*, pg. 1097
CRESTVIEW ADVISORS, L.L.C.—See Crestview Partners, L.P.; *U.S. Private*, pg. 1098
CRESTVIEW PARTNERS, L.P.; *U.S. Private*, pg. 1097
CRI HOTEL INCOME PARTNERS, L.P.; *U.S. Private*, pg. 1100
CRIMSON BIOENERGY LTD.; *Int'l*, pg. 1849
CRIMSON INVESTMENT; *U.S. Private*, pg. 1100
CRISIL RATINGS LIMITED—See S&P Global Inc.; *U.S. Public*, pg. 1830
CRITERION CAPITAL MANAGEMENT LLC; *U.S. Private*, pg. 1101
CRITICAL METALS PLC; *Int'l*, pg. 1851
CRITICALPOINT CAPITAL, LLC; *U.S. Private*, pg. 1102
CROCKER VENTURES LLC; *U.S. Private*, pg. 1102
CRODA OVERSEAS HOLDINGS LTD—See Croda International plc; *Int'l*, pg. 1852
CROSS EQUITY PARTNERS AG; *Int'l*, pg. 1855
CROSSGATE PARTNERS, LLC; *U.S. Private*, pg. 1106
CROSSINGBRIDGE ADVISORS LLC—See ENDI Corp.; *U.S. Public*, pg. 760
CROSSLINK CAPITAL, INC.; *U.S. Private*, pg. 1106
CROSSPLANE CAPITAL MANAGEMENT LP; *U.S. Private*, pg. 1107
CROSSPOINT CAPITAL PARTNERS LP; *U.S. Private*, pg. 1107
CROSSPOINT VENTURE PARTNERS; *U.S. Private*, pg. 1107
CROWN GOLD, INC.—See Rosemore Inc.; *U.S. Private*, pg. 3483
CROWNIA HOLDINGS LTD.; *Int'l*, pg. 1858
CROWN PROPTECH ACQUISITIONS; *U.S. Public*, pg. 600
CRUCIBLE ACQUISITION CORPORATION; *U.S. Public*, pg. 600
CRUX CAPITAL LTD; *U.S. Private*, pg. 1114
CRUZ BATTERY METALS CORP.; *Int'l*, pg. 1859
CRYPTO BLOCKCHAIN INDUSTRIES S.A.; *Int'l*, pg. 1860
CRYPTO FLOW TECHNOLOGY LIMITED; *Int'l*, pg. 1860
CRYPTOSIGN INC.; *U.S. Private*, pg. 1115
CRYSTAL VALLEY FINANCIAL CORP.; *U.S. Public*, pg. 600
CSC FINANCE LTD.—See Capital Securities Corporation; *Int'l*, pg. 1312
CSC FINANCIAL SERVICES LIMITED—See Capital Securities Corporation; *Int'l*, pg. 1312
CSC FUTURES (HK) LTD.—See Capital Securities Corporation; *Int'l*, pg. 1312
CSC INTERNATIONAL HOLDINGS LTD.—See Capital Securities Corporation; *Int'l*, pg. 1312
CSC SECURITIES (HK) LTD.—See Capital Securities Corporation; *Int'l*, pg. 1312
CSI PROPERTIES LIMITED; *Int'l*, pg. 1865
CSL CAPITAL MANAGEMENT, LLC; *U.S. Private*, pg. 1117
CSL CAPITAL (UK) LIMITED—See FCMB Group Plc; *Int'l*, pg. 2628
CSLM ACQUISITION CORP.; *U.S. Public*, pg. 601
CSL STOCKBROKERS LIMITED—See FCMB Group Plc; *Int'l*, pg. 2628
CTB AUSTRALIA LIMITED—See Commonwealth Bank of Australia; *Int'l*, pg. 1719
CTBC ASIA LIMITED—See CTBC Financial Holding Co., Ltd.; *Int'l*, pg. 1869
CT DEVELOPERS LTD.; *Int'l*, pg. 1868
CT REAL ESTATE INVESTMENT TRUST; *Int'l*, pg. 1868
CTT PHARMACEUTICAL HOLDINGS INC.; *U.S. Public*, pg. 603
CT VISION INVESTMENT LTD; *Int'l*, pg. 1868
CUADRILLA CAPITAL LLC; *U.S. Private*, pg. 1119
CUBE INFRASTRUCTURE MANAGERS SA—See Groupe BPCE; *Int'l*, pg. 3094
CUBICAL FINANCIAL SERVICES LIMITED; *Int'l*, pg. 1875
CULLEN INVESTMENTS LIMITED; *Int'l*, pg. 1876
CUMULEX N.V.; *Int'l*, pg. 1878
CUMULUS FUNDING, INC.—See Enova International, Inc.; *U.S. Public*, pg. 769
CURI WEALTH MANAGEMENT, LLC—See Curi Holdings, Inc.; *U.S. Private*, pg. 1125
CURRENC GROUP INC.; *U.S. Public*, pg. 611
CURRENTA GESCHAFTSFUHRUNGS-GMBH—See Bayer Aktiengesellschaft; *Int'l*, pg. 907
CURRENT CAPITAL LLC; *U.S. Private*, pg. 1125
CUSO FINANCIAL SERVICES, L.P.—See Lee Equity Partners LLC; *U.S. Private*, pg. 2412
CUSTODIAN VENTURES LLC; *U.S. Private*, pg. 1127
CVC ADVISERS LTD.—See CVC Capital Partners SICAV-FIS S.A.; *Int'l*, pg. 1881
CVC ADVISORS (U.S.) INC.—See CVC Capital Partners SICAV-FIS S.A.; *Int'l*, pg. 1884
CVC ASIA PACIFIC (AUSTRALIA) LTD.—See CVC Capital Partners SICAV-FIS S.A.; *Int'l*, pg. 1885
CVC ASIA PACIFIC (JAPAN) KABUSHIKI KAISHA—See CVC Capital Partners SICAV-FIS S.A.; *Int'l*, pg. 1885
CVC ASIA PACIFIC LTD.—See CVC Capital Partners SICAV-FIS S.A.; *Int'l*, pg. 1885
CVC CAPITAL PARTNERS (BENELUX) SA/NV—See CVC Capital Partners SICAV-FIS S.A.; *Int'l*, pg. 1885
CVC CAPITAL PARTNERS (DEUTSCHLAND) GMBH—See CVC Capital Partners SICAV-FIS S.A.; *Int'l*, pg. 1886

CVC CAPITAL PARTNERS (ESPANA) SL—See CVC Capital Partners SICAV-FIS S.A.; *Int'l*, pg. 1886
CVC CAPITAL PARTNERS (FRANCE) SA—See CVC Capital Partners SICAV-FIS S.A.; *Int'l*, pg. 1886
CVC CAPITAL PARTNERS NEDERLAND—See CVC Capital Partners SICAV-FIS S.A.; *Int'l*, pg. 1886
CVC LIMITED; *Int'l*, pg. 1889
CVF CAPITAL PARTNERS, INC.; *U.S. Private*, pg. 1132
CVI DOM MAKLERSKI SP. Z O.O.; *Int'l*, pg. 1889
C&W ACQUISITION CORP.; *U.S. Private*, pg. 704
CWB MCLEAN & PARTNERS WEALTH MANAGEMENT LTD.—See Canadian Western Bank; *Int'l*, pg. 1286
CWT EUROPE B.V. GROUP—See CWT International Limited; *Int'l*, pg. 1891
CYBERMETALS, CORP.—See A-Mark Precious Metals, Inc.; *U.S. Public*, pg. 10
CYBERNORTH VENTURES INC.; *Int'l*, pg. 1893
CYBERZONE PROPERTIES INC.—See Filinvest Development Corporation; *Int'l*, pg. 2663
CYBUS CAPITAL MARKETS—See First National of Nebraska, Inc.; *U.S. Private*, pg. 1524
CYMBRIA CORPORATION; *Int'l*, pg. 1896
CYMI HOLDING, S.A.—See ACS, Actividades de Construccion y Servicios, S.A.; *Int'l*, pg. 111
CYPHER METAVERSE INC.; *Int'l*, pg. 1897
CYPRESS EQUIPMENT FUND A, LLC; *U.S. Private*, pg. 1134
THE CYPRESS GROUP LLC; *U.S. Private*, pg. 4017
CYPRIUM INVESTMENT PARTNERS LLC - NEW YORK—See Cyprium Investment Partners LLC; *U.S. Private*, pg. 1135
CYPRIUM INVESTMENT PARTNERS LLC; *U.S. Private*, pg. 1135
THE CYPRUS INVESTMENT AND SECURITIES CORPORATION LTD—See Bank of Cyprus Holdings Public Limited Company; *Int'l*, pg. 842
CYRUS CAPITAL PARTNERS, L.P.; *U.S. Private*, pg. 1135
CYXTERA TECHNOLOGIES, INC.; *U.S. Public*, pg. 618
CZECH TOP VENTURE FUND B.V.—See Erste Group Bank AG; *Int'l*, pg. 2498
CZERWONE MAKI PROJECT SP. Z.O.O.—See Africa Israel Investments Ltd.; *Int'l*, pg. 190
D1 CAPITAL PARTNERS L.P.; *U.S. Private*, pg. 1143
DA32 LIFE SCIENCE TECH ACQUISITION CORP.; *U.S. Public*, pg. 620
DADAM INVESTMENT CORP.; *Int'l*, pg. 1904
DADCO ALUMINA & CHEMICALS LTD.; *Int'l*, pg. 1904
DAEJAN (CAMBRIDGE) LIMITED—See Centremanor Ltd.; *Int'l*, pg. 1411
DAEJAN ENTERPRISES LIMITED—See Centremanor Ltd.; *Int'l*, pg. 1412
DAEJAN INVESTMENTS (GROVE HALL) LIMITED—See Centremanor Ltd.; *Int'l*, pg. 1412
DAEJAN INVESTMENTS (HARROW) LIMITED—See Centremanor Ltd.; *Int'l*, pg. 1412
DAEJAN INVESTMENTS LIMITED—See Centremanor Ltd.; *Int'l*, pg. 1412
DAEJAN (KINGSTON) LIMITED—See Centremanor Ltd.; *Int'l*, pg. 1411
DAEJAN (LAUDERDALE) LIMITED—See Centremanor Ltd.; *Int'l*, pg. 1411
DAEJAN PROPERTIES LIMITED—See Centremanor Ltd.; *Int'l*, pg. 1412
DAEJAN (READING) LIMITED—See Centremanor Ltd.; *Int'l*, pg. 1411
DAEJAN (TAUNTON) LIMITED—See Centremanor Ltd.; *Int'l*, pg. 1411
DAEJAN (TRADERS) LIMITED—See Centremanor Ltd.; *Int'l*, pg. 1411
DAEJAN (UK) LIMITED—See Centremanor Ltd.; *Int'l*, pg. 1411
DAEJAN (WARWICK) LIMITED—See Centremanor Ltd.; *Int'l*, pg. 1411
DAESUNG PRIVATE EQUITY, INC.—See Daesung Holdings Co., Ltd.; *Int'l*, pg. 1909
DAG DVERGSTEN AS; *Int'l*, pg. 1912
DAG VENTURES, LLC; *U.S. Private*, pg. 1144
DAICEL CHEMICAL (CHINA) INVESTMENT CO., LTD.—See Daicel Corporation; *Int'l*, pg. 1918
DAI FUNDING CORPORATION—See Daikin Industries, Ltd.; *Int'l*, pg. 1932
DAIKIN ACCOUNTING SOLUTIONS CO., LTD—See Daikin Industries, Ltd.; *Int'l*, pg. 1932
DAIMYO AS; *Int'l*, pg. 1938
DAISHIN BALANCE 4TH SPECIAL PURPOSE ACQUISITION CO LTD; *Int'l*, pg. 1941
DAIWA CAPITAL MARKETS INDIA PRIVATE LIMITED—See Daiwa Securities Group Inc.; *Int'l*, pg. 1948
DAIWA CAPITAL MARKETS PHILIPPINES, INC.—See Daiwa Securities Group Inc.; *Int'l*, pg. 1948
DAIWA CORPORATE INVESTMENT CO., LTD.—See Daiwa Securities Group Inc.; *Int'l*, pg. 1948
DAIWA OFFICE INVESTMENT CORPORATION; *Int'l*, pg. 1947
DAIWA PI PARTNERS CO. LTD—See Daiwa Securities Group Inc.; *Int'l*, pg. 1948
DAIWA SECURITIES LIVING INVESTMENT CORPORATION; *Int'l*, pg. 1949

DAIWA SECURITIES SMBC PRINCIPAL INVESTMENTS CO. LTD.—See Daiwa Securities Group Inc.; *Int'l*, pg. 1949
DALE CAPITAL GROUP LIMITED; *Int'l*, pg. 1950
DALFORT CAPITAL PARTNERS, LLC; *U.S. Private*, pg. 1149
DALIAN MEDICAL EQUIPMENT HOLDING BV—See Getinge AB; *Int'l*, pg. 2949
DANFORTH ASSOCIATES, INC.; *U.S. Private*, pg. 1153
DANIELI FINANCE SOLUTION SA—See Danieli & C. Officine Meccaniche S.p.A.; *Int'l*, pg. 1963
DANIMER SCIENTIFIC, INC.; *U.S. Public*, pg. 632
DANSKE INVEST MANAGEMENT A/S—See Danske Bank A/S; *Int'l*, pg. 1969
DAN T. MOORE CO.; *U.S. Private*, pg. 1151
DANU INVESTMENT PARTNERS LTD.; *Int'l*, pg. 1969
DANZAS DEUTSCHLAND HOLDING GMBH—See Deutsche Post AG; *Int'l*, pg. 2079
DAR AL AMAN FOR ISLAMIC FINANCE PLC; *Int'l*, pg. 1971
DARAT JORDAN HOLDINGS; *Int'l*, pg. 1972
DARBY OVERSEAS INVESTMENTS, LTD.—See Franklin Resources, Inc.; *U.S. Public*, pg. 879
DARELLE ONLINE SOLUTIONS INC.; *Int'l*, pg. 1972
DARKOM INVESTMENT CO.; *Int'l*, pg. 1973
DARWIN PRIVATE EQUITY LLP; *Int'l*, pg. 1973
DATAMETREX AI LIMITED; *Int'l*, pg. 1979
DATASCOPE INVESTMENT CORP.—See Getinge AB; *Int'l*, pg. 2951
DATASIGHT CORPORATION; *U.S. Private*, pg. 1166
DATUM VENTURES INC.; *Int'l*, pg. 1982
DAVI LUXURY BRAND GROUP, INC.; *U.S. Public*, pg. 635
DA VINCI CAPITAL LLC; *Int'l*, pg. 1902
DAVIS DISTRIBUTORS, LLC—See Davis Selected Advisors, L.P.; *U.S. Private*, pg. 1174
DAVIS SELECTED ADVISERS-NY, INC.—See Davis Selected Advisors, L.P.; *U.S. Private*, pg. 1174
DAWNEY & CO., LTD.; *Int'l*, pg. 1984
DAWN PATROL PARTNERS, LLC; *U.S. Private*, pg. 1175
DAXOR CORPORATION; *U.S. Public*, pg. 644
DAYNINE CONSULTING INC.—See Accenture plc; *Int'l*, pg. 86
DAYTHREE DIGITAL BERHAD; *Int'l*, pg. 1985
D&B ACQUISITION CORP.—See Cannae Holdings, Inc.; *U.S. Public*, pg. 429
D&B ACQUISITION CORP.—See CC Capital Partners, LLC; *U.S. Private*, pg. 798
D&B ACQUISITION CORP.—See Intercontinental Exchange, Inc.; *U.S. Public*, pg. 1141
DB ALTERNATIVE STRATEGIES LIMITED—See Deutsche Bank Aktiengesellschaft; *Int'l*, pg. 2056
DB BAGHEERA, S.A R.L.—See Deutsche Bank Aktiengesellschaft; *Int'l*, pg. 2056
DB COMMODITIES CANADA LTD.—See Deutsche Bank Aktiengesellschaft; *Int'l*, pg. 2056
DB CONSORZIO S. CONS. A R. L.—See Deutsche Bank Aktiengesellschaft; *Int'l*, pg. 2056
DB CREST LIMITED—See Deutsche Bank Aktiengesellschaft; *Int'l*, pg. 2056
DBD PILGRIM AMERICA CORP.—See Deutsche Bank Aktiengesellschaft; *Int'l*, pg. 2057
DBG BETEILIGUNGSGESELLSCHAFT MBH—See Deutsche Beteiligungs AG; *Int'l*, pg. 2062
DBG NEW FUND MANAGEMENT GMBH & CO. KG—See Deutsche Beteiligungs AG; *Int'l*, pg. 2062
D.B. INTERNATIONAL DELAWARE, INC.—See Deutsche Bank Aktiengesellschaft; *Int'l*, pg. 2056
DB (INTERNATIONAL) STOCK BROKERS LTD.; *Int'l*, pg. 1985
DB INVESTMENT RESOURCES HOLDINGS CORP.—See Deutsche Bank Aktiengesellschaft; *Int'l*, pg. 2056
DBJ ASSET MANAGEMENT CO., LTD.—See Development Bank of Japan, Inc.; *Int'l*, pg. 2087
DBJ SECURITIES CO., LTD.—See Development Bank of Japan, Inc.; *Int'l*, pg. 2087
DBOI GLOBAL SERVICES PRIVATE LIMITED—See Deutsche Bank Aktiengesellschaft; *Int'l*, pg. 2057
DB PRIVATE CLIENTS CORP.—See Deutsche Bank Aktiengesellschaft; *Int'l*, pg. 2056
DB SERVICES AMERICAS, INC.—See Deutsche Bank Aktiengesellschaft; *Int'l*, pg. 2056
DBUSBZ2, LLC—See Deutsche Bank Aktiengesellschaft; *Int'l*, pg. 2057
DBX ADVISORS LLC—See Deutsche Bank Aktiengesellschaft; *Int'l*, pg. 2057
D.C. CAPITAL PARTNERS, LLC; *U.S. Private*, pg. 1141
DC HEALTHCARE HOLDINGS BERHAD; *Int'l*, pg. 1989
D-CLEAR LLC—See DIFC Investments LLC; *Int'l*, pg. 2118
DCM FINANCIAL SERVICES LTD.—See DCM Limited; *Int'l*, pg. 1992
D CUBED GROUP LLC; *U.S. Private*, pg. 1136
DD3 ACQUISITION CORP.; *Int'l*, pg. 1993
DD-ROADMAP UNTERNEHMENSBERATUNG GMBH—See BAWAG Group AG; *Int'l*, pg. 900
DEA CAPITAL SPA—See De Agostini S.p.A.; *Int'l*, pg. 1994
DECEUNINCK HOLDING GERMANY GMBH—See Deceuninck NV; *Int'l*, pg. 1999
DECILLION FINANCE LTD.; *Int'l*, pg. 2000

523999 — MISCELLANEOUS FINAN...   CORPORATE AFFILIATIONS

DECISIVE DIVIDEND CORPORATION; *Int'l*, pg. 2001
DEEP LAKE CAPITAL ACQUISITION CORP.; *U.S. Public*, pg. 645
DEEPMARKIT CORP.; *Int'l*, pg. 2003
DEEP MEDICINE ACQUISITION CORP.; *U.S. Public*, pg. 645
DEEPSPATIAL INC.; *Int'l*, pg. 2003
DEEP VALUE DRILLER AS; *Int'l*, pg. 2002
DEERFIELD MANAGEMENT COMPANY L.P.; *U.S. Private*, pg. 1190
DEE TECH SA; *Int'l*, pg. 2002
DEFINITY FINANCIAL CORP.; *Int'l*, pg. 2004
DE LAGE LANDEN CHILE S.A.—See Cooperatieve Centrale Raiffeisen-Boerenleenbank B.A.; *Int'l*, pg. 1791
DE LAGE LANDEN CO., LTD.—See Cooperatieve Centrale Raiffeisen-Boerenleenbank B.A.; *Int'l*, pg. 1791
DE LAGE LANDEN FAKTORING A.S.—See Cooperatieve Centrale Raiffeisen-Boerenleenbank B.A.; *Int'l*, pg. 1791
DE LAGE LANDEN FINANCIAL SERVICES CANADA INC.—See Cooperatieve Centrale Raiffeisen-Boerenleenbank B.A.; *Int'l*, pg. 1791
DE LAGE LANDEN K.K.—See Cooperatieve Centrale Raiffeisen-Boerenleenbank B.A.; *Int'l*, pg. 1791
DE LAGE LANDEN PTE. LIMITED—See Cooperatieve Centrale Raiffeisen-Boerenleenbank B.A.; *Int'l*, pg. 1791
DELANCEY REAL ESTATE ASSET MANAGEMENT LTD.; *Int'l*, pg. 2010
DE LA RUE HOLDINGS PLC—See De La Rue plc; *Int'l*, pg. 1996
DELAVACO RESIDENTIAL PROPERTIES CORP.; *Int'l*, pg. 2010
DELCAM HOLDINGS, LLC; *U.S. Private*, pg. 1196
DELEK CAPITAL LTD.—See Delek Group Ltd.; *Int'l*, pg. 2011
DELEK EUROPE HOLDINGS LTD.—See Delek Group Ltd.; *Int'l*, pg. 2011
DELEK INVESTMENTS & PROPERTIES LTD.—See Delek Group Ltd.; *Int'l*, pg. 2011
DELIVRA CORP.—See Hygrovest Limited; *Int'l*, pg. 3549
DELOS CAPITAL, LLC; *U.S. Private*, pg. 1198
DELOTA CORP.; *Int'l*, pg. 2015
DELPHI GROWTH CAPITAL CORP.; *U.S. Private*, pg. 1199
DELTA ELECTRONICS INTERNATIONAL (SINGAPORE) PTE LTD.—See Delta Electronics, Inc.; *Int'l*, pg. 2018
DELTA FOR CONSTRUCTION & REBUILDING; *Int'l*, pg. 2018
DELTA GENERALI HOLDING D.O.O.—See Assicurazioni Generali S.p.A.; *Int'l*, pg. 646
DELTA LEASING & FINANCE LIMITED; *Int'l*, pg. 2019
DELTAPOINT CAPITAL MANAGEMENT, LLC; *U.S. Private*, pg. 1202
DELTA-V CAPITAL, LLC; *U.S. Private*, pg. 1202
DELTONA LAND & INVESTMENT CORP.—See The Deltona Corporation; *U.S. Private*, pg. 4020
DENEB INVESTMENTS LIMITED—See E Media Holdings Limited; *Int'l*, pg. 2246
DENHAM CAPITAL MANAGEMENT LP; *U.S. Private*, pg. 1204
DENHAM INVESTMENTS LIMITED—See Barclays PLC; *Int'l*, pg. 862
DENHAM SUSTAINABLE PERFORMANCE ACQUISITION CORP.; *U.S. Public*, pg. 653
DENIZ FINANSAL KIRALAMA A.S.; *Int'l*, pg. 2027
DENIZ YATIRIM MENKUL KIYMETLER A.S.; *Int'l*, pg. 2027
DENSO FINANCE & ACCOUNTING CENTER CO., LTD.—See Denso Corporation; *Int'l*, pg. 2029
DENSO FINANCE HOLLAND B.V.—See Denso Corporation; *Int'l*, pg. 2029
DENTSU HOLDINGS (THAILAND) LTD.—See Dentsu Group Inc.; *Int'l*, pg. 2036
D. E. SHAW & CO. (ASIA PACIFIC) LIMITED—See D. E. Shaw & Co., L.P.; *U.S. Private*, pg. 1139
D. E. SHAW & CO. (BERMUDA), LTD.—See D. E. Shaw & Co., L.P.; *U.S. Private*, pg. 1139
D. E. SHAW & CO. (LONDON), LLP—See D. E. Shaw & Co., L.P.; *U.S. Private*, pg. 1139
D. E. SHAW & CO., L.P.; *U.S. Private*, pg. 1139
D. E. SHAW INDIA SECURITIES PRIVATE LIMITED—See D. E. Shaw & Co., L.P.; *U.S. Private*, pg. 1139
D. E. SHAW INDIA SOFTWARE PRIVATE LIMITED—See D. E. Shaw & Co., L.P.; *U.S. Private*, pg. 1139
D. E. SHAW PRIVATE EQUITY INVESTMENT MANAGEMENT (SHANGHAI) CO., LIMITED—See D. E. Shaw & Co., L.P.; *U.S. Private*, pg. 1139
DESIGNCAPITAL PLC; *Int'l*, pg. 2045
DESKTOP METAL, INC.; *U.S. Public*, pg. 656
DESTINY CORPORATE ENTERPRISES, INC.; *U.S. Private*, pg. 1216
DESTRA U.S. LIQUIDITY ALPHA AND INCOME FUND; *U.S. Private*, pg. 1216
DESUN REAL ESTATE INVESTMENT SERVICES GROUP CO., LTD.; *Int'l*, pg. 2047
DETERRA ROYALTIES LIMITED; *Int'l*, pg. 2048
DEUTSCHE BANK AG - UK REPRESENTATIVE OFFICE—See Deutsche Bank Aktiengesellschaft; *Int'l*, pg. 2058
DEUTSCHE BANK ALEX. BROWN INCORPORATED—See Deutsche Bank Aktiengesellschaft; *Int'l*, pg. 2060
DEUTSCHE BANK AMERICAS FINANCE LLC—See Deutsche Bank Aktiengesellschaft; *Int'l*, pg. 2059
DEUTSCHE BANK PRIVATE WEALTH MANAGEMENT—See Deutsche Bank Aktiengesellschaft; *Int'l*, pg. 2060
DEUTSCHE BANK SECURITIES INC.—See Deutsche Bank Aktiengesellschaft; *Int'l*, pg. 2060
DEUTSCHE BETEILIGUNGS AG; *Int'l*, pg. 2062
DEUTSCHE BORSE AG; *Int'l*, pg. 2063
DEUTSCHE BORSE SERVICES S.R.O.—See Deutsche Borse AG; *Int'l*, pg. 2063
DEUTSCHE GROUP SERVICES PTY LIMITED—See Deutsche Bank Aktiengesellschaft; *Int'l*, pg. 2060
DEUTSCHE HOLDINGS (MALTA) LTD.—See Deutsche Bank Aktiengesellschaft; *Int'l*, pg. 2060
DEUTSCHE INTERNATIONAL CORPORATE SERVICES LIMITED—See Deutsche Bank Aktiengesellschaft; *Int'l*, pg. 2060
DEUTSCHE INVEST CAPITAL PARTNERS GMBH; *Int'l*, pg. 2066
DEUTSCHE INVEST MITTELSTAND GMBH—See Deutsche Invest Capital Partners GmbH; *Int'l*, pg. 2066
DEUTSCHE MITTELSTANDSHOLDING GMBH; *Int'l*, pg. 2071
DEUTSCHE POST DHL BETEILIGUNGEN GMBH—See Deutsche Post AG; *Int'l*, pg. 2079
DEUTSCHE POST INVESTMENTS GMBH—See Deutsche Post AG; *Int'l*, pg. 2079
DEUTSCHER RING BETEILIGUNGSHOLDING GMBH—See Baloise Holding AG; *Int'l*, pg. 811
DEUTSCHER RING FINANCIAL SERVICES GMBH—See Baloise Holding AG; *Int'l*, pg. 811
DEVCO PARTNERS OY; *Int'l*, pg. 2086
DEVELOPMENT INVESTMENT CONSTRUCTION HOI AN JSC; *Int'l*, pg. 2088
DEVINE IMPEX LIMITED; *Int'l*, pg. 2089
DEVIR FAKTORING A.S.; *Int'l*, pg. 2089
DEVKI LEASING & FINANCE PRIVATE LIMITED; *Int'l*, pg. 2089
DEVONSHIRE CAPITAL LTD.; *Int'l*, pg. 2089
DEVONSHIRE INVESTORS, INC.—See FMR LLC; *U.S. Private*, pg. 1554
DEVVSTREAM CORP.; *U.S. Public*, pg. 657
DEWB-IT BETEILIGUNGSGESELLSCHAFT MBH—See Deutsche Effecten- und Wechsel-Beteiligungsgesellschaft AG.; *Int'l*, pg. 2065
DEXIA DELAWARE LLC—See Dexia SA; *Int'l*, pg. 2092
DEXIA FINANCE SA—See Dexia SA; *Int'l*, pg. 2092
DEXIA INGENIERIE SOCIALE S.A—See Dexia SA; *Int'l*, pg. 2092
DEXIA KOMMUNALKREDIT BULGARIA EOOD—See Dexia SA; *Int'l*, pg. 2092
DEXIA SABADELL BANCO LOCAL SA—See Dexia SA; *Int'l*, pg. 2092
DFJ TAMIR FISHMAN VENTURES; *Int'l*, pg. 2095
DF TITLE, LLC—See Dream Finders Homes, Inc.; *U.S. Public*, pg. 687
DFW CAPITAL PARTNERS; *U.S. Private*, pg. 1220
DGB CAPITAL LTD.—See DGB Financial Group Co., Ltd.; *Int'l*, pg. 2096
DGH INVESTMENT COMPANY LTD.—See Dabbagh Group Holding Company Ltd.; *Int'l*, pg. 1902
DG INTERNATIONAL OIL COMPANY LTD.—See Dabbagh Group Holding Company Ltd.; *Int'l*, pg. 1902
DHAKA BANK SECURITIES LIMITED—See Dhaka Bank PLC; *Int'l*, pg. 2097
DHANLAXMI COTEX LTD.; *Int'l*, pg. 2098
DHANLEELA INVESTMENTS & TRADING COMPANY LIMITED; *Int'l*, pg. 2098
DHARANI FINANCE LIMITED; *Int'l*, pg. 2098
DHARNI CAPITAL SERVICES LIMITED; *Int'l*, pg. 2099
DHB CAPITAL CORP.; *U.S. Public*, pg. 657
DHL FINANCE SERVICES B.V.—See Deutsche Post AG; *Int'l*, pg. 2074
DHL GLOBAL MANAGEMENT GMBH—See Deutsche Post AG; *Int'l*, pg. 2072
DHOOT INDUSTRIAL FINANCE LIMITED - SAMPOORNA TRADERS DIVISION—See Dhoot Industrial Finance Limited; *Int'l*, pg. 2100
DH PRIVATE EQUITY PARTNERS LLP; *Int'l*, pg. 2097
DHRUVA CAPITAL SERVICES LIMITED; *Int'l*, pg. 2100
DHUNSERI INVESTMENTS LIMITED; *Int'l*, pg. 2100
DIAGEO CAPITAL BV—See Diageo plc; *Int'l*, pg. 2102
DIAGEO INVESTMENT CORPORATION—See Diageo plc; *Int'l*, pg. 2102
DIAMOND CASTLE HOLDINGS, LLC; *U.S. Private*, pg. 1222
DIAMOND POINT A.S.—See Allianz SE; *Int'l*, pg. 352
DICKSON CONCEPTS LIMITED—See Dickson Concepts (International) Limited; *Int'l*, pg. 2112
DICKSON INVESTMENTS (H.K.) LIMITED—See Dickson Concepts (International) Limited; *Int'l*, pg. 2112
DIE ERSTE IMMOBILIENVERMIETUNGSGESELLSCHAFT M.B.H.—See Erste Group Bank AG; *Int'l*, pg. 2498
DIEGO PELLICER WORLDWIDE, INC.; *U.S. Public*, pg. 661
DIFC INVESTMENTS LLC; *Int'l*, pg. 2118
DIFFERENCE CAPITAL FINANCIAL INC.; *Int'l*, pg. 2118
DIGATRADE FINANCIAL CORP.; *Int'l*, pg. 2118
DIGICANN VENTURES INC; *Int'l*, pg. 2118
DIGITAL 9 INFRASTRUCTURE PLC; *Int'l*, pg. 2120
DIGITAL BRAND MEDIA & MARKETING GROUP, INC.; *U.S. Public*, pg. 662
DIGITAL FUEL, LLC; *U.S. Private*, pg. 1230
DIGITAL MEDIA SOLUTIONS, INC.; *U.S. Public*, pg. 662
DIGITAL PAYMENTS PLC; *Int'l*, pg. 2123
DIMENSIONAL ASSOCIATES, LLC—See JDS Capital Management, Inc.; *U.S. Private*, pg. 2196
DIMENSIONS JORDAN & EMIRATES COMMERCIAL INVESTMENTS CORPORATION; *Int'l*, pg. 2126
DINO ENERGY CORPORATION; *Int'l*, pg. 2127
DIRECCT AG—See Baader Bank AG; *Int'l*, pg. 791
DIRECTA SIM S.P.A.; *Int'l*, pg. 2130
DIRECTED CAPITAL RESOURCES, LLC; *U.S. Private*, pg. 1236
DIRECT INVESTMENT HOLDINGS GROUP, INC.; *U.S. Private*, pg. 1235
DIRECTIONAL CAPITAL LLC; *U.S. Private*, pg. 1236
DIRECT SELLING ACQUISITION CORP.; *U.S. Public*, pg. 667
DISCOVERY HARBOUR RESOURCES CORP.; *Int'l*, pg. 2134
DISRUPTIVE CAPITAL ACQUISITION COMPANY LIMITED; *Int'l*, pg. 2135
DISTOKEN ACQUISITION CORPORATION; *Int'l*, pg. 2136
DITECH HOLDING CORPORATION; *U.S. Private*, pg. 1240
DIVERGER LIMITED—See Count Limited; *Int'l*, pg. 1817
DIVERSIFIED ROYALTY CORP.; *Int'l*, pg. 2137
DIVERSIFIED UNITED INVESTMENT LIMITED; *Int'l*, pg. 2137
DIVERSIS CAPITAL, LLC; *U.S. Private*, pg. 1244
DIVIDE DRIVES, INC.; *U.S. Public*, pg. 670
DIVIDEND SWEDEN AB; *Int'l*, pg. 2137
DIVISO GRUPO FINANCIERO S.A.; *Int'l*, pg. 2138
DIV SERVICES SDN. BHD.—See Dialog Group Berhad; *Int'l*, pg. 2104
DIVVYPAY, LLC—See BILL HOLDINGS, INC.; *U.S. Public*, pg. 331
DIXIE GOLD INC.; *Int'l*, pg. 2138
DIXY GROUP AO; *Int'l*, pg. 2138
DKG CAPITAL, INC.—See Emry Capital Group, Inc.; *U.S. Private*, pg. 1388
DLC HOLDINGS CORP.; *Int'l*, pg. 2140
DMY SQUARED TECHNOLOGY GROUP, INC.; *U.S. Public*, pg. 671
DNB ASSET MANAGEMENT AS—See DNB Bank ASA; *Int'l*, pg. 2147
DNB (UK) LIMITED—See DNB Bank ASA; *Int'l*, pg. 2147
DNCA FINANCE S.P.A—See Groupe BPCE; *Int'l*, pg. 3093
DNCA LUXEMBOURG SA—See Groupe BPCE; *Int'l*, pg. 3094
DNP HOLDING USA CORPORATION—See Dai Nippon Printing Co., Ltd.; *Int'l*, pg. 1914
DNP SELECT INCOME FUND INC.; *U.S. Public*, pg. 671
DNS CAPITAL, LLC; *U.S. Private*, pg. 1249
DOCGO INC.; *U.S. Public*, pg. 672
DODONI PORTFOLIO INVESTMENTS PUBLIC COMPANY LTD.—See Elma Holdings Public Company Ltd; *Int'l*, pg. 2367
DOGIN BUSINESS SERVICE, LTD.—See Hokuhoku Financial Group, Inc.; *Int'l*, pg. 3444
DOGIN CARD CO., LTD.—See Hokuhoku Financial Group, Inc.; *Int'l*, pg. 3444
DOHERTY & ASSOCIATES LTD.—See AGF Management Limited; *Int'l*, pg. 206
DO IT AGAIN CORP.; *U.S. Public*, pg. 672
DOLFIN FINANCIAL (UK) LTD.—See Dolfin Group Ltd.; *Int'l*, pg. 2158
DOLLAR FINANCIAL GROUP, INC.—See Lone Star Global Acquisitions, LLC; *U.S. Private*, pg. 2487
DOLL CAPITAL MANAGEMENT; *U.S. Private*, pg. 1254
DOMA HOLDINGS, INC.; *U.S. Public*, pg. 673
DOMANI WEALTH, LLC—See Savant Capital, LLC; *U.S. Private*, pg. 3556
DOME EQUITIES, LLC; *U.S. Private*, pg. 1255
DOMINARI FINANCIAL INC.—See Alkido Pharma Inc.; *U.S. Public*, pg. 63
DOMINARI SECURITIES LLC—See Alkido Pharma Inc.; *U.S. Public*, pg. 63
DOMINION EQUITY LLC; *U.S. Private*, pg. 1256
DOMINION LENDING CENTRES INC.; *Int'l*, pg. 2161
DOMINUS CAPITAL, L.P.; *U.S. Private*, pg. 1256
DOMOFINANCE SA—See BNP Paribas SA; *Int'l*, pg. 1090
DONGBU ASSET MANAGEMENT CO., LTD.—See Dongbu Group; *Int'l*, pg. 2165
DONGFANG CITY HOLDING GROUP COMPANY LIMITED; *U.S. Private*, pg. 1260
DONGWHA HOLDINGS CO., LTD.; *Int'l*, pg. 2170
DONGXING INTERNATIONAL INC.; *Int'l*, pg. 2171
DOORS ULUSLARARASI YONETIM DANISMANLIGI TICARET A.S.—See Dogus Holding AS; *Int'l*, pg. 2154
DORIC NIMROD AIR ONE LIMITED; *Int'l*, pg. 2176
DORIC NIMROD AIR TWO LIMITED; *Int'l*, pg. 2177
DORIEMUS PLC; *Int'l*, pg. 2177
DORILTON CAPITAL ADVISORS LLC; *U.S. Private*, pg. 2180
DORUK FAKTORING A.S.; *Int'l*, pg. 2180

N.A.I.C.S. INDEX

523999 — MISCELLANEOUS FINAN...

DOUBLEVIEW GOLD CORP.; *Int'l*, pg. 2181
DOUGHERTY'S PHARMACY, INC.; *U.S. Private*, pg. 1266
DOWLING CAPITAL MANAGEMENT, LLC; *U.S. Private*, pg. 1268
DOWN2EARTH CAPITAL NV; *Int'l*, pg. 2184
DOWN2EARTH PARTNERS NV—See Down2Earth Capital NV; *Int'l*, pg. 2184
DOWNER HOLDINGS PTY LTD—See Downer EDI Limited; *Int'l*, pg. 2186
DOWNING RENEWABLES & INFRASTRUCTURE TRUST PLC; *Int'l*, pg. 2186
DOYEN INTERNATIONAL HOLDINGS LIMITED; *Int'l*, pg. 2187
DPCM CAPITAL, INC.—See D-Wave Quantum Inc.; *Int'l*, pg. 1900
DPE DEUTSCHE PRIVATE EQUITY GMBH; *Int'l*, pg. 2187
DPE DEUTSCHE PRIVATE EQUITY MANAGEMENT III GMBH—See DPE Deutsche Private Equity GmbH; *Int'l*, pg. 2187
DPM MELLON LLC—See The Bank of New York Mellon Corporation; *U.S. Public*, pg. 2037
DRA ADVISORS LLC; *U.S. Private*, pg. 1271
DRAGANFLY INVESTMENTS LIMITED; *Int'l*, pg. 2199
DRAGONEER INVESTMENT GROUP, LLC; *U.S. Private*, pg. 1271
DRAGONFLY CAPITAL CORP.; *Int'l*, pg. 2199
DRAGON LEGEND ENTERTAINMENT (CANADA) INC.; *Int'l*, pg. 2199
DRAYTON RICHDALE CORP.; *U.S. Private*, pg. 1272
DREAM INCUBATOR INC.; *Int'l*, pg. 2202
DREYFUS MUNICIPAL INFRASTRUCTURE FUND, INC.; *U.S. Private*, pg. 1277
DRILLING TOOLS INTERNATIONAL CORP.; *U.S. Public*, pg. 688
DRONE DELIVERY CANADA CORP.; *Int'l*, pg. 2205
DRUID CAPITAL PARTNERS, LLC; *U.S. Private*, pg. 1279
DRUMZ PLC; *Int'l*, pg. 2206
DRY FLY CAPITAL LLC; *U.S. Private*, pg. 1280
DSG GLOBAL INC.; *Int'l*, pg. 2209
DSW CAPITAL PLC; *Int'l*, pg. 2216
DT CLOUD ACQUISITION CORP.; *Int'l*, pg. 2216
DTRT HEALTH ACQUISITION CORP.; *U.S. Public*, pg. 689
DTXS SILK ROAD INVESTMENT HOLDINGS COMPANY LIMITED; *Int'l*, pg. 2217
DUBAI INTERNATIONAL CAPITAL, LLC—See Dubai Holding LLC; *Int'l*, pg. 2218
DUBAI INVESTMENT GROUP—See Dubai Holding LLC; *Int'l*, pg. 2218
DUBAI INVESTMENTS PARK DEVELOPMENT COMPANY LLC—See Dubai Investments PJSC; *Int'l*, pg. 2219
DUBIN CLARK & COMPANY, INC.; *U.S. Private*, pg. 1283
DUCHOSSOIS CAPITAL MANAGEMENT LLC—See The Duchossois Group, Inc.; *U.S. Private*, pg. 4023
DUE DILIGENCE CORPORATION—See Houlihan Lokey, Inc.; *U.S. Public*, pg. 1055
DUET ACQUISITION CORP.; *Int'l*, pg. 2223
DUFF & PHELPS UTILITY AND INFRASTRUCTURE FUND INC.; *U.S. Public*, pg. 690
DUFRY HOLDINGS & INVESTMENTS AG—See Avolta AG; *Int'l*, pg. 749
DUKE STREET CAPITAL LIMITED; *Int'l*, pg. 2224
DUN & BRADSTREET INVESTMENTS LIMITED—See Cannae Holdings, Inc.; *U.S. Public*, pg. 429
DUN & BRADSTREET INVESTMENTS LIMITED—See CC Capital Partners, LLC; *U.S. Private*, pg. 798
DUN & BRADSTREET INVESTMENTS LIMITED—See Intercontinental Exchange, Inc.; *U.S. Public*, pg. 1142
DUNCAN LAWRIE (IOM) LIMITED—See Camellia Plc; *Int'l*, pg. 1271
DUNCAN LAWRIE LIMITED—See Camellia Plc; *Int'l*, pg. 1271
DUNCAN LAWRIE OFFSHORE SERVICES LIMITED—See Camellia Plc; *Int'l*, pg. 1271
DUNDON CAPITAL ACQUISITION CORPORATION; *U.S. Private*, pg. 1288
DUNEDIN CAPITAL PARTNERS LIMITED—See Dunedin Enterprise Investment Trust PLC; *Int'l*, pg. 2226
DUNEDIN ENTERPRISE INVESTMENT TRUST PLC; *Int'l*, pg. 2226
DUNES POINT CAPITAL, LLC; *U.S. Private*, pg. 1288
DUNYA VARLIK YONETIM A.S.; *Int'l*, pg. 2227
DUPAMIJ HOLDING GMBH—See Heidelberg Materials AG; *Int'l*, pg. 3310
DUPONT CAPITAL MANAGEMENT CORPORATION—See Corteva, Inc.; *U.S. Public*, pg. 583
DUSSINVEST2 BETEILIGUNGSGESELLSCHAFT MBH—See Erste Abwicklungsanstalt AoR; *Int'l*, pg. 2497
DUTCHDELTA FINANCE SARL—See E.ON SE; *Int'l*, pg. 2252
DUTCH OVEN GOLD GROUP INC.; *Int'l*, pg. 2235
DVSM LLC; *U.S. Public*, pg. 1295
DWS FINANZ-SERVICE GMBH—See Deutsche Bank Aktiengesellschaft; *Int'l*, pg. 2057
DYAL CAPITAL PARTNERS—See Blue Owl Capital Inc.; *U.S. Public*, pg. 364
DYMON ASIA CAPITAL (SINGAPORE) PTE. LTD; *Int'l*, pg. 2238
DYNAM HONG KONG CO., LIMITED—See Dynam Japan Holdings, Co., Ltd.; *Int'l*, pg. 2239
DYNAMIC PORTFOLIO MANAGEMENT & SERVICES LIMITED; *Int'l*, pg. 2240
DYNASIVE ENTERPRISE SDN BHD—See IJM Corporation Berhad; *Int'l*, pg. 3608
DYNASTY EQUITY PARTNERS MANAGEMENT, LLC; *U.S. Private*, pg. 1300
DZETA CONSEIL SAS; *Int'l*, pg. 2245
D & Z MEDIA ACQUISITION CORP.; *U.S. Public*, pg. 619
EAA COVERED BOND BANK PLC—See Erste Abwicklungsanstalt AoR; *Int'l*, pg. 2497
EAA JAPAN K.K.—See Erste Abwicklungsanstalt AoR; *Int'l*, pg. 2497
EAGLE ASSET MANAGEMENT (CP) LIMITED—See Great Eagle Holdings Limited; *Int'l*, pg. 3064
EAGLE FILTERS GROUP OYJ; *Int'l*, pg. 2264
EAGLE FOUR EQUITIES LLC; *U.S. Private*, pg. 1309
EAGLE GROWTH AND INCOME OPPORTUNITIES FUND; *U.S. Private*, pg. 1309
EAGLE HOLDING EUROPE B.V.—See Eagle Industry Co., Ltd.; *Int'l*, pg. 2265
EAGLELINE ACQUISITION CORP.; *U.S. Private*, pg. 1311
EAGLE POINT CREDIT COMPANY INC.; *U.S. Public*, pg. 703
EAGLE PRIVATE CAPITAL, LLC; *U.S. Private*, pg. 1310
EAGLES PERSONAL MANAGEMENT COMPANY—See Live Nation Entertainment, Inc.; *U.S. Public*, pg. 1328
EAGLETREE CAPITAL, LP; *U.S. Private*, pg. 1311
EARLY EQUITY PLC; *Int'l*, pg. 2267
EASO BOLSA, S.A.—See Banco de Sabadell, S.A.; *Int'l*, pg. 821
EAST BALKAN PROPERTIES PLC; *Int'l*, pg. 2269
EAST DUBUQUE NITROGEN FERTILIZERS, LLC—See Icahn Enterprises L.P.; *U.S. Public*, pg. 1084
EAST INDIA SECURITIES LIMITED; *Int'l*, pg. 2270
EASTMAN KODAK INTERNATIONAL CAPITAL COMPANY, INC.—See Eastman Kodak Company; *U.S. Public*, pg. 707
EAST MONEY INFORMATION CO., LTD.; *Int'l*, pg. 2270
EAST STONE ACQUISITION CORPORATION; *U.S. Public*, pg. 703
EAST WEST PARTNERS; *U.S. Private*, pg. 1319
EASY FINCORP LIMITED; *Int'l*, pg. 2275
EASY ONE FINANCIAL GROUP LTD.; *Int'l*, pg. 2275
EAT WELL INVESTMENT GROUP INC.; *Int'l*, pg. 2277
EBBGATE INVESTMENTS LIMITED—See Barclays PLC; *Int'l*, pg. 862
EBB HOTELBETRIEBS GMBH—See Erste Group Bank AG; *Int'l*, pg. 2498
E.BRICKS VENTURES; *Int'l*, pg. 2251
EBS D.A.C.—See AIB Group plc; *Int'l*, pg. 228
EBV-BETEILIGUNGEN GMBH—See Erste Group Bank AG; *Int'l*, pg. 2498
ECA MARCELLUS TRUST I—See Energy Corporation of America; *U.S. Public*, pg. 1394
EC EUROPA IMMOBILIEN FONDS NR. 3 GMBH & CO. KG—See Deutsche Bank Aktiengesellschaft; *Int'l*, pg. 2061
E-CHECK HOLDINGS, INC.; *U.S. Private*, pg. 1302
ECI PARTNERS LLP; *Int'l*, pg. 2289
ECLIPSE RESIDENTIAL MORTGAGE INVESTMENT CORPORATION; *Int'l*, pg. 2291
ECM EQUITY CAPITAL MANAGEMENT GMBH; *Int'l*, pg. 2291
ECOFIN U.S. RENEWABLES INFRASTRUCTURE TRUST PLC; *Int'l*, pg. 2295
ECOLABONE B.V.—See Ecolab Inc.; *U.S. Public*, pg. 714
ECOMAX, INC.—See Clark Orient (BVI) Ltd.; *Int'l*, pg. 1650
ECONOCOM FINANCIAL SERVICES INTERNATIONAL BV—See Econocom Group SA; *Int'l*, pg. 2297
ECONOHOMES, LLC.; *U.S. Private*, pg. 1329
ECOSSE ENERGY CORP.; *Int'l*, pg. 2300
ECP-CENTRAL AFRICA—See Emerging Capital Partners (ECP); *U.S. Private*, pg. 1381
ECP ENVIRONMENTAL GROWTH OPPORTUNITIES CORP.; *U.S. Public*, pg. 717
ECP KARLSKRONA AB—See Eurocommercial Properties N.V.; *Int'l*, pg. 2534
ECP-MOROCCO—See Emerging Capital Partners (ECP); *U.S. Private*, pg. 1381
ECP-NIGERIA—See Emerging Capital Partners (ECP); *U.S. Private*, pg. 1381
ECP-NORTH AFRICA—See Emerging Capital Partners (ECP); *U.S. Private*, pg. 1381
ECP-PARIS—See Emerging Capital Partners (ECP); *U.S. Private*, pg. 1381
ECP-SOUTHERN AFRICA—See Emerging Capital Partners (ECP); *U.S. Private*, pg. 1381
ECP-WEST AFRICA—See Emerging Capital Partners (ECP); *U.S. Private*, pg. 1381
ECRID, INC.; *U.S. Public*, pg. 717
ECT FINANCE LTD.—See Environmental Clean Technologies Limited; *Int'l*, pg. 2454
ECZACIBASI PHARMACEUTICAL & INDUSTRIAL INVESTMENT CO.—See Eczacibasi Holding A.S.; *Int'l*, pg. 2301
EDB INVESTMENTS PTE. LTD.; *Int'l*, pg. 2304
EDELWEISS CAPITAL (SINGAPORE) PTE. LIMITED—See Edelweiss Financial Services Ltd.; *Int'l*, pg. 2306
EDELWEISS FINANCIAL SERVICES INC.—See Edelweiss Financial Services Ltd.; *Int'l*, pg. 2306
EDEN CAPITAL MANAGEMENT LLC; *U.S. Private*, pg. 1333
EDEN EMPIRE INC.; *Int'l*, pg. 2306
EDENRED FINLAND OY—See Edenred S.A.; *Int'l*, pg. 2307
EDENRED ITALIA FIN S.R.L—See Edenred S.A.; *Int'l*, pg. 2308
EDENRED JAPAN CO., LTD.—See Edenred S.A.; *Int'l*, pg. 2308
EDENRED MD S.R.L.—See Edenred S.A.; *Int'l*, pg. 2308
EDENRED ROMANIA SRL—See Edenred S.A.; *Int'l*, pg. 2308
EDENRED SAL—See Edenred S.A.; *Int'l*, pg. 2308
EDENRED SINGAPORE PTE. LTD.—See Edenred S.A.; *Int'l*, pg. 2308
EDF INVEST; *Int'l*, pg. 2308
EDGE ASSET MANAGEMENT INC—See Principal Financial Group, Inc.; *U.S. Public*, pg. 1720
EDGE CAPITAL PARTNERS, LLC; *U.S. Private*, pg. 1333
EDGE NATURAL RESOURCES LLC; *U.S. Private*, pg. 1334
EDGE PERFORMANCE VCT PLC—See Edge Group Limited; *Int'l*, pg. 2309
EDGEWATER CAPITAL PARTNERS, L.P.; *U.S. Private*, pg. 1334
EDGEWATER SERVICES, LLC; *U.S. Private*, pg. 1335
EDG PARTNERS, LLC; *U.S. Private*, pg. 1333
EDIFY ACQUISITION CORP.; *U.S. Public*, pg. 719
THE EDINBURGH INVESTMENT TRUST PLC—See Invesco Ltd.; *U.S. Public*, pg. 1163
EDIP GAYRIMENKUL YATIRIM SANAYI VE TICARET A.S.; *Int'l*, pg. 2310
EDISON CAPITAL—See Edison International; *U.S. Public*, pg. 719
EDISON VENTURE PARTNERS LLC; *U.S. Private*, pg. 1337
EDMOND DE ROTHSCHILD ASSET MANAGEMENT—See Edmond de Rothschild Holding S.A.; *Int'l*, pg. 2313
EDMOND DE ROTHSCHILD ASSET MANAGEMENT (SUISSE) SA—See Edmond de Rothschild Holding S.A.; *Int'l*, pg. 2313
EDMOND DE ROTHSCHILD CORPORATE FINANCE—See Edmond de Rothschild Holding S.A.; *Int'l*, pg. 2313
EDMOND DE ROTHSCHILD ENTERPRISES PATRIMONIALES CROISSANCE—See Edmond de Rothschild Holding S.A.; *Int'l*, pg. 2313
EDMOND DE ROTHSCHILD ENTERPRISES PATRIMONIALES—See Edmond de Rothschild Holding S.A.; *Int'l*, pg. 2313
EDMOND DE ROTHSCHILD INVESTMENT SERVICES LIMITED—See Edmond de Rothschild Holding S.A.; *Int'l*, pg. 2312
EDMOND DE ROTHSCHILD PRIVATE EQUITY MANAGEMENT LTD.—See Edmond de Rothschild Holding S.A.; *Int'l*, pg. 2312
EDOC ACQUISITION CORP.—See Australian Oilseeds Holdings Limited; *Int'l*, pg. 722
EDUCATION GROWTH LLC; *U.S. Private*, pg. 1339
EDWARD LOWE FOUNDATION; *U.S. Private*, pg. 1341
EDWARDS CAPITAL, LLC; *U.S. Private*, pg. 1341
EFANOR INVESTIMENTOS, SGPS, SA; *Int'l*, pg. 2318
EFFICIENT GROUP LIMITED—See Apex Fund Services Holdings Ltd.; *Int'l*, pg. 510
EFFICO PORTUGAL—See BNP Paribas SA; *Int'l*, pg. 1090
EFG ASSET MANAGEMENT HOLDING AG—See EFG International AG; *Int'l*, pg. 2320
EFG BANQUE PRIVEE SA—See EFG International AG; *Int'l*, pg. 2320
EFG HERMES FINANCIAL MANAGEMENT (EGYPT) LTD—See EFG Holding; *Int'l*, pg. 2319
EFG - HERMES JORDAN COMPANY—See EFG Holding; *Int'l*, pg. 2319
EFG - HERMES KENYA LTD.—See EFG Holding; *Int'l*, pg. 2319
EFG- HERMES OMAN LLC—See EFG Holding; *Int'l*, pg. 2319
EFG- HERMES UAE LLC—See EFG Holding; *Int'l*, pg. 2319
EFG - HERMES UK LIMITED—See EFG Holding; *Int'l*, pg. 2319
EFG HERMES USA, INC.—See EFG Holding; *Int'l*, pg. 2319
EFG PLATTS FLELLO LTD—See EFG International AG; *Int'l*, pg. 2320
EFG WEALTH MANAGEMENT (INDIA) PRIVATE LIMITED—See EFG International AG; *Int'l*, pg. 2321
EF HUTTON CORP.; *U.S. Private*, pg. 1343
EF SOLUTIONS LLC—See Allianz SE; *Int'l*, pg. 352
EG CAPITAL GROUP, LLC; *U.S. Private*, pg. 1344
EGERIA CAPITAL MANAGEMENT B.V.; *Int'l*, pg. 2323
EGYPT FOR INFORMATION DISSEMINATION—See Cairo & Alexandria Stock Exchanges; *Int'l*, pg. 1253
EGYPTIANS ABROAD INVESTMENT & DEVELOPMENT CO.; *Int'l*, pg. 2327
EHD ADVISORY SERVICES, INC.—See Savant Capital, LLC; *U.S. Private*, pg. 3556
EIG GLOBAL ENERGY PARTNERS, LLC; *U.S. Private*, pg. 1347
EIGHT PEAKS GROUP LTD.; *Int'l*, pg. 2331

523999 — MISCELLANEOUS FINAN...   CORPORATE AFFILIATIONS

EIGHT ROADS VENTURES—See FMR LLC; *U.S. Private*, pg. 1554
EINHELL HOLDING GESELLSCHAFT M.B.H.—See Einhell Germany AG; *Int'l*, pg. 2333
EJADA FOR FINANCIAL INVESTMENTS PLC; *Int'l*, pg. 2337
EJF ACQUISITION CORP.; *U.S. Public*, pg. 721
EK MITTELSTANDSFINANZIERUNGS AG—See Global Equity Partners Beteiligungs-Management AG; *Int'l*, pg. 2996
EKTTITAB HOLDING COMPANY S.A.K.C.; *Int'l*, pg. 2340
ELAN GROWTH PARTNERS, LLC; *U.S. Private*, pg. 1349
ELANTIS PREMIUM FUNDING (NZ) LIMITED—See Arthur J. Gallagher & Co.; *U.S. Public*, pg. 203
ELARG AGRICULTURAL LAND OPPORTUNITY FUND REIT; *Int'l*, pg. 2343
ELB CAPITAL INVESTMENTS (PTY) LIMITED—See ELB Group Limited; *Int'l*, pg. 2343
ELCID INVESTMENTS LIMITED; *Int'l*, pg. 2345
ELDAN TRANSPORTATION LTD.; *Int'l*, pg. 2346
ELDAV INVESTMENT LTD.; *Int'l*, pg. 2346
ELDFELL INVESTMENTS LIMITED—See Barclays PLC; *Int'l*, pg. 862
ELDRIDGE INDUSTRIES LLC; *U.S. Private*, pg. 1351
ELECTRABEL BLUE SKY INVESTMENTS SCRL—See ENGIE SA; *Int'l*, pg. 2431
ELECTROLUX (MALAYSIA) HOLDINGS SDN. BHD.—See AB Electrolux; *Int'l*, pg. 39
ELECTRONIC SERVITOR PUBLICATION NETWORK, INC.; *U.S. Public*, pg. 724
ELECTRUM SPECIAL ACQUISITION CORPORATION; *U.S. Private*, pg. 1356
ELEMENT ALPHA SA; *Int'l*, pg. 2358
ELEMENT PARTNERS, LLC; *U.S. Private*, pg. 1357
ELEMENTS HEALTH INVESTORS, LLC; *U.S. Private*, pg. 1357
ELEVATION PARTNERS; *U.S. Private*, pg. 1358
ELINX CORPORATION; *U.S. Public*, pg. 734
ELITECON INTERNATIONAL LIMITED; *Int'l*, pg. 2363
ELITE GROUP PROPRIETARY LIMITED—See African Dawn Capital Limited; *Int'l*, pg. 191
ELIT GROUP GMBH—See LKQ Corporation; *U.S. Public*, pg. 1334
ELLERSTON GLOBAL INVESTMENTS LIMITED; *Int'l*, pg. 2365
ELLINAS FINANCE PUBLIC COMPANY LTD; *Int'l*, pg. 2366
ELLINGTON CREDIT COMPANY MANAGEMENT LLC; *U.S. Public*, pg. 734
ELLINGTON FINANCIAL INC.—See Ellington Management Group, L.L.C.; *U.S. Private*, pg. 1364
ELLINGTON HOUSING INC.; *U.S. Private*, pg. 1363
ELLIOTT INVESTMENT MANAGEMENT L.P.—See Elliott Management Corporation; *U.S. Private*, pg. 1365
ELLIS CAPITAL, LLC—See Ellis, McQuary, Stanley & Associates LLC; *U.S. Private*, pg. 1374
ELMA HOLDINGS PUBLIC COMPANY LTD; *Int'l*, pg. 2367
ELM CREEK PARTNERS; *U.S. Private*, pg. 1375
ELMHURST GROUP; *U.S. Private*, pg. 1376
ELRON VENTURES LTD; *Int'l*, pg. 2370
EL WADI FOR INTERNATIONAL AND INVESTMENT DEVELOPMENT SAE; *Int'l*, pg. 2371
ELYSEE DEVELOPMENT CORP.; *Int'l*, pg. 2372
ELYSIAN CAPITAL LLP; *Int'l*, pg. 2372
EMBARK GROUP LIMITED; *Int'l*, pg. 2374
EMBARK TECHNOLOGY, INC.—See Applied Intuition, Inc.; *U.S. Private*, pg. 299
EMBRACE CHANGE ACQUISITION CORP.; *Int'l*, pg. 2375
EMBRAER SPAIN HOLDING CO., SL—See Embraer S.A.; *Int'l*, pg. 2375
EMCON TECHNOLOGIES HUNGARY HOLDINGS KFT—See FORVIA SE; *Int'l*, pg. 2745
EME CAPITAL LLP; *Int'l*, pg. 2376
EMERAM CAPITAL PARTNERS GMBH; *Int'l*, pg. 2378
EMERGE COMMERCE LTD.; *Int'l*, pg. 2378
EMERGENCE CAPITAL PARTNERS; *U.S. Private*, pg. 1380
E.MERGE TECHNOLOGY ACQUISITION CORP.; *U.S. Public*, pg. 701
EMERGEVEST LIMITED; *Int'l*, pg. 2378
EMERGING CAPITAL PARTNERS (ECP); *U.S. Private*, pg. 1381
EMERGING MARKETS HORIZON CORP.; *U.S. Public*, pg. 2379
EMERGING OPPORTUNITIES CORP.; *U.S. Private*, pg. 1381
EMERISQUE BRANDS UK LIMITED; *Int'l*, pg. 2379
EMETALS LIMITED; *Int'l*, pg. 2380
EMF CAPITAL (UK) LIMITED—See EMF Capital Partners Limited; *Int'l*, pg. 2380
EMH PARTNERS GMBH; *Int'l*, pg. 2380
EMIRATES ADVANCED INVESTMENTS GROUP LLC; *Int'l*, pg. 2381
EMIRATES INVESTMENT & DEVELOPMENT COMPANY PSC; *Int'l*, pg. 2381
EMOLEUM ROADS GROUP PTY LIMITED—See Downer EDI Limited; *Int'l*, pg. 2186
EMPEIRIA CAPITAL PARTNERS LLC; *U.S. Private*, pg. 1384
EMPEROR CAPITAL GROUP LIMITED; *Int'l*, pg. 2386

EMP GLOBAL LLC; *U.S. Private*, pg. 1383
EMPIRE INVESTMENT HOLDINGS, LLC; *U.S. Private*, pg. 1385
EMP LATIN AMERICAN MANAGEMENT LLC—See EMP Global LLC; *U.S. Private*, pg. 1384
EMPOWERED VENTURES, INC.; *U.S. Private*, pg. 1387
EMPRESA FINANCIERA EDYFICAR S.A.—See Credicorp Ltd.; *Int'l*, pg. 1834
EMPYRION WEALTH MANAGEMENT, INC.—See Genstar Capital, LLC; *U.S. Private*, pg. 1677
EMPYRION WEALTH MANAGEMENT, INC.—See Keystone Group, L.P.; *U.S. Private*, pg. 2298
EMR CAPITAL PTY LTD; *Int'l*, pg. 2392
EMRO FINANCE IRELAND LIMITED—See BPER BANCA S.p.A; *Int'l*, pg. 1132
EMRY CAPITAL GROUP, INC.; *U.S. Private*, pg. 1388
ENBRIDGE INCOME FUND HOLDINGS INC.—See Enbridge Inc.; *Int'l*, pg. 2397
ENCAVIS AG; *Int'l*, pg. 2401
ENCOMPASS HOLDINGS, INC.; *U.S. Public*, pg. 759
ENCORE CONSUMER CAPITAL LLC—See Encore Associates Inc.; *U.S. Private*, pg. 1390
ENDEAVOUR VENTURES LIMITED; *Int'l*, pg. 2403
ENDI CORP.; *U.S. Public*, pg. 760
ENDLESS LLP; *Int'l*, pg. 2403
ENDONOVO THERAPEUTICS, INC.; *U.S. Public*, pg. 760
ENDURANCE ACQUISITION CORP.; *U.S. Public*, pg. 760
ENEL FINANCE INTERNATIONAL NV—See Enel S.p.A.; *Int'l*, pg. 2413
ENERCARE INC.—See Brookfield Infrastructure Partners L.P.; *Int'l*, pg. 1190
ENERFUND, LLC; *U.S. Private*, pg. 1393
ENERGY CAPITAL PARTNERS MANAGEMENT, LP; *U.S. Private*, pg. 1393
THE ENERGY & MINERALS GROUP LP - DALLAS OFFICE—See The Energy & Minerals Group LP; *U.S. Private*, pg. 4026
THE ENERGY & MINERALS GROUP LP; *U.S. Private*, pg. 4026
ENERGYPATHWAYS PLC; *Int'l*, pg. 2423
ENERGY SERVICES OF AMERICA CORPORATION; *U.S. Public*, pg. 762
ENERGY SPECTRUM SECURITIES CORPORATION; *U.S. Private*, pg. 1396
ENERGY TRANSITION PARTNERS B.V.; *Int'l*, pg. 2423
ENERGY VAULT HOLDINGS, INC.; *U.S. Public*, pg. 765
ENERSPAR CORP.; *Int'l*, pg. 2424
ENGEX, INC.; *U.S. Public*, pg. 768
ENGIE SERVICES U.S. INC—See ENGIE SA; *Int'l*, pg. 2428
ENGILITY CORPORATION—See Science Applications International Corporation; *U.S. Public*, pg. 1848
ENHANCED CAPITAL PARTNERS LLC; *U.S. Private*, pg. 1400
ENI FINANCE INTERNATIONAL SA—See Eni S.p.A.; *Int'l*, pg. 2437
ENI ULT LTD—See Eni S.p.A.; *Int'l*, pg. 2437
ENLIGHTENMENT CAPITAL LLC; *U.S. Private*, pg. 1400
ENNOGIE SOLAR GROUP A/S; *Int'l*, pg. 2443
ENNOX GROUP LTD.; *Int'l*, pg. 2444
E-NOVIA S.P.A.; *Int'l*, pg. 2249
ENOVIX CORPORATION; *U.S. Public*, pg. 774
ENPHYS ACQUISITION CORP.; *U.S. Public*, pg. 774
ENRA GROUP BERHAD; *Int'l*, pg. 2445
ENTERPRISE 4.0 TECHNOLOGY ACQUISITION CORP.; *U.S. Public*, pg. 777
ENTERPRISE FLEET MANAGEMENT EXCHANGE, INC.—See Deutsche Bank Aktiengesellschaft; *Int'l*, pg. 2061
ENTERPRISE INVESTMENT FUND SLHF.; *Int'l*, pg. 2451
ENTERPRISE INVESTORS SP. Z O.O.; *Int'l*, pg. 2451
ENTERRA CORPORATION; *U.S. Public*, pg. 779
ENTREPRENEURIAL EQUITY PARTNERS, LLC; *U.S. Private*, pg. 1406
ENVIRONMENTAL IMPACT ACQUISITION CORP.; *U.S. Public*, pg. 781
ENVIRONMENTAL PACKAGING TECHNOLOGIES HOLDINGS, INC.; *U.S. Public*, pg. 781
ENVOI, LLC—See AiTi Global, Inc.; *U.S. Public*, pg. 87
E. OHMAN J:OR AB; *Int'l*, pg. 2250
E.ON CZECH HOLDING AG—See E.ON SE; *Int'l*, pg. 2252
E.ON ENERGIE 31. BETEILIGUNGSGESELLSCHAFT MBH MUNCHEN—See E.ON SE; *Int'l*, pg. 2252
E.ON ENERGY TRADING HOLDING GMBH—See E.ON SE; *Int'l*, pg. 2254
E.ON GAZDASAGI SZOLGALTATO KFT.—See E.ON SE; *Int'l*, pg. 2254
E.ON INTERNATIONAL FINANCE B.V.—See E.ON SE; *Int'l*, pg. 2254
E.ON INVEST GMBH—See E.ON SE; *Int'l*, pg. 2254
E.ON NA CAPITAL LLC—See E.ON SE; *Int'l*, pg. 2254
E.ON UK HOLDING COMPANY LIMITED—See E.ON SE; *Int'l*, pg. 2256
EOS ENERGY ENTERPRISES, INC.—See B. Riley Financial, Inc.; *U.S. Public*, pg. 260
EOS PARTNERS, L.P.; *U.S. Private*, pg. 1411
EOS SERVIZI FIDUCIARI SPA—See EFG International AG; *Int'l*, pg. 2320
EPE SPECIAL OPPORTUNITIES LIMITED; *Int'l*, pg. 2459

EPIPHANY TECHNOLOGY ACQUISITION CORP.; *U.S. Public*, pg. 783
EPISIL HOLDINGS, INC.; *Int'l*, pg. 2463
EPR PROPERTIES; *U.S. Public*, pg. 784
EPS POLSKA HOLDING SP. Z O.O.—See E.ON SE; *Int'l*, pg. 2256
EPUJA SPIRITECH LTD.; *Int'l*, pg. 2466
EQ HEALTH ACQUISITION CORP.; *U.S. Public*, pg. 784
EQ OYJ; *Int'l*, pg. 2466
EQT FUNDS MANAGEMENT LTD—See EQT AB; *Int'l*, pg. 2475
EQT MANAGEMENT S.A.R.L.—See EQT AB; *Int'l*, pg. 2475
EQT PARTNERS AB—See EQT AB; *Int'l*, pg. 2467
EQT PARTNERS AG—See EQT AB; *Int'l*, pg. 2475
EQT PARTNERS ASIA LTD—See EQT AB; *Int'l*, pg. 2475
EQT PARTNERS A/S—See EQT AB; *Int'l*, pg. 2475
EQT PARTNERS GMBH—See EQT AB; *Int'l*, pg. 2475
EQT PARTNERS INC.—See EQT AB; *Int'l*, pg. 2475
EQT PARTNERS OY—See EQT AB; *Int'l*, pg. 2475
EQT PARTNERS SHANGHAI LTD—See EQT AB; *Int'l*, pg. 2475
EQT PARTNERS SINGAPORE PTE LTD—See EQT AB; *Int'l*, pg. 2475
EQT PARTNERS SP. Z O.O.—See EQT AB; *Int'l*, pg. 2475
EQT PARTNERS UK ADVISORS LLP—See EQT AB; *Int'l*, pg. 2475
EQUILIBRIUM CAPITAL MANAGEMENT LLC; *U.S. Private*, pg. 1415
EQUINOR TECHNOLOGY VENTURES AS—See Equinor ASA; *Int'l*, pg. 2484
EQUIPMENT HOLDING COMPANY K.S.C.C.; *Int'l*, pg. 2485
EQUISOURCE HOTEL FUND I, LLP; *U.S. Private*, pg. 1416
EQUISTONE PARTNERS EUROPE LIMITED; *Int'l*, pg. 2486
THE EQUITIUM GROUP, LLC; *U.S. Private*, pg. 4026
EQUITY38, LLC; *U.S. Private*, pg. 1416
EQUITY DISTRIBUTION ACQUISITION CORP.; *U.S. Public*, pg. 790
EQUITY INVESTMENT SERVICES LTD—See Equity Bank Limited; *Int'l*, pg. 2488
EQUITY STORY GROUP LTD.; *Int'l*, pg. 2488
EQUITY VALUE INVESTMENTS NO.1 LIMITED—See Barclays PLC; *Int'l*, pg. 862
EQUIVEST GMBH & CO—See CBR Management GmbH; *Int'l*, pg. 1366
EQUUS CAPITAL PARTNERS, LTD.; *U.S. Private*, pg. 1416
EQVITEC PARTNERS OY; *Int'l*, pg. 2488
ERGON CAPITAL MANAGEMENT SA—See Groupe Bruxelles Lambert SA; *Int'l*, pg. 3099
ERISBEG HOLDINGS LIMITED; *Int'l*, pg. 2493
ERSTE FAKTOR PENZUGYI SZOLGALTATO ZRT.—See Erste Group Bank AG; *Int'l*, pg. 2498
ERSTE FRANKFURTER HOIST GMBH—See Deutsche Bank Aktiengesellschaft; *Int'l*, pg. 2061
ERSTE KERESKEDOHAZ KFT.—See Erste Group Bank AG; *Int'l*, pg. 2498
ERSTE-SPARINVEST KAPITALANLAGEGESELLSCHAFT M.B.H.—See Erste Group Bank AG; *Int'l*, pg. 2498
ESAAR (INDIA) LIMITED; *Int'l*, pg. 2501
ESCORTS FINANCE LIMITED—See Escorts Kubota Limited; *Int'l*, pg. 2502
ESCUDO CAPITAL CORPORATION; *Int'l*, pg. 2502
ESG GLOBAL IMPACT CAPITAL INC.; *Int'l*, pg. 2503
ESH ACQUISITION CORP.; *U.S. Public*, pg. 794
ESH HOSPITALITY, INC.—See Blackstone Inc.; *U.S. Public*, pg. 350
ESH HOSPITALITY, INC.—See Starwood Capital Group Global I, LLC; *U.S. Private*, pg. 3789
ESI INVESTMENT CO.—See Electro-Sensors, Inc.; *U.S. Public*, pg. 723
ESI VENTURES LLC; *U.S. Private*, pg. 1426
ESM ACQUISITION CORPORATION; *U.S. Public*, pg. 794
ESOMET SAS—See BNP Paribas SA; *Int'l*, pg. 1091
ESO PARTNERS L.P.; *Int'l*, pg. 2504
ESPA-FINANCIAL ADVISORS GMBH—See Erste Group Bank AG; *Int'l*, pg. 2498
ESPIGA CAPITAL GESTION S.G.E.C.R, S.A.; *Int'l*, pg. 2506
ESSAR INVESTMENTS LTD.—See Essar Global Limited; *Int'l*, pg. 2508
ESSEL FINANCE VKC FOREX LIMITED—See Ebix Inc.; *U.S. Public*, pg. 710
ESSENTIAL HOUSING INVESTMENT; *U.S. Private*, pg. 1427
ESSEX WOODLANDS MANAGEMENT, INC.; *U.S. Private*, pg. 1428
ESSTRA INDUSTRIES INC.; *Int'l*, pg. 2517
ESTANCIA CAPITAL MANAGEMENT, LLC; *U.S. Private*, pg. 1428
ESTERAD INVESTMENT COMPANY BSC; *Int'l*, pg. 2518
ESTRELLA INTERNATIONAL ENERGY SERVICES LTD.; *Int'l*, pg. 2518
ESUCO BEHEER B.V.—See BASF SE; *Int'l*, pg. 883
ESW CAPITAL, LLC; *U.S. Private*, pg. 1429
ETC M-A ACQUISITION LLC—See Energy Transfer LP; *U.S. Public*, pg. 763
ETCO DEVELOPMENT INC.; *U.S. Private*, pg. 1431
ETFS ASIAN GOLD TRUST; *U.S. Private*, pg. 1431
ETHOS CAPITAL, LLC; *U.S. Private*, pg. 1432

N.A.I.C.S. INDEX

523999 — MISCELLANEOUS FINAN...

ETHOS PRIVATE EQUITY (PROPRIETARY) LIMITED—See TRG Management LP; *U.S. Private*, pg. 4219
ETRE REIT, LLC; *U.S. Private*, pg. 1432
ETUA OY—See Alma Media Corporation; *Int'l*, pg. 362
EUCRATES BIOMEDICAL ACQUISITION CORP.; *U.S. Public*, pg. 797
EULER GESTION—See Allianz SE; *Int'l*, pg. 352
EULER HERMES CESCOB SERVICE S.R.O.—See Allianz SE; *Int'l*, pg. 352
EULER HERMES MAGYAR KOVETELESKEZELO KFT.—See Allianz SE; *Int'l*, pg. 352
EULER HERMES RISK SERVICES UK LIMITED—See Allianz SE; *Int'l*, pg. 353
EULER HERMES SERVICES INDIA PRIVATE LIMITED—See Allianz SE; *Int'l*, pg. 353
EULER HERMES SVERIGE—See Allianz SE; *Int'l*, pg. 353
EURAZEO NORTH AMERICA INC.—See Eurazeo SE; *Int'l*, pg. 2528
EURAZEO PME SAS—See Eurazeo SE; *Int'l*, pg. 2528
EURAZEO SE; *Int'l*, pg. 2527
EUREAM GMBH—See Commerzbank AG; *Int'l*, pg. 1718
EUREKA 93 INC.; *Int'l*, pg. 2530
EUREKING SA; *Int'l*, pg. 2530
EUREX CLEARING AG—See Deutsche Borse AG; *Int'l*, pg. 2063
EUREX REPO GMBH—See Deutsche Borse AG; *Int'l*, pg. 2063
EUROBANK LEASING SINGLE-MEMBER SA—See Eurobank Ergasias Services and Holdings S.A.; *Int'l*, pg. 2532
EURO CAPITAL SAS—See Groupe BPCE; *Int'l*, pg. 3094
EUROCASTLE INVESTMENT LIMITED; *Int'l*, pg. 2533
EUROCOMMERCIAL PROPERTIES AZUR S.A.R.L—See Eurocommercial Properties N.V.; *Int'l*, pg. 2534
EUROCOMMERCIAL PROPERTIES LTD—See Eurocommercial Properties N.V.; *Int'l*, pg. 2534
EUROFINS FOOD DENMARK HOLDING A/S—See Eurofins Scientific S.E.; *Int'l*, pg. 2541
EUROFINS FOOD TESTING NETHERLANDS HOLDING BV—See Eurofins Scientific S.E.; *Int'l*, pg. 2541
EUROFINS FOOD US HOLDINGS II BV—See Eurofins Scientific S.E.; *Int'l*, pg. 2542
EURO INGATLAN CENTER KFT.—See BayernLB Holding AG; *Int'l*, pg. 913
EURO KAPITAL YATIRIM ORTAKLIGI A.S.; *Int'l*, pg. 2531
EUROLEASE GROUP EAD—See Eurohold Bulgaria AD; *Int'l*, pg. 2553
EUROMEZZANINE CONSEIL SAS; *Int'l*, pg. 2554
EUROMOBILIARE ALTERNATIVE INVESTMENT SGR SPA—See Credito Emiliano S.p.A.; *Int'l*, pg. 1836
EUROPA GROWTH COMPANY; *Int'l*, pg. 2555
EUROPA INVESTIMENTI S.P.A.—See Arrow Global Group PLC; *Int'l*, pg. 579
EUROPEAN HEALTHCARE ACQUISITION & GROWTH COMPANY V.; *Int'l*, pg. 2556
EUROPEAN INVESTMENT FUND—See European Investment Bank; *Int'l*, pg. 2556
EUROPEAN SUSTAINABLE GROWTH ACQUISITION CORP.; *U.S. Public*, pg. 799
EUROPLAY CAPITAL ADVISORS, LLC; *U.S. Private*, pg. 1434
EUROPOLIS AG—See Starwood Capital Group Global I, LLC; *U.S. Private*, pg. 3789
EUROPTRONIC INVESTMENT PTE. LTD.—See Europtronic Group Ltd.; *Int'l*, pg. 2557
EUROVESTECH PLC; *Int'l*, pg. 2558
EVANS & PARTNERS PTY. LIMITED—See E&P Financial Group Limited; *Int'l*, pg. 2247
EVANSTON PARTNERS, LLC; *U.S. Private*, pg. 1435
EV DIGITAL INVEST AG; *Int'l*, pg. 2560
EVE & CO INCORPORATED; *Int'l*, pg. 2561
EVE HEALTH GROUP LIMITED; *Int'l*, pg. 2561
EVE MOBILITY ACQUISITION CORP.; *U.S. Public*, pg. 799
EVERARC HOLDINGS LIMITED; *Int'l*, pg. 2563
EVERCORE CAPITAL PARTNERS—See Evercore, Inc.; *U.S. Public*, pg. 800
EVEREST CONSOLIDATOR ACQUISITION CORPORATION; *U.S. Public*, pg. 800
EVERGRANDE PROPERTY SERVICES GROUP LIMITED; *Int'l*, pg. 2565
EVERGREEN-AGRA, INC.; *U.S. Public*, pg. 800
EVERGREEN COAST CAPITAL CORP.—See Elliott Management Corporation; *U.S. Private*, pg. 1366
EVERGREEN PACIFIC PARTNERS MANAGEMENT CO., INC.; *U.S. Private*, pg. 1440
EVERSTONE CAPITAL ADVISORS PVT. LTD.; *Int'l*, pg. 2569
EVERSTONE CAPITAL ASIA PTE. LTD.—See Everstone Capital Advisors Pvt. Ltd.; *Int'l*, pg. 2569
EVERSTONE CAPITAL LIMITED—See Everstone Capital Advisors Pvt. Ltd.; *Int'l*, pg. 2569
EVERWATCH CAPITAL; *U.S. Private*, pg. 1440
EVERYDAY PEOPLE FINANCIAL CORP.; *Int'l*, pg. 2570
EVGO INC.; *U.S. Public*, pg. 802
EVN UMWELT FINANZ- UND SERVICE-GMBH—See EVN AG; *Int'l*, pg. 2571
EVO ACQUISITION CORP.; *U.S. Public*, pg. 803
EVOLUTIONARY GENOMICS, INC.; *U.S. Public*, pg. 804

EVOLUTION CAPITAL INVESTMENTS LLC—See Evolution Capital Management LLC; *U.S. Private*, pg. 1442
EVOLUTION CAPITAL PARTNERS, LLC; *U.S. Private*, pg. 1443
EVOLUTION TECHNOLOGY RESOURCES, INC.; *Int'l*, pg. 2572
EVOLV TECHNOLOGIES HOLDINGS INC.; *U.S. Public*, pg. 804
EXCALIBUR GLOBAL FINANCIAL GROUP LTD.—See Excalibur Global Financial Holdings Ltd.; *Int'l*, pg. 2577
EXCALIBUR GLOBAL FINANCIAL HOLDINGS LTD.; *Int'l*, pg. 2577
EXCELFIN ACQUISITION CORP.; *U.S. Public*, pg. 805
EXCELLENCE INVESTMENTS LTD.—See Delek Group Ltd.; *Int'l*, pg. 2011
EXCELLERE CAPITAL MANAGEMENT LLC; *U.S. Private*, pg. 1446
EXCELSA ACQUISITION CORP.; *U.S. Private*, pg. 1446
EXCELSIOR CAPITAL ASIA (HK) LIMITED; *Int'l*, pg. 2578
EXCELSIOR CAPITAL KOREA LIMITED—See Excelsior Capital Asia (HK) Limited; *Int'l*, pg. 2578
EXCELSIOR UNITED DEVELOPMENT COMPANIES LIMITED; *Int'l*, pg. 2579
EXCHANGE INCOME CORPORATION; *Int'l*, pg. 2579
EXCOLERE ACQUISITION CORP.; *U.S. Private*, pg. 1447
EXECUTIVE NETWORK PARTNERING CORPORATION; *U.S. Public*, pg. 806
EXEL INVESTMENTS INC.—See Deutsche Post AG; *Int'l*, pg. 2080
EXELIXIS INVESTMENTS PUBLIC LIMITED; *Int'l*, pg. 2583
EXIDE LIFE INSURANCE COMPANY LIMITED—See EXIDE INDUSTRIES LIMITED; *Int'l*, pg. 2585
EXIUM PARTNERS, LLC; *U.S. Private*, pg. 1449
EXO U INC.; *Int'l*, pg. 2586
EXPEDITION CAPITAL PARTNERS LLC; *U.S. Private*, pg. 1449
EXPERIAN INVESTMENT HOLDINGS LIMITED—See Experian plc; *Int'l*, pg. 2587
EXPERT & FINANCE S.A.—See Assicurazioni Generali S.p.A.; *Int'l*, pg. 645
EXPORT INVESTMENT CO. LTD.; *Int'l*, pg. 2590
EXPORTS OF WASHINGTON INCORPORATED; *U.S. Private*, pg. 1451
EXTER-REAL INGATLANFORGALMAZASI KORLATOLT FELELOSSEGU TARSASAG—See BayernLB Holding AG; *Int'l*, pg. 913
EXTRAWELL ENTERPRISES LIMITED—See Extrawell Pharmaceutical Holdings Ltd.; *Int'l*, pg. 2592
EYRIR INVEST HF.; *Int'l*, pg. 2593
F2I - FONDI ITALIANI PER LE INFRASTRUTTURE SGR S.P.A.; *Int'l*, pg. 2597
F2 STRATEGY, INC.—See Renovus Capital Partners; *U.S. Private*, pg. 3399
FABCOS INVESTMENT HOLDING COMPANY (PROPRIETARY) LIMITED—See Hosken Consolidated Investments Limited; *Int'l*, pg. 3485
FABREL LOTOS AG—See Fabrel AG; *Int'l*, pg. 2599
FACILEASING EQUIPMENT, S.A. DE C.V.—See Banco Bilbao Vizcaya Argentaria, S.A.; *Int'l*, pg. 817
FAC PROPERTYS LLC; *U.S. Private*, pg. 1459
FACTOR 89 PARTNERS, LLC; *U.S. Private*, pg. 1460
FAI CAPITAL MANAGEMENT INC.; *U.S. Private*, pg. 1461
FAIRCAP GMBH; *Int'l*, pg. 2605
FAIRCHILD CAPITAL PARTNERS, LLC; *U.S. Private*, pg. 1462
FAIRCOURT GOLD INCOME CORP.; *Int'l*, pg. 2605
FAIRCOURT SPLIT TRUST; *Int'l*, pg. 2605
FAIR EAGLE SECURITIES COMPANY LIMITED—See Chinese Estates Holdings Limited; *Int'l*, pg. 1569
FAIRHAVEN CAPITAL MANAGEMENT, LLC; *U.S. Private*, pg. 1464
FAIR OAKS INCOME LIMITED; *Int'l*, pg. 2605
FAIVELEY TRANSPORT HOLDING GMBH & CO KG—See Westinghouse Air Brake Technologies Corporation; *U.S. Public*, pg. 2357
FALCON ACQUISITION CORP.; *U.S. Private*, pg. 1466
FALCON AFFILIATES, LLC; *U.S. Private*, pg. 1466
FALCONHEAD CAPITAL, LLC; *U.S. Private*, pg. 1467
FALFURRIAS CAPITAL PARTNERS, LP; *U.S. Private*, pg. 1467
FAMILY SECURITY CREDIT UNION; *U.S. Private*, pg. 1471
FAMOUS PAWN, INC.—See FirstCash Holdings, Inc.; *U.S. Public*, pg. 849
FANDIFI TECHNOLOGY CORP.; *Int'l*, pg. 2613
FANLOGIC INTERACTIVE INC.; *Int'l*, pg. 2613
FARALLON CAPITAL MANAGEMENT, L.L.C.; *U.S. Private*, pg. 1473
FAR EAST CONSORTIUM INTERNATIONAL LIMITED; *Int'l*, pg. 2615
FAREAST FINANCE & INVESTMENT LIMITED; *Int'l*, pg. 2618
FAR EAST HOLDINGS INTERNATIONAL LIMITED; *Int'l*, pg. 2616
FAREAST ISLAMI LIFE INSURANCE CO. LTD.; *Int'l*, pg. 2618
FARM CREDIT CANADA; *Int'l*, pg. 2619
FARMLAND PARTNERS INC.; *U.S. Public*, pg. 822
FAROL ASSET MANAGEMENT LP; *U.S. Private*, pg. 1480

FAR PEAK ACQUISITION CORPORATION; *U.S. Public*, pg. 821
FAR POINT ACQUISITION CORPORATION; *U.S. Public*, pg. 821
FAS FINANCE & INVESTMENT LIMITED; *Int'l*, pg. 2620
FAST ACQUISITION CORP.; *U.S. Public*, pg. 823
FAST EJENDOM DANMARK A/S; *Int'l*, pg. 2621
FASTIGHETS AB BALDER; *Int'l*, pg. 2622
FAST LANE ACQUISITION, INC.; *U.S. Private*, pg. 1482
FATCO HOLDINGS, LLC—See First American Financial Corporation; *U.S. Public*, pg. 835
FAT PROJECTS ACQUISITION CORP.; *Int'l*, pg. 2622
FAT PROPHETS GLOBAL CONTRARIAN FUND LTD.; *Int'l*, pg. 2622
FAURECIA NETHERLANDS HOLDING B.V.—See FORVIA SE; *Int'l*, pg. 2747
FB CAPITAL PARTNERS, L.P.; *U.S. Private*, pg. 1485
FCCC, INC.; *U.S. Public*, pg. 824
FC CRESTONE LLC; *U.S. Private*, pg. 1485
FCC VENTURES—See Farm Credit Canada; *Int'l*, pg. 2619
FCE BANK PLC - AUSTRIA—See Ford Motor Company; *U.S. Public*, pg. 865
F&C EMERGING MARKETS LIMITED—See Bank of Montreal; *Int'l*, pg. 847
FCF PARTNERS, LP; *U.S. Private*, pg. 1485
FCFS CO, INC.—See FirstCash Holdings, Inc.; *U.S. Public*, pg. 849
FCMB CAPITAL MARKETS LIMITED—See FCMB Group Plc; *Int'l*, pg. 2628
FCMB MICROFINANCE BANK LIMITED—See FCMB Group Plc; *Int'l*, pg. 2628
F&C PORTUGAL GESTAO DE PATRIMONIOS S.A.—See Bank of Montreal; *Int'l*, pg. 847
FCSTONE TRADING, LLC—See StoneX Group Inc.; *U.S. Public*, pg. 1952
FDG ASSOCIATES LP; *U.S. Private*, pg. 1486
FEATHERINGILL CAPITAL, LLC; *U.S. Private*, pg. 1486
FEDCAP PARTNERS, LLC; *U.S. Private*, pg. 1486
FEDERAL CAPITAL PTE LTD—See Federal International (2000) Ltd; *Int'l*, pg. 2630
FEDERAL LIFE GROUP, INC.; *U.S. Public*, pg. 825
FEDERAL-MOGUL AFTERMARKET ESPANA, SA—See Apollo Global Management, Inc.; *U.S. Public*, pg. 160
FEDERAL-MOGUL AFTERMARKET UK LIMITED—See Apollo Global Management, Inc.; *U.S. Public*, pg. 162
FEDERAL MOGUL ARGENTINA SA.—See Apollo Global Management, Inc.; *U.S. Public*, pg. 160
FEDERAL-MOGUL AUTOMOTIVE PTY LTD.—See Apollo Global Management, Inc.; *U.S. Public*, pg. 160
FEDERAL-MOGUL BRADFORD LIMITED—See Apollo Global Management, Inc.; *U.S. Public*, pg. 162
FEDERAL-MOGUL BURSCHEID BETEILIGUNGS GMBH—See Apollo Global Management, Inc.; *U.S. Public*, pg. 160
FEDERAL-MOGUL CANADA LIMITED—See Apollo Global Management, Inc.; *U.S. Public*, pg. 160
FEDERAL-MOGUL DE MEXICO S.A. DE C.V.—See Apollo Global Management, Inc.; *U.S. Public*, pg. 160
FEDERAL-MOGUL DONGSUH (QINGDAO) PISTONS CO., LTD.—See Apollo Global Management, Inc.; *U.S. Public*, pg. 160
FEDERAL-MOGUL EMEA DISTRIBUTION SERVICES, BVBA—See Apollo Global Management, Inc.; *U.S. Public*, pg. 160
FEDERAL-MOGUL FINANCIAL SERVICES SAS—See Apollo Global Management, Inc.; *U.S. Public*, pg. 160
FEDERAL-MOGUL FRICTION PRODUCTS LIMITED—See Apollo Global Management, Inc.; *U.S. Public*, pg. 162
FEDERAL-MOGUL FRICTION PRODUCTS SA—See Apollo Global Management, Inc.; *U.S. Public*, pg. 161
FEDERAL-MOGUL FRIEDBERG GMBH—See Apollo Global Management, Inc.; *U.S. Public*, pg. 161
FEDERAL-MOGUL GLOBAL AFTERMARKET EMEA, BVBA—See Apollo Global Management, Inc.; *U.S. Public*, pg. 161
FEDERAL-MOGUL GMBH—See Apollo Global Management, Inc.; *U.S. Public*, pg. 161
FEDERAL-MOGUL INDUSTRIA DE AUTOPECAS LTDA.—See Apollo Global Management, Inc.; *U.S. Public*, pg. 161
FEDERAL-MOGUL ITALY S.R.L.—See Apollo Global Management, Inc.; *U.S. Public*, pg. 161
FEDERAL MOGUL JAPAN K.K.—See Apollo Global Management, Inc.; *U.S. Public*, pg. 160
FEDERAL-MOGUL LIMITED—See Apollo Global Management, Inc.; *U.S. Public*, pg. 162
FEDERAL-MOGUL VALVETRAIN GMBH—See Apollo Global Management, Inc.; *U.S. Public*, pg. 161
FEDERAL-MOGUL WORLD TRADE (ASIA) LIMITED—See Apollo Global Management, Inc.; *U.S. Public*, pg. 162
FEDERAL STREET ACQUISITION CORP.—See Thomas H. Lee Partners, L.P.; *U.S. Private*, pg. 4156
FEDERATED HERMES (UK) LLP—See Federated Hermes, Inc.; *U.S. Public*, pg. 827
FEE INVESTMENT MANAGEMENT & CONSULTANCY (SHANGHAI) CO., LTD.—See Federal International (2000) Ltd; *Int'l*, pg. 2630
FELDSCHLOSSCHEN GETRANKE HOLDING AG—See

Carlsberg A/S; *Int'l*, pg. 1340
FELLAZO INC.; *Int'l*, pg. 2633
FELT PRODUCTS MFG. CO.—See Icahn Enterprises L.P.; *U.S. Public*, pg. 1084
FENWAY PARTNERS, LLC; *U.S. Private*, pg. 1495
FERNANDEZ HOLDINGS, INC.; *U.S. Private*, pg. 1497
FERRER FREEMAN & COMPANY, LLC; *U.S. Private*, pg. 1498
FEXCO BUSINESS CONSULTING (SHANGHAI) LTD—See FEXCO Holdings; *Int'l*, pg. 2649
FEXCO DCC SOLUTIONS FZ-LLC—See FEXCO Holdings; *Int'l*, pg. 2649
FEXCO FINANCIAL SERVICES—See FEXCO Holdings; *Int'l*, pg. 2649
FEXCO LTD—See FEXCO Holdings; *Int'l*, pg. 2649
FEXCO PACIFIC NEW ZEALAND—See FEXCO Holdings; *Int'l*, pg. 2649
FFG SECURITIES CO., LTD.—See Fukuoka Financial Group, Inc.; *Int'l*, pg. 2840
FFL PARTNERS, LLC; *U.S. Private*, pg. 1500
FH CAPITAL LIMITED—See Finance House P.J.S.C.; *Int'l*, pg. 2664
FHL LEASE HOLDING COMPANY INC.—See BNP Paribas SA; *Int'l*, pg. 1088
FI360, INC.—See Broadridge Financial Solutions, Inc.; *U.S. Public*, pg. 391
FIAT INDUSTRIAL FINANCE NORTH AMERICA, INC.—See CNH Industrial N.V.; *Int'l*, pg. 1675
FIAT INDUSTRIAL FINANCE S.P.A.—See CNH Industrial N.V.; *Int'l*, pg. 1675
FIBEMI NV; *Int'l*, pg. 2651
FIBRA UNO ADMINISTRACION SA DE CV; *Int'l*, pg. 2653
FIDANTE PARTNERS EUROPE LIMITED—See Challenger Limited; *Int'l*, pg. 1438
FIDEICOMISO ENA NORTE; *Int'l*, pg. 2654
FIDEICOMISO ENA SUR; *Int'l*, pg. 2654
FIDELIS CAPITAL LLC; *U.S. Private*, pg. 1502
FIDELITAS INDUSTRIEHOLDING GMBH; *Int'l*, pg. 2654
FIDELITY ASIAN VALUES PLC; *Int'l*, pg. 2654
FIDELITY HOLDING CORP.—See Clean Vision Corporation; *U.S. Public*, pg. 510
FIDELITY INVESTMENTS INSTITUTIONAL SERVICES COMPANY—See FMR LLC; *U.S. Private*, pg. 1555
FIDELITY JAPAN TRUST PLC; *Int'l*, pg. 2654
FIDELITY PRIVATE CREDIT COMPANY LLC; *U.S. Private*, pg. 1503
FIDELITY SPECIAL VALUES PLC; *Int'l*, pg. 2654
FIDUCIAN FINANCIAL SERVICES PTY. LTD.—See Fiducian Group Limited; *Int'l*, pg. 2655
FIDUCIARY INTERNATIONAL, INC.—See Franklin Resources, Inc.; *U.S. Public*, pg. 880
FIDUCIARY INVESTMENT MANAGEMENT INTERNATIONAL, INC.—See Franklin Resources, Inc.; *U.S. Public*, pg. 880
FIDUCIARY TRUST COMPANY OF CANADA—See Franklin Resources, Inc.; *U.S. Public*, pg. 880
FIDUCIARY TRUST INTERNATIONAL LIMITED—See Franklin Resources, Inc.; *U.S. Public*, pg. 880
FIDUCIARY TRUST INTERNATIONAL OF CALIFORNIA—See Franklin Resources, Inc.; *U.S. Public*, pg. 880
FIDUCIARY TRUST INTERNATIONAL OF DELAWARE—See Franklin Resources, Inc.; *U.S. Public*, pg. 880
FIDUCIARY TRUST INTERNATIONAL OF THE SOUTH—See Franklin Resources, Inc.; *U.S. Public*, pg. 880
FIDUS INVESTMENT CORPORATION; *U.S. Public*, pg. 833
FIDUS MEZZANINE CAPITAL II, L.P.—See Fidus Investment Corporation; *U.S. Public*, pg. 833
FIERA CAPITAL CORPORATION; *Int'l*, pg. 2659
FIERA YMG CAPITAL INC.; *Int'l*, pg. 2660
FIFTH STREET CAPITAL LLC; *U.S. Private*, pg. 1505
FIMAC SOLUTIONS LLC—See BancAdvice, LLC; *U.S. Private*, pg. 464
FIMA GLOBAL INVEST D.O.O; *Int'l*, pg. 2664
FIMAPIERRE—See BNP Paribas SA; *Int'l*, pg. 1091
FINACCESS CAPITAL, S.A. DE C.V.—See Grupo Finaccess S.A.P.I. de C.V.; *Int'l*, pg. 3129
FIN-AG INC.—See CHS INC.; *U.S. Public*, pg. 492
FINANCE HOUSE P.J.S.C.; *Int'l*, pg. 2664
FINANCEIRA ALFA S.A.—See Banco Alfa De Investimento SA; *Int'l*, pg. 816
FINANCEWARE, LLC—See NewSpring Capital LLC; *U.S. Private*, pg. 2917
FINANCIAL BRAIN SYSTEMS INC.—See Business Brain Showa-Ota Inc.; *Int'l*, pg. 1228
FINANCIAL CONTROL SYSTEMS, INC.—See STP Investment Services; *U.S. Private*, pg. 3832
FINANCIAL ENGINES ADVISORS L.L.C.—See Hellman & Friedman LLC; *U.S. Private*, pg. 1908
FINANCIAL GRAVITY COMPANIES, INC.; *U.S. Public*, pg. 834
FINANCIAL INNOVATIONS CENTER INC; *U.S. Private*, pg. 1507
FINANCIAL PLUS CREDIT UNION; *U.S. Private*, pg. 1508
FINANCIAL SERVICES COMPANY SAOG; *Int'l*, pg. 2665

FINANCIAL STRATEGIES ACQUISITION CORP.; *U.S. Public*, pg. 834
FINANCIAL TECHNOLOGY VENTURES MANAGEMENT CO. LLC; *U.S. Private*, pg. 1508
FINANCIARA SA—See Erste Group Bank AG; *Int'l*, pg. 2498
FINANCIERA AYUDAMOS S.A. DE C.V., SOFOMER—See Banco Bilbao Vizcaya Argentaria, S.A.; *Int'l*, pg. 817
FINANCIERA FINACREDIT, S.A.—See Grupo Aliado S.A.; *Int'l*, pg. 3119
FINANCIERA FORTALEZA, S.A DE C.V—See Bayport Management Limited; *Int'l*, pg. 915
FINANCIERA IBEROAMERICANA, S.A.—See Banco de Sabadell, S.A.; *Int'l*, pg. 821
FINANCIERA QAPAQ S.A.; *Int'l*, pg. 2665
FINANCIERE LR SARL; *Int'l*, pg. 2668
FINANSA FUND MANAGEMENT LTD.—See FNS HOLDINGS PUBLIC COMPANY LIMITED; *Int'l*, pg. 2718
FINANSINOS S/A - CREDITO FINANCIAMENTO E INVESTIMENTO; *Int'l*, pg. 2669
FINANZAS E INVERSIONES VALENCIANAS S.A.; *Int'l*, pg. 2669
FINATEM BETEILIGUNGSGESELLSCHAFT—See Groupe BPCE; *Int'l*, pg. 3095
FINAXIS NV—See Ackermans & van Haaren NV; *Int'l*, pg. 106
FINBERG ARASTIRMA GELISTIRME DANISMANLIK YATIRIM HIZMETLERI A.S.—See Fibabanka A.S.; *Int'l*, pg. 2651
FINBOND GROUP INTERNATIONAL LIMITED—See Finbond Group Limited; *Int'l*, pg. 2670
FINBOND GROUP LIMITED; *Int'l*, pg. 2670
FINBOND GROUP NORTH AMERICA, LLC—See Finbond Group Limited; *Int'l*, pg. 2670
FINCHAIN CAPITAL PARTNERS AG; *Int'l*, pg. 2672
FINCH CAPITAL PARTNERS B.V; *Int'l*, pg. 2672
FINCLEAR PTY. LTD.—See Ariadne Australia Limited; *Int'l*, pg. 563
FINCONNECT (AUSTRALIA) PTY. LTD.—See Count Limited; *Int'l*, pg. 1817
FINDEV INC.; *Int'l*, pg. 2672
FINDOS INVESTOR GMBH; *Int'l*, pg. 2672
FINEX CAPITAL MANAGEMENT LLP; *Int'l*, pg. 2674
FINEXT VAGYONKEZELO NYILVANOSAN MUKODO RESZVENYTARSASAG; *Int'l*, pg. 2674
FINITALIA S.P.A.—See BPER BANCA S.p.A; *Int'l*, pg. 1132
FINNOVATE ACQUISITION CORP.; *U.S. Public*, pg. 834
FINROCK GROWTH PARTNERS, LLC; *U.S. Private*, pg. 1511
FINSERV ACQUISITION CORP.; *U.S. Public*, pg. 835
FINSURA HOLDINGS PTY. LTD.—See AUB Group Limited; *Int'l*, pg. 698
FINTECH ASIA LTD.; *Int'l*, pg. 2677
FINTECH ECOSYSTEM DEVELOPMENT CORP.; *U.S. Public*, pg. 835
FINTECH EVOLUTION ACQUISITION GROUP; *U.S. Public*, pg. 835
FINTECNA S.P.A.—See Cassa Depositi e Prestiti S.p.A.; *Int'l*, pg. 1355
FINTERTECH CO. LTD.—See Daiwa Securities Group Inc.; *Int'l*, pg. 1949
FIPROMER SASU—See Groupe BPCE; *Int'l*, pg. 3098
FIREBIRD MANAGEMENT LLC; *U.S. Private*, pg. 1511
FIRELAKE CAPITAL MANAGEMENT, LLC; *U.S. Private*, pg. 1512
FIRELIGHT CAPITAL PARTNERS LLC; *U.S. Private*, pg. 1512
FIREMAN CAPITAL PARTNERS LLC; *U.S. Private*, pg. 1512
FIREMAN'S FUND FINANCIAL SERVICES, LLC—See Allianz SE; *Int'l*, pg. 347
FIREMAN'S FUND INDEMNITY CORPORATION—See Allianz SE; *Int'l*, pg. 347
FIREMAN'S FUND INSURANCE COMPANY OF LOUISIANA, CORP.—See Allianz SE; *Int'l*, pg. 347
FIRE SUPPORT (SSFR) HOLDINGS LTD.—See Bilfinger SE; *Int'l*, pg. 1028
FIRION INVESTMENTS SL—See China Tianying Inc.; *Int'l*, pg. 1559
FIRM CAPITAL MORTGAGE INVESTMENT CORPORATION; *Int'l*, pg. 2679
FIRST AFFIRMATIVE FINANCIAL NETWORK LLC—See FOLIOfn, Inc.; *U.S. Private*, pg. 1559
FIRST AL NOOR MODARABA; *Int'l*, pg. 2681
FIRST AMERICAN SERVICES CORPORATION—See Arch Capital Group Ltd.; *Int'l*, pg. 546
FIRST AMERICA RESOURCES CORPORATION; *U.S. Public*, pg. 835
FIRST ATLANTIC CAPITAL LTD.; *U.S. Private*, pg. 1513
FIRST BROTHERS CAPITAL CO., LTD.—See First Brothers Co., Ltd.; *Int'l*, pg. 2682
FIRST CANADIAN MANAGEMENT CORPORATION; *Int'l*, pg. 2682
FIRST CAPITAL CHINA CORPORATION; *Int'l*, pg. 2682
FIRST CAPITAL PARTNERS, LLC—See Coherent Corp.; *U.S. Public*, pg. 528
FIRST CAPITAL SECURITIES CORPORATION LIMITED; *Int'l*, pg. 2682
FIRST CAPITAL S.P.A.; *Int'l*, pg. 2682

FIRSTCASH HOLDINGS, INC.; *U.S. Public*, pg. 848
FIRST CHOICE PRODUCTS INC.; *Int'l*, pg. 2683
FIRST CITY CREDIT UNION; *U.S. Private*, pg. 1515
FIRSTCITY FINANCIAL CORPORATION—See Varde Partners, Inc.; *U.S. Private*, pg. 4346
FIRST DATA CORPORATION; *U.S. Private*, pg. 1517
FIRST DATA MERCHANT SERVICES MEXICO, S. DE R.L. DE C.V.—See Fiserv, Inc.; *U.S. Public*, pg. 851
FIRST EAGLE ALTERNATIVE CAPITAL BDC, INC.—See Crescent Capital BDC, Inc.; *U.S. Public*, pg. 593
FIRST ELITE CAPITAL MODARABA; *Int'l*, pg. 2683
FIRST FINANCE CO.; *Int'l*, pg. 2683
FIRST FINANCIAL ASSETS MANAGEMENT CO., LTD.—See First Financial Holding Co., Ltd.; *Int'l*, pg. 2683
FIRST FINANCIAL SERVICES, INC.; *U.S. Private*, pg. 1519
FIRST FINANCIAL TRUST, N.A.—See The Savings Bank; *U.S. Public*, pg. 4114
FIRST GLOBAL HOLDINGS LIMITED—See GraceKennedy Limited; *Int'l*, pg. 3048
FIRST GLOBAL TRINIDAD & TOBAGO LIMITED—See GraceKennedy Limited; *Int'l*, pg. 3048
FIRST GREENWICH FINANCIAL, INC.; *U.S. Public*, pg. 844
FIRST GROWTH HOLDINGS LTD.; *Int'l*, pg. 2684
FIRST HABIB MODARABA—See Habib Bank AG Zurich; *Int'l*, pg. 3202
FIRST HEARTLAND CAPITAL JSC; *Int'l*, pg. 2684
FIRST HEARTLAND SECURITIES JSC—See First Heartland Capital JSC; *Int'l*, pg. 2684
FIRST HYDRO FINANCE PLC—See ENGIE SA; *Int'l*, pg. 2432
FIRST INVESTEC MODARABA; *Int'l*, pg. 2684
FIRST INVESTMENT COMPANY K.S.C.C.; *Int'l*, pg. 2685
FIRST ISRAEL MEZZANINE INVESTORS LTD.; *Int'l*, pg. 2685
FIRST ISRAEL TURNAROUND ENTERPRISE; *Int'l*, pg. 2685
FIRST JORDAN INVESTMENT COMPANY PLC; *Int'l*, pg. 2685
FIRST LIGHT ADMINISTRATION SERVICES (PTY) LTD.—See Grant Thornton South Africa (Pty) Ltd.; *Int'l*, pg. 3059
FIRSTMARK HORIZON ACQUISITION CORP.; *U.S. Public*, pg. 849
FIRST MIDWEST TRUST CO.—See Old National Bancorp; *U.S. Public*, pg. 1567
FIRST NATIONAL ASSET MANAGEMENT INC.—See First National Financial Corporation; *Int'l*, pg. 2686
FIRST NATIONAL MORTGAGE INVESTMENT FUND; *Int'l*, pg. 2686
FIRSTPLUS FINANCIAL GROUP PLC—See Barclays PLC; *Int'l*, pg. 860
FIRST PRUDENTIAL MODARABA; *Int'l*, pg. 2686
FIRSTRAND BANK LIMITED - INDIA—See FirstRand Limited; *Int'l*, pg. 2690
FIRSTRAND EMA HOLDINGS LIMITED—See FirstRand Limited; *Int'l*, pg. 2690
FIRSTRAND FINANCE COMPANY LIMITED—See FirstRand Limited; *Int'l*, pg. 2690
FIRST RESERVE INTERNATIONAL LIMITED—See First Reserve Management, L.P.; *U.S. Private*, pg. 1525
FIRST RESERVE MANAGEMENT, L.P. - HOUSTON—See First Reserve Management, L.P.; *U.S. Private*, pg. 1525
FIRST RESERVE MANAGEMENT, L.P.; *U.S. Private*, pg. 1525
FIRST RESERVE SUSTAINABLE GROWTH CORP.; *U.S. Public*, pg. 847
FIRST SECURITY CAPITAL I—See Wells Fargo & Company; *U.S. Public*, pg. 2343
FIRST SENTIER INVESTORS (HONG KONG) LIMITED—See KKR & Co. Inc.; *U.S. Public*, pg. 1243
FIRST SENTIER INVESTORS (SINGAPORE)—See KKR & Co. Inc.; *U.S. Public*, pg. 1243
FIRST VENTURE CAPITAL CO., LTD.—See First Financial Holding Co., Ltd.; *Int'l*, pg. 2683
FIRST WASHINGTON REALTY INC.; *U.S. Private*, pg. 1530
FISERV SOLUTIONS, LLC—See Fiserv, Inc.; *U.S. Public*, pg. 851
FISHER LYNCH CAPITAL, LLC - EAST COAST OFFICE—See Fisher Lynch Capital, LLC; *U.S. Private*, pg. 1534
FISHER LYNCH CAPITAL, LLC; *U.S. Private*, pg. 1534
FISHER & PAYKEL FINANCE LIMITED—See Humm Group Limited; *Int'l*, pg. 3531
FISHER & PAYKEL HEALTHCARE ASIA LIMITED—See Fisher & Paykel Healthcare Corporation Limited; *Int'l*, pg. 2693
FISHER & PAYKEL HOLDINGS GMBH—See Fisher & Paykel Healthcare Corporation Limited; *Int'l*, pg. 2693
FISH POOL ASA—See Euronext N.V.; *Int'l*, pg. 2554
FISKARS AMERICAS HOLDING OY AB—See Fiskars Oyj Abp; *Int'l*, pg. 2693
FISKARS EUROPE HOLDING OY AB—See Fiskars Oyj Abp; *Int'l*, pg. 2694
F.I.T. INVESTMENT JSC; *Int'l*, pg. 2597
FITWEISER HOLDINGS, INC.; *U.S. Private*, pg. 1536
FIVE CROWNS CAPITAL, LLC; *U.S. Private*, pg. 1537

523999 — MISCELLANEOUS FINAN...

FIVE ELMS CAPITAL MANAGEMENT LLC; *U.S. Private*, pg. 1537
FIVE MILE CAPITAL PARTNERS LLC; *U.S. Private*, pg. 1537
FIVE POINT ENERGY LLC; *U.S. Private*, pg. 1537
FIVE-STAR BUSINESS FINANCE LIMITED; *Int'l*, pg. 2696
FIVE X TRADECOM LIMITED; *Int'l*, pg. 2696
FJARDE AP-FONDEN; *Int'l*, pg. 2697
F. J. B. INVESTMENT PTE LTD—See FJ Benjamin Holdings Ltd.; *Int'l*, pg. 2697
FLAG SHIP CORPORATION; *U.S. Private*, pg. 1539
FLAGSHIP INVESTMENTS LIMITED; *Int'l*, pg. 2697
FLAGSHIP VENTURES; *U.S. Private*, pg. 1539
FLAKK INTERNATIONAL AS—See Flakk Holding AS; *Int'l*, pg. 2698
FLATWORLD ACQUISITION CORP.; *Int'l*, pg. 2698
FLEXIBLE FERTIGUNGSTECHNIK GMBH—See ATON GmbH; *Int'l*, pg. 689
FLEXIRENT HOLDINGS PTY LIMITED—See Humm Group Limited; *Int'l*, pg. 3531
FLEXIRENT IRELAND LIMITED—See Humm Group Limited; *Int'l*, pg. 3531
FLEXTRONICS HOLDING GMBH—See Flex Ltd.; *Int'l*, pg. 2702
FLEXTRONICS HOLDINGS MEXICO, S.A. DE C.V.—See Flex Ltd.; *Int'l*, pg. 2702
FLEXTRONICS ODM NETHERLANDS NV—See Flex Ltd.; *Int'l*, pg. 2703
FLITWAYS TECHNOLOGY INC.; *U.S. Public*, pg. 853
FLORIDA CAPITAL PARTNERS, INC.; *U.S. Private*, pg. 1547
FLORIDA GULFSHORE CAPITAL LLC; *U.S. Private*, pg. 1548
THE FLORIDA VALUE FUND LLLP; *U.S. Private*, pg. 4029
FLORIN MINING INVESTMENT COMPANY LIMITED; *Int'l*, pg. 2708
FLORINT B.V.; *Int'l*, pg. 2708
FLORINVEST SA—See Floridienne SA; *Int'l*, pg. 2708
FLOWER ONE HOLDINGS INC.; *Int'l*, pg. 2709
FLOW TRADERS HONG KONG LTD.—See Flow Traders NV; *Int'l*, pg. 2709
FLSMIDTH MINERALS HOLDING APS—See FLSmidth & Co. A/S; *Int'l*, pg. 2711
FLYEXCLUSIVE, INC.; *U.S. Public*, pg. 861
FLYING MONKEY CAPITAL CORP.; *Int'l*, pg. 2716
FLYOVER CAPITAL PARTNERS, LLC—See Mariner Wealth Advisors, LLC; *U.S. Private*, pg. 2575
FMCG BUSINESS PARTNER AB; *Int'l*, pg. 2717
F MEC INTERNATIONAL FINANCIAL SERVICES LTD.; *Int'l*, pg. 2594
FM LEASINGPARTNER GMBH—See Commerzbank AG; *Int'l*, pg. 1718
FMRC, INC.—See Huntington Bancshares Incorporated; *U.S. Public*, pg. 1071
FMR LLC; *U.S. Private*, pg. 1554
FMR RESOURCES LIMITED; *Int'l*, pg. 2717
FNOF PRECIOUS HONOUR LIMITED—See Forebright Capital Management Ltd.; *Int'l*, pg. 2731
FNY SERVICE CORP.—See The First of Long Island Corporation; *U.S. Public*, pg. 2074
FOCUS IMPACT BH3 ACQUISITION COMPANY; *U.S. Public*, pg. 862
FONDATIONS CAPITAL SA; *Int'l*, pg. 2725
FONDATIONS CAPITAL SERVICES FRANCE SA—See Fondations Capital SA; *Int'l*, pg. 2725
FONDO ITALIANO DI INVESTIMENTO SGR S.P.A.—See Cassa Depositi e Prestiti S.p.A.; *Int'l*, pg. 1355
FONDS DE CONSOLIDATION ET DE DEVELOPPEMENT DES ENTREPRISES; *Int'l*, pg. 2725
FONDSMANAGEMENT DUSSELDORF GMBH—See Bilfinger SE; *Int'l*, pg. 1028
FOODFEST INTERNATIONAL 2000 INC.; *U.S. Public*, pg. 863
FORBION EUROPEAN ACQUISITION CORP.; *U.S. Public*, pg. 864
FORBION GROUP HOLDING B.V.—See Affiliated Managers Group, Inc.; *U.S. Public*, pg. 54
FORCE PROTECTION VIDEO EQUIPMENT CORP.; *U.S. Public*, pg. 864
FORD CREDIT DE MEXICO S.A. DE C.V.—See Ford Motor Company; *U.S. Public*, pg. 866
FORD CREDIT S.A.—See Ford Motor Company; *U.S. Public*, pg. 866
FORD CREDIT SPA—See Ford Motor Company; *U.S. Public*, pg. 866
FORD FINANCIAL FUND II, L.P.; *U.S. Private*, pg. 1564
FORD INVESTMENT PARTNERSHIP—See Ford Motor Company; *U.S. Public*, pg. 865
FORD MOTOR COMPANY AB—See Ford Motor Company; *U.S. Public*, pg. 865
FOREMAN CAPITAL B.V.; *Int'l*, pg. 2731
FORESIGHT GROUP HOLDINGS LIMITED; *Int'l*, pg. 2731
FORESIGHT SOLAR FUND LIMITED; *Int'l*, pg. 2732
FORESIGHT SUSTAINABLE FORESTRY COMPANY PLC—See Averon Park Limited; *Int'l*, pg. 739
FORESIGHT VCT PLC; *Int'l*, pg. 2732
FORESITE CAPITAL MANAGEMENT, LLC; *U.S. Private*, pg. 1566

FORESITE LIFE SCIENCES CORP.; *U.S. Private*, pg. 1566
FORESTERS INVESTOR SERVICES, INC.—See Golden Gate Capital Management II, LLC; *U.S. Private*, pg. 1731
FOREST INVESTMENTS, INC.; *U.S. Private*, pg. 1567
FOREST ROAD SECURITIES, LLC; *U.S. Private*, pg. 1567
FORGE CAPITAL PARTNERS LLC; *U.S. Private*, pg. 1567
FORGE GLOBAL HOLDINGS, INC.; *U.S. Public*, pg. 867
FORGE GLOBAL, INC.—See Forge Global Holdings, Inc.; *U.S. Public*, pg. 867
FORGELIGHT, LLC; *U.S. Private*, pg. 1568
FORMATION8 PARTNERS LLC; *U.S. Private*, pg. 1571
FORMATION CAPITAL, LLC; *U.S. Private*, pg. 1569
FORMICA CAPITAL AB—See Formica Capital Holding AB; *Int'l*, pg. 2734
FORMICA FINANCE LIMITED—See HAL Trust N.V.; *Int'l*, pg. 3223
FORMICA HOLDCO UK LIMITED—See HAL Trust N.V.; *Int'l*, pg. 3223
FORSTA AP-FONDEN; *Int'l*, pg. 2737
FORSTMANN LITTLE & CO.; *U.S. Private*, pg. 1573
FORSYTH CAPITAL INVESTORS LLC; *U.S. Private*, pg. 1573
FORT ASHFORD HOLDINGS, LLC; *U.S. Private*, pg. 1574
FORTE CAPITAL ADVISORS, LLC; *U.S. Private*, pg. 1575
FORTIGENT HOLDINGS COMPANY, INC.—See LPL Financial Holdings Inc.; *U.S. Public*, pg. 1343
FORTINO CAPITAL PARTNERS; *Int'l*, pg. 2739
FORTISSIMO CAPITAL MANAGEMENT LTD.; *Int'l*, pg. 2740
FORTISTAR SUSTAINABLE SOLUTIONS CORP.; *U.S. Public*, pg. 869
FORTRESS CAPITAL ACQUISITION CORP.; *U.S. Public*, pg. 872
FORTUM INVEST LLC—See Fortum Oyj; *Int'l*, pg. 2741
FORTUM SMALL HYDRO HOLDING OY—See Fortum Oyj; *Int'l*, pg. 2741
FORTUNA INVESTMENT AG—See Assicurazioni Generali S.p.A.; *Int'l*, pg. 644
FORTUNE JOY INTERNATIONAL ACQUISITION CORP.; *Int'l*, pg. 2743
FORTUNE MANAGEMENT INC.; *Int'l*, pg. 2743
FORTUNE RISE ACQUISITION CORPORATION; *U.S. Public*, pg. 873
FORWARD INTERNET GROUP LTD.; *Int'l*, pg. 2747
FOS CAPITAL LIMITED; *Int'l*, pg. 2748
FOSSE MASTER ISSUER PLC; *Int'l*, pg. 2749
FOUNDATION CAPITAL, LLC; *U.S. Public*, pg. 1579
FOUNDATION FINANCIAL HOLDINGS, INC.; *U.S. Private*, pg. 1579
FOUNDATION INVESTMENT PARTNERS, LLC; *U.S. Private*, pg. 1580
FOUNDERS EQUITY, INC.; *U.S. Private*, pg. 1580
FOUNDERS FUND INC.; *U.S. Private*, pg. 1581
FOUNTAINHEAD CAPITAL MANAGEMENT, LLC; *U.S. Private*, pg. 1581
FOUNTAINVEST PARTNERS (ASIA) LIMITED; *Int'l*, pg. 2754
FOUR LEAF ACQUISITION CORPORATION; *U.S. Public*, pg. 875
FOURSTAR WEALTH ADVISORS LLC; *U.S. Private*, pg. 1583
FOX PAINE & COMPANY, LLC—See Paine Schwartz Partners, LLC; *U.S. Private*, pg. 3075
FOX THREE PARTNERS LLC; *U.S. Private*, pg. 1585
FOXWAYNE ENTERPRISES ACQUISITION CORP.; *U.S. Public*, pg. 877
FRAMEWORK CAPITAL PARTNERS; *U.S. Private*, pg. 1586
FRANCISCO PARTNERS MANAGEMENT, LP; *U.S. Private*, pg. 1587
FRANKFURTER VERMOGENS-TREUHAND GESELLSCHAFT MIT BESCHRANKTER HAFTUNG—See Deutsche Bank Aktiengesellschaft; *Int'l*, pg. 2061
FRANKLIN ADVISORY SERVICES, LLC—See Franklin Resources, Inc.; *U.S. Public*, pg. 880
FRANKLIN BSP REALTY TRUST, INC.—See Franklin Resources, Inc.; *U.S. Public*, pg. 879
FRANKLIN PROPERTY & DEVELOPMENT GROUP LLC; *U.S. Private*, pg. 1597
FRANKLIN SQUARE HOLDINGS, L.P.; *U.S. Private*, pg. 1598
FRANKLIN STREET PARTNERS, INC.—See Fifth Third Bancorp; *U.S. Public*, pg. 833
FRANKLIN TEMPLETON AUSTRIA GMBH—See Franklin Resources, Inc.; *U.S. Public*, pg. 879
FRANKLIN TEMPLETON INSTITUTIONAL, LLC—See Franklin Resources, Inc.; *U.S. Public*, pg. 880
FRANKLIN TEMPLETON INTENATIONAL SERVICES S.A.—See Franklin Resources, Inc.; *U.S. Public*, pg. 880
FRANKLIN TEMPLETON INTERNATIONAL SERVICES S.A.R.L.—See Franklin Resources, Inc.; *U.S. Public*, pg. 880
FRANKLIN TEMPLETON INVESTMENT MANAGEMENT LIMITED—See Franklin Resources, Inc.; *U.S. Public*, pg. 880
FRANKLIN TEMPLETON INVESTMENTS (ASIA) LIMITED—See Franklin Resources, Inc.; *U.S. Public*, pg. 880

FRANKLIN TEMPLETON INVESTMENTS CORP.—See Franklin Resources, Inc.; *U.S. Public*, pg. 880
FRANKLIN TEMPLETON INVESTMENT SERVICES GMBH—See Franklin Resources, Inc.; *U.S. Public*, pg. 880
FRANKLIN TEMPLETON INVESTOR SERVICES, LLC—See Franklin Resources, Inc.; *U.S. Public*, pg. 881
FRANKLIN TEMPLETON SWITZERLAND LTD.—See Franklin Resources, Inc.; *U.S. Public*, pg. 881
FRANSA INVEST BANK SAL—See Fransabank SAL; *Int'l*, pg. 2762
FRASER MACKENZIE ACCELERATOR CORP.—See Forward Water Technologies Corp; *Int'l*, pg. 2747
FRASERS PROPERTY (EUROPE) HOLDINGS PTE LTD—See Frasers Property Limited; *Int'l*, pg. 2766
FRAZIER & COMPANY, INC.; *U.S. Private*, pg. 1599
FRAZIER LIFESCIENCES ACQUISITION CORPORATION; *U.S. Public*, pg. 883
FREDDY HOLDINGS PTY LTD.—See TPG Capital, L.P.; *U.S. Public*, pg. 2176
THE FRED JONES COMPANIES INC.; *U.S. Private*, pg. 4030
FREDONIA MINING INC.; *Int'l*, pg. 2769
FREEDOM 3 CAPITAL, LLC; *U.S. Private*, pg. 1603
FREEMAN INVESTMENT HOLDINGS LIMITED—See Arta TechFin Corporation Limited; *Int'l*, pg. 581
FREEMAN SPOGLI & CO. INCORPORATED; *U.S. Private*, pg. 1605
FREESTONE ACQUISITION CORP.; *U.S. Public*, pg. 884
FREMONT GROUP, LLC; *U.S. Private*, pg. 1608
FREMONT PRIVATE HOLDINGS, LLC—See Fremont Group, LLC; *U.S. Private*, pg. 1608
FRIEND SKOLER & CO., INC.; *U.S. Private*, pg. 1611
FRIHEDEN INVEST A/S; *Int'l*, pg. 2792
FRNT FINANCIAL INC.; *Int'l*, pg. 2794
FRONTENAC COMPANY LLC; *U.S. Private*, pg. 1613
FRONTIER ACQUISITION CORP.; *U.S. Public*, pg. 887
FRONTIER CAPITAL INC.—See Frontier Management Inc.; *Int'l*, pg. 2795
FRONTIER CAPITAL LIMITED; *Int'l*, pg. 2795
FRONTIER CAPITAL LLC; *U.S. Private*, pg. 1615
FRONTIER INVESTMENT CORP.; *U.S. Public*, pg. 888
FRONTIER PHARMA LIMITED; *Int'l*, pg. 2795
FRONTIER REAL ESTATE INVESTMENT CORPORATION; *Int'l*, pg. 2795
FRONTLINE GOLD CORPORATION; *Int'l*, pg. 2796
FRX INNOVATIONS INC.; *U.S. Public*, pg. 888
FSD PHARMA INC.; *Int'l*, pg. 2798
FSP INVESTMENTS LLC—See Franklin Street Properties Corp.; *U.S. Public*, pg. 883
FTAC ATHENA ACQUISITION CORP.; *U.S. Public*, pg. 888
FTAC EMERALD ACQUISITION CORP.; *U.S. Public*, pg. 888
FTAC HERA ACQUISITION CORP.; *U.S. Public*, pg. 888
FTAC OLYMPUS ACQUISITION CORP.—See Payoneer Global Inc.; *U.S. Public*, pg. 1656
FTAC PARNASSUS ACQUISITION CORP.; *U.S. Public*, pg. 888
FTAC ZEUS ACQUISITION CORP.; *U.S. Public*, pg. 888
FT KNOWLEDGE MANAGEMENT COMPANY LIMITED—See 63 moons technologies limited; *Int'l*, pg. 14
FTS FINANCIAL SERVICES OY—See Finnair Plc; *Int'l*, pg. 2675
FUBON FUTURES CO., LTD—See Fubon Financial Holding Co. Ltd.; *Int'l*, pg. 2801
FUGRO FINANCE AG—See Fugro N.V.; *Int'l*, pg. 2806
FUGRO HOLDINGS (HONG KONG) LTD.—See Fugro N.V.; *Int'l*, pg. 2806
FUGRO HOLDINGS (UK) LTD.—See Fugro N.V.; *Int'l*, pg. 2806
FUJIAN SUMPO FOODS HOLDINGS COMPANY LIMITED—See Charoen Pokphand Foods Public Company Limited; *Int'l*, pg. 1452
FUJI HUNT ASIAN PACIFIC HOLDING PTY LTD—See FUJIFILM Holdings Corporation; *Int'l*, pg. 2825
FUJITOMI SECURITIES CO., LTD.; *Int'l*, pg. 2831
FUJITSU EMEA PLC—See Fujitsu Limited; *Int'l*, pg. 2833
FUJITSU SERVICES HOLDINGS PLC—See Fujitsu Limited; *Int'l*, pg. 2836
FUKUGIN REAL ESTATE ASSESSMENT SERVICE CO., LTD.—See Fukuoka Financial Group, Inc.; *Int'l*, pg. 2840
FULCRUM CAPITAL PARTNERS INC.; *Int'l*, pg. 2841
FUNDAMENTAL ADVISORS LP; *U.S. Private*, pg. 1622
FUNDAMENTAL GLOBAL INVESTORS, LLC; *U.S. Private*, pg. 1623
FUNDCORP, INC.; *U.S. Private*, pg. 1623
FUNDERSTONE SECURITIES LIMITED—See G-Resources Group Limited; *Int'l*, pg. 2862
FUNDOS GROUP LLC; *U.S. Private*, pg. 1623
FUNFTE SAB TREUHAND UND VERWALTUNG GMBH & CO. SUHL RIMBACHZENTRUM KG—See Deutsche Bank Aktiengesellschaft; *Int'l*, pg. 2061
FUNFZEHNTE BASF FINANZBETEILIGUNGSGESELLSCHAFT MBH—See BASF SE; *Int'l*, pg. 883
FURAMA LTD.; *Int'l*, pg. 2846
FURTHER GLOBAL CAPITAL MANAGEMENT, L.P.; *U.S. Private*, pg. 1624

523999 — MISCELLANEOUS FINAN...

FUSION MEDIA LTD.; *Int'l*, pg. 2849
FUSION MICRO FINANCE LIMITED; *Int'l*, pg. 2849
FUTURE ARAB INVESTMENT CO.; *Int'l*, pg. 2852
FUTURE FARM TECHNOLOGIES INC.; *Int'l*, pg. 2856
FUTUREGROWTH ASSET MANAGEMENT PTY. LTD.; *Int'l*, pg. 2858
FUTURE HEALTH ESG CORP.; *U.S. Public*, pg. 893
FUTURE MARKET NETWORKS LIMITED; *Int'l*, pg. 2856
FUTURES CAPITAL AD; *Int'l*, pg. 2858
FUTURETEL S.A.; *Int'l*, pg. 2858
FUTURE VENTURE CAPITAL CO., LTD.; *Int'l*, pg. 2857
FWU AG; *Int'l*, pg. 2859
G3 VRM ACQUISITION CORP.; *U.S. Public*, pg. 894
G-7 HOLDINGS INC.; *Int'l*, pg. 2862
GAAS LABS, LLC; *U.S. Private*, pg. 1632
GAIA GROW CORP.; *Int'l*, pg. 2868
GAIN CAPITAL SINGAPORE PTE. LTD.—See StoneX Group Inc.; *U.S. Public*, pg. 1952
GAIN CAPITAL UK LIMITED—See StoneX Group Inc.; *U.S. Public*, pg. 1952
GAIN CITIES LIMITED; *U.S. Private*, pg. 1635
GAINLINE CAPITAL PARTNERS LP; *U.S. Private*, pg. 1635
GAJANAN SECURITIES SERVICES LIMITED; *Int'l*, pg. 2869
GALADA FINANCE LIMITED; *Int'l*, pg. 2870
GALAXY BIOMEDICAL INVESTMENT CO., LTD.; *Int'l*, pg. 2871
GALAXY CONSOLIDATED FINANCE LIMITED; *Int'l*, pg. 2871
GALAXY PARTNERS LLC; *U.S. Private*, pg. 1636
GALENICA FINANCE LIMITED—See CSL Limited; *Int'l*, pg. 1866
GALEN PARTNERS, L.P.; *U.S. Private*, pg. 1637
GALLAGHER ESTATE HOLDINGS LIMITED—See Hosken Consolidated Investments Limited; *Int'l*, pg. 3485
GALLAGHER SECURITY CORP.; *Int'l*, pg. 2873
GALLATIN POINT CAPITAL LLC; *U.S. Private*, pg. 1639
GALLIOT ACQUISITION CORP.; *U.S. Private*, pg. 1639
GAMES & ESPORTS EXPERIENCE ACQUISITION CORP.; *U.S. Public*, pg. 895
GAMING AND LEISURE PROPERTIES, INC.; *U.S. Public*, pg. 896
GAMING & HOSPITALITY ACQUISITION CORP.; *U.S. Public*, pg. 896
GAM INVESTMENTS (AUSTRALIA) PTY LTD—See GAM Holding AG; *Int'l*, pg. 2876
GAM INVESTMENTS (SINGAPORE) PTE. LTD.—See GAM Holding AG; *Int'l*, pg. 2876
GAMMON HOLDINGS B.V.—See Gammon India Limited; *Int'l*, pg. 2879
GAMMON INTERNATIONAL B.V.—See Gammon India Limited; *Int'l*, pg. 2879
GAM (SCHWEIZ) AG—See GAM Holding AG; *Int'l*, pg. 2876
GAMUT CAPITAL MANAGEMENT, L.P.; *U.S. Private*, pg. 1641
GANSU YATE INVESTMENT GROUP CO., LTD.; *Int'l*, pg. 2882
GARANTI FINANSAL KIRALAMA A.S.; *Int'l*, pg. 2883
GARANTI YATIRIM ORTAKLIGI AS; *Int'l*, pg. 2883
GARBI FINVEST LTD; *Int'l*, pg. 2883
GARDINER HEALTHCARE ACQUISITIONS CORP.; *U.S. Public*, pg. 906
GARMIN AUSTRIA HOLDING GMBH—See Garmin Ltd.; *Int'l*, pg. 2885
GARNETT & HELFRICH CAPITAL, LLC; *U.S. Private*, pg. 1645
GARNETT STATION PARTNERS, LLC; *U.S. Private*, pg. 1645
GARRINGTON GROUP OF COMPANIES INC.; *Int'l*, pg. 2886
GARRISON INVESTMENT GROUP LP; *U.S. Private*, pg. 1645
GARY COMMUNITY INVESTMENT COMPANY; *U.S. Private*, pg. 1646
GASTON INVESTMENTS SP. Z O.O.—See CPD S.A.; *Int'l*, pg. 1824
GATEMORE CAPITAL MANAGEMENT LLP; *Int'l*, pg. 2889
GATES GROUP CAPITAL PARTNERS, LLC; *U.S. Private*, pg. 1650
GATEWAY STRATEGIC ACQUISITION CO.; *Int'l*, pg. 2889
GATO INVESTMENTS LP—See Searchlight Capital Partners, L.P.; *U.S. Public*, pg. 3587
GATOR CAPITAL MANAGEMENT LLC; *U.S. Private*, pg. 1651
GAUGE CAPITAL LLC; *U.S. Private*, pg. 1652
GAVEA INVESTIMENTOS LTDA.—See JPMorgan Chase & Co.; *U.S. Public*, pg. 1207
GAZKON AO; *Int'l*, pg. 2891
GAZOO ENERGY GROUP, INC.; *U.S. Private*, pg. 1653
GAZ-SERVIS AO; *Int'l*, pg. 2891
GAZ-TEK PAO; *Int'l*, pg. 2891
GBCORP BSC—See GFH Financial Group B.S.C.; *Int'l*, pg. 2956
GCA CHINA COMPANY, LIMITED—See Houlihan Lokey, Inc.; *U.S. Public*, pg. 1055
GCA INDIA INVESTMENT ADVISERS PRIVATE LIMITED—See Houlihan Lokey, Inc.; *U.S. Public*, pg. 1055
GCA SAVVIAN ADVISORS LLC—See Houlihan Lokey, Inc.; *U.S. Public*, pg. 1055
GCA SAVVIAN LLC—See Houlihan Lokey, Inc.; *U.S. Public*, pg. 1055
GCA SINGAPORE PRIVATE LIMITED—See Houlihan Lokey, Inc.; *U.S. Public*, pg. 1055
GCC GLOBAL CAPITAL CORPORATION; *Int'l*, pg. 2894
GCP CAPITAL PARTNERS EUROPE LIMITED—See GCP Capital Partners Holdings LLC; *U.S. Private*, pg. 1654
GCP CAPITAL PARTNERS LLC—See GCP Capital Partners Holdings LLC; *U.S. Private*, pg. 1654
GCP VENTURE PARTNERS LLC—See GCP Capital Partners Holdings LLC; *U.S. Private*, pg. 1654
GCS CAPITAL (HK) CO., LTD.; *Int'l*, pg. 2895
GC SERVICES LP; *U.S. Private*, pg. 1653
GCT SEMICONDUCTOR HOLDING, INC.; *U.S. Public*, pg. 908
GDF SUEZ GAS NA HOLDINGS LLC—See ENGIE SA; *Int'l*, pg. 2433
GDI PROPERTY GROUP; *Int'l*, pg. 2896
GDL LEASING & FINANCE LIMITED; *Int'l*, pg. 2896
GEA CFS FINANCE B.V.—See GEA Group Aktiengesellschaft; *Int'l*, pg. 2898
GEA CFS HOLDING B.V.—See GEA Group Aktiengesellschaft; *Int'l*, pg. 2898
GEA CFS HOLDING GMBH—See GEA Group Aktiengesellschaft; *Int'l*, pg. 2898
GEA FINANCE B.V.—See GEA Group Aktiengesellschaft; *Int'l*, pg. 2899
GEA GROUP HOLDING GMBH—See GEA Group Aktiengesellschaft; *Int'l*, pg. 2899
GEA GROUP HOLDINGS (UK) LIMITED—See GEA Group Aktiengesellschaft; *Int'l*, pg. 2899
GEA SEGMENT MANAGEMENT HOLDING GMBH—See GEA Group Aktiengesellschaft; *Int'l*, pg. 2903
GEBERIT INTERNATIONAL SALES AG—See Geberit AG; *Int'l*, pg. 2904
GEEFCEE FINANCE LIMITED; *Int'l*, pg. 2911
GEETANJALI CREDIT & CAPITAL LTD.; *Int'l*, pg. 2911
GEF ACQUISITION CORPORATION; *U.S. Private*, pg. 1655
GEFEN BIOMED INVESTMENTS LTD.; *Int'l*, pg. 2911
GEFEN LANDA ACQUISITION CORP.; *Int'l*, pg. 2911
GEIGER COUNTER LIMITED; *Int'l*, pg. 2912
GELECEK VARLIK YONETIMI A.S.; *Int'l*, pg. 2913
GELESIS HOLDINGS, INC.; *U.S. Public*, pg. 910
GELF MANAGEMENT (LUX) SARL—See Goodman Limited; *Int'l*, pg. 3040
GEMFIELDS GROUP LIMITED; *Int'l*, pg. 2916
GEMINI INVESTORS LLC; *U.S. Private*, pg. 1658
GEMISYS FINANCIAL; *U.S. Private*, pg. 1658
GEMSHARES PHYSICAL DIAMOND TRUST; *U.S. Private*, pg. 1658
GEMSPRING CAPITAL MANAGEMENT, LLC; *U.S. Private*, pg. 1658
GEN CAP AMERICA, INC.; *U.S. Private*, pg. 1659
GENEDX HOLDINGS CORP.; *U.S. Public*, pg. 911
GENERAL ATLANTIC L.P.—See General Atlantic Service Company, L.P.; *U.S. Private*, pg. 1661
GENERAL ATLANTIC SERVICE COMPANY, L.P.; *U.S. Private*, pg. 1660
GENERAL ENGINEERING MAURITIUS LIMITED—See General Engineering Public Company Limited; *Int'l*, pg. 2918
GENERAL ENTERPRISE VENTURES, INC.; *U.S. Public*, pg. 920
GENERAL FINANCE CORPORATION—See United Rentals, Inc.; *U.S. Public*, pg. 2235
GENERAL FINANCE & DEVELOPMENT, INC.; *U.S. Public*, pg. 920
GENERALFINANCE S.P.A.; *Int'l*, pg. 2920
GENERALI CAPITAL FINANCE B.V.—See Assicurazioni Generali S.p.A.; *Int'l*, pg. 647
GENERALI FINANZSERVICE GMBH—See Assicurazioni Generali S.p.A.; *Int'l*, pg. 645
GENERALI FUND MANAGEMENT S.A.—See Assicurazioni Generali S.p.A.; *Int'l*, pg. 643
GENERALI INVESTMENTS SCHWEIZ AG—See Assicurazioni Generali S.p.A.; *Int'l*, pg. 644
GENERATION 3 CAPITAL, LLC; *U.S. Private*, pg. 1668
GENERATION DEVELOPMENT GROUP; *Int'l*, pg. 2920
GENERATION PARTNERS; *U.S. Private*, pg. 1668
GENERICS HOLDING GMBH—See Bayer Aktiengesellschaft; *Int'l*, pg. 905
GENESIS CAPITAL REAL ESTATE ADVISORS, INC.—See Rithm Capital Corp.; *U.S. Public*, pg. 1800
GENESIS CAPITAL S.R.O.; *Int'l*, pg. 2921
GENESIS GROWTH TECH ACQUISITION CORP.; *Int'l*, pg. 2921
GENESIS PARK, LP; *U.S. Private*, pg. 1669
GENII CAPITAL SA; *Int'l*, pg. 2923
GENNX360 CAPITAL PARTNERS, L.P.; *U.S. Private*, pg. 1672
GENSTAR CAPITAL, LLC; *U.S. Private*, pg. 1673
GENTING INTERNATIONAL SDN BHD—See Genting Berhad; *Int'l*, pg. 2928
GENTING INTERNATIONAL (SINGAPORE) PTE LTD—See Genting Berhad; *Int'l*, pg. 2928
GENTING (LABUAN) LIMITED—See Genting Berhad; *Int'l*, pg. 2928
GENTING SINGAPORE PLC—See Genting Berhad; *Int'l*, pg. 2929
GENUI GMBH; *Int'l*, pg. 2930
GEOJIT CREDITS PRIVATE LIMITED—See Geojit Financial Services Limited; *Int'l*, pg. 2933
GEOJIT FINANCIAL SERVICES LIMITED; *Int'l*, pg. 2933
GEORGE K. BAUM MERCHANT BANC—See George K. Baum Holdings, Inc.; *U.S. Private*, pg. 1682
GEORGESON LLC—See Computershare Limited; *Int'l*, pg. 1760
GEORGESON SHAREHOLDER COMMUNICATIONS AUSTRALIA PTY. LTD.—See Computershare Limited; *Int'l*, pg. 1760
GEORGESON SHAREHOLDER SAS—See Computershare Limited; *Int'l*, pg. 1760
GEORGESON S.L.—See Computershare Limited; *Int'l*, pg. 1760
GEORGESON S.R.L.—See Computershare Limited; *Int'l*, pg. 1760
GEORG FISCHER FINANZ AG—See Georg Fischer AG; *Int'l*, pg. 2935
GERMAN ASSET MANAGERS AG; *Int'l*, pg. 2942
GERRARD FINANCIAL PLANNING LIMITED—See Barclays PLC; *Int'l*, pg. 862
GERRARD INVESTMENT MANAGEMENT LIMITED—See Barclays PLC; *Int'l*, pg. 862
GERRARD MANAGEMENT SERVICES LIMITED—See Barclays PLC; *Int'l*, pg. 862
GETINGE LETTING AB—See Getinge AB; *Int'l*, pg. 2950
GETINGE-MAQUET GERMANY HOLDING GMBH—See Getinge AB; *Int'l*, pg. 2951
GEV GRUNDSTUCKSGESELLSCHAFT HERZOGENAURACH MBH & CO. KG—See adidas AG; *Int'l*, pg. 146
GFA CO., LTD.; *Int'l*, pg. 2955
GF ACQUISITION CORP.; *U.S. Private*, pg. 1689
GF ASSET MANAGEMENT (HONG KONG) LIMITED—See GF Securities Co., Ltd.; *Int'l*, pg. 2955
GF CANADA HOLDINGS COMPANY LIMITED—See GF Securities Co., Ltd.; *Int'l*, pg. 2955
GF CAPITAL (HONG KONG) LIMITED—See GF Securities Co., Ltd.; *Int'l*, pg. 2955
GF CAPITAL MANAGEMENT & ADVISORS, LLC; *U.S. Private*, pg. 1689
GF COMMODITIES CO., LTD.—See GF Securities Co., Ltd.; *Int'l*, pg. 2955
GF GLOBAL CAPITAL LIMITED—See GF Securities Co., Ltd.; *Int'l*, pg. 2955
GFI ENERGY VENTURES LLC—See Brookfield Corporation; *Int'l*, pg. 1181
GF INVESTMENT MANAGEMENT (HONG KONG) COMPANY LIMITED—See GF Securities Co., Ltd.; *Int'l*, pg. 2955
GF INVESTMENTS (HONG KONG) COMPANY LIMITED—See GF Securities Co., Ltd.; *Int'l*, pg. 2955
GF LIGHTHOUSE CAPITAL MANAGEMENT COMPANY LIMITED—See GF Securities Co., Ltd.; *Int'l*, pg. 2955
GF SECURITIES CO., LTD.; *Int'l*, pg. 2955
GF SECURITIES (HONG KONG) BROKERAGE LIMITED—See GF Securities Co., Ltd.; *Int'l*, pg. 2955
GF WEALTH MANAGEMENT (HONG KONG) LIMITED—See GF Securities Co., Ltd.; *Int'l*, pg. 2955
GHK CAPITAL PARTNERS LP; *U.S. Private*, pg. 1690
GHO CAPITAL PARTNERS LLP; *Int'l*, pg. 2959
GHP GROUP; *Int'l*, pg. 2960
GIANT GROUP LTD.; *U.S. Private*, pg. 1694
GIBRALT CAPITAL CORPORATION; *Int'l*, pg. 2963
GIC HOUSING FINANCE LIMITED; *Int'l*, pg. 2963
GIC REAL ESTATE, INC.—See GIC Pte. Ltd.; *Int'l*, pg. 2964
GIC SPECIAL INVESTMENTS PTE. LTD.—See GIC Pte. Ltd.; *Int'l*, pg. 2964
GILADA FINANCE & INVESTMENTS LTD.; *Int'l*, pg. 2973
GILBERT GLOBAL EQUITY PARTNERS; *U.S. Private*, pg. 1698
GILDE BUY OUT PARTNERS B.V.; *Int'l*, pg. 2974
GILDE EQUITY MANAGEMENT (GEM) BENELUX PARTNERS B.V.; *Int'l*, pg. 2975
GILDE HEALTHCARE PARTNERS B.V.; *Int'l*, pg. 2975
GILDE HEALTHCARE PARTNERS US—See Gilde Healthcare Partners B.V.; *Int'l*, pg. 2975
GILDEMEISTER BETEILIGUNGEN AG—See DMG MORI Co., Ltd.; *Int'l*, pg. 2144
GIL INVESTMENTS LTD.; *Int'l*, pg. 2973
GILO VENTURES, LLC; *U.S. Private*, pg. 1701
GI MANAGER L.P.; *U.S. Private*, pg. 1691
GIMV NV; *Int'l*, pg. 2976
GINKGO BIOWORKS HOLDINGS, INC.; *U.S. Public*, pg. 938
GI PARTNERS U.K. LIMITED—See GI Manager L.P.; *U.S. Private*, pg. 1692
GIP DEVELOPMENT SARL—See Aurelius Equity Opportunities SE & Co. KGaA; *Int'l*, pg. 708
GIVAUDAN HOLDINGS UK LTD—See Givaudan S.A.; *Int'l*, pg. 2980
GI VENTURES; *Int'l*, pg. 2960
GJENSIDIGE FORSIKRING ASA; *Int'l*, pg. 2982
G.K. CONSULTANTS LIMITED; *Int'l*, pg. 2865

N.A.I.C.S. INDEX

523999 — MISCELLANEOUS FINAN...

GKN HOLDINGS PLC—See GKN plc; *Int'l*, pg. 2985
GKN SINTER METALS HOLDINGS LTD—See GKN plc; *Int'l*, pg. 2985
GKN (UNITED KINGDOM) PLC—See GKN plc; *Int'l*, pg. 2983
GLADSTONE LAND CORPORATION—See Gladstone Management Corporation; *U.S. Private*, pg. 1705
GLASS HOUSES ACQUISITION CORP.; *U.S. Public*, pg. 939
GLAXOSMITHKLINE CAPITAL PLC—See GSK plc; *Int'l*, pg. 3147
GLAXOSMITHKLINE HOLDINGS LIMITED—See GSK plc; *Int'l*, pg. 3147
GLENCORE CANADA FINANCIAL CORP.—See Glencore plc; *Int'l*, pg. 2990
GLENCORE GROUP FUNDING LIMITED—See Glencore plc; *Int'l*, pg. 2990
GLENDONTODD CAPITAL LLC; *U.S. Private*, pg. 1710
GLENDOWER CAPITAL LLP; *Int'l*, pg. 2991
GLENFARNE GROUP, LLC; *U.S. Private*, pg. 1710
GLENFARNE MERGER CORP.; *U.S. Public*, pg. 940
GLENNON BITTAN INVESTMENTS; *U.S. Private*, pg. 1711
GLENTRA CAPITAL P/S; *Int'l*, pg. 2992
GLENWOOD PRIVATE EQUITY CO., LTD.; *Int'l*, pg. 2992
GLL REAL ESTATE PARTNERS GMBH (GLL)—See Cinven Limited; *Int'l*, pg. 1616
GLOBAL ACOUSTIC PARTNERS LLC—See Evolution Capital Management LLC; *U.S. Private*, pg. 1442
GLOBAL BLOCKCHAIN ACQUISITION CORP.; *U.S. Public*, pg. 940
GLOBAL CAPITAL MARKETS LIMITED; *Int'l*, pg. 2993
GLOBAL CAPITAL PARTNERS, INC.; *U.S. Public*, pg. 941
GLOBAL CASH CARD, INC.—See Automatic Data Processing, Inc.; *U.S. Public*, pg. 230
GLOBAL CHAMPIONS SPLIT CORP.; *Int'l*, pg. 2994
GLOBAL CONSUMER ACQUISITION CORP.; *U.S. Private*, pg. 1713
GLOBAL CORNERSTONE HOLDINGS LIMITED; *U.S. Private*, pg. 1713
GLOBAL DIVIDEND GROWERS INCOME FUND; *Int'l*, pg. 2994
GLOBAL EQUITY CAPITAL, LLC; *U.S. Private*, pg. 1713
GLOBAL EQUITY PARTNERS BETEILIGUNGSMANAGEMENT AG; *Int'l*, pg. 2996
GLOBAL FINANCE SA; *Int'l*, pg. 2996
GLOBAL FOREX TRADING—See StoneX Group Inc.; *U.S. Public*, pg. 1952
GLOBAL FORTUNE INVESTMENT LIMITED; *Int'l*, pg. 2997
GLOBAL INFRASTRUCTURE MANAGEMENT, LLC—See BlackRock, Inc.; *U.S. Public*, pg. 345
GLOBAL INFRATECH & FINANCE LIMITED; *Int'l*, pg. 2997
GLOBALINK INVESTMENT INC.; *U.S. Public*, pg. 946
GLOBAL INNOVATIVE PLATFORMS INC.; *U.S. Public*, pg. 942
GLOBAL LIGHTS ACQUISITION CORP.; *Int'l*, pg. 2998
GLOBAL MACRO TRUST; *U.S. Private*, pg. 1716
GLOBAL MERCHANT FUND CORP.; *U.S. Private*, pg. 1716
GLOBALM-GROUP PLC; *Int'l*, pg. 3004
GLOBAL ONE REAL ESTATE INVESTMENT CORPORATION; *Int'l*, pg. 2999
GLOBAL REAL ESTATE HOLDINGS, INC.; *U.S. Private*, pg. 1717
GLOBAL REDEMPTION INC.; *U.S. Private*, pg. 1717
GLOBAL SECURITIES (USA), INC.—See Global Yatirim Holding A.S.; *Int'l*, pg. 3003
GLOBAL SPAC PARTNERS CO.—See Gorilla Technology Group Inc.; *Int'l*, pg. 3043
GLOBAL STAR ACQUISITION INC.; *U.S. Public*, pg. 945
GLOBAL SYNERGY ACQUISITION CORP.; *U.S. Public*, pg. 945
GLOBAL SYSTEMS DYNAMIC, INC.; *U.S. Public*, pg. 945
GLOBAL TECH INDUSTRIES GROUP, INC.; *U.S. Public*, pg. 945
GLOBAL YATIRIM HOLDING A.S.; *Int'l*, pg. 3002
GLOBE TRADE CENTRE S.A.; *Int'l*, pg. 3006
GLOBIS ACQUISITION CORP.; *U.S. Public*, pg. 946
GLOBIS CAPITAL PARTNERS & CO.—See Globis Corporation; *Int'l*, pg. 3007
GLOBON CO., LTD.; *Int'l*, pg. 3008
GM CAPITAL CORP; *Int'l*, pg. 3011
GMF CAPITAL LLC; *U.S. Private*, pg. 1721
GMM CAPITAL LLC; *U.S. Private*, pg. 1722
GMT COMMUNICATIONS PARTNERS LLP; *Int'l*, pg. 3015
GMUL INVESTMENT COMPANY, LTD.; *Int'l*, pg. 3015
GMX INC.; *U.S. Private*, pg. 1723
GO ACQUISITION CORP.; *U.S. Public*, pg. 949
GOAL ACQUISITIONS CORP.; *U.S. Public*, pg. 949
GOBI ACQUISITION CORP.; *Int'l*, pg. 3018
GOCO GROUP PLC—See Future plc; *Int'l*, pg. 2857
GODIVA SAVINGS LIMITED—See Coventry Building Society; *Int'l*, pg. 1821
GODSPEED CAPITAL MANAGEMENT LP; *U.S. Private*, pg. 1725
GOFINTECH INNOVATION LIMITED; *Int'l*, pg. 3021
GOGREEN INVESTMENTS CORP.; *U.S. Public*, pg. 949
GOLDBERG LINDSAY & CO., LLC; *U.S. Private*, pg. 1728
GOLDEN ARROW MERGER CORP.; *U.S. Public*, pg. 950
GOLDENBRIDGE ACQUISITION LIMITED; *Int'l*, pg. 3032

GOLDEN EQUITIES, INC.—See Graphic Packaging Holding Company; *U.S. Public*, pg. 958
GOLDEN EQUITY INVESTMENTS LLC; *U.S. Private*, pg. 1730
GOLDENEYE RESOURCES CORP.; *Int'l*, pg. 3033
GOLDEN FALCON ACQUISITION CORP.; *U.S. Public*, pg. 950
GOLDEN GATE CAPITAL MANAGEMENT II, LLC; *U.S. Private*, pg. 1730
GOLDEN SAND RIVER CALIFORNIA CORP.—See Beijing Century GSR Ventures Management Co., Ltd.; *Int'l*, pg. 947
GOLDEN SAND RIVER (HONG KONG) LIMITED—See Beijing Century GSR Ventures Management Co., Ltd.; *Int'l*, pg. 947
GOLDEN STAR ACQUISITION CORP.; *U.S. Public*, pg. 951
GOLDEN STAR CORPORATION; *U.S. Private*, pg. 1733
GOLDENSTONE ACQUISITION LTD.; *U.S. Public*, pg. 951
GOLDEN VENTURES ACQUISITION CORP.; *Int'l*, pg. 3032
GOLD FIELDS OROGEN HOLDING (BVI) LIMITED—See Gold Fields Limited; *Int'l*, pg. 3024
GOLD HORN INTERNATIONAL ENTERPRISES GROUP LIMITED; *Int'l*, pg. 3024
GOLDIN FACTORING LIMITED—See Goldin Financial Holdings Limited; *Int'l*, pg. 3033
GOLDIS WATER SDN BHD—See IGB Berhad; *Int'l*, pg. 3601
GOLDMAN SACHS ASSET MANAGEMENT CO., LTD.—See The Goldman Sachs Group, Inc.; *U.S. Public*, pg. 2081
GOLDMAN SACHS BDC, INC.—See The Goldman Sachs Group, Inc.; *U.S. Public*, pg. 2081
GOLDMAN, SACHS & CO. WERTPAPIER GMBH—See The Goldman Sachs Group, Inc.; *U.S. Public*, pg. 2081
GOLDMAN SACHS DO BRASIL BANCO MULTIPLO S/A—See The Goldman Sachs Group, Inc.; *U.S. Public*, pg. 2076
GOLDMAN SACHS MERCHANT BANKING DIVISION—See The Goldman Sachs Group, Inc.; *U.S. Public*, pg. 2076
GOLDMAN SACHS PRIVATE CREDIT CORP.; *U.S. Private*, pg. 1735
GOLDMAN SACHS URBAN INVESTMENT GROUP—See The Goldman Sachs Group, Inc.; *U.S. Public*, pg. 2081
GOLDNER HAWN JOHNSON & MORRISON INC.; *U.S. Private*, pg. 1735
GOLD ROYALTY CORP.; *Int'l*, pg. 3026
GOLDSTONE INVESTMENT CO., LTD.—See CITIC Securities Co., Ltd.; *Int'l*, pg. 1622
GOLECHHA GLOBAL FINANCE LTD.; *Int'l*, pg. 3035
GOLUB CAPITAL BDC, INC.—See Golub Capital, Inc.; *U.S. Private*, pg. 1736
GOLUB CAPITAL BDC REVOLVER FUNDING LLC—See Golub Capital, Inc.; *U.S. Private*, pg. 1736
GOLUB CAPITAL DIRECT LENDING UNLEVERED CORPORATION; *U.S. Private*, pg. 1736
GOLUB CAPITAL, INC.; *U.S. Private*, pg. 1736
GOODBODY CORPORATE FINANCE—See FEXCO Holdings; *Int'l*, pg. 2649
GOODBODY STOCKBROKERS UC—See AIB Group plc; *Int'l*, pg. 228
GOOD COMMERCE ACQUISITION CORP.; *U.S. Private*, pg. 1737
GOODFOOD MARKET CORP.; *Int'l*, pg. 3040
GOODWILL FINANCE LIMITED; *Int'l*, pg. 3041
GOOD WORKS ACQUISITION CORP.; *U.S. Public*, pg. 951
GORDON BROTHERS EUROPE—See Gordon Brothers Group, LLC; *U.S. Private*, pg. 1742
GORDON HOLDINGS (NETHERLANDS) B.V.—See Barclays PLC; *Int'l*, pg. 862
THE GORES GROUP, LLC - BOULDER BRANCH—See The Gores Group, LLC; *U.S. Private*, pg. 4035
THE GORES GROUP, LLC; *U.S. Private*, pg. 4034
GORES GUGGENHEIM, INC.; *U.S. Public*, pg. 952
GORES TECHNOLOGY PARTNERS, INC.; *U.S. Public*, pg. 952
GOTOBILLING, INC.—See Fortis Payment Systems LLC; *U.S. Private*, pg. 1576
GOVERNANCE FOR OWNERS JAPAN KK—See Governance for Owners LLP; *Int'l*, pg. 3044
GOVERNANCE FOR OWNERS LLP; *Int'l*, pg. 3044
GOVERNANCE FOR OWNERS USA, INC.—See Governance for Owners LLP; *Int'l*, pg. 3044
THE GOVERNOR S RETIREMENT RESORT PTY LTD—See Australian Unity Limited; *Int'l*, pg. 723
GOYAL ASSOCIATES LTD; *Int'l*, pg. 3045
GOZDE GIRISIM SERMAYESI YATIRIM ORTAKLIGI A.S.; *Int'l*, pg. 3045
G&P ACQUISITION CORP.; *U.S. Public*, pg. 893
GPB CAPITAL HOLDINGS, LLC; *U.S. Private*, pg. 1748
GPB-FACTORING LLC—See Gazprombank JSC; *Int'l*, pg. 2892
GP BULLHOUND LLP; *Int'l*, pg. 3045
GP CAPITAL CO., LTD.; *Int'l*, pg. 3045
GP INVESTIMENTOS LTDA.—See GP Investments, Ltd.; *Int'l*, pg. 3045
GP INVESTMENTS, LTD.; *Int'l*, pg. 3045

GP NORTH AMERICA, LLC—See GP Investments, Ltd.; *Int'l*, pg. 3045
GPW BENCHMARK S.A.—See Gielda Papierow Wartosciowych w Warszawie S.A.; *Int'l*, pg. 2968
GQG PARTNERS INC.; *U.S. Public*, pg. 952
GRACE KENNEDY CURRENCY TRADING SERVICES LIMITED—See GraceKennedy Limited; *Int'l*, pg. 3048
GRACE KENNEDY PAYMENT SERVICES LIMITED—See GraceKennedy Limited; *Int'l*, pg. 3048
GRACEKENNEDY REMITTANCE SERVICES (TRINIDAD AND TOBAGO) LTD.—See GraceKennedy Limited; *Int'l*, pg. 3049
GRAFTON CAPITAL LIMITED; *Int'l*, pg. 3050
GRAHAM CAPITAL GROUP, LLC; *U.S. Private*, pg. 1751
GRAHAM PARTNERS, INC.—See The Graham Group, Inc.; *U.S. Private*, pg. 4036
GRAIL PARTNERS LLC; *U.S. Private*, pg. 1751
GRAIN MANAGEMENT, LLC; *U.S. Private*, pg. 1751
GRANADA INVESTMENT GMBH I.L.—See Commerzbank AG; *Int'l*, pg. 1718
GRAND CAPITAL FOR FINANCIAL INVESTMENTS; *Int'l*, pg. 3054
THE GRAND GROUP AB—See FAM AB; *Int'l*, pg. 2611
GRANDLAND HOLDINGS GROUP CO., LTD.; *Int'l*, pg. 3058
GRAND PARADE INVESTMENTS LIMITED; *Int'l*, pg. 3056
GRAND PEAK CAPITAL CORP.; *Int'l*, pg. 3056
GRANDVILLE EQUITIES CORP.; *Int'l*, pg. 3058
GRANITE BRIDGE PARTNERS LLC; *U.S. Private*, pg. 1755
GRANITE CREEK CAPITAL PARTNERS, LLC; *U.S. Private*, pg. 1755
GRANITE EQUITY PARTNERS LLC; *U.S. Private*, pg. 1755
GRANITO ACQUISITION I, INC.; *U.S. Private*, pg. 1756
GRANO RETAIL INVESTMENTS INC.; *Int'l*, pg. 3059
GRANT AVENUE CAPITAL, LLC; *U.S. Private*, pg. 1756
GRANT PARK FUTURES FUND LIMITED PARTNERSHIP; *U.S. Private*, pg. 1756
GRANVILLE GMBH; *Int'l*, pg. 3060
GRAPEVINE SOLUTIONS INC.—See DeepSpatial Inc.; *Int'l*, pg. 2003
GRAPHITE CAPITAL MANAGEMENT LLP; *Int'l*, pg. 3060
GRAPHJET TECHNOLOGY; *Int'l*, pg. 3061
GRASS-AIR HOLDING B.V.—See Atlas Copco AB; *Int'l*, pg. 679
GRAYCLIFF PARTNERS LP; *U.S. Private*, pg. 1760
GRAYSCALE LITECOIN TRUST; *U.S. Public*, pg. 961
GRAYS PEAK CAPITAL LP; *U.S. Private*, pg. 1761
THE GRAYSTONE COMPANY, INC.; *U.S. Public*, pg. 2085
GREAT ELM GROUP, INC.; *U.S. Public*, pg. 961
GREAT HILL PARTNERS, L.P.; *U.S. Private*, pg. 1763
GREAT IDEA CORP.; *U.S. Private*, pg. 1764
GREAT MILL ROCK LLC; *U.S. Private*, pg. 1765
GREAT POINT PARTNERS, LLC; *U.S. Private*, pg. 1767
GREAT WALL SECURITIES CO., LTD.—See China Huaneng Group Co., Ltd.; *Int'l*, pg. 1509
GREENBANK CAPITAL INC.; *Int'l*, pg. 3073
GREENBELT CAPITAL MANAGEMENT L.P.; *U.S. Private*, pg. 1774
GREENBRIAR CAPITAL CORP.; *Int'l*, pg. 3073
GREENBRIAR EQUITY GROUP, L.P.; *U.S. Private*, pg. 1775
GREENCITY ACQUISITION CORPORATION; *Int'l*, pg. 3073
GREENCORE UK HOLDINGS PLC—See Greencore Group plc; *Int'l*, pg. 3074
GREEN COURTE PARTNERS, LLC; *U.S. Private*, pg. 1772
GREENFIELD PARTNERS LLC; *U.S. Private*, pg. 1777
GREENFIRST FOREST PRODUCTS INC.; *Int'l*, pg. 3074
GREENLAND TECHNOLOGIES HOLDING CORPORATION; *Int'l*, pg. 3075
GREENOAKS CAPITAL PARTNERS LLC; *U.S. Private*, pg. 1779
GREENRIDGE INVESTMENT PARTNERS; *U.S. Private*, pg. 1779
GREENROSE HOLDING CO INC.; *U.S. Public*, pg. 965
GREENS FARMS CAPITAL LLC; *U.S. Private*, pg. 1779
GREENSPACE BRANDS INC.; *U.S. Private*, pg. 3076
GREEN STREET CAPITAL CORP.; *U.S. Public*, pg. 964
GREIF PACKAGING FRANCE INVESTMENTS SAS—See Greif Inc.; *U.S. Public*, pg. 968
GREIG MIDDLETON HOLDINGS LIMITED—See Barclays PLC; *Int'l*, pg. 862
GREMI INWESTYCJE S.A.; *Int'l*, pg. 3080
GRENKE INVESTITIONEN VERWALTUNGS KOMMANDITGESELLSCHAFT AUF AKTIEN—See Grenke AG; *Int'l*, pg. 3081
GRENKELEASING MAGYARORSZAG KFT.—See Grenke AG; *Int'l*, pg. 3081
GRENKE LIMITED—See Grenke AG; *Int'l*, pg. 3081
GRENKE RENT S.L.—See Grenke AG; *Int'l*, pg. 3081
GRESHAM HOUSE STRATEGIC PLC; *Int'l*, pg. 3082
GRESHAM PARTNERS LTD.; *Int'l*, pg. 3082
GREYBULL CAPITAL LLP; *Int'l*, pg. 3082
GREYLOCK PARTNERS; *U.S. Private*, pg. 1784
GREY MOUNTAIN PARTNERS, LLC; *U.S. Private*, pg. 1784
GREYROCK CAPITAL GROUP, LLC; *U.S. Private*, pg. 1785
GREYSTONE CAPITAL PARTNERS A/S; *Int'l*, pg. 3082
GREYSTONE HOUSING IMPACT INVESTORS LP—See Greystone & Co., Inc.; *U.S. Private*, pg. 1786

523999 — MISCELLANEOUS FINAN...

GRID DYNAMICS HOLDINGS, INC.; *U.S. Public*, pg. 969
GRIDIRON CAPITAL, LLC; *U.S. Private*, pg. 1786
THE GRIFFIN GROUP, LLC; *U.S. Private*, pg. 4039
GRIFFIN HOLDINGS, LLC; *U.S. Private*, pg. 1788
GRN FUNDS, LLC; *U.S. Private*, pg. 1791
GROEP HEYLEN BUSINESS & BUILDING BV; *Int'l*, pg. 3087
GROSVENOR FINANCIAL SERVICES GROUP LTD.; *Int'l*, pg. 3088
GROTECH VENTURES; *U.S. Private*, pg. 1793
GROUPE MTD FINANCE; *Int'l*, pg. 3109
GROUP NINE ACQUISITION CORP.; *U.S. Public*, pg. 972
GROVE COLLABORATIVE HOLDINGS, INC.; *U.S. Public*, pg. 972
GROVEPOINT CAPITAL LLP; *Int'l*, pg. 3112
GROWN ROGUE INTERNATIONAL INC.; *Int'l*, pg. 3113
GROWN ROGUE UNLIMITED, LLC—See Grown Rogue International Inc.; *Int'l*, pg. 3113
GROWTH COMPANY INVESTOR LTD—See Bonhill Group PLC; *Int'l*, pg. 1107
THE GROWTH FOR GOOD ACQUISITION CORPORATION; *U.S. Private*, pg. 4040
GROWTHPOINT PROPERTIES LIMITED; *Int'l*, pg. 3113
GRUMMAN HILL GROUP, LLC; *U.S. Private*, pg. 1797
GRUNWALD EQUITY MANAGEMENT GMBH; *Int'l*, pg. 3115
GRUPO DE INVERSIONES SURAMERICANA S.A.; *Int'l*, pg. 3125
GRUPO EMES S.A.; *Int'l*, pg. 3126
GRUPO FINANCIERO BANORTE, S.A.B. DE C.V.; *Int'l*, pg. 3129
GRUPO SALINAS, S.A. DE C.V.; *Int'l*, pg. 3135
GRYPHON INVESTORS, LLC; *U.S. Private*, pg. 1798
GSB FINANCE LIMITED; *Int'l*, pg. 3143
GS CAPITAL PARTNERS L.P.—See The Goldman Sachs Group, Inc.; *U.S. Public*, pg. 2076
GSC GROUP; *U.S. Private*, pg. 1800
GS CHAIN PLC; *Int'l*, pg. 3141
GSL SECURITIES LIMITED; *Int'l*, pg. 3150
GSP FINANCE COMPANY (BANGLADESH) LIMITED; *Int'l*, pg. 3150
GSTAAD CAPITAL CORP.; *Int'l*, pg. 3150
GTA FINANCECORP INC.; *Int'l*, pg. 3151
GTCR LLC; *U.S. Private*, pg. 1801
GTIS PARTNERS BRAZIL—See GTIS Partners LP; *U.S. Private*, pg. 1807
GTIS PARTNERS LP; *U.S. Private*, pg. 1807
GTY TECHNOLOGY HOLDINGS INC.—See GI Manager L.P.; *U.S. Private*, pg. 1692
GUANFU HOLDINGS CO., LTD.; *Int'l*, pg. 3152
GUANGDONG INVESTMENT LIMITED—See GDH Limited; *Int'l*, pg. 2896
GUANGXI ORIENTAL INTELLIGENT MANUFACTURING TECHNOLOGY CO., LTD; *Int'l*, pg. 3163
GUAN ZHI HOLDINGS LTD.—See Gunze Limited; *Int'l*, pg. 3185
GUARDCAP ASSET MANAGEMENT LIMITED—See Guardian Capital Group Limited; *Int'l*, pg. 3169
GUARDIAN CAPITAL GROUP LIMITED; *Int'l*, pg. 3169
GUARDIAN CAPITAL LP—See Guardian Capital Group Limited; *Int'l*, pg. 3169
GUARDIAN CAPITAL PARTNERS, LLC; *U.S. Private*, pg. 1810
GUARDIAN INVESTOR SERVICES LLC—See The Guardian Life Insurance Company of America; *U.S. Private*, pg. 4040
GUARDRISK ALLIED PRODUCTS & SERVICES PROPRIETARY LIMITED—See Alexander Forbes Group Holdings Limited; *Int'l*, pg. 307
GUERRILLA RF, INC.; *U.S. Public*, pg. 973
GUIDEPOST GROWTH MANAGEMENT COMPANY LLC; *U.S. Private*, pg. 1813
GUIDON PARTNERS, LP; *U.S. Private*, pg. 1814
GUJARAT INVESTA LIMITED; *Int'l*, pg. 3176
GUJARAT STATE FINANCIAL CORPORATION LTD.; *Int'l*, pg. 3177
GULF INTERNATIONAL SERVICES QSC; *Int'l*, pg. 3181
GULFINVEST INTERNATIONAL K.S.C.C.; *Int'l*, pg. 3182
GULF INVESTMENT HOUSE K.S.C.P.; *Int'l*, pg. 3181
GUNSYND PLC; *Int'l*, pg. 3185
GUOTAI JUNAN SECURITIES CO., LTD.; *Int'l*, pg. 3187
GUOZI ZHONGYU CAPITAL HOLDINGS COMPANY; *U.S. Public*, pg. 975
GURKHAS FINANCE LIMITED; *Int'l*, pg. 3188
GURNET POINT CAPITAL LLC; *U.S. Private*, pg. 1819
GUSBOURNE PLC; *Int'l*, pg. 3188
GVD INDUSTRIES LLC; *U.S. Private*, pg. 1820
GV MANAGEMENT COMPANY, LLC—See Alphabet Inc.; *U.S. Public*, pg. 82
GW & WADE; *U.S. Private*, pg. 1821
GYRODYNE, LLC; *U.S. Public*, pg. 976
H2 EQUITY PARTNERS B.V.; *Int'l*, pg. 3199
H2O ASSET MANAGEMENT LLP—See Groupe BPCE; *Int'l*, pg. 3098
HABIB METROPOLITAN FINANCIAL SERVICES LIMITED—See Habib Bank AG Zurich; *Int'l*, pg. 3202
HABROK MINING PTY LTD; *Int'l*, pg. 3203
HADASIT BIO-HOLDINGS LTD.; *Int'l*, pg. 3205

HAGIN INVESTMENT MANAGMENT; *U.S. Private*, pg. 1840
HAHN & COMPANY; *Int'l*, pg. 3207
HAINAN AIRPORT INFRASTRUCTURE CO LTD; *Int'l*, pg. 3211
HAINAN MANASLU CORP.; *Int'l*, pg. 3212
HAITONG INTERNATIONAL SECURITIES GROUP LIMITED—See Haitong Securities Co., Ltd.; *Int'l*, pg. 3218
HALBERG KAPITAL A/S—See Halberg A/S; *Int'l*, pg. 3227
HALDER BETEILIGUNGSBERATUNG GMBH; *Int'l*, pg. 3227
HALE CAPITAL PARTNERS, L.P.; *U.S. Private*, pg. 1842
HALFORDS FINANCE LIMITED—See Halfords Group plc; *Int'l*, pg. 3229
THE HALIFAX GROUP LLC; *U.S. Private*, pg. 4041
HAL INVESTMENTS BV—See HAL Trust N.V.; *Int'l*, pg. 3223
HALK GAYRIMENKUL YATIRIM ORTAKLIGI A.S.; *Int'l*, pg. 3229
HALL CAPITAL PARTNERS, LP—See Hall Capital, LLC; *U.S. Private*, pg. 1843
HALL FINANCIAL GROUP, LTD.; *U.S. Private*, pg. 1843
THE HALLIARD PROPERTY CO. LIMITED—See Centremanor Ltd.; *Int'l*, pg. 1412
HALL OF FAME RESORT & ENTERTAINMENT COMPANY; *U.S. Public*, pg. 980
HALMAN-ALDUBI INVESTMENT HOUSE LTD.; *Int'l*, pg. 3233
HALMOS CAPITAL PARTNERS; *U.S. Private*, pg. 1845
HALYARD CAPITAL MANAGEMENT, LLC; *U.S. Private*, pg. 1847
HAMA FINANCIAL INSTITUTION LIMITED; *Int'l*, pg. 3234
HAMBRO PERKS ACQUISITION COMPANY LIMITED; *Int'l*, pg. 3236
HAMILTON GLOBAL OPPORTUNITIES PLC; *Int'l*, pg. 3237
HAMILTON ROBINSON LLC; *U.S. Private*, pg. 1848
HAMILTON THORNE LTD.—See Astorg Partners S.A.S.; *Int'l*, pg. 656
HAMMOND, KENNEDY, WHITNEY & COMPANY, INC. - INDIANAPOLIS—See Hammond, Kennedy, Whitney & Company, Inc.; *U.S. Private*, pg. 1850
HAMMOND, KENNEDY, WHITNEY & COMPANY, INC.; *U.S. Private*, pg. 1850
HAMNES INVESTMENTS BV—See Barclays PLC; *Int'l*, pg. 862
HAMPSHIRE EQUITY PARTNERS; *U.S. Private*, pg. 1851
HAMPTON BAY CAPITAL, INC.; *Int'l*, pg. 3239
HAMPTON FINANCIAL CORPORATION; *Int'l*, pg. 3239
HAMPTON SECURITIES LIMITED—See Hampton Financial Corporation; *Int'l*, pg. 3239
HANA ASIA LIMITED—See Hana Financial Group, Inc.; *Int'l*, pg. 3240
HANA F&I, INC.—See Hana Financial Group, Inc.; *Int'l*, pg. 3240
HANA FINANCIAL INVESTMENT CO., LTD.—See Hana Financial Group, Inc.; *Int'l*, pg. 3240
HANA MUST SEVEN SPECIAL PURPOSE ACQUISITION COMPANY; *Int'l*, pg. 3241
HANA MUST SPECIAL PURPOSE ACQUISITION COMPANY; *Int'l*, pg. 3241
HANA TI CO., LTD.—See Hana Financial Group, Inc.; *Int'l*, pg. 3240
HANA VENTURES LLC—See Hana Financial Group, Inc.; *Int'l*, pg. 3240
HANCOCK & GORE LTD.; *Int'l*, pg. 3242
HANCOCK PARK ASSOCIATES, LP; *U.S. Private*, pg. 1852
HANCOCK PARK CORPORATE INCOME, INC.; *U.S. Private*, pg. 1852
HANDSON3, LLC; *U.S. Private*, pg. 1853
HANG LUNG FINANCIAL SERVICES LIMITED—See Hang Lung Group Limited; *Int'l*, pg. 3245
HANG LUNG TREASURY LIMITED—See Hang Lung Group Limited; *Int'l*, pg. 3245
HANG SENG INSURANCE COMPANY LIMITED—See HSBC Holdings plc; *Int'l*, pg. 3506
HANG SENG INVESTMENT MANAGEMENT LIMITED—See HSBC Holdings plc; *Int'l*, pg. 3506
HAN KOOK CAPITAL CO., LTD.; *Int'l*, pg. 3240
HANKUU HANSHIN FINANCIAL SUPPORT CO., LTD.—See Hankyu Hanshin Holdings Inc.; *Int'l*, pg. 3255
HANKYU INVESTMENT PARTNERS, INC.—See Hankyu Hanshin Holdings Inc.; *Int'l*, pg. 3255
HANNON ARMSTRONG SUSTAINABLE INFRASTRUCTURE CAPITAL, INC.; *U.S. Public*, pg. 983
HANNOVER FINANZ GMBH; *Int'l*, pg. 3257
HANNOVER LEASING WACHSTUMSWERTE ASIEN 1 GMBH & CO. KG—See Helaba Landesbank Hessen-Thuringen; *Int'l*, pg. 3328
HANOVER INVESTORS MANAGEMENT LLP; *Int'l*, pg. 3258
HANOVER PARTNERS, INC.; *U.S. Private*, pg. 1855
HANSA INVESTMENT COMPANY LIMITED; *Int'l*, pg. 3259
HANSON FINANCE AUSTRALIA LTD—See Heidelberg Materials AG; *Int'l*, pg. 3312
HANSON FINANCE LIMITED—See Heidelberg Materials AG; *Int'l*, pg. 3312
HANSON FINANCIAL SERVICES LIMITED—See Heidelberg Materials AG; *Int'l*, pg. 3312

HANSON QUARRY PRODUCTS (HOLDINGS) SDN BHD—See Heidelberg Materials AG; *Int'l*, pg. 3312
HANWHA INVESTMENT & SECURITIES CO., LTD.; *Int'l*, pg. 3266
HANWHA INVESTMENT TRUST MANAGEMENT CO., LTD.—See Hanwha Group; *Int'l*, pg. 3266
HARBERT MEZZANINE CAPITAL—See Harbert Management Corporation; *U.S. Private*, pg. 1858
HARBERT VENTURE PARTNERS—See Harbert Management Corporation; *U.S. Private*, pg. 1858
HARBINGER CAPITAL PARTNERS LLC; *U.S. Private*, pg. 1858
THE HARBOR BANK OF MARYLAND—See Harbor Bankshares Corporation; *U.S. Public*, pg. 984
HARBOR BEACH CAPITAL, LLC; *U.S. Private*, pg. 1858
HARBOUR GROUP LIMITED OF DELAWARE—See Harbour Group Industries, Inc.; *U.S. Private*, pg. 1860
HARBOUR POINT MANAGEMENT LLC; *U.S. Private*, pg. 1861
HARBOURVEST GLOBAL PRIVATE EQUITY LIMITED; *Int'l*, pg. 3272
HARDBALL CAPITAL; *U.S. Private*, pg. 1862
HARDT GROUP ADVISORS, INC.—See HARDT GROUP Global Management AG; *Int'l*, pg. 3273
HARDT GROUP GLOBAL MANAGEMENT AG; *Int'l*, pg. 3273
HARDT GROUP GMBH—See HARDT GROUP Global Management AG; *Int'l*, pg. 3273
HARDY CAPITAL CORPORATION; *Int'l*, pg. 3273
HAREL INSURANCE INVESTMENTS & FINANCIAL SERVICES LTD.; *Int'l*, pg. 3273
HARGREAVES LANSDOWN ASSET MANAGEMENT LTD—See Hargreaves Lansdown PLC; *Int'l*, pg. 3274
HARGREAVES LANSDOWN FUND MANAGERS LTD—See Hargreaves Lansdown PLC; *Int'l*, pg. 3274
HARGREAVES LANSDOWN NOMINEES LTD—See Hargreaves Lansdown PLC; *Int'l*, pg. 3274
HARGREAVES LANSDOWN TRUSTEE COMPANY LTD—See Hargreaves Lansdown PLC; *Int'l*, pg. 3275
HARLEY STANFIELD, INC.; *U.S. Private*, pg. 1865
HARMONEY CORP LIMITED; *Int'l*, pg. 3277
HARMONY CAPITAL SERVICES LIMITED; *Int'l*, pg. 3278
HARMONY MERGER CORP.—See NextDecade Corporation; *U.S. Public*, pg. 1526
HARPIA OMEGA PARTICIPACOES S.A.; *Int'l*, pg. 3278
HARRISON STREET REAL ESTATE CAPITAL LLC—See Colliers International Group Inc.; *Int'l*, pg. 1701
HARRIS RIA HOLDINGS, INC.—See Bank of Montreal; *Int'l*, pg. 846
HARTE-HANKS STOCK PLAN, INC.—See Harte Hanks, Inc.; *U.S. Public*, pg. 986
HARVEST CAPITAL CREDIT CORPORATION; *U.S. Public*, pg. 987
HARVEST CAPITAL MANAGEMENT PUBLIC LTD.; *Int'l*, pg. 3280
HARVEST CAPITAL STRATEGIES LLC—See Citizens Financial Group, Inc.; *U.S. Public*, pg. 505
HARVEST HEALTHCARE LEADERS INCOME ETF; *Int'l*, pg. 3280
HARVEST PARTNERS L.P.; *U.S. Private*, pg. 1876
HARWOOD CAPITAL LLP; *Int'l*, pg. 3282
HARYANA CAPFIN LIMITED; *Int'l*, pg. 3282
HARYANA FINANCIAL CORPORATION LTD.; *Int'l*, pg. 3282
HASH SPACE ACQUISITION CORP.; *Int'l*, pg. 3283
HASSO PLATTNER VENTURES AFRICA (PTY) LTD.; *Int'l*, pg. 3283
HASSO PLATTNER VENTURES MANAGEMENT GMBH; *Int'l*, pg. 3284
HASTI FINANCE LIMITED; *Int'l*, pg. 3284
HASTINGS EQUITY PARTNERS, LLC; *U.S. Private*, pg. 1879
HAT SICAF S.P.A; *Int'l*, pg. 3284
HATTINGTON CAPITAL LLP; *Int'l*, pg. 3284
HAUCK & AUFHAUSER INVESTMENT GESELLSCHAFT S.A.—See Fosun International Limited; *Int'l*, pg. 2751
HAUSER CAPITAL MARKETS LLC—See Art Hauser Insurance, Inc.; *U.S. Private*, pg. 339
HAVELI INVESTMENT MANAGEMENT LLC—See Whanau Interests LLC; *U.S. Private*, pg. 4503
HAVENCREST CAPITAL MANAGEMENT, LLC; *U.S. Private*, pg. 1880
HAVSFRUN INVESTMENT AB; *Int'l*, pg. 3287
HAWKS ACQUISITION CORP.; *U.S. Public*, pg. 989
HAWK STREET ACQUISITION CORPORATION; *U.S. Private*, pg. 1882
HAWSGOODWIN INVESTMENT MANAGEMENT, LLC—See Genstar Capital, LLC; *U.S. Private*, pg. 1677
HAWSGOODWIN INVESTMENT MANAGEMENT, LLC—See Keystone Group, L.P.; *U.S. Private*, pg. 2298
HAWTHORNE CORPORATION—See Moelis Asset Management LP; *U.S. Private*, pg. 2764
HAYCARB HOLDINGS AUSTRALIA (PTY) LTD.—See Hayleys PLC; *Int'l*, pg. 3291
HAYFIN CAPITAL MANAGEMENT LLP—See British Columbia Investment Management Corp.; *Int'l*, pg. 1169
HAYMAKER ACQUISITION CORP. II—See Haymaker Acquisition Corp.; *U.S. Private*, pg. 1885

HAYMAKER ACQUISITION CORP.; *U.S. Private*, pg. 1885
HAYS HOLDINGS BV—See Hays PLC; *Int'l*, pg. 3293
HAYS INTERNATIONAL HOLDINGS LIMITED—See Hays PLC; *Int'l*, pg. 3293
HAYS OVERSEAS HOLDINGS LIMITED—See Hays PLC; *Int'l*, pg. 3293
HAYS SPECIALIST RECRUITMENT (HOLDINGS) LIMITED—See Hays PLC; *Int'l*, pg. 3294
HAY TOR CAPITAL LLP; *Int'l*, pg. 3289
HBC ACQUISITION CORP.; *U.S. Private*, pg. 1886
HB EQUITY PARTNERS, L.P.; *U.S. Private*, pg. 1886
HBMA HOLDINGS LLC—See Heidelberg Materials AG; *Int'l*, pg. 3310
HBM HEALTHCARE INVESTMENTS AG; *Int'l*, pg. 3296
HBM HEALTHCARE INVESTMENTS (CAYMAN) LTD.—See HBM Healthcare Investments AG; *Int'l*, pg. 3296
HBM PARTNERS LTD.—See HBM Healthcare Investments AG; *Int'l*, pg. 3297
HB STOCKHOLDINGS LIMITED; *Int'l*, pg. 3295
HCI CENTRAL EUROPE HOLDING B.V.—See BRENNTAG SE; *Int'l*, pg. 1149
HCI EQUITY MANAGEMENT, L.P.; *U.S. Private*, pg. 1888
HCI HANSEATISCHE CAPITALBERATUNGSGESELLSCHAFT MBH—See Ernst Russ AG; *Int'l*, pg. 2495
HCM ACQUISITION CORP.; *U.S. Public*, pg. 1014
HC PRIVATE INVESTMENTS LLC; *U.S. Private*, pg. 1888
HCS BETEILIGUNGSGESELLSCHAFT MBH; *Int'l*, pg. 3299
HDFC ASSET MANAGEMENT COMPANY LIMITED—See Housing Development Finance Corporation Limited; *Int'l*, pg. 3491
HDFC MUTUAL FUND—See Housing Development Finance Corporation Limited; *Int'l*, pg. 3491
HDFC REALTY LIMITED—See Housing Development Finance Corporation Limited; *Int'l*, pg. 3492
HDFC TRUSTEE COMPANY LIMITED—See Housing Development Finance Corporation Limited; *Int'l*, pg. 3492
HDM CAPITAL SDN BHD—See Hwang Capital (Malaysia) Berhad; *Int'l*, pg. 3542
HDM PRIVATE EQUITY SDN. BHD.—See Hwang Capital (Malaysia) Berhad; *Int'l*, pg. 3542
HEADHAUL CAPITAL PARTNERS LLC; *U.S. Private*, pg. 1891
HEADLAND CAPITAL PARTNERS LIMITED; *Int'l*, pg. 3301
HEADWAY CAPITAL, LLC—See Enova International, Inc.; *U.S. Public*, pg. 769
HEALTH ASSURANCE ACQUISITION CORP.; *U.S. Public*, pg. 1014
HEALTHCARE ACTIVOS YIELD SOCIMI, S.A.; *Int'l*, pg. 3303
HEALTHCARE AI ACQUISITION CORP.; *Int'l*, pg. 3303
HEALTHCARE ASSOCIATES CREDIT UNION; *U.S. Private*, pg. 1895
HEALTHCARE CAPITAL CORP.; *U.S. Public*, pg. 1015
HEALTHCARE INTEGRATED TECHNOLOGIES INC.; *U.S. Public*, pg. 1015
HEALTHCARE SERVICES ACQUISITION CORPORATION; *U.S. Public*, pg. 1015
HEALTH COEVO AG—See BAWAG Group AG; *Int'l*, pg. 900
HEALTHEDGE INVESTMENT PARTNERS, LLC; *U.S. Private*, pg. 1896
HEALTH ENTERPRISE PARTNERS LLC; *U.S. Private*, pg. 1893
HEALTH EVOLUTION PARTNERS LLC; *U.S. Private*, pg. 1893
HEALTHPOINTCAPITAL, LLC; *U.S. Private*, pg. 1897
HEARTLAND EQUITY MANAGEMENT LLC; *U.S. Private*, pg. 1900
HEARTLAND, INC.; *U.S. Private*, pg. 1901
HEARTLAND MEDIA ACQUISITION CORP.; *U.S. Private*, pg. 1018
HEARTWOOD PARTNERS, LLC; *U.S. Private*, pg. 1901
HEAVEN-SENT CAPITAL MANAGEMENT GROUP CO. LTD.; *Int'l*, pg. 3305
HEDOSOPHIA EUROPEAN GROWTH; *Int'l*, pg. 3307
HEHMEYER, LLC; *U.S. Private*, pg. 1904
HEIDELBERGCEMENT SWEDEN AB—See Heidelberg Materials AG; *Int'l*, pg. 3315
HEIDELBERG INNOVATION FONDS MANAGEMENT GMBH; *Int'l*, pg. 3308
HEIQ PLC; *Int'l*, pg. 3326
HELIAD EQUITY PARTNERS GMBH & CO. KGAA—See Heliad AG; *Int'l*, pg. 3329
HELIOS INVESTMENT PARTNERS LLP; *Int'l*, pg. 3330
HELIX TECHNOLOGIES, INC.—See Forian Inc.; *U.S. Public*, pg. 868
HELLA VENTURES, LLC—See Hella GmbH & Co. KGaA; *Int'l*, pg. 3332
HELLENIC BANK TRUST AND FINANCE CORP. LTD—See Hellenic Bank Public Company Ltd.; *Int'l*, pg. 3333
HELLMAN & FRIEDMAN EUROPE LIMITED—See Hellman & Friedman LLC; *U.S. Private*, pg. 1910
HELLMAN & FRIEDMAN LLC; *U.S. Private*, pg. 1907
HELPAGE FINLEASE LTD.; *Int'l*, pg. 3338
HELPMAN CAPITAL BV—See Alfa Laval AB; *Int'l*, pg. 310
HELVETIA INVESTMENT FOUNDATION—See Helvetia Holding AG; *Int'l*, pg. 3339
HEMANG RESOURCES LIMITED; *Int'l*, pg. 3340

HENDERSON PARK CAPITAL PARTNERS UK LLP; *Int'l*, pg. 3345
HENG XIN CHINA HOLDINGS LIMITED; *Int'l*, pg. 3345
HENKEL ADHESIVE TECHNOLOGIES (MALAYSIA) HOLDINGS B.V.—See Henkel AG & Co. KGaA; *Int'l*, pg. 3348
HENKEL FINANCE AUSTRALIA L.P.—See Henkel AG & Co. KGaA; *Int'l*, pg. 3349
HENKEL HONG KONG HOLDING LTD.—See Henkel AG & Co. KGaA; *Int'l*, pg. 3349
HENLEY PARK ACQUISITION CORP.; *U.S. Public*, pg. 1025
HERALD INVESTMENTS (CHINA) COMPANY LIMITED—See Herald Holdings Limited; *Int'l*, pg. 3358
HERBOS-INVEST D.D.; *Int'l*, pg. 3360
HERCULES CAPITAL, INC.; *U.S. Public*, pg. 1028
HERCULES CLEAN TECHNOLOGY CAPITAL, INC.; *U.S. Private*, pg. 1921
HERCULES HOLDING SPECIALTY MATERIALS B.V.—See Ashland Inc.; *U.S. Public*, pg. 212
HERCULES TECHNOLOGY SBIC MANAGEMENT, LLC—See Hercules Capital, Inc.; *U.S. Public*, pg. 1028
HERITAGE CANNABIS HOLDINGS CORP.; *Int'l*, pg. 3361
HERITAGE COMMUNITIES L.P.—See UDR, Inc.; *U.S. Public*, pg. 2218
HERITAGE FINANCIAL GROUP, INC.; *U.S. Private*, pg. 1922
HERITAGE GROUP, LLC; *U.S. Private*, pg. 1923
HERITAGE GROUP LTD.; *Int'l*, pg. 3361
HERITAGE INTERNATIONAL FUND SERVICES (MALTA) LIMITED—See Heritage Group Ltd.; *Int'l*, pg. 3362
HERITAGE PARTNERS, INC.; *U.S. Private*, pg. 1924
HERKULES CAPITAL AS; *Int'l*, pg. 3362
HERON STREET ACQUISITION CORPORATION; *U.S. Private*, pg. 1926
HESTA BETEILIGUNGS-GMBH—See Hesta AG; *Int'l*, pg. 3365
HESTIA INSIGHT, INC.; *U.S. Public*, pg. 1030
HGCAPITAL LLP—See HgCapital Trust plc; *Int'l*, pg. 3376
HGGC, LLC; *U.S. Private*, pg. 1928
H&G HIGH CONVICTION LIMITED; *Int'l*, pg. 3191
HHG CAPITAL CORPORATION; *Int'l*, pg. 3379
HIESTAND HOLDINGS (SWITZERLAND) AG—See ARYZTA AG; *Int'l*, pg. 588
H.I.G. ACQUISITION CORP.; *U.S. Public*, pg. 979
H.I.G. CAPITAL, LLC; *U.S. Private*, pg. 1826
H.I.G. EUROPEAN CAPITAL PARTNERS GMBH—See H.I.G. Capital, LLC; *U.S. Private*, pg. 1828
H.I.G. EUROPEAN CAPITAL PARTNERS SAS—See H.I.G. Capital, LLC; *U.S. Private*, pg. 1828
HIGGINS DEVELOPMENT PARTNERS, LLC; *U.S. Private*, pg. 1935
HIGHBRIDGE CAPITAL MANAGEMENT (HONG KONG), LIMITED—See JPMorgan Chase & Co.; *U.S. Public*, pg. 1207
HIGHCROFT INVESTMENTS PLC; *Int'l*, pg. 3387
HIGH DESERT CAPITAL, LLC; *U.S. Private*, pg. 1935
HIGHFIELDS CAPITAL MANAGEMENT LP; *U.S. Private*, pg. 1937
HIGHLAND CAPITAL HOLDING CORP.—See Reverence Capital Partners LLC; *U.S. Private*, pg. 3414
HIGHLAND CAPITAL PARTNERS, LLC; *U.S. Private*, pg. 1938
HIGHLAND CONSUMER PARTNERS MANAGEMENT COMPANY LLC—See Highland Capital Partners, LLC; *U.S. Private*, pg. 1938
HIGHLANDER PARTNERS, LP.; *U.S. Private*, pg. 1939
HIGHLANDER PARTNERS SP. Z O.O.—See Highlander Partners, LP.; *U.S. Private*, pg. 1939
HIGHLAND EUROPE (UK) LLP—See Highland Capital Partners, LLC; *U.S. Private*, pg. 1938
HIGHLAND FINANCIAL TRUST—See Highland Capital Management, LP.; *U.S. Private*, pg. 1938
HIGHLAND TRANSCEND PARTNERS I CORP.; *U.S. Public*, pg. 1035
HIGHPOINT HOLDINGS, LLC; *U.S. Private*, pg. 1941
HIGHPOST CAPITAL, LLC; *U.S. Private*, pg. 1941
HIGH ROAD CAPITAL PARTNERS, LLC; *U.S. Private*, pg. 1936
HIGH SIERRA TECHNOLOGIES, INC.; *U.S. Public*, pg. 1035
HIGHSTREET ASSET MANAGEMENT INC.—See AGF Management Limited; *Int'l*, pg. 206
HIGH STREET CAPITAL MANAGEMENT, INC.; *U.S. Private*, pg. 1936
HIGHTOWER ADVISORS, LLC—See HighTower Holding LLC; *U.S. Private*, pg. 1941
HIGHVIEW CAPITAL, LLC; *U.S. Private*, pg. 1941
HIGHWAY CAPITAL PLC; *Int'l*, pg. 3389
HI GOLD OCEAN KMARIN NO.12 SHIP INVESTMENT COMPANY; *Int'l*, pg. 3379
H.I.G. PRIVATE EQUITY—See H.I.G. Capital, LLC; *U.S. Private*, pg. 1828
THE HIGRO GROUP LLC; *U.S. Private*, pg. 4052
HI INVESTMENT & SECURITIES CO., LTD.—See DGB Financial Group Co., Ltd.; *Int'l*, pg. 2096
HIKARI PRIVATE EQUITY INC—See Hikari Tsushin, Inc.; *Int'l*, pg. 3390

HI-KLASS TRADING & INVESTMENT LIMITED; *Int'l*, pg. 3380
HILCO CONSUMER CAPITAL, LLC—See Hilco Trading, LLC; *U.S. Private*, pg. 1943
HILCO CORPORATE FINANCE, LLC—See Hilco Trading, LLC; *U.S. Private*, pg. 1943
HILCO EQUITY MANAGEMENT, LLC—See Hilco Trading, LLC; *U.S. Private*, pg. 1943
HILCO INDUSTRIAL, LLC—See Hilco Trading, LLC; *U.S. Private*, pg. 1943
HILCO INDUSTRIAL ONLINE, LLC—See Hilco Trading, LLC; *U.S. Private*, pg. 1943
HILCO MERCHANT RESOURCES LLC; *U.S. Private*, pg. 1943
HILCO REAL ESTATE, LLC—See Hilco Trading, LLC; *U.S. Private*, pg. 1943
HILCO RECEIVABLES EUROPE B.V.—See Hilco Trading, LLC; *U.S. Private*, pg. 1944
HILCO RECEIVABLES LLC—See Hilco Trading, LLC; *U.S. Private*, pg. 1944
HILCO TRADING CO., INC.—See Hilco Trading, LLC; *U.S. Private*, pg. 1943
HILCO UK LTD.—See Hilco Trading, LLC; *U.S. Private*, pg. 1944
HILIKS TECHNOLOGIES LTD.; *Int'l*, pg. 3391
HILLSIDE CAPITAL INCORPORATED—See Brookside International Incorporated; *U.S. Private*, pg. 665
HILLSPIRE LLC; *U.S. Private*, pg. 1947
HILLTOP PRIVATE CAPITAL, LLC; *U.S. Private*, pg. 1947
HIND SECURITIES & CREDITS LIMITED; *Int'l*, pg. 3397
HINDUJA BANK (MIDDLE EAST) LTD.—See Hinduja Group Ltd.; *Int'l*, pg. 3399
HINDUJA BANK (SCHWEIZ) AG.—See Hinduja Group Ltd.; *Int'l*, pg. 3399
HINDUJA BANK (SWITZERLAND) LTD—See Hinduja Group Ltd.; *Int'l*, pg. 3399
HINDUJA GROUP LTD.; *Int'l*, pg. 3398
HINDUJA INDIA MAURITIUS HOLDINGS LTD.—See Hinduja Group Ltd.; *Int'l*, pg. 3399
HINDUJA LEYLAND FINANCE LIMITED—See Hinduja Group Ltd.; *Int'l*, pg. 3398
HINES GLOBAL INCOME TRUST, INC.; *U.S. Public*, pg. 1041
HITACHI CONSTRUCTION MACHINERY HOLDING U.S.A CORPORATION.—See Hitachi, Ltd.; *Int'l*, pg. 3416
HITACHI DATA SYSTEMS CREDIT CORPORATION—See Hitachi, Ltd.; *Int'l*, pg. 3414
HITACHI DATA SYSTEMS HOLDING CORPORATION—See Hitachi, Ltd.; *Int'l*, pg. 3414
HITACHI ID SYSTEMS HOLDING, INC—See Hitachi, Ltd.; *Int'l*, pg. 3415
HITECVISION AS; *Int'l*, pg. 3425
HITZ HOLDINGS U.S.A INC—See Hitachi Zosen Corporation; *Int'l*, pg. 3411
HK ACQUISITION CORPORATION; *Int'l*, pg. 3428
HK GRAPHENE TECHNOLOGY CORPORATION; *U.S. Public*, pg. 1042
HL ACQUISITIONS CORP.; *U.S. Public*, pg. 1042
HLD ASSOCIES SA; *Int'l*, pg. 3431
HLI-HUME MANAGEMENT COMPANY—See Hong Leong Investment Holdings Pte. Ltd.; *Int'l*, pg. 3468
HMC CAPITAL LIMITED; *Int'l*, pg. 3431
HMC INVESTORS, LLC—See Harbert Management Corporation; *U.S. Private*, pg. 1858
HNR ACQUISITION CORP.; *U.S. Public*, pg. 1044
HOA PHAT GROUP JOINT STOCK COMPANY; *Int'l*, pg. 3435
HOARDBURST LIMITED—See Barclays PLC; *Int'l*, pg. 862
HO CHI MINH CITY INFRASTRUCTURE INVESTMENT JOINT STOCK COMPANY; *Int'l*, pg. 3434
HOCHKONIG BERGBAHNEN GES.M.B.H—See Erste Group Bank AG; *Int'l*, pg. 2499
HOKUGIN BUSINESS SERVICES CO., LTD.—See Hokuhoku Financial Group, Inc.; *Int'l*, pg. 3444
HOKUGIN LEASE CO., LTD.—See Hokuhoku Financial Group, Inc.; *Int'l*, pg. 3444
HOKURIKU HOSHO SERVICES CO., LTD.—See Hokuhoku Financial Group, Inc.; *Int'l*, pg. 3444
HOLCIM FINANCE (LUXEMBOURG) S.A.—See Holcim Ltd.; *Int'l*, pg. 3448
HOLDING CENTER AD; *Int'l*, pg. 3450
HOLDING VARNA AD-VARNA; *Int'l*, pg. 3450
HOLLOWAY LODGING CORPORATION—See Clarke Inc.; *Int'l*, pg. 1650
HOME PLATE ACQUISITION CORPORATION; *U.S. Public*, pg. 1046
HOME POINT CAPITAL LP—See Stone Point Capital LLC; *U.S. Private*, pg. 3825
HOMES FOR AMERICA HOLDINGS; *U.S. Private*, pg. 1974
HOMEVESTORS OF AMERICA, INC.—See Levine Leichtman Capital Partners, LLC; *U.S. Private*, pg. 2436
HONGCHANG INTERNATIONAL CO LTD.; *Int'l*, pg. 3470
HONOR FINANCE LLC—See CIVC Partners LLC; *U.S. Private*, pg. 907
HONY CAPITAL ACQUISITION CORP.; *Int'l*, pg. 3472
HONYE FINANCIAL SERVICES LTD.; *Int'l*, pg. 3472
HOPU INVESTMENT MANAGEMENT CO., LTD.; *Int'l*, pg. 3474

HORIZON ACQUISITION CORPORATION II; *U.S. Public,* pg. 1053
HORIZON ACQUISITION CORPORATION; *U.S. Public,* pg. 1053
HORIZON CAPITAL LLP; *Int'l,* pg. 3479
HORIZON COPPER CORP.; *Int'l,* pg. 3479
HORIZON PARTNERS LTD.; *U.S. Private,* pg. 1982
HORIZONS HOLDINGS INTERNATIONAL, INC.; *U.S. Public,* pg. 1053
HORIZON TECHNOLOGY FINANCE CORPORATION; *U.S. Public,* pg. 1053
HORIZON TECHNOLOGY FINANCE MANAGEMENT LLC—See Monroe Capital LLC; *U.S. Private,* pg. 2773
HORMANNSHOFER FASSADEN GMBH & CO. HALLE KG—See BayernLB Holding AG; *Int'l,* pg. 914
HORMANNSHOFER FASSADEN SUD GMBH & CO. KG—See BayernLB Holding AG; *Int'l,* pg. 914
HORVIK LIMITED; *Int'l,* pg. 3482
HOSKEN CONSOLIDATED INVESTMENTS LIMITED; *Int'l,* pg. 3485
HOSKING PARTNERS LLP; *Int'l,* pg. 3485
HOSPITALITY INVESTMENTS LP; *U.S. Private,* pg. 1987
HOTBED LIMITED; *Int'l,* pg. 3487
HOTEL PROPERTY INVESTMENTS LIMITED; *Int'l,* pg. 3488
HOTUNG INVESTMENT HOLDINGS LIMITED; *Int'l,* pg. 3490
HOUSATONIC PARTNERS MANAGEMENT CO., INC.; *U.S. Private,* pg. 1991
HOUSTON VENTURES; *U.S. Private,* pg. 1994
HOVDE PRIVATE EQUITY ADVISORS LLC; *U.S. Private,* pg. 1994
HOYA HOLDINGS (ASIA) B.V.—See Hoya Corporation; *Int'l,* pg. 3496
H&Q ASIA PACIFIC, LTD.; *U.S. Private,* pg. 1823
HQ CAPITAL (DEUTSCHLAND) GMBH—See Harald Quandt Holding GmbH; *Int'l,* pg. 3269
HQ CAPITAL PRIVATE EQUITY LLC—See Harald Quandt Holding GmbH; *Int'l,* pg. 3269
HQ EQUITA GMBH—See Harald Quandt Holding GmbH; *Int'l,* pg. 3269
HRAM HOLDING DD; *Int'l,* pg. 3501
HSBC BANK ARMENIA CJSC—See HSBC Holdings plc; *Int'l,* pg. 3503
HSBC BANK A.S.—See HSBC Holdings plc; *Int'l,* pg. 3503
HSBC BANK (CHILE) SA—See HSBC Holdings plc; *Int'l,* pg. 3503
HSBC BANK MALTA P.L.C.—See HSBC Holdings plc; *Int'l,* pg. 3503
HSBC BRASIL HOLDING S.A.—See HSBC Holdings plc; *Int'l,* pg. 3505
HSBC CONTINENTAL EUROPE S.A.—See HSBC Holdings plc; *Int'l,* pg. 3505
HSBC GLOBAL ASSET MANAGEMENT (CANADA) LIMITED—See HSBC Holdings plc; *Int'l,* pg. 3504
HSBC GLOBAL ASSET MANAGEMENT (OESTERREICH) GMBH—See HSBC Holdings plc; *Int'l,* pg. 3504
HSBC GLOBAL ASSET MANAGEMENT (SWITZERLAND) AG—See HSBC Holdings plc; *Int'l,* pg. 3504
HSBC GLOBAL ASSET MANAGEMENT (USA) INC.—See HSBC Holdings plc; *Int'l,* pg. 3504
HSBC INSURANCE (SINGAPORE) PTE. LIMITED—See HSBC Holdings plc; *Int'l,* pg. 3505
HSBC LIFE ASSURANCE (MALTA) LIMITED—See HSBC Holdings plc; *Int'l,* pg. 3505
HSBC PRIVATE TRUSTEE (HONG KONG) LIMITED—See HSBC Holdings plc; *Int'l,* pg. 3505
HSBC QIANHAI SECURITIES LIMITED—See HSBC Holdings plc; *Int'l,* pg. 3505
HSBC SECURITIES BROKERS (ASIA) LIMITED—See HSBC Holdings plc; *Int'l,* pg. 3506
HSBC SECURITIES (TAIWAN) CORPORATION LIMITED—See HSBC Holdings plc; *Int'l,* pg. 3505
HSBC SERVICE DELIVERY (POLSKA) SP. Z O.O.—See HSBC Holdings plc; *Int'l,* pg. 3506
HSBC TRANSACTION SERVICES GMBH—See HSBC Holdings plc; *Int'l,* pg. 3506
HSBC TRINKAUS INVESTMENT MANAGERS S.A.—See HSBC Holdings plc; *Int'l,* pg. 3506
HSBC YATIRIM MENKUL DEGERLER A.S.—See HSBC Holdings plc; *Int'l,* pg. 3506
H.T.P. INVESTMENTS BV; *Int'l,* pg. 3196
HUABANG SECURITIES LIMITED—See Huabang Technology Holdings Limited; *Int'l,* pg. 3510
HUAIBEI GREENGOLD INDUSTRY INVESTMENT CO. LTD.; *Int'l,* pg. 3512
HUA NAN INVESTMENT TRUST CORPORATION—See Hua Nan Financial Holdings Co., Ltd.; *Int'l,* pg. 3509
HUA NAN SECURITIES INVESTMENT TRUST CO. LTD.—See Hua Nan Financial Holdings Co., Ltd.; *Int'l,* pg. 3510
HUA NAN VENTURE CAPITAL CO., LTD.—See Hua Nan Financial Holdings Co., Ltd.; *Int'l,* pg. 3510
HUANENG CAPITAL SERVICES CO., LTD.—See China Huaneng Group Co., Ltd.; *Int'l,* pg. 1509
HUANENG GUICHENG TRUST CO., LTD.—See China Huaneng Group Co., Ltd.; *Int'l,* pg. 1509
HUATAI SECURITIES CO., LTD.; *Int'l,* pg. 3514

HUA YIN INTERNATIONAL HOLDINGS LTD.; *Int'l,* pg. 3510
HUAYI TENCENT ENTERTAINMENT COMPANY LIMITED; *Int'l,* pg. 3516
HUBPER GROUP INC.; *U.S. Public,* pg. 2001
HUDACO INVESTMENT COMPANY LIMITED—See Hudaco Industries Limited; *Int'l,* pg. 3521
HUDSON CLEAN ENERGY PARTNERS; *U.S. Private,* pg. 2001
HUDSON EXECUTIVE CAPITATL LP; *U.S. Public,* pg. 1068
HUDSON HILL CAPITAL LLC; *U.S. Private,* pg. 2002
HUDSON RIVER MINERALS LTD.; *Int'l,* pg. 3522
HUHTAMAKI (NZ) HOLDINGS LTD—See Huhtamaki Oyj; *Int'l,* pg. 3524
HUMACYTE, INC.; *U.S. Public,* pg. 1068
HUMANA VENTURES—See Humana, Inc.; *U.S. Public,* pg. 1070
HUMANCO ACQUISITION CORP.; *U.S. Public,* pg. 1070
HUMANCO LLC; *U.S. Private,* pg. 2006
HUMBERCLYDE COMMERCIAL INVESTMENTS LTD.—See BNP Paribas SA; *Int'l,* pg. 1091
HUMILIS HOLDINGS CAPITAL MANAGEMENT COMPANY LLC; *U.S. Private,* pg. 2007
HUNTER & HARP HOLDINGS, LLC; *U.S. Private,* pg. 2009
HUNTINGTON DISTRIBUTION FINANCE, INC.—See Huntington Bancshares Incorporated; *U.S. Public,* pg. 1071
HUNTINGTON PREFERRED CAPITAL, INC.—See Huntington Bancshares Incorporated; *U.S. Public,* pg. 1071
HUNT INVESTMENT GROUP, L.P.—See Hunt Consolidated, Inc.; *U.S. Private,* pg. 2008
HUNTLEIGH HOLDINGS BV.—See Getinge AB; *Int'l,* pg. 2949
HUNTLEIGH INTERNATIONAL HOLDINGS LTD.—See Getinge AB; *Int'l,* pg. 2949
HUNTLEIGH (SST) LTD—See Getinge AB; *Int'l,* pg. 2949
HUNT REALTY CORPORATION—See Hunt Consolidated, Inc.; *U.S. Private,* pg. 2009
HUNTSMAN FAMILY INVESTMENTS, LLC; *U.S. Private,* pg. 2010
HUNTSMAN MA INVESTMENTS (NETHERLANDS) CV—See Huntsman Corporation; *U.S. Public,* pg. 1074
HURON CAPITAL PARTNERS LLC; *U.S. Private,* pg. 2011
HUSQVARNA HOLDING AB—See Husqvarna AB; *Int'l,* pg. 3539
HUY PLC; *Int'l,* pg. 3541
HWGB EV SDN. BHD.—See Ho Wah Genting Berhad; *Int'l,* pg. 3435
HWI PARTNERS, LLC; *U.S. Private,* pg. 2015
HYAS GROUP—See Morgan Stanley; *U.S. Public,* pg. 1472
HYBRID FINANCIAL SERVICES LIMITED; *Int'l,* pg. 3544
HYDE PARK CAPITAL PARTNERS, LLC; *U.S. Private,* pg. 2016
HYDROGENONE CAPITAL GROWTH PLC; *Int'l,* pg. 3547
HYDROMAC ENERGY BV—See Enel S.p.A.; *Int'l,* pg. 2414
HYPERWALLET SYSTEMS INC.—See PayPal Holdings, Inc.; *U.S. Public,* pg. 1656
HYPROP INVESTMENTS LIMITED; *Int'l,* pg. 3554
HYUNDAI CAPITAL CORPORATION—See Hyundai Motor Company; *Int'l,* pg. 3559
HYUNDAI CAPITAL EUROPE GMBH—See Hyundai Motor Company; *Int'l,* pg. 3559
HYUNDAI COMMERCIAL INC.—See Hyundai Motor Company; *Int'l,* pg. 3559
HYUNDAI CORPORATION (CAMBODIA) CO., LTD.—See Hyundai Corporation; *Int'l,* pg. 3555
HYUNDAI MARINE & FIRE INSURANCE CO., LTD.; *Int'l,* pg. 3557
HYUNDAI MOTOR SECURITIES CO. LTD.; *Int'l,* pg. 3560
HYZON MOTORS INC.; *U.S. Public,* pg. 1080
I2 CAPITAL PARTNERS SGR SPA; *Int'l,* pg. 3566
IAM REAL ESTATE GROUP—See Fiera Capital Corporation; *Int'l,* pg. 2660
IANTE INVESTMENTS SOCIMI, S.A.; *Int'l,* pg. 3569
IBERDROLA FINANCIACION, S.A.—See Iberdrola, S.A.; *Int'l,* pg. 3572
IBERE PHARMACEUTICALS; *U.S. Public,* pg. 1083
IBERICA DE COMPRAS CORPORATIVAS, S.L.—See Banco Santander, S.A.; *Int'l,* pg. 826
IBIDEN ASIA HOLDINGS PTE. LTD.—See Ibiden Co., Ltd.; *Int'l,* pg. 3575
IBI INVESTMENT HOUSE LTD.; *Int'l,* pg. 3574
IBKS NO. 14 SPECIAL PURPOSE ACQUISITION CO., LTD.; *Int'l,* pg. 3576
IBM SOUTHEAST EMPLOYEES' CREDIT UNION; *U.S. Private,* pg. 2028
IBRAHIM LEASING LTD.—See Ibrahim Fibres Limited; *Int'l,* pg. 3576
IBUYNEW GROUP LIMITED; *Int'l,* pg. 3577
ICANDY INTERACTIVE LIMITED; *Int'l,* pg. 3578
ICAP AMERICA INVESTMENTS LIMITED—See CME Group, Inc.; *U.S. Public,* pg. 516
ICAPITAL.BIZ BERHAD; *Int'l,* pg. 3578
ICAP SCANDINAVIA FONDSMAEGLERSELSKAB A/S—See CME Group, Inc.; *U.S. Public,* pg. 517
ICBC PORTFOY YONETIMI A.S.—See ICBC Turkey Bank A.S.; *Int'l,* pg. 3578
ICBC TURKEY YATIRIM MENKUL DEGERLER A.S.—See ICBC Turkey Bank A.S.; *Int'l,* pg. 3578
ICC LABS INC.—See Aurora Cannabis Inc.; *Int'l,* pg. 713

ICE CLEAR NETHERLANDS B.V.—See Intercontinental Exchange, Inc.; *U.S. Public,* pg. 1142
ICG HYPERSONIC ACQUISITION CORP.; *U.S. Public,* pg. 1086
ICHIGO OFFICE REIT INVESTMENT CORPORATION; *Int'l,* pg. 3580
ICICI PRUDENTIAL ASSET MANAGEMENT COMPANY LIMITED—See ICICI Bank Limited; *Int'l,* pg. 3581
ICIMB (MSC) SDN BHD—See CIMB Group Holdings Berhad; *Int'l,* pg. 1608
ICL FINCORP LIMITED; *Int'l,* pg. 3581
ICON CAPITAL, CORP.; *U.S. Private,* pg. 2031
ICON ECI FUND FIFTEEN, L.P.; *U.S. Private,* pg. 2032
ICON ECI FUND SIXTEEN; *U.S. Private,* pg. 2032
ICONIC SPORTS ACQUISITION CORP.; *Int'l,* pg. 3586
ICON INFRASTRUCTURE LLP; *Int'l,* pg. 3583
ICONIQ CAPITAL, LLC; *U.S. Private,* pg. 2032
ICONIX ACQUISITION LLC; *U.S. Private,* pg. 2032
ICP LTD.; *Int'l,* pg. 3586
ICV PARTNERS, LLC; *U.S. Private,* pg. 2033
IDEALAB, INC.—See Idealab Holdings, LLC; *U.S. Private,* pg. 2036
IDFC INVESTMENT ADVISORS LIMITED—See IDFC Limited; *Int'l,* pg. 3593
IDFC LIMITED; *Int'l,* pg. 3593
IDFC PRIVATE EQUITY (IDFC PE)—See IDFC Limited; *Int'l,* pg. 3593
IDFC PROJECT EQUITY COMPANY LIMITED—See IDFC Limited; *Int'l,* pg. 3593
IDFC PROJECT FINANCE—See IDFC Limited; *Int'l,* pg. 3593
IDG CAPITAL; *Int'l,* pg. 3593
IDI EMERGING MARKETS S.A.—See IDI SCA; *Int'l,* pg. 3595
IDINVEST PARTNERS SA—See Eurazeo SE; *Int'l,* pg. 2529
IDJ VIETNAM INVESTMENT JOINT STOCK COMPANY; *Int'l,* pg. 3595
IEH ARI HOLDINGS LLC—See Icahn Enterprises L.P.; *U.S. Public,* pg. 1084
IEH AUTO PARTS LLC—See Icahn Enterprises L.P.; *U.S. Public,* pg. 1084
IEH GH MANAGEMENT LLC—See Icahn Enterprises L.P.; *U.S. Public,* pg. 1084
IE LIMITED; *Int'l,* pg. 3597
IEMR RESOURCES INC.; *Int'l,* pg. 3597
IES ENGINEERING SYSTEMS SDN. BHD.—See Annica Holdings Limited; *Int'l,* pg. 474
IFAN FINANCIAL, INC.; *U.S. Public,* pg. 1095
IFC NATIONAL MARKETING INC.—See Integrity Marketing Group LLC; *U.S. Private,* pg. 2103
IFG ASIA LIMITED—See Epiris Managers LLP; *Int'l,* pg. 2461
IFL PROMOTERS LIMITED; *Int'l,* pg. 3599
IFS CAPITAL (MALAYSIA) SDN. BHD.—See IFS Capital Limited; *Int'l,* pg. 3600
IFS SCHWEIZ AG—See EQT AB; *Int'l,* pg. 2478
IG ACQUISITION CORP.; *U.S. Public,* pg. 1095
IGEN NETWORKS CORP.; *U.S. Public,* pg. 1095
IG INDEX PLC—See IG Group Holdings plc; *Int'l,* pg. 3601
IGNITION PARTNERS LLC; *U.S. Private,* pg. 2039
IGP INDUSTRIES, LLC; *U.S. Private,* pg. 2039
IIFL ASSET MANAGEMENT (MAURITIUS) LTD.—See 360 ONE WAM Limited; *Int'l,* pg. 6
IIFL CAPITAL (CANADA) LIMITED—See 360 ONE WAM Limited; *Int'l,* pg. 6
IIFL CAPITAL PTE. LTD.—See 360 ONE WAM Limited; *Int'l,* pg. 6
IIFL PRIVATE WEALTH MANAGEMENT (DUBAI) LTD.—See 360 ONE WAM Limited; *Int'l,* pg. 6
IKIGAI VENTURES LTD.; *Int'l,* pg. 3610
IK INVESTMENT PARTNERS AB—See IK Investment Partners Limited; *Int'l,* pg. 3609
IK INVESTMENT PARTNERS LIMITED; *Int'l,* pg. 3609
ILEARNINGENGINES, INC.; *U.S. Public,* pg. 1101
ILION CAPITAL PARTNERS; *U.S. Private,* pg. 2041
ILLIMITY SGR S.P.A.—See illimity Bank S.p.A.; *Int'l,* pg. 3615
ILLUMINATOR INVESTMENT COMPANY LIMITED; *Int'l,* pg. 3615
ILLUMIN HOLDINGS INC.; *Int'l,* pg. 3615
ILLYRIA (PTY) LTD.; *Int'l,* pg. 3615
ILP FUNDS; *Int'l,* pg. 3616
IMAGIN MEDICAL INC.; *Int'l,* pg. 3619
IMANAGE LLC; *U.S. Private,* pg. 2046
IMARKETS LIMITED—See CK Hutchison Holdings Limited; *Int'l,* pg. 1638
IM+ CAPITALS LIMITED; *Int'l,* pg. 3617
IMCAP PARTNERS AG; *Int'l,* pg. 3621
IMC INVESTMENTS PTE. LTD.—See IMC Pan Asia Alliance Pte. Ltd.; *Int'l,* pg. 3621
IMES S.R.L.—See Heidelberg Materials AG; *Int'l,* pg. 3316
IM GLOBAL PARTNER SAS—See Eurazeo SE; *Int'l,* pg. 2530
IMIN PARTNERS, L.P.; *U.S. Private,* pg. 2047
IMMEDIS, LTD—See Clune Technology Group; *Int'l,* pg. 1664
IMMOBILIARE GLOBAL INVESTMENTS, INC.; *U.S. Private,* pg. 2047

N.A.I.C.S. INDEX

IMMORENT-MOBILIENVERMIETUNGSGESELLSCHAFT M.B.H. & CO LEASING 89 KG—See Erste Group Bank AG; *Int'l*, pg. 2499
IMMORENT-RAMON GRUNDVERWERTUNGSGESELLSCHAFT M.B.H.—See Erste Group Bank AG; *Int'l*, pg. 2499
IMMORENT S-IMMOBILIENMANAGEMENT GESMBH—See Erste Group Bank AG; *Int'l*, pg. 2499
IMPERIUM PARTNERS GROUP, LLC; *U.S. Private*, pg. 2050
INCAPTA, INC.; *U.S. Public*, pg. 1114
INCENTER, LLC; *U.S. Private*, pg. 2053
INCEPTION GROWTH ACQUISITION LIMITED; *U.S. Public*, pg. 1114
INCLINE MGMT CORP.; *U.S. Private*, pg. 2053
INDEPENDENCE HOLDINGS CORP.; *U.S. Public*, pg. 1115
INDIGO PARTNERS LLC; *U.S. Private*, pg. 2063
INDIGO SOUTH CAPITAL, INC.; *U.S. Private*, pg. 2063
INDIVIDUALIZED APPAREL GROUP; *U.S. Private*, pg. 2064
INDUSIND INTERNATIONAL HOLDINGS LIMITED—See Hinduja Group Ltd.; *Int'l*, pg. 3399
INDUSTRIAL HUMAN CAPITAL, INC.; *U.S. Private*, pg. 2066
INDUSTRIAL OPPORTUNITY PARTNERS, LLC; *U.S. Private*, pg. 2067
INDUSTRIAL TECH ACQUISITIONS, INC.; *U.S. Public*, pg. 1117
INDUSTRIVARDEN SERVICE AB—See AB Industrivarden; *Int'l*, pg. 41
INFI GAMMA HOLDING SAL—See Bank Audi sal; *Int'l*, pg. 837
INFINEDI PARTNERS LP; *U.S. Private*, pg. 2070
INFINITE ACQUISITION CORP.; *U.S. Public*, pg. 1117
INFINITY ASSOCIATES LLC; *U.S. Private*, pg. 2071
INFOR GLOBAL SOLUTIONS, INC. - COLORADO SPRINGS—See Koch Industries, Inc.; *U.S. Private*, pg. 2330
INFRASTRUCTURE CAPITAL GROUP LTD.—See Foresight Group Holdings Limited; *Int'l*, pg. 2731
INFRASTRUCTURE & ENERGY ALTERNATIVES INC.—See MasTec, Inc.; *U.S. Public*, pg. 1393
INGEPAR SA—See Groupe BPCE; *Int'l*, pg. 3098
INGERSOLL-RAND IRISH HOLDINGS—See Ingersoll Rand Inc.; *U.S. Public*, pg. 1121
INGLESIDE CAPITAL CO., INC.—See A.C. Israel Enterprises, Inc.; *U.S. Private*, pg. 24
INITIATIVE & FINANCE—See Groupe BPCE; *Int'l*, pg. 3095
INKSTONE FEIBO ACQUISITION CORPORATION; *U.S. Private*, pg. 2078
INLIGN CAPITAL PARTNERS, LLC; *U.S. Private*, pg. 2079
INNOVATUS CAPITAL PARTNERS LLC; *U.S. Private*, pg. 2083
INNOVATUS LIFE SCIENCES ACQUISITION CORP.; *U.S. Private*, pg. 2083
INNOVEST INVESTMENT CORP—See CTCI Corporation; *Int'l*, pg. 1870
INSAGE (MSC) SDN BHD—See ExcelForce MSC Berhad; *Int'l*, pg. 2578
INSIGHT ACQUISITION CORP.; *U.S. Public*, pg. 1129
INSIGHT EQUITY HOLDINGS LLC; *U.S. Private*, pg. 2086
INSIGHT INVESTMENT FUNDS MANAGEMENT LIMITED—See The Bank of New York Mellon Corporation; *U.S. Public*, pg. 2037
INSIGHT INVESTMENT MANAGEMENT LIMITED—See The Bank of New York Mellon Corporation; *U.S. Public*, pg. 2037
INSIGHT VENTURE MANAGEMENT, LLC; *U.S. Private*, pg. 2087
INSIGNIA CAPITAL GROUP, L.P.; *U.S. Private*, pg. 2091
INSPIRATO INCORPORATED; *U.S. Public*, pg. 1131
INSPIRED ENTERTAINMENT INC; *U.S. Public*, pg. 1131
INSTITUTIONAL VENTURE PARTNERS; *U.S. Private*, pg. 2094
INSULATION SOLUTIONS HOLDINGS PTY LIMITED—See Fletcher Building Limited; *Int'l*, pg. 2700
INTECH INVESTMENT MANAGEMENT LLC; *U.S. Private*, pg. 2097
INTEGRATED ASSET MANAGEMENT CORP.—See Fiera Capital Corporation; *Int'l*, pg. 2660
INTEGRATED ENERGY TRANSITION ACQUISITION CORP.; *U.S. Public*, pg. 1136
INTEGRATED FINANCIAL SETTLEMENTS, INC.; *U.S. Private*, pg. 2099
INTEGRATED RAIL & RESOURCES ACQUISITION CORP.; *U.S. Public*, pg. 1136
INTEGRATED WELLNESS ACQUISITION CORP.; *U.S. Public*, pg. 1136
INTEGRITY GAMING ULC—See PlayAGS, Inc.; *U.S. Public*, pg. 1697
INTEL CAPITAL CORPORATION—See Intel Corporation; *U.S. Public*, pg. 1138
INTELLIGENT MEDICINE ACQUISITION CORP.; *U.S. Public*, pg. 1140
INTERCORE, INC.; *U.S. Private*, pg. 2110
INTERDEAN HOLDINGS LIMITED—See EAC Invest AS; *Int'l*, pg. 2261
INTERDYNE COMPANY, INC.; *U.S. Public*, pg. 1144

INTERMEDIA ADVISORS, LLC; *U.S. Private*, pg. 2112
INTERMEDIA PARTNERS, L.P.—See InterMedia Advisors, LLC; *U.S. Private*, pg. 2112
INTERNATIONAL ENDESA BV—See Enel S.p.A.; *Int'l*, pg. 2412
INTERNATIONAL FUND SERVICES (IRELAND) LIMITED—See State Street Corporation; *U.S. Public*, pg. 1941
INTERNATIONAL HARVESTER EMPLOYEE CREDIT UNION, INC.; *U.S. Private*, pg. 2117
INTERNATIONAL MACGREGOR-NAVIRE HOLDING BV—See Cargotec Corporation; *Int'l*, pg. 1328
INTERNATIONAL MEDIA ACQUISITION CORP.; *U.S. Public*, pg. 1154
INTERNATIONAL POWER AUSTRALIA FINANCE—See ENGIE SA; *Int'l*, pg. 2434
INTERNATIONAL RESEARCH & ASSET MANAGEMENT, INC.—See EP Wealth Advisors, LLC; *U.S. Private*, pg. 1411
INTERNATIONAL TRADING AND FINANCE (ITF) B.V.—See Heidelberg Materials AG; *Int'l*, pg. 3316
INTERNET COWBOY VENTURES LLC; *U.S. Private*, pg. 2122
INTERPACIFIC GROUP INC.; *U.S. Private*, pg. 2122
INTERSOUTH PARTNERS; *U.S. Private*, pg. 2123
INTERVALE CAPITAL, LLC - HOUSTON—See Intervale Capital, LLC; *U.S. Private*, pg. 2127
INTERVALE CAPITAL, LLC; *U.S. Private*, pg. 2127
INTL CAPITAL LIMITED—See StoneX Group Inc.; *U.S. Public*, pg. 1952
INTL CAPITAL S.A.—See StoneX Group Inc.; *U.S. Public*, pg. 1952
INTL FCSTONE CAPITAL ASSESSORIA FINANCEIRA LTDA.—See StoneX Group Inc.; *U.S. Public*, pg. 1952
INTL GLOBAL CURRENCIES LIMITED—See StoneX Group Inc.; *U.S. Public*, pg. 1952
INTREPID CAPITAL CORP.; *U.S. Public*, pg. 1159
INVECH HOLDINGS, INC.; *U.S. Public*, pg. 1161
INVENTABIOTECH INC.; *U.S. Private*, pg. 2131
INVERAHORRO, S.L.—See Banco Bilbao Vizcaya Argentaria, S.A.; *Int'l*, pg. 818
INVERFIATC S.A.—See FIATC Mutua de Seguros y de Reaseguros APF; *Int'l*, pg. 2651
INVERNESS GRAHAM INVESTMENTS, INC.—See The Graham Group, Inc.; *U.S. Private*, pg. 4037
INVERNESS MANAGEMENT, LLC; *U.S. Private*, pg. 2131
INVERSIONES COLQUIJIRCA S.A.—See Compania de Minas Buenaventura SAA; *Int'l*, pg. 1748
INVERSIONES EN CONCESIONES FERROVIARIAS, S.A.—See Construcciones y Auxiliar de Ferrocarriles S.A.; *Int'l*, pg. 1777
INVERSIONES INIMA, S.A.—See GS Holdings Corp.; *Int'l*, pg. 3142
INVERSIONES MEXIMEX, S.A. DE C.V.—See Cydsa S.A.B. de C.V.; *Int'l*, pg. 1895
INVESCO ASSET MANAGEMENT (JAPAN) LTD.—See Invesco Ltd.; *U.S. Public*, pg. 1161
INVESCO ASSET MANAGEMENT LIMITED—See Invesco Ltd.; *U.S. Public*, pg. 1162
INVESCO ASSET MANAGEMENT SINGAPORE LTD.—See Invesco Ltd.; *U.S. Public*, pg. 1162
INVESCO INVESTMENT SERVICES, INC.—See Invesco Ltd.; *U.S. Public*, pg. 1162
INVESCO MORTGAGE CAPITAL, INC.—See Invesco Ltd.; *U.S. Public*, pg. 1163
INVESCO PUERTO RICO—See Invesco Ltd.; *U.S. Public*, pg. 1163
INVESCO RUIHE (SHANGHAI) PRIVATE EQUITY INVESTMENT MANAGEMENT COMPANY LIMITED—See Invesco Ltd.; *U.S. Public*, pg. 1163
INVESTIA FINANCIAL SERVICES INC.—See iA Financial Corporation Inc.; *Int'l*, pg. 3567
INVESTINDUSTRIAL S.A.—See BI-Invest Advisors S.A.; *Int'l*, pg. 1016
INVESTIRE SGR S.P.A.—See Banca Finnat Euramerica S.p.A.; *Int'l*, pg. 814
INVESTITORI SGR S.P.A.—See Allianz SE; *Int'l*, pg. 350
INVESTMENT DAR COMPANY K.S.C.C.—See Efad Real Estate Company; *Int'l*, pg. 2318
THE INVUS GROUP, LLC; *U.S. Private*, pg. 4057
ION ACQUISITION CORP 1 LTD.—See Taboola.com Ltd.; *U.S. Public*, pg. 1978
IOOF LTD—See Australian Unity Limited; *Int'l*, pg. 723
IOS FINANCE EFC, S.A.—See Banca Farmafactoring S.p.A.; *Int'l*, pg. 814
IPCONCEPT (LUXEMBURG) S.A.—See DZ BANK AG Deutsche Zentral-Genossenschaftsbank; *Int'l*, pg. 2244
IPCONCEPT (SCHWEIZ) AG—See DZ BANK AG Deutsche Zentral-Genossenschaftsbank; *Int'l*, pg. 2244
IPI PARTNERS, LLC—See ICONIQ Capital, LLC; *U.S. Private*, pg. 2032
IPI PARTNERS, LLC—See Iron Point Partners, LLC; *U.S. Private*, pg. 2139
THE IPS PARTNERSHIP PLC—See Epiris Managers LLP; *Int'l*, pg. 2461
IRON HORSE ACQUISITION CORP.; *U.S. Private*, pg. 2139
IRON POINT PARTNERS, LLC; *U.S. Private*, pg. 2139
IRON SPARK I INC.; *U.S. Private*, pg. 2139

523999 — MISCELLANEOUS FINAN...

IRONWOOD PARTNERS LLC; *U.S. Private*, pg. 2140
IRRADIANT PARTNERS, LP; *U.S. Private*, pg. 2140
IRVING PLACE CAPITAL MANAGEMENT, L.P.; *U.S. Private*, pg. 2141
ISE ETF VENTURES LLC—See Nasdaq, Inc.; *U.S. Public*, pg. 1491
ISHARES GOLD BULLION FUND; *U.S. Public*, pg. 1174
ISHARES GOLD TRUST; *U.S. Public*, pg. 1174
ISLEWORTH HEALTHCARE ACQUISITION CORP.; *U.S. Public*, pg. 1174
ISOCHEM HOLDING GMBH—See Aurelius Equity Opportunities SE & Co. KGaA; *Int'l*, pg. 708
ISOS ACQUISITION CORP.; *U.S. Public*, pg. 1174
ISRAEL ACQUISITIONS CORP.; *U.S. Public*, pg. 1175
ISRAEL AMPLIFY PROGRAM CORP.; *U.S. Public*, pg. 1175
ISTITHMAR PJSC—See Dubai World Corporation; *Int'l*, pg. 2222
ISUN, INC.; *U.S. Public*, pg. 1175
ISWILL ACQUISITION CORPORATION; *U.S. Private*, pg. 2147
ITALCEMENTI FINANCE—See Heidelberg Materials AG; *Int'l*, pg. 3317
ITE MANAGEMENT L.P.; *U.S. Private*, pg. 2149
ITF SUISSE AG—See DZ BANK AG Deutsche Zentral-Genossenschaftsbank; *Int'l*, pg. 2244
ITIQUIRA ACQUISITION CORP.; *U.S. Public*, pg. 1175
IVECO CAPITAL LIMITED—See Barclays PLC; *Int'l*, pg. 862
IVECO CAPITAL SERVICES S.R.L.—See CNH Industrial N.V.; *Int'l*, pg. 1675
IVECO FINANCE GMBH—See Barclays PLC; *Int'l*, pg. 862
IVECO FINANCE HOLDINGS LIMITED—See Barclays PLC; *Int'l*, pg. 862
IVECO FINANZIARIA S.P.A.—See Barclays PLC; *Int'l*, pg. 861
IVECO INTERNATIONAL TRADE FINANCE S.A.—See CNH Industrial N.V.; *Int'l*, pg. 1675
IVY CREDIT OPPORTUNITIES FUND; *U.S. Private*, pg. 2151
JACKSON ACQUISITION COMPANY; *U.S. Public*, pg. 1183
JACKSON SQUARE VENTURES, LLC; *U.S. Private*, pg. 2178
JACOBS CAPITAL, LLC; *U.S. Private*, pg. 2179
JADE GLOBAL HOLDINGS, INC; *U.S. Public*, pg. 1186
JAHANGIR SIDDIQUI SECURITIES SERVICES LIMITED—See EFU Life Assurance Limited; *Int'l*, pg. 2321
JAPAN SECURITIES INCORPORATED—See Aizawa Securities Group Co., Ltd.; *Int'l*, pg. 255
JAWS HURRICANE ACQUISITION CORPORATION; *U.S. Public*, pg. 1187
JAWS JUGGERNAUT ACQUISITION CORPORATION; *U.S. Public*, pg. 1188
JAWS MUSTANG ACQUISITION CORPORATION; *U.S. Public*, pg. 1188
JAWS WILDCAT ACQUISITION CORPORATION; *U.S. Private*, pg. 2191
JAY SOLUTIONS OY—See CapMan PLC; *Int'l*, pg. 1315
JCB FINANCE SAS—See BNP Paribas SA; *Int'l*, pg. 1091
J.C. FLOWERS & CO. LLC; *U.S. Private*, pg. 2159
J.C. FLOWERS & CO. UK LTD.—See J.C. Flowers & Co. LLC; *U.S. Private*, pg. 2159
J. D. MELLBERG FINANCIAL; *U.S. Private*, pg. 2155
JDS CAPITAL MANAGEMENT, INC.; *U.S. Private*, pg. 2196
JEFFERIES (AUSTRALIA) PTY. LTD.—See Jefferies Financial Group Inc.; *U.S. Public*, pg. 1188
JEFFERIES CAPITAL PARTNERS LLC—See Jefferies Financial Group Inc.; *U.S. Public*, pg. 1188
JEN PARTNERS, LLC; *U.S. Private*, pg. 2199
J.F. LEHMAN & COMPANY, INC.; *U.S. Private*, pg. 2162
JG TAX GROUP; *U.S. Private*, pg. 2207
J.H. ELLWOOD & ASSOCIATES; *U.S. Private*, pg. 2165
JH PARTNERS LLC; *U.S. Private*, pg. 2207
J.H. WHITNEY CAPITAL PARTNERS, LLC—See J.H. Whitney & Co., LLC; *U.S. Private*, pg. 2166
J.H. WHITNEY & CO., LLC; *U.S. Private*, pg. 2166
JIMARI INTERNATIONAL, INC.; *U.S. Private*, pg. 2210
JINDAL PHOTO INVESTMENTS LIMITED—See Consolidated Finvest & Holdings Limited; *Int'l*, pg. 1770
JITNEYTRADE INC.—See Canaccord Genuity Group Inc.; *Int'l*, pg. 1277
JIYA ACQUISITION CORP.; *U.S. Public*, pg. 1190
JJ OPPORTUNITY CORP.; *U.S. Public*, pg. 1211
JLL PARTNERS, LLC; *U.S. Private*, pg. 2212
JLS INVESTMENT GROUP LLC; *U.S. Private*, pg. 2213
JLT INVESTMENT MANAGEMENT LIMITED—See Marsh & McLennan Companies, Inc.; *U.S. Public*, pg. 1376
JLT RISK SOLUTIONS AB—See Marsh & McLennan Companies, Inc.; *U.S. Public*, pg. 1376
JLT WEALTH MANAGEMENT LIMITED—See Marsh & McLennan Companies, Inc.; *U.S. Public*, pg. 1376
JMB REALTY CORPORATION; *U.S. Private*, pg. 2215
JMC CAPITAL PARTNERS LLC; *U.S. Private*, pg. 2215
JMG REALTY, INC.; *U.S. Private*, pg. 2215
JMH CAPITAL; *U.S. Private*, pg. 2215
J.M. HUBER INVESTMENT (CHINA) LTD—See J.M. Huber Corporation; *U.S. Private*, pg. 2169
JMI EQUITY—See JMI Services, Inc.; *U.S. Private*, pg. 2215
JMI EQUITY—See JMI Services, Inc.; *U.S. Private*, pg. 2216

523999 — MISCELLANEOUS FINAN...

JMI SPORTS LLC—See JMI Services, Inc.; *U.S. Private*, pg. 2216
JMP CREDIT ADVISORS LLC—See Medalist Partners, LP; *U.S. Private*, pg. 2650
JOFF FINTECH ACQUISITION CORP.; *U.S. Public*, pg. 1190
JOGAN, INC.; *U.S. Private*, pg. 2219
JOHN D. DOVICH & ASSOCIATES, LLC—See Keystone Group, L.P.; *U.S. Private*, pg. 2297
JOHN HANCOCK HEDGED EQUITY & INCOME FUND; *U.S. Public*, pg. 1192
JOHNSON & JOHNSON INNOVATION - JJDC, INC.—See Johnson & Johnson; *U.S. Public*, pg. 1198
JOHNSON HOMES OF MERIDIAN; *U.S. Private*, pg. 2228
JONES CAPITAL, LLC; *U.S. Private*, pg. 2231
JORDAN-BLANCHARD CAPITAL, LLC—See The Jordan Company; *U.S. Private*, pg. 4059
THE JORDAN COMPANY CHINA—See The Jordan Company, L.P.; *U.S. Private*, pg. 4062
THE JORDAN COMPANY, L.P.; *U.S. Private*, pg. 4059
JOSHUA PARTNERS, LLC; *U.S. Private*, pg. 2237
JOULE ASSETS, INC.; *U.S. Private*, pg. 2238
JOULE CAPITAL, LLC—See Joule Assets, Inc.; *U.S. Private*, pg. 2238
JOVIAN CAPITAL CORPORATION—See iA Financial Corporation Inc.; *Int'l*, pg. 3567
J.P. KOTTS & CO.; *U.S. Private*, pg. 2170
JP LAWRENCE BIOMEDICAL, INC.; *U.S. Private*, pg. 2239
J.P. MORGAN ADMINISTRATIVE SERVICES AUSTRALIA LIMITED—See JPMorgan Chase & Co.; *U.S. Public*, pg. 1208
J.P. MORGAN AG—See JPMorgan Chase & Co.; *U.S. Public*, pg. 1208
JPMORGAN ASSET MANAGEMENT HOLDINGS (LUXEMBOURG) S.A R.L.—See JPMorgan Chase & Co.; *U.S. Public*, pg. 1209
JPMORGAN ASSET MANAGEMENT (KOREA) COMPANY LIMITED—See JPMorgan Chase & Co.; *U.S. Public*, pg. 1209
JPMORGAN ASSET MANAGEMENT LUXEMBOURG S.A.—See JPMorgan Chase & Co.; *U.S. Public*, pg. 1209
JPMORGAN ASSET MANAGEMENT (TAIWAN) LIMITED—See JPMorgan Chase & Co.; *U.S. Public*, pg. 1209
J.P. MORGAN AUSTRALIA GROUP PTY LIMITED—See JPMorgan Chase & Co.; *U.S. Public*, pg. 1208
J.P. MORGAN BANK (IRELAND) PLC—See JPMorgan Chase & Co.; *U.S. Public*, pg. 1208
J.P. MORGAN BANK—See JPMorgan Chase & Co.; *U.S. Public*, pg. 1209
JPMORGAN CHASE BANK (CHINA) COMPANY LIMITED—See JPMorgan Chase & Co.; *U.S. Public*, pg. 1209
JPMORGAN CHASE BANK, DEARBORN—See JPMorgan Chase & Co.; *U.S. Public*, pg. 1209
JPMORGAN CHASE & CO.; *U.S. Public*, pg. 1206
J.P. MORGAN CHILE LIMITADA—See JPMorgan Chase & Co.; *U.S. Public*, pg. 1208
J.P. MORGAN CORRETORA DE CAMBIO E VALORES MOBILIARIOS S.A.—See JPMorgan Chase & Co.; *U.S. Public*, pg. 1208
J.P. MORGAN EQUITIES LIMITED—See JPMorgan Chase & Co.; *U.S. Public*, pg. 1208
J.P. MORGAN EUROPE LIMITED—See JPMorgan Chase & Co.; *U.S. Public*, pg. 1208
J.P. MORGAN FONDS SERVICES GMBH—See JPMorgan Chase & Co.; *U.S. Public*, pg. 1208
JPMORGAN FUNDS (ASIA) LIMITED—See JPMorgan Chase & Co.; *U.S. Public*, pg. 1209
J.P. MORGAN NOMINEES AUSTRALIA LIMITED—See JPMorgan Chase & Co.; *U.S. Public*, pg. 1208
J.P. MORGAN PHYSICAL COPPER TRUST; *U.S. Private*, pg. 2170
J.P. MORGAN (S.E.A.) LIMITED—See JPMorgan Chase & Co.; *U.S. Public*, pg. 1208
J.P. MORGAN SECURITIES INDIA PRIVATE LIMITED—See JPMorgan Chase & Co.; *U.S. Public*, pg. 1209
JPMORGAN SECURITIES JAPAN CO., LTD.—See JPMorgan Chase & Co.; *U.S. Public*, pg. 1209
J.P. MORGAN SECURITIES LLC—See JPMorgan Chase & Co.; *U.S. Public*, pg. 1208
J.P. MORGAN SECURITIES SINGAPORE PRIVATE LIMITED—See JPMorgan Chase & Co.; *U.S. Public*, pg. 1208
J.P. MORGAN SERVICES INC.—See JPMorgan Chase & Co.; *U.S. Public*, pg. 1208
JPMORGAN SERVICIOS AUXILIARES, S.A.—See JPMorgan Chase & Co.; *U.S. Public*, pg. 1210
J.P. MORGAN VENTURES ENERGY CORPORATION—See JPMorgan Chase & Co.; *U.S. Public*, pg. 1208
JSC HALYK GLOBAL MARKETS—See Halyk Bank of Kazakhstan JSC; *Int'l*, pg. 3234
JTL CAPITAL, LLC; *U.S. Private*, pg. 2242
JUHACHI CAPITAL CO., LTD.—See Fukuoka Financial Group, Inc.; *Int'l*, pg. 2840
JULIANI KENNEY INVESTMENT CAPITAL, LLC; *U.S. Private*, pg. 2243

JUNIPER INVESTMENT COMPANY, LLC; *U.S. Private*, pg. 2244
JUNO INVESTMENTS LLC; *U.S. Private*, pg. 2244
JUPITER ACQUISITION CORPORATION; *U.S. Public*, pg. 1211
JUPITER PORTFOLIO INVESTMENTS PUBLIC COMPANY LTD.—See Elma Holdings Public Company Ltd; *Int'l*, pg. 2367
JUPITER WELLNESS ACQUISITION CORP.; *U.S. Public*, pg. 1211
JURA-HOLDING AG—See CRH plc; *Int'l*, pg. 1844
JUST ANOTHER ACQUISITION CORP.; *U.S. Public*, pg. 2245
JZ PARTNERS, LLC—See Jordan/Zalaznick Advisers, Inc.; *U.S. Private*, pg. 2235
KADEM SUSTAINABLE IMPACT CORPORATION; *U.S. Public*, pg. 1213
KAH CAPITAL MANAGEMENT, LLC—See Chimera Investment Corp.; *U.S. Public*, pg. 489
KAHN VENTURES, INC.—See Berkshire Hathaway Inc.; *U.S. Public*, pg. 308
KAIN CAPITAL, LLC; *U.S. Private*, pg. 2254
KAINOS CAPITAL, LLC; *U.S. Private*, pg. 2254
KAINOS PARTNERS INC.—See GTCR LLC; *U.S. Private*, pg. 1803
KAIROS ACQUISITION CORP.; *U.S. Public*, pg. 1213
KAIVAL BRANDS INNOVATIONS GROUP, INC.; *U.S. Public*, pg. 1213
KALEYRA, INC.; *U.S. Public*, pg. 1213
KANALY TRUST—See Genstar Capital, LLC; *U.S. Private*, pg. 1677
KANALY TRUST—See Keystone Group, L.P.; *U.S. Private*, pg. 2298
KARPREILLY, LLC; *U.S. Private*, pg. 2263
KARSTENS INVESTMENT COUNSEL, INC.—See The Cap-Financial Group, LLC; *U.S. Private*, pg. 4004
KASSEL EQUITY GROUP, LLC; *U.S. Private*, pg. 2264
KAWA CAPITAL MANAGEMENT, INC.; *U.S. Private*, pg. 2265
KAYNE ANDERSON CAPITAL ADVISORS, L.P.; *U.S. Private*, pg. 2267
KAYNE DL 2021, INC.; *U.S. Private*, pg. 2267
KAZAKHSTAN IJARA COMPANY JOINT STOCK COMPANY—See Aktif Yatirim Bankasi A.S.; *Int'l*, pg. 267
KBC ANCORA SCA—See Cera SCRL; *Int'l*, pg. 1421
KBS CORPORATE SALES LIMITED—See Sun Capital Partners, Inc.; *U.S. Private*, pg. 3861
KBS LEGACY PARTNERS APARTMENT REIT, INC.; *U.S. Private*, pg. 2268
KBS REAL ESTATE INVESTMENT TRUST III, INC.; *U.S. Public*, pg. 1217
KBW, INC.—See Stifel Financial Corp.; *U.S. Public*, pg. 1949
KCB MANAGEMENT LLC; *U.S. Private*, pg. 2269
KCM CAPITAL PARTNERS, LLC; *U.S. Private*, pg. 2270
KEB CAPITAL INC.—See Hana Financial Group, Inc.; *Int'l*, pg. 3240
KEB FUTURES CO., LTD.—See Hana Financial Group, Inc.; *Int'l*, pg. 3240
KEB INVESTORS SERVICES COMPANY—See Hana Financial Group, Inc.; *Int'l*, pg. 3240
KEEL POINT ADVISORS, LLC—See Blue Creek Investment Partners; *U.S. Private*, pg. 586
KEEN VISION ACQUISITION CORPORATION; *U.S. Public*, pg. 1217
KELLY CAPITAL, LLC; *U.S. Private*, pg. 2276
KELSO & COMPANY, L.P.; *U.S. Private*, pg. 2277
KENNEDY LEWIS INVESTMENT MANAGEMENT LLC; *U.S. Private*, pg. 2285
KENNER & COMPANY, INC.; *U.S. Private*, pg. 2285
KENSINGTON CAPITAL PARTNERS LIMITED—See AGF Management Limited; *Int'l*, pg. 207
KENSINGTON CAPITAL PARTNERS, LLC; *U.S. Private*, pg. 2288
KENTUCKY HIGHLANDS INVESTMENT CORP.; *U.S. Private*, pg. 2288
KERNEL GROUP HOLDINGS, INC.; *U.S. Public*, pg. 1224
KETER1 ACQUISITION CORP.; *U.S. Public*, pg. 1224
KEYARCH ACQUISITION CORPORATION; *U.S. Public*, pg. 1225
KEYBANK N.A. - KEY CORPORATE BANK DIVISION—See KeyCorp; *U.S. Public*, pg. 1225
KEY COMMUNITY DEVELOPMENT CORPORATION—See KeyCorp; *U.S. Public*, pg. 1225
KEYSTONE CAPITAL, INC.; *U.S. Private*, pg. 2295
KEYSTONE NATIONAL GROUP LLC; *U.S. Private*, pg. 2300
K-F MANAGEMENT COMPANY, INC.; *U.S. Private*, pg. 2250
KHOSLA VENTURES ACQUISITION CO.; *U.S. Public*, pg. 1227
KHOSLA VENTURES, LLC; *U.S. Private*, pg. 2301
KIAN CAPITAL PARTNERS, LLC; *U.S. Private*, pg. 2302
KICKSTART VENTURES, INC.—See Globe Telecom, Inc.; *Int'l*, pg. 3006
KIDD & COMPANY LLC; *U.S. Private*, pg. 2302
KIER GROUP HOLDINGS, LLC; *U.S. Private*, pg. 2303
KIMBELL TIGER ACQUISITION CORP.; *U.S. Public*, pg. 1228

KIMMERIDGE ENERGY MANAGEMENT COMPANY, LLC; *U.S. Private*, pg. 2305
KINDERHOOK INDUSTRIES, LLC; *U.S. Private*, pg. 2306
KINETIK HOLDINGS INC.—See Kayne Anderson Capital Advisors, L.P.; *U.S. Private*, pg. 2267
KING NUTS HOLDING B.V.—See ACOMO N.V.; *Int'l*, pg. 108
KING STREET CAPITAL MANAGEMENT, L.P.; *U.S. Private*, pg. 2310
KINGSWOOD ACQUISITION CORP.; *U.S. Public*, pg. 1235
KINGSWOOD CAPITAL MANAGEMENT LLC; *U.S. Private*, pg. 2312
KINZIE CAPITAL PARTNERS LP; *U.S. Private*, pg. 2313
KIRTLAND CAPITAL PARTNERS LLC; *U.S. Private*, pg. 2315
KKR ASIA LIMITED—See KKR & Co. Inc.; *U.S. Public*, pg. 1255
KKR & CO. INC.; *U.S. Public*, pg. 1237
KKR CREDIT ADVISORS (EMEA) LLP—See KKR & Co. Inc.; *U.S. Public*, pg. 1256
KKR INDIA FINANCIAL SERVICES PRIVATE LIMITED—See KKR & Co. Inc.; *U.S. Public*, pg. 1256
KKR LUXEMBOURG S.A R.L.—See KKR & Co. Inc.; *U.S. Public*, pg. 1256
KKR MENA LIMITED—See KKR & Co. Inc.; *U.S. Public*, pg. 1256
KKR PRIVATE EQUITY CONGLOMERATE LLC; *U.S. Private*, pg. 2317
KKR SAUDI LIMITED—See KKR & Co. Inc.; *U.S. Public*, pg. 1256
KL ACQUISITION CORP.; *U.S. Public*, pg. 1267
KLEINER PERKINS CAUFIELD & BYERS; *U.S. Private*, pg. 2319
KLEINPARTNERS CAPITAL CORP.; *U.S. Public*, pg. 2319
KLEVENS CAPITAL MANAGEMENT, INC.—See Mariner Wealth Advisors, LLC; *U.S. Private*, pg. 2575
KLH CAPITAL LP; *U.S. Private*, pg. 2319
KLINE HILL PARTNERS LLC; *U.S. Private*, pg. 2320
KLINGENSTEIN, FIELDS & CO., L.P.; *U.S. Private*, pg. 2320
KLK LAND SDN BHD—See Batu Kawan Berhad; *Int'l*, pg. 891
KLM FINANCIAL SERVICES B.V.—See Air France-KLM S.A.; *Int'l*, pg. 237
KNIGHTHEAD CAPITAL MANAGEMENT LLC; *U.S. Private*, pg. 2322
KNIGHTSWAN ACQUISITION CORPORATION; *U.S. Public*, pg. 1270
KNOX CAPITAL HOLDINGS, LLC; *U.S. Private*, pg. 2324
KNOX LANE LP; *U.S. Private*, pg. 2324
KOA CAPITAL PARTNERS LLC; *U.S. Private*, pg. 2325
KOCH EQUITY DEVELOPMENT LLC—See Koch Industries, Inc.; *U.S. Private*, pg. 2332
KODIAK VENTURE PARTNERS, L.P.; *U.S. Private*, pg. 2336
KOHLBERG & COMPANY, LLC; *U.S. Private*, pg. 2337
KOHLBERG KRAVIS ROBERTS & CO. LIMITED—See KKR & Co. Inc.; *U.S. Public*, pg. 1257
KOHLBERG KRAVIS ROBERTS & CO. PARTNERS LLP—See KKR & Co. Inc.; *U.S. Public*, pg. 1257
KOHLBERG KRAVIS ROBERTS & CO. SAS—See KKR & Co. Inc.; *U.S. Public*, pg. 1257
KOMUNO GMBH—See Helaba Landesbank Hessen-Thuringen; *Int'l*, pg. 3328
KONIAG INC.; *U.S. Private*, pg. 2342
KONZA VALLEY CAPITAL INC.; *U.S. Private*, pg. 2343
KOREA NON-BANK LEASE FINANCING CO. LTD—See DGB Financial Group Co., Ltd.; *Int'l*, pg. 2096
KPM ANALYTICS, INC.—See Union Park Capital; *U.S. Private*, pg. 4285
KPS CAPITAL PARTNERS, LP; *U.S. Private*, pg. 2346
KRG CAPITAL MANAGEMENT, L.P.; *U.S. Private*, pg. 2351
KRIYA CAPITAL, LLC; *U.S. Private*, pg. 2352
K ROAD POWER, INC.; *U.S. Private*, pg. 2249
KROKUS PRIVATE EQUITY SP. Z O.O.—See Groupe BPCE; *Int'l*, pg. 3095
KSL CAPITAL PARTNERS, LLC; *U.S. Private*, pg. 2354
KUDU INVESTMENT MANAGEMENT LLC; *U.S. Private*, pg. 2356
KYPROU FINANCE (NL) B.V.—See Bank of Cyprus Holdings Public Limited Company; *Int'l*, pg. 842
L2 CAPITAL PARTNERS; *U.S. Private*, pg. 2367
LABRADOR VENTURES, L.P.; *U.S. Private*, pg. 2370
LABUAN INTERNATIONAL FINANCIAL EXCHANGE INC.—See Bursa Malaysia Berhad; *Int'l*, pg. 1227
LACLEDE INVESTMENT LLC—See Spire, Inc; *U.S. Public*, pg. 1918
LA COMPAGNIE BENJAMIN DE ROTHSCHILD S.A.—See Edmond de Rothschild Holding S.A.; *Int'l*, pg. 2313
LA COMPAGNIE FINANCIERE EDMOND DE ROTHSCHILD BANQUE—See Edmond de Rothschild Holding S.A.; *Int'l*, pg. 2313
LADENBURG, THALMANN & CO. INC.—See Reverence Capital Partners LLC; *U.S. Private*, pg. 3414
LAFAYETTE SQUARE USA, INC.; *U.S. Private*, pg. 2372
LAIRD NORTON COMPANY, LLC; *U.S. Private*, pg. 2374
LAKESHORE CAPITAL PARTNERS LLC; *U.S. Private*, pg. 2377

N.A.I.C.S. INDEX

523999 — MISCELLANEOUS FINAN...

LAKEVIEW ACQUISITION CORPORATION; *U.S. Public*, pg. 1289
LAKEVIEW CAPITAL, INC.; *U.S. Private*, pg. 2378
LAKEVIEW EQUITY PARTNERS, LLC; *U.S. Private*, pg. 2378
LAKEWOOD CAPITAL, LLC; *U.S. Private*, pg. 2378
LAKSON INVESTMENTS LIMITED—See COLGATE-PALMOLIVE (PAKISTAN) LTD; *Int'l*, pg. 1698
LAMAR PARTNERING CORPORATION; *U.S. Private*, pg. 2379
LAMF GLOBAL VENTURES CORP. I—See Holdco Nuvo Group D.G Ltd.; *U.S. Public*, pg. 1044
LAMINEX US HOLDINGS PTY LIMITED—See Fletcher Building Limited; *Int'l*, pg. 2700
LAMPE EQUITY MANAGEMENT GMBH—See Dr. August Oetker KG; *Int'l*, pg. 2190
LAMPE PRIVATINVEST MANAGEMENT GMBH—See Dr. August Oetker KG; *Int'l*, pg. 2190
LANCASTER POLLARD HOLDINGS, INC.; *U.S. Private*, pg. 2381
LANDAU, NASELLA & KLATSKY, LLC; *U.S. Private*, pg. 2384
LANDON CAPITAL PARTNERS, LLC; *U.S. Private*, pg. 2386
THE LARAMAR GROUP, LLC; *U.S. Private*, pg. 4067
LARCO ENTERPRISES INC.; *U.S. Private*, pg. 2391
LARIAT PARTNERS LP; *U.S. Private*, pg. 2392
LARIS MEDIA ACQUISITION CORP.; *U.S. Public*, pg. 1293
LARRY MATHIS FINANCIAL PLANNING, LLC; *U.S. Private*, pg. 2393
LARSON-JUHL US LLC—See Berkshire Hathaway Inc.; *U.S. Public*, pg. 298
LASALLE CAPITAL GROUP PARTNERS, LLC—See LSCG Management, Inc.; *U.S. Private*, pg. 2508
LATCH, INC.; *U.S. Public*, pg. 1294
LAUD COLLIER & COMPANY, LLC; *U.S. Private*, pg. 2397
LAUNCHEQUITY PARTNERS, LLC; *U.S. Private*, pg. 2398
LAVA MEDTECH ACQUISITION CORP.; *U.S. Public*, pg. 1294
L CATTERTON LATIN AMERICA ACQUISITION CORP.; *U.S. Public*, pg. 1278
LCP ACQUISITION CORP.; *U.S. Private*, pg. 2403
LCP HOLDINGS AND INVESTMENTS PUBLIC LTD.—See Bank of Cyprus Holdings Public Limited Company; *Int'l*, pg. 842
LCV CAPITAL MANAGEMENT, LLC; *U.S. Private*, pg. 2404
LDR GROWTH PARTNERS; *U.S. Private*, pg. 2404
LEAD EDGE CAPITAL MANAGEMENT, LLC; *U.S. Private*, pg. 2405
LEAD EDGE GROWTH OPPORTUNITIES, LTD.; *U.S. Public*, pg. 1296
LEADING RIDGE MANAGEMENT, LLC; *U.S. Private*, pg. 2406
LEAF OF FAITH BEVERAGE INC.; *U.S. Public*, pg. 1296
LEAP PARTNERS; *U.S. Public*, pg. 2407
LEARN CW INVESTMENT CORP.; *U.S. Public*, pg. 1298
LEBANESE LEASING COMPANY SAL—See Fransabank SAL; *Int'l*, pg. 2762
LEBARONBROWN INDUSTRIES LLC; *U.S. Private*, pg. 2409
LEBENTHAL & CO. LLC; *U.S. Private*, pg. 2409
LE CLAIRE INVESTMENT INC.—See RiverStone Group, Inc.; *U.S. Private*, pg. 3447
LEEDS EQUITY PARTNERS, LLC; *U.S. Private*, pg. 2414
LEE EQUITY PARTNERS LLC; *U.S. Private*, pg. 2411
LEFTERIS ACQUISITION CORP.; *U.S. Public*, pg. 1301
LEGATO MERGER CORP.; *U.S. Public*, pg. 1301
LEGG MASON INVESTMENTS (EUROPE) LIMITED—See Franklin Resources, Inc.; *U.S. Public*, pg. 882
LEGG MASON INVESTMENTS (SWITZERLAND) GMBH—See Franklin Resources, Inc.; *U.S. Public*, pg. 881
LEISURE ACQUISITION CORP.; *U.S. Public*, pg. 1304
LENDING SCIENCE DM, INC.; *U.S. Private*, pg. 2421
LEONARD GREEN & PARTNERS, L.P.; *U.S. Private*, pg. 2423
LEONE ASSET MANAGEMENT, INC.; *U.S. Public*, pg. 1308
LERER HIPPEAU ACQUISITION CORP.; *U.S. Public*, pg. 1308
L.E. SIMMONS & ASSOCIATES, INC.; *U.S. Private*, pg. 2365
LEUMI LEASING AND INVESTMENTS LTD.—See Bank Leumi Le-Israel B.M.; *Int'l*, pg. 839
LEUMI PARTNERS LTD.—See Bank Leumi Le-Israel B.M.; *Int'l*, pg. 839
LEUMITECH LTD.—See Bank Leumi Le-Israel B.M.; *Int'l*, pg. 839
LEVINE LEICHTMAN CAPITAL PARTNERS, LLC; *U.S. Private*, pg. 2435
LEWIS & CLARK CAPITAL LLC; *U.S. Private*, pg. 2437
LF FINANCE (SUISSE) S.A.—See Banque Libano-Francaise S.A.L.; *Int'l*, pg. 854
LFM CAPITAL LLC; *U.S. Private*, pg. 2441
LFTD PARTNERS, INC.; *U.S. Public*, pg. 1309
LGAM PRIVATE CREDIT LLC; *U.S. Private*, pg. 2441
LH CARGO HOLDING GMBH—See Deutsche Lufthansa AG; *Int'l*, pg. 2066
LHI ACQUISITION CORPORATION; *U.S. Private*, pg. 2442

LIBERTY HALL CAPITAL PARTNERS, L.P.; *U.S. Private*, pg. 2444
LIBERTY LANE PARTNERS LLC; *U.S. Private*, pg. 2444
LIBERTY MEDIA ACQUISITION CORPORATION; *U.S. Public*, pg. 1311
LIBERTY RESOURCES ACQUISITION CORP.; *U.S. Public*, pg. 1311
LIFE CARD CO., LTD.—See AIFUL Corporation; *Int'l*, pg. 232
LIFE CLIPS, INC.; *U.S. Public*, pg. 1312
LIFE & LONGEVITY LTD.—See Bumrungrad Hospital Public Company Limited; *Int'l*, pg. 1215
LIFEPLAN AUSTRALIA BUILDING SOCIETY LIMITED—See Australian Unity Limited; *Int'l*, pg. 723
LIFE STORAGE, INC.—See Extra Space Storage, Inc.; *U.S. Public*, pg. 813
LIFESTYLE MEDICAL NETWORK INC.; *U.S. Public*, pg. 1313
LIGHTBOX—See Battery Ventures, L.P.; *U.S. Private*, pg. 489
LIGHTBOX—See Silver Lake Group, LLC; *U.S. Private*, pg. 3658
LIGHTHOUSE POINT, LLC—See Caesars Entertainment, Inc.; *U.S. Public*, pg. 421
LIGHT MASTER TECHNOLOGY INC.—See Ezconn Corporation; *Int'l*, pg. 2593
LIGHTSPEED MANAGEMENT COMPANY, LLC; *U.S. Private*, pg. 2453
LIGHTVIEW CAPITAL LLC; *U.S. Private*, pg. 2453
LIGHTYEAR CAPITAL LLC; *U.S. Private*, pg. 2454
LIMBACH HOLDINGS, INC.; *U.S. Public*, pg. 1315
LIME ROCK PARTNERS, LLC; *U.S. Private*, pg. 2456
LIMESTONE CAPITAL AG—See 029 Group SE; *Int'l*, pg. 1
LINCOLN INVESTMENT PLANNING INC.; *U.S. Private*, pg. 2457
LINCOLN PEAK CAPITAL MANAGEMENT, LLC; *U.S. Private*, pg. 2458
LINCOLNSHIRE MANAGEMENT, INC.; *U.S. Private*, pg. 2459
LINDEN LLC; *U.S. Private*, pg. 2459
LINEAGE FINANCIAL NETWORK, INC.; *U.S. Private*, pg. 2460
LINGERIE FIGHTING CHAMPIONSHIPS, INC.; *U.S. Public*, pg. 1320
LINSALATA CAPITAL PARTNERS, LLC; *U.S. Private*, pg. 2463
LION EQUITY PARTNERS, LLC; *U.S. Private*, pg. 2463
LIONHEART VENTURES; *U.S. Private*, pg. 2464
LIQUIDPOWER SPECIALTY PRODUCTS INC.—See Berkshire Hathaway Inc.; *U.S. Public*, pg. 308
LITTLEJOHN & CO., LLC; *U.S. Private*, pg. 2469
LIVENTO GROUP, INC.; *U.S. Public*, pg. 1332
LIVE OAK CRESTVIEW CLIMATE ACQUISITION CORP.; *U.S. Public*, pg. 1331
LIVE OAK MOBILITY ACQUISITION CORP.; *U.S. Public*, pg. 1331
LKCM HEADWATER INVESTMENTS; *U.S. Private*, pg. 2474
LLC NCC-ALABUGA—See Aksa Akrilik Kimya Sanayii A.S.; *Int'l*, pg. 264
LLR PARTNERS, INC.—See Independence Capital Partners, LLC; *U.S. Private*, pg. 2056
LMP MANAGEMENT GROUP, INC.; *U.S. Private*, pg. 2476
LNC PARTNERS; *U.S. Private*, pg. 2476
LOCKMAN ELECTRONIC HOLDINGS LIMITED—See Advent International Corporation; *U.S. Private*, pg. 100
LOCORR FUND MANAGEMENT LLC—See Octavus Group LLC; *U.S. Private*, pg. 2993
LOCUST WALK ACQUISITION CORP.; *U.S. Public*, pg. 1339
LOGAN CIRCLE PARTNERS, L.P.—See MetLife, Inc.; *U.S. Public*, pg. 1430
LOGAN RIDGE FINANCE CORPORATION; *U.S. Public*, pg. 1340
LOGISTICS INNOVATION TECHNOLOGIES CORP.; *U.S. Public*, pg. 1341
LONDON BAY CAPITAL LLC; *U.S. Private*, pg. 2483
LONDON INDUSTRIAL LEASING LIMITED—See Deutsche Bank Aktiengesellschaft; *Int'l*, pg. 2061
LONE STAR AMERICAS ACQUISITIONS, LLC—See Lone Star Funds; *U.S. Private*, pg. 2485
LONE STAR GLOBAL ACQUISITIONS, LLC; *U.S. Private*, pg. 2487
LONE STAR INVESTMENT ADVISORS, LLC; *U.S. Private*, pg. 2489
LONE STAR NEW MARKETS LP; *U.S. Private*, pg. 2489
LONGEVITY ACQUISITION CORPORATION—See 4D Pharma PLC; *Int'l*, pg. 11
LONGITUDE CAPITAL MANAGEMENT CO., LLC; *U.S. Private*, pg. 2492
LONG PATH PARTNERS, LP; *U.S. Private*, pg. 2491
LONG POINT CAPITAL LLC; *U.S. Private*, pg. 2491
LONGRANGE CAPITAL L.P.; *U.S. Private*, pg. 2492
LONGUEVUE CAPITAL, LLC; *U.S. Private*, pg. 2493
LONGWATER OPPORTUNITIES LLC; *U.S. Private*, pg. 2493
LONGWEN GROUP CORP.; *U.S. Public*, pg. 1342

LONGWOOD CAPITAL GROUP, INC.; *U.S. Private*, pg. 2493
LOOMIS SAYLES INVESTMENTS ASIA PTE. LTD.—See Groupe BPCE; *Int'l*, pg. 3098
LOOMIS SAYLES INVESTMENTS LTD.—See Groupe BPCE; *Int'l*, pg. 3098
LORD BALTIMORE CAPITAL CORP.; *U.S. Private*, pg. 2495
LORD BUDDHA FINANCE LIMITED—See Global IME Bank Limited; *Int'l*, pg. 2997
LORRAINE CAPITAL LLC; *U.S. Private*, pg. 2495
LOTUS INFRASTRUCTURE PARTNERS LLC; *U.S. Private*, pg. 2497
LOTUS INNOVATIONS LLC; *U.S. Private*, pg. 2497
LOVELL MINNICK PARTNERS LLC; *U.S. Private*, pg. 2501
L&P FINANCIAL SERVICES CO.—See Leggett & Platt, Incorporated; *U.S. Public*, pg. 1302
LSC ACQUISITION CORPORATION; *U.S. Private*, pg. 2508
LUBAR & CO., INC.; *U.S. Private*, pg. 2510
LUBRIZOL GROUP, LLP—See Berkshire Hathaway Inc.; *U.S. Public*, pg. 319
LUCERNE CAPITAL MANAGEMENT, LP.; *U.S. Private*, pg. 2510
LUDVIK HOLDINGS, INC.; *U.S. Private*, pg. 2512
LUFTHANSA MALTA PENSION HOLDING LTD.—See Deutsche Lufthansa AG; *Int'l*, pg. 2069
LUFTHANSA TECHNIK AIRMOTIVE IRELAND HOLDINGS LTD.—See Deutsche Lufthansa AG; *Int'l*, pg. 2070
LUMENT FINANCE TRUST, INC.; *U.S. Public*, pg. 1348
LUMINATE CAPITAL MANAGEMENT, INC.; *U.S. Private*, pg. 2514
LUMINUS MANAGEMENT, LLC; *U.S. Private*, pg. 2514
LURIE INVESTMENTS, INC; *U.S. Private*, pg. 2516
LUX CAPITAL, LLC; *U.S. Private*, pg. 2518
LUX HEALTH TECH ACQUISITION CORP.; *U.S. Public*, pg. 2518
LUXON FINANCIAL LLC; *U.S. Private*, pg. 2518
LUXOR CAPITAL GROUP, LP; *U.S. Private*, pg. 2518
LWC, LLC—See FirstCash Holdings, Inc.; *U.S. Public*, pg. 849
LYNCH HOLDINGS, LLC; *U.S. Private*, pg. 2520
LZG INTERNATIONAL, INC.—See Genius Group Limited; *Int'l*, pg. 2924
MABECO NV—See Ackermans & van Haaren NV; *Int'l*, pg. 106
MACQUARIE CAPITAL VENTURE STUDIO—See The Interpublic Group of Companies, Inc.; *U.S. Public*, pg. 2104
MACROSHARES HOUSING DEPOSITOR, LLC—See MacroMarkets LLC; *U.S. Public*, pg. 2538
MADISON DEARBORN PARTNERS, LLC; *U.S. Private*, pg. 2540
MADISON INDUSTRIES HOLDINGS LLC; *U.S. Private*, pg. 2543
MADISON INTERNATIONAL REALTY, LLC; *U.S. Private*, pg. 2543
MADISON PARKER CAPITAL; *U.S. Private*, pg. 2544
MADISON TAX CAPITAL, LLC—See JPMorgan Chase & Co.; *U.S. Public*, pg. 1210
MAERSK HOLDING B.V.—See A.P. Moller-Maersk A/S; *Int'l*, pg. 27
MAERSK SUPPLY SERVICE HOLDINGS UK LIMITED—See A.P. Moller-Maersk A/S; *Int'l*, pg. 27
MAGHREBAIL SA—See Bank of Africa; *Int'l*, pg. 839
MAGIC JOHNSON ENTERPRISES; *U.S. Private*, pg. 2546
MAGNATE CAPITAL PARTNERS, LLC; *U.S. Private*, pg. 2547
MAGNETI MARELLI HOLDING U.S.A. INC.—See KKR & Co. Inc.; *U.S. Public*, pg. 1261
MAGNOLIA OIL & GAS CORPORATION; *U.S. Public*, pg. 1354
MAI CAPITAL MANAGEMENT, LLC—See Keystone Group, L.P.; *U.S. Private*, pg. 2297
MAIN LINE EQUITY PARTNERS, LLC; *U.S. Private*, pg. 2551
MAIN POST PARTNERS, L.P.; *U.S. Private*, pg. 2551
MAINSAIL MANAGEMENT COMPANY, LLC; *U.S. Private*, pg. 2553
MAINSTAY MACKAY DEFINEDTERM MUNICIPAL OPPORTUNITIES FUND; *U.S. Public*, pg. 1355
MAIN STREET CAPITAL CORPORATION; *U.S. Public*, pg. 1354
MAIN STREET CAPITAL HOLDINGS, LLC; *U.S. Private*, pg. 2551
MAKAI CAPITAL PARTNERS LLC; *U.S. Private*, pg. 2556
MALAYSIA DERIVATIVES EXCHANGE BERHAD—See Bursa Malaysia Berhad; *Int'l*, pg. 1227
MALAYSIAN CENTRAL DEPOSITORY SDN BHD—See Bursa Malaysia Berhad; *Int'l*, pg. 1227
MALKIN PROPERTIES, L.L.C.; *U.S. Private*, pg. 2557
MALLARD ACQUISITION CORP.; *U.S. Public*, pg. 1356
MALONEY INVESTMENTS LIMITED—See Barclays PLC; *Int'l*, pg. 862
MA MANAGED FUTURES FUND, LP; *U.S. Private*, pg. 2530
MANAGED FUTURES PREMIER WARRINGTON L.P.; *U.S. Private*, pg. 2559
MANAGEMENT CAPITAL, LLC; *U.S. Private*, pg. 2560
MANHATTAN PARTNERS; *U.S. Private*, pg. 2563

523999 — MISCELLANEOUS FINAN...

MANHATTAN SCIENTIFICS, INC.; *U.S. Public*, pg. 1356
MANNHEIM, LLC; *U.S. Private*, pg. 2565
MANSA CAPITAL MANAGEMENT, LLC; *U.S. Private*, pg. 2566
MAPLE LIFE FINANCIAL, INC.; *U.S. Private*, pg. 2568
MAQUET FINANCIAL SERVICES GMBH—See Getinge AB; *Int'l*, pg. 2951
MARANON CAPITAL, L.P.—See Eldridge Industries LLC; *U.S. Private*, pg. 1351
MARATHON ASSET MANAGEMENT LP; *U.S. Private*, pg. 2569
MARBAS MENKUL DEGERLER A.S.—See Gedik Yatirim Menkul Degerler A.S.; *Int'l*, pg. 2910
MARBLEGATE ACQUISITION CORP.; *U.S. Public*, pg. 1364
MARCATO CAPITAL MANAGEMENT, LP; *U.S. Private*, pg. 2571
MARCUM WEALTH LLC; *U.S. Private*, pg. 2572
MARCUS PARTNERS, INC.; *U.S. Private*, pg. 2573
MARINER WEALTH ADVISORS LLC—See Mariner Wealth Advisors, LLC; *U.S. Private*, pg. 2575
MARKEL VENTURES, INC.—See Markel Group Inc.; *U.S. Public*, pg. 1368
MARKET MORTGAGE LIMITED—See Capita plc; *Int'l*, pg. 1309
MARKET VECTORS REDEEMABLE SILVER TRUST—See Van Eck Associates Corp.; *U.S. Private*, pg. 4340
MARKETWISE, INC.; *U.S. Public*, pg. 1369
MARKFORGED HOLDING CORPORATION; *U.S. Public*, pg. 1369
MARLIN EQUITY PARTNERS, LLC; *U.S. Private*, pg. 2583
MARLIN TECHNOLOGY CORPORATION; *U.S. Public*, pg. 1370
MARQUETTE CAPITAL PARTNERS, LLC—See Pohlad Companies; *U.S. Private*, pg. 3220
MARS ACQUISITION CORP.; *U.S. Public*, pg. 1374
MARSHALL JUNCTION PARTNERS, LLC; *U.S. Private*, pg. 2592
MARSH ISRAEL (HOLDINGS) LTD.—See Marsh & McLennan Companies, Inc.; *U.S. Public*, pg. 1383
MARSH & MCLENNAN, INCORPORATED—See Marsh & McLennan Companies, Inc.; *U.S. Public*, pg. 1378
MARTIS CAPITAL MANAGEMENT LLC; *U.S. Private*, pg. 2597
MARWIT CAPITAL; *U.S. Private*, pg. 2598
THE MARYJANE GROUP, INC.; *U.S. Private*, pg. 4075
MASON INDUSTRIAL TECHNOLOGY, INC.; *U.S. Public*, pg. 1392
MASON WELLS, INC.; *U.S. Private*, pg. 2602
MASSACHUSETTS BUSINESS DEVELOPMENT CORP.; *U.S. Public*, pg. 1392
MASSACHUSETTS CAPITAL RESOURCE COMPANY; *U.S. Private*, pg. 2603
MASSEY QUICK SIMON & CO., LLC; *U.S. Private*, pg. 2606
MASTRY MANAGEMENT LLC; *U.S. Private*, pg. 2608
MASY BIOSERVICES, INC.; *U.S. Private*, pg. 2608
THE MATHER GROUP, LLC; *U.S. Private*, pg. 4075
MATLINPATTERSON GLOBAL ADVISERS LLC; *U.S. Private*, pg. 2611
MATRIX PARTNERS; *U.S. Private*, pg. 2612
MATTERPORT, INC.; *U.S. Public*, pg. 1399
MAVENHILL CAPITAL; *U.S. Private*, pg. 2615
MAVIK CAPITAL MANAGEMENT, LP; *U.S. Private*, pg. 2616
MAYFIELD FUND; *U.S. Private*, pg. 2621
MAY RIVER CAPITAL, LLC; *U.S. Private*, pg. 2620
MBF HEALTHCARE PARTNERS, L.P.; *U.S. Private*, pg. 2624
MCC INVESTMENT SA.—See Enka Insaat ve Sanayi A.S.; *Int'l*, pg. 2440
MCCOMBS ENTERPRISES; *U.S. Private*, pg. 2629
MCCORMICK SWITZERLAND GMBH—See McCormick & Company, Incorporated; *U.S. Public*, pg. 1404
MCG GLOBAL, LLC; *U.S. Private*, pg. 2634
MCH PRIVATE EQUITY ASESORES, S.L.—See Groupe BPCE; *Int'l*, pg. 3095
MCKAFKA DEVELOPMENT GROUP, LLC; *U.S. Private*, pg. 2637
MCLAREN TECHNOLOGY ACQUISITION CORP.; *U.S. Public*, pg. 1409
MCLEAN CAPITAL MANAGEMENT; *U.S. Private*, pg. 2640
MCNALLY CAPITAL, LLC; *U.S. Private*, pg. 2643
MC PARTNERS INC.; *U.S. Private*, pg. 2625
M/C VENTURE PARTNERS, LLC—See TAC Partners, Inc.; *U.S. Private*, pg. 3920
MCWHORTER CAPITAL PARTNERS, LLC; *U.S. Private*, pg. 2645
MDC CORPORATE (US) INC.—See Stagwell, Inc.; *U.S. Public*, pg. 1927
MDH ACQUISITION CORP.; *U.S. Public*, pg. 1409
M.D. SASS HOLDINGS, INC.; *U.S. Private*, pg. 2528
MECOM FINANCE LIMITED—See DPG Media Group NV; *Int'l*, pg. 2189
MEDA GERMANY HOLDING GMBH—See Viatris Inc.; *U.S. Public*, pg. 2293
MEDALIST PARTNERS, LP; *U.S. Private*, pg. 2650
MEDALLION CAPITAL, INC.—See Medallion Financial Corp.; *U.S. Public*, pg. 1411
MEDEXPRESS JSIC—See Allianz SE; *Int'l*, pg. 354
MEDIA SATURN HOLDING POLSKA SP. Z. O. O.—See Ceconomy AG; *Int'l*, pg. 1385
MEDICAL SUPPLY INTERNATIONAL USA, INC.; *U.S. Public*, pg. 1412
MEDICUS SCIENCES ACQUISITION CORP.; *U.S. Public*, pg. 1412
MEDIMMUNE VENTURES, INC.—See AstraZeneca PLC; *Int'l*, pg. 661
MEDINA CAPITAL PARTNERS, INC; *U.S. Private*, pg. 2657
MEDIOLANUM COMUNICAZIONE S.P.A.—See Banca Mediolanum S.p.A.; *Int'l*, pg. 815
MEDIPORT VENTURE FONDS ZWEI GMBH—See BayernLB Holding AG; *Int'l*, pg. 914
MEDITECHNIK HOLDING GMBH—See Getinge AB; *Int'l*, pg. 2952
MEDLINE INDUSTRIES HOLDINGS, L.P.—See Medline Industries, LP; *U.S. Private*, pg. 2657
MEDPROPERTIES HOLDINGS, LLC; *U.S. Private*, pg. 2658
MEGGITT-USA HOLDINGS LLC—See Parker Hannifin Corporation; *U.S. Public*, pg. 1642
MELI KASZEK PIONEER CORP.; *U.S. Public*, pg. 1414
MELVIN CAPITAL MANAGEMENT LP; *U.S. Private*, pg. 2663
MERAGE INVESTMENT GROUP; *U.S. Private*, pg. 2667
MERCATO PARTNERS ACQUISITION CORP.; *U.S. Public*, pg. 1414
MERCER CONSULTING GROUP, INC.—See Marsh & McLennan Companies, Inc.; *U.S. Public*, pg. 1384
MERCHANT INVESTMENT MANAGEMENT, LLC; *U.S. Private*, pg. 2669
MERCURY ADVISORS LLC; *U.S. Private*, pg. 2670
MERCURY CAPITAL CORP.; *U.S. Private*, pg. 2670
MERCURY CAPITAL PARTNERS, L.P.; *U.S. Private*, pg. 2670
MERIDIAN VENTURE PARTNERS; *U.S. Private*, pg. 2673
MERIT CAPITAL PARTNERS; *U.S. Private*, pg. 2674
MERIT ENERGY COMPANY INC.; *U.S. Private*, pg. 2674
MERITURN PARTNERS, LLC - SAN FRANCISCO—See Meriturn Partners, LLC; *U.S. Private*, pg. 2675
MERITURN PARTNERS, LLC; *U.S. Private*, pg. 2675
MERQUE FINANCIAL SERVICES PROPRIETARY LIMITED—See Barclays PLC; *Int'l*, pg. 862
MERRYMEETING, INC.; *U.S. Private*, pg. 2676
MERUELO CAPITAL INVESTMENTS, INC.—See Meruelo Group LLC; *U.S. Private*, pg. 2677
MESA ACQUIRER LLC—See Repay Holdings Corporation; *U.S. Public*, pg. 1784
MESIROW FINANCIAL, INC.—See Mesirow Financial Holdings, Inc.; *U.S. Private*, pg. 2678
MESO NUMISMATICS, INC.; *U.S. Public*, pg. 1426
METALLURG HOLDINGS CORPORATION—See AMG Critical Materials N.V.; *Int'l*, pg. 426
METALMARK CAPITAL HOLDINGS LLC; *U.S. Private*, pg. 2681
METALS ACQUISITION CORP.; *U.S. Public*, pg. 1427
METAL SKY STAR ACQUISITION CORPORATION; *U.S. Public*, pg. 1427
METAMORPHIC VENTURES; *U.S. Private*, pg. 2682
METAPOINT PARTNERS LP; *U.S. Private*, pg. 2682
METAURUS EQUITY COMPONENT TRUST; *U.S. Public*, pg. 1427
METAVERSE CORPORATION; *U.S. Private*, pg. 2683
METEORA CAPITAL LLC; *U.S. Private*, pg. 2683
METLIFE SECURITIES, INC.—See MetLife, Inc.; *U.S. Public*, pg. 1431
METROLOG SP. Z O.O.—See CEZ, a.s.; *Int'l*, pg. 1428
METROPOULOS & CO.; *U.S. Private*, pg. 2690
METTRUM HEALTH CORP.—See Canopy Growth Corporation; *Int'l*, pg. 1298
METZLER ASSET MANAGEMENT (JAPAN) LTD.—See B. Metzler seel. Sohn & Co. Holding AG; *Int'l*, pg. 788
METZLER IRELAND LIMITED—See B. Metzler seel. Sohn & Co. Holding AG; *Int'l*, pg. 788
MGP FINANCE CO-ISSUER INC.—See VICI Properties Inc.; *U.S. Public*, pg. 2296
MG VENTURE CAPITAL AG—See GEA Group Aktiengesellschaft; *Int'l*, pg. 2904
MH PRIVATE EQUITY FUND, LLC; *U.S. Private*, pg. 2695
MHT PROPERTIES VII INC.—See MHT Housing, Inc.; *U.S. Private*, pg. 2695
MIAMI SUBS CAPITAL PARTNERS I, INC.; *U.S. Private*, pg. 2697
MICHELIN FINANCE (PAYS-BAS) B.V.—See Compagnie Generale des Etablissements Michelin SCA; *Int'l*, pg. 1744
MICHELIN THAI HOLDING CO., LTD.—See Compagnie Generale des Etablissements Michelin SCA; *Int'l*, pg. 1743
MICROCLOUD HOLOGRAM INC.; *U.S. Public*, pg. 1437
MICROMOBILITY.COM INC.; *U.S. Public*, pg. 1437
MICROVAST HOLDINGS, INC.; *U.S. Public*, pg. 1444
MIDCAP FINANCIAL SERVICES, LLC; *U.S. Private*, pg. 2710
MIDDLEBURG INVESTMENT GROUP, INC.—See Atlantic Union Bankshares Corporation; *U.S. Public*, pg. 223
MIDMARK CAPITAL; *U.S. Private*, pg. 2715
MID OAKS INVESTMENTS LLC; *U.S. Private*, pg. 2706
MIDT FACTORING A/S—See Groupe BPCE; *Int'l*, pg. 3098
MIDWEST GROWTH PARTNERS, LLLP; *U.S. Private*, pg. 2721
MIG ABSOLUTE RETURN—See Merage Investment Group; *U.S. Private*, pg. 2667
MIGDAL UNDERWRITING BUSINESS—See Assicurazioni Generali S.p.A.; *Int'l*, pg. 647
MIG PRIVATE EQUITY—See Merage Investment Group; *U.S. Private*, pg. 2667
MILESTONE CAPITAL, INC.; *U.S. Private*, pg. 2728
MILESTONE PARTNERS LTD.; *U.S. Private*, pg. 2728
MILLBROOK CAPITAL MANAGEMENT, INC.; *U.S. Private*, pg. 2730
MILL CITY CAPITAL, L.P.; *U.S. Private*, pg. 2729
MILL CITY VENTURES III, LTD.; *U.S. Public*, pg. 1446
MILLENIUM BROKERAGE GROUP, LLC; *U.S. Private*, pg. 2731
MILLENNIUM SUSTAINABLE VENTURES CORP.; *U.S. Public*, pg. 1446
MILLER/HOWARD HIGH INCOME EQUITY FUND; *U.S. Public*, pg. 1446
MILL POINT CAPITAL LLC—See Guggenheim Partners, LLC; *U.S. Private*, pg. 1811
MILL ROAD CAPITAL MANAGEMENT LLC; *U.S. Private*, pg. 2730
MILLSTREET CAPITAL ACQUISITION CORP.; *U.S. Public*, pg. 1448
MILL STREET PARTNERS LLC; *U.S. Private*, pg. 2730
MINAT TEGUH SDN BHD—See IJM Corporation Berhad; *Int'l*, pg. 3609
MINELLA CAPITAL MANAGEMENT LLC; *U.S. Private*, pg. 2741
MINMETALS FINANCE COMPANY—See China Rare Earth Resources And Technology Co., Ltd.; *Int'l*, pg. 1546
MINORITY EQUALITY OPPORTUNITIES ACQUISITION INC.; *U.S. Public*, pg. 1449
MIROVA S.A.—See Groupe BPCE; *Int'l*, pg. 3096
MISR FOR CENTRAL CLEARING, DEPOSITORY & REGISTRY SAE—See Cairo & Alexandria Stock Exchanges; *Int'l*, pg. 1253
MISSION ADVANCEMENT CORP.; *U.S. Public*, pg. 1450
MISSION CONSUMER CAPITAL; *U.S. Private*, pg. 2747
MISSION HILLS CAPITAL PARTNERS INC—See iA Financial Corporation Inc.; *Int'l*, pg. 3567
MISTICO ACQUISITION CORP.; *U.S. Public*, pg. 2750
MISTRAL EQUITY PARTNERS LLC; *U.S. Private*, pg. 2750
MITCO GROUP LTD.—See CIEL Ltd.; *Int'l*, pg. 1605
MITESCO, INC.; *U.S. Public*, pg. 1452
MMF CAPITAL MANAGEMENT LLC; *U.S. Private*, pg. 2754
MOBILE INFRASTRUCTURE CORPORATION; *U.S. Public*, pg. 1453
MOBILEPAY FINLAND OY—See Danske Bank A/S; *Int'l*, pg. 1969
MOBIUS VENTURE CAPITAL, INC.; *U.S. Private*, pg. 2758
MOBIX LABS, INC.; *U.S. Public*, pg. 1454
MODERN EKONOMI SVERIGE AB—See TowerBrook Capital Partners, L.P.; *U.S. Public*, pg. 4195
MOELIS CAPITAL PARTNERS LLC—See Moelis Asset Management LP; *U.S. Private*, pg. 2764
MOHR DAVIDOW VENTURES; *U.S. Private*, pg. 2765
MOJO DIGITAL ASSETS INC.; *U.S. Public*, pg. 1458
MOLLENHOUR GROSS LLC; *U.S. Private*, pg. 2767
MOLOKAI PROPERTIES LIMITED—See Hong Leong Investment Holdings Pte. Ltd.; *Int'l*, pg. 3468
MONDEE HOLDINGS, INC.; *U.S. Public*, pg. 1460
MONDIAL SERVICE- BELGIUM S.A.—See Allianz SE; *Int'l*, pg. 354
MONEYLION INC.; *U.S. Public*, pg. 1464
THE MONEY TREE INC.; *U.S. Private*, pg. 4080
MONEYWISE WEALTH MANAGEMENT; *U.S. Private*, pg. 2770
MONITOR CLIPPER PARTNERS GMBH—See Monitor Clipper Partners, LLC; *U.S. Private*, pg. 2770
MONITOR CLIPPER PARTNERS, LLC; *U.S. Private*, pg. 2770
MONITOR CLIPPER PARTNERS (UK), LLC—See Monitor Clipper Partners, LLC; *U.S. Private*, pg. 2770
MONOMOY CAPITAL PARTNERS LLC; *U.S. Private*, pg. 2771
MONROE CAPITAL LLC; *U.S. Private*, pg. 2772
MONTAGE PARTNERS, INC.; *U.S. Private*, pg. 2774
MONTAGUE INTERNATIONAL HOLDING LTD.; *U.S. Public*, pg. 1465
MONTEREY INNOVATION ACQUISITION CORP.; *U.S. Public*, pg. 1466
MONTES ARCHIMEDES ACQUISITION CORP.; *U.S. Public*, pg. 1466
MONUMENT CIRCLE ACQUISITION CORP.; *U.S. Public*, pg. 1466
MOOLA SYSTEMS LIMITED—See Marsh & McLennan Companies, Inc.; *U.S. Public*, pg. 1386
MOONBEAM CAPITAL INVESTMENTS, LLC; *U.S. Private*, pg. 2779
MOONEY SERVIZI S.P.A.—See Enel S.p.A.; *Int'l*, pg. 2414
MOONEY S.P.A.—See Enel S.p.A.; *Int'l*, pg. 2414

N.A.I.C.S. INDEX
523999 — MISCELLANEOUS FINAN...

MOONLAKE IMMUNOTHERAPEUTICS; *U.S. Public,* pg. 1471
MORGAN STANLEY CAPITAL PARTNERS—See Morgan Stanley; *U.S. Public,* pg. 1474
MORGAN STANLEY INFRASTRUCTURE, INC.—See Morgan Stanley; *U.S. Public,* pg. 1472
MORGAN STANLEY INTERNATIONAL HOLDINGS INC.—See Morgan Stanley; *U.S. Public,* pg. 1473
MORGAN STANLEY MENKUL DEGERLER A.S.—See Morgan Stanley; *U.S. Public,* pg. 1475
MORGAN STANLEY PRIVATE EQUITY ASIA INC.—See Morgan Stanley; *U.S. Public,* pg. 1473
MORGENS WATERFALL VINTIADIS & CO. INC.; *U.S. Private,* pg. 2785
MORINGA ACQUISITION CORP.; *U.S. Public,* pg. 1476
MORTGAGE ASSETS MANAGEMENT LLC—See Waterfall Asset Management LLC; *U.S. Private,* pg. 4452
MOSAIC CAPITAL CORPORATION—See Fairfax Financial Holdings Limited; *Int'l,* pg. 2607
MOSAIC MEDIA INVESTMENT PARTNERS LLC; *U.S. Private,* pg. 2792
MOTIVE PARTNERS GP, LLC; *U.S. Private,* pg. 2796
MOTOR CITY ACQUISITION CORP.; *U.S. Public,* pg. 1477
MOTOROLA FINANCE EMEA LIMITED—See Motorola Solutions, Inc.; *U.S. Public,* pg. 1478
MOTOROLA SOLUTIONS VENTURE CAPITAL—See Motorola Solutions, Inc.; *U.S. Public,* pg. 1478
MOUNTAIN CAPITAL PARTNERS, LP; *U.S. Private,* pg. 2799
MOUNTAINGATE CAPITAL MANAGEMENT, L.P.; *U.S. Private,* pg. 2801
MOUNT KELLETT CAPITAL MANAGEMENT LP; *U.S. Private,* pg. 2798
MOUNT RAINIER ACQUISITION CORP.; *U.S. Public,* pg. 1479
MPE PARTNERS, LLC; *U.S. Private,* pg. 2803
MPK EQUITY PARTNERS; *U.S. Private,* pg. 2804
MPM CAPITAL LLC; *U.S. Private,* pg. 2804
MPM CAPITAL - SAN FRANCISCO—See MPM Capital LLC; *U.S. Private,* pg. 2804
MQ MEDICAL TECHNOLOGIES CORPORATION; *U.S. Private,* pg. 2804
MRG MASSNAHMETRAGER MUNCHEN-RIEM GMBH—See BayernLB Holding AG; *Int'l,* pg. 914
M SCIENCE LLC—See Jefferies Financial Group Inc.; *U.S. Public,* pg. 1189
MSCI INC.; *U.S. Public,* pg. 1483
MSC INCOME FUND, INC.; *U.S. Public,* pg. 1482
MSCI SERVICES PRIVATE LIMITED—See MSCI Inc.; *U.S. Public,* pg. 1483
MSD ACQUISITION CORP.; *U.S. Private,* pg. 2806
MSD CAPITAL, L.P.; *U.S. Private,* pg. 2806
MSD INVESTMENT CORP.; *U.S. Private,* pg. 2807
MSHARIE LLC—See Dubai Investments PJSC; *Int'l,* pg. 2219
MSI CAPITAL PARTNERS LLC; *U.S. Private,* pg. 2807
M-STORES PROPRIETARY LIMITED—See Bayport Management Limited; *Int'l,* pg. 915
MTN CAPITAL PARTNERS LLC; *U.S. Private,* pg. 2809
MTX WEALTH MANAGEMENT, LLC—See Keystone Group, L.P.; *U.S. Private,* pg. 2297
MUDRICK CAPITAL ACQUISITION CORPORATION II; *U.S. Public,* pg. 1484
MULTIPLAN CORP.; *U.S. Public,* pg. 1486
MULTI SOLUTIONS II, INC.; *U.S. Public,* pg. 1486
MURPHREE VENTURE PARTNERS; *U.S. Private,* pg. 2815
MURRAY HOUSE INVESTMENTS LIMITED—See Barclays PLC; *Int'l,* pg. 862
THE MUSIC ACQUISITION CORPORATION; *U.S. Public,* pg. 2116
THE MUSTANG GROUP, LLC; *U.S. Private,* pg. 4081
MUZINICH BDC, INC.; *U.S. Private,* pg. 2821
MVC ACQUISITION CORP.; *U.S. Public,* pg. 2821
MVC FINANCIAL SERVICES, INC.—See Barings BDC, Inc.; *U.S. Public,* pg. 276
MV CREDIT LIMITED—See Groupe BPCE; *Int'l,* pg. 3098
MV PORTFOLIOS, INC.; *U.S. Public,* pg. 2821
M W RECYCLING, LLC—See Icahn Enterprises L.P.; *U.S. Public,* pg. 1084
M.W. TRADE S.A.—See Getin Holding S.A.; *Int'l,* pg. 2947
MYERS GROVE INVESTMENTS LIMITED—See Barclays PLC; *Int'l,* pg. 862
MYGO GAMES HOLDING CO.; *U.S. Private,* pg. 2825
N2 ACQUISITION HOLDINGS CORP.; *U.S. Private,* pg. 2828
NAJAFI COMPANIES, LLC; *U.S. Private,* pg. 2831
THE NAJAFI COMPANIES; *U.S. Private,* pg. 4081
NAMASTE WORLD ACQUISITION CORPORATION; *U.S. Public,* pg. 1490
NANT CAPITAL, LLC; *U.S. Private,* pg. 2833
NAOC HOLDINGS; *U.S. Private,* pg. 2834
NAOS SMALL CAP OPPORTUNITIES COMPANY LIMITED—See Contango Group Pty. Ltd.; *Int'l,* pg. 1779
THE NAPLES TRUST COMPANY—See The Sanibel Captiva Trust Company; *U.S. Private,* pg. 4114
NATAM MANAGEMENT COMPANY S.A.—See Banca Finnat Euramerica S.p.A.; *Int'l,* pg. 815
NATCORE TECHNOLOGY INC.; *U.S. Public,* pg. 1492

NATIOCREDIMURS SNC—See BNP Paribas SA; *Int'l,* pg. 1092
NATIONAL ART EXCHANGE, INC.; *U.S. Public,* pg. 1493
NATIONAL ENERGY SERVICES REUNITED CORP.; *U.S. Public,* pg. 1494
NATIXIS INVESTISSEMENT PARTNERS—See Groupe BPCE; *Int'l,* pg. 3095
NATIXIS INVESTMENT MANAGERS INTERNATIONAL SA—See Groupe BPCE; *Int'l,* pg. 3098
NATIXIS INVESTMENT MANAGERS, NEDERLANDS S.A.—See Groupe BPCE; *Int'l,* pg. 3098
NATIXIS INVESTMENT MANAGERS SA—See Groupe BPCE; *Int'l,* pg. 3098
NATIXIS LIFE SA—See Groupe BPCE; *Int'l,* pg. 3098
NATIXIS PAYMENT SOLUTIONS SA—See Groupe BPCE; *Int'l,* pg. 3098
NATIXIS PRIVATE EQUITY INTERNATIONAL—See Groupe BPCE; *Int'l,* pg. 3095
NATIXIS - PRIVATE EQUITY & PRIVATE BANKING—See Groupe BPCE; *Int'l,* pg. 3095
NATIXIS PRIVATE EQUITY—See Groupe BPCE; *Int'l,* pg. 3095
NATIXIS WEALTH MANAGEMENT LUXEMBOURG SA—See Groupe BPCE; *Int'l,* pg. 3098
NATSOURCE LLC; *U.S. Private,* pg. 2867
NATURAL ORDER ACQUISITION CORP.; *U.S. Public,* pg. 1499
NATURALSHRIMP, INC.; *U.S. Public,* pg. 1499
NAVIGATION CAPITAL PARTNERS, INC.; *U.S. Private,* pg. 2873
NAVIS HOLDING LLC—See Cargotec Corporation; *Int'l,* pg. 1329
NAXICAP PARTNERS SA—See Groupe BPCE; *Int'l,* pg. 3095
NAYA VENTURES LLC; *U.S. Private,* pg. 2874
NB RENAISSANCE PARTNERS—See Neuberger Berman Group LLC; *U.S. Private,* pg. 2890
NCA PARTNERS, INC.; *U.S. Private,* pg. 2875
NCK CAPITAL LLC; *U.S. Private,* pg. 2876
NCT VENTURES LLC; *U.S. Private,* pg. 2876
NDS CO., LTD.—See COMSYS Holdings Corporation; *Int'l,* pg. 1761
NEAR INTELLIGENCE, INC.—See Blue Torch Capital, LP; *U.S. Private,* pg. 594
NEBULA CARAVEL ACQUISITION CORP.; *U.S. Public,* pg. 1504
NEMPARTNERS—See Groupe BPCE; *Int'l,* pg. 3096
NEOASISTENCIA MANOTERAS S.L.—See Allianz SE; *Int'l,* pg. 354
NEOCARTA VENTURES, INC. - BOSTON—See Neocarta Ventures, Inc.; *U.S. Private,* pg. 2884
NEOCARTA VENTURES, INC.; *U.S. Private,* pg. 2884
NEO TECHNOLOGY ACQUISITION CORP.; *U.S. Public,* pg. 1505
NEOVEST, INC.—See JPMorgan Chase & Co.; *U.S. Public,* pg. 1210
NEPAL HOUSING & MERCHANT FINANCE LTD.—See Citizens Bank International Limited; *Int'l,* pg. 1625
NERDWALLET INC; *U.S. Public,* pg. 1506
NERDY INC.; *U.S. Public,* pg. 1506
NESTLE WATERS NORTH AMERICA HOLDINGS, INC.—See Metropoulos & Co.; *U.S. Private,* pg. 2690
NESTLE WATERS NORTH AMERICA HOLDINGS, INC.—See One Rock Capital Partners, LLC; *U.S. Private,* pg. 3021
NETFIN ACQUISITION CORP.; *U.S. Public,* pg. 1507
NEUHEIM LUX GROUP HOLDING V S.A.R.L—See Sun Capital Partners, Inc.; *U.S. Private,* pg. 3862
NEWBURY PARTNERS LLC—See Bridge Investment Group Holdings Inc.; *U.S. Public,* pg. 381
NEWBURY STREET ACQUISITION CORP.; *U.S. Public,* pg. 1513
NEW CAPITAL PARTNERS; *U.S. Private,* pg. 2892
NEWCASTLE PARTNERS LLC; *U.S. Private,* pg. 2914
NEWCASTLE PARTNERS LP; *U.S. Private,* pg. 2914
NEWCOURT ACQUISITION CORP.; *U.S. Public,* pg. 1513
NEWCREST FINANCE PTY LTD—See Newmont Corporation; *U.S. Public,* pg. 1517
NEW ENGLAND CAPITAL PARTNERS, INC.; *U.S. Private,* pg. 2894
NEW ENGLAND SPORTS ENTERPRISES, LLC—See Fenway Sports Group Holdings, LLC; *U.S. Private,* pg. 1496
NEW ENTERPRISE ASSOCIATES, LLC; *U.S. Private,* pg. 2895
NEW EVOLUTION VENTURES, LLC; *U.S. Private,* pg. 2896
NEWFOCUS FINANCIAL GROUP LLC—See EP Wealth Advisors, LLC; *U.S. Private,* pg. 1411
NEW FRONTIER PARTNERS CO LTD—See AIFUL Corporation; *Int'l,* pg. 232
NEW HARBOR CAPITAL MANAGEMENT LLC; *U.S. Private,* pg. 2896
NEW HERITAGE CAPITAL LLC; *U.S. Private,* pg. 2896
NEW HILL MANAGEMENT, LLC; *U.S. Private,* pg. 2897
NEW MOUNTAIN CAPITAL, LLC; *U.S. Private,* pg. 2899
NEW MOUNTAIN FINANCE CORPORATION—See New Mountain Capital, LLC; *U.S. Private,* pg. 2903

NEWPORT GLOBAL ADVISORS, L.P.; *U.S. Private,* pg. 2916
NEW SEABURY PROPERTIES, LLC—See Icahn Enterprises L.P.; *U.S. Public,* pg. 1084
NEW SENIOR INVESTMENT GROUP INC.—See Ventas, Inc.; *U.S. Public,* pg. 2278
NEWSPRING CAPITAL LLC; *U.S. Private,* pg. 2917
NEW STATE CAPITAL PARTNERS LLC; *U.S. Private,* pg. 2906
NEWSTONE CAPITAL PARTNERS, LLC; *U.S. Private,* pg. 2918
NEWTON CAPITAL MANAGEMENT LIMITED—See The Bank of New York Mellon Corporation; *U.S. Public,* pg. 2037
NEW VALUE CAPITAL LLC; *U.S. Private,* pg. 2907
NEW VISTA ACQUISITION CORP.; *U.S. Public,* pg. 1512
NEW WATER CAPITAL, L.P.; *U.S. Private,* pg. 2907
NEW WORLD CHINA LAND LIMITED—See Chow Tai Fook Enterprises Limited; *Int'l,* pg. 1585
NEW YORK CITY HOUSING DEVELOPMENT CORPORATION; *U.S. Private,* pg. 2909
NEXCORE HEALTHCARE CAPITAL CORP.; *U.S. Public,* pg. 1522
NEXE BLOCKCHAIN, INC.; *U.S. Private,* pg. 2919
NEX EXCHANGE LIMITED—See CME Group, Inc.; *U.S. Public,* pg. 516
NEXIEN BIOPHARMA INC.—See Intiva Inc.; *U.S. Private,* pg. 2129
NEXITY GLOBAL SA—See Graviton Capital S.A.; *Int'l,* pg. 3062
NEXPHASE CAPITAL, LP—See Moelis Asset Management LP; *U.S. Private,* pg. 2764
NEXTDOOR HOLDINGS, INC.; *U.S. Public,* pg. 1526
NEXTERA ENERGY CAPITAL HOLDINGS, INC.—See NextEra Energy, Inc.; *U.S. Public,* pg. 1526
NEXTNAV INC.; *U.S. Public,* pg. 1526
NEXTPOINT ACQUISITION CORP.; *U.S. Public,* pg. 1527
NEXT WORLD CAPITAL LLC—See Next World Capital Partners LLC; *U.S. Private,* pg. 2920
NEXT WORLD CAPITAL PARTNERS LLC; *U.S. Private,* pg. 2920
NEXUS CAPITAL MANAGEMENT LP; *U.S. Private,* pg. 2922
NEXXUS VENTURES; *U.S. Private,* pg. 2922
NGA HOLDCO, LLC; *U.S. Private,* pg. 2923
NGP ENERGY CAPITAL MANAGEMENT, LLC; *U.S. Private,* pg. 2923
NICOLAS BERGGRUEN HOLDINGS GMBH—See Berggruen Holdings, Inc.; *U.S. Private,* pg. 531
NICOLET CAPITAL PARTNERS, LLC; *U.S. Private,* pg. 2926
NIELSEN INNOVATE FUND, LP—See Brookfield Corporation; *Int'l,* pg. 1179
NIELSEN INNOVATE FUND, LP—See Elliott Management Corporation; *U.S. Private,* pg. 1371
NIGHTDRAGON ACQUISITION CORP.; *U.S. Public,* pg. 1528
N.I.S. FINANCIAL SERVICES, INC.—See Prosperity Group Holdings, LP; *U.S. Private,* pg. 3289
NNG FINANCIAL CORPORATION—See Northwest Natural Holding Company; *U.S. Public,* pg. 1542
NN INVESTMENT PARTNERS BELGIUM N.V.—See The Goldman Sachs Group, Inc.; *U.S. Public,* pg. 2082
NN INVESTMENT PARTNERS (FRANCE) S.A.—See The Goldman Sachs Group, Inc.; *U.S. Public,* pg. 2082
NN INVESTMENT PARTNERS SPAIN—See The Goldman Sachs Group, Inc.; *U.S. Public,* pg. 2082
NOBEL BIOCARE HOLDING USA INC.—See Danaher Corporation; *U.S. Public,* pg. 629
NOBLE EDUCATION ACQUISITION CORP.; *U.S. Public,* pg. 1531
NOCTURNE ACQUISITION CORPORATION; *U.S. Public,* pg. 1531
NOGIN, INC.; *U.S. Public,* pg. 1532
NONANTUM CAPITAL PARTNERS LLC; *U.S. Private,* pg. 2934
NOOTEBOOM BIDCO B.V.—See BENCIS Capital Partners B.V.; *Int'l,* pg. 970
NORMACO LTD.—See Axel Johnson Gruppen AB; *Int'l,* pg. 765
NORMANDY REAL ESTATE MANAGEMENT, LLC—See Allianz SE; *Int'l,* pg. 346
NORTH AMERICA FRAC SAND, INC.; *U.S. Public,* pg. 1536
NORTH BRANCH CAPITAL, LLC; *U.S. Private,* pg. 2942
NORTH BRIDGE VENTURE MANAGEMENT COMPANY, INC.; *U.S. Private,* pg. 2942
NORTH CASTLE PARTNERS, LLC; *U.S. Private,* pg. 2943
NORTH CENTRAL EQUITY LLC; *U.S. Private,* pg. 2943
NORTH COAST TECHNOLOGY INVESTORS, L.P.; *U.S. Private,* pg. 2944
NORTH COVE PARTNERS; *U.S. Private,* pg. 2944
NORTHERN PACIFIC GROUP; *U.S. Private,* pg. 2954
THE NORTHERN TRUST COMPANY OF NEW YORK—See Northern Trust Corporation; *U.S. Public,* pg. 1539
NORTHERN TRUST LUXEMBOURG MANAGEMENT COMPANY S.A.—See Northern Trust Corporation; *U.S. Public,* pg. 1538

523999 — MISCELLANEOUS FINAN... CORPORATE AFFILIATIONS

NORTHERN TRUST SECURITIES SERVICES (IRELAND) LIMITED—See Northern Trust Corporation; *U.S. Public*, pg. 1538
NORTH EUROPEAN OIL ROYALTY TRUST; *U.S. Public*, pg. 1536
NORTHLAND INVESTMENT CORPORATION; *U.S. Private*, pg. 2955
NORTHLANE CAPITAL PARTNERS, LLC; *U.S. Private*, pg. 2955
NORTH MOUNTAIN MERGER CORP.; *U.S. Public*, pg. 1537
NORTHRIDGE CORP.; *U.S. Private*, pg. 2957
NORTHRIDGE FINANCE LTD.—See Bank of Ireland Group plc; *Int'l*, pg. 845
NORTH RIVER CAPITAL LLC; *U.S. Private*, pg. 2946
NORTHSIGHT CAPITAL, INC.; *U.S. Public*, pg. 1541
NORTH SQUARE INVESTMENTS, LLC—See Estancia Capital Management, LLC; *U.S. Private*, pg. 1428
NORTHSTAR CAPITAL, LLC; *U.S. Private*, pg. 2957
NORTHVIEW ACQUISITION CORPORATION; *U.S. Public*, pg. 1541
NORTHWEST BANK & TRUST COMPANY; *U.S. Private*, pg. 2959
NORTHWEST COMMUNITY CREDIT UNION; *U.S. Private*, pg. 2959
NORTHWESTERN MUTUAL INVESTMENT SERVICES, LLC—See The Northwestern Mutual Life Insurance Company; *U.S. Private*, pg. 4085
NORWEST EQUITY PARTNERS IX, LP—See Wells Fargo & Company; *U.S. Public*, pg. 2344
NORWEST MEZZANINE PARTNERS—See Wells Fargo & Company; *U.S. Public*, pg. 2344
NORWEST VENTURE CAPITAL MANAGEMENT, INC.—See Wells Fargo & Company; *U.S. Public*, pg. 2344
NORWEST VENTURE PARTNERS; *U.S. Private*, pg. 2964
NOVA INFRASTRUCTURE MANAGEMENT, LLC; *U.S. Private*, pg. 2965
NOVAK BIDDLE VENTURE PARTNERS, LP; *U.S. Private*, pg. 2966
NOVAQUEST CAPITAL MANAGEMENT, LLC; *U.S. Private*, pg. 2967
NOVA TECH ENTERPRISES, INC.; *U.S. Public*, pg. 1547
NOVATION HOLDINGS, INC.; *U.S. Private*, pg. 2967
NOVIDAM CAPITAL LLC; *U.S. Private*, pg. 2968
NRC GROUP HOLDINGS CORP.—See Republic Services, Inc.; *U.S. Public*, pg. 1788
NRD CAPITAL MANAGEMENT, LLC; *U.S. Private*, pg. 2969
N.R. INVESTMENTS INC; *U.S. Private*, pg. 2828
N.R. INVESTMENTS, INC.—See N.R. Investments Inc.; *U.S. Private*, pg. 2828
NRX PHARMACEUTICALS, INC.; *U.S. Public*, pg. 1551
NTK IMMOBILIEN GMBH & CO. MANAGEMENT KG—See DZ BANK AG Deutsche Zentral-Genossenschaftsbank; *Int'l*, pg. 2244
NTP (CHINA) INVESTMENT CO., LTD.—See China NT Pharma Group Company Limited; *Int'l*, pg. 1536
NUBURU, INC.; *U.S. Public*, pg. 1553
NUETERRA CAPITAL MANAGEMENT, LLC; *U.S. Private*, pg. 2972
NUKKLEUS INC; *U.S. Public*, pg. 1555
NURAL ENTERPRISE SDN BHD—See Berjaya Corporation Berhad; *Int'l*, pg. 983
NUSCALE POWER CORPORATION—See Fluor Corporation; *U.S. Public*, pg. 859
NUSENDA CREDIT UNION; *U.S. Private*, pg. 2973
NUVEEN DIVERSIFIED COMMODITY FUND—See Teachers Insurance Association - College Retirement Fund; *U.S. Private*, pg. 3946
NUVEEN INVESTMENTS, INC.—See Teachers Insurance Association - College Retirement Fund; *U.S. Private*, pg. 3947
NUVEEN LONG/SHORT COMMODITY TOTAL RETURN FUND—See Teachers Insurance Association - College Retirement Fund; *U.S. Private*, pg. 3946
NUVEEN NEW YORK SELECT TAX-FREE INCOME PORTFOLIO—See Teachers Insurance Association - College Retirement Fund; *U.S. Private*, pg. 3946
NUVEEN SELECT TAX FREE INCOME PORT 2—See Teachers Insurance Association - College Retirement Fund; *U.S. Private*, pg. 3947
NWL FINANCIAL, INC.—See Prosperity Group Holdings, LP; *U.S. Private*, pg. 3289
NYSE TECHNOLOGIES, INC.—See Intercontinental Exchange, Inc.; *U.S. Public*, pg. 1143
O2 AERO ACQUISITIONS LLC; *U.S. Private*, pg. 2981
O2 INVESTMENT PARTNERS, LLC; *U.S. Private*, pg. 2982
OAK HILL ADVISORS SARL—See T. Rowe Price Group Inc.; *U.S. Public*, pg. 1978
OAK HILL CAPITAL MANAGEMENT, LLC—See Keystone Group, L.P.; *U.S. Private*, pg. 2299
OAK HILL CAPITAL PARTNERS, L.P.—See Keystone Group, L.P.; *U.S. Private*, pg. 2296
OAKLAND STANDARD CO., LLC; *U.S. Private*, pg. 2984
OAK LANE PARTNERS, LLC; *U.S. Private*, pg. 2983
OAK STREET REAL ESTATE CAPITAL, LLC—See Blue Owl Capital Inc.; *U.S. Public*, pg. 364

OAKTREE CAPITAL (BEIJING) LTD.—See Brookfield Corporation; *Int'l*, pg. 1182
OAKTREE CAPITAL (HONG KONG) LTD.—See Brookfield Corporation; *Int'l*, pg. 1182
OAKTREE CAPITAL MANAGEMENT LIMITED—See Brookfield Corporation; *Int'l*, pg. 1182
OAKTREE CAPITAL MANAGEMENT, L.P.—See Brookfield Corporation; *Int'l*, pg. 1181
OAKTREE CAPITAL MANAGEMENT PTE. LTD.—See Brookfield Corporation; *Int'l*, pg. 1182
OAKTREE CAPITAL (SEOUL) LIMITED—See Brookfield Corporation; *Int'l*, pg. 1182
OAKTREE FRANCE S.A.S.—See Brookfield Corporation; *Int'l*, pg. 1182
OAKTREE GARDENS OLP, LLC; *U.S. Private*, pg. 2985
OAKTREE GMBH—See Brookfield Corporation; *Int'l*, pg. 1182
OAKTREE JAPAN, GK—See Brookfield Corporation; *Int'l*, pg. 1182
OAKTREE OVERSEAS INVESTMENT FUND MANAGEMENT (SHANGHAI) CO., LTD.—See Brookfield Corporation; *Int'l*, pg. 1182
OBRA CAPITAL, INC.; *U.S. Private*, pg. 2987
OBSERVER CAPITAL LLC; *U.S. Private*, pg. 2987
OBSIDIAN HOLDINGS LLC—See Goff Capital, Inc.; *U.S. Private*, pg. 1726
OCA ACQUISITION CORP.; *U.S. Public*, pg. 1560
OCEAN DRIVE ACQUISITION CORP.; *U.S. Private*, pg. 2989
OCEAN GROUP INVESTMENTS LIMITED—See Deutsche Post AG; *Int'l*, pg. 2082
OCEANSOUND PARTNERS, LP; *U.S. Private*, pg. 2990
OCEANTECH ACQUISITIONS I CORP.; *U.S. Public*, pg. 1563
OCE-FRANCE FINANCEMENT S.A.—See Canon Inc.; *Int'l*, pg. 1294
OCONEE FINANCIAL CORP.; *U.S. Public*, pg. 1563
OCTAGON HOLDINGS, LLC; *U.S. Private*, pg. 2992
ODYSSEY INVESTMENT PARTNERS, LLC; *U.S. Private*, pg. 2994
OERLIKON VACUUM HOLDING GMBH—See Atlas Copco AB; *Int'l*, pg. 684
OFB BETEILIGUNGEN GMBH—See Helaba Landesbank Hessen-Thuringen; *Int'l*, pg. 3328
OFS CAPITAL CORPORATION; *U.S. Public*, pg. 1564
OFS CREDIT COMPANY, INC; *U.S. Public*, pg. 1564
OHA INVESTMENT CORPORATION—See Portman Ridge Finance Corporation; *U.S. Public*, pg. 1702
OICCO ACQUISITION III, INC.; *U.S. Private*, pg. 3006
OKAPI VENTURE CAPITAL, LLC; *U.S. Private*, pg. 3006
OLB-BETEILIGUNGSGESELLSCHAFT MBH—See Allianz SE; *Int'l*, pg. 354
OLB-SERVICE GMBH—See Allianz SE; *Int'l*, pg. 355
OLIVER WYMAN S.L.—See Marsh & McLennan Companies, Inc.; *U.S. Public*, pg. 1387
OLYMPUS CAPITAL HOLDINGS ASIA; *U.S. Private*, pg. 3012
OLYMPUS CAPITAL INVESTMENTS, LLC—See Olympus Holdings, LLC; *U.S. Private*, pg. 3013
OLYMPUS PARTNERS; *U.S. Private*, pg. 3013
OMEGA ALPHA SPAC; *U.S. Public*, pg. 1571
OMEGA FINANCIAL, LLC—See GI Manager L.P.; *U.S. Private*, pg. 1694
OMEGA III INVESTMENT CO.—See Tristar Holdings Inc.; *U.S. Private*, pg. 4238
OMEGA OPTICAL HOLDINGS INC.—See EssilorLuxottica SA; *Int'l*, pg. 2513
OMNIAB, INC.; *U.S. Public*, pg. 1572
OMNICAS MANAGEMENT AG—See BAWAG Group AG; *Int'l*, pg. 900
OMNICHANNEL ACQUISITION CORP.; *U.S. Public*, pg. 1573
OMNICOM CAPITAL INC—See Omnicom Group Inc.; *U.S. Public*, pg. 1589
OMNI HEALTH, INC.; *U.S. Private*, pg. 3016
OMNI INVESTORS PTE. LTD—See Adval Tech Holding AG; *Int'l*, pg. 155
OMNI VENTURES, INC.; *U.S. Private*, pg. 3016
THE ONCOLOGY INSTITUTE, INC.; *U.S. Public*, pg. 2118
ONE2ONE LIVING CORPORATION; *U.S. Private*, pg. 3024
THE ONE GROUP HOSPITALITY, INC.; *U.S. Public*, pg. 2118
ONELIFE TECHNOLOGIES CORP.; *U.S. Public*, pg. 1602
ONEMAIN FINANCE CORPORATION; *U.S. Private*, pg. 3025
ONEPATH FUNDS MANAGEMENT LIMITED—See Australia & New Zealand Banking Group Limited; *Int'l*, pg. 720
ONE ROCK CAPITAL PARTNERS, LLC; *U.S. Private*, pg. 3020
ONE STONE ENERGY PARTNERS, L.P.; *U.S. Private*, pg. 3023
ONEY POLSKA S.A.—See Groupe BPCE; *Int'l*, pg. 3099
ON FINANCE SA—See EFG International AG; *Int'l*, pg. 2321
ONLINE 401(K); *U.S. Private*, pg. 3026
ON-POINT GROUP, LLC; *U.S. Private*, pg. 3018
ONS ACQUISITION CORP.; *U.S. Public*, pg. 1605
ONSLOW BAY FINANCIAL LLC—See Annaly Capital Management, Inc.; *U.S. Public*, pg. 138

ONTARIO LIMITED—See Allianz SE; *Int'l*, pg. 355
ONTHEMARKET PLC—See CoStar Group, Inc.; *U.S. Public*, pg. 586
ON THE MOVE CORP.; *U.S. Private*, pg. 3018
ONWARD CAPITAL LLC; *U.S. Private*, pg. 3028
OPAL ISLAND ACQUISITION CORPORATION; *U.S. Private*, pg. 3028
OPB VERWALTUNGS- UND TREUHAND GMBH—See Deutsche Bank Aktiengesellschaft; *Int'l*, pg. 2061
OPENDEAL INC.; *U.S. Private*, pg. 3030
OPENGATE CAPITAL MANAGEMENT, LLC; *U.S. Private*, pg. 3030
OPEN LENDING CORPORATION; *U.S. Public*, pg. 1606
THE OPERAND GROUP II LLC; *U.S. Private*, pg. 4088
OPES ADVISORS, INC.—See New York Community Bancorp, Inc.; *U.S. Public*, pg. 1513
OPPFI INC.; *U.S. Public*, pg. 1608
OPTIMAL INVESTMENT SERVICES S.A.—See Banco Santander, S.A.; *Int'l*, pg. 826
OPTIONABLE, INC.; *U.S. Private*, pg. 3035
THE OPTIONS CLEARING CORP.; *U.S. Private*, pg. 4089
OPTUM FINANCIAL, INC.—See UnitedHealth Group Incorporated; *U.S. Public*, pg. 2248
OPUS CAPITAL LLC; *U.S. Private*, pg. 3036
ORANCO, INC.; *U.S. Public*, pg. 1614
ORANGE CAPITAL VENTURES GP, LLC; *U.S. Private*, pg. 3036
ORANGEHOOK, INC.; *U.S. Public*, pg. 1614
ORANGEWOOD PARTNERS LLC; *U.S. Private*, pg. 3038
ORBIMED ADVISORS LLC; *U.S. Private*, pg. 3038
ORBIS INVESTMENT LTD.—See Amdocs Limited; *Int'l*, pg. 420
ORCHARD HOLDINGS GROUP LLC; *U.S. Private*, pg. 3039
ORCHID ISLAND CAPITAL, INC.; *U.S. Public*, pg. 1615
ORCHID VENTURES, INC.; *U.S. Public*, pg. 1615
O'REILLY ALPHATECH VENTURES—See O'Reilly Media, Inc.; *U.S. Private*, pg. 2980
OREY FINANCIAL - INSTITUICAO FINANCEIRA DE CREDITO, SA—See Caixa Geral de Depositos S.A.; *Int'l*, pg. 1260
ORIENTAL MAGIC SOUP, INC.; *U.S. Public*, pg. 1617
ORIGIN MATERIALS, INC.; *U.S. Public*, pg. 1617
ORIGO ACQUISITION CORPORATION; *U.S. Private*, pg. 3042
ORION ACQUISITION CORP.; *U.S. Public*, pg. 1617
ORION BIOTECH OPPORTUNITIES CORP.; *U.S. Public*, pg. 1617
ORION FINANCIAL CORP.; *U.S. Private*, pg. 3043
ORISUN ACQUISITION CORP.—See Ucommune International Ltd.; *U.S. Public*, pg. 2217
ORIZZONTE SGR S.P.A.—See HAT Sicaf S.p.A; *Int'l*, pg. 3284
THE OROGEN GROUP; *U.S. Private*, pg. 4089
ORTEL MOBILE HOLDING B.V.—See CVC Capital Partners SICAV-FIS S.A.; *Int'l*, pg. 1884
ORTHOPEDIE INVESTMENTS EUROPE B.V.—See HAL Trust N.V.; *Int'l*, pg. 3224
OS ACQUISITION CORP.; *U.S. Public*, pg. 1619
OSHKOSH ITALY B.V.—See Oshkosh Corporation; *U.S. Public*, pg. 1621
OSPREY CAPITAL LLC; *U.S. Private*, pg. 3048
OSSIAM SA—See Groupe BPCE; *Int'l*, pg. 3099
OTIS GMBH & CO. OHG—See Otis Worldwide Corporation; *U.S. Public*, pg. 1623
OTR ACQUISITION CORP.; *U.S. Public*, pg. 1623
OTTAWA AVENUE PRIVATE CAPITAL, LLC—See RDV Corporation; *U.S. Private*, pg. 3364
OUDART GESTION SA—See EFG International AG; *Int'l*, pg. 2320
OU SKIP BELEGGINGS PROPRIETARY LIMITED—See Barclays PLC; *Int'l*, pg. 862
OVER FIFTY FUNDS MANAGEMENT PTY LTD—See Centuria Capital Limited; *Int'l*, pg. 1416
OWNER RESOURCE GROUP, LLC; *U.S. Private*, pg. 3055
OXFORD FINANCIAL GROUP LTD.; *U.S. Private*, pg. 3057
THE OXFORD INVESTMENT GROUP, INC.; *U.S. Private*, pg. 4089
OXFORD LANE CAPITAL CORP.; *U.S. Public*, pg. 1629
OYSTER ENTERPRISES ACQUISITION CORP.; *U.S. Public*, pg. 1629
P2 CAPITAL PARTNERS, LLC; *U.S. Private*, pg. 3061
P3 HEALTH PARTNERS INC.; *U.S. Public*, pg. 1630
P4G CAPITAL MANAGEMENT, LLC; *U.S. Private*, pg. 3062
PACELINE EQUITY PARTNERS LLC; *U.S. Private*, pg. 3064
PACER CORPORATION; *U.S. Private*, pg. 3064
PACIFIC AVENUE CAPITAL PARTNERS, LLC; *U.S. Private*, pg. 3065
PACIFIC COAST OIL TRUST—See Pacific Coast Energy Company LP; *U.S. Private*, pg. 3066
PACIFIC NORTHWEST CAPITAL CORP.; *U.S. Private*, pg. 3069
PACIFICO ACQUISITION CORP.—See Caravelle International Group; *Int'l*, pg. 1320
PACIFIC PROPERTIES III; *U.S. Private*, pg. 3070
P.A.G. CAPITAL PARTNERS, LLC; *U.S. Private*, pg. 3060

N.A.I.C.S. INDEX 523999 — MISCELLANEOUS FINAN...

PAINE SCHWARTZ PARTNERS, LLC; *U.S. Private*, pg. 3075

PALADIN HEALTHCARE CAPITAL, LLC; *U.S. Private*, pg. 3076

PALESTINE DEVELOPMENT & INVESTMENT LTD.—See Arab Supply & Trading Co.; *Int'l*, pg. 532

PALISADE CAPITAL MANAGEMENT, LLC; *U.S. Private*, pg. 3077

PALISADES ASSOCIATES, INC.; *U.S. Private*, pg. 3077

PALISADES GROWTH CAPITAL, LLC; *U.S. Private*, pg. 3077

PALLADIAN CAPITAL PARTNERS LLC; *U.S. Private*, pg. 3077

PALLADIN CONSUMER RETAIL PARTNERS, LLC; *U.S. Private*, pg. 3077

PALLADIUM EQUITY PARTNERS, LLC; *U.S. Private*, pg. 3077

PALLADYNE AI CORP.; *U.S. Public*, pg. 1634

PALLINGHURST ADVISORS LLP—See Gemfields Group Limited; *Int'l*, pg. 2916

PALM BEACH CAPITAL PARTNERS LLC; *U.S. Private*, pg. 3079

PALMER CAPITAL FONDSENBEHEER B.V.—See Fiera Capital Corporation; *Int'l*, pg. 2660

PALMER CAPITAL NEDERLAND N.V.—See Fiera Capital Corporation; *Int'l*, pg. 2660

PALO DURO CAPITAL, LLC; *U.S. Private*, pg. 3082

PALOMAR HOLDINGS, INC.; *U.S. Public*, pg. 1635

PANORAMA CAPITAL, LLC; *U.S. Private*, pg. 3087

PAPPAS VENTURES; *U.S. Private*, pg. 3088

PARABELLUM ACQUISITION CORP.; *U.S. Public*, pg. 1636

PARADIGM CAPITAL PARTNERS; *U.S. Private*, pg. 3089

PARALLAX CAPITAL PARTNERS, LLC; *U.S. Private*, pg. 3092

PARALLEL INVESTMENT PARTNERS LLC; *U.S. Private*, pg. 3092

PAR CAPITAL MANAGEMENT, INC.; *U.S. Private*, pg. 3089

PAREX ASSET MANAGEMENT RUSSIA—See AS Reverta; *Int'l*, pg. 591

PAREX ASSET MANAGEMENT—See AS Reverta; *Int'l*, pg. 591

PAREX ASSET MANAGEMENT UKRAINE—See AS Reverta; *Int'l*, pg. 591

PARICOMI 2 (EX-PARICOMI)—See BNP Paribas SA; *Int'l*, pg. 1092

PARILEASE SAS—See BNP Paribas SA; *Int'l*, pg. 1092

PARK AVENUE EQUITY PARTNERS, L.P.; *U.S. Private*, pg. 3095

PARK AVENUE FUNDING, LLC—See The Lightstone Group, LLC; *U.S. Private*, pg. 4070

PARKER HANNIFIN GLOBAL CAPITAL MANAGEMENT S.A R.L.—See Parker Hannifin Corporation; *U.S. Public*, pg. 1647

PARK HILL GROUP LLC—See Blackstone Inc.; *U.S. Public*, pg. 356

PARK SOUND ACQUISITION CORPORATION; *U.S. Private*, pg. 3096

PARKVIEW CAPITAL CREDIT, INC.; *U.S. Private*, pg. 3098

PARSEC CAPITAL ACQUISITION CORP.; *U.S. Public*, pg. 1650

PARTHENON CAPITAL PARTNERS - WEST COAST OFFICE—See PCP Enterprise, L.P.; *U.S. Private*, pg. 3121

PARTICIPATIE MAATSCHAPPIJ TRANSHOL B.V.—See Assicurazioni Generali S.p.A.; *Int'l*, pg. 648

PARTNER ONE SOFTWARE INC.—See Fonds de Solidarite des Travailleurs du Quebec; *Int'l*, pg. 2725

PARTNERS WEALTH MANAGEMENT LLP—See Caledonia Investments plc; *Int'l*, pg. 1262

PASSAGE SERVICES HOLDING GMBH—See Deutsche Lufthansa AG; *Int'l*, pg. 2070

PATIENT SQUARE CAPITAL, L.P.; *U.S. Private*, pg. 3106

PATRIARCH PARTNERS, LLC; *U.S. Private*, pg. 3109

PATRICIA ACQUISITION CORP.; *U.S. Private*, pg. 3110

PATRIOT FINANCIAL PARTNERS, L.P.—See Independence Capital Partners, LLC; *U.S. Private*, pg. 2056

PATTON ALBERTSON & MILLER GROUP, LLC—See Clayton, Dubilier & Rice, LLC; *U.S. Private*, pg. 923

PATTON ALBERTSON & MILLER GROUP, LLC—See Stone Point Capital LLC; *U.S. Private*, pg. 3824

PATUS 216 GMBH—See Barclays PLC; *Int'l*, pg. 862

PAXION CAPITAL, LP; *U.S. Private*, pg. 3115

PAYMENTECH SALEM SERVICES, LLC—See JPMorgan Chase & Co.; *U.S. Public*, pg. 1209

PAYONEER GLOBAL INC.; *U.S. Public*, pg. 1656

PBM CAPITAL GROUP, LLC; *U.S. Private*, pg. 3118

PCM FLOW TECHNOLOGY INC—See Gevelot S.A.; *Int'l*, pg. 2954

PCP ENTERPRISE, L.P.; *U.S. Private*, pg. 3121

PCT LTD; *U.S. Public*, pg. 1658

PEAKEQUITY PARTNERS; *U.S. Private*, pg. 3125

PEAK ROCK CAPITAL LLC; *U.S. Private*, pg. 3123

PEARL HOLDINGS ACQUISITION CORP.; *U.S. Private*, pg. 1660

PEARLMARK REAL ESTATE PARTNERS LLC; *U.S. Private*, pg. 3125

PEAR THERAPEUTICS, INC.; *U.S. Public*, pg. 1659

PEERLESS VALUE OPPORTUNITY FUND; *U.S. Private*, pg. 3129

PEGASUS INVESTMENT COMPANY LIMITED—See Centremanor Ltd.; *Int'l*, pg. 1412

PEKAO LEASING HOLDING S.A.—See Bank Polska Kasa Opieki Spolka Akcyjna; *Int'l*, pg. 849

PELOTON EQUITY LLC; *U.S. Private*, pg. 3131

PENINSULA CAPITAL PARTNERS LLC; *U.S. Private*, pg. 3133

PENINSULA PACIFIC STRATEGIC PARTNERS, LLC; *U.S. Private*, pg. 3133

PENNSPRING CAPITAL, LLC; *U.S. Private*, pg. 3136

PENTA LAS AMERICAS ADMINISTRADORA DE FONDOS DE INVERSION SA—See Empresas Penta S.A.; *Int'l*, pg. 2391

PEONY GROVE ACQUISITION CORP; *U.S. Private*, pg. 3140

PEPPERLIME HEALTH ACQUISITION CORPORATION; *U.S. Public*, pg. 1668

PEPPERTREE CAPITAL MANAGEMENT, INC.; *U.S. Private*, pg. 3145

PE PROJEKT-ENTWICKLUNGSGESELLSCHAFT MBH—See Erste Abwicklungsanstalt AoR; *Int'l*, pg. 2497

PERCEPTIVE ADVISORS, LLC; *U.S. Private*, pg. 3146

PERELLA WEINBERG PARTNERS LP; *U.S. Public*, pg. 1674

PERELLA WEINBERG UK LIMITED—See Perella Weinberg Partners LP; *U.S. Public*, pg. 1674

PERFICIENT, INC. - NEW YORK—See EQT AB; *Int'l*, pg. 2483

PERFORMANT MANAGEMENT COMPANY, LLC; *U.S. Private*, pg. 3150

PERGO HOLDING B. V.—See Mohawk Industries, Inc.; *U.S. Public*, pg. 1458

PERIGON WEALTH MANAGEMENT LLC; *U.S. Private*, pg. 3150

PERIPHAS CAPITAL PARTNERING CORPORATION; *U.S. Public*, pg. 1676

PERISCOPE EQUITY LLC; *U.S. Private*, pg. 3151

PERLOWIN DEVELOPMENT CORP.; *U.S. Private*, pg. 3152

PERMAL CAPITAL MANAGEMENT, LLC; *U.S. Private*, pg. 3152

PERMAL GROUP LTD.—See Franklin Resources, Inc.; *U.S. Public*, pg. 882

PERMANENT EQUITY MANAGEMENT, LLC; *U.S. Private*, pg. 3152

PERMIT CAPITAL ADVISORS, LLC—See Genstar Capital, LLC; *U.S. Private*, pg. 1676

PERPETUAL CAPITAL, LLC; *U.S. Private*, pg. 3152

PERRY HILL ACQUISITION CORPORATION; *U.S. Private*, pg. 3154

PERSEPHONE CAPITAL PARTNERS LLC; *U.S. Private*, pg. 3154

PERSEUS LLC; *U.S. Private*, pg. 3155

PERSHING SQUARE TONTINE HOLDINGS, LTD.; *U.S. Public*, pg. 1677

PERSIL-ALTERSUNTERSTUTZUNG GMBH—See Henkel AG & Co. KGaA; *Int'l*, pg. 3354

PETER J. SOLOMON COMPANY—See Groupe BPCE; *Int'l*, pg. 3095

PETER P. BOLLINGER INVESTMENT CO.; *U.S. Private*, pg. 3159

PETERSON PARTNERS, INC.; *U.S. Private*, pg. 3160

PETRA ACQUISITION, INC.; *U.S. Private*, pg. 3161

PETRA CAPITAL MANAGEMENT LLC; *U.S. Private*, pg. 3161

PETRA CAPITAL PARTNERS, LLC; *U.S. Private*, pg. 3161

PETRON ENERGY II, INC.; *U.S. Public*, pg. 3163

PETRUS RESOURCES CORPORATION; *U.S. Private*, pg. 3163

PFINGSTEN PARTNERS, LLC; *U.S. Private*, pg. 3164

PFISTER HOLDING GMBH—See FLSmidth & Co. A/S; *Int'l*, pg. 2712

PFM FINANCIAL ADVISORS LLC—See Public Financial Management, Inc.; *U.S. Private*, pg. 3299

PFO GLOBAL, INC.; *U.S. Public*, pg. 1683

PFS INVESTMENTS, INC.—See Primerica, Inc.; *U.S. Public*, pg. 1717

PFSL INVESTMENTS CANADA LTD.—See Primerica, Inc.; *U.S. Public*, pg. 1717

PG&E ENERGY RECOVERY FUNDING LLC—See PG&E Corporation; *U.S. Public*, pg. 1684

PGIM QUANTITATIVE SOLUTIONS LLC—See Prudential Financial, Inc.; *U.S. Public*, pg. 1731

PGIM WADHWANI LLP—See Prudential Financial, Inc.; *U.S. Public*, pg. 1731

PHAROS CAPITAL GROUP, LLC; *U.S. Private*, pg. 3166

PHENIXFIN CORP.; *U.S. Public*, pg. 1684

PHI CAPITAL HOLDINGS, INC.—See Philux Global Group Inc; *U.S. Public*, pg. 1689

PHILLIPS EDISON GROCERY CENTER REIT II, INC.—See Phillips Edison & Company LLC; *U.S. Private*, pg. 3170

PHILUX GLOBAL GROUP INC; *U.S. Public*, pg. 1688

PHOENIX ASSET MANAGEMENT LLC; *U.S. Private*, pg. 3172

PHOENIX BIOTECH ACQUISITION CORP.; *U.S. Public*, pg. 1689

PHOENIX COCA-COLA BOTTLING COMPANY—See The Coca-Cola Company; *U.S. Public*, pg. 2065

PHX AP ACQUISITIONS LLC; *U.S. Private*, pg. 3174

PHYSICIANS REALTY TRUST—See Healthpeak Properties, Inc.; *U.S. Public*, pg. 1016

THE PICERNE GROUP, INC.; *U.S. Private*, pg. 4095

PIERMONT WEALTH MANAGEMENT, INC.—See TA Associates, Inc.; *U.S. Private*, pg. 3919

PILGRIM CAPITAL PARTNERS, LLC; *U.S. Private*, pg. 3180

PILLARSTONE EUROPE LLP—See KKR & Co. Inc.; *U.S. Public*, pg. 1263

PILLARSTONE GREECE—See KKR & Co. Inc.; *U.S. Public*, pg. 1263

PILLARSTONE ITALY S.P.A.—See KKR & Co. Inc.; *U.S. Public*, pg. 1263

PILOT GROUP, LLC; *U.S. Private*, pg. 3181

PIMCO ASIA LTD.—See Allianz SE; *Int'l*, pg. 346

PIMCO ASIA PTE. LTD.—See Allianz SE; *Int'l*, pg. 346

PIMCO AUSTRALIA PTY LTD.—See Allianz SE; *Int'l*, pg. 346

PIMCO CANADA CORP.—See Allianz SE; *Int'l*, pg. 346

PIMCO CAPITAL SOLUTIONS BDC CORP.; *U.S. Private*, pg. 3181

PIMCO DEUTSCHLAND GMBH—See Allianz SE; *Int'l*, pg. 347

PIMCO DYNAMIC CREDIT INCOME FUND; *U.S. Private*, pg. 3181

PIMCO DYNAMIC INCOME FUND; *U.S. Public*, pg. 1690

PIMCO EUROPE LTD.—See Allianz SE; *Int'l*, pg. 346

PIMCO GLOBAL ADVISORS (IRELAND) LTD.—See Allianz SE; *Int'l*, pg. 355

PIMCO JAPAN LTD.—See Allianz SE; *Int'l*, pg. 346

PIMCO (SWITZERLAND) LLC—See Allianz SE; *Int'l*, pg. 347

PIMCO TAIWAN LTD.—See Allianz SE; *Int'l*, pg. 355

PINE BROOK PARTNERS, LLC; *U.S. Private*, pg. 3182

PINE CREEK PARTNERS, LLC; *U.S. Private*, pg. 3182

PINECREST CAPITAL PARTNERS, LLC; *U.S. Private*, pg. 3183

PINE ISLAND ACQUISITION CORP.; *U.S. Public*, pg. 1691

PINE ISLAND CAPITAL PARTNERS LLC; *U.S. Private*, pg. 3182

PINE RIVER CAPITAL MANAGEMENT, LP; *U.S. Private*, pg. 3182

PINE STREET ALTERNATIVE ASSET MANAGEMENT LP; *U.S. Private*, pg. 3183

PINE TECHNOLOGY ACQUISITION CORP.; *U.S. Public*, pg. 1691

PINNACLE CAPITAL PARTNERS, LLC—See Alliance Funding Group, Inc.; *U.S. Private*, pg. 182

PINNACLE HOLDINGS LIMITED—See Alviva Holdings Limited; *Int'l*, pg. 402

PINNACLE INVESTMENT SERVICES, INC.—See Pinnacle Financial Corporation; *U.S. Private*, pg. 3185

PIONEER ELECTRONICS ASIACENTRE PTE. LTD.—See EQT AB; *Int'l*, pg. 2470

PISCES NOMINEES LIMITED—See Commerzbank AG; *Int'l*, pg. 1719

PIVOTAL ACQUISITION CORP.; *U.S. Private*, pg. 3192

PIVOTAL GROUP, INC.; *U.S. Private*, pg. 3192

PIVOTAL GROUP, INC.; *U.S. Private*, pg. 3192

PLANET FINANCIAL GROUP, LLC; *U.S. Private*, pg. 3196

PLANET HOME LENDING, LLC—See Planet Financial Group, LLC; *U.S. Private*, pg. 3196

PLATFORM CAPITAL, LLC; *U.S. Private*, pg. 3200

PLATFORM PARTNERS LLC; *U.S. Private*, pg. 3200

PLATINUM EAGLE MORTGAGE, LLC—See Rithm Capital Corp.; *U.S. Public*, pg. 1800

PLATINUM EQUITY, LLC - NEW YORK—See Platinum Equity, LLC; *U.S. Private*, pg. 3207

PLATINUM EQUITY, LLC; *U.S. Private*, pg. 3200

PLATINUM TAX DEFENDERS, LLC—See Cardiff Lexington Corporation; *U.S. Public*, pg. 433

PLATTE RIVER VENTURES, LLC; *U.S. Private*, pg. 3211

PLAYSTUDIOS, INC.; *U.S. Public*, pg. 1698

PLAZA BELMONT MANAGEMENT GROUP II LLC; *U.S. Private*, pg. 3212

PLBY GROUP, INC.; *U.S. Public*, pg. 1698

PLEDGE PETROLEUM CORP.; *U.S. Private*, pg. 3213

PLEXUS CAPITAL, LLC; *U.S. Private*, pg. 3214

P & LS HOLDING GMBH—See BWT Aktiengesellschaft; *Int'l*, pg. 1233

PLUM ACQUISITION CORP. III; *U.S. Public*, pg. 1699

PLURIBUS CAPITAL MANAGEMENT LLC; *U.S. Private*, pg. 3215

PLUTONIAN ACQUISITION CORP.; *U.S. Public*, pg. 1699

PLYMOUTH HEALTH—See CareNex Health Services; *U.S. Private*, pg. 753

PMV CONSUMER ACQUISITION CORP.; *U.S. Public*, pg. 1700

PNC CAPITAL FINANCE, LLC—See The PNC Financial Services Group, Inc.; *U.S. Public*, pg. 2119

PNC COMMUNITY DEVELOPMENT CORP.—See The PNC Financial Services Group, Inc.; *U.S. Public*, pg. 2120

PNC INVESTMENT CORP.—See The PNC Financial Services Group, Inc.; *U.S. Public*, pg. 2120

PNC RIVERARCH CAPITAL—See The PNC Financial Services Group, Inc.; *U.S. Public*, pg. 2119

POEMA GLOBAL HOLDINGS CORP.; *U.S. Public*, pg. 1700

523999 — MISCELLANEOUS FINAN... CORPORATE AFFILIATIONS

POINCARE CAPITAL MANAGEMENT LTD.—See Groupe BPCE; *Int'l*, pg. 3099
POINT JUDITH CAPITAL PARTNERS, LLC; *U.S. Private*, pg. 3222
POLARIS VENTURE MANAGEMENT CO., LLC; *U.S. Private*, pg. 3223
POLARIS VENTURE PARTNERS—See Polaris Venture Management Co., LLC; *U.S. Private*, pg. 3223
POLHEM INFRA AB—See Fjarde AP-fonden; *Int'l*, pg. 2697
POLHEM INFRA AB—See Forsta AP-fonden; *Int'l*, pg. 2737
POLISERVICE B.V.—See ASR Nederland N.V.; *Int'l*, pg. 632
POLLACK SHORES REAL ESTATE GROUP, LLC; *U.S. Private*, pg. 3224
POLY (CHONGQING) INVESTMENT INDUSTRY CO., LTD.—See China Poly Group Corporation; *Int'l*, pg. 1541
POLY (GUANGZHOU) INTERNATIONAL TRADE INVESTMENT CO., LTD.—See China Poly Group Corporation; *Int'l*, pg. 1541
POLY (HONG KONG) HOLDINGS LIMITED—See China Poly Group Corporation; *Int'l*, pg. 1541
PONO CAPITAL TWO, INC.; *U.S. Public*, pg. 1701
PONTEM CORPORATION; *U.S. Public*, pg. 1701
POPLAR CAPITAL PARTNERS LLC; *U.S. Private*, pg. 3228
POPULAR GESTION SGIIC, S.A.—See Allianz SE; *Int'l*, pg. 355
POPULATION HEALTH INVESTMENT CO., INC.; *U.S. Public*, pg. 1702
PORCH GROUP, INC.; *U.S. Public*, pg. 1702
PORTFOLIO SOLUTIONS, LLC.; *U.S. Private*, pg. 3232
PORTIGON FINANCIAL SERVICES GMBH—See Erste Abwicklungsanstalt AoR; *Int'l*, pg. 2497
PORTMAN RIDGE FINANCE CORPORATION; *U.S. Public*, pg. 1702
POST ACUTE PARTNERS, LLC; *U.S. Private*, pg. 3234
POST CAPITAL PARTNERS, LLC; *U.S. Private*, pg. 3234
POST HOLDINGS PARTNERING CORPORATION; *U.S. Public*, pg. 1703
POST OFFICE FINANCIAL & TRAVEL SERVICES—See Bank of Ireland Group plc; *Int'l*, pg. 844
POTOMAC EQUITY PARTNERS, LLC; *U.S. Private*, pg. 3235
POUSCHINE COOK CAPITAL MANAGEMENT LLC; *U.S. Private*, pg. 3236
POWERCOMM HOLDINGS INC.; *U.S. Private*, pg. 3239
POWER & DIGITAL INFRASTRUCTURE ACQUISITION CORP.; *U.S. Public*, pg. 1705
POWERED BRANDS; *U.S. Public*, pg. 1705
POWERGEN LUXEMBOURG HOLDINGS SARL—See E.ON SE; *Int'l*, pg. 2258
POWERUP ACQUISITION CORP.; *U.S. Public*, pg. 1706
PPC INVESTMENT PARTNERS LP—See The Pritzker Group - Chicago, LLC; *U.S. Private*, pg. 4098
PRAETORIAN PROPERTY, INC.; *U.S. Public*, pg. 1712
PRAMERICA INVESTMENT MANAGEMENT LIMITED—See Prudential Financial, Inc.; *U.S. Public*, pg. 1732
PRAMERICA SYSTEMS IRELAND LIMITED—See Prudential Financial, Inc.; *U.S. Public*, pg. 1732
PRAZSKA PLYNARENSKA HOLDING A.S.—See E.ON SE; *Int'l*, pg. 2259
PRECISION FRANCHISING LLC—See Icahn Enterprises L.P.; *U.S. Public*, pg. 1085
PREMIA HOLDINGS LTD—See Kelso & Company, L.P.; *U.S. Private*, pg. 2279
PRENTICE CAPITAL MANAGEMENT, LP; *U.S. Private*, pg. 3252
PRESIDENTIAL REALTY CORPORATION; *U.S. Public*, pg. 1715
THE PRESIDIO GROUP LLC; *U.S. Private*, pg. 4098
PRESIDIO INVESTORS LLC; *U.S. Private*, pg. 3254
PRESIDIO PARTNERS; *U.S. Private*, pg. 3255
PRESTICINQUE S.P.A.—See BPER BANCA S.p.A; *Int'l*, pg. 1132
PRESTIGE CAPITAL CORPORATION; *U.S. Private*, pg. 3255
PRESTON HOLLOW COMMUNITY CAPITAL, INC.; *U.S. Public*, pg. 1716
PRETIUM PARTNERS, LLC; *U.S. Private*, pg. 3257
PRIMARY ENERGY VENTURES LLC—See EPCOR Utilities, Inc.; *Int'l*, pg. 2459
PRIMAVERA CAPITAL ACQUISITION CORPORATION—See Fosun International Limited; *Int'l*, pg. 2751
PRIMUS AUTOMOTIVE FINANCIAL SERVICES, INC.—See Ford Motor Company; *U.S. Public*, pg. 866
PRIMUS AUTOMOTIVE FINANCIAL SERVICES LIMITED—See Ford Motor Company; *U.S. Public*, pg. 866
PRIMUS CAPITAL PARTNERS, INC.; *U.S. Private*, pg. 3263
PRINCETON CAPITAL CORPORATION; *U.S. Public*, pg. 1719
PRINCIPAL ASSET MANAGEMENT BERHAD—See Principal Financial Group, Inc.; *U.S. Public*, pg. 1720
PRINCIPAL PENSIONES, S.A. DE C.V.—See Principal Financial Group, Inc.; *U.S. Public*, pg. 1721
PRIORITY TECHNOLOGY HOLDINGS, INC.; *U.S. Public*, pg. 1722

PRISM VENTURE MANAGEMENT, LLC; *U.S. Private*, pg. 3267
PRITCHARD EQUITY LIMITED—See Bendigo & Adelaide Bank Ltd.; *Int'l*, pg. 971
THE PRITZKER GROUP - CHICAGO, LLC; *U.S. Private*, pg. 4098
THE PRITZKER GROUP - LA, LLC—See The Pritzker Group - Chicago, LLC; *U.S. Private*, pg. 4098
PRIVATE EQUITY CAPITAL CORPORATION; *U.S. Private*, pg. 3268
PRIVATE EQUITY GROUP; *U.S. Private*, pg. 3268
PRIVATE VISTA LLC; *U.S. Private*, pg. 3268
PRIVET FUND MANAGEMENT, LLC; *U.S. Private*, pg. 3268
PROBILITY MEDIA CORPORATION; *U.S. Public*, pg. 1723
PRODOS CAPITAL MANAGEMENT LLC; *U.S. Private*, pg. 3272
PROFICIENT ALPHA ACQUISITION CORP.; *U.S. Public*, pg. 1724
PROFIDIS—See Carrefour SA; *Int'l*, pg. 1346
PROGRESS ACQUISITION CORP.; *U.S. Public*, pg. 1724
PROGRESS EQUITY PARTNERS, LLC; *U.S. Private*, pg. 3278
PROGRESSIVE GREEN SOLUTIONS, INC.; *U.S. Public*, pg. 1726
PROGRESS PARTNERS, INC.; *U.S. Private*, pg. 3278
PROGRESS VENTURES, INC.—See Progress Partners, Inc.; *U.S. Private*, pg. 3278
PROJECT ENERGY REIMAGINED ACQUISITION CORP.; *U.S. Public*, pg. 1726
PROJECT HOLLYWOOD LLC; *U.S. Private*, pg. 3280
PROJEKTENTWICKLUNGSGESELLSCHAFT GARTENSTADT WILDAU ROTHEGRUND II MBH—See Erste Abwicklungsanstalt AoR; *Int'l*, pg. 2497
PROMETHEUM, INC.; *U.S. Public*, pg. 3282
PROMETHEUS PARTNERS, L.P.; *U.S. Private*, pg. 3283
PROMUS EQUITY PARTNERS, LLC—See Promus Holdings, LLC; *U.S. Private*, pg. 3283
PROPEL EQUITY PARTNERS, LLC; *U.S. Private*, pg. 3284
THE PROPERTY DIRECTORY LIMITED—See Coventry Building Society; *Int'l*, pg. 1821
PROPERTY RESOURCES CORP.; *U.S. Private*, pg. 3285
PROPHET EQUITY L.P.; *U.S. Private*, pg. 3286
PROSPECT HILL GROWTH PARTNERS, L.P.; *U.S. Private*, pg. 3288
PROSPECT PARTNERS, LLC; *U.S. Private*, pg. 3288
PROSPECT PROPERTY GROUP; *U.S. Private*, pg. 3288
PROTECTAGROUP ACQUISITIONS LTD—See CCV Risk Solutions Limited; *Int'l*, pg. 1370
PROTEK CAPITAL, INC.; *U.S. Public*, pg. 1729
PROTERRA, INC.; *U.S. Public*, pg. 1729
PROTERRA INVESTMENT PARTNERS LP; *U.S. Private*, pg. 3290
PROVIDENCE EQUITY ADVISORS INDIA PRIVATE LIMITED—See Providence Equity Partners L.L.C.; *U.S. Private*, pg. 3293
PROVIDENCE EQUITY ASIA LIMITED—See Providence Equity Partners L.L.C.; *U.S. Private*, pg. 3293
PROVIDENCE EQUITY INVESTMENT CONSULTING (BEIJING) CO., LTD.—See Providence Equity Partners L.L.C.; *U.S. Private*, pg. 3293
PROVIDENCE EQUITY LLC—See Providence Equity Partners L.L.C.; *U.S. Private*, pg. 3293
PROVIDENCE EQUITY LLP—See Providence Equity Partners L.L.C.; *U.S. Private*, pg. 3293
PROVIDENCE EQUITY PARTNERS L.L.C.; *U.S. Private*, pg. 3291
PRUDENTIAL ANNUITIES LIFE ASSURANCE CORPORATION—See The Carlyle Group Inc.; *U.S. Public*, pg. 2047
PRUDENTIAL ANNUITIES—See Prudential Financial, Inc.; *U.S. Public*, pg. 1732
PRUDENTIAL EQUITY GROUP, LLC—See Prudential Financial, Inc.; *U.S. Public*, pg. 1732
PRUDENTIAL INVESTMENTS, INC—See Bank of the Philippine Islands; *Int'l*, pg. 849
PSC METALS - ALLIANCE, LLC—See Icahn Enterprises L.P.; *U.S. Public*, pg. 1084
PSC METALS - METALLICS, LLC—See Icahn Enterprises L.P.; *U.S. Public*, pg. 1085
PSC METALS - MITCO, LLC—See Icahn Enterprises L.P.; *U.S. Public*, pg. 1085
PSG EQUITY L.L.C.; *U.S. Private*, pg. 3297
PSILOS GROUP MANAGERS, LLC; *U.S. Private*, pg. 3297
PSP CAPITAL PARTNERS, LLC; *U.S. Private*, pg. 3297
PT ASURANSI JIWA GENERALI INDONESIA—See Assicurazioni Generali S.p.A.; *Int'l*, pg. 647
PT AXA MANDIRI FINANCIAL SERVICES—See AXA S.A.; *Int'l*, pg. 759
PT BANK ANZ INDONESIA—See Australia & New Zealand Banking Group Limited; *Int'l*, pg. 720
P.T. DBS VICKERS SEKURITAS INDONESIA—See DBS Group Holdings Ltd.; *Int'l*, pg. 1988
PT FEDERAL INTERNATIONAL—See Federal International (2000) Ltd; *Int'l*, pg. 2630
PT. IFS CAPITAL INDONESIA—See IFS Capital Limited; *Int'l*, pg. 3600
PTK ACQUISITION CORP.; *U.S. Public*, pg. 1735
PUBLIC JOINT STOCK COMPANY "BANK FORUM"—See Commerzbank AG; *Int'l*, pg. 1719

PUBLIC PENSION CAPITAL, LLC; *U.S. Private*, pg. 3300
PULTE ACQUISITION CORP.; *U.S. Private*, pg. 3303
PUREBASE CORPORATION; *U.S. Public*, pg. 1738
PURE PORTFOLIOS HOLDINGS, LLC—See tru Independce LLC; *U.S. Private*, pg. 4244
PWP GROWTH EQUITY LLC—See Perella Weinberg Partners LP; *U.S. Public*, pg. 1674
PYRAMID ADVISORS LLC; *U.S. Private*, pg. 3309
PYRAMIS GLOBAL ADVISORS, LLC—See FMR LLC; *U.S. Private*, pg. 1555
PYROPHYTE ACQUISITION CORP.; *U.S. Public*, pg. 1739
Q BLACK, LLC; *U.S. Private*, pg. 3311
QELL ACQUISITION CORP.; *U.S. Public*, pg. 1742
QHP CAPITAL, L.P.; *U.S. Private*, pg. 3313
QIANSUI INTERNATIONAL GROUP CO., LTD.; *U.S. Public*, pg. 1743
QOMOLANGMA ACQUISITION CORP.; *U.S. Public*, pg. 1743
QONTIGO INDEX GMBH—See Deutsche Borse AG; *Int'l*, pg. 2064
QUAD-C MANAGEMENT, INC.; *U.S. Private*, pg. 3315
QUAD PARTNERS, LLC; *U.S. Private*, pg. 3314
QUADRANGLE GROUP LLC; *U.S. Private*, pg. 3316
QUADRANT MANAGEMENT, INC.; *U.S. Private*, pg. 3316
QUADRO ACQUISITION ONE CORP.; *U.S. Public*, pg. 1745
QUAESTUS HOLDINGS, LLC; *U.S. Private*, pg. 3316
QUAKER PARTNERS MANAGEMENT, L.P.—See Independence Capital Partners, LLC; *U.S. Private*, pg. 2057
QUALCOMM VENTURES—See QUALCOMM Incorporated; *U.S. Public*, pg. 1748
QUALITY MOTORS LIMITED—See Honda Motor Co., Ltd.; *Int'l*, pg. 3464
QUALTEK SERVICES INC.; *U.S. Public*, pg. 1748
QUANTITATIVE BROKERS LLC—See Deutsche Borse AG; *Int'l*, pg. 2064
QUANTITATIVE BROKERS UK LIMITED—See Deutsche Borse AG; *Int'l*, pg. 2064
QUANTUM FINTECH ACQUISITION CORPORATION; *U.S. Public*, pg. 1754
QUANTUMSCAPE CORPORATION; *U.S. Public*, pg. 1754
QUANTUM-SI INCORPORATED; *U.S. Public*, pg. 1754
QUARRY CAPITAL MANAGEMENT LLC; *U.S. Private*, pg. 3324
QUEEN'S GAMBIT GROWTH CAPITAL; *U.S. Public*, pg. 1755
QUESADA KAPITALFORVALTNING AB—See EFG International AG; *Int'l*, pg. 2321
QUETTA ACQUISITION CORPORATION; *U.S. Public*, pg. 1756
QUINTANA CAPITAL GROUP, L.P.; *U.S. Private*, pg. 3328
QUINZEL ACQUISITION COMPANY; *U.S. Public*, pg. 3328
QUODD FINANCIAL INFORMATION SERVICES, INC—See NewSpring Capital LLC; *U.S. Private*, pg. 2917
QURUM BUSINESS GROUP GEOJIT SECURITIES LLC—See Geojit Financial Services Limited; *Int'l*, pg. 2933
RABO PRIVATE EQUITY—See Cooperatieve Centrale Raiffeisen-Boerenleenbank B.A.; *Int'l*, pg. 1792
RACEBROOK CAPITAL ADVISORS, LLC; *U.S. Private*, pg. 3341
RADLER ENTERPRISES INC.; *U.S. Private*, pg. 3345
RAF INDUSTRIES, INC.; *U.S. Private*, pg. 3345
RAGLAN RESOURCES LIMITED—See Dickson Concepts (International) Limited; *Int'l*, pg. 2112
RAIFF PARTNERS, INC.; *U.S. Private*, pg. 3346
RAINSBERGER WEALTH ADVISORS, INC.—See Affiliated Managers Group, Inc.; *U.S. Public*, pg. 56
RAINSBERGER WEALTH ADVISORS, INC.—See HGGC, LLC; *U.S. Private*, pg. 1930
RAKUTEN SECURITIES AUSTRALIA PTY. LTD.—See AT Global Markets (UK) Limited; *Int'l*, pg. 664
RAMEX, INC.; *U.S. Private*, pg. 3351
RAMPART STUDIOS INC.—See Rampart Capital Corporation; *U.S. Private*, pg. 3352
RAND CAPITAL CORPORATION; *U.S. Public*, pg. 1762
RAND CAPITAL SBIC, INC.—See Rand Capital Corporation; *U.S. Public*, pg. 1762
RAND LOGISTICS, INC.—See AIP, LLC; *U.S. Private*, pg. 135
RANGE LIGHT LLC; *U.S. Private*, pg. 3354
RANPAK HOLDINGS CORP.; *U.S. Public*, pg. 1763
RAPID THERAPEUTIC SCIENCE LABORATORIES, INC.; *U.S. Public*, pg. 1763
RAVEN CAPITAL MANAGEMENT LLC—See MetLife, Inc.; *U.S. Public*, pg. 1430
RAVENNA KRAKOW SP. Z.O.O.—See Commerzbank AG; *Int'l*, pg. 1719
RAYCLIFF CAPITAL; *U.S. Private*, pg. 3359
RAYMOND JAMES CAPITAL, INC.—See Raymond James Financial, Inc.; *U.S. Public*, pg. 1764
RB FIDUCIARIA S.P.A—See Allianz SE; *Int'l*, pg. 355
RCF ACQUISITION CORP.; *U.S. Public*, pg. 1767
RCF MANAGEMENT LLC; *U.S. Private*, pg. 3361
RCM CAPITAL MANAGEMENT PTY LTD—See Allianz SE; *Int'l*, pg. 346
RCM (UK) LTD.—See Allianz SE; *Int'l*, pg. 355
R&D BUSINESS FACTORY CO., LTD.—See Fukuoka Fi-

N.A.I.C.S. INDEX 523999 — MISCELLANEOUS FINAN...

N.A.I.C.S. Index

nancial Group, Inc.; *Int'l*, pg. 2840
READY CREDIT CORP.; *U.S. Public*, pg. 1768
REAL FINANCE ASSET MANAGEMENT JSC—See Holding Varna AD-Varna; *Int'l*, pg. 3450
REALIGN CAPITAL STRATEGIES; *U.S. Private*, pg. 3368
REAL I.S. MANAGEMENT SA—See BayernLB Holding AG; *Int'l*, pg. 914
RECHARGE ACQUISITION CORP.; *U.S. Public*, pg. 1769
RECOGNISE BANK LIMITED—See City of London Group PLC; *Int'l*, pg. 1627
RED ARTS CAPITAL, LLC; *U.S. Private*, pg. 3373
REDBALL ACQUISITION CORP.; *U.S. Public*, pg. 1770
REDBIRD CAPITAL PARTNERS L.P.; *U.S. Private*, pg. 3377
REDBOX ENTERTAINMENT INC.—See Chicken Soup for the Soul Entertainment, Inc.; *U.S. Public*, pg. 488
RED CELL DRM ACQUISITION CORP.; *U.S. Public*, pg. 1769
RED DOG EQUITY LLC; *U.S. Private*, pg. 3374
RED MOUNTAIN CAPITAL PARTNERS LLC; *U.S. Private*, pg. 3375
REDWOOD CAPITAL GROUP, LLC; *U.S. Private*, pg. 3380
REDWOOD CAPITAL INVESTMENTS, LLC; *U.S. Private*, pg. 3380
REDWOOD FINANCIAL, INC.; *U.S. Public*, pg. 1771
REDWOOD INVESTMENTS LLC; *U.S. Private*, pg. 3381
REDWOODS ACQUISITION CORP.; *U.S. Public*, pg. 1771
RED ZONE LLC; *U.S. Private*, pg. 3376
REGATTA MEDICAL HOLDINGS LLC—See GTCR LLC; *U.S. Private*, pg. 1806
REGENCY AFFILIATES, INC.; *U.S. Public*, pg. 1774
REGENT, L.P.; *U.S. Private*, pg. 3387
REGENT SQUARE CAPITAL, LLC; *U.S. Private*, pg. 3387
REGUS ADVISORS, INC.; *U.S. Private*, pg. 3389
RELATIVE VALUE INVESTMENTS UK LIMITED LIABILITY PARTNERSHIP—See Barclays PLC; *Int'l*, pg. 862
RELEASE S.P.A.—See Banco BPM S.p.A.; *Int'l*, pg. 819
RELIABILITY INCORPORATED; *U.S. Public*, pg. 1778
RELIANCE AEROTECH INC.; *U.S. Private*, pg. 3394
REMITLY U.K., LTD.—See Remitly Global, Inc.; *U.S. Public*, pg. 1782
RENAISSANCE ASSET FINANCE LIMITED—See Arbuthnot Banking Group plc; *Int'l*, pg. 539
THE RENAISSANCE GROUP LLC; *U.S. Private*, pg. 4104
RENEWABLE ENERGY ACQUISITION CORP.; *U.S. Private*, pg. 3398
RENEWAL FUELS, INC.; *U.S. Public*, pg. 1783
RENOSUN INTERNATIONAL SDN. BHD.—See Annica Holdings Limited; *Int'l*, pg. 474
RENOSY FINANCE INC.—See GAtechnologies Co., Ltd.; *Int'l*, pg. 2889
RENOVO CAPITAL, LLC; *U.S. Private*, pg. 3399
RENSBURG FUND MANAGEMENT LIMITED—See Franklin Resources, Inc.; *U.S. Public*, pg. 883
REORG RESEARCH, INC.—See Warburg Pincus LLC; *U.S. Private*, pg. 4439
REPAY HOLDINGS CORPORATION; *U.S. Public*, pg. 1784
RESERVE GROUP MANAGEMENT COMPANY; *U.S. Private*, pg. 3404
RESERVOIR CAPITAL GROUP, L.L.C.; *U.S. Private*, pg. 3405
RESILIENCE CAPITAL PARTNERS, LLC; *U.S. Private*, pg. 3405
RESOLUTE ADMINISTRATION, INC.; *U.S. Private*, pg. 3406
RESONANCE EMERGING MARKETS MACRO TRUST; *U.S. Private*, pg. 3406
RESOURCE AMERICA, INC.—See Island Capital Group LLC; *U.S. Private*, pg. 2144
RESURGENS TECHNOLOGY PARTNERS, LLC; *U.S. Private*, pg. 3410
RETAILCO, LLC—See TxEx Energy Investments, LLC; *U.S. Private*, pg. 4267
RETAIL OPPORTUNITY INVESTMENTS CORP.; *U.S. Public*, pg. 1792
REVELATION BIOSCIENCES, INC.; *U.S. Public*, pg. 1792
REVELSTOKE CAPITAL PARTNERS LLC; *U.S. Private*, pg. 3413
REVELSTONE CAPITAL ACQUISITION CORP.; *U.S. Public*, pg. 1792
REVERENCE ACQUISITION CORP.; *U.S. Public*, pg. 1793
REVERENCE CAPITAL PARTNERS LLC; *U.S. Private*, pg. 3414
REVOLUTION CAPITAL GROUP, LLC; *U.S. Private*, pg. 3416
REVOLUTION HEALTHCARE ACQUISITION CORP.; *U.S. Public*, pg. 1793
REVOLUTION II WI HOLDING COMPANY, LLC—See Mountain Capital Partners, LP; *U.S. Private*, pg. 2799
REVOLUTION, LLC; *U.S. Private*, pg. 3416
REX AMERICAN RESOURCES CORPORATION; *U.S. Public*, pg. 1795
REXIT, INC.; *U.S. Private*, pg. 3417
RFE INVESTMENT PARTNERS; *U.S. Private*, pg. 3419
R/GA VENTURES LLC—See The Interpublic Group of Companies, Inc.; *U.S. Public*, pg. 2104
R. HASLER AG—See Heliad AG; *Int'l*, pg. 3329
RHEA, S.A.—See Allianz SE; *Int'l*, pg. 355
RHEINENERGIE WINDKRAFT GMBH—See Electricite de France S.A.; *Int'l*, pg. 2350
RHINO NOVI, INC.; *U.S. Public*, pg. 1796
RHO CAPITAL PARTNERS, INC.; *U.S. Private*, pg. 3421
RHODE INVESTMENTS LLC—See Goff Capital, Inc.; *U.S. Private*, pg. 1726
RHONE CAPITAL LLC—See Rhone Group, LLC; *U.S. Private*, pg. 3422
RHON-INNOVATIONS GMBH—See Asklepios Kliniken GmbH & Co. KGaA; *Int'l*, pg. 624
RHO VENTURES LLC—See Rho Capital Partners, Inc.; *U.S. Private*, pg. 3421
RH RETAIL HOLDING GMBH—See Aurelius Equity Opportunities SE & Co. KGaA; *Int'l*, pg. 709
RIBBIT LEAP, LTD.; *U.S. Public*, pg. 1796
RICEPOINT ADMINISTRATION INC.—See Computershare Limited; *Int'l*, pg. 1760
RICHSPACE ACQUISITION CORP.; *U.S. Public*, pg. 1798
RIDGEFIELD ACQUISITION CORP.; *U.S. Public*, pg. 1798
RIDGEMONT PARTNERS MANAGEMENT LLC; *U.S. Private*, pg. 3432
RIFT VALLEY EQUITY PARTNERS, LLC; *U.S. Private*, pg. 3435
RIGEL RESOURCE ACQUISITION CORP.; *U.S. Public*, pg. 1798
RIGHT LANE ACQUISITION I, INC.; *U.S. Private*, pg. 3435
THE RIKOON GROUP, LLC—See Lee Equity Partners LLC; *U.S. Private*, pg. 2412
RIORDAN, LEWIS & HADEN, INC.; *U.S. Private*, pg. 3439
RIPPLE INDUSTRIES LLC; *U.S. Private*, pg. 3439
RIPPLEWOOD HOLDINGS LLC; *U.S. Private*, pg. 3439
THE RISE FUND—See TPG Capital, L.P.; *U.S. Public*, pg. 2177
RISKMETRICS GROUP, LLC—See MSCI Inc.; *U.S. Public*, pg. 1483
RISKMETRICS (UK) LTD.—See MSCI Inc.; *U.S. Public*, pg. 1483
RIVENROCK CAPITAL LLC; *U.S. Private*, pg. 3443
RIVER ASSOCIATES INVESTMENTS, LLC; *U.S. Private*, pg. 3443
RIVER CITIES CAPITAL FUNDS; *U.S. Private*, pg. 3443
RIVER OAKS BANK BUILDING, INC.—See Banco Bilbao Vizcaya Argentaria, S.A.; *Int'l*, pg. 818
THE RIVERSIDE COMPANY - CLEVELAND OFFICE—See The Riverside Company; *U.S. Private*, pg. 4110
THE RIVERSIDE COMPANY - DALLAS OFFICE—See The Riverside Company; *U.S. Private*, pg. 4110
THE RIVERSIDE COMPANY; *U.S. Private*, pg. 4107
RIVERSIDE PARTNERS, LLC; *U.S. Private*, pg. 3445
RIVERSTONE HOLDINGS LLC - HOUSTON OFFICE—See Riverstone Holdings LLC; *U.S. Private*, pg. 3447
RIVERSTONE HOLDINGS LLC; *U.S. Private*, pg. 3447
RIVERTY GROUP GMBH—See Bertelsmann SE & Co. KGaA; *Int'l*, pg. 996
RIVERVIEW ACQUISITION CORP.—See Westrock Coffee Company; *U.S. Public*, pg. 2361
RIVERWOOD CAPITAL LP; *U.S. Private*, pg. 3448
RIZVI TRAVERSE MANAGEMENT LLC; *U.S. Private*, pg. 3449
RLJ EQUITY PARTNERS LLC—See The RLJ Companies, LLC; *U.S. Private*, pg. 4110
RMB ASSET MANAGEMENT (PTY) LIMITED—See FirstRand Limited; *Int'l*, pg. 2690
RMB CORVEST (PTY) LTD.—See FirstRand Limited; *Int'l*, pg. 2690
RMBL MISSOURI, LLC—See RumbleON, Inc.; *U.S. Public*, pg. 1826
RMB PRIVATE EQUITY HOLDINGS (PTY) LTD—See FirstRand Limited; *Int'l*, pg. 2690
RMG ACQUISITION CORP.; *U.S. Public*, pg. 1802
RML - RESIDENCIA MEDICALIZADA DE LOURES, SGPS, S.A.—See Fosun International Limited; *Int'l*, pg. 2751
RMR PREFERRED INCOME FUND; *U.S. Private*, pg. 3452
ROARK CAPITAL GROUP INC.; *U.S. Private*, pg. 3454
ROARK CAPITAL MANAGEMENT, LLC—See Roark Capital Group Inc.; *U.S. Private*, pg. 3455
ROBERT FLEMING HOLDINGS LIMITED—See JPMorgan Chase & Co.; *U.S. Public*, pg. 1210
ROCH CAPITAL INC.; *U.S. Private*, pg. 3463
ROCKBRIDGE GROWTH EQUITY, LLC; *U.S. Private*, pg. 3465
ROCKEFELLER CAPITAL MANAGEMENT; *U.S. Private*, pg. 3466
ROCKET COMPANIES, INC.; *U.S. Public*, pg. 1804
ROCKET GLOBAL ACQUISTION CORP.; *U.S. Private*, pg. 3466
ROCK GATE PARTNERS LLC; *U.S. Private*, pg. 3464
ROCK HILL CAPITAL GROUP, LLC; *U.S. Private*, pg. 3464
ROCK ISLAND CAPITAL LLC; *U.S. Private*, pg. 3464
ROCKLAND CAPITAL, LLC; *U.S. Private*, pg. 3467
ROCKWOOD EQUITY PARTNERS, LLC; *U.S. Private*, pg. 3468
ROEBLING MANAGEMENT COMPANY, LLC; *U.S. Private*, pg. 3470
RORINE INTERNATIONAL HOLDING CORPORATION; *U.S. Public*, pg. 1814
ROSE HILL ACQUISITION CORPORATION; *U.S. Public*, pg. 1814
ROSE PARK ADVISORS LLC; *U.S. Private*, pg. 3481
THE ROSEVIEW GROUP LLC—See Madison Marquette Development Corporation; *U.S. Private*, pg. 2544
ROSTER FINANCIAL LLC—See Allianz SE; *Int'l*, pg. 355
ROTH CH ACQUISITION CO.; *U.S. Public*, pg. 1815
ROTUNDA CAPITAL PARTNERS LLC; *U.S. Private*, pg. 3487
ROUND TABLE CAPITAL MANAGEMENT, LP; *U.S. Private*, pg. 3488
ROUNDTABLE HEALTHCARE MANAGEMENT, INC.; *U.S. Private*, pg. 3488
ROWENA AG.—See Hinduja Group Ltd.; *Int'l*, pg. 3399
ROYAL GOLD, INC.; *U.S. Public*, pg. 1815
ROYALTY MANAGEMENT HOLDING CORPORATION—See American Acquisition Opportunity, Inc.; *U.S. Public*, pg. 95
RPC PACKAGING HOLDINGS BV—See Berry Global Group, Inc; *U.S. Public*, pg. 324
RREEF MANAGEMENT LLC—See Deutsche Bank Aktiengesellschaft; *Int'l*, pg. 2057
RREEF MANAGEMENT LLC—See Deutsche Bank Aktiengesellschaft; *Int'l*, pg. 2057
RREEF PROPERTY TRUST, INC.—See Deutsche Bank Aktiengesellschaft; *Int'l*, pg. 2058
RREEF SPEZIAL INVEST GMBH—See Deutsche Bank Aktiengesellschaft; *Int'l*, pg. 2061
RTW BIOTECH OPPORTUNITIES LTD.—See RTW Investments, LP; *U.S. Private*, pg. 3498
RTW INVESTMENTS, LP; *U.S. Private*, pg. 3498
RUBICON TECHNOLOGY PARTNERS, LLC; *U.S. Private*, pg. 3499
RUCKER ITALIA S.R.L.—See ATON GmbH; *Int'l*, pg. 689
RUCKER SR SPOL.S.R.O. I.L.—See ATON GmbH; *Int'l*, pg. 689
RUIYUAN CAPITAL ASSET MANAGEMENT CO., LTD.—See GF Securities Co., Ltd.; *Int'l*, pg. 2955
RUMBLEON, INC.; *U.S. Public*, pg. 1825
RUPE INVESTMENT CORPORATION; *U.S. Private*, pg. 3504
RUSTIC CANYON PARTNERS; *U.S. Private*, pg. 3507
RUTHENIUM INVESTMENTS LIMITED—See Barclays PLC; *Int'l*, pg. 863
RXR ACQUISITION CORP.; *U.S. Public*, pg. 1827
SABAL FINANCIAL EUROPE LIMITED—See Brookfield Corporation; *Int'l*, pg. 1182
SABAL FINANCIAL GROUP, L.P.—See Brookfield Corporation; *Int'l*, pg. 1182
SABAL TRUST COMPANY—See Sabal Holdings Inc.; *U.S. Private*, pg. 3520
SABAN CAPITAL GROUP, INC.; *U.S. Private*, pg. 3520
SAB BIOTHERAPEUTICS, INC.; *U.S. Public*, pg. 1832
SABER REAL ESTATE ADVISORS, LLC; *U.S. Private*, pg. 3520
SABIDO INVESTMENTS (PROPRIETARY) LIMITED—See Hosken Consolidated Investments Limited; *Int'l*, pg. 3485
SACE FCT S.P.A.—See Cassa Depositi e Prestiti S.p.A.; *Int'l*, pg. 1355
SACHEM ACQUISITION CORP.; *U.S. Public*, pg. 1834
SACK LUNCH PRODUCTIONS INC.; *U.S. Public*, pg. 1834
SACKVILLE TPEN PROPERTY (GP) LTD.—See Ameriprise Financial, Inc.; *U.S. Public*, pg. 114
SACKVILLE TSP PROPERTY (GP) LTD.—See Ameriprise Financial, Inc.; *U.S. Public*, pg. 114
SAF GAYRIMENKUL YATIRIM ORTAKLIGI A.S.—See Akis Gayrimenkul Yatirim Ortakligi A.S.; *Int'l*, pg. 263
SAGALIAM ACQUISITION CORP.; *U.S. Public*, pg. 1835
SAGE CAPITAL LLC; *U.S. Private*, pg. 3526
SAGE PARK, INC.; *U.S. Private*, pg. 3526
SAGEVIEW CAPITAL LP; *U.S. Private*, pg. 3527
SAGEWIND CAPITAL LLC; *U.S. Private*, pg. 3527
SAGREX HOLDING B.V.—See Heidelberg Materials AG; *Int'l*, pg. 3319
SAINT JAMES HOLDING & INVESTMENT COMPANY TRUST; *U.S. Private*, pg. 3529
SAINTS CAPITAL, LLC; *U.S. Private*, pg. 3530
SALLYPORT COMMERCIAL FINANCE, LLC; *U.S. Private*, pg. 3533
SALT CREEK CAPITAL MANAGEMENT, LLC; *U.S. Private*, pg. 3533
SAME DEUTZ-FAHR FINANCE SAS—See BNP Paribas SA; *Int'l*, pg. 1092
SAMSON CAPITAL ADVISORS LLC—See Fiera Capital Corporation; *Int'l*, pg. 2660
SAMUEL SCOTT FINANCIAL GROUP; *U.S. Private*, pg. 3538
SANCEM INVESTMENT PTE LTD—See EnGro Corporation Limited; *Int'l*, pg. 2435
SANDBRIDGE CAPITAL LLC; *U.S. Private*, pg. 3543
SANDBRIDGE X2 CORP.; *U.S. Public*, pg. 1839
SANDERLING VENTURES; *U.S. Private*, pg. 3543
SANDHURST TRUSTEES LIMITED—See Bendigo & Adelaide Bank Ltd.; *Int'l*, pg. 971
SANDLAPPER SECURITIES, LLC; *U.S. Private*, pg. 3544
SANDLER O'NEILL MORTGAGE FINANCE L.P.—See Piper Sandler Companies; *U.S. Public*, pg. 1694
SANDRIDGE MISSISSIPPIAN TRUST II—See SandRidge Energy, Inc.; *U.S. Public*, pg. 1840
SANDRIDGE MISSISSIPPIAN TRUST I—See SandRidge

523999 — MISCELLANEOUS FINAN...

Energy, Inc.; *U.S. Public*, pg. 1839
SANFORD C. BERNSTEIN LIMITED—See Equitable Holdings, Inc.; *U.S. Public*, pg. 789
SAN FRANCISCO EQUITY PARTNERS; *U.S. Private*, pg. 3540
SANIBEL CAPTIVA INVESTMENT ADVISERS, INC.—See The Sanibel Captiva Trust Company; *U.S. Private*, pg. 4114
THE SANIBEL CAPTIVA TRUST COMPANY; *U.S. Private*, pg. 4114
SAN LOTUS HOLDING INC.; *U.S. Private*, pg. 3541
SANTA BARBARA ASSET MANAGEMENT, LLC—See Teachers Insurance Association - College Retirement Fund; *U.S. Private*, pg. 3947
SANTA FE FINANCIAL CORPORATION—See InterGroup Corporation; *U.S. Public*, pg. 1144
SANTANDER CONSUMER BANK AG—See Banco Santander, S.A.; *Int'l*, pg. 826
SANTANDER CONSUMER, EFC, S.A.—See Banco Santander, S.A.; *Int'l*, pg. 827
SANTANDER CONSUMER FINANCE BENELUX B.V.—See Banco Santander, S.A.; *Int'l*, pg. 827
SANTANDER CONSUMER HOLDING GMBH—See Banco Santander, S.A.; *Int'l*, pg. 827
SANTANDER CONSUMER S.A.S.—See Banco Santander, S.A.; *Int'l*, pg. 827
SANTANDER CORPORATE & INVESTMENT BANKING—See Banco Santander, S.A.; *Int'l*, pg. 827
SAOTHAIR CAPITAL PARTNERS LLC; *U.S. Private*, pg. 3548
SARATOGA PARTNERS L.P.; *U.S. Private*, pg. 3549
SARDALEASING S.P.A.—See BPER BANCA S.p.A; *Int'l*, pg. 1132
SARISSA CAPITAL ACQUISITION CORP.; *U.S. Public*, pg. 1841
SATORI CAPITAL, LLC; *U.S. Private*, pg. 3553
SAUGATUCK CAPITAL COMPANY; *U.S. Private*, pg. 3554
SAVI FINANCIAL CORPORATION; *U.S. Public*, pg. 1842
THE SAVINGS BANK OF ROCKVILLE; *U.S. Private*, pg. 4114
SBI-HIKARI P.E. CO., LTD.—See Hikari Tsushin, Inc.; *Int'l*, pg. 3390
SCALECO MANAGEMENT LLC; *U.S. Private*, pg. 3560
SCANCEM CENTRAL AFRICA HOLDING 3 AB—See Heidelberg Materials AG; *Int'l*, pg. 3319
SCANLANKEMPERBARD COMPANIES, LLC; *U.S. Private*, pg. 3561
SCAPA (HK) HOLDINGS LTD—See Mativ Holdings, Inc.; *U.S. Public*, pg. 1397
SC BUCHAREST FINANCIAL PLAZZA SRL—See Erste Group Bank AG; *Int'l*, pg. 2499
S.C. GENAGRICOLA ROMANIA—See Assicurazioni Generali S.p.A.; *Int'l*, pg. 647
SC HOLDINGS CORP.; *U.S. Public*, pg. 1842
SCHOUW & CO. FINANS A/S—See Aktieselskabet Schouw & Co.; *Int'l*, pg. 266
SCHULTZE ASSET MANAGEMENT, LLC; *U.S. Private*, pg. 3570
SCHULTZE SPECIAL PURPOSE ACQUISITION CORP.; *U.S. Public*, pg. 1848
SCIENCE STRATEGIC ACQUISITION CORP. ALPHA; *U.S. Public*, pg. 1848
SCIENS CAPITAL MANAGEMENT LLC; *U.S. Private*, pg. 3574
SCIENS WATER OPPORTUNITIES MANAGEMENT, LLC—See Sciens Capital Management LLC; *U.S. Private*, pg. 3574
SCI PARCOLOG ISLE D'ABEAU 3—See Assicurazioni Generali S.p.A.; *Int'l*, pg. 647
SCOOBEEZ GLOBAL, INC.; *U.S. Public*, pg. 1849
SCOTT HILL ACQUISITION CORPORATION; *U.S. Private*, pg. 3577
SCOTTISH AMERICAN CAPITAL LLC; *U.S. Private*, pg. 3578
SCOTTISH AMERICAN INSURANCE GENERAL AGENCY, INC.; *U.S. Private*, pg. 3578
SCOTTISH BORDERS EDUCATION PARTNERSHIP HOLDINGS LTD.—See Bilfinger SE; *Int'l*, pg. 1028
SCOTTISHPOWER OVERSEAS HOLDINGS, LTD.—See Iberdrola, S.A.; *Int'l*, pg. 3574
SCOTTISH POWER UK HOLDINGS, LTD.—See Iberdrola, S.A.; *Int'l*, pg. 3573
SCOTT-MCRAE INVESTMENTS INC.—See Scott-McRae Automotive Group Inc.; *U.S. Private*, pg. 3578
SCOTTS-SIERRA INVESTMENTS, INC.—See The Scotts Miracle-Gro Company; *U.S. Public*, pg. 2127
SCP WORLDWIDE; *U.S. Private*, pg. 3579
SCREAMING EAGLE ACQUISITION CORP.; *U.S. Public*, pg. 1849
SCULPTOR CAPITAL MANAGEMENT EUROPE LIMITED—See Rithm Capital Corp.; *U.S. Public*, pg. 1800
SCVX CORP.; *U.S. Public*, pg. 1850
SDCL EDGE ACQUISITION CORPORATION; *U.S. Private*, pg. 3581
SEACOAST CAPITAL - SAN FRANCISCO—See Seacoast Capital; *U.S. Private*, pg. 3583
SEACOAST CAPITAL; *U.S. Private*, pg. 3583

SEALAND NATURAL RESOURCES INC.; *U.S. Private*, pg. 3584
SEAMLESS GROUP INC.—See Currenc Group Inc.; *U.S. Public*, pg. 611
SEAPORT CALIBRE MATERIALS ACQUISITION CORP.; *U.S. Public*, pg. 1855
SEAPORT CAPITAL, LLC; *U.S. Private*, pg. 3586
SEARCHLIGHT CAPITAL PARTNERS, L.P.; *U.S. Private*, pg. 3586
SEBASTIAN HOLDINGS, INC.; *U.S. Private*, pg. 3593
SE CAPITAL, LLC; *U.S. Private*, pg. 3582
SECOND CURVE CAPITAL, LLC; *U.S. Private*, pg. 3593
SECURCAPITAL HOLDINGS CORP.; *U.S. Public*, pg. 1855
SECURE INTERNATIONAL FINANCE CO. INC.—See Edward B. Beharry & Co. Ltd.; *Int'l*, pg. 2316
SECURISTYLE GROUP HOLDINGS LIMITED—See ASSA ABLOY AB; *Int'l*, pg. 640
SECURITIES AMERICA ADVISORS, INC.—See Reverence Capital Partners LLC; *U.S. Private*, pg. 3415
SECURITIES AMERICA FINANCIAL CORPORATION—See Reverence Capital Partners LLC; *U.S. Private*, pg. 3415
SECURITIES CLEARING AUTOMATED NETWORK SERVICES SDN BHD—See Bursa Malaysia Berhad; *Int'l*, pg. 1227
SECURITY CAPITAL RESEARCH & MANAGEMENT INCORPORATED—See JPMorgan Chase & Co.; *U.S. Public*, pg. 1210
SEEYOND SA—See Groupe BPCE; *Int'l*, pg. 3099
THE SEIDLER COMPANY, LLC; *U.S. Private*, pg. 4116
SEI EUROPEAN SERVICES LIMITED—See SEI Investments Company; *U.S. Public*, pg. 1856
SEI INVESTMENTS GLOBAL, LIMITED—See SEI Investments Company; *U.S. Public*, pg. 1857
SEI NOVUS UK—See SEI Investments Company; *U.S. Public*, pg. 1857
SELCO COMMUNITY CREDIT UNION; *U.S. Private*, pg. 3600
SELECTA GROUP B.V.—See Allianz SE; *Int'l*, pg. 355
SELECTA HOLDING AB—See Allianz SE; *Int'l*, pg. 355
SELECTA HOLDING LTD.—See Allianz SE; *Int'l*, pg. 355
SELECTA S.A.—See Allianz SE; *Int'l*, pg. 355
SEMCO ENERGY VENTURES, INC.—See AltaGas Ltd.; *Int'l*, pg. 384
SEMENTI ROSS S.R.L.—See Assicurazioni Generali S.p.A.; *Int'l*, pg. 648
SEMINOLE CAPITAL, LLC—See Seminole Holdings Group, LLC; *U.S. Private*, pg. 3604
SEMINOLE EQUITY INVESTMENTS, LLC—See Seminole Holdings Group, LLC; *U.S. Private*, pg. 3604
SEMPER PARATUS ACQUISITION CORPORATION; *U.S. Public*, pg. 1863
SENECA GLOBAL FUND, L.P.; *U.S. Private*, pg. 3606
SENIOR CREDIT INVESTMENTS, LLC; *U.S. Private*, pg. 3606
SENIOR FINANCE PROPRIETARY LIMITED—See Alexander Forbes Group Holdings Limited; *Int'l*, pg. 307
SENIOR LIFESTYLE CORPORATION; *U.S. Private*, pg. 3607
SENSIBILL INC.—See Q2 Holdings, Inc.; *U.S. Public*, pg. 1741
SENTINEL CAPITAL PARTNERS, L.L.C.; *U.S. Private*, pg. 3608
THE SENTINEL COMPANY—See NewSpring Capital LLC; *U.S. Private*, pg. 2918
SENTINEL ENERGY SERVICES INC.; *U.S. Private*, pg. 3609
SENTINEL HOLDINGS B.V.—See Eurocommercial Properties N.V.; *Int'l*, pg. 2534
SENTRY INVESTMENTS INC.—See CI Financial Corporation; *Int'l*, pg. 1601
SEP ACQUISITION CORP.; *U.S. Public*, pg. 1868
SEP GROWTH HOLDINGS CORP.; *U.S. Public*, pg. 3611
SEQUOIA CAPITAL CHINA—See Sequoia Capital Operations, LLC; *U.S. Private*, pg. 3612
SEQUOIA CAPITAL INDIA—See Sequoia Capital Operations, LLC; *U.S. Private*, pg. 3612
SEQUOIA CAPITAL ISRAEL—See Sequoia Capital Operations, LLC; *U.S. Private*, pg. 3612
SEQUOIA CAPITAL OPERATIONS, LLC; *U.S. Private*, pg. 3612
SERCOO GROUP GMBH—See CEZ, a.s.; *Int'l*, pg. 1427
SEREMBAN TWO HOLDINGS SDN BHD—See IJM Corporation Berhad; *Int'l*, pg. 3609
SERENT CAPITAL MANAGEMENT COMPANY, LLC; *U.S. Private*, pg. 3613
SERIESONE, LLC; *U.S. Private*, pg. 3613
SERVICE FINANCIAL, LLC; *U.S. Private*, pg. 3615
SERVICES LOGICIELS D'INTEGRATION BOURSIERE SA—See BNP Paribas SA; *Int'l*, pg. 1092
SES ADVISORS, INC.; *U.S. Private*, pg. 3617
SEVEN ACES LIMITED—See Trive Capital Inc.; *U.S. Private*, pg. 4240
SEVEN ISLANDS, INC.; *U.S. Public*, pg. 1873
SEVEN MILE CAPITAL PARTNERS, LLC; *U.S. Private*, pg. 3618
SEVEN POINT EQUITY PARTNERS, LLC; *U.S. Private*, pg. 3618

SEVENTURE PARTNERS—See Groupe BPCE; *Int'l*, pg. 3095
SEVENTY2 CAPITAL WEALTH MANAGEMENT LLC; *U.S. Private*, pg. 3619
SFW CAPITAL PARTNERS LLC; *U.S. Private*, pg. 3622
SHACKLETON EQUITY PARTNERS LLC; *U.S. Private*, pg. 3622
SHAMROCK CAPITAL ADVISORS, LLC; *U.S. Private*, pg. 3624
SHANDONG HI-SPEED NEW ENERGY GROUP LIMITED—See Beijing Enterprises Water Group Limited; *Int'l*, pg. 950
SHANGHAI FOSUN CAPITAL INVESTMENT MANAGEMENT CO., LTD.—See Fosun International Limited; *Int'l*, pg. 2752
SHANGHAI HANDPAL TRADING CO., LTD.—See 99 Loyalty Limited; *Int'l*, pg. 16
SHARECARE, INC.—See Altaris Capital Partners, LLC; *U.S. Private*, pg. 206
SHARESPOST, INC.; *U.S. Private*, pg. 3626
SHARIAH CAPITAL, INC.; *U.S. Private*, pg. 3626
SHARP FINANCE CORPORATION—See Hon Hai Precision Industry Co., Ltd.; *Int'l*, pg. 3458
SHARP INTERNATIONAL FINANCE (U.K.) PLC—See Hon Hai Precision Industry Co., Ltd.; *Int'l*, pg. 3458
SHEARSON AMERICAN REIT, INC.; *U.S. Private*, pg. 3629
SHELLPOINT PARTNERS LLC—See Rithm Capital Corp.; *U.S. Public*, pg. 1800
SHELTON CAPITAL MANAGEMENT; *U.S. Private*, pg. 3632
SHERBORNE INVESTORS MANAGEMENT LP; *U.S. Private*, pg. 3633
SHERBROOKE CAPITAL LLC; *U.S. Private*, pg. 3633
SHIDLER INVESTMENT COMPANY, LLC; *U.S. Private*, pg. 3635
SHORE CAPITAL PARTNERS, LLC; *U.S. Private*, pg. 3640
SHOREHILL CAPITAL LLC; *U.S. Private*, pg. 3641
SHORELINE EQUITY PARTNERS, LLC; *U.S. Private*, pg. 3641
SHOREVIEW INDUSTRIES, LLC; *U.S. Private*, pg. 3641
SHOULDERUP TECHNOLOGY ACQUISITION CORP.; *U.S. Public*, pg. 1875
SIBANNAC, INC.; *U.S. Public*, pg. 1876
SIDDHI ACQUISITION CORP.; *U.S. Public*, pg. 1876
SIENNA CAPITAL INTERNATIONAL LTD.—See Groupe Bruxelles Lambert SA; *Int'l*, pg. 3100
SIENNA CAPITAL S.A R.L.—See Groupe Bruxelles Lambert SA; *Int'l*, pg. 3101
SIERRA LAKE ACQUISITION CORP.; *U.S. Public*, pg. 1877
SIERRA VENTURES; *U.S. Private*, pg. 3648
SIGMABLEYZER INVESTMENT GROUP LLC; *U.S. Private*, pg. 3649
SIGMA MARINE & PROTECTIVE COATINGS HOLDING B.V—See PPG Industries, Inc.; *U.S. Public*, pg. 1710
SIGMA PARTNERS; *U.S. Private*, pg. 3648
SIGMA PRIME VENTURES, LLC—See Sigma Partners; *U.S. Private*, pg. 3649
SIGMA SYSTEMS GROUP (USA) INC.—See Hansen Technologies Limited; *Int'l*, pg. 3260
SIGNA 12 VERWALTUNGS GMBH—See Allianz SE; *Int'l*, pg. 355
SIGNAL HILL ACQUISITION CORP.; *U.S. Public*, pg. 1878
SIGNAL LAKE MANAGEMENT LLC; *U.S. Private*, pg. 3649
SIGNAL PEAK VENTURE PARTNERS, LLC; *U.S. Private*, pg. 3649
SIGNET ARMORLITE GERMANY HOLDING GMBH—See EssilorLuxottica SA; *Int'l*, pg. 2516
SIGNET LLC; *U.S. Private*, pg. 3650
SIKORSKY FINANCIAL CREDIT UNION; *U.S. Private*, pg. 3651
SILICON VALLEY BANK UK LIMITED—See Federal Deposit Insurance Corporation; *U.S. Private*, pg. 1487
SILLARS HOLDINGS LIMITED—See Downer EDI Limited; *Int'l*, pg. 2186
SILVERFERN CAPITAL MANAGEMENT, LLC; *U.S. Private*, pg. 3663
SILVERHAWK CAPITAL PARTNERS, LLC; *U.S. Private*, pg. 3663
SILVER LAKE ASIA LIMITED—See Silver Lake Group, LLC; *U.S. Private*, pg. 3655
SILVER LAKE EUROPE, LLP—See Silver Lake Group, LLC; *U.S. Private*, pg. 3655
SILVER LAKE GROUP, LLC; *U.S. Private*, pg. 3653
SILVER LAKE KRAFTWERK MANAGEMENT COMPANY, LLC—See Silver Lake Group, LLC; *U.S. Private*, pg. 3655
SILVER LAKE MANAGEMENT COMPANY SUMERU, LLC—See Silver Lake Group, LLC; *U.S. Private*, pg. 3655
SILVER LAKE MANAGEMENT, LLC—See Silver Lake Group, LLC; *U.S. Private*, pg. 3655
SILVER LANE ADVISORS LLC—See Raymond James Financial, Inc.; *U.S. Public*, pg. 1765
SILVERLEAF ADVISORS LLC; *U.S. Private*, pg. 3663
SILVER OAK SERVICES PARTNERS, LLC; *U.S. Private*, pg. 3661
SILVER PEAK PARTNERS; *U.S. Private*, pg. 3661

N.A.I.C.S. INDEX

523999 — MISCELLANEOUS FINAN...

SILVERPEAK STRATEGIC PARTNERS LP; *U.S. Private*, pg. 3663
SILVERSMITH MANAGEMENT, L.P.; *U.S. Private*, pg. 3663
SILVERSPAC INC.; *U.S. Public*, pg. 1880
SILVER SPIKE INVESTMENT CORP.; *U.S. Public*, pg. 1880
SILVER STAR PROPERTIES REIT, INC.; *U.S. Private*, pg. 3662
SILVERSTREAM CAPITAL, LLC; *U.S. Private*, pg. 3664
SILVER SUSTAINABLE SOLUTIONS CORP.; *U.S. Private*, pg. 3662
SILVER VENTURES, INC.; *U.S. Private*, pg. 3662
SIMA PRIVATE EQUITY 1 BETEILIGUNGS GMBH—See Deutsche Bank Aktiengesellschaft; *Int'l*, pg. 2061
SIMA PRIVATE EQUITY 1 GMBH & CO. KG—See Deutsche Bank Aktiengesellschaft; *Int'l*, pg. 2062
SIMEST S.P.A.—See Cassa Depositi e Prestiti S.p.A.; *Int'l*, pg. 1355
S-IMMOBILIEN WEINVIERTLER SPARKASSE GMBH—See Erste Group Bank AG; *Int'l*, pg. 2499
SIMONDS-SHIELDS-THEIS GRAIN CO.; *U.S. Private*, pg. 3666
SIMON PROPERTY GROUP ACQUISITION HOLDINGS, INC.; *U.S. Public*, pg. 1881
SIMPLE MANAGEMENT GROUP, INC.; *U.S. Private*, pg. 3666
SINCLAIR INSURANCE GROUP INC.; *U.S. Private*, pg. 3669
SINGAPORE UNITED RUBBER PLANTATIONS LIMITED—See Bukit Sembawang Estates Ltd; *Int'l*, pg. 1213
SINOMAX SECURITIES LIMITED—See Fu Shek Financial Holdings Limited; *Int'l*, pg. 2801
SI PARTICIPATIONS S.C.A.—See Groupe Siparex; *Int'l*, pg. 3111
SIRIS CAPITAL GROUP, LLC; *U.S. Private*, pg. 3672
SISTEMA 4B, S.A.—See Banco Santander, S.A.; *Int'l*, pg. 828
SITIO ROYALTIES CORP.; *U.S. Public*, pg. 1889
SIXTH STREET LENDING PARTNERS; *U.S. Private*, pg. 3677
SIXTH STREET PARTNERS LLC; *U.S. Private*, pg. 3677
SIZZLE ACQUISITION CORP.—See European Lithium Limited; *Int'l*, pg. 2556
SK CAPITAL PARTNERS, LP; *U.S. Private*, pg. 3678
SK GROWTH OPPORTUNITIES CORPORATION; *U.S. Public*, pg. 1891
SKILLZ INC.; *U.S. Public*, pg. 1892
SKINOVATION PHARMACEUTICAL INCORPORATED; *U.S. Private*, pg. 3682
SKYBRIDGE CAPITAL; *U.S. Private*, pg. 3684
SKYDECK ACQUISITION CORP.; *U.S. Public*, pg. 1892
SKY ISLAND CAPITAL LLC; *U.S. Private*, pg. 3684
SKYKNIGHT CAPITAL LLC; *U.S. Private*, pg. 3684
SKYVIEW CAPITAL, LLC; *U.S. Private*, pg. 3686
SKYWAY CAPITAL PARTNERS, LLC; *U.S. Private*, pg. 3686
SLAM CORP.; *U.S. Public*, pg. 1894
SLATE CAPITAL GROUP LLC; *U.S. Private*, pg. 3687
SLOVENSKE ELEKTRARNE FINANCE BV—See Enel S.p.A.; *Int'l*, pg. 2412
SLR SENIOR INVESTMENT CORP.—See SLR Investment Corp.; *U.S. Public*, pg. 1895
SMARTAG INTERNATIONAL, INC.; *U.S. Public*, pg. 1895
SMART DECISION, INC.; *U.S. Public*, pg. 1895
SMARTNEY SP. Z O.O—See Groupe BPCE; *Int'l*, pg. 3099
SMARTPITCH VENTURES, LLC; *U.S. Private*, pg. 3692
SMARTSTOP SELF STORAGE REIT, INC.—See Strategic Capital Holdings, LLC; *U.S. Private*, pg. 3834
SMART WATCH ASSETS LIMITED—See China COSCO Shipping Corporation Limited; *Int'l*, pg. 1496
SMH CUMMER/MOYERS—See Lee Equity Partners LLC; *U.S. Private*, pg. 2412
SMSA CRANE ACQUISITION CORP.; *U.S. Public*, pg. 1896
SM SUMMIT INVESTMENT PTE. LTD.—See Centurion Corporation Limited; *Int'l*, pg. 1417
SMTC MEX HOLDINGS, INC.—See H.I.G. Capital, LLC; *U.S. Private*, pg. 1834
SNAP ADVANCES; *U.S. Private*, pg. 3699
SNC-LAVALIN CAPITAL INC.—See AtkinsRealis Group Inc.; *Int'l*, pg. 671
SNOW PHIPPS GROUP, LLC—See TruArc Partners, L.P.; *U.S. Private*, pg. 4245
SOAR TECHNOLOGY ACQUISITION CORP.; *U.S. Public*, pg. 1899
SODEMEX DEVELOPPEMENT—See Caisse de Depot et Placement du Quebec; *Int'l*, pg. 1255
SOFIDER SASU—See Groupe BPCE; *Int'l*, pg. 3099
SOFINIM N.V.—See Ackermans & van Haaren NV; *Int'l*, pg. 106
SOFINNOVA VENTURES, INC.; *U.S. Private*, pg. 3704
SOFTWARE AG AUSTRALIA (HOLDINGS) PTY LTD—See Silver Lake Group, LLC; *U.S. Private*, pg. 3659
SOLACE CAPITAL PARTNERS, LLC; *U.S. Private*, pg. 3706
SOLEBURY TROUT LLC—See The PNC Financial Services Group, Inc.; *U.S. Public*, pg. 2120
SOLE SOURCE CAPITAL LLC; *U.S. Private*, pg. 3708

SOLIDIA FINANCE ET PATRIMONIE S.A.—See EFG International AG; *Int'l*, pg. 2320
SOLLENSYS CORP.; *U.S. Public*, pg. 1901
SONIC FINANCIAL CORPORATION; *U.S. Private*, pg. 3713
SONOMA BRANDS LLC; *U.S. Private*, pg. 3714
SORENSON CAPITAL PARTNERS; *U.S. Private*, pg. 3715
SOROS FUND MANAGEMENT LLC; *U.S. Private*, pg. 3715
SOUNDCORE CAPITAL PARTNERS, LLC; *U.S. Private*, pg. 3717
SOUNDHOUND AI, INC.; *U.S. Public*, pg. 1910
SOUND PARTNERS, LLC; *U.S. Private*, pg. 3717
SOURCE CAPITAL, LLC; *U.S. Private*, pg. 3717
SOURCE ROCK, INC.; *U.S. Private*, pg. 3718
SOUTH CHINA INTERNATIONAL LEASING COMPANY LIMITED—See Capital Industrial Financial Services Group Limited; *Int'l*, pg. 1311
SOUTHFIELD CAPITAL ADVISORS, LLC; *U.S. Private*, pg. 3735
SOUTHLAKE EQUITY GROUP LLC; *U.S. Private*, pg. 3736
SOUTHPORT ACQUISITION CORPORATION; *U.S. Public*, pg. 1912
SOWELL & CO., INC.; *U.S. Private*, pg. 3743
SPANOS BARBER JESSE & CO.; *U.S. Private*, pg. 3745
SPARKASSENBETEILIGUNGS UND SERVICE AG FUR OBEROSTERREICH UND SALZBURG—See Erste Group Bank AG; *Int'l*, pg. 2499
SPARTACUS ACQUISITION CORPORATION; *U.S. Private*, pg. 3746
SPARTA HEALTHCARE ACQUISITION CORP.; *U.S. Public*, pg. 1914
SPECTRUM EQUITY INVESTORS, L.P.; *U.S. Private*, pg. 3752
SPELL CAPITAL PARTNERS, LLC; *U.S. Private*, pg. 3754
SPENCER CAPITAL HOLDINGS, LTD.; *U.S. Private*, pg. 3754
SPEYSIDE EQUITY LLC; *U.S. Private*, pg. 3756
SPGL ACQUISITION CORPORATION; *U.S. Private*, pg. 3756
SPICE PRIVATE EQUITY LTD.—See GP Investments, Ltd.; *Int'l*, pg. 3045
SPINDLETOP HEALTH ACQUISITION CORP.; *U.S. Public*, pg. 1918
SPIRE CAPITAL PARTNERS, LLC; *U.S. Private*, pg. 3757
SPIRE GLOBAL, INC.; *U.S. Public*, pg. 1918
SPOOKFISH LIMITED—See Vista Equity Partners, LLC; *U.S. Private*, pg. 4396
SPORTS ENTERTAINMENT ACQUISITION CORP.; *U.S. Public*, pg. 1919
SPORTSMAP TECH ACQUISITION CORP.; *U.S. Public*, pg. 1919
SPORTSTEK ACQUISITION CORP.; *U.S. Public*, pg. 1919
SPORTS VENTURES ACQUISITION CORP.; *U.S. Public*, pg. 1919
SPOTLIGHT INNOVATION INC.; *U.S. Private*, pg. 3761
SPOUTING ROCK ALTERNATIVE CREDIT, LLC—See Spouting Rock Financial Partners LLC; *U.S. Private*, pg. 3762
SPOUTING ROCK ASSET MANAGEMENT LLC—See Spouting Rock Financial Partners LLC; *U.S. Private*, pg. 3762
SPP MANAGEMENT SERVICES, LLC; *U.S. Private*, pg. 3762
SPRINGBIG HOLDINGS, INC.; *U.S. Public*, pg. 1919
SPRINGBOARD CAPITAL, LLC; *U.S. Private*, pg. 3763
SPRINGBOARD CORPORATE FINANCE LLP—See Begbies Traynor Group plc; *Int'l*, pg. 941
SPRUCE POWER HOLDING CORPORATION; *U.S. Public*, pg. 1920
SPT FINANCIAL SERVICES PTY. LTD.—See AUB Group Limited; *Int'l*, pg. 698
SPUTNIK ENTERPRISES INC.; *U.S. Public*, pg. 1920
S-REAL MORAVA SPOL. S.R.O.—See Erste Group Bank AG; *Int'l*, pg. 2499
SRIRAMA ASSOCIATES LLC; *U.S. Private*, pg. 3768
SR ONE LIMITED—See GSK plc; *Int'l*, pg. 3149
SS & C FINANCIAL SERVICES LLC—See SS&C Technologies Holdings, Inc.; *U.S. Public*, pg. 1923
SS&C FUND SERVICES (UK) LIMITED—See SS&C Technologies Holdings, Inc.; *U.S. Public*, pg. 1923
SS&C GLOBEOP S.A.R.L—See SS&C Technologies Holdings, Inc.; *U.S. Public*, pg. 1923
SSW PARTNERS LP; *U.S. Private*, pg. 3770
STAGE EQUITY PARTNERS, LLC; *U.S. Private*, pg. 3775
THE STAGE FUND, LLC; *U.S. Private*, pg. 4120
STANDARD DIVERSIFIED INC.—See Turning Point Brands, Inc.; *U.S. Public*, pg. 2205
STANDARD GENERAL LP; *U.S. Private*, pg. 3778
STANDARD LIFE WEALTH LIMITED—See abrdn PLC; *Int'l*, pg. 69
STAPLE STREET CAPITAL LLC; *U.S. Private*, pg. 3783
STAR EAGLE HOLDINGS LIMITED—See Genting Berhad; *Int'l*, pg. 2929
STAR ESTATE SRL—See Africa Israel Investments Ltd.; *Int'l*, pg. 190
STARK & ROTH, INC.; *U.S. Private*, pg. 3786
STARKS FINANCIAL GROUP INC.—See Genstar Capital, LLC; *U.S. Private*, pg. 1677

STARKS FINANCIAL GROUP INC.—See Keystone Group, L.P.; *U.S. Private*, pg. 2298
STAR NUTRITION, INC.; *U.S. Public*, pg. 1938
START:BAUSPARKASSE AG—See BAWAG Group AG; *Int'l*, pg. 900
START:BAUSPARKASSE AG—See BAWAG Group AG; *Int'l*, pg. 900
STARTENGINE CROWDFUNDING, INC.; *U.S. Private*, pg. 3788
STARWOOD CAPITAL GROUP GLOBAL I, LLC; *U.S. Private*, pg. 3788
STATER BROS DEVELOPMENT INC—See La Cadena Investments; *U.S. Private*, pg. 2368
STATE STREET GLOBAL ADVISORS IRELAND LIMITED—See State Street Corporation; *U.S. Public*, pg. 1941
STATHOLDING AS—See Equinor ASA; *Int'l*, pg. 2485
ST. CLOUD CAPITAL, LLC; *U.S. Private*, pg. 3771
STEADFAST INCOME REIT, INC.—See Steadfast Companies; *U.S. Private*, pg. 3794
STEEL EXCEL INC.—See Steel Partners Holdings L.P.; *U.S. Public*, pg. 1943
STEEL PARTNERS LLC—See Steel Partners Holdings L.P.; *U.S. Public*, pg. 1943
STEEL PIER CAPITAL ADVISORS LLC; *U.S. Private*, pg. 3796
STEELPOINT CAPITAL PARTNERS, LP; *U.S. Private*, pg. 3797
STEIN INVESTMENT GROUP; *U.S. Private*, pg. 3798
STELLAR VALUE CHAIN SOLUTIONS PVT. LTD.—See CMA CGM S.A.; *Int'l*, pg. 1667
STELLEX CAPITAL MANAGEMENT LP; *U.S. Private*, pg. 3800
STEM, INC.; *U.S. Public*, pg. 1945
STEPHENS CAPITAL PARTNERS LLC—See SF Holding Corp.; *U.S. Private*, pg. 3621
THE STEPHENS GROUP, LLC; *U.S. Private*, pg. 4121
STEPSTONE GROUP LP; *U.S. Private*, pg. 3803
STERLING AMERICAN PROPERTY INC.; *U.S. Private*, pg. 3804
STERLING COMMERCIAL CREDIT; *U.S. Private*, pg. 3804
STERLING INVESTMENT PARTNERS, L.P.; *U.S. Private*, pg. 3805
STERLING ORGANIZATION; *U.S. Private*, pg. 3806
STERLING PARTNERS - CHICAGO OFFICE—See Sterling Partners; *U.S. Private*, pg. 3806
STERLING PARTNERS; *U.S. Private*, pg. 3806
STEWARD PARTNERS GLOBAL ADVISORY, LLC; *U.S. Private*, pg. 3811
STEWART CAPITAL PARTNERS LLC; *U.S. Private*, pg. 3811
STHEALTH CAPITAL INVESTMENT CORP.; *U.S. Private*, pg. 3812
STIFEL SCHWEIZ AG—See Stifel Financial Corp.; *U.S. Public*, pg. 1950
STOIC HOLDINGS LLC; *U.S. Private*, pg. 3816
STONE ARCH CAPITAL, LLC; *U.S. Private*, pg. 3816
STONEBRIDGE PARTNERS, LLC; *U.S. Private*, pg. 3827
STONECALIBRE, LLC; *U.S. Private*, pg. 3827
STONECOURT CAPITAL LP; *U.S. Private*, pg. 3828
STONECREEK CAPITAL, INC.; *U.S. Private*, pg. 3828
STONE-GOFF PARTNERS, LLC; *U.S. Private*, pg. 3826
STONE HARBOR EMERGING MARKETS INCOME FUND; *U.S. Private*, pg. 1951
STONEHENGE GROWTH EQUITY PARTNERS—See Stonehenge Capital Corp.; *U.S. Private*, pg. 3828
STONEHENGE PARTNERS, INC.; *U.S. Private*, pg. 3828
STONEPEAK PARTNERS L.P.; *U.S. Private*, pg. 3828
STONE POINT CAPITAL LLC; *U.S. Private*, pg. 3818
STONE POINTE, LLC; *U.S. Private*, pg. 3826
STONE RIVER CAPITAL PARTNERS, LLC; *U.S. Private*, pg. 3826
STONEX BANCO DE CAMBIO S.A.—See StoneX Group Inc.; *U.S. Public*, pg. 1953
STONEX EUROPE LTD.—See StoneX Group Inc.; *U.S. Public*, pg. 1953
STONEX FINANCIAL EUROPE S.A.—See StoneX Group Inc.; *U.S. Public*, pg. 1953
STONEX FINANCIAL GMBH—See StoneX Group Inc.; *U.S. Public*, pg. 1953
STONEX INVESTIMENTOS LTDA.—See StoneX Group Inc.; *U.S. Public*, pg. 1953
STONEX SECURITIES S.A.—See StoneX Group Inc.; *U.S. Public*, pg. 1953
STONY POINT GROUP, INC.; *U.S. Private*, pg. 3830
STRAIT LANE CAPITAL PARTNERS, LLC; *U.S. Private*, pg. 3833
STRAITS FINANCIAL GROUP PTE LTD—See CWT International Limited; *Int'l*, pg. 1891
STRAITS FINANCIAL LLC—See CWT International Limited; *Int'l*, pg. 1891
STRATEGIC ACQUISITIONS, INC.; *U.S. Public*, pg. 1953
STRATEGIC REALTY CAPITAL, LLC; *U.S. Private*, pg. 3835
STRATEGIC REALTY TRUST, INC.; *U.S. Private*, pg. 3835
STRATEGIC VALUE PARTNERS, LLC; *U.S. Private*, pg. 3835
STRATHCLYDE INNOVATION FUND LP—See Braveheart

523999 — MISCELLANEOUS FINAN...

Investment Group Plc; *Int'l*, pg. 1141
STRATIM CLOUD ACQUISITION CORP.; *U.S. Public*, pg. 1954
STRATTAM CAPITAL, LLC; *U.S. Private*, pg. 3837
STREAMLINE CAPITAL, INC.; *U.S. Private*, pg. 3838
STREETERVILLE CAPITAL LLC; *U.S. Private*, pg. 3838
STROTHMANN SPIRITUOSEN VERWALTUNG GMBH—See Berentzen-Gruppe AG; *Int'l*, pg. 978
STRUCTHERM HOLDINGS LIMITED—See Heidelberg Materials AG; *Int'l*, pg. 3319
STUART KING CAPITAL CORP.; *U.S. Private*, pg. 3843
SUBENSAMBLES INTERNACIONALES SA DE CV—See Apollo Global Management, Inc.; *U.S. Public*, pg. 162
SUCCESSION CAPITAL PARTNERS; *U.S. Private*, pg. 3849
SUCCESSION RESOURCE GROUP, INC.; *U.S. Private*, pg. 3849
SUDAMIN HOLDINGS SA—See AMG Critical Materials N.V.; *Int'l*, pg. 426
SUMERU EQUITY PARTNERS LLC; *U.S. Private*, pg. 3852
SUMMER STREET CAPITAL PARTNERS LLC; *U.S. Private*, pg. 3853
SUMMIT AGRICULTURAL GROUP, LLC; *U.S. Private*, pg. 3853
SUMMIT INDUSTRIAL INCOME REIT—See Dream Unlimited Corp.; *Int'l*, pg. 2203
SUMMIT INDUSTRIAL INCOME REIT—See GIC Pte. Ltd.; *Int'l*, pg. 2968
SUMMIT PARTNERS, L.P. - PALO ALTO OFFICE—See Summit Partners, L.P.; *U.S. Private*, pg. 3856
SUMMIT PARTNERS, L.P.; *U.S. Private*, pg. 3855
SUMRIDGE PARTNERS, LLC—See Raymond James Financial, Inc.; *U.S. Public*, pg. 1765
SUN CAPITAL ADVISERS, LLC—See Guggenheim Partners, LLC; *U.S. Private*, pg. 1813
SUN CAPITAL PARTNERS, INC.; *U.S. Private*, pg. 3858
SUN CAPITAL PARTNERS JAPAN K.K.—See Sun Capital Partners, Inc.; *U.S. Private*, pg. 3861
SUN CAPITAL PARTNERS SOURCING, LLC—See Sun Capital Partners, Inc.; *U.S. Private*, pg. 3861
SUNDANCE STRATEGIES, INC.; *U.S. Public*, pg. 1964
SUN EUROPEAN PARTNERS GMBH—See Sun Capital Partners, Inc.; *U.S. Private*, pg. 3862
SUN EUROPEAN PARTNERS, LLP—See Sun Capital Partners, Inc.; *U.S. Private*, pg. 3861
SUN EUROPEAN PARTNERS, SAS—See Sun Capital Partners, Inc.; *U.S. Private*, pg. 3862
SUNFIRE ACQUISITION CORP LIMITED; *U.S. Public*, pg. 1964
SUNLIGHT FINANCIAL HOLDINGS INC.; *U.S. Public*, pg. 1964
SUNLIGHT FINANCIAL LLC—See Sunlight Financial Holdings Inc.; *U.S. Public*, pg. 1964
SUNRISE CAPITAL PARTNERS LP; *U.S. Private*, pg. 3869
SUNSTOCK, INC.; *U.S. Public*, pg. 1966
SUNSTONE PARTNERS MANAGEMENT LLC; *U.S. Private*, pg. 3873
SUNTX CAPITAL PARTNERS, L.P.; *U.S. Private*, pg. 3874
SUOMEN ASIAKASTIETO OY—See Enento Group Plc; *Int'l*, pg. 2415
SUPERIOR CAPITAL PARTNERS LLC; *U.S. Private*, pg. 3876
SUPERIOR FINANCE COMPANY—See Arvest Bank Group, Inc.; *U.S. Private*, pg. 344
SUPERIOR INVESTMENTS HOLDINGS PTE LTD—See Crown Holdings, Inc.; *U.S. Public*, pg. 599
SUPER PLUS ACQUISITION CORPORATION; *U.S. Private*, pg. 3874
SURGE PRIVATE EQUITY LLC; *U.S. Private*, pg. 3884
SURGE VENTURES, LLC; *U.S. Private*, pg. 3884
SURO CAPITAL CORP.; *U.S. Public*, pg. 1967
SURROZEN, INC.; *U.S. Public*, pg. 1968
SUSQUEHANNA COMMUNITY FINANCIAL, INC.; *U.S. Public*, pg. 1968
SUSQUEHANNA PRIVATE CAPITAL, LLC—See Susquehanna International Group, LLP; *U.S. Private*, pg. 3885
SUSTINERE HOLDINGS, INC.; *U.S. Private*, pg. 3886
SVB ANALYTICS, INC.—See SVB Financial Group; *U.S. Public*, pg. 1968
SVERICA CAPITAL MANAGEMENT LP; *U.S. Private*, pg. 3888
SVERICA INTERNATIONAL (BOSTON) LLC—See Sverica Capital Management LP; *U.S. Private*, pg. 3888
SVF INVESTMENT CORP.; *U.S. Public*, pg. 1968
SV HEALTH INVESTORS, LLP; *U.S. Private*, pg. 3887
SV INVESTMENT PARTNERS; *U.S. Private*, pg. 3888
SVOBODA CAPITAL PARTNERS LLC; *U.S. Private*, pg. 3889
SWANDER PACE CAPITAL, LLC; *U.S. Private*, pg. 3889
THE SWEET LAKE LAND & OIL CO. LLC; *U.S. Private*, pg. 4125
SWEETVIEW PARTNERS, INC.; *U.S. Private*, pg. 3892
SW FINANCIAL—See Live Ventures Incorporated; *U.S. Public*, pg. 1332
SWISSALP SA—See Compagnie des Alpes S.A.; *Int'l*, pg. 1738
SWK HOLDINGS CORPORATION—See Carlson Capital, L.P.; *U.S. Private*, pg. 764

S WOHNFINANZIERUNG BERATUNGS GMBH—See Erste Group Bank AG; *Int'l*, pg. 2499
SW POST BEHEER B.V.—See Deutsche Post AG; *Int'l*, pg. 2082
SYCAMORE PARTNERS MANAGEMENT, LP; *U.S. Private*, pg. 3895
SYMBOTIC, INC.; *U.S. Public*, pg. 1969
SYMPHONY INNOVATION, LLC; *U.S. Private*, pg. 3899
SYMPHONY TECHNOLOGY GROUP, LLC; *U.S. Private*, pg. 3900
SYNCHRONY ASSET MANAGEMENT SA—See Banque Cantonale de Geneve S.A.; *Int'l*, pg. 852
SYNGENTA (CHINA) INVESTMENT COMPANY LIMITED—See China National Chemical Corporation; *Int'l*, pg. 1529
SYNGENTA FINANCE N.V.—See China National Chemical Corporation; *Int'l*, pg. 1530
SYNGENTA TREASURY N.V.—See China National Chemical Corporation; *Int'l*, pg. 1530
SYNOVUS TRUST COMPANY, NATIONAL ASSOCIATION—See Synovus Financial Corp.; *U.S. Public*, pg. 1971
SYNOVUS TRUST COMPANY, NATIONAL ASSOCIATION—See Synovus Financial Corp.; *U.S. Public*, pg. 1972
SYSTM BRANDS, LLC; *U.S. Private*, pg. 3908
TA ASSOCIATES ADVISORY PVT. LTD.—See TA Associates, Inc.; *U.S. Private*, pg. 3918
TA ASSOCIATES ASIA PACIFIC LTD.—See TA Associates, Inc.; *U.S. Private*, pg. 3918
TA ASSOCIATES, INC.; *U.S. Private*, pg. 3913
TA ASSOCIATES LTD.—See TA Associates, Inc.; *U.S. Private*, pg. 3918
TABUA INVESTMENTS LIMITED—See Hong Leong Investment Holdings Pte. Ltd.; *Int'l*, pg. 3468
TAC PARTNERS, INC.; *U.S. Private*, pg. 3920
TAGLICH PRIVATE EQUITY LLC; *U.S. Private*, pg. 3922
TAG NEWCO LIMITED—See Dentsu Group Inc.; *Int'l*, pg. 2039
TAI FUNG BANK LIMITED—See Bank of China, Ltd.; *Int'l*, pg. 842
TAILWATER CAPITAL LLC; *U.S. Private*, pg. 3923
TAILWIND CAPITAL GROUP, LLC; *U.S. Private*, pg. 3923
TAILWIND INTERNATIONAL ACQUISITION CORP.; *U.S. Private*, pg. 3924
TALISMAN CAPITAL PARTNERS LLC; *U.S. Private*, pg. 3926
TALON LLC; *U.S. Private*, pg. 3927
TALON REAL ESTATE HOLDING CORP.; *U.S. Public*, pg. 1980
THE TAMPA BAY TRUST COMPANY—See The Sanibel Captiva Trust Company; *U.S. Private*, pg. 4114
TANGENT FUND MANAGEMENT LLC; *U.S. Private*, pg. 3930
TANGLEWOOD INVESTMENTS INC.; *U.S. Private*, pg. 3931
TANGNEY INVESTMENTS (PROPRIETARY) LIMITED—See Hosken Consolidated Investments Limited; *Int'l*, pg. 3485
TANGO THERAPEUTICS, INC.; *U.S. Public*, pg. 1981
TANMIAH COMMERCIAL GROUP LTD.—See Dabbagh Group Holding Company Ltd.; *Int'l*, pg. 1903
TAPCO CREDIT UNION; *U.S. Private*, pg. 3932
TARGA RESOURCES FINANCE CORP.—See Targa Resources Corp.; *U.S. Public*, pg. 1981
TASACIONES HIPOTECARIAS SA—See BNP Paribas SA; *Int'l*, pg. 1093
TAT HONG EQUIPMENT (CHINA) PTE. LTD.—See Affirma Capital Limited; *Int'l*, pg. 187
TAT HONG (V.N.) PTE LTD—See Affirma Capital Limited; *Int'l*, pg. 187
TAURUS INVESTMENTS LLC—See Goff Capital, Inc.; *U.S. Private*, pg. 1726
TAUTACHROME INC.; *U.S. Public*, pg. 1983
TAVERNIER LIMITED—See City of London Group PLC; *Int'l*, pg. 1627
TAVISTOCK GROUP, INC.; *U.S. Private*, pg. 3937
TAX SYSTEMS PLC—See Bowmark Capital LLP; *Int'l*, pg. 1124
TAYLOR NELSON SOFRES GROUP HOLDINGS LTD—See Bain Capital, LP; *U.S. Private*, pg. 448
TBG TRANSPORTBETON REICHENBACH VERWALTUNGS-GMBH—See Heidelberg Materials AG; *Int'l*, pg. 3320
T & B WHITWOOD HOLDINGS LIMITED—See Deutsche Post AG; *Int'l*, pg. 2082
TCC INVESTMENT CORP.—See Technical Communications Corporation; *U.S. Public*, pg. 1988
TCG GROWTH OPPORTUNITIES CORP.; *U.S. Public*, pg. 1983
TC GROUP, LLC - LOS ANGELES—See The Carlyle Group Inc.; *U.S. Public*, pg. 2055
TC GROUP, LLC - NEW YORK—See The Carlyle Group Inc.; *U.S. Public*, pg. 2055
TC GROUP, LLC - SAN FRANCISCO—See The Carlyle Group Inc.; *U.S. Public*, pg. 2055
TC GROUP, LLC—See The Carlyle Group Inc.; *U.S. Public*, pg. 2054

TCMI, INC.; *U.S. Private*, pg. 3942
TCV ACQUISITION CORP.; *U.S. Public*, pg. 1983
THE TCW GROUP, INC.—See The Carlyle Group Inc.; *U.S. Public*, pg. 2055
TCW SPECIAL PURPOSE ACQUISITION CORP.; *U.S. Public*, pg. 1983
TDMY TECHNOLOGY GROUP, INC.; *U.S. Public*, pg. 1987
TEAKWOOD CAPITAL, L.P.; *U.S. Private*, pg. 3948
TEALL CAPITAL PARTNERS, LLC; *U.S. Private*, pg. 3948
TEAMSHARES INC.; *U.S. Private*, pg. 3951
TEB TUKETICI FINANSMAN AS—See BNP Paribas SA; *Int'l*, pg. 1093
TECH CREDIT UNION CORPORATION; *U.S. Private*, pg. 3951
TECH & ENERGY TRANSITION CORPORATION; *U.S. Public*, pg. 1988
TECHNOLOGY CROSSOVER VENTURES L.P. - MILLBURN—See TCMI, Inc.; *U.S. Private*, pg. 3943
TECHSTACKERY, INC.; *U.S. Private*, pg. 3956
TECUM CAPITAL PARTNERS, LLC; *U.S. Private*, pg. 3957
T.E. FINANCIAL CONSULTANTS LTD.—See iA Financial Corporation Inc.; *Int'l*, pg. 3567
TEKKORP DIGITAL ACQUISITION CORP.; *U.S. Public*, pg. 1991
TE KRONOS GMBH—See Helaba Landesbank Hessen-Thuringen; *Int'l*, pg. 3328
TELEGRAPH HILL PARTNERS MANAGEMENT COMPANY, LLC; *U.S. Private*, pg. 3960
TELEO CAPITAL MANAGEMENT, LLC; *U.S. Private*, pg. 3961
TELHIO CREDIT UNION; *U.S. Private*, pg. 3962
TEMPLETON ASSET MANAGEMENT LTD.—See Franklin Resources, Inc.; *U.S. Public*, pg. 883
TENAYA ACQUISITIONS COMPANY; *U.S. Private*, pg. 3965
TENAYA CAPITAL, LLC; *U.S. Private*, pg. 3965
TENGRAM CAPITAL PARTNERS, LIMITED PARTNERSHIP; *U.S. Private*, pg. 3967
TENNENBAUM CAPITAL PARTNERS, LLC—See BlackRock, Inc.; *U.S. Public*, pg. 347
TEN OAKS GROUP; *U.S. Private*, pg. 3964
TENTH STREET CAPITAL, LLC; *U.S. Private*, pg. 3968
TERAWULF INC.; *U.S. Public*, pg. 2018
TERRAMAR CAPITAL LLC; *U.S. Private*, pg. 3971
TERRAPIN 3 ACQUISITION CORPORATION; *U.S. Private*, pg. 3972
TERRAPIN 4 ACQUISITION CORPORATION; *U.S. Private*, pg. 3972
TERRAPIN ASSET MANAGEMENT, LLC—See Terrapin Partners LLC; *U.S. Private*, pg. 3972
TERRAPIN PARTNERS LLC; *U.S. Private*, pg. 3972
TETON ADVISORS, INC.; *U.S. Public*, pg. 2021
TEUCRIUM AGRICULTURAL FUND; *U.S. Public*, pg. 2025
TEUCRIUM CORN FUND; *U.S. Public*, pg. 2025
TEUCRIUM NATURAL GAS FUND; *U.S. Private*, pg. 3974
TEUCRIUM SOYBEAN FUND; *U.S. Public*, pg. 2025
TEUCRIUM SUGAR FUND; *U.S. Public*, pg. 2025
TEUCRIUM WHEAT FUND; *U.S. Public*, pg. 2025
TEXAS ENERGY HOLDINGS INC.; *U.S. Private*, pg. 3975
TEXAS GULF ENERGY, INCORPORATED; *U.S. Public*, pg. 2025
TEXAS SOUTH ENERGY, INC.; *U.S. Private*, pg. 3977
TEXTRON ACQUISITION LIMITED—See Textron Inc.; *U.S. Public*, pg. 2028
TFS FINANCIAL CORPORATION; *U.S. Public*, pg. 2029
TG VENTURE ACQUISITION CORP.; *U.S. Public*, pg. 2030
THAMES RIVER CAPITAL UK LIMITED—See Bank of Montreal; *Int'l*, pg. 847
THAMES RIVER MULTI-CAPITAL LLP—See Bank of Montreal; *Int'l*, pg. 847
THEGLOBE.COM, INC.; *U.S. Public*, pg. 2144
THINK ELEVATION CAPITAL GROWTH OPPORTUNITIES; *U.S. Public*, pg. 2155
THIRD COAST COMMERCIAL CAPITAL, INC.—See Third Coast Bancshares, Inc.; *U.S. Public*, pg. 2155
THIRD LEAF PARTNERS; *U.S. Private*, pg. 4145
THIRD SECURITY, LLC; *U.S. Private*, pg. 4145
TH LEE PUTNAM VENTURES; *U.S. Private*, pg. 3979
THOMA BRAVO ADVANTAGE; *U.S. Public*, pg. 2156
THOMA BRAVO, L.P.; *U.S. Private*, pg. 4145
THOMAS H. LEE PARTNERS, L.P.; *U.S. Private*, pg. 4155
THOMAS, MCNERNEY & PARTNERS II, LLC; *U.S. Private*, pg. 4158
THOMPSON STREET CAPITAL MANAGER LLC; *U.S. Private*, pg. 4160
THOMVEST ASSET MANAGEMENT LTD.—See Thomvest Ventures LLC; *U.S. Private*, pg. 4162
THOMVEST VENTURES LLC; *U.S. Private*, pg. 4162
THREADNEEDLE ASSET MANAGEMENT HOLDINGS LIMITED—See Ameriprise Financial, Inc.; *U.S. Public*, pg. 114
THREADNEEDLE ASSET MANAGEMENT LTD.—See Ameriprise Financial, Inc.; *U.S. Public*, pg. 114
THREADNEEDLE INTERNATIONAL LTD.—See Ameriprise Financial, Inc.; *U.S. Public*, pg. 114
THREADNEEDLE INVESTMENT SERVICES GMBH—See Ameriprise Financial, Inc.; *U.S. Public*, pg. 114
THREADNEEDLE INVESTMENT SERVICES LTD.—See Ameriprise Financial, Inc.; *U.S. Public*, pg. 114

N.A.I.C.S. INDEX

523999 — MISCELLANEOUS FINAN...

THREADNEEDLE MANAGEMENT SERVICES LTD.—See Ameriprise Financial, Inc.; *U.S. Public*, pg. 114
THRESHOLD VENTURES III, L.P.; *U.S. Private*, pg. 4164
THRIVE ACQUISITION CORPORATION; *U.S. Public*, pg. 2157
THURSTON GROUP, LLC; *U.S. Private*, pg. 4166
TIDE ROCK HOLDINGS, LLC; *U.S. Private*, pg. 4167
TIGER GLOBAL MANAGEMENT LLC; *U.S. Private*, pg. 4169
TIGO ENERGY, INC; *U.S. Public*, pg. 2158
TILIA HOLDINGS LLC; *U.S. Private*, pg. 4170
TILLERY CAPITAL LLC; *U.S. Private*, pg. 4171
TILT HOLDINGS INC.; *U.S. Public*, pg. 2159
TIMBERFENCE CAPITAL PARTNERS, LLC; *U.S. Private*, pg. 4171
TIMESSQUARE CAPITAL MANAGEMENT, LLC—See Affiliated Managers Group, Inc.; *U.S. Public*, pg. 56
TIMONEER STRATEGIC PARTNERS, LLC; *U.S. Private*, pg. 4173
TIMPANI CAPITAL MANAGEMENT, LLC—See Calamos Asset Management, Inc.; *U.S. Private*, pg. 716
TINICUM INCORPORATED—See Tinicum Enterprises, Inc.; *U.S. Private*, pg. 4173
TIRSCHWELL & LOEWY, INC.—See Provident Financial Services, Inc.; *U.S. Public*, pg. 1730
TITANIUM HEALTHCARE, INC.; *U.S. Private*, pg. 4177
TITUS WEALTH MANAGEMENT, INC.—See TA Associates, Inc.; *U.S. Private*, pg. 3919
T.K. MAXX HOLDING GMBH—See The TJX Companies, Inc.; *U.S. Public*, pg. 2134
TL CANNON CORPORATION; *U.S. Public*, pg. 4178
TLGY ACQUISITION CORPORATION; *U.S. Public*, pg. 2161
TLH LLC—See Icahn Enterprises L.P.; *U.S. Public*, pg. 1085
TL VENTURES INC.; *U.S. Private*, pg. 4178
TMB INDUSTRIES INC.; *U.S. Private*, pg. 4179
TMF ADMINISTRATIVE SERVICES MALAYSIA SDN. BHD.—See icapital.biz Berhad; *Int'l*, pg. 3578
TMT ACQUISITION CORP.; *U.S. Public*, pg. 4180
TMW ENTERPRISES INC.; *U.S. Private*, pg. 4180
TONKA BAY EQUITY PARTNERS LLC; *U.S. Private*, pg. 4184
TOPSPIN PARTNERS, L.P.; *U.S. Private*, pg. 4188
TOPSTEPTRADER, LLC; *U.S. Private*, pg. 4188
TOP VORSORGE-MANAGEMENT GMBH—See Allianz SE; *Int'l*, pg. 356
TORCH ENERGY ADVISORS INCORPORATED; *U.S. Private*, pg. 4188
TORQUE CAPITAL GROUP, LLC; *U.S. Private*, pg. 4189
TOSEI CORPORATION—See Electrolux Professional AB; *Int'l*, pg. 2353
TOTTA (IRELAND), PLC—See Banco Santander, S.A.; *Int'l*, pg. 828
TOWER ARCH CAPITAL LLC; *U.S. Private*, pg. 4193
TOWERBROOK CAPITAL PARTNERS, L.P.; *U.S. Private*, pg. 4194
TOWERBROOK CAPITAL PARTNERS (U.K.) L.L.P.—See TowerBrook Capital Partners, L.P.; *U.S. Private*, pg. 4196
TOWER GENERAL PARTNER LIMITED—See BlackRock, Inc.; *U.S. Public*, pg. 347
TOWER REALTY PARTNERS, INC.; *U.S. Private*, pg. 4194
TOWNE INVESTMENTS, LLC—See Towne Bank; *U.S. Public*, pg. 2166
TOWNSEND CAPITAL, LLC; *U.S. Private*, pg. 4198
TPG CAPITAL, L.P.; *U.S. Public*, pg. 2166
TPG GROWTH - SAN FRANCISCO OFFICE—See TPG Capital, L.P.; *U.S. Public*, pg. 2177
TPG GROWTH—See TPG Capital, L.P.; *U.S. Public*, pg. 2175
TPG PACE BENEFICIAL FINANCE CORP.; *U.S. Public*, pg. 2177
TPG PACE SOLUTIONS CORP.—See Vacasa, Inc.; *U.S. Public*, pg. 2270
TRADEUP 88 CORP.; *U.S. Public*, pg. 2178
TRADEWINDS GLOBAL INVESTORS, LLC—See Teachers Insurance Association - College Retirement Fund; *U.S. Private*, pg. 3948
TRADE X PARTNERS LLC—See Stagwell, Inc.; *U.S. Public*, pg. 1928
TRADING COVE ASSOCIATES—See Waterford Group, LLC; *U.S. Private*, pg. 4453
TRANSCENDENT INVESTMENT MANAGEMENT; *U.S. Private*, pg. 4207
TRANSFORMATIONAL CPG ACQUISITION CORP.; *U.S. Private*, pg. 4208
TRANSITION CAPITAL PARTNERS LTD.; *U.S. Private*, pg. 4208
TRANSOCEAN HOLDING CORPORATION—See Assicurazioni Generali S.p.A.; *Int'l*, pg. 648
TRANSOM CAPITAL GROUP, LLC; *U.S. Private*, pg. 4209
TRANSPORTATION RESOURCE PARTNERS, LP; *U.S. Private*, pg. 4211
TRAUB CAPITAL—See Marvin Traub Associates, Inc.; *U.S. Private*, pg. 2598
TREGARON MANAGEMENT, LLC; *U.S. Private*, pg. 4217
TRENT CAPITAL PARTNERS, LLC; *U.S. Private*, pg. 4218
TRIA CAPITAL PARTNERS, LLC; *U.S. Private*, pg. 4225
TRIAD HYBRID SOLUTIONS, LLC—See Reverence Capital Partners LLC; *U.S. Private*, pg. 3415
TRI-CONTINENTAL CORPORATION; *U.S. Public*, pg. 2188
TRIDENT BRANDS INCORPORATED; *U.S. Public*, pg. 2189
TRIDENT CAPITAL, INC.; *U.S. Private*, pg. 4229
TRIDENT CAPITAL—See Trident Capital, Inc.; *U.S. Private*, pg. 4229
TRI-FROST CORPORATION—See Cullen/Frost Bankers, Inc.; *U.S. Public*, pg. 604
TRIGATE CAPITAL, LLC; *U.S. Private*, pg. 4230
TRILANTIC CAPITAL PARTNERS LLP—See Trilantic Capital Management L.P.; *U.S. Private*, pg. 4231
TRILINC GLOBAL IMPACT FUND, LLC; *U.S. Public*, pg. 2189
TRIMARAN CAPITAL PARTNERS, LLC; *U.S. Private*, pg. 4232
TRIMBLE TRAILBLAZER GMBH—See Trimble, Inc.; *U.S. Public*, pg. 2193
TRINITY HUNT MANAGEMENT, L.P.; *U.S. Private*, pg. 4234
TRINITY MERGER CORP.—See Waterfall Asset Management LLC; *U.S. Private*, pg. 4453
TRINITY PRIVATE EQUITY GROUP, LLC; *U.S. Private*, pg. 4235
TRINITY VENTURES; *U.S. Private*, pg. 4236
TRIPLEPOINT VENTURE GROWTH BDC CORP.; *U.S. Public*, pg. 2195
TRISALUS LIFE SCIENCES, INC.; *U.S. Public*, pg. 2195
TRISTAR HOLDINGS INC.; *U.S. Private*, pg. 4238
TRITIUM PARTNERS, LLC; *U.S. Private*, pg. 4238
TRITON CAPITAL PARTNERS LIMITED; *U.S. Private*, pg. 4238
TRITON PACIFIC CAPITAL PARTNERS LLC; *U.S. Private*, pg. 4239
TRIVE CAPITAL INC.; *U.S. Private*, pg. 4239
TRIVEST PARTNERS, LP; *U.S. Private*, pg. 4240
TROPICANA LAUGHLIN, LLC—See Caesars Entertainment, Inc.; *U.S. Public*, pg. 421
TRUARC PARTNERS, L.P.; *U.S. Private*, pg. 4244
TRUE GREEN CAPITAL MANAGEMENT LLC; *U.S. Private*, pg. 4247
TRUE VENTURES; *U.S. Private*, pg. 4248
TRUE WIND CAPITAL MANAGEMENT, L.P.; *U.S. Private*, pg. 4248
TRU INDEPENDCE LLC; *U.S. Private*, pg. 4244
TRUMP ORGANIZATION LLC—See The Trump Organization, Inc.; *U.S. Private*, pg. 4128
TRUST COMPANY OF THE WEST—See The Carlyle Group Inc.; *U.S. Public*, pg. 2056
TRYTO CORPORATION—See AIFUL Corporation; *Int'l*, pg. 232
TSG CONSUMER PARTNERS LLC - NEW YORK OFFICE—See TSG Consumer Partners LLC; *U.S. Private*, pg. 4253
TSG CONSUMER PARTNERS LLC; *U.S. Private*, pg. 4252
TUBE CITY IMS HOLDING B.V.—See The Pritzker Organization, LLC; *U.S. Private*, pg. 4100
TUDOR CAPITAL EUROPE LLP—See Tudor Investment Corporation; *U.S. Public*, pg. 4257
TUDOR, PICKERING, HOLT & CO., LLC—See Perella Weinberg Partners LP; *U.S. Public*, pg. 1674
TUDOR, PICKERING, HOLT & CO. SECURITIES-CANADA ULC—See Perella Weinberg Partners LP; *U.S. Public*, pg. 1674
TURMERIC ACQUISITION CORP.; *U.S. Public*, pg. 2205
TURNBRIDGE CAPITAL, LLC; *U.S. Private*, pg. 4260
TURNKEY CAPITAL, INC.; *U.S. Public*, pg. 2205
TURN/RIVER MANAGEMENT LLC; *U.S. Private*, pg. 4259
TURNSPIRE CAPITAL PARTNERS LLC; *U.S. Private*, pg. 4261
TURNSTONE CAPITAL MANAGEMENT LLC; *U.S. Private*, pg. 4261
TURQUINO EQUITY LLC; *U.S. Private*, pg. 4261
TVC CAPITAL LLC; *U.S. Private*, pg. 4264
T-VENTURE HOLDING GMBH—See Deutsche Telekom AG; *Int'l*, pg. 2085
T-VENTURE OF AMERICA, INC.—See Deutsche Telekom AG; *Int'l*, pg. 2085
TWIN POINT CAPITAL, LLC; *U.S. Private*, pg. 4265
TWIN RIDGE CAPITAL ACQUISITION CORP.; *U.S. Public*, pg. 2207
TWIST INVESTMENT CORPORATION; *U.S. Private*, pg. 4266
TWO RIVER GROUP MANAGEMENT, LLC—See Two River Group Holdings, LLC; *U.S. Private*, pg. 4266
TWO; *U.S. Public*, pg. 2207
TWS PARTNERSHIP LLC; *U.S. Private*, pg. 4267
TXEX ENERGY INVESTMENTS, LLC; *U.S. Private*, pg. 4267
TYGON PEAK CAPITAL; *U.S. Private*, pg. 4267
TYGRIS ASSET FINANCE, INC—See Teachers Insurance Association - College Retirement Fund; *U.S. Private*, pg. 3948
TZERO ATS, LLC—See Beyond, Inc.; *U.S. Public*, pg. 327
TZP GROUP LLC; *U.S. Private*, pg. 4269
TZP STRATEGIES ACQUISITION CORP.; *U.S. Public*, pg. 2211
UAN POWER CORP.; *U.S. Public*, pg. 2217
UB GROUP LIMITED—See Barclays PLC; *Int'l*, pg. 863
UBIQUITY MANAGEMENT, L.P.; *U.S. Private*, pg. 4273
UBI TRUSTEE SA—See EFG International AG; *Int'l*, pg. 2321
UD TRUCKS JAPAN CO., LTD. - HANYU PLANT—See AB Volvo; *Int'l*, pg. 45
UD TRUCKS JAPAN CO., LTD. - KONOSU PLANT—See AB Volvo; *Int'l*, pg. 46
UFP PURCHASING, INC.—See UFP Industries, Inc.; *U.S. Public*, pg. 2220
UFS BETEILIGUNGS-GMBH—See Allianz SE; *Int'l*, pg. 356
UGE INTERNATIONAL LTD.—See Nova Infrastructure Management, LLC; *U.S. Public*, pg. 2965
UKRAINIAN NATIONAL ASSOCIATION, INC.; *U.S. Private*, pg. 4275
ULTIMATE ACQUISITION PARTNERS, L.P.; *U.S. Private*, pg. 4277
ULTIMATE TECHNOLOGIES GROUP, INC.; *U.S. Private*, pg. 4277
ULTRALAT CAPITAL MARKET INC.—See Credicorp Ltd.; *Int'l*, pg. 1834
ULYSSES MANAGEMENT, LLC; *U.S. Private*, pg. 4278
UMEWORLD, LIMITED; *U.S. Public*, pg. 2224
UNDERSCORE.VC MANAGEMENT CO. LLC; *U.S. Private*, pg. 4279
UNICOIN INC.; *U.S. Private*, pg. 4281
UNIFI FINANCIAL, INC.; *U.S. Private*, pg. 4282
UNION PARK CAPITAL; *U.S. Private*, pg. 4284
UNIQUE FINANCE LIMITED—See Civil Bank Limited; *Int'l*, pg. 1630
UNITED ARAB JORDAN COMPANY FOR INVESTMENT & FINANCIAL BROKERAGE—See Arab Jordan Investment Bank; *Int'l*, pg. 530
UNITED ENERGIES DEVELOPMENT CORPORATION; *U.S. Public*, pg. 4291
UNITED HOMES GROUP, INC; *U.S. Public*, pg. 2231
UNITED STATES BITCOIN AND TREASURY INVESTMENT TRUST; *U.S. Private*, pg. 4298
UNITED STATES BRENT OIL FUND, LP—See The Marygold Companies, Inc.; *U.S. Public*, pg. 2112
UNITED STATES COMMODITY FUNDS, LLC—See The Marygold Companies, Inc.; *U.S. Public*, pg. 2112
UNITED STATES COMMODITY INDEX FUNDS TRUST—See The Marygold Companies, Inc.; *U.S. Public*, pg. 2112
UNITED STATES GASOLINE FUND, LP—See The Marygold Companies, Inc.; *U.S. Public*, pg. 2112
UNITED STATES GOLD AND TREASURY INVESTMENT TRUST; *U.S. Private*, pg. 4298
UNITED STATES OIL & GAS CORPORATION; *U.S. Private*, pg. 4299
UNITY PARTNERS LP; *U.S. Public*, pg. 2253
UNIVERSAL GLOBAL HUB INC.; *U.S. Public*, pg. 2255
UNIVERSITY VENTURES FUNDS MANAGEMENT LLC; *U.S. Private*, pg. 4310
UNI-WORLD CAPITAL, L.P.; *U.S. Private*, pg. 4281
UNSDG ACQUISITION CORP.; *U.S. Private*, pg. 4311
UPDATA PARTNERS; *U.S. Private*, pg. 4311
UPD HOLDING CORP.; *U.S. Public*, pg. 2263
UPFRONT VENTURES; *U.S. Private*, pg. 4311
UPHEALTH, INC.; *U.S. Public*, pg. 2264
UPONOR BETEILIGUNGS GMBH—See Georg Fischer AG; *Int'l*, pg. 2937
UPPER STREET MARKETING, INC.; *U.S. Public*, pg. 2264
UPROMISE, INC.—See Great Hill Partners, L.P.; *U.S. Private*, pg. 1763
USAA ACCEPTANCE, LLC—See United Services Automobile Association; *U.S. Private*, pg. 4297
USA CAPITAL MANAGEMENT, INC.; *U.S. Private*, pg. 4321
USCF INVESTMENTS, INC.—See The Marygold Companies, Inc.; *U.S. Public*, pg. 2112
USHG ACQUISITION CORP.; *U.S. Public*, pg. 2267
USPP-TRI LAKES, LLC; *U.S. Private*, pg. 4323
U.S. RETIREMENT PARTNERS, INC.—See Kohlberg & Company, LLC; *U.S. Private*, pg. 2339
USRG MANAGEMENT COMPANY, LLC; *U.S. Private*, pg. 4323
U.S. WELL SERVICES, INC.—See ProFrac Holding Corp.; *U.S. Public*, pg. 1724
UTA ACQUISITION CORPORATION; *U.S. Public*, pg. 2267
UTXO ACQUISITION INC.; *U.S. Private*, pg. 4327
UTZ BRANDS, INC.; *U.S. Public*, pg. 2267
THE VALENCE GROUP, LLC—See Piper Sandler Companies; *U.S. Public*, pg. 1694
VALENT CAPITAL PARTNERS LLC; *U.S. Private*, pg. 4331
VALER, INC.; *U.S. Private*, pg. 4331
VALESCO INDUSTRIES, INC; *U.S. Private*, pg. 4331
VALHALLA PARTNERS INC.; *U.S. Private*, pg. 4331
VALLEY CAPITAL CORPORATION; *U.S. Private*, pg. 4332
VALOR EQUITY PARTNERS L.P.; *U.S. Private*, pg. 4336
VALORE VENTURES, INC.; *U.S. Private*, pg. 4337
VALOR LATITUDE ACQUISITION CORP.; *U.S. Public*, pg. 2274
VALSTONE PARTNERS, LLC; *U.S. Private*, pg. 4337
VALUEACT CAPITAL MANAGEMENT, L.P.; *U.S. Private*, pg. 4338
VALUE MANAGEMENT INSTITUTE, INC.—See Development Bank of Japan, Inc.; *Int'l*, pg. 2088

523999 — MISCELLANEOUS FINAN...

VAN BREDA CAR FINANCE NV—See Ackermans & van Haaren NV; *Int'l*, pg. 106
VANCE STREET CAPITAL LLC; *U.S. Private*, pg. 4342
VANECK MERK GOLD TRUST; *U.S. Public*, pg. 2275
VANGUARD INVESTMENTS—See The Vanguard Group, Inc.; *U.S. Private*, pg. 4130
VANTAGE ENERGY ACQUISITION CORP.; *U.S. Private*, pg. 4345
VANTAGEPOINT CAPITAL PARTNERS; *U.S. Private*, pg. 4345
VANTAGE WEST CREDIT UNION; *U.S. Private*, pg. 4345
VARAGON CAPITAL CORPORATION; *U.S. Private*, pg. 4345
VARDE PARTNERS, INC.; *U.S. Private*, pg. 4346
VARIANT EQUITY ADVISORS, LLC; *U.S. Private*, pg. 4346
VARSITY MANAGEMENT COMPANY, LP; *U.S. Private*, pg. 4347
VAULT CREDIT CORPORATION—See Chesswood Group Limited; *Int'l*, pg. 1473
VAULT INTELLIGENCE LIMITED—See Damstra Holdings Ltd.; *Int'l*, pg. 1957
VAULT PAYMENT SYSTEMS LLC—See Chesswood Group Limited; *Int'l*, pg. 1473
V BLOCKCHAIN GROUP INC.; *U.S. Private*, pg. 4327
VECTOR CAPITAL MANAGEMENT, L.P.; *U.S. Private*, pg. 4349
VEEDER-ROOT FINANCE COMPANY—See Danaher Corporation; *U.S. Public*, pg. 631
VELA ABS S.R.L—See BNP Paribas SA; *Int'l*, pg. 1093
VELOCITY ACQUISITION CORP.; *U.S. Public*, pg. 2277
VELOCITY MERGER CORP.; *U.S. Private*, pg. 4354
VEMANTI GROUP, INC.; *U.S. Public*, pg. 2277
VENCOR INTERNATIONAL, INC.; *U.S. Private*, pg. 4356
VENQUEST CAPITAL PARTNERS LLC; *U.S. Private*, pg. 4356
VENROCK ASSOCIATES; *U.S. Private*, pg. 4356
VENROCK ASSOCIATES—See Venrock Associates; *U.S. Private*, pg. 4357
VENTECH—See Groupe BPCE; *Int'l*, pg. 3096
VERACEN FUNDS LP; *U.S. Private*, pg. 4359
VERDE CLEAN FUELS, INC.; *U.S. Public*, pg. 2280
VERGANI & ASSOCIATES, LLC; *U.S. Private*, pg. 4359
VERIFACTS LLC—See TransUnion; *U.S. Public*, pg. 2185
VERIFIER CAPITAL LLC; *U.S. Private*, pg. 4360
VERITAS CAPITAL FUND MANAGEMENT, LLC; *U.S. Private*, pg. 4360
VERONIS SUHLER STEVENSON INTERNATIONAL LTD.—See Veronis Suhler Stevenson Partners LLC; *U.S. Private*, pg. 4368
VERRA MOBILITY CORPORATION; *U.S. Public*, pg. 2286
VERSA CAPITAL MANAGEMENT, LLC—See Independence Capital Partners, LLC; *U.S. Private*, pg. 2057
VERTIV (AUSTRALIA) PTY. LTD.—See Vertiv Holdings Co; *U.S. Public*, pg. 2288
VERTIV CANADA ULC—See Vertiv Holdings Co; *U.S. Public*, pg. 2288
VERTIV CZECH REPUBLIC S.R.O—See Vertiv Holdings Co; *U.S. Public*, pg. 2288
VERTIV ENERGY PRIVATE LIMITED—See Vertiv Holdings Co; *U.S. Public*, pg. 2288
VERTIV GMBH—See Vertiv Holdings Co; *U.S. Public*, pg. 2288
VERTIV HOLDINGS CO; *U.S. Public*, pg. 2287
VERTIV INTEGRATED SYSTEMS GMBH—See Vertiv Holdings Co; *U.S. Public*, pg. 2289
VERTIV INTERNATIONAL DESIGNATED ACTIVITY COMPANY—See Vertiv Holdings Co; *U.S. Public*, pg. 2289
VERTIV MIDDLE EAST DMCC—See Vertiv Holdings Co; *U.S. Public*, pg. 2289
VERTIV (SINGAPORE) PTE. LTD.—See Vertiv Holdings Co; *U.S. Public*, pg. 2288
VERTIV SWEDEN AB—See Vertiv Holdings Co; *U.S. Public*, pg. 2289
VESTA EQUITY, LLC; *U.S. Private*, pg. 4371
VESTAR CAPITAL PARTNERS, LLC; *U.S. Private*, pg. 4371
VESTOR CAPITAL, LLC—See Clayton, Dubilier & Rice, LLC; *U.S. Private*, pg. 924
VESTOR CAPITAL, LLC—See Stone Point Capital LLC; *U.S. Private*, pg. 3824
VFS CANADA INC—See AB Volvo; *Int'l*, pg. 44
VFS DENMARK AS—See AB Volvo; *Int'l*, pg. 44
VFS DEUTSCHLAND GMBH—See AB Volvo; *Int'l*, pg. 44
VFS FINANCE FRANCE S.A.S.—See AB Volvo; *Int'l*, pg. 44
VFS FINANCIAL SERVICES (AUSTRIA) GMBH—See AB Volvo; *Int'l*, pg. 44
VFS FINANCIAL SERVICES BELGIUM NV—See AB Volvo; *Int'l*, pg. 44
VFS FINANCIAL SERVICES BV—See AB Volvo; *Int'l*, pg. 44
VFS FINANCIAL SERVICES CZECH REPUBLIC, S.R.O.—See AB Volvo; *Int'l*, pg. 44
VFS FINANCIAL SERVICES SLOVAKIA, S.R.O.—See AB Volvo; *Int'l*, pg. 44
VFS FINANCIAL SERVICES SPAIN EFC, SA—See AB Volvo; *Int'l*, pg. 44
VFS FINANSAL KIRALAMA A.S.—See AB Volvo; *Int'l*, pg. 44
VFS FINLAND AB—See AB Volvo; *Int'l*, pg. 44

VFS FRANCE—See AB Volvo; *Int'l*, pg. 44
VFS INTERNATIONAL AB—See AB Volvo; *Int'l*, pg. 44
VFS JAPAN CO., LTD.—See AB Volvo; *Int'l*, pg. 44
VFS LATVIA SIA—See AB Volvo; *Int'l*, pg. 44
VFS PENZUGYI SZOLGALTATO KFT.—See AB Volvo; *Int'l*, pg. 44
VFS US LLC—See AB Volvo; *Int'l*, pg. 44
VFS USLUGI FINANSOWE POLSKA SP. Z O.O.—See AB Volvo; *Int'l*, pg. 44
VFS VOSTOK—See AB Volvo; *Int'l*, pg. 44
VGFS FINANCIAL SERVICES ESTONIA OU—See AB Volvo; *Int'l*, pg. 44
VICENTE CAPITAL PARTNERS, LLC; *U.S. Private*, pg. 4376
VICTORIAN SECURITIES—See Bendigo & Adelaide Bank Ltd.; *Int'l*, pg. 971
VICTORY DEVELOPERS INC.; *U.S. Private*, pg. 4378
VIDA FLASH ACQUISITIONS; *U.S. Private*, pg. 4380
THE VILLAGE BANK; *U.S. Public*, pg. 4131
VINTAGE CAPITAL GROUP LLC; *U.S. Private*, pg. 4386
VINTAGE CAPITAL MANAGEMENT LLC; *U.S. Private*, pg. 4386
VINTAGE WINE ESTATES, INC.; *U.S. Public*, pg. 2298
VIOLA FINANZA SRL—See BNP Paribas SA; *Int'l*, pg. 1093
VIOLED INTERNATIONAL PTE. LTD—See Allgreentech International PLC; *Int'l*, pg. 338
VIRESCENT RENEWABLE ENERGY TRUST—See KKR & Co. Inc.; *U.S. Public*, pg. 1266
VIRGO CAPITAL; *U.S. Private*, pg. 4388
VIRGO INVESTMENT GROUP LLC; *U.S. Private*, pg. 4388
VIRTU FINANCIAL GLOBAL SERVICES SINGAPORE PTE LTD.—See Virtu Financial, Inc.; *U.S. Public*, pg. 2300
VIRTUS DIVIDEND, INTEREST & PREMIUM STRATEGY FUND; *U.S. Public*, pg. 2300
VIRTUS REAL ESTATE CAPITAL; *U.S. Private*, pg. 4389
VISA, INC.; *U.S. Public*, pg. 2301
VISCOGLIOSI BROTHERS ACQUISITION CORP.; *U.S. Public*, pg. 2302
VISION CAPITAL - GENEVA—See Vision Capital LP; *U.S. Private*, pg. 4390
VISION INVESTMENTS, LLC; *U.S. Private*, pg. 4391
VISION RIDGE PARTNERS, LLC; *U.S. Private*, pg. 4391
VISION SENSING ACQUISITION CORP.; *U.S. Public*, pg. 2304
VISKASE BRASIL EMBALAGENS LTDA.—See Icahn Enterprises L.P.; *U.S. Public*, pg. 1085
VISKASE GMBH—See Icahn Enterprises L.P.; *U.S. Public*, pg. 1085
VISTA CREDIT STRATEGIC LENDING CORP.; *U.S. Private*, pg. 4394
VISTA DESARROLLO, S.A. SCR DE REGIMEN SIMPLIFICADO—See Banco Santander, S.A.; *Int'l*, pg. 828
VISTA EQUITY PARTNERS, LLC; *U.S. Private*, pg. 4394
VISTAS MEDIA ACQUISITION COMPANY INC.; *U.S. Public*, pg. 2305
THE VISTRIA GROUP, LP; *U.S. Private*, pg. 4131
VITAL HUMAN CAPITAL, INC.; *U.S. Private*, pg. 2306
VIVEON HEALTH ACQUISITION CORP.; *U.S. Private*, pg. 2307
VIVINT SMART HOME, INC.—See NRG Energy, Inc.; *U.S. Public*, pg. 1551
VIVTERA GLOBAL BUSINESS LLP—See Warburg Pincus LLC; *U.S. Private*, pg. 4440
VMG CONSUMER ACQUISITION CORP.; *U.S. Public*, pg. 2307
VMG PARTNERS, LLC; *U.S. Private*, pg. 4408
VOC ENERGY TRUST; *U.S. Public*, pg. 2308
VOLITION CAPITAL LLC; *U.S. Private*, pg. 4410
VOLKSFURSORGE 1. IMMOBILIEN AG & CO. KG—See Cinven Limited; *Int'l*, pg. 1616
VOLVO AUTOMOTIVE FINANCE (CHINA) LTD—See AB Volvo; *Int'l*, pg. 42
VOLVO BUSINESS SERVICES AB—See AB Volvo; *Int'l*, pg. 43
VOLVO FINANCE (SUISSE) SA VAUD—See AB Volvo; *Int'l*, pg. 44
VOLVO FINANCIAL SERVICES GMBH—See AB Volvo; *Int'l*, pg. 44
VOLVO FINANS NORGE AS—See AB Volvo; *Int'l*, pg. 44
VOLVO HOLDING FRANCE SA—See AB Volvo; *Int'l*, pg. 44
VOLVO HOLDING MEXICO, S.A. DE C.V.—See AB Volvo; *Int'l*, pg. 44
VOLVO INDIA LTD - VOLVO FINANCIAL SERVICES INDIA DIVISION—See AB Volvo; *Int'l*, pg. 46
VOM, LLC—See Velocity Portfolio Group, Inc.; *U.S. Private*, pg. 4354
VORA VENTURES LLC; *U.S. Private*, pg. 4412
VOYA EMERGING MARKETS HIGH DIVIDEND EQUITY FUND; *U.S. Public*, pg. 2311
VOYAGER CAPITAL, LLC; *U.S. Private*, pg. 4414
VOYAGER INTERESTS, LLC; *U.S. Private*, pg. 4414
VPR BRANDS, L.P.; *U.S. Public*, pg. 2312
VR HOLDINGS, INC.; *U.S. Private*, pg. 4415
VSEE HEALTH, INC.; *U.S. Public*, pg. 2313
VSPEED CAPITAL, LLC; *U.S. Private*, pg. 4415
VSPEED CAPITAL, LLC—See AG Hill Partners LLC; *U.S. Private*, pg. 124

VULCAN CAPITAL—See Vulcan Inc.; *U.S. Private*, pg. 4416
VULCAN INVESTMENT PARTNERS, LLC; *U.S. Private*, pg. 4416
WAG! GROUP CO.; *U.S. Public*, pg. 2321
WAITR HOLDINGS INC.; *U.S. Public*, pg. 2321
WALDENCAST PLC; *U.S. Public*, pg. 2321
WALDEN VENTURE CAPITAL; *U.S. Private*, pg. 4428
WALLEYE CAPITAL, LLC; *U.S. Private*, pg. 4431
WALL STREET ACQUISITIONS CORP.; *U.S. Private*, pg. 4430
WALLSTREET SECURITIES, INC.; *U.S. Public*, pg. 2324
THE WALNUT GROUP; *U.S. Private*, pg. 4133
WALSH INVESTMENT COMPANY INC.; *U.S. Private*, pg. 4433
WANXIANG AMERICA CAPITAL, LLC; *U.S. Private*, pg. 4436
WARBA CAPITAL HOLDING COMPANY K.S.C.P.—See Boubyan Petrochemical Co. KSC; *Int'l*, pg. 1119
WARBURG PINCUS LLC; *U.S. Private*, pg. 4436
WARM SPRINGS ECONOMIC DEVELOPMENT CORPORATION—See Confederated Tribes of; *U.S. Private*, pg. 1013
WARRIOR TECHNOLOGIES ACQUISITION COMPANY; *U.S. Public*, pg. 2329
WASATCH ADVANTAGE GROUP, LLC; *U.S. Private*, pg. 4445
WASHINGTON CROSSING ADVISORS, LLC—See Stifel Financial Corp.; *U.S. Public*, pg. 1950
WASHINGTON EQUITY PARTNERS L.L.C.; *U.S. Private*, pg. 4447
WASHINGTON GAS RESOURCES CORP.—See AltaGas Ltd.; *Int'l*, pg. 384
WASSERSTEIN & CO., LP; *U.S. Private*, pg. 4450
WATER ASSET MANAGEMENT, LLC; *U.S. Private*, pg. 4451
WATERFORD GAMING FINANCE CORP.—See Waterford Group, LLC; *U.S. Private*, pg. 4453
WATERMILL VENTURES, LTD.—See HMK Enterprises, Inc.; *U.S. Private*, pg. 1955
WATER STREET HEALTHCARE PARTNERS, LLC; *U.S. Private*, pg. 4451
WAUD CAPITAL PARTNERS LLC; *U.S. Private*, pg. 4456
WAVELAND INVESTMENTS, LLC; *U.S. Private*, pg. 4458
WAY HOLDING LTD; *U.S. Private*, pg. 4459
WAYNE HUMMER INVESTMENTS LLC—See Wintrust Financial Corporation; *U.S. Public*, pg. 2375
WAYNE HUMMER TRUST COMPANY, N.A.—See Wintrust Financial Corporation; *U.S. Public*, pg. 2375
WAYZATA INVESTMENT PARTNERS LLC; *U.S. Private*, pg. 4461
WBK 1, INC.; *U.S. Private*, pg. 4461
WEALTHBAR FINANCIAL SERVICES INC.—See CI Financial Corporation; *Int'l*, pg. 1601
WEALTHSOURCE PARTNERS, LLC—See New Mountain Capital, LLC; *U.S. Private*, pg. 2901
WEBSTER EQUITY PARTNERS, LLC; *U.S. Private*, pg. 4466
WEBSTER MORTGAGE COMPANY—See Webster Financial Corporation; *U.S. Public*, pg. 2341
WEBSTER MORTGAGE INVESTMENT CORPORATION—See Webster Financial Corporation; *U.S. Public*, pg. 2341
WECHTER FELDMAN WEALTH MANAGEMENT, INC.; *U.S. Private*, pg. 4468
WEIGHT WATCHERS EUROPEAN HOLDING AB—See WW International, Inc.; *U.S. Public*, pg. 2384
WEINBERG CAPITAL GROUP, INC.; *U.S. Private*, pg. 4471
WELCOME FINANCIAL SERVICES LIMITED—See Cattles Limited; *Int'l*, pg. 1361
WELLS FARGO COMMERCIAL DISTRIBUTION FINANCE, LLC—See Wells Fargo & Company; *U.S. Public*, pg. 2346
WELLS FARGO ENERGY GROUP—See Wells Fargo & Company; *U.S. Public*, pg. 2346
WELLS FARGO VENDOR FINANCIAL SERVICES, LLC—See Wells Fargo & Company; *U.S. Public*, pg. 2347
WELLSPRING CAPITAL MANAGEMENT LLC; *U.S. Private*, pg. 4477
WELSBACH TECHNOLOGY METALS ACQUISITION CORP.; *U.S. Public*, pg. 2349
WELSH, CARSON, ANDERSON & STOWE; *U.S. Private*, pg. 4479
WEMBLY ENTERPRISES LLC; *U.S. Private*, pg. 4480
WEST-ANTANTIC PARTNERS LLC; *U.S. Private*, pg. 4488
WEST BULL SECURITIES LIMITED—See Furniweb Holdings Limited; *Int'l*, pg. 2846
WEST COAST CAPITAL LLC; *U.S. Private*, pg. 4484
WEST COAST VENTURES GROUP CORP.; *U.S. Public*, pg. 2352
WEST CREEK FINANCIAL, INC.; *U.S. Private*, pg. 4484
WESTECH CAPITAL CORP.; *U.S. Private*, pg. 4489
WEST EDGE PARTNERS, LLC; *U.S. Private*, pg. 4485
WEST END HOLDINGS LLC; *U.S. Private*, pg. 4485
WESTERN ACQUISITION VENTURES CORP.; *U.S. Public*, pg. 2354
WESTERN ASSET HIGH YIELD DEFINED OPPORTUNITY

N.A.I.C.S. INDEX

FUND INC.—See Franklin Resources, Inc.; *U.S. Public*, pg. 882
WESTERN ASSET MIDDLE MARKET INCOME FUND INC.—See Franklin Resources, Inc.; *U.S. Public*, pg. 883
WESTERN ASSET MORTGAGE CAPITAL CORPORATION—See TPG Capital, L.P.; *U.S. Public*, pg. 2166
WESTERN EXPLORATION INC.; *U.S. Public*, pg. 2356
WESTERN INTERNATIONAL UNIVERSITY, INC.—See Apollo Global Management, Inc.; *U.S. Public*, pg. 146
WESTERN INTERNATIONAL UNIVERSITY, INC.—See The Vistria Group, LP; *U.S. Private*, pg. 4131
WESTFERRY INVESTMENTS LIMITED—See Barclays PLC; *Int'l*, pg. 863
WESTGKA MANAGEMENT GESELLSCHAFT FUR KOMMUNALE ANLAGEN MBH—See Erste Abwicklungsanstalt AoR; *Int'l*, pg. 2497
WESTLAKE FINANCIAL SERVICES, LLC—See Hankey Group; *U.S. Private*, pg. 1853
WESTLOCK CONTROLS HOLDINGS, INC.—See Crane NXT, Co.; *U.S. Public*, pg. 589
WESTON PRESIDIO CAPITAL; *U.S. Private*, pg. 4500
WESTPOINT HOME (BAHRAIN) W.L.L.—See Icahn Enterprises L.P.; *U.S. Public*, pg. 1085
WESTSHORE CAPITAL PARTNERS LLC; *U.S. Private*, pg. 4500
WESTVIEW CAPITAL PARTNERS, L.P.; *U.S. Private*, pg. 4501
WESTWICKE PARTNERS, LLC—See ICR, LLC; *U.S. Private*, pg. 2033
WEXFORD CAPITAL LIMITED PARTNERSHIP; *U.S. Private*, pg. 4502
WFN CREDIT COMPANY, LLC—See Bread Financial Holdings Inc.; *U.S. Public*, pg. 381
WGI HOLDINGS, INC.; *U.S. Public*, pg. 2365
WHEELER REAL ESTATE INVESTMENT TRUST, INC.; *U.S. Public*, pg. 2365
WHEELOCK STREET CAPITAL L.L.C.; *U.S. Private*, pg. 4506
WHIPPOORWILL ASSOCIATES, INC.; *U.S. Private*, pg. 4506
WHISKEY ACQUISITION, INC.; *U.S. Private*, pg. 4507
WHITECLIFF CAPITAL PARTNERS, INC.; *U.S. Private*, pg. 4511
WHITE DEER MANAGEMENT LLC; *U.S. Private*, pg. 4508
WHITEHORSE FINANCE, INC.; *U.S. Public*, pg. 2369
WHITE OAK GLOBAL ADVISORS, LLC; *U.S. Private*, pg. 4509
WHITESTONE COMMUNICATIONS, INC.; *U.S. Private*, pg. 4512
WHITE WOLF CAPITAL LLC; *U.S. Private*, pg. 4510
WHITING USA TRUST II; *U.S. Public*, pg. 2369
WHOLESOME HOLDINGS GROUP, LLC; *U.S. Private*, pg. 4515
THE WICKS GROUP OF COMPANIES, LLC; *U.S. Private*, pg. 4135
WI HARPER GROUP; *U.S. Private*, pg. 4515
WILKS BROTHERS LLC; *U.S. Private*, pg. 4521
WILLAMETTE BEVERAGE COMPANY; *U.S. Private*, pg. 4521
WILLANDRA VILLAGE MANAGEMENT PTY LTD—See Australian Unity Limited; *Int'l*, pg. 723
WILLCREST PARTNERS; *U.S. Private*, pg. 4521
WILLEMSBRUG B.V.—See Allianz SE; *Int'l*, pg. 356
WILLIAM BLAIR & COMPANY LLC; *U.S. Private*, pg. 4522
THE WILLIAMS CAPITAL GROUP, L.P.; *U.S. Private*, pg. 4136
WILLIAMS ROWLAND ACQUISITION CORP.; *U.S. Public*, pg. 2371
WILLICH BETEILIGUNGEN GMBH—See Bilfinger SE; *Int'l*, pg. 1029
WILLIS & SMITH CAPITAL, LLC; *U.S. Private*, pg. 4527
WILLIS STEIN & PARTNERS, LLC; *U.S. Private*, pg. 4528
WILMINGTON SECURITIES INC—See The Hillman Company; *U.S. Private*, pg. 4053
WILMINGTON TRUST COMPANY—See M&T Bank Corporation; *U.S. Public*, pg. 1351
WILSQUARE CAPITAL LLC; *U.S. Private*, pg. 4532
WINCHESTER CAPITAL PARTNERS, LLC—See Winchester Capital Investment Management Corporation; *U.S. Private*, pg. 4533
WINCHESTO FINANCE COMPANY LIMITED—See CK Hutchison Holdings Limited; *Int'l*, pg. 1638
WINDJAMMER CAPITAL INVESTORS, LLC; *U.S. Private*, pg. 4537
WIND POINT ADVISORS LLC; *U.S. Private*, pg. 4533
WINDROSE HEALTH INVESTORS, LLC—See MTS Health Partners, L.P.; *U.S. Private*, pg. 2809
WINDWARD CAPITAL PARTNERS LP; *U.S. Private*, pg. 4539
WINFIELD ASSOCIATES, INC.—See Keystone Group, L.P.; *U.S. Private*, pg. 2298
WINGAS HOLDING GMBH—See BASF SE; *Int'l*, pg. 885
WINGAS VERWALTUNGS-GMBH—See BASF SE; *Int'l*, pg. 885
WINGATE PARTNERS, LLP; *U.S. Private*, pg. 4541
WINGS & THINGS, INC.; *U.S. Public*, pg. 2374
WINKLEVOSS BITCOIN TRUST; *U.S. Private*, pg. 4542

WINONA CAPITAL MANAGEMENT, LLC—See Laird Norton Company, LLC; *U.S. Private*, pg. 2374
WINTERSHALL RUSSIA HOLDING GMBH—See BASF SE; *Int'l*, pg. 886
THE WINTHROP CORPORATION; *U.S. Private*, pg. 4137
WINTHROP FINANCIAL ASSOCIATES LP; *U.S. Private*, pg. 4545
WINVEST ACQUISITION CORP.; *U.S. Public*, pg. 2376
WISDOMTREE, INC.; *U.S. Public*, pg. 2376
WISER CAPITAL LLC; *U.S. Private*, pg. 4550
WISVEST LLC—See WEC Energy Group, Inc.; *U.S. Public*, pg. 2342
WJ PARTNERS, LLC; *U.S. Private*, pg. 4551
W.L. ROSS & CO., LLC—See Invesco Ltd.; *U.S. Public*, pg. 1163
WM PARTNERS LP; *U.S. Private*, pg. 4552
WM TECHNOLOGY, INC.; *U.S. Public*, pg. 2376
WODA CORP.; *U.S. Public*, pg. 2376
WOLSELEY HOLDINGS DENMARK A/S—See Ferguson plc; *Int'l*, pg. 2638
WOLVERINE CAPITAL PARTNERS LLC; *U.S. Private*, pg. 4555
WOMEN'S COLLEGE PARTNERSHIP—See Bilfinger SE; *Int'l*, pg. 1029
WOODARD TECHNOLOGY & INVESTMENTS LLC; *U.S. Private*, pg. 4557
WOODLAWN PARTNERS, INC.; *U.S. Private*, pg. 4559
WOODSIDE CAPITAL PARTNERS; *U.S. Private*, pg. 4560
WOOSHIN VENTURE INVESTMENT CO., LTD.—See Asia Holdings Co., Ltd.; *Int'l*, pg. 613
WORKLYN PARTNERS; *U.S. Private*, pg. 4564
WORLDNET, INC. OF NEVADA; *U.S. Private*, pg. 4569
WORLDPORT LLC—See Decurion Corp.; *U.S. Private*, pg. 1188
WORLD TRADE & MARKETING, LTD.—See Tootsie Roll Industries, Inc.; *U.S. Public*, pg. 2163
W.P. CAREY INC.; *U.S. Public*, pg. 2315
WPS ADVISORS, INC.—See Equitable Holdings, Inc.; *U.S. Public*, pg. 789
WRENN FINANCIAL STRATEGIES, INC.—See Genstar Capital, LLC; *U.S. Private*, pg. 1677
WRENN FINANCIAL STRATEGIES, INC.—See Keystone Group, L.P.; *U.S. Private*, pg. 2298
WRIGHT INVESTORS' SERVICE HOLDINGS, INC.; *U.S. Public*, pg. 2383
WYNCREST GROUP, INC.; *U.S. Public*, pg. 2384
WYNDHAM CONSUMER FINANCE, INC.—See Travel & Leisure Co.; *U.S. Public*, pg. 2185
WYNNCHURCH CAPITAL, L.P.; *U.S. Private*, pg. 4576
XANGE PRIVATE EQUITY, S.A.—See Groupe Siparex; *Int'l*, pg. 3111
XEROX FINANCIAL SERVICES BELUX NV—See Xerox Holdings Corporation; *U.S. Public*, pg. 2390
XEROX FINANCIAL SERVICES B.V.—See Xerox Holdings Corporation; *U.S. Public*, pg. 2390
XEROX FINANCIAL SERVICES SVERIGE AB—See Xerox Holdings Corporation; *U.S. Public*, pg. 2390
XL FINANCIAL SERVICES (IRELAND) LTD—See AXA S.A.; *Int'l*, pg. 760
XL INVESTMENT MANAGEMENT LTD—See AXA S.A.; *Int'l*, pg. 761
XRX INTERNATIONAL ENTERTAINMENT HOLDING GROUP, INC.; *U.S. Public*, pg. 2393
XS FINANCIAL, INC.—See Axar Capital Management L.P.; *U.S. Private*, pg. 412
XS FINANCIAL, INC.—See Mavik Capital Management, LP; *U.S. Private*, pg. 2616
X-TREME INVESTMENTS, INC.; *U.S. Private*, pg. 4579
YABEZ (HONG KONG) COMPANY LIMITED—See Greenpro Capital Corp.; *Int'l*, pg. 3076
YAYASAN BURSA MALAYSIA—See Bursa Malaysia Berhad; *Int'l*, pg. 1227
YELLOW WOOD PARTNERS LLC; *U.S. Private*, pg. 4587
YENNI CAPITAL, INC.; *U.S. Private*, pg. 4588
YIELDSTREET, INC.; *U.S. Public*, pg. 4589
YORK MANAGEMENT SERVICES, INC.; *U.S. Private*, pg. 4590
YORK STREET CAPITAL PARTNERS; *U.S. Private*, pg. 4591
YOTTA ACQUISITION CORPORATION; *U.S. Public*, pg. 2399
YOUNT, HYDE & BARBOUR PC; *U.S. Private*, pg. 4594
YUKON PARTNERS MANAGEMENT LLC; *U.S. Private*, pg. 4595
THE ZABEL COMPANIES, LLC; *U.S. Private*, pg. 4140
ZALATORIS ACQUISITION CORP.; *U.S. Public*, pg. 2401
ZALATORIS II ACQUISITION CORP.; *U.S. Public*, pg. 2401
Z CAPITAL GROUP, LLC; *U.S. Private*, pg. 4595
Z CAPITAL PARTNERS, LLC—See Z Capital Group, LLC; *U.S. Private*, pg. 4595
ZEBAN NOMINEES LIMITED—See Barclays PLC; *Int'l*, pg. 863
ZELNICKMEDIA CORP.; *U.S. Private*, pg. 4600
ZENSHIN CAPITAL PARTNERS LLC; *U.S. Private*, pg. 4601
ZEPHYR MANAGEMENT, L.P.; *U.S. Private*, pg. 4602
ZHEJIANG SILICON PARADISE ASSET MANAGEMENT GROUP CO., LTD.—See Heaven-Sent Capital Management Group Co. Ltd.; *Int'l*, pg. 3305

ZICURO TECHNOLOGIES PRIVATE LIMITED—See ABans Enterprises Limited; *Int'l*, pg. 48
ZIMMER ENERGY TRANSITION ACQUISITION CORP.; *U.S. Public*, pg. 2408
ZM FINANCIAL SYSTEMS, LLC—See Moody's Corporation; *U.S. Public*, pg. 1469
ZNERGY, INC.; *U.S. Public*, pg. 4607
ZOOM COMPANIES, INC.; *U.S. Private*, pg. 4608
ZS FUND L.P.; *U.S. Private*, pg. 4609
ZT CORPORATE; *U.S. Public*, pg. 4609
ZULU MARKETING, LLC; *U.S. Private*, pg. 4610
Z-WORK ACQUISITION CORP.; *U.S. Public*, pg. 2400

524113 — DIRECT LIFE INSURANCE CARRIERS

1075 PEACHTREE, LLC—See MetLife, Inc.; *U.S. Public*, pg. 1429
655 WEST BROADWAY, LLC—See MetLife, Inc.; *U.S. Public*, pg. 1429
AAA LIFE INSURANCE COMPANY—See The American Automobile Association, Inc.; *U.S. Private*, pg. 3985
ABACUS LIFE, INC.; *U.S. Public*, pg. 13
ABSA MANX INSURANCE COMPANY LIMITED—See Absa Group Limited; *Int'l*, pg. 69
ACACIA LIFE INSURANCE COMPANY—See Ameritas Mutual Holding Company; *U.S. Public*, pg. 261
ACCORDIA LIFE AND ANNUITY COMPANY—See KKR & Co. Inc.; *U.S. Public*, pg. 1251
ADAMJEE LIFE ASSURANCE COMPANY LIMITED—See Adamjee Insurance Company Limited; *Int'l*, pg. 124
ADONIS INSURANCE COMPANY SYRIA S.A.—See Byblos Bank S.A.L.; *Int'l*, pg. 1233
ADRIATICA DE SEGUROS C.A.—See Allianz SE; *Int'l*, pg. 342
ADVANTAGE INSURANCE INC.; *U.S. Private*, pg. 94
AEGON LEVENSVERZEKERING N.V.—See ASR Nederland N.V.; *Int'l*, pg. 632
AEGON SCOTTISH EQUITABLE PLC—See Aegon N.V.; *Int'l*, pg. 174
AEGON USA, INC.—See Aegon N.V.; *Int'l*, pg. 174
AEGON USA, INC.—See Aegon N.V.; *Int'l*, pg. 174
AEGON USA-MONUMENTAL DIVISION—See Aegon N.V.; *Int'l*, pg. 174
AEON ALLIANZ LIFE INSURANCE CO., LTD.—See AEON Co., Ltd.; *Int'l*, pg. 177
AETNA BETTER HEALTH INC.—See CVS Health Corporation; *U.S. Public*, pg. 614
AETNA HEALTH INC. (CONNECTICUT)—See CVS Health Corporation; *U.S. Public*, pg. 614
AETNA HEALTH SERVICES (UK) LIMITED—See CVS Health Corporation; *U.S. Public*, pg. 615
AETNA SPECIALTY PHARMACY, LLC—See CVS Health Corporation; *U.S. Public*, pg. 614
AETNA STUDENT HEALTH AGENCY INC.—See CVS Health Corporation; *U.S. Public*, pg. 614
AFLAC HEARTFUL SERVICES COMPANY LIMITED—See Aflac Incorporated; *U.S. Public*, pg. 57
AFLAC INCORPORATED; *U.S. Public*, pg. 57
AGEAS FRANCE S.A.—See Ageas SA/NV; *Int'l*, pg. 204
AGEAS UK LTD.—See Ageas SA/NV; *Int'l*, pg. 205
AGESA HAYAT VE EMEKLILIK AS; *Int'l*, pg. 206
AGF LIFE LUXEMBOURG S.A—See Allianz SE; *Int'l*, pg. 342
AGF S.A.—See Allianz SE; *Int'l*, pg. 342
AG INSURANCE N.V.—See Ageas SA/NV; *Int'l*, pg. 204
AG INSURANCE SA/NV—See Ageas SA/NV; *Int'l*, pg. 204
AIA EVEREST LIFE COMPANY LIMITED—See AIA Group Limited; *Int'l*, pg. 227
AIA LIFE INSURANCE CO. LTD.—See AIA Group Limited; *Int'l*, pg. 227
AIG DIRECT INSURANCE SERVICES, INC.; *U.S. Private*, pg. 132
AIG FINANCIAL PRODUCTS CORP—See American International Group, Inc.; *U.S. Public*, pg. 104
AIG STAR LIFE INSURANCE CO., LTD.—See Prudential Financial, Inc.; *U.S. Public*, pg. 1733
ALABAMA REASSURANCE CO. INC.—See Greene Group Inc.; *U.S. Private*, pg. 1776
ALFA LIFE INSURANCE CORPORATION—See Alfa Corporation; *U.S. Private*, pg. 164
ALFASTRAKHOVANIE PLC; *Int'l*, pg. 315
ALICO ASIGURARI ROMANIA S.A—See MetLife, Inc.; *U.S. Public*, pg. 1429
ALICO CIA DE SEGUROS S.A.—See MetLife, Inc.; *U.S. Public*, pg. 1429
ALICO ITALIA S.P.A.—See MetLife, Inc.; *U.S. Public*, pg. 1429
ALINMA TOKIO MARINE CO.—See Alinma Bank; *Int'l*, pg. 329
ALLEANZA ASSICURAZIONI S.P.A.—See Assicurazioni Generali S.p.A.; *Int'l*, pg. 643
ALLIANZ AUSTRALIA LIFE INSURANCE LIMITED—See Allianz SE; *Int'l*, pg. 343
ALLIANZ AYUDHYA ASSURANCE PCL.—See Allianz Ayudhya Capital Public Company Limited; *Int'l*, pg. 341

524113 — DIRECT LIFE INSURAN...

CORPORATE AFFILIATIONS

ALLIANZ AYUDHYA ASSURANCE PCL.—See Allianz SE; *Int'l*, pg. 344
ALLIANZ BURKINA ASSURANCES VIE—See Allianz SE; *Int'l*, pg. 344
ALLIANZ CHINA LIFE INSURANCE CO., LTD.—See Allianz SE; *Int'l*, pg. 344
ALLIANZ ELEMENTAR LEBENSVERSICHERUNGS AG—See Allianz SE; *Int'l*, pg. 344
ALLIANZ GLOBAL LIFE LTD.—See Allianz SE; *Int'l*, pg. 348
ALLIANZ LEBENSVERSICHERUNGS-AG—See Allianz SE; *Int'l*, pg. 348
ALLIANZ LIFE ASSURANCE COMPANY-EGYPT S.A.E.—See Allianz SE; *Int'l*, pg. 348
ALLIANZ LIFE (BERMUDA) LTD.—See Allianz SE; *Int'l*, pg. 348
ALLIANZ LIFE FINANCIAL SERVICES LLC—See Allianz SE; *Int'l*, pg. 348
ALLIANZ LIFE INSURANCE COMPANY OF GHANA LIMITED—See Allianz SE; *Int'l*, pg. 348
ALLIANZ LIFE INSURANCE COMPANY OF NEW YORK—See Allianz SE; *Int'l*, pg. 347
ALLIANZ LIFE INSURANCE COMPANY OF NORTH AMERICA—See Allianz SE; *Int'l*, pg. 347
ALLIANZ LIFE INSURANCE COMPANY S.A.—See Allianz SE; *Int'l*, pg. 348
ALLIANZ LIFE INSURANCE COMPANY—See Allianz SE; *Int'l*, pg. 348
ALLIANZ LIFE INSURANCE JAPAN LTD.—See Allianz SE; *Int'l*, pg. 348
ALLIANZ LIFE INSURANCE MALAYSIA BERHAD—See Allianz SE; *Int'l*, pg. 348
ALLIANZ LIFE LUXEMBOURG S.A.—See Allianz SE; *Int'l*, pg. 348
ALLIANZ MADAGASCAR—See Allianz SE; *Int'l*, pg. 349
ALLIANZ MEXICO S.A.—See Allianz SE; *Int'l*, pg. 349
ALLIANZ ROSNO LIFE—See Allianz SE; *Int'l*, pg. 354
ALLIANZ SERVICES PRIVATE LTD.—See Allianz SE; *Int'l*, pg. 350
ALLIANZ-SLOVENSKA DSS A.S.—See Allianz SE; *Int'l*, pg. 351
ALLIANZ SLOVENSKA POISTOVNA, A.S.—See Allianz SE; *Int'l*, pg. 350
ALLIANZ TAKAFUL B.S.C (C)—See Allianz SE; *Int'l*, pg. 350
ALLIED COOPERATIVE INSURANCE GROUP; *Int'l*, pg. 357
ALPHA PROPERTIES, INC.—See MetLife, Inc.; *U.S. Public*, pg. 1429
AMANA TAKAFUL (MALDIVES) PLC—See Amana Takaful PLC; *Int'l*, pg. 409
AMANA TAKAFUL PLC; *Int'l*, pg. 409
AMASSURANCE BERHAD—See AMMB Holdings Berhad; *Int'l*, pg. 429
AME LIFE LUX SA—See Enstar Group Limited; *Int'l*, pg. 2449
AMERICAN-AMICABLE LIFE INSURANCE COMPANY OF TEXAS—See iA Financial Corporation Inc.; *Int'l*, pg. 3567
AMERICAN BANKERS LIFE ASSURANCE COMPANY OF FLORIDA—See Assurant, Inc.; *U.S. Public*, pg. 214
AMERICAN CONTINENTAL INSURANCE COMPANY—See CVS Health Corporation; *U.S. Public*, pg. 615
AMERICAN EQUITY INVESTMENT LIFE INSURANCE COMPANY OF NEW YORK—See Brookfield Reinsurance Ltd.; *Int'l*, pg. 1193
AMERICAN EQUITY INVESTMENT LIFE INSURANCE COMPANY—See Brookfield Reinsurance Ltd.; *Int'l*, pg. 1193
AMERICAN FAMILY INSURANCE COMPANY—See American Family Mutual Insurance Company; *U.S. Private*, pg. 233
AMERICAN FAMILY LIFE ASSURANCE COMPANY OF NEW YORK—See Aflac Incorporated; *U.S. Public*, pg. 57
AMERICAN FAMILY LIFE ASSURANCE CO.—See American Family Mutual Insurance Company; *U.S. Private*, pg. 233
AMERICAN FAMILY MUTUAL INSURANCE COMPANY; *U.S. Private*, pg. 233
AMERICAN FIDELITY ASSURANCE COMPANY—See American Fidelity Corporation; *U.S. Private*, pg. 233
AMERICAN FIDELITY INTERNATIONAL HOLDINGS, INC.—See American Fidelity Corporation; *U.S. Private*, pg. 233
AMERICAN GENERAL ASSURANCE COMPANY—See American International Group, Inc.; *U.S. Public*, pg. 104
AMERICAN GENERAL FINANCE ADVISORS—See American International Group, Inc.; *U.S. Public*, pg. 106
AMERICAN GENERAL LIFE & ACCIDENT INSURANCE COMPANY—See American International Group, Inc.; *U.S. Public*, pg. 105
AMERICAN GENERAL LIFE & ACCIDENT INSURANCE COMPANY—See American International Group, Inc.; *U.S. Public*, pg. 105
AMERICAN GENERAL LIFE COMPANIES SPRINGFIELD—See American International Group, Inc.; *U.S. Public*, pg. 105
AMERICAN GENERAL LIFE INSURANCE COMPANY—See American International Group, Inc.; *U.S. Public*, pg. 105
AMERICAN LIFE & SECURITY CORP.—See Antarctica Capital, LLC; *U.S. Private*, pg. 287
AMERICAN NATIONAL INSURANCE COMPANY OF NEW YORK—See Brookfield Corporation; *Int'l*, pg. 1174
AMERICAN NATIONAL INSURANCE COMPANY—See Brookfield Corporation; *Int'l*, pg. 1174
AMERICO FINANCIAL LIFE & ANNUITY INSURANCE COMPANY—See Financial Holding Corp.; *U.S. Private*, pg. 1507
AMERICO LIFE, INC.—See Financial Holding Corp.; *U.S. Private*, pg. 1507
AMERITAS LIFE INSURANCE CORP.—See Ameritas Mutual Holding Company; *U.S. Private*, pg. 261
AMP SERVICES (NZ) LIMITED—See AMP Limited; *Int'l*, pg. 432
ANBANG LIFE INSURANCE INC.—See Anbang Insurance Group Co., Ltd.; *Int'l*, pg. 447
ANDA INSURANCE AGENCIES PTE. LTD.—See Marsh & McLennan Companies, Inc.; *U.S. Public*, pg. 1374
ANHEUSER-BUSCH BUSCH EMPLOYEES BENEFIT TRUST; *U.S. Private*, pg. 283
ANNUITY INVESTORS LIFE INSURANCE COMPANY—See Massachusetts Mutual Life Insurance Company; *U.S. Private*, pg. 2605
ANNUITY & LIFE RE (HOLDINGS), LTD.; *Int'l*, pg. 474
AON BENFIELD CANADA—See Aon plc; *Int'l*, pg. 489
APEXA CORP.—See MIB Group Inc.; *U.S. Private*, pg. 2697
AP PENSION LIVSFORSIKRINGSAKTIESELSKAB—See Foreningen AP Pension f.m.b.a.; *Int'l*, pg. 2731
APRIL GERMANY AG—See CVC Capital Partners SICAV-FIS S.A.; *Int'l*, pg. 1882
ARENA SA—See Enstar Group Limited; *Int'l*, pg. 2448
ARES INSURANCE SOLUTIONS LLC—See Ares Management Corporation; *U.S. Public*, pg. 187
ASKO-STRAKHOVANIE PJSC; *Int'l*, pg. 625
ASPF II - VERWALTUNGS - GMBH & CO. KG—See Prudential Financial, Inc.; *U.S. Public*, pg. 1731
ASR VERZEKERINGEN N.V.—See ASR Nederland N.V.; *Int'l*, pg. 632
ASSOCIATED INDEMNITY CORP.—See Allianz SE; *Int'l*, pg. 347
ASSOCIATION FOR ADVANCED LIFE UNDERWRITING; *U.S. Private*, pg. 358
ASSUMPTION MUTUAL LIFE INSURANCE COMPANY; *Int'l*, pg. 649
ASSURANCE IQ, LLC—See Prudential Financial, Inc.; *U.S. Public*, pg. 1731
ASSURANT SOLUTIONS - PRENEED DIVISION—See Assurant, Inc.; *U.S. Public*, pg. 215
ASSURED GUARANTY CORP.—See Assured Guaranty Ltd.; *Int'l*, pg. 649
ASSURED GUARANTY US HOLDINGS INC—See Assured Guaranty Ltd.; *Int'l*, pg. 649
ASSURIA LEVENSVERZEKERING N.V.—See Assuria N.V.; *Int'l*, pg. 650
ATHENE ANNUITY & LIFE ASSURANCE COMPANY OF NEW YORK—See Apollo Global Management, Inc.; *U.S. Public*, pg. 147
ATHENE ANNUITY & LIFE ASSURANCE COMPANY—See Apollo Global Management, Inc.; *U.S. Public*, pg. 147
ATLANTA LIFE INSURANCE COMPANY—See Atlanta Life Financial Group; *U.S. Private*, pg. 371
ATLANTICLUX LEBENSVERSICHERUNG S.A.—See FWU AG; *Int'l*, pg. 2859
AUSA LIFE INSURANCE CO.—See Aegon N.V.; *Int'l*, pg. 174
AVETAS VERSICHERUNGS-AKTIENGESELLSCHAFT—See Baloise Holding AG; *Int'l*, pg. 811
AVIVA-COFCO LIFE INSURANCE CO., LTD.—See COFCO Limited; *Int'l*, pg. 1691
AWP ASSISTANCE UK LTD.—See Allianz SE; *Int'l*, pg. 343
AWP P&C S.A.—See Allianz SE; *Int'l*, pg. 343
AXA ASSURANCE MAROC—See AXA S.A.; *Int'l*, pg. 755
AXA BELGIUM S.A.—See AXA S.A.; *Int'l*, pg. 756
AXA DISTRIBUTORS, LLC.—See Equitable Holdings, Inc.; *U.S. Public*, pg. 788
AXA GENERAL INSURANCE HONG KONG—See AXA S.A.; *Int'l*, pg. 756
AXA GLOBAL STRUCTURED PRODUCTS INC.—See Equitable Holdings, Inc.; *U.S. Public*, pg. 788
AXA INSURANCE PLC—See AXA S.A.; *Int'l*, pg. 758
AXA INSURANCE SINGAPORE PTE LTD—See AXA S.A.; *Int'l*, pg. 756
AXA INTERLIFE S.P.A.—See AXA S.A.; *Int'l*, pg. 757
AXA LIFE INSURANCE COMPANY LIMITED—See AXA S.A.; *Int'l*, pg. 757
AXA LIFE LTD.—See AXA S.A.; *Int'l*, pg. 757
AXA PORTUGAL COMPANHIA DE SEGUROS DE VIDA SA—See AXA S.A.; *Int'l*, pg. 758
AXA TOWARZYSTWO UBEZPIECZEN S.A.—See AXA S.A.; *Int'l*, pg. 758
AXA WEALTH MANAGEMENT SINGAPORE PTE LTD—See AXA S.A.; *Int'l*, pg. 759
AXA ZIVOTNI POJISTOVNA, A.S.—See AXA S.A.; *Int'l*, pg. 759
AXA ZYCIE TOWARZYSTWO UBEZPIECZEN S.A.—See AXA S.A.; *Int'l*, pg. 759
AXERIA PREVOYANCE SARL—See CVC Capital Partners SICAV-FIS S.A.; *Int'l*, pg. 1882
AXIS RE SE—See AXIS Capital Holdings Limited; *Int'l*, pg. 769
AZIMUT LIFE DAC—See Azimut Holding SpA; *Int'l*, pg. 779
BAC INSURANCE CORP—See Banco Bradesco S.A.; *Int'l*, pg. 819
BAJAJ ALLIANZ LIFE INSURANCE CO. LTD.—See Allianz SE; *Int'l*, pg. 351
BAJAJ ALLIANZ LIFE INSURANCE CO. LTD.—See Bajaj Auto Ltd.; *Int'l*, pg. 803
BALOISE BELGIUM SA—See Baloise Holding AG; *Int'l*, pg. 811
BALOISE LIFE LTD.—See Baloise Holding AG; *Int'l*, pg. 811
BALTIMORE LIFE COMPANY—See Baltimore Life Insurance Company Inc.; *U.S. Private*, pg. 462
BALTIMORE LIFE INSURANCE COMPANY INC.; *U.S. Private*, pg. 462
BANCFIRST INSURANCE SERVICES, INC.—See BancFirst Corporation; *U.S. Public*, pg. 269
BANKERS FIDELITY LIFE INSURANCE COMPANY—See Atlantic American Corporation; *U.S. Public*, pg. 222
BANKIA MAPFRE VIDA, S.A. DE SEGUROS Y REASEGUROS—See Lone Star Funds; *U.S. Private*, pg. 2485
BASLER LEBENSVERSICHERUNGS-AG—See Baloise Holding AG; *Int'l*, pg. 811
BASLER VERSICHERUNGS-GESELLSCHAFT—See Baloise Holding AG; *Int'l*, pg. 811
BCC VITA S.P.A.—See Iccrea Holding S.p.A.; *Int'l*, pg. 3578
BCI SEGUROS VIDA S.A.—See Empresas Juan Yarur S.A.C.; *Int'l*, pg. 2391
BEECH UNDERWRITING AGENCIES LIMITED—See Brown & Brown, Inc.; *U.S. Public*, pg. 397
BENEFICIAL LIFE INSURANCE COMPANY—See Deseret Management Corporation; *U.S. Private*, pg. 2128
BENEFICIAL STANDARD LIFE INSURANCE COMPANY—See CNO Financial Group, Inc.; *U.S. Public*, pg. 519
BERKSHIRE HATHAWAY LIFE INSURANCE COMPANY OF NEBRASKA—See Berkshire Hathaway Inc.; *U.S. Public*, pg. 301
BERKSHIRE LIFE INSURANCE COMPANY OF AMERICA—See The Guardian Life Insurance Company of America; *U.S. Private*, pg. 4040
BETA CAPITAL CORP.—See Security National Financial Corporation; *U.S. Public*, pg. 1856
BEYKOZ GAYRIMENKUL YATIRIM INSAAT TURIZM SANAYI VE TICARET A.S.—See Allianz SE; *Int'l*, pg. 351
BHSF, INC.—See Berkshire Hathaway Inc.; *U.S. Public*, pg. 299
BLUEBONNET LIFE INSURANCE COMPANY—See Blue Cross & Blue Shield of Mississippi; *U.S. Private*, pg. 587
BLUE INSURANCE, LIMITED—See Hillhouse Investment Management Limited; *Int'l*, pg. 3393
BLUE SHIELD OF CALIFORNIA LIFE & HEALTH INSURANCE COMPANY—See Blue Shield of California; *U.S. Private*, pg. 593
BNP PARIBAS CARDIF - PORTUGAL—See BNP Paribas SA; *Int'l*, pg. 1083
BOCOM MSIG LIFE INSURANCE COMPANY LIMITED—See Bank of Communications Co., Ltd.; *Int'l*, pg. 842
BORDERLAND INVESTMENTS LIMITED—See MetLife, Inc.; *U.S. Public*, pg. 1430
BOSTON MUTUAL LIFE INSURANCE COMPANY; *U.S. Private*, pg. 622
BOULEVARD RESIDENTIAL, LLC—See MetLife, Inc.; *U.S. Public*, pg. 1429
BPI AIA LIFE ASSURANCE CORPORATION—See AIA Group Limited; *Int'l*, pg. 227
BPI-PHILAM LIFE ASSURANCE CORPORATION—See AIA Group Limited; *Int'l*, pg. 227
BPI-PHILAM LIFE ASSURANCE CORPORATION—See Bank of the Philippine Islands; *Int'l*, pg. 848
BRIGHTHOUSE FINANCIAL, INC.; *U.S. Public*, pg. 383
BROAD STREET GLOBAL ADVISORS LLC—See Prudential Financial, Inc.; *U.S. Public*, pg. 1731
CALIFORNIA CASUALTY MANAGEMENT COMPANY; *U.S. Private*, pg. 718
CALIFORNIA LIFE & HEALTH INSURANCE GUARANTEE ASSOCIATION; *U.S. Private*, pg. 719
CAPITOL LIFE INSURANCE COMPANY—See National Health Corporation; *U.S. Private*, pg. 2855
CARDIF VITA S.P.A.—See BNP Paribas SA; *Int'l*, pg. 1083
CARRES BLUES—See CNP Assurances SA; *Int'l*, pg. 1678
CATHOLIC FINANCIAL LIFE; *U.S. Private*, pg. 788
CATHOLIC LIFE INSURANCE; *U.S. Private*, pg. 792
CATHOLIC ORDER OF FORESTERS; *U.S. Private*, pg. 792
CATHOLIC UNITED FINANCIAL; *U.S. Private*, pg. 792
CATLIN AUSTRALIA PTY LIMITED—See AXA S.A.; *Int'l*, pg. 760
CATLIN CANADA INC.—See AXA S.A.; *Int'l*, pg. 760
CATLIN GUERNSEY—See AXA S.A.; *Int'l*, pg. 760
CATLIN HONG KONG LTD.—See AXA S.A.; *Int'l*, pg. 760
CENTURY HEALTHCARE LLC—See Fringe Benefit Group LP; *U.S. Private*, pg. 1612
CHAMPIONS LIFE INSURANCE CO.—See Maximum Corporation; *U.S. Private*, pg. 2618
CHCS SERVICES INC.—See Capgemini SE; *Int'l*, pg. 1303

N.A.I.C.S. INDEX

524113 — DIRECT LIFE INSURAN...

THE CHESAPEAKE LIFE INSURANCE CO.—See Blackstone Inc.; *U.S. Public*, pg. 354
CHINA PACIFIC INSURANCE (GROUP) CO., LTD.; *Int'l*, pg. 1539
CHINA TAIPING INSURANCE (SINGAPORE) PTE. LTD.—See China Taiping Insurance Holdings Company Limited; *Int'l*, pg. 1557
CHINA UNITED INSURANCE SERVICE, INC.; *Int'l*, pg. 1561
CHUBB INSURANCE AUSTRALIA LIMITED—See Chubb Limited; *Int'l*, pg. 1592
CHUBB INSURANCE JAPAN—See Chubb Limited; *Int'l*, pg. 1592
CHUBB INSURANCE NEW ZEALAND LIMITED—See Chubb Limited; *Int'l*, pg. 1592
CHUBB LIFE INSURANCE VIETNAM COMPANY LIMITED—See Chubb Limited; *Int'l*, pg. 1592
CICA LIFE INSURANCE COMPANY OF AMERICA—See Citizens, Inc.; *U.S. Public*, pg. 506
CIGNA HEALTHCARE OF ARIZONA, INC.—See The Cigna Group; *U.S. Public*, pg. 2060
CIGNA HEALTHCARE OF COLORADO, INC.—See The Cigna Group; *U.S. Public*, pg. 2060
CIGNA INTERNATIONAL CORPORATION—See The Cigna Group; *U.S. Public*, pg. 2060
CIGNA LIFE INSURANCE COMPANY OF CANADA—See The Cigna Group; *U.S. Public*, pg. 2060
THE CINCINNATI LIFE INSURANCE COMPANY—See Cincinnati Financial Corporation; *U.S. Public*, pg. 495
CITIC SECURITIES SOUTH CHINA COMPANY LIMITED—See CITIC Securities Co., Ltd.; *Int'l*, pg. 1622
CITIZENS NATIONAL LIFE INSURANCE COMPANY—See Citizens, Inc.; *U.S. Public*, pg. 506
CITIZENS SECURITY LIFE INSURANCE COMPANY—See Citizens Financial Corporation; *U.S. Public*, pg. 505
CITY OF WESTMINSTER ASSURANCE COMPANY LIMITED—See Chesnara Plc; *Int'l*, pg. 1472
C & J FINANCIAL, LLC—See Security National Financial Corporation; *U.S. Public*, pg. 1856
CLASSIC LIFE INSURANCE—See Assicurazioni Generali S.p.A.; *Int'l*, pg. 646
CLIENTELE LIFE ASSURANCE COMPANY LIMITED—See Clientele Limited; *Int'l*, pg. 1659
C.M. LIFE INSURANCE COMPANY—See Massachusetts Mutual Life Insurance Company; *U.S. Private*, pg. 2605
C&N FINANCIAL SERVICES CORPORATION—See Citizens & Northern Corporation; *U.S. Public*, pg. 504
CNL FINANCIAL CORPORATION—See Securian Financial Group, Inc.; *U.S. Private*, pg. 3594
CNP VITA ASSICURA S.P.A.—See Aviva plc; *Int'l*, pg. 746
COFACE ARGENTINA SA—See Groupe BPCE; *Int'l*, pg. 3092
COFACE AUSTRALIA PTY LTD.—See Groupe BPCE; *Int'l*, pg. 3092
COFACE BELGIUM SA—See Groupe BPCE; *Int'l*, pg. 3093
COFACE BULGARIA EOOD—See Groupe BPCE; *Int'l*, pg. 3093
COFACE CANADA INC.—See Groupe BPCE; *Int'l*, pg. 3093
COFACE CHILE SA—See Groupe BPCE; *Int'l*, pg. 3093
COFACE DEBITOREN GMBH—See Groupe BPCE; *Int'l*, pg. 3093
COFACE DO BRASIL SEGUROS DE CREDITO S.A.—See Groupe BPCE; *Int'l*, pg. 3093
COFACE SERVICIOS ESPANA S.L.—See Groupe BPCE; *Int'l*, pg. 3093
COLONIAL LIFE & ACCIDENT INSURANCE COMPANY—See Unum Group; *U.S. Public*, pg. 2263
COLORADO BANKERS LIFE INSURANCE COMPANY—See Eli Global, LLC; *U.S. Private*, pg. 1360
COLUMBIAN LIFE INSURANCE COMPANY—See Columbian Mutual Life Insurance Company; *U.S. Private*, pg. 978
COLUMBIAN MUTUAL LIFE INSURANCE COMPANY—See Columbian Mutual Life Insurance Company; *U.S. Private*, pg. 978
COLUMBIAN MUTUAL LIFE INSURANCE COMPANY - SYRACUSE—See Columbian Mutual Life Insurance Company; *U.S. Private*, pg. 978
COLUMBUS LIFE INSURANCE CO.—See Western & Southern Financial Group, Inc.; *U.S. Private*, pg. 4490
COMBINED INSURANCE COMPANY OF AMERICA - CHICAGO—See Chubb Limited; *Int'l*, pg. 1591
COMBINED INSURANCE COMPANY OF AMERICA—See Chubb Limited; *Int'l*, pg. 1591
COMBINED LIFE INSURANCE COMPANY OF NEW YORK—See Chubb Limited; *Int'l*, pg. 1591
COMMERCIAL TRAVELERS MUTUAL INSURANCE COMPANY; *U.S. Private*, pg. 984
COMPANION LIFE INSURANCE COMPANY—See Blue Cross & Blue Shield of South Carolina; *U.S. Private*, pg. 587
COMPANION LIFE INSURANCE CO.—See Mutual of Omaha Insurance Company; *U.S. Private*, pg. 2820
CONSECO LIFE INSURANCE COMPANY OF TEXAS—See CNO Financial Group, Inc.; *U.S. Public*, pg. 520
CONSECO SENIOR HEALTH INSURANCE COMPANY—See CNO Financial Group, Inc.; *U.S. Public*, pg. 520

CONSTITUTION LIFE INSURANCE CO.—See Golden Gate Capital Management II, LLC; *U.S. Private*, pg. 1731
THE CONTINENTAL INSURANCE COMPANY—See Loews Corporation; *U.S. Public*, pg. 1340
CONTINENTAL LIFE INSURANCE COMPANY OF BRENTWOOD, TENNESSEE—See CVS Health Corporation; *U.S. Public*, pg. 615
COOPERATIVA DE SEGUROS DE VIDA; *U.S. Private*, pg. 1042
COREBRIDGE FINANCIAL, INC.—See American International Group, Inc.; *U.S. Public*, pg. 105
CORONA DIRECT—See Dexia SA; *Int'l*, pg. 2092
COUNTRY INVESTORS LIFE ASSURANCE COMPANY—See COUNTRY Financial; *U.S. Private*, pg. 1066
COUNTRY LIFE INSURANCE COMPANY—See COUNTRY Financial; *U.S. Private*, pg. 1067
CREDEMVITA SPA—See Credito Emiliano S.p.A.; *Int'l*, pg. 1836
CREDITRAS VITA S.P.A.—See Allianz SE; *Int'l*, pg. 352
CUMMINGS POINT INVESTORS CORP—See Geneve Holdings Corp.; *U.S. Private*, pg. 1670
THE DAI-ICHI FRONTIER LIFE INSURANCE CO., LTD.—See Dai-ichi Life Holdings, Inc.; *Int'l*, pg. 1918
THE DAI-ICHI LIFE INFORMATION SYSTEMS CO., LTD.—See Dai-ichi Life Holdings, Inc.; *Int'l*, pg. 1918
DAI-ICHI LIFE INSURANCE (CAMBODIA) PLC.—See Dai-ichi Life Holdings, Inc.; *Int'l*, pg. 1917
DAI-ICHI LIFE INSURANCE COMPANY OF VIETNAM, LIMITED—See Dai-ichi Life Holdings, Inc.; *Int'l*, pg. 1917
DAI-ICHI LIFE INSURANCE MYANMAR LTD.—See Dai-ichi Life Holdings, Inc.; *Int'l*, pg. 1917
DAI-ICHI LIFE INTERNATIONAL (ASIAPACIFIC) LIMITED—See Dai-ichi Life Holdings, Inc.; *Int'l*, pg. 1917
DAI-ICHI LIFE INTERNATIONAL (EUROPE) LIMITED—See Dai-ichi Life Holdings, Inc.; *Int'l*, pg. 1917
DAI-ICHI LIFE INTERNATIONAL (U.S.A.) INC.—See Dai-ichi Life Holdings, Inc.; *Int'l*, pg. 1917
DAKOTA CAPITAL LIFE INSURANCE CORPORATION—See US Alliance Corporation; *U.S. Private*, pg. 4317
DAS LEGAL PROTECTION INSURANCE COMPANY LTD.—See ARAG SE; *Int'l*, pg. 534
DB INSURANCE CO., LTD.—See Dongbu Group; *Int'l*, pg. 2165
DEARBORN NATIONAL LIFE INSURANCE COMPANY—See Health Care Service Corporation; *U.S. Private*, pg. 1892
DEGREE OF HONOR PROTECTIVE ASSOCIATION—See Catholic Financial Life; *U.S. Private*, pg. 789
DELAWARE AMERICAN LIFE INSURANCE COMPANY—See American International Group, Inc.; *U.S. Public*, pg. 106
DELTA LIFE INSURANCE CO.; *U.S. Private*, pg. 1201
DENCAP DENTAL PLANS, INC.; *U.S. Private*, pg. 1204
DEUTSCHE LEBENSVERSICHERUNGS-AG—See Allianz SE; *Int'l*, pg. 352
DIRECTORS HOLDING CORPORATION—See Directors Investment Group Inc.; *U.S. Private*, pg. 1236
DIRECTORS INVESTMENT GROUP INC.; *U.S. Private*, pg. 1236
DLI ASIA PACIFIC PTE. LTD.—See Dai-ichi Life Holdings, Inc.; *Int'l*, pg. 1917
DNB LIVSFORSIKRING AS—See DNB Bank ASA; *Int'l*, pg. 2148
THE DOCTORS' LIFE INSURANCE COMPANY INC.—See The Doctors Company; *U.S. Private*, pg. 4022
DONGBU LIFE INSURANCE CO., LTD.—See Dongbu Group; *Int'l*, pg. 2165
DREI-BANKEN-VERSICHERUNGS AG—See Bank fur Tirol und Vorarlberg Ag; *Int'l*, pg. 838
DUBAI INSURANCE COMPANY (PSC); *Int'l*, pg. 2218
DUBAI NATIONAL INSURANCE & REINSURANCE PSC; *Int'l*, pg. 2220
EAGLE REALTY GROUP, LLC—See Western & Southern Financial Group, Inc.; *U.S. Private*, pg. 4490
EAST WEST LIFE ASSURANCE COMPANY LIMITED; *Int'l*, pg. 2270
ECHELON GENERAL INSURANCE COMPANY AUTOMOBILE DIVISION—See CAA Club Group; *Int'l*, pg. 1245
ECHELON GENERAL INSURANCE COMPANY NICHE PRODUCTS DIVISION—See CAA Club Group; *Int'l*, pg. 1245
ECHELON GENERAL INSURANCE COMPANY—See CAA Club Group; *Int'l*, pg. 1245
EGYPTIAN LIFE TAKAFUL—See Fairfax Financial Holdings Limited; *Int'l*, pg. 2607
EL CORTE INGLES LIFE, PENSIONS AND INSURANCE, S.A.—See El Corte Ingles, S.A.; *Int'l*, pg. 2340
EMPIRE FIDELITY INVESTMENTS LIFE INSURANCE COMPANY—See FMR LLC; *U.S. Private*, pg. 1555
THE EMPIRE LIFE INSURANCE COMPANY—See E-L Financial Corporation Limited; *Int'l*, pg. 2248
EMPLOYEES LIFE COMPANY MUTUAL; *U.S. Private*, pg. 1386
THE EPIC LIFE INSURANCE CO.—See Wisconsin Physicians Service Insurance Corporation; *U.S. Private*, pg. 4549

EQUITABLE FINANCIAL LIFE INSURANCE COMPANY OF AMERICA—See Equitable Holdings, Inc.; *U.S. Public*, pg. 790
EQUITABLE LIFE & CASUALTY INSURANCE COMPANY; *U.S. Private*, pg. 1416
EQUITRUST LIFE INSURANCE COMPANY—See Magic Johnson Enterprises; *U.S. Private*, pg. 2546
ERIE FAMILY LIFE INSURANCE COMPANY—See Erie Indemnity Company; *U.S. Public*, pg. 792
ERIE INSURANCE COMPANY—See Erie Indemnity Company; *U.S. Public*, pg. 792
ERIE INSURANCE PROPERTY & CASUALTY COMPANY—See Erie Indemnity Company; *U.S. Public*, pg. 792
ERIE & NIAGARA INSURANCE ASSOCIATION; *U.S. Private*, pg. 1420
EUROCORE GP S A R.L.—See Prudential Financial, Inc.; *U.S. Public*, pg. 1731
EUROLIFE LTD—See Bank of Cyprus Holdings Public Limited Company; *Int'l*, pg. 842
EUROP ASSISTANCE VAI S.P.A.—See Assicurazioni Generali S.p.A.; *Int'l*, pg. 644
EUROVITA ASSICURAZIONI S.P.A—See Cinven Limited; *Int'l*, pg. 1612
EVEREST GROUP, LTD.; *Int'l*, pg. 2564
EXCEPTIONAL RISK ADVISORS, LLC; *U.S. Private*, pg. 1446
FAJR AL-GULF INSURANCE & REINSURANCE COMPANY—See Fairfax Financial Holdings Limited; *Int'l*, pg. 2607
FALCON LEVEN N.V.—See ASR Nederland N.V.; *Int'l*, pg. 632
FAMILY BENEFIT LIFE INSURANCE COMPANY—See FIRST TRINITY FINANCIAL CORPORATION; *U.S. Private*, pg. 1530
FAMILY HERITAGE LIFE INSURANCE COMPANY OF AMERICA—See Globe Life Inc.; *U.S. Public*, pg. 946
FAMILY LIFE INSURANCE CO—See The Manhattan Insurance Group; *U.S. Private*, pg. 4074
FARM BUREAU LIFE INSURANCE COMPANY OF MISSOURI, INC.—See Missouri Farm Bureau; *U.S. Private*, pg. 2749
FARM BUREAU LIFE INSURANCE COMPANY—See Iowa Farm Bureau Federation; *U.S. Private*, pg. 2134
FARMERS AUTOMOBILE INSURANCE ASSOCIATION; *U.S. Private*, pg. 1476
FATUM LIFE NV—See Guardian Holdings Limited; *Int'l*, pg. 3171
FBL MARKETING SERVICES, L.L.C.—See Iowa Farm Bureau Federation; *U.S. Private*, pg. 2134
FEDERAL LIFE INSURANCE COMPANY; *U.S. Private*, pg. 1489
FIBA EMEKLILIK VE HAYAT A.S.—See Fiba Holding A.S.; *Int'l*, pg. 2651
FIDELITY & GUARANTY LIFE INSURANCE COMPANY—See Fidelity National Financial, Inc.; *U.S. Public*, pg. 831
FIDELITY INVESTMENTS LIFE INSURANCE COMPANY—See FMR LLC; *U.S. Private*, pg. 1555
FIDELITY SECURITY LIFE INSURANCE COMPANY; *U.S. Private*, pg. 1503
FINANCIAL ASSURANCE LIFE INSURANCE COMPANY—See Financial Holding Corp.; *U.S. Private*, pg. 1507
FIRST AMERITAS LIFE INSURANCE CORP. OF NEW YORK—See Ameritas Mutual Holding Company; *U.S. Private*, pg. 261
THE FIRST CATHOLIC SLOVAK LADIES ASSOCIATION; *U.S. Private*, pg. 4029
FIRST NATIONAL LIFE INSURANCE COMPANY OF THE USA, INC.—See Nelnet, Inc.; *U.S. Public*, pg. 1504
FIRST PENN-PACIFIC LIFE INSURANCE COMPANY—See Lincoln National Corporation; *U.S. Public*, pg. 1319
FLAGSHIP CITY INSURANCE COMPANY—See Erie Indemnity Company; *U.S. Public*, pg. 792
FLORIDA COMBINED LIFE INSURANCE COMPANY INC.—See GuideWell Mutual Holding Corporation; *U.S. Private*, pg. 1813
FLT PRIME INSURANCE CORPORATION—See Ayalaland Logistics Holdings Corp.; *Int'l*, pg. 774
FOLKSAM OMSESIDIG LIVFORSAKRING—See Folksam omsesidig sakforsakring; *Int'l*, pg. 2721
FOLKSAM SKADEFORSAKRING AB—See Fennia Group; *Int'l*, pg. 2634
FORENADE LIV GRUPPFORSAKRING AB—See Folksam omsesidig sakforsakring; *Int'l*, pg. 2721
FORESTERS LIFE INSURANCE & ANNUITY COMPANY—See Golden Gate Capital Management II, LLC; *U.S. Private*, pg. 1731
FORETHOUGHT FINANCIAL GROUP, INC.—See KKR & Co. Inc.; *U.S. Public*, pg. 1251
FORTISSIMO CO., LTD.—See MetLife, Inc.; *U.S. Public*, pg. 1430
FORTUNA LEBENS-VERSICHERUNGS AG VADUZ—See FWU AG; *Int'l*, pg. 2859
FTLIFE INSURANCE COMPANY LIMITED—See Chow Tai Fook Enterprises Limited; *Int'l*, pg. 1585
FUBON LIFE ASSURANCE CO., LTD.—See Fubon Finan-

4421

524113 — DIRECT LIFE INSURAN...

cial Holding Co. Ltd.; *Int'l*, pg. 2802
FUBON LIFE INSURANCE (HONG KONG) COMPANY LIMITED—See Fubon Financial Holding Co. Ltd.; *Int'l*, pg. 2802
FUKOKU LIFE INTERNATIONAL (AMERICA) INC.—See Fukoku Mutual Life Insurance Company; *Int'l*, pg. 2839
FUKOKU LIFE INTERNATIONAL (U.K.) LTD.—See Fukoku Mutual Life Insurance Company; *Int'l*, pg. 2839
FUKOKU MUTUAL LIFE INSURANCE COMPANY; *Int'l*, pg. 2839
FUNERAL DIRECTORS CAPITAL VENTURES INC.—See Directors Investment Group Inc.; *U.S. Private*, pg. 1236
FUNERAL DIRECTORS LIFE INSURANCE CO. INC.—See Directors Investment Group Inc.; *U.S. Private*, pg. 1236
GAN ITALIA VITA S.P.A.—See Groupama SA; *Int'l*, pg. 3090
GBU FINANCIAL LIFE; *U.S. Private*, pg. 1653
GENERALI BUSINESS SOLUTIONS S.C.P.A.—See Assicurazioni Generali S.p.A.; *Int'l*, pg. 644
GENERALI HELLAS INSURANCE COMPANY S.A.—See Assicurazioni Generali S.p.A.; *Int'l*, pg. 645
GENERALI OSIGURANJE SRBIJA A.D.O.—See Assicurazioni Generali S.p.A.; *Int'l*, pg. 645
GENERALI PATRIMOINE—See Assicurazioni Generali S.p.A.; *Int'l*, pg. 645
GENERALI PERSONENVERSICHERUNGEN AG—See Assicurazioni Generali S.p.A.; *Int'l*, pg. 644
GENERALI POWSZECHNE TOWARZYSTWO EMERYTALNE S.A.—See Assicurazioni Generali S.p.A.; *Int'l*, pg. 646
GENERALI VIE S.A.—See Assicurazioni Generali S.p.A.; *Int'l*, pg. 645
GENERALI ZAVAROVALNICA D.D.—See Assicurazioni Generali S.p.A.; *Int'l*, pg. 646
GENWORTH FINANCIAL, INC.; *U.S. Public*, pg. 933
GENWORTH LIFE AND ANNUITY INSURANCE COMPANY—See Genworth Financial, Inc.; *U.S. Public*, pg. 934
GERBER LIFE INSURANCE COMPANY—See Western & Southern Financial Group, Inc.; *U.S. Private*, pg. 4490
GLEANER LIFE INSURANCE SOCIETY INC.; *U.S. Private*, pg. 1708
THE GLOBAL ATLANTIC FINANCIAL GROUP LLC—See KKR & Co. Inc.; *U.S. Public*, pg. 1264
GLOBE LIFE & ACCIDENT INSURANCE COMPANY—See Globe Life Inc.; *U.S. Public*, pg. 946
GLOBE LIFE INSURANCE COMPANY OF NEW YORK—See Globe Life Inc.; *U.S. Public*, pg. 946
GOLDEN & COHEN LLC—See Aon plc; *Int'l*, pg. 496
GOLDEN RULE FINANCIAL CORP.—See UnitedHealth Group Incorporated; *U.S. Public*, pg. 2251
GOVERNMENT PERSONNEL MUTUAL LIFE INSURANCE COMPANY; *U.S. Private*, pg. 1746
GRANGE LIFE INSURANCE COMPANY—See Kansas City Life Insurance Company; *U.S. Public*, pg. 1214
GREAT AMERICAN LIFE INSURANCE COMPANY—See Massachusetts Mutual Life Insurance Company; *U.S. Private*, pg. 2605
GREAT SOUTHERN LIFE INSURANCE COMPANY—See Financial Holding Corp.; *U.S. Private*, pg. 1507
GREEK CATHOLIC UNION OF THE U.S.A.; *U.S. Private*, pg. 1770
GROUPAMA PJ SOCIETE DE PROTECTION JURIDIQUE—See Groupama SA; *Int'l*, pg. 3091
GROUPAMA SEGUROS Y REASEGUROS SA—See Grupo Catalana Occidente, S.A.; *U.S. Private*, pg. 3124
GRUPO NACIONAL PROVINCIAL—See Grupo BAL; *Int'l*, pg. 3121
GUARANTY INCOME LIFE INSURANCE COMPANY—See Kuvare US Holdings, Inc.; *U.S. Private*, pg. 2358
GUARANTY REAL ESTATE MANAGEMENT COMPANY, LLC—See Guaranty Corporation; *U.S. Public*, pg. 973
GUARDIAN GENERAL INSURANCE LTD.—See Guardian Holdings Limited; *Int'l*, pg. 3171
GUARDIAN GENERAL LTD—See Guardian Holdings Limited; *Int'l*, pg. 3171
THE GUARDIAN INSURANCE & ANNUITY COMPANY, INC.—See The Guardian Life Insurance Company of America; *U.S. Private*, pg. 4040
GUARDIAN LIFE OF THE CARIBBEAN LTD—See Guardian Holdings Limited; *Int'l*, pg. 3171
GUGGENHEIM LIFE AND ANNUITY COMPANY—See Guggenheim Partners, LLC; *U.S. Private*, pg. 1811
GULF LIFE INSURANCE COMPANY—See Fairfax Financial Holdings Limited; *Int'l*, pg. 2607
GWG HOLDINGS, INC.; *U.S. Public*, pg. 975
HAMISHMAR INSURANCE AGENCY LTD.—See Harel Insurance Investments & Financial Services Ltd.; *Int'l*, pg. 3273
HANA HSBC LIFE INSURANCE CO., LTD.—See Hana Financial Group, Inc.; *Int'l*, pg. 3240
HANA HSBC LIFE INSURANCE CO., LTD.—See HSBC Holdings plc; *Int'l*, pg. 3506
HANSARD EUROPE DESIGNATED ACTIVITY COMPANY—See Hansard Global plc; *Int'l*, pg. 3259
HANSARD EUROPE LIMITED—See Hansard Global plc; *Int'l*, pg. 3259
HANWA ALPHA BUSINESS CO., LTD.—See Hanwa Co., Ltd.; *Int'l*, pg. 3262

HANWHA LIFE INSURANCE CO., LTD.—See Hanwha Group; *Int'l*, pg. 3266
HAREL INSURANCE COMPANY LTD.—See Harel Insurance Investments & Financial Services Ltd.; *Int'l*, pg. 3274
HARTFORD INTERNATIONAL INSURANCE COMPANY—See The Hartford Financial Services Group, Inc.; *U.S. Public*, pg. 2088
HEALTHY LIFE AGRITEC LIMITED; *Int'l*, pg. 3304
HEIDELBERGER LEBENSVERSICHERUNG AG—See Cinven Limited; *Int'l*, pg. 1616
HELVETIA SCHWEIZERISCHE LEBENSVERSICHERUNGS AG—See Helvetia Holding AG; *Int'l*, pg. 3339
HELVETIA SCHWEIZERISCHE VERSICHERUNGSGESELLSCHAFT AG—See Helvetia Holding AG; *Int'l*, pg. 3339
HELVETIA SWISS LIFE INSURANCE COMPANY LTD—See Helvetia Holding AG; *Int'l*, pg. 3340
HERMAN AGENCY INC.—See Principal Financial Group, Inc.; *U.S. Public*, pg. 1721
HM LIFE INSURANCE COMPANY—See Highmark Health; *U.S. Private*, pg. 1940
HOLLARD SPECIALIST LIFE LIMITED—See Hollard Insurance Company Ltd; *Int'l*, pg. 3451
HOMESTEADERS LIFE CO. INC.; *U.S. Private*, pg. 1974
HONOR CAPITAL CORP.—See Geneve Holdings Corp.; *U.S. Private*, pg. 1671
HORACE MANN LIFE INSURANCE COMPANY—See Horace Mann Educators Corporation; *U.S. Public*, pg. 1053
HORIZON MANAGEMENT GROUP, LLC—See The Hartford Financial Services Group, Inc.; *U.S. Public*, pg. 2088
HSBC LIFE UK LIMITED—See HSBC Holdings plc; *Int'l*, pg. 3504
IA AMERICAN LIFE INSURANCE COMPANY—See iA Financial Corporation Inc.; *Int'l*, pg. 3567
IBC LIFE INSURANCE COMPANY—See International Bancshares Corporation; *U.S. Public*, pg. 1145
ICBC-AXA-MINMETALS ASSURANCE CO., LTD.—See AXA S.A.; *Int'l*, pg. 759
ICBC-AXA-MINMETALS ASSURANCE CO., LTD.—See China Rare Earth Resources And Technology Co., Ltd.; *Int'l*, pg. 1545
ICICI PRUDENTIAL LIFE INSURANCE COMPANY LTD.—See ICICI Bank Limited; *Int'l*, pg. 3581
IGI LIFE INSURANCE LIMITED—See IGI Holdings Limited; *Int'l*, pg. 3602
ILLINOIS MUTUAL LIFE INSURANCE COMPANY; *U.S. Private*, pg. 2042
INDEPENDENZIA COMPANY OF LIFE INSURANCE—See W.R. Berkley Corporation; *U.S. Public*, pg. 2316
INDIANA FARM BUREAU INSURANCE—See Indiana Farm Bureau Inc.; *U.S. Private*, pg. 2062
INDUSTRIAL ALLIANCE INSURANCE AND FINANCIAL SERVICES INC.—See iA Financial Corporation Inc.; *Int'l*, pg. 3567
INDUSTRIAL ALLIANCE PACIFIC LIFE INSURANCE COMPANY—See iA Financial Corporation Inc.; *Int'l*, pg. 3567
ING VYSYA LIFE INSURANCE COMPANY LTD.—See EXIDE INDUSTRIES LIMITED; *Int'l*, pg. 2585
INNOVATIVE UNDERWRITERS INC.—See The Guardian Life Insurance Company of America; *U.S. Private*, pg. 4040
INSMARK COMPANY—See Maximum Corporation; *U.S. Private*, pg. 2618
INSPRO, INC.—See Marsh & McLennan Companies, Inc.; *U.S. Public*, pg. 1380
INSURANCE HOUSE; *U.S. Private*, pg. 2095
INTEGRITY LIFE INSURANCE COMPANY—See Western & Southern Financial Group, Inc.; *U.S. Private*, pg. 4490
INTERCONTINENTAL LIFE ASSURANCE COMPANY LIMITED—See Access Corporation; *Int'l*, pg. 89
INTERNATIONAL LIFE INVESTORS INSURANCE COMPANY—See Aegon N.V.; *Int'l*, pg. 174
INVESTORS CONSOLIDATED INSURANCE COMPANY—See The Manhattan Insurance Group; *U.S. Private*, pg. 4074
INVESTORS HERITAGE LIFE INSURANCE COMPANY—See Investors Heritage Capital Corp.; *U.S. Private*, pg. 2132
INVESTORS LIFE INSURANCE COMPANY OF NORTH AMERICA—See Financial Holding Corp.; *U.S. Private*, pg. 1507
ITALO SVIZZERA DI ASSICURAZIONI SULLA VITA S.P.A.—See Helvetia Holding AG; *Int'l*, pg. 3340
JACKSON NATIONAL LIFE INSURANCE COMPANY—See Jackson Financial Inc.; *U.S. Public*, pg. 1183
JAUCH & HUEBENER SPOL. S.R.O.—See Aon plc; *Int'l*, pg. 491
JONATHAN HIND FINANCIAL GROUP—See Principal Financial Group, Inc.; *U.S. Public*, pg. 1721
JSC RUSSIAN STANDARD INSURANCE—See CJSC Russian Standard Corporation; *Int'l*, pg. 1634
THE JUBILEE INSURANCE COMPANY LTD—See Aga Khan Development Network; *Int'l*, pg. 199
THE JUBILEE INSURANCE COMPANY OF TANZANIA LTD—See Aga Khan Development Network; *Int'l*, pg. 199
THE JUBILEE INSURANCE COMPANY OF UGANDA

LTD—See Aga Khan Development Network; *Int'l*, pg. 199
JUBILEE INSURANCE (MAURITIUS) LTD—See Aga Khan Development Network; *Int'l*, pg. 199
JUBILEE LIFE INSURANCE COMPANY LIMITED—See Aga Khan Development Network; *Int'l*, pg. 199
KEMPER HOME SERVICE COMPANIES—See Kemper Corporation; *U.S. Public*, pg. 1220
KEMPER INDEPENDENCE INSURANCE COMPANY—See Kemper Corporation; *U.S. Public*, pg. 1221
KENTUCKY HOME LIFE INSURANCE COMPANY—See Forcht Group of Kentucky, Inc.; *U.S. Private*, pg. 1564
KILPATRICK LIFE INSURANCE CO.; *U.S. Private*, pg. 2304
KPA PENSIONSFORSAKRING AB—See Folksam omsesidig sakforsakring; *Int'l*, pg. 2721
KRUNGTHAI-AXA LIFE INSURANCE CO., LTD.—See AXA S.A.; *Int'l*, pg. 759
KYOEI DO BRASIL COMPANHIA DE SEGUROS—See Prudential Financial, Inc.; *U.S. Public*, pg. 1733
KYOEI KASAI SHINRAI LIFE INSURANCE CO. LTD—See Fukoku Mutual Life Insurance Company; *Int'l*, pg. 2839
THE LAFAYETTE LIFE INSURANCE COMPANY—See Western & Southern Financial Group, Inc.; *U.S. Private*, pg. 4490
LA FEDERATION CONTINENTALE COMPAGNIE D'ASSURANCES SUR LA VIE S.A.—See Assicurazioni Generali S.p.A.; *Int'l*, pg. 645
LAGUNA LIFE D.A.C.—See Enstar Group Limited; *Int'l*, pg. 2449
LATTICE STRATEGIES LLC—See The Hartford Financial Services Group, Inc.; *U.S. Public*, pg. 2088
LA VENEZIA ASSICURAZIONI S.P.A.—See Assicurazioni Generali S.p.A.; *Int'l*, pg. 643
LEGAL CHILE S.A.—See MetLife, Inc.; *U.S. Public*, pg. 1430
LIBERTY NATIONAL INSURANCE CO—See Globe Life Inc.; *U.S. Public*, pg. 946
LIBERTY NATIONAL LIFE INSURANCE CO.—See Globe Life Inc.; *U.S. Public*, pg. 946
LIFE DESIGN PARTNERS CO., LTD.—See Aizawa Securities Group Co., Ltd.; *Int'l*, pg. 255
LIFE INSURANCE COMPANIES OF THE SOUTHWEST—See National Life Insurance Company; *U.S. Private*, pg. 2858
LIFE INSURANCE COMPANY OF ALABAMA INC.; *U.S. Private*, pg. 2448
LIFE INVESTORS INSURANCE COMPANY OF AMERICA—See Aegon N.V.; *Int'l*, pg. 174
LIFE SALES LLC—See Allianz SE; *Int'l*, pg. 347
LINCOLN HERITAGE LIFE INSURANCE CO.—See Londen Insurance Group, Inc.; *U.S. Private*, pg. 2483
THE LINCOLN NATIONAL LIFE INSURANCE CO.—See Lincoln National Corporation; *U.S. Public*, pg. 1319
LION OF AFRICA HOLDINGS COMPANY (PTY) LTD—See Brimstone Investment Corporation Ltd.; *Int'l*, pg. 1164
LONDEN INSURANCE GROUP, INC.; *U.S. Private*, pg. 2483
LOUISIANA DEALER SERVICES INSURANCE; *U.S. Private*, pg. 2499
LOYAL AMERICAN LIFE INSURANCE COMPANY—See The Cigna Group; *U.S. Public*, pg. 2061
LOYAL CHRISTIAN BENEFIT ASSOCIATION; *U.S. Private*, pg. 2506
LUXLIFE—See Groupama SA; *Int'l*, pg. 3091
LV INSURANCE MANAGEMENT LIMITED—See Allianz SE; *Int'l*, pg. 354
MADISON NATIONAL LIFE INSURANCE CO., INC.—See Geneve Holdings Corp.; *U.S. Private*, pg. 1670
MAXIMUM CORPORATION; *U.S. Private*, pg. 2618
MCS LIFE INSURANCE CO.—See JLL Partners, LLC; *U.S. Private*, pg. 2213
MEDLINE DYNACOR DIVISION—See Medline Industries, LP; *U.S. Private*, pg. 2657
THE MEGA LIFE AND HEALTH INSURANCE COMPANY—See Blackstone Inc.; *U.S. Public*, pg. 354
MEMBERS LIFE INSURANCE COMPANY—See CMFG Life Insurance Company; *U.S. Private*, pg. 950
METLIFE ADMINISTRADORA DE FUNDOS MULTIPATROCINADOS LTDA.—See MetLife, Inc.; *U.S. Public*, pg. 1430
METLIFE COMMERCIAL MORTGAGE INCOME FUND GP, LLC—See MetLife, Inc.; *U.S. Public*, pg. 1430
METLIFE GENERAL INSURANCE LIMITED—See MetLife, Inc.; *U.S. Public*, pg. 1430
METLIFE INSURANCE COMPANY OF CONNECTICUT—See MetLife, Inc.; *U.S. Public*, pg. 1431
METLIFE INSURANCE LIMITED—See MetLife, Inc.; *U.S. Public*, pg. 1430
METLIFE INVESTMENT MANAGEMENT LIMITED—See MetLife, Inc.; *U.S. Public*, pg. 1430
METLIFE INVESTMENTS ASIA LIMITED—See MetLife, Inc.; *U.S. Public*, pg. 1430
METLIFE MAS, S.A. DE C.V.—See MetLife, Inc.; *U.S. Public*, pg. 1430
METLIFE SAENGMYOUNG INSURANCE CO. LTD.—See MetLife, Inc.; *U.S. Public*, pg. 1431
METLIFE SLOVAKIA S.R.O.—See MetLife, Inc.; *U.S. Public*, pg. 1430

N.A.I.C.S. INDEX

524113 — DIRECT LIFE INSURAN...

METLIFE WORLDWIDE HOLDINGS, INC.—See MetLife, Inc.; *U.S. Public*, pg. 1430
MIDLAND NATIONAL LIFE INSURANCE CO.—See Sammons Enterprises, Inc.; *U.S. Private*, pg. 3537
MID-WEST NATIONAL LIFE INSURANCE COMPANY OF TENNESSEE—See Blackstone Inc.; *U.S. Public*, pg. 354
THE MINNESOTA LIFE INSURANCE COMPANY—See Securian Financial Group, Inc.; *U.S. Private*, pg. 3594
MISSOURI FARM BUREAU SERVICES—See Missouri Farm Bureau; *U.S. Private*, pg. 2749
MISSOURI FARM BUREAU; *U.S. Private*, pg. 2749
MITHRAS UNDERWRITING LTD.—See Brown & Brown, Inc.; *U.S. Public*, pg. 401
MMA S.A.—See Covea Groupe S.A.S.; *Int'l*, pg. 1820
MML BAY STATE LIFE INSURANCE COMPANY—See Massachusetts Mutual Life Insurance Company; *U.S. Private*, pg. 2605
MODERN WOODMEN OF AMERICA; *U.S. Private*, pg. 2763
MONARCH LIFE INSURANCE CO.; *U.S. Private*, pg. 2769
MONITOR LIFE INSURANCE COMPANY OF NEW YORK—See Commercial Travelers Mutual Insurance Company; *U.S. Private*, pg. 985
MONUMENTAL LIFE INSURANCE COMPANY—See Aegon N.V.; *Int'l*, pg. 174
MONUMENTAL LIFE—See Aegon N.V.; *Int'l*, pg. 174
MOTORISTS LIFE INSURANCE COMPANY—See Motorists Mutual Insurance Co.; *U.S. Private*, pg. 2797
MOUNTAIN LIFE INSURANCE COMPANY—See Forcht Group of Kentucky, Inc.; *U.S. Private*, pg. 1564
MTL INSURANCE COMPANY; *U.S. Private*, pg. 2809
MTL LEASING, LLC—See MetLife, Inc.; *U.S. Public*, pg. 1430
MUTUAL BENEFICIAL ASSOCIATION, INC.; *U.S. Private*, pg. 2819
MUTUAL OF AMERICA LIFE INSURANCE COMPANY; *U.S. Private*, pg. 2820
MUTUAL OF OMAHA INVESTOR SERVICES, INC.—See Mutual of Omaha Insurance Company; *U.S. Private*, pg. 2820
MUTUAL SAVINGS LIFE INSURANCE CO. INC.—See Kemper Corporation; *U.S. Public*, pg. 1220
MUTUAL SAVINGS LIFE INSURANCE COMPANY—See Kemper Corporation; *U.S. Public*, pg. 1220
MY LIFE COVERED LLC—See Reinsurance Group of America, Inc.; *U.S. Public*, pg. 1778
NATIONAL BENEFIT LIFE INSURANCE COMPANY—See Primerica, Inc.; *U.S. Public*, pg. 1717
NATIONAL FAMILY CARE LIFE INSURANCE; *U.S. Private*, pg. 2853
NATIONAL FARMERS UNION LIFE INSURANCE COMPANY—See Financial Holding Corp.; *U.S. Private*, pg. 1507
NATIONAL GUARDIAN LIFE INSURANCE COMPANY; *U.S. Private*, pg. 2855
NATIONAL INSURANCE COMPANY; *U.S. Private*, pg. 2858
NATIONAL LIFE INSURANCE COMPANY; *U.S. Private*, pg. 2858
NATIONAL MUTUAL BENEFIT; *U.S. Private*, pg. 2859
NATIONAL MUTUAL LIFE ASSOCIATION OF AUSTRALIA LTD.—See AMP Limited; *Int'l*, pg. 432
NATIONAL TEACHERS ASSOCIATES LIFE INSURANCE COMPANY—See Horace Mann Educators Corporation; *U.S. Public*, pg. 1053
NATIONAL WESTERN LIFE INSURANCE COMPANY—See Prosperity Group Holdings, LP; *U.S. Private*, pg. 3289
THE NEO FIRST LIFE INSURANCE COMPANY, LIMITED—See Dai-ichi Life Holdings, Inc.; *Int'l*, pg. 1918
NEUFLIZE VIE S.A.—See ABN AMRO Group N.V.; *Int'l*, pg. 65
NEW ENGLAND LIFE INSURANCE CO.—See MetLife, Inc.; *U.S. Public*, pg. 1431
NEW IRELAND ASSURANCE COMPANY PLC—See Bank of Ireland Group plc; *Int'l*, pg. 844
THE NEWPORT GROUP, INC.—See Aquiline Capital Partners LLC; *U.S. Public*, pg. 304
THE NEWPORT GROUP, INC.—See Genstar Capital, LLC; *U.S. Private*, pg. 1675
NEW YORK LIFE FOUNDATION—See New York Life Insurance Company; *U.S. Private*, pg. 2910
NEW YORK LIFE & HEALTH INSURANCE COMPANY INC.—See New York Life Insurance Company; *U.S. Private*, pg. 2910
NEW YORK LIFE INSURANCE COMPANY; *U.S. Private*, pg. 2910
NEW YORK LIFE INSURANCE COMPANY—See New York Life Insurance Company; *U.S. Private*, pg. 2910
NEW YORK LIFE INTERNATIONAL INC.—See New York Life Insurance Company; *U.S. Private*, pg. 2910
NEW YORK LIFE INVESTMENT MANAGEMENT LLC—See New York Life Insurance Company; *U.S. Private*, pg. 2910
NEW YORK LIFE STRUCTURED ASSET MANAGEMENT COMPANY LLC—See New York Life Insurance Company; *U.S. Private*, pg. 2911
NEXTIA LIFE INSURANCE CO., LTD.—See AXA S.A.; *Int'l*, pg. 757
NGL AMERICAN LIFE—See National Guardian Life Insurance Company; *U.S. Private*, pg. 2855
NGL HOLDINGS INC.—See National Guardian Life Insurance Company; *U.S. Private*, pg. 2855
NGL INVESTMENT SERVICES INC.—See National Guardian Life Insurance Company; *U.S. Private*, pg. 2855
NISSAY-GREATWALL LIFE INSURANCE CO., LTD.—See China Great Wall Asset Management Corporation; *Int'l*, pg. 1505
NORTH AMERICAN FIRE AND GENERAL INSURANCE COMPANY—See Edward B. Beharry & Co. Ltd.; *Int'l*, pg. 2316
NORTH CAROLINA JOINT UNDERWRITING ASSOCIATION; *U.S. Private*, pg. 2943
NORTH CAROLINA MUTUAL LIFE INSURANCE COMPANY; *U.S. Private*, pg. 2943
NORTHWEST DENTISTS INSURANCE COMPANY INC.—See Health Services Group, Inc.; *U.S. Private*, pg. 1894
THE NORTHWESTERN MUTUAL LIFE INSURANCE COMPANY; *U.S. Private*, pg. 4084
NPB INSURANCE SERVICES, INC.—See ABRY Partners, LLC; *U.S. Public*, pg. 43
NUCLEUS UNDERWRITING LIMITED—See Brown & Brown, Inc.; *U.S. Public*, pg. 401
NWL SERVICES, INC.—See Prosperity Group Holdings, LP; *U.S. Private*, pg. 3289
OAK RIVER INSURANCE COMPANY—See Berkshire Hathaway Inc.; *U.S. Public*, pg. 313
OCCAM UNDERWRITING LIMITED—See Brown & Brown, Inc.; *U.S. Public*, pg. 401
OCEAN LIFE INSURANCE CO., LTD.—See Dai-ichi Life Holdings, Inc.; *Int'l*, pg. 1917
THE OHIO STATE LIFE INSURANCE COMPANY—See Financial Holding Corp.; *U.S. Private*, pg. 1507
OKKAR LIFTRYGGINGAR HF.—See Arion Bank hf.; *Int'l*, pg. 565
OLD AMERICAN INSURANCE COMPANY—See Kansas City Life Insurance Company; *U.S. Public*, pg. 1214
OLD DOMINION LIFE INSURANCE CO.—See Shenandoah Life Insurance Company; *U.S. Private*, pg. 3632
OLD RELIABLE CASUALTY CO.—See Kemper Corporation; *U.S. Public*, pg. 1221
OLD UNITED CASUALTY COMPANY—See Berkshire Hathaway Inc.; *U.S. Public*, pg. 313
OMNILIFE INSURANCE COMPANY, LIMITED—See Reinsurance Group of America, Inc.; *U.S. Public*, pg. 1777
ONE DIRECT (IRELAND) LIMITED—See An Post LLC; *Int'l*, pg. 443
OZARK NATIONAL LIFE INSURANCE COMPANY—See Prosperity Group Holdings, LP; *U.S. Private*, pg. 3289
PACIFICARE LIFE & HEALTH INSURANCE COMPANY—See UnitedHealth Group Incorporated; *U.S. Public*, pg. 2249
PACIFIC LIFE & ANNUITY COMPANY—See Pacific Mutual Holding Company; *U.S. Private*, pg. 3069
PACIFIC LIFE INSURANCE COMPANY—See Pacific Mutual Holding Company; *U.S. Private*, pg. 3068
PACIFIC PROPERTY AND CASUALTY COMPANY—See Brookfield Corporation; *Int'l*, pg. 1174
PAN-AMERICAN LIFE INSURANCE DE COSTA RICA, S.A.—See Pan-American Life Insurance Group, Inc.; *U.S. Private*, pg. 3084
PAN-AMERICAN LIFE INSURANCE GROUP, INC.; *U.S. Private*, pg. 3084
PARK AVENUE LIFE INSURANCE COMPANY—See The Guardian Life Insurance Company of America; *U.S. Private*, pg. 4040
PEKIN LIFE INSURANCE CO; *U.S. Public*, pg. 1661
THE PENN MUTUAL LIFE INSURANCE COMPANY; *U.S. Private*, pg. 4092
PFP/SCHMITT-SUSSMAN ENTERPRISES; *U.S. Private*, pg. 3165
PGIM, INC.—See Prudential Financial, Inc.; *U.S. Public*, pg. 1731
PGIM IRELAND LIMITED—See Prudential Financial, Inc.; *U.S. Public*, pg. 1731
PGIM LIMITED—See Prudential Financial, Inc.; *U.S. Public*, pg. 1731
PGIM REAL ESTATE (JAPAN) LTD.—See Prudential Financial, Inc.; *U.S. Public*, pg. 1731
PGIM REAL ESTATE LUXEMBOURG S.A.—See Prudential Financial, Inc.; *U.S. Public*, pg. 1731
PGIM REAL ESTATE MEXICO S.C.—See Prudential Financial, Inc.; *U.S. Public*, pg. 1731
PGIM REAL ESTATE (UK) LIMITED—See Prudential Financial, Inc.; *U.S. Public*, pg. 1731
THE PHARMACISTS LIFE INSURANCE COMPANY INC.—See Pharmacists Mutual Companies; *U.S. Private*, pg. 3165
PHILADELPHIA AMERICAN LIFE INSURANCE—See New Era Life Insurance Company of the Midwest; *U.S. Private*, pg. 2896
PHL VARIABLE INSURANCE COMPANY—See Golden Gate Capital Management II, LLC; *U.S. Private*, pg. 1731
PHOENIX FOUNDERS, INC.—See Golden Gate Capital Management II, LLC; *U.S. Private*, pg. 1731
THE PHOENIX INSURANCE COMPANY LTD.—See Delek Group Ltd.; *Int'l*, pg. 2011
PIONEER AMERICAN INSURANCE COMPANY—See iA Financial Corporation Inc.; *Int'l*, pg. 3567
PIONEER SECURITY LIFE INSURANCE COMPANY—See iA Financial Corporation Inc.; *Int'l*, pg. 3567
PIVOTAL FINANCIAL ADVISERS LIMITED—See Dai-ichi Life Holdings, Inc.; *Int'l*, pg. 1918
PLUM UNDERWRITING LIMITED—See Brown & Brown, Inc.; *U.S. Public*, pg. 402
POINTENORTH INSURANCE GROUP LLC; *U.S. Private*, pg. 3222
POLISH NATIONAL ALLIANCE OF US; *U.S. Private*, pg. 3224
POLISH NATIONAL UNION OF AMERICA; *U.S. Private*, pg. 3224
PRAMERICA FOSUN LIFE INSURANCE CO., LTD.—See Prudential Financial, Inc.; *U.S. Public*, pg. 1731
PREFERRED PRODUCT NETWORK, INC.—See Principal Financial Group, Inc.; *U.S. Public*, pg. 1720
PREPAR-VIE SA—See Groupe BPCE; *Int'l*, pg. 3099
PRICOA CAPITAL MANAGEMENT LIMITED—See Prudential Financial, Inc.; *U.S. Public*, pg. 1731
PRIMERICA LIFE INSURANCE COMPANY OF CANADA—See Primerica, Inc.; *U.S. Public*, pg. 1717
PRIMERICA LIFE INSURANCE COMPANY OF CANADA—See Primerica, Inc.; *U.S. Public*, pg. 1717
PRIMERICA LIFE INSURANCE COMPANY OF CANADA—See Primerica, Inc.; *U.S. Public*, pg. 1717
PRIMERICA LIFE INSURANCE COMPANY OF CANADA—See Primerica, Inc.; *U.S. Public*, pg. 1717
PRIMERICA LIFE INSURANCE COMPANY—See Primerica, Inc.; *U.S. Public*, pg. 1717
PRINCIPAL COMPANIA DE SEGUROS DE VIDA CHILE S.A.—See Principal Financial Group, Inc.; *U.S. Public*, pg. 1720
PRINCIPAL LIFE INSURANCE COMPANY—See Principal Financial Group, Inc.; *U.S. Public*, pg. 1721
PRINCIPAL MEXICO COMPANIA DE SEGUROS S.A. DE C.V.—See Principal Financial Group, Inc.; *U.S. Public*, pg. 1721
THE PRODUCERS CHOICE LLC—See Raymond James Financial, Inc.; *U.S. Public*, pg. 1765
PROFESSIONAL LIFE UNDERWRITERS SERVICES, LLC—See The Albrecht Companies, Inc.; *U.S. Private*, pg. 3983
PRO FINANCIAL SERVICES, LLC—See Aon plc; *Int'l*, pg. 497
PROGRESSIVE AMERICAN INSURANCE COMPANY—See The Progressive Corporation; *U.S. Public*, pg. 2125
PROTECTIVE LIFE & ANNUITY INSURANCE COMPANY—See Dai-ichi Life Holdings, Inc.; *Int'l*, pg. 1917
PROVIDENCE LIFE ASSURANCE COMPANY LTD.—See Alpha Growth PLC; *Int'l*, pg. 368
PRUDENTIAL DEFINED CONTRIBUTION SERVICES—See Prudential Financial, Inc.; *U.S. Public*, pg. 1732
PRUDENTIAL FINANCIAL, INC.; *U.S. Public*, pg. 1731
THE PRUDENTIAL INSURANCE COMPANY OF AMERICA—See Prudential Financial, Inc.; *U.S. Public*, pg. 1733
PRUDENTIAL INSURANCE—See Prudential Financial, Inc.; *U.S. Public*, pg. 1732
THE PRUDENTIAL LIFE INSURANCE CO. LTD.—See Prudential Financial, Inc.; *U.S. Public*, pg. 1733
PRUDENTIAL SEGUROS, S.A.—See Prudential Financial, Inc.; *U.S. Public*, pg. 1733
PT ASURANSI CIGNA—See Chubb Limited; *Int'l*, pg. 1592
PT PFI MEGA LIFE INSURANCE—See Prudential Financial, Inc.; *U.S. Public*, pg. 1731
REGENCE LIFE & HEALTH INSURANCE CO.—See Cambia Health Solutions, Inc.; *U.S. Private*, pg. 726
REINSURANCE GROUP OF AMERICA, INC.; *U.S. Public*, pg. 1777
THE RELIABLE LIFE INSURANCE COMPANY—See Kemper Corporation; *U.S. Public*, pg. 1221
RELIASTAR LIFE INSURANCE COMPANY OF NEW YORK—See Voya Financial, Inc.; *U.S. Public*, pg. 2311
RELIASTAR LIFE INSURANCE COMPANY—See Voya Financial, Inc.; *U.S. Public*, pg. 2311
REPUBLIC FINANCE LLC; *U.S. Private*, pg. 3402
RESERVE NATIONAL INSURANCE COMPANY—See Medical Mutual of Ohio; *U.S. Private*, pg. 2655
REVITI LIMITED—See Philip Morris International Inc.; *U.S. Public*, pg. 1687
RGA LIFE REINSURANCE COMPANY OF CANADA—See Reinsurance Group of America, Inc.; *U.S. Public*, pg. 1777
RGA LIFE REINSURANCE COMPANY OF CANADA—See Reinsurance Group of America, Inc.; *U.S. Public*, pg. 1777
RGAX LLC—See Reinsurance Group of America, Inc.; *U.S. Public*, pg. 1778
RIVERSOURCE LIFE INSURANCE COMPANY—See Ameriprise Financial, Inc.; *U.S. Public*, pg. 114
RIVERSOURCE LIFE INSURANCE CO. OF NEW YORK—See Ameriprise Financial, Inc.; *U.S. Public*, pg. 114

524113 — DIRECT LIFE INSURAN...

RMA WATANIYA—See Groupama SA; *Int'l*, pg. 3091
RMB STRUCTURED INSURANCE LIMITED—See FirstRand Limited; *Int'l*, pg. 2690
ROLAND SCHUTZBRIEF-VERSICHERUNG AG—See AXA S.A.; *Int'l*, pg. 759
ROYAL NEIGHBORS OF AMERICA; *U.S. Private*, pg. 3493
ROYAL STATE INSURANCE—See Mutual Benefit Association Hawaii; *U.S. Private*, pg. 2819
SAGICOR INTERNATIONAL MANAGEMENT SERVICES, INC.—See Alignvest Management Corporation; *Int'l*, pg. 328
SAGICOR LIFE INC.—See Alignvest Management Corporation; *Int'l*, pg. 328
SAGICOR LIFE INSURANCE COMPANY—See Alignvest Management Corporation; *Int'l*, pg. 328
SAGICOR LIFE JAMAICA LIMITED—See Alignvest Management Corporation; *Int'l*, pg. 328
SAIF CORP.; *U.S. Private*, pg. 3529
SALT ASSOCIATES LLC—See Reinsurance Group of America, Inc.; *U.S. Public*, pg. 1778
SBLI USA MUTUAL LIFE INSURANCE COMPANY, INC.—See Prosperity Group Holdings, LP; *U.S. Private*, pg. 3289
SC EFG EUROLIFE ASIGURARI DE VIATA S.A.—See Eurobank Ergasias Services and Holdings S.A.; *Int'l*, pg. 2533
SECURITY BENEFIT LIFE INSURANCE COMPANY—See Guggenheim Partners, LLC; *U.S. Private*, pg. 1812
SECURITY LIFE OF DENVER INSURANCE COMPANY—See Voya Financial, Inc.; *U.S. Public*, pg. 2311
SECURITY MUTUAL LIFE INSURANCE COMPANY OF NEW YORK; *U.S. Private*, pg. 3596
SECURITY NATIONAL FINANCIAL CORPORATION; *U.S. Public*, pg. 1856
SECURITY NATIONAL LIFE INSURANCE COMPANY—See Security National Financial Corporation; *U.S. Public*, pg. 1856
SECURITY PLAN LIFE INSURANCE COMPANY—See Citizens, Inc.; *U.S. Public*, pg. 506
SEGUROS VENEZUELA C.A.—See MetLife, Inc.; *U.S. Public*, pg. 1431
SELECTED FUNERAL & LIFE INSURANCE CO.; *U.S. Private*, pg. 3601
SENTRY LIFE INSURANCE COMPANY—See Sentry Insurance Group; *U.S. Private*, pg. 3611
SERVICE LIFE & CASUALTY INSURANCE CO.; *U.S. Private*, pg. 3615
SERVICE LLOYDS INSURANCE COMPANY; *U.S. Private*, pg. 3615
SETTLERS LIFE INSURANCE COMPANY—See National Guardian Life Insurance Company; *U.S. Private*, pg. 2855
SHENANDOAH LIFE INSURANCE COMPANY; *U.S. Private*, pg. 3632
SIERRA HEALTH & LIFE INSURANCE COMPANY, INC.—See UnitedHealth Group Incorporated; *U.S. Public*, pg. 2252
SKANDIA AUSTRIA HOLDING AG—See FWU AG; *Int'l*, pg. 2859
SKANDIA LEBENSVERSICHERUNG AG—See Cinven Limited; *Int'l*, pg. 1616
SKANDIA VERSICHERUNG MANAGEMENT & SERVICE GMBH—See Cinven Limited; *Int'l*, pg. 1616
SLAVONIC BENEVOLENT ORDER OF THE STATE OF TEXAS; *U.S. Private*, pg. 3687
SLOVENE NATIONAL BENEFIT SOCIETY; *U.S. Private*, pg. 3689
SOCAPI—See Confederation Nationale du Credit Mutuel; *Int'l*, pg. 1767
SOUTHERN FARM BUREAU LIFE INSURANCE CO, INC.; *U.S. Private*, pg. 3731
SOUTHERN NATIONAL LIFE INSURANCE COMPANY INC.—See Louisiana Health Service & Indemnity Company, Inc.; *U.S. Private*, pg. 2499
SOUTHLAND NATIONAL INSURANCE CORPORATION—See Eli Global, LLC; *U.S. Private*, pg. 1360
STABLE VISION CORPORATION SDN BHD—See AIA Group Limited; *Int'l*, pg. 227
STANDARD GUARANTY INSURANCE COMPANY—See Assurant, Inc.; *U.S. Public*, pg. 215
STANDARD LIFE ASIA LIMITED—See abrdn, PLC; *Int'l*, pg. 69
STANDARD SECURITY LIFE INSURANCE COMPANY OF NEW YORK—See Geneve Holdings Corp.; *U.S. Private*, pg. 1670
STARMOUNT LIFE INSURANCE COMPANY; *U.S. Private*, pg. 3787
STAR UNION DAI-ICHI LIFE INSURANCE COMPANY LIMITED—See Dai-ichi Life Holdings, Inc.; *Int'l*, pg. 1918
STATE FARM ANNUITY & LIFE INSURANCE CO.—See State Farm Mutual Automobile Insurance Company; *U.S. Private*, pg. 3792
STATE FARM LIFE & ACCIDENT ASSURANCE CO.—See State Farm Mutual Automobile Insurance Company; *U.S. Private*, pg. 3792
STERLING HOLDINGS INC.; *U.S. Private*, pg. 3805

SUN LIFE ASSURANCE COMPANY OF CANADA - U.S. OPERATIONS HOLDINGS, INC.—See Guggenheim Partners, LLC; *U.S. Private*, pg. 1812
SUN LIFE EVERBRIGHT LIFE INSURANCE COMPANY LIMITED—See Anshan Iron & Steel Group Corporation; *Int'l*, pg. 479
SUN LIFE EVERBRIGHT LIFE INSURANCE COMPANY LIMITED—See China Everbright Group Limited; *Int'l*, pg. 1501
SUN LIFE EVERBRIGHT LIFE INSURANCE COMPANY LIMITED—See China North Industries Group Corporation; *Int'l*, pg. 1536
SUN LIFE FINANCIAL EMPLOYEE BENEFITS GROUP—See Guggenheim Partners, LLC; *U.S. Private*, pg. 1813
SUNSET LIFE INSURANCE COMPANY—See Kansas City Life Insurance Company; *U.S. Public*, pg. 1214
SUPERIOR VISION OF NEW JERSEY, INC.—See MetLife, Inc.; *U.S. Public*, pg. 1431
TALCOTT RESOLUTION LIFE INSURANCE COMPANY—See Sixth Street Specialty Lending, Inc.; *U.S. Public*, pg. 1891
TAL DAI-ICHI LIFE AUSTRALIA PTY LTD.—See Dai-ichi Life Holdings, Inc.; *Int'l*, pg. 1918
TAL DIRECT PTY LIMITED—See Dai-ichi Life Holdings, Inc.; *Int'l*, pg. 1918
TAL LIFE LIMITED—See Dai-ichi Life Holdings, Inc.; *Int'l*, pg. 1918
TAL LIMITED-VICTORIA—See Dai-ichi Life Holdings, Inc.; *Int'l*, pg. 1918
TATIL LIFE ASSURANCE LIMITED—See ANSA McAL Limited; *Int'l*, pg. 477
TEACHERS INSURANCE COMPANY—See Horace Mann Educators Corporation; *U.S. Public*, pg. 1053
TERNIAN INSURANCE GROUP LLC—See AXIS Capital Holdings Limited; *Int'l*, pg. 770
TEXAS DIRECTORS LIFE INSURANCE COMPANY INC.—See Directors Investment Group Inc.; *U.S. Private*, pg. 1236
TEXAS LIFE INSURANCE COMPANY—See Vestar Capital Partners, LLC; *U.S. Private*, pg. 4373
THISTLE INSURANCE SERVICES LIMITED—See Apax Partners LLP; *Int'l*, pg. 505
THRIVENT LIFE INSURANCE COMPANY—See Thrivent Financial for Lutherans Foundation; *U.S. Private*, pg. 4165
TIAA-CREF LIFE INSURANCE COMPANY—See Teachers Insurance Association - College Retirement Fund; *U.S. Private*, pg. 3948
TOTAL FINANCIAL & INSURANCE SERVICES, LLC—See Simplicity Financial Marketing Holdings Inc.; *U.S. Private*, pg. 3667
TRANSAMERICA ADVISORS LIFE INSURANCE COMPANY—See Aegon N.V.; *Int'l*, pg. 174
TRANSAMERICA LIFE CANADA—See Vestar Capital Partners, LLC; *U.S. Private*, pg. 4373
TRANSAMERICA LIFE INSURANCE COMPANY—See Aegon N.V.; *Int'l*, pg. 174
TRANSATLANTIC REINSURANCE COMPANY—See Berkshire Hathaway Inc.; *U.S. Public*, pg. 299
TRANS WORLD ASSURANCE INC.; *U.S. Private*, pg. 4205
TRAVELERS UNDERWRITING AGENCY LIMITED—See The Travelers Companies, Inc.; *U.S. Public*, pg. 2136
TRIPLE-S MANAGEMENT CORP.; *U.S. Public*, pg. 2195
TRIPLE-S VIDA, INC.—See Triple-S Management Corp.; *U.S. Public*, pg. 2195
TURK NIPPON SIGORTA A.S.—See Harel Insurance Investments & Financial Services Ltd.; *Int'l*, pg. 3274
THE UNION LABOR LIFE INSURANCE CO.—See Ullico Inc.; *U.S. Private*, pg. 4276
UNION SECURITY INSURANCE COMPANY—See Assurant, Inc.; *U.S. Public*, pg. 216
UNITED AMERICAN INSURANCE COMPANY—See Globe Life Inc.; *U.S. Public*, pg. 946
UNITED FIDELITY LIFE INSURANCE COMPANY—See Financial Holding Corp.; *U.S. Private*, pg. 1507
UNITEDHEALTHCARE INSURANCE COMPANY—See UnitedHealth Group Incorporated; *U.S. Public*, pg. 2252
UNITED LIFE INSURANCE COMPANY—See Kuvare US Holdings, Inc.; *U.S. Private*, pg. 2359
UNITED OF OMAHA LIFE INSURANCE COMPANY—See Mutual of Omaha Insurance Company; *U.S. Private*, pg. 2820
UNITED SECURITY LIFE AND HEALTH INSURANCE COMPANY; *U.S. Private*, pg. 4297
UNITED SECURITY LIFE INSURANCE CO.—See United Security Life and Health Insurance Company; *U.S. Private*, pg. 4297
UNITED SERVICE PROTECTION, INC.—See Assurant, Inc.; *U.S. Public*, pg. 216
THE UNITED STATES LIFE INSURANCE COMPANY IN THE CITY OF NEW YORK—See American International Group, Inc.; *U.S. Public*, pg. 105
UNITED WORLD LIFE INSURANCE COMPANY—See Mutual of Omaha Insurance Company; *U.S. Private*, pg. 2820
UNITY FINANCIAL LIFE INSURANCE COMPANY; *U.S. Private*, pg. 4302

CORPORATE AFFILIATIONS

UNIVERSAL FIDELITY LIFE INSURANCE CO.—See Universal Fidelity Holding Co., Inc.; *U.S. Private*, pg. 4305
UNIVERSAL GUARANTEE LIFE INSURANCE—See UTG, Inc.; *U.S. Public*, pg. 2267
UNUM LIMITED—See Unum Group; *U.S. Public*, pg. 2263
UNUM—See Unum Group; *U.S. Public*, pg. 2263
USABLE LIFE INSURANCE COMPANY—See USAble Corporation; *U.S. Public*, pg. 4322
US ALLIANCE CORPORATION; *U.S. Private*, pg. 4317
US ALLIANCE LIFE & SECURITY COMPANY—See US Alliance Corporation; *U.S. Private*, pg. 4317
US HEALTH AND LIFE INSURANCE CO—See US Health Holdings Ltd.; *U.S. Private*, pg. 4319
US LETTER CARRIERS MUTUAL BENEFIT ASSOCIATION; *U.S. Private*, pg. 4319
VERA FINANCIAL DESIGNATED ACTIVITY COMPANY—See Assicurazioni Generali S.p.A.; *Int'l*, pg. 648
VERA VITA S.P.A.—See Assicurazioni Generali S.p.A.; *Int'l*, pg. 648
VERSANT HEALTH HOLDCO, INC.—See MetLife, Inc.; *U.S. Public*, pg. 1431
VERUS TITLE INC.—See Fathom Holdings Inc.; *U.S. Public*, pg. 824
VITALIA VIE—See Groupe BPCE; *Int'l*, pg. 3096
VOYA FINANCIAL, INC. - SERVICE CENTER—See Voya Financial, Inc.; *U.S. Public*, pg. 2311
VOYA SERVICES CO.—See Voya Financial, Inc.; *U.S. Public*, pg. 2312
WASHINGTON NATIONAL INSURANCE CO.—See CNO Financial Group, Inc.; *U.S. Public*, pg. 520
WEALINS S.A.—See Foyer S.A.; *Int'l*, pg. 2756
WEST COAST LIFE INSURANCE COMPANY—See Dai-ichi Life Holdings, Inc.; *Int'l*, pg. 1918
WESTERN AMERICAN LIFE INSURANCE CO.—See Maximum Corporation; *U.S. Private*, pg. 2618
WESTERN CATHOLIC UNION; *U.S. Private*, pg. 4491
WESTERN FRATERNAL LIFE ASSOCIATION; *U.S. Private*, pg. 4493
WESTERN UNITED LIFE ASSURANCE COMPANY; *U.S. Private*, pg. 4497
WESTMINSTER INSURANCE AGENCY, INC.—See Toll Brothers, Inc.; *U.S. Public*, pg. 2162
WING LUNG INSURANCE CO. LTD.—See China Merchants Group Limited; *Int'l*, pg. 1520
WISCONSIN REINSURANCE CORP.; *U.S. Private*, pg. 4549
WOJTA-HANSEN INSURANCE AGENCY—See Ansay & Associates, LLC.; *U.S. Private*, pg. 285
WOMAN'S LIFE INSURANCE SOCIETY; *U.S. Private*, pg. 4555
WOODMEN OF THE WORLD LIFE INSURANCE SOCIETY, INC.; *U.S. Private*, pg. 4559
WORKMENS CIRCLE INC.; *U.S. Private*, pg. 4564
W.S. VOGEL AGENCY, INC.; *U.S. Private*, pg. 4423
XL SEGUROS BRASIL S.A.—See AXA S.A.; *Int'l*, pg. 761
ZENITH INSURANCE PLC—See Guardian Holdings Limited; *Int'l*, pg. 3171

524114 — DIRECT HEALTH AND MEDICAL INSURANCE CARRIERS

ACCOLADE, INC.; *U.S. Public*, pg. 33
ACCOUNTABLE CARE COALITION OF SOUTHEAST TEXAS, INC.—See Centene Corporation; *U.S. Public*, pg. 471
ACCURATE RX PHARMACY CONSULTING, LLC—See UnitedHealth Group Incorporated; *U.S. Public*, pg. 2247
ACURITY HEALTH GROUP LIMITED—See Evolution Healthcare Pty. Ltd.; *Int'l*, pg. 2572
ADVANTICA; *U.S. Private*, pg. 95
AETNA BETTER HEALTH OF FLORIDA INC.—See CVS Health Corporation; *U.S. Public*, pg. 614
AETNA BETTER HEALTH OF MICHIGAN INC.—See CVS Health Corporation; *U.S. Public*, pg. 614
AETNA GLOBAL BENEFITS (ASIA PACIFIC) LIMITED—See CVS Health Corporation; *U.S. Public*, pg. 614
AETNA GLOBAL BENEFITS (EUROPE) LIMITED—See CVS Health Corporation; *U.S. Public*, pg. 614
AETNA HEALTH INC. (NEW YORK)—See CVS Health Corporation; *U.S. Public*, pg. 614
AETNA HEALTH INC. (PENNSYLVANIA)—See CVS Health Corporation; *U.S. Public*, pg. 614
AETNA HEALTH INC.—See CVS Health Corporation; *U.S. Public*, pg. 614
AETNA HEALTH INC.—See CVS Health Corporation; *U.S. Public*, pg. 614
AETNA HEALTH INSURANCE (THAILAND) PUBLIC COMPANY LIMITED—See CVS Health Corporation; *U.S. Public*, pg. 615
AETNA HEALTH OF CALIFORNIA INC.—See CVS Health Corporation; *U.S. Public*, pg. 614
AETNA HEALTH OF UTAH INC.—See CVS Health Corporation; *U.S. Public*, pg. 614
AETNA INC.—See CVS Health Corporation; *U.S. Public*, pg. 614

N.A.I.C.S. INDEX

524114 — DIRECT HEALTH AND M...

AETNA INSURANCE COMPANY LIMITED—See CVS Health Corporation; *U.S. Public*, pg. 615
AETNA INSURANCE (SINGAPORE) PTE. LTD.—See CVS Health Corporation; *U.S. Public*, pg. 615
AETNA INTELIHEALTH INC.—See CVS Health Corporation; *U.S. Public*, pg. 615
AGATE RESOURCES, INC.—See Centene Corporation; *U.S. Public*, pg. 468
AGILE TECHNOLOGY SOLUTIONS, INC.—See Humana, Inc.; *U.S. Public*, pg. 1069
AHI-HEALTHLINK—See Elevance Health, Inc.; *U.S. Public*, pg. 728
ALASKA COMPREHENSIVE HEALTH INSURANCE ASSOCIATION; *U.S. Private*, pg. 150
ALLIANCE HEALTHCARD, INC.—See Aon plc; *Int'l*, pg. 489
ALLIANZ GENERAL LAOS LTD.—See Allianz SE; *Int'l*, pg. 345
ALLIANZ HELLAS INSURANCE COMPANY S.A.—See Allianz SE; *Int'l*, pg. 348
ALLIANZ SAUDE S.A.—See Allianz SE; *Int'l*, pg. 350
ALLIANZ WORLDWIDE CARE LIMITED—See Allianz SE; *Int'l*, pg. 350
ALLIED SOLUTIONS LLC; *U.S. Private*, pg. 188
ALPINE AGENCY INC.—See Blue Cross & Blue Shield of South Carolina; *U.S. Private*, pg. 587
AMBETTER OF MAGNOLIA, INC.—See Centene Corporation; *U.S. Public*, pg. 468
AMBETTER OF NORTH CAROLINA, INC.—See Centene Corporation; *U.S. Public*, pg. 468
AMBETTER OF PEACH STATE INC.—See Centene Corporation; *U.S. Public*, pg. 468
AMERICAN EAR HEARING AND AUDIOLOGY, LLC; *U.S. Private*, pg. 231
AMERICAN FAMILY LIFE ASSURANCE COMPANY OF COLUMBUS—See Aflac Incorporated; *U.S. Public*, pg. 57
AMERICAN FIDELITY CORPORATION; *U.S. Private*, pg. 233
AMERICAN FINANCIAL & AUTOMOTIVE SERVICES, INC.—See Assurant, Inc.; *U.S. Public*, pg. 214
AMERICAN MEDICAL SECURITY LIFE INSURANCE COMPANY—See UnitedHealth Group Incorporated; *U.S. Public*, pg. 2251
AMERICAN REPUBLIC INSURANCE COMPANY—See American Enterprise Mutual Holding Company; *U.S. Private*, pg. 232
AMERICAN SPECIALTY HEALTH, INC.; *U.S. Private*, pg. 255
AMERIGROUP COMMUNITY CARE OF NEW MEXICO, INC.—See Elevance Health, Inc.; *U.S. Public*, pg. 728
AMERIGROUP CORPORATION—See Elevance Health, Inc.; *U.S. Public*, pg. 728
AMERIGROUP LOUISIANA, INC.—See Elevance Health, Inc.; *U.S. Public*, pg. 728
AMERIGROUP MARYLAND, INC.—See Elevance Health, Inc.; *U.S. Public*, pg. 728
AMERIGROUP NEW JERSEY, INC.—See Elevance Health, Inc.; *U.S. Public*, pg. 728
AMERIGROUP NEW YORK, LLC—See Elevance Health, Inc.; *U.S. Public*, pg. 728
AMERIGROUP TENNESSEE, INC.—See Elevance Health, Inc.; *U.S. Public*, pg. 728
AMERIGROUP TEXAS, INC.—See Elevance Health, Inc.; *U.S. Public*, pg. 728
AMERIGROUP WASHINGTON, INC.—See Elevance Health, Inc.; *U.S. Public*, pg. 728
AMERIHEALTH NEW JERSEY; *U.S. Private*, pg. 259
AMERIPLAN CORPORATION; *U.S. Private*, pg. 260
AMGP GEORGIA MANAGED CARE COMPANY, INC.—See Elevance Health, Inc.; *U.S. Public*, pg. 728
AMIL PARTICIPACOES SA; *Int'l*, pg. 427
ANGIOGRAFIA E HEMODINAMICA MADRE THEODORA LTDA.—See UnitedHealth Group Incorporated; *U.S. Public*, pg. 2239
ANTHEM BLUE CROSS LIFE AND HEALTH INSURANCE COMPANY—See Elevance Health, Inc.; *U.S. Public*, pg. 729
THE ANTHEM COMPANIES, INC.—See Elevance Health, Inc.; *U.S. Public*, pg. 730
ANTHEM CREDENTIALING SERVICES, INC.—See Elevance Health, Inc.; *U.S. Public*, pg. 729
ANTHEM HEALTH PLANS OF MAINE, INC.—See Elevance Health, Inc.; *U.S. Public*, pg. 729
ANTHEM HEALTH PLANS OF VIRGINIA—See Elevance Health, Inc.; *U.S. Public*, pg. 729
ANTHEM INSURANCE COMPANIES, INC.—See Elevance Health, Inc.; *U.S. Public*, pg. 729
APS - ASSISTENCIA PERSONALIZADA A SAUDE LTDA.—See UnitedHealth Group Incorporated; *U.S. Public*, pg. 2238
APS HEALTHCARE, INC.—See Centene Corporation; *U.S. Public*, pg. 471
ARABIA INSURANCE COMPANY S.A.L.—See Arabia Insurance Company; *Int'l*, pg. 533
ARGUS DENTAL PLAN, INC.; *U.S. Private*, pg. 322
ARISE HEALTH PLAN—See Wisconsin Physicians Service Insurance Corporation; *U.S. Private*, pg. 4549
ARKANSAS BLUE CROSS AND BLUE SHIELD—See US-

Able Corporation; *U.S. Private*, pg. 4322
ARKANSAS HEALTH & WELLNESS HEALTH PLAN, INC.—See Centene Corporation; *U.S. Public*, pg. 468
ARKANSAS TOTAL CARE, INC.—See Centene Corporation; *U.S. Public*, pg. 468
ARROHEALTH—See New Mountain Capital, LLC; *U.S. Private*, pg. 2901
ARTEX RISK SOLUTIONS (SINGAPORE) PTE. LTD.—See Arthur J. Gallagher & Co.; *U.S. Public*, pg. 202
ASIA GLOBAL HEALTH LTD.—See Bumrungrad Hospital Public Company Limited; *Int'l*, pg. 1215
ASSISTED 4 LIVING, INC.; *U.S. Public*, pg. 214
ASSURANCES MEDICALES SA—See Allianz SE; *Int'l*, pg. 351
ASSURIA MEDISCHE VERZEKERING N.V.—See Assuria N.V.; *Int'l*, pg. 650
ATLANTA PLUMBERS & STEAMFITTERS; *U.S. Private*, pg. 371
AT MEDICS LTD.—See Centene Corporation; *U.S. Public*, pg. 467
AUSTRALIAN UNITY HEALTH LIMITED—See Australian Unity Limited; *Int'l*, pg. 723
AUTO INJURY SOLUTIONS, INC.—See Advent International Corporation; *U.S. Private*, pg. 98
AVAILITY, L.L.C.—See Humana, Inc.; *U.S. Public*, pg. 1069
AVERA HEALTH; *U.S. Private*, pg. 405
AVESIS, INC.—See The Guardian Life Insurance Company of America; *U.S. Private*, pg. 4040
AVMED HEALTH PLANS—See SantaFe Healthcare, Inc.; *U.S. Private*, pg. 3547
AXA LUXEMBOURG SA—See AXA S.A.; *Int'l*, pg. 757
AXA MANSARD HEALTH LIMITED—See AXA S.A.; *Int'l*, pg. 757
AXA PPP HEALTHCARE GROUP PLC—See AXA S.A.; *Int'l*, pg. 758
AXA SPACE, INC.—See Equitable Holdings, Inc.; *U.S. Public*, pg. 788
BANKERS LIFE & CASUALTY COMPANY—See CNO Financial Group, Inc.; *U.S. Public*, pg. 519
BEACON HEALTH STRATEGIES LLC—See Beacon Health Holdings LLC; *U.S. Private*, pg. 504
BENEFIS HEALTH SYSTEM; *U.S. Private*, pg. 525
BENEFIT RESOURCE GROUP—See GTCR LLC; *U.S. Private*, pg. 1802
BENEFITS MANAGEMENT CORPORATION—See The Cigna Group; *U.S. Public*, pg. 2060
BERKLEY ACCIDENT & HEALTH LLC—See W.R. Berkley Corporation; *U.S. Public*, pg. 2316
BERKLEY HEALTHCARE PROFESSIONAL INSURANCE SERVICES, LLC—See W.R. Berkley Corporation; *U.S. Public*, pg. 2316
BIDV METLIFE LIFE INSURANCE LIMITED LIABILITY COMPANY—See MetLife, Inc.; *U.S. Public*, pg. 1429
BIENVIVIR SENIOR HEALTH SERVICES; *U.S. Private*, pg. 551
BIODAROU PLC—See Grifols, S.A.; *Int'l*, pg. 3084
BLUE CARE NETWORK OF MICHIGAN—See Blue Cross Blue Shield of Michigan; *U.S. Private*, pg. 587
BLUE CHOICE HEALTH PLAN—See Blue Cross & Blue Shield of South Carolina; *U.S. Private*, pg. 587
BLUE CROSS BLUE SHIELD HEALTHCARE PLAN OF GEORGIA, INC.—See Elevance Health, Inc.; *U.S. Public*, pg. 729
BLUE CROSS & BLUE SHIELD OF ALABAMA; *U.S. Private*, pg. 586
BLUE CROSS & BLUE SHIELD OF ARIZONA, INC.; *U.S. Private*, pg. 586
BLUE CROSS & BLUE SHIELD OF FLORIDA, INC.—See GuideWell Mutual Holding Corporation; *U.S. Private*, pg. 1813
BLUE CROSS & BLUE SHIELD OF ILLINOIS—See Health Care Service Corporation; *U.S. Private*, pg. 1892
BLUE CROSS & BLUE SHIELD OF KANSAS CITY, INC.; *U.S. Private*, pg. 586
BLUE CROSS & BLUE SHIELD OF MASSACHUSETTS, INC.; *U.S. Private*, pg. 587
BLUE CROSS BLUE SHIELD OF MICHIGAN; *U.S. Private*, pg. 587
BLUE CROSS & BLUE SHIELD OF MISSISSIPPI; *U.S. Private*, pg. 587
BLUE CROSS & BLUE SHIELD OF NEBRASKA; *U.S. Private*, pg. 587
BLUE CROSS & BLUE SHIELD OF NEW MEXICO—See Health Care Service Corporation; *U.S. Private*, pg. 1892
BLUE CROSS & BLUE SHIELD OF NORTH CAROLINA INC; *U.S. Private*, pg. 587
BLUE CROSS & BLUE SHIELD OF RHODE ISLAND; *U.S. Private*, pg. 587
BLUE CROSS & BLUE SHIELD OF SOUTH CAROLINA; *U.S. Private*, pg. 587
BLUE CROSS & BLUE SHIELD OF TEXAS, INC.—See Health Care Service Corporation; *U.S. Private*, pg. 1892
BLUE CROSS BLUE SHIELD OF WISCONSIN—See Elevance Health, Inc.; *U.S. Public*, pg. 729
BLUE CROSS-BLUE SHIELD WYOMING; *U.S. Private*, pg. 588
BLUE CROSS LIFE & HEALTH INSURANCE

COMPANY—See Elevance Health, Inc.; *U.S. Public*, pg. 729
BLUE SHIELD OF CALIFORNIA - LARGE GROUP BUSINESS UNIT—See Blue Shield of California; *U.S. Private*, pg. 593
BLUE SHIELD OF CALIFORNIA; *U.S. Private*, pg. 592
BMEC (MALAYSIA) SDN. BHD.—See Boustead Singapore Limited; *Int'l*, pg. 1120
BP INC.—See UnitedHealth Group Incorporated; *U.S. Public*, pg. 2239
BRADESCO SAUDE S.A.—See Banco Bradesco S.A.; *Int'l*, pg. 819
BUNKER HILL INSURANCE CASUALTY COMPANY—See The Plymouth Rock Co.; *U.S. Private*, pg. 4097
CAMBRIDGE ARIZONA INSURANCE COMPANY; *U.S. Private*, pg. 726
CAPITAL AREA SERVICE CO. INC.—See CareFirst, Inc.; *U.S. Private*, pg. 753
CAPITAL BLUECROSS INC.; *U.S. Private*, pg. 738
CAPITAL HEALTH PLAN, INC.—See GuideWell Mutual Holding Corporation; *U.S. Private*, pg. 1813
CARDEA HEALTH SOLUTONS LIMITED—See Aon plc; *Int'l*, pg. 494
CARDIF VIE & CARDIF RD—See BNP Paribas SA; *Int'l*, pg. 1083
CARDINAL HEALTH 127, INC.—See Cardinal Health, Inc.; *U.S. Public*, pg. 433
CARE 1ST HEALTH PLAN ARIZONA, INC.—See Centene Corporation; *U.S. Public*, pg. 471
CAREFIRST OF MARYLAND, INC.—See CareFirst, Inc.; *U.S. Private*, pg. 753
CAREFREE INSURANCE SERVICES, INC.—See CVS Health Corporation; *U.S. Public*, pg. 614
CARE IMPROVEMENT PLUS GROUP MANAGEMENT, LLC—See UnitedHealth Group Incorporated; *U.S. Public*, pg. 2239
CAREMARK, LLC—See CVS Health Corporation; *U.S. Public*, pg. 615
CAREMORE HEALTH PLAN—See Elevance Health, Inc.; *U.S. Public*, pg. 729
CAREMORE HEALTH SYSTEM—See Elevance Health, Inc.; *U.S. Public*, pg. 729
CAREPLUS HEALTH PLANS, INC.—See Humana, Inc.; *U.S. Public*, pg. 1069
CARIBBEAN AMERICAN PROPERTY INSURANCE COMPANY—See Assurant, Inc.; *U.S. Public*, pg. 215
CATERPILLAR LIFE INSURANCE COMPANY—See Caterpillar, Inc.; *U.S. Public*, pg. 451
CELTIC GROUP, INC.—See Centene Corporation; *U.S. Public*, pg. 468
CELTIC LIFE INSURANCE COMPANY INC.—See Centene Corporation; *U.S. Public*, pg. 468
CENPATICO OF ARIZONA INC.—See Centene Corporation; *U.S. Public*, pg. 468
CENTENE CORPORATION; *U.S. Public*, pg. 467
CENTERWELL SENIOR PRIMARY CARE (FL), INC.—See Humana, Inc.; *U.S. Public*, pg. 1069
CENTRAL OHIO HEALTH CARE CONSORTIUM; *U.S. Private*, pg. 824
CERULEAN COMPANIES, INC.—See Elevance Health, Inc.; *U.S. Public*, pg. 729
CHINA SHINEWAY PHARMACEUTICAL GROUP LTD.; *Int'l*, pg. 1551
CHOQI CO., LTD.—See EM Systems Co., Ltd.; *Int'l*, pg. 2372
CHRISTIAN FIDELITY LIFE INSURANCE COMPANY—See U-Haul Holding Company; *U.S. Public*, pg. 2211
CIGNA DENTAL HEALTH, INC.—See The Cigna Group; *U.S. Public*, pg. 2060
CIGNA DENTAL HEALTH OF KANSAS, INC.—See The Cigna Group; *U.S. Public*, pg. 2060
CIGNA EUROPEAN SERVICES (UK) LIMITED—See The Cigna Group; *U.S. Public*, pg. 2060
CIGNA EUROPE INSURANCE COMPANY S.A.-N.V.—See The Cigna Group; *U.S. Public*, pg. 2060
CIGNA HEALTHCARE OF CALIFORNIA, INC.—See The Cigna Group; *U.S. Public*, pg. 2060
CIGNA HEALTHCARE OF CONNECTICUT, INC.—See The Cigna Group; *U.S. Public*, pg. 2060
CIGNA HEALTHCARE OF FLORIDA, INC.—See The Cigna Group; *U.S. Public*, pg. 2060
CIGNA HEALTHCARE OF GEORGIA, INC.—See The Cigna Group; *U.S. Public*, pg. 2060
CIGNA HEALTHCARE OF ILLINOIS, INC.—See The Cigna Group; *U.S. Public*, pg. 2060
CIGNA HEALTHCARE OF INDIANA—See The Cigna Group; *U.S. Public*, pg. 2060
CIGNA HEALTHCARE OF MASSACHUSETTS, INC.—See The Cigna Group; *U.S. Public*, pg. 2060
CIGNA HEALTHCARE OF NEW HAMPSHIRE, INC.—See The Cigna Group; *U.S. Public*, pg. 2060
CIGNA HEALTHCARE OF NEW JERSEY, INC.—See The Cigna Group; *U.S. Public*, pg. 2060
CIGNA HEALTHCARE OF OHIO, INC.—See The Cigna Group; *U.S. Public*, pg. 2060
CIGNA HEALTHCARE OF ST. LOUIS, INC.—See The Cigna Group; *U.S. Public*, pg. 2060
CIGNA HEALTHCARE OF TENNESSEE, INC.—See The

524114 — DIRECT HEALTH AND M... — CORPORATE AFFILIATIONS

Cigna Group; *U.S. Public*, pg. 2060
CIGNA HEALTHCARE OF TEXAS, INC.—See The Cigna Group; *U.S. Public*, pg. 2060
CIGNA HEALTHCARE OF VIRGINIA, INC.—See The Cigna Group; *U.S. Public*, pg. 2061
CIGNA HEALTH CORPORATION—See The Cigna Group; *U.S. Public*, pg. 2060
CIGNA INSURANCE MIDDLE EAST S.A.L.—See The Cigna Group; *U.S. Public*, pg. 2061
CIGNA INSURANCE PUBLIC COMPANY LIMITED—See The Cigna Group; *U.S. Public*, pg. 2060
CIGNA INTEGRATEDCARE, INC.—See The Cigna Group; *U.S. Public*, pg. 2061
CIGNA INTERNATIONAL HEALTH SERVICES BVBA—See The Cigna Group; *U.S. Public*, pg. 2061
CIGNATTK HEALTH INSURANCE COMPANY LIMITED—See The Cigna Group; *U.S. Public*, pg. 2061
CIGNA WORLDWIDE INSURANCE COMPANY—See The Cigna Group; *U.S. Public*, pg. 2060
CIRCLE INTERNATIONAL—See Centene Corporation; *U.S. Public*, pg. 468
CLAL HEALTH INSURANCE COMPANY LTD.—See IDB Development Corporation Ltd.; *Int'l*, pg. 3588
COBALT SOFTWARE, LLC—See Centene Corporation; *U.S. Public*, pg. 469
COLLEGIATE RISK MANAGEMENT, LLC; *U.S. Private*, pg. 968
COLONIAL PENN LIFE INSURANCE COMPANY—See CNO Financial Group, Inc.; *U.S. Public*, pg. 520
COMBINED INSURANCE COMPANY OF AMERICA - CANADA—See Chubb Limited; *Int'l*, pg. 1591
COMBINED LIFE INSURANCE COMPANY OF AUSTRALIA, LTD.—See Chubb Limited; *Int'l*, pg. 1591
COMMERCIAL INVESTMENT CORPORATION (PTY) LIMITED—See CIC Holdings Limited; *Int'l*, pg. 1602
COMMUNITYCARE, INC.; *U.S. Private*, pg. 997
COMMUNITY HEALTH PLAN OF WASHINGTON; *U.S. Private*, pg. 994
COMPBENEFITS CORP.—See Humana, Inc.; *U.S. Public*, pg. 1069
COMPDENT OF GEORGIA, INC.; *U.S. Private*, pg. 1000
CONCENTRA AKRON, LLC—See Select Medical Holdings Corporation; *U.S. Public*, pg. 1857
CONCENTRA AKRON, LLC—See Welsh, Carson, Anderson & Stowe; *U.S. Private*, pg. 4479
CONCENTRA HEALTH SERVICES, INC.—See Select Medical Holdings Corporation; *U.S. Public*, pg. 1857
CONCENTRA HEALTH SERVICES, INC.—See Welsh, Carson, Anderson & Stowe; *U.S. Private*, pg. 4479
CONNECTICARE, INC.—See EmblemHealth, Inc.; *U.S. Private*, pg. 1378
CONTINUCARE CORPORATION—See Humana, Inc.; *U.S. Public*, pg. 1070
CONVIVA CARE SOLUTIONS, LLC—See Humana, Inc.; *U.S. Public*, pg. 1069
CONVIVA PHYSICIAN GROUP, LLC—See Humana, Inc.; *U.S. Public*, pg. 1069
CORESOURCE INC.—See Trustmark Mutual Holding Company; *U.S. Private*, pg. 4251
CORVEL CORPORATION; *U.S. Public*, pg. 585
COSALUD, SA DE SEGUROS—See Grupo Catalana Occidente, S.A.; *Int'l*, pg. 3124
COUNT FINANCIAL LIMITED—See Count Limited; *Int'l*, pg. 1817
COVENTRY HEALTH CARE OF DELAWARE, INC.—See CVS Health Corporation; *U.S. Public*, pg. 614
COVENTRY HEALTH CARE OF GEORGIA, INC.—See CVS Health Corporation; *U.S. Public*, pg. 614
COVENTRY HEALTH CARE OF IOWA, INC.—See CVS Health Corporation; *U.S. Public*, pg. 615
COVENTRY HEALTH CARE OF MISSOURI, INC.—See CVS Health Corporation; *U.S. Public*, pg. 615
COVENTRY HEALTH CARE OF NEBRASKA, INC.—See CVS Health Corporation; *U.S. Public*, pg. 615
COVENTRY HEALTH CARE OF VIRGINIA, INC.—See CVS Health Corporation; *U.S. Public*, pg. 615
COVENTRY HEALTH CARE OF WEST VIRGINIA, INC.—See CVS Health Corporation; *U.S. Public*, pg. 615
COVENTRY HEALTH PLAN OF FLORIDA, INC.—See CVS Health Corporation; *U.S. Public*, pg. 615
COVENTRY PRESCRIPTION MANAGEMENT SERVICES, INC.—See CVS Health Corporation; *U.S. Public*, pg. 615
CROATIA OSIGURANJE D.D.—See Adris Grupa d.d.; *Int'l*, pg. 153
DAVASO GMBH—See IQVIA Holdings Inc.; *U.S. Public*, pg. 1168
DECARE DENTAL; *U.S. Private*, pg. 1186
THE DENTAL CARE PLUS GROUP; *U.S. Private*, pg. 4020
DENTALPLANS.COM, INC.—See KKR & Co. Inc.; *U.S. Public*, pg. 1253
DFV DEUTSCHE FAMILIENVERSICHERUNG AG; *Int'l*, pg. 2096
DHC CORPORATION—See Chubb Limited; *Int'l*, pg. 1591
DISABILITY MANAGEMENT SERVICES INC.; *U.S. Private*, pg. 1237
DISCOVERY HEALTH (PROPRIETARY) LIMITED—See Discovery Limited; *Int'l*, pg. 2134

DOCKSIDE SERVICES, INC.—See ATAR Capital, LLC; *U.S. Private*, pg. 364
THE DOCTORS COMPANY—See The Doctors Company; *U.S. Private*, pg. 1181
D. W. VAN DYKE & CO. OF CONNECTICUT INC.—See DDR Holdings Inc.; *U.S. Private*, pg. 1181
EAR PROFESSIONALS INTERNATIONAL CORPORATION—See UnitedHealth Group Incorporated; *U.S. Public*, pg. 2240
EKOCORP PLC.; *Int'l*, pg. 2339
ELITE INSURANCE PARTNERS, LLC; *U.S. Private*, pg. 1361
ELIXIR INSURANCE COMPANY—See New Rite Aid, LLC; *U.S. Private*, pg. 2905
EMBLEMHEALTH, INC.; *U.S. Private*, pg. 1378
EMI HEALTH; *U.S. Private*, pg. 1382
EMPIRE BLUE CROSS & BLUE SHIELD—See Elevance Health, Inc.; *U.S. Public*, pg. 730
EMPIRE HEALTHCHOICE ASSURANCE, INC.—See Elevance Health, Inc.; *U.S. Public*, pg. 730
EMPIRE HEALTHCHOICE HMO, INC.—See Elevance Health, Inc.; *U.S. Public*, pg. 730
ENHANZ DCE, LLC—See Humana, Inc.; *U.S. Public*, pg. 1069
ENROLL AMERICA; *U.S. Private*, pg. 1401
ENSURITYGROUP, L.L.C.; *U.S. Private*, pg. 1402
ENVOLVE DENTAL OF TEXAS, INC.—See Centene Corporation; *U.S. Public*, pg. 468
ENVOLVE VISION BENEFITS, INC.—See Centene Corporation; *U.S. Public*, pg. 468
ENVOLVE VISION, INC.—See Centene Corporation; *U.S. Public*, pg. 468
EVERENCE; *U.S. Private*, pg. 1437
EVERNORTH BEHAVIORAL HEALTH, INC.—See The Cigna Group; *U.S. Public*, pg. 2061
EVERNORTH BEHAVIORAL HEALTH OF CALIFORNIA, INC.—See The Cigna Group; *U.S. Public*, pg. 2061
EVERNORTH HEALTH, INC.—See The Cigna Group; *U.S. Public*, pg. 2061
EXACTUS PHARMACY SOLUTIONS, INC.—See Centene Corporation; *U.S. Public*, pg. 471
THE EXCELLENCE LIFE INSURANCE COMPANY—See iA Financial Corporation Inc.; *Int'l*, pg. 3568
EXCELLUS HEALTH PLAN, INC.—See The Lifetime Healthcare Companies; *U.S. Private*, pg. 4070
EXCESS REINSURANCE UNDERWRITERS, INC.—See Aon plc; *Int'l*, pg. 496
EXPACARE LIMITED—See Marsh & McLennan Companies, Inc.; *U.S. Public*, pg. 1376
EXTENSIA PTY. LTD.—See Hills Limited; *Int'l*, pg. 3393
FAIR HEALTH, INC.; *U.S. Private*, pg. 1462
FAMILY NURSE CARE, LLC—See Centene Corporation; *U.S. Public*, pg. 468
FI HEALTH INSURANCE AD—See First Investment Bank AD; *Int'l*, pg. 2685
FINERGY SOLUTIONS PTY. LTD.—See Arthur J. Gallagher & Co.; *U.S. Public*, pg. 204
FIRST FAMILY INSURANCE, LLC—See UnitedHealth Group Incorporated; *U.S. Public*, pg. 2240
FIRST HEALTH GROUP CORP.—See CVS Health Corporation; *U.S. Public*, pg. 615
FIRST REHABILITATION LIFE INSURANCE CO. OF AMERICA INC.—See ShelterPoint Group, Inc.; *U.S. Private*, pg. 3632
FLORIDA HEALTH CARE PLAN, INC.—See GuideWell Mutual Holding Corporation; *U.S. Private*, pg. 1813
FLORIDA TRUE HEALTH INC.—See GuideWell Mutual Holding Corporation; *U.S. Private*, pg. 1813
FORTIFIED PROVIDER NETWORK, INC.—See UnitedHealth Group Incorporated; *U.S. Public*, pg. 2240
FREE FOR ALL, INC.; *U.S. Private*, pg. 1602
FREELANCERS CONSUMER OPERATED & ORIENTED PROGRAM OF NEW JERSEY, INC.; *U.S. Private*, pg. 1605
FRESENIUS KABI LOGISTIK GMBH—See Fresenius SE & Co. KGaA; *Int'l*, pg. 2778
FULL ALLIANCE GROUP, INC.; *U.S. Public*, pg. 892
GATEWAY HEALTH PLAN, INC.—See Highmark Health; *U.S. Private*, pg. 1940
GEISINGER HEALTH PLAN—See Geisinger Health System; *U.S. Private*, pg. 1656
GENERALI HEALTH SOLUTIONS GMBH—See Assicurazioni Generali S.p.A.; *Int'l*, pg. 645
GENERALI LIFE ASSURANCE PHILIPPINES, INC.—See Assicurazioni Generali S.p.A.; *Int'l*, pg. 647
GENERAL STAR INDEMNITY COMPANY—See Berkshire Hathaway Inc.; *U.S. Public*, pg. 301
GENERATION VIE S.A.—See Allianz SE; *Int'l*, pg. 353
GETHEALTHINSURANCE.COM AGENCY INC.—See UnitedHealth Group Incorporated; *U.S. Public*, pg. 2253
GLADLE ASSOCIATES, INC.—See Dairy Farmers of America, Inc.; *U.S. Private*, pg. 1145
GLAXOSMITHKLINE ALGERIE S.P.A.—See GSK plc; *Int'l*, pg. 3146
GOLDEN OUTLOOK, INC.—See UnitedHealth Group Incorporated; *U.S. Public*, pg. 2241
GOLDEN RULE INSURANCE COMPANY INC.—See UnitedHealth Group Incorporated; *U.S. Public*, pg. 2251

GOLDEN TRIANGLE PHYSICIAN ALLIANCE—See Centene Corporation; *U.S. Public*, pg. 471
GOVERNMENT HEALTH SERVICES, L.L.C.—See Elevance Health, Inc.; *U.S. Public*, pg. 730
GREATER SACRAMENTO SURGERY CENTER LIMITED PARTNERSHIP—See Centene Corporation; *U.S. Public*, pg. 469
GREEN SHIELD CANADA; *Int'l*, pg. 3072
GROUPAMA PHOENIX ASFALISTIKI—See Groupama SA; *Int'l*, pg. 3091
GROUPAMA PHOENIX ASFALISTIKI—See Groupama SA; *Int'l*, pg. 3091
GROUPE DES ASSURANCES DE TUNISIE (GAT)—See Groupama SA; *Int'l*, pg. 3091
GROUP HEALTH SERVICE OF OKLAHOMA, INC.—See Health Care Service Corporation; *U.S. Private*, pg. 1892
HABIB INSURANCE COMPANY LIMITED—See Habib Group of Companies; *Int'l*, pg. 3203
HAPVIDA PARTICIPACOES E INVESTIMENTOS S.A.; *Int'l*, pg. 3269
HARMONY HEALTH PLAN INC.—See Centene Corporation; *U.S. Public*, pg. 471
HARMONY HEALTH PLAN OF INDIANA—See Centene Corporation; *U.S. Public*, pg. 471
HARVARD PILGRIM HEALTH CARE, INC.; *U.S. Private*, pg. 1875
HAWAII HEALTH CONNECTOR; *U.S. Private*, pg. 1881
HAWAII MEDICAL SERVICE ASSOCIATION; *U.S. Private*, pg. 1881
HBF HEALTH LTD.; *Int'l*, pg. 3295
HEALTH ALLIANCE PLAN OF MICHIGAN—See Henry Ford Health System; *U.S. Private*, pg. 1918
HEALTHAMERICA PENNSYLVANIA, INC.—See CVS Health Corporation; *U.S. Public*, pg. 615
HEALTH CARE ENTERPRISES, LLC—See Centene Corporation; *U.S. Public*, pg. 469
HEALTHCARE SOLUTIONS, INC.—See UnitedHealth Group Incorporated; *U.S. Public*, pg. 2247
HEALTHEASE OF FLORIDA INC.—See Centene Corporation; *U.S. Public*, pg. 471
HEALTHFIRST, INC.; *U.S. Private*, pg. 1896
HEALTHGUARD HEALTH BENEFITS FUND LTD—See HBF Health Ltd.; *Int'l*, pg. 3295
HEALTHGUARD OF LANCASTER—See Highmark Health; *U.S. Private*, pg. 1940
HEALTH INSURANCE PLAN OF GREATER NEW YORK—See EmblemHealth, Inc.; *U.S. Private*, pg. 1378
HEALTHKEEPERS, INC.—See Elevance Health, Inc.; *U.S. Public*, pg. 729
HEALTH MANAGEMENT CORPORATION—See Elevance Health, Inc.; *U.S. Public*, pg. 730
HEALTH NETWORK GROUP, LLC—See The Allstate Corporation; *U.S. Public*, pg. 2033
HEALTH OPTIONS, INC.—See GuideWell Mutual Holding Corporation; *U.S. Private*, pg. 1814
HEALTHPARTNERS, INC.; *U.S. Private*, pg. 1897
HEALTH PLAN ADMINISTRATORS, INC.—See Geneve Holdings Corp.; *U.S. Private*, pg. 1670
HEALTH PLAN OF NEVADA, INC.—See UnitedHealth Group Incorporated; *U.S. Public*, pg. 2252
HEALTHPLEX, INC.—See Managed Care of North America, Inc.; *U.S. Private*, pg. 2559
HEALTH SERVICES GROUP, INC.; *U.S. Private*, pg. 1894
HEALTHSPAN, INC.—See Catholic Healthcare Partners; *U.S. Private*, pg. 792
HEALTHWAYS INTERNATIONAL, GMBH—See Stone Point Capital LLC; *U.S. Private*, pg. 3825
HEALTHY STATE, INC.—See HCA Healthcare, Inc.; *U.S. Public*, pg. 998
HELIOS AUKAMM-KLINIK WIESBADEN GMBH—See Fresenius SE & Co. KGaA; *Int'l*, pg. 2779
HELIOS BORDEKLINIK GMBH—See Fresenius SE & Co. KGaA; *Int'l*, pg. 2779
HELIOS FACHKLINIK VOGELSANG-GOMMERN GMBH—See Fresenius SE & Co. KGaA; *Int'l*, pg. 2779
HELIOS HEALTH GMBH—See Fresenius SE & Co. KGaA; *Int'l*, pg. 2779
HELIOS KLINIK BLANKENHAIN GMBH—See Fresenius SE & Co. KGaA; *Int'l*, pg. 2779
HELIOS KLINIK SCHKEUDITZ GMBH—See Fresenius SE & Co. KGaA; *Int'l*, pg. 2779
HELIOS KLINIKUM BERLIN-BUCH GMBH—See Fresenius SE & Co. KGaA; *Int'l*, pg. 2780
HELIOS KLINIKUM GOTHA GMBH—See Fresenius SE & Co. KGaA; *Int'l*, pg. 2780
HELIOS KLINIKUM HILDESHEIM GMBH—See Fresenius SE & Co. KGaA; *Int'l*, pg. 2780
HELIOS KLINIKUM SCHWELM GMBH—See Fresenius SE & Co. KGaA; *Int'l*, pg. 2780
HELIOS KLINIK ZERBST/ANHALT GMBH—See Fresenius SE & Co. KGaA; *Int'l*, pg. 2779
HELIOS PARK-KLINIKUM LEIPZIG GMBH—See Fresenius SE & Co. KGaA; *Int'l*, pg. 2780
HELIOS SPITAL UBERLINGEN GMBH—See Fresenius SE & Co. KGaA; *Int'l*, pg. 2780
HELIOS ST. ELISABETH KLINIK OBERHAUSEN GMBH—See Fresenius SE & Co. KGaA; *Int'l*, pg. 2780
HELIOS ST. ELISABETH-KRANKENHAUS BAD KISSIN-

N.A.I.C.S. INDEX 524114 — DIRECT HEALTH AND M...

GEN GMBH—See Fresenius SE & Co. KGaA; *Int'l*, pg. 2780

HELVETIA ITALIA ASSICURAZIONI S.P.A.—See Helvetia Holding AG; *Int'l*, pg. 3339

HELVETIA LEBEN MAKLERSERVICE GMBH—See Helvetia Holding AG; *Int'l*, pg. 3339

HELVETIA SCHWEIZERISCHE LEBENSVERSICHERUNGSGESELLSCHAFT AG—See Helvetia Holding AG; *Int'l*, pg. 3339

HELVETIA VITA - COMPAGNIA ITALO SVIZZERA DI ASSICURAZIONI SULLA VITA S.P.A.—See Helvetia Holding AG; *Int'l*, pg. 3340

HIGHMARK BLUE CROSS BLUE SHIELD DELAWARE—See Highmark Health; *U.S. Private*, pg. 1940

HIGHMARK BLUE CROSS BLUE SHIELD WEST VIRGINIA—See Highmark Health; *U.S. Private*, pg. 1940

HIGHMARK INC.—See Highmark Health; *U.S. Private*, pg. 1940

HIGHMARK SENIOR RESOURCES INC.—See Highmark Health; *U.S. Private*, pg. 1941

HMO OF LOUISIANA, INC.—See Louisiana Health Service & Indemnity Company, Inc.; *U.S. Private*, pg. 2499

HOLIDAY CVS, L.L.C.—See CVS Health Corporation; *U.S. Public*, pg. 616

HOMELAND HEALTHCARE, INC.; *U.S. Private*, pg. 1973

HOMESCRIPTS.COM, LLC—See Centene Corporation; *U.S. Public*, pg. 469

HORIZON HEALTHCARE SERVICES, INC.; *U.S. Private*, pg. 1981

HOSPITAL AMA S.A.—See UnitedHealth Group Incorporated; *U.S. Public*, pg. 2241

HOSPITAL CARLOS CHAGAS S.A.—See UnitedHealth Group Incorporated; *U.S. Public*, pg. 2241

HOSPITAL E MATERNIDADE SAINT-VIVANT LTDA.—See UnitedHealth Group Incorporated; *U.S. Public*, pg. 2241

HOSPITAL GERAL E MATERNIDADE MADRE MARIA THEODORA LTDA.—See UnitedHealth Group Incorporated; *U.S. Public*, pg. 2241

HPP - MEDICINA MOLECULAR, S.A.—See UnitedHealth Group Incorporated; *U.S. Public*, pg. 2241

HUMANA AT HOME, INC.—See Humana, Inc.; *U.S. Public*, pg. 1070

HUMANA EMPLOYERS HEALTH PLAN OF GEORGIA, INC.—See Humana, Inc.; *U.S. Public*, pg. 1069

HUMANA HEALTH BENEFIT PLAN OF LOUISIANA, INC.—See Humana, Inc.; *U.S. Public*, pg. 1070

HUMANA HEALTH INSURANCE COMPANY OF FLORIDA, INC.—See Humana, Inc.; *U.S. Public*, pg. 1070

HUMANA HEALTH PLAN, INC.—See Humana, Inc.; *U.S. Public*, pg. 1070

HUMANA HEALTH PLAN OF OHIO, INC.—See Humana, Inc.; *U.S. Public*, pg. 1070

HUMANA HEALTH PLAN OF TEXAS, INC.—See Humana, Inc.; *U.S. Public*, pg. 1070

HUMANA HEALTH PLANS OF PUERTO RICO, INC.—See Humana, Inc.; *U.S. Public*, pg. 1070

HUMANA MEDICAL PLAN, INC.—See Humana, Inc.; *U.S. Public*, pg. 1070

HUMANA WISCONSIN HEALTH ORGANIZATION INSURANCE CORPORATION—See Humana, Inc.; *U.S. Public*, pg. 1070

HYGEIA CORPORATION—See UnitedHealth Group Incorporated; *U.S. Public*, pg. 2241

HYGEIA CORPORATION—See UnitedHealth Group Incorporated; *U.S. Public*, pg. 2241

IAH OF FLORIDA, LLC—See Centene Corporation; *U.S. Public*, pg. 469

ICBC-AXA LIFE ASSURANCE—See AXA S.A.; *Int'l*, pg. 759

IMED STAR SERVICOS DE DESEMPENHO ORGANIZACIONAL LTDA.—See UnitedHealth Group Incorporated; *U.S. Public*, pg. 2241

INDEPENDENT CARE HEALTH PLAN, INC.—See Humana, Inc.; *U.S. Public*, pg. 1070

INDEPENDENT CARE HEALTH PLAN, INC.—See Milwaukee Center for Independence, Inc.; *U.S. Private*, pg. 2739

INDIANA COMPREHENSIVE HEALTH INSURANCE ASSOCIATION; *U.S. Private*, pg. 2062

INETICO, INC.; *U.S. Private*, pg. 2070

INTEGRAL QUALITY CARE; *U.S. Private*, pg. 2098

INTERDENT, INC.—See H.I.G. Capital, LLC; *U.S. Private*, pg. 1829

INTERNATIONAL RISK - IRC, INC.—See Aon plc; *Int'l*, pg. 496

INTOTAL HEALTH—See Inova Health System; *U.S. Private*, pg. 2084

IOA RE, LLC—See ELMC Holdings, LLC; *U.S. Private*, pg. 1376

IOWA COMPREHENSIVE HEALTH ASSOCIATION; *U.S. Private*, pg. 2134

ISAPRE BANMEDICA S.A.—See UnitedHealth Group Incorporated; *U.S. Public*, pg. 2242

ISAPRE VIDA TRES S.A.—See UnitedHealth Group Incorporated; *U.S. Public*, pg. 2242

JLT INSURANCE BROKERS IRELAND LIMITED—See Marsh & McLennan Companies, Inc.; *U.S. Public*, pg. 1376

KAISER FOUNDATION HEALTH PLAN, INC.—See Kaiser Permanente; *U.S. Private*, pg. 2255

KAISER FOUNDATION HEALTH PLAN OF GEORGIA, INC.—See Kaiser Permanente; *U.S. Private*, pg. 2255

KAISER FOUNDATION HEALTH PLAN OF THE MID-ATLANTIC STATES, INC.—See Kaiser Permanente; *U.S. Private*, pg. 2255

KAISER FOUNDATION HEALTH PLAN OF THE NORTHWEST—See Kaiser Permanente; *U.S. Private*, pg. 2255

KAISER PERMANENTE, COLORADO REGION—See Kaiser Permanente; *U.S. Private*, pg. 2256

KAISER PERMANENTE, GEORGIA REGION—See Kaiser Permanente; *U.S. Private*, pg. 2256

KAISER PERMANENTE INSURANCE COMPANY—See Kaiser Permanente; *U.S. Private*, pg. 2256

KANSAS MEDICAL MUTUAL INSURANCE CO; *U.S. Private*, pg. 2261

KEYSTONE HEALTH PLAN CENTRAL, INC.—See Capital BlueCross Inc.; *U.S. Private*, pg. 739

KEYSTONE HEALTH PLAN WEST, INC.—See Highmark Health; *U.S. Private*, pg. 1941

LABORATORIO ROE S.A.—See UnitedHealth Group Incorporated; *U.S. Public*, pg. 2242

LAS PALMAS DEL SOL URGENT CARE, PLLC—See HCA Healthcare, Inc.; *U.S. Public*, pg. 1000

LE RESEAU SANTE SOCIALE SAS—See CompuGroup Medical SE & Co. KGaA; *Int'l*, pg. 1757

LIBERTY INTERNATIONAL INSURANCE LTD.—See Liberty Mutual Holding Company Inc.; *U.S. Private*, pg. 2445

LIFECOURSE MANAGEMENT SERVICE; *U.S. Private*, pg. 2449

LIFEMAP ASSURANCE COMPANY—See Cambia Health Solutions, Inc.; *U.S. Private*, pg. 726

LIGHTNING HEALTHCARE, INC.—See The Ensign Group, Inc.; *U.S. Public*, pg. 2071

LLOYD & PARTNERS LIMITED—See Marsh & McLennan Companies, Inc.; *U.S. Public*, pg. 1377

LMN LABORATORIO DE MEDICINA NUCLEAR, UNIPESSOAL, LDA.—See UnitedHealth Group Incorporated; *U.S. Public*, pg. 2242

LONG BEACH MEMORIAL MEDICAL CENTER—See Memorial Health Services; *U.S. Private*, pg. 2664

LOUISIANA HEALTHCARE CONNECTIONS, INC.—See Centene Corporation; *U.S. Public*, pg. 469

LOUISIANA HEALTH SERVICE & INDEMNITY COMPANY, INC.; *U.S. Private*, pg. 2499

LUMENOS—See Elevance Health, Inc.; *U.S. Public*, pg. 730

LUSIADAS-PARCERIAS CASCAIS, S.A.—See UnitedHealth Group Incorporated; *U.S. Public*, pg. 2242

LUSIADAS, SGPS, S.A.—See UnitedHealth Group Incorporated; *U.S. Public*, pg. 2242

MAGNOLIA HEALTH PLAN INC.—See Centene Corporation; *U.S. Public*, pg. 470

MAHKOTA MEDICAL CENTRE SDN. BHD.—See EQT AB; *Int'l*, pg. 2475

MAISHA HEALTH FUND (PRIVATE) LIMITED—See EcoCash Holdings Zimbabwe Limited; *Int'l*, pg. 2295

MANAGED CARE OF NORTH AMERICA, INC.; *U.S. Private*, pg. 2559

MANAGED HEALTH SERVICES—See Centene Corporation; *U.S. Public*, pg. 470

MANNHEIMER KRANKENVERSICHERUNG AG—See Continentale Holding AG; *Int'l*, pg. 1784

MANSON WARNER HEALTHCARE LIMITED—See Marsh & McLennan Companies, Inc.; *U.S. Public*, pg. 1377

MARRICK MEDICAL; *U.S. Private*, pg. 2588

MARSHALL PIERSON, INC.—See Inszone Insurance Services, LLC; *U.S. Private*, pg. 2096

MASSMUTUAL INTERNATIONAL LLC—See Massachusetts Mutual Life Insurance Company; *U.S. Private*, pg. 2605

MATRIX HEALTHCARE SERVICES, INC.—See The Cigna Group; *U.S. Public*, pg. 2061

MATTHEW THORNTON HEALTH PLAN, INC.—See Elevance Health, Inc.; *U.S. Public*, pg. 730

MCNA HEALTH CARE HOLDINGS, LLC—See Managed Care of North America, Inc.; *U.S. Private*, pg. 2559

MCNA INSURANCE COMPANY—See Managed Care of North America, Inc.; *U.S. Private*, pg. 2559

MCS ADVANTAGE, INC.—See JLL Partners, LLC; *U.S. Private*, pg. 2213

MCS HEALTH MANAGEMENT OPTIONS, INC.—See JLL Partners, LLC; *U.S. Private*, pg. 2213

MEDEX INSURANCE SERVICES, INC.—See UnitedHealth Group Incorporated; *U.S. Public*, pg. 2242

MEDICA HEALTHCARE PLANS, INC.—See UnitedHealth Group Incorporated; *U.S. Public*, pg. 2251

MEDICA, INC.; *U.S. Private*, pg. 2654

MEDICAL BENEFITS MUTUAL LIFE INSURANCE CO. INC.; *U.S. Private*, pg. 2654

MEDICAL MUTUAL OF OHIO; *U.S. Private*, pg. 2655

MEDICAL PROTECTIVE CORPORATION—See Berkshire Hathaway Inc.; *U.S. Public*, pg. 312

MEDICA US, INC.—See IK Investment Partners Limited; *Int'l*, pg. 3609

MEDICO INSURANCE COMPANY—See American Enterprise Mutual Holding Company; *U.S. Private*, pg. 232

MEDSYNERGIES NORTH TEXAS, INC.—See UnitedHealth Group Incorporated; *U.S. Public*, pg. 2242

MEMORIALCARE SURGICAL CENTER AT ORANGE COAST, LLC—See Memorial Health Services; *U.S. Private*, pg. 2664

MEMORIALCARE SURGICAL CENTER AT SADDLEBACK, LLC—See Memorial Health Services; *U.S. Private*, pg. 2664

METHODIST AMBULATORY SURGERY CENTER OF BOERNE, LLC—See HCA Healthcare, Inc.; *U.S. Public*, pg. 1002

METHODIST CARENOW URGENT CARE, PLLC—See HCA Healthcare, Inc.; *U.S. Public*, pg. 1002

METLIFE, LIFE INSURANCE COMPANY—See MetLife, Inc.; *U.S. Public*, pg. 1430

METRACOMP, INC.—See CVS Health Corporation; *U.S. Public*, pg. 615

METROPOLITAN HEALTH NETWORKS, INC.—See Humana, Inc.; *U.S. Public*, pg. 1070

MHN SERVICES—See Centene Corporation; *U.S. Public*, pg. 469

MID-ATLANTIC PERMANENTE MEDICAL GROUP, P.C.—See Kaiser Permanente; *U.S. Private*, pg. 2256

MIDWEST MEDICAL INSURANCE COMPANY—See Curi Holdings, Inc.; *U.S. Private*, pg. 1125

MISSISSIPPI COMPREHENSIVE HEALTH INSURANCE RISK POOL ASSOCIATION; *U.S. Private*, pg. 2748

MMM MULTI HEALTH, LLC—See Elevance Health, Inc.; *U.S. Public*, pg. 730

MOLINA HEALTHCARE OF MICHIGAN, INC.—See Molina Healthcare, Inc.; *U.S. Public*, pg. 1459

MOLINA HEALTHCARE OF NEW MEXICO, INC.—See Molina Healthcare, Inc.; *U.S. Public*, pg. 1459

MOLINA HEALTHCARE OF NEW YORK, INC.—See Molina Healthcare, Inc.; *U.S. Public*, pg. 1459

MOLINA HEALTHCARE OF OHIO, INC.—See Molina Healthcare, Inc.; *U.S. Public*, pg. 1459

MOLINA HEALTHCARE OF PUERTO RICO, INC.—See Molina Healthcare, Inc.; *U.S. Public*, pg. 1459

MOLINA HEALTHCARE OF SOUTH CAROLINA, LLC—See Molina Healthcare, Inc.; *U.S. Public*, pg. 1459

MOLINA HEALTHCARE OF TEXAS, INC.—See Molina Healthcare, Inc.; *U.S. Public*, pg. 1459

MOLINA HEALTHCARE OF UTAH, INC.—See Molina Healthcare, Inc.; *U.S. Public*, pg. 1459

MOLINA HEALTHCARE OF WASHINGTON, INC.—See Molina Healthcare, Inc.; *U.S. Public*, pg. 1459

MPI GENERALI INSURANS BERHAD—See Assicurazioni Generali S.p.A.; *Int'l*, pg. 647

MR CENTRUM MELNICK, S.R.O.—See Centene Corporation; *U.S. Public*, pg. 469

MSO OF PUERTO RICO, LLC—See Elevance Health, Inc.; *U.S. Public*, pg. 730

MULTIPLAN, INC.—See MultiPlan Corp.; *U.S. Public*, pg. 1486

NATIONAL CAPITAL ADMINISTRATIVE SERVICES INC.—See CareFirst, Inc.; *U.S. Private*, pg. 753

NATIONAL HEALTH CORPORATION; *U.S. Private*, pg. 2855

NATIONAL HEALTH INSURANCE CO—See National Health Corporation; *U.S. Private*, pg. 2856

NATIONAL HEALTH PARTNERS, INC.; *U.S. Private*, pg. 2856

NEIGHBORHOOD HEALTH PLAN INC.; *U.S. Private*, pg. 2881

NEPHROCARE MUNCHEN-OST GMBH—See Fresenius Medical Care AG; *Int'l*, pg. 2776

NEUEHEALTH, INC.; *U.S. Public*, pg. 1510

NEVADA PACIFIC DENTAL—See UnitedHealth Group Incorporated; *U.S. Public*, pg. 2242

NEWBRIDGE GLOBAL VENTURES, INC.; *U.S. Public*, pg. 1513

THE NEW YORK STATE CATHOLIC HEALTH PLAN, INC.—See Centene Corporation; *U.S. Public*, pg. 470

NEXTCARE LEBANON SAL—See Allianz SE; *Int'l*, pg. 354

NEXTCARE UAE, AGHS LLC—See Allianz SE; *Int'l*, pg. 354

NIRVANAHEALTH, LLC—See Centene Corporation; *U.S. Public*, pg. 471

NORIDIAN MUTUAL INSURANCE COMPANY; *U.S. Private*, pg. 2937

NORTH TEXAS STROKE CENTER, PLLC—See HCA Healthcare, Inc.; *U.S. Public*, pg. 1004

NOVUS ACQUISITION & DEVELOPMENT CORPORATION; *U.S. Public*, pg. 1549

OBJECTIVE MEDICAL ASSESSMENTS CORPORATION—See Stone Point Capital LLC; *U.S. Private*, pg. 3824

ODS HEALTH PLAN INC.—See Health Services Group, Inc.; *U.S. Private*, pg. 1894

OHANA HEALTH PLAN, INC.—See Centene Corporation; *U.S. Public*, pg. 471

OHIC INSURANCE COMPANY—See The Doctors Company; *U.S. Private*, pg. 4021

OLD REPUBLIC INSURANCE COMPANY—See Old Republic International Corporation; *U.S. Public*, pg. 1568

OPTIMUM HEALTHCARE, INC.; *U.S. Private*, pg. 3035

OPTIMUM RE CORPORATION; *U.S. Private*, pg. 3035

OPTUM BIOMETRICS, INC.—See UnitedHealth Group Incorporated; *U.S. Public*, pg. 2243

524114 — DIRECT HEALTH AND M... CORPORATE AFFILIATIONS

N.A.I.C.S. Index

OPTUM CLINICAL SOLUTIONS, INC.—See UnitedHealth Group Incorporated; *U.S. Public*, pg. 2243
OPTUM CLINICAL SOLUTIONS, LTD.—See UnitedHealth Group Incorporated; *U.S. Public*, pg. 2243
OPTUM GLOBAL SOLUTIONS INTERNATIONAL B.V.—See UnitedHealth Group Incorporated; *U.S. Public*, pg. 2243
OPTUMHEALTH CARE SOLUTIONS, INC.—See UnitedHealth Group Incorporated; *U.S. Public*, pg. 2248
OPTUMHEALTH HOLDINGS, LLC—See UnitedHealth Group Incorporated; *U.S. Public*, pg. 2248
OPTUM PALLIATIVE AND HOSPICE CARE, INC.—See UnitedHealth Group Incorporated; *U.S. Public*, pg. 2243
OPTUM PUBLIC SECTOR SOLUTIONS, INC.—See UnitedHealth Group Incorporated; *U.S. Public*, pg. 2243
OREGON MUTUAL INSURANCE COMPANY, INC.; *U.S. Private*, pg. 3040
OSCAR HEALTH AGENCY INC.; *U.S. Private*, pg. 3046
OXFORD HEALTH PLANS (CT), INC.—See UnitedHealth Group Incorporated; *U.S. Public*, pg. 2249
OXFORD HEALTH PLANS LLC—See UnitedHealth Group Incorporated; *U.S. Public*, pg. 2249
OXFORD HEALTH PLANS (NY), INC.—See UnitedHealth Group Incorporated; *U.S. Public*, pg. 2249
PACIFICARE DENTAL—See UnitedHealth Group Incorporated; *U.S. Public*, pg. 2249
PACIFICARE OF COLORADO, INC.—See UnitedHealth Group Incorporated; *U.S. Public*, pg. 2249
PACIFICARE OF OKLAHOMA, INC.—See UnitedHealth Group Incorporated; *U.S. Public*, pg. 2249
PACIFICARE OF TEXAS, INC.—See UnitedHealth Group Incorporated; *U.S. Public*, pg. 2249
PACIFICO S.A. ENTIDAD PRESTADORA DE SALUD—See UnitedHealth Group Incorporated; *U.S. Public*, pg. 2249
PACIFICSOURCE HEALTH PLANS; *U.S. Private*, pg. 3072
PARAMOUNT HEALTH SYSTEMS—See American Healthcare Systems Corp., Inc.; *U.S. Private*, pg. 236
PARTNERS IN INTEGRATED CARE, INC.—See Humana, Inc.; *U.S. Public*, pg. 1070
PATHWAYS COMMUNITY SERVICES LLC—See ATAR Capital, LLC; *U.S. Private*, pg. 364
PATHWAYS OF DELAWARE, INC.—See ATAR Capital, LLC; *U.S. Private*, pg. 364
THE PAVILION CLINIC LTD.—See Centene Corporation; *U.S. Public*, pg. 470
PAYMENT RESOLUTION SERVICES, LLC—See UnitedHealth Group Incorporated; *U.S. Public*, pg. 2249
PEARSANTA, INC.—See Aditxt, Inc.; *U.S. Public*, pg. 41
PEOPLES HEALTH, INC.—See UnitedHealth Group Incorporated; *U.S. Public*, pg. 2249
PETFIRST HEALTHCARE; *U.S. Private*, pg. 3160
PHYS HOLDING CORP.—See UnitedHealth Group Incorporated; *U.S. Public*, pg. 2249
PHYSICIANS CHOICE INSURANCE SERVICE, LLC—See UnitedHealth Group Incorporated; *U.S. Public*, pg. 2249
PHYSICIANS HEALTH CHOICE OF TEXAS, LLC—See UnitedHealth Group Incorporated; *U.S. Public*, pg. 2249
PLANO DE SAUDE ANA COSTA LTDA.—See UnitedHealth Group Incorporated; *U.S. Public*, pg. 2249
PLAZA SPECIALTY HOSPITAL, LLC—See HCA Healthcare, Inc.; *U.S. Public*, pg. 1006
PMSLIC INSURANCE COMPANY—See ProAssurance Corporation; *U.S. Public*, pg. 1723
PORTUGAL TELECOM - ASSOCIACAO DE CUIDADOS DE SAUDE—See Altice Europe N.V.; *Int'l*, pg. 393
POSITIVE PHYSICIANS INSURANCE COMPANY—See Positive Physicians Holdings, Inc.; *U.S. Public*, pg. 1703
PREAMED S.R.O.—See Centene Corporation; *U.S. Public*, pg. 470
PREFERRED CARE PARTNERS, INC.—See UnitedHealth Group Incorporated; *U.S. Public*, pg. 2251
PREFERRED CHOICE MANAGEMENT SYSTEMS INC.; *U.S. Private*, pg. 3247
PREFERRED HEALTH CARE, INC.; *U.S. Private*, pg. 3248
PREFERRED HEALTH SYSTEMS INC.—See Blue Cross & Blue Shield of South Carolina; *U.S. Private*, pg. 587
PREFERRED MEDICAL PLAN, INC.; *U.S. Private*, pg. 3248
PREMERA BLUE CROSS; *U.S. Private*, pg. 3249
PRIMEROSALUD, S.L.—See Centene Corporation; *U.S. Public*, pg. 470
PRINCETON INSURANCE COMPANY—See Berkshire Hathaway Inc.; *U.S. Public*, pg. 302
PRINCIPAL FINANCIAL GROUP (AUSTRALIA) PTY. LTD.—See Principal Financial Group, Inc.; *U.S. Public*, pg. 1720
PRINCIPAL FINANCIAL SERVICES, INC.—See Principal Financial Group, Inc.; *U.S. Public*, pg. 1721
PRINCIPAL GENERA S.A. DE C.V.—See Principal Financial Group, Inc.; *U.S. Public*, pg. 1721
PROASSURANCE MID-CONTINENT UNDERWRITERS, INC.—See ProAssurance Corporation; *U.S. Public*, pg. 1723
PROHEALTH FITNESS OF LAKE SUCCESS, LLC—See UnitedHealth Group Incorporated; *U.S. Public*, pg. 2249
PRO MAGNET, S.R.O—See Centene Corporation; *U.S. Public*, pg. 470
PROSPECT MEDICAL HOLDINGS, INC.—See Leonard Green & Partners, L.P.; *U.S. Private*, pg. 2428
PRUDENTIAL HEALTH INSURANCE LTD—See Discovery Limited; *Int'l*, pg. 2134
P.T. JAKARTA KYOAI MEDICAL CENTER—See Prudential Financial, Inc.; *U.S. Public*, pg. 1733
PTZ INSURANCE AGENCY, LTD.—See Fairfax Financial Holdings Limited; *Int'l*, pg. 2608
QUALCARE ALLIANCE NETWORKS, INC.—See The Cigna Group; *U.S. Public*, pg. 2061
QUALCARE, INC.—See The Cigna Group; *U.S. Public*, pg. 2061
THE REDCO GROUP, INC.—See ATAR Capital, LLC; *U.S. Private*, pg. 365
REGENCE BLUECROSS BLUESHIELD OF OREGON—See Cambia Health Solutions, Inc.; *U.S. Private*, pg. 726
REGENCE BLUECROSS BLUESHIELD OF UTAH—See Cambia Health Solutions, Inc.; *U.S. Private*, pg. 726
REGENCE HMO OREGON, INC.—See Cambia Health Solutions, Inc.; *U.S. Private*, pg. 726
RIBERA LAB, S.L.U.—See Centene Corporation; *U.S. Public*, pg. 470
RITE AID OF CONNECTICUT, INC.—See New Rite Aid, LLC; *U.S. Private*, pg. 2905
RX DIRECT, INC.—See Centene Corporation; *U.S. Public*, pg. 470
RXHELPLINE, LLC—See Madison Dearborn Partners, LLC; *U.S. Private*, pg. 2540
SAFEGUARD HEALTH ENTERPRISES, INC.—See MetLife, Inc.; *U.S. Public*, pg. 1431
SAFEGUARD HEALTH PLANS, INC.—See MetLife, Inc.; *U.S. Public*, pg. 1431
SAG-AFTRA HEALTH PLAN; *U.S. Private*, pg. 3525
SAINT MARY'S PREFERRED HEALTH INSURANCE COMPANY, INC.—See Catholic Health Initiatives; *U.S. Private*, pg. 790
SANTAFE HEALTHCARE, INC.; *U.S. Private*, pg. 3547
SANTA HELENA ASSISTENCIA MEDICA S.A.—See UnitedHealth Group Incorporated; *U.S. Public*, pg. 2250
SCAN HEALTH PLAN—See SCAN Group; *U.S. Private*, pg. 3561
SCOTT RIDDLE AGENCY—See Integrity Marketing Group LLC; *U.S. Private*, pg. 2104
SCRIP WORLD, INC.—See CVS Health Corporation; *U.S. Public*, pg. 615
SEGUROS DE VIDA Y PENSIONES ANTARES, S.A.—See Grupo Catalana Occidente, S.A.; *Int'l*, pg. 3124
SELECTCARE OF TEXAS, INC.—See Centene Corporation; *U.S. Public*, pg. 471
SHELTERPOINT GROUP, INC.; *U.S. Private*, pg. 3632
SIERRA HEALTH-CARE OPTIONS, INC.—See UnitedHealth Group Incorporated; *U.S. Public*, pg. 2252
SIMPLE MEDS, LLC—See SelectQuote, Inc.; *U.S. Public*, pg. 1863
SIMPLY HEALTHCARE PLANS, INC.—See Elevance Health, Inc.; *U.S. Public*, pg. 730
SMARTLIFE CARE AG—See Helvetia Holding AG; *Int'l*, pg. 3340
SOLSTICE BENEFITS, INC.; *U.S. Private*, pg. 3710
SOLUCIA PROTECTION JURIDIQUE SARL—See CVC Capital Partners SICAV-FIS S.A.; *Int'l*, pg. 1882
THE SOUTHEAST PERMANENTE MEDICAL GROUP, INC.—See Kaiser Permanente; *U.S. Private*, pg. 2256
STANDARD LIFE & ACCIDENT INSURANCE COMPANY—See Core Specialty Insurance Holdings, Inc.; *U.S. Private*, pg. 1049
STARMARK—See Trustmark Mutual Holding Company; *U.S. Private*, pg. 4251
STONEWOOD INSURANCE COMPANY—See D. E. Shaw & Co., L.P.; *U.S. Private*, pg. 1139
SUNSHINE STATE HEALTH PLAN, INC.—See Centene Corporation; *U.S. Public*, pg. 470
SUPERIOR DENTAL CARE ALLIANCE, INC.; *U.S. Private*, pg. 3876
SUPERIOR HEALTHPLAN INC.—See Centene Corporation; *U.S. Public*, pg. 470
SUPERIOR VISION SERVICES, INC.—See Centerbridge Partners, L.P.; *U.S. Private*, pg. 816
SYSTEMS PRODUCTS AND SOLUTIONS, INC.; *U.S. Private*, pg. 3908
TAKECARE INSURANCE COMPANY INC.; *U.S. Private*, pg. 3925
TIVITY HEALTH, INC.—See Stone Point Capital LLC; *U.S. Private*, pg. 3825
TOTAL INSURANCE BROKERS, LLC—See Madison Dearborn Partners, LLC; *U.S. Private*, pg. 2540
TOTAL VISION, INC.—See Centene Corporation; *U.S. Public*, pg. 471
TOWER INSURANCE (PNG) LIMITED—See Alpha Insurance Limited; *Int'l*, pg. 368
TRILLIUM COMMUNITY HEALTH PLAN, INC.—See Centene Corporation; *U.S. Public*, pg. 471
TRIPLE-S, INC.—See Triple-S Management Corp.; *U.S. Public*, pg. 2195
TRUE HEALTH NEW MEXICO, INC.—See NeueHealth, Inc.; *U.S. Public*, pg. 1510
TRUESHORE S.R.L—See Humana, Inc.; *U.S. Public*, pg. 1070
TRUSTED HEALTH PLAN, INC.; *U.S. Private*, pg. 4251
TRUSTED HEALTH PLAN MICHIGAN, INC.—See Henry Ford Health System; *U.S. Private*, pg. 1918
UHC OF CALIFORNIA—See UnitedHealth Group Incorporated; *U.S. Public*, pg. 2251
UHC OF CALIFORNIA—See UnitedHealth Group Incorporated; *U.S. Public*, pg. 2251
UMR, INC.—See UnitedHealth Group Incorporated; *U.S. Public*, pg. 2251
UNICARE HEALTH PLAN OF KANSAS, INC.—See Elevance Health, Inc.; *U.S. Public*, pg. 730
UNI-CARE, INC.—See Arthur J. Gallagher & Co.; *U.S. Public*, pg. 207
UNION STANDARD OF AMERICA LIFE INSURANCE CO.—See Ullico Inc.; *U.S. Private*, pg. 4276
UNISON HEALTH PLAN OF DELAWARE, INC.—See UnitedHealth Group Incorporated; *U.S. Public*, pg. 2251
UNITED CONCORDIA COMPANIES INC.—See Highmark Health; *U.S. Private*, pg. 1941
UNITEDHEALTHCARE ARIZONA PHYSICIANS IPA—See UnitedHealth Group Incorporated; *U.S. Public*, pg. 2252
UNITEDHEALTHCARE GLOBAL—See UnitedHealth Group Incorporated; *U.S. Public*, pg. 2241
UNITEDHEALTHCARE, INC.—See UnitedHealth Group Incorporated; *U.S. Public*, pg. 2251
UNITEDHEALTHCARE LIFE INSURANCE COMPANY—See UnitedHealth Group Incorporated; *U.S. Public*, pg. 2251
UNITEDHEALTHCARE NEVADA—See UnitedHealth Group Incorporated; *U.S. Public*, pg. 2252
UNITEDHEALTHCARE OF ARKANSAS, INC.—See UnitedHealth Group Incorporated; *U.S. Public*, pg. 2252
UNITEDHEALTHCARE OF COLORADO, INC.—See UnitedHealth Group Incorporated; *U.S. Public*, pg. 2252
UNITEDHEALTHCARE OF FLORIDA, INC.—See UnitedHealth Group Incorporated; *U.S. Public*, pg. 2252
UNITEDHEALTHCARE OF GEORGIA, INC.—See UnitedHealth Group Incorporated; *U.S. Public*, pg. 2252
UNITEDHEALTHCARE OF ILLINOIS, INC.—See UnitedHealth Group Incorporated; *U.S. Public*, pg. 2252
UNITEDHEALTHCARE OF MISSISSIPPI, INC.—See UnitedHealth Group Incorporated; *U.S. Public*, pg. 2252
UNITEDHEALTHCARE OF NEW ENGLAND, INC.—See UnitedHealth Group Incorporated; *U.S. Public*, pg. 2252
UNITEDHEALTHCARE OF NORTH CAROLINA, INC.—See UnitedHealth Group Incorporated; *U.S. Public*, pg. 2252
UNITEDHEALTHCARE OF OHIO, INC.—See UnitedHealth Group Incorporated; *U.S. Public*, pg. 2252
UNITEDHEALTHCARE OF OKLAHOMA, INC.—See UnitedHealth Group Incorporated; *U.S. Public*, pg. 2251
UNITEDHEALTHCARE OF OREGON, INC.—See UnitedHealth Group Incorporated; *U.S. Public*, pg. 2251
UNITEDHEALTHCARE OF TEXAS, INC.—See UnitedHealth Group Incorporated; *U.S. Public*, pg. 2251
UNITEDHEALTHCARE OF THE MIDLANDS, INC.—See UnitedHealth Group Incorporated; *U.S. Public*, pg. 2252
UNITEDHEALTHCARE OF THE MIDWEST, INC.—See UnitedHealth Group Incorporated; *U.S. Public*, pg. 2252
UNITEDHEALTHCARE OF WISCONSIN, INC.—See UnitedHealth Group Incorporated; *U.S. Public*, pg. 2252
UNITED HEALTHCARE SERVICES, INC.—See UnitedHealth Group Incorporated; *U.S. Public*, pg. 2251
UNITED TEACHER ASSOCIATES INSURANCE COMPANY—See INNOVATE Corp.; *U.S. Public*, pg. 1126
UNIVERSAL FIDELITY HOLDING CO., INC.; *U.S. Private*, pg. 4305
UNIVERSAL HEALTH CARE, INC.; *U.S. Private*, pg. 4305
UNUM DENTAL—See Unum Group; *U.S. Public*, pg. 2263
UNUM LIFE INSURANCE COMPANY OF AMERICA—See Unum Group; *U.S. Public*, pg. 2263
UPMC HEALTH PLAN, INC.—See University of Pittsburgh Medical Center; *U.S. Private*, pg. 4309
UPMC WORKPARTNERS; *U.S. Private*, pg. 4312
USABLE MUTUAL INSURANCE COMPANY—See USAble Corporation; *U.S. Private*, pg. 4322
VALOR HEALTHCARE, INC.—See Humana, Inc.; *U.S. Public*, pg. 1070
VAMED ENGINEERING NICARAGUA, SOCIEDAD ANONIMA—See Fresenius SE & Co. KGaA; *Int'l*, pg. 2781
VAMED HEALTHCARE SERVICES SA (PTY) LTD.—See Fresenius SE & Co. KGaA; *Int'l*, pg. 2781
VAMED HEALTH PROJECT GMBH—See Fresenius SE & Co. KGaA; *Int'l*, pg. 2781
VAMED HEALTH PROJECTS MALAYSIA SDN. BHD.—See Fresenius SE & Co. KGaA; *Int'l*, pg. 2781
VAMED MEDITERRA, A.S.—See Fresenius SE & Co. KGaA; *Int'l*, pg. 2781
VANBREDA INTERNATIONAL LLC—See The Cigna Group; *U.S. Public*, pg. 2061
VANTAGE INSURANCE SERVICES LIMITED—See White Mountains Insurance Group, Ltd.; *U.S. Public*, pg. 2369
VERMONT ACCIDENT INSURANCE CO., INC.—See Concord General Mu; *U.S. Private*, pg. 1010
VISION PLUS OF AMERICA INC.—See Medical Benefits Mutual Life Insurance Co. Inc.; *U.S. Private*, pg. 2654
THE VITALITY GROUP INC—See Discovery Limited; *Int'l*, pg. 2134

N.A.I.C.S. INDEX

524126 — DIRECT PROPERTY AND...

VIVAMED S.R.O.—See Centene Corporation; *U.S. Public*, pg. 471
VYNLEADS, INC.; *U.S. Public*, pg. 2315
WALLACH & COMPANY—See LM Funding America, Inc.; *U.S. Public*, pg. 1337
WAVEMARK, INC.—See Cardinal Health, Inc.; *U.S. Public*, pg. 434
WB COMMUNITY HEALTH; *U.S. Private*, pg. 4461
WELLCARE HEALTH PLANS INC.—See Centene Corporation; *U.S. Public*, pg. 471
WELLCARE OF GEORGIA, INC.—See Centene Corporation; *U.S. Public*, pg. 471
WELLMARK BLUE CROSS & BLUE SHIELD; *U.S. Private*, pg. 4475
WELLTHIE, INC.—See Aflac Incorporated; *U.S. Public*, pg. 57
WESTERN SKY COMMUNITY CARE, INC.—See Centene Corporation; *U.S. Public*, pg. 471
WINNING SECURITY, S.L.—See Centene Corporation; *U.S. Public*, pg. 471
WISCONSIN PHYSICIANS SERVICE INSURANCE CORPORATION; *U.S. Private*, pg. 4548
WORLDWIDE INSURANCE SERVICES LLC—See GuideWell Mutual Holding Corporation; *U.S. Private*, pg. 1814

524126 — DIRECT PROPERTY AND CASUALTY INSURANCE CARRIERS

8121 INSURANCE MANAGEMENT, INC.—See Clayton, Dubilier & Rice, LLC; *U.S. Private*, pg. 927
8121 INSURANCE MANAGEMENT, INC.—See Stone Point Capital LLC; *U.S. Private*, pg. 3825
ABSCO LTD. CORP.; *U.S. Private*, pg. 44
ACE INSURANCE COMPANY OF THE MIDWEST—See Chubb Limited; *Int'l*, pg. 1590
ACE PROPERTY AND CASUALTY INSURANCE COMPANY—See Chubb Limited; *Int'l*, pg. 1590
ACMAT COMPANIES, INC.—See ACMAT Corporation; *U.S. Public*, pg. 35
ACMAT OF TEXAS, INC.—See ACMAT Corporation; *U.S. Public*, pg. 35
ACSTAR INSURANCE COMPANY—See ACMAT Corporation; *U.S. Public*, pg. 35
ACUITY; *U.S. Private*, pg. 71
ADAC AUTOVERSICHERUNG AG—See Allianz SE; *Int'l*, pg. 341
ADLP ASSURANCES SAS—See ADLPartner SA; *Int'l*, pg. 151
ADMIRAL INDEMNITY COMPANY—See W.R. Berkley Corporation; *U.S. Public*, pg. 2316
ADMIRAL INSURANCE COMPANY—See W.R. Berkley Corporation; *U.S. Public*, pg. 2318
ADMIRAL INSURANCE GROUP, LLC—See W.R. Berkley Corporation; *U.S. Public*, pg. 2316
ADVANCED MARKETING & PROCESSING, INC.—See Crestview Partners, L.P.; *U.S. Private*, pg. 1098
ADVANTAGE COMP, INC.; *U.S. Private*, pg. 94
ADVENT CAPITAL (HOLDINGS) PLC—See Fairfax Financial Holdings Limited; *Int'l*, pg. 2605
AEGIS SECURITY INSURANCE CO.—See Warburg Pincus LLC; *U.S. Private*, pg. 4438
AEGON ESPANA S.A.—See Aegon N.V.; *Int'l*, pg. 174
AEGON SCHADEVERZEKERING N.V.—See ASR Nederland N.V.; *Int'l*, pg. 632
AFFILIATED FM INSURANCE COMPANY—See Factory Mutual Insurance Company; *U.S. Private*, pg. 1460
AFFIRMATIVE PROPERTY HOLDINGS, INC.—See J.C. Flowers & Co. LLC; *U.S. Private*, pg. 2159
AFR INSURANCE; *U.S. Private*, pg. 124
AFS INSURANCE SERVICES, INC.—See Associated Food Stores, Inc.; *U.S. Private*, pg. 355
AGA SERVICE COMPANY CORP.—See Allianz SE; *Int'l*, pg. 341
AGCS RESSEGUROS BRASIL S.A.—See Allianz SE; *Int'l*, pg. 341
AGENTCUBED, LLC—See The Allstate Corporation; *U.S. Public*, pg. 2033
AGENZIA1 S.R.L.—See AUTO1 Group SE; *Int'l*, pg. 725
AGRI GENERAL INSURANCE COMPANY—See Chubb Limited; *Int'l*, pg. 1592
AGRILOGIC CONSULTING, LLC—See Apollo Global Management, Inc.; *U.S. Public*, pg. 147
AIG ASIA PACIFIC INSURANCE PTE. LTD.—See American International Group, Inc.; *U.S. Public*, pg. 105
AIG CLAIMS, INC.—See American International Group, Inc.; *U.S. Public*, pg. 104
AIG CYPRUS LIMITED—See American International Group, Inc.; *U.S. Public*, pg. 105
AIG EGYPT INSURANCE COMPANY S.A.E.—See American International Group, Inc.; *U.S. Public*, pg. 105
AIG FEDERAL SAVINGS BANK—See American International Group, Inc.; *U.S. Public*, pg. 104
AIG GENERAL INSURANCE CO., LTD.—See American International Group, Inc.; *U.S. Public*, pg. 104
AIG INSURANCE COMPANY CHINA LIMITED—See American International Group, Inc.; *U.S. Public*, pg. 104

AIG INSURANCE COMPANY, JSC—See American International Group, Inc.; *U.S. Public*, pg. 104
AIG INSURANCE COMPANY-PUERTO RICO—See American International Group, Inc.; *U.S. Public*, pg. 105
AIG INSURANCE HONG KONG LIMITED—See American International Group, Inc.; *U.S. Public*, pg. 105
AIG INVESTMENTS UK LIMITED—See American International Group, Inc.; *U.S. Public*, pg. 104
AIG ISRAEL INSURANCE COMPANY LIMITED—See American International Group, Inc.; *U.S. Public*, pg. 104
AIG KOREA INC.—See American International Group, Inc.; *U.S. Public*, pg. 105
AIG LEBANON SAL—See American International Group, Inc.; *U.S. Public*, pg. 104
AIG MATCHED FUNDING CORP.—See American International Group, Inc.; *U.S. Public*, pg. 104
AIG MEA LIMITED—See American International Group, Inc.; *U.S. Public*, pg. 106
AIG-METROPOLITANA CIA DE SEGUROS Y REASEGUROS S.A.—See American International Group, Inc.; *U.S. Public*, pg. 106
AIG PROPERTY CASUALTY COMPANY—See American International Group, Inc.; *U.S. Public*, pg. 105
AIG PROPERTY CASUALTY INC.—See American International Group, Inc.; *U.S. Public*, pg. 105
AIG PROPERTY CASUALTY INTERNATIONAL, LLC—See American International Group, Inc.; *U.S. Public*, pg. 105
AIG PROPERTY CASUALTY U.S., INC.—See American International Group, Inc.; *U.S. Public*, pg. 106
AIG RE-TAKAFUL (L) BERHAD—See American International Group, Inc.; *U.S. Public*, pg. 105
AIG SEGUROS MEXICO, S.A. DE C.V.—See American International Group, Inc.; *U.S. Public*, pg. 106
AIG SPECIALTY INSURANCE COMPANY—See American International Group, Inc.; *U.S. Public*, pg. 106
AIG TRADING GROUP INC.—See American International Group, Inc.; *U.S. Public*, pg. 106
AIG UKRAINE INSURANCE COMPANY PJSC—See American International Group, Inc.; *U.S. Public*, pg. 106
AIWA INSURANCE SERVICE CO., LTD.—See Bunka Shutter Co., Ltd.; *Int'l*, pg. 1216
AKCIONARSKO DRUSTVO ZA REOSIGURANJE GENERALI REOSIGURANJE SRBIJA—See Assicurazioni Generali S.p.A.; *Int'l*, pg. 643
ALASKA NATIONAL INSURANCE COMPANY—See Alaska National Corporation; *U.S. Private*, pg. 151
ALFA ALLIANCE INSURANCE CORP.—See Alfa Corporation; *U.S. Private*, pg. 164
ALFA INSURANCE CORP.—See Alfa Corporation; *U.S. Private*, pg. 164
ALFALAH INSURANCE COMPANY LIMITED—See Abu Dhabi Group; *Int'l*, pg. 71
ALLEANZA TORO S.P.A.—See Assicurazioni Generali S.p.A.; *Int'l*, pg. 643
ALLEGHANY INSURANCE HOLDINGS LLC—See Berkshire Hathaway Inc.; *U.S. Public*, pg. 298
ALLIANT INSURANCE SERVICES HOUSTON LLC—See Stone Point Capital LLC; *U.S. Private*, pg. 3818
ALLIANZ ALAPKEZELO ZRT.—See Allianz SE; *Int'l*, pg. 343
ALLIANZ AYUDHYA CAPITAL PUBLIC COMPANY LIMITED; *Int'l*, pg. 341
ALLIANZ CAMEROUN ASSURANCES SA—See Allianz SE; *Int'l*, pg. 344
ALLIANZ COTE D'IVOIRE ASSURANCES VIE SA—See Allianz SE; *Int'l*, pg. 344
ALLIANZ DIRECT VERSICHERUNGS-AG—See Allianz SE; *Int'l*, pg. 344
ALLIANZ ELEMENTAR VERSICHERUNGS-AKTIENGESELLSCHAFT—See Allianz SE; *Int'l*, pg. 345
ALLIANZ GLOBAL ASSISTANCE (AGA) INTERNATIONAL S.A.—See Allianz SE; *Int'l*, pg. 342
ALLIANZ GLOBAL ASSISTANCE—See Allianz SE; *Int'l*, pg. 342
ALLIANZ GLOBAL ASSISTANCE—See Allianz SE; *Int'l*, pg. 342
ALLIANZ GLOBAL CORPORATE & SPECIALTY AG—See Allianz SE; *Int'l*, pg. 345
ALLIANZ GLOBAL CORPORATE & SPECIALTY AUSTRALIA—See Allianz SE; *Int'l*, pg. 345
ALLIANZ GLOBAL CORPORATE & SPECIALTY - AUSTRIA—See Allianz SE; *Int'l*, pg. 345
ALLIANZ GLOBAL CORPORATE & SPECIALTY BELGIUM—See Allianz SE; *Int'l*, pg. 345
ALLIANZ GLOBAL CORPORATE & SPECIALTY - CANADA—See Allianz SE; *Int'l*, pg. 345
ALLIANZ GLOBAL CORPORATE & SPECIALTY (FRANCE) S.A.—See Allianz SE; *Int'l*, pg. 345
ALLIANZ GLOBAL CORPORATE & SPECIALTY - IRELAND—See Allianz SE; *Int'l*, pg. 345
ALLIANZ GLOBAL CORPORATE & SPECIALTY - NETHERLANDS—See Allianz SE; *Int'l*, pg. 349
ALLIANZ GLOBAL CORPORATE & SPECIALTY - SINGAPORE—See Allianz SE; *Int'l*, pg. 345
ALLIANZ GLOBAL CORPORATE & SPECIALTY - UK—See Allianz SE; *Int'l*, pg. 345
ALLIANZ GLOBAL RISKS US INSURANCE COMPANY—See Allianz SE; *Int'l*, pg. 345

ALLIANZ MALAYSIA BERHAD—See Allianz SE; *Int'l*, pg. 349
ALLIANZ PARTNERS DEUTSCHLAND GMBH—See Allianz SE; *Int'l*, pg. 349
ALLIANZ PRIVATE KRANKENVERSICHERUNGS-AKTIEN—See Allianz SE; *Int'l*, pg. 349
ALLIANZ SUISSE VERSICHERUNGEN—See Allianz SE; *Int'l*, pg. 350
ALLIANZ SUISSE VERSICHERUNGS-GESELLSCHAFT AG—See Allianz SE; *Int'l*, pg. 350
ALLIANZ VERSICHERUNGS AG—See Allianz SE; *Int'l*, pg. 350
ALLIANZ VERSICHERUNGS AG—See Allianz SE; *Int'l*, pg. 350
ALLIANZ VORSORGEKASSE AG—See Allianz SE; *Int'l*, pg. 350
ALLIANZ YASAM VE EMEKLILIK A.S.—See Allianz SE; *Int'l*, pg. 351
ALLIED WORLD ASSURANCE COMPANY (EUROPE) DESIGNATED ACTIVITY COMPANY—See Fairfax Financial Holdings Limited; *Int'l*, pg. 2605
ALLIED WORLD ASSURANCE COMPANY HOLDINGS, LTD—See Fairfax Financial Holdings Limited; *Int'l*, pg. 2605
ALLIED WORLD REINSURANCE COMPANY—See Fairfax Financial Holdings Limited; *Int'l*, pg. 2606
ALLIED WORLD SYNDICATE SERVICES (SINGAPORE) PTE. LTD.—See Fairfax Financial Holdings Limited; *Int'l*, pg. 2606
ALLSECUR B.V.—See Allianz SE; *Int'l*, pg. 343
ALLSECUR DEUTSCHLAND AG—See Allianz SE; *Int'l*, pg. 343
THE ALLSTATE CORPORATION; *U.S. Public*, pg. 2032
ALLSTATE INSURANCE COMPANY OF CANADA—See The Allstate Corporation; *U.S. Public*, pg. 2032
ALLSTATE INSURANCE COMPANY—See The Allstate Corporation; *U.S. Public*, pg. 2032
ALLSTATE LIFE INSURANCE COMPANY OF NEW YORK—See Vestar Capital Partners, LLC; *U.S. Private*, pg. 4373
ALLSTATE NEW JERSEY INSURANCE COMPANY—See The Allstate Corporation; *U.S. Public*, pg. 2032
ALL TRANS RISK SOLUTIONS, LLC—See Ambac Financial Group, Inc.; *U.S. Public*, pg. 92
ALLTRUST INSURANCE COMPANY OF CHINA LIMITED—See China Huaneng Group Co., Ltd.; *Int'l*, pg. 1509
ALPHA PROPERTY & CASUALTY INSURANCE COMPANY—See Kemper Corporation; *U.S. Public*, pg. 1220
AMERICAN ACCESS CASUALTY COMPANY—See Kemper Corporation; *U.S. Public*, pg. 1220
AMERICAN AUTOMOBILE INSURANCE COMPANY, CORP.—See Allianz SE; *Int'l*, pg. 351
AMERICAN BANKERS INSURANCE COMPANY OF FLORIDA—See Assurant, Inc.; *U.S. Public*, pg. 215
AMERICAN CASUALTY COMPANY OF READING, PENNSYLVANIA—See Loews Corporation; *U.S. Public*, pg. 1339
AMERICAN COLONIAL INSURANCE COMPANY—See Conifer Holdings, Inc.; *U.S. Public*, pg. 567
AMERICAN EMPIRE INSURANCE COMPANY—See American Financial Group, Inc.; *U.S. Public*, pg. 102
AMERICAN EMPIRE SURPLUS LINES INSURANCE COMPANY—See American Financial Group, Inc.; *U.S. Public*, pg. 102
AMERICAN EUROPEAN GROUP, INC.; *U.S. Private*, pg. 232
AMERICAN FIRE & CASUALTY CO.—See Liberty Mutual Holding Company Inc.; *U.S. Public*, pg. 2446
AMERICAN HALLMARK INSURANCE COMPANY OF TEXAS—See Hallmark Financial Services, Inc.; *U.S. Public*, pg. 981
AMERICAN HIGHWAYS INSURANCE AGENCY, INC.—See American Financial Group, Inc.; *U.S. Public*, pg. 103
AMERICAN HOME ASSURANCE CO., LTD.—See American International Group, Inc.; *U.S. Public*, pg. 104
AMERICAN HOME ASSURANCE COMPANY—See American International Group, Inc.; *U.S. Public*, pg. 106
AMERICAN INTEGRITY INSURANCE COMPANY OF FLORIDA, INC.; *U.S. Private*, pg. 238
AMERICAN INTERNATIONAL GROUP UK LIMITED—See American International Group, Inc.; *U.S. Public*, pg. 106
AMERICAN INTERNATIONAL LIFE ASSURANCE COMPANY OF NEW YORK—See American International Group, Inc.; *U.S. Public*, pg. 105
AMERICAN MANAGEMENT CORPORATION—See Novatae Risk Group, LLC; *U.S. Private*, pg. 2967
AMERICAN MANUFACTURERS MUTUAL INSURANCE COMPANY—See Lumbermens Mutual Group; *U.S. Private*, pg. 2514
AMERICAN MERCHANTS CASUALTY CO.—See Motorists Mutual Insurance Co.; *U.S. Private*, pg. 2797
AMERICAN MERCURY INSURANCE COMPANY—See Mercury General Corporation; *U.S. Public*, pg. 1421
AMERICAN MERCURY MGA, INC.—See Mercury General Corporation; *U.S. Public*, pg. 1421
AMERICAN MOTORISTS INSURANCE CO.—See Lumber-

524126 — DIRECT PROPERTY AND... CORPORATE AFFILIATIONS

N.A.I.C.S. Index

mens Mutual Group; *U.S. Private*, pg. 2514
AMERICAN PHYSICIANS ASSURANCE CORPORATION—See The Doctors Company; *U.S. Private*, pg. 4021
AMERICAN RELIABLE INSURANCE COMPANY—See Paine Schwartz Partners, LLC; *U.S. Private*, pg. 3075
AMERICAN SAFETY INSURANCE COMPANY—See Atlantic American Corporation; *U.S. Public*, pg. 222
AMERICAN SERVICE INSURANCE COMPANY—See Atlas Financial Holdings, Inc.; *U.S. Public*, pg. 224
AMERICAN SOUTHERN INSURANCE COMPANY—See Atlantic American Corporation; *U.S. Public*, pg. 222
AMERICAN STRATEGIC INSURANCE CORP.; *U.S. Private*, pg. 256
AMERICAN SUMMIT INSURANCE COMPANY—See Re-Align Capital Strategies; *U.S. Private*, pg. 3368
AMERISURE INSURANCE COMPANY INC—See Amerisure Mutual Insurance Company; *U.S. Private*, pg. 260
AMERISURE MUTUAL INSURANCE COMPANY; *U.S. Private*, pg. 260
AM HOLDINGS LLC—See American International Group, Inc.; *U.S. Public*, pg. 106
AMICA LLOYD'S OF TEXAS—See Amica Mutual Insurance Co.; *U.S. Private*, pg. 263
AMICA MUTUAL INSURANCE CO.; *U.S. Private*, pg. 263
AMTRUST AGRICULTURE INSURANCE SERVICES, LLC—See Stone Point Capital LLC; *U.S. Private*, pg. 3820
AMTRUST EUROPE LTD.—See Stone Point Capital LLC; *U.S. Private*, pg. 3820
AMTRUST GESTION BOLIVIA S.R.L.—See Stone Point Capital LLC; *U.S. Private*, pg. 3820
AMTRUST GESTION PARAGUAY S.A.—See Stone Point Capital LLC; *U.S. Private*, pg. 3820
AMTRUST GESTION PERU S.A.C.—See Stone Point Capital LLC; *U.S. Private*, pg. 3820
AMVENTURE INSURANCE AGENCY, INC.—See Stone Point Capital LLC; *U.S. Private*, pg. 3820
ANBANG INSURANCE GROUP CO., LTD.; *Int'l*, pg. 447
ANCHENG PROPERTY & CASUALTY INSURANCE CO., LTD.; *Int'l*, pg. 448
ANDERSON INSURANCE & INVESTMENT AGENCY—See Associated Banc-Corp; *U.S. Public*, pg. 214
ANEXO GROUP PLC; *Int'l*, pg. 459
ANGEL RISK MANAGEMENT LIMITED—See AXA S.A.; *Int'l*, pg. 760
AON PHILIPPINES, INC.—See Aon plc; *Int'l*, pg. 492
AON (SCHWEIZ) AG—See Aon plc; *Int'l*, pg. 491
APO ASSET MANAGEMENT GMBH—See Deutsche Apotheker- und Arztebank eG; *Int'l*, pg. 2049
APOLLO CASUALTY INSURANCE CO.; *U.S. Private*, pg. 294
ARABIAN SHIELD COOPERATIVE INSURANCE COMPANY; *Int'l*, pg. 533
ARAB INSURANCE GROUP B.S.C.; *Int'l*, pg. 530
ARAB MISR INSURANCE GROUP—See Fairfax Financial Holdings Limited; *Int'l*, pg. 2607
ARBELLA INCORPORATED—See Arbella Insurance Group; *U.S. Private*, pg. 308
ARBELLA SERVICE COMPANY INC.—See Arbella Insurance Group; *U.S. Private*, pg. 308
ARBOUR NATIONAL; *U.S. Private*, pg. 309
ARCH EXCESS & SURPLUS INSURANCE COMPANY—See Arch Capital Group Ltd.; *Int'l*, pg. 546
ARCH INDEMNITY INSURANCE COMPANY—See Arch Capital Group Ltd.; *Int'l*, pg. 546
ARCH MI ASIA LIMITED—See Arch Capital Group Ltd.; *Int'l*, pg. 546
ARCH MORTGAGE INSURANCE COMPANY—See Arch Capital Group Ltd.; *Int'l*, pg. 546
ARCH SPECIALTY INSURANCE COMPANY—See Arch Capital Group Ltd.; *Int'l*, pg. 546
ARCH UNDERWRITERS INC.—See Arch Capital Group Ltd.; *Int'l*, pg. 546
ARCH U.S. MI HOLDINGS INC.—See Arch Capital Group Ltd.; *Int'l*, pg. 546
ARCOA RISK RETENTION GROUP, INC.—See U-Haul Holding Company; *U.S. Public*, pg. 2211
ARC SPECIALTY BROKERAGE, LLC—See ARC Excess & Surplus LLC; *U.S. Private*, pg. 309
ARGOGLOBAL ASSICURAZIONI S.P.A.—See Brookfield Reinsurance Ltd.; *Int'l*, pg. 1194
ARGO MANAGING AGENCY LIMITED—See Brookfield Reinsurance Ltd.; *Int'l*, pg. 1193
ARGONAUT INSURANCE COMPANY—See Brookfield Reinsurance Ltd.; *Int'l*, pg. 1194
ARGO RE, LTD.—See Brookfield Reinsurance Ltd.; *Int'l*, pg. 1194
ARIEL RE BDA LIMITED—See Brookfield Reinsurance Ltd.; *Int'l*, pg. 1194
ARK ROYAL INSURANCE COMPANY; *U.S. Private*, pg. 325
ARMTECH, INC.; *U.S. Private*, pg. 332
ARNOLD CLARK INSURANCE SERVICES LIMITED—See Arnold Clark Automobiles Limited; *Int'l*, pg. 576
AROPE INSURANCE SAL—See BLOM Bank, S.A.L.; *Int'l*, pg. 1064
ARROWHEAD GENERAL INSURANCE AGENCY, INC.—See Brown & Brown, Inc.; *U.S. Public*, pg. 396
ARROWHEAD WHOLESALE INSURANCE SERVICES, LLC—See Brown & Brown, Inc.; *U.S. Public*, pg. 397
ARROWOOD INDEMNITY COMPANY—See Arrowpoint Capital Corp.; *U.S. Private*, pg. 336
ARROWPOINT CAPITAL CORP.; *U.S. Private*, pg. 336
ASPEN INSURANCE HOLDINGS LIMITED—See Apollo Global Management, Inc.; *U.S. Public*, pg. 147
ASPEN INSURANCE UK LIMITED—See Apollo Global Management, Inc.; *U.S. Public*, pg. 147
ASPEN SINGAPORE PTE. LTD.—See Apollo Global Management, Inc.; *U.S. Public*, pg. 147
ASSA COMPANIA DE SEGUROS, S.A.—See Grupo ASSA, S.A.; *Int'l*, pg. 3121
ASSOCIATED INDUSTRIES OF MASSACHUSETTS MUTUAL INSURANCE COMPANY; *U.S. Private*, pg. 356
ASSURANCES CONTINENTALES - CONTINENTALE VERZEKERINGEN N.V.—See The Hartford Financial Services Group, Inc.; *U.S. Public*, pg. 2088
ASSURED GUARANTY (LONDON) PLC—See Assured Guaranty Ltd.; *Int'l*, pg. 649
ASSURED GUARANTY MORTGAGE INSURANCE COMPANY—See Assured Guaranty Ltd.; *Int'l*, pg. 650
ASSURIA SCHADEVERZEKERING N.V.—See Assuria N.V.; *Int'l*, pg. 650
ATAIN INSURANCE COMPANIES—See H.W. Kaufman Financial Group, Inc.; *U.S. Private*, pg. 1836
ATLANTA ASSURANCES; *Int'l*, pg. 674
ATLANTA INTERNATIONAL INSURANCE COMPANY—See Aon plc; *Int'l*, pg. 488
ATLANTIC AMERICAN CORPORATION; *U.S. Public*, pg. 222
ATLANTIC MUTUAL COMPANIES; *U.S. Private*, pg. 373
ATLANTIC MUTUAL INSURANCE COMPANY—See Atlantic Mutual Companies; *U.S. Private*, pg. 373
ATLANTIC STATES INSURANCE COMPANY—See Donegal Group Inc.; *U.S. Public*, pg. 676
ATLANTIC STATES INSURANCE COMPANY—See Donegal Group Inc.; *U.S. Public*, pg. 676
ATLANTIC STATES INSURANCE COMPANY—See Donegal Group Inc.; *U.S. Public*, pg. 676
ATLANTIC STATES INSURANCE COMPANY—See Donegal Group Inc.; *U.S. Public*, pg. 676
ATRADIUS TRADE CREDIT INSURANCE, INC.—See Grupo Catalana Occidente, S.A.; *Int'l*, pg. 3124
AUSTIN MUTUAL INSURANCE GROUP; *U.S. Private*, pg. 396
AUTOCLAIMS DIRECT, INC.; *U.S. Private*, pg. 398
AUTO-OWNERS INSURANCE COMPANY—See Auto-Owners Insurance Group; *U.S. Private*, pg. 397
AUTO-OWNERS LIFE INSURANCE CO.—See Auto-Owners Insurance Group; *U.S. Private*, pg. 397
AUTOSAINT LIMITED—See White Mountains Insurance Group, Ltd.; *U.S. Public*, pg. 2368
AVIVA INSURANCE COMPANY OF CANADA—See Aviva plc; *Int'l*, pg. 745
AVIVA INSURANCE EUROPE SE—See Aviva plc; *Int'l*, pg. 745
AVOMARK INSURANCE CO.—See Liberty Mutual Holding Company Inc.; *U.S. Private*, pg. 2446
AXA CORPORATE SOLUTIONS DUBAI—See AXA S.A.; *Int'l*, pg. 755
AXA CORPORATE SOLUTIONS GERMANY—See AXA S.A.; *Int'l*, pg. 755
AXA CORPORATE SOLUTIONS HONG KONG—See AXA S.A.; *Int'l*, pg. 755
AXA CORPORATE SOLUTIONS INSURANCE—See Equitable Holdings, Inc.; *U.S. Public*, pg. 788
AXA CORPORATE SOLUTIONS—See AXA S.A.; *Int'l*, pg. 755
AXA CORPORATE SOLUTIONS UK—See AXA S.A.; *Int'l*, pg. 755
AXA TIANPING PROPERTY & CASUALTY INSURANCE COMPANY LTD. (AXATP)—See AXA S.A.; *Int'l*, pg. 758
AXIS REINSURANCE COMPANY—See AXIS Capital Holdings Limited; *Int'l*, pg. 769
BANKERS INSURANCE COMPANY—See Bankers International Financial Corporation; *U.S. Private*, pg. 467
BANKERS INSURANCE SERVICES INC.—See Bankers International Financial Corporation; *U.S. Private*, pg. 467
BARBON INSURANCE GROUP LIMITED—See The Carlyle Group Inc.; *U.S. Public*, pg. 2045
BATTLE CREEK MUTUAL INSURANCE COMPANY—See Nodak Insurance Company; *U.S. Private*, pg. 2933
BAY AREA INSURANCE SERVICES; *U.S. Private*, pg. 491
BAY STATE INSURANCE COMPANY—See The Andover Companies; *U.S. Private*, pg. 3986
BCC ASSICURAZIONI S.P.A.—See Iccrea Holding S.p.A.; *Int'l*, pg. 3578
BCI SEGUROS GENERALES S.A.—See Empresas Juan Yarur S.A.C.; *Int'l*, pg. 2391
B.C.S. FINANCIAL CORP.; *U.S. Private*, pg. 420
B.C.S. INSURANCE COMPANY INC.—See B.C.S. Financial Corp.; *U.S. Private*, pg. 420
BDML CONNECT LIMITED—See Capita plc; *Int'l*, pg. 1308
BEAUFORT UNDERWRITING AGENCY LIMITED—See Cincinnati Financial Corporation; *U.S. Public*, pg. 495
BEIJING CAPITAL LAND LTD.; *Int'l*, pg. 947
BERKLEY ALLIANCE MANAGERS, LLC—See W.R. Berkley Corporation; *U.S. Public*, pg. 2316
BERKLEY ARGENTINA DE REASEGUROS S.A.—See W.R. Berkley Corporation; *U.S. Public*, pg. 2316
BERKLEY ASSET PROTECTION UNDERWRITERS, LLC—See W.R. Berkley Corporation; *U.S. Public*, pg. 2316
BERKLEY CAPITAL INVESTORS, LP—See W.R. Berkley Corporation; *U.S. Public*, pg. 2316
BERKLEY CUSTOM INSURANCE MANAGERS, LLC—See W.R. Berkley Corporation; *U.S. Public*, pg. 2316
BERKLEY FINSECURE, LLC—See W.R. Berkley Corporation; *U.S. Public*, pg. 2316
BERKLEY INSURANCE COMPANY—See W.R. Berkley Corporation; *U.S. Public*, pg. 2318
BERKLEY INTERNATIONAL DO BRASIL SEGUROS S. A.—See W.R. Berkley Corporation; *U.S. Public*, pg. 2317
BERKLEY INTERNATIONAL LATINOAMERICA S. A.—See W.R. Berkley Corporation; *U.S. Public*, pg. 2316
BERKLEY INTERNATIONAL, LLC—See W.R. Berkley Corporation; *U.S. Public*, pg. 2317
BERKLEY INTERNATIONAL SEGUROS COLOMBIA S.A.—See W.R. Berkley Corporation; *U.S. Public*, pg. 2316
BERKLEY INTERNATIONAL SEGUROS, S. A.—See W.R. Berkley Corporation; *U.S. Public*, pg. 2316
BERKLEY INTERNATIONAL SEGUROS, S. A.—See W.R. Berkley Corporation; *U.S. Public*, pg. 2316
BERKLEY LIFE SCIENCES, LLC—See W.R. Berkley Corporation; *U.S. Public*, pg. 2317
BERKLEY LS INSURANCE SOLUTIONS, LLC—See W.R. Berkley Corporation; *U.S. Public*, pg. 2317
BERKLEY MID-ATLANTIC GROUP—See W.R. Berkley Corporation; *U.S. Public*, pg. 2318
BERKLEY NET UNDERWRITERS L.L.C.—See W.R. Berkley Corporation; *U.S. Public*, pg. 2317
BERKLEY NORTH PACIFIC GROUP, LLC—See W.R. Berkley Corporation; *U.S. Public*, pg. 2317
BERKLEY OFFSHORE UNDERWRITING MANAGERS, LLC—See W.R. Berkley Corporation; *U.S. Public*, pg. 2317
BERKLEY OFFSHORE UNDERWRITING MANAGERS UK, LIMITED—See W.R. Berkley Corporation; *U.S. Public*, pg. 2317
BERKLEY OIL & GAS SPECIALTY SERVICES, LLC—See W.R. Berkley Corporation; *U.S. Public*, pg. 2317
BERKLEY PROFESSIONAL LIABILITY, LLC—See W.R. Berkley Corporation; *U.S. Public*, pg. 2317
BERKLEY PROGRAM SPECIALISTS, LLC—See W.R. Berkley Corporation; *U.S. Public*, pg. 2317
BERKLEY PUBLIC ENTITY MANAGERS, LLC—See W.R. Berkley Corporation; *U.S. Public*, pg. 2317
BERKLEY REGIONAL SPECIALTY INSURANCE COMPANY—See W.R. Berkley Corporation; *U.S. Public*, pg. 2317
BERKLEY SELECT, LLC—See W.R. Berkley Corporation; *U.S. Public*, pg. 2317
BERKLEY SOUTHEAST INSURANCE GROUP, LLC—See W.R. Berkley Corporation; *U.S. Public*, pg. 2317
BERKLEY TECHNOLOGY UNDERWRITERS, LLC—See W.R. Berkley Corporation; *U.S. Public*, pg. 2317
BITCO CORPORATION—See Old Republic International Corporation; *U.S. Public*, pg. 1567
BITUMINOUS CASUALTY CORPORATION—See Old Republic International Corporation; *U.S. Public*, pg. 1567
BITUMINOUS FIRE AND MARINE INSURANCE COMPANY—See Old Republic International Corporation; *U.S. Public*, pg. 1567
BOARDWALK PIPELINES, LP—See Loews Corporation; *U.S. Public*, pg. 1339
BOK FINANCIAL ASSET MANAGEMENT, INC.—See BOK Financial Corporation; *U.S. Public*, pg. 367
BPI/MS INSURANCE CORPORATION—See Bank of the Philippine Islands; *Int'l*, pg. 848
BRACHT, DECKERS & MACKELBERT N.V.—See The Hartford Financial Services Group, Inc.; *U.S. Public*, pg. 2088
BRIDGEFIELD CASUALTY INSURANCE COMPANY—See American Financial Group, Inc.; *U.S. Public*, pg. 102
BROOKLYN UNDERWRITING PTY LIMITED—See AXA S.A.; *Int'l*, pg. 760
BUCKEYE STATE MUTUAL INSURANCE CO.; *U.S. Private*, pg. 677
BURNS & WILCOX LTD.—See H.W. Kaufman Financial Group, Inc.; *U.S. Private*, pg. 1836
BURNS & WILCOX LTD.—See H.W. Kaufman Financial Group, Inc.; *U.S. Private*, pg. 1836
BURNS & WILCOX—See H.W. Kaufman Financial Group, Inc.; *U.S. Private*, pg. 1836
BXM INSURANCE SERVICES, INC.—See W.R. Berkley Corporation; *U.S. Public*, pg. 2316
C.A. DE SEGUROS AMERICAN INTERNATIONAL—See American International Group, Inc.; *U.S. Public*, pg. 106
CAISSE REGIONALE DE CREDIT AGRICOLE MUTUEL DE NORMANDIE SEINE SC; *Int'l*, pg. 1259
CALIFORNIA AUTOMOBILE INSURANCE COMPANY—See Mercury General Corporation; *U.S. Public*, pg. 1421
CALIFORNIA GENERAL UNDERWRITERS INSURANCE

N.A.I.C.S. INDEX

524126 — DIRECT PROPERTY AND...

COMPANY, INC.—See Mercury General Corporation; *U.S. Public*, pg. 1421
CAMARGUE UNDERWRITING MANAGERS (PTY) LIMITED—See Hollard Insurance Company Ltd; *Int'l*, pg. 3451
CAMBRIDGE MUTUAL FIRE INSURANCE COMPANY; *U.S. Private*, pg. 727
CAMBRIDGE UNDERWRITERS LIMITED; *U.S. Private*, pg. 727
CAPACITY MARINE CORPORATION—See Ambac Financial Group, Inc.; *U.S. Public*, pg. 92
CAPITAL ADVANTAGE INSURANCE COMPANY—See Capital BlueCross Inc.; *U.S. Private*, pg. 739
CAPITAL CITY INSURANCE CO. INC.; *U.S. Private*, pg. 739
CAPITOL COUNTY MUTUAL FIRE INSURANCE CO.—See Kemper Corporation; *U.S. Public*, pg. 1221
CAPITOL INDEMNITY CORPORATION—See Berkshire Hathaway Inc.; *U.S. Public*, pg. 298
CAPSPECIALTY—See Berkshire Hathaway Inc.; *U.S. Public*, pg. 298
CARIBBEAN AMERICAN LIFE ASSURANCE COMPANY—See Assurant, Inc.; *U.S. Public*, pg. 215
CAROLINA CASUALTY INSURANCE COMPANY—See W.R. Berkley Corporation; *U.S. Public*, pg. 2318
CASTLE INSURANCE SERVICES (NORTH EAST) LIMITED—See Brown & Brown, Inc.; *U.S. Public*, pg. 400
CATHOLIC CHURCH INSURANCE LIMITED; *Int'l*, pg. 1361
CATHOLIC MUTUAL GROUP; *U.S. Private*, pg. 792
CATLIN EUROPE SE—See AXA S.A.; *Int'l*, pg. 760
CATLIN, INC—See AXA S.A.; *Int'l*, pg. 760
CATLIN, INC.—See AXA S.A.; *Int'l*, pg. 760
CATLIN INSURANCE COMPANY LTD—See AXA S.A.; *Int'l*, pg. 760
CATLIN INSURANCE COMPANY LTD.—See AXA S.A.; *Int'l*, pg. 760
CATLIN (NORTH AMERICAN) HOLDINGS LTD.—See AXA S.A.; *Int'l*, pg. 760
CATLIN RE SCHWEIZ AG—See AXA S.A.; *Int'l*, pg. 760
CATLIN SINGAPORE PTE LTD.—See AXA S.A.; *Int'l*, pg. 760
CBIZ INSURANCE SERVICES, INC.—See CBIZ, Inc.; *U.S. Public*, pg. 456
CELINA INSURANCE GROUP; *U.S. Private*, pg. 807
CENTAURI SPECIALTY INSURANCE HOLDINGS INC.—See Quadrant Management, Inc.; *U.S. Private*, pg. 3316
CENTRAL MUTUAL INSURANCE COMPANY; *U.S. Private*, pg. 822
CENTREPOINT ALLIANCE LIMITED; *Int'l*, pg. 1412
CENTURY INSURANCE GROUP—See Fosun International Limited; *Int'l*, pg. 2752
CENTURY-NATIONAL INSURANCE COMPANY—See The Allstate Corporation; *U.S. Public*, pg. 2033
CHARTIS INSURANCE COMPANY CHINA LIMITED—See American International Group, Inc.; *U.S. Public*, pg. 105
CHARTIS KAZAKHSTAN INSURANCE COMPANY—See American International Group, Inc.; *U.S. Public*, pg. 106
CHARTIS TAKAFUL-ENAYA B.S.C.—See American International Group, Inc.; *U.S. Public*, pg. 106
CHARTIS VIETNAM INSURANCE COMPANY LIMITED—See American International Group, Inc.; *U.S. Public*, pg. 105
CHINA CONTINENT PROPERTY & CASUALTY INSURANCE COMPANY LTD.—See China Reinsurance (Group) Corporation; *Int'l*, pg. 1547
CHINA PACIFIC PROPERTY INSURANCE CO., LTD.—See China Pacific Insurance (Group) Co., Ltd.; *Int'l*, pg. 1539
CHINA TAIPING INSURANCE (HK) COMPANY LIMITED—See China Taiping Insurance Holdings Company Limited; *Int'l*, pg. 1557
CHINA TAIPING INSURANCE (UK) COMPANY LIMITED—See China Taiping Insurance Holdings Company Limited; *Int'l*, pg. 1557
CHOICE HOME WARRANTY; *U.S. Private*, pg. 888
CHRISTOPHER TRIGG LIMITED—See Brown & Brown, Inc.; *U.S. Public*, pg. 400
CHUBB AGRIBUSINESS—See Chubb Limited; *Int'l*, pg. 1592
CHUBB ATLANTIC INDEMNITY, LTD.—See Chubb Limited; *Int'l*, pg. 1591
CHUBB INSURANCE COMPANY OF NEW JERSEY—See Chubb Limited; *Int'l*, pg. 1591
CHUBB INSURANCE COMPANY OF NEW JERSEY—See Chubb Limited; *Int'l*, pg. 1591
CHUBB INSURANCE SOUTH AFRICA LIMITED—See Chubb Limited; *Int'l*, pg. 1592
CHUBB LLOYDS INSURANCE COMPANY OF TEXAS—See Chubb Limited; *Int'l*, pg. 1591
CHUBB NATIONAL INSURANCE COMPANY—See Chubb Limited; *Int'l*, pg. 1591
CHUBB SEGUROS ARGENTINA S.A.—See Chubb Limited; *Int'l*, pg. 1591
CHUBB SEGUROS COLOMBIA S.A.—See Chubb Limited; *Int'l*, pg. 1592
CHUBB & SON INC.—See Chubb Limited; *Int'l*, pg. 1591
CHUBB TEMPEST RE USA LLC—See Chubb Limited; *Int'l*, pg. 1590
CHUBB UNDERWRITING (DIFC) LIMITED—See Chubb Limited; *Int'l*, pg. 1590
CHUBB US HOLDINGS INC.—See Chubb Limited; *Int'l*, pg. 1591
CHURCH & CASUALTY INSURANCE AGENCY INC.; *U.S. Private*, pg. 894
CHURCHILL INSURANCE COMPANY LIMITED—See Direct Line Insurance Group plc; *Int'l*, pg. 2129
THE CINCINNATI CASUALTY COMPANY—See Cincinnati Financial Corporation; *U.S. Public*, pg. 495
THE CINCINNATI INDEMNITY COMPANY—See Cincinnati Financial Corporation; *U.S. Public*, pg. 495
THE CINCINNATI INSURANCE COMPANY—See Cincinnati Financial Corporation; *U.S. Public*, pg. 495
CITIZENS INSURANCE COMPANY OF AMERICA—See The Hanover Insurance Group, Inc.; *U.S. Public*, pg. 2087
CITIZENS PROPERTY INSURANCE CORPORATION; *U.S. Private*, pg. 904
CIVIL SERVICE EMPLOYEES INSURANCE COMPANY—See CSE Insurance Group; *U.S. Private*, pg. 1116
CLAIMCOR, LLC—See FedNat Holding Company; *U.S. Public*, pg. 828
CLAL CREDIT INSURANCE LTD.—See IDB Development Corporation Ltd.; *Int'l*, pg. 3588
CLAL INSURANCE COMPANY LTD.—See IDB Development Corporation Ltd.; *Int'l*, pg. 3588
CLEAR BLUE SPECIALTY INSURANCE COMPANY—See Clear Blue Financial Holdings LLC; *U.S. Private*, pg. 932
CLINE WOOD AGENCY, INC.—See Marsh & McLennan Companies, Inc.; *U.S. Public*, pg. 1380
CMI LLOYDS—See Central Mutual Insurance Company; *U.S. Private*, pg. 822
CNA INSURANCE COMPANY LIMITED—See Loews Corporation; *U.S. Public*, pg. 1340
CNA INSURANCE - OHIO BRANCH—See Loews Corporation; *U.S. Public*, pg. 1339
CNA SURETY CORPORATION—See Loews Corporation; *U.S. Public*, pg. 1340
CNA SURETY CORPORATION—See Loews Corporation; *U.S. Public*, pg. 1340
COASTAL CASUALTY INSURANCE COMPANY—See Strickland Insurance Group Inc.; *U.S. Private*, pg. 3839
COLINA GENERAL INSURANCE AGENCY & BROKERS LIMITED—See Colina Holdings Bahamas Limited; *Int'l*, pg. 1698
COLINA MORTGAGE CORPORATION LTD.—See Colina Holdings Bahamas Limited; *Int'l*, pg. 1698
COLLEGIATE MANAGEMENT SERVICES LIMITED—See Stone Point Capital LLC; *U.S. Private*, pg. 3820
COLONNADE INSURANCE S.A.—See Fairfax Financial Holdings Limited; *Int'l*, pg. 2606
COLONY INSURANCE COMPANY—See Brookfield Reinsurance Ltd.; *Int'l*, pg. 1194
COLONY INSURANCE GROUP—See Brookfield Reinsurance Ltd.; *Int'l*, pg. 1194
COLORADO FARM BUREAU MUTUAL INSURANCE CO.; *U.S. Private*, pg. 973
COLUMBIA CASUALTY COMPANY—See Loews Corporation; *U.S. Public*, pg. 1340
COLUMBIA INSURANCE CO.—See Berkshire Hathaway Inc.; *U.S. Public*, pg. 302
COLUMBIA INSURANCE GROUP, INC.; *U.S. Private*, pg. 977
COLUMBIA INSURANCE GROUP INC.—See Columbia Insurance Group, Inc.; *U.S. Private*, pg. 977
COLUMBIA NATIONAL INSURANCE CO. INC.—See Columbia Insurance Group, Inc.; *U.S. Private*, pg. 977
COMMUNITY ASSOCIATION UNDERWRITERS OF AMERICA; *U.S. Private*, pg. 989
COMPANHIA DE SEGUROS TRANQUILIDADE, S.A.—See Apollo Global Management, Inc.; *U.S. Public*, pg. 150
COMPANION PROPERTY & CASUALTY INSURANCE GROUP—See Enstar Group Limited; *Int'l*, pg. 2448
COMPARE.COM INSURANCE AGENCY LLC—See Admiral Group plc; *Int'l*, pg. 151
COMPWEST INSURANCE COMPANY; *U.S. Private*, pg. 1006
CONCORD GENERAL MUTUAL INSURANCE CO., INC.; *U.S. Private*, pg. 1009
CONNECTICUT MEDICAL INSURANCE COMPANY INC.; *U.S. Private*, pg. 1016
CONSTRUCTION RISK PARTNERS LLC—See The Baldwin Insurance Group, Inc.; *U.S. Public*, pg. 2036
CONTESSA LIMITED—See AXIS Capital Holdings Limited; *Int'l*, pg. 770
CONTINENTAL CAR CLUB, INC.—See Tiptree Inc.; *U.S. Public*, pg. 2159
CONTINENTAL CASUALTY COMPANY—See Loews Corporation; *U.S. Public*, pg. 1340
CONTINENTAL DIVIDE INSURANCE COMPANY—See Berkshire Hathaway Inc.; *U.S. Public*, pg. 301
CONTINENTAL WESTERN INSURANCE COMPANY—See W.R. Berkley Corporation; *U.S. Public*, pg. 2318
CONTINENTAL WESTERN INSURANCE CO—See W.R. Berkley Corporation; *U.S. Public*, pg. 2318
CONTRACTORS BONDING AND INSURANCE COMPANY—See RLI Corp.; *U.S. Public*, pg. 1801
THE CONTRIBUTIONSHIP COMPANIES; *U.S. Private*, pg. 4014
COOPERATIVE OF AMERICAN PHYSICIANS, INC.; *U.S. Private*, pg. 1042
COPIC TRUST; *U.S. Private*, pg. 1044
COPPERPOINT INSURANCE COMPANY—See CopperPoint Mutual Insurance Holding Company; *U.S. Private*, pg. 1045
CORALISLE GROUP LTD.; *Int'l*, pg. 1795
COREPOINTE INSURANCE COMPANY—See Stone Point Capital LLC; *U.S. Private*, pg. 3820
CORE SPECIALTY INSURANCE HOLDINGS, INC.; *U.S. Private*, pg. 1049
CORNERSTONE MANAGEMENT PARTNERS, INC.; *U.S. Private*, pg. 1052
COUNTRY-WIDE INSURANCE COMPANY; *U.S. Private*, pg. 1067
COVANTA HOLDING CORPORATION—See EQT AB; *Int'l*, pg. 2473
COVERYS; *U.S. Private*, pg. 1072
CRESCENT STAR INSURANCE LIMITED; *Int'l*, pg. 1839
CROP RISK SERVICES, INC.—See American Financial Group, Inc.; *U.S. Public*, pg. 102
CRUM & FORSTER INSURANCE—See Fairfax Financial Holdings Limited; *Int'l*, pg. 2606
CRUSADER INSURANCE COMPANY—See Unico American Corporation; *U.S. Public*, pg. 2225
CSE INSURANCE GROUP; *U.S. Private*, pg. 1116
CULVER INSURANCE BROKERS LTD.—See CCV Risk Solutions Limited; *Int'l*, pg. 1370
CUMBERLAND INSURANCE GROUP; *U.S. Private*, pg. 1122
CUNA MUTUAL INSURANCE GROUP—See CMFG Life Insurance Company; *U.S. Private*, pg. 950
CYPRESS INSURANCE COMPANY—See Berkshire Hathaway Inc.; *U.S. Public*, pg. 304
CYPRESS PROPERTY & CASUALTY INSURANCE COMPANY; *U.S. Private*, pg. 1135
DAIRYLAND INSURANCE CO.—See Sentry Insurance Group; *U.S. Private*, pg. 3611
DALE BARTON AGENCY—See Hellman & Friedman LLC; *U.S. Private*, pg. 1908
DATA & STAFF SERVICE CO.—See RLI Corp.; *U.S. Public*, pg. 1801
DB&T INSURANCE, INC.—See Heartland Financial USA, Inc.; *U.S. Public*, pg. 1018
DDOR NOVI SAD A.D.O.; *Int'l*, pg. 1993
DEALERS ASSURANCE COMPANY—See iA Financial Corporation Inc.; *Int'l*, pg. 3567
DENT WIZARD VENTURES LIMITED—See Stone Point Capital LLC; *U.S. Private*, pg. 3821
DEUTSCHER RING SACHVERSICHERUNGS-AG—See Baloise Holding AG; *Int'l*, pg. 811
DIAMOND STATE INSURANCE COMPANY—See Paine Schwartz Partners, LLC; *U.S. Private*, pg. 3075
DIRECT GENERAL CORPORATION—See The Allstate Corporation; *U.S. Public*, pg. 2033
DIRECT RESPONSE CORPORATION—See Kemper Corporation; *U.S. Public*, pg. 1221
THE DISTINGUISHED PROGRAM GROUP; *U.S. Private*, pg. 4021
THE DOCTORS COMPANY INSURANCE SERVICES—See The Doctors Company; *U.S. Private*, pg. 4021
THE DOCTORS COMPANY/NORTHWEST PHYSICIANS—See The Doctors Company; *U.S. Private*, pg. 4022
THE DOMINION OF CANADA GENERAL INSURANCE COMPANY—See The Travelers Companies, Inc.; *U.S. Public*, pg. 2136
DONEGAL INSURANCE GROUP—See Donegal Group Inc.; *U.S. Public*, pg. 676
DONEGAL MUTUAL INSURANCE COMPANY—See Donegal Group Inc.; *U.S. Public*, pg. 676
DORINCO REINSURANCE COMPANY—See Dow Inc.; *U.S. Public*, pg. 683
DRIVE NEW JERSEY INSURANCE COMPANY—See The Progressive Corporation; *U.S. Public*, pg. 2124
DRYDEN MUTUAL INSURANCE COMPANY; *U.S. Private*, pg. 1281
DUAL GROUP AMERICAS INC—See Howden Group Holdings Limited; *Int'l*, pg. 3493
DUAL IBERICA RIESGOS PROFESIONALES S.A.—See Howden Group Holdings Limited; *Int'l*, pg. 3493
DUNAV OSIGURANJE AD BANJA LUKA; *Int'l*, pg. 2225
DZ VERSICHERUNGSVERMITTLUNG GESELLSCHAFT MBH—See DZ BANK AG Deutsche Zentral-Genossenschaftsbank; *Int'l*, pg. 2244
EASTERN ALLIANCE INSURANCE COMPANY—See ProAssurance Corporation; *U.S. Public*, pg. 1723
EAST WEST INSURANCE COMPANY LIMITED; *Int'l*, pg. 2270
EBS MORTGAGE FINANCE—See AIB Group plc; *Int'l*, pg. 228
ECICS LIMITED—See IFS Capital Limited; *Int'l*, pg. 3599
EL AGUILA, COMPANIA DE SEGUROS, S.A. DE C.V.—See American Financial Group, Inc.; *U.S. Public*, pg. 103
ELECTRIC INSURANCE COMPANY—See Fairfax Financial

524126 — DIRECT PROPERTY AND... CORPORATE AFFILIATIONS

Holdings Limited; *Int'l*, pg. 2608
ELEPHANT INSURANCE SERVICES LLC—See Admiral Group plc; *Int'l*, pg. 151
ELVIA REISEVERSICHERUNG AG—See Allianz SE; *Int'l*, pg. 342
ELVIA SOCIETE D'ASSURANCES DE VOYAGES—See Allianz SE; *Int'l*, pg. 342
EMCASCO INSURANCE COMPANY—See Employers Mutual Casualty Company; *U.S. Private*, pg. 1387
EMC INSURANCE COMPANIES—See Employers Mutual Casualty Company; *U.S. Private*, pg. 1387
EMC UNDERWRITERS, LLC.—See Employers Mutual Casualty Company; *U.S. Private*, pg. 1387
E.M.I. - EZER MORTGAGE INSURANCE COMPANY LTD.—See Harel Insurance Investments & Financial Services Ltd.; *Int'l*, pg. 3274
EMPLOYERS INSURANCE COMPANY OF WAUSAU—See Liberty Mutual Holding Company Inc.; *U.S. Private*, pg. 2445
EMPLOYERS SECURITY INSURANCE COMPANY—See ProAssurance Corporation; *U.S. Public*, pg. 1723
ENCOMPASS INSURANCE COMPANY—See The Allstate Corporation; *U.S. Public*, pg. 2033
ENERGOPROJEKT GARANT A.D.O.—See Energoprojekt Holding a.d.; *Int'l*, pg. 2421
EPSILON INSURANCE BROKING SERVICES PTY. LTD.—See BGC Group, Inc.; *U.S. Public*, pg. 328
ESIS CANADA, INC.—See Chubb Limited; *Int'l*, pg. 1592
ESURE INSURANCE LTD.—See Bain Capital, LP; *U.S. Private*, pg. 453
EULER HERMES ACI—See Allianz SE; *Int'l*, pg. 352
EULER HERMES ACMAR SA—See Allianz SE; *Int'l*, pg. 352
EULER HERMES COLOMBIA—See Allianz SE; *Int'l*, pg. 352
EULER HERMES EMPORIKI S.A.—See Allianz SE; *Int'l*, pg. 352
EULER HERMES HONG KONG SERVICE LIMITED—See Allianz SE; *Int'l*, pg. 353
EULER HERMES KOREA NON-LIFE BROKER COMPANY LIMITED—See Allianz SE; *Int'l*, pg. 353
EULER HERMES SERVICE AB—See Allianz SE; *Int'l*, pg. 353
EULER HERMES SERVICES AG—See Allianz SE; *Int'l*, pg. 353
EULER HERMES SERVICIOS S.A.—See Allianz SE; *Int'l*, pg. 353
EULER HERMES TRADE CREDIT LIMITED—See Allianz SE; *Int'l*, pg. 353
EULER HERMES TRADE CREDIT UNDERWRITING AGENTS PTY LTD—See Allianz SE; *Int'l*, pg. 353
EULER HERMES WORLD AGENCY SASU—See Allianz SE; *Int'l*, pg. 353
EUROLIFE ERB GENERAL INSURANCE S.A.—See Fairfax Financial Holdings Limited; *Int'l*, pg. 2606
EUROPEAN RELIANCE GENERAL INSURANCE S.A.; *Int'l*, pg. 2557
EVANSTON INSURANCE COMPANY—See Markel Group Inc.; *U.S. Public*, pg. 1368
EVEREN LIMITED—See Energy Transfer LP; *U.S. Public*, pg. 764
EVEREN SPECIALTY LTD.—See Energy Transfer LP; *U.S. Public*, pg. 764
EVEREST ADVISORS (UK), LTD.—See Everest Group, Ltd.; *Int'l*, pg. 2564
EVEREST GLOBAL SERVICES, INC.—See Everest Group, Ltd.; *Int'l*, pg. 2564
EVEREST INSURANCE COMPANY OF CANADA—See Everest Group, Ltd.; *Int'l*, pg. 2564
EVEREST REINSURANCE (BERMUDA), LTD.—See Everest Group, Ltd.; *Int'l*, pg. 2564
EVEREST REINSURANCE COMPANY - ESCRITORIO DE REPRESENTA CAO NO BRASIL LTDA.—See Everest Group, Ltd.; *Int'l*, pg. 2564
EVEREST REINSURANCE COMPANY (IRELAND), LIMITED—See Everest Group, Ltd.; *Int'l*, pg. 2564
EVEREST REINSURANCE COMPANY—See Everest Group, Ltd.; *Int'l*, pg. 2564
EVEREST REINSURANCE COMPANY—See Everest Group, Ltd.; *Int'l*, pg. 2564
EVEREST SECURITY INSURANCE COMPANY—See Everest Group, Ltd.; *Int'l*, pg. 2564
EVEREST SPECIALTY UNDERWRITERS, LLC—See Everest Group, Ltd.; *Int'l*, pg. 2564
EXECUTIVE RISK SPECIALTY INSURANCE COMPANY—See Chubb Limited; *Int'l*, pg. 1591
EXPLORER RV INSURANCE AGENCY, INC.—See American Financial Group, Inc.; *U.S. Public*, pg. 103
FACTORY MUTUAL INSURANCE COMPANY - CANADA—See Factory Mutual Insurance Company; *U.S. Private*, pg. 1461
FACTORY MUTUAL INSURANCE COMPANY - CANADA—See Factory Mutual Insurance Company; *U.S. Private*, pg. 1461
FACTORY MUTUAL INSURANCE COMPANY; *U.S. Private*, pg. 1460
FAITEC CORPORATION—See DTS Corporation; *Int'l*, pg. 2217
FARM BUREAU CASUALTY INSURANCE CO.—See Arkansas Farm Bureau Federation; *U.S. Private*, pg. 325

FARM BUREAU FINANCE COMPANY INC.—See Farm Bureau Mutual Insurance Company of Idaho, Inc.; *U.S. Private*, pg. 1474
FARM BUREAU MUTUAL INSURANCE COMPANY OF IDAHO, INC.; *U.S. Private*, pg. 1474
FARM BUREAU MUTUAL INSURANCE COMPANY OF MICHIGAN INC.; *U.S. Private*, pg. 1474
FARM BUREAU MUTUAL INSURANCE CO. OF ARKANSAS—See Arkansas Farm Bureau Federation; *U.S. Private*, pg. 326
FARM BUREAU TOWN & COUNTRY INSURANCE CO. OF MISSOURI—See Missouri Farm Bureau; *U.S. Private*, pg. 2749
FARMERS ALLIANCE MUTUAL INSURANCE CO., INC.; *U.S. Private*, pg. 1476
FARMERS MUTUAL FIRE INSURANCE; *U.S. Private*, pg. 1478
FARMERS MUTUAL HAIL INSURANCE COMPANY OF IOWA; *U.S. Private*, pg. 1478
FARMERS MUTUAL INSURANCE COMPANY OF NEBRASKA INC.; *U.S. Private*, pg. 1478
FARMERS MUTUAL PROTECTIVE ASSOCIATION TEXAS; *U.S. Private*, pg. 1478
FARMERS UNION MUTUAL INSURANCE CO.; *U.S. Private*, pg. 1479
FARM FAMILY CASUALTY INSURANCE COMPANY—See Brookfield Corporation; *Int'l*, pg. 1174
THE FB INSURANCE COMPANY INC.—See Kentucky Farm Bureau Mutual Insurance Company Inc.; *U.S. Private*, pg. 2288
FCIA MANAGEMENT COMPANY INC.—See American Financial Group, Inc.; *U.S. Public*, pg. 103
FEDERATED MUTUAL INSURANCE COMPANY; *U.S. Private*, pg. 1492
FGIC UK LIMITED—See Financial Guaranty Insurance Company; *U.S. Private*, pg. 1507
FIATC MUTUA DE SEGUROS Y DE REASEGUROS APF; *Int'l*, pg. 2651
FIDELITY NATIONAL INSURANCE COMPANY—See Fidelity National Financial, Inc.; *U.S. Public*, pg. 831
FIREMAN FUND SPECIATIES—See Allianz SE; *Int'l*, pg. 347
FIREMAN'S FUND INSURANCE COMPANY—See Allianz SE; *Int'l*, pg. 347
FIREMAN'S FUND INSURANCE COMPANY—See Allianz SE; *Int'l*, pg. 347
FIREMAN'S FUND INSURANCE CO. OF GEORGIA—See Allianz SE; *Int'l*, pg. 347
FIREMAN'S FUND INSURANCE CO. OF TEXAS—See Allianz SE; *Int'l*, pg. 347
FIRST AMERICAN PROPERTY & CASUALTY INSURANCE—See First American Financial Corporation; *U.S. Public*, pg. 836
FIRST AMERICAN TITLE INSURANCE COMPANY OF LOUISIANA—See First American Financial Corporation; *U.S. Public*, pg. 838
FIRST FINANCIAL INSURANCE INDIANA—See First Financial Bancorp.; *U.S. Public*, pg. 843
FIRSTLINE NATIONAL INSURANCE COMPANY—See The Harford Mutual Insurance Company Inc.; *U.S. Private*, pg. 4043
FIRST MERCURY FINANCIAL CORPORATION—See Fairfax Financial Holdings Limited; *Int'l*, pg. 2606
FIRST MERCURY INSURANCE COMPANY—See Fairfax Financial Holdings Limited; *Int'l*, pg. 2606
FIRST PROPERTY AND CASUALTY INSURANCE AGENCY CO., LTD.—See First Financial Holding Co., Ltd.; *Int'l*, pg. 2683
FIRST TAKAFUL INSURANCE COMPANY K.S.C.C.; *Int'l*, pg. 2688
FLORIDA FAMILY INSURANCE COMPANY; *U.S. Private*, pg. 1548
FLORIDA PENINSULA INSURANCE COMPANY; *U.S. Private*, pg. 1550
FLORIDA PREFERRED ADMINISTRATORS, INC.—See Fosun International Limited; *Int'l*, pg. 2752
FLYING J INSURANCE—See FJ Management, Inc.; *U.S. Private*, pg. 1538
FM DO BRASIL SERVICOS DE PREVENCAO DE PERDAS LTDA—See Factory Mutual Insurance Company; *U.S. Private*, pg. 1461
FM ENGINEERING INTERNATIONAL LIMITED—See Factory Mutual Insurance Company; *U.S. Private*, pg. 1460
FM INSURANCE COMPANY LIMITED—See Factory Mutual Insurance Company; *U.S. Private*, pg. 1461
FM INSURANCE COMPANY LIMITED—See Factory Mutual Insurance Company; *U.S. Private*, pg. 1461
FM INSURANCE COMPANY LIMITED—See Factory Mutual Insurance Company; *U.S. Private*, pg. 1461
FM INSURANCE COMPANY LIMITED—See Factory Mutual Insurance Company; *U.S. Private*, pg. 1461
FM INSURANCE COMPANY LIMITED—See Factory Mutual Insurance Company; *U.S. Private*, pg. 1461
FM INSURANCE COMPANY LIMITED—See Factory Mutual Insurance Company; *U.S. Private*, pg. 1461
FM INSURANCE COMPANY LIMITED—See Factory Mutual Insurance Company; *U.S. Private*, pg. 1461

FOOD SERVICE INSURANCE MANAGERS; *U.S. Private*, pg. 1561
FOUNDATION RESERVE INSURANCE CO.—See New Mexico Mutual Casualty Company; *U.S. Private*, pg. 2898
FOUR CORNERS INSURANCE SERVICES—See Topa Equities Ltd., Inc.; *U.S. Private*, pg. 4186
FRANDISCO PROPERTY & CASUALTY INSURANCE—See 1st Franklin Financial Corporation; *U.S. Private*, pg. 4
FRANKENMUTH MUTUAL INSURANCE CO.; *U.S. Private*, pg. 1596
FRANKLIN INSURANCE COMPANY—See United Fire Group, Inc.; *U.S. Public*, pg. 2230
THE FRANKLIN MUTUAL INSURANCE COMPANY; *U.S. Private*, pg. 4030
FRESH INSURANCE SERVICES GROUP LIMITED—See White Mountains Insurance Group, Ltd.; *U.S. Public*, pg. 2369
GAINSCO, INC.—See State Farm Mutual Automobile Insurance Company; *U.S. Private*, pg. 3792
GATEWAY INSURANCE COMPANY—See Buckle Agency LLC; *U.S. Private*, pg. 678
GEICO GENERAL INSURANCE COMPANY—See Berkshire Hathaway Inc.; *U.S. Public*, pg. 305
GEICO INDEMNITY COMPANY—See Berkshire Hathaway Inc.; *U.S. Public*, pg. 305
GEMINI TRANSPORTATION UNDERWRITERS, LLC—See W.R. Berkley Corporation; *U.S. Public*, pg. 2317
GENERALI CESKA POJISTOVNA A.S.—See Assicurazioni Generali S.p.A.; *Int'l*, pg. 644
GENERALI ITALIA S.P.A.—See Assicurazioni Generali S.p.A.; *Int'l*, pg. 646
GENERAL INSURANCE CORPORATION OF INDIA; *Int'l*, pg. 2918
GENERAL INSURANCE OF CYPRUS LTD—See Bank of Cyprus Holdings Public Limited Company; *Int'l*, pg. 842
GENERAL REINSURANCE CORPORATION—See Berkshire Hathaway Inc.; *U.S. Public*, pg. 301
GENERAL REINSURANCE CORPORATION—See Berkshire Hathaway Inc.; *U.S. Public*, pg. 302
GENWORTH MORTGAGE INSURANCE CORPORATION OF NORTH CAROLINA—See Genworth Financial, Inc.; *U.S. Public*, pg. 934
GEORGIA FARM BUREAU MUTUAL INSURANCE CO.; *U.S. Private*, pg. 1684
GERMANIA FARM MUTUAL INSURANCE ASSOCIATION; *U.S. Private*, pg. 1687
GESTIO D'ACTIUS TITULITZATS, S.G.F.T.H.—See Banco Bilbao Vizcaya Argentaria, S.A.; *Int'l*, pg. 817
GLOBAL EXCESS PARTNERS—See H.W. Kaufman Financial Group, Inc.; *U.S. Private*, pg. 1836
GLOBAL TRANSPORT & AUTOMOTIVE INSURANCE SOLUTIONS PTY LIMITED—See Allianz SE; *Int'l*, pg. 353
GMF ASSURANCES S.A.—See Covea Groupe S.A.S.; *Int'l*, pg. 1820
GOLDEN EAGLE INSURANCE CORP.—See Liberty Mutual Holding Company Inc.; *U.S. Private*, pg. 2445
GONARMEX, S.A. DE C.V.—See Grupo Televisa, S.A.B.; *Int'l*, pg. 3136
GORE MUTUAL INSURANCE COMPANY; *Int'l*, pg. 3043
GP CONSULTING PENZUGYI TANACSADO KFT.—See Assicurazioni Generali S.p.A.; *Int'l*, pg. 644
GRAIN DEALERS MUTUAL INSURANCE COMPANY INC.—See American Family Mutual Insurance Company; *U.S. Private*, pg. 233
GRANGE PROPERTY & CASUALTY INSURANCE COMPANY—See Grange Mutual Casualty Company; *U.S. Private*, pg. 1754
GRAPHIC ARTS MUTUAL INSURANCE CO.—See Utica National Insurance Group; *U.S. Private*, pg. 4325
GRAY INSURANCE COMPANY; *U.S. Private*, pg. 1759
GREAT AMERICAN ADVISORS, INC.—See American Financial Group, Inc.; *U.S. Public*, pg. 102
GREAT AMERICAN ALLIANCE INSURANCE COMPANY—See American Financial Group, Inc.; *U.S. Public*, pg. 103
GREAT AMERICAN ASSURANCE COMPANY—See American Financial Group, Inc.; *U.S. Public*, pg. 103
GREAT AMERICAN HOLDING, INC.—See American Financial Group, Inc.; *U.S. Public*, pg. 102
GREAT AMERICAN INSURANCE COMPANY—See American Financial Group, Inc.; *U.S. Public*, pg. 103
GREAT AMERICAN SPIRIT INSURANCE CO.—See American Financial Group, Inc.; *U.S. Public*, pg. 103
GREAT NORTHERN INSURANCE COMPANY—See Chubb Limited; *Int'l*, pg. 1591
GREAT WEST CASUALTY COMPANY—See Old Republic International Corporation; *U.S. Public*, pg. 1567
GRINNELL MUTUAL REINSURANCE COMPANY INC.; *U.S. Private*, pg. 1790
GROUPAMA ASIGURARI SA—See Groupama SA; *Int'l*, pg. 3090
GROUPAMA INSURANCE COMPANY LIMITED—See Ageas SA/NV; *Int'l*, pg. 205
GUARDIAN INSURANCE COMPANY, INC.—See Lockhart Companies Inc.; *U.S. Private*, pg. 2478
GULF CO-OPERATION INSURANCE COMPANY LTD.,

4432

EC—See Dabbagh Group Holding Company Ltd.; *Int'l*, pg. 1902
GULF INSURANCE COMPANY—See The Travelers Companies, Inc.; *U.S. Public*, pg. 2136
GULF INSURANCE GROUP K.S.C.P.—See Fairfax Financial Holdings Limited; *Int'l*, pg. 2606
GULF SIGORTA A.S.—See Fairfax Financial Holdings Limited; *Int'l*, pg. 2607
HACHSHARA INSURANCE COMPANY LTD.; *Int'l*, pg. 3203
HALLMARK INSURANCE COMPANY—See Hallmark Financial Services, Inc.; *U.S. Public*, pg. 981
HAMILTON MUTUAL INSURANCE COMPANY—See Employers Mutual Casualty Company; *U.S. Private*, pg. 1387
HANOVER FIRE & CASUALTY INSURANCE COMPANY; *U.S. Private*, pg. 1855
THE HANOVER INSURANCE COMPANY—See The Hanover Insurance Group, Inc.; *U.S. Public*, pg. 2087
HANOVER LLOYD'S INSURANCE COMPANY—See The Hanover Insurance Group, Inc.; *U.S. Public*, pg. 2087
HANOVER MANUFACTURING PLANT—See REA Magnet Wire Company, Inc.; *U.S. Private*, pg. 3365
HANWHA GENERAL INSURANCE CO., LTD.—See Hanwha Group; *Int'l*, pg. 3266
HARCO NATIONAL INSURANCE COMPANY, INC.—See IAT Reinsurance Company, Ltd.; *U.S. Private*, pg. 2028
THE HARFORD MUTUAL INSURANCE COMPANY INC.; *U.S. Private*, pg. 4043
HARLEY-DAVIDSON INSURANCE SERVICES OF ILLINOIS, INC.—See Harley-Davidson, Inc.; *U.S. Public*, pg. 985
HARTFORD FIRE INSURANCE CO.—See The Hartford Financial Services Group, Inc.; *U.S. Public*, pg. 2088
HAULERS INSURANCE COMPANY, INC.—See Shelter Mutual Insurance Company; *U.S. Private*, pg. 3631
HCC SURETY GROUP; *U.S. Private*, pg. 1888
HCI GROUP, INC.; *U.S. Public*, pg. 1014
HEALTH DIRECT, INC.—See American International Group, Inc.; *U.S. Public*, pg. 107
HERITAGE PROPERTY & CASUALTY INSURANCE COMPANY—See Heritage Insurance Holdings, Inc.; *U.S. Public*, pg. 1028
HIGHLANDS INSURANCE GROUP INC.; *U.S. Private*, pg. 1940
THE HILB GROUP OF INDIANA, LLC—See ABRY Partners, LLC; *U.S. Public*, pg. 43
HOCHHEIM PRAIRIE FARM MUTUAL INSURANCE; *U.S. Private*, pg. 1958
THE HOME AGENCY; *U.S. Private*, pg. 4054
HOMEOWNERS CHOICE PROPERTY & CASUALTY INSURANCE COMPANY, INC.—See HCI Group, Inc.; *U.S. Public*, pg. 1014
HOME-OWNERS INSURANCE CO.—See Auto-Owners Insurance Group; *U.S. Private*, pg. 397
HORACE MANN EDUCATORS CORPORATION; *U.S. Public*, pg. 1052
HORACE MANN INSURANCE COMPANY—See Horace Mann Educators Corporation; *U.S. Public*, pg. 1053
HSBC INSURANCE (ASIA-PACIFIC) HOLDINGS LIMITED—See HSBC Holdings plc; *Int'l*, pg. 3506
HUDSON INSURANCE GROUP—See Fairfax Financial Holdings Limited; *Int'l*, pg. 2607
HUMCO, INC.—See Humana, Inc.; *U.S. Public*, pg. 1070
ICARE ASSURANCE S.A.—See BNP Paribas SA; *Int'l*, pg. 1083
ICI MUTUAL INSURANCE COMPANY; *U.S. Private*, pg. 2031
ICPEI HOLDINGS INC.; *Int'l*, pg. 3586
IDS PROPERTY CASUALTY INSURANCE COMPANY—See Ameriprise Financial, Inc.; *U.S. Public*, pg. 114
ILLINOIS INSURANCE GUARANTY FUND; *U.S. Private*, pg. 2042
IMOBILE SOLUTIONS, INC.—See SPARTA COMMERCIAL SERVICES, INC.; *U.S. Public*, pg. 1914
IMT INSURANCE COMPANY; *U.S. Private*, pg. 2051
INDEPENDENT SPECIALTY INSURANCE COMPANY—See Markel Group Inc.; *U.S. Public*, pg. 1369
INDIANA INSURANCE COMPANY—See Liberty Mutual Holding Company Inc.; *U.S. Private*, pg. 2445
INDUSTRIAL ALLIANCE AUTO & HOME INSURANCE—See iA Financial Corporation Inc.; *Int'l*, pg. 3567
INFINITY CASUALTY INSURANCE COMPANY—See Kemper Corporation; *U.S. Public*, pg. 1220
INFINITY PROPERTY & CASUALTY CORPORATION—See Kemper Corporation; *U.S. Public*, pg. 1220
INFINITY SPECIALTY INSURANCE COMPANY—See Kemper Corporation; *U.S. Public*, pg. 1220
INJURED WORKERS' INSURANCE FUND; *U.S. Private*, pg. 2077
INSURANCE COMPANY OF GREATER NEW YORK—See Greater New York Mutual Insurance Company; *U.S. Private*, pg. 1770
INSURANCE MARKETING AGENCIES, INC.; *U.S. Private*, pg. 2095
INSURANCE NETWORKS ALLIANCE, LLC—See W.R. Berkley Corporation; *U.S. Public*, pg. 2317
INSURE MY VILLA LIMITED—See Arthur J. Gallagher & Co.; *U.S. Public*, pg. 206
INTEGRAND INSURANCE COMPANY; *U.S. Private*, pg. 2098
INTERBORO INSURANCE COMPANY—See American Coastal Insurance Corporation; *U.S. Public*, pg. 98
INTERNATIONAL FIDELITY INSURANCE COMPANY; *U.S. Private*, pg. 2116
INTERSTATE FIRE & CASUALTY COMPANY—See Allianz SE; *Int'l*, pg. 347
INTRAMERICA LIFE INSURANCE COMPANY—See The Allstate Corporation; *U.S. Public*, pg. 2033
INTREPID DIRECT INSURANCE AGENCY, LLC—See W.R. Berkley Corporation; *U.S. Public*, pg. 2317
IOWA MUTUAL INSURANCE COMPANY; *U.S. Private*, pg. 2135
IRONSHORE INC.—See Liberty Mutual Holding Company Inc.; *U.S. Private*, pg. 2445
IRONSHORE INSURANCE LTD.—See Liberty Mutual Holding Company Inc.; *U.S. Private*, pg. 2445
ISBA MUTUAL INSURANCE COMPANY; *U.S. Private*, pg. 2143
ISLAND INSURANCE COMPANY, LTD.—See Island Holdings, Inc.; *U.S. Private*, pg. 2145
JALINAN MASYHUR SDN BHD—See IJM Corporation Berhad; *Int'l*, pg. 3609
JAMES A. SCOTT & SON INC.; *U.S. Private*, pg. 2183
JAMES RIVER GROUP, INC.—See D. E. Shaw & Co., L.P.; *U.S. Private*, pg. 1139
JEWELERS MUTUAL INSURANCE COMPANY; *U.S. Private*, pg. 2204
J.H. FERGUSON & ASSOCIATES, LLC—See Paine Schwartz Partners, LLC; *U.S. Private*, pg. 3075
KEEN BATTLE MEAD & CO.; *U.S. Private*, pg. 2272
KEMPER CORPORATION; *U.S. Public*, pg. 1220
KEMPER SPECIALTY—See Kemper Corporation; *U.S. Public*, pg. 1221
KENTUCKY EMPLOYERS MUTUAL INSURANCE; *U.S. Private*, pg. 2288
KENTUCKY FARM BUREAU MUTUAL INSURANCE COMPANY INC.; *U.S. Private*, pg. 2288
KENTUCKY NATIONAL INSURANCE COMPANY—See Forcht Group of Kentucky, Inc.; *U.S. Private*, pg. 1564
KEY RISK INSURANCE COMPANY—See W.R. Berkley Corporation; *U.S. Public*, pg. 2317
KIBBLE & PRENTICE HOLDING COMPANY—See CPCM, LLC; *U.S. Public*, pg. 1080
KINGSWAY AMIGO INSURANCE COMPANY—See Kingsway Financial Services Inc.; *U.S. Public*, pg. 1234
KLEIN AGENCY, INC.—See Marsh & McLennan Companies, Inc.; *U.S. Public*, pg. 1381
KMRD PARTNERS, INC.; *U.S. Private*, pg. 2321
KRAMER-WILSON CO. INC.; *U.S. Private*, pg. 2349
LAFAYETTE INSURANCE COMPANY—See United Fire Group, Inc.; *U.S. Public*, pg. 2230
LA MERIDIONAL COMPANIA ARGENTINA DE SEGUROS S.A.—See Fairfax Financial Holdings Limited; *Int'l*, pg. 2607
LAVALIER INSURANCE SERVICES, LLC—See W.R. Berkley Corporation; *U.S. Public*, pg. 2318
LEXINGTON INSURANCE COMPANY—See American International Group, Inc.; *U.S. Public*, pg. 107
LIBERTY INSURANCE PTE. LTD.—See Liberty Mutual Holding Company Inc.; *U.S. Private*, pg. 2445
LIBERTY MUTUAL FIRE INSURANCE CO.—See Liberty Mutual Holding Company Inc.; *U.S. Private*, pg. 2446
LIBERTY MUTUAL INSURANCE COMPANY—See Liberty Mutual Holding Company Inc.; *U.S. Private*, pg. 2446
LIBERTY MUTUAL MID-ATLANTIC INSURANCE COMPANY—See Liberty Mutual Holding Company Inc.; *U.S. Private*, pg. 2446
LIBERTY NORTHWEST INSURANCE CORP.—See Liberty Mutual Holding Company Inc.; *U.S. Private*, pg. 2446
LIGHTNING ROD MUTUAL INSURANCE CO.; *U.S. Private*, pg. 2453
LINCOLN GENERAL INSURANCE COMPANY—See Financiere Pinault SCA; *Int'l*, pg. 2669
LINCOLN GENERAL INSURANCE COMPANY—See Kingsway Financial Services Inc.; *U.S. Public*, pg. 1235
LITITZ MUTUAL INSURANCE COMPANY; *U.S. Private*, pg. 2468
LIVINGSTON MUTUAL INSURANCE COMPANY—See Lititz Mutual Insurance Company; *U.S. Private*, pg. 2468
LJ STEIN & COMPANY INC.—See GTCR LLC; *U.S. Private*, pg. 1803
LONDEN LAND COMPANY, L.L.C.—See Londen Insurance Group, Inc.; *U.S. Private*, pg. 2483
LOUISIANA HOME BUILDERS ASSOCIATION; *U.S. Private*, pg. 2499
LOUISIANA MEDICAL MUTUAL INSURANCE COMPANY; *U.S. Private*, pg. 2499
LOUISIANA WORKERS COMPENSATION CORP.; *U.S. Private*, pg. 2500
L.T. SERVICE CORPORATION—See Old Republic International Corporation; *U.S. Public*, pg. 1569
LUMBER INSURANCE CO.; *U.S. Private*, pg. 2513
LUMBERMEN'S MUTUAL CASUALTY COMPANY—See Lumbermens Mutual Group; *U.S. Private*, pg. 2514
LUMBERMEN'S UNDERWRITING ALLIANCE; *U.S. Private*, pg. 2513
LUMENLAB MALAYSIA SDN. BHD.—See MetLife, Inc.; *U.S. Public*, pg. 1430
MAAF ASSURANCES S.A.—See Covea Groupe S.A.S.; *Int'l*, pg. 1820
MAGELLAN LIFE INSURANCE COMPANY—See Centene Corporation; *U.S. Public*, pg. 470
MAG MUTUAL INSURANCE COMPANY; *U.S. Private*, pg. 2545
MAGNA CARTA COMPANIES; *U.S. Private*, pg. 2546
MAINE EMPLOYERS MUTUAL INSURANCE CO.; *U.S. Private*, pg. 2552
MANNHEIMER AG HOLDING—See Continentale Holding AG; *Int'l*, pg. 1784
MANNHEIMER VERSICHERUNG AG—See Continentale Holding AG; *Int'l*, pg. 1784
MANUFACTURERS ALLIANCE INSURANCE COMPANY—See Old Republic International Corporation; *U.S. Public*, pg. 1568
MARINERS INSURANCE AGENCY INC.—See Marsh & McLennan Companies, Inc.; *U.S. Public*, pg. 1381
MARKEL INSURANCE COMPANY—See Markel Group Inc.; *U.S. Public*, pg. 1368
MARKEL MIDWEST—See Markel Group Inc.; *U.S. Public*, pg. 1368
MARKEL SERVICE, INC.—See Markel Group Inc.; *U.S. Public*, pg. 1368
MASSACHUSETTS BAY INSURANCE CO.—See The Hanover Insurance Group, Inc.; *U.S. Public*, pg. 2087
M.B.A. HOLDINGS, INC.; *U.S. Private*, pg. 2528
MBIA INC.; *U.S. Public*, pg. 1403
MBIA INSURANCE CORPORATION—See MBIA Inc.; *U.S. Public*, pg. 1403
MBIA MEXICO, S.A. DE C.V.—See MBIA Inc.; *U.S. Public*, pg. 1403
M&C GENERAL INSURANCE CO. LTD.—See Arthur J. Gallagher & Co.; *U.S. Public*, pg. 206
MCM CORPORATION; *U.S. Private*, pg. 2642
MEADOWBROOK INSURANCE AGENCY FLORIDA—See Fosun International Limited; *Int'l*, pg. 2752
MEADOWBROOK INSURANCE AGENCY, INC.—See Arthur J. Gallagher & Co.; *U.S. Public*, pg. 206
MEADOWBROOK INSURANCE, INC.—See Fosun International Limited; *Int'l*, pg. 2752
THE MEDICAL ASSURANCE COMPANY, INC.—See ProAssurance Corporation; *U.S. Public*, pg. 1723
THE MEDICAL ASSURANCE COMPANY—See ProAssurance Corporation; *U.S. Public*, pg. 1723
MEDICAL LIABILITY MUTUAL INSURANCE CO. LATHAM—See Berkshire Hathaway Inc.; *U.S. Public*, pg. 312
MEDICAL LIABILITY MUTUAL INSURANCE COMPANY—See Berkshire Hathaway Inc.; *U.S. Public*, pg. 312
MEDICAL MUTUAL LIABILITY INSURANCE SOCIETY OF MARYLAND; *U.S. Private*, pg. 2655
THE MEDICAL PROTECTIVE COMPANY—See Berkshire Hathaway Inc.; *U.S. Public*, pg. 302
MEEMIC INSURANCE COMPANY—See The American Automobile Association, Inc.; *U.S. Private*, pg. 3985
THE MEMBERS INSURANCE COMPANY—See Carolina Motor Club, Inc.; *U.S. Public*, pg. 768
MENDOTA INSURANCE COMPANY—See Centene Corporation; *U.S. Public*, pg. 470
MERASTAR INSURANCE CO.—See Kemper Corporation; *U.S. Public*, pg. 1221
MERCER INSURANCE COMPANY OF NEW JERSEY, INC.—See United Fire Group, Inc.; *U.S. Public*, pg. 2231
MERCHANTS BONDING COMPANY; *U.S. Private*, pg. 2669
MERCHANTS GROUP, INC.—See American European Group, Inc.; *U.S. Private*, pg. 232
MERCHANTS MUTUAL INSURANCE COMPANY—See American European Group, Inc.; *U.S. Private*, pg. 232
MERCURY CASUALTY COMPANY—See Mercury General Corporation; *U.S. Public*, pg. 1421
MERCURY COUNTY MUTUAL INSURANCE COMPANY—See Mercury General Corporation; *U.S. Public*, pg. 1421
MERCURY GENERAL CORPORATION; *U.S. Public*, pg. 1421
MERCURY INSURANCE SERVICES, LLC—See Mercury General Corporation; *U.S. Public*, pg. 1421
MERRIMACK MUTUAL FIRE INSURANCE CO.—See The Andover Companies; *U.S. Private*, pg. 3986
METLIFE AUTO & HOME INSURANCE AGENCY, INC.—See MetLife, Inc.; *U.S. Public*, pg. 1430
METROPOLITAN CASUALTY INSURANCE CO.—See MetLife, Inc.; *U.S. Public*, pg. 1431
METROPOLITAN GENERAL INSURANCE CO.—See MetLife, Inc.; *U.S. Public*, pg. 1431
MGIC ASSURANCE CORPORATION—See MGIC Investment Corporation; *U.S. Public*, pg. 1434
MGIC CREDIT ASSURANCE CORPORATION—See MGIC Investment Corporation; *U.S. Public*, pg. 1434
MGIC INVESTMENT CORPORATION; *U.S. Public*, pg. 1434

524126 — DIRECT PROPERTY AND...

MICHIGAN BASIC PROPERTY INSURANCE ASSOCIATION; *U.S. Private*, pg. 2700
MICHIGAN PROPERTY & CASUALTY GUARANTY ASSOCIATION; *U.S. Private*, pg. 2701
MICO INSURANCE COMPANY—See Motorists Mutual Insurance Co.; *U.S. Private*, pg. 2797
MID-CONTINENT ASSURANCE COMPANY—See American Financial Group, Inc.; *U.S. Public*, pg. 102
MID-CONTINENT CASUALTY CO.—See American Financial Group, Inc.; *U.S. Public*, pg. 102
MID-CONTINENT EXCESS AND SURPLUS INSURANCE COMPANY—See American Financial Group, Inc.; *U.S. Public*, pg. 103
MIDDLESEX MUTUAL ASSURANCE COMPANY—See COUNTRY Financial; *U.S. Private*, pg. 1067
MIDWEST EMPLOYER'S CASUALTY COMPANY—See W.R. Berkley Corporation; *U.S. Public*, pg. 2318
MILLERS CAPITAL INSURANCE CO.; *U.S. Private*, pg. 2736
MISSOURI EMPLOYERS MUTUAL INSURANCE CO., INC.; *U.S. Private*, pg. 2749
MMG INSURANCE COMPANY; *U.S. Private*, pg. 2754
MONDIAL ASSISTANCE PORTUGAL—See Allianz SE; *Int'l*, pg. 342
MOREFAR MARKETING, INC.—See American International Group, Inc.; *U.S. Public*, pg. 107
MORTGAGE GUARANTY INSURANCE CORPORATION—See MGIC Investment Corporation; *U.S. Public*, pg. 1434
MOTORISTS MUTUAL INSURANCE CO.; *U.S. Private*, pg. 2797
MOUNTAIN FINANCIAL, INC.—See Nobility Homes, Inc.; *U.S. Public*, pg. 1531
MOUNTAIN STATES INSURANCE COMPANY—See Donegal Group Inc.; *U.S. Public*, pg. 676
MOUNTAIN WEST FARM BUREAU MUTUAL INSURANCE COMPANY INC.; *U.S. Private*, pg. 2800
MOUNT VERNON FIRE INSURANCE COMPANY—See Berkshire Hathaway Inc.; *U.S. Public*, pg. 319
MRM PROPERTY & LIABILITY TRUST; *U.S. Private*, pg. 2805
MT. HAWLEY INSURANCE COMPANY—See RLI Corp.; *U.S. Public*, pg. 1801
M&T INSURANCE AGENCY, INC—See M&T Bank Corporation; *U.S. Public*, pg. 1350
MT. WASHINGTON ASSURANCE CORPORATION—See The Plymouth Rock Co.; *U.S. Private*, pg. 4097
MUNCHENER UND MAGDEBURGER AGRARVERSICHERUNG AKTIENGESELLSCHAFT—See Allianz SE; *Int'l*, pg. 354
MUTUAL BENEFIT INSURANCE COMPANY; *U.S. Private*, pg. 2819
MUTUAL BOILER RE—See Factory Mutual Insurance Company; *U.S. Private*, pg. 1461
MUTUAL OF ENUMCLAW INSURANCE CO. INC.; *U.S. Private*, pg. 2820
MUTUAL SAVINGS FIRE INSURANCE CO. INC.—See Kemper Corporation; *U.S. Public*, pg. 1220
NATIONAL AMERICAN INSURANCE COMPANY OF CALIFORNIA—See EQT AB; *Int'l*, pg. 2474
NATIONAL CROP INSURANCE SERVICES INC.; *U.S. Private*, pg. 2852
NATIONAL ELDERCARE REFERRAL SYSTEMS, LLC—See Genworth Financial, Inc.; *U.S. Public*, pg. 934
NATIONALE WAARBORG B.V.—See Stone Point Capital LLC; *U.S. Private*, pg. 3821
NATIONAL FARMERS UNION PROPERTY & CASUALTY COMPANY—See The Allstate Corporation; *U.S. Public*, pg. 2034
NATIONAL FIRE & MARINE INSURANCE COMPANY—See Berkshire Hathaway Inc.; *U.S. Public*, pg. 302
NATIONAL FLOOD SERVICES, INC.—See Aon plc; *Int'l*, pg. 489
NATIONAL GENERAL INSURANCE COMPANY—See The Allstate Corporation; *U.S. Public*, pg. 2034
NATIONAL GENERAL MANAGEMENT CORP.—See The Allstate Corporation; *U.S. Public*, pg. 2034
NATIONAL INDEMNITY COMPANY OF THE SOUTH—See Berkshire Hathaway Inc.; *U.S. Public*, pg. 302
NATIONAL INDEMNITY COMPANY—See Berkshire Hathaway Inc.; *U.S. Public*, pg. 302
NATIONAL INTERSTATE INSURANCE COMPANY OF HAWAII, INC.—See American Financial Group, Inc.; *U.S. Public*, pg. 103
NATIONAL LLOYDS INSURANCE CORPORATION—See ReAlign Capital Strategies; *U.S. Private*, pg. 3368
NATIONAL MERIT INSURANCE CO.—See Kemper Corporation; *U.S. Public*, pg. 1221
NATIONAL SECURITY FIRE AND CASUALTY COMPANY—See The National Security Group, Inc.; *U.S. Public*, pg. 2116
NATIONAL SECURITY INSURANCE COMPANY—See The National Security Group, Inc.; *U.S. Public*, pg. 2116
NATIONAL SURETY CORPORATION—See Allianz SE; *Int'l*, pg. 354
NATIONAL UNION FIRE INSURANCE COMPANY OF PITTSBURGH, PA.—See American International Group, Inc.; *U.S. Public*, pg. 107

NAU COUNTRY INSURANCE COMPANY—See NAU Holding Company; *U.S. Private*, pg. 2868
NAU HOLDING COMPANY; *U.S. Private*, pg. 2868
NAU INSURANCE COMPANY—See NAU Holding Company; *U.S. Private*, pg. 2868
NAUTILUS INSURANCE COMPANY—See W.R. Berkley Corporation; *U.S. Public*, pg. 2318
NAUTILUS INSURANCE GROUP, LLC—See W.R. Berkley Corporation; *U.S. Public*, pg. 2318
NAVIGATORS (ASIA) LTD.—See The Hartford Financial Services Group, Inc.; *U.S. Public*, pg. 2088
NAVIGATORS INSURANCE COMPANY—See The Hartford Financial Services Group, Inc.; *U.S. Public*, pg. 2088
NAVIGATORS MANAGEMENT UK LTD.—See The Hartford Financial Services Group, Inc.; *U.S. Public*, pg. 2088
NAVIGATORS UNDERWRITING AGENCY LTD.—See The Hartford Financial Services Group, Inc.; *U.S. Public*, pg. 2088
NCCI HOLDINGS INC.; *U.S. Private*, pg. 2875
N.C. FARM BUREAU MUTUAL INSURANCE CO. INC.; *U.S. Private*, pg. 2827
NEVADA GENERAL INSURANCE COMPANY; *U.S. Private*, pg. 2891
NEVADA GENERAL INSURANCE CO—See Nevada General Insurance Company; *U.S. Private*, pg. 2891
NEW JERSEY MANUFACTURERS INSURANCE COMPANY; *U.S. Private*, pg. 2898
NEW LONDON COUNTY MUTUAL INSURANCE COMPANY, INC.; *U.S. Private*, pg. 2898
NEW MEXICO MUTUAL CASUALTY COMPANY; *U.S. Private*, pg. 2898
NEW YORK CENTRAL MUTUAL FIRE INSURANCE COMPANY INC.; *U.S. Private*, pg. 2908
NGM INSURANCE COMPANY—See American Family Mutual Insurance Company; *U.S. Private*, pg. 233
NIELSON & COMPANY INCORPORATED; *U.S. Private*, pg. 2927
NKFE INSURANCE AGENCY COMPANY LIMITED—See Assicurazioni Generali S.p.A.; *Int'l*, pg. 647
NLASCO NATIONAL LLOYDS, INC.—See Align Financial Group, LLC; *U.S. Private*, pg. 168
NODAK INSURANCE COMPANY; *U.S. Private*, pg. 2933
NORCAL MUTUAL INSURANCE CO.—See ProAssurance Corporation; *U.S. Public*, pg. 1723
NORGUARD INSURANCE COMPANY—See Berkshire Hathaway Inc.; *U.S. Public*, pg. 302
NORTHBRIDGE COMMERCIAL INSURANCE CORPORATION—See Fairfax Financial Holdings Limited; *Int'l*, pg. 2607
NORTHBRIDGE GENERAL INSURANCE CORPORATION—See Fairfax Financial Holdings Limited; *Int'l*, pg. 2607
NORTHBRIDGE INDEMNITY INSURANCE CORPORATION—See Fairfax Financial Holdings Limited; *Int'l*, pg. 2607
NORTHBRIDGE INDEMNITY INSURANCE CORPORATION—See Fairfax Financial Holdings Limited; *Int'l*, pg. 2607
NORTHERN SECURITY INSURANCE CO. INC.—See Vermont Mutual Insurance Co., Inc.; *U.S. Private*, pg. 4367
NORTHLAND CASUALTY COMPANY—See The Travelers Companies, Inc.; *U.S. Public*, pg. 2136
NORTHLAND INSURANCE COMPANY—See The Travelers Companies, Inc.; *U.S. Public*, pg. 2136
THE NORTH RIVER INSURANCE COMPANY—See Fairfax Financial Holdings Limited; *Int'l*, pg. 2606
NORTH STAR MUTUAL INSURANCE CO.; *U.S. Private*, pg. 2947
NSM INSURANCE GROUP, INC.—See The Carlyle Group Inc.; *U.S. Public*, pg. 2050
OCCIDENTAL FIRE & CASUALTY COMPANY OF NORTH CAROLINA INC.—See MCM Corporation; *U.S. Private*, pg. 2642
THE OHIO CASUALTY INSURANCE COMPANY—See Liberty Mutual Holding Company Inc.; *U.S. Private*, pg. 2446
OHIO INDEMNITY COMPANY—See BancInsurance Corporation; *U.S. Public*, pg. 464
OKLAHOMA FARM BUREAU MUTUAL INSURANCE CO.; *U.S. Private*, pg. 3007
OKLAHOMA PROPERTY & CASUALTY INSURANCE GUARANTY ASSOCIATION; *U.S. Private*, pg. 3007
OKLAHOMA SURETY COMPANY—See American Financial Group, Inc.; *U.S. Public*, pg. 103
OLD REPUBLIC DEALER SERVICE CORPORATION—See Old Republic International Corporation; *U.S. Public*, pg. 1567
OLD REPUBLIC LIFE INSURANCE COMPANY—See Old Republic International Corporation; *U.S. Public*, pg. 1568
ORCHID UNDERWRITERS AGENCY, LLC—See Brown & Brown, Inc.; *U.S. Public*, pg. 401
OVERBY-SEAWELL COMPANY—See W.R. Berkley Corporation; *U.S. Public*, pg. 2318
OWNERS INSURANCE COMPANY—See Auto-Owners Insurance Group; *U.S. Private*, pg. 398
PACIFIC COMPENSATION INSURANCE COMPANY—See CopperPoint Mutual Insurance Holding Company; *U.S. Private*, pg. 1045
PACIFIC EMPLOYERS INSURANCE COMPANY—See

CORPORATE AFFILIATIONS

Chubb Limited; *Int'l*, pg. 1593
PACIFIC UNDERWRITING CORPORATION PTY LTD—See The Hanover Insurance Group, Inc.; *U.S. Public*, pg. 2087
PAFCO GENERAL INSURANCE COMPANY—See Goran Capital Inc.; *Int'l*, pg. 3042
PAFCO INSURANCE COMPANY—See The Allstate Corporation; *U.S. Public*, pg. 2034
PALMETTO HOSPITAL TRUST; *U.S. Private*, pg. 3081
PARKER SERVICES, L.L.C.—See Sentry Insurance Group; *U.S. Private*, pg. 3610
PARTNERS MUTUAL INSURANCE CO.; *U.S. Private*, pg. 3102
THE PAUL REVERE LIFE INSURANCE COMPANY—See Unum Group; *U.S. Public*, pg. 2263
PCG AGENCIES, INC.—See Berkshire Hathaway Inc.; *U.S. Public*, pg. 313
PEAK INSURANCE ADVISORS, LLC—See Yardi Systems, Inc.; *U.S. Public*, pg. 4586
PEAK PROPERTY AND CASUALTY INSURANCE CORP.—See Sentry Insurance Group; *U.S. Private*, pg. 3611
PEERLESS INSURANCE COMPANY—See Liberty Mutual Holding Company Inc.; *U.S. Private*, pg. 2446
PEMBRIDGE INSURANCE COMPANY—See The Allstate Corporation; *U.S. Public*, pg. 2034
PEMCO INSURANCE COMPANY INC.—See PEMCO Mutual Insurance Co. Inc.; *U.S. Private*, pg. 3132
PEMCO MUTUAL INSURANCE CO. INC.; *U.S. Private*, pg. 3132
PENINSULA INDEMNITY COMPANY—See Donegal Group Inc.; *U.S. Public*, pg. 676
PENN-AMERICA INSURANCE COMPANY—See Paine Schwartz Partners, LLC; *U.S. Private*, pg. 3075
PENN NATIONAL SECURITY INSURANCE COMPANY—See Pennsylvania National Mutual Casualty Insurance Company; *U.S. Public*, pg. 3137
PENN-STAR INSURANCE COMPANY—See Paine Schwartz Partners, LLC; *U.S. Private*, pg. 3075
PENNSYLVANIA LUMBERMENS MUTUAL INSURANCE COMPANY; *U.S. Public*, pg. 1663
PENNSYLVANIA MANUFACTURERS' ASSOCIATION INSURANCE COMPANY—See Old Republic International Corporation; *U.S. Public*, pg. 1568
PENNSYLVANIA MANUFACTURERS INDEMNITY COMPANY—See Old Republic International Corporation; *U.S. Public*, pg. 1568
PENNSYLVANIA NATIONAL MUTUAL CASUALTY INSURANCE COMPANY; *U.S. Private*, pg. 3137
PETER D. JAMES LIMITED—See White Mountains Insurance Group, Ltd.; *U.S. Public*, pg. 2369
PHARMACISTS MUTUAL INSURANCE CO., INC.—See Pharmacists Mutual Companies; *U.S. Private*, pg. 3165
PHT SERVICES LTD.—See Palmetto Hospital Trust; *U.S. Private*, pg. 3081
PINNACOL ASSURANCE; *U.S. Private*, pg. 3186
PIONEER STATE MUTUAL INSURANCE CO.; *U.S. Private*, pg. 3188
PLATTE RIVER INSURANCE COMPANY—See Berkshire Hathaway Inc.; *U.S. Public*, pg. 298
PLAZA INSURANCE COMPANY—See State Automobile Mutual Insurance Company; *U.S. Private*, pg. 3791
POROWNEO.PL SP. Z O.O—See Aviva plc; *Int'l*, pg. 746
PREFERRED MUTUAL INSURANCE CO. INC.; *U.S. Private*, pg. 3248
PREFERRED MUTUAL INSURANCE CO.—See Preferred Mutual Insurance Co. Inc.; *U.S. Private*, pg. 3248
PREPARED INSURANCE COMPANY—See Lighthouse Property Insurance Corp.; *U.S. Private*, pg. 2453
PRESTIGE INTERNATIONAL MANAGEMENT PTE. LTD.—See Advancer Global Limited; *Int'l*, pg. 163
PRIMACY UNDERWRITING MANAGEMENT PTY LIMITED—See Allianz SE; *Int'l*, pg. 347
PROASSURANCE CORPORATION - MOBILE—See ProAssurance Corporation; *U.S. Public*, pg. 1723
PROASSURANCE CORPORATION—See ProAssurance Corporation; *U.S. Public*, pg. 1723
PROASSURANCE CORPORATION—See ProAssurance Corporation; *U.S. Public*, pg. 1723
PROASSURANCE INDEMNITY LLC—See ProAssurance Corporation; *U.S. Public*, pg. 1723
PROASSURANCE—See ProAssurance Corporation; *U.S. Public*, pg. 1723
PROCURA MANAGEMENT, INC.—See UnitedHealth Group Incorporated; *U.S. Public*, pg. 2247
PROFESSIONAL LIABILITY INSURANCE COMPANY OF AMERICA—See Berkshire Hathaway Inc.; *U.S. Public*, pg. 312
PROFESSIONAL UNDERWRITERS LIABILITY INSURANCE COMPANY—See The Doctors Company; *U.S. Private*, pg. 4021
PROGRESSIVE ADVANCED INSURANCE COMPANY—See The Progressive Corporation; *U.S. Public*, pg. 2125
PROGRESSIVE CASUALTY INSURANCE COMPANY—See The Progressive Corporation; *U.S. Public*, pg. 2125
PROGRESSIVE CONSUMER INSURANCE—See The Pro-

gressive Corporation; *U.S. Public*, pg. 2125
PROGRESSIVE COUNTY MUTUAL INSURANCE CO.—See The Progressive Corporation; *U.S. Public*, pg. 2125
PROGRESSIVE GULF INSURANCE COMPANY—See The Progressive Corporation; *U.S. Public*, pg. 2125
PROGRESSIVE HALCYON INSURANCE CO.—See The Progressive Corporation; *U.S. Public*, pg. 2125
PROGRESSIVE INSURANCE AGENCY, INC.—See The Progressive Corporation; *U.S. Public*, pg. 2125
PROGRESSIVE PREFERRED INSURANCE COMPANY—See The Progressive Corporation; *U.S. Public*, pg. 2125
PROGRESSIVE SOUTHEASTERN INSURANCE COMPANY—See The Progressive Corporation; *U.S. Public*, pg. 2125
PROGRESSIVE WEST INSURANCE COMPANY—See The Progressive Corporation; *U.S. Public*, pg. 2125
PRONATIONAL INSURANCE COMPANY—See ProAssurance Corporation; *U.S. Public*, pg. 1723
PRONATIONAL INSURANCE COMPANY—See ProAssurance Corporation; *U.S. Public*, pg. 1723
PRONTO GENERAL AGENCY , LTD.—See Arthur J. Gallagher & Co.; *U.S. Public*, pg. 207
PROTECTIVE INSURANCE COMPANY—See The Progressive Corporation; *U.S. Public*, pg. 2125
PROTECTIVE INSURANCE CORPORATION—See The Progressive Corporation; *U.S. Public*, pg. 2125
PROTEQ LEVENSVERZEKERINGEN N.V.—See Apollo Global Management, Inc.; *U.S. Public*, pg. 147
PSA FINANCE ARGENTINA COMPANIA FINANCIERA SA—See Banco Bilbao Vizcaya Argentaria, S.A.; *Int'l*, pg. 818
PT AIG INSURANCE INDONESIA—See American International Group, Inc.; *U.S. Public*, pg. 105
PT CHINA TAIPING INSURANCE INDONESIA—See China Taiping Insurance Holdings Company Limited; *Int'l*, pg. 1557
PULIC INSURANCE SERVICES, INC.—See The Doctors Company; *U.S. Private*, pg. 4021
QUINCY MUTUAL FIRE INSURANCE COMPANY; *U.S. Private*, pg. 3327
RADIAN GROUP, INC.; *U.S. Public*, pg. 1759
RADIAN SERVICES LLC—See Radian Group, Inc.; *U.S. Public*, pg. 1759
RAIN AND HAIL INSURANCE SERVICE, INC.—See Chubb Limited; *Int'l*, pg. 1592
RASTREATOR.COM LIMITED—See Admiral Group plc; *Int'l*, pg. 151
REPUBLIC FINANCIAL INDEMNITY GROUP, INC.—See Old Republic International Corporation; *U.S. Public*, pg. 1569
REPUBLIC FRANKLIN INSURANCE CO.—See Utica National Insurance Group; *U.S. Private*, pg. 4325
THE REPUBLIC GROUP—See Delek Group Ltd.; *Int'l*, pg. 2011
REPUBLIC INDEMNITY COMPANY OF CALIFORNIA—See American Financial Group, Inc.; *U.S. Public*, pg. 103
REPWEST INSURANCE COMPANY—See U-Haul Holding Company; *U.S. Public*, pg. 2211
RESOLUTE REINSURANCE COMPANY—See Berkshire Hathaway Inc.; *U.S. Public*, pg. 305
RESPONSE INSURANCE COMPANY—See Kemper Corporation; *U.S. Public*, pg. 1221
RISK INSURANCE SERVICES OF INDIANA, INC—See US 1 Industries, Inc.; *U.S. Private*, pg. 4317
RISKTRAC INC.—See Liberty Mutual Holding Company Inc.; *U.S. Private*, pg. 2446
RLI INSURANCE COMPANY—See RLI Corp.; *U.S. Public*, pg. 1801
RLI NORTHERN CALIFORNIA REGIONAL OFFICE—See RLI Corp.; *U.S. Public*, pg. 1802
RLI SPECIAL RISK—See RLI Corp.; *U.S. Public*, pg. 1802
RMIC CORPORATION—See Old Republic International Corporation; *U.S. Public*, pg. 1569
ROCKFORD MUTUAL INSURANCE COMPANY; *U.S. Private*, pg. 3466
ROCKHILL INSURANCE COMPANY—See State Automobile Mutual Insurance Company; *U.S. Private*, pg. 3791
ROCKINGHAM MUTUAL INSURANCE COMPANY; *U.S. Private*, pg. 3467
ROCKWOOD CASUALTY INSURANCE CO.—See Brookfield Reinsurance Ltd.; *Int'l*, pg. 1194
ROLAND ASSISTANCE GMBH—See AXA S.A.; *Int'l*, pg. 759
ROOT, INC.; *U.S. Public*, pg. 1810
ROUNDPOINT MORTGAGE SERVICING LLC—See Two Harbors Investment Corp.; *U.S. Public*, pg. 2207
ROYAL INDEMNITY CO.—See Arrowpoint Capital Corp.; *U.S. Private*, pg. 336
RTW, INC.—See State Automobile Mutual Insurance Company; *U.S. Private*, pg. 3791
RURAL MUTUAL INSURANCE COMPANY INC.; *U.S. Private*, pg. 3504
RUTGERS CASUALTY INSURANCE CO—See American European Group, Inc.; *U.S. Private*, pg. 232
R+V DIREKTVERSICHERUNG AG—See DZ BANK AG Deutsche Zentral-Genossenschaftsbank; *Int'l*, pg. 2244

RVOS FARM MUTUAL INSURANCE COMPANY; *U.S. Private*, pg. 3508
RYAN SPECIALTY GROUP, LLC - DENMARK—See Ryan Specialty Holdings, Inc.; *U.S. Public*, pg. 1828
SAFECO INSURANCE COMPANY OF AMERICA-CENTRAL REGION—See Liberty Mutual Holding Company Inc.; *U.S. Private*, pg. 2446
SAFECO INSURANCE COMPANY OF AMERICA-NORTHEAST REGION—See Liberty Mutual Holding Company Inc.; *U.S. Private*, pg. 2446
SAFECO INSURANCE COMPANY OF AMERICA-NORTHWEST REGION—See Liberty Mutual Holding Company Inc.; *U.S. Private*, pg. 2446
SAFECO INSURANCE COMPANY OF AMERICA—See Liberty Mutual Holding Company Inc.; *U.S. Private*, pg. 2446
SAFECO INSURANCE COMPANY OF AMERICA—See Liberty Mutual Holding Company Inc.; *U.S. Private*, pg. 2446
SAFECO INSURANCE COMPANY OF AMERICA-SOUTHEAST REGION—See Liberty Mutual Holding Company Inc.; *U.S. Private*, pg. 2446
SAFECO INSURANCE COMPANY OF AMERICA-SOUTHWEST REGION—See Liberty Mutual Holding Company Inc.; *U.S. Private*, pg. 2446
SAFETY, CLAIMS & LITIGATION SERVICES, LLC—See American Financial Group, Inc.; *U.S. Public*, pg. 103
SAFETY INSURANCE CO., INC.—See Safety Insurance Group, Inc.; *U.S. Public*, pg. 1835
SAFETY INSURANCE GROUP, INC.; *U.S. Public*, pg. 1834
SAFEWAY INSURANCE COMPANY; *U.S. Private*, pg. 3525
SAGICOR ASSET MANAGEMENT INC.—See Alignvest Management Corporation; *Int'l*, pg. 327
SAGICOR AT LLOYD'S LIMITED—See Alignvest Management Corporation; *Int'l*, pg. 328
SAGICOR CLAIMS MANAGEMENT, INC.—See Alignvest Management Corporation; *Int'l*, pg. 328
SAGICOR LIFE INC.—See Alignvest Management Corporation; *Int'l*, pg. 328
SAGICOR SYNDICATE HOLDINGS LIMITED—See Alignvest Management Corporation; *Int'l*, pg. 328
SAGICOR UNDERWRITING LIMITED—See Alignvest Management Corporation; *Int'l*, pg. 328
SAINT GOBAIN AUTOVER FRANCE S.A.—See Compagnie de Saint-Gobain SA; *Int'l*, pg. 1729
SASKATCHEWAN GOVERNMENT INSURANCE—See Crown Investments Corporation of Saskatchewan; *Int'l*, pg. 1857
SBI SEGUROS URUGUAY S.A.—See Fairfax Financial Holdings Limited; *Int'l*, pg. 2608
SBS SEGUROS COLOMBIA S.A.—See Fairfax Financial Holdings Limited; *Int'l*, pg. 2608
SEABRIGHT INSURANCE COMPANY—See Enstar Group Limited; *Int'l*, pg. 2449
SECURA INSURANCE COMPANY; *U.S. Private*, pg. 3593
SECURITY FIRST INSURANCE COMPANY, INC.; *U.S. Private*, pg. 3595
SECURITY ONE INSURANCE AGENCY—See Kemper Corporation; *U.S. Public*, pg. 1221
SECURITY PLAN FIRE INSURANCE COMPANY—See Citizens, Inc.; *U.S. Public*, pg. 506
SEEMAN HOLTZ PROPERTY & CASUALTY, LLC; *U.S. Private*, pg. 3598
SEGUROS LOGO S.A.—See Apollo Global Management, Inc.; *U.S. Public*, pg. 150
SEGUROS SURA (BRASIL) S.A.—See Grupo de Inversiones Suramericana S.A.; *Int'l*, pg. 3125
SEGUROS SURA S.A.—See Grupo de Inversiones Suramericana S.A.; *Int'l*, pg. 3126
SEGUROS TRIPLE-S, INC.—See Triple-S Management Corp.; *U.S. Public*, pg. 2195
SEIBELS, BRUCE & COMPANY—See The Seibels Bruce Group, Inc.; *U.S. Private*, pg. 4116
THE SEIBELS BRUCE GROUP, INC.; *U.S. Private*, pg. 4116
SELECTIVE AUTO INSURANCE COMPANY OF NEW JERSEY—See Selective Insurance Group, Inc.; *U.S. Public*, pg. 1862
SELECTIVE INSURANCE COMPANY OF AMERICA—See Selective Insurance Group, Inc.; *U.S. Public*, pg. 1862
SELECTIVE INSURANCE COMPANY OF SOUTH CAROLINA—See Selective Insurance Group, Inc.; *U.S. Public*, pg. 1863
SENECA INSURANCE COMPANY INC.—See Fairfax Financial Holdings Limited; *Int'l*, pg. 2606
SENTRY CASUALTY COMPANY—See Sentry Insurance Group; *U.S. Private*, pg. 3611
SENTRY INSURANCE—See Sentry Insurance Group; *U.S. Private*, pg. 3611
SENTRY SELECT INSURANCE COMPANY—See Sentry Insurance Group; *U.S. Private*, pg. 3611
SERVICE NET WARRANTY, LLC—See American International Group, Inc.; *U.S. Public*, pg. 106
SERWIS UBEZPIECZENIOWY SP. Z O.O.—See Alior Bank S.A.; *Int'l*, pg. 329
SFM MUTUAL INSURANCE COMPANY; *U.S. Private*, pg. 3621
SHELTER MUTUAL INSURANCE COMPANY; *U.S. Private*, pg. 3631
SKOGMAN RALSTON & CARLSON INC.—See Skogman

Construction Company of Iowa Inc.; *U.S. Private*, pg. 3683
SOCIETY INSURANCE; *U.S. Private*, pg. 3704
SOUTH BAY ACCEPTANCE CORPORATION—See Tiptree Inc.; *U.S. Public*, pg. 2159
SOUTHBRIDGE COMPANIA DE SEGUROS GENERALES S.A.—See Fairfax Financial Holdings Limited; *Int'l*, pg. 2608
SOUTH CAROLINA FARM BUREAU MUTUAL INSURANCE COMPANY; *U.S. Private*, pg. 3720
SOUTH CHINA INSURANCE CO., LTD.—See Hua Nan Financial Holdings Co., Ltd.; *Int'l*, pg. 3510
SOUTH COAST SURETY INSURANCE SERVICES, LLC—See Boston Omaha Corporation; *U.S. Public*, pg. 372
SOUTHEASTERN UNDERWRITERS, INC.—See W.R. Berkley Corporation; *U.S. Public*, pg. 2318
SOUTHERN FARM BUREAU CASUALTY INSURANCE COMPANY; *U.S. Private*, pg. 3731
SOUTHERN FIDELITY INSURANCE CO.; *U.S. Private*, pg. 3731
SOUTHERN GENERAL INSURANCE CO.—See Insurance House; *U.S. Private*, pg. 2095
SOUTHERN INSURANCE COMPANY OF VIRGINIA—See Donegal Group Inc.; *U.S. Public*, pg. 676
SOUTHERN OAK INSURANCE COMPANY; *U.S. Private*, pg. 3734
SOUTHERN-OWNERS INSURANCE COMPANY—See Auto-Owners Insurance Group; *U.S. Private*, pg. 398
SOUTHERN UNITED FIRE INSURANCE COMPANY—See Kingsway Financial Services Inc.; *U.S. Public*, pg. 1235
SOUTH RISK MANAGEMENT LLC—See Edwards Capital, LLC; *U.S. Private*, pg. 1342
SPECIAL RISK INSURANCE MANAGERS LTD.—See Brown & Brown, Inc.; *U.S. Public*, pg. 402
SPECTERA INC.—See UnitedHealth Group Incorporated; *U.S. Public*, pg. 2250
THE STANDARD FIRE INSURANCE COMPANY—See The Travelers Companies, Inc.; *U.S. Public*, pg. 2136
STANDARD INSURANCE AGENCY, INC.—See Cavco Industries, Inc.; *U.S. Public*, pg. 455
STANDARD PROPERTY & CASUALTY INSURANCE COMPANY—See The Allstate Corporation; *U.S. Public*, pg. 2034
STATE AUTO INSURANCE COMPANY—See State Automobile Mutual Insurance Company; *U.S. Private*, pg. 3791
STATE AUTOMOBILE MUTUAL INSURANCE COMPANY; *U.S. Private*, pg. 3790
STATE AUTO P & C—See State Automobile Mutual Insurance Company; *U.S. Private*, pg. 3791
STATE AUTO PROPERTY AND CASUALTY INSURANCE COMPANY—See State Automobile Mutual Insurance Company; *U.S. Private*, pg. 3791
STATE FARM FIRE & CASUALTY CO.—See State Farm Mutual Automobile Insurance Company; *U.S. Private*, pg. 3792
STATE FARM FLORIDA INSURANCE COMPANY—See State Farm Mutual Automobile Insurance Company; *U.S. Private*, pg. 3792
STATE FARM GENERAL INSURANCE COMPANY—See State Farm Mutual Automobile Insurance Company; *U.S. Private*, pg. 3792
STATE FARM MUTUAL AUTOMOBILE INSURANCE COMPANY; *U.S. Private*, pg. 3791
STATE FUND MUTUAL INSURANCE CO.; *U.S. Private*, pg. 3792
STATE NATIONAL COMPANIES, INC.—See Markel Group Inc.; *U.S. Public*, pg. 1369
STATE VOLUNTEER MUTUAL INSURANCE CO.; *U.S. Private*, pg. 3793
STEWART MILLER MCCULLOCH & CO. LIMITED—See White Mountains Insurance Group, Ltd.; *U.S. Public*, pg. 2369
ST. PAUL FIRE AND MARINE INSURANCE COMPANY—See The Travelers Companies, Inc.; *U.S. Public*, pg. 2136
ST. PAUL FIRE & MARINE INSURANCE COMPANY—See The Travelers Companies, Inc.; *U.S. Public*, pg. 2136
STRATEGICCLAIM; *U.S. Private*, pg. 3836
STRATFORD INSURANCE COMPANY—See American International Group, Inc.; *U.S. Public*, pg. 107
SUNTRUST INSURANCE COMPANY—See Truist Financial Corporation; *U.S. Public*, pg. 2200
SURETY BONDING COMPANY OF AMERICA—See Loews Corporation; *U.S. Public*, pg. 1340
SURETY SOLUTIONS INSURANCE SERVICES INC.—See GTCR LLC; *U.S. Private*, pg. 1804
SURETY SUPPORT SERVICES, LLC—See Boston Omaha Corporation; *U.S. Public*, pg. 372
SUTTER INSURANCE COMPANY; *U.S. Private*, pg. 3887
SYDKRAFT FORSAKRING AB—See Fortum Oyj; *Int'l*, pg. 2742
SYMONS INTERNATIONAL GROUP, INC.—See Goran Capital Inc.; *Int'l*, pg. 3042
SYNCIER GMBH—See Allianz SE; *Int'l*, pg. 356
TALENT KEEPERS, INC.—See Quantum Market Research, Inc.; *U.S. Private*, pg. 3323
TBA INSURANCE INC.; *U.S. Private*, pg. 3941

524126 — DIRECT PROPERTY AND...

TEXAS BUILDERS INSURANCE COMPANY—See Hallmark Financial Services, Inc.; *U.S. Public*, pg. 981
TEXAS MUTUAL INSURANCE COMPANY; *U.S. Private*, pg. 3976
TEXAS PROPERTY & CASUALTY INSURANCE GUARANTY ASSOCIATION; *U.S. Private*, pg. 3977
THOMAS RUTHERFOORD INC.—See Marsh & McLennan Companies, Inc.; *U.S. Public*, pg. 1388
TIG HOLDINGS, INC.—See Fairfax Financial Holdings Limited; *Int'l*, pg. 2608
TIG INSURANCE CO.—See Fairfax Financial Holdings Limited; *Int'l*, pg. 2608
TITAN PROPERTY & CASUALTY INSURANCE COMPANY—See Western National Mutual Insurance Co.; *U.S. Private*, pg. 4494
TOPA INSURANCE COMPANY—See Topa Equities Ltd, Inc.; *U.S. Private*, pg. 4186
TOWARZYSTWO UBEZPIECZEN I REASEKURACJI ALLIANZ POLSKA S.A.—See Allianz SE; *Int'l*, pg. 356
TRANSATLANTIC HOLDINGS, INC.—See Berkshire Hathaway Inc.; *U.S. Public*, pg. 299
TRANSPORTATION INSURANCE COMPANY—See Loews Corporation; *U.S. Public*, pg. 1340
TRANSPROTECTION SERVICE COMPANY—See American Financial Group, Inc.; *U.S. Public*, pg. 103
TRAVELERS CASUALTY AND SURETY COMPANY—See The Travelers Companies, Inc.; *U.S. Public*, pg. 2136
TRAVELERS CONSTITUTION STATE INSURANCE COMPANY—See The Travelers Companies, Inc.; *U.S. Public*, pg. 2136
THE TRAVELERS INDEMNITY COMPANY OF AMERICA—See The Travelers Companies, Inc.; *U.S. Public*, pg. 2136
TRAVELERS INSURANCE COMPANY LIMITED—See The Travelers Companies, Inc.; *U.S. Public*, pg. 2136
TRAVELERS INSURANCE COMPANY OF CANADA—See The Travelers Companies, Inc.; *U.S. Public*, pg. 2136
TRAVELERS INSURANCE DESIGNATED ACTIVITY COMPANY—See The Travelers Companies, Inc.; *U.S. Public*, pg. 2136
TRAVELERS LLOYDS OF TEXAS INSURANCE COMPANY—See The Travelers Companies, Inc.; *U.S. Public*, pg. 2136
TRAVELERS LONDON LIMITED—See The Travelers Companies, Inc.; *U.S. Public*, pg. 2136
TRAVELERS MANAGEMENT LIMITED—See The Travelers Companies, Inc.; *U.S. Public*, pg. 2136
THE TRAVELERS MARINE CORPORATION—See The Travelers Companies, Inc.; *U.S. Public*, pg. 2136
TRAVELERS PROPERTY CASUALTY COMPANY OF AMERICA—See The Travelers Companies, Inc.; *U.S. Public*, pg. 2136
TRAVELERS PROPERTY CASUALTY CORP.—See The Travelers Companies, Inc.; *U.S. Public*, pg. 2136
TRAVELERS—See The Travelers Companies, Inc.; *U.S. Public*, pg. 2136
TRAVELERS SYNDICATE MANAGEMENT LIMITED—See The Travelers Companies, Inc.; *U.S. Public*, pg. 2136
TRAVELERS SYNDICATE MANAGEMENT LIMITED—See The Travelers Companies, Inc.; *U.S. Public*, pg. 2136
TRAVEL GUARD EMEA LIMITED—See American International Group, Inc.; *U.S. Public*, pg. 106
TRAVEL GUARD WORLDWIDE, INC.—See American International Group, Inc.; *U.S. Public*, pg. 106
TRIANGLE LIFE INSURANCE—See First Citizens BancShares, Inc.; *U.S. Public*, pg. 842
TRINITY UNIVERSAL INSURANCE CO.—See Kemper Corporation; *U.S. Public*, pg. 1221
TRIPLE-S PROPIEDAD, INC.—See Triple-S Management Corp.; *U.S. Public*, pg. 2195
TRI POINTE ADVANTAGE INSURANCE SERVICES, INC.—See Tri Pointe Homes, Inc.; *U.S. Public*, pg. 2188
TRUENORTH COMPANIES L.C.; *U.S. Private*, pg. 4248
TRUSTGARD INSURANCE COMPANY—See Grange Mutual Casualty Company; *U.S. Private*, pg. 1754
TUDOR INSURANCE COMPANY—See American International Group, Inc.; *U.S. Public*, pg. 107
TYPTAP INSURANCE COMPANY—See HCI Group, Inc.; *U.S. Public*, pg. 1014
ULICO STANDARD OF AMERICA CASUALTY COMPANY—See Ullico Inc.; *U.S. Private*, pg. 4276
ULLICO CASUALTY COMPANY—See Ullico Inc.; *U.S. Private*, pg. 4276
ULLICO CASUALTY GROUP, INC.—See Ullico Inc.; *U.S. Private*, pg. 4276
ULLICO INC.—See Ullico Inc.; *U.S. Private*, pg. 4276
ULLICO INDEMNITY—See Ullico Inc.; *U.S. Private*, pg. 4276
ULTIMATE SERVICES AGENCY, LLC—See BancInsurance Corporation; *U.S. Private*, pg. 464
UNDERWRITER FOR THE PROFESSIONS INSURANCE COMPANY—See The Doctors Company; *U.S. Private*, pg. 4022
UNION MUTUAL FIRE INSURANCE CO.; *U.S. Private*, pg. 4284
UNITED AUTOMOBILE INSURANCE GROUP, INC.; *U.S. Private*, pg. 4287
UNITED CASUALTY & SURETY INSURANCE COMPANY—See Boston Omaha Corporation; *U.S. Public*, pg. 372
UNITED COASTAL INSURANCE COMPANY—See ACMAT Corporation; *U.S. Public*, pg. 35
UNITED FIRE & CASUALTY COMPANY—See United Fire Group, Inc.; *U.S. Public*, pg. 2230
UNITED FIRE & INDEMNITY COMPANY—See United Fire Group, Inc.; *U.S. Public*, pg. 2231
UNITED FIRE LLOYDS—See United Fire Group, Inc.; *U.S. Public*, pg. 2231
UNITED GUARANTY COMMERCIAL INSURANCE COMPANY OF NORTH CAROLINA—See Arch Capital Group Ltd.; *Int'l*, pg. 546
UNITED GUARANTY CORPORATION—See Arch Capital Group Ltd.; *Int'l*, pg. 546
UNITED GUARANTY CREDIT INSURANCE COMPANY—See Arch Capital Group Ltd.; *Int'l*, pg. 546
UNITEDHEALTHCARE OF ALABAMA, INC.—See UnitedHealth Group Incorporated; *U.S. Public*, pg. 2252
UNITED INTERNATIONAL INSURANCE CO.—See American European Group, Inc.; *U.S. Private*, pg. 232
UNITED NATIONAL GROUP LTD.—See Paine Schwartz Partners, LLC; *U.S. Private*, pg. 3076
UNITED NATIONAL INSURANCE COMPANY—See Paine Schwartz Partners, LLC; *U.S. Private*, pg. 3076
UNITED PROPERTY & CASUALTY INSURANCE COMPANY—See HCI Group, Inc.; *U.S. Public*, pg. 1014
UNITED SERVICES AUTOMOBILE ASSOCIATION; *U.S. Private*, pg. 4297
UNITED STATES AIRCRAFT INSURANCE GROUP—See Berkshire Hathaway Inc.; *U.S. Public*, pg. 302
UNITED STATES FIRE INSURANCE COMPANY—See Fairfax Financial Holdings Limited; *Int'l*, pg. 2606
UNITED STATES LIABILITY INSURANCE COMPANY—See Berkshire Hathaway Inc.; *U.S. Public*, pg. 319
UNITRIN ADVANTAGE INSURANCE COMPANY—See Kemper Corporation; *U.S. Public*, pg. 1221
UNITRIN DIRECT PROPERTY & CASUALTY COMPANY—See Kemper Corporation; *U.S. Public*, pg. 1221
UNIVERSAL INSURANCE COMPANY—See Carolina Motor Club, Inc.; *U.S. Private*, pg. 768
UNIVISTA INSURANCE CORPORATION; *U.S. Private*, pg. 4310
USAA LIFE GENERAL AGENCY INC.—See United Services Automobile Association; *U.S. Private*, pg. 4297
USI INSURANCE SERVICES LLC - FORT LAUDERDALE—See Caisse de Depot et Placement du Quebec; *Int'l*, pg. 1257
USI INSURANCE SERVICES LLC - FORT LAUDERDALE—See KKR & Co. Inc.; *U.S. Public*, pg. 1266
U.S. INVESTMENT CORPORATION—See Berkshire Hathaway Inc.; *U.S. Public*, pg. 319
U.S. SECURITY INSURANCE CO.—See Kingsway Financial Services Inc.; *U.S. Public*, pg. 1235
U.S. UNDERWRITERS INSURANCE COMPANY—See Berkshire Hathaway Inc.; *U.S. Public*, pg. 319
UTAH FARM BUREAU FINANCIAL SERVICES (INC.)—See Iowa Farm Bureau Federation; *U.S. Private*, pg. 2134
UTICA LLOYDS OF TEXAS—See Utica National Insurance Group; *U.S. Private*, pg. 4325
UTICA MUTUAL INSURANCE COMPANY—See Utica National Insurance Group; *U.S. Private*, pg. 4325
UTICA NATIONAL INSURANCE CO. OF TEXAS—See Utica National Insurance Group; *U.S. Private*, pg. 4326
VERA ASSICURAZIONI S.P.A.—See Assicurazioni Generali S.p.A.; *Int'l*, pg. 648
VERA PROTEZIONE S.P.A.—See Assicurazioni Generali S.p.A.; *Int'l*, pg. 648
VERMONT MUTUAL INSURANCE CO., INC.; *U.S. Private*, pg. 4367
VICTOR INSURANCE MANAGERS INC.—See Marsh & McLennan Companies, Inc.; *U.S. Public*, pg. 1388
VIGILANT INSURANCE COMPANY—See Chubb Limited; *Int'l*, pg. 1591
VIKING BOND SERVICE, INC.—See Arthur J. Gallagher & Co.; *U.S. Public*, pg. 207
THE VILLAGES INSURANCE PARTNERS, LLC—See The Baldwin Insurance Group, Inc.; *U.S. Public*, pg. 2036
VINET HOLDINGS INC.; *U.S. Private*, pg. 4385
VIRGINIA FARM BUREAU MUTUAL INSURANCE COMPANY; *U.S. Private*, pg. 4387
VIRGINIA SURETY COMPANY, INC.—See Assurant, Inc.; *U.S. Public*, pg. 216
VOLKSWAGEN AUTOVERSICHERUNG AG—See Allianz SE; *Int'l*, pg. 356
VOLKSWAGEN FINANCIAL SERVICES COMPANIA FINANCIERA SA—See Banco Bilbao Vizcaya Argentaria, S.A.; *Int'l*, pg. 818
WALSH COUNTY MUTUAL INSURANCE COMPANY; *U.S. Private*, pg. 4432
WAPIC INSURANCE PLC—See Access Corporation; *Int'l*, pg. 89
WARRANTY SOLUTIONS MANAGEMENT CORPORATION—See Stone Point Capital LLC; *U.S. Private*, pg. 3821
WAUSAU INSURANCE CO.—See Liberty Mutual Holding Company Inc.; *U.S. Private*, pg. 2445
WAYNE COUNTY BANK; *U.S. Private*, pg. 4459
WEST BEND MUTUAL INSURANCE COMPANY INC.; *U.S. Private*, pg. 4483
WESTCHESTER FIRE INSURANCE COMPANY—See Chubb Limited; *Int'l*, pg. 1592
WESTERN DAKOTA INSURERS INC.; *U.S. Private*, pg. 4492
WESTERN FARM BUREAU SERVICE CO., INC.—See Mountain West Farm Bureau Mutual Insurance Company Inc.; *U.S. Private*, pg. 2800
WESTERN MUTUAL INSURANCE GROUP; *U.S. Private*, pg. 4494
WESTERN NATIONAL MUTUAL INSURANCE CO.; *U.S. Private*, pg. 4494
WESTERN RESERVE MUTUAL CASUALTY CO., INC.; *U.S. Private*, pg. 4496
WESTERN SURETY COMPANY—See Loews Corporation; *U.S. Public*, pg. 1340
WESTERN WORLD INSURANCE COMPANY—See American International Group, Inc.; *U.S. Public*, pg. 107
WESTFIELD INSURANCE COMPANY—See Ohio Farmers Insurance Company; *U.S. Private*, pg. 3004
WESTMINSTER AMERICAN INSURANCE COMPANY—See NI Holdings, Inc.; *U.S. Public*, pg. 1527
WEST VIRGINIA NATIONAL AUTO INSURANCE CO, INC.—See Warrior Insurance Network, Inc; *U.S. Private*, pg. 4445
WILSHIRE INSURANCE CO. INC.—See MCM Corporation; *U.S. Private*, pg. 2642
WILSON & MUIR BANCORP INC - MORTGAGE DIVISION—See Wilson & Muir Bancorp Inc; *U.S. Private*, pg. 4530
WINDHAM INJURY MANAGEMENT GROUP, INC.; *U.S. Private*, pg. 4537
WINDSOR-MOUNT JOY MUTUAL INSURANCE CO.; *U.S. Private*, pg. 4539
WISCONSIN MUTUAL INSURANCE CO.; *U.S. Private*, pg. 4548
WOLVERINE MUTUAL INSURANCE COMPANY; *U.S. Private*, pg. 4555
THE WOODLANDS FINANCIAL GROUP—See Texans Credit Union; *U.S. Private*, pg. 3974
WORKMEN'S AUTO INSURANCE COMPANY—See Mercury General Corporation; *U.S. Public*, pg. 1422
WORLDWIDE CASUALTY INSURANCE COMPANY—See American Financial Group, Inc.; *U.S. Public*, pg. 103
WRBC SUPPORT SERVICES, LLC—See W.R. Berkley Corporation; *U.S. Public*, pg. 2318
W. R. BERKLEY EUROPE AG—See W.R. Berkley Corporation; *U.S. Public*, pg. 2318
W. R. BERKLEY SPAIN, S. L. U.—See W.R. Berkley Corporation; *U.S. Public*, pg. 2318
W. R. BERKLEY SYNDICATE LIMITED—See W.R. Berkley Corporation; *U.S. Public*, pg. 2318
WRIGHT NATIONAL FLOOD INSURANCE COMPANY—See Brown & Brown, Inc.; *U.S. Public*, pg. 402
XL BERMUDA LTD.—See AXA S.A.; *Int'l*, pg. 760
XL CATLIN JAPAN KK—See AXA S.A.; *Int'l*, pg. 760
XL CATLIN MIDDLE EAST—See AXA S.A.; *Int'l*, pg. 760
XL GROUP LTD.—See AXA S.A.; *Int'l*, pg. 760
XL INNOVATE, LLC—See AXA S.A.; *Int'l*, pg. 760
XL INSURANCE COMPANY SE—See AXA S.A.; *Int'l*, pg. 760
XL INSURANCE COMPANY SE—See AXA S.A.; *Int'l*, pg. 761
XL RE EUROPE SE—See AXA S.A.; *Int'l*, pg. 761
XL REINSURANCE AMERICAN—See AXA S.A.; *Int'l*, pg. 761
XL REINSURANCE CORPORATION—See AXA S.A.; *Int'l*, pg. 761
XL RE LATIN AMERICA (ARGENTINA SA)—See AXA S.A.; *Int'l*, pg. 760
Y-RISK, LLC—See The Hartford Financial Services Group, Inc.; *U.S. Public*, pg. 2088
ZAD VICTORIA AD—See Assicurazioni Generali S.p.A.; *Int'l*, pg. 648
ZENSURANCE INC.—See The Travelers Companies, Inc.; *U.S. Public*, pg. 2136
ZEPHYR ACQUISITION COMPANY—See Heritage Insurance Holdings, Inc.; *U.S. Public*, pg. 1028
ZEPHYR INSURANCE COMPANY, INC.—See Heritage Insurance Holdings, Inc.; *U.S. Public*, pg. 1028

524127 — DIRECT TITLE INSURANCE CARRIERS

AIM UNDERWRITING LIMITED—See Allianz SE; *Int'l*, pg. 345
ALLIANZ UNDERWRITERS INSURANCE COMPANY, CORP.—See Allianz SE; *Int'l*, pg. 350
ALLIED WARRANTY LLC—See NRG Energy, Inc.; *U.S. Public*, pg. 1549
ALL NEW YORK TITLE AGENCY, INC.—See Stewart Information Services Corporation; *U.S. Public*, pg. 1947

N.A.I.C.S. INDEX

524127 — DIRECT TITLE INSURA...

AMERICAN GOVERNMENT SERVICES CORP.; *U.S. Private*, pg. 235
AMERICAN GUARANTY TITLE INSURANCE COMPANY—See Old Republic International Corporation; *U.S. Public*, pg. 1568
AN POST DIRECT LIMITED—See An Post LLC; *Int'l*, pg. 443
ARGOGLOBAL SE—See Brookfield Reinsurance Ltd.; *Int'l*, pg. 1194
ATTORNEYS' TITLE GUARANTY FUND, INC.; *U.S. Private*, pg. 383
ATTORNEYS' TITLE GUARANTY FUND, INC.—See Guaranteed Rate, Inc.; *U.S. Private*, pg. 1809
ATTORNEYS' TITLE INSURANCE FUND; *U.S. Private*, pg. 383
BAKING TECHNOLOGY SYSTEMS, INC.—See Markel Group Inc.; *U.S. Public*, pg. 1367
BDR TITLE CORPORATION—See Mercedes Homes Inc.; *U.S. Private*, pg. 2668
BROKERS TITLE, LLC—See Stewart Information Services Corporation; *U.S. Public*, pg. 1947
BURNET TITLE LLC—See Anywhere Real Estate Inc.; *U.S. Public*, pg. 142
CALIFORNIA TITLE COMPANY—See Orange Coast Title Company Inc.; *U.S. Private*, pg. 3036
CF TITLE CO.—See U.S. Bancorp; *U.S. Public*, pg. 2212
CHARTER TITLE COMPANY INC.—See Fidelity National Financial, Inc.; *U.S. Public*, pg. 831
CHICAGO TITLE AND TRUST COMPANY—See Fidelity National Financial, Inc.; *U.S. Public*, pg. 831
CHICAGO TITLE INSURANCE COMPANY—See Fidelity National Financial, Inc.; *U.S. Public*, pg. 831
CHUBB DE MEXICO, COMPANIA AFIANZADORA, S.A. DE C.V.—See Chubb Limited; *Int'l*, pg. 1591
COBRA UNDERWRITING AGENCIES LIMITED—See Apax Partners LLP; *Int'l*, pg. 505
COMMONWEALTH LAND TITLE INSURANCE COMPANY—See Fidelity National Financial, Inc.; *U.S. Public*, pg. 831
COMMONWEALTH TITLE OF DALLAS, INC.—See Fidelity National Financial, Inc.; *U.S. Public*, pg. 831
CONNECTICUT ATTORNEYS TITLE INSURANCE CO.; *U.S. Private*, pg. 1015
CRUM-HALSTED AGENCY, INC.—See New Mountain Capital, LLC; *U.S. Private*, pg. 2901
DATAQUICK TITLE LLC—See Insight Venture Management, LLC; *U.S. Private*, pg. 2089
DATAQUICK TITLE LLC—See Stone Point Capital LLC; *U.S. Private*, pg. 3822
DHI TITLE OF ARIZONA, INC.—See D.R. Horton, Inc.; *U.S. Public*, pg. 619
DHI TITLE OF MINNESOTA, INC.—See D.R. Horton, Inc.; *U.S. Public*, pg. 619
ENACT CONVEYANCING LIMITED—See First American Financial Corporation; *U.S. Public*, pg. 838
ENTITLE INSURANCE COMPANY—See Radian Group, Inc.; *U.S. Public*, pg. 1759
EQUITY TITLE CO. INC.—See Anywhere Real Estate Inc.; *U.S. Public*, pg. 142
ESSEX MANAGEMENT CORPORATION—See Essex Property Trust, Inc.; *U.S. Public*, pg. 796
EVOLVE CONSULTING GROUP INC.—See GTCR LLC; *U.S. Private*, pg. 1803
FIDELITY NATIONAL TITLE GROUP, INC.—See Fidelity National Financial, Inc.; *U.S. Public*, pg. 831
FIDELITY TITLE INSURANCE CORPORATION—See Fidelity National Financial, Inc.; *U.S. Public*, pg. 831
FIRST AMERICAN FINANCIAL CORPORATION; *U.S. Public*, pg. 835
FIRST AMERICAN NATIONAL DEFAULT TITLE SERVICES—See First American Financial Corporation; *U.S. Public*, pg. 836
FIRST AMERICAN SHOSHONE TITLE—See First American Financial Corporation; *U.S. Public*, pg. 836
FIRST AMERICAN SPECIALTY INSURANCE COMPANY—See First American Financial Corporation; *U.S. Public*, pg. 836
FIRST AMERICAN TITLE COMPANY INC.—See First American Financial Corporation; *U.S. Public*, pg. 836
FIRST AMERICAN TITLE COMPANY-NATIONAL VACATION OWNERSHIP—See First American Financial Corporation; *U.S. Public*, pg. 836
FIRST AMERICAN TITLE COMPANY OF HOT SPRINGS COUNTY—See First American Financial Corporation; *U.S. Public*, pg. 836
FIRST AMERICAN TITLE COMPANY OF IDAHO, INC.—See First American Financial Corporation; *U.S. Public*, pg. 836
FIRST AMERICAN TITLE COMPANY OF NEVADA (RENO)—See First American Financial Corporation; *U.S. Public*, pg. 836
FIRST AMERICAN TITLE COMPANY OF NEVADA—See First American Financial Corporation; *U.S. Public*, pg. 836
FIRST AMERICAN TITLE COMPANY OF OREGON—See First American Financial Corporation; *U.S. Public*, pg. 836
FIRST AMERICAN TITLE COMPANY OF OREGON—See First American Financial Corporation; *U.S. Public*, pg. 836
FIRST AMERICAN TITLE COMPANY—See First American Financial Corporation; *U.S. Public*, pg. 836
FIRST AMERICAN TITLE CO. OF SPOKANE-ESCROW OPERS—See First American Financial Corporation; *U.S. Public*, pg. 836
FIRST AMERICAN TITLE INSURANCE COMPANY OF AUSTRALIA PTY LIMITED—See First American Financial Corporation; *U.S. Public*, pg. 838
FIRST AMERICAN TITLE INSURANCE COMPANY OF NEW YORK—See First American Financial Corporation; *U.S. Public*, pg. 837
FIRST AMERICAN TITLE INSURANCE COMPANY OF TEXAS—See First American Financial Corporation; *U.S. Public*, pg. 837
FIRST AMERICAN TITLE INSURANCE COMPANY OF THE CARIBBEAN & LATIN AMERICA—See First American Financial Corporation; *U.S. Public*, pg. 837
FIRST AMERICAN TITLE INSURANCE COMPANY—See First American Financial Corporation; *U.S. Public*, pg. 836
FIRST AMERICAN TITLE INSURANCE COMPANY—See First American Financial Corporation; *U.S. Public*, pg. 836
FIRST AMERICAN TITLE INSURANCE COMPANY—See First American Financial Corporation; *U.S. Public*, pg. 836
FIRST AMERICAN TITLE INSURANCE COMPANY—See First American Financial Corporation; *U.S. Public*, pg. 836
FIRST AMERICAN TITLE INSURANCE COMPANY—See First American Financial Corporation; *U.S. Public*, pg. 837
FIRST AMERICAN TITLE INSURANCE COMPANY—See First American Financial Corporation; *U.S. Public*, pg. 837
FIRST AMERICAN TITLE INSURANCE COMPANY—See First American Financial Corporation; *U.S. Public*, pg. 837
FIRST AMERICAN TITLE INSURANCE COMPANY—See First American Financial Corporation; *U.S. Public*, pg. 837
FIRST AMERICAN TITLE INSURANCE COMPANY—See First American Financial Corporation; *U.S. Public*, pg. 837
FIRST AMERICAN TITLE INSURANCE COMPANY—See First American Financial Corporation; *U.S. Public*, pg. 837
FIRST AMERICAN TITLE INSURANCE COMPANY—See First American Financial Corporation; *U.S. Public*, pg. 837
FIRST AMERICAN TITLE INSURANCE COMPANY—See First American Financial Corporation; *U.S. Public*, pg. 837
FIRST AMERICAN TITLE INSURANCE COMPANY—See First American Financial Corporation; *U.S. Public*, pg. 837
FIRST AMERICAN TITLE INSURANCE COMPANY—See First American Financial Corporation; *U.S. Public*, pg. 837
FIRST AMERICAN TITLE INSURANCE COMPANY—See First American Financial Corporation; *U.S. Public*, pg. 837
FIRST AMERICAN TITLE INSURANCE COMPANY—See First American Financial Corporation; *U.S. Public*, pg. 837
FIRST AMERICAN TITLE—See First American Financial Corporation; *U.S. Public*, pg. 836
FIRST AMERICAN TITLE & TRUST COMPANY—See First American Financial Corporation; *U.S. Public*, pg. 836
FIRST AMERICAN VACATION OWNERSHIP SERVICES, INC.—See First American Financial Corporation; *U.S. Public*, pg. 838
FIRST HONG KONG TITLE LTD.—See First American Financial Corporation; *U.S. Public*, pg. 837
FIRST OHIO TITLE INSURANCE AGENCY, LTD.—See Stewart Information Services Corporation; *U.S. Public*, pg. 1947
FIRST TITLE INSURANCE PLC—See First American Financial Corporation; *U.S. Public*, pg. 838
FIRST TITLE PLC—See First American Financial Corporation; *U.S. Public*, pg. 837
FIRST WESTERN TITLE COMPANY—See Colonial Savings, F.A.; *U.S. Private*, pg. 972
FLORIDA AGENCY NETWORK, LLC; *U.S. Private*, pg. 1547
FNL INSURANCE COMPANY—See Wells Fargo & Company; *U.S. Public*, pg. 2343
FORWARD SETTLEMENT SOLUTIONS, INC.—See Redfin Corporation; *U.S. Public*, pg. 1770
GRAYSTONE TITLE COMPANY, LLC—See Stewart Information Services Corporation; *U.S. Public*, pg. 1947
GRS TITLE SERVICES, LLC—See Clayton, Dubilier & Rice, LLC; *U.S. Private*, pg. 927
GRS TITLE SERVICES, LLC—See Stone Point Capital LLC; *U.S. Private*, pg. 3826
GUARANTEE TITLE & TRUST COMPANY; *U.S. Private*, pg. 1809
GUARDIAN TITLE COMPANY—See Anywhere Real Estate Inc.; *U.S. Public*, pg. 142
HARDENBURGH TITLE AGENCY—See Hill-N-Dale Abstracters, Inc.; *U.S. Private*, pg. 1946
HEXTER-FAIR / FIRST AMERICAN TITLE COMPANY, LLC—See First American Financial Corporation; *U.S. Public*, pg. 838
HILL-N-DALE ABSTRACTERS, INC.; *U.S. Private*, pg. 1946
IDRECO B.V.—See Markel Group Inc.; *U.S. Public*, pg. 1368
INDEPENDENT TITLE SERVICES, INC.—See Independent Bank Corporation; *U.S. Public*, pg. 1116
INVESTORS TITLE INSURANCE COMPANY—See Investors Title Company; *U.S. Public*, pg. 1165
LANDSAFE, INC.—See Bank of America Corporation; *U.S. Public*, pg. 272
LANDWOOD TITLE CO. INC.—See Tarbell Financial Corporation; *U.S. Public*, pg. 3933
LAWLINK (UK) LTD.—See Daily Mail & General Trust plc; *Int'l*, pg. 1938
LAWYERS TITLE INSURANCE CORPORATION—See Fidelity National Financial, Inc.; *U.S. Public*, pg. 831
LAWYERS TITLE OF ARIZONA—See Fidelity National Financial, Inc.; *U.S. Public*, pg. 831
LAWYERS TITLE OF EL PASO, INC.—See Fidelity National Financial, Inc.; *U.S. Public*, pg. 831
LENDERS TITLE COMPANY—See Knox Capital Holdings, LLC; *U.S. Private*, pg. 2324
LEX TERRAE, LTD.—See Old Republic International Corporation; *U.S. Public*, pg. 1569
LIVE LETTING EXCHANGE LIMITED—See First American Financial Corporation; *U.S. Public*, pg. 838
MARKEL CANADA LIMITED—See Markel Group Inc.; *U.S. Public*, pg. 1368
MARKEL SEGURADORA DO BRASIL SA—See Markel Group Inc.; *U.S. Public*, pg. 1368
MARKEL SURETY CORPORATION—See Markel Group Inc.; *U.S. Public*, pg. 1368
MERIDIAN LAND SETTLEMENT SERVICES, LLC—See Meridian Corporation; *U.S. Public*, pg. 1424
MISSISSIPPI VALLEY TITLE INSURANCE COMPANY—See Old Republic International Corporation; *U.S. Public*, pg. 1569
MIT NATIONAL LAND SERVICES LLC—See Newmark Group, Inc.; *U.S. Public*, pg. 1515
MORRIS HARDWICK SCHNEIDER & LANDCASTLE TITLE; *U.S. Private*, pg. 2787
MORTGAGE GUARANTEE & TITLE COMPANY—See First American Financial Corporation; *U.S. Public*, pg. 837
MOTHER LODE HOLDING COMPANY—See First American Financial Corporation; *U.S. Public*, pg. 838
MOUNTAIN VIEW TITLE & ESCROW CO.—See Old Republic International Corporation; *U.S. Public*, pg. 1569
MT. SHASTA TITLE & ESCROW COMPANY—See First American Financial Corporation; *U.S. Public*, pg. 838
NATIONAL EQUITY TITLE AGENCY; *U.S. Private*, pg. 2853
NATIONAL INVESTORS TITLE INSURANCE COMPANY—See Investors Title Company; *U.S. Public*, pg. 1165
NEBRASKA TITLE COMPANY; *U.S. Private*, pg. 2879
NOBLE TITLE & TRUST—See Stock Development, LLC; *U.S. Private*, pg. 3814
NORTH AMERICAN TITLE COMPANY (MD)—See Doma Holdings, Inc.; *U.S. Public*, pg. 673
NORTH AMERICAN TITLE COMPANY OF COLORADO—See Doma Holdings, Inc.; *U.S. Public*, pg. 673
NORTH AMERICAN TITLE COMPANY—See Doma Holdings, Inc.; *U.S. Public*, pg. 673
NORTH AMERICAN TITLE INSURANCE COMPANY—See Doma Holdings, Inc.; *U.S. Public*, pg. 673
NORTH CAROLINA TITLE CENTER, LLC—See First Horizon Corporation; *U.S. Public*, pg. 844
OHIO BAR TITLE INSURANCE COMPANY—See First American Financial Corporation; *U.S. Public*, pg. 838
OLD REPUBLIC NATIONAL TITLE INSURANCE COMPANY—See Old Republic International Corporation; *U.S. Public*, pg. 1569
OLD REPUBLIC SPECIALIZED AGENCY SOLUTIONS—See Old Republic International Corporation; *U.S. Public*, pg. 1569
ORANGE COAST TITLE COMPANY OF LOS ANGELES—See Orange Coast Title Company Inc.; *U.S. Private*, pg. 3037
OSN TEXAS LLC—See Opendoor Technologies Inc.; *U.S. Public*, pg. 1606
PIONEER TITLE COMPANY OF ADA COUNTY; *U.S. Private*, pg. 3188
PIONEER TITLE COMPANY; *U.S. Private*, pg. 3188
PLACER TITLE CO. INC.—See First American Financial Corporation; *U.S. Public*, pg. 838
PRIME TITLE SERVICES, INC.—See Hometown Financial Group, Inc.; *U.S. Public*, pg. 1975
REDVISION SYSTEMS, INC; *U.S. Private*, pg. 3380

524127 — DIRECT TITLE INSURA...

REGENCY ESCROW CORPORATION—See First American Financial Corporation; *U.S. Public*, pg. 838
REPUBLIC TITLE OF TEXAS, INC.—See First American Financial Corporation; *U.S. Public*, pg. 838
THE SECURITY TITLE GUARANTEE CORP; *U.S. Private*, pg. 4115
SOUTHERN TITLE INSURANCE CORP.—See ALPS Corporation; *U.S. Private*, pg. 202
STEWART TITLE COMPANY - KISSIMMEE—See Stewart Information Services Corporation; *U.S. Public*, pg. 1948
STEWART TITLE COMPANY—See Stewart Information Services Corporation; *U.S. Public*, pg. 1948
STEWART TITLE INSURANCE AGENCY OF UTAH, INC.—See Stewart Information Services Corporation; *U.S. Public*, pg. 1948
STEWART TITLE INSURANCE COMPANY—See Stewart Information Services Corporation; *U.S. Public*, pg. 1948
STEWART TITLE OF CALIFORNIA, INC.—See Stewart Information Services Corporation; *U.S. Public*, pg. 1948
STEWART TITLE OF OKLAHOMA, INC.—See Stewart Information Services Corporation; *U.S. Public*, pg. 1948
STEWART TITLE PUERTO RICO, INC.—See Stewart Information Services Corporation; *U.S. Public*, pg. 1948
STONEBRIDGE CASUALTY INSURANCE COMPANY—See Aegon N.V.; *Int'l*, pg. 174
TEAM CONVEYANCING LIMITED—See First American Financial Corporation; *U.S. Public*, pg. 838
TEXAS AMERICAN TITLE COMPANY—See Anywhere Real Estate Inc.; *U.S. Public*, pg. 142
TEXAS ESCROW COMPANY, INC.—See First American Financial Corporation; *U.S. Public*, pg. 838
TITLE365 COMPANY—See Mr. Cooper Group Inc.; *U.S. Public*, pg. 1480
THE TITLE COMPANY OF NORTH CAROLINA—See Old Republic International Corporation; *U.S. Public*, pg. 1569
TITLE FIRST AGENCY, INC.; *U.S. Private*, pg. 4177
TITLE SECURITY AGENCY OF PINAL COUNTY, LLC—See First American Financial Corporation; *U.S. Public*, pg. 838
THE TITLE SECURITY GROUP, INC.—See First American Financial Corporation; *U.S. Public*, pg. 838
TITLE SOURCE, INC.—See RockBridge Growth Equity, LLC; *U.S. Private*, pg. 3465
TITLEVEST AGENCY, INC.—See First American Financial Corporation; *U.S. Public*, pg. 837
TOTAL TITLE SOLUTIONS, LLC—See Florida Agency Network, LLC; *U.S. Private*, pg. 1547
TRANSCOUNTY TITLE AGENCY LLC—See Heartland BancCorp; *U.S. Public*, pg. 1017
TRANSOHIO RESIDENTIAL TITLE AGENCY, LTD.—See M/I Homes, Inc.; *U.S. Public*, pg. 1351
TROMP GROUP AMERICAS, LLC—See Markel Group Inc.; *U.S. Public*, pg. 1369
UNITED TITLE OF LOUISIANA, INC.—See Knox Capital Holdings, LLC; *U.S. Private*, pg. 2324
UNIVERSITY TITLE COMPANY—See Investors Title Company; *U.S. Public*, pg. 1165
US TITLE AGENCY, INC.—See Erie Title Agency, Inc.; *U.S. Private*, pg. 1420
VIDA CAPITAL, INC.—See RedBird Capital Partners L.P.; *U.S. Private*, pg. 3377
VIDA CAPITAL, INC.—See Reverence Capital Partners LLC; *U.S. Private*, pg. 3415
WESTCOR LAND TITLE INSURANCE COMPANY—See The Orogen Group; *U.S. Private*, pg. 4089
WFG NATIONAL TITLE INSURANCE COMPANY—See Williston Financial Group, LLC; *U.S. Private*, pg. 4528
WILLISTON FINANCIAL GROUP, LLC; *U.S. Private*, pg. 4528
WISCONSIN TITLE SERVICE COMPANY, INC.—See First American Financial Corporation; *U.S. Public*, pg. 838

524128 — OTHER DIRECT INSURANCE (EXCEPT LIFE, HEALTH, AND MEDICAL) CARRIERS

2-10 HOME BUYERS WARRANTY CORP.; *U.S. Private*, pg. 4
4WARRANTY CORPORATION—See Tiptree Inc.; *U.S. Public*, pg. 2159
ADAMJEE INSURANCE COMPANY LIMITED; *Int'l*, pg. 124
ADVANCED DIGITAL DISTRIBUTION COMPANY LIMITED—See Advanced Info Service Plc; *Int'l*, pg. 159
ADVANCE PLANNING LIMITED—See Dignity plc; *Int'l*, pg. 2124
AEGON BELGIUM—See ASR Nederland N.V.; *Int'l*, pg. 632
AEGON MAGYARORSZAG ALTALANOS BIZTOSITO ZRT.—See Aegon N.V.; *Int'l*, pg. 174
AEGON NEDERLAND N.V.—See ASR Nederland N.V.; *Int'l*, pg. 632
AEROSPACE INSURANCE MANAGERS, INC.—See Hallmark Financial Services, Inc.; *U.S. Public*, pg. 981
AEROSPACE SPECIAL RISK, INC.—See Hallmark Financial Services, Inc.; *U.S. Public*, pg. 981
AFLAC INSURANCE SERVICE COMPANY, LTD.—See Aflac Incorporated; *U.S. Public*, pg. 57
AFLAC JAPAN—See Aflac Incorporated; *U.S. Public*, pg. 57
AFLAC PAYMENT SERVICE COMPANY, LTD.—See Aflac Incorporated; *U.S. Public*, pg. 57
AGF ALLIANZ CHILE COMPANIA DE SEGUROS GENERALES S.A.—See Allianz SE; *Int'l*, pg. 342
AGF BRASIL SEGUROS SA—See Allianz SE; *Int'l*, pg. 342
AIG AEROSPACE INSURANCE SERVICES, INC.—See American International Group, Inc.; *U.S. Public*, pg. 106
AIG EUROPE, SA—See American International Group, Inc.; *U.S. Public*, pg. 104
AIG LIFE INSURANCE COMPANY (SWITZERLAND) LTD.—See American International Group, Inc.; *U.S. Public*, pg. 105
AIG LIFE LIMITED—See American International Group, Inc.; *U.S. Public*, pg. 105
AIG RESSEGUROS BRASIL S.A.—See American International Group, Inc.; *U.S. Public*, pg. 106
AIG SOUTH AFRICA LIMITED—See American International Group, Inc.; *U.S. Public*, pg. 106
ALLIANZ AUSTRALIA LIMITED—See Allianz SE; *Int'l*, pg. 343
ALLIANZ BELGIUM S.A.—See Allianz SE; *Int'l*, pg. 343
ALLIANZ COMPANIA DE SEGUROS Y REASEGUROS SA—See Allianz SE; *Int'l*, pg. 344
ALLIANZ DRESDNER BAUSPAR AG—See Allianz SE; *Int'l*, pg. 344
ALLIANZ FIRE AND MARINE INSURANCE JAPAN LTD.—See Allianz SE; *Int'l*, pg. 345
ALLIANZ GENERAL INSURANCE COMPANY S.A.—See Allianz SE; *Int'l*, pg. 345
ALLIANZ INSURANCE MANAGEMENT ASIA PACIFIC PTE. LTD.—See Allianz SE; *Int'l*, pg. 344
ALLIANZ NEDERLAND ASSET MANAGEMENT B.V.—See Allianz SE; *Int'l*, pg. 349
ALLIANZ NEW ZEALAND LTD.—See Allianz SE; *Int'l*, pg. 343
ALLIANZ POJISTOVNA A/S—See Allianz SE; *Int'l*, pg. 349
ALLIANZ PORTUGAL—See Allianz SE; *Int'l*, pg. 349
ALLIANZ—See Allianz SE; *Int'l*, pg. 343
ALLIANZ VERSICHERUNGS-AG (DUBAI BRANCH)—See Allianz SE; *Int'l*, pg. 350
ALLIANZ VERSICHERUNGS-AG—See Allianz SE; *Int'l*, pg. 350
ALLIANZ VERSICHERUNGS-AG—See Allianz SE; *Int'l*, pg. 350
ALLSTATE NORTHERN IRELAND LIMITED—See The Allstate Corporation; *U.S. Public*, pg. 2033
ALPHALIFE A.A.E.Z.—See Alpha Services and Holdings S.A.; *Int'l*, pg. 369
ALPS CORPORATION; *U.S. Private*, pg. 202
ALTE LEIPZIGER AUTOVERSICHERUNG—See Alte Leipziger Versicherung AG; *Int'l*, pg. 388
ALTE LEIPZIGER VERSICHERUNG AG; *Int'l*, pg. 388
AMERICAN FINANCIAL WARRANTY CORPORATION—See Assurant, Inc.; *U.S. Public*, pg. 214
AMERICAN HALLMARK INSURANCE SERVICES, INC.—See Hallmark Financial Services, Inc.; *U.S. Public*, pg. 981
AMERICAN HOME SHIELD CORPORATION—See frontdoor, inc.; *U.S. Public*, pg. 887
AMERICAN INCOME HOLDING, INC.—See Globe Life Inc.; *U.S. Public*, pg. 946
AMERICAN INCOME LIFE INSURANCE COMPANY—See Globe Life Inc.; *U.S. Public*, pg. 946
AMERICAN LIFE INSURANCE COMPANY—See MetLife, Inc.; *U.S. Public*, pg. 1429
THE AMERICAN ROAD INSURANCE COMPANY—See Ford Motor Company; *U.S. Public*, pg. 867
AMERICAN SECURITY LIFE INSURANCE COMPANY—See American International Group, Inc.; *U.S. Public*, pg. 106
AMERICAN SHARE INSURANCE; *U.S. Private*, pg. 253
AMTRUST NORTH AMERICA—See Stone Point Capital LLC; *U.S. Private*, pg. 3820
AON HEALTHCARE—See Aon plc; *Int'l*, pg. 491
ARBELLA INDEMNITY INSURANCE CO.—See Arbella Insurance Group; *U.S. Private*, pg. 308
ARBELLA MUTUAL INSURANCE CO.—See Arbella Insurance Group; *U.S. Private*, pg. 308
ARCH INSURANCE (EU) DESIGNATED ACTIVITY COMPANY—See Arch Capital Group Ltd.; *Int'l*, pg. 546
ARDANTA N.V.—See ASR Nederland N.V.; *Int'l*, pg. 632
ASEGURADORA GENERAL S.A.; *Int'l*, pg. 605
ASPERA INSURANCE SERVICES, INC.—See Kinsale Capital Group, Inc.; *U.S. Public*, pg. 1235
ASSET MARKETING SYSTEMS INSURANCE SERVICES, LLC; *U.S. Private*, pg. 354
ASSURANT SERVICES CANADA, INC.—See Assurant, Inc.; *U.S. Public*, pg. 215
ASSURED GUARANTY CORP.—See Assured Guaranty Ltd.; *Int'l*, pg. 650
ASURANSI AXA INDONESIA—See AXA S.A.; *Int'l*, pg. 759
AVIVA CANADA INC.—See Aviva plc; *Int'l*, pg. 745
AVIVA FRANCE—See Aema Groupe; *Int'l*, pg. 175
AVIVA LIFE & PENSIONS IRELAND LTD.—See Aviva plc; *Int'l*, pg. 745
AVIVA LIFE & PENSIONS UK LIMITED—See Aviva plc; *Int'l*, pg. 746

AXA ASSICURAZIONI—See AXA S.A.; *Int'l*, pg. 754
AXA ASSISTANCE FRANCE—See AXA S.A.; *Int'l*, pg. 754
AXA ASSURANCES GABON—See AXA S.A.; *Int'l*, pg. 755
AXA ASSURANCES SENEGAL—See AXA S.A.; *Int'l*, pg. 755
AXA ASSURANCES—See AXA S.A.; *Int'l*, pg. 755
AXA ASSURANCES VIE LUXEMBOURG—See AXA S.A.; *Int'l*, pg. 755
AXA CHINA REGION LTD.—See AXA S.A.; *Int'l*, pg. 755
AXA COLONIA INSURANCE LIMITED—See AXA S.A.; *Int'l*, pg. 755
AXA CONSEIL—See AXA S.A.; *Int'l*, pg. 755
AXA CORPORATE SOLUTIONS—See AXA S.A.; *Int'l*, pg. 755
AXA COTE D'IVOIRE—See AXA S.A.; *Int'l*, pg. 755
AXA FRANCE ASSURANCE SAS—See AXA S.A.; *Int'l*, pg. 756
AXA INSURANCE PCL—See AXA S.A.; *Int'l*, pg. 756
AXA INSURANCE PTE. LTD.—See HSBC Holdings plc; *Int'l*, pg. 3506
AXA INSURANCE (SAUDI ARABIA) B.S.C.—See AXA S.A.; *Int'l*, pg. 756
AXA INVESTMENT MANAGERS UK LIMITED—See AXA S.A.; *Int'l*, pg. 756
AXA KONZERN AG—See AXA S.A.; *Int'l*, pg. 757
AXA MEDITERRANEAN HOLDING, S.A.—See AXA S.A.; *Int'l*, pg. 757
AXA PORTUGAL - COMPANHIA DE SEGUROS S.A.—See AXA S.A.; *Int'l*, pg. 758
AXA SEGUROS MEXICO—See AXA S.A.; *Int'l*, pg. 758
AXA SEGUROS URUGUAY SA—See AXA S.A.; *Int'l*, pg. 758
AXA SUN LIFE PLC—See AXA S.A.; *Int'l*, pg. 758
AXA UK PLC—See AXA S.A.; *Int'l*, pg. 758
AXA VERSICHERUNG AG—See AXA S.A.; *Int'l*, pg. 758
AXA VIE GABON—See AXA S.A.; *Int'l*, pg. 758
AXA WINTERTHUR PENSIONES—See AXA S.A.; *Int'l*, pg. 758
AXENT/AEGON N.V.—See Aegon N.V.; *Int'l*, pg. 174
AXERIA IARD S.A.—See Arch Capital Group Ltd.; *Int'l*, pg. 547
BAHRAIN KUWAIT INSURANCE COMPANY B.S.C.—See Fairfax Financial Holdings Limited; *Int'l*, pg. 2607
BAHRAIN KUWAIT INSURANCE COMPANY B.S.C.—See Fairfax Financial Holdings Limited; *Int'l*, pg. 2607
BAILLIE GIFFORD LTD.—See Baillie Gifford & Co.; *Int'l*, pg. 803
BAILLIE GIFFORD LTD.—See The Guardian Life Insurance Company of America; *U.S. Private*, pg. 4040
BALOISE ASSURANCES LUXEMBOURG S.A.—See Baloise Holding AG; *Int'l*, pg. 811
BALOISE EUROPE VIE SA—See Baloise Holding AG; *Int'l*, pg. 811
BANCO MERCEDES-BENZ DO BRASIL S.A.—See Daimler Truck Holding AG; *Int'l*, pg. 1938
BAOVIET TOKIO MARINE INSURANCE JOINT VENTURE COMPANY—See Bao Viet Holdings; *Int'l*, pg. 855
BEDFORD INSURANCE SERVICES, INC.—See Unico American Corporation; *U.S. Public*, pg. 2225
BERKLEY INTERNATIONAL ARGENTINA, S.A.—See W.R. Berkley Corporation; *U.S. Public*, pg. 2316
BERKLEY INTERNATIONAL LIFE INSURANCE COMPANY, INC.—See W.R. Berkley Corporation; *U.S. Public*, pg. 2316
BERKSHIRE HATHAWAY HOMESTATE INSURANCE COMPANY—See Berkshire Hathaway Inc.; *U.S. Public*, pg. 301
BIDV BAC BO INSURANCE COMPANY—See BIDV Insurance Corporation; *Int'l*, pg. 1019
BIDV BAC TAY NGUYEN INSURANCE COMPANY—See BIDV Insurance Corporation; *Int'l*, pg. 1019
BIDV BAC TRUNG BO INSURANCE COMPANY—See BIDV Insurance Corporation; *Int'l*, pg. 1019
BIDV BINH DINH INSURANCE COMPANY—See BIDV Insurance Corporation; *Int'l*, pg. 1019
BIDV BINH DUONG INSURANCE COMPANY—See BIDV Insurance Corporation; *Int'l*, pg. 1019
BIDV DA NANG INSURANCE COMPANY—See BIDV Insurance Corporation; *Int'l*, pg. 1019
BIDV DONG BAC INSURANCE COMPANY—See BIDV Insurance Corporation; *Int'l*, pg. 1019
BIDV HAI DUONG INSURANCE COMPANY—See BIDV Insurance Corporation; *Int'l*, pg. 1019
BIDV HAI PHONG INSURANCE COMPANY—See BIDV Insurance Corporation; *Int'l*, pg. 1019
BIDV HA NOI INSURANCE COMPANY—See BIDV Insurance Corporation; *Int'l*, pg. 1019
BIDV HO CHI MINH INSURANCE COMPANY—See BIDV Insurance Corporation; *Int'l*, pg. 1019
BIDV MIEN DONG BIDV INSURANCE COMPANY—See BIDV Insurance Corporation; *Int'l*, pg. 1019
BIDV MIEN TAY INSURANCE COMPANY—See BIDV Insurance Corporation; *Int'l*, pg. 1019
BIDV QUANG NINH INSURANCE COMPANY—See BIDV Insurance Corporation; *Int'l*, pg. 1019
BIDV SAI GON INSURANCE COMPANY—See BIDV Insurance Corporation; *Int'l*, pg. 1019
BIDV TAY BAC INSURANCE COMPANY—See BIDV Insurance Corporation; *Int'l*, pg. 1019

N.A.I.C.S. INDEX

524128 — OTHER DIRECT INSURA...

BIDV TAY NGUYEN INSURANCE COMPANY—See BIDV Insurance Corporation; *Int'l*, pg. 1019
BIDV THAI NGUYEN INSURANCE COMPANY—See BIDV Insurance Corporation; *Int'l*, pg. 1019
BIDV THANG LONG INSURANCE COMPANY—See BIDV Insurance Corporation; *Int'l*, pg. 1019
BIDV VUNG TAU INSURANCE COMPANY—See BIDV Insurance Corporation; *Int'l*, pg. 1019
BLUE SHIELD OF CALIFORNIA—See Blue Shield of California; *U.S. Private*, pg. 593
BOC WEALTH MANAGEMENT CO., LTD.—See Bank of China, Ltd.; *Int'l*, pg. 841
BONDED BUILDERS WARRANTY GROUP—See Bankers International Financial Corporation; *U.S. Private*, pg. 468
BURN & WILCOX LTD.—See H.W. Kaufman Financial Group, Inc.; *U.S. Private*, pg. 1836
CARE CONSULT VERSICHERUNGSMAKLER GMBH—See Assicurazioni Generali S.p.A.; *Int'l*, pg. 645
CAREFIRST BLUECROSS BLUESHIELD—See CareFirst, Inc.; *U.S. Private*, pg. 753
C.A.R.S. PROTECTION PLUS, INC.—See Cornell Capital LLC; *U.S. Private*, pg. 1051
CATAWBA INSURANCE COMPANY—See The Seibels Bruce Group, Inc.; *U.S. Private*, pg. 4116
CESVI FRANCE—See Groupama SA; *Int'l*, pg. 3090
CHERRY CREEK BENEFITS—See New Mountain Capital, LLC; *U.S. Private*, pg. 2901
CHIARA ASSICURAZIONI S P A—See Banco Di Desio e Della Brianza S.p.A.; *Int'l*, pg. 822
CHUBB BERMUDA INSURANCE LTD.—See Chubb Limited; *Int'l*, pg. 1590
CHUBB CUSTOM INSURANCE COMPANY—See Chubb Limited; *Int'l*, pg. 1591
CHUBB INDEMNITY INSURANCE COMPANY—See Chubb Limited; *Int'l*, pg. 1591
CHUBB INSURANCE COMPANY OF CANADA—See Chubb Limited; *Int'l*, pg. 1591
C.J. COLEMAN & COMPANY LIMITED; *Int'l*, pg. 1243
CNA INSURANCE COMPANIES—See Loews Corporation; *U.S. Public*, pg. 1339
COLEMAN & LARGE LTD.—See C.J. Coleman & Company Limited; *Int'l*, pg. 1243
CONCOURSE FINANCIAL GROUP AGENCY, INC.—See Dai-ichi Life Holdings, Inc.; *Int'l*, pg. 1917
THE CONTINENTAL INSURANCE COMPANY OF NEW JERSEY—See Loews Corporation; *U.S. Public*, pg. 1340
CO-OPERATIVE INSURANCE SOCIETY LIMITED; *Int'l*, pg. 1679
COUNTRY PREFERRED INSURANCE COMPANY—See COUNTRY Financial; *U.S. Private*, pg. 1067
COVENTRY BUILDING SOCIETY; *Int'l*, pg. 1820
CRUM & FORSTER PET INSURANCE GROUP—See Fairfax Financial Holdings Limited; *U.S. Public*, pg. 2606
CUNA CARIBBEAN INSURANCE SOCIETY LIMITED—See CMFG Life Insurance Company; *U.S. Public*, pg. 950
CYPRESS CARE, INC.—See UnitedHealth Group Incorporated; *U.S. Public*, pg. 2247
DAIMLER TRUCK FINANCIAL SERVICES BELGIUM N.V.—See Daimler Truck Holding AG; *Int'l*, pg. 1938
DAIMLER TRUCK FINANCIAL SERVICES CANADA CORPORATION—See Daimler Truck Holding AG; *Int'l*, pg. 1938
DAIMLER TRUCK FINANCIAL SERVICES ITALIA S.P.A.—See Daimler Truck Holding AG; *Int'l*, pg. 1938
DAIMLER TRUCK FINANCIAL SERVICES NEDERLAND B.V.—See Daimler Truck Holding AG; *Int'l*, pg. 1938
DAIMLER TRUCK FINANCIAL SERVICES UK LIMITED—See Daimler Truck Holding AG; *Int'l*, pg. 1938
DAIMLER TRUCK NEDERLAND B.V.—See Daimler Truck Holding AG; *Int'l*, pg. 1938
DEALERS ALLIANCE CORPORATION; *U.S. Private*, pg. 1182
DE AMERSFOORTSE VERZEKERINGEN N.V.—See ASR Nederland N.V.; *Int'l*, pg. 632
DIRECT ASIA (THAILAND) CO., LTD.—See Hiscox Ltd.; *Int'l*, pg. 3407
DIRECT ASSURANCE—See AXA S.A.; *Int'l*, pg. 759
DIRECT LINE INSURANCE PLC—See Direct Line Insurance Group plc; *Int'l*, pg. 2129
THE DOCTORS COMPANY; *U.S. Private*, pg. 4021
D.R. HORTON INSURANCE AGENCY, INC.—See D.R. Horton, Inc.; *U.S. Public*, pg. 619
DUAL DEUTSCHLAND GMBH—See Howden Group Holdings Limited; *Int'l*, pg. 3493
DUAL INTERNATIONAL LIMITED—See Howden Group Holdings Limited; *Int'l*, pg. 3493
DUAL ITALIA S.P.A—See Howden Group Holdings Limited; *Int'l*, pg. 3493
DUAL SPECIALTY UNDERWRITERS INC.—See Howden Group Holdings Limited; *Int'l*, pg. 3493
DUAL UNDERWRITING AGENCY (HONG KONG) LIMITED—See Howden Group Holdings Limited; *Int'l*, pg. 3493
DUAL UNDERWRITING AGENCY (SINGAPORE) PTE. LIMITED—See Howden Group Holdings Limited; *Int'l*, pg. 3493
ELITE UNDERWRITING LIMITED—See Highway Insurance Holdings Plc; *Int'l*, pg. 3389

ELSEY & ASSOCIATES SURETY INSURANCE AGENCY, INC.—See Marsh & McLennan Companies, Inc.; *U.S. Public*, pg. 1380
EMIRATES INSURANCE COMPANY; *Int'l*, pg. 2381
ENTERPRISE FINANCIAL GROUP, INC.; *U.S. Private*, pg. 1403
EULER HERMES CREDIT INSURANCE NORDIC AB—See Allianz SE; *Int'l*, pg. 352
EURO ACCIDENT LIVFORSAKRING AB—See The Allstate Corporation; *U.S. Public*, pg. 2033
EUROAMERICA SEGUROS DE VIDA, S.A.; *Int'l*, pg. 2532
EUROMEX N.V.—See Baloise Holding AG; *Int'l*, pg. 811
EUROPA-GAN BIZTOSITO—See Groupama SA; *Int'l*, pg. 3090
EUROPAISCHE REISEVERSICHERUNGS AG—See Assicurazioni Generali S.p.A.; *Int'l*, pg. 645
EUROPAI UTAZASI BIZTOSITO RT.—See Assicurazioni Generali S.p.A.; *Int'l*, pg. 645
EUROPEENNE DE PROTECTION JURIDIQUE S.A.—See Assicurazioni Generali S.p.A.; *Int'l*, pg. 644
EVERGREEN NATIONAL INDEMNITY CO.—See ProAlliance Corporation; *U.S. Public*, pg. 3271
FARADAY REINSURANCE COMPANY LTD.—See Berkshire Hathaway Inc.; *U.S. Public*, pg. 301
FARADAY UNDERWRITING LIMITED—See Berkshire Hathaway Inc.; *U.S. Public*, pg. 301
FEDERAL DEPOSIT INSURANCE CORPORATION; *U.S. Private*, pg. 1487
FEDERATED INSURANCE COMPANY OF CANADA—See Fairfax Financial Holdings Limited; *Int'l*, pg. 2607
FFVA MUTUAL INSURANCE CO.; *U.S. Private*, pg. 1500
FIDELIDADE - COMPANHIA DE SEGUROS SA—See Fosun International Limited; *Int'l*, pg. 2751
FIRST ACCEPTANCE CORPORATION; *U.S. Public*, pg. 835
FIRST AMERICAN HOME BUYERS PROTECTION CORPORATION—See First American Financial Corporation; *U.S. Public*, pg. 836
FIRST AMERICAN VEHICLE TITLE INSURANCE—See First American Financial Corporation; *U.S. Public*, pg. 837
FIRST TRENTON INDEMNITY CO.—See The Travelers Companies, Inc.; *U.S. Public*, pg. 4116
FORTUNA RECHTSSCHUTZ-VERSICHERUNG-GESELLSCHAFT AG—See Assicurazioni Generali S.p.A.; *Int'l*, pg. 644
FP MARINE RISKS (AUSTRALIA) PTY LIMITED—See Howden Group Holdings Limited; *Int'l*, pg. 3493
FP MARINE RISKS LIMITED—See Howden Group Holdings Limited; *Int'l*, pg. 3493
GAN PACIFIQUE—See Groupama SA; *Int'l*, pg. 3090
GAN PACIFIQUE—See Groupama SA; *Int'l*, pg. 3090
GENERALI ASIGURARI S.A.—See Assicurazioni Generali S.p.A.; *Int'l*, pg. 645
GENERALI ASSURANCES GENERALES—See Assicurazioni Generali S.p.A.; *Int'l*, pg. 644
GENERALI BELGIUM S.A.—See Apollo Global Management, Inc.; *U.S. Public*, pg. 147
GENERALI ECUADOR COMPANIA DE SEGUROS S.A.—See Assicurazioni Generali S.p.A.; *Int'l*, pg. 644
GENERALI FRANCE ASSURANCES S.A.—See Assicurazioni Generali S.p.A.; *Int'l*, pg. 644
GENERALI HELLAS A.E.A.Z. PROPERTY & CASUALTY INSURANCE CO.—See Assicurazioni Generali S.p.A.; *Int'l*, pg. 645
GENERALI LEBENSVERSICHERUNG AG—See Cinven Limited; *Int'l*, pg. 1616
GENERALI POJISTOVNA A.S.—See Assicurazioni Generali S.p.A.; *Int'l*, pg. 646
GENERALI PROVIDENCIA BIZTOSITO RT.—See Assicurazioni Generali S.p.A.; *Int'l*, pg. 646
GENERALI (SCHWEIZ) HOLDING AG—See Assicurazioni Generali S.p.A.; *Int'l*, pg. 644
GENERALI SIGORTA A.S.—See Assicurazioni Generali S.p.A.; *Int'l*, pg. 647
GENERALI SLOVENSKO POIST'OVNA A.S.—See Assicurazioni Generali S.p.A.; *Int'l*, pg. 646
GENERTEL S.P.A.—See Assicurazioni Generali S.p.A.; *Int'l*, pg. 647
GENWORTH FINANCIAL CANADA—See Genworth Financial, Inc.; *U.S. Public*, pg. 933
THE GIBRALTAR LIFE INSURANCE COMPANY, LTD.—See Prudential Financial, Inc.; *U.S. Public*, pg. 1733
GIE BNP PARIBAS CARDIF S.A.—See BNP Paribas SA; *Int'l*, pg. 1083
GORAN CAPITAL INC.; *Int'l*, pg. 3042
GREENVAL INSURANCE DAC—See BNP Paribas SA; *Int'l*, pg. 1091
GROUPAMA ASSURANCES ET SERVICES—See Groupama SA; *Int'l*, pg. 3090
GROUPAMA GAN VIE—See Groupama SA; *Int'l*, pg. 3090
GROUPAMA INSURANCE (CHINA) LTD—See Groupama SA; *Int'l*, pg. 3091
GROUPAMA SEGUROS PORTUGAL—See Groupama SA; *Int'l*, pg. 3091
GROUPAMA VIE BENIN—See Groupama SA; *Int'l*, pg. 3091
GRUPPO GENERALI SERVIZI S.R.L.—See Assicurazioni Generali S.p.A.; *Int'l*, pg. 647

GULF INSURANCE GROUP (GIG) GULF—See AXA S.A.; *Int'l*, pg. 759
GUNES SIGORTA—See Groupama SA; *Int'l*, pg. 3091
HALLMARK FINANCIAL SERVICES, INC.; *U.S. Public*, pg. 981
HARWORTH INSURANCE COMPANY LIMITED—See Harworth Group plc; *Int'l*, pg. 3282
HELVETIA ASSURANCES S.A. - LE HAVRE—See Helvetia Holding AG; *Int'l*, pg. 3339
HENDRICKS & CO GMBH—See Howden Group Holdings Limited; *Int'l*, pg. 3493
HILO DIRECT SEGUROS Y REASEGUROS S.A.—See AXA S.A.; *Int'l*, pg. 757
HISCOX LTD.; *Int'l*, pg. 3406
HOKUDEN KOGYO—See Hokkaido Electric Power Co., Inc.; *Int'l*, pg. 3443
HOLLARD SPECIALIST INSURANCE LIMITED—See Hollard Insurance Company Ltd; *Int'l*, pg. 3451
HOME SECURITY OF AMERICA, INC.—See frontdoor, inc.; *U.S. Public*, pg. 887
HOME WARRANTY OF AMERICA, INC.—See NRG Energy, Inc.; *U.S. Public*, pg. 1549
HOWDEN FORSIKRINGSMEGLING AS—See Howden Group Holdings Limited; *Int'l*, pg. 3493
HOWDEN INSURANCE BROKERS AB—See Howden Group Holdings Limited; *Int'l*, pg. 3494
HOWDEN INSURANCE BROKERS LIMITED—See Howden Group Holdings Limited; *Int'l*, pg. 3494
HOWDEN INSURANCE BROKERS (S.) PTE. LIMITED—See Howden Group Holdings Limited; *Int'l*, pg. 3494
THE INSURANCE COMPANY OF THE STATE OF PENNSYLVANIA—See American International Group, Inc.; *U.S. Public*, pg. 107
INTEGON SERVICE CO, S.A. DE C.V.—See The Allstate Corporation; *U.S. Public*, pg. 2033
INTERSTATE NATIONAL DEALER SERVICES, INC.—See Dai-ichi Life Holdings, Inc.; *Int'l*, pg. 1917
INVESTORS HERITAGE CAPITAL CORP.; *U.S. Private*, pg. 2132
IPET INSURANCE CO., LTD.—See Dream Incubator Inc.; *Int'l*, pg. 2202
JURIDICA—See AXA S.A.; *Int'l*, pg. 759
KAPLANSKY INSURANCE AGENCY, INC.; *U.S. Private*, pg. 2261
KINGSWAY AMERICA INC.—See Kingsway Financial Services Inc.; *U.S. Public*, pg. 1234
KINSALE BROKERS LIMITED—See Enstar Group Limited; *Int'l*, pg. 2449
KIRBY OCEAN TRANSPORT CO. - HOUSTON OFFICE—See Kirby Corporation; *U.S. Public*, pg. 1236
THE KYOEI ANNUITY HOME CO., LTD.—See Prudential Financial, Inc.; *U.S. Public*, pg. 1733
THE KYOEI BUILDING MANAGEMENT CO., LTD.—See Prudential Financial, Inc.; *U.S. Public*, pg. 1733
LANCET INDEMNITY RISK RETENTION GROUP, INC.; *U.S. Private*, pg. 2382
LAVARETUS UNDERWRITING AB—See Marsh & McLennan Companies, Inc.; *U.S. Public*, pg. 1377
LAWLEY AUTOMOTIVE—See Lawley Service Inc.; *U.S. Private*, pg. 2401
LEE & ASSOCIATES COMMERCIAL REAL ESTATE; *U.S. Private*, pg. 2411
L'EQUITE COMPAGNIE D'ASSURANCES ET DE REASSURANCES CONTRE LES RISQUES DE TOUTE NATURE S.A.—See Assicurazioni Generali S.p.A.; *Int'l*, pg. 645
LIBRA INSURANCE SERVICES LIMITED—See Marsh & McLennan Companies, Inc.; *U.S. Public*, pg. 1377
LIFESTYLE SERVICES GROUP LIMITED—See Assurant, Inc.; *U.S. Public*, pg. 215
LLOYD ADRIATICO S.P.A.—See Allianz SE; *Int'l*, pg. 354
LOCKTON COMPANIES LLP - BIRMINGHAM—See The Lockton Companies, LLC; *U.S. Private*, pg. 4071
LOCKTON COMPANIES LLP - MANCHESTER—See The Lockton Companies, LLC; *U.S. Private*, pg. 4071
LONDON GENERAL INSURANCE COMPANY LIMITED—See Assurant, Inc.; *U.S. Public*, pg. 215
LUBRICO WARRANTY INC.—See iA Financial Corporation Inc.; *Int'l*, pg. 3568
LYNDON PROPERTY INSURANCE COMPANY—See Dai-ichi Life Holdings, Inc.; *Int'l*, pg. 1917
MARKEL INSURANCE S.E.—See Markel Group Inc.; *U.S. Public*, pg. 1368
MARSH MANAGEMENT SERVICES (BERMUDA) LTD.—See Marsh & McLennan Companies, Inc.; *U.S. Public*, pg. 1379
MARSH MANAGEMENT SERVICES (CAYMAN) LTD.—See Marsh & McLennan Companies, Inc.; *U.S. Public*, pg. 1379
MARSH PTY LTD—See Marsh & McLennan Companies, Inc.; *U.S. Public*, pg. 1379
MARSH UK LIMITED—See Marsh & McLennan Companies, Inc.; *U.S. Public*, pg. 1380
MCKINLEY FINANCIAL SERVICES, INC.; *U.S. Private*, pg. 2639
MENZIS—See Allianz SE; *Int'l*, pg. 354

524128 — OTHER DIRECT INSURA...

MONDIAL ASSISTANCE BRAZIL—See Allianz SE; *Int'l*, pg. 354
MONDIAL ASSISTANCE FRANCE—See Allianz SE; *Int'l*, pg. 354
MONITOR LIABILITY MANAGERS, INC.—See W.R. Berkley Corporation; *U.S. Public*, pg. 2318
MUTUAIDE ASSISTANCE—See Groupama SA; *Int'l*, pg. 3091
MUTUELLE SAINT-CHRISTOPHE—See AXA S.A.; *Int'l*, pg. 759
NATIONAL GENERAL MOTOR CLUB, INC.—See The Allstate Corporation; *U.S. Public*, pg. 2034
NATIONAL INSURANCE AND GUARANTEE CORPORATION LIMITED—See Direct Line Insurance Group plc; *Int'l*, pg. 2130
NATIONAL TRUCK PROTECTION CO, INC.—See Kinderhook Industries, LLC; *U.S. Private*, pg. 2307
NAU CA CROP INS—See NAU Holding Company; *U.S. Private*, pg. 2868
THE NAVAKIJ INSURANCE CO., LTD.—See Allianz SE; *Int'l*, pg. 356
NETCOMP INSURANCE CORP.—See Marsh & McLennan Companies, Inc.; *U.S. Public*, pg. 1386
NEW ENERGY RISK, INC.—See AXA S.A.; *Int'l*, pg. 760
NEW YORK LIFE ANNUITY INC—See New York Life Insurance Company; *U.S. Private*, pg. 2910
NEW YORK LIFE INC—See New York Life Insurance Company; *U.S. Private*, pg. 2910
NEW YORK LIFE INSURANCE & ANNUITY CORPORATION—See New York Life Insurance Company; *U.S. Private*, pg. 2910
NEW YORK LIFE LONG TERM CARE INSURANCE—See New York Life Insurance Company; *U.S. Private*, pg. 2911
NORTH AMERICAN COMPANY FOR LIFE & HEALTH INSURANCE—See Sammons Enterprises, Inc.; *U.S. Private*, pg. 3537
N.V. NATIONALE BORG-MAATSCHAPPIJ—See Egeria Capital Management B.V.; *Int'l*, pg. 2323
N.V. NATIONALE BORG-MAATSCHAPPIJ—See HAL Trust N.V.; *Int'l*, pg. 3224
OAKFIRST LIFE INSURANCE CORPORATION—See First United Corporation; *U.S. Public*, pg. 848
OLD REPUBLIC HOME PROTECTION COMPANY, INC.—See Old Republic International Corporation; *U.S. Public*, pg. 1568
ORIENTAL LIFE INSURANCE CULTURAL DEVELOPMENT CENTER—See Prudential Financial, Inc.; *U.S. Public*, pg. 1733
ORIENT TAKAFUL PJSC—See Abu Dhabi Commercial Bank PJSC; *Int'l*, pg. 71
PATRIOT NATIONAL, INC.; *U.S. Public*, pg. 3110
PATRONS OXFORD INSURANCE COMPANY—See Quincy Mutual Fire Insurance Company; *U.S. Public*, pg. 3327
PENN WARRANTY CORPORATION; *U.S. Public*, pg. 3135
PETPARTNERS, INC.; *U.S. Private*, pg. 3161
PET PLAN LTD.—See Allianz SE; *Int'l*, pg. 355
THE PHILIPPINE AMERICAN LIFE & GENERAL INSURANCE COMPANY—See AIA Group Limited; *Int'l*, pg. 227
PLATINUM WARRANTY CORPORATION; *U.S. Private*, pg. 3210
PLYMOUTH ROCK ASSURANCE; *U.S. Private*, pg. 3216
PREFERRED WARRANTIES, INC.—See OPENLANE, Inc.; *U.S. Public*, pg. 1607
PRESENCE VERTE SA—See Groupama SA; *Int'l*, pg. 3091
PRINCIPAL INTERNATIONAL ARGENTINA, S.A.—See Principal Financial Group, Inc.; *U.S. Public*, pg. 1721
PROGRESSIVE NORTHERN INSURANCE COMPANY—See The Progressive Corporation; *U.S. Public*, pg. 2125
PRUCO LIFE INSURANCE COMPANY—See Prudential Financial, Inc.; *U.S. Public*, pg. 1733
P.T. ASURANSI ALLIANZ LIFE INDONESIA—See Allianz SE; *Int'l*, pg. 355
P.T. ASURANSI ALLIANZ UTAMA INDONESIA—See Allianz SE; *Int'l*, pg. 355
RAS TUTELA GIUDIZIARIA S.P.A.—See Allianz SE; *Int'l*, pg. 350
RECHTSSCHUTZ UNION VERSICHERUNGS-AG—See Alte Leipziger Versicherung AG; *Int'l*, pg. 388
RELEVANT MARKETING (HK) LIMITED—See Great Wall Terroir Holdings Limited; *Int'l*, pg. 3066
REPUBLIC INDEMNITY COMPANY OF AMERICA—See American Financial Group, Inc.; *U.S. Public*, pg. 103
REPUBLIC MORTGAGE INSURANCE COMPANY—See Arch Capital Group Ltd.; *Int'l*, pg. 546
RESOURCE AUTOMOTIVE, INC.—See Assurant, Inc.; *U.S. Public*, pg. 215
SETTLEMENT PLANNERS INC.; *U.S. Private*, pg. 3618
SGI CANADA INSURANCE SERVICES LTD.—See Crown Investments Corporation of Saskatchewan; *Int'l*, pg. 1857
SHELBOURNE GROUP LIMITED—See Enstar Group Limited; *Int'l*, pg. 2449
SOCIETE TUNISIENNE D'ASSURANCES ET DE REASSURANCES—See Groupama SA; *Int'l*, pg. 3091
SONSIO, LLC—See SimpleTire, LLC; *U.S. Private*, pg. 3667
SQUAREMOUTH INC.—See Hellman & Friedman LLC; *U.S. Private*, pg. 1909

SQUARETRADE HOLDING COMPANY, INC.—See The Allstate Corporation; *U.S. Public*, pg. 2034
SQUARETRADE LIMITED—See The Allstate Corporation; *U.S. Public*, pg. 2034
STARNET INSURANCE COMPANY—See W.R. Berkley Corporation; *U.S. Public*, pg. 2318
STATE FARM GUARANTY INSURANCE COMPANY—See State Farm Mutual Automobile Insurance Company; *U.S. Private*, pg. 3792
STATE FARM LLOYDS, INC.—See State Farm Mutual Automobile Insurance Company; *U.S. Private*, pg. 3792
ST. HILAIRE AG INSURANCE, INC.—See CHS INC.; *U.S. Public*, pg. 492
STRUCSURE HOME WARRANTY, LLC—See Milestone Partners Ltd.; *U.S. Private*, pg. 2729
THRIVUR HEALTH, LLC—See Corecivic, Inc.; *U.S. Public*, pg. 577
TOUCHSTONE SECURITIES, INC.—See Western & Southern Financial Group, Inc.; *U.S. Private*, pg. 4490
TRAVEL CARE INC.—See Allianz SE; *Int'l*, pg. 356
TRUPANION, INC.; *U.S. Public*, pg. 2201
TWG REPAIR SERVICES (SHANGHAI) CO., LTD.—See Assurant, Inc.; *U.S. Public*, pg. 215
TWG SERVICES LIMITED—See Assurant, Inc.; *U.S. Public*, pg. 215
UAT—See AXA S.A.; *Int'l*, pg. 759
U A VIE—See AXA S.A.; *Int'l*, pg. 759
UGAR—See AXA S.A.; *Int'l*, pg. 759
UMS-GENERALI MARINE S.P.A.—See Assicurazioni Generali S.p.A.; *Int'l*, pg. 648
UNION BERKLEY, COMPANIA DE SEGUROS S.A.—See W.R. Berkley Corporation; *U.S. Public*, pg. 2318
UNITED FINANCIAL CASUALTY COMPANY—See The Progressive Corporation; *U.S. Public*, pg. 2125
UNITED FIRE GROUP, INC.; *U.S. Public*, pg. 2230
UNITRIN COUNTY MUTUAL INSURANCE COMPANY—See Kemper Corporation; *U.S. Public*, pg. 1221
UNUM ZYCIE TOWARZYSTWO UBEZPIECZEN I REASEKURACJI SPOLKA AKCYJNA—See Unum Group; *U.S. Public*, pg. 2263
THE VARIABLE ANNUITY LIFE INSURANCE COMPANY—See American International Group, Inc.; *U.S. Public*, pg. 105
VESTED HEALTH LLC; *U.S. Private*, pg. 4373
WARRANTECH CONSUMER PRODUCT SERVICES GROUP—See Stone Point Capital LLC; *U.S. Private*, pg. 3821
WARRANTECH CORPORATION—See Stone Point Capital LLC; *U.S. Private*, pg. 3821
WARRANTECH DIRECT, INC.—See Stone Point Capital LLC; *U.S. Private*, pg. 3821
WARRANTY CORPORATION AMERICA; *U.S. Private*, pg. 4443
WELCOME FUNDS, INC.; *U.S. Private*, pg. 4473
WESTERN SERVICE CONTRACT CORP.—See The McGraw Group; *U.S. Private*, pg. 4076
WHITE EAGLE ASSURANCE COMPANY—See Helmerich & Payne, Inc.; *U.S. Public*, pg. 1024
WINDSOR LIFE ASSURANCE LTD.—See New York Life Insurance Company; *U.S. Private*, pg. 2911
WINTERTHUR INSURANCE CO—See AXA S.A.; *Int'l*, pg. 758
WINTERTHUR LIFE & PENSIONS AG—See AXA S.A.; *Int'l*, pg. 758
XL INSURANCE ARGENTINA S.A.—See AXA S.A.; *Int'l*, pg. 760
XL INSURANCE COMPANY LIMITED—See AXA S.A.; *Int'l*, pg. 760
XL INSURANCE SWITZERLAND—See AXA S.A.; *Int'l*, pg. 761

524130 — REINSURANCE CARRIERS

ACUMEN RE MANAGEMENT CORPORATION—See Brown & Brown, Inc.; *U.S. Public*, pg. 396
ADNIC INTERNATIONAL LTD.—See Abu Dhabi National Insurance Company; *Int'l*, pg. 72
AGCS DUBAI—See Allianz SE; *Int'l*, pg. 345
ALLIANZ RE DUBLIN LTD.—See Allianz SE; *Int'l*, pg. 351
ALLSTATE LIFE INSURANCE COMPANY—See The Allstate Corporation; *U.S. Public*, pg. 2032
ALPHA CONSULTANTS LIMITED—See Marsh & McLennan Companies, Inc.; *U.S. Public*, pg. 1374
AMERICAN CONCEPT INSURANCE COMPANY—See Enstar Group Limited; *Int'l*, pg. 2448
AMERICAN INTERNATIONAL REINSURANCE COMPANY, LTD.—See American International Group, Inc.; *U.S. Public*, pg. 106
AMP SUPERANNUATION (NZ) LIMITED—See AMP Limited; *Int'l*, pg. 432
ANNUITY & LIFE REASSURANCE, LTD.—See Annuity & Life Re (Holdings), Ltd.; *Int'l*, pg. 474
AON BENFIELD INC—See Aon plc; *Int'l*, pg. 489
AON BENFIELD LIMITED—See Aon plc; *Int'l*, pg. 489
AON BENFIELD (NEW ZEALAND) LTD.—See Aon plc; *Int'l*, pg. 489

AON BENFIELD PTE. LTD.—See Aon plc; *Int'l*, pg. 490
AON BENFIELD PTY. LTD.—See Aon plc; *Int'l*, pg. 490
AON BENFIELD S.A. DE C.V.—See Aon plc; *Int'l*, pg. 490
AON BENFIELD (SOUTH AFRICA) PTY LTD.—See Aon plc; *Int'l*, pg. 489
ARCH CAPITAL GROUP (U.S.) INC.—See Arch Capital Group Ltd.; *Int'l*, pg. 546
ARCH INSURANCE (UK) LIMITED—See Arch Capital Group Ltd.; *Int'l*, pg. 546
ARCH RE ACCIDENT & HEALTH APS—See Arch Capital Group Ltd.; *Int'l*, pg. 546
ARCH RE FACULTATIVE UNDERWRITERS INC.—See Arch Capital Group Ltd.; *Int'l*, pg. 546
ARCH REINSURANCE EUROPE UNDERWRITING LIMITED—See Arch Capital Group Ltd.; *Int'l*, pg. 546
ARCH SOLUTIONS AGENCY LLC—See Reinsurance Group of America, Inc.; *U.S. Public*, pg. 1777
ARCH UNDERWRITING AGENCY (AUSTRALIA) PTY. LTD.—See Arch Capital Group Ltd.; *Int'l*, pg. 546
ARCH UNDERWRITING AT LLOYD'S (AUSTRALIA) PTY LTD—See Arch Capital Group Ltd.; *Int'l*, pg. 547
ARGOGLOBAL UNDERWRITING ASIA PACIFIC PTE LTD.—See Brookfield Reinsurance Ltd.; *Int'l*, pg. 1194
ARGO GROUP US, INC.—See Brookfield Reinsurance Ltd.; *Int'l*, pg. 1193
ARIG CAPITAL LIMITED—See Arab Insurance Group B.S.C.; *Int'l*, pg. 530
ASPEN RISK MANAGEMENT LIMITED—See Apollo Global Management, Inc.; *U.S. Public*, pg. 147
ASSURED GUARANTY RE LTD.—See Assured Guaranty Ltd.; *Int'l*, pg. 649
ATHENE LIFE RE LTD.—See Apollo Global Management, Inc.; *U.S. Public*, pg. 147
ATHORA HOLDING LTD.—See Apollo Global Management, Inc.; *U.S. Public*, pg. 147
AXA ASSURANCES LUXEMBOURG S.A.—See AXA S.A.; *Int'l*, pg. 755
AXA CORPORATE SOLUTIONS LIFE REINSURANCE COMPANY—See Equitable Holdings, Inc.; *U.S. Public*, pg. 788
AXA FRANCE IARD—See AXA S.A.; *Int'l*, pg. 756
AXA GLOBAL RE SA—See AXA S.A.; *Int'l*, pg. 756
AXA INSURANCE—See Equitable Holdings, Inc.; *U.S. Public*, pg. 788
AXA LIABILITIES MANAGERS BELGIUM—See AXA S.A.; *Int'l*, pg. 757
AXA LIABILITIES MANAGERS UK LIMITED—See AXA S.A.; *Int'l*, pg. 757
AXA XL GROUP LTD.—See AXA S.A.; *Int'l*, pg. 759
BALLANTYNE MCKEAN & SULLIVAN LTD.—See BMS Group Ltd.; *Int'l*, pg. 1077
BALOISE INSURANCE COMPANY (I.O.M.) LTD.—See Baloise Holding AG; *Int'l*, pg. 811
BARBICAN REINSURANCE COMPANY LIMITED—See Arch Capital Group Ltd.; *Int'l*, pg. 547
BBPS LIMITED—See Brown & Brown, Inc.; *U.S. Public*, pg. 397
BDB LIMITED—See Brown & Brown, Inc.; *U.S. Public*, pg. 397
BENEFICIOS INTEGRALES OPORTUNOS SA—See Marsh & McLennan Companies, Inc.; *U.S. Public*, pg. 1374
BERKLEY RE AMERICA, LLC—See W.R. Berkley Corporation; *U.S. Public*, pg. 2317
BERKLEY RE SOLUTIONS—See W.R. Berkley Corporation; *U.S. Public*, pg. 2317
BERKLEY RE UK LIMITED—See W.R. Berkley Corporation; *U.S. Public*, pg. 2317
BMO REINSURANCE LIMITED—See Bank of Montreal; *Int'l*, pg. 846
BMS GROUP LTD.; *Int'l*, pg. 1077
BMS RE LTD.—See BMS Group Ltd.; *Int'l*, pg. 1077
BROOKFIELD REINSURANCE LTD.; *Int'l*, pg. 1193
CALPE INSURANCE COMPANY LIMITED—See Berkshire Hathaway Inc.; *U.S. Public*, pg. 299
CANOPIUS BERMUDA LIMITED—See Centerbridge Partners, L.P.; *U.S. Private*, pg. 813
CASTLEWOOD REINSURANCE COMPANY—See Reinsurance Group of America, Inc.; *U.S. Public*, pg. 1777
CENTRAL REINSURANCE CORPORATION; *Int'l*, pg. 1409
CENTRAL SECURITY LIFE INSURANCE CO.—See Maximum Corporation; *U.S. Private*, pg. 2618
CHAUCER MENA LIMITED—See China Reinsurance (Group) Corporation; *Int'l*, pg. 1547
CHINA LIFE REINSURANCE COMPANY LTD.—See China Reinsurance (Group) Corporation; *Int'l*, pg. 1547
CHINA RE NEW YORK LIAISON OFFICE INC.—See China Reinsurance (Group) Corporation; *Int'l*, pg. 1547
CHINA RE UK LIMITED—See China Reinsurance (Group) Corporation; *Int'l*, pg. 1547
CHUBB RE, INC.—See Chubb Limited; *Int'l*, pg. 1591
CHUBB REINSURANCE (SWITZERLAND) LIMITED—See Chubb Limited; *Int'l*, pg. 1592
CHUBB TEMPEST LIFE REINSURANCE LIMITED—See Chubb Limited; *Int'l*, pg. 1591
CHUBB TEMPEST LIFE RE - USA—See Chubb Limited; *Int'l*, pg. 1592
CHUBB TEMPEST RE GROUP—See Chubb Limited; *Int'l*, pg. 1591

N.A.I.C.S. INDEX

524130 — REINSURANCE CARRIER...

CHUBB TEMPEST REINSURANCE LTD.—See Chubb Limited; *Int'l*, pg. 1591
CHUBB TEMPEST RE USA LLC—See Chubb Limited; *Int'l*, pg. 1592
CIBC REINSURANCE COMPANY LIMITED—See Canadian Imperial Bank of Commerce; *Int'l*, pg. 1283
CLEARWATER SELECT INSURANCE COMPANY—See Fairfax Financial Holdings Limited; *Int'l*, pg. 2607
COFACE ASSICURAZIONI S.P.A.—See Coface S.A.; *Int'l*, pg. 1691
COFACE KREDITVERSICHERUNG AG—See Coface S.A.; *Int'l*, pg. 1691
COFACE NORTH AMERICA INSURANCE COMPANY, INC.—See Coface S.A.; *Int'l*, pg. 1691
COLONY SPECIALTY INSURANCE COMPANY—See Brookfield Reinsurance Ltd.; *Int'l*, pg. 1194
COMMONWEALTH ANNUITY & LIFE INSURANCE COMPANY—See KKR & Co. Inc.; *U.S. Public*, pg. 1251
CRANMORE (US) INC.—See Enstar Group Limited; *Int'l*, pg. 2448
CROATIA LLOYD D.D.; *Int'l*, pg. 1851
CX REINSURANCE COMPANY LIMITED—See Financiere Pinault SCA; *Int'l*, pg. 2669
DARAG GROUP LIMITED; *Int'l*, pg. 1972
DDR HOLDINGS INC.; *U.S. Private*, pg. 1181
DELTA GENERALI RE A.D.—See Assicurazioni Generali S.p.A.; *Int'l*, pg. 646
DEUTSCHE RUCKVERSICHERUNG SWITZERLAND LTD.—See Deutsche Ruckversicherung AG; *Int'l*, pg. 2083
DUNAV RE A.D.; *Int'l*, pg. 2225
DVA - DEUTSCHE VERKEHRS-ASSEKURANZ-VERMITTLUNGS GMBH—See Marsh & McLennan Companies, Inc.; *U.S. Public*, pg. 1374
EAST ISLES REINSURANCE, LTD.—See W.R. Berkley Corporation; *U.S. Public*, pg. 2317
ELITE SALES PROCESSING, INC.—See Reinsurance Group of America, Inc.; *U.S. Public*, pg. 1777
ENSTAR (EU) LIMITED—See Enstar Group Limited; *Int'l*, pg. 2448
EQUINOR INSURANCE AS—See Equinor ASA; *Int'l*, pg. 2484
EREINSURE.COM, INC.—See AmWINS Group, Inc.; *U.S. Private*, pg. 270
EREINSURE (UK) LIMITED—See AmWINS Group, Inc.; *U.S. Private*, pg. 270
EULER HERMES REINSURANCE AG—See Allianz SE; *Int'l*, pg. 353
EUREKO RE N.V.—See Achmea B.V.; *Int'l*, pg. 103
EVEREST DENALI INSURANCE COMPANY—See Everest Group, Ltd.; *Int'l*, pg. 2564
EVEREST INSURANCE (IRELAND), DESIGNATED ACTIVITY COMPANY—See Everest Group, Ltd.; *Int'l*, pg. 2564
FAIR AMERICAN INSURANCE & REINSURANCE COMPANY—See Berkshire Hathaway Inc.; *U.S. Public*, pg. 299
FBC HOLDINGS LIMITED; *Int'l*, pg. 2627
FBC REINSURANCE LIMITED—See FBC Holdings Limited; *Int'l*, pg. 2627
FORSAKRINGSAKTIEBOLAGET ASSURANSINVEST MF—See Enstar Group Limited; *Int'l*, pg. 2449
FP REINSURANCE BROKERS LIMITED—See Howden Group Holdings Limited; *Int'l*, pg. 3493
GENERALCOLOGNE RE—See Berkshire Hathaway Inc.; *U.S. Public*, pg. 301
GENERALI RUCKVERSICHERUNG AG—See Assicurazioni Generali S.p.A.; *Int'l*, pg. 647
GENERAL LIFE RE UK LIMITED—See Berkshire Hathaway Inc.; *U.S. Public*, pg. 301
GENERAL RE CORPORATION—See Berkshire Hathaway Inc.; *U.S. Public*, pg. 301
GENERAL REINSURANCE AG—See Berkshire Hathaway Inc.; *U.S. Public*, pg. 301
GENERAL REINSURANCE AUSTRALIA LTD.—See Berkshire Hathaway Inc.; *U.S. Public*, pg. 302
GENERAL REINSURANCE CORPORATION—See Berkshire Hathaway Inc.; *U.S. Public*, pg. 302
GENERAL REINSURANCE CORPORATION—See Berkshire Hathaway Inc.; *U.S. Public*, pg. 302
GENERAL REINSURANCE CORPORATION—See Berkshire Hathaway Inc.; *U.S. Public*, pg. 302
GENERAL REINSURANCE CORPORATION—See Berkshire Hathaway Inc.; *U.S. Public*, pg. 302
GENERAL REINSURANCE CORPORATION—See Berkshire Hathaway Inc.; *U.S. Public*, pg. 302
GENERAL REINSURANCE CORPORATION—See Berkshire Hathaway Inc.; *U.S. Public*, pg. 302
GENERAL REINSURANCE CORPORATION—See Berkshire Hathaway Inc.; *U.S. Public*, pg. 302
GENERAL REINSURANCE CORPORATION—See Berkshire Hathaway Inc.; *U.S. Public*, pg. 302
GENERAL REINSURANCE LIFE AUSTRALIA LTD.—See Berkshire Hathaway Inc.; *U.S. Public*, pg. 302
GEROVA FINANCIAL GROUP, LTD.; *Int'l*, pg. 2943
GLOBALE RUECKVERSICHERUNGS-AG; *Int'l*, pg. 3004
GLOBALE RUECKVERSICHERUNGS-AG—See GLOBALE Rueckversicherungs-AG; *Int'l*, pg. 3004
GLOBALE RUECKVERSICHERUNGS-AG—See GLOBALE Rueckversicherungs-AG; *Int'l*, pg. 3004
GLOBAL GENERAL & REINSURANCE COMPANY LTD.—See GLOBALE Rueckversicherungs-AG; *Int'l*, pg. 3004
GLOBAL INTERNATIONAL REINSURANCE COMPANY LTD.—See GLOBALE Rueckversicherungs-AG; *Int'l*, pg. 3004
GLOBAL LIFE REINSURANCE COMPANY OF AUSTRALIA PTY. LTD.—See GLOBALE Rueckversicherungs-AG; *Int'l*, pg. 3004
GLOBAL REINSURANCE COMPANY—See GLOBALE Rueckversicherungs-AG; *Int'l*, pg. 3004
GLOBAL REINSURANCE COMPANY—See GLOBALE Rueckversicherungs-AG; *Int'l*, pg. 3004
GRANGE INDEMNITY INSURANCE COMPANY—See Grange Mutual Casualty Company; *U.S. Private*, pg. 1754
GRANITE RE, INC.—See Federated Mutual Insurance Company; *U.S. Private*, pg. 1492
GRECO INTERNATIONAL HOLDING AG—See Marsh & McLennan Companies, Inc.; *U.S. Public*, pg. 1375
GREENE GROUP INC.; *U.S. Private*, pg. 1776
GREENLIGHT CAPITAL RE, LTD.; *Int'l*, pg. 3075
GREENLIGHT REINSURANCE, LTD.—See Greenlight Capital Re, Ltd.; *Int'l*, pg. 3075
GUARANTEE INSURANCE COMPANY—See Guarantee Insurance Group, Inc.; *U.S. Private*, pg. 1809
GUY CARPENTER BERMUDA LTD.—See Marsh & McLennan Companies, Inc.; *U.S. Public*, pg. 1375
GUY CARPENTER & CIA., S.A.—See Marsh & McLennan Companies, Inc.; *U.S. Public*, pg. 1375
GUY CARPENTER COLOMBIA LTDA.—See Marsh & McLennan Companies, Inc.; *U.S. Public*, pg. 1375
GUY CARPENTER & COMPANY AB—See Marsh & McLennan Companies, Inc.; *U.S. Public*, pg. 1375
GUY CARPENTER & COMPANY B.V.—See Marsh & McLennan Companies, Inc.; *U.S. Public*, pg. 1375
GUY CARPENTER & COMPANY CORREDORES DE REASEGUROS LTDA—See Marsh & McLennan Companies, Inc.; *U.S. Public*, pg. 1375
GUY CARPENTER & COMPANY GMBH—See Marsh & McLennan Companies, Inc.; *U.S. Public*, pg. 1375
GUY CARPENTER & COMPANY LIMITED—See Marsh & McLennan Companies, Inc.; *U.S. Public*, pg. 1375
GUY CARPENTER & COMPANY LIMITED—See Marsh & McLennan Companies, Inc.; *U.S. Public*, pg. 1375
GUY CARPENTER & COMPANY LIMITED—See Marsh & McLennan Companies, Inc.; *U.S. Public*, pg. 1375
GUY CARPENTER & COMPANY, LLC—See Marsh & McLennan Companies, Inc.; *U.S. Public*, pg. 1375
GUY CARPENTER & COMPANY, LTDA.—See Marsh & McLennan Companies, Inc.; *U.S. Public*, pg. 1375
GUY CARPENTER & COMPANY, LTD.—See Marsh & McLennan Companies, Inc.; *U.S. Public*, pg. 1375
GUY CARPENTER & COMPANY PERU CORREDORES DE REASEGUROS S.A.—See Marsh & McLennan Companies, Inc.; *U.S. Public*, pg. 1375
GUY CARPENTER & COMPANY (PTY) LIMITED—See Marsh & McLennan Companies, Inc.; *U.S. Public*, pg. 1375
GUY CARPENTER & COMPANY PTY. LIMITED—See Marsh & McLennan Companies, Inc.; *U.S. Public*, pg. 1375
GUY CARPENTER & COMPANY, S.A.—See Marsh & McLennan Companies, Inc.; *U.S. Public*, pg. 1375
GUY CARPENTER & COMPANY, S.A.—See Marsh & McLennan Companies, Inc.; *U.S. Public*, pg. 1375
GUY CARPENTER & COMPANY, S.A.—See Marsh & McLennan Companies, Inc.; *U.S. Public*, pg. 1375
GUY CARPENTER & COMPANY, S.A.—See Marsh & McLennan Companies, Inc.; *U.S. Public*, pg. 1375
GUY CARPENTER & COMPANY S.R.L.—See Marsh & McLennan Companies, Inc.; *U.S. Public*, pg. 1375
GUY CARPENTER JAPAN, INC.—See Marsh & McLennan Companies, Inc.; *U.S. Public*, pg. 1376
GUY CARPENTER MEXICO, INTERMEDIARO DE REASUGURO, S.A. DE C.V.—See Marsh & McLennan Companies, Inc.; *U.S. Public*, pg. 1376
GUY CARPENTER (MIDDLE EAST) LIMITED—See Marsh & McLennan Companies, Inc.; *U.S. Public*, pg. 1376
HAAKON AG—See Howden Group Holdings Limited; *Int'l*, pg. 3493
HAAKON (ASIA) LTD—See Howden Group Holdings Limited; *Int'l*, pg. 3493
HAMPDEN INSURANCE GROUP BV—See Hampden Holdings Limited; *Int'l*, pg. 3239
HARDY GUERNSEY LIMITED—See Loews Corporation; *U.S. Public*, pg. 1340
HAWAII EMPLOYERS' MUTUAL INSURANCE COMPANY, INC.; *U.S. Private*, pg. 1881
HORSESHOE INSURANCE SERVICES HOLDINGS LTD.—See Arthur J. Gallagher & Co.; *U.S. Public*, pg. 206
HOWDEN INSURANCE & REINSURANCE BROKERS (PHIL.), INC.—See Howden Group Holdings Limited; *Int'l*, pg. 3493
IBEX REINSURANCE COMPANY LIMITED—See Markel Group Inc.; *U.S. Public*, pg. 1367
INDEPENDENT FINANCIAL SYSTEMS, INC.; *U.S. Private*, pg. 2059
INDUSTRIAL RISKS PROTECTION CONSULTANTS—See Marsh & McLennan Companies, Inc.; *U.S. Public*, pg. 1376
JARDINE LLOYD THOMPSON LIMITED—See Marsh & McLennan Companies, Inc.; *U.S. Public*, pg. 1377
JLT ADVISORY LIMITED—See Marsh & McLennan Companies, Inc.; *U.S. Public*, pg. 1376
JLT INDEPENDENT INSURANCE BROKERS PRIVATE LIMITED—See Marsh & McLennan Companies, Inc.; *U.S. Public*, pg. 1376
JLT REINSURANCE BROKERS LIMITED—See Marsh & McLennan Companies, Inc.; *U.S. Public*, pg. 1376
JOHN SUTAK INSURANCE BROKERS, INC.—See Brookfield Reinsurance Ltd.; *Int'l*, pg. 1194
THE KANSAS BANKERS SURETY COMPANY—See Berkshire Hathaway Inc.; *U.S. Public*, pg. 316
KANSAS CITY LIFE INSURANCE COMPANY; *U.S. Public*, pg. 1214
KINGSWAY REINSURANCE CORPORATION—See Kingsway Financial Services Inc.; *U.S. Public*, pg. 1235
LCL ACQUISITIONS LIMITED—See Lovell Minnick Partners LLC; *U.S. Private*, pg. 2502
LCL GROUP LIMITED—See Lovell Minnick Partners LLC; *U.S. Private*, pg. 2502
LEWER LIFE INSURANCE COMPANY INC.; *U.S. Private*, pg. 2437
LINCOLN NATIONAL CORPORATION; *U.S. Public*, pg. 1318
LOGIQ3 INC.—See Reinsurance Group of America, Inc.; *U.S. Public*, pg. 1777
LOMBARD INSURANCE COMPANY LIMITED—See Hollard Insurance Company Ltd; *Int'l*, pg. 3451
LYNCH INSURANCE BROKERS LIMITED—See Marsh & McLennan Companies, Inc.; *U.S. Public*, pg. 1377
MAG SPA—See Marsh & McLennan Companies, Inc.; *U.S. Public*, pg. 1377
MARKEL AMERICAN INSURANCE COMPANY—See Markel Group Inc.; *U.S. Public*, pg. 1368
MARKEL INTERNATIONAL (DUBAI) LIMITED—See Markel Group Inc.; *U.S. Public*, pg. 1368
MARKEL INTERNATIONAL SINGAPORE PTE. LIMITED—See Markel Group Inc.; *U.S. Public*, pg. 1368
MARSH KOREA, INC.—See Marsh & McLennan Companies, Inc.; *U.S. Public*, pg. 1383
MARSH SERVICES SPOLKA Z.O.O.—See Marsh & McLennan Companies, Inc.; *U.S. Public*, pg. 1384
MENA RE UNDERWRITERS LTD.—See Doha Insurance Group QPSC; *Int'l*, pg. 2155
MERCER (CHINA) LIMITED—See Marsh & McLennan Companies, Inc.; *U.S. Public*, pg. 1384
MERCER (COLOMBIA) LTDA.—See Marsh & McLennan Companies, Inc.; *U.S. Public*, pg. 1384
MERCER INDIA PRIVATE LIMITED—See Marsh & McLennan Companies, Inc.; *U.S. Public*, pg. 1386
MERCER ITALIA SRL—See Marsh & McLennan Companies, Inc.; *U.S. Public*, pg. 1386
MERCER JAPAN LTD—See Marsh & McLennan Companies, Inc.; *U.S. Public*, pg. 1386
MERCER KOREA CO. LTD.—See Marsh & McLennan Companies, Inc.; *U.S. Public*, pg. 1386
MERCER LIMITED—See Marsh & McLennan Companies, Inc.; *U.S. Public*, pg. 1386
MERCER (NEDERLAND) B.V.—See Marsh & McLennan Companies, Inc.; *U.S. Public*, pg. 1384
MERCER PHILIPPINES, INC.—See Marsh & McLennan Companies, Inc.; *U.S. Public*, pg. 1386
MERCER (PORTUGAL) LDA—See Marsh & McLennan Companies, Inc.; *U.S. Public*, pg. 1384
MERCER SOUTH AFRICA (PTY) LTD.—See Marsh & McLennan Companies, Inc.; *U.S. Public*, pg. 1386
MERCER (SWITZERLAND) SA—See Marsh & McLennan Companies, Inc.; *U.S. Public*, pg. 1384
MONY LIFE INSURANCE COMPANY OF THE AMERICAS, LTD.—See Equitable Holdings, Inc.; *U.S. Public*, pg. 790
MUTUAL REINSURANCE BUREAU; *U.S. Private*, pg. 2820
NACION REASEGUROS S.A—See Banco de la Nacion Argentina; *Int'l*, pg. 820
THE NATIONAL SECURITY GROUP, INC.; *U.S. Public*, pg. 2116
NEPHILA CAPITAL LTD.—See Markel Group Inc.; *U.S. Public*, pg. 1369
NEPHILA SYNDICATE MANAGEMENT LTD.—See Markel Group Inc.; *U.S. Public*, pg. 1369
ODYSSEY AMERICA REINSURANCE CORPORATION—See Fairfax Financial Holdings Limited; *Int'l*, pg. 2607
ODYSSEY RE HOLDINGS CORP.—See Fairfax Financial Holdings Limited; *Int'l*, pg. 2607
ODYSSEY REINSURANCE COMPANY—See Fairfax Financial Holdings Limited; *Int'l*, pg. 2607
ODYSSEY REINSURANCE EUROASIA DIVISION—See Fairfax Financial Holdings Limited; *Int'l*, pg. 2607
OLIVER WYMAN LIMITED LIABILITY COMPANY—See

524130 — REINSURANCE CARRIER...

Marsh & McLennan Companies, Inc.; *U.S. Public*, pg. 1386
OXFORD LIFE INSURANCE COMPANY—See U-Haul Holding Company; *U.S. Public*, pg. 2211
PARAGON STRATEGIC SOLUTIONS INC.—See Aon plc; *Int'l*, pg. 490
PARTNER CONNECTICUT INC.—See Covea Groupe S.A.S.; *Int'l*, pg. 1820
PARTNERRE FINANCE A LLC—See Covea Groupe S.A.S.; *Int'l*, pg. 1820
PARTNERRE FINANCE B LLC—See Covea Groupe S.A.S.; *Int'l*, pg. 1820
PARTNERRE HOLDINGS EUROPE LIMITED—See Covea Groupe S.A.S.; *Int'l*, pg. 1820
PARTNERRE HOLDINGS SA—See Covea Groupe S.A.S.; *Int'l*, pg. 1820
PARTNER REINSURANCE ASIA PTE. LTD.—See Covea Groupe S.A.S.; *Int'l*, pg. 1820
PARTNER REINSURANCE COMPANY LTD.—See Covea Groupe S.A.S.; *Int'l*, pg. 1820
PARTNER REINSURANCE COMPANY OF THE U.S.—See Covea Groupe S.A.S.; *Int'l*, pg. 1820
PARTNER REINSURANCE EUROPE SE—See Covea Groupe S.A.S.; *Int'l*, pg. 1820
PARTNERRE LIFE REINSURANCE COMPANY OF CANADA—See Covea Groupe S.A.S.; *Int'l*, pg. 1820
PARTNERRE LTD.—See Covea Groupe S.A.S.; *Int'l*, pg. 1820
PARTNERRE U.S. CORPORATION—See Covea Groupe S.A.S.; *Int'l*, pg. 1820
PELEUS REINSURANCE, LTD.—See Brookfield Reinsurance Ltd.; *Int'l*, pg. 1194
PHYSICIANS LIFE INSURANCE COMPANY—See Physicians Mutual Insurance Co.; *U.S. Private*, pg. 3175
PROSIGHT SPECIALTY INSURANCE GROUP, INC.—See TPG Capital, L.P.; *U.S. Public*, pg. 2175
PROTECTIVE LIFE INSURANCE COMPANY—See Dai-ichi Life Holdings, Inc.; *Int'l*, pg. 1917
PWS EAST ASIA PTE LIMITED—See AmWINS Group, Inc.; *U.S. Private*, pg. 270
RAM REINSURANCE COMPANY LTD.—See American Overseas Group Limited; *Int'l*, pg. 422
REINSURANCE SOLUTIONS INTERNATIONAL, L.L.C.—See Marsh & McLennan Companies, Inc.; *U.S. Public*, pg. 1376
RESIDENTIAL WARRANTY SERVICES, INC.—See Porch Group, Inc.; *U.S. Public*, pg. 1702
RGA CAPITAL LIMITED U.K.—See Reinsurance Group of America, Inc.; *U.S. Public*, pg. 1777
RGA GLOBAL REINSURANCE COMPANY, LTD.—See Reinsurance Group of America, Inc.; *U.S. Public*, pg. 1777
RGA INTERNATIONAL REINSURANCE COMPANY LIMITED—See Reinsurance Group of America, Inc.; *U.S. Public*, pg. 1777
RGA REINSURANCE COMPANY MIDDLE EAST LIMITED—See Reinsurance Group of America, Inc.; *U.S. Public*, pg. 1777
RGA REINSURANCE COMPANY OF AUSTRALIA LIMITED—See Reinsurance Group of America, Inc.; *U.S. Public*, pg. 1777
RGA REINSURANCE COMPANY OF SOUTH AFRICA, LIMITED—See Reinsurance Group of America, Inc.; *U.S. Public*, pg. 1778
RGA REINSURANCE COMPANY—See Reinsurance Group of America, Inc.; *U.S. Public*, pg. 1777
RGA SERVICES INDIA PRIVATE LIMITED—See Reinsurance Group of America, Inc.; *U.S. Public*, pg. 1778
RGA SERVICES (SINGAPORE) PTE. LTD.—See Reinsurance Group of America, Inc.; *U.S. Public*, pg. 1778
RGA UK SERVICES LIMITED—See Reinsurance Group of America, Inc.; *U.S. Public*, pg. 1778
RIVERS GROUP LIMITED—See Marsh & McLennan Companies, Inc.; *U.S. Public*, pg. 1388
RMIC COMPANIES, INC.—See Arch Capital Group Ltd.; *Int'l*, pg. 546
SEDGWICK (DEUTSCHLAND) GMBH—See Marsh & McLennan Companies, Inc.; *U.S. Public*, pg. 1388
SEDGWICK LIMITED—See Marsh & McLennan Companies, Inc.; *U.S. Public*, pg. 1388
SEDGWICK PTE LTD—See Marsh & McLennan Companies, Inc.; *U.S. Public*, pg. 1388
SENECA REINSURANCE COMPANY, LLC—See Antarctica Capital, LLC; *U.S. Private*, pg. 287
SINGAPORE REINSURANCE CORPORATION LIMITED—See Fairfax Financial Holdings Limited; *Int'l*, pg. 2608
SIRIUS AMERICA INSURANCE CO.—See White Mountains Insurance Group, Ltd.; *U.S. Public*, pg. 2369
SOBC CORP.; *U.S. Private*, pg. 3702
SONOMA RISK MANAGEMENT, LLC—See Brookfield Reinsurance Ltd.; *Int'l*, pg. 1194
SR-CHINA ADVISORY SERVICES CO LTD—See Fairfax Financial Holdings Limited; *Int'l*, pg. 2608
STI TECHNOLOGIES LIMITED—See IQVIA Holdings Inc.; *U.S. Public*, pg. 1170
TAIPING REINSURANCE BROKERS LIMITED—See China Taiping Insurance Holdings Company Limited; *Int'l*, pg. 1557
TAIPING REINSURANCE (CHINA) COMPANY LIMITED—See China Taiping Insurance Holdings Company Limited; *Int'l*, pg. 1557
TAIPING REINSURANCE COMPANY LIMITED—See China Taiping Insurance Holdings Company Limited; *Int'l*, pg. 1557
TALBOT RISK SERVICES (LABUAN) PTE. LTD.—See American International Group, Inc.; *U.S. Public*, pg. 107
TALBOT UNDERWRITING (LATAM) S.A.—See American International Group, Inc.; *U.S. Public*, pg. 107
TALBOT UNDERWRITING (LATAM) S.A.—See American International Group, Inc.; *U.S. Public*, pg. 107
TALBOT UNDERWRITING SERVICES, LTD.—See American International Group, Inc.; *U.S. Public*, pg. 107
TALBOT UNDERWRITING SERVICES (US), LTD.—See American International Group, Inc.; *U.S. Public*, pg. 107
THOMPSON HEATH & BOND LIMITED - EUROPEAN DIVISION—See AmWINS Group, Inc.; *U.S. Private*, pg. 270
TOP LAYER REINSURANCE LTD.—See State Farm Mutual Automobile Insurance Company; *U.S. Private*, pg. 3792
TRANSATLANTIC RE (ARGENTINA) S.A.—See Berkshire Hathaway Inc.; *U.S. Public*, pg. 299
TRANSRE S.A.—See Berkshire Hathaway Inc.; *U.S. Public*, pg. 299
TRANSRE ZURICH LTD.—See Berkshire Hathaway Inc.; *U.S. Public*, pg. 299
TRANS RE ZURICH REINSURANCE COMPANY LTD—See Berkshire Hathaway Inc.; *U.S. Public*, pg. 299
USAA LIFE INSURANCE CO.—See United Services Automobile Association; *U.S. Private*, pg. 4297
VALIDUS REASEGUROS, INC.—See American International Group, Inc.; *U.S. Public*, pg. 107
VALIDUS REINSURANCE, LTD.—See American International Group, Inc.; *U.S. Public*, pg. 107
VALIDUS REINSURANCE (SWITZERLAND) LTD—See American International Group, Inc.; *U.S. Public*, pg. 107
VALIDUS RISK SERVICES (IRELAND) LIMITED—See American International Group, Inc.; *U.S. Public*, pg. 107
VICTOR DEUTSCHLAND GMBH—See Marsh & McLennan Companies, Inc.; *U.S. Public*, pg. 1388
VOYA INSURANCE & ANNUITY COMPANY—See Voya Financial, Inc.; *U.S. Public*, pg. 2311
VOYA REINSURANCE—See Voya Financial, Inc.; *U.S. Public*, pg. 2311
VOYA RETIREMENT INSURANCE & ANNUITY COMPANY—See Voya Financial, Inc.; *U.S. Public*, pg. 2311
WESTCO CLAIMS MANAGEMENT SERVICES, INC.—See American International Group, Inc.; *U.S. Public*, pg. 107
WIND RIVER REINSURANCE COMPANY LTD—See Paine Schwartz Partners, LLC; *U.S. Private*, pg. 3076
XL REINSURANCE AMERICA INC.—See AXA S.A.; *Int'l*, pg. 761
XL REINSURANCE INC.—See AXA S.A.; *Int'l*, pg. 761
XL REINSURANCE LIMITED—See AXA S.A.; *Int'l*, pg. 761
ZON RE-USA, LLC—See B.P. Marsh & Partners PLC; *Int'l*, pg. 790

524210 — INSURANCE AGENCIES AND BROKERAGES

1ST SOURCE INSURANCE, INC.—See 1st Source Corporation; *U.S. Public*, pg. 3
A&A UNDERWRITING SERVICES INC.—See Aon plc; *Int'l*, pg. 488
ABA INSURANCE SERVICES INC.—See American Financial Group, Inc.; *U.S. Public*, pg. 102
ABBEY LEGAL PROTECTION LIMITED—See Markel Group Inc.; *U.S. Public*, pg. 1367
ABBEY PROTECTION GROUP LIMITED—See Markel Group Inc.; *U.S. Public*, pg. 1367
ABBEY TAX & CONSULTANCY SERVICES LIMITED—See Markel Group Inc.; *U.S. Public*, pg. 1367
ABB INSURANCE BROKERS LTD—See ABB Ltd.; *Int'l*, pg. 54
ABB INSURANCE LIMITED—See ABB Ltd.; *Int'l*, pg. 52
ABD INSURANCE & FINANCIAL SERVICES, INC.; *U.S. Private*, pg. 37
ABD INSURANCE & FINANCIAL SERVICES INC. - WALNUT CREEK—See ABD Insurance & Financial Services, Inc.; *U.S. Private*, pg. 37
A&B INSURANCE AND FINANCIAL, LLC—See Genstar Capital, LLC; *U.S. Private*, pg. 1674
A & B INSURANCE & REINSURANCE S.R.L.—See Assiteca SpA; *Int'l*, pg. 648
ABLE INSURANCE SERVICES LIMITED—See Admiral Group plc; *Int'l*, pg. 151
ABRAM INTERSTATE INSURANCE SERVICES, INC.—See Arthur J. Gallagher & Co.; *U.S. Public*, pg. 202
ABSA IDIRECT LIMITED—See Absa Group Limited; *Int'l*, pg. 69
ABSA INSURANCE AND FINANCIAL ADVISERS PROPRIETARY LIMITED—See Absa Group Limited; *Int'l*, pg. 69
ABSA INSURANCE COMPANY LIMITED—See Absa Group Limited; *Int'l*, pg. 69
ACADIA INSURANCE COMPANY—See W.R. Berkley Corporation; *U.S. Public*, pg. 2318
ACCELERATED BENEFITS—See Caisse de Depot et Placement du Quebec; *Int'l*, pg. 1256
ACCELERATED BENEFITS—See KKR & Co. Inc.; *U.S. Public*, pg. 1264
THE ACCEL GROUP LLC; *U.S. Private*, pg. 3981
ACCEPTANCE INSURANCE AGENCY OF TENNESSEE, INC.—See Stone Point Capital LLC; *U.S. Private*, pg. 3818
ACCESS INSURANCE COMPANY; *U.S. Private*, pg. 52
ACCIDENT & HEALTH UNDERWRITING LTD.—See White Mountains Insurance Group, Ltd.; *U.S. Public*, pg. 2368
ACCLARA SOLUTIONS, LLC—See R1 RCM Inc.; *U.S. Public*, pg. 1758
ACCUQUOTE; *U.S. Private*, pg. 55
ACCUTRUST MORTGAGE INC.; *U.S. Private*, pg. 56
ACE AMERICAN INSURANCE COMPANY—See Chubb Limited; *Int'l*, pg. 1590
ACE SERVICIOS S.A.—See Chubb Limited; *Int'l*, pg. 1590
ACG INSURANCE AGENCY, LLC—See The Auto Club Group; *U.S. Private*, pg. 3990
ACHIEVA INSURANCE AGENCY, LLC—See Achieva Credit Union; *U.S. Private*, pg. 58
ACHILLES & ASSOCIATES PC—See Aon plc; *Int'l*, pg. 495
ACL INTERNATIONAL LTD.; *Int'l*, pg. 106
ACNB INSURANCE SERVICES INC.—See ACNB Corporation; *U.S. Public*, pg. 35
ACORN INTERNATIONAL NETWORK PTE. LTD.—See Brown & Brown, Inc.; *U.S. Public*, pg. 396
ACREDIA VERSICHERUNG AG—See Allianz SE; *Int'l*, pg. 352
ACRISURE, LLC; *U.S. Private*, pg. 65
ACSIA PARTNERS LLC—See LTC Global, Inc.; *U.S. Private*, pg. 2509
ACW GROUP, LLC—See GCP Capital Partners Holdings LLC; *U.S. Private*, pg. 1654
ADIDAS INSURANCE & RISK CONSULTANTS GMBH—See adidas AG; *Int'l*, pg. 147
ADMIRAL INSURANCE (GIBRALTAR) LIMITED—See Admiral Group plc; *Int'l*, pg. 151
ADONIS INSURANCE & REINSURANCE CO. (ADIR) SAL—See Byblos Bank S.A.L.; *Int'l*, pg. 1233
ADONIS INSURANCE & REINSURANCE SYRIA S.A.—See Byblos Bank S.A.L.; *Int'l*, pg. 1233
ADVANCE CREATE CO., LTD.; *Int'l*, pg. 155
ADVANCED GLASSFIBER YARNS LLC; *U.S. Private*, pg. 89
ADVANCED INSURANCE UNDERWRITERS LLC—See Kelso & Company, L.P.; *U.S. Public*, pg. 2279
ADVANCED PATIENT ADVOCACY LLC—See GrowthCurve Capital LP; *U.S. Private*, pg. 1796
ADVANCED PATIENT ADVOCACY, LLC—See Riverside Partners, LLC; *U.S. Private*, pg. 3446
ADVANTAGE BENEFIT SOLUTIONS; *U.S. Private*, pg. 94
ADVANTA INSURANCE PARTNERS; *U.S. Private*, pg. 93
ADVENTIST RISK MANAGEMENT INC.; *U.S. Private*, pg. 109
ADVOCATE INSURANCE SERVICES CORP.—See Brown & Brown, Inc.; *U.S. Public*, pg. 396
A.E. BARNES INSURANCE AGENCY, INC.—See Cross Financial Corporation; *U.S. Private*, pg. 1104
AEGIS CORP.—See Lovell Minnick Partners LLC; *U.S. Private*, pg. 2502
AEGON EMEKLILIK VE HAYAT A.S.—See Aegon N.V.; *Int'l*, pg. 174
AEGON PENSII SOCIETATE DE ADMINISTRARE A FONDURILOR DE PENSII PRIVATE S.A.—See Aegon N.V.; *Int'l*, pg. 175
AEGON POWSZECHNE TOWARZYSTWO EMERYTAINE SPOLKA AKCYJNA—See Aegon N.V.; *Int'l*, pg. 175
AEGON TOWARZYSTWO UBEZPIECZEN NA ZYCIE SPOLKA AKCYJNA—See Aegon N.V.; *Int'l*, pg. 175
AEGON USA-SPECIAL MARKETS GROUP-CONSUMER DIRECT—See Aegon N.V.; *Int'l*, pg. 174
AES GLOBAL INSURANCE COMPANY—See The AES Corporation; *U.S. Public*, pg. 2030
AFFINITY INSURANCE SERVICES, INC.—See Aon plc; *Int'l*, pg. 488
AFFIRMATIVE INSURANCE COMPANY—See J.C. Flowers & Co, LLC; *U.S. Private*, pg. 2159
AFFIRMATIVE PREMIUM FINANCE, INC.—See J.C. Flowers & Co, LLC; *U.S. Private*, pg. 2159
AFIN BROKER DE ASIGURARE - REASIGURARE S.R.L.—See CNH Industrial N.V.; *Int'l*, pg. 1674
AFLAC INTERNATIONAL, INCORPORATED—See Aflac Incorporated; *U.S. Public*, pg. 57
AFLAC - LEHIGH VALLEY; *U.S. Private*, pg. 123
AFLAC PET SMALL-AMOUNT-AND-SHORT-TERM INSURANCE CO., LTD.—See Aflac Incorporated; *U.S. Public*, pg. 57
AGA FINANCIAL GROUP INC.; *Int'l*, pg. 198
AGAPE INSURANCE SERVICES—See Inszone Insurance Services, LLC; *U.S. Private*, pg. 2096
AGCS AMERICAS—See Allianz SE; *Int'l*, pg. 341
AGCS ARGENTINA—See Allianz SE; *Int'l*, pg. 341
AGCS AUSTRALIA—See Allianz SE; *Int'l*, pg. 341
AGCS LEBANON—See Allianz SE; *Int'l*, pg. 341
AGCS NORTH AMERICA—See Allianz SE; *Int'l*, pg. 341

524210 — INSURANCE AGENCIES ...

AGENCE SARADAR D'ASSURANCES SAL—See Bank Audi sal; *Int'l*, pg. 837
AGENCY INSURANCE COMPANY OF MARYLAND, INC.—See Agency Holding Company of Maryland Inc.; *U.S. Private*, pg. 126
AGENCY SERVICES OF ARKANSAS, INC.—See Stone Point Capital LLC; *U.S. Private*, pg. 3819
AGENT SUPPORT SERVICES INC.; *U.S. Private*, pg. 127
AGF 2X, S.A.—See Allianz SE; *Int'l*, pg. 342
AG STATES AGENCY, LLC—See CHS INC.; *U.S. Public*, pg. 491
AIA AUSTRALIA LIMITED—See AIA Group Limited; *Int'l*, pg. 227
AIA BHD.—See AIA Group Limited; *Int'l*, pg. 227
AIA NEW ZEALAND LIMITED—See AIA Group Limited; *Int'l*, pg. 227
AIA SINGAPORE PRIVATE LIMITED—See AIA Group Limited; *Int'l*, pg. 227
AIA (VIETNAM) LIFE INSURANCE COMPANY LIMITED—See AIA Group Limited; *Int'l*, pg. 227
AIB FINANCIAL GROUP; *U.S. Private*, pg. 131
AIB INSURANCE SERVICES LIMITED—See AIB Group plc; *Int'l*, pg. 228
AIC AMERICA—See Nevada General Insurance Company; *U.S. Private*, pg. 2891
AIG ASSET MANAGEMENT (U.S.), LLC—See American International Group, Inc.; *U.S. Public*, pg. 104
AIG CREDIT CORP.—See American International Group, Inc.; *U.S. Public*, pg. 104
AIG INSURANCE (THAILAND) PUBLIC COMPANY LIMITED—See American International Group, Inc.; *U.S. Public*, pg. 104
AIG PHILIPPINES INSURANCE, INC.—See American International Group, Inc.; *U.S. Public*, pg. 105
AIG RISK MANAGEMENT, INC.—See American International Group, Inc.; *U.S. Public*, pg. 106
AIM SWEDEN AB—See Aon plc; *Int'l*, pg. 488
AIRSOUTH INSURANCE, INC.—See GTCR LLC; *U.S. Private*, pg. 1802
AIR-SUR, INC.—See Arthur J. Gallagher & Co.; *U.S. Public*, pg. 202
A & J INSURANCE, INC.—See Seeman Holtz Property & Casualty, LLC; *U.S. Private*, pg. 3598
AKSIGORTA A.S.; *Int'l*, pg. 264
AL AIN AHLIA INSURANCE COMPANY; *Int'l*, pg. 275
ALANDALE INSURANCE AGENCY INC.; *U.S. Private*, pg. 150
ALAN KAYE INSURANCE AGENCY, INC.—See Aon plc; *Int'l*, pg. 495
ALAN & THOMAS INSURANCE BROKERS LIMITED—See Brown & Brown, Inc.; *U.S. Public*, pg. 396
ALBINGIA SA—See Eurazeo SE; *Int'l*, pg. 2527
THE ALBRECHT COMPANIES, INC.; *U.S. Private*, pg. 3983
ALEXANDER BONHILL LIMITED—See HML Holdings plc; *Int'l*, pg. 3432
ALEXANDER FORBES INTERNATIONAL LTD.—See Alexander Forbes Group Holdings Limited; *Int'l*, pg. 307
ALFA AGENCY—See Alfa Corporation; *U.S. Private*, pg. 164
ALFORD BURTON AND COMPANY LIMITED—See Brown & Brown, Inc.; *U.S. Public*, pg. 396
ALICO AIG LIFE UKRAINE—See MetLife, Inc.; *U.S. Public*, pg. 1429
ALICO A.S.—See MetLife, Inc.; *U.S. Public*, pg. 1429
ALICO BULGARIA—See MetLife, Inc.; *U.S. Public*, pg. 1429
ALIGN GENERAL INSURANCE AGENCY, LLC—See Align Financial Group, LLC; *U.S. Private*, pg. 168
ALKEME INSURANCE SERVICES, INC.—See GCP Capital Partners Holdings LLC; *U.S. Private*, pg. 1654
AL KOOT INSURANCE & REINSURANCE COMPANY P.J.S.C.—See Gulf International Services QSC; *Int'l*, pg. 3181
ALL AMERICA INSURANCE COMPANY—See Central Mutual Insurance Company; *U.S. Private*, pg. 822
ALLEANZA TORO SERVIZI ASSICURATIVI S.R.L—See Assicurazioni Generali S.p.A.; *Int'l*, pg. 643
ALLEATO ASSEKURANZMAKLER GMBH—See adesso SE; *Int'l*, pg. 144
ALLEGHENY INSURANCE SERVICE INC.; *U.S. Private*, pg. 176
ALLEGIAN INSURANCE COMPANY—See Tenet Healthcare Corporation; *U.S. Public*, pg. 2014
ALLIANCE BROKERAGE CORP.; *U.S. Private*, pg. 181
ALLIANCE BUSINESS & COMMERCIAL INSURANCE SERVICES—See Inszone Insurance Services, LLC; *U.S. Private*, pg. 2096
ALLIANCE FINANCIAL GROUP, INC.; *U.S. Private*, pg. 182
ALLIANCE INDEMNITY COMPANY INC.—See Farmers Alliance Mutual Insurance Co., Inc.; *U.S. Private*, pg. 1476
ALLIANCE MARINE RISK MANAGERS OF FLORIDA, INC.—See GTCR LLC; *U.S. Private*, pg. 1802
ALLIANCE TITLE & ESCROW CORPORATION—See Futura Corporation; *U.S. Private*, pg. 1626
ALLIANT INSURANCE SERVICES, INC.—See Stone Point Capital LLC; *U.S. Private*, pg. 3818
ALLIANT/MESIROW INSURANCE SERVICES—See Stone Point Capital LLC; *U.S. Private*, pg. 3818

ALLIANT NATIONAL TITLE INSURANCE COMPANY; *U.S. Private*, pg. 185
ALLIANT SPECIALTY INSURANCE SERVICES, INC.—See Stone Point Capital LLC; *U.S. Private*, pg. 3818
ALLIANZ AFRICA S.A.—See Allianz SE; *Int'l*, pg. 343
ALLIANZ ARGENTINA COMPANIA DE SEGUROS S.A.—See Allianz SE; *Int'l*, pg. 343
ALLIANZ AUSTRALIA ADVANTAGE LTD.—See Allianz SE; *Int'l*, pg. 343
ALLIANZ AUSTRALIA INSURANCE LIMITED—See Allianz SE; *Int'l*, pg. 343
ALLIANZ AVIATION MANAGERS LLC—See Allianz SE; *Int'l*, pg. 344
ALLIANZ AYUDHYA GENERAL INSURANCE PUBLIC COMPANY LIMITED—See Allianz SE; *Int'l*, pg. 344
ALLIANZ BENELUX S.A.—See Allianz SE; *Int'l*, pg. 344
ALLIANZ CAMEROUN ASSURANCES VIE S.A.—See Allianz SE; *Int'l*, pg. 344
ALLIANZ CENTRAFRIQUE ASSURANCES—See Allianz SE; *Int'l*, pg. 344
ALLIANZ DIRECT NEW EUROPE SP. Z O.O.—See Allianz SE; *Int'l*, pg. 344
ALLIANZ DIRECT S.P.A.—See Allianz SE; *Int'l*, pg. 344
ALLIANZ DIRECT S.R.O.—See Allianz SE; *Int'l*, pg. 344
ALLIANZ GLOBAL ASSISTANCE - CANADA—See Allianz SE; *Int'l*, pg. 345
ALLIANZ GLOBAL ASSISTANCE INC.—See Allianz SE; *Int'l*, pg. 342
ALLIANZ GLOBAL ASSISTANCE USA—See Allianz SE; *Int'l*, pg. 345
ALLIANZ GLOBAL CORPORATE & SPECIALTY—See Allianz SE; *Int'l*, pg. 345
ALLIANZ GLOBAL CORPORATE & SPECIALTY—See Allianz SE; *Int'l*, pg. 345
ALLIANZ GLOBAL CORPORATE & SPECIALTY—See Allianz SE; *Int'l*, pg. 345
ALLIANZ GLOBAL CORPORATE & SPECIALTY—See Allianz SE; *Int'l*, pg. 345
ALLIANZ GLOBAL CORPORATE & SPECIALTY—See Allianz SE; *Int'l*, pg. 345
ALLIANZ GLOBAL CORPORATE & SPECIALTY—See Allianz SE; *Int'l*, pg. 345
ALLIANZ GLOBAL CORPORATE & SPECIALTY—See Allianz SE; *Int'l*, pg. 345
ALLIANZ GLOBAL CORPORATE & SPECIALTY SOUTH AFRICA LTD.—See Allianz SE; *Int'l*, pg. 346
ALLIANZ GLOBAL INVESTORS ASSET MANAGEMENT (SHANGHAI) LIMITED—See Allianz SE; *Int'l*, pg. 347
ALLIANZ GLOBAL INVESTORS U.S. LLC—See Allianz SE; *Int'l*, pg. 347
ALLIANZ GROUP GREECE—See Allianz SE; *Int'l*, pg. 348
ALLIANZ HAYAT VE EMEKLILIK AS—See Allianz SE; *Int'l*, pg. 348
ALLIANZ HELLAS SINGLE MEMBER INSURANCE S.A.—See Allianz SE; *Int'l*, pg. 348
ALLIANZ HUNGARIA BIZTOSITO ZRT.—See Allianz SE; *Int'l*, pg. 348
ALLIANZ IARD S.A.—See Allianz SE; *Int'l*, pg. 348
ALLIANZ INSURANCE COMPANY-EGYPT S.A.E.—See Allianz SE; *Int'l*, pg. 348
ALLIANZ INSURANCE COMPANY LANKA LIMITED—See Allianz SE; *Int'l*, pg. 348
ALLIANZ INSURANCE LANKA LIMITED—See Allianz SE; *Int'l*, pg. 348
ALLIANZ INSURANCE LAOS CO. LTD.—See Allianz SE; *Int'l*, pg. 348
ALLIANZ INSURANCE LUXEMBOURG—See Allianz SE; *Int'l*, pg. 348
ALLIANZ INSURANCE NEW ZEALAND—See Allianz SE; *Int'l*, pg. 348
ALLIANZ INVESTMENT MANAGEMENT SE—See Allianz SE; *Int'l*, pg. 348
ALLIANZ JINGDONG GENERAL INSURANCE COMPANY LTD.—See Allianz SE; *Int'l*, pg. 348
ALLIANZ KUNDE UND MARKT GMBH—See Allianz SE; *Int'l*, pg. 348
ALLIANZ LIETUVA GYVYBES DRAUDIMAS UAB—See Allianz SE; *Int'l*, pg. 348
ALLIANZ LIFE INSURANCE LANKA LTD.—See Allianz SE; *Int'l*, pg. 348
ALLIANZ MEXICO S.A. COMPANIA DE SEGUROS—See Allianz SE; *Int'l*, pg. 349
ALLIANZ NIGERIA INSURANCE PLC—See Allianz SE; *Int'l*, pg. 349
ALLIANZ OF ASIA-PACIFIC AND AFRICA GMBH—See Allianz SE; *Int'l*, pg. 351
ALLIANZ OF NEW YORK—See Allianz SE; *Int'l*, pg. 347
ALLIANZ ONE - BUSINESS SOLUTIONS GMBH—See Allianz SE; *Int'l*, pg. 349
ALLIANZ PARTNERS S.A.S.—See Allianz SE; *Int'l*, pg. 349
ALLIANZ PENZIJNI SPOLECNOST A.S.—See Allianz SE; *Int'l*, pg. 351
ALLIANZ PNB LIFE INSURANCE INC.—See Allianz SE; *Int'l*, pg. 349
ALLIANZ POLSKA SERVICES SP. Z O.O.—See Allianz SE; *Int'l*, pg. 349
ALLIANZ POPULAR S.L.—See Allianz SE; *Int'l*, pg. 349

ALLIANZ REINSURANCE AMERICA INC.—See Allianz SE; *Int'l*, pg. 349
ALLIANZ RISK CONSULTING GMBH—See Allianz SE; *Int'l*, pg. 349
ALLIANZ RISK TRANSFER AG—See Allianz SE; *Int'l*, pg. 349
ALLIANZ RISK TRANSFER N.V.—See Allianz SE; *Int'l*, pg. 350
ALLIANZ RISK TRANSFER (UK) LIMITED—See Allianz SE; *Int'l*, pg. 349
ALLIANZ SEGUROS DE VIDA S.A.—See Allianz SE; *Int'l*, pg. 350
ALLIANZ SEGUROS S.A.—See Allianz SE; *Int'l*, pg. 350
ALLIANZ SENEGAL ASSURANCES VIE—See Allianz SE; *Int'l*, pg. 350
ALLIANZ SENEGAL DOMMAGES—See Allianz SE; *Int'l*, pg. 350
ALLIANZ SENEGAL VIE—See Allianz SE; *Int'l*, pg. 350
ALLIANZ SERVICE CENTER GMBH—See Allianz SE; *Int'l*, pg. 350
ALLIANZ SNA SAL—See Allianz SE; *Int'l*, pg. 350
ALLIANZ SP. Z O.O.—See Allianz SE; *Int'l*, pg. 350
ALLIANZ US PRIVATE REIT LP—See Allianz SE; *Int'l*, pg. 350
ALLIANZ VIVA S.P.A.—See Allianz SE; *Int'l*, pg. 350
ALLIED INSURANCE BROKERS LTD.—See GraceKennedy Limited; *Int'l*, pg. 3048
ALLIED INTERNATIONAL HOLDINGS INC.—See AXA S.A.; *Int'l*, pg. 760
ALLIED SOLUTIONS LLC—See Allied Solutions LLC; *U.S. Private*, pg. 188
ALLIED SPECIALTY INSURANCE INC.—See AXA S.A.; *Int'l*, pg. 760
ALLIED WORLD ASSURANCE COMPANY—See Fairfax Financial Holdings Limited; *Int'l*, pg. 2605
ALL MOTORISTS INSURANCE AGENCY INC.—See Western General Insurance Co., Inc.; *U.S. Private*, pg. 4493
ALL NATION INSURANCE COMPANY; *U.S. Private*, pg. 171
ALLOCATION SERVICES, INC.—See Brown & Brown, Inc.; *U.S. Public*, pg. 396
ALL RISKS, LTD.—See Ryan Specialty Holdings, Inc.; *U.S. Public*, pg. 1827
ALLTRUST INSURANCE INC.; *U.S. Private*, pg. 194
AL MADINA TAKAFUL CO. SAOG; *Int'l*, pg. 281
ALMEIDA & CARLSON INSURANCE AGENCY; *U.S. Private*, pg. 195
ALMONDZ INSURANCE BROKERS PVT. LTD.—See Almondz Global Securities Limited; *Int'l*, pg. 364
ALMONDZ REINSURANCE BROKERS PRIVATE LIMITED—See Almondz Global Securities Limited; *Int'l*, pg. 364
ALPHABET AUSTRIA FUHRPARKMANAGEMENT GMBH—See Bayerische Motoren Werke Aktiengesellschaft; *Int'l*, pg. 910
ALPHABET FRANCE FLEET MANAGEMENT S.N.C.—See Bayerische Motoren Werke Aktiengesellschaft; *Int'l*, pg. 910
ALPHABET FUHRPARKMANAGEMENT (SCHWEIZ) AG—See Bayerische Motoren Werke Aktiengesellschaft; *Int'l*, pg. 910
ALPHABET (GB) LTD.—See Bayerische Motoren Werke Aktiengesellschaft; *Int'l*, pg. 910
ALPHABET LUXEMBOURG S.A.—See Bayerische Motoren Werke Aktiengesellschaft; *Int'l*, pg. 910
ALPHABET POLSKA FLEET MANAGEMENT SP. Z O.O.—See Bayerische Motoren Werke Aktiengesellschaft; *Int'l*, pg. 910
ALPHA INSURANCE LIMITED; *Int'l*, pg. 368
ALPHA INSURANCE LTD—See Alpha Services and Holdings S.A.; *Int'l*, pg. 369
AL PURMORT INSURANCE INC.; *U.S. Private*, pg. 147
AL SAGR COOPERATIVE INSURANCE COMPANY—See Al-Sagr National Insurance Company; *Int'l*, pg. 288
ALTIG INTERNATIONAL; *U.S. Private*, pg. 209
ALTRUIS BENEFITS CONSULTING, INC.—See Reliance Global Group, Inc.; *U.S. Public*, pg. 1778
AMAAL COMMERCIAL BROKER LLC—See Belhasa Group of Companies; *Int'l*, pg. 963
AMANA COOPERATIVE INSURANCE COMPANY; *Int'l*, pg. 409
AMAZON INSURANCE NV—See Baloise Holding AG; *Int'l*, pg. 811
A.M. BEST COMPANY—See State Automobile Mutual Insurance Company; *U.S. Private*, pg. 3790
AMBRIDGE PARTNERS, LLC—See Fairfax Financial Holdings Limited; *Int'l*, pg. 2606
AMERICAN AGENCY INC.; *U.S. Private*, pg. 222
AMERICAN BENEFITS GROUP—See Aon plc; *Int'l*, pg. 495
AMERICAN CLAIMS MANAGEMENT - ATLANTIC REGION, LLC—See Brown & Brown, Inc.; *U.S. Public*, pg. 396
AMERICAN CLAIMS MANAGEMENT, INC.—See Brown & Brown, Inc.; *U.S. Public*, pg. 397
AMERICAN COLLECTORS INSURANCE, INC.—See The Carlyle Group LP; *U.S. Public*, pg. 2050
AMERICAN COMPENSATION INSURANCE COMPANY—See State Automobile Mutual Insurance Company; *U.S. Private*, pg. 3790

524210 — INSURANCE AGENCIES ...

AMERICAN EMPIRE UNDERWRITERS, INC.—See American Financial Group, Inc.; *U.S. Public*, pg. 102
THE AMERICAN EQUITY UNDERWRITERS, INC.—See AmWINS Group, Inc.; *U.S. Private*, pg. 270
AMERICAN FAMILY BROKERAGE, INC.—See American Family Mutual Insurance Company; *U.S. Private*, pg. 233
AMERICAN FINANCIAL MARKETING INC.—See Allianz SE; *Int'l*, pg. 351
AMERICAN FUNERAL FINANCIAL, LLC—See Security National Financial Corporation; *U.S. Public*, pg. 1856
AMERICAN GUARANTEE INSURANCE COMPANY—See First Citizens BancShares, Inc.; *U.S. Public*, pg. 842
AMERICAN HERITAGE AGENCY INC.—See Inszone Insurance Services, LLC; *U.S. Private*, pg. 2096
AMERICAN HERITAGE LIFE INSURANCE COMPANY—See The Allstate Corporation; *U.S. Public*, pg. 2033
AMERICAN INDEPENDENT MARKETING, INC.—See Integrity Marketing Group LLC; *U.S. Private*, pg. 2103
AMERICAN INSURANCE ADMINISTRATORS, INC.—See Genstar Capital, LLC; *U.S. Private*, pg. 1674
AMERICAN INSURANCE BROKERS, INC.—See Unico American Corporation; *U.S. Public*, pg. 2225
THE AMERICAN INSURANCE COMPANY, CORP.—See Allianz SE; *Int'l*, pg. 356
AMERICAN INSURANCE MANAGEMENT GROUP; *U.S. Private*, pg. 238
AMERICAN INSURANCE MARKETING SERVICES, INC.—See LTC Global, Inc.; *U.S. Private*, pg. 2509
AMERICAN INTERNATIONAL INSURANCE COMPANY OF PUERTO RICO—See American International Group, Inc.; *U.S. Public*, pg. 106
AMERICAN INTERSTATE INSURANCE COMPANY INC.—See AMERISAFE, Inc.; *U.S. Public*, pg. 115
AMERICAN LIBERTY INSURANCE COMPANY—See Altaris Capital Partners, LLC; *U.S. Private*, pg. 206
AMERICAN LIFE & ACCIDENT INSURANCE COMPANY—See Globe Life Inc.; *U.S. Public*, pg. 946
AMERICAN MEMORIAL LIFE INSURANCE COMPANY—See Assurant, Inc.; *U.S. Public*, pg. 214
AMERICAN NATIONAL COUNTY MUTUAL INSURANCE COMPANY—See Brookfield Corporation; *Int'l*, pg. 1174
AMERICAN NATIONAL LIFE INSURANCE COMPANY OF NEW YORK—See Brookfield Corporation; *Int'l*, pg. 1174
AMERICAN PLATINUM PROPERTY & CASUALTY INSURANCE COMPANY—See Universal Insurance Holdings, Inc.; *U.S. Public*, pg. 2261
AMERICAN SECURITY LIFE INSURANCE COMPANY LIMITED—See American International Group, Inc.; *U.S. Public*, pg. 106
AMERICAN SENIOR BENEFITS, LLC—See Integrity Marketing Group LLC; *U.S. Private*, pg. 2103
AMERICAN SOUTHWEST INSURANCE MANAGERS, INC.—See AmWINS Group, Inc.; *U.S. Private*, pg. 269
AMERICAN SPECIALTY INSURANCE & RISK SERVICES, INC.—See Brown & Brown, Inc.; *U.S. Public*, pg. 396
AMERICAN STANDARD INSURANCE COMPANY OF WISCONSIN—See American Family Mutual Insurance Company; *U.S. Private*, pg. 233
AMERICAN TRANSIT INSURANCE COMPANY—See United Security Life and Health Insurance Company; *U.S. Private*, pg. 4297
AMERICAN WESTBROOK INSURANCE SERVICES, LLC—See GTCR LLC; *U.S. Private*, pg. 1802
AMERICAN WEST INSURANCE COMPANY—See Nodak Insurance Company; *U.S. Private*, pg. 2933
AMERICA'S 1ST CHOICE OF SOUTH CAROLINA, INC.—See Elevance Health, Inc.; *U.S. Public*, pg. 728
AMERICA'S FLOOD SERVICES, INC.—See The Seibels Bruce Group, Inc.; *U.S. Private*, pg. 4116
AMERILIFE GROUP, LLC—See Thomas H. Lee Partners, L.P.; *U.S. Private*, pg. 4156
AMERI LIFE & HEALTH SERVICES; *U.S. Private*, pg. 220
AMERIPRISE TRUST COMPANY—See Ameriprise Financial, Inc.; *U.S. Public*, pg. 114
AMERISTAR AGENCY, INC.—See Marsh & McLennan Companies, Inc.; *U.S. Public*, pg. 1380
AMERMAN INSURANCE SERVICES, LLC—See Galiot Insurance Services, Inc.; *U.S. Private*, pg. 1638
AMETROS FINANCIAL CORPORATION—See Webster Financial Corporation; *U.S. Public*, pg. 2341
AMFI CORP.; *Int'l*, pg. 424
AMICUS INSURANCE SOLUTIONS LIMITED—See Brown & Brown, Inc.; *U.S. Public*, pg. 396
AMITY INSURANCE AGENCY, INC.—See Brown & Brown, Inc.; *U.S. Public*, pg. 399
AMK INSURANCE AGENCY, INC.; *U.S. Private*, pg. 263
AMMETLIFE INSURANCE BERHAD—See MetLife, Inc.; *U.S. Public*, pg. 1429
AMROCK TITLE INSURANCE COMPANY—See Rocket Companies, Inc.; *U.S. Public*, pg. 1804
AMS OSIGURANJE A.D.; *Int'l*, pg. 440
AMT ASSURANCES SARL—See CVC Capital Partners SICAV-FIS S.A.; *Int'l*, pg. 1882
AMTRUST CENTRAL BUREAU OF SERVICES LTD.—See Stone Point Capital LLC; *U.S. Private*, pg. 3820
AMTRUST FINANCIAL SERVICES, INC.—See Stone Point Capital LLC; *U.S. Private*, pg. 3819

AMTRUST INSURANCE SERVICES NORWAY AS—See Stone Point Capital LLC; *U.S. Private*, pg. 3820
AMTRUST INTERNATIONAL INSURANCE LTD.—See Stone Point Capital LLC; *U.S. Private*, pg. 3820
AMTRUST NORTH AMERICA, INC.—See Stone Point Capital LLC; *U.S. Private*, pg. 3820
AMTRUST UNDERWRITERS, INC.—See Stone Point Capital LLC; *U.S. Private*, pg. 3820
AMWINS GROUP, INC. - REDONDO BEACH—See AmWINS Group, Inc.; *U.S. Private*, pg. 269
ANCHOR AGENCY, INC.—See Pioneer Savings Bank; *U.S. Private*, pg. 3188
ANCHOR GENERAL INSURANCE AGENCY, INC.; *U.S. Private*, pg. 273
ANCO INSURANCE MANAGERS INC.; *U.S. Private*, pg. 274
ANCO INSURANCE SERVICES—See Anco Insurance Managers Inc.; *U.S. Private*, pg. 274
ANDERSON ASHCROFT LIMITED—See Brown & Brown, Inc.; *U.S. Public*, pg. 396
ANDREINI & COMPANY—See PCF Insurance Services of The West, LLC; *U.S. Private*, pg. 3120
ANDRE-ROMBERG INSURANCE AGENCY, INC.—See Stone Point Capital LLC; *U.S. Private*, pg. 3818
ANDREW INSURANCE ASSOCIATES, INC.—See Arthur J. Gallagher & Co.; *U.S. Public*, pg. 202
ANDY'S ASSURANCE AGENCY; *U.S. Private*, pg. 281
ANGLO HIBERNIAN BLOODSTOCK INSURANCE SERVICES LIMITED—See Brown & Brown, Inc.; *U.S. Public*, pg. 396
ANICOM INSURANCE, INC.—See Anicom Holdings, Inc.; *Int'l*, pg. 471
ANIELLO INSURANCE AGENCY, INC.—See GTCR LLC; *U.S. Private*, pg. 1802
ANN ARBOR ANNUITY EXCHANGE INC.—See Allianz SE; *Int'l*, pg. 351
THE ANNUITY STORE FINANCIAL & INSURANCE SERVICES LLC—See Allianz SE; *Int'l*, pg. 356
ANSAY & ASSOCIATES INC.; *U.S. Private*, pg. 285
ANSAY & ASSOCIATES, LLC; *U.S. Private*, pg. 285
ANSVAR INSURANCE LIMITED—See Ecclesiastical Insurance Office plc; *Int'l*, pg. 2288
ANTEPRIMA SRL—See Credito Emiliano S.p.A.; *Int'l*, pg. 1836
ANTHEM BLUE CROSS & BLUE SHIELD OF MISSOURI—See Elevance Health, Inc.; *U.S. Public*, pg. 729
ANV SERVICES US INC.—See ACNOVER, S.L.; *Int'l*, pg. 107
AON ADJUDICATION SERVICES LTD—See Aon plc; *Int'l*, pg. 490
AON AFFINITY CHILE LTDA.—See Aon plc; *Int'l*, pg. 489
AON AFFINITY SP ZOO—See Aon plc; *Int'l*, pg. 489
AON/ALBERT G. RUBEN INSURANCE SERVICES, INC.—See Aon plc; *Int'l*, pg. 494
AON ASIA PACIFIC LIMITED—See Aon plc; *Int'l*, pg. 489
AON AUSTRIA VERSICHERUNGSMAKLER GMBH—See Aon plc; *Int'l*, pg. 489
AON BAHRAIN W.L.L.—See Aon plc; *Int'l*, pg. 489
AON BELGIUM NV—See Aon plc; *Int'l*, pg. 489
AON BENFIELD (CHILE) CORREDORES DE REASEGUROS LTDA.—See Aon plc; *Int'l*, pg. 489
AON BENFIELD CHINA LIMITED—See Aon plc; *Int'l*, pg. 489
AON BENFIELD COLOMBIA LTDA. CORREDORES DE REASEGUROS—See Aon plc; *Int'l*, pg. 489
AON BENFIELD FAC INC.—See Aon plc; *Int'l*, pg. 489
AON BENFIELD GREECE SA—See Aon plc; *Int'l*, pg. 489
AON BENFIELD IBERIA, CORREDURIA DE REASEGUROS SA—See Aon plc; *Int'l*, pg. 489
AON BENFIELD, INC.—See Aon plc; *Int'l*, pg. 489
AON BENFIELD ISRAEL LIMITED—See Aon plc; *Int'l*, pg. 489
AON BENFIELD ITALIA SPA—See Aon plc; *Int'l*, pg. 489
AON BENFIELD MALAYSIA LIMITED—See Aon plc; *Int'l*, pg. 489
AON BENFIELD NETHERLANDS CV—See Aon plc; *Int'l*, pg. 489
AON BENFIELD PERU CORREDORES REASEGUROS SA—See Aon plc; *Int'l*, pg. 489
AON BENFIELD RUCKVERSICHERUNGSMAKLER GES.MBH—See Aon plc; *Int'l*, pg. 490
AON BENFIELD SECURITIES, INC.—See Aon plc; *Int'l*, pg. 490
AON BOLIVIA SA CORREDORES DE SEGUROS—See Aon plc; *Int'l*, pg. 490
AON BULGARIA EOOD—See Aon plc; *Int'l*, pg. 490
AON BUSINESS CONSULTING LTD.—See Aon plc; *Int'l*, pg. 490
AON CENTRAL AND EASTERN EUROPE AS—See Aon plc; *Int'l*, pg. 490
AON-COFCO INSURANCE BROKERAGE CO., LTD.—See COFCO Limited; *Int'l*, pg. 1691
AON-COFCO INSURANCE BROKERS CO., LTD.—See Aon plc; *Int'l*, pg. 494
AON CONSULTING ARGENTINA SA—See Aon plc; *Int'l*, pg. 490

CORPORATE AFFILIATIONS

AON CONSULTING & INSURANCE SERVICES—See Aon plc; *Int'l*, pg. 490
AON CONSULTING LESOTHO (PTY) LTD.—See Aon plc; *Int'l*, pg. 490
AON CONSULTING (PNG) LTD.—See Aon plc; *Int'l*, pg. 490
AON CONSULTING - SAN FRANCISCO—See Aon plc; *Int'l*, pg. 490
AON CONSULTING SOUTH AFRICA (PTY) LTD.—See Aon plc; *Int'l*, pg. 490
AON CONSULTING (THAILAND) LTD.—See Aon plc; *Int'l*, pg. 490
AON CORP.—See Aon plc; *Int'l*, pg. 491
AON CR SRL—See Aon plc; *Int'l*, pg. 490
AON DENMARK A/S—See Aon plc; *Int'l*, pg. 491
AON DIRECT GROUP ESPANA SL—See Aon plc; *Int'l*, pg. 491
AON FINLAND OY—See Aon plc; *Int'l*, pg. 491
AON FRANCE FINANCE SA—See Aon plc; *Int'l*, pg. 491
AON GIL Y CARVAJAL CORREDURIA DE SEGUROS SA—See Aon plc; *Int'l*, pg. 491
AON GLOBAL RISK CONSULTING LUXEMBOURG SARL—See Aon plc; *Int'l*, pg. 491
AON GROUP, INC.—See Aon plc; *Int'l*, pg. 491
AON GROUP JAPAN LTD.—See Aon plc; *Int'l*, pg. 490
AON HEALTHCARE—See Aon plc; *Int'l*, pg. 491
AON HEWITT CONSULTING KOREA INC.—See Aon plc; *Int'l*, pg. 490
AON HEWITT GMBH—See Alight, Inc.; *U.S. Public*, pg. 76
AON HEWITT RISK & CONSULTING SRL—See Alight, Inc.; *U.S. Public*, pg. 76
AON HOLDINGS CORRETORES DE SEGUROS LTDA—See Aon plc; *Int'l*, pg. 491
AON HOLDINGS NORWAY AS—See Aon plc; *Int'l*, pg. 491
AON HUNTINGTON T BLOCK INSURANCE AGENCY—See Aon plc; *Int'l*, pg. 493
AON INSURANCE BROKERS (MALAYSIA) SDN BHD—See Aon plc; *Int'l*, pg. 491
AON INSURANCE BROKERS (PVT) LTD.—See Aon plc; *Int'l*, pg. 491
AON INSURANCE MANAGERS (BARBADOS) LTD.—See Aon plc; *Int'l*, pg. 491
AON INSURANCE MANAGERS GIBRALTAR LTD.—See Aon plc; *Int'l*, pg. 492
AON INSURANCE MANAGERS (LUXEMBOURG) SA—See Aon plc; *Int'l*, pg. 492
AON INSURANCE SERVICES—See Aon plc; *Int'l*, pg. 490
AON INTERNATIONAL HOLDINGS, INC.—See Aon plc; *Int'l*, pg. 492
AON ITALIA SPA—See Aon plc; *Int'l*, pg. 492
AON JAUCH & HUBENER EMPLOYEE BENEFIT CONSULTING GES.MBH—See Aon plc; *Int'l*, pg. 491
AON KOREA INC.—See Aon plc; *Int'l*, pg. 492
AON LATVIA SIA—See Aon plc; *Int'l*, pg. 492
AON LESOTHO (PTY) LTD.—See Aon plc; *Int'l*, pg. 492
AON LUXEMBOURG SA—See Aon plc; *Int'l*, pg. 492
AON MACDONAGH BOLAND GROUP LTD—See Aon plc; *Int'l*, pg. 492
AON MONIA OY—See Aon plc; *Int'l*, pg. 492
AON NAMIBIA (PTY) LTD.—See Aon plc; *Int'l*, pg. 492
AON NETHERLANDS OPERATIONS BV—See Aon plc; *Int'l*, pg. 492
AON NEW ZEALAND—See Aon plc; *Int'l*, pg. 492
AON NORWAY AS—See Aon plc; *Int'l*, pg. 492
AON OF ARIZONA INC.—See Aon plc; *Int'l*, pg. 494
AON PARIZEAU INC.—See Aon plc; *Int'l*, pg. 492
AON PENSIONS INSURANCE BROKERS GMBH—See Aon plc; *Int'l*, pg. 492
AON POLSKA SP ZOO—See Aon plc; *Int'l*, pg. 492
AON PRIVATE CONSULTING A/S—See Aon plc; *Int'l*, pg. 492
AON QATAR LLC—See Aon plc; *Int'l*, pg. 492
AON RE MIDDLE EAST WLL—See Aon plc; *Int'l*, pg. 492
AON RE SWITZERLAND—See Aon plc; *Int'l*, pg. 492
AON RISK INSURANCE SERVICES WEST, INC.—See Aon plc; *Int'l*, pg. 493
AON RISK SERVICE OF TEXAS INC.—See Aon plc; *Int'l*, pg. 493
AON RISK SERVICES AUSTRALIA LTD.—See Aon plc; *Int'l*, pg. 493
AON RISK SERVICES (CHILE) SA—See Aon plc; *Int'l*, pg. 493
AON RISK SERVICES COMPANIES, INC.—See Aon plc; *Int'l*, pg. 492
AON RISK SERVICES INC. FLORIDA—See Aon plc; *Int'l*, pg. 493
AON RISK SERVICES INC. (LA)—See Aon plc; *Int'l*, pg. 493
AON RISK SERVICES, INC. OF CENTRAL CALIFORNIA—See Aon plc; *Int'l*, pg. 493
AON RISK SERVICES INC. OF COLORADO—See Aon plc; *Int'l*, pg. 493
AON RISK SERVICES INC. OF INDIANA—See Aon plc; *Int'l*, pg. 493
AON RISK SERVICES, INC. OF MASSACHUSETTS—See Aon plc; *Int'l*, pg. 493
AON RISK SERVICES INC. OF NJ—See Aon plc; *Int'l*, pg. 493
AON RISK SERVICES INC.—See Aon plc; *Int'l*, pg. 492
AON RISK SERVICES INC.—See Aon plc; *Int'l*, pg. 493

524210 — INSURANCE AGENCIES ...

AON RISK SERVICES INC.—See Aon plc; *Int'l*, pg. 493
AON RISK SERVICES INC.—See Aon plc; *Int'l*, pg. 493
AON RISK SERVICES INC.—See Aon plc; *Int'l*, pg. 493
AON RISK SERVICES INC.—See Aon plc; *Int'l*, pg. 493
AON RISK SERVICES INC.—See Aon plc; *Int'l*, pg. 493
AON RISK SERVICES INC.—See Aon plc; *Int'l*, pg. 493
AON RISK SERVICES INC.—See Aon plc; *Int'l*, pg. 493
AON RISK SERVICES INC.—See Aon plc; *Int'l*, pg. 493
AON RISK SERVICES INC.—See Aon plc; *Int'l*, pg. 493
AON RISK SERVICES OF OREGON—See Aon plc; *Int'l*, pg. 493
AON RISK SERVICES OF PUERTO RICO INC—See Aon plc; *Int'l*, pg. 493
AON RISK SERVICES OF TEXAS—See Aon plc; *Int'l*, pg. 493
AON RISK SERVICES—See Aon plc; *Int'l*, pg. 493
AON RISK SERVICES SOUTHWEST, INC.—See Aon plc; *Int'l*, pg. 493
AON RISK SERVICES TAIWAN LTD.—See Aon plc; *Int'l*, pg. 493
AON RISK SERVICES (THAILAND) LTD.—See Aon plc; *Int'l*, pg. 493
AON RISK SOLUTIONS (CAYMAN) LTD.—See Aon plc; *Int'l*, pg. 493
AON ROMANIA BROKER DE ASIGURARE - RE ASIGURARE SRL—See Aon plc; *Int'l*, pg. 494
AON RUS INSURANCE BROKERS LLC—See Aon plc; *Int'l*, pg. 494
AON SOLUTIONS IRELAND LIMITED—See Alight, Inc.; *U.S. Public*, pg. 76
AON SOLUTIONS JAPAN LTD—See Alight, Inc.; *U.S. Public*, pg. 76
AON SWEDEN AB—See Aon plc; *Int'l*, pg. 494
AON TAIWAN LTD.—See Aon plc; *Int'l*, pg. 494
AON TANZANIA LTD.—See Aon plc; *Int'l*, pg. 494
AON (THAILAND) LTD.—See Aon plc; *Int'l*, pg. 489
AON UK LIMITED—See Aon plc; *Int'l*, pg. 494
AON VERSICHERUNGSMAKLER DEUTSCHLAND GMBH—See Aon plc; *Int'l*, pg. 494
AON VIETNAM LIMITED—See Aon plc; *Int'l*, pg. 494
AON ZAMBIA LTD—See Aon plc; *Int'l*, pg. 494
APEX INSURANCE AGENCY, INC.—See Brown & Brown, Inc.; *U.S. Public*, pg. 396
APEX OUTSOURCING, INC.; *U.S. Private*, pg. 293
A PLUS ASSET ADVISOR CO., LTD.; *Int'l*, pg. 18
APPALACHIAN UNDERWRITERS, INC. - OAK RIDGE—See Appalachian Underwriters, Inc.; *U.S. Private*, pg. 295
APPALACHIAN UNDERWRITERS, INC.; *U.S. Private*, pg. 295
APPLEBY & STERLING, INC.; *U.S. Private*, pg. 297
APPLEBY & WYMAN INSURANCE AGENCY, INC.—See Cross Financial Corporation; *U.S. Private*, pg. 1104
APPLING INSURANCE AGENCY—See Inszone Insurance Services, LLC; *U.S. Private*, pg. 2096
APPROFRAIS S.A.—See Allianz SE; *Int'l*, pg. 351
APRIL COVER SARL—See CVC Capital Partners SICAV-FIS S.A.; *Int'l*, pg. 1882
APRIL ENTREPRISE LYON—See CVC Capital Partners SICAV-FIS S.A.; *Int'l*, pg. 1882
APRIL IARD SARL—See CVC Capital Partners SICAV-FIS S.A.; *Int'l*, pg. 1882
APRIL IBERIA SARL—See CVC Capital Partners SICAV-FIS S.A.; *Int'l*, pg. 1882
APRIL MARINE—See CVC Capital Partners SICAV-FIS S.A.; *Int'l*, pg. 1882
APRIL MARKETING SOLUTIONS SARL—See CVC Capital Partners SICAV-FIS S.A.; *Int'l*, pg. 1882
APRIL MON ASSURANCE LYON—See CVC Capital Partners SICAV-FIS S.A.; *Int'l*, pg. 1882
APRIL PATRIMOINE SARL—See CVC Capital Partners SICAV-FIS S.A.; *Int'l*, pg. 1882
AQUILLA INSURANCE BROKERS LIMITED—See Brown & Brown, Inc.; *U.S. Public*, pg. 396
A QUOTE INSURANCE SERVICES LIMITED—See Highway Insurance Holdings Plc; *Int'l*, pg. 3389
ARABIA INSURANCE COOPERATIVE COMPANY; *Int'l*, pg. 533
ARAG INSURANCE COMPANY INC.; *U.S. Private*, pg. 307
ARAG SERVICES LLC—See Arag Insurance Company Inc.; *U.S. Private*, pg. 307
ARAMARK HEALTHCARE TECHNOLOGIES, LLC—See Ascension Health Alliance; *U.S. Private*, pg. 346
ARBELLA INSURANCE GROUP—See Arbella Insurance Group; *U.S. Private*, pg. 308
ARBELLA PROTECTION INSURANCE COMPANY INC.—See Arbella Insurance Group; *U.S. Private*, pg. 308
ARC EXCESS & SURPLUS LLC; *U.S. Private*, pg. 309
ARC EXCESS & SURPLUS OF MIDSOUTH, LLC—See ARC Excess & Surplus LLC; *U.S. Private*, pg. 309
ARC EXCESS & SURPLUS OF NEW ENGLAND, LLC—See ARC Excess & Surplus LLC; *U.S. Private*, pg. 309
ARCH CAPITAL SERVICES INC—See Arch Capital Group Ltd.; *Int'l*, pg. 546
ARCHENFIELD INSURANCE MANAGEMENT LIMITED—See Brown & Brown, Inc.; *U.S. Public*, pg. 396

ARCHER A. ASSOCIATES, INC.—See GTCR LLC; *U.S. Private*, pg. 1802
ARCH INSURANCE CANADA LTD.—See Arch Capital Group Ltd.; *Int'l*, pg. 546
ARCH INSURANCE COMPANY—See Arch Capital Group Ltd.; *Int'l*, pg. 546
ARCH INVESTMENT MANAGEMENT LTD.—See Arch Capital Group Ltd.; *Int'l*, pg. 546
ARCH LMI PTY LTD—See Arch Capital Group Ltd.; *Int'l*, pg. 546
ARCH MORTGAGE ASSURANCE COMPANY—See Arch Capital Group Ltd.; *Int'l*, pg. 546
ARCH MORTGAGE INSURANCE LIMITED—See Arch Capital Group Ltd.; *Int'l*, pg. 546
ARCH SPECIALTY INSURANCE AGENCY INC.—See Arch Capital Group Ltd.; *Int'l*, pg. 546
ARC LEGAL ASSISTANCE LIMITED—See Stone Point Capital LLC; *U.S. Private*, pg. 3820
ARC MIDATLANTIC—See ARC Excess & Surplus LLC; *U.S. Private*, pg. 309
ARC SOUTH, LLC—See ARC Excess & Surplus LLC; *U.S. Private*, pg. 309
ARCW INSURANCE, INC.; *U.S. Private*, pg. 316
ARENA BROKER S.R.L.—See Banco BPM S.p.A.; *Int'l*, pg. 818
ARGENIA, LLC—See Truist Financial Corporation; *U.S. Public*, pg. 2200
ARGOGLOBAL UNDERWRITING (DUBAI) LIMITED—See Brookfield Reinsurance Ltd.; *Int'l*, pg. 1194
ARGO GROUP INTERNATIONAL HOLDINGS, LTD. - ALTERIS PUBLIC RISK SOLUTIONS DIVISION—See Brookfield Reinsurance Ltd.; *Int'l*, pg. 1193
ARGO PRO—See Brookfield Reinsurance Ltd.; *Int'l*, pg. 1193
ARGO RE DIFC, LTD.—See Brookfield Reinsurance Ltd.; *Int'l*, pg. 1193
ARGYLL INSURANCE SERVICES LIMITED—See Marsh & McLennan Companies, Inc.; *U.S. Public*, pg. 1374
ARH III INSURANCE CO., INC.—See NJ Transit Corporation; *U.S. Private*, pg. 2930
ARI CASUALTY COMPANY—See Stone Point Capital LLC; *U.S. Private*, pg. 3820
ARIS TITLE INSURANCE CORPORATION—See Brookfield Reinsurance Ltd.; *Int'l*, pg. 1193
ARMFIELD, HARRISON & THOMAS, INC.—See The Baldwin Insurance Group, Inc.; *U.S. Public*, pg. 2035
ARMSTRONG/ROBITAILLE/RIEGLE BUSINESS & INSURANCE SOLUTIONS—See Genstar Capital, LLC; *U.S. Private*, pg. 1674
ARNONE LOWTH WILSON & LEIBOWITZ INC—See Aon plc; *Int'l*, pg. 495
ARPICO INSURANCE PLC; *Int'l*, pg. 578
ARRIVA INSURANCE A/S—See I Squared Capital Advisors (US) LLC; *U.S. Private*, pg. 2024
ARRIVA INSURANCE COMPANY (GIBRALTAR) LIMITED—See I Squared Capital Advisors (US) LLC; *U.S. Private*, pg. 2024
ARROWHEAD GENERAL INSURANCE AGENCY HOLDING CORP.—See Brown & Brown, Inc.; *U.S. Public*, pg. 396
ARROWHEAD INSURANCE RISK MANAGERS, LLC—See Brown & Brown, Inc.; *U.S. Public*, pg. 396
ARTEX RISK SOLUTIONS (GIBRALTAR) LIMITED—See Arthur J. Gallagher & Co.; *U.S. Public*, pg. 202
ARTEX RISK SOLUTIONS (MALTA) LIMITED—See Arthur J. Gallagher & Co.; *U.S. Public*, pg. 202
ART HAUSER INSURANCE, INC.; *U.S. Private*, pg. 339
ARTHUR J. GALLAGHER (AUS) PTY. LTD.—See Arthur J. Gallagher & Co.; *U.S. Public*, pg. 203
ARTHUR J. GALLAGHER AUSTRALASIA HOLDINGS PTY. LTD.—See Arthur J. Gallagher & Co.; *U.S. Public*, pg. 203
ARTHUR J. GALLAGHER BROKERAGE & RISK MANAGEMENT SERVICES, LLC—See Arthur J. Gallagher & Co.; *U.S. Public*, pg. 203
ARTHUR J. GALLAGHER & CO. (AUS) LTD—See Arthur J. Gallagher & Co.; *U.S. Public*, pg. 203
ARTHUR J. GALLAGHER & CO. (ILLINOIS)—See Arthur J. Gallagher & Co.; *U.S. Public*, pg. 203
ARTHUR J. GALLAGHER & CO. INSURANCE BROKERS OF CALIFORNIA, INC.—See Arthur J. Gallagher & Co.; *U.S. Public*, pg. 202
ARTHUR J. GALLAGHER & CO. NEWPORT BEACH—See Arthur J. Gallagher & Co.; *U.S. Public*, pg. 202
ARTHUR J. GALLAGHER & CO. ROCKVILLE—See Arthur J. Gallagher & Co.; *U.S. Public*, pg. 205
ARTHUR J. GALLAGHER HOUSING LIMITED—See Arthur J. Gallagher & Co.; *U.S. Public*, pg. 202
ARTHUR J. GALLAGHER REINSURANCE AUSTRALASIA PTY. LTD.—See Arthur J. Gallagher & Co.; *U.S. Public*, pg. 203
ARTHUR J. GALLAGHER RISK MANAGEMENT SERVICES (HAWAII), INC.—See Arthur J. Gallagher & Co.; *U.S. Public*, pg. 203
ARTHUR J. GALLAGHER RISK MANAGEMENT SERVICES, INC.—See Arthur J. Gallagher & Co.; *U.S. Public*, pg. 203
ARTHUR J. GALLAGHER SWEDEN AB—See Arthur J. Gallagher & Co.; *U.S. Public*, pg. 203

ARTHUR J. GLATFELTER AGENCY INC.—See American International Group, Inc.; *U.S. Public*, pg. 106
ARX INSURANCE COMPANY—See Fairfax Financial Holdings Limited; *Int'l*, pg. 2605
A S ARBURY & SONS, INC.—See Hellman & Friedman LLC; *U.S. Private*, pg. 1908
ASCENSION COLLEGIATE SOLUTIONS—See Aquiline Capital Partners LLC; *U.S. Private*, pg. 305
ASH BROKERAGE CORP.; *U.S. Private*, pg. 349
ASHTON STATE BANK AGENCY, INC.—See Ashton Bancshares, Inc.; *U.S. Private*, pg. 350
ASN BROKER PCL; *Int'l*, pg. 628
ASPECT MANAGEMENT, LLC—See Integrity Marketing Group LLC; *U.S. Private*, pg. 2103
ASPEN INSURANCE U.S. SERVICES INC.—See Apollo Global Management, Inc.; *U.S. Public*, pg. 147
ASPEN SPECIALTY INSURANCE COMPANY—See Apollo Global Management, Inc.; *U.S. Public*, pg. 147
ASSCOM INSURANCE BROKERS SRL—See Aon plc; *Int'l*, pg. 494
ASSET PROTECTION, INC.—See Hellman & Friedman LLC; *U.S. Private*, pg. 1908
ASSISTANCE COURTAGE D'ASSURANCE ET DE REASSURANCE S.A.—See Allianz SE; *Int'l*, pg. 351
ASSITECA AGRICOLTURA S.R.L.—See Assiteca SpA; *Int'l*, pg. 648
ASSITECA BSA S.R.L.—See Assiteca SpA; *Int'l*, pg. 648
ASSITECA CONSULTING S.R.L.—See Assiteca SpA; *Int'l*, pg. 648
ASSITECA SPA; *Int'l*, pg. 648
ASSOCIATED AGENCY GROUP, LLC—See Aon plc; *Int'l*, pg. 495
ASSOCIATED FINANCIAL GROUP, LLC—See Caisse de Depot et Placement du Quebec; *Int'l*, pg. 1256
ASSOCIATED FINANCIAL GROUP, LLC—See KKR & Co. Inc.; *U.S. Public*, pg. 1264
ASSOCIATED INDUSTRIES INSURANCE COMPANY, INC.—See Stone Point Capital LLC; *U.S. Private*, pg. 3820
ASSOCIATED INSURANCE AGENTS, INC.—See CBIZ, Inc.; *U.S. Public*, pg. 456
ASSOCIATES INSURANCE AGENCY, INC.; *U.S. Private*, pg. 358
ASSOCIATION CASUALTY INSURANCE COMPANY—See Columbia Insurance Group, Inc.; *U.S. Private*, pg. 977
ASSOCIATION MEMBER BENEFITS ADVISORS, LLC; *U.S. Private*, pg. 358
ASSURANCE VIE ET PREVOYANCE (AVIP) S.A.—See Allianz SE; *Int'l*, pg. 351
ASSURED GUARANTY (EUROPE) PLC—See Assured Guaranty Ltd.; *Int'l*, pg. 649
ASSURESOUTH, INC.—See GTCR LLC; *U.S. Private*, pg. 1802
ASSURITY LIFE INSURANCE COMPANY—See Assurity Security Group Inc.; *U.S. Private*, pg. 359
ASU GROUP; *U.S. Private*, pg. 362
ASURANSI DAYIN MITRA TBK; *Int'l*, pg. 663
ATHENS ADMINISTRATORS; *U.S. Private*, pg. 367
ATLANTIC EMPLOYERS INSURANCE COMPANY—See Chubb Limited; *Int'l*, pg. 1590
ATLANTIC RISK SPECIALISTS, INC.—See AmWINS Group, Inc.; *U.S. Private*, pg. 269
ATLANTIC SECURITY INSURANCE COMPANY INC.—See Strickland Insurance Group Inc.; *U.S. Private*, pg. 3839
ATLANTIC SPECIALTY LINES, INC.—See Ryan Specialty Holdings, Inc.; *U.S. Public*, pg. 1828
ATLAS GENERAL HOLDINGS, LLC—See Arthur J. Gallagher & Co.; *U.S. Public*, pg. 203
ATLAS INSURANCE LIMITED; *Int'l*, pg. 685
ATLAS MORTGAGE & INSURANCE CO., INC.; *U.S. Private*, pg. 379
ATRIUM UNDERWRITING GROUP LTD.—See Enstar Group Limited; *Int'l*, pg. 2448
AUB GROUP NZ LIMITED—See AUB Group Limited; *Int'l*, pg. 698
AURA OSIGURANJE A.D.; *Int'l*, pg. 706
AUSTAGENCIES PTY. LTD.—See AUB Group Limited; *Int'l*, pg. 698
AUSTBROKERS CANBERRA PTY. LTD.—See AUB Group Limited; *Int'l*, pg. 698
AUSTBROKERS CENTRAL COAST PTY. LTD.—See AUB Group Limited; *Int'l*, pg. 698
AUSTBROKERS PREMIER PTY. LTD.—See AUB Group Limited; *Int'l*, pg. 698
AUSTBROKERS RWA PTY. LTD.—See AUB Group Limited; *Int'l*, pg. 698
AUSTBROKERS TERRACE INSURANCE BROKERS PTY. LTD.—See AUB Group Limited; *Int'l*, pg. 698
AUSTBROKERS TERRACE INSURANCE PTY LTD.—See AUB Group Limited; *Int'l*, pg. 698
AUSTBROKERS TRADE CREDIT PTY. LTD.—See AUB Group Limited; *Int'l*, pg. 698
AUSTIN CONSULTING GROUP, INC.—See Arthur J. Gallagher & Co.; *U.S. Public*, pg. 203
AUTO & GENERAL INSURANCE COMPANY LIMITED—See BGL Group Limited; *Int'l*, pg. 1008
AUTO INSURANCE SPECIALISTS, LLC—See Mercury

524210 — INSURANCE AGENCIES ...

General Corporation; *U.S. Public*, pg. 1421
AUTO INSURANCE SPECIALISTS—See Mercury General Corporation; *U.S. Public*, pg. 1421
AUTOMATED BENEFIT SERVICES—See US Health Holdings Corp.; *U.S. Private*, pg. 4319
AUTOMOBILE INSURANCE PLANS SERVICE OFFICE; *U.S. Private*, pg. 400
AUTOMOTIVE ASSURANCE GROUP, LLC—See Stone Point Capital LLC; *U.S. Private*, pg. 3820
AVALON RISK MANAGEMENT, INC.; *U.S. Private*, pg. 403
AVANSSUR S.A.—See AXA S.A.; *Int'l*, pg. 759
AVENUE 365 LENDER SERVICES, LLC—See Rithm Capital Corp.; *U.S. Public*, pg. 1799
AVIATION SOLUTIONS, LLC—See Marsh & McLennan Companies, Inc.; *U.S. Public*, pg. 1380
THE AVI GROUP; *U.S. Private*, pg. 3990
AVIVA CENTRAL SERVICES UK LIMITED—See Aviva plc; *Int'l*, pg. 745
AVIVA PLC; *Int'l*, pg. 745
THE AVON-DIXON AGENCY, LLC—See Genstar Capital, LLC; *U.S. Private*, pg. 1675
AVSURANCE CORPORATION—See Avfuel Corporation; *U.S. Private*, pg. 406
A.W. AYRES AGENCY, INC.—See The Ayres Group, LLC; *U.S. Private*, pg. 3990
AWP AUSTRALIA PTY. LTD.—See Allianz SE; *Int'l*, pg. 343
AWP FRANCE SAS—See Allianz SE; *Int'l*, pg. 343
AXA-ARAG RECHTSSCHUTZ AG.—See AXA S.A.; *Int'l*, pg. 759
AXA ASSISTANCE MEXICO SA DE CV—See AXA S.A.; *Int'l*, pg. 754
AXA ASSISTANCE OCEAN INDIEN LTD—See AXA S.A.; *Int'l*, pg. 754
AXA AURORA VIDA SA DE SEGUROS Y REASEGUROS—See AXA S.A.; *Int'l*, pg. 757
AXA CESKA REPUBLIKA S.R.O—See AXA S.A.; *Int'l*, pg. 755
AXA COOPERATIVE INSURANCE COMPANY; *Int'l*, pg. 754
AXA CORPORATE SOLUTIONS—See Equitable Holdings, Inc.; *U.S. Public*, pg. 788
AXA CORP. SOLUTIONS INSURANCE COMPANY—See Equitable Holdings, Inc.; *U.S. Public*, pg. 788
AXA EQUITABLE LIFE ASSURANCE COMPANY—See Equitable Holdings, Inc.; *U.S. Public*, pg. 788
AXA FRANCE VIE S.A—See AXA S.A.; *Int'l*, pg. 756
AXA GENERAL INSURANCE - LTD.—See AXA S.A.; *Int'l*, pg. 759
AXA INSURANCE GULF—See AXA S.A.; *Int'l*, pg. 756
AXA INSURANCE S.A.—See Assicurazioni Generali S.p.A.; *Int'l*, pg. 643
AXA INSURANCE—See AXA S.A.; *Int'l*, pg. 756
AXA IRELAND LIMITED—See AXA S.A.; *Int'l*, pg. 757
AXA KRANKENVERSICHERUNG AG—See AXA S.A.; *Int'l*, pg. 757
AXA LIABILITIES MANAGERS INC.—See Equitable Holdings, Inc.; *U.S. Public*, pg. 788
AXA NETWORK, LLC—See Equitable Holdings, Inc.; *U.S. Public*, pg. 788
AXA SEGUROS SA DE CV—See AXA S.A.; *Int'l*, pg. 758
AXA SIGORTA A.S.—See AXA S.A.; *Int'l*, pg. 758
AXA SR—See AXA S.A.; *Int'l*, pg. 758
AXA UBEZPIECZENIA TOWARZYSTWO UBEZPIECZEN I REASEKURACJI S.A.—See AXA S.A.; *Int'l*, pg. 758
AXA UKRAINE—See AXA S.A.; *Int'l*, pg. 758
AXA ZIVOTNI POJISTOVNA A.S.—See AXA S.A.; *Int'l*, pg. 759
AXIOM RE, INC.—See Aquiline Capital Partners LLC; *U.S. Private*, pg. 304
AXIS GROUP SERVICES, INC.—See AXIS Capital Holdings Limited; *Int'l*, pg. 769
AXIS INSURANCE COMPANY—See AXIS Capital Holdings Limited; *Int'l*, pg. 769
AXIS SPECIALTY INSURANCE CO.—See AXIS Capital Holdings Limited; *Int'l*, pg. 770
AXIS SURPLUS INSURANCE COMPANY—See AXIS Capital Holdings Limited; *Int'l*, pg. 770
AYRES-RICE INSURANCE AGENCY, INC.—See The Ayres Group, LLC; *U.S. Private*, pg. 3990
AZIMUT FINANCIAL INSURANCE S.P.A.—See Azimut Holding SpA; *Int'l*, pg. 779
BAC FLORIDA INVESTMENTS—See Banco Bradesco S.A.; *Int'l*, pg. 819
BADGE AGENCY, INC.—See ABRY Partners, LLC; *U.S. Private*, pg. 41
BAGATTA ASSOCIATES, INC.—See GI Manager L.P.; *U.S. Private*, pg. 1693
BAGATTA ASSOCIATES, INC.—See Summit Partners, L.P.; *U.S. Private*, pg. 3856
BAHRAIN NATIONAL INSURANCE COMPANY B.S.C.—See Bahrain National Holding Company BSC; *Int'l*, pg. 800
BAHRAIN NATIONAL LIFE ASSURANCE COMPANY B.S.C.—See Bahrain National Holding Company BSC; *Int'l*, pg. 800
BAIRD MACGREGOR INSURANCE BROKERS LP; *Int'l*, pg. 803

BAJA AUTO INSURANCE—See Stone Point Capital LLC; *U.S. Private*, pg. 3818
BALOISE LEBENSVERSICHERUNG AG—See Baloise Holding AG; *Int'l*, pg. 811
BALOISE SACHVERSICHERUNG AG—See Baloise Holding AG; *Int'l*, pg. 811
BALOISE VIE LUXEMBOURG S.A—See Baloise Holding AG; *Int'l*, pg. 811
BALTIMORE FINANCIAL SERVICES CORPORATION—See Baltimore Life Insurance Company Inc.; *U.S. Private*, pg. 462
BANCO SANTANDER CONSUMER PORTUGAL, S.A.—See Banco Santander, S.A.; *Int'l*, pg. 825
BANGKOK PREMIER LIFE INSURANCE BROKER CO., LTD.—See Bangkok Dusit Medical Services Public Company Limited; *Int'l*, pg. 834
BANGLADESH NATIONAL INSURANCE CO., LTD.; *Int'l*, pg. 836
BANKERS INSURANCE GROUP, INC.—See Bankers International Financial Corporation; *U.S. Private*, pg. 467
BANKERS INTERNATIONAL FINANCIAL CORPORATION; *U.S. Private*, pg. 467
BANKERS LIFE INSURANCE COMPANY—See Bankers International Financial Corporation; *U.S. Private*, pg. 467
BANK MAKRAMAH LIMITED; *Int'l*, pg. 839
BANK OF IRELAND INSURANCE & INVESTMENTS LTD.—See Bank of Ireland Group plc; *Int'l*, pg. 844
THE BANK OF SAN ANTONIO INSURANCE GROUP, INC.—See Southwest Bancshares, Inc.; *U.S. Private*, pg. 3738
BANKSERVE INSURANCE SERVICES LTD.—See BMS Group Ltd.; *Int'l*, pg. 1077
BANSABADELL CORREDURIA DE SEGUROS SA—See Banco de Sabadell, S.A.; *Int'l*, pg. 821
BAO VIET INSURANCE CORPORATION—See Bao Viet Holdings; *Int'l*, pg. 855
BARBARY INSURANCE BROKERAGE—See Heffernan Insurance Brokers; *U.S. Private*, pg. 1904
BARBEE JACKSON INSURANCE COMPANY; *U.S. Private*, pg. 472
BARCLAYS INSURANCE SERVICES CO. LTD.—See Barclays PLC; *Int'l*, pg. 860
BARCLAYS VIE SA—See Barclays PLC; *Int'l*, pg. 861
BARNEY & BARNEY, INC.—See Marsh & McLennan Companies, Inc.; *U.S. Public*, pg. 1380
BARPAX ASSOCIATES LIMITED—See Brown & Brown, Inc.; *U.S. Public*, pg. 397
BAR-ZIV RAVID INSURANCE AGENCY LIMITED—See Howden Group Holdings Limited; *Int'l*, pg. 3493
BASE BRASIL B.I. CORRETORA DE SEGUROS LTDA.—See Alper Consultoria e Corretora de Seguros S.A.; *Int'l*, pg. 366
BAYLISS & COOKE LIMITED—See Brown & Brown, Inc.; *U.S. Public*, pg. 397
BAYSTATE FINANCIAL SERVICES, LLC; *U.S. Private*, pg. 497
BAYWA ASSEKURANZ-VERMITTLUNG GMBH—See BayWa AG; *Int'l*, pg. 916
BBC INSURANCE AGENCY, INC.—See Best Buy Co., Inc.; *U.S. Public*, pg. 326
B & B PROTECTOR PLANS, INC.—See Brown & Brown, Inc.; *U.S. Public*, pg. 397
BB&T INSURANCE SERVICES, INC. - BURKEY RISK SERVICES—See Clayton, Dubilier & Rice, LLC; *U.S. Private*, pg. 927
BB&T INSURANCE SERVICES, INC. - BURKEY RISK SERVICES—See Stone Point Capital LLC; *U.S. Private*, pg. 3826
BB&T INSURANCE SERVICES, INC.—See Clayton, Dubilier & Rice, LLC; *U.S. Private*, pg. 927
BB&T INSURANCE SERVICES, INC.—See Stone Point Capital LLC; *U.S. Private*, pg. 3826
BB&T INSURANCE SERVICES, INC. - TOFC—See Clayton, Dubilier & Rice, LLC; *U.S. Private*, pg. 927
BB&T INSURANCE SERVICES, INC. - TCFC—See Stone Point Capital LLC; *U.S. Private*, pg. 3826
BB&T - JOHN BURNHAM INSURANCE SERVICES—See Clayton, Dubilier & Rice, LLC; *U.S. Private*, pg. 927
BB&T - JOHN BURNHAM INSURANCE SERVICES—See Stone Point Capital LLC; *U.S. Private*, pg. 3826
BB&T - J. ROLFE DAVIS INSURANCE—See Clayton, Dubilier & Rice, LLC; *U.S. Private*, pg. 927
BB&T - J. ROLFE DAVIS INSURANCE—See Stone Point Capital LLC; *U.S. Private*, pg. 3826
BB&T - J.V. ARTHUR—See Clayton, Dubilier & Rice, LLC; *U.S. Private*, pg. 927
BB&T - J.V. ARTHUR—See Stone Point Capital LLC; *U.S. Private*, pg. 3826
BDB (UK) LIMITED—See Brown & Brown, Inc.; *U.S. Public*, pg. 397
BDO INSURANCE BROKERS, INC.—See BDO Unibank, Inc.; *Int'l*, pg. 930
BEAR INSURANCE SERVICE—See First Bancorp; *U.S. Public*, pg. 839
BEAUMONTS INSURANCE BROKERS LIMITED—See Marsh & McLennan Companies, Inc.; *U.S. Public*, pg. 1374
BEAZLEY HOLDINGS, INC.—See Beazley plc; *Int'l*, pg. 935

BEAZLEY INSURANCE DAC—See Beazley plc; *Int'l*, pg. 935
BEAZLEY LIMITED—See Beazley plc; *Int'l*, pg. 935
BEAZLEY PTE. LIMITED—See Beazley plc; *Int'l*, pg. 935
BEAZLEY UNDERWRITING PTY LTD—See Beazley plc; *Int'l*, pg. 936
BEDROCK TITLE COMPANY, LLC—See Stewart Information Services Corporation; *U.S. Public*, pg. 1947
BEECHER CARLSON HOLDINGS, INC.—See Brown & Brown, Inc.; *U.S. Public*, pg. 397
BEECHER CARLSON MANAGEMENT, LTD.—See Brown & Brown, Inc.; *U.S. Public*, pg. 397
BEEHIVE INSURANCE AGENCY, INC.—See Clyde Companies Inc.; *U.S. Private*, pg. 949
BEIMDIEK INSURANCE AGENCY, INC.—See GTCR LLC; *U.S. Private*, pg. 1802
BELL-ANDERSON INSURANCE, INC.; *U.S. Private*, pg. 519
BELWAY INSURANCE SERVICE, INC.—See Belcorp Inc.; *U.S. Private*, pg. 517
BENEFIT MARKETING SOLUTIONS, L.L.C.—See Aon plc; *Int'l*, pg. 494
BENEFIT PLANNERS & ASSOCIATES INC.—See Managed Care of America Inc.; *U.S. Private*, pg. 2559
BENEFITS ALLIANCE INSURANCE SERVICES, LLC—See GI Manager L.P.; *U.S. Private*, pg. 1693
BENEFITS ALLIANCE INSURANCE SERVICES, LLC—See Summit Partners, L.P.; *U.S. Private*, pg. 3856
BENEFIT SERVICES GROUP, INC.—See Wirtz Corporation; *U.S. Private*, pg. 4547
BENEFITTER INSURANCE SOLUTIONS, INC.—See UnitedHealth Group Incorporated; *U.S. Public*, pg. 2239
BENEFLEX INSURANCE SERVICES, INC.—See New Mountain Capital, LLC; *U.S. Private*, pg. 2901
BENEFYTT TECHNOLOGIES, INC.—See Madison Dearborn Partners, LLC; *U.S. Private*, pg. 2540
BENEUSA LLC—See Warner Pacific Insurance Services, Inc.; *U.S. Private*, pg. 4442
BENICO, LTD.—See Genstar Capital, LLC; *U.S. Private*, pg. 1674
BENIX LIMITED—See Humanica Public Company Limited; *Int'l*, pg. 3530
BENTON & PARKER CO. INC.; *U.S. Private*, pg. 528
BERKELEY INSURANCE GROUP LIMITED—See Brown & Brown, Inc.; *U.S. Public*, pg. 397
BERKELEY INSURANCE GROUP UK LIMITED—See Brown & Brown, Inc.; *U.S. Public*, pg. 397
BERKLEY AVIATION, LLC—See W.R. Berkley Corporation; *U.S. Public*, pg. 2316
BERKLEY RISK MANAGERS—See W.R. Berkley Corporation; *U.S. Public*, pg. 2317
BERKLEY TECHNOLGY SERVICES—See W.R. Berkley Corporation; *U.S. Public*, pg. 2317
BERKSHIRE AGENCY, INC.—See ABRY Partners, LLC; *U.S. Private*, pg. 41
BERKSHIRE HATHAWAY INTERNATIONAL INSURANCE LIMITED—See Berkshire Hathaway Inc.; *U.S. Public*, pg. 301
BERKSHIRE INSURANCE GROUP, INC.—See Berkshire Hills Bancorp, Inc.; *U.S. Public*, pg. 320
BERNARD WILLIAMS & CO.; *U.S. Private*, pg. 536
THE BERT COMPANY—See Caisse de Depot et Placement du Quebec; *Int'l*, pg. 1256
THE BERT COMPANY—See KKR & Co. Inc.; *U.S. Public*, pg. 1265
BESSO GRIMME INSURANCE BROKERSGMBH—See BGC Group, Inc.; *U.S. Public*, pg. 328
BESSO INSURANCE GROUP LIMITED—See BGC Group, Inc.; *U.S. Public*, pg. 328
BESSO RE BRASIL CORRETORA DE RESSEGUROS LTDA.—See BGC Group, Inc.; *U.S. Public*, pg. 328
BESSO SIGORTA VE REASURANS BROKERLIGI LTD.—See BGC Group, Inc.; *U.S. Public*, pg. 328
BEST HOMES TITLE AGENCY, LLC; *U.S. Private*, pg. 543
BESTPARK INTERNATIONAL LIMITED; *Int'l*, pg. 1000
BEST RATE INSURANCE AGENCY, INC.—See Stone Point Capital LLC; *U.S. Private*, pg. 3818
BF&G INSURANCE LIMITED—See Arthur J. Gallagher & Co.; *U.S. Public*, pg. 204
BGA INSURANCE AGENCY, INC.—See Cross Financial Corporation; *U.S. Private*, pg. 1104
B & H INSURANCE, LLC—See GTCR LLC; *U.S. Private*, pg. 1802
BHK INSURANCE SERVICES LIMITED—See Brown & Brown, Inc.; *U.S. Public*, pg. 397
BIDDLE INSURANCE SERVICES, INC.—See GTCR LLC; *U.S. Private*, pg. 1802
BIG I ADVANTAGE, INC.—See Independent Insurance Agents & Brokers of America, Inc.; *U.S. Private*, pg. 2059
BIG INSURANCE LIMITED—See Brown & Brown, Inc.; *U.S. Public*, pg. 397
BIG SAVINGS INSURANCE AGENCY INC.—See Dowling Capital Management, LLC; *U.S. Private*, pg. 1268
BIG SAVINGS INSURANCE AGENCY INC.—See Keystone Group, L.P.; *U.S. Private*, pg. 2298
BILAN SERVICES S.N.C.—See Allianz SE; *Int'l*, pg. 351
BILBAO HIPOTECARIA, S.A., E.F.C.—See Grupo Catalana Occidente, S.A.; *Int'l*, pg. 3124

524210 — INSURANCE AGENCIES ...

BILBAO VIDA Y GESTORES FINANCIEROS, S.A.—See Grupo Catalana Occidente, S.A.; *Int'l*, pg. 3124
BILL MARKVE & ASSOCIATES GROUP; *U.S. Private*, pg. 557
BIM INSURANCE BROKER SPA—See Banca Intermobiliare di Investimenti e Gestioni S.p.A.; *Int'l*, pg. 815
BIPIEMME VITA S.P.A.—See Banco BPM S.p.A.; *Int'l*, pg. 819
BISNETT INSURANCE, INC.—See Kelso & Company, L.P.; *U.S. Private*, pg. 2279
BISON INSURANCE AGENCY—See Duke Energy Corporation; *U.S. Public*, pg. 690
B.J. PETRUSO AGENCY & ASSOCIATES, INC.—See Northwest Bancshares, Inc.; *U.S. Public*, pg. 1542
BKCW, L.P.; *U.S. Private*, pg. 568
BLACK DAVIS & SHUE AGENCY INC.; *U.S. Private*, pg. 570
THE BLAIR AGENCY, INC.—See LTC Global, Inc.; *U.S. Private*, pg. 2509
B&L BROKERAGE SERVICES, INC.—See The Progressive Corporation; *U.S. Public*, pg. 2125
BLOOMINGTON COMPENSATION INSURANCE COMPANY—See State Automobile Mutual Insurance Company; *U.S. Private*, pg. 3791
BLUE LABEL DISTRIBUTION PROPRIETARY LIMITED—See Blue Label Telecoms Limited; *Int'l*, pg. 1068
BLV VERSICHERUNGSMANAGEMENT GMBH—See Benteler International AG; *Int'l*, pg. 976
BMI FINANCIAL GROUP, INC.; *U.S. Private*, pg. 600
BMT INSURANCE ADVISORS INC.—See Bryn Mawr Bank Corporation; *U.S. Public*, pg. 408
BMW AUSTRIA BANK GMBH—See Bayerische Motoren Werke Aktiengesellschaft; *Int'l*, pg. 911
BMW FINANCIAL SERVICES B.V.—See Bayerische Motoren Werke Aktiengesellschaft; *Int'l*, pg. 911
BMW FINANCIAL SERVICES DENMARK A/S—See Bayerische Motoren Werke Aktiengesellschaft; *Int'l*, pg. 911
BMW INSURANCE SERVICES KOREA CO. LTD.—See Bayerische Motoren Werke Aktiengesellschaft; *Int'l*, pg. 911
BNC INSURANCE AGENCY, INC.; *U.S. Private*, pg. 601
BNPP CARDIF GENERAL INSURANCE CO., LTD.—See BNP Paribas SA; *Int'l*, pg. 1088
BNPP CARDIF SEGUROS DE VIDA SA—See BNP Paribas SA; *Int'l*, pg. 1088
BOC GROUP LIFE ASSURANCE CO., LTD.—See Bank of China, Ltd.; *Int'l*, pg. 841
BOCOMMLIFE INSURANCE COMPANY LIMITED—See Bank of Communications Co., Ltd.; *Int'l*, pg. 842
BOC-SAMSUNG LIFE INSURANCE CO., LTD.—See Bank of China, Ltd.; *Int'l*, pg. 841
BOLTON & COMPANY—See IMA Financial Group, Inc.; *U.S. Private*, pg. 2043
BONDING INSURANCE AGENCY & INSURANCE FACTORS—See Vinet Holdings Inc.; *U.S. Private*, pg. 4385
BONDS, INC.—See Kelso & Company, L.P.; *U.S. Private*, pg. 2279
THE BORDEN-PERLMAN INSURANCE AGENCY, INC.; *U.S. Private*, pg. 3996
BORDEN PERLMAN INSURANCE AGENCY, INC.—See CBIZ, Inc.; *U.S. Public*, pg. 456
BORDER INSURANCE SERVICES, INC.—See Marsh & McLennan Companies, Inc.; *U.S. Public*, pg. 1380
BORISOFF INSURANCE SERVICES, INC.—See Hellman & Friedman LLC; *U.S. Private*, pg. 1909
THE BOSTONIAN GROUP INSURANCE AGENCY, INC.—See Marsh & McLennan Companies, Inc.; *U.S. Public*, pg. 1382
BOWEN, MICLETTE & BRITT, INC.; *U.S. Private*, pg. 625
BOWERSOX INSURANCE AGENCY COMPANY—See Keystone Agency Investors LLC; *U.S. Private*, pg. 2295
BOYD INSURANCE & INVESTMENT SERVICES, INC.; *U.S. Private*, pg. 627
BPI PHILAM LIFE ASSURANCE CORPORATION—See Bank of the Philippine Islands; *Int'l*, pg. 848
BPW INSURANCE SERVICES LIMITED—See Brown & Brown, Inc.; *U.S. Public*, pg. 397
BRADLEY INSURANCE AGENCY.—See Marsh & McLennan Companies, Inc.; *U.S. Public*, pg. 1380
BRADY RISK MANAGEMENT, INC.—See Hellman & Friedman LLC; *U.S. Private*, pg. 1908
THE BRAUN AGENCY, INC.; *U.S. Private*, pg. 4000
BRB - ADMINISTRADORA E CORRETORA DE SEGUROS S.A.—See BRB BCO DE BRASILIA S.A.; *Int'l*, pg. 1143
BRECKENRIDGE INSURANCE GROUP, INC—See W.R. Berkley Corporation; *U.S. Public*, pg. 2317
BRECKENRIDGE INSURANCE SERVICES—See Breckenridge IS, Inc.; *U.S. Private*, pg. 644
BREMER INSURANCE AGENCIES, INC.—See Bremer Financial Corporation; *U.S. Private*, pg. 645
BRENNAN & ASSOCIATES RISK MANAGEMENT & INSURANCE SERVICES, INC.—See Aon plc; *Int'l*, pg. 495
BRIDGEFIELD EMPLOYERS INSURANCE COMPANY—See American Financial Group, Inc.; *U.S. Public*, pg. 103

BRIDGEPORT BENEFITS—See GI Manager L.P.; *U.S. Private*, pg. 1693
BRIDGEPORT BENEFITS—See Summit Partners, L.P.; *U.S. Private*, pg. 3856
BRIDGER INSURANCE AGENCY, INC.; *U.S. Private*, pg. 649
BRIGHT & ASSOCIATES, INC.—See Brown & Brown, Inc.; *U.S. Public*, pg. 397
BRIGHTCLAIM, INC.—See Genpact Limited; *Int'l*, pg. 2926
BRIGHTHOUSE LIFE INSURANCE COMPANY—See MetLife, Inc.; *U.S. Public*, pg. 1430
BRIGHT INSURANCE AGENCY, INC.—See Sun Communities, Inc.; *U.S. Public*, pg. 1961
BRIGHTWAY INSURANCE, INC.; *U.S. Private*, pg. 653
BRIM AB—See Arthur J. Gallagher & Co.; *U.S. Public*, pg. 204
BRINCKERHOFF & NEUVILLE, INC.—See Rhinebeck Bank; *U.S. Private*, pg. 3421
BRIO BENEFIT CONSULTING, INC.—See Genstar Capital, LLC; *U.S. Private*, pg. 1674
BRITAM - COMPANHIA DE SEGUROS DE MOZAMBIQUE S.A.—See Britam Holdings Plc; *Int'l*, pg. 1164
BRITAM INSURANCE COMPANY LIMITED—See Britam Holdings Plc; *Int'l*, pg. 1165
BRITAM INSURANCE COMPANY LIMITED—See Britam Holdings Plc; *Int'l*, pg. 1165
BRITAM INSURANCE COMPANY (TANZANIA) LIMITED—See Britam Holdings Plc; *Int'l*, pg. 1165
BRIT GROUP SERVICES LIMITED—See Fairfax Financial Holdings Limited; *Int'l*, pg. 2606
BRIT INSURANCE LIMITED—See Fairfax Financial Holdings Limited; *Int'l*, pg. 2606
BRIT LIMITED—See Fairfax Financial Holdings Limited; *Int'l*, pg. 2606
BRIT SYNDICATES LIMITED—See Fairfax Financial Holdings Limited; *Int'l*, pg. 2606
BRIT UW LIMITED—See Fairfax Financial Holdings Limited; *Int'l*, pg. 2606
BROAD-MINDED CO., LTD.; *Int'l*, pg. 1171
BROCK INSURANCE AGENCY; *U.S. Private*, pg. 660
BROKEN ARROW INSURANCE AGENCY, INC.—See Stone Point Capital LLC; *U.S. Private*, pg. 3818
BROKER INS LTD.—See Alfa Finance Holding AD; *Int'l*, pg. 307
BROKERS INTERNATIONAL, LTD.—See Integrity Marketing Group LLC; *U.S. Private*, pg. 2103
BROKERS RISK PLACEMENT SERVICE, INC.—See One80 Intermediaries LLC; *U.S. Private*, pg. 3024
BROKERS TRUST INSURANCE GROUP INC.; *Int'l*, pg. 1173
BROOKS GROUP INSURANCE AGENCY, LLC.—See CCP Fund III Management LLC; *U.S. Public*, pg. 801
BROWN & BROWN ABSENCE SERVICES GROUP, LLC—See Brown & Brown, Inc.; *U.S. Public*, pg. 397
BROWN & BROWN AGENCY OF INSURANCE PROFESSIONALS, INC.—See Brown & Brown, Inc.; *U.S. Public*, pg. 397
BROWN & BROWN DISASTER RELIEF FOUNDATION, INC.—See Brown & Brown, Inc.; *U.S. Public*, pg. 397
BROWN & BROWN (EUROPE) LIMITED—See Brown & Brown, Inc.; *U.S. Public*, pg. 397
BROWN & BROWN INSURANCE AGENCY OF VIRGINIA, INC.—See Brown & Brown, Inc.; *U.S. Public*, pg. 397
BROWN & BROWN INSURANCE BROKERS OF SACRAMENTO, INC.—See Brown & Brown, Inc.; *U.S. Public*, pg. 397
BROWN & BROWN INSURANCE OF ARIZONA, INC.—See Brown & Brown, Inc.; *U.S. Public*, pg. 398
BROWN & BROWN INSURANCE OF GEORGIA, INC.—See Brown & Brown, Inc.; *U.S. Public*, pg. 398
BROWN & BROWN INSURANCE OF NEVADA, INC.—See Brown & Brown, Inc.; *U.S. Public*, pg. 398
BROWN & BROWN INSURANCE SERVICES OF CALIFORNIA, INC.—See Brown & Brown, Inc.; *U.S. Public*, pg. 398
BROWN & BROWN INSURANCE SERVICES OF SAN ANTONIO, INC.—See Brown & Brown, Inc.; *U.S. Public*, pg. 398
BROWN & BROWN INSURANCE SERVICES OF TEXAS, INC.—See Brown & Brown, Inc.; *U.S. Public*, pg. 398
BROWN & BROWN INSURANCE—See Brown & Brown, Inc.; *U.S. Public*, pg. 398
BROWN & BROWN LONE STAR INSURANCE SERVICES, INC.—See Brown & Brown, Inc.; *U.S. Public*, pg. 398
BROWN & BROWN METRO, INC. - MOUNT LAUREL—See Brown & Brown, Inc.; *U.S. Public*, pg. 398
BROWN & BROWN METRO, INC.—See Brown & Brown, Inc.; *U.S. Public*, pg. 398
BROWN & BROWN OF ARKANSAS, INC.—See Brown & Brown, Inc.; *U.S. Public*, pg. 398
BROWN & BROWN OF CENTRAL MICHIGAN, INC.—See Brown & Brown, Inc.; *U.S. Public*, pg. 398
BROWN & BROWN OF CENTRAL OKLAHOMA, INC.—See Brown & Brown, Inc.; *U.S. Public*, pg. 398
BROWN & BROWN OF COLORADO, INC.—See Brown & Brown, Inc.; *U.S. Public*, pg. 398
BROWN & BROWN OF CONNECTICUT, INC.—See Brown & Brown, Inc.; *U.S. Public*, pg. 398

BROWN & BROWN OF DELAWARE, INC.—See Brown & Brown, Inc.; *U.S. Public*, pg. 398
BROWN & BROWN OF DETROIT, INC.—See Brown & Brown, Inc.; *U.S. Public*, pg. 398
BROWN & BROWN OF FLORIDA, INC. - BREVARD—See Brown & Brown, Inc.; *U.S. Public*, pg. 398
BROWN & BROWN OF FLORIDA, INC. - BROOKSVILLE—See Brown & Brown, Inc.; *U.S. Public*, pg. 398
BROWN & BROWN OF FLORIDA, INC. - FT. LAUDERDALE—See Brown & Brown, Inc.; *U.S. Public*, pg. 398
BROWN & BROWN OF FLORIDA, INC. - FT. MYERS—See Brown & Brown, Inc.; *U.S. Public*, pg. 398
BROWN & BROWN OF FLORIDA, INC. - JACKSONVILLE—See Brown & Brown, Inc.; *U.S. Public*, pg. 398
BROWN & BROWN OF FLORIDA, INC. - LEESBURG—See Brown & Brown, Inc.; *U.S. Public*, pg. 398
BROWN & BROWN OF FLORIDA, INC. - MIAMI—See Brown & Brown, Inc.; *U.S. Public*, pg. 398
BROWN & BROWN OF FLORIDA, INC. - MONTICELLO—See Brown & Brown, Inc.; *U.S. Public*, pg. 398
BROWN & BROWN OF FLORIDA, INC. - NAPLES—See Brown & Brown, Inc.; *U.S. Public*, pg. 398
BROWN & BROWN OF FLORIDA, INC. - ORLANDO—See Brown & Brown, Inc.; *U.S. Public*, pg. 398
BROWN & BROWN OF FLORIDA, INC. - SARASOTA—See Brown & Brown, Inc.; *U.S. Public*, pg. 398
BROWN & BROWN OF FLORIDA, INC.—See Brown & Brown, Inc.; *U.S. Public*, pg. 398
BROWN & BROWN OF FLORIDA, INC. - TAMPA—See Brown & Brown, Inc.; *U.S. Public*, pg. 398
BROWN & BROWN OF FLORIDA, INC. - WEST PALM BEACH—See Brown & Brown, Inc.; *U.S. Public*, pg. 398
BROWN & BROWN OF GARDEN CITY, INC.—See Brown & Brown, Inc.; *U.S. Public*, pg. 399
BROWN & BROWN OF ILLINOIS, INC.—See Brown & Brown, Inc.; *U.S. Public*, pg. 399
BROWN & BROWN OF INDIANA, INC.—See Brown & Brown, Inc.; *U.S. Public*, pg. 399
BROWN & BROWN OF KENTUCKY, INC.—See Brown & Brown, Inc.; *U.S. Public*, pg. 399
BROWN & BROWN OF LEHIGH VALLEY, INC.—See Brown & Brown, Inc.; *U.S. Public*, pg. 399
BROWN & BROWN OF LOUISIANA, INC.—See Brown & Brown, Inc.; *U.S. Public*, pg. 399
BROWN & BROWN OF MASSACHUSETTS, LLC—See Brown & Brown, Inc.; *U.S. Public*, pg. 399
BROWN & BROWN OF MICHIGAN, INC.—See Brown & Brown, Inc.; *U.S. Public*, pg. 399
BROWN & BROWN OF MINNESOTA, INC. - RETAIL DIVISION—See Brown & Brown, Inc.; *U.S. Public*, pg. 399
BROWN & BROWN OF MINNESOTA, INC.—See Brown & Brown, Inc.; *U.S. Public*, pg. 399
BROWN & BROWN OF MISSISSIPPI, LLC—See Brown & Brown, Inc.; *U.S. Public*, pg. 399
BROWN & BROWN OF MISSOURI, INC.—See Brown & Brown, Inc.; *U.S. Public*, pg. 399
BROWN & BROWN OF NEW MEXICO, INC. - ALBUQUERQUE—See Brown & Brown, Inc.; *U.S. Public*, pg. 399
BROWN & BROWN OF NEW MEXICO, INC.—See Brown & Brown, Inc.; *U.S. Public*, pg. 399
BROWN & BROWN OF NEW YORK, INC.—See Brown & Brown, Inc.; *U.S. Public*, pg. 399
BROWN & BROWN OF NEW YORK, INC. - SYRACUSE—See Brown & Brown, Inc.; *U.S. Public*, pg. 399
BROWN & BROWN OF NORTHERN CALIFORNIA, INC.—See Brown & Brown, Inc.; *U.S. Public*, pg. 399
BROWN & BROWN OF NORTHERN ILLINOIS, INC.—See Brown & Brown, Inc.; *U.S. Public*, pg. 399
BROWN & BROWN OF OKLAHOMA, INC.—See Brown & Brown, Inc.; *U.S. Public*, pg. 399
BROWN & BROWN OF OREGON, LLC—See Brown & Brown, Inc.; *U.S. Public*, pg. 399
BROWN & BROWN OF PENNSYLVANIA, INC.—See Brown & Brown, Inc.; *U.S. Public*, pg. 399
BROWN & BROWN OF SOUTH CAROLINA, INC.—See Brown & Brown, Inc.; *U.S. Public*, pg. 399
BROWN & BROWN OF SOUTHWEST INDIANA, INC.—See Brown & Brown, Inc.; *U.S. Public*, pg. 400
BROWN & BROWN OF TENNESSEE, INC.—See Brown & Brown, Inc.; *U.S. Public*, pg. 400
BROWN & BROWN OF WASHINGTON, INC. - LYNDEN-SSK—See Brown & Brown, Inc.; *U.S. Public*, pg. 400
BROWN & BROWN OF WASHINGTON, INC. - SEATTLE—See Brown & Brown, Inc.; *U.S. Public*, pg. 400
BROWN & BROWN OF WASHINGTON, INC.—See Brown & Brown, Inc.; *U.S. Public*, pg. 400
BROWN & BROWN OF WISCONSIN, INC.—See Brown & Brown, Inc.; *U.S. Public*, pg. 400
BROWN & BROWN PACIFIC INSURANCE SERVICES, INC.—See Brown & Brown, Inc.; *U.S. Public*, pg. 398

524210 — INSURANCE AGENCIES ...

BROWN & CO INSURANCE SERVICES LP—See Galiot Insurance Services, Inc.; *U.S. Private*, pg. 1638
BROWNLEE AGENCY, INC.—See Brown & Brown, Inc.; *U.S. Public*, pg. 400
BRUMFIELD & PETERS INSURANCE SERVICES, INC.—See Inszone Insurance Services, LLC; *U.S. Private*, pg. 2096
BRYN MAWR BROKERAGE CO., INC.—See Bryn Mawr Bank Corporation; *U.S. Public*, pg. 408
BRYTE INSURANCE COMPANY LTD.—See Fairfax Financial Holdings Limited; *Int'l*, pg. 2606
BUCKINGHAM BADLER ASSOCIATES, INC.—See Scottish American Capital LLC; *U.S. Private*, pg. 3578
BUCKMAN-MITCHELL, INC.—See Arthur J. Gallagher & Co.; *U.S. Public*, pg. 204
BUDGET INSURANCE COMPANY LIMITED—See BGL Group Limited; *Int'l*, pg. 1008
BUITEN & ASSOCIATES, LLC—See Brown & Brown, Inc.; *U.S. Public*, pg. 399
BUNKER HILL INSURANCE COMPANY—See The Plymouth Rock Co.; *U.S. Private*, pg. 4097
BUPA ARABIA FOR COOPERATIVE INSURANCE COMPANY; *Int'l*, pg. 1220
BUREAU D'ASSURANCES ET DEPRETS—See Apollo Global Management, Inc.; *U.S. Public*, pg. 147
BUREAU D'EXPERTISES DESPRETZ S.A.—See Allianz SE; *Int'l*, pg. 351
BURKE INSURANCE GROUP, LLC—See Kelso & Company, L.P.; *U.S. Private*, pg. 2279
THE BURLINGTON INSURANCE COMPANY—See IFG Companies; *U.S. Private*, pg. 2038
BURNETT & CO. INC.; *U.S. Private*, pg. 689
BURNHAM BENEFITS INSURANCE SERVICES, INC.; *U.S. Private*, pg. 689
BURNS & WILCOX CANADA—See H.W. Kaufman Financial Group, Inc.; *U.S. Private*, pg. 1836
BURNS & WILCOX OF SAN FRANCISCO—See H.W. Kaufman Financial Group, Inc.; *U.S. Private*, pg. 1836
BURNS & WILCOX—See H.W. Kaufman Financial Group, Inc.; *U.S. Private*, pg. 1836
BURUJ COOPERATIVE INSURANCE COMPANY; *Int'l*, pg. 1227
BUSH AND ROE FINANCIAL, INC.—See Madison County Financial, Inc.; *U.S. Public*, pg. 1353
BUSINESS MENS INSURANCE CORPORATION—See BMI Financial Group, Inc.; *U.S. Private*, pg. 600
BUSINESS OWNERS LIABILITY TEAM LLC—See CVC Capital Partners SICAV-FIS S.A.; *Int'l*, pg. 1885
BUSINESS UNDERWRITERS ASSOCIATES, LLC—See Hellman & Friedman LLC; *U.S. Private*, pg. 1909
BYARS-WRIGHT, INC.—See Galiot Insurance Services, Inc.; *U.S. Private*, pg. 1638
CAA CLUB GROUP; *Int'l*, pg. 1245
CADENCE INSURANCE, INC.—See Arthur J. Gallagher & Co.; *U.S. Public*, pg. 204
CAJA DE SEGUROS S.A.—See Assicurazioni Generali S.p.A.; *Int'l*, pg. 643
CALEDONIAN INSURANCE GROUP, INC.—See Truist Financial Corporation; *U.S. Public*, pg. 2200
CALHOUN AGENCY, INC.—See World Insurance Associates LLC; *U.S. Private*, pg. 4565
CALVO ENTERPRISES, INC.; *U.S. Private*, pg. 725
CAMEO INSURANCE SERVICES, INC.—See Inszone Insurance Services, LLC; *U.S. Private*, pg. 2096
CAMERON GENERAL CORPORATION; *U.S. Private*, pg. 728
CAMPION INSURANCE INC.—See Maury, Donnelly & Parr, Inc.; *U.S. Private*, pg. 2615
CAMPMED CASUALTY & INDEMNITY COMPANY, INC.—See The Hanover Insurance Group, Inc.; *U.S. Public*, pg. 2087
CANADIAN RESOURCES INSURANCE SOLUTIONS INC.—See Hellman & Friedman LLC; *U.S. Private*, pg. 1909
CANNELLA INSURANCE SERVICES INC.—See Achieva Credit Union; *U.S. Private*, pg. 58
CANOPIUS UNDERWRITING AGENCY INC.—See Centerbridge Partners, L.P.; *U.S. Private*, pg. 813
CANOPY INC.; *U.S. Private*, pg. 735
CAPACITY COVERAGE CO.—See Insurance Resource Brokerage Group; *U.S. Private*, pg. 2095
CAPAX MANAGEMENT & INSURANCE SERVICES, INC.—See Hellman & Friedman LLC; *U.S. Private*, pg. 1908
CAP INSURANCE COMPANY INC.—See Pacific Marine & Supply Co. Ltd. Inc.; *U.S. Private*, pg. 3068
CAPITAL INSURANCE ADVISORY CORP.—See Capital Securities Corporation; *Int'l*, pg. 1312
CAPITAL INSURANCE AGENCY CORP.—See Capital Securities Corporation; *Int'l*, pg. 1312
CAPIZZI INSURANCE AGENCY—See Inszone Insurance Services, LLC; *U.S. Private*, pg. 2096
CAPPER'S INSURANCE SERVICE INC.—See The Nutting Company, Inc.; *U.S. Private*, pg. 4086
CAPPS INSURANCE AGENCY-MT. PLEASANT LTD.—See Galiot Insurance Services, Inc.; *U.S. Private*, pg. 1638
CAPSICUM RE LATIN AMERICA CORRETORA DE RESSEGUROS LTDA.—See Arthur J. Gallagher & Co.; *U.S. Public*, pg. 204
CAPSTONE BROKERAGE, INC.; *U.S. Private*, pg. 746
CAPSTONE INSURANCE BROKERS LIMITED—See Brown & Brown, Inc.; *U.S. Public*, pg. 400
CARBONE AUTOMOTIVE GROUP—See Lithia Motors, Inc.; *U.S. Public*, pg. 1321
CAR CARE CONSULT VERSICHERUNGSMAKLER GMBH—See Assicurazioni Generali S.p.A.; *Int'l*, pg. 646
CARDIF BIZTOSITO MAGYARORSZAG ZRT—See BNP Paribas SA; *Int'l*, pg. 1083
CARDIF COLOMBIA SEGUROS GENERALES S.A.—See BNP Paribas SA; *Int'l*, pg. 1083
CARDIF DEL PERU SA COMPANIA DE SEGUROS—See BNP Paribas SA; *Int'l*, pg. 1083
CARDIF I-SERVICES—See BNP Paribas SA; *Int'l*, pg. 1083
CARDIF LUX VIE SA—See BNP Paribas SA; *Int'l*, pg. 1083
CARDIF MEXICO SEGUROS DE VIDA SA DE CV—See BNP Paribas SA; *Int'l*, pg. 1083
CAREXPERT KFZ-SACHVERSTANDIGEN GMBH—See DZ BANK AG Deutsche Zentral-Genossenschaftsbank; *Int'l*, pg. 2245
CARGEAS ASSICURAZIONI SPA—See BNP Paribas SA; *Int'l*, pg. 1089
CARIBOU INSURANCE AGENCY, INC.—See PointeNorth Insurance Group LLC; *U.S. Private*, pg. 3222
CARMICHAEL ASSOCIATES, INC.—See Inszone Insurance Services, LLC; *U.S. Private*, pg. 2096
CARPENTER TURNER SA—See Marsh & McLennan Companies, Inc.; *U.S. Public*, pg. 1375
CARTIER AGENCY, INC.—See Keystone Agency Investors LLC; *U.S. Private*, pg. 2295
CASCADE INSURANCE CENTER LLC—See Inszone Insurance Services, LLC; *U.S. Private*, pg. 2096
CASH.LIFE AG; *Int'l*, pg. 1352
CASSIDY DAVIS EUROPE BV—See Guardian Holdings Limited; *Int'l*, pg. 3171
CASTLE CAIRN (INSURANCE BROKERS) LIMITED—See Marsh & McLennan Companies, Inc.; *U.S. Public*, pg. 1374
CATERPILLAR INSURANCE HOLDINGS, INC.—See Caterpillar, Inc.; *U.S. Public*, pg. 451
CAUNCE O'HARA & COMPANY LIMITED—See Markel Group Inc.; *U.S. Public*, pg. 1367
CAVANAH ASSOCIATES, INC.—See Caisse de Depot et Placement du Quebec; *Int'l*, pg. 1256
CAVANAH ASSOCIATES, INC.—See KKR & Co. Inc.; *U.S. Public*, pg. 1265
CAVENDISH MUNRO PROFESSIONAL RISKS LIMITED—See Brown & Brown, Inc.; *U.S. Public*, pg. 400
CBC SETTLEMENT FUNDING, LLC—See Asta Funding, Inc.; *U.S. Public*, pg. 360
CBIZ LIFE INSURANCE SOLUTIONS, INC.—See CBIZ, Inc.; *U.S. Public*, pg. 456
CBIZ SLATON INSURANCE—See CBIZ, Inc.; *U.S. Public*, pg. 457
C B S INSURANCE, L.L.P.—See Arthur J. Gallagher & Co.; *U.S. Public*, pg. 204
CDOC, INC.—See CNO Financial Group, Inc.; *U.S. Public*, pg. 519
CEC INSURANCE AGENCY, LLC—See Perdoceo Education Corporation; *U.S. Public*, pg. 1673
CEGEDIM ACTIV SASU—See Cegedim S.A.; *Int'l*, pg. 1390
CENTENNIAL SURETY ASSOCIATES, INC.—See GTCR LLC; *U.S. Private*, pg. 1802
CENTER OF INSURANCE—See Houchens Industries, Inc.; *U.S. Private*, pg. 1989
CENTRAL INSURANCE COMPANY LIMITED; *Int'l*, pg. 1408
CENTRAL NEW YORK AGENCY, LLC; *U.S. Private*, pg. 823
CENTRAL STATES INDEMNITY CO. OF OMAHA—See Berkshire Hathaway Inc.; *U.S. Public*, pg. 301
CENTRO PROCESSI ASSICURATIVI S.R.L.—See Gruppo MutuiOnline S.p.A; *Int'l*, pg. 3140
CFR, INC.; *U.S. Public*, pg. 844
CGCA SARL—See CVC Capital Partners SICAV-FIS S.A.; *Int'l*, pg. 1882
CGM GALLAGHER INSURANCE BROKERS (BARBADOS) LIMITED—See Arthur J. Gallagher & Co.; *U.S. Public*, pg. 204
CGM GALLAGHER INSURANCE BROKERS JAMAICA LTD.—See Arthur J. Gallagher & Co.; *U.S. Public*, pg. 204
CGM GALLAGHER INSURANCE BROKERS ST. KITTS & NEVIS LTD.—See Arthur J. Gallagher & Co.; *U.S. Public*, pg. 204
CHALLENGING FINANCIAL CAREERS INSURANCE MARKETING CORP., LLC—See Allianz SE; *Int'l*, pg. 351
CHARITY FIRST INSURANCE SERVICES, INC.—See Arthur J. Gallagher & Co.; *U.S. Public*, pg. 202
CHARLES L. CRANE AGENCY; *U.S. Private*, pg. 852
CHARLES TAYLOR ADJUSTING LIMITED—See Lovell Minnick Partners LLC; *U.S. Private*, pg. 2502
CHARLES TAYLOR CONSULTING (AUSTRALIA) PTY LTD—See Lovell Minnick Partners LLC; *U.S. Private*, pg. 2502
CHARLES TAYLOR CONSULTING (JAPAN) LIMITED—See Lovell Minnick Partners LLC; *U.S. Private*, pg. 2502
CHARLES TAYLOR INSURANCE SERVICES LIMITED—See Lovell Minnick Partners LLC; *U.S. Private*, pg. 2502
CHARTER BROKERAGE LLC—See Berkshire Hathaway Inc.; *U.S. Public*, pg. 304
CHASE, CLARKE, STEWART & FONTANA, INC.; *U.S. Private*, pg. 860
CHASE & LUNT INSURANCE AGENCY LLC—See Arthur J. Gallagher & Co.; *U.S. Public*, pg. 204
CHAS H. BILZ INSURANCE AGENCY, INC.; *U.S. Private*, pg. 859
CHAUCER HOLDINGS LIMITED—See China Reinsurance (Group) Corporation; *Int'l*, pg. 1547
CHAUCER UNDERWRITING A/S—See China Reinsurance (Group) Corporation; *Int'l*, pg. 1547
CHB INSURANCE BROKERAGE COMPANY, LTD.—See Chang Hwa Commercial Bank Ltd.; *Int'l*, pg. 1441
CHB LIFE INSURANCE AGENCY COMPANY, LTD.—See Chang Hwa Commercial Bank Ltd.; *Int'l*, pg. 1441
CHERGEY INSURANCE—See GCP Capital Partners Holdings LLC; *U.S. Private*, pg. 1654
CHERNOMORSKI HOLDING AD; *Int'l*, pg. 1472
CHEVALIER (INSURANCE BROKERS) LIMITED—See Chevalier International Holdings Limited; *Int'l*, pg. 1473
CHEVALIER INSURANCE COMPANY LIMITED—See Chevalier International Holdings Limited; *Int'l*, pg. 1473
CHICAGO INSURANCE COMPANY, CORP.—See Allianz SE; *Int'l*, pg. 351
CHINABANK INSURANCE BROKERS, INC.—See China Banking Corporation; *Int'l*, pg. 1484
CHINA BOCOM INSURANCE CO., LTD.—See Bank of Communications Co., Ltd.; *Int'l*, pg. 842
CHINA LIFE PENSION COMPANY LIMITED—See China Life Insurance Company Limited; *Int'l*, pg. 1515
CHINA MERCHANTS INSURANCE COMPANY LIMITED—See China Merchants Group Limited; *Int'l*, pg. 1521
CHINA RE UNDERWRITING AGENCY LIMITED—See China Reinsurance (Group) Corporation; *Int'l*, pg. 1547
CHINATRUST INSURANCE BROKERS CO., LTD.—See CTBC Financial Holding Co., Ltd.; *Int'l*, pg. 1869
CHOICEMARK INSURANCE SERVICES, INC.—See SelectQuote, Inc.; *U.S. Public*, pg. 1863
CHRISTIE, OWEN & DAVIES LTD.—See Christie Group plc; *Int'l*, pg. 1587
CHUBB ARABIA COOPERATIVE INSURANCE COMPANY—See Chubb Limited; *Int'l*, pg. 1590
CHUBB GROUP OF INSURANCE COMPANY - OREGON—See Chubb Limited; *Int'l*, pg. 1591
CHUBB GROUP OF INSURANCE COMPANY—See Chubb Limited; *Int'l*, pg. 1591
CHUBB INSURANCE COMPANY LIMITED—See Chubb Limited; *Int'l*, pg. 1591
CHUBB INSURANCE COMPANY OF PUERTO RICO—See Chubb Limited; *Int'l*, pg. 1592
CHUBB INSURANCE HONG KONG LIMITED—See Chubb Limited; *Int'l*, pg. 1590
CHUBB INSURANCE MALAYSIA BERHAD—See Chubb Limited; *Int'l*, pg. 1592
CHUBB INSURANCE SOLUTIONS AGENCY INC.—See Chubb Limited; *Int'l*, pg. 1591
CHUBB INSURANCE VIETNAM COMPANY LIMITED—See Chubb Limited; *Int'l*, pg. 1592
CHUBB LIFE ASSURANCE PUBLIC COMPANY LIMITED—See Chubb Limited; *Int'l*, pg. 1592
CHUBB LIFE INSURANCE COMPANY OF CANADA—See Chubb Limited; *Int'l*, pg. 1592
CHUBB PERU S.A. COMPANIA DE SEGUROS Y REASEGUROS—See Chubb Limited; *Int'l*, pg. 1590
CHUBB SEGURADORA MACAU S.A.—See Chubb Limited; *Int'l*, pg. 1592
CHUBB SEGUROS CHILE SA—See Chubb Limited; *Int'l*, pg. 1592
CHUBB SEGUROS DE VIDA CHILE S.A.—See Chubb Limited; *Int'l*, pg. 1592
CHUBB SEGUROS ECUADOR S.A.—See Chubb Limited; *Int'l*, pg. 1592
CHUBB SEGUROS MEXICO, S.A.—See Chubb Limited; *Int'l*, pg. 1590
CHUBB SEGUROS PANAMA S.A.—See Chubb Limited; *Int'l*, pg. 1592
CHUBB SERVICES UK LIMITED—See Chubb Limited; *Int'l*, pg. 1592
CHUOU INTERNATIONAL GROUP CO., LTD.; *Int'l*, pg. 1600
CHURCH INSURANCE & FINANCIAL SERVICES, INC.—See GTCR LLC; *U.S. Private*, pg. 1802
CHURCH MUTUAL INSURANCE COMPANY; *U.S. Private*, pg. 894
CIA SEGUROS ALIANCA DA BAHIA; *Int'l*, pg. 1602
CIC INSURANCE GROUP LIMITED; *Int'l*, pg. 1602
CIGI DIRECT INSURANCE SERVICES, INC.; *U.S. Private*, pg. 897
CIGNA CORPORATE SERVICES, LLC—See The Cigna Group; *U.S. Public*, pg. 2060
CIGNA HEALTHCARE OF NORTH CAROLINA, INC.—See The Cigna Group; *U.S. Public*, pg. 2060

N.A.I.C.S. INDEX 524210 — INSURANCE AGENCIES ...

CIS INC.; *U.S. Private*, pg. 900
CITADEL INSURANCE SERVICES, LC; *U.S. Private*, pg. 901
CITICORP INSURANCE AGENCY CO., LTD.—See Citigroup Inc.; *U.S. Public*, pg. 503
CITI INTERNATIONAL FINANCIAL SERVICES, LLC—See Citigroup Inc.; *U.S. Public*, pg. 502
CITIZENS INSURANCE AGENCY OF TEXAS, INC.—See Prosperity Bancshares, Inc.; *U.S. Public*, pg. 1728
CLAIMIFY, LLC; *U.S. Private*, pg. 910
CLARK ASSOCIATES, INC.—See GTCR LLC; *U.S. Private*, pg. 1802
CLARK & ASSOCIATES OF NEVADA, INC.—See Peter C. Foy & Associates Insurance Services, Inc.; *U.S. Private*, pg. 3157
CLARKE & SAMPSON, INC.—See ABRY Partners, LLC; *U.S. Private*, pg. 41
CLARK FARLEY INSURANCE AGENCY, INC.—See Aquiline Capital Partners LLC; *U.S. Private*, pg. 305
CLARK-MORTENSON AGENCY, INC.—See ABRY Partners, LLC; *U.S. Private*, pg. 43
CLASSIC INSURANCE SERVICES LIMITED—See White Mountains Insurance Group, Ltd.; *U.S. Public*, pg. 2368
CLEARWATER UNDERWRITERS, INC.—See AmWINS Group, Inc.; *U.S. Private*, pg. 270
CLEGG INSURANCE GROUP, INC.; *U.S. Private*, pg. 939
CLEMENS & ASSOCIATES INSURANCE AGENCY INC.; *U.S. Private*, pg. 939
CLEMENTS & CO.—See Arthur J. Gallagher & Co.; *U.S. Public*, pg. 204
CLERMONT SPECIALTY MANAGERS, LTD.—See W.R. Berkley Corporation; *U.S. Public*, pg. 2317
C.L. FRATES AND COMPANY; *U.S. Private*, pg. 708
CLIFFORD R. ZINN & SON, INC.—See Genstar Capital, LLC; *U.S. Private*, pg. 1674
CLINICAL TRIALS INSURANCE SERVICES LIMITED—See Howden Group Holdings Limited; *Int'l*, pg. 3493
CLJM LLC; *U.S. Private*, pg. 945
CLJM LLC - SPRINGFIELD OFFICE—See CLJM LLC; *U.S. Private*, pg. 945
CLS PARTNERS—See Stone Point Capital LLC; *U.S. Private*, pg. 3818
CME GROUP SINGAPORE OPERATIONS PTE.LTD.—See CME Group, Inc.; *U.S. Public*, pg. 516
C & M FIRST SERVICES, INC.—See One80 Intermediaries LLC; *U.S. Private*, pg. 3024
CM INSURANCE COMPANY, INC.—See Columbus McKinnon Corporation; *U.S. Public*, pg. 535
C.M. SMITH AGENCY, LLC—See Genstar Capital, LLC; *U.S. Private*, pg. 1674
CNA FINANCIAL CORPORATION - CHICAGO BRANCH—See Loews Corporation; *U.S. Public*, pg. 1339
CNA INSURANCE - READING BRANCH—See Loews Corporation; *U.S. Public*, pg. 1340
CNA NATIONAL WARRANTY CORPORATION—See Loews Corporation; *U.S. Public*, pg. 1340
CNH INDUSTRIAL CAPITAL AMERICA LLC—See CNH Industrial N.V.; *Int'l*, pg. 1674
CNH INDUSTRIAL CAPITAL CANADA LTD.—See CNH Industrial N.V.; *Int'l*, pg. 1674
CNO SERVICES, LLC—See CNO Financial Group, Inc.; *U.S. Public*, pg. 520
CNP ASFALISTIKI LTD.—See CNP Assurances SA; *Int'l*, pg. 1677
CNP CYPRUS INSURANCE HOLDINGS LIMITED—See CNP Assurances SA; *Int'l*, pg. 1677
CNP EUROPE LIFE LTD—See CNP Assurances SA; *Int'l*, pg. 1677
CNP IAM—See CNP Assurances SA; *Int'l*, pg. 1677
CNP LUXEMBOURG SA—See CNP Assurances SA; *Int'l*, pg. 1678
CNP VIDA—See CNP Assurances SA; *Int'l*, pg. 1678
CNP ZOIS S.A—See CNP Assurances SA; *Int'l*, pg. 1678
COASTAL AMERICAN INSURANCE COMPANY—See Gulf States Holdings, Inc.; *U.S. Private*, pg. 1817
COASTAL HOMEOWNERS INSURANCE SPECIALISTS, INC.—See Universal Insurance Holdings, Inc.; *U.S. Public*, pg. 2261
COBB-HALL INSURANCE AGENCIES, INC.; *U.S. Private*, pg. 957
COBBS, ALLEN & HALL INC.; *U.S. Private*, pg. 957
COBRA NETWORK LIMITED—See Apax Partners LLP; *Int'l*, pg. 505
COBRA UK & IRELAND LIMITED—See Apax Partners LLP; *Int'l*, pg. 505
COCA-COLA REINSURANCE SERVICES LIMITED—See The Coca-Cola Company; *U.S. Public*, pg. 2065
COFACE GRECE SA—See Groupe BPCE; *Int'l*, pg. 3093
COFACE HUNGARY KFT—See Groupe BPCE; *Int'l*, pg. 3093
COFACE IRELAND LIMITED—See Groupe BPCE; *Int'l*, pg. 3093
COFACE JAPAN CO., LTD.—See Groupe BPCE; *Int'l*, pg. 3093
COFACE SEGURO DE CREDITO MEXICO S.A. DE C.V.—See Groupe BPCE; *Int'l*, pg. 3093

COFACE SIGORTA TURQUIE A.S—See Groupe BPCE; *Int'l*, pg. 3093
COFACE SWITZERLAND SA—See Groupe BPCE; *Int'l*, pg. 3093
COFACE TAIWAN LIMITED—See Groupe BPCE; *Int'l*, pg. 3093
COHEN PARTNERS, LLC—See World Insurance Associates LLC; *U.S. Private*, pg. 4565
COHEN-SELTZER, INC.—See Caisse de Depot et Placement du Quebec; *Int'l*, pg. 1256
COHEN-SELTZER, INC.—See KKR & Co. Inc.; *U.S. Public*, pg. 1265
THE COLBURN CORP.—See Caisse de Depot et Placement du Quebec; *Int'l*, pg. 1256
THE COLBURN CORP.—See KKR & Co. Inc.; *U.S. Public*, pg. 1265
COLEMONT FINLAND OY—See Howden Group Holdings Limited; *Int'l*, pg. 3493
COLINA GENERAL INSURANCE AGENTS & BROKERS LIMITED—See Colina Holdings Bahamas Limited; *Int'l*, pg. 1698
COLLECTIBLES INSURANCE SERVICES, LLC—See Paine Schwartz Partners, LLC; *U.S. Private*, pg. 3075
COLLINS BENEFITS SOLUTIONS INC.—See Advantage Benefit Solutions; *U.S. Private*, pg. 94
COLLINSWORTH, ALTER, FOWLER DOWLING & FRENCH GROUP INC; *U.S. Private*, pg. 969
THE COLONIAL GROUP, INC.—See Brown & Brown, Inc.; *U.S. Public*, pg. 401
COLONIAL INSURANCE—See Colonial Company; *U.S. Private*, pg. 970
COLONY AGENCY SERVICES, INC.—See Brookfield Reinsurance Ltd.; *Int'l*, pg. 1194
COLONY SPECIALTY—See Brookfield Reinsurance Ltd.; *Int'l*, pg. 1194
COLORADO BROKERAGE GROUP, LLC—See Leisure, Werden & Terry Agency, Inc.; *U.S. Private*, pg. 2420
COLORADO INSURANCE SALES & SERVICE—See Peter C. Foy & Associates Insurance Services, Inc.; *U.S. Private*, pg. 3157
COLT INSURANCE AGENCY, INC.—See Cross Financial Corporation; *U.S. Private*, pg. 1104
COLUMBIAN FAMILY LIFE INSURANCE COMPANY—See Columbian Mutual Life Insurance Company; *U.S. Private*, pg. 978
COLUMBIAN FINANCIAL GROUP—See Columbian Mutual Life Insurance Company; *U.S. Private*, pg. 978
COLUMBIAN MUTUAL LIFE INSURANCE COMPANY; *U.S. Private*, pg. 978
COMBINED GROUP INSURANCE SERVICES, INC.—See Brown & Brown, Inc.; *U.S. Public*, pg. 400
COMEGYS INSURANCE AGENCY, INC.; *U.S. Private*, pg. 981
COMERICA INSURANCE SERVICES, INC.—See Comerica Incorporated; *U.S. Public*, pg. 542
COMMERCIAL CARRIERS INSURANCE AGENCY, INC.—See Fosun International Limited; *Int'l*, pg. 2752
COMMERCIAL INSURANCE BROKERS (PVT) LIMITED—See Commercial Bank of Ceylon PLC; *Int'l*, pg. 1715
COMMERCIAL INSURANCE SERVICE CORP; *U.S. Private*, pg. 983
COMMERCIAL INSURANCE SERVICES, INC.—See GTCR LLC; *U.S. Private*, pg. 1802
COMMERCIAL INSURANCE UNDERWRITERS, INC.—See Arthur J. Gallagher & Co.; *U.S. Public*, pg. 204
COMMODORE INSURANCE SERVICES; *U.S. Private*, pg. 985
COMMUNITY SERVICE ACCEPTANCE COMPANY—See Farm Bureau Mutual Insurance Company of Michigan Inc.; *U.S. Private*, pg. 1474
COMMVESCO LEVINSON VINER GROUP INC; *Int'l*, pg. 1721
COMPANIA DE SEGUROS DE VIDA CAMARA SA; *Int'l*, pg. 1749
COMPASS ADJUSTERS & INVESTIGATORS, INC.; *U.S. Private*, pg. 998
COMPASS INSURANCE AGENCY, INC.—See The PNC Financial Services Group, Inc.; *U.S. Public*, pg. 2119
COMPLETE BENEFIT ALLIANCE, LLC—See Arthur J. Gallagher & Co.; *U.S. Public*, pg. 204
COMPOSITE LEGAL SERVICES LIMITED—See Stone Point Capital LLC; *U.S. Private*, pg. 3820
COMPRE GROUP HOLDINGS LTD.—See British Columbia Investment Management Corp.; *Int'l*, pg. 1169
COMPRE GROUP HOLDINGS LTD.—See Cinven Limited; *Int'l*, pg. 1611
CONFIDENCE PLUS INSURANCE SERVICES; *U.S. Private*, pg. 1013
CONIFER INSURANCE COMPANY—See RedBird Capital Partners L.P.; *U.S. Private*, pg. 3377
CONNECTED RISK SOLUTIONS, LLC—See AmWINS Group, Inc.; *U.S. Private*, pg. 269
CONNECTED WORLD SERVICES NETHERLANDS BV—See Currys plc; *Int'l*, pg. 1879
CONNER INSURANCE AGENCY INC.; *U.S. Private*, pg. 1017
CONNER STRONG & BUCKELEW; *U.S. Private*, pg. 1017

CONOVER INSURANCE, INC.—See Hellman & Friedman LLC; *U.S. Private*, pg. 1908
CONSOLIDATED INSURANCE CENTER, INC.—See JBO Holding Company; *U.S. Private*, pg. 2194
CONSTANTIA LIFE LIMITED—See CONDUIT CAPITAL LIMITED; *Int'l*, pg. 1766
CONSULTATIVE INSURANCE GROUP INC.—See Aquiline Capital Partners LLC; *U.S. Private*, pg. 305
CONSUMER UNITED; *U.S. Private*, pg. 1025
CONTEGO SERVICES GROUP, LLC—See Patriot National, Inc.; *U.S. Private*, pg. 3110
CONTEGO UNDERWRITING LIMITED—See Arthur J. Gallagher & Co.; *U.S. Public*, pg. 202
CONTINENTAL AMERICAN INSURANCE COMPANY—See Aflac Incorporated; *U.S. Public*, pg. 57
CONTINENTAL INSURANCE LIMITED; *Int'l*, pg. 1784
CONTINENTAL RISK INSURANCE SERVICES—See Caisse de Depot et Placement du Quebec; *Int'l*, pg. 1256
CONTINENTAL RISK INSURANCE SERVICES—See KKR & Co. Inc.; *U.S. Public*, pg. 1265
CONTINENTAL WESTERN INSURANCE COMPANY - LINCOLN—See W.R. Berkley Corporation; *U.S. Public*, pg. 2318
CONTRACTOR MANAGING GENERAL INSURANCE AGENCY, INC.—See Stone Point Capital LLC; *U.S. Private*, pg. 3820
COOL INSURING AGENCY, INC.—See Arthur J. Gallagher & Co.; *U.S. Public*, pg. 204
COOPER GAY & COMPANY LTD—See Lightyear Capital LLC; *U.S. Private*, pg. 2454
COOPER GAY RE, LTD.—See Lightyear Capital LLC; *U.S. Private*, pg. 2454
CORCORAN & HAVLIN INSURANCE GROUP—See Cross Financial Corporation; *U.S. Private*, pg. 1104
CORINS B.V.—See ASR Nederland N.V.; *Int'l*, pg. 632
CORKILL INSURANCE AGENCY, INC.—See GTCR LLC; *U.S. Private*, pg. 1802
CORNERSTONE PROFESSIONAL LIABILITY CONSULTANTS, INC.; *U.S. Private*, pg. 1052
CORPORATE BENEFIT MARKETING—See GI Manager L.P.; *U.S. Private*, pg. 1693
CORPORATE BENEFIT MARKETING—See Summit Partners, L.P.; *U.S. Private*, pg. 3856
THE CORY GROUP, INC.; *U.S. Private*, pg. 4015
COSCO SHIPPING (HONG KONG) INSURANCE BROKERS LIMITED—See China COSCO Shipping Corporation Limited; *Int'l*, pg. 1492
COSTCO INSURANCE AGENCY, INC.—See Costco Wholesale Corporation; *U.S. Public*, pg. 586
COUNTER SERVICE CO., LTD.—See C.P. All Public Company Limited; *Int'l*, pg. 1244
COUNTRY & COMMERCIAL INSURANCE BROKERS LIMITED—See Brown & Brown, Inc.; *U.S. Public*, pg. 400
COUNTRY FINANCIAL - CENTRAL REGION—See COUNTRY Financial; *U.S. Private*, pg. 1066
COUNTRY FINANCIAL; *U.S. Private*, pg. 1066
COUNTRY FINANCIAL—See COUNTRY Financial; *U.S. Private*, pg. 1066
COUNTRY MEDICAL PLANS, INC.—See COUNTRY Financial; *U.S. Private*, pg. 1067
COUNTRY MUTUAL INSURANCE COMPANY—See COUNTRY Financial; *U.S. Private*, pg. 1067
COUNTY INSURANCE CONSULTANTS LIMITED—See Brown & Brown, Inc.; *U.S. Public*, pg. 400
COVEA INSURANCE PLC—See Covea Groupe S.A.S.; *Int'l*, pg. 1820
COVEA RISKS S.A.—See Covea Groupe S.A.S.; *Int'l*, pg. 1820
COVERDELL & COMPANY, INC.—See Vertrue Inc.; *U.S. Private*, pg. 4370
COVERRA INSURANCE SERVICES, INC.—See Keystone Insurers Group, Inc.; *U.S. Private*, pg. 2300
CRANBROOK UNDERWRITING LIMITED—See H.W. Kaufman Financial Group, Inc.; *U.S. Private*, pg. 1836
CRANMORE EUROPE BVBA—See Enstar Group Limited; *Int'l*, pg. 2448
CRAWFORD & COMPANY (CANADA), INC.—See Crawford & Company; *U.S. Public*, pg. 592
CRB INSURANCE AGENCY, INC.; *U.S. Private*, pg. 1086
CRC INSURANCE SERVICES, INC.—See Truist Financial Corporation; *U.S. Public*, pg. 2200
CRECER SEGUROS; *Int'l*, pg. 1834
CREDEMASSICURAZIONI SPA—See Credito Emiliano S.p.A.; *Int'l*, pg. 1836
CREDITOR RESOURCES, INC.—See Aegon N.V.; *Int'l*, pg. 174
CRENDON INSURANCE BROKERS LIMITED—See Brown & Brown, Inc.; *U.S. Public*, pg. 400
CRES INSURANCE SERVICE, LLC—See Arthur J. Gallagher & Co.; *U.S. Public*, pg. 204
CRESS INSURANCE CONSULTANTS, INC.—See Galiot Insurance Services, Inc.; *U.S. Private*, pg. 1638
CROMBIE LOCKWOOD (NZ) LIMITED—See Arthur J. Gallagher & Co.; *U.S. Public*, pg. 203
CROSBY INSURANCE INC.; *U.S. Private*, pg. 1103
CROSS INSURANCE INC.—See Cross Financial Corporation; *U.S. Private*, pg. 1104
CROSS INSURANCE TPA, INC.—See Cross Financial Cor-

524210 — INSURANCE AGENCIES ...

poration; *U.S. Private*, pg. 1104
CROSS SURETY, INC.—See Cross Financial Corporation; *U.S. Private*, pg. 1105
CROSSTATES INSURANCE CONSULTANTS; *U.S. Private*, pg. 1108
CROTTY INSURANCE BROKERS LIMITED—See Brown & Brown, Inc.; *U.S. Public*, pg. 400
CRUM & FORSTER INSURANCE COMPANY—See Fairfax Financial Holdings Limited; *Int'l*, pg. 2606
CRUMP INSURANCE SERVICES, INC.—See Truist Financial Corporation; *U.S. Public*, pg. 2200
CRUMP LIFE INSURANCE SERVICES, INC.—See Truist Financial Corporation; *U.S. Public*, pg. 2200
CRUSADERSTERLING PENSIONS LTD.—See Custodian Investment PLC; *Int'l*, pg. 1880
CSE SAFEGUARD INSURANCE COMPANY—See CSE Insurance Group; *U.S. Private*, pg. 1116
C&S INSURANCE AGENCY, INC.; *U.S. Private*, pg. 704
CULTURAL INSURANCE SERVICES INTERNATIONAL, INC.—See American Institute for Foreign Study, Inc.; *U.S. Private*, pg. 237
CUMBERLAND CASUALTY & SURETY COMPANY—See Cumberland Technologies, Inc.; *U.S. Private*, pg. 1122
CUNA MUTUAL INSURANCE AGENCY, INC.—See CMFG Life Insurance Company; *U.S. Private*, pg. 950
CURLEY ASSOCIATES, INC.—See ABRY Partners, LLC; *U.S. Private*, pg. 42
CURNEAL & HIGNITE INSURANCE, INC.—See Houchens Industries, Inc.; *U.S. Private*, pg. 1990
CUSTODIAN INVESTMENT PLC; *Int'l*, pg. 1880
CW BAKER INSURANCE AGENCY, INC.—See Stone Point Capital LLC; *U.S. Private*, pg. 3818
DAHLMEIER INSURANCE AGENCY, INC.—See Aquiline Capital Partners LLC; *U.S. Private*, pg. 305
DAH SING GENERAL INSURANCE COMPANY LIMITED—See Dah Sing Financial Holdings Limited; *Int'l*, pg. 1913
DAH SING INSURANCE COMPANY (1976) LIMITED—See Dah Sing Financial Holdings Limited; *Int'l*, pg. 1913
DAIRYLAND COUNTY MUTUAL INSURANCE CO.—See Sentry Insurance Group; *U.S. Private*, pg. 3611
DAISHI HOKUETSU SECURITIES CO., LTD.—See Daishi Hokuetsu Financial Group, Inc.; *Int'l*, pg. 1941
DAIWABO LIFESUPPORT CO., LTD.—See Daiwabo Holdings Co., Ltd.; *Int'l*, pg. 1949
DAIWA HOUSE INSURANCE CO., LTD.—See Daiwa House Industry Co., Ltd.; *Int'l*, pg. 1945
DALE GROUP INC.; *U.S. Private*, pg. 1148
DALLAS FINANCIAL WHOLESALERS—See Thomas H. Lee Partners, L.P.; *U.S. Private*, pg. 4156
DALTON TIMMIS INSURANCE GROUP, INC.—See Aon plc; *Int'l*, pg. 495
DALY MERRITT, INC.—See GTCR LLC; *U.S. Private*, pg. 1802
DANA INSURANCE COMPANY; *Int'l*, pg. 1957
DANSK TANDFORSIKRING A/S—See Gjensidige Forsikring ASA; *Int'l*, pg. 2982
DAUL INSURANCE AGENCY, INC.—See Caisse de Depot et Placement du Quebec; *Int'l*, pg. 1256
DAUL INSURANCE AGENCY, INC.—See KKR & Co, Inc.; *U.S. Public*, pg. 1265
DAVE CUTRIGHT INSURANCE AGENCY—See Seeman Holtz Property & Casualty, LLC; *U.S. Private*, pg. 3598
DAVID JOHN GLUCKLE INSURANCE AGENCY LLC; *U.S. Private*, pg. 1170
DAVIS-GARVIN AGENCY, INC.—See GTCR LLC; *U.S. Private*, pg. 1802
DAVISON & ASSOCIATES (NI) LIMITED—See Brown & Brown, Inc.; *U.S. Public*, pg. 400
DAVISON INSURANCE AGENCY, LLC—See Origin Bancorp, Inc.; *U.S. Public*, pg. 1617
DAWOOD FAMILY TAKAFUL LIMITED—See B.R.R. Guardian Modaraba; *Int'l*, pg. 790
DAWSON COMPANIES—See GTCR LLC; *U.S. Private*, pg. 1803
DBV DEUTSCHE BEAMTENVERSICHERUNG AG—See AXA S.A.; *Int'l*, pg. 759
DBV DEUTSCHE BEAMTENVERSICHERUNG LEBENSVERSICHERUNG AG—See AXA S.A.; *Int'l*, pg. 759
DB VITA S.A.—See Deutsche Bank Aktiengesellschaft; *Int'l*, pg. 2057
DBV-WINTERTHUR HOLDING AG—See AXA S.A.; *Int'l*, pg. 758
DEAN & DRAPER INSURANCE AGENCY, LP; *U.S. Private*, pg. 1183
DEEP SOUTH INSURANCE; *U.S. Private*, pg. 1189
DEERFIELD INSURANCE COMPANY—See Markel Group Inc.; *U.S. Public*, pg. 1368
DELIMA MARSH S.A. - LOS CORREDORES DE SEGUROS S.A.—See Marsh & McLennan Companies, Inc.; *U.S. Public*, pg. 1378
DELMARVA SURETY ASSOCIATES, INC.—See Kelso & Company, L.P.; *U.S. Private*, pg. 2279
DELOTT & ASSOCIATES, INC.—See Aon plc; *Int'l*, pg. 495
DELPHI INSURANCE LIMITED—See Aptiv PLC; *Int'l*, pg. 525
DELTA CREDIT SPV; *Int'l*, pg. 2016

DELTA DENTAL PLAN OF VIRGINIA INC.; *U.S. Private*, pg. 1200
DELTA GENERALI OSIGURANJE AD—See Assicurazioni Generali S.p.A.; *Int'l*, pg. 646
DELTA LIFE INSURANCE COMPANY LIMITED; *Int'l*, pg. 2019
DEMPSEY & SIDERS INSURANCE AGENCY—See American Financial Group, Inc.; *U.S. Public*, pg. 102
DENISON YACHTING, LLC—See OneWater Marine Inc.; *U.S. Public*, pg. 1604
DENTAL SELECT; *U.S. Private*, pg. 1206
DENVER AGENCY COMPANY—See Arthur J. Gallagher & Co.; *U.S. Public*, pg. 204
DEPSA, SA DE SEGUROS Y REASEGUROS—See Grupo Catalana Occidente, S.A.; *Int'l*, pg. 3124
DESANCTIS INSURANCE AGENCY, INC.; *U.S. Private*, pg. 1211
DESCO, INC.—See Globeride, Inc.; *Int'l*, pg. 3007
DESIGN BENEFIT PLANS, INC.—See CNO Financial Group, Inc.; *U.S. Public*, pg. 520
DESIGN BENEFITS INC.—See Principal Financial Group, Inc.; *U.S. Public*, pg. 1721
DEUTSCHE BANK INSURANCE AGENCY OF DELAWARE, INC.—See Deutsche Bank Aktiengesellschaft; *Int'l*, pg. 2059
DEUTSCHE RUCKVERSICHERUNG AG; *Int'l*, pg. 2083
DEVK SERVICE GMBH; *Int'l*, pg. 2089
DICKENSHIED CRAVILLION INSURANCE SERVICES, INC.—See Seeman Holtz Property & Casualty, LLC; *U.S. Private*, pg. 3598
DICKSTEIN ASSOCIATES AGENCY LLC—See Kelso & Company, L.P.; *U.S. Private*, pg. 2279
DIGNEY GRANT LIMITED—See Brown & Brown, Inc.; *U.S. Public*, pg. 400
DINAMIK ISI MAKINA YALITIM MALZEMELERI SANAYI VE TICARET A.S.; *Int'l*, pg. 2126
DIPLOMAT RISK SERVICES—See Diplomat Hotel Corporation; *U.S. Private*, pg. 1234
DIRECT ASIA INSURANCE (SINGAPORE) PTE LIMITED—See Hiscox Ltd.; *Int'l*, pg. 3407
DIRECT BENEFITS, INC.—See Genstar Capital, LLC; *U.S. Private*, pg. 1674
DIRECT MOTORLINE LIMITED—See Highway Insurance Holdings Plc; *Int'l*, pg. 3389
DIRECTPATH, LLC—See CNO Financial Group, Inc.; *U.S. Public*, pg. 520
DISTINCTIVE INSURANCE—See Genstar Capital, LLC; *U.S. Private*, pg. 1674
DIVERSIFIED DENTAL SERVICES INC—See Principal Financial Group, Inc.; *U.S. Public*, pg. 1720
DIVERSIFIED INSURANCE SOLUTIONS, INC.; *U.S. Private*, pg. 1242
DIVIRGILIO INSURANCE & FINANCIAL GROUP; *U.S. Private*, pg. 1244
DLALA BROKERAGE AND INVESTMENTS HOLDING COMPANY Q.S.C; *Int'l*, pg. 2140
DLG LEGAL SERVICES LIMITED—See Direct Line Insurance Group plc; *Int'l*, pg. 2129
D.M. LOVITT INSURANCE AGENCY—See GTCR LLC; *U.S. Private*, pg. 1802
DOGUS SIGORTA ARACILIK HIZMETLERI A.S.—See Dogus Holding AS; *Int'l*, pg. 2154
DOHA BANK ASSURANCE COMPANY W.L.L—See Doha Bank Q.S.C.; *Int'l*, pg. 2155
DOHRMANN INSURANCE AGENCY INC.—See Genstar Capital, LLC; *U.S. Private*, pg. 1674
DOLLAR BANK INSURANCE AGENCY, INC.—See Dollar Mutual Bancorp; *U.S. Private*, pg. 1254
DOMENICK & ASSOCIATES—See Bryn Mawr Bank Corporation; *U.S. Public*, pg. 408
DONALD C. BOWERS INSURANCE, INC.—See Farmers National Banc Corp.; *U.S. Public*, pg. 822
DONALD J. FAGER & ASSOCIATES; *U.S. Private*, pg. 1260
DONEGAL INSURANCE GROUP—See Donegal Group Inc.; *U.S. Public*, pg. 676
DONORIA SPOLKA AKCYJNA—See Howden Group Holdings Limited; *Int'l*, pg. 3493
DORCHESTER INSURANCE COMPANY—See Topa Equities Ltd, Inc.; *U.S. Private*, pg. 4186
THE DOUGHERTY COMPANY INC.—See GI Manager L.P.; *U.S. Private*, pg. 1693
THE DOUGHERTY COMPANY INC.—See Summit Partners, L.P.; *U.S. Private*, pg. 3856
DOUGLAS COUNTY INSURANCE SERVICES; *U.S. Private*, pg. 1267
DOUGLAS INSURANCE AGENCY, INC.—See New York Community Bancorp, Inc.; *U.S. Public*, pg. 1512
DOUGLAS INSURANCE BROKERS LIMITED—See Brown & Brown, Inc.; *U.S. Public*, pg. 400
DOVETAIL MANAGING GENERAL AGENCY CORPORATION—See Marsh & McLennan Companies, Inc.; *U.S. Public*, pg. 1374
DOWNLANDS LIABILITY MANAGEMENT LTD.—See Apollo Global Management, Inc.; *U.S. Public*, pg. 148
DOXA INSURANCE HOLDINGS LLC; *U.S. Private*, pg. 1269
DRESSANDER BHC INC.—See Simplicity Financial Marketing Holdings Inc.; *U.S. Private*, pg. 3667

CORPORATE AFFILIATIONS

DRINA OSIGURANJE A.D.; *Int'l*, pg. 2204
THE DRISCOLL AGENCY, INC.—See Cross Financial Corporation; *U.S. Private*, pg. 1105
DUAL AUSTRALIA PTY LIMITED—See Howden Group Holdings Limited; *Int'l*, pg. 3493
DUAL NEW ZEALAND LIMITED—See Howden Group Holdings Limited; *Int'l*, pg. 3493
DUANE SAMMONS INSURANCE CENTER, INC.—See Stone Point Capital LLC; *U.S. Private*, pg. 3818
DUBLIN INSURANCE SERVICES, INC.—See Aon plc; *Int'l*, pg. 496
DUBRASKI & ASSOCIATES INSURANCE SERVICES, LLC—See Kelso & Company, L.P.; *U.S. Private*, pg. 2279
DUMONT GROUP INCORPORATED—See *U.S. Private*, pg. 1287
DUNN INSURANCE, INC.—See Aquiline Capital Partners LLC; *U.S. Private*, pg. 305
DURAMERICA BROKERAGE INC; *U.S. Private*, pg. 1292
DVA - DEUTSCHE VERKEHRS-ASSEKURANZ-VERMITTLUNGS GMBH—See Deutsche Bahn AG; *Int'l*, pg. 2051
DVA - DEUTSCHE VERKEHRS-ASSEKURANZ-VERMITTLUNGS GMBH—See DEVK Service GmbH; *Int'l*, pg. 2089
DVA - DEUTSCHE VERKEHRS-ASSEKURANZ-VERMITTLUNGS GMBH—See Marsh & McLennan Companies, Inc.; *U.S. Public*, pg. 1379
DWIGHT W. ANDRUS INSURANCE INC.—See Hellman & Friedman LLC; *U.S. Private*, pg. 1908
EAGA INSURANCE SERVICES LIMITED—See Carillion plc; *Int'l*, pg. 1331
EAGAN INSURANCE AGENCY, INC.—See Galiot Insurance Services, Inc.; *U.S. Private*, pg. 1638
EAGLE CONSTRUCTION OF VA., LLC—See Markel Group Inc.; *U.S. Public*, pg. 1367
EAGLE INSURANCE COMPANY LTD.; *Int'l*, pg. 2266
EAGLE REALTY OF VIRGINIA, LLC—See Markel Group Inc.; *U.S. Public*, pg. 1368
EARLY, CASSIDY & SCHILLING, LLC—See GTCR LLC; *U.S. Private*, pg. 1803
EAST BAY INSURANCE AGENCY INC.; *U.S. Private*, pg. 1315
EAST COAST BENEFIT PLANS, INC.—See New Mountain Capital, LLC; *U.S. Private*, pg. 2901
EASTERN INSURANCE COMPANY LIMITED; *Int'l*, pg. 2272
EASTERN INSURANCE GROUP, LLC—See Arthur J. Gallagher & Co.; *U.S. Public*, pg. 204
EASTLAND INSURANCE COMPANY LIMITED; *Int'l*, pg. 2274
EASTWOOD INSURANCE SERVICES; *U.S. Private*, pg. 1322
EASY STREET INSURANCE, LLC—See Integrity Marketing Group LLC; *U.S. Private*, pg. 2103
EBAY INSURANCE SERVICES, INC.—see eBay Inc.; *U.S. Public*, pg. 709
EBERLE VIVIAN, INC.—See Liberty Mutual Holding Company Inc.; *U.S. Private*, pg. 2445
EBS-RMSCO, INC.—See The Lifetime Healthcare Companies; *U.S. Private*, pg. 4070
ECC INSURANCE BROKERS, INC.—See Brown & Brown, Inc.; *U.S. Public*, pg. 400
ED BROKING MIAMI INC.—See BGC Group, Inc.; *U.S. Public*, pg. 328
EDELWEISS GENERAL INSURANCE COMPANY LIMITED—See Edelweiss Financial Services Ltd.; *Int'l*, pg. 2306
EDELWEISS INSURANCE BROKERS LIMITED—See Edelweiss Financial Services Ltd.; *Int'l*, pg. 2306
EDELWEISS TOKIO LIFE INSURANCE COMPANY LIMITED—See Edelweiss Financial Services Ltd.; *Int'l*, pg. 2306
EDGEWOOD PARTNERS INSURANCE CENTER—See Keystone Group, L.P.; *U.S. Private*, pg. 2297
EDMONDSONS LIMITED—See Brown & Brown, Inc.; *U.S. Public*, pg. 400
EDWARD E. HALL & COMPANY—See One80 Intermediaries LLC; *U.S. Private*, pg. 3024
EFINANCIAL, LLC; *U.S. Private*, pg. 1343
EFU GENERAL INSURANCE LTD - CENTRAL DIVISION—See EFU General Insurance Ltd.; *Int'l*, pg. 2321
EFU LIFE ASSURANCE LIMITED; *Int'l*, pg. 2321
EGI INSURANCE MANAGERS INC.—See ICPEI Holdings Inc.; *Int'l*, pg. 3586
EGYPT LIFE TAKAFUL INSURANCE COMPANY S.A.E.—See Fairfax Financial Holdings Limited; *Int'l*, pg. 2607
EHEALTHINSURANCE SERVICES, INC.—See eHealth, Inc.; *U.S. Public*, pg. 721
ELAN GROUP INC.—See Principal Financial Group, Inc.; *U.S. Public*, pg. 1721
ELEMENT RISK MANAGEMENT LLC; *U.S. Private*, pg. 1357
ELITE INSURANCE GROUP, INC.—See Porch Group, Inc.; *U.S. Public*, pg. 1702
ELLIOTT SPECIAL RISKS LP—See Markel Group Inc.; *U.S. Public*, pg. 1368

N.A.I.C.S. INDEX 524210 — INSURANCE AGENCIES ...

ELLSWORTH CORPORATION; *U.S. Private*, pg. 1375
EMBRACE PET INSURANCE AGENCY, LLC—See The Carlyle Group Inc.; *U.S. Public*, pg. 2050
EMERSON REID LLC; *U.S. Private*, pg. 1382
EMPLOY AMERICA, LLC; *U.S. Private*, pg. 1386
EMPLOYEE PLANS, LLC—See Old National Bancorp; *U.S. Public*, pg. 1567
EMPLOYER'S COMP ASSOCIATES, INC.—See American Financial Group, Inc.; *U.S. Public*, pg. 103
EMPLOYERS MUTUAL CASUALTY COMPANY; *U.S. Private*, pg. 1386
EMPLOYERS UNITY INC.; *U.S. Private*, pg. 1387
ENCON GROUP INC.—See Marsh & McLennan Companies, Inc.; *U.S. Public*, pg. 1374
ENDEAVOR INSURANCE SERVICES, INC.—See ABRY Partners, LLC; *U.S. Private*, pg. 43
ENEOS INSURANCE SERVICE CORPORATION—See ENEOS Holdings, Inc.; *Int'l*, pg. 2415
ENERGY INSURANCE AGENCY, INC.—See The American Automobile Association, Inc.; *U.S. Private*, pg. 3985
ENERGY & MARINE UNDERWRITERS, INC.—See Brown & Brown, Inc.; *U.S. Public*, pg. 400
ENGLE-HAMBRIGHT & DAVIES INC.; *U.S. Private*, pg. 1399
ENGLE, PAXSON & HAWTHORNE INSURANCE SERVICES, LLC—See ABRY Partners, LLC; *U.S. Private*, pg. 43
ENSTAR AUSTRALIA LIMITED—See Enstar Group Limited; *Int'l*, pg. 2448
ENSTAR NEW YORK, INC—See Enstar Group Limited; *Int'l*, pg. 2448
ENTERPRISE UNDERWRITING SVCS—See Managed Care of America Inc.; *U.S. Private*, pg. 2559
ENVISION INSURANCE COMPANY—See New Rite Aid, LLC; *U.S. Public*, pg. 2905
EPIC INSURANCE SOLUTIONS AGENCY LLC—See Fifth Third Bancorp; *U.S. Public*, pg. 833
EQUITY PARTNERS INSURANCE SERVICES, INC.—See One80 Intermediaries LLC; *U.S. Private*, pg. 3024
ERIC RAWLINS & CO., LTD.—See Brown & Brown, Inc.; *U.S. Public*, pg. 400
ERICSON INSURANCE SERVICES, LLC—See Arthur J. Gallagher & Co.; *U.S. Public*, pg. 204
ERIE INSURANCE COMPANY OF NEW YORK—See Erie Indemnity Company; *U.S. Public*, pg. 792
ESA EUROSHIP GMBH—See Allianz SE; *Int'l*, pg. 356
ESSENTIA INSURANCE COMPANY—See Markel Group Inc.; *U.S. Public*, pg. 1368
ESS NEXTIER INSURANCE GROUP, LLC—See IMA Financial Group, Inc.; *U.S. Private*, pg. 2043
ESTLICK-GIRVIN & LEFEVER INC.; *U.S. Private*, pg. 1429
ESTRELLA INSURANCE INC.—See Stone Point Capital LLC; *U.S. Private*, pg. 3818
ESURANCE INSURANCE SERVICES, INC.—See The Allstate Corporation; *U.S. Public*, pg. 2033
ETHIAS SA—See Ethias Finance SA/NV; *Int'l*, pg. 2523
EULER HERMES SEGUROS S.A.—See Allianz SE; *Int'l*, pg. 353
EULER HERMES SERVICES ITALIA S.R.L.—See Allianz SE; *Int'l*, pg. 353
EULER HERMES SERVICOS DE GESTAO DE RISCOS LTDA.—See Allianz SE; *Int'l*, pg. 353
EUNISURE LTD.—See Edwards Capital, LLC; *U.S. Private*, pg. 1341
EUROBROKERS S.A.; *Int'l*, pg. 2533
EUROCROSS ASSISTANCE NETHERLANDS B.V.—See Achmea B.V.; *Int'l*, pg. 103
EUROCROSS INTERNATIONAL CENTRAL EUROPE S.R.O.—See Achmea B.V.; *Int'l*, pg. 103
EURO EKSPERTS AD; *Int'l*, pg. 2531
EURO GARANTIE AG—See Allianz SE; *Int'l*, pg. 353
EUROHERC OSIGURANJE D.D.; *Int'l*, pg. 2552
EUROINS GEORGIA AD—See Eurohold Bulgaria AD; *Int'l*, pg. 2553
EUROINS INSURANCE GROUP AD—See Eurohold Bulgaria AD; *Int'l*, pg. 2553
EUROPASSUR SARL—See CVC Capital Partners SICAV-FIS S.A.; *Int'l*, pg. 1882
THE EVANS AGENCY, LLC—See Arthur J. Gallagher & Co.; *U.S. Public*, pg. 207
EVEREST INDEMNITY INSURANCE COMPANY—See Everest Group, Ltd.; *Int'l*, pg. 2564
EVEREST INSURANCE (IRELAND), DAC—See Everest Group, Ltd.; *Int'l*, pg. 2564
EVEREST NATIONAL INSURANCE COMPANY—See Everest Group, Ltd.; *Int'l*, pg. 2564
EVERETT CASH MUTUAL INSURANCE CO.; *U.S. Private*, pg. 1438
EVERINSURANCE, INC.—See Teachers Insurance Association - College Retirement Fund; *U.S. Private*, pg. 3948
EVOLUTION TECHNOLOGY SERVICES LIMITED—See Arthur J. Gallagher & Co.; *U.S. Public*, pg. 204
EVOLVE CYBER INSURANCE SERVICES LLC—See Brown & Brown, Inc.; *U.S. Public*, pg. 400
EWING-LEAVITT INSURANCE AGENCY, INC.; *U.S. Private*, pg. 1444
EWI RE, INC.—See Arthur J. Gallagher & Co.; *U.S. Public*, pg. 203

EXCHANGE UNDERWRITERS, INCORPORATED—See World Insurance Associates LLC; *U.S. Private*, pg. 4565
EXECUTIVE RISK INDEMNITY INC.—See Chubb Limited; *Int'l*, pg. 1591
EXPEDITORS CARGO INSURANCE BROKERS B.V.—See Expeditors International of Washington, Inc.; *U.S. Public*, pg. 810
EXPERIEN INSURANCE SERVICES PTY. LTD.—See AUB Group Limited; *Int'l*, pg. 698
EXPLORATION INSURANCE GROUP, LLC—See Galiot Insurance Services, Inc.; *U.S. Private*, pg. 1638
EXXARO INSURANCE COMPANY LIMITED—See Exxaro Resources Ltd.; *Int'l*, pg. 2592
FACULTATIVE RESOURCES, INC.—See W.R. Berkley Corporation; *U.S. Public*, pg. 2318
FAI ALLIANZ LTD.—See Allianz SE; *Int'l*, pg. 353
FAIR AMERICAN SELECT INSURANCE COMPANY—See Berkshire Hathaway Inc.; *U.S. Public*, pg. 299
FAIRFIRST INSURANCE LIMITED—See Fairfax Financial Holdings Limited; *Int'l*, pg. 2606
FAIRMONT SPECIALTY—See Fairfax Financial Holdings Limited; *Int'l*, pg. 2606
FAIRVIEW INSURANCE AGENCY ASSOCIATES INC; *U.S. Private*, pg. 1464
FALCON INSURANCE COMPANY (HONG KONG) LIMITED—See Fairfax Financial Holdings Limited; *Int'l*, pg. 2606
FALCON INSURANCE COMPANY SAOC—See Al Yousef Group; *Int'l*, pg. 283
FANHUA INC.; *Int'l*, pg. 2613
FARM BUREAU INSURANCE AGENCY OF COLORADO, INC.—See Colorado Farm Bureau Mutual Insurance Co.; *U.S. Private*, pg. 973
FARM BUREAU MUTUAL INSURANCE CO.—See Iowa Farm Bureau Federation; *U.S. Private*, pg. 2134
FARMERS CROP INSURANCE ALLIANCE, INC.—See American Financial Group, Inc.; *U.S. Public*, pg. 103
FARM FAMILY LIFE INSURANCE COMPANY—See Brookfield Corporation; *Int'l*, pg. 1174
FARMIN ROTHROCK & PARROTT, INC.—See Stone Point Capital LLC; *U.S. Private*, pg. 3819
FARMWEB LIMITED—See Direct Line Insurance Group plc; *Int'l*, pg. 2129
FATUM GENERAL INSURANCE NV—See Guardian Holdings Limited; *Int'l*, pg. 3171
FBC INSURANCE COMPANY (PRIVATE) LIMITED—See FBC Holdings Limited; *Int'l*, pg. 2627
FBC SECURITIES (PRIVATE) LIMITED—See FBC Holdings Limited; *Int'l*, pg. 2627
FBD INSURANCE BROKERS LIMITED—See Marsh & McLennan Companies, Inc.; *U.S. Public*, pg. 1376
FBD LIFE & PENSIONS LIMITED—See FBD Holdings plc; *Int'l*, pg. 2627
FBN INSURANCE BROKERS LIMITED—See FBN Holdings PLC; *Int'l*, pg. 2627
FCCI INSURANCE GROUP INC.—See FCCI Mutual Insurance Holding Company; *U.S. Private*, pg. 1485
FDL CORPORATION; *U.S. Private*, pg. 1486
THE FEDELI GROUP, INC.; *U.S. Private*, pg. 4028
FEDERAL INSURANCE COMPANY LIMITED; *Int'l*, pg. 2630
FEDERAL INSURANCE COMPANY—See Chubb Limited; *Int'l*, pg. 1591
FEDERATED NATIONAL INSURANCE COMPANY—See FedNat Holding Company; *U.S. Public*, pg. 828
FEIGHNER INSURANCE INC.; *U.S. Private*, pg. 1493
FELISON ASSURADEUREN B.V.—See ASR Nederland N.V.; *Int'l*, pg. 632
THE FESSLER AGENCY INC.; *U.S. Private*, pg. 4028
FFG INSURANCE SERVICE CO., LTD.—See Fukuoka Financial Group, Inc.; *Int'l*, pg. 2840
FIDELIA ASSISTANCE SA—See Covea Groupe S.A.S.; *Int'l*, pg. 2630
FIDELITY ASSURANCE, INC.; *U.S. Private*, pg. 1502
FIDELITY GUARANTY AND ACCEPTANCE CORP.—See Lennar Corporation; *U.S. Public*, pg. 1306
FIDELITY INSURANCE AGENCY, INC.—See Fidelity Financial Corporation; *U.S. Private*, pg. 1503
FIESTA AUTO INSURANCE CENTER; *U.S. Private*, pg. 1504
FINANCE INSURANCE LTD.—See Finance Factors, Limited 1952; *U.S. Public*, pg. 1506
FINANCIAL ARTS INC.—See Inszone Insurance Services, LLC; *U.S. Private*, pg. 2096
FINANCIAL DESIGN ASSOCIATES—See Massachusetts Mutual Life Insurance Company; *U.S. Private*, pg. 2605
FINANCIAL MARKETS, INC.; *U.S. Private*, pg. 1508
FINANCIAL PACIFIC INSURANCE COMPANY—See United Fire Group, Inc.; *U.S. Public*, pg. 2230
FINANCIAL PROFESSIONAL RISK SOLUTIONS, INC.—See Aon plc; *Int'l*, pg. 494
FINANCIAL RISK SOLUTIONS, INC.—See DOXA Insurance Holdings LLC; *U.S. Private*, pg. 1270
FINANCIAL SECURITY ASSOCIATES, INC.—See Simplicity Financial Marketing Holdings Inc.; *U.S. Private*, pg. 3667
FINPROM INSURANCE S.R.L.—See Gruppo MutuiOnline S.p.A; *Int'l*, pg. 3141
FINSURE FINANCE & INSURANCE PTY LTD—See BNK Banking Corporation Limited; *Int'l*, pg. 1079
FIREMAN'S FUND INSURANCE CO. OF HAWAII, INC.—See Allianz SE; *Int'l*, pg. 347
FIREMAN'S FUND INSURANCE CO. OF NEW JERSEY—See Allianz SE; *Int'l*, pg. 347
FIRM, INC.—See Genstar Capital, LLC; *U.S. Private*, pg. 1674
FIRST ACCEPTANCE INSURANCE COMPANY, INC.—See First Acceptance Corporation; *U.S. Public*, pg. 835
FIRST ACCEPTANCE SERVICES, INC.—See First Acceptance Corporation; *U.S. Public*, pg. 835
FIRST AMERICAN PROPERTY & CASUALTY INSURANCE COMPANY—See First American Financial Corporation; *U.S. Public*, pg. 836
FIRST AMERICAN TITLE COMPANY OF BELLINGHAM—See First American Financial Corporation; *U.S. Public*, pg. 836
FIRST AMERICAN TITLE INSURANCE DE MEXICO, S.A. DE C.V.—See First American Financial Corporation; *U.S. Public*, pg. 838
FIRSTBANK INSURANCE AGENCY, INC.—See First Bancorp; *U.S. Public*, pg. 839
FIRST BANK INSURANCE SERVICES, INC.—See First Bancorp; *U.S. Public*, pg. 839
FIRST CAPITAL-AWIS LLC—See Brown & Brown, Inc.; *U.S. Public*, pg. 397
FIRST CATHOLIC SLOVAK UNION US; *U.S. Private*, pg. 1515
FIRST COMMUNITY INSURANCE SERVICES, INC.—See First Community Bankshares, Inc.; *U.S. Public*, pg. 842
FIRST FINANCIAL GROUP OF AMERICA—See American Fidelity Corporation; *U.S. Private*, pg. 233
FIRST FINANCIAL INSURANCE AGENCY, INC.—See First Financial Bankshares, Inc.; *U.S. Public*, pg. 843
FIRST FLORIDA INSURANCE NETWORK; *U.S. Private*, pg. 1519
FIRST GLOBAL FINANCIAL & INSURANCE SERVICES INC.—See Aon plc; *Int'l*, pg. 496
FIRST GLOBAL INSURANCE BROKERS LIMITED—See GraceKennedy Limited; *Int'l*, pg. 3048
FIRST INSURANCE FUNDING OF CANADA, INC.—See Wintrust Financial Corporation; *U.S. Public*, pg. 2375
FIRST INSURANCE GROUP OF THE MIDWEST, INC.—See Kelso & Company, L.P.; *U.S. Private*, pg. 2279
FIRST INSURANCE NETWORK INC.—See Align Financial Group, LLC; *U.S. Private*, pg. 168
FIRST INSURANCE NETWORK INC.—See Excellere Capital Management LLC; *U.S. Private*, pg. 1446
FIRST INSURANCE PARTNERS LLC; *U.S. Private*, pg. 1520
FIRST JERSEY TITLE SERVICES, INC.—See Columbia Financial, Inc.; *U.S. Public*, pg. 534
FIRST LIFE INSURANCE CO., LTD.—See First Financial Holding Co., Ltd.; *Int'l*, pg. 2683
FIRST LINE INSURANCE SERVICES, INC.—See Virtus LLC; *U.S. Public*, pg. 4389
FIRST MANISTIQUE AGENCY, INC.—See Mackinac Financial Corporation; *U.S. Private*, pg. 1352
FIRST NATIONWIDE TITLE AGENCY LLC—See Stone Point Capital LLC; *U.S. Private*, pg. 3821
FIRST NATIONWIDE TITLE AGENCY OF TEXAS, LLC—See Stone Point Capital LLC; *U.S. Private*, pg. 3821
FIRST SECURITY COMPANY, INC.—See ABRY Partners, LLC; *U.S. Private*, pg. 42
FIRST SERVICE INSURANCE AGENTS & BROKERS, INC.—See GTCR LLC; *U.S. Private*, pg. 1803
FIRST TENNESSEE BROKERAGE, INC.—See First Horizon Corporation; *U.S. Public*, pg. 844
FIRST TITLE ABSTRACT & SERVICES, LLC; *U.S. Private*, pg. 1530
FIRST TITLE CEE (BIZTOSITASKOZVETITO KORLATOLT FELELOSSEGU TARSASAG)—See First American Financial Corporation; *U.S. Public*, pg. 838
F&I SENTINEL, LLC; *U.S. Public*, pg. 1455
FISHER BROWN BOTTRELL INSURANCE, INC. - PENSACOLA OFFICE—See Marsh & McLennan Companies, Inc.; *U.S. Public*, pg. 1380
FISHER BROWN BOTTRELL INSURANCE, INC.—See Marsh & McLennan Companies, Inc.; *U.S. Public*, pg. 1380
FITNESS INSURANCE, LLC—See Brown & Brown, Inc.; *U.S. Public*, pg. 400
FIVE INSURANCE BROKERS LIMITED—See Brown & Brown, Inc.; *U.S. Public*, pg. 400
FIVE POINTS BENEFITS SOLUTIONS, LLC—See Arthur J. Gallagher & Co.; *U.S. Public*, pg. 204
THE FLAGSHIP GROUP, LTD.—See Brown & Brown, Inc.; *U.S. Public*, pg. 402
FLEET RISK MANAGEMENT, INC.—See GTCR LLC; *U.S. Private*, pg. 1803
FLEISCHER-JACOBS & ASSOCIATES INC.—See Aon plc; *Int'l*, pg. 496
FLEWWELLING INSURANCE BROKERS LIMITED; *Int'l*, pg. 2701
FLORIDA FARM BUREAU CASUALTY INSURANCE COMPANY, MAIN OFFICE—See Southern Farm Bureau Ca-

524210 — INSURANCE AGENCIES ...

sualty Insurance Company; *U.S. Private*, pg. 3731
FLOWERS INSURANCE AGENCY, LLC—See Galiot Insurance Services, Inc.; *U.S. Private*, pg. 1638
FM ENGINEERING INTERNATIONAL LTD—See Factory Mutual Insurance Company; *U.S. Private*, pg. 1460
FM ENGINEERING INTERNATIONAL LTD—See Factory Mutual Insurance Company; *U.S. Private*, pg. 1460
FM ENGINEERING INTERNATIONAL LTD—See Factory Mutual Insurance Company; *U.S. Private*, pg. 1460
FM ENGINEERING INTERNATION LTD—See Factory Mutual Insurance Company; *U.S. Private*, pg. 1460
FM GLOBAL DE MEXICO—See Factory Mutual Insurance Company; *U.S. Private*, pg. 1460
FM INSURANCE COMPANY LIMITED—See Factory Mutual Insurance Company; *U.S. Private*, pg. 1461
FM INSURANCE COMPANY LIMITED—See Factory Mutual Insurance Company; *U.S. Private*, pg. 1461
FM INSURANCE COMPANY LIMITED—See Factory Mutual Insurance Company; *U.S. Private*, pg. 1461
FMP FORDERUNGSMANAGEMENT POTSDAM GMBH—See BayernLB Holding AG; *Int'l*, pg. 914
FNL INSURANCE COMPANY, LTD—See Wells Fargo & Company; *U.S. Public*, pg. 2343
FOA & SON CORPORATION; *U.S. Private*, pg. 1556
FORD CAPITAL B.V.—See Ford Motor Company; *U.S. Public*, pg. 864
FORESTERS LIFE INSURANCE COMPANY—See Golden Gate Capital Management II, LLC; *U.S. Private*, pg. 1731
FORREST T. JONES & COMPANY, INC.; *U.S. Private*, pg. 1572
FORTA FINANCIAL GROUP, INC.—See Financial Gravity Companies, Inc.; *U.S. Public*, pg. 834
FORTMAN INSURANCE AGENCY, INC.—See Reliance Global Group, Inc.; *U.S. Public*, pg. 1778
FOUNDATION TITLE, LLC; *U.S. Private*, pg. 1580
FOUNDERS INSURANCE CO.—See Nationwide Group; *U.S. Private*, pg. 2866
FOUNTAIN FINANCIAL, INC.—See Ameris Bancorp; *U.S. Public*, pg. 114
FOY INSURANCE GROUP, INC.—See World Insurance Associates LLC; *U.S. Private*, pg. 4566
FRANCIS M. WALLEY INSURANCE AGENCY, INC.—See C&S Insurance Agency, Inc.; *U.S. Private*, pg. 704
FRANK CRYSTAL & CO. INC.—See Stone Point Capital LLC; *U.S. Private*, pg. 3819
FRANK E. NEAL & CO., INC.—See Brown & Brown, Inc.; *U.S. Public*, pg. 400
FRANK H. REIS INC.; *U.S. Private*, pg. 1594
FRANK VITALE INSURANCE AGENCY—See Inszone Insurance Services, LLC; *U.S. Private*, pg. 2096
FRASER MACANDREW RYAN LIMITED—See Arthur J. Gallagher & Co.; *U.S. Public*, pg. 203
FRED A. MORETON & COMPANY; *U.S. Private*, pg. 1600
FRED C. CHURCH INC.; *U.S. Private*, pg. 1600
FRED DANIEL & SONS, INC.—See Stone Point Capital LLC; *U.S. Private*, pg. 3819
FRED LOYA INSURANCE AGENCY; *U.S. Private*, pg. 1601
FREEMAN INSURANCE SERVICES LIMITED—See Arta TechFin Corporation Limited; *Int'l*, pg. 581
FREEWAY INSURANCE SERVICES INC.—See Stone Point Capital LLC; *U.S. Private*, pg. 3819
FRENKEL BENEFITS, LLC—See Keystone Group, L.P.; *U.S. Private*, pg. 2297
FRENKEL & COMPANY - BOSTON—See Keystone Group, L.P.; *U.S. Private*, pg. 2297
FRENKEL & COMPANY - JERSEY CITY—See Keystone Group, L.P.; *U.S. Private*, pg. 2297
FRENKEL & COMPANY—See Keystone Group, L.P.; *U.S. Private*, pg. 2297
FRETT BARRINGTON LTD.—See R&R Insurance Services, Inc.; *U.S. Private*, pg. 3333
FRIENDS LIFE MANAGEMENT SERVICES LIMITED—See Aviva plc; *Int'l*, pg. 746
FRIENDS PROVIDENT INTERNATIONAL LIMITED—See Cinven Limited; *Int'l*, pg. 1612
FRONT RANGE INSURANCE GROUP, LLC—See GTCR LLC; *U.S. Private*, pg. 1803
FSB INSURANCE SERVICE LIMITED—See Markel Group Inc.; *U.S. Public*, pg. 1368
FUBON INSURANCE (VIETNAM) CO., LTD—See Fubon Financial Holding Co. Ltd.; *Int'l*, pg. 2802
FUBON LIFE INSURANCE COMPANY HONG KONG LIMITED—See Fubon Financial Holding Co. Ltd.; *Int'l*, pg. 2802
FUJI OFFICE & LIFE SERVICE, CO., LTD.—See Fuji Electric Co., Ltd.; *Int'l*, pg. 2812
FULCRUM PARTNERS, LLC—See New Mountain Capital, LLC; *U.S. Private*, pg. 2901
FULL SERVICE INSURANCE, INC.—See Caisse de Depot et Placement du Quebec; *Int'l*, pg. 1256
FULL SERVICE INSURANCE, INC.—See KKR & Co. Inc.; *U.S. Public*, pg. 1265
FULTON INSURANCE AGENCIES LTD.; *Int'l*, pg. 2843
FURUNO LIFE BEST CO., LTD.—See Furuno Electric Co., Ltd.; *Int'l*, pg. 2848
FU SHENG INSURANCE AGENCY CO., LTD.—See Fubon Financial Holding Co. Ltd.; *Int'l*, pg. 2801
GALLAGHER BASSETT SERVICES, INC.—See Arthur J. Gallagher & Co.; *U.S. Public*, pg. 205
GALLAGHER HEALTHCARE INSURANCE SERVICES, INC.—See Arthur J. Gallagher & Co.; *U.S. Public*, pg. 205
GALLAGHER INSURANCE BROKERS (ST. LUCIA) LIMITED—See Arthur J. Gallagher & Co.; *U.S. Public*, pg. 205
GALLAGHER INSURANCE BROKERS (ST. VINCENT) LIMITED—See Arthur J. Gallagher & Co.; *U.S. Public*, pg. 205
GAMEPLAN FINANCIAL MARKETING, LLC; *U.S. Private*, pg. 1640
GARDEN STATE LIFE INSURANCE COMPANY—See Brookfield Corporation; *Int'l*, pg. 1174
GARDNER & WHITE CORPORATION; *U.S. Private*, pg. 1643
GARNER & GLOVER COMPANY—See Arthur J. Gallagher & Co.; *U.S. Public*, pg. 205
GARRETT-STOTZ COMPANY, LLC—See Arthur J. Gallagher & Co.; *U.S. Public*, pg. 205
GARY G. OETGEN, INC.—See Fidelity National Financial, Inc.; *U.S. Public*, pg. 831
GARY WOOD ASSOCIATES, INC.; *U.S. Private*, pg. 1647
GATEWAY INSURANCE SERVICES, INC.—See TrueNorth Companies L.C.; *U.S. Private*, pg. 4249
GAUNTLET INSURANCE SERVICES LIMITED—See Brown & Brown, Inc.; *U.S. Public*, pg. 400
GBS ADMINISTRATORS, INC.—See Arthur J. Gallagher & Co.; *U.S. Public*, pg. 205
GBS INSURANCE AND FINANCIAL SERVICES, INC.—See Arthur J. Gallagher & Co.; *U.S. Public*, pg. 205
GCG FINANCIAL, LLC—See Genstar Capital, LLC; *U.S. Private*, pg. 1674
GCG RISK MANAGEMENT, INC.—See Aon plc; *Int'l*, pg. 496
GCUBE INSURANCE SERVICES INC.—See Marsh & McLennan Companies, Inc.; *U.S. Public*, pg. 1375
GD VERSICHERUNGSSERVICE GMBH—See The Goodyear Tire & Rubber Company; *U.S. Public*, pg. 2083
THE GEHRING GROUP, INC.—See Kelso & Company, L.P.; *U.S. Private*, pg. 2280
GENCORP INSURANCE GROUP, INC.—See ABRY Partners, LLC; *U.S. Private*, pg. 43
GENERAL DE SEGUROS, S. A.—See Banco General, S.A.; *Int'l*, pg. 822
GENERALI CAR CARE S.R.O.—See Assicurazioni Generali S.p.A.; *Int'l*, pg. 646
GENERALI CEE HOLDING B.V.—See Assicurazioni Generali S.p.A.; *Int'l*, pg. 644
GENERALI DEUTSCHLAND KRANKENVERSICHERUNG AG—See Assicurazioni Generali S.p.A.; *Int'l*, pg. 644
GENERALI DEUTSCHLAND LEBENSVERSICHERUNG AG—See Assicurazioni Generali S.p.A.; *Int'l*, pg. 644
GENERALI ENGAGEMENT SOLUTIONS GMBH—See Assicurazioni Generali S.p.A.; *Int'l*, pg. 644
GENERALI ESPANA, S.A. DE SEGUROS Y REASEGUROS—See Assicurazioni Generali S.p.A.; *Int'l*, pg. 644
GENERALI FINANCE SPOLKA Z OGRANICZONA ODPOWIEDZIALNOSCIA—See Assicurazioni Generali S.p.A.; *Int'l*, pg. 644
GENERALI FRANCE S.A.—See Assicurazioni Generali S.p.A.; *Int'l*, pg. 645
GENERALI GERANCE S.A.—See Assicurazioni Generali S.p.A.; *Int'l*, pg. 645
GENERALI IARD S.A.—See Assicurazioni Generali S.p.A.; *Int'l*, pg. 645
GENERALI INSURANCE AD—See Assicurazioni Generali S.p.A.; *Int'l*, pg. 644
GENERALI INSURANCE (THAILAND) CO., LTD.—See Assicurazioni Generali S.p.A.; *Int'l*, pg. 646
GENERALI LIFE (HONG KONG) LIMITED—See Assicurazioni Generali S.p.A.; *Int'l*, pg. 647
GENERALI LUXEMBOURG S.A.—See Assicurazioni Generali S.p.A.; *Int'l*, pg. 645
GENERAL INDEMNITY GROUP, LLC—See Boston Omaha Corporation; *U.S. Public*, pg. 372
GENERALI OSIGURANJE D.D.—See Assicurazioni Generali S.p.A.; *Int'l*, pg. 646
GENERALI PARTNER GMBH—See Cinven Limited; *Int'l*, pg. 1616
GENERALI PENSIONSFONDS AG—See Assicurazioni Generali S.p.A.; *Int'l*, pg. 646
GENERALI PENSIONS- UND SICHERUNGSMANAGEMENT GMBH—See Assicurazioni Generali S.p.A.; *Int'l*, pg. 646
GENERALI PENZIJNI SPOLECNOST, A.S.—See Assicurazioni Generali S.p.A.; *Int'l*, pg. 647
GENERALI SEGUROS, S.A.—See Assicurazioni Generali S.p.A.; *Int'l*, pg. 647
GENERALI SICHERUNGSTREUHAND GMBH—See Assicurazioni Generali S.p.A.; *Int'l*, pg. 647
GENERALI TELEFON- + AUFTRAGSSERVICE GMBH—See Assicurazioni Generali S.p.A.; *Int'l*, pg. 645
GENERALI VIS INFORMATIK GMBH—See Assicurazioni Generali S.p.A.; *Int'l*, pg. 646
GENERALI WARRANTY SERVICES, LLC—See Assicurazioni Generali S.p.A.; *Int'l*, pg. 644
GENERAL REINSURANCE CORPORATION—See Berkshire Hathaway Inc.; *U.S. Public*, pg. 302
GENERAL SOUTHWEST INSURANCE AGENCY, INC.—See Arthur J. Gallagher & Co.; *U.S. Public*, pg. 205
GENERAL STAR NATIONAL INSURANCE COMPANY—See Berkshire Hathaway Inc.; *U.S. Public*, pg. 301
GENERATIONS AGENCY, INC.—See Generations Bancorp NY, Inc.; *U.S. Public*, pg. 930
GENERTELLIFE S.P.A.—See Assicurazioni Generali S.p.A.; *Int'l*, pg. 647
GENESIS ABSTRACT, LLC—See Old Republic International Corporation; *U.S. Public*, pg. 1567
GENESIS INDEMNITY INSURANCE COMPANY—See Berkshire Hathaway Inc.; *U.S. Public*, pg. 301
GENESIS INSURANCE COMPANY—See Berkshire Hathaway Inc.; *U.S. Public*, pg. 301
GENESIS UNDERWRITING MANAGEMENT COMPANY—See Berkshire Hathaway Inc.; *U.S. Public*, pg. 301
GENEVE CAPITAL GROUP INC.—See Geneve Holdings Corp.; *U.S. Private*, pg. 1670
GENTRY INSURANCE AGENCY, INC.—See ABRY Partners, LLC; *U.S. Private*, pg. 43
GENWORTH FINANCIAL INDIA PRIVATE LIMITED—See Genworth Financial, Inc.; *U.S. Public*, pg. 934
GENWORTH OPERACIONES COLOMBIA S.A.S.—See Genworth Financial, Inc.; *U.S. Public*, pg. 934
GEO V BULLEN & SON, INC.—See Kelso & Company, L.P.; *U.S. Private*, pg. 2279
GEOVERA INSURANCE COMPANY INC.—See Edwards Capital, LLC; *U.S. Private*, pg. 1341
GERALD EVE FINANCIAL SERVICES LIMITED—See Alkido Pharma Inc.; *U.S. Public*, pg. 63
GERARD B TRACY ASSOCIATES, INC.—See Kelso & Company, L.P.; *U.S. Private*, pg. 2279
GFA CARAIBES SA—See Assicurazioni Generali S.p.A.; *Int'l*, pg. 645
G&G AGENCY LTD.—See Principal Financial Group, Inc.; *U.S. Public*, pg. 1721
GIBRALTAR BSN LIFE BERHAD—See Prudential Financial, Inc.; *U.S. Public*, pg. 1733
GIBSON INSURANCE AGENCY INC.; *U.S. Private*, pg. 1696
GIC RE SOUTH AFRICA LTD.—See General Insurance Corporation Of India; *Int'l*, pg. 2918
GIE AXA—See AXA S.A.; *Int'l*, pg. 759
GIG GULF—See AXA S.A.; *Int'l*, pg. 759
GIG OF MISSOURI INC.—See American International Group, Inc.; *U.S. Public*, pg. 106
GILES INSURANCE BROKERS LTD.—See Arthur J. Gallagher & Co.; *U.S. Public*, pg. 202
GILLIS, ELLIS & BAKER, INC.—See Arthur J. Gallagher & Co.; *U.S. Public*, pg. 205
GIO GENERAL LIMITED—See Dai-ichi Life Holdings, Inc.; *Int'l*, pg. 1918
GK INSURANCE BROKERS LIMITED—See GraceKennedy Limited; *Int'l*, pg. 3048
GLACIER INSURANCE OF LIBBY, INC.—See Hellman & Friedman LLC; *U.S. Private*, pg. 1908
GLATFELTER BROKERAGE SERVICE—See American International Group, Inc.; *U.S. Public*, pg. 106
GLATFELTER INSURANCE GROUP—See American International Group, Inc.; *U.S. Public*, pg. 106
GLATFELTER UNDERWRITING SERVICES, INC.—See American International Group, Inc.; *U.S. Public*, pg. 106
GLENMOORE CAPITAL REIT; *Int'l*, pg. 2992
GLENN/DAVIS & ASSOCIATES, INC.—See GTCR LLC; *U.S. Private*, pg. 1803
GLENN HARRIS & ASSOCIATES, INC.—See Galiot Insurance Services, Inc.; *U.S. Private*, pg. 1638
GLOBAL AG INSURANCE SERVICES, LLC—See Farmers Mutual Hail Insurance Company of Iowa; *U.S. Private*, pg. 1478
GLOBAL ASSET PROTECTION SERVICES, LLC—See AXA S.A.; *Int'l*, pg. 760
GLOBAL INDEMNITY INSURANCE AGENCY, INC.; *U.S. Private*, pg. 1714
GLOBAL MENKUL DEGERLER A.S—See Global Yatirim Holding A.S.; *Int'l*, pg. 3002
GLOBAL SIGORTA ARACILIK HIZMETLERI A.S—See Global Yatirim Holding A.S.; *Int'l*, pg. 3003
GLOBAL SPECIAL RISKS, LLC—See Ryan Specialty Holdings, Inc.; *U.S. Public*, pg. 1828
GLOBE UNDERWRITING LIMITED—See BGC Group, Inc.; *U.S. Public*, pg. 329
GLOBOS OSIGURANJE A.D.; *Int'l*, pg. 3008
GM CORRETORA DE SEGUROS LTDA.—See General Motors Company; *U.S. Public*, pg. 924
GODWIN & REESE INSURANCE AGENCY, INC.; *U.S. Private*, pg. 1725
GOLDEN WEST DENTAL & VISION HEALTH PLANS, INC.—See Elevance Health, Inc.; *U.S. Public*, pg. 730
GOLDEN WEST HEALTH PLAN, INC.—See Elevance Health, Inc.; *U.S. Public*, pg. 730
GOODHART NATIONAL GORMAN AGENCY, INC.; *U.S. Private*, pg. 1739
GOOSEHEAD INSURANCE, INC.; *U.S. Public*, pg. 952

N.A.I.C.S. INDEX

524210 — INSURANCE AGENCIES ...

GORDON B. ROBERTS AGENCY, LLC—See Community Bank System, Inc.; *U.S. Public*, pg. 550
GRACEKENNEDY MONEY SERVICES (ANGUILLA) LIMITED—See GraceKennedy Limited; *Int'l*, pg. 3049
GRACEKENNEDY REMITTANCE SERVICES (GUYANA) LIMITED—See GraceKennedy Limited; *Int'l*, pg. 3049
GRAHAM-ROGERS, INC.—See Brown & Brown, Inc.; *U.S. Public*, pg. 398
GRANA Y ASOCIADOS CORREDORES DE SEGUROS SA—See Aon plc; *Int'l*, pg. 494
GRAY-STONE & COMPANY—See The Liberty Company Insurance Brokers, Inc.; *U.S. Public*, pg. 4069
GREAT AMERICAN CUSTOM INSURANCE SERVICES, INC.—See American Financial Group, Inc.; *U.S. Public*, pg. 103
GREAT AMERICAN LLOYDS INC.—See Massachusetts Mutual Life Insurance Company; *U.S. Private*, pg. 2605
GREAT AMERICAN PROTECTION INSURANCE COMPANY—See American Financial Group, Inc.; *U.S. Public*, pg. 103
GREATER TEXAS INSURANCE MANAGERS & AGENCY, INC.—See BKCW, L.P.; *U.S. Private*, pg. 568
GREENLIGHT REINSURANCE IRELAND, LIMITED—See Greenlight Capital Re, Ltd.; *Int'l*, pg. 3075
GREEN MOUNTAIN INSURANCE COMPANY, INC.—See Concord General Mu; *U.S. Private*, pg. 1010
GREEN-OWENS INSURANCE—See Keystone Group, L.P.; *U.S. Private*, pg. 2299
GREENWICH INSURANCE COMPANY—See AXA S.A.; *Int'l*, pg. 761
GREMESCO OF NEW JERSEY, LLC—See Brown & Brown, Inc.; *U.S. Public*, pg. 400
GRESHAM & ASSOCIATES, INC.—See AmWINS Group, Inc.; *U.S. Private*, pg. 269
GRIFFIN UNDERWRITING SERVICES—See Ryan Specialty Holdings, Inc.; *U.S. Public*, pg. 1828
GRIGGS NELSON MUTUAL INSURANCE CO.—See Walsh County Mutual Insurance Company; *U.S. Private*, pg. 4432
GRINNELL SELECT INSURANCE COMPANY—See Grinnell Mutual Reinsurance Company Inc.; *U.S. Private*, pg. 1790
GROCERS INSURANCE AGENCY, INC.—See Brookfield Reinsurance Ltd.; *Int'l*, pg. 1194
GROSSLIGHT INSURANCE, INC.—See Peter C. Foy & Associates Insurance Services, Inc.; *U.S. Private*, pg. 3157
GROUP ALTERNATIVES INC.—See GTCR LLC; *U.S. Private*, pg. 1803
GROUPAMA ASSICURAZIONI SPA—See Groupama SA; *Int'l*, pg. 3090
GROUPAMA EMEKLILIK A.S.—See Groupama SA; *Int'l*, pg. 3090
GROUPAMA GARANCIA BIZTOSITO ZRT—See Groupama SA; *Int'l*, pg. 3090
GROUPAMA GARANCIA POISTOVNA, A. S.—See Groupama SA; *Int'l*, pg. 3090
GROUPAMA ZASTRAHOVANE EAD—See Groupama SA; *Int'l*, pg. 3091
GROUP ASSOCIATES, INC.—See Marpai, Inc; *U.S. Public*, pg. 1370
GROUP BENEFIT SERVICES INC.—See AmWINS Group, Inc.; *U.S. Private*, pg. 269
GROUPE APICIL; *Int'l*, pg. 3091
GROUPE-CONSEIL AON INC.—See Aon plc; *Int'l*, pg. 494
GROUPHEALTHFLORIDA.COM; *U.S. Private*, pg. 1794
GROUP INSURANCE, INCORPORATED OF LOUISIANA—See Stone Point Capital LLC; *U.S. Private*, pg. 3819
GROUP SERVICES, LLC—See Genstar Capital, LLC; *U.S. Private*, pg. 1674
GRUPO ASSA, S.A.; *Int'l*, pg. 3121
GRUPO CATALANA OCCIDENTE SERVICIOS TECNOLOGICOS, AIE—See Grupo Catalana Occidente, S.A.; *Int'l*, pg. 3124
GUARDIAN IB LIMITED—See Brown & Brown, Inc.; *U.S. Public*, pg. 400
GUARDIAN ROYAL EXCHANGE PLC—See AXA S.A.; *Int'l*, pg. 758
GUIAN S.A.—See Marsh & McLennan Companies, Inc.; *U.S. Public*, pg. 1375
GUIDED INSURANCE SOLUTIONS, LLC—See The Baldwin Insurance Group, Inc.; *U.S. Public*, pg. 2036
GULF REINSURANCE LIMITED—See Arch Capital Group Ltd.; *Int'l*, pg. 547
GULFSHORE INSURANCE, INC.; *U.S. Private*, pg. 1817
GULF STATES HOLDINGS, INC.; *U.S. Private*, pg. 1817
GULF STATES INSURANCE COMPANY, INC.—See Gulf States Holdings, Inc.; *U.S. Private*, pg. 1817
GUMTREE WHOLESALE INSURANCE BROKERS, INC.—See Caisse de Depot et Placement du Quebec; *Int'l*, pg. 1256
GUMTREE WHOLESALE INSURANCE BROKERS, INC.—See KKR & Co. Inc.; *U.S. Public*, pg. 1265
GUNDERMANN & GUNDERMANN—See Keystone Group, L.P.; *U.S. Private*, pg. 2297
GUNN-MOWERY, LLC; *U.S. Private*, pg. 1818

GUNTHER LUBSEN GMBH—See BGC Group, Inc.; *U.S. Public*, pg. 329
GUOTAI JUNAN FUTURES (HONG KONG) LIMITED—See Guotai Junan Securities Co., Ltd.; *Int'l*, pg. 3187
GUOTAI JUNAN FX LIMITED—See Guotai Junan Securities Co., Ltd.; *Int'l*, pg. 3187
GUY CARPENTER & CO. LABUAN LTD.—See Marsh & McLennan Companies, Inc.; *U.S. Public*, pg. 1375
GUY CARPENTER & COMPANY INC. OF PENNSYLVANIA—See Marsh & McLennan Companies, Inc.; *U.S. Public*, pg. 1375
GUY CARPENTER INSURANCE BROKERS (BEIJING) CO. LTD.—See Marsh & McLennan Companies, Inc.; *U.S. Public*, pg. 1375
HACKETT VALINE & MACDONALD, INC.—See Aon plc; *Int'l*, pg. 496
HADLEY INSURIT GROUP INSURANCE, INC.—See Narragansett Financial Corp.; *U.S. Private*, pg. 2835
HADLEY & LYDEN, INC.—See World Insurance Associates LLC; *U.S. Private*, pg. 4566
HAE INSURANCE SERVICES LIMITED—See Marsh & McLennan Companies, Inc.; *U.S. Public*, pg. 1376
HAGERTY INSURANCE AGENCY, LLC—See Hagerty, Inc.; *U.S. Public*, pg. 979
HAGERTY INTERNATIONAL LIMITED—See Hagerty, Inc.; *U.S. Public*, pg. 979
HALE & ASSOCIATES, INC.—See PCF Insurance Services of The West, LLC; *U.S. Private*, pg. 3120
HALSTEAD INSURANCE AGENCY, INC.—See GTCR LLC; *U.S. Private*, pg. 1803
HAMILTON RISK MANAGEMENT CO.—See Kingsway Financial Services Inc.; *U.S. Public*, pg. 1234
HAMMAN-MILLER-BEAUCHAMP-DEEBLE, INC.—See Hellman & Friedman LLC; *U.S. Private*, pg. 1909
HAMMERBERG INVESTMENTS, INC.—See Arthur J. Gallagher & Co.; *U.S. Public*, pg. 205
HANA INSURANCE. CO., LTD.—See Hana Financial Group, Inc.; *Int'l*, pg. 3240
HANASAB INSURANCE SERVICES, INC.—See ABRY Partners, LLC; *U.S. Private*, pg. 42
HANOVER EXCESS & SURPLUS, INC.—See Arthur J. Gallagher & Co.; *U.S. Public*, pg. 205
HANWHA LIFE CO., LTD—See Hanwha Group; *Int'l*, pg. 3266
HANWHA LIFE INSURANCE VIETNAM LTD.—See Hanwha Group; *Int'l*, pg. 3266
HARBORWAY INSURANCE AGENCY, LLC—See The Travelers Companies, Inc.; *U.S. Public*, pg. 2136
HARCO INSURANCE SERVICES; *U.S. Private*, pg. 1861
HARDEN & ASSOCIATES, INC.—See Arthur J. Gallagher & Co.; *U.S. Public*, pg. 205
HARDENBERGH INSURANCE GROUP, INC.; *U.S. Private*, pg. 1862
HAREL INSURANCE, FINANCING & ISSUING LTD.—See Harel Insurance Investments & Financial Services Ltd.; *Int'l*, pg. 3274
HAREL (UK) LTD.—See Harel Insurance Investments & Financial Services Ltd.; *Int'l*, pg. 3274
HARIYALI INSURANCE BROKING LIMITED—See DCM Shriram Limited; *Int'l*, pg. 1992
HAROLD DIERS & CO.—See Brown & Brown, Inc.; *U.S. Public*, pg. 397
HARRINGTON BENEFIT SERVCES, INC.—See Fiserv, Inc.; *U.S. Public*, pg. 851
HARRIS FOWLER INSURANCE COMPANY, INC.—See Leavitt Group Enterprises, Inc.; *U.S. Private*, pg. 2409
HARTLEY CYLKE PACIFIC INSURANCE SERVICES, INC.—See Arthur J. Gallagher & Co.; *U.S. Public*, pg. 205
HATHAWAY AGENCY, INC.—See NBT Bancorp Inc.; *U.S. Public*, pg. 1500
HAUSMANN JOHNSON INSURANCE, INC.—See The Benefit Services Group, Inc.; *U.S. Private*, pg. 3993
HAVELAAR ET VAN STOLK B.V.—See Allianz SE; *Int'l*, pg. 353
HAYAH INSURANCE COMPANY P.J.S.C—See AXA S.A.; *Int'l*, pg. 759
HAYS COMPANIES INC.—See Brown & Brown, Inc.; *U.S. Public*, pg. 400
HAYS COMPANIES OF NEW JERSEY, INC.—See Brown & Brown, Inc.; *U.S. Public*, pg. 401
HAYS GROUP OF WISCONSIN LLC—See Brown & Brown, Inc.; *U.S. Public*, pg. 401
HAYS INSURANCE BROKERAGE OF NEW ENGLAND, LLC—See Brown & Brown, Inc.; *U.S. Public*, pg. 401
HAYS OF UTAH INSURANCE SERVICES INC—See Brown & Brown, Inc.; *U.S. Public*, pg. 401
HBI TITLE SERVICES, INC.—See Huntington Bancshares Incorporated; *U.S. Public*, pg. 1071
HEALTHCARE INSURANCE PROFESSIONALS, INC.—See Brown & Brown, Inc.; *U.S. Public*, pg. 401
HEALTHCOMPARE INSURANCE SERVICES, INC.—See The Allstate Corporation; *U.S. Public*, pg. 2033
HEALTHPLANONE, LLC—See Peloton Equity LLC; *U.S. Private*, pg. 3131
HEALTH SPECIAL RISK, INC.—See Brown & Brown, Inc.; *U.S. Public*, pg. 401
HEARTLAND SPECIALTY INSURANCE—See Texans

Credit Union; *U.S. Private*, pg. 3974
HECHT & HECHT INSURANCE AGENCY, INC.—See Stone Point Capital LLC; *U.S. Private*, pg. 3819
HEFFERNAN INSURANCE BROKERS; *U.S. Private*, pg. 1903
HEFFERNAN NETWORK INSURANCE BROKERS—See Heffernan Insurance Brokers; *U.S. Private*, pg. 1904
HELP SEGUROS DE VIDA S.A.—See UnitedHealth Group Incorporated; *U.S. Public*, pg. 2241
HELVETIA CONSULTA AG—See Helvetia Holding AG; *Int'l*, pg. 3339
HELVETIA LATIN AMERICA LLC—See Helvetia Holding AG; *Int'l*, pg. 3339
HELVETIA SWISS INSURANCE COMPANY IN LIECHTENSTEIN LTD.—See Helvetia Holding AG; *Int'l*, pg. 3340
HELVETIA SWISS INSURANCE COMPANY (LABUAN BRANCH) LTD.—See Helvetia Holding AG; *Int'l*, pg. 3340
HELVETIA SWISS INSURANCE COMPANY LTD—See Helvetia Holding AG; *Int'l*, pg. 3340
HENTSCHELL & ASSOCIATES INC.; *U.S. Private*, pg. 1920
HERBERT L. JAMISON & CO., LLC—See GTCR LLC; *U.S. Private*, pg. 1803
HERBIE WILES INSURANCE, INC.; *U.S. Private*, pg. 1921
HERITAGE INSURANCE SERVICE INC.—See Marsh & McLennan Companies, Inc.; *U.S. Public*, pg. 1380
HESSE & PATRNER, AG—See Arthur J. Gallagher & Co.; *U.S. Public*, pg. 206
HEUNGKUK FIRE & MARINE INSURANCE CO., LTD.; *Int'l*, pg. 3366
HEWITT ASSOCIATES KOREA YUHAN HOESA—See Alight, Inc.; *U.S. Public*, pg. 76
HFG (SINGAPORE) PTE. LTD.—See High Finance Ltd.; *Int'l*, pg. 3385
H&H AGENCY, INC.; *U.S. Private*, pg. 1822
H.H.V. WHITCHURCH & CO. LTD.; *Int'l*, pg. 3195
HIBBS-HALLMARK & COMPANY; *U.S. Private*, pg. 1932
HIGGINBOTHAM INSURANCE AGENCY, LLC—See Galiot Insurance Services, Inc.; *U.S. Private*, pg. 1637
HIGHLAND CAPITAL BROKERAGE, INC.—See Reverence Capital Partners LLC; *U.S. Private*, pg. 3414
THE HILB GROUP, LLC—See ABRY Partners, LLC; *U.S. Private*, pg. 43
THE HILB GROUP OF VIRGINIA, LLC—See ABRY Partners, LLC; *U.S. Private*, pg. 43
HIMCO DISTRIBUTION SERVICES COMPANY—See The Hartford Financial Services Group, Inc.; *U.S. Public*, pg. 2088
HINRICHS FLANAGAN FINANCIAL; *U.S. Private*, pg. 1949
HISCOX INSURANCE COMPANY (GUERNSEY) LIMITED—See Hiscox Ltd.; *Int'l*, pg. 3407
HISCOX INSURANCE COMPANY INC.—See Hiscox Ltd.; *Int'l*, pg. 3407
HISCOX RE INSURANCE LINKED STRATEGIES LTD.—See Hiscox Ltd.; *Int'l*, pg. 3407
HITACHI INSURANCE AGENCY (CHINA) LIMITED—See Hitachi, Ltd.; *Int'l*, pg. 3419
HITACHI INSURANCE SERVICES (HONG KONG) LTD.—See Hitachi, Ltd.; *Int'l*, pg. 3419
HITACHI INSURANCE SERVICES, LTD.—See Hitachi, Ltd.; *Int'l*, pg. 3419
HMK INSURANCE—See Genstar Capital, LLC; *U.S. Private*, pg. 1674
HMS INSURANCE ASSOCIATES, INC.—See Marsh & McLennan Companies, Inc.; *U.S. Public*, pg. 1380
HNB GENERAL INSURANCE LIMITED—See HNB Assurance PLC; *Int'l*, pg. 3434
HOCKLEY & O'DONNELL INSURANCE AGENCY, LLC—See ACNB Corporation; *U.S. Public*, pg. 35
HOCKMAN INSURANCE AGENCY, INC.—See ABRY Partners, LLC; *U.S. Private*, pg. 43
HOLLARD BOTSWANA (PTY) LTD—See Hollard Insurance Company Ltd; *Int'l*, pg. 3451
HOLLARD INSURANCE COMPANY LTD; *Int'l*, pg. 3451
HOLLARD INSURANCE COMPANY OF NAMIBIA LIMITED—See Hollard Insurance Company Ltd; *Int'l*, pg. 3451
HOLLARD INSURANCE ZAMBIA LIMITED—See Hollard Insurance Company Ltd; *Int'l*, pg. 3451
HOLLARD LIFE ASSURANCE ZAMBIA LIMITED—See Hollard Insurance Company Ltd; *Int'l*, pg. 3451
HOLLARD MOCAMBIQUE COMPANHIA DE SEGUROS SARL—See Hollard Insurance Company Ltd; *Int'l*, pg. 3451
HOLLIS D. SEGUR INC.; *U.S. Private*, pg. 1965
HOLMES MURPHY & ASSOCIATES, INC.; *U.S. Private*, pg. 1967
HOLMES SHAW, INC.—See PointeNorth Insurance Group LLC; *U.S. Private*, pg. 3222
HOME COUNTIES INSURANCE SERVICES LIMITED—See Brown & Brown, Inc.; *U.S. Public*, pg. 401
HOMEINSURANCE.COM LLC—See Red Ventures, LLC; *U.S. Private*, pg. 3376
HOME & LEGACY INSURANCE SERVICES LIMITED—See Allianz SE; *Int'l*, pg. 353
HOMER WARREN PROCTOR INC.; *U.S. Private*, pg. 1973
HORIZON AGENCY, INC.—See Hellman & Friedman LLC; *U.S. Private*, pg. 1909

524210 — INSURANCE AGENCIES ...

HORIZON INSURANCE SERVICES, INC.—See Horizon Bancorp, Inc.; *U.S. Public*, pg. 1053
HORST INSURANCE AGENCY—See The Horst Group Inc.; *U.S. Private*, pg. 4054
HORTICA INSURANCE; *U.S. Public*, pg. 1984
THE HORTON GROUP INC.—See Marsh & McLennan Companies, Inc.; *U.S. Public*, pg. 1382
HOTCHKISS INSURANCE AGENCY; *U.S. Private*, pg. 1989
HOULDER INSURANCE SERVICES LTD.; *Int'l*, pg. 3490
HOUSE OF INSURTECH SWITZERLAND AG—See Assicurazioni Generali S.p.A.; *Int'l*, pg. 644
HOUSING NEW YORK CORPORATION—See New York City Housing Development Corporation; *U.S. Private*, pg. 2909
HOUSKA INSURANCE SERVICES INC.—See New Mountain Capital, LLC; *U.S. Private*, pg. 2901
HOUSTON BUSINESS INSURANCE AGENCY, INC.—See GTCR LLC; *U.S. Private*, pg. 1803
HOUSTON SURPLUS LINES, INC.—See XPT Group LLC; *U.S. Private*, pg. 4582
HOVG, LLC—See Exela Technologies, Inc.; *U.S. Public*, pg. 806
HOVIS & ASSOCIATES—See Integrity Marketing Group LLC; *U.S. Private*, pg. 2103
HOWDEN CORRETORA DE RESSEGUROS LTDA—See Howden Group Holdings Limited; *Int'l*, pg. 3493
HOWDEN GROUP HOLDINGS LIMITED; *Int'l*, pg. 3493
HOWDEN IBERIA S.A.—See Howden Group Holdings Limited; *Int'l*, pg. 3493
HOWDEN INSURANCE BROKERS (2002) LIMITED—See Howden Group Holdings Limited; *Int'l*, pg. 3493
HOWDEN INSURANCE BROKERS (BERMUDA) LIMITED—See Howden Group Holdings Limited; *Int'l*, pg. 3494
HOWDEN INSURANCE BROKERS (HK) LIMITED—See Howden Group Holdings Limited; *Int'l*, pg. 3494
HOWDEN INSURANCE BROKERS LIMITED—See Howden Group Holdings Limited; *Int'l*, pg. 3494
HOWDEN INSURANCE BROKERS NEDERLAND B.V.—See Howden Group Holdings Limited; *Int'l*, pg. 3494
HOWDEN INSURANCE BROKERS OY—See Howden Group Holdings Limited; *Int'l*, pg. 3494
HOWDEN INSURANCE, LLC—See Howden Group Holdings Limited; *Int'l*, pg. 3494
HOWDEN INSURANCE SERVICES, INC—See Howden Group Holdings Limited; *Int'l*, pg. 3494
HOWDEN SIGORTA BROKERLIGI ANONIM SIRKETI—See Howden Group Holdings Limited; *Int'l*, pg. 3494
HOWDEN URUGUAY CORREDORES DE REASEGUROS S.A—See Howden Group Holdings Limited; *Int'l*, pg. 3494
HOWELL SHONE INSURANCE BROKERS LIMITED—See Marsh & McLennan Companies, Inc.; *U.S. Public*, pg. 1376
HPB INSURANCE GROUP, INC.—See Pinnacle Financial Partners, Inc.; *U.S. Public*, pg. 1692
HQ INSURANCE CORPORATION—See HireQuest, Inc.; *U.S. Public*, pg. 1042
HR OWEN INSURANCE SERVICES LIMITED—See Arthur J. Gallagher & Co.; *U.S. Public*, pg. 205
HSBC INSURANCE SERVICES—See HSBC Holdings plc; *Int'l*, pg. 3505
HUATAI INSURANCE AGENCY & CONSULTANT SERVICE LIMITED—See China Reinsurance (Group) Corporation; *Int'l*, pg. 1547
HUATAI SURVEYORS & ADJUSTERS COMPANY LIMITED—See China Reinsurance (Group) Corporation; *Int'l*, pg. 1547
HUAXIA LIFE INSURANCE CO., LTD.; *Int'l*, pg. 3515
HUB INTERNATIONAL GREAT PLAINS, LLC—See Hellman & Friedman LLC; *U.S. Private*, pg. 1909
HUB INTERNATIONAL INSURANCE SERVICES, INC.—See Hellman & Friedman LLC; *U.S. Private*, pg. 1909
HUB INTERNATIONAL LIMITED—See Hellman & Friedman LLC; *U.S. Private*, pg. 1908
HUB INTERNATIONAL MIDWEST LIMITED—See Hellman & Friedman LLC; *U.S. Private*, pg. 1909
HUB INTERNATIONAL MOUNTAIN STATES LIMITED—See Hellman & Friedman LLC; *U.S. Private*, pg. 1909
HUB INTERNATIONAL NEW ENGLAND, LLC—See Hellman & Friedman LLC; *U.S. Private*, pg. 1909
HUB INTERNATIONAL QUEBEC LIMITED—See Hellman & Friedman LLC; *U.S. Private*, pg. 1909
HUB INTERNATIONAL SOUTHEAST LIMITED—See Hellman & Friedman LLC; *U.S. Private*, pg. 1909
HUB INTERNATIONAL TEXAS, INC. - DALLAS; *U.S. Private*, pg. 2000
HUB INTERNATIONAL TEXAS, INC.—See Hellman & Friedman LLC; *U.S. Private*, pg. 1909
HUDSON VALLEY INSURANCE COMPANY—See PepsiCo, Inc.; *U.S. Public*, pg. 1669
HUGHES INSURANCE AGENCY, INC.—See Arthur J. Gallagher & Co.; *U.S. Public*, pg. 206
HUGH WOOD, INC.—See Kelso & Company, L.P.; *U.S. Private*, pg. 2280

HULL & COMPANY, LLC—See Brown & Brown, Inc.; *U.S. Public*, pg. 401
HUNTINGTON PACIFIC INSURANCE AGENCY, INC.—See Inszone Insurance Services, LLC; *U.S. Private*, pg. 2096
HUNT INSURANCE GROUP, LLC; *U.S. Private*, pg. 2009
HYATT LEGAL PLANS, INC.—See MetLife, Inc.; *U.S. Public*, pg. 1430
HYLANT GROUP - ANN ARBOR—See Hylant Group Inc.; *U.S. Private*, pg. 2019
HYLANT GROUP INC.; *U.S. Private*, pg. 2018
HYLANT GROUP - INDIANAPOLIS—See Hylant Group Inc.; *U.S. Private*, pg. 2019
HYLANT—See Hylant Group Inc.; *U.S. Private*, pg. 2019
HYUNDAI INSURANCE BROKERS PTE. LTD.—See Hyundai Marine & Fire Insurance Co., Ltd.; *Int'l*, pg. 3558
HYUNDAI INSURANCE (CHINA) COMPANY LTD.—See Hyundai Marine & Fire Insurance Co., Ltd.; *Int'l*, pg. 3558
HYUNDAI U.K UNDERWRITING LTD.—See Hyundai Marine & Fire Insurance Co., Ltd.; *Int'l*, pg. 3558
IA CLARINGTON INVESTMENTS INC.—See iA Financial Corporation Inc.; *Int'l*, pg. 3567
ICC INSURANCE AGENCY, INC.—See RCAP Holdings, LLC; *U.S. Private*, pg. 3361
IC EUROINS-LIFE EAD—See Eurohold Bulgaria AD; *Int'l*, pg. 2553
ICICI LOMBARD GENERAL INSURANCE CO. LTD.—See Fairfax Financial Holdings Limited; *Int'l*, pg. 2607
ICICI LOMBARD GENERAL INSURANCE CO. LTD.—See ICICI Bank Limited; *Int'l*, pg. 3581
ICI MUTUAL INSURANCE BROKERS—See ICI Mutual Insurance Company; *U.S. Private*, pg. 2031
ICS GROUP HOLDINGS INC.—See INNOVATE Corp.; *U.S. Public*, pg. 1126
I.G.I. UNDERWRITING AGENCY, INC.—See Stone Point Capital LLC; *U.S. Private*, pg. 3821
IHC ADMINISTRATIVE SERVICES, INC.—See Geneve Holdings Corp.; *U.S. Private*, pg. 1670
IHC FINANCIAL GROUP, INC.—See Geneve Holdings Corp.; *U.S. Private*, pg. 1670
IHL HOME INSURANCE AGENCY, LLC—See Century Communities, Inc.; *U.S. Public*, pg. 475
IIAA AGENCY ADMINISTRATIVE SERVICES, INC.—See Independent Insurance Agents & Brokers of America, Inc.; *U.S. Private*, pg. 2059
IIAA MEMBERSHIP SERVICES, INC.—See Independent Insurance Agents & Brokers of America, Inc.; *U.S. Private*, pg. 2059
IINO BUSINESS SERVICE CO., LTD.—See Iino Kaiun Kaisha Ltd.; *Int'l*, pg. 3608
ILLINOIS UNION INSURANCE COMPANY—See Chubb Limited; *Int'l*, pg. 1593
IMA FINANCIAL GROUP, INC.; *U.S. Private*, pg. 2043
IMA INC.—See IMA Financial Group, Inc.; *U.S. Private*, pg. 2043
IMA, KANSAS INC.—See IMA Financial Group, Inc.; *U.S. Private*, pg. 2043
IMA OF COLORADO INC.—See IMA Financial Group, Inc.; *U.S. Private*, pg. 2043
IMPACT FORECASTING, L.L.C.—See Aon plc; *Int'l*, pg. 494
IMPENDULO LIMITED—See Vista Equity Partners, LLC; *U.S. Private*, pg. 4395
INDEPENDENT INSURANCE AGENTS & BROKERS OF AMERICA, INC.; *U.S. Private*, pg. 2059
INDEPENDENT INSURANCE CENTER, INC.; *U.S. Private*, pg. 2059
INDEPENDER SERVICES B.V.—See DPG Media Group NV; *Int'l*, pg. 2188
INDIAN HARBOR INSURANCE COMPANY—See AXA S.A.; *Int'l*, pg. 761
INDIGO INSURANCE (CAYMAN) LIMITED—See Colina Holdings Bahamas Limited; *Int'l*, pg. 1698
INDUSTRY CONSULTING GROUP, INC.—See Brown & Brown, Inc.; *U.S. Public*, pg. 401
INFANTINE INSURANCE, INC.—See Cross Financial Corporation; *U.S. Private*, pg. 1105
INFINITY AUTO INSURANCE COMPANY—See Kemper Corporation; *U.S. Public*, pg. 1220
INFINITY INSURANCE AGENCY INC.—See Kemper Corporation; *U.S. Public*, pg. 1220
INFORMA HIS GMBH—See Bertelsmann SE & Co. KGaA; *Int'l*, pg. 997
INNOVATE360, INC.—See GTCR LLC; *U.S. Private*, pg. 1803
INNOVATIVE SOLUTIONS INSURANCE SERVICES, LLC; *U.S. Private*, pg. 2083
INNSLAKE TITLE AGENCY, LLC—See Markel Group Inc.; *U.S. Public*, pg. 1368
INO24 AG—See Hubert Burda Media Holding Kommanditgesellschaft; *Int'l*, pg. 3520
INPRO INSURANCE GROUP, LLC—See ABRY Partners, LLC; *U.S. Public*, pg. 42
INSENTIAL, INC.—See Hendricks Holding Company, Inc.; *U.S. Private*, pg. 1915
INSERVCO INSURANCE SERVICES, INC.—See Pennsylvania National Mutual Casualty Insurance Company; *U.S. Private*, pg. 3137
INSGROUP, INC.—See The Baldwin Insurance Group, Inc.; *U.S. Public*, pg. 2036

INSOLUTIONS LIMITED—See Marsh & McLennan Companies, Inc.; *U.S. Public*, pg. 1377
INSPHERE INSURANCE SOLUTIONS, INC.—See Blackstone Inc.; *U.S. Public*, pg. 354
INSTRAT INSURANCE BROKERS LTD—See Arthur J. Gallagher & Co.; *U.S. Public*, pg. 203
INSURAMATCH, LLC—See The Travelers Companies, Inc.; *U.S. Public*, pg. 2136
INSURANCE APPLICATIONS GROUP, LLC; *U.S. Private*, pg. 2094
INSURANCE ASSOCIATES INC.; *U.S. Private*, pg. 2095
INSURANCE & BENEFITS GROUP LLC—See GTCR LLC; *U.S. Private*, pg. 1803
INSURANCE BROKERS & AGENTS OF THE WEST—See Independent Insurance Agents & Brokers of America, Inc.; *U.S. Private*, pg. 2059
INSURANCE BROKERS OF NIGERIA LIMITED—See Marsh & McLennan Companies, Inc.; *U.S. Public*, pg. 1376
INSURANCE BROKERS WEST INC.; *U.S. Private*, pg. 2095
INSURANCE BY KEN BROWN, INC.—See Arthur J. Gallagher & Co.; *U.S. Public*, pg. 206
INSURANCE CENTER FOR EXCELLENCE, LLC—See Madison Dearborn Partners, LLC; *U.S. Private*, pg. 2540
INSURANCE CENTER, INC.; *U.S. Private*, pg. 2095
T.H.E. INSURANCE CO. INC.—See AXA S.A.; *Int'l*, pg. 760
INSURANCE COMPANY EURASIA JSC—See Eurasian Bank JSC; *Int'l*, pg. 2527
INSURANCE COMPANY MEDICO 21 AD—See Doverie United Holding AD; *Int'l*, pg. 2182
INSURANCE DIALOGUE LIMITED—See Arthur J. Gallagher & Co.; *U.S. Public*, pg. 203
THE INSURANCE EXCHANGE, INC.—See Cross Financial Corporation; *U.S. Private*, pg. 1105
INSURANCE LICENSING SERVICES-AMERICA—See Re-Source Pro, LLC; *U.S. Private*, pg. 3407
INSURANCE MARKETING CENTER, INC.—See GTCR LLC; *U.S. Private*, pg. 1803
INSURANCE NETWORK, LC—See Gibson Insurance Agency Inc.; *U.S. Private*, pg. 1696
INSURANCE NETWORK OF TEXAS, INC.; *U.S. Private*, pg. 2095
INSURANCE OF AMERICA AGENCY; *U.S. Private*, pg. 2095
INSURANCE OFFICE OF AMERICA, INC.; *U.S. Private*, pg. 2095
INSURANCE PARTNERS OF TEXAS—See Marsh & McLennan Companies, Inc.; *U.S. Public*, pg. 1381
INSURANCE RESOURCE BROKERAGE GROUP; *U.S. Private*, pg. 2095
INSURANCE RISK MANAGEMENT GROUP, INC.—See Williams Industries, Inc.; *U.S. Private*, pg. 4526
INSURANCE SERVICES GROUP; *U.S. Private*, pg. 2095
INSURANCE SERVICES OF AMERICA INC.—See Stone Point Capital LLC; *U.S. Private*, pg. 3819
INSURANCE SPECIALISTS—See Houchens Industries, Inc.; *U.S. Private*, pg. 1990
INSURANCE SYSTEMS, INC.—See GTCR LLC; *U.S. Private*, pg. 1803
INSURE-LINK, INC.—See NSI Insurance Group; *U.S. Private*, pg. 2970
INSUREON; *U.S. Private*, pg. 2095
INSYNC INSURANCE SOLUTIONS LIMITED—See Brown & Brown, Inc.; *U.S. Public*, pg. 401
INTERAMERICAN HELLENIC LIFE INSURANCE COMPANY S.A.—See Achmea B.V.; *Int'l*, pg. 103
INTERASCO SOCIETE ANONYME GENERAL INSURANCE COMPANY—See Harel Insurance Investments & Financial Services Ltd.; *Int'l*, pg. 3274
INTERLINE INSURANCE SERVICES, INC.—See Fosun International Limited; *Int'l*, pg. 2752
INTERNATIONAL EXCESS PROGRAMS MANAGERS—See One80 Intermediaries LLC; *U.S. Private*, pg. 3024
INTERNATIONAL INSURANCE BROKERS, LTD.—See Kelso & Company, L.P.; *U.S. Private*, pg. 2280
INTERNATIONAL INSURANCE GROUP, INC.—See Aon plc; *Int'l*, pg. 496
INTERNATIONAL PLANNING ALLIANCE, LLC; *U.S. Private*, pg. 2119
INTERNATIONAL SPECIAL RISKS; *U.S. Private*, pg. 2121
INTERNATIONAL SPECIALTY INSURANCE—See Ryan Specialty Holdings, Inc.; *U.S. Public*, pg. 1828
INTERNET FOR CONTINUING EDUCATION INC.; *U.S. Private*, pg. 2122
INTERPARK PITTSBURGH, LLC—See Brookfield Corporation; *Int'l*, pg. 1174
INTER PARTNER ASSISTENZA SERVIZI SPA—See AXA S.A.; *Int'l*, pg. 755
INTERSECTIONS INSURANCE SERVICES INC.—See General Catalyst Partners; *U.S. Private*, pg. 1664
INTERSECTIONS INSURANCE SERVICES INC.—See iSubscribed Inc.; *U.S. Private*, pg. 2147
INTERSECTIONS INSURANCE SERVICES INC.—See WndrCo Holdings, LLC; *U.S. Private*, pg. 4552
INTERSTATE INSURANCE MANAGEMENT, INC.—See Ryan Specialty Holdings, Inc.; *U.S. Public*, pg. 1828

N.A.I.C.S. INDEX

524210 — INSURANCE AGENCIES ...

INTERWEST INSURANCE SERVICES, INC.; *U.S. Private,* pg. 2128
INVESTAR HOLDINGS INC.; *U.S. Private,* pg. 2131
INVESTORS FINANCIAL GROUP, INC.—See Citizens Financial Group, Inc.; *U.S. Public,* pg. 505
IPA SINGAPORE PTE LTD—See AXA S.A.; *Int'l,* pg. 759
IPIPELINE, INC.—See Roper Technologies, Inc.; *U.S. Public,* pg. 1814
IQS INSURANCE RETENTION GROUP, INC.—See Covenant Logistics Group, Inc.; *U.S. Public,* pg. 588
IRONSHORE CANADA LTD.—See Liberty Mutual Holding Company Inc.; *U.S. Private,* pg. 2445
IRONSHORE EUROPE DAC—See Hamilton Insurance Group, Ltd.; *Int'l,* pg. 3238
IRONSHORE INSURANCE LTD. - SINGAPORE—See Liberty Mutual Holding Company Inc.; *U.S. Private,* pg. 2445
IRONWOOD INSURANCE SERVICES LLC—See Marsh & McLennan Companies, Inc.; *U.S. Public,* pg. 1381
IRVING WEBER ASSOCIATES, INC.—See Brown & Brown, Inc.; *U.S. Public,* pg. 401
ISURE INSURANCE BROKERS; *U.S. Private,* pg. 2147
ITALIANO INSURANCE SERVICES, INC.—See GTCR LLC; *U.S. Private,* pg. 1803
IZZO INSURANCE SERVICES, INC.—See Brown & Brown, Inc.; *U.S. Public,* pg. 401
JACK RICE INSURANCE, INC.; *U.S. Private,* pg. 2174
JACKSON NATIONAL LIFE DISTRIBUTORS LLC—See Jackson Financial Inc.; *U.S. Public,* pg. 1183
J.A. COUNTER & ASSOCIATES, INC.—See Genstar Capital, LLC; *U.S. Private,* pg. 1674
JAEGER & HAINES, INC.—See Oklahoma General Agency, Inc.; *U.S. Private,* pg. 3007
JAMES C. JENKINS INSURANCE; *U.S. Private,* pg. 2183
JAMES G. PARKER INSURANCE ASSOCIATES; *U.S. Private,* pg. 2184
JAMES L. MINITER INSURANCE AGENCY, INC.—See Hellman & Friedman LLC; *U.S. Private,* pg. 1909
JARDINE LLOYD THOMPSON ASIA PRIVATE LIMITED—See Marsh & McLennan Companies, Inc.; *U.S. Public,* pg. 1376
JARDINE LLOYD THOMPSON KOREA LIMITED—See Marsh & McLennan Companies, Inc.; *U.S. Public,* pg. 1377
JARDINE LLOYD THOMPSON LIMITED—See Marsh & McLennan Companies, Inc.; *U.S. Public,* pg. 1377
JARDINE LLOYD THOMPSON LIMITED—See Marsh & McLennan Companies, Inc.; *U.S. Public,* pg. 1377
JARDINE LLOYD THOMPSON LIMITED—See Marsh & McLennan Companies, Inc.; *U.S. Public,* pg. 1377
JARDINE LLOYD THOMPSON PTE LIMITED—See Marsh & McLennan Companies, Inc.; *U.S. Public,* pg. 1377
JARDINE LLOYD THOMPSON SDN BHD—See Marsh & McLennan Companies, Inc.; *U.S. Public,* pg. 1377
JARDINE LLOYD THOMPSON S.P.A.—See Marsh & McLennan Companies, Inc.; *U.S. Public,* pg. 1377
J. BERG & ASSOCIATES, INC.—See Integrity Marketing Group LLC; *U.S. Private,* pg. 2103
JBO HOLDING COMPANY; *U.S. Private,* pg. 2194
J. DEMPSEY INC.—See Principal Financial Group, Inc.; *U.S. Public,* pg. 1721
J DEUTSCH ASSOCIATES INC.—See Aquiline Capital Partners LLC; *U.S. Private,* pg. 305
JELF CLARKE ROXBURGH—See Marsh & McLennan Companies, Inc.; *U.S. Public,* pg. 1378
JELF INSURANCE BROKERS LIMITED—See Marsh & McLennan Companies, Inc.; *U.S. Public,* pg. 1378
JELF LAMPIER—See Marsh & McLennan Companies, Inc.; *U.S. Public,* pg. 1378
JELF MANSON—See Marsh & McLennan Companies, Inc.; *U.S. Public,* pg. 1378
JENCAP INSURANCE SERVICES INC.—See The Carlyle Group Inc.; *U.S. Public,* pg. 2047
JEWELL INSURANCE ASSOCIATES, INC.—See TrueNorth Companies L.C.; *U.S. Private,* pg. 4249
J.G. ELLIOTT INSURANCE CENTER—See Platte Valley Financial Service Companies Inc.; *U.S. Private,* pg. 3211
J.H. BLADES & CO., INC.—See Lightyear Capital LLC; *U.S. Private,* pg. 2454
J. H. BLADES & CO., INC.—See Truist Financial Corporation; *U.S. Public,* pg. 2200
JIMCOR AGENCY INC.; *U.S. Private,* pg. 2210
JJ WADE & ASSOCIATES, INC.; *U.S. Private,* pg. 2211
JL MARINE INSURANCE-BROKERS GMBH & CO. KG—See Marsh & McLennan Companies, Inc.; *U.S. Public,* pg. 1376
JLS GROUP INC.; *U.S. Private,* pg. 2213
JLT BERMUDA LTD.—See Marsh & McLennan Companies, Inc.; *U.S. Public,* pg. 1376
JLT HOLDINGS JAPAN LIMITED—See Marsh & McLennan Companies, Inc.; *U.S. Public,* pg. 1376
JLT INSURANCE MANAGEMENT (BERMUDA) LIMITED—See Marsh & McLennan Companies, Inc.; *U.S. Public,* pg. 1376
JLT INSURANCE MANAGEMENT (SINGAPORE) PTE LTD—See Marsh & McLennan Companies, Inc.; *U.S. Public,* pg. 1377
JLT JAPAN LIMITED—See Marsh & McLennan Companies, Inc.; *U.S. Public,* pg. 1376
JLT RE LIMITED—See Marsh & McLennan Companies, Inc.; *U.S. Public,* pg. 1376
JLT RISK SERVICES JAPAN LIMITED—See Marsh & McLennan Companies, Inc.; *U.S. Public,* pg. 1377
JLT RISK SOLUTIONS ASIA PTE LIMITED—See Marsh & McLennan Companies, Inc.; *U.S. Public,* pg. 1377
JLT SPECIALTY LIMITED—See Marsh & McLennan Companies, Inc.; *U.S. Public,* pg. 1376
JMIB HOLDINGS BV—See Marsh & McLennan Companies, Inc.; *U.S. Public,* pg. 1376
J.M. THOMPSON INSURANCE, INC.—See McGowan Insurance Group Inc.; *U.S. Private,* pg. 2635
JOHN ADAMS LIFE CORPORATION; *U.S. Public,* pg. 1190
JOHN ADCOCK INSURANCE AGENCY, INC.; *U.S. Private,* pg. 2220
JOHN BUTTINE INC.—See Kelso & Company, L.P.; *U.S. Private,* pg. 2280
JOHN E. PEAKES INSURANCE AGENCY, INC.—See PCF Insurance Services of The West, LLC; *U.S. Private,* pg. 3120
JOHN HENSHALL LIMITED—See Brown & Brown, Inc.; *U.S. Public,* pg. 401
JOHN J HOLDEN INSURANCE COMPANY—See Reading Anthracite Company; *U.S. Private,* pg. 3366
JOHN L. WORTHAM & SON LLP—See Marsh & McLennan Companies, Inc.; *U.S. Public,* pg. 1383
JOHNS MANVILLE EUROPE GMBH—See Berkshire Hathaway Inc.; *U.S. Public,* pg. 308
JOHNS MANVILLE GMBH—See Berkshire Hathaway Inc.; *U.S. Public,* pg. 308
JOHNSON INSURANCE SERVICES, INC.—See S.C. Johnson & Son, Inc.; *U.S. Private,* pg. 3516
JOHNSON-LOCKLIN & ASSOCIATES INSURANCE CORPORATION—See GTCR LLC; *U.S. Private,* pg. 1803
JOHNSONS ROONEY WELCH, INC.—See Aon plc; *Int'l,* pg. 494
JOHNSTON LEWIS ASSOCIATES, INC.—See Hellman & Friedman LLC; *U.S. Private,* pg. 1909
JOHN TRAYLOR INSURANCE—See Advanta Insurance Partners; *U.S. Private,* pg. 93
JOINT INSURANCE BROKER CO., LTD.—See China United Insurance Service, Inc.; *Int'l,* pg. 1561
JONES BROWN INC.—See Arthur J. Gallagher & Co.; *U.S. Public,* pg. 206
JORDAN EMIRATES INSURANCE COMPANY—See Al-Sagr National Insurance Company; *Int'l,* pg. 288
JOSEPH G. PULITANO INSURANCE AGENCY INC.; *U.S. Private,* pg. 2236
JP TECH INSURANCE SERVICES INC.—See Arthur J. Gallagher & Co.; *U.S. Public,* pg. 206
J. RYAN BONDING, INC.—See GTCR LLC; *U.S. Private,* pg. 1803
JSC INSURANCE COMPANY KAZKOMMERTS POLICY—See Halyk Bank of Kazakhstan JSC; *Int'l,* pg. 3234
J. SMITH LANIER & CO.—See Marsh & McLennan Companies, Inc.; *U.S. Public,* pg. 1381
JUBILEE GENERAL INSURANCE COMPANY LIMITED—See Aga Khan Development Network; *Int'l,* pg. 199
JUNGE & CO. VERSICHERUNGSMAKLER GMBH—See Lightyear Capital LLC; *U.S. Private,* pg. 2454
JURPARTNER SERVICES GESELLSCHAFT FUR RECHTSSCHUTZ-SCHADENREGULIERUNG MBH—See AXA S.A.; *Int'l,* pg. 759
JURS MONTGOMERY BROKERAGE, LLC—See Simplicity Financial Marketing Holdings Inc.; *U.S. Private,* pg. 3667
JUST LANDLORDS INSURANCE SERVICES LTD.—See Arthur J. Gallagher & Co.; *U.S. Public,* pg. 206
KAHN-CARLIN + CO., INC.—See Kelso & Company, L.P.; *U.S. Private,* pg. 2280
KAI YURCONIC INSURANCE AGENCY, LLC—See Bain Capital, LP; *U.S. Private,* pg. 441
KAI YURCONIC INSURANCE AGENCY, LLC—See Keystone Insurers Group, Inc.; *U.S. Private,* pg. 2300
KALIFF INSURANCE—See Scottish American Insurance General Agency, Inc.; *U.S. Private,* pg. 3578
KBI INSURANCE COMPANY, INC.—See Stock Yards Bancorp, Inc.; *U.S. Public,* pg. 1951
THE KEANE INSURANCE GROUP, INC.—See ABRY Partners, LLC; *U.S. Public,* pg. 43
KEENAN & ASSOCIATES INC.—See New Mexico Mutual Casualty Company; *U.S. Private,* pg. 2898
KEEP SERVICES, INC.; *U.S. Private,* pg. 2273
KELLY & ASSOCIATES INSURANCE GROUP, INC.; *U.S. Private,* pg. 2276
KELLY, NANEY INSURANCE AGENCY, INC.—See Inszone Insurance Services, LLC; *U.S. Private,* pg. 2096
KEMBERTON HEALTHCARE SERVICES LLC—See GrowthCurve Capital LP; *U.S. Private,* pg. 1796
KEMBERTON HEALTHCARE SERVICES LLC—See Riverside Partners, LLC; *U.S. Private,* pg. 3446
KEMMONS WILSON INSURANCE GROUP, LLC—See Virtus LLC; *U.S. Private,* pg. 4389
KEMPKEY INSURANCE SERVICES, INC.—See Aon plc; *Int'l,* pg. 496
KENSINGTON VANGUARD NATIONAL LAND SERVICES, LLC—See Clayton, Dubilier & Rice, LLC; *U.S. Private,* pg. 927
KENSINGTON VANGUARD NATIONAL LAND SERVICES, LLC—See Stone Point Capital LLC; *U.S. Private,* pg. 3826
KEN TAME & ASSOCIATES PTY LTD—See Allianz SE; *Int'l,* pg. 353
KENTUCKY FARM BUREAU INSURANCE AGENCY INC.—See Kentucky Farm Bureau Mutual Insurance Company Inc.; *U.S. Private,* pg. 2288
KESSLER & CO AG—See Marsh & McLennan Companies, Inc.; *U.S. Public,* pg. 1377
KESSLER PREVOYANCE SA—See Marsh & McLennan Companies, Inc.; *U.S. Public,* pg. 1377
KESTEN-BROWN INSURANCE, LLC—See GTCR LLC; *U.S. Private,* pg. 1803
KEY INSURANCE COMPANY LIMITED—See GraceKennedy Limited; *Int'l,* pg. 3049
KEYSTONE AGENCY INVESTORS LLC; *U.S. Private,* pg. 2295
KEYSTONE RISK PARTNERS, LLC—See Ryan Specialty Holdings, Inc.; *U.S. Public,* pg. 1827
KGS INSURANCE SERVICES, LLC—See Aon plc; *Int'l,* pg. 496
KING INSURANCE PARTNERS, LLC; *U.S. Private,* pg. 2309
KINGSTONE COMPANIES, INC.; *U.S. Public,* pg. 1234
KINSALE CAPITAL GROUP, INC.; *U.S. Public,* pg. 1235
KIRBY KANOY & ASSOCIATES, INC.; *U.S. Private,* pg. 2314
K & K INSURANCE GROUP, INC.—See Aon plc; *Int'l,* pg. 494
KLANT CONTACT SERVICES B.V—See Achmea B.V.; *Int'l,* pg. 103
KLEIN & COSTA INSURANCE SERVICES—See Western Security Surplus Insurance Brokers, Inc.; *U.S. Private,* pg. 4496
KLEINSCHMIDT AGENCY, INC.—See Arthur J. Gallagher & Co.; *U.S. Public,* pg. 206
KNAPP SCHENCK & CO. INSURANCE AGENCY, INC.—See Cross Financial Corporation; *U.S. Private,* pg. 1105
KNIGHT PLANNING CORP.—See Winged Keel Group, LLC; *U.S. Private,* pg. 4541
KNIGHTS OF COLUMBUS; *U.S. Private,* pg. 2322
KNOWLES ASSOCIATES, LLC; *U.S. Private,* pg. 2324
KOFSTAD AGENCY INC.—See Principal Financial Group, Inc.; *U.S. Public,* pg. 1720
KOROTKIN-SCHLESINGER & ASSOCIATES, INC.; *U.S. Private,* pg. 2344
KPD INSURANCE, INC.—See IMA Financial Group, Inc.; *U.S. Private,* pg. 2043
KPTI LIMITED—See Brown & Brown, Inc.; *U.S. Public,* pg. 401
KRAUS-ANDERSON INSURANCE—See Kraus-Anderson Incorporated; *U.S. Private,* pg. 2349
KRAUTER & COMPANY, LLC—See Kelso & Company, L.P.; *U.S. Private,* pg. 2280
KRB MANAGEMENT, INC.—See Caisse de Depot et Placement du Quebec; *Int'l,* pg. 1256
KRB MANAGEMENT, INC.—See KKR & Co. Inc.; *U.S. Public,* pg. 1265
KRONHOLM INSURANCE SERVICES—See Brown & Brown, Inc.; *U.S. Public,* pg. 401
KUYKENDALL GARDNER; *U.S. Private,* pg. 2359
KYOUEI SHOKUSAN CO., LTD.—See Daicel Corporation; *Int'l,* pg. 1919
LA/BEACH STRATEGIC ALLIANCE, LLC—See Marsh & McLennan Companies, Inc.; *U.S. Public,* pg. 1381
LACHER & ASSOCIATES INSURANCE AGENCY, INC.; *U.S. Private,* pg. 2371
LACKAWANNA CASUALTY COMPANY—See Group One Thousand One, LLC; *U.S. Private,* pg. 1794
LAKE OKEECHOBEE REAL ESTATE MAGAZINE—See Independent Newspapers, Inc.; *U.S. Private,* pg. 2060
LAMBERT, RIDDLE, SCHIMMEL & COMPANY, LLLP—See Brown & Brown, Inc.; *U.S. Public,* pg. 397
LAMMICO INSURANCE AGENCY INC.—See Louisiana Medical Mutual Insurance Company; *U.S. Private,* pg. 2500
LANCER CLAIMS SERVICES, INC.—See Brown & Brown, Inc.; *U.S. Public,* pg. 401
LANDER VAN GUNDY AGENCY, INC.; *U.S. Private,* pg. 2385
LANDMARK GROUP OF BRIGHTON, INC.—See Aon plc; *Int'l,* pg. 497
LANDRY HARRIS & CO. INC.; *U.S. Private,* pg. 2386
LANDSTAR TITLE AGENCY INC.; *U.S. Private,* pg. 2387
LAND TITLE GUARANTEE COMPANY INC.; *U.S. Private,* pg. 2384
LANDY COURTAGE S.A.S.—See Assicurazioni Generali S.p.A.; *Int'l,* pg. 647
LANGLEY AGENCY, INC.—See GTCR LLC; *U.S. Private,* pg. 1803
LANIER UPSHAW, INC.; *U.S. Private,* pg. 2390
LARRY FU INSURANCE AGENCY INC—See Inszone Insurance Services, LLC; *U.S. Private,* pg. 2096

524210 — INSURANCE AGENCIES ...

LA SEGUNDA S.A.—See Asociacion de Cooperativas Argentinas C.L.; *Int'l*, pg. 628
LASSITER-WARE INC.; *U.S. Private*, pg. 2395
LAWLEY BENEFITS GROUP, LLC—See Lawley Service Inc.; *U.S. Private*, pg. 2401
LAWLEY SERVICE INC.; *U.S. Private*, pg. 2401
LAWRENCE FRASER BROKERS LIMITED—See Brown & Brown, Inc.; *U.S. Public*, pg. 401
LAYA HEALTHCARE LIMITED—See AXA S.A.; *Int'l*, pg. 759
LCL SERVICES (IOM) LIMITED—See Lovell Minnick Partners LLC; *U.S. Private*, pg. 2502
LCL SERVICES (IRELAND) LIMITED—See Lovell Minnick Partners LLC; *U.S. Private*, pg. 2502
LEADVILLE INSURANCE COMPANY—See Macy's, Inc.; *U.S. Public*, pg. 1353
LEAVITT GROUP ENTERPRISES, INC.; *U.S. Private*, pg. 2409
LEAVITT GROUP FOUR CORNERS INSURANCE INC.—See Leavitt Group Enterprises, Inc.; *U.S. Private*, pg. 2409
LEGACY MARKETING GROUP—See Regan Holding Corporation; *U.S. Private*, pg. 3386
LEH INSURANCE GROUP, LLC—See Sharing Services Global Corporation; *U.S. Public*, pg. 1873
LEIDSCHE VERZEKERING MAATSCHAPIJ N.V.—See Reinsurance Group of America, Inc.; *U.S. Public*, pg. 1777
LEISURE, WERDEN & TERRY AGENCY, INC.; *U.S. Private*, pg. 2420
LELYNX S.A.S.—See Gruppo MutuiOnline S.p.A; *Int'l*, pg. 3141
LE MARS INSURANCE COMPANY—See Donegal Group Inc.; *U.S. Public*, pg. 676
LEONARD INSURANCE SERVICES AGENCY INC.—See GTCR LLC; *U.S. Private*, pg. 1803
L'EQUITE S.A.—See Assicurazioni Generali S.p.A.; *Int'l*, pg. 645
LERCARI INTERNATIONAL LTD.—See Gruppo MutuiOnline S.p.A; *Int'l*, pg. 3141
LERCARI S.R.L.—See Gruppo MutuiOnline S.p.A; *Int'l*, pg. 3141
LE SPHINX ASSURANCES LUXEMBOURG SA—See BNP Paribas SA; *Int'l*, pg. 1091
LEWIS HYMANSON SMALL SOLICITORS LLP—See Markel Group Inc.; *U.S. Public*, pg. 1367
LEX TERRAE NATIONAL TITLE SERVICES, INC.—See Old Republic International Corporation; *U.S. Public*, pg. 1569
LIBERTY BENEFIT INSURANCE SERVICES, INC.—See Clayton, Dubilier & Rice, LLC; *U.S. Private*, pg. 927
LIBERTY BENEFIT INSURANCE SERVICES, INC.—See Stone Point Capital LLC; *U.S. Private*, pg. 3826
THE LIBERTY COMPANY INSURANCE BROKERS, INC.; *U.S. Private*, pg. 4069
LIBERTY INSURANCE AGENCY INC.—See Liberty Bank for Savings Inc.; *U.S. Private*, pg. 2443
LIBERTY INSURANCE ASSOCIATES; *U.S. Private*, pg. 2444
LIBERTY MUTUAL AGENCY CORPORATION—See Liberty Mutual Holding Company Inc.; *U.S. Private*, pg. 2446
LIBERTY SEGUROS—See Liberty Mutual Holding Company Inc.; *U.S. Private*, pg. 2446
LIFE INSURANCE COMPANY OF BOSTON & NEW YORK—See Boston Mutual Life Insurance Company; *U.S. Private*, pg. 622
LIFE OF THE SOUTH INSURANCE COMPANY—See Tiptree Inc.; *U.S. Public*, pg. 2159
LIFEPLANS LLC—See ABRY Partners, LLC; *U.S. Private*, pg. 42
LIFE QUOTES, INC.—See Bain Capital, LP; *U.S. Private*, pg. 441
LIFE QUOTES, INC.—See Keystone Insurers Group, Inc.; *U.S. Private*, pg. 2300
LIFESECURE INSURANCE COMPANY—See Blue Cross Blue Shield of Michigan; *U.S. Private*, pg. 588
LINCOLN FINANCIAL BENEFIT PARTNERS—See Lincoln National Corporation; *U.S. Public*, pg. 1319
LINCOLN HARRIS, LLC—See Lincoln Property Company; *U.S. Private*, pg. 2458
LINCOLN INSURANCE—See King Insurance Partners, LLC; *U.S. Private*, pg. 2309
LIPSCOMB & PITTS INSURANCE, LLC—See Galiot Insurance Services, Inc.; *U.S. Private*, pg. 1638
LIVINGSTON INSURANCE AGENCY, INC.—See World Insurance Associates LLC; *U.S. Private*, pg. 4566
LLC CHUBB INSURANCE COMPANY—See Chubb Limited; *Int'l*, pg. 1592
LLOYD BEDFORD COX, INC.—See Arthur J. Gallagher & Co.; *U.S. Public*, pg. 206
LOCKHART COMPANIES INC.; *U.S. Private*, pg. 2478
THE LOCKTON COMPANIES, LLC; *U.S. Private*, pg. 4071
LOCKTON COMPANIES LLP - BELFAST—See The Lockton Companies, LLC; *U.S. Private*, pg. 4071
LOCKTON COMPANIES OF COLORADO, INC.—See The Lockton Companies, LLC; *U.S. Private*, pg. 4071
LOCKTON DUNNING BENEFIT COMPANY—See The Lockton Companies, LLC; *U.S. Private*, pg. 4071
THE LOCKTON INSURANCE AGENCY, INC.—See The Lockton Companies, LLC; *U.S. Private*, pg. 4071
LOCKTON INSURANCE BROKERS LLC—See The Lockton Companies, LLC; *U.S. Private*, pg. 4071
LOCKWOOD AGENCY, INC.—See Stone Point Capital LLC; *U.S. Private*, pg. 3819
LODGEPINE CAPITAL MANAGEMENT LIMITED—See Markel Group Inc.; *U.S. Public*, pg. 1368
LONDEN MEDIA GROUP, L.L.C.—See Londen Insurance Group, Inc.; *U.S. Private*, pg. 2483
LONDON AND EDINBURGH INSURANCE COMPANY LIMITED—See Aviva plc; *Int'l*, pg. 746
LONMAR GLOBAL RISKS LIMITED—See Brown & Brown, Inc.; *U.S. Public*, pg. 401
LOOMIS COMPANY; *U.S. Private*, pg. 2494
LOOMIS & LAPANN, INC.—See Arrow Financial Corporation; *U.S. Public*, pg. 200
LOUGEE INSURANCE AGENCY, LLC—See Cross Financial Corporation; *U.S. Private*, pg. 1104
LOUIS A. WILLIAMS & ASSOCIATES; *U.S. Private*, pg. 2498
LOUISIANA COMPANIES; *U.S. Private*, pg. 2499
LOUISIANA FARM BUREAU CASUALTY INSURANCE COMPANY—See Southern Farm Bureau Casualty Insurance Company; *U.S. Private*, pg. 3731
LOVINGER INSURANCE, INC—See Purmort & Martin Insurance Agency, LLC; *U.S. Private*, pg. 3306
LOVITT & TOUCHE, INC.—See Marsh & McLennan Companies, Inc.; *U.S. Public*, pg. 1381
LPL INSURANCE AGENCY, INC.—See Inszone Insurance Services, LLC; *U.S. Private*, pg. 2096
LP RISK, INC.—See XPT Group LLC; *U.S. Private*, pg. 4582
LRT RECORD SERVICES, INC.—See Fidelity National Financial, Inc.; *U.S. Public*, pg. 831
LSG INSURANCE—See Assurant, Inc.; *U.S. Public*, pg. 215
LTC GLOBAL, INC.; *U.S. Private*, pg. 2509
LTCI PARTNERS, LLC—See Aon plc; *Int'l*, pg. 496
LUBRIZOL OILFIELD SOLUTIONS, INC.—See Berkshire Hathaway Inc.; *U.S. Public*, pg. 319
LUCURA RUCKVERSICHERUNGS AG—See BASF SE; *Int'l*, pg. 884
LUHN-MCCAIN INSURANCE AGENCY, LTD.—See Southwest Bancshares, Inc.; *U.S. Private*, pg. 3738
LUMBERMENS MUTUAL GROUP; *U.S. Private*, pg. 2514
LUNDSTROM INSURANCE AGENCY, INC.—See GTCR LLC; *U.S. Private*, pg. 1803
LYKES INSURANCE, INC.—See Lykes Brothers Inc.; *U.S. Private*, pg. 2519
LYNDON SOUTHERN INSURANCE COMPANY—See Tiptree Inc.; *U.S. Public*, pg. 2159
M3 FINANCIAL, INC.—See Simplicity Financial Marketing Holdings Inc.; *U.S. Private*, pg. 3667
M3 INSURANCE SOLUTIONS, INC.; *U.S. Private*, pg. 2530
MACAU INSURANCE COMPANY LIMITED—See Dah Sing Financial Holdings Limited; *Int'l*, pg. 1913
MACK MACK & WALTZ INSURANCE GROUP, INC.—See GTCR LLC; *U.S. Private*, pg. 1803
MADANES INSURANCE AGENCY LTD.—See Harel Insurance Investments & Financial Services Ltd.; *Int'l*, pg. 3274
THE MADISON GROUP, INC.—See Winged Keel Group, LLC; *U.S. Private*, pg. 4541
MAERSK INSURANCE A/S—See A.P. Moller-Maersk A/S; *Int'l*, pg. 27
MAGDEBURGER SIGORTA A.S.—See Allianz SE; *Int'l*, pg. 354
MAG JLT SPA—See Marsh & McLennan Companies, Inc.; *U.S. Public*, pg. 1377
MAGUIRE FINANCIAL ADVISORS, LLC—See Aon plc; *Int'l*, pg. 496
MAHOWALD INSURANCE AGENCY, LLC—See Arthur J. Gallagher & Co.; *U.S. Public*, pg. 206
MAIDSTONE INSURANCE COMPANY—See Turning Point Brands, Inc.; *U.S. Public*, pg. 2205
MAISON INSURANCE COMPANY—See FedNat Holding Company; *U.S. Public*, pg. 829
MAKEFET FINANCIAL SERVICES - INSURANCE AGENCY LTD.—See Assicurazioni Generali S.p.A.; *Int'l*, pg. 647
MANAGED CARE CONSULTANTS LLC—See Aon plc; *Int'l*, pg. 496
MANAGED CARE OF AMERICA INC.; *U.S. Private*, pg. 2559
MANAGED INSURANCE OPERATIONS B.V.—See Allianz SE; *Int'l*, pg. 354
MANAGEMENT BROKERS, INC.—See Aon plc; *Int'l*, pg. 496
MANG INSURANCE AGENCY, LLC—See NBT Bancorp Inc.; *U.S. Public*, pg. 1500
MANGROVE COBRASOURCE, LLC—See Asure Software, Inc.; *U.S. Public*, pg. 218
MANHATTAN LIFE INSURANCE COMPANY—See The Manhattan Insurance Group; *U.S. Private*, pg. 4074
MANHATTAN NATIONAL LIFE INSURANCE COMPANY—See Massachusetts Mutual Life Insurance Company; *U.S. Private*, pg. 2605
MANRY-RAWLS, LLC—See Towne Bank; *U.S. Public*, pg. 2166
MANUEL LUJAN INSURANCE, INC.; *U.S. Private*, pg. 2567
MARCOTTE INSURANCE AGENCY, INC.—See Caisse de Depot et Placement du Quebec; *Int'l*, pg. 1256
MARCOTTE INSURANCE AGENCY, INC.—See KKR & Co. Inc.; *U.S. Public*, pg. 1265
MARINE, AVIATION & GENERAL (LONDON) LIMITED—See Marsh & McLennan Companies, Inc.; *U.S. Public*, pg. 1377
MARK EDWARD PARTNERS LLC—See GCP Capital Partners Holdings LLC; *U.S. Private*, pg. 1654
MARKEL CORP. - WOODLAND HILLS—See Markel Group Inc.; *U.S. Public*, pg. 1368
MARKEL LAW LLP—See Markel Group Inc.; *U.S. Public*, pg. 1368
MARKEL (UK) LIMITED—See Markel Group Inc.; *U.S. Public*, pg. 1368
MARKET FINDERS INSURANCE CORP.; *U.S. Private*, pg. 2579
MARKETING AND COMMERCIAL AGENCIES COMPANY LTD.—See Dabbagh Group Holding Company Ltd.; *Int'l*, pg. 1902
MARKS & SPENCER FINANCIAL SERVICES PLC—See HSBC Holdings plc; *Int'l*, pg. 3503
MARQUEE MANAGED CARE SOLUTIONS, INC.—See Brown & Brown, Inc.; *U.S. Public*, pg. 401
MARQUIS AGENCY—See NIP Group, Inc.; *U.S. Private*, pg. 2928
MARSH AB—See Marsh & McLennan Companies, Inc.; *U.S. Public*, pg. 1379
MARSH ADVANTAGE INSURANCE PTY LTD.—See Marsh & McLennan Companies, Inc.; *U.S. Public*, pg. 1378
MARSH AG—See Marsh & McLennan Companies, Inc.; *U.S. Public*, pg. 1379
MARSHALL & STERLING, INC.—See Marshall & Sterling Enterprises, Inc.; *U.S. Private*, pg. 2592
MARSHALL WOOLDRIDGE LIMITED—See Brown & Brown, Inc.; *U.S. Public*, pg. 401
MARSHA SALDANA INC; *U.S. Private*, pg. 2592
MARSH A/S—See Marsh & McLennan Companies, Inc.; *U.S. Public*, pg. 1378
MARSH AUSTRIA G.M.B.H.—See Marsh & McLennan Companies, Inc.; *U.S. Public*, pg. 1379
MARSH (BAHRAIN) COMPANY SPC—See Marsh & McLennan Companies, Inc.; *U.S. Public*, pg. 1378
MARSH BOTSWANA (PROPRIETARY) LIMITED—See Marsh & McLennan Companies, Inc.; *U.S. Public*, pg. 1378
MARSH BROKERS LIMITED—See Marsh & McLennan Companies, Inc.; *U.S. Public*, pg. 1380
MARSH B.V.—See Marsh & McLennan Companies, Inc.; *U.S. Public*, pg. 1379
MARSH (CHINA) INSURANCE BROKERS CO., LTD.—See Marsh & McLennan Companies, Inc.; *U.S. Public*, pg. 1378
MARSH D.O.O. BEOGRAD—See Marsh & McLennan Companies, Inc.; *U.S. Public*, pg. 1383
MARSH D.O.O. ZA POSREDOVANJE U OSIGURANJU—See Marsh & McLennan Companies, Inc.; *U.S. Public*, pg. 1383
MARSH EUROPE - ORGANIZACNA ZLOZKA SLOVENSKO—See Marsh & McLennan Companies, Inc.; *U.S. Public*, pg. 1379
MARSH GMBH—See Marsh & McLennan Companies, Inc.; *U.S. Public*, pg. 1379
MARSH GSC ADMINISTRACAO E CORRETAGEM DE SEGUROS LTDA.—See Marsh & McLennan Companies, Inc.; *U.S. Public*, pg. 1378
MARSH (HONG KONG) LIMITED—See Marsh & McLennan Companies, Inc.; *U.S. Public*, pg. 1378
MARSH INC—See Marsh & McLennan Companies, Inc.; *U.S. Public*, pg. 1378
MARSH INDIA INSURANCE BROKERS PVT. LIMITED—See Marsh & McLennan Companies, Inc.; *U.S. Public*, pg. 1383
MARSH INSCO LLC—See Marsh & McLennan Companies, Inc.; *U.S. Public*, pg. 1379
MARSH INSURANCE AND RISK MANAGEMENT CONSULTANTS LTD.—See Marsh & McLennan Companies, Inc.; *U.S. Public*, pg. 1379
MARSH (INSURANCE BROKERS) LLP—See Marsh & McLennan Companies, Inc.; *U.S. Public*, pg. 1378
MARSH INTERNATIONAL HOLDINGS, INC.—See Marsh & McLennan Companies, Inc.; *U.S. Public*, pg. 1383
MARSH IRELAND LIMITED—See Marsh & McLennan Companies, Inc.; *U.S. Public*, pg. 1379
MARSH (ISLE OF MAN) LIMITED—See Marsh & McLennan Companies, Inc.; *U.S. Public*, pg. 1380
MARSH ISRAEL INSURANCE AGENCY LTD.—See Marsh & McLennan Companies, Inc.; *U.S. Public*, pg. 1379
MARSH JAPAN, INC.—See Marsh & McLennan Companies, Inc.; *U.S. Public*, pg. 1379
MARSH JCS INC.—See Marsh & McLennan Companies, Inc.; *U.S. Public*, pg. 1383
MARSH KINDLUSTUSMAAKLER AS—See Marsh & McLennan Companies, Inc.; *U.S. Public*, pg. 1379
MARSH LIMITED—See Marsh & McLennan Companies, Inc.; *U.S. Public*, pg. 1379
MARSH LIMITED—See Marsh & McLennan Companies, Inc.; *U.S. Public*, pg. 1379
MARSH LLC INSURANCE BROKERS—See Marsh & McLennan Companies, Inc.; *U.S. Public*, pg. 1379

N.A.I.C.S. INDEX 524210 — INSURANCE AGENCIES ...
N.A.I.C.S. Index

MARSH LLC—See Marsh & McLennan Companies, Inc.; *U.S. Public*, pg. 1379
MARSH LLC—See Marsh & McLennan Companies, Inc.; *U.S. Public*, pg. 1383
MARSH LORANT AGENTE DE SEGUROS Y DE FIANZAS, S.A. DE C.V.—See Marsh & McLennan Companies, Inc.; *U.S. Public*, pg. 1383
MARSH LTD. TAIWAN BRANCH—See Marsh & McLennan Companies, Inc.; *U.S. Public*, pg. 1379
MARSH LUXEMBOURG SA—See Marsh & McLennan Companies, Inc.; *U.S. Public*, pg. 1379
MARSH (MALAWI) LIMITED—See Marsh & McLennan Companies, Inc.; *U.S. Public*, pg. 1378
MARSH MANAGEMENT SERVICES (BARBADOS) LTD.—See Marsh & McLennan Companies, Inc.; *U.S. Public*, pg. 1379
MARSH MARINE & ENERGY AS—See Marsh & McLennan Companies, Inc.; *U.S. Public*, pg. 1379
MARSH MARINE NEDERLAND B.V.—See Marsh & McLennan Companies, Inc.; *U.S. Public*, pg. 1383
MARSH & MCLENNAN AGENCIES AS—See Marsh & McLennan Companies, Inc.; *U.S. Public*, pg. 1377
MARSH & MCLENNAN AGENCY LLC - MIDWEST REGION—See Marsh & McLennan Companies, Inc.; *U.S. Public*, pg. 1381
MARSH & MCLENNAN AGENCY LLC—See Marsh & McLennan Companies, Inc.; *U.S. Public*, pg. 1380
MARSH & MCLENNAN COMPANIES UK LIMITED—See Marsh & McLennan Companies, Inc.; *U.S. Public*, pg. 1377
MARSH MEDICAL CONSULTING GMBH—See Marsh & McLennan Companies, Inc.; *U.S. Public*, pg. 1383
MARSH (NAMIBIA) (PROPRIETARY) LIMITED—See Marsh & McLennan Companies, Inc.; *U.S. Public*, pg. 1378
MARSH NORWAY AS—See Marsh & McLennan Companies, Inc.; *U.S. Public*, pg. 1379
MARSH PB CO., LTD.—See Marsh & McLennan Companies, Inc.; *U.S. Public*, pg. 1379
MARSH PERU SA CORREDORES DE SEGUROS—See Marsh & McLennan Companies, Inc.; *U.S. Public*, pg. 1379
MARSH PHILIPPINES, INC.—See Marsh & McLennan Companies, Inc.; *U.S. Public*, pg. 1379
MARSH RESOLUTIONS PTY LIMITED—See Marsh & McLennan Companies, Inc.; *U.S. Public*, pg. 1383
MARSH SALDANA INC.—See Marsh & McLennan Companies, Inc.; *U.S. Public*, pg. 1382
MARSH, S.A. MEDIADORES DE SEGUROS—See Marsh & McLennan Companies, Inc.; *U.S. Public*, pg. 1383
MARSH S.A.—See Marsh & McLennan Companies, Inc.; *U.S. Public*, pg. 1379
MARSH SA—See Marsh & McLennan Companies, Inc.; *U.S. Public*, pg. 1380
MARSH SA—See Marsh & McLennan Companies, Inc.; *U.S. Public*, pg. 1384
MARSH SAUDI ARABIA INSURANCE & REINSURANCE BROKERS—See Marsh & McLennan Companies, Inc.; *U.S. Public*, pg. 1384
MARSH SIA—See Marsh & McLennan Companies, Inc.; *U.S. Public*, pg. 1380
MARSH SIGORTA VE REASURANS BROKERLIGI A.S.—See Marsh & McLennan Companies, Inc.; *U.S. Public*, pg. 1380
MARSH SINGAPORE PTE LTD.—See Marsh & McLennan Companies, Inc.; *U.S. Public*, pg. 1380
MARSH—See Marsh & McLennan Companies, Inc.; *U.S. Public*, pg. 1377
MARSH S.P.A.—See Marsh & McLennan Companies, Inc.; *U.S. Public*, pg. 1380
MARSH SPOLKA Z.O.O.—See Marsh & McLennan Companies, Inc.; *U.S. Public*, pg. 1380
MARSH S.R.O.—See Marsh & McLennan Companies, Inc.; *U.S. Public*, pg. 1383
MARSH USA INC. - ALABAMA—See Marsh & McLennan Companies, Inc.; *U.S. Public*, pg. 1382
MARSH USA INC. - ALASKA—See Marsh & McLennan Companies, Inc.; *U.S. Public*, pg. 1382
MARSH USA INC. - CONNECTICUT—See Marsh & McLennan Companies, Inc.; *U.S. Public*, pg. 1382
MARSH USA INC. - IDAHO—See Marsh & McLennan Companies, Inc.; *U.S. Public*, pg. 1382
MARSH USA INC. - ILLINOIS—See Marsh & McLennan Companies, Inc.; *U.S. Public*, pg. 1382
MARSH USA INC. - INDIANA—See Marsh & McLennan Companies, Inc.; *U.S. Public*, pg. 1382
MARSH USA INC. - KENTUCKY—See Marsh & McLennan Companies, Inc.; *U.S. Public*, pg. 1382
MARSH USA INC. - MICHIGAN—See Marsh & McLennan Companies, Inc.; *U.S. Public*, pg. 1382
MARSH USA INC. - NEVADA—See Marsh & McLennan Companies, Inc.; *U.S. Public*, pg. 1382
MARSH USA INC. - PENNSYLVANIA—See Marsh & McLennan Companies, Inc.; *U.S. Public*, pg. 1382
MARSH USA INC.—See Marsh & McLennan Companies, Inc.; *U.S. Public*, pg. 1380
MARSH USA INC. - TENNESSEE—See Marsh & McLennan Companies, Inc.; *U.S. Public*, pg. 1382
MARSH USA INC. - TEXAS—See Marsh & McLennan Companies, Inc.; *U.S. Public*, pg. 1382
MARSH USA INC. - UTAH—See Marsh & McLennan Companies, Inc.; *U.S. Public*, pg. 1382
MARSH USA INC. - VIRGINIA—See Marsh & McLennan Companies, Inc.; *U.S. Public*, pg. 1382
THE MARTIN AGENCY INC.—See ABRY Partners, LLC; *U.S. Private*, pg. 43
MARTIN FINANCIAL GROUP; *U.S. Private*, pg. 2595
MARVELL TOWER INSURANCE AGENCIES; *U.S. Private*, pg. 2597
MARYLAND AUTOMOBILE INSURANCE FUND; *U.S. Private*, pg. 2600
MARY ROACH INSURANCE AGENCY, INC.—See Stone Point Capital LLC; *U.S. Private*, pg. 3819
MASON & MASON TECHNOLOGY INSURANCE SERVICES, INC.—See The Baldwin Insurance Group, Inc.; *U.S. Public*, pg. 2035
MATEWAN REALTY CORPORATION—See Truist Financial Corporation; *U.S. Public*, pg. 2200
MATRIX INSURANCE & REINSURANCE BROKERS S.A.—See Howden Group Holdings Limited; *Int'l*, pg. 3494
MATTIS INSURANCE AGENCY—See Inszone Insurance Services, LLC; *U.S. Private*, pg. 2096
MAURICE TAYLOR INSURANCE BROKERS INC.—See Inszone Insurance Services, LLC; *U.S. Private*, pg. 2096
MAURY, DONNELLY & PARR, INC.; *U.S. Private*, pg. 2615
MAWISTA GMBH—See Allianz SE; *Int'l*, pg. 354
MAXIM INSURANCE AGENCY INC.; *U.S. Private*, pg. 2618
MAY, BONEE & CLARK INSURANCE—See Kelso & Company, L.P.; *U.S. Private*, pg. 2280
MAZZOLA FINANCIAL SERVICES; *U.S. Private*, pg. 2623
MBR MEDICAL BILLING INC.—See Radiation Billing Solutions, Inc.; *U.S. Private*, pg. 3343
MBS INSURANCE SERVICES INC.; *U.S. Private*, pg. 2625
MBSL INSURANCE COMPANY LIMITED—See Bank of Ceylon; *Int'l*, pg. 841
MCANALLY WILKINS LLC—See Stone Point Capital LLC; *U.S. Private*, pg. 3819
MCBRAYER INSURANCE CENTER—See Platte Valley Financial Service Companies Inc.; *U.S. Private*, pg. 3211
MCCLELLAND & HINE—See AmWINS Group, Inc.; *U.S. Private*, pg. 270
MCCLOSKEY SURPLUS & EXCESS, INC.—See Arthur J. Gallagher & Co.; *U.S. Public*, pg. 207
MCCRILLIS & ELDREDGE INSURANCE, INC.—See Michaud & Sammon Insurance, Inc.; *U.S. Private*, pg. 2699
MCDERMOTT-COSTA CO., INC.; *U.S. Private*, pg. 2632
MCDONALD ZARING INSURANCE, INC.—See Marsh & McLennan Companies, Inc.; *U.S. Public*, pg. 1381
MCGEE & THIELEN INSURANCE BROKERS; *U.S. Private*, pg. 2634
MCGINTY-GORDON & ASSOCIATES; *U.S. Private*, pg. 2635
MCGRADY LIMITED—See Brown & Brown, Inc.; *U.S. Public*, pg. 401
THE MCGRAW GROUP; *U.S. Private*, pg. 4076
MCGRAW INSURANCE, INC.—See The McGraw Group; *U.S. Private*, pg. 4077
MCGRIFF, SEIBELS AND WILLIAMS OF TEXAS, INC.—See Truist Financial Corporation; *U.S. Public*, pg. 2201
MCGRIFF SEIBELS OF TEXAS, INC.—See Truist Financial Corporation; *U.S. Public*, pg. 2201
MCGRIFF, SEIBELS & WILLIAMS, INC.—See Truist Financial Corporation; *U.S. Public*, pg. 2200
MCGRIFF, SEIBELS & WILLIAMS OF GEORGIA, INC.—See Truist Financial Corporation; *U.S. Public*, pg. 2201
MCINTYRE & ASSOCIATES INC.; *U.S. Private*, pg. 2637
MCLAUGHLIN BRUNSON INSURANCE AGENCY, LLP—See Kelso & Company, L.P.; *U.S. Private*, pg. 2280
THE MCLAUGHLIN COMPANY; *U.S. Private*, pg. 4077
MCMAHON INSURANCE INC.; *U.S. Private*, pg. 2642
MCNAMARA, CO.—See Brown & Brown, Inc.; *U.S. Public*, pg. 401
MCNAUGHTON GARDINER INSURANCE BROKERS PTY. LTD.—See AUB Group Limited; *Int'l*, pg. 698
MCNEIL & COMPANY, INC.—See Arch Capital Group Ltd.; *Int'l*, pg. 547
MCNERNEY MANAGEMENT GROUP, INC.—See Integrity Marketing Group LLC; *U.S. Private*, pg. 2103
MCSWEENEY RICCI INSURANCE AGENCY INC.; *U.S. Private*, pg. 2644
MEADOWBROOK, INC.—See Fosun International Limited; *Int'l*, pg. 2752
THE MECHANIC GROUP, INC.—See Hellman & Friedman LLC; *U.S. Private*, pg. 1909
MEDIA ASSURANCES S.A.—See Bertelsmann SE & Co. KGaA; *Int'l*, pg. 993
MEDICARE ADVANTAGE SPECIALISTS, LLC—See Integrity Marketing Group LLC; *U.S. Private*, pg. 2103
MEDINSIGHTS, INC.—See Arthur J. Gallagher & Co.; *U.S. Public*, pg. 206
MEDIOINSURANCE S.R.L.—See Duna House Holding Public Company Limited; *Int'l*, pg. 2225
MEDITERRANEO VIDA S.A.—See Banco de Sabadell, S.A.; *Int'l*, pg. 821
MEDMAL DIRECT INSURANCE COMPANY—See Basler Sachversicherungs-AG; *Int'l*, pg. 887
MELCHER & PRESCOTT INSURANCE; *U.S. Private*, pg. 2662
MENATH INSURANCE, AN ALERA GROUP AGENCY, LLC—See Genstar Capital, LLC; *U.S. Private*, pg. 1674
MERCER CONSULTING, S.L.U.—See Marsh & McLennan Companies, Inc.; *U.S. Public*, pg. 1384
MERCER HEALTH & BENEFITS (SINGAPORE) PTE. LTD.—See Marsh & McLennan Companies, Inc.; *U.S. Public*, pg. 1384
MERCIER & KOSINSKI INSURANCE, INC.—See Thompson Insurance Group; *U.S. Private*, pg. 4160
MERIDIAN INSURANCE SERVICE, INC.; *U.S. Private*, pg. 2673
MERIT BENEFITS GROUP, INC.—See Group RHI; *U.S. Private*, pg. 1794
MERRELL-BENCO AGENCY LLC; *U.S. Private*, pg. 2675
MESIROW FINANCIAL, INC. - OAKBROOK—See Mesirow Financial Holdings, Inc.; *U.S. Private*, pg. 2679
METLIFE ALICO CYPRUS—See MetLife, Inc.; *U.S. Public*, pg. 1429
METLIFE ALICO MUTUAL FUNDS COMPANY—See MetLife, Inc.; *U.S. Public*, pg. 1429
METLIFE AMERICAN INTERNATIONAL GROUP AND ARAB NATIONAL BANK COOPERATIVE INSURANCE COMPANY—See MetLife, Inc.; *U.S. Public*, pg. 1430
METLIFE COLOMBIA SEGUROS DE VIDA S.A.—See MetLife, Inc.; *U.S. Public*, pg. 1430
METLIFE CORE PROPERTY REIT, LLC—See MetLife, Inc.; *U.S. Public*, pg. 1430
METLIFE EUROPE INSURANCE LIMITED—See MetLife, Inc.; *U.S. Public*, pg. 1430
METLIFE INSURANCE K.K.—See MetLife, Inc.; *U.S. Public*, pg. 1430
METLIFE POJISTOVNA A.S.—See MetLife, Inc.; *U.S. Public*, pg. 1430
METLIFE PROPERTIES VENTURES, LLC—See MetLife, Inc.; *U.S. Public*, pg. 1430
METLIFE SEGUROS S.A.—See MetLife, Inc.; *U.S. Public*, pg. 1430
METLIFE SEGUROS S.A.—See MetLife, Inc.; *U.S. Public*, pg. 1430
METLIFE SERVICES CYPRUS LIMITED—See MetLife, Inc.; *U.S. Public*, pg. 1430
METLIFE UK LIMITED—See MetLife, Inc.; *U.S. Public*, pg. 1431
METRO ACCIDENT & HEALTH AGENCY, INC.—See Principal Financial Group, Inc.; *U.S. Public*, pg. 1721
METRO INSURANCE SERVICES, INC.—See Stone Point Capital LLC; *U.S. Private*, pg. 3819
METROPOLITAN LIFE SOCIETATE DE ADMINISTRARE A UNUI FOND DE PENSII ADMINISTRAT PRIVAT S—See MetLife, Inc.; *U.S. Public*, pg. 1430
THE M.E. WILSON COMPANY, INC.; *U.S. Private*, pg. 4073
MEYERS-REYNOLDS & ASSOCIATES, INC.—See Arthur J. Gallagher & Co.; *U.S. Public*, pg. 206
MGI INSURANCE BROKERAGE INC.—See iA Financial Corporation Inc.; *Int'l*, pg. 3567
M GROUP INC.—See Penns Woods Bancorp, Inc.; *U.S. Public*, pg. 1663
MHBT, INC.—See Marsh & McLennan Companies, Inc.; *U.S. Public*, pg. 1377
MICHAUD & SAMMON INSURANCE, INC.; *U.S. Private*, pg. 2699
MICHELETTI & ASSOCIATES INC.; *U.S. Private*, pg. 2699
MICHIGAN INSURANCE COMPANY—See Donegal Group Inc.; *U.S. Public*, pg. 676
MICROPLAN FINANCIAL SERVICES (PRIVATE) LIMITED—See FBC Holdings Limited; *Int'l*, pg. 2627
MID-AMERICA RISK MANAGERS, LLC—See Warburg Pincus LLC; *U.S. Private*, pg. 4438
MIDDLESEX INSURANCE CO.—See Sentry Insurance Group; *U.S. Private*, pg. 3611
MIDWEST AGENCIES, INC.—See Peter Kiewit Sons', Inc.; *U.S. Private*, pg. 3158
MIDWESTONE INSURANCE SERVICES—See MidWestOne Financial Group, Inc.; *U.S. Public*, pg. 1446
M/I INSURANCE AGENCY, LLC—See M/I Homes, Inc.; *U.S. Public*, pg. 1351
MILENIJUM OSIGURANJE A.D.—See Adris Grupa d.d.; *Int'l*, pg. 153
MILESTONE INSURANCE BROKERS, LLC—See ABRY Partners, LLC; *U.S. Private*, pg. 42
MILLENNIUM SETTLEMENTS, INC.—See Sage Settlement Consulting, LLC; *U.S. Private*, pg. 3527
MILLER INSURANCE, INC.—See Keystone Insurers Group, Inc.; *U.S. Private*, pg. 2300
MILLER INSURANCE SERVICES LLP—See GIC Pte. Ltd.; *Int'l*, pg. 2967
MILLER & LOUGHRY, INC.—See Pinnacle Financial Partners, Inc.; *U.S. Public*, pg. 1692
MILLSTREAM UNDERWRITING LIMITED—See Brown & Brown, Inc.; *U.S. Public*, pg. 401
MINET BOTSWANA—See Aon plc; *Int'l*, pg. 495
MISSION WEALTH MANAGEMENT, LLC; *U.S. Private*, pg. 2748
MITCHELL, REED & SCHMITTEN INSURANCE, INC.—See

524210 — INSURANCE AGENCIES ...

Cashmere Valley Bank; *U.S. Public*, pg. 446
MITHRAS UNDERWRITING EUROPE S.R.L.—See Brown & Brown, Inc.; *U.S. Public*, pg. 401
MITHRAS UNDERWRITING ITALIA S.R.L.—See Brown & Brown, Inc.; *U.S. Public*, pg. 401
MIVTACH-SIMON INSURANCE AGENCIES LTD.—See Assicurazioni Generali S.p.A.; *Int'l*, pg. 647
MLMIC INSURANCE COMPANY—See Berkshire Hathaway Inc.; *U.S. Public*, pg. 308
MMA HOLDINGS UK PLC—See Covea Groupe S.A.S.; *Int'l*, pg. 1820
M & M BROKERAGE SERVICES, INC.—See Aon plc; *Int'l*, pg. 496
MODERNA FORSAKRINGAR LIV AB—See Chesnara Plc; *Int'l*, pg. 1472
MODERN INSURANCE MARKETING, INC.—See Integrity Marketing Group LLC; *U.S. Private*, pg. 2103
MOLHOLM FORSIKRING A/S—See Gjensidige Forsikring ASA; *Int'l*, pg. 2982
MOMENTOUS INSURANCE BROKERAGE, INC.—See Marsh & McLennan Companies, Inc.; *U.S. Public*, pg. 1381
MONAGHAN, TILGHMAN & HOYLE, INC.—See Aon plc; *Int'l*, pg. 496
MONARCH MANAGEMENT CORPORATION—See Players Health Cover USA Inc.; *U.S. Private*, pg. 3212
MONDIAL ASSISTANCE AGENT DE ASIGURARE SRL—See Allianz SE; *Int'l*, pg. 354
MONDIAL ASSISTANCE SARL—See Allianz SE; *Int'l*, pg. 354
MONDICS INSURANCE GROUP INC; *U.S. Private*, pg. 2769
MORAL CARAIBES SARL—See CVC Capital Partners SICAV-FIS S.A.; *Int'l*, pg. 1882
MOSCKER INSURANCE AGENCY, INC.—See GTCR LLC; *U.S. Private*, pg. 1803
MOTEN ASSOCIATES—See Brown & Brown, Inc.; *U.S. Public*, pg. 401
MOULTON INSURANCE AGENCY, INC.—See Peter C. Foy & Associates Insurance Services, Inc.; *U.S. Public*, pg. 3158
MOVESTIC KAPITALFORVALTNING AB—See Chesnara Plc; *Int'l*, pg. 1472
MSU MANAGEMENT - SERVICE - UND UNTERNEHMENSBERATUNG GMBH—See DZ BANK AG Deutsche Zentral-Genossenschaftsbank; *Int'l*, pg. 2244
M.T.D. ASSOCIATES, L.L.C.—See Aon plc; *Int'l*, pg. 496
MT. LOGAN RE, LTD.—See Everest Group, Ltd.; *Int'l*, pg. 2564
MT. MCKINLEY MANAGERS, LLC—See Everest Group, Ltd.; *Int'l*, pg. 2564
MUANG THAI LIFE ASSURANCE CO., LTD.—See Ageas SA/NV; *Int'l*, pg. 205
MUNICIPAL ASSURANCE CORP.—See Assured Guaranty Ltd.; *Int'l*, pg. 650
MUTANT ASSURANCES SARL—See CVC Capital Partners SICAV-FIS S.A.; *Int'l*, pg. 1882
MUTUAL MED, INC.—See Truist Financial Corporation; *U.S. Public*, pg. 2199
MVP HEALTH CARE INC.—See MVP Health Care Inc.; *U.S. Private*, pg. 2821
MVP HEALTH CARE INC.—See MVP Health Care Inc.; *U.S. Private*, pg. 2822
MYERS-STEVENS & CO. INC.; *U.S. Private*, pg. 2824
MYRON F. STEVES & COMPANY; *U.S. Private*, pg. 2826
MYRON F. STEVES & COMPANY—See Myron F. Steves & Company; *U.S. Private*, pg. 2826
NAIS, INC—See Inszone Insurance Services, LLC; *U.S. Private*, pg. 2096
NARAGANSETT BAY INSURANCE COMPANY—See Heritage Insurance Holdings, Inc.; *U.S. Public*, pg. 1028
NATIO ASSURANCE, SA—See BNP Paribas SA; *Int'l*, pg. 1092
NATIONAL ADVANTAGE INSURANCE SERVICES, INC.—See R.E. Chaix & Associates Insurance Brokers, Inc.; *U.S. Private*, pg. 3335
NATIONAL AGENTS ALLIANCE—See Integrity Marketing Group LLC; *U.S. Private*, pg. 2103
NATIONAL AMERICAN INSURANCE COMPANY; *U.S. Private*, pg. 2839
NATIONAL ENROLLMENT SERVICES, INC.—See Aon plc; *Int'l*, pg. 497
NATIONAL FINANCIAL INSURANCE AGENCY INC.—See iA Financial Corporation Inc.; *Int'l*, pg. 3567
NATIONAL INSURANCE AGENCY—See Assurant, Inc.; *U.S. Public*, pg. 215
NATIONAL INSURANCE BROKERAGE, LLC—See Aon plc; *Int'l*, pg. 497
NATIONAL INSURANCE SERVICES, INC.; *U.S. Private*, pg. 2858
NATIONAL INSURANCE SOLUTIONS INC.—See Seeman Holtz Property & Casualty, LLC; *U.S. Private*, pg. 3598
NATIONAL INTERSTATE INSURANCE AGENCY, INC.—See American Financial Group, Inc.; *U.S. Public*, pg. 103
NATIONAL INVESTORS TITLE INSURANCE COMPANY—See Investors Title Company; *U.S. Public*, pg. 1165

NATIONAL LIABILITY AND FIRE INSURANCE COMPANY—See Berkshire Hathaway Inc.; *U.S. Public*, pg. 303
NATIONAL LIABILITY & FIRE INSURANCE COMPANY—See Berkshire Hathaway Inc.; *U.S. Public*, pg. 313
NATIONAL MADISON GROUP, INC.—See Aon plc; *Int'l*, pg. 497
NATIONAL MORTGAGE & FINANCE CO. LTD.; *U.S. Private*, pg. 2859
NATIONAL PARTNERS PFCO, LLC—See Steel Partners Holdings L.P.; *U.S. Public*, pg. 1943
NATIONAL TRUCK UNDERWRITING MANAGERS, INC.—See AmWINS Group, Inc.; *U.S. Private*, pg. 269
NAVIGATORS CALIFORNIA INSURANCE SERVICES, INC.—See The Hartford Financial Services Group, Inc.; *U.S. Public*, pg. 2088
NAVIGATORS MANAGEMENT COMPANY, INC.—See The Hartford Financial Services Group, Inc.; *U.S. Public*, pg. 2088
NCMIC INSURANCE CO.—See NCMIC Group Inc.; *U.S. Private*, pg. 2876
NEASE LAGANA EDEN & CULLEY, INC.—See Winged Keel Group, LLC; *U.S. Private*, pg. 4541
NEAT MANAGEMENT GROUP—See Integrity Marketing Group LLC; *U.S. Private*, pg. 2103
NEBCO INC.; *U.S. Private*, pg. 2878
NEDASCO B.V.—See Aegon N.V.; *Int'l*, pg. 175
NEIGHBORHOOD HEALTH PLAN OF RHODE ISLAND, INC.; *U.S. Private*, pg. 2881
NEIGHBOR INSURANCE SERVICES; *U.S. Private*, pg. 2881
NEK INSURANCE INC.—See Arthur J. Gallagher & Co.; *U.S. Public*, pg. 206
NEMCO BROKERAGE, INC.—See Aon plc; *Int'l*, pg. 497
NEM INSURANCE IRELAND LIMITED—See Allianz SE; *Int'l*, pg. 354
NEM (WEST INDIES) INSURANCE LTD—See Guardian Holdings Limited; *Int'l*, pg. 3171
NETRISK.HU—See TA Associates, Inc.; *U.S. Private*, pg. 3916
NETWORK HOLDINGS INC.—See Align Financial Group, LLC; *U.S. Private*, pg. 168
NETWORK HOLDINGS INC.—See Excellere Capital Management LLC; *U.S. Private*, pg. 1446
NEVADA PACIFIC INSURANCE SERVICES—See Topa Equities Ltd; *U.S. Private*, pg. 4187
NEWCREST INSURANCE PTE LTD—See Newmont Corporation; *U.S. Public*, pg. 1517
NEW ERA FINANCIAL ADVISORS, INC.—See TA Associates, Inc.; *U.S. Private*, pg. 3919
NEW ERA LIFE INSURANCE COMPANY OF THE MIDWEST; *U.S. Private*, pg. 2895
NEWFRONT INSURANCE, INC.; *U.S. Private*, pg. 2914
NEW HORIZONS INSURANCE MARKETING INC.—See Integrity Marketing Group LLC; *U.S. Private*, pg. 2103
NEWINS INSURANCE AGENCY HOLDINGS, LLC—See Kemper Corporation; *U.S. Public*, pg. 1221
NEWKIRK, DENNIS & BUCKLES, INC.; *U.S. Private*, pg. 2915
NEWMAN CRANE & ASSOCIATES INSURANCE, INC.—See ABRY Partners, LLC; *U.S. Private*, pg. 43
NEWMAN FINANCIAL SERVICES, LLC—See Thrivent Financial for Lutherans Foundation; *U.S. Public*, pg. 4165
NEW OCEAN CAPITAL MANAGEMENT LIMITED—See AXA S.A.; *Int'l*, pg. 760
NEWSTEAD INSURANCE BROKERS LIMITED—See Brown & Brown, Inc.; *U.S. Public*, pg. 401
NEWTOWN INSURANCE SERVICE, LLC—See Manzi Insurance; *U.S. Private*, pg. 2567
NEW YORK LIFE SECURITIES INC.—See New York Life Insurance Company; *U.S. Private*, pg. 2911
NEXT INSURANCE, INC.; *U.S. Private*, pg. 2920
NFC HOLDINGS, INC.—See Hikari Tsushin, Inc.; *Int'l*, pg. 3390
NFP BENEFIT PLANNING SERVICES, INC.—See Aon plc; *Int'l*, pg. 496
NFP BROKERAGE INSURANCE SERVICES, INC.—See Aon plc; *Int'l*, pg. 496
NFP CLIPPINGER FINANCIAL GROUP, LLC—See Aon plc; *Int'l*, pg. 496
NFP CORPORATE SERVICES—See Aon plc; *Int'l*, pg. 496
NFP MITCHELL & MORONESO INSURANCE SERVICES, INC.—See Aon plc; *Int'l*, pg. 497
NFP-NATIONAL ACCOUNT SERVICES, INC.—See Aon plc; *Int'l*, pg. 497
NFP PROPERTY & CASUALTY SERVICES, INC.—See Aon plc; *Int'l*, pg. 497
NFP THE BENEFITS SOLUTION GROUP, INC.—See Aon plc; *Int'l*, pg. 497
NFP THE HARTFIELD COMPANY, INC.—See Aon plc; *Int'l*, pg. 497
NICO INSURANCE SERVICES, INC.—See Marsh & McLennan Companies, Inc.; *U.S. Public*, pg. 1381
NIP GROUP, INC.; *U.S. Private*, pg. 2928
NOECKER AGENCY LLC—See The Ayres Group, LLC; *U.S. Private*, pg. 3990
NORMAN-SPENCER AGENCY, INC.; *U.S. Private*, pg. 2938

CORPORATE AFFILIATIONS

NORTEHISPANA, SA DE SEGUROS Y REASEGUROS—See Grupo Catalana Occidente, S.A.; *Int'l*, pg. 3124
NORTH AMERICAN ADVANTAGE INSURANCE SERVICES, LLC—See Doma Holdings, Inc.; *U.S. Public*, pg. 673
NORTH AMERICAN TITLE COMPANY (AZ)—See Doma Holdings, Inc.; *U.S. Public*, pg. 673
NORTHBRIDGE INSURANCE AGENCY INC.—See Arthur J. Gallagher & Co.; *U.S. Public*, pg. 204
NORTH COUNTRY INSURANCE CO.; *U.S. Private*, pg. 2944
NORTH COUNTY INSURANCE—See Stone Point Capital LLC; *U.S. Private*, pg. 3819
NORTHEAST AGENCIES INC.—See The Allstate Corporation; *U.S. Public*, pg. 2034
NORTH LIGHT SPECIALTY INSURANCE COMPANY—See The Allstate Corporation; *U.S. Public*, pg. 2034
NORTH STAR MARKETING CORPORATION—See Assurant, Inc.; *U.S. Public*, pg. 215
NORTHSTAR RISK MANAGEMENT & INSURANCE SERVICES INC.; *U.S. Private*, pg. 2958
NORWEGIAN INSURANCE PARTNERS AS—See Howden Group Holdings Limited; *Int'l*, pg. 3493
NOTHERN CAPITAL INC.; *U.S. Private*, pg. 2965
NOVA AMERICAN GROUP, INC.—See The Hanover Insurance Group, Inc.; *U.S. Public*, pg. 2087
NOVATAE RISK GROUP, LLC; *U.S. Private*, pg. 2967
NOYLE W. JOHNSON INSURANCE AGENCY, INC.—See Genstar Capital, LLC; *U.S. Private*, pg. 1674
NPMIC INSURANCE AGENCY, INC.—See The Doctors Company; *U.S. Private*, pg. 4022
NSI INSURANCE GROUP; *U.S. Private*, pg. 2970
NUVISION FINANCIAL CORPORATION, INC.—See Aon plc; *Int'l*, pg. 497
NW HOLDING CO.; *U.S. Private*, pg. 2975
NYLIFE INSURANCE COMPANY OF ARIZONA—See New York Life Insurance Company; *U.S. Public*, pg. 2910
OAKES AGENCY INC.; *U.S. Private*, pg. 2984
OAMPS (UK) LIMITED—See Arthur J. Gallagher & Co.; *U.S. Public*, pg. 203
OASIS SOUTH INSURANCE SERVICES INC.—See Dowling Capital Management, LLC; *U.S. Private*, pg. 1268
OASIS SOUTH INSURANCE SERVICES INC.—See Keystone Group, L.P.; *U.S. Private*, pg. 2298
OBS REIT, LLC—See MetLife, Inc.; *U.S. Public*, pg. 1431
O'CONNOR TITLE SERVICES, INC.—See Near North National Title, LLC; *U.S. Private*, pg. 2877
ODYSSEY INSURANCE, INC.—See Howden Group Holdings Limited; *Int'l*, pg. 3494
OHIO NATIONAL LIFE ASSURANCE CORPORATION—See Caisse de Depot et Placement du Quebec; *Int'l*, pg. 1254
OIL INSURANCE COMPANY—See Chevron Corporation; *U.S. Public*, pg. 487
OKLAHOMA GENERAL AGENCY, INC.; *U.S. Private*, pg. 3007
OLD REPUBLIC AGRIBUSINESS UNDERWRITERS, INC.—See Old Republic International Corporation; *U.S. Public*, pg. 1568
OLD REPUBLIC CONTRACTORS INSURANCE GROUP, INC.—See Old Republic International Corporation; *U.S. Public*, pg. 1567
OLD REPUBLIC PROFESSIONAL LIABILITY, INC.—See Old Republic International Corporation; *U.S. Public*, pg. 1568
OLD REPUBLIC SPECIALTY INSURANCE UNDERWRITERS, INC.—See Old Republic International Corporation; *U.S. Public*, pg. 1568
OLD REPUBLIC SURETY GROUP, INC.—See Old Republic International Corporation; *U.S. Public*, pg. 1568
OLD REPUBLIC TITLE COMPANY OF CONROE—See Old Republic International Corporation; *U.S. Public*, pg. 1569
OLD REPUBLIC TITLE COMPANY OF HOUSTON—See Old Republic International Corporation; *U.S. Public*, pg. 1569
OLD REPUBLIC TITLE COMPANY OF NEVADA—See Old Republic International Corporation; *U.S. Public*, pg. 1569
OLD REPUBLIC TITLE COMPANY OF OKLAHOMA—See Old Republic International Corporation; *U.S. Public*, pg. 1569
OLD REPUBLIC TITLE COMPANY OF ST. LOUIS, INC.—See Old Republic International Corporation; *U.S. Public*, pg. 1569
OLD REPUBLIC TITLE INFORMATION CONCEPTS—See Old Republic International Corporation; *U.S. Public*, pg. 1569
OLD SPARTAN LIFE INSURANCE CO.—See Continental Holding Company; *U.S. Private*, pg. 1029
O'LEARY INSURANCES GALWAY LIMITED—See Brown & Brown, Inc.; *U.S. Public*, pg. 401
O'LEARY INSURANCES WATERFORD LIMITED—See Brown & Brown, Inc.; *U.S. Public*, pg. 401
OLIVER WYMAN SDN. BHD.—See Marsh & McLennan Companies, Inc.; *U.S. Public*, pg. 1388
OLIVER WYMAN SP. Z O.O.—See Marsh & McLennan Companies, Inc.; *U.S. Public*, pg. 1388
OLTMAN INSURANCE AGENCY, INC.—See S&V Insurance

N.A.I.C.S. INDEX 524210 — INSURANCE AGENCIES ...

Services LLC; *U.S. Private*, pg. 3514
ONE RESOURCE GROUP, LLC—See Integrity Marketing Group LLC; *U.S. Private*, pg. 2104
ONEY INSURANCE (PCC) LIMITED—See Groupe BPCE; *Int'l*, pg. 3099
ONI RISK PARTNERS, INC.—See Keystone Group, L.P.; *U.S. Private*, pg. 2299
ONPOINT UNDERWRITING, INC.—See Brown & Brown, Inc.; *U.S. Public*, pg. 401
OONA INSURANCE PTE LTD—See Warburg Pincus LLC; *U.S. Private*, pg. 4439
OPTISURE RISK PARTNERS, LLC; *U.S. Private*, pg. 3035
OPTUMRX PBM OF ILLINOIS, INC.—See UnitedHealth Group Incorporated; *U.S. Public*, pg. 2247
OPTUMRX PD OF PENNSYLVANIA, LLC—See UnitedHealth Group Incorporated; *U.S. Public*, pg. 2247
ORION RISK MANAGEMENT INSURANCE SERVICES, INC.—See Genstar Capital, LLC; *U.S. Private*, pg. 1674
ORIZON UNDERWRITERS SL—See Marsh & McLennan Companies, Inc.; *U.S. Public*, pg. 1381
OS NATIONAL LLC—See Opendoor Technologies Inc.; *U.S. Public*, pg. 1606
OSWALD COMPANIES; *U.S. Private*, pg. 3048
OSWEGO VALLEY INSURANCE AGENCIES LLC; *U.S. Private*, pg. 3048
OTC BRANDS, INC.—See Berkshire Hathaway Inc.; *U.S. Public*, pg. 313
OTIS-MAGIE INSURANCE AGENCY, INC.—See Marsh & McLennan Companies, Inc.; *U.S. Public*, pg. 1381
OTTAWA-KENT INSURANCE AGENCY, INC.—See ABRY Partners, LLC; *U.S. Private*, pg. 42
OTTERSTEDT INSURANCE AGENCY, INC.—See Sasco Insurance Services Inc.; *U.S. Private*, pg. 3552
OUTSURANCE LIMITED—See FirstRand Limited; *Int'l*, pg. 2690
OWL MARINE INSURANCE-BROKERS GMBH & CO. KG—See Marsh & McLennan Companies, Inc.; *U.S. Public*, pg. 1386
PACE PROFESSIONAL SERVICES, LTD.—See Kelso & Company, L.P.; *U.S. Private*, pg. 2280
THE PACIFIC INSURANCE BERHAD—See Fairfax Financial Holdings Limited; *Int'l*, pg. 2608
PACIFIC PIONEER INSURANCE GROUP INC.; *U.S. Private*, pg. 3070
PACIFIC REDWOOD INSURANCE AGENCY, INC.—See Inszone Insurance Services, LLC; *U.S. Private*, pg. 2096
PACIFIC RESOURCES BENEFITS ADVISORS, LLC—See Brown & Brown, Inc.; *U.S. Public*, pg. 401
PACIFIC SERVICES CANADA LIMITED—See Pacific Mutual Holding Company; *U.S. Private*, pg. 3069
PACIFIC SPECIALITY INSURANCE COMPANY—See The McGraw Group; *U.S. Private*, pg. 4077
PACIFIC WESTERN INSURANCE, LLC—See Essex Property Trust, Inc.; *U.S. Public*, pg. 796
PACO ASSURANCE COMPANY, INC.—See ProAssurance Corporation; *U.S. Public*, pg. 1723
PAGET REINSURANCE LTD—See Chubb Limited; *Int'l*, pg. 1590
PAINTER & JOHNSON FINANCIAL—See Galiot Insurance Services, Inc.; *U.S. Private*, pg. 1638
PALLAS VERSICHERUNG AG—See Bayer Aktiengesellschaft; *Int'l*, pg. 910
PALMS SC INSURANCE COMPANY, LLC—See NextEra Energy, Inc.; *U.S. Public*, pg. 1526
PALMS SPECIALTY INSURANCE COMPANY, INC.—See NextEra Energy, Inc.; *U.S. Public*, pg. 1526
PALOMAR INSURANCE CORP.; *U.S. Private*, pg. 3082
PANALPINA INSURANCE BROKER LTD.—See DSV A/S; *Int'l*, pg. 2214
PAOLINO INSURANCE AGENCY, INC.—See Starkweather & Shepley Insurance Brokerage, Inc.; *U.S. Private*, pg. 3787
P.A. POST AGENCY, LLC—See ABRY Partners, LLC; *U.S. Private*, pg. 43
PARAGON HOTELBETRIEBS GMBH—See Erste Group Bank AG; *Int'l*, pg. 2499
PARAGON UNDERWRITERS, INC.—See ABRY Partners, LLC; *U.S. Private*, pg. 42
PARKER ASSURANCE, LTD.—See Sentry Insurance Group; *U.S. Private*, pg. 3610
PARKER CENTENNIAL ASSURANCE COMPANY—See Sentry Insurance Group; *U.S. Private*, pg. 3610
PARKER, SMITH & FEEK, INC.—See IMA Financial Group, Inc.; *U.S. Private*, pg. 2043
PARKER STEVENS AGENCY, L.L.C.—See Sentry Insurance Group; *U.S. Private*, pg. 3611
PARTNERRE INSURANCE COMPANY OF NEW YORK—See Employers Holdings, Inc.; *U.S. Public*, pg. 754
PARTNERRE MIAMI INC.—See Covea Groupe S.A.S.; *Int'l*, pg. 1820
PARTNERS ADVANTAGE INSURANCE SERVICES—See AMZ Financial Insurance Services, LLC; *U.S. Private*, pg. 270
THE PARTNERS GROUP, LTD.; *U.S. Private*, pg. 4091
PARTNERS INSURANCE GROUP LLC—See Narragansett Financial Corp.; *U.S. Private*, pg. 2835
PARTNERS SPECIALTY GROUP LLC—See AmWINS Group, Inc.; *U.S. Private*, pg. 269
PATRIOT GENERAL INSURANCE CO.—See Sentry Insurance Group; *U.S. Private*, pg. 3611
PATRIOT GROWTH PARTNERS, LLC—See GI Manager L.P.; *U.S. Private*, pg. 1693
PATRIOT GROWTH PARTNERS, LLC—See Summit Partners, L.P.; *U.S. Private*, pg. 3856
PAUL PETERS AGENCY INC.; *U.S. Private*, pg. 3113
PAVESE-MCCORMICK AGENCY, INC.—See King Insurance Partners, LLC; *U.S. Private*, pg. 2309
PAYNEWEST INSURANCE, INC. - HELENA, CEDAR STREET—See Marsh & McLennan Companies, Inc.; *U.S. Public*, pg. 1381
PAYNEWEST INSURANCE, INC. - KALISPELL—See Marsh & McLennan Companies, Inc.; *U.S. Public*, pg. 1382
PAYNEWEST INSURANCE, INC. - MISSOULA, FRONT STREET—See Marsh & McLennan Companies, Inc.; *U.S. Public*, pg. 1382
PAYNEWEST INSURANCE, INC. - MISSOULA (PALMER STREET) CORPORATE OFFICE—See Marsh & McLennan Companies, Inc.; *U.S. Public*, pg. 1381
PAYNEWEST INSURANCE, INC.—See Marsh & McLennan Companies, Inc.; *U.S. Public*, pg. 1381
PCF INSURANCE SERVICES OF THE WEST, LLC; *U.S. Private*, pg. 3120
PDP GROUP, INCORPORATED—See Stone Point Capital LLC; *U.S. Private*, pg. 3821
PEACHES INSURANCE AGENCY INC—See Align Financial Group, LLC; *U.S. Private*, pg. 168
PEACHES INSURANCE AGENCY INC—See Excellere Capital Management LLC; *U.S. Private*, pg. 1446
PEACHTREE CASUALTY INSURANCE COMPANY—See Align Financial Group, LLC; *U.S. Private*, pg. 168
PEACHTREE CASUALTY INSURANCE COMPANY—See Excellere Capital Management LLC; *U.S. Private*, pg. 1446
PEACHTREE SPECIAL RISK BROKERS, LLC—See Brown & Brown, Inc.; *U.S. Public*, pg. 401
PEAK REINSURANCE COMPANY LIMITED—See Fosun International Limited; *Int'l*, pg. 2752
PEARSON INSURANCE COMPANY, LTD—See TPG Capital, L.P.; *U.S. Public*, pg. 2168
PEART INSURANCE BROKERS LIMITED—See Marsh & McLennan Companies, Inc.; *U.S. Public*, pg. 1388
PENINSULA INSURANCE COMPANY—See Donegal Group Inc.; *U.S. Public*, pg. 676
PENN-AMERICA GROUP, INC.—See Paine Schwartz Partners, LLC; *U.S. Private*, pg. 3075
THE PENNOYER GROUP, INC.—See ABRY Partners, LLC; *U.S. Private*, pg. 43
PENUNDERWRITING GROUP PTY LTD.—See Arthur J. Gallagher & Co.; *U.S. Public*, pg. 203
PEN UNDERWRITING LIMITED—See Arthur J. Gallagher & Co.; *U.S. Public*, pg. 207
PEOPLES INSURANCE AGENCY, LLC—See Peoples Bancorp Inc.; *U.S. Public*, pg. 1667
PEOPLE'S UNITED INSURANCE AGENCY, INC.—See GTCR LLC; *U.S. Private*, pg. 1803
PERFORMANCE MATTERS ASSOCIATES OF TEXAS, INC.—See CNO Financial Group, Inc.; *U.S. Public*, pg. 520
PERSONABLE GENERAL INSURANCE AGENCY, INC.—See Align Financial Group, LLC; *U.S. Private*, pg. 168
PERSONABLE GENERAL INSURANCE AGENCY, INC.—See Excellere Capital Management LLC; *U.S. Private*, pg. 1446
PERSONALIZED BROKERAGE SERVICE LLC—See Allianz SE; *Int'l*, pg. 355
PETER C. FOY & ASSOCIATES INSURANCE SERVICES, INC.; *U.S. Private*, pg. 3157
PETHERWICK INSURANCE BROKERS LIMITED—See Brown & Brown, Inc.; *U.S. Public*, pg. 402
PHILLIPS INSURANCE ASSOCIATES, INC.; *U.S. Private*, pg. 3171
PHYSICIANS INSURANCE, A MUTUAL COMPANY; *U.S. Private*, pg. 3175
PIB GROUP LIMITED—See Apax Partners LLP; *Int'l*, pg. 505
PIERCE GROUP BENEFITS, LLC—See GTCR LLC; *U.S. Private*, pg. 1804
PILGRIM INSURANCE COMPANY—See The Plymouth Rock Co.; *U.S. Private*, pg. 4097
PIM MULIER B.V.—See Achmea B.V.; *Int'l*, pg. 103
THE PINNACLE BENEFITS GROUP, LLC.—See Integrity Marketing Group LLC; *U.S. Private*, pg. 2104
PINNACLE INSURANCE & FINANCIAL SERVICES, LLC; *U.S. Private*, pg. 3185
PIONEER SPECIALTY INSURANCE COMPANY—See Western National Mutual Insurance Co.; *U.S. Private*, pg. 4494
PIONEER TITLE COMPANY—See First American Financial Corporation; *U.S. Public*, pg. 837
PIPER JORDAN, LLC—See Brown & Brown, Inc.; *U.S. Public*, pg. 402
PLACER TITLE INSURANCE AGENCY OF UTAH, INC.—See First American Financial Corporation; *U.S. Public*, pg. 838
PLANNED ADMINISTRATORS INC.—See Blue Cross & Blue Shield of South Carolina; *U.S. Private*, pg. 587
THE PLASTRIDGE AGENCY, INC.; *U.S. Private*, pg. 4096
THE PLYMOUTH ROCK CO.; *U.S. Private*, pg. 4096
PNB METLIFE INDIA INSURANCE COMPANY LIMITED—See MetLife, Inc.; *U.S. Public*, pg. 1431
PODIATRY INSURANCE COMPANY OF AMERICA—See ProAssurance Corporation; *U.S. Public*, pg. 1723
POINT INSURANCE AGENCY, LLC—See Sentry Insurance Group; *U.S. Private*, pg. 3611
POMS & ASSOCIATES INSURANCE BROKERS, INC.; *U.S. Private*, pg. 3227
POOLE PROFESSIONAL LTD.—See Brown & Brown, Inc.; *U.S. Public*, pg. 399
POTOMAC BASIN GROUP ASSOCIATES, LLC—See Aon plc; *Int'l*, pg. 497
POTTER-HOLDEN & CO.—See Arthur J. Gallagher & Co.; *U.S. Public*, pg. 207
POULOS INSURANCE, INC.—See Aon plc; *Int'l*, pg. 497
POWDERHORN AGENCY, INC.—See GTCR LLC; *U.S. Private*, pg. 1804
PRAMERICA ASIA FUND MANAGEMENT LIMITED—See Prudential Financial, Inc.; *U.S. Public*, pg. 1732
PRAMERICA FIXED INCOME (ASIA) LIMITED—See Prudential Financial, Inc.; *U.S. Public*, pg. 1732
PRAMERICA LIFE INSURANCE COMPANY LIMITED—See Prudential Financial, Inc.; *U.S. Public*, pg. 1731
PRAXIS CONSULTING INC.—See Crawford & Company; *U.S. Public*, pg. 592
PRECISION HEALTHCARE, INC.—See IVX Health, Inc.; *U.S. Private*, pg. 2151
PREFERRED CONCEPTS, LLC—See Stone Point Capital LLC; *U.S. Private*, pg. 3819
PREFERRED GOVERNMENTAL CLAIM SOLUTIONS, INC.—See Brown & Brown, Inc.; *U.S. Public*, pg. 402
PREFERRED GUARDIAN INSURANCE—See GTCR LLC; *U.S. Private*, pg. 1804
PREMIER CHOICE HEALTHCARE LIMITED—See Brown & Brown, Inc.; *U.S. Public*, pg. 402
PREMIER INSURANCE SERVICES INC.—See Dowling Capital Management, LLC; *U.S. Private*, pg. 1268
PREMIER INSURANCE SERVICES INC.—See Keystone Group, L.P.; *U.S. Private*, pg. 2298
PRENEED REINSURANCE COMPANY OF AMERICA—See National Guardian Life Insurance Company; *U.S. Private*, pg. 2855
PREPERSA, PERITACION Y PREVENCION DE SEGUROS AIE—See Grupo Catalana Occidente, S.A.; *Int'l*, pg. 3124
PRESCOTT JONES LIMITED—See Brown & Brown, Inc.; *U.S. Public*, pg. 402
PRESIDIO BENEFITS GROUP, INC.—See Marsh & McLennan Companies, Inc.; *U.S. Public*, pg. 1382
PRICOA CONSULTING (SHANGHAI) CO., LTD.—See Prudential Financial, Inc.; *U.S. Public*, pg. 1731
PRIME FINANCIAL ASIA LTD.—See China United Insurance Service, Inc.; *Int'l*, pg. 1561
PRIMEGROUP INSURANCE, INC.; *U.S. Private*, pg. 3263
PRIMELENDING VENTURES, LLC—See Hilltop Holdings Inc.; *U.S. Public*, pg. 1039
PRIMERICA FINANCIAL SERVICES (CANADA) LTD.—See Primerica, Inc.; *U.S. Public*, pg. 1717
PRIMERICA FINANCIAL SERVICES, INC.—See Primerica, Inc.; *U.S. Public*, pg. 1717
PRINCIPAL GLOBAL SERVICES PRIVATE LIMITED—See Principal Financial Group, Inc.; *U.S. Public*, pg. 1721
PRITCHARD INSURANCE INC.—See Lovell Minnick Partners LLC; *U.S. Private*, pg. 2503
PRITCHETT-MOORE, INC.—See Galiot Insurance Services, Inc.; *U.S. Private*, pg. 1638
PRIVATE CLIENT SERVICES BY MERCER CHINA LIMITED—See Marsh & McLennan Companies, Inc.; *U.S. Public*, pg. 1388
PRIVATE CLIENT SERVICES BY MERCER LIMITED—See Marsh & McLennan Companies, Inc.; *U.S. Public*, pg. 1388
PRIVATE CLIENT SERVICES BY MERCER PTE. LTD.—See Marsh & McLennan Companies, Inc.; *U.S. Public*, pg. 1388
PRIVATE CLIENT SERVICES BY MERCER SA—See Marsh & McLennan Companies, Inc.; *U.S. Public*, pg. 1388
PRO ADVANTAGE SERVICES, INC.—See Pharmacists Mutual Companies; *U.S. Private*, pg. 3165
PROASSURANCE - BIRMINGHAM—See ProAssurance Corporation; *U.S. Public*, pg. 1723
PROASSURANCE CASUALTY COMPANY—See ProAssurance Corporation; *U.S. Public*, pg. 1723
PROASSURANCE CORPORATION—See ProAssurance Corporation; *U.S. Public*, pg. 1723
PROASSURANCE INDEMNITY COMPANY INC—See ProAssurance Corporation; *U.S. Public*, pg. 1723
PROASSURANCE WISCONSIN INSURANCE COMPANY—See ProAssurance Corporation; *U.S. Public*, pg. 1723
PROCTOR FINANCIAL, INC.—See Brown & Brown, Inc.; *U.S. Public*, pg. 402
PROFESSIONAL BENEFIT SERVICES, INC.—See IMA Financial Group, Inc.; *U.S. Private*, pg. 2043

524210 — INSURANCE AGENCIES ...

PROFESSIONAL INSURANCE ASSOCIATES; U.S. Private, pg. 3275
PROFESSIONAL LIFE INTERLINK SECURITIES—See Comerica Incorporated; U.S. Public, pg. 542
PROFESSIONAL & MEDICAL INSURANCE SOLUTIONS LIMITED—See Brown & Brown, Inc.; U.S. Public, pg. 402
PROFESSIONAL RISK, AN ALERA GROUP AGENCY, LLC—See Genstar Capital, LLC; U.S. Private, pg. 1674
PROFESSIONAL RISK ASSOCIATES, INC.—See Kelso & Company, L.P.; U.S. Private, pg. 2280
PROGRESS-GARANT INSURANCE COMPANY OJSC—See Allianz SE; Int'l, pg. 355
PROGRESSIVE CORP. - AGENCY GROUP—See The Progressive Corporation; U.S. Public, pg. 2125
PROINOVA AB—See Arthur J. Gallagher & Co.; U.S. Public, pg. 207
PROMOVE CORRETORA DE SEGUROS LTDA.—See Alper Consultoria e Corretora de Seguros S.A.; Int'l, pg. 366
PROPEL INSURANCE AGENCY, LLC—See Edwards Capital, LLC; U.S. Private, pg. 1342
PROPERTY-OWNERS INSURANCE CO.—See Auto-Owners Insurance Group; U.S. Private, pg. 398
PROSIGHT GLOBAL, INC.—See Further Global Capital Management, L.P.; U.S. Private, pg. 1625
PROSIGHT GLOBAL, INC.—See TowerBrook Capital Partners, L.P.; U.S. Private, pg. 4195
PROSURANCE GROUP, INC.—See One80 Intermediaries LLC; U.S. Private, pg. 3024
PROSURANCE/REDEKER GROUP LTD.—See Kelso & Company, L.P.; U.S. Private, pg. 2280
PROTECTA INSURANCE NEW ZEALAND LTD.—See Assurant, Inc.; U.S. Public, pg. 215
PROTECTIVE SPECIALTY INSURANCE COMPANY—See The Progressive Corporation; U.S. Public, pg. 2125
PROTECTOR HOLDINGS LLC—See Dowling Capital Management, LLC; U.S. Private, pg. 1268
PROTECTOR HOLDINGS LLC—See Keystone Group, L.P.; U.S. Private, pg. 2298
PROTEGRITY HOLDINGS, INC; U.S. Private, pg. 3289
THE PROVIDENCE INSURANCE GROUP, INC.—See New Mountain Capital, LLC; U.S. Private, pg. 2901
PROVINSURE, INC.; U.S. Private, pg. 3295
PRUDENTIAL AGRICULTURAL CREDIT, INC.—See Prudential Financial, Inc.; U.S. Public, pg. 1732
PRUDENTIAL AGRICULTURAL PROPERTY HOLDING COMPANY, LLC—See Prudential Financial, Inc.; U.S. Public, pg. 1732
PRUDENTIAL GIBRALTAR AGENCY CO., LTD.—See Prudential Financial, Inc.; U.S. Public, pg. 1732
THE PRUDENTIAL GIBRALTAR FINANCIAL LIFE INSURANCE CO., LTD.—See Prudential Financial, Inc.; U.S. Public, pg. 1733
PRUDENTIAL MORTGAGE CAPITAL COMPANY II, LLC—See Prudential Financial, Inc.; U.S. Public, pg. 1733
PRUDENTIAL RELOCATION LTD.—See Prudential Financial, Inc.; U.S. Public, pg. 1733
PRUDENTIAL RETIREMENT INSURANCE AND ANNUITY COMPANY—See Prudential Financial, Inc.; U.S. Public, pg. 1733
PRW ASSOCIATES INSURANCE AGENCY, INC.—See Aon plc; Int'l, pg. 497
PSA FINANCE POLSKA SP. Z O.O.—See Banco Santander, S.A.; Int'l, pg. 826
PSA FINANCE UK LIMITED—See Banco Santander, S.A.; Int'l, pg. 826
P.S.A. INSURANCE, INC.—See PSA Holdings, Inc.; U.S. Private, pg. 3297
PT. AIA FINANCIAL—See AIA Group Limited; Int'l, pg. 227
PT AON INDONESIA—See Aon plc; Int'l, pg. 495
PT ASURANSI CHUBB SYARIAH INDONESIA—See Chubb Limited; Int'l, pg. 1592
PT CHUBB GENERAL INSURANCE INDONESIA—See Chubb Limited; Int'l, pg. 1592
PT CHUBB GENERAL INSURANCE INDONESIA—See Chubb Limited; Int'l, pg. 1593
PT CHUBB LIFE INSURANCE INDONESIA—See Chubb Limited; Int'l, pg. 1593
PT. HANWHA LIFE INSURANCE—See Hanwha Group; Int'l, pg. 3266
PT HOWDEN INSURANCE BROKERS INDONESIA—See Howden Group Holdings Limited; Int'l, pg. 3494
PT. IBS INSURANCE BROKING SERVICE—See Arthur J. Gallagher & Co.; U.S. Public, pg. 206
PT. MARSH INDONESIA—See Marsh & McLennan Companies, Inc.; U.S. Public, pg. 1383
PT MARSH REINSURANCE BROKERS INDONESIA—See Marsh & McLennan Companies, Inc.; U.S. Public, pg. 1388
PT RADITA HUTAMA INTERNUSA—See Lovell Minnick Partners LLC; U.S. Private, pg. 2502
PUBLIC RISK UNDERWRITERS INSURANCE SERVICES OF TEXAS, LLC—See Brown & Brown, Inc.; U.S. Public, pg. 402
PUBLIC RISK UNDERWRITERS OF FLORIDA, INC.—See Brown & Brown, Inc.; U.S. Public, pg. 402
PUBLIC RISK UNDERWRITERS OF INDIANA, LLC—See Brown & Brown, Inc.; U.S. Public, pg. 402
PUBLIC RISK UNDERWRITERS OF THE NORTHWEST, INC.—See Brown & Brown, Inc.; U.S. Public, pg. 402
PURMORT & MARTIN INSURANCE AGENCY, LLC; U.S. Private, pg. 3306
THE PURPLE PARTNERSHIP LIMITED—See Brown & Brown, Inc.; U.S. Public, pg. 397
PWA INSURANCE SERVICES, LLC—See Genstar Capital, LLC; U.S. Private, pg. 1674
QATAR TAKAFUL COMPANY S.O.C.—See Al Khaleej Takaful Insurance Company Q.P.S.C.; Int'l, pg. 280
QUAKER AGENCY, INC.—See The Carlyle Group Inc.; U.S. Public, pg. 2047
QUALITY 1 AG—See Allianz SE; Int'l, pg. 355
QUESTAR AGENCY INC.—See Allianz SE; Int'l, pg. 355
RABO AGRIINSURANCE SERVICES, INC.—See Cooperatieve Centrale Raiffeisen-Boerenleenbank B.A.; Int'l, pg. 1791
RADIAN TITLE INSURANCE INC.—See Radian Group, Inc.; U.S. Public, pg. 1759
RAIN AND HAIL INSURANCE SERVICE, LTD.—See Chubb Limited; Int'l, pg. 1592
RAIN & HAIL LLC—See Chubb Limited; Int'l, pg. 1592
RALPH C WILSON AGENCY, INC.—See Kelso & Company, L.P.; U.S. Private, pg. 2280
RAMPART GROUP; U.S. Private, pg. 3352
RAMSEY INSURANCE AGENCY, INC.—See GTCR LLC; U.S. Private, pg. 1804
RAND-TEC INSURANCE AGENCY, INC.—See GTCR LLC; U.S. Private, pg. 1804
THE RANEW INSURANCE AGENCY, INC.—See GTCR LLC; U.S. Private, pg. 1804
RA ROSSBOROUGH (INSURANCE BROKERS) LTD—See Arthur J. Gallagher & Co.; U.S. Public, pg. 207
RATHBONE, KING & SEELEY INSURANCE SERVICES—See H.W. Kaufman Financial Group, Inc.; U.S. Private, pg. 1836
RAYMOND JAMES INSURANCE GROUP, INC.—See Raymond James Financial, Inc.; U.S. Public, pg. 1764
RCC INSURANCE BROKERS PLC—See Christie Group plc; Int'l, pg. 1587
R. C. WILLEY HOME FURNISHINGS—See Berkshire Hathaway Inc.; U.S. Public, pg. 316
REALCARE INSURANCE MARKETING, INC.—See Aon plc; Int'l, pg. 497
REAL ESTATE SECURITY AGENCY, LLC—See Towne Bank; U.S. Public, pg. 2166
REALTY SUPPORT SERVICES, LLC—See Stone Point Capital LLC; U.S. Private, pg. 3819
THE REAVES AGENCY, LLC—See New Mountain Capital, LLC; U.S. Private, pg. 2901
R.E. BULLOCK & COMPANY; U.S. Private, pg. 3335
R.E. CHAIX & ASSOCIATES INSURANCE BROKERS, INC.; U.S. Private, pg. 3335
RED BANK TITLE AGENCY INC.—See Foundation Title, LLC; U.S. Private, pg. 1580
RED CEDAR INSURANCE COMPANY—See Conifer Holdings, Inc.; U.S. Public, pg. 567
REDMOND GENERAL INSURANCE AGENCY, INC.—See GTCR LLC; U.S. Private, pg. 1804
REGENCY INSURANCE BROKERAGE SERVICES, INC.—See Caisse de Depot et Placement du Quebec; Int'l, pg. 1257
REGENCY INSURANCE BROKERAGE SERVICES, INC.—See KKR & Co. Inc.; U.S. Public, pg. 1265
REGENERSIS DIGITAL CARE AB—See Francisco Partners Management, LP; U.S. Private, pg. 1588
REGISTRY MONITORING INSURANCE SERVICES, INC.—See Internet Truckstop Group, LLC; U.S. Private, pg. 2122
REIFF & ASSOCIATES, LLC—See Kelso & Company, L.P.; U.S. Private, pg. 2280
RELATION INSURANCE SERVICES INC.—See Aquiline Capital Partners LLC; U.S. Private, pg. 305
RELIABLE LIFE INSURANCE COMPANY—See Old Republic International Corporation; U.S. Public, pg. 1569
RELIABLE POLICY MANAGEMENT, LLC—See Truist Financial Corporation; U.S. Public, pg. 2201
RELIAQUOTE, INC.—See Fiserv, Inc.; U.S. Public, pg. 851
REPUBLIC MORTGAGE INSURANCE COMPANY OF NORTH CAROLINA—See Old Republic International Corporation; U.S. Public, pg. 1569
RESOLUTION SARL—See CVC Capital Partners SICAV-FIS S.A.; Int'l, pg. 1882
RESOURCE UNDERWRITING PACIFIC PTY LTD—See Arch Capital Group Ltd.; Int'l, pg. 547
RESTAURANT COVERAGE ASSOCIATES, INC.—See Patriot National, Inc.; U.S. Private, pg. 3110
RETIREMENT STRATEGIES, INC.—See TA Associates, Inc.; U.S. Private, pg. 3919
REUNION TITLE, INC.; U.S. Private, pg. 3412
R.G. MCGRAW INSURANCE AGENCY, INC.—See Fifth Third Bancorp; U.S. Public, pg. 834
RIB GROUP LIMITED—See Brown & Brown, Inc.; U.S. Public, pg. 402
RICHARDS HOGG LINDLEY (INDIA) LTD—See Lovell Minnick Partners LLC; U.S. Private, pg. 2502
RICHARDS, INCORPORATED; U.S. Private, pg. 3429
RICH & CARTMILL, INC.; U.S. Private, pg. 3425
RICK YOUNG & ASSOCIATES, INC.—See Genstar Capital, LLC; U.S. Private, pg. 1674
RIGGS, COUNSELMAN, MICHAELS & DOWNES, INC.—See JBO Holding Company; U.S. Private, pg. 2194
RIGHTSURE INSURANCE GROUP; U.S. Private, pg. 3436
RINGLER ASSOCIATES INC.; U.S. Private, pg. 3438
RISK MANAGEMENT SOLUTIONS - MIDWEST US—See Moody's Corporation; U.S. Public, pg. 1469
RISKPOINT INSURANCE ADVISORS, LLC—See IMA Financial Group, Inc.; U.S. Private, pg. 2043
RISK SERVICES-VERMONT, INC.—See Stone Point Capital LLC; U.S. Private, pg. 3821
RISK SPECIALISTS COMPANIES, INC.—See American International Group, Inc.; U.S. Public, pg. 107
RITMAN & ASSOCIATES, INC.—See Caisse de Depot et Placement du Quebec; Int'l, pg. 1256
RITMAN & ASSOCIATES, INC.—See KKR & Co. Inc.; U.S. Public, pg. 1265
RIVER FALLS MUTUAL INSURANCE COMPANY; U.S. Private, pg. 3443
RLI SOUTHEAST REGIONAL OFFICE—See RLI Corp.; U.S. Public, pg. 1802
R.L. MILSNER, INC. INSURANCE BROKERAGE—See Peter C. Foy & Associates Insurance Services, Inc.; U.S. Private, pg. 3158
RMA BROKERAGE LLC; U.S. Private, pg. 3451
RMB FINANCIAL SERVICES LIMITED—See FirstRand Limited; Int'l, pg. 2690
RMB STRUCTURED INSURANCE LIMITED PCC—See FirstRand Limited; Int'l, pg. 2690
R. MCCLOSKEY INSURANCE AGENCY; U.S. Private, pg. 3334
RMC REINSURANCE, LTD—See Regional Management Corp.; U.S. Public, pg. 1776
ROANOKE TRADE SERVICES INC.; U.S. Private, pg. 3453
ROBBI DAVIS AGENCY INC.—See Arthur J. Gallagher & Co.; U.S. Public, pg. 207
ROBERT ALAN AGENCY, INC.—See Kelso & Company, L.P.; U.S. Private, pg. 2280
ROBERT BELL INSURANCE BROKERS, INC.—See GCP Capital Partners Holdings LLC; U.S. Private, pg. 1654
ROBERT S. MAXAM INC.—See American International Group, Inc.; U.S. Public, pg. 107
ROBINHOOD MARKETS, INC.; U.S. Public, pg. 1804
ROBLIN INSURANCE AGENCY, INC.—See Keystone Group, L.P.; U.S. Private, pg. 2299
ROCHDALE INSURANCE COMPANY—See Stone Point Capital LLC; U.S. Private, pg. 3821
ROCKY MOUNTAIN HEALTH MAINTENANCE ORGANIZATION INCORPORATED; U.S. Private, pg. 3469
RODMAN INSURANCE AGENCY, INC.—See Brown & Brown, Inc.; U.S. Public, pg. 399
RODNEY D. YOUNG INSURANCE AGENCY, INC.; U.S. Private, pg. 3470
ROEDING GROUP COMPANIES, INC.; U.S. Private, pg. 3470
ROEHRS & COMPANY, INC.—See GTCR LLC; U.S. Private, pg. 1804
ROGER BOUCHARD INSURANCE, INC.—See Marsh & McLennan Companies, Inc.; U.S. Public, pg. 1382
THE ROLLINS AGENCY, INC.—See Brown & Brown, Inc.; U.S. Public, pg. 399
ROONEY INSURANCE AGENCY, INC.—See Rooney Holdings, Inc.; U.S. Private, pg. 3479
ROSE & KIERNAN INC.—See Aon plc; Int'l, pg. 497
ROSENFELD EINSTEIN & ASSOCIATES, INC.—See Marsh & McLennan Companies, Inc.; U.S. Public, pg. 1382
ROSENZWEIG INSURANCE AGENCY, INC.—See Arthur J. Gallagher & Co.; U.S. Public, pg. 207
ROSNO INSURANCE COMPANY OJSC—See Allianz SE; Int'l, pg. 355
ROSSBOROUGH INSURANCE (IOM) LTD.—See Arthur J. Gallagher & Co.; U.S. Public, pg. 207
ROTH AGENCY INC.—See Seeman Holtz Property & Casualty, LLC; U.S. Private, pg. 3598
R.O. WILLIAMS & CO., INC; U.S. Private, pg. 3339
ROYAL INSURANCE AGENCY INC.—See Mutual Benefit Association Hawaii; U.S. Private, pg. 2819
ROYAL PREMIUM BUDGET, INC.—See H.W. Kaufman Financial Group, Inc.; U.S. Private, pg. 1836
RPS EXCEL—See Arthur J. Gallagher & Co.; U.S. Public, pg. 207
R&R INSURANCE SERVICES, INC.; U.S. Private, pg. 3333
RSC INSURANCE BROKERAGE, INC.—See Kelso & Company, L.P.; U.S. Private, pg. 2279
RT NEW DAY—See Ryan Specialty Holdings, Inc.; U.S. Public, pg. 1828
R-T SPECIALTY, LLC—See Ryan Specialty Holdings, Inc.; U.S. Public, pg. 1828
RUNACRES LIMITED—See AUB Group Limited; Int'l, pg. 698
RUSSELL BOND & CO. INC.; U.S. Private, pg. 3506
THE RUSSO FINANCIAL GROUP—See The Northwestern Mutual Life Insurance Company; U.S. Public, pg. 4085
RUV AGENTURBERATUNGS GMBH—See DZ BANK AG Deutsche Zentral-Genossenschaftsbank; Int'l, pg. 2244

524210 — INSURANCE AGENCIES ...

RYUGIN HOSHO CO., LTD.—See Bank of The Ryukyus, Ltd.; *Int'l*, pg. 849
SA CARENE ASSURANCE—See Allianz SE; *Int'l*, pg. 355
SAFEGUARD INSURANCE LLC—See GTCR LLC; *U.S. Private*, pg. 1804
SAFE HARBOR FINANCIAL, INC.; *U.S. Private*, pg. 3523
SAFE HARBOUR UNDERWRITERS, LLC—See The Progressive Corporation; *U.S. Public*, pg. 2124
SAFEHOLD SPECIAL RISK, INC.—See Wells Fargo & Company; *U.S. Private*, pg. 2345
SAGAMORE INSURANCE COMPANY—See The Progressive Corporation; *U.S. Public*, pg. 2125
SAGICOR INSURANCE BROKERS LIMITED—See Alignvest Management Corporation; *Int'l*, pg. 328
SAGICOR LIFE OF THE CAYMAN ISLANDS LIMITED—See Alignvest Management Corporation; *Int'l*, pg. 328
SAINT-BARTH ASSURANCES S.A R.L.—See Allianz SE; *Int'l*, pg. 355
SALE INSURANCE AGENCY, INC.—See Hellman & Friedman LLC; *U.S. Private*, pg. 1909
SALERNO 94 S.A.—See Grupo Catalana Occidente, S.A.; *Int'l*, pg. 3124
SAMBA FEDERAL EMPLOYEE BENEFIT ASSOCIATION; *U.S. Private*, pg. 3536
SANDY SPRING INSURANCE CORPORATION—See Sandy Spring Bancorp, Inc.; *U.S. Public*, pg. 1840
SANFILIPPO & SONS INSURANCE SERVICES LLC—See Inszone Insurance Services, LLC; *U.S. Private*, pg. 2096
SANILAC MUTUAL INSURANCE CO, INC.—See Farmers Alliance Mutual Insurance Co., Inc.; *U.S. Private*, pg. 1476
SANTANDER GENERALES SEGUROS Y REASEGUROS, S.A.—See Aegon N.V.; *Int'l*, pg. 175
SANTANDER INSURANCE AGENCY, U.S., LLC—See Banco Santander, S.A.; *Int'l*, pg. 827
SANTANDER SEGUROS Y REASEGUROS, COMPANIA ASEGURADORA, S.A.—See Banco Santander, S.A.; *Int'l*, pg. 827
SANTANDER TOTTA SEGUROS, COMPANHIA DE SEGUROS DE VIDA, S.A.—See Banco Santander, S.A.; *Int'l*, pg. 827
SANTECLAIR—See Covea Groupe S.A.S.; *Int'l*, pg. 1820
SAPOZNIK INSURANCE & ASSOCIATES, INC.—See World Insurance Associates LLC; *U.S. Private*, pg. 4566
SASCO INSURANCE SERVICES INC.; *U.S. Private*, pg. 3552
SASCO SARL—See CVC Capital Partners SICAV-FIS S.A.; *Int'l*, pg. 1882
SASID; *U.S. Private*, pg. 3552
SC EFG EUROLIFE ASIGURARI GENERALE S.A.—See Eurobank Ergasias Services and Holdings S.A.; *Int'l*, pg. 2533
SC EUROINS ROMANIA INSURANCE REINSURANCE SA—See Eurohold Bulgaria AD; *Int'l*, pg. 2553
SCHAEFER AGENCY, INC.—See Inszone Insurance Services, LLC; *U.S. Private*, pg. 2096
SCHEETZ & HOGAN INSURANCE AGENCY, INC.—See Caisse de Depot et Placement du Quebec; *Int'l*, pg. 1256
SCHEETZ & HOGAN INSURANCE AGENCY, INC.—See KKR & Co. Inc.; *U.S. Public*, pg. 1265
THE SCHINNERER GROUP, INC.—See Marsh & McLennan Companies, Inc.; *U.S. Public*, pg. 1388
SCHONNING INSURANCE SERVICES, INC.—See Cross Financial Corporation; *U.S. Private*, pg. 1105
SCHWARTZ BENEFIT SERVICES, INC.—See Aon plc; *Int'l*, pg. 497
SCHWARZ INSURANCE, INC.—See Seeman Holtz Property & Casualty, LLC; *U.S. Private*, pg. 3598
SCOTTISH & YORK INSURANCE CO. LIMITED—See Aviva plc; *Int'l*, pg. 745
SDN INSURANCE AGENCY, LLC—See Aon plc; *Int'l*, pg. 497
SEABURY & SMITH, INC.—See Marsh & McLennan Companies, Inc.; *U.S. Public*, pg. 1388
SEARCH INFLUENCE, LLC; *U.S. Private*, pg. 3586
SEASHORE INSURANCE & ASSOCIATION; *U.S. Private*, pg. 3591
SEASIDE INSURANCE, INC.—See United Community Banks, Inc.; *U.S. Public*, pg. 2230
SECOND OPINION INSURANCE SERVICES—See Marsh & McLennan Companies, Inc.; *U.S. Public*, pg. 1383
SECURITY BUILDERS LTD. INC.—See Mazzola Financial Services; *U.S. Private*, pg. 2623
SECURITY FEDERAL INSURANCE, INC.—See Security Federal Corporation; *U.S. Public*, pg. 1856
SECURON HANSE VERSICHERUNGSMAKLER GMBH—See DZ BANK AG Deutsche Zentral-Genossenschaftsbank; *Int'l*, pg. 2244
SECURON VERSICHERUNGSMAKLER GMBH—See DZ BANK AG Deutsche Zentral-Genossenschaftsbank; *Int'l*, pg. 2244
SEGAL SELECT INSURANCE SERVICES, INC.—See The Segal Group, Inc.; *U.S. Private*, pg. 4116
SEGURO DIRECTO GERE COMPANHIA DE SEGUROS SA—See AXA S.A.; *Int'l*, pg. 757
SEGUROS BBVA BANCOMER SA DE CV—See Banco Bilbao Vizcaya Argentaria, S.A.; *Int'l*, pg. 818
SEGUROS CATALANA OCCIDENTE, S.A.—See Grupo Catalana Occidente, S.A.; *Int'l*, pg. 3124
SEGUROS E INVERSIONES, S.A.—See Citigroup Inc.; *U.S. Public*, pg. 504
SEGUROS PROVINCIAL CA—See Banco Bilbao Vizcaya Argentaria, S.A.; *Int'l*, pg. 818
SEGUROS SIN BARRERAS INSURANCE AGENCY, INC.—See Stone Point Capital LLC; *U.S. Private*, pg. 3819
SELECT GENERAL AGENCY, LLC—See Brown & Brown, Inc.; *U.S. Public*, pg. 401
SELECTIVE INSURANCE COMPANY OF THE SOUTHEAST—See Selective Insurance Group, Inc.; *U.S. Public*, pg. 1863
SELECTQUOTE INSURANCE SERVICES; *U.S. Public*, pg. 3601
SENEX INSURANCE SERVICES, INC.—See Peter C. Foy & Associates Insurance Services, Inc.; *U.S. Private*, pg. 3158
SENIOR INSURANCE SPECIALISTS—See Integrity Marketing Group LLC; *U.S. Private*, pg. 2104
SENIORS ADVISORY SERVICES INC.—See Stone Point Capital LLC; *U.S. Private*, pg. 3819
SENTINEL ADMINISTRATIVE SERVICES, INC.—See National Life Insurance Company; *U.S. Private*, pg. 2858
SENTRY ABSTRACT COMPANY—See Old Republic International Corporation; *U.S. Public*, pg. 1569
SENTRY INSURANCE BROKERS LTD.—See Canadian Imperial Bank of Commerce; *Int'l*, pg. 1283
SENTRY INSURANCE GROUP; *U.S. Private*, pg. 3610
SERNA INSURANCE AGENCY, INC.—See Arthur J. Gallagher & Co.; *U.S. Public*, pg. 207
SETNOR, BYER, BOGDANOFF, INC.—See Kelso & Company, L.P.; *U.S. Private*, pg. 2280
SEUBERT & ASSOCIATES INSURANCE; *U.S. Private*, pg. 3618
SHATTUCK & GRUMMETT INC.; *U.S. Private*, pg. 3627
SHAWHANKINS, INC.; *U.S. Private*, pg. 3628
SHAW & PETERSEN INSURANCE INC.; *U.S. Private*, pg. 3627
SHEARWATER INSURANCE SERVICES LIMITED—See Brown & Brown, Inc.; *U.S. Public*, pg. 402
SHEBOYGAN FALLS INSURANCE COMPANY—See Donegal Group Inc.; *U.S. Public*, pg. 676
SHEPARD INSURANCE—See Aquiline Capital Partners LLC; *U.S. Private*, pg. 305
SHEPARD WALTON KING INSURANCE GROUP; *U.S. Private*, pg. 3632
SHGINS INSURANCE SOLUTIONS LLC; *U.S. Private*, pg. 3635
SHIELDS BROKERAGE LLC—See Integrity Marketing Group LLC; *U.S. Private*, pg. 2104
SHIRAZI BENEFITS LLC—See Genstar Capital, LLC; *U.S. Private*, pg. 1675
SHOREWEST INSURANCE ASSOCIATES, LLC—See Marsh & McLennan Companies, Inc.; *U.S. Public*, pg. 1388
S&H UNDERWRITERS, INC.—See XPT Group LLC; *U.S. Private*, pg. 4582
SIAC SERVICES SRL—See Allianz SE; *Int'l*, pg. 355
SIERRA INSURANCE ASSOCIATES INC.—See Heffernan Insurance Brokers; *U.S. Private*, pg. 1904
SIERRA SPECIALTY INSURANCE SERVICES, INC.—See XPT Group LLC; *U.S. Private*, pg. 4582
SIFCOM ASSURANCES—See Allianz SE; *Int'l*, pg. 355
SIGNATOR INVESTORS INC.—See Reverence Capital Partners LLC; *U.S. Private*, pg. 3415
SIGORTAYERI SIGORTA VE REASURANS BROKERLIGI A.S.—See Aktif Yatirim Bankasi A.S.; *Int'l*, pg. 267
SILVER OAK CASUALTY, INC.—See AMERISAFE, Inc.; *U.S. Public*, pg. 115
SIMPLICITY FINANCIAL MARKETING HOLDINGS INC.; *U.S. Private*, pg. 3667
SIMPLY BUSINESS, INC.—See The Travelers Companies, Inc.; *U.S. Public*, pg. 2136
SIMPSON & MCCRADY LLC; *U.S. Private*, pg. 3668
SINGER NELSON CHARLMERS—See Kelso & Company, L.P.; *U.S. Private*, pg. 2280
SINO-US UNITED METLIFE INSURANCE CO—See MetLife, Inc.; *U.S. Public*, pg. 1431
SIRIUS INTERNATIONAL INSURANCE CORPORATION—See White Mountains Insurance Group, Ltd.; *U.S. Public*, pg. 2369
SITZMANN, MORRIS & LAVIS INSURANCE AGENCY, INC.—See Brown & Brown, Inc.; *U.S. Public*, pg. 399
SIX & GEVING INSURANCE, INC.—See Galiot Insurance Services, Inc.; *U.S. Private*, pg. 1638
SMART DRIVER CLUB LTD.—See CalAmp Corp.; *U.S. Public*, pg. 422
SMART INSURANCE & IT SOLUTIONS GMBH—See Helvetia Holding AG; *Int'l*, pg. 3340
SME INSURANCE SERVICES LIMITED—See Marsh & McLennan Companies, Inc.; *U.S. Public*, pg. 1388
SMITH FEIKE MINTON, INC.; *U.S. Private*, pg. 3694
SMITH INSURANCE ASSOCIATES, INC.—See Brown & Brown, Inc.; *U.S. Public*, pg. 400
SMITH'S INSURANCE AGENCY INC.—See Element Risk Management LLC; *U.S. Private*, pg. 1357
SML AGENCY SERVICES, INC.—See Security Mutual Life Insurance Company of New York; *U.S. Private*, pg. 3596
SMP HOLDINGS, INC.—See Prudential Financial, Inc.; *U.S. Public*, pg. 1733
SNAPP & ASSOCIATES—See GCP Capital Partners Holdings LLC; *U.S. Private*, pg. 1654
SNYDER INSURANCE AGENCY, INC.—See R&R Insurance Services, Inc.; *U.S. Private*, pg. 3333
SOCIETE FRANCAISE DE GARANTIE S.A.—See Brookfield Corporation; *Int'l*, pg. 1189
SOCIUS INSURANCE SERVICES INC.—See Ryan Specialty Holdings, Inc.; *U.S. Public*, pg. 1828
SOENEN VERZEKERINGSKANTOOR NV—See Apollo Global Management, Inc.; *U.S. Public*, pg. 147
SOMERSET CONSUMER SERVICE CORP.—See Somerset Savings Bank, SLA; *U.S. Private*, pg. 3712
SONORAN NATIONAL INSURANCE GROUP—See Franchise Services of North America Inc.; *U.S. Private*, pg. 1587
SORCI INSURANCE BROKERAGE, INC.—See Keystone Group, L.P.; *U.S. Private*, pg. 2298
SORENSEN FLEXIBLE BENEFITS, LTD.; *U.S. Private*, pg. 3715
SOTHEBY'S INTERNATIONAL REALTY—See Anywhere Real Estate Inc.; *U.S. Public*, pg. 141
SOUTH COUNTY INSURANCE AGENCY, LLC—See The Ayres Group, LLC; *U.S. Private*, pg. 3990
SOUTHEASTERN RISK SPECIALISTS—See American International Group, Inc.; *U.S. Public*, pg. 107
SOUTH EAST RISK SPECIALTY PROPERTIES—See American International Group, Inc.; *U.S. Public*, pg. 107
SOUTHERN CROSS INSURANCE SERVICES, INC.—See Truist Financial Corporation; *U.S. Public*, pg. 2200
SOUTHERN HARVEST INSURANCE AGENCY INC.—See Stone Point Capital LLC; *U.S. Private*, pg. 3818
SOUTHERN INSURANCE UNDERWRITERS INC.; *U.S. Private*, pg. 3732
SOUTHERN PIONEER PROPERTY & CASUALTY INSURANCE COMPANY—See Biglari Holdings Inc.; *U.S. Public*, pg. 331
SOUTHERN PROTECTIVE GROUP, LLC—See The Baldwin Insurance Group, Inc.; *U.S. Public*, pg. 2036
SOUTH ESSEX INSURANCE BROKERS LIMITED—See Ecclesiastical Insurance Office plc; *Int'l*, pg. 2288
SOUTHPOINT RISK ADVISORS LLC; *U.S. Private*, pg. 3737
SOUTHWEST BUSINESS CORPORATION; *U.S. Private*, pg. 3738
SOUTHWESTERN FINANCIAL CORPORATION; *U.S. Private*, pg. 3741
SOUTH & WESTERN GENERAL AGENCY, INC.—See Brown & Brown, Inc.; *U.S. Public*, pg. 401
SOUTHWEST FLORIDA INSURANCE ASSOCIATES, INC.; *U.S. Private*, pg. 3739
SOUTHWEST GENERAL INSURANCE COMPANY—See Gurley Motor Company; *U.S. Private*, pg. 1819
SOUTHWEST RISK SERVICES INC.—See W.R. Berkley Corporation; *U.S. Public*, pg. 2318
SOVEREIGN GROUP INTERNATIONAL; *U.S. Private*, pg. 3743
SPARTA INSURANCE HOLDINGS, INC.—See Apollo Global Management, Inc.; *U.S. Public*, pg. 148
SPA UNDERWRITING SERVICES SELECT LIMITED—See Howden Group Holdings Limited; *Int'l*, pg. 3494
SPECIAL CONTINGENCY RISKS LIMITED—See GIC Pte. Ltd.; *Int'l*, pg. 2967
SPECIAL RISKS FACILITIES INC.; *U.S. Private*, pg. 3748
SPECIALTY CONTRACTOR'S INSURANCE SERVICES—See Inszone Insurance Services, LLC; *U.S. Private*, pg. 2096
SPECIALTY LINES OF PENNSYLVANIA, LLC—See Ryan Specialty Holdings, Inc.; *U.S. Public*, pg. 1828
SPECIALTY PROGRAM GROUP LLC—See Hellman & Friedman LLC; *U.S. Private*, pg. 1909
SPECK INSURANCE & FINANCIAL SERVICES PLLC—See Inszone Insurance Services, LLC; *U.S. Private*, pg. 2096
SPECTRUM DIRECT INSURANCE SERVICES, INC.; *U.S. Private*, pg. 3752
SPECTRUM RISK MANAGEMENT AND REINSURANCE DMCC—See Brown & Brown, Inc.; *U.S. Public*, pg. 402
SPETNER ASSOCIATES, INC.; *U.S. Private*, pg. 3756
SP&G INSURANCE BROKERS SDN BHD—See Arthur J. Gallagher & Co.; *U.S. Public*, pg. 207
THE SPRINGS COMPANY; *U.S. Private*, pg. 4120
SPROUTLOUD MEDIA NETWORKS, LLC—See Ansira Partners, Inc.; *U.S. Private*, pg. 286
SQUARE CIRCLE BROKERS LIMITED—See Brown & Brown, Inc.; *U.S. Public*, pg. 402
SSB INSURANCE CORP.—See SouthState Corporation; *U.S. Public*, pg. 1913
S SERVIS, S.R.O.—See Erete Group Bank AG; *Int'l*, pg. 2499
SSI CROSS, INC.—See Cross Financial Corporation; *U.S. Private*, pg. 1105
STAHL & ASSOCIATES INSURANCE, INC.—See Galiot Insurance Services, Inc.; *U.S. Private*, pg. 1638
STAHL & ASSOCIATES INSURANCE INC.—See Galiot Insurance Services, Inc.; *U.S. Private*, pg. 1638
STAHL & ASSOCIATES INSURANCE—See Galiot Insur-

524210 — INSURANCE AGENCIES ...

ance Services, Inc.; *U.S. Private*, pg. 1638
STAHL, BOWLES & ASSOCIATES, INC.—See Galiot Insurance Services, Inc.; *U.S. Private*, pg. 1638
STALLARD FINANCIAL STRATEGIES, INC.—See Aon plc; *Int'l*, pg. 497
STAMMEN INSURANCE GROUP, LLC; *U.S. Private*, pg. 3777
STAMS LTD.—See Assurant, Inc.; *U.S. Public*, pg. 215
STANDARD CASUALTY COMPANY—See Cavco Industries, Inc.; *U.S. Public*, pg. 455
STARKWEATHER & SHEPLEY INSURANCE BROKERAGE, INC.; *U.S. Private*, pg. 3787
STAR RISK SERVICES INC.—See Deutsche Lufthansa AG; *Int'l*, pg. 2070
STATE FARM INDEMNITY COMPANY—See State Farm Mutual Automobile Insurance Company; *U.S. Private*, pg. 3792
STATE MUTUAL INSURANCE CO., INC.—See Concord General Mu; *U.S. Private*, pg. 1010
STERLING CASUALTY INSURANCE COMPANY INC.—See H&H Agency, Inc.; *U.S. Private*, pg. 1822
STEWART, BRIMNER, PETERS & COMPANY, INC.—See Arthur J. Gallagher & Co.; *U.S. Public*, pg. 207
STEWART TITLE OF ALABAMA, LLC—See Stewart Information Services Corporation; *U.S. Public*, pg. 1948
S.T. GOOD INSURANCE, INC.—See Aquiline Capital Partners LLC; *U.S. Private*, pg. 305
STIFEL NICOLAUS INSURANCE AGENCY, INCORPORATED—See Stifel Financial Corp.; *U.S. Public*, pg. 1950
STOLTE INSURANCE AGENCY, INC.—See Ewing-Leavitt Insurance Agency, Inc.; *U.S. Private*, pg. 1444
STONEWOOD INSURANCE SERVICES, INC.—See Stone Point Capital LLC; *U.S. Private*, pg. 3819
STONEX COMMODITIES DMCC—See StoneX Group Inc.; *U.S. Public*, pg. 1953
STONEX DIGITAL INTERNATIONAL LIMITED—See StoneX Group Inc.; *U.S. Public*, pg. 1953
STONEX DTVM LTDA.—See StoneX Group Inc.; *U.S. Public*, pg. 1953
STONEX POLAND SP. Z O.O.—See StoneX Group Inc.; *U.S. Public*, pg. 1953
STONEX (SHANGHAI) TRADING CO., LTD.—See StoneX Group Inc.; *U.S. Public*, pg. 1953
STOUDT ADVISORS, INC.—See GTCR LLC; *U.S. Private*, pg. 1804
ST. PAUL SURPLUS LINES INSURANCE COMPANY—See The Travelers Companies, Inc.; *U.S. Public*, pg. 2136
STRATEGIC RESOURCE COMPANY—See CVS Health Corporation; *U.S. Public*, pg. 615
STRATTON AGENCY—See ABRY Partners, LLC; *U.S. Private*, pg. 42
STRAUSSER INSURANCE AGENCY, INC.; *U.S. Private*, pg. 3837
STRICKLAND INSURANCE BROKERS INC.—See Strickland Insurance Group Inc.; *U.S. Private*, pg. 3840
STRICKLAND INSURANCE GROUP INC.; *U.S. Private*, pg. 3839
STRONG ADVISORY GROUP, INC.—See Arthur J. Gallagher & Co.; *U.S. Public*, pg. 207
SULLIVANCURTISMONROE INSURANCE SERVICES, LLC; *U.S. Private*, pg. 3852
SUMIRE AGENCY, INC.—See H2O Retailing Corp.; *Int'l*, pg. 3201
SUMISHIN LIFE CARD COMPANY, LIMITED—See AIFUL Corporation; *Int'l*, pg. 232
SUMMERS THOMPSON LOWRY, INC.—See Aquiline Capital Partners LLC; *U.S. Private*, pg. 305
SUMMIT INSURANCE SERVICES, LLC—See ABRY Partners, LLC; *U.S. Private*, pg. 43
SUNAPEE MUTUAL FIRE INSURANCE CO., INC.—See Concord General Mu; *U.S. Private*, pg. 1010
SUNSHINE SECURITY INSURANCE AGENCY, INC.—See The Progressive Corporation; *U.S. Public*, pg. 2124
SUPERGARANT VERZEKERINGEN B.V.—See ASR Nederland N.V.; *Int'l*, pg. 632
SUPERIOR ACCESS INSURANCE SERVICES, INC.—See CVC Capital Partners SICAV-FIS S.A.; *Int'l*, pg. 1885
SURETY SOLUTIONS, LLC—See Arthur J. Gallagher & Co.; *U.S. Public*, pg. 207
SURVIVAL INSURANCE, INC.—See Stone Point Capital LLC; *U.S. Private*, pg. 3819
S.USA LIFE INSURANCE COMPANY, INC.—See Prosperity Group Holdings, LP; *U.S. Private*, pg. 3289
SUTTER, MCLELLAN & GILBREATH, INC.—See Genstar Capital, LLC; *U.S. Private*, pg. 1675
SUTTON JAMES INCORPORATED—See Optisure Risk Partners, LLC; *U.S. Private*, pg. 3035
SUZUKA ROBO CARE CENTER CO., LTD.—See Cyberdyne Inc.; *Int'l*, pg. 1893
THE SWETT & CRAWFORD GROUP, INC.—See Lightyear Capital LLC; *U.S. Private*, pg. 2454
SWIMC, INC.—See The Sherwin-Williams Company; *U.S. Public*, pg. 2128
SYNAPSE SERVICES, LLC—See IAC Inc.; *U.S. Public*, pg. 1083
SYNERGY ABSTRACT, LP—See Banco Santander, S.A.; *Int'l*, pg. 827

TAILORED ADJUSTMENT SERVICES, INC.—See Global Risk Solutions, Inc.; *U.S. Private*, pg. 1717
TAILORWELL INC.—See Cambia Health Solutions, Inc.; *U.S. Private*, pg. 726
TAKAFUL INTERNATIONAL COMPANY B.S.C—See Fairfax Financial Holdings Limited; *Int'l*, pg. 2607
TALBOT RISK SERVICES PTE LTD.—See American International Group, Inc.; *U.S. Public*, pg. 107
TANENBAUM HARBER OF FLORIDA, LLC—See Kelso & Company, L.P.; *U.S. Private*, pg. 2280
TAPCO UNDERWRITERS, INC.—See Truist Financial Corporation; *U.S. Public*, pg. 2200
TARBELL REALTORS—See Tarbell Financial Corporation; *U.S. Private*, pg. 3933
TARGET INSURANCE SERVICES INC.—See Ash Brokerage Corp.; *U.S. Private*, pg. 349
TARGET PROFESSIONAL PROGRAMS—See Truist Financial Corporation; *U.S. Public*, pg. 2200
TAYLOR & ASSOCIATES BENEFITS—See Aquiline Capital Partners LLC; *U.S. Private*, pg. 305
TCOR INSURANCE MANAGEMENT, LTD.—See Stone Point Capital LLC; *U.S. Private*, pg. 3819
TECHNOLOGY INSURANCE ASSOCIATES, LLC; *U.S. Private*, pg. 3955
TECSEFIN GUATEMALA—See Aon plc; *Int'l*, pg. 495
TED TODD INSURANCE, INC.; *U.S. Private*, pg. 3957
TEJAS AMERICAN GENERAL AGENCY, LLC—See Arthur J. Gallagher & Co.; *U.S. Public*, pg. 207
TERRACE INSURANCE BROKERS PTY. LTD.—See AUB Group Limited; *Int'l*, pg. 698
TEXAS ALL RISK GENERAL AGENCY, INC.—See Brown & Brown, Inc.; *U.S. Public*, pg. 401
TEXAS BANKERS INSURANCE AGENCY, INC.—See Texas Bankers Association; *U.S. Private*, pg. 3974
TEXAS FARM BUREAU MUTUAL INSURANCE; *U.S. Private*, pg. 3975
TEXAS INSURANCE MANAGERS, INC.—See Arthur J. Gallagher & Co.; *U.S. Public*, pg. 207
TEXAS REPUBLIC LIFE INSURANCE COMPANY—See Texas Republic Capital Corporation; *U.S. Private*, pg. 3977
TEXAS REPUBLIC LIFE SOLUTIONS—See Texas Republic Capital Corporation; *U.S. Private*, pg. 3977
TEXAS SECURITY GENERAL INSURANCE AGENCY, INC.—See Brown & Brown, Inc.; *U.S. Public*, pg. 402
THAXTON BARCLAY GROUP; *U.S. Private*, pg. 3980
THB UK LIMITED—See AmWINS Group, Inc.; *U.S. Private*, pg. 270
THERIUM INC.—See Stone Point Capital LLC; *U.S. Private*, pg. 3821
THOMAS SAGAR INSURANCES LIMITED—See Brown & Brown, Inc.; *U.S. Public*, pg. 402
THOMPSON BROTHERS INSURANCE CONSULTANTS LIMITED—See Brown & Brown, Inc.; *U.S. Public*, pg. 402
THOMPSON HEATH & BOND LIMITED—See AmWINS Group, Inc.; *U.S. Private*, pg. 270
THOMPSON INSURANCE ENTERPRISES, LLC—See Markel Group Inc.; *U.S. Public*, pg. 1368
THOMPSON & PECK INC.; *U.S. Private*, pg. 4158
THREE DEEP, INC.—See Bold Orange Company, LLC; *U.S. Private*, pg. 610
THREE SIXTY INSURE LIMITED—See Brown & Brown, Inc.; *U.S. Public*, pg. 402
THURINGIA GENERALI 2. IMMOBILIEN AG & CO. KG—See Cinven Limited; *Int'l*, pg. 1616
TICOR TITLE INSURANCE COMPANY—See Fidelity National Financial, Inc.; *U.S. Public*, pg. 831
TIDEWATER MANAGEMENT GROUP—See Integrity Marketing Group LLC; *U.S. Private*, pg. 2104
TIS INSURANCE SERVICES INC.—See Edwards Capital, LLC; *U.S. Private*, pg. 1342
TK SPECIALTY RISKS PTY.—See Ensurance Ltd.; *Int'l*, pg. 2449
TLG INSURANCE CO., LTD.—See CTBC Financial Holding Co., Ltd.; *Int'l*, pg. 1869
TMS CONTACT SARL—See CVC Capital Partners SICAV-FIS S.A.; *Int'l*, pg. 1882
THE TODD AGENCY, INC.—See Reverence Capital Partners, LLC; *U.S. Private*, pg. 3415
TODD AND CASSANELLI INC.; *U.S. Private*, pg. 4181
TOKIO MARINE PACIFIC INSURANCE LIMITED—See Calvo Enterprises, Inc.; *U.S. Public*, pg. 725
TOMPKINS INSURANCE AGENCIES, INC.—See Tompkins Financial Corporation; *U.S. Public*, pg. 2162
TOPA INSURANCE SERVICES—See Topa Equities Ltd, Inc.; *U.S. Private*, pg. 4187
TOP VERSICHERUNGSSERVICE GMBH—See Allianz SE; *Int'l*, pg. 356
TOP VERSICHERUNGS-VERMITTLER SERVICE GMBH—See Allianz SE; *Int'l*, pg. 356
TORRENT GOVERNMENT CONTRACTING SERVICES, LLC—See Marsh & McLennan Companies, Inc.; *U.S. Public*, pg. 1388
TORRES INSURANCE AGENCY, INC.; *U.S. Private*, pg. 4190
TOTAL DOLLAR MANAGEMENT EFFORT LTD; *U.S. Private*, pg. 4190
TOTAL PROGRAM MANAGEMENT, LLC—See Stone Point Capital LLC; *U.S. Private*, pg. 3821
TOTTEN INSURANCE GROUP INC.—See Hellman & Friedman LLC; *U.S. Private*, pg. 1909
TOWARZYSTWO UBEZPIECZEN EULER HERMES S.A.—See Allianz SE; *Int'l*, pg. 356
TOWER HILL INSURANCE GROUP; *U.S. Private*, pg. 4194
TOWERSTONE, INC.—See IMA Financial Group, Inc.; *U.S. Private*, pg. 2043
TOWN & COUNTRY AGENCY LLC—See Community Bank System, Inc.; *U.S. Public*, pg. 550
TOWNE INSURANCE AGENCY, LLC—See Towne Bank; *U.S. Public*, pg. 2166
TRACY-DRISCOLL & CO., INC.—See ABRY Partners, LLC; *U.S. Private*, pg. 42
TRADE LAKE MUTUAL INSURANCE CO, INC.—See River Falls Mutual Insurance Company; *U.S. Private*, pg. 3444
TRADEWIND INSURANCE COMPANY, LTD.—See Island Holdings, Inc.; *U.S. Private*, pg. 2145
TRAFALGAR INSURANCE PUBLIC LIMITED COMPANY—See Allianz SE; *Int'l*, pg. 356
TRANSAMERICA BROKERAGE GROUP—See Aegon N.V.; *Int'l*, pg. 174
TRANSAMERICA LIFE (BERMUDA) LTD.—See Aegon N.V.; *Int'l*, pg. 175
TRANSRE EUROPE S.A.—See Berkshire Hathaway Inc.; *U.S. Public*, pg. 299
TRANSRE LONDON LIMITED—See Berkshire Hathaway Inc.; *U.S. Public*, pg. 299
TRANSURE SERVICES, INC.—See Aquiline Capital Partners LLC; *U.S. Private*, pg. 305
TRAVCO SERVICES INC.; *U.S. Private*, pg. 4212
TRAVELERS SEGUROS BRASIL S.A.—See The Travelers Companies, Inc.; *U.S. Public*, pg. 2136
TRAVEL GUARD GROUP, INC.—See American International Group, Inc.; *U.S. Public*, pg. 106
TREAN CORPORATION—See Altaris Capital Partners, LLC; *U.S. Private*, pg. 206
TRIAD FINANCIAL SERVICE, INC—See ECN Capital Corp.; *Int'l*, pg. 2292
TRICOR, INC.; *U.S. Private*, pg. 4229
TRIDENT INSURANCE SERVICES, LLC—See Paragon Insurance Holdings, LLC; *U.S. Private*, pg. 3091
TRILOGY RISK SPECIALISTS, INC.—See Regions Financial Corporation; *U.S. Public*, pg. 1776
TRINITY BENEFIT ADVISORS, INC.—See The Baldwin Insurance Group, Inc.; *U.S. Public*, pg. 2036
TRINITY UNDERWRITING MANAGERS, INC.—See AmWINS Group, Inc.; *U.S. Private*, pg. 270
TRIPLE-S INSURANCE AGENCY, INC.—See Triple-S Management Corp.; *U.S. Public*, pg. 2195
TRIPOL AS—See Marsh & McLennan Companies, Inc.; *U.S. Public*, pg. 1376
TRISSEL, GRAHAM & TOOLE INC.; *U.S. Private*, pg. 4238
TRISTAR MANAGING GENERAL AGENCY; *U.S. Private*, pg. 4238
TRISURE CORPORATION—See Hellman & Friedman LLC; *U.S. Private*, pg. 1910
TROY FAIN INSURANCE INC.—See Loews Corporation; *U.S. Public*, pg. 1340
TRUCK INSURANCE MART INC.—See Aquiline Capital Partners LLC; *U.S. Private*, pg. 305
TRUSTED CHOICE, INC.—See Independent Insurance Agents & Brokers of America, Inc.; *U.S. Private*, pg. 2059
TRUSTED SENIOR SPECIALISTS—See Integrity Marketing Group LLC; *U.S. Private*, pg. 2104
TSA, INC.—See Cross Financial Corporation; *U.S. Public*, pg. 1105
TSG PREMIUM FINANCE, LLC—See Brown & Brown, Inc.; *U.S. Public*, pg. 402
TUTTON INSURANCE SERVICES, INC.—See GTCR LLC; *U.S. Private*, pg. 1804
T.W. COOPER INSURANCE, LLC—See Russ Smale, Inc.; *U.S. Private*, pg. 3506
TYLER INSURANCE AGENCY, LLC—See Arthur J. Gallagher & Co.; *U.S. Public*, pg. 207
TYNET CORPORATION—See Tyson Foods, Inc.; *U.S. Public*, pg. 2210
ULLICO MORTGAGE CORPORATION—See Ullico Inc.; *U.S. Private*, pg. 4276
UMPQUA INSURANCE AGENCY INC.; *U.S. Private*, pg. 4279
UNDERWRITERS MARINE SERVICES, INC.—See Aon plc; *Int'l*, pg. 495
UNDERWRITERS SAFETY AND CLAIMS, INC.; *U.S. Private*, pg. 4280
UNIFAX INSURANCE SYSTEMS, INC.—See Unico American Corporation; *U.S. Public*, pg. 2225
UNIFIED LIFE INSURANCE COMPANY—See Obra Capital, Inc.; *U.S. Private*, pg. 2987
UNION AGENCY, INC.—See Farmers & Merchants Investment, Inc.; *U.S. Private*, pg. 1476
UNION BAY RISK ADVISORS LLC; *U.S. Private*, pg. 4284
UNION INSURANCE CO. P.S.C.—See Al-Sagr National Insurance Company; *Int'l*, pg. 288
UNION INSURANCE GROUP, LLC—See Atlantic Union Bankshares Corporation; *U.S. Public*, pg. 223
UNION POIST'OVNA A.S.—See Achmea B.V.; *Int'l*, pg. 104

N.A.I.C.S. INDEX

524210 — INSURANCE AGENCIES ...

UNIRISC, INC.—See Kelso & Company, L.P.; *U.S. Private*, pg. 2280
UNI-SERVICE OPERATIONS CORPORATION—See Utica National Insurance Group; *U.S. Private*, pg. 4325
UNITED AMERICAN HEALTHCARE CORP.; *U.S. Public*, pg. 2229
UNITED BANK INSURANCE AGENCY—See United Community Financial; *U.S. Private*, pg. 4290
UNITED CASUALTY INSURANCE COMPANY OF AMERICA—See Kemper Corporation; *U.S. Public*, pg. 1221
UNITED FARM FAMILY INSURANCE COMPANY—See Brookfield Corporation; *Int'l*, pg. 1175
UNITED FIRE GROUP, INC.—See United Fire Group, Inc.; *U.S. Public*, pg. 2231
UNITED GUARANTY SERVICES, INC.—See Arch Capital Group Ltd.; *Int'l*, pg. 547
UNITED INSURANCE COMPANY—See Barbados Shipping & Trading Co. Ltd.; *Int'l*, pg. 858
UNITED INSURANCE MANAGEMENT, L.C.—See American Coastal Insurance Corporation; *U.S. Public*, pg. 98
UNITED UNDERWRITERS INSURANCE; *U.S. Private*, pg. 4301
UNIVERSAL INSPECTION CORPORATION—See Universal Insurance Holdings, Inc.; *U.S. Public*, pg. 2261
UNIVERSAL INSURANCE SERVICES OF FLORIDA, INC.—See Keystone Group, L.P.; *U.S. Private*, pg. 2298
UNIVERSAL PROPERTY & CASUALTY INSURANCE CO. (UPCIC)—See Universal Insurance Holdings, Inc.; *U.S. Public*, pg. 2261
UNIWILL INSURANCE BROKER CO., LTD.—See China United Insurance Service, Inc.; *Int'l*, pg. 1561
UNUM INSURANCE AGENCY, LLC—See Unum Group; *U.S. Public*, pg. 2263
UPSTATE AGENCY, LLC—See Arrow Financial Corporation; *U.S. Public*, pg. 200
URM INSURANCE AGENCY—See URM Stores, Inc.; *U.S. Private*, pg. 4316
USAA INSURANCE AGENCY INC.—See United Services Automobile Association; *U.S. Private*, pg. 4297
USAGENCIES CASUALTY INSURANCE—See J.C. Flowers & Co. LLC; *U.S. Private*, pg. 2159
USAGENCIES, LLC—See J.C. Flowers & Co. LLC; *U.S. Private*, pg. 2159
US BENEFITS ALLIANCE, LLC—See Reliance Global Group, Inc.; *U.S. Public*, pg. 1778
US E & O BROKERS—See Caisse de Depot et Placement du Quebec; *Int'l*, pg. 1257
US E & O BROKERS—See KKR & Co. Inc.; *U.S. Public*, pg. 1265
USI COLORADO LLC—See Caisse de Depot et Placement du Quebec; *Int'l*, pg. 1257
USI COLORADO LLC—See KKR & Co. Inc.; *U.S. Public*, pg. 1265
USI INSURANCE SERVICES LLC - AUSTIN—See Caisse de Depot et Placement du Quebec; *Int'l*, pg. 1257
USI INSURANCE SERVICES LLC - AUSTIN—See KKR & Co. Inc.; *U.S. Public*, pg. 1265
USI INSURANCE SERVICES LLC - DALLAS—See Caisse de Depot et Placement du Quebec; *Int'l*, pg. 1257
USI INSURANCE SERVICES LLC - DALLAS—See KKR & Co. Inc.; *U.S. Public*, pg. 1265
USI INSURANCE SERVICES LLC - HOUSTON—See Caisse de Depot et Placement du Quebec; *Int'l*, pg. 1257
USI INSURANCE SERVICES LLC - HOUSTON—See KKR & Co. Inc.; *U.S. Public*, pg. 1266
USI INSURANCE SERVICES LLC - PHOENIX—See Caisse de Depot et Placement du Quebec; *Int'l*, pg. 1257
USI INSURANCE SERVICES LLC - PHOENIX—See KKR & Co. Inc.; *U.S. Public*, pg. 1266
USI INSURANCE SERVICES LLC - SAN ANGELO—See Caisse de Depot et Placement du Quebec; *Int'l*, pg. 1257
USI INSURANCE SERVICES LLC - SAN ANGELO—See KKR & Co. Inc.; *U.S. Public*, pg. 1266
USI INSURANCE SERVICES LLC—See Caisse de Depot et Placement du Quebec; *Int'l*, pg. 1256
USI INSURANCE SERVICES LLC—See KKR & Co. Inc.; *U.S. Public*, pg. 1264
USI INSURANCE SERVICES LLC - SOUTH PORTLAND—See Caisse de Depot et Placement du Quebec; *Int'l*, pg. 1257
USI INSURANCE SERVICES LLC - SOUTH PORTLAND—See KKR & Co. Inc.; *U.S. Public*, pg. 1266
U.S.I. INSURANCE SERVICES OF MASSACHUSETTS, INC.—See Caisse de Depot et Placement du Quebec; *Int'l*, pg. 1257
U.S.I. INSURANCE SERVICES OF MASSACHUSETTS, INC.—See KKR & Co. Inc.; *U.S. Public*, pg. 1265
U.S. INSURANCE SERVICES, INC.—See Paine Schwartz Partners, LLC; *U.S. Private*, pg. 3076
USLP UNDERWRITING SOLUTIONS LP—See Aon plc; *Int'l*, pg. 495
U.S. RISK BROKERS, INC.—See Caisse de Depot et Placement du Quebec; *Int'l*, pg. 1256
U.S. RISK BROKERS, INC.—See KKR & Co. Inc.; *U.S. Public*, pg. 1265
U.S. RISK FINANCIAL SERVICES, INC.—See Caisse de Depot et Placement du Quebec; *Int'l*, pg. 1257
U.S. RISK FINANCIAL SERVICES, INC.—See KKR & Co. Inc.; *U.S. Public*, pg. 1265
U.S. RISK, LLC—See Caisse de Depot et Placement du Quebec; *Int'l*, pg. 1256
U.S. RISK, LLC—See KKR & Co. Inc.; *U.S. Public*, pg. 1265
U-SURE INSURANCE SERVICES LIMITED—See Brown & Brown, Inc.; *U.S. Public*, pg. 402
VAN BEURDEN INSURANCE SERVICES; *U.S. Private*, pg. 4338
VANBREDA INTERNATIONAL N.V.—See The Cigna Group; *U.S. Public*, pg. 2061
VAN DEN HEUVEL & FOUNTAIN INC.—See Aon plc; *Int'l*, pg. 498
VAN DYK & COMPANY, INC.; *U.S. Private*, pg. 4339
VAN DYKE RANKIN & COMPANY INC.; *U.S. Private*, pg. 4339
VANLINER INSURANCE COMPANY—See American Financial Group, Inc.; *U.S. Public*, pg. 103
VAN METER INSURANCE GROUP—See Houchens Industries, Inc.; *U.S. Private*, pg. 1990
VANNER INSURANCE AGENCY; *U.S. Private*, pg. 4344
VARNEY AGENCY, INC.; *U.S. Private*, pg. 4347
VASEK INSURANCE SERVICES LIMITED—See Arthur J. Gallagher & Co.; *U.S. Public*, pg. 207
VCS GROUP INC.—See Benefits Network Inc.; *U.S. Private*, pg. 525
VELA INSURANCE SERVICES, INC.—See W.R. Berkley Corporation; *U.S. Public*, pg. 2318
VELOCITY RISK UNDERWRITERS, LLC—See Brookfield Corporation; *Int'l*, pg. 1182
VENNEBERG INSURANCE, INC.—See Caisse de Depot et Placement du Quebec; *Int'l*, pg. 1257
VENNEBERG INSURANCE, INC.—See KKR & Co. Inc.; *U.S. Public*, pg. 1266
VENTIV TECHNOLOGY—See Symphony Technology Group, LLC; *U.S. Private*, pg. 3902
VENTURA PACIFIC INSURANCE SERVICES—See GTCR LLC; *U.S. Private*, pg. 1804
VERBAG AG—See Arthur J. Gallagher & Co.; *U.S. Public*, pg. 206
VERITAS RISK SERVICES, LLC—See New Mountain Capital, LLC; *U.S. Private*, pg. 2901
VERN FONK INSURANCE, INC.—See Stone Point Capital LLC; *U.S. Private*, pg. 3819
VEZINA ASSURANCES INC.—See Marsh & McLennan Companies, Inc.; *U.S. Public*, pg. 1388
VICTOR O. SCHINNERER & COMPANY, INC.—See Marsh & McLennan Companies, Inc.; *U.S. Public*, pg. 1383
VICTORY FINANCIAL GROUP, INC.; *U.S. Private*, pg. 4378
VIKCO INSURANCE SERVICES, INC.; *U.S. Private*, pg. 4382
VIKING INSURANCE COMPANY OF WISCONSIN—See Sentry Insurance Group; *U.S. Private*, pg. 3611
VILLAGE INSURANCE AGENCY, INC.—See Village Bank & Trust Financial Corp.; *U.S. Public*, pg. 2297
VINCENT, URBAN, WALKER & ASSOCIATES, INC.—See Seeman Holtz Property & Casualty, LLC; *U.S. Private*, pg. 3598
VIRGINIA FARM BUREAU FIRE & CASUALTY INSURANCE COMPANY—See Virginia Farm Bureau Mutual Insurance Company; *U.S. Private*, pg. 4387
VIRTUS BENEFITS, LLC—See Genstar Capital, LLC; *U.S. Private*, pg. 1675
VISTA INSURANCE PARTNERS OF ILLINOIS, INC.—See Caisse de Depot et Placement du Quebec; *Int'l*, pg. 1257
VISTA INSURANCE PARTNERS OF ILLINOIS, INC.—See KKR & Co. Inc.; *U.S. Public*, pg. 1266
VOLUNTEER FIREMEN'S INSURANCE SERVICES, INC.—See American International Group, Inc.; *U.S. Public*, pg. 107
VOLVO GROUP INSURANCE FORSAKRINGS AB—See AB Volvo; *Int'l*, pg. 44
V.SCOPE RISK MANAGEMENT LTD.—See Ackermans & van Haaren NV; *Int'l*, pg. 106
WAARD VERZEKERINGEN B.V.—See Chesnara Plc; *Int'l*, pg. 1472
WAFD INSURANCE GROUP, INC.—See WaFd, Inc.; *U.S. Public*, pg. 2321
WALLACE SPECIALTY INSURANCE GROUP, LLC—See Kelso & Company, L.P.; *U.S. Private*, pg. 2280
WALLACE WELCH & WILLINGHAM, INC.—See IMA Financial Group, Inc.; *U.S. Private*, pg. 2044
WALL STREET INSURANCE INC.—See ABRY Partners, LLC; *U.S. Private*, pg. 42
WALSDORF AGENCY, INC.—See Arthur J. Gallagher & Co.; *U.S. Public*, pg. 208
WALSH DUFFIELD COMPANIES, INC.; *U.S. Private*, pg. 4433
WALTER L. CLARK & ASSOCIATES, INC.—See Aquiline Capital Partners LLC; *U.S. Private*, pg. 305
WARD FINANCIAL GROUP, INC.—See Aon plc; *Int'l*, pg. 495
WAREHEIM INSURANCE CONSULTANTS, INC.; *U.S. Private*, pg. 4441
WARNER PACIFIC INSURANCE SERVICES, INC.; *U.S. Private*, pg. 4442
THE WARNOCK AGENCY, INC.—See Boston Omaha Corporation; *U.S. Public*, pg. 372
WARRANTECH HOME SERVICE COMPANY—See Stone Point Capital LLC; *U.S. Private*, pg. 3821
WARRIOR INSURANCE NETWORK, INC; *U.S. Private*, pg. 4444
WASHINGTON NATIONAL INSURANCE COMPANY—See CNO Financial Group, Inc.; *U.S. Public*, pg. 520
WATKINS INSURANCE GROUP INC.; *U.S. Private*, pg. 4455
WAVIN ASSURANTIE B.V.—See Bharti Enterprises Limited; *Int'l*, pg. 1012
WAYPOINT INSURANCE GROUP, INC.—See Banco Santander, S.A.; *Int'l*, pg. 827
WEBER'S INSURANCE SERVICES, INC.—See Aon plc; *Int'l*, pg. 498
WEB SHAW LIMITED—See Brown & Brown, Inc.; *U.S. Public*, pg. 402
WELCH INSURANCE LLC—See Knowles Associates, LLC; *U.S. Private*, pg. 2324
WELLS FARGO INSURANCE SERVICES, INC.—See Wells Fargo & Company; *U.S. Public*, pg. 2346
WELLS INSURANCE AGENCY, INC.—See Citizens Community Bancorp, Inc.; *U.S. Public*, pg. 505
W.E. LOVE & ASSOCIATES INC.—See XPT Group LLC; *U.S. Private*, pg. 4582
WESBANCO INSURANCE SERVICES, INC.—See WesBanco, Inc.; *U.S. Public*, pg. 2350
WESTCHESTER SURPLUS LINES INSURANCE COMPANY—See Chubb Limited; *Int'l*, pg. 1593
WEST COAST INSURANCE SERVICES, INC.—See Stone Point Capital LLC; *U.S. Private*, pg. 3819
WESTERN INSURANCE—See Western State Agency, Inc.; *U.S. Private*, pg. 4497
WESTERN PROTECTORS INSURANCE COMPANY—See Oregon Mutual Insurance Company, Inc.; *U.S. Private*, pg. 3040
WESTERN RE/MANAGERS INSURANCE SERVICES, INC.—See Align Financial Group, LLC; *U.S. Private*, pg. 168
WESTERN SECURITY SURPLUS INSURANCE BROKERS, INC.; *U.S. Private*, pg. 4496
WEST JAPAN SERVICE COMPANY LIMITED—See Coca-Cola Bottlers Japan Holdings Inc.; *Int'l*, pg. 1684
WEST TEXAS INSURANCE EXCHANGE, INC.; *U.S. Private*, pg. 4487
WESTWOOD INSURANCE AGENCY, INC.—See The Baldwin Insurance Group, Inc.; *U.S. Public*, pg. 2036
WETZEL & LANZI INC.—See Maury, Donnelly & Parr, Inc.; *U.S. Private*, pg. 2615
WHARTON LYON & LYON—See GCP Capital Partners Holdings LLC; *U.S. Public*, pg. 1654
WHEATMAN INSURANCE SERVICES, LLC—See Arthur J. Gallagher & Co.; *U.S. Public*, pg. 208
WHITBOY, INC.—See Stone Point Capital LLC; *U.S. Private*, pg. 3819
WHITE PINE INSURANCE COMPANY—See Conifer Holdings, Inc.; *U.S. Public*, pg. 567
WHITNEY INSURANCE AGENCY, INC.; *U.S. Private*, pg. 4513
WHOLESALE TRADING INSURANCE SERVICES, LLC—See The Carlyle Group Inc.; *U.S. Public*, pg. 2048
WIGMORE INSURANCE AGENCY, INC.—See Arthur J. Gallagher & Co.; *U.S. Public*, pg. 208
WILBER-PRICE INSURANCE GROUP LTD.—See PCF Insurance Services of The West, LLC; *U.S. Private*, pg. 3120
WILLIAMS INSURANCE SERVICES, INC.—See Inszone Insurance Services, LLC; *U.S. Private*, pg. 2097
WILLIAMS & WILLIAMS, INC.—See GTCR LLC; *U.S. Private*, pg. 1804
WILLIS RE, INC.—See Arthur J. Gallagher & Co.; *U.S. Public*, pg. 208
WILLOW GLEN INSURANCE AGENCY, INC.—See Inszone Insurance Services, LLC; *U.S. Private*, pg. 2097
WILSON GREGORY AGENCY INC.—See Arch Capital Group Ltd.; *Int'l*, pg. 547
WILSON H. FLOCK INSURANCE, INC.—See GTCR LLC; *U.S. Private*, pg. 1804
WILSON, WASHBURN & FORSTER, INC.—See Genstar Capital, LLC; *U.S. Private*, pg. 1675
WINGED KEEL GROUP, LLC; *U.S. Private*, pg. 4541
WINNOCK ZORG B.V.—See Achmea B.V.; *Int'l*, pg. 104
WINTER GROUP, INC.—See Kelso & Company, L.P.; *U.S. Private*, pg. 2280
WIRTZ INSURANCE AGENCY, INC.—See Wirtz Corporation; *U.S. Private*, pg. 4547
WITKEMPER INSURANCE GROUP—See GTCR LLC; *U.S. Private*, pg. 1804
W. JOSEPH MCPHILLIPS, INC.—See Arrow Financial Corporation; *U.S. Public*, pg. 200
WM BROKERS LIMITED—See Brown & Brown, Inc.; *U.S. Public*, pg. 402
WM K LYONS AGENCY, INC.—See Stone Point Capital LLC; *U.S. Private*, pg. 3819
WOOD GUTMANN & BOGART INSURANCE BROKERS; *U.S. Private*, pg. 4556
THE WOODITCH COMPANY INSURANCE SERVICES,

524210 — INSURANCE AGENCIES ...

INC.—See Hellman & Friedman LLC; *U.S. Private*, pg. 1909
WOODROW W. CROSS AGENCY—See Cross Financial Corporation; *U.S. Private*, pg. 1104
WOODRUFF-SAWYER & CO.; *U.S. Private*, pg. 4560
WORD & BROWN, INSURANCE ADMINISTRATORS, INC.; *U.S. Private*, pg. 4562
WORLCO MANAGEMENT SERVICES, INC.—See Centene Corporation; *U.S. Public*, pg. 471
WORLD ACCESS SERVICE CORP.—See Allianz SE; *Int'l*, pg. 342
WORLD INSURANCE ASSOCIATES LLC; *U.S. Private*, pg. 4565
WORLDSOURCE INSURANCE NETWORK INC.—See Guardian Capital Group Limited; *Int'l*, pg. 3170
WORLDWIDE FACILITIES, LLC—See AmWINS Group, Inc.; *U.S. Public*, pg. 270
WRAPID SPECIALTY, INC.—See Aon plc; *Int'l*, pg. 495
THE WRIGHT INSURANCE GROUP LLC—See Brown & Brown, Inc.; *U.S. Public*, pg. 402
WRIGHTMAN, INC.—See Arthur J. Gallagher & Co.; *U.S. Public*, pg. 208
WRIGHT & PERCY INSURANCE AGENCY INC.; *U.S. Private*, pg. 4572
WRIGHT PROGRAM MANAGEMENT, LLC—See Brown & Brown, Inc.; *U.S. Public*, pg. 402
WRIGHT RISK CONSULTING, LLC—See Brown & Brown, Inc.; *U.S. Public*, pg. 402
WRIGHT RISK MANAGEMENT COMPANY, LLC—See Brown & Brown, Inc.; *U.S. Public*, pg. 402
WRIGHT SPECIALTY INSURANCE AGENCY, LLC—See Brown & Brown, Inc.; *U.S. Public*, pg. 402
WRI INSURANCE BROKERS PTY LTD—See AUB Group Limited; *Int'l*, pg. 698
WTC INSURANCE CORPORATION, LTD.—See International Business Machines Corporation; *U.S. Public*, pg. 1151
WYOMING FINANCIAL INSURANCE COMPANY—See Hellman & Friedman LLC; *U.S. Private*, pg. 1910
XBRIDGE LIMITED—See The Travelers Companies, Inc.; *U.S. Public*, pg. 2136
XENIA BROKING GROUP LIMITED—See Brown & Brown, Inc.; *U.S. Public*, pg. 402
XENIA BROKING LIMITED—See Brown & Brown, Inc.; *U.S. Public*, pg. 402
XL INDIA BUSINESS SERVICES PRIVATE LIMITED—See AXA S.A.; *Int'l*, pg. 760
XL INSURANCE COMPANY SE—See AXA S.A.; *Int'l*, pg. 761
XL INSURANCE—See AXA S.A.; *Int'l*, pg. 760
XL INSURANCE SWITZERLAND LTD—See AXA S.A.; *Int'l*, pg. 761
XL LONDON MARKET GROUP LTD—See AXA S.A.; *Int'l*, pg. 761
YEELIM INSURANCE AGENCY LTD.—See Harel Insurance Investments & Financial Services Ltd.; *Int'l*, pg. 3274
YORK AGENCY, INC.—See Matthews International Corporation; *U.S. Public*, pg. 1401
YORK BRUKAN B.I. ASSESSORIA ADMINISTRACAO E CORRETAGEM DE SEGUROS LTDA.—See Alper Consultoria e Corretora de Seguros S.A.; *Int'l*, pg. 366
THE YORKE AGENCY INC.—See ABRY Partners, LLC; *U.S. Private*, pg. 42
YOUZOOM INSURANCE SERVICES, INC.—See Brown & Brown, Inc.; *U.S. Public*, pg. 402
YVC HOLDINGS, INC; *U.S. Public*, pg. 2400
ZARAT BETEILIGUNGSGESELLSCHAFT MBH & CO. OBJEKT LEBEN II KG—See Deutsche Bank Aktiengesellschaft; *Int'l*, pg. 2062
ZEILER INSURANCE INC.; *U.S. Private*, pg. 4599
ZENSURANCE BROKERS INC.—See The Travelers Companies, Inc.; *U.S. Public*, pg. 2136
ZITO INSURANCE AGENCY, INC.—See Kelso & Company, L.P.; *U.S. Private*, pg. 2280

524291 — CLAIMS ADJUSTING

ADJUSTERS INTERNATIONAL INC.; *U.S. Private*, pg. 79
ADMIRAL LAW LIMITED—See Admiral Group plc; *Int'l*, pg. 151
AEROSPACE CLAIMS MANAGEMENT GROUP, INC.—See Hallmark Financial Services, Inc.; *U.S. Public*, pg. 981
AI CLAIMS SOLUTIONS (UK) LIMITED—See AI Claims Solutions Plc; *Int'l*, pg. 226
ALEX N SILL COMPANY—See CNL Strategic Capital Management LLC; *U.S. Private*, pg. 952
AMERICAN ROAD SERVICES COMPANY LLC—See Ford Motor Company; *U.S. Public*, pg. 864
AMMETLIFE TAKAFUL BERHAD—See MetLife, Inc.; *U.S. Public*, pg. 1429
AON BENFIELD BRATISLAVA S.R.O.—See Aon plc; *Int'l*, pg. 489
AON (DIFC) GULF LLC—See Aon plc; *Int'l*, pg. 489
AON HEWITT ESPANA S.A.U.—See Alight, Inc.; *U.S. Public*, pg. 76
AON TUNISIA SO.CAR.GEST S.A.—See Aon plc; *Int'l*, pg. 494

APEX CLAIMS SERVICES OF NEW ENGLAND—See Aquiline Capital Partners LLC; *U.S. Private*, pg. 305
BDE LAW LIMITED—See Admiral Group plc; *Int'l*, pg. 151
BPO TECHNICAL SERVICES LLC—See The Carlyle Group Inc.; *U.S. Public*, pg. 2054
BRIDGEWATER GROUP, LLC—See Field Pros Direct LLC; *U.S. Private*, pg. 1504
CARL WARREN & COMPANY; *U.S. Private*, pg. 763
CARSTENS I SCHUES POLAND SP. Z O.O.—See Aon plc; *Int'l*, pg. 494
CHARLES TAYLOR ADJUSTING (AUSTRALIA) PTY LTD—See Lovell Minnick Partners LLC; *U.S. Private*, pg. 2502
CLAIM MANAGEMENT SERVICES, INC.—See Elevance Health, Inc.; *U.S. Public*, pg. 729
CORPORATE CLAIMS MANAGEMENT, INC.; *U.S. Private*, pg. 1054
CRAWFORD & COMPANY ADJUSTERS LIMITED—See Crawford & Company; *U.S. Public*, pg. 592
CRP RISK MANAGEMENT LIMITED; *Int'l*, pg. 1858
CUSTARD INSURANCE ADJUSTERS INC.; *U.S. Private*, pg. 1127
DAVID MORSE & ASSOCIATES; *U.S. Private*, pg. 1171
DEKRA BELGIUM N.V.—See DEKRA e.V.; *Int'l*, pg. 2006
DEKRA CLAIMS SERVICES MAROC S.A.R.L.—See DEKRA e.V.; *Int'l*, pg. 2006
DIMONT & ASSOCIATES, LLC—See Metro Public Adjustment, Inc.; *U.S. Private*, pg. 2686
EAGLE ADJUSTING SERVICES, INC.—See SE Capital, LLC; *U.S. Private*, pg. 3582
ENGLE MARTIN & ASSOCIATES, LLC; *U.S. Private*, pg. 1399
EPS SETTLEMENTS GROUP INC.; *U.S. Private*, pg. 1414
EUROPEJSKIE CENTRUM ODSZKODOWAN S.A.; *Int'l*, pg. 2557
FIELD PROS DIRECT LLC; *U.S. Private*, pg. 1504
FRONTIER ADJUSTERS, INC.—See HGGC, LLC; *U.S. Private*, pg. 1929
FUNDACION AON ESPANA—See Aon plc; *Int'l*, pg. 494
GLATFELTER CLAIMS MANAGEMENT, INC.—See American International Group, Inc.; *U.S. Public*, pg. 106
THE GREENSPAN COMPANY; *U.S. Private*, pg. 4039
GRUPO MULTIASISTENCIA S.A.—See Allianz SE; *Int'l*, pg. 353
HMG-PCMS LIMITED—See Arthur J. Gallagher & Co.; *U.S. Public*, pg. 205
HOMESERVE CLAIMS MANAGEMENT—See Brookfield Corporation; *Int'l*, pg. 1188
IAS CLAIM SERVICES—See IAS Services Group LLC; *U.S. Private*, pg. 2028
INSURANCE NETWORK SERVICES, INC.—See The Seibels Bruce Group, Inc.; *U.S. Private*, pg. 4116
JOHN MULLEN & CO, INC.; *U.S. Private*, pg. 2223
JOHNS EASTERN COMPANY INC.—See HGGC, LLC; *U.S. Private*, pg. 1929
LAMORTE BURNS & CO INC.; *U.S. Private*, pg. 2380
LAUREATE INSURANCE PARTNERS, LLC—See The Baldwin Insurance Group, Inc.; *U.S. Public*, pg. 2036
MASON CLAIM SERVICES, INC.; *U.S. Private*, pg. 2601
MCLARENS YOUNG INTERNATIONAL—See McLarens, Inc.; *U.S. Private*, pg. 2640
METRO PUBLIC ADJUSTMENT, INC.; *U.S. Private*, pg. 2686
MICHIGAN CATASTROPHIC CLAIMS ASSOCIATION; *U.S. Private*, pg. 2700
MOTORS INSURANCE COMPANY LIMITED—See Stone Point Capital LLC; *U.S. Private*, pg. 3821
NATIONAL CATASTROPHE ADJUSTERS LLC—See Aquiline Capital Partners LLC; *U.S. Private*, pg. 305
NATIONAL VENDOR, INC.; *U.S. Private*, pg. 2864
NETWORK ADJUSTERS INC.; *U.S. Private*, pg. 2888
NFP STRUCTURED SETTLEMENTS, INC.—See Aon plc; *Int'l*, pg. 497
NORDIC FORSAKRING & RISKHANTERING AB—See Arthur J. Gallagher & Co.; *U.S. Public*, pg. 206
OPTUMRX DISCOUNT CARD SERVICES, LLC—See UnitedHealth Group Incorporated; *U.S. Public*, pg. 2247
PACESETTER CLAIMS SERVICE; *U.S. Private*, pg. 3064
THE PHIA GROUP LLC; *U.S. Private*, pg. 4094
PILOT AND ASSOCIATES INC.—See Pilot Catastrophe Services Inc.; *U.S. Private*, pg. 3181
PILOT CATASTROPHE SERVICES INC.; *U.S. Private*, pg. 3181
PINNACLE RISK MANAGEMENT SERVICES, INC.; *U.S. Private*, pg. 3185
PREMIER ADJUSTERS, INC.—See Location Services, LLC; *U.S. Private*, pg. 2478
PROFESSIONAL DENTAL REVIEWERS—See Aon plc; *Int'l*, pg. 489
PROTECTIVE MARKETING ENTERPRISES—See Aon plc; *Int'l*, pg. 495
RAILWAY CLAIM SERVICES INC.; *U.S. Private*, pg. 3346
REID, JONES, MCRORIE & WILLIAMS, INC.—See Aquiline Capital Partners LLC; *U.S. Private*, pg. 305
RENEWABLE ENERGY LOSS ADJUSTERS LIMITED—See Marsh & McLennan Companies, Inc.; *U.S. Public*, pg. 1388
THE RICHARDS HOGG LINDLEY GROUP LIMITED—See Lovell Minnick Partners LLC; *U.S. Private*, pg. 2502
ROGERSGRAY INC.—See The Baldwin Insurance Group, Inc.; *U.S. Public*, pg. 2036
RYZE CLAIM SOLUTIONS LLC; *U.S. Private*, pg. 3511
SCIBAL ASSOCIATES, INC.—See The Cigna Group; *U.S. Public*, pg. 2061
SEDGWICK CLAIMS MANAGEMENT SERVICES, INC.—See The Carlyle Group Inc.; *U.S. Public*, pg. 2053
SMITH & CARSON; *U.S. Private*, pg. 3693
STATE FARM INSURANCE CO.—See State Farm Mutual Automobile Insurance Company; *U.S. Private*, pg. 3792
SUPERVIELLE SEGUROS S.A.—See Grupo Supervielle S.A.; *Int'l*, pg. 3135
TENCO SERVICES, INC.; *U.S. Private*, pg. 3965
TOENSMEIER ADJUSTMENT SERVICE; *U.S. Private*, pg. 4181
TRAVELERS LIABILITY INSURANCE—See The Travelers Companies, Inc.; *U.S. Public*, pg. 2136
TREEFROG DATA SOLUTIONS; *U.S. Private*, pg. 4217
VERICLAIM UK LIMITED—See The Carlyle Group Inc.; *U.S. Public*, pg. 2054
VITALITY CORPORATE SERVICES LIMITED—See Discovery Limited; *Int'l*, pg. 2134
WINKLER TREGER & ASSOCIATES LLC; *U.S. Private*, pg. 4542
WORLEY CLAIMS SERVICES, LLC—See Aquiline Capital Partners LLC; *U.S. Private*, pg. 305
ZELIS CLAIMS INTEGRITY, INC.—See PCP Enterprise, L.P.; *U.S. Private*, pg. 3121

524292 — THIRD PARTY ADMINISTRATION OF INSURANCE AND PENSION FUNDS

ACA FINANCIAL GUARANTY CORPORATION—See Manifold Capital Corp.; *U.S. Private*, pg. 2564
ACCELERATED CLAIMS INC.; *U.S. Private*, pg. 49
ACMG, INC.; *U.S. Private*, pg. 62
ADMINISTRADORA DE FONDOS DE PENSIONES PROVIDA S.A.—See MetLife, Inc.; *U.S. Public*, pg. 1429
ADVOCATE CAPITAL, INC.—See Pinnacle Financial Partners, Inc.; *U.S. Public*, pg. 1692
AEGON UK PLC—See Aegon N.V.; *Int'l*, pg. 174
AFP GENESIS ADMINISTRADORA DE FONDOS Y FIDEICOMISOS S.A.—See MetLife, Inc.; *U.S. Public*, pg. 1429
AFP HORIZONTE SA—See Banco Bilbao Vizcaya Argentaria, S.A.; *Int'l*, pg. 816
AJ BELL PLC.; *Int'l*, pg. 255
ALAN GRAY LLC; *U.S. Private*, pg. 149
ALBERTA INVESTMENT MANAGEMENT CORPORATION; *Int'l*, pg. 297
ALBERTA PENSION SERVICES CORPORATION; *Int'l*, pg. 298
ALECTA PENSIONSFORSAKRING, OMSESIDIGT; *Int'l*, pg. 305
ALEGEUS TECHNOLOGIES, LLC—See Vista Equity Partners, LLC; *U.S. Private*, pg. 4395
ALLIANCE BENEFIT GROUP CAROLINAS, INC.—See Alliance Benefit Group, LLC; *U.S. Private*, pg. 181
ALLIANCE BENEFIT GROUP MIDATLANTIC, LLC—See Alliance Benefit Group, LLC; *U.S. Private*, pg. 181
ALLIANCE BENEFIT GROUP OF HOUSTON, INC.—See Alliance Benefit Group, LLC; *U.S. Private*, pg. 181
ALLIANCE BENEFIT GROUP OF ILLINOIS, INC.—See Alliance Benefit Group, LLC; *U.S. Private*, pg. 181
ALLIANCE BENEFIT GROUP OF MICHIGAN, INC.—See Alliance Benefit Group, LLC; *U.S. Private*, pg. 181
ALLIED WORLD INSURANCE COMPANY—See Fairfax Financial Holdings Limited; *Int'l*, pg. 2606
AMERICAN BENEFIT PLAN ADMINISTRATORS, INC.—See Water Street Healthcare Partners, LLC; *U.S. Private*, pg. 4452
AMTRUST UNDERWRITING LIMITED—See Stone Point Capital LLC; *U.S. Private*, pg. 3820
ANTHEM BENEFIT ADMINISTRATORS INC.—See Elevance Health, Inc.; *U.S. Public*, pg. 728
AON GLOBAL SERVICES, INC.—See Aon plc; *Int'l*, pg. 491
APRIO BENEFIT ADVISORS, LLC—See Aprio, LLP; *U.S. Private*, pg. 301
ARBEJDSMARKEDETS TILLAEGSPENSION; *Int'l*, pg. 537
ARISTA INVESTORS CORP.; *U.S. Private*, pg. 323
ARMY WELFARE TRUST LLC; *Int'l*, pg. 575
ASCENSUS, LLC—See Aquiline Capital Partners LLC; *U.S. Private*, pg. 303
ASCENSUS, LLC—See Genstar Capital, LLC; *U.S. Private*, pg. 1675
ASSOCIATED CLAIMS ENTERPRISES INC.—See Cameron General Corporation; *U.S. Private*, pg. 728
ASSOCIAZIONE DEI FONOGRAFICI ITALIANI; *Int'l*, pg. 649
ASSURANCE SERVICES CORPORATION—See Marsh & McLennan Companies, Inc.; *U.S. Public*, pg. 1374
ATLAS ADMINISTRATORS INC.—See USA Managed Care Organization; *U.S. Private*, pg. 4321
AURORA NATIONAL LIFE ASSURANCE COMPANY—See Financiere Pinault SCA; *U.S. Private*, pg. 2668
AUSTRALIAN UNITY NOMINEES PTY LTD—See Australian Unity Limited; *Int'l*, pg. 723

N.A.I.C.S. INDEX

524292 — THIRD PARTY ADMINIS...

AVISENA, INC.; *U.S. Private*, pg. 408
AWARE SUPER PTY LTD; *Int'l*, pg. 752
BAILLIE GIFFORD & CO.; *Int'l*, pg. 802
BANKIA PENSIONES, S.A., E.G.F.P.—See Lone Star Funds; *U.S. Private*, pg. 2485
BANK OF COMMUNICATIONS TRUSTEE LIMITED—See Bank of Communications Co., Ltd.; *Int'l*, pg. 842
BANK OF IRELAND LIFE—See Bank of Ireland Group plc; *Int'l*, pg. 844
BENEFIT RESOURCE, INC.—See ABRY Partners, LLC; *U.S. Private*, pg. 42
BENESYS, INC.; *U.S. Private*, pg. 525
BLUE CROSS & BLUE SHIELD ASSOCIATION GOVERNMENT RELATIONS—See Blue Cross & Blue Shield Association; *U.S. Private*, pg. 586
BOV FUND SERVICES LTD.—See Bank of Valletta p.l.c.; *Int'l*, pg. 849
BOWDITCH MARINE, INC.—See Lovell Minnick Partners LLC; *U.S. Private*, pg. 2502
BRAISHFIELD ASSOCIATES, INC.—See Brown & Brown, Inc.; *U.S. Public*, pg. 397
BROWN BROTHERS HARRIMAN (LUXEMBOURG) S.A.—See Brown Brothers Harriman & Co.; *U.S. Private*, pg. 666
BROWN & BROWN BENEFIT ADVISORS, INC.—See Brown & Brown, Inc.; *U.S. Public*, pg. 397
BUSINESSFIRST INSURANCE COMPANY—See American Financial Group, Inc.; *U.S. Public*, pg. 103
C2C SOLUTIONS, INC.; *U.S. Private*, pg. 709
CALVERT ADMINISTRATIVE SERVICES COMPANY—See Ameritas Mutual Holding Company; *U.S. Private*, pg. 261
CANADA PENSION PLAN INVESTMENT BOARD; *Int'l*, pg. 1278
CAPITA LIFE & PENSIONS LIMITED—See Capita plc; *Int'l*, pg. 1308
CAPITA LIFE & PENSIONS REGULATED SERVICES LIMITED—See Capita plc; *Int'l*, pg. 1308
CARECENTRIX, INC.—See Walgreens Boots Alliance, Inc.; *U.S. Public*, pg. 2322
CBCA ADMINISTRATORS, INC.—See Simplifi, Inc.; *U.S. Private*, pg. 3667
CDM RETIREMENT CONSULTANTS, INC.—See Northwest Plan Services, Inc.; *U.S. Private*, pg. 2961
THE CEI GROUP INC.—See CSI Holdings Inc.; *U.S. Private*, pg. 1117
CHARD, SNYDER & ASSOCIATES, LLC—See WEX, Inc.; *U.S. Public*, pg. 2364
CHARLES TAYLOR ADJUSTING SARL—See Lovell Minnick Partners LLC; *U.S. Private*, pg. 2502
CHARLES TAYLOR (JAPAN) LIMITED—See Lovell Minnick Partners LLC; *U.S. Private*, pg. 2502
CHARLES TAYLOR P&I MANAGEMENT (AMERICAS) INC.—See Lovell Minnick Partners LLC; *U.S. Private*, pg. 2502
CHARLES TAYLOR RSLAC INC.—See Lovell Minnick Partners LLC; *U.S. Private*, pg. 2502
CJA & ASSOCIATES, INC.; *U.S. Private*, pg. 909
CLAIMS COMPENSATION BUREAU, LLC—See PRA Group, Inc.; *U.S. Public*, pg. 1712
CLAIMS MANAGEMENT OF MISSOURI, LLC—See Brown & Brown, Inc.; *U.S. Public*, pg. 400
COLLEGIATE ASSOCIATION RESOURCE OF THE SOUTHWEST; *U.S. Private*, pg. 968
COMPCOST INC.—See State Fund Mutual Insurance Co.; *U.S. Private*, pg. 3792
COMPLETE CLAIMS PROCESSING, INC.—See Targeted Medical Pharma, Inc.; *U.S. Public*, pg. 1982
CONFERENCE ASSOCIATES, INC.; *U.S. Private*, pg. 1013
CONTROLEXPERT HOLDING GMBH—See Allianz SE; *Int'l*, pg. 351
CORPORATE CLAIMS MANAGEMENT, INC.—See Patriot National, Inc.; *U.S. Private*, pg. 3110
CRITERION ADJUSTERS LIMITED—See Lovell Minnick Partners LLC; *U.S. Private*, pg. 2502
CRITERION SURVEYORS LIMITED—See Lovell Minnick Partners LLC; *U.S. Private*, pg. 2502
CRUSADER STERLING PENSION LIMITED—See Custodian Investment PLC; *Int'l*, pg. 1880
C.T. HELLMUTH & ASSOCIATES, LLC—See New Mountain Capital, LLC; *U.S. Private*, pg. 2901
DBS ASSET MANAGEMENT (UNITED STATES) PTE LTD—See DBS Group Holdings Ltd.; *Int'l*, pg. 1988
DEKRA CLAIMS & EXPERT SERVICES (SWITZERLAND) SA—See DEKRA e.V.; *Int'l*, pg. 2009
DEKRA CLAIMS SERVICES AUSTRIA GMBH—See DEKRA e.V.; *Int'l*, pg. 2008
DEKRA CLAIMS SERVICES CZ S.R.O.—See DEKRA e.V.; *Int'l*, pg. 2008
DEKRA CLAIMS SERVICES FINLAND—See DEKRA e.V.; *Int'l*, pg. 2008
DEKRA CLAIMS SERVICES HUNGARY SERVICE LTD.—See DEKRA e.V.; *Int'l*, pg. 2008
DEKRA CLAIMS SERVICES INTERNATIONAL BVBA—See DEKRA e.V.; *Int'l*, pg. 2008
DEKRA CLAIMS SERVICES LUXEMBOURG S.A.—See DEKRA e.V.; *Int'l*, pg. 2008
DEKRA CLAIMS SERVICES PORTUGAL S.A.—See DEKRA e.V.; *Int'l*, pg. 2008
DEKRA CLAIMS SERVICES SPAIN, S.A.—See DEKRA e.V.; *Int'l*, pg. 2008
DEKRA CLAIMS SERVICES TURKEY LTD.—See DEKRA e.V.; *Int'l*, pg. 2008
DEKRA CLAIMS SERVICES UK LTD.—See DEKRA e.V.; *Int'l*, pg. 2008
DEKRA CLAIMS SERVICES UKRAINE—See DEKRA e.V.; *Int'l*, pg. 2008
DEKRA EXPERTS B.V.—See DEKRA e.V.; *Int'l*, pg. 2008
DEKRA EXPERTS NV—See DEKRA e.V.; *Int'l*, pg. 2008
DEKRA PEOPLE B.V.—See DEKRA e.V.; *Int'l*, pg. 2009
DEKRA RUSS O.O.O.—See DEKRA e.V.; *Int'l*, pg. 2009
DIGITAL INSURANCE, LLC—See New Mountain Capital, LLC; *U.S. Private*, pg. 2901
EBMS; *U.S. Private*, pg. 1324
EBS PENSION LIMITED—See Embark Group Limited; *Int'l*, pg. 2374
ECHELON AUSTRALIA PTY LIMITED—See Marsh & McLennan Companies, Inc.; *U.S. Public*, pg. 1374
ENTERPRISE RISK STRATEGIES, LLC—See Mariner Wealth Advisors, LLC; *U.S. Private*, pg. 2575
ERSTE ASSET MANAGEMENT GMBH—See Erste Group Bank AG; *Int'l*, pg. 2498
ERSTE SECURITIES ISTANBUL MENKUL DEGERLER AS—See Erste Group Bank AG; *Int'l*, pg. 2498
EVERQUOTE, INC.; *U.S. Public*, pg. 801
FAIRPAY SOLUTIONS, INC.—See Stone Point Capital LLC; *U.S. Private*, pg. 3823
FGR HANNA LIMITADA—See Lovell Minnick Partners LLC; *U.S. Private*, pg. 2502
FINANCIAL RESOURCE MANAGEMENT GROUP, INC.—See Caisse de Depot et Placement du Quebec; *Int'l*, pg. 1256
FINANCIAL RESOURCE MANAGEMENT GROUP, INC.—See KKR & Co. Inc.; *U.S. Public*, pg. 1265
FINOVO AG—See Helvetia Holding AG; *Int'l*, pg. 3339
FIRST LIFE ASSURANCE COMPANY LTD.—See Achmea B.V.; *Int'l*, pg. 103
FLEXIBLE BENEFIT ADMINISTRATORS INC.; *U.S. Private*, pg. 1544
FLORIDA HOSPITAL HEALTHCARE SYSTEM, INC.—See Adventist Health System Sunbelt Healthcare Corporation; *U.S. Public*, pg. 109
FLORIDA WORKERS' COMPENSATION INSURANCE GUARANTY ASSOCIATION, INC.; *U.S. Private*, pg. 1551
FM APPROVALS, LLC—See Factory Mutual Insurance Company; *U.S. Private*, pg. 1460
FONDACTION, LE FONDS DE DEVELOPPEMENT DE LA CONFEDERATION DES SYNDICATS NATIONAUX POUR LA COOPERATION ET L'EMPLOI; *Int'l*, pg. 2724
FRANKFURTER LEBENSVERSICHERUNG AG—See Fosun International Limited; *Int'l*, pg. 2751
FREEDOM HEALTH INC.; *U.S. Private*, pg. 1603
FRONTIER CLAIMS SERVICES, INC.—See Evans Bancorp, Inc.; *U.S. Public*, pg. 799
GOVERNMENT EMPLOYEES ASSOCIATION—See One80 Intermediaries LLC; *U.S. Private*, pg. 3024
HEALTHCOMP LLC—See New Mountain Capital, LLC; *U.S. Private*, pg. 2902
HEALTH E SYSTEMS, LLC; *U.S. Private*, pg. 1893
HEALTHSMART BENEFIT SOLUTIONS, INC.—See HealthSmart Holdings, Inc.; *U.S. Private*, pg. 1897
HEALTHSMART CASUALTY CLAIMS SOLUTIONS—See HealthSmart Holdings, Inc.; *U.S. Private*, pg. 1897
HELMSMAN MANAGEMENT SERVICES, LLC—See Liberty Mutual Holding Company Inc.; *U.S. Private*, pg. 2445
HERMES FUND MANAGERS LIMITED—See Federated Hermes, Inc.; *U.S. Public*, pg. 827
HFG BENEFITS CORP.—See Arthur J. Gallagher & Co.; *U.S. Public*, pg. 205
ILMARINEN MUTUAL PENSION INSURANCE COMPANY; *Int'l*, pg. 3615
INSURANCE ADMINISTRATIVE SOLUTIONS, LLC—See Integrity Marketing Group LLC; *U.S. Private*, pg. 2103
INSURANCE CARE DIRECT INC; *U.S. Private*, pg. 2095
INSURANCE CLUB, INC.—See Unico American Corporation; *U.S. Public*, pg. 2225
INSURERS ADMINISTRATIVE CORPORATION—See Geneve Holdings Corp.; *U.S. Private*, pg. 1670
INTELLICENTS INC.; *U.S. Private*, pg. 2105
IPS PENSIONS LIMITED—See Epiris Managers LLP; *Int'l*, pg. 2461
ITM TWENTYFIRST, LLC; *U.S. Private*, pg. 2150
JUAN A. CALZADO S.A.R.L.—See DEKRA e.V.; *Int'l*, pg. 2010
KB PENSION SERVICES, INC.—See Kerkering, Barberio & Co.; *U.S. Private*, pg. 2290
LAKE NORMAN BENEFITS, INC.—See ABRY Partners, LLC; *U.S. Private*, pg. 43
LIFE PARTNERS HOLDINGS, INC.; *U.S. Private*, pg. 2448
LIFE PARTNERS, INC.—See Life Partners Holdings, Inc.; *U.S. Private*, pg. 2448
LIFEPLAN AUSTRALIA FRIENDLY SOCIETY LIMITED—See Australian Unity Limited; *Int'l*, pg. 723
LOMBARD INTERNATIONAL ADMINISTRATION SERVICES COMPANY, LLC—See Blackstone Inc.; *U.S. Public*, pg. 356
LONG TERM CARE GROUP, INC.—See ABRY Partners, LLC; *U.S. Private*, pg. 42
LT PLAN SERVICES, INC.—See LT Trust Company; *U.S. Private*, pg. 2509
LWP CLAIMS SOLUTIONS, INC.; *U.S. Private*, pg. 2519
MANAGED CARE NETWORK INC.; *U.S. Private*, pg. 2559
MANN & WATTERS, INC.—See New Mountain Capital, LLC; *U.S. Private*, pg. 2901
MASSACHUSETTS MUTUAL LIFE INSURANCE COMPANY; *U.S. Private*, pg. 2604
MCGREGOR & ASSOCIATES, INC.; *U.S. Private*, pg. 2635
MEDIMPACT HEALTHCARE SYSTEMS, INC.; *U.S. Private*, pg. 2657
MEDTRAK SERVICES, LLC—See New Rite Aid, LLC; *U.S. Private*, pg. 2905
MERITAIN HEALTH, INC.—See CVS Health Corporation; *U.S. Public*, pg. 615
MOORE FUND ADMINISTRATION (IOM) LIMITED—See AnaCap Financial Partners LLP; *Int'l*, pg. 445
MOORE FUND ADMINISTRATION (JERSEY) LIMITED—See AnaCap Financial Partners LLP; *Int'l*, pg. 445
MULTIPLAN INC.—See MultiPlan Corp.; *U.S. Public*, pg. 1486
THE MYR CORPORATION—See EqualizeRCM; *U.S. Private*, pg. 1415
NATIONAL GOVERNMENT SERVICES, INC.—See Elevance Health, Inc.; *U.S. Public*, pg. 730
NATIONAL UNDERWRITING AGENCIES PTY. LTD.—See Assurant, Inc.; *U.S. Public*, pg. 215
NATIXIS DISTRIBUTORS, L.P.—See Groupe BPCE; *Int'l*, pg. 3096
NEXTCARE CLAIMS MANAGEMENT LLC—See Allianz SE; *Int'l*, pg. 354
NORMAN & COMPANY, INC.; *U.S. Private*, pg. 2938
NORTHWEST PLAN SERVICES, INC.; *U.S. Private*, pg. 2961
THE NYHART COMPANY INC.; *U.S. Private*, pg. 4087
PACIFIC BENEFITS CONSULTANTS, INC.—See ABRY Partners, LLC; *U.S. Private*, pg. 42
PACIFIC SELECT DISTRIBUTORS, INC.—See Pacific Mutual Holding Company; *U.S. Private*, pg. 3069
PAYFLEX SYSTEMS USA, INC.—See ABRY Partners, LLC; *U.S. Private*, pg. 42
PBM-PLUS, INC.—See Consonance Capital Partners LLC; *U.S. Private*, pg. 1023
PEN-CAL ADMINISTRATORS, INC.—See Voya Financial, Inc.; *U.S. Public*, pg. 2311
PINNACLE INSURANCE PLC—See BNP Paribas SA; *Int'l*, pg. 1092
PMA MANAGEMENT CORPORATION OF NEW ENGLAND—See Old Republic International Corporation; *U.S. Public*, pg. 1568
PMA MANAGEMENT CORP.—See Old Republic International Corporation; *U.S. Public*, pg. 1568
PREMIUM CREDIT LIMITED—See Cinven Limited; *Int'l*, pg. 1613
PRINCIPAL FINANCIAL GROUP, INC. - APPLETON—See Principal Financial Group, Inc.; *U.S. Public*, pg. 1720
PROMED A.S.—See CompuGroup Medical SE & Co. KGaA; *Int'l*, pg. 1757
PTE ALLIANZ POLSKA S.A.—See Allianz SE; *Int'l*, pg. 356
QUINTILLION LIMITED—See U.S. Bancorp; *U.S. Public*, pg. 2212
RETIREMENT, LLC - SERIES TWO, OPERATIONS OFFICE—See Retirement, LLC - Series Two; *U.S. Private*, pg. 3412
RETIREMENT, LLC - SERIES TWO; *U.S. Private*, pg. 3412
THE RETIREMENT SYSTEMS OF ALABAMA; *U.S. Private*, pg. 4105
RICHARD HOGGS LINDLEY (HELLAS) GREECE LIMITED—See Lovell Minnick Partners LLC; *U.S. Private*, pg. 2502
RICHARD HOGGS LINDLEY (INDIA) LIMITED—See Lovell Minnick Partners LLC; *U.S. Private*, pg. 2502
RIGHTCHOICE BENEFIT ADMINISTRATORSSM—See Elevance Health, Inc.; *U.S. Public*, pg. 730
RISK MANAGEMENT CLAIM SERVICES—See Landstar System, Inc.; *U.S. Public*, pg. 1292
ROYAL HEALTH CARE OF LONG ISLAND, LLC—See Independent Living Systems, LLC.; *U.S. Private*, pg. 2059
SCHULKE INC.—See EQT AB; *Int'l*, pg. 2479
SECURITY ADMINISTRATORS, INC.—See Security Mutual Life Insurance Company of New York; *U.S. Private*, pg. 3596
SELMAN & COMPANY—See One80 Intermediaries LLC; *U.S. Private*, pg. 3024
SIMPLIFI, INC.; *U.S. Private*, pg. 3667
SPECTRUM PENSION CONSULTANTS, INC.—See Alliance Benefit Group, LLC; *U.S. Private*, pg. 181
ST. JAMES INSURANCE GROUP, INC.; *U.S. Private*, pg. 3771
TANGERINE PENSIONS LIMITED—See AXA S.A.; *Int'l*, pg. 757
TEACHER RETIREMENT SYSTEM OF TEXAS; *U.S. Private*, pg. 3944
TEDRO & ASSOCIATES, INC.—See Water Street Healthcare Partners, LLC; *U.S. Private*, pg. 4452

524292 — THIRD PARTY ADMINIS...

THREADNEEDLE PENSIONS LTD.—See Ameriprise Financial, Inc.; *U.S. Public*, pg. 114
TWG BENEFITS, INC.; *U.S. Private*, pg. 4264
UNITED GOVERNMENT SERVICES, LLC—See Elevance Health, Inc.; *U.S. Public*, pg. 730
UNITED RETIREMENT PLAN CONSULTANTS, INC.—See Aquiline Capital Partners LLC; *U.S. Private*, pg. 304
UNITED RETIREMENT PLAN CONSULTANTS, INC.—See Genstar Capital, LLC; *U.S. Private*, pg. 1675
USA MANAGED CARE ORGANIZATION; *U.S. Private*, pg. 4321
U.S. BANCORP FUND SERVICES, LTD.—See U.S. Bancorp; *U.S. Public*, pg. 2213
US HEALTH HOLDINGS LTD.; *U.S. Private*, pg. 4318
VANBRIDGE LLC—See Keystone Group, L.P.; *U.S. Private*, pg. 2298
VOYA INSTITUTIONAL PLAN SERVICES, LLC—See Voya Financial, Inc.; *U.S. Public*, pg. 2312
VOYA INSTITUTIONAL PLAN SERVICES, LLC—See Voya Financial, Inc.; *U.S. Public*, pg. 2312
THE WARRANTY GROUP DE MEXICO S.A. DE C.V.—See Assurant, Inc.; *U.S. Public*, pg. 216
THE WARRANTY GROUP KOREA, INC.—See Assurant, Inc.; *U.S. Public*, pg. 215
WELLS FARGO AUTO FINANCE—See Wells Fargo & Company; *U.S. Public*, pg. 2346
WESTERN ASSET MANAGEMENT COMPANY LIMITED—See Franklin Resources, Inc.; *U.S. Public*, pg. 882
WESTERN LITIGATION, INC.—See Arthur J. Gallagher & Co.; *U.S. Public*, pg. 208
WIMBERLY CLAIM SERVICES—See RYZE Claim Solutions LLC; *U.S. Private*, pg. 3511
WORKSITE COMMUNICATIONS—See Arthur J. Gallagher & Co.; *U.S. Public*, pg. 205
XEROX PENSIONS LTD—See Xerox Holdings Corporation; *U.S. Public*, pg. 2389

524298 — ALL OTHER INSURANCE RELATED ACTIVITIES

1-888-OHIOCOMP, INC.; *U.S. Private*, pg. 1
1ST GUARD CORPORATION—See Biglari Holdings Inc.; *U.S. Public*, pg. 331
AAA ALLIED INSURANCE SERVICES, INC.—See The American Automobile Association, Inc.; *U.S. Private*, pg. 3985
AAS GJENSIDIGE BALTIC—See Gjensidige Forsikring ASA; *Int'l*, pg. 2982
ABC AGENCY NETWORK, INC.—See The Allstate Corporation; *U.S. Public*, pg. 2033
ABC AGENCY NETWORK OF TEXAS, LLC—See The Allstate Corporation; *U.S. Public*, pg. 2033
ABDA INSURANCE; *Int'l*, pg. 58
ABN AMRO VERZEKERINGEN B.V.—See ABN AMRO Group N.V.; *Int'l*, pg. 65
ABN ASSURANTIE HOLDING B.V.—See ABN AMRO Group N.V.; *Int'l*, pg. 65
ABSA LIFE LIMITED—See Absa Group Limited; *Int'l*, pg. 69
ABU DHABI NATIONAL INSURANCE COMPANY; *Int'l*, pg. 72
ABU DHABI NATIONAL TAKAFUL CO. P.S.C; *Int'l*, pg. 73
ACCESS PLANS, INC.—See Aon plc; *Int'l*, pg. 489
ACCESS PLANS USA, INC.—See Aon plc; *Int'l*, pg. 489
ACCIDENT EXCHANGE LIMITED—See Accident Exchange Group Plc; *Int'l*, pg. 90
ACCIDENT FUND INSURANCE COMPANY OF AMERICA; *U.S. Private*, pg. 53
ACCURISK SOLUTIONS LLC—See Ryan Specialty Holdings, Inc.; *U.S. Public*, pg. 1827
ACE CAPITAL TITLE REINSURANCE COMPANY—See Chubb Limited; *Int'l*, pg. 1590
ACE FIRE UNDERWRITERS INSURANCE COMPANY—See Chubb Limited; *Int'l*, pg. 1590
ACE UNDERWRITING GROUP; *U.S. Private*, pg. 57
ACNOVER, S.L.; *Int'l*, pg. 107
ADAMJEE INSURANCE COMPANY LIMITED—See Adamjee Insurance Company Limited; *Int'l*, pg. 124
AD INSURANCE POLICY; *Int'l*, pg. 122
ADMINISTRATORS FOR THE PROFESSIONS, INC.; *U.S. Private*, pg. 81
ADP NATIONAL ACCOUNT SERVICES—See Automatic Data Processing, Inc.; *U.S. Public*, pg. 230
ADRIATIC OSIGURANJE D.D.; *Int'l*, pg. 153
AEGON DIRECT MARKETING SERVICES, INC.—See Aegon N.V.; *Int'l*, pg. 174
AEI INSURANCE GROUP PTY LTD—See AUB Group Limited; *Int'l*, pg. 697
AEMA GROUPE; *Int'l*, pg. 175
AEON INSURANCE SERVICE CO., LTD.—See AEON Co., Ltd.; *Int'l*, pg. 176
AGA ASSISTANCE AUSTRALIA PTY LTD—See Allianz SE; *Int'l*, pg. 342
AGA ASSISTANCE (INDIA) PRIVATE LIMITED—See Allianz SE; *Int'l*, pg. 341
AGAPE HEALTHCARE PARTNERS, LP—See CoVerica, Inc.; *U.S. Private*, pg. 1072

AGA SERVICES (THAILAND) CO., LTD.—See Allianz SE; *Int'l*, pg. 342
AGC INSURANCE MANAGEMENT CO., LTD.—See AGC Inc.; *Int'l*, pg. 202
AGCS HONG KONG—See Allianz SE; *Int'l*, pg. 344
AGCS MARINE INSURANCE COMPANY—See Allianz SE; *Int'l*, pg. 341
AGCS SINGAPORE—See Allianz SE; *Int'l*, pg. 341
AGCS SOUTH AFRICA LIMITED—See Allianz SE; *Int'l*, pg. 342
AGEAS INSURANCE LIMITED—See Ageas SA/NV; *Int'l*, pg. 205
AGENCY INTERMEDIARIES, INC.—See The Carlyle Group Inc.; *U.S. Public*, pg. 2047
AGENT ALLIANCE INSURANCE COMPANY—See The Allstate Corporation; *U.S. Public*, pg. 2033
AGF ASSURANCES LUXEMBOURG S.A.—See Allianz SE; *Int'l*, pg. 342
AGF BURKINA ASSURANCES—See Allianz SE; *Int'l*, pg. 342
AGF BURKINA ASSURANCES VIE—See Allianz SE; *Int'l*, pg. 342
AGF CAMEROUN ASSURANCES—See Allianz SE; *Int'l*, pg. 342
AGF CAMEROUN ASSURANCES VIE—See Allianz SE; *Int'l*, pg. 342
AGF CENTRAFRIQUE ASSURANCES—See Allianz SE; *Int'l*, pg. 342
AGF COTE D'IVOIRE ASSURANCES VIE—See Allianz SE; *Int'l*, pg. 342
AGF SENEGAL ASSURANCES VIE—See Allianz SE; *Int'l*, pg. 342
AGOSTINI INSURANCE BROKERS GRENADA LTD—See Aon plc; *Int'l*, pg. 489
AGOSTINI INSURANCE BROKERS LTD—See Aon plc; *Int'l*, pg. 489
AGOSTINI INSURANCE BROKERS ST. LUCIA LTD—See Aon plc; *Int'l*, pg. 489
AGRANI INSURANCE COMPANY LIMITED; *Int'l*, pg. 214
AGRI-SERVICES AGENCY, LLC—See Dairy Farmers of America, Inc.; *U.S. Private*, pg. 1145
AHLIA INSURANCE COMPANY (S.A.); *Int'l*, pg. 223
AIA COMPANY, LIMITED—See AIA Group Limited; *Int'l*, pg. 227
AIG CAPITAL CORPORATION—See American International Group, Inc.; *U.S. Public*, pg. 104
AIG EUROPE LIMITED—See American International Group, Inc.; *U.S. Public*, pg. 104
AIG EUROPE (U.K.) LIMITED—See American International Group, Inc.; *U.S. Public*, pg. 104
AIG INSURANCE COMPANY OF CANADA—See American International Group, Inc.; *U.S. Public*, pg. 104
AIG INSURANCE LIMITED—See American International Group, Inc.; *U.S. Public*, pg. 105
AIG INSURANCE NEW ZEALAND LIMITED—See American International Group, Inc.; *U.S. Public*, pg. 105
AIG KENYA INSURANCE COMPANY LIMITED—See American International Group, Inc.; *U.S. Public*, pg. 105
AIG LIFE SOUTH AFRICA LIMITED—See American International Group, Inc.; *U.S. Public*, pg. 105
AIG MALAYSIA INSURANCE BERHAD—See American International Group, Inc.; *U.S. Public*, pg. 105
AIG PROPERTY CASUALTY INSURANCE AGENCY, INC.—See American International Group, Inc.; *U.S. Public*, pg. 106
AIG SEGUROS BRASIL S.A.—See American International Group, Inc.; *U.S. Public*, pg. 106
AIG TAIWAN INSURANCE CO., LTD.—See American International Group, Inc.; *U.S. Public*, pg. 105
AIG TRAVEL ASSIST, INC.—See American International Group, Inc.; *U.S. Public*, pg. 106
AIG UGANDA LIMITED—See American International Group, Inc.; *U.S. Public*, pg. 106
AIG VIETNAM INSURANCE COMPANY LIMITED—See American International Group, Inc.; *U.S. Public*, pg. 105
AIM GIBRALTAR LTD.—See Aon plc; *Int'l*, pg. 488
AIR CAPITAL INSURANCE, LLC—See GTCR LLC; *U.S. Private*, pg. 1802
AIRPORT ASSEKURANZ VERMITTLUNGS-GMBH—See Fraport AG; *Int'l*, pg. 2764
AIR WORLDWIDE CORPORATION—See Verisk Analytics, Inc.; *U.S. Public*, pg. 2282
AIS MANAGEMENT LLC—See Mercury General Corporation; *U.S. Public*, pg. 1421
AIX HOLDINGS, INC.—See The Hanover Insurance Group, Inc.; *U.S. Public*, pg. 2087
AIX, INC.—See The Hanover Insurance Group, Inc.; *U.S. Public*, pg. 2087
AIX SPECIALTY INSURANCE COMPANY—See The Hanover Insurance Group, Inc.; *U.S. Public*, pg. 2087
AKZO NOBEL INSURANCE MANAGEMENT B.V.—See Akzo Nobel N.V.; *Int'l*, pg. 271
AL AMEEN INSURANCE COMPANY; *Int'l*, pg. 275
ALBA ALLGEMEINE VERSICHERUNGS-GESELLSCHAFT—See Allianz SE; *Int'l*, pg. 350
ALBATRAOS VERSICHERUNGSDIENSTE GMBH—See Deutsche Lufthansa AG; *Int'l*, pg. 2066
ALBORZ INSURANCE COMPANY; *Int'l*, pg. 299

AL BUHAIRA NATIONAL INSURANCE COMPANY P.S.C.; *Int'l*, pg. 276
ALDHAFRA INSURANCE COMPANY P.S.C.; *Int'l*, pg. 304
ALE SOLUTIONS, INC.—See Corpay, Inc.; *U.S. Public*, pg. 579
ALEXANDER FORBES COMPENSATION TECHNOLOGIES (PTY) LTD—See Alexander Forbes Group Holdings Limited; *Int'l*, pg. 306
AL FUJAIRAH NATIONAL INSURANCE COMPANY (P.S.C.); *Int'l*, pg. 277
AL-HAMARA'A INSURANCE COMPANY; *Int'l*, pg. 285
ALIGHT HEALTH MARKET INSURANCE SOLUTIONS INC.—See Alight, Inc.; *U.S. Public*, pg. 75
AL JAZIRA TAKAFUL TA'AWUNI COMPANY; *Int'l*, pg. 280
AL KHALEEJ TAKAFUL INSURANCE COMPANY Q.P.S.C.; *Int'l*, pg. 280
AL KHAZNA INSURANCE COMPANY - ABU DHABI TRAFFIC—See Al Khazna Insurance Company P.S.C.; *Int'l*, pg. 280
AL KHAZNA INSURANCE COMPANY - AL AIN BRANCH—See Al Khazna Insurance Company P.S.C.; *Int'l*, pg. 280
AL KHAZNA INSURANCE COMPANY - AL AIN TRAFFIC—See Al Khazna Insurance Company P.S.C.; *Int'l*, pg. 281
AL KHAZNA INSURANCE COMPANY - AL MUSSAFAH LIGHT VEHICLE—See Al Khazna Insurance Company P.S.C.; *Int'l*, pg. 281
AL KHAZNA INSURANCE COMPANY - AL MUSSAFAH—See Al Khazna Insurance Company P.S.C.; *Int'l*, pg. 281
AL KHAZNA INSURANCE COMPANY - AL WAGAN—See Al Khazna Insurance Company P.S.C.; *Int'l*, pg. 281
AL KHAZNA INSURANCE COMPANY - BEDA ZAYED—See Al Khazna Insurance Company P.S.C.; *Int'l*, pg. 281
AL KHAZNA INSURANCE COMPANY - DUBAI—See Al Khazna Insurance Company P.S.C.; *Int'l*, pg. 281
AL KHAZNA INSURANCE COMPANY P.S.C.; *Int'l*, pg. 280
ALLEGIANCE TITLE COMPANY—See First Title Abstract & Services, LLC; *U.S. Private*, pg. 1530
ALLIANCE INSURANCE (PSC); *Int'l*, pg. 340
ALLIANCE UNITED INSURANCE SERVICES, INC.—See Kemper Corporation; *U.S. Public*, pg. 1220
ALLIANZ AUTOMOTIVE SERVICES GMBH—See Allianz SE; *Int'l*, pg. 344
ALLIANZ AUTOWELT GMBH—See Allianz SE; *Int'l*, pg. 344
ALLIANZ BERATUNGS- UND VERTRIEBS-AG—See Allianz SE; *Int'l*, pg. 344
ALLIANZ BULGARIA HOLDING—See Allianz SE; *Int'l*, pg. 344
ALLIANZ BUSINESS SERVICES LIMITED—See Allianz SE; *Int'l*, pg. 348
ALLIANZ CAPITAL PARTNERS GMBH—See Allianz SE; *Int'l*, pg. 344
ALLIANZ CHINA GENERAL INSURANCE COMPANY LTD.—See Allianz SE; *Int'l*, pg. 344
ALLIANZ CLIMATE SOLUTIONS GMBH—See Allianz SE; *Int'l*, pg. 346
ALLIANZ COTE D'IVOIRE ASSURANCES—See Allianz SE; *Int'l*, pg. 344
ALLIANZ C.P. GENERAL INSURANCE CO., LTD.—See Allianz SE; *Int'l*, pg. 344
ALLIANZ C.P. GENERAL INSURANCE CO., LTD.—See Charoen Pokphand Group Co., Ltd.; *Int'l*, pg. 1453
ALLIANZ ELEMENTAR VERSICHERUNGS AG—See Allianz SE; *Int'l*, pg. 344
ALLIANZ FRANCE—See Allianz SE; *Int'l*, pg. 345
ALLIANZ GLOBAL ASSISTANCE S.A.S.—See Allianz SE; *Int'l*, pg. 345
ALLIANZ GLOBAL BENEFITS GMBH—See Allianz SE; *Int'l*, pg. 345
ALLIANZ GLOBAL CORPORATE & SPECIALTY, NATIONAL INSURANCE COMPANY—See Allianz SE; *Int'l*, pg. 346
ALLIANZ HAYAT VE EMEKLILIK A.S.—See Allianz SE; *Int'l*, pg. 345
ALLIANZ INSURANCE COMPANY OF SINGAPORE PTE LTD—See Allianz SE; *Int'l*, pg. 348
ALLIANZ INSURANCE PLC—See Allianz SE; *Int'l*, pg. 348
ALLIANZ MALI ASSURANCES—See Allianz SE; *Int'l*, pg. 349
ALLIANZ NEDERLAND GROEP NV—See Allianz SE; *Int'l*, pg. 349
ALLIANZ NEDERLAND LEVENSVERZEKERING NV—See Allianz SE; *Int'l*, pg. 349
ALLIANZ NEDERLAND SCHADEVERZEKERING NV—See Allianz SE; *Int'l*, pg. 349
ALLIANZ NORTHERN IRELAND LTD—See Allianz SE; *Int'l*, pg. 349
ALLIANZ PRIVATE KRANKENVERSICHERUNGS-AG—See Allianz SE; *Int'l*, pg. 349
ALLIANZ RISK AUDIT—See Allianz SE; *Int'l*, pg. 348
ALLIANZ SAUDI FRANSI COOPERATIVE INSURANCE COMPANY—See Allianz SE; *Int'l*, pg. 345
ALLIANZ SENEGAL ASSURANCES—See Allianz SE; *Int'l*, pg. 350
ALLIANZ SIGORTA A.S.—See Allianz SE; *Int'l*, pg. 345
ALLIANZ S.P.A.—See Allianz SE; *Int'l*, pg. 350

N.A.I.C.S. INDEX 524298 — ALL OTHER INSURANCE...

ALLIANZ SUISSE INSURANCE COMPANY—See Allianz SE; *Int'l*, pg. 350
ALLIANZ TAIWAN LIFE INSURANCE COMPANY LTD.—See Allianz SE; *Int'l*, pg. 350
ALLIANZ-TIRIAC ASIGURARI S.A.—See Allianz SE; *Int'l*, pg. 351
ALLIANZ TOGO ASSURANCES—See Allianz SE; *Int'l*, pg. 350
ALLIANZ (UK) LIMITED—See Allianz SE; *Int'l*, pg. 343
ALLIANZ UKRAINE SLC—See Allianz SE; *Int'l*, pg. 354
ALLIANZ ZAGREB D.D.—See Allianz SE; *Int'l*, pg. 351
ALLIANZ ZENTRUM FUER TECHNIK GMBH—See Allianz SE; *Int'l*, pg. 351
ALLIED RISK MANAGEMENT LIMITED—See Arthur J. Gallagher & Co.; *U.S. Public*, pg. 203
ALLIED WORLD ASSURANCE COMPANY, LTD—See Fairfax Financial Holdings Limited; *Int'l*, pg. 2606
ALLIED WORLD ASSURANCE COMPANY (U.S.) INC.—See Fairfax Financial Holdings Limited; *Int'l*, pg. 2605
ALLIED WORLD ASSURANCE HOLDINGS (IRELAND) LTD—See Fairfax Financial Holdings Limited; *Int'l*, pg. 2606
ALLIED WORLD ASSURANCE HOLDINGS (U.S.) INC.—See Fairfax Financial Holdings Limited; *Int'l*, pg. 2606
ALLIED WORLD SPECIALTY INSURANCE COMPANY—See Fairfax Financial Holdings Limited; *Int'l*, pg. 2606
ALLIED WORLD SURPLUS LINES INSURANCE COMPANY—See Fairfax Financial Holdings Limited; *Int'l*, pg. 2606
ALLSTATE NORTHBROOK INDEMNITY COMPANY—See The Allstate Corporation; *U.S. Public*, pg. 115
ALL WEB LEADS, INC.—See Great Hill Partners, L.P.; *U.S. Private*, pg. 1763
AL MADINA INSURANCE COMPANY SAOG; *Int'l*, pg. 281
AL-MANARA INSURANCE PLC CO.; *Int'l*, pg. 286
AL MASHRIQ FINANCIAL INVESTMENT CO. S.A.L.—See Arabia Insurance Co.; *Int'l*, pg. 533
AL-NISR AL-ARABI INSURANCE—See Arab Bank plc; *Int'l*, pg. 529
ALPER CONSULTORIA E CORRETORA DE SEGUROS S.A.; *Int'l*, pg. 366
ALPHACAT MANAGERS LTD.—See American International Group, Inc.; *U.S. Public*, pg. 107
ALPHA INSURANCE SA—See Enstar Group Limited; *Int'l*, pg. 2449
ALPINE INSURANCE ASSOCIATES, INC.—See GTCR LLC; *U.S. Private*, pg. 1802
AL RAJHI COMPANY FOR COOPERATIVE INSURANCE; *Int'l*, pg. 282
AL-SAGR NATIONAL INSURANCE COMPANY; *Int'l*, pg. 288
AL-SALAMA INSURANCE CO., LTD.; *Int'l*, pg. 288
ALTERIS INSURANCE SERVICES, INC.—See Brookfield Reinsurance Ltd.; *Int'l*, pg. 1193
ALTERNATIVE RISK MANAGEMENT LTD.; *U.S. Private*, pg. 207
AL-WATANIA INSURANCE COMPANY YSC; *Int'l*, pg. 289
AL WATHBA NATIONAL INSURANCE COMPANY P.S.C.; *Int'l*, pg. 283
AMCICO POJISTOVNA A.S.—See MetLife, Inc.; *U.S. Public*, pg. 1429
AMCOM INSURANCE SERVICES, INC.—See Stone Point Capital LLC; *U.S. Private*, pg. 3820
AMERICAN ACCEPTANCE CORP.—See Unico American Corporation; *U.S. Public*, pg. 2225
AMERICAN COASTAL INSURANCE COMPANY—See American Coastal Insurance Corporation; *U.S. Public*, pg. 98
AMERICAN CORNERSTONE INSURANCE LLC—See RightSure Insurance Group; *U.S. Private*, pg. 3436
AMERICAN FIRE RESTORATION, LLC; *U.S. Private*, pg. 234
AMERICAN HERITAGE LIFE INVESTMENT CORPORATION—See The Allstate Corporation; *U.S. Public*, pg. 2033
AMERICAN INDEPENDENT NETWORK INSURANCE COMPANY OF NEW YORK—See Penn Treaty American Corporation; *U.S. Private*, pg. 3135
AMERICAN INSURANCE ACQUISITION INC.—See Atlas Financial Holdings, Inc.; *U.S. Public*, pg. 224
AMERICAN MERCURY LLOYDS INSURANCE COMPANY—See Mercury General Corporation; *U.S. Public*, pg. 1421
AMERICAN NATIONAL LIFE INSURANCE COMPANY OF TEXAS—See Brookfield Corporation; *Int'l*, pg. 1174
AMERICAN NATIONAL PROPERTY & CASUALTY COMPANY—See Brookfield Corporation; *Int'l*, pg. 1174
AMERICAN NETWORK INSURANCE COMPANY—See Penn Treaty American Corporation; *U.S. Private*, pg. 3135
AMERICAN PENSION SERVICES, INC.; *U.S. Private*, pg. 243
AMERICAP INSURANCE GROUP, LLC—See Galiot Insurance Services, Inc.; *U.S. Private*, pg. 1637
AMERICA'S HEALTH CARE PLAN/RX AGENCY, INC.—See Aon plc; *Int'l*, pg. 489
AMERIPRISE AUTO & HOME INSURANCE AGENCY INC.—See American Family Mutual Insurance Company; *U.S. Private*, pg. 233
AMERISAFE RISK SERVICES, INC.—See AMERISAFE, Inc.; *U.S. Public*, pg. 115
AMFED COMPANIES, LLC; *U.S. Private*, pg. 262
AMG INSURANCE BERHAD—See AMMB Holdings Berhad; *Int'l*, pg. 429
AMP INSURANCE INVESTMENT HOLDINGS PTY LIMITED—See AMP Limited; *Int'l*, pg. 432
AMTRUST AT LLOYD'S LIMITED—See Stone Point Capital LLC; *U.S. Private*, pg. 3820
AMTRUST CLAIMS MANAGEMENT SRL.—See Stone Point Capital LLC; *U.S. Private*, pg. 3820
AMTRUST CORPORATE MEMBER LIMITED—See Stone Point Capital LLC; *U.S. Private*, pg. 3820
AMTRUST EUROPE LEGAL, LTD.—See Stone Point Capital LLC; *U.S. Private*, pg. 3820
AMTRUST INSURANCE LUXEMBOURG S.A—See Stone Point Capital LLC; *U.S. Private*, pg. 3820
AMTRUST INSURANCE SPAIN, S. L.—See Liberty Mutual Holding Company Inc.; *U.S. Private*, pg. 2445
AMTRUST INTERNATIONAL UNDERWRITERS LIMITED—See Stone Point Capital LLC; *U.S. Private*, pg. 3820
AMTRUST NORDIC AB—See Stone Point Capital LLC; *U.S. Private*, pg. 3820
AMTRUST NORTH AMERICA OF FLORIDA, INC.—See Stone Point Capital LLC; *U.S. Private*, pg. 3820
AMTRUST RE ARIES S.A.—See Stone Point Capital LLC; *U.S. Private*, pg. 3820
AMWINS GROUP, INC.; *U.S. Private*, pg. 269
AMYNTA AGENCY, INC.—See Fairfax Financial Holdings Limited; *Int'l*, pg. 2606
AMYNTA SURETY SOLUTIONS—See Fairfax Financial Holdings Limited; *Int'l*, pg. 2606
AMZ FINANCIAL INSURANCE SERVICES, LLC; *U.S. Private*, pg. 270
ANADOLU ANONIM TURK SIGORTA SIRKETI; *Int'l*, pg. 445
ANICOM HOLDINGS, INC.; *Int'l*, pg. 471
ANSWER FINANCIAL, INC.—See The Allstate Corporation; *U.S. Public*, pg. 2033
ANTHEM BEHAVIORAL HEALTH—See Elevance Health, Inc.; *U.S. Public*, pg. 729
ANTHEM DENTAL—See Elevance Health, Inc.; *U.S. Public*, pg. 729
ANTHEM HEALTH PLANS, INC.—See Elevance Health, Inc.; *U.S. Public*, pg. 729
ANTHEM HEALTH PLANS OF KENTUCKY—See Elevance Health, Inc.; *U.S. Public*, pg. 729
ANTHEM HEALTH PLANS OF NEW HAMPSHIRE—See Elevance Health, Inc.; *U.S. Public*, pg. 729
ANTHEM VISION—See Elevance Health, Inc.; *U.S. Public*, pg. 729
ANTICIMEX FORSAKRINGAR AB—See EQT AB; *Int'l*, pg. 2468
ANV SYNDICATE MANAGEMENT LIMITED—See ACNOVER, S.L.; *Int'l*, pg. 107
AON (BERMUDA) LTD.—See Aon plc; *Int'l*, pg. 489
AON BETEILIGUNGSMANAGEMENT DEUTSCHLAND GMBH & CO. KG—See Aon plc; *Int'l*, pg. 490
AON CANADA INC.—See Aon plc; *Int'l*, pg. 490
AON CENTRE FOR INNOVATION AND ANALYTICS LTD—See Aon plc; *Int'l*, pg. 490
AON CONSULTING (BENEFITS) LIMITED—See Aon plc; *Int'l*, pg. 490
AON CORPORATION—See Aon plc; *Int'l*, pg. 488
AON CORP.—See Aon plc; *Int'l*, pg. 491
AON CREDIT INTERNATIONAL SCHWEIZ AG—See Aon plc; *Int'l*, pg. 491
AON DEUTSCHLAND BETEILIGUNGS GMBH—See Aon plc; *Int'l*, pg. 491
AON DIRECT GROUP INC.—See Aon plc; *Int'l*, pg. 491
AON GREECE S.A.—See Aon plc; *Int'l*, pg. 491
AON HEWITT FINANCIAL ADVICE LTD.—See Aon plc; *Int'l*, pg. 491
AON HEWITT MALAYSIA SDN. BHD—See Alight, Inc.; *U.S. Public*, pg. 76
AON HEWITT (PNG) LTD.—See Alight, Inc.; *U.S. Public*, pg. 76
AON HEWITT (SWITZERLAND) S.A.—See Alight, Inc.; *U.S. Public*, pg. 76
AON HOLDING DEUTSCHLAND GMBH—See Aon plc; *Int'l*, pg. 491
AON HOLDINGS HONG KONG LIMITED—See Aon plc; *Int'l*, pg. 491
AON HOLDINGS LIMITED—See Aon plc; *Int'l*, pg. 491
AON INSURANCE MANAGERS (DUBLIN) LTD.—See Aon plc; *Int'l*, pg. 492
AON INSURANCE MANAGERS (ISLE OF MAN) LTD.—See Aon plc; *Int'l*, pg. 492
AON INSURANCE MANAGERS (LIECHTENSTEIN) AG—See Aon plc; *Int'l*, pg. 492
AON INSURANCE MANAGERS (MALTA) —See Aon plc; *Int'l*, pg. 492
AON INSURANCE MANAGERS (SHANNON) LIMITED—See Aon plc; *Int'l*, pg. 492
AON INSURANCE MANAGERS (SINGAPORE) PTE LTD—See Aon plc; *Int'l*, pg. 492
AON INSURANCE MANAGERS (SWITZERLAND) AG—See Aon plc; *Int'l*, pg. 492
AON JAUCH & HUEBENER GMBH—See Aon plc; *Int'l*, pg. 491
AON JAUCH & HUEBENER GMBH—See Aon plc; *Int'l*, pg. 491
AON KENYA INSURANCE BROKERS LTD—See Aon plc; *Int'l*, pg. 492
AON LIMPOPO (PTY) LTD—See Aon plc; *Int'l*, pg. 492
AON MAJAN LLC—See Aon plc; *Int'l*, pg. 492
AON MANAGEMENT SOLUTIONS SAU—See Aon plc; *Int'l*, pg. 492
AON MIDDLE EAST CO LLC—See Aon plc; *Int'l*, pg. 492
AON NATIONAL FLOOD SERVICES, INC.—See Aon plc; *Int'l*, pg. 492
AON PMI INTERNATIONAL LIMITED—See Aon plc; *Int'l*, pg. 492
AON POLSKA SERVICES SP. Z.O.O.—See Aon plc; *Int'l*, pg. 492
AON PREMIUM FINANCE, LLC—See Aon plc; *Int'l*, pg. 492
AON REED STENHOUSE, INC.—See Aon plc; *Int'l*, pg. 491
AON REINSURANCE SOLUTIONS MENA LIMITED—See Aon plc; *Int'l*, pg. 490
AON RISK SERVICES INC.—See Aon plc; *Int'l*, pg. 493
AON RISK SERVICES INC.—See Aon plc; *Int'l*, pg. 493
AON RISK SERVICES (NI) LIMITED—See Aon plc; *Int'l*, pg. 492
AON SINGAPORE (BROKING CENTRE) PTE. LTD.—See Aon plc; *Int'l*, pg. 494
AON SINGAPORE PTE LTD—See Aon plc; *Int'l*, pg. 493
AON SLOVAKIA—See Aon plc; *Int'l*, pg. 491
AON SOLUTIONS SWEDEN AB—See Alight, Inc.; *U.S. Public*, pg. 76
AON SPECIALIST SERVICES PRIVATE LIMITED—See Aon plc; *Int'l*, pg. 494
AON SPECIALTY RE, INC.—See Aon plc; *Int'l*, pg. 494
AON TARIZEAU INC.—See Aon plc; *Int'l*, pg. 490
AON US HOLDINGS, INC.—See Aon plc; *Int'l*, pg. 494
AON VERSICHERUNGSAGENTUR DEUTSCHLAND GMBH—See Aon plc; *Int'l*, pg. 494
ARABIA INSURANCE COMPANY; *Int'l*, pg. 533
ARABIA INSURANCE COMPANY - SYRIA S.A.—See Arabia Insurance Co.; *Int'l*, pg. 533
ARABIA INSURANCE CO.; *Int'l*, pg. 533
ARAB JORDANIAN INSURANCE GROUP; *Int'l*, pg. 530
ARAB LIFE & ACCIDENT INSURANCE COMPANY P.S.C.; *Int'l*, pg. 531
ARAB ORIENT INSURANCE CO. LTD.—See Fairfax Financial Holdings Limited; *Int'l*, pg. 2607
ARAB UNION INTERNATIONAL INSURANCE CO. LTD.; *Int'l*, pg. 532
ARCH INSURANCE COMPANY (EUROPE) LTD.—See Arch Capital Group Ltd.; *Int'l*, pg. 546
ARCH INSURANCE GROUP, INC.—See Arch Capital Group Ltd.; *Int'l*, pg. 546
ARCH REINSURANCE COMPANY INC.—See Arch Capital Group Ltd.; *Int'l*, pg. 546
ARGO DIRECT, LTD.—See Brookfield Reinsurance Ltd.; *Int'l*, pg. 1193
ARGONAUT CLAIMS MANAGEMENT, LLC—See Brookfield Reinsurance Ltd.; *Int'l*, pg. 1194
ARGONAUT LIMITED RISK INSURANCE COMPANY—See Brookfield Reinsurance Ltd.; *Int'l*, pg. 1194
ARGONAUT-MIDWEST INSURANCE COMPANY—See Brookfield Reinsurance Ltd.; *Int'l*, pg. 1194
ARGONAUT-SOUTHWEST INSURANCE COMPANY—See Brookfield Reinsurance Ltd.; *Int'l*, pg. 1194
ARGO SEGURAS BRASIL, SA—See GP Investments, Ltd.; *Int'l*, pg. 3045
ARGO SOLUTIONS, SA—See Brookfield Reinsurance Ltd.; *Int'l*, pg. 1194
ARGUS GROUP HOLDINGS LIMITED; *Int'l*, pg. 563
ARTEX RISK SOLUTIONS, INC.—See Arthur J. Gallagher & Co.; *U.S. Public*, pg. 202
ARTHUR J. GALLAGHER & CO. (BERMUDA) LIMITED—See Arthur J. Gallagher & Co.; *U.S. Public*, pg. 202
ARTHUR J. GALLAGHER INTERMEDIARIES (BERMUDA) LIMITED—See Arthur J. Gallagher & Co.; *U.S. Public*, pg. 202
ARTHUR J. GALLAGHER MANAGEMENT (BERMUDA) LIMITED—See Arthur J. Gallagher & Co.; *U.S. Public*, pg. 202
ARTHUR J. GALLAGHER MIDDLE EAST BSC—See Arthur J. Gallagher & Co.; *U.S. Public*, pg. 202
ARTHUR J. GALLAGHER (UK) LIMITED—See Arthur J. Gallagher & Co.; *U.S. Public*, pg. 202
ASCENSION BENEFITS & INSURANCE SOLUTIONS—See Aquiline Capital Partners LLC; *U.S. Private*, pg. 305
ASIA INSURANCE CO.; *Int'l*, pg. 613
ASIA INSURANCE LIMITED; *Int'l*, pg. 613
ASIAN LIFE INSURANCE COMPANY; *Int'l*, pg. 618

524298 — ALL OTHER INSURANCE...

ASIA PACIFIC GENERAL INSURANCE CO. LIMITED; *Int'l*, pg. 613
ASKARI GENERAL INSURANCE COMPANY LIMITED; *Int'l*, pg. 621
ASPEN SPECIALTY INSURANCE SOLUTIONS, LLC—See Apollo Global Management, Inc.; *U.S. Public*, pg. 147
ASPIRE FINANCIAL SERVICES, LLC—See PCS Retirement, LLC; *U.S. Private*, pg. 3121
ASPIRION HEALTH RESOURCES, LLC—See Linden LLC; *U.S. Private*, pg. 2460
ASPIS INSURANCE BROKERAGE SA—See Eurobank Ergasias Services and Holdings S.A.; *Int'l*, pg. 2533
ASSICURAZIONI GENERALI—See Assicurazioni Generali S.p.A.; *Int'l*, pg. 643
ASSICURAZIONI GENERALI S.P.A. - GENERALI GLOBAL LONDON UNIT—See Assicurazioni Generali S.p.A.; *Int'l*, pg. 643
ASSIGNED RISK SOLUTIONS LTD.—See The Allstate Corporation; *U.S. Public*, pg. 2033
ASSOCIATED ACCEPTANCE, INC.—See Rush Enterprises, Inc.; *U.S. Public*, pg. 1826
ASSOCIATED FUIG LLC; *U.S. Private*, pg. 355
ASSOCIATED PENSION CONSULTANTS, INC.—See Lightyear Capital LLC; *U.S. Private*, pg. 2454
ASSURANCEAMERICA CORPORATION; *U.S. Private*, pg. 359
ASSURANCES BIAT—See Banque Internationale Arabe de Tunisie; *Int'l*, pg. 854
ASSURANCES GENERALES DU LAOS—See Allianz SE; *Int'l*, pg. 343
ASSURANT ARGENTINA COMPANIA DE SEGUROS SOCIEDAD ANONIMA—See Assurant, Inc.; *U.S. Public*, pg. 214
ASSURANT DEUTSCHLAND GMBH—See Assurant, Inc.; *U.S. Public*, pg. 215
ASSURANT LIFE OF CANADA—See Assurant, Inc.; *U.S. Public*, pg. 215
ASSURANT SERVICES IRELAND, LTD.—See Assurant, Inc.; *U.S. Public*, pg. 215
ASSURANT SOLUTIONS—See Assurant, Inc.; *U.S. Public*, pg. 215
ASSURANT SOLUTIONS SPAIN, S.A.—See Assurant, Inc.; *U.S. Public*, pg. 215
ASSURANT SPECIALTY PROPERTY—See Assurant, Inc.; *U.S. Public*, pg. 215
ASSURE AMERICA CORP.; *U.S. Private*, pg. 359
ASSURIA LIFE (GY) INC.—See Assuria N.V.; *Int'l*, pg. 650
ASTREE ASSURANCES—See Allianz SE; *Int'l*, pg. 343
ASURANSI MULTI ARTHA GUNA TBK; *Int'l*, pg. 663
ATHENE LEBENSVERSICHERUNG AG—See Apollo Global Management, Inc.; *U.S. Public*, pg. 147
ATHENE USA CORPORATION—See Apollo Global Management, Inc.; *U.S. Public*, pg. 147
ATLANTICA COMPANHIA DE SEGUROS S.A.—See Banco Bradesco S.A.; *Int'l*, pg. 819
ATLANTIC INSURANCE COMPANY PUBLIC LTD; *Int'l*, pg. 675
ATLAS COPCO REINSURANCE SA—See Atlas Copco AB; *Int'l*, pg. 680
ATRADIUS CREDIT INSURANCE NV—See Grupo Catalana Occidente, S.A.; *Int'l*, pg. 3124
ATRADIUS—See Grupo Catalana Occidente, S.A.; *Int'l*, pg. 3124
ATRADIUS—See Grupo Catalana Occidente, S.A.; *Int'l*, pg. 3124
ATRIUM RISK MANAGEMENT SERVICES (WASHINGTON) LTD.—See Enstar Group Limited; *Int'l*, pg. 2448
ATRIUM UNDERWRITERS LTD.—See Enstar Group Limited; *Int'l*, pg. 2448
AUDATEX CANADA, ULC—See Vista Equity Partners, LLC; *U.S. Private*, pg. 4400
AUDATEX NORTH AMERICA, INC.—See Vista Equity Partners, LLC; *U.S. Private*, pg. 4400
AUDATEX SWITZERLAND GMBH—See Vista Equity Partners, LLC; *U.S. Private*, pg. 4400
AUDATEX (UK) LIMITED—See Vista Equity Partners, LLC; *U.S. Private*, pg. 4399
AUDIT SERVICES, INC.—See Aquiline Capital Partners LLC; *U.S. Private*, pg. 305
AUL REINSURANCE MANAGEMENT SERVICES, LLC—See American United Mutual Insurance Holding Company; *U.S. Private*, pg. 258
AUSTBROKERS CE MCDONALD PTY. LTD.—See AUB Group Limited; *Int'l*, pg. 698
AUSTBROKERS CORPORATE PTY. LTD.—See AUB Group Limited; *Int'l*, pg. 698
AUSTBROKERS PTY. LTD.—See AUB Group Limited; *Int'l*, pg. 698
AUSTRALIAN ASSOCIATED MOTOR INSURERS LIMITED; *Int'l*, pg. 721
AUTO CLUB INSURANCE ASSOCIATION—See The American Automobile Association, Inc.; *U.S. Private*, pg. 3985
AUTOTOTAL BIZTOSITASI SZOLGALTATO KFT.—See Assicurazioni Generali S.p.A.; *Int'l*, pg. 646
AVIVA ANNUITY UK LIMITED—See Aviva plc; *Int'l*, pg. 745
AVIVA ASSURANCES SA—See Aema Groupe; *Int'l*, pg. 175
AVIVA HEALTH UK LIMITED—See Aviva plc; *Int'l*, pg. 745
AVIVA INSURANCE IRELAND DESIGNATED ACTIVITY COMPANY—See Aviva plc; *Int'l*, pg. 745
AVIVA INSURANCE LIMITED—See Aviva plc; *Int'l*, pg. 745
AVIVA INSURANCE UK LIMITED—See Aviva plc; *Int'l*, pg. 745
AVIVA ITALIA HOLDING S.P.A.—See Aviva plc; *Int'l*, pg. 746
AVIVA ITALIA S.P.A—See Allianz SE; *Int'l*, pg. 350
AVIVA LIMITED—See Aviva plc; *Int'l*, pg. 746
AVIVA TOWARZYSTWO UBEZPIECZEN NA ZYCIE SA—See Aviva plc; *Int'l*, pg. 746
AVIVA TOWARZYSTWO UBEZPIECZEN OGOLNYCH SA—See Aviva plc; *Int'l*, pg. 746
AVIVA VIE S.A.—See Aema Groupe; *Int'l*, pg. 175
AVLA PERU COMPANIA DE SEGUROS SA; *Int'l*, pg. 748
AW UNDERWRITERS INC.—See Fairfax Financial Holdings Limited; *Int'l*, pg. 2606
AXA ART FRANCE—See AXA S.A.; *Int'l*, pg. 754
AXA ART INSURANCE CORPORATION - CANADA—See AXA S.A.; *Int'l*, pg. 754
AXA ART INSURANCE CORPORATION—See AXA S.A.; *Int'l*, pg. 754
AXA ART LUXEMBOURG—See AXA S.A.; *Int'l*, pg. 754
AXA ART - NEDERLAND—See AXA S.A.; *Int'l*, pg. 754
AXA ART—See AXA S.A.; *Int'l*, pg. 754
AXA ART VERSICHERUNG AG—See AXA S.A.; *Int'l*, pg. 754
AXA ART VERSICHERUNG AG—See AXA S.A.; *Int'l*, pg. 757
AXA ASSISTANCE CHILE S.A.—See AXA S.A.; *Int'l*, pg. 754
AXA ASSISTANCE DEUTSCHLAND GMBH—See AXA S.A.; *Int'l*, pg. 754
AXA ASSISTANCE JAPAN CO., LTD.—See AXA S.A.; *Int'l*, pg. 754
AXA ASSISTANCE PANAMA SA—See AXA S.A.; *Int'l*, pg. 754
AXA ASSISTANCE—See AXA S.A.; *Int'l*, pg. 754
AXA ASSISTANCE (UK) LTD—See AXA S.A.; *Int'l*, pg. 754
AXA AURORA IBERICA S.A. DE SEGUROS Y REASEGUROS—See AXA S.A.; *Int'l*, pg. 757
AXA CESSIONS—See AXA S.A.; *Int'l*, pg. 755
AXA CHINA REGION INSURANCE COMPANY (BERMUDA) LIMITED—See AXA S.A.; *Int'l*, pg. 755
AXA CORPORATE SOLUTIONS ASSURANCE S.A—See AXA S.A.; *Int'l*, pg. 755
AXA CORPORATE SOLUTIONS AUSTRALIA—See AXA S.A.; *Int'l*, pg. 755
AXA CORPORATE SOLUTIONS—See AXA S.A.; *Int'l*, pg. 755
AXA CORPORATE SOLUTIONS SWITZERLAND—See AXA S.A.; *Int'l*, pg. 755
AXA CZECH REPUBLIC INSURANCE—See AXA S.A.; *Int'l*, pg. 755
AXA DIRECT KOREA—See AXA S.A.; *Int'l*, pg. 756
AXA DIRECT—See AXA S.A.; *Int'l*, pg. 756
AXA EPARGNE ENTREPRISE—See AXA S.A.; *Int'l*, pg. 756
AXA FINE ART CHINA—See AXA S.A.; *Int'l*, pg. 754
AXA FINE ART HONG KONG—See AXA S.A.; *Int'l*, pg. 754
AXA FINE ART SINGAPORE—See AXA S.A.; *Int'l*, pg. 754
AXA GENERAL INSURANCE CO., LTD.—See AXA S.A.; *Int'l*, pg. 756
AXA INSURANCE A.E.—See AXA S.A.; *Int'l*, pg. 757
AXA INSURANCE GULF—See AXA S.A.; *Int'l*, pg. 756
AXA INSURANCE LIMITED—See AXA S.A.; *Int'l*, pg. 756
AXA INSURANCE UK PLC—See AXA S.A.; *Int'l*, pg. 758
AXA ITALIA S.P.A.—See AXA S.A.; *Int'l*, pg. 757
AXA JAPAN HOLDING CO.—See AXA S.A.; *Int'l*, pg. 757
AXA LIFE EUROPE LIMITED—See AXA S.A.; *Int'l*, pg. 757
AXA MANSARD INSURANCE PLC—See AXA S.A.; *Int'l*, pg. 757
AXA MBASK IC OJSC—See AXA S.A.; *Int'l*, pg. 757
AXA MIDDLE EAST—See AXA S.A.; *Int'l*, pg. 757
AXA PHILIPPINES—See AXA S.A.; *Int'l*, pg. 757
AXA POJISOVNA A.S.—See AXA S.A.; *Int'l*, pg. 759
AXA PROTECTION JURIDIQUE—See AXA S.A.; *Int'l*, pg. 758
AXA SEGUROS GENERALES SA DE SEGUROS Y REASEGUROS—See AXA S.A.; *Int'l*, pg. 757
AXA VERSICHERUNGEN AG—See AXA S.A.; *Int'l*, pg. 758
AXA WEALTH UK—See AXA S.A.; *Int'l*, pg. 759
AXENT NABESTAANDENZORG N.V.—See Egeria Capital Management B.V.; *Int'l*, pg. 2323
AXIOMA INSURANCE (CYPRUS) LTD—See Allianz SE; *Int'l*, pg. 343
AXIS CAPITAL HOLDINGS LIMITED - AXIS GLOBAL ACCIDENT & HEALTH DIVISION—See AXIS Capital Holdings Limited; *Int'l*, pg. 769
AXIS RE LIMITED—See AXIS Capital Holdings Limited; *Int'l*, pg. 769
AXIS SPECIALTY EUROPE LIMITED—See AXIS Capital Holdings Limited; *Int'l*, pg. 770
AXIS SPECIALTY FINANCE LLC—See AXIS Capital Holdings Limited; *Int'l*, pg. 770
AXIS SPECIALTY LIMITED—See AXIS Capital Holdings Limited; *Int'l*, pg. 770
BADGER MUTUAL INSURANCE COMPANY; *U.S. Private*, pg. 424
BAHRAIN NATIONAL HOLDING COMPANY BSC; *Int'l*, pg. 800

BAJAJ ALLIANZ GENERAL INSURANCE CO. LTD.—See Allianz SE; *Int'l*, pg. 351
BAJAJ ALLIANZ GENERAL INSURANCE CO. LTD.—See Bajaj Auto Ltd.; *Int'l*, pg. 803
BALDWIN KRYSTYN SHERMAN PARTNERS, LLC—See The Baldwin Insurance Group, Inc.; *U.S. Public*, pg. 2035
BALOISE ASSURANCES IARD S.A.—See Baloise Holding AG; *Int'l*, pg. 811
BALOISE BELGIUM SA - BRUSSEL—See Baloise Holding AG; *Int'l*, pg. 811
BALOISE LIFE (LIECHTENSTEIN) AG—See Baloise Holding AG; *Int'l*, pg. 811
BANCA POPOLARE PUGLIESE S.C.P.A.; *Int'l*, pg. 816
BANGKOK INSURANCE PUBLIC COMPANY LTD.; *Int'l*, pg. 834
BANGKOK UNION INSURANCE PUBLIC COMPANY LIMITED; *Int'l*, pg. 835
BANGLADESH GENERAL INSURANCE COMPANY LIMITED; *Int'l*, pg. 835
BANKERS INSURANCE SERVICE, INC.—See Aon plc; *Int'l*, pg. 494
BANKERS STANDARD INSURANCE COMPANY—See Chubb Limited; *Int'l*, pg. 1590
BANKERS SURETY SERVICES—See Bankers International Financial Corporation; *U.S. Public*, pg. 467
BANKGUAM INSURANCE UNDERWRITERS LTD.—See BankGuam Holding Company; *U.S. Public*, pg. 274
BANKINTER SEGUROS DE VIDA, DE SEGUROS Y REASEGUROS SA—See Bankinter, S.A.; *Int'l*, pg. 850
BAO MINH INSURANCE CORPORATION; *Int'l*, pg. 855
BARBICAN CORPORATE MEMBER LIMITED—See Arch Capital Group Ltd.; *Int'l*, pg. 547
BARHORST INSURANCE GROUP; *U.S. Private*, pg. 474
BARNES INSURANCE & FINANCIAL SERVICES—See Genstar Capital, LLC; *U.S. Private*, pg. 1674
BASLER SACHVERSICHERUNGS-AG; *Int'l*, pg. 887
BASLER SECURITAS VERSICHERUNGS-AKTIENGESELLSCHAFT—See Baloise Holding AG; *Int'l*, pg. 811
BASLER VERSICHERUNGS-GESELLSCHAFT—See Baloise Holding AG; *Int'l*, pg. 811
BAVARIA WIRTSCHAFTSAGENTUR GMBH—See Bayerische Motoren Werke Aktiengesellschaft; *Int'l*, pg. 912
BAWAG PSK VERSICHERUNG AG—See Assicurazioni Generali S.p.A.; *Int'l*, pg. 645
BAY MILL SPECIALTY INSURANCE ADJUSTERS INC.—See Aviva plc; *Int'l*, pg. 746
BAY OF QUINTE MUTUAL INSURANCE CO.; *Int'l*, pg. 901
BB&T INSURANCE SERVICES, INC. - FREDERICK UNDERWRITERS—See Clayton, Dubilier & Rice, LLC; *U.S. Private*, pg. 927
BB&T INSURANCE SERVICES, INC. - FREDERICK UNDERWRITERS—See Stone Point Capital LLC; *U.S. Private*, pg. 3826
BEACON AVIATION INSURANCE SERVICES, INC.; *U.S. Private*, pg. 504
BEAZLEY DEDICATED LTD.—See Beazley plc; *Int'l*, pg. 935
BEAZLEY DEDICATED NO.2 LIMITED—See Beazley plc; *Int'l*, pg. 935
BEAZLEY FURLONGE HOLDINGS LIMITED—See Beazley plc; *Int'l*, pg. 935
BEAZLEY FURLONGE LIMITED—See Beazley plc; *Int'l*, pg. 935
BEAZLEY PLC; *Int'l*, pg. 935
BEAZLEY UNDERWRITING SERVICES LTD.—See Beazley plc; *Int'l*, pg. 936
BEE INSURANCE MANAGEMENT SERVICES LIMITED—See Arthur J. Gallagher & Co.; *U.S. Public*, pg. 203
BEEMA-PAKISTAN COMPANY LIMITED; *Int'l*, pg. 939
BELFIUS INSURANCE—See Belfius Bank SA/NV; *Int'l*, pg. 963
BELGIBO N.V.—See Exmar N.V.; *Int'l*, pg. 2585
BELLINGHAM UNDERWRITERS, INC.—See Brown & Brown, Inc.; *U.S. Public*, pg. 397
BENEFICIAL INSURANCE SERVICES, LLC—See Caisse de Depot et Placement du Quebec; *Int'l*, pg. 1256
BENEFICIAL INSURANCE SERVICES, LLC—See KKR & Co. Inc.; *U.S. Public*, pg. 1265
BENEFIT CONSULTANTS GROUP, INC.—See Horace Mann Educators Corporation; *U.S. Public*, pg. 1053
BENEFIT MANAGEMENT INC.—See Nueterra Capital Management, LLC; *U.S. Private*, pg. 2972
BENEFIT SERVICES GROUP—See Aon plc; *Int'l*, pg. 495
BENEFIT SOURCE, INC.; *U.S. Private*, pg. 525
BENEPLACE, LLC—See Entertainment Benefits Group, LLC; *U.S. Private*, pg. 1404
BERKLEY RISK SOLUTIONS, INC.—See W.R. Berkley Corporation; *U.S. Public*, pg. 2317
BERKLEY SPECIALTY UNDERWRITING MANAGERS, LLC—See W.R. Berkley Corporation; *U.S. Public*, pg. 2317
BERKLEY SURETY GROUP, INC.—See W.R. Berkley Corporation; *U.S. Public*, pg. 2317
BESTOW, INC.; *U.S. Private*, pg. 544
B.F. LORENZETTI & ASSOCIATES; *Int'l*, pg. 789
BF&M LIMITED; *Int'l*, pg. 1006
BICKFORD AT MISSION SPRINGS I, L.L.C.—See National

N.A.I.C.S. INDEX
524298 — ALL OTHER INSURANCE...

Health Investors, Inc.; *U.S. Public*, pg. 1495
BICKFORD OF CARMEL, LLC—See National Health Investors, Inc.; *U.S. Public*, pg. 1495
BICKFORD OF MIDDLETOWN, LLC—See National Health Investors, Inc.; *U.S. Public*, pg. 1495
BICKFORD OF OVERLAND PARK, L.L.C.—See National Health Investors, Inc.; *U.S. Public*, pg. 1495
BIDV INSURANCE CORPORATION; *Int'l*, pg. 1019
BILBAO, COMPANIA ANONIMA DE SEGUROS Y REASEGUROS—See Grupo Catalana Occidente, S.A.; *Int'l*, pg. 3124
BKD INSURANCE, LLC—See BKD, LLP; *U.S. Private*, pg. 568
BLUE CROSS OF CALIFORNIA—See Elevance Health, Inc.; *U.S. Public*, pg. 729
BLUEFIN ADVISORY SERVICES LIMITED—See AXA S.A.; *Int'l*, pg. 759
BLUEFIN GROUP LIMITED—See AXA S.A.; *Int'l*, pg. 758
BMO LIFE ASSURANCE COMPANY—See Bank of Montreal; *Int'l*, pg. 846
BMO LIFE INSURANCE COMPANY—See Bank of Montreal; *Int'l*, pg. 846
BMS ASIA INTERMEDIARIES LTD.—See BMS Group Ltd.; *Int'l*, pg. 1077
BMS ASIA INTER-MEDIARIES PTE., LTD.—See BMS Group Ltd.; *Int'l*, pg. 1077
BMS ASSOCIATES LTD.—See BMS Group Ltd.; *Int'l*, pg. 1077
BMS BERMUDA LTD.—See BMS Group Ltd.; *Int'l*, pg. 1077
BMS FACULTATIVE LTD.—See BMS Group Ltd.; *Int'l*, pg. 1077
BMS HARRIS & DIXON LTD.—See BMS Group Ltd.; *Int'l*, pg. 1077
BMS HARRIS & DIXON MARINE LTD.—See BMS Group Ltd.; *Int'l*, pg. 1077
BMS HARRIS & DIXON REINSURANCE BROKERS LTD.—See BMS Group Ltd.; *Int'l*, pg. 1077
BMS INTERNATIONAL INTERMEDIARIES LTD.—See BMS Group Ltd.; *Int'l*, pg. 1077
BMS SPECIAL RISK SERVICES LTD.—See BMS Group Ltd.; *Int'l*, pg. 1077
BMS VISION RE LTD.—See BMS Group Ltd.; *Int'l*, pg. 1077
BOETGER ACQUISITION CORP.—See Northwest Bancshares, Inc.; *U.S. Public*, pg. 1542
BOLEY-FEATHERSTON-HUFFMAN & DEAL CO.—See Arthur J. Gallagher & Co.; *U.S. Public*, pg. 204
BONDED BUILDERS INSURANCE SERVICES—See Bankers International Financial Corporation; *U.S. Private*, pg. 468
BOSNA REOSIGURANJE D.D.; *Int'l*, pg. 1116
BOWRING MARSH (BERMUDA) LTD.—See Marsh & McLennan Companies, Inc.; *U.S. Public*, pg. 1374
BOWRING MARSH LIMITED—See Marsh & McLennan Companies, Inc.; *U.S. Public*, pg. 1374
BPA ASSEGURANCES, SA—See Banca Privada D'Andorra, SA; *Int'l*, pg. 816
BP AUSTRALIA CAPITAL MARKETS LIMITED—See BP plc; *Int'l*, pg. 1128
BRADESCO ARGENTINA DE SEGUROS S.A—See Banco Bradesco S.A.; *Int'l*, pg. 819
BRADESCO AUTO/RE COMPANHIA DE SEGUROS—See Banco Bradesco S.A.; *Int'l*, pg. 819
BRADESCO CAPITALIZACAO S.A.—See Banco Bradesco S.A.; *Int'l*, pg. 819
BRADESCO VIDA E PREVIDENCIA S.A.—See Banco Bradesco S.A.; *Int'l*, pg. 819
THE BRALEY & WELLINGTON INSURANCE AGENCY CORPORATION—See Workers' Credit Union; *U.S. Private*, pg. 4563
BRECKENRIDGE IS, INC.; *U.S. Private*, pg. 644
BRIDGE ABSTRACT LLC—See Dime Community Bancshares, Inc.; *U.S. Public*, pg. 666
BRINCH AGENCY, LLC—See Inszone Insurance Services, LLC; *U.S. Private*, pg. 2096
BRITAM COMPANHIA DE SEGUROS DE MOCAMBIQUE SA—See Britam Holdings Plc; *Int'l*, pg. 1164
BRITAM GENERAL INSURANCE COMPANY (KENYA) LIMITED—See Britam Holdings Plc; *Int'l*, pg. 1164
BRITAM INSURANCE COMPANY (RWANDA) LIMITED—See Britam Holdings Plc; *Int'l*, pg. 1165
BRITAM INSURANCE COMPANY (UGANDA) LIMITED—See Britam Holdings Plc; *Int'l*, pg. 1165
BRITAM INSURANCE (TANZANIA) LIMITED—See Britam Holdings Plc; *Int'l*, pg. 1164
BROKERS' SERVICE MARKETING GROUP—See Hellman & Friedman LLC; *U.S. Private*, pg. 1909
BROOKLAWN INSURANCE AGENCY, INC.—See Kaplansky Insurance Agency, Inc.; *U.S. Private*, pg. 2261
BROWN & BROWN INSURANCE OF ARIZONA, INC. - PRESCOTT—See Brown & Brown, Inc.; *U.S. Public*, pg. 398
BROWN & BROWN OF NEW JERSEY, LLC—See Brown & Brown, Inc.; *U.S. Public*, pg. 399
BROWN & BROWN OF OHIO, INC.—See Brown & Brown, Inc.; *U.S. Public*, pg. 399
BRUNNER INSURANCE, INC.—See Lacher & Associates Insurance Agency, Inc.; *U.S. Private*, pg. 2371
BUCKLE AGENCY LLC; *U.S. Private*, pg. 678

THE BUCKNER COMPANY, INC.—See RiskProNet International Inc.; *U.S. Private*, pg. 3441
BUILDERS INSURANCE SERVICES, LLC—See Stone Point Capital LLC; *U.S. Private*, pg. 3820
BUILDERS & TRADESMEN'S INSURANCE SERVICES, INC.—See Stone Point Capital LLC; *U.S. Private*, pg. 3820
BURNHAM BENEFIT ADVISORS—See Genstar Capital, LLC; *U.S. Private*, pg. 1674
BURNS & WILCOX LIMITED—See Arch Capital Group Ltd.; *Int'l*, pg. 547
BUSINESS & INDUSTRIAL INSURANCE COMPANY LTD.; *Int'l*, pg. 1228
BUYERS VEHICLE PROTECTION PLAN, INC.—See Credit Acceptance Corporation; *U.S. Public*, pg. 593
CAIXA SEGUROS—See CNP Assurances SA; *Int'l*, pg. 1678
THE CALEY GROUP LIMITED—See Berkshire Hathaway Inc.; *U.S. Public*, pg. 315
CALIFORNIA CHOICE BENEFIT ADMINISTRATORS, INC.—See Word & Brown, Insurance Administrators, Inc.; *U.S. Private*, pg. 4562
CALIFORNIA FRINGE BENEFIT AND INSURANCE MARKETING CORPORATION—See Lincoln National Corporation; *U.S. Public*, pg. 1319
CALIFORNIA INSURANCE COMPANY—See Berkshire Hathaway Inc.; *U.S. Public*, pg. 304
CAL INSPECTION BUREAU, INC.—See XPT Group LLC; *U.S. Private*, pg. 4582
CALIPSO SPA—See Banca Finnat Euramerica S.p.A.; *Int'l*, pg. 814
CALYPSO—See Allianz SE; *Int'l*, pg. 342
CAMICO MUTUAL INSURANCE COMPANY; *U.S. Private*, pg. 729
CAMS INSURANCE REPOSITORY SERVICES LIMITED—See Computer Age Management Services Limited; *Int'l*, pg. 1759
CANARY BLOMSTROM INSURANCE AGENCY, INC.—See GTCR LLC; *U.S. Private*, pg. 1803
CANOPIUS MANAGING AGENTS LTD.—See Centerbridge Partners, L.P.; *U.S. Private*, pg. 813
CAPE ANN INSURANCE, INC.—See Salem Five Bancorp; *U.S. Public*, pg. 3531
CAPITA INSURANCE SERVICES LIMITED—See Capita plc; *Int'l*, pg. 1308
CAPITAL CDPQ—See Caisse de Depot et Placement du Quebec; *Int'l*, pg. 1254
CAP RECHTSSCHUTZ VERSICHERUNG—See Allianz SE; *Int'l*, pg. 350
CAPSPECIALTY, INC.—See Berkshire Hathaway Inc.; *U.S. Public*, pg. 298
CAPTIVE INSURANCE SERVICES, INC.—See Tenet Healthcare Corporation; *U.S. Public*, pg. 2001
CAR CARE PLAN LIMITED—See Stone Point Capital LLC; *U.S. Private*, pg. 3820
CARDIF GERMANY—See BNP Paribas SA; *Int'l*, pg. 1083
CARDIF POLSKA S.A.—See BNP Paribas SA; *Int'l*, pg. 1083
CARDIF SOCIETE VIE TAIWAN—See BNP Paribas SA; *Int'l*, pg. 1081
CARDIF—See BNP Paribas SA; *Int'l*, pg. 1083
CARDIF—See BNP Paribas SA; *Int'l*, pg. 1083
CARDIF SPAIN—See BNP Paribas SA; *Int'l*, pg. 1083
CAREATC; *U.S. Private*, pg. 752
CARLSBERG INSURANCE A/S—See Carlsberg A/S; *Int'l*, pg. 1340
CASTELAN LTD.; *Int'l*, pg. 1356
CATALINA WORTHING INSURANCE LIMITED—See Apollo Global Management, Inc.; *U.S. Public*, pg. 148
CBIZ BENEFITS & INSURANCE SERVICES, INC.—See CBIZ, Inc.; *U.S. Public*, pg. 456
CCV RISK SOLUTIONS LIMITED; *Int'l*, pg. 1370
CDP TECHNOLOGIES—See Caisse de Depot et Placement du Quebec; *Int'l*, pg. 1253
CEDAR FALLS BICKFORD COTTAGE, L.L.C.—See National Health Investors, Inc.; *U.S. Public*, pg. 1495
CENTRAL ANALYSIS BUREAU, INC.—See Aurora Capital Group; *U.S. Private*, pg. 394
CENTRAL RESERVE LIFE INSURANCE COMPANY—See American Financial Group, Inc.; *U.S. Public*, pg. 102
CENTRAL STATES OF OMAHA COMPANIES, INC.—See Berkshire Hathaway Inc.; *U.S. Public*, pg. 304
CENTRE CDP CAPITAL—See Caisse de Depot et Placement du Quebec; *Int'l*, pg. 1254
CENTURION LIFE INSURANCE COMPANY—See Bestow, Inc.; *U.S. Private*, pg. 544
CENTURY INDEMNITY COMPANY—See Chubb Limited; *Int'l*, pg. 1590
CERTUS MANAGEMENT GROUP—See United Claim Solutions, LLC; *U.S. Private*, pg. 4289
CFC UNDERWRITING LIMITED; *Int'l*, pg. 1429
CGU UNDERWRITING LIMITED—See Aviva plc; *Int'l*, pg. 746
CHAPMAN & HOGAN INSURANCE GROUP—See Reverence Capital Partners LLC; *U.S. Private*, pg. 3415
CHARAN INSURANCE PUBLIC COMPANY LIMITED; *Int'l*, pg. 1448
CHARLES TAYLOR CONSULTING (CANADA) INC—See Lovell Minnick Partners LLC; *U.S. Private*, pg. 2502

CHARLES TAYLOR PLC—See Lovell Minnick Partners LLC; *U.S. Private*, pg. 2501
CHARTER NATIONAL LIFE INSURANCE COMPANY—See The Allstate Corporation; *U.S. Public*, pg. 2033
CHAUCER LATIN AMERICA S.A—See China Reinsurance (Group) Corporation; *Int'l*, pg. 1547
CHAUCER SINGAPORE PTE LIMITED—See China Reinsurance (Group) Corporation; *Int'l*, pg. 1547
CHAUCER SYNDICATE SERVICES LIMITED—See The Hanover Insurance Group, Inc.; *U.S. Public*, pg. 2087
CHESAPEAKE EMPLOYERS' INSURANCE COMPANY; *U.S. Private*, pg. 875
CHI MICROINSURANCE LIMITED—See Consolidated Hallmark Insurance Plc.; *Int'l*, pg. 1770
CHINA LIFE INSURANCE ASSET MANAGEMENT COMPANY LIMITED—See China Life Insurance Company Limited; *Int'l*, pg. 1515
CHINATRUST LIFE INSURANCE CO., LTD.—See CTBC Financial Holding Co., Ltd.; *Int'l*, pg. 1869
CHUBB ALTERNATIVE RISK LTD.—See Chubb Limited; *Int'l*, pg. 1590
CHUBB ASIA PACIFIC SERVICES PTE. LTD.—See Chubb Limited; *Int'l*, pg. 1590
CHUBB CUSTOM MARKET, INC.—See Chubb Limited; *Int'l*, pg. 1591
CHUBB EUROPEAN GROUP LIMITED—See Chubb Limited; *Int'l*, pg. 1590
CHUBB INSURANCE EGYPT S.A.E.—See Chubb Limited; *Int'l*, pg. 1592
CHUBB INSURANCE SOLUTIONS AGENCY INC.—See Chubb Limited; *Int'l*, pg. 1592
CHUBB INSURANCE (SWITZERLAND) LIMITED—See Chubb Limited; *Int'l*, pg. 1592
CHUBB RESSEGURADORA BRASIL S.A.—See Chubb Limited; *Int'l*, pg. 1592
CHUBB SERVICES CORPORATION—See Chubb Limited; *Int'l*, pg. 1591
CHUBB TEMPEST RE CANADA, INC.—See Chubb Limited; *Int'l*, pg. 1591
CHUBB UNDERWRITING (DIFC) LIMITED—See Chubb Limited; *Int'l*, pg. 1590
CIGNA & CMB LIFE INSURANCE COMPANY LIMITED—See The Cigna Group; *U.S. Public*, pg. 2060
CIGNA FINANS EMEKLILIK VE HAYAT A.S.—See The Cigna Group; *U.S. Public*, pg. 2060
CIGNA INSURANCE SERVICES (EUROPE) LIMITED—See The Cigna Group; *U.S. Public*, pg. 2061
CIGNA LIFE INSURANCE COMPANY OF EUROPE S.A.-N.V.—See The Cigna Group; *U.S. Public*, pg. 2060
CIGNA LIFE INSURANCE NEW ZEALAND LIMITED—See The Cigna Group; *U.S. Public*, pg. 2061
CIGNA WORLDWIDE LIFE INSURANCE COMPANY LIMITED—See Chubb Limited; *Int'l*, pg. 1592
CINCINNATI GLOBAL UNDERWRITING LIMITED—See Cincinnati Financial Corporation; *U.S. Public*, pg. 495
CITIBANK INVESTMENTS LIMITED—See Citigroup Inc.; *U.S. Public*, pg. 503
CITY GENERAL INSURANCE COMPANY LIMITED; *Int'l*, pg. 1626
CKD GLOBAL SERVICE CORPORATION—See CKD Corporation; *Int'l*, pg. 1639
CKP INSURANCE, LLC—See Brown & Brown, Inc.; *U.S. Public*, pg. 400
CLEAR BLUE INSURANCE SERVICES, INC.—See Clear Blue Financial Holdings LLC; *U.S. Private*, pg. 932
CLEARWATER INSURANCE COMPANY—See Fairfax Financial Holdings Limited; *Int'l*, pg. 2607
CLUB MARINE LTD.—See Allianz SE; *Int'l*, pg. 342
CNA INSURANCE - NEW YORK CITY BRANCH—See Loews Corporation; *U.S. Public*, pg. 1339
CNP ASSURANCES COMPANIA DE SEGUROS DE VIDA S.A—See CNP Assurances SA; *Int'l*, pg. 1677
CNP ASSURANCES SA; *Int'l*, pg. 1677
CNP CHINA—See CNP Assurances SA; *Int'l*, pg. 1677
CNP ITALIA SPA—See CNP Assurances SA; *Int'l*, pg. 1678
COASTAL DENTAL, INC.; *U.S. Private*, pg. 955
COASTAL INSURANCE UNDERWRITERS, INC.—See Clayton, Dubilier & Rice, LLC; *U.S. Private*, pg. 927
COASTAL INSURANCE UNDERWRITERS, INC.—See Stone Point Capital LLC; *U.S. Private*, pg. 3826
COBRA HOLDINGS LTD—See Apax Partners LLP; *Int'l*, pg. 505
COFINTEX 6 SA—See Groupama SA; *Int'l*, pg. 3090
COLINA INSURANCE LIMITED—See Colina Holdings Bahamas Limited; *Int'l*, pg. 1698
COMBINED BENEFITS ADMINISTRATORS, LLC—See Hellman & Friedman LLC; *U.S. Private*, pg. 1908
COMBINED UNDERWRITERS OF MIAMI—See Kelso & Company, L.P.; *U.S. Private*, pg. 2279
COMERICA INSURANCE GROUP, INC.—See Comerica Incorporated; *U.S. Public*, pg. 542
COMMBANK MANAGEMENT CONSULTING (ASIA) CO LIMITED—See Commonwealth Bank of Australia; *Int'l*, pg. 1720
COMMERCE INSURANCE SERVICES, INC.—See Commerce Bancshares, Inc.; *U.S. Public*, pg. 545
COMMERCIAL INVESTIGATION INCORPORATED; *U.S. Private*, pg. 984

524298 — ALL OTHER INSURANCE...

COMMONWEALTH UNDERWRITERS LTD.—See Hellman & Friedman LLC; *U.S. Private*, pg. 1909
COMMUNITY INSURANCE COMPANY—See Elevance Health, Inc.; *U.S. Public*, pg. 729
COMPAGNIE BELGE D'ASSURANCES AVIATION NV/SA—See AXIS Capital Holdings Limited; *Int'l*, pg. 770
COMPANHIA DE SEGUROS ALIANCA DA BAHIA; *Int'l*, pg. 1747
COMPANHIA DE SEGUROS ALLIANZ PORTUGAL S.A.—See Allianz SE; *Int'l*, pg. 351
COMPANIA COLOMBIANA DE INVERSION COLSEGUROS S.A.—See Allianz SE; *Int'l*, pg. 342
COMPANIA DE SEGUROS BOLIVAR S.A.—See Grupo Bolivar S.A.; *Int'l*, pg. 3123
COMPANIA DE SEGUROS DE VIDA CRUZ DEL SUR S.A; *Int'l*, pg. 1749
COMPASS ABSTRACT, INC.—See Old Republic International Corporation; *U.S. Public*, pg. 1568
COMPASS CONSULTING GROUP, LLC—See New Mountain Capital, LLC; *U.S. Private*, pg. 2901
COMPOSITE ASSISTANCE LIMITED—See Stone Point Capital LLC; *U.S. Private*, pg. 3820
COMPOSITE LEGAL EXPENSES LIMITED—See Stone Point Capital LLC; *U.S. Private*, pg. 3820
CONCENTRIX INSURANCE ADMINISTRATION SOLUTIONS CORPORATION—See Concentrix Corporation; *U.S. Public*, pg. 564
CONFIE HOLDING II CO.—See Stone Point Capital LLC; *U.S. Private*, pg. 3818
CONSOLIDATED HALLMARK INSURANCE PLC.; *Int'l*, pg. 1770
CONSOLIDATED SERVICES GROUP; *U.S. Private*, pg. 1022
CONSTANTIA INSURANCE COMPANY LIMITED—See CONDUIT CAPITAL LIMITED; *Int'l*, pg. 1766
CONSTELLATION AFFILIATED PARTNERS LLC—See Clayton, Dubilier & Rice, LLC; *U.S. Private*, pg. 927
CONSTELLATION AFFILIATED PARTNERS LLC—See Stone Point Capital LLC; *U.S. Private*, pg. 3826
CONSTITUTION STATE SERVICE LLC—See The Travelers Companies, Inc.; *U.S. Public*, pg. 2136
CONTINENTAL S.A. SOCIEDAD ADMINISTRADORA DE FONDOS—See Banco Bilbao Vizcaya Argentaria, S.A.; *Int'l*, pg. 817
CORE ASSURANCE PARTNERS, INC.; *U.S. Private*, pg. 1048
CORELOGIC FLOOD SERVICES, LLC—See Insight Venture Management, LLC; *U.S. Private*, pg. 2088
CORELOGIC FLOOD SERVICES, LLC—See Stone Point Capital LLC; *U.S. Private*, pg. 3822
COREPOINTE INSURANCE AGENCY, INC.—See Stone Point Capital LLC; *U.S. Private*, pg. 3820
CORPORATE CONSULTING SERVICES—See Marsh & McLennan Companies, Inc.; *U.S. Public*, pg. 1380
CORREDURIA DE SEGUROS, S.A.—See El Corte Ingles, S.A.; *Int'l*, pg. 2340
CORVEL HEALTHCARE CORPORATION—See CorVel Corporation; *U.S. Public*, pg. 585
COSEC COMPANHIA DE SEGURO DE CREDITOS, S.A.—See Allianz SE; *Int'l*, pg. 352
COSEV@D SAS—See Assicurazioni Generali S.p.A.; *Int'l*, pg. 645
COSMOS INSURANCE COMPANY PUBLIC LTD; *Int'l*, pg. 1813
COVERICA, INC.; *U.S. Private*, pg. 1072
COVERXSPECIALTY—See Fairfax Financial Holdings Limited; *Int'l*, pg. 2606
CPI QUALIFIED PLAN CONSULTANTS INC.—See CMFG Life Insurance Company; *U.S. Private*, pg. 950
CRANMORE (UK) LIMITED—See Enstar Group Limited; *Int'l*, pg. 2448
CRAWFORD & COMPANY (BERMUDA) LIMITED—See Crawford & Company; *U.S. Public*, pg. 592
CRAWFORD & COMPANY (CANADA) INC.—See Crawford & Company; *U.S. Public*, pg. 592
CRAWFORD & COMPANY; *U.S. Public*, pg. 592
CRAWFORD & COMPANY UK—See Crawford & Company; *U.S. Public*, pg. 592
CRAWFORDSVILLE BICKFORD COTTAGE, L.L.C.—See National Health Investors, Inc.; *U.S. Public*, pg. 1495
CR CO., LTD.—See Chugai Ro Co., Ltd.; *Int'l*, pg. 1594
CREDIT ASSEGURANCES—See Credit Andorra, S.A.; *Int'l*, pg. 1835
CREDIT GUARD OF FLORIDA INC.; *U.S. Private*, pg. 1091
CRETCHER HEARTLAND LLC; *U.S. Private*, pg. 1099
CRINSURANCE S.A.S.; *Int'l*, pg. 1850
CSG ACTUARIAL, LLC—See Integrity Marketing Group LLC; *U.S. Private*, pg. 2103
CTBC LIFE INSURANCE CO., LTD.—See CTBC Financial Holding Co., Ltd.; *Int'l*, pg. 1869
CYPRIALIFE LTD.—See Bank of Cyprus Holdings Public Limited Company; *Int'l*, pg. 842
DAI-ICHI LIFE RESEARCH INSTITUTE INC.,—See Dai-ichi Life Holdings, Inc.; *Int'l*, pg. 1917
DAR AL SALAM INSURANCE COMPANY—See Fairfax Financial Holdings Limited; *Int'l*, pg. 2607
DAR AL TAKAFUL HOUSE PJSC; *Int'l*, pg. 1971

DARTA SAVING LIFE ASSURANCE LTD.—See Allianz SE; *Int'l*, pg. 352
DASH & LOVE, INC.—See Kelso & Company, L.P.; *U.S. Private*, pg. 2279
DAS LEGAL EXPENSES INSURANCE COMPANY LIMITED—See ARAG SE; *Int'l*, pg. 534
D.A.S. POISTOVNA PRAVNEJ OCHRANY, A.S.—See Allianz SE; *Int'l*, pg. 352
DATACEDE LLC; *U.S. Private*, pg. 1165
DCR (FI) LIMITED—See Howden Group Holdings Limited; *Int'l*, pg. 3493
DECARE DENTAL INSURANCE IRELAND, LTD.—See Elevance Health, Inc.; *U.S. Public*, pg. 729
DEERBROOK INSURANCE COMPANY—See The Allstate Corporation; *U.S. Public*, pg. 2033
DEFT RESEARCH, LLC—See Integrity Marketing Group LLC; *U.S. Private*, pg. 2103
DEGGINGER, MCINTOSH & ASSOCIATES, INC.—See Stone Point Capital LLC; *U.S. Private*, pg. 3819
DE GOUDSE N.V.; *Int'l*, pg. 1995
DELTA DENTAL PLAN OF NEW HAMPSHIRE, INC.; *U.S. Private*, pg. 1199
DELTA INSURANCE COMPANY LTD.; *Int'l*, pg. 2019
DELTA INSURANCE—See Egypt Kuwait Holding Co. S.A.E; *Int'l*, pg. 2327
DELVAG LUFTFAHRTVERSICHERUNGS-AG—See Deutsche Lufthansa AG; *Int'l*, pg. 2068
DENTAL HEALTH ALLIANCE, L.L.C.—See Assurant, Inc.; *U.S. Public*, pg. 216
DENTEMAX, LLC—See Health Care Service Corporation; *U.S. Private*, pg. 1892
DESERT CORNERSTONE INSURANCE SERVICE, INC.—See Inszone Insurance Services, LLC; *U.S. Private*, pg. 2096
DEUTSCHE NIEDERLASSUNG DER FRIDAY INSURANCE S.A.—See Baloise Holding AG; *Int'l*, pg. 811
DEUTSCHE POST REINSURANCE S.A.—See Deutsche Post AG; *Int'l*, pg. 2079
DEXIA EPARGNE PENSION SA—See Dexia SA; *Int'l*, pg. 2092
DHAKA INSURANCE LIMITED; *Int'l*, pg. 2097
DHOFAR INSURANCE COMPANY S.A.O.G; *Int'l*, pg. 2099
DIRECTED SERVICES LLC—See Voya Financial, Inc.; *U.S. Public*, pg. 2312
DIRECT RESPONSE INSURANCE ADMINISTRATIVE SERVICES, INC.; *U.S. Private*, pg. 1235
DISCOVERY BENEFITS, INC.—See WEX, Inc., *U.S. Public*, pg. 2364
DIVALL INSURED INCOME PROPERTIES 2 LIMITED PARTNERSHIP; *U.S. Private*, pg. 1240
DOHA INSURANCE GROUP QPSC; *Int'l*, pg. 2155
DOMESTIC & GENERAL INSURANCE PLC—See CVC Capital Partners SICAV-FIS S.A.; *Int'l*, pg. 1883
DOMESTIC & GENERAL INSURANCE SERVICES LIMITED—See CVC Capital Partners SICAV-FIS S.A.; *Int'l*, pg. 1883
DOMESTIC & GENERAL SERVICE GMBH—See CVC Capital Partners SICAV-FIS S.A.; *Int'l*, pg. 1883
DOMESTIC & GENERAL SERVICES LIMITED—See CVC Capital Partners SICAV-FIS S.A.; *Int'l*, pg. 1883
DONATELLO INTERMEDIAZIONE SRL—See Assicurazioni Generali S.p.A.; *Int'l*, pg. 643
DORE UNDERWRITING SERVICES LIMITED—See Stone Point Capital LLC; *U.S. Private*, pg. 3821
DOVETAIL INSURANCE CORP.—See Marsh & McLennan Companies, Inc.; *U.S. Public*, pg. 1374
DOWLING & O'NEIL INSURANCE AGENCY, INC.—See ABRY Partners, LLC; *U.S. Private*, pg. 43
DOWNEAST PENSION SERVICES, INC.—See NBT Bancorp Inc.; *U.S. Public*, pg. 1500
DOWNEAST PENSION SERVICES, INC.—See NBT Bancorp Inc.; *U.S. Public*, pg. 1501
DOWNER EDI GROUP INSURANCE PTE. LTD.—See Downer EDI Limited; *Int'l*, pg. 2185
DRAPER & KRAMER REALTY ADVISORS, INC.—See DKH, Incorporated; *U.S. Private*, pg. 1247
DRIVE INSURANCE HOLDINGS, INC.—See The Progressive Corporation; *U.S. Public*, pg. 2124
DRIVERS HISTORY; *U.S. Private*, pg. 1278
DSV INSURANCE A/S—See DSV A/S; *Int'l*, pg. 2212
DUBAI ISLAMIC INSURANCE & REINSURANCE COMPANY P.S.C.; *Int'l*, pg. 2220
DUBOSE & ASSOCIATES INSURANCE COMPANY—See Colonial Savings, F.A.; *U.S. Private*, pg. 972
DUDEK INSURANCE AGENCY GROUP—See ABRY Partners, LLC; *U.S. Private*, pg. 42
DUNHOUR AGENCY, INC.—See World Insurance Associates LLC; *U.S. Private*, pg. 4565
DURFEE-BUFFINTON INSURANCE AGENCY INC.—See World Insurance Associates LLC; *U.S. Private*, pg. 4565
EBS/FORAN INSURANCE & ADVISORY SERVICES, INC.—See Aon plc; *Int'l*, pg. 496
ECC DO BRASIL CIA DE SEGUROS—See Embraer S.A.; *Int'l*, pg. 2375
ECCLESIASTICAL INSURANCE OFFICE PLC; *Int'l*, pg. 2288
E-CIE VIE S.A.—See Assicurazioni Generali S.p.A.; *Int'l*, pg. 645

CORPORATE AFFILIATIONS

ECONET INSURANCE (PRIVATE) LIMITED—See EcoCash Holdings Zimbabwe Limited; *Int'l*, pg. 2294
EDUCATORS INSURANCE AGENCY, INC.—See The Hanover Insurance Group, Inc.; *U.S. Public*, pg. 2087
ELLIOTT-HARTMAN AGENCY—See ABRY Partners, LLC; *U.S. Private*, pg. 42
ELSECO LIMITED; *Int'l*, pg. 2370
EMPLOYEE BENEFITS ADMINISTRATORS LTD.—See Alignvest Management Corporation; *Int'l*, pg. 327
EMPLOYEE BENEFITS INTERNATIONAL; *U.S. Private*, pg. 1386
EMPLOYERS COMPENSATION INSURANCE CO.—See Employers Holdings, Inc.; *U.S. Public*, pg. 754
EMPLOYERS DENTAL SERVICES, INC.—See Principal Financial Group, Inc.; *U.S. Public*, pg. 1720
EMPLOYERS GROUP, INC.—See Employers Holdings, Inc.; *U.S. Public*, pg. 754
EMPLOYERS INSURANCE COMPANY OF NEVADA—See Employers Holdings, Inc.; *U.S. Public*, pg. 754
ENSTAR GROUP LIMITED; *Int'l*, pg. 2448
ENSURANCE LTD.; *Int'l*, pg. 2449
ENSURANCE UNDERWRITING PTY. LIMITED—See Ensurance Ltd.; *Int'l*, pg. 2449
ENTERPRISE GROUP PLC; *Int'l*, pg. 2451
E.ON RISK CONSULTING GMBH—See E.ON SE; *Int'l*, pg. 2255
EQUIAN, LLC—See New Mountain Capital, LLC; *U.S. Private*, pg. 2902
E.R. QUINN CO., INC.—See CVC Capital Partners SICAV-FIS S.A.; *Int'l*, pg. 1884
ESA ALLIANZ—See Allianz SE; *Int'l*, pg. 356
ESA EUROSHIP ASSEKURADEURGESELLSCHAFT MBH & CO. KG—See Allianz SE; *Int'l*, pg. 350
ESIS, INC.—See Chubb Limited; *Int'l*, pg. 1591
ESSENT GUARANTY, INC.—See Essent Group Ltd.; *Int'l*, pg. 2510
ESURANCE PROPERTY & CASUALTY INSURANCE COMPANY—See The Allstate Corporation; *U.S. Public*, pg. 2033
ETHICARE ADVISORS, INC.—See PCP Enterprise, L.P.; *U.S. Private*, pg. 3121
EUCLID INSURANCE SERVICES, INC.; *U.S. Private*, pg. 1433
EULER HERMES AKTIENGESELLSCHAFT—See Allianz SE; *Int'l*, pg. 352
EULER HERMES CESCOB UVEROVA POJISTOVNA A.S.—See Allianz SE; *Int'l*, pg. 352
EULER HERMES CONSULTING (SHANGHAI) CO., LTD.—See Allianz SE; *Int'l*, pg. 352
EULER HERMES CREDIT MANAGEMENT OOO—See Allianz SE; *Int'l*, pg. 352
EULER HERMES CREDIT MANAGEMENT SERVICES IRELAND LTD.—See Allianz SE; *Int'l*, pg. 352
EULER HERMES CREDIT SERVICES (JP) LTD.—See Allianz SE; *Int'l*, pg. 352
EULER HERMES DANMARK—See Allianz SE; *Int'l*, pg. 352
EULER HERMES GROUP SA—See Allianz SE; *Int'l*, pg. 352
EULER HERMES HELLAS CREDIT INSURANCE SA—See Allianz SE; *Int'l*, pg. 352
EULER HERMES HOLDINGS UK PLC—See Allianz SE; *Int'l*, pg. 352
EULER HERMES HONG KONG SERVICES LTD.—See Allianz SE; *Int'l*, pg. 352
EULER HERMES INDIA PVT. LTD.—See Allianz SE; *Int'l*, pg. 352
EULER HERMES IRELAND—See Allianz SE; *Int'l*, pg. 352
EULER HERMES NEW ZEALAND LTD.—See Allianz SE; *Int'l*, pg. 352
EULER HERMES NORGE—See Allianz SE; *Int'l*, pg. 352
EULER HERMES NORTH AMERICA INSURANCE COMPANY—See Allianz SE; *Int'l*, pg. 352
EULER HERMES RISK YONETIMI VE DANISMANLIK HIZMETLERI LIMITED SIRKETI—See Allianz SE; *Int'l*, pg. 353
EULER HERMES SEGUROS DE CREDITO SA—See Allianz SE; *Int'l*, pg. 353
EULER HERMES SERVICES BELGIUM S.A.—See Allianz SE; *Int'l*, pg. 353
EULER HERMES SERVICES B.V.—See Allianz SE; *Int'l*, pg. 353
EULER HERMES SERVICII FINANCIARE S.R.L.—See Allianz SE; *Int'l*, pg. 353
EULER HERMES SIGORTA A.S.—See Allianz SE; *Int'l*, pg. 353
EULER HERMES SINGAPORE SERVICES PTE LTD.—See Allianz SE; *Int'l*, pg. 353
EULER HERMES SUOMI—See Allianz SE; *Int'l*, pg. 353
EURCO RE LTD.—See Belfius Bank SA/NV; *Int'l*, pg. 963
EURCO SA—See Belfius Bank SA/NV; *Int'l*, pg. 963
EUREKO SIGORTA A.S.—See Achmea B.V.; *Int'l*, pg. 103
EURO ARAB INSURANCE; *Int'l*, pg. 2530
EUROGUARB INSURANCE COMPANY PCC LIMITED—See Alexander Forbes Group Holdings Limited; *Int'l*, pg. 307
EUROINS INSURANCE AD SKOPJE—See Eurohold Bulgaria AD; *Int'l*, pg. 2553
EUROINS INSURANCE PLC; *Int'l*, pg. 2553
EUROPAISCHE REISEVERSICHERUNGS AG—See Helve-

N.A.I.C.S. INDEX

524298 — ALL OTHER INSURANCE...

tia Holding AG; *Int'l*, pg. 3339
EUROVITA S.P.A.—See Cinven Limited; *Int'l*, pg. 1612
EVEREST INSURANCE COMPANY LTD.—See Himalayan Everest Insurance Limited; *Int'l*, pg. 3396
EXECUTIVE PERILS INSURANCE SERVICES; *U.S. Private*, pg. 1448
EXPERTA ART S.A.—See Gregorio, Numo y Noel Werthein S.A.; *Int'l*, pg. 3078
EXUDE BENEFITS GROUP, INC.; *U.S. Private*, pg. 1453
EXZEO SOFTWARE PRIVATE LIMITED—See HCI Group, Inc.; *U.S. Public*, pg. 1014
EXZEO USA, INC.—See HCI Group, Inc.; *U.S. Public*, pg. 1014
FAIRFAX BRASIL SEGUROS CORPORATIVOS S.A.—See Fairfax Financial Holdings Limited; *Int'l*, pg. 2606
FAIRLANE FINANCIAL CORPORATION; *U.S. Private*, pg. 1464
FAIRWAYS INSURANCE SERVICES, INC.—See World Insurance Associates LLC; *U.S. Private*, pg. 4566
FARRELL & ASSOCIATES INSURANCE SERVICES—See The Carlyle Group Inc.; *U.S. Public*, pg. 2054
FARRELL INSURANCE ASSOCIATES, INC.—See Union Bay Risk Advisors LLC; *U.S. Private*, pg. 4284
THE FAWCETT GROUP, INC.—See The Baldwin Insurance Group, Inc.; *U.S. Public*, pg. 2036
FBD INSURANCE PLC—See FBD Holdings plc; *Int'l*, pg. 2627
FEDNAT UNDERWRITERS, INC.—See FedNat Holding Company; *U.S. Public*, pg. 828
FENIX DIRECTO COMPANIA DE SEGUROS Y REASEGUROS S.A.—See Allianz SE; *Int'l*, pg. 343
FENNIA GROUP; *Int'l*, pg. 2634
FIDEA NV—See Baloise Holding AG; *Int'l*, pg. 811
FIELD UNDERWRITERS AGENCY, INC.—See Aon plc; *Int'l*, pg. 496
FIJICARE INSURANCE LIMITED; *Int'l*, pg. 2662
FINNAT SERVIZI ASSICURATIVI S.R.L.—See Banca Finnat Euramerica S.p.A.; *Int'l*, pg. 814
FIREMAN'S FUND MCGEE UNDERWRITERS—See Allianz SE; *Int'l*, pg. 347
FIRST AMERICAN MORTGAGE SOLUTIONS, LLC—See First American Financial Corporation; *U.S. Public*, pg. 836
FIRST ATLANTIC TITLE INSURANCE CORP.—See Stone Point Capital LLC; *U.S. Private*, pg. 3821
FIRST CANADIAN TITLE INSURANCE COMPANY LTD.—See First American Financial Corporation; *U.S. Public*, pg. 837
FIRSTCAUTION SA; *Int'l*, pg. 2688
FIRST COLONIAL INSURANCE COMPANY—See The Allstate Corporation; *U.S. Public*, pg. 2033
FIRSTCOMP UNDERWRITERS GROUP, INC.—See Markel Group Inc.; *U.S. Public*, pg. 1368
FIRST INSURANCE CO.; *Int'l*, pg. 2684
FIRST NONPROFIT COMPANIES, INC.—See Stone Point Capital LLC; *U.S. Private*, pg. 3821
FIRST NONPROFIT INSURANCE COMPANY—See Stone Point Capital LLC; *U.S. Private*, pg. 3821
FIRST UNDERWRITING LTD.—See White Mountains Insurance Group, Ltd.; *U.S. Public*, pg. 2369
FIVE STAR SPECIALTY PROGRAMS—See Truist Financial Corporation; *U.S. Public*, pg. 2200
FLOR-AG CORPORATION—See Prudential Financial, Inc.; *U.S. Public*, pg. 1732
FLORIDA INTRACOASTAL UNDERWRITERS, LIMITED COMPANY—See Brown & Brown, Inc.; *U.S. Public*, pg. 400
FMG SUITE, LLC; *U.S. Private*, pg. 1554
FOLKSAM OMSESIDIG SAKFORSAKRING; *Int'l*, pg. 2721
FONGEPAR—See CNP Assurances SA; *Int'l*, pg. 1678
FORD CREDIT B.V.—See Ford Motor Company; *U.S. Public*, pg. 866
FOSTER & CRANFIELD LTD.—See Epiris Managers LLP; *Int'l*, pg. 2461
FOYER S.A.; *Int'l*, pg. 2756
FRANCO SIGNOR LLC—See Verisk Analytics, Inc.; *U.S. Public*, pg. 2282
FRANKLIN MADISON GROUP LLC—See Guggenheim Partners, LLC; *U.S. Public*, pg. 1811
FREO GROUP PTY LTD—See Berkshire Hathaway Inc.; *U.S. Public*, pg. 305
FRIENDS FIRST IRELAND—See Achmea B.V.; *Int'l*, pg. 103
FRONT STREET FINANCING LLC—See The Hanover Insurance Group, Inc.; *U.S. Public*, pg. 2087
FUBON DIRECT MARKETING CONSULTING CO., LTD—See Fubon Financial Holding Co. Ltd.; *Int'l*, pg. 2801
FUBON INSURANCE CO., LTD.—See Fubon Financial Holding Co. Ltd.; *Int'l*, pg. 2802
FUBON LIFE INSURANCE CO., LTD—See Fubon Financial Holding Co. Ltd.; *Int'l*, pg. 2802
FUJISANKEI AGENCY CO., LTD.—See Fuji Media Holdings, Inc.; *Int'l*, pg. 2814
FULMAR INSURANCE COMPANY LTD.—See Compagnie de Saint-Gobain SA; *Int'l*, pg. 1725
GABLER AS; *Int'l*, pg. 2867
GAINSCO SERVICE CORP.—See State Farm Mutual Automobile Insurance Company; *U.S. Private*, pg. 3792

GALIOT INSURANCE SERVICES, INC.; *U.S. Private*, pg. 1637
GALLAGHER BASSETT CANADA, INC.—See Arthur J. Gallagher & Co.; *U.S. Public*, pg. 205
GALLAGHER BASSETT INTERNATIONAL LTD. (UK)—See Arthur J. Gallagher & Co.; *U.S. Public*, pg. 205
GALLAGHER BASSETT SERVICES PTY. LTD.—See Arthur J. Gallagher & Co.; *U.S. Public*, pg. 205
GALLAGHER BASSETT SERVICES PTY LTD.—See Arthur J. Gallagher & Co.; *U.S. Public*, pg. 205
GALLAGHER BASSETT SERVICES WORKERS COMPENSATION VICTORIA PTY. LTD.—See Arthur J. Gallagher & Co.; *U.S. Public*, pg. 205
G.A. MAVON & COMPANY—See Arthur J. Gallagher & Co.; *U.S. Public*, pg. 205
GAM CONSULTORIA ECONOMICA LTDA.—See Prudential Financial, Inc.; *U.S. Public*, pg. 1731
GAN OUTRE MER IARD—See Groupama SA; *Int'l*, pg. 3090
GAP PRUDENTIAL ALOCACAO DE RECURSOS LTDA.—See Prudential Financial, Inc.; *U.S. Public*, pg. 1731
GAUDREAU GROUP INC.—See Caisse de Depot et Placement du Quebec; *Int'l*, pg. 1256
GAUDREAU GROUP INC.—See KKR & Co. Inc.; *U.S. Public*, pg. 1265
GCUBE UNDERWRITING LIMITED—See Marsh & McLennan Companies, Inc.; *U.S. Public*, pg. 1375
GDS RISK SOLUTION CORREDURIA DE SEGUROS S.L.—See Aon plc; *Int'l*, pg. 494
G.D. VAN WAGENEN FINANCIAL SERVICES, INC.—See Bankers International Financial Corporation; *U.S. Private*, pg. 468
GEICO CHOICE INSURANCE COMPANY—See Berkshire Hathaway Inc.; *U.S. Public*, pg. 305
GENERALCOLOGNE RE IBERICA CORRESDORES DE REASEGUROS, S.A.—See Berkshire Hathaway Inc.; *U.S. Public*, pg. 301
GENERAL & COLOGNE RE (SUR) COMPANIA DE REASEGUROS S.A.—See Berkshire Hathaway Inc.; *U.S. Public*, pg. 301
GENERALI ALLGEMEINE VERSICHERUNGEN AG—See Assicurazioni Generali S.p.A.; *Int'l*, pg. 644
GENERALI ARGENTINA S.A.—See Assicurazioni Generali S.p.A.; *Int'l*, pg. 644
GENERALI ASIA N.V.—See Assicurazioni Generali S.p.A.; *Int'l*, pg. 647
GENERALI FINANCE B.V.—See Assicurazioni Generali S.p.A.; *Int'l*, pg. 647
GENERALI GROUP INSURANCE AG—See Assicurazioni Generali S.p.A.; *Int'l*, pg. 645
GENERALI HELLAS INSURANCE COMPANY S.A.—See Assicurazioni Generali S.p.A.; *Int'l*, pg. 645
GENERALI INVESTMENTS EUROPE S.P.A.—See Assicurazioni Generali S.p.A.; *Int'l*, pg. 646
GENERAL INSURANCE COMPANY (SUDAN) LIMITED; *Int'l*, pg. 2918
GENERALI TURKEY HOLDING B.V.—See Assicurazioni Generali S.p.A.; *Int'l*, pg. 647
GENERALI VIETNAM LIFE INSURANCE LTD—See Assicurazioni Generali S.p.A.; *Int'l*, pg. 647
GENERALI ZYCIE TOWARZYSTWO UBEZPIECZEN S.A.—See Assicurazioni Generali S.p.A.; *Int'l*, pg. 647
GENERAL RE AUSTRALIA LTD.—See Berkshire Hathaway Inc.; *U.S. Public*, pg. 302
GENERAL RE BEIRUT S.A.L.—See Berkshire Hathaway Inc.; *U.S. Public*, pg. 301
GENERAL REINSURANCE AFRICA LTD.—See Berkshire Hathaway Inc.; *U.S. Public*, pg. 301
GENERAL REINSURANCE AG—See Berkshire Hathaway Inc.; *U.S. Public*, pg. 306
GENERAL REINSURANCE AUSTRALIA LTD.—See Berkshire Hathaway Inc.; *U.S. Public*, pg. 302
GENERAL REINSURANCE CORPORATION—See Berkshire Hathaway Inc.; *U.S. Public*, pg. 302
GENERAL REINSURANCE SCANDINAVIA A/S—See Berkshire Hathaway Inc.; *U.S. Public*, pg. 301
GENERAL REINSURANCE UK LIMITED—See Berkshire Hathaway Inc.; *U.S. Public*, pg. 302
GENERAL RE LIFE CORPORATION—See Berkshire Hathaway Inc.; *U.S. Public*, pg. 306
GENERAL RE RIGA SIA—See Berkshire Hathaway Inc.; *U.S. Public*, pg. 301
GENERTEL BIZTOSITO ZRT—See Assicurazioni Generali S.p.A.; *Int'l*, pg. 646
GENERTEL SERVIZI ASSICURATIVI S.R.L.—See Assicurazioni Generali S.p.A.; *Int'l*, pg. 647
GENIALLOYD SPA—See Allianz SE; *Int'l*, pg. 350
GEN RE CORPORATION—See Berkshire Hathaway Inc.; *U.S. Public*, pg. 301
GEN RE MEXICO, S.A—See Berkshire Hathaway Inc.; *U.S. Public*, pg. 301
GI GENERAL INSURANCE LIMITED—See IGI Holdings Limited; *Int'l*, pg. 3602
GILSBAR INC.; *U.S. Public*, pg. 1701
GJENSIDIGE BALTIC—See Gjensidige Forsikring ASA; *Int'l*, pg. 2982
GLAXOSMITHKLINE INSURANCE LTD.—See GSK plc; *Int'l*, pg. 3148

GLB INSURANCE GROUP OF NEVADA—See Genstar Capital, LLC; *U.S. Private*, pg. 1674
GLOBAL INSURANCE LIMITED; *Int'l*, pg. 2997
GLOBAL RISK SOLUTIONS, INC.; *U.S. Private*, pg. 1717
GLOBAL WARRANTY GROUP, LLC; *U.S. Private*, pg. 1718
GMAC INTERNATIONAL INSURANCE SERVICES LIMITED—See Stone Point Capital LLC; *U.S. Private*, pg. 3821
G&M PTE LTD.; *Int'l*, pg. 2862
GOLDLINK INSURANCE PLC.; *Int'l*, pg. 3033
GOLDRUSH INSURANCE SERVICES, INC.—See Prism Technologies Group, Inc.; *U.S. Public*, pg. 1722
GOODWORKS FINANCIAL GROUP—See GTCR LLC; *U.S. Private*, pg. 1803
GOVERNMENT EMPLOYEES INSURANCE COMPANY—See Berkshire Hathaway Inc.; *U.S. Public*, pg. 302
GPA-IARD S.A.—See Assicurazioni Generali S.p.A.; *Int'l*, pg. 644
GRAINGER LIMITED—See Grainger plc; *Int'l*, pg. 3052
GRANDPARENTS INSURANCE SOLUTIONS LLC—See Grandparents.com, Inc.; *U.S. Private*, pg. 1754
GRANITE STATE HEALTH PLAN, INC.—See Centene Corporation; *U.S. Public*, pg. 469
GREAT AMERICAN CASUALTY INSURANCE COMPANY—See American Financial Group, Inc.; *U.S. Public*, pg. 103
GREAT AMERICAN CONTEMPORARY INSURANCE COMPANY—See American Financial Group, Inc.; *U.S. Public*, pg. 103
GREAT DIVIDE INSURANCE COMPANY—See W.R. Berkley Corporation; *U.S. Public*, pg. 2318
GREAT NIGERIA INSURANCE PLC; *Int'l*, pg. 3065
GREAT NORTHWEST INSURANCE COMPANY; *U.S. Private*, pg. 1766
GREEN DELTA INSURANCE COMPANY LIMITED; *Int'l*, pg. 3070
GREEN FLAG LIMITED—See Direct Line Insurance Group plc; *Int'l*, pg. 2129
GROUPAMA SA; *Int'l*, pg. 3090
GROUP & PENSION ADMINISTRATORS, INC.; *U.S. Private*, pg. 1793
GRUNDSTUCKSGESELLSCHAFT DER VEREINTEN VERSICHERUNGEN MBH—See Allianz SE; *Int'l*, pg. 353
GRUPO CATALANA OCCIDENTE, S.A.; *Int'l*, pg. 3124
THE GUARDIAN LIFE INSURANCE COMPANY OF AMERICA; *U.S. Private*, pg. 4040
GUIDEONE INSURANCE COMPANY; *U.S. Private*, pg. 1813
GUINEA INSURANCE PLC; *Int'l*, pg. 3174
GULF GENERAL COOPERATIVE INSURANCE COMPANY; *Int'l*, pg. 3180
GULF INSURANCE CO.; *Int'l*, pg. 3181
GULF INSURANCE LIMITED—See Assuria N.V.; *Int'l*, pg. 650
GULF UNION ALAHLIA COOPERATIVE INSURANCE CO.; *Int'l*, pg. 3182
GUNN, STEERS & COMPANY, LLC—See Keystone Group, L.P.; *U.S. Private*, pg. 2299
GURANS LIFE INSURANCE COMPANY LTD.; *Int'l*, pg. 3187
GUY CARPENTER & CO. LABUAN LTD.—See Marsh & McLennan Companies, Inc.; *U.S. Public*, pg. 1375
GUY CARPENTER & COMPANY CORRETORA DE RESSEGUROS LTDA.—See Marsh & McLennan Companies, Inc.; *U.S. Public*, pg. 1375
GUY CARPENTER & COMPANY, LIMITED—See Marsh & McLennan Companies, Inc.; *U.S. Public*, pg. 1375
GUY CARPENTER & COMPANY PRIVATE LIMITED—See Marsh & McLennan Companies, Inc.; *U.S. Public*, pg. 1375
GUY CARPENTER & COMPANY, S.A.S.—See Marsh & McLennan Companies, Inc.; *U.S. Public*, pg. 1375
GUY CARPENTER MEXICO INTERMEDIARIO DE REASEGURO, S.A. DE C.V.—See Marsh & McLennan Companies, Inc.; *U.S. Public*, pg. 1376
HALCYON UNDERWRITERS, INC.—See Brown & Brown, Inc.; *U.S. Public*, pg. 400
HALLMAN & LORBER ASSOCIATES, INC.; *U.S. Private*, pg. 1844
HALLMARK CLAIMS SERVICE INC.—See Hallmark Financial Services, Inc.; *U.S. Public*, pg. 981
HALLMARK SPECIALTY INSURANCE COMPANY—See Hallmark Financial Services, Inc.; *U.S. Public*, pg. 981
HAMBURGER HOF VERSICHERUNGS-AKTIENGESELLSCHAFT—See E.ON SE; *Int'l*, pg. 2258
HAMMERMAN & GAINER INC.; *U.S. Private*, pg. 1849
HAMPDEN CORPORATE MEMBER LIMITED—See Helios Underwriting PLC; *Int'l*, pg. 3330
HARDY UNDERWRITING LIMITED—See Loews Corporation; *U.S. Public*, pg. 1340
HARLEY-DAVIDSON INSURANCE SERVICES, INC.—See Harley-Davidson, Inc.; *U.S. Public*, pg. 985
HARTZELL INSURANCE ASSOCIATES, INC.—See ABRY Partners, LLC; *U.S. Private*, pg. 42
HAUTEVILLE INSURANCE COMPANY LTD.—See Allianz SE; *Int'l*, pg. 342
HAWAIIAN INSURANCE & GUARANTY COMPANY,

524298 — ALL OTHER INSURANCE...

LTD.—See Great Northwest Insurance Company; *U.S. Private*, pg. 1766
HCV UNDERWRITING MANAGERS (PTY) LIMITED—See Hollard Insurance Company Ltd; *Int'l*, pg. 3451
HDFC ERGO GENERAL INSURANCE COMPANY LTD.—See Housing Development Finance Corporation Limited; *Int'l*, pg. 3492
HDFC STANDARD LIFE INSURANCE COMPANY LTD.—See abrdn PLC; *Int'l*, pg. 68
HDFC STANDARD LIFE INSURANCE COMPANY LTD.—See Housing Development Finance Corporation Limited; *Int'l*, pg. 3492
THE HEALTHCARE UNDERWRITING COMPANY, A RISK RETENTION GROUP—See Tenet Healthcare Corporation; *U.S. Public*, pg. 2009
HEALTHLINK HMO, INC.—See Elevance Health, Inc.; *U.S. Public*, pg. 730
HEALTHOME INC.; *U.S. Public*, pg. 1897
HEALTHSCOPE BENEFITS, INC.; *U.S. Private*, pg. 1897
HEARTLAND FINANCIAL GROUP, INC—See Integrity Marketing Group LLC; *U.S. Private*, pg. 2103
HEATH XS, LLC—See Hallmark Financial Services, Inc.; *U.S. Public*, pg. 981
HELVETIA ASSURANCES S.A.—See Helvetia Holding AG; *Int'l*, pg. 3339
HELVETIA COMPAGNIE SUISSE D'ASSURANCES SA—See Helvetia Holding AG; *Int'l*, pg. 3339
HELVETIA COMPANIA SUIZA SOCIEDAD ANONIMA DE SEGUROS Y REASEGUROS—See Helvetia Holding AG; *Int'l*, pg. 3339
HELVETIA VERSICHERUNGEN AG—See Helvetia Holding AG; *Int'l*, pg. 3340
HELVETIA VERSICHERUNGEN—See Helvetia Holding AG; *Int'l*, pg. 3340
HELVETIA VERSICHERUNGS-AG—See Helvetia Holding AG; *Int'l*, pg. 3340
HELVETIC WARRANTY GMBH—See Helvetia Holding AG; *Int'l*, pg. 3340
HELVIASS VERZEKERINGEN B.V.—See Allianz SE; *Int'l*, pg. 353
HESTIS SAS—See Blackfin Capital Partners SAS; *Int'l*, pg. 1060
HIBARI DEVELOPMENT CO., LTD.—See Bain Capital, LP; *U.S. Private*, pg. 444
HIGH STREET INSURANCE PARTNERS, INC.—See ABRY Partners, LLC; *U.S. Private*, pg. 41
HIMALAYAN EVEREST INSURANCE LIMITED; *Int'l*, pg. 3396
H.J. HEINZ FINANCE UK PLC—See 3G Capital Inc.; *U.S. Private*, pg. 10
H.J. HEINZ FINANCE UK PLC—See Berkshire Hathaway Inc.; *U.S. Public*, pg. 318
HOCHTIEF INSURANCE BROKING & RISK MANAGEMENT SOLUTIONS GMBH—See ACS, Actividades de Construccion y Servicios, S.A.; *Int'l*, pg. 114
HOMESERVE CARE SOLUTIONS LIMITED—See Brookfield Corporation; *Int'l*, pg. 1188
HOMESERVE ENTERPRISES LIMITED—See Brookfield Corporation; *Int'l*, pg. 1188
HONG LEONG ASSURANCE BHD.—See Hong Leong Investment Holdings Pte. Ltd.; *Int'l*, pg. 3468
HOOPER, SPUHLER & STURGEON INSURANCE SERVICES, INC.—See Aquiline Capital Partners LLC; *U.S. Private*, pg. 305
HORAI CO., LTD.; *Int'l*, pg. 3474
HORAK INSURANCE, INC—See Arthur J. Gallagher & Co.; *U.S. Public*, pg. 206
HOSPITAL UNDERWRITING GROUP, INC.—See Tenet Healthcare Corporation; *U.S. Public*, pg. 2004
HOUSING AUTHORITY RISK RETENTION GROUP INC.; *U.S. Private*, pg. 1992
HOWDEN EMPLOYEE BENEFITS LIMITED—See Howden Group Holdings Limited; *Int'l*, pg. 3494
HSBC INSURANCE (ASIA) LIMITED—See HSBC Holdings plc; *Int'l*, pg. 3505
HSBC INSURANCE (IRELAND) LIMITED—See HSBC Holdings plc; *Int'l*, pg. 3505
HSBC REINSURANCE LTD—See HSBC Holdings plc; *Int'l*, pg. 3505
HTK/HUNT TRAINA KENNARD INSURANCE AGENCY, INC.—See World Insurance Associates LLC; *U.S. Private*, pg. 4566
HUB INTERNATIONAL ONTARIO LIMITED—See Hellman & Friedman LLC; *U.S. Private*, pg. 1909
HULL & COMPANY, INC. - TAMPA—See Brown & Brown, Inc.; *U.S. Public*, pg. 401
IAS SERVICES GROUP LLC; *U.S. Private*, pg. 2028
IC GUARDIA—See American International Group, Inc.; *U.S. Public*, pg. 107
IGI PRUDENTIAL INSURANCE LIMITED; *Int'l*, pg. 3602
IMA GROUP MANAGEMENT COMPANY, LLC; *U.S. Private*, pg. 2044
IMERITI, INC.—See Simplicity Financial Marketing Holdings Inc.; *U.S. Private*, pg. 3667
IMPERIAL INSURANCE MANAGERS, LLC—See The Allstate Corporation; *U.S. Public*, pg. 2033
IMPERIUM INSURANCE COMPANY—See SKYWARD SPECIALTY INSURANCE GROUP, INC.; *U.S. Public*, pg. 1893
INDEPENDENT MEDICAL EXPERT CONSULTING SERVICES, INC.—See Apax Partners LLP; *Int'l*, pg. 504
INDUSTRIAL ALLIANCE PACIFIC INSURANCE AND FINANCIAL SERVICES INC.—See iA Financial Corporation Inc.; *Int'l*, pg. 3567
INFINITY INSURANCE AGENCY, INC.—See Kemper Corporation; *U.S. Public*, pg. 1220
INFINITY PROPERTY & CASUALTY SERVICES—See Kemper Corporation; *U.S. Public*, pg. 1220
ING ADMINISTRADORA DE FONDOS DE PENSIONES Y CESANTIAS S.A.—See Grupo de Inversiones Suramericana S.A.; *Int'l*, pg. 3125
INNOVATIVE AFTERMARKET SYSTEMS L.P.—See iA Financial Corporation Inc.; *Int'l*, pg. 3568
INORA LIFE DAC—See Enstar Group Limited; *Int'l*, pg. 2449
INSIA A.S.—See Marsh & McLennan Companies, Inc.; *U.S. Public*, pg. 1376
INSIA EUROPE SE—See Marsh & McLennan Companies, Inc.; *U.S. Public*, pg. 1376
INSIA SK S.R.O.—See Marsh & McLennan Companies, Inc.; *U.S. Public*, pg. 1376
INSIGHT INSURANCE SERVICES, INC.—See Brookfield Reinsurance Ltd.; *Int'l*, pg. 1194
INSURANCEAGENTS.COM; *U.S. Private*, pg. 2095
INSURANCE ANSWER CENTER, LLC—See The Allstate Corporation; *U.S. Public*, pg. 2033
INSURANCE.COM, INC.; *U.S. Private*, pg. 2095
INSURANCE COMPANY OF THE BAHAMAS LIMITED—See Aon plc; *Int'l*, pg. 494
INSURANCE MANAGEMENT COMPANY—See Hellman & Friedman LLC; *U.S. Private*, pg. 1909
THE INSURANCENTER—See American International Group, Inc.; *U.S. Public*, pg. 107
INSURAPRISE INC.; *U.S. Private*, pg. 2095
INSURICA, INC.; *U.S. Private*, pg. 2095
INSZONE INSURANCE SERVICES, LLC; *U.S. Private*, pg. 2096
INTEGON INDEMNITY CORPORATION—See The Allstate Corporation; *U.S. Public*, pg. 2033
INTEGON NATIONAL INSURANCE COMPANY—See The Allstate Corporation; *U.S. Public*, pg. 2033
INTEGRITY MARKETING GROUP LLC; *U.S. Private*, pg. 2103
INTEGRO USA INC.—See Keystone Group, L.P.; *U.S. Private*, pg. 2297
INTERGUARD, LTD.—See Berkshire Hathaway Inc.; *U.S. Public*, pg. 302
INTERNATIONAL CMA RETIREMENT CORP.; *U.S. Private*, pg. 2115
INTERNATIONAL FILM GUARANTORS LLC—See Allianz SE; *Int'l*, pg. 347
INTERNATIONAL FILM GUARANTORS LTD.—See Allianz SE; *Int'l*, pg. 353
INTERNATIONAL FINANCIAL GROUP, INC.—See Assurant, Inc.; *U.S. Public*, pg. 215
INTER PARTNER ASSISTANCE S.A—See AXA S.A.; *Int'l*, pg. 754
INTERSOURCE INSURANCE COMPANY—See MDU Resources Group, Inc.; *U.S. Public*, pg. 1410
INTERSTATE INSURANCE GROUP—See Allianz SE; *Int'l*, pg. 347
INTERSTATE NATIONAL CORPORATION—See Dai-ichi Life Holdings, Inc.; *Int'l*, pg. 1917
INVENSURE INSURANCE BROKERS, INC.—See Hellman & Friedman LLC; *U.S. Private*, pg. 1909
INVESTORS TITLE EXCHANGE CORPORATION—See Investors Title Company; *U.S. Public*, pg. 1165
INVESTORS UNDERWRITING MANAGERS, INC.—See Markel Group Inc.; *U.S. Public*, pg. 1368
INVISION BENEFIT, INC.—See Stone Point Capital LLC; *U.S. Private*, pg. 3819
ISLAMIC ARAB INSURANCE CO. (P.S.C.)—See Dallah Al Baraka Holding Company E.C.; *Int'l*, pg. 1954
ISLAND PREMIER INSURANCE COMPANY, LTD.—See Island Holdings, Inc.; *U.S. Private*, pg. 2145
ISO CLAIMS SERVICES, INC.—See Verisk Analytics, Inc.; *U.S. Public*, pg. 2283
ISZAO PPF INSURANCE—See Assicurazioni Generali S.p.A.; *Int'l*, pg. 646
IVANTAGE INSURANCE BROKERS INC.—See The Allstate Corporation; *U.S. Public*, pg. 2033
IWS ACQUISITION CORPORATION—See Kingsway Financial Services Inc.; *U.S. Public*, pg. 1234
JACKSON SUMNER & ASSOCIATES, INC.; *U.S. Private*, pg. 2178
JACOBS FINANCIAL GROUP, INC.; *U.S. Private*, pg. 2180
JAMAICA INTERNATIONAL INSURANCE COMPANY LIMITED—See GraceKennedy Limited; *Int'l*, pg. 3049
JAMES M. JOHNSTON & ASSOCIATES INC.—See AlphaCore Capital LLC; *U.S. Private*, pg. 200
JAMES RIVER INSURANCE COMPANY—See D. E. Shaw & Co., L.P.; *U.S. Public*, pg. 1139
JARDINE LLOYD THOMPSON AUSTRALIA PTY LIMITED—See Marsh & McLennan Companies, Inc.; *U.S. Public*, pg. 1377
JARDINE LLOYD THOMPSON GROUP PLC—See Marsh & McLennan Companies, Inc.; *U.S. Public*, pg. 1376
JARDINE LLOYD THOMPSON RISK & INSURANCE GROUP—See Marsh & McLennan Companies, Inc.; *U.S. Public*, pg. 1377
JARDINE LLOYD THOMPSON—See Marsh & McLennan Companies, Inc.; *U.S. Public*, pg. 1376
JLT SERVICES CORP.—See Aon plc; *Int'l*, pg. 489
JOHN HACKNEY AGENCY, INC.—See Genstar Capital, LLC; *U.S. Private*, pg. 1674
JONES-WILSON INSURANCE & INVESTMENTS, INC.—See Inszone Insurance Services, LLC; *U.S. Private*, pg. 2096
JRG ADVISORS, LLC—See Emerson Reid LLC; *U.S. Private*, pg. 1382
K2 INSURANCE SERVICES, LLC—See Warburg Pincus LLC; *U.S. Public*, pg. 4438
KAKUTAMA SERVICE CO., LTD.—See Arakawa Chemical Industries, Ltd.; *Int'l*, pg. 534
KALISTRUT AEROSPACE S.A.S.—See Berkshire Hathaway Inc.; *U.S. Public*, pg. 314
KAZAKHINTRAKH JSC—See Halyk Bank of Kazakhstan JSC; *Int'l*, pg. 3234
KB INSURANCE COMPANY LTD.; *U.S. Private*, pg. 2268
KEMPER COST MANAGEMENT, INC.—See Commercial Warranty Solutions, LLC; *U.S. Public*, pg. 985
KENTUCKY SPIRIT HEALTH PLAN, INC.—See Centene Corporation; *U.S. Public*, pg. 469
KEYSTONE AGENCY PARTNERS, LLC—See Bain Capital, LP; *U.S. Private*, pg. 441
KEYSTONE AGENCY PARTNERS, LLC—See Keystone Insurers Group, Inc.; *U.S. Private*, pg. 2300
KILROY REALTY FINANCE PARTNERSHIP, L.P.—See Kilroy Realty Corporation; *U.S. Public*, pg. 1228
KINGSWAY INSURANCE SERVICES LIMITED—See Brown & Brown, Inc.; *U.S. Public*, pg. 401
THE KIRKSEY AGENCY, INC.—See Arthur J. Gallagher & Co.; *U.S. Public*, pg. 207
KISTLER TIFFANY BENEFITS CO.—See New Mountain Capital, LLC; *U.S. Private*, pg. 2901
K&K INSURANCE BROKERS, INC. CANADA—See Aon plc; *Int'l*, pg. 495
K.P.R., INC.—See Northlane Capital Partners, LLC; *U.S. Private*, pg. 2956
KRAMER DIRECT; *U.S. Private*, pg. 2349
KRAVAG UMWELTSCHUTZ UND SICHERHEITSTECHNIK GMBH—See DZ BANK AG Deutsche Zentral-Genossenschaftsbank; *Int'l*, pg. 2244
KYOBO AXA GENERAL INSURANCE CO. LTD.—See AXA S.A.; *Int'l*, pg. 759
KYOEI SHOKUSAN CO. LTD.—See Daicel Corporation; *Int'l*, pg. 1919
KYPROU INSURANCE SERVICES LTD—See Bank of Cyprus Holdings Public Limited Company; *Int'l*, pg. 842
LACLEDE GAS FAMILY SERVICES, INC.—See Spire, Inc; *U.S. Public*, pg. 1918
LACLEDE INSURANCE RISK SERVICES, INC.—See Spire, Inc; *U.S. Public*, pg. 1918
LAIMING INSURANCE GROUP—See Lander Van Gundy Agency, Inc.; *U.S. Private*, pg. 2385
LALANCE FINANCIAL GROUP, INC.—See State Farm Mutual Automobile Insurance Company; *U.S. Private*, pg. 3792
LANDERS UNDERWRITING INC.—See Jackson Sumner & Associates, Inc.; *U.S. Private*, pg. 2178
LAS SERENAS SENIOR APARTMENTS LP—See Berkshire Hathaway Inc.; *U.S. Public*, pg. 298
LCP LIBERA AG—See Alexander Forbes Group Holdings Limited; *Int'l*, pg. 307
LEGACYTEXAS TITLE CO.—See Prosperity Bancshares, Inc.; *U.S. Public*, pg. 1728
LEGAL ACCESS PLANS LLC; *U.S. Private*, pg. 2417
LEGAL & GENERAL (FRANCE) SA—See Groupe Apicil; *Int'l*, pg. 3091
LENFEST GROUP LLC; *U.S. Private*, pg. 2422
L'EQUITE IARD S.A.—See Assicurazioni Generali S.p.A.; *Int'l*, pg. 645
LEZAOLA THOMPSON INSURANCE, INC.—See Thompson Insurance Group; *U.S. Private*, pg. 4160
LIBERTY INSURANCE UNDERWRITERS, INC.—See Liberty Mutual Holding Company Inc.; *U.S. Private*, pg. 2445
LIBERTY INTERNATIONAL UNDERWRITERS—See Liberty Mutual Holding Company Inc.; *U.S. Private*, pg. 2445
LIBERTY SEGUROS—See Liberty Mutual Holding Company Inc.; *U.S. Private*, pg. 2446
LIFE ASSURANCE BANK OF IRELAND LIFE HOLDINGS PLC—See Bank of Ireland Group plc; *Int'l*, pg. 845
LIFE EXCHANGE, INC.; *U.S. Private*, pg. 2448
LIFE INSURANCE COMPANY OF NORTH AMERICA—See The Cigna Group; *U.S. Public*, pg. 2061
LIGHTHOUSE PROPERTY INSURANCE CORP.; *U.S. Private*, pg. 2453
LILYPAD INSURANCE COMPANY—See Arbol Inc.; *U.S. Private*, pg. 308
LINCOLN FINANCIAL ADVISORS CORPORATION—See Lincoln National Corporation; *U.S. Public*, pg. 1319
LINCOLN FINANCIAL LIMITED LIABILITY COMPANY I—See Lincoln National Corporation; *U.S. Public*, pg. 1319

N.A.I.C.S. INDEX

524298 — ALL OTHER INSURANCE...

LINCOLN LIFE & ANNUITY COMPANY OF NEW YORK—See Lincoln National Corporation; *U.S. Public*, pg. 1319

LIONMARK INSURANCE COMPANY—See Ameris Bancorp; *U.S. Public*, pg. 114

LIVERPOOL VICTORIA INSURANCE COMPANY LIMITED—See Allianz SE; *Int'l*, pg. 353

LOCKTON COMPANIES INTERNATIONAL LIMITED—See The Lockton Companies, LLC; *U.S. Private*, pg. 4071

LONDON VERZEKERINGEN N.V.—See Allianz SE; *Int'l*, pg. 349

LOTSOLUTIONS, INC.—See Tiptree Inc.; *U.S. Public*, pg. 2159

LR3 ENTERPRISES INC.; *U.S. Private*, pg. 2507

LSG INSURANCE PARTNERS, INC.—See Arthur J. Gallagher & Co.; *U.S. Public*, pg. 206

LTC FINANCIAL PARTNERS, LLC.—See LTC Global, Inc.; *U.S. Private*, pg. 2509

LUBA MUTUAL HOLDING COMPANY; *U.S. Private*, pg. 2510

LYNX SERVICES, LLC—See Vista Equity Partners, LLC; *U.S. Private*, pg. 4400

THE LYONS COMPANIES; *U.S. Private*, pg. 4073

MACDUFF UNDERWRITERS, INC.—See Brown & Brown, Inc.; *U.S. Public*, pg. 401

MAGNOLIA HEALTH PLAN, INC.—See Centene Corporation; *U.S. Public*, pg. 470

MAJESTIC UNDERWRITERS LLC—See Geneve Holdings Corp.; *U.S. Private*, pg. 1671

MANZI INSURANCE; *U.S. Private*, pg. 2567

MARCH CORREDURIA DE SEGUROS S.A.—See Alba Grupo March; *Int'l*, pg. 292

MARCH-JLT CORREDURIA DE SEGUROS, SA—See Alba Grupo March; *Int'l*, pg. 292

MARKEL CORPORATION; *U.S. Private*, pg. 2578

MARKETFORM HOLDINGS LIMITED—See American Financial Group, Inc.; *U.S. Public*, pg. 103

THE MARKETING ALLIANCE, INC.; *U.S. Public*, pg. 2112

MARSH AS—See Marsh & McLennan Companies, Inc.; *U.S. Public*, pg. 1378

MARSH (BEIJING) INSURANCE BROKERS CO., LTD.—See Marsh & McLennan Companies, Inc.; *U.S. Public*, pg. 1378

MARSH BROCKMAN Y SCHUH AGENTE DE SEGUROS Y DE FIANZAS, S.A. DE C.V.—See Marsh & McLennan Companies, Inc.; *U.S. Public*, pg. 1378

MARSH BROKER DE ASIGURARE-REASIGURARE S.R.L.—See Marsh & McLennan Companies, Inc.; *U.S. Public*, pg. 1378

MARSH BROKERS (HONG KONG) LIMITED—See Marsh & McLennan Companies, Inc.; *U.S. Public*, pg. 1378

MARSH CANADA LIMITED—See Marsh & McLennan Companies, Inc.; *U.S. Public*, pg. 1379

MARSH CORRETORA DE SEGUROS LTDA.—See Marsh & McLennan Companies, Inc.; *U.S. Public*, pg. 1378

MARSH EOOD—See Marsh & McLennan Companies, Inc.; *U.S. Public*, pg. 1378

MARSH EUROFINANCE B.V.—See Marsh & McLennan Companies, Inc.; *U.S. Public*, pg. 1378

MARSH EUROPE S.A.—See Marsh & McLennan Companies, Inc.; *U.S. Public*, pg. 1379

MARSH FINANCE B.V.—See Marsh & McLennan Companies, Inc.; *U.S. Public*, pg. 1378

MARSH FOR INSURANCE SERVICES—See Marsh & McLennan Companies, Inc.; *U.S. Public*, pg. 1378

MARSH GMBH—See Marsh & McLennan Companies, Inc.; *U.S. Public*, pg. 1379

MARSH HOLDINGS B.V.—See Marsh & McLennan Companies, Inc.; *U.S. Public*, pg. 1378

MARSH INSURANCE AND REINSURANCE BROKERS LLC—See Marsh & McLennan Companies, Inc.; *U.S. Public*, pg. 1383

MARSH INSURANCE BROKERS (MALAYSIA) SDN BHD—See Marsh & McLennan Companies, Inc.; *U.S. Public*, pg. 1383

MARSH INVESTMENT B.V.—See Marsh & McLennan Companies, Inc.; *U.S. Public*, pg. 1383

MARSH ISRAEL CONSULTANTS LTD.—See Marsh & McLennan Companies, Inc.; *U.S. Public*, pg. 1383

MARSH KOREA, INC.—See Marsh & McLennan Companies, Inc.; *U.S. Public*, pg. 1383

MARSH, LDA.—See Marsh & McLennan Companies, Inc.; *U.S. Public*, pg. 1384

MARSH LIMITED—See Marsh & McLennan Companies, Inc.; *U.S. Public*, pg. 1379

MARSH LIMITED—See Marsh & McLennan Companies, Inc.; *U.S. Public*, pg. 1383

MARSH LTD.—See Marsh & McLennan Companies, Inc.; *U.S. Public*, pg. 1383

MARSH MANAGEMENT SERVICES INC.—See Marsh & McLennan Companies, Inc.; *U.S. Public*, pg. 1383

MARSH MANAGEMENT SERVICES ISLE OF MAN LIMITED—See Marsh & McLennan Companies, Inc.; *U.S. Public*, pg. 1383

MARSH MANAGEMENT SERVICES MALTA LIMITED—See Marsh & McLennan Companies, Inc.; *U.S. Public*, pg. 1383

MARSH MANAGEMENT SERVICES SWEDEN AB—See Marsh & McLennan Companies, Inc.; *U.S. Public*, pg. 1383

MARSH & MCLENNAN AGENCY AB—See Marsh & McLennan Companies, Inc.; *U.S. Public*, pg. 1377

MARSH & MCLENNAN AGENCY PTY LTD.—See Marsh & McLennan Companies, Inc.; *U.S. Public*, pg. 1377

MARSH & MCLENNAN DEUTSCHLAND GMBH—See Marsh & McLennan Companies, Inc.; *U.S. Public*, pg. 1378

MARSH & MCLENNAN SERVICIOS, S.A. DE C.V.—See Marsh & McLennan Companies, Inc.; *U.S. Public*, pg. 1378

MARSH & MCLENNAN SWEDEN AB—See Marsh & McLennan Companies, Inc.; *U.S. Public*, pg. 1378

MARSH OMAN LLC—See Marsh & McLennan Companies, Inc.; *U.S. Public*, pg. 1383

MARSH OY—See Marsh & McLennan Companies, Inc.; *U.S. Public*, pg. 1383

MARSH PRIVATE CLIENT LIFE INSURANCE SERVICES—See Marsh & McLennan Companies, Inc.; *U.S. Public*, pg. 1383

MARSH (QLD) PTY LTD.—See Marsh & McLennan Companies, Inc.; *U.S. Public*, pg. 1378

MARSH RISK CONSULTING LIMITADA—See Marsh & McLennan Companies, Inc.; *U.S. Public*, pg. 1384

MARSH RISK CONSULTING, S.L.—See Marsh & McLennan Companies, Inc.; *U.S. Public*, pg. 1384

MARSH RISK & INSURANCE SERVICES—See Marsh & McLennan Companies, Inc.; *U.S. Public*, pg. 1382

MARSH S.A. CORREDORES DE SEGUROS—See Marsh & McLennan Companies, Inc.; *U.S. Public*, pg. 1380

MARSH SA—See Marsh & McLennan Companies, Inc.; *U.S. Public*, pg. 1384

MARSH S.A.S.—See Marsh & McLennan Companies, Inc.; *U.S. Public*, pg. 1384

MARSH UGANDA LIMITED—See Marsh & McLennan Companies, Inc.; *U.S. Public*, pg. 1384

MARSH UK HOLDINGS LIMITED—See Marsh & McLennan Companies, Inc.; *U.S. Public*, pg. 1380

MARSH ZAMBIA LIMITED—See Marsh & McLennan Companies, Inc.; *U.S. Public*, pg. 1384

MASON & MASON INSURANCE AGENCY, INC.—See The Baldwin Insurance Group, Inc.; *U.S. Public*, pg. 2035

MATTHIESSEN ASSURANS AB—See Marsh & McLennan Companies, Inc.; *U.S. Public*, pg. 1384

MAXIS GBN S.A.S.—See AXA S.A.; *Int'l*, pg. 759

MAXIS GBN S.A.S.—See MetLife, Inc.; *U.S. Public*, pg. 1430

MAY INSURANCE SERVICES, INC.—See Emerson Reid LLC; *U.S. Private*, pg. 1382

MCCRARY DANIELS INSURANCE AGENCY—See PointeNorth Insurance Group LLC; *U.S. Private*, pg. 3222

MCGOWAN INSURANCE GROUP INC.; *U.S. Private*, pg. 2635

MCGRIFF INSURANCE SERVICES, INC.—See Truist Financial Corporation; *U.S. Public*, pg. 2199

MCLARENS, INC.; *U.S. Private*, pg. 2640

MCLEAN INSURANCE AGENCY—See Arthur J. Gallagher & Co.; *U.S. Public*, pg. 206

MEDCOM CARE MANAGEMENT, INC.—See Gilsbar Inc.; *U.S. Private*, pg. 1701

MEDIOLANUM INTERNATIONAL LIFE—See Banca Mediolanum S.p.A.; *Int'l*, pg. 815

MEDIOLANUM VITA SPA—See Banca Mediolanum S.p.A.; *Int'l*, pg. 815

MERCER, AGENTE DE SEGUROS, S.A. DE C.V.—See Marsh & McLennan Companies, Inc.; *U.S. Public*, pg. 1386

MERCER (BELGIUM) SA-NV—See Marsh & McLennan Companies, Inc.; *U.S. Public*, pg. 1384

MERCER (CANADA) LIMITED—See Marsh & McLennan Companies, Inc.; *U.S. Public*, pg. 1384

MERCER (CZECH) A.S.—See Marsh & McLennan Companies, Inc.; *U.S. Public*, pg. 1384

MERCER HEALTH & BENEFITS ADMINISTRATION LLC—See Marsh & McLennan Companies, Inc.; *U.S. Public*, pg. 1385

MERCER HEALTH & BENEFITS LLC—See Marsh & McLennan Companies, Inc.; *U.S. Public*, pg. 1385

MERCER ITALIA SRL—See Marsh & McLennan Companies, Inc.; *U.S. Public*, pg. 1386

MERCER (NEDERLAND) B.V.—See Marsh & McLennan Companies, Inc.; *U.S. Public*, pg. 1384

MERCER PHILIPPINES, INC.—See Marsh & McLennan Companies, Inc.; *U.S. Public*, pg. 1386

MERCER (PORTUGAL) LDA—See Marsh & McLennan Companies, Inc.; *U.S. Public*, pg. 1384

MERCER SIGORTA BROKERLIGI ANONIM SIRKETI—See Marsh & McLennan Companies, Inc.; *U.S. Public*, pg. 1386

MERCER (SWITZERLAND) SA—See Marsh & McLennan Companies, Inc.; *U.S. Public*, pg. 1385

MERCER TREUHAND GMBH—See Marsh & McLennan Companies, Inc.; *U.S. Public*, pg. 1386

MERCURY INDEMNITY COMPANY OF AMERICA—See Mercury General Corporation; *U.S. Public*, pg. 1421

MERIDIAN CITIZENS MUTUAL INSURANCE COMPANY—See State Automobile Mutual Insurance Company; *U.S. Private*, pg. 3791

MESA UNDERWRITERS SPECIALTY INSURANCE COMPANY—See Selective Insurance Group, Inc.; *U.S. Public*, pg. 1862

MESIROW FINANCIAL STRUCTURED SETTLEMENTS, LLC—See Mesirow Financial Holdings, Inc.; *U.S. Private*, pg. 2678

METLIFE DIRECT CO., LTD.—See MetLife, Inc.; *U.S. Public*, pg. 1431

METLIFE INDIA INSURANCE COMPANY PRIVATE LIMITED—See MetLife, Inc.; *U.S. Public*, pg. 1429

METLIFE INSURANCE LIMITED—See MetLife, Inc.; *U.S. Public*, pg. 1431

METLIFE INVESTORS DISTRIBUTION COMPANY—See MetLife, Inc.; *U.S. Public*, pg. 1431

METLIFE LIMITED—See MetLife, Inc.; *U.S. Public*, pg. 1431

METLIFE MEXICO S.A.—See MetLife, Inc.; *U.S. Public*, pg. 1431

METLIFE POLICYHOLDER TRUST—See MetLife, Inc.; *U.S. Public*, pg. 1431

METROPOLITAN LIFE SEGUROS DE VIDA, S.A.—See MetLife, Inc.; *U.S. Public*, pg. 1431

METROPOLITAN LIFE SEGUROS E PREVIDENCIA PRIVADA S.A.—See MetLife, Inc.; *U.S. Public*, pg. 1431

MFI COMPANIES, LLC—See GTCR LLC; *U.S. Private*, pg. 1803

M HAYES & ASSOCIATES, LLC—See Stone Point Capital LLC; *U.S. Private*, pg. 3823

MIB GROUP INC.; *U.S. Private*, pg. 2697

MICHAEL J. HALL & CO.—See GTCR LLC; *U.S. Private*, pg. 1803

MIDTOWN INSURANCE COMPANY—See The New York Times Company; *U.S. Public*, pg. 2116

MIDWESTONE INSURANCE SERVICES, INC.—See MidWestOne Financial Group, Inc.; *U.S. Public*, pg. 1446

MILLENNIUM MARKETING GROUP, LLC; *U.S. Private*, pg. 2732

MILLIMAN GMBH—See Milliman, Inc.; *U.S. Private*, pg. 2737

MILLIMAN, INC.—See Milliman, Inc.; *U.S. Private*, pg. 2737

MINET INC.—See Aon plc; *Int'l*, pg. 495

MMC UK GROUP LIMITED—See Marsh & McLennan Companies, Inc.; *U.S. Public*, pg. 1378

MMC UK PENSION FUND TRUSTEE LIMITED—See Marsh & McLennan Companies, Inc.; *U.S. Public*, pg. 1378

MONDIAL ASSISTANCE ASIA PACIFIC LTD.—See Allianz SE; *Int'l*, pg. 354

MONDIAL ASSISTANCE/AUTO ASSIST CO., LTD.—See Allianz SE; *Int'l*, pg. 354

MONDIAL ASSISTANCE BELGIUM—See Allianz SE; *Int'l*, pg. 354

MONDIAL ASSISTANCE GMBH—See Allianz SE; *Int'l*, pg. 354

MONDIAL ASSISTANCE GREECE—See Allianz SE; *Int'l*, pg. 354

MONDIAL ASSISTANCE GROUP—See Allianz SE; *Int'l*, pg. 342

MONDIAL ASSISTANCE IRELAND LIMITED—See Allianz SE; *Int'l*, pg. 354

MONDIAL ASSISTANCE OOO—See Allianz SE; *Int'l*, pg. 354

MONDIAL ASSISTANCE REUNION S.A.—See Allianz SE; *Int'l*, pg. 354

MONDIAL ASSISTANCE SIGORTA ARACILIK HIZMETLERI LIMITED SIRKETI, LS—See Allianz SE; *Int'l*, pg. 354

MONDIAL ASSISTANCE SINGAPORE—See Allianz SE; *Int'l*, pg. 342

MONDIAL ASSISTANCE SP. Z O.O.—See Allianz SE; *Int'l*, pg. 354

MONDIAL ASSISTANCE S.R.O—See Allianz SE; *Int'l*, pg. 354

MONDIAL SERVICE ITALIA S.R.L—See Allianz SE; *Int'l*, pg. 354

MONDIAL SERVICES (INDIA) PVT. LTD.—See Allianz SE; *Int'l*, pg. 354

MONDIAL SERVICIOS S.A. DE C.V.—See Allianz SE; *Int'l*, pg. 342

MONTEREY BENEFITS LLC—See S.C. Johnson & Son, Inc.; *U.S. Private*, pg. 3516

MONUMENT ASSURANCE LUXEMBOURG S.A.—See Enstar Group Limited; *Int'l*, pg. 2449

MONUMENT RE LIMITED—See Enstar Group Limited; *Int'l*, pg. 2449

MORGAN INSURANCE SERVICES LIMITED—See Arthur J. Gallagher & Co.; *U.S. Public*, pg. 203

MOSAIC INSURANCE ALLIANCE, LLC—See Inszone Insurance Services, LLC; *U.S. Private*, pg. 2096

MOST INSURANCE AGENCY—See Stone Point Capital LLC; *U.S. Private*, pg. 3819

MOTOR VEHICLE ACCIDENT INDEMNIFICATION CORPORATION; *U.S. Private*, pg. 2797

MRC MARSH RISK CONSULTING GMBH—See Marsh & McLennan Companies, Inc.; *U.S. Public*, pg. 1377

MUBELL FINANCE, LLC—See Shore Bancshares, Inc.; *U.S. Public*, pg. 1875

MUELLER SERVICES, INC.; *U.S. Private*, pg. 2810

MUTUAL CAPITAL HOLDINGS, INC.—See Mutual Capital Group, Inc.; *U.S. Private*, pg. 2819

MYRIAD DEVELOPMENT, INC.; *U.S. Private*, pg. 2825

524298 — ALL OTHER INSURANCE...

NATIONAL ASSOCIATION OF INSURANCE AND FINANCIAL ADVISORS; *U.S. Private*, pg. 2847
NATIONAL AUTOMOTIVE INSURANCE COMPANY—See The Allstate Corporation; *U.S. Public*, pg. 2034
NATIONAL BROKERAGE SERVICES, INC.; *U.S. Private*, pg. 2849
NATIONAL INDEMNITY COMPANY OF MID-AMERICA—See Berkshire Hathaway Inc.; *U.S. Public*, pg. 302
NATIONAL TAKAFUL COMPANY (WATANIA) PJSC—See Dar Al Takaful House PJSC; *Int'l*, pg. 1971
NEIGHBOR'S INSURANCE ADVISORS, INC.—See Seeman Holtz Property & Casualty, LLC; *U.S. Private*, pg. 3598
NETQUOTE, INC.—See Red Ventures, LLC; *U.S. Private*, pg. 3376
NEVADA WEST BUSINESS INSURANCE SERVICES—See GTCR LLC; *U.S. Private*, pg. 1803
NEW ENGLAND RISK SPECIALISTS—See American International Group, Inc.; *U.S. Public*, pg. 107
NEW YORK COMPENSATION INSURANCE RATING BOARD; *U.S. Private*, pg. 2909
NEW YORK MUNICIPAL POWER AGENCY; *U.S. Private*, pg. 2911
NEXTCARE EGYPT LLC—See Allianz SE; *Int'l*, pg. 354
NFP-AIS INSURANCE SERVICES, INC.—See Aon plc; *Int'l*, pg. 497
NFP MID-ATLANTIC SG, LLC—See Aon plc; *Int'l*, pg. 497
NIF GROUP, INC.—See The Carlyle Group Inc.; *U.S. Public*, pg. 2047
NORTH AMERICAN CASUALTY CO.—See Berkshire Hathaway Inc.; *U.S. Public*, pg. 313
NORTHCOAST WARRANTY SERVICES, INC.—See Stone Point Capital LLC; *U.S. Private*, pg. 3821
NORTHERN STAR MANAGEMENT, INC.—See Norman-Spencer Agency, Inc.; *U.S. Private*, pg. 2938
NORTHSHORE INTERNATIONAL INSURANCE SERVICES INC.—See HGGC, LLC; *U.S. Private*, pg. 1929
NORTHWESTERN LONG TERM CARE INSURANCE COMPANY—See The Northwestern Mutual Life Insurance Company; *U.S. Private*, pg. 4085
NORTHWESTERN MUTUAL ATLANTIC BENEFIT GROUP—See The Northwestern Mutual Life Insurance Company; *U.S. Private*, pg. 4085
NORTON INSURANCE LIMITED—See Compagnie de Saint-Gobain SA; *Int'l*, pg. 1731
NOVA INSURANCE CONSULTANTS LIMITED—See FSE Services Group Limited; *Int'l*, pg. 2798
OBERLIN MARKETING CO., INC.—See Integrity Marketing Group LLC; *U.S. Private*, pg. 2104
OJSC ROSNO—See Allianz SE; *Int'l*, pg. 354
OLD REPUBLIC AEROSPACE, INC.—See Old Republic International Corporation; *U.S. Public*, pg. 1568
OLD REPUBLIC GENERAL INSURANCE CORPORATION—See Old Republic International Corporation; *U.S. Public*, pg. 1568
OLD REPUBLIC INSURANCE COMPANY OF CANADA—See Old Republic International Corporation; *U.S. Public*, pg. 1568
OLD REPUBLIC INSURED AUTOMOTIVE SERVICES, INC.—See Old Republic International Corporation; *U.S. Public*, pg. 1568
OLD REPUBLIC RISK MANAGEMENT, INC.—See Old Republic International Corporation; *U.S. Public*, pg. 1568
OLD REPUBLIC TITLE INSURANCE AGENCY, INC.—See Old Republic International Corporation; *U.S. Public*, pg. 1569
OLIVER WYMAN AB—See Marsh & McLennan Companies, Inc.; *U.S. Public*, pg. 1387
OMEGA INSURANCE AGENCY, INC.—See HCI Group, Inc.; *U.S. Public*, pg. 1014
ONE80 INTERMEDIARIES LLC; *U.S. Private*, pg. 3024
ONEDIGITAL HEALTH & BENEFITS—See New Mountain Capital, LLC; *U.S. Private*, pg. 2901
ONEGROUP NY, INC.—See Community Bank System, Inc.; *U.S. Public*, pg. 550
OPTIKA A/S—See Aon plc; *Int'l*, pg. 495
OPTUMRX PBM OF WISCONSIN, LLC—See UnitedHealth Group Incorporated; *U.S. Public*, pg. 2247
ORBITA, AGENCIA DE SEGUROS—See Grupo Catalana Occidente, S.A.; *Int'l*, pg. 3124
ORGANIZACION BROCKMAN Y SCHUH S.A. DE C.V.—See Marsh & McLennan Companies, Inc.; *U.S. Public*, pg. 1388
ORIENT INSURANCE PJSC—See Al-Futtaim Private Company LLC; *Int'l*, pg. 285
ORIGENES SEGUROS DE RETIRO, S.A.—See Grupo EMES S.A.; *Int'l*, pg. 3126
OWNERGUARD CORPORATION—See Stone Point Capital LLC; *U.S. Private*, pg. 3821
OXBOW MARKETING COMPANY—See Simplicity Financial Marketing Holdings Inc.; *U.S. Private*, pg. 3667
PACIFIC LIFE RE LIMITED—See Pacific Mutual Holding Company; *U.S. Private*, pg. 3069
PACIFIC LIFE RE LIMITED—See Pacific Mutual Holding Company; *U.S. Private*, pg. 3069
PANDIAS RE AG—See Bayer Aktiengesellschaft; *Int'l*, pg. 910

PARAGON INSURANCE HOLDINGS, LLC; *U.S. Private*, pg. 3091
PATRIOT UNDERWRITERS, INC.—See Patriot National, Inc.; *U.S. Private*, pg. 3110
PCC AIRFOILS LLC—See Berkshire Hathaway Inc.; *U.S. Public*, pg. 314
PELTOURS INSURANCE AGENCIES LTD.—See Assicurazioni Generali S.p.A.; *Int'l*, pg. 647
PEMBROKE MANAGING AGENCY LIMITED—See Hamilton Insurance Group, Ltd.; *Int'l*, pg. 3238
PENN TREATY NETWORK AMERICA INSURANCE COMPANY—See Penn Treaty American Corporation; *U.S. Private*, pg. 3135
PENSION BENEFITS UNLIMITED, INC.—See Lightyear Capital LLC; *U.S. Private*, pg. 2454
PETHEALTH INC.—See Fairfax Financial Holdings Limited; *Int'l*, pg. 2608
PGIM JAPAN CO,. LTD.—See Prudential Financial, Inc.; *U.S. Public*, pg. 1732
PHARMACISTS MUTUAL COMPANIES; *U.S. Private*, pg. 3165
PHENIX COMPAGNIE D'ASSURANCES—See Allianz SE; *Int'l*, pg. 342
PHYSICIANS RECIPROCAL INSURERS—See Administrators for the Professions, Inc.; *U.S. Private*, pg. 81
PILOT INSURANCE COMPANY—See Aviva plc; *Int'l*, pg. 745
PINE HILL GROUP LLC—See The Carlyle Group Inc.; *U.S. Public*, pg. 2045
PINNACLE UNDERWRITING LIMITED—See BNP Paribas SA; *Int'l*, pg. 1092
THE PLEXUS GROUPE, INC.; *U.S. Private*, pg. 4096
POINTER LOCALIZACION Y ASISTENCIA S.A—See PowerFleet, Inc.; *U.S. Public*, pg. 1706
POLENZANI BENEFITS & INSURANCE SERVICES, LLC—See IMA Financial Group, Inc.; *U.S. Private*, pg. 2043
POLISEEK AIS INSURANCE SOLUTIONS, INC.—See Mercury General Corporation; *U.S. Public*, pg. 1422
POLSKIE TOWARZYSTWO REASEKURACJI SPOLKA AKCYJNA—See Fairfax Financial Holdings Limited; *Int'l*, pg. 2608
POLYCOMP ADMINISTRATIVE SERVICES, INC.—See Aquiline Capital Partners LLC; *U.S. Private*, pg. 304
POLYCOMP ADMINISTRATIVE SERVICES, INC.—See Genstar Capital, LLC; *U.S. Private*, pg. 1675
PRAMERICA ZYCIE TOWARZYSTWO UBEZPIECZEN I REASEKURACJI SPOLKA AKCYJNA—See Unum Group; *U.S. Public*, pg. 2263
PREFERRED EMPLOYERS INSURANCE COMPANY—See W.R. Berkley Corporation; *U.S. Public*, pg. 2318
PREFERRED HEALTH PROFESSIONALS, INC.—See Blue Cross & Blue Shield of Kansas City, Inc.; *U.S. Private*, pg. 587
PREFERRED MOTOR SPORTS RISK PURCHASING GROUP, LLC—See Wells Fargo & Company; *U.S. Public*, pg. 2345
PREMIER INSURANCE CORPORATION, INC.—See GTCR LLC; *U.S. Private*, pg. 1804
PREMIUM ASSIGNMENT CORPORATION—See IPFS Corporation; *U.S. Private*, pg. 2136
PREMIUM FINANCE COMPANY (E.C.) LTD.—See Lockhart Companies Inc.; *U.S. Private*, pg. 2478
PRIMELUX INSURANCE S.A.—See Deutsche Bank Aktiengesellschaft; *Int'l*, pg. 2061
PRIME PENSIONS, INC.—See Lightyear Capital LLC; *U.S. Private*, pg. 2454
PRIMERO SEGUROS, S.A. DE C.V.—See Stone Point Capital LLC; *U.S. Private*, pg. 3821
PRINCETON RISK PROTECTION, INC.—See Berkshire Hathaway Inc.; *U.S. Public*, pg. 302
PRINCIPAL FINANCIAL GROUP, INC. INDIANAPOLIS—See Principal Financial Group, Inc.; *U.S. Public*, pg. 1720
PRINCIPAL FINANCIAL GROUP, INC. - RALEIGH—See Principal Financial Group, Inc.; *U.S. Public*, pg. 1721
PROASSURANCE INDEMNITY COMPANY—See ProAssurance Corporation; *U.S. Public*, pg. 1723
PROFESSIONAL LINES UNDERWRITING SPECIALISTS, INC.—See IMA Financial Group, Inc.; *U.S. Private*, pg. 2044
PROFESSIONAL PENSIONS, INC.—See Principal Financial Group, Inc.; *U.S. Public*, pg. 1722
PROFESSIONAL RISK MANAGEMENT SERVICES, INC.—See Berkshire Hathaway Inc.; *U.S. Public*, pg. 299
PROFESSIONAL WARRANTY SERVICE CORPORATION—See PCF Insurance Services of The West, LLC; *U.S. Private*, pg. 3120
PROGRESSIVE HAWAII INSURANCE CORP.—See The Progressive Corporation; *U.S. Public*, pg. 2124
PROGRESSIVE PREMIER INSURANCE COMPANY OF ILLINOIS—See The Progressive Corporation; *U.S. Public*, pg. 2125
PROGRESSIVE SPECIALTY INSURANCE COMPANY—See The Progressive Corporation; *U.S. Public*, pg. 2125

PROPEL INSURANCE-SEATTLE—See Edwards Capital, LLC; *U.S. Private*, pg. 1342
PROSPERITY GROUP HOLDINGS, LP; *U.S. Private*, pg. 3289
PRUDENCE CREOLE S.A.—See Assicurazioni Generali S.p.A.; *Int'l*, pg. 645
PRUDENTIAL SEGUROS MEXICO, S.A.—See Prudential Financial, Inc.; *U.S. Public*, pg. 1732
PRUDENTIAL SERVICIOS, S. DE R.L. DE C.V.—See Prudential Financial, Inc.; *U.S. Public*, pg. 1732
PT. FLO-BEND INDONESIA—See Berkshire Hathaway Inc.; *U.S. Public*, pg. 314
PT MERCER INDONESIA—See Marsh & McLennan Companies, Inc.; *U.S. Public*, pg. 1388
PT TECPROTEC—See Stone Point Capital LLC; *U.S. Private*, pg. 3821
PURDUM GRAY INGLEDUE BECK, INC.—See First Mid Bancshares, Inc.; *U.S. Public*, pg. 846
QUALITY PLANNING CORPORATION—See Verisk Analytics, Inc.; *U.S. Public*, pg. 2283
QUINSTREET INSURANCE AGENCY, INC.—See QuinStreet, Inc.; *U.S. Public*, pg. 1757
QUOTEWIZARD.COM LLC—See LendingTree, Inc.; *U.S. Public*, pg. 1305
RAC INSURANCE PARTNERS, LLC—See The Allstate Corporation; *U.S. Public*, pg. 2034
RADIAN GUARANTY INC.—See Radian Group, Inc.; *U.S. Public*, pg. 1759
RBS CITIZENS INSURANCE AGENCY, INC.—See Citizens Financial Group, Inc.; *U.S. Public*, pg. 506
REAAL SCHADEVERZEKERINGEN N.V.—See Apollo Global Management, Inc.; *U.S. Public*, pg. 147
RECOVERY SERVICES INTERNATIONAL, INC.—See Chubb Limited; *Int'l*, pg. 1593
REGAL AVIATION INSURANCE—See GTCR LLC; *U.S. Private*, pg. 1804
REGIONAL REPORTING INC.; *U.S. Private*, pg. 3389
REHABILITATIONSKLINIK BARBY BESITZGESELLSCHAFT MBH—See Advent International Corporation; *U.S. Private*, pg. 97
REHABILITATIONSKLINIK BARBY BESITZGESELLSCHAFT MBH—See Centerbridge Partners, L.P.; *U.S. Private*, pg. 813
REKORD VERSICHERUNGVERMITTLUNGS-UND BETREUUNGSGESELLSCHAFT FUR SELBSTANDIGE MBH & CO. KG—See Dexia SA; *Int'l*, pg. 2092
RELATION INSURANCE, INC.—See Aquiline Capital Partners LLC; *U.S. Private*, pg. 305
RENTERS LEGAL LIABILITY LLC.—See DOXA Insurance Holdings LLC; *U.S. Private*, pg. 1270
RGA INTERNATIONAL REINSURANCE COMPANY—See Reinsurance Group of America, Inc.; *U.S. Public*, pg. 1777
RGA REINSURANCE UK LIMITED—See Reinsurance Group of America, Inc.; *U.S. Public*, pg. 1778
RICHARDS HOGG LINDLEY (HELLAS) LTD.—See Lovell Minnick Partners LLC; *U.S. Private*, pg. 2502
RIGHT ANSWER INSURANCE AGENCY, LLC—See The Allstate Corporation; *U.S. Public*, pg. 2034
RISCO INSURANCE SERVICES, INC.—See Inszone Insurance Services, LLC; *U.S. Private*, pg. 2096
RISK ENTERPRISE MANAGEMENT LIMITED; *U.S. Private*, pg. 3440
RISK & INSURANCE S.A.—See Achmea B.V.; *Int'l*, pg. 103
RISK INTERNATIONAL SERVICES INC.—See Arthur J. Gallagher & Co.; *U.S. Public*, pg. 202
RISK MANAGEMENT PARTNERS LTD.—See Arthur J. Gallagher & Co.; *U.S. Public*, pg. 203
RISK PLANNERS, INC.—See Arthur J. Gallagher & Co.; *U.S. Public*, pg. 207
RISKRIGHTER, LLC—See Truist Financial Corporation; *U.S. Public*, pg. 2200
RISK SERVICES, LLC—See Stone Point Capital LLC; *U.S. Private*, pg. 3821
RITTER INSURANCE MARKETING; *U.S. Private*, pg. 3442
RIVERSTONE INSURANCE (UK) LIMITED—See CVC Capital Partners SICAV-FIS S.A.; *Int'l*, pg. 1884
RIVERSTONE MANAGING AGENCY LIMITED—See Fairfax Financial Holdings Limited; *Int'l*, pg. 2608
RLI CORP.; *U.S. Public*, pg. 1801
R. MEES & ZOONEN ASSURADEUREN B.V.—See Marsh & McLennan Companies, Inc.; *U.S. Public*, pg. 1388
RMTS, LLC; *U.S. Private*, pg. 3452
ROADZEN, INC.; *U.S. Public*, pg. 1802
ROSENBAUM FINANCIAL, INC.—See Hersman Serles Almond PLLC; *U.S. Private*, pg. 1927
ROSENBAUM FINANCIAL, INC.—See Seidman Insurance Consultants LLC; *U.S. Private*, pg. 3599
ROUTE MOBIEL—See Apollo Global Management, Inc.; *U.S. Public*, pg. 148
ROUX AGENCY, INC.—See Aon plc; *Int'l*, pg. 497
ROYAL OAK UNDERWRITERS, INC.—See AmWINS Group, Inc.; *U.S. Private*, pg. 270
RRS, INC.; *U.S. Private*, pg. 3496
RSG UNDERWRITING MANAGERS, LLC—See Ryan Specialty Holdings, Inc.; *U.S. Public*, pg. 1828
RSUI GROUP, INC.—See Berkshire Hathaway Inc.; *U.S. Public*, pg. 299

N.A.I.C.S. INDEX

524298 — ALL OTHER INSURANCE...

R+V SERVICE CENTER GMBH—See DZ BANK AG Deutsche Zentral-Genossenschaftsbank; *Int'l*, pg. 2244
RYAN SPECIALTY GROUP, LLC - SWEDEN—See Ryan Specialty Holdings, Inc.; *U.S. Public*, pg. 1828
SAFECO SURETY—See Liberty Mutual Holding Company Inc.; *U.S. Private*, pg. 2446
SAFE-GUARD PRODUCTS INTERNATIONAL, LLC—See Stone Point Capital LLC; *U.S. Private*, pg. 3825
SAGICOR GENERAL INSURANCE INC.—See Alignvest Management Corporation; *Int'l*, pg. 327
SAGICOR PANAMA SA—See Alignvest Management Corporation; *Int'l*, pg. 328
SANTANDER INSURANCE SERVICES UK LIMITED—See Banco Santander, S.A.; *Int'l*, pg. 827
SANTO INSURANCE & FINANCIAL SERVICES, INC.—See Aquiline Capital Partners LLC; *U.S. Private*, pg. 305
SCHLATHER INSURANCE AGENCY INC.—See Northlane Capital Partners, LLC; *U.S. Private*, pg. 2956
SCHUSTER VERSICHERUNGSMAKLER GMBH—See DZ BANK AG Deutsche Zentral-Genossenschaftsbank; *Int'l*, pg. 2244
SCILDON N.V.—See Chesnara Plc; *Int'l*, pg. 1472
S.C. LA QUERCIA S.R.L.—See Assicurazioni Generali S.p.A.; *Int'l*, pg. 647
SEACOAST SPECIALTY ADMINISTRATORS, INC.—See One80 Intermediaries LLC; *U.S. Private*, pg. 3024
SEACOAST UNDERWRITERS, INC.—See Arthur J. Gallagher & Co.; *U.S. Public*, pg. 207
SEACURUS LIMITED—See Arch Capital Group Ltd.; *Int'l*, pg. 547
SECURIAN FINANCIAL SERVICES, INC.—See Securian Financial Group, Inc.; *U.S. Private*, pg. 3594
SEDGWICK BELGIUM SA—See The Carlyle Group Inc.; *U.S. Public*, pg. 2053
SEDGWICK FRANCE S.A.—See The Carlyle Group Inc.; *U.S. Public*, pg. 2053
SEDGWICK INTERNATIONAAL B.V.—See Marsh & McLennan Companies, Inc.; *U.S. Public*, pg. 1388
SEDGWICK INTERNATIONAL UK—See The Carlyle Group Inc.; *U.S. Public*, pg. 2054
SEDGWICK NEDERLAND B.V.—See The Carlyle Group Inc.; *U.S. Public*, pg. 2053
SEDGWICK RISK SERVICES LIMITED—See The Carlyle Group Inc.; *U.S. Public*, pg. 2054
SEGURCAIXA ADESLAS, S.A. DE SEGUROS Y REASEGUROS—See Lone Star Funds; *U.S. Private*, pg. 2485
SEGUROS BANAMEX, S.A. DE C.V.—See Citigroup Inc.; *U.S. Public*, pg. 504
SEGUROS BILBAO FONDOS S.G.I.I.C.—See Grupo Catalana Occidente, S.A.; *Int'l*, pg. 3124
SEGUROS DE RIESGOS PROFESIONALES SURAMERICANA S.A.—See Grupo de Inversiones Suramericana S.A.; *Int'l*, pg. 3126
SEGUROS GENESIS, S.A.—See Liberty Mutual Holding Company Inc.; *U.S. Private*, pg. 2446
SEGUROS MONTERREY NEW YORK LIFE, S.A.—See New York Life Insurance Company; *U.S. Private*, pg. 2910
SEGUROS SURAMERICANA S.A.—See Grupo de Inversiones Suramericana S.A.; *Int'l*, pg. 3126
SEGUROS SURA, S.A DE C.V.—See Grupo de Inversiones Suramericana S.A.; *Int'l*, pg. 3126
SEIB INSURANCE BROKERS LIMITED—See Ecclesiastical Insurance Office plc; *Int'l*, pg. 2288
SELECTIVE CASUALTY INSURANCE COMPANY—See Selective Insurance Group, Inc.; *U.S. Public*, pg. 1862
SENIOR MARKET SALES, INC.—See Stone Point Capital LLC; *U.S. Private*, pg. 3819
SENTRY GROUP—See Sentry Insurance Group; *U.S. Private*, pg. 3611
SEQUOIA INSURANCE COMPANY—See Stone Point Capital LLC; *U.S. Private*, pg. 3821
SERVICIOS REUNIDOS, S.A.—See Banco de Sabadell, S.A.; *Int'l*, pg. 821
SHINSTROM & NORMAN, INC.—See Hellman & Friedman LLC; *U.S. Private*, pg. 1909
SIA "AON CONSULTING"—See Aon plc; *Int'l*, pg. 495
SICA FLETCHER, LLC; *U.S. Private*, pg. 3645
SIGNATURE INSURANCE AGENCY, INC.—See Triple-S Management Corp.; *U.S. Public*, pg. 2195
SIGNATURE MOTOR CLUB, INC.—See The Allstate Corporation; *U.S. Public*, pg. 2034
SIGNET STAR HOLDINGS, INC.—See W.R. Berkley Corporation; *U.S. Public*, pg. 2318
SIG SPORTS, LEISURE AND ENTERTAINMENT RISK PURCHASING GROUP, LLC—See Everest Group, Ltd.; *Int'l*, pg. 2564
SKANDIA A/S—See Foreningen AP Pension f.m.b.a.; *Int'l*, pg. 2731
SLEEPER SEWELL INSURANCE SERVICES, INC.—See Aquiline Capital Partners LLC; *U.S. Private*, pg. 305
SLE WORLDWIDE PTY LIMITED—See The Hanover Insurance Group, Inc.; *U.S. Public*, pg. 2087
SMITH BROTHERS INSURANCE, LLC; *U.S. Private*, pg. 3694
SOCIEDAD MUNDIAL DE ASISTENCIA S.A.—See Allianz SE; *Int'l*, pg. 355

SOCIETE NATIONALE D'ASSURANCES S.A.L.—See Allianz SE; *Int'l*, pg. 342
SOLIDARITY BAHRAIN B.S.C.—See First Insurance Co.; *Int'l*, pg. 2684
SOLIDARITY SAUDI TAKAFUL COMPANY—See Al Jazira Takaful Ta'awuni Company; *Int'l*, pg. 280
SOMERSET CASUALTY INSURANCE COMPANY—See Brookfield Reinsurance Ltd.; *Int'l*, pg. 1194
SOVEREIGN RISK INSURANCE LIMITED—See Chubb Limited; *Int'l*, pg. 1590
SPECIALTY INSURANCE GROUP, INC.—See Everest Group, Ltd.; *Int'l*, pg. 2564
SPRING VENTURE GROUP, LLC; *U.S. Private*, pg. 3763
SSDC SERVICES CORP.; *U.S. Private*, pg. 3768
STAFFORD & COMPANY INSURANCE LTD.; *U.S. Private*, pg. 3775
STARSEED MEDICINAL INC.—See Entourage Health Corp.; *Int'l*, pg. 2452
STARSTONE INSURANCE SE—See Enstar Group Limited; *Int'l*, pg. 2449
STARSTONE NATIONAL INSURANCE COMPANY—See Enstar Group Limited; *Int'l*, pg. 2449
STARSTONE SPECIALTY INSURANCE COMPANY—See Enstar Group Limited; *Int'l*, pg. 2449
S&T-EVERGREEN INSURANCE, LLC—See S&T Bancorp, Inc.; *U.S. Public*, pg. 1832
STEWART C MILLER & CO. INC.; *U.S. Private*, pg. 3811
STEWART TITLE GUARANTY COMPANY—See Stewart Information Services Corporation; *U.S. Public*, pg. 1948
ST. PAUL MERCURY INSURANCE COMPANY—See The Travelers Companies, Inc.; *U.S. Public*, pg. 2136
STRATEGIC RISK SOLUTIONS INC.—See Strategic Risk Solutions Inc.; *U.S. Private*, pg. 3835
STRAUS, ITZKOWITZ & LECOMPTE INSURANCE AGENCY, INC.—See Towne Bank; *U.S. Public*, pg. 2166
SUMMIT CONSULTING, LLC—See American Financial Group, Inc.; *U.S. Public*, pg. 103
SUMMIT GROUP, INC.—See Retirement, LLC - Series Two; *U.S. Private*, pg. 3412
SUNZ INSURANCE COMPANY; *U.S. Private*, pg. 3874
SUSSEX INSURANCE COMPANY—See Enstar Group Limited; *Int'l*, pg. 2449
S&V INSURANCE SERVICES LLC; *U.S. Private*, pg. 3514
SYRIA INTERNATIONAL INSURANCE COMPANY—See BLOM Bank, S.A.L.; *Int'l*, pg. 1064
SYRIAN KUWAITI INSURANCE COMPANY—See Fairfax Financial Holdings Limited; *Int'l*, pg. 2607
TALBOT UNDERWRITING LTD.—See American International Group, Inc.; *U.S. Public*, pg. 107
TALBOT UNDERWRITING (MENA) LTD.—See American International Group, Inc.; *U.S. Public*, pg. 107
TALBOT UNDERWRITING RISK SERVICES LTD.—See American International Group, Inc.; *U.S. Public*, pg. 107
TAL SERVICES LIMITED—See Dai-ichi Life Holdings, Inc.; *Int'l*, pg. 1918
TAWA MANAGEMENT LTD.—See Financière Pinault SCA; *Int'l*, pg. 2669
TAYLOR BUILDING CORPORATION OF AMERICA; *U.S. Private*, pg. 3937
TEACHERS INSURANCE & ANNUITY ASSOCIATION OF AMERICA—See Teachers Insurance Association - College Retirement Fund; *U.S. Private*, pg. 3945
TECH-COR, LLC—See The Allstate Corporation; *U.S. Public*, pg. 2034
TECPROTEC ASIA PRIVATE LIMITED—See Stone Point Capital LLC; *U.S. Private*, pg. 3821
TECPROTEC SDN BHD—See Stone Point Capital LLC; *U.S. Private*, pg. 3821
TEXSTAR INSURANCE SERVICES, INC.—See Inszone Insurance Services, LLC; *U.S. Private*, pg. 2096
THB RISK SOLUTIONS LIMITED—See AmWINS Group, Inc.; *U.S. Private*, pg. 270
THERIUM CAPITAL MANAGEMENT LIMITED—See Stone Point Capital LLC; *U.S. Private*, pg. 3821
THOMPSON INSURANCE GROUP; *U.S. Private*, pg. 4160
TIC INTERNATIONAL CORPORATION; *U.S. Private*, pg. 4167
TITLEONE CORP.—See Anywhere Real Estate Inc.; *U.S. Public*, pg. 142
TML INTERGOVERNMENTAL RISK POOL; *U.S. Private*, pg. 4179
TONGYANG LIFE INSURANCE CO., LTD.—See Anbang Insurance Group Co., Ltd.; *Int'l*, pg. 447
TORUS CORPORATE CAPITAL LTD.—See Enstar Group Limited; *Int'l*, pg. 2449
TORUS NATIONAL INSURANCE COMPANY—See Enstar Group Limited; *Int'l*, pg. 2449
TORUS UNDERWRITING MANAGEMENT LTD.—See Enstar Group Limited; *Int'l*, pg. 2449
TORUS US INTERMEDIARIES INC—See Enstar Group Limited; *Int'l*, pg. 2449
TRANSAMERICA CORPORATION—See Aegon N.V.; *Int'l*, pg. 174
TRANS-NEMWIL INSURANCE (GRENADA) LTD—See Guardian Holdings Limited; *Int'l*, pg. 3171
TRAUTMANN, MAHER & ASSOCIATES, INC.—See Northwest Plan Services, Inc.; *U.S. Private*, pg. 2961
TRAVEL GUARD AMERICAS LLC—See American International Group, Inc.; *U.S. Public*, pg. 106
TRICENTURION INC.—See GuideWell Mutual Holding Corporation; *U.S. Private*, pg. 1814
TRIDENT INSURANCE COMPANY LIMITED—See ANSA McAL Limited; *Int'l*, pg. 476
TRINIDAD & TOBAGO INSURANCE LIMITED—See ANSA McAL Limited; *Int'l*, pg. 477
TRIPLE-C, INC.—See Triple-S Management Corp.; *U.S. Public*, pg. 2195
TRISTAR INSURANCE GROUP, INC.; *U.S. Private*, pg. 4238
TRISTAR RISK MANAGEMENT INC.; *U.S. Private*, pg. 4238
TSB LOSS CONTROL CONSULTANTS, INC.—See Factory Mutual Insurance Company; *U.S. Private*, pg. 1461
T&T2 INC—See Hellman & Friedman LLC; *U.S. Private*, pg. 1909
TU ALLIANZ ZYCIE POLSKA S.A.—See Allianz SE; *Int'l*, pg. 356
TUSCARORA WAYNE INSURANCE CO.—See Mutual Capital Group, Inc.; *U.S. Private*, pg. 2819
UADBB AON BALTIC—See Aon plc; *Int'l*, pg. 495
UAD BB MARSH LIETUVA—See Marsh & McLennan Companies, Inc.; *U.S. Public*, pg. 1388
UNDERWRITING RISK SERVICES S.A.—See American International Group, Inc.; *U.S. Public*, pg. 107
UNICO SIGORTA A.S.—See EMF Capital Partners Limited; *Int'l*, pg. 2380
UNIFIED GROCERS INSURANCE SERVICES—See Stone Point Capital LLC; *U.S. Private*, pg. 3821
UNIFORMED SERVICES BENEFIT ASSOCIATION; *U.S. Private*, pg. 4283
UNION SECURITY LIFE INSURANCE COMPANY OF NEW YORK—See Assurant, Inc.; *U.S. Public*, pg. 216
UNION STANDARD INSURANCE COMPANY—See W.R. Berkley Corporation; *U.S. Public*, pg. 2318
UNION TITLE COMPANY, LLC—See Farmers & Merchants Investment Inc.; *U.S. Private*, pg. 1476
UNITED EDUCATORS INSURANCE, A RECIPROCAL RISK RETENTION GROUP, INC.; *U.S. Private*, pg. 4291
UNITED HOME INSURANCE COMPANY, A RISK RETENTION GROUP—See Beazer Homes USA, Inc.; *U.S. Public*, pg. 288
UNITED INSURANCE CO.—See Hayel Saeed Anam Group of Companies; *Int'l*, pg. 3291
UNITED LEASING COMPANY LIMITED—See Camellia Plc; *Int'l*, pg. 1271
UNITED WISCONSIN INSURANCE COMPANY—See Accident Fund Insurance Company of America; *U.S. Private*, pg. 53
THE UNIVERSAL INSURANCE COMPANY LIMITED—See Bibojee Services Private Limited; *Int'l*, pg. 1018
UNIVERSAL WARRANTY CORP.; *U.S. Private*, pg. 4307
UNIVERSITY HEALTH PLANS, INC—See Kelso & Company, L.P.; *U.S. Private*, pg. 2280
UNIVEST INSURANCE, INC.—See Univest Financial Corporation; *U.S. Public*, pg. 2263
USABLE MCO—See USAble Corporation; *U.S. Private*, pg. 4322
USI AFFINITY—See Caisse de Depot et Placement du Quebec; *Int'l*, pg. 1257
USI AFFINITY—See KKR & Co. Inc.; *U.S. Public*, pg. 1265
USI INSURANCE SERVICES OF CONNECTICUT, LLC—See Caisse de Depot et Placement du Quebec; *Int'l*, pg. 1257
USI INSURANCE SERVICES OF CONNECTICUT, LLC—See KKR & Co. Inc.; *U.S. Public*, pg. 1266
USIS, INC.—See Brown & Brown, Inc.; *U.S. Public*, pg. 402
U.S. RISK MANAGEMENT, INC.—See Caisse de Depot et Placement du Quebec; *Int'l*, pg. 1257
U.S. RISK MANAGEMENT, INC.—See KKR & Co. Inc.; *U.S. Public*, pg. 1266
VALIDUS RESEARCH INC.—See American International Group, Inc.; *U.S. Public*, pg. 107
VANDER HAEGHEN & CO SA—See Enstar Group Limited; *Int'l*, pg. 2449
VAUGHT WRIGHT & BOND, INC.—See Inszone Insurance Services, LLC; *U.S. Private*, pg. 2096
VECTOR SECURITY, INC.—See The Philadelphia Contributionship; *U.S. Private*, pg. 4094
VEHICLE ADMINISTRATIVE SERVICES, LTD.—See Brown & Brown, Inc.; *U.S. Public*, pg. 402
VEREINTE SPEZIAL KRANKENVERSICHERUNG AKTIENGESELLSCHAFT—See Allianz SE; *Int'l*, pg. 356
VERHAGEN GLENDENNING & WALKER LLP—See Brown & Brown, Inc.; *U.S. Public*, pg. 398
VIDACAIXA, S.A. DE SEGUROS Y REASEGUROS—See Lone Star Funds; *U.S. Private*, pg. 2485
VIRTUS LLC; *U.S. Private*, pg. 4389
VISTA SURETY INSURANCE SOLUTIONS, LLC—See Stone Point Capital LLC; *U.S. Private*, pg. 3821
VK UNDERWRITERS LLC—See Howden Group Holdings Limited; *U.S. Private*, pg. 3494
VOLANKA INSURANCE SERVICES (PVT) LTD.—See Hayleys PLC; *Int'l*, pg. 3292
VOYA FUNDS SERVICES, LLC—See Voya Financial, Inc.; *U.S. Public*, pg. 2311

524298 — ALL OTHER INSURANCE...

VOYA INVESTMENTS, LLC—See Voya Financial, Inc.; *U.S. Public*, pg. 2311
VRX, LLC—See Centene Corporation; *U.S. Public*, pg. 470
WALNUT STREET ABSTRACT, L.P.—See Pennsylvania Real Estate Investment Trust; *U.S. Public*, pg. 1664
WARRANTY DIRECT LTD—See BNP Paribas SA; *Int'l*, pg. 1093
WEAVER BROS. INSURANCE ASSOCIATES, INC.—See Kelso & Company, L.P.; *U.S. Private*, pg. 2280
WEBBROKER S.A.—See Apollo Global Management, Inc.; *U.S. Public*, pg. 147
WELLCARE SPECIALTY PHARMACY, INC.—See Centene Corporation; *U.S. Public*, pg. 471
WELLPOINT PHARMACY MANAGEMENT—See Elevance Health, Inc.; *U.S. Public*, pg. 730
WELLS FARGO WEALTH BROKERAGE INSURANCE AGENCY, LLC—See Wells Fargo & Company; *U.S. Public*, pg. 2347
WENTWORTH INSURANCE COMPANY LTD.—See Fairfax Financial Holdings Limited; *Int'l*, pg. 2608
WESTERN GENERAL INSURANCE CO., INC.; *U.S. Private*, pg. 4493
WEST INDIES ALLIANCE INSURANCE LIMITED—See Guardian Holdings Limited; *Int'l*, pg. 3171
WHITE MOUNTAINS SOLUTIONS, INC.—See White Mountains Insurance Group, Ltd.; *U.S. Public*, pg. 2369
WHITE ROCK INSURANCE (EUROPE) PCC LIMITED—See Aon plc; *Int'l*, pg. 495
WORKPLACE HEALTH SOLUTIONS INC.—See Community Bank System, Inc.; *U.S. Public*, pg. 550
WRM GROUP, LLC—See Galiot Insurance Services, Inc.; *U.S. Private*, pg. 1638
WR SIMS AGENCY INCORPORATED—See Bain Capital, LP; *U.S. Private*, pg. 441
WR SIMS AGENCY INCORPORATED—See Keystone Insurers Group, Inc.; *U.S. Private*, pg. 2300
WTC INSURANCE CORP, LTD.—See International Business Machines Corporation; *U.S. Public*, pg. 1151
WYATT INSURANCE SERVICES, INC.—See Hellman & Friedman LLC; *U.S. Private*, pg. 1910
XCHANGE BENEFITS, LLC—See Ambac Financial Group, Inc.; *U.S. Public*, pg. 92
XCHANGE GROUP LLC; *U.S. Private*, pg. 4580
XL DESIGN PROFESSIONAL—See AXA S.A.; *Int'l*, pg. 761
XL GROUP - INSURANCE - ENVIRONMENTAL INTERNATIONAL DIVISION—See AXA S.A.; *Int'l*, pg. 760
XL GROUP - INSURANCE - NEW YORK ENVIRONMENTAL DIVISION—See AXA S.A.; *Int'l*, pg. 760
XL GROUP - INSURANCE—See AXA S.A.; *Int'l*, pg. 760
XL INDIA BUSINESS SERVICES PVT LTD—See AXA S.A.; *Int'l*, pg. 760
XL INSURANCE AMERICA INC.—See AXA S.A.; *Int'l*, pg. 761
XL INSURANCE (CHINA) COMPANY LIMITED—See AXA S.A.; *Int'l*, pg. 760
XL INSURANCE COMPANY OF NEW YORK, INC—See AXA S.A.; *Int'l*, pg. 761
XL INSURANCE COMPANY—See AXA S.A.; *Int'l*, pg. 760
XL LONDON MARKET LTD.—See AXA S.A.; *Int'l*, pg. 761
XL REINSURANCE AMERICA—See AXA S.A.; *Int'l*, pg. 761
XL REINSURANCE AMERICA—See AXA S.A.; *Int'l*, pg. 761
XL RE LTD—See AXA S.A.; *Int'l*, pg. 761
XL SEGUROS MEXICO S.A. DE C.V.—See AXA S.A.; *Int'l*, pg. 761
XL SERVICES UK LTD.—See AXA S.A.; *Int'l*, pg. 761
XPT GROUP LLC; *U.S. Private*, pg. 4582
YEDIDIM PENSION ARRANGEMENTS INSURANCE AGENCY LTD.—See Harel Insurance Investments & Financial Services Ltd.; *Int'l*, pg. 3274
YUZZU SA—See AXA S.A.; *Int'l*, pg. 761
ZENITH INSURANCE COMPANY—See Fairfax Financial Holdings Limited; *Int'l*, pg. 2609
ZURICH INSURANCE (TAIWAN) LTD.—See Hotai Motor Co., Ltd.; *Int'l*, pg. 3487

525110 — PENSION FUNDS

401KEXCHANGE.COM INC.; *U.S. Private*, pg. 14
ACCESS PENSION FUND CUSTODIAN LIMITED—See FBN Holdings PLC; *Int'l*, pg. 2627
AEGON CAPPITAL B.V.—See Aegon N.V.; *Int'l*, pg. 174
AFORE INBURSA S.A. DE C.V.—See Grupo Financiero Inbursa, S.A. de C.V.; *Int'l*, pg. 3129
AIZAWA ASSET MANAGEMENT CO., LTD.—See Aizawa Securities Group Co., Ltd.; *Int'l*, pg. 255
AKZO NOBEL PENSIONS GMBH—See Akzo Nobel N.V.; *Int'l*, pg. 272
ALBERTA TEACHERS RETIREMENT FUND; *Int'l*, pg. 298
ALLETE & AFFILIATED COMPANIES RETIREE HEALTH PLAN A; *U.S. Private*, pg. 180
ALLIANZ DRESDNER PENSION CONSULT GMBH—See Allianz SE; *Int'l*, pg. 344
ALLIANZ PENSIONSFONDS AKTIENGESELLSCHAFT—See Allianz SE; *Int'l*, pg. 349
ALLIANZ PENSIONSKASSE AG—See Allianz SE; *Int'l*, pg. 349
ALLIANZ PENZIJNI FOND A.S.—See Allianz SE; *Int'l*, pg. 351
ALLIANZ SLOVENSKA DOCHODKOVA SPRAVCOVSA SPOLOCNOST, A.S.—See Allianz SE; *Int'l*, pg. 350
ALLIANZ-TIRIAC PENSII PRIVATE—See Allianz SE; *Int'l*, pg. 351
THE AMALGAMATED LIFE INSURANCE CO. INC.—See Amalgamated Insurance Fund; *U.S. Private*, pg. 215
AMERICAN TRUST—See Mid Atlantic Capital Group, Inc.; *U.S. Private*, pg. 2705
AON ZAMBIA PENSION FUND ADMINISTRATORS LIMITED—See Aon plc; *Int'l*, pg. 494
APAC RESOURCES ASIA LIMITED—See APAC Resources Limited; *Int'l*, pg. 500
ATM INWESTYCJE SP. Z.O.O.—See ATM Grupa S.A.; *Int'l*, pg. 687
AUSTRALIANSUPER PTY LTD; *Int'l*, pg. 723
AVON RUBBER PENSION TRUST LIMITED—See Avon Protection plc; *Int'l*, pg. 750
AXA CZECH REPUBLIC PENSION FUNDS—See AXA S.A.; *Int'l*, pg. 755
AXA MERKENS FONDS GMBH—See AXA S.A.; *Int'l*, pg. 757
AXA PENSION SOLUTIONS AG—See AXA S.A.; *Int'l*, pg. 757
AXA POLAND PENSION FUNDS—See AXA S.A.; *Int'l*, pg. 758
AXA POWSZECHNE TOWARZYSTWO EMERYTALNE S.A.—See AXA S.A.; *Int'l*, pg. 758
BANK CONSORTIUM TRUST COMPANY LIMITED—See Dah Sing Financial Holdings Limited; *Int'l*, pg. 1913
BLUE BENEFITS CONSULTING INC.; *U.S. Private*, pg. 585
BOK FINANCIAL INSURANCE, INC.—See Caisse de Depot et Placement du Quebec; *Int'l*, pg. 1256
BOK FINANCIAL INSURANCE, INC.—See KKR & Co. Inc.; *U.S. Public*, pg. 1265
CHARLES TAYLOR & CO LTD—See Lovell Minnick Partners LLC; *U.S. Private*, pg. 2502
CHEMIE PENSIONSFONDS AG—See DZ BANK AG Deutsche Zentral-Genossenschaftsbank; *Int'l*, pg. 2243
CHEROKEE NATIONAL LIFE INSURANCE CO.—See Securian Financial Group, Inc.; *U.S. Private*, pg. 3594
COLLEGE RETIREMENT EQUITIES FUND—See Teachers Insurance Association - College Retirement Fund; *U.S. Private*, pg. 3945
COMMERZTRUST GMBH—See Commerzbank AG; *Int'l*, pg. 1717
COMPERTIS BERATUNGSGESELLSCHAFT FUR BETRIEBLICHES VORSORGEMANAGEMENT MBH—See DZ BANK AG Deutsche Zentral-Genossenschaftsbank; *Int'l*, pg. 2245
CONDOR ALLGEMEINE VERSICHERUNGS-AKTIENGESELLSCHAFT—See DZ BANK AG Deutsche Zentral-Genossenschaftsbank; *Int'l*, pg. 2243
CONDOR LEBENSVERSICHERUNGS—See DZ BANK AG Deutsche Zentral-Genossenschaftsbank; *Int'l*, pg. 2243
DANICA PENSION—See Danske Bank A/S; *Int'l*, pg. 1969
DCP, INC.—See Arthur J. Gallagher & Co.; *U.S. Public*, pg. 204
DEUTSCHE POST PENSIONSFONDS AG—See Deutsche Post AG; *Int'l*, pg. 2079
DEUTSCHE POST PENSIONS-TREUHAND GMBH & CO. KG—See Deutsche Post AG; *Int'l*, pg. 2079
DEUTSCHES INSTITUT FUR ALTERSVORSORGE GMBH—See Deutsche Bank Aktiengesellschaft; *Int'l*, pg. 2061
DHL EMPLOYEE BENEFIT FUND OFP—See Deutsche Post AG; *Int'l*, pg. 2073
DHL PENSIONS INVESTMENT FUND LIMITED—See Deutsche Post AG; *Int'l*, pg. 2077
EAGLE MANAGED CARE CORP.—See New Rite Aid, LLC; *U.S. Private*, pg. 2905
EBS PENSIONEER TRUSTEES LIMITED—See Embark Group Limited; *Int'l*, pg. 2374
EBS SELF-ADMINISTERED PERSONAL PENSION PLAN TRUSTEES LIMITED—See Embark Group Limited; *Int'l*, pg. 2374
ENERGIE-PENSIONS-MANAGEMENT GMBH—See Fortum Oyj; *Int'l*, pg. 2742
EQUITY STORY PTY LTD.—See Equity Story Group Ltd.; *Int'l*, pg. 2488
EXXONMOBIL PENSIONS-VERWALTUNGSGESELLSCHAFT MBH—See Exxon Mobil Corporation; *U.S. Public*, pg. 816
FCMB PENSIONS LIMITED—See FCMB Group Plc; *Int'l*, pg. 2628
FIJI NATIONAL PROVIDENT FUND; *Int'l*, pg. 2661
FJC & ASSOCIATES, INC.—See Stone Point Capital LLC; *U.S. Private*, pg. 3819
FRAGWILHELM GMBH—See DZ BANK AG Deutsche Zentral-Genossenschaftsbank; *Int'l*, pg. 2245
GARANTI BBVA EMEKLILIK AS—See Banco Bilbao Vizcaya Argentaria, S.A.; *Int'l*, pg. 818
GARDENS PENSION TRUSTEES LIMITED—See 3i Group plc; *Int'l*, pg. 8
GENERALI PENSIONSKASSE AG—See Assicurazioni Generali S.p.A.; *Int'l*, pg. 646
GENERALI PENSIONSMANAGEMENT GMBH—See Cinven Limited; *Int'l*, pg. 1616
GENERALI PENZIJNI FOND A.S.—See Assicurazioni Generali S.p.A.; *Int'l*, pg. 646
GENERALI SOCIETATE DE ADMINISTRARE A FONDURILOR DE PENSII PRIVATE S.A.—See Assicurazioni Generali S.p.A.; *Int'l*, pg. 647
GENERALI TVG VORSORGEMANAGEMENT GMBH—See Assicurazioni Generali S.p.A.; *Int'l*, pg. 646
GLOBAL MARINE SYSTEMS PENSION TRUSTEE, LTD—See INNOVATE Corp.; *U.S. Public*, pg. 1126
GROUP RHI; *U.S. Private*, pg. 1794
HARGREAVES LANSDOWN PENSIONS DIRECT LTD—See Hargreaves Lansdown PLC; *Int'l*, pg. 3274
HARGREAVES LANSDOWN PENSIONS TRUSTEES LTD—See Hargreaves Lansdown PLC; *Int'l*, pg. 3275
HIPS (TRUSTEES) LIMITED—See Heidelberg Materials AG; *Int'l*, pg. 3311
HOLDEN EMPLOYEES SUPERANNUATION FUND PTY LTD—See General Motors Company; *U.S. Public*, pg. 926
HQDA ELDERLY LIFE NETWORK CORP.; *U.S. Public*, pg. 1065
INDIANA BENEFITS INC.—See Blue Benefits Consulting Inc.; *U.S. Private*, pg. 585
INVESCO PENSIONS LIMITED—See Invesco Ltd.; *U.S. Public*, pg. 1163
IRISH PENSIONS TRUST LIMITED—See Marsh & McLennan Companies, Inc.; *U.S. Public*, pg. 1376
JLT BENEFIT SOLUTIONS LIMITED—See Marsh & McLennan Companies, Inc.; *U.S. Public*, pg. 1376
LOCAL AUTHORITIES PENSION PLAN—See Alberta Pension Services Corporation; *Int'l*, pg. 298
MASSEY FERGUSON WORKS PENSION TRUST LTD.—See AGCO Corporation; *U.S. Public*, pg. 59
MG ALTERSVERSORGUNG GMBH—See GEA Group Aktiengesellschaft; *Int'l*, pg. 2904
NATIONAL RETIREMENT SERVICES, INC.—See Aquiline Capital Partners LLC; *U.S. Private*, pg. 304
NATIONAL RETIREMENT SERVICES, INC.—See Genstar Capital, LLC; *U.S. Private*, pg. 1675
NEW ENGLAND PENSION PLAN SYSTEMS, LLC—See Hellman & Friedman LLC; *U.S. Private*, pg. 1908
NOW: PENSIONS LTD.—See Marsh & McLennan Companies, Inc.; *U.S. Public*, pg. 1384
ORIENTAL PENSION CONSULTANTS, INC.—See OFG Bancorp; *U.S. Public*, pg. 1564
PAREX OPEN PENSION FUND—See AS Reverta; *Int'l*, pg. 591
PENSION CONSULT-BERATUNGSGESELLSCHAFT FUR ALTERSVORSORGE MBH—See DZ BANK AG Deutsche Zentral-Genossenschaftsbank; *Int'l*, pg. 2244
PENTEGRA RETIREMENT SERVICES—See Pentegra Retirement Services; *U.S. Private*, pg. 3140
PENZIJNI FOND CESKE SPORITELNY, A.S—See Erste Group Bank AG; *Int'l*, pg. 2498
PIONEER MUTUAL LIFE INSURANCE COMPANY—See American United Mutual Insurance Holding Company; *U.S. Private*, pg. 258
PRINCIPAL RETIREMENT ADVISORS PRIVATE LIMITED—See Principal Financial Group, Inc.; *U.S. Public*, pg. 1722
PROFUTURO GNP—See Grupo BAL; *Int'l*, pg. 3122
PTE ALLIANZ POLSKA SA—See Allianz SE; *Int'l*, pg. 355
R+V LUXEMBOURG LEBENSVERSICHERUNG S.A.—See DZ BANK AG Deutsche Zentral-Genossenschaftsbank; *Int'l*, pg. 2244
THE SHAW GROUP UK PENSION PLAN LIMITED—See The Shaw Group Inc.; *U.S. Private*, pg. 4117
SOUTHWEST ADMINISTRATORS INC.; *U.S. Private*, pg. 3738
STATE TEACHERS RETIREMENT SYSTEM OF OHIO; *U.S. Public*, pg. 3793
TKP PENSIOEN B.V.—See Aegon N.V.; *Int'l*, pg. 175
UNITED ADMINISTRATIVE SERVICES; *U.S. Private*, pg. 4287
VDM-HILFE GMBH—See GEA Group Aktiengesellschaft; *Int'l*, pg. 2903
VESTUS GROUP; *U.S. Private*, pg. 4373
VMB VORSORGEMANAGEMENT FUR BANKEN GMBH—See DZ BANK AG Deutsche Zentral-Genossenschaftsbank; *Int'l*, pg. 2245
VOLUNTARY PENSION FUND M.DELTA—See Assicurazioni Generali S.p.A.; *Int'l*, pg. 646
WOODMONT REAL ESTATE SERVICES LTD.; *U.S. Private*, pg. 4559
WOODMONT REALTY ADVISORS INC.—See Woodmont Real Estate Services Ltd.; *U.S. Private*, pg. 4559
ZENITH ADMINISTRATORS, INC.—See Ullico Inc.; *U.S. Private*, pg. 4276
ZENITH AMERICAN SOLUTIONS INC.—See Advanced Solutions International Inc.; *U.S. Private*, pg. 92

525120 — HEALTH AND WELFARE FUNDS

ACCIDENT FUND HOLDINGS, INC.—See Blue Cross Blue Shield of Michigan; *U.S. Private*, pg. 587

N.A.I.C.S. INDEX

525910 — OPEN-END INVESTMENT...

ACTION INC.; *U.S. Private*, pg. 67
AETNA BETTER HEALTH PREMIER PLAN MMAI INC.—See CVS Health Corporation; *U.S. Public*, pg. 613
AETNA CAPITAL MANAGEMENT, LLC—See CVS Health Corporation; *U.S. Public*, pg. 614
AETNA GLOBAL BENEFITS LIMITED—See CVS Health Corporation; *U.S. Public*, pg. 614
AETNA (SHANGHAI) ENTERPRISE SERVICES CO. LTD.—See CVS Health Corporation; *U.S. Public*, pg. 614
AIAI GROUP CORPORATION; *Int'l*, pg. 227
ALAMO WORKFORCE DEVELOPMENT, INC.; *U.S. Private*, pg. 149
AMALGAMATED INSURANCE FUND; *U.S. Private*, pg. 215
ASTERON PORTFOLIO SERVICES LIMITED—See Dai-ichi Life Holdings, Inc.; *Int'l*, pg. 1918
AUTOMOTIVE PETROLEUM AND ALLIED INDUSTRIES EMPLOYEES WELFARE FUND; *U.S. Private*, pg. 400
BENEFIT COMMERCE GROUP—See Genstar Capital, LLC; *U.S. Public*, pg. 1674
BLUE CROSS COMPLETE OF MICHIGAN; *U.S. Private*, pg. 588
BROTHERHOOD'S RELIEF AND COMPENSATION FUND; *U.S. Private*, pg. 665
CALIFORNIA STATE EMPLOYEES ASSOCIATION; *U.S. Private*, pg. 720
CAPITAL DISTRICT PHYSICIANS' HEALTH PLAN, INC.; *U.S. Private*, pg. 739
CARDINAL CUSHING CENTERS, INC.; *U.S. Private*, pg. 750
CAREFIRST ADMINISTRATORS—See CareFirst, Inc.; *U.S. Private*, pg. 753
CARPENTERS' HEALTH AND WELFARE FUND OF PHILADELPHIA AND VICINITY; *U.S. Private*, pg. 770
THE CENTRE FOR HEALTH & DISABILITY ASSESSMENTS LTD.—See MAXIMUS, Inc.; *Int'l*, pg. 1402
CENTURYLINK INVESTMENT MANAGEMENT COMPANY—See Lumen Technologies, Inc.; *U.S. Public*, pg. 1345
CHINESE COMMUNITY HEALTH CARE ASSOCIATION; *U.S. Private*, pg. 886
COCORPORT, INC.; *Int'l*, pg. 1687
CONMED HEALTHCARE MANAGEMENT, INC.—See H.I.G. Capital, LLC; *U.S. Public*, pg. 1829
CONNECTICUT CARPENTERS BENEFIT FUNDS; *U.S. Private*, pg. 1015
CONTAINER ROYALTY SUPPLEMENTAL CASH BENEFIT PLAN; *U.S. Private*, pg. 1027
COVENTRY HEALTH CARE OF ILLINOIS, INC.—See CVS Health Corporation; *U.S. Public*, pg. 614
DAIHEN WELFARE ENTERPRISE CO., LTD.—See Daihen Corporation; *Int'l*, pg. 1926
DELAWARE CHARTER GUARANTEE & TRUST CO.—See Principal Financial Group, Inc.; *U.S. Public*, pg. 1720
DELTA FOUNDATION—See Delta Holding; *Int'l*, pg. 2018
EDENRED EMPLOYEE BENEFITS UK LTD—See Edenred S.A.; *Int'l*, pg. 2307
ELECTRICAL INSURANCE TRUSTEES; *U.S. Private*, pg. 1353
EMPLOYEES OF MUNICIPAL & OTHER PUBLIC EMPLOYERS; *U.S. Private*, pg. 1386
FAUJI FOUNDATION; *Int'l*, pg. 2623
FDK LIFETEC CORPORATION—See Fujitsu Limited; *Int'l*, pg. 2832
FIRST COMMERCE CREDIT UNION; *U.S. Private*, pg. 1516
FOUNDATION FOR SURGICAL FELLOWSHIP; *U.S. Private*, pg. 1580
GAROFALO HEALTH CARE SPA; *Int'l*, pg. 2886
GIORGIO HEALTH & WELFARE PLAN; *U.S. Private*, pg. 1702
GOLDBERRY WEALTH GMBH—See Franklin Resources, Inc.; *U.S. Public*, pg. 881
HARGREAVES LANSDOWN EBT TRUSTEES LTD—See Hargreaves Lansdown PLC; *Int'l*, pg. 3274
HAYEL SAEED ANAM & ASSOCIATES WELFARE CORPORATION—See Hayel Saeed Anam Group of Companies; *Int'l*, pg. 3290
IMPACT COAL SUBTRUST; *U.S. Private*, pg. 2048
INTERNATIONAL FOUNDATION OF EMPLOYEE BENEFIT PLANS; *U.S. Private*, pg. 2117
ISAPRE SAN LORENZO LTDA—See Corporacion Nacional del Cobre de Chile; *Int'l*, pg. 1805
KEY BENEFIT ADMINISTRATORS, INC.—See Key Family of Companies; *U.S. Private*, pg. 2293
KEY BENEFIT ADMINISTRATORS—See Key Family of Companies; *U.S. Private*, pg. 2293
KEY FAMILY OF COMPANIES; *U.S. Private*, pg. 2293
KEY FINANCIAL ADMINISTRATORS, LTD.—See Key Family of Companies; *U.S. Private*, pg. 2293
KEY PARTNERS, INC.—See Key Family of Companies; *U.S. Private*, pg. 2293
LABOR-MANAGEMENT HEALTHCARE FUND; *U.S. Private*, pg. 2370
LAW ENFORCEMENT HEALTH BENEFITS, INC.; *U.S. Private*, pg. 2400
LAW ENFORCEMENT OFFICERS & FIREFIGHTERS HEALTH AND WELFARE TRUST; *U.S. Private*, pg. 2400
LOUISIANA HEALTH PLAN; *U.S. Private*, pg. 2499
MASSACHUSETTS LABORERS BENEFIT FUNDS; *U.S. Private*, pg. 2604
MEDICAL BENEFITS ADMINISTRATORS INC—See Medical Benefits Mutual Life Insurance Co. Inc.; *U.S. Private*, pg. 2654
MEDICAL SECURITY CARD COMPANY, LLC—See MedImpact Healthcare Systems, Inc.; *U.S. Private*, pg. 2657
METAIRIE PHYSICIAN SERVICES, INC.; *U.S. Private*, pg. 2679
METROPOLITAN EMPLOYEES BENEFITS ASSOCIATION; *U.S. Private*, pg. 2688
MICHIGAN ELECTRICAL EMPLOYEES HEALTH PLAN; *U.S. Private*, pg. 2700
MICHIGAN LABORERS FRINGE BENEFIT FUNDS; *U.S. Private*, pg. 2701
MOTION PICTURE INDUSTRY PENSION & HEALTH PLANS; *U.S. Private*, pg. 2795
NEW YORK STATE CORRECTIONAL OFFICERS & POLICE BENEVOLENT ASSOCIATION, INC.; *U.S. Private*, pg. 2912
NFG DISTRIBUTION CORP NYD VEBA FOR COLLECTIVELY BARGAINED EES; *U.S. Private*, pg. 2922
NORTHWEST ADMINISTRATORS INC.; *U.S. Private*, pg. 2958
NORTHWESTERN REGION EMPLOYEE BENEFIT TRUST; *U.S. Private*, pg. 2963
OHIO CARPENTERS' HEALTH FUND; *U.S. Private*, pg. 3004
OKLAHOMA CITY OTHER POST EMPLOYMENT BENEFITS; *U.S. Private*, pg. 3007
THE PENNSYLVANIA EMPLOYEES BENEFIT TRUST FUND; *U.S. Private*, pg. 4093
PHILADELPHIA FEDERATION OF TEACHERS HEALTH AND WELFARE FUND; *U.S. Private*, pg. 3169
PORTER COUNTY SCHOOL EMPLOYEES' INSURANCE TRUST; *U.S. Private*, pg. 3231
PUBLIC EDUCATION HEALTH TRUST; *U.S. Private*, pg. 3299
RISK MANAGEMENT ADVISORS, INC.—See Kelso & Company, L.P.; *U.S. Private*, pg. 2280
ROSE COMMUNITY FOUNDATION; *U.S. Private*, pg. 3481
SAN DIEGO CITY EMPLOYEES RETIREE MEDICAL TRUST; *U.S. Private*, pg. 3539
SANTA FE COMMUNITY FOUNDATION; *U.S. Private*, pg. 3547
SEAFARERS WELFARE PLAN INC.; *U.S. Private*, pg. 3584
SPRINGPOINT SENIOR LIVING; *U.S. Private*, pg. 3764
SUNSYSTEM DEVELOPMENT CORPORATION; *U.S. Private*, pg. 3873
TRI-STATE JOINT FUND; *U.S. Private*, pg. 4224
UNION PACIFIC RAILROAD EMPLOYEE HEALTH SYSTEMS INC.; *U.S. Private*, pg. 4284
UNITED FOOD & COMMERCIAL WORKERS & EMPS ARIZONA HEALTH & WELFARE TRUST; *U.S. Private*, pg. 4292
UNITED ISRAEL APPEAL, INC.; *U.S. Private*, pg. 4293
UNITE HERE HEALTH; *U.S. Private*, pg. 4287
URBAN STRATEGIES INC.; *U.S. Private*, pg. 4315
WISCONSIN PIPE TRADES HEALTH FUND; *U.S. Private*, pg. 4549

525190 — OTHER INSURANCE FUNDS

ADMINISTRADORA DE FONDOS DE PENSIONES CUPRUM S.A.—See Principal Financial Group, Inc.; *U.S. Public*, pg. 1720
ALLIANZ AUSTRALIA WORKERS COMPENSATION (NSW) LIMITED—See Allianz SE; *Int'l*, pg. 343
ALLIANZ AUSTRALIA WORKERS COMPENSATION (SA) LIMITED—See Allianz SE; *Int'l*, pg. 344
ALLIANZ AUSTRALIA WORKERS COMPENSATION (VICTORIA) LIMITED—See Allianz SE; *Int'l*, pg. 344
AMERICAN MINING INSURANCE GROUP, LLC—See W.R. Berkley Corporation; *U.S. Public*, pg. 2316
APPLIED UNDERWRITERS, INC.—See Quadrant Management, Inc.; *U.S. Private*, pg. 3316
ASSURANT, INC.; *U.S. Public*, pg. 214
BERKLEY RISK ADMINISTRATORS COMPANY, LLC—See W.R. Berkley Corporation; *U.S. Public*, pg. 2317
BIOGEN NEW VENTURES INC.—See Biogen Inc.; *U.S. Public*, pg. 336
BOV ASSET MANAGEMENT LIMITED—See Bank of Valletta p.l.c.; *Int'l*, pg. 849
CCCC FUND MANAGEMENT CO., LTD.—See China Communications Construction Company Limited; *Int'l*, pg. 1490
CENTRAL STATES HEALTH & LIFE CO. OF OMAHA INC.; *U.S. Private*, pg. 825
CERIFONDS (LUXEMBOURG) SA—See Banque Cantonale Vaudoise; *Int'l*, pg. 853
COFACE NORTH AMERICA POLITICAL RISK—See Coface S.A.; *Int'l*, pg. 1691
DANSKE INVEST ASSET MANAGEMENT AS—See Danske Bank A/S; *Int'l*, pg. 1969
DONEGAL GROUP INC.; *U.S. Public*, pg. 676
EFU GENERAL INSURANCE LTD.; *Int'l*, pg. 2321
FINANCIAL CONCEPTS, INC.—See Aon plc; *Int'l*, pg. 496
FLORIDA INSURANCE GUARANTY ASSOCIATION, INC.; *U.S. Private*, pg. 1549
FUNDEX INVESTMENTS INC.—See iA Financial Corporation Inc.; *Int'l*, pg. 3567
GALICIA SECURITIES S.A.—See Grupo Financiero Galicia S.A.; *Int'l*, pg. 3129
GLOBAL WELLNESS STRATEGIES INC.; *Int'l*, pg. 3002
GRACEKENNEDY (TRINIDAD AND TOBAGO) LIMITED—See GraceKennedy Limited; *Int'l*, pg. 3049
HUMANA, INC.; *U.S. Public*, pg. 1069
LOMBARD INTERNATIONAL LIFE ASSURANCE COMPANY—See Blackstone Inc.; *U.S. Public*, pg. 356
MERCER INSURANCE GROUP, INC.—See United Fire Group, Inc.; *U.S. Public*, pg. 2230
NEW RIVER VALLEY BENEFITS CONSORTIUM; *U.S. Private*, pg. 2906
NFP NATIONAL MADISON GROUP, INC.—See Aon plc; *Int'l*, pg. 497
NORTH CAROLINA RATE BUREAU; *U.S. Private*, pg. 2943
PENNSYLVANIA COMPENSATION RATING BUREAU; *U.S. Private*, pg. 3136
PHYSICIANS MUTUAL INSURANCE CO.; *U.S. Private*, pg. 3175
SAMMONS ANNUITY GROUP—See Sammons Enterprises, Inc.; *U.S. Private*, pg. 3537
SARACEN FUND MANAGERS LIMITED—See AssetCo plc; *Int'l*, pg. 643
SHIPSURANCE INSURANCE SERVICES, INC.—See Assurant, Inc.; *U.S. Public*, pg. 215
STATE AUTO FINANCIAL CORPORATION—See State Automobile Mutual Insurance Company; *U.S. Private*, pg. 3791
SUNSTONE ASSURANCE, LLC; *U.S. Private*, pg. 3873
UNITED COMMERCIAL TRAVELERS OF AMERICA; *U.S. Private*, pg. 4289
WELLNZ LIMITED—See Marsh & McLennan Companies, Inc.; *U.S. Public*, pg. 1388

525910 — OPEN-END INVESTMENT FUNDS

3M (EAST) AG—See 3M Company; *U.S. Public*, pg. 5
ABERDEEN ASSET MANAGERS LTD.—See abrdn PLC; *Int'l*, pg. 68
ABERDEEN DO BRASIL GESTAO DE RECURSOS LTD.—See abrdn PLC; *Int'l*, pg. 68
ABERDEEN STANDARD ASSET MANAGEMENT (SHANGHAI) CO., LTD.—See abrdn PLC; *Int'l*, pg. 68
ABERDEEN STANDARD ASSET MANAGEMENT (THAILAND) LIMITED—See abrdn PLC; *Int'l*, pg. 68
ABERDEEN STANDARD FUND MANAGERS LIMITED—See abrdn PLC; *Int'l*, pg. 68
ABERDEEN STANDARD INVESTMENTS (CANADA) LIMITED—See abrdn PLC; *Int'l*, pg. 68
ABERDEEN STANDARD INVESTMENTS CO. LTD.—See abrdn PLC; *Int'l*, pg. 68
ABERDEEN STANDARD INVESTMENTS DEUTSCHLAND AG—See abrdn PLC; *Int'l*, pg. 68
ABERDEEN STANDARD INVESTMENTS (HONG KONG) LIMITED—See abrdn PLC; *Int'l*, pg. 68
ABERDEEN STANDARD INVESTMENTS LUXEMBOURG S.A.—See abrdn PLC; *Int'l*, pg. 68
ABERDEEN STANDARD INVESTMENTS (SWITZERLAND) AG—See abrdn PLC; *Int'l*, pg. 68
ABERDEEN STANDARD INVESTMENTS TAIWAN LIMITED—See abrdn PLC; *Int'l*, pg. 68
ABERDEEN STANDARD ISLAMIC INVESTMENTS (MALAYSIA) SDN. BHD.—See abrdn PLC; *Int'l*, pg. 68
ABG SUNDAL COLLIER ASSET MANAGEMENT AS—See ABG Sundal Collier Holding ASA; *Int'l*, pg. 60
ABRDN ASIA LIMITED—See abrdn PLC; *Int'l*, pg. 68
ABRDN AUSTRALIA LTD.—See abrdn PLC; *Int'l*, pg. 68
ABRDN SILVER ETF TRUST; *U.S. Public*, pg. 27
ACASTA ENTERPRISES, INC.; *Int'l*, pg. 78
ACKERMANS & VAN HAAREN NV; *Int'l*, pg. 104
ACORN CAPITAL INVESTMENT FUND LIMITED—See Acorn Capital Limited; *Int'l*, pg. 108
ADVANCE ASSET MANAGEMENT LIMITED—See Marsh & McLennan Companies, Inc.; *U.S. Public*, pg. 1384
AGF ASSET MANAGEMENT ASIA LTD.—See AGF Management Limited; *Int'l*, pg. 206
AGF FUNDS INC.—See AGF Management Limited; *Int'l*, pg. 206
AIC VENTURES, LP; *U.S. Private*, pg. 131
AIG MARKETING, INC.—See American International Group, Inc.; *U.S. Public*, pg. 105
ALARIS EQUITY PARTNERS INCOME TRUST; *Int'l*, pg. 291
ALLIANCEBERNSTEIN HOLDING L.P.—See Equitable Holdings, Inc.; *U.S. Public*, pg. 788
ALLVEST GMBH—See Allianz SE; *Int'l*, pg. 351
ALPHA ASSET MANAGEMENT A.E.D.A.K.—See Alpha Services and Holdings S.A.; *Int'l*, pg. 369
ALPHAMETRIX, LLC; *U.S. Private*, pg. 200
ALPHASIMPLEX GROUP, LLC—See Virtus Investment Partners, Inc.; *U.S. Public*, pg. 2300

525910 — OPEN-END INVESTMENT...

ARMA GROUP HOLDINGS PTY. LTD.—See Credit Clear Limited; *Int'l*, pg. 1835
ARTISAN PARTNERS LIMITED PARTNERSHIP—See Artisan Partners Asset Management Inc; *U.S. Public*, pg. 208
ASHMORE GLOBAL OPPORTUNITIES LTD.; *Int'l*, pg. 607
ASSET PLUS FUND MANAGEMENT COMPANY LIMITED—See Asia Plus Group Holdings Public Company Limited; *Int'l*, pg. 614
AVENIR FINANCE INVESTMENT MANAGERS (AFIM)—See Advenis; *Int'l*, pg. 166
AZIMUT INVESTMENTS SA AGF—See Azimut Holding SpA; *Int'l*, pg. 779
BAIRD FUNDS, INC.—See Baird Financial Group, Inc.; *U.S. Private*, pg. 454
BARCLAYS GLOBAL INVESTORS CANADA LTD.—See Barclays PLC; *Int'l*, pg. 860
BARONSMEAD SECOND VENTURE TRUST PLC; *Int'l*, pg. 867
BAYERNINVEST LUXEMBOURG S.A.—See BayernLB Holding AG; *Int'l*, pg. 913
BELLEVUE ASSET MANAGEMENT AG—See Bellevue Group AG; *Int'l*, pg. 967
BENDURA FUND MANAGEMENT ALPHA AG—See Citychamp Watch & Jewellery Group Limited; *Int'l*, pg. 1628
BENDURA FUND MANAGEMENT BETA AG—See Citychamp Watch & Jewellery Group Limited; *Int'l*, pg. 1628
BLACKROCK 2022 GLOBAL INCOME OPPORTUNITY TRUST; *U.S. Public*, pg. 342
BLACKROCK ARGENTINA ASESORIAS LTDA.—See BlackRock, Inc.; *U.S. Public*, pg. 344
BLACKROCK CREDIT ALLOCATION INCOME TRUST; *U.S. Public*, pg. 342
BLACKROCK INVESTMENTS CANADA, INC.—See BlackRock, Inc.; *U.S. Public*, pg. 345
BOYD GROUP SERVICES INC; *Int'l*, pg. 1124
BPA FONS, SA—See Banca Privada D'Andorra, SA; *Int'l*, pg. 816
BROCKMAN MINING (MANAGEMENT) LIMITED—See Brockman Mining Limited; *Int'l*, pg. 1173
BURNHAM ASSET MANAGEMENT CORP.; *U.S. Private*, pg. 689
CALVERT DISTRIBUTORS, INC.—See Ameritas Mutual Holding Company; *U.S. Private*, pg. 261
CANBANK VENTURE CAPITAL FUND LIMITED—See Canara Bank; *Int'l*, pg. 1287
CANDRIAM INVESTORS GROUP—See New York Life Insurance Company; *U.S. Private*, pg. 2911
CAPITAL GROWTH MANAGEMENT, L.P.—See Groupe BPCE; *Int'l*, pg. 3096
CAPMAN AB—See CapMan PLC; *Int'l*, pg. 1315
CAPMAN (GUERNSEY) LTD.—See CapMan PLC; *Int'l*, pg. 1315
CAPMAN NORWAY AS—See CapMan PLC; *Int'l*, pg. 1315
CARNEGIE FONDER AB—See Altor Equity Partners AB; *Int'l*, pg. 394
CASSADAY & COMPANY, INC.; *U.S. Private*, pg. 783
CENTRIA CAPITAL—See Centria Inc.; *Int'l*, pg. 1412
CENTRIA INC.; *Int'l*, pg. 1412
CENTURIA PROPERTY FUNDS LIMITED—See Centuria Capital Limited; *Int'l*, pg. 1416
CENTURIA PROPERTY FUNDS NO. 2 LIMITED—See Centuria Capital Limited; *Int'l*, pg. 1416
CF MANAGEMENT SERVICES PTY. LTD.—See Earlypay Ltd.; *Int'l*, pg. 2267
CHENAVARI TORO INCOME FUND LIMITED; *Int'l*, pg. 1465
CHUBB ASSET MANAGEMENT INC.—See Chubb Limited; *Int'l*, pg. 1591
CIBC PRIVATE WEALTH GROUP, LLC—See Canadian Imperial Bank of Commerce; *Int'l*, pg. 1283
CIBRO MANAGEMENT INC.; *U.S. Private*, pg. 896
CITIGROUP INVESTOR SERVICES, INC.—See Citigroup Inc.; *U.S. Public*, pg. 503
CIVIL PENSION FUND INVESTMENT CO.; *Int'l*, pg. 1630
COLUMBIA MANAGEMENT GROUP, LLC—See Bank of America Corporation; *U.S. Public*, pg. 271
C-QUADRAT INVESTMENT AG; *Int'l*, pg. 1239
CROMWELL PROPERTY SECURITIES LIMITED—See Cromwell Property Group; *Int'l*, pg. 1854
DAIWA ASSET MANAGEMENT CO. LTD.—See Daiwa Securities Group Inc.; *Int'l*, pg. 1947
DANSKE CAPITAL AS—See Danske Bank A/S; *Int'l*, pg. 1969
DFA INVESTMENT DIMENSIONS GROUP INC.—See Dimensional Fund Advisors LP; *U.S. Private*, pg. 1233
DIGITAL UTILITIES VENTURES, INC.; *U.S. Public*, pg. 664
DIMELING, SCHREIBER & PARK; *U.S. Private*, pg. 1232
DIMENSIONAL FUND ADVISORS LP; *U.S. Private*, pg. 1233
DIMENSIONAL JAPAN LTD.—See Dimensional Fund Advisors LP; *U.S. Private*, pg. 1233
THE DIREXION FUNDS—See Rafferty Holdings, LLC; *U.S. Private*, pg. 3345
DKR CAPITAL INC.; *U.S. Private*, pg. 1247
D NALOZBE D.D.; *Int'l*, pg. 1899
DOMACOM LIMITED; *Int'l*, pg. 2159
DOWNING LLP; *Int'l*, pg. 2186

EASTNINE AB; *Int'l*, pg. 2274
EC POHL & CO PTY. LTD.—See Global Masters Fund Limited; *Int'l*, pg. 2999
ELECTA VENTURES S.R.L.—See Azimut Holding SpA; *Int'l*, pg. 779
ELLIOTT ASSOCIATES, L.P.—See Elliott Management Corporation; *U.S. Private*, pg. 1365
ELLIOTT INTERNATIONAL, L.P.—See Elliott Management Corporation; *U.S. Private*, pg. 1365
EQT NORTHERN EUROPE PRIVATE EQUITY FUNDS—See EQT AB; *Int'l*, pg. 2475
EQT PARTNERS AUSTRALIA PTY. LTD.—See EQT AB; *Int'l*, pg. 2475
EQT PARTNERS JAPAN KK—See EQT AB; *Int'l*, pg. 2475
EQT PARTNERS KOREA CO., LTD.—See EQT AB; *Int'l*, pg. 2475
EQT PARTNERS NETHERLANDS B.V.—See EQT AB; *Int'l*, pg. 2475
EUROBANK EFG FUND MANAGEMENT COMPANY (LUXEMBOURG) S.A.—See Eurobank Ergasias Services and Holdings S.A.; *Int'l*, pg. 2532
EUROBANK EFG MUTUAL FUNDS MANAGEMENT COMPANY S.A.—See Eurobank Ergasias Services and Holdings S.A.; *Int'l*, pg. 2532
EUROMOBILIARE ASSET MANAGEMENT SGR SPA—See Credito Emiliano S.p.A.; *Int'l*, pg. 1836
FACTS MANAGEMENT AUS PTY. LTD.—See Nelnet, Inc.; *U.S. Private*, pg. 1504
FCMB TRUSTEES LIMITED—See FCMB Group Plc; *Int'l*, pg. 2628
FIDELITY INVESTMENTS CANADA LTD.—See FMR LLC; *U.S. Private*, pg. 1555
FONDI ALLEANZA S.G.R.P.A.—See Assicurazioni Generali S.p.A.; *Int'l*, pg. 643
FORCE LEGAL PTY. LTD.—See Credit Clear Limited; *Int'l*, pg. 1835
FOREMOST INCOME FUND; *Int'l*, pg. 2731
FP FUND MANAGERS LIMITED—See Bank of Montreal; *Int'l*, pg. 847
FRIESS ASSOCIATES, LLC—See Affiliated Managers Group, Inc.; *U.S. Public*, pg. 55
FRIESS ASSOCIATES OF DELAWARE, LLC—See Affiliated Managers Group, Inc.; *U.S. Public*, pg. 55
FRONTIER FUNDS; *U.S. Private*, pg. 1615
GALLIARD CAPITAL MANAGEMENT, INC.—See Wells Fargo & Company; *U.S. Public*, pg. 2343
GARUDA CAPITAL CORP.; *Int'l*, pg. 2886
GATEWAY INVESTMENT ADVISERS, L.P.—See Groupe BPCE; *Int'l*, pg. 3096
GCP ASSET BACKED INCOME FUND LTD.; *Int'l*, pg. 2895
GEAR ASSET MANAGEMENT LIMITED—See ETS Group Limited; *Int'l*, pg. 2524
GEAR SECURITIES INVESTMENT LIMITED—See ETS Group Limited; *Int'l*, pg. 2524
GENERALI ASSET MANAGEMENT S.P.A.—See Assicurazioni Generali S.p.A.; *Int'l*, pg. 644
GLENNON SMALL COMPANIES LIMITED; *Int'l*, pg. 2992
GOLDSTREAM CAPITAL MANAGEMENT LIMITED—See Goldstream Investment Limited; *Int'l*, pg. 3034
GORE STREET ENERGY STORAGE FUND PLC; *Int'l*, pg. 3043
GRESHAM HOUSE ENERGY STORAGE FUND PLC; *Int'l*, pg. 3082
GUOTAI JUNAN ALLIANZ FUND MANAGEMENT CO., LTD.—See Allianz SE; *Int'l*, pg. 346
GUOTAI JUNAN ALLIANZ FUND MANAGEMENT CO., LTD.—See Guotai Junan Securities Co., Ltd.; *Int'l*, pg. 3187
GUOTAI JUNAN SECURITIES (HONG KONG) LIMITED—See Guotai Junan Securities Co., Ltd.; *Int'l*, pg. 3187
HARBOURVEST INVESTMENT CONSULTING (BEIJING) COMPANY LIMITED—See HarbourVest Partners, LLC; *U.S. Private*, pg. 1861
HARTFORD FUNDS MANAGEMENT COMPANY, LLC—See The Hartford Financial Services Group, Inc.; *U.S. Public*, pg. 2088
HARTFORD FUNDS MANAGEMENT GROUP, INC.—See The Hartford Financial Services Group, Inc.; *U.S. Public*, pg. 2088
HAVSFRUN CAPITAL AB—See Havsfrun Investment AB; *Int'l*, pg. 3287
HEALTHCARE REALTY TRUST INCORPORATED; *U.S. Public*, pg. 1015
HEARTS AND MINDS INVESTMENTS LIMITED; *Int'l*, pg. 3304
HERCULES FUNDING I LLC—See Hercules Capital, Inc.; *U.S. Public*, pg. 1028
HIAG HOLDING AG—See HIAG Immobilen Holding AG; *Int'l*, pg. 3382
HIAG IMMOBILIEN SCHWEIZ AG—See HIAG Immobilen Holding AG; *Int'l*, pg. 3382
HIROGIN SECURITIES CO., LTD.—See Hirogin Holdings, Inc.; *Int'l*, pg. 3404
HOLLARD LIFE PROPERTIES (PTY) LIMITED—See Hollard Insurance Company Ltd; *Int'l*, pg. 3451
HORIZONS ALPHAPRO GARTMAN ETF; *Int'l*, pg. 3479
HUAAN FUNDS MANAGEMENT CO., LTD.—See Guotai

Junan Securities Co., Ltd.; *Int'l*, pg. 3187
HUNTER PREMIUM FUNDING LTD.—See Allianz SE; *Int'l*, pg. 342
I4VENTURES SP. Z O.O.; *Int'l*, pg. 3567
IBF SECURITIES CO., LTD.—See IBF Financial Holdings Co., Ltd.; *Int'l*, pg. 3574
IBF VENTURE CAPITAL CO., LTD.—See IBF Financial Holdings Co., Ltd.; *Int'l*, pg. 3574
INTERNATIONAL BILLS FINANCE CORP.—See IBF Financial Holdings Co., Ltd.; *Int'l*, pg. 3574
INTER-RISCO - SOCIEDADE DE CAPITAL DE RISCO, S.A.—See Lone Star Funds; *U.S. Private*, pg. 2484
INVESCO ASSET MANAGEMENT DEUTSCHLAND GMBH—See Invesco Ltd.; *U.S. Public*, pg. 1163
INVESCO ASSET MANAGEMENT GMBH—See Invesco Ltd.; *U.S. Public*, pg. 1163
INVESCO ASSET MANAGEMENT OSTERREICH GMBH—See Invesco Ltd.; *U.S. Public*, pg. 1162
INVESCO ASSET MANAGEMENT S.A.—See Invesco Ltd.; *U.S. Public*, pg. 1162
INVESCO ASSET MANAGEMENT S.A.—See Invesco Ltd.; *U.S. Public*, pg. 1162
INVESCO ASSET MANAGEMENT S.A.—See Invesco Ltd.; *U.S. Public*, pg. 1162
INVESCO ASSET MANAGEMENT (SWITZERLAND) LTD.—See Invesco Ltd.; *U.S. Public*, pg. 1162
INVESCO AUSTRALIA LTD—See Invesco Ltd.; *U.S. Public*, pg. 1162
INVESCO CONTINENTAL EUROPE SERVICES S.A.—See Invesco Ltd.; *U.S. Public*, pg. 1162
INVESCO DUBLIN—See Invesco Ltd.; *U.S. Public*, pg. 1162
INVESCO GESTION S.A.—See Invesco Ltd.; *U.S. Public*, pg. 1162
INVESCO HIGH INCOME 2024 TARGET TERM FUND; *U.S. Public*, pg. 1161
INVESCO INSTITUTIONAL—See Invesco Ltd.; *U.S. Public*, pg. 1162
INVESCO INTERNATIONAL LTD.—See Invesco Ltd.; *U.S. Public*, pg. 1162
INVESCO INVESTMENT SERVICES, INC.—See Invesco Ltd.; *U.S. Public*, pg. 1162
INVESCO REAL ESTATE LTD.—See Invesco Ltd.; *U.S. Public*, pg. 1163
INVESCO TAIWAN LTD.—See Invesco Ltd.; *U.S. Public*, pg. 1163
INVISTA REAL ESTATE INVESTMENT MANAGEMENT HOLDINGS LIMITED—See Fiera Capital Corporation; *Int'l*, pg. 2659
IOWA PACIFIC HOLDINGS, LLC; *U.S. Private*, pg. 2135
JEFFERIES FUNDING LLC—See Jefferies Financial Group Inc.; *U.S. Public*, pg. 1188
JPMORGAN ASSET MANAGEMENT HOLDINGS INC.—See JPMorgan Chase & Co.; *U.S. Public*, pg. 1208
J.P. MORGAN INVESTMENT MANAGEMENT—See JPMorgan Chase & Co.; *U.S. Public*, pg. 1208
LAZARD WORLD DIVIDEND & INCOME FUND, INC.; *U.S. Private*, pg. 2402
MARINE PETROLEUM TRUST; *U.S. Public*, pg. 1366
MARKET VECTORS-RUSSIA EFT—See Van Eck Associates Corp.; *U.S. Private*, pg. 4339
MERCER PRIVATE MARKETS AG—See Marsh & McLennan Companies, Inc.; *U.S. Public*, pg. 1386
METAVESCO, INC.; *U.S. Public*, pg. 1428
MFS INVESTMENT MANAGEMENT—See Guggenheim Partners, LLC; *U.S. Private*, pg. 1812
MINING INVESTMENTS JERSEY LTD—See Barrick Gold Corporation; *Int'l*, pg. 869
M&I SERVICING CORP.—See Bank of Montreal; *Int'l*, pg. 2402
MONTANA CAPITAL PARTNERS AG—See Prudential Financial, Inc.; *U.S. Public*, pg. 1731
MORNINGSTAR INVESTMENT MANAGEMENT AUSTRALIA LIMITED—See Morningstar, Inc.; *U.S. Public*, pg. 1476
MOUSAM VENTURES LLC; *U.S. Private*, pg. 2801
MT. LOGAN MANAGEMENT, LTD.—See Everest Group, Ltd.; *Int'l*, pg. 2564
NEWTON CAPITAL PARTNERS, L.P.—See Juniper Investment Company, LLC; *U.S. Private*, pg. 2244
NISA INVESTMENT ADVISORS LLC; *U.S. Private*, pg. 2928
NUVEEN DIVERSIFIED DIVIDEND & INCOME FUND—See Teachers Insurance Association - College Retirement Fund; *U.S. Private*, pg. 3946
NUVEEN LLC—See Teachers Insurance Association - College Retirement Fund; *U.S. Private*, pg. 3945
OAKBRIDGE LAWYERS PTY. LTD.—See Credit Clear Limited; *Int'l*, pg. 1835
OPPENHEIMERFUNDS, INC. - ROCHESTER OFFICE—See Invesco Ltd.; *U.S. Public*, pg. 1163
OPPENHEIM KAPITALANLAGEGESELLSCHAFT MBH—See Deutsche Bank Aktiengesellschaft; *Int'l*, pg. 2062
OPPENHEIM PRAMERICA ASSET MANAGEMENT S.A R.L.—See Fosun International Limited; *Int'l*, pg. 2751
PARAMETRIC PORTFOLIO ASSOCIATES LLC—See Morgan Stanley; *U.S. Public*, pg. 1471

N.A.I.C.S. INDEX

525990 — OTHER FINANCIAL VEH...

PEGASUS CAPITAL ADVISORS, L.P.; *U.S. Private*, pg. 3129
PGIM INDIA ASSET MANAGEMENT PRIVATE LIMITED—See Prudential Financial, Inc.; *U.S. Public*, pg. 1731
P.J. DOHERTY & ASSOCIATES CO. LTD.—See AGF Management Limited; *Int'l*, pg. 207
PT ABERDEEN STANDARD INVESTMENT—See abrdn PLC; *Int'l*, pg. 69
PUTNAM ADVISORY COMPANY, LLC—See Franklin Resources, Inc.; *U.S. Public*, pg. 883
PUTNAM INVESTMENTS, LLC—See Franklin Resources, Inc.; *U.S. Public*, pg. 883
QUANTUM VENTURES OF MICHIGAN, LLC; *U.S. Private*, pg. 3323
SCARBOROUGH EQUITIES PTY. LIMITED—See Bentley Capital Ltd.; *Int'l*, pg. 977
SCM STRATEGIC CAPITAL MANAGEMENT ASIA LTD—See Marsh & McLennan Companies, Inc.; *U.S. Public*, pg. 1388
SICAVONLINE SA—See Ageas SA/NV; *Int'l*, pg. 205
SINGLIFE FINANCIAL ADVISERS PTE. LTD—See Aviva plc; *Int'l*, pg. 746
SNYDER CAPITAL MANAGEMENT, L.P.—See Groupe BPCE; *Int'l*, pg. 3096
SOCIETE POUR LA GESTION DE PLACEMENTS COLLECTIFS GEP SA—See Banque Cantonale Vaudoise; *Int'l*, pg. 853
STRATEGIA ITALIA SGR SPA—See Agenzia Nazionale per l'Attrazione degli Investimenti e lo Sviluppo d'Impresa SpA; *Int'l*, pg. 206
TALENT TECH LABS, LLC—See Allegis Group, Inc.; *U.S. Private*, pg. 177
TOSCANA ENERGY INCOME CORPORATION—See i3 Energy Plc; *Int'l*, pg. 3566
TRANSAMERICA CAPITAL, INC.—See Aegon N.V.; *Int'l*, pg. 174
TREASURE ISLAND ROYALTY TRUST; *U.S. Public*, pg. 2186
TRILOGY FUNDS MANAGEMENT LIMITED—See Balmain Corp.; *Int'l*, pg. 810
T. ROWE PRICE ASSOCIATES, INC.—See T. Rowe Price Group Inc.; *U.S. Public*, pg. 1978
UNION INVESTMENT SERVICE BANK AG—See DZ BANK AG Deutsche Zentral-Genossenschaftsbank; *Int'l*, pg. 2245
UNITED STATES 12 MONTH NATURAL GAS FUND, LP—See The Marygold Companies, Inc.; *U.S. Public*, pg. 2112
UNITED STATES 12 MONTH OIL FUND, LP—See The Marygold Companies, Inc.; *U.S. Public*, pg. 2112
UNITED STATES DIESEL-HEATING OIL FUND, LP—See The Marygold Companies, Inc.; *U.S. Public*, pg. 2112
UNITED STATES NATURAL GAS FUND, LP—See The Marygold Companies, Inc.; *U.S. Public*, pg. 2113
UNITED STATES SHORT OIL FUND, LP—See The Marygold Companies, Inc.; *U.S. Public*, pg. 2113
U.S. BANCORP FUND SERVICES, LLC—See U.S. Bancorp; *U.S. Public*, pg. 2212
VALLEY FORGE INVESTMENT CORP.; *U.S. Private*, pg. 4334
VANGUARD ATLANTIC LTD.; *U.S. Private*, pg. 4343
THE VANGUARD GROUP, INC.; *U.S. Private*, pg. 4130
WARBURG - HENDERSON KAPITALANLAGEGESELLSCHAFT FUR IMMOBILIEN MBH—See Teachers Insurance Association - College Retirement Fund; *U.S. Private*, pg. 3945
WARDS COVE PACKING COMPANY; *U.S. Private*, pg. 4441
WESTOZ FUNDS MANAGEMENT PTY. LTD.—See Euroz Hartleys Group Limited; *Int'l*, pg. 2559

525920 — TRUSTS, ESTATES, AND AGENCY ACCOUNTS

ARGENT TRUST COMPANY, N.A.—See Argent Financial Group, Inc.; *U.S. Private*, pg. 320
ARGENT TRUST COMPANY OF TENNESSEE—See Argent Financial Group, Inc.; *U.S. Private*, pg. 320
AVI GLOBAL TRUST PLC; *Int'l*, pg. 740
BASIC PROPERTIES B.V.—See BasicNet S.p.A.; *Int'l*, pg. 886
BCI HOLDING, INC.; *U.S. Private*, pg. 499
BLACKROCK RESOURCES & COMMODITIES STRATEGY TRUST; *U.S. Public*, pg. 344
BLACKROCK TAXABLE MUNICIPAL BOND TRUST; *U.S. Public*, pg. 344
BLACKROCK UTILITIES, INFRASTRUCTURE & POWER OPPORTUNITIES TRUST; *U.S. Public*, pg. 344
CALDWELL TRUST COMPANY—See Trust Companies of America, Inc.; *U.S. Private*, pg. 4250
CALTEX AUSTRALIA INVESTMENTS PTY LTD—See Ampol Limited; *Int'l*, pg. 436
CANDOVER INVESTMENTS PLC; *Int'l*, pg. 1289
CHAUCER LABUAN LIMITED—See China Reinsurance (Group) Corporation; *Int'l*, pg. 1547
DAITO MIRAI TRUST CO., LTD.—See Daito Trust Construction Co., Ltd.; *Int'l*, pg. 1943
DATA INFRASTRUCTURE TRUST; *Int'l*, pg. 1976
EMIGRANT CAPITAL CORP.—See New York Private Bank & Trust Corporation; *U.S. Private*, pg. 2911
EMIGRANT FUNDING CORPORATION—See New York Private Bank & Trust Corporation; *U.S. Private*, pg. 2911
ESSEX CATALINA GARDENS, LLC—See Essex Property Trust, Inc.; *U.S. Public*, pg. 796
ESSEX REXFORD, LLC—See Essex Property Trust, Inc.; *U.S. Public*, pg. 796
FIRST HAWAIIAN CAPITAL 1—See BNP Paribas SA; *Int'l*, pg. 1088
FIRST PROPERTY ASSET MANAGEMENT LTD.—See First Property Group Plc; *Int'l*, pg. 2686
FORTUNE SUN (CHINA) HOLDINGS LIMITED; *Int'l*, pg. 2744
HAL TRUST N.V.; *Int'l*, pg. 3223
H&M HENNES & MAURITZ INTERNATIONAL B.V.—See H&M Hennes & Mauritz AB; *Int'l*, pg. 3192
H&M HENNES & MAURITZ USA BV—See H&M Hennes & Mauritz AB; *Int'l*, pg. 3192
HYFLUX WATER TRUST MANAGEMENT PTE LTD—See Hyflux Ltd; *Int'l*, pg. 3548
INVESTORS' SECURITY TRUST COMPANY—See First Busey Corporation; *U.S. Public*, pg. 840
LOW AND BONAR (NEDERLAND) BV—See Freudenberg SE; *Int'l*, pg. 2789
MACRO BANK LTD—See Banco Macro S.A.; *Int'l*, pg. 823
MESA ROYALTY TRUST; *U.S. Public*, pg. 1426
MONTE PASCHI FIDUCIARIA S.P.A.—See Banca Monte dei Paschi di Siena S.p.A.; *Int'l*, pg. 815
MV OIL TRUST; *U.S. Public*, pg. 1487
OPPENHEIM VERMOGENSTREUHAND GMBH—See Deutsche Bank Aktiengesellschaft; *Int'l*, pg. 2062
PARISH GROUP LIMITED—See APQ Global Limited; *Int'l*, pg. 522
PRA RECEIVABLES MANAGEMENT, LLC—See PRA Group, Inc.; *U.S. Public*, pg. 1712
SOLO OIL AUSTRALIA PTY LTD—See Ampol Limited; *Int'l*, pg. 436
STERLING TRUST COMPANY—See Equity Trust Company; *U.S. Private*, pg. 1416
STRYKER JAPAN HOLDINGS BV—See Stryker Corporation; *U.S. Public*, pg. 1957
THE STURM FINANCIAL GROUP, INC.; *U.S. Private*, pg. 4124
THERMO FISHER SCIENTIFIC VERMOGENSVERWALTUNGS GMBH—See Thermo Fisher Scientific Inc.; *U.S. Public*, pg. 2154
TRUST COMPANIES OF AMERICA, INC.; *U.S. Private*, pg. 4250
THE TRUST COMPANY—See Argent Financial Group, Inc.; *U.S. Private*, pg. 320
WINTHROP REALTY LIQUIDATING TRUST; *U.S. Public*, pg. 2374

525990 — OTHER FINANCIAL VEHICLES

16TH STREET PARTNERS, LLC—See Starwood Property Trust, Inc.; *U.S. Public*, pg. 1939
360 CAPITAL MORTGAGE REIT; *Int'l*, pg. 6
360 CAPITAL REIT—See Centuria Capital Limited; *Int'l*, pg. 1416
786 INVESTMENTS LIMITED; *Int'l*, pg. 14
AAFA OF MISSISSIPPI, INC.—See Grupo Salinas, S.A. de C.V.; *Int'l*, pg. 3135
ABA RESOURCES PTY. LTD.; *Int'l*, pg. 47
ABC ARBITRAGE S.A.; *Int'l*, pg. 57
ABDULLAH AL-OTHAIM INVESTMENT & REAL ESTATE DEVELOPMENT COMPANY—See Al-Othaim Holding Company; *Int'l*, pg. 288
ABERDEEN ASSET MANAGEMENT FINLAND OY—See abrdn PLC; *Int'l*, pg. 68
ABERDEEN EMERGING MARKETS EQUITY INCOME, INC.; *Int'l*, pg. 60
ABERDEEN GLOBAL INCOME FUND, INC.; *U.S. Public*, pg. 25
ABERDEEN PROPERTY INVESTORS FRANCE SAS—See abrdn PLC; *Int'l*, pg. 68
ABERDEEN PROPERTY INVESTORS SWEDEN AB—See abrdn PLC; *Int'l*, pg. 68
ABERDEEN PROPERTY INVESTORS THE NETHERLANDS B.V.—See abrdn PLC; *Int'l*, pg. 68
ABERDEEN UNIT TRUST MANAGERS LTD.—See abrdn PLC; *Int'l*, pg. 68
ABERFORTH SMALLER COMPANIES TRUST PLC; *Int'l*, pg. 60
ABRDN GLOBAL DYNAMIC DIVIDEND FUND; *U.S. Public*, pg. 26
ABRDN GLOBAL PREMIER PROPERTIES FUND; *U.S. Public*, pg. 26
ABRDN HEALTHCARE OPPORTUNITIES FUND; *U.S. Public*, pg. 26
ABRDN JAPAN EQUITY FUND INC.; *U.S. Public*, pg. 26
ABRDN NEW INDIA INVESTMENT TRUST PLC; *Int'l*, pg. 68
ABRDN TOTAL DYNAMIC DIVIDEND FUND; *U.S. Public*, pg. 27
ABRDN UK SMALLER COMPANIES GROWTH TRUST PLC; *Int'l*, pg. 69
ACADIA REALTY TRUST; *U.S. Public*, pg. 31
ACCELERATE PROPERTY FUND LTD.; *Int'l*, pg. 80
ACCESS CAPITAL SERVICES, INC.; *U.S. Private*, pg. 50
ACCESS CASH GENERAL PARTNERSHIP—See Morgan Stanley; *U.S. Public*, pg. 1474
ACCORD FINANCIAL CORP.; *Int'l*, pg. 92
ACCORDIA GOLF TRUST; *Int'l*, pg. 93
ACER PROPERTY DEVELOPMENT, INC.—See Acer Incorporated; *Int'l*, pg. 99
ACRES COMMERCIAL REALTY CORP.; *U.S. Public*, pg. 36
ADAMS NATURAL RESOURCES FUND, INC.; *U.S. Public*, pg. 38
ADEUS AKTIENREGISTER-SERVICE GMBH—See Allianz SE; *Int'l*, pg. 343
AD-MANUM FINANCE LTD.; *Int'l*, pg. 123
ADVANCE RESIDENCE INVESTMENT CORPORATION; *Int'l*, pg. 156
AEI CORE PROPERTY INCOME TRUST, INC.; *U.S. Private*, pg. 117
AEP INDUSTRIES FINANCE INC.—See Berry Global Group, Inc; *U.S. Public*, pg. 320
AERCAP FINANCIAL SERVICES (IRELAND) LTD—See AerCap Holdings N.V.; *Int'l*, pg. 179
AEW CAPITAL MANAGEMENT, L.P.—See Groupe BPCE; *Int'l*, pg. 3096
AEW EUROPE—See Groupe BPCE; *Int'l*, pg. 3096
AEW GLOBAL LIMITED—See Groupe BPCE; *Int'l*, pg. 3096
AFRICA ISRAEL (EAST EUROPE) INVESTMENTS B.V.—See Africa Israel Investments Ltd.; *Int'l*, pg. 190
AFRICAN ALLIANCE INSURANCE PLC; *Int'l*, pg. 191
AFRICAN EQUITY EMPOWERMENT INVESTMTS LIMITED; *Int'l*, pg. 191
AGARTHA REAL ESTATE SOCIMI, S.A.U.; *Int'l*, pg. 200
AGELLAN COMMERCIAL REAL ESTATE INVESTMENT TRUST—See El-Ad Group, Ltd.; *U.S. Private*, pg. 1349
AG FINANCIAL INVESTMENT TRUST, INC.; *U.S. Private*, pg. 124
AG MORTGAGE INVESTMENT TRUST, INC.—See TPG Capital, L.P.; *U.S. Public*, pg. 2166
AGREE REALTY CORPORATION; *U.S. Public*, pg. 62
AIMS PROPERTY SECURITIES FUND; *Int'l*, pg. 234
AKTIV KAPITAL FINANCIAL SERVICES AS—See PRA Group, Inc.; *U.S. Public*, pg. 1712
ALBERTA TREASURY BRANCHES; *Int'l*, pg. 298
ALBIS HITEC LEASING GMBH—See ALBIS Leasing AG; *Int'l*, pg. 299
ALBIS SERVICE GMBH—See ALBIS Leasing AG; *Int'l*, pg. 299
ALCENTRA CAPITAL CORPORATION—See Crescent Capital BDC, Inc.; *U.S. Public*, pg. 593
ALDA OFFICE PROPERTIES, INC.; *U.S. Private*, pg. 154
ALEXANDER'S, INC.; *U.S. Public*, pg. 75
ALEXANDRIA ADVANTAGE WARRANTY COMPANY; *U.S. Public*, pg. 75
ALEXANDRIA REAL ESTATE EQUITIES, INC.; *U.S. Public*, pg. 75
ALINA HOLDINGS PLC; *Int'l*, pg. 328
ALINMA RETAIL REIT FUND; *Int'l*, pg. 329
ALLBODEN AG ALLGEMEINE GRUNDSTUCKS-AKTIENGESELLSCHAFT—See Aroundtown SA; *Int'l*, pg. 578
ALLETTI GESTIELLE SGR S.P.A.—See Banco BPM S.p.A.; *Int'l*, pg. 818
ALLIANCEBERNSTEIN GLOBAL HIGH INCOME FUND, INC.; *U.S. Public*, pg. 79
ALLIANCEBERNSTEIN NATIONAL MUNICIPAL INCOME FUND, INC.; *U.S. Public*, pg. 79
ALLIANT COMPANY LLC; *U.S. Private*, pg. 184
ALLIANZ GLOBAL INVESTORS (FRANCE) S.A.—See Allianz SE; *Int'l*, pg. 346
ALLIANZ PROZESSFINANZ GMBH—See Allianz SE; *Int'l*, pg. 349
ALLIANZ RISK CONSULTANTS B.V.—See Allianz SE; *Int'l*, pg. 349
ALLIANZ RISK TRANSFER AG—See Allianz SE; *Int'l*, pg. 345
ALLIANZ RISK TRANSFER (BERMUDA) LIMITED—See Allianz SE; *Int'l*, pg. 345
ALLIANZ RISK TRANSFER, INC.—See Allianz SE; *Int'l*, pg. 345
ALLIANZ SUISSE VERSICHERUNGEN - ALLIANZ SUISSE LEBEN—See Allianz SE; *Int'l*, pg. 350
ALLSPRING GLOBAL DIVIDEND OPPORTUNITY FUND; *U.S. Public*, pg. 81
ALLSPRING INCOME OPPORTUNITIES FUND; *U.S. Public*, pg. 81
ALLSPRING UTILITIES & HIGH INCOME FUND; *U.S. Public*, pg. 81
ALSTRIA OFFICE REIT-AG; *Int'l*, pg. 383
ALTABA INC.; *U.S. Public*, pg. 86
ALTAREA SCA; *Int'l*, pg. 385
ALTUR INVESTISSEMENT S.C.A.; *Int'l*, pg. 399
AMATI AIM VCT PLC; *Int'l*, pg. 413
AMBAC ASSURANCE UK LIMITED-MILAN BRANCH—See

525990 — OTHER FINANCIAL VEH...

Ambac Financial Group, Inc.; *U.S. Public*, pg. 92
AMBAC ASSURANCE UK LIMITED—See Ambac Financial Group, Inc.; *U.S. Public*, pg. 92
AMERICAN ASSETS TRUST, INC.; *U.S. Public*, pg. 96
AMERICAN CAMPUS COMMUNITIES, INC.—See Blackstone Inc.; *U.S. Public*, pg. 347
AMERICAN HEALTHCARE REIT, INC.—See American Healthcare Investors LLC; *U.S. Private*, pg. 236
AMERICAN HEALTHCARE REIT, INC.—See Griffin Capital Corporation; *U.S. Private*, pg. 1787
AMERICAN HOTEL INCOME PROPERTIES REIT LP; *Int'l*, pg. 422
AMERICAN LAND LEASE, INC.—See Green Courte Partners, LLC; *U.S. Private*, pg. 1772
AMERICAN PACIFIC INVESTCORP, LP; *U.S. Private*, pg. 242
AMERICAN REALTY CAPITAL DAILY NET ASSET VALUE TRUST, INC.—See AR Global Investments, LLC; *U.S. Private*, pg. 306
AMERICAN REALTY CAPITAL GLOBAL TRUST II, INC.—See AR Global Investments, LLC; *U.S. Private*, pg. 306
AMERICAN REALTY CAPITAL NEW YORK CITY REIT II, INC.—See AR Global Investments, LLC; *U.S. Private*, pg. 306
AMERICAN REALTY CAPITAL - RETAIL CENTERS OF AMERICA II, INC.—See AR Global Investments, LLC; *U.S. Private*, pg. 306
AMERICAN REALTY INVESTORS, INC.; *U.S. Public*, pg. 108
AMERICAN STRATEGIC INVESTMENT CO.—See AR Global Investments, LLC; *U.S. Private*, pg. 306
AMERICAN TOWER CORPORATION; *U.S. Public*, pg. 110
AMERICAN WATER CAPITAL CORPORATION—See American Water Works Company, Inc.; *U.S. Public*, pg. 112
AMERICOLD REALTY TRUST, INC.; *U.S. Public*, pg. 113
AMERICREDIT FINANCIAL SERVICES, INC.—See General Motors Company; *U.S. Public*, pg. 925
AMERISERV TRUST & FINANCIAL SERVICES CO.—See Ameriserv Financial, Inc.; *U.S. Public*, pg. 115
AMLI RESIDENTIAL PROPERTIES TRUST—See Morgan Stanley; *U.S. Public*, pg. 1475
AMPROPERTY TRUST MANAGEMENT BERHAD—See AMMB Holdings Berhad; *Int'l*, pg. 429
ANF IMMOBILIER—See Caisse des Depots et Consignations; *Int'l*, pg. 1258
ANSAR FINANCIAL AND DEVELOPMENT CORPORATION; *Int'l*, pg. 478
ANTARES, INC.; *U.S. Private*, pg. 287
ANTHEM PROPERTIES GROUP, LTD.—See Anthem Works Ltd.; *Int'l*, pg. 483
ANWORTH MORTGAGE ASSET CORPORATION—See Waterfall Asset Management LLC; *U.S. Private*, pg. 4453
APARTMENT INCOME REIT LLC—See Blackstone Inc.; *U.S. Public*, pg. 349
APARTMENT INVESTMENT AND MANAGEMENT COMPANY; *U.S. Public*, pg. 143
APHEX BIOCLEANSE SYSTEMS, INC; *U.S. Public*, pg. 144
APOLLO COMMERCIAL REAL ESTATE FINANCE, INC.—See Apollo Global Management, Inc.; *U.S. Public*, pg. 146
APOLLO GLOBAL REAL ESTATE MANAGEMENT, L.P.—See Apollo Global Management, Inc.; *U.S. Public*, pg. 146
APOLLO TACTICAL INCOME FUND INC.—See Apollo Global Management, Inc.; *U.S. Public*, pg. 147
APPLE HOSPITALITY REIT, INC.—See Apple Suites Realty Group, Inc.; *U.S. Private*, pg. 297
APRIL DEUTSCHLAND AG—See CVC Capital Partners SICAV-FIS S.A.; *Int'l*, pg. 1882
ARBOR REALTY TRUST, INC.; *U.S. Public*, pg. 178
ARCALIS—See Allianz SE; *Int'l*, pg. 342
ARCO TOWERS REIT; *Int'l*, pg. 549
ARENA REIT—See Arena Investment Management Limited; *Int'l*, pg. 558
ARES COMMERCIAL REAL ESTATE CORPORATION—See Ares Management Corporation; *U.S. Public*, pg. 187
ARES DYNAMIC CREDIT ALLOCATION FUND, INC.—See Ares Management Corporation; *U.S. Public*, pg. 188
ARMADALE CAPITAL INC.; *U.S. Private*, pg. 329
ARMOUR RESIDENTIAL REIT, INC.; *U.S. Public*, pg. 193
ARRENDADORA VALMEX—See Grupo BAL; *Int'l*, pg. 3121
ASA ALEASING D.O.O.—See ASA Holding d.o.o.; *Int'l*, pg. 591
ASCENCIO S.A.; *Int'l*, pg. 601
ASCENDAS HOSPITALITY TRUST; *Int'l*, pg. 601
ASEANA PROPERTIES LTD.; *Int'l*, pg. 605
ASEGURADORA PORVENIR GNP—See Grupo BAL; *Int'l*, pg. 3121
ASHEVILLE MALL CMBS, LLC—See CBL & Associates Properties, Inc.; *U.S. Public*, pg. 457
ASHFORD HOSPITALITY TRUST, INC.; *U.S. Public*, pg. 211
ASPEN PROPERTY MANAGEMENT LTD.—See CML Global Capital Ltd.; *Int'l*, pg. 1671
ASSEMBLY ROW CONDOMINIUM, INC.—See Federal Realty Investment Trust; *U.S. Public*, pg. 825
ASSOCIATED ESTATES REALTY CORPORATION—See Brookfield Corporation; *Int'l*, pg. 1175
ATA GAYRIMENKUL YATIRIM ORTAKLIGI AS; *Int'l*, pg. 665
ATLANTA LIFE FINANCIAL GROUP; *U.S. Private*, pg. 371
ATLANTIC LEAF PROPERTIES LIMITED; *Int'l*, pg. 675
ATMEQUIPMENT.COM—See Grant Victor; *U.S. Private*, pg. 1757
AURORA PROPERTY BUY-WRITE INCOME TRUST—See Aurora Funds Management Limited; *Int'l*, pg. 713
AUSTRALIAN REIT INCOME FUND—See Harvest Portfolios Group Inc.; *Int'l*, pg. 3281
AUTHORISED INVESTMENT FUND LTD.; *Int'l*, pg. 724
AVENUE CAPITAL MORTGAGE REIT INC.—See Avenue Capital Group, LLC; *U.S. Private*, pg. 405
BAJAJ FINANCE LTD.—See Bajaj Auto Ltd.; *Int'l*, pg. 804
BANCROFT FUND LTD.—See GAMCO Investors, Inc.; *U.S. Public*, pg. 895
BANKRATE, LLC—See Red Ventures, LLC; *U.S. Private*, pg. 3376
BANQUE AGF—See Allianz SE; *Int'l*, pg. 342
BANVIDA SA; *Int'l*, pg. 855
BARINGS CORPORATE INVESTORS—See Massachusetts Mutual Life Insurance Company; *U.S. Private*, pg. 2605
BARINGS EMERGING EMEA OPPORTUNITIES PLC—See Massachusetts Mutual Life Insurance Company; *U.S. Private*, pg. 2604
BARINGS GLOBAL SHORT DURATION HIGH YIELD FUND—See Massachusetts Mutual Life Insurance Company; *U.S. Private*, pg. 2605
BARINGS PARTICIPATION INVESTORS—See Massachusetts Mutual Life Insurance Company; *U.S. Private*, pg. 2605
BARRATT EAST ANGLIA LIMITED—See Barratt Developments PLC; *Int'l*, pg. 868
BARRATT LONDON LIMITED—See Barratt Developments PLC; *Int'l*, pg. 868
BAY GROUP HOLDINGS SDN BHD; *Int'l*, pg. 900
BAYVIEW HOLDING LTD.—See Morgan Stanley; *U.S. Public*, pg. 1471
BEHSHAHR INDUSTRIAL GROUP INVESTMENT COMPANY; *Int'l*, pg. 942
BELHASA REAL ESTATE—See Belhasa Group of Companies; *Int'l*, pg. 964
BENCHMARK FINANCIAL GROUPS, LLC; *U.S. Private*, pg. 523
BENEFIT STREET PARTNERS BDC, INC.—See Franklin Resources, Inc.; *U.S. Public*, pg. 879
BENEFITWORKS, INC.—See Fulton Financial Corporation; *U.S. Public*, pg. 892
BENJAMIN HORNIGOLD LTD.; *Int'l*, pg. 974
BERKSHIRE INCOME REALTY LLC—See Berkshire Group, LLC; *U.S. Private*, pg. 533
BHOME MORTGAGE, LLC—See Green Brick Partners, Inc.; *U.S. Public*, pg. 962
BIBBY FACTORING SERVICES (MALAYSIA) SDN BHD—See Bibby Line Group Limited; *Int'l*, pg. 1017
BIBBY FACTORING SLOVAKIA A.S.—See Bibby Line Group Limited; *Int'l*, pg. 1018
BIBBY FINANCIAL SERVICES (ASIA) LIMITED—See Bibby Line Group Limited; *Int'l*, pg. 1018
BIBBY FINANCIAL SERVICES A.S.—See Bibby Line Group Limited; *Int'l*, pg. 1018
BIBBY FINANCIAL SERVICES (CANADA), INC—See Bibby Line Group Limited; *Int'l*, pg. 1018
BIBBY FINANCIAL SERVICES GMBH—See Bibby Line Group Limited; *Int'l*, pg. 1018
BIBBY FINANCIAL SERVICES (INDIA) PVT LIMITED—See Bibby Line Group Limited; *Int'l*, pg. 1018
BIBBY FINANCIAL SERVICES (IRELAND) LIMITED—See Bibby Line Group Limited; *Int'l*, pg. 1018
BIBBY FINANCIAL SERVICES LIMITED—See Bibby Line Group Limited; *Int'l*, pg. 1017
BIBBY FINANCIAL SERVICES (SINGAPORE) PTE LIMITED—See Bibby Line Group Limited; *Int'l*, pg. 1018
BIBBY FINANCIAL SERVICES S.P. Z.O.O.—See Bibby Line Group Limited; *Int'l*, pg. 1018
BIG PHARMA SPLIT CORP.; *Int'l*, pg. 1021
BIMINI CAPITAL MANAGEMENT, INC.; *U.S. Public*, pg. 331
BLACKHAWK NETWORK HOLDINGS, INC.—See P2 Capital Partners, LLC; *U.S. Private*, pg. 3061
BLACKHAWK NETWORK HOLDINGS, INC.—See Silver Lake Group, LLC; *U.S. Private*, pg. 3656
BLACKROCK CORPORATE HIGH YIELD FUND, INC.; *U.S. Public*, pg. 342
BLACKROCK DEBT STRATEGIES FUND, INC.; *U.S. Public*, pg. 342
BLACKROCK ENHANCED CAPITAL & INCOME FUND, INC.; *U.S. Public*, pg. 342
BLACKROCK ENHANCED EQUITY DIVIDEND TRUST; *U.S. Public*, pg. 342
BLACKROCK ENHANCED GLOBAL DIVIDEND TRUST; *U.S. Public*, pg. 342
BLACKROCK ENHANCED GOVERNMENT FUND, INC.; *U.S. Public*, pg. 342
BLACKROCK ENHANCED INTERNATIONAL DIVIDEND TRUST; *U.S. Public*, pg. 342
BLACKROCK FLOATING RATE INCOME STRATEGIES FUND, INC.; *U.S. Public*, pg. 342
BLACKROCK FLOATING RATE INCOME TRUST; *U.S. Public*, pg. 342
BLACKROCK FRONTIERS INVESTMENT TRUST PLC; *Int'l*, pg. 1061
BLACKROCK INVESTMENT QUALITY MUNI TR; *U.S. Public*, pg. 342
BLACKROCK LONG-TERM MUNICIPAL ADTGTRUST; *U.S. Public*, pg. 342
BLACKROCK MARYLAND MUNICIPAL BOND TRUST; *U.S. Public*, pg. 342
BLACKROCK MASSACHUSETTS TAX-EXEMPT TRUST; *U.S. Public*, pg. 342
BLACKROCK MUNIASSETS FUND, INC.; *U.S. Public*, pg. 342
BLACKROCK MUNICIPAL INCOME FUND, INC.; *U.S. Public*, pg. 343
BLACKROCK MUNICIPAL INCOME INVESTMENT QUALITY TRUST; *U.S. Public*, pg. 343
BLACKROCK MUNICIPAL INCOME INVESTMENT TRUST; *U.S. Public*, pg. 343
BLACKROCK MUNICIPAL INCOME QUALITY TRUST; *U.S. Public*, pg. 343
BLACKROCK MUNICIPAL INCOME TRUST II; *U.S. Public*, pg. 343
BLACKROCK MUNIENHANCED FUND, INC.; *U.S. Public*, pg. 343
BLACKROCK MUNIHOLDINGS CALIFORNIA QUALITY FUND, INC.; *U.S. Public*, pg. 343
BLACKROCK MUNIHOLDINGS FUND II, INC.; *U.S. Public*, pg. 343
BLACKROCK MUNIHOLDINGS FUND, INC.; *U.S. Public*, pg. 343
BLACKROCK MUNIHOLDINGS INVESTMENT QUALITY FUND; *U.S. Public*, pg. 343
BLACKROCK MUNIHOLDINGS NEW JERSEY QUALITY FUND, INC.; *U.S. Public*, pg. 343
BLACKROCK MUNIHOLDINGS QUALITY FUND II, INC.; *U.S. Public*, pg. 343
BLACKROCK MUNIHOLDINGS QUALITY FUND, INC.; *U.S. Public*, pg. 343
BLACKROCK MUNI NEW YORK INTERMEDIATE DURATION FUND, INC.; *U.S. Public*, pg. 342
BLACKROCK MUNIVEST FUND II, INC.; *U.S. Public*, pg. 343
BLACKROCK MUNIYIELD ARIZONA FUND, INC.; *U.S. Public*, pg. 343
BLACKROCK MUNIYIELD CALIFORNIA FUND, INC.; *U.S. Public*, pg. 343
BLACKROCK MUNIYIELD CALIFORNIA QUALITY FUND, INC.; *U.S. Public*, pg. 343
BLACKROCK MUNIYIELD FUND, INC.; *U.S. Public*, pg. 343
BLACKROCK MUNIYIELD INVESTMENT QUALITY FUND; *U.S. Public*, pg. 343
BLACKROCK MUNIYIELD INVSTMT FD; *U.S. Public*, pg. 343
BLACKROCK MUNIYIELD MICHIGAN QUALITY FUND, INC.; *U.S. Public*, pg. 343
BLACKROCK MUNIYIELD NEW JERSEY FUND, INC.; *U.S. Public*, pg. 344
BLACKROCK MUNIYIELD PENNSYLVANIA QUALITY FUND; *U.S. Public*, pg. 344
BLACKROCK MUNIYIELD QUALITY FUND II; *U.S. Public*, pg. 344
BLACKROCK MUNIYIELD QUALITY FUND, INC.; *U.S. Public*, pg. 344
BLACKROCK NEW YORK MUNICIPAL BOND TRUST; *U.S. Public*, pg. 344
BLACKROCK NEW YORK MUNICIPAL INCOME QUALITY TRUST; *U.S. Public*, pg. 344
BLACKROCK SCIENCE & TECHNOLOGY TRUST; *U.S. Public*, pg. 344
BLACKROCK STRATEGIC MUNICIPAL TRUST; *U.S. Public*, pg. 344
BLACKROCK VIRGINIA MUNICIPAL BOND TRUST; *U.S. Public*, pg. 344
BLACKSTONE / GSO STRATEGIC CREDIT FUND—See Blackstone Inc.; *U.S. Public*, pg. 348
BLACKSTONE LONG-SHORT CREDIT INCOME FUND; *U.S. Public*, pg. 361
BLACKSTONE MORTGAGE TRUST, INC.—See Blackstone Inc.; *U.S. Public*, pg. 349
BLACKSTONE PRIVATE CREDIT FUND—See Blackstone Inc.; *U.S. Public*, pg. 349
BLACKSTONE SENIOR FLOATING RATE 2027 TERM FUND; *U.S. Public*, pg. 361
BLOCKMATE VENTURES, INC.; *Int'l*, pg. 1064
BLOK TECHNOLOGIES, INC.; *Int'l*, pg. 1064
BLOOM SELECT INCOME FUND—See Bloom Investment Counsel, Inc.; *Int'l*, pg. 1065
BLUEFIN PAYMENT SYSTEMS; *U.S. Private*, pg. 596
BLUE OWL CAPITAL CORPORATION III—See Blue Owl Capital Inc.; *U.S. Public*, pg. 364
BLUE OWL CAPITAL CORPORATION II—See Blue Owl Capital Inc.; *U.S. Public*, pg. 364
BLUE RIBBON INCOME FUND; *Int'l*, pg. 1069

N.A.I.C.S. INDEX

525990 — OTHER FINANCIAL VEH...

BLUEROCK RESIDENTIAL GROWTH REIT, INC.; *U.S. Public*, pg. 366
BMH INVESTMENT GROUP, LLC—See U.S. Financial Services, LLC; *U.S. Private*, pg. 4270
BMO GLOBAL WATER SOLUTIONS TACTIC FUND—See Bank of Montreal; *Int'l*, pg. 846
BNP LEASE GROUP S.P.A.—See BNP Paribas SA; *Int'l*, pg. 1087
BNP PARIBAS LEASING SOLUTIONS SPA—See BNP Paribas SA; *Int'l*, pg. 1086
BNP PARIBAS REAL ESTATE INVESTMENT MANAGEMENT GERMANY GMBH—See BNP Paribas SA; *Int'l*, pg. 1086
BNP PARIBAS WEALTH MANAGEMENT—See BNP Paribas SA; *Int'l*, pg. 1088
BOARDWALK REAL ESTATE INVESTMENT TRUST; *Int'l*, pg. 1094
BONITA LAKES MALL LIMITED PARTNERSHIP—See CBL & Associates Properties, Inc.; *U.S. Public*, pg. 457
BOSTON PIZZA ROYALTIES INCOME FUND; *Int'l*, pg. 1118
BOSTON PROPERTIES, INC.; *U.S. Public*, pg. 372
BOULDER GROWTH & INCOME FUND INC.; *U.S. Public*, pg. 375
B.P. MARSH & PARTNERS PLC; *Int'l*, pg. 790
BRAEMAR HOTELS & RESORTS, INC.; *U.S. Public*, pg. 379
BRAND LEADERS INCOME FUND—See Harvest Portfolios Group Inc.; *Int'l*, pg. 3281
BRANDYWINE REALTY TRUST; *U.S. Public*, pg. 380
BREDERODE S.A.; *Int'l*, pg. 1144
BRE DIAMOND HOTEL LLC—See Blackstone Inc.; *U.S. Public*, pg. 350
BRE RETAIL CENTERS CORP—See Blackstone Inc.; *U.S. Public*, pg. 350
BRIDGEWELL INCOME TRUST INC.; *U.S. Private*, pg. 650
BRIXMOR PROPERTY GROUP INC.-CONSHOHOCKEN—See Blackstone Inc.; *U.S. Public*, pg. 352
BROMPTON SPLIT BANC CORP.—See Brompton Funds Limited; *Int'l*, pg. 1173
BROOKFIELD DTLA FUND OFFICE TRUST INVESTOR, INC.; *U.S. Public*, pg. 395
BROOKFIELD GLOBAL INFRASTRUCTURE SECURITIES INCOME FUND; *Int'l*, pg. 1189
BROOKFIELD INVESTMENTS CORPORATION—See Brookfield Corporation; *Int'l*, pg. 1184
BROOKFIELD OFFICE PROPERTIES INC.—See Brookfield Corporation; *Int'l*, pg. 1186
BROOKFIELD PROPERTIES, INC.—See Brookfield Corporation; *Int'l*, pg. 1186
BROOKFIELD PROPERTY REIT INC.—See Brookfield Corporation; *Int'l*, pg. 1186
BROOKFIELD REAL ASSETS INCOME FUND INC.—See Brookfield Corporation; *Int'l*, pg. 1184
BROOKFIELD SQUARE PARCEL, LLC—See CBL & Associates Properties, Inc.; *U.S. Public*, pg. 457
BRT APARTMENTS CORP.; *U.S. Public*, pg. 403
BTB REAL ESTATE INVESTMENT TRUST; *Int'l*, pg. 1204
BT LEASING TRANSILVANIA IFN S.A.—See Banca Transilvania S.A.; *Int'l*, pg. 816
THE BUSINESS FINANCE STORE—See The Finance Store; *U.S. Private*, pg. 4028
BUY-OUT CENTRAL EUROPE II BETEILIGUNGS-INVEST AG—See Global Equity Partners Beteiligungs-Management AG; *Int'l*, pg. 2996
CA IMMO DEUTSCHLAND GMBH—See Starwood Capital Group Global I, LLC; *U.S. Private*, pg. 3789
CALAMOS CONVERTIBLE & HIGH INCOME FUND; *U.S. Public*, pg. 421
CALAMOS GLOBAL DYNAMIC INCOME FUND; *U.S. Public*, pg. 421
CALAMOS GLOBAL TOTAL RETURN FUND; *U.S. Public*, pg. 421
CALAMOS STRATEGIC TOTAL RETURN FUND; *U.S. Public*, pg. 421
CALEDONIA INVESTMENTS PLC; *Int'l*, pg. 1262
CALLAHAN CAPITAL PARTNERS; *U.S. Private*, pg. 722
CAMDEN PROPERTY TRUST; *U.S. Public*, pg. 426
CAMDEN SUMMIT, INC.—See Camden Property Trust; *U.S. Public*, pg. 426
CANACCORD GENUITY SECURITIES LLC—See Canaccord Genuity Group Inc.; *Int'l*, pg. 1277
CANADIAN APARTMENT PROPERTIES REAL ESTATE INVESTMENT TRUST; *Int'l*, pg. 1282
CANADIAN HIGH YIELD FOCUS FUND—See Fiera Capital Corporation; *Int'l*, pg. 2659
CANADIAN SOLAR INFRASTRUCTURE FUND, INC.; *Int'l*, pg. 1286
CANADIAN UTILITIES & TELECOM INCOME FUND; *Int'l*, pg. 1286
CANOE EIT INCOME FUND—See Canoe Financial LP; *Int'l*, pg. 1292
CANSO CREDIT INCOME FUND; *Int'l*, pg. 1298
CANSO SELECT OPPORTUNITIES CORP.; *Int'l*, pg. 1299
CAPITALAND COMMERCIAL TRUST—See CapitaLand Investment Limited; *Int'l*, pg. 1313
CAPITALAND INTEGRATED COMMERCIAL TRUST—See CapitaLand Investment Limited; *Int'l*, pg. 1313

CAPITALAND INVESTMENT LIMITED; *Int'l*, pg. 1313
CAPITAL AUTOMOTIVE REAL ESTATE SERVICES, INC.; *U.S. Private*, pg. 738
CAPITAL CITY INVESTMENT B.V.—See Enka Insaat ve Sanayi A.S.; *Int'l*, pg. 2440
CAPITAL FINANCIAL GLOBAL, INC.; *U.S. Public*, pg. 431
CAPITAL MARKET SERVICES LLC; *U.S. Private*, pg. 741
CAPITAL ONE SERVICES (CANADA) INC.—See Capital One Financial Corporation; *U.S. Public*, pg. 431
CAPITAL PROCESSING INT'L INC.; *U.S. Private*, pg. 741
CAPRI CAPITAL PARTNERS, LLC; *U.S. Private*, pg. 745
CAPSTEAD MORTGAGE CORPORATION—See Franklin Resources, Inc.; *U.S. Public*, pg. 879
CARCHEX; *U.S. Private*, pg. 748
CAR FINANCIAL SERVICES, INC.—See ATLANTICUS HOLDINGS CORPORATION; *U.S. Public*, pg. 223
CARINDALE PROPERTY TRUST; *Int'l*, pg. 1331
CARMAX ENTERPRISE SERVICES, LLC—See CarMax, Inc.; *U.S. Public*, pg. 437
CAROUSEL CHECKS INC.; *U.S. Private*, pg. 770
CARRUTH CAPITAL LLC; *U.S. Private*, pg. 774
CARTER VALIDUS MISSION CRITICAL REIT, INC.—See Carter & Associates, LLC; *U.S. Private*, pg. 775
CASEY RESEARCH, LLC; *U.S. Private*, pg. 782
CASHGATE AG—See Cembra Money Bank AG; *Int'l*, pg. 1396
CASTLELAKE, L.P.; *U.S. Private*, pg. 785
CASTLEVIEW PROPERTY FUND LTD.; *Int'l*, pg. 1357
CBL & ASSOCIATES PROPERTIES, INC.; *U.S. Public*, pg. 457
CBL/FOOTHILLS PLAZA PARTNERSHIP—See CBL & Associates Properties, Inc.; *U.S. Public*, pg. 458
CBL-FRIENDLY CENTER, LLC—See CBL & Associates Properties, Inc.; *U.S. Public*, pg. 458
CBL/YORK, INC.—See CBL & Associates Properties, Inc.; *U.S. Public*, pg. 458
CC JAPAN INCOME & GROWTH TRUST PLC; *Int'l*, pg. 1366
CEDAR REALTY TRUST, INC.—See Wheeler Real Estate Investment Trust, Inc.; *U.S. Public*, pg. 2365
CENTERPOINT PROPERTIES TRUST; *U.S. Private*, pg. 817
CENTERSPACE; *U.S. Public*, pg. 472
CENTRALA PEKAO FACTORING SP. Z O.O.—See Bank Polska Kasa Opieki Spolka Akcyjna; *Int'l*, pg. 849
CENTRAL PENNSYLVANIA MEDICAL FOUNDATION; *U.S. Private*, pg. 824
CENTRIA COMMERCE—See Centria Inc.; *Int'l*, pg. 1412
CENTRUM KART S.A.—See Bank Polska Kasa Opieki Spolka Akcyjna; *Int'l*, pg. 849
CENTURIA INDUSTRIAL REIT—See Centuria Capital Limited; *Int'l*, pg. 1416
CENTURIA OFFICE REIT—See Centuria Capital Limited; *Int'l*, pg. 1416
CERBERUS MORTGAGE CAPITAL, INC.—See Cerberus Capital Management, L.P.; *U.S. Private*, pg. 837
CFB COMMERZ FONDS BETEILIGUNGS GMBH—See Commerzbank AG; *Int'l*, pg. 1717
CHALLENGER DIVERSIFIED PROPERTY GROUP—See Challenger Limited; *Int'l*, pg. 1438
CHALLENGER LIMITED; *Int'l*, pg. 1438
CHAMPION REAL ESTATE INVESTMENT TRUST; *Int'l*, pg. 1440
CHARFEN INSTITUTE; *U.S. Private*, pg. 850
CHARTER HALL LIMITED; *Int'l*, pg. 1454
CHARTER HALL LONG WALE REIT—See Charter Hall Limited; *Int'l*, pg. 1454
CHARTER HALL SOCIAL INFRASTRUCTURE REIT—See Charter Hall Limited; *Int'l*, pg. 1454
CHASE MORTGAGE HOLDINGS, INC.—See JPMorgan Chase & Co.; *U.S. Public*, pg. 1206
CHATHAM LODGING TRUST; *U.S. Public*, pg. 483
CHECKSMART FINANCIAL COMPANY—See Community Choice Financial Inc.; *U.S. Private*, pg. 991
CHEEMINMET FINANCE LIMITED—See China Rare Earth Resources And Technology Co., Ltd.; *Int'l*, pg. 1545
CHELSEA INVESTMENTS CORPORATION; *U.S. Private*, pg. 870
CHELVERTON GROWTH TRUST PLC; *Int'l*, pg. 1460
CHELVERTON UK DIVIDEND TRUST PLC; *Int'l*, pg. 1460
CHERRY HILL MORTGAGE INVESTMENT CORPORATION; *U.S. Public*, pg. 485
CHERRYVALE MALL, LLC—See CBL & Associates Properties, Inc.; *U.S. Public*, pg. 458
CHESAPEAKE LODGING TRUST—See Park Hotels & Resorts Inc.; *U.S. Public*, pg. 1638
CHICAGO OAKBROOK FINANCIAL GROUP; *U.S. Private*, pg. 878
CHIMERA INVESTMENT CORP.; *U.S. Public*, pg. 489
CHINA HOUSING & LAND DEVELOPMENT, INC.; *Int'l*, pg. 1508
CHINA MERCHANTS CHINA DIRECT INVESTMENTS LIMITED—See China Merchants Group Limited; *Int'l*, pg. 1520
CHINA MERCHANTS SHEKOU INDUSTRIAL ZONE CO., LTD.—See China Merchants Group Limited; *Int'l*, pg. 1521
CHINA MINING UNITED FUND; *Int'l*, pg. 1524

CHINA NEW ECONOMY FUND LIMITED; *Int'l*, pg. 1534
CHINA RESOURCES LAND LIMITED—See China Resources (Holdings) Co., Ltd.; *Int'l*, pg. 1548
CHINESE ESTATES HOLDINGS LIMITED; *Int'l*, pg. 1569
CHINESE ESTATES LIMITED—See Chinese Estates Holdings Limited; *Int'l*, pg. 1569
THE CHOICE GROUP, LLC; *U.S. Private*, pg. 4009
CHOICE PROPERTIES REAL ESTATE INVESTMENT TRUST—See George Weston Limited; *Int'l*, pg. 2938
THE CHRISKEN RESIDENTIAL TRUST; *U.S. Private*, pg. 4009
CIM GROUP, LLC; *U.S. Private*, pg. 897
CIM REAL ESTATE FINANCE TRUST, INC.—See CIM Group, LLC; *U.S. Private*, pg. 897
CIP CAPITAL FUND, L.P.; *U.S. Private*, pg. 899
CIT HEALTHCARE LLC—See First Citizens BancShares, Inc.; *U.S. Public*, pg. 841
CITIZENS ASSET FINANCE, INC.—See Citizens Financial Group, Inc.; *U.S. Public*, pg. 505
CI TOWER INVESTMENTS LIMITED—See CLS Holdings plc; *Int'l*, pg. 1664
CLARENDON CENTER LLC—See Saul Centers, Inc.; *U.S. Public*, pg. 1842
CLEARBRIDGE ENERGY MIDSTREAM OPPORTUNITY FUND INC.—See Franklin Resources, Inc.; *U.S. Public*, pg. 881
CLEARBRIDGE MLP & MIDSTREAM FUND INC.—See Franklin Resources, Inc.; *U.S. Public*, pg. 881
CLIFTON ASSET MANAGEMENT PLC; *Int'l*, pg. 1659
CLOSE PREMIUM FINANCE IRELAND—See Close Brothers Group plc; *Int'l*, pg. 1661
CLOSE PREMIUM FINANCE—See Close Brothers Group plc; *Int'l*, pg. 1661
CLOUGH GLOBAL DIVIDEND & INCOME FUND; *U.S. Public*, pg. 515
CLOUGH GLOBAL EQUITY FUND; *U.S. Public*, pg. 515
CLOUGH GLOBAL OPPORTUNITIES FUND; *U.S. Public*, pg. 515
CNL GROWTH PROPERTIES, INC.—See CNL Financial Group, Inc.; *U.S. Private*, pg. 952
CNL HEALTHCARE PROPERTIES II, INC.—See CNL Financial Group, Inc.; *U.S. Private*, pg. 952
CNL HEALTHCARE PROPERTIES, INC.—See CNL Financial Group, Inc.; *U.S. Private*, pg. 952
CNL LIFESTYLE PROPERTIES, INC.—See CNL Financial Group, Inc.; *U.S. Private*, pg. 952
COASTAL GRAND, LLC—See CBL & Associates Properties, Inc.; *U.S. Public*, pg. 458
COFINIMMO S.A./N.V.; *Int'l*, pg. 1692
COHEN & STEERS LIMITED DURATION PREFERRED AND INCOME FUND, INC.; *U.S. Public*, pg. 526
COHEN & STEERS REIT & PREFERRED INCOME FUND, INC.; *U.S. Public*, pg. 526
COHEN & STEERS SELECT PREFERRED & INCOME FUND, INC.; *U.S. Public*, pg. 526
COHEN & STEERS TOTAL RETURN REALTY FUND, INC.; *U.S. Public*, pg. 526
COLLEGE STATION PARTNERS, LTD.—See CBL & Associates Properties, Inc.; *U.S. Public*, pg. 458
COLLINEO ASSET MANAGEMENT GMBH—See Deutsche Bank Aktiengesellschaft; *Int'l*, pg. 2062
COLUMBIA SELIGMAN PREMIUM TECHNOLOGY GROWTH FUND, INC.; *U.S. Public*, pg. 534
COMERICA WIRE TRANSFER—See Comerica Incorporated; *U.S. Public*, pg. 542
COMINAR REAL ESTATE INVESTMENT TRUST—See Canderel Management Inc.; *Int'l*, pg. 1289
COMMERZBANK HOLDINGS (UK) LIMITED—See Commerzbank AG; *Int'l*, pg. 1717
COMMERZ REAL FONDS BETEILIGUNGS- GESELLSCHAFT MBH—See Commerzbank AG; *Int'l*, pg. 1716
COMMONWEALTH PREMIUM FINANCE CORPORATION—See Unified Financial Services, Inc.; *U.S. Private*, pg. 4282
COMMONWEALTH REALTY PARTNERS, INC.; *U.S. Private*, pg. 987
COMMUNITY CHOICE FINANCIAL INC.; *U.S. Private*, pg. 990
COMMUNITY HEALTHCARE TRUST INCORPORATED; *U.S. Public*, pg. 557
COMPLETE MERCHANT SOLUTIONS (CMS); *U.S. Private*, pg. 1001
CONAFI PRESTITO S.P.A.; *Int'l*, pg. 1763
CONAM INVESTMENT GROUP—See The ConAm Group of Companies; *U.S. Private*, pg. 4013
CONDOR HOSPITALITY TRUST, INC.; *U.S. Public*, pg. 566
CONIHASSET CAPTIAL PARTNERS, INC.; *U.S. Public*, pg. 567
THE CONNECTICUT CARPENTERS PENSION FUND—See Connecticut Carpenters Benefit Funds; *U.S. Private*, pg. 1015
CONSENSYS, INC.; *U.S. Private*, pg. 1019
CONSULTANTS GROUP COMMERCIAL FINANCE—See Blue Owl Capital Inc.; *U.S. Public*, pg. 364
COPT DEFENSE PROPERTIES; *U.S. Public*, pg. 575
CORE ECONOMY INVESTMENT GROUP LIMITED; *Int'l*, pg. 1797
CORELOGIC SOLUTIONS, LLC—See Insight Venture Man-

4481

525990 — OTHER FINANCIAL VEH...

agement, LLC; *U.S. Private*, pg. 2089
CORELOGIC SOLUTIONS, LLC—See Stone Point Capital LLC; *U.S. Private*, pg. 3822
CORESITE REALTY CORPORATION—See American Tower Corporation; *U.S. Public*, pg. 111
CORNERSTONE STRATEGIC VALUE FUND, INC.; *U.S. Public*, pg. 577
CORNERSTONE TOTAL RETURN FUND, INC.; *U.S. Public*, pg. 577
CORPORACION FINANCIERA DE INVERSIONES SA; *Int'l*, pg. 1803
CORPORATE CAPITAL TRUST, INC.—See Franklin Square Holdings, L.P.; *U.S. Private*, pg. 1598
CORPORATE PROPERTY ASSOCIATES 17 - GLOBAL INCORPORATED—See W.P. Carey Inc.; *U.S. Public*, pg. 2315
CORPORATE PROPERTY ASSOCIATES 18 GLOBAL INC; *U.S. Private*, pg. 1055
CORPOREX COMPANIES, INC.; *U.S. Private*, pg. 1058
COUSINS PROPERTIES INCORPORATED; *U.S. Public*, pg. 587
COUSINS - SAN JACINTO CENTER LLC—See Cousins Properties Incorporated; *U.S. Public*, pg. 587
CRANE INVESTMENT CO.—See Crane Group Co.; *U.S. Private*, pg. 1085
CREATIVE PAYMENT SOLUTIONS, INC.—See Truist Financial Corporation; *U.S. Public*, pg. 2200
CREDEM PRIVATE EQUITY SGR SPA—See Credito Emiliano S.p.A.; *Int'l*, pg. 1836
CRESUD SOCIEDAD ANONIMA, COMERCIAL, INMOBILIARIA, FINANCIERA Y AGROPECUARIA; *Int'l*, pg. 1842
CROMBIE REIT—See Empire Company Limited; *Int'l*, pg. 2387
CROMWELL PROPERTY GROUP; *Int'l*, pg. 1853
CRYSTAL AMBER FUND LIMITED—See Crystal Amber Asset Management (Guernsey) LLP; *Int'l*, pg. 1860
CT UK HIGH INCOME TRUST PLC; *Int'l*, pg. 1868
CUBESMART; *U.S. Public*, pg. 603
CUBESMART WILTON, LLC—See CubeSmart; *U.S. Public*, pg. 603
CUKIERMAN & CO. REAL ESTATE LTD.—See Cukierman & Co. Investment House Ltd.; *Int'l*, pg. 1876
THE CUSHING ENERGY INCOME FUND—See Swank Capital, LLC; *U.S. Private*, pg. 3890
CYRUSONE INC.—See BlackRock, Inc.; *U.S. Public*, pg. 346
CYRUSONE INC.—See KKR & Co. Inc.; *U.S. Public*, pg. 1244
DAH SING NOMINEES LTD—See Dah Sing Financial Holdings Limited; *Int'l*, pg. 1913
DAIWA HOUSE REIT MANAGEMENT CO., LTD.—See Daiwa House Industry Co., Ltd.; *Int'l*, pg. 1945
DARR FAMILY FOUNDATION; *U.S. Private*, pg. 1159
DAVENHAM GROUP HOLDINGS PLC—See Davenham Group Plc; *Int'l*, pg. 1983
DAVICTUS PLC; *Int'l*, pg. 1983
DB REAL ESTATE INVESTMENT GMBH—See Deutsche Bank Aktiengesellschaft; *Int'l*, pg. 2058
DCT INDUSTRIAL TRUST INC.—See Prologis, Inc.; *U.S. Public*, pg. 1726
DCT MEXICO REIT LLC—See Prologis, Inc.; *U.S. Public*, pg. 1726
DE 100 WILSHIRE, LLC—See Douglas Emmett, Inc.; *U.S. Public*, pg. 678
DE 8484 WILSHIRE, LLC—See Douglas Emmett, Inc.; *U.S. Public*, pg. 678
DEBT FREE ASSOCIATES; *U.S. Private*, pg. 1186
DE LAGE LANDEN LEASING GMBH—See Cooperatieve Centrale Raiffeisen-Boerenleenbank B.A.; *Int'l*, pg. 1791
DE LAGE LANDEN LEASING LTD.—See Cooperatieve Centrale Raiffeisen-Boerenleenbank B.A.; *Int'l*, pg. 1791
DE LAGE LANDEN LEASING LTD.—See Cooperatieve Centrale Raiffeisen-Boerenleenbank B.A.; *Int'l*, pg. 1791
DE LAGE LANDEN LEASING N.V.—See Cooperatieve Centrale Raiffeisen-Boerenleenbank B.A.; *Int'l*, pg. 1791
DE LAGE LANDEN LEASING S.P.A.—See Cooperatieve Centrale Raiffeisen-Boerenleenbank B.A.; *Int'l*, pg. 1791
DELAWARE ENHANCED GLOBAL DIVIDEND & INCOME FUND; *U.S. Public*, pg. 648
DELAWARE INVESTMENTS COLORADO INSURED MUNICIPAL INCOME FUND; *U.S. Public*, pg. 648
DELAWARE INVESTMENTS DIV & INCOME FUND; *U.S. Public*, pg. 648
DELTA PROPERTY FUND LIMITED; *Int'l*, pg. 2020
DEMAND POOLING, INC.; *U.S. Private*, pg. 1203
DEMIRE DEUTSCHE MITTELSTAND REAL ESTATE AG; *Int'l*, pg. 2025
DEMOTELLER SYSTEMS, INC.—See ASSA ABLOY AB; *Int'l*, pg. 637
DEVELOPERS INVESTORS, INC.—See W.C. Bradley Co.; *U.S. Private*, pg. 4419
DEXUS CONVENIENCE RETAIL REIT—See DEXUS; *Int'l*, pg. 2093
DEXUS INDUSTRIA REIT—See DEXUS; *Int'l*, pg. 2093
DHL MANAGEMENT (SCHWEIZ) AG—See Deutsche Post AG; *Int'l*, pg. 2077
DIAMOND MIND INC.; *U.S. Private*, pg. 1223

DIESEL LTD.—See Starwood Property Trust, Inc.; *U.S. Public*, pg. 1939
DIGITALBRIDGE GROUP, INC.; *U.S. Public*, pg. 664
DIGITAL REALTY TRUST, INC.; *U.S. Public*, pg. 663
DIGITAL REALTY TRUST, L.P.—See Digital Realty Trust, Inc.; *U.S. Public*, pg. 663
DIPULA INCOME FUND LIMITED; *Int'l*, pg. 2129
DIREKTSERVICE COMMERZ GMBH—See Commerzbank AG; *Int'l*, pg. 1717
DIVERSIFIED HEALTHCARE TRUST; *U.S. Public*, pg. 670
DIVIDEND CAPITAL ADVISORS LLC—See Prologis, Inc.; *U.S. Public*, pg. 1726
DIVIDEND GROWTH SPLIT CORP.—See Brompton Funds Limited; *Int'l*, pg. 1173
DIVIDEND & INCOME FUND; *U.S. Public*, pg. 670
DO DEUTSCHE OFFICE AG—See alstria office REIT-AG; *Int'l*, pg. 383
DOMESTIC & GENERAL GROUP LIMITED—See CVC Capital Partners SICAV-FIS S.A.; *Int'l*, pg. 1883
DONGBUKA NO 12 SHIP INVESTMENT CO., LTD.; *Int'l*, pg. 2166
DONGBUKA NO.13 SHIP INVESTMENT CO., LTD.; *Int'l*, pg. 2166
DOUBLELINE INCOME SOLUTIONS FUND—See DoubleLine Capital LP; *U.S. Private*, pg. 1266
DOUBLELINE INCOME SOLUTIONS TRUST—See Bank of Montreal; *Int'l*, pg. 846
DOUBLELINE OPPORTUNISTIC CREDIT FUND—See DoubleLine Capital LP; *U.S. Private*, pg. 1266
DOUGLAS EMMETT, INC.; *U.S. Public*, pg. 677
DOWNING ONE VCT PLC; *Int'l*, pg. 2186
DREAM GLOBAL REAL ESTATE INVESTMENT TRUST—See Blackstone Inc.; *U.S. Public*, pg. 350
DREAM INDUSTRIAL REAL ESTATE INVESTMENT TRUST—See Dream Unlimited Corp.; *Int'l*, pg. 2203
DREAM OFFICE REAL ESTATE INVESTMENT TRUST—See Dream Unlimited Corp.; *Int'l*, pg. 2203
DRUMMOND VENTURES CORP.; *Int'l*, pg. 2206
DTF TAX-FREE INCOME 2028 TERM FUND INC.; *U.S. Public*, pg. 689
DUBAI INVESTMENTS REAL ESTATE COMPANY—See Dubai Investments PJSC; *Int'l*, pg. 2219
DUKE CAPITAL CORPORATION—See Duke Energy Corporation; *U.S. Public*, pg. 690
DUNEDIN INCOME GROWTH INVESTMENT TRUST PLC; *Int'l*, pg. 2226
DUSIT THANI FREEHOLD & LEASEHOLD REIT; *Int'l*, pg. 2234
DWS MUNICIPAL INCOME TRUST; *U.S. Public*, pg. 694
DWS STRATEGIC MUNICIPAL INCOME TRUST; *U.S. Public*, pg. 694
DYNEX CAPITAL, INC.; *U.S. Public*, pg. 700
E4E FINANCIAL SERVICES—See e4e Inc.; *U.S. Private*, pg. 1308
EARN CMO LLC—See Ellington Credit Company Management LLC; *U.S. Public*, pg. 734
EARTHTECH CONTRACTING, INC.—See Kinderhook Industries, LLC; *U.S. Private*, pg. 2307
EASTBRIDGE INVESTMENTS PLC; *Int'l*, pg. 2271
EASTERLY GOVERNMENT PROPERTIES, INC.; *U.S. Public*, pg. 703
EASTERN BAY ENERGY TRUST; *Int'l*, pg. 2271
EASTERN COMMERCIAL LEASING PUBLIC COMPANY LIMITED; *Int'l*, pg. 2272
EASTGROUP PROPERTIES, INC.; *U.S. Public*, pg. 704
EATON VANCE CALIFORNIA MUNICIPAL INCOME TRUST; *U.S. Public*, pg. 708
EATON VANCE ENHANCED EQUITY INCOME FUND; *U.S. Public*, pg. 708
EATON VANCE ENHANCED EQUITY INCOME II; *U.S. Public*, pg. 708
EATON VANCE FLOATING-RATE 2022 TARGET TERM TRUST; *U.S. Public*, pg. 708
EATON VANCE FLOATING-RATE INCOME PLUS FUND; *U.S. Public*, pg. 708
EATON VANCE FLOATING-RATE INCOME TRUST; *U.S. Public*, pg. 708
EATON VANCE LIMITED DURATION INCOME FUND; *U.S. Public*, pg. 708
EATON VANCE MUNICIPAL BOND FUND; *U.S. Public*, pg. 708
EATON VANCE MUNICIPAL INCOME 2028 TERM TRUST—See Morgan Stanley; *U.S. Public*, pg. 1472
EATON VANCE MUNICIPAL INCOME TRUST; *U.S. Public*, pg. 708
EATON VANCE NATIONAL MUNICIPAL OPPORTUNITIES TRUST; *U.S. Public*, pg. 708
EATON VANCE RISK-MANAGED DIVERSIFIED EQUITY INCOME FUND; *U.S. Public*, pg. 708
EATON VANCE SENIOR FLOATING-RATE TRUST; *U.S. Public*, pg. 708
EATON VANCE SENIOR INCOME TRUST; *U.S. Public*, pg. 708
EATON VANCE SHORT DURATION DIVERSIFIED INCOME FUND; *U.S. Public*, pg. 708
EATON VANCE TAX-ADVANTAGED DIVIDEND INCOME FUND; *U.S. Public*, pg. 708
EATON VANCE TAX-ADVANTAGED GLOBAL DIVIDEND INCOME FUND; *U.S. Public*, pg. 709
EATON VANCE TAX-ADVANTAGED GLOBAL DIVIDEND OPPORTUNITIES FUND; *U.S. Public*, pg. 709
EATON VANCE TAX-MANAGED BUY-WRITE INCOME FUND; *U.S. Public*, pg. 709
EATON VANCE TAX-MANAGED BUY-WRITE OPPORTUNITIES FUND; *U.S. Public*, pg. 709
EATON VANCE TAX-MANAGED DIVERSIFIED EQUITY INCOME FUND; *U.S. Public*, pg. 709
EATON VANCE TAX MANAGED GLOBAL BUY WRITE OPPORTUNITIES FUND; *U.S. Public*, pg. 709
EBSCO INCOME PROPERTIES LLC—See EBSCO Industries, Inc.; *U.S. Private*, pg. 1324
ECC CAPITAL CORPORATION; *U.S. Public*, pg. 710
ECL FINANCE LIMITED—See Edelweiss Financial Services Ltd.; *Int'l*, pg. 2306
EDCO INVESTMENT B.V.—See Enka Insaat ve Sanayi A.S.; *Int'l*, pg. 2440
EDINBURGH WORLDWIDE INVESTMENT TRUST PLC; *Int'l*, pg. 2310
EGLOBAL; *U.S. Private*, pg. 1344
EGYPTIAN KUWAITI HOLDING; *Int'l*, pg. 2327
EILDON CAPITAL LIMITED—See CVC Limited; *Int'l*, pg. 1889
E.J. VESTCO INDUSTRIES, LLC; *U.S. Private*, pg. 1306
ELANOR INVESTORS GROUP; *Int'l*, pg. 2343
ELANOR RETAIL PROPERTY FUND; *Int'l*, pg. 2343
ELEPHANT INSURANCE COMPANY—See Admiral Group plc; *Int'l*, pg. 151
ELLIOTT ADVISORS (UK) LIMITED—See Elliott Management Corporation; *U.S. Private*, pg. 1364
ELME COMMUNITIES; *U.S. Public*, pg. 734
ELOIGNE COMPANY—See Xcel Energy Inc.; *U.S. Public*, pg. 2385
ELSO HAZAI ENERGIA-PORTFOLIO PLC; *Int'l*, pg. 2370
EMIRA PROPERTY FUND; *Int'l*, pg. 2381
EMIRATES REIT (CEIC) PLC; *Int'l*, pg. 2382
EMPIRE STATE REALTY OP, L.P.—See Empire State Realty Trust, Inc.; *U.S. Public*, pg. 753
EMPIRE STATE REALTY TRUST, INC.; *U.S. Public*, pg. 753
ENDESA FINANCIACION FILIALES SAU—See Enel S.p.A.; *Int'l*, pg. 2412
ENERGY LEADERS INCOME FUND—See Harvest Portfolios Group Inc.; *Int'l*, pg. 3281
ENKA ADAPAZARI POWER INVESTMENT B.V.—See Enka Insaat ve Sanayi A.S.; *Int'l*, pg. 2440
ENKA CONSTRUCTION & DEVELOPMENT B.V.—See Enka Insaat ve Sanayi A.S.; *Int'l*, pg. 2440
ENKA GEBZE POWER INVESTMENT B.V.—See Enka Insaat ve Sanayi A.S.; *Int'l*, pg. 2440
ENKA IZMIR POWER INVESTMENT B.V.—See Enka Insaat ve Sanayi A.S.; *Int'l*, pg. 2440
ENKA POWER INVESTMENT B.V.—See Enka Insaat ve Sanayi A.S.; *Int'l*, pg. 2440
ENOVA INTERNATIONAL, INC.; *U.S. Public*, pg. 769
ENRU DEVELOPMENT B.V.—See Enka Insaat ve Sanayi A.S.; *Int'l*, pg. 2440
EQUINOR SERVICE CENTER BELGIUM NV—See Equinor ASA; *Int'l*, pg. 2484
EQUITES PROPERTY FUND LIMITED; *Int'l*, pg. 2488
EQUITRUST USA—See UDG, Inc.; *U.S. Private*, pg. 4274
EQUITY CAPITAL MANAGEMENT, LLC; *U.S. Private*, pg. 1416
EQUITY COMMONWEALTH; *U.S. Public*, pg. 790
EQUITY RESIDENTIAL; *U.S. Public*, pg. 790
ERP OPERATING LIMITED PARTNERSHIP—See Equity Residential; *U.S. Public*, pg. 792
ERSTE ABWICKLUNGSANSTALT AOR; *Int'l*, pg. 2497
ESCROW.COM, INC.—See Freelancer Ltd.; *Int'l*, pg. 2770
ESR-LOGOS REIT—See ESR Investment Management (S) Pte. Ltd.; *Int'l*, pg. 2508
ESSEX PORTFOLIO, L.P.—See Essex Property Trust, Inc.; *U.S. Public*, pg. 796
ESSEX PROPERTY TRUST, INC.; *U.S. Public*, pg. 795
ESTUARY INVESTMENT CORP.; *U.S. Private*, pg. 1429
EULER HERMES AUSTRALIA PTY LTD.—See Allianz SE; *Int'l*, pg. 352
EULER HERMES EUROPE SA—See Allianz SE; pg. 352
EULER HERMES SFAC—See Allianz SE; *Int'l*, pg. 353
EUROCOMMERCIAL PROPERTIES ITALIA S.R.L.—See Eurocommercial Properties N.V.; *Int'l*, pg. 2534
EUROFIMA; *Int'l*, pg. 2535
EURO-FINANCE LTD.; *Int'l*, pg. 2531
EXCEL TRUST, L.P.—See Blackstone Inc.; *U.S. Public*, pg. 350
EXCLAMATION INVESTMENTS CORP.; *Int'l*, pg. 2580
EXPANDER ADVISORS SP. Z O.O.—See Aviva plc; *Int'l*, pg. 746
EXTRA SPACE STORAGE LP—See Extra Space Storage, Inc.; *U.S. Public*, pg. 813
FACTORTRUST, INC.—See TransUnion; *U.S. Public*, pg. 2184
FAIR VALUE REIT-AG—See DEMIRE Deutsche Mittelstand Real Estate AG; *Int'l*, pg. 2025
FAR EAST DEVELOPMENT B.V.—See Enka Insaat ve Sanayi A.S.; *Int'l*, pg. 2440

N.A.I.C.S. INDEX

525990 — OTHER FINANCIAL VEH...

FAR EAST HOSPITALITY TRUST—See Far East Organization Pte. Ltd.; *Int'l*, pg. 2616
FAT PROPHETS GLOBAL PROPERTY FUND; *Int'l*, pg. 2622
FBD PROPERTY & LEISURE LIMITED—See Farmer Business Developments plc; *Int'l*, pg. 2619
F&C INVESTMENT TRUST PLC; *Int'l*, pg. 2595
FEDERAL REALTY INVESTMENT TRUST; *U.S. Public*, pg. 825
FEDERATED HERMES PREMIER MUNICIPAL INCOME FUND; *U.S. Public*, pg. 827
FERAX CAPITAL AG; *Int'l*, pg. 2635
FERRELLGAS PARTNERS FINANCE CORP.—See Ferrellgas Partners, L.P.; *U.S. Public*, pg. 829
FIBERSOFT LIMITED—See Hines Global REIT, Inc.; *U.S. Private*, pg. 1949
FIDELITY EMERGING MARKETS LIMITED; *Int'l*, pg. 2654
FIDELITY EUROPEAN TRUST PLC; *Int'l*, pg. 2654
FILIPINO FUND, INC.; *Int'l*, pg. 2663
FILLMORE CAPITAL PARTNERS, LLC; *U.S. Private*, pg. 1506
THE FINANCE STORE; *U.S. Private*, pg. 4028
FINANCIAL COMPANY REAL-INVEST.KZ JSC; *Int'l*, pg. 2665
FINANCIAL PACIFIC LEASING, INC.—See Columbia Banking System, Inc.; *U.S. Public*, pg. 534
FINANCIAL PACIFIC LEASING, INC.—See Columbia Banking System, Inc.; *U.S. Public*, pg. 534
FINITI GROUP, LLC—See Insight Venture Management, LLC; *U.S. Private*, pg. 2089
FINITI GROUP, LLC—See Stone Point Capital LLC; *U.S. Private*, pg. 3822
FINSHORE MANAGEMENT SERVICES LTD.; *Int'l*, pg. 2676
FIRST ANGUILLA TRUST COMPANY LIMITED; *Int'l*, pg. 2682
FIRST CAPITAL REAL ESTATE TRUST INCORPORATED; *U.S. Private*, pg. 1515
FIRST FEDERAL FINANCE CORPORATION—See First BanCorp; *U.S. Public*, pg. 839
FIRST FINANCE LIMITED; *Int'l*, pg. 2683
FIRST FINANCIAL DIVERSIFIED CORPORATION—See First Financial Northwest, Inc.; *U.S. Public*, pg. 844
FIRST GLOBAL FINANCIAL SERVICES LTD.—See GraceKennedy Limited; *Int'l*, pg. 3048
FIRSTHAND TECHNOLOGY VALUE FUND, INC.—See Firsthand Capital Management, Inc.; *U.S. Private*, pg. 1532
FIRST INDUSTRIAL FINANCING PARTNERSHIP, L.P.—See First Industrial Realty Trust, Inc.; *U.S. Public*, pg. 845
FIRST INDUSTRIAL REALTY TRUST, INC.; *U.S. Public*, pg. 845
THE FIRST OF LONG ISLAND REIT, INC.—See The First of Long Island Corporation; *U.S. Public*, pg. 2074
FIRST REAL ESTATE INVESTMENT TRUST NEW JERSEY CO.; *U.S. Public*, pg. 847
FIRST REAL ESTATE INVESTMENT TRUST; *Int'l*, pg. 2687
FIRST REGISTRARS NIGERIA LIMITED—See FBN Holdings PLC; *Int'l*, pg. 2627
FIRST REPUBLIC PREFERRED CAPITAL CORPORATION—See JPMorgan Chase & Co.; *U.S. Public*, pg. 1207
FIRST SPONSOR GROUP LIMITED; *Int'l*, pg. 2688
FIRST TRUST ABERDEEN EMERGING OPPORTUNITY FUND; *U.S. Public*, pg. 848
FIRST TRUST/ABRDN GLOBAL OPPORTUNITY INCOME FUND; *U.S. Public*, pg. 848
FIRST TRUST ENERGY INFRASTRUCTURE FUND—See First Trust Portfolios L.P.; *U.S. Private*, pg. 1530
FIRST TRUST ENHANCED EQUITY INCOME FUND; *U.S. Public*, pg. 848
FIRST TRUST INTER DUR PREF& INCOME FUND; *U.S. Public*, pg. 848
FIRST TRUST MLP AND ENERGY INCOME FUND—See First Trust Portfolios L.P.; *U.S. Private*, pg. 1530
FIRST TRUST SENIOR FLOATING RATE 2022 TARGET TERM FUND; *U.S. Public*, pg. 848
FIRST TRUST SPECIALTY FINANCE & FINANCIAL OPPORTUNITIES FUND; *U.S. Public*, pg. 848
FLAHERTY & CRUMRINE PREFERRED & INCOME SECURITIES FUND, INC.; *U.S. Public*, pg. 852
FOCUSED MONEY SOLUTIONS INC.; *Int'l*, pg. 2720
FONDO DE VALORES INMOBILIARIOS S.A.C.A.; *Int'l*, pg. 2725
FONDS NATIONAL D'INVESTISSEMENT; *Int'l*, pg. 2725
FONTERELLI GMBH & CO KGAA; *Int'l*, pg. 2726
FORBO FINANZ AG—See Forbo Holding Ltd.; *Int'l*, pg. 2729
FOREST CITY REALTY TRUST, INC.—See Brookfield Corporation; *Int'l*, pg. 1187
FORTH SMART SERVICE PUBLIC COMPANY LIMITED; *Int'l*, pg. 2738
FORTRESS REIT LIMITED; *Int'l*, pg. 2740
FORTUNEBUILDERS INC.; *U.S. Private*, pg. 1577
FOSTER FINANCIAL GROUP; *U.S. Private*, pg. 1578
FRANKLIN LIMITED DURATION INCOME TRUST; *U.S. Public*, pg. 879

FRASERS HOSPITALITY TRUST—See Frasers Property Limited; *Int'l*, pg. 2766
FRASERS PROPERTY AHL LIMITED—See Frasers Property Limited; *Int'l*, pg. 2766
FS ENERGY & POWER FUND—See Franklin Square Holdings, L.P.; *U.S. Private*, pg. 1598
FS KKR CAPITAL CORP.—See Franklin Square Holdings, L.P.; *U.S. Private*, pg. 1598
FUNDCORE INSTITUTIONAL INCOME TRUST INC.; *U.S. Private*, pg. 1623
FUNDIMO, S.A.—See Caixa Geral de Depositos S.A.; *Int'l*, pg. 1260
FUNDING CIRCLE HOLDINGS PLC; *Int'l*, pg. 2845
GABELLI DIVIDEND & INCOME TRUST; *U.S. Public*, pg. 894
THE GABELLI EQUITY TRUST INC.—See GAMCO Investors, Inc.; *U.S. Public*, pg. 895
THE GABELLI GLOBAL SMALL & MID CAP VALUE TRUST; *U.S. Public*, pg. 2074
GABELLI GLOBAL UTILITY & INCOME TRUST—See GAMCO Investors, Inc.; *U.S. Public*, pg. 895
THE GABELLI GO ANYWHERE TRUST; *U.S. Public*, pg. 2074
GABELLI HEALTHCARE & WELLNESSRX TRUST; *U.S. Public*, pg. 894
GABELLI MULTIMEDIA TRUST, INC.; *U.S. Public*, pg. 894
GABLES RESIDENTIAL TRUST—See Franklin Resources, Inc.; *U.S. Public*, pg. 881
GALJADEN FASTIGHETER AB—See Bronsstadet AB; *Int'l*, pg. 1174
GALLIFORD TRY INVESTMENTS LIMITED—See Galliford Try Holdings plc; *Int'l*, pg. 2874
GAMCO NATURAL RESOURCES, GOLD & INCOME TRUST—See GAMCO Investors, Inc.; *U.S. Public*, pg. 895
GAZELLE ASSET MANAGEMENT PTE LTD.; *Int'l*, pg. 2891
G CITY EUROPE LIMITED—See G City Ltd.; *Int'l*, pg. 2861
G CITY LTD.; *Int'l*, pg. 2861
GE CAPITAL BANK LIMITED—See General Electric Company; *U.S. Public*, pg. 920
GECINA S.A.; *Int'l*, pg. 2909
GEFINOR FINANCE S.A.—See Gefinor S.A.; *Int'l*, pg. 2911
GEFINOR U.S.A., INC.—See Gefinor S.A.; *Int'l*, pg. 2911
GENERAL ELECTRIC CAPITAL CORPORATION—See General Electric Company; *U.S. Public*, pg. 920
GETTY PROPERTIES CORP.—See Getty Realty Corp.; *U.S. Public*, pg. 935
GINKGO RESIDENTIAL TRUST INC.; *U.S. Private*, pg. 1701
GLADSTONE CAPITAL CORPORATION—See Gladstone Management Corporation; *U.S. Private*, pg. 1705
GLADSTONE COMMERCIAL CORPORATION—See Gladstone Management Corporation; *U.S. Private*, pg. 1705
GLADSTONE COMMERCIAL PARTNERS, LLC—See Gladstone Management Corporation; *U.S. Private*, pg. 1705
GLADSTONE INVESTMENT CORPORATION—See Gladstone Management Corporation; *U.S. Private*, pg. 1705
GLAXO FINANCE BERMUDA LIMITED—See GSK plc; *Int'l*, pg. 3145
GLOBAL CAPITAL LIMITED; *U.S. Private*, pg. 1712
GLOBAL DIVERSIFIED INVESTMENT GRADE INCOME TRUST II; *Int'l*, pg. 2994
GLOBAL MASTERS FUND LIMITED; *Int'l*, pg. 2999
GLOBAL NET LEASE, INC.—See AR Global Investments, LLC; *U.S. Private*, pg. 306
GLOBAL OPPORTUNITIES TRUST PLC; *Int'l*, pg. 2999
GLOBAL SERVICE SOLUTIONS, INC.; *U.S. Private*, pg. 1717
GLOBAL TELECOM & UTILITIES INCOME FUND—See Harvest Portfolios Group Inc.; *Int'l*, pg. 3281
GLORY GLOBAL SOLUTIONS ASIA PACIFIC—See GLORY Ltd.; *Int'l*, pg. 3010
G&L REALTY CORP.; *U.S. Public*, pg. 1629
GMAC DE VENEZUELA, C.A.—See General Motors Company; *U.S. Public*, pg. 925
GOLDMAN SACHS MLP & ENERGY RENAISSANCE FUND; *U.S. Public*, pg. 951
GOOD.BEE HOLDING GMBH—See Erste Group Bank AG; *Int'l*, pg. 2499
GOULD INVESTORS, L.P.; *U.S. Public*, pg. 952
GOWING BROTHERS LIMITED; *Int'l*, pg. 3044
GPT GROUP; *Int'l*, pg. 3047
GRAMERCY PROPERTY TRUST—See Blackstone Inc.; *U.S. Public*, pg. 350
GRANITE REAL ESTATE INVESTMENT TRUST; *Int'l*, pg. 3059
GRAVITON CAPITAL S.A.; *Int'l*, pg. 3062
GREAT AJAX CORP.; *U.S. Public*, pg. 961
GREAT RANGE CAPITAL, LLC; *U.S. Private*, pg. 1767
GREEN REIT PLC—See Henderson Park Capital Partners UK LLP; *U.S. Private*, pg. 3345
THE GREENWICH GROUP INTERNATIONAL LLC - CALIFORNIA—See The Greenwich Group International LLC; *U.S. Private*, pg. 4039
THE GREENWICH GROUP INTERNATIONAL LLC - VIRGINIA—See The Greenwich Group International LLC; *U.S. Private*, pg. 4039
GREYSTAR GROWTH & INCOME FUND, LP—See Greys-

tar Real Estate Partners, LLC; *U.S. Private*, pg. 1785
GRIFFIN-AMERICAN HEALTHCARE REIT III, INC.—See American Healthcare Investors LLC; *U.S. Private*, pg. 236
GRIFFIN-AMERICAN HEALTHCARE REIT III, INC.—See Griffin Capital Corporation; *U.S. Private*, pg. 1787
GRIFFIN CAPITAL ESSENTIAL ASSET REIT II, INC.—See Griffin Capital Corporation; *U.S. Private*, pg. 1787
GROWTHFORCE, LLC; *U.S. Private*, pg. 1796
GROWTHPOINT PROPERTIES AUSTRALIA LIMITED—See Growthpoint Properties Limited; *Int'l*, pg. 3113
GTC REAL ESTATE INVESTMENTS SERBIA B.V.—See Globe Trade Centre S.A.; *Int'l*, pg. 3006
GTC REAL ESTATE INVESTMENTS UKRAINE B.V.—See Globe Trade Centre S.A.; *Int'l*, pg. 3006
GUANDAO PUER INVESTMENT CO., LTD.; *Int'l*, pg. 3152
GUGGENHEIM CREDIT ALLOCATION FUND; *U.S. Public*, pg. 974
GUGGENHEIM CREDIT INCOME FUND—See Guggenheim Partners, LLC; *U.S. Private*, pg. 1811
GUGGENHEIM ENHANCED EQUITY INCOME FUND; *U.S. Public*, pg. 974
GUGGENHEIM TAXABLE MUNICIPAL BOND & INVESTMENT GRADE DEBT TRUST—See Guggenheim Partners, LLC; *U.S. Private*, pg. 1812
GULF NORTH AFRICA HOLDING CO. K.S.C.; *Int'l*, pg. 3181
HALCOM VIETNAM JSC; *Int'l*, pg. 3227
HAMAGIN FINANCE CO., LTD.—See Concordia Financial Group, Ltd.; *Int'l*, pg. 1765
HAMBORNER REIT AG; *Int'l*, pg. 3236
HAMERSLEY INTERNATIONAL BV—See CLS Holdings plc; *Int'l*, pg. 1664
HANG LUNG PROPERTIES LIMITED—See Hang Lung Group Limited; *Int'l*, pg. 3245
HANKYU REIT, INC.—See Hankyu Hanshin Holdings Inc.; *Int'l*, pg. 3255
HARBOUR DIGITAL ASSET CAPITAL LIMITED; *Int'l*, pg. 3271
HARDWOOD FUNDING LLC—See National Basketball Association; *U.S. Private*, pg. 2848
HARVEST SUSTAINABLE INCOME FUND—See Harvest Portfolios Group Inc.; *Int'l*, pg. 3281
HEALTHCARE SPECIAL OPPORTUNITIES FUND; *Int'l*, pg. 3304
HEALTHPEAK PROPERTIES, INC.; *U.S. Public*, pg. 1016
HEARTLAND PROPERTIES, INC.; *U.S. Private*, pg. 1900
HENDERSON EUROPEAN TRUST PLC; *Int'l*, pg. 3344
HENDERSON OPPORTUNITIES TRUST PLC; *Int'l*, pg. 3345
HENDERSON SMALLER COMPANIES INVESTMENT TRUST PLC; *Int'l*, pg. 3345
HERITAGE FINANCIAL CONSULTANTS, LLC; *U.S. Private*, pg. 1922
HERSHA HOSPITALITY TRUST—See KSL Capital Partners, LLC; *U.S. Private*, pg. 2355
HERZFELD CARIBBEAN BASIN FUND, INC.; *U.S. Public*, pg. 1029
HGCAPITAL TRUST PLC; *Int'l*, pg. 3376
HHY FUND; *Int'l*, pg. 3379
HIBERNIA REIT PLC—See Brookfield Corporation; *Int'l*, pg. 1188
HICL INFRASTRUCTURE PLC; *Int'l*, pg. 3383
HIGHWOODS PROPERTIES, INC.; *U.S. Public*, pg. 1035
HILLHOUSE INVESTMENT MANAGEMENT LIMITED; *Int'l*, pg. 3392
HINES GLOBAL REIT, INC.; *U.S. Private*, pg. 1949
HINES GLOBAL REIT MARLBOROUGH CAMPUS I LLC—See Hines Global REIT, Inc.; *U.S. Private*, pg. 1949
HINES REAL ESTATE INVESTMENT TRUST, INC.; *U.S. Private*, pg. 1949
HI REAL SPA; *Int'l*, pg. 3379
HISPANIA ACTIVOS INMOBILIARIOS SOCIMI, S.A.—See Blackstone Inc.; *U.S. Public*, pg. 354
HMG/COURTLAND PROPERTIES, INC.; *U.S. Public*, pg. 1042
HOIST FINANCE AB; *Int'l*, pg. 3442
HOIST FINANCE SPAIN S.L.—See Hoist Finance AB; *Int'l*, pg. 3442
HOIST ITALIA S.R.L.—See Hoist Finance AB; *Int'l*, pg. 3442
THE HOKUETSU LEASING CO., LTD.—See Daishi Hokuetsu Financial Group, Inc.; *Int'l*, pg. 1941
HOSHINO RESORTS REIT, INC.—See Hoshino Resorts Inc.; *Int'l*, pg. 3483
HOSPITALITY INVESTORS TRUST, INC.—See AR Global Investments, LLC; *U.S. Private*, pg. 306
HOST HOTELS & RESORTS, INC.; *U.S. Public*, pg. 1054
HOWARD HUGHES HOLDINGS INC.; *U.S. Public*, pg. 1060
H&R REAL ESTATE INVESTMENT TRUST; *Int'l*, pg. 3193
HRTI, LLC—See Healthcare Realty Trust Incorporated; *U.S. Public*, pg. 1015
HSC HANSEATISCHE SACHWERT CONCEPT GMBH—See Ernst Russ AG; *Int'l*, pg. 2496
HUDSON 6922 HOLLYWOOD, LLC—See Hudson Pacific Properties, Inc.; *U.S. Public*, pg. 1068

525990 — OTHER FINANCIAL VEH...

HUDSON PACIFIC PROPERTIES, INC.; *U.S. Public*, pg. 1068
HUTCHISON PORT HOLDINGS TRUST; *Int'l*, pg. 3540
HVC INVESTMENT & TECHNOLOGY JSC; *Int'l*, pg. 3541
HWANG CAPITAL (MALAYSIA) BERHAD; *Int'l*, pg. 3542
HYFCO DEVELOPMENT COMPANY LIMITED—See Henderson Land Development Co. Ltd.; *Int'l*, pg. 3344
ICADE S.A.—See Caisse des Depots et Consignations; *Int'l*, pg. 1258
ICAP HOLDINGS (NEDERLAND) B.V.—See CME Group, Inc.; *U.S. Public*, pg. 516
IDACORP FINANCIAL SERVICES, INC.—See IDACORP, Inc.; *U.S. Public*, pg. 1088
IDSUD SA; *Int'l*, pg. 3596
IFAST CORPORATION LIMITED; *Int'l*, pg. 3598
IFS CAPITAL ASSETS PTE. LTD.—See IFS Capital Limited; *Int'l*, pg. 3600
IFS CAPITAL (THAILAND) PCL—See IFS Capital Limited; *Int'l*, pg. 3600
IJM OVERSEAS VENTURES SDN BHD—See IJM Corporation Berhad; *Int'l*, pg. 3609
IMPAC COMMERCIAL ASSETS CORPORATION—See Drive Shack Inc.; *U.S. Public*, pg. 688
IMPAC MORTGAGE HOLDINGS, INC.; *U.S. Public*, pg. 1113
IMPERIAL BANK LIMITED—See Dubai World Corporation; *Int'l*, pg. 2221
IMPERIAL PFS—See IPFS Corporation; *U.S. Private*, pg. 2136
IMPLENIA TESCH GMBH—See Bilfinger SE; *Int'l*, pg. 1024
INCOME OPPORTUNITY REALTY INVESTORS, INC.; *U.S. Public*, pg. 1114
INDEPENDENCE MORTGAGE TRUST, INC.; *U.S. Private*, pg. 2058
INDEPENDENCE REALTY TRUST, INC.; *U.S. Public*, pg. 1115
INDUS REALTY TRUST, INC.—See Centerbridge Partners, L.P.; *U.S. Private*, pg. 815
INDUS REALTY TRUST, INC.—See GIC Pte. Ltd.; *Int'l*, pg. 2964
INDUSTRIAL LOGISTICS PROPERTIES TRUST—See The RMR Group Inc.; *U.S. Public*, pg. 2126
INDUSTRIAL PROPERTY TRUST INC.—See Prologis, Inc.; *U.S. Public*, pg. 1727
INLAND RESIDENTIAL PROPERTIES TRUST, INC.—See The Inland Real Estate Group of Companies, Inc.; *U.S. Private*, pg. 4056
INNKEEPERS USA TRUST; *U.S. Private*, pg. 2080
INNOVO INC.; *U.S. Private*, pg. 2084
INNSUITES HOSPITALITY TRUST; *U.S. Public*, pg. 1127
INSIGHT SELECT INCOME FUND; *U.S. Public*, pg. 1130
INTEGRITY FUNDING, LLC; *U.S. Private*, pg. 2103
INTER-AMERICAN INVESTMENT CORPORATION—See Inter-American Development Bank; *U.S. Private*, pg. 2107
INTERNATIONAL HOUSING SOLUTIONS S.A R.L—See Fundamental Advisors LP; *U.S. Private*, pg. 1622
INTERNATIONAL MANAGEMENT (MAURITIUS) LIMITED—See Cim Financial Services Limited; *Int'l*, pg. 1607
INTERNATIONAL MARKET CENTERS, INC.—See Blackstone Inc.; *U.S. Public*, pg. 350
INTERSHOP HOLDING AG—See BZ Bank Aktiengesellschaft; *Int'l*, pg. 1237
INTRACORP COMPANIES; *U.S. Private*, pg. 2129
INVENTRUST PROPERTIES CORP.; *U.S. Public*, pg. 1161
INVESCO ADVANTAGE MUNICIPAL INCOME TRUST II; *U.S. Public*, pg. 1161
INVESCO BOND FUND; *U.S. Public*, pg. 1161
INVESCO BOND INCOME PLUS LIMITED—See Invesco Ltd.; *U.S. Public*, pg. 1163
INVESCO CALIFORNIA VALUE MUNICIPAL INCOME TRUST; *U.S. Public*, pg. 1161
INVESCO CURRENCYSHARES AUSTRALIAN DOLLAR TRUST—See Invesco Ltd.; *U.S. Public*, pg. 1162
INVESCO CURRENCYSHARES BRITISH POUND STERLING TRUST—See Invesco Ltd.; *U.S. Public*, pg. 1162
INVESCO CURRENCYSHARES CANADIAN DOLLAR TRUST—See Invesco Ltd.; *U.S. Public*, pg. 1162
INVESCO CURRENCYSHARES EURO TRUST—See Invesco Ltd.; *U.S. Public*, pg. 1162
INVESCO CURRENCYSHARES JAPANESE YEN TRUST—See Invesco Ltd.; *U.S. Public*, pg. 1162
INVESCO CURRENCYSHARES SWISS FRANC TRUST—See Invesco Ltd.; *U.S. Public*, pg. 1162
INVESCO DYNAMIC CREDIT OPPORTUNITIES FUND; *U.S. Public*, pg. 1161
INVESCO HIGH INCOME 2023 TARGET TERM FUND; *U.S. Public*, pg. 1161
INVESCO HIGH INCOME TRUST II; *U.S. Public*, pg. 1161
INVESCO MUNICIPAL OPPORTUNITY TRUST; *U.S. Public*, pg. 1164
INVESCO MUNICIPAL TRUST; *U.S. Public*, pg. 1164
INVESCO MUNI INCOME OPPS TRUST; *U.S. Public*, pg. 1164
INVESCO PENNSYLVANIA VALUE MUNICIPAL INCOME TRUST; *U.S. Public*, pg. 1164

INVESCO QUALITY MUNICIPAL INCOME TRUST; *U.S. Public*, pg. 1164
INVESCO REAL ESTATE—See Invesco Ltd.; *U.S. Public*, pg. 1163
INVESCO SENIOR INCOME TRUST; *U.S. Public*, pg. 1164
INVESCO TRUST FOR INVESTMENT GRADE MUNICIPALS; *U.S. Public*, pg. 1164
INVESCO TRUST FOR INVESTMENT GRADE NEW YORK MUNICIPALS; *U.S. Public*, pg. 1164
INVESCO VALUE MUNICIPAL INCOME TRUST; *U.S. Public*, pg. 1164
INVESQUE INC.; *U.S. Public*, pg. 1164
INVESTCORP CREDIT MANAGEMENT BDC, INC.; *U.S. Public*, pg. 1165
IRC RETAIL CENTERS INC.—See DRA Advisors LLC; *U.S. Private*, pg. 1271
IRON MOUNTAIN INCORPORATED; *U.S. Public*, pg. 1171
ISRAEL INFRASTRUCTURE FUND—See Harel Insurance Investments & Financial Services Ltd.; *Int'l*, pg. 3274
ITALEASE FINANCE S.P.A.—See Banco BPM S.p.A.; *Int'l*, pg. 818
ITEB B.V.—See Allianz SE; *Int'l*, pg. 349
IVY HIGH INCOME OPPORTUNITIES FUND; *U.S. Public*, pg. 1179
JACKSON HUNTER MORRIS & KNIGHT LLP; *U.S. Private*, pg. 2177
JANA PARTNERS, LLC; *U.S. Private*, pg. 2186
JAPAN SMALLER CAPITALIZATION FUND, INC.; *U.S. Public*, pg. 1187
JAVELIN MORTGAGE INVESTMENT CORP.—See ARMOUR Residential REIT, Inc.; *U.S. Public*, pg. 193
JER INVESTORS TRUST INC.; *U.S. Private*, pg. 2201
JERNIGAN CAPITAL, INC.; *U.S. Private*, pg. 2201
JFT STRATEGIES FUND—See First Asset Investment Management Inc.; *Int'l*, pg. 2682
J.G. WENTWORTH SSC, L.P.—See JLL Partners, LLC; *U.S. Private*, pg. 2213
JLG FINANCIAL SOLUTIONS—See Oshkosh Corporation; *U.S. Public*, pg. 1620
JLL INCOME PROPERTY TRUST, INC.; *U.S. Private*, pg. 2212
JMI REALTY LLC—See JMI Services, Inc.; *U.S. Private*, pg. 2216
JOHN HANCOCK STRATEGIC DIVERSIFIED INCOME FUND; *U.S. Private*, pg. 2222
JOHNSON & JOHNSON FINANCE LIMITED—See Johnson & Johnson; *U.S. Public*, pg. 1198
KASCO CORPORATION; *U.S. Private*, pg. 2263
KAYNE ANDERSON ENERGY INFRASTRUCTURE FUND, INC.—See Kayne Anderson Capital Advisors, L.P.; *U.S. Private*, pg. 2267
KAYNE ANDERSON NEXTGEN ENERGY & INFRASTRUCTURE, INC.—See Kayne Anderson Capital Advisors, L.P.; *U.S. Private*, pg. 2267
KBS GROWTH & INCOME REIT, INC.; *U.S. Public*, pg. 1216
KFN SENTINEL REIT LLC—See KKR & Co. Inc.; *U.S. Public*, pg. 1254
KILROY REALTY CORPORATION; *U.S. Public*, pg. 1228
KILROY REALTY, L.P.—See Kilroy Realty Corporation; *U.S. Public*, pg. 1228
KIMCO, INC.—See Kimco Realty Corporation; *U.S. Public*, pg. 1232
KIMCO REALTY CORPORATION; *U.S. Public*, pg. 1231
KIMCO REALTY INC—See Kimco Realty Corporation; *U.S. Public*, pg. 1231
KIMCO REALTY INC—See Prometheus Real Estate Group, Inc.; *U.S. Private*, pg. 3283
KIMCO REALTY OP, LLC—See Kimco Realty Corporation; *U.S. Public*, pg. 1231
KITE REALTY GROUP TRUST; *U.S. Public*, pg. 1236
KLAFF REALTY, L.P.; *U.S. Private*, pg. 2317
KYTO TECHNOLOGY & LIFE SCIENCE, INC.; *U.S. Public*, pg. 1278
LAMAR ADVERTISING COMPANY; *U.S. Public*, pg. 1290
LANDMARK INFRASTRUCTURE PARTNERS LP—See DigitalBridge Group, Inc.; *U.S. Public*, pg. 665
LASALLE HOTEL PROPERTIES—See Pebblebrook Hotel Trust; *U.S. Public*, pg. 1660
LBC CREDIT PARTNERS, INC.—See Independence Capital Partners, LLC; *U.S. Private*, pg. 2055
LEAF FINANCIAL CORP.—See Island Capital Group LLC; *U.S. Private*, pg. 2144
LENDIO INC.; *U.S. Private*, pg. 2421
LEVIN FINANCIAL GROUP, INC.; *U.S. Private*, pg. 2435
LEXINGTON FINANCE—See LXP Industrial Trust; *U.S. Public*, pg. 1349
LEXINGTON ISS HOLDINGS—See LXP Industrial Trust; *U.S. Public*, pg. 1349
LEXINGTON OLIVE BRANCH MANAGER LLC—See LXP Industrial Trust; *U.S. Public*, pg. 1349
LEXINGTON REAL ESTATE INCOME TRUST—See LXP Industrial Trust; *U.S. Public*, pg. 1349
LIBERTY ALL-STAR EQUITY FUND; *U.S. Public*, pg. 1310
LIG ASSETS, INC.; *U.S. Public*, pg. 1314
LIGHTSTONE VALUE PLUS REIT III, INC.—See The Lightstone Group, LLC; *U.S. Private*, pg. 4070
LIGHTSTONE VALUE PLUS REIT II, INC.—See The Light-

CORPORATE AFFILIATIONS

stone Group, LLC; *U.S. Private*, pg. 4070
LIGHTSTONE VALUE PLUS REIT I, INC.—See The Lightstone Group, LLC; *U.S. Private*, pg. 4070
LIGHTSTONE VALUE PLUS REIT IV, INC.—See The Lightstone Group, LLC; *U.S. Private*, pg. 4070
LIGHTSTONE VALUE PLUS REIT V, INC.—See The Lightstone Group, LLC; *U.S. Private*, pg. 4070
LINX PARTNERS, LP; *U.S. Public*, pg. 2463
LM FUNDING AMERICA, INC.; *U.S. Public*, pg. 1337
LNR SCOTTS VALLEY HOTEL LLC—See Starwood Property Trust, Inc.; *U.S. Public*, pg. 1940
LOANCORE REALTY TRUST, INC.; *U.S. Private*, pg. 2477
LODGECAP, INC.; *U.S. Private*, pg. 2479
LRA MKP TRS L.P.—See LXP Industrial Trust; *U.S. Public*, pg. 1349
LTC PROPERTIES, INC.; *U.S. Public*, pg. 1344
LXP INDUSTRIAL TRUST; *U.S. Public*, pg. 1349
THE MACERICH COMPANY; *U.S. Public*, pg. 2109
MACQUARIE/FIRST TRUST GLOBAL INFRASTRUCTURE/UTILITIES DIVIDEND & INCOME FUND; *U.S. Public*, pg. 1352
MACQUARIE GLOBAL INFRASTRUCTURE TOTAL RETURN FUND INC.; *U.S. Public*, pg. 1352
MAINSTREET PROPERTY GROUP; *U.S. Private*, pg. 2554
MARLIN BUSINESS SERVICES CORP—See HPS Investment Partners, LLC; *U.S. Private*, pg. 1997
MARQUEE BRANDS LLC; *U.S. Private*, pg. 2586
MARRET HIGH YIELD STRATEGIES FUND—See CI Financial Corporation; *Int'l*, pg. 1601
MARRET MULTI-STRATEGY INCOME FUND—See CI Financial Corporation; *Int'l*, pg. 1601
MAXUS REALTY TRUST, INC.; *U.S. Public*, pg. 1403
MCARE SOLUTIONS, LLC—See New Mountain Capital, LLC; *U.S. Private*, pg. 2904
MCDOUGAL COMPANIES; *U.S. Private*, pg. 2633
MEDALLION FINANCIAL CORP.; *U.S. Public*, pg. 1411
MEDALLION FUNDING LLC—See Medallion Financial Corp.; *U.S. Public*, pg. 1411
MELODY INVESTMENT ADVISORS LP; *U.S. Private*, pg. 2662
MEMBERS TRUST COMPANY; *U.S. Private*, pg. 2663
MENTOR CAPITAL, INC.; *U.S. Public*, pg. 1414
MERIDIAN ASSET SERVICES, LLC—See Stone Point Capital LLC; *U.S. Private*, pg. 3825
METRO PARK V, LLC—See Blackstone Inc.; *U.S. Public*, pg. 356
METWEST REALTY ADVISORS LLC; *U.S. Private*, pg. 2691
MFA FINANCIAL, INC.; *U.S. Public*, pg. 1433
MFS CHARTER INCOME TRUST; *U.S. Public*, pg. 1434
MFS GOVERNMENT MARKETS INCOME TRUST; *U.S. Public*, pg. 1434
MFS HIGH INCOME MUNICIPAL TRUST; *U.S. Public*, pg. 1434
MFS HIGH YIELD MUNICIPAL TRUST; *U.S. Public*, pg. 1434
MFS INTERMEDIATE HIGH INCOME FUND; *U.S. Public*, pg. 1434
MFS INTERMEDIATE INCOME TRUST; *U.S. Public*, pg. 1434
MFS INVESTMENT GRADE MUNICIPAL TRUST; *U.S. Public*, pg. 1434
MFS MULTIMARKET INCOME TRUST; *U.S. Public*, pg. 1434
MFS MUNICIPAL INCOME TRUST; *U.S. Public*, pg. 1434
MFS SPECIAL VALUE TRUST; *U.S. Public*, pg. 1434
MGA CONSULTANTS, INC.—See Aquiline Capital Partners LLC; *U.S. Private*, pg. 304
MGA CONSULTANTS, INC.—See Genstar Capital, LLC; *U.S. Private*, pg. 1675
MHI HOSPITALITY TRS HOLDING, INC.—See Sotherly Hotels Inc.; *U.S. Public*, pg. 1910
MID-AMERICA APARTMENT COMMUNITIES, INC.; *U.S. Public*, pg. 1444
MIDCAP FINANCIAL INVESTMENT CORPORATION—See Apollo Global Management, Inc.; *U.S. Public*, pg. 153
THE MILLS PROPERTIES—See Simon Property Group, Inc.; *U.S. Public*, pg. 1882
MLP UNIT PLEDGE L.P.—See LXP Industrial Trust; *U.S. Public*, pg. 1349
MMA CREDIT HOLDINGS, LLC—See Fundamental Advisors LP; *U.S. Private*, pg. 1622
MOBILE INFRASTRUCTURE CORPORATION—See Mobile Infrastructure Corporation; *U.S. Public*, pg. 1453
MOLA ADMINISTRATION GMBH—See Apex Fund Services Holdings Ltd.; *Int'l*, pg. 510
MONMOUTH REAL ESTATE INVESTMENT CORPORATION—See The RMR Group Inc.; *U.S. Public*, pg. 2126
MOODY NATIONAL REIT II, INC.; *U.S. Private*, pg. 2778
MOODY NATIONAL REIT I, INC.; *U.S. Private*, pg. 2778
MORENO, PEELEN, PINTO & CLARK (MPC); *U.S. Private*, pg. 2782
MORGAN PROPERTIES TRUST; *U.S. Private*, pg. 2784
MOTUS, LLC—See Thoma Bravo, L.P.; *U.S. Private*, pg. 4150
MOUNTAIN AGENCY INC.; *U.S. Private*, pg. 2798

N.A.I.C.S. INDEX 525990 — OTHER FINANCIAL VEH...

N.A.I.C.S. Index

MPT OF ALLEN FCER, LLC—See Medical Properties Trust, Inc.; *U.S. Public*, pg. 1412
MPT OF DALLAS, LLC—See Medical Properties Trust, Inc.; *U.S. Public*, pg. 1412
MSREF REAL ESTATE ADVISOR, INC.—See Morgan Stanley; *U.S. Public*, pg. 1472
MUNDUS GROUP, INC.; *U.S. Public*, pg. 1487
MUNI FUNDING COMPANY OF AMERICA, LLC—See Tiptree Inc.; *U.S. Public*, pg. 2159
MURRAY WISE ASSOCIATES LLC—See Farmland Partners Inc.; *U.S. Public*, pg. 823
MVC CAPITAL, INC.—See Barings BDC, Inc.; *U.S. Public*, pg. 276
THE NASDAQ PRIVATE MARKET, LLC—See Nasdaq, Inc.; *U.S. Public*, pg. 1492
NATIONAL AIRCRAFT FINANCE COMPANY—See Lake Michigan Credit Union; *U.S. Private*, pg. 2375
NATIONAL FUNDING INC.; *U.S. Private*, pg. 2855
NATIONAL HEALTHCARE PROPERTIES, INC.; *U.S. Public*, pg. 1497
NATIONAL HEALTH INVESTORS, INC.; *U.S. Public*, pg. 1494
NATIONAL RURAL UTILITIES COOPERATIVE FINANCE CORPORATION; *U.S. Public*, pg. 1497
NATIONAL STORAGE AFFILIATES TRUST; *U.S. Public*, pg. 1497
NATIXIS INTEREPARGNE S.A.—See Groupe BPCE; *Int'l*, pg. 3097
NBT FINANCIAL SERVICES, INC.—See NBT Bancorp Inc.; *U.S. Public*, pg. 1501
THE NECESSITY RETAIL REIT, INC.—See AR Global Investments, LLC; *U.S. Private*, pg. 306
NEUBERGER BERMAN ENERGY INFRASTRUCTURE AND INCOME FUND INC.—See Neuberger Berman Group LLC; *U.S. Private*, pg. 2890
NEW AGC LLC—See Drive Shack Inc.; *U.S. Public*, pg. 688
NEW AMERICA HIGH INCOME FUND, INC.; *U.S. Public*, pg. 1511
NEW SCHOOL PROPERTIES, INC.; *U.S. Private*, pg. 2906
NEW YORK MORTGAGE TRUST, INC.; *U.S. Public*, pg. 1513
NEXPOINT CAPITAL, INC.—See Highland Capital Management, L.P.; *U.S. Private*, pg. 1938
NEXPOINT HOSPITALITY TRUST, INC.—See Highland Capital Management, L.P.; *U.S. Private*, pg. 1938
NEXPOINT MULTIFAMILY CAPITAL TRUST, INC.—See Highland Capital Management, L.P.; *U.S. Private*, pg. 1938
NEXPOINT RESIDENTIAL TRUST, INC.—See Highland Capital Management, L.P.; *U.S. Private*, pg. 1938
NGP REALTY SUB GP, LLC—See Drive Shack Inc.; *U.S. Public*, pg. 688
NNN REIT, INC.; *U.S. Public*, pg. 1531
NOMU PAY—See Finch Capital Partners B.V; *Int'l*, pg. 2672
NORTH HAVEN PRIVATE INCOME FUND LLC; *U.S. Private*, pg. 2945
NORTHSTAR HEALTHCARE INCOME, INC.—See DigitalBridge Group, Inc.; *U.S. Public*, pg. 665
NORTHSTAR REALTY EUROPE CORP.—See AXA S.A.; *Int'l*, pg. 757
NORTHSTAR/RXR NEW YORK METRO REAL ESTATE, INC.; *U.S. Private*, pg. 2958
NUVEEN AMT-FREE MUNICIPAL CREDIT INCOME FUND—See Teachers Insurance Association - College Retirement Fund; *U.S. Private*, pg. 3945
NUVEEN AMT-FREE MUNICIPAL VALUE FUND—See Teachers Insurance Association - College Retirement Fund; *U.S. Private*, pg. 3945
NUVEEN AMT-FREE QUALITY MUNICIPAL INCOME FUND—See Teachers Insurance Association - College Retirement Fund; *U.S. Private*, pg. 3945
NUVEEN ARIZONA QUALITY MUNICIPAL INCOME FUND—See Teachers Insurance Association - College Retirement Fund; *U.S. Private*, pg. 3945
NUVEEN CALIFORNIA AMT-FREE QUALITY MUNICIPAL INCOME FUND—See Teachers Insurance Association - College Retirement Fund; *U.S. Private*, pg. 3945
NUVEEN CALIFORNIA MUNICIPAL VALUE FUND 2—See Teachers Insurance Association - College Retirement Fund; *U.S. Private*, pg. 3945
NUVEEN CALIFORNIA MUNICIPAL VALUE FUND, INC.—See Teachers Insurance Association - College Retirement Fund; *U.S. Private*, pg. 3945
NUVEEN CALIFORNIA QUALITY MUNICIPAL INCOME FUND—See Teachers Insurance Association - College Retirement Fund; *U.S. Private*, pg. 3945
NUVEEN CORE EQUITY ALPHA FUND—See Teachers Insurance Association - College Retirement Fund; *U.S. Private*, pg. 3945
NUVEEN CREDIT STRATEGIES INCOME FUND—See Teachers Insurance Association - College Retirement Fund; *U.S. Private*, pg. 3946
NUVEEN DOW 30SM DYNAMIC OVERWRITE FUND—See Teachers Insurance Association - College Retirement Fund; *U.S. Private*, pg. 3946
NUVEEN ENHANCED MUNICIPAL VALUE FUND—See Teachers Insurance Association - College Retirement Fund; *U.S. Private*, pg. 3946
NUVEEN FLOATING RATE INCOME FUND—See Teachers Insurance Association - College Retirement Fund; *U.S. Private*, pg. 3946
NUVEEN GLOBAL HIGH INCOME FUND—See Teachers Insurance Association - College Retirement Fund; *U.S. Private*, pg. 3946
NUVEEN MASSACHUSETTS QUALITY MUNICIPAL INCOME FUND—See Teachers Insurance Association - College Retirement Fund; *U.S. Private*, pg. 3946
NUVEEN MICHIGAN QUALITY MUNICIPAL INCOME FUND—See Teachers Insurance Association - College Retirement Fund; *U.S. Private*, pg. 3946
NUVEEN MINNESOTA QUALITY MUNICIPAL INCOME FUND—See Teachers Insurance Association - College Retirement Fund; *U.S. Private*, pg. 3946
NUVEEN MISSOURI QUALITY MUNICIPAL INCOME FUND—See Teachers Insurance Association - College Retirement Fund; *U.S. Private*, pg. 3946
NUVEEN MORTGAGE OPPORTUNITY TERM FUND 2—See Teachers Insurance Association - College Retirement Fund; *U.S. Private*, pg. 3946
NUVEEN MULTI-MARKET INCOME FUND—See Teachers Insurance Association - College Retirement Fund; *U.S. Private*, pg. 3946
NUVEEN MUNICIPAL 2021 TARGET TERM FUND—See Teachers Insurance Association - College Retirement Fund; *U.S. Private*, pg. 3946
NUVEEN MUNICIPAL CREDIT INCOME FUND—See Teachers Insurance Association - College Retirement Fund; *U.S. Private*, pg. 3946
NUVEEN MUNICIPAL HIGH INCOME OPP FUND—See Teachers Insurance Association - College Retirement Fund; *U.S. Private*, pg. 3946
NUVEEN MUNICIPAL INCOME FUND, INC.—See Teachers Insurance Association - College Retirement Fund; *U.S. Private*, pg. 3946
NUVEEN MUNICIPAL VALUE FUND, INC.—See Teachers Insurance Association - College Retirement Fund; *U.S. Private*, pg. 3946
NUVEEN NASDAQ 100 DYNAMIC OVERWRITE FUND—See Teachers Insurance Association - College Retirement Fund; *U.S. Private*, pg. 3946
NUVEEN NEW JERSEY QUALITY MUNICIPAL INCOME FUND—See Teachers Insurance Association - College Retirement Fund; *U.S. Private*, pg. 3946
NUVEEN NEW YORK AMT-FREE QUALITY MUNICIPAL INCOME FUND—See Teachers Insurance Association - College Retirement Fund; *U.S. Private*, pg. 3946
NUVEEN NEW YORK MUNICIPAL VALUE FUND, INC.—See Teachers Insurance Association - College Retirement Fund; *U.S. Private*, pg. 3946
NUVEEN NEW YORK QUALITY MUNICIPAL INCOME FUND—See Teachers Insurance Association - College Retirement Fund; *U.S. Private*, pg. 3946
NUVEEN NJ MUNICIPAL VALUE FUND—See Teachers Insurance Association - College Retirement Fund; *U.S. Private*, pg. 3946
NUVEEN NY MUNICIPAL VALUE FUND 2—See Teachers Insurance Association - College Retirement Fund; *U.S. Private*, pg. 3946
NUVEEN OHIO QUALITY MUNICIPAL INCOME FUND—See Teachers Insurance Association - College Retirement Fund; *U.S. Private*, pg. 3946
NUVEEN PENNSYLVANIA MUNICIPAL VALUE FUND—See Teachers Insurance Association - College Retirement Fund; *U.S. Private*, pg. 3946
NUVEEN PENNSYLVANIA QUALITY MUNICIPAL INCOME FUND—See Teachers Insurance Association - College Retirement Fund; *U.S. Private*, pg. 3947
NUVEEN PREFERRED & INCOME 2022 TERM—See Teachers Insurance Association - College Retirement Fund; *U.S. Private*, pg. 3947
NUVEEN PREFERRED & INCOME OPPORTUNITIES FUND—See Teachers Insurance Association - College Retirement Fund; *U.S. Private*, pg. 3947
NUVEEN PREFERRED & INCOME TERM FUND—See Teachers Insurance Association - College Retirement Fund; *U.S. Private*, pg. 3947
NUVEEN PREFERRED SECURITIES INCOME FUND—See Teachers Insurance Association - College Retirement Fund; *U.S. Private*, pg. 3947
NUVEEN QUALITY MUNICIPAL INCOME FUND—See Teachers Insurance Association - College Retirement Fund; *U.S. Private*, pg. 3947
NUVEEN REAL ASSET INCOME AND GROWTH FUND—See Teachers Insurance Association - College Retirement Fund; *U.S. Private*, pg. 3947
NUVEEN REAL ESTATE INCOME FUND—See Teachers Insurance Association - College Retirement Fund; *U.S. Private*, pg. 3947
NUVEEN SELECT MATURITIES MUNICIPAL FUND—See Teachers Insurance Association - College Retirement Fund; *U.S. Private*, pg. 3947
NUVEEN S&P 500 BUY-WRITE INCOME FUND—See Teachers Insurance Association - College Retirement Fund; *U.S. Private*, pg. 3947
NUVEEN S&P 500 DYNAMIC OVERWRITE FUND—See Teachers Insurance Association - College Retirement Fund; *U.S. Private*, pg. 3947
NUVEEN TAXABLE MUNICIPAL INCOME FUND—See Teachers Insurance Association - College Retirement Fund; *U.S. Private*, pg. 3947
NUVEEN TAX-ADVANTAGED DIVIDEND GROWTH FUND—See Teachers Insurance Association - College Retirement Fund; *U.S. Private*, pg. 3947
NUVEEN TAX-ADVANTAGED TOTAL RETURN STRATEGY FUND—See Teachers Insurance Association - College Retirement Fund; *U.S. Private*, pg. 3947
NUVEEN VIRGINIA QUALITY MUNICIPAL INCOME FUND—See Teachers Insurance Association - College Retirement Fund; *U.S. Private*, pg. 3947
NXG NEXTGEN INFRASTRUCTURE INCOME FUND—See Swank Capital, LLC; *U.S. Private*, pg. 3890
O'DONNELL STRATEGIC INDUSTRIAL REIT, INC.; *U.S. Private*, pg. 2978
OFFICE PROPERTIES INCOME TRUST—See The RMR Group Inc.; *U.S. Public*, pg. 2126
OMEGA HEALTHCARE INVESTORS, INC.; *U.S. Public*, pg. 1571
OMNEX GROUP, INC.—See Nexxar Group Inc.; *U.S. Private*, pg. 2922
ONCOR NTU HOLDINGS COMPANY LLC—See Sempra; *U.S. Public*, pg. 1863
ONE1 FINANCIAL LIMITED—See GraceKennedy Limited; *Int'l*, pg. 3049
ONE FIVE ONE PROPERTY PTY LTD.—See Blackstone Inc.; *U.S. Public*, pg. 360
ONE FREEDOM SQUARE, L.L.C.—See Boston Properties, Inc.; *U.S. Public*, pg. 373
ONE LIBERTY PROPERTIES, INC.; *U.S. Public*, pg. 1602
ORIGEN FINANCIAL, INC.; *U.S. Private*, pg. 3041
OWENS MORTGAGE INVESTMENT FUND, A CALIFORNIA LIMITED PARTNERSHIP; *U.S. Private*, pg. 3055
OWENS REALTY MORTGAGE, INC.—See Waterfall Asset Management LLC; *U.S. Private*, pg. 4453
PACIFIC OAK STRATEGIC OPPORTUNITY REIT, INC.; *U.S. Public*, pg. 1632
PACIFIC REALTY ASSOCIATES, LP; *U.S. Private*, pg. 3070
PACIFIC RIM CAPITAL, INC.—See Fuyo General Lease Co., Ltd.; *Int'l*, pg. 2859
PARAMOUNT GROUP INC.; *U.S. Public*, pg. 1637
PAREX LEASING & FACTORING—See AS Reverta; *Int'l*, pg. 591
PARK HOTELS & RESORTS INC.; *U.S. Public*, pg. 1637
PCM FUND, INC.; *U.S. Public*, pg. 1658
PEAKSTONE REALTY TRUST—See Griffin Capital Corporation; *U.S. Private*, pg. 1787
PEBBLEBROOK HOTEL TRUST; *U.S. Public*, pg. 1660
PEKAO FINANCIAL SERVICES SP. Z O.O.—See Bank Polska Kasa Opieki Spolka Akcyjna; *Int'l*, pg. 850
PEKAO FUNDUSZ KAPITALOWY SP. Z O.O.—See Bank Polska Kasa Opieki Spolka Akcyjna; *Int'l*, pg. 850
PEKAO PIONEER POWSZECHNED TOWARZYSTWO EMERYTALNE S.A.—See Bank Polska Kasa Opieki Spolka Akcyjna; *Int'l*, pg. 850
PEMBROOK REALTY CAPITAL LLC; *U.S. Private*, pg. 3131
PENNANTPARK FLOATING RATE CAPITAL LTD.; *U.S. Public*, pg. 1663
PENNANTPARK INVESTMENT CORPORATION; *U.S. Public*, pg. 1663
PERFORMANCE OPPORTUNITIES FUND, L.P.—See General Motors Company; *U.S. Public*, pg. 928
PERSPECTIVE PARTNERS, LLC—See Callodine Acquisition Corporation; *U.S. Public*, pg. 424
PGA PROFESSIONAL CENTER PROPERTY OWNERS ASSOCIATION—See LXP Industrial Trust; *U.S. Public*, pg. 1349
PGIM HIGH YIELD BOND FUND, INC.; *U.S. Public*, pg. 1684
PHILIPS INTERNATIONAL REALTY CORP.; *U.S. Private*, pg. 3170
PHILLIPS EDISON & COMPANY INC.—See Phillips Edison & Company LLC; *U.S. Private*, pg. 3170
PIEDMONT OFFICE REALTY TRUST, INC.; *U.S. Public*, pg. 1690
PILLARSTONE CAPITAL REIT; *U.S. Private*, pg. 3180
PIMCO CA MUNI INCOME FUND II; *U.S. Public*, pg. 1690
PIMCO CORPORATE & INCOME OPPORTUNITY FUND; *U.S. Public*, pg. 1690
PIMCO CORPORATE & INCOME STRATEGY FUND; *U.S. Public*, pg. 1690
PIMCO GLOBAL STOCKSPLUS & INCOME FUND; *U.S. Public*, pg. 1690
PIMCO INCOME OPPORTUNITY FUND; *U.S. Public*, pg. 1690
PIMCO INCOME STRATEGY FUND II; *U.S. Public*, pg. 1690
PIMCO INVESTMENTS LLC—See Allianz SE; *Int'l*, pg. 347
PIMCO MUNICIPAL INCOME FUND II; *U.S. Public*, pg. 1690
PIMCO NEW YORK MUNICIPAL INCOME FUND III; *U.S. Public*, pg. 1691
PIMCO NEW YORK MUNICIPAL INCOME FUND; *U.S. Public*, pg. 1691
PIMCO REIT, INC.; *U.S. Private*, pg. 3181

525990 — OTHER FINANCIAL VEH... CORPORATE AFFILIATIONS

PIONEER DIVERSIFIED HIGH INCOME FUND, INC; *U.S. Public*, pg. 1692
PIONEER FLOATING RATE FUND, INC; *U.S. Public*, pg. 1692
PIONEER HIGH INCOME FUND, INC.; *U.S. Public*, pg. 1692
PIONEER MUNICIPAL HIGH INCOME ADVANTAGE FUND, INC.; *U.S. Public*, pg. 1693
PIONEER MUNICIPAL HIGH INCOME FUND, INC.; *U.S. Public*, pg. 1693
PIRELLI SERVIZI FINANZIARI S.P.A.—See China National Chemical Corporation; *Int'l*, pg. 1528
PITTSBURGH & WEST VIRGINIA RAILROAD—See Power REIT; *U.S. Public*, pg. 1705
PLYMOUTH INDUSTRIAL REIT, INC.; *U.S. Public*, pg. 1699
PMA FINANCIAL NETWORK, LLC; *U.S. Private*, pg. 3217
POTLATCHDELTIC CORPORATION; *U.S. Public*, pg. 1704
POTOMAC MORTGAGE GROUP, INC.—See Intercoastal Mortgage, LLC; *U.S. Private*, pg. 2109
POWER REIT; *U.S. Public*, pg. 1705
PRA GROUP POLAND SP. Z OO—See PRA Group, Inc.; *U.S. Public*, pg. 1712
PREFERRED APARTMENT COMMUNITIES, INC.—See Blackstone Inc.; *U.S. Public*, pg. 351
PREFERRED APARTMENT COMMUNITIES OPERATING PARTNERSHIP, L.P.—See Blackstone Inc.; *U.S. Public*, pg. 351
PRIME PROPERTY INVESTORS, LTD.; *U.S. Private*, pg. 3262
PRIME RATE PREMIUM FINANCE CORPORATION, INC.—See Truist Financial Corporation; *U.S. Public*, pg. 2201
PRIME REALTY INCOME TRUST, INC.; *U.S. Private*, pg. 3262
PRINCIPAL GLOBAL INVESTORS—See Principal Financial Group, Inc.; *U.S. Public*, pg. 1721
PRINCIPAL REAL ESTATE INVESTORS, LLC—See Principal Financial Group, Inc.; *U.S. Public*, pg. 1721
PR MORTGAGE INVESTMENT MANAGEMENT, LLC—See Merchants Bancorp; *U.S. Public*, pg. 1415
THE PROCACCIANTI GROUP; *U.S. Private*, pg. 4100
PROFIT PLANNERS MANAGEMENT, INC.; *U.S. Public*, pg. 1724
PROLOGIS, INC.; *U.S. Public*, pg. 1726
PROLOGIS PROPERTY FRANCE S.A.R.L.—See Prologis, Inc.; *U.S. Public*, pg. 1727
PROVIDENT MORTGAGE CAPITAL ASSOCIATES, INC.; *U.S. Private*, pg. 3295
PS BUSINESS PARKS, INC.—See Blackstone Inc.; *U.S. Public*, pg. 356
P. SCHOENFELD ASSET MANAGEMENT LLC; *U.S. Private*, pg. 3060
PT KENCANA INTERNUSA ARTHA FINANCE—See CIMB Group Holdings Berhad; *Int'l*, pg. 1608
PUBLIC STORAGE; *U.S. Public*, pg. 1736
PURE INDUSTRIAL REAL ESTATE TRUST—See Blackstone Inc.; *U.S. Public*, pg. 350
PURE MULTI-FAMILY REIT LP—See Cortland Partners, LLC; *U.S. Private*, pg. 1061
PUTNAM MORTGAGE OPPORTUNITIES FUND—See Franklin Resources, Inc.; *U.S. Public*, pg. 883
PYRAMID HOTELS & RESORTS, INC.; *U.S. Private*, pg. 3310
PYXIS FINVEST LIMITED—See Centrum Capital Ltd.; *Int'l*, pg. 1415
PZENA FINANCIAL SERVICES, LLC—See Pzena Investment Management, Inc.; *U.S. Public*, pg. 1741
QTS REALTY TRUST, INC.—See Blackstone Inc.; *U.S. Public*, pg. 351
QUALITYTECH, LP—See Blackstone Inc.; *U.S. Public*, pg. 351
RAFFLES HOLDINGS LIMITED—See CapitaLand Investment Limited; *Int'l*, pg. 1314
THE RAINMAKER GROUP VENTURES, LLC; *U.S. Private*, pg. 4102
RAIT FINANCIAL TRUST; *U.S. Private*, pg. 3348
RAIT-MELODY 2016 HOLDINGS TRUST—See RAIT Financial Trust; *U.S. Private*, pg. 3349
RAS ASSET MANAGEMENT SGR S.P.A.—See Allianz SE; *Int'l*, pg. 350
RAYONIER INC.; *U.S. Public*, pg. 1765
RCAP SECURITIES, INC.—See Annaly Capital Management, Inc.; *U.S. Public*, pg. 138
RDI REIT P.L.C.—See Starwood Capital Group Global I, LLC; *U.S. Private*, pg. 3789
READY CAPITAL CORPORATION—See Waterfall Asset Management LLC; *U.S. Public*, pg. 4452
REALTY INCOME CORPORATION; *U.S. Public*, pg. 1768
REALTY SYSTEMS, INC.—See Equity LifeStyle Properties, Inc.; *U.S. Public*, pg. 790
RECKSON OPERATING PARTNERSHIP, L.P.—See SL Green Realty Corp.; *U.S. Public*, pg. 1894
RED STONE TAX EXEMPT PARTNERS LP; *U.S. Private*, pg. 3376
REDWOOD TRUST, INC.; *U.S. Public*, pg. 1771
REGENCY CENTERS CORPORATION; *U.S. Public*, pg. 1774

REGIONAL HEALTH PROPERTIES, INC.; *U.S. Public*, pg. 1775
REG-UB PROPERTIES, LLC—See Regency Centers Corporation; *U.S. Public*, pg. 1774
RENEGADE VENTURES, INC.; *U.S. Private*, pg. 3397
RENN FUND, INC.; *U.S. Public*, pg. 1783
RESCAP LIQUIDATING TRUST; *U.S. Public*, pg. 1789
RES DIRECT, LLC—See Insight Venture Management, LLC; *U.S. Private*, pg. 2089
RES DIRECT, LLC—See Stone Point Capital LLC; *U.S. Private*, pg. 3823
RESEARCH CORPORATION TECHNOLOGIES, INC.; *U.S. Private*, pg. 3403
RESOURCE INNOVATION OFFICE REIT, INC.—See Island Capital Group LLC; *U.S. Private*, pg. 2144
RESOURCE REAL ESTATE OPPORTUNITY REIT, INC.—See Island Capital Group LLC; *U.S. Private*, pg. 2144
RESOURCE REIT, INC.—See Blackstone Inc.; *U.S. Public*, pg. 351
RETAIL CREDIT PROPERTY TRUST, INC.—See AR Global Investments, LLC; *U.S. Public*, pg. 306
RETAIL PROPERTIES OF AMERICA, INC.—See Kite Realty Group Trust; *U.S. Public*, pg. 1236
REUNION HOSPITALITY TRUST, INC.; *U.S. Private*, pg. 3412
REVERSE MORTGAGE INVESTMENT TRUST INC.; *U.S. Private*, pg. 3416
RHP HOTEL PROPERTIES, LP—See Ryman Hospitality Properties, Inc.; *U.S. Public*, pg. 1829
RIALTO CAPITAL MANAGEMENT, LLC—See Stone Point Capital LLC; *U.S. Private*, pg. 3825
RICHMOND HONAN MEDICAL PROPERTIES INC.; *U.S. Private*, pg. 3430
RIFCO INC.—See Chesswood Group Limited; *Int'l*, pg. 1472
RINCON CENTER COMMERCIAL, LLC—See Hudson Pacific Properties, Inc.; *U.S. Public*, pg. 1068
RITHM CAPITAL CORP.; *U.S. Public*, pg. 1799
RIVERNORTH/DOUBLELINE STRATEGIC OPPORTUNITY FUND, INC.; *U.S. Public*, pg. 1801
RIVERNORTH OPPORTUNITIES FUND, INC.; *U.S. Public*, pg. 1801
RLJ LODGING TRUST—See The RLJ Companies, LLC; *U.S. Private*, pg. 4111
RNY PROPERTY TRUST—See Aurora Funds Management Limited; *Int'l*, pg. 713
ROBUSTWEALTH, INC.—See Principal Financial Group, Inc.; *U.S. Public*, pg. 1722
ROYCE GLOBAL VALUE TRUST, INC.; *U.S. Public*, pg. 1816
ROYCE MICRO-CAP TRUST, INC.; *U.S. Public*, pg. 1816
RPT REALTY—See Kimco Realty Corporation; *U.S. Public*, pg. 1232
RYMAN HOSPITALITY PROPERTIES, INC.; *U.S. Public*, pg. 1829
SABRA HEALTH CARE REIT, INC.; *U.S. Public*, pg. 1833
SAGA SERVICES LIMITED—See Charterhouse Capital Partners LLP; *Int'l*, pg. 1455
SAGA SERVICES LIMITED—See CVC Capital Partners SICAV-FIS S.A.; *Int'l*, pg. 1882
SALESSTAFF, LLC; *U.S. Private*, pg. 3532
SALIENT MIDSTREAM & MLP FUND—See Salient Partners, L.P.; *U.S. Private*, pg. 3532
SALIENT MLP & ENERGY INFRASTRUCTURE FUND—See Salient Partners, L.P.; *U.S. Private*, pg. 3532
SALUS CAPITAL PARTNERS LLC—See Spectrum Brands Holdings, Inc.; *U.S. Public*, pg. 1915
SANTANDER CONSUMER BANK GMBH—See Banco Santander, S.A.; *Int'l*, pg. 826
SARATOGA INVESTMENT CORP.; *U.S. Public*, pg. 1841
SAWYER REALTY HOLDINGS LLC; *U.S. Private*, pg. 3558
SCALE FINANCE LLC—See Belay, Inc.; *U.S. Private*, pg. 516
SCHNITZER WEST, LLC; *U.S. Private*, pg. 3567
SCHOTTENSTEIN PROPERTY GROUP, INC.; *U.S. Private*, pg. 3568
SECURITY CREDIT SERVICES, LLC; *U.S. Private*, pg. 3595
SECURITY CREDIT SERVICES—See Security Credit Services, LLC; *U.S. Private*, pg. 3595
SELECT INCOME REIT—See The RMR Group Inc.; *U.S. Public*, pg. 2126
SEMBLE, INC.; *U.S. Private*, pg. 3603
SENTINEL HOLDINGS II B.V.—See Eurocommercial Properties N.V.; *Int'l*, pg. 2534
SERITAGE GROWTH PROPERTIES; *U.S. Public*, pg. 1869
SERVICE PROPERTIES TRUST; *U.S. Public*, pg. 1872
SESAME SERVICES LTD—See Aviva plc; *Int'l*, pg. 746
SEVEN HILLS REALTY TRUST—See The RMR Group Inc.; *U.S. Public*, pg. 2126
SHEFFIELD FINANCIAL, LLC—See Truist Financial Corporation; *U.S. Public*, pg. 2201
SILA REALTY TRUST, INC.—See Carter & Associates, LLC; *U.S. Private*, pg. 775
SIMON PROPERTY GROUP (ILLINOIS), L.P.—See Simon Property Group, Inc.; *U.S. Public*, pg. 1881
SIMON PROPERTY GROUP, INC.; *U.S. Public*, pg. 1881

SIMON PROPERTY GROUP, L.P.—See Simon Property Group, Inc.; *U.S. Public*, pg. 1881
SIMON PROPERTY GROUP (TEXAS), L.P.—See Simon Property Group, Inc.; *U.S. Public*, pg. 1881
SITE CENTERS CORP.; *U.S. Public*, pg. 1888
SITUS EUROPE LIMITED—See Stone Point Capital LLC; *U.S. Private*, pg. 3825
SKYLON ALL ASSET TRUST—See CI Financial Corporation; *Int'l*, pg. 1601
SKYLON INTERNATIONAL ADVANTAGE YIELD TRUST—See CI Financial Corporation; *Int'l*, pg. 1601
SL GREEN REALTY CORP.; *U.S. Public*, pg. 1893
SLOAN FINANCIAL GROUP, LLC; *U.S. Public*, pg. 3689
SMUGGLERS' NOTCH INVESTMENT CO.; *U.S. Private*, pg. 3699
SNC COGEDIM GRAND LYON—See Altarea SCA; *Int'l*, pg. 385
SOLID POWER, INC.; *U.S. Public*, pg. 1900
SOMERA CAPITAL MANAGEMENT, LLC; *U.S. Private*, pg. 3711
SPECIAL OPPORTUNITIES FUND, INC.; *U.S. Public*, pg. 1914
SPECTRUM BUSINESS SOLUTIONS, LLC; *U.S. Private*, pg. 3752
SPEEDPAY, INC.—See ACI Worldwide, Inc.; *U.S. Public*, pg. 35
SPIRIT REALTY CAPITAL, INC.; *U.S. Public*, pg. 1919
SPOUTING ROCK FINANCIAL PARTNERS LLC; *U.S. Private*, pg. 3762
SPRING GARDENS LIMITED—See CLS Holdings plc; *Int'l*, pg. 1664
SRS REAL ESTATE PARTNERS, LLC - SAN JOSE OFFICE—See Jones Lang LaSalle Incorporated; *U.S. Public*, pg. 1205
STAG INDUSTRIAL, INC.; *U.S. Public*, pg. 1925
STARLIGHT U.S. MULTI-FAMILY (NO. 5) CORE FUND—See Blackstone Inc.; *U.S. Public*, pg. 352
STARWOOD PROPERTY TRUST, INC.; *U.S. Public*, pg. 1939
STEADFAST APARTMENT REIT, INC.—See Independence Realty Trust, Inc.; *U.S. Public*, pg. 1116
STELLUS CAPITAL INVESTMENT CORPORATION—See Stellus Capital Management, LLC; *U.S. Private*, pg. 3801
STERLING CAPITAL MANAGEMENT LLC—See Guardian Capital Group Limited; *Int'l*, pg. 3170
STERLING CAPITAL MANAGEMENT LLC - WASHINGTON—See Guardian Capital Group Limited; *Int'l*, pg. 3170
STERLING EQUITIES, INC.; *U.S. Private*, pg. 3805
STG PARTNERS, LLC—See Symphony Technology Group, LLC; *U.S. Private*, pg. 3901
STONE HARBOR EMG MKTS TOTAL INCOME FUND; *U.S. Public*, pg. 1951
STORE CAPITAL CORPORATION—See Blue Owl Capital Inc.; *U.S. Public*, pg. 364
STORE CAPITAL CORPORATION—See GIC Pte. Ltd.; *Int'l*, pg. 2964
S-TOURISMUSFONDS MANAGEMENT AKTIENGESELLSCHAFT—See Erste Group Bank AG; *Int'l*, pg. 2499
STRADA CAPITAL, CORP.; *U.S. Private*, pg. 3832
STRATEGIC COMMUNICATIONS—See FTI Consulting, Inc.; *U.S. Public*, pg. 890
STRATEGIC INCOME ALLOCATION FUND—See Fiera Capital Corporation; *Int'l*, pg. 2660
STRATHSPEY CROWN LLC—See ALPHAEON Corporation; *U.S. Private*, pg. 200
STREET RETAIL, INC.—See Federal Realty Investment Trust; *U.S. Public*, pg. 826
SUMMIT HOTEL PROPERTIES, INC.; *U.S. Public*, pg. 1959
SUN COMMUNITIES, INC.; *U.S. Public*, pg. 1961
SUNSTONE HOTEL INVESTORS, INC.; *U.S. Public*, pg. 1966
SWISS HELVETIA FUND, INC.; *U.S. Public*, pg. 1968
SYMPHONY FLOATING RATE SENIOR LOAN FUND—See Brompton Funds Limited; *Int'l*, pg. 1173
SYNCHRONY FINANCIAL; *U.S. Public*, pg. 1970
TALON FIRST TRUST, LLC—See Talon Real Estate Holding Corp.; *U.S. Public*, pg. 1980
TANGER PROPERTIES LIMITED PARTNERSHIP—See Tanger Inc.; *U.S. Public*, pg. 1981
TCW CAPITAL INVESTMENT CORPORATION—See The Carlyle Group Inc.; *U.S. Public*, pg. 2056
TCW STRATEGIC INCOME FUND, INC.; *U.S. Public*, pg. 1983
TEMPLETON DRAGON FUND, INC.; *U.S. Public*, pg. 1999
TEMPLETON GLOBAL INCOME FUND; *U.S. Public*, pg. 1999
TERRA SECURED INCOME TRUST, INC.; *U.S. Private*, pg. 3970
TERRENO 3601 PENNSY LLC—See Terreno Realty Corporation; *U.S. Public*, pg. 2021
TERRENO AIRGATE LLC—See Terreno Realty Corporation; *U.S. Public*, pg. 2021
TERRENO REALTY CORPORATION; *U.S. Public*, pg. 2020
THAI CORP INTERNATIONAL CO., LTD.—See Berli Jucker Public Co. Ltd.; *Int'l*, pg. 985
THESTREET.COM RATINGS, INC.—See The Arena Group

N.A.I.C.S. INDEX 531110 — LESSORS OF RESIDENT...

Holdings, Inc; *U.S. Public*, pg. 2035
THL CREDIT SENIOR LOAN FUND; *U.S. Public*, pg. 2156
TIAA REAL ESTATE ACCOUNT—See Teachers Insurance Association - College Retirement Fund; *U.S. Private*, pg. 3948
TIER REIT, INC.—See Cousins Properties Incorporated; *U.S. Public*, pg. 587
TIME EQUITIES, INC.; *U.S. Private*, pg. 4172
TORTOISE ENERGY INDEPENDENCE FUND, INC.—See Lovell Minnick Partners LLC; *U.S. Private*, pg. 2503
TORTOISE ENERGY INFRASTRUCTURE CORPORATION—See Lovell Minnick Partners LLC; *U.S. Private*, pg. 2503
TORTOISE MIDSTREAM ENERGY FUND, INC.—See Lovell Minnick Partners LLC; *U.S. Private*, pg. 2503
TORTOISE PIPELINE & ENERGY FUND, INC.—See Lovell Minnick Partners LLC; *U.S. Private*, pg. 2503
TORTOISE POWER & ENERGY INFRASTRUCTURE FUND, INC.—See Lovell Minnick Partners LLC; *U.S. Private*, pg. 2503
TRADEWEB LLC—See Tradeweb Markets Inc.; *U.S. Public*, pg. 2178
TRANSATLANTIC CAPITAL INC.; *U.S. Public*, pg. 2179
TRANSCONTINENTAL REALTY INVESTORS, INC.—See American Realty Investors, Inc.; *U.S. Public*, pg. 108
TREMONT MORTGAGE TRUST—See The RMR Group Inc.; *U.S. Public*, pg. 2126
TRIDENT ROYALTIES PLC—See Deterra Royalties Limited; *Int'l*, pg. 2048
TRINITY COMMERCIAL SERVICES, INC.; *U.S. Private*, pg. 4233
TWO HARBORS INVESTMENT CORP.; *U.S. Public*, pg. 2207
UDR, INC.; *U.S. Public*, pg. 2217
UIL LIMITED—See ICM Limited; *Int'l*, pg. 3581
UNBOUND GROUP PLC—See Epiris Managers LLP; *Int'l*, pg. 2461
THE UNICORN GROUP; *U.S. Private*, pg. 4129
UNITED CAPITAL MARKETS HOLDINGS, INC.; *U.S. Private*, pg. 4288
UNITED DEVELOPMENT FUNDING INCOME FUND V; *U.S. Private*, pg. 4291
UNITED DEVELOPMENT FUNDING IV; *U.S. Private*, pg. 4291
UNITED DOMINION REALTY L.P.—See UDR, Inc.; *U.S. Public*, pg. 2218
UNITI GROUP INC.; *U.S. Public*, pg. 2253
UNIVERSAL HEALTH REALTY INCOME TRUST; *U.S. Public*, pg. 2255
UNIVERSAL LEVEN N.V.—See Allianz SE; *Int'l*, pg. 349
US FEDERAL PROPERTIES TRUST, INC.; *U.S. Private*, pg. 4318
UTILICO EMERGING MARKETS LIMITED—See ICM Limited; *Int'l*, pg. 3582
UTILICO EMERGING MARKETS TRUST PLC—See ICM Limited; *Int'l*, pg. 3582
UTILITY FINANCIAL CORP.—See Southwest Gas Holdings, Inc.; *U.S. Public*, pg. 1913
VALAD PROPERTY HOLDINGS (UK) LIMITED—See Blackstone Inc.; *U.S. Public*, pg. 360
VENTAS HEALTHCARE PROPERTIES, INC.—See Ventas, Inc.; *U.S. Public*, pg. 2279
VENTAS, INC.; *U.S. Public*, pg. 2277
VEREIT, INC.—See Realty Income Corporation; *U.S. Public*, pg. 1768
VESTIN REALTY MORTGAGE II, INC.; *U.S. Private*, pg. 4373
VESTIN REALTY MORTGAGE I, INC.—See Vestin Group, Inc.; *U.S. Private*, pg. 4373
VFS RENTING SOCIEDADE UNIPESSOAL LDA.—See AB Volvo; *Int'l*, pg. 42
VIAMERICAS CORPORATION; *U.S. Private*, pg. 4375
VIRGINIA INVESTMENT COUNSELORS, INC.—See Guardian Capital Group Limited; *Int'l*, pg. 3170
VIRTUS CONVERTIBLE & INCOME FUND II; *U.S. Public*, pg. 2300
VIRTUS EQUITY & CONVERTIBLE INCOME FUND; *U.S. Public*, pg. 2300
VIRTUS TOTAL RETURN FUND, INC.; *U.S. Public*, pg. 2301
VORNADO REALTY L.P.—See Vornado Realty Trust; *U.S. Public*, pg. 2309
VORNADO REALTY TRUST; *U.S. Public*, pg. 2309
VOYA ASIA PACIFIC HIGH DIVIDEND EQUITY INCOME FUND; *U.S. Public*, pg. 2311
VOYA GLOBAL ADVANTAGE & PREMIUM OPPORTUNITY FUND; *U.S. Public*, pg. 2312
VOYA GLOBAL EQUITY DIVIDEND & PREMIUM OPPORTUNITY FUND; *U.S. Public*, pg. 2312
VOYA INFRASTRUCTURE, INDUSTRIALS & MATERIALS FUND; *U.S. Public*, pg. 2312
VOYA INTERNATIONAL HIGH DIVIDEND EQUITY INCOME FUND; *U.S. Public*, pg. 2312
VOYA NATURAL RESOURCES EQUITY INCOME FUND; *U.S. Public*, pg. 2312
VOYA PRIME RATE TRUST; *U.S. Public*, pg. 2312
VR EQUITYPARTNER GMBH—See DZ BANK AG Deutsche Zentral-Genossenschaftsbank; *Int'l*, pg. 2245
WALTRUST PROPERTIES, INC.—See Walgreens Boots Alliance, Inc.; *U.S. Public*, pg. 2323
WARI INC.; *U.S. Private*, pg. 4442
WASHINGTON PRIME GROUP INC.; *U.S. Private*, pg. 4448
WASHINGTON PRIME GROUP, L.P.—See Washington Prime Group Inc.; *U.S. Private*, pg. 4449
WATERMARK LODGING TRUST, INC.—See W.P. Carey Inc.; *U.S. Public*, pg. 2316
WEBSTER PREFERRED CAPITAL CORPORATION—See Webster Financial Corporation; *U.S. Public*, pg. 2341
WEED GROWTH FUND, INC.; *U.S. Public*, pg. 2342
WELLS FARGO CAPITAL FINANCE (UK) LIMITED—See Wells Fargo & Company; *U.S. Public*, pg. 2346
WELLS FARGO MULTI-SECTOR INCOME FUND; *U.S. Public*, pg. 2347
WELLS FARGO REAL ESTATE INVESTMENT CORPORATION—See Wells Fargo & Company; *U.S. Public*, pg. 2346
WELLS REAL ESTATE FUNDS, INC.; *U.S. Private*, pg. 4476
WELLTOWER CCRC OPCO LLC—See Welltower Inc.; *U.S. Public*, pg. 2349
WELLTOWER INC.; *U.S. Public*, pg. 2347
WELSH PROPERTY TRUST, INC.; *U.S. Private*, pg. 4479
WESTBROOK REAL ESTATE PARTNERS, LLC; *U.S. Private*, pg. 4488
WEST COAST REALTY TRUST, INC.; *U.S. Private*, pg. 4484
WESTERN ALLIANCE EQUIPMENT FINANCE, INC.—See Western Alliance Bancorporation; *U.S. Public*, pg. 2354
WESTERN ASSET CORPORATE LOAN FUND, INC.—See Franklin Resources, Inc.; *U.S. Public*, pg. 882
WESTERN ASSET GLOBAL CORPORATE DEFINED OPPORTUNITY FUND, INC.—See Franklin Resources, Inc.; *U.S. Public*, pg. 882
WESTERN ASSET HIGH INCOME FUND II, INC.—See Franklin Resources, Inc.; *U.S. Public*, pg. 882
WESTERN ASSET INFLATION-LINKED INCOME FUND; *U.S. Public*, pg. 2354
WESTERN ASSET INFLATION-LINKED OPPORTUNITIES & INCOME FUND; *U.S. Public*, pg. 2354
WESTERN ASSET INTERMEDIATE MUNI FUND, INC.—See Franklin Resources, Inc.; *U.S. Public*, pg. 882
WESTERN ASSET INVESTMENT GRADE DEFINED OPPORTUNITY TRUST, INC.—See Franklin Resources, Inc.; *U.S. Public*, pg. 882
WESTERN ASSET INVESTMENT GRADE INCOME FUND, INC.—See Franklin Resources, Inc.; *U.S. Public*, pg. 882
WESTERN ASSET MANAGEMENT COMPANY—See Franklin Resources, Inc.; *U.S. Public*, pg. 882
WESTERN ASSET MUNICIPAL HIGH INCOME FUND, INC.—See Franklin Resources, Inc.; *U.S. Public*, pg. 883
WESTERN ASSET PREMIER BOND FUND—See Franklin Resources, Inc.; *U.S. Public*, pg. 883
WEYERHAEUSER REALTY INVESTORS, INC.—See Weyerhaeuser Company; *U.S. Public*, pg. 2365
WHITEHALL STREET REAL ESTATE L.P.—See The Goldman Sachs Group, Inc.; *U.S. Public*, pg. 2082
WHITESTONE PINNACLE OF SCOTTSDALE, LLC—See Whitestone REIT; *U.S. Public*, pg. 2369
WHITESTONE REIT; *U.S. Public*, pg. 2369
WHM LLC—See Blackstone Inc.; *U.S. Public*, pg. 351
WINDROSE SIERRA PROPERTIES, LTD.—See Welltower Inc.; *U.S. Public*, pg. 2349
WING LUNG BANK (TRUSTEE) LTD.—See China Merchants Group Limited; *Int'l*, pg. 1520
WING LUNG FINANCE LTD.—See China Merchants Group Limited; *Int'l*, pg. 1520
WISDOMTREE INTERNATIONAL REAL ESTATE FUND—See WisdomTree, Inc.; *U.S. Public*, pg. 2376
WORLD FINANCIAL CAPITAL BANK—See Bread Financial Holdings Inc.; *U.S. Public*, pg. 381
WPF HOLDINGS, INC.; *U.S. Public*, pg. 2383
WPT INDUSTRIAL REAL ESTATE INVESTMENT TRUST—See Blackstone Inc.; *U.S. Public*, pg. 352
XOOM CORPORATION—See PayPal Holdings, Inc.; *U.S. Public*, pg. 1657
YANTIS COMPANY; *U.S. Private*, pg. 4586
YIELD ADVANTAGE INCOME TRUST—See CI Financial Corporation; *Int'l*, pg. 1601
YOUNAN PROPERTIES, INC.; *U.S. Private*, pg. 4592
ZETA RESOURCES LIMITED—See ICM Limited; *Int'l*, pg. 3582
ZIMMER LUCAS CAPITAL LLC.; *U.S. Private*, pg. 4605

531110 — LESSORS OF RESIDENTIAL BUILDINGS AND DWELLINGS

1200 BROADWAY, LLC—See UDR, Inc.; *U.S. Public*, pg. 2218
13TH & MARKET PROPERTIES LLC—See UDR, Inc.; *U.S. Public*, pg. 2218
1620 CENTRAL LLC—See Highlands REIT, Inc.; *U.S. Private*, pg. 1940
1740 BROADWAY ASSOCIATES L.P.—See Vornado Realty Trust; *U.S. Public*, pg. 2310
200 EAST 87TH STREET COMPANY, LLC—See Equitable Holdings, Inc.; *U.S. Public*, pg. 788
20 LAMBOURNE LLC—See UDR, Inc.; *U.S. Public*, pg. 2218
20 VIC MANAGEMENT INC.; *Int'l*, pg. 4
300 BROADWAY, LLC—See Ryman Hospitality Properties, Inc.; *U.S. Public*, pg. 1829
3535 N. HALL STREET, LLC—See Welltower Inc.; *U.S. Public*, pg. 2347
399 FREMONT LLC—See UDR, Inc.; *U.S. Public*, pg. 2218
9108-9458 QUEBEC INC.—See Welltower Inc.; *U.S. Public*, pg. 2347
AERC ARROWHEAD STATION, INC.—See Brookfield Corporation; *Int'l*, pg. 1175
AERC DORAL WEST, LLC—See Brookfield Corporation; *Int'l*, pg. 1174
AFG IMMOBILIEN AG—See Arbonia AG; *Int'l*, pg. 537
AFRICA GROWTH CORPORATION; *U.S. Private*, pg. 124
AH4R MANAGEMENT-GA, LLC—See American Homes 4 Rent; *U.S. Public*, pg. 104
AH4R MANAGEMENT-NC, LLC—See American Homes 4 Rent; *U.S. Public*, pg. 104
AH4R MANAGEMENT-TX, LLC—See American Homes 4 Rent; *U.S. Public*, pg. 104
AH4R PROPERTIES, LLC—See American Homes 4 Rent; *U.S. Public*, pg. 104
AHTNA DEVELOPMENT CORPORATION—See Ahtna Incorporated; *U.S. Private*, pg. 131
AIMCO ANGELES GP, LLC—See Apartment Investment and Management Company; *U.S. Public*, pg. 143
AIMCO ANTIOCH, L.L.C.—See Apartment Investment and Management Company; *U.S. Public*, pg. 143
AIMCO/BETHESDA GP, L.L.C.—See Apartment Investment and Management Company; *U.S. Public*, pg. 144
AIMCO ESPLANADE AVENUE APARTMENTS, LLC—See Apartment Investment and Management Company; *U.S. Public*, pg. 143
AIMCO KEY TOWERS, L.P.—See Apartment Investment and Management Company; *U.S. Public*, pg. 143
AIMCO MONTEREY GROVE APARTMENTS, LLC—See Blackstone Inc.; *U.S. Public*, pg. 350
AIMCO/NASHUA, L.L.C.—See Blackstone Inc.; *U.S. Public*, pg. 350
AIMCO WARWICK, L.L.C.—See Apartment Investment and Management Company; *U.S. Public*, pg. 143
ALEXANDER'S, INC.—See Vornado Realty Trust; *U.S. Public*, pg. 2310
AMBITION DX HOLDINGS CO., LTD.; *Int'l*, pg. 415
AMERICAN ASSETS TRUST, L.P.—See American Assets Trust, Inc.; *U.S. Public*, pg. 96
AMERICAN REALTY TRUST, INC.—See American Realty Investors, Inc.; *U.S. Public*, pg. 108
AMH PORTFOLIO ONE, LLC—See American Homes 4 Rent; *U.S. Public*, pg. 104
AMPLUS ASSET DEVELOPMENT INC.—See AK Holdings, Inc.; *Int'l*, pg. 259
ANDORVER PLACE APTS. L.L.C.—See Veris Residential, Inc.; *U.S. Public*, pg. 2281
ANDOVER HOUSE LLC—See UDR, Inc.; *U.S. Public*, pg. 2218
ANNA MARIA VACATIONS; *U.S. Private*, pg. 284
APARTMENT LIST; *U.S. Private*, pg. 290
APARTMENTS OF MANDALAY BAY, LLC—See RAIT Financial Trust; *U.S. Private*, pg. 3348
ARAM GROUP P.J.S.C; *Int'l*, pg. 535
ARCHSTONE CRONIN'S LANDING LLC—See Equity Residential; *U.S. Public*, pg. 791
ARCHSTONE REDWOOD SHORES LLC—See Equity Residential; *U.S. Public*, pg. 791
ARDEPRO CO. LTD.; *Int'l*, pg. 554
AREALINK CO. LTD.; *Int'l*, pg. 557
THE ARMCO GROUP INC.; *U.S. Private*, pg. 3988
ARNS, INC.—See Ares Management Corporation; *U.S. Public*, pg. 191
ARNS, INC.—See Pretium Partners, LLC; *U.S. Private*, pg. 3257
ARRIS SINGAPORE PTE. LTD.—See CommScope Holding Company, Inc.; *U.S. Public*, pg. 548
ARTISAN (UK) DEVELOPMENTS LIMITED—See Artisan (UK) plc; *Int'l*, pg. 584
ARTISAN (UK) PROJECTS LIMITED—See Artisan (UK) plc; *Int'l*, pg. 584
ARTISAN (UK) PROPERTIES LIMITED—See Artisan (UK) plc; *Int'l*, pg. 584
ARVADA HOUSE PRESERVATION LIMITED PARTNERSHIP—See Apartment Investment and Management Company; *U.S. Public*, pg. 144
THE ASCOTT LIMITED—See CapitaLand Investment Limited; *Int'l*, pg. 1314
ASEANA HOLDINGS, INC.—See DM Wenceslao & Associates, Inc.; *Int'l*, pg. 2142
ASPEN APARTMENTS—See American Management Services LLC; *U.S. Private*, pg. 240
ASPEN PLACE, INC.—See Webster Financial Corporation; *U.S. Public*, pg. 2341
ASPENWOOD SQUARE APARTMENTS, LP—See Synovus Financial Corp.; *U.S. Public*, pg. 1971
ASPENWOOD SQUARE APARTMENTS, LP—See Synovus Financial Corp.; *U.S. Public*, pg. 1971

N.A.I.C.S. Index

531110 — LESSORS OF RESIDENT... CORPORATE AFFILIATIONS

ASTAKOS TERMINAL S.A.—See AEGEK Group; *Int'l*, pg. 173
ATLAND VOISIN SAS—See Fonciere Atland SA; *Int'l*, pg. 2724
ATRIUM REAL ESTATE INVESTMENT TRUST; *Int'l*, pg. 694
AUBURN MANOR APARTMENTS LP—See Edison International; *U.S. Public*, pg. 719
AUDUBON URBAN INVESTMENTS, LLC—See Bank of America Corporation; *U.S. Public*, pg. 270
AUFBAU UND HANDELSGESELLSCHAFT MBH—See DZ BANK AG Deutsche Zentral-Genossenschaftsbank; *Int'l*, pg. 2243
AUGUSTA APARTMENTS NEVADA, LLC—See RAIT Financial Trust; *U.S. Private*, pg. 3348
AUXIDEICO GESTION, S.A.—See ECE Projektmanagement GmbH & Co KG; *Int'l*, pg. 2288
AVALONBAY ASSEMBLY ROW, INC.—See AvalonBay Communities, Inc.; *U.S. Public*, pg. 240
AVALON BONTERRA, LLC—See AvalonBay Communities, Inc.; *U.S. Public*, pg. 240
AVALON CAMPBELL SOLAR, LLC—See AvalonBay Communities, Inc.; *U.S. Public*, pg. 240
AVALON CERRITOS, L.P.—See AvalonBay Communities, Inc.; *U.S. Public*, pg. 240
AVALON PORTICO AT SILVER SPRING METRO, LLC—See AvalonBay Communities, Inc.; *U.S. Public*, pg. 240
AVALON SOMERVILLE STATION URBAN RENEWAL, LLC—See AvalonBay Communities, Inc.; *U.S. Public*, pg. 240
AVA PASADENA SOLAR, LLC—See AvalonBay Communities, Inc.; *U.S. Public*, pg. 240
AXIS REAL ESTATE INVESTMENT TRUST; *Int'l*, pg. 770
BAIC BLUEPARK NEW ENERGY TECHNOLOGY CO., LTD.; *Int'l*, pg. 801
BAILEY & COMPANY BENEFITS GROUP—See Genstar Capital, LLC; *U.S. Private*, pg. 1674
BAKER HOUSE APARTMENTS LLC—See Duke Energy Corporation; *U.S. Public*, pg. 690
BALLARD REALTY CO INC.; *U.S. Private*, pg. 460
BATH PROPERTY LETTING LIMITED—See Bath Building Society; *Int'l*, pg. 889
BATIGERE NORD EST; *Int'l*, pg. 889
BAUBECON BIO GMBH—See Barclays PLC; *Int'l*, pg. 862
BAUMANN PROPERTY COMPANY INC.; *U.S. Private*, pg. 490
BAYVIEW CLUB APARTMENTS INDIANA, LLC—See Independence Realty Trust, Inc.; *U.S. Public*, pg. 1115
BEDFORD HOUSE, LTD.—See Apartment Investment and Management Company; *U.S. Public*, pg. 144
BEIH-PROPERTY CO., LTD.; *Int'l*, pg. 942
BEIJING ZODI INVESTMENT CO., LTD.; *Int'l*, pg. 961
BELGARDE ENTERPRISES; *U.S. Private*, pg. 517
BELLE CREEK APARTMENTS COLORADO, LLC—See RAIT Financial Trust; *U.S. Private*, pg. 3348
BELMONT CROSSING, LLC—See Bluerock Residential Growth REIT, Inc.; *U.S. Public*, pg. 366
BELMONT VILLAGE TURTLE CREEK TENANT, LLC—See Welltower Inc.; *U.S. Public*, pg. 2348
BELMONT VILLAGE WEST LAKE HILLS TENANT, LLC—See Welltower Inc.; *U.S. Public*, pg. 2348
BENNINGTON POND LLC—See Independence Realty Trust, Inc.; *U.S. Public*, pg. 1115
BESSEMER TRUST COMPANY OF CALIFORNIA, N.A.—See The Bessemer Group, Incorporated; *U.S. Private*, pg. 3994
BGI GROUP AD; *Int'l*, pg. 1008
BH MANAGEMENT SERVICES, LLC; *U.S. Private*, pg. 549
BOEING CAPITAL CORPORATION—See The Boeing Company; *U.S. Public*, pg. 2039
BOI CARLSBAD LLC—See Brandywine Realty Trust; *U.S. Public*, pg. 380
BOZZUTO MANAGEMENT COMPANY—See The Bozzuto Group; *U.S. Private*, pg. 3999
BRADLEE DANVERS LLC—See UDR, Inc.; *U.S. Public*, pg. 2218
BREM HOLDING BERHAD; *Int'l*, pg. 1144
BRESLER & REINER, INC.; *U.S. Public*, pg. 381
BRISTOL DEVELOPMENT LLC; *U.S. Private*, pg. 656
BROOKDALE CASTLE HILLS, LLC—See Brookdale Senior Living Inc.; *U.S. Public*, pg. 393
BROOKDALE PLACE OF WILTON, LLC—See Brookdale Senior Living Inc.; *U.S. Public*, pg. 394
BR PROPERTIES S.A.—See GP Investments, Ltd.; *Int'l*, pg. 3045
BRUNSWICK POINT NORTH CAROLINA, LLC—See Independence Realty Trust, Inc.; *U.S. Public*, pg. 1115
BSF-ARBORS RIVER OAKS—See Independence Realty Trust, Inc.; *U.S. Public*, pg. 1115
BUILDERS INC.; *U.S. Public*, pg. 682
BURROAKCOMMONSPLUS, LLC—See Welltower Inc.; *U.S. Public*, pg. 2348
BUTLER & BUTLER INVESTMENTS; *U.S. Private*, pg. 696
BUTTERFIELD TRAIL VILLAGE, INC.; *U.S. Private*, pg. 698
BW REAL ESTATE, INC.—See Western Alliance Bancorporation; *U.S. Public*, pg. 2354

BZ WBK FINANSE & LEASING S.A.—See Banco Santander, S.A.; *Int'l*, pg. 826
CALVERT'S WALK LLC—See UDR, Inc.; *U.S. Public*, pg. 2218
CAMBRIDGE CENTER NORTH TRUST—See Boston Properties, Inc.; *U.S. Public*, pg. 373
CAMBRIDGE HEIGHTS APARTMENTS LIMITED PARTNERSHIP—See Apartment Investment and Management Company; *U.S. Public*, pg. 144
CAMDEN OPERATING, L.P.—See Camden Property Trust; *U.S. Public*, pg. 426
CANE ISLAND, LLC—See D.R. Horton, Inc.; *U.S. Public*, pg. 619
CANTERBURY APARTMENTS, L.L.C.—See Equity Residential; *U.S. Public*, pg. 791
CAPREIT.; *U.S. Private*, pg. 745
CARR PROPERTIES—See JPMorgan Chase & Co.; *U.S. Public*, pg. 1206
CASCADES APARTMENTS, LTD—See American Realty Investors, Inc.; *U.S. Public*, pg. 108
C&B HOLDINGS, LLC—See Compass Group PLC; *Int'l*, pg. 1750
CENTRAL SQUARE AT FRISCO LLC—See UDR, Inc.; *U.S. Public*, pg. 2218
CHERRY GROVE SOUTH CAROLINA, LLC—See Independence Realty Trust, Inc.; *U.S. Public*, pg. 1115
CHESTER WOODS INC.—See LCS Holdings Inc.; *U.S. Private*, pg. 2404
CHINA BAOAN GROUP CO., LTD.; *Int'l*, pg. 1485
CHINESE ESTATES (HARCOURT HOUSE) LIMITED—See Chinese Estates Holdings Limited; *Int'l*, pg. 1569
CHRISTIAN CARE COMPANIES, INC.; *U.S. Private*, pg. 890
CINCINNATI METROPOLITAN HOUSING AUTHORITY; *U.S. Private*, pg. 898
CINDA REAL ESTATE CO., LTD.—See China Cinda Asset Management Co., Ltd.; *Int'l*, pg. 1488
CIRCLE TOWERS LLC—See UDR, Inc.; *U.S. Public*, pg. 2218
CITY EMPIRIA A.S.—See Assicurazioni Generali S.p.A.; *Int'l*, pg. 643
CITYVIEW APARTMENTS AND COMMERCIAL CENTRE LIMITED—See Aspial Corporation Limited; *Int'l*, pg. 630
CITYVIEW APARTMENTS AND COMMERCIAL CENTRE LIMITED—See Fragrance Group Limited; *Int'l*, pg. 2758
CITY VIEW—See Essex Property Trust, Inc.; *U.S. Public*, pg. 795
THE COLLIER COMPANIES, INC.; *U.S. Private*, pg. 4011
COLONIAL PARC APARTMENTS ARKANSAS, LLC—See RAIT Financial Trust; *U.S. Private*, pg. 3348
COMMERZ REAL AG—See Commerzbank AG; *Int'l*, pg. 1716
CONCORD MANAGEMENT LTD.; *U.S. Private*, pg. 1010
CONDOMINIUM CONCEPTS MANAGEMENT, LLC—See FirstService Corporation; *Int'l*, pg. 2691
COOL CHIPS PLC; *Int'l*, pg. 1789
COPT NORTHCREEK, LLC—See COPT Defense Properties; *U.S. Public*, pg. 575
COPT PROPERTY MANAGEMENT SERVICES, LLC—See COPT Defense Properties; *U.S. Public*, pg. 575
CORESITE, L.P.—See American Tower Corporation; *U.S. Public*, pg. 111
CORPORATE HOUSING—See Woodlands Operating Company LP; *U.S. Private*, pg. 4559
COUNTRY CLUB CONDOMINIUM, L.L.C.—See Equity Residential; *U.S. Public*, pg. 791
COURTYARDS AT 65TH, L.P.—See Essex Property Trust, Inc.; *U.S. Public*, pg. 796
CREEKSIDE ASSOCIATES LIMITED—See Feit Management Company; *U.S. Private*, pg. 1493
CREEKSIDE CORNERS GEORGIA, LLC—See Independence Realty Trust, Inc.; *U.S. Public*, pg. 1115
CRUZ MANAGEMENT INC.; *U.S. Private*, pg. 1114
CSM CORPORATION; *U.S. Private*, pg. 1117
CSR - MONTICELLO CROSSINGS, LLC—See Centerspace; *U.S. Public*, pg. 472
CWS CAPITAL PARTNERS, LLC; *U.S. Private*, pg. 1133
THE DAISHI LEASE CO., LTD.—See Daishi Hokuetsu Financial Group, Inc.; *Int'l*, pg. 1941
DAKOTA ARMS, LTD—See American Realty Investors, Inc.; *U.S. Public*, pg. 108
DA LI DEVELOPMENT USA LLC—See Da-Li Development Co., Ltd.; *Int'l*, pg. 1902
DA-LY REALTY & INSURANCE INC.; *U.S. Private*, pg. 1143
DARBY TOWNHOUSES PRESERVATION, LP—See Apartment Investment and Management Company; *U.S. Public*, pg. 144
DAVID DRYE COMPANY LLC; *U.S. Private*, pg. 1169
DAVIDSON PROPERTIES, INC.—See Apartment Investment and Management Company; *U.S. Public*, pg. 144
DCG DEVELOPMENT CO.; *U.S. Private*, pg. 1179
DENVER MERCHANDISE MART, INC.—See American Realty Investors, Inc.; *U.S. Public*, pg. 108
DESERT WIND APARTMENTS ARIZONA, LLC—See RAIT Financial Trust; *U.S. Private*, pg. 3348
D HLM NOTRE LOGIS; *Int'l*, pg. 1899
DIAL EQUITIES INC.—See Dial Companies Corporation; *U.S. Private*, pg. 1222

DIGGI MULTITRADE LIMITED; *Int'l*, pg. 2118
DIXON RIVER APARTMENTS, L.P.—See Apartment Investment and Management Company; *U.S. Public*, pg. 144
DKLS SIGNATUREHOMES SDN. BHD.—See DKLS Industries Berhad; *Int'l*, pg. 2139
DLF FINANCIAL SERVICES LIMITED—See DLF Limited; *Int'l*, pg. 2141
DLF LIMITED; *Int'l*, pg. 2140
DOMINION KINGS PLACE LLC—See UDR, Inc.; *U.S. Public*, pg. 2218
THE DOUBLE B PARTNERSHIP—See Boston Properties, Inc.; *U.S. Public*, pg. 373
DOUGLAS EMMETT 1998, LLC—See Douglas Emmett, Inc.; *U.S. Public*, pg. 678
DOUGLAS EMMETT MANAGEMENT HAWAII, LLC—See Douglas Emmett, Inc.; *U.S. Public*, pg. 678
DOUGLAS EMMETT MANAGEMENT, LLC—See Douglas Emmett, Inc.; *U.S. Public*, pg. 678
D.R. HORTON - COLORADO, LLC—See D.R. Horton, Inc.; *U.S. Public*, pg. 619
D.R. HORTON - GEORGIA, LLC—See D.R. Horton, Inc.; *U.S. Public*, pg. 619
D.R. HORTON - INDIANA, LLC—See D.R. Horton, Inc.; *U.S. Public*, pg. 619
DUNDEE REALTY MANAGEMENT (SASK) CORP.—See Dundee Corporation; *Int'l*, pg. 2226
EAGLE RIDGE APARTMENTS CALIFORNIA, LLC—See RAIT Financial Trust; *U.S. Private*, pg. 3348
EASTCO MANAGEMENT CORPORATION; *U.S. Private*, pg. 1319
EAVES CREEKSIDE SOLAR, LLC—See AvalonBay Communities, Inc.; *U.S. Public*, pg. 240
ECE PROJEKTMANAGEMENT AUSTRIA GMBH—See ECE Projektmanagement GmbH & Co KG; *Int'l*, pg. 2288
ECE PROJEKTMANAGEMENT BUDAPEST KFT.—See ECE Projektmanagement GmbH & Co KG; *Int'l*, pg. 2288
ECE PROJEKTMANAGEMENT POLSKA SP. Z O.O.—See ECE Projektmanagement GmbH & Co KG; *Int'l*, pg. 2288
ECE RUSSLAND OOO—See ECE Projektmanagement GmbH & Co KG; *Int'l*, pg. 2288
ECE TURKIYE PROJE YONETIMI A.S.—See ECE Projektmanagement GmbH & Co KG; *Int'l*, pg. 2288
EC-MISSION VERDE, LLC—See Equity Residential; *U.S. Public*, pg. 791
EC OPCO WASHINGTON TOWNSHIP, LLC—See Ventas, Inc.; *U.S. Public*, pg. 2278
EC OPCO XENIA, LLC—See Ventas, Inc.; *U.S. Public*, pg. 2278
ECUMENICAL ENTERPRISES INC.; *U.S. Private*, pg. 1331
EDR AUBURN, LLC—See Greystar Real Estate Partners, LLC; *U.S. Private*, pg. 1785
EDWARD ROSE & SONS, LLC—See Edward Rose Company; *U.S. Private*, pg. 1341
ELCO LANDMARK RESIDENTIAL HOLDINGS LLC—See Elco Limited; *Int'l*, pg. 2345
ELDORADO AT SANTA FE—See AMREP Corporation; *U.S. Public*, pg. 133
ELME DULLES LLC—See Elme Communities; *U.S. Public*, pg. 735
ELME EAGLES LANDING 860 LLC—See Elme Communities; *U.S. Public*, pg. 735
ELME GERMANTOWN LLC—See Elme Communities; *U.S. Public*, pg. 735
ELME HERNDON LLC—See Elme Communities; *U.S. Public*, pg. 735
ELME PARK ADAMS APARTMENTS LLC—See Elme Communities; *U.S. Public*, pg. 735
ELME ROOSEVELT TOWERS LLC—See Elme Communities; *U.S. Public*, pg. 735
EL PASO LEGENDS, LTD—See American Realty Investors, Inc.; *U.S. Public*, pg. 108
ELTOFI AS—See W.P. Carey Inc.; *U.S. Public*, pg. 2315
EMBARCADERO CENTER ASSOCIATES—See Boston Properties, Inc.; *U.S. Public*, pg. 373
EMERALD BAY APARTMENTS NEVADA, LLC—See RAIT Financial Trust; *U.S. Private*, pg. 3348
EQR-1500 MASS, LLC—See Equity Residential; *U.S. Public*, pg. 791
EQR-175 KENT AVENUE A, LLC—See Equity Residential; *U.S. Public*, pg. 791
EQR-228 WEST 71ST, LLC—See Equity Residential; *U.S. Public*, pg. 791
EQR-425 MASSACHUSETTS, LLC—See Equity Residential; *U.S. Public*, pg. 791
EQR-600 WASHINGTON, L.L.C.—See Equity Residential; *U.S. Public*, pg. 791
EQR-77 PARK AVENUE LLC—See Equity Residential; *U.S. Public*, pg. 791
EQR-ACADEMY VILLAGE, L.L.C.—See Equity Residential; *U.S. Public*, pg. 791
EQR-CAPE HOUSE I, LP—See Equity Residential; *U.S. Public*, pg. 791
EQR-GALLERY APARTMENTS LIMITED PARTNERSHIP—See Equity Residential; *U.S. Public*, pg. 791
EQR-GATEWAY AT MALDEN CENTER, LLC—See Equity Residential; *U.S. Public*, pg. 791

N.A.I.C.S. INDEX
531110 — LESSORS OF RESIDENT...

EQR-GLO APARTMENTS, LLC—See Equity Residential; *U.S. Public*, pg. 791

EQR-HEIGHTS ON CAPITOL HILL LLC—See Equity Residential; *U.S. Public*, pg. 791

EQR-HERITAGE RIDGE, L.L.C.—See Equity Residential; *U.S. Public*, pg. 791

EQR-HUDSON CROSSING, LLC—See Equity Residential; *U.S. Public*, pg. 791

EQR-HUDSON POINTE, L.L.C.—See Equity Residential; *U.S. Public*, pg. 791

EQR-IVORY WOOD, L.L.C.—See Equity Residential; *U.S. Public*, pg. 791

EQR-KELVIN COURT, LLC—See Equity Residential; *U.S. Public*, pg. 791

EQR-KINGS COLONY, L.L.C.—See Equity Residential; *U.S. Public*, pg. 791

EQR-LEXINGTON FARM, L.L.C.—See Equity Residential; *U.S. Public*, pg. 791

EQR-LIBERTY TOWER, LLC—See Equity Residential; *U.S. Public*, pg. 791

EQR-LINDLEY, LLC—See Equity Residential; *U.S. Public*, pg. 791

EQR-LUNA UPPER WESTSIDE LLC—See Equity Residential; *U.S. Public*, pg. 791

EQR-MARK ON 8TH LLC—See Equity Residential; *U.S. Public*, pg. 791

EQR-METRO ON FIRST LLC—See Equity Residential; *U.S. Public*, pg. 791

EQR-MIDTOWN 24, LLC—See Equity Residential; *U.S. Public*, pg. 791

EQR-MILL CREEK, L.L.C.—See Equity Residential; *U.S. Public*, pg. 791

EQR-MIRAMAR LAKES, L.L.C.—See Equity Residential; *U.S. Public*, pg. 791

EQR-NORTHPARK, LLC—See Equity Residential; *U.S. Public*, pg. 791

EQR-OAK MILL, L.L.C.—See Equity Residential; *U.S. Public*, pg. 791

EQR-OAKS AT FALLS CHURCH, LLC—See Equity Residential; *U.S. Public*, pg. 791

EQR-PALM TRACE LANDING, L.L.C.—See Equity Residential; *U.S. Public*, pg. 791

EQR-PEGASUS, LLC—See Equity Residential; *U.S. Public*, pg. 791

EQR-RIVERTOWER, LLC—See Equity Residential; *U.S. Public*, pg. 791

EQR-SIENA TERRACE, L.L.C.—See Equity Residential; *U.S. Public*, pg. 792

EQR-SKYLINE TERRACE LIMITED PARTNERSHIP—See Equity Residential; *U.S. Public*, pg. 792

EQR-SOUTHWOOD LIMITED PARTNERSHIP—See Equity Residential; *U.S. Public*, pg. 792

EQR-UWAJIMAYA VILLAGE, L.L.C.—See Equity Residential; *U.S. Public*, pg. 792

EQR-VIRGINIA SQUARE LLC—See Equity Residential; *U.S. Public*, pg. 792

EQR-WATERFORD PLACE, L.L.C.—See Equity Residential; *U.S. Public*, pg. 792

EQR-WELLINGTON GREEN, L.L.C.—See Equity Residential; *U.S. Public*, pg. 792

EQUITY APARTMENT MANAGEMENT, LLC—See Equity Residential; *U.S. Public*, pg. 792

EQUITY COMMONWEALTH EQC—See Equity Commonwealth; *U.S. Public*, pg. 790

EQUITY RESIDENTIAL MANAGEMENT, L.L.C.—See Equity Residential; *U.S. Public*, pg. 792

ESSEX ANAVIA, L.P.—See Essex Property Trust, Inc.; *U.S. Public*, pg. 796

ESSEX BELLA VILLAGIO, L.P.—See Essex Property Trust, Inc.; *U.S. Public*, pg. 796

ESSEX BELLERIVE, L.P.—See Essex Property Trust, Inc.; *U.S. Public*, pg. 796

ESSEX BERNARD, L.P.—See Essex Property Trust, Inc.; *U.S. Public*, pg. 796

ESSEX BRIARWOOD, L.P.—See Essex Property Trust, Inc.; *U.S. Public*, pg. 796

ESSEX BRIDLE TRAILS, L.P.—See Essex Property Trust, Inc.; *U.S. Public*, pg. 796

ESSEX BRIGHTON RIDGE, L.P.—See Essex Property Trust, Inc.; *U.S. Public*, pg. 796

ESSEX CANYON OAKS APARTMENTS, L.P.—See Essex Property Trust, Inc.; *U.S. Public*, pg. 796

ESSEX CANYON POINTE, L.P.—See Essex Property Trust, Inc.; *U.S. Public*, pg. 796

ESSEX CARLYLE, L.P.—See Essex Property Trust, Inc.; *U.S. Public*, pg. 796

ESSEX DAVEY GLEN APARTMENTS, L.P.—See Essex Property Trust, Inc.; *U.S. Public*, pg. 796

ESSEX ESPLANADE, L.P.—See Essex Property Trust, Inc.; *U.S. Public*, pg. 796

ESSEX FAIRWOOD POND, L.P.—See Essex Property Trust, Inc.; *U.S. Public*, pg. 796

ESSEX FOUNTAIN PARK APARTMENTS, L.P.—See Essex Property Trust, Inc.; *U.S. Public*, pg. 796

ESSEX HUNTINGTON BREAKERS, L.P.—See Essex Property Trust, Inc.; *U.S. Public*, pg. 796

ESSEX INGLENOOK COURT, LLC—See Essex Property Trust, Inc.; *U.S. Public*, pg. 796

ESSEX KINGS ROAD, L.P.—See Essex Property Trust, Inc.; *U.S. Public*, pg. 796

ESSEX MARBRISA LONG BEACH, L.P.—See Essex Property Trust, Inc.; *U.S. Public*, pg. 796

ESSEX MARINA CITY CLUB, L.P.—See Essex Property Trust, Inc.; *U.S. Public*, pg. 796

ESSEX MONTEREY VILLAS, L.P.—See Essex Property Trust, Inc.; *U.S. Public*, pg. 796

ESSEX PARCWOOD APARTMENTS, L.P.—See Essex Property Trust, Inc.; *U.S. Public*, pg. 796

ESSEX REGENCY TOWER APARTMENTS, L.P.—See Essex Property Trust, Inc.; *U.S. Public*, pg. 796

ESSEX SAMMAMISH VIEW, L.P.—See Essex Property Trust, Inc.; *U.S. Public*, pg. 796

ESSEX SANTEE COURT, L.P.—See Essex Property Trust, Inc.; *U.S. Public*, pg. 796

ESSEX STONEHEDGE VILLAGE, L.P.—See Essex Property Trust, Inc.; *U.S. Public*, pg. 796

ESSEX SUMMERHILL PARK, L.P.—See Essex Property Trust, Inc.; *U.S. Public*, pg. 796

ESSEX THE COMMONS, L.P.—See Essex Property Trust, Inc.; *U.S. Public*, pg. 796

ESSEX THE POINTE, L.P.—See Essex Property Trust, Inc.; *U.S. Public*, pg. 796

ESSEX TIERRA VISTA, L.P.—See Essex Property Trust, Inc.; *U.S. Public*, pg. 796

ESSEX TOWNSHIP, L.P.—See Essex Property Trust, Inc.; *U.S. Public*, pg. 796

ESSEX VELO RAY, L.P.—See Essex Property Trust, Inc.; *U.S. Public*, pg. 796

ESSEX VISTA BELVEDERE, L.P.—See Essex Property Trust, Inc.; *U.S. Public*, pg. 796

ESSEX WANDERING CREEK, LLC—See Essex Property Trust, Inc.; *U.S. Public*, pg. 796

ESSEX WATERFORD, L.P.—See Essex Property Trust, Inc.; *U.S. Public*, pg. 796

ESSEX WHARFSIDE POINTE, L.P.—See Essex Property Trust, Inc.; *U.S. Public*, pg. 796

EUROBANK EFG EQUITIES INVESTMENT FIRM S.A.—See Eurobank Ergasias Services and Holdings S.A.; *Int'l*, pg. 2532

FAIRFAX SQUARE PARKING LLC—See Vornado Realty Trust; *U.S. Public*, pg. 2310

FALCON LAKES, LTD—See American Realty Investors, Inc.; *U.S. Public*, pg. 108

THE FARASH CORPORATION; *U.S. Private*, pg. 4027

FEDERAL CAPITAL PARTNERS; *U.S. Private*, pg. 1487

FEDERAL RESERVE BANK-SAN ANTONIO—See Federal Reserve Bank of Dallas; *U.S. Public*, pg. 825

FENALU GESTAO DE INVESTIMENTOS E PARTICIPACOES SA; *Int'l*, pg. 2633

FHB REAL ESTATE LEASING LTD.—See FHB Mortgage Bank Public Limited Company; *Int'l*, pg. 2650

FIDELITY DEVELOPMENT, INC.—See Fidelity Financial Corporation; *U.S. Private*, pg. 1503

FIDELITY MANAGEMENT CORPORATION—See Fidelity Financial Corporation; *U.S. Private*, pg. 1503

FILISTER ENTERPRISES; *U.S. Private*, pg. 1505

FINBAR TO RENT PTY. LTD.—See Finbar Group Limited; *Int'l*, pg. 2670

FINGER COMPANIES INC.; *U.S. Private*, pg. 1509

FIRST PLAZA INC.—See CV Industries Inc.; *U.S. Private*, pg. 1132

FISCHBACH & DOUGHERTY, INC.; *U.S. Private*, pg. 1532

FLAGSTONE APARTMENT PROPERTY, LLC—See Wells Fargo & Company; *U.S. Public*, pg. 2343

FLATS AT PALISADES LLC—See UDR, Inc.; *U.S. Public*, pg. 2218

FOOTHILL RIDGE APARTMENTS; *U.S. Private*, pg. 1562

FORESTAL, CONSTRUCTORA Y COMERCIAL DEL PACIFICO SUR S.A.; *Int'l*, pg. 2732

FOREST REALTY MANAGEMENT INC.; *U.S. Private*, pg. 1567

FORRENT, LLC—See CoStar Group, Inc.; *U.S. Public*, pg. 586

FOUR CORNERS PROPERTY TRUST, INC.; *U.S. Public*, pg. 875

FOUR SPRINGS CAPITAL TRUST; *U.S. Private*, pg. 1582

FOXBOROUGH LODGE LIMITED PARTNERSHIP—See UDR, Inc.; *U.S. Public*, pg. 2218

FOX RUN APARTMENTS, LTD.—See Apartment Investment and Management Company; *U.S. Public*, pg. 144

FRANKS EIENDOM AS—See Expro Group Holdings N.V.; *Int'l*, pg. 2591

FREEDOM MANAGEMENT; *U.S. Private*, pg. 1603

FREEDOM PLAZA LTD.; *U.S. Private*, pg. 1604

FRIENDS HOMES INC.; *U.S. Private*, pg. 1611

FRIENDSWOOD DEVELOPMENT COMPANY, LLC—See Lennar Corporation; *U.S. Public*, pg. 1306

FRIT SHOPS AT SUNSET PLACE, LLC—See Federal Realty Investment Trust; *U.S. Public*, pg. 825

FRIT SOLAR, INC.—See Federal Realty Investment Trust; *U.S. Public*, pg. 825

FRONTIER ADJUSTERS OF AMERICA, INC.—See Merrymeeting, Inc.; *U.S. Private*, pg. 2677

FUNDAMENTA ERTEKLANC INGATLANKOZVETITO ES SZOLGALTATO KFT.—See DZ BANK AG Deutsche Zentral-Genossenschaftsbank; *Int'l*, pg. 2244

FW IL-RIVERSIDE/RIVERS EDGE, LLC—See Regency Centers Corporation; *U.S. Public*, pg. 1774

GALESI GROUP—See Galesi Group; *U.S. Private*, pg. 1637

GATE MANOR APARTMENTS, LTD., A TENNESSEE LIMITED PARTNERSHIP—See Apartment Investment and Management Company; *U.S. Public*, pg. 144

GENERAL SERVICES CORPORATION (GSC); *U.S. Private*, pg. 1667

GEORGETOWN WOODS SENIOR APARTMENTS, L.P.—See Apartment Investment and Management Company; *U.S. Public*, pg. 144

GID INVESTMENT ADVISOR LLC; *U.S. Private*, pg. 1697

GLENVEAGH PROPERTIES PLC; *Int'l*, pg. 2992

GOTHAM APARTMENTS, LIMITED PARTNERSHIP—See Apartment Investment and Management Company; *U.S. Public*, pg. 144

GOTSE DELCHEV TABAC AD; *Int'l*, pg. 3044

GRANDCORP INC—See Grandparents.com, Inc.; *U.S. Private*, pg. 1754

GRAND TERRACE APARTMENTS CALIFORNIA, LLC—See RAIT Financial Trust; *U.S. Private*, pg. 3348

GREYWALL CLUB L.L.C.—See Lennar Corporation; *U.S. Public*, pg. 1306

GR-HIGHLAND GLEN, L.P.—See Equity Residential; *U.S. Public*, pg. 792

GRIFFIN PARTNERS CO.—See ASIAN STAR CO.; *Int'l*, pg. 619

GRUPE MANAGEMENT COMPANY—See Grupe Holding Company; *U.S. Private*, pg. 1797

GUARDIAN/KW HAYWARD LLC—See Kennedy-Wilson Holdings, Inc.; *U.S. Public*, pg. 1223

HABITAT BEAUJOLAIS VAL DE SAONE; *Int'l*, pg. 3203

HABITAT DU GARD; *Int'l*, pg. 3203

H.A. LANGER & ASSOCIATES; *U.S. Private*, pg. 1825

HANGZHOU BINJIANG REAL ESTATE GROUP CO., LTD.; *Int'l*, pg. 3246

HARSCH INVESTMENT CORP.; *U.S. Private*, pg. 1872

HARSCH INVESTMENT INC.—See Harsch Investment Corp.; *U.S. Private*, pg. 1872

HAVENWOOD-HERITAGE HEIGHTS RETIREMENT COMMUNITY; *U.S. Private*, pg. 1880

HAVERFORD PLACE APARTMENTS OWNER, LLC—See Independence Realty Trust, Inc.; *U.S. Public*, pg. 1115

HAWTHORNECOMMONSPLUS, LLC—See Welltower Inc.; *U.S. Public*, pg. 2348

HCN DOWNREIT MEMBER, LLC—See Welltower Inc.; *U.S. Public*, pg. 2348

HCN-REVERA LESSEE (ARNPRIOR VILLA) GP INC.—See Welltower Inc.; *U.S. Public*, pg. 2348

HCN-REVERA LESSEE (INGLEWOOD) LP—See Welltower Inc.; *U.S. Public*, pg. 2348

HCN-REVERA LESSEE (JARDINS DU COUVENT) LP—See Welltower Inc.; *U.S. Public*, pg. 2348

HCN-REVERA LESSEE (MANOIR LAFONTAINE) LP—See Welltower Inc.; *U.S. Public*, pg. 2348

HCN-REVERA LESSEE (MCKENZIE TOWNE) LP—See Welltower Inc.; *U.S. Public*, pg. 2348

HCN-REVERA LESSEE (RIVER RIDGE) GP INC.—See Welltower Inc.; *U.S. Public*, pg. 2348

HCN-REVERA LESSEE (SCENIC ACRES) GP INC.—See Welltower Inc.; *U.S. Public*, pg. 2348

HCN-REVERA LESSEE (THE CHURCHILL) GP INC.—See Welltower Inc.; *U.S. Public*, pg. 2348

HEALTHCARE REALTY SERVICES INCORPORATED—See Healthcare Realty Trust Incorporated; *U.S. Public*, pg. 1015

HEATHER CREEK APARTMENTS MESQUITE, LTD—See American Realty Investors, Inc.; *U.S. Public*, pg. 108

HEFEI URBAN CONSTRUCTION DEVEL CO., LTD.; *Int'l*, pg. 3308

HEIWA REAL ESTATE CO. LTD.; *Int'l*, pg. 3327

HEKTAR REAL ESTATE INVESTMENT TRUST; *Int'l*, pg. 3327

HELP USA INC.; *U.S. Private*, pg. 1912

HERITAGE TRACE APARTMENTS VIRGINIA, LLC—See RAIT Financial Trust; *U.S. Private*, pg. 3348

H.H. HUNT CORPORATION; *U.S. Private*, pg. 1826

HHHUNT PROPERTY MANAGEMENT, INC.; *U.S. Private*, pg. 1931

HIDEAWAY BAY MARINA, INC.—See Sun Communities, Inc.; *U.S. Public*, pg. 1963

HILLIARD GRAND APARTMENTS, LLC—See Independence Realty Trust, Inc.; *U.S. Public*, pg. 1115

HILLTOP GARDENS RETIREMENT VILLAGE LIMITED—See AX Investments PLC; *Int'l*, pg. 754

HLM DU COTENTIN; *Int'l*, pg. 3431

HM MANAGEMENT COMPANY INC; *U.S. Private*, pg. 1954

HOLIDAY RETIREMENT (CLEVEDON) LIMITED—See Welltower Inc.; *U.S. Public*, pg. 2348

HOMEAWAY PTY LTD—See Expedia Group, Inc.; *U.S. Public*, pg. 809

HOMEFED CORPORATION—See Jefferies Financial Group Inc.; *U.S. Public*, pg. 1188

HOME FORWARD; *U.S. Private*, pg. 1970

HOME IN SCOTLAND LIMITED—See Home Group Limited; *Int'l*, pg. 3454

HOME PROPERTIES CAMBRIDGE VILLAGE, LLC—See

531110 — LESSORS OF RESIDENT... CORPORATE AFFILIATIONS

N.A.I.C.S. Index

Lone Star Global Acquisitions, LLC; *U.S. Private*, pg. 2488
HOME PROPERTIES CHARLESTON, LLC—See Lone Star Global Acquisitions, LLC; *U.S. Private*, pg. 2488
HOME PROPERTIES CIDER MILL, LLC—See Lone Star Global Acquisitions, LLC; *U.S. Private*, pg. 2488
HOME PROPERTIES COUNTRY VILLAGE LLC—See Lone Star Global Acquisitions, LLC; *U.S. Private*, pg. 2488
HOME PROPERTIES CRESCENT CLUB, LLC—See Lone Star Global Acquisitions, LLC; *U.S. Private*, pg. 2488
HOME PROPERTIES DE WOODMONT, LLC—See Lone Star Global Acquisitions, LLC; *U.S. Private*, pg. 2488
HOME PROPERTIES FALCON CREST TOWNHOUSES, LLC—See Lone Star Global Acquisitions, LLC; *U.S. Private*, pg. 2488
HOME PROPERTIES FALKLAND CHASE, LLC—See Lone Star Global Acquisitions, LLC; *U.S. Private*, pg. 2488
HOME PROPERTIES HERITAGE SQUARE, LLC—See Lone Star Global Acquisitions, LLC; *U.S. Private*, pg. 2488
HOME PROPERTIES HOLIDAY SQUARE, LLC—See Lone Star Global Acquisitions, LLC; *U.S. Private*, pg. 2488
HOME PROPERTIES LAKE GROVE, LLC—See Lone Star Global Acquisitions, LLC; *U.S. Private*, pg. 2488
HOME PROPERTIES, L.P.—See Lone Star Global Acquisitions, LLC; *U.S. Private*, pg. 2488
HOME PROPERTIES MID-ISLAND, LLC—See Lone Star Global Acquisitions, LLC; *U.S. Private*, pg. 2488
HOME PROPERTIES MORNINGSIDE HEIGHTS LLC—See Lone Star Global Acquisitions, LLC; *U.S. Private*, pg. 2488
HOME PROPERTIES NEWPORT VILLAGE, LLC—See Lone Star Global Acquisitions, LLC; *U.S. Private*, pg. 2488
HOME PROPERTIES PLEASANT VIEW, LLC—See Lone Star Global Acquisitions, LLC; *U.S. Private*, pg. 2488
HOME PROPERTIES RIDGEVIEW AT WAKEFIELD VALLEY—See Lone Star Global Acquisitions, LLC; *U.S. Private*, pg. 2488
HOME PROPERTIES SAYVILLE, LLC—See Lone Star Global Acquisitions, LLC; *U.S. Private*, pg. 2488
HOME PROPERTIES SOUTH BAY MANOR, LLC—See Lone Star Global Acquisitions, LLC; *U.S. Private*, pg. 2488
HOME PROPERTIES TAMARRON, LLC—See Lone Star Global Acquisitions, LLC; *U.S. Private*, pg. 2488
HOME PROPERTIES TOPFIELD, LLC—See Lone Star Global Acquisitions, LLC; *U.S. Private*, pg. 2488
HOME PROPERTIES VILLAGE SQUARE, LLC—See Lone Star Global Acquisitions, LLC; *U.S. Private*, pg. 2488
HOME PROPERTIES WESTBROOKE, LLC—See Lone Star Global Acquisitions, LLC; *U.S. Private*, pg. 2488
HOME PROPERTIES WESTCHESTER WEST, LLC—See Lone Star Global Acquisitions, LLC; *U.S. Private*, pg. 2488
HOME PROPERTIES WOODHOLME MANOR, LLC—See Lone Star Global Acquisitions, LLC; *U.S. Private*, pg. 2488
HOME PROPERTIES WOODMONT VILLAGE, LLC—See Lone Star Global Acquisitions, LLC; *U.S. Private*, pg. 2488
HOME RENT SP. Z O.O.—See City Service SE; *Int'l*, pg. 1627
HORST PROPERTY MANAGEMENT—See The Horst Group Inc.; *U.S. Private*, pg. 4054
HOST HOTELS & RESORTS L.P.—See Host Hotels & Resorts, Inc.; *U.S. Public*, pg. 1055
HPI COLLIER PARK LLC—See Independence Realty Trust, Inc.; *U.S. Public*, pg. 1115
HPI HARTSHIRE LLC—See Independence Realty Trust, Inc.; *U.S. Public*, pg. 1115
HPI KENSINGTON COMMONS LLC—See Independence Realty Trust, Inc.; *U.S. Public*, pg. 1115
HPI RIVERCHASE LLC—See Independence Realty Trust, Inc.; *U.S. Public*, pg. 1115
HPI SCHIRM FARMS LLC—See Independence Realty Trust, Inc.; *U.S. Public*, pg. 1115
HUBER INVESTMENT CORPORATION; *U.S. Private*, pg. 2000
HUNT ENTERPRISES INC.; *U.S. Private*, pg. 2009
ID PROPERTY CO., LTD.—See Dear Life Co., Ltd.; *Int'l*, pg. 1998
IGD SIIQ S.P.A; *Int'l*, pg. 3602
INGLENOOK AT BRIGHTON; *U.S. Private*, pg. 2075
INGRAM SQUARE PRESERVATION, L.P.—See Apartment Investment and Management Company; *U.S. Public*, pg. 144
INLET BAY AT GATEWAY, LLC—See UDR, Inc.; *U.S. Public*, pg. 2218
INNOHUBS GMBH—See 3U Holding AG; *Int'l*, pg. 10
INTEGRATED PROPERTIES, INC.—See Apartment Investment and Management Company; *U.S. Public*, pg. 144
INTERGROUP CORPORATION; *U.S. Public*, pg. 1144
INTERGROUP MEADOWBROOK GARDENS, INC.—See InterGroup Corporation; *U.S. Public*, pg. 1144
INTERGROUP PINE LAKE, INC.—See InterGroup Corporation; *U.S. Public*, pg. 1144
INVESTORS MANAGEMENT TRUST REAL ESTATE GROUP INC.; *U.S. Private*, pg. 2132
IRET - VALLEY PARK MANOR, LLC—See Centerspace; *U.S. Public*, pg. 472
I'ROM PM CO., LTD.—See I'rom Group Co., Ltd.; *Int'l*, pg. 3562
IRONWOOD COURT, INC.—See Webster Financial Corporation; *U.S. Public*, pg. 2341
IRT LIVE OAK TRACE LOUISIANA, LLC—See Independence Realty Trust, Inc.; *U.S. Public*, pg. 1115
IRT STONEBRIDGE CROSSING APARTMENTS OWNER, LLC—See Independence Realty Trust, Inc.; *U.S. Public*, pg. 1115
IRT WATERFORD LANDING APARTMENTS, LLC—See Independence Realty Trust, Inc.; *U.S. Public*, pg. 1115
IRVINE APARTMENT COMMUNITIES INCORPORATED—See The Irvine Company Inc.; *U.S. Private*, pg. 4057
I STAY MANAGEMENT SDN. BHD.—See AME Elite Consortium Berhad; *Int'l*, pg. 420
IZENBERG APPRAISAL ASSOCIATES, INC.—See BBG Inc.; *U.S. Private*, pg. 498
IZTOK PARKSIDE EOOD—See Arco Vara AS; *Int'l*, pg. 550
JACKSON SCHOOL VILLAGE, L.P.—See Essex Property Trust, Inc.; *U.S. Public*, pg. 796
JACOB FORD VILLAGE, LLC—See Lone Star Global Acquisitions, LLC; *U.S. Private*, pg. 2488
JAMES BATMASIAN; *U.S. Private*, pg. 2183
JAMESTOWN CRA-B1, LLC—See Independence Realty Trust, Inc.; *U.S. Public*, pg. 1115
J. A. PETERSON ENTERPRISES; *U.S. Private*, pg. 2155
JEFFERSON AT MARINA DEL REY, L.P.—See UDR, Inc.; *U.S. Public*, pg. 2218
J&H ASSET PROPERTY MANAGEMENT INC.; *U.S. Private*, pg. 2154
K. HOVNANIAN ASPIRE AT APRICOT GROVE, LLC—See Hovnanian Enterprises, Inc.; *U.S. Public*, pg. 1056
K. HOVNANIAN ASPIRE AT PORT ST. LUCIE, LLC—See Hovnanian Enterprises, Inc.; *U.S. Public*, pg. 1056
K. HOVNANIAN ASPIRE AT STONES THROW, LLC—See Hovnanian Enterprises, Inc.; *U.S. Public*, pg. 1056
K. HOVNANIAN AT BELLEWOOD, LLC—See Hovnanian Enterprises, Inc.; *U.S. Public*, pg. 1058
K. HOVNANIAN AT COOPER'S LANDING, LLC—See Hovnanian Enterprises, Inc.; *U.S. Public*, pg. 1058
K. HOVNANIAN AT DORADO AT TWELVE BRIDGES, LLC—See Hovnanian Enterprises, Inc.; *U.S. Public*, pg. 1058
K. HOVNANIAN AT FIREFLY AT WINDING CREEK, LLC—See Hovnanian Enterprises, Inc.; *U.S. Public*, pg. 1058
K. HOVNANIAN AT FORK LANDING, LLC—See Hovnanian Enterprises, Inc.; *U.S. Public*, pg. 1058
K. HOVNANIAN AT GLEN OAKS, LLC—See Hovnanian Enterprises, Inc.; *U.S. Public*, pg. 1058
K. HOVNANIAN AT HARBOR'S EDGE AT BAYSIDE, LLC—See Hovnanian Enterprises, Inc.; *U.S. Public*, pg. 1059
K. HOVNANIAN AT LAUREL HILLS CROSSING, LLC—See Hovnanian Enterprises, Inc.; *U.S. Public*, pg. 1059
K. HOVNANIAN AT MCCARTNEY RANCH, LLC—See Hovnanian Enterprises, Inc.; *U.S. Public*, pg. 1059
K. HOVNANIAN AT SUN CITY WEST, LLC—See Hovnanian Enterprises, Inc.; *U.S. Public*, pg. 1059
K. HOVNANIAN AT TOWNSEND FIELDS, LLC—See Hovnanian Enterprises, Inc.; *U.S. Public*, pg. 1060
K. HOVNANIAN AT VICTORY AT VERRADO, LLC—See Hovnanian Enterprises, Inc.; *U.S. Public*, pg. 1060
K. HOVNANIAN DFW ASCEND AT JUSTIN CROSSING, LLC—See Hovnanian Enterprises, Inc.; *U.S. Public*, pg. 1056
K. HOVNANIAN HOMES AT SUMMIT POINTE, LLC—See Hovnanian Enterprises, Inc.; *U.S. Public*, pg. 1057
K. HOVNANIAN HOUSTON BALMORAL, LLC—See Hovnanian Enterprises, Inc.; *U.S. Public*, pg. 1057
K. HOVNANIAN HOUSTON ELDRIDGE PARK, LLC—See Hovnanian Enterprises, Inc.; *U.S. Public*, pg. 1057
K. HOVNANIAN HOUSTON LAKES OF BELLA TERRA WEST, LLC—See Hovnanian Enterprises, Inc.; *U.S. Public*, pg. 1057
K. HOVNANIAN HOUSTON SUNSET RANCH, LLC—See Hovnanian Enterprises, Inc.; *U.S. Public*, pg. 1057
K. HOVNANIAN HOUSTON TERRA DEL SOL, LLC—See Hovnanian Enterprises, Inc.; *U.S. Public*, pg. 1057
K. HOVNANIAN HOUSTON WESTWOOD, LLC—See Hovnanian Enterprises, Inc.; *U.S. Public*, pg. 1057
K. HOVNANIAN PRESERVE AT AVONLEA, LLC—See Hovnanian Enterprises, Inc.; *U.S. Public*, pg. 1058
KING'S LANDING LLC—See Independence Realty Trust, Inc.; *U.S. Public*, pg. 1115
KING TOWER INC.—See Harsch Investment Corp.; *U.S. Private*, pg. 1872
KINNICKINNIC REALTY CO.; *U.S. Private*, pg. 2313
KLEPIERRE MANAGEMENT MAGYARORSZAG KFT.—See BNP Paribas SA; *Int'l*, pg. 1091
KONOVER RESIDENTIAL CORPORATION—See The Simon Konover Company; *U.S. Private*, pg. 4118
K.P.A. COMPANY LIMITED—See China Financial Services Holdings Limited; *Int'l*, pg. 1503
KRG RIVERS EDGE, LLC—See Kite Realty Group Trust; *U.S. Public*, pg. 1236
KW CANTATA TRAIL, LLC—See Kennedy-Wilson Holdings, Inc.; *U.S. Public*, pg. 1223
THE LAFAYETTE DENVER, LLC—See Highlands REIT, Inc.; *U.S. Private*, pg. 1940
LAFAYETTE ENGLISH APARTMENTS, LP—See RAIT Financial Trust; *U.S. Private*, pg. 3349
LAKE CAMERON, LLC—See DRA Advisors LLC; *U.S. Private*, pg. 1271
LAKE CAMERON, LLC—See Fogelman Properties, LLC; *U.S. Private*, pg. 1557
LAKE FOREST AM, LTD—See American Realty Investors, Inc.; *U.S. Public*, pg. 108
LAKESIDE MILL LLC—See UDR, Inc.; *U.S. Public*, pg. 2218
LAKES OF NORTHDALE APARTMENTS LLC—See Independence Realty Trust, Inc.; *U.S. Public*, pg. 1115
LANDURA, LLC—See UFP Industries, Inc.; *U.S. Public*, pg. 2219
LASALLE FUNDS MANAGEMENT LIMITED—See Jones Lang LaSalle Incorporated; *U.S. Public*, pg. 1203
LEFRAK ORGANIZATION INC.; *U.S. Private*, pg. 2415
LEISURE CARE, INC.; *U.S. Private*, pg. 2420
LENNAR ARIZONA CONSTRUCTION, INC.—See Lennar Corporation; *U.S. Public*, pg. 1306
LENNAR HOMES OF TEXAS LAND AND CONSTRUCTION, LTD.—See Lennar Corporation; *U.S. Public*, pg. 1306
LENNAR MORTGAGE, LLC—See Lennar Corporation; *U.S. Public*, pg. 1306
LENNAR TITLE, INC.—See Lennar Corporation; *U.S. Public*, pg. 1306
LENNAR TITLE, LLC—See Lennar Corporation; *U.S. Public*, pg. 1306
LENOX FARMS LIMITED PARTNERSHIP—See UDR, Inc.; *U.S. Public*, pg. 2218
LEVINE MANAGEMENT GROUP INC.; *U.S. Private*, pg. 2436
LEWISBURG ASSOCIATES LIMITED PARTNERSHIP—See Apartment Investment and Management Company; *U.S. Public*, pg. 144
LEWIS-MCCHORD COMMUNITIES, LLC—See Equity Residential; *U.S. Public*, pg. 792
LEXINGTON KNOXVILLE LLC—See LXP Industrial Trust; *U.S. Public*, pg. 1349
LEX PHOENIX L.P.—See LXP Industrial Trust; *U.S. Public*, pg. 1349
LEX PROPERTIES INC.—See Davidson Health Care, Inc.; *U.S. Private*, pg. 1171
LIFE CARE SERVICES LLC—See LCS Holdings Inc.; *U.S. Private*, pg. 2404
LMF COMMERCIAL, LLC—See Lennar Corporation; *U.S. Public*, pg. 1306
LODGE AT AMES POND LIMITED PARTNERSHIP—See UDR, Inc.; *U.S. Public*, pg. 2218
LOFTS AT CHARLES RIVER LANDING, LLC—See UDR, Inc.; *U.S. Public*, pg. 2218
LONGVIEW PLACE, LLC—See Equity Residential; *U.S. Public*, pg. 792
LS DAVOL SQUARE, LLC—See Ventas, Inc.; *U.S. Public*, pg. 2278
LUCERNE APARTMENTS TAMPA, LLC—See Independence Realty Trust, Inc.; *U.S. Public*, pg. 1115
LUXURBAN HOTELS INC.; *U.S. Public*, pg. 1349
LV CHARRIERES LIMITED—See Aedifica SA; *Int'l*, pg. 173
MADISON APARTMENT GROUP, LP—See Equus Capital Partners, Ltd.; *U.S. Private*, pg. 1416
MAKAAN.COM PRIVATE LIMITED—See News Corporation; *U.S. Public*, pg. 1519
MALEK MANAGEMENT CORPORATION; *U.S. Private*, pg. 2557
MANCELLE D'HABITATION SA—See Groupe BPCE; *Int'l*, pg. 3094
MANDALAY OWNER TEXAS, LLC—See RAIT Financial Trust; *U.S. Private*, pg. 3349
MARTIN MODERN PTE. LTD.—See Hong Leong Investment Holdings Pte. Ltd.; *Int'l*, pg. 3468
MASON PARK, LTD—See American Realty Investors, Inc.; *U.S. Public*, pg. 108
MASTRO PROPERTIES; *U.S. Private*, pg. 2608
MCDOWELL MOUNTAIN ARIZONA, LLC—See RAIT Financial Trust; *U.S. Private*, pg. 3349
MCGRATH SALES PADDINGTON PTY LTD—See Bayleys Corporation Limited; *Int'l*, pg. 914
MCKEE GROUP REALTY, LLC; *U.S. Private*, pg. 2638
MCKINLEY ASSOCIATES INC.; *U.S. Private*, pg. 2638
MEADOWS CRA-B1, LLC—See Independence Realty Trust, Inc.; *U.S. Public*, pg. 1115
MEDICAL CARE DEVELOPMENT INC.; *U.S. Private*, pg. 2654
MEGAWORLD CORPORATION—See Alliance Global Group, Inc.; *Int'l*, pg. 339
MERIDIAN GROUP INC.; *U.S. Private*, pg. 2673
MESIROW REALTY SERVICES, INC.—See Mesirow Financial Holdings, Inc.; *U.S. Private*, pg. 2679
METRO PARK I, L.L.C.—See Blackstone Inc.; *U.S. Public*, pg. 356
MEYER MANSION PTE. LTD.—See Hong Leong Invest-

N.A.I.C.S. INDEX

531110 — LESSORS OF RESIDENT...

ment Holdings Pte. Ltd.; *Int'l*, pg. 3468
MGM GROWTH PROPERTIES OPERATING PARTNERSHIP LP—See VICI Properties Inc.; *U.S. Public*, pg. 2295
MIAMI INTERNATIONAL COMMERCE CENTER—See Blackstone Inc.; *U.S. Public*, pg. 356
MICHAELS MILITARY HOUSING, LLC—See The Michael's Development Company Inc.; *U.S. Private*, pg. 4079
MID-AMERICA APARTMENTS, L.P.—See Mid-America Apartment Communities, Inc.; *U.S. Public*, pg. 1444
MIDBORO MANAGEMENT, INC.—See FirstService Corporation; *Int'l*, pg. 2691
MIDTOWN BAY PTE. LTD.—See Hong Leong Investment Holdings Pte. Ltd.; *Int'l*, pg. 3468
MIDWEST REAL ESTATE DEVELOPMENT; *U.S. Private*, pg. 2723
MILESTONE MANAGEMENT—See Olympus Real Estate Corp.; *U.S. Private*, pg. 3014
MILLENIA 700, LLC—See Independence Realty Trust, Inc.; *U.S. Public*, pg. 1115
MISSISSIPPI METHODIST SENIOR SERVICES; *U.S. Private*, pg. 2748
MONACO NORTH URBAN RENEWAL L.L.C.—See Veris Residential, Inc.; *U.S. Public*, pg. 2281
MONTICELLO MANOR, LTD.—See Apartment Investment and Management Company; *U.S. Public*, pg. 144
MORTGAGE INVESTMENT CORPORATION; *U.S. Private*, pg. 2791
M & P DEVELOPMENT COMPANY—See Apartment Investment and Management Company; *U.S. Public*, pg. 144
MUNSON HILL TOWERS, L.L.C.—See Elme Communities; *U.S. Public*, pg. 735
MURPHEY TAYLOR AND ELLIS INC.; *U.S. Private*, pg. 2815
MYND PROPERTY MANAGEMENT, INC.; *U.S. Private*, pg. 2825
NATH MANAGEMENT INC—See Nath Companies Incorporated; *U.S. Private*, pg. 2838
NC MAX WORLD CO., LTD.—See Fantasista Co., Ltd.; *Int'l*, pg. 2614
NESTAWAY TECHNOLOGIES PRIVATE LIMITED—See Aurum PropTech Ltd.; *Int'l*, pg. 715
NEW ENGLAND REALTY ASSOCIATES LIMITED PARTNERSHIP; *U.S. Public*, pg. 1511
NIC 15 KIRKWOOD CORNERS LEASING LLC—See Ventas, Inc.; *U.S. Public*, pg. 2278
NIC 15 PINES OF NEW MARKET LEASING LLC—See Ventas, Inc.; *U.S. Public*, pg. 2278
NIC 20 GRAND VIEW LEASING LLC—See Ventas, Inc.; *U.S. Public*, pg. 2278
OH FRIENDLY VILLAGE, LLC—See UMH Properties, Inc.; *U.S. Public*, pg. 2224
OHIO PRESBYTERIAN RETIREMENT SERVICE; *U.S. Private*, pg. 3005
OH MEADOWS OF PERRYSBURG, LLC—See UMH Properties, Inc.; *U.S. Public*, pg. 2224
OH PERRYSBURG ESTATES, LLC—See UMH Properties, Inc.; *U.S. Public*, pg. 2224
OH PIKEWOOD MANOR, LLC—See UMH Properties, Inc.; *U.S. Public*, pg. 2225
OKABE NORTH AMERICA, INC.—See APA Holdings Co., Ltd.; *Int'l*, pg. 500
ONE CRANS-MONTANA SA—See CPI Property Group, S.A.; *Int'l*, pg. 1825
ORLANDO LUTHERAN TOWERS; *U.S. Private*, pg. 3044
OXFORD REALTY FINANCIAL GROUP; *U.S. Private*, pg. 3057
OXMOOR CRA-B1, LLC—See Independence Realty Trust, Inc.; *U.S. Public*, pg. 1116
OYSTER POINT APARTMENTS VIRGINIA, LLC—See RAIT Financial Trust; *U.S. Private*, pg. 3349
PAC PARKSIDE AT THE BEACH, LLC—See Blackstone Inc.; *U.S. Public*, pg. 351
PALMETTO RESIDENTIAL RENTALS, LLC—See Berkshire Hathaway Inc.; *U.S. Public*, pg. 304
PALMS AT PECCOLE RANCH—See Kennedy-Wilson Holdings, Inc.; *U.S. Public*, pg. 1223
PALOMA SUMMIT APARTMENTS—See Sequoia Equities Inc.; *U.S. Private*, pg. 3612
PAN-AM EQUITIES, INC.; *U.S. Private*, pg. 3084
PANORAMA; *U.S. Private*, pg. 3087
PARC AT MAUMELLE, LP—See American Realty Investors, Inc.; *U.S. Public*, pg. 109
PARC AT METRO CENTER, LP—See American Realty Investors, Inc.; *U.S. Public*, pg. 109
PARC AT ROGERS, LP—See American Realty Investors, Inc.; *U.S. Public*, pg. 109
PARK HAVEN APARTMENTS; *U.S. Private*, pg. 3096
PEPPERTREE VILLAGE OF AVON PARK, LIMITED—See Apartment Investment and Management Company; *U.S. Public*, pg. 144
PERLEN IMMOBILIEN AG—See CPH Chemie + Papier Holding AG; *Int'l*, pg. 1824
PHOENIX AT AVONDALE APARTMENTS—See Olympus Real Estate Corp.; *U.S. Private*, pg. 3014
PINEWOOD PARK APARTMENTS, A LIMITED PARTNERSHIP—See Apartment Investment and Management Company; *U.S. Public*, pg. 144

PLAZA PROPERTIES INC.; *U.S. Private*, pg. 3213
POINTE AT CANYON RIDGE, LLC—See Independence Realty Trust, Inc.; *U.S. Public*, pg. 1116
POINTE EAST CONDOMINIUM, LLC—See Equity Residential; *U.S. Public*, pg. 792
PORTMAN SQUARE PROPERTIES LIMITED—See Great Portland Estates Plc; *Int'l*, pg. 3065
POST SOUTH END, L.P.—See Mid-America Apartment Communities, Inc.; *U.S. Public*, pg. 1445
PREMIER SUPPLY CHAIN IMPROVEMENT, INC.—See Premier, Inc.; *U.S. Public*, pg. 1715
PRESBYTERIAN HOMES INC.; *U.S. Private*, pg. 3253
PRESBYTERIAN RETIREMENT COMMUNITIES NORTHWEST; *U.S. Private*, pg. 3253
PRESTON LAKE REALTY—See Presidential Realty Corporation; *U.S. Public*, pg. 1716
PROMENADE PLACE, LLC—See Veritex Holdings, Inc.; *U.S. Public*, pg. 2283
PROPERTY RESOURCES CORP.; *U.S. Private*, pg. 3285
PROSPECT PARK CRA-B1, LLC—See Independence Realty Trust, Inc.; *U.S. Public*, pg. 1116
PT KENCANA UNGGUL SUKSES—See Agung Podomoro Land Tbk; *Int'l*, pg. 222
QUANTUM MANAGEMENT SERVICES, INC.—See Hoban & Associates, Llc; *U.S. Private*, pg. 1958
QUEEN'S ENTERPRISES LTD. INC.—See HTH Corporation; *U.S. Private*, pg. 1999
RAAMCO INTERNATIONAL INCORPORATED; *U.S. Private*, pg. 3341
RAINTREE VILLAGE, L.L.C.—See Lennar Corporation; *U.S. Public*, pg. 1307
RANCHO VIEJO PROPERTIES—See Pinnacle West Capital Corporation; *U.S. Public*, pg. 1692
THE RANDALL GROUP INC.; *U.S. Private*, pg. 4102
RE/MAX ONTARIO-ATLANTIC CANADA, INC.—See RE/MAX Holdings, Inc.; *U.S. Public*, pg. 1768
RENT SOLUTIONS; *U.S. Private*, pg. 3400
RENTWERX, LLC; *U.S. Private*, pg. 3400
RESIDENCE BELGICKA, S.R.O.—See CPI Property Group, S.A.; *Int'l*, pg. 1825
RESIDENCE DU MARCHE INC.—See Ventas, Inc.; *U.S. Public*, pg. 2278
RESIDENCE IZABELLA, ZRT.—See CPI Property Group, S.A.; *Int'l*, pg. 1825
RESIDENTIAL INSURANCE AGENCY, LLC—See Equity Residential; *U.S. Public*, pg. 792
R. FRIEDRICH & SONS INC.; *U.S. Private*, pg. 3333
RICHLAND PROPERTIES INC.; *U.S. Private*, pg. 3430
RIPPON HOMES LIMITED—See Artisan (UK) plc; *Int'l*, pg. 584
RIVER POINTE (DE), LLC—See Greystar Real Estate Partners, LLC; *U.S. Private*, pg. 1785
ROCHDALE VILLAGE INC.; *U.S. Private*, pg. 3463
RODGERS FORGE CONDOMINIUMS, INC.—See UDR, Inc.; *U.S. Public*, pg. 2218
ROOM BANK INSURE., LTD.—See Good Com Asset Co., Ltd.; *Int'l*, pg. 3038
ROYAL AMERICAN MANAGEMENT, INC.; *U.S. Private*, pg. 3491
ROYAL PALMS SENIOR RESIDENCE; *U.S. Private*, pg. 3493
R+V ALLGEMEINE VERSICHERUNG AKTIENGESELLSCHAFT—See DZ BANK AG Deutsche Zentral-Genossenschaftsbank; *Int'l*, pg. 2244
SAFEGARD MINI STORAGE, LLC—See National Storage Affiliates Trust; *U.S. Public*, pg. 1498
SAINT BERNARD PROPERTIES COMPANY LLC—See Valero Energy Corporation; *U.S. Public*, pg. 2272
SAN CAMILLO INC.; *U.S. Private*, pg. 3539
SANDSTONE CREEK, LLC—See Blackstone Inc.; *U.S. Public*, pg. 351
SAUGUS AVALON RETAIL, LLC—See AvalonBay Communities, Inc.; *U.S. Public*, pg. 240
SAVOYE LLC—See UDR, Inc.; *U.S. Public*, pg. 2218
SCHOOL STREET ASSOCIATES LIMITED PARTNERSHIP—See Boston Properties, Inc.; *U.S. Public*, pg. 373
SEAVIEW SUMMIT APARTMENTS—See Sequoia Equities Inc.; *U.S. Private*, pg. 3612
SECURCARE SELF STORAGE, INC.—See National Storage Affiliates Trust; *U.S. Public*, pg. 1498
SEGALL BRYANT & HAMILL LLC—See Thoma Bravo, L.P.; *U.S. Private*, pg. 4153
SEQUOIA EQUITIES INC.; *U.S. Private*, pg. 3612
SEVEN KINGS HOLDINGS, INC.; *U.S. Private*, pg. 3618
SHK MANAGEMENT INC.; *U.S. Private*, pg. 3638
SILVER CITY HOUSING LP—See Edison International; *U.S. Public*, pg. 719
SIMPSON PROPERTY GROUP, LP—See Simpson Housing Limited Partnership; *U.S. Private*, pg. 3668
SIMSBURY ASSOCIATES INC.; *U.S. Private*, pg. 3669
SKYVIEW OWNERS CORPORATION; *U.S. Private*, pg. 3686
SLG IRP REALTY LLC—See SL Green Realty Corp.; *U.S. Public*, pg. 1894
SMITH MANAGEMENT CO., INC.; *U.S. Private*, pg. 3695
SOCIETE NATIONALE IMMOBILIERE—See Caisse des Depots et Consignations; *Int'l*, pg. 1258

SO HUDSON 555 MANAGEMENT, INC.—See Vornado Realty Trust; *U.S. Public*, pg. 2310
SOUTH STREET SEAPORT LIMITED PARTNERSHIP—See Howard Hughes Holdings Inc.; *U.S. Public*, pg. 1060
SPACE CENTER, INC.—See Helmerich & Payne, Inc.; *U.S. Public*, pg. 1024
SPOKANE UNITED METHODIST HOMES; *U.S. Private*, pg. 3760
SPT WAH WELLINGTON LLC—See Starwood Property Trust, Inc.; *U.S. Public*, pg. 1940
SRHI LLC—See D.R. Horton, Inc.; *U.S. Public*, pg. 620
STAG MEBANE 1, LLC—See STAG Industrial, Inc.; *U.S. Public*, pg. 1925
STAG READING, LLC—See STAG Industrial, Inc.; *U.S. Public*, pg. 1925
ST. BARNABAS INC.; *U.S. Private*, pg. 3770
STERLING HOUSING LLC; *U.S. Private*, pg. 3805
STESSA, INC.—See Roofstock, Inc.; *U.S. Private*, pg. 3479
STONE CREEK APARTMENTS COLORADO, LLC—See RAIT Financial Trust; *U.S. Private*, pg. 3349
STONERIDGE FARMS HUNT CLUB, LLC—See Blackstone Inc.; *U.S. Public*, pg. 351
STONERIDGE - PRESCOTT VALLEY LLC—See Pinnacle West Capital Corporation; *U.S. Public*, pg. 1692
STOREY PARK CLUB, LLC—See Lennar Corporation; *U.S. Public*, pg. 1307
STRATA PROPERTIES, LLC—See UDR, Inc.; *U.S. Public*, pg. 2218
STRATEGIC HOLDINGS, INC.—See Lennar Corporation; *U.S. Public*, pg. 1307
SUMAR REALTORS; *U.S. Private*, pg. 3852
SURU HOMES LTD—See Haldane McCall PLC; *Int'l*, pg. 3227
SUSSEX HALL APARTMENTS—See Revona Properties; *U.S. Private*, pg. 3417
TABERNA CAPITAL MANAGEMENT, LLC—See RAIT Financial Trust; *U.S. Private*, pg. 3349
TANGLEWOOD PARK—See Peabody Properties, Inc.; *U.S. Private*, pg. 3122
TCC PROPERTIES INC.; *U.S. Private*, pg. 3942
TENPO RYUTSUU NET, INC.—See Hurxley Corporation; *Int'l*, pg. 3538
TICON, INC.; *U.S. Private*, pg. 4167
TIDES AT CALABASH NORTH CAROLINA, LLC—See Independence Realty Trust, Inc.; *U.S. Public*, pg. 1116
TIMES SQUARE PROPERTIES; *U.S. Private*, pg. 4172
TOLL BROTHERS CANADA USA, INC.—See Toll Brothers, Inc.; *U.S. Public*, pg. 2162
TOWERVIEW, LLC—See COPT Defense Properties; *U.S. Public*, pg. 575
TOWN CENTER SELF STORAGE, LLC—See National Storage Affiliates Trust; *U.S. Public*, pg. 1498
TOWN SQUARE COMMONS, LLC—See UDR, Inc.; *U.S. Public*, pg. 2218
TOWSON PROMENADE, LLC—See UDR, Inc.; *U.S. Public*, pg. 2218
TRAILS AT NORTHPOINT MISSISSIPPI MEMBER, LLC—See RAIT Financial Trust; *U.S. Private*, pg. 3349
TRAMMELL CROW SERVICES, INC.—See CBRE Group, Inc.; *U.S. Public*, pg. 460
TRANSCON BUILDERS INC.; *U.S. Private*, pg. 4207
TRC PINNACLE TOWERS, L.L.C.—See COPT Defense Properties; *U.S. Public*, pg. 575
TREASURE ISLAND RESORT FLORIDA, LLC—See RAIT Financial Trust; *U.S. Private*, pg. 3349
TRESA AT ARROWHEAD ARIZONA, LLC—See RAIT Financial Trust; *U.S. Private*, pg. 3349
TRI CITY RENTAL; *U.S. Private*, pg. 4220
TRUMP PALACE—See The Trump Organization, Inc.; *U.S. Private*, pg. 4128
TS BIG CREEK, LLC—See Independence Realty Trust, Inc.; *U.S. Public*, pg. 1116
TS BRIER CREEK, LLC—See Independence Realty Trust, Inc.; *U.S. Public*, pg. 1116
TS CRAIG RANCH, LLC—See Independence Realty Trust, Inc.; *U.S. Public*, pg. 1116
TS CREEKSTONE, LLC—See Independence Realty Trust, Inc.; *U.S. Public*, pg. 1116
TS GOOSECREEK, LLC—See Independence Realty Trust, Inc.; *U.S. Public*, pg. 1116
TS MILLER CREEK, LLC—See Independence Realty Trust, Inc.; *U.S. Public*, pg. 1116
TS TALISON ROW, LLC—See Independence Realty Trust, Inc.; *U.S. Public*, pg. 1116
TS WESTMONT, LLC—See Independence Realty Trust, Inc.; *U.S. Public*, pg. 1116
TUSCANY BAY APARTMENTS FLORIDA, LLC—See RAIT Financial Trust; *U.S. Private*, pg. 3349
TWO FREEDOM SQUARE, L.L.C.—See Boston Properties, Inc.; *U.S. Public*, pg. 373
UDR BRIO LLC—See UDR, Inc.; *U.S. Public*, pg. 2218
UDR CANAL I LLC—See UDR, Inc.; *U.S. Public*, pg. 2218
UDR CANTERBURY LLC—See UDR, Inc.; *U.S. Public*, pg. 2218
UDR COOL SPRINGS I LLC—See UDR, Inc.; *U.S. Public*, pg. 2218

531110 — LESSORS OF RESIDENT...

UDR CURRENTS ON THE CHARLES LLC—See UDR, Inc.; *U.S. Public*, pg. 2218
UDR INWOOD LLC—See UDR, Inc.; *U.S. Public*, pg. 2218
UDR LEONARD POINTE LLC—See UDR, Inc.; *U.S. Public*, pg. 2218
UDR PERIDOT PALMS LLC—See UDR, Inc.; *U.S. Public*, pg. 2218
UDR PRESERVE AT GATEWAY LLC—See UDR, Inc.; *U.S. Public*, pg. 2218
UDR PRESIDENTIAL GREENS, L.L.C.—See UDR, Inc.; *U.S. Public*, pg. 2218
UDR SMITH LLC—See UDR, Inc.; *U.S. Public*, pg. 2218
UDR UNION PLACE LLC—See UDR, Inc.; *U.S. Public*, pg. 2218
UMB UNTERNEHMENS-MANAGEMENTBERATUNGS GMBH—See DZ BANK AG Deutsche Zentral-Genossenschaftsbank; *Int'l*, pg. 2245
UMH IN SUMMIT VILLAGE, LLC—See UMH Properties, Inc.; *U.S. Public*, pg. 2225
UMH MI NORTHTOWNE MEADOWS, LLC—See UMH Properties, Inc.; *U.S. Public*, pg. 2225
UMH PA HIGHLAND ESTATES. LLC—See UMH Properties, Inc.; *U.S. Public*, pg. 2225
UNION HILL APARTMENTS, L.P.—See Synovus Financial Corp.; *U.S. Public*, pg. 1971
UNION HILL APARTMENTS, L.P.—See Synovus Financial Corp.; *U.S. Public*, pg. 1972
UNION MEADOWS ASSOCIATES LLC—See Edison International; *U.S. Public*, pg. 719
UNION PROPERTIES PJSC—See Emirates NBD PJSC; *Int'l*, pg. 2382
THE UNIT SERVICED APARTMENTS LIMITED—See Emperor International Holdings Limited; *Int'l*, pg. 2386
UNIVERSITY VILLAGE TOWERS, LLC—See Greystar Real Estate Partners, LLC; *U.S. Private*, pg. 1785
UNIVESCO INC.; *U.S. Private*, pg. 4310
URBAN EDGE CAGUAS LP—See URBAN EDGE PROPERTIES; *U.S. Public*, pg. 2265
US SUITES OF SAN DIEGO INC.—See The Armco Group Inc.; *U.S. Private*, pg. 3988
US SUITES OF SEATTLE INC.—See The Armco Group Inc.; *U.S. Private*, pg. 3988
VACATION PALM SPRINGS REAL ESTATE, INC.—See Travel & Leisure Co.; *U.S. Public*, pg. 2185
VAIL BEAVER CREEK RESORT PROPERTIES INC.—See Vail Resorts, Inc.; *U.S. Public*, pg. 2271
VAN NUYS APARTMENTS—See Apartment Investment and Management Company; *U.S. Public*, pg. 144
VENTAS AMBERLEIGH, LLC—See Ventas, Inc.; *U.S. Public*, pg. 2279
VERDES DEL ORIENTE PRESERVATION, L.P.—See Apartment Investment and Management Company; *U.S. Public*, pg. 144
VERIS RESIDENTIAL, INC.; *U.S. Public*, pg. 2281
VILLA ANGELINA APARTMENT FUND, LTD—See Essex Property Trust, Inc.; *U.S. Public*, pg. 796
VILLA AT SAN MATEO—See LCS Holdings Inc.; *U.S. Private*, pg. 2404
VILLAS VALRICHE RESORTS LTD.—See ENL Limited; *Int'l*, pg. 2442
VISTA LAGO CONDOS, LLC—See RAIT Financial Trust; *U.S. Private*, pg. 3349
VISTAS OF VANCE JACKSON, LTD—See American Realty Investors, Inc.; *U.S. Public*, pg. 109
WALNUT HILLS PRESERVATION, L.P.—See Apartment Investment and Management Company; *U.S. Public*, pg. 144
WARREN PROPERTIES, INC.; *U.S. Private*, pg. 4444
WASCO ARMS—See Apartment Investment and Management Company; *U.S. Public*, pg. 144
WATERSIDE TOWERS, L.L.C.—See UDR, Inc.; *U.S. Public*, pg. 2218
WATERVIEW AT HANOVER, LLC—See Lennar Corporation; *U.S. Public*, pg. 1307
WESTERN RIM PROPERTY SERVICES; *U.S. Private*, pg. 4496
WESTLAKE ASSOCIATES INC.; *U.S. Private*, pg. 4498
WESTMINSTER MANAGEMENT—See Kushner Companies; *U.S. Private*, pg. 2358
WESTMINSTER VILLAGE, INC.; *U.S. Private*, pg. 4499
WESTSIDE RENTALS, LLC—See CoStar Group, Inc.; *U.S. Public*, pg. 586
WHETSTONE COMPANY; *U.S. Private*, pg. 4506
WHISPERING WOODS LLC—See Deutsche Bank Aktiengesellschaft; *Int'l*, pg. 2062
WILDFLOWER VILLAS, LTD—See American Realty Investors, Inc.; *U.S. Public*, pg. 109
WILKES TOWERS LIMITED PARTNERSHIP—See Apartment Investment and Management Company; *U.S. Public*, pg. 144
WILLOW CREEK APARTMENTS INVESTOR, LLC—See RAIT Financial Trust; *U.S. Private*, pg. 3349
WINDEMERE AT SYCAMORE HIGHLANDS, LLC—See UDR, Inc.; *U.S. Public*, pg. 2218
WINRIDGE APARTMENTS—See Deutsche Bank Aktiengesellschaft; *Int'l*, pg. 2058
WINTER GARDEN PRESERVATION, L.P.—See Apartment Investment and Management Company; *U.S. Public*, pg. 144
WIRTZ REALTY CORPORATION—See Wirtz Corporation; *U.S. Public*, pg. 4547
WOODBINE PROPERTIES—See Equity Residential; *U.S. Public*, pg. 792
WORLD REAL ESTATE S.R.L.—See Atlas Estates Limited; *Int'l*, pg. 685
WORLD-WIDE HOLDINGS CORP.; *U.S. Private*, pg. 4568
W. P. CAREY EQUITY INVESTMENT MANAGEMENT (SHANGHAI) CO., LTD.—See W.P. Carey Inc.; *U.S. Public*, pg. 2316
WPC MAN-STRASSE 1 GMBH—See W.P. Carey Inc.; *U.S. Public*, pg. 2316

531120 — LESSORS OF NONRESIDENTIAL BUILDINGS (EXCEPT MINIWAREHOUSES)

3L ENTRANCE, INC.—See Apaman Co., Ltd.; *Int'l*, pg. 500
518 PROPERTY MANAGEMENT AND LEASING, LLC—See State Automobile Mutual Insurance Company; *U.S. Private*, pg. 3791
7 WEST 34TH STREET LLC—See Vornado Realty Trust; *U.S. Public*, pg. 2310
ACCIONA APARCAMIENTOS, S.L.—See Acciona, S.A.; *Int'l*, pg. 90
ADAPTEO OYJ; *Int'l*, pg. 125
AEON INTEGRATED BUSINESS SERVICE CO., LTD—See AEON Co., Ltd.; *Int'l*, pg. 176
AEON MALL CO., LTD.—See AEON Co., Ltd.; *Int'l*, pg. 177
AFBA - THE 5 STAR ASSOCIATION; *U.S. Private*, pg. 121
AFFINE S.A.; *Int'l*, pg. 186
AGS FINANCIAL CORPORATION—See A.G. Spanos Companies; *U.S. Private*, pg. 26
AIRPORT FACILITIES CO., LTD.; *Int'l*, pg. 248
ALAMANCE CROSSING, LLC—See CBL & Associates Properties, Inc.; *U.S. Public*, pg. 457
AL-'AQAR HEALTHCARE REIT; *Int'l*, pg. 283
ALCOM SA TIMISOARA; *Int'l*, pg. 302
ALLEE-CENTER HAMM KG—See Deutsche EuroShop AG; *Int'l*, pg. 2065
ALLEN DANIEL ASSOCIATES INC.; *U.S. Private*, pg. 178
ALLIED REALTY COMPANY; *U.S. Private*, pg. 187
ALL-PHASE ELECTRIC SUPPLY CO.—See Blackfriars Corp.; *U.S. Private*, pg. 574
ALMEDA MALL, INC.—See Buchanan Street Partners, Inc.; *U.S. Private*, pg. 676
AMANAH HARTA TANAH PNB; *Int'l*, pg. 409
AMANDA STORESENTER AS—See BNP Paribas SA; *Int'l*, pg. 1079
AMBASE CORPORATION; *U.S. Public*, pg. 92
AMC, INC.—See Blackstone Inc.; *U.S. Public*, pg. 350
AMERICAN INTERNATIONAL REALTY CORP.—See American International Group, Inc.; *U.S. Public*, pg. 106
ANCHOR COMMERCIAL REALTY CORP.; *U.S. Private*, pg. 272
ANGROPREDUZECE D.D.; *Int'l*, pg. 463
ANIMAS VALLEY MALL, LLC—See Brookfield Corporation; *Int'l*, pg. 1185
AOC TRANSPORT, INC.—See Getty Realty Corp.; *U.S. Public*, pg. 935
ARBORETUM MALL, LLC—See Washington Prime Group Inc.; *U.S. Private*, pg. 4448
ARBOR WALK MALL, LLC—See Washington Prime Group Inc.; *U.S. Private*, pg. 4448
ARIZONA MILLS—See Simon Property Group, Inc.; *U.S. Public*, pg. 1882
ARKADY WROCLAWSKIE S.A.—See Develia S.A.; *Int'l*, pg. 2087
ARROWHEAD TOWNE CENTER LLC—See The Macerich Company; *U.S. Public*, pg. 2109
ARTSPACE PROJECTS INC; *U.S. Public*, pg. 344
ARUNDEL MILLS—See Simon Property Group, Inc.; *U.S. Public*, pg. 1882
ATKINSON INVESTMENT CORPORATION—See Dilmar Oil Company Inc.; *U.S. Private*, pg. 1232
ATLANTIC INVESTMENT COMPANY; *U.S. Private*, pg. 373
ATRIA MANAGEMENT CANADA, ULC—See Ventas, Inc.; *U.S. Public*, pg. 2278
ATRIUM MALL LLC—See Winthrop Realty Liquidating Trust; *U.S. Public*, pg. 2374
ATWOOD ENTERPRISES INC.; *U.S. Private*, pg. 384
THE AVENUE AT WHITE MARSH BUSINESS TRUST—See Federal Realty Investment Trust; *U.S. Public*, pg. 826
AVR REALTY COMPANY, LLC; *U.S. Private*, pg. 410
A.W. PERRY INC.; *U.S. Private*, pg. 29
AZLE ANTIQUE MALL; *U.S. Private*, pg. 415
BAILEY PROPERTIES LLC; *U.S. Private*, pg. 426
BAILIAN NANQIAO SHOPPING MALL—See Bailian Group Co., Ltd.; *Int'l*, pg. 802
BAILIAN OUTLETS PLAZA—See Bailian Group Co., Ltd.; *Int'l*, pg. 802
BAILIAN YOUYICHENG SHOPPING MALL—See Bailian Group Co., Ltd.; *Int'l*, pg. 802
BAL HARBOUR SHOPS, LLLP; *U.S. Private*, pg. 457
BALLYVESEY HOLDINGS POLSKA LTD—See Ballyvesey Holdings Limited; *Int'l*, pg. 809
BALTIMORE SYMPHONY ORCHESTRA; *U.S. Private*, pg. 463
BAOJI SHOPPING MALL CO., LTD—See Hainan Traffic Administration Holding Co., Ltd.; *Int'l*, pg. 3213
BARCLAYS GROUP PROPERTY SERVICES—See Barclays PLC; *Int'l*, pg. 860
BARRINGTON DEVELOPMENT CORP.; *U.S. Private*, pg. 480
BARRISTER EXECUTIVE SUITES; *U.S. Private*, pg. 480
BAY SHORE MALL, LP—See Brookfield Corporation; *Int'l*, pg. 1185
BECK PROPERTIES INC.; *U.S. Private*, pg. 510
BEIJING HOMYEAR CAPITAL HOLDINGS CO., LTD.; *Int'l*, pg. 951
BEIJING HUALIAN DEPARTMENT STORE CO., LTD.; *Int'l*, pg. 952
BELGER REALTY CO. INC.—See Belcorp Inc.; *U.S. Private*, pg. 517
BELVEDERE CORPORATION; *U.S. Private*, pg. 521
BELZ ENTERPRISES; *U.S. Private*, pg. 522
THE BENCHMARK FINANCIAL GROUP; *U.S. Private*, pg. 3993
BENTALL KENNEDY RETAIL SERVICES LP—See Bentall Kennedy LP; *Int'l*, pg. 975
BERJAYA TIMES SQUARE SDN. BHD.—See Berjaya Assets Berhad; *Int'l*, pg. 981
BERTHEL FISHER & CO. MANAGEMENT CORP.—See Berthel Fisher & Company Inc.; *U.S. Private*, pg. 539
BIG SHOPPING CENTERS LTD.; *Int'l*, pg. 1021
BKS IMMOBILIEN-SERVICE GESELLSCHAFT MBH—See Bank fur Tirol und Vorarlberg Ag; *Int'l*, pg. 838
BKS ZENTRALE-ERRICHTUNGS- U. VERMIETUNGSGESELLSCHAFT MBH—See Bank fur Tirol und Vorarlberg Ag; *Int'l*, pg. 838
BLDG MANAGEMENT INC.; *U.S. Private*, pg. 580
BOE LAND CO., LTD.—See BOE Technology Group Co., Ltd.; *Int'l*, pg. 1099
BOSTON WHARF COMPANY—See Dubai World Corporation; *Int'l*, pg. 2220
BOWEN BUILDING, L.P.—See Vornado Realty Trust; *U.S. Public*, pg. 2310
BOWIE MALL COMPANY, LLC—See Washington Prime Group Inc.; *U.S. Private*, pg. 4448
BOWMAN DEVELOPMENT CORPORATION—See Bowman Group LLP; *U.S. Private*, pg. 626
BOXER PROPERTY MANAGEMENT CORPORATION; *U.S. Private*, pg. 626
THE BOYER COMPANY, LLC; *U.S. Private*, pg. 3999
BOYNTON BEACH MALL, LLC—See Washington Prime Group Inc.; *U.S. Private*, pg. 4448
BRANCH CAPITAL PARTNERS LP; *U.S. Private*, pg. 635
BRANDYWINE SPORTS, INC.; *U.S. Private*, pg. 639
BRE/PEARLRIDGE, LLC—See Washington Prime Group Inc.; *U.S. Private*, pg. 4448
BRH & ASSOCIATES; *U.S. Private*, pg. 647
BRIDGE COMMERCIAL REAL ESTATE LLC—See Bridge Investment Group Holdings Inc.; *U.S. Public*, pg. 381
BRIDGEVIEW MANAGEMENT CO. INC.—See Grupo Mexico, S.A.B. de C.V.; *Int'l*, pg. 3132
BRIXMOR LLC, SOUTHWEST—See Blackstone Inc.; *U.S. Public*, pg. 352
BR MALLS PARTICIPACOES S.A.—See Allos SA; *Int'l*, pg. 359
BR MALLS SERVICOS COMPARTILHADOS LTDA.—See Allos SA; *Int'l*, pg. 359
THE BROE COMPANIES, INC.; *U.S. Private*, pg. 4000
BROOKFIELD FINANCIAL PROPERTIES, L.P.—See Brookfield Corporation; *Int'l*, pg. 1186
BROTHERS INTERNATIONAL CORP; *U.S. Private*, pg. 665
BRUNSWICK SQUARE MALL, LLC—See Washington Prime Group Inc.; *U.S. Private*, pg. 4448
BT PROPERTY LTD.—See BT Group plc; *Int'l*, pg. 1203
BUNKER PROPERTIES INC.—See PBI/Gordon Corporation; *U.S. Private*, pg. 3118
BURNAM HOLDING COMPANIES INC; *U.S. Private*, pg. 689
BUTLER ENTERPRISES; *U.S. Private*, pg. 697
THE CAFARO CO.; *U.S. Private*, pg. 4003
CAMELBACK COLONNADE ASSOCIATES LIMITED PARTNERSHIP—See The Macerich Company; *U.S. Public*, pg. 2109
CANAL WALK SHOPPING CENTRE—See Hyprop Investments Limited; *Int'l*, pg. 3554
CANON FINANCE AUSTRALIA PTY. LTD.—See Canon Inc.; *Int'l*, pg. 1293
CANON FINANCE NEW ZEALAND LTD.—See Canon Inc.; *Int'l*, pg. 1293
CAPITALAND ASCOTT TRUST MANAGEMENT LIMITED; *Int'l*, pg. 1313
CAPITALAND CHINA TRUST; *Int'l*, pg. 1313
CAPITAL & COUNTIES USA, INC.; *U.S. Private*, pg. 738
CAPLAND ASCENDAS REIT; *Int'l*, pg. 1314
CASTLEWOOD REALTY COMPANY; *U.S. Private*, pg. 785
CBL/MONROEVILLE, L.P.—See CBL & Associates Properties, Inc.; *U.S. Public*, pg. 458
CBL/PARK PLAZA MALL, LLC—See CBL & Associates Properties, Inc.; *U.S. Public*, pg. 458

N.A.I.C.S. INDEX
531120 — LESSORS OF NONRESID...

CBL/STROUD, INC.—See CBL & Associates Properties, Inc.; *U.S. Public*, pg. 458

CBRE GLOBAL INVESTORS, LLC - BOSTON—See CBRE Group, Inc.; *U.S. Public*, pg. 460

CCGI / MALL OF AMERICA, LLC—See Blink Charging Co.; *U.S. Public*, pg. 361

CCP VALENCIA LLC—See The Macerich Company; *U.S. Public*, pg. 2109

CEETRUS HUNGARY KFT.—See Auchan Holding S.A.; *Int'l*, pg. 699

CEETRUS POLSKA SP ZOO—See Auchan Holding S.A.; *Int'l*, pg. 699

CENCOSUD SHOPPING CENTER S.A.—See Cencosud S.A.; *Int'l*, pg. 1400

CENTURY INVESTMENTS INC—See Caruso Affiliated; *U.S. Private*, pg. 777

CESC PARK TWO L.L.C.—See Vornado Realty Trust; *U.S. Public*, pg. 2310

CHAGALA MANAGEMENT LLP—See Chagala Group Limited; *Int'l*, pg. 1436

CHARLES E. SMITH COMMERCIAL REALTY, L.P.—See Vornado Realty Trust; *U.S. Public*, pg. 2310

CHARLOTTESVILLE FASHION SQUARE, LLC—See Washington Prime Group Inc.; *U.S. Private*, pg. 4448

CHASE G.P. CORPORATION—See Chase Enterprises, Inc.; *U.S. Private*, pg. 859

CHAUTAUQUA MALL, LLC—See Washington Prime Group Inc.; *U.S. Private*, pg. 4448

CHELCO REALTY CORP.—See Chelco Group of Companies Inc.; *U.S. Private*, pg. 869

CHESAPEAKE MALL, LLC—See Washington Prime Group Inc.; *U.S. Private*, pg. 4448

CHIPPEWA ENTERPRISES INCORPORATED; *U.S. Private*, pg. 886

CHULA VISTA CENTER, LP—See Brookfield Corporation; *Int'l*, pg. 1185

CITIZEN PLAZA CO., LTD.—See Citizen Watch Co., Ltd.; *Int'l*, pg. 1624

CITY CENTER STF, LP—See City Office REIT, Inc.; *Int'l*, pg. 1627

CITYCON JAKOBSBERGS CENTRUM AB—See Citycon Oyj; *Int'l*, pg. 1629

CITYCON LILJEHOLMSTORGET GALLERIA AB—See Citycon Oyj; *Int'l*, pg. 1629

CITY-GALERIE WOLFSBURG KG—See Deutsche EuroShop AG; *Int'l*, pg. 2065

CLARE ROSE INC.; *U.S. Private*, pg. 910

CLAY TERRACE PARTNERS, LLC—See Washington Prime Group Inc.; *U.S. Private*, pg. 4448

CLOVER FINANCIAL CORPORATION; *U.S. Private*, pg. 947

CLSH MANAGEMENT LIMITED—See CLS Holdings plc; *Int'l*, pg. 1664

CODDING ENTERPRISES; *U.S. Private*, pg. 960

COLDWELL BANKER BAIN ASSOCIATES, INC.—See Anywhere Real Estate Inc.; *U.S. Public*, pg. 140

COLLIN CREEK MALL, LLC—See Brookfield Corporation; *Int'l*, pg. 1185

COLONY SQUARE MALL, LLC—See Brookfield Corporation; *Int'l*, pg. 1185

COLUMBUS ASSOCIATION FOR THE PERFORMING ARTS CORPORATION; *U.S. Private*, pg. 978

COLUMBUS PROPERTIES LP; *U.S. Private*, pg. 979

COMMUNICATION SITE MANAGEMENT CORP.—See Chase Enterprises, Inc.; *U.S. Private*, pg. 859

COMPANHIA FLUMINENSE DE ADMINISTRACAO E COMERCIO—See Allos SA; *Int'l*, pg. 359

COMPCO HOLDING COMPANY INC.—See S-P Company Inc.; *U.S. Private*, pg. 3514

COMPCO LAND COMPANY INC.—See S-P Company Inc.; *U.S. Private*, pg. 3514

CONVENE PHILADELPHIA—See Sentry Centers Holdings LLC; *U.S. Private*, pg. 3610

CORD MEYER DEVELOPMENT LLC; *U.S. Private*, pg. 1047

COROC/MYRTLE BEACH L.L.C.—See Tanger Inc.; *U.S. Public*, pg. 1980

COROC/PARK CITY L.L.C.—See Tanger Inc.; *U.S. Public*, pg. 1980

CORTE MADERA VILLAGE, LLC—See The Macerich Company; *U.S. Public*, pg. 2109

CORTLANDT TOWN CENTER LLC—See Acadia Realty Trust; *U.S. Public*, pg. 31

THE COUNTY LINE ENTERPRISES, INC.; *U.S. Private*, pg. 4015

COUSINS PROPERTIES LP—See Cousins Properties Incorporated; *U.S. Public*, pg. 587

CPB PROPERTIES, INC.—See Central Pacific Financial Corporation; *U.S. Public*, pg. 473

CRAWFORD STREET CORP.—See Radius Recycling, Inc.; *U.S. Public*, pg. 1760

CROSS CREEK MALL, LLC—See CBL & Associates Properties, Inc.; *U.S. Public*, pg. 458

CROSSROADS MALL—See Pennsylvania Real Estate Investment Trust; *U.S. Public*, pg. 1663

C&S LAND CO.—See S-P Company Inc.; *U.S. Private*, pg. 3514

CUMBERLAND MALL ASSOCIATES—See Pennsylvania Real Estate Investment Trust; *U.S. Public*, pg. 1663

CUSTOM INDEX INC.; *U.S. Private*, pg. 1129

DAHLEM COMPANIES, INC.; *U.S. Private*, pg. 1144

DALLAS MARKET CENTER COMPANY; *U.S. Private*, pg. 1150

DASIN RETAIL TRUST MANAGEMENT PTE LTD.; *Int'l*, pg. 1974

DAVID MARTIN & ASSOCIATES; *U.S. Private*, pg. 1170

DAVIS ENTERPRISES; *U.S. Private*, pg. 1173

DEAD RIVER COMPANY; *U.S. Private*, pg. 1182

DEAD RIVER PROPERTIES—See Dead River Company; *U.S. Private*, pg. 1182

DELMAR HALL, LLC—See Live Nation Entertainment, Inc.; *U.S. Public*, pg. 1328

DE PARK AVENUE 10880, LLC—See Douglas Emmett, Inc.; *U.S. Public*, pg. 678

DE PARK AVENUE 10960, LLC—See Douglas Emmett, Inc.; *U.S. Public*, pg. 678

DERMODY PROPERTIES INC.; *U.S. Private*, pg. 1210

DESERT SKY MALL, LLC—See The Macerich Company; *U.S. Public*, pg. 2109

DESHANO CONSTRUCTION COMPANY; *U.S. Private*, pg. 1213

DEZER PROPERTIES, INC.; *U.S. Private*, pg. 1220

DIAGNOSTIC CLINIC MED GROUP; *U.S. Private*, pg. 1222

DIAL COMPANIES CORPORATION; *U.S. Private*, pg. 1222

DIC PROPERTIES LLC—See Eighteen Seventy Corporation; *U.S. Private*, pg. 1347

DIGITALUM N.V.—See Alan Allman Associates SA; *Int'l*, pg. 290

DILL INVESTMENTS, LLC; *U.S. Private*, pg. 1231

DMB PROPERTY VENTURE LP; *U.S. Private*, pg. 1248

DNAL CO., LTD.—See BTS Group Holdings Public Company Limited; *Int'l*, pg. 1205

DOHOME GROUP COMPANY LIMITED—See DoHome Public Company Limited; *Int'l*, pg. 2156

DOLPHIN MALL ASSOCIATES LLC—See Simon Property Group, Inc.; *U.S. Public*, pg. 1881

DONAHUE SCHRIBER REALTY GROUP, INC.—See First Washington Realty Inc.; *U.S. Private*, pg. 1530

DOWWAY HOLDINGS LTD.; *Int'l*, pg. 2187

DRURY DEVELOPMENT CORP.; *U.S. Private*, pg. 1280

DRURY DEVELOPMENT—See Drury Development Corp.; *U.S. Private*, pg. 1280

DUNA PLAZA ZRT—See BNP Paribas SA; *Int'l*, pg. 1090

DUNDRUM TOWN CENTRE MANAGEMENT LIMITED—See Hammerson plc; *Int'l*, pg. 3238

EAGLECARE INC.; *U.S. Private*, pg. 1311

EASTFIELD ASSOCIATES, LLC—See Mountain Development Corp.; *U.S. Private*, pg. 2799

EAST HOUSTON MEDICAL PLAZA, LLC—See Ventas, Inc.; *U.S. Public*, pg. 2278

EASTLAND MALL, LLC—See CBL & Associates Properties, Inc.; *U.S. Public*, pg. 458

EAST MEADOW PLAZA REGENCY, LLC—See Regency Centers Corporation; *U.S. Public*, pg. 1774

EATONTOWN MONMOUTH MALL LLC—See Vornado Realty Trust; *U.S. Public*, pg. 2310

ECE PROJEKTMANAGEMENT PRAHA S.R.O. —See ECE Projektmanagement GmbH & Co KG; *Int'l*, pg. 2288

ECP COLLESTRADA S.R.L.—See Eurocommercial Properties N.V.; *Int'l*, pg. 2534

EDD INVESTMENT CO.; *U.S. Private*, pg. 1332

EDISON MALL, LLC—See Washington Prime Group Inc.; *U.S. Private*, pg. 4448

EMGP—See Caisse des Depots et Consignations; *Int'l*, pg. 1258

EMPIRE STATE BUILDING COMPANY LLC—See Malkin Properties, L.L.C.; *U.S. Private*, pg. 2557

EMPRESAS PUERTORRIQUENAS DE DESARROLLO INC.; *U.S. Private*, pg. 1388

ENKA TC LLC—See Enka Insaat ve Sanayi A.S.; *Int'l*, pg. 2440

ENSTOA, INC.; *U.S. Private*, pg. 1402

EPT WATERPARKS, INC.—See EPR Properties; *U.S. Public*, pg. 784

EQUITY INVESTMENT GROUP; *U.S. Private*, pg. 1416

ERNEST N. MORIAL CONVENTION CTR NEW ORLEANS; *U.S. Private*, pg. 1421

ESTEIN & ASSOCIATES USA LTD.; *U.S. Private*, pg. 1429

FAIRGREEN CAPITAL L.P.; *U.S. Private*, pg. 1464

FAIRGROUND HOLDINGS (PTY) LTD—See Botswana Development Corporation Limited; *Int'l*, pg. 1118

FARMERS MARKETING ASSOCIATION OF HOUSTON TEXAS, INC.—See MLB Capital Partners, LLC; *U.S. Private*, pg. 2754

FHB PROPERTIES, INC.—See BNP Paribas SA; *Int'l*, pg. 1088

FILINVEST SUPERMALL INC.—See Filinvest Development Corporation; *Int'l*, pg. 2663

FIRST SHIP LEASE TRUST; *Int'l*, pg. 2688

FIRST STERLING CORPORATION; *U.S. Private*, pg. 1529

THE FITZGERALD THEATER COMPANY INC.—See American Public Media Group; *U.S. Public*, pg. 245

FLAGSTAFF MALL SPE LLC—See The Macerich Company; *U.S. Public*, pg. 2110

FLATIRON PROPERTY HOLDING, LLC—See The Macerich Company; *U.S. Public*, pg. 2110

FOOTHILLS MALL, INC.—See CBL & Associates Properties, Inc.; *U.S. Public*, pg. 458

FOREST CITY RENTAL PROPERTIES CORPORATION—See Brookfield Corporation; *Int'l*, pg. 1187

FOREST MALL, LLC—See Washington Prime Group Inc.; *U.S. Private*, pg. 4448

FORSSAN HAMEENTIE 3 KOY—See Citycon Oyj; *Int'l*, pg. 1629

FORTIS PROPERTIES BRUNSWICK SQUARE LTD.—See Fortis Inc.; *Int'l*, pg. 2739

FOURTH CRYSTAL PARK ASSOCIATES LIMITED PARTNERSHIP—See Vornado Realty Trust; *U.S. Public*, pg. 2310

FRANK INVESTMENT INC.; *U.S. Private*, pg. 1594

FRASERS COMMERCIAL TRUST—See Frasers Property Limited; *Int'l*, pg. 2766

FR MERCER MALL, LLC—See Federal Realty Investment Trust; *U.S. Public*, pg. 825

FR SAN ANTONIO CENTER, LLC—See Federal Realty Investment Trust; *U.S. Public*, pg. 825

GALERIE LIPPE GMBH & CO. KG—See Helaba Landesbank Hessen-Thuringen; *Int'l*, pg. 3328

THE GARDENS ON EL PASEO LLC—See Simon Property Group, Inc.; *U.S. Public*, pg. 1882

GATE RIVERPLACE COMPANY—See Gate Petroleum Company; *U.S. Private*, pg. 1649

GENERALI-INGATLAN VAGYONKEZELO ES SZOLGALTATO KFT.—See Assicurazioni Generali S.p.A.; *Int'l*, pg. 647

GENERALI VELKY SPALICEK S.R.O.—See Assicurazioni Generali S.p.A.; *Int'l*, pg. 645

GENET PROPERTY GROUP, INC.; *U.S. Private*, pg. 1670

GERMAN CENTRE FOR INDUSTRY AND TRADE SHANGHAI CO. LTD.—See BayernLB Holding AG; *Int'l*, pg. 914

GGP-GATEWAY MALL L.L.C.—See Brookfield Corporation; *Int'l*, pg. 1185

GIBRALTAR TRADE CENTER INC.; *U.S. Private*, pg. 1696

GIBSON PROPERTIES INC.—See Gibson Merchandise Group Inc.; *U.S. Private*, pg. 1696

GLENPOINTE ASSOCIATES II LLC; *U.S. Private*, pg. 1711

GLOBAL LINK PARTNERS INC.—See Global Link Management, Inc.; *Int'l*, pg. 2998

GONG'S MARKET OF SANGER INC.; *U.S. Private*, pg. 1737

GORDON STREET CORPORATION—See Martin Supply Company Inc.; *U.S. Private*, pg. 2596

THE GRAHAM GROUP, INC.; *U.S. Private*, pg. 4036

GRAND TRAVERSE MALL, LLC—See Brookfield Corporation; *Int'l*, pg. 1185

GRAPEVINE MILLS—See Simon Property Group, Inc.; *U.S. Public*, pg. 1882

GREAT ESCAPE OF NITRO, LLC—See Cineworld Group plc; *Int'l*, pg. 1611

GREEN ACRES MALL, L.L.C.—See The Macerich Company; *U.S. Public*, pg. 2110

GREENBRIER MALL, LLC—See CBL & Associates Properties, Inc.; *U.S. Public*, pg. 458

GREEN TREE MALL LLC—See The Macerich Company; *U.S. Public*, pg. 2110

GROOTHANDELSGEBOUWEN N.V.; *Int'l*, pg. 3088

GROVE ARCADE RESTORATION LLC—See Duke Energy Corporation; *U.S. Public*, pg. 691

GRUBB & ELLIS NEW YORK, INC.—See BGC Group, Inc.; *U.S. Public*, pg. 329

GULF COAST TOWN CENTER CMBS, LLC—See CBL & Associates Properties, Inc.; *U.S. Public*, pg. 458

GULF VIEW SQUARE, LLC—See Washington Prime Group Inc.; *U.S. Private*, pg. 4448

GVA OXFORD—See Oxford Development Company; *U.S. Private*, pg. 3057

HABBERSTAD BMW INC.; *U.S. Private*, pg. 1837

HABITAT PROIECT S.A.; *Int'l*, pg. 3203

HAESUNG INDUSTRIAL CO., LTD.; *Int'l*, pg. 3205

HAMILTON PLACE MALL GENERAL PARTNERSHIP—See CBL & Associates Properties, Inc.; *U.S. Public*, pg. 458

HAMMERSON MARKETING ET COMMUNICATION SAS—See Hammerson plc; *Int'l*, pg. 3238

HAMMOCK LANDING/WEST MELBOURNE, LLC—See CBL & Associates Properties, Inc.; *U.S. Public*, pg. 458

HAMPTON ENTERPRISES INC.; *U.S. Private*, pg. 1851

HANKYU REALTY CO., LTD.—See Hankyu Hanshin Holdings Inc.; *Int'l*, pg. 3255

HANSORD AGENCY INC.—See Luther Holding Company; *U.S. Private*, pg. 2517

HAP SENG LAND SDN. BHD.—See Hap Seng Consolidated Berhad; *Int'l*, pg. 3268

HAP SENG PROPERTIES DEVELOPMENT SDN. BHD.—See Hap Seng Consolidated Berhad; *Int'l*, pg. 3268

HAP SENG REALTY (KK I) SDN. BHD.—See Hap Seng Consolidated Berhad; *Int'l*, pg. 3268

HARRIS CAPITAL GROUP, INC.; *U.S. Private*, pg. 1869

HCP LIFE SCIENCE ESTATES, INC.—See Healthpeak Properties, Inc.; *U.S. Public*, pg. 1016

HCP MOB SCOTTSDALE LLC—See Healthpeak Properties, Inc.; *U.S. Public*, pg. 1016

531120 — LESSORS OF NONRESID... CORPORATE AFFILIATIONS

HD SYMMCO INC.—See Symmco Group Inc.; *U.S. Private*, pg. 3899
HEALTH CARE REIT, LLC—See Welltower Inc.; *U.S. Public*, pg. 2348
HEIKINTORI OY—See Citycon Oyj; *Int'l*, pg. 1629
HELMSLEY ENTERPRISES, INC.; *U.S. Private*, pg. 1912
H.E. PROPERTIES, INC.—See Hyatt Hotels Corporation; *U.S. Public*, pg. 1077
HERBERT YENTIS & COMPANY; *U.S. Private*, pg. 1920
HIGHLAND LAKES CENTER, LLC—See Washington Prime Group Inc.; *U.S. Private*, pg. 4448
HILL CREST DEVELOPMENT; *U.S. Private*, pg. 1945
H&J INC.—See The Hagadone Corporation; *U.S. Private*, pg. 4041
HOKUGIN REAL ESTATE SERVICES CO., LTD.—See Hokuhoku Financial Group, Inc.; *Int'l*, pg. 3444
HOLIDAY PROPERTIES; *U.S. Private*, pg. 1963
HOMETOWN AMERICA MANAGEMENT CORP.; *U.S. Private*, pg. 1975
HONEY CREEK MALL, LLC—See CBL & Associates Properties, Inc.; *U.S. Public*, pg. 458
HOTEL VENTURE LP—See Circa Capital Corporation; *U.S. Private*, pg. 899
HPD HOLDINGS CORP.—See WD-40 Company; *U.S. Public*, pg. 2338
HRS EDUCATION SERVICES, INC.—See Hawk Management & Financial Services Inc.; *U.S. Private*, pg. 1882
HUDSON 901 MARKET, LLC—See Hudson Pacific Properties, Inc.; *U.S. Public*, pg. 1068
HUDSON MET PARK NORTH, LLC—See Hudson Pacific Properties, Inc.; *U.S. Public*, pg. 1068
HYATTSVILLE LAND CO., INC.—See The Hillman Company; *U.S. Private*, pg. 4053
ICHIGO GREEN INFRASTRUCTURE INVESTMENT CORPORATION; *Int'l*, pg. 3580
THE IDI GROUP COMPANIES; *U.S. Private*, pg. 4055
IINO ENTERPRISE CO., LTD.—See Iino Kaiun Kaisha Ltd.; *Int'l*, pg. 3608
IMAGE LOCATIONS INC.; *U.S. Private*, pg. 2044
IMPACT EXHIBITION MANAGEMENT COMPANY LIMITED—See Bangkok Land Public Company Limited; *Int'l*, pg. 835
IMPERIAL REALTY COMPANY INC.; *U.S. Private*, pg. 2049
IMPERIAL VALLEY MALL, L.P.—See CBL & Associates Properties, Inc.; *U.S. Public*, pg. 458
INFOMART DALLAS, LP—See Equinix, Inc.; *U.S. Public*, pg. 788
INLAND AMERICAN COMMUNITIES GROUP INC.; *U.S. Private*, pg. 2078
INTEGRAL FACILITY SERVICES LIMITED—See Jones Lang LaSalle Incorporated; *U.S. Public*, pg. 1202
IVANHOE CAMBRIDGE, INC.—See Caisse de Depot et Placement du Quebec; *Int'l*, pg. 1254
JACOBSON CAPITAL SERVICES INC.; *U.S. Private*, pg. 2180
THE J.A.M.S. AGENCY CORPORATION—See Glockner Chevrolet Co. Inc.; *U.S. Private*, pg. 1720
JANESVILLE MALL LIMITED PARTNERSHIP—See CBL & Associates Properties, Inc.; *U.S. Public*, pg. 458
J.C. PENNEY PROPERTIES, INC.—See J.C. Penney Company, Inc.; *U.S. Private*, pg. 2160
JLH PROPERTIES, INC.—See Tupperware Brands Corporation; *U.S. Public*, pg. 2204
JLL MORTGAGE SERVICES PTY LTD—See Jones Lang LaSalle Incorporated; *U.S. Public*, pg. 1202
JMB/245 PARK AVENUE ASSOCIATES, LTD.—See JMB Realty Corporation; *U.S. Private*, pg. 2215
JOHN BUCK COMPANY; *U.S. Private*, pg. 2220
JONES LANG LASALLE HOTELS & HOSPITALITY—See Jones Lang LaSalle Incorporated; *U.S. Public*, pg. 1203
JONES LANG LASALLE INVESTMENT MANAGEMENT—See Jones Lang LaSalle Incorporated; *U.S. Public*, pg. 1203
JONES LANG LASALLE KENYA LTD—See Jones Lang LaSalle Incorporated; *U.S. Public*, pg. 1204
JONES LANG LASALLE SPOKA Z OGRANICZON ODPOWIEDZIALNOCECI—See Jones Lang LaSalle Incorporated; *U.S. Public*, pg. 1205
JUJAMCYN THEATRES CORP.; *U.S. Private*, pg. 2243
J.W. MAYS, INC.; *U.S. Public*, pg. 1180
JYVASKYLAN KAUPPAKATU 31 KOY—See Citycon Oyj; *Int'l*, pg. 1629
KATY MILLS—See Simon Property Group, Inc.; *U.S. Public*, pg. 1882
KAUPPAKESKUS ISOKARHU OY—See Citycon Oyj; *Int'l*, pg. 1629
KENNEDY-WILSON PROPERTIES, LTD.; *U.S. Private*, pg. 2285
KINGSTON COLLECTION—See Pyramid Management Group, Inc.; *U.S. Private*, pg. 3310
KNOTEL AHOY! BERLIN GMBH—See Newmark Group, Inc.; *U.S. Public*, pg. 1515
KNOXVILLE CENTER, LLC—See Washington Prime Group Inc.; *U.S. Private*, pg. 4448
KOSSMAN DEVELOPMENT COMPANY; *U.S. Private*, pg. 2344
KOURY CORPORATION; *U.S. Private*, pg. 2345
KRAVCO SIMON COMPANY; *U.S. Private*, pg. 2350

KRISTIINE KESKUS OU—See Citycon Oyj; *Int'l*, pg. 1629
KW SACRAMENTO, LLC—See Kennedy-Wilson Holdings, Inc.; *U.S. Public*, pg. 1223
L8 SOUTH COAST PLAZA LLC—See Fosun International Limited; *Int'l*, pg. 2751
LAKELAND SQUARE MALL, LLC—See Brookfield Corporation; *Int'l*, pg. 1185
LAKELINE PLAZA, LLC—See Washington Prime Group Inc.; *U.S. Private*, pg. 4448
LANCO CORP.; *U.S. Private*, pg. 2382
LANDMARK MALL L.L.C.—See Howard Hughes Holdings Inc.; *U.S. Public*, pg. 1060
LANSING MALL, LLC—See Brookfield Corporation; *Int'l*, pg. 1185
LASALLE INVESTMENT MANAGEMENT AUSTRALIA PTY LTD—See Jones Lang LaSalle Incorporated; *U.S. Public*, pg. 1205
LASALLE REIT ADVISORS K.K.—See Jones Lang LaSalle Incorporated; *U.S. Public*, pg. 1205
LBS LIMITED PARTNERSHIP—See Ventas, Inc.; *U.S. Public*, pg. 2278
LEEMAH PROPERTY INC—See Leemah Corporation; *U.S. Private*, pg. 2415
LEGACY COMMERCIAL PROPERTY—See Highland Ventures, Ltd.; *U.S. Private*, pg. 1939
LEGACY GOLF MANAGEMENT LLC; *U.S. Private*, pg. 2416
LEVCOR, INC.; *U.S. Private*, pg. 2433
LEXINGTON CENTER CORPORATION; *U.S. Public*, pg. 2440
LEXINGTON LAC LENEXA L.P.—See LXP Industrial Trust; *U.S. Public*, pg. 1349
LIFETIME, INC.; *U.S. Private*, pg. 2451
LINCOLNWOOD TOWN CENTER, LLC—See Washington Prime Group Inc.; *U.S. Private*, pg. 4448
LINDALE MALL, LLC—See Washington Prime Group Inc.; *U.S. Private*, pg. 4448
LOBLAW PROPERTIES LIMITED—See George Weston Limited; *Int'l*, pg. 2938
LOCKARD DEVELOPMENT INC.—See LLJ Inc.; *U.S. Private*, pg. 2475
LOFFLER BUSINESS SYSTEMS INC.; *U.S. Private*, pg. 2480
LOGICOM, INC.—See CRE, Inc.; *Int'l*, pg. 1830
LOGJAM PRESENTS, LLC—See Live Nation Entertainment, Inc.; *U.S. Public*, pg. 1330
LONE STAR EQUITIES, INC.; *U.S. Private*, pg. 2484
LORDAE INC.; *U.S. Private*, pg. 2495
MACARTHUR SHOPPING CENTER LLC—See Simon Property Group, Inc.; *U.S. Public*, pg. 1881
MACERICH BROADWAY PLAZA LLC—See The Macerich Company; *U.S. Public*, pg. 2110
MACERICH DEPTFORD LLC—See The Macerich Company; *U.S. Public*, pg. 2110
MACERICH LAKE SQUARE MALL LLC—See The Macerich Company; *U.S. Public*, pg. 2110
MACERICH LAKEWOOD, LLC—See The Macerich Company; *U.S. Public*, pg. 2110
MACERICH LUBBOCK GP CORP.—See The Macerich Company; *U.S. Public*, pg. 2110
MACERICH NORTH PARK MALL LLC—See The Macerich Company; *U.S. Public*, pg. 2110
MACERICH NORTHRIDGE LP—See The Macerich Company; *U.S. Public*, pg. 2110
MACERICH OAKS LLC—See The Macerich Company; *U.S. Public*, pg. 2110
MACERICH PANORAMA LP—See The Macerich Company; *U.S. Public*, pg. 2110
MACERICH RIMROCK GP CORP.—See The Macerich Company; *U.S. Public*, pg. 2110
MACERICH SANTA MONICA LP—See The Macerich Company; *U.S. Public*, pg. 2110
MACERICH SANTA MONICA PLACE CORP.—See The Macerich Company; *U.S. Public*, pg. 2110
MACERICH SOUTH PARK MALL LLC—See The Macerich Company; *U.S. Public*, pg. 2110
MACERICH SOUTH PLAINS LP—See The Macerich Company; *U.S. Public*, pg. 2110
MACERICH SOUTHRIDGE MALL LLC—See The Macerich Company; *U.S. Public*, pg. 2110
MACERICH STONEWOOD, LLC—See The Macerich Company; *U.S. Public*, pg. 2110
MACERICH TWENTY NINTH STREET LLC—See The Macerich Company; *U.S. Public*, pg. 2110
MACERICH TYSONS LLC—See The Macerich Company; *U.S. Public*, pg. 2110
MACERICH VALLEY RIVER CENTER LLC—See The Macerich Company; *U.S. Public*, pg. 2110
MACERICH VICTOR VALLEY LLC—See The Macerich Company; *U.S. Public*, pg. 2110
MACERICH VINTAGE FAIRE LIMITED PARTNERSHIP—See The Macerich Company; *U.S. Public*, pg. 2110
MACERICH WESTSIDE GP CORP.—See The Macerich Company; *U.S. Public*, pg. 2110
MACERICH WESTSIDE PAVILION PROPERTY LLC—See The Macerich Company; *U.S. Public*, pg. 2110
MADISON/EAST TOWNE, LLC—See CBL & Associates Properties, Inc.; *U.S. Public*, pg. 458
MAGISTRAL KAUBANDUSKESKUSE OU—See EfTEN Capital AS; *Int'l*, pg. 2321
MALKIN SECURITIES CORP.—See Malkin Properties, L.L.C.; *U.S. Private*, pg. 2557
MALL AT JEFFERSON VALLEY, LLC—See Washington Prime Group Inc.; *U.S. Private*, pg. 4448
MALL AT JOHNSON CITY REIT, LLC—See Washington Prime Group Inc.; *U.S. Private*, pg. 4448
MALL AT LONGVIEW, LLC—See Washington Prime Group Inc.; *U.S. Private*, pg. 4448
MALL AT VALLE VISTA, LLC—See Washington Prime Group Inc.; *U.S. Private*, pg. 4448
MALL DEL NORTE, LLC—See CBL & Associates Properties, Inc.; *U.S. Public*, pg. 458
MALL PLAZA COLOMBIA S.A.S.—See Falabella S.A.; *Int'l*, pg. 2610
MALL PLAZA PERU S.A.—See Falabella S.A.; *Int'l*, pg. 2610
MALL ST. VINCENT, LLC—See Brookfield Corporation; *Int'l*, pg. 1185
MARKETPLACE AT CONCORD MILLS, LLC—See Washington Prime Group Inc.; *U.S. Private*, pg. 4448
MARKLAND MALL, LLC—See Washington Prime Group Inc.; *U.S. Private*, pg. 4448
MARKLAND PLAZA, LLC—See Washington Prime Group Inc.; *U.S. Private*, pg. 4448
MAR PROPERTIES INC.—See Sun Capital Partners, Inc.; *U.S. Private*, pg. 3860
MASKINKLIPPET AB—See BHG Group AB; *Int'l*, pg. 1015
MASSACHUSETTS CONVENTION CENTER AUTHORITY; *U.S. Private*, pg. 2603
MAX FINKELSTEIN INC.; *U.S. Private*, pg. 2617
MAYFAIRE TOWN CENTER, LP—See CBL & Associates Properties, Inc.; *U.S. Public*, pg. 458
MB REAL ESTATE; *U.S. Private*, pg. 2624
MCBARSCOT COMPANY; *U.S. Private*, pg. 2625
MCCURDY & COMPANY INC; *U.S. Private*, pg. 2631
MCDONALD INDUSTRIAL LAND CO.—See McDonald Steel Corporation; *U.S. Private*, pg. 2632
MCGEE TIRE STORES INC.; *U.S. Public*, pg. 2634
MCKENNA HAWAII INC.; *U.S. Private*, pg. 2638
MELBOURNE SQUARE, LLC—See Washington Prime Group Inc.; *U.S. Private*, pg. 4448
MENARA HAP SENG SDN. BHD.—See Hap Seng Consolidated Berhad; *Int'l*, pg. 3268
THE MENKITI GROUP; *U.S. Private*, pg. 4077
MERIDIAN MALL COMPANY, INC.—See CBL & Associates Properties, Inc.; *U.S. Public*, pg. 458
METRONATIONAL CORPORATION; *U.S. Private*, pg. 2687
METROPLEX HOLDINGS INC.; *U.S. Private*, pg. 2687
METROPOLITAN PROPERTIES AMERICA INCORPORATED; *U.S. Private*, pg. 2689
MHI INVESTMENTS, LLC—See Healthpeak Properties, Inc.; *U.S. Public*, pg. 1016
MID ATLANTIC PETROLEUM PROPERTIES LLC; *U.S. Private*, pg. 2705
MIDWAY SHOPPING CENTER, L.P.—See Regency Centers Corporation; *U.S. Public*, pg. 1774
MIE PROPERTIES INC.; *U.S. Private*, pg. 2724
MILESTONE PROPERTIES INC.; *U.S. Private*, pg. 2729
MISKOLC 2002 KFT.—See BNP Paribas SA; *Int'l*, pg. 1092
MJ HOLDINGS, INC.; *U.S. Private*, pg. 1452
MODULAIRE GROUP—See Brookfield Corporation; *Int'l*, pg. 1176
MOORESTOWN MALL LLC—See Pennsylvania Real Estate Investment Trust; *U.S. Public*, pg. 1663
MORII APPRAISAL & INVESTMENT CONSULTING INC.—See Jones Lang LaSalle Incorporated; *U.S. Public*, pg. 1205
MSB REAL ESTATE CORP.—See M&T Bank Corporation; *U.S. Public*, pg. 1351
MUNCIE MALL, LLC—See Washington Prime Group Inc.; *U.S. Private*, pg. 4448
MVEC EXHIBITION AND EVENT SERVICES SDN. BHD.—See IGB Berhad; *Int'l*, pg. 3601
NATURALLY FRESH, INC.—See TreeHouse Foods, Inc.; *U.S. Public*, pg. 2187
NEOSTREET INC.—See Akebono Brake Industry Co., Ltd.; *Int'l*, pg. 262
NEVINS-ADAMS-LEWBEL-SCHELL PROPERTIES INC; *U.S. Private*, pg. 2891
NEWPARK MALL, LP—See Brookfield Corporation; *Int'l*, pg. 1185
NEWPORT NEWS GENERAL AND NON SECTARIAN HOSPITAL ASSOCIATION INC.; *U.S. Private*, pg. 2916
NEW WATER STREET CORP.; *U.S. Private*, pg. 2908
NORTH BRIDGE CHICAGO LLC—See The Macerich Company; *U.S. Public*, pg. 2110
NORTHGATE MALL ASSOCIATES—See The Macerich Company; *U.S. Public*, pg. 2110
NORTHLAKE MALL, LLC—See Washington Prime Group Inc.; *U.S. Private*, pg. 4448
NORTH PLAINS MALL, LLC—See Brookfield Corporation; *Int'l*, pg. 1185
OAK COURT MALL, LLC—See Washington Prime Group Inc.; *U.S. Private*, pg. 4448
OAK HILL PROPERTIES LLC; *U.S. Private*, pg. 2983
OAK LEAF MANAGEMENT INC.; *U.S. Private*, pg. 2983

N.A.I.C.S. INDEX 531120 — LESSORS OF NONRESID...
N.A.I.C.S. Index

THE OFFICE GROUP LIMITED—See Blackstone Inc.; *U.S. Public*, pg. 361
OHI ASSET (CO) MESA, LLC—See Omega Healthcare Investors, Inc.; *U.S. Public*, pg. 1571
OHI HEATH LODGE AND AUTUMN VALE LTD—See Omega Healthcare Investors, Inc.; *U.S. Public*, pg. 1571
OHI HILLINGS LTD—See Omega Healthcare Investors, Inc.; *U.S. Public*, pg. 1571
OHIO BUILDING AUTHORITY; *U.S. Private*, pg. 3004
OKC CLASSEN CURVE, LLC—See Washington Prime Group Inc.; *U.S. Private*, pg. 4449
OLEN PROPERTIES CORP.; *U.S. Private*, pg. 3010
OMAN ENTERPRISES INC.; *U.S. Private*, pg. 3014
OOO INFORM FUTURE—See Blackstone Inc.; *U.S. Public*, pg. 351
ORANGE PARK MALL, LLC—See Washington Prime Group Inc.; *U.S. Private*, pg. 4448
ORIENT SHOPPING CENTRE - HUAIHAI—See Bailian Group Co., Ltd.; *Int'l*, pg. 802
ORIENT SHOPPING CENTRE - JIADING—See Bailian Group Co., Ltd.; *Int'l*, pg. 802
ORIENT SHOPPING CENTRE LTD.—See Bailian Group Co., Ltd.; *Int'l*, pg. 802
ORIENT SHOPPING CENTRE - NANDONG—See Bailian Group Co., Ltd.; *Int'l*, pg. 802
ORIENT SHOPPING CENTRE - NINGBO—See Bailian Group Co., Ltd.; *Int'l*, pg. 802
ORIENT SHOPPING CENTRE - YANGPU—See Bailian Group Co., Ltd.; *Int'l*, pg. 802
OULUN GALLERIA KOY—See Citycon Oyj; *Int'l*, pg. 1629
OXFORD DEVELOPMENT COMPANY; *U.S. Private*, pg. 3057
PADDOCK MALL, LLC—See Washington Prime Group Inc.; *U.S. Private*, pg. 4448
PAPPAS ENTERPRISES INC.; *U.S. Private*, pg. 3088
PARKDALE MALL, LLC—See CBL & Associates Properties, Inc.; *U.S. Public*, pg. 458
PARTRIDGE CREEK FASHION PARK LLC—See Simon Property Group, Inc.; *U.S. Public*, pg. 1881
PEARLAND TOWN CENTER HOTEL/RESIDENTIAL CONDOMINIUM ASSOCIATION, INC.—See CBL & Associates Properties, Inc.; *U.S. Public*, pg. 459
PENN INSURANCE & ANNUITY CO.—See The Penn Mutual Life Insurance Company; *U.S. Private*, pg. 4092
PERSIS CORPORATION; *U.S. Private*, pg. 3155
PIER 39 L.P.; *U.S. Private*, pg. 3178
PIERRE BOSSIER MALL, LLC—See Brookfield Corporation; *Int'l*, pg. 1185
PIKESVILLE ASSISTED LIVING, LLC—See Healthpeak Properties, Inc.; *U.S. Public*, pg. 1016
PLAZA AT NORTHWOOD, LLC—See Washington Prime Group Inc.; *U.S. Private*, pg. 4448
PLAZAMERICAS MALL TEXAS, LLC—See RAIT Financial Trust; *U.S. Private*, pg. 3349
PM PROPERTIES INC.—See CrossAmerica Partners LP; *U.S. Public*, pg. 596
PNC REALTY SERVICES—See The PNC Financial Services Group, Inc.; *U.S. Public*, pg. 2120
POAG SHOPPING CENTERS, LLC; *U.S. Private*, pg. 3219
POLARIS FASHION PLACE REIT, LLC—See Washington Prime Group Inc.; *U.S. Private*, pg. 4448
POM-COLLEGE STATION, LLC—See CBL & Associates Properties, Inc.; *U.S. Public*, pg. 458
PORIN ISOLINNANKATU 18 KOY—See Citycon Oyj; *Int'l*, pg. 1629
PORT CHARLOTTE MALL LLC—See Washington Prime Group Inc.; *U.S. Private*, pg. 4448
PORT OF TACOMA; *U.S. Private*, pg. 3231
PPR WASHINGTON SQUARE LLC—See The Macerich Company; *U.S. Public*, pg. 2110
PRECISION COMPONENTS, INC.; *U.S. Private*, pg. 3244
PREIT ASSOCIATES, L.P.—See Pennsylvania Real Estate Investment Trust; *U.S. Public*, pg. 1664
PREIT GADSDEN MALL LLC—See Pennsylvania Real Estate Investment Trust; *U.S. Public*, pg. 1664
PREMIER OFFICE CENTERS, LLC; *U.S. Private*, pg. 3250
PRESIDENT ASSET GROUP LLC; *U.S. Private*, pg. 3254
PR EXTON SQUARE PROPERTY L.P.—See Pennsylvania Real Estate Investment Trust; *U.S. Public*, pg. 1663
PR FRANCIS SCOTT KEY LLC—See Pennsylvania Real Estate Investment Trust; *U.S. Public*, pg. 1663
PR GAINESVILLE LLC—See Pennsylvania Real Estate Investment Trust; *U.S. Public*, pg. 1663
PRICE INDUSTRIES INC.; *U.S. Private*, pg. 3258
PRIMEWEST (NORTHLANDS) PTY LTD—See Centuria Capital Limited; *Int'l*, pg. 1416
PRINTELLECTUAL—See Jenkins Group, Inc.; *U.S. Private*, pg. 2199
PR JACKSONVILLE LIMITED PARTNERSHIP—See Pennsylvania Real Estate Investment Trust; *U.S. Public*, pg. 1663
PR LOGAN VALLEY LLC—See Pennsylvania Real Estate Investment Trust; *U.S. Public*, pg. 1663
PR NORTH DARTMOUTH LLC—See Pennsylvania Real Estate Investment Trust; *U.S. Public*, pg. 1663
PROCETEL SA—See ELECTROMAGNETICA S.A.; *Int'l*, pg. 2353
THE PROMENADE D'IBERVILLE, LLC—See CBL & Associates Properties, Inc.; *U.S. Public*, pg. 459
PROPRIETORS OF UNION WHARF; *U.S. Private*, pg. 3286
PROSPECT DEVELOPMENT CO., LTD.—See Bangkok Bank Public Company Limited; *Int'l*, pg. 833
PR PALMER PARK MALL LIMITED PARTNERSHIP—See Pennsylvania Real Estate Investment Trust; *U.S. Public*, pg. 1663
PR VALLEY VIEW LLC—See Pennsylvania Real Estate Investment Trust; *U.S. Public*, pg. 1663
PR VIEWMONT LLC—See Pennsylvania Real Estate Investment Trust; *U.S. Public*, pg. 1663
PR WASHINGTON CROWN LIMITED PARTNERSHIP—See Pennsylvania Real Estate Investment Trust; *U.S. Public*, pg. 1663
PR WIREGRASS COMMONS LLC—See Pennsylvania Real Estate Investment Trust; *U.S. Public*, pg. 1664
PR WYOMING VALLEY LIMITED PARTNERSHIP—See Pennsylvania Real Estate Investment Trust; *U.S. Public*, pg. 1664
PYRAMID MANAGEMENT GROUP, INC.; *U.S. Private*, pg. 3310
QUADRANGLE DEVELOPMENT CORPORATION; *U.S. Private*, pg. 3315
QUEENS CENTER REIT LLC—See The Macerich Company; *U.S. Public*, pg. 2110
QUEMETCO REALTY, INC.—See Quexco Incorporated; *U.S. Private*, pg. 3326
RACINE BROADCASTING LLC—See Adams Publishing Group, LLC; *U.S. Private*, pg. 74
RAMA 9 SQUARE CO., LTD.—See Central Pattana Public Company Limited; *Int'l*, pg. 1409
RDC INC.; *U.S. Private*, pg. 3364
REGENCY CENTERS, L.P.—See Regency Centers Corporation; *U.S. Public*, pg. 1774
REGENCY COMMERCIAL ASSOCIATES LLC—See Regency Management Service LLC; *U.S. Private*, pg. 3386
RESINOID ENGINEERING CORP.; *U.S. Private*, pg. 3406
RETAIL VALUE INC.; *U.S. Public*, pg. 1792
REXTON REALTY COMPANY; *U.S. Private*, pg. 3417
THE RICHARD E. JACOBS GROUP, LLC; *U.S. Private*, pg. 4106
RICHMOND TOWN SQUARE MALL, LLC—See Washington Prime Group Inc.; *U.S. Private*, pg. 4448
RIPARIUS CONSTRUCTION INC.—See Riparius Corporation; *U.S. Private*, pg. 3439
RIPARIUS CORPORATION; *U.S. Private*, pg. 3439
RIVERGATE MALL LIMITED PARTNERSHIP—See CBL & Associates Properties, Inc.; *U.S. Public*, pg. 459
RIVER OAKS CENTER, LLC—See Washington Prime Group Inc.; *U.S. Private*, pg. 4448
RIVERWALK MARKETPLACE (NEW ORLEANS), LLC—See Howard Hughes Holdings Inc.; *U.S. Public*, pg. 1060
ROB-TOM INC.—See Vollers, Inc.; *U.S. Private*, pg. 4411
ROCCA AL MARE KAUBANDUSKESKUSE AS—See Citycon Oyj; *Int'l*, pg. 1629
ROCKAWAY TOWN COURT, LLC—See Washington Prime Group Inc.; *U.S. Private*, pg. 4448
ROEMER INSURANCE, INC.—See GTCR LLC; *U.S. Private*, pg. 1804
ROLLING OAKS MALL, LLC—See Washington Prime Group Inc.; *U.S. Private*, pg. 4449
ROSS INVESTMENT VENTURES; *U.S. Private*, pg. 3485
ROTTERDAM INDUSTRIAL PARK—See Galesi Group; *U.S. Private*, pg. 1637
ROTTERDAM SQUARE, LLC—See The Macerich Company; *U.S. Public*, pg. 2110
ROTTERDAM VENTURES INC.—See Galesi Group; *U.S. Private*, pg. 1637
RUFFIN COMPANIES; *U.S. Private*, pg. 3502
SACHS INVESTING COMPANY; *U.S. Private*, pg. 3521
SACHS PROPERTIES—See Sachs Holding Company; *U.S. Private*, pg. 3521
SADDLEBACK ASSOCIATES INC.; *U.S. Private*, pg. 3522
SADYBA BEST MALL SP ZOO—See BNP Paribas SA; *Int'l*, pg. 1092
SAINT THOMAS HEALTH SERVICES—See Ascension Health Alliance; *U.S. Private*, pg. 347
THE SAMUEL MILLS DAMON ESTATE; *U.S. Private*, pg. 4113
SANDS EXPO & CONVENTION CENTER, INC.—See Las Vegas Sands Corp.; *U.S. Public*, pg. 1293
SAS SOCIEDADE ADMINISTRADORA DE CENTROS COMERCIAIS LTDA.—See Allos SA; *Int'l*, pg. 359
SAVVYSHERPA, LLC—See UnitedHealth Group Incorporated; *U.S. Public*, pg. 2250
SB PARTNERS; *U.S. Private*, pg. 3559
SCHWERMAN REAL ESTATE & DEVELOPMENT CORP.—See Tankstar USA, Inc.; *U.S. Private*, pg. 3931
SCI-ROEV TEXAS PARTNERS LP; *U.S. Private*, pg. 3573
SCOTIA INDUSTRIAL PARK, INC.—See Galesi Group; *U.S. Private*, pg. 1637
SCOTT-MCRAE PROPERTIES INC.—See Scott-McRae Automotive Group Inc.; *U.S. Private*, pg. 3578
SCOTTSDALE FASHION SQUARE LLC—See The Macerich Company; *U.S. Public*, pg. 2110
SCOTTSDALE FASHION SQUARE PARTNERSHIP—See The Macerich Company; *U.S. Public*, pg. 2110
SEA ISLAND PROPERTIES, INC.—See Sea Island Company; *U.S. Private*, pg. 3582
SEGECE ESPANA SLU—See BNP Paribas SA; *Int'l*, pg. 1092
SEGECE POLSKA SP. Z.O.O.—See BNP Paribas SA; *Int'l*, pg. 1092
SELIG ENTERPRISES INC.; *U.S. Private*, pg. 3602
SEMINOLE SHORES LIVING CENTER, LLC—See Healthpeak Properties, Inc.; *U.S. Public*, pg. 1016
SEMINOLE TOWNE CENTER LIMITED PARTNERSHIP—See Washington Prime Group Inc.; *U.S. Private*, pg. 4449
SEN PLEX CORPORATION; *U.S. Private*, pg. 3605
SERRAMONTE CENTER HOLDING CO. LLC—See Regency Centers Corporation; *U.S. Public*, pg. 1774
SHANGHAI FASHION STORE—See Bailian Group Co., Ltd.; *Int'l*, pg. 802
SHANGHAI HUALIAN COMMERCIAL BUILDING - HUANGPU—See Bailian Group Co., Ltd.; *Int'l*, pg. 802
SHANGHAI LADY FASHION DEPARTMENT STORE—See Bailian Group Co., Ltd.; *Int'l*, pg. 802
SHANGHAI NO. 1 DEPARTMENT STORE - HUANGPU—See Bailian Group Co., Ltd.; *Int'l*, pg. 802
SHANGHAI NO. 1 DEPARTMENT STORE - SONGJIANG—See Bailian Group Co., Ltd.; *Int'l*, pg. 802
SHANGHAI NO. 1 YAOHAN CO., LTD.—See Bailian Group Co., Ltd.; *Int'l*, pg. 802
SHANGHAI WESTGATE MALL CO., LTD.—See CK Asset Holdings Limited; *Int'l*, pg. 1635
SHAW ELECTRIC CO.; *U.S. Private*, pg. 3628
SHOPPING CENTER MANAGEMENT; *U.S. Private*, pg. 3640
SHOPPINGTOWN MALL, LLC—See The Macerich Company; *U.S. Public*, pg. 2111
SHOPS AT GRAND AVENUE LLC—See Acadia Realty Trust; *U.S. Public*, pg. 31
SHOPS AT NORTHEAST MALL, LLC—See Washington Prime Group Inc.; *U.S. Private*, pg. 4449
SHORENSTEIN COMPANY, L.P.; *U.S. Private*, pg. 3641
SHORT HILLS ASSOCIATES, LLC—See Simon Property Group, Inc.; *U.S. Public*, pg. 1881
SHUR-MARKET DEVELOPMENT CO., INC.—See C&S Wholesale Grocers, Inc.; *U.S. Private*, pg. 704
SIERRA VISTA MALL, LLC—See Brookfield Corporation; *Int'l*, pg. 1185
SIGNATURE THEATRES LLC; *U.S. Private*, pg. 3650
SIKES SENTER, LLC—See Brookfield Corporation; *Int'l*, pg. 1185
SILVER LAKE MALL, LLC—See Brookfield Corporation; *Int'l*, pg. 1185
SIMON CAPITAL LIMITED PARTNERSHIP—See Simon Property Group, Inc.; *U.S. Public*, pg. 1881
SIMPLYTITLE COMPANY—See Lennar Corporation; *U.S. Public*, pg. 1307
SLG 609 FIFTH LLC—See SL Green Realty Corp.; *U.S. Public*, pg. 1894
SM EASTLAND MALL, LLC—See The Macerich Company; *U.S. Public*, pg. 2110
SM MESA MALL, LLC—See Washington Prime Group Inc.; *U.S. Private*, pg. 4449
SM RUSHMORE MALL, LLC—See Washington Prime Group Inc.; *U.S. Private*, pg. 4449
SM SOUTHERN HILLS MALL, LLC—See Washington Prime Group Inc.; *U.S. Private*, pg. 4449
SOUTHEASTERN REALTY GROUP INC.; *U.S. Private*, pg. 3728
SOUTHERN PARK MALL, LLC—See Washington Prime Group Inc.; *U.S. Private*, pg. 4449
SOUTHLAND CENTER, LLC—See Brookfield Corporation; *Int'l*, pg. 1185
SOUTH PARK STREET INC.—See Symmco Group Inc.; *U.S. Private*, pg. 3899
SOUTHWEST LANDCOM; *U.S. Private*, pg. 3739
SPATZ CENTERS INC.; *U.S. Private*, pg. 3747
SPELNA, INC.; *U.S. Private*, pg. 3754
SPG ANDERSON MALL, LLC—See Washington Prime Group Inc.; *U.S. Private*, pg. 4449
SPIGEL PROPERTIES INC.; *U.S. Private*, pg. 3756
SPRINGFIELD DEVELOPMENT CORP LLC—See United Natural Foods, Inc.; *U.S. Public*, pg. 2231
SPRING HILL MALL L.L.C.—See Brookfield Corporation; *Int'l*, pg. 1185
STADT-GALERIE HAMELN KG—See Deutsche EuroShop AG; *Int'l*, pg. 2065
STADT-GALERIE PASSAU KG—See Deutsche EuroShop AG; *Int'l*, pg. 2065
STANDARD PROPERTY CORPORATION—See Highmark Health; *U.S. Private*, pg. 1941
STATE STREET CAPITAL REALTY, LLC; *U.S. Private*, pg. 3793
ST. CHARLES TOWNE PLAZA, LLC—See Washington Prime Group Inc.; *U.S. Private*, pg. 4449
ST. CLAIR SQUARE LIMITED PARTNERSHIP—See CBL & Associates Properties, Inc.; *U.S. Public*, pg. 459
STEINHAFEL'S INC.; *U.S. Private*, pg. 3798
STENUNGS TORG FASTIGHETS AB—See Citycon Oyj; *Int'l*, pg. 1629

531120 — LESSORS OF NONRESID...

STEUART INVESTMENT COMPANY; *U.S. Private,* pg. 3807
STONERIDGE APARTMENTS, INC.—See Deutsche Bank Aktiengesellschaft; *Int'l,* pg. 2062
STONY POINT FASHION PARK ASSOCIATES, LLC—See Simon Property Group, Inc.; *U.S. Public,* pg. 1881
STROMPILEN AB—See Citycon Oyj; *Int'l,* pg. 1629
STROUD MALL LLC—See CBL & Associates Properties, Inc.; *U.S. Public,* pg. 459
STUMP CREEK INC—See Symmco Group Inc.; *U.S. Private,* pg. 3899
THE SUBURBAN PAVILION, LLC—See Omega Healthcare Investors, Inc.; *U.S. Public,* pg. 1572
SUHRBIER COMPANY; *U.S. Private,* pg. 3850
SUNLAND PARK MALL, LLC—See Washington Prime Group Inc.; *U.S. Private,* pg. 4449
SUNRISE GOLF DEVELOPMENT CORP.—See CMC Realty Inc.; *U.S. Private,* pg. 950
SUSQUEHANNA PROPERTIES, INC.—See Delaware Otsego Corp.; *U.S. Private,* pg. 1195
SYMMCO REALTY INC—See Symmco Group Inc.; *U.S. Private,* pg. 3899
SZEGED PLAZA KFT.—See BNP Paribas SA; *Int'l,* pg. 1093
SZOLNOK PLAZA KFT.—See BNP Paribas SA; *Int'l,* pg. 1093
TANGER WISCONSIN DELLS, LLC—See Tanger Inc.; *U.S. Public,* pg. 1981
TAUBMAN CHERRY CREEK SHOPPING CENTER, L.L.C.—See Simon Property Group, Inc.; *U.S. Public,* pg. 1882
THE TAUBMAN COMPANY LLC—See Simon Property Group, Inc.; *U.S. Public,* pg. 1882
TAUBMAN PRESTIGE OUTLETS OF CHESTERFIELD LLC—See Simon Property Group, Inc.; *U.S. Public,* pg. 1882
TAUBMAN REALTY GROUP LIMITED PARTNERSHIP—See Simon Property Group, Inc.; *U.S. Public,* pg. 1882
TAYLOR & MATHIS, INC.; *U.S. Private,* pg. 3937
TCG DEVELOPMENTS INDIA PVT. LTD.—See Vornado Realty Trust; *U.S. Public,* pg. 2309
TCG REAL ESTATE INVESTMENT MANAGEMENT COMPANY PVT. LTD.—See Vornado Realty Trust; *U.S. Public,* pg. 2309
T CITY (IPOH) SDN. BHD.—See Goodland Group Limited; *Int'l,* pg. 3040
TCR CORPORATION; *U.S. Private,* pg. 3943
TDI TERRAPLAN DEVELOPMENT; *U.S. Private,* pg. 3944
TEALS EXPRESS INC.; *U.S. Private,* pg. 3949
TEJON RANCH COMPANY; *U.S. Public,* pg. 1991
TELX - DALLAS, LLC—See Digital Realty Trust, Inc.; *U.S. Public,* pg. 663
TENPO INNOVATION CO., LTD.—See Crops Corporation; *Int'l,* pg. 1855
TERRAMAR RETAIL CENTERS, LLC; *U.S. Private,* pg. 3971
THEMART—See Vornado Realty Trust; *U.S. Public,* pg. 2310
THIES & TALLE MANAGEMENT CO.; *U.S. Private,* pg. 4144
THREE RIVERS MALL, L.L.C.—See Brookfield Corporation; *Int'l,* pg. 1185
THRIFTY OIL CO.; *U.S. Private,* pg. 4165
TJ PALM BEACH ASSOCIATES LIMITED PARTNERSHIP—See Simon Property Group, Inc.; *U.S. Public,* pg. 1881
TORRE IBERDROLA, A.I.E.—See Iberdrola, S.A.; *Int'l,* pg. 3574
TOUCHSTONE CORPORATION—See Urban Renaissance Group LLC; *U.S. Private,* pg. 4315
TOWER PROPERTIES COMPANY; *U.S. Public,* pg. 2165
TOWN CENTER AT AURORA, LLC—See Washington Prime Group Inc.; *U.S. Private,* pg. 4449
TOWNE WEST SQUARE, LLC—See Washington Prime Group Inc.; *U.S. Private,* pg. 4449
TRANSWESTERN COMMERCIAL SERVICES—See Pearlmark Real Estate Partners LLC; *U.S. Private,* pg. 3125
TRG CHARLOTTE LLC—See Simon Property Group, Inc.; *U.S. Public,* pg. 1882
TRIANGLE TOWN CENTER, LLC—See CBL & Associates Properties, Inc.; *U.S. Public,* pg. 459
TRY-IT DISTRIBUTING CO. INC.; *U.S. Private,* pg. 4251
TURTLE MAGAZINE FOR PRESCHOOL KIDS—See Saturday Evening Post Society; *U.S. Private,* pg. 3553
TUTUBAN PROPERTIES, INC.—See Ayalaland Logistics Holdings Corp.; *Int'l,* pg. 774
TWC CHANDLER LLC—See The Macerich Company; *U.S. Public,* pg. 2111
TWC II-PRESCOTT MALL, LLC—See The Macerich Company; *U.S. Public,* pg. 2111
TWELVE OAKS MALL LLC—See Simon Property Group, Inc.; *U.S. Public,* pg. 1882
TWENTIETH CENTURY MARKETS, INC.—See The Fiore Companies; *U.S. Private,* pg. 4028
UAB PREKYBOS CENTRAS MANDARINAS—See Citycon Oyj; *Int'l,* pg. 1629
UAB "ECE PROJEKTMANAGEMENT VILNIUS"—See ECE Projektmanagement GmbH & Co KG; *Int'l,* pg. 2288

UE HUDSON MALL HOLDING LLC—See URBAN EDGE PROPERTIES; *U.S. Public,* pg. 2265
UNIFIED PORT OF SAN DIEGO; *U.S. Private,* pg. 4283
UNITED PROPERTIES; *U.S. Private,* pg. 4296
UNITED REALTY CORPORATION—See Atwood Enterprises Inc.; *U.S. Private,* pg. 384
UNIVERSITY PARK MALL CC, LLC—See Washington Prime Group Inc.; *U.S. Private,* pg. 4449
URBAN EDGE PROPERTIES; *U.S. Public,* pg. 2264
URBAN RENAISSANCE GROUP LLC; *U.S. Private,* pg. 4314
UTICA SQUARE SHOPPING CENTER, INC.—See Helmerich & Payne, Inc.; *U.S. Public,* pg. 1024
UTILITY PROPERTIES INC.—See Utility Holdings Inc.; *U.S. Private,* pg. 4326
UTTOXETER ESTATES LIMITED—See Blackstone Inc.; *U.S. Public,* pg. 358
VALLEY STREAM GREEN ACRES LLC—See The Macerich Company; *U.S. Public,* pg. 2111
VAN'S INC.—See C.S. Wo & Sons Ltd.; *U.S. Private,* pg. 709
VANTAGE MANAGEMENT CO., INC.—See Belmont Group Inc.; *U.S. Private,* pg. 520
VAUXHALL CROSS LIMITED—See CLS Holdings plc; *Int'l,* pg. 1664
VBCJ, INC.—See Van Blarcom Closures Inc.; *U.S. Private,* pg. 4339
VENUWORKS; *U.S. Private,* pg. 4358
VILLAGE PARK PLAZA, LLC—See Washington Prime Group Inc.; *U.S. Private,* pg. 4449
VIRGINIA CENTER COMMONS, LLC—See Washington Prime Group Inc.; *U.S. Private,* pg. 4449
VOLUSIA MALL, LLC—See CBL & Associates Properties, Inc.; *U.S. Public,* pg. 459
VOLUSIA MALL SAC, LLC—See CBL & Associates Properties, Inc.; *U.S. Public,* pg. 459
VORA TECHNOLOGY PARK LLC—See Vora Ventures LLC; *U.S. Private,* pg. 4412
VORNADO SPRINGFIELD MALL MANAGER LLC—See Vornado Realty Trust; *U.S. Public,* pg. 2310
VTR LS ODU 2, LLC—See Ventas, Inc.; *U.S. Public,* pg. 2279
VTR SCIENCE & TECHNOLOGY, LLC—See Ventas, Inc.; *U.S. Public,* pg. 2279
WASHINGTON DESIGN CENTER L.L.C.—See Vornado Realty Trust; *U.S. Public,* pg. 2310
WASHINGTON PARK MALL, LLC—See Brookfield Corporation; *Int'l,* pg. 1185
WASHINGTON PRIME PROPERTY LIMITED PARTNERSHIP—See Washington Prime Group Inc.; *U.S. Private,* pg. 4449
WATERFORD LAKES TOWN CENTER, LLC—See Kimco Realty Corporation; *U.S. Public,* pg. 1232
WATKINS ASSOCIATED DEVELOPERS—See Watkins Associated Industries Inc.; *U.S. Private,* pg. 4455
WEIDNER INVESTMENT SERVICES; *U.S. Private,* pg. 4470
WEINSTEIN MINKOFF INVESTMENTS; *U.S. Private,* pg. 4472
WELLINGTON TRUST CO.—See Wellington Management Company, LLP; *U.S. Private,* pg. 4475
WESSEX SERVICE CO., INC.—See Kidder Matthew, LLC; *U.S. Public,* pg. 2303
WEST ACRES DEVELOPMENT, LLP—See The Macerich Company; *U.S. Public,* pg. 2111
WESTERN MORTGAGE & REALTY CO.; *U.S. Private,* pg. 4494
WEST GROUP MANAGEMENT LLC; *U.S. Private,* pg. 4485
WESTLAKE DEVELOPMENT CO., INC.; *U.S. Private,* pg. 4499
WESTMINSTER MALL, LLC—See Washington Prime Group Inc.; *U.S. Private,* pg. 4449
WESTON COMPANIES—See Vantage Companies; *U.S. Private,* pg. 4344
WEST QUAY SHOPPING CENTRE LTD—See Hammerson plc; *Int'l,* pg. 3238
WEST RIDGE MALL, LLC—See Washington Prime Group Inc.; *U.S. Private,* pg. 4449
WEST TOWN CORNERS, LLC—See Washington Prime Group Inc.; *U.S. Private,* pg. 4449
WESTWOOD MALL, LLC—See Brookfield Corporation; *Int'l,* pg. 1185
WG PARK, LP—See Pennsylvania Real Estate Investment Trust; *U.S. Public,* pg. 1664
WHITE MARSH PLAZA, LLC—See Federal Realty Investment Trust; *U.S. Public,* pg. 826
WHITE MOUNTAIN MALL, LLC—See Brookfield Corporation; *Int'l,* pg. 1185
WHITE OAKS PLAZA, LLC—See Washington Prime Group Inc.; *U.S. Private,* pg. 4449
WHITING DOOR MANUFACTURING CORP.; *U.S. Private,* pg. 4512
WILDISH CONSTRUCTION CO., INC.—See Wildish Land Company; *U.S. Private,* pg. 4519
WILDISH EQUIPMENT CO.—See Wildish Land Company; *U.S. Private,* pg. 4519
WILLIAM C. SMITH & COMPANY; *U.S. Private,* pg. 4522
WILLIAM H. LEAHY ASSOCIATES INC.; *U.S. Private,* pg. 4523

WILLOW BEND SHOPPING CENTER LIMITED PARTNERSHIP—See Simon Property Group, Inc.; *U.S. Public,* pg. 1882
WILLOWS CENTER CONCORD, INC.—See Regency Centers Corporation; *U.S. Public,* pg. 1774
WILSON MANAGEMENT COMPANY—See The Wilson Holding Company; *U.S. Private,* pg. 4137
WILTON MALL, LLC—See The Macerich Company; *U.S. Public,* pg. 2111
WINNER GROUP INCORPORATED; *U.S. Private,* pg. 4542
W. LEE FLOWERS & COMPANY INC.; *U.S. Private,* pg. 4418
W&L SALES—See W&L Sales Co., Inc.; *U.S. Private,* pg. 4417
WORLD TRADE CENTER STOCKHOLM AB—See Alecta pensionsforsakring, omsesidigt; *Int'l,* pg. 305
WPG WESTSHORE, LLC—See Washington Prime Group Inc.; *U.S. Private,* pg. 4449
WPG WOLF RANCH, LLC—See Washington Prime Group Inc.; *U.S. Private,* pg. 4449
WRB ENTERPRISES, INC.; *U.S. Private,* pg. 4572
XEROX REALTY CORPORATION—See Xerox Holdings Corporation; *U.S. Public,* pg. 2390
YONG'AN DEPARTMENT STORE—See Bailian Group Co., Ltd.; *Int'l,* pg. 802
YOUNGWORLD INC.—See Youngworld Stores Group Inc.; *U.S. Private,* pg. 4594
ZAMIAS SERVICES INC.; *U.S. Private,* pg. 4597

531130 — LESSORS OF MINIWAREHOUSES AND SELF-STORAGE UNITS

12902 SOUTH 301 HIGHWAY, LLC—See CubeSmart; *U.S. Public,* pg. 603
2701 S. CONGRESS AVENUE, LLC—See CubeSmart; *U.S. Public,* pg. 603
4211 BELLAIRE BLVD., LLC—See CubeSmart; *U.S. Public,* pg. 603
4370 FOUNTAIN HILLS DRIVE NE, LLC—See CubeSmart; *U.S. Public,* pg. 603
500 MILDRED AVENUE PRIMOS, LLC—See CubeSmart; *U.S. Public,* pg. 603
5700 WASHINGTON AVENUE, LLC—See CubeSmart; *U.S. Public,* pg. 603
5715 BURNET ROAD, LLC—See CubeSmart; *U.S. Public,* pg. 603
610 SAWDUST ROAD, LLC—See CubeSmart; *U.S. Public,* pg. 603
ABERDEEN MINI STORAGE, L.L.C.—See National Storage Affiliates Trust; *U.S. Public,* pg. 1497
AIFUL GUARANTEE CO., LTD.—See AIFUL Corporation; *Int'l,* pg. 231
ALL SPANAWAY STORAGE LLC—See National Storage Affiliates Trust; *U.S. Public,* pg. 1498
ALL STOR INDIAN TRAIL, LLC—See National Storage Affiliates Trust; *U.S. Public,* pg. 1498
ALMATYTEMIR JSC; *Int'l,* pg. 363
AMERICAN MINI STORAGE-SAN ANTONIO, LLC—See National Storage Affiliates Trust; *U.S. Public,* pg. 1498
ANGROPROMET TIKVESANKA AD; *Int'l,* pg. 463
THE ASSURED GROUP; *U.S. Private,* pg. 3989
ATLANTIC SELF STORAGE; *U.S. Private,* pg. 374
BIG YELLOW GROUP PLC; *Int'l,* pg. 1022
BROADWAY STORAGE SOLUTIONS, L.L.C.—See National Storage Affiliates Trust; *U.S. Public,* pg. 1498
BRUNDAGE MANAGEMENT COMPANY; *U.S. Private,* pg. 672
BULLHEAD FREEDOM STORAGE, L.L.C.—See National Storage Affiliates Trust; *U.S. Public,* pg. 1498
BURTCO, INC.; *U.S. Private,* pg. 692
CANYON ROAD STORAGE, LLC—See National Storage Affiliates Trust; *U.S. Public,* pg. 1498
COMCM S.A.; *Int'l,* pg. 1709
DAMASCUS MINI STORAGE LLC—See National Storage Affiliates Trust; *U.S. Public,* pg. 1498
DOWTY AEROSPACE PROPELLERS, REPAIR & OVERHAUL—See General Electric Company; *U.S. Public,* pg. 918
EASTERN MEDIA INTERNATIONAL CORPORATION; *Int'l,* pg. 2273
EMOVE, INC.—See U-Haul Holding Company; *U.S. Public,* pg. 2211
EQUINOR STORAGE DEUTSCHLAND GMBH—See Equinor ASA; *Int'l,* pg. 2484
FLETCHER HEIGHTS STORAGE SOLUTIONS, L.L.C.—See National Storage Affiliates Trust; *U.S. Public,* pg. 1498
FONTANA SELF STORAGE TRS, LLC—See CubeSmart; *U.S. Public,* pg. 603
FONTANA UNIVERSAL SELF STORAGE—See National Storage Affiliates Trust; *U.S. Public,* pg. 1498
FOOD CITY DISTRIBUTION CENTER—See K-VA-T Food Stores, Inc.; *U.S. Public,* pg. 2251
FOOTHILLS SELF STORAGE—See TDG Inc.; *U.S. Private,* pg. 3944
FOREST GROVE MINI STORAGE, LLC—See National Storage Affiliates Trust; *U.S. Public,* pg. 1498

N.A.I.C.S. INDEX

GOLDEN STATE STORAGE ONE, LLC—See Ojai Oil Company; *U.S. Public*, pg. 1566
GRESHAM MINI & RV STORAGE, LLC—See National Storage Affiliates Trust; *U.S. Public*, pg. 1498
HANWA LOGISTICS NAGOYA CO., LTD.—See Hanwa Co., Ltd.; *Int'l*, pg. 3262
HIDE-AWAY STORAGE SERVICES INC.; *U.S. Private*, pg. 1934
HIGHLAND MINI STORAGE—See TKG-StorageMart Partners Portfolio, LLC; *U.S. Private*, pg. 4178
HIGHWAY 97 MINI STORAGE, LLC—See National Storage Affiliates Trust; *U.S. Public*, pg. 1498
HIGHWAY 99 MINI STORAGE, LLC—See National Storage Affiliates Trust; *U.S. Public*, pg. 1498
JDL CASTLE CORPORATION; *U.S. Private*, pg. 2195
JKW HOLDINGS, LLC—See WillScot Mobile Mini Holdings Corp.; *U.S. Public*, pg. 2372
LOMA LINDA UNIVERSAL SELF STORAGE—See National Storage Affiliates Trust; *U.S. Public*, pg. 1498
MILLER INDUSTRIES, INC.; *U.S. Private*, pg. 2734
NATIONAL DISTRIBUTION CENTERS; *U.S. Private*, pg. 2852
NSA OP, LP—See National Storage Affiliates Trust; *U.S. Public*, pg. 1498
PRINEVILLE SPE LLC—See National Storage Affiliates Trust; *U.S. Public*, pg. 1498
PS ORANGECO, INC.—See Public Storage; *U.S. Public*, pg. 1736
PUBLIC STORAGE OP, LP—See Public Storage; *U.S. Public*, pg. 1736
ROBERT BARE ASSOCIATES; *U.S. Private*, pg. 3457
SAFEGARD MINI STORAGE-TIGARD—See National Storage Affiliates Trust; *U.S. Public*, pg. 1498
SEATAC STORAGE, LLC—See National Storage Affiliates Trust; *U.S. Public*, pg. 1498
SECURCARE PROPERTIES II, LLC—See National Storage Affiliates Trust; *U.S. Public*, pg. 1498
SHERWOOD STORAGE, LLC—See National Storage Affiliates Trust; *U.S. Public*, pg. 1498
SHURGARD SELF STORAGE S.C.A.—See Public Storage; *U.S. Public*, pg. 1736
SIMPLY STORAGE MANAGEMENT LLC—See Public Storage; *U.S. Public*, pg. 1736
SOUTHERN SELF STORAGE OF DESTIN, LLC—See National Storage Affiliates Trust; *U.S. Public*, pg. 1498
SOUTHERN SELF STORAGE OF EDGEWATER, LLC—See National Storage Affiliates Trust; *U.S. Public*, pg. 1498
STORAGEMART PARTNERS L.L.C.—See TKG-StorageMart Partners Portfolio, LLC; *U.S. Private*, pg. 4178
STORAGE RENTALS OF AMERICA—See Benjamin Macfarland Company, LLC; *U.S. Public*, pg. 526
SZR SAN MATEO LLC—See Ventas, Inc.; *U.S. Public*, pg. 2278
TKG-STORAGEMART PARTNERS PORTFOLIO, LLC; *U.S. Private*, pg. 4178
TROUTDALE MINI STORAGE, LLC—See National Storage Affiliates Trust; *U.S. Public*, pg. 1498
TWISS COLD STORAGE, INC.—See Bulova Technologies Group, Inc.; *U.S. Private*, pg. 685
UNIVERSAL SELF STORAGE HESPERIA LLC—See National Storage Affiliates Trust; *U.S. Public*, pg. 1498
UNIVERSAL SELF STORAGE SAN BERNARDINO LLC—See National Storage Affiliates Trust; *U.S. Public*, pg. 1498
UNIVERSAL SELF STORAGE—See National Storage Affiliates Trust; *U.S. Public*, pg. 1498
UPLAND UNIVERSAL SELF STORAGE—See National Storage Affiliates Trust; *U.S. Public*, pg. 1498
VERIZON COMMUNICATIONS INC. - HAYES, VA—See Verizon Communications Inc.; *U.S. Public*, pg. 2285
WCAL, LLC—See National Storage Affiliates Trust; *U.S. Public*, pg. 1498
WILSONVILLE JUST STORE IT, LLC—See National Storage Affiliates Trust; *U.S. Public*, pg. 1498

531190 — LESSORS OF OTHER REAL ESTATE PROPERTY

029 GROUP SE; *Int'l*, pg. 1
850 THORN ST INC—See Thomson Properties Inc.; *U.S. Private*, pg. 4162
A&B INC.—See Alexander & Baldwin, Inc.; *U.S. Public*, pg. 75
A B N INTERCORP LIMITED; *Int'l*, pg. 17
ABSA FINANCIAL CORP.; *Int'l*, pg. 69
ACE LIBERTY & STONE PLC; *Int'l*, pg. 94
ADAPTIVE MICRO SYSTEMS LLC—See Traffic & Parking Control Co., Inc.; *U.S. Private*, pg. 4203
ADGAR INVESTMENTS AND DEVELOPMENT LIMITED; *Int'l*, pg. 145
ADRIANO CARE SOCIMI S.A.; *Int'l*, pg. 153
ADVANCE LOGISTICS INVESTMENT CORPORATION; *Int'l*, pg. 156
ADVANCE TERRAFUND REIT; *Int'l*, pg. 157
AGP MALAGA SOCIMI, S.A.; *Int'l*, pg. 213

AGROMEC SA; *Int'l*, pg. 220
AKARD HOLDINGS LP—See Sci-Roev Texas Partners LP; *U.S. Private*, pg. 3573
AL (AP) HOLDING LLC—See Ventas, Inc.; *U.S. Public*, pg. 2277
ALDAR PROPERTIES PJSC; *Int'l*, pg. 304
ALHAMRANI REAL ESTATE DEVELOPMENT COMPANY—See Alhamrani Group; *Int'l*, pg. 319
ALIANTA INVESTMENTS GROUP SA; *Int'l*, pg. 323
ALLIANZ REAL ESTATE GMBH—See Allianz SE; *Int'l*, pg. 349
ALONY HETZ PROPERTIES AND INVESTMENTS LTD.; *Int'l*, pg. 365
ALTERNATIVE INCOME REIT PLC; *Int'l*, pg. 391
AMACON CONSTRUCTION LTD; *Int'l*, pg. 403
ANIMALFEEDS INTERNATIONAL CORPORATION; *U.S. Private*, pg. 283
ANNAPOLIS JUNCTION NFM LLC—See Boston Properties, Inc.; *U.S. Public*, pg. 372
ANNINMUIZAS IPASUMS SIA—See Africa-Israel Investments Ltd.; *Int'l*, pg. 190
ANSHIN GUARANTOR SERVICE CO., LTD.; *Int'l*, pg. 479
ANTIQUELAND USA INC.; *U.S. Private*, pg. 288
AOYUAN BEAUTY VALLEY TECHNOLOGY CO., LTD.; *Int'l*, pg. 499
APODACA INVERSIONES INMOBILIARIAS SOCIMI, S.A.; *Int'l*, pg. 517
APPLE CARR VILLAGE MOBILE HOME PARK, LLC—See Sun Communities, Inc.; *U.S. Public*, pg. 1961
ARA US HOSPITALITY TRUST; *Int'l*, pg. 529
ARCTURUS REALTY CORPORATION—See AtkinsRealis Group Inc.; *Int'l*, pg. 671
AREF THALASSA SOCIMI, S.A.U.; *Int'l*, pg. 557
AREIT, INC.; *Int'l*, pg. 558
ARIMELIA ITG SOCIMI, S.A.; *Int'l*, pg. 565
ARLANDASTAD GROUP AB; *Int'l*, pg. 573
AROUNDTOWN SA; *Int'l*, pg. 577
ARRAS GROUP S.P.A.; *Int'l*, pg. 578
ASGARD INVESTMENT HOTELS SOCIMI SA; *Int'l*, pg. 606
ASHFORD PROPERTIES, LLC—See TransDigm Group Incorporated; *U.S. Public*, pg. 2180
ASPHOLMEN FASTIGHETER AB—See Castellum AB; *Int'l*, pg. 1356
ASSET DEVELOPMENT GROUP, INC.—See West Partners LLC; *U.S. Private*, pg. 4486
ASUNTOSALKKU OY; *Int'l*, pg. 663
ATRIUM BIRE, SIGI, S.A.; *Int'l*, pg. 694
AURORA EIENDOM AS; *Int'l*, pg. 713
BALDWIN HEALTH CENTER INC—See Communicare, Inc.; *U.S. Private*, pg. 988
BALTIC CLASSIFIEDS GROUP PLC; *Int'l*, pg. 812
BAMBOO GROVE RECREATIONAL SERVICES LIMITED—See Hysan Development Company Limited; *Int'l*, pg. 3554
BANC OF AMERICA COMMUNITY DEVELOPMENT CORPORATION—See Bank of America Corporation; *U.S. Public*, pg. 270
BASTI SA; *Int'l*, pg. 888
BAYSIDE STREET INCORPORATED—See Omega Healthcare Investors, Inc.; *U.S. Public*, pg. 1571
BENNETT BROTHERS, INC.—See Bennett Brothers, Inc.; *U.S. Private*, pg. 527
BERCY HAMMERSON FRANCE—See Hammerson plc; *Int'l*, pg. 3238
BERGVIK KOPET 3 K.B.—See Eurocommercial Properties N.V.; *Int'l*, pg. 2534
BERMONT DEVELOPMENT SDN. BHD; *Int'l*, pg. 986
BIANCHI LAND CO.; *U.S. Private*, pg. 550
BILFINGER REAL ESTATE GMBH—See Bilfinger SE; *Int'l*, pg. 1027
BLACK SEA PROPERTY AS; *Int'l*, pg. 1060
BLACKWALL FUND SERVICES LIMITED—See BlackWall Limited; *Int'l*, pg. 1062
BLE KEDROS REAL ESTATE INVESTMENT COMPANY SA; *Int'l*, pg. 1063
BONNA ESTATES COMPANY LIMITED—See Hang Lung Group Limited; *Int'l*, pg. 3244
BOSTON PROPERTIES LIMITED PARTNERSHIP—See Boston Properties, Inc.; *U.S. Public*, pg. 372
BPD INDUSTRIAL REAL ESTATE FUND REIT; *Int'l*, pg. 1131
BP KINGSTOWNE OFFICE BUILDING T LLC—See Boston Properties, Inc.; *U.S. Public*, pg. 372
BP MANAGEMENT, L.P.—See Boston Properties, Inc.; *U.S. Public*, pg. 372
BRANDYWINE REALTY SERVICES CORPORATION—See Brandywine Realty Trust; *U.S. Public*, pg. 380
BRICKS NEWCO LIMITED; *Int'l*, pg. 1151
BRIDGEWATER EQUITY RELEASE LIMITED—See Grainger plc; *Int'l*, pg. 3052
BRIGHTLANE CORP.—See Brightlane Acquisition Corp.; *U.S. Private*, pg. 652
BROMLEY PROPERTY INVESTMENTS LIMITED—See Grainger plc; *Int'l*, pg. 3052
BROOKSIDE VILLAGE MOBILE HOME PARK, LLC—See Sun Communities, Inc.; *U.S. Public*, pg. 1961
BRUUN S GALLERI AS—See BNP Paribas SA; *Int'l*, pg. 1089

BUKIT SEMBAWANG VIEW PTE LTD—See Bukit Sembawang Estates Ltd; *Int'l*, pg. 1213
BULGARIAN REAL ESTATE FUND; *Int'l*, pg. 1213
BURLOV CENTRE FASTIGHETS A.B.—See Eurocommercial Properties N.V.; *Int'l*, pg. 2534
CADDO ENTERPRISES, LIMITED—See Hang Lung Group Limited; *Int'l*, pg. 3244
CAJAVEC-MEGA A.D.; *Int'l*, pg. 1260
CAJAVEC SIP A.D.; *Int'l*, pg. 1260
CALIFORNIA PARKING COMPANY, INC.—See Propark, Inc.; *U.S. Private*, pg. 3284
CAMPUS CREST COMMUNITIES, INC.—See Colliers International Group Inc.; *Int'l*, pg. 1701
CANDEREL MANAGEMENT INC.; *Int'l*, pg. 1289
CAPITAL PROPERTIES, INC.; *U.S. Public*, pg. 432
CARASSO REAL ESTATE LTD.; *Int'l*, pg. 1319
CASA ALBA - INDEPENDENTA SA; *Int'l*, pg. 1349
CBL & ASSOCIATES PROPERTIES—See CBL & Associates Properties, Inc.; *U.S. Public*, pg. 457
CDL LAND NEW ZEALAND LIMITED—See CDL Investments New Zealand Limited; *Int'l*, pg. 1371
CENTRE AT LAUREL, LLC—See Kite Realty Group Trust; *U.S. Public*, pg. 1237
CHELSEA JAPAN CO., LTD.—See Simon Property Group, Inc.; *U.S. Public*, pg. 1881
CHENAL PROPERTIES, INC.—See PotlatchDeltic Corporation; *U.S. Public*, pg. 1704
CHENEGA CORPORATION; *U.S. Private*, pg. 872
CHEUK NANG PROPERTY MANAGEMENT COMPANY—See Cheuk Nang (Holdings) Limited; *Int'l*, pg. 1473
CHINA OVERSEAS GRAND OCEANS GROUP LTD.—See China State Construction Engineering Corporation Limited; *Int'l*, pg. 1554
CHINA VANKE CO., LTD.; *Int'l*, pg. 1561
CITICORE ENERGY REIT CORPORATION; *Int'l*, pg. 1622
CITYA IMMOBILIER SAS; *Int'l*, pg. 1628
CITYCON AB—See Citycon Oyj; *Int'l*, pg. 1629
CITYCON FINLAND OY—See Citycon Oyj; *Int'l*, pg. 1629
CLOVELLY CORPORATION; *U.S. Public*, pg. 947
COCREATIV TAMPA BAY LLC; *U.S. Private*, pg. 959
COIMA RES SIIQ S.P.A.; *Int'l*, pg. 1696
COLDWELL BANKER COMMERCIAL AFFILIATES—See Anywhere Real Estate Inc.; *U.S. Public*, pg. 141
COLTON REAL ESTATE GROUP INC.; *U.S. Private*, pg. 976
COMALEX SA; *Int'l*, pg. 1707
COMPAGNIE LA LUCETTE S.A.—See Caisse des Depots et Consignations; *Int'l*, pg. 1258
COMPANIES (TC) LLC.; *U.S. Private*, pg. 998
COMPLEX COMET SA; *Int'l*, pg. 1753
CONIFER INC—See Omega Healthcare Investors, Inc.; *U.S. Public*, pg. 1571
COPLEY HEALTH CENTER INC—See Communicare, Inc.; *U.S. Private*, pg. 988
CORE SPAIN HOLDCO SOCIMI, S.A.U.; *Int'l*, pg. 1798
CORIX BIOSCIENCE, INC.; *U.S. Private*, pg. 1050
THE CORKY MCMILLIN COMPANIES; *U.S. Private*, pg. 4015
CORPFIN CAPITAL PRIME RETAIL III SOCIMI SA; *Int'l*, pg. 1802
CORPFIN CAPITAL PRIME RETAIL II SOCIMI SA; *Int'l*, pg. 1802
COUSINS PROPERTIES PALISADES LLC—See Cousins Properties Incorporated; *U.S. Public*, pg. 587
COUSINS PROPERTIES SERVICES LLC—See Cousins Properties Incorporated; *U.S. Public*, pg. 587
CPI FIM S.A.—See CPI Property Group, S.A.; *Int'l*, pg. 1825
CTP N.V.; *Int'l*, pg. 1872
CWS CORPORATE HOUSING; *U.S. Private*, pg. 1133
DAEHO CO., LTD—See DHSteel; *Int'l*, pg. 2100
DAEJAN ESTATES LIMITED—See Centremanor Ltd.; *Int'l*, pg. 1412
DAIWA INFORMATION SERVICE CO., LTD.—See Daiwa House Industry Co., Ltd.; *Int'l*, pg. 1945
DAMAC INVEST CO. LLC—See DAMAC Group; *Int'l*, pg. 1955
DELTA INVESTORS—See Omega Healthcare Investors, Inc.; *U.S. Public*, pg. 1571
DETALJHANDELSHUSET I HYLLINGE AB—See BNP Paribas SA; *Int'l*, pg. 1090
DEUTSCHE EIGENHEIM UNION AG; *Int'l*, pg. 2065
DEUTSCHE INDUSTRIE REIT-AG; *Int'l*, pg. 2065
DEUTSCHE KONSUM REIT-AG; *Int'l*, pg. 2066
DEWEY SQUARE TOWER ASSOCIATES, LLC—See MetLife, Inc.; *U.S. Public*, pg. 1430
DEXTERS LONDON LIMITED; *Int'l*, pg. 2093
DIAMOND SPARKLING LIMITED—See Daido Group Ltd; *Int'l*, pg. 1920
DIC ESTATE CO., LTD.—See DIC Corporation; *Int'l*, pg. 2107
DIEGEM-KENNEDY; *Int'l*, pg. 2114
DISTRIBUTIVNI CENTAR A.D.; *Int'l*, pg. 2137
DIXON HEALTH CARE CENTER—See Omega Healthcare Investors, Inc.; *U.S. Public*, pg. 1571
DKLS EQUITY SDN BHD—See DKLS Industries Berhad; *Int'l*, pg. 2139

531190 — LESSORS OF OTHER RE...

DOKAY LIMITED—See Hang Lung Group Limited; *Int'l*, pg. 3244
DONGGUAN WINNERWAY INDUSTRY ZONE LTD.; *Int'l*, pg. 2167
DOTHOME, LLC.—See National Association of Realtors; *U.S. Private*, pg. 2847
DOTSTAY S.P.A.; *Int'l*, pg. 2180
DOUGLAS ELLIMAN INC.; *U.S. Public*, pg. 677
DREISBACH ENTERPRISES INC.; *U.S. Private*, pg. 1275
DRUSTVENI STANDARD CAJAVEC A.D.; *Int'l*, pg. 2206
DUKEMOUNT CAPITAL PLC; *Int'l*, pg. 2224
DUSSMANN PROPERTY MANAGEMENT (SHANGHAI) CO. LTD.—See Dussmann Stiftung & Co. KGaA; *Int'l*, pg. 2234
DUTCHWAY FARM MARKET INC.; *U.S. Private*, pg. 1294
DUTTON MILL VILLAGE, LLC—See Sun Communities, Inc.; *U.S. Public*, pg. 1961
EARLY AGE CO., LTD.; *Int'l*, pg. 2267
ECP MORABERG K.B.—See Eurocommercial Properties N.V.; *Int'l*, pg. 2534
EEMERGE, INC.—See SL Green Realty Corp.; *U.S. Public*, pg. 1894
EFTEN REAL ESTATE FUND III AS; *Int'l*, pg. 2321
EGP 2297 OTAY LLC—See Easterly Government Properties, Inc.; *U.S. Public*, pg. 703
EKLANDIA FASTIGHETS AB—See Castellum AB; *Int'l*, pg. 1356
EL CID LAND & CATTLE INC.—See Allsup Enterprises Inc.; *U.S. Private*, pg. 194
ELITE COMMERCIAL REIT; *Int'l*, pg. 2362
THE ELK HORN COAL COMPANY LLC—See Wexford Capital Limited Partnership; *U.S. Private*, pg. 4502
EMAAR PROPERTIES CANADA LTD—See Emaar Properties PJSC; *Int'l*, pg. 2372
EMLAK KATILIM VARLIK KIRALAMA A.S.; *Int'l*, pg. 2384
EMMA VILLAS S.P.A.; *Int'l*, pg. 2384
ENERGETICS & ENERGY SAVINGS FUND - FEEI SPV; *Int'l*, pg. 2420
ERG CAP 3 REIT; *Int'l*, pg. 2490
E-STARCO CO., LTD.; *Int'l*, pg. 2249
EUROCOMMERCIAL PROPERTIES CAUMARTIN S.N.C.—See Eurocommercial Properties N.V.; *Int'l*, pg. 2534
EUROCOMMERCIAL PROPERTIES SWEDEN AB—See Eurocommercial Properties N.V.; *Int'l*, pg. 2534
EUROLOG CANOLA SOCIMI, S.A.U.; *Int'l*, pg. 2553
EUROPEAN REAL ESTATE INVESTMENT TRUST LIMITED; *Int'l*, pg. 2557
EVERBRIGHT GRAND CHINA ASSETS LIMITED; *Int'l*, pg. 2563
EYELEVEL DISTRIBUTION SERVICES—See HH Global Group Limited; *Int'l*, pg. 3378
FABRIKA KOZE LAUS A.D.; *Int'l*, pg. 2599
FAIFEY INVEST SOCIMI, S.A.; *Int'l*, pg. 2604
FAR EAST CONSORTIUM LIMITED—See Far East Consortium International Limited; *Int'l*, pg. 2615
FARMANDSTREDET ANS—See BNP Paribas SA; *Int'l*, pg. 1091
FARMANDSTREDET EIENDOM AS—See BNP Paribas SA; *Int'l*, pg. 1091
FARM BUREAU BUILDING, INC.—See Arkansas Farm Bureau Federation; *U.S. Private*, pg. 325
FARNSWORTH REALTY AND MANAGEMENT CO.—See Farnsworth Development Companies; *U.S. Private*, pg. 1480
FASTIGHETS AB ALLUM—See BNP Paribas SA; *Int'l*, pg. 1091
FASTIGHETS AB BORLANGE KOPCENTRUM—See BNP Paribas SA; *Int'l*, pg. 1091
FASTIGHETS AB BROSTADEN—See Castellum AB; *Int'l*, pg. 1356
FASTIGHETS AB CENTRUMINVEST—See BNP Paribas SA; *Int'l*, pg. 1091
FASTIGHETS AB MARIEBERG CENTRUM—See BNP Paribas SA; *Int'l*, pg. 1091
FASTIGHETS AB OVERBY KOPCENTRUM—See BNP Paribas SA; *Int'l*, pg. 1091
FASTIGHETS AB SOLLENTUNA CENTRUM—See BNP Paribas SA; *Int'l*, pg. 1091
FC TRIDENT, LLC—See Welltower Inc;; *U.S. Public*, pg. 2348
FERTI-LOME DISTRIBUTORS INC.—See Voluntary Purchasing Groups, Inc.; *U.S. Private*, pg. 4411
FIBRA HD SERVICIOS SC; *Int'l*, pg. 2652
FIRST HOSPITALITY GROUP, INC.; *U.S. Private*, pg. 1520
FIRST STAGE CORPORATION; *Int'l*, pg. 2688
FLUGHAFEN WIEN IMMOBILIENVERWERTUNGSGESELLSCHAFT M.B.H—See Flughafen Wien Aktiengesellschaft; *Int'l*, pg. 2712
FONTAINEBLEAU VASTGOED BV—See Carpetright plc; *Int'l*, pg. 1343
FUND ESTATES REIT; *Int'l*, pg. 2845
FU YIK COMPANY LIMITED—See Hang Lung Group Limited; *Int'l*, pg. 3245
GALIMMO SA—See Carmila SA; *Int'l*, pg. 1342
GAMLA HAREL RESIDENTIAL REAL-ESTATE LTD.; *Int'l*, pg. 2878

GANGLONG CHINA PROPERTY GROUP LIMITED; *Int'l*, pg. 2880
GASTRONOM SA; *Int'l*, pg. 2888
GENERALCOM SA; *Int'l*, pg. 2920
GERRITY COMPANY INCORPORATED; *U.S. Private*, pg. 1687
GLOBAL PIELAGO, SOCIMI, S.A.; *Int'l*, pg. 3000
GOLDEN VENTURES LEASEHOLD REAL ESTATE INVESTMENT TRUST; *Int'l*, pg. 3032
GOOD LIFE COMPANY, INC.; *Int'l*, pg. 3038
GOWILY LIMITED—See Hang Lung Group Limited; *Int'l*, pg. 3245
GRADISKA TRZNICA A.D.; *Int'l*, pg. 3049
GRADSKI TRGOVSKI CENTAR AD; *Int'l*, pg. 3050
GRAINGER STUTTGART PORTFOLIO 1 SARL & CO KG—See Grainger plc; *Int'l*, pg. 3052
GRAND BAZAAR LTD.—See ANSA McAL Limited; *Int'l*, pg. 477
GREEN TOWER PROPERTIES, INC.; *Int'l*, pg. 3073
G RENT S.P.A.; *Int'l*, pg. 2861
GROW BIZ GAMES, INC.—See Winmark Corporation; *U.S. Public*, pg. 2374
GRP LIMITED; *Int'l*, pg. 3113
GRUNBERG REALTY; *U.S. Private*, pg. 1797
GUANGZHOU R&F PROPERTIES CO., LTD.; *Int'l*, pg. 3167
GUBER A.D.; *Int'l*, pg. 3171
GULF GENERAL INVESTMENT COMPANY PSC - REAL ESTATE DIVISION—See Gulf General Investment Company PSC; *Int'l*, pg. 3180
HAADTHIP DEVELOPMENT CO., LTD.—See Haad Thip Public Company Limited; *Int'l*, pg. 3201
HAFIZ LIMITED; *Int'l*, pg. 3206
HAINING CHINA LEATHER MARKET CO., LTD.; *Int'l*, pg. 3216
HALMONT PROPERTIES CORPORATION; *Int'l*, pg. 3233
HAMAMATSU TERMINAL DEVELOPMENT CO., LTD.—See Central Japan Railway Company; *Int'l*, pg. 1408
HAMAR STORSENTER AS—See BNP Paribas SA; *Int'l*, pg. 1091
HAMMERSON CENTRE COMMERCIAL ITALIE SAS—See Hammerson plc; *Int'l*, pg. 3238
HAMMERSON MADELEINE SAS—See Hammerson plc; *Int'l*, pg. 3238
HAMMERSON SAS—See Hammerson plc; *Int'l*, pg. 3238
HANG CHUI COMPANY LIMITED—See Hang Lung Group Limited; *Int'l*, pg. 3245
HANG FINE COMPANY LIMITED—See Hang Lung Group Limited; *Int'l*, pg. 3245
HANG KWOK COMPANY LIMITED—See Hang Lung Group Limited; *Int'l*, pg. 3245
HARPER DENNIS HOBBS LIMITED—See Newmark Group, Inc.; *U.S. Public*, pg. 1515
HARRIS PREFERRED CAPITAL CORPORATION; *U.S. Private*, pg. 1870
HARRY SJOGREN AB—See Castellum AB; *Int'l*, pg. 1356
HASEKO CORPORATION; *Int'l*, pg. 3282
HA TAY TRADING JOINT STOCK COMPANY; *Int'l*, pg. 3201
HCI HANSEATISCHE IMMOBILIENBETEILIGUNGSGESELLSCHAFT MBH—See Ernst Russ AG; *Int'l*, pg. 2495
HCP PROPERTIES, INC.—See JPMorgan Chase & Co.; *U.S. Public*, pg. 1207
HEATHER HIGHLANDS MOBILE HOME VILLAGE ASSOCIATES, LP—See UMH Properties, Inc.; *U.S. Public*, pg. 2224
HECKENKEMPER HOMES, LLC.; *U.S. Private*, pg. 1903
HEIMSTADEN AB; *Int'l*, pg. 3323
HEMARAJ LEASEHOLD REAL ESTATE INVESTMENT TRUST; *Int'l*, pg. 3340
HICKORY HILLS VILLAGE, LLC—See Sun Communities, Inc.; *U.S. Public*, pg. 1961
HIDDEN RIDGE AN RV COMMUNITY, LLC—See Sun Communities, Inc.; *U.S. Public*, pg. 1961
HIGHWOODS REALTY LIMITED PARTNERSHIP—See Highwoods Properties, Inc.; *U.S. Public*, pg. 1035
HOMES & HOLIDAY AG; *Int'l*, pg. 3455
HOMETOGO SE; *Int'l*, pg. 3455
HOMIZY S.P.A.; *Int'l*, pg. 3456
HUA YU LIEN DEVELOPMENT CO., LTD.; *Int'l*, pg. 3510
HUDSON 1099 STEWART REIT, LLC—See Hudson Pacific Properties, Inc.; *U.S. Public*, pg. 1068
HUI XIAN ASSET MANAGEMENT LIMITED; *Int'l*, pg. 3526
HUNG CHING DEVELOPMENT & CONSTRUCTION CO., LTD.; *Int'l*, pg. 3535
HUP SENG HUAT LAND PTE LTD—See HupSteel Limited; *Int'l*, pg. 3538
HYSAN LEASING COMPANY LIMITED—See Hysan Development Company Limited; *Int'l*, pg. 3554
HYSAN PROPERTY MANAGEMENT LIMITED—See Hysan Development Company Limited; *Int'l*, pg. 3554
HYSOUNG INVESTMENT & DEVELOPMENT—See Hyosung Corporation; *Int'l*, pg. 3552
ICONIC DEVELOPMENT LLC; *U.S. Private*, pg. 2032
IGIS NEPTUNE BARCELONA HOLDCO SOCIMI, S.A.; *Int'l*, pg. 3602
IGP ADVANTAG AG; *Int'l*, pg. 3603
INTERMOBILIARIA, S.A.—See Bankinter, S.A.; *Int'l*, pg. 850

INTERNATIONAL ENDEAVORS CORPORATION; *U.S. Public*, pg. 1151
IPROPERTY.COM MALAYSIA SDN BHD—See News Corporation; *U.S. Public*, pg. 1521
IVANHOE CAMBRIDGE—See Caisse de Depot et Placement du Quebec; *Int'l*, pg. 1254
JAMES CAMPBELL CORPORATION; *U.S. Private*, pg. 2183
JENSEN'S INC.—See Sun Communities, Inc.; *U.S. Public*, pg. 1961
JONES LANG LASALLE AMERICAS, INC; *U.S. Private*, pg. 2233
KINNEBROOK MOBILE HOME ASSOCIATES LP—See UMH Properties, Inc.; *U.S. Public*, pg. 2224
KLECAR EUROPE SUD SCS—See BNP Paribas SA; *Int'l*, pg. 1091
KLE PROJET 1 SAS—See BNP Paribas SA; *Int'l*, pg. 1091
KRONAN FASTIGHETER I KARLSKRONA AB—See Eurocommercial Properties N.V.; *Int'l*, pg. 2534
KRONOS (US) INC—See Hellman & Friedman LLC; *U.S. Private*, pg. 1910
KS MARKEDET—See BNP Paribas SA; *Int'l*, pg. 1091
LANCOR PROJECTS LIMITED—See Compuage Infocom Ltd.; *Int'l*, pg. 1754
LANDMARK DIVIDEND LLC—See DigitalBridge Group, Inc.; *U.S. Public*, pg. 664
LANDMARK WHITE (GOLD COAST) PTY LTD—See Acumentis Group Limited; *Int'l*, pg. 121
LANDMARK WHITE (VIC) PTY LTD—See Acumentis Group Limited; *Int'l*, pg. 121
LASALLE INVESTMENT MANAGEMENT (CANADA)—See Jones Lang LaSalle Incorporated; *U.S. Public*, pg. 1203
LASALLE INVESTMENT MANAGEMENT SECURITIES, LLC—See Jones Lang LaSalle Incorporated; *U.S. Public*, pg. 1204
LD ACQUISITION COMPANY 8 LLC—See DigitalBridge Group, Inc.; *U.S. Public*, pg. 665
LEE THEATRE REALTY LIMITED—See Hysan Development Company Limited; *Int'l*, pg. 3554
LEO PROPERTY MANAGEMENT PRIVATE LIMITED—See Allgreen Properties Ltd.; *Int'l*, pg. 338
LEUCADIA FINANCIAL CORPORATION—See Jefferies Financial Group Inc.; *U.S. Public*, pg. 1189
LILLIBRIDGE HEALTHCARE SERVICES, INC.—See Ventas, Inc.; *U.S. Public*, pg. 2278
LIVE SMART @ HOME LIMITED—See Home Group Limited; *Int'l*, pg. 3454
LSG SKY CHEFS BUILDING AB—See Deutsche Lufthansa AG; *Int'l*, pg. 2068
LXB HOLDINGS LIMITED—See Hammerson plc; *Int'l*, pg. 3238
MANSITA LIMITED—See Hang Lung Group Limited; *Int'l*, pg. 3245
MATTHEWS REAL ESTATE INVESTMENT SERVICES; *U.S. Private*, pg. 2613
MAUNA KEA AGRIBUSINESS CO., INC.—See C. Brewer & Co. Ltd.; *U.S. Private*, pg. 705
MAXIM ENTERPRISES, INC; *U.S. Private*, pg. 2618
MERCANTILE LEASING S.P.A.—See Banco BPM S.p.A.; *Int'l*, pg. 819
METROSPACES, INC.; *U.S. Public*, pg. 1431
METUCHEN COMMUNITY SERVICES CORPORATION; *U.S. Private*, pg. 2691
MIDPOINT PROPERTIES LIMITED—See Allgreen Properties Ltd.; *Int'l*, pg. 338
MILLCRAFT INVESTMENTS INC.—See Millcraft Industries Inc.; *U.S. Private*, pg. 2731
MINNESOTA POWER—See ALLETE, Inc.; *U.S. Public*, pg. 79
MLB CAPITAL PARTNERS, LLC; *U.S. Private*, pg. 2753
MODERN DEVELOPMENT COMPANY; *U.S. Private*, pg. 2760
MOUNTAIN MANAGERS, INC.—See Hammersmith Data Management, Inc.; *U.S. Private*, pg. 1849
THE MOUNT VERNON COMPANY , INC.; *U.S. Private*, pg. 4081
NERSTRANDA AS—See BNP Paribas SA; *Int'l*, pg. 1092
NET LEASE OFFICE PROPERTIES; *U.S. Public*, pg. 1506
NEWLAKE CAPITAL PARTNERS, INC.; *U.S. Public*, pg. 1515
THE NEW RIVER COMPANY LIMITED—See Derwent London plc; *Int'l*, pg. 2043
NEW WORLD CHINA LAND INVESTMENTS COMPANY LIMITED—See Chow Tai Fook Enterprises Limited; *Int'l*, pg. 1585
NORDBYEN SENTER AS—See BNP Paribas SA; *Int'l*, pg. 1092
NORTH MAN SVERIGE AB—See BNP Paribas SA; *Int'l*, pg. 1092
NORTHUMBERLAND & DURHAM PROPERTY TRUST LIMITED—See Grainger plc; *Int'l*, pg. 3052
NRI REAL ESTATE INVESTMENT & TECHNOLOGY, INC.; *U.S. Private*, pg. 2969
OAK CENTER HOMES PARTNERS, L.P.; *U.S. Private*, pg. 2983
OHI CONNECTICUT INC—See Omega Healthcare Investors, Inc.; *U.S. Public*, pg. 1571
OMEGA HEALTHCARE INVESTORS INC.-

N.A.I.C.S. INDEX

531210 — OFFICES OF REAL EST...

MARYLAND—See Omega Healthcare Investors, Inc.; *U.S. Public*, pg. 1571
ORCO BUDAPEST KFT—See CPI Property Group, S.A.; *Int'l*, pg. 1825
ORION OFFICE REIT, INC.; *U.S. Public*, pg. 1618
OS ALLE 3 AS—See BNP Paribas SA; *Int'l*, pg. 1092
OTAY LAND COMPANY, LLC—See Jefferies Financial Group Inc.; *U.S. Public*, pg. 1188
OTTRINGHAM LIMITED—See Hang Lung Group Limited; *Int'l*, pg. 3245
OXFORD VILLAGE LTD—See UMH Properties, Inc.; *U.S. Public*, pg. 2225
PAC/SIB L.L.C.—See Pacific Realty Associates, LP; *U.S. Private*, pg. 3070
PALM SHADOWS MOBILE HOME & RV RESORT—See Manufactured Housing Properties Inc.; *U.S. Public*, pg. 1362
PBF LOGISTICS LP—See PBF Energy Inc.; *U.S. Public*, pg. 1657
PHOSPHATE RESOURCES (SINGAPORE) PTE LTD—See CI Resources Limited; *Int'l*, pg. 1601
PIER PARK, LLC.; *U.S. Private*, pg. 3178
POCAHONTAS LAND CORPORATION—See Norfolk Southern Corporation; *U.S. Public*, pg. 1536
POCALITON LIMITED—See Hang Lung Group Limited; *Int'l*, pg. 3245
POLY DEVELOPMENTS AND HOLDINGS GROUP CO., LTD.—See China Poly Group Corporation; *Int'l*, pg. 1541
POLY SOUTHERN GROUP CO., LTD.—See China Poly Group Corporation; *Int'l*, pg. 1541
PROIN S.A.—See Banco Macro S.A.; *Int'l*, pg. 823
PT SENTRABOGA INTISELERA—See Asahi Group Holdings Ltd.; *Int'l*, pg. 593
QUIJUL PTE. LTD.—See Platinum Equity, LLC; *U.S. Private*, pg. 3206
REDMAN HEENAN PROPERTIES LIMITED—See Blackstone Inc.; *U.S. Public*, pg. 358
REISTERSTOWN PLAZA ASSOCIATES, LLC—See Kite Realty Group Trust; *U.S. Public*, pg. 1237
RENTBITS.COM; *U.S. Private*, pg. 3400
RIOLOY LIMITED—See Hang Lung Group Limited; *Int'l*, pg. 3245
RMC PROPERTY GROUP LLC; *U.S. Private*, pg. 3451
THE ROCKY RIVER REALTY COMPANY—See Eversource Energy; *U.S. Public*, pg. 802
RPC BRAMLAGE VELKY MEDER S.R.O.—See Berry Global Group, Inc; *U.S. Public*, pg. 324
RUBY WAY LIMITED—See Far East Consortium International Limited; *Int'l*, pg. 2615
RUISLIP AND NORTHWOOD AGED PEOPLE'S HOUSING COMPANY LIMITED—See Home Group Limited; *Int'l*, pg. 3454
RUSSELL SENIORS, LLC.; *U.S. Private*, pg. 3507
RUTAR INTERNATIONAL TRGOVINSKA D.O.O.—See Erste Group Bank AG; *Int'l*, pg. 2499
SAGUNA NETWORKS LTD.—See COMSovereign Holding Corp.; *U.S. Public*, pg. 562
SAMARKANDFASTIGHETER AB—See Eurocommercial Properties N.V.; *Int'l*, pg. 2534
SCHIAVI LEASING CORPORATION—See Vanguard Modular Building Systems, LLC; *U.S. Public*, pg. 4344
SCOPE PROPERTIES, INC.—See ReConserve, Inc.; *U.S. Private*, pg. 3371
SEFERCO DEVELOPMENT S.A.—See Eurobank Ergasias Services and Holdings S.A.; *Int'l*, pg. 2533
SEGECE CESKA REPUBLIKA SRO—See BNP Paribas SA; *Int'l*, pg. 1092
SEQUOIA RESIDENTIAL FUNDING, INC.—See Redwood Trust, Inc.; *U.S. Public*, pg. 1771
SHIZUOKA TERMINAL DEVELOPMENT COMPANY LIMITED—See Central Japan Railway Company; *Int'l*, pg. 1408
SILVER NICETY COMPANY LIMITED—See Hysan Development Company Limited; *Int'l*, pg. 3554
SINGAPORE UNITED ESTATES (PRIVATE) LIMITED—See Bukit Sembawang Estates Ltd; *Int'l*, pg. 1213
SOUTHWOOD VILLAGE MOBILE HOME PARK, LLC—See Sun Communities, Inc.; *U.S. Public*, pg. 1963
STAVANGER STORSENTER AS—See BNP Paribas SA; *Int'l*, pg. 1092
STELLA MARIS INC.; *U.S. Private*, pg. 3799
STERLING ACQUISTION CORP—See Omega Healthcare Investors, Inc.; *U.S. Public*, pg. 1572
STERLING REALTY ORGANIZATION CO.; *U.S. Private*, pg. 3807
STOVNER SENTER AS—See BNP Paribas SA; *Int'l*, pg. 1092
STRATUS CAPITAL CORP.; *U.S. Public*, pg. 1954
SUBURBAN PAVILLION INC.—See Omega Healthcare Investors, Inc.; *U.S. Public*, pg. 1572
SULLIVAN & COGLIANO DESIGNERS INC., RHODE ISLAND—See Sullivan & Cogliano Designers Inc.; *U.S. Private*, pg. 3850
S&W SERVICES, INC.; *U.S. Private*, pg. 3514
SYCAMORE VILLAGE MOBILE HOME PARK, LLC—See Sun Communities, Inc.; *U.S. Public*, pg. 1963
SYNTHES MEDICAL IMMOBILIEN GMBH—See Johnson & Johnson; *U.S. Public*, pg. 1200

TERRAQUEST SOLUTIONS LIMITED—See Apse Capital Ltd.; *Int'l*, pg. 523
THREADNEEDLE CAPITAL MANAGEMENT LTD.—See Ameriprise Financial, Inc.; *U.S. Public*, pg. 114
THREE ALBERT EMBANKMENT LIMITED—See CLS Holdings plc; *Int'l*, pg. 1664
TLC WILDLIFE RANCHES INC.—See Moore Holdings Inc.; *U.S. Private*, pg. 2780
TOMARTA SDN. BHD.—See Far East Consortium International Limited; *Int'l*, pg. 2615
TOP TREND DEVELOPMENTS LIMITED—See Far East Consortium International Limited; *Int'l*, pg. 2615
TORVBYEN SENTER AS—See BNP Paribas SA; *Int'l*, pg. 1093
TORVBYEN UTVIKLING AS—See BNP Paribas SA; *Int'l*, pg. 1093
TORVHJORNET LILLESTROM ANS—See BNP Paribas SA; *Int'l*, pg. 1093
TRANSWEST PARTNERS; *U.S. Private*, pg. 4211
TRAVELERS HAVEN, LLC—See Blueground US Inc; *U.S. Private*, pg. 597
TRIBUNE PROPERTIES, INC.—See Nexstar Media Group, Inc.; *U.S. Public*, pg. 1525
TRILLION DEVELOPMENT CO LTD—See AP (Thailand) Public Company Limited; *Int'l*, pg. 499
TRIPLA GRUNDSTUCKS-VERMIETUNGSGESELLSCHAFT MBH—See Deutsche Bank Aktiengesellschaft; *Int'l*, pg. 2062
TULIP MANAGEMENT SRL—See Africa Israel Investments Ltd.; *Int'l*, pg. 190
UMH IN HIGHLAND, LLC—See UMH Properties, Inc.; *U.S. Public*, pg. 2225
UMH IN HOLIDAY VILLAGE, LLC—See UMH Properties, Inc.; *U.S. Public*, pg. 2225
UMH IN MEADOWS, LLC—See UMH Properties, Inc.; *U.S. Public*, pg. 2225
UMH IN WOODS EDGE, LLC—See UMH Properties, Inc.; *U.S. Public*, pg. 2225
UMH MI CANDLEWICK COURT, LLC—See UMH Properties, Inc.; *U.S. Public*, pg. 2225
UMH NY BROOKVIEW MHP, LLC—See UMH Properties, Inc.; *U.S. Public*, pg. 2225
UMH NY D&R VILLAGE, LLC—See UMH Properties, Inc.; *U.S. Public*, pg. 2225
UMH OH CATALINA, LLC—See UMH Properties, Inc.; *U.S. Public*, pg. 2225
UMH OH HAYDEN HEIGHTS, LLC—See UMH Properties, Inc.; *U.S. Public*, pg. 2225
UMH OH LAKE SHERMAN VILLAGE, LLC—See UMH Properties, Inc.; *U.S. Public*, pg. 2225
UMH OH OLMSTED FALLS, LLC—See UMH Properties, Inc.; *U.S. Public*, pg. 2225
UMH OH WORTHINGTON ARMS, LLC—See UMH Properties, Inc.; *U.S. Public*, pg. 2225
UMH PA CRANBERRY VILLAGE, LLC—See UMH Properties, Inc.; *U.S. Public*, pg. 2225
UMH PA FOREST PARK, LLC—See UMH Properties, Inc.; *U.S. Public*, pg. 2225
UMH PA HOLLY ACRES, LLC—See UMH Properties, Inc.; *U.S. Public*, pg. 2225
UMH PA HUNTINGDON POINTE, LLC—See UMH Properties, Inc.; *U.S. Public*, pg. 2225
UMH PA SUBURBAN ESTATES, LLC—See UMH Properties, Inc.; *U.S. Public*, pg. 2225
UMH PA SUNNY ACRES, LLC—See UMH Properties, Inc.; *U.S. Public*, pg. 2225
UMH PA VALLEY STREAM, LLC—See UMH Properties, Inc.; *U.S. Public*, pg. 2225
UMH PA VOYAGER ESTATES, LLC—See UMH Properties, Inc.; *U.S. Public*, pg. 2225
UMH PROPERTIES, INC.; *U.S. Public*, pg. 2224
UMH TN ALLENTOWN, LLC—See UMH Properties, Inc.; *U.S. Public*, pg. 2225
UMH TN WEATHERLY ESTATES, LLC—See UMH Properties, Inc.; *U.S. Public*, pg. 2225
UNITED MOBILE HOMES OF BUFFALO, INC.—See UMH Properties, Inc.; *U.S. Public*, pg. 2225
UNIVERSITY SQUARE PARKING LLC—See Kite Realty Group Trust; *U.S. Public*, pg. 1237
USAA REAL ESTATE SERVICES—See United Services Automobile Association; *U.S. Private*, pg. 4297
VASTRA TORP MARK AB—See BNP Paribas SA; *Int'l*, pg. 1093
VERMONT LAND TRUST INC.; *U.S. Private*, pg. 4367
VICI PROPERTIES L.P.; *U.S. Public*, pg. 2296
VICTORY PACKAGING DE MEXICO, S. DE R.L. DE C.V—See WestRock Company; *U.S. Public*, pg. 2361
VITALICIO TORRE CERDA S.L.—See Assicurazioni Generali S.p.A.; *Int'l*, pg. 644
WESTREC EQUITIES, INC.—See Centerbridge Partners, L.P.; *U.S. Public*, pg. 816
WILDER CORPORATION; *U.S. Private*, pg. 4519
WILLIAM PITT SOTHEBY'S INTERNATIONAL REALTY; *U.S. Private*, pg. 4524
WORLDWIDE APARTMENT SERVICES PTE LTD—See Allgreen Properties Ltd.; *Int'l*, pg. 338
WRI FLAMINGO PINES, LLC—See Kimco Realty Corporation; *U.S. Public*, pg. 1232

WYNDHAM VACATION OWNERSHIP, INC.—See Travel & Leisure Co.; *U.S. Public*, pg. 2185
WYNNE BUILDING CORPORATION; *U.S. Private*, pg. 4578
ZILLOW GROUP MORTGAGES, INC.—See Zillow Group, Inc.; *U.S. Public*, pg. 2405

531210 — OFFICES OF REAL ESTATE AGENTS AND BROKERS

101 HUDSON LEASING ASSOCIATES—See Veris Residential, Inc.; *U.S. Public*, pg. 2281
1325 AVENUE OF THE AMERICAS, L.P.—See Paramount Group Inc.; *U.S. Public*, pg. 1637
1ST CLASS REAL ESTATE LLC; *U.S. Private*, pg. 4
1ST KNIGHT REALTY, LLC; *U.S. Private*, pg. 4
2350 HARPER HOUSE, L.L.C.—See Starwood Real Estate Income Trust, Inc.; *U.S. Private*, pg. 3789
2390 GRAHAM PARK, L.L.C.—See Starwood Real Estate Income Trust, Inc.; *U.S. Private*, pg. 3789
250 HIGH STREET, L.L.C.—See Starwood Real Estate Income Trust, Inc.; *U.S. Private*, pg. 3789
360 BLUE, LLC—See Natural Retreats US LLC; *U.S. Private*, pg. 2867
4CORNERS HOMES; *U.S. Private*, pg. 15
600 GOODALE, L.L.C.—See Starwood Real Estate Income Trust, Inc.; *U.S. Private*, pg. 3789
801 POLARIS HOLDINGS, L.L.C.—See Starwood Real Estate Income Trust, Inc.; *U.S. Private*, pg. 3790
80 ON THE COMMONS, L.L.C.—See Starwood Real Estate Income Trust, Inc.; *U.S. Private*, pg. 3789
A.A.A. AG ALLGEMEINE ANLAGEVERWALTUNG; *Int'l*, pg. 22
AAL REALTY CORP.—See The Great Atlantic & Pacific Tea Company, Inc.; *U.S. Private*, pg. 4038
ABC DEVELOPMENT CORPORATION—See Asahi Broadcasting Group Holdings Corporation; *Int'l*, pg. 592
ABHI-CROCKETT, INC.—See Matson, Inc.; *U.S. Public*, pg. 1398
ABLE & PARTNERS CO., LTD.; *Int'l*, pg. 62
ABLON GROUP LIMITED; *Int'l*, pg. 63
ABLON SP. Z O.O.—See Ablon Group Limited; *Int'l*, pg. 63
ABU DHABI NATIONAL PROPERTIES PRJC—See First Abu Dhabi Bank P.J.S.C.; *Int'l*, pg. 2681
ACCESSIBLE SPACE INC.; *U.S. Private*, pg. 53
ACRES REAL ESTATE SERVICES INC.; *U.S. Private*, pg. 65
ACUMENTIS BRISBANE PTY LTD—See Acumentis Group Limited; *Int'l*, pg. 121
ACUMENTIS GOLD COAST PTY LTD—See Acumentis Group Limited; *Int'l*, pg. 121
ACUMENTIS MELBOURNE PTY LTD—See Acumentis Group Limited; *Int'l*, pg. 121
ADA INTERNATIONAL REAL ESTATE OWNED BY ABU DHABI AVIATION-SOLE PROPRIETORSHIP CO. L.L.C.—See Abu Dhabi Aviation; *Int'l*, pg. 70
ADAM DEVELOPMENT PROPERTIES, L.P.—See The Adam Corporation/Group; *U.S. Private*, pg. 3981
ADGAR CANADA INC.—See ADGAR INVESTMENTS AND DEVELOPMENT LIMITED; *Int'l*, pg. 145
ADGAR POLAND SP. Z O.O.—See ADGAR INVESTMENTS AND DEVELOPMENT LIMITED; *Int'l*, pg. 145
ADOMOS SA; *Int'l*, pg. 152
ADVANCE REALTY GROUP, LLC; *U.S. Private*, pg. 87
ADVENTURE PROPERTIES INC.; *U.S. Private*, pg. 109
AD WEST END, LLC—See Prologis, Inc.; *U.S. Public*, pg. 1726
AEGON USA REALTY ADVISORS, LLC—See Aegon N.V.; *Int'l*, pg. 174
AEW ASIA LIMITED—See Groupe BPCE; *Int'l*, pg. 3092
AEW INVEST GMBH—See Groupe BPCE; *Int'l*, pg. 3092
AFC GAMMA, INC.; *U.S. Public*, pg. 53
AFFINIA HOSPITALITY; *U.S. Private*, pg. 122
THE AGENCY; *U.S. Private*, pg. 3983
THE AGENT (PROPERTY EXPERT) CO., LTD.—See Ananda Development Public Company Limited; *Int'l*, pg. 447
AGRAM NEKRETNINE D.D.; *Int'l*, pg. 213
AGROENERGY REIT; *Int'l*, pg. 218
AGRO-PROPERTY KFT.—See BayWa AG; *Int'l*, pg. 915
A.G. SPANOS MANAGEMENT—See A.G. Spanos Companies; *U.S. Private*, pg. 26
A&I BROADWAY REALTY; *U.S. Private*, pg. 20
AIRBORNE SECURITY & PROTECTION SERVICES, INC.; *U.S. Public*, pg. 68
AJS REALTY GROUP, INC.; *U.S. Private*, pg. 144
AKYASAM YONETIM HIZMETLERI A.S.—See Akis Gayrimenkul Yatirim Ortakligi A.S.; *Int'l*, pg. 263
ALAIN PINEL REALTORS, INC.—See Compass, Inc.; *U.S. Public*, pg. 561
ALBERT M. GREENFIELD & CO., INC.; *U.S. Private*, pg. 153
ALBERTO HERNANDEZ REAL ESTATE INC.; *U.S. Private*, pg. 153
ALCO REALTY, INC.—See Clayton, Dubilier & Rice, LLC; *U.S. Private*, pg. 928
ALFA REALTY, INC.—See Alfa Corporation; *U.S. Private*, pg. 164

531210 — OFFICES OF REAL EST...

A-LIVING SMART CITY SERVICES CO., LTD.; *Int'l*, pg. 20
ALKAS CONSULTING—See Jones Lang LaSalle Incorporated; *U.S. Public*, pg. 1201
ALLERGAN PHARMACEUTICALS (PROPRIETARY) LIMITED—See AbbVie Inc.; *U.S. Public*, pg. 23
ALLIANCE MANAGEMENT, INC.; *U.S. Private*, pg. 183
ALLIANZ IMMOBILIEN GMBH—See Allianz SE; *Int'l*, pg. 348
ALLISON JAMES ESTATES & HOMES INC.; *U.S. Private*, pg. 192
ALL POINTS NORTH PLC; *Int'l*, pg. 332
ALLREAL HOLDING AG; *Int'l*, pg. 360
ALL SAINTS COMMERCIAL PLC; *Int'l*, pg. 332
ALMA DEVELOPMENT SP. Z O.O.—See Alma Market S.A.; *Int'l*, pg. 361
ALONY HETZ GLOBAL LTD.—See Alony Hetz Properties and Investments Ltd.; *Int'l*, pg. 365
AL-OSAISI REAL ESTATE CO.—See Al-Osais International Holding Company; *Int'l*, pg. 287
ALPHA BARNES REAL ESTATE SERVICES, LLC—See Asset Plus Companies LP; *U.S. Private*, pg. 354
ALPHA REAL TRUST LIMITED; *Int'l*, pg. 369
ALPINE INCOME PROPERTY TRUST, INC.; *U.S. Public*, pg. 85
ALSONS DEVELOPMENT AND INVESTMENT CORPORATION—See Alcantara Group; *Int'l*, pg. 300
ALTA CRP AUBERGENVILLE SNC—See Altarea SCA; *Int'l*, pg. 385
ALTA FINANCIAL SERVICES, INC.—See Hanna Holdings, Inc.; *U.S. Private*, pg. 1854
ALTAIR SOLAR, LLC—See EnBio Holdings Inc.; *Int'l*, pg. 2396
ALTAREA COGEDIM CITALIS—See Altarea SCA; *Int'l*, pg. 385
ALTAREA ESPANA SL—See Altarea SCA; *Int'l*, pg. 385
ALTAREA FRANCE SAS—See Altarea SCA; *Int'l*, pg. 385
ALTAREA ITALIA S.R.L.—See Altarea SCA; *Int'l*, pg. 385
ALTERE SECURITIZADORA S.A.; *Int'l*, pg. 391
THE ALTMAN GROUP; *U.S. Private*, pg. 3985
ALTUS GROUP U.S. INC.—See Altus Group Limited; *Int'l*, pg. 399
AMAG SERVICE GMBH—See AMAG Austria Metall AG; *Int'l*, pg. 408
AMAS LIMITED—See Jones Lang LaSalle Incorporated; *U.S. Public*, pg. 1203
AMELIA BULLOCK REALTORS, INC.—See Kuper Realty Corp.; *U.S. Private*, pg. 2357
AMELKIS RESORTS S.A.—See Emaar Properties PJSC; *Int'l*, pg. 2372
AMERICANA LLC; *U.S. Private*, pg. 258
AMERICAN CAMPUS COMMUNITIES OPERATING PARTNERSHIP, LP—See Blackstone Inc.; *U.S. Public*, pg. 347
AMERICAN ESCROW COMPANY—See First American Financial Corporation; *U.S. Public*, pg. 835
AMERICAN FIDELITY PROPERTY COMPANY—See American Fidelity Corporation; *U.S. Private*, pg. 234
AMERICAN PROPERTY GROUP OF SARASOTA INC.; *U.S. Private*, pg. 244
AMERICAN PROPERTY MANAGEMENT CORPORATION; *U.S. Private*, pg. 244
AMERICAN TRADING & PRODUCTION CORPORATION; *U.S. Private*, pg. 257
AMERIFIRST HOME MORTGAGE; *U.S. Private*, pg. 259
AMURCON CORPORATION; *U.S. Private*, pg. 269
ANCHOR GRUP S.A.—See Fiba Holding A.S.; *Int'l*, pg. 2651
ANDISCH, INC.; *U.S. Private*, pg. 278
ANDREWS REALTY LTD; *Int'l*, pg. 452
ANGEL OAK MORTGAGE REIT, INC.; *U.S. Public*, pg. 136
ANSAL BUILDWELL LTD; *Int'l*, pg. 477
ANSAL CLUBS PVT. LIMITED—See Ansal Housing Ltd; *Int'l*, pg. 478
ANTARIKSH INDUSTRIES LIMITED; *Int'l*, pg. 482
ANTICIPA REAL ESTATE, SLU—See Blackstone Inc.; *U.S. Public*, pg. 360
APAC REALTY LIMITED—See Morgan Stanley; *U.S. Public*, pg. 1471
APARTMENT REALTY ADVISORS OF ARIZONA, LLLP—See BGC Group, Inc.; *U.S. Public*, pg. 327
APARTMENT REALTY ADVISORS OF FLORIDA, INC.—See BGC Group, Inc.; *U.S. Public*, pg. 328
APEX LIMITED PARTNERSHIP; *Int'l*, pg. 511
API FOX PLAZA LLC—See Equity Residential; *U.S. Public*, pg. 791
APM PROPERTY MANAGEMENT PTE. LTD.—See ESR Group Limited; *Int'l*, pg. 2507
APO IMMOBILIEN-KAG—See Deutsche Apotheker- und Arztebank eG; *Int'l*, pg. 2049
APPLETON CORPORATION—See The O'Connell Companies, Incorporated; *U.S. Private*, pg. 4087
APRIL CORPORATE BROKING SARL—See CVC Capital Partners SICAV-FIS S.A.; *Int'l*, pg. 1882
ARA NATIONAL LAND SERVICES, LLC—See BGC Group, Inc.; *U.S. Private*, pg. 328
ARCHSTONE B.V.—See Equity Residential; *U.S. Public*, pg. 791
A&R KATZ MANAGEMENT INC.; *U.S. Private*, pg. 20
ARROYO & COMPANY; *U.S. Private*, pg. 336
THE ARTERY GROUP, LLC; *U.S. Private*, pg. 3988
ARTHUR J. ROGERS & CO; *U.S. Private*, pg. 342

ART-INVEST REAL ESTATE MANAGEMENT GMBH & CO. KG; *Int'l*, pg. 580
ASAS MUTIARA SDN. BHD.—See Asas Dunia Berhad; *Int'l*, pg. 599
ASBURY PARTNERS, LLC—See Safehold Inc.; *U.S. Public*, pg. 1834
ASHIANA HOUSING LTD; *Int'l*, pg. 607
ASHLEY CAPITAL LLC; *U.S. Private*, pg. 349
ASHWICK (VIC) NO 102 PTY. LTD.—See Elders Limited; *Int'l*, pg. 2346
ASKARI REAL ESTATE LTD.—See Army Welfare Trust LLC; *Int'l*, pg. 576
A-SMART PROPERTY HOLDINGS PTE LTD—See A-Smart Holdings Ltd.; *Int'l*, pg. 20
THE ASNY CORPORATION; *U.S. Private*, pg. 3989
ASPEN (GROUP) HOLDINGS LIMITED; *Int'l*, pg. 628
ASPIRE REAL ESTATE INVESTORS, INC.; *U.S. Private*, pg. 352
ASSET REALTY—See Asset Realty Group; *U.S. Private*, pg. 354
ASSET REALTY—See Asset Realty Group; *U.S. Private*, pg. 354
ASTAR PIMA ROADSCOTTSDALE LLC—See Safehold Inc.; *U.S. Public*, pg. 1834
ASWAN VILLAGE ASSOCIATES, LLC—See Bank of America Corporation; *U.S. Public*, pg. 270
ATG TITLE; *U.S. Private*, pg. 367
ATLANTA OUTLET SHOPPES, LLC—See CBL & Associates Properties, Inc.; *U.S. Public*, pg. 457
ATLANTIC REALTY PROFESSIONALS, INC.—See Wilkinson & Associates Real Estate; *U.S. Private*, pg. 4521
ATTORNEYS' TITLE GUARANTY FUND—See Guaranteed Rate, Inc.; *U.S. Private*, pg. 1809
ATWATER REAL ESTATE; *U.S. Private*, pg. 384
AUCKLAND REAL ESTATE TRUST; *Int'l*, pg. 699
AUCTION WORLD USA, LLC; *U.S. Private*, pg. 385
AURUM ANALYTICA PRIVATE LIMITED—See Aurum PropTech Ltd.; *Int'l*, pg. 715
AUSTINREALESTATE.COM; *U.S. Private*, pg. 396
AVALON ANAHEIM STADIUM, L.P.—See AvalonBay Communities, Inc.; *U.S. Public*, pg. 240
AVALON AT BALLSTON, LLC—See AvalonBay Communities, Inc.; *U.S. Public*, pg. 240
AVALON AT DIAMOND HEIGHTS, L.P.—See AvalonBay Communities, Inc.; *U.S. Public*, pg. 240
AVALON AT PROVIDENCE PARK, LLC—See AvalonBay Communities, Inc.; *U.S. Public*, pg. 240
AVALONBAY GROSVENOR, INC.—See AvalonBay Communities, Inc.; *U.S. Public*, pg. 240
AVALON ENCINO, L.P.—See AvalonBay Communities, Inc.; *U.S. Public*, pg. 240
AVALON FASHION VALLEY, L.P.—See AvalonBay Communities, Inc.; *U.S. Public*, pg. 240
AVALON OCEAN AVENUE, L.P.—See AvalonBay Communities, Inc.; *U.S. Public*, pg. 240
AVALON RIVERVIEW NORTH, LLC—See AvalonBay Communities, Inc.; *U.S. Public*, pg. 240
AVALON WEST LONG BRANCH, LLC—See AvalonBay Communities, Inc.; *U.S. Public*, pg. 240
AVALON WOODLAND HILLS, L.P.—See AvalonBay Communities, Inc.; *U.S. Public*, pg. 240
AVENIDA PARTNERS LLC—See Ashmore Group plc; *Int'l*, pg. 608
AVH NORTH FLORIDA, LLC—See Brookfield Corporation; *Int'l*, pg. 1183
AV HOMES OF ARIZONA, LLC—See Brookfield Corporation; *Int'l*, pg. 1183
AVIATION FACILITIES COMPANY, INC.; *U.S. Private*, pg. 406
AVISON YOUNG (CANADA) INC.; *Int'l*, pg. 744
AVISON YOUNG (USA) INC. - LOS ANGELES, NORTH—See Avison Young (Canada) Inc.; *Int'l*, pg. 744
AVISON YOUNG (USA) INC. - NEW JERSEY—See Avison Young (Canada) Inc.; *Int'l*, pg. 744
AVISON YOUNG (USA) INC. - RALEIGH-DURHAM—See Avison Young (Canada) Inc.; *Int'l*, pg. 744
AVISON YOUNG (USA) INC.—See Avison Young (Canada) Inc.; *Int'l*, pg. 744
AVISON YOUNG (USA) INC. - SOUTH FLORIDA-FORT LAUDERDALE—See Avison Young (Canada) Inc.; *Int'l*, pg. 745
AYALA LAND, INC.—See Ayala Corporation; *Int'l*, pg. 774
BAIRD & WARNER REAL ESTATE, INC.; *U.S. Private*, pg. 453
BAIRD & WARNER—See Baird & Warner Real Estate, Inc.; *U.S. Private*, pg. 453
BALFOUR BEATTY CAMPUS SOLUTIONS LLC—See Balfour Beatty plc; *Int'l*, pg. 807
B-A-L GERMANY AG; *Int'l*, pg. 784
BALLEY PACIFIC PETROLEUM; *U.S. Private*, pg. 461
BALMORAL LAND NAUL LTD—See Balmoral International Land Holdings plc; *Int'l*, pg. 810
BALTIC SEA PROPERTIES AS; *Int'l*, pg. 812
BANGKOK LAND AGENCY LIMITED—See Bangkok Land Public Company Limited; *Int'l*, pg. 834
BANKS & ASSOCIATES, LLC—See Seminole Holdings Group, LLC; *U.S. Private*, pg. 3604
BARINGS CORE SPAIN SOCIMI, S.A.; *Int'l*, pg. 865

CORPORATE AFFILIATIONS

BARTON BUSINESS PARK LIMITED—See Blackstone Inc.; *U.S. Public*, pg. 358
BATIMENTS ET LOGEMENTS RESIDENTIELS; *Int'l*, pg. 889
BAYLEYS CORPORATION LIMITED; *Int'l*, pg. 914
BAYSIDE VILLAGE ASSOCIATES, L.P.—See Brookfield Corporation; *Int'l*, pg. 1187
BEACH PROPERTIES OF FLORIDA—See Berkshire Hathaway Inc.; *U.S. Public*, pg. 306
BEAR CREEK STATION LLC—See Phillips Edison & Company LLC; *U.S. Private*, pg. 3170
BEAZER HOMES SALES, INC.—See Beazer Homes USA, Inc.; *U.S. Public*, pg. 287
BECHARD GROUP, INC.; *U.S. Private*, pg. 509
BEITLER & ASSOCIATES INC.; *U.S. Private*, pg. 516
BELKORP INDUSTRIES, INC.; *Int'l*, pg. 965
BELLEVUE TOWERS CONDOMINIUMS, LLC—See Morgan Stanley; *U.S. Public*, pg. 1471
BELL PARTNERS, INC.; *U.S. Private*, pg. 518
BELLWETHER ENTERPRISE REAL ESTATE—See Enterprise Community Partners, Inc.; *U.S. Private*, pg. 1403
BELPOINTE PREP, LLC; *U.S. Public*, pg. 295
BENCHMARK REALTY LLC; *U.S. Private*, pg. 524
BENGUET EBARA REAL ESTATE CORP.—See Benguet Corporation; *Int'l*, pg. 974
BENGUET EBARA REAL ESTATE CORP.—See Ebara Corporation; *Int'l*, pg. 2282
BENJAMIN MACFARLAND COMPANY, LLC; *U.S. Private*, pg. 526
BENTALL KENNEDY REAL ESTATE SERVICES LP—See Bentall Kennedy LP; *Int'l*, pg. 975
BERGER ORGANIZATION, LLC; *U.S. Private*, pg. 530
BERKELEY POINT CAPITAL, LLC—See Newmark Group, Inc.; *U.S. Public*, pg. 1515
BERKSHIRE HATHAWAY HOMESERVICES FOX & ROACH, REALTORS—See Berkshire Hathaway Inc.; *U.S. Public*, pg. 306
BERKSHIRE HATHAWAY HOMESERVICES NEW ENGLAND PROPERTIES—See Berkshire Hathaway Inc.; *U.S. Public*, pg. 306
BERLIN HYP IMMOBILIEN GMBH—See Deutscher Sparkassen- und Giroverband e.V.; *Int'l*, pg. 2085
THE BERNSTEIN COMPANIES; *U.S. Private*, pg. 3994
BERNSTEIN MANAGEMENT CORPORATION; *U.S. Private*, pg. 538
BERWIND PROPERTY GROUP, LTD.—See Berwind Corporation; *U.S. Private*, pg. 541
BEST DEAL PROPERTIES HOLDING PLC; *Int'l*, pg. 999
BEST HOTEL PROPERTIES A.S.; *Int'l*, pg. 999
BEST PROPERTY CO., LTD.—See Biken Techno Corporation Ltd.; *Int'l*, pg. 1023
BETTER HOMES & GARDENS REAL ESTATE LLC—See Anywhere Real Estate Inc.; *U.S. Public*, pg. 140
THE BETZ COMPANIES; *U.S. Private*, pg. 3994
BEVERLY-HANKS & ASSOCIATES INC.—See Hanna Holdings, Inc.; *U.S. Private*, pg. 1854
B. GRIMM INTERNATIONAL SERVICE CO., LTD.—See B. Grimm Group; *Int'l*, pg. 788
BHH AFFILIATES, LLC—See Berkshire Hathaway Inc.; *U.S. Public*, pg. 299
BHW IMMOBILIEN GMBH—See Deutsche Post AG; *Int'l*, pg. 2079
BH-ZACD (TUAS BAY) DEVELOPMENT PTE. LTD.—See CNQC International Holdings Ltd.; *Int'l*, pg. 1678
BIG BANK PRODUCTIONS, INC.; *U.S. Private*, pg. 552
BIG BEN REALTY, INC.; *U.S. Private*, pg. 552
BILL NAITO COMPANY; *U.S. Private*, pg. 558
BILTMORE APARTMENTS, LTD.—See Apartment Investment and Management Company; *U.S. Public*, pg. 144
BIM IMMOBILIARE SRL—See Banca Intermobiliare di Investimenti e Gestioni S.p.A.; *Int'l*, pg. 815
BINSWANGER MANAGEMENT CORP.; *U.S. Private*, pg. 561
BIRGER BOSTAD AB—See Fabege AB; *Int'l*, pg. 2598
BISHOP CAPITAL CORP/WYOMING; *U.S. Public*, pg. 339
BK IMMOBILIEN VERWALTUNG GMBH—See DIC Asset AG; *Int'l*, pg. 2107
BKM CAPITAL PARTNERS, L.P.; *U.S. Private*, pg. 569
BLACKSTONE REAL ESTATE INCOME TRUST, INC.—See Blackstone Inc.; *U.S. Public*, pg. 351
BLADCENTRALENS EIENDOMSSELSKAP AS—See Egmont Fonden; *Int'l*, pg. 2325
BLAKE REAL ESTATE, INC.; *U.S. Private*, pg. 578
BLEACHER SALES COMPANY INC.; *U.S. Private*, pg. 580
BLOSSOM TIME SDN. BHD.—See Atlan Holdings Berhad; *Int'l*, pg. 673
BLOWING ROCK INVESTMENT PROPERTIES, INC.—See Hanna Holdings, Inc.; *U.S. Private*, pg. 1854
BLUE DOG LLC—See Equity CommonWealth; *U.S. Public*, pg. 790
BLUE STAR PROPERTIES, INC.—See Banner Corporation; *U.S. Public*, pg. 275
BLUE VISION A/S; *Int'l*, pg. 1070
BLYTHE VALLEY INNOVATION CENTRE LTD.—See Prologis, Inc.; *U.S. Public*, pg. 1727
BMW INGENIEUR ZENTRUM GMBH & CO.—See Bayerische Motoren Werke Aktiengesellschaft; *Int'l*, pg. 911

N.A.I.C.S. INDEX
531210 — OFFICES OF REAL EST...

BNP PARIBAS REAL ESTATE HOLDING GMBH—See BNP Paribas SA; *Int'l*, pg. 1086
THE BOARDWALK COMPANY; *U.S. Private*, pg. 3995
BOBACK COMMERCIAL GROUP; *U.S. Private*, pg. 606
BOB PARKS REALTY LLC; *U.S. Private*, pg. 604
BOLKAN PROPERTY INSTRUMENTS REIT; *Int'l*, pg. 1102
BON MANAGEMENT INC.; *U.S. Private*, pg. 612
BOOMERANG DIRECT MARKETING, LLC; *U.S. Private*, pg. 616
BORDERPLEX REALTY LLC; *U.S. Private*, pg. 618
BOSSHARDT REALTY SERVICES, INC.; *U.S. Private*, pg. 620
BOSTON PROPERTIES SERVICES, LLC—See Boston Properties, Inc.; *U.S. Public*, pg. 373
BOUWCOMBINATIE INTERMEZZO V.O.F.—See Heijmans N.V.; *Int'l*, pg. 3322
BOWEN AGENCY INC.; *U.S. Private*, pg. 625
BREMNERDUKE MCKINNEY DEVELOPMENT I, LLC—See Prologis, Inc.; *U.S. Public*, pg. 1726
BRG INTERNATIONAL, LLC—See Jones Lang LaSalle Incorporated; *U.S. Public*, pg. 1201
BRH GARVER CONSTRUCTION, L.P.—See Kidd & Company LLC; *U.S. Private*, pg. 2302
BRIDGEMARQ REAL ESTATE SERVICES INC.; *Int'l*, pg. 1153
BRIGHTSPIRE CAPITAL, INC.; *U.S. Public*, pg. 383
BRINOVA FASTIGHETER AB; *Int'l*, pg. 1164
BRIOSCHI FINANZIARIA S.P.A.—See Bastogi S.p.A.; *Int'l*, pg. 888
BROADSTONE NET LEASE, INC.; *U.S. Public*, pg. 392
BROAD STREET REALTY, LLC; *U.S. Private*, pg. 658
BROKERS CONSOLIDATED, INC.; *U.S. Private*, pg. 662
BROOKFIELD PROPERTY GROUP—See Brookfield Corporation; *Int'l*, pg. 1185
BROOKHILL GROUP INC.; *U.S. Private*, pg. 663
BROOKMAY PROPERTIES (PTY) LIMITED—See Esor Limited; *Int'l*, pg. 2504
BROOKS RESOURCES CORPORATION; *U.S. Private*, pg. 664
BROOKVIEW LP—See UMH Properties, Inc.; *U.S. Public*, pg. 2224
BROTHERS PROPERTY CORPORATION—See American Financial Group, Inc.; *U.S. Public*, pg. 103
BROWN HARRIS STEVENS, LLC - COCONUT GROVE OFFICE—See Brown Harris Stevens, LLC; *U.S. Private*, pg. 667
BROWN HARRIS STEVENS, LLC; *U.S. Private*, pg. 667
BROWN STEVENS ELMORE & SPARRE; *U.S. Private*, pg. 669
BSEL INFRASTRUCTURE REALTY FZE—See BSEL Infrastructure Realty Limited; *Int'l*, pg. 1202
BSR REAL ESTATE INVESTMENT TRUST; *U.S. Public*, pg. 409
BTV REAL-LEASING GMBH—See Bank fur Tirol und Vorarlberg Ag; *Int'l*, pg. 838
BUCKEYES HOTEL OWNER LP—See Pebblebrook Hotel Trust; *U.S. Public*, pg. 1660
BULGARIAN INVESTMENT GROUP REIT; *Int'l*, pg. 1213
BULIGO CAPITAL ORD SHS; *Int'l*, pg. 1214
BUNTING MANAGEMENT GROUP, INC.; *U.S. Private*, pg. 686
BURKE REHABILITATION HOSPITAL—See The Winifred Masterson Burke Rehabilitation Hospital, Inc.; *U.S. Private*, pg. 687
BURKI VERPACKUNGSTECHNIK AG; *Int'l*, pg. 1226
BURLINGTON RIVER APARTMENTS, LIMITED PARTNERSHIP—See Apartment Investment and Management Company; *U.S. Public*, pg. 144
BUYATIMESHARE.COM; *U.S. Private*, pg. 699
BUY EFFICIENT, LLC—See Sunstone Hotel Investors, Inc.; *U.S. Public*, pg. 1966
BWP TRUST; *Int'l*, pg. 1232
CABARET EAST—See RCI Hospitality Holdings, Inc.; *U.S. Public*, pg. 1767
CADDO HOLDING COMPANY, LLC—See ALLETE, Inc.; *U.S. Public*, pg. 306
CADU INMOBILIARIA S.A DE C.V.; *Int'l*, pg. 1248
CAIXA-IMOBILIARIO-SOCIEDADE DE GESTAO E INVESTIMENTO IMOBILIARIO S.A.—See Caixa Geral de Depositos S.A.; *Int'l*, pg. 1260
CALATLANTIC TITLE AGENCY, LLC—See Lennar Corporation; *U.S. Public*, pg. 1306
CALETHOS, INC.; *U.S. Public*, pg. 423
CALSTAR PROPERTIES LLC; *U.S. Private*, pg. 723
CAMERON REAL ESTATE SERVICES, INC.; *U.S. Private*, pg. 729
CANADA LAND LIMITED; *Int'l*, pg. 1278
CAN BRIANS 2, S.A.—See ACS, Actividades de Construccion y Servicios, S.A.; *Int'l*, pg. 110
CANNABUSINESS GROUP, INC.; *U.S. Private*, pg. 734
CANTOR FITZGERALD INCOME TRUST, INC.; *U.S. Private*, pg. 735
CAPI FRANCE—See Financiere Pinault SCA; *Int'l*, pg. 2668
CAPITAL AG PROPERTY SERVICES INC.; *U.S. Private*, pg. 738
CAPITAL AGRICULTURAL PROPERTY SERVICES, INC.—See Prudential Financial, Inc.; *U.S. Public*, pg. 1734

CAPITAL FIRST REALTY INCORPORATED; *U.S. Private*, pg. 740
CAPITAL HOLDING GROUP REIT; *Int'l*, pg. 1311
CAPITAL REAL ESTATE PROJECTS B.S.C.—See GFH Financial Group B.S.C.; *Int'l*, pg. 2956
CAPITAL SQUARE SDN. BHD.—See Bandar Raya Developments Berhad; *Int'l*, pg. 829
CAPITOL CROSSING ADVISORS, LLC—See W.R. Berkley Corporation; *U.S. Public*, pg. 2317
CAPTIVA VERDE WELLNESS CORP.; *Int'l*, pg. 1317
CARABETTA MANAGEMENT CO., INC.; *U.S. Private*, pg. 748
CAREY FINANCIAL, LLC—See W.P. Carey Inc.; *U.S. Public*, pg. 2315
CARLSBERG MANAGEMENT COMPANY INC.—See CMC Realty Inc.; *U.S. Private*, pg. 950
CARLSON REAL ESTATE COMPANY—See Carlson Companies Inc.; *U.S. Private*, pg. 765
THE CARLYLE GROUP, INC.; *U.S. Private*, pg. 4005
CARPENTER & COMPANY, INC.; *U.S. Private*, pg. 770
CARPENTER REALTORS; *U.S. Private*, pg. 770
CARRINGTON HOLDING CO.; *U.S. Private*, pg. 772
CARROLL ORGANIZATION, LLC; *U.S. Private*, pg. 773
CARTER & ASSOCIATES, LLC; *U.S. Private*, pg. 775
CARTUS B.V.—See Anywhere Real Estate Inc.; *U.S. Public*, pg. 140
CASA, INC.; *Int'l*, pg. 1349
CASAMIA IMMOBILIARE SAS—See Emeis SA; *Int'l*, pg. 2376
CASCADE SOTHEBY'S INTERNATIONAL REALTY; *U.S. Private*, pg. 781
CASE POMEROY & COMPANY INC.; *U.S. Private*, pg. 782
CASTLEHEAD, INC. ESCROWS; *U.S. Private*, pg. 785
CATELLA BANK SA—See Catella AB; *Int'l*, pg. 1359
CATELLA CORPORATE FINANCE GOTEBORG HB—See Catella AB; *Int'l*, pg. 1359
CATELLA CORPORATE FINANCE MALMO AB—See Catella AB; *Int'l*, pg. 1359
CATELLA CORPORATE FINANCE SIA—See Catella AB; *Int'l*, pg. 1359
CATELLA CORPORATE FINANCE VILNIUS UAB—See Catella AB; *Int'l*, pg. 1359
CATELLA FRANCE SARL—See Catella AB; *Int'l*, pg. 1359
CATELLA INVESTMENT MANAGEMENT A/S—See Catella AB; *Int'l*, pg. 1359
CATELLA PROPERTY BENELUX SA—See Catella AB; *Int'l*, pg. 1359
CATELLA PROPERTY GMBH—See Catella AB; *Int'l*, pg. 1359
CATELLA PROPERTY SPAIN S.A.—See Catella AB; *Int'l*, pg. 1359
CATELLA REAL ESTATE AG—See Catella AB; *Int'l*, pg. 1359
CBL & ASSOCIATES LIMITED PARTNERSHIP—See CBL & Associates Properties, Inc.; *U.S. Public*, pg. 457
CBRE GROUP, INC.; *U.S. Public*, pg. 459
CBRE, INC. - HOUSTON—See CBRE Group, Inc.; *U.S. Public*, pg. 460
CBRE LIMITED; *Int'l*, pg. 1366
CB RICHARD ELLIS, INC. - CHICAGO—See CBRE Group, Inc.; *U.S. Public*, pg. 459
CB RICHARD ELLIS, INC. - LOS ANGELES, DOWNTOWN—See CBRE Group, Inc.; *U.S. Public*, pg. 459
CB RICHARD ELLIS, INC. - NEW YORK CITY—See CBRE Group, Inc.; *U.S. Public*, pg. 459
CB RICHARD ELLIS, INC.—See CBRE Group, Inc.; *U.S. Public*, pg. 459
CB RICHARD ELLIS - N.E. PARTNERS, LP—See CBRE Group, Inc.; *U.S. Public*, pg. 459
CB RICHARD ELLIS OF VIRGINIA, INC.—See Colliers International Group Inc.; *Int'l*, pg. 1700
CB RICHARD ELLIS SERVICES, INC.—See CBRE Group, Inc.; *U.S. Public*, pg. 459
CBSHOME REAL ESTATE—See Berkshire Hathaway Inc.; *U.S. Public*, pg. 306
CB/TCC GLOBAL HOLDINGS LIMITED—See CBRE Group, Inc.; *U.S. Public*, pg. 460
CCIP STERLING, L.P.—See Apartment Investment and Management Company; *U.S. Public*, pg. 144
CDP CAPITAL REAL ESTATE ADVISORY—See Caisse de Depot et Placement du Quebec; *Int'l*, pg. 1253
CDP IMMOBILIARE S.R.L.—See Cassa Depositi e Prestiti S.p.A.; *Int'l*, pg. 1354
CEBU HOLDINGS INC.—See Ayala Corporation; *Int'l*, pg. 774
CEDAR CREEK PROPERTIES LLC—See CRH plc; *Int'l*, pg. 1843
CEDAR CREEK REALTY, LLC—See CRH plc; *Int'l*, pg. 1843
THE CEDARWOOD COMPANIES; *U.S. Private*, pg. 4006
CEDARWOOD DEVELOPMENT, INC.—See The Cedarwood Companies; *U.S. Private*, pg. 4006
CENTRALE KREDIETVERLENING NV; *Int'l*, pg. 1410
CENTRAL GENERAL DEVELOPMENT CO., LTD.; *Int'l*, pg. 1406
CENTURY 21 BEGGINS ENTERPRISES, INC.; *U.S. Private*, pg. 831
CENTURY 21 HOMETOWN REALTY; *U.S. Private*, pg. 831

CENTURY 21 NORTH HOMES REALTY, INC.; *U.S. Private*, pg. 831
CENTURY 21 PROPERTY AGENCY LIMITED—See Huanxi Media Group Limited; *Int'l*, pg. 3513
CENTURY21 REAL ESTATE OF JAPAN LTD.; *Int'l*, pg. 1420
CENTURY 21 RONDEAU; *U.S. Private*, pg. 831
CERNER PROPERTIES, INC.—See Oracle Corporation; *U.S. Public*, pg. 1611
CERVERA REAL ESTATE, INC.; *U.S. Private*, pg. 842
C. G. P., INC.—See Tootsie Roll Industries, Inc.; *U.S. Public*, pg. 2163
CGRN, INC.—See Anywhere Real Estate Inc.; *U.S. Public*, pg. 140
CHAKRATEC ORD SHS; *Int'l*, pg. 1437
CHALET VILLAGE PROPERTIES, INC.—See Cabins For You, LLC; *U.S. Private*, pg. 711
CHAMPION REALTY INC.—See Berkshire Hathaway Inc.; *U.S. Public*, pg. 306
CHANGCHUN VANKE REAL ESTATE DEVELOPMENT COMPANY LIMITED—See China Vanke Co., Ltd.; *Int'l*, pg. 1562
CHARITY & WEISS INTERNATIONAL REALTY, LLC; *U.S. Private*, pg. 851
CHARLES DUNN COMPANY, INC.; *U.S. Private*, pg. 852
CHARLES DUNN REAL ESTATE SERVICES—See Charles Dunn Company, Inc.; *U.S. Private*, pg. 852
CHARLES RUTENBERG REALTY, INC.; *U.S. Private*, pg. 853
CHARLES RUTENBERG REALTY, INC.; *U.S. Private*, pg. 853
CHARLIE EARHART REALTY; *U.S. Private*, pg. 857
CHEN XING DEVELOPMENT HOLDINGS LIMITED; *Int'l*, pg. 1465
CHICAGO ATLANTIC REAL ESTATE FINANCE, INC.; *U.S. Public*, pg. 488
CHINACHEM GROUP; *Int'l*, pg. 1568
CHINA PROPERTIES GROUP LTD; *Int'l*, pg. 1542
CHINA RAILWAY CONSTRUCTION REAL ESTATE GROUP CO., LTD.—See China Railway Construction Corporation Limited; *Int'l*, pg. 1543
CHUDEN AUTO LEASE CO., LTD.—See Chubu Electric Power Co., Inc.; *Int'l*, pg. 1593
CHUDEN REAL ESTATE CO., LTD.—See Chubu Electric Power Co., Inc.; *Int'l*, pg. 1593
CHURSTON HEARD LTD—See Jones Lang LaSalle Incorporated; *U.S. Public*, pg. 1203
CIBC WM REAL ESTATE LTD.—See Canadian Imperial Bank of Commerce; *Int'l*, pg. 1284
CIMINELLI DEVELOPMENT COMPANY, INC.; *U.S. Private*, pg. 897
CIM INTERNATIONAL GROUP, INC.; *Int'l*, pg. 1607
CINCINNATI COMMERCIAL CONTRACTING, LLC.; *U.S. Private*, pg. 897
CIRCA CAPITAL CORPORATION; *U.S. Private*, pg. 899
CIRCLE PROPERTY PLC; *Int'l*, pg. 1617
CIS PROMOTION; *Int'l*, pg. 1618
CITI HABITATS—See Anywhere Real Estate Inc.; *U.S. Public*, pg. 141
CITISCAPE PROPERTY MANAGEMENT GROUP, LLC—See FirstService Corporation; *Int'l*, pg. 2691
CITYLAND DEVELOPMENT CORPORATION; *Int'l*, pg. 1629
CITY SUNSTONE PROPERTIES LLC; *U.S. Private*, pg. 907
CIVITAS SOCIAL HOUSING PLC; *Int'l*, pg. 1630
CLASSIC DREAM PROPERTIES LTD.; *Int'l*, pg. 1652
CLIFF DEVELOPMENT SALES & APPRAISALS, INC.; *U.S. Private*, pg. 943
THE CLIMATIC DEVELOPMENT CORPORATION.—See The Climatic Corporation; *U.S. Private*, pg. 4010
CLIPPER REALTY INC.; *U.S. Public*, pg. 515
CLS LUXEMBOURG SARL—See CLS Holdings plc; *Int'l*, pg. 1664
CMC REALTY INC.; *U.S. Private*, pg. 950
CMN CALGARY INC.—See Colliers International Group Inc.; *Int'l*, pg. 1701
CMR PARTNERS LLP; *U.S. Private*, pg. 951
CMS PROPERTY DEVELOPMENT SDN. BHD.—See Cahya Mata Sarawak Berhad; *Int'l*, pg. 1251
COASTAL PROPERTIES GROUP INTERNATIONAL, LLC; *U.S. Private*, pg. 956
COASTAL REALTY DEVELOPMENT CO. LIMITED—See Coastal Greenland Limited; *Int'l*, pg. 1681
COAST CITIES ESCROW INC.—See First Team Real Estate-Orange County Inc.; *U.S. Private*, pg. 1529
COGEDIM MIDI-PYRENEES—See Altarea SCA; *Int'l*, pg. 385
COGEDIM SAVOIES-LEMAN SNC—See Altarea SCA; *Int'l*, pg. 385
COLDWELL BANKER BURNET RESOURCE CENTER—See Anywhere Real Estate Inc.; *U.S. Public*, pg. 141
COLDWELL BANKER BURNET; *U.S. Private*, pg. 966
COLDWELL BANKER CANADA OPERATIONS ULC—See Anywhere Real Estate Inc.; *U.S. Public*, pg. 140
COLDWELL BANKER COMMERCIAL PACIFIC PROPERTIES LLC—See Anywhere Real Estate Inc.; *U.S. Public*, pg. 141

531210 — OFFICES OF REAL EST...

COLDWELL BANKER LLC—See Anywhere Real Estate Inc.; *U.S. Public*, pg. 140
COLDWELL BANKER PACIFIC PROPERTIES LLC—See Anywhere Real Estate Inc.; *U.S. Public*, pg. 140
COLDWELL BANKER REAL ESTATE LLC—See Anywhere Real Estate Inc.; *U.S. Public*, pg. 140
COLDWELL BANKER REAL ESTATE SERVICES LLC—See Anywhere Real Estate Inc.; *U.S. Public*, pg. 141
COLDWELL BANKER RESIDENTIAL BROKERAGE, INC.—See Anywhere Real Estate Inc.; *U.S. Public*, pg. 141
COLDWELL BANKER RESIDENTIAL BROKERAGE OF UTAH—See Anywhere Real Estate Inc.; *U.S. Public*, pg. 141
COLDWELL BANKER RESIDENTIAL REAL ESTATE INC.—See Anywhere Real Estate Inc.; *U.S. Public*, pg. 141
COLDWELL BANKER RESIDENTIAL REAL ESTATE LLC—See Anywhere Real Estate Inc.; *U.S. Public*, pg. 141
COLDWELL BANKER RESIDENTIAL REAL ESTATE SERVICES INC.—See Anywhere Real Estate Inc.; *U.S. Public*, pg. 141
COLDWELL BANKER—See Anywhere Real Estate Inc.; *U.S. Public*, pg. 140
COLDWELL BANKER SUNSTAR-MORRIS REALTY, INC.—See Coldwell Banker Schmidt Realtors; *U.S. Private*, pg. 966
COLDWELL BANKER UNITED, REALTORS—See Anywhere Real Estate Inc.; *U.S. Public*, pg. 141
COLLIERS INTERNATIONAL - CANADA, TORONTO DOWNTOWN OFFICE—See Colliers International Group Inc.; *Int'l*, pg. 1701
COLLIERS INTERNATIONAL - CENTRAL CALIFORNIA—See Colliers International Group Inc.; *Int'l*, pg. 1700
COLLIERS INTERNATIONAL - COLUMBUS—See Colliers International Group Inc.; *Int'l*, pg. 1700
COLLIERS INTERNATIONAL CT LLC—See Colliers International Group Inc.; *Int'l*, pg. 1701
COLLIERS INTERNATIONAL (HONG KONG) LTD.—See Colliers International Group Inc.; *Int'l*, pg. 1700
COLLIERS INTERNATIONAL (ILLINOIS)—See Colliers International Group Inc.; *Int'l*, pg. 1700
COLLIERS INTERNATIONAL KOREA LTD.—See Colliers International Group Inc.; *Int'l*, pg. 1701
COLLIERS INTERNATIONAL LI INC.—See Colliers International Group Inc.; *Int'l*, pg. 1701
COLLIERS INTERNATIONAL MANAGEMENT-ATLANTA, LLC—See Colliers International Group Inc.; *Int'l*, pg. 1701
COLLIERS INTERNATIONAL NEW ENGLAND, LLC—See Colliers International Group Inc.; *Int'l*, pg. 1701
COLLIERS INTERNATIONAL - NEW YORK—See Colliers International Group Inc.; *Int'l*, pg. 1700
COLLIERS INTERNATIONAL NJ LLC—See Colliers International Group Inc.; *Int'l*, pg. 1701
COLLIERS INTERNATIONAL NORTHEAST FLORIDA, INC.—See Colliers International Group Inc.; *Int'l*, pg. 1701
COLLIERS INTERNATIONAL (NSW) PTY. LIMITED—See Colliers International Group Inc.; *Int'l*, pg. 1701
COLLIERS INTERNATIONAL - PHILADELPHIA—See Colliers International Group Inc.; *Int'l*, pg. 1700
COLLIERS INTERNATIONAL REAL ESTATE MANAGEMENT SERVICES (MI), INC.—See Colliers International Group Inc.; *Int'l*, pg. 1701
COLLIERS INTERNATIONAL - RICHMOND—See Colliers International Group Inc.; *Int'l*, pg. 1700
COLLIERS INTERNATIONAL - SAN DIEGO REGION—See Colliers International Group Inc.; *Int'l*, pg. 1700
COLLIERS INTERNATIONAL - SAN FRANCISCO—See Colliers International Group Inc.; *Int'l*, pg. 1700
COLLIERS INTERNATIONAL (SINGAPORE) PTE. LTD.—See Colliers International Group Inc.; *Int'l*, pg. 1700
COLLIERS INTERNATIONAL (VICTORIA) PTY. LIMITED—See Colliers International Group Inc.; *Int'l*, pg. 1701
COLLIERS MACAULAY NICOLLS INC.—See Colliers International Group Inc.; *Int'l*, pg. 1701
COLLIERS MONROE FRIEDLANDER, INC.—See Colliers International Group Inc.; *Int'l*, pg. 1701
COLLIERS PARAGON, LLC—See Colliers International Group Inc.; *Int'l*, pg. 1701
COLONIAL SQUARE REALTY, INC.; *U.S. Private*, pg. 972
COLONIE VENTURES, INC.—See Galesi Group; *U.S. Private*, pg. 1637
COLONY REALTY PARTNERS, LLC—See DigitalBridge Group, Inc.; *U.S. Public*, pg. 664
COLTER & PETERSON INC.; *U.S. Private*, pg. 976
COLTON ENTERPRISES, INC.—See Dollar Mutual Bancorp; *U.S. Private*, pg. 1254
COLUMBIA PROPERTY TRUST OPERATING PARTNERSHIP, L.P.—See Allianz SE; *Int'l*, pg. 346
COLVILL OFFICE PROPERTIES, LLC—See TPG Capital, L.P.; *U.S. Public*, pg. 2171
COMFORIA RESIDENTIAL REIT, INC.; *Int'l*, pg. 1711

COMMERCIAL ASSET PARTNERS REALTY; *U.S. Private*, pg. 983
COMMERCIAL PARTNERS REALTY INC.—See George F. Young, Inc.; *U.S. Private*, pg. 1682
COMMERCIAL PROPERTY SOUTHWEST FLORIDA, LLC; *U.S. Private*, pg. 984
COMMERCIAL REAL ESTATE CONSULTANTS, LLC; *U.S. Private*, pg. 984
COMMUNITY BUILDERS INC.; *U.S. Private*, pg. 990
COMMUNITY PROPERTIES OF OHIO; *U.S. Private*, pg. 996
COMPAGNIE EUROPEENNE DE GARANTIES ET DE CAUTIONS SA—See Groupe BPCE; *Int'l*, pg. 3093
COMPAGNIE FINANCIERE DE NEUFCOUR S.A.; *Int'l*, pg. 1740
COMPAGNIE HET ZOUTE NV; *Int'l*, pg. 1745
COMPAGNIE IMMOBILIERE D'HARDELOT SAS—See Compagnie Het Zoute NV; *Int'l*, pg. 1745
THE CONAM GROUP OF COMPANIES; *U.S. Private*, pg. 4013
CON AM MANAGEMENT CORPORATION; *U.S. Private*, pg. 1008
CONAM MANAGEMENT CORPORATION—See The ConAm Group of Companies; *U.S. Private*, pg. 4013
CONAM MANAGEMENT—See The ConAm Group of Companies; *U.S. Private*, pg. 4013
CONCORD PACIFIC GROUP—See Adex Securities, Inc.; *Int'l*, pg. 145
CONSERVATIVE CONCEPT AG—See Baader Bank AG; *Int'l*, pg. 791
CONSOLIDATED ANALYTICS, INC.; *U.S. Private*, pg. 1020
CONSTRUTORA ADOLPHO LINDENBERG S.A.; *Int'l*, pg. 1778
CONSUS REAL ESTATE AG; *Int'l*, pg. 1778
CONTINENTAL PROPERTY GROUP, INC.; *U.S. Private*, pg. 1030
CONTINENTAL REAL ESTATE COMPANIES COMMERCIAL PROPERTIES CORP.—See Colliers International Group Inc.; *Int'l*, pg. 1701
CONTINENTAL REALTY CORPORATION; *U.S. Private*, pg. 1030
CONTINENTAL REALTY, LTD.—See Newmark Group, Inc.; *U.S. Public*, pg. 1515
COPPER FUNDING, LLC—See White Mountains Insurance Group, Ltd.; *U.S. Public*, pg. 2369
THE CORCORAN GROUP—See Anywhere Real Estate Inc.; *U.S. Public*, pg. 141
CORE COMMERCIAL GROUP, LLC—See Hilton Grand Vacations Inc.; *U.S. Public*, pg. 1040
CORELOGIC REO ASSET MANAGEMENT—See Insight Venture Management, LLC; *U.S. Private*, pg. 2088
CORELOGIC REO ASSET MANAGEMENT—See Stone Point Capital LLC; *U.S. Private*, pg. 3822
COREPOINT LODGING INC.—See Cerberus Capital Management, L.P.; *U.S. Private*, pg. 837
COREPOINT LODGING INC.—See Highgate Hotels, L.P.; *U.S. Private*, pg. 1937
CORESTATE CAPITAL ADVISORS GMBH—See CORESTATE Capital Holding SA; *Int'l*, pg. 1800
CORESTATE CAPITAL HOLDING SA; *Int'l*, pg. 1799
CORESTATE CAPITAL PARTNERS GMBH—See CORESTATE Capital Holding SA; *Int'l*, pg. 1800
CORESTATE CAPITAL PARTNERS UK LIMITED—See CORESTATE Capital Holding SA; *Int'l*, pg. 1800
CORO REALTY ADVISORS LLC; *U.S. Private*, pg. 1053
CORPORATE OFFICE PROPERTIES, L.P.—See COPT Defense Properties; *U.S. Public*, pg. 575
CORPORATE REALTY INCOME FUND 1 LP; *U.S. Public*, pg. 1055
THE CORUS GROUP OF LONG & FOSTER—See The Long & Foster Companies, Inc.; *U.S. Private*, pg. 4072
COSMO BUSINESS SUPPORT CO., LTD.—See Cosmo Energy Holdings Co., Ltd.; *Int'l*, pg. 1811
COSMOS INITIA CO., LTD.—See Daiwa House Industry Co., Ltd.; *Int'l*, pg. 1945
COTTONTREE HOSPITALITY GROUP; *U.S. Private*, pg. 1064
COTTONWOOD COMMUNITIES, INC.; *U.S. Private*, pg. 1064
COTTONWOOD REALTY SERVICES LLC; *U.S. Private*, pg. 1064
COUNSELOR REALTY INC.; *U.S. Private*, pg. 1066
COUNTRY CLUB BANK; *U.S. Private*, pg. 1066
COUNTRY HOUSES, INC.; *U.S. Private*, pg. 1067
COURTIERS EN DOUANES CARSON LIMITEE; *Int'l*, pg. 1819
CRAIG DEVELOPMENT PTE LTD—See Guthrie GTS Limited; *Int'l*, pg. 3188
CRAVENHURST PROPERTIES LIMITED—See Apollo Global Management, Inc.; *U.S. Public*, pg. 165
THE CRAWFORD GROUP, L.L.C.; *U.S. Private*, pg. 4016
CREDIPASS POLSKA S.A.—See Duna House Holding Public Company Limited; *Int'l*, pg. 2225
CREDIT FONCIER IMMOBILIER SA—See Groupe BPCE; *Int'l*, pg. 3093
CREED ASIA (CAMBODIA) CO., LTD.—See CREED Corporation; *Int'l*, pg. 1837
CREED ASIA DEVELOPMENT (M) SDN. BHD.—See CREED Corporation; *Int'l*, pg. 1837
CREED ASIA INVESTMENT CO., LTD.—See CREED Corporation; *Int'l*, pg. 1837
CREED HOLDINGS PTE.LTD.—See CREED Corporation; *Int'l*, pg. 1837
CREED INVESTMENTS PTE. LTD.—See CREED Corporation; *Int'l*, pg. 1837
CRESSY & EVERETT COMMERCIAL CORPORATION—See Pokagon Band of Potawatomi Indians; *U.S. Private*, pg. 3223
CRE (THAILAND) CO., LTD.—See CRE, Inc.; *Int'l*, pg. 1830
CROSBY & ASSOCIATES, INC.—See National Land Realty, LLC; *U.S. Private*, pg. 2858
THE CROSLAND GROUP INC.; *U.S. Private*, pg. 4016
CROSLAND RETAIL—See The Crosland Group Inc.; *U.S. Private*, pg. 4016
CROSSMAN & COMPANY INC.; *U.S. Private*, pg. 1106
THE CROWLEY GROUP INC.; *U.S. Private*, pg. 4017
CROWN REALTY OF KANSAS INC.; *U.S. Private*, pg. 1112
CRYE-LEIKE INC.; *U.S. Private*, pg. 1115
CSS FARMS INC.; *U.S. Private*, pg. 1117
CTL MANAGEMENT INC.—See The Randall Group Inc.; *U.S. Private*, pg. 4102
CTW GROUP, INC.; *U.S. Private*, pg. 1119
CUBESMART, L.P.—See CubeSmart; *U.S. Public*, pg. 603
CU IMMOBILIEN LAHR AG—See CPH Chemie + Papier Holding AG; *Int'l*, pg. 1824
CULLINAN PROPERTIES, LTD.; *U.S. Private*, pg. 1121
CUMMINGS-BACCUS INTERESTS; *U.S. Private*, pg. 1123
CURRY INVESTMENT COMPANY; *U.S. Private*, pg. 1126
CUSHMAN & WAKEFIELD, INC. - INDIANAPOLIS—See TPG Capital, L.P.; *U.S. Public*, pg. 2173
CUSHMAN & WAKEFIELD, INC.—See TPG Capital, L.P.; *U.S. Public*, pg. 2171
CUSHMAN & WAKEFIELD, INC. - TAMPA—See TPG Capital, L.P.; *U.S. Public*, pg. 2172
CUSHMAN & WAKEFIELD OF ARIZONA, INC.—See TPG Capital, L.P.; *U.S. Public*, pg. 2172
CUSHMAN & WAKEFIELD OF CALIFORNIA, INC.—See TPG Capital, L.P.; *U.S. Public*, pg. 2172
CUSHMAN & WAKEFIELD OF CONNECTICUT, INC.—See TPG Capital, L.P.; *U.S. Public*, pg. 2172
CUSHMAN & WAKEFIELD OF FLORIDA, INC.—See TPG Capital, L.P.; *U.S. Public*, pg. 2172
CUSHMAN & WAKEFIELD OF GEORGIA, INC.—See TPG Capital, L.P.; *U.S. Public*, pg. 2172
CUSHMAN & WAKEFIELD OF ILLINOIS, INC.—See TPG Capital, L.P.; *U.S. Public*, pg. 2172
CUSHMAN & WAKEFIELD OF LONG ISLAND, INC.—See TPG Capital, L.P.; *U.S. Public*, pg. 2172
CUSHMAN & WAKEFIELD OF MARYLAND, INC.—See TPG Capital, L.P.; *U.S. Public*, pg. 2172
CUSHMAN & WAKEFIELD OF MASSACHUSETTS, INC.—See TPG Capital, L.P.; *U.S. Public*, pg. 2172
CUSHMAN & WAKEFIELD OF NEW JERSEY, INC.—See TPG Capital, L.P.; *U.S. Public*, pg. 2172
CUSHMAN & WAKEFIELD OF OREGON, INC.—See TPG Capital, L.P.; *U.S. Public*, pg. 2172
CUSHMAN & WAKEFIELD OF TEXAS, INC. - AUSTIN—See TPG Capital, L.P.; *U.S. Public*, pg. 2172
CUSHMAN & WAKEFIELD OF TEXAS, INC.—See TPG Capital, L.P.; *U.S. Public*, pg. 2172
CUSHMAN & WAKEFIELD OF WASHINGTON D.C., INC.—See TPG Capital, L.P.; *U.S. Public*, pg. 2173
CUSHMAN & WAKEFIELD OF WASHINGTON, INC.—See TPG Capital, L.P.; *U.S. Public*, pg. 2173
CUTLER REAL ESTATE, INC.; *U.S. Private*, pg. 1131
CYPRESS TITLE CORPORATION—See Anywhere Real Estate Inc.; *U.S. Public*, pg. 142
DAC REALTY GROUP, INC.; *U.S. Private*, pg. 1144
DAIWA ESTATE CO., LTD.—See Daiwa House Industry Co., Ltd.; *Int'l*, pg. 1945
DAIWA HOMES ONLINE CO., LTD.—See Daiwa House REIT Investment Corporation; *Int'l*, pg. 1947
DAIWA HOUSE (CHANGZHOU) REAL ESTATE DEVELOPMENT CO., LTD.—See Daiwa House Industry Co., Ltd.; *Int'l*, pg. 1945
DAIWA HOUSE INDUSTRY INDIA PVT. LTD.—See Daiwa House Industry Co., Ltd.; *Int'l*, pg. 1945
DAIWA HOUSE INDUSTRY(THAILAND)CO., LTD.—See Daiwa House Industry Co., Ltd.; *Int'l*, pg. 1945
DAIWA HOUSE REAL ESTATE DEVELOPMENT CO., LTD.—See Daiwa House Industry Co., Ltd.; *Int'l*, pg. 1945
DAIWA HOUSE REAL ESTATE INVESTMENT MANAGEMENT CO., LTD.—See Daiwa House Industry Co., Ltd.; *Int'l*, pg. 1945
DAIWA LIVING NESUTO HOLDINGS PTY LTD—See Daiwa House Industry Co., Ltd.; *Int'l*, pg. 1946
DAIWA ROYAL CO., LTD.—See Daiwa House Industry Co., Ltd.; *Int'l*, pg. 1946
DAKOTA SQUARE MALL CMBS, LLC—See CBL & Associates Properties, Inc.; *U.S. Public*, pg. 458
DALEKOVOD PROFESSIO D.O.O—See Dalekovod d.d.; *Int'l*, pg. 1951
DALIAN VANKE PROPERTY COMPANY LIMITED—See China Vanke Co., Ltd.; *Int'l*, pg. 1562
DALIAN YIHE PROPERTY MANAGEMENT CO., LTD.—See

N.A.I.C.S. INDEX

531210 — OFFICES OF REAL EST...

Daiwa House Industry Co., Ltd.; *Int'l*, pg. 1946
DAMASCUS CENTRE, LLC—See First Real Estate Investment Trust New Jersey Co.; *U.S. Public*, pg. 847
THE DANBERRY, CO.—See Miller Diversified Inc.; *U.S. Private*, pg. 2733
DANIEL REALTY CORPORATION—See Daniel Corporation; *U.S. Private*, pg. 1153
DAT XANH DONG NAM BO SERVICES & INVESTMENT JSC—See Dat Xanh Group Joint Stock Company; *Int'l*, pg. 1975
DAT XANH MIEN BAC SERVICES & REAL ESTATE JSC—See Dat Xanh Group Joint Stock Company; *Int'l*, pg. 1975
DAT XANH MIEN TAY SERVICE AND INVESTMENT JOINT STOCK COMPANY—See Dat Xanh Group Joint Stock Company; *Int'l*, pg. 1975
DAT XANH MIEN TRUNG JSC—See Dat Xanh Group Joint Stock Company; *Int'l*, pg. 1975
DAUPHIN REALTY OF MOBILE, INC.—See Berkshire Hathaway Inc.; *U.S. Public*, pg. 306
DAVID LYNG & ASSOCIATES, INC.; *U.S. Private*, pg. 1170
DAVIDSON REALTY, INC.; *U.S. Private*, pg. 1172
DAWN PROPERTY CONSULTANCY—See Dawn Properties Limited; *Int'l*, pg. 1984
DCT PAN AMERICAN LLC—See Prologis, Inc.; *U.S. Public*, pg. 1726
D&D PLATFORM REIT CO., LTD.; *Int'l*, pg. 1899
DDR REALTY, LLC—See DDR Builders, LLC; *U.S. Private*, pg. 1181
DECAMA CAPITAL LTD.; *Int'l*, pg. 1999
DECORUS REALTY LLC—See One Sotheby's International Realty, Inc.; *U.S. Private*, pg. 3023
DELAWARE COUNTY REAL ESTATE; *U.S. Private*, pg. 1194
DELCO BUILDERS & DEVELOPERS, INC.; *U.S. Private*, pg. 1196
DELMARVA REAL ESTATE—See Independent Newspapers, Inc.; *U.S. Private*, pg. 2060
DENTON HINES PROPERTIES, INC.; *U.S. Private*, pg. 1206
DESARROLLOS MULTIPLES INSULARES, INC.—See CEMEX, S.A.B. de C.V.; *Int'l*, pg. 1399
DEUTSCHE GRUNDSTUECKSAUKTIONEN AG; *Int'l*, pg. 2065
DEVELOPMENT PARTNER AG—See Gateway Real Estate AG; *Int'l*, pg. 2889
DEWAG 1. OBJEKTGESELLSCHAFT MBH—See Equity Residential; *U.S. Public*, pg. 791
DEWAG MANAGEMENT GMBH—See Equity Residential; *U.S. Public*, pg. 791
DH ASIA INVESTMENT PTE. LTD.—See Daiwa House Industry Co., Ltd.; *Int'l*, pg. 1945
DH REALTY PARTNERS INC.; *U.S. Private*, pg. 1221
DIAL REALTY CORP—See Dial Companies Corporation; *U.S. Private*, pg. 1222
DICENEXT INC.—See Daiwa House Industry Co., Ltd.; *Int'l*, pg. 1946
DICKERSON REALTY CORPORATION—See The Dickerson Group, Inc.; *U.S. Private*, pg. 4021
DIGITAL CORE REIT LTD.—See Digital Realty Trust, Inc.; *U.S. Public*, pg. 663
DKH, INCORPORATED; *U.S. Private*, pg. 1247
DLF RECREATIONAL FOUNDATION LIMITED—See DLF Limited; *Int'l*, pg. 2141
DLP REALTY—See Don Wenner Home Selling, Inc.; *U.S. Private*, pg. 1259
DOAN PYRAMID LLC; *U.S. Private*, pg. 1250
THE DOHRING GROUP, INC.; *U.S. Private*, pg. 4022
DOLLAR UNION LIMITED—See Chinese Estates Holdings Limited; *Int'l*, pg. 1569
DONGYANG PARAGON CO., LTD.—See Dongyang Engineering & Construction Corp.; *Int'l*, pg. 2171
DORSEL BAZ LTD.; *Int'l*, pg. 2180
DOUCETTE REALTY LTD.; *Int'l*, pg. 2181
DOWNING-FRYE REALTY, LNC.; *U.S. Private*, pg. 1269
DRAPER & KRAMER, INCORPORATED—See DKH, Incorporated; *U.S. Private*, pg. 1247
DRAPER & KRAMER RETIREMENT PROPERTY SERVICES—See DKH, Incorporated; *U.S. Private*, pg. 1247
DUALTAP CO., LTD.; *Int'l*, pg. 2217
DUKE/HULFISH, LLC—See Prologis, Inc.; *U.S. Public*, pg. 1727
DUKE REALTY OHIO—See Prologis, Inc.; *U.S. Public*, pg. 1726
DVMC PROPERTIES, LLC—See Universal Health Realty Income Trust; *U.S. Public*, pg. 2255
DYNASTY PROPERTIES CO., LTD.—See China Airlines Ltd.; *Int'l*, pg. 1481
EAGLE COMMERCIAL REALTY, LLC—See Markel Group Inc.; *U.S. Public*, pg. 1367
EARN MORTGAGE LLC—See Ellington Credit Company Management LLC; *U.S. Private*, pg. 734
EAST BRUNSWICK STUART LLC—See The Great Atlantic & Pacific Tea Company, Inc.; *U.S. Private*, pg. 4038
EASTERN RURAL PTY LTD—See Elders Limited; *Int'l*, pg. 2346

EASTLAND TITLE SERVICE LLC—See Strattam Capital, LLC; *U.S. Private*, pg. 3837
THE EASTON GROUP; *U.S. Private*, pg. 4024
EASTON SANDERSON & COMPANY; *U.S. Private*, pg. 1322
EAST WEST RESORT MANAGEMENT—See East West Partners; *U.S. Private*, pg. 1319
EBBY HALLIDAY REAL ESTATE, INC.—See Berkshire Hathaway Inc.; *U.S. Public*, pg. 306
EBSCO DEVELOPMENT COMPANY, INC—See EBSCO Industries, Inc.; *U.S. Private*, pg. 1324
ECE ITALIA S.R.L.—See ECE Projektmanagement GmbH & Co KG; *Int'l*, pg. 2288
ECE PROJEKTMANAGEMENT SLOVAKIA S.R.O.—See ECE Projektmanagement GmbH & Co KG; *Int'l*, pg. 2288
ECOMM GROUP, INC.—See Commerce Group Corp.; *U.S. Public*, pg. 545
ECO WORLD INTERNATIONAL BERHAD; *Int'l*, pg. 2293
EDEN HOUSING MANAGEMENT, INC.—See Eden Housing, Inc.; *U.S. Private*, pg. 1333
EDERRA, S.A.—See Banco de Sabadell, S.A.; *Int'l*, pg. 821
EDINA REALTY, INC.—See Berkshire Hathaway Inc.; *U.S. Public*, pg. 306
EDINA REALTY—See Berkshire Hathaway Inc.; *U.S. Public*, pg. 306
EDR SYRACUSE, LLC—See Greystar Real Estate Partners, LLC; *U.S. Private*, pg. 1785
THE EDWARD SUROVELL COMPANY—See Hanna Holdings, Inc.; *U.S. Private*, pg. 1854
EFG EUROBANK PROPERTY SERVICES S.A.—See Eurobank Ergasias Services and Holdings S.A.; *Int'l*, pg. 2532
EFG PROPERTY SERVICES D.O.O. BELGRADE—See Eurobank Ergasias Services and Holdings S.A.; *Int'l*, pg. 2532
EFG PROPERTY SERVICES POLSKA SP.Z.O.O.—See Eurobank Ergasias Services and Holdings S.A.; *Int'l*, pg. 2532
EFG PROPERTY SERVICES UKRAINE LLC—See Eurobank Ergasias Services and Holdings S.A.; *Int'l*, pg. 2532
EGELCRAFT, LLC—See Sun Communities, Inc.; *U.S. Public*, pg. 1961
E-HOUSE (CHINA) ENTERPRISE HOLDINGS LTD.; *Int'l*, pg. 2248
EIK FASTEIGNAFELAG HF; *Int'l*, pg. 2332
E KOCREF CR-REIT CO., LTD.; *Int'l*, pg. 2246
ELDECO HOUSING & INDUSTRIES LTD; *Int'l*, pg. 2346
ELECTRICITE ET EAUX DE MADAGASCAR SA; *Int'l*, pg. 2352
ELITE TEAM REALTY & PROPERTY MANAGEMENT; *U.S. Private*, pg. 1361
ELLIS, RICHARD CB & REICHLE KLEIN; *U.S. Private*, pg. 1374
ELMDALE PARTNERS, LLC; *U.S. Private*, pg. 1376
ELME ALEXANDRIA LLC—See Elme Communities; *U.S. Public*, pg. 735
ELME CONYERS LLC—See Elme Communities; *U.S. Public*, pg. 735
ELME DRUID HILLS LLC—See Elme Communities; *U.S. Public*, pg. 735
ELME KENMORE LLC—See Elme Communities; *U.S. Public*, pg. 735
ELME LEESBURG LLC—See Elme Communities; *U.S. Public*, pg. 735
ELME MANASSAS LLC—See Elme Communities; *U.S. Public*, pg. 735
ELME MARIETTA LLC—See Elme Communities; *U.S. Public*, pg. 735
ELME PARAMOUNT LLC—See Elme Communities; *U.S. Public*, pg. 735
ELME RIVERSIDE APARTMENTS LLC—See Elme Communities; *U.S. Public*, pg. 735
ELME SANDY SPRINGS LLC—See Elme Communities; *U.S. Public*, pg. 735
ELME TROVE LLC—See Elme Communities; *U.S. Public*, pg. 735
ELME WATKINS MILL LLC—See Elme Communities; *U.S. Public*, pg. 735
ELME WELLINGTON LLC—See Elme Communities; *U.S. Public*, pg. 735
ELME YALE WEST LLC—See Elme Communities; *U.S. Public*, pg. 735
ELVIEMEK LAND DEVELOPMENT - LOGISTICS PARKS - ENERGY - RECYCLING SA; *Int'l*, pg. 2371
EMAAR DHA ISLAMABAD LIMITED—See Emaar Properties PJSC; *Int'l*, pg. 2372
EMAAR GIGA KARACHI LIMITED—See Emaar Properties PJSC; *Int'l*, pg. 2372
EMAAR INDIA LIMITED—See Emaar Properties PJSC; *Int'l*, pg. 2372
EMAAR PROPERTIES PJSC; *Int'l*, pg. 2372
EMAAR TECHNOLOGIES LLC—See Emaar Properties PJSC; *Int'l*, pg. 2373
EMBASSY OFFICE PARKS REIT; *Int'l*, pg. 2374
EMIRATES PROPERTIES REIT; *Int'l*, pg. 2382
EMIRATES PROPERTY INVESTMENT CO.—See Al Fahim Group; *Int'l*, pg. 277

EMPIRE COMMERCIAL & INDUSTRIAL CORPORATION; *U.S. Private*, pg. 1384
EMPIRE MANAGEMENT COMPANY; *U.S. Private*, pg. 1385
EMPIRE REALTY ASSOCIATES, INC.—See Pacific Union International, Inc.; *U.S. Private*, pg. 3071
ENBIO REAL ESTATE, INC.—See EnBio Holdings Inc.; *Int'l*, pg. 2396
ENCORE PARTNERS LLC; *U.S. Private*, pg. 1391
ENDURANCE WEALTH MANAGEMENT, INC.—See Clayton, Dubilier & Rice, LLC; *U.S. Private*, pg. 923
ENDURANCE WEALTH MANAGEMENT, INC.—See Stone Point Capital LLC; *U.S. Private*, pg. 3824
ENERGY REALTY, INC.—See CenterPoint Energy, Inc.; *U.S. Public*, pg. 472
ENGEL & VOLKERS AMERICAS, INC.; *U.S. Private*, pg. 1397
ENTREPRISES ET CHEMINS DE FER EN CHINE SA; *Int'l*, pg. 2453
EPH EUROPEAN PROPERTY HOLDINGS PLC; *Int'l*, pg. 2459
EPROPERTYSITES, LLC; *U.S. Private*, pg. 1414
EQR-71 BROADWAY, LLC—See Equity Residential; *U.S. Public*, pg. 791
EQR-VANTAGE POINTE, LLC—See Equity Residential; *U.S. Public*, pg. 792
EQUINIX (REAL ESTATE) GMBH—See Equinix, Inc.; *U.S. Public*, pg. 787
EQUITY CONCEPTS REALTY CORP.; *U.S. Private*, pg. 1416
ERA BROKERS CONSOLIDATED - LAS VEGAS—See Brokers Consolidated, Inc.; *U.S. Private*, pg. 662
ERA BROKERS CONSOLIDATED - MESQUITE—See Brokers Consolidated, Inc.; *U.S. Private*, pg. 662
ERA SUNRISE REALTY; *U.S. Private*, pg. 1417
ERWE IMMOBILIEN AG; *Int'l*, pg. 2500
ESAS GAYRIMENKUL—See ESAS Holding A.S.; *Int'l*, pg. 2501
ESCO GLOBAL REALTY CORP.; *Int'l*, pg. 2502
ES-CON ASSET MANAGEMENT CO., LTD.—See ES-CON JAPAN Ltd.; *Int'l*, pg. 2500
ES-CON LIVING SERVICE LTD.—See ES-CON JAPAN Ltd.; *Int'l*, pg. 2500
ESHENBAUGH LAND COMPANY; *U.S. Private*, pg. 1425
ESPAIS SL—See Banco de Sabadell, S.A.; *Int'l*, pg. 821
ESSENTIAL PROPERTIES REALTY TRUST, INC.; *U.S. Public*, pg. 795
ESSEX FOX PLAZA, L.P.—See Essex Property Trust, Inc.; *U.S. Public*, pg. 796
ESSEX HAVER HILL, L.P.—See Essex Property Trust, Inc.; *U.S. Public*, pg. 796
ESSEX REGENCY ESCUELA, L.P.—See Essex Property Trust, Inc.; *U.S. Public*, pg. 796
ESSLINGER-WOOTEN-MAXWELL REALTORS, INC.—See Berkshire Hathaway Inc.; *U.S. Public*, pg. 306
ESTATE MANAGEMENT COMPANY JSC; *Int'l*, pg. 2517
ETKIN EQUITIES; *U.S. Private*, pg. 1432
EUROCOMMERCIAL PROPERTIES N.V.; *Int'l*, pg. 2534
EUROTERRA BULGARIA AD; *Int'l*, pg. 2558
EVEREST CONSULTING GROUP LP; *U.S. Private*, pg. 1437
EVERGREEN ESCROW, INC.—See Del Toro Loan Servicing, Inc.; *U.S. Private*, pg. 1193
EVER REACH GROUP (HOLDINGS) COMPANY LIMITED; *Int'l*, pg. 2562
EVERS & CO. REAL ESTATE, INC.—See The Long & Foster Companies, Inc.; *U.S. Private*, pg. 4072
EXECUTIVE AFFILIATES INC.; *U.S. Private*, pg. 1447
EXECUTIVE CAPITAL CORP.; *U.S. Private*, pg. 1447
EXP AUSTRALIA PTY. LTD.—See eXp World Holdings, Inc.; *U.S. Public*, pg. 808
EXP REALTY ASSOCIATES, LLC—See eXp World Holdings, Inc.; *U.S. Public*, pg. 808
EXP REALTY OF CANADA, INC.—See eXp World Holdings, Inc.; *U.S. Public*, pg. 808
EXP WORLD UK LIMITED—See eXp World Holdings, Inc.; *U.S. Public*, pg. 808
EXTON RANCH, LLC—See Omega Flex, Inc.; *U.S. Public*, pg. 1571
EYEMAXX REAL ESTATE AG; *Int'l*, pg. 2593
FABEGE AB; *Int'l*, pg. 2598
FAIRBRIDGE PARTNERS LLC; *U.S. Private*, pg. 1462
FAIRFIELD PROPERTIES L.P.; *U.S. Private*, pg. 1463
FANCY ASSET COMPANY LIMITED—See Fancy Wood Industries Public Company Limited; *Int'l*, pg. 2613
FASHION SQUARE MALL CMBS, LLC—See CBL & Associates Properties, Inc.; *U.S. Public*, pg. 458
FATH MANAGEMENT COMPANY; *U.S. Private*, pg. 1483
FAULK & FOSTER REAL ESTATE; *U.S. Private*, pg. 1483
FC MEADOWBROOK LLC—See Sun Communities, Inc.; *U.S. Public*, pg. 1961
FC PEBBLE CREEK LLC—See Sun Communities, Inc.; *U.S. Public*, pg. 1961
FCR IMMOBILIEN AG; *Int'l*, pg. 2628
FDC MANAGEMENT INC.; *U.S. Private*, pg. 1486
FEDIMMO S.A.—See Befimmo SCA; *Int'l*, pg. 940
FEIT MANAGEMENT COMPANY; *U.S. Private*, pg. 1493
FIDELIS ASSET MANAGEMENT, LLC—See Roofstock, Inc.; *U.S. Private*, pg. 3479

4503

531210 — OFFICES OF REAL EST...

FINELAND LIVING SERVICES GROUP LIMITED; *Int'l*, pg. 2674
FIRM CAPITAL APARTMENT REAL ESTATE INVESTMENT TRUST; *Int'l*, pg. 2679
FIRST AMERICAN PROFESSIONAL REAL ESTATE SERVICES, INC—See First American Financial Corporation; *U.S. Public*, pg. 836
FIRST ASSOCIATES LLC—See Equity CommonWealth; *U.S. Public*, pg. 790
FIRST BROKERS REAL ESTATE—See Da-Ly Realty & Insurance Inc.; *U.S. Private*, pg. 1143
FIRST BUSINESS LEASING LLC—See First Business Financial Services, Inc.; *U.S. Public*, pg. 840
FIRST CHOICE PROPERTIES, INC.; *U.S. Private*, pg. 1515
FIRST COAST AUCTION & REALTY, INC.; *U.S. Private*, pg. 1516
FIRST DUBAI REAL ESTATE DEVELOPMENT COMPANY K.S.C.—See Al-Mazaya Holding Company K.S.C.P.; *Int'l*, pg. 287
FIRST PROPERTY ASSET MANAGEMENT ROMANIA SRL—See First Property Group Plc; *Int'l*, pg. 2686
FIRST PROPERTY POLAND SP. Z O.O.—See First Property Group Plc; *Int'l*, pg. 2686
FIRST REALTY/GMAC REAL ESTATE—See Berkshire Hathaway Inc.; *U.S. Public*, pg. 306
FIRST SERVICE REALTY INC.; *U.S. Private*, pg. 1527
FIRSTSERVICE RESIDENTIAL FLORIDA, INC,—See FirstService Corporation; *Int'l*, pg. 2691
FIRST SHANGHAI PROPERTIES LIMITED—See First Shanghai Investments Limited; *Int'l*, pg. 2687
FIRST TEAM REAL ESTATE-ORANGE COUNTY INC.; *U.S. Private*, pg. 1529
FIRST TITLE REAL ESTATE GUARANTY CO., LTD.—See First American Financial Corporation; *U.S. Public*, pg. 838
FIRST WINTHROP CORPORATION—See Winthrop Financial Associates LP; *U.S. Private*, pg. 4545
FITOUTETRIS SA—See Jones Lang LaSalle Incorporated; *Int'l*, pg. 1201
FIVE POINT HOLDINGS, LLC; *U.S. Public*, pg. 852
FIVE POINT OPERATING COMPANY, LP—See Five Point Holdings, LLC; *U.S. Public*, pg. 852
FJ COMMUNITY CO., LTD.—See FJ Next Holdings Co., Ltd.; *Int'l*, pg. 2697
THE FLATLEY COMPANY; *U.S. Private*, pg. 4029
FLETCHER KING SERVICES LIMITED—See Fletcher King Plc; *Int'l*, pg. 2701
FLORIDA EXECUTIVE REALTY; *U.S. Private*, pg. 1548
FLS REAL ESTATE A/S—See FLSmidth & Co. A/S; *Int'l*, pg. 2710
F.M. TARBELL CO. INC.—See Tarbell Financial Corporation; *U.S. Private*, pg. 3933
FOCUS COMMERCIAL, INC.—See The Randall Group Inc.; *U.S. Private*, pg. 4102
FONG CHIEN CONSTRUCTION CO., LTD.; *Int'l*, pg. 2726
FORCE REALTY; *U.S. Private*, pg. 1563
FORD MOTOR LAND SERVICES CORP.—See Ford Motor Company; *U.S. Public*, pg. 866
FOREST CITY BAYSIDE CORPORATION—See Brookfield Corporation; *Int'l*, pg. 1187
FOREST CITY COMMERCIAL GROUP—See Brookfield Corporation; *Int'l*, pg. 1187
FOREST CITY COMMERCIAL MANAGEMENT, INC.—See Brookfield Corporation; *Int'l*, pg. 1187
FOREST CITY EQUITY SERVICES, INC.—See Brookfield Corporation; *Int'l*, pg. 1187
FOREST CITY RESIDENTIAL GROUP, LLC—See Brookfield Corporation; *Int'l*, pg. 1187
FOREST CITY RESIDENTIAL MANAGEMENT, INC.—See Brookfield Corporation; *Int'l*, pg. 1187
FOREST CITY STAPLETON LAND, INC.—See Brookfield Corporation; *Int'l*, pg. 1187
FOREST CITY WASHINGTON, INC.—See Brookfield Corporation; *Int'l*, pg. 1187
FORTH ESTUARY TOWAGE LIMITED—See Arcus Infrastructure Partners LLP; *Int'l*, pg. 552
FORT HOOD FAMILY HOUSING LP.; *U.S. Private*, pg. 1574
FORTH PROPERTIES LIMITED—See Arcus Infrastructure Partners LLP; *Int'l*, pg. 552
FORTH PROPERTY DEVELOPMENTS LTD—See Arcus Infrastructure Partners LLP; *Int'l*, pg. 552
FORTUNE INTERNATIONAL REALTY, INC.; *U.S. Private*, pg. 1577
FORUCOM REIT; *Int'l*, pg. 2744
FOSHAN VANKE PROPERTY COMPANY LIMITED—See China Vanke Co., Ltd.; *Int'l*, pg. 1562
FOUNDERS 3 REAL ESTATE SERVICES; *U.S. Private*, pg. 1580
FOUNDRY COMMERCIAL LLC; *U.S. Private*, pg. 1581
FOXTONS GROUP PLC; *Int'l*, pg. 2756
FP NEWHAVEN TWO LIMITED—See Arcus Infrastructure Partners LLP; *Int'l*, pg. 552
FRANKEL MANAGEMENT INC.; *U.S. Private*, pg. 1596
FRANKLIN INDUSTRIES LIMITED; *Int'l*, pg. 2762
FRANKLIN STREET; *U.S. Private*, pg. 1598
FREMONT REALTY CAPITAL (NEW YORK)—See Fremont Group, LLC; *U.S. Private*, pg. 1608

FREY + GNEHM INGENIEURE AG—See BKW AG; *Int'l*, pg. 1055
FRITZY TECH INC.; *Int'l*, pg. 2794
FS CREDIT REAL ESTATE INCOME TRUST, INC.; *U.S. Private*, pg. 1618
FSP 1999 BROADWAY LLC—See Franklin Street Properties Corp.; *U.S. Public*, pg. 883
FSP 303 EAST WACKER DRIVE CORP.; *U.S. Private*, pg. 1618
FSP PARK TEN LIMITED PARTNERSHIP—See Franklin Street Properties Corp.; *U.S. Public*, pg. 883
FULCRUM COMMERCIAL REAL ESTATE SERVICES LLC—See Newmark Group, Inc.; *U.S. Public*, pg. 1515
FULLER MADISON LLC—See Vornado Realty Trust; *U.S. Public*, pg. 2310
FUNDAMENTA REAL ESTATE AG; *Int'l*, pg. 2845
FUNG YIK SDN. BHD.—See Asas Dunia Berhad; *Int'l*, pg. 599
FURMAN CO., INC.—See CBRE Group, Inc.; *U.S. Public*, pg. 460
GADSDEN GROWTH PROPERTIES, INC.—See Gadsden Properties, Inc.; *U.S. Public*, pg. 894
GAEDEKE HOLDINGS LTD.; *U.S. Private*, pg. 1633
GAG LUDWIGSHAFEN AM RHEIN AKTIENGESELLSCHAFT; *Int'l*, pg. 2868
GANESH INFRASTRUCTURE (INDIA) PVT LTD—See Ganesh Housing Corporation Ltd; *Int'l*, pg. 2880
GARRETT REALTY SERVICES, INC.; *U.S. Private*, pg. 1645
GATEWAY REAL ESTATE AG; *Int'l*, pg. 2889
GATSKI COMMERCIAL REAL ESTATE SERVICES; *U.S. Private*, pg. 1651
GB ACQUISITIONS, LLC—See Universal Health Services, Inc.; *U.S. Public*, pg. 2257
GEHR DEVELOPMENT—See The Gehr Group; *U.S. Private*, pg. 4032
GEHRKI COMMERCIAL REAL ESTATE, LLC—See Colliers International Group Inc.; *Int'l*, pg. 1701
GEMEENTE SINT-PIETERS-LEEUW; *Int'l*, pg. 2915
GENDIS REALTY, INC.—See Gendis Inc.; *Int'l*, pg. 2917
GENE B. GLICK COMPANY, INC.; *U.S. Private*, pg. 1660
GENERATION INCOME PROPERTIES, INC.; *U.S. Public*, pg. 929
GEOPHY B.V.—See Walker & Dunlop, Inc.; *U.S. Public*, pg. 2324
GEO PROPERTY GROUP LIMITED—See AVID Property Group; *Int'l*, pg. 743
GERMAN HIGH STREET PROPERTIES A/S; *Int'l*, pg. 2943
GEWERBEGRUND AIRPORT GMBH & CO. HALLBERGMOOS KG—See BayernLB Holding AG; *Int'l*, pg. 914
GH LII MANAGEMENT, LLC—See Anywhere Real Estate Inc.; *U.S. Public*, pg. 140
GIBSON INTERNATIONAL—See Pacific Union International, Inc.; *U.S. Private*, pg. 3071
GIVAT SAVYON LTD.—See Africa Israel Investments Ltd.; *Int'l*, pg. 190
G&K MANAGEMENT COMPANY; *U.S. Private*, pg. 1629
GLOBAL COMMUNITY CO., LTD.—See Daiwa House Industry Co., Ltd.; *Int'l*, pg. 1946
GLOBAL PROPERTY STRATEGIC ALLIANCE PTE. LTD.—See GPS Alliance Holdings Limited; *Int'l*, pg. 3047
GLOBAL REAL ESTATE GROUP; *Int'l*, pg. 3000
GLOBAL REALTY SERVICES GROUP LLC; *U.S. Private*, pg. 1717
GLOBAL SELF STORAGE, INC.; *U.S. Public*, pg. 945
GLORIA NILSON, INC.; *U.S. Private*, pg. 1720
GMH ASSOCIATES INC.; *U.S. Private*, pg. 1722
GMO SOLUTION PARTNER, INC.—See GMO Internet Group, Inc.; *Int'l*, pg. 3014
GM WESTBERRY, LLC—See Greystar Real Estate Partners, LLC; *U.S. Private*, pg. 1785
GOLF HOST SECURITIES, INC.—See Salamander Innisbrook, LLC; *U.S. Public*, pg. 3530
GOOD COM ASSET CO., LTD.; *Int'l*, pg. 3038
GOODDAYS HOLDINGS, INC.; *Int'l*, pg. 3039
GOODMAN REAL ESTATE (SPAIN) S.L.—See Goodman Limited; *Int'l*, pg. 3041
GPT PTY LTD—See GPT Group; *Int'l*, pg. 3047
GRABLE & ASSOCIATES REALTY; *U.S. Private*, pg. 1748
GRAFENTAL GMBH & CO. KG—See ADLER Group SA; *Int'l*, pg. 150
GRANDEUR PARK SDN. BHD.—See Hua Yang Berhad; *Int'l*, pg. 3510
GRAND RESIDENCES BY MARRIOTT—See Marriott Vacations Worldwide Corporation; *U.S. Public*, pg. 1374
GRANDY HOUSE CORPORATION; *Int'l*, pg. 3058
GRANITE POINT MORTGAGE TRUST INC.; *U.S. Public*, pg. 958
THE GREAT ATLANTIC PROPERTY MANAGEMENT COMPANY; *U.S. Private*, pg. 4038
GREAT UNIVERSAL CAPITAL CORP.—See Lee National Corporation; *U.S. Private*, pg. 2413
GREAT UNIVERSAL INCORPORATED; *U.S. Private*, pg. 1768
GREAT WEST HOUSE LIMITED—See CLS Holdings plc; *Int'l*, pg. 1664
GREC CONVERSIONS—See Fortune Capital Partners, Inc.; *U.S. Private*, pg. 1577

CORPORATE AFFILIATIONS

GREEN 711 THIRD AVENUE LLC—See SL Green Realty Corp.; *U.S. Public*, pg. 1894
GREEN BRICK TITLE, LLC—See Green Brick Partners, Inc.; *U.S. Public*, pg. 962
GREEN TOWN PROJECTS PLC; *Int'l*, pg. 3073
GREENTOWN REAL ESTATE GROUP CO., LTD.—See Greentown China Holdings Limited; *Int'l*, pg. 3077
GRENADIER REALTY CORP.—See Starrett Corporation; *U.S. Private*, pg. 3787
GRIFFIS BLESSING INC.; *U.S. Private*, pg. 1788
GRIMALDI COMMERCIAL REALTY CORP.; *U.S. Private*, pg. 1789
GRIMMER REALTY CO. INC.; *U.S. Private*, pg. 1790
GRIVALIA PROPERTIES REAL ESTATE INVESTMENTS COMPANY S.A.—See Eurobank Ergasias Services and Holdings S.A.; *Int'l*, pg. 2532
GROSSMAN COMPANY PROPERTIES, INC.; *U.S. Private*, pg. 1792
GROUP FIVE PROPERTY DEVELOPMENTS (PROPRIETARY) LIMITED—See Group Five Limited; *Int'l*, pg. 3089
THE GROUP INC.; *U.S. Private*, pg. 4039
GROVE FARM COMPANY INC.; *U.S. Private*, pg. 1794
GROWTH PROPERTIES INVESTMENT MANAGERS, INC.; *U.S. Private*, pg. 1796
GRUPO LAMOSA, SA DE CV—See Grupo Lamosa S.A. de C.V.; *Int'l*, pg. 3131
GRUPO LAR INVERSIONES INMOBILIARIAS, SA; *Int'l*, pg. 3132
G&S REAL ESTATE, INC.—See Sysco Corporation; *U.S. Public*, pg. 1974
GUANGDONG HONGLING GROUP CO., LTD.—See Guangdong Rising Assets Management Co., Ltd.; *Int'l*, pg. 3159
GUANGDONG RISING GROUP INVESTMENT CO., LTD.—See Guangdong Rising Assets Management Co., Ltd.; *Int'l*, pg. 3159
GUIYANG VANKE REAL ESTATE COMPANY LIMITED—See China Vanke Co., Ltd.; *Int'l*, pg. 1562
GULF BREEZE REAL ESTATE; *U.S. Private*, pg. 1814
H2M ARCHITECTS + ENGINEERS; *U.S. Private*, pg. 1837
H 47 GMBH & CO. KG—See Commerzbank AG; *Int'l*, pg. 1718
THE HABITAT COMPANY INC.; *U.S. Private*, pg. 4041
HABITAT EN REGION SERVICES SAS—See Groupe BPCE; *Int'l*, pg. 3098
HAEDRICH & CO., INC.—See Capital Rivers Commercial LLC; *U.S. Private*, pg. 742
HAILAN HOLDINGS LIMITED; *Int'l*, pg. 3211
HALK VARLIK KIRALAMA AS; *Int'l*, pg. 3229
HALSTEAD BROOKLYN, LLC—See Halstead Property, LLC.; *U.S. Private*, pg. 1846
HALSTEAD EAST HAMPTON, LLC—See Halstead Property, LLC.; *U.S. Private*, pg. 1846
HALSTEAD PROPERTY CONNECTICUT, LLC—See Halstead Property, LLC.; *U.S. Private*, pg. 1846
HALSTEAD PROPERTY HUDSON VALLEY, LLC—See Halstead Property, LLC.; *U.S. Private*, pg. 1846
HALSTEAD PROPERTY, LLC.; *U.S. Private*, pg. 1846
HALSTEAD PROPERTY NEW JERSEY, LLC—See Halstead Property, LLC.; *U.S. Private*, pg. 1846
HALSTEAD PROPERTY RIVERDALE, LLC—See Halstead Property, LLC.; *U.S. Private*, pg. 1846
HAMBORNBERG IMMOBILIEN- UND VERWALTUNGSGMBH—See Hamborner REIT AG; *Int'l*, pg. 3236
HAMILTON VALLEY MANAGEMENT, INC.—See BHHH Companies Inc.; *U.S. Private*, pg. 549
HAMMER RETEX AG; *Int'l*, pg. 3238
HAMMERSON (BRENT CROSS) LTD—See Hammerson plc; *Int'l*, pg. 3238
HAMMERSON GROUP MANAGEMENT LTD—See Hammerson plc; *Int'l*, pg. 3238
HAMMERSON INTERNATIONAL HOLDINGS LTD—See Hammerson plc; *Int'l*, pg. 3238
HAMMERSON ORACLE INVESTMENTS LTD—See Hammerson plc; *Int'l*, pg. 3238
HAMMERSON PROPERTY LTD—See Hammerson plc; *Int'l*, pg. 3238
HAMPSHIRE PROPERTIES LLC—See Heidelberg Materials AG; *Int'l*, pg. 3311
HANFORD HOTELS INC.; *U.S. Private*, pg. 1853
HANG LUNG (ADMINISTRATION) LIMITED—See Hang Lung Group Limited; *Int'l*, pg. 3245
HANG LUNG PROPERTY MANAGEMENT LIMITED—See Hang Lung Group Limited; *Int'l*, pg. 3245
HANG LUNG REAL ESTATE AGENCY LIMITED—See Hang Lung Group Limited; *Int'l*, pg. 3245
HANKYU FACILITIES CO., LTD.—See Hankyu Hanshin Holdings Inc.; *Int'l*, pg. 3255
HANNA COMMERCIAL REAL ESTATE—See Hanna Holdings, Inc.; *U.S. Private*, pg. 1854
HAPCO REAL ESTATE INVESTMENT; *U.S. Private*, pg. 1857
HARDAWAY REALTY CO. INC.—See Hardaway Group, Inc.; *U.S. Private*, pg. 1862
HARLEY & ASSOCIATES COMMERCIAL REAL ESTATE, INC.—See Sun Coast Partners, LLC; *U.S. Private*, pg. 3862

N.A.I.C.S. INDEX
531210 — OFFICES OF REAL EST...

HARPE REALTY—See Henderson Properties Inc.; *U.S. Private*, pg. 1914

HARRODS ESTATES—See Harrods Ltd.; *Int'l*, pg. 3279

HARRY E. ROBBINS ASSOCIATES, INC.; *U.S. Private*, pg. 1871

HARRY NORMAN REALTORS—See Berkshire Hathaway Inc.; *U.S. Public*, pg. 306

HARTAMAS REAL ESTATE (KD) SDN BHD—See Hartamas Group Bhd.; *Int'l*, pg. 3279

HARTAMAS REAL ESTATE (OUG) SDN BHD—See Hartamas Group Bhd.; *Int'l*, pg. 3280

HARTAMAS REAL ESTATE (SETIA ALAM) SDN BHD—See Hartamas Group Bhd.; *Int'l*, pg. 3280

HARTFORD ESCROW INC.—See Tarbell Financial Corporation; *U.S. Private*, pg. 3933

HA THUAN HUNG CONSTRUCTION - TRADE - SERVICE LTD. COMPANY—See Dat Xanh Group Joint Stock Company; *Int'l*, pg. 1975

HAUSBAU FINANZ GMBH—See HELMA Eigenheimbau AG; *Int'l*, pg. 3338

HAWAIIANA GROUP, INC.—See Swell International Inc; *U.S. Private*, pg. 3892

HAWAIIAN HOSPITALITY GROUP, INC.; *U.S. Public*, pg. 989

HAWAII COMMERCIAL REAL ESTATE, LLC—See Elite Pacific, LLC; *U.S. Private*, pg. 1361

HAWAII LIFE; *U.S. Private*, pg. 1881

HAW PAR PROPERTIES (SINGAPORE) PRIVATE LIMITED—See Haw Par Corporation Limited; *Int'l*, pg. 3287

HAYES PROPERTY MANAGEMENT CO.; *U.S. Private*, pg. 1884

HAYMAN COMPANY; *U.S. Private*, pg. 1885

HB MANAGEMENT LLC; *U.S. Private*, pg. 1886

HCMC INVESMENT & DEVELOPMENT JSC—See Dat Xanh Group Joint Stock Company; *Int'l*, pg. 1975

HEALTH BIOSCIENCES SPA; *Int'l*, pg. 3303

HEETON ESTATE PTE LTD—See Heeton Holdings Limited; *Int'l*, pg. 3307

HEIJMANS VASTGOED B.V.—See Heijmans N.V.; *Int'l*, pg. 3322

HEIJMANS VASTGOED PARTICIPATIES B.V.—See Heijmans N.V.; *Int'l*, pg. 3322

HEIJMANS VASTGOED REALISATIE B.V.—See Heijmans N.V.; *Int'l*, pg. 3322

HELABA ASSET SERVICES—See Helaba Landesbank Hessen-Thuringen; *Int'l*, pg. 3328

HELABA GESELLSCHAFT FUR IMMOBILIENBEWERTUNG MBH—See Helaba Landesbank Hessen-Thuringen; *Int'l*, pg. 3328

HELLO NET INC.—See Aucnet Inc.; *Int'l*, pg. 700

HELMA FERIENIMMOBILIEN GMBH—See HELMA Eigenheimbau AG; *Int'l*, pg. 3338

HELMSLEY-NOYES CO., LLC—See Helmsley Enterprises, Inc.; *U.S. Private*, pg. 1912

HELMSLEY-SPEAR, LLC; *U.S. Private*, pg. 1912

HELVETIA ASSET MANAGEMENT AG—See Helvetia Holding AG; *Int'l*, pg. 3339

HEMBREE & ASSOCIATES, INC.; *U.S. Private*, pg. 1913

HENDERSON PROPERTIES INC.; *U.S. Private*, pg. 1914

HENDRICKS & PARTNERS, INC.; *U.S. Private*, pg. 1914

HENRY LUST REAL ESTATE CO., INC.; *U.S. Private*, pg. 1918

HENRY S. MILLER BROKERAGE, LLC—See Henry S. Miller Management Corp.; *U.S. Private*, pg. 1919

HENRY S. MILLER COMMERCIAL AUSTIN, INC.—See Henry S. Miller Management Corp.; *U.S. Private*, pg. 1919

HERITAGE DEVELOPMENT GROUP INC.; *U.S. Private*, pg. 1922

THE HERITAGE ESCROW COMPANY—See First American Financial Corporation; *U.S. Public*, pg. 838

HERITAGE TEXAS PROPERTIES, LLC—See Anywhere Real Estate Inc.; *U.S. Public*, pg. 140

HFS.COM REAL ESTATE INCORPORATED—See Anywhere Real Estate Inc.; *U.S. Public*, pg. 142

HFS.COM REAL ESTATE LLC—See Anywhere Real Estate Inc.; *U.S. Public*, pg. 142

HIAG IMMOBILIEN DELTA GMBH—See Hornbach Holding AG & Co. KGaA; *Int'l*, pg. 3481

HIAP HOE LIMITED; *Int'l*, pg. 3382

HIFFMAN SHAFFER ASSOCIATES, INC.—See Island Capital Group LLC; *U.S. Private*, pg. 2144

THE HIGGINS GROUP, INC.; *U.S. Private*, pg. 4052

HIGGINS PROPERTIES LLC—See Equity CommonWealth; *U.S. Public*, pg. 790

HIGHLANDS REIT, INC.; *U.S. Private*, pg. 1940

HIGHPOINT INVESTMENTS, LLC—See The GEO Group, Inc.; *U.S. Public*, pg. 2075

THE HIGNELL COMPANIES; *U.S. Private*, pg. 4052

HILI PROPERTIES PLC; *Int'l*, pg. 3391

HINES INTERESTS LIMITED PARTNERSHIP; *U.S. Private*, pg. 1949

HISTORIC PROPERTIES INC.—See Apartment Investment and Management Company; *U.S. Public*, pg. 144

HISTORIC PROPERTY MANAGEMENT LLC—See Duke Energy Corporation; *U.S. Public*, pg. 691

HITACHI REAL ESTATE PARTNERS, LTD.—See Hitachi, Ltd.; *Int'l*, pg. 3421

HITACHI URBAN SUPPORT, LTD.—See Hitachi, Ltd.; *Int'l*, pg. 3422

H.K. LANE PALM DESERT, INC.; *U.S. Private*, pg. 1835

HOANG QUAN BINH THUAN CONSULTING - TRADING - SERVICE REAL ESTATE CORPORATION—See Hoang Quan Consulting - Trading - Service Real Estate Corporation; *Int'l*, pg. 3436

HOANG QUAN CAN THO INVESTMENT REAL ESTATE CORPORATION—See Hoang Quan Consulting - Trading - Service Real Estate Corporation; *Int'l*, pg. 3436

HOBAN & ASSOCIATES, LLC; *U.S. Private*, pg. 1958

HOETING INC.; *U.S. Private*, pg. 1959

HOFD ASHVILLE PARK LLC—See Jefferies Financial Group Inc.; *U.S. Public*, pg. 1188

HOKUETSU TRADING CORPORATION—See Hokuetsu Corporation; *Int'l*, pg. 3444

HOKURIKU KOSAN CO., LTD.—See Hokuriku Electric Industry Co., Ltd.; *Int'l*, pg. 3445

HOMEBAY RESIDENTIAL PRIVATE LIMITED—See Jones Lang LaSalle Incorporated; *U.S. Public*, pg. 1202

HOME CONSORTIUM LIMITED—See HMC Capital Limited; *Int'l*, pg. 3431

HOMEGENIUS REAL ESTATE LLC—See Radian Group, Inc.; *U.S. Public*, pg. 1759

HOME PROPERTIES CAMBRIDGE COURT, LLC—See Lone Star Global Acquisitions, LLC; *U.S. Private*, pg. 2488

HOME PROPERTIES HUNTERS GLEN, LLC—See Lone Star Global Acquisitions, LLC; *U.S. Private*, pg. 2488

HOME REAL ESTATE INC.—See Berkshire Hathaway Inc.; *U.S. Public*, pg. 306

THE HOME SALES COMPANY; *U.S. Private*, pg. 4054

HOMES.COM, INC.—See Irish Times; *U.S. Private*, pg. 2138

HOMESERVICES OF AMERICA, INC.—See Berkshire Hathaway Inc.; *U.S. Public*, pg. 306

HOMESMART INTERNATIONAL LLC; *U.S. Private*, pg. 1974

HOMETOWN REALTY SERVICES INC.; *U.S. Private*, pg. 1975

HONG KONG LAND HOLDINGS LTD.; *Int'l*, pg. 3466

HOPEFLUENT PROPERTIES LIMITED—See Hopefluent Group Holdings Ltd; *Int'l*, pg. 3473

HOPEWELL REAL ESTATE AGENCY LIMITED—See Hopewell Holdings Limited; *Int'l*, pg. 3473

HOULIHAN LAWRENCE INC.—See Berkshire Hathaway Inc.; *U.S. Public*, pg. 306

HOUSECOM CORPORATION—See Daito Trust Construction Co., Ltd.; *Int'l*, pg. 1944

HOUSING ASSISTANCE OF ORANGE CITY, LTD.—See Apartment Investment and Management Company; *U.S. Public*, pg. 144

HOUSING SUPPORT CORPORATION—See Asahi Broadcasting Group Holdings Corporation; *Int'l*, pg. 592

HOWARD HANNA CO. - MENTOR—See Hanna Holdings, Inc.; *U.S. Private*, pg. 1854

HOWARD HANNA COMPANY—See Hanna Holdings, Inc.; *U.S. Private*, pg. 1854

HOWARDS (ESTATE AGENTS) LIMITED—See HAL Trust N.V.; *Int'l*, pg. 3226

HPB NEKRETNINE D.O.O.—See Hrvatska Postanska banka d.d.; *Int'l*, pg. 3502

HSR PROPERTY CONSULTANTS PTE LTD—See 3Cnergy Limited; *Int'l*, pg. 7

HUB ACQUISITION TRUST—See Equity CommonWealth; *U.S. Public*, pg. 790

HUDSON 1455 MARKET STREET, LLC—See Hudson Pacific Properties, Inc.; *U.S. Public*, pg. 1068

HUNT COMMERCIAL REAL ESTATE CORP.—See Hastings + Cohn Real Estate, LLC; *U.S. Private*, pg. 1879

HUNTER INDUSTRIES INC.—See American Superconductor Corporation; *U.S. Public*, pg. 110

HUNT REAL ESTATE CORPORATION; *U.S. Private*, pg. 2009

HUTCHISON WHAMPOA PROPERTIES (CHENGDU) LIMITED—See CK Asset Holdings Limited; *Int'l*, pg. 1635

HUTCHISON WHAMPOA PROPERTIES (CHONGQING NANAN) LIMITED—See CK Asset Holdings Limited; *Int'l*, pg. 1635

HUTCHISON WHAMPOA PROPERTIES (QINGDAO) LIMITED—See CK Asset Holdings Limited; *Int'l*, pg. 1635

HUTCHISON WHAMPOA PROPERTIES (WUHAN JIANGHAN SOUTH) LIMITED—See CK Asset Holdings Limited; *Int'l*, pg. 1635

HYBRIDGE COMMERCIAL REAL ESTATE; *U.S. Private*, pg. 2016

IAN BLACK REAL ESTATE; *U.S. Private*, pg. 2027

IBERDROLA INMOBILIARIA, S.A.—See Iberdrola, S.A.; *Int'l*, pg. 3572

ICHIGO ECO ENERGY CO., LTD.—See Ichigo, Inc.; *Int'l*, pg. 3580

ICHIGO ESTATE CO., LTD.—See Ichigo, Inc.; *Int'l*, pg. 3580

ICHIGO, INC.; *Int'l*, pg. 3580

ICHIGO INVESTMENT ADVISORS CO., LTD.—See Ichigo, Inc.; *Int'l*, pg. 3580

ICHIGO LAND SHINCHIKU CO., LTD.—See Ichigo, Inc.; *Int'l*, pg. 3580

ICHIGO MARCHE CO., LTD.—See Ichigo, Inc.; *Int'l*, pg. 3580

ICHIGO OWNERS CO., LTD.—See Ichigo, Inc.; *Int'l*, pg. 3580

ICHIGO REAL ESTATE SERVICES FUKUOKA CO., LTD.—See Ichigo, Inc.; *Int'l*, pg. 3580

ICON IMMOBILIEN GMBH & CO. KG—See Allianz SE; *Int'l*, pg. 353

IFM INVESTMENTS LIMITED; *Int'l*, pg. 3599

IGIS RESIDENCE REIT CO., LTD.; *Int'l*, pg. 3602

IGIS VALUE PLUS REIT CO., LTD.; *Int'l*, pg. 3602

IHP CAPITAL PARTNERS INC.; *U.S. Private*, pg. 2040

IKM INVEST AS—See IKM Gruppen AS; *Int'l*, pg. 3611

ILLUSTRATED PROPERTIES REAL ESTATE, INC.—See The Keyes Company; *U.S. Private*, pg. 4065

IMMOBILIARE METANOPOLI S.P.A.—See Eni S.p.A.; *Int'l*, pg. 2437

IMMOBILIEN-VERMIETUNGSGESELLSCHAFT REEDER & CO. OBJEKT AIRPORT BUROCENTER-DRESDEN KG—See Commerzbank AG; *Int'l*, pg. 1718

IMMOBILIEN-VERMIETUNGSGESELLSCHAFT SCHUMACHER&CO OBJEKT BAHNHOFE DEUTSCHLAND KG—See Deutsche Bahn AG; *Int'l*, pg. 2052

IMMOBILIERE DES TECHNODES—See Heidelberg Materials AG; *Int'l*, pg. 3316

IMMOCHAN MAGYARORSZAG KFT.—See Auchan Holding S.A.; *Int'l*, pg. 699

IMMO WAUTERS BVBA—See ADGAR INVESTMENTS AND DEVELOPMENT LIMITED; *Int'l*, pg. 145

INDEPENDENCE REALTY, LLC; *U.S. Private*, pg. 2058

INDOCHINE REAL ESTATE JOINT STOCK COMPANY—See Dat Xanh Group Joint Stock Company; *Int'l*, pg. 1975

INDUSTRIAL REALTY SOLUTIONS, INC.; *U.S. Private*, pg. 2068

INFINITE REALTY; *U.S. Private*, pg. 2071

INLAND REAL ESTATE INCOME TRUST, INC.; *U.S. Public*, pg. 1124

INLANTA MORTGAGE, INC.—See McCarthy Group, LLC; *U.S. Private*, pg. 2627

INMAN GROUP, LLC—See Beringer Capital; *Int'l*, pg. 981

INMOBILIARIA HOTELERA POSADAS, S.A. DE C.V.—See Grupo Posadas S.A.B. de C.V.; *Int'l*, pg. 3134

INMOBILIARIA TEPALCAPA SA DE CV—See Enovis Corporation; *U.S. Public*, pg. 773

INPOINT COMMERCIAL REAL ESTATE INCOME, INC.—See The Inland Real Estate Group of Companies, Inc.; *U.S. Private*, pg. 4056

INTEGRAL PROPERTIES LLC—See The Integral Group LLC; *U.S. Private*, pg. 4057

INTEGRATED PRIVATE DEBT CORP.—See Fiera Capital Corporation; *Int'l*, pg. 2660

INTERNATIONAL PAPER INVESTMENTS FRANCE S.A.—See International Paper Company; *U.S. Public*, pg. 1157

INTERO REAL ESTATE SERVICES, INC.—See Berkshire Hathaway Inc.; *U.S. Public*, pg. 306

INTERSTATE REALTY MANAGEMENT CO.; *U.S. Private*, pg. 2125

INVESTMENT PROPERTIES AND MANAGEMENT—See Tutera Group Inc.; *U.S. Private*, pg. 4262

INVESTMENT PROPERTIES CORPORATION; *U.S. Private*, pg. 2132

INVITATION HOMES INC.; *U.S. Public*, pg. 1165

INVITATION HOMES L.P.—See Invitation Homes Inc.; *U.S. Public*, pg. 1165

IOWA REALTY CO., INC.—See Berkshire Hathaway Inc.; *U.S. Public*, pg. 306

IP COMMERCIAL PROPERTIES INC.—See International Paper Company; *U.S. Public*, pg. 1155

IRET PROPERTIES—See Centerspace; *U.S. Public*, pg. 472

IRISH ESTATES (FACILITIES MANAGEMENT) LIMITED—See Aramark; *U.S. Public*, pg. 177

IRONGATE REALTORS INC.; *U.S. Private*, pg. 2140

IRONSTOB, LLC—See Forestar Group Inc.; *U.S. Public*, pg. 867

ISLAND REALTY INC.; *U.S. Private*, pg. 2145

ISTAR ASSET SERVICES, INC.—See Safehold Inc.; *U.S. Public*, pg. 1834

ISTAR MARLIN LLC—See Safehold Inc.; *U.S. Public*, pg. 1834

ITANDI, INC.—See GAtechnologies Co., Ltd.; *Int'l*, pg. 2888

ITG REALTY LLC—See ITG Holdings LLC; *U.S. Private*, pg. 2149

JACKSON & COOKSEY INC.—See BGC Group, Inc.; *U.S. Public*, pg. 329

JACOBS REAL ESTATE SERVICES LLC—See The Richard E. Jacobs Group, LLC; *U.S. Private*, pg. 4106

JANOVER INC.; *U.S. Public*, pg. 1187

JANSEN COASTAL PROPERTIES GROUP; *U.S. Private*, pg. 2187

JAPAN H. L. LIMITED—See Jones Lang LaSalle Incorporated; *U.S. Public*, pg. 1202

J.B. GOODWIN REAL ESTATE CO. INC.; *U.S. Private*, pg. 2158

JBG SMITH PROPERTIES; *U.S. Public*, pg. 1188

N.A.I.C.S. Index
531210 — OFFICES OF REAL EST... CORPORATE AFFILIATIONS

JB HOWELL; *U.S. Private*, pg. 2193
JCM PARTNERS, LLC; *U.S. Private*, pg. 2195
JEFFERSON MALL CMBS, LLC—See CBL & Associates Properties, Inc.; *U.S. Public*, pg. 458
JENNY MARAGHY TEAM, INC.; *U.S. Private*, pg. 2200
J.E. ROBERT COMPANY; *U.S. Private*, pg. 2162
JEVONS PROPERTIES, LLC—See MYND Property Management, Inc.; *U.S. Private*, pg. 2825
JGB VENTURES INC.; *U.S. Private*, pg. 2207
JIANGXI VANKE YIDA PROPERTY INVESTMENT COMPANY LIMITED—See China Vanke Co., Ltd.; *Int'l*, pg. 1562
JIM WILSON & ASSOCIATES, INC.; *U.S. Private*, pg. 2210
JLL LTD—See Jones Lang LaSalle Incorporated; *U.S. Public*, pg. 1202
JLS INVESTMENT REALTY; *U.S. Private*, pg. 2213
J.L. TODD AUCTION CO.; *U.S. Private*, pg. 2168
JMA PROPERTIES LLC; *U.S. Private*, pg. 2214
J.M. JAYSON & CO., INC.; *U.S. Private*, pg. 2169
JMP REALTY TRUST INC.—See Citizens Financial Group, Inc.; *U.S. Public*, pg. 506
JOE GARRELL & ASSOCIATES INC.; *U.S. Private*, pg. 2218
JOHN DAUGHERTY REALTORS INC.; *U.S. Private*, pg. 2221
JOHN DEERE-LANZ VERWALTUNGS-AKTIENGESELLSCHAFT—See Deere & Company; *U.S. Public*, pg. 647
JOHN L. SCOTT INC.; *U.S. Private*, pg. 2222
JOHN R. WOOD, INC.; *U.S. Private*, pg. 2224
JOHNS HOPKINS REAL ESTATE; *U.S. Private*, pg. 2226
JOHN STEWART CO. INC.; *U.S. Private*, pg. 2224
JONES LANG LASALLE AB—See Jones Lang LaSalle Incorporated; *U.S. Public*, pg. 1202
JONES LANG LASALLE (ACT INTEGRATED) PTY LIMITED—See Jones Lang LaSalle Incorporated; *U.S. Public*, pg. 1202
JONES LANG LASALLE (ACT) PTY LIMITED—See Jones Lang LaSalle Incorporated; *U.S. Public*, pg. 1203
JONES LANG LASALLE AG—See Jones Lang LaSalle Incorporated; *U.S. Public*, pg. 1202
JONES LANG LASALLE AP LIMITED—See Jones Lang LaSalle Incorporated; *U.S. Public*, pg. 1203
JONES LANG LASALLE ARIZONA, LLC—See Jones Lang LaSalle Incorporated; *U.S. Public*, pg. 1202
JONES LANG LASALLE - ATLANTA—See Jones Lang LaSalle Incorporated; *U.S. Public*, pg. 1202
JONES LANG LASALLE AUSTRALIA PTY. LIMITED—See Jones Lang LaSalle Incorporated; *U.S. Public*, pg. 1202
JONES LANG LASALLE (BEIJING) CO., LTD.—See Jones Lang LaSalle Incorporated; *U.S. Public*, pg. 1202
JONES LANG LASALLE BV—See Jones Lang LaSalle Incorporated; *U.S. Public*, pg. 1205
JONES LANG LASALLE CO., LTD.—See Jones Lang LaSalle Incorporated; *U.S. Public*, pg. 1203
JONES LANG LASALLE CONSTRUCTION COMPANY, INC.—See Jones Lang LaSalle Incorporated; *U.S. Public*, pg. 1203
JONES LANG LASALLE ESPANA, S.A.—See Jones Lang LaSalle Incorporated; *U.S. Public*, pg. 1203
JONES LANG LASALLE EUROPE LIMITED—See Jones Lang LaSalle Incorporated; *U.S. Public*, pg. 1203
JONES LANG LASALLE FACILITIES KABUSHIKI KAISHA—See Jones Lang LaSalle Incorporated; *U.S. Public*, pg. 1203
JONES LANG LASALLE FINLAND OY—See Jones Lang LaSalle Incorporated; *U.S. Public*, pg. 1203
JONES LANG LASALLE (GENEVA) SA—See Jones Lang LaSalle Incorporated; *U.S. Public*, pg. 1202
JONES LANG LASALLE HOTELS (QLD) PTY LIMITED—See Jones Lang LaSalle Incorporated; *U.S. Public*, pg. 1203
JONES LANG LASALLE - HOUSTON—See Jones Lang LaSalle Incorporated; *U.S. Public*, pg. 1202
JONES LANG LASALLE (INDIA) PRIVATE LIMITED—See Jones Lang LaSalle Incorporated; *U.S. Public*, pg. 1202
JONES LANG LASALLE ISRAEL LIMITED—See Jones Lang LaSalle Incorporated; *U.S. Public*, pg. 1204
JONES LANG LASALLE KABUSHIKI KAISHA—See Jones Lang LaSalle Incorporated; *U.S. Public*, pg. 1204
JONES LANG LASALLE KFT—See Jones Lang LaSalle Incorporated; *U.S. Public*, pg. 1204
JONES LANG LASALLE LANKA (PRIVATE) LIMITED—See Jones Lang LaSalle Incorporated; *U.S. Public*, pg. 1204
JONES LANG LASALLE LIMITED—See Jones Lang LaSalle Incorporated; *U.S. Public*, pg. 1204
JONES LANG LASALLE LLC—See Jones Lang LaSalle Incorporated; *U.S. Public*, pg. 1204
JONES LANG LASALLE LLP—See Jones Lang LaSalle Incorporated; *U.S. Public*, pg. 1204
JONES LANG LASALLE LTD—See Jones Lang LaSalle Incorporated; *U.S. Public*, pg. 1204
JONES LANG LASALLE (LUXEMBOURG) SECS—See Jones Lang LaSalle Incorporated; *U.S. Public*, pg. 1205
JONES LANG LASALLE MICHIGAN, LLC—See Jones Lang LaSalle Incorporated; *U.S. Public*, pg. 1204
JONES LANG LASALLE (NSW) PTY LIMITED—See Jones Lang LaSalle Incorporated; *U.S. Public*, pg. 1203
JONES LANG LASALLE OF NEW YORK, LLC—See Jones Lang LaSalle Incorporated; *U.S. Public*, pg. 1205
JONES LANG LASALLE (PHILIPPINES), INC.—See Jones Lang LaSalle Incorporated; *U.S. Public*, pg. 1202
JONES LANG LASALLE PROPERTY CONSULTANTS PTE LTD—See Jones Lang LaSalle Incorporated; *U.S. Public*, pg. 1204
JONES LANG LASALLE (PUERTO RICO), INC.—See Jones Lang LaSalle Incorporated; *U.S. Public*, pg. 1202
JONES LANG LASALLE (QLD) PTY LIMITED—See Jones Lang LaSalle Incorporated; *U.S. Public*, pg. 1203
JONES LANG LASALLE REAL ESTATE SERVICES INCORPORATED—See Jones Lang LaSalle Incorporated; *U.S. Public*, pg. 1204
JONES LANG LASALLE RESIDENTIAL PRIVATE LIMITED—See Jones Lang LaSalle Incorporated; *U.S. Public*, pg. 1204
JONES LANG LASALLE - SAN DIEGO—See Jones Lang LaSalle Incorporated; *U.S. Public*, pg. 1202
JONES LANG LASALLE (SA) PTY LIMITED—See Jones Lang LaSalle Incorporated; *U.S. Public*, pg. 1203
JONES LANG LASALLE S.A.—See Jones Lang LaSalle Incorporated; *U.S. Public*, pg. 1204
JONES LANG LASALLE SAS—See Jones Lang LaSalle Incorporated; *U.S. Public*, pg. 1204
JONES LANG LASALLE (SCOTLAND) LIMITED—See Jones Lang LaSalle Incorporated; *U.S. Public*, pg. 1203
JONES LANG LASALLE - SEATTLE—See Jones Lang LaSalle Incorporated; *U.S. Public*, pg. 1202
JONES LANG LASALLE SECS—See Jones Lang LaSalle Incorporated; *U.S. Public*, pg. 1204
JONES LANG LASALLE SERVICES AB—See Jones Lang LaSalle Incorporated; *U.S. Public*, pg. 1204
JONES LANG LASALLE - SILICON VALLEY—See Jones Lang LaSalle Incorporated; *U.S. Public*, pg. 1202
JONES LANG LASALLE, SOCIEDAD ANONIMA DE CAPITAL VARIABLE—See Jones Lang LaSalle Incorporated; *U.S. Public*, pg. 1205
JONES LANG LASALLE, SOCIEDADE DE MEDIACAO IMOBILIARIA, S.A.—See Jones Lang LaSalle Incorporated; *U.S. Public*, pg. 1205
JONES LANG LASALLE SOUTH AFRICA (PROPRIETARY) LTD—See Jones Lang LaSalle Incorporated; *U.S. Public*, pg. 1204
JONES LANG LASALLE S.P.A.—See Jones Lang LaSalle Incorporated; *U.S. Public*, pg. 1204
JONES LANG LASALLE SPRL—See Jones Lang LaSalle Incorporated; *U.S. Public*, pg. 1205
JONES LANG LASALLE SP. Z O.O.—See Jones Lang LaSalle Incorporated; *U.S. Public*, pg. 1204
JONES LANG LASALLE S.R.L.—See Jones Lang LaSalle Incorporated; *U.S. Public*, pg. 1204
JONES LANG LASALLE SRL—See Jones Lang LaSalle Incorporated; *U.S. Public*, pg. 1205
JONES LANG LASALLE TAIWAN LIMITED—See Jones Lang LaSalle Incorporated; *U.S. Public*, pg. 1205
JONES LANG LASALLE - TEXAS, INC.—See Jones Lang LaSalle Incorporated; *U.S. Public*, pg. 1202
JONES LANG LASALLE (THAILAND) LIMITED—See Jones Lang LaSalle Incorporated; *U.S. Public*, pg. 1202
JONES LANG LASALLE (VIC) PTY LIMITED—See Jones Lang LaSalle Incorporated; *U.S. Public*, pg. 1203
JONES LANG LASALLE VIETNAM COMPANY LIMITED—See Jones Lang LaSalle Incorporated; *U.S. Public*, pg. 1205
JONES LANG LASALLE (WA) PTY LIMITED—See Jones Lang LaSalle Incorporated; *U.S. Public*, pg. 1203
JONES PROPERTIES, INC.—See Jones International University; *U.S. Private*, pg. 2233
JOSHUA & CO.; *U.S. Private*, pg. 2237
JPB PARTNERS, LLC—See J.P.B. Enterprises, Inc.; *U.S. Private*, pg. 2170
JP PICCININI REAL ESTATE SERVICES LLC—See Aperion Management; *U.S. Private*, pg. 291
J. ROBERTS & COMPANY; *U.S. Private*, pg. 2157
JULIA B. FEE SOTHEBY'S INTERNATIONAL REALTY—See William Pitt Sotheby's International Realty; *U.S. Private*, pg. 4524
JUMP INC.; *U.S. Private*, pg. 2243
JUSTIZZENTRUM IN HALLE WICHFORD & CO. KG—See Starwood Capital Group Global I, LLC; *U.S. Private*, pg. 3789
JUSTIZZENTRUM IN HALLE WICHFORD VERWALTUNGSGESELLSCHAFT MBH—See Starwood Capital Group Global I, LLC; *U.S. Private*, pg. 3789
J WOOD REALTY, LLC; *U.S. Private*, pg. 2153
KAPALUA REALTY COMPANY, LTD.—See Maui Land & Pineapple Company, Inc.; *U.S. Public*, pg. 1402
KAPPEL & KAPPEL INC.; *U.S. Private*, pg. 2262
KAUPULEHU DEVELOPMENTS—See Barnwell Industries, Inc.; *U.S. Public*, pg. 278
KAVALA, INC.; *U.S. Private*, pg. 2265
K. BARGER REALTY, LLC; *U.S. Private*, pg. 2251
KBS CAPITAL MARKETS GROUP, LLC—See KBS Realty Advisors, LLC; *U.S. Private*, pg. 2269
KEENE'S POINTE REALTY—See Murdock Holdings, LLC; *U.S. Private*, pg. 2814
KEEPING CURRENT MATTERS, INC.; *U.S. Private*, pg. 2273
KEE REAL ESTATE CO. OF DETROIT, INC; *U.S. Private*, pg. 2271
KELLER WILLIAMS CAPITAL PROPERTIES; *U.S. Private*, pg. 2275
KELLER WILLIAMS LEGACY BROKERAGE GROUP; *U.S. Private*, pg. 2275
KELLER WILLIAMS PLATINUM PARTNERS, INC.; *U.S. Private*, pg. 2275
KELLER WILLIAMS REALTY, INC.; *U.S. Private*, pg. 2275
KELLY & PICERNE INC.—See Picerne Real Estate Group; *U.S. Private*, pg. 3176
KENNEDY WILSON AUCTION GROUP INC.—See Kennedy-Wilson Holdings, Inc.; *U.S. Public*, pg. 1223
KENNEDY-WILSON INTERNATIONAL—See Kennedy-Wilson Holdings, Inc.; *U.S. Public*, pg. 1223
KENNEDY WILSON IRELAND LIMITED—See Kennedy-Wilson Holdings, Inc.; *U.S. Public*, pg. 1223
KENSINGTON CA, LLC—See Jones Lang LaSalle Incorporated; *U.S. Public*, pg. 1205
KENTWOOD REAL ESTATE SERVICES LLC—See Berkshire Hathaway Inc.; *U.S. Public*, pg. 306
KESSINGER/HUNTER & CO. LC; *U.S. Private*, pg. 2291
KETTLEY & COMPANY REALTORS-BATAVIA—See Kettley & Company Realtors Inc.; *U.S. Private*, pg. 2292
KETTLEY & COMPANY REALTORS-COMMERCIAL—See Kettley & Company Realtors Inc.; *U.S. Private*, pg. 2292
KETTLEY & COMPANY REALTORS INC.; *U.S. Private*, pg. 2292
KETTLEY & COMPANY REALTORS-OSWEGO—See Kettley & Company Realtors Inc.; *U.S. Private*, pg. 2292
KETTLEY & COMPANY REALTORS-SAINT CHARLES—See Kettley & Company Realtors Inc.; *U.S. Private*, pg. 2292
KETTLEY & COMPANY REALTORS-SANDWICH—See Kettley & Company Realtors Inc.; *U.S. Private*, pg. 2292
KETTLEY & COMPANY REALTORS-YORKVILLE—See Kettley & Company Realtors Inc.; *U.S. Private*, pg. 2292
KETTLEY REALTORS—See Kettley & Company Realtors Inc.; *U.S. Private*, pg. 2292
KEYES ASSET MANAGEMENT—See The Keyes Company; *U.S. Private*, pg. 4065
THE KEYES COMPANY; *U.S. Private*, pg. 4065
KEYES NATIONAL REFERRAL—See The Keyes Company; *U.S. Private*, pg. 4065
KEYS COMMERCIAL REAL ESTATE LLC—See Lowe Enterprises, Inc.; *U.S. Private*, pg. 2504
KEY SOLUTIONS REAL ESTATE GROUP; *U.S. Private*, pg. 2294
KEYSTONE ASSET MANAGEMENT, INC.—See LRES Corp.; *U.S. Private*, pg. 2507
KEYSTONE PROPERTY GROUP; *U.S. Private*, pg. 2300
KIDDER MATTHEW, LLC; *U.S. Private*, pg. 2303
KILLEARN PROPERTIES, INC.; *U.S. Private*, pg. 2304
KILLEARN PROPERTIES OF GEORGIA—See Killearn Properties, Inc.; *U.S. Private*, pg. 2304
KILPATRICK & SCONYERS AGENCY—See Sherman & Hemstreet, Inc.; *U.S. Private*, pg. 3634
KILROY SERVICES, LLC—See Kilroy Realty Corporation; *U.S. Public*, pg. 1228
KINGS HILL ESTATE MANAGEMENT COMPANY LIMITED—See Prologis, Inc.; *U.S. Public*, pg. 1727
KINGSMILL REALTY INC.—See Anheuser-Busch InBev SA/NV; *Int'l*, pg. 465
KIRAZ 1 GAYRIMENKUL YATIRZM DANZSMANLIGI A.S.—See ESAS Holding A.S.; *Int'l*, pg. 2501
KISLAK COMPANY—See J.I. Kislak Inc.; *U.S. Private*, pg. 2167
KITE REALTY GROUP, L.P.—See Kite Realty Group Trust; *U.S. Public*, pg. 1236
KKR REAL ESTATE FINANCE TRUST INC.; *U.S. Public*, pg. 1267
KLEIN & HEUCHAN, INC.; *U.S. Private*, pg. 2318
KLINGBEIL CAPITAL MANAGEMENT; *U.S. Private*, pg. 2320
KLNB, LLC; *U.S. Private*, pg. 2320
KOKURA ENTERPRISE CO., LTD.—See Biken Techno Corporation Ltd.; *Int'l*, pg. 1023
KORMAN SERVICES, L.P.; *U.S. Private*, pg. 2344
KOVACK REALTORS—See Berkshire Hathaway Inc.; *U.S. Public*, pg. 308
KRAUS-ANDERSON REALTY COMPANY—See Kraus-Anderson Incorporated; *U.S. Private*, pg. 2350
KUKUI'ULA DEVELOPMENT COMPANY, INC.—See Alexander & Baldwin, Inc.; *U.S. Public*, pg. 75
KUNKLE REALTY, LLC; *U.S. Private*, pg. 2357
KUPER REALTY CORP.; *U.S. Private*, pg. 2357
KUTLICK REALTY, LLC—See Steve Platz Realty Inc.; *U.S. Private*, pg. 3808
KW FOUR POINTS, LLC—See Kennedy-Wilson Holdings, Inc.; *U.S. Public*, pg. 1223
KW/LF MALIBU SANDS, LLC—See Kennedy-Wilson Holdings, Inc.; *U.S. Public*, pg. 1223
KW MARINA VIEW, LLC—See Kennedy-Wilson Holdings, Inc.; *U.S. Public*, pg. 1223
KW TRICENTER, LLC—See Kennedy-Wilson Holdings, Inc.; *U.S. Public*, pg. 1223

N.A.I.C.S. INDEX

531210 — OFFICES OF REAL EST...

LAFAYETTE REAL ESTATE LLC—See Prologis, Inc.; *U.S. Public*, pg. 1727
LAFFEY INTERNATIONAL REALTY, LLC—See Berkshire Hathaway Inc.; *U.S. Public*, pg. 306
LAKE JEANETTE DEVELOPMENT CO—See Hudson Advisors LLC; *U.S. Private*, pg. 2001
LAMOSA DESARROLLOS INMOBILIARIOS, S.A. DE C.V.—See Grupo Lamosa S.A. de C.V.; *Int'l*, pg. 3132
LANDMARK WHITE (BRISBANE) PTY LTD—See Acumentis Group Limited; *Int'l*, pg. 121
LAND PROPERTIES INC.; *U.S. Private*, pg. 2383
LANDQWEST COMMERCIAL, LLC; *U.S. Private*, pg. 2386
LAND SOLUTIONS, INC.; *U.S. Private*, pg. 2384
LAND SOUTH REALTY, LLC—See Land South Holdings, LLC; *U.S. Private*, pg. 2384
LANDVEST INC.; *U.S. Private*, pg. 2387
LANG REALTY, INC.; *U.S. Private*, pg. 2388
LASALLE INVESTMENT MANAGEMENT BV—See Jones Lang LaSalle Incorporated; *U.S. Public*, pg. 1203
LASALLE INVESTMENT MANAGEMENT HONG KONG LIMITED—See Jones Lang LaSalle Incorporated; *U.S. Public*, pg. 1205
LASALLE INVESTMENT MANAGEMENT, INC.—See Jones Lang LaSalle Incorporated; *U.S. Public*, pg. 1204
LASALLE INVESTMENT MANAGEMENT LUXEMBOURG SARL—See Jones Lang LaSalle Incorporated; *U.S. Public*, pg. 1204
LASALLE INVESTMENT MANAGEMENT S.A.S.—See Jones Lang LaSalle Incorporated; *U.S. Public*, pg. 1203
LASALLE INVESTMENT MANAGEMENT (SHANGHAI) CO., LTD.—See Jones Lang LaSalle Incorporated; *U.S. Public*, pg. 1205
LASALLE INVESTMENT MANAGEMENT—See Jones Lang LaSalle Incorporated; *U.S. Public*, pg. 1203
LAT PURSER & ASSOCIATES, INC.; *U.S. Private*, pg. 2395
LATTER & BLUM, INC.—See Compass, Inc.; *U.S. Public*, pg. 561
LATTER & BLUM OF TEXAS, LLC—See Compass, Inc.; *U.S. Public*, pg. 561
LAURELWOOD PROPERTIES INC.—See The Goodyear Tire & Rubber Company; *U.S. Public*, pg. 2084
LAWRENCE RUBEN CO.; *U.S. Private*, pg. 2402
THE LAWSON COMPANIES, INC.; *U.S. Private*, pg. 4068
L.B. INDUSTRIES, INC.; *U.S. Private*, pg. 2364
L&B REALTY ADVISORS, INC.; *U.S. Private*, pg. 2362
LBS IMMOBILIEN GMBH—See Helaba Landesbank Hessen-Thuringen; *Int'l*, pg. 3328
L.C. LOGISTICS PTE LTD—See Aspial Corporation Limited; *Int'l*, pg. 630
L.C. LOGISTICS PTE LTD—See Fragrance Group Limited; *Int'l*, pg. 2758
LE ARC CORPORATION—See Parigi International Inc.; *U.S. Private*, pg. 3094
LEASINVEST IMMO LUX SA—See Ackermans & van Haaren NV; *Int'l*, pg. 106
LEASINVEST SERVICES NV—See Ackermans & van Haaren NV; *Int'l*, pg. 106
LEDRA ESTATE LTD.—See Bank of Cyprus Holdings Public Limited Company; *Int'l*, pg. 842
LEGACY LANDS, LLC—See Five Point Holdings, LLC; *U.S. Public*, pg. 852
LEGUM & NORMAN INC.; *U.S. Private*, pg. 2418
LEHIGH REALTY COMPANY—See Heidelberg Materials AG; *Int'l*, pg. 3318
LEISURE WORLD OF MARYLAND; *U.S. Private*, pg. 2420
LENNAR COLORADO, LLC—See Lennar Corporation; *U.S. Public*, pg. 1306
LERNER CORPORATION; *U.S. Private*, pg. 2431
LEVY BEFFORT, LLC—See BGC Group, Inc.; *U.S. Public*, pg. 329
LGI HOMES - ARIZONA, LLC—See LGI Homes, Inc.; *U.S. Public*, pg. 1310
LGI HOMES - DEER CREEK, LLC—See LGI Homes, Inc.; *U.S. Public*, pg. 1310
LGI HOMES - E SAN ANTONIO, LLC—See LGI Homes, Inc.; *U.S. Public*, pg. 1310
LGI HOMES - FLORIDA, LLC—See LGI Homes, Inc.; *U.S. Public*, pg. 1310
LGI HOMES - FW, LLC—See LGI Homes, Inc.; *U.S. Public*, pg. 1310
LGI HOMES GROUP, LLC—See LGI Homes, Inc.; *U.S. Public*, pg. 1310
LGI HOMES - LUCKEY RANCH, LLC—See LGI Homes, Inc.; *U.S. Public*, pg. 1310
LGI HOMES - NC, LLC—See LGI Homes, Inc.; *U.S. Public*, pg. 1310
LGI HOMES - OAK HOLLOW, LLC—See LGI Homes, Inc.; *U.S. Public*, pg. 1310
LGI HOMES - PRESIDENTIAL GLEN, LLC—See LGI Homes, Inc.; *U.S. Public*, pg. 1310
LGI HOMES - SONTERRA, LLC—See LGI Homes, Inc.; *U.S. Public*, pg. 1310
LIBERTY AIPO LIMITED PARTNERSHIP—See Prologis, Inc.; *U.S. Public*, pg. 1727
LIBERTY DURHAM, LLC—See Prologis, Inc.; *U.S. Public*, pg. 1727
LIFE STORAGE LP—See Extra Space Storage, Inc.; *U.S. Public*, pg. 813

LIMA LAND, INC.—See Aboitiz Equity Ventures, Inc.; *Int'l*, pg. 66
LINCOLN PROPERTY COMPANY RESIDENTIAL—See Lincoln Property Company; *U.S. Private*, pg. 2458
LINCOLN PROPERTY COMPANY; *U.S. Private*, pg. 2458
LINGERFELT OFFICE PROPERTIES LLC—See Ladder Capital Corp.; *U.S. Public*, pg. 1288
LIONHEART CAPITAL; *U.S. Private*, pg. 2464
LIVING SALINAS EMPREENDIMENTOS IMOBILIARIOS LTDA.—See Cyrela Brazil Realty S.A.; *Int'l*, pg. 1897
L. NAKAGAWA-JOHNSTON; *U.S. Private*, pg. 2364
LOANATIK, LLC; *U.S. Private*, pg. 2476
LOEB PARTNERS REALTY & DEVELOPMENT—See Loeb Holding Corporation; *U.S. Private*, pg. 2479
LOEB PARTNERS REALTY, LLC; *U.S. Private*, pg. 2480
LONG & FOSTER REAL ESTATE, INC.—See The Long & Foster Companies, Inc.; *U.S. Private*, pg. 4072
LONG REALTY COMPANY—See Berkshire Hathaway Inc.; *U.S. Public*, pg. 306
LONNEGAL PROPERTY PTY. LTD.—See Cedar Woods Properties Limited; *Int'l*, pg. 1388
LOUIS HYATT, INC.—See Reliable Contracting Company Inc.; *U.S. Private*, pg. 3394
LOWE ENTERPRISES REAL ESTATE GROUP—See Lowe Enterprises, Inc.; *U.S. Private*, pg. 2504
LOWE ENTERPRISES REAL ESTATE GROUP—See Lowe Enterprises, Inc.; *U.S. Private*, pg. 2504
LOWE ENTERPRISES TEXAS INC.—See Lowe Enterprises, Inc.; *U.S. Private*, pg. 2504
LTL INC.—See Joe Garrell & Associates Inc.; *U.S. Private*, pg. 2218
LUMAS REALTY, INC.; *U.S. Private*, pg. 2513
MAA ARKANSAS REIT, LLC—See Mid-America Apartment Communities, Inc.; *U.S. Public*, pg. 1444
MACERICH DB LLC—See The Macerich Company; *U.S. Public*, pg. 2110
THE MACERICH PARTNERSHIP, L.P.—See The Macerich Company; *U.S. Public*, pg. 2111
MACGREGOR PARK, INC.—See The AES Corporation; *U.S. Public*, pg. 2032
MACK-CALI REALTY, L.P.—See Veris Residential, Inc.; *U.S. Public*, pg. 2281
MACK-CALI WOODBRIDGE L.L.C.—See Veris Residential, Inc.; *U.S. Public*, pg. 2281
MACKENZIE REALTY CAPITAL, INC.; *U.S. Public*, pg. 1352
MACKINAC ISLAND REALTY, INC.; *U.S. Private*, pg. 2537
MAINE MEDICAL PARTNERS—See MaineHealth; *U.S. Private*, pg. 2553
MAKOWSKY RINGEL GREENBERG, LLC; *U.S. Private*, pg. 2556
MALT REALTY & DEVELOPMENT INC.; *U.S. Private*, pg. 2558
MANEKIN LLC—See Colliers International Group Inc.; *Int'l*, pg. 1701
MAPLE BROOK, L.L.C.—See Sun Communities, Inc.; *U.S. Public*, pg. 1961
THE MARK COMPANY / PACIFIC UNION INTERNATIONAL, INC.—See Pacific Union International, Inc.; *U.S. Private*, pg. 3071
MARKET AMERICA REALTY AND INVESTMENTS, INC.; *U.S. Private*, pg. 2578
MARKETPLACE HOMES; *U.S. Private*, pg. 2581
MARQUIS PROPERTIES REALTY; *U.S. Private*, pg. 2587
MARRIOTT OWNERSHIP RESORTS, INC.—See Marriott Vacations Worldwide Corporation; *U.S. Public*, pg. 1374
MARSH & MCLENNAN REAL ESTATE ADVISORS INC.—See Marsh & McLennan Companies, Inc.; *U.S. Public*, pg. 1378
MARTHA TURNER SOTHEBY'S INTERNATIONAL REALTY—See Anywhere Real Estate Inc.; *U.S. Public*, pg. 141
MASELLE & ASSOCIATES, INC.; *U.S. Private*, pg. 2601
MAXIMUM ONE REALTY; *U.S. Private*, pg. 2619
MAXIMUS SECURITIES LIMITED—See Hybrid Financial Services Limited; *Int'l*, pg. 3544
MAYHUGH REALTY, INC.; *U.S. Private*, pg. 2622
MCBRIDE & SON ENTERPRISES INC.; *U.S. Private*, pg. 2625
MCCORMACK BARON MANAGEMENT SERVICES—See McCormack Baron Salazar, Inc.; *U.S. Private*, pg. 2630
MCENEARNEY ASSOCIATES INC.; *U.S. Private*, pg. 2633
MCGEOUGH LAMACCHIA REALTY INC.; *U.S. Private*, pg. 2634
MCGRATH LIMITED—See Bayleys Corporation Limited; *Int'l*, pg. 914
MCGUIRE REAL ESTATE SERVICES GROUP—See McGuire Development Company, LLC; *U.S. Private*, pg. 2636
MCKESSON PROVIDER TECHNOLOGIES—See McKesson Corporation; *U.S. Public*, pg. 1408
MCLEAN FAULCONER INC.; *U.S. Private*, pg. 2641
MCO PROPERTIES INC.—See Maxxam, Inc.; *U.S. Private*, pg. 2620
MCQUAID & COMPANY; *U.S. Private*, pg. 2644
MEDALIST DIVERSIFIED REIT, INC.; *U.S. Public*, pg. 1411
MENLO EQUITIES LLC; *U.S. Private*, pg. 2666

MENTOR MANAGEMENT LIMITED—See CBRE Group, Inc.; *U.S. Public*, pg. 460
MERICLE COMMERCIAL REAL ESTATE SERVICES; *U.S. Private*, pg. 2672
MESIROW FINANCIAL REAL ESTATE BROKERAGE, INC.—See Mesirow Financial Holdings, Inc.; *U.S. Private*, pg. 2678
METCALFE INC.; *U.S. Public*, pg. 2683
MET II OFFICE LLC—See MetLife, Inc.; *U.S. Public*, pg. 1430
METRO ATLANTA PROPERTIES—See Fischbach & Dougherty, Inc.; *U.S. Private*, pg. 1532
METRO REALTY; *U.S. Private*, pg. 2686
M&H PROPERTIES LTD.—See American Motel Management; *U.S. Private*, pg. 241
MICHAEL SAUNDERS & COMPANY; *U.S. Private*, pg. 2698
MIKE MYERS REALTY INC.; *U.S. Private*, pg. 2725
MILLENIUM PROPERTIES, INC.—See First Busey Corporation; *U.S. Public*, pg. 840
MILLER REAL ESTATE INVESTMENTS, LLC—See Kimco Realty Corporation; *U.S. Public*, pg. 1232
MIRAGE LEISURE & DEVELOPMENT INC.—See Emaar Properties PJSC; *Int'l*, pg. 2373
MJB REALTY INC.; *U.S. Private*, pg. 2752
MJKI INDIA PVT. LTD.—See Digilife Technologies Limited; *Int'l*, pg. 2119
MLG COMMERCIAL, LLC—See Newmark Group, Inc.; *U.S. Public*, pg. 1515
THE MODEL GROUP INC.; *U.S. Private*, pg. 4080
MODERN STANDARD CO., LTD.—See GAtechnologies Co., Ltd.; *Int'l*, pg. 2889
MODI INDONESIA 2020 PTE. LTD.—See Digilife Technologies Limited; *Int'l*, pg. 2119
MODIV INDUSTRIAL, INC.; *U.S. Public*, pg. 1455
MOLPUS COMPANY; *U.S. Private*, pg. 2767
MONTEPIO VALOR - SOCIEDADE GESTORA DE FUNDOS DE INVESTIMENTO, S.A.—See Caixa Economica Montepio Geral; *Int'l*, pg. 1259
MONTICELLO MANAGEMENT CO.; *U.S. Private*, pg. 2777
MORECO, INC.—See Modern Group Ltd.; *U.S. Private*, pg. 2761
MORGAN PROPERTIES, LLC—See Raymond James Financial, Inc.; *U.S. Public*, pg. 1764
MORGAN STANLEY REAL ESTATE—See Morgan Stanley; *U.S. Public*, pg. 1475
MORSE PROPERTIES, INC.; *U.S. Private*, pg. 2790
MORTGAGE OIL CORP.; *U.S. Public*, pg. 1477
MOSENKA LLC—See Enka Insaat ve Sanayi A.S.; *Int'l*, pg. 2440
MOSKVA KRASNYE HOLMY LLC—See Enka Insaat ve Sanayi A.S.; *Int'l*, pg. 2440
MOTT & CHACE SOTHEBY'S INTERNATIONAL REALTY; *U.S. Private*, pg. 2797
MOTTO FRANCHISING, LLC—See RE/MAX Holdings, Inc.; *U.S. Public*, pg. 1768
MOVOTO LLC; *U.S. Private*, pg. 2802
MPT OPERATING PARTNERSHIP, L.P.—See Medical Properties Trust, Inc.; *U.S. Public*, pg. 1412
MR. PAYROLL CORPORATION—See FirstCash Holdings, Inc.; *U.S. Public*, pg. 849
MSL PROPERTY MANAGEMENT; *U.S. Private*, pg. 2807
MSP CAPITAL MANAGEMENT, L.L.C.; *U.S. Private*, pg. 2808
M&T PARTNERS—See Pacific Realty Associates, LP; *U.S. Private*, pg. 3070
MULHEARN REALTORS INC.; *U.S. Private*, pg. 2811
MYM COMMUNITY CO., LTD.—See Biken Techno Corporation Ltd.; *Int'l*, pg. 1023
NAI GLOBAL, INC.—See Island Capital Group LLC; *U.S. Private*, pg. 2144
NAI HUNNEMAN—See Island Capital Group LLC; *U.S. Private*, pg. 2144
NAI SOUTHWEST FLORIDA, INC.; *U.S. Private*, pg. 2830
NAI TALCOR; *U.S. Private*, pg. 2830
NALURI CORPORATION BERHAD—See Atlan Holdings Berhad; *Int'l*, pg. 674
NALURI PROPERTIES SDN. BHD.—See Atlan Holdings Berhad; *Int'l*, pg. 674
NANCY PHANEUF COMMERCIAL REALTY & DEVELOPMENT; *U.S. Private*, pg. 2833
NAPLES REALTY SERVICES INC.; *U.S. Private*, pg. 2834
NATERRA LAND—See Naterra Land; *U.S. Private*, pg. 2838
NATERRA LAND TENNESSEE LLC—See Naterra Land; *U.S. Private*, pg. 2838
NATIONAL CHURCH RESIDENCES; *U.S. Private*, pg. 2850
NATIONAL LAND REALTY, LLC; *U.S. Private*, pg. 2858
NATIONAL PROPERTY ANALYSTS; *U.S. Private*, pg. 2861
NATIONAL REALTY & DEVELOPMENT CORP.; *U.S. Private*, pg. 2861
NATIONAL SECURITIES & INVESTMENTS INC.—See National Mortgage & Finance Co. Ltd.; *U.S. Private*, pg. 2859
NATIONAL TAX SEARCH, LLC—See Insight Venture Management, LLC; *U.S. Private*, pg. 2089
NATIONAL TAX SEARCH, LLC—See Stone Point Capital LLC; *U.S. Private*, pg. 3823
NATIXIS PFANDBRIEFBANK AG—See Groupe BPCE; *Int'l*, pg. 3098

531210 — OFFICES OF REAL EST...

NATIXIS ZWEIGNIEDERLASSUNG DEUTSCHLAND SE—See Groupe BPCE; *Int'l*, pg. 3099
NAUMANN GROUP REAL ESTATE INC.; *U.S. Private*, pg. 2868
NEST SEEKERS LLC; *U.S. Private*, pg. 2886
NETSTREIT CORP.; *U.S. Public*, pg. 1509
NEWMARK ASSOCIATES, INC., *U.S. Private*, pg. 2916
NEWMARK BH2 LLP—See Newmark Group, Inc.; *U.S. Public*, pg. 1516
NEWMARK CORNISH & CAREY—See BGC Group, Inc.; *U.S. Public*, pg. 329
NEWMARK GROUP, INC.; *U.S. Public*, pg. 1515
NEWMARK GRUBB KNIGHT FRANK - ATLANTA—See BGC Group, Inc.; *U.S. Public*, pg. 329
NEWMARK GRUBB KNIGHT FRANK - CHICAGO—See BGC Group, Inc.; *U.S. Public*, pg. 329
NEWMARK GRUBB KNIGHT FRANK - DETROIT—See BGC Group, Inc.; *U.S. Public*, pg. 329
NEWMARK GRUBB PHOENIX REALTY GROUP, INC.—See BGC Group, Inc.; *U.S. Public*, pg. 329
NEWMARK KNIGHT FRANK CANADA LIMITED—See Newmark Group, Inc.; *U.S. Public*, pg. 1515
NEWMARK KNIGHT FRANK VALUATION & ADVISORY, LLC—See Newmark Group, Inc.; *U.S. Public*, pg. 1515
NEWMARK REAL ESTATE OF DALLAS, LLC—See BGC Group, Inc., *U.S. Public*, pg. 329
NEWMARK REAL ESTATE OF HOUSTON, LLC—See BGC Group, Inc.; *U.S. Public*, pg. 329
NEWMARK REAL ESTATE OF NEW JERSEY, LLC—See BGC Group, Inc., *U.S. Public*, pg. 329
NEWMARK REAL ESTATE PANAMA, S.A.—See Newmark Group, Inc.; *U.S. Public*, pg. 1516
NEWPOINT FINANCIAL CORP.; *U.S. Public*, pg. 1518
NEW STAR REALTY & INVESTMENT—See Berkshire Hathaway Inc.; *U.S. Public*, pg. 307
NEXACOR REALTY MANAGEMENT INC.—See AtkinsRealis Group Inc.; *Int'l*, pg. 671
NEXPOINT REAL ESTATE FINANCE, INC.; *U.S. Public*, pg. 1522
NEYER MANAGEMENT; *U.S. Private*, pg. 2922
NGA, LLC—See Newmark Group, Inc.; *U.S. Public*, pg. 1516
NH ENTERPRISES (2008) PTE. LTD.—See Blackgold Natural Resources Ltd.; *Int'l*, pg. 1061
NIHON JYUTAKU RYUTU CO., LTD.—See Daiwa House Industry Co., Ltd.; *Int'l*, pg. 1947
NINETY PARK PROPERTY LLC—See Vornado Realty Trust; *U.S. Public*, pg. 2310
NORCAL GOLD, INC. - FAIR OAKS—See Norcal Gold, Inc.; *U.S. Private*, pg. 2935
NORCAL GOLD, INC. - LODI—See Norcal Gold, Inc.; *U.S. Private*, pg. 2935
NORCAL GOLD, INC.; *U.S. Private*, pg. 2935
NORRIS BEGGS & SIMPSON NORTHWEST LIMITED PARTNERSHIP; *U.S. Private*, pg. 2939
NORTH AMERICAN TITLE COMPANY (MN)—See Doma Holdings, Inc.; *U.S. Public*, pg. 673
NORTH AMERICAN TITLE COMPANY (NV)—See Doma Holdings, Inc.; *U.S. Public*, pg. 673
NORTH AMERICAN TITLE COMPANY (TX)—See Doma Holdings, Inc.; *U.S. Public*, pg. 673
NORTHERN VIRGINIA HOMES; *U.S. Private*, pg. 2955
NORTH SHORE REALTY GROUP; *U.S. Private*, pg. 2947
NORTHWOOD REALTY SERVICES—See Everest Consulting Group LP; *U.S. Private*, pg. 1438
NORTON & PROFFITT DEVELOPMENTS LIMITED—See Blackstone Inc.; *U.S. Public*, pg. 358
NOTHNAGLE REALTORS—See Hanna Holdings, Inc.; *U.S. Private*, pg. 1854
NOVAK FORNEY & ASSOCIATES, LLC; *U.S. Private*, pg. 2966
NRT DEVONSHIRE WEST LLC—See Anywhere Real Estate Inc.; *U.S. Public*, pg. 142
NRT LLC—See Anywhere Real Estate Inc.; *U.S. Public*, pg. 141
NRT MISSOURI LLC—See Anywhere Real Estate Inc.; *U.S. Public*, pg. 141
NRT PITTSBURGH LLC—See Anywhere Real Estate Inc.; *U.S. Public*, pg. 141
NRT REOEXPERTS LLC—See Anywhere Real Estate Inc.; *U.S. Public*, pg. 141
NRT ZIPREALTY LLC—See Anywhere Real Estate Inc.; *U.S. Public*, pg. 142
NUVEEN GLOBAL CITIES REIT, INC.—See Teachers Insurance Association - College Retirement Fund; *U.S. Private*, pg. 3947
OAK LEAF PROPERTIES, LLC.; *U.S. Private*, pg. 2983
O'BOYLE PROPERTIES, INC.—See BGC Group, Inc.; *U.S. Public*, pg. 329
OCCIDENTAL MANAGEMENT INC.; *U.S. Private*, pg. 2988
OCEAN PROPERTIES & MANAGEMENT, INC.; *U.S. Private*, pg. 2989
OFFICESCAPE, INC.; *U.S. Private*, pg. 3002
OHI ASSET (IN) GREENSBURG, LLC—See Omega Healthcare Investors, Inc.; *U.S. Public*, pg. 1571
OLD COLONY - GMAC REAL ESTATE; *U.S. Private*, pg. 3008
OLIVER CARR COMPANY; *U.S. Private*, pg. 3010

OLP SELDEN, INC.—See One Liberty Properties, Inc.; *U.S. Public*, pg. 1602
OLYMPIC RESOURCE MANAGEMENT—See Rayonier Inc.; *U.S. Public*, pg. 1765
ONCOR INTERNATIONAL LLC—See Anywhere Real Estate Inc.; *U.S. Public*, pg. 142
OPENDOOR BROKERAGE INC.—See Opendoor Technologies Inc.; *U.S. Public*, pg. 1606
OPPENHEIM VERWALTUNG VON IMMOBILIENVERMOGEN GMBH—See Deutsche Bank Aktiengesellschaft; *Int'l*, pg. 2062
OPTIMA ASSET MANAGEMENT SERVICES; *U.S. Private*, pg. 3034
ORHP MANAGEMENT COMPANY—See Old Republic International Corporation; *U.S. Public*, pg. 1567
ORLANDO INTERNATIONAL RESORT CLUB—See Travel & Leisure Co.; *U.S. Public*, pg. 2186
O,R&L COMMERCIAL, LLC—See O,R&L Construction Corp.; *U.S. Private*, pg. 2981
ORRADA CO., LTD.—See DCON Products Public Company Limited; *Int'l*, pg. 1993
ORSCHELN PROPERTIES CO. L.L.C.—See Orscheln Group; *U.S. Private*, pg. 3045
OSBORNE PROPERTIES CORP.; *U.S. Private*, pg. 3046
OSPREY REAL ESTATE SERVICES, LLC—See Osprey S.A. Limited; *U.S. Private*, pg. 3048
OSPREY S.A. LIMITED; *U.S. Private*, pg. 3048
OTIS & AHEARN INC.; *U.S. Private*, pg. 3049
OUTER BANKS BLUE REALTY SERVICES; *U.S. Private*, pg. 3051
OWNIT MORTGAGE SOLUTIONS OAKMONT; *U.S. Private*, pg. 3055
OXFORD REALTY, INC.; *U.S. Private*, pg. 3057
PACIFICA HOTEL COMPANY—See Invest West Financial Corporation; *U.S. Private*, pg. 2131
PACIFIC BAY HOMES, LLC—See Ford Motor Company; *U.S. Public*, pg. 867
PACIFIC REALTY COMMERCIAL, LLC—See Colliers International Group Inc.; *Int'l*, pg. 1701
PACIFICWIDE BUSINESS GROUP, INC.; *U.S. Private*, pg. 3072
PALM COAST HOLDINGS, INC.—See ALLETE, Inc.; *U.S. Public*, pg. 79
PALMERHOUSE PROPERTIES, LLC- DULUTH—See HomeSmart International LLC; *U.S. Private*, pg. 1974
PALMERHOUSE PROPERTIES, LLC.—See HomeSmart International LLC; *U.S. Private*, pg. 1974
PALMETTO REAL ESTATE TRUST; *U.S. Public*, pg. 1635
PALM HARBOR VILLAGES REAL ESTATE, LLC—See Cavco Industries, Inc.; *U.S. Public*, pg. 455
PANGEA REAL ESTATE; *U.S. Private*, pg. 3086
PAPPAS REALTY CO.; *U.S. Private*, pg. 3088
PARACOM LLC—See Colliers International Group Inc.; *Int'l*, pg. 1701
PAREF SA—See Fosun International Limited; *Int'l*, pg. 2752
PARKING CONCEPTS INC.; *U.S. Private*, pg. 3098
PARTNERS IN BOUWEN—See Heijmans N.V.; *Int'l*, pg. 3323
PATRICK MALLOY COMMUNITIES, INC.; *U.S. Private*, pg. 3110
PATTERSON-SCHWARTZ & ASSOCIATES INC.; *U.S. Private*, pg. 3111
PAUL HEMMER CONSTRUCTION COMPANY; *U.S. Private*, pg. 3113
PAULSCORP, LLC; *U.S. Private*, pg. 3114
PCD REALTY LLC—See PulteGroup, Inc.; *U.S. Public*, pg. 1737
PCI INC.—See Advanced Horizons Inc.; *U.S. Private*, pg. 90
PCS DEVELOPMENT INC.—See Public Communications Services, Inc.; *U.S. Private*, pg. 3298
PDM INTERNATIONAL LIMITED—See Jones Lang LaSalle Incorporated; *U.S. Public*, pg. 1205
PEABODY & PLUM REALTORS, INC.—See Century 21 Hometown Realty; *U.S. Private*, pg. 831
PEARSON SMITH REALTY, LLC—See United Real Estate Group, LLC; *U.S. Private*, pg. 4296
THE PEGASUS GROUP; *U.S. Public*, pg. 4092
PENNANT CONSTRUCTION MANAGEMENT, INC.—See McWhorter Capital Partners, LLC; *U.S. Private*, pg. 2645
PENN CENTER MANAGEMENT CORP.; *U.S. Private*, pg. 3133
PEPITONE PROPERTIES CORP.; *U.S. Private*, pg. 3144
PERRY BROTHERS, INC.; *U.S. Private*, pg. 3153
PHILLIPS EDISON & COMPANY LLC; *U.S. Private*, pg. 3170
PHOENICIAN PROPERTIES REALTY; *U.S. Private*, pg. 3172
PICKFORD REALTY INC.; *U.S. Private*, pg. 3176
PIEDMONT GOVERNMENT SERVICES, LLC—See Piedmont Office Realty Trust, Inc.; *U.S. Public*, pg. 1690
PIMCO MORTGAGE INCOME TRUST INC.; *U.S. Public*, pg. 1690
PINNACLE VACATIONS, INC.—See Hilton Grand Vacations Inc.; *U.S. Public*, pg. 1040
PIONEER REAL ESTATE SERVICES INC.—See Dickerson & Nieman Realtors, Inc.; *U.S. Private*, pg. 1226

PITTSBURGH COMMERCIAL REAL ESTATE, INC.—See Colliers International Group Inc.; *Int'l*, pg. 1701
PLACE2B SERVICOS IMOBILIARIOS LTDA.—See Companhia Brasileira de Distribuicao; *Int'l*, pg. 1746
PLATINUM REALTY, LLC—See United Real Estate Group, LLC; *U.S. Private*, pg. 4296
PLATINUM REALTY R.E. SERVICES—See United Real Estate Group, LLC; *U.S. Private*, pg. 4296
PLAZZA AG—See Bystronic AG; *Int'l*, pg. 1236
PMD PROPERTIES, LLC—See Laboratory Corporation of America Holdings; *U.S. Public*, pg. 1287
PM REALTY GROUP LP; *U.S. Private*, pg. 3217
POLINGER SHANNON & LUCHS COMPANY; *U.S. Private*, pg. 3224
PORTA MALLORQUINA REAL ESTATE S.L.U.—See Homes & Holiday AG; *Int'l*, pg. 3455
PORTSMOUTH SQUARE, INC.—See InterGroup Corporation; *U.S. Public*, pg. 1144
THE PPA GROUP, LLC; *U.S. Private*, pg. 4097
PPR REALTY INC.—See Everest Consulting Group LP; *U.S. Private*, pg. 1438
PRAIRIE RONDE REALTY COMPANY, INC.—See National Tube Holding Company Inc.; *U.S. Private*, pg. 2864
PREFERRED PROPERTIES OF VENICE INC.; *U.S. Private*, pg. 3248
PREFERRED REAL ESTATE GROUP INC.; *U.S. Private*, pg. 3248
PREIT-RUBIN, INC.—See Pennsylvania Real Estate Investment Trust; *U.S. Public*, pg. 1664
PREMIER COMMERCIAL, INC.—See The Scottsdale Co.; *U.S. Private*, pg. 4115
PREMIER SOTHEBY'S INTERNATIONAL REALTY; *U.S. Private*, pg. 3251
PRIAM PROPERTIES INC.; *U.S. Private*, pg. 3258
PRICOA RELOCATION ASIA PTE. LTD.—See Prudential Financial, Inc.; *U.S. Public*, pg. 1731
PRIMAC PTY. LTD.—See Elders Limited; *Int'l*, pg. 2346
PRIME ASSOCIATES, INC.—See Fidelity National Information, Inc.; *U.S. Public*, pg. 833
PRIME PROPERTY CONSULTANTS LIMITED—See Jones Lang LaSalle Incorporated; *U.S. Public*, pg. 1205
PRIMESTOR JORDAN DOWNS, LLC—See Federal Realty Investment Trust; *U.S. Public*, pg. 825
PRINCETON PROPERTY MANAGEMENT; *U.S. Private*, pg. 3264
PRIVATE MINI STORAGE REALTY LP; *U.S. Private*, pg. 3268
PROBITY INTERNATIONAL CORPORATION; *U.S. Private*, pg. 3271
PROCACCIANTI HOTEL REIT, INC.; *U.S. Private*, pg. 3271
PROFESSIONAL COMMUNITY MANAGEMENT; *U.S. Private*, pg. 3274
PROJEK BANDAR SAMARIANG SDN. BHD.—See Cahya Mata Sarawak Berhad; *Int'l*, pg. 1251
PROLOGIS CANADA INCORPORATED—See Prologis, Inc.; *U.S. Public*, pg. 1727
PROLOGIS JAPAN INCORPORATED—See Prologis, Inc.; *U.S. Public*, pg. 1727
PROMETHEUS REAL ESTATE GROUP, INC.; *U.S. Private*, pg. 3283
@PROPERTIES; *U.S. Private*, pg. 17
PROPST PROPERTIES, LLC; *U.S. Private*, pg. 3286
PRUDENTIAL CALIFORNIA REALTY—See Berkshire Hathaway Inc.; *U.S. Public*, pg. 307
PRUDENTIAL FLORIDA WCI REALTY—See Prudential Financial, Inc.; *U.S. Public*, pg. 1732
THE PRUDENTIAL LIFE REALTY GROUP—See Prudential Financial, Inc.; *U.S. Public*, pg. 1734
PRUDENTIAL NEW JERSEY PROPERTIES; *U.S. Private*, pg. 3296
PRUDENTIAL NORTHWEST REALTY ASSOCIATES, LLC—See Berkshire Hathaway Inc.; *U.S. Public*, pg. 307
PRUDENTIAL REAL ESTATE AFFILIATES, INC.—See Prudential Financial, Inc.; *U.S. Public*, pg. 1733
PRUDENTIAL REALTY COMPANY; *U.S. Private*, pg. 3296
PRUDENTIAL UTAH REAL ESTATE; *U.S. Private*, pg. 3296
PRUDENTIAL WOODMONT REALTY INC; *U.S. Private*, pg. 3296
PRU-ONE INC.; *U.S. Private*, pg. 3295
PT BUANA MEGAWISATAMA—See Gallant Venture Ltd.; *Int'l*, pg. 2874
PT ERA GRAHAREALTY TBK—See Morgan Stanley; *U.S. Public*, pg. 1471
P.T. METROTECH JAYA KOMUNIKA INDONESIA—See Digilife Technologies Limited; *Int'l*, pg. 2119
PYRAMID BROKERAGE COMPANY INC.; *U.S. Private*, pg. 3310
QINGDAO VANKE REAL ESTATE COMPANY LIMITED—See China Vanke Co., Ltd.; *Int'l*, pg. 1562
QINGJIAN REALTY (SOUTH PACIFIC) GROUP PTE. LTD.—See CNQC International Holdings Ltd.; *Int'l*, pg. 1678
QUADRANTE S.P.A—See Cassa Depositi e Prestiti S.p.A.; *Int'l*, pg. 1355
QUALITY CHOICE TITLE LLC—See Anywhere Real Estate Inc.; *U.S. Public*, pg. 142
QUALITY INVESTMENT PROPERTIES MIAMI, LLC—See Blackstone Inc.; *U.S. Public*, pg. 351

N.A.I.C.S. INDEX

531210 — OFFICES OF REAL EST...

RABENHORST LIFE INSURANCE COMPANY—See Service Corporation International; *U.S. Public*, pg. 1870
RAMCO/LION VENTURE LP—See Kimco Realty Corporation; *U.S. Public*, pg. 1232
RAMSAY REALTY; *U.S. Private*, pg. 3352
RANCON REAL ESTATE CORPORATION; *U.S. Private*, pg. 3353
RANDALLS PROPERTIES, INC.—See Cerberus Capital Management, L.P.; *U.S. Private*, pg. 836
RAND REALTY LLC; *U.S. Private*, pg. 3353
RAPID REALTY FRANCHISE LLC; *U.S. Private*, pg. 3356
READYCONNECT CONCIERGE—See News Corporation; *U.S. Public*, pg. 1521
REAL ADVISORS, LLC; *U.S. Private*, pg. 3367
REALEN PROPERTIES; *U.S. Private*, pg. 3368
REALESTATE.COM.AU PTY LTD—See News Corporation; *U.S. Public*, pg. 1521
REAL ESTATE DELIVERY, INC.—See BNP Paribas SA; *Int'l*, pg. 1088
REAL ESTATE GROUP INC.; *U.S. Private*, pg. 3367
THE REAL ESTATE GROUP, LLC; *U.S. Private*, pg. 4102
REAL ESTATE III INC.; *U.S. Private*, pg. 3367
REAL ESTATE LENDERS—See Wells Fargo & Company; *U.S. Public*, pg. 2345
REAL ESTATE REFERRALS LLC—See Anywhere Real Estate Inc.; *U.S. Public*, pg. 142
REALIZZA S.R.L.—See Duna House Holding Public Company Limited; *Int'l*, pg. 2225
REAL LIVING CYPRESS REALTY, INC.; *U.S. Private*, pg. 3367
REAL LIVING, INC.; *U.S. Private*, pg. 3368
REAL LIVING PITTMAN PROPERTIES; *U.S. Private*, pg. 3367
REALOGY BROKERAGE GROUP LLC—See Anywhere Real Estate Inc.; *U.S. Public*, pg. 143
REALOGY FRANCHISE GROUP LLC—See Anywhere Real Estate Inc.; *U.S. Public*, pg. 142
REALOGY TITLE GROUP LLC—See Anywhere Real Estate Inc.; *U.S. Public*, pg. 143
REAL PROPERTY MANAGEMENT—See Harvest Partners L.P.; *U.S. Private*, pg. 1876
REAL PROPERTY SERVICES CORP; *U.S. Private*, pg. 3368
REAL SERVICES, INC.—See Anywhere Real Estate Inc.; *U.S. Public*, pg. 141
REALTOR.COM.AU PTY LTD—See Insight Venture Management, LLC; *U.S. Private*, pg. 2089
REALTOR.COM.AU PTY LTD—See Stone Point Capital LLC; *U.S. Private*, pg. 3823
REALTY EXECUTIVES ASSOCIATES INC.; *U.S. Private*, pg. 3369
REALTY EXECUTIVES OF TUCSON, INC.; *U.S. Private*, pg. 3369
REALTY EXECUTIVES, RIVERSIDE; *U.S. Private*, pg. 3369
REALTYSOUTH—See Berkshire Hathaway Inc.; *U.S. Public*, pg. 307
REALTY USA CAPITAL, INC.—See Realty USA LLC; *U.S. Private*, pg. 3369
REALTY USA CNY, INC. - SARATOGA SPRINGS-BROADWAY OFFICE—See Realty USA LLC; *U.S. Private*, pg. 3369
REALTY USA CNY, INC.—See Realty USA LLC; *U.S. Private*, pg. 3369
REALTY USA WNY, INC. - PITTSFORD OFFICE—See Realty USA LLC; *U.S. Private*, pg. 3369
REALTY USA WNY, INC.—See Realty USA LLC; *U.S. Private*, pg. 3369
REALTYWORKS INC.; *U.S. Private*, pg. 3369
REALXDATA GMBH—See Moody's Corporation; *U.S. Public*, pg. 1469
RECON TRUST COMPANY, N.A.—See Bank of America Corporation; *U.S. Public*, pg. 271
RECTOR-HAYDEN REALTORS—See Berkshire Hathaway Inc.; *U.S. Public*, pg. 307
RED BELL REAL ESTATE, LLC—See Radian Group, Inc.; *U.S. Public*, pg. 1759
RED CANYON AT PALOMINO PARK L.L.C.—See Moody's Corporation; *U.S. Public*, pg. 1469
REDEFY, INC.—See Redefy Corporation; *U.S. Public*, pg. 1770
REDFIN CORPORATION; *U.S. Public*, pg. 1770
REECE & NICHOLS REALTORS—See Berkshire Hathaway Inc.; *U.S. Public*, pg. 307
REFERRAL NETWORK PLUS, INC.—See Anywhere Real Estate Inc.; *U.S. Public*, pg. 142
REGENCY-KLEBAN PROPERTIES, LLC—See Regency Centers Corporation; *U.S. Public*, pg. 1774
REGENCY MANAGEMENT SERVICE LLC; *U.S. Private*, pg. 3386
REGIONAL MANAGEMENT, INC.; *U.S. Private*, pg. 3388
REIF 2000 KFT.—See Duna House Holding Public Company Limited; *Int'l*, pg. 2225
REILEY REALTY, INC.; *U.S. Private*, pg. 3391
REI REAL ESTATE SERVICES LLC; *U.S. Private*, pg. 3390
RELATED SALES LLC—See The Related Companies, L.P.; *U.S. Private*, pg. 4104
RELIABLE GROUP, LLC—See Reliable Contracting Company Inc.; *U.S. Private*, pg. 3393

RELIANCE PROPERTY RESOURCES CO.—See LandPark Advisors, LLC; *U.S. Private*, pg. 2386
RELIANT REALTY, LLC; *U.S. Private*, pg. 3395
RE/MAX ACCORD; *U.S. Private*, pg. 3364
RE/MAX ALLEGIANCE; *U.S. Private*, pg. 3364
RE/MAX ALLEGIANCE - VIRGINIA BEACH—See RE/MAX Allegiance; *U.S. Private*, pg. 3364
RE/MAX ALLIANCE GROUP; *U.S. Private*, pg. 3364
RE/MAX BENCH REALTY GROUP—See RE/MAX Holdings, Inc.; *U.S. Public*, pg. 1768
RE/MAX CHOICE PROPERTIES; *U.S. Private*, pg. 3365
RE/MAX HEARTLAND; *U.S. Private*, pg. 3365
RE/MAX, LLC—See RE/MAX Holdings, Inc.; *U.S. Public*, pg. 1768
RE/MAX OF NAPERVILLE INC.; *U.S. Private*, pg. 3365
RE/MAX PROPERTIES EAST, INC.; *U.S. Private*, pg. 3365
RE/MAX REALTORS INC.; *U.S. Private*, pg. 3365
RE/MAX VILLA REALTORS; *U.S. Private*, pg. 3365
RENIN UK CORPORATION—See Hilton Grand Vacations Inc.; *U.S. Public*, pg. 1040
RENOSY ASSET MANAGEMENT CO., LTD.—See GAtechnologies Co., Ltd.; *Int'l*, pg. 2889
RENOSY PLUS CO., LTD.—See GAtechnologies Co., Ltd.; *Int'l*, pg. 2889
RENOSY (THAILAND) CO., LTD.—See GAtechnologies Co., Ltd.; *Int'l*, pg. 2889
RENOSY X CO., LTD.—See GAtechnologies Co., Ltd.; *Int'l*, pg. 2889
RENTERS WAREHOUSE—See Appreciate Holdings, Inc.; *U.S. Public*, pg. 173
REO AMERICA, INC.; *U.S. Private*, pg. 3400
THE RESORT AT LONGBOAT KEY CLUB—See Ocean Properties, Ltd.; *U.S. Private*, pg. 2989
RESORT DEVELOPERS LIMITED—See DEAP Capital Management & Trust plc; *Int'l*, pg. 1998
REUKERS B.V.—See Heijmans N.V.; *Int'l*, pg. 3322
REUKERS B.V.—See Heijmans N.V.; *Int'l*, pg. 3323
REXX INDEX, LLC—See BGC Group, Inc.; *U.S. Public*, pg. 330
RICHARDSON REALTY AUCTION; *U.S. Private*, pg. 3429
RICHLAND TOWERS - SAN ANTONIO, LLC—See American Tower Corporation; *U.S. Public*, pg. 111
RIVERBEND TITLE, LLC—See Anywhere Real Estate Inc.; *U.S. Public*, pg. 142
RIVERSIDE REALTY GROUP, LLC; *U.S. Private*, pg. 3446
RIVERWOODS PRESERVATION, L.P.—See Apartment Investment and Management Company; *U.S. Public*, pg. 144
RJB MANAGEMENT CO.—See World Holdings Inc.; *U.S. Private*, pg. 4565
RJ KING & ASSOCIATES; *U.S. Private*, pg. 3449
RKF GROUP CANADA REALTY—See Newmark Group, Inc.; *U.S. Public*, pg. 1516
RKF GROUP ILLINOIS LLC—See Newmark Group, Inc.; *U.S. Public*, pg. 1516
RKF GROUP NEW JERSEY LLC—See Newmark Group, Inc.; *U.S. Public*, pg. 1516
RLI LOS ANGELES REGIONAL OFFICE—See RLI Corp.; *U.S. Public*, pg. 1802
R&M REALTY INC.; *U.S. Private*, pg. 3332
ROBERT YATES REAL ESTATE, INC.; *U.S. Private*, pg. 3459
ROCKET HOMES REAL ESTATE LLC; *U.S. Private*, pg. 3466
RODIN INCOME TRUST, INC.; *U.S. Private*, pg. 3470
ROLAND LAND INVESTMENT CO., INC.; *U.S. Private*, pg. 3473
ROSEBAY INTERNATIONAL, INC.; *U.S. Private*, pg. 3482
ROSELAND PARTNERS LLC; *U.S. Private*, pg. 3482
ROSELAND RESIDENTIAL TRUST—See Veris Residential, Inc.; *U.S. Private*, pg. 2282
ROSEMONT PROPERTY MANAGEMENT LLC; *U.S. Private*, pg. 3483
ROSEMONT PROPERTY MANAGEMENT OF TEXAS LLC—See Rosemont Property Management LLC; *U.S. Private*, pg. 3483
ROSEN ASSOCIATES MANAGEMENT CORP.; *U.S. Private*, pg. 3483
ROSEWOOD APARTMENTS CORPORATION—See Apartment Investment and Management Company; *U.S. Public*, pg. 144
ROSS REAL ESTATE LTD.—See BGC Group, Inc.; *U.S. Public*, pg. 329
THE ROSS REALTY GROUP, INC.—See RMC Property Group LLC; *U.S. Private*, pg. 3451
ROSS REALTY INC.; *U.S. Private*, pg. 3485
ROUSE KENT (CENTRAL) LIMITED—See Prologis, Inc.; *U.S. Public*, pg. 1727
ROVACABIN LIMITED—See Enviri Corporation; *U.S. Public*, pg. 781
ROYAL COMMERCIAL REALTY INC—See Royal Seal Construction Inc.; *U.S. Private*, pg. 3493
ROYAL LEPAGE REAL ESTATE SERVICES LTD.—See Brookfield Corporation; *Int'l*, pg. 1186
ROYCE HILL REAL ESTATE; *U.S. Private*, pg. 3494
RPAI PACIFIC PROPERTY SERVICES LLC—See Kite Realty Group Trust; *U.S. Public*, pg. 1237
RPAI SOUTHWEST MANAGEMENT LLC—See Kite Realty

Group Trust; *U.S. Public*, pg. 1237
RPAI US MANAGEMENT LLC—See Kite Realty Group Trust; *U.S. Public*, pg. 1237
RPAI WILLISTON MAPLE TREE, L.L.C.—See Kite Realty Group Trust; *U.S. Public*, pg. 1237
RUHL AND RUHL REALTORS LLC; *U.S. Private*, pg. 3502
RWB REAL ESTATE INC.; *U.S. Private*, pg. 3508
SACHEM REAL CORP.; *U.S. Public*, pg. 1834
SAGE PARTNERS, LLC; *U.S. Private*, pg. 3526
SAIGON REAL INVESTMENT AND SERVICE JOINT STOCK COMPANY—See Dat Xanh Group Joint Stock Company; *Int'l*, pg. 1975
SAMSON MANAGEMENT CORP.; *U.S. Private*, pg. 3538
SAN ANN OIL COMPANY—See Supertest Oil Company Inc.; *U.S. Private*, pg. 3881
SANDS INVESTMENT GROUP, INC.; *U.S. Private*, pg. 3545
THE SANKEI BUILDING CO., LTD.—See Fuji Media Holdings, Inc.; *Int'l*, pg. 2814
SARABAY REAL ESTATE, INC.; *U.S. Private*, pg. 3549
SAUDI ARABIA INVESTMENT COMPANY—See Groupe BPCE; *Int'l*, pg. 3099
SBA TOWERS IV, LLC—See SBA Communications Corporation; *U.S. Public*, pg. 1842
SCALZO GROUP; *U.S. Private*, pg. 3561
SCCV CLEF DE SOL—See Altarea SCA; *Int'l*, pg. 385
SCHEPPS NEW MEXICO DEVELOPMENT CORP.—See Julius Schepps Company, Inc.; *U.S. Private*, pg. 2243
SEABROOK ISLAND REALTY—See Club At Seabrook Island Inc.; *U.S. Private*, pg. 948
SEALY REAL ESTATE, INC.—See Tempur Sealy International, Inc.; *U.S. Public*, pg. 2000
SECURED LAND TRANSFERS LLC—See Anywhere Real Estate Inc.; *U.S. Public*, pg. 142
SELIGMAN & ASSOCIATES, INC.; *U.S. Private*, pg. 3602
SEMONIN REALTORS—See Berkshire Hathaway Inc.; *U.S. Public*, pg. 307
SENIOR LIVING INVESTMENT BROKERAGE, INC.; *U.S. Private*, pg. 3607
SENTINEL SALES & MANAGEMENT LLC; *U.S. Private*, pg. 3610
SENTRY MANAGEMENT INC.; *U.S. Private*, pg. 3611
SERVICES & GESTION FRANCE SARL—See Generac Holdings Inc.; *U.S. Public*, pg. 913
SEV PROJECTS PTE LIMITED—See Digilife Technologies Limited; *Int'l*, pg. 2120
SEYMOUR N. LOGAN ASSOCIATES; *U.S. Private*, pg. 3621
SFI ENERGY—See First Reserve Management, L.P.; *U.S. Private*, pg. 1526
SFI WAIPOULI LLC—See Safehold Inc.; *U.S. Public*, pg. 1834
SHAFER PROPERTY COMPANY INC.; *U.S. Private*, pg. 3623
SHAMROCK HOLDINGS, INC.; *U.S. Private*, pg. 3624
SHAMROCK HOLDINGS OF CALIFORNIA, INC.—See Shamrock Holdings, Inc.; *U.S. Private*, pg. 3624
SHANGHAI FU YANG PROPERTY CONSULTANT CO., LIMITED—See Fortune Sun (China) Holdings Limited; *Int'l*, pg. 2744
SHANGHAI HEBAO PROPERTY SERVICE CO., LTD.—See Daiwa House Industry Co., Ltd.; *Int'l*, pg. 1947
SHANGHAI LANSHENG REAL ESTATE CO., LTD.—See DLG Exhibitions & Events Corp Ltd.; *Int'l*, pg. 2141
SHELDON GOOD & COMPANY INTERNATIONAL, LLC—See Racebrook Capital Advisors, LLC; *U.S. Private*, pg. 3341
SHELDON GROSS REALTY INC.; *U.S. Private*, pg. 3631
SHELTER BAY RETAIL GROUP, INC.—See Jones Lang LaSalle Incorporated; *U.S. Public*, pg. 1206
SHENJUMIAOSUAN CO., LTD.—See GAtechnologies Co., Ltd.; *Int'l*, pg. 2889
SHENZHEN HUTCHISON WHAMPOA CATIC PROPERTIES LIMITED—See CK Asset Holdings Limited; *Int'l*, pg. 1635
SHIVAJIMARG PROPERTIES LIMITED—See DLF Limited; *Int'l*, pg. 2141
SHOREWEST REALTORS, INC.; *U.S. Private*, pg. 3642
SIBCY CLINE, INC.; *U.S. Private*, pg. 3645
SIGMA KFT.—See Fotex Holding SE; *Int'l*, pg. 2752
SILVER HORSMAN INC.; *U.S. Private*, pg. 3653
SILVERLEAF RESORTS, INC.—See Kemmons Wilson, Inc.; *U.S. Private*, pg. 2281
SILVESTRI INVESTMENTS INC.; *U.S. Private*, pg. 3664
SIMON MANAGEMENT ASSOCIATES, LLC—See Simon Property Group, Inc.; *U.S. Public*, pg. 1881
SIMPLENEXUS, LLC—See nCino, Inc.; *U.S. Public*, pg. 1501
SINGAPORE BIKEN PTE. LTD.—See Biken Techno Corporation Ltd.; *Int'l*, pg. 1023
SKOGMAN REALTY CO. INC.—See Skogman Construction Company of Iowa Inc.; *U.S. Private*, pg. 3683
SKYLINE EQUITIES REALTY, LLC; *U.S. Private*, pg. 3685
SKYLINE PROPERTIES; *U.S. Private*, pg. 3685
SLG 625 LESSEE LLC—See SL Green Realty Corp.; *U.S. Public*, pg. 1894
SL GREEN MANAGEMENT LLC—See SL Green Realty Corp.; *U.S. Public*, pg. 1894
SL GREEN OPERATING PARTNERSHIP, L.P.—See SL

531210 — OFFICES OF REAL EST... CORPORATE AFFILIATIONS

Green Realty Corp.; *U.S. Public*, pg. 1894
SLIFER SMITH & FRAMPTON; *U.S. Private*, pg. 3688
SMITH & ASSOCIATES REAL ESTATE; *U.S. Private*, pg. 3693
SMITH MACK & CO., INC.—See BGC Group, Inc.; *U.S. Public*, pg. 330
SMYTHE, CRAMER CO.—See Hanna Holdings, Inc.; *U.S. Private*, pg. 1854
SNC COGEDIM ATLANTIQUE—See Altarea SCA; *Int'l*, pg. 385
SNC COGEDIM GRENOBLE—See Altarea SCA; *Int'l*, pg. 385
SNC COGEDIM MEDITERRANEE—See Altarea SCA; *Int'l*, pg. 385
SNC COGEDIM PROVENCE—See Altarea SCA; *Int'l*, pg. 385
SNC COGEDIM VENTE—See Altarea SCA; *Int'l*, pg. 385
SOCFIM SA—See Groupe BPCE; *Int'l*, pg. 3099
SOHGO HOUSING CO. LTD.—See Dai-ichi Life Holdings, Inc.; *Int'l*, pg. 1918
SOLA HOTEL EIENDOM AS—See Avinor AS; *Int'l*, pg. 744
SOLID SOURCE REALTY INC.—See HomeSmart International LLC; *U.S. Private*, pg. 1974
SORCE PROPERTIES INC.; *U.S. Private*, pg. 3715
SOTHEBY'S INTERNATIONAL REALTY, INC.—See Anywhere Real Estate Inc.; *U.S. Public*, pg. 141
SOTHEBY'S INTERNATIONAL REALTY—See Anywhere Real Estate Inc.; *U.S. Public*, pg. 141
SOUTH SHORE HARBOUR DEVELOPMENT, LTD.—See Brookfield Corporation; *Int'l*, pg. 1174
SOUTHWEST RESIDENTIAL PARTNERS, INC.—See BGC Group, Inc.; *U.S. Public*, pg. 330
SPACE CENTER INC.; *U.S. Private*, pg. 3743
SPE HB BROKERS - GESTAO IMOBILIARIA LTDA.—See Helbor Empreendimentos S.A.; *Int'l*, pg. 3328
SPERRY VAN NESS INTERNATIONAL CORP.; *U.S. Private*, pg. 3756
SPIRIT MANAGEMENT COMPANY II—See Spirit Realty Capital, Inc.; *U.S. Public*, pg. 1919
SPIRIT MTA REIT; *U.S. Private*, pg. 3758
SPIRIT REALTY, L.P.—See Spirit Realty Capital, Inc.; *U.S. Public*, pg. 1919
SPRING11 ADVISORY SERVICES LIMITED—See Newmark Group, Inc.; *U.S. Public*, pg. 1516
SPRING 11 LLC—See Newmark Group, Inc.; *U.S. Public*, pg. 1516
SPRINGHILL LAKE INVESTORS LIMITED PARTNERSHIP CO.—See Blackstone Inc.; *U.S. Public*, pg. 350
SREIT CAMRI GREEN APARTMENTS, L.L.C.—See Starwood Real Estate Income Trust, Inc.; *U.S. Private*, pg. 3790
SREIT-COASTAL PARTNERS, L.P.—See Starwood Real Estate Income Trust, Inc.; *U.S. Private*, pg. 3790
SREIT COLUMBIA HILLS, L.L.C.—See Starwood Real Estate Income Trust, Inc.; *U.S. Private*, pg. 3790
SREIT COURTNEY MANOR, L.L.C.—See Starwood Real Estate Income Trust, Inc.; *U.S. Private*, pg. 3790
SREIT CREEKSIDE AT BELLEMEADE, L.P.—See Starwood Real Estate Income Trust, Inc.; *U.S. Private*, pg. 3790
SREIT DOMINION PINES, L.L.C.—See Starwood Real Estate Income Trust, Inc.; *U.S. Private*, pg. 3790
SREIT FALCON POINTE, L.P.—See Starwood Real Estate Income Trust, Inc.; *U.S. Private*, pg. 3790
SREIT FALCON TRACE, L.L.C.—See Starwood Real Estate Income Trust, Inc.; *U.S. Private*, pg. 3790
SREIT GRIFFIN SCOTTSDALE, L.L.C.—See Starwood Real Estate Income Trust, Inc.; *U.S. Private*, pg. 3790
SREIT HATTERAS SOUND, L.L.C.—See Starwood Real Estate Income Trust, Inc.; *U.S. Private*, pg. 3790
SREIT HOLLY COVE APARTMENTS, L.L.C.—See Starwood Real Estate Income Trust, Inc.; *U.S. Private*, pg. 3790
SREIT LAS VILLAS DE KINO, L.L.C.—See Starwood Real Estate Income Trust, Inc.; *U.S. Private*, pg. 3790
SREIT LAS VILLAS DE LEON, L.P.—See Starwood Real Estate Income Trust, Inc.; *U.S. Private*, pg. 3790
SREIT LEIGH MEADOWS APARTMENTS, L.L.C.—See Starwood Real Estate Income Trust, Inc.; *U.S. Private*, pg. 3790
SREIT LEXINGTON CLUB, L.L.C.—See Starwood Real Estate Income Trust, Inc.; *U.S. Private*, pg. 3790
SREIT MADELYN OAKS, L.L.C.—See Starwood Real Estate Income Trust, Inc.; *U.S. Private*, pg. 3790
SREIT OVERLOOK AT SIMMS CREEK, L.P.—See Starwood Real Estate Income Trust, Inc.; *U.S. Private*, pg. 3790
SREIT PATRIOTS POINTE, L.P.—See Starwood Real Estate Income Trust, Inc.; *U.S. Private*, pg. 3790
SREIT PONCE HARBOR, L.L.C.—See Starwood Real Estate Income Trust, Inc.; *U.S. Private*, pg. 3790
SREIT RESERVES AT ARBORETUM, L.L.C.—See Starwood Real Estate Income Trust, Inc.; *U.S. Private*, pg. 3790
SREIT RIVER PARK PLACE, L.L.C.—See Starwood Real Estate Income Trust, Inc.; *U.S. Private*, pg. 3790
SREIT RIVER REACH, L.L.C.—See Starwood Real Estate Income Trust, Inc.; *U.S. Private*, pg. 3790
SREIT SOLDIERS RIDGE, L.L.C.—See Starwood Real Estate Income Trust, Inc.; *U.S. Private*, pg. 3790
SREIT SOUTH MAINE COMMONS, L.L.C.—See Starwood Real Estate Income Trust, Inc.; *U.S. Private*, pg. 3790
SREIT SPINNAKER REACH, L.L.C.—See Starwood Real Estate Income Trust, Inc.; *U.S. Private*, pg. 3790
SREIT STERLING CREST, L.L.C.—See Starwood Real Estate Income Trust, Inc.; *U.S. Private*, pg. 3790
SREIT STONE CREEK, L.P.—See Starwood Real Estate Income Trust, Inc.; *U.S. Private*, pg. 3790
SREIT THOMAS CHASE APARTMENTS, L.L.C.—See Starwood Real Estate Income Trust, Inc.; *U.S. Private*, pg. 3790
SREIT VISTA HAVEN, L.L.C.—See Starwood Real Estate Income Trust, Inc.; *U.S. Private*, pg. 3790
STARWOOD MORTGAGE CAPITAL LLC—See Starwood Property Trust, Inc.; *U.S. Public*, pg. 1940
STARWOOD REAL ESTATE INCOME TRUST, INC.; *U.S. Private*, pg. 3789
STEFFNER COMMERCIAL REAL ESTATE, LLC—See BGC Group, Inc.; *U.S. Public*, pg. 330
STELLINE SERVIZI IMMOBILIARI S.P.A.—See Credito Valtellinese Societa Cooperativa; *Int'l*, pg. 1837
STEM HOLDINGS, INC.; *U.S. Public*, pg. 1944
STERLING REAL ESTATE TRUST; *U.S. Private*, pg. 3807
STEVE PLATZ REALTY INC.; *U.S. Private*, pg. 3808
STI IMMOBILIEN (DEUTSCHLAND) GMBH—See Arbonia AG; *Int'l*, pg. 538
STIRLING PROPERTIES, INC.—See Maurin-Ogden Properties; *U.S. Private*, pg. 2615
STRATEGIC PARTNERS CO., LTD.—See CRE, Inc.; *Int'l*, pg. 1830
STRATEGIC STUDENT & SENIOR HOUSING TRUST, INC.—See Strategic Capital Holdings, LLC; *U.S. Private*, pg. 3834
STRAWBERRY FIELDS REIT, INC.; *U.S. Public*, pg. 1954
STR COLUMBIA SAS—See CoStar Group, Inc.; *U.S. Public*, pg. 586
STUDIO SERENISSIMA SRL—See Clariane SE; *Int'l*, pg. 1645
SUITEY, INC.—See The Agency; *U.S. Private*, pg. 3983
SUMMIT HEALTHCARE REIT, INC.; *U.S. Private*, pg. 3854
SUN BLAZING STAR LLC—See Sun Communities, Inc.; *U.S. Public*, pg. 1963
SUN CAMELOT VILLA LLC—See Sun Communities, Inc.; *U.S. Public*, pg. 1963
SUN COAST PARTNERS, LLC; *U.S. Private*, pg. 3862
SUNNY MODE SDN. BHD.—See Hua Yang Berhad; *Int'l*, pg. 3510
SUNPLANET CO., LTD.—See Eisai Co., Ltd.; *Int'l*, pg. 2335
SUN REALTY & AUCTION SERVICE, LLC; *U.S. Private*, pg. 3864
SUN REALTY USA, INC.; *U.S. Private*, pg. 3864
SUNRISE OF OCEANSIDE CA PROPCO, LLC—See Welltower Inc.; *U.S. Public*, pg. 2349
THE SUNSHINE GROUP, LTD.—See Anywhere Real Estate Inc.; *U.S. Public*, pg. 142
SUNSTONE SAINT CLAIR LESSEE, INC.—See Sunstone Hotel Investors, Inc.; *U.S. Public*, pg. 1966
SUNSTONE SAINT CLAIR, LLC—See Sunstone Hotel Investors, Inc.; *U.S. Public*, pg. 1966
SUNTRUST PROPERTIES, INC.—See Alliance Global Group, Inc.; *Int'l*, pg. 339
SVENSK FASTIGHETSFORMEDLING AB—See DNB Bank ASA; *Int'l*, pg. 2148
SWEETWATER DEVELOPMENT LLC—See Duke Energy Corporation; *U.S. Public*, pg. 691
SYNERGY RELOCATIONS INC.; *U.S. Private*, pg. 3904
SYSTEM PROPERTY DEVELOPMENT COMPANY, INC.; *U.S. Private*, pg. 3907
TAIWAN DAIWA HOUSE CONSTRUCTION CO., LTD.—See Daiwa House Industry Co., Ltd.; *Int'l*, pg. 1947
TAIWAN GOOD COM CO., LTD.—See Good Com Asset Co., Ltd.; *Int'l*, pg. 3038
TAIYO KAIHATSU CO., LTD.—See Hisamitsu Pharmaceutical Co., Inc.; *Int'l*, pg. 3406
TALLAHASSEE LAND COMPANY, INC.; *U.S. Private*, pg. 3927
TALON OP, L.P.—See Talon Real Estate Holding Corp.; *U.S. Public*, pg. 1980
TANGER INC.; *U.S. Public*, pg. 1980
TANGSHAN VANKE REAL ESTATE DEVELOPMENT COMPANY LIMITED—See China Vanke Co., Ltd.; *Int'l*, pg. 1562
TARBELL REALTORS—See Tarbell Financial Corporation; *U.S. Private*, pg. 3933
T-AROUND CO., LTD.—See Iida Group Holdings Co., Ltd.; *Int'l*, pg. 3607
TAUBMAN ASIA LIMITED—See Simon Property Group, Inc.; *U.S. Public*, pg. 1882
TB PROPRIETARY CORP.—See Toll Brothers, Inc.; *U.S. Public*, pg. 2162
TEICHERT LAND CO.—See Teichert, Inc.; *U.S. Private*, pg. 3958
TEJON MOUNTAIN VILLAGE, LLC.—See Tejon Ranch Company; *U.S. Public*, pg. 1991
TELES PROPERTIES; *U.S. Private*, pg. 3961
TELFORD HOMES PLC—See CBRE Group, Inc.; *U.S. Public*, pg. 460
TEN-X, LLC—See CoStar Group, Inc.; *U.S. Public*, pg. 586
TERRA DEVELOPMENT MARKETING, LLC—See Halstead Property, LLC.; *U.S. Private*, pg. 1846
TERRA PROPERTY TRUST, INC.; *U.S. Public*, pg. 2020
TETRIS DESIGN AND BUILD (PTY) LTD.—See Jones Lang LaSalle Incorporated; *U.S. Public*, pg. 1206
TETRIS DESIGN AND BUILD SARL—See Jones Lang LaSalle Incorporated; *U.S. Public*, pg. 1206
TETRIS DESIGN & BUILD BV—See Jones Lang LaSalle Incorporated; *U.S. Public*, pg. 1206
TETRIS DESIGN & BUILD SARL—See Jones Lang LaSalle Incorporated; *U.S. Public*, pg. 1206
TETRIS DESIGN & BUILD SPRL—See Jones Lang LaSalle Incorporated; *U.S. Public*, pg. 1206
TEXAS PACIFIC LAND CORP.; *U.S. Public*, pg. 2027
THUNDERHILL ESTATES, L.L.C.—See Sun Communities, Inc.; *U.S. Public*, pg. 1963
TIANJIN VANKE REAL ESTATE COMPANY LIMITED—See China Vanke Co., Ltd.; *Int'l*, pg. 1562
TICOMO VALLEY CORP; *U.S. Private*, pg. 4167
THE TIME GROUP INC.; *U.S. Private*, pg. 4127
TISHMAN SPEYER PROPERTIES LP; *U.S. Private*, pg. 4176
TJM PROPERTIES, INC.; *U.S. Private*, pg. 4177
TM5 PROPERTIES, LP; *U.S. Private*, pg. 4179
TOLL BROTHERS REAL ESTATE, INC.—See Toll Brothers, Inc.; *U.S. Public*, pg. 2162
TOLL FL XIII LIMITED PARTNERSHIP—See Toll Brothers, Inc.; *U.S. Public*, pg. 2162
TOLL STRATFORD LLC—See Toll Brothers, Inc.; *U.S. Public*, pg. 2162
TOMIE RAINES, INC.—See Berkshire Hathaway Inc.; *U.S. Public*, pg. 307
TOWNE PROPERTIES; *U.S. Private*, pg. 4198
TOWNE REALTY, INC.—See Zilber Ltd.; *U.S. Private*, pg. 4604
TOWNE REALTY, LLC—See Towne Bank; *U.S. Public*, pg. 2166
THE TOWNHOMES OF BEVERLY—See Lone Star Global Acquisitions, LLC; *U.S. Private*, pg. 2488
TRADITAL S.P.A.—See Domus Fin S.A.; *Int'l*, pg. 2162
TRADITION REALTY, LLC—See Hilton Grand Vacations Inc.; *U.S. Public*, pg. 1040
TRAVERS REALTY CORP.; *U.S. Private*, pg. 4214
TRAVERS REALTY CORP.—See Travers Realty Corp.; *U.S. Private*, pg. 4214
TRAVERS REALTY CORP.—See Travers Realty Corp.; *U.S. Private*, pg. 4214
TRAVERS REALTY CORP.—See Travers Realty Corp.; *U.S. Private*, pg. 4214
TRAVERS REALTY CORP.—See Travers Realty Corp.; *U.S. Private*, pg. 4214
TRAVIS COMMERCIAL REAL ESTATE SERVICES, LTD.—See Jones Lang LaSalle Incorporated; *U.S. Public*, pg. 1206
TRIDENT ABSTRACT TITLE AGENCY, LLC—See OceanFirst Financial Corp.; *U.S. Public*, pg. 1563
TRIMONT REAL ESTATE ADVISORS LLC—See Varde Partners, Inc.; *U.S. Private*, pg. 4346
TRINITY PLACE HOLDINGS, INC.; *U.S. Public*, pg. 2194
TRI-STATE DISPLAYS INC.—See Capital Properties, Inc.; *U.S. Public*, pg. 432
TRI-STATE HOME SERVICES LLC—See Morgan Stanley; *U.S. Public*, pg. 1474
TROV INC.—See The Travelers Companies, Inc.; *U.S. Public*, pg. 2136
TRUMP INTERNATIONAL REALTY—See The Trump Organization, Inc.; *U.S. Private*, pg. 4128
TUDOR REALTY SERVICES CORP.—See FirstService Corporation; *Int'l*, pg. 2691
TWIDDY AND COMPANY REALTORS; *U.S. Private*, pg. 4264
TWINEAGLES BROKERAGE INC—See Ronto Group, Inc.; *U.S. Private*, pg. 3478
UAB NIF LIETUVA—See AS Reverta; *Int'l*, pg. 591
UDR RED STONE RANCH LLC—See UDR, Inc.; *U.S. Public*, pg. 2218
UNICO PROPERTIES INC.; *U.S. Private*, pg. 4281
UNIPROP HOMES INC.—See Uniprop, Inc.; *U.S. Private*, pg. 4286
UNITED EL SEGUNDO INC.; *U.S. Private*, pg. 4291
UNITED OIL CO.; *U.S. Private*, pg. 4295
UNITIL REALTY CORP.—See Unitil Corporation; *U.S. Public*, pg. 2253
UNIVERSAL BUILDING NORTH, INC.—See Vornado Realty Trust; *U.S. Public*, pg. 2310
UNIVERSAL PROPERTY MANAGEMENT—See Universal Insurance Holdings, Inc.; *U.S. Public*, pg. 2261
UPARTMENTS REAL ESTATE GMBH—See CORESTATE Capital Holding SA; *Int'l*, pg. 1800
UPNEST, INC.—See News Corporation; *U.S. Public*, pg. 1519
UPWARD TITLE & CLOSING TEXAS LLC—See Anywhere Real Estate Inc.; *U.S. Public*, pg. 143
USAA RELOCATION SERVICES, INC.—See United Services Automobile Association; *U.S. Private*, pg. 4297
UTAH PROPERTY MANAGEMENT ASSOCIATES, LLC—See Deseret Management Corporation; *U.S. Private*, pg. 1212

N.A.I.C.S. INDEX

531311 — RESIDENTIAL PROPERT...

VACATION HOME RENTALS, INC.—See TripAdvisor, Inc.; *U.S. Public*, pg. 2195
VANKE HOLDINGS USA LLC—See China Vanke Co., Ltd.; *Int'l*, pg. 1562
THE VAN METRE COMPANIES; *U.S. Private*, pg. 4130
VANTEX COMMERCIAL PROPERTY GROUP—See Sowell & Co., Inc.; *U.S. Private*, pg. 3743
VELOCITY FINANCIAL, INC.; *U.S. Public*, pg. 2277
VEREIT OPERATING PARTNERSHIP, L.P.—See Realty Income Corporation; *U.S. Public*, pg. 1769
VIETHOMES REAL ESTATE JOINT STOCK COMPANY—See Dat Xanh Group Joint Stock Company; *Int'l*, pg. 1975
VIETNAM BIKEN COMPANY LIMITED—See Biken Techno Corporation Ltd.; *Int'l*, pg. 1023
VIKA PROJECT FINANCE AS—See ABG Sundal Collier Holding ASA; *Int'l*, pg. 60
VILLAGE INVESTMENTS; *U.S. Private*, pg. 4383
VILLA IMMOBILIARE SRL—See Steel Partners Holdings L.P.; *U.S. Public*, pg. 1943
VINEYARDS REALTY INC.; *U.S. Private*, pg. 4385
VIP REALTY GROUP, INC.; *U.S. Private*, pg. 4386
VIRTU INVESTMENTS; *U.S. Private*, pg. 4388
VISTA REAL ESTATE INC.; *U.S. Private*, pg. 4403
VIZCAYA LAKES COMMUNITIES, LLC—See Sun Communities, Inc.; *U.S. Public*, pg. 1963
VOIT COMMERCIAL BROKERAGE LP—See Voit Real Estate Services, Inc.; *U.S. Private*, pg. 4410
VOIT REAL ESTATE SERVICES, INC.; *U.S. Private*, pg. 4410
VORNADO OFFICE INC.—See Vornado Realty Trust; *U.S. Public*, pg. 2310
VORNADO OFFICE MANAGEMENT LLC—See Vornado Realty Trust; *U.S. Public*, pg. 2310
WAGNER REALTY; *U.S. Private*, pg. 4426
WALCHERSE BOUWUNIE B.V.—See Heijmans N.V.; *Int'l*, pg. 3322
WALCHERSE BOUWUNIE B.V.—See Heijmans N.V.; *Int'l*, pg. 3323
WALTERS GROUP; *U.S. Private*, pg. 4434
WAMPLER REALTY, INC.; *U.S. Private*, pg. 4435
WANGARD PARTNERS, INC.; *U.S. Private*, pg. 4435
WASATCH PROPERTY MANAGEMENT, INC.—See Wasatch Advantage Group, LLC; *U.S. Private*, pg. 4445
WATSON REALTY CORP.; *U.S. Private*, pg. 4455
WEICHERT CO.; *U.S. Private*, pg. 4470
THE WELFONT COMPANIES INC.; *U.S. Private*, pg. 4134
WELLINGTON EQUESTRIAN REALTY, LLC; *U.S. Private*, pg. 4475
WELLS FARGO PROPERTIES, INC.—See Wells Fargo & Company; *U.S. Public*, pg. 2347
WELSH COMPANIES LLC; *U.S. Private*, pg. 4479
WESTDALE ASSET MANAGEMENT INC.—See JGB Ventures Inc.; *U.S. Private*, pg. 2207
WESTREC MARINA MANAGEMENT, INC.—See Centerbridge Partners, L.P.; *U.S. Private*, pg. 816
WESTREC MARINAS MANAGEMENT, INC.—See Centerbridge Partners, L.P.; *U.S. Private*, pg. 815
WEST SHELL COMMERCIAL, INC.—See Colliers International Group Inc.; *Int'l*, pg. 1701
WESTWARD360, INC.; *U.S. Private*, pg. 4501
WHH TRICE & CO., INC.—See The Bush Company; *U.S. Private*, pg. 4003
WHIRLPOOL REALTY CORPORATION—See Whirlpool Corporation; *U.S. Public*, pg. 2368
WHITE OAKS STATION LLC—See Phillips Edison & Company LLC; *U.S. Public*, pg. 3171
WIDNES REGENERATION LIMITED—See Blackstone Inc.; *U.S. Public*, pg. 358
WII REALTY MANAGEMENT—See Williams Industries, Inc.; *U.S. Private*, pg. 4526
THE WILDER COMPANIES; *U.S. Private*, pg. 4136
WILDWOOD L.P.—See Sun Communities, Inc.; *U.S. Public*, pg. 1963
WILKINSON & ASSOCIATES REAL ESTATE; *U.S. Private*, pg. 4520
WILLIAM L. LYON & ASSOCIATES, INC.—See Windermere Real Estate Services Company; *U.S. Private*, pg. 4537
WILLIAMSBURG ENTERPRISES LTD.; *U.S. Private*, pg. 4527
WILLIS ALLEN REAL ESTATE COMPANY; *U.S. Private*, pg. 4527
WIMMER BROTHERS REALTY INC.; *U.S. Private*, pg. 4532
WINDSOR REALTY CORP.—See Citizens Financial Group, Inc.; *U.S. Public*, pg. 506
WINGATE & ASSOCIATES REALTY, INC.; *U.S. Private*, pg. 4541
WINN MANAGEMENT CORPORATION; *U.S. Private*, pg. 4542
WISCONSIN MANAGEMENT COMPANY; *U.S. Private*, pg. 4548
W.M. GRACE DEVELOPMENT COMPANY; *U.S. Private*, pg. 4421
WOODS BROS REALTY, INC.—See Berkshire Hathaway Inc.; *U.S. Public*, pg. 307
WOODYARD & ASSOCIATES, LLC; *U.S. Private*, pg. 4561
WORLD CLASS GLOBAL LIMITED—See Aspial Corporation Limited; *Int'l*, pg. 630

WRI GOLDEN STATE, LLC—See Kimco Realty Corporation; *U.S. Public*, pg. 1232
WUHAN VANKE REAL ESTATE COMPANY LIMITED—See China Vanke Co., Ltd.; *Int'l*, pg. 1562
WUHU VANKE REAL ESTATE COMPANY LIMITED—See China Vanke Co., Ltd.; *Int'l*, pg. 1562
WYMAN, GREEN & BLALOCK REAL ESTATE, INC.; *U.S. Private*, pg. 4576
WYNDHAM BRANSON AT THE MEADOWS—See Travel & Leisure Co.; *U.S. Public*, pg. 2185
WYNDHAM PAGOSA—See Travel & Leisure Co.; *U.S. Public*, pg. 2186
WYNDHAM RESORT AT FAIRFIELD BAY—See Travel & Leisure Co.; *U.S. Public*, pg. 2185
WYNDHAM VACATION OWNERSHIP AT PATRIOTS PLACE—See Travel & Leisure Co.; *U.S. Public*, pg. 2185
WYNDHAM VACATION RESORTS, INC.—See Travel & Leisure Co.; *U.S. Public*, pg. 2185
WYNN PROPERTIES, INC.; *U.S. Private*, pg. 4576
WYODAK RESOURCES DEVELOPMENT CORP.—See Black Hills Corporation; *U.S. Public*, pg. 341
YOUR HOME SOLD GUARANTEED REALTY, INC.; *U.S. Private*, pg. 4594
ZEPHYR REAL ESTATE; *U.S. Private*, pg. 4602
ZILBERT REALTY GROUP—See Brown Harris Stevens, LLC; *U.S. Private*, pg. 667
ZOLL DATA SYSTEMS—See Asahi Kasei Corporation; *Int'l*, pg. 597

531311 — RESIDENTIAL PROPERTY MANAGERS

ABBEY, S.R.O.—See Gallagher Holdings Ltd.; *Int'l*, pg. 2873
ABLON S.R.L.—See Ablon Group Limited; *Int'l*, pg. 63
ADLERSHOFER SARL—See CLS Holdings plc; *Int'l*, pg. 1663
ADVANCE SYNERGY REALTY SDN. BHD.—See Advance Synergy Berhad; *Int'l*, pg. 156
A.D.WORKS GROUP CO., LTD.; *Int'l*, pg. 23
AIMCO 21 FITZSIMONS, LLC—See Blackstone Inc.; *U.S. Public*, pg. 350
AIMCO BROADWAY LOFTS, L.P.—See Blackstone Inc.; *U.S. Public*, pg. 350
AIMCO PARK AND 12TH, LLC—See Apartment Investment and Management Company; *U.S. Public*, pg. 143
AIMCO SAN MELIA, LLC—See Apartment Investment and Management Company; *U.S. Public*, pg. 143
AKELIUS RESIDENTIAL AB; *Int'l*, pg. 262
ALARGAN BAHRAIN W.L.L.—See Alargan International Real Estate Co. K.S.C.C.; *Int'l*, pg. 291
ALCO PROPERTIES LIMITED—See Alco Holdings Limited; *Int'l*, pg. 301
ALL HOMES CORP.—See Green Courte Partners, LLC; *U.S. Private*, pg. 1772
ALLIANCE DEVELOPPEMENT CAPITAL SIIC SE; *Int'l*, pg. 338
ALLIANCE REALTY ADVISORS; *U.S. Private*, pg. 184
ALLIED PROPERTIES MANAGEMENT LIMITED PARTNERSHIP—See Allied Properties Real Estate Investment Trust; *Int'l*, pg. 358
ALPHA REAL ESTATE SERVICES LLC—See Alpha Services and Holdings S.A.; *Int'l*, pg. 369
ALPINE PROPERTY MANAGEMENT LLC; *U.S. Private*, pg. 202
ALTUS PROPERTY VENTURES, INC.; *Int'l*, pg. 399
AMBANGAN PURI SDN. BHD—See Eastern & Oriental Berhad; *Int'l*, pg. 2271
AMERICAN HOMES 4 RENT, L.P.—See American Homes 4 Rent; *U.S. Public*, pg. 104
AMERICAN MOTEL MANAGEMENT; *U.S. Private*, pg. 241
ANANT RAJ LIMITED; *Int'l*, pg. 447
AON INC.; *Int'l*, pg. 488
AOYUAN HEALTHY LIFE GROUP COMPANY LIMITED; *Int'l*, pg. 499
APARTMENT INCOME REIT, L.P.—See Blackstone Inc.; *U.S. Public*, pg. 349
APEX EQUITY CAPITAL SDN. BHD.—See Apex Equity Holdings Berhad; *Int'l*, pg. 509
ARAMARK PROPERTY SERVICES LIMITED—See Aramark; *U.S. Public*, pg. 177
ARANETA PROPERTIES, INC.; *Int'l*, pg. 536
ARCHSTONE BOCA RATON REIT LP—See AvalonBay Communities, Inc.; *U.S. Public*, pg. 240
ARR PLANNER CO., LTD.; *Int'l*, pg. 578
ASCOTT INTERNATIONAL MANAGEMENT (2001) PTE LTD—See CapitaLand Investment Limited; *Int'l*, pg. 1314
ASCOTT PROPERTY MANAGEMENT (BEIJING) CO., LTD—See CapitaLand Investment Limited; *Int'l*, pg. 1314
ASCOTT RESIDENCE TRUST MANAGEMENT LIMITED—See CapitaLand Investment Limited; *Int'l*, pg. 1314
ASIA ASSET PROPERTY SERVICES (SHANGHAI) CO., LTD.—See Hopefluent Group Holdings Ltd; *Int'l*, pg. 3473
ASIAN PAC HOLDINGS BERHAD; *Int'l*, pg. 618
ASIA ORIENT COMPANY LIMITED—See Asia Orient Holdings Limited; *Int'l*, pg. 613

ASIA ORIENT HOLDINGS LIMITED; *Int'l*, pg. 613
ASPEN SQUARE MANAGEMENT, INC.; *U.S. Private*, pg. 352
ASSOCIATIONS, INC.; *U.S. Private*, pg. 359
ASSURA PROPERTY MANAGEMENT LIMITED—See Assura plc; *Int'l*, pg. 649
ATLAN HOLDINGS BERHAD; *Int'l*, pg. 673
ATOS PROPERTY MANAGEMENT GMBH—See COR-ESTATE Capital Holding SA; *Int'l*, pg. 1799
ATRIUM 21 SP. Z O.O.—See City Service SE; *Int'l*, pg. 1627
AVESTA HOMES LLC; *U.S. Private*, pg. 406
AZORIM INVESTMENT DEVELOPMENT & CONSTRUCTION CO., LTD.; *Int'l*, pg. 781
AZPLANNING CO., LTD.; *Int'l*, pg. 781
THE BAINBRIDGE COMPANIES LLC; *U.S. Private*, pg. 3991
BALMORAL INTERNATIONAL LAND UK LTD—See Balmoral International Land Holdings plc; *Int'l*, pg. 810
BASF IMMOBILIEN-GESELLSCHAFT MBH—See BASF SE; *Int'l*, pg. 879
BASF PROPERTIES INC.—See BASF SE; *Int'l*, pg. 881
BAY PARC PLAZA APARTMENTS, L.P.—See Blackstone Inc.; *U.S. Public*, pg. 350
BDW EAST SCOTLAND LIMITED—See Barratt Developments PLC; *Int'l*, pg. 867
BEIJING CAPITAL JIAYE PROPERTY SERVICES CO., LIMITED; *Int'l*, pg. 947
BEKASI ASRI PEMULA TBK; *Int'l*, pg. 962
BELCO PROPERTIES LIMITED—See Abengoa S.A.; *Int'l*, pg. 59
BELCO PROPERTIES LIMITED—See Algonquin Power & Utilities Corp.; *Int'l*, pg. 319
BELLWAY (SERVICES) LIMITED—See Bellway plc; *Int'l*, pg. 967
BENCHMARK MANAGEMENT GROUP, INC.—See Community Association Management Specialist, Inc.; *U.S. Private*, pg. 989
BERTAM ALLIANCE BERHAD; *Int'l*, pg. 989
BINJIANG SERVICE GROUP CO., LTD.; *Int'l*, pg. 1034
BLUE ROCK PARTNERS, LLC; *U.S. Private*, pg. 592
BLUFFS AT HIGHLANDS RANCH LLC—See Sares-Regis Group; *U.S. Private*, pg. 3550
BNP PARIBAS REAL ESTATE ADVISORY & PROPERTY MANAGEMENT LUXEMBOURG SA—See BNP Paribas SA; *Int'l*, pg. 1086
BNPP REAL ESTATE ADVISORY & PROPERTY MANAGEMENT IRELAND LTD.—See BNP Paribas SA; *Int'l*, pg. 1088
BNPP REAL ESTATE POLAND SP. Z O.O.—See BNP Paribas SA; *Int'l*, pg. 1088
BOC PROPERTY DEVELOPMENT & MANAGEMENT (PVT) LTD—See Bank of Ceylon; *Int'l*, pg. 840
BONAVA AB; *Int'l*, pg. 1105
BOYUAN HOLDINGS LIMITED; *Int'l*, pg. 1125
BPG RESIDENTIAL SERVICES, LLC—See The Buccini/Pollin Group, Inc.; *U.S. Private*, pg. 4002
BREAKERS WEST DEVELOPMENT CORP.—See Flagler System Inc.; *U.S. Private*, pg. 1539
BRE PROPERTIES, INC.—See Essex Property Trust, Inc.; *U.S. Public*, pg. 795
BROOKFIELD RESIDENTIAL SERVICES LTD.—See Brookfield Corporation; *Int'l*, pg. 1186
BRYDENS INSURANCE INC.—See ANSA McAl Limited; *Int'l*, pg. 476
BUDWORTH PROPERTIES LIMITED; *Int'l*, pg. 1211
BULLET EXPLORATION INC.; *Int'l*, pg. 1214
BUROGEBAUDE DARMSTADTER LANDSTRASSE GMBH & CO. KG—See Helaba Landesbank Hessen-Thuringen; *Int'l*, pg. 3327
BYGGMASTARE ANDERS J AHLSTROM HOLDING AB; *Int'l*, pg. 1235
CAHYA MATA DEVELOPMENT SDN. BHD.—See Cahya Mata Sarawak Berhad; *Int'l*, pg. 1251
CAIRN HOMES PLC; *Int'l*, pg. 1252
CALEDONIAN CITY DEVELOPMENTS LTD.—See Caledonian Trust PLC; *Int'l*, pg. 1263
CALEDONIAN SCOTTISH DEVELOPMENTS LTD.—See Caledonian Trust PLC; *Int'l*, pg. 1263
CAMBRIDGE MANAGEMENT SERVICES, INC.—See LeCesse Development Corporation; *U.S. Private*, pg. 2409
CANDEREL RESIDENTIAL INC.—See Canderel Management Inc.; *Int'l*, pg. 1289
CAPITALAND RESIDENTIAL LIMITED—See CapitaLand Investment Limited; *Int'l*, pg. 1313
CAPITAL CITY PROPERTY SDN BHD—See Capital World Limited; *Int'l*, pg. 1313
CAQ HOLDINGS LIMITED; *Int'l*, pg. 1319
CARREFOUR ESPANA PROPERTIES, S.L.—See Carrefour SA; *Int'l*, pg. 1345
CARREFOUR PROPERTY B.V.—See Carrefour SA; *Int'l*, pg. 1344
CASIN REAL ESTATE DEVELOPMENT GROUP CO., LTD.; *Int'l*, pg. 1352
C&D PROPERTY MANAGEMENT GROUP CO., LTD.; *Int'l*, pg. 1238
CEBU PROPERTY VENTURES AND DEVELOPMENT CORPORATION—See Ayala Corporation; *Int'l*, pg. 774

531311 — RESIDENTIAL PROPERT...   CORPORATE AFFILIATIONS

CEC COMMERCIAL DEVELOPMENT CORPORATION—See Continental Holdings Corp.; *Int'l*, pg. 1784
CELTIC ITALY SRL—See CPD S.A.; *Int'l*, pg. 1824
CENTER PARCS (OPERATING COMPANY) LIMITED—See Brookfield Corporation; *Int'l*, pg. 1187
CENTRAL CHINA MANAGEMENT COMPANY LIMITED; *Int'l*, pg. 1405
CENTRAL CHINA NEW LIFE LIMITED; *Int'l*, pg. 1405
CENTRAL EQUITY LIMITED; *Int'l*, pg. 1406
CENTURION DORMITORIES PTE LTD.—See Centurion Corporation Limited; *Int'l*, pg. 1417
CENTURION DORMITORIES SDN BHD—See Centurion Corporation Limited; *Int'l*, pg. 1417
CENTURION DORMITORY (WESTLITE) PTE LTD.—See Centurion Corporation Limited; *Int'l*, pg. 1417
CENTURY LEGEND MANAGEMENT LIMITED—See Century Legend Holdings Ltd; *Int'l*, pg. 1418
CESC PROPERTIES LIMITED—See CESC Limited; *Int'l*, pg. 1424
CFH GROUP, LLC; *U.S. Private*, pg. 843
CHARTER HALL REAL ESTATE MANAGEMENT SERVICES (NSW) PTY LIMITED—See Charter Hall Limited; *Int'l*, pg. 1454
CHARTER HALL REAL ESTATE MANAGEMENT SERVICES (QLD) PTY LIMITED—See Charter Hall Limited; *Int'l*, pg. 1454
CHINA ENTERPRISE COMPANY LIMITED; *Int'l*, pg. 1500
CHINA MOTOR BUS COMPANY LIMITED; *Int'l*, pg. 1524
CHINA RESOURCES MIXC LIFESTYLE SERVICES LIMITED; *Int'l*, pg. 1549
CH. KARNCHANG REAL ESTATE CO., LTD.—See CH. Karnchang Public Company Limited; *Int'l*, pg. 1435
CIFI EVER SUNSHINE SERVICES GROUP LIMITED; *Int'l*, pg. 1605
CITADINES MELBOURNE ON BOURKE PTY LTD—See CapitaLand Investment Limited; *Int'l*, pg. 1314
CITYBASE PROPERTY MANAGEMENT LIMITED—See CK Asset Holdings Limited; *Int'l*, pg. 1635
CITY OF DREAMS PENANG SDN. BHD.—See Ewein Berhad; *Int'l*, pg. 2576
CITY SITE ESTATES PLC; *Int'l*, pg. 1628
CLIFFORD MODERN LIVING HOLDINGS LIMITED; *Int'l*, pg. 1659
CLOSE ASSET MANAGEMENT HOLDINGS LIMITED—See Close Brothers Group plc; *Int'l*, pg. 1661
COLAB CLOUD PLATFORMS LIMITED; *Int'l*, pg. 1697
COLOUR LIFE SERVICES GROUP CO., LTD.; *Int'l*, pg. 1704
COMMERZ BUILDING AND MANAGEMENT GMBH—See Commerzbank AG; *Int'l*, pg. 1716
COMMON INTEREST MANAGEMENT SERVICES INC.; *U.S. Private*, pg. 986
COUNTRY HEIGHTS HOLDINGS BERHAD; *Int'l*, pg. 1818
CPI IMMOBILIEN AG; *Int'l*, pg. 1825
CRANBERRY PROPERTIES LLC—See Verizon Communications Inc.; *U.S. Public*, pg. 2285
CREATIVE INVESTMENTS PTE LTD—See Amara Holdings Ltd.; *Int'l*, pg. 411
CROMWELL EUROPEAN MANAGEMENT SERVICES LIMITED—See Cromwell Property Group; *Int'l*, pg. 1854
CROSSBRIDGE CONDOMINIUM SERVICES LTD.—See FirstService Corporation; *Int'l*, pg. 2691
CROWN COMMUNITIES, LLC; *U.S. Private*, pg. 1110
C'S CREATE CO., LTD.; *Int'l*, pg. 1239
CUMICA CORPORATION; *Int'l*, pg. 1878
DAEJAN (CARDIFF) LIMITED—See Centremanor Ltd.; *Int'l*, pg. 1411
DAIWA LIFENEXT CO., LTD.—See Daiwa House Industry Co., Ltd.; *Int'l*, pg. 1945
DAIWA MONTHLY CO., LTD.—See Daiwa House Industry Co., Ltd.; *Int'l*, pg. 1946
DAIWA PROPERTY CO., LTD.—See Daiwa Securities Group Inc.; *Int'l*, pg. 1948
DALIAN ACACIA TOWN VILLA CO., LTD.—See Daiwa House Industry Co., Ltd.; *Int'l*, pg. 1946
DAMAC PROPERTIES DUBAI CO PJSC—See DAMAC Group; *Int'l*, pg. 1955
DAMANSARA REALTY MANAGEMENT SERVICES SDN. BHD.—See Damansara Realty Berhad; *Int'l*, pg. 1955
DARULAMAN ASET SDN. BHD.—See Bina Darulaman Berhad; *Int'l*, pg. 1032
DAZHENG PROPERTY GROUP CO., LTD.; *Int'l*, pg. 1985
DDMP REIT, INC.; *Int'l*, pg. 1993
DEALT LIMITED; *Int'l*, pg. 1998
DEBENHAMS PROPERTIES LIMITED—See Debenhams plc; *Int'l*, pg. 1998
DEUTSCHE WOHNEN MANAGEMENT GMBH—See Deutsche Wohnen SE; *Int'l*, pg. 2085
DEVELOP NORTH PLC; *Int'l*, pg. 2087
DEXIN CHINA HOLDINGS CO., LTD.; *Int'l*, pg. 2092
DEXIN SERVICES GROUP LIMITED; *Int'l*, pg. 2093
DKLS INDUSTRIES BERHAD; *Int'l*, pg. 2139
DLF CYBER CITY DEVELOPERS LIMITED—See DLF Limited; *Int'l*, pg. 2141
DLF INFO CITY DEVELOPERS (CHENNAI) LTD.—See DLF Limited; *Int'l*, pg. 2141
DLF UNIVERSAL LIMITED—See DLF Limited; *Int'l*, pg. 2141

DLP REALTY PROPERTY MANAGEMENT—See Don Wenner Home Selling, Inc.; *U.S. Private*, pg. 1259
DOM CONSTRUCTION SP. Z O.O.—See Dom Development S.A.; *Int'l*, pg. 2159
DOM DEVELOPMENT S.A.; *Int'l*, pg. 2159
DOM DEVELOPMENT WROCLAW SP. Z O.O.—See Dom Development S.A.; *Int'l*, pg. 2159
DT REAL ESTATE, LLC—See Hilton Worldwide Holdings Inc.; *U.S. Public*, pg. 1040
DTZ ZADELHOFF V.O.F.—See TPG Capital, L.P.; *U.S. Public*, pg. 2173
DUSIT EXCELLENCE CO., LTD.—See Dusit Thani Public Company Limited; *Int'l*, pg. 2234
EASTERN & ORIENTAL BERHAD; *Int'l*, pg. 2271
EASYKNIT PROPERTIES MANAGEMENT LIMITED—See Easyknit International Holdings Ltd.; *Int'l*, pg. 2276
EAVES BURLINGTON, LLC—See AvalonBay Communities, Inc.; *U.S. Public*, pg. 240
EAVES HUNTINGTON BEACH—See AvalonBay Communities, Inc.; *U.S. Public*, pg. 240
ECHO INVESTMENT S.A.; *Int'l*, pg. 2289
EDGE COMMERCIAL REAL ESTATE LLC—See KLNB, LLC; *U.S. Private*, pg. 2320
EDISTON PROPERTY INVESTMENT COMPANY PLC; *Int'l*, pg. 2311
EDIZIONE PROPERTY S.P.A.—See Edizione S.r.l.; *Int'l*, pg. 2311
EIT ENVIRONMENTAL DEVELOPMENT GROUP CO., LTD.; *Int'l*, pg. 2336
EJADAH ASSET MANAGEMENT GROUP L.L.C—See Dubai Holding LLC; *Int'l*, pg. 2218
ELDERS REAL ESTATE (QLD) PTY. LTD.—See Elders Limited; *Int'l*, pg. 2346
ELEMENT NATIONAL MANAGEMENT COMPANY; *U.S. Private*, pg. 1357
ELMDALE MANAGEMENT GROUP, LLC.—See Elmdale Partners, LLC; *U.S. Private*, pg. 1376
EMERALD STAY S.A.—See 029 Group SE; *Int'l*, pg. 1
ENEOS REAL ESTATE CORPORATION—See ENEOS Holdings, Inc.; *Int'l*, pg. 2415
E&O CUSTOMER SERVICES SDN. BHD.—See Eastern & Oriental Berhad; *Int'l*, pg. 2271
E&O PROPERTY (PENANG) SDN. BHD.—See Eastern & Oriental Berhad; *Int'l*, pg. 2271
EP MANAGEMENT CORPORATION—See Apollo Global Management, Inc.; *U.S. Public*, pg. 165
EPOCH MANAGEMENT, INC.—See Epoch Properties Inc.; *U.S. Private*, pg. 1414
EPRC LIMITED—See Hong Kong Economic Times Holdings Ltd; *Int'l*, pg. 3465
ERNEST WILSONS & CO LIMITED—See Begbies Traynor Group plc; *Int'l*, pg. 940
E-STAR COMMERCIAL MANAGEMENT COMPANY LIMITED; *Int'l*, pg. 2249
EUGENE BURGER MANAGEMENT CORP.; *U.S. Private*, pg. 1433
EURO STYL S.A—See Dom Development S.A.; *Int'l*, pg. 2159
EXCELLENCE COMMERCIAL PROPERTY & FACILITIES MANAGEMENT GROUP LIMITED; *Int'l*, pg. 2578
FACILITA BERLIN GMBH—See Deutsche Wohnen SE; *Int'l*, pg. 2085
FAIRPLAY PROPERTIES REIT; *Int'l*, pg. 2609
FAITHNETWORK CO., LTD.; *Int'l*, pg. 2609
FAJARBARU BUILDER GROUP BHD.; *Int'l*, pg. 2610
FAR EAST ORCHARD LIMITED; *Int'l*, pg. 2616
FASTER ENTERPRISES LTD; *Int'l*, pg. 2622
FCL PROPERTY INVESTMENTS PTE LTD—See Frasers Property Limited; *Int'l*, pg. 2766
FCW HOLDINGS BERHAD; *Int'l*, pg. 2628
FEDERAL LAND, INC.—See GT Capital Holdings, Inc.; *Int'l*, pg. 3150
FENGATE CAPITAL MANAGEMENT LTD.; *Int'l*, pg. 2634
FGV USA PROPERTIES, INC—See FGV Holdings Bhd; *Int'l*, pg. 2649
FHB MANAGEMENT SDN. BHD.—See Fiamma Holdings Berhad; *Int'l*, pg. 2650
FILINVEST ALABANG INC.—See Filinvest Development Corporation; *Int'l*, pg. 2663
FINANCIAL STREET PROPERTY COMPANY LIMITED; *Int'l*, pg. 2665
FIRST OCEANIC PROPERTY MANAGEMENT, INC—See Alliance Global Group, Inc.; *Int'l*, pg. 339
FIRSTONSITE RESTORATION LTD.—See FirstService Corporation; *Int'l*, pg. 2691
FIRSTSERVICE RESIDENTIAL, INC.—See FirstService Corporation; *Int'l*, pg. 2691
FKP RESIDENTIAL DEVELOPMENTS PTY. LTD.—See Brookfield Corporation; *Int'l*, pg. 1186
FLAMINGO LTD.—See Africa Israel Investments Ltd.; *Int'l*, pg. 190
FLOW AMERICA, LLC—See Lone Star Funds; *U.S. Private*, pg. 2485
FOLKESTONE LIMITED—See Charter Hall Limited; *Int'l*, pg. 1454
FONCIERE VOLTA SA; *Int'l*, pg. 2724
FORLIFE CO., LTD.; *Int'l*, pg. 2733

FOX CREEK RESERVE, L.L.C.—See Sun Communities, Inc.; *U.S. Public*, pg. 1961
FPI MANAGEMENT, INC.; *U.S. Private*, pg. 1586
FRANCHI MANAGEMENT COMPANY; *U.S. Private*, pg. 1587
FRASER RESIDENCE ORCHARD PTE LTD—See Frasers Property Limited; *Int'l*, pg. 2766
FRASERS PROPERTY DEVELOPMENTS LTD—See Frasers Property Limited; *Int'l*, pg. 2766
FRASERS PROPERTY (UK) LIMITED—See Frasers Property Limited; *Int'l*, pg. 2766
FREY INVEST S.L.—See Frey S.A.; *Int'l*, pg. 2791
FS BRANDS, INC.—See FirstService Corporation; *Int'l*, pg. 2691
FUJIAN SANMU GROUP CO., LTD.; *Int'l*, pg. 2819
FULTON COUNTY PROPERTIES LLC—See BlueScope Steel Limited; *Int'l*, pg. 1073
GALLANT VENTURE LTD.; *Int'l*, pg. 2873
GARDA PROPERTY GROUP; *Int'l*, pg. 2884
GATECHNOLOGIES CO., LTD.; *Int'l*, pg. 2888
GBST HOLDINGS LIMITED - GBST WEALTH MANAGEMENT DIVISION—See GBST Holdings Limited; *Int'l*, pg. 2893
GENERALI PROPERTIES FUND I GMBH & CO. KG.—See Cinven Limited; *Int'l*, pg. 1616
GENERALI REALTIES LTD—See Assicurazioni Generali S.p.A.; *Int'l*, pg. 646
GENERATIONS GROUP OF COMPANIES INC.—See Genesis Land Development Corp.; *Int'l*, pg. 2921
GENOVA PROPERTY GROUP AB; *Int'l*, pg. 2926
GENTING PLANTATIONS BERHAD—See Genting Berhad; *Int'l*, pg. 2928
GGM GESELLSCHAFT FUR GEBAUDE MANAGEMENT MBH—See Helaba Landesbank Hessen-Thuringen; *Int'l*, pg. 3327
GHAR INC.; *U.S. Private*, pg. 1690
GHG ASSET MANAGEMENT LLC—See Icahn Enterprises L.P.; *U.S. Public*, pg. 1084
GLOBAL DEVELOPMENT KFT.—See Ablon Group Limited; *Int'l*, pg. 63
GLOBAL MUTUAL PROPERTIES LIMITED; *Int'l*, pg. 2999
GLOBAL ORIENTAL BERHAD; *Int'l*, pg. 2999
GLOMAC ALLIANCE SDN. BHD.—See GLOMAC Berhad; *Int'l*, pg. 3008
GLOMAC CITY SDN. BHD.—See GLOMAC Berhad; *Int'l*, pg. 3008
GLOMAC RAWANG SDN. BHD.—See GLOMAC Berhad; *Int'l*, pg. 3008
GOLDEN LONG TENG DEVELOPMENT CO., LTD.; *Int'l*, pg. 3030
GOLDFIELD PROPERTIES LIMITED; *Int'l*, pg. 3033
GOODWELL PROPERTY MANAGEMENT LIMITED—See CK Asset Holdings Limited; *Int'l*, pg. 1635
GOVERNOUR'S SQUARE OF COLUMBUS CO. L.P.—See UDR, Inc.; *U.S. Public*, pg. 2218
G.P.E. (88/104 BISHOPSGATE) LIMITED—See Great Portland Estates Plc; *Int'l*, pg. 3065
GRAPHISOFT PARK SE; *Int'l*, pg. 3060
THE GREAT EAGLE PROPERTIES MANAGEMENT COMPANY, LIMITED—See Great Eagle Holdings Limited; *Int'l*, pg. 3064
GREENTOWN SERVICE GROUP CO. LTD.; *Int'l*, pg. 3077
GREINER REAL ESTATE SP. Z O.O.—See Greiner Holding AG; *Int'l*, pg. 3079
GREYSTAR MANAGEMENT SERVICES, L.P.—See Greystar Real Estate Partners, LLC; *U.S. Private*, pg. 1785
GROMUTUAL BERHAD - MELAKA—See Gromutual Berhad; *Int'l*, pg. 3087
GROMUTUAL BERHAD; *Int'l*, pg. 3087
GROSSGLOCKNER SARL—See CLS Holdings plc; *Int'l*, pg. 1664
GSW IMMOBILIEN AG—See Deutsche Wohnen SE; *Int'l*, pg. 2085
GUANGDONG JADIETE HOLDINGS GROUP CO., LTD.; *Int'l*, pg. 3156
GUTHRIE GTS LIMITED; *Int'l*, pg. 3188
HAINAN HAIDE CAPITAL MANAGEMENT CO., LTD.; *Int'l*, pg. 3212
HANAN MOR GROUP - HOLDING LTD.; *Int'l*, pg. 3241
HARIMA B-STEM CORPORATION; *Int'l*, pg. 3276
HARTAMAS REAL ESTATE SDN. BHD.—See Hartamas Group Bhd.; *Int'l*, pg. 3279
HASEKO LIVENET, INC.—See Haseko Corporation; *Int'l*, pg. 3283
HASEKO PROPERTY MANAGEMENT HOLDINGS INC.—See Haseko Corporation; *Int'l*, pg. 3283
HASEKO URBAN CO., LTD.—See Haseko Corporation; *Int'l*, pg. 3283
HASEKO URBEST, INC.—See Haseko Corporation; *Int'l*, pg. 3283
HATTEN LAND LIMITED; *Int'l*, pg. 3284
HEALTHCO HEALTHCARE & WELLNESS REIT; *Int'l*, pg. 3304
HEETON HOLDINGS LIMITED; *Int'l*, pg. 3307
HELICAL BAR (REX HOUSE) LTD—See Helical Plc; *Int'l*, pg. 3329
HELICAL (BRAMSHOTT PLACE) LTD—See Helical Plc; *Int'l*, pg. 3329

N.A.I.C.S. INDEX

531311 — RESIDENTIAL PROPERT...

HELLOWORLD TECHNOLOGIES INDIA PRIVATE LIMITED—See Aurum PropTech Ltd.; *Int'l*, pg. 715
HEMISPHERE PROPERTIES INDIA LIMITED; *Int'l*, pg. 3341
HEVOL SERVICES GROUP CO. LIMITED; *Int'l*, pg. 3367
HIAG HANDEL IMMOBILIEN AG—See HIAG Immobilien Holding AG; *Int'l*, pg. 3382
HIAWATHA MANOR ASSOCIATION AT LAKE TANSI—See Crown Resorts, Ltd.; *U.S. Private*, pg. 1112
HML ANDERTONS LIMITED—See HML Holdings plc; *Int'l*, pg. 3432
HML SHAW LIMITED—See HML Holdings plc; *Int'l*, pg. 3432
HOMECO DAILY NEEDS REIT; *Int'l*, pg. 3455
HOME MANAGEMENT KFT.—See Duna House Holding Public Company Limited; *Int'l*, pg. 2225
HOMETRACK DATA SYSTEMS LIMITED; *Int'l*, pg. 3456
HONG LAI HUAT GROUP LIMITED; *Int'l*, pg. 3467
HOOSIERS LIVING SERVICE CO., LTD.—See Hoosiers Holdings; *Int'l*, pg. 3472
HORTI MILANO SRL—See BNP Paribas SA; *Int'l*, pg. 1091
HUA YANG BERHAD; *Int'l*, pg. 3510
HUBEI FUXING SCIENCE & TECHNOLOGY CO., LTD.; *Int'l*, pg. 3517
HUNTAVEN PROPERTIES LIMITED—See Hunting Plc; *Int'l*, pg. 3536
HUNT MILITARY COMMUNITIES MGMT., LLC—See Hunt Companies, Inc.; *U.S. Private*, pg. 2008
HYFCO ESTATE MANAGEMENT AND AGENCY LIMITED—See Henderson Land Development Co. Ltd.; *Int'l*, pg. 3344
IGB CORPORATION BERHAD—See IGB Berhad; *Int'l*, pg. 3601
IJM PROPERTIES SDN BHD—See IJM Corporation Berhad; *Int'l*, pg. 3608
INSULA PROPERTIES, LLC; *U.S. Private*, pg. 2094
J.J. GUMBERG CO. INC.; *U.S. Private*, pg. 2167
JONES & FORREST, INC.—See Common Interest Management Services Inc.; *U.S. Private*, pg. 986
JONES LANG LASALLE RESIDENTIAL DEVELOPMENT GMBH—See Jones Lang LaSalle Incorporated; *U.S. Public*, pg. 1204
KAPELLEN SARL—See CLS Holdings plc; *Int'l*, pg. 1664
KEYSEN PROPERTY MANAGEMENT SERVICES LIMITED—See Great Eagle Holdings Limited; *Int'l*, pg. 3064
KIPLE SDN. BHD.—See Green Packet Berhad; *Int'l*, pg. 3072
KIU LOK PROPERTIES (INTERNATIONAL) LIMITED—See FSE Services Group Limited; *Int'l*, pg. 2798
KONOVER SOUTH, LLC—See The Simon Konover Company; *U.S. Private*, pg. 4118
KOREX LIMITED—See Aminex PLC; *Int'l*, pg. 428
KORMAN RESIDENTIAL PROPERTIES, INC.—See Korman Services, L.P.; *U.S. Private*, pg. 2344
KW PROPERTY MANAGEMENT, LLC; *U.S. Private*, pg. 2359
LA INDIAN OAKS QRS INC.—See Apartment Investment and Management Company; *U.S. Public*, pg. 144
LANDSEA HOMES CORP.; *U.S. Public*, pg. 1292
LANE COMPANY; *U.S. Private*, pg. 2387
LCD (INDOCHINA) PTE LTD—See Aspial Corporation Limited; *Int'l*, pg. 630
LCD (INDOCHINA) PTE LTD—See Fragrance Group Limited; *Int'l*, pg. 2758
LCD PROPERTY MANAGEMENT PTE LTD—See Aspial Corporation Limited; *Int'l*, pg. 630
LCD PROPERTY MANAGEMENT PTE LTD—See Fragrance Group Limited; *Int'l*, pg. 2758
LEGACY HOUSING CORPORATION; *U.S. Public*, pg. 1301
LEX DALLAS L.P.—See LXP Industrial Trust; *U.S. Public*, pg. 1349
LIVEWIRE ERGOGENICS, INC.; *U.S. Public*, pg. 1333
LMW RESIDENTIAL PTY LTD—See Acumentis Group Limited; *Int'l*, pg. 121
LOK WING GROUP LIMITED—See China Properties Investment Holdings Limited; *Int'l*, pg. 1542
LUFTHANSA TECHNIK IMMOBILIEN- UND VERWALTUNGSGESELLSCHAFT MBH—See Deutsche Lufthansa AG; *Int'l*, pg. 2070
MAXIMUS PROPERTIES LLC—See MAXIMUS, Inc.; *U.S. Public*, pg. 1402
MCKEE ASSET MANAGEMENT; *U.S. Private*, pg. 2637
MCP PROPERTY MANAGEMENT, LLC—See MetLife, Inc.; *U.S. Public*, pg. 1430
MEM PROPERTY MANAGEMENT CORPORATION; *U.S. Private*, pg. 2663
MICHAELSON GROUP REAL ESTATE, LLC; *U.S. Private*, pg. 2699
MILES PROPERTIES INC.; *U.S. Private*, pg. 2727
MILLER DEVELOPMENTS LIMITED—See Bridgepoint Group Plc; *Int'l*, pg. 1154
MILLER HOMES LIMITED—See Bridgepoint Group Plc; *Int'l*, pg. 1154
MITTBYGGE AB—See Addnode Group AB; *Int'l*, pg. 130
MOBILE MODULAR MANAGEMENT CORPORATION—See McGrath RentCorp.; *U.S. Public*, pg. 1407
MODERN LIVING INVESTMENTS HOLDINGS LIMITED—See Asia Allied Infrastructure Holdings Limited; *Int'l*, pg. 610
MONACHIA AG—See Bayerische Stadte- und Wohnungsbau GmbH & Co. KG; *Int'l*, pg. 913
MUREX PROPERTIES, LLC; *U.S. Private*, pg. 2815
NAM HONG PROPERTIES PTE. LTD.—See Blackgold Natural Resources Ltd.; *Int'l*, pg. 1061
NEWCASTLE CONSTRUCTION MANAGEMENT, LLC—See AvalonBay Communities, Inc.; *U.S. Public*, pg. 240
NEW WORLD DEVELOPMENT COMPANY LIMITED—See Chow Tai Fook Enterprises Limited; *Int'l*, pg. 1584
NORTHWEST CAPITAL GROUP, INC.—See Northwest Bancshares, Inc.; *U.S. Public*, pg. 1542
NRT PROPERTY MANAGEMENT ARIZONA LLC—See Anywhere Real Estate Inc.; *U.S. Public*, pg. 141
NRT PROPERTY MANAGEMENT FLORIDA LLC—See Anywhere Real Estate Inc.; *U.S. Public*, pg. 141
NRT PROPERTY MANAGEMENT TEXAS LLC—See Anywhere Real Estate Inc.; *U.S. Public*, pg. 141
NTS RESIDENTIAL MANAGEMENT COMPANY—See NTS Corporation; *U.S. Private*, pg. 2971
NWJ COMPANIES, INC.; *U.S. Private*, pg. 2975
OCEANIC REALTY GROUP INTERNATIONAL, INC—See Alliance Global Group, Inc.; *Int'l*, pg. 339
OFFICE-MATE CORPORATION—See GSI Creos Corporation; *Int'l*, pg. 3145
OLYMPIA LAND BERHAD—See DutaLand Berhad; *Int'l*, pg. 2235
PAKAR ANGSANA SDN BHD—See Berjaya Corporation Berhad; *Int'l*, pg. 983
PANCHMAHAL PROPERTIES LTD.—See Bengal & Assam Company Ltd.; *Int'l*, pg. 973
PAPIRBREDDEN EIENDOM AS—See Entra ASA; *Int'l*, pg. 2452
PEABODY PROPERTIES, INC.; *U.S. Private*, pg. 3122
PEABODY PROPERTIES SOUTH, LLC—See Peabody Properties, Inc.; *U.S. Private*, pg. 3122
PENN FLORIDA CAPITAL CORP.; *U.S. Private*, pg. 3134
PERMAS JAYA SDN. BHD.—See Bandar Raya Developments Berhad; *Int'l*, pg. 829
PETROVSKY FORT LLC—See ENR Russia Invest SA; *Int'l*, pg. 2444
PGI INCORPORATED; *U.S. Public*, pg. 1684
PINNACLE AT UNION HILLS LLC—See Greystar Real Estate Partners, LLC; *U.S. Private*, pg. 1785
PINNACLE GALLERIA LLC—See FPI Management, Inc.; *U.S. Private*, pg. 1586
PLANO PITANGUEIRAS EMPREENDIMENTOS IMOBILIARIOS LTDA.—See Cyrela Brazil Realty S.A.; *Int'l*, pg. 1897
PL MANAGEMENT LTD—See Harrods Ltd.; *Int'l*, pg. 3279
POLY PROPERTY SERVICES CO., LTD.—See China Poly Group Corporation; *Int'l*, pg. 1541
POSTER PROPERTY LIMITED—See DigitalBridge Group, Inc.; *U.S. Public*, pg. 665
PRIMA SIXTEEN SDN. BHD.—See GLOMAC Berhad; *Int'l*, pg. 3008
PROSPERITY LAND ESTATE MANAGEMENT LIMITED—See Asia Orient Holdings Limited; *Int'l*, pg. 613
PROTECH PROPERTY MANAGEMENT LIMITED—See Allied Group Limited; *Int'l*, pg. 357
PROVIDENCE MANAGEMENT COMPANY, LLC; *U.S. Private*, pg. 3294
PUNCAK LUYANG SDN. BHD.—See B.I.G. Industries Berhad; *Int'l*, pg. 790
QUORUM SERVICES, INC.—See The Ensign Group, Inc.; *U.S. Public*, pg. 2072
REALTECH TITLE LLC—See Anywhere Real Estate Inc.; *U.S. Public*, pg. 143
REALTEX HOUSING MANAGEMENT, LLC—See Realtex Development Corporation; *U.S. Private*, pg. 3369
REALTY AUSTIN, LLC—See Compass, Inc.; *U.S. Public*, pg. 561
RED HOUSE MANAGEMENT COMPANY (NORFOLK) LIMITED—See Barclays PLC; *Int'l*, pg. 862
REDROW HOMES SOUTH WALES LIMITED—See Barratt Developments PLC; *Int'l*, pg. 868
REGAL ESTATE MANAGEMENT LIMITED—See Century City International Holdings Ltd; *Int'l*, pg. 1418
REGENCY LAND SDN. BHD.—See GLOMAC Berhad; *Int'l*, pg. 3008
RESIDENCIAL MONTE CARMELO, S.A—See ACS, Actividades de Construccion y Servicios, S.A.; *Int'l*, pg. 115
RESORT ASSOCIATION MANAGEMENT; *U.S. Private*, pg. 3406
REVALO SPA—See Covivio; *Int'l*, pg. 1821
REVONA PROPERTIES; *U.S. Private*, pg. 3417
RIBEKK AS—See Entra ASA; *Int'l*, pg. 2452
RIVERSTONE RESIDENTIAL GROUP, LLC—See Greystar Real Estate Partners, LLC; *U.S. Private*, pg. 1785
RIVER VALLEY SHOPPING CENTRE PTE LTD—See Frasers Property Limited; *Int'l*, pg. 2766
RIVER VALLEY TOWER PTE LTD—See Frasers Property Limited; *Int'l*, pg. 2766
RIVNOBUD LLC—See Dragon Ukrainian Properties & Development Plc; *Int'l*, pg. 2199
ROBBINS PROPERTY ASSOCIATES, LLC—See Elco Limited; *Int'l*, pg. 2345
RODROCK & ASSOCIATES INC.; *U.S. Private*, pg. 3470
ROHDE OTTMERS SIEGEL REALTY, INC.—See Island Capital Group LLC; *U.S. Private*, pg. 2144
RWF HEALTH & COMMUNITY DEVELOPERS LIMITED—See HICL Infrastructure PLC; *Int'l*, pg. 3383
SADONG DEVELOPMENT SDN. BHD.—See Advance Synergy Berhad; *Int'l*, pg. 157
SANTA INES EMPREENDIMENTOS IMOBILIARIOS LTDA.—See Direcional Engenharia S.A.; *Int'l*, pg. 2129
SARASOTA MANAGEMENT AND LEASING; *U.S. Private*, pg. 3549
SECURISERVICES SDN BHD—See Berjaya Corporation Berhad; *Int'l*, pg. 983
SELEX ENGINEERING SERVICES LIMITED—See Great Eagle Holdings Limited; *Int'l*, pg. 3064
SELIGMAN WESTERN ENTERPRISES LIMITED—See Seligman & Associates, Inc.; *U.S. Private*, pg. 3602
SEVENTY DAMANSARA SDN. BHD.—See Eastern & Oriental Berhad; *Int'l*, pg. 2271
SHANGHAI INTERNATIONAL REALTY CO., LTD.—See Daiwa House Industry Co., Ltd.; *Int'l*, pg. 1947
SHILO MANAGEMENT CORPORATION; *U.S. Private*, pg. 3636
SICHUAN LANGUANG JUSTBON SERVICES GROUP CO., LTD.—See Country Garden Services Holdings Company Limited; *Int'l*, pg. 1818
THE SIMON KONOVER COMPANY; *U.S. Private*, pg. 4118
SKY PARKS BUSINESS CENTER LIMITED—See Flughafen Wien Aktiengesellschaft; *Int'l*, pg. 2713
SKYRUN VACATION RENTALS, LLC; *U.S. Private*, pg. 3686
SOCIETE FRANCAISE DE GESTION ET DE CONSTRUCTION (SFGC) SA—See Barclays PLC; *Int'l*, pg. 863
SOMERSET WEST AUTOPARK PROPRIETARY LIMITED—See Barclays PLC; *Int'l*, pg. 863
SOUTH CASTLE PROPERTIES LTD.—See Caledonian Trust PLC; *Int'l*, pg. 1263
SOUTHPORT FINANCIAL CORPORATION; *U.S. Private*, pg. 3737
SOVEREIGN AOC OPERATIONS PTY LIMITED—See Brookfield Corporation; *Int'l*, pg. 1189
SOVEREIGN GOLDSEA PTY LIMITED—See Brookfield Corporation; *Int'l*, pg. 1189
SOVEREIGN PACIFIC BAY PROPERTY MANAGEMENT PTY LIMITED—See Brookfield Corporation; *Int'l*, pg. 1189
SOVEREIGN WYNYARD FINANCE PTY LIMITED—See Brookfield Corporation; *Int'l*, pg. 1189
SPEED WIN LIMITED—See Chinese Estates Holdings Limited; *Int'l*, pg. 1569
SPRAVBYTKOMFORT, A.S.—See CEZ, a.s.; *Int'l*, pg. 1428
STEADLINK ASSET MANAGEMENT PTE LTD.—See Colour Life Services Group Co., Ltd.; *Int'l*, pg. 1704
STEAM PLANT SQUARE, LLC—See Avista Corporation; *U.S. Public*, pg. 249
STEPHENS PROPERTIES SDN BHD—See Berjaya Corporation Berhad; *Int'l*, pg. 984
SUMMIT DEVELOPMENT CORPORATION SDN. BHD.—See Hexza Corporation Berhad; *Int'l*, pg. 3373
SYARIKAT TENAGA SAHABAT SDN. BHD.—See Global Oriental Berhad; *Int'l*, pg. 3000
TAMAN EQUINE (M) SDN. BHD.—See Global Oriental Berhad; *Int'l*, pg. 3000
TAN & TAN DEVELOPMENTS BERHAD—See IGB Berhad; *Int'l*, pg. 3601
TAPESTRY MANAGEMENT LLC—See Hilton Worldwide Holdings Inc.; *U.S. Public*, pg. 1041
TAYLOR MORRISON OF TEXAS, INC.—See Brookfield Corporation; *Int'l*, pg. 1183
TAYLOR WOODROW HOMES - SOUTHWEST FLORIDA DIVISION, LLC—See Brookfield Corporation; *Int'l*, pg. 1183
T.C.C. COMMERCIAL PROPERTY MANAGEMENT CO., LTD.—See Asset World Corp Public Company Limited; *Int'l*, pg. 643
TIANJIN JIUHE INTERNATIONAL VILLA CO., LTD.—See Daiwa House Industry Co., Ltd.; *Int'l*, pg. 1947
TIRAM JAYA SDN BHD—See Berjaya Corporation Berhad; *Int'l*, pg. 983
TOWER-SERVICE SP. Z O.O.—See CPI Property Group, S.A.; *Int'l*, pg. 1825
TRIBRIDGE RESIDENTIAL PROPERTY MANAGEMENT ADVISORS, LLC—See Tribridge Residential, LLC; *U.S. Private*, pg. 4227
TRICAP CHICAGO, LLC; *U.S. Private*, pg. 4228
TTH DEVELOPMENT PTE LTD—See Amara Holdings Ltd.; *Int'l*, pg. 411
TURNBERRY, LTD.; *U.S. Private*, pg. 4260
TWO BALLSTON PLAZA CO. LLC—See Brookfield Corporation; *Int'l*, pg. 1186
UPI POSLOVNI SISTEM D.D. SARAJEVO—See CID Adriatic Investments GmbH; *Int'l*, pg. 1603
VACATION VILLAGES OF AMERICA, INC.; *U.S. Private*, pg. 4329
VAISHNAVI BUILDERS & DEVELOPERS PRIVATE LIMITED—See Hubtown Limited; *Int'l*, pg. 3521

531311 — RESIDENTIAL PROPERT...

VICTORIA PROPERTIES A/S—See Gefion Group A/S; *Int'l*, pg. 2911
VILLAGE GREEN MANAGEMENT COMPANY; *U.S. Private*, pg. 4383
VIRTUAL PROPERTIES REALTY, LLC—See United Real Estate Group, LLC; *U.S. Private*, pg. 4296
VISTANA SIGNATURE EXPERIENCES, INC.—See Marriott Vacations Worldwide Corporation; *U.S. Public*, pg. 1374
WANGSA TEGAP SDN BHD—See Berjaya Corporation Berhad; *Int'l*, pg. 984
WBG GMBH—See E.ON SE; *Int'l*, pg. 2260
WELK RESORTS SAN DIEGO—See The Welk Group Inc.; *U.S. Private*, pg. 4134
WEST CASTLE PROPERTIES LTD.—See Caledonian Trust PLC; *Int'l*, pg. 1263
WESTWIND MANOR RESORT ASSOCIATION, INC.—See Crown Resorts, Ltd.; *U.S. Private*, pg. 1112
WOODGREEN (BLYTH) RESIDENTS MANAGEMENT COMPANY LIMITED—See Bellway plc; *Int'l*, pg. 968
THE WORKS COMMUNITY MANAGEMENT CO., LTD.—See Ananda Development Public Company Limited; *Int'l*, pg. 447
WORKS FINANCE (NZ) LIMITED—See Downer EDI Limited; *Int'l*, pg. 2186
WRH REALTY SERVICES, INC.; *U.S. Private*, pg. 4572
WYNDHAM SEAWATCH PLANTATION—See Travel & Leisure Co.; *U.S. Public*, pg. 2186
YES INC.; *U.S. Private*, pg. 4588
ZWEITE BASF IMMOBILIEN-GESELLSCHAFT MBH—See BASF SE; *Int'l*, pg. 886

531312 — NONRESIDENTIAL PROPERTY MANAGERS

1ST CHOICE PROPERTY MANAGEMENT & DEVELOPMENT COMPANY, LLC—See 1st Choice Facilities Services Corp.; *U.S. Private*, pg. 4
23RD GROUP LLC; *U.S. Private*, pg. 6
3811 BELL MEDICAL PROPERTIES, LLC—See Universal Health Realty Income Trust; *U.S. Public*, pg. 2255
420 PROPERTY MANAGEMENT LLC; *U.S. Public*, pg. 9
61 SOUTHWARK STREET LTD—See Helical Plc; *Int'l*, pg. 3329
AAREAL GESELLSCHAFT FUR BETEILIGUNGEN UND GRUNDBESITZ DRITTE MBH & CO. KG—See Advent International Corporation; *U.S. Private*, pg. 96
AAREAL GESELLSCHAFT FUR BETEILIGUNGEN UND GRUNDBESITZ DRITTE MBH & CO. KG—See Centerbridge Partners, L.P.; *U.S. Private*, pg. 812
AAREON FRANCE S.A.S.—See Advent International Corporation; *U.S. Private*, pg. 96
AAREON FRANCE S.A.S.—See Centerbridge Partners, L.P.; *U.S. Private*, pg. 812
ABACUS CAPITAL GROUP LLC—See Affiliated Managers Group, Inc.; *U.S. Public*, pg. 53
A&B II, LLC—See Alexander & Baldwin, Inc.; *U.S. Public*, pg. 75
A BROWN COMPANY, INC.; *Int'l*, pg. 17
ACCELL PROPERTY MANAGEMENT INC.—See Seabreeze Management Company, Inc.; *U.S. Private*, pg. 3583
ACCENTIS SA/NV; *Int'l*, pg. 82
ACTION INVESTMENT GROUP, INC.; *U.S. Private*, pg. 67
ADLER REAL ESTATE HOTEL GMBH—See ADLER Group SA; *Int'l*, pg. 150
ADLER REAL ESTATE PROPERTIES GMBH & CO. KG—See ADLER Group SA; *Int'l*, pg. 150
A GROUP OF RETAIL ASSETS SWEDEN AB; *Int'l*, pg. 17
AIRPORT CITY PROPERTY MANAGEMENT D.O.O.—See Africa Israel Investments Ltd.; *Int'l*, pg. 190
ALBION LAND (BUSHEY MILL) LTD—See Helical Plc; *Int'l*, pg. 3329
ALIANSCE SHOPPING CENTERS SA—See Allos SA; *Int'l*, pg. 359
ALMANAC REALTY INVESTORS, LLC—See Neuberger Berman Group LLC; *U.S. Private*, pg. 2890
AMERICAN RENTAL MANAGEMENT COMPANY—See Federal Capital Partners; *U.S. Private*, pg. 1487
ANDERSON REGENERATE—See Anderson Group Limited; *Int'l*, pg. 450
ANGEL GROUP LTD.; *Int'l*, pg. 459
ANTARA MEGAH SDN. BHD.—See Bertam Alliance Berhad; *Int'l*, pg. 989
APPRAISAL PROPERTY MANAGEMENT SDN BHD—See Jones Lang LaSalle Incorporated; *U.S. Public*, pg. 1201
ARAMARK SERVICE INDUSTRIES (CHINA) CO., LTD.—See Aramark; *U.S. Public*, pg. 177
ARTHALAND CORPORATION; *Int'l*, pg. 583
ASIA ASSET PROPERTY GROUP LTD—See Hopefluent Group Holdings Ltd; *Int'l*, pg. 3473
ASSURA PROPERTIES LIMITED—See Assura plc; *Int'l*, pg. 649
ASSURA PROPERTIES UK LIMITED—See Assura plc; *Int'l*, pg. 649
AUSTRALIAN COMMERCIAL PROPERTY MANAGEMENT LIMITED—See Australia & New Zealand Banking Group Limited; *Int'l*, pg. 720

AVIGNON CAPITAL LIMITED; *Int'l*, pg. 743
BABIS VOVOS INTERNATIONAL CONSTRUCTION S.A.; *Int'l*, pg. 793
BANDAR KEPALA BATAS SDN. BHD.—See Hunza Properties Berhad; *Int'l*, pg. 3537
BELLANCA DEVELOPMENTS LTD.—See Dundee Corporation; *Int'l*, pg. 2226
BERTAM DEVELOPMENT SDN. BHD.—See Bertam Alliance Berhad; *Int'l*, pg. 989
BLB RESOURCES, INC.; *U.S. Private*, pg. 580
BLUE VICTORY HOLDINGS, INC.; *U.S. Private*, pg. 594
BNP PARIBAS IMMOBILIER PROMOTION IMMOBILIER D'ENTREPRISE—See BNP Paribas SA; *Int'l*, pg. 1085
BNP PARIBAS REAL ESTATE PROPERTY MANAGEMENT BELGIUM SA—See BNP Paribas SA; *Int'l*, pg. 1086
BNP PARIBAS REAL ESTATE—See BNP Paribas SA; *Int'l*, pg. 1086
BONASUDDEN HOLDING AB; *Int'l*, pg. 1105
BOWMAN GROUP LLP; *U.S. Private*, pg. 626
BOYKIN MANAGEMENT COMPANY, LLC; *U.S. Private*, pg. 628
BPG REAL ESTATE SERVICES LLC—See The Buccini/Pollin Group, Inc.; *U.S. Private*, pg. 4002
BROOKFIELD PROPERTIES MANAGEMENT CORPORATION—See Brookfield Corporation; *Int'l*, pg. 1186
BROOKFIELD PROPERTIES MANAGEMENT LLC—See Brookfield Corporation; *Int'l*, pg. 1186
BROOKFIELD PROPERTIES RETAIL INC.—See Brookfield Corporation; *Int'l*, pg. 1185
BURTON CAROL MANAGEMENT, LLC; *U.S. Private*, pg. 693
CALIFORNIA PROPERTY HOLDINGS III LLC—See Abbott Laboratories; *U.S. Public*, pg. 19
CANTAMAR PROPERTY MANAGEMENT, INC.—See Meruelo Group LLC; *U.S. Private*, pg. 2677
CAPITALAND COMMERCIAL LIMITED—See CapitaLand Investment Limited; *Int'l*, pg. 1313
CARL M. FREEMAN RETAIL LLC—See Carl M. Freeman Associates, Inc.; *U.S. Private*, pg. 762
CARRIANNA GROUP HOLDINGS COMPANY LIMITED; *Int'l*, pg. 1346
CARROLLTON ENTERPRISES LP; *U.S. Private*, pg. 774
CAVALIERS OPERATING COMPANY, LLC; *U.S. Private*, pg. 795
CBZ PROPERTIES (PVT) LIMITED—See CBZ Holdings Limited; *Int'l*, pg. 1366
CCCG REAL ESTATE CORPORATION LIMITED; *Int'l*, pg. 1366
CC REALITY LLC—See Silver Lake Group, LLC; *U.S. Private*, pg. 3654
CC RP LLC—See Sun Communities, Inc.; *U.S. Public*, pg. 1961
CEBU LANDMASTERS, INC.; *Int'l*, pg. 1372
CENTRALAND LIMITED; *Int'l*, pg. 1410
CENTRECORP MANAGEMENT SERVICES LTD.—See North American Development Group; *U.S. Private*, pg. 2940
CENTRO PROPERTIES GROUP - NORTHEAST—See Blackstone Inc.; *U.S. Public*, pg. 352
CEZ SPRAVA MAJETKU, S.R.O.—See CEZ, a.s.; *Int'l*, pg. 1427
CHEMIE UETIKON AG—See CPH Chemie + Papier Holding AG; *Int'l*, pg. 1824
CHINA GEM HOLDINGS LIMITED; *Int'l*, pg. 1504
CHINA NEW CITY COMMERCIAL DEVELOPMENT LIMITED; *Int'l*, pg. 1534
CHINA WORLD TRADE CENTER CO., LTD.; *Int'l*, pg. 1563
CHINA YUANBANG PROPERTY HOLDINGS LIMITED; *Int'l*, pg. 1565
C.I. PROPERTY & INVESTMENTS LIMITED—See Financiere Pinault SCA; *Int'l*, pg. 2668
CITIZENS JMP GROUP, LLC—See Citizens Financial Group, Inc.; *U.S. Public*, pg. 505
CITIZENS JMP SECURITIES, LLC—See Citizens Financial Group, Inc.; *U.S. Public*, pg. 505
CITY AND COUNTRY PROPERTIES (BIRMINGHAM) LIMITED—See Centremanor Ltd.; *Int'l*, pg. 1411
CITY AND COUNTRY PROPERTIES (CAMBERLEY) LIMITED—See Centremanor Ltd.; *Int'l*, pg. 1411
CITY AND COUNTRY PROPERTIES (MIDLANDS) LIMITED—See Centremanor Ltd.; *Int'l*, pg. 1411
CITY PROFESSIONAL MANAGEMENT LIMITED—See Asia Allied Infrastructure Holdings Limited; *Int'l*, pg. 610
COBHAN PROPERTIES LTD—See Bank of Cyprus Holdings Public Limited Company; *Int'l*, pg. 842
COGESA S.P.A.—See ACS, Actividades de Construccion y Servicios, S.A.; *Int'l*, pg. 110
COLLIERS INTERNATIONAL - HAWAII—See Colliers International Group Inc.; *Int'l*, pg. 1700
COLLIN ESTATES LIMITED—See Great Portland Estates Plc; *Int'l*, pg. 3065
CORONADO CENTER—See Brookfield Corporation; *Int'l*, pg. 1185
COUNTRY VIEW BERHAD; *Int'l*, pg. 1819
COUSINS REALTY SERVICES, LLC—See Cousins Properties Incorporated; *U.S. Public*, pg. 587
COVENANT PROPERTIES, LLC—See Covenant Logistics

CORPORATE AFFILIATIONS

Group, Inc.; *U.S. Public*, pg. 588
COVIVIO OFFICE AG—See Covivio; *Int'l*, pg. 1821
CREATIVE ENTERPRISE HOLDINGS LTD.—See China Merchants Group Limited; *Int'l*, pg. 1523
CROMWELL CORPORATION LIMITED—See Cromwell Property Group; *Int'l*, pg. 1853
CROMWELL PROPERTY SERVICES PTY. LTD.—See Cromwell Property Group; *Int'l*, pg. 1854
CULTURECOM CENTRE LIMITED—See Culturecom Holdings Ltd; *Int'l*, pg. 1877
CWI REAL ESTATE AG; *Int'l*, pg. 1891
DAEJAN (BRIGHTON) LIMITED—See Centremanor Ltd.; *Int'l*, pg. 1411
DAEJAN COMMERCIAL PROPERTIES LIMITED—See Centremanor Ltd.; *Int'l*, pg. 1411
DAEJAN (DARTFORD) LIMITED—See Centremanor Ltd.; *Int'l*, pg. 1411
DAEJAN RETAIL PROPERTIES LIMITED—See Centremanor Ltd.; *Int'l*, pg. 1412
DAEJAN (US) LIMITED—See Centremanor Ltd.; *Int'l*, pg. 1411
DAIMAN DEVELOPMENT BERHAD; *Int'l*, pg. 1938
DAIWA SERVICE CO., LTD.—See Daiwa House Industry Co., Ltd.; *Int'l*, pg. 1946
DAKOTA HOSPITALITY COMPANY—See Jones Lang LaSalle Incorporated; *U.S. Public*, pg. 1204
DAMANSARA REALTY BERHAD; *Int'l*, pg. 1955
DDR PUERTO RICO—See SITE Centers Corp.; *U.S. Public*, pg. 1888
DEKA GRUNDSTUCKSVERWALTUNGSGESELLSCHAFT I (GBR)—See DekaBank; *Int'l*, pg. 2005
DEUTSCHE LAND PLC; *Int'l*, pg. 2066
DHI MINERALS LTD.—See Gold Royalty Corp.; *Int'l*, pg. 3026
DKLS PREMIERHOME SDN BHD—See DKLS Industries Berhad; *Int'l*, pg. 2139
DLC MANAGEMENT CORP.; *U.S. Private*, pg. 1247
DLF INTERNATIONAL HOLDINGS PTE LIMITED—See DLF Limited; *Int'l*, pg. 2141
DLF RETAIL DEVELOPERS LIMITED—See DLF Limited; *Int'l*, pg. 2141
DOWNTOWN BUSINESS IMPROVEMENT DISTRICT CORPORATION; *U.S. Private*, pg. 1269
DP REALTY LIMITED—See Domino's Pizza Group plc; *Int'l*, pg. 2162
DRITTE ADLER REAL ESTATE GMBH & CO. KG—See ADLER Group SA; *Int'l*, pg. 150
DUAL COMMERCIAL LLC—See Howden Group Holdings Limited; *Int'l*, pg. 3493
DUAL CORPORATE RISKS LIMITED—See Howden Group Holdings Limited; *Int'l*, pg. 3493
DUBAI PROPERTIES GROUP LLC—See Dubai Holding LLC; *Int'l*, pg. 2218
DUBAI PROPERTIES—See Dubai Holding LLC; *Int'l*, pg. 2218
DUNDEE REALTY MANAGEMENT (B.C.) CORP.—See Dundee Corporation; *Int'l*, pg. 2226
DUTALAND BERHAD; *Int'l*, pg. 2235
DWC 3.0 S.P.A.; *Int'l*, pg. 2236
EAST LAKE, LLC; *U.S. Private*, pg. 1316
ECO WORLD SYDNEY DEVELOPMENT PTY. LTD.—See Eco World International Berhad; *Int'l*, pg. 2293
EDMUND TIE & COMPANY (THAILAND) CO., LTD.—See Edmund Tie & Company (SEA) Pte. Ltd.; *Int'l*, pg. 2313
EHL IMMOBILIEN MANAGEMENT GMBH—See EHL Immobilien GmbH; *Int'l*, pg. 2328
EJENDOMSAKTIESELSKABET AF 4. MARTS 1982—See Carlsberg A/S; *Int'l*, pg. 1340
ELDERS REAL ESTATE (TASMANIA) PTY. LTD.—See Elders Limited; *Int'l*, pg. 2346
ELDERS REAL ESTATE (WA) PTY. LTD.—See Elders Limited; *Int'l*, pg. 2346
EMAAR DEVELOPMENT PJSC—See Emaar Properties PJSC; *Int'l*, pg. 2372
EMAAR INTERNATIONAL MALLS LLC—See Emaar Properties PJSC; *Int'l*, pg. 2372
EMICO HOLDINGS BERHAD; *Int'l*, pg. 2380
EMPRESS LOUISIANA PROPERTIES, L.P.—See Expand Energy Corporation; *U.S. Public*, pg. 808
ENTRA ASA; *Int'l*, pg. 2452
EQUITY ONE PLC—See Carson Cumberbatch PLC; *Int'l*, pg. 1417
EUPE CORPORATION BERHAD; *Int'l*, pg. 2526
EURASIA GROUPE SA; *Int'l*, pg. 2527
FAIRCHECK SCHADENSERVICE GMBH—See Helvetia Holding AG; *Int'l*, pg. 3340
FARLIM GROUP (MALAYSIA) BHD; *Int'l*, pg. 2618
FASHION SHOW MALL—See Brookfield Corporation; *Int'l*, pg. 1185
FASTPARTNER AB; *Int'l*, pg. 2622
FCL CENTREPOINT PTE LTD—See Frasers Property Limited; *Int'l*, pg. 2766
FERRARI PARTNERS LP; *U.S. Private*, pg. 1498
FIFTH STREET MANAGEMENT COMPANY, LLC—See Kim King Associates, LLC; *U.S. Private*, pg. 2305
FIMA CORPORATION BERHAD; *Int'l*, pg. 2663
FIM PROPERTY INVESTMENT LIMITED—See FIMBank p.l.c.; *Int'l*, pg. 2664

531312 — NONRESIDENTIAL PROP...

N.A.I.C.S. INDEX

FIRST CAPITAL REIT—See G City Ltd.; *Int'l*, pg. 2861
FIRST PROPERTY GROUP PLC; *Int'l*, pg. 2686
FOREST CITY MYRTLE ASSOCIATES, LLC—See Brookfield Corporation; *Int'l*, pg. 1187
FOREST CITY RATNER COMPANIES, LLC—See Brookfield Corporation; *Int'l*, pg. 1187
FORMATION DESIGN & BUILD LIMITED—See Formation Group PLC; *Int'l*, pg. 2733
FOTEX NETHERLANDS B.V.—See Fotex Holding SE; *Int'l*, pg. 2752
FRASERS CENTREPOINT PROPERTY MANAGEMENT SERVICES PTE LTD—See Frasers Property Limited; *Int'l*, pg. 2766
FRASERS CITY QUARTER PTY LIMITED—See Frasers Property Limited; *Int'l*, pg. 2766
FRASERS PROPERTY MANAGEMENT AUSTRALIA PTY LIMITED—See Frasers Property Limited; *Int'l*, pg. 2766
FRASERS TOWN HALL PTY LTD—See Frasers Property Limited; *Int'l*, pg. 2766
FRASER SUITE SYDNEY—See Frasers Property Limited; *Int'l*, pg. 2766
FREEDOM VILLAGE OF SUN CITY CENTER, LTD.—See Brookdale Senior Living Inc.; *U.S. Public*, pg. 394
FREEPORT RETAIL LIMITED—See The Carlyle Group Inc.; *U.S. Public*, pg. 2047
FRIT COCOWALK OWNER, LLC—See Federal Realty Investment Trust; *U.S. Public*, pg. 825
FSP PROPERTY MANAGEMENT LLC—See Franklin Street Properties Corp.; *U.S. Public*, pg. 883
GATEWAY ENTERPRISE COMPANY LIMITED—See Aspial Corporation Limited; *Int'l*, pg. 630
GATEWAY ENTERPRISE COMPANY LIMITED—See Fragrance Group Limited; *Int'l*, pg. 2758
GATEWAY HEALTHCARE, INC.—See The Ensign Group, Inc.; *U.S. Public*, pg. 2071
GAV-YAM LANDS CORP. LTD—See IDB Development Corporation Ltd.; *Int'l*, pg. 3588
GCP HOSPITALITY MANAGEMENT LTD.—See Gaw Capital Advisors Limited; *Int'l*, pg. 2891
GEARUP INVESTMENTS LIMITED—See Hysan Development Company Limited; *Int'l*, pg. 3554
GHL ZWEITE GESELLSCHAFT FUR HAFEN- UND LAGEREIIMMOBILIEN-VERWALTUNG MBH—See Hamburger Hafen und Logistik AG; *Int'l*, pg. 3236
GLENRYE PROPERTIES SERVICES LIMITED—See Aramark; *U.S. Public*, pg. 177
GLOBAL LOGISTICS PROPERTIES INC.—See Global Logistic Properties Limited; *Int'l*, pg. 2999
GLP BRASIL EMPREENDIMENTOS E PARTICIPACOES LTDA.—See Global Logistic Properties Limited; *Int'l*, pg. 2999
GLP INVESTMENT MANAGEMENT (CHINA) CO., LTD.—See Global Logistic Properties Limited; *Int'l*, pg. 2999
GLP INVESTMENT MANAGEMENT PTE. LTD.—See Global Logistic Properties Limited; *Int'l*, pg. 2999
GLP US MANAGEMENT LLC—See Global Logistic Properties Limited; *Int'l*, pg. 2999
GOODALL AND BOURNE PROPERTIES (PROPRIETARY) LIMITED—See CONDUIT CAPITAL LIMITED; *Int'l*, pg. 1766
GOODLAND CAPITAL PTE. LTD.—See Goodland Group Limited; *Int'l*, pg. 3040
GOODLAND DEVELOPMENT PTE. LTD.—See Goodland Group Limited; *Int'l*, pg. 3040
GOODLAND GROUP CONSTRUCTION PTE. LTD.—See Goodland Group Limited; *Int'l*, pg. 3040
GOODLAND HOMES PTE. LTD.—See Goodland Group Limited; *Int'l*, pg. 3040
GOODLAND INVESTMENTS PTE. LTD.—See Goodland Group Limited; *Int'l*, pg. 3040
GOTHI PLASCON INDIA LIMITED; *Int'l*, pg. 3043
GPT OPERATING PARTNERSHIP LP—See Blackstone Inc.; *U.S. Public*, pg. 350
GRANDE ASSET HOTELS & PROPERTY PUBLIC COMPANY LIMITED; *Int'l*, pg. 3057
GRAO CASTALIA, S.L.—See Banco de Sabadell, S.A.; *Int'l*, pg. 821
GREENTOWN CHINA HOLDINGS LIMITED; *Int'l*, pg. 3076
GROCON ERSTE GRUNDSTUCKSGESELLSCHAFT MBH—See Baloise Holding AG; *Int'l*, pg. 811
GRUPE COMMERCIAL COMPANY—See Grupe Holding Company; *U.S. Private*, pg. 1797
GTOWER SDN. BHD.—See IGB Berhad; *Int'l*, pg. 3601
GUANGDONG HIGHSUN GROUP CO., LTD.; *Int'l*, pg. 3155
GUTHRIE FMC PTE LTD—See Guthrie GTS Limited; *Int'l*, pg. 3188
GUTHRIE PMS (S) PTE LTD—See Guthrie GTS Limited; *Int'l*, pg. 3189
HANG YICK PROPERTIES MANAGEMENT LIMITED—See Henderson Land Development Co. Ltd.; *Int'l*, pg. 3344
HCI HANSEATISCHE CAPITALBERATUNGSGESELLSCHAFT MBH—See Ernst Russ AG; *Int'l*, pg. 2495
HEIMAR HF.; *Int'l*, pg. 3323
HELICAL BAR DEVELOPMENTS (SOUTH EAST) LTD—See Helical Plc; *Int'l*, pg. 3330
HELICAL (CARDIFF) LTD—See Helical Plc; *Int'l*, pg. 3329
HELICAL (CRAWLEY) LTD—See Helical Plc; *Int'l*, pg. 3329

HELICAL (HAILSHAM) LTD—See Helical Plc; *Int'l*, pg. 3329
HELICAL RETAIL LTD—See Helical Plc; *Int'l*, pg. 3330
HELICAL (SEVENOAKS) LTD—See Helical Plc; *Int'l*, pg. 3329
HELICAL WROCLAW SP. Z.O.O.—See Helical Plc; *Int'l*, pg. 3330
HENRY BOOT 'K' LTD—See Henry Boot PLC; *Int'l*, pg. 3355
HENRY BOOT PROJECTS LIMITED—See Henry Boot PLC; *Int'l*, pg. 3355
HENRY S. MILLER REALTY MANAGEMENT, LLC—See Henry S. Miller Management Corp.; *U.S. Private*, pg. 1919
HERITAGE MANAGEMENT CORP.; *U.S. Private*, pg. 1924
HERMES REAL ESTATE INVESTMENT MANAGEMENT LTD.—See Federated Hermes, Inc.; *U.S. Public*, pg. 827
HIAG IMMOBILIEN BETA GMBH—See Hornbach Holding AG & Co. KGaA; *Int'l*, pg. 3481
HIW-KC ORLANDO, LLC—See Highwoods Properties, Inc.; *U.S. Public*, pg. 1035
HOPEWELL CENTRE MANAGEMENT LIMITED—See Hopewell Holdings Limited; *Int'l*, pg. 3473
HOSTMARK HOSPITALITY GROUP; *U.S. Private*, pg. 1988
HUNTER RESORT VACATIONS, INC.—See Vail Resorts, Inc.; *U.S. Public*, pg. 2271
HUNZA-LAND CORPORATION SDN. BHD.—See Hunza Properties Berhad; *Int'l*, pg. 3537
HUNZA PROPERTIES BERHAD; *Int'l*, pg. 3537
HUNZA PROPERTIES (GURNEY) SDN. BHD.—See Hunza Properties Berhad; *Int'l*, pg. 3537
HUNZA PROPERTIES (WILAYAH) SDN. BHD.—See Hunza Properties Berhad; *Int'l*, pg. 3537
I-BERHAD; *Int'l*, pg. 3562
ICORR PROPERTIES INTERNATIONAL; *Int'l*, pg. 3586
IDI SERVICES GROUP, LLC—See Brookfield Corporation; *Int'l*, pg. 1184
IFM IMMOBILIEN AG; *Int'l*, pg. 3599
I HOMES PROPERTIES SDN. BHD.—See Ideal Capital Berhad; *Int'l*, pg. 3589
IN-REL PROPERTIES, INC.; *U.S. Private*, pg. 2052
INTERNATIONAL TRADEMART COMPANY LIMITED—See Hopewell Holdings Limited; *Int'l*, pg. 3473
INTERSTATE HOTELS & RESORTS, INC.—See Advent International Corporation; *U.S. Private*, pg. 97
JADE EIGHT PROPERTIES LLC—See Safehold Inc.; *U.S. Public*, pg. 1834
JARNGRINDEN PROJEKTUTVECKLING AB—See Genova Property Group AB; *Int'l*, pg. 2926
JIAYU HNA INDUSTRY DEVELOPMENT CO., LTD.—See Hainan Traffic Administration Holding Co., Ltd.; *Int'l*, pg. 3215
JLL KNIGHTSBRIDGE—See Jones Lang LaSalle Incorporated; *U.S. Public*, pg. 1202
JONES PROPERTIES, LLC—See Check Into Cash Inc.; *U.S. Private*, pg. 869
J.S. KARLTON COMPANY, INC.; *U.S. Private*, pg. 2171
KAHN GLOBAL SERVICES, INC.—See Albert Kahn Associates, Inc.; *U.S. Private*, pg. 153
KELLY PROPERTIES, INC.—See Kelly Services, Inc.; *U.S. Public*, pg. 1218
KIMCO OCALA 665, INC.—See Kimco Realty Corporation; *U.S. Public*, pg. 1231
KING STURGE MANAGEMENT SPRL—See Jones Lang LaSalle Incorporated; *U.S. Public*, pg. 1205
KITSON & PARTNERS CLUBS—See Kitson & Partners, LLC; *U.S. Private*, pg. 2316
KNIGHTON ESTATES LIMITED—See Great Portland Estates Plc; *Int'l*, pg. 3065
KONDOSERVIS SDN. BHD.—See IGB Berhad; *Int'l*, pg. 3601
KONOVER COMMERCIAL CORPORATION—See The Simon Konover Company; *U.S. Private*, pg. 4118
KONOVER HOTEL CORPORATION—See The Simon Konover Company; *U.S. Private*, pg. 4118
KUCERA PROPERTIES; *U.S. Private*, pg. 2356
KUCHING RIVERINE RESORT MANAGEMENT SDN BHD—See IJM Corporation Berhad; *Int'l*, pg. 3609
LAS VEGAS SUNSET PROPERTIES—See Western Alliance Bancorporation; *U.S. Public*, pg. 2354
LEAWOOD TCP, LLC—See Washington Prime Group Inc.; *U.S. Private*, pg. 4449
LO & SON LAND INVESTMENT COMPANY LIMITED—See Cheuk Nang (Holdings) Limited; *Int'l*, pg. 1473
LOTOS OCHRONA SP. Z O.O.—See Grupa LOTOS S.A.; *Int'l*, pg. 3117
LOVE HOTEL MANAGEMENT COMPANY—See Love Real Estate Company; *U.S. Private*, pg. 2501
LUBERT-ADLER MANAGEMENT, LLC—See Independence Capital Partners, LLC; *U.S. Private*, pg. 2056
LUFTHANSA TECHNIK OBJEKT- UND VERWALTUNGSGESELLSCHAFT MBH—See Deutsche Lufthansa AG; *Int'l*, pg. 2070
LUWOGE GMBH HAUS BREITNAU—See BASF SE; *Int'l*, pg. 884
LUWOGE GMBH HAUS WESTERLAND—See BASF SE; *Int'l*, pg. 884
LUWOGE GMBH—See BASF SE; *Int'l*, pg. 884
LUWOGE GMBH STUDIENHAUS ST. JOHANN—See BASF SE; *Int'l*, pg. 884

LYNNHAVEN MALL—See Brookfield Corporation; *Int'l*, pg. 1185
MACKLOWE MANAGEMENT, LLC—See Macklowe Properties, L.L.C.; *U.S. Private*, pg. 2537
MAINSTAY GROUP LIMITED—See Equistone Partners Europe Limited; *Int'l*, pg. 2486
MALL ST. MATTHEWS—See Brookfield Corporation; *Int'l*, pg. 1185
MANASOTA GROUP, INC.; *U.S. Private*, pg. 2561
MARTEGO SDN BHD—See Cheuk Nang (Holdings) Limited; *Int'l*, pg. 1473
MASUKA BINA SDN. BHD.—See Hunza Properties Berhad; *Int'l*, pg. 3537
MBG DALLGOW GMBH & CO. KG—See ADLER Group SA; *Int'l*, pg. 150
MEDICLIN IMMOBILIEN VERWALTUNG GMBH—See Asklepios Kliniken GmbH & Co. KGaA; *Int'l*, pg. 623
MEPC LTD.—See Federated Hermes, Inc.; *U.S. Public*, pg. 827
MERRITT PROPERTIES, LLC—See Merritt Management Corporation; *U.S. Private*, pg. 2676
MESIROW FINANCIAL AGRICULTURE MANAGEMENT, LLC—See Mesirow Financial Holdings, Inc.; *U.S. Private*, pg. 2678
MILESTONE PROPERTY MANAGEMENT, INC.—See Milestone Properties Inc.; *U.S. Private*, pg. 2729
THE MILLS AT JERSEY GARDENS—See Simon Property Group, Inc.; *U.S. Public*, pg. 1882
MORGANTOWN MALL ASSOCIATES, LP—See Washington Prime Group Inc.; *U.S. Private*, pg. 4449
MOUNTAIN DEVELOPMENT CORP.; *U.S. Private*, pg. 2799
MUNCHENER BAUGESELLSCHAFT MBH—See ADLER Group SA; *Int'l*, pg. 150
MUSTANG PROPERTY CORPORATION—See BASF SE; *Int'l*, pg. 876
NEARON ENTERPRISES - PROPERTY MANAGEMENT DIVISION—See Nearon Enterprises; *U.S. Private*, pg. 2877
NORIAN REGNSKAP AS—See TowerBrook Capital Partners, L.P.; *U.S. Private*, pg. 4195
NORTHWEST HNA PROPERTY CO., LTD.—See Hainan Traffic Administration Holding Co., Ltd.; *Int'l*, pg. 3215
OAKMONT CAPITAL RESOURCES, INC.; *U.S. Private*, pg. 2985
OMNI PARTNERS, LP; *U.S. Private*, pg. 3016
PACER HEALTH CORPORATION—See Pacer Corporation; *U.S. Private*, pg. 3064
PACIFIC YGNACIO CORPORATION—See Great Eagle Holdings Limited; *Int'l*, pg. 3064
PALMER CAPITAL CZECH REPUBLIC, S.R.O.—See Fiera Capital Corporation; *Int'l*, pg. 2660
PANATTONI DEVELOPMENT COMPANY; *U.S. Private*, pg. 3085
PANDA PLACE MANAGEMENT LIMITED—See Hopewell Holdings Limited; *Int'l*, pg. 3473
PECANLAND MALL—See Brookfield Corporation; *Int'l*, pg. 1185
PERIMETER MALL—See Brookfield Corporation; *Int'l*, pg. 1185
PFP COLUMBUS, LLC—See Washington Prime Group Inc.; *U.S. Private*, pg. 4448
PH ONE DEVELOPMENT (CAMBODIA) LTD.—See Hong Lai Huat Group Limited; *Int'l*, pg. 3467
P&O DEVELOPMENTS LTD.—See Dubai World Corporation; *Int'l*, pg. 2222
POSH PROPERTIES DEVELOPMENT CORPORATION—See Anchor Land Holdings, Inc.; *Int'l*, pg. 448
PPP SCHLOSS SONNENSTEIN GMBH—See Bilfinger SE; *Int'l*, pg. 1028
PRINCE KUHIO PLAZA—See Brookfield Corporation; *Int'l*, pg. 1185
PROPERTY & BUILDINGS COMMERCIAL CENTERS, LTD.—See IDB Development Corporation Ltd.; *Int'l*, pg. 3588
PROP PARK SENDIRIAN BERHAD—See Hua Yang Berhad; *Int'l*, pg. 3510
PT BATAMINDO INVESTMENT CAKRAWALA—See Gallant Venture Ltd.; *Int'l*, pg. 2874
PT BINTAN INTI INDUSTRIAL ESTATE—See Gallant Venture Ltd.; *Int'l*, pg. 2874
PUBLIC HOUSING DEVELOPMENT (CAMBODIA) LTD.—See Hong Lai Huat Group Limited; *Int'l*, pg. 3467
QUADRANGLE MANAGEMENT COMPANY—See Quadrangle Development Corporation; *U.S. Private*, pg. 3315
RAHN CONTRACTING, LLC; *U.S. Private*, pg. 3346
RECOVERY ONE, LLC—See WSFS Financial Corporation; *U.S. Public*, pg. 2383
REGNUM CORP.; *U.S. Public*, pg. 1777
RELATED MANAGEMENT COMPANY, L.P.—See The Related Companies, L.P.; *U.S. Private*, pg. 4104
RELOCATION PROPERTIES MANAGEMENT LLC—See Valvoline Inc.; *U.S. Public*, pg. 2274
RENTGUARD LIMITED—See Arthur J. Gallagher & Co.; *U.S. Public*, pg. 207
RGA UNDERWRITING LIMITED—See Arthur J. Gallagher & Co.; *U.S. Public*, pg. 207

RIA FOOD CENTRE SDN. BHD.—See Eupe Corporation Berhad; *Int'l*, pg. 2526
RODAG PROPERTIES (PTY) LIMITED—See Afrimat Limited; *Int'l*, pg. 193
RPAI CHICAGO BRICKYARD, L.L.C.—See Kite Realty Group Trust; *U.S. Public*, pg. 1237
SAFEGUARD PROPERTIES, INC.; *U.S. Private*, pg. 3524
SAGAX FINLAND ASSET MANAGEMENT OY—See AB Sagax; *Int'l*, pg. 41
SAGAX GERMANY HOLDING GMBH—See AB Sagax; *Int'l*, pg. 41
SAGAX NEDERLAND B.V.—See AB Sagax; *Int'l*, pg. 41
SANYA HNA REA-ESTATE DEVELOPMENT CO., LTD.—See Hainan Traffic Administration Holding Co., Ltd.; *Int'l*, pg. 3216
SEMINOLE REAL ESTATE SERVICES, LLC—See Seminole Holdings Group, LLC; *U.S. Private*, pg. 3604
SHANDONG HNA BUSINESS DEVELOPMENT CO., LTD—See Hainan Traffic Administration Holding Co.; *Int'l*, pg. 3216
THE SHOPS AT MARY BRICKELL VILLAGE—See Caisse de Depot et Placement du Quebec; *Int'l*, pg. 1254
SILVERLINK HOLDINGS LIMITED—See DLF Limited; *Int'l*, pg. 2141
SIMON PREMIUM OUTLETS—See Simon Property Group, Inc.; *U.S. Public*, pg. 1881
SOLEIL MANAGEMENT, LLC—See The Asny Corporation; *U.S. Private*, pg. 3989
SONAE SIERRA SGPS, SA—See Efanor Investimentos, SGPS, SA; *Int'l*, pg. 2319
SPONDA KIINTEISTOT OY—See Blackstone Inc.; *U.S. Public*, pg. 351
SRI SAN ANTONIO, INC.—See Federal Realty Investment Trust; *U.S. Public*, pg. 825
STONECUTTER MILLS CORP.; *U.S. Private*, pg. 3828
STREAM REALTY PARTNERS, L.P.; *U.S. Private*, pg. 3838
STREET RETAIL WEST 6, L.P.—See Federal Realty Investment Trust; *U.S. Public*, pg. 826
STYLES & WOOD LIMITED—See 7FC LLP; *Int'l*, pg. 15
SUNLINK HEALTHCARE PROFESSIONAL PROPERTY, LLC—See SunLink Health Systems, Inc.; *U.S. Public*, pg. 1964
SUNSET PROPERTIES, LLC—See GCC, S.A.B. de C.V.; *Int'l*, pg. 2895
SUNTEC INTERNATIONAL CONVENTION & EXHIBITION SERVICES PTE. LTD.—See ESR Group Limited; *Int'l*, pg. 2508
TETRIS DESIGN AND BUILD S.R.L—See Jones Lang LaSalle Incorporated; *U.S. Public*, pg. 1206
TETRIS PROJECTS GMBH—See Jones Lang LaSalle Incorporated; *U.S. Public*, pg. 1206
TRYON MANAGEMENT, INC.—See Wells Fargo & Company; *U.S. Public*, pg. 2347
TSE WALL ARLIDGE LIMITED—See Downer EDI Limited; *Int'l*, pg. 2186
TWMB ASSOCIATES, LLC—See Tanger Inc.; *U.S. Public*, pg. 1980
UAB AGRO MANAGEMENT TEAM—See AUGA group, AB; *Int'l*, pg. 703
UH INDUSTRIES & DEVELOPMENT SDN. BHD.—See Bertam Alliance Berhad; *Int'l*, pg. 989
URBAN INVESTMENT RESEARCH CORP.; *U.S. Private*, pg. 4314
URBAN RETAIL PROPERTIES, LLC; *U.S. Private*, pg. 4315
USGP DALLAS DEA LP—See Easterly Government Properties, Inc.; *U.S. Public*, pg. 703
UTICA SERVICES INC.—See St. John Health System Inc.; *U.S. Private*, pg. 3771
VEPEMA OY—See Blackstone Inc.; *U.S. Public*, pg. 351
VISION HUAQING (BEIJING) DEVELOPMENT CO., LTD—See Frasers Property Limited; *Int'l*, pg. 2766
WANDA HOTEL DEVELOPMENT COMPANY LIMITED—See Dalian Wanda Group Corporation Ltd.; *Int'l*, pg. 1953
WATERFRONT A, LLC—See Shidler Investment Company, LLC; *U.S. Private*, pg. 3635
WATT PROPERTIES & LEASING—See Watt Companies, Inc.; *U.S. Private*, pg. 4456
WEINGARTEN REALTY MANAGEMENT COMPANY—See Kimco Realty Corporation; *U.S. Public*, pg. 1232
WELL BORN REAL ESTATE MANAGEMENT LIMITED—See Henderson Land Development Co. Ltd.; *Int'l*, pg. 3345
WOLFF URBAN MANAGEMENT, INC.; *U.S. Private*, pg. 4554
YORKSBON DEVELOPMENT LIMITED—See Cheuk Nang (Holdings) Limited; *Int'l*, pg. 1473

531320 — OFFICES OF REAL ESTATE APPRAISERS

ACCURATE GROUP; *U.S. Private*, pg. 55
ACT APPRAISAL MANAGEMENT; *U.S. Private*, pg. 66
ADVANCED COLLATERAL SOLUTIONS, LLC—See Wells Fargo & Company; *U.S. Public*, pg. 2343
ATM CORPORATION OF AMERICA; *U.S. Private*, pg. 381
AUTHENTIC HEROES, INC.—See AUTHENTIC HOLDINGS, INC.; *U.S. Public*, pg. 228
CAPRIGHT PROPERTY ADVISORS, LLC; *U.S. Private*, pg. 745
CATLETT & COMPANY INC.—See BBG Inc.; *U.S. Private*, pg. 498
CERTIFIED APPRAISALS LLC—See C&F Financial Corporation; *U.S. Public*, pg. 414
CLASS VALUATION, LLC—See Gridiron Capital, LLC; *U.S. Private*, pg. 1786
COLLIERS INTERNATIONAL VALUATION & ADVISORY SERVICES INC.—See Colliers International Group Inc.; *Int'l*, pg. 1701
CORELOGIC VALUATION SERVICES, LLC—See Insight Venture Management, LLC; *U.S. Private*, pg. 2089
CORELOGIC VALUATION SERVICES, LLC—See Stone Point Capital LLC; *U.S. Private*, pg. 3822
CORNERSTONE APPRAISAL SERVICES, INC.—See Compass Equity Partners, LLC; *U.S. Private*, pg. 999
CROWN APPRAISAL GROUP—See BBG Inc.; *U.S. Private*, pg. 498
DART APPRAISAL.COM, INC.; *U.S. Private*, pg. 1159
EMORTGAGE LOGIC, LLC—See Assurant, Inc.; *U.S. Public*, pg. 215
ENTREKEN ASSOCIATES, INC.; *U.S. Private*, pg. 1406
E STREET APPRAISAL MANAGEMENT LLC—See Rithm Capital Corp.; *U.S. Public*, pg. 1800
GORDON BROTHERS ASSET ADVISORS, LLC—See Gordon Brothers Group, LLC; *U.S. Private*, pg. 1742
HEIJMANS ENERGIE B.V.—See Heijmans N.V.; *Int'l*, pg. 3322
HEINEN & ASSOCIATES LLC; *U.S. Private*, pg. 1904
INSIDEVALUATION PARTNERS, LLC—See LRES Corp.; *U.S. Private*, pg. 2507
INTEGRA REALTY RESOURCES, INC.; *U.S. Private*, pg. 2098
JACKSON CLAYBORN, INC.; *U.S. Private*, pg. 2176
JAMES REAL ESTATE SERVICES, INC.—See Intelica Commercial Real Estate Company; *U.S. Private*, pg. 2104
JOSEPH J. BLAKE ASSOCIATES, INC.; *U.S. Private*, pg. 2236
KIDDER MATHEWS; *U.S. Private*, pg. 2302
LENDER'S CHOICE INC.—See LRES Corp.; *U.S. Private*, pg. 2507
LPS VALUATION SOLUTIONS, LLC—See Fidelity National Financial, Inc.; *U.S. Public*, pg. 831
LRES CORP.; *U.S. Private*, pg. 2507
LRX GROUP, INC.; *U.S. Private*, pg. 2508
METROPOLITAN VALUATION SERVICES, INC.—See Jones Lang LaSalle Incorporated; *U.S. Public*, pg. 1205
NATIONAL REAL ESTATE INFORMATION SERVICES INC.; *U.S. Public*, pg. 2861
NATIONWIDE APPRAISAL NETWORK (NAN); *U.S. Private*, pg. 2865
NGP REALTY SUB, L.P.—See Drive Shack Inc.; *U.S. Public*, pg. 688
PINDERS PROFESSIONAL & CONSULTANCY SERVICES LTD.—See Christie Group plc; *Int'l*, pg. 1587
PRINCIPLE VALUATION, LLC—See Prism Health Care Services, Inc.; *U.S. Private*, pg. 3267
PROFESSIONAL VALUATION SERVICES, LLC—See Hilton Grand Vacations Inc.; *U.S. Public*, pg. 1039
PRO-TECK SERVICES LTD.—See Stewart Information Services Corporation; *U.S. Public*, pg. 1948
RELATIONAL TECHNOLOGY SERVICES—See Relational LLC; *U.S. Private*, pg. 3392
RELS, LLC—See Insight Venture Management, LLC; *U.S. Private*, pg. 2089
RELS, LLC—See Stone Point Capital LLC; *U.S. Private*, pg. 3823
SCHENBERGER, TAYLOR, MCCORMICK & JECKER INC.—See Valbridge Property Advisors, Inc.; *U.S. Private*, pg. 4330
SERVICELINK IP HOLDING COMPANY LLC.—See Fidelity National Financial, Inc.; *U.S. Public*, pg. 831
SPRINGHOUSE, L.L.C.—See Altisource Portfolio Solutions S.A.; *Int'l*, pg. 393
STEPHAN, COLE & ASSOCIATES, LLC; *U.S. Private*, pg. 3802
STREETLINKS LLC—See Novation Companies, Inc.; *U.S. Public*, pg. 1548
TIMIOS APPRAISAL MANAGEMENT, INC.—See Ideanomics, Inc.; *U.S. Public*, pg. 1088
TINSA—See Advent International Corporation; *U.S. Private*, pg. 107
UNITED STATES APPRAISALS LLC—See Stewart Information Services Corporation; *U.S. Public*, pg. 1948
VR WERT GESELLSCHAFT FUR IMMOBILIENBEWERTUNG MBH—See DZ BANK AG Deutsche Zentral-Genossenschaftsbank; *Int'l*, pg. 2245
WASHINGTON PRIME PROPERTIES LLC—See Washington Prime Group Inc.; *U.S. Private*, pg. 4449
WESTERVELT REALTY—See The Westervelt Company; *U.S. Private*, pg. 4134
ZOOCASA REALTY INC.—See eXp World Holdings, Inc.; *U.S. Public*, pg. 808

531390 — OTHER ACTIVITIES RELATED TO REAL ESTATE

1001 BRICKELL BAY DRIVE, LLC—See Apartment Investment and Management Company; *U.S. Public*, pg. 143
100 FEDERAL SUBSIDIARY REIT LLC—See Boston Properties, Inc.; *U.S. Public*, pg. 372
101069101 SASKATCHEWAN LTD.—See Crown Investments Corporation of Saskatchewan; *Int'l*, pg. 1857
118 HOLDINGS INC.—See Cosco Capital, Inc.; *Int'l*, pg. 1809
11 EAST 68TH STREET LLC—See Vornado Realty Trust; *U.S. Public*, pg. 2309
150 MAIN STREET, L.L.C.—See Veris Residential, Inc.; *U.S. Public*, pg. 2281
1822DIREKT GESELLSCHAFT DER FRANKFURTER SPARKASSE MBH—See Helaba Landesbank Hessen-Thuringen; *Int'l*, pg. 3327
1ST RED AG; *Int'l*, pg. 3
2001 SIXTH LLC—See Digital Realty Trust, Inc.; *U.S. Public*, pg. 663
20 PINE STREET LLC—See Africa Israel Investments Ltd.; *Int'l*, pg. 189
235 HOLDINGS LTD.; *Int'l*, pg. 4
360 ENTERPRISES LLC; *U.S. Private*, pg. 8
3CNERGY LIMITED; *Int'l*, pg. 7
4 SWEET BRIAR ROAD LIMITED—See ANSA McAL Limited; *Int'l*, pg. 476
50 BEALE STREET LLC—See Paramount Group Inc.; *U.S. Public*, pg. 1637
520 BROADWAY PARALLEL REIT LLC—See Vornado Realty Trust; *U.S. Public*, pg. 2310
577 INVESTMENT CORPORATION; *Int'l*, pg. 13
58.COM INC.; *Int'l*, pg. 13
650 MADISON OWNER LLC—See Vornado Realty Trust; *U.S. Public*, pg. 2310
695 ATLANTIC AVENUE COMPANY, LLC—See The Plymouth Rock Co.; *U.S. Private*, pg. 4097
AAMAL COMPANY Q.S.C.; *Int'l*, pg. 36
AAREAL ESTATE AG—See Advent International Corporation; *U.S. Private*, pg. 96
AAREAL ESTATE AG—See Centerbridge Partners, L.P.; *U.S. Private*, pg. 812
AAREAL GESELLSCHAFT FUR BETEILIGUNGEN UND GRUNDBESITZ ERSTE MBH & CO. KG—See Advent International Corporation; *U.S. Private*, pg. 96
AAREAL GESELLSCHAFT FUR BETEILIGUNGEN UND GRUNDBESITZ ERSTE MBH & CO. KG—See Centerbridge Partners, L.P.; *U.S. Private*, pg. 812
AAREON WODIS GMBH—See Advent International Corporation; *U.S. Private*, pg. 96
AAREON WODIS GMBH—See Centerbridge Partners, L.P.; *U.S. Private*, pg. 812
A'AYAN REAL ESTATE COMPANY K.S.C.C.—See A'ayan Leasing and Investment Company KSCC; *Int'l*, pg. 19
ABAAD REAL ESTATE COMPANY B.S.C.—See Bahrain Islamic Bank; *Int'l*, pg. 800
ABACUS GROUP, LLC; *Int'l*, pg. 47
ABB IMMOBILIEN AG—See ABB Ltd.; *Int'l*, pg. 54
ABBVIE REAL ESTATE MANAGEMENT GMBH—See AbbVie Inc.; *U.S. Public*, pg. 21
ABLON KFT.—See Ablon Group Limited; *Int'l*, pg. 63
ABLON S.R.O.—See Ablon Group Limited; *Int'l*, pg. 63
ABN AMRO INVESTMENT SOLUTIONS S.A.—See ABN AMRO Group N.V.; *Int'l*, pg. 65
ABOITIZLAND, INC.—See Aboitiz Equity Ventures, Inc.; *Int'l*, pg. 66
ABP KAKAAKO COMMERCE 1 LLC—See Alexander & Baldwin, Inc.; *U.S. Public*, pg. 75
A&B PROPERTIES, INC.—See Alexander & Baldwin, Inc.; *U.S. Public*, pg. 75
ABRAMS CAPITAL, LLC; *U.S. Private*, pg. 40
AB SAGAX; *Int'l*, pg. 41
ABYAAR REAL ESTATE DEVELOPMENT COMPANY K.S.C.C.; *Int'l*, pg. 74
ACADIAN ASSET MANAGEMENT (SINGAPORE) PTE. LTD.—See BrightSphere Investment Group Inc.; *U.S. Public*, pg. 383
ACANTHE DEVELOPPEMENT SA; *Int'l*, pg. 78
ACAP ASSET MANAGEMENT COMPANY LIMITED—See Asia Capital Public Company Limited; *Int'l*, pg. 610
ACASA GROUP BVBA; *Int'l*, pg. 78
ACCIONA INMOBILIARIA, S.L.—See Acciona, S.A.; *Int'l*, pg. 90
ACCIONA NIERUCHOMOSCI SP. Z O.O.—See Acciona, S.A.; *Int'l*, pg. 90
ACCUCOMP, LLC; *U.S. Private*, pg. 54
ACCU HOLDING AG; *Int'l*, pg. 94
ACHETER LOUER FR SA—See Adomos SA; *Int'l*, pg. 152
ACIERTA ASISTENCIA, S.A.—See Helvetia Holding AG; *Int'l*, pg. 3339
ACOPIO FACILITY GMBH & CO. KG—See Covivio; *Int'l*, pg. 1821
ACRINOVA AB; *Int'l*, pg. 108
ACRON AG; *Int'l*, pg. 109
ACTIVE EDGE SDN BHD—See Fiamma Holdings Berhad; *Int'l*, pg. 2650

N.A.I.C.S. INDEX

531390 — OTHER ACTIVITIES RE...

ACUMENTIS GROUP LIMITED; *Int'l*, pg. 121
ACURE ASSET MANAGEMENT LTD—See Moelis & Company; *U.S. Public*, pg. 1456
ADAMS PLC; *Int'l*, pg. 124
ADDAR REAL ESTATE SERVICES LLC—See ALDAR Properties PJSC; *Int'l*, pg. 304
AD DULAYL INDUSTRIAL PARK & REAL ESTATE CO.; *Int'l*, pg. 122
ADEKA LIFE-CREATE CORP.—See Adeka Corporation; *Int'l*, pg. 142
ADHBHUT INFRASTRUCTURE LIMITED; *Int'l*, pg. 145
ADIB (UK) LIMITED—See Abu Dhabi Islamic Bank PJSC; *Int'l*, pg. 72
ADLER GROUP SA; *Int'l*, pg. 150
ADLER REAL ESTATE AG—See ADLER Group SA; *Int'l*, pg. 150
ADLER WOHNEN SERVICE GMBH—See ADLER Group SA; *Int'l*, pg. 150
A.D. MAKEPEACE COMPANY; *U.S. Public*, pg. 12
ADRENNA PROPERTY GROUP LIMITED; *Int'l*, pg. 152
ADVANCED ENERGY SYSTEMS LIMITED; *Int'l*, pg. 158
ADVANCED HOME CONCEPT DEVELOPMENT CORP.—See ATN Holdings, Inc.; *Int'l*, pg. 687
ADVANCED OXYGEN TECHNOLOGIES, INC.; *U.S. Public*, pg. 49
ADVANCE LIFESTYLES LIMITED; *Int'l*, pg. 156
A.D. WORKS CORPORATION; *Int'l*, pg. 23
AEDAS HOMES; *Int'l*, pg. 173
AEDES SIIQ S.P.A; *Int'l*, pg. 173
AEDIFICA INVEST SA—See Aedifica SA; *Int'l*, pg. 173
AEDIFICA SA; *Int'l*, pg. 173
AEOLIKI OLYMPUS EVIA S.A.—See ELLAKTOR S.A.; *Int'l*, pg. 2364
AEON REIT INVESTMENT CORPORATION; *Int'l*, pg. 179
AERMONT CAPITAL LLP; *Int'l*, pg. 180
AETOS CAPITAL REAL ESTATE, LP; *U.S. Private*, pg. 120
AEW ASIA PTE. LTD.—See Groupe BPCE; *Int'l*, pg. 3092
AFI EUROPE BULGARIA EOOD—See Africa Israel Investments Ltd.; *Int'l*, pg. 189
AFI EUROPE B.V.—See Africa Israel Investments Ltd.; *Int'l*, pg. 190
AFI EUROPE CZECH REPUBLIC, S.R.O.—See Africa Israel Investments Ltd.; *Int'l*, pg. 189
AFI EUROPE INFRASTRUCTURE B.V.—See Africa Israel Investments Ltd.; *Int'l*, pg. 190
AFI EUROPE (ISRAEL BRANCH) LTD.—See Africa Israel Investments Ltd.; *Int'l*, pg. 189
AFI EUROPE MANAGEMENT SRL—See Africa Israel Investments Ltd.; *Int'l*, pg. 190
AFI GERMANY GMBH—See Africa Israel Investments Ltd.; *Int'l*, pg. 190
AFI MANAGEMENT SIA—See Africa Israel Investments Ltd.; *Int'l*, pg. 190
AFI MANAGEMENT SP. Z O.O.—See Africa Israel Investments Ltd.; *Int'l*, pg. 190
AFI PROPERTIES LTD.—See BIG Shopping Centers Ltd.; *Int'l*, pg. 1021
AFI RUS LLC—See AFI Development PLC; *Int'l*, pg. 189
AFRICA ISRAEL INTERNATIONAL PROPERTIES (2002) LTD.—See Africa Israel Investments Ltd.; *Int'l*, pg. 190
AGAT EJENDOMME A/S; *Int'l*, pg. 200
AGENT ELITE, INC.; *U.S. Private*, pg. 127
AGENZIA LA TORRE S.R.L.—See Assicurazioni Generali S.p.A.; *Int'l*, pg. 647
AGILE REAL ESTATE CONSTRUCTION MANAGEMENT GROUP CO., LTD.—See Agile Group Holdings Limited; *Int'l*, pg. 209
AGI PROPERTIES INC.—See Brookfield Reinsurance Ltd.; *Int'l*, pg. 1193
AG REAL ESTATE—See Ageas SA/NV; *Int'l*, pg. 204
AGRICOLA PROPERTIES LIMITED—See Dairygold Co-Operative Society Ltd; *Int'l*, pg. 1940
AGROB IMMOBILIEN AG; *Int'l*, pg. 218
AGUER HAVELOCK ASSOCIATES, INC.—See Avison Young (Canada) Inc.; *Int'l*, pg. 744
AGUNG PODOMORO LAND TBK; *Int'l*, pg. 222
AIMCO 777 SOUTH BROAD, LLC—See Blackstone Inc.; *U.S. Public*, pg. 350
AIMCO BENT TREE, LLC—See Blackstone Inc.; *U.S. Public*, pg. 350
AIMCO LOCUST ON THE PARK, LLC—See Blackstone Inc.; *U.S. Public*, pg. 350
AIMCO SOUTHSTAR LOFTS, LLC—See Apartment Investment and Management Company; *U.S. Public*, pg. 144
AINA LE'A, INC.; *U.S. Private*, pg. 133
AIRBUS REAL ESTATE PREMIUM AEROTEC NORD GMBH & CO. KG—See Airbus SE; *Int'l*, pg. 244
AIRPORT CITY LTD.—See Equital Ltd.; *Int'l*, pg. 2487
AIZAWA INVESTMENTS CO., LTD.—See Aizawa Securities Group Co., Ltd.; *Int'l*, pg. 255
A&J ASSETS LLC—See Postal Realty Trust, Inc.; *U.S. Public*, pg. 1704
A.J. GREEN SHELL PLC; *Int'l*, pg. 24
AJIAL REAL ESTATE ENTERTAINMENT COMPANY K.S.C.C.; *Int'l*, pg. 256
AJMERA REALTY & INFRA INDIA LIMITED; *Int'l*, pg. 258
AJWAN GULF REAL ESTATE CO. (K.S.C.C.); *Int'l*, pg. 259

AKFEN GAYRIMENKUL YATIRIM ORTAKLIGI A.S.; *Int'l*, pg. 263
AKS CORPORATION PUBLIC COMPANY LIMITED; *Int'l*, pg. 264
AKTEK GIYIM SAN. VE TIC. A.S.; *Int'l*, pg. 265
AKTIV PROPERTIES REIT; *Int'l*, pg. 267
AKTOROM SRL—See ELLAKTOR S.A.; *Int'l*, pg. 2364
ALANDALUS PROPERTY COMPANY; *Int'l*, pg. 290
AL-AQARIYA TRADING INVESTMENT COMPANY; *Int'l*, pg. 284
ALARGAN INTERNATIONAL REAL ESTATE CO. K.S.C.C.; *Int'l*, pg. 291
ALARGAN TOWEL INVESTMENT COMPANY LLC—See Alargan International Real Estate Co. K.S.C.C.; *Int'l*, pg. 291
ALARKO GAYRIMENKUL YATIRIM ORTAKLIGI AS; *Int'l*, pg. 291
AL BATINAH DEVELOPMENT & INVESTMENT HOLDING CO. SAOG; *Int'l*, pg. 276
ALCHEMIST REALTY LTD.; *Int'l*, pg. 300
AL-DAR NATIONAL REAL ESTATE COMPANY K.S.C.C.; *Int'l*, pg. 284
ALECTA REAL ESTATE INVESTMENT, LLC—See Alecta pensionsforsakring, omsesidigt; *Int'l*, pg. 305
ALECTA REAL ESTATE USA, LLC—See Alecta pensionsforsakring, omsesidigt; *Int'l*, pg. 305
AL ENTKAEYA FOR INVESTMENT & REAL ESTATE DEVELOPMENT CO. PLC; *Int'l*, pg. 276
ALE PROPERTY GROUP—See Charter Hall Limited; *Int'l*, pg. 1454
ALE PROPERTY GROUP—See Host-Plus Pty. Limited; *Int'l*, pg. 3486
ALFAB JONKOPING 5 AB—See Alecta pensionsforsakring, omsesidigt; *Int'l*, pg. 305
ALFAB VALUTAN 13 AB—See Alecta pensionsforsakring, omsesidigt; *Int'l*, pg. 305
ALFA LAVAL NV—See Alfa Laval AB; *Int'l*, pg. 310
ALFAVISION OVERSEAS (INDIA) LIMITED; *Int'l*, pg. 315
AL-FUTTAIM GROUP REAL ESTATE—See Al-Futtaim Private Company LLC; *Int'l*, pg. 285
ALFUTURO SERVIZI ASSICURATIVI S.R.L.—See Assicurazioni Generali S.p.A.; *Int'l*, pg. 643
ALICO-AGRI, LTD.—See Continental Grain Company; *U.S. Private*, pg. 1029
ALICO LAND DEVELOPMENT, INC.—See Continental Grain Company; *U.S. Private*, pg. 1029
ALLEGHANY PROPERTIES LLC—See Berkshire Hathaway Inc.; *U.S. Public*, pg. 298
ALLGREEN PROPERTIES LTD.; *Int'l*, pg. 338
ALLGREEN PROPERTIES (TIANJIN) PTE. LTD.—See Allgreen Properties Ltd.; *Int'l*, pg. 338
ALLGREEN PROPERTIES (VIETNAM) PTE. LTD.—See Allgreen Properties Ltd.; *Int'l*, pg. 338
ALLIANCES; *Int'l*, pg. 341
ALLIANZ INVESTMENT PROPERTIES LTD.—See Allianz SE; *Int'l*, pg. 348
ALLIANZ PROPERTIES LIMITED—See Allianz SE; *Int'l*, pg. 349
ALLIANZ REAL ESTATE ASIA PACIFIC—See Allianz SE; *Int'l*, pg. 349
ALLIANZ REAL ESTATE GERMANY GMBH—See Allianz SE; *Int'l*, pg. 349
ALLIED CAPITAL AND DEVELOPMENT OF SOUTH FLORIDA LLC; *U.S. Private*, pg. 185
ALLIED HOTEL PROPERTIES INC.—See Allied Holdings Ltd.; *Int'l*, pg. 357
ALL INSPIRE DEVELOPMENT PUBLIC COMPANY LIMITED; *Int'l*, pg. 332
ALL IN WEST! CAPITAL CORPORATION; *Int'l*, pg. 332
ALLREAL FINANCE AG—See Allreal Holding AG; *Int'l*, pg. 360
ALLREAL GENERALUNTERNEHMUNG AG—See Allreal Holding AG; *Int'l*, pg. 360
ALLREAL HOME AG—See Allreal Holding AG; *Int'l*, pg. 360
ALLREAL OFFICE AG—See Allreal Holding AG; *Int'l*, pg. 360
ALLREAL TONI AG—See Allreal Holding AG; *Int'l*, pg. 360
ALLREAL VULKAN AG—See Allreal Holding AG; *Int'l*, pg. 360
ALLREAL WEST AG—See Allreal Holding AG; *Int'l*, pg. 360
AL-MAMOURA COMPANY FOR REAL ESTATE INVESTMENT; *Int'l*, pg. 286
AL MAMOURA REAL ESTATE INVESTMENTS CO.; *Int'l*, pg. 281
AL-MASAKEN INTERNATIONAL FOR REAL ESTATE DEVELOPMENT CO. - K.S.C.; *Int'l*, pg. 286
AL-MASSALEH REAL ESTATE COMPANY K.S.C.C.; *Int'l*, pg. 286
ALMOAYYED CONTRACTING GROUP Y.K.—See Bahrain Duty Free Shop Complex BSC; *Int'l*, pg. 800
AL MUDON INTERNATIONAL REAL ESTATE COMPANY - KPSC; *Int'l*, pg. 281
ALOJAS BIROJI SIA—See Eastnine AB; *Int'l*, pg. 2274
ALPHA ASTIKA AKINITA S.A.—See Alpha Services and Holdings S.A.; *Int'l*, pg. 369
AL-RAKAEZ PLC; *Int'l*, pg. 288
AL RAMZ CORPORATION INVESTMENT & DEVELOPMENT COMPANY PJSC—See Al Ramz Capital LLC; *Int'l*, pg. 282

ALROV PROPERTIES & LODGINGS LTD.; *Int'l*, pg. 377
AL SAFAT REAL ESTATE COMPANY K.P.S.C.; *Int'l*, pg. 282
AL-SHAMEKHA FOR REAL ESTATE & FINANCIAL INVESTMENTS CO., LTD.; *Int'l*, pg. 288
AL SHAMS HOUSING & URBANIZATION; *Int'l*, pg. 282
ALTAREIT SCA—See Altarea SCA; *Int'l*, pg. 385
ALTER ASSET MANAGEMENT, INC—See The Alter Group Ltd.; *U.S. Private*, pg. 3985
ALTER+CARE—See The Alter Group Ltd.; *U.S. Private*, pg. 3985
ALTERCO S.A.; *Int'l*, pg. 391
ALTERON REIT VARNA; *Int'l*, pg. 392
ALTISOURCE ASSET MANAGEMENT CORPORATION; *U.S. Public*, pg. 88
ALTUS GROUP LIMITED; *Int'l*, pg. 399
ALVEEN SA; *Int'l*, pg. 401
AL-WATANIAH TOWERS COMPANY; *Int'l*, pg. 289
AMAD INVESTMENT & REAL ESTATE DEVELOPMENT PLC; *Int'l*, pg. 403
AMASTEN FASTIGHETS AB; *Int'l*, pg. 412
AMATA ASIA LIMITED—See Amata Corporation Public Company Limited; *Int'l*, pg. 412
AMATA CITY CO. LTD.—See Amata Corporation Public Company Limited; *Int'l*, pg. 412
AMATA CITY HALONG JOINT STOCK COMPANY—See Amata Corporation Public Company Limited; *Int'l*, pg. 412
AMATA CITY RAYONG CO., LTD.—See Amata Corporation Public Company Limited; *Int'l*, pg. 412
AMATA GLOBAL PTE. LTD.—See Amata Corporation Public Company Limited; *Int'l*, pg. 412
AMATA VN PCL—See Amata Corporation Public Company Limited; *Int'l*, pg. 413
AMBER RIDGE, LLC—See Hovnanian Enterprises, Inc.; *U.S. Public*, pg. 1056
AME DEVELOPMENT SDN. BHD.—See AME Elite Consortium Berhad; *Int'l*, pg. 420
AMERCO REAL ESTATE COMPANY OF TEXAS, INC.—See U-Haul Holding Company; *U.S. Public*, pg. 2211
AMERCO REAL ESTATE COMPANY—See U-Haul Holding Company; *U.S. Public*, pg. 2211
AMER GROUP HOLDING; *Int'l*, pg. 420
AMERICAN CAMPUS COMMUNITIES SERVICES, INC.—See Blackstone Inc.; *U.S. Public*, pg. 347
AMERICAN HOMES 4 RENT; *U.S. Public*, pg. 104
AMERICAN LAND DEVELOPMENT, LLC—See Peabody Energy Corporation; *U.S. Public*, pg. 1659
AMERICAN MANAGEMENT SERVICES LLC; *U.S. Private*, pg. 240
AMERICAN NEVADA COMPANY—See The Greenspun Corporation; *U.S. Private*, pg. 4039
AMERICAN TITLE INC.—See Assurant, Inc.; *U.S. Public*, pg. 214
AMERICA'S CAPITAL PARTNERS, LLC; *U.S. Private*, pg. 220
AMFUNDS MANAGEMENT BERHAD—See AMMB Holdings Berhad; *Int'l*, pg. 429
AMG HOLDINGS CO., LTD.; *Int'l*, pg. 426
AMOUN INTERNATIONAL FOR INVESTMENT P.L.C; *Int'l*, pg. 431
AMP CAPITAL INVESTORS PROPERTY JAPAN KK—See AMP Limited; *Int'l*, pg. 432
AMPLION ASSET MANAGEMENT OY—See Catella AB; *Int'l*, pg. 1359
AMREIT MANAGERS SDN BHD—See AMMB Holdings Berhad; *Int'l*, pg. 429
AMROCK, LLC—See Rocket Companies, Inc.; *U.S. Public*, pg. 1804
AMSAC RIVERS ESCROW, INC.—See Stewart Information Services Corporation; *U.S. Public*, pg. 1947
ANABUKI KOSAN INC.; *Int'l*, pg. 444
ANADOLU VARLIK YONETIM A.S.—See AG Anadolu Grubu Holding A.S.; *Int'l*, pg. 197
AND ANADOLU GAYRIMENKUL YATIRIMLARI A.S.—See Ag Anadolu Grubu Holding Anonim Sirketi; *Int'l*, pg. 197
AN DUONG THAO DIEN REAL ESTATE TRADING INVESTMENT JOINT STOCK COMPANY; *Int'l*, pg. 443
ANEMOS THRAKIS SA—See ELLAKTOR S.A.; *Int'l*, pg. 2364
ANHUI BAOYE CONSTRUCTION ENGINEERING GROUP CO., LTD.—See Baoye Group Company Limited; *Int'l*, pg. 857
ANIDAPORT - INVESTIMENTOS IMOBILIARIOS, UNIPESSOAL, LTDA—See Banco Bilbao Vizcaya Argentaria, S.A.; *Int'l*, pg. 817
ANNA INFRASTRUCTURES LIMITED; *Int'l*, pg. 473
ANRITSU REAL ESTATE CO., LTD.—See Anritsu Corporation; *Int'l*, pg. 476
ANSLEY ATLANTA REAL ESTATE,LLC; *U.S. Private*, pg. 286
ANTHEM WORKS LTD.; *Int'l*, pg. 483
ANTHON EIENDOM AS—See Fastighets AB Balder; *Int'l*, pg. 2622
ANYWHERE REAL ESTATE GROUP LLC—See Anywhere Real Estate Inc.; *U.S. Public*, pg. 140
APALUX AG—See Allreal Holding AG; *Int'l*, pg. 360

531390 — OTHER ACTIVITIES RE... CORPORATE AFFILIATIONS

APARTMENTS, LLC—See CoStar Group, Inc.; *U.S. Public*, pg. 585
APEX DEVELOPMENT PUBLIC COMPANY LIMITED; *Int'l*, pg. 509
APEX KINGWIN INTERNATIONAL CO., LTD.—See Apex International Financial Engineering Research & Technology Co., Limited; *Int'l*, pg. 511
APEX TOWER LIMITED—See CLS Holdings plc; *Int'l*, pg. 1663
APLEONA REAL ESTATE GMBH—See Bilfinger SE; *Int'l*, pg. 1024
APN EUROPEAN RETAIL PROPERTY GROUP; *Int'l*, pg. 516
APN PROPERTY GROUP LIMITED—See DEXUS; *Int'l*, pg. 2093
APP CORPORATION PTY LIMITED—See Bureau Veritas S.A.; *Int'l*, pg. 1221
APPLE SUITES REALTY GROUP, INC.; *U.S. Private*, pg. 297
APS VERWALTUNGS-GMBH—See Sealed Air Corporation; *U.S. Public*, pg. 1852
AQAR REAL ESTATE INVESTMENTS COMPANY - K.S.C.; *Int'l*, pg. 527
ARAB DEVELOPMENT INVESTMENT COMPANY; *Int'l*, pg. 530
ARAB EAST INVESTMENT COMPANY; *Int'l*, pg. 530
ARAB INVESTORS UNION CO. FOR REAL ESTATES DEVELOPING P.L.C; *Int'l*, pg. 530
ARAB PHOENIX HOLDINGS; *Int'l*, pg. 531
ARAB REAL ESTATE COMPANY K.S.C.C.; *Int'l*, pg. 531
ARBOR REALTY FUNDING, LLC—See Arbor Realty Trust, Inc.; *U.S. Public*, pg. 178
ARBOR REALTY SR, INC.—See Arbor Realty Trust, Inc.; *U.S. Public*, pg. 178
ARBOR TRAILS, LLC—See Hovnanian Enterprises, Inc.; *U.S. Public*, pg. 1056
ARCH FINANCIAL HOLDINGS AUSTRALIA PTY LTD—See Arch Capital Group Ltd.; *Int'l*, pg. 546
ARCHICOM SA—See Echo Investment S.A.; *Int'l*, pg. 2289
ARCO DEVELOPMENT SIA—See Arco Vara AS; *Int'l*, pg. 550
ARCO VARA AS; *Int'l*, pg. 549
ARC TITUCAZ001, LLC—See Realty Income Corporation; *U.S. Public*, pg. 1768
ARCVIA MINERVA SA; *Int'l*, pg. 553
AREA QUEST INC.; *Int'l*, pg. 557
ARGENT PROPERTY SERVICES, LLC—See Argent Financial Group, Inc.; *U.S. Private*, pg. 320
ARGENT VENTURES, LLC; *U.S. Private*, pg. 320
ARGOSY REAL ESTATE MANAGEMENT, LLC—See Argosy Capital Group, LLC; *U.S. Private*, pg. 321
ARHC ATLARFL01 TRS, LLC—See Ventas, Inc.; *U.S. Public*, pg. 2278
ARHC BTFMYFL01 TRS, LLC—See Ventas, Inc.; *U.S. Public*, pg. 2278
ARHC BTNAPFL01 TRS, LLC—See Ventas, Inc.; *U.S. Public*, pg. 2278
ARIHANT FOUNDATIONS & HOUSING LIMITED; *Int'l*, pg. 564
ARIHANT SUPERSTRUCTURES LIMITED; *Int'l*, pg. 564
ARIHANT VATIKA REALTY PRIVATE LIMITED—See Arihant Superstructures Limited; *Int'l*, pg. 565
ARIMA REAL ESTATE SOCIMI SA; *Int'l*, pg. 565
ARINSIRI LAND PUBLIC COMPANY LIMITED; *Int'l*, pg. 565
ARISTEYA LLC—See AFI Development PLC; *Int'l*, pg. 189
ARIXA MANAGEMENT, LLC; *U.S. Private*, pg. 323
ARKAN AL-KUWAIT REAL ESTATE COMPANY KSCC; *Int'l*, pg. 568
ARMADILLO EVEN EMPREENDIMENTOS IMOBILIARIOS LTDA.—See Even Construtora e Incorporadora S.A.; *Int'l*, pg. 2561
ARMSTRONG DEVELOPMENT PROPERTIES, INC.—See Armstrong Holdings, Inc.; *U.S. Private*, pg. 331
ARTEA SA; *Int'l*, pg. 581
ARTEMIS IMMOBILIEN AG—See Artemis Holding AG; *Int'l*, pg. 582
ARTEMIS REAL ESTATE SRL—See Artemis Holding AG; *Int'l*, pg. 582
ARTWELL ENTERPRISES LIMITED—See Asia Cassava Resources Holdings Limited; *Int'l*, pg. 611
ASAHI KASEI HOMES CORP.—See Asahi Kasei Corporation; *Int'l*, pg. 595
AS CAPITAL, INC.; *U.S. Private*, pg. 345
ASCENCIA LIMITED; *Int'l*, pg. 601
THE ASCOTT CAPITAL PTE LTD—See CapitaLand Investment Limited; *Int'l*, pg. 1314
THE ASCOTT (EUROPE) PTE LTD—See CapitaLand Investment Limited; *Int'l*, pg. 1314
A SELF-ADMINISTERED REAL ESTATE INVESTMENT TRUST INC.; *Int'l*, pg. 18
ASF (HONG KONG) LTD.—See ASF Group Limited; *Int'l*, pg. 606
ASHFORD ADVISORS, INC.—See Ashford Inc.; *U.S. Public*, pg. 211
ASHFORD HOSPITALITY ADVISORS LLC—See Ashford Inc.; *U.S. Public*, pg. 211
ASHLAND INC.; *U.S. Public*, pg. 211
ASHLAND MANAGEMENT AGENCY, LLC—See Fifth Third Bancorp; *U.S. Public*, pg. 833
ASIAN GROWTH PROPERTIES LIMITED; *Int'l*, pg. 617
ASIAN STAR CO.; *Int'l*, pg. 619
ASIA - PACIFIC INVESTMENT JOINT STOCK COMPANY; *Int'l*, pg. 609
ASIA-PACIFIC STRATEGIC INVESTMENTS LIMITED; *Int'l*, pg. 616
ASIA PROPERTIES, INC.; *U.S. Public*, pg. 213
ASIA STANDARD INTERNATIONAL GROUP LIMITED; *Int'l*, pg. 615
ASKARI LIFE ASSURANCE COMPANY LIMITED—See Army Welfare Trust LLC; *Int'l*, pg. 575
ASMITA GARDENS SRL—See Alpha Services and Holdings S.A.; *Int'l*, pg. 369
ASR REAL ESTATE B.V.—See ASR Nederland N.V.; *Int'l*, pg. 632
ASSET FIVE GROUP PUBLIC COMPANY LIMITED; *Int'l*, pg. 642
ASSET PLUS COMPANIES LP; *U.S. Private*, pg. 354
ASSET WORLD CORP PUBLIC COMPANY LIMITED; *Int'l*, pg. 642
ASSURA PLC; *Int'l*, pg. 649
ASTECO PROPERTY MANAGEMENT LLC—See ALDAR Properties PJSC; *U.S. Public*, pg. 304
AST GROUPE SA; *Int'l*, pg. 651
ATAL S.A.; *Int'l*, pg. 665
ATC REALTY ONE, LLC—See Wells Fargo & Company; *U.S. Public*, pg. 2343
ATENOR S.A.; *Int'l*, pg. 668
ATHENA PROPERTIES LIMITED—See Centum Investment Company Limited; *Int'l*, pg. 1416
ATHOS IMMOBILIEN AG; *Int'l*, pg. 670
ATIA GROUP LTD.; *U.S. Private*, pg. 369
ATLANTIC CAPITAL GROUP, INC.; *U.S. Private*, pg. 372
ATLANTIC DYNAMICS SDN. BHD.—See Daiman Development Berhad; *Int'l*, pg. 1938
ATLAS CAPITAL GROUP, LLC; *U.S. Private*, pg. 375
ATLAS ESTATES COOPERATIEF U.A.—See Atlas Estates Limited; *Int'l*, pg. 685
ATP EJENDOMME A/S—See Arbejdsmarkedets Tillaegspension; *Int'l*, pg. 537
ATRIA NORTHGATE PARK, LLC—See Ventas, Inc.; *U.S. Public*, pg. 2278
ATRIA VISTA DEL RIO, LLC—See Ventas, Inc.; *U.S. Public*, pg. 2278
ATRIUM LJUNGBERG AB; *Int'l*, pg. 694
ATTACQ LIMITED; *Int'l*, pg. 696
ATTORNEYS' TITLE FUND SERVICES, LLC—See Attorneys' Title Insurance Fund; *U.S. Private*, pg. 383
ATVEXA AB; *Int'l*, pg. 697
AUG. PRIEN IMMOBILIEN PE VERWALTUNG BRAHMSQUARTIER GMBH—See Allianz SE; *Int'l*, pg. 343
AUGUSTE THOUARD EXPERTISE, SAS—See BNP Paribas SA; *Int'l*, pg. 1080
AUSTRALAND HK COMPANY LIMITED—See Frasers Property Limited; *Int'l*, pg. 2766
AUSTRALAND WHOLESALE HOLDINGS LIMITED—See Frasers Property Limited; *Int'l*, pg. 2766
AUTHENTIC CUSTOM HOMES, LLC; *U.S. Private*, pg. 396
AUTOMOTIVE PROPERTIES REAL ESTATE INVESTMENT TRUST; *Int'l*, pg. 731
AUTUMN BUILDERS LIMITED; *Int'l*, pg. 732
AVALON ARUNDEL CROSSING, LLC—See AvalonBay Communities, Inc.; *U.S. Public*, pg. 240
AVALONBAY COMMUNITIES, INC.; *U.S. Public*, pg. 239
AVALON COLUMBIA PIKE, LLC—See AvalonBay Communities, Inc.; *U.S. Public*, pg. 240
AVALON HOBOKEN, LLC—See AvalonBay Communities, Inc.; *U.S. Public*, pg. 240
AVALON IRVINE, L.P.—See AvalonBay Communities, Inc.; *U.S. Public*, pg. 240
AVALON NEW CANAAN, LLC—See AvalonBay Communities, Inc.; *U.S. Public*, pg. 240
AVALON SOMERS, LLC—See AvalonBay Communities, Inc.; *U.S. Public*, pg. 240
AVANTAZH GROUP; *Int'l*, pg. 735
AVH CAROLINAS, LLC—See Brookfield Corporation; *Int'l*, pg. 1183
AVID PROPERTY GROUP; *Int'l*, pg. 743
AVISON YOUNG (USA) INC. - TAMPA—See Avison Young (Canada) Inc.; *Int'l*, pg. 745
AWG PROPERTY LIMITED—See Canada Pension Plan Investment Board; *Int'l*, pg. 1278
AWG PROPERTY LIMITED—See Commonwealth Bank of Australia; *Int'l*, pg. 1720
AWH PARTNERS, LLC—See Winston Harton Holdings, LLC; *U.S. Private*, pg. 4544
A. WILBERT'S SONS, LLC; *U.S. Private*, pg. 24
AXA REAL ESTATE INVESTMENT MANAGERS - HUNGARY—See AXA S.A.; *Int'l*, pg. 757
AXA REAL ESTATE INVESTMENT MANAGERS ITALIA S.R.L.—See AXA S.A.; *Int'l*, pg. 757
AXA REAL ESTATE INVESTMENT MANAGERS JAPAN KK—See AXA S.A.; *Int'l*, pg. 757
AXA REAL ESTATE INVESTMENT MANAGERS NEDERLAND B.V.—See AXA S.A.; *Int'l*, pg. 757
AXA REAL ESTATE INVESTMENT MANAGERS S.A.—See AXA S.A.; *Int'l*, pg. 757
AXA REAL ESTATE INVESTMENT MANAGERS - SPAIN—See AXA S.A.; *Int'l*, pg. 757
AXA REAL ESTATE INVESTMENT MANAGERS - SWITZERLAND—See AXA S.A.; *Int'l*, pg. 757
AXA REAL ESTATE INVESTMENT MANAGERS - UK—See AXA S.A.; *Int'l*, pg. 757
AXFAST AB—See Axel Johnson Gruppen AB; *Int'l*, pg. 762
AXF RESOURCES PTY LTD.; *Int'l*, pg. 767
AYCO GRUPO INMOBILIARIO, S.A.; *Int'l*, pg. 774
AYER HITAM LAND SDN. BHD.—See Gromutual Berhad; *Int'l*, pg. 3087
AZOOM CO., LTD.; *Int'l*, pg. 780
AZUMA HOUSE CO., LTD.; *Int'l*, pg. 781
AZZ HOLDINGS, INC.—See AZZ, Inc.; *U.S. Public*, pg. 259
BAAN ROCK GARDEN PUBLIC COMPANY LIMITED; *Int'l*, pg. 792
BABCOCK LAND LIMITED—See Babcock International Group PLC; *Int'l*, pg. 792
BABER INVESTMENT GROUP, INC.; *U.S. Private*, pg. 422
BAGAPROP LIMITED—See ENL Limited; *Int'l*, pg. 2441
BALDER DANMARK A/S; *Int'l*, pg. 807
BALFOUR BEATTY COMMUNITIES LLC—See Balfour Beatty plc; *Int'l*, pg. 807
BALFOUR BEATTY INFRASTRUCTURE INVESTMENTS LTD—See Balfour Beatty plc; *Int'l*, pg. 808
BALKAN & SEA PROPERTIES REIT; *Int'l*, pg. 808
BALMORAL INTERNATIONAL LAND LIMITED—See Balmoral International Land Holdings plc; *Int'l*, pg. 810
BALWIN PROPERTIES LIMITED; *Int'l*, pg. 812
BANCA CESARE PONTI S.P.A.—See BPER BANCA S.p.A; *Int'l*, pg. 1132
BANDERA/LANTANA III, LP—See Forestar Group Inc.; *U.S. Public*, pg. 867
BANGKOK CITISMART CO., LTD.—See AP (Thailand) Public Company Limited; *Int'l*, pg. 499
BANGKOK LAND PUBLIC COMPANY LIMITED; *Int'l*, pg. 834
BANKOWY DOM HIPOTECZNY SP. Z. O.O.—See Commerzbank AG; *Int'l*, pg. 1715
BANRISUL S.A. CORRETORA DE VM E CAMBIO—See Banco do Estado do Rio Grande do Sul SA; *Int'l*, pg. 822
BA PROPERTIES, INC.—See Bank of America Corporation; *U.S. Public*, pg. 270
BARCLAY DOWNS ASSOCIATES, LP—See Ventas, Inc.; *U.S. Public*, pg. 2278
BARCLAYS HOME FINANCE—See Barclays PLC; *Int'l*, pg. 860
BARCLAYS UNQUOTED PROPERTY INVESTMENTS LIMITED—See Barclays PLC; *Int'l*, pg. 861
BA RIA - VUNG TAU HOUSE DEVELOPMENT JOINT STOCK COMPANY; *Int'l*, pg. 791
BARINGS REAL ESTATE ADVISERS LLC—See Massachusetts Mutual Life Insurance Company; *U.S. Private*, pg. 2605
BARRATT ASSET MANAGEMENT, LLC; *U.S. Private*, pg. 479
BARRETT GRILLO GROUP, INC.; *U.S. Private*, pg. 479
BARWA CITY REAL ESTATE COMPANY WLL—See Barwa Real Estate Company Q.P.S.C.; *Int'l*, pg. 870
BARWA REAL ESTATE COMPANY Q.P.S.C.; *Int'l*, pg. 870
BASEL REAL ESTATE, OJSC—See Basic Element Company; *Int'l*, pg. 886
BATIMAP SA—See Groupe BPCE; *Int'l*, pg. 3092
BATIROC BRETAGNE PAYS DE LOIRE SA—See Groupe BPCE; *Int'l*, pg. 3092
BATTERSEE REAL ESTATE SRL—See Bank of Cyprus Holdings Public Limited Company; *Int'l*, pg. 842
BAUBECON IMMOBILIEN GMBH—See Barclays PLC; *Int'l*, pg. 862
BAY COLONY REALTY, LLC—See iPic Entertainment Inc.; *U.S. Public*, pg. 1167
BAYER REAL ESTATE GMBH—See Bayer Aktiengesellschaft; *Int'l*, pg. 905
BAYFIELD COURT OPERATIONS LIMITED—See Welltower Inc.; *U.S. Public*, pg. 2347
BAYSIDE WEST LIMITED—See ANSA McAL Limited; *Int'l*, pg. 477
BAYSWATER BROKERAGE MASS. LLC—See Icahn Enterprises L.P.; *U.S. Public*, pg. 1084
BAYVIEW ASSET MANAGEMENT, LLC; *U.S. Private*, pg. 497
BBC PROPERTY LIMITED—See British Broadcasting Corporation; *Int'l*, pg. 1168
BBG INC.; *U.S. Private*, pg. 498
BBI DEVELOPMENT SA; *Int'l*, pg. 920
B&B REALTY LIMITED; *Int'l*, pg. 783
BBS VERWALTUNGS GMBH—See Accentis SA/NV; *Int'l*, pg. 82
BBX CAPITAL ASSET MANAGEMENT, LLC—See Hilton Grand Vacations Inc.; *U.S. Public*, pg. 1039
BCB MANAGEMENT SDN. BHD.—See BCB Berhad; *Int'l*, pg. 926
BCC MID VALLEY OPERATIONS, LLC—See Ventas, Inc.; *U.S. Public*, pg. 2278
BCC RISPARMIO & PREVIDENZA SGRPA—See Iccrea Holding S.p.A.; *Int'l*, pg. 3578

N.A.I.C.S. INDEX

531390 — OTHER ACTIVITIES RE...

BCI PROPERTIES, LLC—See Lennar Corporation; *U.S. Public*, pg. 1305
BCL INDUSTRIES LIMITED; *Int'l*, pg. 928
B&D MHP LLC—See Manufactured Housing Properties Inc.; *U.S. Public*, pg. 1362
BDR BUILDCON LIMITED; *Int'l*, pg. 930
BEACON CAPITAL STRATEGIC L.P.—See Cinven Limited; *Int'l*, pg. 1616
BEAN GROUP; *U.S. Private*, pg. 506
BEAZER REALTY LOS ANGELES, INC.—See Beazer Homes USA, Inc.; *U.S. Public*, pg. 288
BEAZER REALTY SERVICES, LLC—See Beazer Homes USA, Inc.; *U.S. Public*, pg. 288
BEBEK VARLIK YONETYM A.S.—See Deutsche Bank Aktiengesellschaft; *Int'l*, pg. 2055
BEEDIE INVESTMENTS LTD.—See Beedie Capital Partners; *Int'l*, pg. 939
BEELK HOLDING AG; *Int'l*, pg. 939
BEFIMMO SCA; *Int'l*, pg. 940
BEHAVIORAL HEALTHCARE REALTY, LLC—See AAC Holdings, Inc.; *U.S. Private*, pg. 31
BEIJING AIRPORT HIGH-TECH PARK CO., LTD.; *Int'l*, pg. 945
BEIJING CAPITAL DEVELOPMENT GROUP CO., LTD.—See Beijing Capital Development Holding Group Co., Ltd; *Int'l*, pg. 947
BEIJING DALONG WEIYE REAL ESTATE DEVELOPMENT CO., LTD.; *Int'l*, pg. 948
BEIJING FRASER SUITES REAL ESTATE MANAGEMENT CO., LTD—See Tishman Speyer Properties LP; *U.S. Private*, pg. 4176
BEIJING NEW CHINA FUSHI ASSET MANAGEMENT CO., LTD.—See HengTai Securities CO., LTD; *Int'l*, pg. 3347
BEIJING URBAN CONSTRUCTION INVESTMENT & DEVELOPMENT CO., LTD.; *Int'l*, pg. 959
BEIJING YEE ZHI REAL ESTATE CONSULTANCY CO., LTD.—See Hong Kong Land Holdings Ltd.; *Int'l*, pg. 3466
BELL ROSE CAPITAL, INC.; *U.S. Public*, pg. 295
BELLWETHER ASSET MANAGEMENT, INC.; *U.S. Private*, pg. 520
BELPOINTE REIT, INC.; *U.S. Public*, pg. 295
BEN BAILEY LTD.—See Gladedale Holdings PLC; *Int'l*, pg. 2987
BENJI INVEST KFT.; *Int'l*, pg. 974
BENTALL KENNEDY (CANADA) LIMITED PARTNERSHIP—See Bentall Kennedy LP; *Int'l*, pg. 975
BEREKET VARLIK KIRALAMA A.S.; *Int'l*, pg. 978
BERGMAN & BEVING FASTIGHETER AB—See Bergman & Beving AB; *Int'l*, pg. 980
BERJAYA 2ND HOMES (MM2H) SDN BHD—See Berjaya Corporation Berhad; *Int'l*, pg. 982
BERJAYA (CHINA) GREAT MALL CO. LTD—See Berjaya Corporation Berhad; *Int'l*, pg. 982
BERJAYA CORPORATION (S) PTE LTD—See Berjaya Corporation Berhad; *Int'l*, pg. 982
BERJAYA LAND DEVELOPMENT SDN BHD—See Berjaya Corporation Berhad; *Int'l*, pg. 982
BERKSHIRE GROUP, LLC; *U.S. Private*, pg. 533
BERKSHIRE HATHAWAY CREDIT CORPORATION—See Berkshire Hathaway Inc.; *U.S. Public*, pg. 300
BERLINOVO IMMOBILIEN GESELLSCHAFT MBH; *Int'l*, pg. 986
BESALCO S.A.; *Int'l*, pg. 998
BESQAB AB; *Int'l*, pg. 998
BFW LIEGENSCHAFTEN AG; *Int'l*, pg. 1006
B.GRIMM ALMA LINK BUILDING CO., LTD.—See B. Grimm Group; *Int'l*, pg. 788
B.GRIMM DR. GERHARD LINK BUILDING CO., LTD.—See B. Grimm Group; *Int'l*, pg. 788
BHAGYANAGAR PROPERTIES LIMITED; *Int'l*, pg. 1010
BHARTI REALTY LIMITED—See Bharti Enterprises Limited; *Int'l*, pg. 1013
BHIRAJ OFFICE LEASEHOLD REIT; *Int'l*, pg. 1015
BI DOLYNA DEVELOPMENT LLC—See Dragon Ukrainian Properties & Development Plc; *Int'l*, pg. 2199
BIG BLOCKCHAIN INTELLIGENCE GROUP INC.; *Int'l*, pg. 1021
BILFINGER REAL ESTATE BV—See Bilfinger SE; *Int'l*, pg. 1027
BILFINGER REAL ESTATE GESERV GMBH—See Bilfinger SE; *Int'l*, pg. 1027
BILFINGER REAL ESTATE INSERV GMBH—See Bilfinger SE; *Int'l*, pg. 1027
BILFINGER TEBODIN NETHERLANDS B.V.—See Bilfinger SE; *Int'l*, pg. 1028
BINA PURI PROPERTIES SDN BHD—See Bina Puri Holdings Bhd; *Int'l*, pg. 1032
BINH CHANH CONSTRUCTION INVESTMENT JOINT STOCK COMPANY; *Int'l*, pg. 1034
BIOMED REALTY, L.P.—See Blackstone Inc.; *U.S. Public*, pg. 350
BIR FINANCIAL LIMITED; *Int'l*, pg. 1045
BIRIKIM VARLIK YONETIM A.S.; *Int'l*, pg. 1047
BISHOP & ASSOCIATES, INC.; *U.S. Private*, pg. 565
BIURO INWESTYCJI KAPITALOWYCH S.A.; *Int'l*, pg. 1052
BK IMMO VORSORGE GMBH—See Capital Bank - GRAWE Gruppe AG; *Int'l*, pg. 1310
BLACK CREEK CAPITAL MARKETS, LLC—See Black Creek Group, LLC; *U.S. Private*, pg. 570
BLACKSTONE REAL ESTATE ADVISORS—See Blackstone Inc.; *U.S. Public*, pg. 349
BLACKSTONE REAL ESTATE ASIA PTE. LTD.—See Blackstone Inc.; *U.S. Public*, pg. 350
BLACKWALL MANAGEMENT SERVICES PTY LTD—See BlackWall Limited; *Int'l*, pg. 1062
BLAKE & SANYU—See Joseph J. Blake Associates, Inc.; *U.S. Private*, pg. 2236
BLAUWHOED HOLDING B.V.; *Int'l*, pg. 1063
BLINDINGQUEEN PROPERTIES SRL—See Bank of Cyprus Holdings Public Limited Company; *Int'l*, pg. 842
B-LOT CO., LTD.; *Int'l*, pg. 785
BLUE COLIBRI AG; *Int'l*, pg. 1067
BLUEGROUND US INC; *U.S. Private*, pg. 597
BLUELIFE LTD.; *Int'l*, pg. 1072
BMO REAL ESTATE PARTNERS GMBH & CO. KG—See Bank of Montreal; *Int'l*, pg. 847
BMO REAL ESTATE PARTNERS LLP—See Bank of Montreal; *Int'l*, pg. 847
B NANJI ENTERPRISES LIMITED; *Int'l*, pg. 783
BNP PARIBAS ASSET MANAGEMENT SGR SPA—See BNP Paribas SA; *Int'l*, pg. 1087
BNP PARIBAS IMMOBILIER RESIDENTIEL PROMOTION MEDITERRANEE—See BNP Paribas SA; *Int'l*, pg. 1085
BNP PARIBAS IMMOBILIER RESIDENTIEL RESIDENCES SERVICES BSA—See BNP Paribas SA; *Int'l*, pg. 1085
BNP PARIBAS IMMOBILIER RESIDENTIEL RESIDENCES SERVICES SOFIANE—See BNP Paribas SA; *Int'l*, pg. 1085
BNP PARIBAS IMMOBILIER RESIDENTIEL S.A.S.—See BNP Paribas SA; *Int'l*, pg. 1085
BNP PARIBAS IMMOBILIER RESIDENTIEL TRANSACTION & CONSEIL—See BNP Paribas SA; *Int'l*, pg. 1085
BNP PARIBAS REAL ESTATE ADVISORY BELGIUM SA—See BNP Paribas SA; *Int'l*, pg. 1086
BNP PARIBAS REAL ESTATE ADVISORY ITALY SPA—See BNP Paribas SA; *Int'l*, pg. 1086
BNP PARIBAS REAL ESTATE ADVISORY SPAIN SA—See BNP Paribas SA; *Int'l*, pg. 1086
BNP PARIBAS REAL ESTATE CONSULT FRANCE—See BNP Paribas SA; *Int'l*, pg. 1086
BNP PARIBAS REAL ESTATE CONSULT GMBH—See BNP Paribas SA; *Int'l*, pg. 1086
BNP PARIBAS REAL ESTATE FACILITIES MANAGEMENT LTD.—See BNP Paribas SA; *Int'l*, pg. 1086
BNP PARIBAS REAL ESTATE FINANCIAL PARTNER—See BNP Paribas SA; *Int'l*, pg. 1086
BNP PARIBAS REAL ESTATE GMBH—See BNP Paribas SA; *Int'l*, pg. 1086
BNP PARIBAS REAL ESTATE INVESTMENT MANAGEMENT LTD.—See BNP Paribas SA; *Int'l*, pg. 1086
BNP PARIBAS REAL ESTATE INVESTMENT MANAGEMENT LUXEMBOURG SA—See BNP Paribas SA; *Int'l*, pg. 1086
BNP PARIBAS REAL ESTATE INVESTMENT MANAGEMENT—See BNP Paribas SA; *Int'l*, pg. 1086
BNP PARIBAS REAL ESTATE JERSEY LTD.—See BNP Paribas SA; *Int'l*, pg. 1086
BNP PARIBAS REAL ESTATE PROPERTY DEVELOPPEMENT UK LTD.—See BNP Paribas SA; *Int'l*, pg. 1086
BNP PARIBAS REAL ESTATE PROPERTY MANAGEMENT GMBH—See BNP Paribas SA; *Int'l*, pg. 1086
BNP PARIBAS REAL ESTATE, S.A.—See BNP Paribas SA; *Int'l*, pg. 1086
BNP PARIBAS REAL ESTATE TRANSACTION FRANCE S.A.—See BNP Paribas SA; *Int'l*, pg. 1086
BOEING REALTY CORPORATION—See The Boeing Company; *U.S. Public*, pg. 2041
BOLONIA REAL ESTATE SL—See Enel S.p.A.; *Int'l*, pg. 2411
BOMBARDIER INC. - REAL ESTATE SERVICES—See Bombardier Inc.; *Int'l*, pg. 1104
BOMBAY POTTERIES & TILES LIMITED; *Int'l*, pg. 1104
BONAVA DANMARK A/S—See Bonava AB; *Int'l*, pg. 1105
BONAVA EESTI OU—See Bonava AB; *Int'l*, pg. 1105
BONAVA LATVIJA SIA—See Bonava AB; *Int'l*, pg. 1105
BONAVA NORGE AS—See Bonava AB; *Int'l*, pg. 1105
BONAVA SUOMI OY—See Bonava AB; *Int'l*, pg. 1105
BON JOUR CAPITAL; *U.S. Private*, pg. 612
BOP 1801 CALIFORNIA STREET LLC—See Brookfield Corporation; *Int'l*, pg. 1186
BOP 650 MASS LLC—See Brookfield Corporation; *Int'l*, pg. 1186
BORDEAUX DEVELOPMENTS CORPORATION; *Int'l*, pg. 1113
BORGOSESIA S.P.A.; *Int'l*, pg. 1114
BOULDER CREEK BUILDERS—See *U.S. Private*, pg. 623
BOUTIQUE CORPORATION PUBLIC COMPANY LIMITED; *Int'l*, pg. 1121
BPT LIMITED—See Grainger plc; *Int'l*, pg. 3052
BRACK CAPITAL PROPERTIES NV—See ADLER Group SA; *Int'l*, pg. 150
BRACK CAPITAL REAL ESTATE; *Int'l*, pg. 1134
BRAEMAR GROUP LIMITED—See Brooks Macdonald Group plc; *Int'l*, pg. 1194
BRAND REALTY SERVICES LTD.; *Int'l*, pg. 1139
BRANDYWINE OPERATING PARTNERSHIP, L.P.—See Brandywine Realty Trust; *U.S. Public*, pg. 380
BRASILAGRO-CIA BRAS DE PROP AGRICOLAS; *Int'l*, pg. 1140
BRASIL BROKERS PARTICIPACOES S.A.; *Int'l*, pg. 1140
BRAZILIAN FINANCE & REAL ESTATE S.A.; *Int'l*, pg. 1143
BRE.LOCUM S.A.—See Commerzbank AG; *Int'l*, pg. 1719
BRENNAN INVESTMENT GROUP, LLC; *U.S. Private*, pg. 645
BRENNTAG REAL ESTATE GMBH—See BRENNTAG SE; *Int'l*, pg. 1148
BRE PROPERTY PARTNER SP. Z O.O.—See Commerzbank AG; *Int'l*, pg. 1719
BRICKLE REALTY GROUP—See Hyman Brickle & Son, Inc.; *U.S. Private*, pg. 2019
BRIDGEWATER TENANCIES LIMITED—See Grainger plc; *Int'l*, pg. 3052
BRIGADE ENTERPRISES LTD.; *Int'l*, pg. 1160
BRIGHTON MANAGEMENT LLC; *U.S. Private*, pg. 652
BRIQ PROPERTIES REIC; *Int'l*, pg. 1164
BROADSHORE CAPITAL PARTNERS LLC—See The Guardian Life Insurance Company of America; *U.S. Private*, pg. 4040
BROADSTONE REAL ESTATE, LLC; *U.S. Private*, pg. 659
BRONSWOOD CEMETERY, INC.—See Axar Capital Management L.P.; *U.S. Private*, pg. 411
BROOKFIELD BUSINESS CORPORATION; *Int'l*, pg. 1174
BROOKFIELD CANADA OFFICE PROPERTIES—See Brookfield Corporation; *Int'l*, pg. 1186
BROOKFIELD INCORPORACOES S.A.—See Brookfield Corporation; *Int'l*, pg. 1175
BROOKFIELD INFRASTRUCTURE CORPORATION—See Brookfield Infrastructure Partners L.P.; *Int'l*, pg. 1189
BROOKFIELD MULTIPLEX CAPITAL LIMITED—See Brookfield Corporation; *Int'l*, pg. 1185
BROOKFIELD MULTIPLEX DEVELOPMENTS—See Brookfield Corporation; *Int'l*, pg. 1185
BROOKFIELD PROPERTY PARTNERS L.P.—See Brookfield Corporation; *Int'l*, pg. 1185
BROOKFIELD RENEWABLE CORPORATION; *U.S. Public*, pg. 395
BROOKFIELD RESIDENTIAL (ALBERTA) LP—See Brookfield Corporation; *Int'l*, pg. 1187
BROOKFIELD RESIDENTIAL PROPERTIES INC.—See Brookfield Corporation; *Int'l*, pg. 1187
BROTHER REAL ESTATE, LTD.—See Brother Industries, Ltd.; *Int'l*, pg. 1197
BRP LEASING, LLC—See Jefferies Financial Group Inc.; *U.S. Public*, pg. 1188
BRYGGEN VEJLE AS—See BNP Paribas SA; *Int'l*, pg. 1089
BSA ADVANCED PROPERTY SOLUTIONS (ACT) PTY LTD—See BSA Limited; *Int'l*, pg. 1201
BSA ADVANCED PROPERTY SOLUTIONS (NT) PTY LTD—See BSA Limited; *Int'l*, pg. 1201
BSA ADVANCED PROPERTY SOLUTIONS (VIC) PTY LTD—See BSA Limited; *Int'l*, pg. 1201
BSA COMMUNICATIONS & UTILITY INFRASTRUCTURE PTY LTD—See BSA Limited; *Int'l*, pg. 1201
BSEL INFRASTRUCTURE REALTY LIMITED; *Int'l*, pg. 1202
BTV CROWN EQUITIES, INC.; *U.S. Private*, pg. 676
BUALUANG OFFICE LEASEHOLD REIT; *Int'l*, pg. 1206
BUDAPESTI INGATLAN NYRT; *Int'l*, pg. 1210
BUDAPEST PROPERTY UTILIZATION AND DEVELOPMENT PLC.; *Int'l*, pg. 1210
BUKIT HITAM DEVELOPMENT SDN. BHD.—See AYER Holdings Berhad; *Int'l*, pg. 775
BULACHGUSS AG—See Allreal Holding AG; *Int'l*, pg. 360
BULDAN TEKSTIL TIC. SAN. LTD. STI.; *Int'l*, pg. 1213
BULLAND INVESTMENTS REIT; *Int'l*, pg. 1214
THE BUNCHER COMPANY; *U.S. Private*, pg. 4002
BURGER PHILLIPS BUILDING, LLC—See Synovus Financial Corp.; *U.S. Public*, pg. 1971
BURGER PHILLIPS BUILDING, LLC—See Synovus Financial Corp.; *U.S. Public*, pg. 1972
BURNAC CORPORATION; *Int'l*, pg. 1226
BURNS BROS., INC.; *U.S. Private*, pg. 690
BUSINESS IMMO S.A.S.—See CoStar Group, Inc.; *U.S. Public*, pg. 585
BUSINESS PARK VARNA AD—See Africa Israel Investments Ltd.; *Int'l*, pg. 190
BUTTERFIELD PROPERTIES LLC—See PulteGroup, Inc.; *U.S. Public*, pg. 1737
BUZZ OATES CONSTRUCTION, LP—See Buzz Oates Companies; *U.S. Private*, pg. 699
B-XI BEDFORD LLC—See Welltower Inc.; *U.S. Public*, pg. 2347
BXP 601 & 651 GATEWAY CENTER LP—See Boston Properties, Inc.; *U.S. Public*, pg. 372
CAFEL INVERSIONES 2008, S.L.—See Assicurazioni Generali S.p.A.; *Int'l*, pg. 643
CA IMMOBILIEN ANLAGEN AG—See Starwood Capital Group Global I, LLC; *U.S. Private*, pg. 3788
CA IMMO REAL ESTATE MANAGEMENT HUNGARY KFT.—See Starwood Capital Group Global I, LLC; *U.S. Private*, pg. 3789
CA IMMO REAL ESTATE MANAGEMENT POLAND SP. Z O.O.—See Starwood Capital Group Global I, LLC; *U.S. Private*, pg. 3789

531390 — OTHER ACTIVITIES RE...

CA IMMO REAL ESTATE MANAGEMENT ROMANIA SRL—See Starwood Capital Group Global I, LLC; *U.S. Private*, pg. 3789
CAITONG SECURITIES CO., LTD.; *Int'l*, pg. 1259
CALCON DEUTSCHLAND GMBH—See Advent International Corporation; *U.S. Private*, pg. 96
CALCON DEUTSCHLAND GMBH—See Centerbridge Partners, L.P.; *U.S. Private*, pg. 812
CALEDONIAN PROPERTIES LIMITED—See Derwent London plc; *Int'l*, pg. 2043
CALEDONIAN TRUST PLC; *Int'l*, pg. 1263
CAM IMMOBILIARE S.P.A.—See Camfin S.p.A.; *Int'l*, pg. 1272
CAMTOR COMMERCIAL REAL ESTATE LENDING, L.P.; *U.S. Private*, pg. 732
CANADA GLOBAL (T.R) LTD; *Int'l*, pg. 1278
CANADIAN NET REAL ESTATE INVESTMENT TRUST; *Int'l*, pg. 1284
CAN-AMERI AGRI CO. INC.; *Int'l*, pg. 1276
CANDEREL COMMERCIAL SERVICES INC.—See Canderel Management Inc.; *Int'l*, pg. 1289
CANDEREL PACIFIC INC.—See Canderel Management Inc.; *Int'l*, pg. 1289
CANDRIAM INVESTORS GROUP-BELGIUM—See New York Life Insurance Company; *U.S. Private*, pg. 2911
THE CANEEL GROUP, LLC; *U.S. Private*, pg. 4004
CAPERA IMMOBILIEN SERVICE GMBH—See COR-ESTATE Capital Holding SA; *Int'l*, pg. 1799
CAPITALAND (CHINA) INVESTMENT CO., LTD—See CapitaLand Investment Limited; *Int'l*, pg. 1313
CAPITALAND GCC HOLDINGS PTE LTD—See CapitaLand Investment Limited; *Int'l*, pg. 1313
CAPITALAND INTERNATIONAL PTE. LTD.—See CapitaLand Investment Limited; *Int'l*, pg. 1313
CAPITALAND (JAPAN) KABUSHIKI KAISHA—See CapitaLand Investment Limited; *Int'l*, pg. 1313
CAPITALAND RESIDENTIAL SINGAPORE PTE LTD—See CapitaLand Investment Limited; *Int'l*, pg. 1313
CAPITALAND SINGAPORE LIMITED—See CapitaLand Investment Limited; *Int'l*, pg. 1313
CAPITALAND TREASURY LIMITED—See CapitaLand Investment Limited; *Int'l*, pg. 1313
CAPITALAND UK MANAGEMENT LTD—See CapitaLand Investment Limited; *Int'l*, pg. 1313
CAPITALAND-VISTA JOINT VENTURE CO., LTD.—See CapitaLand Investment Limited; *Int'l*, pg. 1313
CAPITAL ART APARTMENTS SP. Z O.O.—See Atlas Estates Limited; *Int'l*, pg. 685
CAPITALATWORK FOYER GROUP S.A.—See Foyer S.A.; *Int'l*, pg. 2756
CAPITAL ONE MULTI-ASSET EXECUTION TRUST; *U.S. Private*, pg. 741
CAPITAL PARK S.A.—See Madison International Realty, LLC; *U.S. Private*, pg. 2543
CAPITAL PROPERTY FUND NOMINEES PROPRIETARY LIMITED—See Barclays PLC; *Int'l*, pg. 862
CAPITAL RIVERS COMMERCIAL LLC; *U.S. Private*, pg. 742
CAPITALVALUE HOMES LIMITED—See CapitaLand Investment Limited; *Int'l*, pg. 1313
CAPITOL DEVELOPMENT GROUP LLC; *U.S. Private*, pg. 743
CAPMAN REAL ESTATE DENMARK, FILIAL AV CAPMAN AB—See CapMan PLC; *Int'l*, pg. 1315
CAPMAN REAL ESTATE OY—See CapMan PLC; *Int'l*, pg. 1315
CAPRICORNUS EVEN EMPREENDIMENTOS IMOBILIARIOS LTDA.—See Even Construtora e Incorporadora S.A.; *Int'l*, pg. 2561
CAPSOURCE INC.; *U.S. Private*, pg. 745
CAPSTONE GROUP, INC.; *U.S. Private*, pg. 746
CAPSTONE TITLE, LLC; *U.S. Private*, pg. 746
CAPTIL AUTOMOTIVE REAL ESTATE SERVICES, INC.; *U.S. Private*, pg. 746
CARE PROPERTY INVEST NV; *Int'l*, pg. 1323
CARGO BOAT DEVELOPMENT CO. PLC; *Int'l*, pg. 1325
CARINOS PROPERTIES, LLC—See IMH Financial Corporation; *U.S. Private*, pg. 2047
CARL M. FREEMAN GOLF, LLC—See Carl M. Freeman Associates, Inc.; *U.S. Private*, pg. 762
CARLSBERG EJENDOMME HOLDING A/S—See Carlsberg A/S; *Int'l*, pg. 1340
CARPINIENNE DE PARTICIPATIONS SA—See Finatis SA; *Int'l*, pg. 2670
CARREFOUR PROPERTY DEVELOPMENT SA—See Carrefour SA; *Int'l*, pg. 1345
CARREFOUR PROPERTY GESTION—See Carrefour SA; *Int'l*, pg. 1344
CARRIAGE COVE, LLC—See Sun Communities, Inc.; *U.S. Public*, pg. 1961
CARTER VALIDUS ADVISORS, LLC—See Carter & Associates, LLC; *U.S. Private*, pg. 775
CASALETTO S.R.L.—See Assicurazioni Generali S.p.A.; *Int'l*, pg. 643
C.A.S. ASSET CO., LTD.—See Charoen Aksorn Holding Group Co. Ltd.; *Int'l*, pg. 1451
CASETTE S.R.L.—See Encavis AG; *Int'l*, pg. 2401

CASPI LIMITED LLP—See Chagala Group Limited; *Int'l*, pg. 1436
CASSIDIAN REAL ESTATE MANCHING GMBH & CO. KG—See Airbus SE; *Int'l*, pg. 242
CASSIDIAN REAL ESTATE ULM/UNTERSCHLEISSHEIM GMBH & CO. KG—See Airbus SE; *Int'l*, pg. 242
CASTELLUM AB; *Int'l*, pg. 1356
CASTLE & COOKE, INC.—See Murdock Holdings, LLC; *U.S. Private*, pg. 2814
CASTLE & COOKE PROPERTIES, INC.—See Murdock Holdings, LLC; *U.S. Private*, pg. 2814
CASTLE PEAK REAL ESTATE CO., LTD.—See Castle Peak Holdings Public Company Limited; *Int'l*, pg. 1357
CATALYST ONE PTY LTD—See BSA Limited; *Int'l*, pg. 1201
CAT EVEN EMPREENDIMENTOS IMOBILIARIOS LTDA.—See Even Construtora e Incorporadora S.A.; *Int'l*, pg. 2561
CB AUSTRALIA LIMITED; *Int'l*, pg. 1364
CB EUREGIO GMBH—See Commerzbank AG; *Int'l*, pg. 1715
CBIZ GIBRALTAR REAL ESTATE SERVICES, LLC—See CBIZ, Inc.; *U.S. Public*, pg. 456
C.B. RAGLAND COMPANY; *U.S. Private*, pg. 706
CBRE GLOBAL INVESTORS (ASIA) LIMITED—See CBRE Group, Inc.; *U.S. Public*, pg. 460
CBRE GLOBAL INVESTORS BELGIUM—See CBRE Group, Inc.; *U.S. Public*, pg. 460
CBRE GLOBAL INVESTORS (NL) B.V.—See CBRE Group, Inc.; *U.S. Public*, pg. 460
CBRE GLOBAL INVESTORS (UK) LTD—See CBRE Group, Inc.; *U.S. Public*, pg. 460
CBRE INVESTMENT MANAGEMENT, LLC—See CBRE Group, Inc.; *U.S. Public*, pg. 460
CCHP WAIKIKI LLC—See Host Hotels & Resorts, Inc.; *U.S. Public*, pg. 1054
CCNG REALTY, INC.; *U.S. Private*, pg. 801
CEDAR POINTE CLUB, LLC—See Lennar Corporation; *U.S. Public*, pg. 1306
CEL AUSTRALIA PTY LTD—See Chip Eng Seng Corporation Ltd.; *Int'l*, pg. 1572
CELEBI IPLIK TIC. VE SAN. A.S.; *Int'l*, pg. 1392
CEMAT REAL ESTATE S.A.—See Cemat A/S; *Int'l*, pg. 1396
CENTENNIAL PROPERTIES, INC.—See Cowles Company; *U.S. Private*, pg. 1073
CENTERSQUARE INVESTMENT MANAGEMENT HOLDINGS, INC.—See Lovell Minnick Partners LLC; *U.S. Private*, pg. 2501
CENTRAL BUILDING LTD.—See Hong Kong Land Holdings Ltd.; *Int'l*, pg. 3466
CENTRAL CHINA REAL ESTATE LIMITED; *Int'l*, pg. 1405
CENTRAL SOCIETA DI INVESTIMENTO PER AZIONI A CAPITALO FISSO CENTRAL SICAF S.P.A—See Covivio; *Int'l*, pg. 1821
CENTURIA CAPITAL NZ NO.1 LTD.—See Centuria Capital Limited; *Int'l*, pg. 1416
CENTURION LAND TITLE, INC.; *U.S. Private*, pg. 831
CENTURION - LIAN BENG (PAPAN) PTE. LTD.—See Centurion Corporation Limited; *Int'l*, pg. 1417
CENTURY 21 FRANCE SAS—See Citya Immobilier SAS; *Int'l*, pg. 1628
CENTURY 21 PINNACLE; *U.S. Private*, pg. 831
CENTURY PROPERTIES GROUP, INC.; *Int'l*, pg. 1419
CEO INTERNATIONAL CO., LTD.—See C.E.O Group Joint Stock Company; *Int'l*, pg. 1240
CEPHEUS EVEN EMPREENDIMENTOS IMOBILIARIOS LTDA.—See Even Construtora e Incorporadora S.A.; *Int'l*, pg. 2561
CERAH BAKTI SDN BHD—See Berjaya Corporation Berhad; *Int'l*, pg. 983
CFC, INC.—See Cook Group Incorporated; *U.S. Private*, pg. 1037
CFE IMMO—See Ackermans & van Haaren NV; *Int'l*, pg. 104
CFI-COMPAGNIE FONCIERE INTERNATIONALE; *Int'l*, pg. 1430
CG REAL ESTATE LUXEMBURG S.A.R.L.—See Commerzbank AG; *Int'l*, pg. 1715
CHAGALA GROUP LIMITED; *Int'l*, pg. 1436
CHAMAELEON EVEN EMPREENDIMENTOS IMOBILIARIOS LTDA.—See Even Construtora e Incorporadora S.A.; *Int'l*, pg. 2561
CHAMBERLAIN HOLDINGS LLC; *U.S. Private*, pg. 845
CHAM IMMOBILIEN AG—See Cham Group AG; *Int'l*, pg. 1439
CHAOPRAYA MAHANAKORN PCL; *Int'l*, pg. 1447
CHARLESGATE REALTY GROUP, LLC; *U.S. Private*, pg. 856
CHARNIC CAPITAL TBK PT; *Int'l*, pg. 1451
CHARN ISSARA DEVELOPMENT PUBLIC COMPANY LIMITED; *Int'l*, pg. 1451
CHARN ISSARA VIPHAPOL COMPANY LIMITED—See Charn Issara Development Public Company Limited; *Int'l*, pg. 1451
CHARTER HALL REAL ESTATE INC.—See Charter Hall Limited; *Int'l*, pg. 1454
CHARTER HALL REAL ESTATE MANAGEMENT SERVICES (VIC) PTY LIMITED—See Charter Hall Limited; *Int'l*, pg. 1454
CHARTER HALL RETAIL MANAGEMENT PTY LIMITED—See Charter Hall Limited; *Int'l*, pg. 1454

CORPORATE AFFILIATIONS

CHATHAM PINES MHP LLC—See Manufactured Housing Properties Inc.; *U.S. Public*, pg. 1362
CHATMETER; *U.S. Private*, pg. 868
CHELSFIELD FRANCE LTD—See Chelsfield Partners LLP; *Int'l*, pg. 1460
CHELSFIELD PARTNERS LLP; *Int'l*, pg. 1460
CHENGDU HEZHIHELI PROPERTY MANAGEMENT CO., LTD.—See Country Garden Services Holdings Company Limited; *Int'l*, pg. 1818
CHENGDU HI-TECH DEVELOPMENT CO., LTD.; *Int'l*, pg. 1468
CHENGDU VANKE REAL ESTATE COMPANY LIMITED—See China Vanke Co., Ltd.; *Int'l*, pg. 1562
CHERUBIM INTERESTS, INC.; *U.S. Public*, pg. 485
CHEVALIER PROPERTY MANAGEMENT LIMITED—See Chevalier International Holdings Limited; *Int'l*, pg. 1473
CHEWATHAI PLC; *Int'l*, pg. 1474
CHINA AOYUAN GROUP LIMITED; *Int'l*, pg. 1482
CHINA CALXON GROUP CO., LTD.; *Int'l*, pg. 1487
CHINA EXPAND DEVELOPMENT LTD.—See China Rare Earth Resources And Technology Co., Ltd.; *Int'l*, pg. 1545
CHINA FORTUNE LAND DEVELOPMENT CO., LTD.; *Int'l*, pg. 1503
CHINA GREEN ELECTRICITY INVESTMENT OF TIANJIN CO., LTD.; *Int'l*, pg. 1505
CHINA MERCHANTS PROPERTY DEVELOPMENT CO., LTD.—See China Merchants Group Limited; *Int'l*, pg. 1521
CHINA MERCHANTS PROPERTY OPERATION & SERVICE CO., LTD.—See AVIC International Holdings Limited; *Int'l*, pg. 742
CHINA OVERSEAS LAND & INVESTMENT LIMITED—See China State Construction Engineering Corporation Limited; *Int'l*, pg. 1554
CHINA POLY GROUP CORPORATION; *Int'l*, pg. 1540
CHINA PROSPERITY DEVELOPMENT CORPORATION—See China Steel Corporation; *Int'l*, pg. 1555
CHINA TIANBAO GROUP DEVELOPMENT COMPANY LIMITED; *Int'l*, pg. 1559
CHINA WUYI CO., LTD.; *Int'l*, pg. 1563
CH JANKI SP ZOO—See Cromwell Property Group; *Int'l*, pg. 1853
CHONGQING DIMA INDUSTRY CO., LTD.; *Int'l*, pg. 1579
CHONGQING YUKAIFA CO., LTD.; *Int'l*, pg. 1581
CHONGQING YUZHONG XINHAOJUN REAL ESTATE DEVELOPMENT CO., LTD.—See Hong Leong Investment Holdings Pte. Ltd.; *Int'l*, pg. 3468
CHORI URBAN DEVELOPMENT CO., LTD.—See Chori Co., Ltd.; *Int'l*, pg. 1583
CH REAL ESTATE II, INC.; *U.S. Private*, pg. 844
CHRISTIE & CO AUSTRIA GMBH—See Christie Group plc; *Int'l*, pg. 1586
CHUANG'S CHINA INVESTMENTS LIMITED; *Int'l*, pg. 1590
CI AUSTRALIA PTY LIMITED—See Apollo Global Management, Inc.; *U.S. Public*, pg. 166
CIBUS NORDIC REAL ESTATE AB; *Int'l*, pg. 1602
CI-CO S.A.; *Int'l*, pg. 1601
C-III CAPITAL PARTNERS LLC—See Island Capital Group LLC; *U.S. Private*, pg. 2144
CINCINNATI CENTER CITY DEVELOPMENT CORPORATION; *U.S. Private*, pg. 897
CIO SAN TAN II, LIMITED PARTNERSHIP—See City Office REIT, Inc.; *U.S. Public*, pg. 1627
CIRI SERVICES CORPORATION—See Cook Inlet Region, Inc.; *U.S. Private*, pg. 1038
CITIC NINGBO GROUP—See CITIC Group Corporation; *Int'l*, pg. 1621
CITIC SOUTH CHINA GROUP CO., LTD.—See CITIC Group Corporation; *Int'l*, pg. 1621
CITIGROUP DERIVATIVES MARKETS INC.—See Citigroup Inc.; *U.S. Public*, pg. 503
CITI PROPERTIES REIT; *Int'l*, pg. 1619
CITYCON OYJ; *Int'l*, pg. 1629
CITYFEET.COM—See CoStar Group, Inc.; *U.S. Public*, pg. 586
CITY GATE STUTTGART GMBH—See EPH European Property Holdings PLC; *Int'l*, pg. 2459
CITY HALL PROPERTIES LLC; *U.S. Private*, pg. 906
CITY-HAUSVERWALTUNG GMBH—See Consus Real Estate AG; *Int'l*, pg. 1778
CITY & LAND DEVELOPERS, INC.; *Int'l*, pg. 1626
CITYMARK ANALYS I NORDEN AB—See Byggfakta Group Nordic HoldCo AB; *Int'l*, pg. 1234
CITY NORTH GROUP PLC—See Grainger plc; *Int'l*, pg. 3052
CJSC "SSMQ LENSPETSSMU"—See Etalon Group Plc; *Int'l*, pg. 2520
C.J. SEGERSTROM & SONS, LLC; *U.S. Private*, pg. 708
CK INFRASTRUCTURE HOLDINGS LIMITED—See CK Hutchison Holdings Limited; *Int'l*, pg. 1636
C&K PROPERTIES; *U.S. Private*, pg. 703
CLARION PARTNERS (DEUTSCHLAND) EUROPE GMBH—See Franklin Resources, Inc.; *U.S. Public*, pg. 879
CLARION PARTNERS, LLC - BOSTON—See Franklin Resources, Inc.; *U.S. Public*, pg. 881

N.A.I.C.S. INDEX

531390 — OTHER ACTIVITIES RE...

CLARION PARTNERS, LLC—See Franklin Resources, Inc.; *U.S. Public*, pg. 881
CLARION PARTNERS, LLC - WASHINGTON, DC—See Franklin Resources, Inc.; *U.S. Public*, pg. 881
CLARITAS ADMINISTRACAO DE RECURSOS LTDA.—See Principal Financial Group, Inc.; *U.S. Public*, pg. 1720
CLARK ENTERPRISES, INC.; *U.S. Private*, pg. 912
CLARKE REAL ESTATE LTD.; *Int'l*, pg. 1650
CLARK REALTY CAPITAL, L.L.C.—See Clark Enterprises, Inc.; *U.S. Private*, pg. 913
CL ASSET HOLDINGS, LIMITED; *Int'l*, pg. 1640
CLEAN & CARBON ENERGY S.A.; *Int'l*, pg. 1653
CLEARBELL CAPITAL LLP; *Int'l*, pg. 1656
CLEARCAPITAL.COM, INC.; *U.S. Private*, pg. 932
CLEARWATER DEVELOPMENT INC—See EFO Financial Group LLC; *U.S. Private*, pg. 1343
CLISE PROPERTIES, INC.; *U.S. Private*, pg. 945
CLI SINGAPORE PTE. LTD.—See CapitaLand Investment Limited; *Int'l*, pg. 1313
CLSA FUND SERVICES (ASIA) LIMITED—See CITIC Securities Co., Ltd.; *Int'l*, pg. 1622
THE CLUB AT HIDDEN RIVER, LLC—See D.R. Horton, Inc.; *U.S. Public*, pg. 620
CMS LAND SDN. BHD.—See Cahya Mata Sarawak Berhad; *Int'l*, pg. 1251
COASSETS LIMITED; *Int'l*, pg. 1681
COASTAL DEVELOPMENT LLC; *U.S. Private*, pg. 956
COBALT VENTURES LLC—See Blue Cross & Blue Shield of Kansas City, Inc.; *U.S. Private*, pg. 586
COCA-COLA WEST SERVICE CO., LTD.—See Coca-Cola Bottlers Japan Holdings Inc.; *Int'l*, pg. 1684
COFCO COMMERCIAL PROPERTY INVESTMENT CO., LTD.—See COFCO Limited; *Int'l*, pg. 1691
COFCO (HAINAN) INVESTMENT & DEVELOPMENT CO., LTD.—See COFCO Limited; *Int'l*, pg. 1691
COFCO (HONG KONG) CO., LTD.—See COFCO Limited; *Int'l*, pg. 1691
COFHYLUX SA—See BNP Paribas SA; *Int'l*, pg. 1090
COFRA DUSSELDORF GMBH—See COFRA Holding AG; *Int'l*, pg. 1694
COGEDIM SAS—See Altarea SCA; *Int'l*, pg. 385
COGIFRANCE SA; *Int'l*, pg. 1695
COGIR MANAGEMENT CORPORATION - ONTARIO DIVISION—See COGIR Management Corporation; *Int'l*, pg. 1695
COGIR MANAGEMENT CORPORATION; *Int'l*, pg. 1695
COHEN & STEERS MLP INCOME & ENERGY OPP; *U.S. Public*, pg. 526
COILS PROPERTY MANAGEMENT LIMITED—See CEC International Holdings Limited; *Int'l*, pg. 1372
COIMA RES S.P.A; *Int'l*, pg. 1696
COINSHARES (UK) LIMITED—See CoinShares International Limited; *Int'l*, pg. 1696
COLD RIVER LAND, LLC—See CBRE Group, Inc.; *U.S. Public*, pg. 460
COLDWELL BANKER REAL ESTATE (S) PTE. LTD.—See Morgan Stanley; *U.S. Public*, pg. 1471
COLDWELL BANKER SCHMIDT REALTORS; *U.S. Private*, pg. 966
COLES GROUP PROPERTIES PTY LTD—See Coles Group Limited; *Int'l*, pg. 1698
COLLATERAL INTELLIGENCE, LLC—See Assurant, Inc.; *U.S. Public*, pg. 215
COLLEGIATE HOUSING SERVICES, INC.; *U.S. Private*, pg. 968
COLLIER ENTERPRISES MANAGEMENT, INC.—See Collier Enterprises, Inc.; *U.S. Private*, pg. 969
COLLINS PLACE NO. 2 PTY LTD—See AMP Limited; *Int'l*, pg. 432
COLLINS PLACE PTY LIMITED—See AMP Limited; *Int'l*, pg. 432
COLLINS TECHNOLOGY PARK PARTNERS, LLC—See Digital Realty Trust, Inc.; *U.S. Public*, pg. 663
COLOMBO LAND & DEVELOPMENT CO.; *Int'l*, pg. 1702
COLONIAL FIRST STATE PROPERTY LIMITED—See Commonwealth Bank of Australia; *Int'l*, pg. 1720
COLUMBA EVEN EMPREENDIMENTOS IMOBILIARIOS LTDA.—See Even Construtora e Incorporadora S.A.; *Int'l*, pg. 2561
COLUMBIA EXECUTIVE ASSOCIATES—See Galesi Group; *U.S. Private*, pg. 1637
COLUMBIA PROPERTY TRUST, INC.—See Allianz SE; *Int'l*, pg. 346
COMBINED GROUP ROCKS COMPANY- K.S.C.—See Combined Group Contracting Company KSCC; *Int'l*, pg. 1709
COMBINED INTERNATIONAL REAL ESTATE COMPANY- K.S.C.—See Combined Group Contracting Company KSCC; *Int'l*, pg. 1709
COMLAND COMMERCIAL LIMITED; *Int'l*, pg. 1714
COMMERCE ESCROW COMPANY—See Pacific Premier Bancorp, Inc.; *U.S. Public*, pg. 1632
COMMERCIAL DEVELOPMENT COMPANY LTD.—See Commercial Bank of Ceylon PLC; *Int'l*, pg. 1715
COMMERCIAL REALTY & RESOURCES CORP.—See New Jersey Resources Corporation; *U.S. Public*, pg. 1512
COMMERCIAL TEXAS, LLC—See Avison Young (Canada) Inc.; *Int'l*, pg. 745

COMMERZBANK PROPERTY MANAGEMENT & SERVICES LIMITED—See Commerzbank AG; *Int'l*, pg. 1717
COMMERZ REAL BAUCONTRACT GMBH—See Commerzbank AG; *Int'l*, pg. 1716
COMMERZ REAL DIREKT GMBH I.L.—See Commerzbank AG; *Int'l*, pg. 1716
COMMERZ REAL FINANZIERUNGSLEASING GMBH—See Commerzbank AG; *Int'l*, pg. 1716
COMMERZ REAL INVESTMENTGESELLSCHAFT MBH—See Commerzbank AG; *Int'l*, pg. 1716
COMMERZ REAL MIETKAUF GMBH—See Commerzbank AG; *Int'l*, pg. 1716
COMMERZ REAL PARTNER SUD GMBH—See Commerzbank AG; *Int'l*, pg. 1716
COMMERZ REAL PROJEKTCONSULT GMBH—See Commerzbank AG; *Int'l*, pg. 1716
COMMERZ REAL VERTRIEB GMBH—See Commerzbank AG; *Int'l*, pg. 1716
COMMERZ REAL VERWALTUNG UND TREUHAND GMBH—See Commerzbank AG; *Int'l*, pg. 1716
COMMERZ REAL WESTERN EUROPE GMBH—See Commerzbank AG; *Int'l*, pg. 1716
COMMONWEALTH CRYSTAL HOLDING II, INC.; *U.S. Private*, pg. 986
COMMONWEALTH REALTY GROUP, LLC—See Berkshire Hathaway Inc.; *U.S. Public*, pg. 304
COMPAGNIA IMMOBILIARE AZIONARIA S.P.A.; *Int'l*, pg. 1722
COMPANHIA HABITASUL DE PARTICIPACOES; *Int'l*, pg. 1747
COMPANIA ESPANOLA DE VIVIENDAS EN ALQUILER S.A.; *Int'l*, pg. 1749
COMPANIA URBANIZADORA DEL COTO, S.L.—See Acciona, S.A.; *Int'l*, pg. 90
THE COMPASS MANAGEMENT GROUP, LLC; *U.S. Private*, pg. 4013
COMPASS PROPERTIES, LLC—See F.N.B. Corporation; *U.S. Public*, pg. 818
COMPLEJO PORTUARIO MEJILLONES S.A.—See Corporacion Nacional del Cobre de Chile; *Int'l*, pg. 1805
COMPLEXE LEBOURGNEUF PHASE II INC.—See BTB Real Estate Investment Trust; *Int'l*, pg. 1204
COMRIT INVESTMENTS 1 LP; *Int'l*, pg. 1761
COMSTOCK HOLDING COMPANIES, INC.; *U.S. Public*, pg. 562
COMSTOCK MAXWELL SQUARE, L.C.—See Comstock Holding Companies, Inc.; *U.S. Public*, pg. 562
CONCERTO INC.—See Credit Saison Co., Ltd.; *Int'l*, pg. 1836
CONCRETION LIMITED—See ANSA McAL Limited; *Int'l*, pg. 477
CONDADO PROPERTIES, INC.; *Int'l*, pg. 1766
CONFLUENT DEVELOPMENT, LLC; *U.S. Private*, pg. 1013
CONIFER REALTY, LLC—See Belveron Real Estate Partners, LLC; *U.S. Private*, pg. 522
CONNECTONE PREFERRED FUNDING CORP.—See ConnectOne Bancorp, Inc.; *U.S. Public*, pg. 568
CONSERA HEALTHCARE REAL ESTATE LLC—See Ventas, Inc.; *U.S. Public*, pg. 2278
CONSOLIDATED HCI HOLDINGS CORP.; *Int'l*, pg. 1770
CONSORTIUM AMERICA II, LLC—See Wells Fargo & Company; *U.S. Public*, pg. 2343
CONSULTATIO SA; *Int'l*, pg. 1778
CONSUS DEUTSCHLAND GMBH—See Consus Real Estate AG; *Int'l*, pg. 1778
CONTEMPRO FOR HOUSING PROJECTS PLC; *Int'l*, pg. 1779
CONTINENTAL PROPERTIES MEXICO SA DE CV—See Continental Aktiengesellschaft; *Int'l*, pg. 1783
COOP IMMOBILIEN AG—See Coop-Gruppe Genossenschaft; *Int'l*, pg. 1790
COPLAND ROAD CAPITAL CORPORATION; *Int'l*, pg. 1793
CORCORAN SUNSHINE MARKETING GROUP—See Anywhere Real Estate Inc.; *U.S. Public*, pg. 142
CORELOGIC BACKGROUND DATA, LLC—See Insight Venture Management, LLC; *U.S. Private*, pg. 2088
CORELOGIC BACKGROUND DATA, LLC—See Stone Point Capital LLC; *U.S. Private*, pg. 3822
CORELOGIC NZ LIMITED—See Insight Venture Management, LLC; *U.S. Private*, pg. 2088
CORELOGIC NZ LIMITED—See Stone Point Capital LLC; *U.S. Private*, pg. 3822
CORELOGIC RENTAL PROPERTY SOLUTIONS, LLC—See Insight Venture Management, LLC; *U.S. Private*, pg. 2088
CORELOGIC RENTAL PROPERTY SOLUTIONS, LLC—See Stone Point Capital LLC; *U.S. Private*, pg. 3822
CORELOGIC SOLUTIONS LIMITED—See Insight Venture Management, LLC; *U.S. Private*, pg. 2089
CORELOGIC SOLUTIONS LIMITED—See Stone Point Capital LLC; *U.S. Private*, pg. 3822
CORELOGIC UK LIMITED—See Insight Venture Management, LLC; *U.S. Private*, pg. 2089
CORELOGIC UK LIMITED—See Stone Point Capital LLC; *U.S. Private*, pg. 3822
CORELOGIC VALUATION SOLUTIONS, INC.—See Insight Venture Management, LLC; *U.S. Private*, pg. 2089

CORELOGIC VALUATION SOLUTIONS, INC.—See Stone Point Capital LLC; *U.S. Private*, pg. 3822
COREM PROPERTY GROUP AB; *Int'l*, pg. 1798
CORESTATE BANK GMBH—See CORESTATE Capital Holding SA; *Int'l*, pg. 1800
COREVEST AMERICAN FINANCE LENDER LLC—See Redwood Trust, Inc.; *U.S. Public*, pg. 1771
CORPORACION INMOBILIARIA VESTA, S.A.B. DE C.V.; *Int'l*, pg. 1804
CORTLAND PARTNERS, LLC; *U.S. Private*, pg. 1061
CORUM ECOMMERCE PTY LTD—See Corum Group Limited; *Int'l*, pg. 1808
COSCO (BEIJING) ENTERPRISES CO., LTD.—See China COSCO Shipping Corporation Limited; *Int'l*, pg. 1492
COSCO SHIPPING (HONG KONG) PROPERTY DEVELOPMENT LIMITED—See China COSCO Shipping Corporation Limited; *Int'l*, pg. 1492
COSMOS AUSTRALIA PTY LTD—See Daiwa House Industry Co., Ltd.; *Int'l*, pg. 1945
COSMOS GROUP CO., LTD.; *Int'l*, pg. 1813
COSMOS HEALTH INC.; *U.S. Public*, pg. 585
COSTAR PORTFOLIO STRATEGY, LLC—See CoStar Group, Inc.; *U.S. Public*, pg. 585
COSTAR REALTY INFORMATION, INC.—See CoStar Group, Inc.; *U.S. Public*, pg. 586
COSTAR UK LIMITED—See CoStar Group, Inc.; *U.S. Public*, pg. 585
COSTAR UK LIMITED—See CoStar Group, Inc.; *U.S. Public*, pg. 585
COUNTRY GARDEN DANGA BAY SDN. BHD.—See Country Garden Holdings Company Limited; *Int'l*, pg. 1818
COUNTRY GARDEN PACIFICVIEW SDN. BHD.—See Country Garden Holdings Company Limited; *Int'l*, pg. 1818
COUNTRY GROUP DEVELOPMENT PUBLIC COMPANY LIMITED; *Int'l*, pg. 1818
COURTLAND PARTNERS LTD.—See StepStone Group LP; *U.S. Private*, pg. 3804
COUSINEAU PROPERTIES—See Cousineau Inc.; *U.S. Private*, pg. 1071
COUSINS TERMINUS LLC—See Cousins Properties Incorporated; *U.S. Public*, pg. 587
COVINGTON GROUP, INC.; *U.S. Private*, pg. 1073
COVIVIO IMMOBILIEN SE—See Covivio; *Int'l*, pg. 1821
COVIVIO OFFICE GMBH—See Covivio; *Int'l*, pg. 1821
COVIVIO; *Int'l*, pg. 1821
CPF HONG KONG CO., LTD.—See Charoen Pokphand Foods Public Company Limited; *Int'l*, pg. 1452
CPI ENERGO, A.S.—See CPI Property Group, S.A.; *Int'l*, pg. 1825
CPI HUNGARY KFT.—See CPI Property Group, S.A.; *Int'l*, pg. 1825
CPI IMMO, S.A.R.L.—See CPI Property Group, S.A.; *Int'l*, pg. 1825
CPI MARKETING GMBH—See CPI Immobilien AG; *Int'l*, pg. 1825
CPI METEOR CENTRE, S.R.O.—See CPI Property Group, S.A.; *Int'l*, pg. 1825
CPI POLAND SP. Z O.O.—See CPI Property Group, S.A.; *Int'l*, pg. 1825
CPI PROPERTY GROUP, S.A.; *Int'l*, pg. 1825
CPI RETAIL PORTFOLIO I, A.S.—See CPI Property Group, S.A.; *Int'l*, pg. 1825
CPI WACHSTUMS IMMOBILIEN AG—See CPI Immobilien AG; *Int'l*, pg. 1825
CPI WERTPAPIER BERATUNG UND VERMITTLUNG GMBH—See CPI Immobilien AG; *Int'l*, pg. 1825
C.P. LAND PLC—See Charoen Pokphand Foods Public Company Limited; *Int'l*, pg. 1452
CR2 EMPREENDIMENTOS IMOBILIARIOS S.A.; *Int'l*, pg. 1827
CRANE INFRASTRUCTURE LTD.; *Int'l*, pg. 1828
CR CAPITAL REAL ESTATE AG; *Int'l*, pg. 1827
CREA MADRID NUEVO NORTE S.A.—See Banco Bilbao Vizcaya Argentaria, S.A.; *Int'l*, pg. 817
CRE ASIA PTE. LTD.—See CRE, Inc.; *Int'l*, pg. 1830
CREATD, INC.; *U.S. Public*, pg. 593
CREATIVE MEDIA & COMMUNITY TRUST CORPORATION; *U.S. Public*, pg. 593
CREED CORPORATION; *Int'l*, pg. 1837
CRE, INC.; *Int'l*, pg. 1830
CRE LOGISTICS REIT, INC.; *Int'l*, pg. 1830
CRE PROPERTIES (HONG KONG) LTD.—See China Resources (Holdings) Co., Ltd.; *Int'l*, pg. 1547
CRE REIT ADVISERS, INC.—See CRE, Inc.; *Int'l*, pg. 1830
CRESCENT REAL ESTATE LLC—See Goff Capital, Inc.; *U.S. Private*, pg. 1726
CRESCENT RESOURCES, LLC; *U.S. Private*, pg. 1094
CREST VENTURES LIMITED; *Int'l*, pg. 1841
CRETAN GROUP PLC; *Int'l*, pg. 1842
CRIC REAL ESTATE DATABASE SERVICES—See E-House (China) Holdings Limited; *Int'l*, pg. 2248
CRISTAL IMMO SC—See Groupe BPCE; *Int'l*, pg. 3093
CRI ZWEITE BETEILIGUNGSGESELLSCHAFT MBH—See Commerzbank AG; *Int'l*, pg. 1715
CROCKER PARTNERS LLC; *U.S. Private*, pg. 1102
CROISSANCE LTD.; *Int'l*, pg. 1853
CROMWELL CORPORATE SECRETARIAL LIMITED—See

Cromwell Property Group; *Int'l*, pg. 1853
CROMWELL FRANCE SAS—See W.W. Grainger, Inc.; *U.S. Public*, pg. 2319
CROMWELL POLAND SP. Z O.O.—See W.W. Grainger, Inc.; *U.S. Public*, pg. 2319
CROMWELL PROPERTY GROUP ITALY SRL—See Cromwell Property Group; *Int'l*, pg. 1854
CROMWELL SWEDEN A/B—See Cromwell Property Group; *Int'l*, pg. 1854
CROSSWOOD SA; *Int'l*, pg. 1856
CRYOMASS TECHNOLOGIES INC.; *U.S. Public*, pg. 600
C&S ASSET MANAGEMENT CO., LTD.; *Int'l*, pg. 1239
CSCEC XINJIANG CONSTRUCTION & ENGINEERING (GROUP) CO., LTD.—See China State Construction Engineering Corporation Limited; *Int'l*, pg. 1554
CSE-HANKIN (TAIWAN) LTD.—See CSE Global Ltd.; *Int'l*, pg. 1863
CTO REALTY GROWTH, INC.; *U.S. Public*, pg. 602
CTW GROUP INCORPORATED; *U.S. Private*, pg. 1119
CUBESMART ALEXANDRIA, LLC—See CubeSmart; *U.S. Public*, pg. 603
CUBIC LAND, INC.—See Elliott Management Corporation; *U.S. Private*, pg. 1368
CUBIC LAND, INC.—See Veritas Capital Fund Management, LLC; *U.S. Private*, pg. 4361
CUSHMAN & WAKEFIELD - BRUSSELS—See TPG Capital, L.P.; *U.S. Public*, pg. 2171
CUSHMAN & WAKEFIELD DE MEXICO—See TPG Capital, L.P.; *U.S. Public*, pg. 2172
CUSHMAN & WAKEFIELD (HK) LIMITED—See TPG Capital, L.P.; *U.S. Public*, pg. 2171
CUSHMAN & WAKEFIELD (INDIA) PVT. LTD.—See TPG Capital, L.P.; *U.S. Public*, pg. 2171
CUSHMAN & WAKEFIELD K.K.—See TPG Capital, L.P.; *U.S. Public*, pg. 2171
CUSHMAN & WAKEFIELD LLP—See TPG Capital, L.P.; *U.S. Public*, pg. 2172
CUSHMAN & WAKEFIELD LTD.—See TPG Capital, L.P.; *U.S. Public*, pg. 2172
CUSHMAN & WAKEFIELD - MADRID—See TPG Capital, L.P.; *U.S. Public*, pg. 2171
CUSHMAN & WAKEFIELD (NSW) PTY LIMITED—See TPG Capital, L.P.; *U.S. Public*, pg. 2171
CUSHMAN & WAKEFIELD - SAO PAULO—See TPG Capital, L.P.; *U.S. Public*, pg. 2171
CUSHMAN & WAKEFIELD (SHANGHAI) CO. LTD.—See TPG Capital, L.P.; *U.S. Public*, pg. 2171
CUSHMAN & WAKEFIELD (S) PTE LTD—See TPG Capital, L.P.; *U.S. Public*, pg. 2171
CUSHMAN & WAKEFIELD SWEDEN AB—See TPG Capital, L.P.; *U.S. Public*, pg. 2172
CUSHMAN & WAKEFIELD (U.K.) LTD.—See TPG Capital, L.P.; *U.S. Public*, pg. 2171
CUSHMAN & WAKEFIELD (VIC) PTY LTD—See TPG Capital, L.P.; *U.S. Public*, pg. 2171
CUU LONG PETRO URBAN DEVELOPMENT & INVESTMENT CORPORATION; *Int'l*, pg. 1881
CVF TECHNOLOGIES CORP.; *Int'l*, pg. 1889
CWG INTERNATIONAL LTD; *Int'l*, pg. 1890
CWS APARTMENT HOMES LLC—See CWS Capital Partners, LLC; *U.S. Private*, pg. 1133
CYBER BAY CORPORATION; *Int'l*, pg. 1891
CYPRESS EQUITIES—See Jones Lang LaSalle Incorporated; *U.S. Public*, pg. 1205
CYPRUS LEASING ROMANIA IFN SA—See Bank of Cyprus Holdings Public Limited Company; *Int'l*, pg. 842
CYRELA BRAZIL REALTY S.A.; *Int'l*, pg. 1897
DABACO REAL ESTATE—See DABACO Group Joint Stock Company; *Int'l*, pg. 1902
DACRA DEVELOPMENT CORP.; *U.S. Private*, pg. 1144
DAEJAN DEVELOPMENTS LIMITED—See Centremanor Ltd.; *Int'l*, pg. 1411
DAFA PROPERTIES GROUP LTD.; *Int'l*, pg. 1911
DAHLEM ENTERPRISES, INC.—See Dahlem Companies, Inc.; *U.S. Private*, pg. 1144
DAHLEM REALTY COMPANY, INC.—See Dahlem Companies, Inc.; *U.S. Private*, pg. 1144
THE DAI-ICHI BUILDING CO., LTD.—See Dai-ichi Life Holdings, Inc.; *Int'l*, pg. 1918
DAIICHI KENSETSU CORPORATION; *Int'l*, pg. 1927
DAIWA BAOYE (NANTONG) REAL ESTATE DEVELOPMENT CO., LTD.—See Daiwa House Industry Co., Ltd.; *Int'l*, pg. 1945
DAIWA HOUSE AUSTRALIA PTY LTD.—See Daiwa House REIT Investment Corporation; *Int'l*, pg. 1947
DAIWA HOUSE CALIFORNIA—See Daiwa House REIT Investment Corporation; *Int'l*, pg. 1947
DAIWA HOUSE REIT INVESTMENT CORPORATION; *Int'l*, pg. 1947
DAIWA HOUSE (SUZHOU) REAL ESTATE DEVELOPMENT CO., LTD.—See Daiwa House Industry Co., Ltd.; *Int'l*, pg. 1945
DAIWA HOUSE TEXAS INC.—See Daiwa House Industry Co., Ltd.; *Int'l*, pg. 1945
DAIWA HOUSE VIETNAM CO., LTD.—See Daiwa House REIT Investment Corporation; *Int'l*, pg. 1947
DAIWA HOUSE (WUXI) REAL ESTATE DEVELOPMENT CO., LTD.—See Daiwa House REIT Investment Corporation; *Int'l*, pg. 1947
DAIWA LEASE CO., LTD.—See Daiwa House Industry Co., Ltd.; *Int'l*, pg. 1945
DAIWA REAL ESTATE ASSET MANAGEMENT CO. LTD—See Daiwa Securities Group Inc.; *Int'l*, pg. 1948
DAIWA SECURITIES REALTY CO. LTD.—See Daiwa Securities Group Inc.; *Int'l*, pg. 1949
DA LI DEVELOPMENT LLC—See Da-Li Development Co., Ltd.; *Int'l*, pg. 1902
DANANG HOUSING INVESTMENT AND DEVELOPMENT JOINT STOCK COMPANY; *Int'l*, pg. 1958
DANVILLE DEVELOPMENT, LLC—See PENN Entertainment, Inc.; *U.S. Public*, pg. 1662
DANZAS GRUNDSTUECKSVERWALTUNG GROSS-GERAU GMBH—See Deutsche Post AG; *Int'l*, pg. 2079
DAR AL ARKAN REAL ESTATE DEVELOPMENT COMPANY; *Int'l*, pg. 1971
DAR AL DHABI HOLDING CO. K.S.C.—See Bayan Investment Holding Company K.S.C.C.; *Int'l*, pg. 901
DAR AL THURAYA REAL ESTATE CO KSCP; *Int'l*, pg. 1971
DAS GLOBAL CAPITAL CORP.; *U.S. Private*, pg. 1160
DATA443 RISK MITIGATION, INC.; *U.S. Public*, pg. 635
DAT XANH GROUP JOINT STOCK COMPANY; *Int'l*, pg. 1975
DB REALTY LIMITED—See Dynamix Balwas Group of Companies; *Int'l*, pg. 2241
DBSI DEVELOPMENT LLC—See DBSI, Inc.; *U.S. Private*, pg. 1179
DCI ADVISORS LIMITED; *Int'l*, pg. 1991
DEALCYBER LIMITED—See GSK plc; *Int'l*, pg. 3145
DEAR LIFE CO., LTD.; *Int'l*, pg. 1998
DEAUVILLE DIAMOND PROPERTIES SA; *Int'l*, pg. 1998
DEBARTOLO DEVELOPMENT, LLC—See DeBartolo Holdings, LLC; *U.S. Private*, pg. 1186
DEBEKO IMMOBILIEN GMBH & CO GRUNDBESITZ OHG—See Deutsche Bank Aktiengesellschaft; *Int'l*, pg. 2057
DECORINT SA; *Int'l*, pg. 2001
DEERA INVESTMENT & REAL ESTATE DEVELOPMENT CO.; *Int'l*, pg. 2003
DEG, LLC—See Douglas Emmett, Inc.; *U.S. Public*, pg. 678
DEKA IMMOBILIEN GMBH—See DekaBank; *Int'l*, pg. 2005
DEKA IMMOBILIEN INVESTMENT GMBH—See DekaBank; *Int'l*, pg. 2005
DELTA CORP LTD.; *Int'l*, pg. 2016
DELTA REAL ESTATE D.O.O.—See Delta Holding; *Int'l*, pg. 2018
DEMIRE LEIPZIG AM ALTEN FLUGHAFEN 1 GMBH—See DEMIRE Deutsche Mittelstand Real Estate AG; *Int'l*, pg. 2025
DENGE VARLIK YONETIM A.S.; *Int'l*, pg. 2026
DENIZ GAYRIMENKUL YATIRIM ORTAKLIGI AS; *Int'l*, pg. 2027
DENTSU WORKS INC.—See Dentsu Group Inc.; *Int'l*, pg. 2038
DERWENT LONDON PLC; *Int'l*, pg. 2043
DESANE PROPERTIES PTY. LTD.—See Desane Group Holdings Ltd; *Int'l*, pg. 2043
DEUTSCHE ASSET MANAGEMENT SCHWEIZ—See Deutsche Bank Aktiengesellschaft; *Int'l*, pg. 2058
DEUTSCHE ASSET MANAGEMENT SWITZERLAND—See Deutsche Bank Aktiengesellschaft; *Int'l*, pg. 2058
DEUTSCHE ASSET MANAGEMENT (UK) LTD.—See Deutsche Bank Aktiengesellschaft; *Int'l*, pg. 2059
DEUTSCHE BANK REAL ESTATE (JAPAN) Y.K.—See Deutsche Bank Aktiengesellschaft; *Int'l*, pg. 2060
DEUTSCHE BANK REALTY ADVISORS, INC.—See Deutsche Bank Aktiengesellschaft; *Int'l*, pg. 2060
DEUTSCHE EINKAUFS-CENTER MANAGEMENT G.M.B.H—See ECE Projektmanagement GmbH & Co KG; *Int'l*, pg. 2288
DEUTSCHE EUROSHOP MANAGEMENT GMBH—See Deutsche EuroShop AG; *Int'l*, pg. 2065
DEUTSCHE IMMOBILIEN LEASING GMBH—See Deutsche Bank Aktiengesellschaft; *Int'l*, pg. 2060
DEUTSCHE INTERNET IMMOBILIEN AUKTIONEN GMBH—See Deutsche Grundstuecksauktionen AG; *Int'l*, pg. 2065
DEUTSCHE POST DHL CORPORATE REAL ESTATE MANAGEMENT GMBH—See Deutsche Post AG; *Int'l*, pg. 2079
DEUTSCHE POST GRUNDSTUCKS- VERMIETUNGSGESELLSCHAFT BETA MBH—See Deutsche Post AG; *Int'l*, pg. 2079
DEUTSCHE POST IMMOBILIEN GMBH—See Deutsche Post AG; *Int'l*, pg. 2079
DEVASHRI NIRMAN LLP—See Goa Carbon Ltd.; *Int'l*, pg. 3018
DEVELA S.A.; *Int'l*, pg. 2087
DEVELOPMENT PARTNER IMMOBILIEN CONSULTING GMBH—See Gateway Real Estate AG; *Int'l*, pg. 2889
DEXUS HOLDINGS PTY LIMITED—See DEXUS; *Int'l*, pg. 2093
DEXUS; *Int'l*, pg. 2093
DEYAAR DEVELOPMENT PJSC; *Int'l*, pg. 2093
DHANUKA REALTY LTD.; *Int'l*, pg. 2098
DHI TITLE OF ALABAMA, INC.—See D.R. Horton, Inc.; *U.S. Public*, pg. 619
DHL LESOTHO (PROPRIETARY) LTD.—See Deutsche Post AG; *Int'l*, pg. 2077
DHL SWAZILAND (PROPRIETARY) LTD.—See Deutsche Post AG; *Int'l*, pg. 2078
DHOUSE PATTANA PUBLIC COMPANY LIMITED; *Int'l*, pg. 2100
DHRUV ESTATES LIMITED; *Int'l*, pg. 2100
DIAMONDROCK HOSPITALITY COMPANY; *U.S. Public*, pg. 659
DIANA PROPERTY SP. Z.O.O.—See CPI Property Group, S.A.; *Int'l*, pg. 1825
DIC ASSET AG; *Int'l*, pg. 2107
DICKERSON & NIEMAN REALTORS, INC.; *U.S. Private*, pg. 1226
DIC ONSITE GMBH—See DIC Asset AG; *Int'l*, pg. 2107
DI DEUTSCHE IMMOBILIEN TREUHANDGESELLSCHAFT MBH—See Deutsche Bank Aktiengesellschaft; *Int'l*, pg. 2057
DIERIG TEXTILWERKE GMBH—See Dierig Holding AG; *Int'l*, pg. 2115
DIGITAL EAST CORNELL, LLC—See Digital Realty Trust, Inc.; *U.S. Public*, pg. 663
DIGITAL WINTER, LLC—See Digital Realty Trust, Inc.; *U.S. Public*, pg. 663
DIOK ONE AG; *Int'l*, pg. 2127
DIOS FASTIGHETER AB; *Int'l*, pg. 2128
DIRECIONAL ENGENHARIA S.A.; *Int'l*, pg. 2129
DIT GROUP LIMITED; *Int'l*, pg. 2137
DIVERSE DEVELOPMENT GROUP, INC.; *U.S. Private*, pg. 1240
DIVIDUM OY—See CapMan PLC; *Int'l*, pg. 1315
DJK RESIDENTIAL—See Madison Dearborn Partners, LLC; *U.S. Private*, pg. 2542
DKB WOHNIMMOBILIEN BETEILIGUNGS GMBH & CO. KG—See Helaba Landesbank Hessen-Thuringen; *Int'l*, pg. 3327
DKLS CONSTRUCTION SDN BHD—See DKLS Industries Berhad; *Int'l*, pg. 2139
DKSH HOLDINGS (ASIA) SDN. BHD.—See Diethelm Keller Holding Limited; *Int'l*, pg. 2116
DLALA REAL ESTATE S.P.C.—See Dlala Brokerage and Investments Holding Company Q.S.C; *Int'l*, pg. 2140
DLF ESTATE DEVELOPERS LIMITED—See DLF Limited; *Int'l*, pg. 2141
DLF PROJECTS LIMITED—See DLF Limited; *Int'l*, pg. 2141
DLP CAPITAL ADVISORS—See Don Wenner Home Selling, Inc.; *U.S. Private*, pg. 1259
DLP REAL ESTATE CAPITAL INC.; *U.S. Private*, pg. 1247
DLP RESOURCES INC.; *Int'l*, pg. 2141
DMH REALTY, LLC—See Pacific Oak Strategic Opportunity REIT, Inc.; *U.S. Public*, pg. 1632
DNB NAERINGSEIENDOM AS—See DNB Bank ASA; *Int'l*, pg. 2148
DOGUS GAYRIMENKUL YATIRIM ORTAKLIGI A.S.; *Int'l*, pg. 2174
&DO HOLDINGS CO., LTD.; *Int'l*, pg. 1
DOLOMITE INDUSTRIES COMPANY SDN. BHD.—See Dolomite Corporation Berhad; *Int'l*, pg. 2159
DOLOMITE PROPERTIES SDN. BHD.—See Dolomite Corporation Berhad; *Int'l*, pg. 2159
DONGGUAN VANKE REAL ESTATE COMPANY LIMITED—See China Vanke Co., Ltd.; *Int'l*, pg. 1562
DONG SUNG AMERICA INC.—See Dongsung Chemical Co., Ltd.; *Int'l*, pg. 2169
DONGWON DEVELOPMENT CO., LTD.; *Int'l*, pg. 2170
DON WENNER HOME SELLING, INC.; *U.S. Private*, pg. 1259
DORIC GROUP HOLDINGS PTY LTD—See Alisthe Investments Pty Ltd; *Int'l*, pg. 329
DORNACOM SA; *Int'l*, pg. 2179
DOTLOOP, LLC—See Zillow Group, Inc.; *U.S. Public*, pg. 2405
DOUGLAS EMMETT REALTY FUND, LLC—See Douglas Emmett, Inc.; *U.S. Public*, pg. 678
DOUGLAS WILSON COMPANIES; *U.S. Private*, pg. 1267
DOUJA PROMOTION GROUPE ADDOHA SA; *Int'l*, pg. 2181
DRAGON UKRAINIAN PROPERTIES & DEVELOPMENT PLC; *Int'l*, pg. 2199
DREAM HOMES LIMITED; *U.S. Private*, pg. 1275
DREES & SOMMER COLOGNE GMBH—See Drees & Sommer SE; *Int'l*, pg. 2204
DREES & SOMMER DRESDEN GMBH—See Drees & Sommer SE; *Int'l*, pg. 2204
DREES & SOMMER HAMBURG GMBH—See Drees & Sommer SE; *Int'l*, pg. 2204
DREES & SOMMER LEIPZIG GMBH—See Drees & Sommer SE; *Int'l*, pg. 2204
DREES & SOMMER NETHERLANDS B.V.—See Drees & Sommer SE; *Int'l*, pg. 2204
DREES & SOMMER UK LTD.—See Drees & Sommer SE; *Int'l*, pg. 2204
DREES & SOMMER ULM GMBH—See Drees & Sommer SE; *Int'l*, pg. 2204
DRH HOLDINGS JOINT STOCK COMPANY; *Int'l*, pg. 2204

N.A.I.C.S. INDEX

531390 — OTHER ACTIVITIES RE...

D.R. HORTON - CROWN, LLC—See D.R. Horton, Inc.; *U.S. Public*, pg. 619
D.R. HORTON, INC. -CHICAGO—See D.R. Horton, Inc.; *U.S. Public*, pg. 619
D.R. HORTON, INC. - HUNTSVILLE—See D.R. Horton, Inc.; *U.S. Public*, pg. 619
D.R. HORTON, INC. - MINNESOTA—See D.R. Horton, Inc.; *U.S. Public*, pg. 619
D.R. HORTON REALTY, LLC—See D.R. Horton, Inc.; *U.S. Public*, pg. 619
DRYSDALE PROPERTIES LTD—See Bank of Cyprus Holdings Public Limited Company; *Int'l*, pg. 842
DT DEVELOPMENT VIETNAM LLC—See Daiwa House Industry Co., Ltd.; *Int'l*, pg. 1945
DUBOKO PLAVETNILO UGLJAN PROJEKTANT D.O.O.—See Cubus Lux Plc; *Int'l*, pg. 1876
DUKE REALTY LIMITED PARTNERSHIP—See Prologis, Inc.; *U.S. Public*, pg. 1726
DUNDEE 360 REAL ESTATE CORPORATION—See Dundee Corporation; *Int'l*, pg. 2225
DUNDEE REALTY MANAGEMENT CORPORATION—See Dundee Corporation; *Int'l*, pg. 2225
DUNIEC BROS. LTD.; *Int'l*, pg. 2227
DWS GROUP GMBH & CO. KGAA; *Int'l*, pg. 2236
DZ IMMOBILIEN+TREUHAND GMBH—See DZ BANK AG Deutsche Zentral-Genossenschaftsbank; *Int'l*, pg. 2244
EADS REAL ESTATE TAUFKIRCHEN GMBH & CO. KG—See Airbus SE; *Int'l*, pg. 75
EAGLE & WISE SERVICE S.R.L.—See Gruppo MutuiOnline S.p.A; *Int'l*, pg. 3141
EASTBAY EQUITIES INC.—See State Street Capital Realty, LLC; *U.S. Private*, pg. 3793
EAST BUILDTECH LTD; *Int'l*, pg. 2269
EAST CAMPUS REALTY, LLC—See Mutual of Omaha Insurance Company; *U.S. Private*, pg. 2820
EASTERN HOUSING LIMITED; *Int'l*, pg. 2272
EASTERN STAR REAL ESTATE PUBLIC COMPANY LIMITED; *Int'l*, pg. 2274
EAST MAUI IRRIGATION CO., LTD.—See Alexander & Baldwin, Inc.; *U.S. Public*, pg. 75
EBARA AGENCY CO., LTD.—See Ebara Corporation; *Int'l*, pg. 2282
ECE I, LLC—See EPR Properties; *U.S. Public*, pg. 784
ECE PROJEKTMANAGEMENT GMBH & CO KG; *Int'l*, pg. 2288
ECE REAL ESTATE PARTNERS G.M.B.H.—See ECE Projektmanagement GmbH & Co KG; *Int'l*, pg. 2288
ECE REAL ESTATE PARTNERS S.A R.L.—See ECE Projektmanagement GmbH & Co KG; *Int'l*, pg. 2288
E-CITY PROPERTY MANAGEMENT & SERVICES PVT. LTD.—See Essel Corporate Resources Pvt. Ltd.; *Int'l*, pg. 2509
ECM ASSET MANAGEMENT LIMITED—See Wells Fargo & Company; *U.S. Public*, pg. 2343
ECM REAL ESTATE INVESTMENTS A.G.; *Int'l*, pg. 2292
ECO BOTANIC SDN. BHD.—See Eco World Development Group Berhad; *Int'l*, pg. 2293
ECO BUSINESS PARK 1 SDN. BHD.—See Eco World Development Group Berhad; *Int'l*, pg. 2293
ECO BUSINESS PARK 2 SDN. BHD.—See Eco World Development Group Berhad; *Int'l*, pg. 2293
ECO GREEN CITY SDN. BHD.—See Avaland Berhad; *Int'l*, pg. 734
ECO HORIZON SDN. BHD.—See Eco World Development Group Berhad; *Int'l*, pg. 2293
ECO MAJESTIC DEVELOPMENT SDN. BHD.—See Eco World Development Group Berhad; *Int'l*, pg. 2293
ECO MEADOWS SDN. BHD.—See Eco World Development Group Berhad; *Int'l*, pg. 2293
ECONOS CO., LTD.; *Int'l*, pg. 2298
ECO SANCTUARY SDN. BHD.—See Eco World Development Group Berhad; *Int'l*, pg. 2293
ECO SKY SDN. BHD.—See Eco World Development Group Berhad; *Int'l*, pg. 2293
ECO SUMMER SDN. BHD.—See Eco World Development Group Berhad; *Int'l*, pg. 2293
ECO SYSTEMS LTD.; *Int'l*, pg. 2292
ECO TERRACES SDN. BHD.—See Eco World Development Group Berhad; *Int'l*, pg. 2293
ECO TROPICS DEVELOPMENT SDN. BHD.—See Eco World Development Group Berhad; *Int'l*, pg. 2293
ECO WORLD DEVELOPMENT GROUP BERHAD; *Int'l*, pg. 2293
ECO WORLD DEVELOPMENT MANAGEMENT (BBCC) SDN. BHD.—See Eco World Development Group Berhad; *Int'l*, pg. 2293
EDENS INDUSTRIAL PARK, INC.—See Bee Street Holdings LLC; *U.S. Private*, pg. 513
EDENS REALTY, INC., *U.S. Private*, pg. 1333
ED INVEST S.A.; *Int'l*, pg. 2302
EDMOND DE ROTHSCHILD ADVISORY MANAGEMENT (BEIJING) CO., LTD.—See Edmond de Rothschild Holding S.A.; *Int'l*, pg. 2313
EDMOND DE ROTHSCHILD ASSET MANAGEMENT CHILE S.A.—See Edmond de Rothschild Holding S.A.; *Int'l*, pg. 2313
EDMOND DE ROTHSCHILD ASSET MANAGEMENT (C.I.)

LIMITED—See Edmond de Rothschild Holding S.A.; *Int'l*, pg. 2313
EDMOND DE ROTHSCHILD ASSET MANAGEMENT (LUXEMBOURG) SA—See Edmond de Rothschild Holding S.A.; *Int'l*, pg. 2313
EDMOND DE ROTHSCHILD INVESTMENT PARTNERS (HONG KONG) LTD.—See Edmond de Rothschild Holding S.A.; *Int'l*, pg. 2313
EDMOND DE ROTHSCHILD INVESTMENT PARTNERS (SHANGHAI) LTD.—See Edmond de Rothschild Holding S.A.; *Int'l*, pg. 2313
EDMUND TIE & COMPANY (SEA) PTE. LTD.; *Int'l*, pg. 2313
EDPA KIMYA SAN. VE TIC. A.S.; *Int'l*, pg. 2315
EDPA TEKSTIL TICARET A.S.; *Int'l*, pg. 2315
EDPA USA, INC.; *U.S. Private*, pg. 1338
EDRI-EL ISRAEL ASSETS LTD.; *Int'l*, pg. 2315
EDWARD R. JAMES PARTNERS, LLC; *U.S. Private*, pg. 1341
EFC DEVELOPMENTS LTD.—See Executive Flight Centre Fuel Services Ltd.; *Int'l*, pg. 2580
EFFICIENT SELECT (PTY) LTD—See Apex Fund Services Holdings Ltd.; *Int'l*, pg. 510
EF NOVA OSELYA LLC—See Dragon Ukrainian Properties & Development Plc; *Int'l*, pg. 2199
EFO FINANCIAL GROUP LLC; *U.S. Private*, pg. 1343
EFTEN CAPITAL AS; *Int'l*, pg. 2321
EGYPTIANS FOR HOUSING & DEVELOPMENT CO.; *Int'l*, pg. 2327
EHL IMMOBILIEN GMBH; *Int'l*, pg. 2328
EH PROPERTY MANAGEMENT PTE LTD—See Enviro-Hub Holdings Ltd.; *Int'l*, pg. 2454
THE EIDSON GROUP, LLC—See Avison Young (Canada) Inc.; *Int'l*, pg. 745
EIENDOMSSPAR ASA; *Int'l*, pg. 2329
EIFFAGE IMMOBILIER POLSKA SP. Z OO—See Eiffage S.A.; *Int'l*, pg. 2330
EIFFAGE IMMOBILIER—See Eiffage S.A.; *Int'l*, pg. 2330
EIGHTY EIGHT OIL CO.—See True Companies; *U.S. Private*, pg. 4247
EIGNARHALDSFELAGIO LANDEY EHF.—See Arion Bank hf.; *Int'l*, pg. 565
EJESUR S.A.—See BNP Paribas SA; *Int'l*, pg. 1090
ELANA AGRICULTURAL LAND FUND REIT; *Int'l*, pg. 2343
ELARA INVESTMENTS SP. Z O.O.—See CPD S.A.; *Int'l*, pg. 1824
ELECTRA AMERICA, INC.—See Elco Limited; *Int'l*, pg. 2345
ELECTRA REAL ESTATE LTD.—See Elco Limited; *Int'l*, pg. 2345
ELECTROMINING SA; *Int'l*, pg. 2353
ELITE PACIFIC, LLC; *U.S. Private*, pg. 1361
ELIX VINTAGE RESIDENCIAL SOCIMI S.A.—See Allianz SE; *Int'l*, pg. 352
ELLIMAC PRIME HOLDINGS INC.—See Cosco Capital, Inc.; *Int'l*, pg. 1809
EL MILANILLO, S.A.—See Banco Bilbao Vizcaya Argentaria, S.A.; *Int'l*, pg. 817
EL OBOUR REAL ESTATE INVESTMENT; *Int'l*, pg. 2341
EMAAR INTERNATIONAL JORDAN—See Emaar Properties PJSC; *Int'l*, pg. 2372
EMAAR MGF LAND LIMITED—See Emaar Properties PJSC; *Int'l*, pg. 2372
EMAAR MISR FOR DEVELOPMENT S.A.E.; *Int'l*, pg. 2372
EMAAR PAKISTAN GROUP—See Emaar Properties PJSC; *Int'l*, pg. 2372
EMAAR THE ECONOMIC CITY JSC; *Int'l*, pg. 2373
EMAAR TURKEY—See Emaar Properties PJSC; *Int'l*, pg. 2373
EMAAR USA—See Emaar Properties PJSC; *Int'l*, pg. 2373
EMAMI REALTY LIMITED—See Emami Group; *Int'l*, pg. 2374
E MAN CONSTRUCTION COMPANY LIMITED—See Henderson Land Development Co. Ltd.; *Int'l*, pg. 3344
EMBASSY PROPERTY DEVELOPMENTS PVT. LTD.—See Blackstone Inc.; *U.S. Public*, pg. 350
EMERALD LEISURES LIMITED; *Int'l*, pg. 2377
EMERALD REALTY OF NORTHWEST FLORIDA, LLC—See D.R. Horton, Inc.; *U.S. Public*, pg. 620
EMERGIA INC.; *Int'l*, pg. 2378
EMMAR INVESTMENTS & REAL ESTATE DEVELOPMENT COMPANY; *Int'l*, pg. 2384
EMPIRE PROPERTIES; *U.S. Private*, pg. 1385
ENERGIBYGG AS—See Bravida Holding AB; *Int'l*, pg. 1142
ENFYN MANAGEMENT LIMITED—See ENL Limited; *Int'l*, pg. 2442
ENGLER FINANCIAL GROUP, LLC—See Walker & Dunlop, Inc.; *U.S. Public*, pg. 2324
ENGTEX PROPERTIES SDN. BHD.—See Engtex Group Berhad; *Int'l*, pg. 2436
ENJAZ FOR DEVELOPMENT & MULTI PROJECTS COMPANY P.L.C.; *Int'l*, pg. 2439
ENL PROPERTY LIMITED—See ENL Limited; *Int'l*, pg. 2441
ENSEJOUR LTD.—See ENL Limited; *Int'l*, pg. 2441
ENSTYLE MANAGEMENT LIMITED—See ENL Limited; *Int'l*, pg. 2441
ENTRECAMPOS CUATRO SOCIMI SA; *Int'l*, pg. 2452
E.ON FASTIGHETER SVERIGE AB—See E.ON SE; *Int'l*, pg. 2255
E.ON GRUGA OBJEKTGESELLSCHAFT MBH & CO.

KG—See E.ON SE; *Int'l*, pg. 2254
EON HADAPSAR INFRASTRUCTURE PVT. LTD.; *Int'l*, pg. 2458
E.ON UK PROPERTY SERVICES LIMITED—See E.ON SE; *Int'l*, pg. 2256
E&O PROPERTY DEVELOPMENT BERHAD—See Eastern & Oriental Berhad; *Int'l*, pg. 2271
EP3OIL INC; *U.S. Public*, pg. 782
EPIC SUISSE AG—See Alrov Properties & Lodgings Ltd.; *Int'l*, pg. 377
EPIC SUISSE PROPERTY MANAGEMENT GMBH—See Alrov Properties & Lodgings Ltd.; *Int'l*, pg. 377
EPM SWISS PROPERTY MANAGEMENT AG—See Bilfinger SE; *Int'l*, pg. 1028
EQ1 GIVES, INC.; *U.S. Private*, pg. 1414
EQ LIFE OY—See eQ Oyj; *Int'l*, pg. 2466
EQUIFAX PROPERTY DATA & ANALYTICS—See Equifax Inc.; *U.S. Public*, pg. 786
EQUITY TWO PLC—See Carson Cumberbatch PLC; *Int'l*, pg. 1347
ERA REALTY NETWORK PTE. LTD.—See Morgan Stanley; *U.S. Public*, pg. 1471
ERGON PROPERTIES, INC.—See Ergon, Inc.; *U.S. Private*, pg. 1418
ERIE TITLE AGENCY, INC.; *U.S. Private*, pg. 1420
ERSTE NEKRETNINE D.O.O.—See Erste Group Bank AG; *Int'l*, pg. 2498
ES-CON JAPAN LTD.; *Int'l*, pg. 2500
ESCON JAPAN REIT INVESTMENT CORP.—See ES-CON JAPAN Ltd.; *Int'l*, pg. 2500
ESCROW AGENT JAPAN, INC.; *Int'l*, pg. 2502
ESHRAQ INVESTMENTS PJSC; *Int'l*, pg. 2503
ESKMUIR PROPERTIES LTD; *Int'l*, pg. 2503
ESLEAD CORP.; *Int'l*, pg. 2504
ESPACIO LEON PROPCO S.L.U.—See Commerzbank AG; *Int'l*, pg. 1718
ESPIRE HOSPITALITY LIMITED; *Int'l*, pg. 2506
ESR KENDALL SQUARE REIT CO., LTD.; *Int'l*, pg. 2508
ESRT 1359 BROADWAY, L.L.C.—See Empire State Realty Trust, Inc.; *U.S. Public*, pg. 753
ESTATELY, INC.—See Anywhere Real Estate Inc.; *U.S. Public*, pg. 142
ETALON GROUP PLC; *Int'l*, pg. 2520
ETECH SOLUTIONS LIMITED—See Insight Venture Management, LLC; *U.S. Private*, pg. 2089
ETECH SOLUTIONS LIMITED—See Stone Point Capital LLC; *U.S. Private*, pg. 3823
ETHIKA INVESTMENTS LLC; *U.S. Private*, pg. 1431
ETUDIBEL S.A.—See Ascencio S.A.; *Int'l*, pg. 601
EUREKA GROUP HOLDINGS LIMITED; *Int'l*, pg. 2530
EUROASSET ITALIA S.R.L.—See Commerzbank AG; *Int'l*, pg. 1718
EUROFINS HYGIENE DU BATIMENT PARIS SAS—See Eurofins Scientific S.E.; *Int'l*, pg. 2542
EUROPEAN PROPERTY INVESTMENT CORPORATION LIMITED—See Alrov Properties & Lodgings Ltd.; *Int'l*, pg. 377
EUROSIC S.A.—See Gecina S.A.; *Int'l*, pg. 2909
EVEN CONSTRUTORA E INCORPORADORA S.A.; *Int'l*, pg. 2561
EVEN SP 18/10 EMPREENDIMENTOS IMOBILIARIOS LTDA.—See Even Construtora e Incorporadora S.A.; *Int'l*, pg. 2562
EVEN - SP 35/10 EMPREENDIMENTOS IMOBILIARIOS LTDA.—See Even Construtora e Incorporadora S.A.; *Int'l*, pg. 2561
EVEN - SP 47/10 EMPREENDIMENTOS IMOBILIARIOS LTDA.—See Even Construtora e Incorporadora S.A.; *Int'l*, pg. 2561
EVEN - SP 59/11 EMPREENDIMENTOS IMOBILIARIOS LTDA.—See Even Construtora e Incorporadora S.A.; *Int'l*, pg. 2561
EVERBRIGHT JIABAO CO., LTD.; *Int'l*, pg. 2563
EVEREST ESCROW, INC.—See Escrow Options Group Inc.; *U.S. Private*, pg. 1425
EVERGREEN SUSTAINABLE ENTERPRISES, INC.; *U.S. Public*, pg. 800
EVERLAND PUBLIC COMPANY LIMITED; *Int'l*, pg. 2567
EVERYDAY NETWORK CO., LTD.; *Int'l*, pg. 2569
EXP GLOBAL INDIA—See eXp World Holdings, Inc.; *U.S. Public*, pg. 808
EXPONENTIAL PROPERTY CONSTRUCTION, LLC; *U.S. Private*, pg. 1450
EXP WORLD HOLDINGS, INC.; *U.S. Public*, pg. 808
EXTENSA DEVELOPMENT SA—See Ackermans & van Haaren NV; *Int'l*, pg. 105
EXTENSA ISTANBUL—See Ackermans & van Haaren NV; *Int'l*, pg. 105
EXTENSA LAND II SA—See Ackermans & van Haaren NV; *Int'l*, pg. 106
EXTENSA NV—See Ackermans & van Haaren NV; *Int'l*, pg. 105
EXTENSA ROMANIA S.R.L—See Ackermans & van Haaren NV; *Int'l*, pg. 105
EXTENSA SLOVAKIA S.R.O.—See Ackermans & van Haaren NV; *Int'l*, pg. 106
EXTRA SPACE STORAGE, INC.; *U.S. Public*, pg. 812

531390 — OTHER ACTIVITIES RE...

EYP REALTY, LLC—See Brookfield Corporation; *Int'l*, pg. 1186
EZDAN HOLDING GROUP COMPANY (Q.S.C.); *Int'l*, pg. 2593
EZTEC EMPREENDIMENTOS E PARTICIPACOES S.A.; *Int'l*, pg. 2594
FAB PROPERTIES—See First Abu Dhabi Bank P.J.S.C.; *Int'l*, pg. 2681
FACT ENTERPRISE LIMITED; *Int'l*, pg. 2601
FAIRFIELD RESIDENTIAL COMPANY LLC—See Brookfield Corporation; *Int'l*, pg. 1187
FAIR LAND TITLE COMPANY, INC.—See Hovnanian Enterprises, Inc.; *U.S. Public*, pg. 1056
FAIRPLAY; *U.S. Private*, pg. 1464
FAIRVEST LIMITED; *Int'l*, pg. 2609
FAIRVEST PROPERTY HOLDINGS LIMITED; *Int'l*, pg. 2609
FAIRVIEW PROPERTIES, INC.—See Future plc; *Int'l*, pg. 2857
FAIRWAY INVESTMENTS, LLC; *U.S. Private*, pg. 1465
FANG HOLDINGS LTD.; *Int'l*, pg. 2613
FANTASIA HOLDINGS GROUP CO., LIMITED; *Int'l*, pg. 2613
FARAWAY LAND, LLC—See INSPIRATO INCORPORATED; *U.S. Private*, pg. 1131
FARMLAND PARTNERS OPERATING PARTNERSHIP, L.P.—See Farmland Partners Inc.; *U.S. Public*, pg. 822
FASTEXPERT, INC.; *U.S. Private*, pg. 1482
FASTIGHETS AB CENTRUM VASTERORT—See BNP Paribas SA; *Int'l*, pg. 1091
FASTIGHETS AB OSTERBOTTEN—See Atrium Ljungberg AB; *Int'l*, pg. 694
FASTIGHETS AB TORNET—See Fabege AB; *Int'l*, pg. 2598
FASTIGHETS AB TRIANON; *Int'l*, pg. 2622
FAVO REALTY, INC.; *U.S. Private*, pg. 1484
FAX LITE CO., LTD.—See Advanced Info Service Plc; *Int'l*, pg. 160
FBS REAL ESTATE S.P.A.—See Banca IFIS S.p.A.; *Int'l*, pg. 815
FCC CORPORATION—See Bilfinger SE; *Int'l*, pg. 1028
F&C PROPERTY LIMITED—See Bank of Montreal; *Int'l*, pg. 847
F&C REIT CORPORATE FINANCE LIMITED—See Bank of Montreal; *Int'l*, pg. 847
FDA SDN. BHD.—See GLOMAC Berhad; *Int'l*, pg. 3008
FELDA PROPERTIES SDN. BHD.—See FGV Holdings Bhd; *Int'l*, pg. 2649
FEPA TEKSTIL SANAYI VE PAZARLAMA A.S.; *Int'l*, pg. 2635
FERGO AISA, S.A.; *Int'l*, pg. 2637
F G INGENIERIE ET PROMOTION IMMOBILIERE—See BNP Paribas SA; *Int'l*, pg. 1091
FIBRA DANHOS; *Int'l*, pg. 2652
FIBRA MACQUARIE; *Int'l*, pg. 2652
FIBRA PROLOGIS; *Int'l*, pg. 2652
FIBRA SHOP PORTAFOLIOS INMOBILIARIOS SAPI DE CV; *Int'l*, pg. 2653
FIDELITY NATIONAL FINANCIAL, INC.; *U.S. Public*, pg. 830
FIDUCIAL REAL ESTATE SA; *Int'l*, pg. 2655
FIERA PROPERTIES LIMITED—See Fiera Capital Corporation; *Int'l*, pg. 2659
FILINVEST LAND INC.—See Filinvest Development Corporation; *Int'l*, pg. 2663
FILIOS, INC.—See IAC Inc.; *U.S. Public*, pg. 1082
FINBAR GROUP LIMITED; *Int'l*, pg. 2670
FINCAS ANZIZU SL; *Int'l*, pg. 2672
FINEXIA FINANCIAL GROUP LTD.; *Int'l*, pg. 2674
FINLAY MANAGEMENT, INC.; *U.S. Private*, pg. 1510
THE FIORE COMPANIES; *U.S. Private*, pg. 4028
FIPP S.A.; *Int'l*, pg. 2678
FIRM CAPITAL PROPERTY TRUST; *Int'l*, pg. 2679
FIRST ASIA HOLDINGS LIMITED; *Int'l*, pg. 2682
FIRST ASIA PROPERTIES (M) SDNBHD—See First Asia Holdings Limited; *Int'l*, pg. 2682
FIRST BROTHERS CO., LTD.; *Int'l*, pg. 2682
FIRST DUBAI FOR REAL ESTATE DEVELOPMENT COMPANY K.S.C.C.—See Al-Mazaya Holding Company K.S.C.P.; *Int'l*, pg. 287
FIRST HARTFORD CORPORATION; *U.S. Public*, pg. 844
FIRST INDUSTRIAL L.P.—See First Industrial Realty Trust, Inc.; *U.S. Public*, pg. 845
FIRSTLOGIC INC.; *Int'l*, pg. 2689
FIRST NATIONAL HOUSING TRUST LIMITED—See Henry Boot PLC; *Int'l*, pg. 3355
FIRST TEAM REAL ESTATE-ORANGE COUNTY INC. - FIRST TEAM COMMERCIAL DIVISION—See First Team Real Estate-Orange County Inc.; *U.S. Private*, pg. 1529
FISHER AUCTION COMPANY, INC.; *U.S. Private*, pg. 1534
FISHER PROPERTY GROUP, INC.; *U.S. Private*, pg. 1534
FITAS VERWALTUNG GMBH & CO. VERMIETUNGS-KG—See E.ON SE; *Int'l*, pg. 2257
FIVE FOX MANAGEMENT CO., LTD.—See Fuyo General Lease Co., *Int'l*, pg. 2859
FJ NEXT HOLDINGS CO., LTD.; *Int'l*, pg. 2697
FKP FUNDS MANAGEMENT LIMITED—See Brookfield Corporation; *Int'l*, pg. 1186
FKP LIMITED—See Brookfield Corporation; *Int'l*, pg. 1185

FKP REAL ESTATE PTY. LTD.—See Brookfield Corporation; *Int'l*, pg. 1186
FLAGSHIP RESORT DEVELOPMENT; *U.S. Private*, pg. 1539
FLC GROUP JOINT STOCK COMPANY; *Int'l*, pg. 2698
FLETCHER KING PLC; *Int'l*, pg. 2701
FLEXFUNDS ETP LLC; *U.S. Private*, pg. 1544
FLORENCE REALTY, LLC—See Ventas, Inc.; *U.S. Public*, pg. 2278
FLORIDA CROWN DEVELOPMENT CORP.; *U.S. Private*, pg. 1547
FLYING J, INC-REAL ESTATE DIVISION—See FJ Management, Inc.; *U.S. Private*, pg. 1538
FONCIERE 7 INVESTISSEMENT SA; *Int'l*, pg. 2724
FONCIERE ATLAND SA; *Int'l*, pg. 2724
FONCIERE DE PARIS SIIC—See Gecina S.A.; *Int'l*, pg. 2909
FONCIERE DES MURS SCA—See Covivio; *Int'l*, pg. 1821
FONCIERE EURIS—See Finatis SA; *Int'l*, pg. 2670
FONCIERE INEA SA; *Int'l*, pg. 2724
FONCIERE PARIS NORD SA; *Int'l*, pg. 2724
FONCIERE R-PARIS SCA; *Int'l*, pg. 2724
FONCIERE VINDI SA; *Int'l*, pg. 2724
FONVILLE MORISEY REALTY—See The Long & Foster Companies, Inc.; *U.S. Private*, pg. 4072
FORECLOSURE VENTURE CAPITAL, INC.; *U.S. Private*, pg. 1565
FOREIGN TRADE DEVELOPMENT & INVESTMENT CORPORATION; *Int'l*, pg. 2731
FORESTAR (USA) REAL ESTATE GROUP INC. - ATLANTA—See Forestar Group Inc.; *U.S. Public*, pg. 867
FORESTAR (USA) REAL ESTATE GROUP INC. - LUFKIN—See Forestar Group Inc.; *U.S. Public*, pg. 867
FORESTAR (USA) REAL ESTATE GROUP INC.—See Forestar Group Inc.; *U.S. Public*, pg. 867
FOREST CITY RESIDENTIAL GROUP, INC.—See Brookfield Corporation; *Int'l*, pg. 1187
FORMATION ASSET MANAGEMENT LIMITED—See Formation Group PLC; *Int'l*, pg. 2733
FORT STREET REAL ESTATE CAPITAL PTY. LIMITED—See E&P Financial Group Limited; *Int'l*, pg. 2247
FORUM EQUITY PARTNERS—See Providence Equity Partners L.L.C.; *U.S. Private*, pg. 3293
FORUM IMMOBILIENGESELLSCHAFT MBH—See Commerzbank AG; *Int'l*, pg. 1718
FOUNDERS TITLE AGENCY, INC.—See Hovnanian Enterprises, Inc.; *U.S. Public*, pg. 1056
FOURLIS HOLDINGS S.A.; *Int'l*, pg. 2755
FOUR SALES, LTD.; *U.S. Private*, pg. 1582
FRAGRANCE LAND PTE LTD—See Fragrance Group Limited; *Int'l*, pg. 2758
FRANCONIA REAL ESTATE SERVICES, INC.—See Weichert Co.; *U.S. Private*, pg. 4470
FRANKLIN L. HANEY COMPANY; *U.S. Private*, pg. 1597
FRANKLIN STREET ADVISORS, INC.—See Fifth Third Bancorp; *U.S. Public*, pg. 833
FRAPORT IMMOBILIENSERVICE UND -ENTWICKLUNGS GMBH & CO. KG—See Fraport AG; *Int'l*, pg. 2764
FRAPORT REAL ESTATE 162 163 GMBH & CO. KG—See Fraport AG; *Int'l*, pg. 2764
FRAPORT REAL ESTATE VERWALTUNGS GMBH—See Fraport AG; *Int'l*, pg. 2764
FRAPPANT ALTONA GMBH—See Hypo Real Estate Holding AG; *Int'l*, pg. 3553
FRASERS HOSPITALITY (UK) LIMITED—See Frasers Property Limited; *Int'l*, pg. 2766
FRASERS PROPERTY (APG) PTY. LIMITED—See Frasers Property Limited; *Int'l*, pg. 2766
FRASERS PROPERTY AUSTRALIA PTY LIMITED—See Frasers Property Limited; *Int'l*, pg. 2766
FRASERS PROPERTY LIMITED; *Int'l*, pg. 2765
FRAWO FRANKFURTER WOHNUNGS- UND SIEDLUNGS-GESELLSCHAFT MBH—See Helaba Landesbank Hessen-Thuringen; *Int'l*, pg. 3327
FRAZEL GROUP SDN. BHD.; *Int'l*, pg. 2767
FREUDENBERG REAL ESTATE GMBH—See Freudenberg SE; *Int'l*, pg. 2788
FREY S.A.; *Int'l*, pg. 2791
FRONT YARD RESIDENTIAL CORPORATION—See Ares Management Corporation; *U.S. Public*, pg. 191
FRONT YARD RESIDENTIAL CORPORATION—See Pretium Partners, LLC; *U.S. Private*, pg. 3257
FRP DEVELOPMENT CORP.—See FRP Holdings, Inc.; *U.S. Public*, pg. 888
FRP HOLDINGS, INC.; *U.S. Public*, pg. 888
FSK LAND CORPORATION; *U.S. Private*, pg. 1618
FUJIAN START GROUP CO., LTD.; *Int'l*, pg. 2819
FUKUOKA REIT CORPORATION; *Int'l*, pg. 2840
FUNDIMMO SAS—See Fonciere Atland SA; *Int'l*, pg. 2724
FUNDINGSHIELD LLC; *U.S. Private*, pg. 1623
FURUKAWA CO., LTD. - REAL ESTATE DIVISION—See Furukawa Co., Ltd.; *Int'l*, pg. 2847
FUTURA CONSORCIO INMOBILIARIO SA; *Int'l*, pg. 2852
FUTURELAND, CORP.; *U.S. Public*, pg. 893
FUTURISTIC SOLUTIONS LIMITED; *Int'l*, pg. 2858

CORPORATE AFFILIATIONS

GABAY PROPERTIES AND DEVELOPMENT LTD; *Int'l*, pg. 2867
GABETTI S.P.A.—See Gabetti Property Solutions SpA; *Int'l*, pg. 2867
GAG IMMOBILIEN AG; *Int'l*, pg. 2868
GALATA INVESTMENT COMPANY AD; *Int'l*, pg. 2871
GALESI GROUP; *U.S. Private*, pg. 1637
GAMMAU CONSTRUCTION SDN. BHD.—See Gamuda Berhad; *Int'l*, pg. 2879
GAMUDA LAND SDN. BHD.—See Gamuda Berhad; *Int'l*, pg. 2879
GARBARY SP. Z O.O.—See Commerzbank AG; *Int'l*, pg. 1719
THE GARDENS OF BAGATELLE LTD.—See ENL Limited; *Int'l*, pg. 2442
GARNET CONSTRUCTION LIMITED; *Int'l*, pg. 2885
GATE MARITIME PROPERTIES, INC.—See Gate Petroleum Company; *U.S. Private*, pg. 1649
GAUCHO GROUP HOLDINGS, INC.; *U.S. Public*, pg. 908
GAY-LUSSAC GESTION—See Raymond James Financial, Inc.; *U.S. Public*, pg. 1764
GAZPROMBANK-INVEST LLC—See Gazprombank JSC; *Int'l*, pg. 2892
GBCORP TOWER REAL ESTATE W.L.L.—See GFH Financial Group B.S.C.; *Int'l*, pg. 2956
GB PARTNERSHIPS LIMITED; *Int'l*, pg. 2893
GCCL CONSTRUCTION & REALITIES LTD.; *Int'l*, pg. 2895
GCG CONSTRUCTION, INC.; *U.S. Private*, pg. 1653
GDH REAL ESTATES (CHINA) CO. LIMITED—See GDH Limited; *Int'l*, pg. 2896
GEA CFS REAL ESTATE GMBH—See GEA Group Aktiengesellschaft; *Int'l*, pg. 2898
GEA REAL ESTATE GMBH—See GEA Group Aktiengesellschaft; *Int'l*, pg. 2902
GECINA NOM; *Int'l*, pg. 2909
GEFION GROUP A/S; *Int'l*, pg. 2911
GEI-IMMO AG; *Int'l*, pg. 2912
GEMDALE CORPORATION; *Int'l*, pg. 2915
GEMDALE DONGGUAN COMPANY—See Gemdale Corporation; *Int'l*, pg. 2915
GEMDALE SHAOXING COMPANY—See Gemdale Corporation; *Int'l*, pg. 2915
GEMDALE USA CORPORATION—See Gemdale Corporation; *Int'l*, pg. 2915
GEMEINNUTZIGE WOHNUNGSGESELLSCHAFT MBH HESSEN—See Helaba Landesbank Hessen-Thuringen; *Int'l*, pg. 3328
GENERAL DYNAMICS PROPERTIES, INC.—See General Dynamics Corporation; *U.S. Public*, pg. 915
GENERAL HOMES CORP.—See Wells Fargo & Company; *U.S. Public*, pg. 2343
GENERALI DEUTSCHLAND GESELLSCHAFT FUR BAV MBH—See Assicurazioni Generali S.p.A.; *Int'l*, pg. 644
GENERALI FRANCE IMMOBILIER SAS—See Assicurazioni Generali S.p.A.; *Int'l*, pg. 645
GENERALI IMMOBILIEN AG—See Assicurazioni Generali S.p.A.; *Int'l*, pg. 645
GENERALI INSURANCE AGENCY COMPANY LIMITED—See Assicurazioni Generali S.p.A.; *Int'l*, pg. 646
GENERALI PROPERTIES S.P.A.—See Assicurazioni Generali S.p.A.; *Int'l*, pg. 646
GENERALI REAL ESTATE INVESTMENTS B.V.—See Apollo Global Management, Inc.; *U.S. Public*, pg. 147
GENERALI REAL ESTATE S.P.A.—See Assicurazioni Generali S.p.A.; *Int'l*, pg. 646
GENERALI SAXON LAND DEVELOPMENT COMPANY LIMITED—See Assicurazioni Generali S.p.A.; *Int'l*, pg. 647
GEORG FISCHER LIEGENSCHAFTEN AG—See Georg Fischer AG; *Int'l*, pg. 2936
GEWERBEGRUND AIRPORT GMBH & CO. SCHWAIG KG—See BayernLB Holding AG; *Int'l*, pg. 914
GEWERBESIEDLUNGS-GESELLSCHAFT GMBH—See CPI Property Group, S.A.; *Int'l*, pg. 1825
G-G-B GEBAUDE- UND GRUNDBESITZ GMBH—See Commerzbank AG; *Int'l*, pg. 1718
GGG GESELLSCHAFT FUR GRUNDSTUCKS- UND GE-BAUDENUTZUNG MBH—See E.ON SE; *Int'l*, pg. 2257
GHG FACILITAIR B.V.—See Groothandelsgebouwen N.V.; *Int'l*, pg. 3088
GHP ASSET MANAGEMENT LIMITED—See GHP Group; *Int'l*, pg. 2960
GHP GROUP - REAL ESTATE DIVISION—See GHP Group; *Int'l*, pg. 2960
GIBRALTAR CAPITAL AND ASSET MANAGEMENT, LLC—See Toll Brothers, Inc.; *U.S. Public*, pg. 2161
GIBRALTAR PROPERTIES, INC.—See Prudential Financial, Inc.; *U.S. Public*, pg. 1731
GIBRALTAR REAL ESTATE CAPITAL LLC—See Toll Brothers, Inc.; *U.S. Public*, pg. 2161
GIC REAL ESTATE PTE. LTD.—See GIC Pte. Ltd.; *Int'l*, pg. 2964
GILAT SATELLITE NETWORKS (HOLLAND) B.V.—See Gilat Satellite Networks Ltd.; *Int'l*, pg. 2973
GILBANE DEVELOPMENT COMPANY—See Gilbane, Inc.; *U.S. Private*, pg. 1698
G IMMO SCI—See Groupe BPCE; *Int'l*, pg. 3098

N.A.I.C.S. INDEX

531390 — OTHER ACTIVITIES RE...

GIRISIM VARLIK YONETIMI A.S.—See Fiba Holding A.S.; *Int'l*, pg. 2651
GIZA GENERAL CONTRACTING & REAL ESTATE INVESTMENT; *Int'l*, pg. 2982
G.K. REAL ESTATE (2564) CO., LTD.—See Gunkul Engineering Co., Ltd.; *Int'l*, pg. 3183
GLASMACHERVIERTEL GMBH & CO. KG—See ADLER Group SA; *Int'l*, pg. 150
GLENMARIE PROPERTIES SDN. BHD.—See DRB-HICOM Berhad; *Int'l*, pg. 2201
GLENRISE GROVE, L.L.C.—See Hovnanian Enterprises, Inc.; *U.S. Public*, pg. 1056
GLIMCHER GROUP INCORPORATED; *U.S. Private*, pg. 1711
GLOBAL CENTER KFT.—See Ablon Group Limited; *Int'l*, pg. 63
GLOBAL-ESTATE RESORTS, INC.—See Alliance Global Group, Inc.; *Int'l*, pg. 339
GLOBAL FUND INVESTMENTS LLC; *U.S. Private*, pg. 1714
GLOBAL GATE PROPERTY CORP.; *U.S. Private*, pg. 1714
GLOBAL IMAGING HOLDINGS REALTY, LLC; *U.S. Private*, pg. 1714
GLOBAL JUHAN CORPORATION; *Int'l*, pg. 2998
GLOBAL LAND MASTERS CORPORATION LIMITED; *Int'l*, pg. 2998
GLOBAL LINK MANAGEMENT, INC.; *Int'l*, pg. 2998
GLOBAL MEDICAL REIT INC.; *U.S. Public*, pg. 942
GLOBAL MIAMI ACQUISITION COMPANY, LLC—See Digital Realty Trust, Inc.; *U.S. Public*, pg. 663
GLOBALPORT 900 INC.; *Int'l*, pg. 3004
GLOBAL TRADE CENTRE S.A.; *Int'l*, pg. 3002
GLOBALWORTH POLAND—See Globalworth Real Estate Investments Limited; *Int'l*, pg. 3005
GLOMAC SUTERA SDN. BHD.—See GLOMAC Berhad; *Int'l*, pg. 3008
GMH COMMUNITIES, LP—See Blackstone Inc.; *U.S. Public*, pg. 347
GMO RETECH, INC.—See GMO Internet Group, Inc.; *Int'l*, pg. 3014
GOAT EVEN EMPREENDIMENTOS IMOBILIARIOS LTDA.—See Even Construtora e Incorporadora S.A.; *Int'l*, pg. 2562
GOHOME H.K. CO. LTD.—See News Corporation; *U.S. Public*, pg. 1519
GOLD CREST CO., LTD.; *Int'l*, pg. 3024
GOLDCREST CORPORATION LIMITED; *Int'l*, pg. 3027
GOLDEN LAND PROPERTY DEVELOPMENT PUBLIC COMPANY LIMITED—See Frasers Property Limited; *Int'l*, pg. 2766
GOLD HORSE INTERNATIONAL, INC.; *Int'l*, pg. 3024
GOLDIN PROPERTIES HOLDINGS LIMITED; *Int'l*, pg. 3033
GOLDMAN PROPERTIES; *U.S. Private*, pg. 1735
GOLD POINT LODGING AND REALTY, INC.; *U.S. Private*, pg. 1728
GOLUB REALTY SERVICES LLC—See Golub & Co; *U.S. Private*, pg. 1736
GOODMAN ASIA LIMITED—See Goodman Limited; *Int'l*, pg. 3040
GOODMAN BELGIUM NV—See Goodman Limited; *Int'l*, pg. 3040
GOODMAN FRANCE SARL—See Goodman Limited; *Int'l*, pg. 3040
GOODMAN GERMANY GMBH—See Goodman Limited; *Int'l*, pg. 3040
GOODMAN ITALY S.R.L.—See Goodman Limited; *Int'l*, pg. 3040
GOODMAN JAPAN FUNDS LIMITED—See Goodman Limited; *Int'l*, pg. 3040
GOODMAN JAPAN LIMITED—See Goodman Limited; *Int'l*, pg. 3040
GOODMAN MANAGEMENT CONSULTING (BEIJING) CO., LTD.—See Goodman Limited; *Int'l*, pg. 3040
GOODMAN MANAGEMENT CONSULTING (SHANGHAI) CO., LTD.—See Goodman Limited; *Int'l*, pg. 3040
GOODMAN NETHERLANDS BV—See Goodman Limited; *Int'l*, pg. 3040
GOODMAN OPERATOR (UK) LIMITED—See Goodman Limited; *Int'l*, pg. 3040
GOOD SAM MOB INVESTORS, LLC—See Ventas, Inc.; *U.S. Public*, pg. 2278
GORILLA CAPITAL; *U.S. Private*, pg. 1743
GOTESCO LAND INC.; *Int'l*, pg. 3043
GOVERNMENT LIQUIDATION.COM, LLC—See Liquidity Services, Inc.; *U.S. Public*, pg. 1321
GOZDE GIYIM SAN. VE TIC. A.S.; *Int'l*, pg. 3045
GPG LUPINE PARTNERS—See Greener Pastures Group LLC; *U.S. Private*, pg. 1777
GPLUSMEDIA INC.—See Gakken Holdings Co., Ltd.; *Int'l*, pg. 2869
GRADINA A.D.; *Int'l*, pg. 3049
GRAINGER PLC; *Int'l*, pg. 3052
GRAINGER RESIDENTIAL MANAGEMENT LIMITED—See Grainger plc; *Int'l*, pg. 3052
GRAND CANAL LAND PUBLIC COMPANY LIMITED—See Central Pattana Public Company Limited; *Int'l*, pg. 1409

GRANDJOY HOLDINGS GROUP CO., LTD.—See COFCO Limited; *Int'l*, pg. 1692
GRAND PACIFIC FINANCING CORP.—See Chailease Holding Company Limited; *Int'l*, pg. 1437
GRAND REAL ESTATE PROJECTS CO. K.S.C.C.; *Int'l*, pg. 3056
GRANGE ROC PROPERTY PTY LTD—See Grange Resources Limited; *Int'l*, pg. 3058
GRANITE AUSTRIA GMBH—See Granite Real Estate Investment Trust; *Int'l*, pg. 3059
GRANITE REIT INC.—See Granite Real Estate Investment Trust; *Int'l*, pg. 3059
GRAPHISOFT PARK KFT—See Graphisoft Park SE; *Int'l*, pg. 3060
GREAT CHINA HOLDINGS (HONG KONG) LIMITED; *Int'l*, pg. 3063
GRECAM S.A.S.—See CoStar Group, Inc.; *U.S. Public*, pg. 586
GREENBANK VENTURES INC.; *Int'l*, pg. 3073
GREENER PASTURES GROUP LLC; *U.S. Private*, pg. 1777
GREENHOUSE REAL ESTATE, LLC—See AAC Holdings, Inc.; *U.S. Private*, pg. 31
GREENLAND HOLDINGS CORPORATION LIMITED; *Int'l*, pg. 3075
GREENLINK INTERNATIONAL, INC.; *U.S. Public*, pg. 965
GREEN RESOURCES PUBLIC COMPANY LIMITED; *Int'l*, pg. 3072
GREENSPRING AT MT. SNOW HOMEOWNER'S ASSOCIATION, INC.; *U.S. Private*, pg. 1780
GREENSTREET REAL ESTATE PARTNERS, L.P.; *U.S. Private*, pg. 1780
GREENWORKS SERVICE COMPANY; *U.S. Private*, pg. 1782
GREE REAL ESTATE CO., LTD.; *Int'l*, pg. 3069
GR GRUNDSTUCKS GMBH OBJEKT CORVUS & CO.—See Commerzbank AG; *Int'l*, pg. 1719
GRIFFIN LAND—See Centerbridge Partners, L.P.; *U.S. Private*, pg. 815
GRIFFIN LAND—See GIC Pte. Ltd.; *Int'l*, pg. 2964
GRIFFIN PARTNERS, INC.; *U.S. Private*, pg. 1788
GRIT REAL ESTATE INCOME GROUP LIMITED; *Int'l*, pg. 3087
GROUPAMA ASSET MANAGEMENT—See Groupama SA; *Int'l*, pg. 3090
GROUPAMA IMMOBILIER—See Groupama SA; *Int'l*, pg. 3091
GROUPE CANVAR INC.; *Int'l*, pg. 3101
GROUPE ETPO SA; *Int'l*, pg. 3102
GROUPE VENDOME ROME; *Int'l*, pg. 3112
GROUPIMO S.A.; *Int'l*, pg. 3112
GROVY INDIA LIMITED; *Int'l*, pg. 3112
GROWNERS S.A.; *Int'l*, pg. 3113
GRUBB & ELLIS MANAGEMENT SERVICES, INC.—See BGC Group, Inc.; *U.S. Public*, pg. 329
GRUNDBESITZGESELLSCHAFT BERLIN MBH—See Commerzbank AG; *Int'l*, pg. 1718
GRUNDSTUCKSVERWALTUNGS—See Helaba Landesbank Hessen-Thuringen; *Int'l*, pg. 3328
GRUPO EXP REALTORS MEXICO, S DE R.L. DE C.V.—See eXp World Holdings, Inc.; *U.S. Public*, pg. 808
GRUPO GICSA, S.A.B. DE C.V.; *Int'l*, pg. 3129
GRZYBOWSKA CENTRUM SP. Z O.O.—See Atlas Estates Limited; *Int'l*, pg. 685
GTC BULGARIA—See Globe Trade Centre S.A.; *Int'l*, pg. 3006
GTC CROATIA—See Globe Trade Centre S.A.; *Int'l*, pg. 3006
GTC CZECH REPUBLIC—See Globe Trade Centre S.A.; *Int'l*, pg. 3006
GTC HUNGARY—See Globe Trade Centre S.A.; *Int'l*, pg. 3006
GTC REAL ESTATE INVESTMENTS BULGARIA B.V.—See Globe Trade Centre S.A.; *Int'l*, pg. 3006
GTC REAL ESTATE MANAGEMENT, S.R.O.—See Globe Trade Centre S.A.; *Int'l*, pg. 3007
GTC ROMANIA—See Globe Trade Centre S.A.; *Int'l*, pg. 3007
GTC SERBIA—See Globe Trade Centre S.A.; *Int'l*, pg. 3007
GTJ REIT, INC.; *U.S. Private*, pg. 1807
GTM TEXTILE CO., LTD.—See GTM HOLDINGS CORPORATION; *Int'l*, pg. 3151
GTS JAPAN CO., LTD.—See Chubu Electric Power Co., Inc.; *Int'l*, pg. 1593
GUANGDONG CHANGSHENG ENTERPRISES GROUP CO., LTD.—See Guangdong Rising Assets Management Co., Ltd.; *Int'l*, pg. 3159
GUANGDONG EVER-RISING GROUP CORPORATION LTD.—See Guangdong Rising Assets Management Co., Ltd.; *Int'l*, pg. 3159
GUANGDONG PROVINCE GUANGSHENG ASSETS MANAGEMENT CO., LTD—See Guangdong Rising Assets Management Co., Ltd.; *Int'l*, pg. 3159
GUANGDONG SHIRONGZHAOYE CO., LTD.; *Int'l*, pg. 3160
GUANGXI POLY YUANCHEN REAL ESTATE DEVELOPMENT CO., LTD—See China Poly Group Corporation; *Int'l*, pg. 1541

GUANGZHOU PEARL RIVER INDUSTRIAL DEVELOPMENT HOLDINGS CO., LTD; *Int'l*, pg. 3167
GUANGZHOU VANKE REAL ESTATE COMPANY LIMITED—See China Vanke Co., Ltd.; *Int'l*, pg. 1562
GUANGZHOU YUETAI GROUP CO., LTD.; *Int'l*, pg. 3168
GUARDIAN COMMERCIAL REALTY; *U.S. Private*, pg. 1810
GUH DEVELOPMENT SDN. BHD.—See GUH Holdings Berhad; *Int'l*, pg. 3173
GUH PROPERTIES SDN. BHD.—See GUH Holdings Berhad; *Int'l*, pg. 3173
GULF GENERAL INVESTMENT COMPANY PSC; *Int'l*, pg. 3180
GULF HOLDING COMPANY KSCC—See GFH Financial Group B.S.C.; *Int'l*, pg. 2956
GULSKOGEN PROSJEKT & EIENDOM AS—See BNP Paribas SA; *Int'l*, pg. 1091
GUNDAKER COMMERCIAL GROUP, INC.; *U.S. Private*, pg. 1818
GUOCOLAND BINH DUONG PROPERTY CO., LTD.—See Hong Leong Investment Holdings Pte. Ltd.; *Int'l*, pg. 3468
GUOCOLAND LIMITED—See Hong Leong Investment Holdings Pte. Ltd.; *Int'l*, pg. 3468
GUOCOLAND (MALAYSIA) BERHAD—See Hong Leong Investment Holdings Pte. Ltd.; *Int'l*, pg. 3468
GUOCOLAND (SINGAPORE) PTE. LTD.—See Hong Leong Investment Holdings Pte. Ltd.; *Int'l*, pg. 3468
GUOTAI JUNAN FUTURES CO., LTD.—See Guotai Junan Securities Co., Ltd.; *Int'l*, pg. 3187
GVG GESELLSCHAFT ZUR VERWERTUNG VON GRUNDBESITZ MIT BESCHRANKTER HAFTUNG—See Commerzbank AG; *Int'l*, pg. 1718
GWH BAUPROJEKTE GMBH—See Helaba Landesbank Hessen-Thuringen; *Int'l*, pg. 3327
GWH IMMOBILIEN HOLDING GMBH—See Helaba Landesbank Hessen-Thuringen; *Int'l*, pg. 3328
GWH WERTINVEST GMBH—See Helaba Landesbank Hessen-Thuringen; *Int'l*, pg. 3328
GYAN DEVELOPERS & BUILDERS LIMITED; *Int'l*, pg. 3190
HABIB METRO PAKISTAN (PRIVATE) LIMITED—See House of Habib; *Int'l*, pg. 3491
HABITATION DOMAINE DES TREMBLES INC.—See Welltower Inc.; *U.S. Public*, pg. 2348
HABITATION FAUBOURG GIFFARD INC.—See Welltower Inc.; *U.S. Public*, pg. 2348
HA DO GROUP JOINT STOCK COMPANY; *Int'l*, pg. 3201
HAFENBOGEN GMBH & CO. KG—See Helaba Landesbank Hessen-Thuringen; *Int'l*, pg. 3328
HAGAG GROUP REAL ESTATE ENTREPRENEURSHIP LTD.; *Int'l*, pg. 3206
HAGIBOR OFFICE BUILDING, A.S.—See CPI Property Group, S.A.; *Int'l*, pg. 1825
HAI PHAT INVESTMENT JSC; *Int'l*, pg. 3209
HAIYUAN PROPERTY CO., LTD.—See Hubei Jumpcan Pharmaceutical Co., Ltd.; *Int'l*, pg. 3518
HALE KAUAI, LTD.; *U.S. Private*, pg. 1842
HALLAM LAND MANAGEMENT LIMITED—See Henry Boot PLC; *Int'l*, pg. 3355
HALLMARK ESCROW CO., INC.—See First Team Real Estate-Orange County Inc.; *U.S. Private*, pg. 1529
HAL MANN PROPERTIES LTD.—See Hal Mann Vella Group PLC; *Int'l*, pg. 3223
HALPERN ENTERPRISES, INC.; *U.S. Private*, pg. 1846
HAL REAL ESTATE INC.—See HAL Trust N.V.; *Int'l*, pg. 3227
HALS-DEVELOPMENT JSC; *Int'l*, pg. 3233
HAMAGA AS; *Int'l*, pg. 3234
HAMMERSMITH DATA MANAGEMENT, INC.; *U.S. Private*, pg. 1849
HAMMERSON PLC; *Int'l*, pg. 3238
HANA ASSET TRUST CO., LTD.—See Hana Financial Group, Inc.; *Int'l*, pg. 3240
HANG LUNG GROUP LIMITED; *Int'l*, pg. 3244
HANGZHOU NIAGRA REAL ESTATES COMPANY LIMITED—See China City Infrastructure Group Limited; *Int'l*, pg. 1489
HA NOI SOUTH HOUSING AND URBAN DEVELOPMENT CORPORATION; *Int'l*, pg. 3201
HANSA LUFTBILD AG; *Int'l*, pg. 3259
HANSEATISCHE IMMOBILIEN MANAGEMENT GMBH—See Ernst Russ AG; *Int'l*, pg. 2496
HANSHIN REAL ESTATE CO., LTD.—See Hankyu Hanshin Holdings Inc.; *Int'l*, pg. 3256
HANS HOLTERBOSCH, INC.; *U.S. Private*, pg. 1856
HANWHA ASSET MANAGEMENT CO., LTD.—See Hanwha Group; *Int'l*, pg. 3264
HARBIN POLY REAL ESTATE COMPREHENSIVE DEVELOPMENT CO., LTD—See China Poly Group Corporation; *Int'l*, pg. 1541
HARBOR URBAN, LLC—See Urban Partners, LLC; *U.S. Private*, pg. 4314
HARCOURTS INTERNATIONAL LTD; *Int'l*, pg. 3272
HARIMA TRADING, INC.—See Harima Chemicals Group, Inc.; *Int'l*, pg. 3276
HARMONY PROPERTY SDN. BHD.—See Brem Holding Berhad; *Int'l*, pg. 1144

4525

HARROW ESTATES PLC—See Barratt Developments PLC; *Int'l*, pg. 868
HARTMAN 400 NORTH BELT LLC—See SILVER STAR PROPERTIES REIT, INC.; *U.S. Private*, pg. 3662
HARTMAN COOPER STREET PLAZA, LLC—See SILVER STAR PROPERTIES REIT, INC.; *U.S. Private*, pg. 3662
HARTMAN CORPORATE PARK PLACE LLC—See SILVER STAR PROPERTIES REIT, INC.; *U.S. Private*, pg. 3662
HARTMAN MITCHELLDALE BUSINESS PARK, LLC—See SILVER STAR PROPERTIES REIT, INC.; *U.S. Private*, pg. 3662
HARTMAN SKYMARK TOWER LLC—See SILVER STAR PROPERTIES REIT, INC.; *U.S. Private*, pg. 3662
HARTMAN THREE FOREST PLAZA, LLC—See SILVER STAR PROPERTIES REIT, INC.; *U.S. Private*, pg. 3662
HARTMAN WESTWAY ONE, LLC—See SILVER STAR PROPERTIES REIT, INC.; *U.S. Private*, pg. 3662
HARTZ MOUNTAIN INDUSTRIES, INC.—See The Hartz Group, Inc.; *U.S. Private*, pg. 4043
HARUM INTISARI SDN BHD—See Gamuda Berhad; *Int'l*, pg. 2879
HARWORTH GROUP PLC; *Int'l*, pg. 3282
HASEKO BUSINESS PROXY, INC.—See Haseko Corporation; *Int'l*, pg. 3283
HASTINGS + COHN REAL ESTATE, LLC; *U.S. Private*, pg. 1879
HAUCK & AUFHAUSER (SCHWEIZ) AG—See Fosun International Limited; *Int'l*, pg. 2751
HAUS TALK, INC.; *Int'l*, pg. 3285
HAWAII LIFE REAL ESTATE BROKERS; *U.S. Private*, pg. 1881
HAWKEYE PROPERTIES, INC.; *U.S. Private*, pg. 1882
HAZOOR MULTI PROJECTS LIMITED; *Int'l*, pg. 3295
HB DEVELOPERS LTD.; *Int'l*, pg. 3295
HBS REALTORS PVT. LTD.; *Int'l*, pg. 3297
HCI IMMOBILIEN GESCHAFTSFUHRUNGSGESELLSCHAFT MBH—See Ernst Russ AG; *Int'l*, pg. 2495
HCI REAL ESTATE FINANCE I GMBH & CO. KG—See Ernst Russ AG; *Int'l*, pg. 2496
HDM PROPERTIES SDN BHD—See Hwang Capital (Malaysia) Berhad; *Int'l*, pg. 3542
HEALTHCARE & MEDICAL INVESTMENT CORPORATION; *Int'l*, pg. 3303
HEALTHPEAK OP, LLC—See Healthpeak Properties, Inc.; *U.S. Public*, pg. 1016
HEARTLAND, LLC—See Laird Norton Company, LLC; *U.S. Private*, pg. 2374
HEBA FASTIGHETS AB; *Int'l*, pg. 3305
HEBO LIMITED—See Hang Lung Group Limited; *Int'l*, pg. 3245
HEIDELBERGCEMENT GRUNDSTUCKSGESELLSCHAFT MBH & CO. KG—See Heidelberg Materials AG; *Int'l*, pg. 3314
HEIDELBERGCEMENT GRUNDSTUCKSVERWALTUNGSGESELLSCHAFT MBH—See Heidelberg Materials AG; *Int'l*, pg. 3314
HEILBAD BAD NEUSTADT GMBH—See Asklepios Kliniken GmbH & Co. KGaA; *Int'l*, pg. 624
HEILONGJIANG TRANSPORT DEVELOPMENT CO., LTD.; *Int'l*, pg. 3323
HEITMAN LLC; *U.S. Private*, pg. 1905
HEIWA REAL ESTATE ASSET MANAGEMENT CO., LTD.—See HEIWA REAL ESTATE CO. LTD.; *Int'l*, pg. 3327
HEIWA REAL ESTATE REIT,INC.; *Int'l*, pg. 3327
HELABA DIGITAL GMBH & CO. KG—See Helaba Landesbank Hessen-Thuringen; *Int'l*, pg. 3328
HELBOR EMPREENDIMENTOS S.A.; *Int'l*, pg. 3328
HELICAL PLC; *Int'l*, pg. 3329
HELLENIC QUARRIES SA—See ELLAKTOR S.A.; *Int'l*, pg. 2364
HELONGJIANG POLY AOYU REAL ESTATE DEVELOPMENT CO., LTD—See China Poly Group Corporation; *Int'l*, pg. 1541
HELSINGIN ITAMERENKATU 21 KOY—See Blackstone Inc.; *U.S. Public*, pg. 351
HELVETIA SPORT LTD.—See ENL Limited; *Int'l*, pg. 2441
HENRY BOOT DEVELOPMENTS LIMITED—See Henry Boot PLC; *Int'l*, pg. 3355
HENRY BOOT ESTATES LIMITED—See Henry Boot PLC; *Int'l*, pg. 3355
HENRY BOOT TAMWORTH LIMITED—See Henry Boot PLC; *Int'l*, pg. 3355
HESTA IMMOBILIEN GMBH—See Hesta AG; *Int'l*, pg. 3365
HFF, INC.—See Jones Lang LaSalle Incorporated; *U.S. Public*, pg. 1202
HGI REALTY, INC.—See Heritage Group, Inc.; *U.S. Private*, pg. 1923
H&H CONSTRUCTORS OF FAYETTEVILLE, LLC—See Dream Finders Homes, Inc.; *U.S. Public*, pg. 687
HHLA INTERMODAL VERWALTUNG GMBH—See Hamburger Hafen und Logistik AG; *Int'l*, pg. 3236
HIAG IMMOBILEN HOLDING AG; *Int'l*, pg. 3382
HIBINO SPACETECH CORPORATION—See Hibino Corporation; *Int'l*, pg. 3383
HIGASHINIHON FUDOSAN CO., LTD.—See First Brothers Co., Ltd.; *Int'l*, pg. 2682
HIGH PERFORMANCE REAL ESTATE INVESTMENTS COMPANY PLC; *Int'l*, pg. 3386
HILI PREMIER ESTATE ROMANIA SRL—See Hili Properties PLC; *Int'l*, pg. 3391
HILLPARK DEVELOPMENT SDN. BHD.—See Gromutual Berhad; *Int'l*, pg. 3087
HILLSBORO CLUB, LLC—See Alecta pensionsforsakring, omsesidigt; *Int'l*, pg. 305
HILLSBORO TERRACE, LLC—See Alecta pensionsforsakring, omsesidigt; *Int'l*, pg. 305
HILLSTRAND DEVELOPMENT SDN BHD—See Gadang Holdings Berhad; *Int'l*, pg. 2868
HIRON TRADE INVESTMENT & INDUSTRIAL BUILDINGS LTD.; *Int'l*, pg. 3404
HITACHI LIFE, LTD.—See Hitachi, Ltd.; *Int'l*, pg. 3420
HITACHI URBAN INVESTMENT, LTD.—See Hitachi, Ltd.; *Int'l*, pg. 3422
HITEC VASTGOED B.V.—See Air Water Inc.; *Int'l*, pg. 240
HIYES INTERNATIONAL CO., LTD.; *Int'l*, pg. 3427
HKL (THAI DEVELOPMENTS) LIMITED—See Hong Kong Land Holdings Ltd.; *Int'l*, pg. 3466
HKL (VIETNAM) CONSULTANCY & MANAGEMENT COMPANY LIMITED—See Hong Kong Land Holdings Ltd.; *Int'l*, pg. 3466
HKR INTERNATIONAL LIMITED; *Int'l*, pg. 3429
HLH DEVELOPMENT PTE LTD—See Hong Lai Huat Group Limited; *Int'l*, pg. 3467
HNA PROPERTY MANAGEMENT CO., LTD.—See Hainan Traffic Administration Holding Co., Ltd.; *Int'l*, pg. 3213
HNLC, INC.—See Douglas Emmett, Inc.; *U.S. Public*, pg. 678
HOA BINH HOUSE JSC—See Hoa Binh Construction Group JSC; *Int'l*, pg. 3435
HOANG QUAN CONSULTING - TRADING - SERVICE REAL ESTATE CORPORATION; *Int'l*, pg. 3436
HOCHTIEF PROJEKTENTWICKLUNG GMBH—See ACS, Actividades de Construccion y Servicios, S.A.; *Int'l*, pg. 114
HOCHTIEF PROJEKTENTWICKLUNG HELFMANN PARK GMBH & CO. KG—See ACS, Actividades de Construccion y Servicios, S.A.; *Int'l*, pg. 114
HOIVATILAT OYJ; *Int'l*, pg. 3442
HOLDING GONDOMAR 3 SAS—See BNP Paribas SA; *Int'l*, pg. 1091
HOLLY FAYE MHP LLC—See Manufactured Housing Properties Inc.; *U.S. Public*, pg. 1362
HOME AFRIKA LIMITED; *Int'l*, pg. 3454
HOME A/S—See Danske Bank A/S; *Int'l*, pg. 1969
HOMEFINDER.COM, LLC—See Placester, Inc.; *U.S. Private*, pg. 3194
HOMEGAIN.COM, INC.—See Reply! Inc.; *U.S. Private*, pg. 3401
HOME GROUP DEVELOPMENTS LIMITED—See Home Group Limited; *Int'l*, pg. 3454
HOME INVEST BELGIUM SA; *Int'l*, pg. 3454
HOMELIFE/BAYVIEW REALTY INC.; *Int'l*, pg. 3455
HOME PROPERTIES 1200 EAST WEST, LLC—See Lone Star Global Acquisitions, LLC; *U.S. Private*, pg. 2488
HOMETRACK AUSTRALIA PTY LIMITED—See News Corporation; *U.S. Public*, pg. 1521
HONDA KAIHATSU CO., LTD.—See Honda Motor Co., Ltd.; *Int'l*, pg. 3461
HONGKONG LAND (CHENGDU) INVESTMENT & DEVELOPMENT COMPANY LIMITED—See Hong Kong Land Holdings Ltd.; *Int'l*, pg. 3466
HONGKONG LAND (CHONGQING) INVESTMENT & HOLDING CO., LTD.—See Hong Kong Land Holdings Ltd.; *Int'l*, pg. 3466
HONGKONG LAND (HANGZHOU) SHENGYUE MANAGEMENT CO., LTD.—See Hong Kong Land Holdings Ltd.; *Int'l*, pg. 3466
HONGKONG LAND (NANJING) PUZHI MANAGEMENT CO., LTD.—See Hong Kong Land Holdings Ltd.; *Int'l*, pg. 3466
HONGKONG LAND (PHILIPPINES) CONSULTANCY, INC.—See Hong Kong Land Holdings Ltd.; *Int'l*, pg. 3466
HONGKONG LAND (PREMIUM INVESTMENTS) LIMITED—See Hong Kong Land Holdings Ltd.; *Int'l*, pg. 3466
HONGKONG LAND (SHANGHAI) MANAGEMENT COMPANY LIMITED—See Hong Kong Land Holdings Ltd.; *Int'l*, pg. 3466
HONGKONG LAND (WUHAN) INVESTMENT & DEVELOPMENT COMPANY LIMITED—See Hong Kong Land Holdings Ltd.; *Int'l*, pg. 3467
HOPEWELL HOLDINGS LIMITED; *Int'l*, pg. 3473
HORIZON GROUP PROPERTIES, INC.; *U.S. Public*, pg. 1053
HORNBACH IMMOBILIEN AG—See Hornbach Holding AG & Co. KGaA; *Int'l*, pg. 3481
HOSPITALITY PROPERTY FUND LTD.—See Hosken Consolidated Investments Limited; *Int'l*, pg. 3485
HOUSE VIET NAM JOINT STOCK COMPANY; *Int'l*, pg. 3491
HOUSING AUTHORITY NEW ORLEANS (HANO); *U.S. Private*, pg. 1992
HOUSING AUTHORITY OF THE CITY OF CHARLOTTE; *U.S. Private*, pg. 1992
HOVSITE FIRENZE LLC—See Hovnanian Enterprises, Inc.; *U.S. Public*, pg. 1056
H. PARK GERMANY LP GMBH—See Jones Lang LaSalle Incorporated; *U.S. Public*, pg. 1201
HQ CAPITAL REAL ESTATE L.P.—See Harald Quandt Holding GmbH; *Int'l*, pg. 3269
HR IMMOBILIEN RHO GMBH—See Hornbach Holding AG & Co. KGaA; *Int'l*, pg. 3481
HSBC GLOBAL ASSET MANAGEMENT (UK) LIMITED—See HSBC Holdings plc; *Int'l*, pg. 3504
HSC HANSEATISCHE MANAGEMENT GMBH—See Ernst Russ AG; *Int'l*, pg. 2496
HUARONG REAL ESTATE CO., LTD.—See China CITIC Financial Asset Management Co., Ltd.; *Int'l*, pg. 1489
HUATAI SECURITIES (SHANGHAI) ASSET MANAGEMENT CO., LTD.—See Huatai Securities Co., Ltd.; *Int'l*, pg. 3514
HUATAI SECURITIES (SHANGHAI) ASSETS MANAGEMENT CO., LTD.—See Huatai Securities Co., Ltd.; *Int'l*, pg. 3514
HUA YUAN PROPERTY CO., LTD.; *Int'l*, pg. 3510
HUBILU VENTURE CORPORATION; *U.S. Public*, pg. 1067
HUBTOWN LIMITED; *Int'l*, pg. 3520
HUDSON PACIFIC PROPERTIES, L.P.—See Hudson Pacific Properties, Inc.; *U.S. Public*, pg. 1068
HULIC CO., LTD.; *Int'l*, pg. 3528
HUNG POO REAL ESTATE DEVELOPMENT CO., LTD.; *Int'l*, pg. 3535
HUNG SHENG CONSTRUCTION CO., LTD.; *Int'l*, pg. 3535
HUNT CLUB MHP LLC—See Manufactured Housing Properties Inc.; *U.S. Public*, pg. 1362
HUNT INVESTMENT MANAGEMENT, LLC—See Hunt Companies, Inc.; *U.S. Private*, pg. 2008
HUNTSVILLE HOUSING AUTHORITY; *U.S. Private*, pg. 2011
HUNTWICKE CAPITAL GROUP INC.; *U.S. Public*, pg. 1075
HUPP REALTY ADVISORS, INC.; *U.S. Private*, pg. 2011
HUSER & CO GMBH—See Bilfinger SE; *Int'l*, pg. 1028
HUZHOU DIXI GENGDU ECOLOGICAL AGRICULTURE DEVELOPMENT CO., LTD.—See Asia-Pacific Strategic Investments Limited; *Int'l*, pg. 616
HVI HANDELS- UND VERWERTUNGSGESELLSCHAFT FUR IMMOBILIEN MBH—See Commerzbank AG; *Int'l*, pg. 1718
HYAS & CO., INC.; *Int'l*, pg. 3544
HYPERION INMOBILARIA S.A. DE C.V.—See Deutsche Post AG; *Int'l*, pg. 2081
I2 DEVELOPMENT SA; *Int'l*, pg. 3566
ICA FASTIGHETER AB—See ICA Gruppen AB; *Int'l*, pg. 3577
ICA PROPIEDADES INMUEBLES, S.A. DE C.V.—See Empresas ICA S.A.B. de C.V.; *Int'l*, pg. 2391
ICC REALTY, LLC—See ICC Holdings, Inc.; *U.S. Public*, pg. 1085
ICHIGO HOTEL REIT INVESTMENT CORPORATION; *Int'l*, pg. 3580
ICHIYOSHI BUSINESS SERVICE CO., LTD.—See Ichiyoshi Securities Co., Ltd.; *Int'l*, pg. 3581
IC IMMOBILIEN HOLDING AG; *Int'l*, pg. 3577
ICON EOOD—See Gek Terna Societe Anonyme Holdings Real Estate Constructions; *Int'l*, pg. 2913
IDEA FIMIT SGR—See De Agostini S.p.A.; *Int'l*, pg. 1995
IDEAL GROUP S.A.; *Int'l*, pg. 3589
IDEALIST GAYRIMENKUL YATIRIM ORTAKLIGI A.S.; *Int'l*, pg. 3589
ID HOME CO., LTD.—See Iida Group Holdings Co., Ltd.; *Int'l*, pg. 3607
IDI LOGISTICS, LLC—See Brookfield Corporation; *Int'l*, pg. 1184
IHDATHIAT CO-ORDINATES; *Int'l*, pg. 3603
IIDA HOME MAX CO., LTD.—See Iida Group Holdings Co., Ltd.; *Int'l*, pg. 3607
IINO BUILDING TECHNOLOGY CO., LTD.—See Iino Kaiun Kaisha Ltd.; *Int'l*, pg. 3608
IKATAN FLORA SDN BHD—See IJM Corporation Berhad; *Int'l*, pg. 3609
IMMOBILIENINVEST UND BETRIEBSGESELLSCHAFT HERZO-BASE GMBH & CO. KG—See adidas AG; *Int'l*, pg. 146
IMMOBILIENINVEST UND BETRIEBSGESELLSCHAFT HERZO-BASE VERWALTUNGS GMBH—See adidas AG; *Int'l*, pg. 146
IMMOBILIENVERWALTUNGSGESELLSCHAFT GRAMMOPHON BUROPARK MBH—See Commerzbank AG; *Int'l*, pg. 1718
IMMOBILIENVERWALTUNGS- UND VERTRIEBSGESELLSCHAFT VILLEN AM GLIENICKER HORN MBH—See Commerzbank AG; *Int'l*, pg. 1718
IMMOBILIERE CARREFOUR S.A.S.—See Carrefour SA; *Int'l*, pg. 1345
IMMOBILIERE DASSAULT SA—See Groupe Industriel Marcel Dassault S.A.; *Int'l*, pg. 3105
IMMOBURG N.V.—See China International Marine Containers (Group) Co., Ltd.; *Int'l*, pg. 1511
IMMORENT AKTIENGESELLSCHAFT—See Erste Group Bank AG; *Int'l*, pg. 2499
IMMOWELT AG—See Axel Springer SE; *Int'l*, pg. 766

N.A.I.C.S. INDEX 531390 — OTHER ACTIVITIES RE...

IMMOWELT HAMBURG GMBH—See Axel Springer SE; *Int'l*, pg. 766
IMMOWELT HOLDING AG—See Axel Springer SE; *Int'l*, pg. 766
IMPACT ALAPKEZELO ZRT.—See Duna House Holding Public Company Limited; *Int'l*, pg. 2225
INDEPENDENT SETTLEMENT SERVICES, LLC—See Radian Group, Inc.; *U.S. Public*, pg. 1759
INDLUPLACE PROPERTIES LIMITED—See Fairvest Limited; *Int'l*, pg. 2609
INDRA EHSAN SDN BHD—See Berjaya Corporation Berhad; *Int'l*, pg. 982
INDUSTRIALS REIT LIMITED—See Blackstone Inc.; *U.S. Public*, pg. 354
INFRACORE SA—See AEVIS VICTORIA SA; *Int'l*, pg. 183
THE INLAND REAL ESTATE GROUP, LLC—See The Inland Real Estate Group of Companies, Inc.; *U.S. Private*, pg. 4056
INMOBILIARIA BAJA, S.A. DE C.V.—See Empresas ICA S.A.B. de C.V.; *Int'l*, pg. 2391
INMOBILIARIA MANSO DE VELASCO LTDA—See Enel S.p.A.; *Int'l*, pg. 2414
INNOTION ENTERPRISES, INC.; *U.S. Private*, pg. 2081
INNOVATIVE INDUSTRIAL PROPERTIES, INC.; *U.S. Public*, pg. 1127
INSIGNIA REAL ESTATE COMPANIES, LLC; *U.S. Private*, pg. 2091
INSULA COMPANIES; *U.S. Private*, pg. 2094
INTEGRIS REALTY CORPORATION—See INTEGRIS Health, Inc.; *U.S. Private*, pg. 2102
INTELICA COMMERCIAL REAL ESTATE COMPANY; *U.S. Private*, pg. 2104
INTERCONTINENTAL PROPERTIES LIMITED—See Access Corporation; *Int'l*, pg. 89
INTERNATIONAL LAND ALLIANCE, INC.; *U.S. Public*, pg. 1154
INTERNATIONAL VALUERS LTD.—See ENL Limited; *Int'l*, pg. 2441
INTERVEST OFFICES & WAREHOUSES N.V.—See TPG Capital, L.P.; *U.S. Public*, pg. 2174
INVALANCE LTD.—See Daito Trust Construction Co., Ltd.; *Int'l*, pg. 1944
INVESCO GLOBAL ASSET MANAGEMENT LIMITED—See Invesco Ltd.; *U.S. Public*, pg. 1161
INVESCO REAL ESTATE GMBH—See Invesco Ltd.; *U.S. Public*, pg. 1163
INVESCO REAL ESTATE MANAGEMENT S.A.R.L.—See Invesco Ltd.; *U.S. Public*, pg. 1163
INVESCO REAL ESTATE S.R.O.—See Invesco Ltd.; *U.S. Public*, pg. 1161
INVESTIRE IMMOBILIARE SGR S.P.A.—See Banca Finnat Euramerica S.p.A.; *Int'l*, pg. 814
INVESTOR MANAGEMENT SERVICES, LLC—See Thoma Bravo, L.P.; *U.S. Private*, pg. 4152
INVEST WEST FINANCIAL CORPORATION; *U.S. Private*, pg. 2131
INVISTA REAL ESTATE INVESTMENT MANAGEMENT LIMITED—See Fiera Capital Corporation; *Int'l*, pg. 2659
IPARK DEVELOPMENT SDN. BHD.—See AME Elite Consortium Berhad; *Int'l*, pg. 420
IPROPERTY.COM PTY. LTD.—See News Corporation; *U.S. Public*, pg. 1520
IPROPERTY.COM SINGAPORE PTE. LTD—See News Corporation; *U.S. Public*, pg. 1520
IP STRATEGY LLC—See Eversource Energy; *U.S. Public*, pg. 801
IRIGNY EMPREENDIMENTOS IMOBILIARIOS S.A.—See Even Construtora e Incorporadora S.A.; *Int'l*, pg. 2562
ITW GERMAN REAL ESTATE MANAGEMENT GMBH & CO. KG—See Illinois Tool Works Inc.; *U.S. Public*, pg. 1106
ITW MORTGAGE INVESTMENTS II, INC.—See Illinois Tool Works Inc.; *U.S. Public*, pg. 1106
ITW REAL ESTATE MANAGEMENT GMBH—See Illinois Tool Works Inc.; *U.S. Public*, pg. 1107
JADE IMMOBILIEN MANAGEMENT GMBH—See ADLER Group SA; *Int'l*, pg. 150
JANEWAY PROPERTIES, INC.—See Edison Properties, LLC; *U.S. Private*, pg. 1337
JANFAIR PTY. LTD.—See China Rare Earth Resources And Technology Co., Ltd.; *Int'l*, pg. 1545
JBA CONSULTING ENGINEERS (ASIA) LIMITED—See NV5 Global, Inc.; *U.S. Public*, pg. 1557
JBA CONSULTING ENGINEERS SHANGHAI LIMITED—See NV5 Global, Inc.; *U.S. Public*, pg. 1557
JBA CONSULTING ENGINEERS VIETNAM LIMITED COMPANY—See NV5 Global, Inc.; *U.S. Public*, pg. 1557
JEN FLORIDA II, LLC—See Brookfield Corporation; *Int'l*, pg. 1183
JEROME HAIMS REALTY, INC.—See BBG Inc.; *U.S. Private*, pg. 498
JIANG MEN YUAN HUI PROPERTY CO., LTD.—See China COSCO Shipping Corporation Limited; *Int'l*, pg. 1492
JIUXIN(CHANGZHOU)REAL ESTATE DEVELOPMENT CO., LTD.—See Daiwa House Industry Co., Ltd.; *Int'l*, pg. 1946
JJS PROPERTIES, INC.—See Ventas, Inc.; *U.S. Public*, pg. 2278
J KOMFORT NERUHOMIST LLC—See Dragon Ukrainian Properties & Development Plc; *Int'l*, pg. 2199
JLL CAPITAL MARKETS AB—See Jones Lang LaSalle Incorporated; *U.S. Public*, pg. 1202
JLL CORRETAGEM E TRASACOES IMOBILIARIAS LTDA.—See Jones Lang LaSalle Incorporated; *U.S. Public*, pg. 1202
JLL PROPERTY SERVICES (MALAYSIA) SDN BHD—See Jones Lang LaSalle Incorporated; *U.S. Public*, pg. 1202
JLL VALORACIONES SA—See Jones Lang LaSalle Incorporated; *U.S. Public*, pg. 1202
JLR, INC.—See Equifax Inc.; *U.S. Public*, pg. 786
JMA VENTURES, LLC; *U.S. Private*, pg. 2214
JMD MHC LLC—See JMD Properties Inc.; *U.S. Public*, pg. 1190
JOHBASE DEVELOPMENT SDN. BHD.—See BCB Berhad; *Int'l*, pg. 926
JOHN DEERE RECEIVABLES, INC.—See Deere & Company; *U.S. Public*, pg. 647
JOINT PROPERTY CO., LTD.—See Haseko Corporation; *Int'l*, pg. 3283
JONES LANG LASALLE (CHINA) LIMITED—See Jones Lang LaSalle Incorporated; *U.S. Public*, pg. 1202
JONES LANG LASALLE D.O.O.—See Jones Lang LaSalle Incorporated; *U.S. Public*, pg. 1205
JONES LANG LASALLE GAYRIMENKUL HIZMETLERI TICARET ANONIM SIRKETI—See Jones Lang LaSalle Incorporated; *U.S. Public*, pg. 1203
JONES LANG LASALLE MACHINERY & BUSINESS ASSETS LIMITED—See Jones Lang LaSalle Incorporated; *U.S. Public*, pg. 1203
JONES LANG LASALLE REAL ESTATE SERVICES, INC.—See Jones Lang LaSalle Incorporated; *U.S. Public*, pg. 1204
JONES LANG LASALLE SAUDI ARABIA LIMITED—See Jones Lang LaSalle Incorporated; *U.S. Public*, pg. 1204
JONES LANG LASALLE S.R.O—See Jones Lang LaSalle Incorporated; *U.S. Public*, pg. 1205
JONES LANG LASALLE SSC (PHILIPPINES), INC.—See Jones Lang LaSalle Incorporated; *U.S. Public*, pg. 1204
JONES LANG LASALLE UAE LIMITED—See Jones Lang LaSalle Incorporated; *U.S. Public*, pg. 1205
THE JORDAN COMPANY; *U.S. Private*, pg. 4059
JPMORGAN ASSET MANAGEMENT (ASIA) INC.—See JPMorgan Chase & Co.; *U.S. Public*, pg. 1208
JPMORGAN ASSET MANAGEMENT (AUSTRALIA) LIMITED—See JPMorgan Chase & Co.; *U.S. Public*, pg. 1209
JPMORGAN ASSET MANAGEMENT INDIA PRIVATE LIMITED—See JPMorgan Chase & Co.; *U.S. Public*, pg. 1209
JPMORGAN ASSET MANAGEMENT (SINGAPORE) LIMITED—See JPMorgan Chase & Co.; *U.S. Public*, pg. 1209
JR CENTRAL BUILDING CO., LTD.—See Central Japan Railway Company; *Int'l*, pg. 1408
JR DEVELOPMENT AND MANAGEMENT CORPORATION OF SHIZUOKA—See Central Japan Railway Company; *Int'l*, pg. 1408
JR TOKAI REAL ESTATE CO., LTD.—See Central Japan Railway Company; *Int'l*, pg. 1408
J-VON REALTY—See Hyman Brickle & Son, Inc.; *U.S. Private*, pg. 2019
JWB REAL ESTATE CAPITAL LLC; *U.S. Private*, pg. 2246
KALNIN VENTURES LLC; *U.S. Private*, pg. 2258
KAMES CAPITAL—See Aegon N.V.; *Int'l*, pg. 174
KANIZSA 2002 KFT.—See BNP Paribas SA; *Int'l*, pg. 1091
KB ARBETSSTOLEN 3—See Atrium Ljungberg AB; *Int'l*, pg. 694
KB HOME ORLANDO LLC—See KB Home; *U.S. Public*, pg. 1215
KBS CAPITAL ADVISORS, LLC—See KBS Realty Advisors, LLC; *U.S. Private*, pg. 2269
KBSIII ALMADEN FINANCIAL PLAZA, LLC—See KBS Real Estate Investment Trust III, Inc.; *U.S. Public*, pg. 1217
KBSIII ANCHOR CENTRE, LLC—See KBS Real Estate Investment Trust III, Inc.; *U.S. Public*, pg. 1217
KBSIII ONE WASHINGTONIAN, LLC—See KBS Real Estate Investment Trust III, Inc.; *U.S. Public*, pg. 1217
KBSIII TEN ALMADEN, LLC—See KBS Real Estate Investment Trust III, Inc.; *U.S. Public*, pg. 1217
KBS REALTY ADVISORS, LLC; *U.S. Private*, pg. 2268
KDC REAL ESTATE DEVELOPMENT & INVESTMENTS - SOUTHEAST DIVISION—See KDC Real Estate Development & Investments; *U.S. Private*, pg. 2270
KEDAH HOLDINGS SDN. BHD.—See Bina Darulaman Berhad; *Int'l*, pg. 1032
KEELEY DEVELOPMENT GROUP, INC.—See The Keeley Companies; *U.S. Private*, pg. 4064
KENDRA SAINT PIERRE LIMITED—See ENL Limited; *Int'l*, pg. 2441
KENLOC, INC.; *U.S. Private*, pg. 2284
KENNAMETAL WIDIA REAL ESTATE GMBH & CO. KG—See Kennametal Inc.; *U.S. Public*, pg. 1222
KENNEDY-WILSON, INC.—See Kennedy-Wilson Holdings, Inc.; *U.S. Public*, pg. 1223
KENNEDY WILSON PENNSYLVANIA MANAGEMENT, INC.—See Kennedy-Wilson Holdings, Inc.; *U.S. Public*, pg. 1223
KENNEDY WILSON UK LIMITED—See Kennedy-Wilson Holdings, Inc.; *U.S. Public*, pg. 1223
KENSTONE GMBH—See Commerzbank AG; *Int'l*, pg. 1718
KENT IMMOBILEMANAGEMNT GMBH—See CR Capital Real Estate AG; *Int'l*, pg. 1827
KERMIA PROPERTIES & INVESTMENTS LTD—See Bank of Cyprus Holdings Public Limited Company; *Int'l*, pg. 842
KEY INTERNATIONAL, INC.; *U.S. Private*, pg. 2293
KEY PROPERTY SOLUTIONS, LLC; *U.S. Private*, pg. 2294
KEYSER, LLC; *U.S. Private*, pg. 2295
KGAL ASSET MANAGEMENT OSTERREICH GMBH—See Commerzbank AG; *Int'l*, pg. 1718
K + G COMPLEX PUBLIC COMPANY LIMITED—See G.S. Galatariotis & Sons Ltd.; *Int'l*, pg. 2866
K. HOVNANIAN AT AMBERLEY WOODS, LLC—See Hovnanian Enterprises, Inc.; *U.S. Public*, pg. 1058
K. HOVNANIAN AT ASHBY PLACE, LLC—See Hovnanian Enterprises, Inc.; *U.S. Public*, pg. 1058
K. HOVNANIAN AT BLACKSTONE, LLC—See Hovnanian Enterprises, Inc.; *U.S. Public*, pg. 1058
K. HOVNANIAN AT BRADWELL ESTATES, LLC—See Hovnanian Enterprises, Inc.; *U.S. Public*, pg. 1058
K. HOVNANIAN AT BURCH KOVE, LLC—See Hovnanian Enterprises, Inc.; *U.S. Public*, pg. 1058
K. HOVNANIAN AT CASA DEL MAR, LLC—See Hovnanian Enterprises, Inc.; *U.S. Public*, pg. 1058
K. HOVNANIAN AT CEDAR LANE, LLC—See Hovnanian Enterprises, Inc.; *U.S. Public*, pg. 1058
K. HOVNANIAN AT CORAL LAGO, LLC—See Hovnanian Enterprises, Inc.; *U.S. Public*, pg. 1058
K. HOVNANIAN AT DOYLESTOWN, LLC—See Hovnanian Enterprises, Inc.; *U.S. Public*, pg. 1058
K. HOVNANIAN AT FAIRFIELD RIDGE, LLC—See Hovnanian Enterprises, Inc.; *U.S. Public*, pg. 1058
K. HOVNANIAN AT HILLTOP RESERVE, LLC—See Hovnanian Enterprises, Inc.; *U.S. Public*, pg. 1059
K. HOVNANIAN AT HUNTER'S POND, LLC—See Hovnanian Enterprises, Inc.; *U.S. Public*, pg. 1059
K. HOVNANIAN AT INDIAN WELLS, LLC—See Hovnanian Enterprises, Inc.; *U.S. Public*, pg. 1059
K. HOVNANIAN AT LAKE BURDEN, LLC—See Hovnanian Enterprises, Inc.; *U.S. Public*, pg. 1059
K. HOVNANIAN AT LAKE RANCHO VIEJO, LLC—See Hovnanian Enterprises, Inc.; *U.S. Public*, pg. 1059
K. HOVNANIAN AT LILY ORCHARD, LLC—See Hovnanian Enterprises, Inc.; *U.S. Public*, pg. 1059
K. HOVNANIAN AT MAIN STREET SQUARE, LLC—See Hovnanian Enterprises, Inc.; *U.S. Public*, pg. 1059
K. HOVNANIAN AT MEADOWRIDGE VILLAS, LLC—See Hovnanian Enterprises, Inc.; *U.S. Public*, pg. 1059
K. HOVNANIAN AT PRAIRIE POINTE, LLC—See Hovnanian Enterprises, Inc.; *U.S. Public*, pg. 1059
K. HOVNANIAN AT RANDALL HIGHLANDS, LLC—See Hovnanian Enterprises, Inc.; *U.S. Public*, pg. 1059
K. HOVNANIAN AT RIVER HILLS, LLC—See Hovnanian Enterprises, Inc.; *U.S. Public*, pg. 1059
K. HOVNANIAN AT SAUGANASH GLEN, LLC—See Hovnanian Enterprises, Inc.; *U.S. Public*, pg. 1059
K. HOVNANIAN AT SEASONS LANDING, LLC—See Hovnanian Enterprises, Inc.; *U.S. Public*, pg. 1059
K. HOVNANIAN AT TAMARACK SOUTH LLC—See Hovnanian Enterprises, Inc.; *U.S. Public*, pg. 1056
K. HOVNANIAN AT TANGLEWOOD OAKS, LLC—See Hovnanian Enterprises, Inc.; *U.S. Public*, pg. 1059
K. HOVNANIAN AT THE HIGHLANDS AT SUMMERLAKE GROVE, LLC—See Hovnanian Enterprises, Inc.; *U.S. Public*, pg. 1059
K. HOVNANIAN AT THE PRESERVE, LLC—See Hovnanian Enterprises, Inc.; *U.S. Public*, pg. 1059
K. HOVNANIAN AT UPPER PROVIDENCE, LLC—See Hovnanian Enterprises, Inc.; *U.S. Public*, pg. 1060
K. HOVNANIAN AT VALLETTA, LLC—See Hovnanian Enterprises, Inc.; *U.S. Public*, pg. 1060
K. HOVNANIAN AT VINEYARD HEIGHTS, LLC—See Hovnanian Enterprises, Inc.; *U.S. Public*, pg. 1060
K. HOVNANIAN AT WALKERS GROVE, LLC—See Hovnanian Enterprises, Inc.; *U.S. Public*, pg. 1060
K. HOVNANIAN AT WEST WINDSOR, L.L.C.—See Hovnanian Enterprises, Inc.; *U.S. Public*, pg. 1060
K. HOVNANIAN BELDEN POINTE, LLC—See Hovnanian Enterprises, Inc.; *U.S. Public*, pg. 1056
K. HOVNANIAN DFW AUBURN FARMS, LLC—See Hovnanian Enterprises, Inc.; *U.S. Public*, pg. 1056
K. HOVNANIAN DFW HARMON FARMS, LLC—See Hovnanian Enterprises, Inc.; *U.S. Public*, pg. 1056
K. HOVNANIAN DFW HERON POND, LLC—See Hovnanian Enterprises, Inc.; *U.S. Public*, pg. 1056
K. HOVNANIAN DFW HOMESTEAD, LLC—See Hovnanian Enterprises, Inc.; *U.S. Public*, pg. 1056
K. HOVNANIAN DFW LIBERTY CROSSING, LLC—See Hovnanian Enterprises, Inc.; *U.S. Public*, pg. 1057
K. HOVNANIAN DFW SEVENTEEN LAKES, LLC—See Hovnanian Enterprises, Inc.; *U.S. Public*, pg. 1057
K. HOVNANIAN ESTATES AT WEKIVA, LLC—See Hovnanian Enterprises, Inc.; *U.S. Public*, pg. 1057
K. HOVNANIAN GRAND CYPRESS, LLC—See Hovnanian Enterprises, Inc.; *U.S. Public*, pg. 1057

N.A.I.C.S. Index

531390 — OTHER ACTIVITIES RE... CORPORATE AFFILIATIONS

K. HOVNANIAN HOMES AT BROOK MANOR, LLC—See Hovnanian Enterprises, Inc.; *U.S. Public*, pg. 1057
K. HOVNANIAN HOMES AT CREEKSIDE, LLC—See Hovnanian Enterprises, Inc.; *U.S. Public*, pg. 1057
K. HOVNANIAN HOMES AT SHELL HALL, LLC—See Hovnanian Enterprises, Inc.; *U.S. Public*, pg. 1057
K. HOVNANIAN HOMES AT THE ABBY, LLC—See Hovnanian Enterprises, Inc.; *U.S. Public*, pg. 1057
K. HOVNANIAN HOMES - DFW, L.L.C.—See Hovnanian Enterprises, Inc.; *U.S. Public*, pg. 1057
K. HOVNANIAN HOMES OF MARYLAND I, LLC—See Hovnanian Enterprises, Inc.; *U.S. Public*, pg. 1057
K. HOVNANIAN HOMES OF MINNESOTA AT ARBOR CREEK, LLC—See Hovnanian Enterprises, Inc.; *U.S. Public*, pg. 1057
K. HOVNANIAN HOMES OF MINNESOTA AT AUTUMN MEADOWS, LLC—See Hovnanian Enterprises, Inc.; *U.S. Public*, pg. 1057
K. HOVNANIAN HOMES OF MINNESOTA AT CEDAR HOLLOW, LLC—See Hovnanian Enterprises, Inc.; *U.S. Public*, pg. 1057
K. HOVNANIAN HOMES OF MINNESOTA AT FOUNDER'S RIDGE, LLC—See Hovnanian Enterprises, Inc.; *U.S. Public*, pg. 1057
K. HOVNANIAN HOMES OF MINNESOTA AT HARPERS STREET WOODS, LLC—See Hovnanian Enterprises, Inc.; *U.S. Public*, pg. 1057
K. HOVNANIAN HOMES OF MINNESOTA, L.L.C.—See Hovnanian Enterprises, Inc.; *U.S. Public*, pg. 1057
K. HOVNANIAN LAKE PARKER, LLC—See Hovnanian Enterprises, Inc.; *U.S. Public*, pg. 1057
K. HOVNANIAN LIBERTY ON BLUFF CREEK, LLC—See Hovnanian Enterprises, Inc.; *U.S. Public*, pg. 1057
K. HOVNANIAN OF HOUSTON II, L.L.C.—See Hovnanian Enterprises, Inc.; *U.S. Public*, pg. 1060
K. HOVNANIAN'S FOUR SEASONS AT BAKERSFIELD, L.L.C.—See Hovnanian Enterprises, Inc.; *U.S. Public*, pg. 1056
K. HOVNANIAN'S FOUR SEASONS AT NEW KENT VINEYARDS, L.L.C.—See Hovnanian Enterprises, Inc.; *U.S. Public*, pg. 1060
K. HOVNANIAN'S FOUR SEASONS AT RUSH CREEK, L.L.C.—See Hovnanian Enterprises, Inc.; *U.S. Public*, pg. 1060
K. HOVNANIAN'S FOUR SEASONS AT THE LAKES AT CANE BAY, LLC—See Hovnanian Enterprises, Inc.; *U.S. Public*, pg. 1060
K. HOVNANIAN SHERWOOD AT REGENCY, LLC—See Hovnanian Enterprises, Inc.; *U.S. Public*, pg. 1058
K. HOVNANIAN STERLING RANCH, LLC—See Hovnanian Enterprises, Inc.; *U.S. Public*, pg. 1058
K. HOVNANIAN UNION PARK, LLC—See Hovnanian Enterprises, Inc.; *U.S. Public*, pg. 1058
K. HOVNANIAN WOODRIDGE PLACE, LLC—See Hovnanian Enterprises, Inc.; *U.S. Public*, pg. 1058
KIINTEISTO OY RAISION LUOLASTO—See Elisa Corporation; *Int'l*, pg. 2361
KIINTEISTO OY VANTAAN TAHTAINKUJA 3—See Blackstone Inc.; *U.S. Public*, pg. 351
KINDER REESE; *U.S. Private*, pg. 2306
KINGS CREEK PLANTATION LLC; *U.S. Private*, pg. 2311
KINGS HILL PROPERTY MANAGEMENT LIMITED—See Prologis, Inc.; *U.S. Public*, pg. 1727
KINGS HILL RESIDENTIAL ESTATE MANAGEMENT COMPANY LIMITED—See Prologis, Inc.; *U.S. Public*, pg. 1727
KING STREET REAL ESTATE GP, L.L.C; *U.S. Private*, pg. 2310
KIVEL PROPERTIES LIMITED—See Heidelberg Materials AG; *Int'l*, pg. 3317
KIWS PROPERTY LLC—See dormakaba Holding AG; *Int'l*, pg. 2177
KJR MANAGEMENT—See KKR & Co. Inc.; *U.S. Public*, pg. 1255
KLEBER LA PEROUSE SNC—See BNP Paribas SA; *Int'l*, pg. 1091
KLECAR FONCIER ESPANA SA—See BNP Paribas SA; *Int'l*, pg. 1091
KLECAR FRANCE SNC—See BNP Paribas SA; *Int'l*, pg. 1091
KNESTRICK PROPERTIES, LLC—See Knestrick Contractor Inc.; *U.S. Private*, pg. 2321
KNIGHTSBRIDGE BUSINESS SALES LIMITED—See Sun Capital Partners, Inc.; *U.S. Private*, pg. 3861
KNOXVILLE'S COMMUNITY DEVELOPMENT CORP.; *U.S. Private*, pg. 2325
THE KOMAN GROUP, LLC—See The Keeley Companies; *U.S. Private*, pg. 4064
KOMYAPI INSAAT A.S.—See Bera Holding A.S.; *Int'l*, pg. 978
KORONA DEVELOPMENT LLC—See Dragon Ukrainian Properties & Development Plc; *Int'l*, pg. 2199
KOSKIKESKUKSEN HUOLTO OY—See Citycon Oyj; *Int'l*, pg. 1629
KOTA RAYA DEVELOPMENT SDN BHD—See Berjaya Corporation Berhad; *Int'l*, pg. 983
KOY HELSINGIN ITAKATU 11—See Blackstone Inc.; *U.S. Public*, pg. 351

KOY KUNINKAANKAARI—See Blackstone Inc.; *U.S. Public*, pg. 351
KOY NIMISMIEHENNIITTY—See Blackstone Inc.; *U.S. Public*, pg. 351
KOY ZEPPELININ CITY KESKUS—See Blackstone Inc.; *U.S. Public*, pg. 351
KSA REALTY CORPORATION—See A. Soriano Corporation; *Int'l*, pg. 22
KTR CAPITAL PARTNERS, LLC—See Prologis, Inc.; *U.S. Public*, pg. 1727
KURGAN GRUNDSTUCKSVERWALTUNGSGESELLSCHAFT MBH & CO. OHG—See E.ON SE; *Int'l*, pg. 2258
KURZ GROUP, INC.—See Ryan, LLC; *U.S. Private*, pg. 3511
KVIKMYNDAHOLLIN EHF.—See Heimar hf.; *Int'l*, pg. 3323
LACLEDE DEVELOPMENT COMPANY—See Spire, Inc; *U.S. Public*, pg. 1918
LADDER CAPITAL ASSET MANAGEMENT LLC—See Ladder Capital Corp.; *U.S. Public*, pg. 1288
LAGRANGE ASSOCIATES, LLC—See Wheeler Real Estate Investment Trust, Inc.; *U.S. Public*, pg. 2366
LAHDEN TRIO KOY—See Citycon Oyj; *Int'l*, pg. 1629
LAIRD NORTON PROPERTIES—See Laird Norton Company, LLC; *U.S. Private*, pg. 2374
LAKEFRONT RESIDENCE SDN. BHD.—See Avaland Berhad; *Int'l*, pg. 734
LAKE TANSI VILLAGE INC.—See Equity LifeStyle Properties, Inc.; *U.S. Public*, pg. 790
LANDMARK NETWORK INC.—See Gridiron Capital, LLC; *U.S. Private*, pg. 1786
LANDMARK PROPERTY DEVELOPMENT COMPANY LIMITED—See Dalmia Bharat Limited; *Int'l*, pg. 1954
LANDMARK PROPERTY MANAGEMENT JSC—See Alfa Finance Holding AD; *Int'l*, pg. 307
LANDMARK WHITE (SYDNEY) PTY LTD—See Acumentis Group Limited; *Int'l*, pg. 121
LANDSAFE FLOOD DETERMINATION, INC.—See Bank of America Corporation; *U.S. Public*, pg. 272
LAND SAPPORT INC.—See GENDAI AGENCY INC.; *Int'l*, pg. 2917
LAND SOUTH HOLDINGS, LLC; *U.S. Private*, pg. 2384
LAND TITLE AND ESCROW, INC.—See Anywhere Real Estate Inc.; *U.S. Public*, pg. 142
THE LANDWELL COMPANY LP—See Contran Corporation; *U.S. Private*, pg. 1034
LANKA INDUSTRIAL ESTATES LIMITED—See DFCC Bank PLC; *Int'l*, pg. 2094
LAPPEENRANNAN VILLIMIEHEN VITONEN OY—See Citycon Oyj; *Int'l*, pg. 1629
LARSON MANAGEMENT, INC.; *U.S. Private*, pg. 2394
LASALLE INVESTMENT MANAGEMENT CO., LTD.—See Jones Lang LaSalle Incorporated; *U.S. Public*, pg. 1205
LASALLE PARTNERS, S. DE R.L. DE C.V.—See Jones Lang LaSalle Incorporated; *U.S. Public*, pg. 1205
LA SOCIETE DE PROMOTION DE LA POINTE SIMON ET SES ENVIRONS—See Guardian Holdings Limited; *Int'l*, pg. 3171
LATITUDE MANAGEMENT REAL ESTATE INVESTORS, INC.—See Jones Lang LaSalle Incorporated; *U.S. Public*, pg. 1204
LATT MAXCY CORPORATION; *U.S. Private*, pg. 2397
LAUREL HIGHLANDS, LLC—See Hovnanian Enterprises, Inc.; *U.S. Public*, pg. 1060
LAURUS CORP.—See Ethika Investments LLC; *U.S. Private*, pg. 1431
LBA REALTY LLC; *U.S. Private*, pg. 2403
LB IMMOBILIENBEWERTUNGSGESELLSCHAFT MBH—See BayernLB Holding AG; *Int'l*, pg. 914
LEIGH MARCUS, INC.; *U.S. Private*, pg. 2419
LEISURE LIVING LIMITED—See Blackstone Inc.; *U.S. Public*, pg. 358
LELAND PROPERTIES—See ITT Inc.; *U.S. Public*, pg. 1178
LEM CAPITAL, L.P.—See Independence Capital Partners, LLC; *U.S. Private*, pg. 2056
LENDINGONE, LLC; *U.S. Private*, pg. 2421
LES ALLEES D'HELVETIA COMMERCIAL CENTRE LIMITED—See ENL Limited; *Int'l*, pg. 2441
LESTER DEVELOPMENT CORPORATION—See The Lester Group Inc.; *U.S. Private*, pg. 4069
LEWIS OPERATING CORP.; *U.S. Private*, pg. 2439
LEXINGTON NATIONAL LAND SERVICES, LLC—See Blackstone Inc.; *U.S. Public*, pg. 355
LHPT COLUMBUS THE, LLC—See Ventas, Inc.; *U.S. Public*, pg. 2278
LHRET ASCENSION SJ, LLC—See Ventas, Inc.; *U.S. Public*, pg. 2278
LHRET ASCENSION SV, LLC—See Ventas, Inc.; *U.S. Public*, pg. 2278
LHRET ST. LOUIS, LLC—See Ventas, Inc.; *U.S. Public*, pg. 2278
LIBERTY GROUP OF COMPANIES; *U.S. Private*, pg. 2444
LIBERTY PROPERTY LIMITED PARTNERSHIP; *U.S. Private*, pg. 2447
LIBERTY PROPERTY TRUST—See Prologis, Inc.; *U.S. Public*, pg. 1727
LIBERTY PROPERTY TRUST UK LIMITED—See Prologis, Inc.; *U.S. Public*, pg. 1727
LIGETVAROS KFT—See Atlas Estates Limited; *Int'l*, pg. 685

LIGHT ERA DEVELOPMENT CO., LTD.—See Chunghwa Telecom Co., Ltd.; *Int'l*, pg. 1598
LIGHTHOUSE GLOBAL HOLDINGS, INC.; *U.S. Public*, pg. 1315
LIMA ONE CAPITAL, LLC—See MFA FINANCIAL, INC.; *U.S. Public*, pg. 1434
LIMESTONE PROPERTIES LTD—See Bank of Cyprus Holdings Public Limited Company; *Int'l*, pg. 842
LIMITED REAL ESTATE—See Bath & Body Works, Inc.; *U.S. Public*, pg. 279
LIMONEIRA LEWIS COMMUNITY BUILDERS, LLC—See Limoneira Company; *U.S. Public*, pg. 1316
LINCOLN HARRIS CSG—See Lincoln Property Company; *U.S. Private*, pg. 2458
LINCOLN RACKHOUSE—See Lincoln Property Company; *U.S. Private*, pg. 2458
LIONFISH EVEN EMPREENDIMENTOS IMOBILIARIOS LTDA.—See Even Construtora e Incorporadora S.A.; *Int'l*, pg. 2562
THE LITCHFIELD COMPANY; *U.S. Private*, pg. 4071
LIVING PLUS LIMITED—See City of London Group PLC; *Int'l*, pg. 1627
LIVINGVENTURES, INC.; *U.S. Private*, pg. 2474
LLC BONAVA SAINT-PETERSBURG—See Bonava AB; *Int'l*, pg. 1105
LLC "ETALON-INVEST"—See Etalon Group Plc; *Int'l*, pg. 2520
LMG REALTY PTE. LTD.—See BRC Asia Limited; *Int'l*, pg. 1143
LNR PARTNERS, LLC—See Starwood Property Trust, Inc.; *U.S. Public*, pg. 1939
LNR PROPERTY LLC—See Starwood Property Trust, Inc.; *U.S. Public*, pg. 1939
LOCARE SNC—See Gecina S.A.; *Int'l*, pg. 2909
L-O DEL MAR HOLDING, INC; *U.S. Private*, pg. 2363
LOFRA GMBH & CO.KG—See Commerzbank AG; *Int'l*, pg. 1718
THE LONG & FOSTER COMPANIES, INC. - HARRISON ST—See The Long & Foster Companies, Inc.; *U.S. Private*, pg. 4072
LOOPNET, INC.—See CoStar Group, Inc.; *U.S. Public*, pg. 586
LOTUS ESTATE CO., LTD.—See Astellas Pharma Inc.; *Int'l*, pg. 653
LOVE MANAGEMENT COMPANY, LLC—See Love Real Estate Company; *U.S. Private*, pg. 2501
LOWE COMMERCIAL SERVICES LLC—See Lowe Enterprises, Inc.; *U.S. Private*, pg. 2504
LOWE REAL ESTATE GROUP—See Lowe Enterprises, Inc.; *U.S. Private*, pg. 2504
LOWER HOLDING COMPANY; *U.S. Private*, pg. 2506
LPC SOUTHEAST—See Lincoln Property Company; *U.S. Private*, pg. 2458
LUBERT-ADLER PARTNERS, L.P.—See Independence Capital Partners, LLC; *U.S. Private*, pg. 2056
LUCARA IMMOBILIENVERWALTUNGS GMBH—See BASF SE; *Int'l*, pg. 884
LUWOGE CONSULT GMBH—See BASF SE; *Int'l*, pg. 884
MACKENZIE CAPITAL MANAGEMENT, LP; *U.S. Private*, pg. 2536
MACKLOWE PROPERTIES, L.L.C.; *U.S. Private*, pg. 2537
MACLEH (CHEVALIER) LIMITED—See Chevalier International Holdings Limited; *Int'l*, pg. 1474
MADISON HOSPITALITY GROUP, LLC; *U.S. Private*, pg. 2543
MAGASINET FASTIGHETSSVERIGE AB—See Byggfakta Group Nordic HoldCo AB; *Int'l*, pg. 1234
MAGNOLIA GREEN DEVELOPMENT PARTNERS LLC—See Safehold Inc.; *U.S. Public*, pg. 1834
MAGNOLIA PROPERTIES & INVESTMENTS INC.; *U.S. Private*, pg. 2548
MAHAMERU CONSULTANCY D.O.O.—See Berjaya Corporation Berhad; *Int'l*, pg. 983
MAINE SEABOARD REALTY LLC—See Jefferies Financial Group Inc.; *U.S. Public*, pg. 1188
MAINSTREET PROPERTY GROUP, LLC—See Mainstreet Investment Company, LLC; *U.S. Private*, pg. 2554
MAJULAH INVESTMENT, INC.; *U.S. Private*, pg. 2555
MAKAR PROPERTIES, LLC; *U.S. Private*, pg. 2556
MALL OF (MAURITIUS) AT BAGATELLE LTD.—See ENL Limited; *Int'l*, pg. 2441
MAMMOTH PROPERTY RESERVATIONS—See Mammoth Properties, Inc.; *U.S. Private*, pg. 2559
MANAGED ASSETS CORPORATION—See Hilton Grand Vacations Inc.; *U.S. Public*, pg. 1040
MANTENIMENT I CONSERVACIO DEL VALLES, S.A.—See ACS, Actividades de Construccion y Servicios, S.A.; *Int'l*, pg. 115
MANUFACTURED TECHNOLOGIES CORPORATION—See New Mountain Capital, LLC; *U.S. Private*, pg. 2900
MARA ESCROW COMPANY—See Old Republic International Corporation; *U.S. Public*, pg. 1569
MARAFEQ AL TASHGHEEL COMPANY—See Abdullah Al-Othaim Markets Company; *Int'l*, pg. 59
MARCUS & MILLICHAP REAL ESTATE INVESTMENT SERVICES, INC.—See Marcus & Millichap, Inc.; *U.S. Public*, pg. 1365

N.A.I.C.S. INDEX

531390 — OTHER ACTIVITIES RE...

MARCUS & MILLICHAP REIS OF ATLANTA, INC.—See Marcus & Millichap, Inc.; *U.S. Public*, pg. 1365

MARCUS & MILLICHAP REIS OF CHICAGO, INC.—See Marcus & Millichap, Inc.; *U.S. Public*, pg. 1365

MARCUS & MILLICHAP REIS OF FLORIDA, INC.—See Marcus & Millichap, Inc.; *U.S. Public*, pg. 1365

MARCUS & MILLICHAP REIS OF NEVADA, INC.—See Marcus & Millichap, Inc.; *U.S. Public*, pg. 1365

MARCUS & MILLICHAP REIS OF NORTH CAROLINA, INC.—See Marcus & Millichap, Inc.; *U.S. Public*, pg. 1365

MARCUS & MILLICHAP REIS OF SEATTLE, INC.—See Marcus & Millichap, Inc.; *U.S. Public*, pg. 1365

MARK ONE CAPITAL, INC.—See Marcus & Millichap, Inc.; *U.S. Public*, pg. 1365

MARSHALL & SWIFT/BOECKH, LLC—See Insight Venture Management, LLC; *U.S. Private*, pg. 2089

MARSHALL & SWIFT/BOECKH, LLC—See Stone Point Capital LLC; *U.S. Private*, pg. 3822

MARWEST MANAGEMENT CANADA LTD.—See All in West! Capital Corporation; *Int'l*, pg. 332

THE MARYLAND & DELAWARE GROUP OF LONG & FOSTER; *U.S. Private*, pg. 4075

MASANTO CONTAINERS PRIVATE LIMITED—See Bhagyanagar Properties Limited; *Int'l*, pg. 1010

MATT MARTIN REAL ESTATE MANAGEMENT LLC; *U.S. Private*, pg. 2613

MAXCY DEVELOPMENT GROUP—See Latt Maxcy Corporation; *U.S. Private*, pg. 2397

MB DEVELOPMENT, LLC—See Icahn Enterprises L.P.; *U.S. Public*, pg. 1084

MBG SACHSEN GMBH—See ADLER Group SA; *Int'l*, pg. 150

MCCALL & ALMY, INC.—See Newmark Group, Inc.; *U.S. Public*, pg. 1515

MCCRANEY PROPERTY COMPANY; *U.S. Private*, pg. 2630

MCL LAND (MALAYSIA) SDN. BHD.—See Hong Kong Land Holdings Ltd.; *Int'l*, pg. 3467

MDA INFORMATION PRODUCTS LTD.—See Advent International Corporation; *U.S. Private*, pg. 103

MDA PROPERTIES LTD.—See ENL Limited; *Int'l*, pg. 2441

MEDICAL PROPERTIES TRUST, INC.; *U.S. Public*, pg. 1412

MEDLEY LLC; *U.S. Public*, pg. 1413

MEGAH CAPITAL SDN. BHD.—See Gamuda Berhad; *Int'l*, pg. 2879

MEGAH MANAGEMENT SERVICES SDN. BHD.—See Gamuda Berhad; *Int'l*, pg. 2879

MEGAH SEWA SDN. BHD.—See Gamuda Berhad; *Int'l*, pg. 2879

MELNICK EVEN DESENVOLVIMENTO IMOBILIARIO S.A.—See Even Construtora e Incorporadora S.A.; *Int'l*, pg. 2562

MEMPHIS INVEST GP; *U.S. Private*, pg. 2664

MERCER JAPAN LTD.—See Marsh & McLennan Companies, Inc.; *U.S. Public*, pg. 1386

MEREDITH LODGING LLC; *U.S. Private*, pg. 2671

MERIDIAN PACIFIC PROPERTIES INC.; *U.S. Private*, pg. 2673

MERKUR IMMOBILIEN- UND BETEILIGUNGS GMBH—See Gauselmann AG; *Int'l*, pg. 2890

MESIROW REAL ESTATE INVESTMENTS, INC.—See Mesirow Financial Holdings, Inc.; *U.S. Private*, pg. 2679

METHODIST SERVICES INC.; *U.S. Private*, pg. 2684

METRO TITLE, LLC—See D.R. Horton, Inc.; *U.S. Public*, pg. 620

METZLER NORTH AMERICA CORPORATION—See B. Metzler seel. Sohn & Co. Holding AG; *Int'l*, pg. 788

MEUNIER PROMOTION—See BNP Paribas SA; *Int'l*, pg. 1092

MFC REAL ESTATE LLC—See Erste Abwicklungsanstalt AoR; *Int'l*, pg. 2497

MICHAELSON, CONNOR & BOUL, INC.; *U.S. Private*, pg. 2699

MICROPOLITAN, LLC—See Psomas; *U.S. Private*, pg. 3297

MIDWEST PROPERTIES LLC—See Abbott Laboratories; *U.S. Public*, pg. 20

MIG REAL ESTATE—See Merage Investment Group; *U.S. Private*, pg. 2668

M/I HOMES OF AUSTIN, LLC—See M/I Homes, Inc.; *U.S. Public*, pg. 1351

MILLCRAFT INDUSTRIES INC.; *U.S. Private*, pg. 2731

MILLENNIUM TITLE AGENCY, LTD.—See Hovnanian Enterprises, Inc.; *U.S. Public*, pg. 1060

MILLER REALTY INVESTMENT PARTNERS, INC.—See Henry S. Miller Management Corp.; *U.S. Private*, pg. 1919

MINERVA LTD.—See Delancey Real Estate Asset Management Ltd.; *Int'l*, pg. 2010

MINMETALS LAND LIMITED—See China Rare Earth Resources And Technology Co., Ltd.; *Int'l*, pg. 1546

MINMETALS REAL ESTATE COMPANY—See China Rare Earth Resources And Technology Co., Ltd.; *Int'l*, pg. 1546

MISMAK PROPERTIES CO. LLC—See First Abu Dhabi Bank P.J.S.C.; *Int'l*, pg. 2681

MISTRAS GROUP BVBA—See Mistras Group, Inc.; *U.S. Public*, pg. 1451

M.K. REAL ESTATE DEVELOPMENT PUBLIC COMPANY LIMITED—See Bangkok Bank Public Company Limited; *Int'l*, pg. 833

MOCSA REAL ESTATE BV—See Ascom Holding AG; *Int'l*, pg. 603

MODIS GMBH—See Adecco Group AG; *Int'l*, pg. 141

MOELIS AUSTRALIA ASSET MANAGEMENT LTD—See Moelis & Company; *U.S. Public*, pg. 1456

MONASTIRIOU TECHNICAL DEVELOPMENT S.A.—See Gek Terna Societe Anonyme Holdings Real Estate Constructions; *Int'l*, pg. 2913

MORGAN STANLEY PROPERTIES CORSO VENEZIA S.R.L.—See Morgan Stanley; *U.S. Public*, pg. 1475

MORGAN STANLEY PROPERTIES FRANCE SAS—See Morgan Stanley; *U.S. Public*, pg. 1475

MORGAN STANLEY REALTY INC.—See Morgan Stanley; *U.S. Public*, pg. 1475

MORTENSON DEVELOPMENT, INC.—See M.A. Mortenson Company; *U.S. Private*, pg. 2527

MOSTCHOICE.COM; *U.S. Private*, pg. 2795

MPM PROPERTIES LLC—See Abu Dhabi Islamic Bank PJSC; *Int'l*, pg. 72

MP VENTURES, INC.; *U.S. Private*, pg. 2803

MRS BIOUL S.A.—See Apollo Global Management, Inc.; *U.S. Public*, pg. 147

MS AVON, L.P.—See Welltower Inc.; *U.S. Public*, pg. 2348

MSMC RESIDENTIAL REALTY LLC; *U.S. Private*, pg. 2808

MS MISHAWAKA, L.P.—See Welltower Inc.; *U.S. Public*, pg. 2348

MUSSER-DAVIS LAND COMPANY; *U.S. Private*, pg. 2818

MYHOUSE CO., LTD.—See Apaman Co., Ltd.; *Int'l*, pg. 500

MYTRADE, INC.—See The Charles Schwab Corporation; *U.S. Public*, pg. 2058

MYYRMANNI KOY—See Citycon Oyj; *Int'l*, pg. 1629

NAGA ISTIMEWA SDN. BHD.—See Brem Holding Berhad; *Int'l*, pg. 1144

NAI EXCEL—See Island Capital Group LLC; *U.S. Private*, pg. 2144

NAI MID-MICHIGAN; *U.S. Private*, pg. 2830

NAMI-AEW EUROPE—See Groupe BPCE; *Int'l*, pg. 3096

NATHANTABOR.COM; *U.S. Private*, pg. 2839

NATIONAL CLOSING SOLUTIONS, INC.—See First American Financial Corporation; *U.S. Public*, pg. 838

NATIONAL CLOSING SOLUTIONS, INC. - TEXAS DIVISION—See First American Financial Corporation; *U.S. Public*, pg. 838

NATIONAL CLOSING SOLUTIONS, INC. - UTAH DIVISION—See First American Financial Corporation; *U.S. Public*, pg. 838

NAVIDUL COGENERACION, S.A.—See Iberdrola, S.A.; *Int'l*, pg. 3573

NDC LLC—See Ecolab Inc.; *U.S. Public*, pg. 715

NEARON ENTERPRISES; *U.S. Private*, pg. 2877

NEO PROPERTY SERVICES ZRT.—See AKKO Invest Nyrt.; *Int'l*, pg. 263

NE PACIFIC SHOPPING CENTERS CORP.—See Cosco Capital, Inc.; *Int'l*, pg. 1809

NEVADA REALTY ASSOCIATES, LLC—See Wynn Resorts Limited; *U.S. Public*, pg. 2384

NEW BRUNSWICK DEVELOPMENT CORPORATION; *U.S. Private*, pg. 2892

NEWMAN & GOH PROPERTY CONSULTANTS PTE. LTD.—See Advancer Global Limited; *Int'l*, pg. 163

NEWMARK & COMPANY REAL ESTATE, INC.—See BGC Group, Inc.; *U.S. Public*, pg. 329

NEW WEST REALTY DEVELOPMENT CORP.; *U.S. Private*, pg. 2908

NEXPOINT DIVERSIFIED REAL ESTATE TRUST; *U.S. Public*, pg. 1522

NEXSTAR CAPITAL, LLC—See InterDigital, Inc.; *U.S. Public*, pg. 1144

NEXTENSA NV—See Ackermans & van Haaren NV; *Int'l*, pg. 106

NINGBO DAXIE DEVELOPMENT ZONE—See CITIC Group Corporation; *Int'l*, pg. 1621

NITTO FUDOHSAN CO., LTD.—See Dai Nippon Toryo Co., Ltd.; *Int'l*, pg. 1916

NLT TITLE, LLC—See Guaranteed Rate, Inc.; *U.S. Private*, pg. 1699

NOBLE INVESTMENT GROUP, LLC; *U.S. Private*, pg. 2932

NORCAL GOLD, INC. - SACRAMENTO—See Norcal Gold, Inc.; *U.S. Private*, pg. 2935

NORDBODEN IMMOBILIEN- UND HANDELSGESELLSCHAFT MBH—See Commerzbank AG; *Int'l*, pg. 1718

NORDDEUTSCHE GRUNDSTUCKSAUKTIONEN AG—See Deutsche Grundstuecksauktionen AG; *Int'l*, pg. 2065

NORIT REAL ESTATE B.V.—See Cabot Corporation; *U.S. Public*, pg. 417

NORSK KJOPESENTERFORVALTNING AS—See BNP Paribas SA; *Int'l*, pg. 1092

NORTH AMERICAN DEVELOPMENT GROUP; *U.S. Private*, pg. 2940

NORTH AMERICAN PROPERTIES INC.; *U.S. Private*, pg. 2941

NORTH AMERICAN REAL ESTATE GROUP, LLC—See Lennar Corporation; *U.S. Public*, pg. 1307

NORTH AMERICAN TITLE GROUP, LLC—See Doma Holdings, Inc.; *U.S. Public*, pg. 673

NORTH IDAHO TITLE COMPANY—See First American Financial Corporation; *U.S. Public*, pg. 838

NORTHMARQ CAPITAL, LLC—See Pohlad Companies; *U.S. Private*, pg. 3220

NORTHMARQ CAPITAL, LLC—See Pohlad Companies; *U.S. Private*, pg. 3220

NORTH TERRACE PM LLC; *U.S. Private*, pg. 2948

NOVA IMMO SAS—See Groupe BPCE; *Int'l*, pg. 3099

NOVARE NATIONAL SETTLEMENT SERVICE, LLC—See Starwood Property Trust, Inc.; *U.S. Public*, pg. 1940

NOVO MAAR SP. Z.O.O.—See Africa Israel Investments Ltd.; *Int'l*, pg. 190

NRDC REAL ESTATE ADVISORS—See National Realty & Development Corp.; *U.S. Private*, pg. 2861

NRT DEVELOPMENT ADVISORS LLC—See Anywhere Real Estate Inc.; *U.S. Public*, pg. 141

NRT MISSOURI REFERRAL NETWORK LLC—See Anywhere Real Estate Inc.; *U.S. Public*, pg. 141

NSAM US LLC—See DigitalBridge Group, Inc.; *U.S. Public*, pg. 665

NTS REALTY PARTNERS, LLC—See NTS Corporation; *U.S. Private*, pg. 2971

NYPRO REALTY CORP—See Jabil Inc.; *U.S. Public*, pg. 1182

OAHU PAVING COMPANY, INC—See Alexander & Baldwin, Inc.; *U.S. Public*, pg. 75

OAKLAND HOLDINGS SDN. BHD.—See DutaLand Berhad; *Int'l*, pg. 2235

OAKLAND MANAGEMENT CORP.; *U.S. Private*, pg. 2984

OAKSVILLA SDN. BHD.—See Fiamma Holdings Berhad; *Int'l*, pg. 2650

OBJEKT BURCHARDPLATZ GMBH & CO. KG—See Allianz SE; *Int'l*, pg. 355

OFB PROJEKTENTWICKLUNG GMBH—See Helaba Landesbank Hessen-Thuringen; *Int'l*, pg. 3328

OFFERPAD SOLUTIONS INC.; *U.S. Public*, pg. 1564

OFICEA COMPANY LIMITED—See ENL Limited; *Int'l*, pg. 2442

OHI HEALTHCARE PROPERTIES LIMITED PARTNERSHIP—See Omega Healthcare Investors, Inc.; *U.S. Public*, pg. 1571

OHIO CASHFLOW, LLC; *U.S. Private*, pg. 3004

OIL & GAS ASSET CLEARINGHOUSE, LLC—See OFSCap LLC; *U.S. Private*, pg. 3003

OJAI OIL COMPANY; *U.S. Public*, pg. 1566

OK MINILAGER AS—See Teachers Insurance Association - College Retirement Fund; *U.S. Private*, pg. 3945

OLB-IMMOBILIENDIENST-GMBH—See Allianz SE; *Int'l*, pg. 354

OLDACRE MCDONALD, LLC; *U.S. Private*, pg. 3009

THE OLD FACTORY LIMITED—See ENL Limited; *Int'l*, pg. 2442

OLD REPUBLIC TITLE AND ESCROW OF HAWAII, LTD.—See Old Republic International Corporation; *U.S. Public*, pg. 1569

OLEKSA ENTERPRISES INCORPORATED; *U.S. Private*, pg. 3010

OMAX INTERNATIONAL LIMITED—See Euromax Resources Ltd.; *Int'l*, pg. 2553

O'MEARA HOLDINGS LIMITED—See ANSA McAL Limited; *Int'l*, pg. 477

OMICRON EVEN RIO EMPREENDIMENTOS IMOBILIARIOS LTDA.—See Even Construtora e Incorporadora S.A.; *Int'l*, pg. 2562

ON COLLABORATIVE LLC—See Anywhere Real Estate Inc.; *U.S. Public*, pg. 142

ONE ALLEN CENTER CO. LLC—See Brookfield Corporation; *Int'l*, pg. 1186

ONE EMBARCADERO CENTER VENTURE—See Boston Properties, Inc.; *U.S. Public*, pg. 373

THE O'NEIL GROUP COMPANY, LLC; *U.S. Private*, pg. 4087

ONE SOTHEBY'S INTERNATIONAL REALTY, INC.; *U.S. Private*, pg. 3023

OPAL REAL ESTATE GROUP—See Peter Pan Bus Lines, Inc.; *U.S. Private*, pg. 3159

OPERA RENDEMENT SCPI—See BNP Paribas SA; *Int'l*, pg. 1092

OPHIUCHUS EVEN EMPREENDIMENTOS IMOBILIARIOS LTDA.—See Even Construtora e Incorporadora S.A.; *Int'l*, pg. 2562

OPPENHEIMER DEVELOPMENT CORPORATION—See Oppenheimer Companies, Inc.; *U.S. Private*, pg. 3033

OPUS DEVELOPMENT CORPORATION—See Opus Holding, LLC; *U.S. Private*, pg. 3036

ORANGE LAKE COUNTRY CLUB REALTY, INC.—See Kemmons Wilson, Inc.; *U.S. Private*, pg. 2281

ORBIT PROJECTS PRIVATE LIMITED—See Emami Ltd; *Int'l*, pg. 2374

ORC UTILITY & INFRASTRUCTURE LAND SERVICES, LLC; *U.S. Private*, pg. 3039

ORIEL ASSET MANAGEMENT LLP—See Stifel Financial Corp.; *U.S. Public*, pg. 1950

ORION INVESTMENT & MANAGEMENT LTD. CORP.; *U.S. Private*, pg. 3043

ORPHEUM PROPERTY, INC.; *U.S. Public*, pg. 1618

OSAKA DIAMOND CHIKAGAI CO., LTD.—See Hankyu Hanshin Holdings Inc.; *Int'l*, pg. 3256

531390 — OTHER ACTIVITIES RE...   CORPORATE AFFILIATIONS

OTE ESTATE S.A.—See Hellenic Telecommunications Organization S.A.; *Int'l*, pg. 3334
OTO DEVELOPMENT; *U.S. Private*, pg. 3049
OVERSTOCK.COM REAL ESTATE LLC—See Beyond, Inc..; *U.S. Public*, pg. 327
OXPLUS B.V.—See Bentley Systems, Inc.; *U.S. Public*, pg. 297
PACIFICA COMPANIES, LLC; *U.S. Private*, pg. 3071
PACIFICA REAL ESTATE GROUP, LLC; *U.S. Private*, pg. 3072
PACIFIC EAGLE HOLDINGS CORPORATION—See Great Eagle Holdings Limited; *Int'l*, pg. 3064
PACIFIC OAK RESIDENTIAL TRUST, INC.—See Pacific Oak Strategic Opportunity REIT, Inc.; *U.S. Public*, pg. 1632
PACIFIC TOWER PROPERTIES INC.—See Cook Inlet Region, Inc.; *U.S. Private*, pg. 1038
PACIFIC UNION INTERNATIONAL, INC.; *U.S. Private*, pg. 3071
PAGE MANAGEMENT CO., INC.; *U.S. Private*, pg. 3074
PALAZZO, INC.—See Greener Pastures Group LLC; *U.S. Private*, pg. 1777
PALISADES COLLECTION, LLC—See Asta Funding, Inc.; *U.S. Private*, pg. 360
PALLADIAN LAND DEVELOPMENT INC—See ATN Holdings, Inc.; *Int'l*, pg. 687
PALMER CAPITAL PARTNERS LIMITED—See Fiera Capital Corporation; *Int'l*, pg. 2659
PANATTONI DEVELOPMENT COMPANY—See Panattoni Development Company; *U.S. Private*, pg. 3085
PANATTONI LUXEMBOURG SERVICES S.A.R.L—See Panattoni Development Company; *U.S. Private*, pg. 3085
PARAMOUNT GROUP REAL ESTATE ADVISOR LLC—See Paramount Group Inc.; *U.S. Public*, pg. 1637
PARKWAY, INC.; *U.S. Public*, pg. 1650
PARKWAY PROPERTIES LP—See Parkway, Inc.; *U.S. Public*, pg. 1650
PARKWAY PROPERTY INVESTMENTS, LLC—See Parkway, Inc.; *U.S. Public*, pg. 1650
PARMENTER REALTY & INVESTMENT COMPANY; *U.S. Private*, pg. 3099
PAX ANLAGE AG—See Baloise Holding AG; *Int'l*, pg. 811
PEARL MARINA ESTATES LIMITED—See Centum Investment Company Limited; *Int'l*, pg. 1416
PEGASUS FUNDING, LLC—See Asta Funding, Inc.; *U.S. Private*, pg. 360
PEKAO PROPERTY SA—See Bank Polska Kasa Opieki Spolka Akcyjna; *Int'l*, pg. 849
PENINSULA LAND LIMITED—See Ashok Piramal Group; *Int'l*, pg. 608
PENSAM CAPITAL, LLC; *U.S. Private*, pg. 3138
PEPINE REALTY, LLC; *U.S. Private*, pg. 3144
PERHOPOLIS S.R.L.—See Camfin S.p.A.; *Int'l*, pg. 1272
P F INNI—See Eik Bank P/F; *Int'l*, pg. 2332
PGIM (AUSTRALIA) PTY. LTD.—See Prudential Financial, Inc.; *U.S. Public*, pg. 1731
PGIM (HONG KONG) LTD.—See Prudential Financial, Inc.; *U.S. Public*, pg. 1731
PGIM REAL ESTATE FRANCE SAS—See Prudential Financial, Inc.; *U.S. Public*, pg. 1731
PGIM REAL ESTATE GERMANY AG—See Prudential Financial, Inc.; *U.S. Public*, pg. 1731
PGIM REAL ESTATE S. DE R.L. DE C.V.—See Prudential Financial, Inc.; *U.S. Public*, pg. 1731
PGIM (SHANGHAI) COMPANY LTD.—See Prudential Financial, Inc.; *U.S. Public*, pg. 1731
PGIM (SINGAPORE) PTE. LTD.—See Prudential Financial, Inc.; *U.S. Public*, pg. 1731
PHU QUOC HOUSING & URBAN DEVELOPMENT JSC—See C.E.O Group Joint Stock Company; *Int'l*, pg. 1240
PIASA REAL ESTATE, INC.—See Piasa Motor Fuels LLC; *U.S. Private*, pg. 3175
PINNACLE AMS DEVELOPMENT COMPANY LLC—See American Management Services LLC; *U.S. Private*, pg. 240
PISCES EVEN EMPREENDIMENTOS IMOBILIARIOS LTDA.—See Even Construtora e Incorporadora S.A.; *Int'l*, pg. 2562
PITCH PROMOTION SNC—See Altarea SCA; *Int'l*, pg. 385
PJB MANAGEMENT-GMBH—See Bilfinger SE; *Int'l*, pg. 1028
PLAZA ADVISORS, INC.; *U.S. Private*, pg. 3212
PLETTNER & BRECHT IMMOBILIEN GMBH—See Deutsche Grundstueckauktionen AG; *Int'l*, pg. 2065
PLYMOUTH ROCK MANAGEMENT COMPANY OF NEW JERSEY—See The Plymouth Rock Co.; *U.S. Private*, pg. 4097
PMB REAL ESTATE SERVICES LLC—See Ventas, Inc.; *U.S. Public*, pg. 2278
P&O ESTATES LTD.—See Dubai World Corporation; *Int'l*, pg. 2222
POINTE VISTA DEVELOPMENT LLC; *U.S. Private*, pg. 3222
POLARIS PACIFIC; *U.S. Private*, pg. 3223
POLY (BAOTOU) REAL ESTATE DEVELOPMENT CO., LTD.—See China Poly Group Corporation; *Int'l*, pg. 1541
POLY (BEIJING) REAL ESTATE DEVELOPMENT CO., LTD.—See China Poly Group Corporation; *Int'l*, pg. 1541
POLY (GUANGZHOU) PROPERTY MANAGEMENT CO., LTD.—See China Poly Group Corporation; *Int'l*, pg. 1541
POLY (GUANGZHOU) REAL ESTATE CLUB MANAGEMENT CO., LTD.—See China Poly Group Corporation; *Int'l*, pg. 1541
POLY (GUANGZHOU) REAL ESTATE DEVELOPMENT CO., LTD.—See China Poly Group Corporation; *Int'l*, pg. 1541
POLY GUIZHOU REAL ESTATE DEVELOPMENT CO., LTD—See China Poly Group Corporation; *Int'l*, pg. 1541
POLY (HU'NAN) REAL ESTATE DEVELOPMENT CO., LTD.—See China Poly Group Corporation; *Int'l*, pg. 1541
POLY (SCIENCE CITY, GUANGZHOU) REAL ESTATE DEVELOPMENT CO., LTD.—See China Poly Group Corporation; *Int'l*, pg. 1541
POLY (SHANGHAI) REAL ESTATE DEVELOPMENT CO., LTD.—See China Poly Group Corporation; *Int'l*, pg. 1541
POLY (SHENYANG) REAL ESTATE DEVELOPMENT CO., LTD.—See China Poly Group Corporation; *Int'l*, pg. 1541
POLY SOUTH CHINA INDUSTRY CO., LTD.—See China Poly Group Corporation; *Int'l*, pg. 1541
POLY (WUHAN) REAL ESTATE DEVELOPMENT CO., LTD.—See China Poly Group Corporation; *Int'l*, pg. 1541
POMMERAIE PARC SC—See BNP Paribas SA; *Int'l*, pg. 1092
PORIN ASEMA-AUKIO KOY—See Citycon Oyj; *Int'l*, pg. 1629
PORTE KANAZAWA CO., LTD.—See Hulic Co., Ltd.; *Int'l*, pg. 3528
PORT IMPERIAL SOUTH 15, L.L.C.—See Veris Residential, Inc.; *U.S. Public*, pg. 2281
PORTSIDE APARTMENT DEVELOPERS, L.L.C.—See Veris Residential, Inc.; *U.S. Public*, pg. 2281
PORTZAMPARC GESTION—See BNP Paribas SA; *Int'l*, pg. 1092
POSTAL REALTY TRUST, INC.; *U.S. Public*, pg. 1704
POSTBANK IMMOBILIEN GMBH—See Deutsche Bank Aktiengesellschaft; *Int'l*, pg. 2061
PPMG POTSDAMER PLATZ MANAGEMENT GMBH—See ECE Projektmanagement GmbH & Co KG; *Int'l*, pg. 2288
THE PRAEDIUM GROUP LLC; *U.S. Private*, pg. 4097
PRAIRIE DEVELOPMENT SDN. BHD.—See Gromutual Berhad; *Int'l*, pg. 3087
PRAMERICA REAL ESTATE INVESTORS (ASIA) PTE. LTD.—See Prudential Financial, Inc.; *U.S. Public*, pg. 1733
PRECISION REALTY, LLC—See Markel Group Inc.; *U.S. Public*, pg. 1368
PREI INTERNATIONAL, INC.—See Prudential Financial, Inc.; *U.S. Public*, pg. 1732
PREMIER PARTNERS, LLC—See McCarthy Bush Corporation; *U.S. Private*, pg. 2626
PREMIER REVERSE CLOSINGS—See First American Financial Corporation; *U.S. Public*, pg. 838
PRESCIENT, INC.; *U.S. Private*, pg. 3253
PRESIDIO PROPERTY TRUST, INC.; *U.S. Public*, pg. 1716
PRIMA 200 LIMITED—See HICL Infrastructure PLC; *Int'l*, pg. 3383
PRIMCO MANAGEMENT INC.; *U.S. Private*, pg. 3261
PRINCIPAL GLOBAL INVESTORS, LLC—See Principal Financial Group, Inc.; *U.S. Public*, pg. 1721
PROEQUITY ASSET MANAGEMENT CORPORATION; *U.S. Private*, pg. 3274
THE PROFESSIONAL LANDLORDS, LLC; *U.S. Private*, pg. 4100
PROFIT CONSTRUCT SRL—See ELLAKTOR S.A.; *Int'l*, pg. 2365
PROGREEN US, INC.; *U.S. Private*, pg. 3278
PROLOGIS B.V.—See Prologis, Inc.; *U.S. Public*, pg. 1727
PROLUXE PROPERTIES; *U.S. Private*, pg. 3282
PROMEC SP. Z O.O.—See E.ON SE; *Int'l*, pg. 2259
PROMMIS SOLUTIONS HOLDING CORP.; *U.S. Private*, pg. 3283
PROPERTUNITIES IMMOBILIEN CONSULTING GMBH—See BKW AG; *Int'l*, pg. 1056
PROPERTY AND BUILDING CORP. LTD.—See IDB Development Corporation Ltd.; *Int'l*, pg. 3588
PROPRIUM CAPITAL PARTNERS, L.P.; *U.S. Private*, pg. 3286
PROPTECH GROUP LIMITED—See GI Manager L.P.; *U.S. Private*, pg. 1693
PRO TECK EARNS INC.; *U.S. Private*, pg. 3270
PROTON CITY DEVELOPMENT CORPORATION SDN. BHD.—See DRB-HICOM Berhad; *Int'l*, pg. 2202
PROVISION OPERATION SYSTEMS, INC.; *U.S. Public*, pg. 1731
PRUDENTIAL AMERICANA GROUP REALTORS; *U.S. Private*, pg. 3295
PRUDENTIAL REAL ESTATE INVESTORS INVESTIMENTOS IMOBILIARIOS LTDA.—See Prudential Financial, Inc.; *U.S. Public*, pg. 1733
PRUDENTIAL REAL ESTATE INVESTORS (JAPAN) K.K.—See Prudential Financial, Inc.; *U.S. Public*, pg. 1733
PRUDENTIAL REAL ESTATE INVESTORS, SOCIEDAD RESPONSABILIDAD LIMITADA DE CAPITAL VARIABLE—See Prudential Financial, Inc.; *U.S. Public*, pg. 1733
PT DAIWA LIFE NEXT INDONESIA—See Daiwa House Industry Co., Ltd.; *Int'l*, pg. 1947
PT. FIRST ASIA INDONESIA—See First Asia Holdings Limited; *Int'l*, pg. 2682
PT HONGKONG LAND CONSULTANCY & MANAGEMENT—See Hong Kong Land Holdings Ltd.; *Int'l*, pg. 3467
PT HYUNDAI INTI DEVELOP—See Hyundai Corporation; *Int'l*, pg. 3555
PTP MANAGEMENT INC.—See Cook Inlet Region, Inc.; *U.S. Private*, pg. 1038
PUBLIC STORAGE PROPERTIES—See Public Storage; *U.S. Public*, pg. 1736
PUGH & COMPANY LIMITED—See Begbies Traynor Group plc; *Int'l*, pg. 941
PUJEN LAND DEVELOPMENT CO., LTD.—See China Metal Products Co., Ltd.; *Int'l*, pg. 1523
Q10 CAPITAL, L.L.C.; *U.S. Private*, pg. 3312
QATAR REAL ESTATE INVESTMENT COMPANY Q.P.S.C—See Barwa Real Estate Company Q.P.S.C.; *Int'l*, pg. 870
QHSLAB, INC.; *U.S. Public*, pg. 1742
QUICKEN LOANS, INC.—See RockBridge Growth Equity, LLC; *U.S. Private*, pg. 3465
QUINTAIN LIMITED—See Lone Star Global Acquisitions, LLC; *U.S. Private*, pg. 2489
R7 REAL ESTATE INC.—See Avison Young (Canada) Inc.; *Int'l*, pg. 745
RABBIT EVEN EMPREENDIMENTOS IMOBILIARIOS LTDA.—See Even Construtora e Incorporadora S.A.; *Int'l*, pg. 2562
RAGNAROK VERMOGENSVERWALTUNG AG & CO. KG—See Hypo Real Estate Holding AG; *Int'l*, pg. 3554
RAIN ASSOCIATES; *U.S. Private*, pg. 3347
RAINBOW ENTITY SDN. BHD.—See Gromutual Berhad; *Int'l*, pg. 3087
RANDOLPH ACQUISITIONS, INC.; *U.S. Private*, pg. 3354
RAYDIENT LLC—See Rayonier Inc.; *U.S. Public*, pg. 1765
RAYSUM CO., LTD.—See Hulic Co., Ltd.; *Int'l*, pg. 3528
RAYZOR RANCH, LP—See Forestar Group Inc.; *U.S. Public*, pg. 867
RDI, LLC—See Regent Contracting Corp.; *U.S. Private*, pg. 3387
REAC GROUP, INC.; *U.S. Private*, pg. 3365
REAGAN ASSET MANAGEMENT, LLC; *U.S. Private*, pg. 3367
REALCAPITALMARKETS.COM, LLC; *U.S. Private*, pg. 3368
REAL CAPITAL SOLUTIONS INC.; *U.S. Private*, pg. 3367
REAL ESTATE ECONOMICS—See MidOcean Partners, LLP; *U.S. Private*, pg. 2717
REAL ESTATE INSYNC; *U.S. Private*, pg. 3367
REAL ESTATE RESEARCH CONSULTANTS, INC.—See Comvest Group Holdings LLC; *U.S. Private*, pg. 1007
REAL ESTATE SOLUTION & TECHNOLOGY SRL—See Covivio; *Int'l*, pg. 1821
REAL FOUNDATIONS, INC.; *U.S. Private*, pg. 3367
REALIA GROUP OY—See Altor Equity Partners AB; *Int'l*, pg. 396
REALIA MANAGEMENT OY—See Altor Equity Partners AB; *Int'l*, pg. 396
REALI, INC.; *U.S. Private*, pg. 3368
REAL I.S. AG GESELLSCHAFT FUR IMMOBILIEN ASSETMANAGEMENT—See BayernLB Holding AG; *Int'l*, pg. 914
REAL I.S. MANAGEMENT HAMBURG GMBH—See BayernLB Holding AG; *Int'l*, pg. 914
REAL TRENDS, INC.—See HW Media, LLC; *U.S. Private*, pg. 2015
REALTY INTERNATIONAL ASSOCIATES PTE. LTD.—See Morgan Stanley; *U.S. Public*, pg. 1471
REALTY ONE GROUP, INC.; *U.S. Private*, pg. 3369
REAL VERWALTUNGSGESELLSCHAFT MBH—See Advent International Corporation; *U.S. Private*, pg. 97
REAL VERWALTUNGSGESELLSCHAFT MBH—See Centerbridge Partners, L.P.; *U.S. Private*, pg. 813
REDEFY CORPORATION; *U.S. Public*, pg. 1770
REDEVCO B.V.—See COFRA Holding AG; *Int'l*, pg. 1694
REDEVCO FRANCE S.A.—See COFRA Holding AG; *Int'l*, pg. 1694
REDEVCO NETHERLANDS—See COFRA Holding AG; *Int'l*, pg. 1694
REDEVCO RETAIL ESPANA S.L.U.—See COFRA Holding AG; *Int'l*, pg. 1694
REDEVCO SERVICES DEUTSCHLAND GMBH—See COFRA Holding AG; *Int'l*, pg. 1694
REDEVCO (SUISSE) AG—See COFRA Holding AG; *Int'l*, pg. 1694
REDEVCO UK—See COFRA Holding AG; *Int'l*, pg. 1694
REDFIN MORTGAGE, LLC—See Redfin Corporation; *U.S. Public*, pg. 1770
RED OAK REALTY; *U.S. Private*, pg. 3375
REDSTONE INVESTMENTS; *U.S. Private*, pg. 3380
REDUS FLORIDA COMMERCIAL, LLC—See Wells Fargo & Company; *U.S. Public*, pg. 2345
REDUS FL PROPERTIES, LLC—See Wells Fargo & Company; *U.S. Public*, pg. 2345
REGIONALNOE AGROPROIZVODSTVENNOE OBJEDI-

N.A.I.C.S. INDEX

531390 — OTHER ACTIVITIES RE...

NENIE LLC—See AFI Development PLC; *Int'l*, pg. 189

THE REISER GROUP; *U.S. Private*, pg. 4103

REIS, INC.—See Moody's Corporation; *U.S. Public*, pg. 1469

REIT ASSET MANAGEMENT LIMITED—See Bank of Montreal; *Int'l*, pg. 847

RELATED BEAL, LLC—See The Related Companies, L.P.; *U.S. Private*, pg. 4103

RELATED CALIFORNIA, LLC—See The Related Companies, L.P.; *U.S. Private*, pg. 4103

RELATED GROUP—See The Related Companies, L.P.; *U.S. Private*, pg. 4104

RENEW INDIANAPOLIS, INC.; *U.S. Private*, pg. 3398

RENTPATH, LLC—See Redfin Corporation; *U.S. Public*, pg. 1770

RENT READY, LLC; *U.S. Private*, pg. 3400

RENWOOD REALTYTRAC, LLC—See *U.S. Private*, pg. 3400

REQUIRE LLC—See Covius Holdings, Inc.; *U.S. Private*, pg. 1073

RESORTQUEST INTERNATIONAL, INC.—See Jefferies Financial Group Inc.; *U.S. Public*, pg. 1189

RESOURCE PROPERTY MANAGEMENT, LLC—See Island Capital Group LLC; *U.S. Private*, pg. 2144

RESOURCE REAL ESTATE, INC.—See Island Capital Group LLC; *U.S. Private*, pg. 2144

RETAIL OPPORTUNITY INVESTMENTS PARTNERSHIP, LP—See RETAIL OPPORTUNITY INVESTMENTS CORP.; *U.S. Public*, pg. 1792

REXFORD INDUSTRIAL REALTY, INC.; *U.S. Public*, pg. 1795

R & F PROPERTIES (CAMBODIA) CO., LTD.—See Guangzhou R&F Properties Co., Ltd.; *Int'l*, pg. 3167

R&F PROPERTY AUSTRALIA PTY LTD—See Guangzhou R&F Properties Co., Ltd.; *Int'l*, pg. 3167

R & F PROPERTY PTY LTD—See Guangzhou R&F Properties Co., Ltd.; *Int'l*, pg. 3167

RHP PARTNER, LLC—See Ryman Hospitality Properties, Inc.; *U.S. Public*, pg. 1829

RIDA DEVELOPMENT CORP.; *U.S. Private*, pg. 3431

RIDGEWOOD INFRASTRUCTURE LLC; *U.S. Private*, pg. 3433

RIDGEWOOD REAL ESTATE PARTNERS, LLC; *U.S. Private*, pg. 3434

RIKAZ DEVELOPMENT COMPANY—See HAK Algahtani Group of Companies; *Int'l*, pg. 3219

RISLAND (THAILAND) CO., LTD.—See Country Garden Holdings Company Limited; *Int'l*, pg. 1818

RIVERSIDE PROPERTY PTE LTD—See Frasers Property Limited; *Int'l*, pg. 2766

RIVER VALLEY APARTMENTS PTE LTD—See Frasers Property Limited; *Int'l*, pg. 2766

RIVERWALK G URBAN RENEWAL L.L.C.—See Veris Residential, Inc.; *U.S. Public*, pg. 2282

RJR REALTY RELOCATION SERVICES, INC.—See British American Tobacco plc; *Int'l*, pg. 1168

ROAD LINK (A69) LIMITED—See Henry Boot PLC; *Int'l*, pg. 3355

ROBERT B. AIKENS & ASSOCIATES, LLC; *U.S. Private*, pg. 3457

ROBERT PAUL PROPERTIES, INC.—See Berkshire Hathaway Inc.; *U.S. Public*, pg. 304

ROBYG S.A.—See The Goldman Sachs Group, Inc.; *U.S. Public*, pg. 2080

ROCKPOINT EUROPE LIMITED—See Rockpoint Group, LLC; *U.S. Private*, pg. 3467

ROCKPOINT GROUP, LLC - DALLAS OFFICE—See Rockpoint Group, LLC; *U.S. Private*, pg. 3467

ROCKPOINT GROUP, LLC - SAN FRANCISCO OFFICE—See Rockpoint Group, LLC; *U.S. Private*, pg. 3467

ROCKPOINT GROUP, LLC; *U.S. Private*, pg. 3467

ROCKWELL PROPERTY CO.; *U.S. Private*, pg. 3467

ROCKWOOD CAPITAL, LLC; *U.S. Private*, pg. 3468

RODACOM SARL—See Axel Springer SE; *Int'l*, pg. 766

RODENHURST ESTATES LIMITED—See Highcroft Investments PLC; *Int'l*, pg. 3387

ROEBUCK ASSET MANAGEMENT LLP—See GFH Financial Group B.S.C.; *Int'l*, pg. 2956

ROEDIGER GRUNDBESITZ GMBH—See Bilfinger SE; *Int'l*, pg. 1028

ROOFSTOCK, INC.; *U.S. Private*, pg. 3479

ROSELAND MANAGEMENT CO., LLC—See Veris Residential, Inc.; *U.S. Public*, pg. 2282

ROSELAND MANAGEMENT SERVICES, L.P.—See Veris Residential, Inc.; *U.S. Public*, pg. 2282

ROSEWOOD LAFAYETTE COMMONS, L.L.C.—See Veris Residential, Inc.; *U.S. Public*, pg. 2282

ROUSE KENT (RESIDENTIAL) LIMITED—See Prologis, Inc.; *U.S. Public*, pg. 1727

ROWE ENTERPRISES, INC.; *U.S. Private*, pg. 3490

RP DATA LIMITED—See Insight Venture Management, LLC; *U.S. Private*, pg. 2089

RP DATA LIMITED—See Stone Point Capital LLC; *U.S. Private*, pg. 3823

RP DATA NEW ZEALAND LIMITED—See Insight Venture Management, LLC; *U.S. Private*, pg. 2089

RP DATA NEW ZEALAND LIMITED—See Stone Point Capital LLC; *U.S. Private*, pg. 3823

RP MANAGEMENT, INC.; *U.S. Private*, pg. 3495

RREEF MANAGEMENT GMBH—See Deutsche Bank Aktiengesellschaft; *Int'l*, pg. 2061

R & R PROPERTY MANAGERS—See Reading Anthracite Company; *U.S. Private*, pg. 3366

RSL REAL ESTATE DEVELOPMENT S.R.L.—See Ablon Group Limited; *Int'l*, pg. 63

RUBENSTEIN PARTNERS, L.P.—See Independence Capital Partners, LLC; *U.S. Private*, pg. 2057

RUBLOFF DEVELOPMENT GROUP, INC.; *U.S. Private*, pg. 3500

THE RUBY GROUP; *U.S. Private*, pg. 4113

RUENMONGKOL CO., LTD.—See Bumrungrad Hospital Public Company Limited; *Int'l*, pg. 1215

RUSTHUIS KRUYENBERG NV—See Ackermans & van Haaren NV; *Int'l*, pg. 106

RW NATIONAL HOLDINGS, LLC—See Appreciate Holdings, Inc.; *U.S. Public*, pg. 173

RXR REALTY, LLC; *U.S. Private*, pg. 3509

SACHSISCHE GRUNDSTUCKSAUKTIONEN AG—See Deutsche Grundstuecksauktionen AG; *Int'l*, pg. 2065

SAFE AND GREEN DEVELOPMENT CORPORATION—See Safe & Green Holdings Corp.; *U.S. Public*, pg. 1834

SAFEHOLD INC.; *U.S. Public*, pg. 1834

THE SAILS PATTAYA—See Grande Asset Hotels & Property Public Company Limited; *Int'l*, pg. 3057

SAISON FUNDEX CORPORATION—See Credit Saison Co., Ltd.; *Int'l*, pg. 1836

SAKAE CORPORATION SDN. BHD.—See Gromutual Berhad; *Int'l*, pg. 3087

SAMALAJU HOTEL MANAGEMENT SDN. BHD.—See Cahya Mata Sarawak Berhad; *Int'l*, pg. 1251

SAM-MAN REALTY, INC.—See Hyman Brickle & Son, Inc.; *U.S. Private*, pg. 2019

SAM PAO PETCH CO., LTD.—See BTS Group Holdings Public Company Limited; *Int'l*, pg. 1206

SAN ELIJO HILLS TOWN CENTER, LLC—See Jefferies Financial Group Inc.; *U.S. Public*, pg. 1188

SAN JUAN ABSTRACT COMPANY, INC.—See Stewart Information Services Corporation; *U.S. Public*, pg. 1948

SANSONE GROUP LLC; *U.S. Private*, pg. 3546

SANTANDER GLOBAL PROPERTY, S.L.—See Banco Santander, S.A.; *Int'l*, pg. 827

SARES-REGIS GROUP; *U.S. Private*, pg. 3550

SARL FONCIERE ATLAND REIM—See Fonciere Atland SA; *Int'l*, pg. 2724

SAUNAMAX OY—See Harvia Oyj; *Int'l*, pg. 3281

SAVANNAH PROPERTIES LIMITED—See ENL Limited; *Int'l*, pg. 2441

SBA COMMUNICATIONS CORPORATION; *U.S. Public*, pg. 1842

SB CATTLE LTD.—See ENL Limited; *Int'l*, pg. 2441

S.C BNP PARIBAS REAL ESTATE ADVISORY S.A—See BNP Paribas SA; *Int'l*, pg. 1092

SC CLH ESTATE SRL—See ELLAKTOR S.A.; *Int'l*, pg. 2365

SCG FINANCE CORPORATION LIMITED—See Capital Industrial Financial Services Group Limited; *Int'l*, pg. 1311

SCHLOSS BENSBERG MANAGEMENT GMBH—See Aedifica SA; *Int'l*, pg. 173

SCHOONER BAY REALTY INC.; *U.S. Private*, pg. 3568

SCHULTZ INDUSTRIAL SERVICES, INC.—See New Mountain Capital, LLC; *U.S. Private*, pg. 2900

SCI FLIF CHATEAU LANDON—See BNP Paribas SA; *Int'l*, pg. 1092

SCI FLIF EVRY 2—See BNP Paribas SA; *Int'l*, pg. 1092

SCI FLIF LE GALLO—See BNP Paribas SA; *Int'l*, pg. 1092

SCI REAL ESTATE INVESTMENTS, LLC; *U.S. Private*, pg. 3573

SCOPIA CAPITAL MANAGEMENT LP; *U.S. Private*, pg. 3575

SCOTTISHPOWER SP ENERGYNETWORKS—See Iberdrola, S.A.; *Int'l*, pg. 3574

SCUDO GRUNDSTUCKS-VERMIETUNGSGESELLSCHAFT MBH & CO. OBJEKT KLEINE ALEXANDERSTRASSE KG—See Deutsche Bank Aktiengesellschaft; *Int'l*, pg. 2061

SEALASKA SECURITY HOLDINGS, LLC.—See Sealaska Corporation; *U.S. Private*, pg. 3585

SECURITY LAND AND DEVELOPMENT CORPORATION; *U.S. Private*, pg. 3596

SEDO GRUNDSTUCKS-VERMIETUNGSGESELLSCHAFT MBH—See Deutsche Bank Aktiengesellschaft; *Int'l*, pg. 2061

SEGECE HELLAS REAL ESTATE MANAGEMENT SA—See BNP Paribas SA; *Int'l*, pg. 1092

SELAT MAKMUR SDN BHD—See Berjaya Corporation Berhad; *Int'l*, pg. 983

SELECTIS HEALTH, INC.; *U.S. Public*, pg. 1862

SELECT REALTY GROUP; *U.S. Private*, pg. 3600

SEMANGAT CERGAS SDN BHD—See Berjaya Corporation Berhad; *Int'l*, pg. 983

SENECA INVESTMENTS; *U.S. Private*, pg. 3606

SENTINEL REAL ESTATE CORPORATION; *U.S. Private*, pg. 3609

SERVICE LINK LP—See Fidelity National Financial, Inc.; *U.S. Public*, pg. 831

SERVICELINK—See Fidelity National Financial, Inc.; *U.S. Public*, pg. 831

SESAME CONSEIL SAS—See BNP Paribas SA; *Int'l*, pg. 1092

SHANGHAI FORTE LAND CO., LTD.—See Fosun International Limited; *Int'l*, pg. 2752

SHANGHAI WEITAI PROPERTIES MANAGEMENT CO., LTD.—See Haitong Securities Co., Ltd.; *Int'l*, pg. 3218

SHANGHAI XUYU PROPERTY CO. LTD.—See CIFI Holdings (Group) Co. Ltd.; *Int'l*, pg. 1605

SHANGHAI ZECHUN INVESTMENT & DEVELOPMENT CO., LTD.—See Haitong Securities Co., Ltd.; *Int'l*, pg. 3218

SHAPELL INVESTMENT PROPERTIES, INC.; *U.S. Private*, pg. 3625

SHARED TECHNOLOGY SERVICES GROUP INC.—See The Plymouth Rock Co.; *U.S. Private*, pg. 4097

SHEA PROPERTIES INC.—See J.F. Shea Co., Inc.; *U.S. Private*, pg. 2165

SHELDON GOOD & COMPANY-MOUNTAIN REGION—See Racebrook Capital Advisors, LLC; *U.S. Private*, pg. 3341

SHERMAN & HEMSTREET, INC.; *U.S. Private*, pg. 3633

S-H FORTY-NINE PROPCO VENTURES, LLC—See Healthpeak Properties, Inc.; *U.S. Public*, pg. 1016

SHIN-YOKOHAMA STATION DEVELOPMENT CO., LTD.—See Central Japan Railway Company; *Int'l*, pg. 1408

SHOWINGTIME.COM, INC.—See Zillow Group, Inc.; *U.S. Public*, pg. 2405

S.H. RESOURCES & DEVELOPMENT CORP.; *U.S. Public*, pg. 1832

SIAM FUTURE DEVELOPMENT PCL—See Central Pattana Public Company Limited; *Int'l*, pg. 1409

THE SIEGEL GROUP; *U.S. Private*, pg. 4118

SIGNATUR FASTIGHETER AB—See Fastighets AB Trianon; *Int'l*, pg. 2622

SILVA ESTATE A/S—See Det Danske Hedeselskab; *Int'l*, pg. 2047

SILVER MESA AT PALOMINO PARK L.L.C.—See Moody's Corporation; *U.S. Public*, pg. 1469

SIMPANG MAJU ENTERPRISES SDN. BHD.—See Gromutual Berhad; *Int'l*, pg. 3088

SIMPLEX INVESTMENT ADVISORS INC.—See Hulic Co., Ltd.; *Int'l*, pg. 3528

SIMPSON HOUSING LIMITED PARTNERSHIP; *U.S. Private*, pg. 3668

SIMS URBAN OASIS PTE. LTD.—See Hong Leong Investment Holdings Pte. Ltd.; *U.S. Private*, pg. 3468

SINO SANTA FE REAL ESTATE (BEIJING) CO. LTD.—See EAC Invest AS; *Int'l*, pg. 2262

SJP 1 LIMITED—See Heidelberg Materials AG; *Int'l*, pg. 3319

SKYMARK REAL ESTATE INVESTMENTS; *U.S. Private*, pg. 3686

SMART SERVICE & MANAGEMENT CO., LTD.—See AP (Thailand) Public Company Limited; *Int'l*, pg. 499

SMARTZIP ANALYTICS, INC.—See Constellation Real Estate Group, Inc.; *U.S. Private*, pg. 1023

SMUGGLERS' NOTCH MANAGEMENT COMPANY LTD.—See Smugglers' Notch Investment Co.; *U.S. Private*, pg. 3699

SNAKE EVEN EMPREENDIMENTOS IMOBILIARIOS LTDA.—See Even Construtora e Incorporadora S.A.; *Int'l*, pg. 2562

SNC COGEDIM AQUITAINE—See Altarea SCA; *Int'l*, pg. 385

SNC COGEDIM EST—See Altarea SCA; *Int'l*, pg. 385

SNC COGEDIM LANGUEDOC ROUSSILLON—See Altarea SCA; *Int'l*, pg. 385

SNC COGEDIM MIDI-PYRENEES—See Altarea SCA; *Int'l*, pg. 385

SNC COGEDIM PARIS METROPOLE—See Altarea SCA; *Int'l*, pg. 385

SNC COGEDIM SAVOIES-LEMAN—See Altarea SCA; *Int'l*, pg. 385

SNC FONCIERE ATLAND VALORISATION—See Fonciere Atland SA; *Int'l*, pg. 2724

SOCIETE ALSACIENNE DE DEVELOPPEMENT ET D'EXPANSION S.A.—See BNP Paribas SA; *Int'l*, pg. 1084

SOCIETE DES CENTRES D'OC ET D'OIL - SCOO SC—See BNP Paribas SA; *Int'l*, pg. 1092

SOCIETE GENERALE FONCIERE SAL—See Fransabank SAL; *Int'l*, pg. 2762

SOCIETE INMOBILIERE BBV D—See Banco Bilbao Vizcaya Argentaria, S.A.; *Int'l*, pg. 818

SODEARIF SA—See Bouygues S.A.; *Int'l*, pg. 1123

SOHGOH REAL ESTATE CO., LTD.—See Haseko Corporation; *Int'l*, pg. 3283

SOLID EARTH, INC.; *U.S. Private*, pg. 3709

SOTHERLY HOTELS INC.; *U.S. Public*, pg. 1910

SOUL SPACE PROJECTS LIMITED—See B L Kashyap & Sons Limited; *Int'l*, pg. 783

SOUTH CAN THO INVESTMENT & DEVELOPMENT JSC—See C.E.O Group Joint Stock Company; *Int'l*, pg. 1240

SOUTHEAST LAND CONSULTANTS, INC.; *U.S. Private*, pg. 3726

SOUTHERN OAKS APARTMENT HOMES—See Kennedy-Wilson Holdings, Inc.; *U.S. Public*, pg. 1223
SOUTHERN SELF STORAGE OF GRAYTON, LLC—See National Storage Affiliates Trust; *U.S. Public*, pg. 1498
SOUTHERN SELF STORAGE OF PENSACOLA, LLC—See National Storage Affiliates Trust; *U.S. Public*, pg. 1498
SOVEREIGN PROPERTY FUND PTY LIMITED—See Brookfield Corporation; *Int'l*, pg. 1189
SOVEREIGN REAL ESTATE INVESTMENT TRUST—See Banco Santander, S.A.; *Int'l*, pg. 827
SOVIME S.R.L.—See Gruppo MutuiOnline S.p.A; *Int'l*, pg. 3141
SPANGLER PROPERTIES, LLC—See Spangler Companies, Inc.; *U.S. Private*, pg. 3745
SPARKASSEN-IMMOBILIEN—See Helaba Landesbank Hessen-Thuringen; *Int'l*, pg. 3328
SP ASSET MANAGEMENT LLC—See Steel Partners Holdings L.P.; *U.S. Public*, pg. 1943
SPHERION OBJEKT GMBH & CO. KG—See Allianz SE; *Int'l*, pg. 356
SPONDA OYJ—See Blackstone Inc.; *U.S. Public*, pg. 350
SPORT CLUB 18, S.A—See Banco Bilbao Vizcaya Argentaria, S.A.; *Int'l*, pg. 818
SP PLUS PROPERTY MANAGEMENT, INC.—See Eldridge Industries LLC; *U.S. Private*, pg. 1351
S PROSERV HUNGARY - PROCUREMENT SERVICES HU KFT.—See Erste Group Bank AG; *Int'l*, pg. 2499
S PROSERV SLOVAKIA - PROCUREMENT SERVICES SK, S.R.O.—See Erste Group Bank AG; *Int'l*, pg. 2499
SQLI IMMOBILIER—See DBAY Advisors Limited; *Int'l*, pg. 1987
SQUARE MILE CAPITAL MANAGEMENT LLC; *U.S. Private*, pg. 3766
S REAL SPARKASSE D.O.O.—See Erste Group Bank AG; *Int'l*, pg. 2499
SRI PANGLIMA SDN BHD—See Berjaya Corporation Berhad; *Int'l*, pg. 982
SRS CORE LLC; *U.S. Private*, pg. 3768
SRS REAL ESTATE PARTNERS, LLC—See Jones Lang LaSalle Incorporated; *U.S. Public*, pg. 1205
ST. ANDREW BAY LAND COMPANY, LLC—See Jefferies Financial Group Inc.; *U.S. Public*, pg. 1188
STAN JOHNSON COMPANY; *U.S. Private*, pg. 3777
STANLEY GRUNDSTUCKSVERWALTUNGS GMBH—See Stanley Black & Decker, Inc.; *U.S. Public*, pg. 1935
STARBEV NETHERLANDS BV—See Molson Coors Beverage Company; *U.S. Public*, pg. 1459
STATES TITLE HOLDING, INC.—See Doma Holdings Inc.; *U.S. Public*, pg. 673
STATION PLACE ON MONMOUTH, LLC—See First Real Estate Investment Trust New Jersey Co.; *U.S. Public*, pg. 847
ST. BARTH PROPERTIES, INC.; *U.S. Private*, pg. 3771
STEADFAST CAPITAL MARKETS GROUP, LLC—See Steadfast Companies; *U.S. Private*, pg. 3794
STEADFAST PROPERTIES & DEVELOPMENT, INC.—See Steadfast Companies; *U.S. Private*, pg. 3794
STEINER EQUITIES GROUP LLC; *U.S. Private*, pg. 3798
STENDORREN FASTIGHETER AB—See EQT AB; *Int'l*, pg. 2481
STEPSTONE GROUP REAL ESTATE LP—See StepStone Group LP; *U.S. Private*, pg. 3804
STERLING ADVISORS—See Truist Financial Corporation; *U.S. Public*, pg. 2201
STERLING MOTOR PROPERTIES LIMITED—See General Motors Company; *U.S. Public*, pg. 928
STEWART TITLE OF CAMERON COUNTY, INC.—See Stewart Information Services Corporation; *U.S. Public*, pg. 1948
STEWART TITLE OF MONTGOMERY COUNTY INC.—See Howard Hughes Holdings Inc.; *U.S. Public*, pg. 1060
STIFEL VENTURE CORP.—See Stifel Financial Corp.; *U.S. Public*, pg. 1950
STIRLING CAPITAL PROPERTIES, LLC—See Prologis, Inc.; *U.S. Public*, pg. 1726
ST. JOE CLUB & RESORTS VACATION RENTALS, LLC—See The St. Joe Company; *U.S. Public*, pg. 2131
ST. JOE TIMBERLAND COMPANY OF DELAWARE, L.L.C.—See The St. Joe Company; *U.S. Public*, pg. 2131
ST JOHN'S MANCHESTER LIMITED—See Henry Boot PLC; *Int'l*, pg. 3355
ST. LOUIS RIVERPORT HOLDING COMPANY, INC.; *U.S. Private*, pg. 3770
ST. MARY'S PROPERTIES, INC.—See Omega Healthcare Investors, Inc.; *U.S. Public*, pg. 1571
ST. MODWEN PROPERTIES PLC—See Blackstone Inc.; *U.S. Public*, pg. 358
STOCK PLUS AD; *U.S. Public*, pg. 1950
STORHUB MANAGEMENT PTE LTD—See Warburg Pincus LLC; *U.S. Private*, pg. 4439
STORTPLAATS NOORD EN MIDDEN ZEELAND B.V.—See Delta N.V.; *Int'l*, pg. 2019
STRASBURGER ENTERPRISES, INC.; *U.S. Private*, pg. 3833
STRATEGIC RETAIL ADVISORS, INC.; *U.S. Private*, pg. 3835
STREETSENSE, INC.; *U.S. Private*, pg. 3839
STRONG SOLUTIONS, INC.; *U.S. Public*, pg. 1955

SUBWAY REAL ESTATE CORP.—See Doctor's Associates Inc.; *U.S. Private*, pg. 1251
SUDBURY AVALON, INC.—See AvalonBay Communities, Inc.; *U.S. Public*, pg. 240
SUMMER RANGE SDN. BHD.—See Gromutual Berhad; *Int'l*, pg. 3088
SUNBEAM DEVELOPMENT CORPORATION—See Sunbeam Television Corporation; *U.S. Private*, pg. 3864
SUNRISE TECH PARK CO. LLC—See Brookfield Corporation; *Int'l*, pg. 1186
SUPER ABASTOS CENTRALES Y COMERCIALES, S.A. DE C.V.—See Desarrolladora Homex, S.A. de C.V.; *Int'l*, pg. 2044
SUPERDIS SA—See Carrefour SA; *Int'l*, pg. 1346
SUPER FUNWORLD PTE LTD—See Hiap Hoe Limited; *Int'l*, pg. 3382
SURESNES IMMOBILIER S.A.—See Assicurazioni Generali S.p.A.; *Int'l*, pg. 645
SURETY HOLDINGS CORP.; *U.S. Public*, pg. 1967
SURPLUS ACQUISITION VENTURE, LLC—See Liquidity Services, Inc.; *U.S. Public*, pg. 1321
SWELL INTERNATIONAL INC; *U.S. Private*, pg. 3892
SWISS HEALTHCARE PROPERTIES AG—See AEVIS VICTORIA SA; *Int'l*, pg. 183
SYGECO LIMITED—See ENL Limited; *Int'l*, pg. 2442
SYNEXS GMBH—See ACS, Actividades de Construccion y Servicios, S.A.; *Int'l*, pg. 116
TAAMEER HOSPITALITY FOR HOTEL MANAGEMENT S.A.—See Al-Massaleh Real Estate Company K.S.C.C.; *Int'l*, pg. 287
TAAMEER HOTEL MANAGEMENT COMPANY & CONSULTANCY S.A.—See Al-Massaleh Real Estate Company K.S.C.C.; *Int'l*, pg. 287
TAAMEER LEBANON HOLDING COMPANY-S.A.L.—See Al-Massaleh Real Estate Company K.S.C.C.; *Int'l*, pg. 287
TAAMEER REAL ESTATE INVESTMENT CO. KSCC—See Al-Massaleh Real Estate Company K.S.C.C.; *Int'l*, pg. 287
TACT HOME CO., LTD.—See Iida Group Holdings Co., Ltd.; *Int'l*, pg. 3607
TAKIR GRUNDSTUCKS-VERMIETUNGSGESELLSCHAFT MBH—See Deutsche Bank Aktiengesellschaft; *Int'l*, pg. 2062
TAMPEREEN SUVANTOKATU KOY—See Citycon Oyj; *Int'l*, pg. 1629
TARA IMMOBILIENGESELLSCHAFT MBH—See Commerzbank AG; *Int'l*, pg. 1718
TARA IMMOBILIENPROJEKTE GMBH—See Commerzbank AG; *Int'l*, pg. 1718
TARA PROPERTY MANAGEMENT GMBH—See Commerzbank AG; *Int'l*, pg. 1719
TASHIMA DEVELOPMENT SDN BHD—See EcoFirst Consolidated Bhd; *Int'l*, pg. 2295
TATE CAPITAL REAL ESTATE SOLUTIONS, LLC; *U.S. Private*, pg. 3935
TATWEER DUBAI LLC—See Dubai Holding LLC; *Int'l*, pg. 2218
TAU ATLANTIC, LLC—See Realty Income Corporation; *U.S. Public*, pg. 1768
TAUBMAN CENTERS, INC.—See Simon Property Group, Inc.; *U.S. Public*, pg. 1881
TAUBMAN (HONG KONG) LIMITED—See Simon Property Group, Inc.; *U.S. Public*, pg. 1882
TAYLOR MORRISON OF FLORIDA, INC.—See Brookfield Corporation; *Int'l*, pg. 1183
TECOLOTE RESOURCES, INC.—See Owl Companies; *U.S. Private*, pg. 3055
TECOM INVESTMENTS LLC—See Dubai Holding LLC; *Int'l*, pg. 2218
TEMPLETON SANTA BARBARA, LLC—See Limoneira Company; *U.S. Public*, pg. 1316
TERAS ECO SDN. BHD.—See Axteria Group Berhad; *Int'l*, pg. 772
TERGO GRUNDSTUCKS-VERMIETUNGSGESELLSCHAFT MBH—See Deutsche Bank Aktiengesellschaft; *Int'l*, pg. 2062
TERRA COASTAL ESCROW, INC.—See Anywhere Real Estate Inc.; *U.S. Public*, pg. 143
TERRA FIRMA CAPITAL CORPORATION—See GM Capital Corp; *Int'l*, pg. 3011
TERRAIN-AKTIENGESELLSCHAFT HERZOGPARK—See Advent International Corporation; *U.S. Private*, pg. 97
TERRAIN-AKTIENGESELLSCHAFT HERZOGPARK—See Centerbridge Partners, L.P.; *U.S. Private*, pg. 813
TERRAPOINTE LLC—See Rayonier Inc.; *U.S. Public*, pg. 1765
TERRA REAL ESTATE ADVISORS—See Terra Group; *U.S. Private*, pg. 3970
TERRASURE DEVELOPMENT, LLC—See OceanSound Partners, LP; *U.S. Private*, pg. 2991
TERRA VERDE GROUP, LLC; *U.S. Private*, pg. 3970
TERRA VITRIS EMPREENDIMENTOS IMOBILIARIOS LTDA.—See Even Construtora e Incorporadora S.A.; *Int'l*, pg. 2562
TERRUS GRUNDSTUCKS-VERMIETUNGSGESELLSCHAFT MBH & CO. OBJEKT BERNBACH KG—See Deutsche Bank Aktiengesellschaft; *Int'l*, pg. 2062
TERRUS GRUNDSTUCKS-VERMIETUNGSGESELLSCHAFT MBH—See Deutsche Bank Aktiengesellschaft; *Int'l*, pg. 2062
TFML LIMITED—See BlackWall Limited; *Int'l*, pg. 1062
THAMES PROPERTIES LTD—See Bank of Cyprus Holdings Public Limited Company; *Int'l*, pg. 842
THOMAS DAILY GMBH—See CoStar Group, Inc.; *U.S. Public*, pg. 586
THOMAS INVESTMENT HOLDINGS, LLC—See Immobiliare Global Investments, Inc.; *U.S. Private*, pg. 2047
THOMAS TITLE & ESCROW, LLC—See Stewart Information Services Corporation; *U.S. Public*, pg. 1948
THURINGIA GENERALI 1. IMMOBILIEN AG & CO. KG—See Cinven Limited; *Int'l*, pg. 1616
TIAA HENDERSON REAL ESTATE LTD.—See Teachers Insurance Association - College Retirement Fund; *U.S. Private*, pg. 3945
TIC PROPERTIES, LLC; *U.S. Private*, pg. 4167
TIMIOS TITLE, A CALIFORNIA CORPORATION—See Ideanomics, Inc.; *U.S. Public*, pg. 1088
TISHMAN CONSTRUCTION CORPORATION—See AECOM; *U.S. Public*, pg. 51
TISHMAN REALTY CORPORATION—See AECOM; *U.S. Public*, pg. 52
TITAN HOA MANAGEMENT, LLC; *U.S. Private*, pg. 4177
TITLEONE EXCHANGE COMPANY—See Anywhere Real Estate Inc.; *U.S. Public*, pg. 143
TITLEZOOM COMPANY—See Lennar Corporation; *U.S. Public*, pg. 1307
TOKYO STATION DEVELOPMENT CO., LTD.—See Central Japan Railway Company; *Int'l*, pg. 1408
TOPA MANAGEMENT COMPANY—See Topa Equities Ltd, Inc.; *U.S. Private*, pg. 4187
TOPA PROPERTIES, LTD.—See Topa Equities Ltd, Inc.; *U.S. Private*, pg. 4187
TOPREALITY.SK S.R.O.—See Axel Springer SE; *Int'l*, pg. 767
TOTAL LENDER SOLUTIONS, INC.; *U.S. Private*, pg. 4191
TOUCHSTONE CAPITAL MANAGEMENT CO., LTD.—See Danto Holdings Corporation; *Int'l*, pg. 1969
TOYOHASHI STATION BUILDING CO., LTD.—See Central Japan Railway Company; *Int'l*, pg. 1408
TPG RE FINANCE TRUST, INC.; *U.S. Public*, pg. 2178
TRAFALGAR CORPORATE PTY. LIMITED—See Centuria Capital Limited; *Int'l*, pg. 1416
TRAFON GROUP; *U.S. Private*, pg. 4203
TRB APOPKA LLC—See BRT Apartments Corp.; *U.S. Public*, pg. 403
TRB ARLINGTON LLC—See BRT Apartments Corp.; *U.S. Public*, pg. 403
TRB NO. 1 CORP.—See BRT Apartments Corp.; *U.S. Public*, pg. 403
THE TRENDY CONDOMINIUM—See Grande Asset Hotels & Property Public Company Limited; *Int'l*, pg. 3057
TRIBAL RIDES INTERNATIONAL CORP.; *U.S. Public*, pg. 2189
TRIBRIDGE RESIDENTIAL, LLC; *U.S. Private*, pg. 4227
TRICON AMERICAN HOMES LLC—See Blackstone Inc.; *U.S. Public*, pg. 352
TRICON RESIDENTIAL INC.—See Blackstone Inc.; *U.S. Public*, pg. 351
TRI POINTE COMMUNITIES, INC.—See Tri Pointe Homes, Inc.; *U.S. Public*, pg. 2188
TRN CAPITAL MANAGEMENT, INC.—See Hurxley Corporation; *Int'l*, pg. 3538
TRN INVESTMENT MANAGEMENT, INC.—See Hurxley Corporation; *Int'l*, pg. 3538
TROJAN GENERAL CONTRACTING LLC—See Alpha Dhabi Holding PJSC; *Int'l*, pg. 368
TRUE VIEW REALTY PARTNERS ONE LP; *U.S. Private*, pg. 4248
TRULAND HOMES, LLC—See D.R. Horton, Inc.; *U.S. Public*, pg. 620
TUJUAN EHSAN SDN. BHD.—See Global Oriental Berhad; *Int'l*, pg. 3000
TULARE COUNTY ASSOCIATION OF REALTORS, INC.; *U.S. Private*, pg. 4257
TURCO NEDERLAND B.V.—See Henkel AG & Co. KGaA; *Int'l*, pg. 3351
TURNBERRY ASSOCIATES—See Turnberry, Ltd.; *U.S. Private*, pg. 4260
TURNKEY VENTURES LLC—See Schneider National, Inc.; *U.S. Public*, pg. 1847
TVO GROUPE; *U.S. Private*, pg. 4263
TVO NORTH AMERICA—See TVO Groupe; *U.S. Private*, pg. 4263
UB ORANGEBURG, LLC—See Regency Centers Corporation; *U.S. Public*, pg. 1774
UBS FUND MANAGEMENT (SWITZERLAND) AG—See Northern Trust Corporation; *U.S. Public*, pg. 1539
UBS FUND SERVICES (LUXEMBOURG) S.A.—See Northern Trust Corporation; *U.S. Public*, pg. 1539
ULTIMA HOSPITALITY, LLC—See Waterford Group, LLC; *U.S. Private*, pg. 4453
UNICA IMMOBILIENGESELLSCHAFT MBH—See Commerzbank AG; *Int'l*, pg. 1719

N.A.I.C.S. INDEX

532111 — PASSENGER CAR RENTA...

UNIPHOENIX JAYA SDN. BHD.—See Fiamma Holdings Berhad; *Int'l*, pg. 2650
UNITED CAPITAL CORP.; *U.S. Private*, pg. 4288
UNITED CLASSIFIEDS S.R.O.—See Axel Springer SE; *Int'l*, pg. 767
UNITED PROJECTS COMPANY FOR AVIATION SERVICES K.S.C.P.—See Agility; *Int'l*, pg. 210
UNITED PROPERTIES LLC—See Pohlad Companies; *U.S. Private*, pg. 3221
UNITED REAL ESTATE GROUP, LLC; *U.S. Private*, pg. 4296
UNITED STATES REALTY & INVESTMENT COMPANY; *U.S. Private*, pg. 4299
UNIVERSAL AMERICAN MORTGAGE COMPANY OF CALIFORNIA—See Lennar Corporation; *U.S. Public*, pg. 1307
UNIVERZALNI SPRAVA MAJETKU AS—See Assicurazioni Generali S.p.A.; *Int'l*, pg. 648
UNLIMITED SKY HOLDINGS, INC.; *U.S. Private*, pg. 4310
UPDC PLC.—See Custodian Investment PLC; *Int'l*, pg. 1880
THE UPTURN, INC.; *U.S. Private*, pg. 4129
UPWARD TITLE CO., LTD.—See Anywhere Real Estate Inc.; *U.S. Public*, pg. 143
UPWARD TITLE & ESCROW CO., LTD.—See Anywhere Real Estate Inc.; *U.S. Public*, pg. 143
URBAN PARTNERS, LLC; *U.S. Private*, pg. 4314
URO PROPERTY HOLDINGS SOCIMI SA—See Banco Santander, S.A.; *Int'l*, pg. 828
USAA REAL ESTATE COMPANY; *U.S. Private*, pg. 4321
US APPRAISAL GROUP, INC.; *U.S. Private*, pg. 4317
USGP ALBANY DEA, LLC—See Easterly Government Properties, Inc.; *U.S. Public*, pg. 703
VACATION HOME SWAP, INC.; *U.S. Private*, pg. 4328
VACI UTCA CENTER KFT—See Assicurazioni Generali S.p.A.; *Int'l*, pg. 645
VALBRIDGE PROPERTY ADVISORS, INC.; *U.S. Private*, pg. 4330
VALENCIA DEVELOPMENT SDN. BHD.—See Gamuda Berhad; *Int'l*, pg. 2879
VALETTA LOCOSHED OFFICES LTD.—See ENL Limited; *Int'l*, pg. 2442
VALUAMERICA, INC.—See Radian Group, Inc.; *U.S. Public*, pg. 1759
VAMED ESTATE DEVELOPMENT & ENGINEERING GMBH & CO KG—See Fresenius SE & Co. KGaA; *Int'l*, pg. 2781
VAN BREDA IMMO CONSULT NV—See Ackermans & van Haaren NV; *Int'l*, pg. 106
VANHAN RUUKIN KIINTEISTOPALVELU OY—See Componenta Corporation; *Int'l*, pg. 1753
VANTAGE COMPANIES; *U.S. Private*, pg. 4344
VELA HOME SRL—See BNP Paribas SA; *Int'l*, pg. 1093
VENTAS REALTY, LIMITED PARTNERSHIP—See Ventas, Inc.; *U.S. Public*, pg. 2279
VENTAS SSL, INC.—See Ventas, Inc.; *U.S. Public*, pg. 2279
VENTURA PROPERTY MANAGEMENT, LLC—See Morgan Stanley; *U.S. Public*, pg. 1475
VENTURE REALTY GROUP; *U.S. Private*, pg. 4358
VERTBOIS S.A R.L.—See Allianz SE; *Int'l*, pg. 356
VERUS INTERNATIONAL, INC.; *U.S. Public*, pg. 2290
VESTIN MORTGAGE, LLC—See Vestin Group, Inc.; *U.S. Private*, pg. 4373
VIADOR GMBH—See Starwood Capital Group Global I, LLC; *U.S. Private*, pg. 3789
VICTORIAN CORRECTIONAL INFRASTRUCTURE PARTNERSHIP PTY. LTD.—See Bilfinger SE; *Int'l*, pg. 1029
VILLAGE PARK HOMES, LLC—See Dream Finders Homes, Inc.; *U.S. Public*, pg. 687
VILLAGE SQUARE APARTMENT HOMES—See Kennedy-Wilson Holdings, Inc.; *U.S. Public*, pg. 1223
VILLA WORLD DEVELOPMENTS PTY LTD—See AVID Property Group; *Int'l*, pg. 743
VILLA WORLD HOMES—See AVID Property Group; *Int'l*, pg. 743
VINTAGE SENIOR MANAGEMENT INC.; *U.S. Private*, pg. 4386
THE VIRGINIA PROPERTIES—See The Long & Foster Companies, Inc.; *U.S. Private*, pg. 4072
VIRIDIAN PARTNERS LLC; *U.S. Private*, pg. 4388
VISTANA VACATION OWNERSHIP, INC.—See Marriott International, Inc.; *U.S. Public*, pg. 1372
VITTORIA SRL—See Clariane SE; *Int'l*, pg. 1645
VIVA PARADISE SDN. BHD.—See Eksons Corporation Berhad; *Int'l*, pg. 2340
VIVEICA, S.A. DE C.V.—See Empresas ICA S.A.B. de C.V.; *Int'l*, pg. 2391
VOLVO GROUP REAL ESTATE AB—See AB Volvo; *Int'l*, pg. 44
VOSS GMBH & CO. KG—See BayWa AG; *Int'l*, pg. 919
VRS (MALAYSIA) SDN BHD—See Berjaya Corporation Berhad; *Int'l*, pg. 984
VRX MEDIA GROUP LLC—See Zillow Group, Inc.; *U.S. Public*, pg. 2405
VULCAN PROPERTY MANAGEMENT CO.—See Vulcan International Corporation; *U.S. Private*, pg. 4416
VULCAN REAL ESTATE—See Vulcan Inc.; *U.S. Private*, pg. 4416
WAGON WHEEL REALTY, LLC—See The TJX Companies, Inc.; *U.S. Public*, pg. 2134

WALKER & DUNLOP CAPITAL, LLC—See Walker & Dunlop, Inc.; *U.S. Public*, pg. 2324
WALKER & DUNLOP INVESTMENT PARTNERS, INC.—See Walker & Dunlop, Inc.; *U.S. Public*, pg. 2324
WALLICH RESIDENCE PTE. LTD.—See Hong Leong Investment Holdings Pte. Ltd.; *Int'l*, pg. 3468
WAL-MART REALTY COMPANY—See Walmart Inc.; *U.S. Public*, pg. 2325
WALSRODER CASINGS POLSKA SP.ZO.O—See Icahn Enterprises L.P.; *U.S. Public*, pg. 1085
WALTON STREET CAPITAL, LLC; *U.S. Public*, pg. 4435
WANGFU CENTRAL REAL ESTATE DEVELOPMENT CO. LTD.—See Hong Kong Land Holdings Ltd.; *Int'l*, pg. 3467
WARMINGTON PROPERTIES, INC.—See The Warmington Group; *U.S. Private*, pg. 4133
WARMINGTON RESIDENTIAL—See The Warmington Group; *U.S. Private*, pg. 4133
WASHINGTON DEVELOPMENT—See Washington Corporations; *U.S. Private*, pg. 4446
WASHREIT ALEXANDRIA LLC—See Elme Communities; *U.S. Public*, pg. 735
WASHREIT DULLES LLC—See Elme Communities; *U.S. Public*, pg. 735
WASHREIT GERMANTOWN LLC—See Elme Communities; *U.S. Public*, pg. 735
WASHREIT LANDMARK LLC—See Elme Communities; *U.S. Public*, pg. 735
WASHREIT LEESBURG LLC—See Elme Communities; *U.S. Public*, pg. 735
WASHREIT WATKINS MILL LLC—See Elme Communities; *U.S. Public*, pg. 735
WASSERMAN VORNADO STRATEGIC REAL ESTATE FUND LLC—See Vornado Realty Trust; *U.S. Public*, pg. 2310
WATERSOUND ORIGINS TOWN CENTER, LLC—See The St. Joe Company; *U.S. Public*, pg. 2131
WATERTON ASSOCIATES LLC—See Waterford Group, LLC; *U.S. Private*, pg. 4453
WATT COMPANIES, INC.; *U.S. Private*, pg. 4456
WATT REALTY ADVISORS—See Watt Companies, Inc.; *U.S. Private*, pg. 4456
WCS-333 SOUTH STREET, INC.; *U.S. Private*, pg. 4462
WEICHERT REAL ESTATE AFFILIATES, INC.—See Weichert Co.; *U.S. Private*, pg. 4470
WEINGARTEN REALTY INVESTORS—See Kimco Realty Corporation; *U.S. Public*, pg. 1232
WELLS FARGO CAPITAL FINANCE CORPORATION CANADA—See Wells Fargo & Company; *U.S. Public*, pg. 2346
WELLS FARGO REAL ESTATE TAX SERVICES, LLC—See Wells Fargo & Company; *U.S. Public*, pg. 2347
WESTBODEN-BAU- UND VERWALTUNGSGESELLSCHAFT MBH—See Commerzbank AG; *Int'l*, pg. 1719
WEST COAST ESCROW COMPANY—See Anywhere Real Estate Inc.; *U.S. Public*, pg. 142
WESTDEUTSCHE GRUNDSTUCKSAUKTIONEN AG—See Deutsche Grundstuecksauktionen AG; *Int'l*, pg. 2065
WESTERN PROPERTIES, INC.—See Biglari Holdings Inc.; *U.S. Public*, pg. 331
WESTERN RESOURCES TITLE CO—See First Team Real Estate-Orange County Inc.; *U.S. Private*, pg. 1529
WESTGRUND AG—See ADLER Group SA; *Int'l*, pg. 150
WESTLITE DORMITORY MANAGEMENT PTE. LTD.—See Centurion Corporation Limited; *Int'l*, pg. 1417
WESTLITE DORMITORY MANAGEMENT SDN. BHD.—See Centurion Corporation Limited; *Int'l*, pg. 1417
WESTLITE DORMITORY (TOH GUAN) PTE. LTD.—See Centurion Corporation Limited; *Int'l*, pg. 1417
WESTLITE DORMITORY (WOODLANDS) PTE. LTD.—See Centurion Corporation Limited; *Int'l*, pg. 1417
WESTLITE JUNIPER (MANDAI) PTE. LTD.—See Centurion Corporation Limited; *Int'l*, pg. 1417
WESTMORELAND COUNTY HOUSING AUTHORITY; *U.S. Private*, pg. 4500
WFI NMC CORP.—See Kratos Defense & Security Solutions, Inc.; *U.S. Public*, pg. 1277
WHEELER REAL ESTATE LLC—See Wheeler Real Estate Investment Trust, Inc.; *U.S. Public*, pg. 2366
WHEELER REIT, L.P.—See Wheeler Real Estate Investment Trust, Inc.; *U.S. Public*, pg. 2366
WH PROPERTIES, INC.—See Hovnanian Enterprises, Inc.; *U.S. Public*, pg. 1060
WILLIAM CHARLES REAL ESTATE CO—See William Charles, Ltd.; *U.S. Private*, pg. 4523
WILLIAM MACKLOWE COMPANY LLC; *U.S. Private*, pg. 4523
WILLIAMS TREW REAL ESTATE SERVICES, LLC—See Berkshire Hathaway Inc.; *U.S. Public*, pg. 306
WILSHIRE ENTERPRISES, INC.; *U.S. Private*, pg. 4529
WINDGATE ACQUISITION LTD.; *U.S. Private*, pg. 4537
WING LUNG PROPERTY MANAGEMENT LIMITED—See China Merchants Group Limited; *Int'l*, pg. 1520
WISMA DEVELOPMENT SDN. BHD.—See Gromutual Berhad; *Int'l*, pg. 3088
WNC REAL ESTATE; *U.S. Private*, pg. 4552
WOLFF URBAN DEVELOPMENT, LLC—See Wolff Urban Management, Inc.; *U.S. Private*, pg. 4554
WOLFNET TECHNOLOGIES, LLC—See The Northwestern Mutual Life Insurance Company; *U.S. Private*, pg. 4085
WOODLAKE REALTY, LLC—See Ventas, Inc.; *U.S. Public*, pg. 2279
WOODMONT REAL ESTATE SERVICES LTD. - COMMERCIAL DIVISION—See Woodmont Real Estate Services Ltd.; *U.S. Private*, pg. 4559
WOOLWICH HOMES LIMITED—See Barclays PLC; *Int'l*, pg. 863
WORLDWIDE HOLDINGS CORP.; *U.S. Public*, pg. 2382
WRIT BRADDOCK OFFICE LLC—See Elme Communities; *U.S. Public*, pg. 735
WUHAN FUTURE CITY HOTEL MANAGEMENT COMPANY LIMITED—See China City Infrastructure Group Limited; *Int'l*, pg. 1489
WUHAN FUTURE CITY PROPERTY MANAGEMENT COMPANY LIMITED—See China City Infrastructure Group Limited; *Int'l*, pg. 1489
WYNN DESIGN & DEVELOPMENT, LLC—See Wynn Resorts Limited; *U.S. Public*, pg. 2384
WYOMING TITLE & ESCROW COMPANY, INC.—See First American Financial Corporation; *U.S. Public*, pg. 838
XEMEX GROUP, INC.; *U.S. Public*, pg. 2385
YANGON AMATA SMART & ECO CITY LIMITED—See Amata Corporation Public Company Limited; *Int'l*, pg. 413
YANGTZE RIVER PORT & LOGISTICS LIMITED; *U.S. Public*, pg. 2398
YELLOWFIN ASSET MANAGEMENT GMBH—See Commerzbank AG; *Int'l*, pg. 1719
YUKON TITLE COMPANY, INC.—See Stewart Information Services Corporation; *U.S. Public*, pg. 1948
ZANDU REALTY LIMITED—See Emami Group; *Int'l*, pg. 2374
ZAYANI PROPERTIES WLL—See Al Zayani Investments WLL; *Int'l*, pg. 283
ZIEGLER CAPITAL MANAGEMENT, LLC—See Stifel Financial Corp.; *U.S. Public*, pg. 1950
ZILLOW GROUP MARKETPLACE, INC.—See Zillow Group, Inc.; *U.S. Public*, pg. 2405
ZOB AN DER HACKERBRUCKE GMBH & CO. KG—See ACS, Actividades de Construccion y Servicios, S.A.; *Int'l*, pg. 114
ZOOPLA PROPERTY GROUP LTD.—See Daily Mail & General Trust plc; *Int'l*, pg. 1938
ZUMOT REAL ESTATE MANAGEMENT, INC.; *U.S. Private*, pg. 4610
ZURPLE, INC.; *U.S. Private*, pg. 4610

532111 — PASSENGER CAR RENTAL

A BETTERWAY RENT-A-CAR INC.; *U.S. Private*, pg. 18
ABSOLUTE MOBILITY CENTER—See Edwards Capital, LLC; *U.S. Private*, pg. 1342
ACE RENT A CAR, INC.—See Avis Budget Group, Inc.; *U.S. Public*, pg. 248
ADAMSON CAR & TRUCK RENTAL INC.—See A Betterway Rent-A-Car Inc.; *U.S. Private*, pg. 18
ADVANCED MOBILITY SYSTEMS OF TEXAS, INC.—See Edwards Capital, LLC; *U.S. Private*, pg. 1342
ALAMO RENT-A-CAR—See Enterprise Holdings, Inc.; *U.S. Private*, pg. 1403
ALEA MOBILITA' URBANA S.R.L.—See CogenInfra SpA; *Int'l*, pg. 1694
ALPETOUR - POTOVALNA AGENCIJA D.O.O.—See I Squared Capital Advisors (US) LLC; *U.S. Private*, pg. 2024
ALPHABET BELGIUM LONG TERM RENTAL N.V.—See Bayerische Motoren Werke Aktiengesellschaft; *Int'l*, pg. 910
ALPHABET BELGIUM N.V./S.A.—See Bayerische Motoren Werke Aktiengesellschaft; *Int'l*, pg. 910
ALPHABET NEDERLAND B.V.—See Bayerische Motoren Werke Aktiengesellschaft; *Int'l*, pg. 910
A MACFRUGEL COMPANY INC.; *U.S. Private*, pg. 18
APEX RENT A CAR LTD.—See Avis Budget Group, Inc.; *U.S. Public*, pg. 248
ARMADALE COMMERCIAL LTD.—See Avis Budget Group, Inc.; *U.S. Public*, pg. 248
ARVAL SERVICE GMBH—See BNP Paribas SA; *Int'l*, pg. 1080
ATLANTIC LIMOUSINE INC.; *U.S. Private*, pg. 373
AUTO ESCAPE SA—See Expedia Group, Inc.; *U.S. Public*, pg. 809
AUTO ESCAPE UK—See Expedia Group, Inc.; *U.S. Public*, pg. 809
AUTOHELLAS S.A.; *Int'l*, pg. 727
AUTO HRVATSKA D.D.; *Int'l*, pg. 724
AUTORIDERS INTERNATIONAL LTD.; *Int'l*, pg. 732
AUTOTECHNICA FLEET SERVICES S.R.L.—See AUTOHELLAS S.A.; *Int'l*, pg. 727
AUTOTECHNICA LTD.—See AUTOHELLAS S.A.; *Int'l*, pg. 727
AUTOTECHNICA MONTENEGRO DOO—See AUTOHELLAS S.A.; *Int'l*, pg. 727
AUTOTECHNICA SERBIA DOO—See AUTOHELLAS S.A.; *Int'l*, pg. 727
AUTOTEHNA A.D; *Int'l*, pg. 732

532111 — PASSENGER CAR RENTA...

AVALON GLOBAL GROUP, INC.; *U.S. Private*, pg. 403
AVIS AUTOVERMIETUNG AG—See Avis Budget Group, Inc.; *U.S. Public*, pg. 248
AVIS AUTOVERMIETUNG GESELLSCHAFT M.B.H—See Avis Budget Group, Inc.; *U.S. Public*, pg. 248
AVIS AUTOVERMIETUNG GMBH & CO KG—See Avis Budget Group, Inc.; *U.S. Public*, pg. 248
AVIS BELGIUM SA—See Avis Budget Group, Inc.; *U.S. Public*, pg. 248
AVIS BUDGET AUTO SERVICE GMBH—See Avis Budget Group, Inc.; *U.S. Public*, pg. 248
AVIS BUDGET AUTOVERHUUR BV—See Avis Budget Group, Inc.; *U.S. Public*, pg. 248
AVIS BUDGET AUTOVERMIETUNG AG—See Avis Budget Group, Inc.; *U.S. Public*, pg. 248
AVIS BUDGET DENMARK AS—See Avis Budget Group, Inc.; *U.S. Public*, pg. 248
AVIS BUDGET EMEA LTD—See Avis Budget Group, Inc.; *U.S. Public*, pg. 248
AVIS BUDGET EUROPE INTERNATIONAL REINSURANCE LIMITED—See Avis Budget Group, Inc.; *U.S. Public*, pg. 248
AVIS BUDGET SERVICES LIMITED—See Avis Budget Group, Inc.; *U.S. Public*, pg. 248
AVIS EUROPE PLC—See Avis Budget Group, Inc.; *U.S. Public*, pg. 248
AVIS LOCATION DE VOITURES S.A R.L—See Avis Budget Group, Inc.; *U.S. Public*, pg. 248
AVIS RENT A CAR LIMITED—See Avis Budget Group, Inc.; *U.S. Public*, pg. 248
AVIS RENT A CAR SYSTEM, LLC—See Avis Budget Group, Inc.; *U.S. Public*, pg. 249
AVIS SOUTHERN AFRICA LTD.—See Barloworld Ltd.; *Int'l*, pg. 866
BALZAC CARAVANES; *Int'l*, pg. 813
B&B RV, INC.—See Camping World Holdings, Inc.; *U.S. Public*, pg. 427
BEYAZ FILO OTO KIRALAMA A.S.; *Int'l*, pg. 1005
BILPARTNER AB—See Amplex AB; *Int'l*, pg. 433
BROADWAY RENTAL CARS, INC.—See Broadway Enterprises, Inc.; *U.S. Private*, pg. 660
BUDGET INTERNATIONAL, INC.—See Avis Budget Group, Inc.; *U.S. Public*, pg. 249
BUDGET RENT A CAR AUSTRALIA PTY. LTD.—See Avis Budget Group, Inc.; *U.S. Public*, pg. 249
BUDGET RENT A CAR LICENSOR, LLC—See Avis Budget Group, Inc.; *U.S. Public*, pg. 249
BUDGET RENT-A-CAR OF B.C. LTD; *Int'l*, pg. 1211
BUDGET RENT A CAR SYSTEM, INC.—See Avis Budget Group, Inc.; *U.S. Public*, pg. 249
BUNDY AMERICAN CORPORATION—See JJF Management Services, Inc.; *U.S. Private*, pg. 2211
CALCORP LIMITED; *Int'l*, pg. 1262
CAPPS RENT-A-CAR INC.; *U.S. Private*, pg. 745
CAR RENTAL 8, LLC; *U.S. Private*, pg. 747
CAR RENTALS INC.; *U.S. Private*, pg. 747
CARSHARE AUSTRALIA PTY. LTD.—See Archer Capital Pty. Ltd.; *Int'l*, pg. 547
CARSMARTT; *U.S. Public*, pg. 444
CARTRAWLER LTD.—See BC Partners LLP; *Int'l*, pg. 923
CAR & TRUCK RENTALS, INC.; *U.S. Private*, pg. 747
CE-TUR CELEBI TOURISM TRADE INC.—See Celebi Holding A.S.; *Int'l*, pg. 1391
CEVITAL-MTP SPA—See Cevital S.p.A.; *Int'l*, pg. 1425
CHAPMAN FORD SALES, INC.; *U.S. Private*, pg. 849
CMH CAR HIRE (PTY) LTD—See Combined Motor Holdings Limited; *Int'l*, pg. 1709
COURTESY CAR CITY; *U.S. Private*, pg. 1070
DEMSTAR RENTALS 2005 LTD.—See AUTOHELLAS S.A.; *Int'l*, pg. 727
DIAMONDLEASE LLC—See Al Habtoor Group LLC; *Int'l*, pg. 278
DISCOUNT CAR & TRUCK RENTALS LTD.—See Enterprise Holdings, Inc.; *U.S. Private*, pg. 1403
DOLLAR THRIFTY AUTOMOTIVE GROUP CANADA INC.—See Hertz Global Holdings, Inc.; *U.S. Public*, pg. 1029
DOLLAR THRIFTY AUTOMOTIVE GROUP, INC.—See Hertz Global Holdings, Inc.; *U.S. Public*, pg. 1029
DRB-HICOM EZ-DRIVE SDN. BHD.—See DRB-HICOM Berhad; *Int'l*, pg. 2201
DTG OPERATIONS, INC.—See Hertz Global Holdings, Inc.; *U.S. Public*, pg. 1029
DTG SUPPLY, LLC—See Hertz Global Holdings, Inc.; *U.S. Public*, pg. 1029
EARN-A-CAR, INC.; *Int'l*, pg. 2267
EHI CAR SERVICES LIMITED; *Int'l*, pg. 2328
ELITE LIMOUSINE PLUS, INC.; *U.S. Private*, pg. 1361
ENTERPRISE FLEX-E-RENT—See Enterprise Holdings, Inc.; *U.S. Private*, pg. 1403
ENTERPRISE INTERNATIONAL OPERATIONS—See Enterprise Holdings, Inc.; *U.S. Private*, pg. 1403
ENTERPRISE LEASING COMPANY OF PHILADELPHIA, LLC—See Enterprise Holdings, Inc.; *U.S. Private*, pg. 1403
ENTERPRISE RENT-A-CAR—See Enterprise Holdings, Inc.; *U.S. Private*, pg. 1403
ERWIN HYMER GROUP STUTTGART GMBH—See Thor Industries, Inc.; *U.S. Public*, pg. 2156
EUROPCAR SOUTH AFRICA—See Dubai World Corporation; *Int'l*, pg. 2221
FACEDRIVE, INC.; *Int'l*, pg. 2600
FRANCHISE SERVICES OF NORTH AMERICA INC.; *U.S. Private*, pg. 1587
GARANTI BBVA FILO AS—See Banco Bilbao Vizcaya Argentaria, S.A.; *Int'l*, pg. 818
GARENTA ULASIM COZUMLERI A.S.—See AG Anadolu Grubu Holding A.S.; *Int'l*, pg. 197
GETAROUND, INC.; *U.S. Public*, pg. 935
GILES AUTOMOTIVE GROUP, INC.; *U.S. Private*, pg. 1699
GOLDBELL CAR RENTAL PTE LTD—See Goldbell Corporation; *Int'l*, pg. 3027
HA FLEET PTY LTD.—See Hertz Global Holdings, Inc.; *U.S. Public*, pg. 1029
HERTZ ASIA PACIFIC PTE. LTD.—See Hertz Global Holdings, Inc.; *U.S. Public*, pg. 1029
HERTZ AUSTRALIA PTY. LIMITED—See Hertz Global Holdings, Inc.; *U.S. Public*, pg. 1029
HERTZ AUTOVERMIETUNG GMBH—See Hertz Global Holdings, Inc.; *U.S. Public*, pg. 1029
HERTZ BELGIUM B.V.B.A.—See Hertz Global Holdings, Inc.; *U.S. Public*, pg. 1029
HERTZ CAR SALES LLC—See Hertz Global Holdings, Inc.; *U.S. Public*, pg. 1029
HERTZ DO BRASIL LTDA.—See Hertz Global Holdings, Inc.; *U.S. Public*, pg. 1029
HERTZ HOLDINGS NETHERLANDS B.V.—See Hertz Global Holdings, Inc.; *U.S. Public*, pg. 1029
HERTZ LOCAL EDITION CORP.—See Hertz Global Holdings, Inc.; *U.S. Public*, pg. 1029
HNA SAFE CAR RENTAL CO., LTD.—See Hainan Traffic Administration Holding Co., Ltd.; *Int'l*, pg. 3213
HONGDA FINANCIAL HOLDING LIMITED; *Int'l*, pg. 3470
HSF ENTERPRISES INC.; *U.S. Private*, pg. 1999
HYRECAR, INC.; *U.S. Public*, pg. 1079
IDEA FLEET S.A.—See Getin Holding S.A.; *Int'l*, pg. 2947
JACKIE COOPER BMW MINI; *U.S. Private*, pg. 2175
JIM DUNWORTH INC.; *U.S. Private*, pg. 2208
KORGES ENTERPRISES, INC.—See Lazydays Holdings, Inc.; *U.S. Public*, pg. 1295
LEASAFRIC GHANA LIMITED—See C & I Leasing Plc.; *Int'l*, pg. 1237
LIMOS.COM, INC.—See On Demand iCars, Inc.; *U.S. Private*, pg. 3018
LOCATRICE ITALIANA SPA—See BNP Paribas SA; *Int'l*, pg. 1091
MALCO ENTERPRISES NEVADA INC.; *U.S. Private*, pg. 2556
MCNICOLL VEHICLE SALES LTD.—See Avis Budget Group, Inc.; *U.S. Public*, pg. 249
MIDWAY RENT-A-CAR INC.; *U.S. Private*, pg. 2719
MIDWEST CAR CORPORATION; *U.S. Private*, pg. 2720
MIDWESTERN WHEELS INC.; *U.S. Private*, pg. 2724
MORINI SPA—See Avis Budget Group, Inc.; *U.S. Public*, pg. 249
NATIONAL CAR RENTAL OF PHOENIX; *U.S. Private*, pg. 2850
NATIONAL CAR RENTALS OF CORPUS CHRISTI, INC.—See Enterprise Holdings, Inc.; *U.S. Private*, pg. 1403
NATIONAL CAR RENTAL—See Enterprise Holdings, Inc.; *U.S. Private*, pg. 1404
NAVIGATION SOLUTIONS LLC—See Hertz Global Holdings, Inc.; *U.S. Public*, pg. 1029
NDS LEASE CO., LTD.—See COMSYS Holdings Corporation; *Int'l*, pg. 1761
NEXUS VEHICLE MANAGEMENT LIMITED—See Equistone Partners Europe Limited; *Int'l*, pg. 2486
OVERLAND WEST, INC. - BILLINGS OFFICE—See Overland West, Inc.; *U.S. Private*, pg. 3053
OVERLAND WEST, INC.; *U.S. Private*, pg. 3053
PAYLESS CAR RENTAL CANADA INC.—See Avis Budget Group, Inc.; *U.S. Public*, pg. 249
PAYLESS CAR RENTAL, INC.—See Avis Budget Group, Inc.; *U.S. Public*, pg. 249
PENSKE CAR RENTAL MEMPHIS, LLC—See Penske Automotive Group, Inc.; *U.S. Public*, pg. 1665
PRACTICAR SYSTEMS INC.—See Grandville Equities Corp.; *Int'l*, pg. 3058
PROBUS INSURANCE COMPANY EUROPE DAC—See Hertz Global Holdings, Inc.; *U.S. Public*, pg. 1029
RAC NORWAY AS—See Avis Budget Group, Inc.; *U.S. Public*, pg. 249
RENTAL CAR FINANCE LLC—See Hertz Global Holdings, Inc.; *U.S. Public*, pg. 1029
RIDESHARE CAR RENTALS LLC—See EVmo, Inc.; *U.S. Public*, pg. 803
ROBERT'S HAWAII LEASING INC.—See Robert's Hawaii Inc.; *U.S. Private*, pg. 3459
RODMAN FORD SALES INC.; *U.S. Private*, pg. 3470
RON MARHOFER CHEVROLET INC.; *U.S. Private*, pg. 3477
RUNABOUT, LLC—See Avis Budget Group, Inc.; *U.S. Public*, pg. 249
SANTANDER CONSUMER RENTING, S.L.—See Banco Santander, S.A.; *Int'l*, pg. 827
SHANGHAI HAIBO CO., LTD.—See Bright Food (Group) Co., Ltd.; *Int'l*, pg. 1161
SK RENT A CAR CO., LTD.—See Affinity Equity Partners (HK) Ltd.; *Int'l*, pg. 186
STEVE FOLEY CADILLAC; *U.S. Private*, pg. 3808
STUURGROEP FLEET (NETHERLANDS) B.V.—See Hertz Global Holdings, Inc.; *U.S. Public*, pg. 1029
STVE PTE LTD—See Goldbell Corporation; *Int'l*, pg. 3027
SWEDEN RENT A CAR AB—See Avis Budget Group, Inc.; *U.S. Public*, pg. 249
TAMAROFF LEASING CO.—See Tamaroff Motors, Inc.; *U.S. Private*, pg. 3928
TEB ARVAL ARAC FILO KIRALAMA AS—See BNP Paribas SA; *Int'l*, pg. 1093
THRIFTY CAR SALES INC.—See Hertz Global Holdings, Inc.; *U.S. Public*, pg. 1029
THRIFTY, LLC—See Hertz Global Holdings, Inc.; *U.S. Public*, pg. 1029
TRAVELERS RENTAL CO. INC.; *U.S. Private*, pg. 4214
TRAVELJIGSAW LTD.—See Booking Holdings, Inc.; *U.S. Public*, pg. 368
TURISCAR RENT A CAR, S.A.—See Avis Budget Group, Inc.; *U.S. Public*, pg. 249
UNIQUE LIMOUSINE, INC.; *U.S. Private*, pg. 4286
U-SAVE AUTO RENTAL OF AMERICA, INC.—See Franchise Services of North America Inc.; *U.S. Private*, pg. 1587
VANGUARD CAR RENTAL USA, LLC—See Enterprise Holdings, Inc.; *U.S. Private*, pg. 1403
WARRANTECH AUTOMOTIVE, INC.—See Stone Point Capital LLC; *U.S. Private*, pg. 3821
XEROX ITALIA RENTAL SERVICES SRL—See Xerox Holdings Corporation; *U.S. Public*, pg. 2390
ZIPCAR FRANCE S.A.S.—See Avis Budget Group, Inc.; *U.S. Public*, pg. 249
ZIPCAR, INC. - SEATTLE—See Avis Budget Group, Inc.; *U.S. Public*, pg. 249
ZIPCAR, INC.—See Avis Budget Group, Inc.; *U.S. Public*, pg. 249
ZIPCAR ON CAMPUS, INC.—See Avis Budget Group, Inc.; *U.S. Public*, pg. 249

532112 — PASSENGER CAR LEASING

ABSA VEHICLE MANAGEMENT PROPRIETARY LIMITED—See Absa Group Limited; *Int'l*, pg. 69
ABSA VEHICLE MANAGEMENT SOLUTIONS PROPRIETARY LIMITED—See Absa Group Limited; *Int'l*, pg. 69
ALD AUTOMOTIVE AG—See ALD Automotive; *Int'l*, pg. 303
ALD AUTOMOTIVE D.O.O.—See ALD Automotive; *Int'l*, pg. 303
ALD AUTOMOTIVE D.O.O. ZA.—See ALD Automotive; *Int'l*, pg. 303
ALD AUTOMOTIVE FUHRPARKMANAGEMENT UND LEASING GMBH—See ALD Automotive; *Int'l*, pg. 303
ALD AUTOMOTIVE MAGYARORSZAG AUTOPARK - KEZELO ES FINANSZIROZO KFT—See ALD Automotive; *Int'l*, pg. 303
ALD AUTOMOTIVE OOO—See ALD Automotive; *Int'l*, pg. 303
ALD AUTOMOTIVE OPERATIONAL LEASING DOO—See ALD Automotive; *Int'l*, pg. 303
ALD AUTOMOTIVE POLSKA SP Z O.O.—See ALD Automotive; *Int'l*, pg. 303
ALD AUTOMOTIVE PRIVATE LIMITED—See ALD Automotive; *Int'l*, pg. 303
ALD AUTOMOTIVE S.A. DE C.V.—See ALD Automotive; *Int'l*, pg. 303
ALD AUTOMOTIVE S.A.—See ALD Automotive; *Int'l*, pg. 303
ALD AUTOMOTIVE S.A.U—See ALD Automotive; *Int'l*, pg. 303
ALD AUTOMOTIVE; *Int'l*, pg. 303
ALD AUTOMOTIVE TURIZM TICARET ANONIM SIRKETI—See ALD Automotive; *Int'l*, pg. 303
ALLANE SE—See Banco Santander, S.A.; *Int'l*, pg. 826
ALLANE SE—See Hyundai Motor Company; *Int'l*, pg. 3559
ALLSTATE LEASING, INC.—See Atlantic Automotive Corp.; *U.S. Private*, pg. 371
ALPENA POWER COMPANY; *U.S. Private*, pg. 196
ALPHABET FUHRPARKMANAGEMENT GMBH—See Bayerische Motoren Werke Aktiengesellschaft; *Int'l*, pg. 910
ALPHABET ITALIA FLEET MANAGEMENT S.P.A.—See Bayerische Motoren Werke Aktiengesellschaft; *Int'l*, pg. 910
ALPHABET UK LTD.—See Bayerische Motoren Werke Aktiengesellschaft; *Int'l*, pg. 910
ARNOLD CLARK FINANCE LIMITED—See Arnold Clark Automobiles Limited; *Int'l*, pg. 576
ARVAL AB—See BNP Paribas SA; *Int'l*, pg. 1080
ARVAL AS—See BNP Paribas SA; *Int'l*, pg. 1080
ARVAL BENELUX BV—See BNP Paribas SA; *Int'l*, pg. 1080
ARVAL BRASIL LTDA—See BNP Paribas SA; *Int'l*, pg. 1080
ARVAL CZ S.R.O.—See BNP Paribas SA; *Int'l*, pg. 1080

N.A.I.C.S. INDEX

ARVAL INDIA PRIVATE LTD.—See BNP Paribas SA; *Int'l*, pg. 1080
ARVAL OY—See BNP Paribas SA; *Int'l*, pg. 1080
ARVAL PHH SERVICE LEASE CZ S.R.O—See BNP Paribas SA; *Int'l*, pg. 1080
ARVAL SERVICE LEASE ALUGER OPERATIONAL AUTOMOVEIS SA—See BNP Paribas SA; *Int'l*, pg. 1080
ARVAL SERVICE LEASE ROMANIA SRL—See BNP Paribas SA; *Int'l*, pg. 1080
ARVAL SERVICE LEASE SA—See BNP Paribas SA; *Int'l*, pg. 1080
ARVAL SLOVAKIA, S.R.O.—See BNP Paribas SA; *Int'l*, pg. 1080
ASIA SERMKIJ LEASING PUBLIC COMPANY LIMITED; *Int'l*, pg. 615
ATS PROCESSING SERVICES, L.L.C.—See Verra Mobility Corporation; *U.S. Public*, pg. 2286
BARLOWORLD NETHERLANDS—See Barloworld Ltd.; *Int'l*, pg. 866
BELFIUS AUTO LEASE SA/NV—See Belfius Bank SA/NV; *Int'l*, pg. 963
BMW LEASING CORP.—See Bayerische Motoren Werke Aktiengesellschaft; *Int'l*, pg. 912
BNPP LEASING SERVICES SP. Z O.O.—See BNP Paribas SA; *Int'l*, pg. 1088
BNPP LEASING SOLUTIONS SUISSE SA—See BNP Paribas SA; *Int'l*, pg. 1088
BPCE CAR LEASE SASU—See Groupe BPCE; *Int'l*, pg. 3092
BPI CENTURY TOKYO LEASE & FINANCE CORPORATION—See Bank of the Philippine Islands; *Int'l*, pg. 848
BT OPERATIONAL LEASING SA—See Banca Transilvania S.A.; *Int'l*, pg. 816
CARCADE SERVICE SP. Z O.O.—See Getin Holding S.A.; *Int'l*, pg. 2947
CARILLION FLEET MANAGEMENT LTD—See Carillion plc; *Int'l*, pg. 1330
CITYLIMO LEASING (M) SDN. BHD.—See ComfortDelGro Corporation Limited; *Int'l*, pg. 1712
COMFORTDELGRO RENT-A-CAR PTE. LTD.—See ComfortDelGro Corporation Limited; *Int'l*, pg. 1713
COMMERZ REAL AUTOSERVICE GMBH I.L.—See Commerzbank AG; *Int'l*, pg. 1716
CONKLIN FANGMAN INVESTMENT CO.; *U.S. Private*, pg. 1014
CREDIT EUROPE LEASING LLC—See Fiba Holding A.S.; *Int'l*, pg. 2651
CREDIT EUROPE LEASING LLC—See Fiba Holding A.S.; *Int'l*, pg. 2651
CTI FLEET MANAGEMENT PTY LTD—See CTI Logistics Limited; *Int'l*, pg. 1871
DAN PERKINS LEASING INC.—See Dan Perkins Auto Group; *U.S. Private*, pg. 1151
DIRECT ACCIDENT MANAGEMENT LIMITED—See Anexo Group Plc; *Int'l*, pg. 459
D & L LEASING, INC.—See Lykins Companies, Inc.; *U.S. Private*, pg. 2520
DONDELINGER CHEVROLET CADILLAC; *U.S. Private*, pg. 1260
DONLEN CORPORATION—See Apollo Global Management, Inc.; *U.S. Public*, pg. 147
DONLEN FSHCO COMPANY—See Hertz Global Holdings, Inc.; *U.S. Public*, pg. 1029
EBRAHIM K. KANOO COMPANY B.S.C - KANOO VEHICLE LEASING DIVISION—See Ebrahim K. Kanoo Company B.S.C.; *Int'l*, pg. 2286
EFG AUTO LEASING E.O.O.D.—See Eurobank Ergasias Services and Holdings S.A.; *Int'l*, pg. 2532
EL CAJON FORD; *U.S. Private*, pg. 1348
ENTERPRISE FLEET SERVICES—See Enterprise Holdings, Inc.; *U.S. Private*, pg. 1403
EUROBANK FIN AND RENT S.A.—See Eurobank Ergasias Services and Holdings S.A.; *Int'l*, pg. 2532
EURO LEASE AUTO AD—See Eurohold Bulgaria AD; *Int'l*, pg. 2553
EXECUTIVE CAR LEASING CO.; *U.S. Private*, pg. 1447
FIBA AIR HAVA TASIMACILIK VE HIZMETLERI A.S.—See Fiba Holding A.S.; *Int'l*, pg. 2651
FLEET PARTNERS PTY. LTD.—See FleetPartners Group Limited; *Int'l*, pg. 2699
FLOTTENMANAGEMENT GMBH—See Erste Group Bank AG; *Int'l*, pg. 2498
FOLKUP DEVELOPMENT INC.; *Int'l*, pg. 2721
FORD LEASING SPA—See Ford Motor Company; *U.S. Public*, pg. 866
FUYO AUTO LEASE CO., LTD.—See Fuyo General Lease Co., Ltd.; *Int'l*, pg. 2859
GARANTI BBVA FILO YONETIM HIZMETLERI A.S.—See Garanti Finansal Kiralama A.S.; *Int'l*, pg. 2883
GENERALI LEASING GMBH—See Assicurazioni Generali S.p.A.; *Int'l*, pg. 646
GRIDRESERVE LTD.—See Gresham House Energy Storage Fund PLC; *Int'l*, pg. 3082
HEMPSTEAD AUTO CO. INC.; *U.S. Private*, pg. 1913
HIROGIN LEASE CO., LTD.—See Hirogin Holdings, Inc.; *Int'l*, pg. 3404
JAKE SWEENEY AUTO LEASING, INC.—See Jake Sweeney Automotive Inc.; *U.S. Private*, pg. 2182
LITHIA FINANCIAL CORPORATION—See Lithia Motors, Inc.; *U.S. Public*, pg. 1324
MAIB-LEASING SA—See BC Moldova Agroindbank S.A.; *Int'l*, pg. 922
MARSHALL LEASING LIMITED—See Bank of Ireland Group plc; *Int'l*, pg. 844
MAYFAIR RENT-A-CAR, LLC - WAUKESHA—See Ewald Automotive Group, LLC; *U.S. Private*, pg. 1444
MB LEASING CORP.—See Mercedes-Benz of Coral Gables; *U.S. Private*, pg. 2668
MEDALLION AUTO MANAGEMENT LLC—See Ameritrans Capital Corporation; *U.S. Public*, pg. 115
MIKE ALBERT LEASING, INC.; *U.S. Private*, pg. 2724
MILLER ALL LINE LEASING INC.—See Miller Enterprises; *U.S. Private*, pg. 2734
MOBILITY CONCEPT GMBH—See HgCapital Trust plc; *Int'l*, pg. 3377
MOBILITY SOLUTIONS AG—See Die Schweizerische Post AG; *Int'l*, pg. 2113
MOBILITY SOLUTIONS MANAGEMENT AG—See Die Schweizerische Post AG; *Int'l*, pg. 2113
THE MOTORLEASE CORPORATION; *U.S. Private*, pg. 4081
MOTORWORLD AUTOMOTIVE GROUP—See Atlantic Automotive Corp.; *U.S. Private*, pg. 371
N AUTO SOFIA EAD—See Eurohold Bulgaria AD; *Int'l*, pg. 2553
OGDEN LINCOLN MERCURY INC.; *U.S. Private*, pg. 3003
OU HANSATEE KINNISVARA—See AS Infortar; *Int'l*, pg. 590
PACJETS FINANCIAL LTD.—See Nordic Group of Companies, Ltd.; *U.S. Private*, pg. 2937
PEKAO LEASING SP. Z O.O.—See Bank Polska Kasa Opieki Spolka Akcyjna; *Int'l*, pg. 850
POPULAR AUTO LLC—See Popular, Inc.; *U.S. Public*, pg. 1702
POST COMPANY CARS AG—See Die Schweizerische Post AG; *Int'l*, pg. 2113
PREMIER AUTO FINANCE INC.—See Aon plc; *Int'l*, pg. 495
RM RAILCARS LLC—See Interstate Commodities Inc.; *U.S. Private*, pg. 2124
SANTANDER CONSUMER LEASING GMBH—See Banco Santander, S.A.; *Int'l*, pg. 827
SANTANDER CONSUMER LEASING S.R.O.—See Banco Santander, S.A.; *Int'l*, pg. 827
SENTRY LEASING INC—See Don Hill Automotive Associates Inc.; *U.S. Private*, pg. 1257
TASHEELAT CAR LEASING COMPANY W.L.L.—See Bahrain Commercial Facilities Company BSC; *Int'l*, pg. 800
TRANSPORTATION LEASING CO.; *U.S. Private*, pg. 4211
VADEN HOLDING INC.; *U.S. Private*, pg. 4329
VELCOR LEASING CORPORATION; *U.S. Private*, pg. 4354
WHEELS INC.—See Frank Consolidated Enterprises; *U.S. Private*, pg. 1594
WILLIAM LEHMAN LEASING CORP.—See Lithia Motors, Inc.; *U.S. Public*, pg. 1323
ZAYANI LEASING W.L.L.—See Al Zayani Investments WLL; *Int'l*, pg. 283
ZAYANI MOTORS WLL—See Al Zayani Investments WLL; *Int'l*, pg. 283
ZEDA CAR LEASING (PTY) LIMITED—See Barloworld Ltd.; *Int'l*, pg. 866

532120 — TRUCK, UTILITY TRAILER, AND RV (RECREATIONAL VEHICLE) RENTAL AND LEASING

AA TRUCK RENTING CORPORATION; *U.S. Private*, pg. 30
ABC FINANCIAL SERVICES—See ABC Bus Companies, Inc.; *U.S. Private*, pg. 35
ADAMS MACHINERY MOVERS, INC.—See Olympus Partners; *U.S. Private*, pg. 3013
ADA SA—See G7 Entreprises; *Int'l*, pg. 2867
AIM LEASING CO.; *U.S. Private*, pg. 132
AIROLDI BROTHERS INC.; *U.S. Private*, pg. 142
ALBAN RENTS, LLC—See Carter Machinery Company, Inc.; *U.S. Private*, pg. 776
ALL STAR INTERNATIONAL TRUCKS INC.—See Yancey Bros. Co.; *U.S. Private*, pg. 4585
ALL STOR MH—See National Storage Affiliates Trust; *U.S. Public*, pg. 1498
A & M ASSOCIATES, INC—See U-Haul Holding Company; *U.S. Public*, pg. 2211
AMERICAN TRAILER RENTAL GROUP—See Wind Point Advisors LLC; *U.S. Private*, pg. 4533
APEX TOWING COMPANY—See Apex Oil Company, Inc.; *U.S. Private*, pg. 293
ARTEGY LTD.—See BNP Paribas SA; *Int'l*, pg. 1079
ARTEGY SAS—See BNP Paribas SA; *Int'l*, pg. 1079
ARVAL AUSTRIA GMBH—See BNP Paribas SA; *Int'l*, pg. 1080
ARVAL BELGIUM—See BNP Paribas SA; *Int'l*, pg. 1080
ARVAL B.V.—See BNP Paribas SA; *Int'l*, pg. 1080
ARVAL ECL SAS—See BNP Paribas SA; *Int'l*, pg. 1080
ARVAL FRANCE—See BNP Paribas SA; *Int'l*, pg. 1080

532120 — TRUCK, UTILITY TRAI...

ARVAL LUXEMBOURG—See BNP Paribas SA; *Int'l*, pg. 1080
ARVAL MAGYARORSZAG KFT.—See BNP Paribas SA; *Int'l*, pg. 1080
ARVAL OOO—See BNP Paribas SA; *Int'l*, pg. 1080
ARVAL PORTUGAL—See BNP Paribas SA; *Int'l*, pg. 1080
ARVAL SCHWEIZ AG—See BNP Paribas SA; *Int'l*, pg. 1080
ARVAL SERVICE LEASE ITALIA S.P.A.—See BNP Paribas SA; *Int'l*, pg. 1080
ARVAL SERVICE LEASE POLSKA SP. Z O.O.—See BNP Paribas SA; *Int'l*, pg. 1080
ARVAL SERVICE LEASE, S.A.—See BNP Paribas SA; *Int'l*, pg. 1080
ARVAL UK LTD.—See BNP Paribas SA; *Int'l*, pg. 1080
A & S RV CENTER, INC.—See Redwood Capital Investments, LLC; *U.S. Private*, pg. 3380
AUTOMOTIVE RENTALS, INC.—See Holman Automotive Group, Inc.; *U.S. Private*, pg. 1967
AVIS BUDGET TECHNOLOGY INNOVATIONS PRIVATE LIMITED—See Avis Budget Group, Inc.; *U.S. Public*, pg. 248
BASE CRAFT LLC; *U.S. Private*, pg. 484
BAWAG LEASING & FLEET S.R.O.—See BAWAG Group AG; *Int'l*, pg. 900
BIG TRUCK RENTAL, LLC; *U.S. Private*, pg. 554
BMW AUSTRIA LEASING GMBH—See Bayerische Motoren Werke Aktiengesellschaft; *Int'l*, pg. 911
BMW FINANCIAL SERVICES DE MEXICO S.A. DE C.V.—See Bayerische Motoren Werke Aktiengesellschaft; *Int'l*, pg. 911
BMW FINANCIAL SERVICES NEW ZEALAND LTD.—See Bayerische Motoren Werke Aktiengesellschaft; *Int'l*, pg. 911
BOWMAN SALES & EQUIPMENT INC.—See Bowman Group LLP; *U.S. Private*, pg. 626
BOWMAN TRUCK LEASING, LLC—See Bowman Group LLP; *U.S. Private*, pg. 626
BROWN TRUCK LEASING CORP; *U.S. Private*, pg. 669
BRS LTD—See AB Volvo; *Int'l*, pg. 42
BRUCKNER LEASING CO. INC.—See Bruckner Truck Sales, Inc.; *U.S. Private*, pg. 671
BUDGET TRUCK RENTAL LLC—See Avis Budget Group, Inc.; *U.S. Public*, pg. 249
BULK LOGISTICS INC.—See Tankstar USA, Inc.; *U.S. Private*, pg. 3931
CALMONT LEASING LTD; *Int'l*, pg. 1265
CALMONT TRUCK CENTRE LTD.—See Calmont Leasing Ltd; *Int'l*, pg. 1265
CAMEX EQUIPMENT SALES & RENTALS LTD.—See Brandt Industries Ltd.; *Int'l*, pg. 1140
CAMP-OUT, INC.; *U.S. Private*, pg. 730
CAPSTONE EQUIPMENT LEASING LLC—See Wolf Energy Services Inc.; *U.S. Public*, pg. 2376
CARCO CAPITAL CORPORATION; *U.S. Private*, pg. 749
CARCO INTERNATIONAL, INC.—See Carco Capital Corporation; *U.S. Private*, pg. 749
CARCO RENTALS, INC.—See Carco Capital Corporation; *U.S. Private*, pg. 749
CARMICHAEL LEASING CO. INC.; *U.S. Private*, pg. 766
CARRIER TRUCK SALES, LLC; *U.S. Private*, pg. 772
CHECKER LEASING INCORPORATED; *U.S. Private*, pg. 869
CHROME CAPITAL, LLC; *U.S. Private*, pg. 892
CHUDEN TRANSPORTATION SERVICE CO., LTD.—See Chubu Electric Power Co., Inc.; *Int'l*, pg. 1593
COLTON VB, L.P.—See National Storage Affiliates Trust; *U.S. Public*, pg. 1498
CONSOLIDATED DISPOSAL SYSTEMS—See H.I.G. Capital, LLC; *U.S. Private*, pg. 1833
CONWAY BEAM LEASING INC.—See Beam Mack Sales & Service, Inc.; *U.S. Private*, pg. 506
COPART OF TEXAS, INC.—See Copart, Inc.; *U.S. Public*, pg. 575
CRUISE AMERICA, INC.; *U.S. Private*, pg. 1113
CRUISE CANADA, INC.—See Cruise America, Inc.; *U.S. Private*, pg. 1113
CUSTOM LEASING OF IOWA INC—See North American Truck & Trailer, Inc.; *U.S. Private*, pg. 2941
CUSTOM TRUCK & EQUIPMENT, LLC—See North American Truck & Trailer, Inc.; *U.S. Private*, pg. 2941
CUSTOM TRUCK LEASING, INC.—See North American Truck & Trailer, Inc.; *U.S. Private*, pg. 2941
DANA CONTAINER INC.—See Dana Transport Inc.; *U.S. Private*, pg. 1152
DECAROLIS TRUCK RENTAL INC.—See Penske Automotive Group, Inc.; *U.S. Public*, pg. 1665
DECAROLIS TRUCK RENTAL INC.—See Penske Corporation; *U.S. Private*, pg. 3139
DJ LEASING LLC; *U.S. Private*, pg. 1246
DRAEGER LEASING INC.—See Draeger Oil Co. Inc.; *U.S. Private*, pg. 1271
DRAGON ESP, LTD.; *U.S. Private*, pg. 1271
DSU LEASING, INC.—See DSU Peterbilt & GMC Truck, Inc.; *U.S. Private*, pg. 1282
EAGLE LEASING COMPANY; *U.S. Private*, pg. 1309
EDMONTON KENWORTH LTD. - KENWORTH LEDUC DIVISION—See Edmonton Kenworth Ltd.; *Int'l*, pg. 2313
EDMONTON KENWORTH LTD. - KENWORTH LLOYDMIN-

532120 — TRUCK, UTILITY TRAI...

STER DIVISION—See Edmonton Kenworth Ltd.; *Int'l*, pg. 2313
EDMONTON KENWORTH LTD.; *Int'l*, pg. 2313
EFFICIENCY ENTERPRISES INC.—See Breakthru Beverage Group, LLC; *U.S. Private*, pg. 643
ENERGY MAHANAKHON CO., LTD.—See Energy Absolute Public Company Limited; *Int'l*, pg. 2422
ENTERPRISE RENT-A-CAR CANADA CO.—See Enterprise Holdings, Inc.; *U.S. Private*, pg. 1403
ENTERPRISE RENT-A-TRUCK—See Enterprise Holdings, Inc.; *U.S. Private*, pg. 1403
EXCEL LEASING & SALES COMPANY—See The Kretsinger Group, Inc.; *U.S. Private*, pg. 4066
FACILEASING S.A. DE C.V.—See Banco Bilbao Vizcaya Argentaria, S.A.; *Int'l*, pg. 817
FLEET LEASE INC.—See Boerner Truck Center; *U.S. Private*, pg. 609
FORTIS LEASE CAR & TRUCK S.A.—See BNP Paribas SA; *Int'l*, pg. 1085
FRED TAYLOR COMPANY INC.; *U.S. Private*, pg. 1601
FREETRAILER GROUP A/S; *Int'l*, pg. 2771
GEORGIA MOTOR TRUCKS INC.; *U.S. Private*, pg. 1684
G&H TRUCK LEASING INC.—See Astleford International Trucks, Inc.; *U.S. Private*, pg. 360
GRAND POWER EXPRESS INTERNATIONAL (SHENZHEN) LIMITED—See Grand Power Logistics Group Limited; *Int'l*, pg. 3056
GREAT LAKES CONSULTING GROUP INC.—See Rockwood Holding Company Inc.; *U.S. Private*, pg. 3468
GREAT WESTERN LEASING & SALES, LLC; *U.S. Private*, pg. 1768
HANKYU KANKO BUS CO., LTD.—See Hankyu Hanshin Holdings Inc.; *Int'l*, pg. 3255
HANSHIN BUS CO., LTD.—See Hankyu Hanshin Holdings Inc.; *Int'l*, pg. 3255
HEATHROW TRUCK CENTRE LTD—See Ballyvesey Holdings Limited; *Int'l*, pg. 809
H & K EQUIPMENT COMPANY INC.—See Diamond Group Inc.; *U.S. Private*, pg. 1223
HOGAN MOTOR LEASING INC.; *U.S. Private*, pg. 1961
HUB TRUCK RENTAL CORP.; *U.S. Private*, pg. 2000
IDEALEASE DE MEXICO SA DE CV—See Idealease, Inc.; *U.S. Private*, pg. 2037
IDEALEASE, INC.; *U.S. Private*, pg. 2037
IDEALEASE OF ATLANTA, L.L.C.—See Idealease, Inc.; *U.S. Private*, pg. 2037
IDEALEASE OF CHICAGO LLC—See Rush Enterprises, Inc.; *U.S. Public*, pg. 1826
IDEALEASE OF FLINT INC.—See C&S Motors, Inc.; *U.S. Private*, pg. 704
IDEALEASE OF HOUSTON, L.L.C.—See Idealease, Inc.; *U.S. Private*, pg. 2037
IMPERIAL CAPITAL LIMITED—See Dubai World Corporation; *Int'l*, pg. 2221
INBOUND PLATFORM CORP.—See AirTrip Corp.; *Int'l*, pg. 250
IVECO PARTICIPATIONS S.A.S.—See CNH Industrial N.V.; *Int'l*, pg. 1675
JX PACLEASE—See JX Enterprises Inc.; *U.S. Private*, pg. 2247
KENWORTH OF JACKSON INC.; *U.S. Private*, pg. 2289
KIRK NATIONALEASE CO. INC.—See KNL Holdings Inc.; *U.S. Private*, pg. 2322
KRIS-WAY TRUCK LEASING INC.—See Penske Automotive Group, Inc.; *U.S. Public*, pg. 1665
KRIS-WAY TRUCK LEASING INC.—See Penske Corporation; *U.S. Private*, pg. 3139
KYOTO KANKYO CO., LTD.—See Daiei Kankyo Co., Ltd.; *Int'l*, pg. 1924
LEASCO INC—See Transwood Carriers Inc.; *U.S. Private*, pg. 4211
LEASE LINE INC.; *U.S. Private*, pg. 2408
LEASEWAY OF PUERTO RICO INC.; *U.S. Private*, pg. 2408
LEROY HOLDING CO., INC.; *U.S. Private*, pg. 2431
LUCKY'S LEASE, INC.—See Lucky's Trailer Sales, Inc.; *U.S. Private*, pg. 2511
MACK LEASING SYSTEM—See AB Volvo; *Int'l*, pg. 45
MAVERICK LEASING, LLC—See Maverick USA, Inc.; *U.S. Private*, pg. 2616
MCCOY NATIONALEASE, INC.—See McCoy Group, Inc.; *U.S. Private*, pg. 2630
MCKINNEY TRAILERS & CONTAINERS; *U.S. Private*, pg. 2639
MEARS MOTOR LIVERY CORPORATION; *U.S. Private*, pg. 2647
MENDON LEASING CORPORATION—See Groupe Petit Forestier SAS; *Int'l*, pg. 3109
MHC TRUCK LEASING INC.—See Murphy-Hoffman Company; *U.S. Private*, pg. 2816
MIAMI INDUSTRIAL TRUCKS INC.—See Miami Industrial Trucks, Inc.; *U.S. Private*, pg. 2696
MPG TRUCK & TRACTOR, INC.—See Maine Potato Growers, Inc.; *U.S. Private*, pg. 2552
NATIONAL TRUCK LEASING SYSTEM—See AmeriQuest Business Services; *U.S. Private*, pg. 260
NORTHLAND TRUCKING INC.; *U.S. Private*, pg. 2955
NOVAE CORPORATION—See Brightstar Capital Partners, L.P.; *U.S. Private*, pg. 653

NU WAY SERVICE STATION INC.—See NW Holding Co.; *U.S. Private*, pg. 2975
O/B LEASING COMPANY—See Universal Logistics Holdings, Inc.; *U.S. Public*, pg. 2261
OLD DOMINION TRUCK LEASING INC.; *U.S. Public*, pg. 3008
OMNI AMERICAN INC.—See Global Capital Corp.; *U.S. Private*, pg. 1712
OSHKOSH/MCNEILUS FINANCIAL SERVICES PARTNERSHIP—See Bank of America Corporation; *U.S. Public*, pg. 272
PACCAR FINANCIAL CORP.—See PACCAR Inc.; *U.S. Public*, pg. 1630
PACCAR FINANCIAL DEUTSCHLAND GMBH—See PACCAR Inc.; *U.S. Public*, pg. 1630
PACCAR LEASING CO.—See PACCAR Inc.; *U.S. Public*, pg. 1631
PACCAR LEASING GMBH—See PACCAR Inc.; *U.S. Public*, pg. 1631
PARSEC INC.—See Universal Logistics Holdings, Inc.; *U.S. Public*, pg. 2261
PATSY'S, INC.; *U.S. Private*, pg. 3111
PAULCAMPER GMBH—See Camplify Holdings Limited; *Int'l*, pg. 1275
PENSKE CADILLAC OF CALIFORNIA, INC.—See Penske Automotive Group, Inc.; *U.S. Public*, pg. 1665
PENSKE CORPORATION; *U.S. Private*, pg. 3138
PENSKE LOGISTICS, LLC—See Penske Corporation; *U.S. Private*, pg. 3138
PENSKE TRUCK LEASING COMPANY, L.P.—See Penske Automotive Group, Inc.; *U.S. Public*, pg. 1665
PENSKE TRUCK LEASING COMPANY, L.P.—See Penske Corporation; *U.S. Private*, pg. 3139
PENSKE TRUCK RENTAL—See Penske Automotive Group, Inc.; *U.S. Public*, pg. 1666
PENSKE TRUCK RENTAL—See Penske Corporation; *U.S. Private*, pg. 3139
PETERBILT OF MEMPHIS—See Daco Corporation; *U.S. Private*, pg. 1144
PREFERRED LEASING INC.—See Taylor & Martin Enterprises Inc.; *U.S. Private*, pg. 3937
PREMIER TRAILER LEASING, INC.—See Redwood Capital Investments, LLC; *U.S. Private*, pg. 3380
PREMIER TRUCK GROUP—See Penske Automotive Group, Inc.; *U.S. Public*, pg. 1666
PRIMMS LP; *U.S. Private*, pg. 3263
RAPID LEASING, INC.—See CRST International, Inc.; *U.S. Private*, pg. 1113
RBL LEASING CORP.—See Bergeys Inc.; *U.S. Private*, pg. 531
RENTAL EQUIPMENT INVESTMENT CORP.—See Kinderhook Industries, LLC; *U.S. Private*, pg. 2307
RENT-A-WRECK OF AMERICA, INC.—See JJF Management Services, Inc.; *U.S. Private*, pg. 2211
REPUBLIC LEASING CORPORATION—See Luther Holding Company; *U.S. Private*, pg. 2517
R&R TRANSPORTATION, INC.; *U.S. Private*, pg. 3333
RUSH GMC TRUCK CENTER OF TUCSON, INC.—See Rush Enterprises, Inc.; *U.S. Public*, pg. 1826
RUSH TRUCK LEASING, INC.—See Rush Enterprises, Inc.; *U.S. Public*, pg. 1827
RV WORLD, LLC—See Camping World Holdings, Inc.; *U.S. Public*, pg. 428
RWBT INC.; *U.S. Private*, pg. 3508
RYDER CONTAINER TERMINALS—See Ryder System, Inc.; *U.S. Public*, pg. 1828
RYDER CRSA LOGISTICS (HK) LIMITED—See Ryder System, Inc.; *U.S. Public*, pg. 1828
RYDER DE MEXICO S.A. DE C.V.—See Ryder System, Inc.; *U.S. Public*, pg. 1828
RYDER FUEL SERVICES, LLC—See Ryder System, Inc.; *U.S. Public*, pg. 1828
RYDER, INC. OF FLORIDA—See Ryder System, Inc.; *U.S. Public*, pg. 1828
RYDER LIMITED—See Ryder System, Inc.; *U.S. Public*, pg. 1828
RYDER TRUCK RENTAL CANADA LTD.—See Ryder System, Inc.; *U.S. Public*, pg. 1828
RYDER TRUCK RENTAL, INC.—See Ryder System, Inc.; *U.S. Public*, pg. 1828
SALEM HOLDING COMPANY; *U.S. Private*, pg. 3531
SALEM LEASING CORP.—See Salem Holding Company; *U.S. Private*, pg. 3531
SALEM NATIONALLEASE—See Salem Holding Company; *U.S. Private*, pg. 3531
SALEM TRUCK LEASING INC.; *U.S. Private*, pg. 3531
SCHILLI LEASING, INC.—See Daseke, Inc.; *U.S. Private*, pg. 1161
SIVA TRUCK LEASING INC.—See Badger Truck and Automotive Group, Inc.; *U.S. Private*, pg. 424
SOMMER'S MOBILE LEASING, INC.—See WillScot Mobile Mini Holdings Corp.; *U.S. Public*, pg. 2372
SOUTHERN FREIGHT INC.; *U.S. Private*, pg. 3732
SPARTA COMMERCIAL SERVICES, INC.; *U.S. Public*, pg. 1914
SSV ENVIRONNEMENT S.A.S.—See Bucher Industries AG; *Int'l*, pg. 1209

CORPORATE AFFILIATIONS

STAR LEASING CO.—See I Squared Capital Advisors (US) LLC; *U.S. Private*, pg. 2026
STAR TRUCK RENTALS INC.—See Penske Automotive Group, Inc.; *U.S. Public*, pg. 1666
STAR TRUCK RENTALS INC.—See Penske Corporation; *U.S. Private*, pg. 3139
STOOPS NATIONALEASE INC—See Stoops Freightliner Quality Trailer; *U.S. Private*, pg. 3830
SWIFT LEASING CO., LLC—See Knight-Swift Transportation Holdings Inc.; *U.S. Public*, pg. 1269
TOTAL TRANSPORTATION SERVICES, INC.—See UniGroup, Inc.; *U.S. Private*, pg. 4283
TRAILER BOSS; *U.S. Private*, pg. 4203
TRAIN TRAILER RENTALS LIMITED—See Bravia Capital Hong Kong Limited; *Int'l*, pg. 1141
TRANSCO LEASING INC.—See P&S Investment Company Inc.; *U.S. Private*, pg. 3059
TRANSPEC LEASING INC.—See TSL Companies; *U.S. Private*, pg. 4254
TRANSPORT LEASING COMPANY LLP; *U.S. Private*, pg. 4210
TRANSPORT SERVICES INC.; *U.S. Private*, pg. 4210
TRI-LIFT INC.; *U.S. Private*, pg. 4222
TRUCKWAY LEASING INC.; *U.S. Private*, pg. 4246
TSI EQUIPMENT INC.—See Transportation Services, Inc.; *U.S. Private*, pg. 4211
TURO INC.—See General Motors Company; *U.S. Public*, pg. 929
T.W.L CORP; *U.S. Private*, pg. 3912
U-HAUL CO. OF ALABAMA, INC.—See U-Haul Holding Company; *U.S. Public*, pg. 2211
U-HAUL CO. OF ALASKA, INC.—See U-Haul Holding Company; *U.S. Public*, pg. 2211
U-HAUL CO. OF ARIZONA—See U-Haul Holding Company; *U.S. Public*, pg. 2211
U-HAUL CO. OF ARKANSAS—See U-Haul Holding Company; *U.S. Public*, pg. 2211
U-HAUL CO. OF CHARLESTON—See U-Haul Holding Company; *U.S. Public*, pg. 2211
U-HAUL CO. OF COLORADO—See U-Haul Holding Company; *U.S. Public*, pg. 2211
U-HAUL CO. OF DISTRICT OF COLUMBIA, INC.—See U-Haul Holding Company; *U.S. Public*, pg. 2211
U-HAUL CO. OF FLORIDA—See U-Haul Holding Company; *U.S. Public*, pg. 2211
U-HAUL CO. OF GEORGIA—See U-Haul Holding Company; *U.S. Public*, pg. 2211
U-HAUL CO. OF IDAHO, INC.—See U-Haul Holding Company; *U.S. Public*, pg. 2211
U-HAUL CO. OF INDIANA, INC.—See U-Haul Holding Company; *U.S. Public*, pg. 2211
U-HAUL CO. OF KANSAS, INC.—See U-Haul Holding Company; *U.S. Public*, pg. 2211
U-HAUL CO. OF KENTUCKY—See U-Haul Holding Company; *U.S. Public*, pg. 2211
U-HAUL, CO. OF LOUISIANA—See U-Haul Holding Company; *U.S. Public*, pg. 2211
U-HAUL CO. OF MAINE, INC.—See U-Haul Holding Company; *U.S. Public*, pg. 2211
U-HAUL CO. OF MARYLAND, INC.—See U-Haul Holding Company; *U.S. Public*, pg. 2211
U-HAUL CO. OF MICHIGAN—See U-Haul Holding Company; *U.S. Public*, pg. 2211
U-HAUL CO. OF MINNESOTA—See U-Haul Holding Company; *U.S. Public*, pg. 2211
U-HAUL CO. OF MISSISSIPPI—See U-Haul Holding Company; *U.S. Public*, pg. 2211
U-HAUL CO. OF NEBRASKA—See U-Haul Holding Company; *U.S. Public*, pg. 2211
U-HAUL CO. OF NEVADA, INC.—See U-Haul Holding Company; *U.S. Public*, pg. 2211
U-HAUL CO. OF NEW JERSEY, INC.—See U-Haul Holding Company; *U.S. Public*, pg. 2211
U-HAUL CO. OF NEW YORK AND VERMONT, INC.—See U-Haul Holding Company; *U.S. Public*, pg. 2211
U-HAUL CO. OF PENNSYLVANIA—See U-Haul Holding Company; *U.S. Public*, pg. 2211
U-HAUL CO. OF SOUTH CAROLINA, INC.—See U-Haul Holding Company; *U.S. Public*, pg. 2212
U-HAUL CO. OF SOUTH DAKOTA, INC.—See U-Haul Holding Company; *U.S. Public*, pg. 2212
U-HAUL CO. OF UTAH, INC.—See U-Haul Holding Company; *U.S. Public*, pg. 2212
U-HAUL CO. OF VIRGINIA—See U-Haul Holding Company; *U.S. Public*, pg. 2212
U-HAUL CO. OF WISCONSIN, INC.—See U-Haul Holding Company; *U.S. Public*, pg. 2212
U-HAUL INTERNATIONAL, INC.—See U-Haul Holding Company; *U.S. Public*, pg. 2211
U-HAUL OF HAWAII, INC.—See U-Haul Holding Company; *U.S. Public*, pg. 2212
ULTIMATE POWER TRUCK, LLC—See Cool Technologies, Inc.; *U.S. Public*, pg. 573
VFS LOCATION FRANCE S.A.S.—See AB Volvo; *Int'l*, pg. 44
VOLVO TRUCKS OF OMAHA INC.—See North American Truck & Trailer, Inc.; *U.S. Private*, pg. 2941

N.A.I.C.S. INDEX

532289 — ALL OTHER CONSUMER ...

W.C. EQUIPMENT COMPANY INC.—See William Charles, Ltd.; *U.S. Private*, pg. 4522
WESTERN PACIFIC PACLEASE—See Greenbriar Equity Group, L.P.; *U.S. Private*, pg. 1776
WEST POINT CHEVROLET, INC.—See North American Truck & Trailer, Inc.; *U.S. Private*, pg. 2941
WORLDWIDE EQUIPMENT, INC. - LEXINGTON DIVISION—See Worldwide Equipment, Inc.; *U.S. Private*, pg. 4569
XTRA CORPORATION—See Berkshire Hathaway Inc.; *U.S. Public*, pg. 319
XTRA LEASE LLC—See Berkshire Hathaway Inc.; *U.S. Public*, pg. 319

532210 — CONSUMER ELECTRONICS AND APPLIANCES RENTAL

AARON'S SALES & LEASE OWNERSHIP—See Aaron's Company, Inc.; *U.S. Public*, pg. 13
ABC TELEVISION & APPLIANCE RENTAL; *U.S. Private*, pg. 36
A CONTACT ELECTRIC RENTALS, L.P.—See I Squared Capital Advisors (US) LLC; *U.S. Private*, pg. 2021
A D LIFT TRUCK—See Wolter Group LLC; *U.S. Private*, pg. 4554
ALCOA INESPAL, S.A.—See Alcoa Corporation; *U.S. Public*, pg. 74
ARVADA RENT-ALLS; *U.S. Private*, pg. 344
ATAG HEATING B.V.—See Ariston Holding N.V.; *Int'l*, pg. 567
AVI SYSTEMS COMPANY—See AVI Systems, Inc.; *U.S. Private*, pg. 406
A V MATTERS—See Harbor Beach Capital, LLC; *U.S. Private*, pg. 1858
BAYER PLC—See Bayer Aktiengesellschaft; *Int'l*, pg. 906
BEECRUISE INC.—See BEENOS Inc.; *Int'l*, pg. 939
BEIJING ZHONGKE I/E COMPANY LTD.—See China Science Publishing & Media Ltd.; *Int'l*, pg. 1550
BEXEMA GMBH—See HORIBA Ltd; *Int'l*, pg. 3475
BISSETT EQUIPMENT CORP.—See SiteOne Landscape Supply, Inc.; *U.S. Public*, pg. 1889
CARLTON-BATES COMPANY DE MEXICO S.A. DE C.V.—See WESCO International, Inc.; *U.S. Public*, pg. 2351
EAST COAST RIGGING & CONTRACTING COMPANY, INC.—See Incorp Holdings, LLC; *U.S. Private*, pg. 2054
ELECTRO RENT CORPORATION (EASTERN REGIONAL OFFICE)—See Platinum Equity, LLC; *U.S. Private*, pg. 3202
ELMEN ENTERPRISES; *U.S. Private*, pg. 1376
FREEMAN AUDIO VISUAL, INC.—See Freeman Decorating Co.; *U.S. Private*, pg. 1605
GASTECH-ENERGI A/S—See Ariston Holding N.V.; *Int'l*, pg. 567
GAZELLE, INC.; *U.S. Private*, pg. 1652
GOEASY LTD.; *Int'l*, pg. 3021
HAIER AMERICA TRADING, LLC—See Haier Smart Home Co., Ltd.; *Int'l*, pg. 3210
HPI DISTRIBUTION GMBH—See HPI AG; *Int'l*, pg. 3500
IK INVESTMENT PARTNERS GMBH—See IK Investment Partners Limited; *Int'l*, pg. 3609
INGRADO S.R.L.—See Ariston Holding N.V.; *Int'l*, pg. 567
ISMAIL ABUDAWOOD PROCTER & GAMBLE - DAMMAM—See The Procter & Gamble Company; *U.S. Public*, pg. 2120
LEBAKKENS, INC. OF WISCONSIN; *U.S. Private*, pg. 2409
MAC EQUIPMENT, LLC—See Herc Holdings Inc.; *U.S. Public*, pg. 1028
MEETING TOMORROW, INC.; *U.S. Private*, pg. 2660
THE MODAL SHOP INC.—See Amphenol Corporation; *U.S. Public*, pg. 131
MSP EQUIPMENT RENTALS, INC.—See Ashtead Group Plc; *Int'l*, pg. 609
RR APPLIANCE SERVICES, INC.; *U.S. Private*, pg. 3496
SAFETY ADHERENCE TECHNOLOGY (PTY) LTD—See CSG Holdings Limited; *Int'l*, pg. 1864
SANMINA CORPORATION; *U.S. Public*, pg. 1840
SCREENWORKS LLC—See The Carlyle Group Inc.; *U.S. Public*, pg. 2049
SHOWPLACE INC.; *U.S. Private*, pg. 3643
SMARTSOURCE COMPUTER & AUDIO VISUAL RENTALS—See Abcom Computer Rental, Inc.; *U.S. Private*, pg. 37
TLH ENTERPRISES INC.; *U.S. Private*, pg. 4178
TRINITY INDUSTRIES, INC.; *U.S. Public*, pg. 2193
VERIZON CREDIT INC.—See Verizon Communications Inc.; *U.S. Public*, pg. 2285
WEATHERFORD ASIA PACIFIC PTE. LTD.—See Weatherford International plc; *U.S. Public*, pg. 2340
XEROX DE VENEZUELA, C.A.—See Xerox Holdings Corporation; *U.S. Public*, pg. 2390

532281 — FORMAL WEAR AND COSTUME RENTAL

ANDERSON'S FORMAL WEAR INC.—See Frana & Associates Inc.; *U.S. Private*, pg. 1586
BINZAGR COMPANY; *Int'l*, pg. 1035
DICK BRUHN INCORPORATED; *U.S. Private*, pg. 1225
FRANA & ASSOCIATES INC.; *U.S. Private*, pg. 1586
HOUSE OF BRIDES INC.; *U.S. Private*, pg. 1991
ICHIKURA CO., LTD.; *Int'l*, pg. 3580
JIM'S FORMAL WEAR CO.; *U.S. Private*, pg. 2210
MR. FORMAL INC.; *U.S. Private*, pg. 2805
RENT THE RUNWAY, INC.; *U.S. Public*, pg. 1784

532282 — VIDEO TAPE AND DISC RENTAL

ALL MOBILE VIDEO; *U.S. Private*, pg. 171
BLOCKBUSTER AUSTRALIA PTY. LTD.—See Franchise Entertainment Group Pty Ltd.; *Int'l*, pg. 2760
BLOCKBUSTER DE MEXICO, S.A. DE C.V.—See Grupo Salinas, S.A. de C.V.; *Int'l*, pg. 3135
BLOCKBUSTER ENTERTAINMENT LIMITED—See Gordon Brothers Group, LLC; *U.S. Private*, pg. 1742
CAPITAL VIDEO CORPORATION; *U.S. Private*, pg. 742
CAPITOL ENTERTAINMENT MANAGEMENT CO.; *U.S. Private*, pg. 743
CRITICS' CHOICE VIDEO, INC.—See Infinity Resources, Inc.; *U.S. Private*, pg. 2072
DELTAMAC (TAIWAN) CO., LTD.; *Int'l*, pg. 2020
DIGITAL BROS SPA; *Int'l*, pg. 2120
DOUGLAS VIDEO WAREHOUSE; *U.S. Private*, pg. 1267
FAMILY VIDEO MOVIE CLUB INC.—See Highland Ventures, Ltd.; *U.S. Private*, pg. 1939
FRANCHISE ENTERTAINMENT GROUP PTY LTD.; *Int'l*, pg. 2760
GAMEFLY, INC.; *U.S. Private*, pg. 1640
GEO HOLDINGS CORPORATION; *Int'l*, pg. 2932
GEO NETWORKS CORPORATION—See GEO Holdings Corporation; *Int'l*, pg. 2932
HAPPY LAND ENTERTAINMENT (W.L.L.)—See Future Kid Entertainment and Real Estate Co. K.S.C.C.; *Int'l*, pg. 2856
HIBINO BESCO CORPORATION—See Hibino Corporation; *Int'l*, pg. 3383
LOVEFILM UK LTD.—See Amazon.com, Inc.; *U.S. Public*, pg. 90
MARCH NETWORKS S.R.L.—See Delta Electronics, Inc.; *Int'l*, pg. 2018
MOVIE BRANDS INC.; *U.S. Private*, pg. 2802
MOVIE TRADING COMPANY—See Live Ventures Incorporated; *U.S. Public*, pg. 1332
NETFLIX, INC.; *U.S. Public*, pg. 1508
OVERWATCH LEAGUE, LLC—See Microsoft Corporation; *U.S. Public*, pg. 1439
SNOWED IN STUDIOS, INC.—See Canada Pension Plan Investment Board; *Int'l*, pg. 1280
SNOWED IN STUDIOS, INC.—See EQT AB; *Int'l*, pg. 2483
TLA ENTERTAINMENT GROUP, INC.; *U.S. Private*, pg. 4178
THE TRAILERFARM LIMITED—See Canada Pension Plan Investment Board; *Int'l*, pg. 1281
THE TRAILERFARM LIMITED—See EQT AB; *Int'l*, pg. 2483
TS OPERATIONS LIMITED—See Gordon Brothers Group, LLC; *U.S. Private*, pg. 1742
UNITED ENTERTAINMENT CORP.; *U.S. Private*, pg. 4291
VUDU INC.—See Comcast Corporation; *U.S. Public*, pg. 540
XTRA-VISION LIMITED—See Hilco Trading, LLC; *U.S. Private*, pg. 1944

532283 — HOME HEALTH EQUIPMENT RENTAL

AEROCARE HOLDINGS, INC.—See AdaptHealth Corp.; *U.S. Public*, pg. 38
AGILITI HEALTH, INC.—See Thomas H. Lee Partners, L.P.; *U.S. Private*, pg. 4155
ARCADIAN HEALTHCARE INC.; *U.S. Private*, pg. 310
ARJOHUNTLEIGH HEALTHCARE POLSKA SP. Z O.O.—See Getinge AB; *Int'l*, pg. 2948
ARJOHUNTLEIGH IBERICA S.L.—See Getinge AB; *Int'l*, pg. 2948
BLUEGRASS OXYGEN, INC.—See AdaptHealth Corp.; *U.S. Public*, pg. 38
CENTRAL MEDICAL EQUIPMENT RENTALS; *U.S. Private*, pg. 822
CENTRAL MEDICAL SUPPLY, INC.—See Osceola Capital Management, LLC; *U.S. Private*, pg. 3047
CHILDREN'S HOME HEALTHCARE—See Children's Hospital & Medical Center; *U.S. Private*, pg. 884
COASTAL MED TECH, INC.—See Quipt Home Medical Corp.; *U.S. Public*, pg. 1757
CONSOLIDATED MEDICAL & SURGICAL SUPPLY CO, INC.—See Osceola Capital Management, LLC; *U.S. Private*, pg. 3047
CORNERSTONE MEDICAL SERVICES - AKRON—See Catholic Health Initiatives; *U.S. Private*, pg. 789
CORNERSTONE MEDICAL SERVICES—See Catholic Health Initiatives; *U.S. Private*, pg. 789
DYNASPLINT SYSTEMS INC.; *U.S. Private*, pg. 1300
FREEDOM MEDICAL, INC.—See Freeman Spogli & Co. Incorporated; *U.S. Private*, pg. 1606
FRONTIER MEDICAL, INC.; *U.S. Private*, pg. 1615
GE HEALTHCARE FINANCIAL SERVICES—See GE HealthCare Technologies Inc.; *U.S. Public*, pg. 909
HOME CARE SPECIALISTS, INC.; *U.S. Private*, pg. 1970
HOMETOWN OXYGEN, CHARLOTTE, LLC—See The Halifax Group LLC; *U.S. Private*, pg. 4042
HUNTLEIGH HEALTHCARE PTE LTD—See Getinge AB; *Int'l*, pg. 2948
LEGACY MEDICAL EQUIPMENT—See Catholic Health Initiatives; *U.S. Private*, pg. 789
LEHIGH VALLEY RESPIRATORY CARE - LANCASTER, INC.—See AdaptHealth Corp.; *U.S. Public*, pg. 39
LYNAY HEALTHCARE INC.; *U.S. Private*, pg. 2520
MCCLELLAND HEALTH SYSTEMS; *U.S. Private*, pg. 2628
MED ONE CAPITAL INCORPORATED; *U.S. Private*, pg. 2650
PACIFIC PULMONARY SERVICE—See PPSC, Inc.; *U.S. Private*, pg. 3241
RESPIRATORY THERAPY HOME CARE—See New Mountain Capital, LLC; *U.S. Private*, pg. 2903
SOUTHEASTERN MEDEQUIP, INC.; *U.S. Private*, pg. 3728
SPECIALIZED MEDICAL SERVICES, INC.—See New Mountain Capital, LLC; *U.S. Private*, pg. 2903
TAYLOR HOME HEALTH INC.—See Rotech Healthcare, Inc.; *U.S. Private*, pg. 3486
TRILOGY HEALTH SERVICES LLC—See American Healthcare Investors LLC; *U.S. Private*, pg. 236
TRILOGY HEALTH SERVICES LLC—See DigitalBridge Group, Inc.; *U.S. Public*, pg. 665
TRILOGY HEALTH SERVICES LLC—See Griffin Capital Corporation; *U.S. Private*, pg. 1787

532284 — RECREATIONAL GOODS RENTAL

AMANCRUISES COMPANY LIMITED—See DLF Limited; *Int'l*, pg. 2141
AOSKGL, INC.—See Christy Sports LLC; *U.S. Private*, pg. 892
B-CYCLE, LLC—See Humana, Inc.; *U.S. Public*, pg. 1069
BEAVER CREEK ASSOCIATES, INC.—See Vail Resorts, Inc.; *U.S. Public*, pg. 2271
CABINS FOR YOU, LLC; *U.S. Private*, pg. 711
FRASER YACHTS CALIFORNIA—See MarineMax, Inc.; *U.S. Public*, pg. 1366
GREENFIELDS SPORTS & LEISURE PTY LTD.—See ABN AMRO Group N.V.; *Int'l*, pg. 64
GREENFIELDS SPORTS & LEISURE PTY LTD.—See Gilde Buy Out Partners B.V.; *Int'l*, pg. 2974
GYG PLC; *Int'l*, pg. 3190
HEIFERMAN, INC.—See Dubin Clark & Company, Inc.; *U.S. Private*, pg. 1283
HUNYVERS SA; *Int'l*, pg. 3537
IGY MALAGA MARINA—See MarineMax, Inc.; *U.S. Public*, pg. 1366
K1 SPEED, LLC; *U.S. Private*, pg. 2253
PUBLIBIKE SA—See Die Schweizerische Post AG; *Int'l*, pg. 2113
SEVEN CROWN RESORTS INC.; *U.S. Private*, pg. 3618
TAOS SKI & BOOT COMPANY—See Taos Ski Valley, Inc.; *U.S. Private*, pg. 3932
YOUBIKE CO., LTD.—See Giant Manufacturing Co., Ltd.; *Int'l*, pg. 2961

532289 — ALL OTHER CONSUMER GOODS RENTAL

ACTION PARTY RENTALS; *U.S. Private*, pg. 67
ADVANCE YOUR REACH LLC; *U.S. Private*, pg. 87
ALL CHEMICAL LEASING, INC.; *U.S. Private*, pg. 170
ARONA CORPORATION; *U.S. Private*, pg. 334
ATH APLICACIONES TECNICAS HIDRAULICAS S.L.—See Fluidra SA; *Int'l*, pg. 2713
BALDWIN GLOBALTEC LTD.—See Forsyth Capital Investors LLC; *U.S. Private*, pg. 1573
BBJ RENTALS INC.; *U.S. Private*, pg. 498
THE BIG VIEW; *U.S. Private*, pg. 3995
BRIDGEPORT EQUIPMENT & TOOL; *U.S. Private*, pg. 649
BROOK FURNITURE RENTAL, INC.; *U.S. Private*, pg. 663
BUCYRUS EQUIPMENT LLC—See Caterpillar, Inc.; *U.S. Public*, pg. 449
BUNGOBOX; *U.S. Private*, pg. 685
CAI INTERNATIONAL GMBH—See CAI International, Inc.; *U.S. Public*, pg. 421
CAMPUS BOOK RENTALS, INC.; *U.S. Private*, pg. 732
CANON SOUTH AFRICA PTY. LTD.—See Canon Inc.; *Int'l*, pg. 1295
CAPITAL PARTY RENTALS LLC—See Dubin Clark & Company, Inc.; *U.S. Private*, pg. 1283
CE RENTAL, INC.—See Dubin Clark & Company, Inc.; *U.S. Private*, pg. 1283
CINEQUIPT INC.; *U.S. Private*, pg. 898
CLASSIC PARTY RENTALS, INC. - DALLAS—See Apollo Global Management, Inc.; *U.S. Public*, pg. 149
CLASSIC PARTY RENTALS, INC. - EL SEGUNDO—See Apollo Global Management, Inc.; *U.S. Public*, pg. 149

532289 — ALL OTHER CONSUMER ...

CLASSIC PARTY RENTALS, INC. - PHOENIX—See Apollo Global Management, Inc.; *U.S. Public*, pg. 149
CLASSIC PARTY RENTALS, INC. - SAN DIEGO—See Apollo Global Management, Inc.; *U.S. Public*, pg. 149
CLASSIC PARTY RENTALS, INC.—See Apollo Global Management, Inc.; *U.S. Public*, pg. 149
COLORTONE AUDIO VISUAL STAGING & RENTALS, INC.; *U.S. Private*, pg. 975
COLUMBIA VENDING SERVICE INC.; *U.S. Private*, pg. 978
CORT BUSINESS SERVICES CORPORATION—See Berkshire Hathaway Inc.; *U.S. Public*, pg. 303
CREATIVE TECHNOLOGY LOS ANGELES—See The Carlyle Group Inc.; *U.S. Public*, pg. 2049
CUCKOO HOMESYS CO LTD.; *Int'l*, pg. 1876
CULINARY VENTURES VENDING; *U.S. Private*, pg. 1121
CUYAHOGA VENDING CO. INC.; *U.S. Private*, pg. 1132
DIAMOND SHARP SERVICES, INC.—See Birch Hill Equity Partners Management Inc.; *Int'l*, pg. 1046
DORFIN INC.; *Int'l*, pg. 2176
ELMEN ENTERPRISES INC. - MENOMINEE—See Elmen Enterprises; *U.S. Private*, pg. 1376
HAMILTON & COMPANY LIMITED; *Int'l*, pg. 3237
ICE HOUSE AMERICA, LLC—See Ulysses Management, LLC; *U.S. Public*, pg. 4278
INTEGRAL SHOPPER FZ LLC—See HighCo S.A.; *Int'l*, pg. 3387
J&S AUDIO VISUAL COMMUNICATIONS, LLC—See Ashford Inc.; *U.S. Public*, pg. 211
KARL'S RENTAL CENTER INC.; *U.S. Private*, pg. 2263
KIRBY RENTALS, LLC—See PRO EM Operations, LLC; *U.S. Private*, pg. 3269
KVL AUDIO VISUAL SERVICES; *U.S. Private*, pg. 2359
LOLLIPROPS INC.; *U.S. Private*, pg. 2483
LOSBERGER SHANGHAI CO., LTD.—See Gilde Buy Out Partners B.V.; *Int'l*, pg. 2975
MAHAFFEY FABRIC STRUCTURES.; *U.S. Private*, pg. 2550
MARKEYS AUDIO VISUAL INC.; *U.S. Private*, pg. 2581
MART FINANCIAL GROUP INCORPORATED; *U.S. Private*, pg. 2593
MASQUE SOUND & RECORDING CORP.; *U.S. Private*, pg. 2603
M&M RENTAL CENTER, INC.—See Dubin Clark & Company, Inc.; *U.S. Private*, pg. 1283
PARTY RENTAL LTD.; *U.S. Private*, pg. 3103
PIEDMONT BOBCAT LLC; *U.S. Private*, pg. 3177
PJJ ENTERPRISES INC.—See John Lenore & Company, Inc.; *U.S. Private*, pg. 2223
PRG DALLAS—See The Jordan Company, L.P.; *U.S. Private*, pg. 4061
PROJECTION PRESENTATION TECHNOLOGY; *U.S. Private*, pg. 3281
QUIXOTE STUDIOS, LLC—See Hudson Pacific Properties, Inc.; *U.S. Public*, pg. 1068
Q/W COIN SERVICES LTD.; *U.S. Private*, pg. 3312
RAC NATIONAL PRODUCT SERVICE, LLC—See Upbound Group, Inc.; *U.S. Public*, pg. 2263
RAPHAELS PARTY RENTALS INC.; *U.S. Private*, pg. 3355
RENT-A-CENTER CORPORATE LEASING—See Upbound Group, Inc.; *U.S. Public*, pg. 2263
ROYAL CROWN LEASING INC.; *U.S. Private*, pg. 3492
RTO ASSET MANAGEMENT INC.—See goeasy Ltd.; *Int'l*, pg. 3021
SKC ENTERPRISES INC.; *U.S. Private*, pg. 3681
SOUTH JERSEY CHILDCARE CORP.; *U.S. Private*, pg. 3722
STYLEWEST; *U.S. Private*, pg. 3846
TAYLOR RENTAL—See ACON Investments, LLC; *U.S. Private*, pg. 63
TRANSITIONS GROUP INC.; *U.S. Private*, pg. 4208
TRAUBE TENT COMPANY, INC.; *U.S. Private*, pg. 4212
VISUAL AIDS ELECTRONICS CORP.; *U.S. Private*, pg. 4404
WAKE UP NOW, INC.; *U.S. Public*, pg. 2321
WARNING LITES INC OF COLORADO—See Kohlberg & Company, LLC; *U.S. Private*, pg. 2337
WATERS INC.; *U.S. Private*, pg. 4454
WORLDSTAGE, INC.; *U.S. Private*, pg. 4569

532310 — GENERAL RENTAL CENTERS

AARON'S COMPANY, INC.; *U.S. Public*, pg. 13
AIM HIGH EQUIPMENT RENTALS, INC.—See Kinderhook Industries, LLC; *U.S. Public*, pg. 2307
AMES TAPING TOOL SYSTEMS CO.—See Sun Capital Partners, Inc.; *U.S. Private*, pg. 3858
AUGUST HALL, LLC—See Live Nation Entertainment, Inc.; *U.S. Public*, pg. 1328
BI-RITE COMPANY INC.; *U.S. Private*, pg. 550
DAIWA LIVING CALIFORNIA INC—See Daiwa House Industry, Co., Ltd.; *Int'l*, pg. 1945
FBL LEASING SERVICES, INC.—See Iowa Farm Bureau Federation; *U.S. Private*, pg. 2134
FOUNTAIN LEASING LLC—See SmartFinancial, Inc.; *U.S. Public*, pg. 1895
KEYSTONE EQUIPMENT FINANCE CORP.—See BDT Capital Partners, LLC; *U.S. Private*, pg. 502

NICHII CARENET CO., LTD.—See Bain Capital, LP; *U.S. Private*, pg. 442
NICHII CAREPALACE CAMPANY—See Bain Capital, LP; *U.S. Private*, pg. 442
RELIANT ASSET MANAGEMENT LLC; *U.S. Private*, pg. 3395
SMARTEX SP. Z O.O.—See Dekpol S.A.; *Int'l*, pg. 2006
SNC COGEDIM GESTION—See Altarea SCA; *Int'l*, pg. 385
SUNSHINE RENTALS, INC.; *U.S. Private*, pg. 3872
UPBOUND GROUP, INC.; *U.S. Public*, pg. 2263

532411 — COMMERCIAL AIR, RAIL, AND WATER TRANSPORTATION EQUIPMENT RENTAL AND LEASING

1104816 ONTARIO LIMITED—See Custom Truck One Source, Inc.; *U.S. Public*, pg. 612
ACC AVIATION LTD.; *Int'l*, pg. 78
ACCIPITER HOLDINGS DESIGNATED ACTIVITY COMPANY—See CK Asset Holdings Limited; *Int'l*, pg. 1635
ADLER TANK RENTALS, LLC—See Kinderhook Industries, LLC; *U.S. Private*, pg. 2306
AERCAP AVIATION SOLUTIONS—See Cerberus Capital Management, L.P.; *U.S. Private*, pg. 835
AERCAP GROUP SERVICES B.V.—See AerCap Holdings N.V.; *Int'l*, pg. 179
AERCAP IRELAND LTD.—See Cerberus Capital Management, L.P.; *U.S. Private*, pg. 836
AERCAP SINGAPORE PTE. LTD.—See AerCap Holdings N.V.; *Int'l*, pg. 179
AERGO CAPITAL LTD.; *Int'l*, pg. 179
AEROTURBINE ASIA PTE LTD—See AerCap Holdings N.V.; *Int'l*, pg. 179
AEROTURBINE EUROPE LIMITED—See AerCap Holdings N.V.; *Int'l*, pg. 179
AEROTURBINE, INC.—See AerCap Holdings N.V.; *Int'l*, pg. 179
AERSALE, INC.—See Leonard Green & Partners, L.P.; *U.S. Private*, pg. 2423
AIRBUS CHINA—See Airbus SE; *Int'l*, pg. 244
AIRBUS JAPAN KK—See Airbus SE; *Int'l*, pg. 244
AIRCRAFT LEASING & MANAGEMENT LIMITED—See Fuyo General Lease Co., Ltd.; *Int'l*, pg. 2859
AIRCRAFT LOGISTICS PTY. LTD.—See Bristow Group, Inc.; *U.S. Public*, pg. 387
AIR KILROE LIMITED—See Bristow Group, Inc.; *U.S. Public*, pg. 387
AIR LEASE CORPORATION; *U.S. Public*, pg. 64
AIRLINE CONTAINER LEASING, LLC - NEW YORK—See Ranger Aerospace LLC; *U.S. Private*, pg. 3354
AIRLINE CONTAINER LEASING, LLC—See Ranger Aerospace LLC; *U.S. Private*, pg. 3354
AIR SHOP B.V.—See Ranger Aerospace LLC; *U.S. Private*, pg. 3354
AK FINANSAL KIRALAMA A.S.—See Akbank T.A.S.; *Int'l*, pg. 261
ALL NOW LOGISTICS CO., LTD.—See C.P. All Public Company Limited; *Int'l*, pg. 1243
ALLTERRA CENTRAL, INC.; *U.S. Private*, pg. 194
AMERICAN RAILCAR LEASING, LLC—See ITE Management L.P.; *U.S. Private*, pg. 2149
ANGEL TRAINS LIMITED—See AMP Limited; *Int'l*, pg. 432
ARIES MARINE CORPORATION; *U.S. Private*, pg. 323
ARISTON THERMO USA LLC—See Ariston Holding N.V.; *Int'l*, pg. 567
ARISTON THERMO VIETNAM LTD.—See Ariston Holding N.V.; *Int'l*, pg. 567
ARMOUR TRANSPORTATION SYSTEMS; *Int'l*, pg. 575
ARRIVA BUS & COACH LTD.—See I Squared Capital Advisors (US) LLC; *U.S. Private*, pg. 2024
ASIA JET SDN. BHD.—See Berjaya Corporation Berhad; *Int'l*, pg. 982
AS SPACECOM—See Globaltrans Investment PLC; *Int'l*, pg. 3004
ATAG HEIZUNGSTECHNIK GMBH—See Ariston Holding N.V.; *Int'l*, pg. 567
ATEL LEASING CORPORATION—See ATEL Capital Group; *U.S. Private*, pg. 366
AVATION PLC; *Int'l*, pg. 737
AVES ONE AG; *Int'l*, pg. 739
AVIAAM LEASING AB; *Int'l*, pg. 741
AVIATION EQUIPMENT LEASING (AUSTRALIA) PTY LTD—See Goldbell Corporation; *Int'l*, pg. 3027
AVIATION EQUIPMENT LEASING PTE LTD—See Goldbell Corporation; *Int'l*, pg. 3027
AVOLON HOLDINGS LIMITED—See Hainan Traffic Administration Holding Co., Ltd.; *Int'l*, pg. 3213
AXIOM RAIL (STOKE) LIMITED—See Deutsche Bahn AG; *Int'l*, pg. 2050
BCI AIRCRAFT LEASING, INC; *U.S. Public*, pg. 499
BGI AVIATION TECHNICAL SERVICES (OVERSEAS) LIMITED—See Bristow Group, Inc.; *U.S. Public*, pg. 387
BHNA HOLDINGS INC.—See Bristow Group, Inc.; *U.S. Public*, pg. 387
BLACKSTONE IRELAND LIMITED—See Blackstone Inc.; *U.S. Public*, pg. 349

BLACKSTONE SINGAPORE PTE. LTD.—See Blackstone Inc.; *U.S. Public*, pg. 352
BLUE BEACON TRUCK WUSHEA—See Blue Beacon International, Inc.; *U.S. Private*, pg. 585
BOC AVIATION—See Bank of China, Ltd.; *Int'l*, pg. 841
BRISTOW TRAVEL PROPRIETARY LIMITED—See Bristow Group, Inc.; *U.S. Public*, pg. 387
CAPITEQ LIMITED—See Bristow Group, Inc.; *U.S. Public*, pg. 387
CARLYLE AVIATION GROUP, LLC—See The Carlyle Group Inc.; *U.S. Public*, pg. 2045
CDB AVIATION LEASE FINANCE DESIGNATED ACTIVITY COMPANY—See China Development Bank Financial Leasing Co., Ltd.; *Int'l*, pg. 1497
CHAPMAN FREEBORN AIRCHARTERING BV—See Chapman Freeborn Airchartering Ltd.; *Int'l*, pg. 1447
CHAPMAN FREEBORN AIRCHARTERING CONSULTING (SHANGHAI) CO., LTD.—See Chapman Freeborn Airchartering Ltd.; *Int'l*, pg. 1447
CHAPMAN FREEBORN AIRCHARTERING LIMITED—See Chapman Freeborn Airchartering Ltd.; *Int'l*, pg. 1447
CHAPMAN FREEBORN AIRCHARTERING S.L—See Chapman Freeborn Airchartering Ltd.; *Int'l*, pg. 1447
CHINA AIRCRAFT LEASING GROUP HOLDINGS LIMITED; *Int'l*, pg. 1481
CHINA DEVELOPMENT BANK FINANCIAL LEASING CO., LTD.; *Int'l*, pg. 1497
C.H. ROBINSON FREIGHT SERVICES MIDDLE EAST DMCC—See C.H. Robinson Worldwide, Inc.; *U.S. Public*, pg. 415
CIT AEROSPACE ASIA PTE LTD.—See First Citizens BancShares, Inc.; *U.S. Public*, pg. 841
CITIC OCEAN HELECOPTER CO., LTD.—See CITIC Group Corporation; *Int'l*, pg. 1621
CLASSIC AVIATION INC.; *U.S. Private*, pg. 916
CONSOLIDATED FASTFRATE INC.; *Int'l*, pg. 1770
CONTAINER APPLICATIONS INTERNATIONAL (U.K.) LIMITED—See CAI International, Inc.; *U.S. Public*, pg. 421
CONTAINERPOOL—See Stonepeak Partners L.P.; *U.S. Private*, pg. 3829
CRONOS HOLDING CO LTD.—See Kelso & Company, L.P.; *U.S. Private*, pg. 2278
CRONOS LTD.—See Kelso & Company, L.P.; *U.S. Private*, pg. 2278
CSSC (HONG KONG) SHIPPING COMPANY LIMITED—See China State Shipbuilding Corporation; *Int'l*, pg. 1554
DALLAS AIRMOTIVE SOUTH AFRICA PTY LIMITED—See BlackRock, Inc.; *U.S. Public*, pg. 346
DALLAS AIRMOTIVE SOUTH AFRICA PTY LIMITED—See Blackstone Inc.; *U.S. Public*, pg. 358
DALLAS AIRMOTIVE SOUTH AFRICA PTY LIMITED—See Cascade Investment LLC; *U.S. Private*, pg. 780
DP AIRCRAFT I LIMITED; *Int'l*, pg. 2187
EAGLE AVIATION INC.; *U.S. Private*, pg. 1308
EAGLE COPTERS AUSTRALASIA PTY. LTD.—See Eagle Copters Ltd.; *Int'l*, pg. 2264
EASTERN AIRWAYS (UK) LIMITED—See Bristow Group, Inc.; *U.S. Public*, pg. 387
EASTERN MARINE SYSTEM CO., LTD.—See Azuma Shipping Co., Ltd.; *Int'l*, pg. 782
EAST SHORE AIRCRAFT LLC—See Stifel Financial Corp.; *U.S. Public*, pg. 1949
ECC LEASING COMPANY LTD.—See Embraer S.A.; *Int'l*, pg. 2375
ERMEWA BERLIN—See Ermewa Interservices Sarl; *Int'l*, pg. 2494
ERMEWA LIMITED—See Ermewa Interservices Sarl; *Int'l*, pg. 2494
ERMEWA SRL—See Ermewa Interservices Sarl; *Int'l*, pg. 2494
ERMEWA S.R.L.—See Ermewa Interservices Sarl; *Int'l*, pg. 2494
FERROCARRIL ANTOFAGASTA A BOLIVIA SA—See Antofagasta plc; *Int'l*, pg. 484
FGL AIRCRAFT IRELAND LIMITED—See Fuyo General Lease Co., Ltd.; *Int'l*, pg. 2859
FINNAIR AIRCRAFT FINANCE OY—See Finnair Plc; *Int'l*, pg. 2676
FLIGHT OPTIONS LLC—See Directional Capital LLC; *U.S. Private*, pg. 1236
FLIGHT OPTIONS LLC—See Resilience Capital Partners, LLC; *U.S. Private*, pg. 3405
FPG AMENTUM LIMITED—See Financial Partners Group Co., Ltd.; *Int'l*, pg. 2665
FRASER YACHTS FLORIDA, INC.—See MarineMax, Inc.; *U.S. Public*, pg. 1366
GAS/WILSON, L.P.—See G.A.S. Capital, Inc.; *U.S. Private*, pg. 1630
GATX RAIL AUSTRIA GMBH—See GATX Corporation; *U.S. Public*, pg. 908
GATX RAIL CANADA—See GATX Corporation; *U.S. Public*, pg. 908
GATX RAIL GERMANY GMBH—See GATX Corporation; *U.S. Public*, pg. 908
GATX RAIL—See GATX Corporation; *U.S. Public*, pg. 908
GENERAL HELICOPTERS INTERNATIONAL, INC.—See

N.A.I.C.S. INDEX

532412 — CONSTRUCTION, MININ...

G.A.S. Capital, Inc.; *U.S. Private*, pg. 1630
GLOBAL GUARDIAN AIR AMBULANCE—See Global Guardian, LLC; *U.S. Private*, pg. 1714
GLOBAL SHIP LEASE SERVICES LIMITED—See Global Ship Lease, Inc.; *Int'l*, pg. 3001
GMT GLOBAL REPUBLIC AVIATION LTD.—See Republic Financial Corporation; *U.S. Private*, pg. 3402
GOAL GERMAN OPERATING AIRCRAFT LEASING GMBH—See Commerzbank AG; *Int'l*, pg. 1718
GOAL GERMAN OPERATING AIRCRAFT LEASING GMBH—See Deutsche Lufthansa AG; *Int'l*, pg. 2066
GRAND POWER EXPRESS INTERNATIONAL (CHINA) LIMITED—See Grand Power Logistics Group Limited; *Int'l*, pg. 3056
GRAND POWER EXPRESS INTERNATIONAL LIMITED—See Grand Power Logistics Group Limited; *Int'l*, pg. 3056
GRC LOGISTICS LLP—See Globe International Carriers Ltd.; *Int'l*, pg. 3006
GREENBRIER RAILCAR LLC—See The Greenbrier Companies, Inc.; *U.S. Public*, pg. 2086
GROUPE PETIT FORESTIER SAS; *Int'l*, pg. 3109
HAMBURGER GESELLSCHAFT FUR FLUGHAFENANLAGEN MBH—See Deutsche Lufthansa AG; *Int'l*, pg. 2070
HONG KONG INTERNATIONAL AVIATION LEASING CO., LTD.—See Hainan Traffic Administration Holding Co., Ltd.; *Int'l*, pg. 3215
I-77 MOBILITY PARTNERS LLC—See Ferrovial S.A.; *Int'l*, pg. 2644
ILYUSHIN FINANCE CO.; *Int'l*, pg. 3617
INTERLAKEN CAPITAL AVIATION SERVICES, INC.—See W.R. Berkley Corporation; *U.S. Public*, pg. 2318
KALITTA TURBINE LEASING, LLC—See Kalitta Air, LLC; *U.S. Private*, pg. 2257
KENN BOREK AIR LTD.—See Borek Construction, Ltd.; *Int'l*, pg. 1114
LUFTHANSA LEASING GMBH & CO. ECHO-ZULU OHG—See Deutsche Lufthansa AG; *Int'l*, pg. 2068
LUFTHANSA LEASING GMBH—See Commerzbank AG; *Int'l*, pg. 1718
LUFTHANSA LEASING GMBH—See Deutsche Lufthansa AG; *Int'l*, pg. 2069
MARCON GRUPPEN I SVERIGE AB—See Endur ASA; *Int'l*, pg. 2410
MAVERICK BOAT GROUP, INC.—See Malibu Boats, Inc.; *U.S. Public*, pg. 1356
MCRAE AVIATION SERVICES INC—See Abrams International LLP; *U.S. Private*, pg. 40
MEGA MATRIX CORP.; *U.S. Public*, pg. 1414
MILESTONE AVIATION GROUP LIMITED—See General Electric Company; *U.S. Public*, pg. 919
MILESTONE AVIATION GROUP LLC—See General Electric Company; *U.S. Public*, pg. 919
NOMAD DIGITAL PTY LIMITED—See Alstom S.A.; *Int'l*, pg. 381
OK3 AIR; *U.S. Private*, pg. 3006
PACIFIC COAST GROUP INC.; *U.S. Private*, pg. 3066
PBJV GROUP SDN. BHD—See Barakah Offshore Petroleum Berhad; *Int'l*, pg. 858
PORTERBROOK LEASING COMPANY LIMITED—See Alberta Investment Management Corporation; *Int'l*, pg. 298
PORTERBROOK LEASING COMPANY LIMITED—See Allianz SE; *Int'l*, pg. 344
PORTERBROOK LEASING COMPANY LIMITED—See Electricite de France S.A.; *Int'l*, pg. 2352
PORT KLANG—See Stonepeak Partners L.P.; *U.S. Private*, pg. 3829
PRIVE JETS, LLC; *U.S. Private*, pg. 3268
PROCOR LIMITED—See Berkshire Hathaway Inc.; *U.S. Public*, pg. 311
REH HOLDINGS INC—See REH Holdings Inc.; *U.S. Private*, pg. 3389
ROBERTS AIRCRAFT COMPANY; *U.S. Private*, pg. 3459
SAFAIR OPERATIONS (PTY) LIMITED—See Aergo Capital Ltd.; *Int'l*, pg. 179
SARI SA—See Ermewa Interservices Sarl; *Int'l*, pg. 2494
SEACO AMERICA LLC—See Hainan Traffic Administration Holding Co., Ltd.; *Int'l*, pg. 3213
SEACO ASIA PTE LTD—See Hainan Traffic Administration Holding Co., Ltd.; *Int'l*, pg. 3213
SEACO BRITISH ISLES LTD.—See Hainan Traffic Administration Holding Co., Ltd.; *Int'l*, pg. 3213
SEACO CHINA LTD.—See Hainan Traffic Administration Holding Co., Ltd.; *Int'l*, pg. 3213
SEACO FRANCE SARL—See Hainan Traffic Administration Holding Co., Ltd.; *Int'l*, pg. 3213
SEACO GLOBAL AUSTRALIA PTY. LTD.—See Hainan Traffic Administration Holding Co., Ltd.; *Int'l*, pg. 3213
SEACO GLOBAL LTD.—See Hainan Traffic Administration Holding Co., Ltd.; *Int'l*, pg. 3213
SEACO INTERNATIONAL LEASING GMBH—See Hainan Traffic Administration Holding Co., Ltd.; *Int'l*, pg. 3213
SEACO ITALIA SRL—See Hainan Traffic Administration Holding Co., Ltd.; *Int'l*, pg. 3213
SEALITE SHIPPING CO., LTD.—See Stonepeak Partners L.P.; *U.S. Private*, pg. 3829
SEFA TRANSPORTATION, LLC—See Heidelberg Materials AG; *Int'l*, pg. 3319
SEGI SA—See Ermewa Interservices Sarl; *Int'l*, pg. 2494
SHENZHEN CIMC INVESTMENT HOLDING COMPANY—See China International Marine Containers (Group) Co., Ltd.; *Int'l*, pg. 1512
SKY NIGHT LLC—See flyExclusive, Inc.; *U.S. Public*, pg. 861
SLR LEASING CORP.—See Brookfield Infrastructure Partners L.P.; *Int'l*, pg. 1193
SLR LEASING CORP.—See GIC Pte. Ltd.; *Int'l*, pg. 2967
SMIT LAMNALCO TOWAGE (AUSTRALIA) PTY. LTD.—See HAL Trust N.V.; *Int'l*, pg. 3227
STERLING AIR SERVICES, LLC—See Brookfield Corporation; *Int'l*, pg. 1188
STJM-AIR INC.—See Stimson Lumber Company; *U.S. Private*, pg. 3812
TAMPA INTERNATIONAL JET CENTER—See Sheltair Aviation Center, LLC; *U.S. Private*, pg. 3631
TEM AGENCIES CC—See Stonepeak Partners L.P.; *U.S. Private*, pg. 3829
TEM (H.K.) LIMITED—See Stonepeak Partners L.P.; *U.S. Private*, pg. 3829
TEXTAINER EQUIPMENT MANAGEMENT—See Stonepeak Partners L.P.; *U.S. Private*, pg. 3829
TEXTAINER EQUIPMENT MANAGEMENT (U.S.) LIMITED—See Stonepeak Partners L.P.; *U.S. Private*, pg. 3829
TEXTAINER EQUIPMENT—See Stonepeak Partners L.P.; *U.S. Private*, pg. 3829
TEXTAINER JAPAN LIMITED—See Stonepeak Partners L.P.; *U.S. Private*, pg. 3829
TOPSHEEN SHIPPING SINGAPORE PTE. LTD.—See Caravelle International Group; *Int'l*, pg. 1320
TRINITY INDUSTRIES LEASING COMPANY—See Trinity Industries, Inc.; *U.S. Public*, pg. 2194
VOTG NORTH AMERICA INC.—See Morgan Stanley; *U.S. Public*, pg. 1476
VOTG TANKTAINER GMBH—See Morgan Stanley; *U.S. Public*, pg. 1476
VTG DEUTSCHLAND GMBH - BELGIUM REPRESENTATIVE OFFICE—See Morgan Stanley; *U.S. Public*, pg. 1476
VTG DEUTSCHLAND GMBH - NETHERLANDS REPRESENTATIVE OFFICE—See Morgan Stanley; *U.S. Public*, pg. 1476
WATER MOVERS, INC.—See WillScot Mobile Mini Holdings Corp.; *U.S. Public*, pg. 2372
WELLS FARGO RAIL CORPORATION—See Wells Fargo & Company; *U.S. Public*, pg. 2347
WORLDLINK CORPORATION—See Stonepeak Partners L.P.; *U.S. Private*, pg. 3829
XTRA LLC—See Berkshire Hathaway Inc.; *U.S. Public*, pg. 319

532412 — CONSTRUCTION, MINING, AND FORESTRY MACHINERY AND EQUIPMENT RENTAL AND LEASING

ABIRD HOLDING BV; *Int'l*, pg. 62
ADMAR SUPPLY CO. INC.; *U.S. Private*, pg. 80
AERIAL WORK PLATFORMS, INC.—See Herc Holdings Inc.; *U.S. Public*, pg. 1028
AHERN RENTALS, INC.—See United Rentals, Inc.; *U.S. Public*, pg. 2235
AJOS A/S—See Hojgaard Holding A/S; *Int'l*, pg. 3442
AKTIO MALAYSIA SDN BHD—See Aktio Holdings Corporation; *Int'l*, pg. 267
AKTIO PACIFIC PTE. LTD.—See Aktio Holdings Corporation; *Int'l*, pg. 267
AKTIO TAIWAN CO., LTD.—See Aktio Holdings Corporation; *Int'l*, pg. 267
AKTIO THAILAND CO., LTD.—See Aktio Holdings Corporation; *Int'l*, pg. 267
AL ASHER & SONS, INC.; *U.S. Private*, pg. 147
ALL-AMERICAN SCAFFOLD, LLC—See Brand Industrial Services, Inc.; *U.S. Private*, pg. 636
ALL ERECTION & CRANE RENTAL CORP.; *U.S. Private*, pg. 170
ALP LEASING CORPORATION—See ALP Industries, Inc.; *U.S. Private*, pg. 196
ALTERMAN ENTERPRISES INC.—See Alterman, Inc.; *U.S. Private*, pg. 207
ALVA TECHNIKA, UAB—See Cramo Plc; *Int'l*, pg. 1827
AMECO MEXICO ADMINISTRACION Y SERVICIOS S DE RL/CV—See OEP Capital Advisors, L.P.; *U.S. Private*, pg. 2998
AMECO SERVICES, INC.—See OEP Capital Advisors, L.P.; *U.S. Private*, pg. 2998
AMECO SERVICES, INC.—See OEP Capital Advisors, L.P.; *U.S. Private*, pg. 2998
AMECO SERVICES S DE RL DE CV—See OEP Capital Advisors, L.P.; *U.S. Private*, pg. 2998
AMECO SERVICES, S. DE R.L. DE C.V.—See OEP Capital Advisors, L.P.; *U.S. Private*, pg. 2998
AMECO SERVICES SRL—See OEP Capital Advisors, L.P.; *U.S. Private*, pg. 2998
AMECO SERVICES SRL—See OEP Capital Advisors, L.P.; *U.S. Private*, pg. 2998
AMECO SERVICES SRL—See OEP Capital Advisors, L.P.; *U.S. Private*, pg. 2998
AMECO SERVICES SRL—See OEP Capital Advisors, L.P.; *U.S. Private*, pg. 2998
AMECO SERVICES SRL—See OEP Capital Advisors, L.P.; *U.S. Private*, pg. 2998
AMECO SERVICES SRL—See OEP Capital Advisors, L.P.; *U.S. Private*, pg. 2998
AMERACRANE & HOIST, LLC.—See Balance Point Capital Advisors, LLC; *U.S. Public*, pg. 457
AMQUIP CRANE—See Apollo Global Management, Inc.; *U.S. Public*, pg. 153
ANDERSON EQUIPMENT CO., INC.; *U.S. Private*, pg. 276
AP EQUIPMENT RENTALS (SINGAPORE) PTE. LTD.—See AP Rentals Holdings Ltd.; *Int'l*, pg. 499
API SUPPLY, INC.—See APi Group Corporation; *Int'l*, pg. 513
ARCOMET ASIA PTE LTD—See Arcomet & Co.; *Int'l*, pg. 550
ARCOMET DEUTSCHLAND GMBH & CO. KG—See Arcomet & Co.; *Int'l*, pg. 550
ARCOMET (HONG KONG) LTD—See Arcomet & Co.; *Int'l*, pg. 550
ARCOMET ITALIA SPA—See Arcomet & Co.; *Int'l*, pg. 550
ARCOMET TORENKRANEN NEDERLAND BV—See Arcomet & Co.; *Int'l*, pg. 550
ARMSTRONG CRANE & RIGGING INC.—See Barnhart Crane & Rigging Co.; *U.S. Private*, pg. 478
ASCO EQUIPMENT SAN ANTONIO—See Associated Supply Company Inc.; *U.S. Private*, pg. 357
AS CRAMO ESTONIA—See Cramo Plc; *Int'l*, pg. 1827
ATLAS COPCO ANLEGG- OG GRUVETEKNIKK A/S—See Atlas Copco AB; *Int'l*, pg. 677
ATLAS COPCO A/S—See Atlas Copco AB; *Int'l*, pg. 677
ATLAS COPCO (N.Z.) LTD—See Atlas Copco AB; *Int'l*, pg. 677
ATLAS COPCO RENTAL B.V.—See Atlas Copco AB; *Int'l*, pg. 679
ATLAS COPCO SPECIALTY RENTAL LLC—See Atlas Copco AB; *Int'l*, pg. 680
BAKER ATLAS—See Baker Hughes Company; *U.S. Public*, pg. 264
BAUER EQUIPMENT GULF FZE.—See BAUER Aktiengesellschaft; *Int'l*, pg. 892
BAUER EQUIPMENT SOUTH ASIA PTE. LTD.—See BAUER Aktiengesellschaft; *Int'l*, pg. 892
BAY CRANE SERVICE, INC.; *U.S. Private*, pg. 492
BEST LINE LEASING INC.; *U.S. Private*, pg. 543
B&G CRANE SERVICE, LLC—See Apollo Global Management, Inc.; *U.S. Public*, pg. 153
BHHH COMPANIES INC.; *U.S. Private*, pg. 549
BIGGE EQUIPMENT CO.—See Bigge Crane & Rigging Company; *U.S. Private*, pg. 555
BIS GERATETECHNIK DEUTSCHLAND GMBH—See Bilfinger SE; *Int'l*, pg. 1025
BIS GERATETECHNIK GMBH—See Bilfinger SE; *Int'l*, pg. 1025
BLACK DIAMOND ENERGY SERVICES INC.—See Black Diamond Group Limited; *Int'l*, pg. 1059
BLUE MOUNTAIN EQUIPMENT RENTAL CORPORATION—See United Rentals, Inc.; *U.S. Public*, pg. 2235
BOBCAT OF NEW YORK INC.; *U.S. Private*, pg. 606
BOOM LOGISTICS LIMITED; *Int'l*, pg. 1110
BOTTOM LINE EQUIPMENT, L.L.C.; *U.S. Private*, pg. 623
BRAGG CRANE SERVICE—See Bragg Investment Company, Inc.; *U.S. Private*, pg. 634
BRAMCO INC. - CERTIFIED RENTAL DIVISION—See Bramco Inc.; *U.S. Private*, pg. 635
BRAND ENERGY & INFRASTRUCTURE SERVICES AUSTRALIA PTY LTD—See Brand Industrial Services, Inc.; *U.S. Private*, pg. 636
BRAND ENERGY & INFRASTRUCTURE SERVICES (GLADSTONE) PTY. LTD.—See Brand Industrial Services, Inc.; *U.S. Private*, pg. 636
BRAND ENERGY & INFRASTRUCTURE SERVICES GMBH—See Brand Industrial Services, Inc.; *U.S. Private*, pg. 636
BRAND ENERGY & INFRASTRUCTURE SERVICES (HUNTER VALLEY) PTY. LTD.—See Brand Industrial Services, Inc.; *U.S. Private*, pg. 636
BRAND FRANCE S.A.S.—See Brand Industrial Services, Inc.; *U.S. Private*, pg. 636
BRAND ITALIA S.P.A.—See Brand Industrial Services, Inc.; *U.S. Private*, pg. 636
B.T. EQUIPMENT CO., INC.—See Hallamore Corporation; *U.S. Private*, pg. 1844
BT EQUIPMENT PTY LIMITED—See Affirma Capital Limited; *Int'l*, pg. 187
BUBLITZ MATERIAL HANDLING, INC.; *U.S. Private*, pg. 676
BUCK & KNOBBY EQUIPMENT CO.; *U.S. Private*, pg. 676
BUCKNER HEAVYLIFT CRANES, LLC—See Markel Group Inc.; *U.S. Public*, pg. 1367
CAROLINA TRACTOR & EQUIPMENT CO. - PINNACLE

N.A.I.C.S. Index

532412 — CONSTRUCTION, MININ... CORPORATE AFFILIATIONS

CRANES DIVISION—See Carolina Tractor &; *U.S. Private*, pg. 769
CARRIER RENTAL SYSTEMS—See Carrier Global Corporation; *U.S. Public*, pg. 442
CARTER MACHINERY COMPANY, INC.; *U.S. Private*, pg. 776
CATE EQUIPMENT COMPANY INC.; *U.S. Private*, pg. 788
CATERPILLAR FINANCIAL AUSTRALIA LIMITED—See Caterpillar, Inc.; *U.S. Public*, pg. 450
CATERPILLAR LEASING GMBH (LEIPZIG)—See Caterpillar, Inc.; *U.S. Public*, pg. 450
THE CAT RENTAL STORE—See Ohio Machinery Co.; *U.S. Private*, pg. 3004
CHAILEASE INTERNATIONAL FINANCIAL LEASING CORP.—See Chailease Holding Company Limited; *Int'l*, pg. 1437
CHIGASAKI RENTAL CO., LTD.—See Aktio Holdings Corporation; *Int'l*, pg. 267
CINTAC S.A.—See CAP S.A.; *Int'l*, pg. 1301
CISCO EQUIPMENT - ARTESIA—See Cisco Ford Equipment, Inc.; *U.S. Private*, pg. 900
CLOSE BROTHERS LIMITED—See Close Brothers Group plc; *Int'l*, pg. 1661
CLOVERDALE EQUIPMENT CO.; *U.S. Private*, pg. 948
COASTAL MACHINERY COMPANY, INC.; *U.S. Private*, pg. 956
COLTMAN PRECAST CONCRETE LIMITED—See Ibstock plc; *Int'l*, pg. 3577
CONTRACTORS RENTAL CORPORATION; *U.S. Private*, pg. 1033
CONTRACT PLANT RENTAL LTD—See Ballyvesey Holdings Limited; *Int'l*, pg. 809
CORPORACION MULTI INVERSIONES SA; *Int'l*, pg. 1804
CRAIG TAYLOR EQUIPMENT COMPANY; *U.S. Private*, pg. 1083
CRAMO AB—See Cramo Plc; *Int'l*, pg. 1827
CRAMO AG—See Cramo Plc; *Int'l*, pg. 1827
CRAMO A/S—See Cramo Plc; *Int'l*, pg. 1827
CRAMO INSTANT AB—See Cramo Plc; *Int'l*, pg. 1827
CRAMO INSTANT AS—See Cramo Plc; *Int'l*, pg. 1827
CRAMO KALININGRAD OOO—See Cramo Plc; *Int'l*, pg. 1827
CRAMO NEW HOLDING AB—See Cramo Plc; *Int'l*, pg. 1827
CRAMO PLC; *Int'l*, pg. 1827
CRAMO S.R.O—See Cramo Plc; *Int'l*, pg. 1827
CRAMO SVERIGE AB—See Cramo Plc; *Int'l*, pg. 1827
CROSS ENTERPRISES INC.; *U.S. Private*, pg. 1104
CTI LEASING INC.—See CTI Corp.; *U.S. Private*, pg. 1118
DAITO CORPORATE SERVICE CO., LTD.—See Daito Trust Construction Co., Ltd.; *Int'l*, pg. 1943
DAITO FINANCE CO., LTD.—See Daito Trust Construction Co., Ltd.; *Int'l*, pg. 1943
DANELLA RENTAL SYSTEMS INC.—See The Danella Companies Inc.; *U.S. Private*, pg. 4018
DOGGETT HEAVY MACHINERY SERVICES—See Doggett Equipment Services, Ltd.; *U.S. Private*, pg. 1253
DOGGETT MACHINERY SERVICES—See Doggett Equipment Services, Ltd.; *U.S. Private*, pg. 1253
DURANTE RENTALS, LLC—See Clairvest Group Inc.; *Int'l*, pg. 1641
DYNAMIC DRILL & BLAST PTY. LTD.—See Dynamic Group Holdings Limited; *Int'l*, pg. 2240
ECCO EQUIPMENT CORPORATION; *U.S. Private*, pg. 1326
ECM ENERGY SERVICES, INC.; *U.S. Private*, pg. 1328
EDGE CONSTRUCTION SUPPLY, LLC—See NEFCO Corp.; *U.S. Private*, pg. 2880
ELB EQUIPMENT LIMITED - CONSTRUCTION EQUIPMENT DIVISION—See ELB Group Limited; *Int'l*, pg. 2343
ELB EQUIPMENT LIMITED - EARTHMOVING EQUIPMENT DIVISION—See ELB Group Limited; *Int'l*, pg. 2343
ELEMENT FLEET MANAGEMENT CORPORATION MEXICO S.A. DE C.V—See Element Fleet Management Corporation; *Int'l*, pg. 2358
ELEMENT FLEET MANAGEMENT CORPORATION; *Int'l*, pg. 2358
EMECO HOLDINGS LIMITED; *Int'l*, pg. 2376
ENGEL HOLDINGS INCORPORATED—See Brand Industrial Services, Inc.; *U.S. Private*, pg. 637
ENHANCED PETROLEUM SERVICES PARTNERSHIP - CHANDEL EQUIPMENT RENTALS DIVISION—See Ensign Energy Services Inc.; *Int'l*, pg. 2446
ESI ENERGY SERVICES INC.—See Battery Mineral Resources Corp.; *Int'l*, pg. 890
FARMERS EQUIPMENT COMPANY; *U.S. Private*, pg. 1478
FLORIDA DIRECTIONAL BORING EQUIPMENT & SUPPLIES, INC.—See Spivey Utility Construction Co. Inc.; *U.S. Private*, pg. 3759
F&M MAFCO INC.—See OEP Capital Advisors, L.P.; *U.S. Private*, pg. 2998
FOLEY INCORPORATED; *U.S. Private*, pg. 1558
FOUR SEASON EQUIPMENT; *U.S. Private*, pg. 1582
GAZ METRO PLUS INC.—See Caisse de Depot et Placement du Quebec; *Int'l*, pg. 1256
GENERAL AGGREGATE EQUIPMENT SALES ULC—See General Equipment & Supplies Inc.; *U.S. Private*, pg. 1664
GEODRILL LIMITED—See Geodrill Limited; *Int'l*, pg. 2933
GEORGE P. BANE, INC.; *U.S. Private*, pg. 1682
G.H.M. (GROUP) LIMITED; *Int'l*, pg. 2865
GILES & RANSOME, INC. - ALLENTOWN FACILITY—See Giles & Ransome, Inc.; *U.S. Private*, pg. 1699
GOLD COAST HI-LIFT, INC.—See Skyworks LLC; *U.S. Private*, pg. 3686
GREAT PLAINS OILFIELD RENTAL, L.L.C.—See Patterson-UTI Energy, Inc.; *U.S. Public*, pg. 1654
GREGORY POOLE EQUIPMENT COMPANY INC.—See Panther Summit Industries Inc.; *U.S. Private*, pg. 3087
GSV MATERIELUDLEJNING AS—See Access Capital Partners SA; *Int'l*, pg. 88
GSV MATERIELUDLEJNING AS—See Catacap Management AS; *Int'l*, pg. 1358
GUARDIAN COMPANIES INC.—See Guardian Companies Inc.; *U.S. Private*, pg. 1810
GUAY INC.; *Int'l*, pg. 3171
THE G.W. VAN KEPPEL CO. - OKLAHOMA CITY—See The G.W. Van Keppel Company; *U.S. Private*, pg. 4031
HASPER EQUIPMENT CO.—See Cloverdale Equipment Co.; *U.S. Private*, pg. 948
HEAVY & HIGHWAY INC.—See Trierweiler Construction & Supply Co. Inc.; *U.S. Private*, pg. 4230
H&E EQUIPMENT SERVICES INC. - PHOENIX—See H&E Equipment Services, Inc.; *U.S. Public*, pg. 976
H&E EQUIPMENT SERVICES (MID-ATLANTIC), INC.—See H&E Equipment Services, Inc.; *U.S. Public*, pg. 976
HERC RENTALS INC.—See Herc Holdings Inc.; *U.S. Public*, pg. 1027
HING MING HOLDINGS LIMITED; *Int'l*, pg. 3401
HITACHI CONSTRUCTION MACHINERY JAPAN CO., LTD.—See Hitachi, Ltd.; *Int'l*, pg. 3416
HOLT CAT COMPANY OF TEXAS INC.; *U.S. Private*, pg. 1968
IMPERIAL CRANE SERVICES INC.; *U.S. Private*, pg. 2049
INDUSTRIAL LIFT TRUCK & EQUIPMENT CO., INC.—See Gibson Energy Inc.; *Int'l*, pg. 2963
INTERNATIONAL DIRECTIONAL SERVICES, L.L.C.—See Granite Construction Incorporated; *U.S. Public*, pg. 957
IRON SOURCE, LLC—See Clairvest Group Inc.; *Int'l*, pg. 1641
JOE JOHNSON EQUIPMENT LLC—See Federal Signal Corporation; *U.S. Public*, pg. 826
JOHNSON ACCESS (PROPRIETARY) LIMITED—See Hosken Consolidated Investments Limited; *Int'l*, pg. 3485
JOYCE STEEL ERECTION, LLC—See Berkshire Hathaway Inc.; *U.S. Public*, pg. 309
KELLY TRACTOR CO. INC.; *U.S. Private*, pg. 2277
KIRBY-SMITH MACHINERY INC.; *U.S. Private*, pg. 2314
KOYO KENKI LEASE CO., LTD.—See Aktio Holdings Corporation; *Int'l*, pg. 267
KYN CAPITAL GROUP, INC.; *U.S. Public*, pg. 1278
KYOSEI RENTEMU CO., LTD.—See Aktio Holdings Corporation; *Int'l*, pg. 267
LAMPSON AUSTRALIA PTY LTD—See Lampson International, LLC; *U.S. Private*, pg. 2381
LAMPSON CANADA, LTD—See Lampson International, LLC; *U.S. Private*, pg. 2381
LAMPSON INTERNATIONAL, LLC; *U.S. Private*, pg. 2381
LARAMIE ENTERPRISES, INC.; *U.S. Private*, pg. 2391
LEPPO INC.; *U.S. Private*, pg. 2431
L.E.W. EQUIPMENT CO., INC.—See L.E.W. Holding Co. Inc.; *U.S. Private*, pg. 2365
LIZZY LIFT, INC.—See BigRentz, Inc.; *U.S. Private*, pg. 556
MARCO CRANE & RIGGING CO.; *U.S. Private*, pg. 2571
MARKS CRANE & RIGGING CO. LTD.; *U.S. Private*, pg. 2582
MARR COMPANIES; *U.S. Private*, pg. 2588
MEDICO INDUSTRIES, INC.; *U.S. Private*, pg. 2656
MID SOUTH MACHINERY INC.; *U.S. Private*, pg. 2706
MIDWEST EQUIPMENT LEASING CORP.—See Midco Construction Corporation; *U.S. Private*, pg. 2710
MILESTONE EQUIPMENT HOLDINGS, LLC—See Massachusetts Mutual Life Insurance Company; *U.S. Private*, pg. 2605
MINING, ROCK EXCAVATION & CONSTRUCTION LLC—See Atlas Copco AB; *Int'l*, pg. 681
MORROW EQUIPMENT CO. LLC; *U.S. Private*, pg. 2790
MOULDAGRAPH CORPORATION; *U.S. Private*, pg. 2797
MUSTANG RENTAL SERVICES INC.—See Mustang Tractor & Equipment Company; *U.S. Private*, pg. 2819
NATIONAL PUMP & ENERGY LTD.—See Atlas Copco AB; *Int'l*, pg. 683
NESCO LLC—See Custom Truck One Source, Inc.; *U.S. Public*, pg. 612
NEW-COM INC.; *U.S. Private*, pg. 2913
NOBLE IRON INC.—See Uptake Technologies, LLC; *U.S. Private*, pg. 4313
NOBLE IRON TEXAS—See Uptake Technologies, LLC; *U.S. Private*, pg. 4313
NORCAL RENTAL GROUP LLC; *U.S. Private*, pg. 2935
NORTHERN OFFSHORE LTD.; *U.S. Private*, pg. 2953
NWE MANAGEMENT COMPANY—See Northwestern Engineering Company; *U.S. Private*, pg. 2962
ODESSA PACKER SERVICE, INC.—See Intervale Capital, LLC; *U.S. Private*, pg. 2127
OFFSHORE CRANE & SERVICE COMPANY; *U.S. Private*, pg. 3002
OOO ELMETA—See BLRT Grupp AS; *Int'l*, pg. 1066
OOO ELME TRANS UKRAINE—See BLRT Grupp AS; *Int'l*, pg. 1066
PATTERSON SERVICES, INC.—See RPC, Inc.; *U.S. Public*, pg. 1816
PENHALL COMPANY—See H.I.G. Capital, LLC; *U.S. Private*, pg. 1833
PENHALL CO.—See H.I.G. Capital, LLC; *U.S. Private*, pg. 1833
PI-SYSTEM GMBH—See BKW AG; *Int'l*, pg. 1056
PITNEY BOWES OF CANADA LTD.-LEASING DIVISION—See Pitney Bowes Inc.; *U.S. Public*, pg. 1695
P & J ARCOMET LLC—See Arcomet & Co.; *Int'l*, pg. 550
PLANT IMPROVEMENT CO. INC.; *U.S. Private*, pg. 3197
POWER EQUIPMENT LEASING COMPANY—See Utility Sales & Service, Inc.; *U.S. Private*, pg. 4326
PRECISION DRILLING SERVICES M.E. W.L.L.—See Weatherford International plc; *U.S. Public*, pg. 2339
PRECISION ENERGY SERVICES SAUDI ARABIA CO. LTD.—See Weatherford International plc; *U.S. Public*, pg. 2340
PRIME OPERATING COMPANY—See PrimeEnergy Resources Corporation; *U.S. Public*, pg. 1717
PROCRANE SALES INC.—See Berkshire Hathaway Inc.; *U.S. Public*, pg. 309
PROFESSIONAL PLAYGROUND—See Hesscor, Inc.; *U.S. Private*, pg. 1928
PROVIDENCE CAPITAL FUNDING, INC.; *U.S. Private*, pg. 3291
PT. AKTIO EQUIPMENT INDONESIA—See Aktio Holdings Corporation; *Int'l*, pg. 267
PT. WEATHERFORD INDONESIA—See Weatherford International plc; *U.S. Public*, pg. 2339
RABERN RENTALS, LP—See Manitex International, Inc.; *U.S. Public*, pg. 1356
RAMIRENT A/S—See Access Capital Partners SA; *Int'l*, pg. 88
RAMIRENT A/S—See Catacap Management AS; *Int'l*, pg. 1358
RANSOME RENTS—See Giles & Ransome, Inc.; *U.S. Private*, pg. 1699
REC EQUIPMENT CORP.—See The Rados Companies; *U.S. Private*, pg. 4102
RENTALS UNLIMITED INC.; *U.S. Private*, pg. 3400
REVITRANS, A.S.—See CEZ, a.s.; *Int'l*, pg. 1428
R.H. WHITE CONSTRUCTION COMPANY, INC.—See R.H. White Companies Inc.; *U.S. Private*, pg. 3336
RIG TOOLS, INC.—See Gibson Energy Inc.; *Int'l*, pg. 2963
ROCKY MOUNTAIN STRUCTURES INC.—See First Reserve Management, L.P.; *U.S. Private*, pg. 1526
RUSH PETERBILT TRUCK CENTER—See Rush Enterprises, Inc.; *U.S. Public*, pg. 1826
SAINICHI CO., LTD.—See Aktio Holdings Corporation; *Int'l*, pg. 267
SAMOBA GMBH—See 3U Holding AG; *Int'l*, pg. 10
SGB ALUMA MALAYSIA SDN. BHD.—See Brand Industrial Services, Inc.; *U.S. Private*, pg. 636
SGB ALUMA SINGAPORE PTE. LTD.—See Brand Industrial Services, Inc.; *U.S. Private*, pg. 636
SHANGHAI TAT HONG EQUIPMENT RENTAL CO., LTD.—See Affirma Capital Limited; *Int'l*, pg. 187
SHAWMUT EQUIPMENT COMPANY INC.; *U.S. Private*, pg. 3628
SHEEDY DRAYAGE CO.; *U.S. Private*, pg. 3629
SIA ELME TRANS L—See BLRT Grupp AS; *Int'l*, pg. 1066
SIMS CRANE & EQUIPMENT COMPANY; *U.S. Private*, pg. 3669
SOKUTO CO., LTD.—See Aktio Holdings Corporation; *Int'l*, pg. 267
SOUTHWORTH-MILTON INC.; *U.S. Private*, pg. 3743
SRS CO., LTD.—See Aktio Holdings Corporation; *Int'l*, pg. 267
STAR INDUSTRIES INC.; *U.S. Private*, pg. 3784
STERLING CRANE - CONTRACT LIFTING DIVISION—See Berkshire Hathaway Inc.; *U.S. Public*, pg. 309
STERLING CRANE - RENTALS DIVISION—See Berkshire Hathaway Inc.; *U.S. Public*, pg. 309
STERLING CRANE—See Berkshire Hathaway Inc.; *U.S. Public*, pg. 309
STREIF BAULOGISTIK GMBH—See ACS, Actividades de Construccion y Servicios, S.A.; *Int'l*, pg. 114
SUN WELL SERVICE, INC.—See Steel Partners Holdings L.P.; *U.S. Public*, pg. 1943
SWING STAGING LLC—See Brand Industrial Services, Inc.; *U.S. Private*, pg. 637
TAK CONSTRUCTION, INC.; *U.S. Private*, pg. 3925
TAT HONG HEAVY EQUIPMENT (HONG KONG) LIMITED—See Affirma Capital Limited; *Int'l*, pg. 187
TAT HONG HEAVYLIFT PTE LTD—See Affirma Capital Limited; *Int'l*, pg. 187
TAT HONG (VIETNAM) CO., LTD.—See Affirma Capital Limited; *Int'l*, pg. 187
TECHNI BHARATHI PRIVATE LIMITED—See IGC Pharma, Inc.; *U.S. Public*, pg. 1095
THL FOUNDATION EQUIPMENT PTE. LTD.—See CSC Holdings Limited; *Int'l*, pg. 1863

N.A.I.C.S. INDEX

532490 — OTHER COMMERCIAL AN...

TNT CRANE & RIGGING, INC. - OKLAHOMA CITY—See First Reserve Management, L.P.; *U.S. Private*, pg. 1526
TNT CRANE & RIGGING, INC.—See First Reserve Management, L.P.; *U.S. Private*, pg. 1526
TNT CRANE & RIGGING, INC.—See First Reserve Management, L.P.; *U.S. Private*, pg. 1526
TOPLAK GMBH—See EVN AG; *Int'l*, pg. 2571
TRANSERVICE LEASE CORP.—See ZS Fund L.P.; *U.S. Private*, pg. 4609
TRENCH PLATE RENTAL COMPANY—See Brookfield Corporation; *Int'l*, pg. 1184
TUTT BRYANT GROUP LIMITED - CARADEL HIRE—See Affirma Capital Limited; *Int'l*, pg. 188
TUTT BRYANT HEAVY LIFT & SHIFT—See Affirma Capital Limited; *Int'l*, pg. 188
TUTT BRYANT HEAVY LIFT & SHIFT—See Affirma Capital Limited; *Int'l*, pg. 188
TUTT BRYANT HIRE PORTSMITH—See Affirma Capital Limited; *Int'l*, pg. 188
TUTT BRYANT HIRE—See Affirma Capital Limited; *Int'l*, pg. 188
UNITED RENTALS (NORTH AMERICA), INC.—See United Rentals, Inc.; *U.S. Public*, pg. 2235
UNITED RENTALS NORTHWEST, INC.—See United Rentals, Inc.; *U.S. Public*, pg. 2235
UNITED RENTALS OF CANADA, INC.—See United Rentals, Inc.; *U.S. Public*, pg. 2235
U.S. SHORING & EQUIPMENT CO.—See Road Machinery & Supplies Company; *U.S. Private*, pg. 3453
VALTRA VOUKRAUS OY—See AGCO Corporation; *U.S. Public*, pg. 59
WEATHERFORD INDUSTRIA E COMERCIO LTDA.—See Weatherford International plc; *U.S. Public*, pg. 2340
WEATHERFORD INTERNATIONAL DE ARGENTINA S.A.—See Weatherford International plc; *U.S. Public*, pg. 2340
WEATHERFORD INTERNATIONAL, LLC—See Weatherford International plc; *U.S. Public*, pg. 2340
WEATHERFORD LATIN AMERICA, S.C.A.—See Weatherford International plc; *U.S. Public*, pg. 2340
WEATHERFORD TRINIDAD LIMITED—See Weatherford International plc; *U.S. Public*, pg. 2340
WELLS FARGO EQUIPMENT FINANCE COMPANY—See Wells Fargo & Company; *U.S. Public*, pg. 2346
WELLTONIC ASIA PTE LIMITED—See Hunting Plc; *Int'l*, pg. 3537
WESTERNONE RENTALS & SALES—See United Rentals, Inc.; *U.S. Public*, pg. 2235
WESTERN RENTALS INCORPORATED—See Scott Equipment Incorporated; *U.S. Private*, pg. 3576
WHITE CRANE CO, INC.—See Barnhart Crane & Rigging Co.; *U.S. Private*, pg. 478
WILLIAMS EQUIPMENT CORPORATION—See Williams Industries, Inc.; *U.S. Private*, pg. 4526
WISCO, INC.—See Gibson Energy Inc.; *Int'l*, pg. 2963
W.O. GRUBB STEEL ERECTION INC.; *U.S. Private*, pg. 4422
WORLDWIDE MACHINERY INC.; *U.S. Private*, pg. 4570
YVONNE MOBILIEN-LEASING GMBH—See Asklepios Kliniken GmbH & Co. KGaA; *Int'l*, pg. 623

532420 — OFFICE MACHINERY AND EQUIPMENT RENTAL AND LEASING

ABCOM COMPUTER RENTAL, INC.; *U.S. Private*, pg. 36
AIDA BUSINESS CORP.—See AIDA Engineering, Ltd.; *Int'l*, pg. 230
AJ NETWORKS CO LTD; *Int'l*, pg. 255
APERLEASING SRL—See Econocom Group SA; *Int'l*, pg. 2297
BESTWAY, INC.; *U.S. Private*, pg. 544
BNP PARIBAS LEASE GROUP S.A.—See BNP Paribas SA; *Int'l*, pg. 1085
BTV REAL-LEASING II GMBH—See Bank fur Tirol und Vorarlberg Ag; *Int'l*, pg. 838
CANON PRINT SQUARE INC.—See Canon Inc.; *Int'l*, pg. 1296
CENTIA TECHNOLOGIES SDN BHD—See Digilife Technologies Limited; *Int'l*, pg. 2119
THE CHUGIN LEASE COMPANY, LIMITED—See Chugin Financial Group, Inc.; *Int'l*, pg. 1595
C&L MANAGEMENT INC.; *U.S. Private*, pg. 703
COMMONWEALTH CAPITAL CORP.; *U.S. Private*, pg. 986
COMPRENDIUM STRUCTURED FINANCING GMBH; *Int'l*, pg. 1754
COMPUGEN FINANCE INC.—See Compugen Inc.; *Int'l*, pg. 1755
CONTINENTAL LEASING COMPANY, INC.—See Continental Resources, Inc.; *U.S. Public*, pg. 573
CORINTHIAN LEASING CORPORATION—See Cannae Holdings, Inc.; *U.S. Public*, pg. 429
CORINTHIAN LEASING CORPORATION—See CC Capital Partners, LLC; *U.S. Private*, pg. 798
CORINTHIAN LEASING CORPORATION—See Intercontinental Exchange, Inc.; *U.S. Public*, pg. 1141
CREDITEX - ALUGUER DE EQUIPAMENTOS S.A.—See Xerox Holdings Corporation; *U.S. Public*, pg. 2387
CTS CO., LTD.; *Int'l*, pg. 1872
DYVENTIVE INC.; *U.S. Private*, pg. 1300
ECONOCOM LOCATION SAS—See Econocom Group SA; *Int'l*, pg. 2297
ELECTRO RENT (BEIJING) TEST & MEASUREMENT EQUIPMENT RENTAL CO., LTD.—See Platinum Equity, LLC; *U.S. Private*, pg. 3202
ELECTRO RENT CORPORATION—See Platinum Equity, LLC; *U.S. Private*, pg. 3202
ELECTRO RENT EUROPE NV—See Platinum Equity, LLC; *U.S. Private*, pg. 3202
EPLUS GROUP, INC.—See ePlus Inc.; *U.S. Public*, pg. 784
EPLUS—See ePlus Inc.; *U.S. Public*, pg. 784
EVENT TECHNOLOGY, LLC; *U.S. Private*, pg. 1437
EVOLV SOLUTIONS, LLC; *U.S. Private*, pg. 1443
FINA FINANCE & TRADING CO., LTD.—See Chailease Holding Company Limited; *Int'l*, pg. 1437
FIRST EQUIPMENT CO.; *U.S. Private*, pg. 1517
FIRST TECHNOLOGY CAPITAL, INC.; *U.S. Private*, pg. 1529
FLEXIGROUP (NZ) LTD—See Humm Group Limited; *Int'l*, pg. 3531
FLEXIRENT SPV NO 2 PTY LIMITED—See Humm Group Limited; *Int'l*, pg. 3531
GC CREDIT-BAIL QUEBEC INC.—See Grenke AG; *Int'l*, pg. 3080
GC FACTORING AAF SRL—See Grenke AG; *Int'l*, pg. 3080
GC FINANCIAL SOLUTIONS LTD.—See Grenke AG; *Int'l*, pg. 3080
GC LEASE SINGAPORE PTE. LTD.—See Grenke AG; *Int'l*, pg. 3080
GC LEASING D.O.O.—See Grenke AG; *Int'l*, pg. 3080
GC LEASING MELBOURNE PTY. LTD.—See Grenke AG; *Int'l*, pg. 3080
GC LEASING MIDDLE EAST FZCO—See Grenke AG; *Int'l*, pg. 3080
GC LEASING ONTARIO INC.—See Grenke AG; *Int'l*, pg. 3080
GC LEASING SYDNEY PTY. LTD.—See Grenke AG; *Int'l*, pg. 3080
GF FAKTOR ZRT.—See Grenke AG; *Int'l*, pg. 3080
GL LEASING BRITISH COLUMBIA INC.—See Grenke AG; *Int'l*, pg. 3080
GLORY SERVICE CO., LTD.—See GLORY Ltd.; *Int'l*, pg. 3010
GRENKE ALQUILER S.A—See Grenke AG; *Int'l*, pg. 3080
GRENKE BUSINESS SOLUTIONS GMBH CO. KG—See Grenke AG; *Int'l*, pg. 3081
GRENKE DIGITAL GMBH—See Grenke AG; *Int'l*, pg. 3081
GRENKEFACTORING AG—See Grenke AG; *Int'l*, pg. 3081
GRENKE FINANCE PLC—See Grenke AG; *Int'l*, pg. 3081
GRENKE HRVATSKA D.O.O.—See Grenke AG; *Int'l*, pg. 3081
GRENKELEASING AB—See Grenke AG; *Int'l*, pg. 3081
GRENKELEASING AG—See Grenke AG; *Int'l*, pg. 3081
GRENKELEASING APS—See Grenke AG; *Int'l*, pg. 3081
GRENKELEASING GMBH—See Grenke AG; *Int'l*, pg. 3081
GRENKELEASING OY—See Grenke AG; *Int'l*, pg. 3081
GRENKELEASING SP. Z O.O—See Grenke AG; *Int'l*, pg. 3081
GRENKELEASING S.R.O.—See Grenke AG; *Int'l*, pg. 3081
GRENKELOCATION SARL—See Grenke AG; *Int'l*, pg. 3081
GRENKE LOCATION SAS—See Grenke AG; *Int'l*, pg. 3081
GRENKE LOCAZIONE S.R.L.—See Grenke AG; *Int'l*, pg. 3081
GRENKE RENT S.A.—See Grenke AG; *Int'l*, pg. 3081
GWFACT - INVOICE SOLUTIONS, LDA.—See Grenke AG; *Int'l*, pg. 3081
HAMILTON RENTALS LTD.; *Int'l*, pg. 3238
HEWLETT-PACKARD FINANCIAL SERVICES CANADA COMPANY—See Hewlett Packard Enterprise Company; *U.S. Public*, pg. 1031
HEWLETT-PACKARD FINANCIAL SERVICES (INDIA) PRIVATE LIMITED—See Hewlett Packard Enterprise Company; *U.S. Public*, pg. 1031
HIRE INTELLIGENCE INTERNATIONAL LIMITED; *Int'l*, pg. 3404
HIS EQUIPMENT MARKETING CO.; *U.S. Private*, pg. 1951
INNERWORKINGS DEUTSCHLAND GMBH—See HH Global Group Limited; *Int'l*, pg. 3378
LASALLE SYSTEMS LEASING, INC.—See American Securities LLC; *U.S. Private*, pg. 250
LEWIS BROTHERS LEASING CO. INC.—See Lewis Management Inc.; *U.S. Private*, pg. 2439
MARKETEX COMPUTER CORP.; *U.S. Private*, pg. 2579
MARUZEN SYSTEM SERVICE CO., LTD.—See Dai Nippon Printing Co., Ltd.; *Int'l*, pg. 1916
MCCALL-THOMAS ENGINEERING COMPANY, INC.; *U.S. Private*, pg. 2626
MILNER DOCUMENT PRODUCTS, INC.—See Milner Document Products, Inc.; *U.S. Public*, pg. 2738
M & J ENGINEERS LIMITED—See Gallagher Holdings Ltd.; *Int'l*, pg. 2873
MODULAR DOCUMENT SOLUTIONS, LLC—See Sycamore Partners Management, LP; *U.S. Private*, pg. 3896
NATIONAL MICRO RENTAL; *U.S. Private*, pg. 2859
NORDANIA LEASING—See Danske Bank A/S; *Int'l*, pg. 1969
OCE-DEUTSCHLAND LEASING GMBH—See Canon Inc.; *Int'l*, pg. 1294
PCRC CORP.; *U.S. Private*, pg. 3121
PEREMEX COMPUTER SYSTEMS PVT LTD—See Digilife Technologies Limited; *Int'l*, pg. 2119
POLYVISION NV—See Steelcase Inc.; *U.S. Public*, pg. 1944
PRICE SYSTEMS, LLC—See The Carlyle Group Inc.; *U.S. Public*, pg. 2056
PRICE SYSTEMS LTD.—See The Carlyle Group Inc.; *U.S. Public*, pg. 2056
REARDON OFFICE EQUIPMENT, INC.—See Loffler Companies, Inc.; *U.S. Private*, pg. 2480
RENT-A-PC, INC.—See Abcom Computer Rental, Inc.; *U.S. Private*, pg. 37
RESOLUTE PARTNERS LLC; *U.S. Private*, pg. 3406
REYNA CAPITAL CORPORATION—See The Reynolds & Reynolds Company; *U.S. Private*, pg. 4106
RUSH COMPUTER RENTALS INC.—See Platinum Equity, LLC; *U.S. Private*, pg. 3203
RYUKYU LEASING CO., LTD.—See Bank of The Ryukyus, Ltd.; *Int'l*, pg. 849
SHANGHAI EAST BEST CONVENTION & EXHIBITION MANAGEMENT CO., LTD.—See DLG Exhibitions & Events Corp Ltd.; *Int'l*, pg. 2141
SIA GC LEASING BALTIC—See Grenke AG; *Int'l*, pg. 3081
SOMERSET CAPITAL GROUP, LTD.; *U.S. Private*, pg. 3711
STANDARD DISTRIBUTORS LIMITED—See ANSA McAL Limited; *Int'l*, pg. 477
STANDARD DISTRIBUTORS & SALES BARBADOS LIMITED—See ANSA McAL Limited; *Int'l*, pg. 477
SUBSPLIT SERVICES GROUP, L.P.; *U.S. Private*, pg. 3847
TECHNOLOGY INVESTMENT PARTNERS, LLC—See Pathward Financial, Inc.; *U.S. Public*, pg. 1652
TEMP-POWER, INC.—See Herc Holdings Inc.; *U.S. Public*, pg. 1028
USM CAPITAL, INC.—See U.S. Micro Corporation; *U.S. Private*, pg. 4271
VERMEER MID ATLANTIC, LLC—See All Roads Company; *U.S. Private*, pg. 172
VISUAL TECHNOLOGIES CORP.; *U.S. Private*, pg. 4404
WINMARK CAPITAL CORPORATION—See Winmark Corporation; *U.S. Public*, pg. 2374
XEROX FINANCIAL SERVICES INTERNATIONAL LIMITED—See Xerox Holdings Corporation; *U.S. Public*, pg. 2391
XEROX LEASING DEUTSCHLAND GMBH—See Xerox Holdings Corporation; *U.S. Public*, pg. 2389
XEROX RENTING S.A.U.—See Xerox Holdings Corporation; *U.S. Public*, pg. 2390

532490 — OTHER COMMERCIAL AND INDUSTRIAL MACHINERY AND EQUIPMENT RENTAL AND LEASING

ABACORE CAPITAL HOLDINGS, INC.; *Int'l*, pg. 47
ABLE EQUIPMENT RENTAL, INC.; *U.S. Private*, pg. 39
ABN AMRO LEASE N.V.—See ABN AMRO Group N.V.; *Int'l*, pg. 64
ADTRAN NETWORKS INDIA PRIVATE LIMITED—See ADTRAN Holdings, Inc.; *U.S. Public*, pg. 43
ADVANTEST FINANCE INC—See Advantest Corporation; *Int'l*, pg. 166
AGGREKO, LLC—See I Squared Capital Advisors (US) LLC; *U.S. Private*, pg. 2021
AIGIN LEASE CO., LTD.—See Aichi Financial Group Co., Ltd.; *Int'l*, pg. 229
AIRPORT EQUIPMENT RENTALS INC.; *U.S. Private*, pg. 142
AIRTEL CONGO RDC S.A.—See Airtel Africa Plc; *Int'l*, pg. 249
AIRTEL MONEY TANZANIA LIMITED—See Airtel Africa Plc; *Int'l*, pg. 249
AIRTEL MONEY TRANSFER LIMITED—See Airtel Africa Plc; *Int'l*, pg. 249
ALD AUTOMOTIVE ALGERIE SPA—See ALD Automotive; *Int'l*, pg. 303
ALD AUTOMOTIVE EESTI AS—See ALD Automotive; *Int'l*, pg. 303
ALD AUTOMOTIVE EOOD—See ALD Automotive; *Int'l*, pg. 303
ALD AUTOMOTIVE LIMITADA.—See ALD Automotive; *Int'l*, pg. 303
ALD AUTOMOTIVE PERU S.A.C.—See ALD Automotive; *Int'l*, pg. 303
ALD AUTOMOTIVE S.A.S—See ALD Automotive; *Int'l*, pg. 303
ALD AUTOMOTIVE SIA—See ALD Automotive; *Int'l*, pg. 303
ALD AUTOMOTIVE SLOVAKIA S.R.O—See ALD Automotive; *Int'l*, pg. 303
ALD AUTOMOTIVE SRL—See ALD Automotive; *Int'l*, pg. 303
ALD AUTOMOTIVE UKRAINE LIMITED LIABILITY COMPANY—See ALD Automotive; *Int'l*, pg. 303
ALGHANIM INTERNATIONAL FOR RENTAL EQUIPMENT CO. W.L.L—See Fouad Alghanim & Sons Group of Companies; *Int'l*, pg. 2753
ALINCO SCAFFOLDING RENTAL SERVICE CO.,

532490 — OTHER COMMERCIAL AN...

LTD.—See Alinco Incorporated; *Int'l*, pg. 329
ALINCO SCAFFOLDING (THAILAND) CO., LTD.—See Alinco Incorporated; *Int'l*, pg. 329
ALINCO (THAILAND) CO., LTD.—See Alinco Incorporated; *Int'l*, pg. 329
ALLIANCE FUNDING GROUP, INC.; *U.S. Private*, pg. 182
ALTRAD HAVICO N.V.—See Altrad Investment Authority SAS; *Int'l*, pg. 397
AMECO SERVICES, INC.—See OEP Capital Advisors, L.P.; *U.S. Private*, pg. 2998
AMERICAN EQUIPMENT COMPANY, INC.—See OEP Capital Advisors, L.P.; *U.S. Private*, pg. 2998
ANDARA TOOLS AND PLANT HIRE LTD—See Bryen & Langley Ltd.; *Int'l*, pg. 1201
ASHTEAD GROUP PLC; *Int'l*, pg. 609
ASHTEAD PLANT HIRE CO. LTD.—See Ashtead Group Plc; *Int'l*, pg. 609
ASHTEAD TECHNOLOGY HOLDINGS PLC; *Int'l*, pg. 609
ASHTEAD TECHNOLOGY LTD.—See Ashtead Technology Holdings Plc; *Int'l*, pg. 609
ASPIS LEASING S.A.—See Eurobank Ergasias Services and Holdings S.A.; *Int'l*, pg. 2533
ATEL CAPITAL GROUP; *U.S. Private*, pg. 366
ATLAS COPCO FRANCE SAS—See Atlas Copco AB; *Int'l*, pg. 678
ATLAS COPCO RENTAL EUROPE N.V.—See Atlas Copco AB; *Int'l*, pg. 678
ATLAS COPCO (SHANGHAI) EQUIPMENT RENTAL CO LTD—See Atlas Copco AB; *Int'l*, pg. 677
ATM SYSTEM SP. Z.O.O.—See ATM Grupa S.A.; *Int'l*, pg. 687
A TOOL SHED INC.; *U.S. Private*, pg. 19
AVFX, LLC—See Harbor Beach Capital, LLC; *U.S. Private*, pg. 1858
AZTEC EVENTS & TENTS, INC.—See Milestone Capital, Inc.; *U.S. Private*, pg. 2728
BABYLON PUMP & POWER LIMITED; *Int'l*, pg. 793
BA LEASING BSC, LLC—See Bank of America Corporation; *U.S. Public*, pg. 270
BANCLEASING INC.—See BancVue, Ltd.; *U.S. Private*, pg. 464
BDO RENTAL, INC.—See BDO Unibank, Inc.; *Int'l*, pg. 930
BERTHEL FISHER & CO LEASING—See Berthel Fisher & Company Inc.; *U.S. Private*, pg. 539
BLITZ COMMUNICATIONS GROUP LIMITED—See Viad Corp.; *U.S. Public*, pg. 2290
BLUCHER (AUSTRALIA) PTY. LTD.—See E&A Limited; *Int'l*, pg. 2246
BLUELINE RENTAL, LLC—See United Rentals, Inc.; *U.S. Public*, pg. 2235
BLUEWATER TECHNOLOGIES INC.; *U.S. Private*, pg. 598
BMO HARRIS EQUIPMENT FINANCE COMPANY—See Bank of Montreal; *Int'l*, pg. 846
BNP PARIBAS-DALLAS—See BNP Paribas SA; *Int'l*, pg. 1087
BNP PARIBAS LEASE GROUP GMBH & CO KG—See BNP Paribas SA; *Int'l*, pg. 1085
BNP PARIBAS LEASING CORPORATION—See BNP Paribas SA; *Int'l*, pg. 1087
BNP PARIBAS LEASING SOLUTIONS—See BNP Paribas SA; *Int'l*, pg. 1085
BOB'S BARRICADES INC.; *U.S. Private*, pg. 605
BOEMER RENTAL SERVICES GROUP—See Egeria Capital Management B.V.; *Int'l*, pg. 2323
BOK FINANCIAL EQUIPMENT FINANCE, INC.—See BOK Financial Corporation; *U.S. Public*, pg. 367
BOSTON BARRICADE CO., INC.—See Mosaic Capital Partners; *U.S. Private*, pg. 2792
BPH EQUIPMENT LIMITED—See Balfour Beatty plc; *Int'l*, pg. 807
BRADY A/S—See Brady Corporation; *U.S. Public*, pg. 378
BRADY B.V.—See Brady Corporation; *U.S. Public*, pg. 378
BRADY CORPORATION ASIA PACIFIC PTE. LTD.—See Brady Corporation; *U.S. Public*, pg. 378
BRADY GROUPE S.A.S—See Brady Corporation; *U.S. Public*, pg. 378
BRADY S.R.O.—See Brady Corporation; *U.S. Public*, pg. 379
BRAMBLES ENTERPRISES LIMITED—See Brambles Limited; *Int'l*, pg. 1138
BRIDGE FUNDING GROUP, INC.—See BankUnited, Inc.; *U.S. Public*, pg. 274
BRIGGS EQUIPMENT, INC.—See Sammons Enterprises, Inc.; *U.S. Private*, pg. 3537
BRIGGS EQUIPMENT UK LIMITED—See Sammons Enterprises, Inc.; *U.S. Private*, pg. 3537
BRIGGS EQUIPMENT UK LIMITED—See Sammons Enterprises, Inc.; *U.S. Private*, pg. 3537
BRIN FINANCIAL CORPORATION; *U.S. Private*, pg. 654
BUDCO GROUP, INC.; *U.S. Private*, pg. 679
BULAB REALTY OF MISSOURI, LLC—See Bulab Holdings, Inc.; *U.S. Private*, pg. 684
BULAB REALTY OF TENNESSEE, LLC—See Bulab Holdings, Inc.; *U.S. Private*, pg. 684
BUSINESS ALLIANCE JSC; *Int'l*, pg. 1228
CANON FINANCIAL SERVICES, INC.—See Canon Inc.; *Int'l*, pg. 1297

CAPITAL CITY GROUP, INC.—See Bay Crane Service, Inc.; *U.S. Private*, pg. 492
CENTRAL MISSOURI AGRISERVICE LLC; *U.S. Private*, pg. 822
CENTRON TELECOM INTERNATIONAL HOLDING LTD; *Int'l*, pg. 1414
CENTURION TRUCK RENTAL LTD—See Ballyvesey Holdings Limited; *Int'l*, pg. 809
CFC INVESTMENT COMPANY—See Cincinnati Financial Corporation; *U.S. Public*, pg. 494
CHAILEASE INTERNATIONAL LEASING COMPANY LIMITED—See Chailease Holding Company Limited; *Int'l*, pg. 1436
CHAILEASE INTERNATIONAL TRADING COMPANY LIMITED—See Chailease Holding Company Limited; *Int'l*, pg. 1436
CHAPMAN/LEONARD STUDIO EQUIPMENT, INC.; *U.S. Private*, pg. 850
CHEP AUSTRALIA LIMITED—See Brambles Limited; *Int'l*, pg. 1138
CHEP BENELUX NEDERLAND BV—See Brambles Limited; *Int'l*, pg. 1138
CHEP BENELUX N.V.—See Brambles Limited; *Int'l*, pg. 1138
CHEP CANADA, INC.—See Brambles Limited; *Int'l*, pg. 1138
CHEP CHILE SA—See Brambles Limited; *Int'l*, pg. 1138
CHEP DENMARK—See Brambles Limited; *Int'l*, pg. 1138
CHEP DEUTSCHLAND GMBH—See Brambles Limited; *Int'l*, pg. 1138
CHEP ESPANA SA—See Brambles Limited; *Int'l*, pg. 1138
CHEP FINLAND—See Brambles Limited; *Int'l*, pg. 1138
CHEP FRANCE S.A.—See Brambles Limited; *Int'l*, pg. 1138
CHEP INDIA PVT. LTD.—See Brambles Limited; *Int'l*, pg. 1138
CHEP ITALIA SRL—See Brambles Limited; *Int'l*, pg. 1138
CHEP (MALAYSIA) SDN BHD—See Brambles Limited; *Int'l*, pg. 1138
CHEP MEXICO SA DE CV—See Brambles Limited; *Int'l*, pg. 1138
CHEP NEW ZEALAND—See Brambles Limited; *Int'l*, pg. 1138
CHEP NORWAY—See Brambles Limited; *Int'l*, pg. 1138
CHEP OSTERREICH GMBH—See Brambles Limited; *Int'l*, pg. 1138
CHEP PORTUGAL—See Brambles Limited; *Int'l*, pg. 1138
CHEP SCHWEIZ BV—See Brambles Limited; *Int'l*, pg. 1138
CHEP (SHANGHAI) CO., LTD.—See Brambles Limited; *Int'l*, pg. 1138
CHEP SINGAPORE PTE. LTD.—See Brambles Limited; *Int'l*, pg. 1138
CHEP SWEDEN—See Brambles Limited; *Int'l*, pg. 1139
CHEP UK LIMITED—See Brambles Limited; *Int'l*, pg. 1139
CHEP USA—See Brambles Limited; *Int'l*, pg. 1138
CHINA HUARONG FINANCIAL LEASING CO LTD—See China CITIC Financial Asset Management Co., Ltd.; *Int'l*, pg. 1489
CHS CONTAINER HANDEL GMBH; *Int'l*, pg. 1589
CINELEASE, INC.—See Herc Holdings Inc.; *U.S. Public*, pg. 1028
CITIZENS MECHANICAL SERVICES, LLC—See Citizens Energy Group; *U.S. Private*, pg. 903
CJ LOGGING EQUIPMENT LLC; *U.S. Private*, pg. 908
CLEANAWAY ENTERPRISE COMPANY LIMITED—See Cleanaway Company Limited; *Int'l*, pg. 1654
CLINICHAIN HOLDING B.V.—See ADDvise Group AB; *Int'l*, pg. 136
CLOSE BREWERY RENTALS LIMITED—See Close Brothers Group plc; *Int'l*, pg. 1661
COCA-COLA FOUNTAIN INC.—See The Coca-Cola Company; *U.S. Public*, pg. 2063
COLUMBUS MCKINNON DO BRAZIL LTDA.—See Columbus McKinnon Corporation; *U.S. Public*, pg. 536
COLUMBUS MCKINNON (HANGZHOU) INDUSTRIAL PRODUCTS CO. LTD.—See Columbus McKinnon Corporation; *U.S. Public*, pg. 535
COLUMBUS MCKINNON HUNGARY KFT.—See Columbus McKinnon Corporation; *U.S. Public*, pg. 536
COLUMBUS MCKINNON INDUSTRIAL PRODUCTS GMBH—See Columbus McKinnon Corporation; *U.S. Public*, pg. 535
COLUMBUS MCKINNON INDUSTRIAL PRODUCTS ME FZE—See Columbus McKinnon Corporation; *U.S. Public*, pg. 536
COMMERZ REAL MOBILIENLEASING GMBH—See Commerzbank AG; *Int'l*, pg. 1716
COMPREHENSIVE LEASING CO.; *Int'l*, pg. 1754
COMSYS TSUSAN CO., LTD.—See COMSYS Holdings Corporation; *Int'l*, pg. 1762
CONTRACT ASSOCIATES INC.—See Furniture Marketing Group Inc.; *U.S. Private*, pg. 1624
CONTRACTORS CHOICE EQUIPMENT RENTAL INC.—See J&L Building Materials Inc.; *U.S. Private*, pg. 2154
CONTRACTORS EQUIPMENT INC.—See Mosser Construction Inc.; *U.S. Private*, pg. 2794
COPERION S.R.L.—See Hillenbrand, Inc.; *U.S. Public*, pg. 1036
CRAMO AS—See Cramo Plc; *Int'l*, pg. 1827

THE CRANE LAEM CHABANG CO., LTD.—See Chu Kai Public Company Limited; *Int'l*, pg. 1589
THE CRANE RAYONG CO., LTD.—See Chu Kai Public Company Limited; *Int'l*, pg. 1589
THE CRANE SERVICE CO., LTD.—See Chu Kai Public Company Limited; *Int'l*, pg. 1589
CREATIVE TECHNOLOGY GROUP, INC—See The Carlyle Group Inc.; *U.S. Public*, pg. 2049
CROM EQUIPMENT RENTALS INC.—See The Crom Corporation; *U.S. Public*, pg. 4016
CROSSFIRE SOUND PRODUCTIONS, LLC; *U.S. Private*, pg. 1106
C&T AFFILIATES INC.; *U.S. Private*, pg. 704
CTI TOWERS, INC.—See Melody Investment Advisors LP; *U.S. Private*, pg. 2663
DANE EQUIPMENT LLC—See Dane Construction Inc.; *U.S. Private*, pg. 1153
DEGER VARLIK KIRALAMA A.S.—See Albaraka Turk Katilim Bankasi A.S.; *Int'l*, pg. 293
DENVER WEST LEASING—See Stevinson Automotive Inc.; *U.S. Private*, pg. 3810
DE WIT LAS- EN SNIJTECHNIEK BV—See ABIRD Holding BV; *Int'l*, pg. 62
DIVERSIFIED CAPITAL CREDIT CORP.; *U.S. Private*, pg. 1241
DUSKIN SERVE KYUSU CO., LTD.—See Duskin Co., Ltd.; *Int'l*, pg. 2234
DUSKIN SERVE TOHOKU CO., LTD.—See Duskin Co., Ltd.; *Int'l*, pg. 2234
DUSKIN SERVE TOKAI HOKURIKU CO., LTD.—See Duskin Co., Ltd.; *Int'l*, pg. 2234
THE EIGHTEENTH LEASE CO., LTD.—See Fukuoka Financial Group, Inc.; *Int'l*, pg. 2840
ELIS TEXTIL SERVICE AB—See Eurazeo SE; *Int'l*, pg. 2528
ENERGOINVEST AUTOMATIKA A.D.; *Int'l*, pg. 2421
ENTERPRISE PRODUCTS OPERATING LLC - BEATRICE OFFICE—See Enterprise Products Partners L.P.; *U.S. Public*, pg. 779
EPBIZ CO., LTD.—See EPS Holdings, Inc.; *Int'l*, pg. 2465
EQUILEASE HOLDING CORP.; *U.S. Private*, pg. 1415
EVANS CONSOLES, INC.—See Carl Marks & Co., Inc.; *U.S. Private*, pg. 762
EVENT EQUIPMENT LEASING, LLC—See National Association for Stock Car Auto Racing, Inc.; *U.S. Private*, pg. 2845
EVERGREEN TANK SOLUTIONS, INC.—See WillScot Mobile Mini Holdings Corp.; *U.S. Public*, pg. 2372
FACILITIES BY ADF PLC; *Int'l*, pg. 2600
FARISSIA BTP EURL—See Haulotte Group SA; *Int'l*, pg. 3285
FARM CREDIT LEASING SERVICES CORPORATION—See Federal Farm Credit Banks Funding Corporation; *U.S. Public*, pg. 1487
FASTORQ, LLC—See Superior Energy Services, Inc.; *U.S. Private*, pg. 3877
FJORDS PROCESSING AUSTRALIA PTY LTD—See NOV, Inc.; *U.S. Public*, pg. 1544
FLEXI-VAN LEASING, INC.—See Murdock Holdings, LLC; *U.S. Private*, pg. 2814
FLORENS ASSET MANAGEMENT (USA), LIMITED—See China COSCO Shipping Corporation Limited; *Int'l*, pg. 1492
FOOTHILL ENGINEERING & DEWATERING, INC.—See Crossplane Capital Management LP; *U.S. Private*, pg. 1107
FORD FINANCIAL SERVICES, INC.; *U.S. Private*, pg. 1564
FORTIS LEASE GROUP SERVICES S.A.—See BNP Paribas SA; *Int'l*, pg. 1085
FOX STUDIOS AUSTRALIA PTY LIMITED—See Fox Corporation; *U.S. Public*, pg. 876
FRESENIUS MEDICAL CARE RENAL SERVICES LTD—See Fresenius Medical Care AG; *Int'l*, pg. 2774
FUJITSU AUSTRALIA LTD.—See Fujitsu Limited; *Int'l*, pg. 2833
FUYO GENERAL LEASE (ASIA) PTE. LTD.—See Fuyo General Lease Co., Ltd.; *Int'l*, pg. 2859
FUYO GENERAL LEASE (HK) LIMITED—See Fuyo General Lease Co., Ltd.; *Int'l*, pg. 2859
FUYO GENERAL LEASE (USA) INC.—See Fuyo General Lease Co., Ltd.; *Int'l*, pg. 2859
FUYO LEASE SALES CO., LTD.—See Fuyo General Lease Co., Ltd.; *Int'l*, pg. 2859
GC FACTORING LIMITED—See Grenke AG; *Int'l*, pg. 3080
GC LEASING AZ LLC—See Grenke AG; *Int'l*, pg. 3080
GC LEASING NORWAY AS—See Grenke AG; *Int'l*, pg. 3080
GC LOCACAO DE EQUIPAMENTOS LTDA.—See Grenke AG; *Int'l*, pg. 3080
GC RENT CHILE SPA—See Grenke AG; *Int'l*, pg. 3080
GEARHOUSE ACTIS SAS—See Gravity Media Group Limited; *Int'l*, pg. 3062
GENERAL DE ALQUILER DE MAQUINARIA, S.A.; *Int'l*, pg. 2918
GMDI LEASING CORP.; *U.S. Private*, pg. 1721
GOLDBELL CORPORATION; *Int'l*, pg. 3026
GOLDBELL EQUIPMENT (VIETNAM) CO., LTD—See Goldbell Corporation; *Int'l*, pg. 3027
GOLDBELL LEASING (DALIAN) CO., LTD—See Goldbell Corporation; *Int'l*, pg. 3027

GOLDBELL LEASING PTE LTD—See Goldbell Corporation; *Int'l*, pg. 3027
GOLDBELL LEASING (SHANGHAI) CO., LTD—See Goldbell Corporation; *Int'l*, pg. 3027
GOLDEN LEGAND LEASING & FINANCE LTD.; *Int'l*, pg. 3030
GREENLEAF COMPACTION, INC.—See Waste Management, Inc.; *U.S. Public*, pg. 2331
GRENKEFINANCE N.V.—See Grenke AG; *Int'l*, pg. 3081
GRENKE KIRALAMA LTD. STI.—See Grenke AG; *Int'l*, pg. 3081
GRENKE LEASE SPRL—See Grenke AG; *Int'l*, pg. 3081
GRENKE LEASING LTD.—See Grenke AG; *Int'l*, pg. 3081
GRENKELEASING S.R.O.—See Grenke AG; *Int'l*, pg. 3081
GRENKE RENTING LTD.—See Grenke AG; *Int'l*, pg. 3081
GRENKE RENTING, S.A.—See Grenke AG; *Int'l*, pg. 3081
GRENKE RENTING S.R.L.—See Grenke AG; *Int'l*, pg. 3081
GRIFFIN PUMP & EQUIPMENT, INC.—See Crossplane Capital Management LP; *U.S. Private*, pg. 1107
GROUPE SOLOTECH, INC.; *Int'l*, pg. 3111
GSD DENIZCILIK GAYRIMENKUL INSAAT SANAYI VE TICARET AS—See GSD Holding A.S.; *Int'l*, pg. 3144
HAITONG UNITRUST INTERNATIONAL LEASING CORPORATION—See Feishang Anthracite Resources Limited; *Int'l*, pg. 2632
HANSLER INDUSTRIES; *Int'l*, pg. 3260
HB RENTALS—See Superior Energy Services, Inc.; *U.S. Private*, pg. 3877
HEALTHLINE MEDICAL EQUIPMENT, INC.—See AdaptHealth Corp.; *U.S. Public*, pg. 39
HEF & HIJS NEDERLAND B.V.—See ABIRD Holding BV; *Int'l*, pg. 62
HERKULES S.A.; *Int'l*, pg. 3362
THE HERTZ CORPORATION—See Hertz Global Holdings, Inc.; *U.S. Public*, pg. 1029
HIGHWAY TECHNOLOGIES, INC.—See Wynnchurch Capital, L.P.; *U.S. Private*, pg. 4577
H L EQUIPMENTS INC.—See HLE Glascoat Limited; *Int'l*, pg. 3431
HOLLAND MOUNTING SYSTEMS B.V.—See Brady Corporation; *U.S. Public*, pg. 379
HOLLYWOOD RENTALS PRODUCTION SERVICES LLC; *U.S. Private*, pg. 1966
HOLT TEXAS, LTD.; *U.S. Private*, pg. 1968
HORMANN KMT KOMMUNIKATIONS- UND MELDETECHNIK GMBH—See Hormann Holding GmbH & Co. KG; *Int'l*, pg. 3480
HSS HIRE GROUP PLC—See Exponent Private Equity LLP; *Int'l*, pg. 2589
HUDSON TANK TERMINALS CORPORATION; *U.S. Private*, pg. 2002
HYSTER-YALE UK PENSION CO. LIMITED—See Hyster-Yale Materials Handling, Inc.; *U.S. Public*, pg. 1080
ICE FAR EAST (HK) LIMITED—See CSC Holdings Limited; *Int'l*, pg. 1862
ICE FAR EAST PTE. LTD.—See CSC Holdings Limited; *Int'l*, pg. 1862
ICE FAR EAST SDN. BHD.—See CSC Holdings Limited; *Int'l*, pg. 1862
ICE FAR EAST (THAILAND) CO., LTD.—See CSC Holdings Limited; *Int'l*, pg. 1862
ICS TERMINALS (UK) LIMITED—See Brookfield Infrastructure Partners L.P.; *Int'l*, pg. 1190
IKM LABORATORIUM AS—See IKM Gruppen AS; *Int'l*, pg. 3611
IMT-THL INDIA PRIVATE LIMITED—See CSC Holdings Limited; *Int'l*, pg. 1862
INAG-NIEVERGELT AG—See BKW AG; *Int'l*, pg. 1055
INDIAN NATIONS FIBER OPTICS, INC.—See Chickasaw Holding Company; *U.S. Private*, pg. 880
INDU-TOOLS B.V.—See United Rentals, Inc.; *U.S. Public*, pg. 2235
INDU-TOOLS N.V.—See United Rentals, Inc.; *U.S. Public*, pg. 2235
INDU-TOOLS SAS—See United Rentals, Inc.; *U.S. Public*, pg. 2235
INGERSOLL-RAND FINLAND OY—See Ingersoll Rand Inc.; *U.S. Public*, pg. 1121
INMARSAT LEASING (TWO) LIMITED—See ViaSat, Inc.; *U.S. Public*, pg. 2292
INTERNATIONAL LEASING COMPANY LLC—See Illinois Tool Works Inc.; *U.S. Public*, pg. 1108
IRONGATE ENERGY SERVICES, LLC—See Clearlake Capital Group, L.P.; *U.S. Private*, pg. 935
ITUB AS—See Berry Global Group, Inc; *U.S. Public*, pg. 326
ITUB DANMARK APS—See Berry Global Group, Inc; *U.S. Public*, pg. 326
ITUB EHF—See Berry Global Group, Inc; *U.S. Public*, pg. 322
JLG INDUSTRIES INDIA PRIVATE LIMITED—See Oshkosh Corporation; *U.S. Public*, pg. 1620
JM EQUIPMENT COMPANY INC.; *U.S. Private*, pg. 2213
JORLEASE INC.—See Jordano's, Inc.; *U.S. Private*, pg. 2236
JS LEASING COMPANY INC.—See Slay Industries Inc.; *U.S. Private*, pg. 3687
KAMPHUIS LASTECHNIEK BV—See ABIRD Holding BV; *Int'l*, pg. 62

KDS KOMPRESSOREN- UND DRUCKLUFTSERVICE GMBH—See Atlas Copco AB; *Int'l*, pg. 683
KING CAPITAL CORP.; *U.S. Private*, pg. 2309
KOMATSU TOCHIGI INC.—See Fujii Sangyo Corporation; *Int'l*, pg. 2826
KRAUS-ANDERSON CAPITAL INC—See Kraus-Anderson Incorporated; *U.S. Private*, pg. 2349
LEASE ONE CORP.; *U.S. Private*, pg. 2408
THE LEASING EXPERTS INC.; *U.S. Private*, pg. 4068
LEASING INNOVATIONS INC.; *U.S. Private*, pg. 2408
LIFTONE LLC—See Carolina Tractor &; *U.S. Private*, pg. 769
LIGHT TOWER RENTALS, LLC—See Clearlake Capital Group, L.P.; *U.S. Private*, pg. 935
LONE STAR TANK RENTAL INC.—See United Rentals, Inc.; *U.S. Public*, pg. 2235
LPM FORKLIFT SALES & SERVICE, INC.; *U.S. Private*, pg. 2507
M2 LEASE FUNDS, LLC—See QCR Holdings, Inc.; *U.S. Public*, pg. 1742
MARLIN LEASING CORPORATION—See HPS Investment Partners, LLC; *U.S. Private*, pg. 1997
MAXIM CRANE WORKS, L.P.—See Apollo Global Management, Inc.; *U.S. Public*, pg. 153
MCGRATH RENTCORP.; *U.S. Public*, pg. 1406
MERRION FLEET MANAGEMENT LIMITED—See ALD Automotive; *Int'l*, pg. 303
METRO TRAILER LEASING INC.; *U.S. Private*, pg. 2686
MINING SERVICES LIMITED—See Harworth Group plc; *Int'l*, pg. 3282
MINISTER DONUT TAIWAN CO., LTD.—See Duskin Co., Ltd.; *Int'l*, pg. 2234
MITEL LEASE SA—See Searchlight Capital Partners, L.P.; *U.S. Private*, pg. 3589
MITEL LEASING, INC.—See Searchlight Capital Partners, L.P.; *U.S. Private*, pg. 3589
MMI SERVICES LLC—See Mining Machinery Inc.; *U.S. Private*, pg. 2742
MOBILE STEAM BOILER RENTAL CORP.—See Miller Proctor Nickolas Inc.; *U.S. Private*, pg. 2735
MONGOLIA HOLDINGS, INC.; *U.S. Private*, pg. 2770
MOR-SON LEASING INC.—See Morrison Industrial Equipment Company; *U.S. Private*, pg. 2789
MOUNTAIN PRODUCTIONS, INC.; *U.S. Private*, pg. 2799
MULTIAIR BELUX NV—See Atlas Copco AB; *Int'l*, pg. 683
NATIONAL LEASING GROUP INC.—See Canadian Western Bank; *Int'l*, pg. 1287
NATIONAL TRENCH SAFETY, LLC—See Brookfield Corporation; *Int'l*, pg. 1184
NEPTUNE PLANT HIRE (PTY) LIMITED—See enX Group Limited; *Int'l*, pg. 2456
NEW JAPAN MACHINERY CO. LTD.—See Denyo Co., Ltd.; *Int'l*, pg. 2040
NF FLEET AB—See ALD Automotive; *Int'l*, pg. 303
NF FLEET AS—See ALD Automotive; *Int'l*, pg. 303
NF FLEET A/S—See ALD Automotive; *Int'l*, pg. 303
NF FLEET OY—See ALD Automotive; *Int'l*, pg. 303
OMA-VYNMSA AERO INDUSTRIAL PARK, S.A. DE C.V.—See Grupo Aeroportuario del Centro Norte, S.A.B. de C.V.; *Int'l*, pg. 3118
OMEGA/CINEMA PROPS INC.; *U.S. Private*, pg. 3015
ON SERVICES HOUSTON—See Viad Corp.; *U.S. Public*, pg. 2291
OSLO STILLASUTLEIE AS—See AF Gruppen ASA; *Int'l*, pg. 184
PACIFIC MOBILE STRUCTURES INC.—See Pacific Mobile Structures Inc.; *U.S. Private*, pg. 3068
PACKAGING LEASING SYSTEMS INC.—See Illinois Tool Works Inc.; *U.S. Public*, pg. 1110
PASKAL LIGHTING, INC.—See The Jordan Company, L.P.; *U.S. Private*, pg. 4061
PATIENTLINE EXPLOITATIE BV—See Marlin Equity Partners, LLC; *U.S. Private*, pg. 2584
PAWNEE LEASING CORPORATION—See Chesswood Group Limited; *Int'l*, pg. 1472
PECO PALLET, INC.—See The Pritzker Group - Chicago, LLC; *U.S. Private*, pg. 4099
PEOPLE'S CAPITAL & LEASING CORP.—See M&T Bank Corporation; *U.S. Public*, pg. 1351
PFAFF BETEILIGUNGS GMBH—See Columbus McKinnon Corporation; *U.S. Public*, pg. 536
PHILIPPINE GAMING MANAGEMENT CORPORATION—See Berjaya Corporation Berhad; *Int'l*, pg. 983
PIEDMONT POWER, LLC—See Piedmont Office Realty Trust, Inc.; *U.S. Public*, pg. 1690
PIPELINE SUPPLY & SERVICE HOLDINGS, LLC—See Cadent Energy Partners, LLC; *U.S. Private*, pg. 713
PM CENTER CO., LTD.—See CMO Public Company Limited; *Int'l*, pg. 1671
PRIORITY LEASING, INC.; *U.S. Private*, pg. 3266
PRODUCTION RESOURCE GROUP LLC—See The Jordan Company, L.P.; *U.S. Private*, pg. 4061
PROGRESS RAIL EQUIPMENT LEASING CORPORATION—See Paceline Equity Partners LLC; *U.S. Private*, pg. 3064
QUEST BUILDING PRODUCTS INC—See Incline MGMT Corp.; *U.S. Private*, pg. 2053

RAC ACCEPTANCE EAST, LLC—See Upbound Group, Inc.; *U.S. Public*, pg. 2263
RAC MEXICO OPERACIONES, S. DE R.L. DE C.V.—See Upbound Group, Inc.; *U.S. Public*, pg. 2263
RAND AIR SOUTH AFRICA PTY LTD—See Atlas Copco AB; *Int'l*, pg. 684
RAPID MANUFACTURING, LCR; *U.S. Private*, pg. 3356
REGAL AUSTRALIA PTY LTD—See Regal Rexnord Corporation; *U.S. Public*, pg. 1773
RENTAL MAX LLC; *U.S. Private*, pg. 3400
RIVER BEND MATERIALS INC.—See GMS Inc.; *U.S. Public*, pg. 948
RMS RENTALS COMPANY—See Road Machinery & Supplies Company; *U.S. Private*, pg. 3453
RNI-DALBO—See Lincolnshire Management, Inc.; *U.S. Private*, pg. 2459
ROBYN MEREDITH, INC.; *U.S. Private*, pg. 3463
ROMLIFT SERV S.R.L.—See Group Thermote & Vanhalst; *Int'l*, pg. 3089
RPC ENERGY SERVICES OF CANADA, LTD—See RPC, Inc.; *U.S. Public*, pg. 1816
SAM HIRE LIMITED—See Grafton Group plc; *Int'l*, pg. 3051
SCAFFOLDING RENTAL & ERECTION SERVICES, LLC—See Bernhard Capital Partners Management, LP; *U.S. Private*, pg. 537
SCAFFOLDING RENTAL & ERECTION SERVICES, LLC—See KBR, Inc.; *U.S. Public*, pg. 1216
SEA FIBRE NETWORKS LIMITED—See Digital 9 Infrastructure Plc; *Int'l*, pg. 2120
SHINTECHNO CORPORATION—See Aktio Holdings Corporation; *Int'l*, pg. 267
SHOPCO LEASING INC—See BHX Inc.; *U.S. Private*, pg. 549
SKYWORKS LLC; *U.S. Private*, pg. 3686
SPEECH DESIGN CARRIER SYSTEMS GMBH—See Bogen Communications International Inc.; *U.S. Public*, pg. 367
SPS INDUSTRIAL INC.; *U.S. Private*, pg. 3765
S&S SUPPLIES AND SOLUTIONS, INC.—See Littlejohn & Co., LLC; *U.S. Private*, pg. 2472
STRATES HOLDING CORP—See Strates Enterprises Inc.; *U.S. Private*, pg. 3837
SUB SURFACE TOOLS, LLC—See Superior Energy Services, Inc.; *U.S. Private*, pg. 3877
SUMMIT COMMERCIAL FINANCE COMPANY—See Mintaka Financial, LLC; *U.S. Private*, pg. 2745
SUNBELT RENTALS, INC.—See Ashtead Group Plc; *Int'l*, pg. 609
SWIFTY GLOBAL; *U.S. Public*, pg. 1968
SYSCO ARIZONA LEASING, INC.—See Sysco Corporation; *U.S. Public*, pg. 1975
TAT HONG PLANT LEASING PTE LTD—See Affirma Capital Limited; *Int'l*, pg. 187
TAYCOR LLC; *U.S. Private*, pg. 3937
TELAG AG—See Capita plc; *Int'l*, pg. 1309
TELEASSETS CO., LTD.—See Charoen Pokphand Group Co., Ltd.; *Int'l*, pg. 1453
TEMP-AIR, INC.; *U.S. Private*, pg. 3963
TETRA FINANCIAL SERVICES, INC.—See TETRA Technologies, Inc.; *U.S. Public*, pg. 2024
TEXADIA SYSTEMS LLC; *U.S. Private*, pg. 3974
TEXAS UNITED SUPPLY COMPANY INC.—See United Salt Corporation; *U.S. Private*, pg. 4297
TEXTRON FINANCIAL CORPORATION—See Textron Inc.; *U.S. Public*, pg. 2029
THL FOUNDATION EQUIPMENT (MYANMAR) COMPANY LIMITED—See CSC Holdings Limited; *Int'l*, pg. 1862
THL FOUNDATION EQUIPMENT (PHILIPPINES) INC.—See CSC Holdings Limited; *Int'l*, pg. 1863
THL VIETNAM COMPANY LIMITED—See CSC Holdings Limited; *Int'l*, pg. 1863
TOOLSRENT24 VERMIETUNGS- UND HANDELSGESELLSCHAFT MBH—See United Rentals, Inc.; *U.S. Public*, pg. 2235
TRAFCON INC.—See Constructors Inc.; *U.S. Private*, pg. 1025
TRANSAMERICA LIFE INSURANCE OF NEW YORK—See Aegon N.V.; *Int'l*, pg. 174
TRANSPORT ENTERPRISE LEASING, LLC—See Covenant Logistics Group, Inc.; *U.S. Public*, pg. 588
TRANSPOSAFE SYSTEMS HOLLAND B.V.—See Brady Corporation; *U.S. Public*, pg. 379
TRANSPOSAFE SYSTEMS POLSKA SP. Z.O.O.—See Brady Corporation; *U.S. Public*, pg. 379
TREMONT GROUP, INC.; *U.S. Private*, pg. 4218
TRINITY VALLEY ELECTRIC COOP (CEDAR CREEK SUB-OFFICE)—See Trinity Valley Electric Coop; *U.S. Private*, pg. 4236
TRITON CONTAINER INTERNATIONAL B.V.—See Brookfield Infrastructure Partners L.P.; *Int'l*, pg. 1190
TRITON CONTAINER INTERNATIONAL, GMBH—See Brookfield Infrastructure Partners L.P.; *Int'l*, pg. 1190
TRITON CONTAINER INTERNATIONAL LIMITED—See Brookfield Infrastructure Partners L.P.; *Int'l*, pg. 1190
TRITON CONTAINER SOUTH AFRICA (PTY) LTD—See Brookfield Infrastructure Partners L.P.; *Int'l*, pg. 1190
TRITON CONTAINER (S) PTE LTD—See Brookfield Infrastructure Partners L.P.; *Int'l*, pg. 1190

532490 — OTHER COMMERCIAL AN...

TRITON CONTAINER SUL AMERICANA-TRANSPORTE E COMERCIO LTDA.—See Brookfield Infrastructure Partners L.P.; *Int'l*, pg. 1190
TRITON CONTAINER UK LIMITED—See Brookfield Infrastructure Partners L.P.; *Int'l*, pg. 1190
TRITON INTERNATIONAL AUSTRALIA PTY LTD—See Brookfield Infrastructure Partners L.P.; *Int'l*, pg. 1190
TRITON INTERNATIONAL LIMITED—See Brookfield Infrastructure Partners L.P.; *Int'l*, pg. 1189
TRITON ITALY S.R.L.—See Brookfield Infrastructure Partners L.P.; *Int'l*, pg. 1190
TRITON LIMITED—See Brookfield Infrastructure Partners L.P.; *Int'l*, pg. 1190
TRS-RENTELCO INC.—See McGrath RentCorp.; *U.S. Public*, pg. 1407
TURNER EQUIPMENT DIVISION—See Turner Industries Group, L.L.C.; *U.S. Private*, pg. 4260
TURNER INDUSTRIES—See Turner Industries Group, L.L.C.; *U.S. Private*, pg. 4260
TURNER SCAFFOLDING SERVICES—See Turner Industries Group, L.L.C.; *U.S. Private*, pg. 4261
TYGA-BOX SYSTEMS, INC.; *U.S. Private*, pg. 4267
TYO TECHNICAL RANCH INC.—See AOI TYO Holdings Inc.; *Int'l*, pg. 488
TYSAN MACHINERY HIRE LIMITED—See Blackstone Inc.; *U.S. Public*, pg. 351
UAB ALD AUTOMOTIVE—See ALD Automotive; *Int'l*, pg. 304
UNITED RENTALS BELGIUM BV—See United Rentals, Inc.; *U.S. Public*, pg. 2235
UNITED RENTALS GMBH—See United Rentals, Inc.; *U.S. Public*, pg. 2235
UNITED RENTALS INTERNATIONAL B.V.—See United Rentals, Inc.; *U.S. Public*, pg. 2235
UNITEK SOLVENT SERVICES INC.; *U.S. Private*, pg. 4302
UNIVERSAL BUILDERS SUPPLY LTD.—See Universal Builders Supply, Inc.; *U.S. Private*, pg. 4304
USA HOIST CO., INC.—See Mid-American Elevator Equipment Co., Inc.; *U.S. Private*, pg. 2707
VARILEASE TECHNOLOGY FINANCE GROUP INC.; *U.S. Private*, pg. 4347
VIKING FINANCIAL SERVICES INC.—See Viking Engineering and Development Incorporated; *U.S. Private*, pg. 4382
WEDBUSH LEASING, INC.—See Wedbush Capital Partners; *U.S. Private*, pg. 4468
WEST COAST ENERGY SYSTEMS LLC—See Generac Holdings Inc.; *U.S. Public*, pg. 913
WESTERN OILFIELDS SUPPLY CO.; *U.S. Private*, pg. 4495
WESTROCK SERVICES POLAND SP.Z O.O.—See WestRock Company; *U.S. Public*, pg. 2363
WHOLESALE EQUIPMENT OF FRESNO; *U.S. Private*, pg. 4514
WIDE SHINE DEVELOPMENT LIMITED—See China Merchants Group Limited; *Int'l*, pg. 1523
WINDSOR SERVICE, INC.—See Haines & Kibblehouse Inc.; *U.S. Private*, pg. 1841
WORKSTRINGS INTERNATIONAL, L.L.C.—See Superior Energy Services, Inc.; *U.S. Private*, pg. 3877
WORKSTRINGS, LLC—See Superior Energy Services, Inc.; *U.S. Private*, pg. 3877
WORLDWIDE POWER PRODUCTS, LLC; *U.S. Private*, pg. 4570
XEROX FINANCE LIMITED—See Xerox Holdings Corporation; *U.S. Public*, pg. 2390
YALE LIFTING & MINING PRODUCTS (PTY.) LTD.—See Columbus McKinnon Corporation; *U.S. Public*, pg. 536
YF LEASING CO., LTD.—See Fuyo General Lease Co., Ltd.; *Int'l*, pg. 2859
ZEP INDUSTRIES N.V.—See New Mountain Capital, LLC; *U.S. Private*, pg. 2904
ZEP ITALIA S.R.L.—See New Mountain Capital, LLC; *U.S. Private*, pg. 2904
ZOHARI LEASING LIMITED—See Centum Investment Company Limited; *Int'l*, pg. 1416

533110 — LESSORS OF NONFINANCIAL INTANGIBLE ASSETS (EXCEPT COPYRIGHTED WORKS)

ABM FRANCHISING GROUP, LLC—See ABM Industries, Inc.; *U.S. Public*, pg. 25
ABRA FRANCHISE SERVICES LP—See Hellman & Friedman LLC; *U.S. Private*, pg. 1907
ACCORD INC.; *U.S. Private*, pg. 53
ALAMEDA JUICE LLC; *U.S. Private*, pg. 149
ALLIANCE FRANCHISE BRANDS LLC; *U.S. Private*, pg. 182
ALTERNATIF FINANSAL KIRALAMA AS; *Int'l*, pg. 391
ANCHOR WALL SYSTEMS—See CRH plc; *Int'l*, pg. 1845
APEX GLOBAL BRANDS INC.; *U.S. Private*, pg. 292
ARTHUR MURRAY ENTERPRISES, INC.—See Arthur Murray International, Inc.; *U.S. Private*, pg. 342
ARTHUR MURRAY INTERNATIONAL, INC.; *U.S. Private*, pg. 342
ASHLEY HOMESTORES, LTD.—See Ashley Furniture Industries, Inc.; *U.S. Private*, pg. 350
A SQUARED ENTERTAINMENT LLC—See Kartoon Studios, Inc.; *U.S. Public*, pg. 1214
ATARI, INC.—See Atari, SA; *Int'l*, pg. 666
ATWORKGROUP LLC; *U.S. Private*, pg. 384
AUDIOMICRO, INC.—See Zealot Networks, Inc.; *U.S. Private*, pg. 4598
AUTHENTIC BRANDS GROUP LLC—See Leonard Green & Partners, L.P.; *U.S. Private*, pg. 2424
AWI LICENSING COMPANY—See Armstrong World Industries, Inc.; *U.S. Public*, pg. 194
BASKIN-ROBBINS FRANCHISING LLC—See Roark Capital Group Inc.; *U.S. Private*, pg. 3455
BCT INTERNATIONAL, INC.; *U.S. Private*, pg. 500
BENESSE MUSIC PUBLISHING CO.—See EQT AB; *Int'l*, pg. 2467
BILL BLASS GROUP, LLC; *U.S. Private*, pg. 556
BLUE CROSS & BLUE SHIELD ASSOCIATION; *U.S. Private*, pg. 586
BMG RIGHTS MANAGEMENT GMBH—See Bertelsmann SE & Co. KGaA; *Int'l*, pg. 990
BOWMO, INC.; *U.S. Public*, pg. 377
BRIGHT & BEAUTIFUL UK LIMITED—See Harvest Partners L.P.; *U.S. Private*, pg. 1877
BRIGHTSTAR FRANCHISING LLC; *U.S. Private*, pg. 653
BROADCAST MUSIC INC.—See New Mountain Capital, LLC; *U.S. Private*, pg. 2900
BUFFALO'S FRANCHISE CONCEPTS, INC.—See Fog Cutter Capital Group Inc.; *U.S. Private*, pg. 1556
BU HOLDINGS, LLC—See Tregaron Management, LLC; *U.S. Private*, pg. 4217
CEJA CORPORATION; *U.S. Private*, pg. 806
CENTUM FINANCIAL GROUP INC.—See Charlwood Pacific Group; *Int'l*, pg. 1450
CENTURY 21 CANADA LIMITED PARTNERSHIP—See Charlwood Pacific Group; *Int'l*, pg. 1450
CENTURY 21 REAL ESTATE LLC—See Anywhere Real Estate Inc.; *U.S. Public*, pg. 140
CERTAPRO PAINTERS, LTD.—See FirstService Corporation; *Int'l*, pg. 2691
CHAILEASE FINANCE INTERNATIONAL CORP.—See Chailease Holding Company Limited; *Int'l*, pg. 1436
CHOICE HOTELS INTERNATIONAL SERVICES CORP—See Choice Hotels International, Inc.; *U.S. Public*, pg. 490
C & I LEASING PLC; *Int'l*, pg. 1237
CLOCKWORK, INC.—See Apax Partners LLP; *Int'l*, pg. 502
COLLECTIVE LICENSING INTERNATIONAL, LLC—See Payless Holdings LLC; *U.S. Private*, pg. 3117
COLOR ME MINE FRANCHISING, INC.—See Color Me Mine Enterprises, Inc.; *U.S. Private*, pg. 973
COOKIES BY DESIGN, INC.; *U.S. Private*, pg. 1039
COUNTRY INNS & SUITES BY CARLSON INC.—See Carlson Companies Inc.; *U.S. Private*, pg. 764
COVERALL NORTH AMERICA, INC.; *U.S. Private*, pg. 1072
CRUISESHIPCENTERS INTERNATIONAL INC.—See Expedia Group, Inc.; *U.S. Public*, pg. 809
CRUISESHIPCENTERS USA INC.—See Expedia Group, Inc.; *U.S. Public*, pg. 809
DAIDO SHIZAI SERVICE CO., LTD.—See Daido Steel Co., Ltd.; *Int'l*, pg. 1923
DASHGO, INC.—See Zealot Networks, Inc.; *U.S. Private*, pg. 4599
DICK SMITH ELECTRONICS FRANCHISING PTY. LTD.—See Anchorage Capital Partners Pty. Limited; *Int'l*, pg. 448
DIPPIN' DOTS FRANCHISING, LLC—See J&J Snack Foods Corporation; *U.S. Public*, pg. 1179
DISTRIBUTION ROYALTY INC.; *U.S. Private*, pg. 1239
DOLBY LABORATORIES LICENSING CORPORATION—See Dolby Laboratories, Inc.; *U.S. Public*, pg. 672
DOUBLE P CORPORATION; *U.S. Private*, pg. 1266
DUNKIN' BRANDS, INC.—See Roark Capital Group Inc.; *U.S. Private*, pg. 3455
DUNKIN' DONUTS LLC—See Roark Capital Group Inc.; *U.S. Private*, pg. 3455
DURACLEAN INTERNATIONAL, INC.; *U.S. Private*, pg. 1292
D.V.F. STUDIO; *U.S. Private*, pg. 1143
EAST OF CHICAGO PIZZA INC.; *U.S. Private*, pg. 1317
ERA FRANCHISE SYSTEMS LLC—See Anywhere Real Estate Inc.; *U.S. Public*, pg. 141
FAMILY INNS OF AMERICA, INC.; *U.S. Private*, pg. 1470
FASTSIGNS INTERNATIONAL, INC.—See Freeman Spogli & Co. Incorporated; *U.S. Private*, pg. 1606
FASTSIGNS INTERNATIONAL, INC.—See LightBay Management, LLC; *U.S. Private*, pg. 2452
FIP PORTUGAL, UNIPESSOAL, LDA.—See Frontier IP Group plc; *Int'l*, pg. 2795
FLOOR COVERINGS INTERNATIONAL, LTD.—See FirstService Corporation; *Int'l*, pg. 2691
FRANCHISE SERVICES, INC.—See KOA Holdings Inc.; *U.S. Private*, pg. 2325
FRONTIER IP GROUP PLC; *Int'l*, pg. 2795
FTI FOODTECH INTERNATIONAL INC.; *Int'l*, pg. 2800
FUN-BRANDS HQ CAROUSEL, LLC—See Tregaron Management, LLC; *U.S. Private*, pg. 4217
GAC FRANCHISING, LLC—See Fog Cutter Capital Group Inc.; *U.S. Private*, pg. 1557
GALARDI GROUP, INC.; *U.S. Private*, pg. 1636
GALAXY BRANDS LLC—See Sequential Brands Group, Inc.; *U.S. Public*, pg. 1868
GARAGETEK INC.; *U.S. Private*, pg. 1642
GEOFFREY, LLC—See WHP Global; *U.S. Public*, pg. 4515
GLOBAL PET FOOD STORES INC.—See Franchise Bancorp Inc.; *Int'l*, pg. 2760
GOIN' POSTAL FRANCHISE CORPORATION; *U.S. Private*, pg. 1726
GOLDEN ROYAL DEVELOPMENT, INC.; *U.S. Private*, pg. 1733
HALK FINANSAL KIRALAMA A.S.; *Int'l*, pg. 3229
HOLLYWOOD TANNING SYSTEMS, INC.; *U.S. Private*, pg. 1966
HOME INSTEAD SENIOR CARE; *U.S. Private*, pg. 1971
HOWARD JOHNSON INTERNATIONAL, INC.—See Travel & Leisure Co.; *U.S. Public*, pg. 2185
HUARONG FINANCIAL LEASING CO., LTD.—See China CITIC Financial Asset Management Co., Ltd.; *Int'l*, pg. 1489
ICONIX LATIN AMERICA LLC—See Iconix Acquisition LLC; *U.S. Private*, pg. 2033
IHOP PROPERTY LEASING, LLC—See Dine Brands Global, Inc.; *U.S. Public*, pg. 667
INDUSTRIEVERWALTUNGSGESELLSCHAFT CHAM AG—See Cham Group AG; *Int'l*, pg. 1439
INFOGROUP LICENSING—See CCMP Capital Advisors, LP; *U.S. Private*, pg. 800
INSIGNIAM PERFORMANCE, L.P.—See Elixirr International plc; *Int'l*, pg. 2363
INSTANTWHIP FOODS, INC.; *U.S. Private*, pg. 2092
INTERNATIONAL CENTER FOR ENTREPRENEURIAL DEVELOPMENT, INC.; *U.S. Private*, pg. 2115
INTROMARK, INC.—See Technosystems Consolidated Corporation; *U.S. Private*, pg. 3956
INVENTERGY, INC.—See Inventergy Global, Inc.; *U.S. Public*, pg. 1161
IPR LICENSING, INC.—See InterDigital, Inc.; *U.S. Public*, pg. 1144
IPVALUE MANAGEMENT, INC.—See Vector Capital Management, L.P.; *U.S. Private*, pg. 4351
JANI KING FRANCHISING, INC.—See Jani-King International, Inc.; *U.S. Private*, pg. 2186
JANI KING, INC.—See Jani-King International, Inc.; *U.S. Private*, pg. 2187
JANI KING LEASING CORP.—See Jani-King International, Inc.; *U.S. Private*, pg. 2187
JANI KING OF CALIFORNIA, INC.—See Jani-King International, Inc.; *U.S. Private*, pg. 2187
JANI KING OF CINCINNATI, INC.—See Jani-King International, Inc.; *U.S. Private*, pg. 2187
JANI KING OF CLEVELAND, INC.—See Jani-King International, Inc.; *U.S. Private*, pg. 2187
JANI KING OF COLORADO, INC.—See Jani-King International, Inc.; *U.S. Private*, pg. 2187
JANI KING OF FLORIDA, INC.—See Jani-King International, Inc.; *U.S. Private*, pg. 2187
JANI KING OF HARTFORD, INC.—See Jani-King International, Inc.; *U.S. Private*, pg. 2187
JANI KING OF MIAMI, INC.—See Jani-King International, Inc.; *U.S. Private*, pg. 2187
JANI KING OF MICHIGAN, INC.—See Jani-King International, Inc.; *U.S. Private*, pg. 2187
JANI KING OF NEW JERSEY, INC.—See Jani-King International, Inc.; *U.S. Private*, pg. 2187
JANI KING OF OKLAHOMA, INC.—See Jani-King International, Inc.; *U.S. Private*, pg. 2187
JANI KING OF PHILADELPHIA, INC.—See Jani-King International, Inc.; *U.S. Private*, pg. 2187
JANI KING OF ST. LOUIS, INC.—See Jani-King International, Inc.; *U.S. Private*, pg. 2187
JANI KING OF WASHINGTON D.C., INC.—See Jani-King International, Inc.; *U.S. Private*, pg. 2187
JAZZERCISE, INC.; *U.S. Private*, pg. 2193
JEWELRY REPAIR ENTERPRISES, INC.; *U.S. Private*, pg. 2205
JIMMY JOHN'S FRANCHISOR SPV, LLC—See Roark Capital Group Inc.; *U.S. Private*, pg. 3455
JM DIGITAL WORKS—See Jazzercise, Inc.; *U.S. Private*, pg. 2193
KITCHEN INVESTMENT GROUP; *U.S. Private*, pg. 2316
KOA HOLDINGS INC.; *U.S. Private*, pg. 2325
LAMP POST FRANCHISE CORPORATION; *U.S. Private*, pg. 2380
LA ROSA'S, INC.; *U.S. Private*, pg. 2369
LAWN DOCTOR INC.; *U.S. Private*, pg. 2401
LEARFIELD COMMUNICATIONS, LLC—See Atairos Group, Inc.; *U.S. Private*, pg. 363
LEARFIELD LICENSING PARTNERS, LLC—See Atairos Group, Inc.; *U.S. Private*, pg. 363
LEE & ASSOCIATES LICENSING AND ADMINISTRATION CO., LP; *U.S. Private*, pg. 2411
LIVE NATION MERCHANDISE INC.—See Live Nation Entertainment, Inc.; *U.S. Public*, pg. 1329

N.A.I.C.S. INDEX

LIVING LIGHTING INC.—See Franchise Bancorp Inc.; *Int'l*, pg. 2760
LYNX FRANCHISING, LLC—See MidOcean Partners, LLP; *U.S. Private*, pg. 2717
MAGGIEMOO'S FRANCHISING, LLC—See Fog Cutter Capital Group Inc.; *U.S. Private*, pg. 1557
THE MAIDS INTERNATIONAL, LLC—See Gladstone Management Corporation; *U.S. Private*, pg. 1705
MARBLE SLAB FRANCHISING, LLC—See Fog Cutter Capital Group Inc.; *U.S. Private*, pg. 1557
MAZZIO'S CORPORATION; *U.S. Private*, pg. 2623
MCDONALD'S INTERNATIONAL—See McDonald's Corporation; *U.S. Public*, pg. 1406
MICROSOFT LICENSING, GP—See Microsoft Corporation; *U.S. Public*, pg. 1441
MICROSOFT SERVER & TOOLS DIVISION—See Microsoft Corporation; *U.S. Public*, pg. 1441
MIGHTY DISTRIBUTING SYSTEM OF AMERICA; *U.S. Private*, pg. 2724
MINUTEMAN PRESS INTERNATIONAL, INC.; *U.S. Private*, pg. 2745
MOSAIC IMMUNOENGINEERING, INC.; *U.S. Public*, pg. 1477
MPEG LA LLC; *U.S. Private*, pg. 2804
MRS. FIELDS FAMOUS BRANDS, LLC—See Capricorn Holdings, Inc.; *U.S. Private*, pg. 745
MTI ENTERPRISES INC.; *U.S. Private*, pg. 2809
MUSCLE MAKER FRANCHISING LLC—See American Restaurant Holdings, Inc.; *U.S. Private*, pg. 246
NATIONAL FOOTBALL LEAGUE PLAYERS INCORPORATED—See National Football League Players Association; *U.S. Private*, pg. 2854
NAVAJO PIPELINE GP, LLC—See HF Sinclair Corporation; *U.S. Public*, pg. 1034
NAVAJO PIPELINE LP, LLC—See HF Sinclair Corporation; *U.S. Public*, pg. 1034
NAVAJO SOUTH, INC.—See HF Sinclair Corporation; *U.S. Public*, pg. 1034
NEIGHBORLY, INC.—See Harvest Partners L.P.; *U.S. Private*, pg. 1876
NEW HORIZONS COMPUTER LEARNING CENTERS, INC.—See Camden Partners Holdings, LLC; *U.S. Private*, pg. 728
PACPIZZA LLC; *U.S. Private*, pg. 3073
THE PASTA HOUSE COMPANY FRANCHISES, INC.—See The Pasta House Co.; *U.S. Private*, pg. 4091
PAUL DAVIS RESTORATION, INC.—See FirstService Corporation; *Int'l*, pg. 2691
PICK-UPS PLUS, INC.; *U.S. Public*, pg. 1690
PIGGLY WIGGLY, LLC—See C&S Wholesale Grocers, Inc.; *U.S. Private*, pg. 704
PINCH A PENNY, INC.; *U.S. Private*, pg. 3181
PIZZA PAN GROUP PTY. LTD.—See Allegro Funds Pty. Ltd.; *Int'l*, pg. 336
PM FRANCHISING, LLC—See Fog Cutter Capital Group Inc.; *U.S. Private*, pg. 1557
POTBELLY FRANCHISING, LLC—See Potbelly Corporation; *U.S. Public*, pg. 1704
PRIMROSE SCHOOL FRANCHISING COMPANY—See Roark Capital Group Inc.; *U.S. Private*, pg. 3455
PROPERTY LINK INTERNATIONAL; *U.S. Private*, pg. 3285
PUBLIX ASSET MANAGEMENT COMPANY—See Publix Super Markets, Inc.; *U.S. Private*, pg. 3301
QUALCOMM TECHNOLOGY LICENSING—See QUALCOMM Incorporated; *U.S. Public*, pg. 1748
THE QUIZNO'S OPERATING COMPANY LLC—See QCE Finance LLC; *U.S. Private*, pg. 3312
REMINGTON LICENSING CORPORATION—See Spectrum Brands Holdings, Inc.; *U.S. Public*, pg. 1916
RHINO 7 FRANCHISE DEVELOPMENT CORPORATION; *U.S. Private*, pg. 3421
RUNZA NATIONAL INC.—See Runza Drive-Inns of America Inc.; *U.S. Private*, pg. 3504
RUTH'S CHRIS STEAK HOUSE FRANCHISE, LLC—See Darden Restaurants, Inc.; *U.S. Public*, pg. 633
SCOPE ENERGY RESOURCES, INC.—See ReConserve, Inc.; *U.S. Private*, pg. 3371
SCOPE LEASING, INC.—See Park National Corporation; *U.S. Public*, pg. 1638
SIGN-A-RAMA INC.—See UFG Group, Inc.; *U.S. Private*, pg. 4274
SINCERELY YOGURT FRANCHISING LLC—See Ablak Holdings, LLC; *U.S. Private*, pg. 39
SINNSUPTAWEE ASSET MANAGEMENT CO., LTD.—See Bangkok Bank Public Company Limited; *Int'l*, pg. 833
SIR SPEEDY, INC.—See KOA Holdings Inc.; *U.S. Private*, pg. 2325
SMOOTHIE KING FRANCHISES, INC.—See Affirma Capital Limited; *Int'l*, pg. 187
TACO JOHN'S INTERNATIONAL, INC.; *U.S. Private*, pg. 3920
TCBY SYSTEMS, LLC—See Capricorn Holdings, Inc.; *U.S. Private*, pg. 745
TECHNIS, INC.; *U.S. Private*, pg. 3954
TRISTRATA TECHNOLOGY INC—See Tristrata Inc.; *U.S. Private*, pg. 4238
UNIGLOBE TRAVEL INTERNATIONAL LIMITED PARTNERSHIP—See Charlwood Pacific Group; *Int'l*, pg. 1450
UNITED MEDIA, INC.—See The E.W. Scripps Company; *U.S. Public*, pg. 2069
VALVOLINE INSTANT OIL CHANGE FRANCHISING, INC.—See Valvoline Inc.; *U.S. Public*, pg. 2274
VOSTA LMG IP & SOFTWARE B.V.—See ASL Marine Holdings Ltd; *Int'l*, pg. 625
WATHNE IMPORTS LTD.; *U.S. Private*, pg. 4454
WPT ENTERPRISE INC.—See Allied Gaming & Entertainment, Inc.; *U.S. Public*, pg. 80
XCEL BRANDS, INC.; *U.S. Public*, pg. 2385

541110 — OFFICES OF LAWYERS

1031 SOLUTIONS, LLC—See First American Financial Corporation; *U.S. Public*, pg. 835
3M INNOVATIVE PROPERTIES COMPANY—See 3M Company; *U.S. Public*, pg. 6
ABRIL ABOGADOS SLU; *Int'l*, pg. 69
ADAMS AND REESE LLP; *U.S. Private*, pg. 73
ADVANZ FIDELIS IP SDN BHD—See Adamantem Capital Management Pty Limited; *Int'l*, pg. 123
AEON LAW PLLC; *U.S. Private*, pg. 117
AKERMAN LLP - DALLAS—See Akerman LLP; *U.S. Private*, pg. 145
AKERMAN LLP - HOUSTON—See Akerman LLP; *U.S. Private*, pg. 145
AKERMAN LLP - MIAMI—See Akerman LLP; *U.S. Private*, pg. 145
AKERMAN LLP; *U.S. Private*, pg. 144
AKIN GUMP STRAUSS HAUER & FELD LLP; *U.S. Private*, pg. 145
ALLEN, ALLEN, ALLEN & ALLEN; *U.S. Private*, pg. 180
ALLEN MATKINS LECK GAMBLE MALLORY & NATSIS LLP; *U.S. Private*, pg. 179
ALLEN OVERY SHEARMAN STERLING LLP; *Int'l*, pg. 336
ALSTON & BIRD LLP; *U.S. Private*, pg. 203
A&M BACON LIMITED—See Frenkel Topping Group plc; *Int'l*, pg. 2773
AMUNDSEN DAVIS LLC; *U.S. Private*, pg. 269
ANTON CASTRO LAW, LLC; *U.S. Private*, pg. 288
ARENTFOX SCHIFF LLP; *U.S. Private*, pg. 318
ARMSTRONG TEASDALE LLP; *U.S. Private*, pg. 332
ARNECKE SIEBOLD RECHTSANWALTE PARTNER-SCHAFTSGESELLSCHAFT; *Int'l*, pg. 576
ARNOLD & PORTER KAYE SCHOLER LLP; *U.S. Private*, pg. 332
ATTEA & ATTEA, P.C.; *U.S. Private*, pg. 383
AXIOM AUTOMOTIVE TECHNOLOGIES, INC; *U.S. Private*, pg. 413
AXIOM LEGAL, INC.-SAN FRANCISCO—See Axiom Automotive Technologies, Inc; *U.S. Private*, pg. 413
AXIOM LEGAL LONDON—See Axiom Automotive Technologies, Inc; *U.S. Private*, pg. 413
BAILEY KENNEDY LLP; *U.S. Private*, pg. 425
BAKER BOTTS L.L.P.; *U.S. Private*, pg. 455
BAKER DONELSON BEARMAN CALDWELL & BERKOWITZ PC; *U.S. Private*, pg. 456
BAKER & HOSTETLER LLP; *U.S. Private*, pg. 454
BAKER & MCKENZIE LLP; *U.S. Private*, pg. 454
BALLARD SPAHR LLP; *U.S. Private*, pg. 460
BARCLAY DAMON, LLP; *U.S. Private*, pg. 473
BARLEY SNYDER LLC; *U.S. Private*, pg. 476
BARNES & THORNBURG LP; *U.S. Private*, pg. 477
BEAUMIER, TROGDON, ORMAN, HURD & VIEGAS, PLLP; *U.S. Private*, pg. 508
BECKER LLC; *U.S. Private*, pg. 511
BECKER & POLIAKOFF, P.A.; *U.S. Private*, pg. 510
BENNETT, BRICKLIN & SALTZBURG LLC; *U.S. Private*, pg. 527
BERGER SINGERMAN PA; *U.S. Private*, pg. 530
BIDWELL HENDERSON COSTS CONSULTANTS LIMITED—See Frenkel Topping Group plc; *Int'l*, pg. 2773
BINGHAM GREENEBAUM DOLL LLP; *U.S. Private*, pg. 560
BIRD & BIRD LLP; *Int'l*, pg. 1046
BLALOCK WALTERS P.A.; *U.S. Private*, pg. 578
BLANK ROME LLP; *U.S. Private*, pg. 579
BLETHEN, GAGE & KRAUSE, PLLP; *U.S. Private*, pg. 581
BOIES SCHILLER FLEXNER LLP; *U.S. Private*, pg. 609
BOND, SCHOENECK & KING, PLLC; *U.S. Private*, pg. 613
BOND TURNER LIMITED—See Anexo Group Plc; *Int'l*, pg. 459
BONE MCALLESTER NORTON PLLC—See Spencer Fane LLP; *U.S. Private*, pg. 3755
BRACEWELL & GIULIANI LLP; *U.S. Private*, pg. 630
BRADLEY ARANT BOULT CUMMINGS LLP; *U.S. Private*, pg. 632
BRADSHAW, FOWLER, PROCTOR & FAIRGRAVE, PC—See Dickinson, Mackaman, Tyler & Hagen, P.C.; *U.S. Private*, pg. 1227
BREAZEALE, SACHSE & WILSON, LLP; *U.S. Private*, pg. 643
BROWN RUDNICK LLP; *U.S. Private*, pg. 668
BRUNS, CONNELL, VOLLMAR & ARMSTRONG, LLC; *U.S. Private*, pg. 672

541110 — OFFICES OF LAWYERS

BRYAN CAVE LLP; *U.S. Private*, pg. 673
BUCHALTER, NEMER, FIELDS & YOUNGER LLP; *U.S. Private*, pg. 676
BUCHANAN INGERSOLL & ROONEY PC; *U.S. Private*, pg. 676
BUCKLEYSANDLER LLP.; *U.S. Private*, pg. 678
BURR & FORMAN LLP; *U.S. Private*, pg. 691
BUTLER SNOW LLP; *U.S. Private*, pg. 697
CADWALADER, WICKERSHAM & TAFT LLP; *U.S. Private*, pg. 713
CAHILL GORDON & REINDEL LLP; *U.S. Private*, pg. 714
CALABRESE HUFF; *U.S. Private*, pg. 715
CALDWELL LESLIE & PROCTOR PC—See Boies Schiller Flexner LLP; *U.S. Private*, pg. 609
CARLTON FIELDS JORDEN BURT, P.A. - SIMSBURY—See Carlton Fields Jorden Burt, P.A.; *U.S. Private*, pg. 765
CARLTON FIELDS JORDEN BURT, P.A.; *U.S. Private*, pg. 765
CARMODY TORRANCE SANDAK & HENNESSEY LLP; *U.S. Private*, pg. 766
CARRUTHERS & ROTH, P.A.; *U.S. Private*, pg. 774
CELLER LAW, P.A.—See The Celler Organization; *U.S. Private*, pg. 4006
THE CENTER FOR REPRODUCTIVE RIGHTS, INC.; *U.S. Private*, pg. 4006
CETRULO LLP; *U.S. Private*, pg. 843
CHAD T. WILSON LAW FIRM PLLC; *U.S. Private*, pg. 845
CHAPMAN & CUTLER LLP; *U.S. Private*, pg. 849
CHARLES ADAMS RITCHIE & DUCKWORTH—See Collas Crill; *Int'l*, pg. 1698
CHARLES RUSSELL SPEECHLYS LLP; *Int'l*, pg. 1450
THE CHARTWELL LAW OFFICES, LLP - HARRISBURG—See The Chartwell Law Offices, LLP; *U.S. Private*, pg. 4007
THE CHARTWELL LAW OFFICES, LLP - NEW YORK—See The Chartwell Law Offices, LLP; *U.S. Private*, pg. 4007
THE CHARTWELL LAW OFFICES, LLP; *U.S. Private*, pg. 4007
CHOATE HALL & STEWART LLP; *U.S. Private*, pg. 887
CLARK HILL PLC; *U.S. Private*, pg. 913
CLEARY GOTTLIEB STEEN & HAMILTON LLP; *U.S. Private*, pg. 939
CLI LAWYERS PTY. LTD.—See Archer Capital Pty. Ltd.; *Int'l*, pg. 547
CLYDE & CO LLP; *Int'l*, pg. 1664
CLYDE & CO US LLP—See Clyde & Co LLP; *Int'l*, pg. 1664
CMS CAMERON MCKENNA NABARRO OLSWANG LLP; *Int'l*, pg. 1672
COATS ROSE, P.C.; *U.S. Private*, pg. 957
COHEN & GRIGSBY, P.C.—See Dentons Group; *U.S. Private*, pg. 1207
COLLAS CRILL; *Int'l*, pg. 1698
COLORADO LEGAL SERVICES; *U.S. Private*, pg. 974
THE COMMON SOURCE; *U.S. Private*, pg. 4012
COMPASS LEXECON SPAIN, S.L.—See FTI Consulting, Inc.; *U.S. Public*, pg. 890
CONRAD O'BRIEN, P.C.—See Clark Hill PLC; *U.S. Private*, pg. 913
COOLEY LLP - RESTON—See Cooley LLP; *U.S. Private*, pg. 1040
COOLEY LLP; *U.S. Private*, pg. 1039
COOLEY LLP - WASHINGTON, DC—See Cooley LLP; *U.S. Private*, pg. 1040
CO-OPERATIVE LEGAL SERVICES LIMITED—See Co-operative Group Limited; *Int'l*, pg. 1679
COUNSEL PRESS, INC—See Align Capital Partners, LLC; *U.S. Private*, pg. 167
COVINGTON & BURLING LLP; *U.S. Private*, pg. 1072
COZEN O'CONNOR; *U.S. Private*, pg. 1079
CRABBE BROWN & JAMES, LLP—See Amundsen Davis LLC; *U.S. Private*, pg. 269
CRAVATH, SWAINE & MOORE LLP; *U.S. Private*, pg. 1086
CREDISSIMO SA—See BNP Paribas SA; *Int'l*, pg. 1090
CREDIT INFONET GROUP, INC.—See Stone Point Capital LLC; *U.S. Private*, pg. 3823
CULLEN & DYKMAN LLP; *U.S. Private*, pg. 1121
CURTIS, MALLET-PREVOST, COLT & MOSLE LLP; *U.S. Private*, pg. 1127
DAVIS & KUELTHAU, S.C.—See Amundsen Davis LLC; *U.S. Private*, pg. 269
DAVIS POLK & WARDWELL LLP; *U.S. Private*, pg. 1174
DAVIS WRIGHT TREMAINE LLP; *U.S. Private*, pg. 1174
DAY KETTERER LTD.; *U.S. Private*, pg. 1176
DAY PITNEY LLP; *U.S. Private*, pg. 1176
DAY PITNEY LLP; *U.S. Private*, pg. 1176
DEBEVOISE & PLIMPTON LLP; *U.S. Private*, pg. 1186
DECHERT LLP; *U.S. Private*, pg. 1187
DENTONS BOEKEL N.V.—See Dentons Group; *U.S. Private*, pg. 1207
DENTONS CANADA LLP—See Dentons Group; *U.S. Private*, pg. 1207
DENTONS EUROPE LLP—See Dentons Group; *U.S. Private*, pg. 1207
DENTONS UKMEA LLP—See Dentons Group; *U.S. Private*, pg. 1207
DENTONS US LLP—See Dentons Group; *U.S. Private*, pg. 1207
DESPACHO DE ABOGADOS MIEMBRO DE HOGAN

541110 — OFFICES OF LAWYERS

LOVELLS—See Hogan Lovells International LLP; *Int'l*, pg. 3441
DEVINE, MILLIMET & BRANCH PROFESSIONAL ASSOCIATION; *U.S. Private*, pg. 1218
DEWITT MACKALL CROUNSE & MOORE S.C.—See DeWitt Ross & Stevens S.C.; *U.S. Private*, pg. 1219
DEWITT ROSS & STEVENS S.C.; *U.S. Private*, pg. 1219
DICKINSON, MACKAMAN, TYLER & HAGEN, P.C.; *U.S. Private*, pg. 1227
DICKINSON WRIGHT PLLC; *U.S. Private*, pg. 1227
DINSMORE & SHOHL LLP; *U.S. Private*, pg. 1233
DLA PIPER AUSTRALIA - MELBOURNE—See DLA Piper Global; *Int'l*, pg. 2140
DLA PIPER AUSTRALIA—See DLA Piper Global; *Int'l*, pg. 2140
DLA PIPER BAZ NLD SPA; *Int'l*, pg. 2140
DLA PIPER (CANADA) LLP—See DLA Piper Global; *Int'l*, pg. 2140
DLA PIPER DENMARK LAW FIRM P/S—See DLA Piper Global; *Int'l*, pg. 2140
DLA PIPER KUWAIT—See DLA Piper Global; *Int'l*, pg. 2140
DLA PIPER LLP (US)—See DLA Piper Global; *Int'l*, pg. 2140
DLA PIPER LLP (US) - WASHINGTON, D.C.—See DLA Piper Global; *Int'l*, pg. 2140
DLA PIPER RUS LTD.—See DLA Piper Global; *Int'l*, pg. 2140
DLA PIPER UK LLP—See DLA Piper Global; *Int'l*, pg. 2140
DONAHUE DURHAM & NOONAN PC—See Carmody Torrance Sandak & Hennessey LLP; *U.S. Private*, pg. 766
DORSEY & WHITNEY LLP; *U.S. Private*, pg. 1263
DOWLING AARON INCORPORATED—See Fennemore Craig, P.C.; *U.S. Private*, pg. 1495
DUANE MORRIS LLP; *U.S. Private*, pg. 1282
DURHAM JONES & PINEGAR, P.C.—See Dentons Group; *U.S. Private*, pg. 1207
DWC LAW FIRM PS—See Aeon Law PLLC; *U.S. Private*, pg. 117
DYKEMA GOSSETT PLLC; *U.S. Private*, pg. 1296
EASTHAM, WATSON, DALE & FORNEY, LLP—See Schouest, Bamdas, Soshea & BenMaier, PLLC; *U.S. Private*, pg. 3569
ECKERT SEAMANS CHERIN & MELLOTT, LLC; *U.S. Private*, pg. 1328
EPSTEIN BECKER & GREEN, P.C.; *U.S. Private*, pg. 1414
EQUAL JUSTICE WORKS; *U.S. Private*, pg. 1415
EVERSHEDS ATTORNEYS LTD.—See Eversheds LLP; *Int'l*, pg. 2568
EVERSHEDS LLP; *Int'l*, pg. 2568
EVERSHEDS SUTHERLAND (US) LLP—See Eversheds LLP; *Int'l*, pg. 2568
FAEGRE DRINKER BIDDLE & REATH LLP; *U.S. Private*, pg. 1461
FARRIS BOBANGO PLC—See Phelps Dunbar LLP; *U.S. Private*, pg. 3167
FENNEMORE CRAIG, P.C.; *U.S. Private*, pg. 1495
FERENCIK LIBANOFF BRANDT BUSTAMANTE & GOLDSTEIN, P.A.—See Hinckley, Allen & Snyder LLP; *U.S. Private*, pg. 1948
FIELDFISHER RYSER—See Field Fisher Waterhouse LLP; *Int'l*, pg. 2655
FIELD FISHER WATERHOUSE LLP; *Int'l*, pg. 2655
FINERS STEPHENS INNOCENT LLP; *Int'l*, pg. 2674
FINNEGAN, HENDERSON, FARABOW, GARRETT & DUNNER, L.L.P.; *U.S. Private*, pg. 1510
FISHER & PHILLIPS LLP; *U.S. Private*, pg. 1533
FISH & RICHARDSON PC; *U.S. Private*, pg. 1533
FITZPATRICK CELLA HARPER & SCINTO—See Venable LLP; *U.S. Private*, pg. 4355
FITZPATRICK & HUNT, PAGANO, AUBERT, LLP; *U.S. Private*, pg. 1536
FLETCHER VAN GILDER LLP; *U.S. Private*, pg. 1543
FOLEY HOAG LLP; *U.S. Private*, pg. 1558
FOLEY & LARDNER LLP; *U.S. Private*, pg. 1558
FOX ROTHSCHILD LLP - SAN FRANCISCO, CA-FRONT STREET—See Fox Rothschild LLP; *U.S. Private*, pg. 1584
FOX ROTHSCHILD LLP; *U.S. Private*, pg. 1584
FPA PATENT ATTORNEYS ASIA PTE LTD.—See Adamantem Capital Management Pty Limited; *Int'l*, pg. 124
THE FRAN HAASCH LAW GROUP; *U.S. Private*, pg. 4030
FREEMAN, FREEMAN & SMILEY, LLP—See Saul Ewing Arnstein & Lehr LLP; *U.S. Private*, pg. 3554
FREEMAN MATHIS & GARY, LLP; *U.S. Private*, pg. 1605
FROST BROWN TODD LLC; *U.S. Private*, pg. 1616
FUTTERMAN, LANZA & PASCULLI, LLP; *U.S. Private*, pg. 1626
GARDERE WYNNE SEWELL LLP—See Foley & Lardner LLP; *U.S. Private*, pg. 1558
GELLER & COMPANY; *U.S. Private*, pg. 1656
GGI GENEVA GROUP INTERNATIONAL AG; *Int'l*, pg. 2957
GIBBONS P.C.; *U.S. Private*, pg. 1695
GIBSON, DUNN & CRUTCHER LLP; *U.S. Private*, pg. 1697
GIBSON, DUNN & CRUTCHER; *U.S. Private*, pg. 1697
GIFFEN & KAMINSKI, LLC—See Perez & Morris LLC; *U.S. Private*, pg. 3147
GODFREY & KAHN, S.C.; *U.S. Private*, pg. 1724
GOLDBERG & OSBORNE; *U.S. Private*, pg. 1728

GOLDMAN & ROSEN, LTD.—See Day Ketterer Ltd.; *U.S. Private*, pg. 1176
GONZALEZ LUNA, MORENO Y ARMIDA, S.C.—See DLA Piper Global; *Int'l*, pg. 2140
GOODWIN PROCTER LLP; *U.S. Private*, pg. 1741
GORDON & REES LLP; *U.S. Private*, pg. 1741
GOULSTON & STORRS PC; *U.S. Private*, pg. 1745
GOWLING WLG (CANADA) LLP—See Gowling WLG International Limited; *Int'l*, pg. 3045
GOWLING WLG (UK) LLP—See Gowling WLG International Limited; *Int'l*, pg. 3045
GRAYROBINSON, P.A.; *U.S. Private*, pg. 1761
GREENBERG TRAURIG, LLP; *U.S. Private*, pg. 1775
GREENBERG TRAURIG, P.A.—See Greenberg Traurig, LLP; *U.S. Private*, pg. 1775
GREENSFELDER, HEMKER & GALE, P.C.—See UB Greensfelder LLP; *U.S. Private*, pg. 4273
GREENSPOON MARDER LLP; *U.S. Private*, pg. 1780
GREGORY PARTNERS, LLC—See I Squared Capital Advisors (US) LLC; *U.S. Private*, pg. 2025
GRUBER HURST ELROD JOHANSEN HAIL SHANK LLP; *U.S. Private*, pg. 1796
GUNSTER, YOAKLEY & STEWART, P.A.; *U.S. Private*, pg. 1818
HAIGHT BROWN & BONESTEEL, LLP; *U.S. Private*, pg. 1840
HAILE SHAW & PFAFFENBERGER, P.A.—See Nason, Yeager, Gerson, Harris & Fumero P.A.; *U.S. Private*, pg. 2837
HARPER MACLEOD LLP; *Int'l*, pg. 3278
HAYNES & BOONE LLP; *U.S. Private*, pg. 1885
HENDERSON, FRANKLIN, STARNES & HOLT, P.A.; *U.S. Private*, pg. 1914
HERRICK, FEINSTEIN LLP; *U.S. Private*, pg. 1926
HILL WARD HENDERSON; *U.S. Private*, pg. 1945
HINCKLEY, ALLEN & SNYDER LLP; *U.S. Private*, pg. 1948
HINSHAW & CULBERTSON LLP; *U.S. Private*, pg. 1950
HIRSCHLER FLEISCHER, A PROFESSIONAL CORPORATION; *U.S. Private*, pg. 1951
HODGSON RUSS LLP; *U.S. Private*, pg. 1959
HOGAN LOVELLS (ALICANTE) S.L. & CIA.—See Hogan Lovells International LLP; *Int'l*, pg. 3441
HOGAN LOVELLS BSTL, S.C.—See Hogan Lovells International LLP; *Int'l*, pg. 3441
HOGAN LOVELLS CIS LLC—See Hogan Lovells International LLP; *Int'l*, pg. 3441
HOGAN LOVELLS INTERNATIONAL LLP; *Int'l*, pg. 3441
HOGAN LOVELLS (LUXEMBOURG) LLP—See Hogan Lovells International LLP; *Int'l*, pg. 3441
HOGAN LOVELLS (MIDDLE EAST) LLP—See Hogan Lovells International LLP; *Int'l*, pg. 3441
HOGAN LOVELLS (MONGOLIA) LLP—See Hogan Lovells International LLP; *Int'l*, pg. 3441
HOGAN LOVELLS (PARIS) LLP—See Hogan Lovells International LLP; *Int'l*, pg. 3441
HOGAN LOVELLS SOUTH AFRICA—See Hogan Lovells International LLP; *Int'l*, pg. 3441
HOGAN LOVELLS STUDIO LEGALE—See Hogan Lovells International LLP; *Int'l*, pg. 3441
HOGAN LOVELLS US LLP—See Hogan Lovells International LLP; *Int'l*, pg. 3441
HOGAN LOVELLS (WARSZAWA) LLP—See Hogan Lovells International LLP; *Int'l*, pg. 3441
HOLLAND & HART LLP; *U.S. Private*, pg. 1963
HOLLAND & KNIGHT LLP; *U.S. Private*, pg. 1963
HONIGMAN MILLER SCHWARTZ & COHN LLP - CHICAGO—See Honigman Miller Schwartz & Cohn LLP; *U.S. Private*, pg. 1977
HONIGMAN MILLER SCHWARTZ & COHN LLP; *U.S. Private*, pg. 1976
HUSCH BLACKWELL LLP; *U.S. Private*, pg. 2013
HWW WIENBERG WILHELM RECHTSANWALTE PARTNERSCHAFT; *Int'l*, pg. 3543
ICE MILLER LLP; *U.S. Private*, pg. 2030
IRELL & MANELLA LLP; *U.S. Private*, pg. 2137
JACKSON KELLY PLLC - EVANSVILLE—See Jackson Kelly PLLC; *U.S. Private*, pg. 2177
JACKSON KELLY PLLC; *U.S. Private*, pg. 2177
JACKSON WALKER LLP; *U.S. Private*, pg. 2178
JACOBACCI & PARTNERS S.P.A.—See Abril Abogados SLU; *Int'l*, pg. 69
JACOBY & MEYERS ATTORNEYS LLP—See Jacoby & Meyers, P.C.; *U.S. Private*, pg. 2180
JACOBY & MEYERS, LLP—See Jacoby & Meyers, P.C.; *U.S. Private*, pg. 2180
JAENSCH IMMIGRATION LAW FIRM; *U.S. Private*, pg. 2181
JEFFER MANGELS BUTLER & MITCHELL LLP; *U.S. Private*, pg. 2197
JILL S. SCHWARTZ & ASSOCIATES, P.A.; *U.S. Private*, pg. 2208
JM ENTERPRISES 1, INC.—See Cardiff Lexington Corporation; *U.S. Public*, pg. 433
JODAT LAW GROUP, P.A.; *U.S. Private*, pg. 2217
JONES DAY; *U.S. Private*, pg. 2232
JONES KING LAWYERS PTY LTD—See Collection House Limited; *Int'l*, pg. 1699
KASOWITZ BENSON TORRES & FRIEDMAN LLP; *U.S. Private*, pg. 2264

KATTEN MUCHIN ROSENMAN LLP; *U.S. Private*, pg. 2265
KEATING, MUETHING & KLEKAMP PLL; *U.S. Private*, pg. 2271
KELLEY CAWTHORNE, LLC; *U.S. Private*, pg. 2275
KELLEY DRYE & WARREN LLP; *U.S. Private*, pg. 2275
KEMP & RUGE LAW GROUP; *U.S. Private*, pg. 2282
KEYSTONE CASE MANAGEMENT LIMITED—See Frenkel Topping Group plc; *Int'l*, pg. 2773
KILPATRICK TOWNSEND & STOCKTON LLP; *U.S. Private*, pg. 2304
KING & SPALDING LLP; *U.S. Private*, pg. 2308
KIRKLAND & ELLIS LLP; *U.S. Private*, pg. 2314
K&L GATES LLP; *U.S. Private*, pg. 2249
KNOBBE MARTENS OLSON & BEAR LLP; *U.S. Private*, pg. 2323
KRAMER LEVIN NAFTALIS & FRANKEL LLP; *U.S. Private*, pg. 2349
KUNKEL MILLER & HAMENT; *U.S. Private*, pg. 2357
KUTAK ROCK LLP; *U.S. Private*, pg. 2358
LADAS & PARRY, CALIFORNIA—See Ladas & Parry; *U.S. Private*, pg. 2372
LADAS & PARRY, ILLINOIS—See Ladas & Parry; *U.S. Private*, pg. 2372
LADAS & PARRY; *U.S. Private*, pg. 2372
LAND & LEGAL SOLUTIONS; *U.S. Private*, pg. 2382
LANE POWELL PC; *U.S. Private*, pg. 2388
LARKIN INGRASSIA, PLLC; *U.S. Private*, pg. 2392
LATHAM & WATKINS LLP; *U.S. Private*, pg. 2396
LATHROP & GAGE LLP; *U.S. Private*, pg. 2396
THE LAW FIRM OF ANIDJAR & LEVINE, P.A.; *U.S. Private*, pg. 4068
LEGAL AID BUREAU, INC.; *U.S. Private*, pg. 2417
LEGAL AID FOUNDATION OF LOS ANGELES; *U.S. Private*, pg. 2417
LEGAL AID SERVICES OF OKLAHOMA, INC.; *U.S. Private*, pg. 2417
THE LEGAL GROUP INC.—See Noor, Inc.; *U.S. Private*, pg. 2935
LEWIS BRISBOIS BISGAARD & SMITH LLP; *U.S. Private*, pg. 2438
LEWIS ROCA ROTHGERBER CHRISTIE LLP; *U.S. Private*, pg. 2439
LEWIS, THOMASON, KING, KRIEG & WALDROP, P.C. - MEMPHIS—See Lewis, Thomason, King, Krieg & Waldrop, P.C.; *U.S. Private*, pg. 2440
LEWIS, THOMASON, KING, KRIEG & WALDROP, P.C.; *U.S. Private*, pg. 2440
LIFE CERTAIN WEALTH STRATEGIES, LLC—See Reverence Capital Partners LLC; *U.S. Private*, pg. 3415
LINER LLP—See DLA Piper Global; *Int'l*, pg. 2140
LIPPES MATHIAS WEXLER FRIEDMAN LLP - ALBANY—See Lippes Mathias Wexler Friedman LLP; *U.S. Private*, pg. 2465
LIPPES MATHIAS WEXLER FRIEDMAN LLP; *U.S. Private*, pg. 2465
LITCHNEY LAW FIRM; *U.S. Private*, pg. 2467
LITTLER MENDELSON P.C.; *U.S. Private*, pg. 2472
LOCKE LORD EDWARDS LLP; *U.S. Private*, pg. 2478
LOEB & LOEB LLP; *U.S. Private*, pg. 2479
LOWENSTEIN SANDLER PC; *U.S. Private*, pg. 2505
LUHRSEN LAW GROUP, P.L.; *U.S. Private*, pg. 2512
MANATT, PHELPS & PHILLIPS LLP; *U.S. Private*, pg. 2561
MANNING GROSS + MASSENBURG LLP; *U.S. Private*, pg. 2565
MARSHALL DENNEHEY WARNER COLEMAN & GOGGIN, P.C.; *U.S. Private*, pg. 2592
MATEER & HARBERT, P.A.—See Dinsmore & Shohl LLP; *U.S. Private*, pg. 1234
MAYER BROWN LLP; *U.S. Private*, pg. 2621
MAYNARD, COOPER & GALE, P.C.; *U.S. Private*, pg. 2622
MCCARTER & ENGLISH LLP; *U.S. Private*, pg. 2626
MCDERMOTT WILL & EMERY LLP; *U.S. Private*, pg. 2631
MCELROY, DEUTSCH, MULVANEY & CARPENTER, LLP; *U.S. Private*, pg. 2633
MCGUIREWOODS LLP; *U.S. Private*, pg. 2636
MCINTYRE, PANZARELLA, THANASIDES, BRINGGOLD & TODD, P.A.; *U.S. Private*, pg. 2637
MCNAIR LAW FIRM P.A.—See Burr & Forman LLP; *U.S. Private*, pg. 691
MEHAFFY & WEBER, A PROFESSIONAL CORPORATION; *U.S. Private*, pg. 2660
MENTER, RUDIN & TRIVELPIECE, P.C.—See Barclay Damon, LLP; *U.S. Private*, pg. 473
MERCURY INSURANCE COMPANY—See Mercury General Corporation; *U.S. Public*, pg. 1421
MICHAEL, BEST & FRIEDRICH LLP; *U.S. Private*, pg. 2699
MID-MINNESOTA LEGAL AID; *U.S. Private*, pg. 2708
MILBANK, TWEED, HADLEY & MCCLOY LLP; *U.S. Private*, pg. 2727
MILLER, CANFIELD, PADDOCK AND STONE, P.L.C.; *U.S. Private*, pg. 2736
MINTZ, LEVIN, COHN, FERRIS, GLOVSKY & POPEO, P.C.; *U.S. Private*, pg. 2745
MITCHELL SILBERBERG & KNUPP LLP; *U.S. Private*, pg. 2751
MOORE & VAN ALLEN PLLC; *U.S. Private*, pg. 2779
MORGAN, LEWIS & BOCKIUS LLP; *U.S. Private*, pg. 2784
MORRIS, MANNING & MARTIN LLP; *U.S. Private*, pg. 2788

N.A.I.C.S. INDEX

541191 — TITLE ABSTRACT AND ...

MORRISON & FOERSTER LLP; *U.S. Private*, pg. 2788
MUNGER TOLLES & OLSON LLP; *U.S. Private*, pg. 2813
MURTHY LAW FIRM; *U.S. Private*, pg. 2817
MYSTERY GUILD—See Bertelsmann SE & Co. KGaA; *Int'l*, pg. 992
NABARRO LLP—See CMS Cameron McKenna Nabarro Olswang LLP; *Int'l*, pg. 1672
N-ABLE SERVICES LIMITED—See Frenkel Topping Group plc; *Int'l*, pg. 2773
NASON, YEAGER, GERSON, HARRIS & FUMERO P.A.; *U.S. Private*, pg. 2837
NELSON MULLINS RILEY & SCARBOROUGH LLP; *U.S. Private*, pg. 2883
NELSONS SOLICITORS LIMITED—See Blixt Group Limited; *Int'l*, pg. 1064
NEW ENGLAND LAW BOSTON; *U.S. Private*, pg. 2894
NEW YORK LEGAL ASSISTANCE GROUP; *U.S. Private*, pg. 2910
NIERENGARTEN & HIPPERT LTD.—See Blethen, Gage & Krause, PLLP; *U.S. Private*, pg. 581
NIXON PEABODY LLP; *U.S. Private*, pg. 2930
NOVACK AND MACEY LLP—See Armstrong Teasdale LLP; *U.S. Private*, pg. 332
OFFIT KURMAN; *U.S. Private*, pg. 3002
OGLETREE, DEAKINS, NASH, SMOAK & STEWART, P.C.; *U.S. Private*, pg. 3003
OLDER & LUNDY; *U.S. Private*, pg. 3010
OLSWANG LLP—See CMS Cameron McKenna Nabarro Olswang LLP; *Int'l*, pg. 1672
O'MELVENY & MYERS LLP; *U.S. Private*, pg. 2979
ORRICK, HERRINGTON & SUTCLIFFE LLP; *U.S. Private*, pg. 3044
PAHL & MCCAY A PROFESSIONAL CORPORATION—See Spencer Fane LLP; *U.S. Private*, pg. 3755
PARTNERS IN COSTS LIMITED—See Frenkel Topping Group plc; *Int'l*, pg. 2773
PATTERSON BELKNAP WEBB & TYLER LLP; *U.S. Private*, pg. 3111
PATTERSON THUENTE PEDERSEN, P.A.—See Husch Blackwell LLP; *U.S. Private*, pg. 2013
PAUL HASTINGS LLP; *U.S. Private*, pg. 3112
PAUL, WEISS, RIFKIND, WHARTON & GARRISON LLP; *U.S. Private*, pg. 3113
PEPPER HAMILTON LLP; *U.S. Private*, pg. 3144
PEREZ & MORRIS LLC; *U.S. Private*, pg. 3147
PERKINS COIE LLP; *U.S. Private*, pg. 3151
PHELPS DUNBAR LLP; *U.S. Private*, pg. 3167
PILLSBURY WINTHROP SHAW PITTMAN LLP; *U.S. Private*, pg. 3180
POOLE & SHAFFERY, LLP; *U.S. Private*, pg. 3228
PORTER WRIGHT MORRIS & ARTHUR LLP; *U.S. Private*, pg. 3232
POWELL, CARNEY, MALLER, P.A.; *U.S. Private*, pg. 3237
POZNAK LAW FIRM LTD.—See Winick & Gallaher, PC; *U.S. Private*, pg. 4542
PROSKAUER ROSE LLP; *U.S. Private*, pg. 3287
PUERTO RICO LEGAL SERVICES, INC.; *U.S. Private*, pg. 3302
QUARLES & BRADY LLP; *U.S. Private*, pg. 3324
QUINN EMANUEL URQUHART & SULLIVAN, LLP; *U.S. Private*, pg. 3326
QUIROGA LAW OFFICE, PLLC; *U.S. Private*, pg. 3329
RACKEMANN, SAWYER & BREWSTER PROFESSIONAL CORPORATION—See Verrill Dana LLP; *U.S. Private*, pg. 4368
RATNER & PRESTIA PC—See Buchanan Ingersoll & Rooney PC; *U.S. Private*, pg. 676
REED SMITH LLP; *U.S. Private*, pg. 3382
RIVKIN RADLER LLP; *U.S. Private*, pg. 3448
RLI ATLANTA - P/C—See RLI Corp.; *U.S. Public*, pg. 1801
ROBERTS MARKEL WEINBERG BUTLER HAILEY PC; *U.S. Private*, pg. 3459
ROBINS KAPLAN LLP - LOS ANGELES—See Robins, Kaplan, Miller & Ciresi L.L.P.; *U.S. Private*, pg. 3461
ROBINS, KAPLAN, MILLER & CIRESI L.L.P. - ATLANTA—See Robins, Kaplan, Miller & Ciresi L.L.P.; *U.S. Private*, pg. 3461
ROBINS, KAPLAN, MILLER & CIRESI L.L.P. - BOSTON—See Robins, Kaplan, Miller & Ciresi L.L.P.; *U.S. Private*, pg. 3461
ROBINS, KAPLAN, MILLER & CIRESI L.L.P. - NAPLES—See Robins, Kaplan, Miller & Ciresi L.L.P.; *U.S. Private*, pg. 3461
ROBINS, KAPLAN, MILLER & CIRESI L.L.P. - NEW YORK—See Robins, Kaplan, Miller & Ciresi L.L.P.; *U.S. Private*, pg. 3461
ROBINS, KAPLAN, MILLER & CIRESI L.L.P.; *U.S. Private*, pg. 3460
ROBINSON & COLE LLP; *U.S. Private*, pg. 3461
ROBINSON GRAY STEPP & LAFFITTE, LLC; *U.S. Private*, pg. 3463
ROCK FUSCO & CONNELLY, LLC; *U.S. Private*, pg. 3464
ROCKVILLE ENTERPRISES LLC—See Limoneira Company; *U.S. Public*, pg. 1316
RODYK & DAVIDSON LLP—See Dentons Group; *U.S. Private*, pg. 1207
ROETZEL & ANDRESS; *U.S. Private*, pg. 3471
ROPES & GRAY LLP; *U.S. Private*, pg. 3480
RUMBERGER, KIRK & CALDWELL PROFESSIONAL ASSOCIATION; *U.S. Private*, pg. 3503
SALEM & GREEN CORP.—See Weintraub Tobin Chediak Coleman Grodin Law Corporation; *U.S. Private*, pg. 4472
SANDLER LLC; *U.S. Private*, pg. 3544
SAUL EWING ARNSTEIN & LEHR LLP; *U.S. Private*, pg. 3554
SCARINCI HOLLENBECK, LLC; *U.S. Private*, pg. 3561
SCHIFF HARDIN LLP—See ArentFox Schiff LLP; *U.S. Private*, pg. 318
SCHOUEST, BAMDAS, SOSHEA & BENMAIER, PLLC; *U.S. Private*, pg. 3569
SCHOX, PLC; *U.S. Private*, pg. 3569
SCHULTE, ROTH & ZABEL LLP; *U.S. Private*, pg. 3570
SCHUSTER AGUILO LLC—See Littler Mendelson P.C.; *U.S. Private*, pg. 2472
SEIGER GFELLER LAURIE LLP; *U.S. Private*, pg. 3599
SEILER WATERMAN LLC; *U.S. Private*, pg. 3599
SEYFARTH SHAW; *U.S. Private*, pg. 3620
SHAPIRO, LIFSCHITZ AND SCHRAM, P.C.—See Barclay Damon, LLP; *U.S. Private*, pg. 473
SHEARMAN & STERLING LLP—See Allen Overy Shearman Sterling LLP; *Int'l*, pg. 336
SHEPPARD MULLIN RICHTER & HAMPTON LLP; *U.S. Private*, pg. 3632
SHOOK, HARDY & BACON LLP; *U.S. Private*, pg. 3640
SHUTTS & BOWEN LLP; *U.S. Private*, pg. 3644
SIBETH PARTNERSCHAFT—See Arnecke Siebold Rechtsanwalte Partnerschaftsgesellschaft; *Int'l*, pg. 576
SIDLEY AUSTIN LLP; *U.S. Private*, pg. 3646
SILLS CUMMIS & GROSS P.C.; *U.S. Private*, pg. 3653
SIMPSON MILLAR LLP—See Fairpoint Group Plc; *Int'l*, pg. 2609
SIMPSON THACHER & BARTLETT LLP; *U.S. Private*, pg. 3668
SLATER & GORDON LIMITED—See Allegro Funds Pty. Ltd.; *Int'l*, pg. 336
SLATER & GORDON (UK) LLP—See Allegro Funds Pty. Ltd.; *Int'l*, pg. 336
SMITH, GAMBRELL & RUSSELL, LLP; *U.S. Private*, pg. 3696
SMITH MOORE LLP; *U.S. Private*, pg. 3695
SMOLKER BARTLETT SCHLOSSER LOEB & HINDS, P.A.; *U.S. Private*, pg. 3698
SNELL & WILMER LLP; *U.S. Private*, pg. 3700
SNOW, CHRISTENSEN & MARTINEAU, P.C.—See Spencer Fane LLP; *U.S. Private*, pg. 3755
SOMEK & ASSOCIATES LIMITED—See Frenkel Topping Group plc; *Int'l*, pg. 2773
SPENCER FANE LLP; *U.S. Private*, pg. 3755
SQUIRE PATTON BOGGS (US) LLP; *U.S. Private*, pg. 3766
SQUIRE PATTON BOGGS (US) LLP - WASHINGTON, DC—See Squire Patton Boggs (US) LLP; *U.S. Private*, pg. 3766
STANLEY DAVIS GROUP LIMITED—See Dye & Durham Limited; *Int'l*, pg. 2238
STATE FARM INSURANCE CO.—See State Farm Mutual Automobile Insurance Company; *U.S. Private*, pg. 3792
STEPTOE & JOHNSON LLP; *U.S. Private*, pg. 3804
STEVENS & LEE, P.C.—See The Stevens & Lee Companies, LLC; *U.S. Private*, pg. 4123
STINSON LEONARD STREET LLP - MINNEAPOLIS—See Stinson Leonard Street LLP; *U.S. Private*, pg. 3813
STINSON LEONARD STREET LLP; *U.S. Private*, pg. 3813
STOEL RIVES LLP; *U.S. Private*, pg. 3815
STOLL KEENON OGDEN PLLC; *U.S. Private*, pg. 3816
STONESIFER & KELLEY, P.C.—See Barley Snyder LLC; *U.S. Private*, pg. 476
STRASBURGER & PRICE, LLP; *U.S. Private*, pg. 3833
STRATA SOLICITORS LTD.—See Arthur J. Gallagher & Co.; *U.S. Public*, pg. 205
STROOCK & STROOCK & LAVAN LLP; *U.S. Private*, pg. 3841
SULLIVAN & CROMWELL LLP; *U.S. Private*, pg. 3850
SULLIVAN & WORCESTER LLP; *U.S. Private*, pg. 3851
TAFT STETTINIUS & HOLLISTER LLP - CHICAGO—See Taft Stettinius & Hollister LLP; *U.S. Private*, pg. 3922
TAFT STETTINIUS & HOLLISTER LLP; *U.S. Private*, pg. 3921
TAYLOR & ASSOCIATES LAW GROUP, PLLC; *U.S. Private*, pg. 3937
TAYLOR & CARLS, P.A.—See Becker & Poliakoff, P.A.; *U.S. Private*, pg. 510
THOMAS P. PAPPAS & ASSOCIATES—See Kelley Cawthorne, LLC; *U.S. Private*, pg. 2275
THOMPSON HINE LLP; *U.S. Private*, pg. 4159
THOMPSON & KNIGHT LLP—See Holland & Knight LLP; *U.S. Private*, pg. 1964
THOMSEN & NYBECK, P.A.—See DeWitt Ross & Stevens S.C.; *U.S. Private*, pg. 1219
TODAY'S CAR WASH, L.L.C.—See Red Dog Equity LLC; *U.S. Private*, pg. 3374
TOP CLASS ACTIONS LLC; *U.S. Private*, pg. 4186
TORKZADEH LAW FIRM, PLC; *U.S. Private*, pg. 4189
TRILBY MISSO LAWYERS LIMITED—See Allegro Funds Pty. Ltd.; *Int'l*, pg. 336
TROUTMAN PEPPER HAMILTON SANDERS LLP; *U.S. Private*, pg. 4243
TROUTMAN SANDERS LLP; *U.S. Private*, pg. 4243
TULLY RINCKEY PLLC; *U.S. Private*, pg. 4258
UB GREENSFELDER LLP; *U.S. Private*, pg. 4273
VEDDER PRICE P.C.; *U.S. Private*, pg. 4353
VENABLE LLP; *U.S. Private*, pg. 4355
VERRILL DANA LLP; *U.S. Private*, pg. 4368
VINSON & ELKINS LLP; *U.S. Private*, pg. 4386
VOIPLINK CORPORATION; *U.S. Private*, pg. 4409
VORYS, SATER, SEYMOUR & PEASE LLP; *U.S. Private*, pg. 4413
WACHTELL LIPTON ROSEN & KATZ; *U.S. Private*, pg. 4424
WALLER LANSDEN DORTCH & DAVIS LLP—See Holland & Knight LLP; *U.S. Private*, pg. 1964
WEBER & ROSE, PSC—See Seiller Waterman LLC; *U.S. Private*, pg. 3599
WEIL, GOTSHAL & MANGES LLP; *U.S. Private*, pg. 4471
WEINTRAUB TOBIN CHEDIAK COLEMAN GRODIN LAW CORPORATION; *U.S. Private*, pg. 4472
WENDEL, ROSEN, BLACK & DEAN LLP—See Fennemore Craig, P.C.; *U.S. Private*, pg. 1495
WHITE & CASE LLP; *U.S. Private*, pg. 4507
WHITE & WILLIAMS LLP; *U.S. Private*, pg. 4508
WILEY REIN LLP; *U.S. Private*, pg. 4520
WILLIAMS & CONNOLLY, LLP; *U.S. Private*, pg. 4525
WILLIAMS MULLEN; *U.S. Private*, pg. 4526
WILLKIE FARR & GALLAGHER LLP; *U.S. Private*, pg. 4528
WILMER CUTLER PICKERING HALE & DORR LLP; *U.S. Private*, pg. 4529
WILSON ELSER MOSKOWITZ EDELMAN & DICKER; *U.S. Private*, pg. 4530
WILSON SONSINI GOODRICH & ROSATI; *U.S. Private*, pg. 4531
WILTSHIRE & GRANNIS LLP; *U.S. Private*, pg. 4532
WINICK & GALLAHER, PC; *U.S. Private*, pg. 4541
WINSTEAD PC; *U.S. Private*, pg. 4543
WINSTON & STRAWN LLP; *U.S. Private*, pg. 4543
WOMBLE CARLYLE SANDRIDGE & RICE, LLP; *U.S. Private*, pg. 4555
WOODEN MCLAUGHLIN LLP—See Dinsmore & Shohl LLP; *U.S. Private*, pg. 1234
WOODS ROGERS PLC; *U.S. Private*, pg. 4560
XEROX CORP.—See Xerox Holdings Corporation; *U.S. Public*, pg. 2390
YEPREMYAN LAW FIRM INC.; *U.S. Private*, pg. 4588

541191 — TITLE ABSTRACT AND SETTLEMENT OFFICES

ABSTRACTERS' INFORMATION SERVICE, INC.—See First American Financial Corporation; *U.S. Public*, pg. 835
ACCUTITLE LLC; *U.S. Private*, pg. 55
ACTION TITLE RESEARCH, LLC—See Strattam Capital, LLC; *U.S. Private*, pg. 3837
ADVANTAGE TITLE OF FT. BEND, LC—See Stewart Information Services Corporation; *U.S. Public*, pg. 1947
AMERICAN TITLE COMPANY OF HOUSTON—See Anywhere Real Estate Inc.; *U.S. Public*, pg. 142
BARNEY ABSTRACT & TITLE CO.—See Nebraska Title Company; *U.S. Private*, pg. 2879
BESSEMER TRUST CO. - WASHINGTON, DC—See The Bessemer Group, Incorporated; *U.S. Private*, pg. 3994
BOSTON NATIONAL TITLE AGENCY, LLC—See Incenter, LLC; *U.S. Private*, pg. 2053
BURNET TITLE OF INDIANA, LLC—See Anywhere Real Estate Inc.; *U.S. Public*, pg. 142
CONTRACT LAND STAFF LP—See Hammond, Kennedy, Whitney & Company, Inc.; *U.S. Private*, pg. 1850
COREA TITLE COMPANY—See First American Financial Corporation; *U.S. Public*, pg. 835
CORNERSTONE TITLE COMPANY—See Anywhere Real Estate Inc.; *U.S. Public*, pg. 142
CPT SC TITLE HOLDING CORPORATION; *U.S. Private*, pg. 1081
DECISIONQUEST, INC.—See U.S. Legal Support, Inc.; *U.S. Private*, pg. 4271
DIRECT TITLE SOLUTIONS, INC.; *U.S. Private*, pg. 1235
DONA ANA TITLE COMPANY, INC.—See First American Financial Corporation; *U.S. Public*, pg. 835
EASTERN TITLE AGENCY, INC.—See Hovnanian Enterprises, Inc.; *U.S. Private*, pg. 1056
EDINA REALTY TITLE—See Berkshire Hathaway Inc.; *U.S. Public*, pg. 306
EQUITY TITLE COMPANY—See Anywhere Real Estate Inc.; *U.S. Public*, pg. 142
FIDELITY NATIONAL TITLE INSURANCE COMPANY OF NEW YORK—See Fidelity National Financial, Inc.; *U.S. Public*, pg. 831
FIRST ADVANTAGE TITLE, LLC—See Anywhere Real Estate Inc.; *U.S. Public*, pg. 142
FIRST AMERICAN ABSTRACT COMPANY—See First American Financial Corporation; *U.S. Public*, pg. 836
FIRST AMERICAN SMS, LLC—See First American Financial Corporation; *U.S. Public*, pg. 836
FIRST AMERICAN TITLE & ABSTRACT CO.—See First American Financial Corporation; *U.S. Public*, pg. 836

541191 — TITLE ABSTRACT AND ...

FIRST AMERICAN TITLE COMPANY OF LARAMIE COUNTY—See First American Financial Corporation; *U.S. Public*, pg. 836
FIRST AMERICAN TITLE INSURANCE AGENCY OF PINAL—See First American Financial Corporation; *U.S. Public*, pg. 836
FIRST AMERICAN TITLE INSURANCE COMPANY—See First American Financial Corporation; *U.S. Public*, pg. 836
FIRST AMERICAN TITLE INSURANCE COMPANY—See First American Financial Corporation; *U.S. Public*, pg. 837
FIRST AMERICAN TITLE INSURANCE COMPANY—See First American Financial Corporation; *U.S. Public*, pg. 837
FIRST AMERICAN TITLE INSURANCE COMPANY—See First American Financial Corporation; *U.S. Public*, pg. 837
FIRST AMERICAN TITLE INSURANCE COMPANY—See First American Financial Corporation; *U.S. Public*, pg. 837
FIRST AMERICAN TITLE INSURANCE COMPANY—See First American Financial Corporation; *U.S. Public*, pg. 837
FIRST AMERICAN TITLE INSURANCE COMPANY—See First American Financial Corporation; *U.S. Public*, pg. 837
FIRST AMERICAN TITLE INSURANCE COMPANY - WYOMING—See First American Financial Corporation; *U.S. Public*, pg. 837
FIRST CALIFORNIA ESCROW CORPORATION—See Anywhere Real Estate Inc.; *U.S. Public*, pg. 142
GOSHEN COUNTY ABSTRACT & TITLE COMPANY—See First American Financial Corporation; *U.S. Public*, pg. 837
GUARDIAN TITLE AGENCY, LLC—See Anywhere Real Estate Inc.; *U.S. Public*, pg. 141
HEART OF AMERICA TITLE & ESCROW, LLC—See Stewart Information Services Corporation; *U.S. Public*, pg. 1947
HILLSBOROUGH TITLE INC.; *U.S. Private*, pg. 1947
INSITE CO., LTD.—See Actcall Inc.; *Int'l*, pg. 117
ISGN FULFILLMENT SERVICES, INC.—See CESC Limited; *Int'l*, pg. 1424
I & S HOLDINGS, LLC—See Stewart Information Services Corporation; *U.S. Public*, pg. 1947
KEYSTONE CLOSING SERVICES LLC—See Anywhere Real Estate Inc.; *U.S. Public*, pg. 141
LANDON TITLE COMPANY, LLC—See Stewart Information Services Corporation; *U.S. Public*, pg. 1947
LANDSAFE TITLE AGENCY, INC.—See Bank of America Corporation; *U.S. Public*, pg. 272
MARKET STREET SETTLEMENT GROUP LLC—See Anywhere Real Estate Inc.; *U.S. Public*, pg. 142
MBK REAL ESTATE LTD.; *U.S. Private*, pg. 2624
MERCURY TITLE LLC—See Anywhere Real Estate Inc.; *U.S. Public*, pg. 142
MID-ATLANTIC SETTLEMENT SERVICES LLC—See Anywhere Real Estate Inc.; *U.S. Public*, pg. 142
MID-VALLEY TITLE AND ESCROW COMPANY—See First American Financial Corporation; *U.S. Public*, pg. 837
MILLENNIUM TITLE OF HOUSTON, LC—See Stewart Information Services Corporation; *U.S. Public*, pg. 1947
MONROE-GORMAN TITLE AGENCY, LLC—See Stewart Information Services Corporation; *U.S. Public*, pg. 1947
NEAR NORTH NATIONAL TITLE, LLC; *U.S. Private*, pg. 2877
NEW LAND TITLE AGENCY, L.L.C.—See Hovnanian Enterprises, Inc.; *U.S. Public*, pg. 1060
NORTH AMERICAN TITLE COMPANY, INC.—See Doma Holdings, Inc.; *U.S. Public*, pg. 673
NRT ARIZONA LLC—See Anywhere Real Estate Inc.; *U.S. Public*, pg. 141
OKLAHOMA LAND TITLE SERVICES, LLC—See Stewart Information Services Corporation; *U.S. Public*, pg. 1947
ORANGE COAST TITLE COMPANY INC.; *U.S. Private*, pg. 3036
ORANGE COAST TITLE COMPANY—See Orange Coast Title Company Inc.; *U.S. Private*, pg. 3037
PROMINENT TITLE LLC; *U.S. Private*, pg. 3283
RED RIVER TITLE SERVICES, INC.—See Stewart Information Services Corporation; *U.S. Public*, pg. 1948
THE SEAPORT TITLE AGENCY LTD.—See LandStar Title Agency Inc.; *U.S. Private*, pg. 2387
SOLUTIONSTAR SETTLEMENT SERVICES LLC—See Mr. Cooper Group Inc.; *U.S. Public*, pg. 1480
STEWART TITLE GROUP, LLC—See Stewart Information Services Corporation; *U.S. Public*, pg. 1948
STEWART TITLE LTD.—See Stewart Information Services Corporation; *U.S. Public*, pg. 1948
STEWART TITLE OF ALBUQUERQUE, LLC—See Stewart Information Services Corporation; *U.S. Public*, pg. 1948
STEWART TITLE OF ARKANSAS, LLC—See Stewart Information Services Corporation; *U.S. Public*, pg. 1948
STEWART TITLE OF LUBBOCK, INC.—See Stewart Information Services Corporation; *U.S. Public*, pg. 1948
STEWART TITLE OF MINNESOTA, LLC—See Stewart Information Services Corporation; *U.S. Public*, pg. 1948
STEWART TITLE OF NEVADA HOLDINGS, INC.—See Stewart Information Services Corporation; *U.S. Public*, pg. 1948

STEWART TITLE S.R.O.—See Stewart Information Services Corporation; *U.S. Public*, pg. 1948
STEWART TITLE & TRUST OF TUCSON—See Stewart Information Services Corporation; *U.S. Public*, pg. 1948
ST. MARY'S TITLE SERVICES, LLC—See Anywhere Real Estate Inc.; *U.S. Public*, pg. 142
SYC SETTLEMENT SERVICES, INC.—See Orrstown Financial Services, Inc.; *U.S. Public*, pg. 1619
TIMIOS, INC.—See Ideanomics, Inc.; *U.S. Public*, pg. 1088
TITLE RESOURCE GROUP LLC—See Anywhere Real Estate Inc.; *U.S. Public*, pg. 142
TITLE RESOURCE GROUP SETTLEMENT SERVICES, LLC—See Anywhere Real Estate Inc.; *U.S. Public*, pg. 142
TITLE RESOURCES GUARANTY COMPANY—See Centerbridge Partners, L.P.; *U.S. Private*, pg. 816
TRADITION TITLE COMPANY, LLC—See Hilton Grand Vacations Inc.; *U.S. Public*, pg. 1040
UINTA TITLE AND INSURANCE, INC.—See First American Financial Corporation; *U.S. Public*, pg. 837
UNITED TITLE GUARANTY AGENCY, LLC—See Stewart Information Services Corporation; *U.S. Public*, pg. 1948
U.S. TITLE GUARANTY COMPANY—See Anywhere Real Estate Inc.; *U.S. Public*, pg. 142
WESTMINSTER TITLE COMPANY, INC.—See Toll Brothers, Inc.; *U.S. Public*, pg. 2162
WILCOX ABSTRACT & TITLE GUARANTY AGENCY—See First American Financial Corporation; *U.S. Public*, pg. 837
YANKTON TITLE COMPANY, INC.—See Stewart Information Services Corporation; *U.S. Public*, pg. 1948

541199 — ALL OTHER LEGAL SERVICES

ABOINGO SERVICES—See Aquiline Capital Partners LLC; *U.S. Private*, pg. 304
ADVANCEMENT PROJECT; *U.S. Private*, pg. 93
ADVOKATFIRMAET SCHJODT AS; *Int'l*, pg. 168
AKERMAN LLP - FORT LAUDERDALE—See Akerman LLP; *U.S. Private*, pg. 145
AMERICAN LEGAL SEARCH, LLC; *U.S. Private*, pg. 239
AMERIX CORPORATION—See Ascend One Corporation; *U.S. Private*, pg. 346
APPRISS, INC.—See Appriss Holdings, Inc.; *U.S. Private*, pg. 300
ASCEND ONE CORPORATION; *U.S. Private*, pg. 346
ASCENSION CAPITAL GROUP, INC.—See Encore Capital Group, Inc.; *U.S. Public*, pg. 759
ATLANTA LEGAL AID SOCIETY, INC.; *U.S. Private*, pg. 370
AXIOM, INC.; *U.S. Private*, pg. 413
BARBRI, INC.—See Francisco Partners Management, LP; *U.S. Private*, pg. 1588
BENGO4.COM, INC.; *Int'l*, pg. 974
BFFI GROUP INC.; *Int'l*, pg. 1006
BLACK LETTER DISCOVERY, INC.—See Milestone Partners Ltd.; *U.S. Private*, pg. 2728
BROWNSTEIN HYATT FARBER SCHRECK, LLP.; *U.S. Private*, pg. 670
CASE CENTRAL; *U.S. Private*, pg. 781
CEREBRA LPO INDIA LIMITED.—See Cerebra Integrated Technologies Ltd.; *Int'l*, pg. 1422
CMEC (BEIJING) INTERNATIONAL ECONOMIC & LEGAL ADVISORS INC.—See China Machinery Engineering Corporation; *Int'l*, pg. 1515
COMMUNITY JUSTICE PROJECT; *U.S. Private*, pg. 995
COMMUNITY LEGAL SERVICES OF MID-FLORIDA, INC.; *U.S. Private*, pg. 995
CONNECTICUT BAR FOUNDATION, INC; *U.S. Private*, pg. 1015
CONSILIO HL (UK) LIMITED—See GI Manager L.P.; *U.S. Private*, pg. 1692
CONSILIO, LLC—See GI Manager L.P.; *U.S. Private*, pg. 1692
CORPORATION SERVICE COMPANY; *U.S. Private*, pg. 1056
CPA GLOBAL (ASIA) LIMITED—See Clarivate PLC; *Int'l*, pg. 1649
CPA GLOBAL (LANDON IP), INC.—See Clarivate PLC; *Int'l*, pg. 1649
CPA GLOBAL PATENT RESEARCH LIMITED—See Clarivate PLC; *Int'l*, pg. 1649
CPA GLOBAL PATENT RESEARCH LLC—See Clarivate PLC; *Int'l*, pg. 1649
CPA GLOBAL SUPPORT SERVICES INDIA PVT. LIMITED—See Clarivate PLC; *Int'l*, pg. 1649
THE CRIMINAL JUSTICE INSTITUTE, INC.; *U.S. Private*, pg. 4016
CROWELL & MORING LLP; *U.S. Private*, pg. 1109
D4 LLC—See Adecco Group AG; *Int'l*, pg. 141
D.A.S. LEGAL SERVICES S.R.L.—See Assicurazioni Generali S.p.A.; *Int'l*, pg. 643
DAS UK HOLDINGS LIMITED—See ARAG SE; *Int'l*, pg. 534
DAVIES COLLISON CAVE ASIA PTE LTD—See Adamantem Capital Management Pty Limited; *Int'l*, pg. 124
DELOITTE LEGAL BV—See Deloitte Holding B.V.; *Int'l*, pg. 2014
DENNEMEYER SA; *Int'l*, pg. 2028

DEPOSITION SOLUTIONS, LLC - RECORDS RETRIEVAL DIVISION—See Apax Partners LLP; *Int'l*, pg. 503
DISCOVERY SERVICES LLC; *U.S. Private*, pg. 1238
DSI, DOCUMENT SOLUTIONS, INC.; *U.S. Private*, pg. 1281
ESQUIRE ASSIST LTD.—See Apax Partners LLP; *Int'l*, pg. 503
EVERYTHING LEGAL LTD.—See ARAG SE; *Int'l*, pg. 534
EVOLVE DISCOVERY LLC—See Fronteo, Inc.; *Int'l*, pg. 2794
THE FEDERALIST SOCIETY FOR LAW & PUBLIC POLICY STUDIES; *U.S. Private*, pg. 4028
FENWICK & WEST LLP; *U.S. Private*, pg. 1496
FIONDELLA, MILONE & LASARACINA LLP; *U.S. Private*, pg. 1511
FIRST NAMES (JERSEY) LIMITED—See AnaCap Financial Partners LLP; *Int'l*, pg. 445
FIRST NATIONAL TRUSTEE COMPANY LIMITED—See Epiris Managers LLP; *Int'l*, pg. 2461
THE FLORIDA BAR FOUNDATION, INC.; *U.S. Private*, pg. 4029
FNTC AMERICA LIMITED—See Epiris Managers LLP; *Int'l*, pg. 2461
THE FOCAL POINT, LLC—See Trinity Hunt Management, L.P.; *U.S. Private*, pg. 4234
FONDIA OYJ; *Int'l*, pg. 2725
FOSTER GARVEY PC; *U.S. Private*, pg. 1578
FPA PATENT ATTORNEYS PTY LTD—See Adamantem Capital Management Pty Limited; *Int'l*, pg. 124
FRAGOMEN, DEL REY, BERNSEN & LOEWY, LLP; *U.S. Private*, pg. 1586
FRONTEO KOREA, INC.—See Fronteo, Inc.; *Int'l*, pg. 2794
GATELEY (HOLDINGS) PLC; *Int'l*, pg. 2889
GEMINI LEGAL SUPPORT, INC.; *U.S. Private*, pg. 1658
GEORGIA LEGAL SERVICES PROGRAM; *U.S. Private*, pg. 1684
GREATER BOSTON LEGAL SERVICES, INC.; *U.S. Private*, pg. 1769
GTM DEVELOPMENT LTD.—See Aurelius Equity Opportunities SE & Co. KGaA; *Int'l*, pg. 708
HALFORD, NIEMIEC & FREEMAN, L.L.P.; *U.S. Private*, pg. 1842
HALLIBURTON WORLDWIDE GMBH—See Halliburton Company; *U.S. Public*, pg. 981
HANDAL & ASSOCIATES, INC.—See Greenspoon Marder LLP; *U.S. Private*, pg. 1780
H&H LTD.—See Steel Partners Holdings L.P.; *U.S. Public*, pg. 1942
HIGBEE & ASSOCIATES; *U.S. Private*, pg. 1934
HUGHES HUBBARD & REED LLP; *U.S. Private*, pg. 2003
IDEALEASE RISK SERVICES, INC.—See Idealease, Inc.; *U.S. Private*, pg. 2037
IMMIGRANT LEGAL RESOURCE CENTER; *U.S. Private*, pg. 2047
IMS CONSULTING & EXPERT SERVICES, LLC—See Trinity Hunt Management, L.P.; *U.S. Private*, pg. 4234
IPICS CORPORATION—See Denso Corporation; *Int'l*, pg. 2032
JACKSON GILMOUR & DOBBS, P.C.—See Kelley Drye & Warren LLP; *U.S. Private*, pg. 2275
JACKSON LEWIS LLP; *U.S. Private*, pg. 2177
JENNER & BLOCK LLP; *U.S. Private*, pg. 2199
JUDICIAL WATCH, INC.; *U.S. Private*, pg. 2242
KIND, INC.; *U.S. Private*, pg. 2306
KINSELLA MEDIA, LLC—See Exela Technologies, Inc.; *U.S. Public*, pg. 806
KIRKLAND & ELLIS INTERNATIONAL LLP—See Kirkland & Ellis LLP; *U.S. Private*, pg. 2315
LABCORP - CHEYENNE—See Laboratory Corporation of America Holdings; *U.S. Public*, pg. 1287
LADAS & PARRY, ENGLAND—See Ladas & Parry; *U.S. Private*, pg. 2372
LADAS & PARRY, LLP, GERMANY—See Ladas & Parry; *U.S. Private*, pg. 2372
LAWFRONT GROUP LIMITED—See Blixt Group Limited; *Int'l*, pg. 1064
LEARNERS EDGE, INC.—See Quad-C Management, Inc.; *U.S. Private*, pg. 3315
LEGAL AID CENTER OF SOUTHERN NEVADA; *U.S. Private*, pg. 2417
LEGAL AID OF NORTHWEST TEXAS; *U.S. Private*, pg. 2417
LEGAL AID SOCIETY OF SUFFOLK COUNTY INC.; *U.S. Private*, pg. 2417
LEGAL RESEARCH CENTER, INC.; *U.S. Private*, pg. 2418
LEGAL SERVICES NYC; *U.S. Private*, pg. 2418
LEGAL SERVICES OF NEW JERSEY; *U.S. Private*, pg. 2418
LEGALZOOM.COM, INC.; *U.S. Public*, pg. 1301
LEGILITY, LLC; *U.S. Private*, pg. 2418
LIGHTHOUSE DOCUMENT TECHNOLOGIES, INC.—See Lightyear Capital LLC; *U.S. Private*, pg. 2454
LITIGATION SOLUTIONS, LLC—See MCMC LLC; *U.S. Private*, pg. 2642
LONE STAR LEGAL AID; *U.S. Private*, pg. 2489
MAGNA LEGAL SERVICES—See Odyssey Investment Partners, LLC; *U.S. Private*, pg. 2995
THE MASSACHUSETTS LEGAL ASSISTANCE CORPORATION; *U.S. Private*, pg. 4075

N.A.I.C.S. INDEX

MAXENE WEINBERG AGENCY—See Huseby, LLC; *U.S. Private*, pg. 2013
MCKENZIE LAIRD OTTINGER LEACH, PLLC—See Maynard, Cooper & Gale, P.C.; *U.S. Private*, pg. 2622
MCSAM HOTEL GROUP LLC; *U.S. Private*, pg. 2644
MCS GROUP INC.; *U.S. Private*, pg. 2644
MEDICINES 360; *U.S. Private*, pg. 2656
MEDRECS, INC.—See U.S. Legal Support, Inc.; *U.S. Private*, pg. 4271
MILLER LAW GROUP; *U.S. Private*, pg. 2734
NATIONAL BUSINESS INSTITUTE; *U.S. Private*, pg. 2849
NATIONAL CONSUMER LAW CENTER, INC.; *U.S. Private*, pg. 2851
NATIONAL COUNCIL OF JUVENILE & FAMILY COURT JUDGES; *U.S. Private*, pg. 2852
NATIONAL JUVENILE DEFENDER CENTER; *U.S. Private*, pg. 2858
NATIONWIDE COURT SERVICES, INC.; *U.S. Private*, pg. 2865
NEIGHBORHOOD LEGAL SERVICES OF LOS ANGELES COUNTY; *U.S. Private*, pg. 2881
NEW YORK CITY CRIMINAL JUSTICE AGENCY, INC.; *U.S. Private*, pg. 2909
NEW YORK STATE BAR ASSOCIATION; *U.S. Private*, pg. 2912
NODAL EXCHANGE, LLC—See Deutsche Borse AG; *Int'l*, pg. 2064
NOLO INC.—See KKR & Co. Inc.; *U.S. Public*, pg. 1253
NORTHWEST JUSTICE PROJECT; *U.S. Private*, pg. 2961
ORMAN, NORD & HURD, P.L.L.P.—See Beaumier, Trogdon, Orman, Hurd & Viegas, PLLP; *U.S. Private*, pg. 508
PANGEA3 LEGAL DATABASE SYSTEMS PVT. LTD.—See Ernst & Young Pvt Ltd.; *Int'l*, pg. 2494
PANGEA3, LLC—See Ernst & Young LLP; *U.S. Private*, pg. 1422
PARADIGM DKD GROUP, L.L.C.—See Ryan, LLC; *U.S. Private*, pg. 3511
PEARL LAW GROUP; *U.S. Private*, pg. 3125
PENNSYLVANIA BAR INSTITUTE; *U.S. Private*, pg. 3136
POLSINELLI PC; *U.S. Private*, pg. 3225
PRE-PAID LEGAL SERVICES, INC.—See Stone Point Capital LLC; *U.S. Private*, pg. 3825
PROSEARCH STRATEGIES, INC.—See Consello Management LP; *U.S. Private*, pg. 1019
PROVEST LLC; *U.S. Private*, pg. 3291
QANTM INTELLECTUAL PROPERTY LIMITED—See Adamantem Capital Management Pty Limited; *Int'l*, pg. 123
REPARIO—See JLL Partners, LLC; *U.S. Private*, pg. 2213
ROCKET LAWYER INCORPORATED; *U.S. Private*, pg. 3466
ROLAND RECHTSSCHUTZ-VERSICHERUNGS-AG - AMSTERDAM—See AXA S.A.; *Int'l*, pg. 759
ROLAND RECHTSSCHUTZ VERSICHERUNGS AG—See AXA S.A.; *Int'l*, pg. 759
ROLAND RECHTSSCHUTZ-VERSICHERUNGS-AG - VIENNA—See AXA S.A.; *Int'l*, pg. 759
SALT LAKE LEGAL DEFENDER ASSOCIATION; *U.S. Private*, pg. 3533
SAYLER LEGAL SERVICE, INC.—See Gemini Legal Support, Inc.; *U.S. Private*, pg. 1658
SEIFER, MURKEN, DESPINA, JAMES & TEICHMAN, ALC—See SD Mayer & Associates LLP; *U.S. Private*, pg. 3581
SENSEI ENTERPRISES, INC.; *U.S. Private*, pg. 3607
SEYFARTH SHAW (UK) LLP—See Seyfarth Shaw; *U.S. Private*, pg. 3620
SIGNATURE CLOSERS, LLC—See Stewart Information Services Corporation; *U.S. Public*, pg. 1948
SIMMONS HANLY CONROY LLP; *U.S. Private*, pg. 3665
SIMPLURIS, INC.; *U.S. Private*, pg. 3668
SMITH BRANDON INTERNATIONAL, INC.—See Kreller Group Inc.; *U.S. Private*, pg. 2351
SOVEREIGN PALM COVE DEVELOPMENT NOMINEES PTY LIMITED—See Brookfield Corporation; *Int'l*, pg. 1189
SPECTOR & EHRENWORTH, P.C.—See Scarinci Hollenbeck, LLC; *U.S. Private*, pg. 3561
SUSTAIN TECHNOLOGIES, INC.—See Daily Journal Corporation; *U.S. Public*, pg. 620
THOMPSON COBURN LLP; *U.S. Private*, pg. 4159
TRANSPERFECT LEGAL SOLUTIONS—See TransPerfect Global, Inc.; *U.S. Private*, pg. 4210
TRIAL EXHIBITS, INC.—See U.S. Legal Support, Inc.; *U.S. Private*, pg. 4271
TRIALGRAPHIX INC.—See Odyssey Investment Partners, LLC; *U.S. Private*, pg. 2995
TRIAL PARTNERS, INC.—See U.S. Legal Support, Inc.; *U.S. Private*, pg. 4271
TRUSTPOINT INTERNATIONAL, LLC; *U.S. Private*, pg. 4251
UNITED STATES JUSTICE FOUNDATION; *U.S. Private*, pg. 4299
U.S. LEGAL SUPPORT, INC.; *U.S. Private*, pg. 4271
VERISTAR LLC; *U.S. Private*, pg. 4360
VIENNA AIRCRAFT HANDLING GESELLSCHAFT M.B.H.—See Flughafen Wien Aktiengesellschaft; *Int'l*, pg. 2713
ZAMBRA LEGAL PTY LIMITED—See Parker Hannifin Corporation; *U.S. Public*, pg. 1643

541211 — OFFICES OF CERTIFIED PUBLIC ACCOUNTANTS

AAFCPAS, INC.; *U.S. Private*, pg. 31
ABIP, PC; *U.S. Private*, pg. 38
ADAMS BROWN, LLC; *U.S. Private*, pg. 73
ADVOKATFIRMAET PRICEWATERHOUSECOOPERS AS; *Int'l*, pg. 168
AGRESTA STORMS & O'LEARY P.C.; *U.S. Private*, pg. 129
ALLISON & CHUMNEY, PC.; *U.S. Private*, pg. 192
AMADEUS FIRE SERVICES GMBH—See Amadeus Fire AG; *Int'l*, pg. 405
AMBITION GROUP LIMITED; *Int'l*, pg. 415
AMERICAN PACESETTERS ENTERPRISE LLC.; *U.S. Private*, pg. 242
ANCHIN, BLOCK & ANCHIN LLP; *U.S. Private*, pg. 272
ANDERSON ZURMUEHLEN & CO., PC; *U.S. Private*, pg. 277
ANTON COLLINS MITCHELL, LLP—See BDO USA, LLP; *U.S. Private*, pg. 501
APPLE BELL JOHNSON & CO. PA—See Gilliam Bell Moser LLP; *U.S. Private*, pg. 1700
APPLE GROWTH PARTNERS; *U.S. Private*, pg. 296
APRIO, LLP; *U.S. Private*, pg. 301
ARMANINO LLP; *U.S. Private*, pg. 330
AS PRICEWATERHOUSECOOPERS; *Int'l*, pg. 591
BAHAMAS UNDERWRITERS SERVICES LIMITED—See National Amusements, Inc.; *U.S. Private*, pg. 2839
BAKER TILLY UK AUDIT LLP—See Baker Tilly UK Holdings Limited; *Int'l*, pg. 805
BAKER TILLY US, LLP; *U.S. Private*, pg. 456
BALDWIN CPAS, PLLC; *U.S. Private*, pg. 458
BARATZ & ASSOCIATES, PA; *U.S. Private*, pg. 471
BASHOR & LEGENDRE, LLP; *U.S. Private*, pg. 484
BDO AG WIRTSCHAFTSPRUFUNGSGESELLSCHAFT; *Int'l*, pg. 929
BDO DUNWOODY LLP; *Int'l*, pg. 929
BDO KENDALLS; *Int'l*, pg. 930
BDO PUERTO RICO, P.S.C.; *U.S. Private*, pg. 500
BDO USA, LLP; *U.S. Private*, pg. 500
BENNETT THRASHER; *U.S. Private*, pg. 527
BERDON LLP; *U.S. Private*, pg. 529
BERKOWITZ POLLACK BRANT; *U.S. Private*, pg. 533
BERNARD ROBINSON & COMPANY, L.L.P.; *U.S. Private*, pg. 536
BIEGLER & ASSOCIATES, P.C.—See Kositzka & Wicks Co.; *U.S. Private*, pg. 2344
BKD, LLP - INDIANAPOLIS—See BKD, LLP; *U.S. Private*, pg. 568
BKD, LLP; *U.S. Private*, pg. 568
BLUE & CO. LLC; *U.S. Private*, pg. 585
BOLGER & ASSOCIATES, INC.; *U.S. Private*, pg. 610
BONADIO & CO. LLP; *U.S. Private*, pg. 613
BOYER AND RITTER LLC; *U.S. Private*, pg. 628
BOY SCOUTS OF AMERICA; *U.S. Private*, pg. 627
BREGMAN & COMPANY, PC—See Fiondella, Milone & LaSaracina LLP; *U.S. Private*, pg. 1511
BRIGGS & VESELKA CO.; *U.S. Private*, pg. 651
BRIMMER, BUREK & KEELAN, LLP; *U.S. Private*, pg. 654
BRIXEY & MEYER, INC.; *U.S. Private*, pg. 658
BRONIEC ASSOCIATES INC.; *U.S. Private*, pg. 662
BROWN SMITH WALLACE LLC; *U.S. Private*, pg. 668
BRUNO, DIBELLO & CO., LLC; *U.S. Private*, pg. 672
BRYANT & WELBORN L.L.P.; *U.S. Private*, pg. 673
BUCHBINDER TUNICK & COMPANY LLP; *U.S. Private*, pg. 676
BURR, PILGER & MAYER LLP; *U.S. Private*, pg. 691
CARLSON HIGHLAND & CO., LLP; *U.S. Private*, pg. 765
CARR, RIGGS & INGRAM, LLC - ATLANTA, GA—See Carr, Riggs & Ingram, LLC; *U.S. Private*, pg. 771
CARR, RIGGS & INGRAM, LLC - CONROE—See Carr, Riggs & Ingram, LLC; *U.S. Private*, pg. 771
CARR, RIGGS & INGRAM, LLC; *U.S. Private*, pg. 771
CARR, RIGGS & INGRAM, LLC - THE WOODLANDS, TX—See Carr, Riggs & Ingram, LLC; *U.S. Private*, pg. 771
CAVANAUGH & CO., LLP; *U.S. Private*, pg. 795
CBIZ ACCOUNTING, TAX & ADVISORY OF OHIO, LLC—See CBIZ, Inc.; *U.S. Public*, pg. 456
CBIZ MHM, LLC - BAKERSFIELD—See CBIZ, Inc.; *U.S. Public*, pg. 456
CBIZ MHM, LLC—See CBIZ, Inc.; *U.S. Public*, pg. 456
CBIZ MHM, LLC - TAMPA BAY—See CBIZ, Inc.; *U.S. Public*, pg. 457
CBIZ SOUTHERN CALIFORNIA, L.L.C.—See CBIZ, Inc.; *U.S. Public*, pg. 457
CENDROWSKI CORPORATE ADVISORS, LLC—See Unity Partners LP; *U.S. Public*, pg. 2253
CHAS P. SMITH & ASSOCIATES, PA, CPA'S; *U.S. Private*, pg. 859
CHERRY BEKAERT LLP; *U.S. Private*, pg. 873
CHRISTOPHER, SMITH, LEONARD, BRISTOW & STANELL, P.A.; *U.S. Private*, pg. 892
CITRIN COOPERMAN & COMPANY, LLP - MARYLAND—See Citrin Cooperman & Company, LLP; *U.S. Private*, pg. 904
CITRIN COOPERMAN & COMPANY, LLP - MASSACHUSETTS—See Citrin Cooperman & Company, LLP; *U.S. Private*, pg. 904
CITRIN COOPERMAN & COMPANY, LLP - RHODE ISLAND—See Citrin Cooperman & Company, LLP; *U.S. Private*, pg. 904
CITRIN COOPERMAN & COMPANY, LLP; *U.S. Private*, pg. 904
CJBS, LLC; *U.S. Private*, pg. 909
CLARK, SCHAEFER, HACKETT & CO.; *U.S. Private*, pg. 914
CLIFTONLARSONALLEN LLP; *U.S. Private*, pg. 943
COHEN & COMPANY; *U.S. Private*, pg. 962
COHEN & COMPANY - ST. CLAIR SHORES—See Cohen & Company; *U.S. Private*, pg. 962
COHEN & COMPANY - YOUNGSTOWN OFFICE—See Cohen & Company; *U.S. Private*, pg. 962
COHNREZNICK LLP - ATLANTA—See CohnReznick LLP; *U.S. Private*, pg. 963
COHNREZNICK LLP - BALTIMORE—See CohnReznick LLP; *U.S. Private*, pg. 963
COHNREZNICK LLP - BETHESDA—See CohnReznick LLP; *U.S. Private*, pg. 963
COHNREZNICK LLP - CHARLOTTE—See CohnReznick LLP; *U.S. Private*, pg. 963
COHNREZNICK LLP - EDISON—See CohnReznick LLP; *U.S. Private*, pg. 964
COHNREZNICK LLP - GLASTONBURY—See CohnReznick LLP; *U.S. Private*, pg. 964
COHNREZNICK LLP - ROSELAND—See CohnReznick LLP; *U.S. Private*, pg. 964
COHNREZNICK LLP - SACRAMENTO—See CohnReznick LLP; *U.S. Private*, pg. 964
COHNREZNICK LLP; *U.S. Private*, pg. 963
CONCANNON MILLER & CO., P.C.; *U.S. Private*, pg. 1008
CORE ASSOCIATES, LLC—See AvidXchange Holdings, Inc.; *U.S. Public*, pg. 246
CORRIGAN KRAUSE CPA; *U.S. Private*, pg. 1058
COULTER & JUSTUS, P.C.; *U.S. Private*, pg. 1065
COUNTING HOUSE ASSOCIATES, LLC—See AcuityCFO, LLC; *U.S. Private*, pg. 71
CREESE, SMITH, HUNE & CO., LLC—See Herbein + Company, Inc.; *U.S. Private*, pg. 1920
CROSS, FERNANDEZ & RILEY, LLP; *U.S. Private*, pg. 1105
CROWE HORWATH AUSTRALASIA LTD.—See Financial Index Australia Pty Ltd.; *Int'l*, pg. 2665
CROWE HORWATH LLP; *U.S. Private*, pg. 1109
DASZKAL BOLTON LLP—See CohnReznick LLP; *U.S. Private*, pg. 964
DELOITTE AUDIT OOD—See Deloitte Bulgaria EOOD; *Int'l*, pg. 2014
DELOITTE CHILE; *Int'l*, pg. 2014
DELOITTE LLP; *Int'l*, pg. 2014
DELOITTE & TOUCHE LLP—See Deloitte LLP; *U.S. Private*, pg. 1198
DEMBO JONES, P.C.; *U.S. Private*, pg. 1203
DENNIS, GARTLAND & NIERGARTH, CPA; *U.S. Private*, pg. 1205
DMJ & CO., PLLC; *U.S. Private*, pg. 1249
DMJ & CO., PLLC—See DMJ & Co., PLLC; *U.S. Private*, pg. 1249
DOEREN MAYHEW & CO., P.C.; *U.S. Private*, pg. 1252
E. COHEN AND COMPANY; *U.S. Private*, pg. 1303
EGIS CAPITAL PARTNERS LLC; *U.S. Private*, pg. 1344
E&H CERTIFIED PUBLIC ACCOUNTANTS & MANAGEMENT CONSULTANTS P.C.—See Mbe Cpas LLP; *U.S. Private*, pg. 2624
EHRHARDT, KEEFE, STEINER & HOTTMAN, P.C.; *U.S. Private*, pg. 1346
EIDE BAILLY LLP; *U.S. Private*, pg. 1346
ELLIOTT DAVIS DECOSIMO, LLC; *U.S. Private*, pg. 1364
ENNIS, PELLUM & ASSOCIATES, CPAS; *U.S. Private*, pg. 1401
ERNST & YOUNG GMBH WIRTSCHAFTSPRUFUNGSGESELLSCHAFT; *Int'l*, pg. 2494
ERNST & YOUNG INC.; *Int'l*, pg. 2494
ERNST & YOUNG LLP; *Int'l*, pg. 2494
ERNST & YOUNG LLP; *U.S. Private*, pg. 1422
ERNST & YOUNG PVT LTD; *Int'l*, pg. 2494
ESPIJNEIRA, PACHECO Y ASOCIADOS; *Int'l*, pg. 2506
EXLER & COMPANY, INC.—See Horovitz, Rudoy & Roteman, LLC; *U.S. Private*, pg. 1984
FOELGNER, RONZ & STRAW, P.A.; *U.S. Private*, pg. 1556
FRAZER FROST, PLC; *U.S. Private*, pg. 1599
FRAZIER & DEETER, LLC; *U.S. Private*, pg. 1599
FRAZIER & DEETER, LLC - TAMPA OFFICE—See Frazier & Deeter, LLC; *U.S. Private*, pg. 1600
FRIEDMAN LLP; *U.S. Private*, pg. 1611
FROST & CO. PLLC—See CliftonLarsonAllen LLP; *U.S. Private*, pg. 943
GALAZ, YAMAZAKI, RUIZ URQUIZA, S.C.; *Int'l*, pg. 2872
GARCIA & ORTIZ, PA; *U.S. Private*, pg. 1642
GELFAND RENNERT & FELDMAN LLP; *U.S. Private*, pg. 1656
GETTRY MARCUS CPA, P.C. - NEW YORK CITY (EAST

541211 — OFFICES OF CERTIFIE...

SIDE) OFFICE—See Citrin Cooperman & Company, LLP; *U.S. Private*, pg. 904
GETTRY MARCUS CPA, P.C. - NEW YORK CITY (WEST SIDE) OFFICE—See Citrin Cooperman & Company, LLP; *U.S. Private*, pg. 904
GETTRY MARCUS CPA, P.C.—See Citrin Cooperman & Company, LLP; *U.S. Private*, pg. 904
GILLIAM COBLE & MOSER LLP—See Gilliam Bell Moser LLP; *U.S. Private*, pg. 1700
G&J SEIBERLICH & CO., LLP; *U.S. Private*, pg. 1629
GOMERDINGER & ASSOCIATES, LLC—See Aprio, LLP; *U.S. Private*, pg. 301
GRANT THORNTON LLP - CANADA; *Int'l*, pg. 3059
GRANT THORNTON LLP - USA; *U.S. Private*, pg. 1756
GRANT THORNTON SOUTH AFRICA (PTY) LTD.; *Int'l*, pg. 3059
GRANT THORNTON UK LLP; *Int'l*, pg. 3059
GRAY, GRAY & GRAY, LLP—See Antares Group, Inc.; *U.S. Private*, pg. 287
GREAT VALLEY ADVISOR GROUP, INC.; *U.S. Private*, pg. 1768
GREGORY, SHARER & STUART, P.A.; *U.S. Private*, pg. 1783
GROSSDUKENELSON & CO., P.C.—See Brady Ware & Schoenfeld Inc.; *U.S. Private*, pg. 633
HACKER, JOHNSON & SMITH PA; *U.S. Private*, pg. 1838
HANNIS T. BOURGEOIS, LLP; *U.S. Private*, pg. 1855
HARBOR PAYMENTS, INC.—See American Express Company; *U.S. Public*, pg. 100
HAWKINS CONRAD & CO., PLLC—See BGW CPA, PLLC; *U.S. Private*, pg. 549
HBE LLP; *U.S. Private*, pg. 1887
HEMMING MORSE, INC.; *U.S. Private*, pg. 1913
HERSMAN SERLES ALMOND PLLC; *U.S. Private*, pg. 1927
HILL, BARTH & KING LLC; *U.S. Private*, pg. 1945
HLB AZERBAIJAN LLC; *Int'l*, pg. 3430
HLB CHILE - CONSULTORES Y AUDITORES DE EMPRESAS LTDA.; *Int'l*, pg. 3430
HLB CINNAMON, JANG, WILLOUGHBY & CO.; *Int'l*, pg. 3430
HLB DEUTSCHLAND GMBH; *Int'l*, pg. 3430
HLB EL SALVADOR, S.A. DE C.V.; *Int'l*, pg. 3430
HLB MANN JUDD (WA) PTY LTD—See HLB Mann Judd Australasian Association; *Int'l*, pg. 3430
HLB TECHNOLOGIES (MUMBAI) PRIVATE LIMITED; *Int'l*, pg. 3430
HLB (THAILAND) LTD.; *Int'l*, pg. 3430
HLB UKRAINE LLC; *Int'l*, pg. 3431
HLB USA, INC.; *U.S. Private*, pg. 1954
HOLTHOUSE CARLIN VAN TRIGT LLP; *U.S. Private*, pg. 1969
HONKAMP KRUEGER & CO., PC; *U.S. Private*, pg. 1977
HORNE LLP; *U.S. Private*, pg. 1983
HSMC ORIZON LLC; *U.S. Private*, pg. 1999
HUBERTY & ASSOCIATES, S.C.; *U.S. Private*, pg. 2001
IAB SOLUTIONS, LLC; *U.S. Private*, pg. 2027
INSERO & CO. CPAS, LLP; *U.S. Private*, pg. 2085
JACKSON THORNTON & CO. PC; *U.S. Private*, pg. 2178
JAMES MOORE & CO., P.L.; *U.S. Private*, pg. 2184
JANSEN VALK THOMPSON & REAHM PC; *U.S. Private*, pg. 2187
JARRARD, NOWELL & RUSSELL, LLC; *U.S. Private*, pg. 2188
JOHNSON HICKEY MURCHISON, PC; *U.S. Private*, pg. 2228
JOHNSON O'CONNOR FERON & CARUCCI, LLP; *U.S. Private*, pg. 2228
JONES, MARESCA & MCQUADE, P.A.; *U.S. Private*, pg. 2234
KATZ SAPPER & MILLER LLP; *U.S. Private*, pg. 2265
KAUFMAN, ROSSIN & CO., PROFESSIONAL ASSOCIATION; *U.S. Private*, pg. 2265
KCOE ISOM, LLP; *U.S. Private*, pg. 2270
KEMPER CPA GROUP LLP; *U.S. Private*, pg. 2282
KEMPER TECHNOLOGY CONSULTING—See Kemper CPA Group LLP; *U.S. Private*, pg. 2282
KERKERING, BARBERIO & CO.; *U.S. Private*, pg. 2290
KEY & ASSOCIATES PC; *U.S. Private*, pg. 2292
KIRKPATRICK SPRECKER & COMPANY, LLP—See Regier Carr & Monroe LLP; *U.S. Private*, pg. 3388
KLINGLER & ASSOCIATES PC—See Smith Elliott Kearns & Company, LLC; *U.S. Private*, pg. 3694
KOSITZKA & WICKS CO.; *U.S. Private*, pg. 2344
KPMG LLP; *U.S. Private*, pg. 2346
LARKIN ERVIN & SHIRLEY, LLP—See Calvetti Ferguson, P.C.; *U.S. Private*, pg. 724
LASSUS WHERLEY & ASSOCIATES, P.C.—See Peapack-Gladstone Financial Corporation; *U.S. Public*, pg. 1659
LAURUS TRANSACTION ADVISORS L.L.C.—See CBIZ, Inc.; *U.S. Public*, pg. 457
LEGACY PROFESSIONALS LLP; *U.S. Private*, pg. 2416
LEGIER & COMPANY—See Cherry Bekaert LLP; *U.S. Private*, pg. 874
LS & COMPANY; *U.S. Private*, pg. 2508
MARCUM LLP—See CBIZ, Inc.; *U.S. Public*, pg. 457
MARGOLIN, WINER & EVENS LLP; *U.S. Private*, pg. 2573
MARKHAM NORTON MOSTELLER WRIGHT & COMPANY, P.A.; *U.S. Private*, pg. 2581
MARK M. JONES & ASSOCIATES P.C.—See Calvetti Ferguson, P.C.; *U.S. Private*, pg. 724
MARKSNELSON LLC; *U.S. Private*, pg. 2582
MARKS PANETH LLP; *U.S. Private*, pg. 2582
MARRIOTT INTERNATIONAL HOTELS—See Marriott International, Inc.; *U.S. Public*, pg. 1371
MATHER & CO., CPAS, LLC; *U.S. Private*, pg. 2610
MAULDIN & JENKINS, LLC; *U.S. Private*, pg. 2615
MAYER HOFFMAN MCCANN, P.C.; *U.S. Private*, pg. 2621
MCGUIGAN TOMBS & CO.—See WithumSmith+Brown PC; *U.S. Private*, pg. 4551
MENGALI ACCOUNTANCY—See Moss Adams LLP; *U.S. Private*, pg. 2793
METTER & CO.—See Baratz & Associates, PA; *U.S. Private*, pg. 471
MICHAEL L. CROSS & CO LTD—See Herbein + Company, Inc.; *U.S. Private*, pg. 1920
MIDDLETON RAINES + ZAPATA LLP—See Baker Tilly US, LLP; *U.S. Private*, pg. 457
MITCHELL & TITUS LLP; *U.S. Private*, pg. 2750
MIZE HOUSER & CO., P.A.; *U.S. Private*, pg. 2752
MORRISON, BROWN, ARGIZ & FARRA, LLC—See BDO USA, LLP; *U.S. Private*, pg. 501
MORRISON & HEAD LP—See Ryan, LLC; *U.S. Private*, pg. 3511
THE MORRISSEY GROUP LLC; *U.S. Private*, pg. 4080
MOSS ADAMS LLP - FRESNO—See Moss Adams LLP; *U.S. Private*, pg. 2794
MOSS ADAMS LLP - SACRAMENTO—See Moss Adams LLP; *U.S. Private*, pg. 2794
MOSS ADAMS LLP - SANTA ROSA—See Moss Adams LLP; *U.S. Private*, pg. 2794
MOSS ADAMS LLP; *U.S. Private*, pg. 2793
MOSS ADAMS LLP - SPOKANE—See Moss Adams LLP; *U.S. Private*, pg. 2794
MOSS ADAMS LLP - YAKIMA—See Moss Adams LLP; *U.S. Private*, pg. 2794
MOUNTJOY CHILTON MEDLEY LLP; *U.S. Private*, pg. 2801
MURRAY, JONSON, WHITE & ASSOCIATES, LTD., P.C.—See Yount, Hyde & Barbour PC; *U.S. Private*, pg. 4594
NATIONAL HEALTHCARE REVIEW INC.; *U.S. Private*, pg. 2856
OLSEN THIELEN & CO. LTD.; *U.S. Private*, pg. 3011
ON-TIME PAYROLL, INC.—See DiVirgilio Insurance & Financial Group; *U.S. Private*, pg. 1244
PANNELL KERR FORSTER OF TEXAS, P.C.; *U.S. Private*, pg. 3086
PARESKY FLITT & COMPANY, LLP—See UHY LLP; *U.S. Private*, pg. 4275
PDR CERTIFIED PUBLIC ACCOUNTANTS; *U.S. Private*, pg. 3122
PEAK INVESTMENT SOLUTIONS, LLC; *U.S. Private*, pg. 3123
PERKINS & COMPANY, P.C.; *U.S. Private*, pg. 3151
PETER LI, INC.—See Peter Li Education Group; *U.S. Private*, pg. 3158
PKF O'CONNOR DAVIES, LLP; *U.S. Private*, pg. 3193
PLANTE & MORAN, PLLC—See Aquiline Capital Partners LLC; *U.S. Private*, pg. 304
PORTE BROWN LLC; *U.S. Private*, pg. 3231
POWERS & SULLIVAN, LLC—See CBIZ, Inc.; *U.S. Public*, pg. 457
PRAGER METIS CPAS, LLC; *U.S. Private*, pg. 3241
PRGR BELGIUM, INC.—See PRGX Global, Inc.; *U.S. Private*, pg. 3257
PRGX INDIA PRIVATE LIMITED—See PRGX Global, Inc.; *U.S. Private*, pg. 3257
PRGX PORTUGAL, INC.—See PRGX Global, Inc.; *U.S. Private*, pg. 3257
PRICEWATERHOUSECOOPERS LANKA (PRIVATE) LIMITED—See Deloitte Touche Tohmatsu Limited; *Int'l*, pg. 2015
PRICEWATERHOUSECOOPERS LLP (USA); *U.S. Private*, pg. 3259
PRIDA GUIDA & COMPANY, P.A.; *U.S. Private*, pg. 3259
REA & ASSOCIATES, INC.; *U.S. Private*, pg. 3365
REDMILE GROUP LLC; *U.S. Private*, pg. 3379
REGIER CARR & MONROE LLP; *U.S. Private*, pg. 3388
REHMANN ROBSON PC; *U.S. Private*, pg. 3389
RICHARD P. MORTENSON P. C.; *U.S. Private*, pg. 3428
RIDOUT BARRETT & CO PC—See Aprio, LLP; *U.S. Private*, pg. 301
RIVERO, GORDIMER & COMPANY, P.A.; *U.S. Private*, pg. 3445
ROCKY MOUNTAIN ADVISORY, LLC—See Marshall & Stevens Inc.; *U.S. Private*, pg. 2592
RSM US LLP; *U.S. Private*, pg. 3497
RUBINBROWN LLP; *U.S. Private*, pg. 3500
RVG PARTNERS, LLC—See Porte Brown LLC; *U.S. Private*, pg. 3231
SALTMARSH CLEAVELAND & GUND CPAS; *U.S. Private*, pg. 3534
SAREEN & ASSOCIATES, INC.; *U.S. Private*, pg. 3550
SCANLAN & LEO, LTD.—See Sikich LLP; *U.S. Private*, pg. 3651

SC&H GROUP, LLC; *U.S. Private*, pg. 3560
SCHNEIDER DOWNS & CO., INC.; *U.S. Private*, pg. 3566
SCOTT A. GOFFSTEIN & ASSOCIATES, LLP—See AAFCPAs, Inc.; *U.S. Private*, pg. 31
SEVENICH BUTLER GERLACH BRAZIL, LTD.—See Nepsis Inc.; *U.S. Private*, pg. 2885
SEYMOUR TAYLOR AUDIT LIMITED—See Hampden Holdings Limited; *Int'l*, pg. 3239
SHINN & COMPANY, LLC—See Carr, Riggs & Ingram, LLC; *U.S. Private*, pg. 771
SIKICH LLP; *U.S. Private*, pg. 3651
SINGER LEWAK GREENBAUM & GOLDSTEIN; *U.S. Private*, pg. 3670
SKODA, MINOTTI & CO., CERTIFIED PUBLIC ACCOUNTANTS; *U.S. Private*, pg. 3683
THE SLEETER GROUP, INC.—See Diversified Communications; *U.S. Private*, pg. 1241
SMITH ELLIOTT KEARNS & COMPANY, LLC; *U.S. Private*, pg. 3694
SMITH SCHAFER AND ASSOCIATES, LTD.; *U.S. Private*, pg. 3695
SQUAR MILNER LLP; *U.S. Private*, pg. 3766
STRATUS GROUP LLC—See Unity Partners LP; *U.S. Public*, pg. 2253
SUBY, VON HADEN & ASSOCIATES, S.C.; *U.S. Private*, pg. 3848
SUPERCOMM INC.—See The Walt Disney Company; *U.S. Public*, pg. 2139
SWINDOLL, JANZEN, HAWK & LLOYD, LLC; *U.S. Private*, pg. 3893
TIDWELL GROUP, LLC; *U.S. Private*, pg. 4168
TJS & COMPANY, LLC—See TJS Deemer Dana LLP; *U.S. Private*, pg. 4178
TJS DEEMER DANA - DULUTH—See TJS Deemer Dana LLP; *U.S. Private*, pg. 4178
TJS DEEMER DANA LLP; *U.S. Private*, pg. 4178
UHY LLP; *U.S. Private*, pg. 4275
U.S. BANK BUSINESS CREDIT—See U.S. Bancorp; *U.S. Public*, pg. 2213
VAVRINEK, TRINE, DAY AND CO., LLP; *U.S. Private*, pg. 4348
VERDI CONSULTING INC; *U.S. Private*, pg. 4359
VOLT INFORMATION SCIENCES-WEST—See American CyberSystems, Inc.; *U.S. Private*, pg. 230
VONFELDT, BAUER, & VONFELDT CHARTERED—See Adams Brown, LLC; *U.S. Private*, pg. 74
THE WAGNER COMPANIES, INC.; *U.S. Private*, pg. 4132
WARREN AVERETT, LLC; *U.S. Private*, pg. 4443
WEAVER & TIDWELL, L.L.P.; *U.S. Private*, pg. 4463
WHITLEY PENN LLP; *U.S. Private*, pg. 4512
WHITTLESEY & HADLEY, P.C. - HAMDEN OFFICE—See Whittlesey & Hadley, P.C.; *U.S. Private*, pg. 4514
WHITTLESEY & HADLEY, P.C. - HOLYOKE OFFICE—See Whittlesey & Hadley, P.C.; *U.S. Private*, pg. 4514
WHITTLESEY & HADLEY, P.C.; *U.S. Private*, pg. 4514
WINDES, INC.; *U.S. Private*, pg. 4537
WITHUMSMITH+BROWN PC; *U.S. Private*, pg. 4550
WOLF & COMPANY, P.C.—See BKD, LLP; *U.S. Private*, pg. 568
WOODCOCK & ASSOCIATES, PC—See Yount, Hyde & Barbour PC; *U.S. Private*, pg. 4594
WSRP, LLC; *U.S. Private*, pg. 4574
YEO & YEO, P.C.; *U.S. Private*, pg. 4588

541213 — TAX PREPARATION SERVICES

2ND STORY SOFTWARE, INC.—See Genstar Capital, LLC; *U.S. Private*, pg. 1676
ACCOUNTAX CONSULTING LIMITED—See Markel Group Inc.; *U.S. Public*, pg. 1367
ADVENT FINANCIAL SERVICES—See Novation Companies, Inc.; *U.S. Public*, pg. 1548
AMSCOT CORPORATION—See Amscot Holdings Inc.; *U.S. Private*, pg. 267
AMSCOT HOLDINGS INC.; *U.S. Private*, pg. 267
BANKER EXCHANGE, LLC—See TIC Properties, LLC; *U.S. Private*, pg. 4167
BDO SCHLESWIG-HOLSTEINISCHE TREUHANDGESELLSCHAFT MBH WIRTSCHAFTSPRUFUNGSGESELLSCHAFT STEUERBERATUNGSGESELLSCHAFT—See BDO AG Wirtschaftsprufungsgesellschaft; *Int'l*, pg. 929
BEIJING AEROSPACE GOLDEN CARD CO.—See Aisino Corporation; *Int'l*, pg. 254
BLEVINS FRANKS TAX LIMITED—See Blevins Franks Financial Management Limited; *Int'l*, pg. 1063
DANERICA ENTERPRISES, INC.; *U.S. Private*, pg. 1153
DELOITTE TAX LLP—See Deloitte LLP; *U.S. Private*, pg. 1198
ELIZABETH MORELAND CONSULTING, INC.—See Stone Point Capital LLC; *U.S. Private*, pg. 3825
EPS FINANCIAL, LLC—See Pathward Financial, Inc.; *U.S. Public*, pg. 1652
EQUINOX BUSINESS SOLUTIONS; *U.S. Private*, pg. 1415
EQUITA LIMITED—See Capita plc; *Int'l*, pg. 1309
FARM BUSINESS CONSULTANTS INC.; *Int'l*, pg. 2619

N.A.I.C.S. INDEX

541219 — OTHER ACCOUNTING SE...

FUHRMAN, SMOLSKY & FUREY, INC.—See HBE LLP; *U.S. Private*, pg. 1887
GEBERIT SERVICE SP. Z O.O.—See Geberit AG; *Int'l*, pg. 2905
HRB CORPORATE SERVICES LLC—See H&R Block, Inc.; *U.S. Public*, pg. 976
HRB DIGITAL LLC—See H&R Block, Inc.; *U.S. Public*, pg. 976
H&R BLOCK COMPANY OF UTAH—See H&R Block, Inc.; *U.S. Public*, pg. 976
H&R BLOCK EASTERN ENTERPRISES, INC.—See H&R Block, Inc.; *U.S. Public*, pg. 976
H&R BLOCK GROUP, INC.—See H&R Block, Inc.; *U.S. Public*, pg. 976
H&R BLOCK (INDIA) PRIVATE LIMITED—See H&R Block, Inc.; *U.S. Public*, pg. 976
H&R BLOCK TAX AND BUSINESS SERVICES, INC.—See H&R Block, Inc.; *U.S. Public*, pg. 976
H&R BLOCK TAX SERVICES LLC—See H&R Block, Inc.; *U.S. Public*, pg. 976
JACKSON HEWITT TAX SERVICE INC.; *U.S. Private*, pg. 2177
JTH TAX, INC.—See B. Riley Financial, Inc.; *U.S. Public*, pg. 261
JTH TAX, INC.—See Irradiant Partners, LP; *U.S. Private*, pg. 2140
LOPEZ TAX SERVICE, INC.; *U.S. Private*, pg. 2494
MARKEL CONSULTANCY SERVICES LIMITED—See Markel Group Inc.; *U.S. Public*, pg. 1368
MEADOWS URQUHART ACREE & COOK, LLP; *U.S. Private*, pg. 2647
THE NANNY TAX COMPANY; *U.S. Private*, pg. 4081
OPPORTUNE LLP; *U.S. Private*, pg. 3033
ORIGAMI LOGIC LTD.—See Intuit Inc.; *U.S. Public*, pg. 1160
PAYROLL TAX FILING SERVICES, INC.—See NCR Voyix Corporation.; *U.S. Public*, pg. 1502
PLYMOUTH PARK TAX SERVICES LLC—See JPMorgan Chase & Co.; *U.S. Public*, pg. 1210
PROFIT SENSE INNOVATIONS; *U.S. Private*, pg. 3277
REAL PROPERTY TAX ADVISORS; *U.S. Private*, pg. 3368
RELOCATION TAXES, LLC—See Orion Mobility; *U.S. Private*, pg. 3043
RNL & ASSOCIATES—See Berkshire Hills Bancorp, Inc.; *U.S. Public*, pg. 320
ROSS & ROBERTS LIMITED—See Capita plc; *Int'l*, pg. 1309
RYAN, LLC; *U.S. Private*, pg. 3510
TAXBREAK LLC; *U.S. Private*, pg. 3937
TAX GUARD, INC.—See Bertram Capital Management, LLC; *U.S. Private*, pg. 540
TAXOPS LLC; *U.S. Private*, pg. 3937
TCA FINANCIAL, LLC; *U.S. Private*, pg. 3942
TRUE PARTNERS CONSULTING LLC—See Baker Tilly US, LLP; *U.S. Private*, pg. 457
WALL STREET CONCEPTS—See Fidelity National Infor.; *U.S. Public*, pg. 832
WORLDWIDE TRADE PARTNERS, LLC—See Ryan, LLC; *U.S. Private*, pg. 3511

541214 — PAYROLL SERVICES

ACLINE HR—See New Mountain Capital, LLC; *U.S. Private*, pg. 2901
ADP CANADA CO.—See Automatic Data Processing, Inc.; *U.S. Public*, pg. 230
ADP EUROPE S.A.—See Automatic Data Processing, Inc.; *U.S. Public*, pg. 229
ADP NATIONAL ACCOUNT SERVICES—See Automatic Data Processing, Inc.; *U.S. Public*, pg. 230
ADP PRIVATE LIMITED—See Automatic Data Processing, Inc.; *U.S. Public*, pg. 230
ADVANCED BUSINESS SOFTWARE & SOLUTIONS LTD.; *Int'l*, pg. 157
ADVANTAGE PAYROLL SERVICES INC.—See Paychex, Inc.; *U.S. Public*, pg. 1655
AFRICA HR SOLUTIONS LTD.—See ADvTECH Limited; *Int'l*, pg. 168
AMANO BUSINESS SOLUTIONS CORP.—See Amano Corporation; *Int'l*, pg. 410
AMERICAN AUTOMATED PAYROLL; *U.S. Private*, pg. 223
A RAIZE-INSTITUICAO DE PAGAMENTOS S.A.; *Int'l*, pg. 18
ASSOCIATED DATA SERVICES, INC.—See Asure Software, Inc.; *U.S. Public*, pg. 218
ASURE PAYROLL TAX MANAGEMENT LLC—See Asure Software, Inc.; *U.S. Public*, pg. 218
AUTOMATIC DATA PROCESSING INSURANCE AGENCY, INC.—See Automatic Data Processing, Inc.; *U.S. Public*, pg. 230
AUTOMATIC DATA PROCESSING LIMITED—See Automatic Data Processing, Inc.; *U.S. Public*, pg. 230
BABEL MEDIA INDIA PRIVATE LIMITED—See Canada Pension Plan Investment Board; *Int'l*, pg. 1280
BABEL MEDIA INDIA PRIVATE LIMITED—See EQT AB; *Int'l*, pg. 2482
BOARDROOM CORPORATE SERVICES (HK) LIMITED—See G. K. Goh Holdings Limited; *Int'l*, pg. 2864
BOARDROOM CORPORATE SERVICES (JOHOR) SDN BHD—See G. K. Goh Holdings Limited; *Int'l*, pg. 2864
BOARDROOM CORPORATE SERVICES (PENANG) SDN BHD—See G. K. Goh Holdings Limited; *Int'l*, pg. 2864
BOARDROOM LSC BEIJING LIMITED—See G. K. Goh Holdings Limited; *Int'l*, pg. 2864
BOARDROOM LSC CHINA LIMITED—See G. K. Goh Holdings Limited; *Int'l*, pg. 2864
BOARDROOM PTY LIMITED—See G. K. Goh Holdings Limited; *Int'l*, pg. 2864
CAST & CREW ENTERTAINMENT SERVICES LLC—See EQT AB; *Int'l*, pg. 2473
CELERGO; *U.S. Private*, pg. 806
CENTERSTONE INSURANCE & FINANCIAL SERVICES, INC.—See Truist Financial Corporation; *U.S. Public*, pg. 2199
CERIDIAN BENEFITS SERVICES—See Fidelity National Financial, Inc.; *U.S. Public*, pg. 831
CERIDIAN BENEFITS SERVICES—See Thomas H. Lee Partners, L.P.; *U.S. Private*, pg. 4156
CERIDIAN CORPORATION—See Fidelity National Financial, Inc.; *U.S. Public*, pg. 830
CERIDIAN CORPORATION—See Thomas H. Lee Partners, L.P.; *U.S. Private*, pg. 4156
CHECKS AND BALANCES INC—See Employment Enterprises Inc.; *U.S. Private*, pg. 1387
DEEL, INC.; *U.S. Private*, pg. 1189
DENSO WELL CORPORATION—See Denso Corporation; *Int'l*, pg. 2031
DENTSU MANAGEMENT SERVICES INC.—See Dentsu Group Inc.; *Int'l*, pg. 2038
DOHERTY EMPLOYER SERVICES—See Paychex, Inc.; *U.S. Public*, pg. 1655
DOMINION PAYROLL SERVICES; *U.S. Private*, pg. 1256
ECIT WLCOM AS—See TowerBrook Capital Partners, L.P.; *U.S. Private*, pg. 4195
ECOMIC CO LTD; *Int'l*, pg. 2296
EFG BUSINESS SERVICES D.O.O. BEOGRAD—See Eurobank Ergasias Services and Holdings S.A.; *Int'l*, pg. 2532
ELECTRONIC COMMERCE INC.; *U.S. Private*, pg. 1355
ESCALON SERVICES INC.; *U.S. Private*, pg. 1424
ESG REPUBLIC; *U.S. Private*, pg. 1425
EUROBANK EFG BUSINESS SERVICES S.A.—See Eurobank Ergasias Services and Holdings S.A.; *Int'l*, pg. 2532
EXECUPAY, INC.—See Vensure Employer Services, Inc.; *U.S. Private*, pg. 4357
EXPATICORE SERVICES LLC—See Clune Technology Group; *Int'l*, pg. 1664
EXPERCASH GMBH—See Mastercard Incorporated; *U.S. Public*, pg. 1394
FMS SOLUTIONS HOLDINGS, LLC—See New Heritage Capital LLC; *U.S. Private*, pg. 2896
GALAXY PAYROLL GROUP LIMITED; *Int'l*, pg. 2871
GTM PAYROLL SERVICES INC.; *U.S. Private*, pg. 1807
HEARTLAND PAYROLL SOLUTIONS, INC.—See Global Payments Inc.; *U.S. Public*, pg. 944
HITACHI MANAGEMENT PARTNER, CORP.—See Hitachi, Ltd.; *Int'l*, pg. 3420
I3-AXIA, LLC—See i3 Verticals, Inc.; *U.S. Public*, pg. 1081
I3-EZPAY, LLC—See i3 Verticals, Inc.; *U.S. Public*, pg. 1081
I3-RS, LLC—See i3 Verticals, Inc.; *U.S. Public*, pg. 1081
INOVA PAYROLL, INC.; *U.S. Private*, pg. 2084
INTECT APS—See TowerBrook Capital Partners, L.P.; *U.S. Private*, pg. 4195
JETPAY ISO SERVICES, LLC—See NCR Voyix Corporation.; *U.S. Public*, pg. 1502
JETPAY MERCHANT SERVICES, LLC—See NCR Voyix Corporation.; *U.S. Public*, pg. 1502
JX NIPPON BUSINESS SERVICES CORPORATION—See ENEOS Holdings, Inc.; *Int'l*, pg. 2416
KELLY PAYROLL SERVICES LIMITED—See Kelly Services, Inc.; *U.S. Public*, pg. 1219
LYONS HR, INC.—See New Mountain Capital, LLC; *U.S. Private*, pg. 2901
MASTERCARD ASIA/PACIFIC (AUSTRALIA) PTY. LTD.—See Mastercard Incorporated; *U.S. Public*, pg. 1394
MASTERCARD ASIA/PACIFIC PTE. LTD.—See Mastercard Incorporated; *U.S. Public*, pg. 1394
MODIS INTERNATIONAL LIMITED—See Adecco Group AG; *Int'l*, pg. 140
MONEY WISE PAYROLL SOLUTIONS—See Blue Ridge Bankshares, Inc.; *U.S. Public*, pg. 365
MORGAN WHITE GROUP, INC.; *U.S. Private*, pg. 2784
MPAY, INC.; *U.S. Private*, pg. 2803
NATIONAL PAYROLL SYSTEMS PTY. LTD.—See Allegis Group, Inc.; *U.S. Private*, pg. 177
NEXTIMAGE MEDICAL, INC.—See Chrysalis Ventures; *U.S. Private*, pg. 893
NORIAN ACCOUNTING AB—See TowerBrook Capital Partners, L.P.; *U.S. Private*, pg. 4195
NORIAN ACCOUNTING SP. Z O.O.—See TowerBrook Capital Partners, L.P.; *U.S. Private*, pg. 4195
NORIAN ACCOUNTING UAB—See TowerBrook Capital Partners, L.P.; *U.S. Private*, pg. 4195
OPTIMUM OUTSOURCING LLC; *U.S. Private*, pg. 3035
PAI SERVICES LLC; *U.S. Private*, pg. 3075
PAXSAL BUSINESS PROCESS OUTSOURCING (PTY) LTD—See Adcorp Holdings Limited; *Int'l*, pg. 127
PAXSAL PAYROLL OUTSOURCING (PTY) LTD—See Adcorp Holdings Limited; *Int'l*, pg. 127
PAYCHEX, INC.; *U.S. Public*, pg. 1655
PAYCHEX MANAGEMENT CORP.—See Paychex, Inc.; *U.S. Public*, pg. 1656
PAYCHEX TIME & ATTENDANCE INC.—See Paychex, Inc.; *U.S. Public*, pg. 1656
PAYCOR, INC.; *U.S. Private*, pg. 3116
PAYCOR, INC.—See Paycor, Inc.; *U.S. Private*, pg. 3116
PAYDAY PAYROLL SERVICES; *U.S. Private*, pg. 3116
PAYPAL AUSTRALIA PTY LIMITED—See PayPal Holdings, Inc.; *U.S. Public*, pg. 1656
PAYPLUS, LLC; *U.S. Private*, pg. 3117
PAYROC LLC—See PCP Enterprise, L.P.; *U.S. Private*, pg. 3121
PAYROLL 1, INC.—See Global Payments Inc.; *U.S. Public*, pg. 944
PAYROLL MAXX, LLC—See Asure Software, Inc.; *U.S. Public*, pg. 218
PAYROLL SERVICES PLUS, INC.; *U.S. Private*, pg. 3117
PRIMEPAY, LLC; *U.S. Private*, pg. 3263
PROFESSIONAL OUTSOURCING SOLUTIONS LIMITED—See Humanica Public Company Limited; *Int'l*, pg. 3530
PROLIANT; *U.S. Private*, pg. 3282
PUREPAYMENTS LLC—See Rev19, LLC; *U.S. Private*, pg. 3413
RUE DE LA PAYE SAS—See Cegedim S.A.; *Int'l*, pg. 1390
SAN DIEGO COUNTY TOBACCO SECURITIZATION CORPORATION; *U.S. Private*, pg. 3539
SERVICIOS ADMINISTRATIVOS VOLARIS, S.A. DE C.V.—See Controladora Vuela Compania de Aviacion, S.A.B. de C.V.; *Int'l*, pg. 1786
SUREPAYROLL, INC.—See Paychex, Inc.; *U.S. Public*, pg. 1656
TALENT2 K.K.—See Allegis Group, Inc.; *U.S. Private*, pg. 177
TALENT PARTNERS; *U.S. Private*, pg. 3926
TALENT PARTNERS—See Talent Partners; *U.S. Private*, pg. 3926
TELEPASS PAY SPA—See Edizione S.r.l.; *Int'l*, pg. 2312
TELEPAYROLL, INC.—See Asure Software, Inc.; *U.S. Public*, pg. 218
TP ASSOCIATES INC.—See Timber Products Company, LP; *U.S. Private*, pg. 4171
TRUPAY; *U.S. Private*, pg. 4250
USA PAYROLLS INC.—See Asure Software, Inc.; *U.S. Public*, pg. 218
VENMO INC.—See eBay Inc.; *U.S. Public*, pg. 709
VENTURO TECHNOLOGIES S.A.R.L.—See Corpay, Inc.; *U.S. Public*, pg. 580
VISUAL LEASE, LLC—See CoStar Group, Inc.; *U.S. Public*, pg. 586
WEX AUSTRALIA PTY LTD—See WEX, Inc.; *U.S. Public*, pg. 2364
WEX EUROPE LIMITED—See WEX, Inc.; *U.S. Public*, pg. 2365
WISE CONSULTING ASSOCIATES, LLC—See RSM US LLP; *U.S. Private*, pg. 3497
WOODLAND RESORT CONFERENCE CENTRE—See Woodlands Operating Company LP; *U.S. Private*, pg. 4559
XACCT ACCOUNTING AS—See TowerBrook Capital Partners, L.P.; *U.S. Private*, pg. 4195

541219 — OTHER ACCOUNTING SERVICES

ABACI AS—See TowerBrook Capital Partners, L.P.; *U.S. Private*, pg. 4194
ABC FINANCIAL SERVICES, INC.—See Thoma Bravo, L.P.; *U.S. Private*, pg. 4145
ACCOUNTANTS IN TRANSITION, INC.; *U.S. Private*, pg. 54
ACCOUNTING MANAGEMENT SOLUTIONS, INC.; *U.S. Private*, pg. 54
ACOM MEDICAL BILLING—See ACOM Solutions Inc.; *U.S. Private*, pg. 62
ACUITYCFO, LLC; *U.S. Private*, pg. 71
AGRI STATS, INC.—See Eli Lilly & Company; *U.S. Public*, pg. 731
AIRAN AUSTRALIA PTY LIMITED—See AIRAN Limited; *Int'l*, pg. 241
AIRAN GLOBAL PRIVATE LIMITED—See AIRAN Limited; *Int'l*, pg. 241
AIRLINE ACCOUNTING CENTER DE MEXICO S.A. DE C.V.—See Deutsche Lufthansa AG; *Int'l*, pg. 2069
AKADEMIE FUR INTERNATIONALE RECHNUNGSLEGUNG (AKIR) GMBH—See Amadeus Fire AG; *Int'l*, pg. 405
ALDANA & ASSOCIATES PSC LTD.; *U.S. Private*, pg. 155
ALEA INZENIRING DOO; *Int'l*, pg. 305
ALLIED PHYSICIANS OF MICHIANA, LLC—See The South

541219 — OTHER ACCOUNTING SE...

Bend Clinic, LLP; *U.S. Private*, pg. 4119
ALLOY, SILVERSTEIN, SHAPIRO, ADAMS, MULFORD, CICALESE, WILSON & COMPANY; *U.S. Private*, pg. 193
ALLY SERVICING, LLC—See Ally Financial Inc.; *U.S. Public*, pg. 81
ALPHA REVIEW CORPORATION—See Stone Point Capital LLC; *U.S. Private*, pg. 3823
AMADEUS FIRE INTERIM- UND PROJEKTMANAGEMENT GMBH—See Amadeus Fire AG; *Int'l*, pg. 405
AMERICAN SUPPORT LLC; *U.S. Private*, pg. 256
ANDERSON ANDERSON & BROWN LLP; *Int'l*, pg. 450
ANESTHESIA BUSINESS CONSULTANTS; *U.S. Private*, pg. 281
ANTARES GROUP, INC.; *U.S. Private*, pg. 287
APEX ACCOUNTING AND TAX, INC.; *U.S. Private*, pg. 291
ARC CONSULTING LLC—See CBIZ, Inc.; *U.S. Public*, pg. 456
ARGY, WILTSE & ROBINSON, P.C.; *U.S. Private*, pg. 322
ARLA FOODS FINANCIAL SERVICES CENTRE SP. Z O.O.—See Arla Foods amba; *Int'l*, pg. 572
ARROW BUSINESS CONSULTING CORPORATION—See Chiyoda Corporation; *Int'l*, pg. 1574
ASSOCIATED BILLING SERVICES, INC.—See Northwell Health, Inc.; *U.S. Private*, pg. 2958
ASSURANCE FORENSIC ACCOUNTING CPAS, LLC; *U.S. Private*, pg. 359
ATAG PRIVATE CLIENT SERVICES AG—See Basellandschaftliche Kantonalbank; *Int'l*, pg. 871
AUDITWERX—See Carr, Riggs & Ingram, LLC; *U.S. Private*, pg. 771
BADEN GAGE & SCHROEDER, LLC; *U.S. Private*, pg. 424
BARRACLOUGH & ASSOCIATES, PC—See Carr, Riggs & Ingram, LLC; *U.S. Private*, pg. 771
BARZ, GOWIE, AMON & FULTZ LLC; *U.S. Private*, pg. 484
BDO DR. LAUTER & FISCHER GMBH WIRTSCHAFTSPRUFUNGS-GESELLSCHAFT—See BDO AG Wirtschaftsprufungsgesellschaft; *Int'l*, pg. 929
BDO SCHURMANN & GLASHOFF STEUERBERATUNGSGESELLSCHAFT MBH—See BDO AG Wirtschaftsprufungsgesellschaft; *Int'l*, pg. 929
BDO WESTFALEN-REVISION GMBH WIRTSCHAFTSPRUFUNGSGESELLSCHAFT—See BDO AG Wirtschaftsprufungsgesellschaft; *Int'l*, pg. 929
BEDERSON & COMPANY LLP; *U.S. Private*, pg. 512
BERGAN PAULSEN & COMPANY PC; *U.S. Private*, pg. 530
BGW CPA, PLLC; *U.S. Private*, pg. 549
BILLING SERVICES, INC.—See Fellow Health Partners, Inc.; *U.S. Private*, pg. 1494
BLANSKI PETER KRONLAGE & ZACH, P.A.—See Smith Schafer and Associates, Ltd.; *U.S. Private*, pg. 3695
BOARDROOM BUSINESS SOLUTIONS PTE. LTD.—See G. K. Goh Holdings Limited; *Int'l*, pg. 2864
BODINE AND COMPANY, LLC; *U.S. Private*, pg. 608
BORLAND BENEFIELD, P.C.; *U.S. Private*, pg. 618
THE BOSMA GROUP, PC; *U.S. Private*, pg. 3997
BPA WORLDWIDE, INC.—See Alliance for Audited Media; *U.S. Private*, pg. 182
BRADY WARE & SCHOENFELD INC.; *U.S. Private*, pg. 633
BRANDYWINE FINANCIAL SERVICES CORPORATION—See The Brandywine Companies, LLC; *U.S. Private*, pg. 4000
BRIGHTREE LLC—See ResMed Inc.; *U.S. Public*, pg. 1790
BROUSSARD PARTNERS & ASSOCIATES—See Guggenheim Partners, LLC; *U.S. Private*, pg. 1812
BROUSSARD POCHE LEWIS BREAUX LLC; *U.S. Private*, pg. 665
BST & CO. CPA LLP; *U.S. Private*, pg. 675
CADE, LTD.; *U.S. Private*, pg. 712
CAJAVEC USLUZNE DJELATNOSTI A.D.—See Cajavec SIP a.d.; *Int'l*, pg. 1260
CALVETTI FERGUSON, P.C.; *U.S. Private*, pg. 724
CANOPY FINANCIAL; *U.S. Private*, pg. 735
CARLSBERG ACCOUNTING SERVICE CENTRE SP. Z.O.O.—See Carlsberg A/S; *Int'l*, pg. 1339
CAROLINAS MEDICAL ALLIANCE, INC.—See Medical University Of South Carolina; *U.S. Private*, pg. 2656
CBIZ ACCOUNTING, TAX & ADVISORY OF SOUTHWEST FLORIDA, LLC—See CBIZ, Inc.; *U.S. Public*, pg. 456
CBIZ ACCOUNTING, TAX & ADVISORY OF TOPEKA, LLC—See CBIZ, Inc.; *U.S. Public*, pg. 456
CBIZ BEATTY SATCHELL, LLC—See CBIZ, Inc.; *U.S. Public*, pg. 456
CBIZ, INC.; *U.S. Public*, pg. 456
CBIZ MHM, LLC - KANSAS CITY—See CBIZ, Inc.; *U.S. Public*, pg. 456
CERIMELE, MEYER & WRAY, LLC—See Bodine and Company, LLC; *U.S. Private*, pg. 608
CFGI, LLC—See The Carlyle Group Inc.; *U.S. Public*, pg. 2045
CHARLES A LUTHER, C.P.A.; *U.S. Private*, pg. 851
COLLECTIVE POINT OF SALE SOLUTIONS LTD.—See U.S. Bancorp; *U.S. Public*, pg. 2212
COMCOUNT INC.; *U.S. Private*, pg. 981
COMPREHENSIVE MEDICAL PRACTICE MANAGEMENT, INC.; *U.S. Private*, pg. 1003
CONCEPT RESTAURANTS INC.; *U.S. Private*, pg. 1009

CONFIDENCE FUTURISTIC ENERGETECH LIMITED; *Int'l*, pg. 1767
CONIFER PHYSICIAN SERVICES, INC.—See Tenet Healthcare Corporation; *U.S. Public*, pg. 2002
CORRIGAN FINANCIAL INC.; *U.S. Private*, pg. 1058
COTTON & CO.—See Sikich LLP; *U.S. Private*, pg. 3651
COWAN, BOLDUC, DOHERTY & COMPANY, LLC—See Blum, Shapiro & Company, P.C.; *U.S. Private*, pg. 599
CPA SITE SOLUTIONS; *U.S. Private*, pg. 1079
CRAWFORD FINANCIAL CONSULTING, LLC—See B. Riley Financial, Inc.; *U.S. Public*, pg. 260
CREDITE CONSULTING AB—See TowerBrook Capital Partners, L.P.; *U.S. Private*, pg. 4194
CROSSLIN & ASSOCIATES PC; *U.S. Private*, pg. 1106
CROWE LLP; *U.S. Private*, pg. 1109
CWBJ, PLLC—See CBIZ, Inc.; *U.S. Public*, pg. 457
DAENEN HENDERSON & CO.—See Hannis T. Bourgeois, LLP; *U.S. Private*, pg. 1855
DAVID T. CHASE ENTERPRISES INC.—See Chase Enterprises, Inc.; *U.S. Private*, pg. 859
DB SCHENKER GLOBAL SERVICES EUROPE S.R.L.—See Deutsche Bahn AG; *Int'l*, pg. 2052
DEAN DORTON ALLEN FORD, PLLC; *U.S. Private*, pg. 1183
DELLING ENTERPRISES; *U.S. Private*, pg. 1197
DHL PARCEL PORTUGAL, UNIPESSOAL LDA.—See Deutsche Post AG; *Int'l*, pg. 2078
DIVERSIFIED HEALTH CARE MANAGEMENT, INC.—See ModuleMD LLC; *U.S. Private*, pg. 2764
DNT BUSINESS SERVICE CO., LTD.—See Dai Nippon Toryo Co., Ltd.; *Int'l*, pg. 1916
DOMINION LEASING SOFTWARE LLC—See Banyan Software, Inc.; *U.S. Private*, pg. 470
DUNLAPSLK, P.C.; *U.S. Private*, pg. 1290
DWS INVESTMENTS SHANGHAI LIMITED—See Deutsche Bank Aktiengesellschaft; *Int'l*, pg. 2057
DYNAMIC HEALTHIER CONSULTANT; *U.S. Private*, pg. 1298
ECODE SOLUTIONS, LLC—See UnitedHealth Group Incorporated; *U.S. Public*, pg. 2253
E.C. ORTIZ & CO., LLP; *U.S. Private*, pg. 1304
ELEMENT 78 LLC; *U.S. Private*, pg. 1357
EMBS, INC.—See Intercontinental Exchange, Inc.; *U.S. Public*, pg. 1142
EMPLOYER ADVANTAGE, LLC—See G&A Outsourcing, Inc.; *U.S. Private*, pg. 1628
ENVIRONMENTAL PRODUCTS; *U.S. Private*, pg. 1408
ESSEDIESSE SOCIETA DI SERVIZI SPA—See Edizione S.r.l.; *Int'l*, pg. 2312
ESSILOR EUROPEAN SHARED SERVICE CENTER LTD.—See EssilorLuxottica SA; *Int'l*, pg. 2512
EUROSERVICES BAYER GMBH—See Bayer Aktiengesellschaft; *Int'l*, pg. 907
EXECUTIVE MONETARY MANAGEMENT, LLC—See Genstar Capital, LLC; *U.S. Private*, pg. 1676
FACTOR SYSTEMS, INC.—See EQT AB; *Int'l*, pg. 2472
F.A.S.B., INC.—See Stewart Information Services Corporation; *U.S. Public*, pg. 1947
FEB D.D. SARAJEVO; *Int'l*, pg. 2629
FEDERMAN, LALLY & REMIS LLC—See CBIZ, Inc.; *U.S. Public*, pg. 457
FELLOW HEALTH PARTNERS, INC.; *U.S. Private*, pg. 1494
FIDUCIAL EXPERTISE S.A.—See Fiducial; *Int'l*, pg. 2655
FIDUCIAL, INC.—See Fiducial; *Int'l*, pg. 2655
FIDUCIAL SA—See Fiducial; *Int'l*, pg. 2655
FINANCIAL ACCOUNTING FOUNDATION; *U.S. Private*, pg. 1506
FISHER HERBST & KEMBLE, PC—See Whitley Penn LLP; *U.S. Private*, pg. 4513
FISKARS SERVICES OY AB—See Fiskars Oyj Abp; *Int'l*, pg. 2694
FLEXFIN, LLC—See PhenixFIN Corp.; *U.S. Public*, pg. 1684
FORENSIC RESOLUTIONS, INC.—See Kelso & Company, L.P.; *U.S. Private*, pg. 2278
FOSTER & FOSTER CONSULTING ACTUARIES INC.; *U.S. Private*, pg. 1578
FRIEDMAN & FRIEDMAN—See Kelso & Company, L.P.; *U.S. Private*, pg. 2279
FULLY ACCOUNTABLE, LLC; *U.S. Private*, pg. 1621
GARDEN MEDICAL CENTRE LIMITED—See Bamboos Health Care Holdings Limited; *Int'l*, pg. 813
GBST HOLDINGS LIMITED; *Int'l*, pg. 2893
GIELDA PRAW MAJATKOWYCH VINDEXUS S.A.; *Int'l*, pg. 2969
GILLIAM BELL MOSER LLP; *U.S. Private*, pg. 1700
GLORY DENSHI KOGYO (SUZHOU) LTD.—See GLORY Ltd.; *Int'l*, pg. 3009
GLORY ENGINEERING LTD.—See GLORY Ltd.; *Int'l*, pg. 3009
GLORY PRODUCTS LTD.—See GLORY Ltd.; *Int'l*, pg. 3010
GRACEKENNEDY MONEY SERVICES CARIBBEAN SRL—See GraceKennedy Limited; *Int'l*, pg. 3049
GRACE, KENNEDY REMITTANCE SERVICES (GUYANA) LIMITED—See GraceKennedy Limited; *Int'l*, pg. 3048
GROVE MUELLER & SWANK PC—See Redw Stanley Financial Advisors LLC; *U.S. Private*, pg. 3380

GRUNENTHAL GES. M. B. H.—See Grunenthal GmbH; *Int'l*, pg. 3114
GS YUASA ACCOUNTING SERVICE LTD.—See GS Yuasa Corporation; *Int'l*, pg. 3143
HALT BUZAS & POWELL LTD.—See Sikich LLP; *U.S. Private*, pg. 3651
HANKYU ACT FOR—See H2O Retailing Corp.; *Int'l*, pg. 3200
HBK CPAS & CONSULTANTS—See Hill, Barth & King LLC; *U.S. Private*, pg. 1945
HERBEIN + COMPANY, INC.; *U.S. Private*, pg. 1920
HMI BUYING GROUP INC.; *U.S. Private*, pg. 1955
HOLBROOK & MANTER INC.; *U.S. Private*, pg. 1961
HOROVITZ, RUDOY & ROTEMAN, LLC; *U.S. Private*, pg. 1984
HOUSE BUSINESS PARTNERS CORPORATION—See House Foods Group Inc.; *Int'l*, pg. 3490
HPG LLC—See Spectrum Brands Holdings, Inc.; *U.S. Public*, pg. 1916
HURWITZ GELLER PTY. LTD.—See Azimut Holding SpA; *Int'l*, pg. 779
HUTCHINSON & BLOODGOOD LLP; *U.S. Private*, pg. 2014
ICSGLOBAL LIMITED; *Int'l*, pg. 3586
IDEA GLOBAL LLC—See Expolanka Holdings PLC; *U.S. Private*, pg. 2589
IINO MANAGEMENT DATA PROCESSING CO., LTD.—See Iino Kaiun Kaisha Ltd.; *Int'l*, pg. 3608
INFOSYNC SERVICES LLC; *U.S. Private*, pg. 2074
INTERACTIVE SOLUTIONS, LLC; *U.S. Private*, pg. 2108
INTERSTATE BILLING SERVICE INC.—See BancIndependent Inc.; *U.S. Private*, pg. 464
INVESTORS FINANCIAL SERVICES, INC.—See Citizens Financial Group, Inc.; *U.S. Public*, pg. 505
ISIGMA, LLC—See Energy Services Group, LLC; *U.S. Private*, pg. 1396
I-WELLNESS MARKETING GROUP, INC.; *U.S. Public*, pg. 1081
JANZEN JOHNSTON & ROCKWELL EMERGENCY MEDICINE MANAGEMENT SERVICES, INC.; *U.S. Private*, pg. 2188
JIM OLIVER & ASSOCIATES—See Calvetti Ferguson, P.C.; *U.S. Private*, pg. 724
JS FINANCIAL SERVICES CO., INC.—See Stevens Group, Inc.; *U.S. Private*, pg. 3809
KELIN KRAFT AS—See Arendals Fossekompani ASA; *Int'l*, pg. 559
KELLAWAY CRIDLAND PTY. LTD.—See Azimut Holding SpA; *Int'l*, pg. 779
KENTUCKY MEDICAL SERVICES FOUNDATION INC.; *U.S. Private*, pg. 2288
KERN DEWENTER VIERE, LTD.—See Bergan Paulsen & Company PC; *U.S. Private*, pg. 530
KIRSCH KOHN & BRIDGE LLP—See Aprio, LLP; *U.S. Private*, pg. 301
KUTCHINS, ROBBINS & DIAMOND, LTD.; *U.S. Private*, pg. 2358
LERETA LLC—See Edwards Capital, LLC; *U.S. Private*, pg. 1342
LERETA LLC—See Vestar Capital Partners, LLC; *U.S. Private*, pg. 4372
LIBERTY BILLING & CONSULTING SERVICES, INC.—See Linden LLC; *U.S. Private*, pg. 2460
MARKET IMPROVEMENT CORPORATION—See United Natural Foods, Inc.; *U.S. Public*, pg. 2232
MATSON, DRISCOLL & DAMICO; *U.S. Private*, pg. 2612
MAYER ELECTRIC SUPPLY SERVICE CO. INC.—See Mayer Electric Supply Company Inc.; *U.S. Private*, pg. 2621
MBE CPAS LLP; *U.S. Private*, pg. 2624
MBS VALUE PARTNERS, LLC; *U.S. Private*, pg. 2625
MC2 CONSULTING SERVICES, INC.—See The Graham Group, Inc.; *U.S. Private*, pg. 4037
MCCLATCHY SHARED SERVICES, INC.—See Chatham Asset Management, LLC; *U.S. Private*, pg. 867
MD OPS, INC.—See UnitedHealth Group Incorporated; *U.S. Public*, pg. 2242
MDSCRIPTS, INC.; *U.S. Private*, pg. 2646
MEDASSIST, INC.—See Firstsource Solutions Limited; *Int'l*, pg. 2691
MEDDATA, INC.—See MEDNAX, Inc.; *U.S. Public*, pg. 1413
MEDIA PLATFORM LIMITED—See Emperor Culture Group Limited; *Int'l*, pg. 2386
MEDICAL BILLING MANAGEMENT EAST; *U.S. Private*, pg. 2654
MEDICAL BUSINESS SERVICE INC.; *U.S. Private*, pg. 2654
MEDICAL DATA SYSTEMS INC.; *U.S. Private*, pg. 2654
MEDICAL MANAGEMENT SYSTEMS INC.; *U.S. Private*, pg. 2655
MEDICAL REIMBURSEMENTS OF AMERICA, INC.—See GrowthCurve Capital LP; *U.S. Private*, pg. 1796
MEDICAL REIMBURSEMENTS OF AMERICA, INC.—See Riverside Partners, LLC; *U.S. Private*, pg. 3446
MEDI CORP, INC.—See Aquiline Capital Partners LLC; *U.S. Private*, pg. 304
MEDIWARE REIMBURSEMENT SERVICES—See Leonard Green & Partners, L.P.; *U.S. Private*, pg. 2430

N.A.I.C.S. INDEX

541310 — ARCHITECTURAL SERVI...

MEDIWARE REIMBURSEMENT SERVICES—See TPG Capital, L.P.; *U.S. Public*, pg. 2177
MED SYSTEMS ASSOCIATES LP; *U.S. Private*, pg. 2650
MEEPOS & CO.—See CPAmerica, Inc.; *U.S. Private*, pg. 1080
MERIDIAN RESOURCE COMPANY, LLC—See Elevance Health, Inc.; *U.S. Public*, pg. 730
MILLENNIUM ACCOUNT SERVICES, LLC—See Exelon Corporation; *U.S. Public*, pg. 807
MIR, MITCHELL & COMPANY, LLP; *U.S. Private*, pg. 2745
MOORE BUSINESS SERVICE INC.; *U.S. Private*, pg. 2779
MOSS ADAMS LLP - BELLINGHAM—See Moss Adams LLP; *U.S. Private*, pg. 2794
MOSS ADAMS LLP - EUGENE—See Moss Adams LLP; *U.S. Private*, pg. 2794
MOSS ADAMS LLP - EVERETT—See Moss Adams LLP; *U.S. Private*, pg. 2794
MOSS ADAMS LLP - LOS ANGELES—See Moss Adams LLP; *U.S. Private*, pg. 2794
MOSS ADAMS LLP - ORANGE COUNTY—See Moss Adams LLP; *U.S. Private*, pg. 2794
MOSS ADAMS LLP - PORTLAND—See Moss Adams LLP; *U.S. Private*, pg. 2794
MOSS ADAMS LLP - SAN FRANCISCO—See Moss Adams LLP; *U.S. Private*, pg. 2794
MOSS ADAMS LLP - TACOMA—See Moss Adams LLP; *U.S. Private*, pg. 2794
MUNISERVICES, LLC—See Guggenheim Partners, LLC; *U.S. Private*, pg. 1812
MUTUAL SHAREHOLDER SERVICES, LLC (MSS); *U.S. Private*, pg. 2820
NAGANO MORITA LLP—See Prager Metis CPAs, LLC; *U.S. Private*, pg. 3241
NAVITAIRE LLC—See Amadeus IT Group, S.A.; *Int'l*, pg. 406
NDH ADVISORS LLC—See Unity Partners LP; *U.S. Public*, pg. 2253
NEWMONT AUSTRALIA SUPERANNUATION PLAN PTY LTD—See Newmont Corporation; *U.S. Public*, pg. 1517
NOELL, AGNEW & MORSE—See KCoe Isom, LLP; *U.S. Private*, pg. 2270
NORTHERN RV PTY. LTD.—See Fleetwood Limited; *Int'l*, pg. 2699
NUMERATIS SP. Z O.O.—See Ergis S.A.; *Int'l*, pg. 2491
OKAW PROPERTIES INC.; *U.S. Private*, pg. 3006
ORTHOBANC LLC; *U.S. Private*, pg. 3045
PARADIGM PARTNERS; *U.S. Private*, pg. 3089
PARTNER REGNSKAP AS—See TowerBrook Capital Partners, L.P.; *U.S. Private*, pg. 4195
PAY SYSTEMS OF AMERICA INC.—See Asure Software, Inc.; *U.S. Public*, pg. 218
PBMARES, LLP; *U.S. Private*, pg. 3118
PEPPER ENVIRONMENTAL TECHNOLOGIES, INC.—See Pepper Construction Group, LLC; *U.S. Private*, pg. 3144
PETROLEDGER LLC—See Avisto Capital Partners, LLC; *U.S. Private*, pg. 409
PHASES ACCOUNTING & TAX SERVICES—See Apex Accounting And Tax, Inc.; *U.S. Private*, pg. 291
PHYSICIANS BILLING & SUPPORT SERVICES—See Central Georgia Health System Inc.; *U.S. Private*, pg. 821
PHYSICIANS GROUP MANAGEMENT, INC.; *U.S. Private*, pg. 3175
PONTIFF & ASSOCIATES, P.C.—See Aprio, LLP; *U.S. Private*, pg. 301
POPOWCER KATTEN LTD.—See Kutchins, Robbins & Diamond, Ltd.; *U.S. Private*, pg. 2358
PORTFOLIOS FINANCIAL SERVICES, INC.; *U.S. Private*, pg. 3232
PRACTICEFORCES; *U.S. Private*, pg. 3241
QUADAX INC.; *U.S. Private*, pg. 3315
RADNET MANAGEMENT INC.—See RadNet, Inc.; *U.S. Public*, pg. 1761
RED HILLS FINANCE, LLC—See Acciona, S.A.; *Int'l*, pg. 90
REMITTANCE PROCESSING SERVICES, LLC—See The AES Corporation; *U.S. Public*, pg. 2032
RESERVATION DATA MAINTENANCE INDIA PRIVATE LTD.—See Deutsche Lufthansa AG; *Int'l*, pg. 2070
RETAIL FINANCIAL SERVICES—See New Heritage Capital LLC; *U.S. Private*, pg. 2897
REVENUE DISCOVERY SYSTEMS—See Guggenheim Partners, LLC; *U.S. Private*, pg. 1812
RGL-FORENSIC ACCOUNTANTS & CONSULTANTS; *U.S. Private*, pg. 3420
RIGHT NETWORKS, LLC; *U.S. Private*, pg. 3435
SALO, LLC—See Korn Ferry; *U.S. Public*, pg. 1275
SCHENCK SC—See CliftonLarsonAllen LLP; *U.S. Private*, pg. 943
SD MAYER & ASSOCIATES LLP; *U.S. Private*, pg. 3581
SECORE & NIEDZIALEK P.C.—See Eide Bailly LLP; *U.S. Private*, pg. 1347
SENSIBA SAN FILIPPO LLP; *U.S. Private*, pg. 3607
SERVICES GENERAUX DE GESTION S.A.—See Astorg Partners S.A.S.; *Int'l*, pg. 657
SGA GROUP, PC; *U.S. Private*, pg. 3622
SHARRARD, MCGEE & CO., P.A.—See Carr, Riggs & Ingram, LLC; *U.S. Private*, pg. 771
SLATER MOFFAT ASSOCIATES, LLP—See Sensiba San Filippo LLP; *U.S. Private*, pg. 3607
SMALLBIZPROS, INC.; *U.S. Private*, pg. 3690

SMITH, LINDEN & BASSO, LLP—See Windes, Inc.; *U.S. Private*, pg. 4537
SOUTHEASTERN DATA COOPERATIVE; *U.S. Private*, pg. 3727
SPENCE, MARSTON, BUNCH, MORRIS & CO.; *U.S. Private*, pg. 3754
S.R. SNODGRASS, A.C.; *U.S. Private*, pg. 3518
STRATEGIC CONSULTING SOLUTIONS, INC.; *U.S. Private*, pg. 3834
STRATEGIC RESOURCE ALTERNATIVES—See Arena Investors, LP; *U.S. Private*, pg. 318
SUDACO INC.; *U.S. Private*, pg. 3849
SYNTELLECT TECHNOLOGY CORP.—See Enghouse Systems Limited; *Int'l*, pg. 2428
TAX CARE S.A.—See Getin Holding S.A.; *Int'l*, pg. 2947
TAXGROUP PARTNERS INC.—See Cherry Bekaert LLP; *U.S. Private*, pg. 874
TAX TRILOGY, LLC; *U.S. Private*, pg. 3937
TEAM ACQUISITION CORPORATION; *U.S. Private*, pg. 3949
TGG ACCOUNTING; *U.S. Private*, pg. 3979
THOMPSON COBB BAZILIO ASSOCIATES PC; *U.S. Private*, pg. 4159
TICKETECH, INC.—See FlashParking, Inc.; *U.S. Private*, pg. 1540
TMDG, LLC—See PBMares, LLP; *U.S. Private*, pg. 3119
TOBIN & COLLINS CPA, PA.—See Aprio, LLP; *U.S. Private*, pg. 301
TOMBOLA INTERNATIONAL MALTA PLC—See Flutter Entertainment plc; *Int'l*, pg. 2715
TRANSPORT FINANCIAL SERVICES—See AB Volvo; *Int'l*, pg. 42
TREFZ CORPORATION; *U.S. Private*, pg. 4217
UHY ADVISORS, INC.; *U.S. Private*, pg. 4275
UNIVERSITY OF VIRGINIA PHYSICIANS GROUP; *U.S. Private*, pg. 4310
UNTRACHT EARLY, LLC; *U.S. Private*, pg. 4311
UT PHYSICIANS; *U.S. Private*, pg. 4324
VALUE RECOVERY GROUP, INC.; *U.S. Private*, pg. 4337
VENTURITY FINANCIAL PARTNERS; *U.S. Private*, pg. 4358
VERSCEND TECHNOLOGIES, INC.—See Veritas Capital Fund Management, LLC; *U.S. Private*, pg. 4365
WINTER, KLOMAN, MOTER & REPP, S.C.; *U.S. Private*, pg. 4545
XACT ERP SOLUTIONS (PTY) LTD—See ARB HOLDINGS LIMITED; *Int'l*, pg. 537
XIMANTIX SOFTWARE GMBH—See Cegedim S.A.; *Int'l*, pg. 1390
ZELIS PAYMENTS, INC.—See PCP Enterprise, L.P.; *U.S. Private*, pg. 3121

541310 — ARCHITECTURAL SERVICES

505DESIGN CHARLOTTE, INC.—See Cooper Carry, Inc; *U.S. Private*, pg. 1041
AAI ARCHITECTS, P.C.—See Adamson Associates Architects; *Int'l*, pg. 124
AAIC, INC.; *U.S. Private*, pg. 31
ACAI ASSOCIATES; *U.S. Private*, pg. 47
ACLA LTD.—See ARCADIS N.V.; *Int'l*, pg. 541
AC MARTIN PARTNERS, INC.; *U.S. Private*, pg. 45
ADAMSON ASSOCIATES ARCHITECTS; *Int'l*, pg. 124
ADAMSON ASSOCIATES, INC.—See Adamson Associates Architects; *Int'l*, pg. 124
ADAMSON ASSOCIATES (INTERNATIONAL) LIMITED—See Adamson Associates Architects; *Int'l*, pg. 124
AECOM—See AECOM; *U.S. Public*, pg. 50
AECOM—See AECOM; *U.S. Public*, pg. 50
AF SANDELLSANDBERG ARKITEKTER AB—See AFRY AB; *Int'l*, pg. 193
AI COLLABORATIVE, INC.; *U.S. Private*, pg. 131
ALA HOSPITALITY LLC—See Sphere Entertainment Co.; *U.S. Public*, pg. 1918
ALBERT KAHN ASSOCIATES, INC.; *U.S. Private*, pg. 153
ALFONSO ARCHITECTS, INC. - ITALY OFFICE—See Alfonso Architects, Inc.; *U.S. Private*, pg. 165
ALFONSO ARCHITECTS, INC.; *U.S. Private*, pg. 165
AL FORSAN TADBEER CENTER LLC—See Alpha Dhabi Holding PJSC; *Int'l*, pg. 367
ALLEN & HOSHALL—See Allen & Hoshall, Inc.; *U.S. Private*, pg. 178
ALLEVATO ARCHITECTS INC—See Harrison French & Associates, Ltd.; *U.S. Private*, pg. 1870
THE ALLIANCE, INC.; *U.S. Private*, pg. 3984
ALUMINIUM & LIGHT INDUSTRIES CO. LTD.—See GIBCA Limited; *Int'l*, pg. 2962
AMB DEVELOPMENT GROUP LLC; *U.S. Private*, pg. 217
ANDERSON DESIGN & BUILD—See Anderson Group Limited; *Int'l*, pg. 450
ANEL ELEKTRIK PROJE TAAHHUT TIC. A.S—See Anel Electrical Project Contracting Trade Inc.; *Int'l*, pg. 457
ANEL ELEKTRIK PROJE TAAHHUT VE TICARET A.S—See Anel Electrical Project Contracting Trade Inc.; *Int'l*, pg. 457
ANEL ELEKTRIK PROJE TAAHHUT VE TICARET A.S—See

Anel Electrical Project Contracting Trade Inc.; *Int'l*, pg. 457
ANEL ELEKTRIK PROJE TAAHHUT VE TICARET A.S—See Anel Electrical Project Contracting Trade Inc.; *Int'l*, pg. 458
ANELEMIRATES GENERAL CONTRACTING LLC—See Anel Electrical Project Contracting Trade Inc.; *Int'l*, pg. 458
ANEL ENGINEERING & CONTRACTING LIMITED—See Anel Electrical Project Contracting Trade Inc.; *Int'l*, pg. 458
ANHUI PROVINCIAL ARCHITECTURAL DESIGN & RESEARCH INSTITUTE CO., LTD.; *Int'l*, pg. 469
ARC3 ARCHITECTURE, INC.; *U.S. Private*, pg. 309
ARCHITECTS ORANGE LLP; *U.S. Private*, pg. 311
ARCHITECTS STUDIO JAPAN INC.; *Int'l*, pg. 549
ARCHITECTURE DESIGN COLLABORATIVE, INC.; *U.S. Private*, pg. 311
ARCHITECTUREPLUS INTERNATIONAL, INC.; *U.S. Private*, pg. 311
ARCHITRAVE DESIGN & PLANNING SERVICES PTE. LTD.—See Banyan Tree Holdings Ltd.; *Int'l*, pg. 855
ARRASMITH, JUDD, RAPP, CHOVAN, INC.—See Schmidt Associates, Inc.; *U.S. Private*, pg. 3565
ASAHI ARCHITECTS OFFICE CO., LTD.—See Adeka Corporation; *Int'l*, pg. 142
ASSOCIATED CONSULTING INTERNATIONAL, INC.; *U.S. Private*, pg. 355
ATOM LIVIN TECH CO., LTD.; *Int'l*, pg. 687
AUKETT FITZROY ROBINSON SP. Z.O.O.—See Aukett Swanke Group Plc; *Int'l*, pg. 704
AUKETT SRO—See Aukett Swanke Group Plc; *Int'l*, pg. 704
AUSTIN-SMITH:LORD ABU DHABI—See Austin-Smith:Lord LLP; *Int'l*, pg. 718
AUSTIN-SMITH:LORD LLP; *Int'l*, pg. 718
AUSTIN-SMITH:LORD LLP—See Austin-Smith:Lord LLP; *Int'l*, pg. 718
AUSTIN-SMITH:LORD LLP—See Austin-Smith:Lord LLP; *Int'l*, pg. 718
AUSTIN-SMITH:LORD LLP—See Austin-Smith:Lord LLP; *Int'l*, pg. 718
AUSTIN-SMITH:LORD LLP—See Austin-Smith:Lord LLP; *Int'l*, pg. 718
AXIO-NET GMBH—See Trimble, Inc.; *U.S. Public*, pg. 2190
BAKER BARRIOS ARCHITECTS, INC.; *U.S. Private*, pg. 455
BARBARA THAYER PE ARCH, LANDSCAPE ARCHITECTURE, L S, PC—See PS&S Integrated Services; *U.S. Private*, pg. 3296
BARLOW EDDY JENKINS PA—See Eley Guild Hardy Architects, PA; *U.S. Private*, pg. 1358
BARTON MALOW DESIGN—See Barton Malow Enterprises, Inc.; *U.S. Private*, pg. 483
BAXTER HODELL DONNELLY PRESTON INC.; *U.S. Private*, pg. 491
BBH DESIGN—See EwingCole, Inc.; *U.S. Private*, pg. 1444
BCS DESIGN, INC.—See Butler National Corporation; *U.S. Public*, pg. 413
BCWH, INC.—See Quinn Evans Architects Inc.; *U.S. Private*, pg. 3328
BDG ARCHITECTS LLP; *U.S. Private*, pg. 500
BEARSCH COMPEAU KNUDSON, ARCHITECTS & ENGINEERS, PC—See ARCADIS N.V.; *Int'l*, pg. 541
BEERS & HOFFMAN, LTD.; *U.S. Private*, pg. 514
BESSOLO DESIGN GROUP, INC.; *U.S. Private*, pg. 542
BLAIR COMPANIES, INC.; *U.S. Private*, pg. 578
BLDD ARCHITECTS, INC.; *U.S. Private*, pg. 580
BOARMAN KROOS VOGEL GROUP INC.; *U.S. Private*, pg. 602
BOMBARDIER TRANSPORTATION—See Alstom S.A.; *Int'l*, pg. 382
BONSALL SHAFFERMAN ARCHITECTS AND SPACE PLANNERS, PC—See Serfass Construction Company Inc.; *U.S. Private*, pg. 3613
BRACKE HAYES MILLER MAHON, ARCHITECTS LLP—See Bray Associates Architects Inc.; *U.S. Private*, pg. 641
BRASS CO., LTD.; *Int'l*, pg. 1140
BRAY ASSOCIATES ARCHITECTS INC.; *U.S. Private*, pg. 641
BRENNAN BEER GORMAN ARCHITECTS LLP; *U.S. Private*, pg. 645
BROWN CRAIG TURNER; *U.S. Private*, pg. 667
BRPH COMPANIES, INC.; *U.S. Private*, pg. 670
BSSW ARCHITECTS, INC.—See Bernhard Capital Partners Management, LP; *U.S. Private*, pg. 537
BUILDING EXTERIOR SOLUTIONS—See Terracon Consultants, Inc.; *U.S. Private*, pg. 3970
BUILDING SOLUTIONS, LLC; *U.S. Private*, pg. 683
BUILD LLC; *U.S. Private*, pg. 681
BULLOCK TICE ASSOCIATES, INC.—See Bernhard Capital Partners Management, LP; *U.S. Private*, pg. 537
BYUCKSAN ENGINEERING & CONSTRUCTION CO., LTD.; *Int'l*, pg. 1237
C A DESIGN SERVICES LTD—See HAL Trust N.V.; *Int'l*, pg. 3226
CALLISONRTKL, INC.—See ARCADIS N.V.; *Int'l*, pg. 541
CALLISONRTKL, INC.—See ARCADIS N.V.; *Int'l*, pg. 541

4553

541310 — ARCHITECTURAL SERVI...

CALLISONRTKL-UK LTD.—See ARCADIS N.V.; *Int'l*, pg. 541
CALTHORPE ASSOCIATES, INC.—See HDR, Inc.; *U.S. Private*, pg. 1890
CAMARGOCOPELAND ARCHITECTS, LLP; *U.S. Private*, pg. 725
CAMPBELLSPORT BUILDING SUPPLY; *U.S. Private*, pg. 731
CANERDAY BELFSKY & ARROYO ARCHITECTS INC.; *U.S. Private*, pg. 734
CANNON DESIGN, INC.; *U.S. Private*, pg. 734
CAPITA SYMONDS LIMITED—See Capita plc; *Int'l*, pg. 1308
CBRE HEERY, INC.—See CBRE Group, Inc.; *U.S. Public*, pg. 460
C CHENG HOLDINGS LIMITED; *Int'l*, pg. 1237
CDGGR, P.C.—See Ghafari Associates, L.L.C.; *U.S. Private*, pg. 1690
CDI-INFRASTRUCTURE, LLC—See Management Recruiters International, Inc.; *U.S. Private*, pg. 2560
CEDARWOOD ARCHITECTURAL, INC.—See The Cedarwood Companies; *U.S. Private*, pg. 4006
C.E.O GROUP JOINT STOCK COMPANY; *Int'l*, pg. 1240
CHA ARCHITECTURE, P.C.—See H.I.G. Capital, LLC; *U.S. Private*, pg. 1827
CHANCEY DESIGN PARTNERSHIP, INC.; *U.S. Private*, pg. 847
CHANGZHOU ARCHITECTURAL RESEARCH INSTITUTE GROUP CO., LTD.; *Int'l*, pg. 1445
CHBA-IBI INC.—See ARCADIS N.V.; *Int'l*, pg. 541
CHICAGO ARCHITECTURE FOUNDATION; *U.S. Private*, pg. 877
CHINA 9D CONSTRUCTION GROUP, INC.; *Int'l*, pg. 1481
CHINA ARCHITECTURE DESIGN & RESEARCH GROUP; *Int'l*, pg. 1483
CHINA COME RIDE NEW ENERGY GROUP LIMITED; *Int'l*, pg. 1490
COLLMAN & KARSKY ARCHITECTS, INC.; *U.S. Private*, pg. 970
COMMONWEALTH ARCHITECTS, P.C.; *U.S. Private*, pg. 986
CONSORT NT SA; *Int'l*, pg. 1772
COOPER CARRY, INC; *U.S. Private*, pg. 1041
COOPER JOHNSON SMITH ARCHITECTS, INC.; *U.S. Private*, pg. 1041
COTERA REED ARCHITECTS INC.—See Dykema Architects Inc.; *U.S. Private*, pg. 1296
CPL ARCHITECTS, ENGINEERS & LANDSCAPE ARCHITECT D.P.C.; *U.S. Private*, pg. 1080
CREMONESI WORKSHOP S.R.L.—See Ferrovie dello Stato Italiane S.p.A.; *Int'l*, pg. 2645
CRJA-IBI GROUP—See ARCADIS N.V.; *Int'l*, pg. 541
CSHQA, INC.; *U.S. Private*, pg. 1117
CSM ENGINEERING LTD.—See ARCADIS N.V.; *Int'l*, pg. 541
CUBE 3 STUDIO; *U.S. Private*, pg. 1120
CUHACI & PETERSON ARCHITECTS LLC; *U.S. Private*, pg. 1120
CURTS GAINES HALL JONES ARCHITECTS, INC.; *U.S. Private*, pg. 1127
CUSHING TERRELL; *U.S. Private*, pg. 1127
DAT XANH MIEN NAM INVESTMENT & SERVICES JSC—See Dat Xanh Group Joint Stock Company; *Int'l*, pg. 1975
DAVIS BEWS DESIGN GROUP, INC.; *U.S. Private*, pg. 1173
DAVIS BRODY BOND, LLP.—See Page Southerland Page, Inc.; *U.S. Private*, pg. 3074
DAVIS LANGDON LLP—See AECOM; *U.S. Public*, pg. 51
DESIGN RESOURCES GROUP ARCHITECTS, A.I.A., INC.; *U.S. Private*, pg. 1214
DESIGN STYLES INC.; *U.S. Private*, pg. 1214
DETI CO., LTD.—See Applicad Public Company Limited; *Int'l*, pg. 521
DEVELOPMENT DESIGN GROUP INC.—See Brown Craig Turner; *U.S. Private*, pg. 667
DICKINSON HUSSMAN ARCHITECTS, P.C.—See BLDD Architects, Inc.; *U.S. Private*, pg. 580
DLR GROUP INC.—See DLR Holding, LLC; *U.S. Private*, pg. 1247
DLR GROUP (SHANGHAI) ARCHITECTURAL DESIGN CONSULTING CO., LTD.—See DLR Holding, LLC; *U.S. Private*, pg. 1247
DONALD L. BLOUNT & ASSOCIATES, INC.—See Leidos Holdings, Inc.; *U.S. Public*, pg. 1304
DOUGLAS ARCHITECTS, INC—See TBA Studio Architecture, A Professional Corporation; *U.S. Private*, pg. 3941
DULL OLSON WEEKES ARCHITECTS, INC.—See ARCADIS N.V.; *Int'l*, pg. 542
DYKAB VARV & MEK AB—See Endur ASA; *Int'l*, pg. 2409
DYKEMA ARCHITECTS INC.; *U.S. Private*, pg. 1296
EASTLAKE STUDIO INC.—See geniant, LLC; *U.S. Private*, pg. 1671
EBERT NORMAN BRADY ARCHITECTS PA—See LS3P Associates Ltd.; *U.S. Private*, pg. 2508
ECOSIAN CO., LTD.—See HanmiGlobal Co., LTD.; *Int'l*, pg. 3257
EINHORN YAFFEE & PRESCOTT; *U.S. Private*, pg. 1347
ELEY GUILD HARDY ARCHITECTS, PA; *U.S. Private*, pg. 1358
ELITE MODULAR LEASING & SALES, INC.—See WillScot Mobile Mini Holdings Corp.; *U.S. Public*, pg. 2372
ELPEC AS—See Eesti Energia AS; *Int'l*, pg. 2317
EMIRATES SAFETY LABORATORY LLC—See Alpha Dhabi Holding PJSC; *Int'l*, pg. 367
ENGLISH + ASSOCIATES ARCHITECTS, INC.; *U.S. Private*, pg. 1400
ENTECH ENGINEERING INC.—See Entech Engineering Inc.; *U.S. Private*, pg. 1402
EPCO (HK) LIMITED—See EPCO Co., Ltd.; *Int'l*, pg. 2459
EPCO (JILIN) LTD.—See EPCO Co., Ltd.; *Int'l*, pg. 2459
EPCO (SHENZHEN) LTD.—See EPCO Co., Ltd.; *Int'l*, pg. 2459
EPPSTEIN UHEN ARCHITECTS, INC.; *U.S. Private*, pg. 1414
EP URBANIZAM I ARH. A.D.—See Energoprojekt Holding a.d.; *Int'l*, pg. 2421
EQUATOR DESIGN, INC.—See Matthews International Corporation; *U.S. Public*, pg. 1399
EVERYDAY GREEN LLC—See Steven Winter Associates, Inc.; *U.S. Private*, pg. 3809
EWINGCOLE, INC.; *U.S. Private*, pg. 1444
EXP FEDERAL INC.—See exp Global Inc.; *Int'l*, pg. 2586
EXPLORATION INVESTMENT RESOURCES II AS—See CGG; *Int'l*, pg. 1431
EXP U.S. SERVICES INC.—See exp Global Inc.; *Int'l*, pg. 2586
EYP ARCHITECTURE & ENGINEERING, P.C.—See EYP, Inc.; *U.S. Private*, pg. 1454
F5 FINISHES, INC.; *U.S. Private*, pg. 1458
FAWLEY BRYANT ARCHITECTS, INC.; *U.S. Private*, pg. 1484
FBV CONSTRUCTION JSC; *Int'l*, pg. 2627
FENTRESS ARCHITECTS; *U.S. Private*, pg. 1495
FISHER & ASSOCIATES, LLC; *U.S. Private*, pg. 1533
FLAD ARCHITECTS; *U.S. Private*, pg. 1539
FLEISCHMAN & GARCIA ARCHITECTS & PLANNERS, AIA—See BDG Architects LLP; *U.S. Private*, pg. 500
FORMATION ARCHITECTURAL DESIGN LIMITED—See Formation Group PLC; *Int'l*, pg. 2733
FOSTER + PARTNERS LTD.; *Int'l*, pg. 2749
FUJI ART, INC.—See Fuji Media Holdings, Inc.; *Int'l*, pg. 2813
GANFLEC ARCHITECTS & ENGINEERS, INC.—See OceanSound Partners, LP; *U.S. Private*, pg. 2991
GAUDREAU, INC.—See EwingCole, Inc.; *U.S. Private*, pg. 1444
GECI INGENIERIA S.L.—See GECI International SA; *Int'l*, pg. 2909
GENESIS ARCHITECTURE LLC—See Welsh Companies LLC; *U.S. Private*, pg. 4479
GEORGE F. YOUNG, INC.; *U.S. Private*, pg. 1682
GHAFARI ASSOCIATES LLC—See Ghafari Associates, L.L.C.; *U.S. Private*, pg. 1690
GKKWORKS CONSTRUCTION SERVICES, INC; *U.S. Private*, pg. 1704
GLOBAL WALL MALAYSIA SDN. BHD.—See Atlas Holdings, LLC; *U.S. Private*, pg. 377
GORA/MCGAHEY ARCHITECTS; *U.S. Private*, pg. 1741
GOTTLIEB PALUDAN ARCHITECTS A/S—See AFRY AB; *Int'l*, pg. 194
GOULD EVANS AFFILIATES P.A.; *U.S. Private*, pg. 1745
GOULD EVANS ASSOCIATES LLC—See Gould Evans Affiliates P.A.; *U.S. Private*, pg. 1745
GPD GROUP; *U.S. Private*, pg. 1748
GRACE HEBERT CURTIS ARCHITECTS, LLC—See Bernhard Capital Partners Management, LP; *U.S. Private*, pg. 537
GREELEY & HANSEN LLC, TAMPA—See T.Y. Lin International Group Ltd.; *U.S. Private*, pg. 3913
GREENBERG FARROW ARCHITECTURE INC., CALIFORNIA—See Greenberg Farrow Architecture Incorporated; *U.S. Private*, pg. 1775
GREENBERG FARROW ARCHITECTURE INC., ILLINOIS—See Greenberg Farrow Architecture Incorporated; *U.S. Private*, pg. 1775
GREENBERG FARROW ARCHITECTURE INC., NEW YORK—See Greenberg Farrow Architecture Incorporated; *U.S. Private*, pg. 1775
GREENBERG FARROW ARCHITECTURE INC., TEXAS—See Greenberg Farrow Architecture Incorporated; *U.S. Private*, pg. 1775
GREEN INDUSTRY SOLUTIONS INC.—See Munro Companies, Inc.; *U.S. Private*, pg. 2814
GRESHAM, SMITH & PARTNERS, ATLANTA OFFICE—See Gresham, Smith & Partners; *U.S. Private*, pg. 1784
GRESHAM, SMITH & PARTNERS, BIRMINGHAM OFFICE—See Gresham, Smith & Partners; *U.S. Private*, pg. 1784
GRESHAM, SMITH & PARTNERS, CHARLOTTE OFFICE—See Gresham, Smith & Partners; *U.S. Private*, pg. 1784
GRESHAM, SMITH & PARTNERS, DALLAS OFFICE—See Gresham, Smith & Partners; *U.S. Private*, pg. 1784
GRESHAM, SMITH & PARTNERS, JACKSONVILLE OFFICE—See Gresham, Smith & Partners; *U.S. Private*, pg. 1784
GRESHAM, SMITH & PARTNERS, LOUISVILLE OFFICE—See Gresham, Smith & Partners; *U.S. Private*, pg. 1784
GRESHAM, SMITH & PARTNERS, MEMPHIS OFFICE—See Gresham, Smith & Partners; *U.S. Private*, pg. 1784
GRESHAM, SMITH & PARTNERS, RICHMOND OFFICE—See Gresham, Smith & Partners; *U.S. Private*, pg. 1784
GRESHAM, SMITH & PARTNERS; *U.S. Private*, pg. 1783
GRESHAM, SMITH & PARTNERS, TAMPA OFFICE—See Gresham, Smith & Partners; *U.S. Private*, pg. 1784
GROUNDS FOR SCULPTURE; *U.S. Private*, pg. 1793
GRUSKIN GROUP; *U.S. Private*, pg. 1797
GRYPHON MARINE, LLC—See AE Industrial Partners, LP; *U.S. Private*, pg. 112
GSC ARCHITECTS; *U.S. Private*, pg. 1800
GUANGDONG ADWAY CONSTRUCTION (GROUP) HOLDINGS COMPANY LIMITED; *Int'l*, pg. 3152
GULF METAL CRAFT (GMC)—See Dubai Investments PJSC; *Int'l*, pg. 2219
HAGART SP. Z O.O.—See Figene Capital SA; *Int'l*, pg. 2661
HANJIA DESIGN GROUP CO., LTD.; *Int'l*, pg. 3252
HANSON PRECAST PTY LTD - MULGRAVE FACTORY—See Heidelberg Materials AG; *Int'l*, pg. 3312
HANSON PRECAST PTY LTD—See Heidelberg Materials AG; *Int'l*, pg. 3312
HARLEY ELLIS DEVEREAUX CORPORATION; *U.S. Private*, pg. 1865
HARRIMAN ASSOCIATES; *U.S. Private*, pg. 1868
HARRISON FRENCH & ASSOCIATES, LTD.; *U.S. Private*, pg. 1870
HARVARD JOLLY, INC.; *U.S. Private*, pg. 1875
HARVARD JOLLY INC.—See Harvard Jolly, Inc.; *U.S. Private*, pg. 1875
HDR, INC.; *U.S. Private*, pg. 1890
HEERIM ARCHITECTS & PLANNERS CO., LTD.; *Int'l*, pg. 3307
HELLMUTH, OBATA & KASSABAUM, INC.; *U.S. Private*, pg. 1911
HERSCHMAN ARCHITECTS, INC.; *U.S. Private*, pg. 1926
HERZOG & DE MEURON BASEL LTD.; *Int'l*, pg. 3365
HGA MID-ATLANTIC, INC.—See Hammel, Green & Abrahamson, Inc.; *U.S. Private*, pg. 1849
HI-TECH CONCRETE PRODUCTS LLC—See Alpha Dhabi Holding PJSC; *Int'l*, pg. 367
HKS, INC.; *U.S. Private*, pg. 1953
HLW INTERNATIONAL LLP; *U.S. Private*, pg. 1954
HLW INTERNATIONAL LLP—See HLW International LLP; *U.S. Private*, pg. 1954
HLW INTERNATIONAL LTD.—See HLW International LLP; *U.S. Private*, pg. 1954
HNTB ARCHITECTURE—See HNTB Corporation; *U.S. Private*, pg. 1956
HNTB-ARLINGTON—See HNTB Corporation; *U.S. Private*, pg. 1956
HNTB-ORLANDO—See HNTB Corporation; *U.S. Private*, pg. 1957
HOA BINH ARCHITECTURE CO., LTD.—See Hoa Binh Construction Group JSC; *Int'l*, pg. 3435
HOCHTIEF VSB A/S—See ACS, Actividades de Construccion y Servicios, S.A.; *Int'l*, pg. 114
HOFFMAN ARCHITECTS, P.A.; *U.S. Private*, pg. 1960
HOFFMANN ARCHITECTS, INC.—See Wannemacher Jensen Architects Inc.; *U.S. Private*, pg. 4435
HOH ARCHITECTS, INC.—See The HOH Group; *U.S. Private*, pg. 4053
HSS BIM SOLUTIONS PRIVATE LIMITED—See HSS Engineers Berhad; *Int'l*, pg. 3507
HUATU CENDES CO., LTD.; *Int'l*, pg. 3514
HUCKABEE ARCHITECTS LP—See Godspeed Capital Management LP; *U.S. Private*, pg. 1725
HUGHES GROUP ARCHITECTS, INC.—See Little Diversified Architectural Consulting, Inc.; *U.S. Private*, pg. 2468
HUMPHREYS & PARTNERS ARCHITECTS, L.P.; *U.S. Private*, pg. 2007
HWA KOON ENGINEERING PTE. LTD.—See Hke Holdings Ltd.; *Int'l*, pg. 3428
HWP PLANUNGS GMBH; *Int'l*, pg. 3543
HYUNDAI ARCHITECTS & ENGINEERS ASSOCIATES CO., LTD.—See Hyundai Motor Company; *Int'l*, pg. 3558
IBIKEN CO., LTD.—See Ibiden Co., Ltd.; *Int'l*, pg. 3576
IBI TAYLOR YOUNG LTD.—See ARCADIS N.V.; *Int'l*, pg. 542
IKESHITA SEKKEI CO. LTD.; *Int'l*, pg. 3610
ILLBRUCK GMBH; *Int'l*, pg. 3615
INGENHOVEN ARCHITECTS INTERNATIONAL GMBH & CO. KG—See BKW AG; *Int'l*, pg. 1055
INGENIEURBURO PROF. DR.-ING. VOGT PLANUNGSGESELLSCHAFT MBH—See BKW AG; *Int'l*, pg. 1055
INTERIOR ARCHITECTS, INC.; *U.S. Private*, pg. 2111
JACK ROUSE ASSOCIATES, INC.—See RWS & Associates Entertainment, Inc.; *U.S. Private*, pg. 3509
JAN SNEL HD B.V.—See Daiwa House Industry Co., Ltd.; *Int'l*, pg. 1946

N.A.I.C.S. INDEX

541310 — ARCHITECTURAL SERVI...

JARMEL KIZEL ARCHITECTS & ENGINEERS, INC.; *U.S. Private*, pg. 2188
JCJ ARCHITECTURE; *U.S. Private*, pg. 2195
JIGSAW SEARCH PTY. LTD.—See Bain Capital, LP; *U.S. Private*, pg. 434
JOHN F. WATSON & COMPANY—See Peak Rock Capital LLC; *U.S. Private*, pg. 3124
JORDY-CARTER INC.; *U.S. Private*, pg. 2236
JR CENTRAL CONSULTANTS COMPANY—See Central Japan Railway Company; *Int'l*, pg. 1408
JUNTO DESIGN STUDIO, LLC; *U.S. Private*, pg. 2245
KAHN DO BRASIL LTDA.—See Albert Kahn Associates, Inc.; *U.S. Private*, pg. 153
KAHN SOUTH, INC.—See Albert Kahn Associates, Inc.; *U.S. Private*, pg. 153
KENNEDY ASSOCIATES/ARCHITECTS, INC.; *U.S. Private*, pg. 2284
KEN ROSS ARCHITECTS INC.—See Clark Nexsen, Inc.; *U.S. Private*, pg. 913
KIREI INC.—See Amuse Inc.; *Int'l*, pg. 442
KORTE DESIGNS, INC.—See Korte Construction Company Inc.; *U.S. Private*, pg. 2344
KOSINSKI ARCHITECTURE, INC.; *U.S. Private*, pg. 2344
KREI ARCHITECTURE INC—See Parametrix, Inc.; *U.S. Private*, pg. 3092
KWAN HENMI ARCHITECTURE & PLANNING, INC.—See DLR Holding, LLC; *U.S. Private*, pg. 1247
LAMVIN, INC.—See Sound Seal, Inc.; *U.S. Private*, pg. 3717
LARSON DESIGN GROUP; *U.S. Private*, pg. 2393
THE LARSON GROUP, INC.; *U.S. Private*, pg. 4067
LAWN TECH INC.—See Green Group Holdings LLC; *U.S. Private*, pg. 1773
LEGACY STRUCTURES, LLC—See Maugel Architects Inc; *U.S. Private*, pg. 2614
LIGHT BUREAU AS—See AFRY AB; *Int'l*, pg. 194
LINDSCHULTE PLANUNGSGESELLSCHAFT MBH—See BKW AG; *Int'l*, pg. 1055
THE LIRO GROUP; *U.S. Private*, pg. 4070
LITTLE DIVERSIFIED ARCHITECTURAL CONSULTING, INC.; *U.S. Private*, pg. 2468
LONG & ASSOCIATES ARCHITECTS/ENGINEERS, INC.; *U.S. Private*, pg. 2490
LORD, AECK & SARGENT, INC.; *U.S. Private*, pg. 2495
L. ROBERT KIMBALL & ASSOCIATES, INC.—See Ocean-Sound Partners, LP; *U.S. Private*, pg. 2991
LS3P ASSOCIATES LTD.; *U.S. Private*, pg. 2508
LUCKETT & FARLEY ARCHITECTS, ENGINEERS AND CONSTRUCTION MANAGERS, INC.; *U.S. Private*, pg. 2511
LUNZ PREBOR FOWLER ARCHITECTS; *U.S. Private*, pg. 2515
LYMAN DAVIDSON DOOLEY, INC.; *U.S. Private*, pg. 2520
LYMAN DAVIDSON DOOLEY INC.—See Lyman Davidson Dooley, Inc.; *U.S. Private*, pg. 2520
MADE BY PROSPER LIMITED—See HAL Trust N.V.; *Int'l*, pg. 3226
MAKOVICH & PUSTI ARCHITECTS INC.—See CPL Architects, Engineers & Landscape Architect D.P.C.; *U.S. Private*, pg. 1080
MARC TRUANT & ASSOCIATES, INC.; *U.S. Private*, pg. 2571
M. ARTHUR GENSLER JR. & ASSOCIATES INC.; *U.S. Private*, pg. 2526
MASER CONSULTING—See Colliers International Group Inc.; *Int'l*, pg. 1700
MASON BLAU & ASSOCIATES, INC.—See Godspeed Capital Management LP; *U.S. Private*, pg. 1725
THE MASON & HANGER GROUP INC.—See The Day & Zimmermann Group, Inc.; *U.S. Private*, pg. 4019
MAUGEL ARCHITECTS INC; *U.S. Private*, pg. 2614
MAWARID HOLDING INVESTMENT LLC—See Alpha Dhabi Holding PJSC; *Int'l*, pg. 367
MEAD & HUNT, INC.; *U.S. Private*, pg. 2646
M.E /IBI GROUP—See ARCADIS N.V.; *Int'l*, pg. 542
METHOD ARCHITECTURE, PLLC; *U.S. Private*, pg. 2683
MICHAEL GRAVES & ASSOCIATES, INC.; *U.S. Private*, pg. 2698
MICHAEL MALTZAN ARCHITECTURE, INC.; *U.S. Private*, pg. 2698
MILLER LEGG & ASSOCIATES INC.; *U.S. Private*, pg. 2734
MILOSI, INC.; *U.S. Private*, pg. 2738
MITHUN INC.; *U.S. Private*, pg. 2751
MKSD ARCHITECTS; *U.S. Private*, pg. 2753
MOLZEN-CORBIN & ASSOCIATES, P.A.; *U.S. Private*, pg. 2767
MOLZEN-CORBIN & ASSOCIATES, P.A.—See Molzen-Corbin & Associates, P.A.; *U.S. Private*, pg. 2767
MOODY.NOLAN, INC; *U.S. Private*, pg. 2778
MORRIS ARCHITECTS, INC. See Huitt Zollars, Inc.; *U.S. Private*, pg. 2004
MOSELEY ARCHITECTS P.C.; *U.S. Private*, pg. 2793
MUHLENBERG GREENE ARCHITECTS LTD.; *U.S. Private*, pg. 2811
MULTIWAVE GEOPHYSICAL COMPANY AS—See CGG; *Int'l*, pg. 1431
MUSTANG AL-HEJAILAN DAR PI—See Al-Hejailan Group; *Int'l*, pg. 286

NAC, INC.; *U.S. Private*, pg. 2829
NADEL ARCHITECTS, INC.; *U.S. Private*, pg. 2830
NATIONAL PROJECTS AND CONSTRUCTION LLC—See Alpha Dhabi Holding PJSC; *Int'l*, pg. 367
NBBJ GROUP; *U.S. Private*, pg. 2874
NBBJ—See NBBJ Group; *U.S. Private*, pg. 2874
NICHOLS BROSCH WURTE WOLFE & ASSOCIATES, INC.; *U.S. Private*, pg. 2925
NIGHTINGALE ARCHITECTS LIMITED—See ARCADIS N.V.; *Int'l*, pg. 542
NISSOKEN ARCHITECTS/ENGINEERS INC.—See CTI Engineering Co., Ltd.; *Int'l*, pg. 1871
OEM ENERGY SP. Z O.O.—See CEZ, a.s.; *Int'l*, pg. 1428
OLIVERI ARCHITECTS INC.; *U.S. Private*, pg. 3011
THE ONYX GROUP; *U.S. Private*, pg. 4088
OPUS AE GROUP, INC.—See Opus Holding, LLC; *U.S. Private*, pg. 3036
OPUS DESIGN BUILD, L.L.C.—See Opus Holding, LLC; *U.S. Private*, pg. 3036
OWEN-AMES-KIMBALL ENGINEERING, INC.—See Owen-Ames-Kimball Company; *U.S. Private*, pg. 3055
PACIFIC CORNERSTONE ARCHITECTS INC.—See Harley Ellis Devereaux Corporation; *U.S. Private*, pg. 1865
PAGE SOUTHERLAND PAGE, INC; *U.S. Private*, pg. 3074
PAGE + STEELE / IBI GROUP ARCHITECTS—See ARCADIS N.V.; *Int'l*, pg. 542
PARKHILL, SMITH & COOPER, INC.; *U.S. Private*, pg. 3098
PATRIOT CONTRACTORS, INC; *U.S. Private*, pg. 3110
PAULUS, SOKOLOWSKI & SARTOR LLC; *U.S. Private*, pg. 3114
PAYETTE ASSOCIATES INC.; *U.S. Private*, pg. 3117
PERKINS EASTMAN ARCHITECTS P.C.; *U.S. Private*, pg. 3151
THE PERKINS + WILL GROUP, LTD.; *U.S. Private*, pg. 4093
PERKINS + WILL - RESEARCH TRIANGLE PARK—See The Perkins + Will Group, Ltd.; *U.S. Private*, pg. 4093
PERMASTEELISA-GARTNER TAIWAN LTD.—See Atlas Holdings, LLC; *U.S. Private*, pg. 378
PERMASTEELISA (THAILAND) LTD.—See Atlas Holdings, LLC; *U.S. Private*, pg. 378
PETERSON BRUSTAD INC.—See Sterling Investment Partners, L.P.; *U.S. Private*, pg. 3806
PGAV INC.; *U.S. Private*, pg. 3165
PHILLIPS ARCHITECTURE PA—See Redline Design Group, P.A.; *U.S. Private*, pg. 3379
PK STUDIOS INC.; *U.S. Private*, pg. 3193
PLANTSTREAM INC.—See Chiyoda Corporation; *Int'l*, pg. 1575
POOLE & POOLE ARCHITECTURE, LLC; *U.S. Private*, pg. 3228
PORTAL PARTNERSHIP INCORPORATED—See Basil Read Holdings Limited; *Int'l*, pg. 887
THE PRESTON PARTNERSHIP, LLC; *U.S. Private*, pg. 4098
PROGRESSIVE ARCHITECTURE ENGINEERING PLANNING, INC.; *U.S. Private*, pg. 3278
PROTELCO SAS—See Iliad S.A.; *Int'l*, pg. 3614
PS&S INTEGRATED SERVICES; *U.S. Private*, pg. 3296
PUCHLIK DESIGN ASSOCIATES, INC.—See Harley Ellis Devereaux Corporation; *U.S. Private*, pg. 1865
Q. GRADY MINOR & ASSOCIATES, P.A.—See Palm Beach Capital Partners LLC; *U.S. Private*, pg. 3079
QUINN EVANS ARCHITECTS INC.; *U.S. Private*, pg. 3328
QUORUM ARCHITECTS, INC.; *U.S. Private*, pg. 3329
RANDALL/BAYLON ARCHITECTS, INC.—See JCJ Architecture; *U.S. Private*, pg. 2195
RAND ENGINEERING & ARCHITECTURE, PC; *U.S. Private*, pg. 3353
RANON & PARTNERS INC.; *U.S. Private*, pg. 3355
RATIO ARCHITECTS, INC.; *U.S. Private*, pg. 3357
REDLINE DESIGN GROUP, P.A.; *U.S. Private*, pg. 3379
RELIANT POOLS, INC.—See Reliant Holdings, Inc.; *U.S. Public*, pg. 1782
RENKER-EICH-PARKS ARCHITECTS, INC.; *U.S. Private*, pg. 3398
REYNOLDS, SMITH & HILLS INC.; *U.S. Private*, pg. 3418
RH BUILD & DESIGN, INC.—See RH; *U.S. Public*, pg. 1796
ROBERT REID WEDDING ARCHITECTS & PLANNERS, AIA, INC.; *U.S. Private*, pg. 3459
ROJO ARCHITECTURE, LLC; *U.S. Private*, pg. 3473
ROSSDRULISCUSENBERY ARCHITECTURE, INC.—See DLR Holding, LLC; *U.S. Private*, pg. 1247
ROSSER INTERNATIONAL, INC.; *U.S. Private*, pg. 3486
RQAW CORP.—See White Wolf Capital LLC; *U.S. Private*, pg. 4510
RSP ARCHITECTS, LTD.; *U.S. Private*, pg. 3497
RTKL INTERNATIONAL LTD.—See ARCADIS N.V.; *Int'l*, pg. 541
RUSSELL SWINTON OATMAN DESIGN ASSOCIATES, INC.; *U.S. Private*, pg. 3507
SABER POWER SERVICES, LLC—See Greenbelt Capital Management L.P.; *U.S. Private*, pg. 1774
THE SANKEI BLDG TECHNO CO., LTD.—See Fuji Media Holdings, Inc.; *Int'l*, pg. 2814
SASAKI ASSOCIATES INC.; *U.S. Private*, pg. 3552
SAUDI AMERICAN GLASS COMPANY—See Dubai Investments PJSC; *Int'l*, pg. 2219

SCHENKEL & SHULTZ INC.; *U.S. Private*, pg. 3564
THE SCHIMBERG GROUP INC.; *U.S. Private*, pg. 4114
SCHMIDT ASSOCIATES, INC.; *U.S. Private*, pg. 3565
SCHOTT NORTH AMERICA, INC. - ARCHITECTURE DIVISION—See Carl-Zeiss-Stiftung; *Int'l*, pg. 1337
SGA-IBI GROUP ARCHITECTS—See ARCADIS N.V.; *Int'l*, pg. 542
SHAFER, KLINE & WARREN, INC.; *U.S. Private*, pg. 3623
SHANKLAND COX LIMITED—See Aukett Swanke Group Plc; *Int'l*, pg. 704
SHEELEY ARCHITECTS, INC.; *U.S. Private*, pg. 3630
SHERMAN-CARTER-BARNHART, PSC; *U.S. Private*, pg. 3634
SHIVE-HATTERY GROUP INC.; *U.S. Private*, pg. 3638
SKIDMORE OWINGS & MERRILL LLP; *U.S. Private*, pg. 3681
SLI DESIGN INC.—See SLI Group Inc.; *U.S. Private*, pg. 3688
SMITH CONSULTING ARCHITECTS—See Godspeed Capital Management LP; *U.S. Private*, pg. 1725
SMITHGROUP, INC. - PHOENIX—See SmithGroup Companies, Inc.; *U.S. Private*, pg. 3697
SMITHGROUP, INC. - SAN FRANCISCO—See SmithGroup Companies, Inc.; *U.S. Private*, pg. 3697
SMITHGROUP, INC.—See SmithGroup Companies, Inc.; *U.S. Private*, pg. 3697
SMITHGROUP, INC. - WASHINGTON, DC—See SmithGroup Companies, Inc.; *U.S. Private*, pg. 3698
SOLSTICE PLANNING AND ARCHITECTURE; *U.S. Private*, pg. 3710
SPRING ENGINEERING, INC.; *U.S. Private*, pg. 3763
SSOE GROUP; *U.S. Private*, pg. 3769
STABIPLAN B.V.—See Trimble, Inc.; *U.S. Public*, pg. 2191
STABIPLAN GMBH—See Trimble, Inc.; *U.S. Public*, pg. 2191
STABIPLAN S.R.L.—See Trimble, Inc.; *U.S. Public*, pg. 2191
STENGEL HILL ARCHITECTURE, INC—See Godspeed Capital Management LP; *U.S. Private*, pg. 1725
STEVENS & WILKINSON GA, INC.—See SSOE Group; *U.S. Private*, pg. 3769
STEVENS & WILKINSON SC, INC.—See SSOE Group; *U.S. Private*, pg. 3769
STEVEN WINTER ASSOCIATES, INC.; *U.S. Private*, pg. 3809
STRUXTURE ARCHITECTS, P.L.C.; *U.S. Private*, pg. 3842
STUDIO 951—See Shive-Hattery Group Inc.; *U.S. Private*, pg. 3638
STUDIO FOUR DESIGN INC.—See Michael Graves & Associates, Inc.; *U.S. Private*, pg. 2698
STUDIO PLUS ARCHITECTURE CORP.; *U.S. Private*, pg. 3843
STV/GWD INC—See STV Group, Inc.; *U.S. Private*, pg. 3846
STV INC/RALPH WHITEHEAD ASSOCIATES—See STV Group, Inc.; *U.S. Private*, pg. 3846
STV INC.—See STV Group, Inc.; *U.S. Private*, pg. 3845
STV INC.—See STV Group, Inc.; *U.S. Private*, pg. 3845
STV INC.—See STV Group, Inc.; *U.S. Private*, pg. 3845
STV INC.—See STV Group, Inc.; *U.S. Private*, pg. 3845
STV INC.—See STV Group, Inc.; *U.S. Private*, pg. 3845
STV INC.—See STV Group, Inc.; *U.S. Private*, pg. 3845
STV INC.—See STV Group, Inc.; *U.S. Private*, pg. 3845
STV INC.—See STV Group, Inc.; *U.S. Private*, pg. 3845
STV INC.—See STV Group, Inc.; *U.S. Private*, pg. 3845
STV INC.—See STV Group, Inc.; *U.S. Private*, pg. 3845
STV INC.—See STV Group, Inc.; *U.S. Private*, pg. 3845
STV INC.—See STV Group, Inc.; *U.S. Private*, pg. 3845
STV INC—See STV Group, Inc.; *U.S. Private*, pg. 3845
STV, INC.—See STV Group, Inc.; *U.S. Private*, pg. 3846
STV/RALPH WHITEHEAD ASSOCIATES—See STV Group, Inc.; *U.S. Private*, pg. 3846
STV/RALPH WHITEHEAD ASSOCIATES—See STV Group, Inc.; *U.S. Private*, pg. 3846
STV/RALPH WHITEHEAD ASSOCIATES—See STV Group, Inc.; *U.S. Private*, pg. 3846
STV/RALPH WHITEHEAD ASSOCIATES—See STV Group, Inc.; *U.S. Private*, pg. 3846
STV/RALPH WHITEHEAD ASSOCIATES—See STV Group, Inc.; *U.S. Private*, pg. 3846
STV/RALPH WHITEHEAD ASSOCIATES—See STV Group, Inc.; *U.S. Private*, pg. 3846
SWEET SPARKMAN ARCHITECTS, INC.; *U.S. Private*, pg. 3892
SYMMES MAINI & MCKEE ASSOCIATES, INC.; *U.S. Private*, pg. 3899
TBA STUDIO ARCHITECTURE, A PROFESSIONAL CORPORATION; *U.S. Private*, pg. 3941
TECNEL S.R.L.—See Antares Vision SpA; *Int'l*, pg. 482
TETRA - IBI GROUP ARCHITECTURE PLANNING—See ARCADIS N.V.; *Int'l*, pg. 542
TEXAS - IBI GROUP, INC.—See ARCADIS N.V.; *Int'l*, pg. 542
THORNTON-TOMASETTI, INC.; *U.S. Private*, pg. 4163
TIGROUP—See Thompson Industrial Services, LLC; *U.S. Private*, pg. 4160

541310 — ARCHITECTURAL SERVI...

TITSCH & ASSOCIATES ARCHITECTS, INC.; *U.S. Private*, pg. 4177
TPS CONSULT LIMITED—See Carillion plc; *Int'l*, pg. 1330
TRINITY HEALTH GROUP, LTD.—See NAC, Inc.; *U.S. Private*, pg. 2829
TRI POINTE HOMES ARIZONA, LLC—See Tri Pointe Homes, Inc.; *U.S. Public*, pg. 2188
TRI POINTE HOMES DC METRO, INC.—See Tri Pointe Homes, Inc.; *U.S. Public*, pg. 2188
TRI POINTE HOMES WASHINGTON, INC.—See Tri Pointe Homes, Inc.; *U.S. Public*, pg. 2188
TROJAN CONSTRUCTION GROUP - SOLE PROPRIETORSHIP LLC—See Alpha Dhabi Holding PJSC; *Int'l*, pg. 368
UDG, INC. - ATLANTA STUDIO—See UDG, Inc.; *U.S. Private*, pg. 4274
UDG, INC.; *U.S. Private*, pg. 4274
URBAN STUDIO ARCHITECTS, INC.; *U.S. Private*, pg. 4315
VAMED ENGINEERING GMBH & CO KG—See Fresenius SE & Co. KGaA; *Int'l*, pg. 2781
VAN AUKEN AKINS ARCHITECTS LLC; *U.S. Private*, pg. 4338
THE VAUGHN COLLABORATIVE INC—See Design Resources Group Architects, A.I.A., Inc.; *U.S. Private*, pg. 1214
VBN CHINA - BEIJING—See STV Group, Inc.; *U.S. Private*, pg. 3846
VBN CORP.—See STV Group, Inc.; *U.S. Private*, pg. 3846
VERETEC LIMITED—See Aukett Swanke Group Plc; *Int'l*, pg. 704
VERSATEX BUILDING PRODUCTS, LLC—See The AZEK Company Inc.; *U.S. Public*, pg. 2035
WALDON STUDIO ARCHITECTS & PLANNERS, PC—See Michael Graves & Associates, Inc.; *U.S. Private*, pg. 2698
WALLACE ROBERTS & TODD LLC; *U.S. Private*, pg. 4431
WANNEMACHER JENSEN ARCHITECTS INC.; *U.S. Private*, pg. 4435
WARE MALCOMB; *U.S. Private*, pg. 4441
WCIT ARCHITECTURE, INC.; *U.S. Private*, pg. 4461
WEBIM SERVICES CO., LTD.—See CHIEN KUO CONSTRUCTION CO., LTD.; *Int'l*, pg. 1477
WHL ARCHITECTS & PLANNERS, INC.—See Architects Orange LLP; *U.S. Private*, pg. 311
WHR ARCHITECTS, INC.—See EYP, Inc.; *U.S. Private*, pg. 1454
WILDER ARCHITECTURE, INC.; *U.S. Private*, pg. 4519
WILLIAAM COX LTD.—See CRH plc; *Int'l*, pg. 1849
WILLIAMSON DACAR ASSOCIATES INC.; *U.S. Private*, pg. 4527
WIMBERLY ALLISON TONG & GOO INC.; *U.S. Private*, pg. 4532
WODPOL SP. Z O.O.—See Apator S.A.; *Int'l*, pg. 501
WOLD ARCHITECTS, INC.; *U.S. Private*, pg. 4553
WTW ARCHITECT, INC.—See AE Works Ltd.; *U.S. Private*, pg. 112
ZABALA ERICKSON, LLC; *U.S. Private*, pg. 4596
ZIMMER GUNSUL FRASCA PARTNERSHIP; *U.S. Private*, pg. 4605
ZIMMERMAN ARCHITECTURAL STUDIOS, INC.; *U.S. Private*, pg. 4605
ZROKA ENGINEERING, P.C.—See Milhouse Engineering & Construction, Inc.; *U.S. Private*, pg. 2729
ZYSCOVICH INC.; *U.S. Private*, pg. 4611

541320 — LANDSCAPE ARCHITECTURAL SERVICES

ACCUSWEEP SERVICES, INC.—See Warburg Pincus LLC; *U.S. Private*, pg. 4439
AD GREEN CO., LTD.—See AISIN Corporation; *Int'l*, pg. 251
AECON CONCESSIONS—See Aecon Group Inc.; *Int'l*, pg. 172
AGROMEC SA; *Int'l*, pg. 220
AGROMEC SA; *Int'l*, pg. 220
AMERISCAPE USA, INC.; *U.S. Private*, pg. 260
ARABI AGRICULTURE CO.—See Arabi Holding Group Company K.S.C.C.; *Int'l*, pg. 532
AUKETT SWANKE GROUP PLC; *Int'l*, pg. 704
A YARD & A HALF LANDSCAPING LLC; *U.S. Private*, pg. 19
BAYSHORE CENTER AT BIVALVE; *U.S. Private*, pg. 496
BEIJING ORIENT LANDSCAPE & ENVIRONMENT CO., LTD.; *Int'l*, pg. 954
BEIJING QIANJING LANDSCAPE CO., LTD.; *Int'l*, pg. 955
BELHASA ANTHONY POOLS CONTRACTING—See Belhasa Group of Companies; *Int'l*, pg. 963
BENCHMARK LANDSCAPES, LLC—See BrightView Holdings, Inc.; *U.S. Public*, pg. 383
BENEFLEX HR RESOURCES, INC.—See Paylocity Holding Corporation; *U.S. Public*, pg. 1656
BRIGHTVIEW LANDSCAPES, LLC—See KKR & Co. Inc.; *U.S. Public*, pg. 1242
CACDO CO., LTD.—See Dentsu Group Inc.; *Int'l*, pg. 2034
CARDNO CHRISTCHURCH—See Cardno Limited; *Int'l*, pg. 1322
CARILLION ENERGY SERVICES LIMITED—See Carillion plc; *Int'l*, pg. 1330
CENTROPROJEKT-ARCHITECTURE, ENGINEERING & STRUCTURAL SYSTEMS LTD.; *Int'l*, pg. 1414
CHANHIGH HOLDINGS LIMITED; *Int'l*, pg. 1446
CHATEAU LANDSCAPE, INC.—See Landscape Developmental Inc.; *U.S. Private*, pg. 2387
CHENGBANG ECO-ENVIRONMENT CO., LTD.; *Int'l*, pg. 1466
CHINA GREENLAND BROAD GREENSTATE GROUP CO., LTD.; *Int'l*, pg. 1505
CHIPPERS, INC.—See The Davey Tree Expert Company; *U.S. Private*, pg. 4018
CHRISTY WEBBER LANDSCAPES; *U.S. Private*, pg. 892
CONFLUENCE; *U.S. Private*, pg. 1013
CONVERSANO ASSOCIATES INC.—See Cobepa S.A.; *Int'l*, pg. 1683
CYPARK RESOURCES BERHAD; *Int'l*, pg. 1896
THE DAVEY TREE EXPERT COMPANY; *U.S. Private*, pg. 4018
DONGZHU ECOLOGICAL ENVIRONMENT PROTECTION CO., LTD.; *Int'l*, pg. 2172
DOUBLE TAKE LLC—See Take-Two Interactive Software, Inc.; *U.S. Public*, pg. 1979
EASTERN LAND MANAGEMENT (ELM); *U.S. Private*, pg. 1320
EASYGRASS LLC—See Sentinel Capital Partners, L.L.C.; *U.S. Private*, pg. 3609
EDSA; *U.S. Private*, pg. 1338
ENVIROLOK, LLC—See Agrecol, LLC; *U.S. Private*, pg. 129
ENVIRONMENT ECOLOGY HOLDING COMPANY OF CHINA; *Int'l*, pg. 2454
FRANCISCO TAVARES INC.; *U.S. Private*, pg. 1593
GATEWAY HOME & GARDEN CENTER, LLC—See SiteOne Landscape Supply, Inc.; *U.S. Public*, pg. 1888
GEORGIA SCAPES, INC.—See Centre Partners Management LLC; *U.S. Private*, pg. 829
GEORGIA SCAPES, INC.—See LP First Capital; *U.S. Private*, pg. 2507
GEOSCAPE CORPORATION—See Hazama Ando Corporation; *Int'l*, pg. 3294
GRAPHEX GROUP LIMITED; *Int'l*, pg. 3060
HALVORSON DESIGN PARTNERSHIP—See Tighe & Bond, Inc.; *U.S. Private*, pg. 4170
HANGZHOU LANDSCAPE ARCHITECTURE DESIGN INSTITUTE CO., LTD.; *Int'l*, pg. 3249
HEDEDANMARK A/S—See Det Danske Hedeselskab; *Int'l*, pg. 2047
HERITAGE LINKS—See Lexicon, Inc.; *U.S. Private*, pg. 2440
IDVERDE UK LTD.; *Int'l*, pg. 3597
IN BLOOM, INC.; *U.S. Private*, pg. 2052
INNOVAR ENVIRONMENTAL, INC.; *U.S. Private*, pg. 2081
INTERMOUNTAIN PLANTINGS, INC.—See BrightView Holdings, Inc.; *U.S. Public*, pg. 384
J.C. CHEEK CONTRACTORS, INC.; *U.S. Private*, pg. 2159
JUNIPER LANDSCAPING, INC.; *U.S. Private*, pg. 2244
LAKE CITY PARTNERSHIP COUNCIL; *U.S. Private*, pg. 2374
LANDSCAPE CONCEPTS MANAGEMENT, INC.; *U.S. Private*, pg. 2387
LANDSCAPE MAINTENANCE PROFESSIONALS, INC.; *U.S. Private*, pg. 2387
THE LANDSCAPE PARTNERS, LTD.—See Aspen Grove Landscape Companies, LLC; *U.S. Private*, pg. 352
LANDSCAPE SERVICE PROFESSIONALS, INC.—See Centre Partners Management LLC; *U.S. Private*, pg. 829
LANDSCAPE SERVICE PROFESSIONALS, INC.—See LP First Capital; *U.S. Private*, pg. 2507
MAIN STREET MARKET SQUARE REDEVELOPMENT AUTHORITY; *U.S. Private*, pg. 2552
MASER CONSULTING—See Colliers International Group Inc.; *Int'l*, pg. 1700
MASER CONSULTING—See Colliers International Group Inc.; *Int'l*, pg. 1700
MASER CONSULTING—See Colliers International Group Inc.; *Int'l*, pg. 1700
MASER CONSULTING—See Colliers International Group Inc.; *Int'l*, pg. 1700
MIJULAND CO., LTD.—See DHSteel; *Int'l*, pg. 2100
MUNICIPAL IMPROVEMENT CORPORATION OF LOS ANGELES; *U.S. Private*, pg. 2814
NATIVE LAND DESIGN, LLC; *U.S. Private*, pg. 2866
NICKLAUS DESIGN, LLC—See Nicklaus Companies, LLC; *U.S. Private*, pg. 2926
OUTDOOR LIVING SUPPLY LLC—See Trilantic Capital Management L.P.; *U.S. Private*, pg. 4231
PARKER INTERIOR PLANTSCAPE, INC.; *U.S. Private*, pg. 3097
PLANT FANTASIES INCORPORATED; *U.S. Private*, pg. 3197
PRACTIS INC.—See 424 Capital, LLC; *U.S. Private*, pg. 15
PRACTIS INC.—See Eagle Private Capital, LLC; *U.S. Private*, pg. 1310
PRACTIS INC.—See Plexus Capital, LLC; *U.S. Private*, pg. 3214
THE RECREATIONAL GROUP LLC—See Sentinel Capital Partners, L.L.C.; *U.S. Private*, pg. 3609
RVE, INC.; *U.S. Private*, pg. 3508
SCHILL LANDSCAPING & LAWN SERVICES, INC.; *U.S. Private*, pg. 3565
SEA TRAIL CORPORATION; *U.S. Private*, pg. 3582
SGB PACKAGING GROUP, INC.—See Ares Management Corporation; *U.S. Public*, pg. 191
SMITHGROUP, INC. - CHICAGO—See SmithGroup Companies, Inc.; *U.S. Private*, pg. 3697
SMITHGROUP, INC. - MADISON—See SmithGroup Companies, Inc.; *U.S. Private*, pg. 3697
STUDIOINSITE LLC—See Confluence; *U.S. Private*, pg. 1013
SWANKE HAYDEN CONNELL MIMARLIK AS—See Aukett Swanke Group Plc; *Int'l*, pg. 704
TCLANDSCAPES LTD.—See idverde UK Ltd.; *Int'l*, pg. 3597
TERRACARE ASSOCIATES, LLC—See One Rock Capital Partners, LLC; *U.S. Private*, pg. 3023
TERRA PACIFIC LANDSCAPE, INC.—See Gothic Landscape, Inc.; *U.S. Private*, pg. 1745
TILDEN FARM NURSERY, LLC—See SiteOne Landscape Supply, Inc.; *U.S. Public*, pg. 1889
THE T.L.C. GROUP, LTD.; *U.S. Private*, pg. 4126
TYGAR MANUFACTURING, INC.; *U.S. Private*, pg. 4267
WARD ASSOCIATES, PC—See KB Engineering, PC; *U.S. Private*, pg. 2268
WOLVERTON & ASSOCIATES, INC.—See H.I.G. Capital, LLC; *U.S. Private*, pg. 1827
YAMASATO, FUJIWARA, HIGA & ASSOCIATES, INC.—See Fortive Corporation; *U.S. Public*, pg. 871
YELLOWSTONE LANDSCAPE GROUP, INC.—See Harvest Partners L.P.; *U.S. Private*, pg. 1877

541330 — ENGINEERING SERVICES

2IS INC.; *U.S. Private*, pg. 7
302 ENLISA S.A.—See Energoprojekt Holding a.d.; *Int'l*, pg. 2421
3ANGLE EPCM V.O.F.—See Fluor Corporation; *U.S. Public*, pg. 857
3DENT TECHNOLOGY, LLC—See Ocean Power Technologies, Inc.; *U.S. Public*, pg. 1562
450477 ONTARIO LTD; *Int'l*, pg. 11
4. SEPTEMBAR A,D.; *Int'l*, pg. 11
5-D SYSTEMS, INC.—See Kratos Defense & Security Solutions, Inc.; *U.S. Public*, pg. 1276
A1 ELEKTRO AG—See BKW AG; *Int'l*, pg. 1054
A1 SERVICES (MANCHESTER) LIMITED—See Heidelberg Materials AG; *Int'l*, pg. 3308
A2Z INFRASTRUCTURE LIMITED—See A2Z Infra Engineering Limited; *Int'l*, pg. 30
AAIMCONTROLS, INC.—See Danfoss A/S; *Int'l*, pg. 1960
AANNEMINGEN VAN WELLEN—See Ackermans & van Haaren NV; *Int'l*, pg. 104
AANNEMINGSMAATSCHAPPIJ MARKUS B.V.—See HAL Trust N.V.; *Int'l*, pg. 3224
AAPICO ENGINEERING SDN. BHD.—See AAPICO Hitech plc; *Int'l*, pg. 37
AASKI TECHNOLOGY, INC.; *U.S. Private*, pg. 33
ABB ALGERIA SPA—See ABB Ltd.; *Int'l*, pg. 50
ABB BUSINESS SERVICES GMBH—See ABB Ltd.; *Int'l*, pg. 50
ABB CONTRACTING COMPANY LTD.—See ABB Ltd.; *Int'l*, pg. 54
ABB ELECTRICAL INDUSTRIES LTD.—See ABB Ltd.; *Int'l*, pg. 54
ABB ENERGY AUTOMATION S.P.A.—See ABB Ltd.; *Int'l*, pg. 51
ABB ENGINEERING TECHNOLOGIES CO. (KSCC)—See ABB Ltd.; *Int'l*, pg. 50
ABB HOLDINGS (PTY) LTD.—See ABB Ltd.; *Int'l*, pg. 55
ABB LLC—See ABB Ltd.; *Int'l*, pg. 53
ABB LTD.; *Int'l*, pg. 49
ABB LTD.—See ABB Ltd.; *Int'l*, pg. 53
ABB (PTY) LTD.—See ABB Ltd.; *Int'l*, pg. 49
ABB S.A. DE CV—See ABB Ltd.; *Int'l*, pg. 54
ABB SUSA INC.—See ABB Ltd.; *Int'l*, pg. 52
ABB SWITZERLAND LTD - MANUFACTURING & ROBOTICS—See ABB Ltd.; *Int'l*, pg. 54
ABB TRANSMISSION & DISTRIBUTION LTD.—See ABB Ltd.; *Int'l*, pg. 51
ABC COSTRUZIONI SRL—See Argo Finanziaria S.p.A.; *Int'l*, pg. 562
ABCO ENGINEERING CORP.—See Ei Companies; *U.S. Private*, pg. 1346
ABDUL AALI AL AJMI CO. LTD.; *Int'l*, pg. 58
ABDULLAH A M AL-KHODARI SONS CO JSC; *Int'l*, pg. 59
AB DYNAMICS GK—See AB Dynamics plc; *Int'l*, pg. 39
AB DYNAMICS INC.—See AB Dynamics plc; *Int'l*, pg. 39
ABENGOA S.A.; *Int'l*, pg. 59
ABHISHEK INFRAVENTURES LIMITED; *Int'l*, pg. 61
ABK-CONCRETE PLANT LLP—See Build Investments Group JSC; *Int'l*, pg. 1212
ABLE ENGINEERING HOLDINGS LIMITED; *Int'l*, pg. 62
ABLEVETS LLC—See Oracle Corporation; *U.S. Public*, pg. 1610
ABO ERG—See ABO-Group NV/SA; *Int'l*, pg. 66
ABU DHABI COMMERCIAL ENGINEERING SERVICES

N.A.I.C.S. INDEX

541330 — ENGINEERING SERVICE...

LLC—See Abu Dhabi Commercial Bank PJSC; *Int'l*, pg. 71
ACADEMY OF ENVIRONMENTAL PLANNING & DESIGN, CO., LTD.; *Int'l*, pg. 77
ACADEMY SOLUTIONS GROUP, LLC.; *U.S. Private*, pg. 46
ACCEDO GROUP LTD.; *Int'l*, pg. 79
ACCELERATED DESIGNS, INC.—See EMA Design Automation, Inc.; *U.S. Public*, pg. 1377
ACCORD LIFT SERVICES LTD.—See CNIM Constructions Industrielles de la Mediterranee SA; *Int'l*, pg. 1676
ACHATZ SERVICE GMBH—See Bilfinger SE; *Int'l*, pg. 1024
ACIEROID S.A.—See Bouygues S.A.; *Int'l*, pg. 1121
ACME INDUSTRIAL PIPING, LLC—See Limbach Holdings, Inc.; *U.S. Public*, pg. 1316
ACOUSTI ENGINEERING CO.—See Ardian SAS; *Int'l*, pg. 554
ACQYRE B.V.—See Fluor Corporation; *U.S. Public*, pg. 857
ACROMEC ENGINEERS PTE LTD.; *Int'l*, pg. 109
ACROMETA GROUP LIMITED; *Int'l*, pg. 109
ACS, ACTIVIDADES DE CONSTRUCCION Y SERVICIOS, S.A.; *Int'l*, pg. 109
ACS INTEGRATED SYSTEMS, INC.; *U.S. Private*, pg. 66
ACTA, LLC—See Advanced Core Concepts, LLC; *U.S. Private*, pg. 89
ACTER CO., LTD.; *Int'l*, pg. 117
ACTER TECHNOLOGY CO., LTD.—See Acter Co., Ltd.; *Int'l*, pg. 117
ACTIA AUTOMOTIVE JOINT STOCK COMPANY—See Actia Group SA; *Int'l*, pg. 118
ACTIA CHINA CO., LTD.—See Actia Group SA; *Int'l*, pg. 118
ACTIA COLOMIERS SA—See Actia Group SA; *Int'l*, pg. 118
ACTIA DO BRASIL LTDA.—See Actia Group SA; *Int'l*, pg. 118
ACTIA ENGINEERING SERVICES SA—See Actia Group SA; *Int'l*, pg. 118
ACTIA JAPAN K.K.—See Actia Group SA; *Int'l*, pg. 118
ACTIA SYSTEMS S.A.U.—See Actia Group SA; *Int'l*, pg. 118
ACTIA TUNISIE SA—See Actia Group SA; *Int'l*, pg. 118
ACT INDUSTRIAL PROCESS SERVICES LLC—See ACS, Actividades de Construccion y Servicios, S.A.; *Int'l*, pg. 111
ACTIVE ENERGY GROUP PLC; *Int'l*, pg. 120
ACUTE TECHNOLOGICAL SERVICES, INC.—See Oil States International, Inc.; *U.S. Public*, pg. 1565
ADAPTIVE ENERGY LLC—See AE Industrial Partners, LP; *U.S. Private*, pg. 112
ADASTRIA LOGISTICS CO., LTD.—See Adastria Co., Ltd.; *Int'l*, pg. 126
ADE TP—See FAYAT SAS; *Int'l*, pg. 2624
ADEX MACHINING TECHNOLOGIES, LLC; *U.S. Private*, pg. 78
ADFAST CORP.; *Int'l*, pg. 145
ADICORA SERVICIOS DE INGENIERIA, S.L.—See Iberdrola, S.A.; *Int'l*, pg. 3570
AD SERVO MIHALJ INZENJERING; *Int'l*, pg. 122
ADS SYSTEM SAFETY CONSULTING, LLC—See DSS Sustainable Solutions Switzerland SA; *Int'l*, pg. 2210
ADVANCECON HOLDINGS BERHAD; *Int'l*, pg. 157
ADVANCED APPLIED ENGINEERING, INC.—See Bowman Consulting Group Ltd.; *U.S. Public*, pg. 376
ADVANCED CONTROL SOLUTIONS—See Applied Industrial Technologies, Inc.; *U.S. Public*, pg. 170
ADVANCED CORE CONCEPTS, LLC; *U.S. Private*, pg. 88
ADVANCED DYNAMICS CORPORATION LTD.; *Int'l*, pg. 158
ADVANCED ENERGY SOLUTIONS LLC—See Irex Corporation; *U.S. Private*, pg. 2137
ADVANCED ENGINEERING CONSULTANTS; *U.S. Private*, pg. 89
ADVANCED GOVERNMENT SOLUTIONS, INC.; *U.S. Private*, pg. 90
ADVANCED INDUSTRIAL SERVICES—See Irex Corporation; *U.S. Private*, pg. 2137
ADVANCED NUCLEAR—See Irex Corporation; *U.S. Private*, pg. 2137
ADVANCED SOLUTIONS, INC.—See Rocket Lab USA, Inc.; *U.S. Public*, pg. 1804
ADVANCED SYSTEMS ENGINEERING CORPORATION—See Sterling Investment Partners, L.P.; *U.S. Private*, pg. 3806
ADVENS AG—See Alpiq Holding AG; *Int'l*, pg. 372
AECOM CANADA—See AECOM; *U.S. Public*, pg. 50
AECOM CANADA—See AECOM; *U.S. Public*, pg. 50
AECOM ENVIRONMENT—See AECOM; *U.S. Public*, pg. 50
AECOM-LATHAM—See AECOM; *U.S. Public*, pg. 51
AECOM; *U.S. Public*, pg. 50
AECOM—See AECOM; *U.S. Public*, pg. 50
AECOM—See AECOM; *U.S. Public*, pg. 50
AECOM—See AECOM; *U.S. Public*, pg. 50
AECOM—See AECOM; *U.S. Public*, pg. 50
AECOM—See AECOM; *U.S. Public*, pg. 50
AECOM—See AECOM; *U.S. Public*, pg. 50
AECOM—See AECOM; *U.S. Public*, pg. 50
AECOM USA, INC.—See AECOM; *U.S. Public*, pg. 50
AECON CONSTRUCTION GROUP INC.—See Aecon Group Inc.; *Int'l*, pg. 172
AECON CONSTRUCTION & MATERIALS LTD.—See Aecon Group Inc.; *Int'l*, pg. 172

AECON MATERIALS ENGINEERING CORP.—See Aecon Group Inc.; *Int'l*, pg. 172
AECON UTILITY ENGINEERING—See Aecon Group Inc.; *Int'l*, pg. 172
AEDGE GROUP LIMITED; *Int'l*, pg. 173
AEGIS SIMULATION TECHNOLOGIES UK, LTD.—See Arlington Capital Partners LLC; *U.S. Private*, pg. 327
AEG WEST, INC.—See Tetra Tech, Inc.; *U.S. Public*, pg. 2022
AEI ENGINEERING PTE LTD—See Ascent Bridge Limited; *Int'l*, pg. 602
AEL HOLDCO LIMITED—See AECI Limited; *Int'l*, pg. 171
AENZA S.A.A.; *Int'l*, pg. 176
AEOLIKI PARNONOS SA—See ELLAKTOR S.A.; *Int'l*, pg. 2364
A. EPSTEIN & SONS INTERNATIONAL, INC.; *U.S. Private*, pg. 23
AERODYN ENGINEERING, INC.; *U.S. Private*, pg. 118
AEROSPATIALE MATRA ATR—See Airbus SE; *Int'l*, pg. 246
AEROSTAR SES LLC—See Bristol Bay Native Corporation; *U.S. Private*, pg. 655
AESA AIR ENGINEERING PRIVATE LIMITED—See Batliboi Ltd.; *Int'l*, pg. 890
AE WORKS LTD.; *U.S. Private*, pg. 112
AF-COLENCO THAILAND LTD.—See AFRY AB; *Int'l*, pg. 193
AF-CONSULT INDIA PVT. LTD.—See AFRY AB; *Int'l*, pg. 193
AF-CONSULT SWITZERLAND LTD.—See AFRY AB; *Int'l*, pg. 193
AF-CONSULT UAB—See AFRY AB; *Int'l*, pg. 193
AF-ENGINEERING OY—See AFRY AB; *Int'l*, pg. 193
AF-ENGINEERING S.R.O—See AFRY AB; *Int'l*, pg. 193
AFFILIATED ENGINEERS, INC.; *U.S. Private*, pg. 121
AF GRUPPEN NORGE AS—See AF Gruppen ASA; *Int'l*, pg. 184
AF-HANSEN & HENNEBERG A/S—See AFRY AB; *Int'l*, pg. 194
AFRY AUSTRIA GMBH—See AFRY AB; *Int'l*, pg. 194
AFRY CANADA INC.—See AFRY AB; *Int'l*, pg. 194
AFRY CAPITAL LIMITED—See AFRY AB; *Int'l*, pg. 194
AFRY CZ S.R.O.—See AFRY AB; *Int'l*, pg. 194
AFRY DEUTSCHLAND GMBH—See AFRY AB; *Int'l*, pg. 194
AFRY ENGINEERING INDIA PRIVATE LIMITED—See AFRY AB; *Int'l*, pg. 194
AFRY EROTERV ZRT.—See AFRY AB; *Int'l*, pg. 194
AFRY ESTONIA OU—See AFRY AB; *Int'l*, pg. 194
AFRY FINLAND OY—See AFRY AB; *Int'l*, pg. 194
AFRY INDIA PRIVATE LIMITED—See AFRY AB; *Int'l*, pg. 194
AFRY IRELAND LIMITED—See AFRY AB; *Int'l*, pg. 194
AFRY ITALY S.R.L.—See AFRY AB; *Int'l*, pg. 194
AFRY MANAGEMENT CONSULTING AUSTRIA GMBH—See AFRY AB; *Int'l*, pg. 194
AFRY MANAGEMENT CONSULTING INC.—See AFRY AB; *Int'l*, pg. 194
AFRY MANAGEMENT CONSULTING S.R.L.—See AFRY AB; *Int'l*, pg. 194
AFRY POLAND SP. Z.O.O.—See AFRY AB; *Int'l*, pg. 194
AFRY RUS LLC—See AFRY AB; *Int'l*, pg. 194
AFRY SOLUTIONS SPAIN, S.A.U.—See AFRY AB; *Int'l*, pg. 194
AFRY SOLUTIONS UK LIMITED—See AFRY AB; *Int'l*, pg. 194
AFRY USA LLC—See AFRY AB; *Int'l*, pg. 194
AFRY VIETNAM LTD.—See AFRY AB; *Int'l*, pg. 194
AGC AUSTRALIA PTY LTD—See AusGroup Limited; *Int'l*, pg. 716
AGC ENGINEERING CO., LTD.—See AGC Inc.; *Int'l*, pg. 201
AGC INDUSTRIES PTY LTD—See AusGroup Limited; *Int'l*, pg. 716
AGC TECHNOLOGY SOLUTIONS CO., LTD.—See AGC Inc.; *Int'l*, pg. 203
AGC TECHNOLOGY SOLUTIONS (KUNSHAN) CO., LTD.—See AGC Inc.; *Int'l*, pg. 203
AGC TECHNOLOGY SOLUTIONS (THAILAND) CO., LTD.—See AGC Inc.; *Int'l*, pg. 203
AGENCIJA ZA POSEBNI OTPAD D.O.O.—See Hrvatska elektroprivreda d.d.; *Int'l*, pg. 3502
AGENSI PEKERJAAN TRS MALAYSIA SDN. BHD.—See Fluor Corporation; *U.S. Public*, pg. 857
AGIDENS AG—See Ackermans & van Haaren NV; *Int'l*, pg. 104
AGIDENS INC.—See Ackermans & van Haaren NV; *Int'l*, pg. 104
AGNOLI, BARBER & BRUNDAGE, INC.—See LJA Engineering, Inc.; *U.S. Private*, pg. 2474
AGORA A.d.; *Int'l*, pg. 212
AGRA INDUSTRIES, INC.; *U.S. Private*, pg. 128
AGRIPHAR DE COLOMBIA SAS—See Element Solutions Inc.; *U.S. Public*, pg. 725
AGRIPHAR HELLAS SA—See Element Solutions Inc.; *U.S. Public*, pg. 725
AHLUWALIA CONTRACTS (INDIA) LIMITED; *Int'l*, pg. 225
AHNTECH, INC.; *U.S. Private*, pg. 131
AHRENS GROUP PTY. LTD.; *Int'l*, pg. 225
AHTNA CONTRACTORS, LLC—See Ahtna Incorporated; *U.S. Private*, pg. 131

AHTNA DESIGN-BUILD, INC.—See Ahtna Incorporated; *U.S. Private*, pg. 131
AHTNA ENGINEERING SERVICES, LLC—See Ahtna Incorporated; *U.S. Private*, pg. 131
AHTNA ENVIRONMENTAL, INC.—See Ahtna Incorporated; *U.S. Private*, pg. 131
AHTNA GOVERNMENT SERVICES CORPORATION—See Ahtna Incorporated; *U.S. Private*, pg. 131
AHTNA, INC.; *U.S. Private*, pg. 131
AHTNA PROFESSIONAL SERVICES, INC.—See Ahtna Incorporated; *U.S. Private*, pg. 131
AHTNA TECHNOLOGIES, INC.—See Ahtna Incorporated; *U.S. Private*, pg. 131
AIA ENGINEERING LTD.; *Int'l*, pg. 227
AI INTERNATIONAL, INC.—See Avis Industrial Corporation; *U.S. Private*, pg. 407
AIM ENGINEERING & SURVEYING INC.; *U.S. Private*, pg. 132
AIOLOS INC; *Int'l*, pg. 234
AIRBUS DEFENCE & SPACE SAS—See Airbus SE; *Int'l*, pg. 246
AIRBUS DS OPTRONICS (PTY) LTD.—See Airbus SE; *Int'l*, pg. 242
AIRBUS GROUP LIMITED—See Airbus SE; *Int'l*, pg. 243
AIR KING INDUSTRIAL CO., LTD.—See Allis Electric Co., Ltd.; *Int'l*, pg. 359
AIRMOTIVE ENGINEERING CORP.—See Danbury Aero-Space, Inc.; *U.S. Private*, pg. 1152
AIRPORT INTERNATIONAL GROUP P.S.C.—See Aeroports de Paris S.A.; *Int'l*, pg. 181
AIR WATER AMERICA INC.—See Air Water Inc.; *Int'l*, pg. 239
A.J. BAYLISS PETROLEUM ENGINEERS LTD—See Sun Capital Partners, Inc.; *U.S. Private*, pg. 3861
AJT ENGINEERING LIMITED—See Camellia Plc; *Int'l*, pg. 1270
AKER ENGINEERING MALAYSIA SDN BHD—See Aker Solutions ASA; *Int'l*, pg. 262
AKER ENGINEERING & TECHNOLOGY AS—See Aker Solutions ASA; *Int'l*, pg. 262
AKER SOLUTIONS FINLAND OY—See Aker Solutions ASA; *Int'l*, pg. 262
AKFEN INSAAT TURIZM VE TICARET A.S.—See Akfen Holding A.S.; *Int'l*, pg. 263
AKKA BELGIUM SA—See Adecco Group AG; *Int'l*, pg. 139
AKKA MIDDLE EAST DMCC—See Adecco Group AG; *Int'l*, pg. 139
AKKA TECHNOLOGIES BEIJING LTD.—See Adecco Group AG; *Int'l*, pg. 139
AKKODIS GROUP AG—See Adecco Group AG; *Int'l*, pg. 139
AKT II LIMITED—See Tetra Tech, Inc.; *U.S. Public*, pg. 2024
AKTOR CONCESSIONS S.A—See ELLAKTOR S.A.; *Int'l*, pg. 2364
AKTOR FACILITY MANAGEMENT S.A.—See ELLAKTOR S.A.; *Int'l*, pg. 2364
ALAM HIDRO (M) SDN. BHD.—See Alam Maritim Resources Berhad; *Int'l*, pg. 290
ALAMO AEROSPACE, LP—See Greenwich AeroGroup, Inc.; *U.S. Private*, pg. 1781
ALBAN TRACTOR COMPANY INC. - ALBAN MACHINING & HYDRAULICS DIVISION—See Carter Machinery Company, Inc.; *U.S. Private*, pg. 776
ALBAN TRACTOR COMPANY INC. - ALBAN RENTAL SOLUTIONS DIVISION—See Carter Machinery Company, Inc.; *U.S. Private*, pg. 776
AL BATIN BUSINESS CENTRE L.L.C.—See STV Group, Inc.; *U.S. Private*, pg. 3845
ALBERICI WESTERN CONSTRUCTORS, LTD.—See Alberici Corporation; *U.S. Private*, pg. 152
ALCO ENGINEERING, INC.—See Thielsch Engineering, Inc.; *U.S. Private*, pg. 4144
AL DAWLIYAH FOR HOTELS & MALLS PLC; *Int'l*, pg. 276
ALDEN RESEARCH LABORATORY, INC.—See Round Table Capital Management, LP; *U.S. Private*, pg. 3488
ALDRICH & ELLIOTT PC; *U.S. Private*, pg. 160
A-LERT CONSTRUCTION SERVICES INC.—See Centurion Industries Inc.; *U.S. Private*, pg. 831
ALEX - MECHKOV OOD—See Doppelmayr Group; *Int'l*, pg. 2174
ALFA LAVAL NIAGARA INC.—See Alfa Laval AB; *Int'l*, pg. 312
ALFA LAVAL SLOVAKIA SPOL, S.R.O.—See Alfa Laval AB; *Int'l*, pg. 311
ALFRED BENESCH & COMPANY - MILWAUKEE—See Alfred Benesch & Company; *U.S. Private*, pg. 165
ALFRED BENESCH & COMPANY; *U.S. Private*, pg. 165
ALFRED BENESCH & COMPANY—See Alfred Benesch & Company; *U.S. Private*, pg. 165
ALFRED BENESCH & COMPANY—See Alfred Benesch & Company; *U.S. Private*, pg. 165
ALFRED BENESCH & COMPANY—See Alfred Benesch & Company; *U.S. Private*, pg. 165
ALFRED BENESCH & COMPANY—See Alfred Benesch & Company; *U.S. Private*, pg. 165
ALFRED BENESCH & COMPANY—See Alfred Benesch & Company; *U.S. Private*, pg. 165
ALFRED BENESCH & COMPANY—See Alfred Benesch & Company; *U.S. Private*, pg. 165
ALFRED BENESCH & COMPANY—See Alfred Benesch & Company; *U.S. Private*, pg. 165

ALFRED BENESCH & COMPANY—See Alfred Benesch & Company; *U.S. Private*, pg. 165
ALGOR, S.L.—See Alten S.A.; *Int'l*, pg. 390
AL HAMAS TRADING COMPANY LLC—See Al Hassan Engineering Company S.A.O.G.; *Int'l*, pg. 278
AL HASSAN ELECTRICALS LLC—See Al Hassan Engineering Company S.A.O.G.; *Int'l*, pg. 278
AL HASSAN ENGINEERING CO. ABU DHABI LLC—See Al Hassan Engineering Company S.A.O.G.; *Int'l*, pg. 278
AL HASSAN ENGINEERING CO. DUBAI LLC—See Al Hassan Engineering Company S.A.O.G.; *Int'l*, pg. 278
AL HASSAN ENGINEERING CO. SAOG—See Al Hassan Engineering Company S.A.O.G.; *Int'l*, pg. 279
AL HASSAN POWER INDUSTRIES—See Al Hassan Engineering Company S.A.O.G.; *Int'l*, pg. 279
AL HASSAN SWITCHGEAR MANUFACTURING—See Al Hassan Engineering Company S.A.O.G.; *Int'l*, pg. 279
ALION SCIENCE AND TECHNOLOGY CORPORATION—See Veritas Capital Fund Management, LLC; *U.S. Private*, pg. 4360
ALLANA BUICK & BERS, INC.; *U.S. Private*, pg. 174
ALLAN R. NELSON ENGINEERING (1997) INC.; *Int'l*, pg. 332
ALLEN & HOSHALL INC - NASHVILLE—See Allen & Hoshall, Inc.; *U.S. Private*, pg. 178
ALLEN & HOSHALL, INC.; *U.S. Private*, pg. 178
ALLEN & HOSHALL—See Allen & Hoshall, Inc.; *U.S. Private*, pg. 178
ALLGEIER, MARTIN & ASSOCIATES, INC.; *U.S. Private*, pg. 181
ALLIANCE ENGINEERING INC.; *U.S. Private*, pg. 182
ALLIANCE SPACESYSTEMS, LLC—See AE Industrial Partners, LP; *U.S. Private*, pg. 111
ALLIED ASSOCIATES INTERNATIONAL, INC.—See Redhorse Corporation; *U.S. Private*, pg. 3378
ALLIED POWER GROUP, LLC; *U.S. Private*, pg. 187
ALLPLAN GMBH—See EVN AG; *Int'l*, pg. 2570
ALL SYSTEMS GO, LLC; *U.S. Private*, pg. 173
ALLTAINER AB; *Int'l*, pg. 360
AL MAROUF AND AL BARJAS COMBINED FOR GENERAL TRADING AND CONTRACTING COMPANY - ABDUL RAHMAN MOUSAA AL MAROUF AND PARTNER'S - W.L.L.—See Combined Group Contracting Company KSCC; *Int'l*, pg. 1709
AL-MUNTASER TRADING & CONTRACTING CO. W.L.L. - CONTRACTING DIVISION—See Al-Muntaser Trading & Contracting Co. W.L.L.; *Int'l*, pg. 287
AL-OSAIS MCM CO. LTD.—See Al-Osais International Holding Company; *Int'l*, pg. 287
ALPHA AEOLIKI MOLAON LAKONIA S.A—See ELLAKTOR S.A.; *Int'l*, pg. 2364
ALPHA-PLAN AG ROTHRIST—See Burkhalter Holding AG; *Int'l*, pg. 1224
ALPHA TESTING, INC.—See Universal Engineering Sciences, LLC; *U.S. Private*, pg. 4304
ALPINE-ENERGIE HOLDING AG—See ALPINE Bau GmbH; *Int'l*, pg. 371
ALPINE MAYREDER CONSTRUCTION CO., LTD.—See ALPINE Bau GmbH; *Int'l*, pg. 371
AL SAHWA TRADING CO. LLC—See Al Hassan Engineering Company S.A.O.G.; *Int'l*, pg. 279
ALSIM ALARKO SAN. TES. VE TIC, A.S.—See Alarko Holding A.S.; *Int'l*, pg. 291
ALSIM ALARKO S.R.L.—See Alarko Holding A.S.; *Int'l*, pg. 291
ALS INDUSTRIAL AUSTRALIA PTY. LTD.—See ALS Limited; *Int'l*, pg. 378
ALTAIR ENGINEERING AB—See Altair Engineering, Inc.; *U.S. Public*, pg. 86
ALTAIR ENGINEERING CANADA, LTD.—See Altair Engineering, Inc.; *U.S. Public*, pg. 86
ALTAIR ENGINEERING FRANCE S.A.S.—See Altair Engineering, Inc.; *U.S. Public*, pg. 86
ALTAIR ENGINEERING (PTY.) LTD.—See Altair Engineering, Inc.; *U.S. Public*, pg. 86
ALTAIR ENGINEERING SDN. BHD.—See Altair Engineering, Inc.; *U.S. Public*, pg. 86
ALTAIR SOFTWARE AND SERVICES S.L.—See Altair Engineering, Inc.; *U.S. Public*, pg. 86
ALTAMIRA TECHNOLOGIES CORPORATION; *U.S. Private*, pg. 204
ALTA VISTA SOLUTIONS—See GI Manager L.P.; *U.S. Private*, pg. 1691
ALTEN AUSTRIA SUD GMBH—See Alten S.A.; *Int'l*, pg. 389
ALTEN BELGIUM SPRL—See Alten S.A.; *Int'l*, pg. 389
ALTEN CALSOFT LABS INDIA PRIVATE LTD.—See Alten S.A.; *Int'l*, pg. 389
ALTEN GMBH—See Alten S.A.; *Int'l*, pg. 389
ALTEN LTD—See Alten S.A.; *Int'l*, pg. 389
ALTEN S.A.; *Int'l*, pg. 389
ALTEN SUD OUEST SAS—See Alten S.A.; *Int'l*, pg. 390
ALTEN SWEDEN AB—See Alten S.A.; *Int'l*, pg. 389
ALTEN SWITZERLAND SARL AG—See Alten S.A.; *Int'l*, pg. 389
ALTEN TECHNOLOGY GMBH—See Alten S.A.; *Int'l*, pg. 389
ALTIFORT FRANCE SAS; *Int'l*, pg. 393
ALTITUDE AEROSPACE INTERIORS LIMITED—See Air New Zealand Limited; *Int'l*, pg. 239
ALTITUDE, INC.—See Accenture plc; *Int'l*, pg. 86
ALTRAN BELGIUM SA—See Capgemini SE; *Int'l*, pg. 1304
ALTRAN CANADA INC—See Capgemini SE; *Int'l*, pg. 1304
ALTRAN SOLUTIONS CORP.—See Capgemini SE; *Int'l*, pg. 1305
AMANO MAINTENANCE ENGINEERING CORP.—See Amano Corporation; *Int'l*, pg. 410
AMART S.A.—See Ackermans & van Haaren NV; *Int'l*, pg. 104
AMAZON ENERGY LIMITED—See Computacenter plc; *Int'l*, pg. 1758
AMBANG WIRA SDN. BHD.—See AWC Berhad; *Int'l*, pg. 752
AMCORP PROPERTIES BERHAD—See Amcorp Group Berhad; *Int'l*, pg. 418
AME CONSTRUCTION SDN. BHD.—See AME Elite Consortium Berhad; *Int'l*, pg. 420
AM ENGINEERING, INC.; *U.S. Private*, pg. 214
AMENTUM SERVICES, INC.; *U.S. Private*, pg. 218
AMERANT MORTGAGE, LLC—See Amerant Bancorp Inc.; *U.S. Public*, pg. 94
AMERICAN COMPLIANCE TECHNOLOGIES, INC.; *U.S. Private*, pg. 227
AMERICAN ELECTRONICS, INC.—See Ducommun Incorporated; *U.S. Public*, pg. 689
AMERICAN ENGINEERING ASSOCIATES - SOUTHEAST, P.A.; *U.S. Private*, pg. 232
AMERICAN PETROLEUM EQUIPMENT & CONSTRUCTION COMPANY, INC.; *U.S. Private*, pg. 243
AMERICAN STRUCTUREPOINT INC.; *U.S. Private*, pg. 256
AMETEK MIDDLE EAST FZE—See AMETEK, Inc.; *U.S. Public*, pg. 119
AMODIAG ENVIRONNEMENT—See Hiolle Industries S.A.; *Int'l*, pg. 3401
AM PIERCE & ASSOCIATES, INC.; *U.S. Private*, pg. 214
AMPIRICAL SOLUTIONS LLC; *U.S. Private*, pg. 266
AMSEC LLC—See Huntington Ingalls Industries, Inc.; *U.S. Public*, pg. 1072
AMS MARINE PTE. LTD.—See Destini Berhad; *Int'l*, pg. 2046
AMYX, INC.; *U.S. Private*, pg. 270
ANADARKO INDUSTRIES, LLC; *U.S. Private*, pg. 271
ANAFI PLUS—See Assystem S.A.; *Int'l*, pg. 650
ANALYTICAL SERVICES & MATERIALS, INC.; *U.S. Private*, pg. 271
ANAND PROJECTS LIMITED; *Int'l*, pg. 446
ANAS INTERNATIONAL ENTERPRISE S.P.A.—See Ferrovie dello Stato Italiane S.p.A.; *Int'l*, pg. 2645
ANCOM NYLEX TERMINALS SDN. BHD.—See Ancom Logistics Berhad; *Int'l*, pg. 449
ANC RESEARCH & DEVELOPMENT LLC - CONSTRUCTION DIVISION—See Cook Inlet Region, Inc.; *U.S. Private*, pg. 1038
ANDERSONPENNA PARTNERS, INC.—See Littlejohn & Co., LLC; *U.S. Private*, pg. 2469
THE ANDREWS ENGINEERING COMPANY INCORPORATED—See Davis & Floyd, Inc.; *U.S. Private*, pg. 1172
ANDRITZ INC.—See ANDRITZ AG; *Int'l*, pg. 453
ANDRITZ METALS USA INC—See ANDRITZ AG; *Int'l*, pg. 454
ANDRITZ OY—See ANDRITZ AG; *Int'l*, pg. 454
ANDROMEDA SYSTEMS INC.; *U.S. Private*, pg. 280
ANEL ELECTRICAL PROJECT CONTRACTING TRADE INC.; *Int'l*, pg. 457
ANELSIS MUHENDISLIK SAN. VE TIC, LTD. STI.—See Anel Electrical Project Contracting Trade Inc.; *Int'l*, pg. 458
ANEMOS ATALANTIS SA—See ELLAKTOR S.A.; *Int'l*, pg. 2364
ANEST IWATA SCANDINAVIA AKTIEBOLAG—See ANEST IWATA Corporation; *Int'l*, pg. 458
ANEWA ENGINEERING PRIVATE LIMITED—See Alpha Dhabi Holding PJSC; *Int'l*, pg. 367
ANGLO AMERICAN AUSTRALIA LIMITED—See Anglo American PLC; *Int'l*, pg. 461
ANGLO AMERICAN RESOURCES TRADING (CHINA) CO. LTD.—See Anglo American PLC; *Int'l*, pg. 461
ANGLO COAL (GERMAN CREEK) PTY LTD—See Anglo American PLC; *Int'l*, pg. 461
ANGLO OPERATIONS (PTY) LTD.—See Anglo American PLC; *Int'l*, pg. 461
ANGLO PLATINUM MARKETING LIMITED—See Anglo American PLC; *Int'l*, pg. 461
ANHUI CONSTRUCTION ENGINEERING GROUP CORPORATION LIMITED; *Int'l*, pg. 467
ANHUI DONGHUA ENVIRONMENT & MUNICIPAL ENGINEERING CO., LTD.—See East China Engineering Science & Technology Co., Ltd.; *Int'l*, pg. 2269
ANHUI HUAQI ENVIRONMENTAL PROTECTION & TECHNOLOGY CO., LTD.; *Int'l*, pg. 468
ANHUI TRANSPORT CONSULTING & DESIGN INSTITUTE CO., LTD.; *Int'l*, pg. 470
ANI INTEGRATED SERVICES LIMITED; *Int'l*, pg. 471
ANION QUIMICA INDUSTRIAL S.A.—See Element Solutions Inc.; *U.S. Public*, pg. 725
ANSALDO ENERGY INC.—See Hanwha Group; *Int'l*, pg. 3265
ANSALDO NUCLEARE SPA—See Cassa Depositi e Prestiti S.p.A.; *Int'l*, pg. 1354
ANSALDO THOMASSEN GULF LLC—See Cassa Depositi e Prestiti S.p.A.; *Int'l*, pg. 1354
ANTHONY BEST DYNAMICS LIMITED—See AB Dynamics plc; *Int'l*, pg. 39
ANTICLINE DISPOSAL, LLC—See NGL Energy Partners LP; *U.S. Public*, pg. 1527
ANTON BORER IMMOBILIEN AG; *Int'l*, pg. 484
ANUBHAV INFRASTRUCTURE LIMITED; *Int'l*, pg. 485
AOYAMA KIKO CO., LTD.—See Hazama Ando Corporation; *Int'l*, pg. 3294
APEX ADVANCED TECHNOLOGY LLC—See Cadsys (India) Ltd.; *Int'l*, pg. 1248
APEX MACHINE TOOL COMPANY, INC.—See Hanwha Group; *Int'l*, pg. 3264
APLEONA R&M AUSBAU BERLIN GMBH—See Bilfinger SE; *Int'l*, pg. 1024
APLEONA R&M AUSBAU MANNHEIM GMBH—See Bilfinger SE; *Int'l*, pg. 1024
APLEONA R&M AUSBAU STUTTGART GMBH—See Bilfinger SE; *Int'l*, pg. 1024
APLICACIONES TECNICAS DE LA ENERGIA, S.L.—See Elecnor, S.A.; *Int'l*, pg. 2347
A.P.M. AUTOMATION SOLUTIONS LTD.—See Emerson Electric Co.; *U.S. Public*, pg. 745
APOLLO HOLDING B.V.—See Newell Brands Inc.; *U.S. Public*, pg. 1513
A-POWER ENERGY GENERATION SYSTEMS, LTD.; *Int'l*, pg. 20
APPLIED CONTROL TECHNOLOGY, LLC.—See ACS, Actividades de Construccion y Servicios, S.A.; *Int'l*, pg. 111
APPLIED RESEARCH ASSOCIATES MIDWEST DIVISION—See Applied Research Associates, Inc.; *U.S. Private*, pg. 299
APPLIED RESEARCH ASSOCIATES SHOCK PHYSICS DIVISION—See Applied Research Associates, Inc.; *U.S. Private*, pg. 299
APPLIED RESEARCH ASSOCIATES SOUTHEAST DIVISION—See Applied Research Associates, Inc.; *U.S. Private*, pg. 299
APPLY LEIRVIK INTERNATIONAL PTE LTD—See Apply ASA; *Int'l*, pg. 522
APPLY POLAND SP. Z O.O.—See Apply ASA; *Int'l*, pg. 522
APPLY RIG & MODULES AS—See Apply ASA; *Int'l*, pg. 522
APPLY SORCO AS—See Apply ASA; *Int'l*, pg. 522
APS TECHNOLOGY, INC.; *U.S. Private*, pg. 302
APTITO, LLC—See Mullen Automotive, Inc.; *U.S. Public*, pg. 1486
AQ1 SYSTEMS S.A.—See Aktieselskabet Schouw & Co.; *Int'l*, pg. 265
AQUALISBRAEMAR TECHNICAL SERVICES (ADJUSTING) LIMITED—See ABL Group ASA; *Int'l*, pg. 62
AQUALISBRAEMAR TECHNICAL SERVICES LTD.—See ABL Group ASA; *Int'l*, pg. 62
ARABI ENERTECH COMPANY K.S.C.—See Arabi Holding Group Company K.S.C.C.; *Int'l*, pg. 532
ARABI ENGINEERING CO.—See Arabi Holding Group Company K.S.C.C.; *Int'l*, pg. 532
ARABTEC ENGINEERING SERVICES L.L.C.—See Arabtec Holding PJSC; *Int'l*, pg. 534
ARCADIS ASIA—See ARCADIS N.V.; *Int'l*, pg. 540
ARCADIS BELGIUM N.V.—See ARCADIS N.V.; *Int'l*, pg. 540
ARCADIS BOUW BV—See ARCADIS N.V.; *Int'l*, pg. 541
ARCADIS CHILE SA—See ARCADIS N.V.; *Int'l*, pg. 540
ARCADIS CZ A.S.—See ARCADIS N.V.; *Int'l*, pg. 540
ARCADIS DEUTSCHLAND GMBH—See ARCADIS N.V.; *Int'l*, pg. 540
ARCADIS ESG—See ARCADIS N.V.; *Int'l*, pg. 540
ARCADIS EUROMETUDES S.A.—See ARCADIS N.V.; *Int'l*, pg. 540
ARCADIS G&M, INC.—See ARCADIS N.V.; *Int'l*, pg. 541
ARCADIS INFRA B.V.—See ARCADIS N.V.; *Int'l*, pg. 541
ARCADIS ITALIA SRL—See ARCADIS N.V.; *Int'l*, pg. 540
ARCADIS, LTD.—See ARCADIS N.V.; *Int'l*, pg. 541
ARCADIS - MIDDLE EAST—See ARCADIS N.V.; *Int'l*, pg. 541
ARCADIS NEDERLAND BV—See ARCADIS N.V.; *Int'l*, pg. 541
ARCADIS PERU—See ARCADIS N.V.; *Int'l*, pg. 540
ARCADIS - PHILIPPINES—See ARCADIS N.V.; *Int'l*, pg. 541
ARCADIS SPATIAL INFORMATION—See ARCADIS N.V.; *Int'l*, pg. 541
ARCADIS SP. Z.O.O.—See ARCADIS N.V.; *Int'l*, pg. 541
ARCADIS (UK) LIMITED—See ARCADIS N.V.; *Int'l*, pg. 541
ARCADIS U.S., INC. - TAMPA—See ARCADIS N.V.; *Int'l*, pg. 541
ARC FABRICATORS, LLC—See MDU Resources Group, Inc.; *U.S. Public*, pg. 1409
ARCO CONSTRUCTION COMPANY INC.; *U.S. Private*, pg. 315
ARDAMAN & ASSOCIATES, INC.—See Tetra Tech, Inc.; *U.S. Public*, pg. 2022
ARDMORE CONSTRUCTION LIMITED; *Int'l*, pg. 556
ARDMORE SHIPPING SERVICES (IRELAND)

N.A.I.C.S. INDEX

541330 — ENGINEERING SERVICE...

LIMITED—See Ardmore Shipping Corporation; *Int'l*, pg. 556
AREHNA ENGINEERING, INC.; *U.S. Private*, pg. 318
AREIAS SYSTEMS, INC.; *U.S. Private*, pg. 318
ARGEO AS; *Int'l*, pg. 561
ARI JACKSON MANUFACTURING—See ITE Management L.P.; *U.S. Private*, pg. 2149
ARK RESOURCES HOLDINGS SDN BHD; *Int'l*, pg. 568
ARMSTRONG AEROSPACE, INC.—See Astronics Corporation; *U.S. Public*, pg. 217
ARMSTRONG CONSULTANTS, INC.—See H.W. Lochner, Inc.; *U.S. Private*, pg. 1836
ARMSTRONG MECHANICAL COMPONENTS COMPANY LIMITED—See Armstrong Industrial Corporation Ltd.; *Int'l*, pg. 575
ARMSTRONG ODENWALD CHANGCHUN (AOC) TECHNOLOGY CO LTD—See Armstrong Industrial Corporation Ltd.; *Int'l*, pg. 575
ARMSTRONG ODENWALD TECHNOLOGY (TIANJIN) CO LTD—See Armstrong Industrial Corporation Ltd.; *Int'l*, pg. 575
ARMSTRONG ODENWALD TECHNOLOGY (WUHAN) CO LTD—See Armstrong Industrial Corporation Ltd.; *Int'l*, pg. 575
ARMSTRONG RUBBER TECHNOLOGY (THAILAND) COMPANY LIMITED—See Armstrong Industrial Corporation Ltd.; *Int'l*, pg. 575
ARMSTRONG TECHNOLOGY (SUZHOU) CO LTD—See Armstrong Industrial Corporation Ltd.; *Int'l*, pg. 575
ARMSTRONG TECHNOLOGY (WUXI) CO LTD—See Armstrong Industrial Corporation Ltd.; *Int'l*, pg. 575
ARNEST ONE CORPORATION—See Iida Group Holdings Co., Ltd.; *Int'l*, pg. 3607
ARNOLD & O'SHERIDAN, INC.; *U.S. Private*, pg. 332
ARORA ENGINEERS, INC.; *U.S. Private*, pg. 334
ARO RECRUITMENT (SINGAPORE) PTE. LTD.—See Bain Capital, LP; *U.S. Private*, pg. 433
ARREDONDO, ZEPEDA & BRUNZ, LLC—See Littlejohn & Co., LLC; *U.S. Private*, pg. 2469
ARTEFACT PROJECTS LTD.; *Int'l*, pg. 581
ARTELIA HOLDING SA; *Int'l*, pg. 581
ARTEMIS RESOURCES LTD; *Int'l*, pg. 583
ARTS GROUP CO., LTD.; *Int'l*, pg. 585
ARTSON ENGINEERING LTD; *Int'l*, pg. 586
ARUP ADVISORY INC.—See Arup Group Ltd.; *Int'l*, pg. 586
ARUP AMERICAS, INC.—See Arup Group Ltd.; *Int'l*, pg. 586
ARUP ASSOCIATES LIMITED—See Arup Group Ltd.; *Int'l*, pg. 586
ARUP BOTSWANA LIMITED—See Arup Group Ltd.; *Int'l*, pg. 586
ARUP BRASIL CONSULTORIA LTDA—See Arup Group Ltd.; *Int'l*, pg. 586
ARUP B.V.—See Arup Group Ltd.; *Int'l*, pg. 586
ARUP CANADA INC.—See Arup Group Ltd.; *Int'l*, pg. 586
ARUP CHINA LIMITED—See Arup Group Ltd.; *Int'l*, pg. 586
ARUP COLOMBIA S.A.S.—See Arup Group Ltd.; *Int'l*, pg. 586
ARUP DEUTSCHLAND GMBH—See Arup Group Ltd.; *Int'l*, pg. 586
ARUP D.O.O.—See Arup Group Ltd.; *Int'l*, pg. 587
ARUP GOVERNMENT PROJECTS INC.—See Arup Group Ltd.; *Int'l*, pg. 586
ARUP GROUP LTD.; *Int'l*, pg. 586
ARUP IRELAND LIMITED—See Arup Group Ltd.; *Int'l*, pg. 586
ARUP ITALIA S.R.L.—See Arup Group Ltd.; *Int'l*, pg. 586
ARUP LATIN AMERICA S.A.U.—See Arup Group Ltd.; *Int'l*, pg. 586
ARUP MUHENDISLIK VE MUSAVIRLIK LIMITED SIRKETI—See Arup Group Ltd.; *Int'l*, pg. 586
ARUP NEW ZEALAND LIMITED—See Arup Group Ltd.; *Int'l*, pg. 586
ARUP PARTNER PTY LIMITED—See Arup Group Ltd.; *Int'l*, pg. 587
ARUP (PTY) LIMITED—See Arup Group Ltd.; *Int'l*, pg. 586
ARUP PTY LIMITED—See Arup Group Ltd.; *Int'l*, pg. 587
ARUP - S.I.G.M.A. LTD—See Arup Group Ltd.; *Int'l*, pg. 586
ARUP SINGAPORE PRIVATE LIMITED—See Arup Group Ltd.; *Int'l*, pg. 587
ARUP TEXAS INC.—See Arup Group Ltd.; *Int'l*, pg. 587
ARUP VIETNAM LIMITED—See Arup Group Ltd.; *Int'l*, pg. 587
ASAHI SYNCHROTECH CO., LTD.—See Chubu Electric Power Co., Inc.; *Int'l*, pg. 1593
ASAKA MISONO UTILITY SERVICES CORPORATION—See Hitachi, Ltd.; *Int'l*, pg. 3412
ASAN TECHNO VALLEY CO., LTD.—See Hanwha Group; *Int'l*, pg. 3264
ASANUMA CONSTRUCTION LTD.—See Asanuma Corporation; *Int'l*, pg. 599
ASCO CONSTRUCTION LTD.; *Int'l*, pg. 602
ASFALTOS Y CONSTRUCCIONES ELSAN, S.A.—See Grupo Villar Mir, S.A.U.; *Int'l*, pg. 3138
THE ASH GROUP, INC.; *U.S. Private*, pg. 3989
ASIAN MICRO CO. LTD.—See Asian Micro Holdings Ltd.; *Int'l*, pg. 618
ASIAN MICRO TECHNOLOGY CO. LTD.—See Asian Micro Holdings Ltd.; *Int'l*, pg. 618

ASIA PROCESS INDUSTRIES PTE. LTD.—See Hiap Seng Engineering Limited; *Int'l*, pg. 3382
ASISTENCIA OFFSHORE, S.A.—See ACS, Actividades de Construccion y Servicios, S.A.; *Int'l*, pg. 110
AS MERKO EHITUS; *Int'l*, pg. 590
ASMO DETROIT, INC—See Denso Corporation; *Int'l*, pg. 2028
ASM WAFER PROCESS EQUIPMENT SINGAPORE PTE LTD—See ASM INTERNATIONAL N.V.; *Int'l*, pg. 626
ASPROFOS ENGINEERING S.A.—See HELLENIQ ENERGY Holdings S.A.; *Int'l*, pg. 3334
ASSEMBLIN AB; *Int'l*, pg. 642
ASSOCIATED BRITISH ENGINEERING PLC; *Int'l*, pg. 648
ASSOCIATED ENGINEERS, LTD.; *Int'l*, pg. 648
ASSOCIATED ENGINEERS ZHUHAI S.E.Z. LTD.—See Associated Engineers, Ltd.; *Int'l*, pg. 648
ASSOCIATED SUBSTATION ENGINEERING INC.—See Aubrey Silvey Enterprises Inc.; *U.S. Private*, pg. 385
AS STUBER, ZNL DER SERGIO LO STANCO ELEKTRO AG—See Burkhalter Holding AG; *Int'l*, pg. 1224
ASSURANCE TECHNOLOGY CORPORATION; *U.S. Private*, pg. 359
ASSURED FLOW SOLUTIONS LLC—See Sentinel Capital Partners, L.L.C.; *U.S. Private*, pg. 3609
ASSYSTEMBRIME PORTUGAL—See Assystem S.A.; *Int'l*, pg. 651
ASSYSTEM DEUTSCHLAND HOLDING GMBH—See Assystem S.A.; *Int'l*, pg. 650
ASSYSTEM DEVELOPPEMENT—See Assystem S.A.; *Int'l*, pg. 650
ASSYSTEM ENGINEERING & CONSULTING (SHANGHAI) CO , LTD—See Assystem S.A.; *Int'l*, pg. 650
ASSYSTEM ENVIRONNEMENT—See Assystem S.A.; *Int'l*, pg. 650
ASSYSTEM ENVY A.S.—See Assystem S.A.; *Int'l*, pg. 650
ASSYSTEM FACILITIES—See Assystem S.A.; *Int'l*, pg. 650
ASSYSTEM FRANCE—See Assystem S.A.; *Int'l*, pg. 650
ASSYSTEM GMBH—See Assystem S.A.; *Int'l*, pg. 650
ASSYSTEM GROUP UK LTD—See Assystem S.A.; *Int'l*, pg. 651
ASSYSTEM IBERIA—See Assystem S.A.; *Int'l*, pg. 651
ASSYSTEM INDIA PVT LTD—See Assystem S.A.; *Int'l*, pg. 651
ASSYSTEM (IOM) LTD—See Assystem S.A.; *Int'l*, pg. 650
ASSYSTEM ITALIA SRL—See Assystem S.A.; *Int'l*, pg. 651
ASSYSTEM PORTUGAL—See Assystem S.A.; *Int'l*, pg. 651
ASSYSTEM S.A.; *Int'l*, pg. 650
ASSYSTEM SERVICES DEUTSCHLAND GMBH—See Assystem S.A.; *Int'l*, pg. 650
ASSYSTEM TECHNOLOGIES & SERVICES SA—See Assystem S.A.; *Int'l*, pg. 651
AS TALLINNA TEED—See AS Merko Ehitus; *Int'l*, pg. 590
ASTON MARTIN LAGONDA—See Efad Real Estate Company; *Int'l*, pg. 2318
ASTRAL ASIA BERHAD; *Int'l*, pg. 658
ASTRIUM GMBH—See Airbus SE; *Int'l*, pg. 245
ASTRIUM SPACE TRANSPORTATION GMBH—See Airbus SE; *Int'l*, pg. 245
ASTRIUM (UK) LIMITED—See Airbus SE; *Int'l*, pg. 245
ATAL REALTECH LIMITED; *Int'l*, pg. 665
ATE ENERGY INTERNATIONAL CO., LTD.; *Int'l*, pg. 667
ATELJE A.D.; *Int'l*, pg. 668
ATEXIS FRANCE SAS—See Alten S.A.; *Int'l*, pg. 390
ATEXIS GMBH—See Alten S.A.; *Int'l*, pg. 390
ATEXIS SPAIN SL—See Alten S.A.; *Int'l*, pg. 390
ATEXIS SRL—See Alten S.A.; *Int'l*, pg. 390
AT&F MARINE—See American Tank & Fabricating Company; *U.S. Private*, pg. 256
ATG ACCESS LTD.—See Hill & Smith PLC; *Int'l*, pg. 3391
ATIL-COBRA, S.A.—See ACS, Actividades de Construccion y Servicios, S.A.; *Int'l*, pg. 110
ATKINS AUSTRALASIA PTY LTD.—See AtkinsRealis Group Inc.; *Int'l*, pg. 673
ATKINS CHINA LIMITED—See AtkinsRealis Group Inc.; *Int'l*, pg. 673
ATKINS DANMARK A/S—See AtkinsRealis Group Inc.; *Int'l*, pg. 671
ATKINS NORTH AMERICA INC.—See AtkinsRealis Group Inc.; *Int'l*, pg. 673
ATKINS NORTH AMERICA—See AtkinsRealis Group Inc.; *Int'l*, pg. 673
ATKINS NORTH AMERICA—See AtkinsRealis Group Inc.; *Int'l*, pg. 673
ATLANTA DEVCON LIMITED; *Int'l*, pg. 674
ATLANTIC MARINE ELECTRONICS, INC—See Viking Yacht Company; *U.S. Private*, pg. 4382
ATLANTIC PROJECTS COMPANY, INC.—See Argan, Inc.; *U.S. Public*, pg. 191
ATLANTIC PROJECTS COMPANY LIMITED—See Argan, Inc.; *U.S. Public*, pg. 191
ATLANTIC TESTING LABORATORIES, LTD.; *U.S. Private*, pg. 374
ATLAS INTERMEDIATE HOLDINGS LLC—See GI Manager L.P.; *U.S. Private*, pg. 1691
ATL TECHNOLOGY, INC.; *U.S. Private*, pg. 369
ATREM S.A.; *Int'l*, pg. 693
ATSL HOLDINGS B.V.—See Gammon India Limited; *Int'l*, pg. 2879

ATTIKI ODOS S.A—See ELLAKTOR S.A.; *Int'l*, pg. 2364
ATV PROJECTS INDIA LIMITED; *Int'l*, pg. 697
ATWELL AZ, LLC—See Atwell, LLC; *U.S. Private*, pg. 384
ATWELL, LLC; *U.S. Private*, pg. 384
AUDUBON ENGINEERING; *U.S. Private*, pg. 391
AURORA CIVIL ENGINEERING INC.; *U.S. Private*, pg. 394
AURORA TECHNOLOGY B.V.—See GomSpace Group AB; *Int'l*, pg. 3037
AUSENCO LIMITED—See RCF Management LLC; *U.S. Private*, pg. 3362
AUSENCO SERVICES PTY. LTD.—See RCF Management LLC; *U.S. Private*, pg. 3362
AUSINO PTY LTD.—See China Machinery Engineering Corporation; *Int'l*, pg. 1515
AUSLEY ASSOCIATES INC.—See MAG DS Corp.; *U.S. Private*, pg. 2545
AUSTBORE PTY. LTD.—See Austin Engineering Ltd.; *Int'l*, pg. 718
AUSTIN BROCKENBROUGH & ASSOCIATES, LLP—See Godspeed Capital Management LP; *U.S. Private*, pg. 1725
AUTOBAHNPLUS SERVICES GMBH—See BERGER Holding GmbH; *Int'l*, pg. 979
AUTOMOBILE CONTROLE TECHNIQUE S.A.R.L.—See DEKRA e.V.; *Int'l*, pg. 2007
AUXITEC BATIMENT SAS—See Artelia Holding SA; *Int'l*, pg. 581
AVADA GROUP LIMITED; *Int'l*, pg. 733
AVANCEON LP—See Endress+Hauser (International) Holding AG; *Int'l*, pg. 2405
AVANCEON LTD.; *U.S. Private*, pg. 403
AVAS ENGINEERING LLC—See Endress+Hauser (International) Holding AG; *Int'l*, pg. 2405
AVAX S.A.; *Int'l*, pg. 737
AVENG E+PC ENGINEERING & PROJECTS COMPANY LIMITED—See Aveng Limited; *Int'l*, pg. 738
AVERTEX UTILITY SOLUTIONS INC.; *Int'l*, pg. 739
AVIC INTERNATIONAL MARITIME HOLDINGS LIMITED—See China Merchants Group Limited; *Int'l*, pg. 1520
AVID TECHNOLOGIES, INC.—See Avnet, Inc.; *U.S. Public*, pg. 254
AVNET ASIC ISRAEL LTD—See Avnet, Inc.; *U.S. Public*, pg. 250
AVT SIMULATION INC.; *U.S. Private*, pg. 410
AWARE SECURITY CORPORATION—See Aware, Inc.; *U.S. Public*, pg. 254
AX CONSTRUCTION LIMITED—See AX Investments PLC; *Int'l*, pg. 754
AXEN SARL—See Alten S.A.; *Int'l*, pg. 389
AXFLOW B.V.—See Axel Johnson Gruppen AB; *Int'l*, pg. 763
AXISCADES GMBH—See Axiscades Technologies Ltd.; *Int'l*, pg. 770
AXISCADES INC.—See Axiscades Technologies Ltd.; *Int'l*, pg. 770
AXISCADES TECHNOLOGIES LTD.; *Int'l*, pg. 770
AXISCADES TECHNOLOGY CANADA INC.—See Axiscades Technologies Ltd.; *Int'l*, pg. 770
AXISCADES UK LIMITED—See Axiscades Technologies Ltd.; *Int'l*, pg. 770
AXIS GEOSPATIAL LLC—See Peak Rock Capital LLC; *U.S. Private*, pg. 3124
AXPO HOLZ + ENERGIE AG—See Axpo Holding AG; *Int'l*, pg. 771
AYRES ASSOCIATES INC.; *U.S. Private*, pg. 414
AYRO, INC.; *U.S. Public*, pg. 256
AYSON GEOTEKNIK VE DENIZ INSAAT A.S.—See Dogus Holding AS; *Int'l*, pg. 2154
AYYAN INVESTMENT CO.; *Int'l*, pg. 776
AZEVEDO & TRAVASSOS S.A.; *Int'l*, pg. 778
AZIENDA BRESCIANA PETROLI NOCIVELLI S.P.A.; *Int'l*, pg. 778
AZZ ENCLOSURE SYSTEMS - CHATTANOOGA LLC—See AZZ, Inc.; *U.S. Public*, pg. 258
AZZ GALVANIZING - BRISTOL LLC—See AZZ, Inc.; *U.S. Public*, pg. 258
AZZ TEXAS WELDED WIRE, LLC—See AZZ, Inc.; *U.S. Public*, pg. 259
B2I AUTOMOTIVE—See Alten S.A.; *Int'l*, pg. 390
BABCOCK AFRICA (PTY) LTD—See Babcock International Group PLC; *Int'l*, pg. 792
BABCOCK AFRICA SERVICES (PTY) LIMITED—See Babcock International Group PLC; *Int'l*, pg. 792
BABCOCK BORSIG POWER USLUGE D.O.O.—See Bilfinger SE; *Int'l*, pg. 1024
BABCOCK BORSIG STEINMULLER GMBH—See Bilfinger SE; *Int'l*, pg. 1024
BABCOCK DESIGN & TECHNOLOGY LIMITED—See Babcock International Group PLC; *Int'l*, pg. 792
BABCOCK INTEGRATED TECHNOLOGY LIMITED—See Babcock International Group PLC; *Int'l*, pg. 792
BABCOCK INTERNATIONAL FRANCE AVIATION SAS—See Babcock International Group PLC; *Int'l*, pg. 792
BABCOCK INTERNATIONAL GROUP PLC; *Int'l*, pg. 792
BABCOCK INTERNATIONAL ITALY S.P.A.—See Babcock International Group PLC; *Int'l*, pg. 792
BABCOCK INTERNATIONAL LIMITED—See Babcock Inter-

541330 — ENGINEERING SERVICE...

national Group PLC; *Int'l*, pg. 792
BABCOCK INTERNATIONAL SPAIN S.L.U.—See Babcock International Group PLC; *Int'l*, pg. 792
BABCOCK MARINE (CLYDE) LIMITED—See Babcock International Group PLC; *Int'l*, pg. 792
BABCOCK NTUTHUKO ENGINEERING (PTY) LIMITED—See Babcock International Group PLC; *Int'l*, pg. 792
BABCOCK (NZ) LTD—See Babcock International Group PLC; *Int'l*, pg. 792
BABCOCK POWER ENVIRONMENTAL INC.—See Babcock Power, Inc.; *U.S. Private*, pg. 422
BABCOCK POWER SERVICES INC.—See Babcock Power, Inc.; *U.S. Private*, pg. 422
BABCOCK PTY LTD—See Babcock International Group PLC; *Int'l*, pg. 792
BABCOCK RAIL—See Babcock International Group PLC; *Int'l*, pg. 792
BABCOCK WANSON MAROC—See CNIM Constructions Industrielles de la Mediterranee SA; *Int'l*, pg. 1677
BA CONSULTING GROUP LTD.; *Int'l*, pg. 791
BAE-NEWPLAN GROUP LIMITED—See AtkinsRealis Group Inc.; *Int'l*, pg. 671
BAE SYSTEMS-APPLIED TECHNOLOGIES—See BAE Systems plc; *Int'l*, pg. 797
BAGGERMAATSCHAPPIJ BOSKALIS B.V.—See HAL Trust N.V.; *Int'l*, pg. 3224
BAKER & PROVAN PTY. LTD.; *Int'l*, pg. 805
BALFOUR BEATTY CIVIL ENGINEERING LTD—See Balfour Beatty plc; *Int'l*, pg. 807
BALFOUR BEATTY CONSTRUCTION GROUP INC—See Balfour Beatty plc; *Int'l*, pg. 807
BALFOUR BEATTY ENGINEERING SERVICES LIMITED—See Balfour Beatty plc; *Int'l*, pg. 808
BALFOUR BEATTY GROUND ENGINEERING LTD—See Balfour Beatty plc; *Int'l*, pg. 808
BALFOUR BEATTY PLC; *Int'l*, pg. 807
BALL AEROSPACE & TECHNOLOGIES CORP.—See Ball Corporation; *U.S. Public*, pg. 266
BALZER INGENIEURE AG—See BKW AG; *Int'l*, pg. 1054
BANC3, INC.; *U.S. Private*, pg. 464
BANKS ENGINEERING, INC.; *U.S. Private*, pg. 468
BANTREL CO.; *Int'l*, pg. 855
BANTREL MANAGEMENT SERVICES CO.—See Bantrel Co.; *Int'l*, pg. 855
BARAN CHILE SPA—See Baran Group Ltd.; *Int'l*, pg. 858
BARAN CONSTRUCTION AND INFRASTRUCTURE LTD.—See Baran Group Ltd.; *Int'l*, pg. 858
BARAN ENGINEERING SOUTH AFRICA (PTY) LTD.—See Baran Group Ltd.; *Int'l*, pg. 858
BARAN GROUP LTD.; *Int'l*, pg. 858
BARAN INDUSTRIES (91) LTD.—See Baran Group Ltd.; *Int'l*, pg. 858
BARANMEX, S.A. DE C.V.—See Baran Group Ltd.; *Int'l*, pg. 858
BARAN-OIL & PETROCHEMICAL (1987) PROJECTS LTD.—See Baran Group Ltd.; *Int'l*, pg. 858
BARAN PROJECTS SOUTH AFRICA (PTY) LTD.—See Baran Group Ltd.; *Int'l*, pg. 858
BARAN-ROMANIA LLC—See Baran Group Ltd.; *Int'l*, pg. 858
BARAN SOUTH EAST ASIA LTD.—See Baran Group Ltd.; *Int'l*, pg. 858
BARAN VIETNAM LTD.—See Baran Group Ltd.; *Int'l*, pg. 858
BARCO SILEX SAS—See Barco N.V.; *Int'l*, pg. 863
BARD, RAO + ATHANAS CONSULTING ENGINEERS, LLC - NEW YORK—See Bard, Rao + Athanas Consulting Engineers, LLC; *U.S. Private*, pg. 473
BARD, RAO + ATHANAS CONSULTING ENGINEERS, LLC; *U.S. Private*, pg. 473
BARGE WAGGONER SUMNER & CANNON INC.; *U.S. Private*, pg. 474
BARMAC (CONSTRUCTION) LIMITED—See Barclays PLC; *Int'l*, pg. 862
BARRA DO PEIXE MONTAGENS E SERVICOS, LTDA.—See ACS, Actividades de Construccion y Servicios, S.A.; *Int'l*, pg. 110
BARRATT DEVELOPMENTS PLC; *Int'l*, pg. 867
BARR ENGINEERING COMPANY, ANN ARBOR—See Barr Engineering Company; *U.S. Private*, pg. 479
BARR ENGINEERING COMPANY, DULUTH—See Barr Engineering Company; *U.S. Private*, pg. 479
BARR ENGINEERING COMPANY, HIBBING—See Barr Engineering Company; *U.S. Private*, pg. 479
BARR ENGINEERING COMPANY, JEFFERSON CITY—See Barr Engineering Company; *U.S. Private*, pg. 479
BARR ENGINEERING COMPANY; *U.S. Private*, pg. 479
BARRIOS TECHNOLOGY LTD.; *U.S. Private*, pg. 480
BARRY ISETT & ASSOCIATES INC.; *U.S. Private*, pg. 481
BARRY-WEHMILLER DESIGN GROUP, INC.—See Barry-Wehmiller Companies, Inc.; *U.S. Private*, pg. 481
BARRY-WEHMILLER DESIGN GROUP—See Barry-Wehmiller Companies, Inc.; *U.S. Private*, pg. 481
BARTEC ENGINEERING LLC—See Baran Group Ltd.; *Int'l*, pg. 858
BASE ENGINEERING INC.; *U.S. Private*, pg. 484

BASIC COMMERCE AND INDUSTRIES, INC.; *U.S. Private*, pg. 485
BASS ENGINEERING—See HM International; *U.S. Private*, pg. 1954
BASSI ELEKTRO AG—See Burkhalter Holding AG; *Int'l*, pg. 1224
BATTELLE UK LIMITED—See Battelle Memorial Institute; *U.S. Private*, pg. 487
BAUER ENGINEERING INDIA PRIVATE LIMITED—See BAUER Aktiengesellschaft; *Int'l*, pg. 891
BAUER FOUNDATION CORP.—See BAUER Aktiengesellschaft; *Int'l*, pg. 891
BAUER FOUNDATIONS CANADA INC.—See BAUER Aktiengesellschaft; *Int'l*, pg. 891
BAUER FOUNDATIONS PHILIPPINES, INC.—See BAUER Aktiengesellschaft; *Int'l*, pg. 891
BAUER FUNDACIONES PANAMA S.A.—See BAUER Aktiengesellschaft; *Int'l*, pg. 892
BAUER HONG KONG LIMITED—See BAUER Aktiengesellschaft; *Int'l*, pg. 892
BAUER SPECIAL FOUNDATIONS CAMBODIA CO., LTD.—See BAUER Aktiengesellschaft; *Int'l*, pg. 892
BAUER SPEZIALTIEFBAU SCHWEIZ AG.—See BAUER Aktiengesellschaft; *Int'l*, pg. 892
BAUER UMWELT GMBH.—See BAUER Aktiengesellschaft; *Int'l*, pg. 892
BAUMANN ELECTRO AG—See Burkhalter Holding AG; *Int'l*, pg. 1224
BAU-UNION POTSDAM GMBH—See Bilfinger SE; *Int'l*, pg. 1024
BAY ENGINEERING, INC.—See Atwell, LLC; *U.S. Private*, pg. 384
BB GOVERNMENT SERVICES GMBH—See BAVARIA Industries Group AG; *Int'l*, pg. 899
BB GOVERNMENT SERVICES S.R.L.—See BAVARIA Industries Group AG; *Int'l*, pg. 899
BB INFRASTRUCTURE SERVICES GMBH—See Bilfinger SE; *Int'l*, pg. 1024
BBL BUILDINGS & COMPONENTS, LTD.—See MacArthur Co.; *U.S. Private*, pg. 2534
BBPI SENTINEL PTY LTD—See Bilfinger SE; *Int'l*, pg. 1024
BBR CONSTRUCTION SYSTEMS (M) SDN. BHD.—See BBR Holdings (S) Ltd.; *Int'l*, pg. 921
BBR CONSTRUCTION SYSTEMS PTE LTD—See BBR Holdings (S) Ltd.; *Int'l*, pg. 921
BBS SCHALUNGSBAU GMBH—See Bilfinger SE; *Int'l*, pg. 1024
BBV SYSTEMS GMBH—See Bilfinger SE; *Int'l*, pg. 1024
BCC ENGINEERING, INC.—See Parsons Corporation; *U.S. Public*, pg. 1650
BCE ENGINEERS, INC.—See OceanSound Partners, LP; *U.S. Private*, pg. 2991
BCEG ENVIRONMENTAL REMEDIATION CO., LTD.; *Int'l*, pg. 928
BCE KRAKOW SP. Z O.O.—See Bjornsen Beratende Ingenieure GmbH; *Int'l*, pg. 1054
BCER ENGINEERING, INC.; *U.S. Private*, pg. 499
BCG ENGINEERING & CONSULTING, INC.—See Littlejohn & Co., LLC; *U.S. Private*, pg. 2469
BCI ASIA VIETNAM CO, LTD.—See Byggfakta Group Nordic HoldCo AB; *Int'l*, pg. 1234
BCI CENTRAL LTD.—See Byggfakta Group Nordic HoldCo AB; *Int'l*, pg. 1234
BCI CENTRAL SDN BHD.—See Byggfakta Group Nordic HoldCo AB; *Int'l*, pg. 1234
BCI CENTRAL SINGAPORE PTE. LTD.—See Byggfakta Group Nordic HoldCo AB; *Int'l*, pg. 1234
BCI NEW ZEALAND PTY. LTD.—See Byggfakta Group Nordic HoldCo AB; *Int'l*, pg. 1234
BDB SYNERGY SDN. BHD.—See Bina Darulaman Berhad; *Int'l*, pg. 1032
BEAR SCOTLAND LIMITED—See Jacobs Engineering Group, Inc.; *U.S. Public*, pg. 1185
BECA APPLIED TECHNOLOGIES LTD—See Beca Group Limited; *Int'l*, pg. 936
BECA CARTER HOLLINGS & FERNER LTD—See Beca Group Limited; *Int'l*, pg. 936
BECA GROUP LIMITED; *Int'l*, pg. 936
BECA PTY. LTD.—See Beca Group Limited; *Int'l*, pg. 936
BEC CONSTRUCTION CHAMPAGNE—See FAYAT SAS; *Int'l*, pg. 2624
BEC CONSTRUCTION LANGUEDOC ROUSSILLON—See FAYAT SAS; *Int'l*, pg. 2624
BEC CONSTRUCTION PROVENCE—See FAYAT SAS; *Int'l*, pg. 2624
BECHTEL CIVIL, INC.—See Bechtel Group, Inc.; *U.S. Private*, pg. 510
BECHTEL ENTERPRISES, INC.—See Bechtel Group, Inc.; *U.S. Private*, pg. 510
BECHTEL GROUP, INC.; *U.S. Private*, pg. 509
BECHTEL HANFORD INC.—See Bechtel Group, Inc.; *U.S. Private*, pg. 510
BECHTEL NATIONAL, INC.—See Bechtel Group, Inc.; *U.S. Private*, pg. 510
BECHTEL POWER CORPORATION—See Bechtel Group, Inc.; *U.S. Private*, pg. 510
BE ENGINEERING SERVICES INDIA PRIVATE LIMITED—See RTX Corporation; *U.S. Public*, pg. 1822

BEIJING BOSSCO ENVIRONMENTAL PROTECTION TECHNOLOGY CO., LTD—See Guangxi Bossco Environmental Protection Technology Co., Ltd.; *Int'l*, pg. 3162
BEIJING HITACHI CONTROL SYSTEMS CO., LTD.—See Hitachi, Ltd.; *Int'l*, pg. 3412
BEIJING HITACHI HUASUN INFORMATION SYSTEMS CO., LTD.—See Hitachi, Ltd.; *Int'l*, pg. 3412
BEIJING NATIONAL RAILWAY RESEARCH & DESIGN INSTITUTE OF SIGNAL & COMMUNICATION CO., LTD.—See China Railway Signal & Communication Corporation Ltd.; *Int'l*, pg. 1544
BEIJING SINODATA TECH CO., LTD.; *Int'l*, pg. 957
BEIJING SNLN HP NEW SYNTC FBR SER CO LTD; *Int'l*, pg. 957
BELCAN LLC—See AE Industrial Partners, LP; *U.S. Private*, pg. 111
BELHASA ENGINEERING & CONTRACTING COMPANY—See Belhasa Group of Companies; *Int'l*, pg. 964
BELLECCI & ASSOCIATES, INC.—See Sanderson Bellecci, Inc.; *U.S. Private*, pg. 3543
BELLWAY HOMES LIMITED—See Bellway plc; *Int'l*, pg. 967
BEML LIMITED - AEROSPACE MANUFACTURING DIVISION—See BEML Limited; *Int'l*, pg. 969
BEML LIMITED - BANGALORE COMPLEX—See BEML Limited; *Int'l*, pg. 969
BEML LIMITED - TECHNOLOGY DIVISION—See BEML Limited; *Int'l*, pg. 969
BEML LIMITED - TRUCK DIVISION—See BEML Limited; *Int'l*, pg. 969
BEML (MALAYSIA) SDN.BHD.—See BEML Limited; *Int'l*, pg. 969
BENALEC SDN BHD—See Benalec Holdings Berhad; *Int'l*, pg. 969
BENCHMARK BUILDERS, INC.—See FTE Networks, Inc.; *U.S. Public*, pg. 889
BENCHMARK CIVIL ENGINEERING SERVICES INC.; *U.S. Private*, pg. 523
BENDALLS ENGINEERING—See Carr's Group PLC; *Int'l*, pg. 1343
BENELMAT SA—See Ackermans & van Haaren NV; *Int'l*, pg. 104
BENNETT & PLESS, INC.; *U.S. Private*, pg. 526
BENSON LTD.—See Berkshire Hathaway Inc.; *U.S. Public*, pg. 312
BENTELER ENGINEERING CHENNAI PRIVATE LIMITED—See Benteler International AG; *Int'l*, pg. 976
BENYAN DEVELOPMENT CO. L.L.C.—See Finance House P.J.S.C.; *Int'l*, pg. 2664
BERGEN GROUP SERVICES AS - INDUSTRIAL SERVICE—See Endur ASA; *Int'l*, pg. 2409
BERGEN GROUP SERVICES AS - MARITIME SERVICE—See Endur ASA; *Int'l*, pg. 2409
BERGEN GROUP SERVICES AS—See Endur ASA; *Int'l*, pg. 2409
BERGERABAM INC.—See The Louis Berger Group, Inc.; *U.S. Private*, pg. 4073
BERGER BAU POLSKA SP. Z O.O.—See BERGER Holding GmbH; *Int'l*, pg. 979
BERGMANN ASSOCIATES, ARCHITECTS, ENGINEERS, LANDSCAPE ARCHITECTS & SURVEYORS, D.P.C.; *U.S. Private*, pg. 531
BERLI JUCKER LOGISTICS LIMITED—See Berli Jucker Public Co. Ltd.; *Int'l*, pg. 985
BERNARD PAYSAGE & ENVIRONNEMENT—See FAYAT SAS; *Int'l*, pg. 2624
BERNDORF METALL- UND BADERBAU GMBH—See Berndorf AG; *Int'l*, pg. 987
BERNHARD, LLC—See DIF Management Holding B.V.; *Int'l*, pg. 2117
BERRIEHILL RESEARCH CORPORATION—See Applied Research Associates, Inc.; *U.S. Private*, pg. 299
BERTRANDT AG; *Int'l*, pg. 997
BERTRANDT CESKA REPUBLIKA ENGINEERING TECHNOLOGIES S.R.O.—See Bertrandt AG; *Int'l*, pg. 997
BERTRANDT ENGINEERING SHANGHAI CO., LTD.—See Bertrandt AG; *Int'l*, pg. 997
BERTRANDT FAHRERPROBUNG SUD GMBH—See Bertrandt AG; *Int'l*, pg. 997
BERTRANDT PROJEKTGESELLSCHAFT MBH—See Bertrandt AG; *Int'l*, pg. 998
BERTRANDT SAS BETRIEBSSTATTE—See Bertrandt AG; *Int'l*, pg. 998
BERTRANDT S.A.S.—See Bertrandt AG; *Int'l*, pg. 998
BERTRANDT UK LTD.—See Bertrandt AG; *Int'l*, pg. 998
BERTRANDT US INC.—See Bertrandt AG; *Int'l*, pg. 998
BERTRANDT VERWALTUNGS GMBH—See Bertrandt AG; *Int'l*, pg. 998
BES ENGINEERING CORPORATION; *Int'l*, pg. 998
BESTTECHNICA TM - RADOMIR; *Int'l*, pg. 1000
BETONTIR S.P.A.—See Heidelberg Materials AG; *Int'l*, pg. 3309
BEUTLER & LANG SCHALUNGS- UND BEHALTER-BAU GMBH; *Int'l*, pg. 1004
BEVILACQUA-KNIGHT, INC.—See Gas Technology Institute; *U.S. Private*, pg. 1647
BGR ENERGY SYSTEMS LIMITED - ELECTRICAL PROJ-

N.A.I.C.S. INDEX

541330 — ENGINEERING SERVICE...

ECTS DIVISION—See BGR Energy Systems Limited; *Int'l*, pg. 1008
BGR ENERGY SYSTEMS LIMITED - INFRASTRUCTURE DIVISION—See BGR Energy Systems Limited; *Int'l*, pg. 1008
BHAGWAN MARINE; *Int'l*, pg. 1009
BHARAT BIJLEE LTD; *Int'l*, pg. 1010
BHATIA BROTHERS LLC - INDUSTRIAL SUPPLIES DIVISION—See Bhatia Brothers Group; *Int'l*, pg. 1013
BHI ENERGY I POWER SERVICES LLC—See Bernhard Capital Partners Management, LP; *U.S. Private*, pg. 537
BHILAI ENGINEERING CORP LTD.; *Int'l*, pg. 1015
BIA-PHILLIPSBURG—See Barry Isett & Associates Inc.; *U.S. Private*, pg. 481
BIBUS ITALIA SRL—See Daikin Industries, Ltd.; *Int'l*, pg. 1932
BI-CEMENT LLP—See Build Investments Group JSC; *Int'l*, pg. 1212
BI-CON SERVICES, INC.; *U.S. Private*, pg. 549
BIERI ELEKTROTECHNIK AG—See Burkhalter Holding AG; *Int'l*, pg. 1224
BIGGE POWER CONSTRUCTORS—See Bigge Crane & Rigging Company; *U.S. Private*, pg. 555
BIG RED DOG, INC.—See Wantman Group, Inc.; *U.S. Private*, pg. 4436
BIG STREET CONSTRUCTION, INC.; *U.S. Private*, pg. 554
BILFINGER BERGER AMBIENTE S.R.L.—See Bilfinger SE; *Int'l*, pg. 1024
BILFINGER BERGER BUDOWNICTWO S.A.—See Bilfinger SE; *Int'l*, pg. 1025
BILFINGER BERGER BUILDING POLSKA SP. Z O.O.—See Bilfinger SE; *Int'l*, pg. 1025
BILFINGER BERGER INGENIEURBAU GMBH—See Bilfinger SE; *Int'l*, pg. 1026
BILFINGER BERGER PI CORPORATE SERVICES GMBH—See Bilfinger SE; *Int'l*, pg. 1026
BILFINGER BERGER REGIOBAU GMBH—See Bilfinger SE; *Int'l*, pg. 1026
BILFINGER BERGER SPEZIALTIEFBAU GMBH—See Bilfinger SE; *Int'l*, pg. 1026
BILFINGER BRABANT MOBIEL B.V.—See Bilfinger SE; *Int'l*, pg. 1027
BILFINGER EMS GMBH—See Bilfinger SE; *Int'l*, pg. 1026
BILFINGER ENGINEERING & MAINTENANCE NORDICS AB—See Bilfinger SE; *Int'l*, pg. 1027
BILFINGER ENGINEERING & MAINTENANCE NORDICS AS—See Bilfinger SE; *Int'l*, pg. 1027
BILFINGER ENGINEERING & MAINTENANCE NORDICS OY—See Bilfinger SE; *Int'l*, pg. 1027
BILFINGER INDUSTRIAL AUTOMATION SERVICES LTD.—See Bilfinger SE; *Int'l*, pg. 1026
BILFINGER INDUSTRIAL SERVICES BELGIE N.V.—See Bilfinger SE; *Int'l*, pg. 1027
BILFINGER INDUSTRIAL SERVICES INC.—See Bilfinger SE; *Int'l*, pg. 1027
BILFINGER INDUSTRIAL SERVICES NEDERLAND B.V.—See Bilfinger SE; *Int'l*, pg. 1027
BILFINGER LIFE SCIENCE AUTOMATION GMBH—See Bilfinger SE; *Int'l*, pg. 1027
BILFINGER LTM INDUSTRIE SAS—See Bilfinger SE; *Int'l*, pg. 1027
BILFINGER PETERS ENGINEERING SAS—See Bilfinger SE; *Int'l*, pg. 1027
BILFINGER SHARED SERVICES GMBH—See Bilfinger SE; *Int'l*, pg. 1027
BILFINGER TEBODIN BELGIUM NV—See Bilfinger SE; *Int'l*, pg. 1027
BILFINGER TEBODIN HUNGARY KFT.—See Bilfinger SE; *Int'l*, pg. 1028
BILFINGER TEBODIN ROMANIA S.R.L.—See Bilfinger SE; *Int'l*, pg. 1028
BILFINGER TEBODIN—See Bilfinger SE; *Int'l*, pg. 1026
BILFINGER UK LIMITED—See Bilfinger SE; *Int'l*, pg. 1026
BILLER REINHART STRUCTURAL GROUP INC.; *U.S. Private*, pg. 559
BINAWANI SDN BHD—See Ekovest Berhad; *Int'l*, pg. 2339
BIOFIN HOLDING INTERNATIONAL BV—See DiaSorin S.p.A.; *Int'l*, pg. 2106
BIOGAS NORD AG; *Int'l*, pg. 1038
BIRSE GROUP—See Balfour Beatty plc; *Int'l*, pg. 807
BIRSE PROCESS ENGINEERING LIMITED—See Balfour Beatty plc; *Int'l*, pg. 807
BIS BRABANT MOBIEL B.V.—See Bilfinger SE; *Int'l*, pg. 1025
BIS ENTECH GMBH—See Bilfinger SE; *Int'l*, pg. 1025
BIS IKF GMBH—See Bilfinger SE; *Int'l*, pg. 1025
BIS INDUSTRIAL SERVICES NEDERLAND B.V.—See Bilfinger SE; *Int'l*, pg. 1025
BIS INDUSTRIAL SERVICES OSTERREICH GMBH—See Bilfinger SE; *Int'l*, pg. 1025
BIS ISOLIERTECHNIK NORD GMBH—See Bilfinger SE; *Int'l*, pg. 1025
BIS IZOMAR SP. Z O.O.—See Bilfinger SE; *Int'l*, pg. 1025
BIS MAINSERV SP. Z O.O.—See Bilfinger SE; *Int'l*, pg. 1025
BIS MAINTENANCE NORD GMBH—See Bilfinger SE; *Int'l*, pg. 1025
BIS PRODUCTION PARTNER IPEC AS—See Bilfinger SE; *Int'l*, pg. 1025
BIS WILLICH GMBH—See Bilfinger SE; *Int'l*, pg. 1026
BIT SYSTEMS, INC.—See CACI International Inc.; *U.S. Public*, pg. 418
BIWATER USA INC.—See Biwater Holdings Limited; *Int'l*, pg. 1052
BJC ENGINEERING COMPANY LIMITED—See Berli Jucker Public Co. Ltd.; *Int'l*, pg. 985
BJORNSEN CONSULTING ENGINEERING ERFURT GMBH—See Bjornsen Beratende Ingenieure GmbH; *Int'l*, pg. 1054
BKI GABON S.A.—See HAL Trust N.V.; *Int'l*, pg. 3224
BLACK EAGLE CONSULTING, INC.—See OceanSound Partners, LP; *U.S. Private*, pg. 2991
BLACK IPO, INC.; *U.S. Private*, pg. 572
BLACK PEONY (GROUP) CO., LTD.; *Int'l*, pg. 1059
BLACK & VEATCH LTD.—See Black & Veatch Holding Company; *U.S. Private*, pg. 569
BLAYLOCK, THREET, PHILLIPS & ASSOCIATES, INC.; *U.S. Private*, pg. 580
B L KASHYAP & SONS LIMITED; *Int'l*, pg. 783
BLUE CANYON TECHNOLOGIES LLC; *U.S. Private*, pg. 586
BLUE ENGINEERING S.R.L.—See CRRC Corporation Limited; *Int'l*, pg. 1858
BLUEFIN, LLC—See O2 Investment Partners, LLC; *U.S. Private*, pg. 2982
BLUEHALO, LLC—See Arlington Capital Partners LLC; *U.S. Private*, pg. 327
BLUELINE; *U.S. Private*, pg. 597
BLUESCOPE BUILDINGS NORTH AMERICA INC.—See BlueScope Steel Limited; *Int'l*, pg. 1073
BLUESCOPE CONSTRUCTION INC.—See BlueScope Steel Limited; *Int'l*, pg. 1073
BLUE STAR DESIGN & ENGINEERING LTD.—See Blue Star Limited; *Int'l*, pg. 1070
BLUE STAR M & E ENGINEERING SDN BHD—See Amcorp Group Berhad; *Int'l*, pg. 418
BLUMAUERPLATZ BETEILIGUNGS-HOLDING GMBH—See Fresenius SE & Co. KGaA; *Int'l*, pg. 2777
B. MAIER ZERKLEINERUNGSTECHNIK GMBH—See Diefenbacher Holding GmbH & Co. KG; *Int'l*, pg. 2114
BMB PROPERTY SERVICES—See Bahrain Middle East Bank BSC; *Int'l*, pg. 800
BMT DEFENCE SERVICES (AUSTRALIA) PTY. LTD.—See BMT Group Limited; *Int'l*, pg. 1077
BMT DESIGNERS & PLANNERS, INC.—See BMT Group Limited; *Int'l*, pg. 1077
BMT DESIGN & TECHNOLOGY PTY LTD—See BMT Group Limited; *Int'l*, pg. 1077
BMT ENERGY AND ENVIRONMENT—See BMT Group Limited; *Int'l*, pg. 1077
BMT ENERGY—See BMT Group Limited; *Int'l*, pg. 1077
BMT FLUID MECHANICS LIMITED—See BMT Group Limited; *Int'l*, pg. 1078
BMT JFA CONSULTANTS PTY LTD—See BMT Group Limited; *Int'l*, pg. 1078
BMT RELIABILITY CONSULTANTS LTD.—See BMT Group Limited; *Int'l*, pg. 1078
BMT SCIENTIFIC MARINE SERVICES INC—See BMT Group Limited; *Int'l*, pg. 1078
BMT SCIENTIFIC MARINE SERVICES LTDA—See BMT Group Limited; *Int'l*, pg. 1078
BMT SURVEYS (AMSTERDAM) B.V.—See BMT Group Limited; *Int'l*, pg. 1078
BMT SURVEYS (ANTWERP) NV—See BMT Group Limited; *Int'l*, pg. 1078
BMT SURVEYS (LONDON) LIMITED—See BMT Group Limited; *Int'l*, pg. 1078
BMT SURVEYS (ROTTERDAM) B.V.—See BMT Group Limited; *Int'l*, pg. 1078
BMT WBM INC.—See BMT Group Limited; *Int'l*, pg. 1078
BMT WBM PTY. LTD.—See BMT Group Limited; *Int'l*, pg. 1078
BNG SPECIALIZED ENGINEERING SERVICES LTD—See Tetra Tech, Inc.; *U.S. Public*, pg. 2022
BNS NUCLEAR SERVICES LIMITED—See Babcock International Group PLC; *Int'l*, pg. 792
BOCHUM PERSPEKTIVE 2022 GMBH—See General Motors Company; *U.S. Public*, pg. 926
BODAK-CAMERON ENGINEERING—See Cameron Engineering & Associates, LLP; *U.S. Private*, pg. 728
BODE BYG A/S—See Hojgaard Holding A/S; *Int'l*, pg. 3442
BOECORE, INC.—See Enlightenment Capital LLC; *U.S. Private*, pg. 1400
BOEING AEROSPACE OPERATIONS, INC.—See The Boeing Company; *U.S. Public*, pg. 2039
BOG'ART S.R.L.; *Int'l*, pg. 1100
BOLD THINKING, LLC—See The Boldt Group Inc.; *U.S. Private*, pg. 3996
BOLDT TECHNICAL SERVICES—See The Boldt Group Inc.; *U.S. Private*, pg. 3996
BOLTON PEREZ & ASSOCIATES, INC.—See Colliers International Group Inc.; *Int'l*, pg. 1700
BOMBARD ELECTRIC, LLC—See MDU Resources Group, Inc.; *U.S. Public*, pg. 1409
BOMESC OFFSHORE ENGINEERING COMPANY LIMITED; *Int'l*, pg. 1104
BORGWARNER ENGINEERING SERVICES SWITZERLAND AG—See BorgWarner Inc.; *U.S. Public*, pg. 369
BORNEO GEOTECHNIC SDN. BHD.—See CSC Holdings Limited; *Int'l*, pg. 1862
BORTON-LAWSON ENGINEERING, INC.—See Sterling Investment Partners, L.P.; *U.S. Private*, pg. 3806
BOSKALIS AUSTRALIA PTY LTD—See HAL Trust N.V.; *Int'l*, pg. 3225
BOSKALIS DREDGING INDIA PVT. LTD.—See HAL Trust N.V.; *Int'l*, pg. 3225
BOSKALIS INFRA B.V.—See HAL Trust N.V.; *Int'l*, pg. 3224
BOSKALIS INTERNATIONAL (S) PTE LTD—See HAL Trust N.V.; *Int'l*, pg. 3225
BOSKALIS INTERNATIONAL URUGUAY S.A.—See HAL Trust N.V.; *Int'l*, pg. 3225
BOSKALIS ITALIA S.R.L.—See HAL Trust N.V.; *Int'l*, pg. 3225
BOSKALIS NEDERLAND B.V.—See HAL Trust N.V.; *Int'l*, pg. 3225
BOSKALIS NEDERLAND INFRA B.V.—See HAL Trust N.V.; *Int'l*, pg. 3225
BOSKALIS OFFSHORE CONTRACTING B.V.—See HAL Trust N.V.; *Int'l*, pg. 3225
BOSKALIS OFFSHORE GMBH—See HAL Trust N.V.; *Int'l*, pg. 3225
BOSKALIS OFFSHORE MARINE SERVICES B.V.—See HAL Trust N.V.; *Int'l*, pg. 3225
BOSKALIS OFFSHORE SUBSEA CONTRACTING AZERBAIJAN LLC—See HAL Trust N.V.; *Int'l*, pg. 3225
BOSKALIS OFFSHORE TRANSPORT SERVICES N.V.—See HAL Trust N.V.; *Int'l*, pg. 3225
BOSKALIS PANAMA S.A.—See HAL Trust N.V.; *Int'l*, pg. 3225
BOSKALIS SMIT INDIA LLP—See HAL Trust N.V.; *Int'l*, pg. 3225
BOSKALIS SOUTH AFRICA (PTY) LTD.—See HAL Trust N.V.; *Int'l*, pg. 3225
BOSKALIS S.R.L.—See HAL Trust N.V.; *Int'l*, pg. 3225
BOSKALIS WESTMINSTER CONTRACTING LIMITED—See HAL Trust N.V.; *Int'l*, pg. 3225
BOSKALIS WESTMINSTER LTD.—See HAL Trust N.V.; *Int'l*, pg. 3225
BOSKALIS WESTMINSTER SHIPPING B.V.—See HAL Trust N.V.; *Int'l*, pg. 3225
BOSKALIS ZINKCON LTD.—See HAL Trust N.V.; *Int'l*, pg. 3225
BOSSARD, INC.—See Bossard Holding AG; *Int'l*, pg. 1117
BOS SOLUTIONS LTD.—See Advent International Corporation; *U.S. Private*, pg. 98
BOSWELL ENGINEERING; *U.S. Private*, pg. 622
BOSWELL ENGINEERING—See Boswell Engineering; *U.S. Private*, pg. 622
BOSWELL MCCLAVE ENGINEERING—See Boswell Engineering; *U.S. Private*, pg. 622
BOSWELL UNDERWATER ENGINEERING—See Boswell Engineering; *U.S. Private*, pg. 622
BOURNS SENSORS GMBH—See Bourns, Inc.; *U.S. Private*, pg. 624
BOUSTEAD HEAVY INDUSTRIES CORPORATION BERHAD; *Int'l*, pg. 1120
BOUSTEAD INFRASTRUCTURES PTE. LTD.—See Boustead Singapore Limited; *Int'l*, pg. 1120
BOUSTEAD PROJECTS INVESTMENTS PTE LTD—See Boustead Singapore Limited; *Int'l*, pg. 1120
BOUSTEAD SALCON PTE LTD—See Boustead Singapore Limited; *Int'l*, pg. 1120
BOUTHILLETTE PARIZEAU; *Int'l*, pg. 1121
BOUYGUES ENERGIES & SERVICES GABON—See Bouygues S.A.; *Int'l*, pg. 1122
BOUYGUES E&S CONTRACTING UK LIMITED—See Bouygues S.A.; *Int'l*, pg. 1122
BOUYGUES E&S INTEC SWITZERLAND LTD—See Bouygues S.A.; *Int'l*, pg. 1123
BOUYGUES INMOBILIARIA S.A.—See Bouygues S.A.; *Int'l*, pg. 1122
BOWMAN CONSULTING GROUP LTD.; *U.S. Public*, pg. 376
BP CONSTRUCTION—See FAYAT SAS; *Int'l*, pg. 2624
BPC SA/NV—See Ackermans & van Haaren NV; *Int'l*, pg. 104
BPGS CONSTRUCTION LLC—See The Buccini/Pollin Group, Inc.; *U.S. Private*, pg. 4002
BPI SA/NV—See Ackermans & van Haaren NV; *Int'l*, pg. 104
BPR-BATIMENT INC.—See Tetra Tech, Inc.; *U.S. Public*, pg. 2022
BPR CSO SOLUTIONS INC.—See Tetra Tech, Inc.; *U.S. Public*, pg. 2022
BPR-ENERGIE INC.—See Tetra Tech, Inc.; *U.S. Public*, pg. 2022
BPR GROUPE-CONSEIL, S.E.N.C.—See Tetra Tech, Inc.; *U.S. Public*, pg. 2022
BPR-INFRASTRUCTURE INC.—See Tetra Tech, Inc.; *U.S. Public*, pg. 2022
BPR-TRIAX INC.—See Tetra Tech, Inc.; *U.S. Public*, pg. 2022
BPU INGENIEURUNTERNEHMUNG AG—See BKW AG; *Int'l*, pg. 1054
BRABANTS DAGBLAD BV—See DPG Media Group NV; *Int'l*, pg. 2189

541330 — ENGINEERING SERVICE...

BRACKEN ENGINEERING, INC; *U.S. Private*, pg. 630
BRADKEN LTD.—See Hitachi, Ltd.; *Int'l*, pg. 3415
BRADKEN UK LIMITED—See Hitachi, Ltd.; *Int'l*, pg. 3415
BRAEMAR ADJUSTING PTE LTD—See Braemar PLC; *Int'l*, pg. 1135
BRAEMAR FALCONER PTE LIMITED—See Braemar PLC; *Int'l*, pg. 1135
BRAEMAR FALCONER PTY LIMITED—See Braemar PLC; *Int'l*, pg. 1135
BRAEMAR FALCONER (SHANGHAI) PTE LTD—See Braemar PLC; *Int'l*, pg. 1135
BRAEMAR FALCONER—See Braemar PLC; *Int'l*, pg. 1135
BRAEMAR STEEGE CANADA LIMITED—See ABL Group ASA; *Int'l*, pg. 62
BRAEMAR STEEGE, LLC—See ABL Group ASA; *Int'l*, pg. 62
BRAEMAR STEEGE PTE. LTD.—See Braemar PLC; *Int'l*, pg. 1135
BRAEMAR STEEGE RIO DE JANEIRO—See ABL Group ASA; *Int'l*, pg. 62
BRAEMAR STEEGE SHANGHAI—See ABL Group ASA; *Int'l*, pg. 62
BRAEMAR TECHNICAL SERVICED (OFFSHORE) SDN BHD—See Braemar PLC; *Int'l*, pg. 1136
BRAEMAR TECHNICAL SERVICES (OFFSHORE) INDIA PVT LTD—See Braemar PLC; *Int'l*, pg. 1135
BRAEMAR WAVESPEC USA INC.—See Braemar PLC; *Int'l*, pg. 1136
BRAINSELL TECHNOLOGIES, LLC; *U.S. Private*, pg. 634
BRAMCO-MPS—See Bramco Inc.; *U.S. Private*, pg. 635
BRANDYWINE COMMUNICATIONS, INC.—See Cache Creek Industries, LLC; *U.S. Private*, pg. 712
BRANDYWINE COMMUNICATIONS, INC.—See Rockmont Capital Partners Ltd.; *U.S. Private*, pg. 3467
BRAVIDA PRENAD AB—See Bravida Holding AB; *Int'l*, pg. 1142
BREEN INTERNATIONAL (HK) CO LTD—See Breen International Pte. Ltd.; *Int'l*, pg. 1144
BREIJN B.V.—See Heijmans N.V.; *Int'l*, pg. 3322
BRGM—See Bureau de Recherches Geologiques et Miniere; *Int'l*, pg. 1221
BRIDGE DESIGN, INC.—See SV Health Investors, LLP; *U.S. Private*, pg. 3888
BRIDGENET INTERNATIONAL—See Tetra Tech, Inc.; *U.S. Public*, pg. 2022
BRIGHT INTERNATIONAL, LLC—See Aterian Investment Management, L.P.; *U.S. Private*, pg. 366
BRINDERSON SERVICES, LLC—See New Mountain Capital, LLC; *U.S. Private*, pg. 2899
BRISTOL FUEL SYSTEMS, LLC—See Bristol Bay Native Corporation; *U.S. Private*, pg. 656
BRITCON; *Int'l*, pg. 1165
BRITISH ENGINES LTD.; *Int'l*, pg. 1171
BRITON ENGINEERING DEVELOPMENTS LTD.—See Doppelmayr Group; *Int'l*, pg. 2174
BRIXHAM MARINE SERVICES LTD—See Damen Shipyards Group; *Int'l*, pg. 1956
BRK SPECIALIS MELYEPITO KFT.—See BAUER Aktiengesellschaft; *Int'l*, pg. 892
BROADDUS & ASSOCIATES, INC.; *U.S. Private*, pg. 659
BROADSPECTRUM (AUSTRALIA) PTY. LTD.—See Apollo Global Management, Inc.; *U.S. Public*, pg. 166
BROADSPECTRUM AUSTRALIA (QLD) PTY LIMITED—See Apollo Global Management, Inc.; *U.S. Public*, pg. 166
BROADSPECTRUM (NEW ZEALAND) LIMITED—See Apollo Global Management, Inc.; *U.S. Public*, pg. 166
BROADSPECTRUM (WA) PTY LIMITED—See Apollo Global Management, Inc.; *U.S. Public*, pg. 166
BROOKS LIFE SCIENCE SYSTEMS—See Azenta, Inc.; *U.S. Public*, pg. 257
BROWN AND CALDWELL; *U.S. Private*, pg. 666
BROWN & GAY ENGINEERS, INC.; *U.S. Private*, pg. 666
BROWN, MITCHELL & ALEXANDER, INC.; *U.S. Private*, pg. 669
BROWN & ROOT INDUSTRIAL SERVICES, LLC—See Bernhard Capital Partners Management, LP; *U.S. Private*, pg. 537
BROWN & ROOT INDUSTRIAL SERVICES, LLC—See KBR, Inc.; *U.S. Public*, pg. 1216
BRUCKENBAU PLAUEN GMBH—See GEA Group Aktiengesellschaft; *Int'l*, pg. 2897
BRUNEL AUSTRIA GMBH—See Brunel International N.V.; *Int'l*, pg. 1199
BRUNEL CAR SYNERGIES GMBH—See Brunel International N.V.; *Int'l*, pg. 1199
BRUNEL ENERGY KOREA LTD.—See Brunel International N.V.; *Int'l*, pg. 1199
BRUNEL ENERGY MALAYSIA SDN BHD—See Brunel International N.V.; *Int'l*, pg. 1199
BRUNEL ICT NV—See Brunel International N.V.; *Int'l*, pg. 1199
BRUNEL RECRUITMENT KAZAKHSTAN LLP—See Brunel International N.V.; *Int'l*, pg. 1200
BRUNEL SWITZERLAND AG—See Brunel International N.V.; *Int'l*, pg. 1200
BRUNEL VIETNAM COMPANY LTD.—See Brunel International N.V.; *Int'l*, pg. 1200

BRUNS-PAK INC.; *U.S. Private*, pg. 672
BRYANT-DURHAM ELECTRIC CO., INC. - EASTERN DIVISION—See Bryant-Durham Electric Co., Inc.; *U.S. Private*, pg. 674
BS BAUFACHHANDEL BRANDS & SCHNITZLER GMBH & CO. KG—See BayWa AG; *Int'l*, pg. 919
BS&B MID ATLANTIC—See BS&B Safety Systems, LLC; *U.S. Private*, pg. 674
BS&B PRESSURE SAFETY MANAGEMENT, L.L.C.—See BS&B Safety Systems, LLC; *U.S. Private*, pg. 674
BSC GROUP, INC.; *U.S. Private*, pg. 674
BSI ENGINEERING, INC.; *U.S. Private*, pg. 675
BST NANOCARBON LLC; *U.S. Private*, pg. 675
BT ASIA MARKETING & ENGINEERING PTE LTDBT ASIA MARKETING & ENGINEERING PTE LTD—See Beng Kuang Marine Limited; *Int'l*, pg. 973
BTM ENGINEERING INC.—See Bowman Consulting Group Ltd.; *U.S. Public*, pg. 376
BTN BARAN TELECOM NETWORKS GMBH—See Baran Group Ltd.; *Int'l*, pg. 858
BTU OVERSEAS, LTD.—See Amtech Systems, Inc.; *U.S. Public*, pg. 133
BUCHART HORN INC—See Pace Resources, Inc.; *U.S. Private*, pg. 3064
BUCHART HORN INC—See Pace Resources, Inc.; *U.S. Private*, pg. 3064
BUDIMEX BAU GMBH—See Ferrovial S.A.; *Int'l*, pg. 2644
BUECHEL HANDELS-UND BETEILIGUNGS-KG; *Int'l*, pg. 1211
BUILD INVESTMENTS GROUP JSC - ASTANA MDU DIVISION—See Build Investments Group JSC; *Int'l*, pg. 1212
BUILD INVESTMENTS GROUP JSC - CONSTRUCTION MATERIALS PRODUCTION DIVISION—See Build Investments Group JSC; *Int'l*, pg. 1212
BULLDOG MARINE; *U.S. Private*, pg. 684
BUMI ARMADA ENGINEERING SDN BHD—See Bumi Armada Berhad; *Int'l*, pg. 1215
BUMYANG CONSTRUCTION CO., LTD.; *Int'l*, pg. 1215
BUNDABERG WALKERS ENGINEERING LTD.—See Finasucre S.A.; *Int'l*, pg. 2670
BUREAU DE RECHERCHES GEOLOGIQUES ET MINIERE; *Int'l*, pg. 1221
BURGERS ERGON B.V.—See Heijmans N.V.; *Int'l*, pg. 3322
BURGESS & NIPLE, INC. - CHANTILLY—See Burgess & Niple, Inc.; *U.S. Private*, pg. 687
BURGESS & NIPLE, INC. - FORTH WORTH—See Burgess & Niple, Inc.; *U.S. Private*, pg. 687
BURGESS & NIPLE, INC. - PAINESVILLE—See Burgess & Niple, Inc.; *U.S. Private*, pg. 687
BURGESS & NIPLE, INC.; *U.S. Private*, pg. 687
BURGESS & NIPLE, INC.—See Burgess & Niple, Inc.; *U.S. Private*, pg. 687
BURGESS-NORTON MANUFACTURING COMPANY—See AMSTED Industries Incorporated; *U.S. Private*, pg. 268
BURKE NEWCO S.L.—See Alten S.A.; *Int'l*, pg. 390
BURKHALTER ELEKTROTECHNIK AG—See Burkhalter Holding AG; *Int'l*, pg. 1224
BURKHALTER SERVICES AG—See Burkhalter Holding AG; *Int'l*, pg. 1224
BURKHALTER TECHNICS AG—See Burkhalter Holding AG; *Int'l*, pg. 1224
BURNS & McDONNELL, INC.; *U.S. Private*, pg. 689
BURO HAPPOLD APS—See Buro Happold Engineers Limited; *Int'l*, pg. 1226
BURO HAPPOLD CONSULTING ENGINEERS (BEIJING) LIMITED—See Buro Happold Engineers Limited; *Int'l*, pg. 1226
BURO HAPPOLD CONSULTING ENGINEERS, INC.—See Buro Happold Engineers Limited; *Int'l*, pg. 1226
BURO HAPPOLD CONSULTING ENGINEERS LIMITED—See Buro Happold Engineers Limited; *Int'l*, pg. 1226
BURO HAPPOLD ENGINEERS INDIA PVT. LTD.—See Buro Happold Engineers Limited; *Int'l*, pg. 1226
BURO HAPPOLD ENGINEERS LIMITED; *Int'l*, pg. 1226
BURO HAPPOLD INTERNATIONAL (HONG KONG) LIMITED—See Buro Happold Engineers Limited; *Int'l*, pg. 1226
BURO HAPPOLD LIMITED—See Buro Happold Engineers Limited; *Int'l*, pg. 1226
BURO HAPPOLD & PARTNER FOR ENGINEERING CONSULTANCY CO—See Buro Happold Engineers Limited; *Int'l*, pg. 1226
BURO HAPPOLD POLSKA SP. Z O.O.—See Buro Happold Engineers Limited; *Int'l*, pg. 1226
BURROW GLOBAL, LLC; *U.S. Private*, pg. 692
BURSICH ASSOCIATES, INC.; *U.S. Private*, pg. 692
BW IDEOL AS; *Int'l*, pg. 1231
BWT PHARMA & BIOTECH AB—See BWT Aktiengesellschaft; *Int'l*, pg. 1233
BWT PHARMA & BIOTECH GMBH—See BWT Aktiengesellschaft; *Int'l*, pg. 1233
BYGGFAKTA A/S—See Byggfakta Group Nordic HoldCo AB; *Int'l*, pg. 1234
BYSTRONIC POLSKA SP. Z O.O.—See Bystronic AG; *Int'l*, pg. 1235
BYT HOLDINGS LTD.; *Int'l*, pg. 1236

BYUCKSAN AMERICA INC.—See Byucksan Engineering & Construction Co., Ltd.; *Int'l*, pg. 1237
CABINET D'EXPERTISE R.TANFERRI S.A.S.—See DEKRA e.V.; *Int'l*, pg. 2007
CAD ENTERPRISES, INC.—See Crawford United Corporation; *U.S. Public*, pg. 592
CA DESIGN, INC.—See CyberAgent, Inc.; *Int'l*, pg. 1892
CADES STUDEC TECHNOLOGIES (INDIA) PRIVATE LIMITED—See Axiscades Technologies Ltd.; *Int'l*, pg. 770
CAE AUTOMOTIVE GMBH; *Int'l*, pg. 1248
CAF TURNKEY & ENGINEERING, S.L.U.—See Construcciones y Auxiliar de Ferrocarriles S.A.; *Int'l*, pg. 1776
CALEDONIAN PETROLEUM SERVICES LTD.—See Global Energy (Holdings) Ltd.; *Int'l*, pg. 2995
CALEDONIAN TOWAGE LTD—See Global Energy (Holdings) Ltd.; *Int'l*, pg. 2995
CAL ENGINEERING & GEOLOGY INC—See Haley & Aldrich Inc.; *U.S. Private*, pg. 1842
CALIBRE GROUP LTD; *Int'l*, pg. 1264
CALIFORNIA CODE CHECK, INC.—See Bureau Veritas S.A.; *Int'l*, pg. 1222
CALSOFT LABS UK PRIVATE LTD.—See Alten S.A.; *Int'l*, pg. 390
CALTROP CORPORATION—See TRC Companies, Inc.; *U.S. Private*, pg. 4215
CALVIN, GIORDANO & ASSOCIATES, INC.; *U.S. Private*, pg. 724
CAMCORP INC.—See Camrost-Felcorp Inc.; *Int'l*, pg. 1275
CAMERON ENGINEERING & ASSOCIATES, LLP; *U.S. Private*, pg. 728
CAN AS—See CAN (Offshore) Ltd; *Int'l*, pg. 1275
CAN GLOBAL ANGOLA LDA—See CAN (Offshore) Ltd; *Int'l*, pg. 1276
CAN MIDDLE EAST L.L.C.—See CAN (Offshore) Ltd; *Int'l*, pg. 1276
CANNING GUMM LLC—See Element Solutions Inc.; *U.S. Public*, pg. 725
CANNOCK CHASE B.V.—See ARCADIS N.V.; *Int'l*, pg. 541
CAN (OFFSHORE) LTD; *Int'l*, pg. 1275
CANSEL SURVEY EQUIPMENT, LTD.; *Int'l*, pg. 1298
CAN STRUCTURES LTD—See CAN (Offshore) Ltd; *Int'l*, pg. 1276
CAN USA, INC.—See CAN (Offshore) Ltd; *Int'l*, pg. 1276
CAN USA, INC.—See CAN (Offshore) Ltd; *Int'l*, pg. 1276
CAPACIT'E INFRAPROJECTS LIMITED; *Int'l*, pg. 1301
CAPGEMINI ENGINEERING—See Capgemini SE; *Int'l*, pg. 1304
CARDINAL ENGINEERING CORPORATION - OHIO—See Cardinal Engineering Corporation; *U.S. Private*, pg. 750
CARDINAL ENGINEERING CORPORATION; *U.S. Private*, pg. 750
CARDINAL ENGINEERING, INC.—See Enviro Clean Services LLC; *U.S. Private*, pg. 1406
CARDINAL MECHANICAL, INC.—See Primoris Services Corporation; *U.S. Public*, pg. 1718
CARDNO ALEXANDER BROWNE PTY. LTD.—See Cardno Limited; *Int'l*, pg. 1322
CARDNO BOWLER PTY. LTD.—See Cardno Limited; *Int'l*, pg. 1322
CARDNO BOWLER—See Cardno Limited; *Int'l*, pg. 1322
CARDNO ECOLOGY LAB PTY. LTD.—See Cardno Limited; *Int'l*, pg. 1322
CARDNO EMERGING MARKETS (AUSTRALIA) PTY. LTD.—See Cardno Limited; *Int'l*, pg. 1322
CARDNO EMERGING MARKETS BELGIUM S.A.—See Cardno Limited; *Int'l*, pg. 1322
CARDNO EMERGING MARKETS (USA), LTD.—See Cardno Limited; *Int'l*, pg. 1322
CARDNO ENTRIX (COLOMBIA) S.A.S.—See Cardno Limited; *Int'l*, pg. 1322
CARDNO HAYNES WHALEY, INC.—See Cardno Limited; *Int'l*, pg. 1322
CARDNO ITC PTY. LTD.—See Cardno Limited; *Int'l*, pg. 1322
CARDNO ITC (QLD) PTY. LTD.—See Cardno Limited; *Int'l*, pg. 1322
CARDNO ITC (VIC) PTY. LTD.—See Cardno Limited; *Int'l*, pg. 1322
CARDNO ITC (WA) PTY. LTD.—See Cardno Limited; *Int'l*, pg. 1322
CARDNO LOW & HOOKE PTY. LTD.—See Cardno Limited; *Int'l*, pg. 1322
CARDNO (NSW/ACT) PTY. LTD.—See Cardno Limited; *Int'l*, pg. 1322
CARDNO (NZ) LIMITED—See Cardno Limited; *Int'l*, pg. 1322
CARDNO (PNG) LTD.—See Cardno Limited; *Int'l*, pg. 1322
CARDNO PTY. LTD.—See Cardno Limited; *Int'l*, pg. 1322
CARDNO (QLD) PTY. LTD.—See Cardno Limited; *Int'l*, pg. 1322
CARDNO TBE (MICHIGAN), INC.—See Cardno Limited; *Int'l*, pg. 1322
CARDNO TBE—See Cardno Limited; *Int'l*, pg. 1322
CARDNO UK LIMITED—See Cardno Limited; *Int'l*, pg. 1322
CARDNO ULLMAN & NOLAN PTY. LTD.—See Cardno Limited; *Int'l*, pg. 1322

N.A.I.C.S. INDEX

541330 — ENGINEERING SERVICE...

CARDNO UNITED STATES OF AMERICA—See Cardno Limited; *Int'l*, pg. 1322
CARDNO (WA) PTY. LTD.—See Cardno Limited; *Int'l*, pg. 1322
CARDNO WRG, INC.—See Cardno Limited; *Int'l*, pg. 1322
CARGOTEC POLAND SP. Z O.O.—See Cargotec Corporation; *Int'l*, pg. 1326
CARI AQUITAINE—See FAYAT SAS; *Int'l*, pg. 2625
CARIATIDE, S.A.—See ACS, Actividades de Construccion y Servicios, S.A.; *Int'l*, pg. 110
CARILLION CONSTRUCTION LTD—See Carillion plc; *Int'l*, pg. 1330
CARILLION PILING—See Carillion plc; *Int'l*, pg. 1330
CARILLION SERVICES LTD—See Carillion plc; *Int'l*, pg. 1330
CARI LORRAINE—See FAYAT SAS; *Int'l*, pg. 2625
CARI MENUISERIE—See FAYAT SAS; *Int'l*, pg. 2625
CARI PROVENCE—See FAYAT SAS; *Int'l*, pg. 2625
CARI RHONE LYON—See FAYAT SAS; *Int'l*, pg. 2625
CARLIT SANGYO CO., LTD.—See Carlit Co., Ltd.; *Int'l*, pg. 1338
CARLO GAVAZZI INC.—See Carlo Gavazzi Holding AG; *Int'l*, pg. 1339
CARMAGEN ENGINEERING, INC.—See Mistras Group, Inc.; *U.S. Public*, pg. 1451
CARMICHAEL ENGINEERING, INC.—See Universal Engineering Sciences, LLC; *U.S. Private*, pg. 4304
CARNEGIE DEVELOPMENT, INC.; *U.S. Private*, pg. 437
CAROLLO ENGINEERS, INC.; *U.S. Private*, pg. 769
CARPENTER TECHNOLOGY ASIA PACIFIC PTE. LTD.—See Carpenter Technology Corporation; *U.S. Public*, pg. 439
CARROLL ENGINEERING CORP.; *U.S. Private*, pg. 773
CASCADE DESIGN PROFESSIONALS, INC.—See Cooper Zietz Engineers, Inc.; *U.S. Private*, pg. 1041
CASCADE ENGINEERING SERVICES INC.; *U.S. Private*, pg. 779
CASCADE RENEWABLE ENERGY—See Cascade Engineering, Inc.; *U.S. Private*, pg. 779
CASCO SIGNAL LTD.—See Alstom S.A.; *Int'l*, pg. 381
CASCO SIGNAL LTD.—See China National Railway Signal & Communication Corp.; *Int'l*, pg. 1534
CASE FORENSICS CORP.—See Gryphon Investors, LLC; *U.S. Private*, pg. 1798
CASSIDIAN BELGIUM N.V.—See Airbus SE; *Int'l*, pg. 242
CASSIDIAN FINLAND OY—See Airbus SE; *Int'l*, pg. 242
CASSIDIAN HONG KONG LIMITED—See Airbus SE; *Int'l*, pg. 242
CASSIDIAN MEXICO S.A DE C.V.—See Airbus SE; *Int'l*, pg. 242
CASTEL ALU JARNAC—See FAYAT SAS; *Int'l*, pg. 2625
CASTEL ALU—See FAYAT SAS; *Int'l*, pg. 2625
CASTEL ET FROMAGET ASIA—See FAYAT SAS; *Int'l*, pg. 2625
CASTEL ET FROMAGET REUNION—See FAYAT SAS; *Int'l*, pg. 2625
CASTEL ET FROMAGET—See FAYAT SAS; *Int'l*, pg. 2625
CAT TECH ASIA PACIFIC PTE LTD.—See Clean Harbors, Inc.; *U.S. Public*, pg. 509
CAVIEZEL AG—See Burkhalter Holding AG; *Int'l*, pg. 1224
CAVOTEC CIS LTD.—See Cavotec SA; *Int'l*, pg. 1363
CAVOTEC ENGINEERING SERVICES INDIA PVT. LTD.—See Cavotec SA; *Int'l*, pg. 1363
CAVOTEC IBERICA S.L.—See Cavotec SA; *Int'l*, pg. 1362
CAVOTEC MSL HOLDINGS LIMITED - CAVOTEC ITALIA DIVISION—See Cavotec SA; *Int'l*, pg. 1363
CBI CONSTRUCTORS PTY. LTD. (PERTH)—See McDermott International, Inc.; *U.S. Public*, pg. 1405
CBI CONSTRUCTORS PTY. LTD—See McDermott International, Inc.; *U.S. Public*, pg. 1405
CB&I LUMMUS B.V.—See McDermott International, Inc.; *U.S. Public*, pg. 1405
CB&I LUMMUS GMBH—See McDermott International, Inc.; *U.S. Public*, pg. 1405
CB&I LUMMUS S.R.O.—See McDermott International, Inc.; *U.S. Public*, pg. 1405
CB&I NEDERLAND B.V.—See McDermott International, Inc.; *U.S. Public*, pg. 1405
CB&I SINGAPORE PTE LTD.—See McDermott International, Inc.; *U.S. Public*, pg. 1405
CB&I S.R.O.—See McDermott International, Inc.; *U.S. Public*, pg. 1405
CBRE UK—See CBRE Group, Inc.; *U.S. Public*, pg. 460
CCCC FIRST HARBOUR CONSULTANTS CO., LTD.—See China Communications Construction Company Limited; *Int'l*, pg. 1490
CCECC (BOTSWANA) (PTY) LTD.—See China Railway Construction Corporation Limited; *Int'l*, pg. 1542
CCECC INTERNATIONAL TRADING CO. LTD.—See China Railway Construction Corporation Limited; *Int'l*, pg. 1542
CCECC NIGERIA LTD.—See China Railway Construction Corporation Limited; *Int'l*, pg. 1542
C.C. JOHNSON & MALHOTRA, P.C.; *U.S. Private*, pg. 706
CCTEC ENGINEERING CO.—See China Rare Earth Resources And Technology Co., Ltd.; *Int'l*, pg. 1545
C & C TOWERS LTD—See C & C Constructions Limited; *Int'l*, pg. 1237

C&D HOLSIN ENGINEERING CONSULTING CO., LTD; *Int'l*, pg. 1238
CDI ENGINEERING SOLUTIONS, LLC—See AE Industrial Partners, LP; *U.S. Private*, pg. 112
CDM FEDERAL PROGRAMS CORPORATION—See CDM Smith Inc.; *U.S. Private*, pg. 803
CDM SMITH INC.; *U.S. Private*, pg. 802
CDM SMITH IRELAND LTD.—See CDM Smith Inc.; *U.S. Private*, pg. 803
CDM SMITH SP. Z O.O.—See CDM Smith Inc.; *U.S. Private*, pg. 803
CDR MAGUIRE INC. - CONNECTICUT OFFICE—See CDR Maguire Inc.; *U.S. Private*, pg. 803
CDR MAGUIRE INC. - PENNSYLVANIA OFFICE—See CDR Maguire Inc.; *U.S. Private*, pg. 803
CDR MAGUIRE INC. - RHODE ISLAND OFFICE—See CDR Maguire Inc.; *U.S. Private*, pg. 803
CDR MAGUIRE INC.; *U.S. Private*, pg. 803
CDR MAGUIRE INC. - VIRGIN ISLANDS OFFICE—See CDR Maguire Inc.; *U.S. Private*, pg. 803
CEC CONSTRUCTION ENGINEERING + CONTRACTING GMBH—See Bilfinger SE; *Int'l*, pg. 1028
CECEP TECHAND ECOLOGY & ENVIRONMENT CO., LTD.; *Int'l*, pg. 1373
CEC INTERNATIONAL MALAYSIA SDN. BHD.—See Continental Holdings Corp.; *Int'l*, pg. 1784
CECS INC.—See The Crom Corporation; *U.S. Private*, pg. 4016
CEDAR CORPORATION—See Steel Partners Holdings L.P.; *U.S. Public*, pg. 1943
CEGEDIM RX LIMITED—See Cegedim S.A.; *Int'l*, pg. 1390
CELEO REDES, S.L.U.—See Elecnor, S.A.; *Int'l*, pg. 2347
CENERGY CORP.; *U.S. Private*, pg. 808
CENTAR ZA PUTEVE VOJVODINE A.D.; *Int'l*, pg. 1402
CENTENNIAL CONTRACTORS ENTERPRISES, INC.—See Bilfinger SE; *Int'l*, pg. 1028
CENTERPLAN CONSTRUCTION COMPANY; *U.S. Private*, pg. 816
CENTRAL ENGINEERING CO., LTD.—See Central Glass Co., Ltd.; *Int'l*, pg. 1406
CENTRAL HOLDING GROUP CO., LTD.; *Int'l*, pg. 1407
CENTRO REVISIONE AUTO S.C.A.R.L.—See DEKRA e.V.; *Int'l*, pg. 2007
CENTROSLAVIJA A.D.; *Int'l*, pg. 1414
CENTURY MECHANICAL SOLUTIONS, INC.—See Comfort Systems USA, Inc.; *U.S. Public*, pg. 543
CE POWER ENGINEERED SERVICES, LLC—See New Mountain Capital, LLC; *U.S. Private*, pg. 2903
CERAMI & ASSOCIATES, INC.—See Keystone Group, L.P.; *U.S. Private*, pg. 2299
CERCLE ENTREPRISE; *Int'l*, pg. 1421
CES, INC.; *U.S. Private*, pg. 842
C E S N W INC—See PACE Engineers, Inc.; *U.S. Private*, pg. 3063
CESTNE STAVBY AS; *Int'l*, pg. 1424
CFA, INC.—See Bowman Consulting Group Ltd.; *U.S. Public*, pg. 376
CFE BRABANT—See Ackermans & van Haaren NV; *Int'l*, pg. 104
CFE HUNGARY EPITOIPARI KFT.—See Ackermans & van Haaren NV; *Int'l*, pg. 104
CFE INTERNATIONAL—See Ackermans & van Haaren NV; *Int'l*, pg. 104
CFE POLSKA SP. Z O.O.—See Ackermans & van Haaren NV; *Int'l*, pg. 104
CFE TUNISIA—See Ackermans & van Haaren NV; *Int'l*, pg. 105
CFG SERVICES SA—See Bureau de Recherches Geologiques et Miniere; *Int'l*, pg. 1221
CF STEEL MOROCCO—See FAYAT SAS; *Int'l*, pg. 2625
CGG EXPLO SARL—See CGG; *Int'l*, pg. 1431
CGG I SA—See CGG; *Int'l*, pg. 1431
CGG MARINE RESOURCES NORGE AS—See CGG; *Int'l*, pg. 1431
CH2M HILL ALASKA, INC.—See Jacobs Engineering Group, Inc.; *U.S. Public*, pg. 1183
CH2M HILL COMPANIES, LTD.—See Jacobs Engineering Group, Inc.; *U.S. Public*, pg. 1183
CH2M HILL ENGINEERS, INC.—See Jacobs Engineering Group, Inc.; *U.S. Public*, pg. 1183
CH2M HILL, INC.—See Jacobs Engineering Group, Inc.; *U.S. Public*, pg. 1183
CH2M HILL SINGAPORE PTE. LTD.—See Jacobs Engineering Group, Inc.; *U.S. Public*, pg. 1184
CH2M HILL UNITED KINGDOM—See Jacobs Engineering Group, Inc.; *U.S. Public*, pg. 1183
CHA CANADA—See H.I.G. Capital, LLC; *U.S. Private*, pg. 1827
CHA CONSULTING, INC.—See H.I.G. Capital, LLC; *U.S. Private*, pg. 1827
CHAINQUI CONSTRUCTION DEVELOPMENT CO., LTD.; *Int'l*, pg. 1437
CHANG JIA M&E ENGINEERING CORP.; *Int'l*, pg. 1441
CHANGZHENG ENGINEERING CO., LTD.; *Int'l*, pg. 1445
CHAPOMED LTD—See Charilaos Apostolides Public Ltd.; *Int'l*, pg. 1450
CHARILAOS APOSTOLIDES PUBLIC LTD.; *Int'l*, pg. 1450

CHARTER ENGINEERING, INC.—See HEICO Corporation; *U.S. Public*, pg. 1021
CHASTAIN-SKILLMAN, INC.—See White Wolf Capital LLC; *U.S. Private*, pg. 4510
CHAVDA INFRA LIMITED; *Int'l*, pg. 1457
C.H. BAILEY PLC; *Int'l*, pg. 1240
CHEMITECHNIK PHARMA KFT—See Gedeon Richter Plc.; *Int'l*, pg. 2909
CHEMOPROJEKT, A.S.; *Int'l*, pg. 1463
CHEMRING ENERGETICS UK LIMITED—See Chemring Group PLC; *Int'l*, pg. 1463
CHEMTURA COLUMBIA LTDA—See Element Solutions Inc.; *U.S. Public*, pg. 725
CHEN & ASSOCIATES CIVIL & ENVIRONMENTAL ENGINEERS, INC.; *U.S. Private*, pg. 872
CHEUNG HO ELECTRIC CO., LIMITED; *Int'l*, pg. 1473
CHEVALIER (ENVIROTECH) LIMITED—See Chevalier International Holdings Limited; *Int'l*, pg. 1473
CHG GROUP, INC.—See Chemring Group PLC; *Int'l*, pg. 1463
CHICAGO BRIDGE & IRON COMPANY B.V.—See McDermott International, Inc.; *U.S. Public*, pg. 1405
CHICAGO BRIDGE & IRON COMPANY—See McDermott International, Inc.; *U.S. Public*, pg. 1405
CHICAGO RIVET & MACHINE CO.—See Chicago Rivet & Machine Company; *U.S. Public*, pg. 488
CHI ENGINEERING SERVICES, INC.—See NV5 Global, Inc.; *U.S. Public*, pg. 1557
CHINA AUTOMATION GROUP LIMITED; *Int'l*, pg. 1483
CHINA BLUESTAR LEHIGH ENGINEERING CORP—See Bluestar Adisseo Company Limited; *Int'l*, pg. 1074
CHINA BUILDING MATERIAL TEST & CERTIFICATION GROUP CO., LTD; *Int'l*, pg. 1487
CHINA CAMC ENGINEERING CO., LTD.—See China National Machinery Industry Corporation; *Int'l*, pg. 1531
CHINA CGAME, INC.; *Int'l*, pg. 1488
CHINA CHEMICAL ENGINEERING SECOND CONSTRUCTION CORPORATION—See China National Chemical Engineering Co., Ltd.; *Int'l*, pg. 1530
CHINA CHEMICAL GUILIN ENGINEERING CO., LTD.—See China National Chemical Engineering Co., Ltd.; *Int'l*, pg. 1530
CHINA CIVIL ENGINEERING CONSTRUCTION COMPANY-(MACAU) LTD.—See China Railway Construction Corporation Limited; *Int'l*, pg. 1543
CHINA CIVIL ENGINEERING CONSTRUCTION CORPORATION—See China Railway Construction Corporation Limited; *Int'l*, pg. 1542
CHINA COAL XI'AN ENGINEERING DESIGN CO., LTD.—See China Coal Energy Company Limited; *Int'l*, pg. 1490
CHINA CONSTRUCTION DECORATION ENGINEERING CO.—See China State Construction Engineering Corporation Limited; *Int'l*, pg. 1554
CHINA DESIGN GROUP CO., LTD.; *Int'l*, pg. 1497
CHINA ELEVENTH CHEMICAL CONSTRUCTION CO., LTD.—See China National Chemical Engineering Co., Ltd.; *Int'l*, pg. 1530
CHINA ENERGY ENGINEERING CORPORATION LIMITED; *Int'l*, pg. 1500
CHINA GEZHOUBA GROUP COMPANY LIMITED; *Int'l*, pg. 1504
CHINA HAOHUA ENGINEERING CO., LTD.—See China National Chemical Corporation; *Int'l*, pg. 1526
CHINA HARBOUR ENGINEERING COMPANY LTD.—See China Communications Construction Company Limited; *Int'l*, pg. 1490
CHINA MERCHANTS INDUSTRY HOLDINGS CO., LTD.—See China Merchants Group Limited; *Int'l*, pg. 1520
CHINA MERCHANTS ZHANGZHOU DEVELOPMENT ZONE CO., LTD.—See China Merchants Group Limited; *Int'l*, pg. 1521
CHINA NATIONAL CHEMICAL ENGINEERING CO., LTD.; *Int'l*, pg. 1530
CHINA NATIONAL CHEMICAL ENGINEERING NO.14 CONSTRUCTION CO., LTD.—See China National Chemical Engineering Co., Ltd.; *Int'l*, pg. 1530
CHINA NATIONAL CHEMICAL ENGINEERING NO.16 CONSTRUCTION COMPANY—See China National Chemical Engineering Co., Ltd.; *Int'l*, pg. 1530
CHINA NATIONAL CHEMICAL ENGINEERING NO.7 CONSTRUCTION COMPANY LTD.—See China National Chemical Engineering Co., Ltd.; *Int'l*, pg. 1530
CHINA NATIONAL CHEMICAL ENGINEERING SIXTH CONSTRUCTION CO., LTD.—See China National Chemical Engineering Co., Ltd.; *Int'l*, pg. 1530
CHINA NATIONAL ELECTRIC ENGINEERING CO., LTD.—See China Machinery Engineering Corporation; *Int'l*, pg. 1516
CHINA NERIN ENGINEERING CO. LTD—See China Nonferrous Metal Mining (Group) Co., Ltd.; *Int'l*, pg. 1535
CHINA NUCLEAR ENGINEERING CORPORATION LIMITED; *Int'l*, pg. 1536
CHINA RAILWAY 11TH BUREAU GROUP CO., LTD.—See China Railway Construction Corporation Limited; *Int'l*, pg. 1543
CHINA RAILWAY 23RD BUREAU GROUP CO., LTD.—See

China Railway Construction Corporation Limited; *Int'l*, pg. 1543
CHINA RAILWAY ENGINEERING CONSULTING GROUP CO., LTD.—See China Railway Group Limited; *Int'l*, pg. 1543
CHINA RAILWAY FIFTH SURVEY & DESIGN INSTITUTE GROUP CO., LTD.—See China Railway Construction Corporation Limited; *Int'l*, pg. 1543
CHINA RAILWAY FIRST SURVEY & DESIGN INSTITUTE GROUP CO., LTD.—See China Railway Construction Corporation Limited; *Int'l*, pg. 1543
CHINA RAILWAY FOURTH SURVEY AND DESIGN INSTITUTE GROUP CO., LTD—See China Railway Construction Corporation Limited; *Int'l*, pg. 1543
CHINA RAILWAY HUATIE ENGINEERING DESIGNING GROUP CO., LTD.—See China Railway Group Limited; *Int'l*, pg. 1543
CHINA RAILWAY MAJOR BRIDGE RECONNAISSANCE & DESIGN INSTITUTE CO., LTD.—See China Railway Group Limited; *Int'l*, pg. 1543
CHINA RAILWAY SHANGHAI DESIGN INSTITUTE GROUP CO., LTD.—See China Railway Construction Corporation Limited; *Int'l*, pg. 1543
CHINA RAILWAY SOUTHWEST RESEARCH INSTITUTE CO., LTD.—See China Railway Group Limited; *Int'l*, pg. 1543
CHINA SHIPBUILDING NDRI ENGINEERING CO., LTD.—See China State Shipbuilding Corporation; *Int'l*, pg. 1554
CHINA STATE CONSTRUCTION INTERNATIONAL HOLDINGS LIMITED; *Int'l*, pg. 1554
CHINA TIANCHEN ENGINEERING CORPORATION—See China National Chemical Engineering Co., Ltd.; *Int'l*, pg. 1531
CHINA TRIUMPH INTERNATIONAL ENGINEERING CO., LTD.—See China National Building Material Group Co., Ltd.; *Int'l*, pg. 1525
CHINA WUZHOU ENGINEERING CORPORATION LTD.—See China North Industries Group Corporation; *Int'l*, pg. 1535
CHINA ZHONGYUAN ENGINEERING CORPORATION—See China National Nuclear Corporation; *Int'l*, pg. 1532
CHINHUNG INTERNATIONAL (INC.); *Int'l*, pg. 1570
CHIYODA ADVANCED SOLUTIONS CORPORATION—See Chiyoda Corporation; *Int'l*, pg. 1574
CHIYODA ALMANA ENGINEERING LLC—See Chiyoda Corporation; *Int'l*, pg. 1574
CHIYODA KOSHO CO., LTD.—See Chiyoda Corporation; *Int'l*, pg. 1574
CHIYODA MALAYSIA SDN. BHD.—See Chiyoda Corporation; *Int'l*, pg. 1574
CHIYODA PHILIPPINES CORPORATION.—See Chiyoda Corporation; *Int'l*, pg. 1574
CHIYODA SYSTEM TECHNOLOGIES CORPORATION—See Chiyoda Corporation; *Int'l*, pg. 1574
CHIYODA TECHNOACE CO., LTD.—See Chiyoda Corporation; *Int'l*, pg. 1575
CHODAI CO., LTD.; *Int'l*, pg. 1577
CHONG HONG CONSTRUCTION CO., LTD.; *Int'l*, pg. 1578
CHONGQING CONSTRUCTION ENGING GRP CO LTD; *Int'l*, pg. 1579
CHRIST NISHOTECH WATER SYSTEMS PTE. LTD.—See BWT Aktiengesellschaft; *Int'l*, pg. 1233
CHRISTOF ELECTRICS GMBH & CO KG—See Clayton, Dubilier & Rice, LLC; *U.S. Private*, pg. 926
CHRISTOPHER B. BURKE ENGINEERING, LLC—See Christopher B. Burke Engineering Ltd.; *U.S. Private*, pg. 892
CHRISTOPHER B. BURKE ENGINEERING LTD.; *U.S. Private*, pg. 891
CHROMAGE PYRENEEN SA.—See Arbonia AG; *U.S. Private*, pg. 538
CHUDENKO CORPORATION; *Int'l*, pg. 1594
CHUGACH INDUSTRIES, INC.—See Chugach Alaska Corporation; *U.S. Private*, pg. 894
CHUN WO CIVIL ENGINEERING LIMITED—See Asia Allied Infrastructure Holdings Limited; *Int'l*, pg. 610
CHUN WO E & M ENGINEERING LIMITED—See Asia Allied Infrastructure Holdings Limited; *Int'l*, pg. 610
CHUO KAIHATSU CORPORATION—See Chudenko Corporation; *Int'l*, pg. 1594
CIE AMENAGEMENT COTEAUX DE GASCOGNE; *Int'l*, pg. 1603
C & I ENGINEERING, LLC; *U.S. Private*, pg. 701
CII ENGINEERING & CONSTRUCTION JSC—See Ho Chi Minh City Infrastructure Investment Joint Stock Company; *Int'l*, pg. 3434
CIMETRIX JAPAN KK—See PDF Solutions, Inc.; *U.S. Public*, pg. 1658
CIMETRIX SOFTWARE (SHANGHAI) CO., LTD.—See PDF Solutions, Inc.; *U.S. Public*, pg. 1658
CIMTAS STEEL METAL KONSTRUKSIYA MMC—See Enka Insaat ve Sanayi A.S.; *Int'l*, pg. 2440
CINDA ENGINEERING & CONSTRUCTION PVT. LTD.—See CTCI Corporation; *Int'l*, pg. 1870
CITEC INFORMATION & ENGINEERING GMBH—See Cyient Limited; *Int'l*, pg. 1895
CITEC OY AB—See Cyient Limited; *Int'l*, pg. 1896
CITELUM SA—See Electricite de France S.A.; *Int'l*, pg. 2350
CITIC INSTITUTE OF ARCHITECTURE & DESIGN RESEARCH—See CITIC Group Corporation; *Int'l*, pg. 1620
CITIC INTERNATIONAL CONTRACTING INC.—See CITIC Group Corporation; *Int'l*, pg. 1620
CITYWIDE SERVICE SOLUTIONS PTY LTD; *Int'l*, pg. 1630
CIVES ENGINEERING CORPORATION—See Cives Corporation; *U.S. Private*, pg. 908
CIVILCORP, LLC—See Strength Capital Partners, LLC; *U.S. Private*, pg. 3839
CIVILTECH ENGINEERING, INC.—See Woolpert Inc.; *U.S. Private*, pg. 4562
CJ ENGINEERING & CONSTRUCTION CORP.—See CJ Corporation; *Int'l*, pg. 1632
CJ O'SHEA (PLANT HIRE) LTD—See C J O'Shea Group Ltd; *Int'l*, pg. 1238
CJSC GIPROBUM-POYRY—See AFRY AB; *Int'l*, pg. 195
CJ SYSTEMS CO., LTD.—See CJ Corporation; *Int'l*, pg. 1633
CKGP/PW & ASSOCIATES, INC.—See ATON GmbH; *Int'l*, pg. 689
CLARK ENGINEERING & SURVEYING, P.C.—See Ryan Biggs Clark Davis, Engineering & Surveying, P.C.; *U.S. Private*, pg. 3509
CLARKE SOLUTIONS, LLC—See Lightview Capital LLC; *U.S. Private*, pg. 2454
CLARK NEXSEN, INC.; *U.S. Private*, pg. 913
CLASSIC INDUSTRIAL SERVICES, INC.—See APi Group Corporation; *Int'l*, pg. 513
CLEANTECH ALPHA CORPORATION; *U.S. Public*, pg. 511
CLEAR ENVIRONMENTAL SOLUTIONS INC.—See CES Energy Solutions Corp.; *Int'l*, pg. 1423
CLEMENS GMBH—See Avantor, Inc.; *U.S. Public*, pg. 242
CLEMESSY EMCS—See Eiffage S.A.; *Int'l*, pg. 2329
CLE S.A.—See Ackermans & van Haaren NV; *Int'l*, pg. 105
CLI CORPORATION; *U.S. Private*, pg. 942
CLINTON ENGINEERING CO., INC.—See McCarthy Bush Corporation; *U.S. Private*, pg. 2626
THE CLOROX COMPANY - KENNESAW PLANT—See The Clorox Company; *U.S. Public*, pg. 2062
CLP ENGINEERING LIMITED—See CLP Holdings Limited; *Int'l*, pg. 1663
CLUNE CONSTRUCTION CO.; *U.S. Private*, pg. 949
CME ASSOCIATES, INC.—See H.I.G. Capital, LLC; *U.S. Private*, pg. 1827
CMEC ENGINEERING C.A.—See China Machinery Engineering Corporation; *Int'l*, pg. 1515
CMEC NAMIBIA (PROPRIETARY) LIMITED—See China Machinery Engineering Corporation; *Int'l*, pg. 1516
CMEC NIGERIA DEVELOPMENT LTD.—See China Machinery Engineering Corporation; *Int'l*, pg. 1516
CMEC SENEGAL S.A.—See China Machinery Engineering Corporation; *Int'l*, pg. 1516
CMI NESA—See Euremis Holding SA; *Int'l*, pg. 2530
CMTA INC.; *U.S. Private*, pg. 951
C.M.V. S.R.L.—See Certina Holding AG; *Int'l*, pg. 1423
CNA ENGINEERING PVT LTD—See CNA Group Ltd.; *Int'l*, pg. 1763
CNIM BABCOCK CENTRAL EUROPE S.R.O.—See CNIM Constructions Industrielles de la Mediterranee SA; *Int'l*, pg. 1677
CNIM ECS LTD—See CNIM Constructions Industrielles de la Mediterranee SA; *Int'l*, pg. 1677
CNIM ENVIRONNEMENT SA—See CNIM Constructions Industrielles de la Mediterranee SA; *Int'l*, pg. 1677
CNIM TRANSPORT HOLDING SRL—See CNIM Constructions Industrielles de la Mediterranee SA; *Int'l*, pg. 1677
COASTAL CONTRACTS BHD.; *Int'l*, pg. 1681
COASTAL ENGINEERING CO. INC.—See Tighe & Bond, Inc.; *U.S. Private*, pg. 4170
COBB, FENDLEY & ASSOCIATES, INC.; *U.S. Private*, pg. 957
COBITO (PTY) LIMITED—See AECI Limited; *Int'l*, pg. 171
COBRA PERU, S.A.—See ACS, Actividades de Construccion y Servicios, S.A.; *Int'l*, pg. 110
CODA OCTOPUS COLMEK, INC.—See Coda Octopus Group, Inc.; *U.S. Public*, pg. 521
CODA OCTOPUS MARTECH LTD.—See Coda Octopus Group, Inc.; *U.S. Public*, pg. 521
CODENATURE CO., LTD.; *Int'l*, pg. 1688
COFCO TECHNOLOGY & INDUSTRY CO., LTD.; *Int'l*, pg. 1692
COFELY FABRICOM S.A.—See ENGIE SA; *Int'l*, pg. 2429
COFELY INEO—See ENGIE SA; *Int'l*, pg. 2430
COFELY TERMIKA—See ENGIE SA; *Int'l*, pg. 2430
COFFMAN ENGINEERS, INC. - ANCHORAGE OFFICE—See Coffman Engineers, Inc.; *U.S. Private*, pg. 961
COFFMAN ENGINEERS, INC. - HONOLULU OFFICE—See Coffman Engineers, Inc.; *U.S. Private*, pg. 961
COFFMAN ENGINEERS, INC.; *U.S. Private*, pg. 961
COFFMAN ENGINEERS, INC. - SPOKANE OFFICE—See Coffman Engineers, Inc.; *U.S. Private*, pg. 961
COFRA LIMITED—See HAL Trust N.V.; *Int'l*, pg. 3226
COLAS DANMARK A/S—See Bouygues S.A.; *Int'l*, pg. 1122
COLAS GABON—See Bouygues S.A.; *Int'l*, pg. 1122
COLAS-HUNGARIA ZRT.—See Bouygues S.A.; *Int'l*, pg. 1122
COLEMAN ENGINEERING, INC.—See Sanderson Bellecci, Inc.; *U.S. Private*, pg. 3543
COLLIERS ENGINEERING & DESIGN, INC.—See Colliers International Group Inc.; *U.S. Public*, pg. 1700
COLORADO ENGINEERING INC.—See Advent International Corporation; *U.S. Private*, pg. 99
COMAL S.P.A.; *Int'l*, pg. 1707
COMBINED GROUP TRADING AND CONTRACTING GLOBAL - L.L.C.—See Combined Group Contracting Company KSCC; *Int'l*, pg. 1709
COMER GMBH—See Comer Industries S.p.A.; *Int'l*, pg. 1710
COMER INDUSTRIES DO BRASIL LTDA.—See Comer Industries S.p.A.; *Int'l*, pg. 1710
COMER INDUSTRIES GMBH—See Comer Industries S.p.A.; *Int'l*, pg. 1710
COMER INDUSTRIES S.P.A.; *Int'l*, pg. 1710
COMER (SHANGHAI) TRADING COMPANY LTD—See Comer Industries S.p.A.; *Int'l*, pg. 1710
COMMAND BUILDING SERVICES LIMITED—See Christchurch City Holdings Ltd.; *Int'l*, pg. 1586
COMO ENGINEERS PTY. LTD.; *Int'l*, pg. 1721
COMPAGNIE INDUSTRIELLE DES COMPOSANTS BETON—See FAYAT SAS; *Int'l*, pg. 2625
COMPASS TECHNOLOGY SERVICES, INC.—See Jacobs Engineering Group, Inc.; *U.S. Public*, pg. 1184
COMPLERE ENGINEERING GROUP, INC.; *U.S. Private*, pg. 1000
COMPLIANCE CORPORATION; *U.S. Private*, pg. 1001
COMPRESSOR CONTROLS SAUDI ARABIA, LLC—See Roper Technologies, Inc.; *U.S. Public*, pg. 1811
COMSA ALTYAPI LTD.STI—See COMSA EMTE S.L.; *Int'l*, pg. 1761
COMSA BRAZIL LTDA.—See COMSA EMTE S.L.; *Int'l*, pg. 1761
COMSA DE ARGENTINA SA—See COMSA EMTE S.L.; *Int'l*, pg. 1761
COMSA EMTE CHINA—See COMSA EMTE S.L.; *Int'l*, pg. 1761
COMSA EMTE-ECUADOR—See COMSA EMTE S.L.; *Int'l*, pg. 1761
COMSA EMTE FRANCE—See COMSA EMTE S.L.; *Int'l*, pg. 1761
COMSA EMTE PERU S.A.C.—See COMSA EMTE S.L.; *Int'l*, pg. 1761
COMSA EMTE, S.A. DE C.V.—See COMSA EMTE S.L.; *Int'l*, pg. 1761
COMSA EMTE SAS—See COMSA EMTE S.L.; *Int'l*, pg. 1761
COMSA EMTE USA, INC.—See COMSA EMTE S.L.; *Int'l*, pg. 1761
COMSA SUISSE SA—See COMSA EMTE S.L.; *Int'l*, pg. 1761
COMSYS ENGINEERING CO., LTD.—See COMSYS Holdings Corporation; *Int'l*, pg. 1762
CONALVIAS SERVICIOS S.A.S.—See Conalvias S.A.; *Int'l*, pg. 1763
CONALVIAS USA, LLC.—See Conalvias S.A.; *Int'l*, pg. 1763
CONCH CONSTRUCTION & ROOFING INC.—See Anhui Conch Cement Company Limited; *Int'l*, pg. 467
CONCH VENTURE ENVIRONMENTAL PROTECTION TECHNOLOGY (SHANGHAI) CO., LTD.—See China Conch Venture Holdings Limited; *Int'l*, pg. 1491
CONCORD PROJECTS LTD.; *Int'l*, pg. 1765
CONCORD WEST—See RTM & Associates, Inc.; *U.S. Private*, pg. 3498
CONDURIL, ENGENHARIA S.A.; *Int'l*, pg. 1767
CONEX PRAHOVA SA; *Int'l*, pg. 1767
CONGRUEX LLC—See Crestview Partners, L.P.; *U.S. Private*, pg. 1098
CONOPS INDUSTRIAL LTD.—See Fluor Corporation; *U.S. Public*, pg. 858
CONSOLIDATED CONSTRUCTION CONSORTIUM LTD; *Int'l*, pg. 1770
CONSOLIDATED CONTRACTORS INTERNATIONAL COMPANY S.A.L.; *Int'l*, pg. 1770
CONSOLIDATED POWER PROJECTS AUSTRALIA LTD—See Quanta Services, Inc.; *U.S. Public*, pg. 1750
CONSOR ENGINEERS, LLC—See Keystone Capital, Inc.; *U.S. Private*, pg. 2295
CONSORZIO DEKRA REVISIONI—See DEKRA e.V.; *Int'l*, pg. 2007
CONSTRUCTION ENGINEERING GROUP CO., LTD.; *Int'l*, pg. 1777
CONSTRUCTION MANAGEMENT SA/NV—See Ackermans & van Haaren NV; *Int'l*, pg. 105
CONSTRUCTION PARTNERS, INC.; *U.S. Public*, pg. 572
CONSTRUCTION PROFESSIONALS PTE LTD—See Downer EDI Limited; *Int'l*, pg. 2185
CONSTRUCTORA CONCONCRETO SA; *Int'l*, pg. 1778
CONSTRUCTORA SAN JOSE PORTUGAL S.A.—See Grupo Empresarial San Jose, S.A.; *U.S. Private*, pg. 3128
CONSTRUCTORAS ICA, S. A. DE C. V.—See Empresas ICA S.A.B. de C.V.; *Int'l*, pg. 2390
CONSTRUTORA UDRA LTDA.—See Grupo Empresarial

N.A.I.C.S. INDEX

541330 — ENGINEERING SERVICE...

San Jose, S.A.; *Int'l*, pg. 3128
CONSUL SYSTEM S.P.A.—See A2A S.p.A.; *Int'l*, pg. 29
CONSULTING ENGINEERING BUREAU ABDULLAH DABBAGH PARTNERS—See Dabbagh Group Holding Company Ltd.; *Int'l*, pg. 1902
CONSULTING ENGINEERING SERVICES LLC.—See Jacobs Engineering Group, Inc.; *U.S. Public*, pg. 1184
CONSULTING ENGINEERS GROUP, INC.; *U.S. Private*, pg. 1025
CONTINENTAL DATAGRAPHICS LTD.—See The Boeing Company; *U.S. Public*, pg. 2041
CONTINENTAL DATAGRAPHICS—See The Boeing Company; *U.S. Public*, pg. 2041
CONTINENTAL DESIGN & MANAGEMENT GROUP INC.—See Stevens Engineers & Constructors; *U.S. Private*, pg. 3809
CONTINENTAL ENGINEERING CORPORATION—See Continental Holdings Corp.; *Int'l*, pg. 1784
CONTINENTAL MAPPING CONSULTANTS, INC.—See Bluestone Investment Partners, LLC; *U.S. Private*, pg. 598
CONTRACT PROFESSIONALS—See Contract Professionals Inc.; *U.S. Private*, pg. 1032
CONTROL & APPLICATIONS GROUP; *Int'l*, pg. 1785
CONTROL ENGINEERING, INC.—See root9B Holdings, Inc.; *U.S. Public*, pg. 1810
THE CONVERSE PROFESSIONAL GROUP, INC.; *U.S. Private*, pg. 4014
COOPER PERKINS, INC.—See The Carlyle Group Inc.; *U.S. Public*, pg. 2051
COOPER ZIETZ ENGINEERS, INC. - BATTLE GROUND—See Cooper Zietz Engineers, Inc.; *U.S. Private*, pg. 1041
COOPER ZIETZ ENGINEERS, INC.; *U.S. Private*, pg. 1041
CORDELL INFORMATION PTY LTD—See Insight Venture Management, LLC; *U.S. Private*, pg. 2088
CORDELL INFORMATION PTY LTD—See Stone Point Capital LLC; *U.S. Private*, pg. 3822
CORE CONSTRUCTION INDIANA, LLC—See Core Construction; *U.S. Private*, pg. 1048
CORE CONSTRUCTION SERVICES, LLC—See Core Construction; *U.S. Private*, pg. 1048
CORE CONSTRUCTION SERVICES OF NEVADA, INC.—See Core Construction; *U.S. Private*, pg. 1048
CORE CONSTRUCTION SERVICES OF TEXAS, INC.—See Core Construction; *U.S. Private*, pg. 1048
CORESTATES, INC.; *U.S. Private*, pg. 1049
COREVALUE—See Avenga; *Int'l*, pg. 738
CORNERSTONE GEOTECHNICAL, INC.—See Robinson Noble, Inc.; *U.S. Private*, pg. 3462
COROMANDEL ENGINEERING COMPANY LIMITED; *Int'l*, pg. 1802
CORROSION SERVICE COMPANY INC—See Corrosion Service Company Limited; *Int'l*, pg. 1807
CORROSION SERVICE COMPANY LIMITED; *Int'l*, pg. 1806
CORVEN ENGINEERING, INC.—See Hardesty & Hanover, LLC; *U.S. Private*, pg. 1863
COSENTINI ASSOCIATES, INC.—See Tetra Tech, Inc.; *U.S. Public*, pg. 2023
COSTAIN (AFRICA) LIMITED—See Costain Group PLC; *Int'l*, pg. 1814
COSTAIN CIVIL ENGINEERING LTD.—See Costain Group PLC; *Int'l*, pg. 1814
COSTAIN INTERNATIONAL LIMITED—See Costain Group PLC; *Int'l*, pg. 1815
COSTAIN LTD—See Costain Group PLC; *Int'l*, pg. 1815
COTANA CONSULTANT CONSTRUCTION JOINT STOCK COMPANY—See Cotana Group Joint Stock Company; *Int'l*, pg. 1815
COTEG—See FAYAT SAS; *Int'l*, pg. 2625
COUGAR MACHINE LTD.—See Gevelot S.A.; *Int'l*, pg. 2954
COUGAR WELLHEAD SERVICES INC.—See Gevelot S.A.; *Int'l*, pg. 2954
COUTURIER—See FAYAT SAS; *Int'l*, pg. 2625
CPDC GREEN TECHNOLOGY CORP.—See China Petrochemical Development Corp.; *Int'l*, pg. 1540
CPG ADVISORY (SHANGHAI) CO. LTD.—See China Architecture Design & Research Group; *Int'l*, pg. 1483
CPG CONSULTANTS PTE LTD.—See China Architecture Design & Research Group; *Int'l*, pg. 1483
CPG CORPORATION PTE LTD.—See China Architecture Design & Research Group; *Int'l*, pg. 1483
CPG ENVIRONMENTAL ENGINEERING CO. LTD—See Downer EDI Limited; *Int'l*, pg. 2185
CPG NEW ZEALAND—See Downer EDI Limited; *Int'l*, pg. 2185
CPG TRAFFIC PTY LTD—See Downer EDI Limited; *Int'l*, pg. 2185
CPG VIETNAM CO LTD—See China Architecture Design & Research Group; *Int'l*, pg. 1483
CRAIG TESTING LABORATORIES, INC.—See Colliers International Group Inc.; *Int'l*, pg. 1700
CRANE COMPANY; *U.S. Public*, pg. 589
CREATIVE ADVANCED TECHNOLOGY CENTER—See Creative Technology Ltd.; *Int'l*, pg. 1833
THE CRE GROUP, INC.—See BGC Group, Inc.; *U.S. Public*, pg. 329
CREIGHTON MANNING ENGINEERING, LLP.—See Comvest Group Holdings LLC; *U.S. Private*, pg. 1007
CREST BUILDER HOLDINGS BERHAD; *Int'l*, pg. 1840
CRESTTEK LLC—See Alten S.A.; *Int'l*, pg. 390
CRIADO & ASSOCIATES, INC.—See Dunaway Associates, LLC; *U.S. Private*, pg. 1287
CSBC COATING SOLUTIONS CO., LTD.—See CSBC Corp. Taiwan; *Int'l*, pg. 1862
CSC HOLDINGS LIMITED; *Int'l*, pg. 1862
CS CONSTRUCTION & GEOTECHNIC PTE. LTD.—See CSC Holdings Limited; *Int'l*, pg. 1862
CSE SYSTEMS & ENGINEERING (THAILAND) LIMITED—See CSE Global Ltd.; *Int'l*, pg. 1864
CSE-TRANSTEL PTY LTD—See CSE Global Ltd.; *Int'l*, pg. 1863
CS GEOTECHNIC PTE. LTD.—See CSC Holdings Limited; *Int'l*, pg. 1862
CSI TECHNOLOGIES—See Superior Energy Services, Inc.; *U.S. Private*, pg. 3877
CTAG-IDIADA SAFETY TECHNOLOGY, S.L.—See I Squared Capital Advisors (US) LLC; *U.S. Private*, pg. 2022
CTCI ADVANCED SYSTEMS INC.; *Int'l*, pg. 1869
CTCI CORPORATION—See CTCI Corporation; *Int'l*, pg. 1870
CTCI TRADING SHANGHAI CO., LTD.—See CTCI Corporation; *Int'l*, pg. 1870
CTCI VIETNAM COMPANY LIMITED—See CTCI Corporation; *Int'l*, pg. 1870
CTI AURA CO., LTD.—See CTI Engineering Co., Ltd.; *Int'l*, pg. 1870
CTI ENGINEERING CO., LTD.; *Int'l*, pg. 1870
CTI ENGINEERING INTERNATIONAL CO., LTD.—See CTI Engineering Co., Ltd.; *Int'l*, pg. 1870
CTI GROUND PLANNING CO., LTD.—See CTI Engineering Co., Ltd.; *Int'l*, pg. 1871
CT INGENIEROS AAISL; *Int'l*, pg. 1868
CTI PILIPINAS, INC.—See CTI Engineering Co., Ltd.; *Int'l*, pg. 1871
CTL ENGINEERING, INC.; *U.S. Private*, pg. 1119
CUBIC SIMULATION SYSTEMS, INC.—See Elliott Management Corporation; *U.S. Private*, pg. 1368
CUBIC SIMULATION SYSTEMS, INC.—See Veritas Capital Fund Management, LLC; *U.S. Private*, pg. 4361
CUMBEY & FAIR, INC.; *U.S. Private*, pg. 1123
CUMBRA INGENIERIA S.A.—See Aenza S.A.A.; *Int'l*, pg. 176
CUMMINS TURBO TECHNOLOGIES—See Cummins Inc.; *U.S. Public*, pg. 607
CUMMINS TURBO TECHNOLOGIES—See Cummins Inc.; *U.S. Public*, pg. 607
CURTIS CANADA INC.—See CNIM Constructions Industrielles de la Mediterranee SA; *Int'l*, pg. 1677
CUSTOM ENGINEERING AND DESIGNS, INC.—See Marotta Controls, Inc.; *U.S. Private*, pg. 2586
CUSTOMIZED ENGINEERING & DEPOT SUPPORT—See RTX Corporation; *U.S. Public*, pg. 1825
CUSTOM MMIC DESIGN SERVICES, INC.—See Qorvo, Inc.; *U.S. Public*, pg. 1743
C. VARGAS & ASSOCIATES, LTD.; *U.S. Private*, pg. 705
C&W SECURE SERVICES INC.—See ACS, Actividades de Construccion y Servicios, S.A.; *Int'l*, pg. 113
CYBER CLOUD TECHNOLOGIES, LLC—See T-Rex Solutions, LLC; *U.S. Private*, pg. 3911
CYBERNET MBSE CO., LTD.—See FUJISOFT INCORPORATED; *Int'l*, pg. 2830
CYIENT AUSTRALIA PTY LIMITED—See Cyient Limited; *Int'l*, pg. 1896
CYIENT BENELUX BV—See Cyient Limited; *Int'l*, pg. 1896
CYIENT EUROPE LIMITED—See Cyient Limited; *Int'l*, pg. 1896
CYIENT SCHWEIZ GMBH—See Cyient Limited; *Int'l*, pg. 1896
CYIENT SINGAPORE PTE LIMITED—See Cyient Limited; *Int'l*, pg. 1896
CYIENT SRO—See Cyient Limited; *Int'l*, pg. 1896
D3 TECHNICAL SERVICES, LLC—See Addnode Group AB; *Int'l*, pg. 130
DABACO SUBSTRUCTURE DEVELOPMENT & BUILDING INVESTMENT COMPANY LIMITED—See DABACO Group Joint Stock Company; *Int'l*, pg. 1902
DADABHAI CONSTRUCTION W.L.L.—See Dadabhai Group; *Int'l*, pg. 1904
DAELIM INDUSTRIAL CO., LTD.; *Int'l*, pg. 1907
DAELIM (MALAYSIA) SDN. BHD.—See Daelim Industrial Co., Ltd.; *Int'l*, pg. 1908
DAELIM SAUDI ARABIA CO., LTD.—See Daelim Industrial Co., Ltd.; *Int'l*, pg. 1908
DAIHO CORPORATION; *Int'l*, pg. 1927
DAIHO TOSO KOGYO CORP.—See DAIHO CORPORATION; *Int'l*, pg. 1927
DAIICHI MECHA-TECH CORPORATION—See Daiichi Jitsugyo Co. Ltd.; *Int'l*, pg. 1927
DAISEI ENGINEERING CO., LTD.—See Bain Capital, LP; *U.S. Private*, pg. 434
DAISUE CONSTRUCTION CO., LTD.; *Int'l*, pg. 1942
D AKADEMIE S.R.L.—See DEKRA e.V.; *Int'l*, pg. 2007
DALEKOVOD D.D.; *Int'l*, pg. 1950
DALEKOVOD-PROJEKT D.O.O.—See Dalekovod d.d.; *Int'l*, pg. 1951
DALIAN ES MARINE & OFFSHORE ENGINEERING CO., LTD.—See ES Group (Holdings) Limited; *Int'l*, pg. 2500
DAMEN SCHELDE GEARS BV—See Damen Shipyards Group; *Int'l*, pg. 1956
DANELLA ASSOCIATES—See The Danella Companies Inc.; *U.S. Private*, pg. 4018
DANELLA ATLANTIC CORPORATION—See The Danella Companies Inc.; *U.S. Private*, pg. 4018
DANELLA CONSTRUCTION CORPORATION OF NEW JERSEY, INC.—See The Danella Companies Inc.; *U.S. Private*, pg. 4018
DANELLA ENGINEERING AND CONSTRUCTION CORPORATION—See The Danella Companies Inc.; *U.S. Private*, pg. 4018
DANELLA UTILITY CONSTRUCTION, INC.—See The Danella Companies Inc.; *U.S. Private*, pg. 4018
DANIELI CORUS, INC.—See Danieli & C. Officine Meccaniche S.p.A.; *Int'l*, pg. 1963
DANIELI CORUS TECHNICAL SERVICES BV—See Danieli & C. Officine Meccaniche S.p.A.; *Int'l*, pg. 1963
DANUM ENGINEERING PTY. LTD.—See EVZ Limited; *Int'l*, pg. 2574
DARCHEM ENGINEERING LIMITED—See TransDigm Group Incorporated; *U.S. Public*, pg. 2181
DARNUZER INGENIEURE AG—See BKW AG; *Int'l*, pg. 1055
DARRAS ET JOUANIN—See FAYAT SAS; *Int'l*, pg. 2625
DARWISH CONSULTING ENGINEERS—See ARCADIS N.V.; *Int'l*, pg. 541
DATA SCIENCE AUTOMATION, INC.—See Blackford Capital LLC; *U.S. Private*, pg. 574
DATBIM SA; *Int'l*, pg. 1981
DAVIDSON ENGINEERING, INC.; *U.S. Private*, pg. 1171
DAVIS & FLOYD, INC.; *U.S. Private*, pg. 1172
DAVIS H. ELLIOT CONSTRUCTION COMPANY, INC.—See Davis H. Elliot Company Inc.; *U.S. Private*, pg. 1173
DAVIS STRATEGIC INNOVATIONS, INC.; *U.S. Private*, pg. 1174
DAXCON ENGINEERING, INC.; *U.S. Private*, pg. 1176
DAYA CMT SDN. BHD.; *Int'l*, pg. 1985
DAY AUTOMATION SYSTEMS, INC.; *U.S. Private*, pg. 1176
DAY & ZIMMERMANN INTERNATIONAL, INC.—See The Day & Zimmermann Group, Inc.; *U.S. Private*, pg. 4019
DB DESIGN GROUP, INC.—See AEM Holdings Ltd.; *Int'l*, pg. 175
DB ENGINEERING & CONSULTING USA INC.—See Deutsche Bahn AG; *Int'l*, pg. 2050
DB PROJEKTBAU GMBH—See Deutsche Bahn AG; *Int'l*, pg. 2050
DB SERVICES GMBH—See Deutsche Bahn AG; *Int'l*, pg. 2051
DB SYSTEMTECHNIK GMBH—See Deutsche Bahn AG; *Int'l*, pg. 2051
D.C.R. SERVICES; *U.S. Private*, pg. 1141
DEANGELO BROTHERS INC.—See Sterling Partners; *U.S. Private*, pg. 3806
DECISION TECHNOLOGIES, INC.; *U.S. Private*, pg. 1187
DEEP BLUE MARINE, INC.; *U.S. Public*, pg. 645
DEEPMALA INFRASTRUCTURE PRIVATE LIMITED—See Gammon India Limited; *Int'l*, pg. 2879
DEEP SOUTH INDUSTRIAL SERVICES, INC.—See Carylon Corporation; *U.S. Private*, pg. 777
DEEP SPACE SYSTEMS, INC.—See Redwire Corporation; *U.S. Public*, pg. 1771
DEERE & AULT CONSULTANTS INC.—See Schnabel Engineering, Inc.; *U.S. Private*, pg. 3566
DEERNS ITALIA SPA—See Deerns Raadgevende Ingenieurs B.V; *Int'l*, pg. 2003
DEGENKOLB ENGINEERS; *U.S. Private*, pg. 1191
DEIMOS SPACE, S.L.U.—See Elecnor, S.A.; *Int'l*, pg. 2347
DEJEAN-SERVIERES—See FAYAT SAS; *Int'l*, pg. 2625
DEKRA AUTOMOTIVE AB—See DEKRA e.V.; *Int'l*, pg. 2007
DEKRA AUTOMOTIVE OOD—See DEKRA e.V.; *Int'l*, pg. 2007
DEKRA AUTOMOTIVE S.A.—See DEKRA e.V.; *Int'l*, pg. 2007
DEKRA AUTOMOTIVE SOLUTIONS GERMANY GMBH—See DEKRA e.V.; *Int'l*, pg. 2007
DEKRA EKSPERT D.O.O.—See DEKRA e.V.; *Int'l*, pg. 2008
DEKRA EXPERTISES LTDA.—See DEKRA e.V.; *Int'l*, pg. 2008
DEKRA EXPERTISE SPAIN S.L.U.—See DEKRA e.V.; *Int'l*, pg. 2008
DEKRA FRANCE S.A.S.—See DEKRA e.V.; *Int'l*, pg. 2008
DEKRA PORTUGAL EXPERTISES-PERITAGEM AUTOMOVEL S.A.—See DEKRA e.V.; *Int'l*, pg. 2009
DEKRA (SHANGHAI) CO., LTD.—See DEKRA e.V.; *Int'l*, pg. 2007
DEL CARPIO ANALISIS Y ASESORIAS LTDA.—See HORIBA Ltd; *Int'l*, pg. 3475
DELETE SWEDEN AB—See Axcel Management A/S; *Int'l*, pg. 762
DELON HAMPTON & ASSOCIATES, CHARTERED; *U.S. Private*, pg. 1198
DELPHI AUTOMOTIVE CUSTOMER TECHNOLOGY CENTER—See Aptiv PLC; *Int'l*, pg. 524

541330 — ENGINEERING SERVICE...

DELTAMARIN (CHINA) CO., LTD.—See China Merchants Group Limited; *Int'l*, pg. 1520
DELTA RESOURCES, INC.—See Alvarez & Marsal, Inc.; *U.S. Private*, pg. 213
DEMCO PUBLIC COMPANY LIMITED; *Int'l*, pg. 2025
DEME ENVIRONMENTAL NV—See Ackermans & van Haaren NV; *Int'l*, pg. 105
DEME INFRA MARINE CONTRACTORS B.V.—See Ackermans & van Haaren NV; *Int'l*, pg. 105
DEME NV—See Ackermans & van Haaren NV; *Int'l*, pg. 105
DERICHEBOURG ENERGIE SA—See Derichebourg S.A.; *Int'l*, pg. 2042
DERUNGS AG—See Burkhalter Holding AG; *Int'l*, pg. 1224
DESARROLLADORA DE CASAS DEL NOROESTE, S.A. DE C.V.—See Desarrolladora Homex, S.A. de C.V.; *Int'l*, pg. 2044
DESARROLLO DE CONCESIONARIAS VIARIAS DOS, S.L.—See ACS, Actividades de Construccion y Servicios, S.A.; *Int'l*, pg. 111
DESARROLLOS EOLICOS PROMOCION, S.A.—See EDP - Energias de Portugal, S.A.; *Int'l*, pg. 2314
DESERT MECHANICAL INC.—See Tutor Perini Corporation; *U.S. Public*, pg. 2205
DESIGN SOUTH PROFESSIONALS, INC.—See Littlejohn & Co., LLC; *U.S. Private*, pg. 2469
DESIGNWORKS USA—See Bayerische Motoren Werke Aktiengesellschaft; *Int'l*, pg. 912
DEUTSCHE BABCOCK AL JABER W.L.L.—See Al Jaber Group; *Int'l*, pg. 280
DEUTSCHE BAHN ENGINEERING&CONSULTING INDIA PRIVATE LIMITED—See Deutsche Bahn AG; *Int'l*, pg. 2051
DEUTSCHE VAN RIETSCHOTEN & HOUWENS GMBH—See Electricite de France S.A.; *Int'l*, pg. 2351
DEWBERRY & DAVIS, INC.—See Dewberry LLC; *U.S. Private*, pg. 1219
DEWBERRY-GOODKIND, INC.—See Dewberry LLC; *U.S. Private*, pg. 1219
DEWBERRY LLC; *U.S. Private*, pg. 1219
DF DO BRASIL DESENVOLVIMENTO DE PROJETOS LTDA.—See Duro Felguera, S.A.; *Int'l*, pg. 2228
DFR SOLUTIONS, LLC—See ANSYS, Inc.; *U.S. Public*, pg. 139
DGB ASIA BERHAD; *Int'l*, pg. 2096
DGE INC.—See FEV GmbH; *Int'l*, pg. 2648
DHENIN—See FAYAT SAS; *Int'l*, pg. 2625
D. H. GRIFFIN CONTRACTING CO., INC.—See D.H. Griffin Wrecking Co. Inc.; *U.S. Private*, pg. 1142
D.H. GRIFFIN WRECKING CO. INC. - ASHEVILLE DIVISION—See D.H. Griffin Wrecking Co. Inc.; *U.S. Private*, pg. 1142
D.H. GRIFFIN WRECKING CO. INC. - CRUSHING DIVISION—See D.H. Griffin Wrecking Co. Inc.; *U.S. Private*, pg. 1142
DIALOG E & C SDN. BHD.—See Dialog Group Berhad; *Int'l*, pg. 2104
DIEDRICHS & ASSOCIATES, INC.; *U.S. Private*, pg. 1228
D-I-E ELEKTRO AG—See CEZ, a.s.; *Int'l*, pg. 1427
DIETRICH DESIGN GROUP INC.—See Worthington Industries, Inc.; *U.S. Public*, pg. 2382
DIETRICH DESIGN GROUP INC.—See Worthington Industries, Inc.; *U.S. Public*, pg. 2382
DIETSMANN AD—See Dietsmann N.V.; *Int'l*, pg. 2117
DIGIOIA, GRAY & ASSOCIATES, LLC—See OceanSound Partners, LP; *U.S. Private*, pg. 2991
DILIP BUILDCON LIMITED; *Int'l*, pg. 2125
DILLING GROUP, INC.—See Comfort Systems USA, Inc.; *U.S. Public*, pg. 543
DI-NIKKO ENGINEERING CO., LTD.; *Int'l*, pg. 2101
DISENOS Y PROYECTOS TECNICOS SA; *Int'l*, pg. 2135
DIS-TRAN PACKAGED SUBSTATIONS, LLC—See Crest Industries, LLC; *U.S. Private*, pg. 1096
DIVERSIFIED TECHNOLOGY CONSULTANTS, INC.; *U.S. Private*, pg. 1243
DIVOSTA BUILDING, LLC—See PulteGroup, Inc.; *U.S. Public*, pg. 1737
DIXON NETWORKS CORPORATION; *Int'l*, pg. 2138
D&M CONSULTING ENGINEERS, INC.—See AECOM; *U.S. Public*, pg. 51
D.M. CONSUNJI, INC.—See DMCI Holdings, Inc.; *Int'l*, pg. 2142
DME ALLIANCE, INC.—See O'Neal Inc.; *U.S. Private*, pg. 2979
DMG MORI GLOBAL SERVICE MILLING GMBH—See DMG MORI Co., Ltd.; *Int'l*, pg. 2144
DMG MORI GLOBAL SERVICE TURNING GMBH—See DMG MORI Co., Ltd.; *Int'l*, pg. 2144
DMI DALIAN LTD—See DMI UK Ltd.; *Int'l*, pg. 2145
DMI MARINE INC.—See DMI UK Ltd.; *Int'l*, pg. 2145
DMK ASSOCIATES, INC.; *U.S. Private*, pg. 1249
DMR HYDROENGINEERING & INFRASTRUCTURES LTD.; *Int'l*, pg. 2146
DOAN VIET CO. LTD—See Doppelmayr Group; *Int'l*, pg. 2174
DOBLETHOMAS & ASSOCIATES, INC.—See Laco Associates, Inc.; *U.S. Private*, pg. 2372
DOBLE TRANSINOR AS—See ESCO Technologies, Inc.; *U.S. Public*, pg. 793

DOERFER CORPORATION; *U.S. Private*, pg. 1252
DOMIKI AKINITON S.A.—See Domiki Kritis S.A.; *Int'l*, pg. 2161
DOMINION ENGINEERING, INC.—See Bernhard Capital Partners Management, LP; *U.S. Private*, pg. 536
DOMINION TECHNICAL SOLUTIONS, INC.—See Dominion Energy, Inc.; *U.S. Public*, pg. 674
DONALD F DICKERSON ASSOCIATES—See Coffman Engineers, Inc.; *U.S. Private*, pg. 961
DONGAH GEOLOGICAL ENGINEERING CO., LTD.; *Int'l*, pg. 2165
DONGAH GEOLOGICAL ENGINEERING INDIA PRIVATE LTD.—See DongAh Geological Engineering Co., Ltd.; *Int'l*, pg. 2165
DONGBU CORPORATION—See Dongbu Group; *Int'l*, pg. 2166
DONGBU ENGINEERING CO., LTD .—See Dongbu Group; *Int'l*, pg. 2166
DONGBU SOLAR CO., LTD.—See Dongbu Group; *Int'l*, pg. 2166
DONGSEO CONSTRUCTION CO., LTD.—See Daesang Corporation; *Int'l*, pg. 1909
DONGSHIN ENGINEERING & CONSTRUCTION CO., LTD.; *Int'l*, pg. 2169
DOOSAN ATS AMERICA, LLC—See Doosan Corporation; *Int'l*, pg. 2172
DOOSAN HF CONTROLS CORP.—See E2S Co., Ltd.; *Int'l*, pg. 2261
DOOSAN POWER SYSTEMS INDIA PRIVATE LTD.—See Doosan Corporation; *Int'l*, pg. 2173
DOPPELMAYR CANADA LTD.—See Doppelmayr Group; *Int'l*, pg. 2174
DOPPELMAYR DO BRASIL SISTEMAS DE TRANSPORTE LTDA.—See Doppelmayr Group; *Int'l*, pg. 2175
DOPPELMAYR POLSKA SP Z O.O.—See Doppelmayr Group; *Int'l*, pg. 2174
DOPPELMAYR TURKEY ASANSOR TELEFERIK VE KABLOLU TASIMA SISTEMLERI INS. TAAH. LTD. STI—See Doppelmayr Group; *Int'l*, pg. 2175
DORNERWORKS, LTD.; *U.S. Private*, pg. 1263
DORNIER CONSULTING GMBH—See Airbus SE; *Int'l*, pg. 242
DOUCET & ASSOCIATES, INC.—See Goldberg Lindsay & Co., LLC; *U.S. Private*, pg. 1729
DOUG VEERKAMP GENERAL ENGINEERING, INC.; *U.S. Private*, pg. 1266
DOUNREAY SITE RESTORATION LIMITED—See Babcock International Group PLC; *Int'l*, pg. 792
DOWA TECHNO-RESEARCH CO., LTD.—See Dowa Holdings Co., Ltd.; *Int'l*, pg. 2184
DOW DIVERSIFIED, INC.—See H2I Group, Inc.; *U.S. Private*, pg. 1837
DOWNER CONSTRUCTION (FIJI) LIMITED—See Downer EDI Limited; *Int'l*, pg. 2185
DOWNER EDI ENGINEERING GROUP PTY LIMITED—See Downer EDI Limited; *Int'l*, pg. 2185
DOWNER EDI ENGINEERING HOLDINGS PTY LTD—See Downer EDI Limited; *Int'l*, pg. 2185
DOWNER EDI ENGINEERING - PROJECTS PTY LTD—See Downer EDI Limited; *Int'l*, pg. 2185
DOWNER EDI ENGINEERING (S) PTE LTD—See Downer EDI Limited; *Int'l*, pg. 2185
DOWNER EDI GROUP (NZ) LTD—See Downer EDI Limited; *Int'l*, pg. 2185
DOWNER EDI MINING PTY LTD.—See Downer EDI Limited; *Int'l*, pg. 2185
DOWNER EDI SERVICES PTY LTD—See Downer EDI Limited; *Int'l*, pg. 2185
DOWNER EDI (USA) PTY LTD—See Downer EDI Limited; *Int'l*, pg. 2185
DOWNER ENGINEERING POWER PTY LIMITED—See Downer EDI Limited; *Int'l*, pg. 2186
DOWNER MBL PTY LIMITED—See Downer EDI Limited; *Int'l*, pg. 2186
DRACE GEOCISA, S.A.—See ACS, Actividades de Construccion y Servicios, S.A.; *Int'l*, pg. 111
DRA GROUP HOLDINGS PROPRIETARY LIMITED; *Int'l*, pg. 2196
DRAKE, INC.; *U.S. Private*, pg. 1272
DRAVENSA C.A.—See HAL Trust N.V.; *Int'l*, pg. 3226
DREES & SOMMER BELGIUM S.P.R.L—See Drees & Sommer SE; *Int'l*, pg. 2204
DREES & SOMMER BERLIN GMBH—See Drees & Sommer SE; *Int'l*, pg. 2204
DREES & SOMMER ESPANA S.L.—See Drees & Sommer SE; *Int'l*, pg. 2204
DREES & SOMMER FRANCE SARL—See Drees & Sommer SE; *Int'l*, pg. 2204
DREES & SOMMER ITALIA ENGINEERING S.R.L.—See Drees & Sommer SE; *Int'l*, pg. 2204
DREES & SOMMER LUXEMBOURG SARL—See Drees & Sommer SE; *Int'l*, pg. 2204
DREES & SOMMER NORDIC A/S—See Drees & Sommer SE; *Int'l*, pg. 2204
DREES & SOMMER POLSKA SP.Z.O.O.—See Drees & Sommer SE; *Int'l*, pg. 2204
DREES & SOMMER PROJECT MANAGEMENT & CONSULTING (BEIJING) CO., LTD.—See Drees & Sommer SE; *Int'l*, pg. 2204

DREES & SOMMER PROJEKTMANAGEMENT UND BAUTECHNISCHE BERATUNG GMBH—See Drees & Sommer SE; *Int'l*, pg. 2204
DREES & SOMMER ROMANIA S.R.L.—See Drees & Sommer SE; *Int'l*, pg. 2204
DREES & SOMMER RUSSIA & CIS—See Drees & Sommer SE; *Int'l*, pg. 2204
DREES & SOMMER SCHWEIZ GMBH—See Drees & Sommer SE; *Int'l*, pg. 2204
DREES & SOMMER TURKIYE LTD.—See Drees & Sommer SE; *Int'l*, pg. 2204
DREES & SOMMER UKRAINE—See Drees & Sommer SE; *Int'l*, pg. 2204
DRILLING RESEARCH & DEVELOPMENT CORPORATION—See Weatherford International plc; *U.S. Public*, pg. 2339
DRIVER CONSULT LIMITED—See Diales; *Int'l*, pg. 2104
DRIVER CONSULT (OMAN) LLC—See Diales; *Int'l*, pg. 2104
DSI TUNNELING LLC—See Frank Calandra, Inc.; *U.S. Private*, pg. 1594
DSPACE GMBH; *Int'l*, pg. 2210
D S S COMPANY—See MDU Resources Group, Inc.; *U.S. Public*, pg. 1410
DTECH LABS, INC.—See Elliott Management Corporation; *U.S. Private*, pg. 1368
DTECH LABS, INC.—See Veritas Capital Fund Management, LLC; *U.S. Private*, pg. 4362
DTP TERRASSEMENT SA—See Bouygues S.A.; *Int'l*, pg. 1123
DUERR CYPLAN LIMITED—See Durr AG; *Int'l*, pg. 2230
DUFFIELD ASSOCIATES INC.—See Round Table Capital Management, LP; *U.S. Private*, pg. 3488
DUNAWAY ASSOCIATES, LLC; *U.S. Private*, pg. 1287
DUNGAN ENGINEERING PA; *U.S. Private*, pg. 1289
DUNHAM ENGINEERING—See Tailwind Capital Group, LLC; *U.S. Private*, pg. 3924
DUNKELBERGER ENGINEERING & TESTING, INC. - SARASOTA OFFICE—See Terracon Consultants, Inc.; *U.S. Private*, pg. 3970
DUNKELBERGER ENGINEERING & TESTING, INC.—See Terracon Consultants, Inc.; *U.S. Private*, pg. 3970
DURATEC LIMITED; *Int'l*, pg. 2228
THE DURBIN GROUP, LLC—See The Goldman Sachs Group, Inc.; *U.S. Public*, pg. 2080
DURO DAKOVIC INZENJERING D.D.—See Duro Dakovic Holding d.d.; *Int'l*, pg. 2228
DURO DAKOVIC PROIZVODNJA OPREME D.O.O.—See Duro Dakovic Holding d.d.; *Int'l*, pg. 2228
DURO DAKOVIC SLOBODNA ZONA D.O.O.—See Duro Dakovic Holding d.d.; *Int'l*, pg. 2228
DURO DAKOVIC SPECIJALNA VOZILA D.D.—See Duro Dakovic Holding d.d.; *Int'l*, pg. 2228
DURO DAKOVIC STROJNA OBRADA D.O.O.—See Duro Dakovic Holding d.d.; *Int'l*, pg. 2228
DURO FELGUERA INDUSTRIAL PROJECTS CONSULTING CO., LTD.—See Duro Felguera, S.A.; *Int'l*, pg. 2228
DURO FELGUERA, S.A.; *Int'l*, pg. 2228
DUTA TECHNIC SDN. BHD.—See HeiTech Padu Berhad; *Int'l*, pg. 3326
DV CONSTRUCTION SA—See Bouygues S.A.; *Int'l*, pg. 1122
DYNA-MAC OFFSHORE SERVICES PTE. LTD.—See Hanwha Group; *Int'l*, pg. 3264
DYNA-MAC OFFSHORE SERVICES PTE. LTD.—See Hanwha Ocean Co., Ltd.; *Int'l*, pg. 3266
DYNAMIC RESEARCH, INC.—See AB Dynamics plc; *Int'l*, pg. 39
DYNA TEN CORPORATION—See Comfort Systems USA, Inc.; *U.S. Public*, pg. 544
DYNNIQ NEDERLAND BV—See Egeria Capital Management B.V.; *Int'l*, pg. 2323
DYTECNA ENGINEERING LTD—See Dytecna Limited; *Int'l*, pg. 2243
DYTECNA LIMITED; *Int'l*, pg. 2243
E&A CONTRACTORS PTY. LTD.—See E&A Limited; *Int'l*, pg. 2246
EADS CHILE—See Airbus SE; *Int'l*, pg. 246
EADS CHINA—See Airbus SE; *Int'l*, pg. 246
EADS COMPOSITES AQUITAINE—See Airbus SE; *Int'l*, pg. 246
EADS FRANCE S.A.S. - INNOVATION WORKS—See Airbus SE; *Int'l*, pg. 246
EADS INDIA PVT LTD—See Airbus SE; *Int'l*, pg. 246
EADS INDONESIA—See Airbus SE; *Int'l*, pg. 246
EADS KOREA CO., LTD.—See Airbus SE; *Int'l*, pg. 246
EADS MEXICO, S.A. DE C.V.—See Airbus SE; *Int'l*, pg. 246
EADS SINGAPORE PTE LTD—See Airbus SE; *Int'l*, pg. 247
EADS SOUTH AFRICA PTY. LTD.—See Airbus SE; *Int'l*, pg. 246
EADS SYSTEMS & DEFENSE ELECTRONICS—See Airbus SE; *Int'l*, pg. 246
EADS THAILAND—See Airbus SE; *Int'l*, pg. 246
EADS TURKEY—See Airbus SE; *Int'l*, pg. 246
EA ENGINEERING, P.C.—See EA Engineering, Science & Technology, Inc.; *U.S. Private*, pg. 1308

N.A.I.C.S. INDEX

541330 — ENGINEERING SERVICE...

EA ENGINEERING, SCIENCE, AND TECHNOLOGY (MI) PLC.—See EA Engineering, Science & Technology, Inc.; *U.S. Private*, pg. 1308
EARTH EXPLORATION, INC.—See Terracon Consultants, Inc.; *U.S. Private*, pg. 3970
EAST CHINA ENGINEERING SCIENCE & TECHNOLOGY CO., LTD.; *Int'l*, pg. 2269
EAST ENGINEERING LTD OY—See AFRY AB; *Int'l*, pg. 195
EASTERN SOLDAR (SINGAPORE) PTE. LTD.—See Harbour-Link Group Berhad; *Int'l*, pg. 3272
EASTERN TECHNICAL ENGINEERING PUBLIC CO., LTD.; *Int'l*, pg. 2274
EASY MIX SDN. BHD.—See Bina Puri Holdings Bhd; *Int'l*, pg. 1032
EBA S.L.—See Grupo Empresarial San Jose, S.A.; *Int'l*, pg. 3128
EBI INTERNATIONAL, INC.—See Everything Blockchain, Inc.; *U.S. Public*, pg. 802
EBNOTHER ELEKTRO AG—See Burkhalter Holding AG; *Int'l*, pg. 1224
EC DRIVER & ASSOCIATES, INC.—See AECOM; *U.S. Public*, pg. 51
E&C ENGINEERING CORPORATION—See CTCI Corporation; *Int'l*, pg. 1870
ECHEVERRIA IZQUIERDO S.A.; *Int'l*, pg. 2289
ECHEZABAL & ASSOCIATES, INC.—See Peak Rock Capital LLC; *U.S. Private*, pg. 3124
ECHOSTAR UKRAINE, LLC—See EchoStar Corporation; *U.S. Public*, pg. 711
ECKHARD GARBE GMBH—See Heidelberg Materials AG; *Int'l*, pg. 3310
ECKLER ENGINEERING INC—See H.I.G. Capital, LLC; *U.S. Private*, pg. 1827
ECLIPSE ENGINEERING, P.C.—See Cushing Terrell; *U.S. Private*, pg. 1127
ECM INGENIEUR-UNTERNEHMEN FUR ENERGIE- UND UMWELTTECHNIK GMBH—See Alpiq Holding AG; *Int'l*, pg. 372
ECM ING.UNTERNEHMEN FUR ENERGIE-UND UMWELTTECHNIK GMBH—See Alpiq Holding AG; *Int'l*, pg. 372
ECO ENGINEERING, INC.; *U.S. Private*, pg. 1328
ECON SOUTH, LLC—See Land South Holdings, LLC; *U.S. Private*, pg. 2384
ECOREM—See ABO-Group NV/SA; *Int'l*, pg. 66
ECOSCIENCE INTERNATIONAL BERHAD; *Int'l*, pg. 2299
ECOTEC S.R.L.; *Int'l*, pg. 2300
ECS, INC.—See Coffman Engineers, Inc.; *U.S. Private*, pg. 961
EC SOURCE SERVICES, LLC—See MasTec, Inc.; *U.S. Public*, pg. 1393
EDAG PRODUCTION SOLUTIONS INDIA PRIV. LTD.—See ATON GmbH; *Int'l*, pg. 689
EDC IRELAND—See Chevron Corporation; *U.S. Public*, pg. 487
EDISCOVERY INC.—See ArcherHall, LLC; *U.S. Private*, pg. 311
EDP INOVACAO, S.A.—See EDP - Energias de Portugal, S.A.; *Int'l*, pg. 2314
EDRASIS - C. PSALLIDAS S.A.; *Int'l*, pg. 2315
EE-HWA CONSTRUCTION CO., LTD.; *Int'l*, pg. 2317
EFACEC ENGENHARIA E SISTEMAS, S.A.—See Efacec Capital, SGPS, S.A.; *Int'l*, pg. 2318
EGIS S.A.—See Caisse des Depots et Consignations; *Int'l*, pg. 1257
E-GLOBE S.P.A.; *Int'l*, pg. 2247
EHISA CONSTRUCCIONES Y OBRAS, S.A.U.—See Elecnor, S.A.; *Int'l*, pg. 2347
EIC ACTIVITIES PTY LTD—See ACS, Actividades de Construccion y Servicios, S.A.; *Int'l*, pg. 111
EIFFAGE CONSTRUCTION ALSACE FRANCHE COMTE S.N.C—See Eiffage S.A.; *Int'l*, pg. 2329
EIFFAGE CONSTRUCTION ARTOIS HAINAUT S.N.C—See Eiffage S.A.; *Int'l*, pg. 2329
EIFFAGE CONSTRUCTION AUVERGNE SNC—See Eiffage S.A.; *Int'l*, pg. 2329
EIFFAGE CONSTRUCTION LIMOUSIN—See Eiffage S.A.; *Int'l*, pg. 2329
EIFFAGE CONSTRUCTION LORRAINE S.N.C—See Eiffage S.A.; *Int'l*, pg. 2329
EIFFAGE CONSTRUCTION MIDI PYRENEES S.N.C—See Eiffage S.A.; *Int'l*, pg. 2329
EIFFAGE CONSTRUCTION NORD—See Eiffage S.A.; *Int'l*, pg. 2329
EIFFAGE CONSTRUCTION PARIS PATRIMOINE—See Eiffage S.A.; *Int'l*, pg. 2329
EIFFAGE CONSTRUCTION PROVENCE S.N.C—See Eiffage S.A.; *Int'l*, pg. 2330
EIFFAGE CONSTRUCTION RHONE-ALPES S.N.C—See Eiffage S.A.; *Int'l*, pg. 2330
EIFFAGE CONSTRUCTION VAL DE SEINE S.N.C—See Eiffage S.A.; *Int'l*, pg. 2330
EIFFAGE ENERGIE NORD—See Eiffage S.A.; *Int'l*, pg. 2330
EIFFAGE ENERGIE POITOU-CHARENTES S.A.S.—See Eiffage S.A.; *Int'l*, pg. 2330
EIFFAGE ENERGIE VAL DE LOIRE S.A.S.—See Eiffage S.A.; *Int'l*, pg. 2330

EIFFAGE TRAVAUX PUBLICS MEDITERRANEE—See Eiffage S.A.; *Int'l*, pg. 2331
EIFFAGE TRAVAUX PUBLICS SUD OUEST S.N.C—See Eiffage S.A.; *Int'l*, pg. 2331
EIFFEL INDUSTRIE S.A.S—See Eiffage S.A.; *Int'l*, pg. 2331
EIGENMANN AG—See Burkhalter Holding AG; *Int'l*, pg. 1224
EI RISK MANAGEMENT CORP.—See Ei Companies; *U.S. Private*, pg. 1346
EIS INC.—See Audax Group, Limited Partnership; *U.S. Private*, pg. 387
EJM ENGINEERING, INC.—See GI Manager L.P.; *U.S. Private*, pg. 1691
EK DESIGN SERVICES, INC.—See Jacobs Engineering Group, Inc.; *U.S. Public*, pg. 1184
EKOVEST BERHAD; *Int'l*, pg. 2339
ELB ENGINEERING SERVICES (PTY) LIMITED—See ELB Group Limited; *Int'l*, pg. 2343
ELB GROUP LIMITED; *Int'l*, pg. 2343
ELECDOR, S.A.—See Elecnor, S.A.; *Int'l*, pg. 2347
ELECNOR CHILE, S.A.—See Elecnor, S.A.; *Int'l*, pg. 2347
ELECNOR, S.A.; *Int'l*, pg. 2347
ELECTRA BUIN SA—See Burkhalter Holding AG; *Int'l*, pg. 1224
ELECTRAWATCH INC.—See Austal Limited; *Int'l*, pg. 716
ELECTREN, S.A.—See ACS, Actividades de Construccion y Servicios, S.A.; *Int'l*, pg. 111
ELECTRICAL & CONTROL SPECIALISTS LTD—See Forges Tardieu Ltd; *Int'l*, pg. 2733
ELECTRICAL DESIGN & CONTROL CO. INC.—See DASCAN Industrial Controls; *Int'l*, pg. 1973
ELECTRICAL RELIABILITY SERVICES, INC.—See Emerson Electric Co.; *U.S. Public*, pg. 746
ELECTRIC POWER ENGINEERS, LLC—See Lime Rock Partners, LLC; *U.S. Private*, pg. 2456
ELECTROCONSTRUCTIA ELCO ALBA IULIA SA; *Int'l*, pg. 2353
ELECTROCONSTRUCTIA ELCO SA; *Int'l*, pg. 2353
ELECTRO-MAG INC.—See Graybar Electric Company, Inc.; *U.S. Private*, pg. 1760
ELECVEN CONSTRUCCIONES, S.A.—See Elecnor, S.A.; *Int'l*, pg. 2347
ELEKTRO ARBER AG—See Burkhalter Holding AG; *Int'l*, pg. 1224
ELEKTRO-BAU AG ROTHRIST—See Burkhalter Holding AG; *Int'l*, pg. 1225
ELEKTRO BURKHALTER AG—See Burkhalter Holding AG; *Int'l*, pg. 1224
ELEKTRO CHRISTOFFEL, ZNL DER CAVIEZEL AG—See Burkhalter Holding AG; *Int'l*, pg. 1224
ELEKTRO GUTZWILLER AG—See Burkhalter Holding AG; *Int'l*, pg. 1224
ELEKTRO HUNZIKER AG—See Burkhalter Holding AG; *Int'l*, pg. 1224
ELEKTROHUUS VON ALLMEN AG—See Burkhalter Holding AG; *Int'l*, pg. 1225
ELEKTRO KALIN AG—See Burkhalter Holding AG; *Int'l*, pg. 1224
ELEKTRO NIKLAUS AG—See Burkhalter Holding AG; *Int'l*, pg. 1224
ELEKTRO PIZOL AG—See Burkhalter Holding AG; *Int'l*, pg. 1224
ELEKTRO RUEGG AG—See Burkhalter Holding AG; *Int'l*, pg. 1224
ELEKTRO SCHMIDLIN AG—See Burkhalter Holding AG; *Int'l*, pg. 1225
ELEKTRO SIEGRIST AG—See Burkhalter Holding AG; *Int'l*, pg. 1225
ELEKTROS, INC.; *Int'l*, pg. 2357
ELEKTRO STAMPFL AG—See Burkhalter Holding AG; *Int'l*, pg. 1225
ELEKTRO ZURICHSEE AG—See Burkhalter Holding AG; *Int'l*, pg. 1225
ELETTRO CELIO SA—See Burkhalter Holding AG; *Int'l*, pg. 1225
ELEVION GMBH—See CEZ, a.s.; *Int'l*, pg. 1427
ELIA ENGINEERING SA—See Elia Group SA; *Int'l*, pg. 2360
ELITYS CONSULTING SARL—See Alten S.A.; *Int'l*, pg. 390
ELLINIKI TECHNODOMIKI ANEMOS S.A—See ELLAKTOR S.A.; *Int'l*, pg. 2365
ELLINIKI TECHNODOMIKI ENERGIAKI S.A—See ELLAKTOR S.A.; *Int'l*, pg. 2365
ELLIOT ENGINEERING, INC.—See Davis H. Elliot Company Inc.; *U.S. Private*, pg. 1173
ELLISDON SERVICES INC.—See EllisDon Corporation; *Int'l*, pg. 2367
ELOMATIC OY; *Int'l*, pg. 2368
ELRINGKLINGER ABSCHIRMTECHNIK (SCHWEIZ) AG—See ElringKlinger AG; *Int'l*, pg. 2369
ELSPEC ANDINA S.A.S—See Elspec Engineering Ltd.; *Int'l*, pg. 2370
ELTEL SISA, ZNL DER ELEKTROHUUS VON ALLMEN AG—See Burkhalter Holding AG; *Int'l*, pg. 1225
ELTON ANDERSON ASSOCIATES—See Ghafari Associates, L.L.C.; *U.S. Private*, pg. 1690
EMAS AMC—See Ezra Holdings Ltd.; *Int'l*, pg. 2594
EMATS, INC.; *U.S. Private*, pg. 1378
EMC ANALYTICAL SERVICES, LLC; *U.S. Private*, pg. 1379

EMC MANAGEMENT CONCEPTS—See EMC Analytical Services, LLC; *U.S. Private*, pg. 1379
EMCOR GROUP (UK) PLC—See EMCOR Group, Inc.; *U.S. Public*, pg. 737
EMERALD COAST ASSOCIATES, INC.—See GeoPoint Surveying, Inc.; *U.S. Private*, pg. 1681
EMERSON NETWORK POWER SURGE PROTECTION, INC.—See Vertiv Holdings Co; *U.S. Public*, pg. 2289
EMERSON PROCESS MANAGEMENT CSI—See Emerson Electric Co.; *U.S. Public*, pg. 746
EMERSON PROCESS MANAGEMENT DISTRIBUTION N.V.—See Emerson Electric Co.; *U.S. Public*, pg. 746
EMERSON PROCESS MANAGEMENT LLLP—See Emerson Electric Co.; *U.S. Public*, pg. 748
EMERSON PROCESS MANAGEMENT POWER & WATER SOLUTIONS INDIA PRIVATE LIMITED—See Emerson Electric Co.; *U.S. Public*, pg. 748
EMERSON PROCESS MANAGEMENT ROMANIA S.R.L.—See Emerson Electric Co.; *U.S. Public*, pg. 747
EMERSON PROCESS MANAGEMENT—See Emerson Electric Co.; *U.S. Public*, pg. 746
EMERSON PROCESS MANAGEMENT—See Emerson Electric Co.; *U.S. Public*, pg. 746
EMERSON PROCESS MANAGEMENT—See Emerson Electric Co.; *U.S. Public*, pg. 746
EMERSON PROCESS MANAGEMENT—See Emerson Electric Co.; *U.S. Public*, pg. 747
EMIRATES DISTRICT COOLING COMPANY LLC—See Dubai Investments PJSC; *Int'l*, pg. 2219
EMIRATES NATIONAL ELECTROMECHANICAL L.L.C.—See Finance House P.J.S.C.; *Int'l*, pg. 2664
EMK CONSULTANTS OF FLORIDA, INC.; *U.S. Private*, pg. 1383
EMP. CONST. MOLLER Y PEREZ-COTAPOS S.A.; *Int'l*, pg. 2385
EMS LIMITED; *Int'l*, pg. 2392
EMTE ANDORRA, S.A.—See COMSA EMTE S.L.; *Int'l*, pg. 1761
EMTE CLEANROOM S.A.—See COMSA EMTE S.L.; *Int'l*, pg. 1761
EMTE INSTALACIONES—See COMSA EMTE S.L.; *Int'l*, pg. 1761
EMTE, LDA—See COMSA EMTE S.L.; *Int'l*, pg. 1761
EMTE ME ZONA FRANCA S.A.—See COMSA EMTE S.L.; *Int'l*, pg. 1761
E.M.T.E. S.A.R.L.—See COMSA EMTE S.L.; *Int'l*, pg. 1761
ENCOM GMBH—See Energoprojekt Holding a.d.; *Int'l*, pg. 2421
ENCORE CONSTRUCTION GROUP, INC.—See Garney Holding Company, Inc.; *U.S. Private*, pg. 1645
ENDRESS+HAUSER AG—See Endress+Hauser (International) Holding AG; *Int'l*, pg. 2406
ENDRESS+HAUSER AUSTRALIA PTY LTD.—See Endress+Hauser (International) Holding AG; *Int'l*, pg. 2406
ENDRESS+HAUSER (IRELAND) LTD.—See Endress+Hauser (International) Holding AG; *Int'l*, pg. 2406
EN ENGINEERING, LLC—See General Atlantic Service Company, L.P.; *U.S. Private*, pg. 1662
ENERCON SERVICES, INC.—See Brookfield Corporation; *Int'l*, pg. 1182
ENERFIN ENERVENTO, S.L.U.—See Elecnor, S.A.; *Int'l*, pg. 2347
ENERGENZE CONSULTING, LLC—See NV5 Global, Inc.; *U.S. Public*, pg. 1557
ENERGENZE CONSULTING LTD.—See NV5 Global, Inc.; *U.S. Public*, pg. 1557
ENERGOINVEST, D.D.; *Int'l*, pg. 2421
ENERGO NIGERIJA LTD.—See Energoprojekt Holding a.d.; *Int'l*, pg. 2421
ENERGOPROJEKT - ENTEL A.D.—See Energoprojekt Holding a.d.; *Int'l*, pg. 2421
ENERGOPROJEKT HIDROINZENJERING A.D.—See Energoprojekt Holding a.d.; *Int'l*, pg. 2422
ENERGOPROJEKT HOLDING A.D.; *Int'l*, pg. 2421
ENERGOPROJEKT INDUSTRIJA A.D.; *Int'l*, pg. 2422
ENERGOPROJEKT OPREMA A.D.—See Energoprojekt Holding a.d.; *Int'l*, pg. 2422
ENERGOPROJEKT URBANIZAM I ARHITEKTURA A.D.; *Int'l*, pg. 2422
ENERGOPROJEKT VISOKOGRADNJA A.D.; *Int'l*, pg. 2422
ENERGY CONTROL SYSTEMS ENGINEERING INC.—See CODA Holdings, Inc.; *U.S. Private*, pg. 959
ENERGY FRONTIER—See Hokkaido Electric Power Co., Inc.; *Int'l*, pg. 3442
ENERGY SYSTEMS GROUP, LLC—See Brookfield Corporation; *Int'l*, pg. 1182
ENERGY TECHNOLOGIES LIMITED; *Int'l*, pg. 2423
ENERGY TRANSFER SOLUTIONS, LLC—See Madison Dearborn Partners, LLC; *U.S. Private*, pg. 2541
ENERPEAK AG—See BKW AG; *Int'l*, pg. 1055
ENERSENSE INTERNATIONAL OYJ; *Int'l*, pg. 2424
ENERTIS COLOMBIA S.A.S.—See I Squared Capital Advisors (US) LLC; *U.S. Private*, pg. 2022
ENERTIS UK LIMITED—See I Squared Capital Advisors (US) LLC; *U.S. Private*, pg. 2022
ENGENCO LIMITED; *Int'l*, pg. 2426
ENGIE SERVICES INC.—See ENGIE SA; *Int'l*, pg. 2431

541330 — ENGINEERING SERVICE...

ENGINEERED CONCEPTS CONSULTING SERVICES INC.—See Terracon Consultants, Inc.; *U.S. Private*, pg. 3970
ENGINEERING DESIGN & MANUFACTURING SERVICES, INC.—See Park-Ohio Holdings Corp.; *U.S. Public*, pg. 1639
ENGINEERING & ENVIRONMENTAL CONSULTANTS, INC.—See Civil & Environmental Consultants, Inc.; *U.S. Private*, pg. 908
ENGINEERING INGEGNERIA INFORMATICA S.P.A.—See Apax Partners LLP; *Int'l*, pg. 504
ENGINEERING SERVICE, INC.; *U.S. Private*, pg. 1399
ENGINEERING SERVICES NETWORK, INC.; *U.S. Private*, pg. 1399
ENGLEKIRK INSTITUTIONAL—See Englekirk Partners Consulting Structural Engineers, Inc.; *U.S. Private*, pg. 1400
ENGLEKIRK PARTNERS CONSULTING STRUCTURAL ENGINEERS, INC.; *U.S. Private*, pg. 1400
ENGLEKIRK & SABOL, INC.—See Englekirk Partners Consulting Structural Engineers, Inc.; *U.S. Private*, pg. 1400
ENGLEKIRK SYSTEMS DEVELOPMENT, INC.—See Englekirk Partners Consulting Structural Engineers, Inc.; *U.S. Private*, pg. 1400
ENGLOBAL U.S., INC.—See ENGlobal Corporation; *U.S. Public*, pg. 768
ENG SOON ENGINEERING (1999) PTE LTD—See ES Group (Holdings) Limited; *Int'l*, pg. 2500
ENG TEKNOLOGI HOLDINGS BHD.—See Giovanni Agnelli B.V.; *Int'l*, pg. 2978
ENKA PAZARLAMA IHRACAT ITHALAT AS—See Enka Insaat ve Sanayi A.S.; *Int'l*, pg. 2440
ENRICH TECH CO., LTD.—See Acter Co., Ltd.; *Int'l*, pg. 117
ENROBES 34—See FAYAT SAS; *Int'l*, pg. 2625
ENSHAM RESOURCES PTY. LTD.—See Idemitsu Kosan Co., Ltd.; *Int'l*, pg. 3590
ENSIGN DRILLING PARTNERSHIP - ENGINEERING, PROCUREMENT & CONSTRUCTION DIVISION—See Ensign Energy Services Inc.; *Int'l*, pg. 2446
ENSITE, INC.; *U.S. Private*, pg. 1402
ENTECH ENGINEERING INC.—See Entech Engineering Inc.; *U.S. Private*, pg. 1402
ENTERPRISE MARINE SERVICES LLC—See Enterprise Products Partners L.P.; *U.S. Public*, pg. 778
ENTERTAINMENT ENGINEERING INC.; *U.S. Private*, pg. 1404
ENTRIX AMERICAS, SA—See Cardno Limited; *Int'l*, pg. 1323
ENVAR ENGINEERS AND CONTRACTORS PTY. LTD.—See Downer EDI Limited; *Int'l*, pg. 2186
ENVERITY ENGINEERING, LLC; *U.S. Private*, pg. 1406
ENVIRO-HUB HOLDINGS LTD.; *Int'l*, pg. 2454
ENVIRONMENTAL ENGINEERING CONSULTANTS, INC.; *U.S. Private*, pg. 1407
ENVIRONMENTAL TECHNIQUES LIMITED—See New Mountain Capital, LLC; *U.S. Private*, pg. 2899
ENVOLVE ENGINEERING, LLC—See HomeValet, Inc.; *U.S. Private*, pg. 1975
E.ON NEW BUILD & TECHNOLOGY GMBH—See E.ON SE; *Int'l*, pg. 2254
EPADYM S.A.—See ELLAKTOR S.A.; *Int'l*, pg. 2365
EPCO CO., LTD.; *Int'l*, pg. 2458
EP-HOLDING GUINEE S.A.—See Energoprojekt Holding a.d.; *Int'l*, pg. 2421
EPIC SYSTEMS, INC.; *U.S. Private*, pg. 1413
EPIROC ARGENTINA S.A.C.I.—See Epiroc AB; *Int'l*, pg. 2461
EPIROC ARMENIA LLC—See Epiroc AB; *Int'l*, pg. 2461
EPIROC AUSTRALIA PTY LTD.—See Epiroc AB; *Int'l*, pg. 2461
EPIROC B-H D.O.O.—See Epiroc AB; *Int'l*, pg. 2461
EPIROC BOLIVIA EQUIPOS Y SERVICIOS S.A.—See Epiroc AB; *Int'l*, pg. 2461
EPIROC BOTSWANA (PTY) LTD.—See Epiroc AB; *Int'l*, pg. 2461
EPIROC BRASIL COMERCIALIZACAO DE PRODUTOS E SERVICOS PARA MINERACAO E CONSTRUCAO LTDA.—See Epiroc AB; *Int'l*, pg. 2461
EPIROC BURKINA FASO SARL—See Epiroc AB; *Int'l*, pg. 2461
EPIROC CANADA INC.—See Epiroc AB; *Int'l*, pg. 2461
EPIROC CHILE S.A.C.—See Epiroc AB; *Int'l*, pg. 2462
EPIROC COLOMBIA S.A.S.—See Epiroc AB; *Int'l*, pg. 2462
EPIROC CROATIA D.O.O.—See Epiroc AB; *Int'l*, pg. 2462
EPIROC CZECH REPUBLIC S.R.O.—See Epiroc AB; *Int'l*, pg. 2462
EPIROC DRC SARL—See Epiroc AB; *Int'l*, pg. 2462
EPIROC EASTERN AFRICA LTD.—See Epiroc AB; *Int'l*, pg. 2462
EPIROC HELLAS S.A.—See Epiroc AB; *Int'l*, pg. 2462
EPIROC HONG KONG LTD.—See Epiroc AB; *Int'l*, pg. 2462
EPIROC ITALIA S.R.L.—See Epiroc AB; *Int'l*, pg. 2462
EPIROC MEXICO, S.A. DE C. V.—See Epiroc AB; *Int'l*, pg. 2462
EPIROC MEYCO AG—See Epiroc AB; *Int'l*, pg. 2462
EPIROC MOCAMBIQUE LIMITADA—See Epiroc AB; *Int'l*, pg. 2462
EPIROC MONGOLIA LLC—See Epiroc AB; *Int'l*, pg. 2462

EPSILON SYSTEMS SOLUTIONS; *U.S. Private*, pg. 1414
EPSTEIN ARCHITECTURE & ENGINEERING SRL—See A. Epstein & Sons International, Inc.; *U.S. Private*, pg. 23
EPSTEIN CIVIL ENGINEERING, INC.—See A. Epstein & Sons International, Inc.; *U.S. Private*, pg. 23
EPSTEIN SP. Z O.O.—See A. Epstein & Sons International, Inc.; *U.S. Private*, pg. 23
EPTISA SERVICIOS DE INGENIERIA S.A.—See ARCADIS N.V.; *Int'l*, pg. 541
ERC INCORPORATED; *U.S. Private*, pg. 1417
ERDEMIR MUHENDISLIK YONETIM VE DANISMANLIK HIZMETLERI A.S.—See Eregli Demir Ve Celik Fabrikalari T.A.S.; *Int'l*, pg. 2490
ERICPOL AB—See Ericpol Sp. z o.o.; *Int'l*, pg. 2493
ERICPOL TZOV—See Ericpol Sp. z o.o.; *Int'l*, pg. 2493
ERIN ENGINEERING & RESEARCH INC.—See Gryphon Investors, LLC; *U.S. Private*, pg. 1798
ERNEST LOWE—See Hudaco Industries Limited; *Int'l*, pg. 3521
ERS—See FAYAT SAS; *Int'l*, pg. 2625
ESA PWA—See Environmental Science Associates; *U.S. Private*, pg. 1408
ESE CONSULTANTS, INC.—See Toll Brothers, Inc.; *U.S. Public*, pg. 2161
ESE CONSULTANTS, INC.—See Toll Brothers, Inc.; *U.S. Public*, pg. 2161
ESE ENERGY SDN. BHD.—See Harbour-Link Group Berhad; *Int'l*, pg. 3272
E&S ENVIRONMENTAL SERVICES LTD—See Sun Capital Partners, Inc.; *U.S. Private*, pg. 3861
E.S. FOX LIMITED; *Int'l*, pg. 2260
ESNAD COMPANY—See Alinma Bank; *Int'l*, pg. 329
ESOR AFRICA (PTY) LIMITED—See Esor Limited; *Int'l*, pg. 2504
ESORFRANKI CIVILS (PTY) LIMITED—See Esor Limited; *Int'l*, pg. 2504
ESOR LIMITED; *Int'l*, pg. 2504
ESPA CORP, INC.—See KCI Holdings Inc.; *U.S. Private*, pg. 2269
ESP ASSOCIATES, INC.—See Strength Capital Partners, LLC; *U.S. Private*, pg. 3839
ESPEC ENVIRONMENTAL CHAMBERS SALES & ENGINEERING LTD. STI.—See ESPEC Corp.; *Int'l*, pg. 2505
ESRG, LLC—See Caterpillar, Inc.; *U.S. Public*, pg. 452
ESSAI, INC.—See Advantest Corporation; *Int'l*, pg. 166
ESSEX WINDERMERE CORPORATION—See Northrop Grumman Corporation; *U.S. Public*, pg. 1540
ESS LABORATORY—See Thielsch Engineering, Inc.; *U.S. Private*, pg. 4144
ESTRELLA GROUP LTD; *Int'l*, pg. 2518
ESYS AUTOMATION, LLC—See Hitachi, Ltd.; *Int'l*, pg. 3423
ETABO ENERGIETECHNIK UND ANLAGENSERVICE GMBH—See ELKA Beteiligungs GmbH; *Int'l*, pg. 2364
ETC GROUP INC—See DIF Management Holding B.V.; *Int'l*, pg. 2117
ETCM SA—See Eiffage S.A.; *Int'l*, pg. 2331
ETHERIOS DESIGN SERVICES INC.—See Digi International Inc.; *U.S. Public*, pg. 662
ETION LIMITED; *Int'l*, pg. 2523
E T MACKENZIE OF FLORIDA INC—See E.T. Mackenzie Company; *U.S. Private*, pg. 1307
E-T-M ENTERPRISES INC.; *U.S. Private*, pg. 1303
ETS EFFICIENT TECHNICAL SOLUTIONS GMBH—See CEZ, a.s.; *Int'l*, pg. 1427
ETTE-CONSULTING OY—See Etteplan Oyj; *Int'l*, pg. 2524
ETTE-ENGINEERING OY—See Etteplan Oyj; *Int'l*, pg. 2524
ETTEPLAN CONSULTING (SHANGHAI) CO., LTD—See Etteplan Oyj; *Int'l*, pg. 2524
ETTEPLAN DESIGN CENTER OY—See Etteplan Oyj; *Int'l*, pg. 2524
ETTEPLAN INDUSTRITEKNIK AB—See Etteplan Oyj; *Int'l*, pg. 2525
ETTEPLAN INDUSTRY AB—See Etteplan Oyj; *Int'l*, pg. 2525
ETTEPLAN—See Etteplan Oyj; *Int'l*, pg. 2524
ETTEPLAN TECHNICAL SYSTEMS AB—See Etteplan Oyj; *Int'l*, pg. 2525
ETT PROYECTOS S.A.—See AFRY AB; *Int'l*, pg. 195
ETV-EROTERV RT.—See AFRY AB; *Int'l*, pg. 195
EUGENE ENGINEERING CO. LIMITED—See Hitachi, Ltd.; *Int'l*, pg. 3412
EURAFRICA BAUGESELLSCHAFT MBH—See ACS, Actividades de Construccion y Servicios, S.A.; *Int'l*, pg. 113
EURASIA CONSULT—See ARCADIS N.V.; *Int'l*, pg. 541
EURO AUTOMATION S.R.L.—See EuroGroup Laminations S.p.A.; *Int'l*, pg. 2552
EURO ENGINEERING AG—See Adecco Group AG; *Int'l*, pg. 141
EUROFINS EAG SANTA CLARA—See Eurofins Scientific S.E.; *Int'l*, pg. 2549
EUROINSTRUMENTS CIA. LTDA.—See Endress+Hauser (International) Holding AG; *Int'l*, pg. 2408
EUROPEAN AERONAUTIC DEFENSE AND SPACE CO.—See Airbus SE; *Int'l*, pg. 247
EUROSOND GMBH—See BERGER Holding GmbH; *Int'l*, pg. 979
EUROSYN DEVELOPPEMENT SAS—See Assystem S.A.; *Int'l*, pg. 651

CORPORATE AFFILIATIONS

EUTEK SYSTEMS, INC—See CRH plc; *Int'l*, pg. 1846
EVER-CLEAR ENVIRONMENTAL ENG CORP.; *Int'l*, pg. 2563
EVEREST EQUIPMENT CO.—See Alamo Group Inc.; *U.S. Public*, pg. 71
E-VOLVE SYSTEMS LLC—See The Graham Group, Inc.; *U.S. Private*, pg. 4036
EVOTECH S.A.S.—See Durr AG; *Int'l*, pg. 2232
EVZ LIMITED; *Int'l*, pg. 2574
EWE OFFSHORE SERVICE & SOLUTIONS GMBH—See EWE Aktiengesellschaft; *Int'l*, pg. 2575
EXCEL CORPORATION—See Cargill, Inc.; *U.S. Private*, pg. 758
EXCEL ENGINEERING, INCORPORATED—See Excel Group, Inc.; *U.S. Private*, pg. 1445
EXCEL INDUSTRIAL ELECTRONICS, INC.—See Regal Rexnord Corporation; *U.S. Public*, pg. 1772
EXCEL MIDSTREAM SOLUTIONS, INCORPORATED—See Excel Group, Inc.; *U.S. Private*, pg. 1445
EXIDA.COM LLC; *U.S. Private*, pg. 1448
EXODYNE, INC.; *U.S. Private*, pg. 1449
EXOSTRATEGIES, INC.—See Ensco Inc.; *U.S. Private*, pg. 1402
EXP GLOBAL INC.; *Int'l*, pg. 2586
EXPLEO ENGINEERING UK LTD—See Assystem S.A.; *Int'l*, pg. 651
EXPO GAS CONTAINERS LTD.; *Int'l*, pg. 2589
EXPONENT GMBH—See Exponent, Inc.; *U.S. Public*, pg. 812
EXPONENT, INC.-BOSTON AREA—See Exponent, Inc.; *U.S. Public*, pg. 812
EXPONENT, INC.-DETROIT AREA—See Exponent, Inc.; *U.S. Public*, pg. 812
EXPONENT, INC.-LOS ANGELES—See Exponent, Inc.; *U.S. Public*, pg. 812
EXPONENT, INC.-NEW YORK—See Exponent, Inc.; *U.S. Public*, pg. 812
EXPONENT, INC., PHILADELPHIA—See Exponent, Inc.; *U.S. Public*, pg. 812
EXPONENT INC.—See Exponent, Inc.; *U.S. Public*, pg. 812
EXPONENT—See Exponent, Inc.; *U.S. Public*, pg. 812
EXTIA—See Alten S.A.; *Int'l*, pg. 390
EXTREME ENGINEERING SOLUTIONS, INC.; *U.S. Private*, pg. 1452
EZLO, INC.; *U.S. Private*, pg. 1454
FABCOR TARGETCO LTD.—See MasTec, Inc.; *U.S. Public*, pg. 1393
FABRE ENGINEERING, INC.—See Bowman Consulting Group Ltd.; *U.S. Public*, pg. 376
FABRICOM OFFSHORE SERVICES LTD.—See ENGIE SA; *Int'l*, pg. 2429
FABRICOM OIL, GAS & POWER LIMITED—See ENGIE SA; *Int'l*, pg. 2429
FACILITY SOLUTIONS GROUP, INC.; *U.S. Private*, pg. 1460
FAIRWINDS INTERNATIONAL; *U.S. Private*, pg. 1465
FALLER, DAVIS & ASSOCIATES, INC.; *U.S. Private*, pg. 1468
FALLS CITY MACHINE TECHNOLOGY—See PMC Capital Partners, LLC; *U.S. Private*, pg. 3218
FAMIS GMBH—See E.ON SE; *Int'l*, pg. 2257
FARADAY TECHNOLOGY, INC.—See Physical Sciences Inc.; *U.S. Private*, pg. 3175
FAR EAST ENGINEERING SERVICES LIMITED—See FSE Services Group Limited; *Int'l*, pg. 2798
FAR EAST TECHNICAL SERVICES (MACAO) LIMITED—See FSE Services Group Limited; *Int'l*, pg. 2798
FARECO—See FAYAT SAS; *Int'l*, pg. 2625
FAURECIA USA HOLDINGS, INC.—See FORVIA SE; *Int'l*, pg. 2747
FAYAT BATIMENT SAS—See FAYAT SAS; *Int'l*, pg. 2625
FAYAT CONSTRUCTION ACHATS INVESTISSEMENTS—See FAYAT SAS; *Int'l*, pg. 2625
FAYAT SYSTEME D'INFORMATION—See FAYAT SAS; *Int'l*, pg. 2625
FAYAT TP—See FAYAT SAS; *Int'l*, pg. 2625
FAY, SPOFFORD & THORNDIKE, INC.; *U.S. Private*, pg. 1484
FBS GLOBAL LIMITED; *Int'l*, pg. 2627
FCAB INGENIERIA Y SERVICIOS LIMITADA—See Antofagasta plc; *Int'l*, pg. 484
FEDERAL CONTRACTING INC; *U.S. Private*, pg. 1487
FEDERAL HARDWARE ENGINEERING CO PTE LTD—See Federal International (2000) Ltd; *Int'l*, pg. 2630
FEDERAL-MOGUL (CHINA) CO., LTD.—See Apollo Global Management, Inc.; *U.S. Public*, pg. 160
FEDERAL-MOGUL ENGINEERING LIMITED—See Apollo Global Management, Inc.; *U.S. Public*, pg. 162
FEDERAL RESOURCES SERVICES PTE LTD—See Federal International (2000) Ltd; *Int'l*, pg. 2630
FEINTOOL EQUIPMENT CORP.—See Artemis Holding AG; *U.S. Public*, pg. 582
FELGUERA GRUAS INDIA PRIVATE LIMITED—See Duro Felguera, S.A.; *Int'l*, pg. 2228
FELGUERA-IHI S.A.—See Duro Felguera, S.A.; *Int'l*, pg. 2229

N.A.I.C.S. INDEX

541330 — ENGINEERING SERVICE...

FELGUERA-IHI S.A.—See IHI Corporation; *Int'l*, pg. 3604
FELICITY SCIENTIFIC CO., LTD.—See FEV GmbH; *Int'l*, pg. 2648
FELIX CONSTRUCTIONS SA—See FAYAT SAS; *Int'l*, pg. 2625
FERROVIAL SERVICES US, INC.—See Apollo Global Management, Inc.; *U.S. Public*, pg. 166
FERROVIAL SERVICIOS AMBIENTALES S.A.—See Apollo Global Management, Inc.; *U.S. Public*, pg. 166
FEV AMERICA LATINA LTDA.—See FEV GmbH; *Int'l*, pg. 2648
FEV CHINA CO., LTD.—See FEV GmbH; *Int'l*, pg. 2648
FEV FRANCE S.A.S.—See FEV GmbH; *Int'l*, pg. 2648
FEV GMBH; *Int'l*, pg. 2648
FEV IBERIA SL—See FEV GmbH; *Int'l*, pg. 2648
FEV, INC.—See FEV GmbH; *Int'l*, pg. 2648
FEV INDIA PRIVATE LIMITED—See FEV GmbH; *Int'l*, pg. 2648
FEV INDIA PVT. LTD.—See FEV GmbH; *Int'l*, pg. 2648
FEV ITALIA S.R.L—See FEV GmbH; *Int'l*, pg. 2648
FEV JAPAN CO., LTD.—See FEV GmbH; *Int'l*, pg. 2648
FEV KOREA LTD.—See FEV GmbH; *Int'l*, pg. 2648
FEV NORTH AMERICA, INC.; *U.S. Private*, pg. 1500
FEV POLSKA SP. Z O.O.—See FEV GmbH; *Int'l*, pg. 2648
FEV SVERIGE AB—See FEV GmbH; *Int'l*, pg. 2648
FEV TR OTOMOTIV VE ENERJI ARASTIRMA VE MUHENDISLIK LTD. STI.—See FEV GmbH; *Int'l*, pg. 2648
FEV UK LTD.—See FEV GmbH; *Int'l*, pg. 2648
FFE INVEST A/S—See FLSmidth & Co. A/S; *Int'l*, pg. 2710
FFT ESPANA TECNOLOGIAS DE AUTOMOCION S.A.—See Fosun International Limited; *Int'l*, pg. 2750
FFT MEXICO S.A. DE C.V.—See Fosun International Limited; *Int'l*, pg. 2750
FFT PRODUCTION SYSTEMS, INC.—See Fosun International Limited; *Int'l*, pg. 2751
FFT PRODUCTION SYSTEMS (SHANGHAI) CO., LTD.—See Fosun International Limited; *Int'l*, pg. 2750
FFT PRODUCTION SYSTEMS S.R.L.—See Fosun International Limited; *Int'l*, pg. 2751
F.H. PAPENMEIER GMBH & CO. KG; *Int'l*, pg. 2596
FIDELITY ENGINEERING CORP. - ASHBURN—See Fidelity Engineering LLC; *U.S. Private*, pg. 1502
FIDELITY ENGINEERING LLC; *U.S. Private*, pg. 1502
FIELDAIR HOLDINGS LIMITED—See Freightways Group Limited; *Int'l*, pg. 2771
FIELDDATA.IO GMBH—See BAUER Aktiengesellschaft; *Int'l*, pg. 893
FIGEAC AERO NORTH AMERICA, INC—See Figeac-Aero SA; *Int'l*, pg. 2660
FIMA TECHNOLOGY SDN. BHD.—See Fima Corporation Berhad; *Int'l*, pg. 2663
FINCANTIERI (SHANGHAI) TRADING CO. LTD.—See Fincantieri S.p.A.; *Int'l*, pg. 2671
FINELLI CONSULTING ENGINEERS, INC.; *U.S. Private*, pg. 1509
FINFROCK; *U.S. Private*, pg. 1509
FIRST BROTHERS DEVELOPMENT CO., LTD.—See First Brothers Co., Ltd.; *Int'l*, pg. 2682
THE FITZPATRICK COMPANY EUROPE N.V.—See IDEX Corp; *U.S. Public*, pg. 1092
FITZPATRICK ENGINEERING GROUP, PLLC—See Structura, Inc.; *U.S. Private*, pg. 3841
FIVES, SOCIETE ANONYME; *Int'l*, pg. 2696
FLAGSHIP CONSTRUCTION CO., LLC—See National Construction Enterprises Inc.; *U.S. Private*, pg. 2851
FLETCHER BUILDING NETHERLANDS B.V.—See Fletcher Building Limited; *Int'l*, pg. 2700
FLETCHER CONSTRUCTION COMPANY (FIJI) LIMITED—See Fletcher Building Limited; *Int'l*, pg. 2700
FLEXTRONICS CANADA DESIGN SERVICES, INC.—See Flex Ltd.; *Int'l*, pg. 2702
FLEXTRONICS DESIGN SRL—See Flex Ltd.; *Int'l*, pg. 2702
FLEXTRONICS EMS CANADA INC.—See Flex Ltd.; *Int'l*, pg. 2702
FLEXTRONICS INTERNATIONAL GMBH—See Flex Ltd.; *Int'l*, pg. 2702
FLEXTRONICS INTERNATIONAL LTD. - ASIA PACIFIC REGIONAL HEADQUARTERS—See Flex Ltd.; *Int'l*, pg. 2702
FLEXTRONICS INTERNATIONAL—See Flex Ltd.; *Int'l*, pg. 2702
FLEXTRONICS INTERNATIONAL SWEDEN AB—See Flex Ltd.; *Int'l*, pg. 2703
FLEXTRONICS INTERNATIONAL TECHNOLOGIA LTDA.—See Flex Ltd.; *Int'l*, pg. 2703
FLIRI & CONRAD ELECTRO, ZNL DER ELECTRA BUIN S.A.—See Burkhalter Holding AG; *Int'l*, pg. 1225
FLI WATER LIMITED—See FLI International Limited; *Int'l*, pg. 2705
FLORIDA DESIGN CONSULTANTS, INC.; *U.S. Private*, pg. 1548
FLOTA PROYECTOS SINGULARES, S.A—See ACS, Actividades de Construccion y Servicios, S.A.; *Int'l*, pg. 111
FLOTRON AG—See BKW AG; *Int'l*, pg. 1055
FLOWSERVE - AL MANSOORI SERVICES COMPANY LTD.—See Flowserve Corporation; *U.S. Public*, pg. 855
FLOYD PCL; *Int'l*, pg. 2709

FLSMIDTH A/S—See FLSmidth & Co. A/S; *Int'l*, pg. 2710
FLSMIDTH INDUSTRIAL SOLUTIONS (CANADA) INC.—See FLSmidth & Co. A/S; *Int'l*, pg. 2710
FLS PLAST A/S—See FLSmidth & Co. A/S; *Int'l*, pg. 2710
FLUGPLATZ WERNEUCHEN GMBH—See BERGER Holding GmbH; *Int'l*, pg. 979
FLUOR BRASIL, LTDA.—See Fluor Corporation; *U.S. Public*, pg. 858
FLUOR CANADA LTD—See Fluor Corporation; *U.S. Public*, pg. 858
FLUOR CHILE INGENIERIA Y CONSTRUCCION S.A.—See Fluor Corporation; *U.S. Public*, pg. 858
FLUOR CHILE S.A.—See Fluor Corporation; *U.S. Public*, pg. 858
FLUOR CONSTRUCTORS CANADA LTD—See Fluor Corporation; *U.S. Public*, pg. 858
FLUOR DANIEL CARIBBEAN, INC—See Fluor Corporation; *U.S. Public*, pg. 858
FLUOR DANIEL ENGINEERS & CONSTRUCTORS, INC—See Fluor Corporation; *U.S. Public*, pg. 858
FLUOR DANIEL INDIA PRIVATE LIMITED—See Fluor Corporation; *U.S. Public*, pg. 858
FLUOR ENGENHARIA E PROJETOS S.A—See Fluor Corporation; *U.S. Public*, pg. 858
FLUOR FEDERAL SERVICES INC.—See Fluor Corporation; *U.S. Public*, pg. 858
FLUOR HEAVY CIVIL, LLC—See Fluor Corporation; *U.S. Public*, pg. 859
FLUOR PLANT ENGINEERING, S.A.—See Fluor Corporation; *U.S. Public*, pg. 859
FLUOR SUPPLY CHAIN SOLUTIONS LLC—See Fluor Corporation; *U.S. Public*, pg. 859
FOCUS DYNAMICS GROUP BERHAD; *Int'l*, pg. 2719
FONTANIE—See Eiffage S.A.; *Int'l*, pg. 2331
FORCLUMECA ANTILLES GUYANE—See Eiffage S.A.; *Int'l*, pg. 2331
FORD, BACON AND DAVIS, LLC—See S&B Engineers & Constructors, Ltd.; *U.S. Private*, pg. 3512
FORESITE GROUP, INC.; *U.S. Private*, pg. 1566
FORGE ENGINEERING, INC.—See Cobepa S.A.; *Int'l*, pg. 1683
FORGES TARDIEU LTD; *Int'l*, pg. 2733
FORMAPHARM ENGINEERING GROUP D.O.O.; *Int'l*, pg. 2733
FORMAPHARM ENGINEERING GROUP—See FormaPharm Engineering Group d.o.o.; *Int'l*, pg. 2733
FORMEL D GMBH—See 3i Group plc; *Int'l*, pg. 8
FORMWORK & SCAFFOLDING PTY LIMITED—See Anchorage Capital Partners Pty. Limited; *Int'l*, pg. 448
FORTACO ZRT.; *Int'l*, pg. 2737
FORTUNE ELECTRIC EXTRA HIGH VOLTAGE CO., LTD.—See Fortune Electric Co., Ltd.; *Int'l*, pg. 2743
FORTUNE TRIUMPH SDN. BHD.—See Dayang Enterprise Holdings Berhad; *Int'l*, pg. 1985
FOSTER AND PARTNERS (HONG KONG) LIMITED—See Foster + Partners Ltd.; *Int'l*, pg. 2749
FOTH PRODUCTION SOLUTIONS, LLC—See Foth & Van Dyke & Associates Inc.; *U.S. Private*, pg. 1579
FOTH & VAN DYKE & ASSOCIATES INC.; *U.S. Private*, pg. 1579
THE FOURTH CONSTRUCTION CORPORATION—See China National Chemical Engineering Co., Ltd.; *Int'l*, pg. 1531
FOWLERS ASPHALTING PTY. LIMITED—See Downer EDI Limited; *Int'l*, pg. 2186
FPCO ENGINEERING, LTD.—See FP Corporation; *Int'l*, pg. 2756
FRANKI AFRICA (PTY) LIMITED—See Esor Limited; *Int'l*, pg. 2504
FRANKI FONDATION—See FAYAT SAS; *Int'l*, pg. 2625
FRANK M. BOOTH DESIGN BUILD CO.—See Frank M. Booth Inc.; *U.S. Private*, pg. 1595
FRANK'S INTERNATIONAL AS—See Expro Group Holdings N.V.; *Int'l*, pg. 2591
FRANK'S INTERNATIONAL C.V.—See Expro Group Holdings N.V.; *Int'l*, pg. 2591
FRANK'S INTERNATIONAL, LLC—See Expro Group Holdings N.V.; *Int'l*, pg. 2591
FRASER & CHALMERS SIYAKHA (PTY) LIMITED—See Aveng Limited; *Int'l*, pg. 738
FRAZER-NASH AUSTRALIA PTY. LTD.—See KBR, Inc.; *U.S. Public*, pg. 1215
FRAZER-NASH CONSULTANCY (AUSTRALIA) PTY LTD—See KBR, Inc.; *U.S. Public*, pg. 1215
FRAZER-NASH CONSULTANCY LTD.—See KBR, Inc.; *U.S. Public*, pg. 1215
FREEDOM FUELS AUSTRALIA PTY. LTD.—See Idemitsu Kosan Co., Ltd.; *Int'l*, pg. 3590
THE FREEDOM GROUP OF COMPANIES LIMITED—See Grovepoint Capital LLP; *Int'l*, pg. 3112
FREELANCE TECHNICAL ASSOCIATES, INC.; *U.S. Private*, pg. 1604
FREELAND & KAUFFMAN, INC.—See LJA Engineering, Inc.; *U.S. Private*, pg. 2474
FREESE & NICHOLS INC.; *U.S. Private*, pg. 1607
FREESIA TRADING CO., LTD.—See Freesia Macross Corporation; *Int'l*, pg. 2771

FRENCKEN AMERICA INC.—See Frencken Group Limited; *Int'l*, pg. 2772
FRENCKEN ENGINEERING B.V.—See Frencken Group Limited; *Int'l*, pg. 2772
FRENCKEN EUROPE B.V.—See Frencken Group Limited; *Int'l*, pg. 2772
FRITZ WEGMANN ELEKTRISCHE ANLAGEN AG—See Burkhalter Holding AG; *Int'l*, pg. 1225
FROG DESIGN S.R.L—See Flex Ltd.; *Int'l*, pg. 2704
FST ENGINEERS, INC.—See Fay, Spofford & Thorndike, Inc.; *U.S. Private*, pg. 1484
FTC SOLAR, INC.; *U.S. Public*, pg. 888
FTT DEUTSCHLAND GMBH—See Kratos Defense & Security Solutions, Inc.; *U.S. Public*, pg. 1276
FUDO TETRA CORPORATION; *Int'l*, pg. 2804
FUELING SYSTEMS CONTRACTORS, LLC—See Quanta Services, Inc.; *U.S. Public*, pg. 1751
FUELPOSITIVE CORPORATION; *Int'l*, pg. 2804
FUGRO CHANCE, INC.—See Fugro N.V.; *Int'l*, pg. 2805
FUGRO CONSULTANTS, INC.—See Fugro N.V.; *Int'l*, pg. 2805
FUGRO CONSULTANTS, INC.—See Fugro N.V.; *Int'l*, pg. 2805
FUGRO CONSULT KFT.—See Fugro N.V.; *Int'l*, pg. 2805
FUGRO-ELBOCON B.V.—See Fugro N.V.; *Int'l*, pg. 2807
FUGRO FRANCE S.A.S.—See Fugro N.V.; *Int'l*, pg. 2806
FUGRO GEOCONSULTING, INC.—See Fugro N.V.; *Int'l*, pg. 2805
FUGRO GEOTECHNIQUE; *Int'l*, pg. 2805
FUGRO GEOTECH (PVT) LTD.—See Fugro N.V.; *Int'l*, pg. 2806
FUGRO GHANA LIMITED—See Fugro N.V.; *Int'l*, pg. 2806
FUGRO HONG KONG, LTD.—See Fugro N.V.; *Int'l*, pg. 2806
FUGRO-INPARK B.V.—See Fugro N.V.; *Int'l*, pg. 2807
FUGRO INTERSITE B.V.—See Fugro N.V.; *Int'l*, pg. 2807
FUGRO JAPAN CO., LTD.—See Fugro N.V.; *Int'l*, pg. 2806
FUGRO LTD.—See Fugro N.V.; *Int'l*, pg. 2806
FUGRO MALAYSIA—See Fugro N.V.; *Int'l*, pg. 2806
FUGRO MIDDLE EAST B.V.—See Fugro N.V.; *Int'l*, pg. 2806
FUGRO NETHERLANDS MARINE BV—See Fugro N.V.; *Int'l*, pg. 2807
FUGRO PENINSULAR—See Fugro N.V.; *Int'l*, pg. 2806
FUGRO RUE AS—See Fugro N.V.; *Int'l*, pg. 2807
FUGRO SINGAPORE PTE LTD.—See Fugro N.V.; *Int'l*, pg. 2807
FUGRO SUBSEA SERVICES AUSTRALIA PTY LTD.—See Fugro N.V.; *Int'l*, pg. 2807
FUGRO VASTGOED B.V.—See Fugro N.V.; *Int'l*, pg. 2807
FUGRO WILLIAM LETTIS & ASSOCIATES, INC.—See Fugro N.V.; *Int'l*, pg. 2805
FUJIAN TENDERING CO., LTD.; *Int'l*, pg. 2820
FUJIAN YONGFU POWER ENGINEERING CO., LTD.; *Int'l*, pg. 2820
FUJI CAC JOINT STOCK COMPANY—See Fuji Electric Co., Ltd.; *Int'l*, pg. 2811
FUJIFILM ENGINEERING CO., LTD.—See FUJIFILM Holdings Corporation; *Int'l*, pg. 2824
FUJI FURUKAWA E&C (CAMBODIA) CO. LTD.—See Fuji Furukawa Engineering & Construction Co., Ltd.; *Int'l*, pg. 2813
FUJI FURUKAWA E&C (MALAYSIA) SDN. BHD.—See Fuji Furukawa Engineering & Construction Co., Ltd.; *Int'l*, pg. 2813
FUJI FURUKAWA E&C (MYANMAR) CO., LTD.—See Fuji Furukawa Engineering & Construction Co., Ltd.; *Int'l*, pg. 2813
FUJI FURUKAWA E&C (VIETNAM) CO., LTD.—See Fuji Furukawa Engineering & Construction Co., Ltd.; *Int'l*, pg. 2813
FUJI FURUKAWA ENGINEERING & CONSTRUCTION CO., LTD.; *Int'l*, pg. 2813
FUJI P.S CORPORATION; *Int'l*, pg. 2816
FUKUYAMA CONSULTANTS COMPANY LIMITED; *Int'l*, pg. 2841
FULGHUM MACINDOE & ASSOCIATES, INC.—See Littlejohn & Co., LLC; *U.S. Private*, pg. 2469
FULL SERVICE FACILITY SOLUTIONS—See M.A. Mortenson Company; *U.S. Private*, pg. 2527
FULLWEALTH INTERNATIONAL GROUP HOLDINGS LIMITED; *Int'l*, pg. 2843
FUNA INTERNATIONAL B.V.—See L3Harris Technologies, Inc.; *U.S. Public*, pg. 1281
FURGO-SUHAIMI LTD.—See Fugro N.V.; *Int'l*, pg. 2806
FURMANITE AB—See Team, Inc.; *U.S. Public*, pg. 1987
FURMANITE AS—See Team, Inc.; *U.S. Public*, pg. 1987
FURMANITE BV—See Team, Inc.; *U.S. Public*, pg. 1987
FURMANITE CANADA CORP—See Team, Inc.; *U.S. Public*, pg. 1987
FURMANITE GMBH—See Team, Inc.; *U.S. Public*, pg. 1988
FURMANITE (MALAYSIA) SDN. BHD.—See Team, Inc.; *U.S. Public*, pg. 1987
FURMANITE SAS—See Team, Inc.; *U.S. Public*, pg. 1987
FURMANITE SINGAPORE PTE LTD.—See Team, Inc.; *U.S. Public*, pg. 1987
FURUNO CIRCUITECH CO., LTD.—See Furuno Electric Co., Ltd.; *Int'l*, pg. 2847
FUTURE ELECTRICAL CONTROL CO., LTD.—See Gunkul Engineering Co., Ltd.; *Int'l*, pg. 3183

541330 — ENGINEERING SERVICE...

FUTURE RESEARCH, CORPORATION; *U.S. Private*, pg. 1627
GABRIELLE—See FAYAT SAS; *Int'l*, pg. 2625
GAI CONSULTANTS, INC.—See Comvest Group Holdings LLC; *U.S. Private*, pg. 1007
GAI CONSULTANTS INC.—See Comvest Group Holdings LLC; *U.S. Private*, pg. 1007
GAI CONSULTANTS INC.—See Comvest Group Holdings LLC; *U.S. Private*, pg. 1007
GALFAR ENGINEERING & CONTRACTING SAOG; *Int'l*, pg. 2872
GALLATI AG—See Burkhalter Holding AG; *Int'l*, pg. 1225
GALLIFORD TRY PARTNERSHIPS LIMITED—See Galliford Try Holdings plc; *Int'l*, pg. 2874
GALLIFORD TRY PLANT LIMITED—See Galliford Try Holdings plc; *Int'l*, pg. 2874
GAME INGENIERIE S.A.S—See Eiffage S.A.; *Int'l*, pg. 2331
GAMMON AND BILLIMORIA LLC—See Gammon India Limited; *Int'l*, pg. 2879
GAMMON INTERNATIONAL, FZE—See Gammon India Limited; *Int'l*, pg. 2879
GAMMON PAKISTAN LIMITED; *Int'l*, pg. 2879
GAN CORPORATION; *U.S. Private*, pg. 1641
GANNETT FLEMING, INC. - BALTIMORE—See OceanSound Partners, LP; *U.S. Private*, pg. 2991
GANNETT FLEMING, INC. - ROSEVILLE—See OceanSound Partners, LP; *U.S. Private*, pg. 2991
GANNETT FLEMING, INC.—See OceanSound Partners, LP; *U.S. Private*, pg. 2991
GANNETT FLEMING, INC. - TAMPA (CORPORATE LAKE DRIVE), FL—See OceanSound Partners, LP; *U.S. Private*, pg. 2991
GANTECH, INC.—See Sagewind Capital LLC; *U.S. Private*, pg. 3527
GARAVENTA AG—See Doppelmayr Group; *Int'l*, pg. 2175
GARAVENTA ALGERIE SARL—See Doppelmayr Group; *Int'l*, pg. 2175
GARDEN REACH SHIPBUILDERS & ENGINEERS LTD.; *Int'l*, pg. 2884
THE GARDNER ZEMKE COMPANY - MECHANICAL DIVISION—See The Gardner Zemke Company; *U.S. Private*, pg. 4032
GARRY STRUTHERS ASSOCIATES, INC.; *U.S. Private*, pg. 1646
GAS TRANSMISSION SYSTEMS, INC.—See Goldberg Lindsay & Co., LLC; *U.S. Private*, pg. 1729
GAS TURBINE EFFICIENCY, LLC; *U.S. Private*, pg. 1647
GATEWAY CONSTRUCTION & ENGINEERING LTD.; *Int'l*, pg. 2889
GAUDET ASSOCIATES, INC.—See NV5 Global, Inc.; *U.S. Public*, pg. 1557
GAUDFRIN; *Int'l*, pg. 2890
GAVAN & BARKER, INC.—See Huitt-Zollars, Inc.; *U.S. Private*, pg. 2004
GAYATRI PROJECTS LTD; *Int'l*, pg. 2891
GAZTRANSPORT ET TECHNIGAZ SA; *Int'l*, pg. 2892
GDB GEOTECHNICS SDN. BHD.—See GDB Holdings Berhad; *Int'l*, pg. 2896
GEA ENGENHARIA DE PROCESSOS E SISTEMAS INDUSTRIAIS LTDA.—See GEA Group Aktiengesellschaft; *Int'l*, pg. 2898
GEA FILTRATION INC.—See GEA Group Aktiengesellschaft; *Int'l*, pg. 2899
GEA GROUP AKTIENGESELLSCHAFT; *Int'l*, pg. 2897
GEA MESSO PT—See GEA Group Aktiengesellschaft; *Int'l*, pg. 2901
GEA NIRO PT B.V.—See GEA Group Aktiengesellschaft; *Int'l*, pg. 2901
GEA PROCESS ENGINEERING CHINA LIMITED—See GEA Group Aktiengesellschaft; *Int'l*, pg. 2901
GEA PROCESS ENGINEERING IRELAND LTD—See GEA Group Aktiengesellschaft; *Int'l*, pg. 2901
GEA PROCESS ENGINEERING PTY. LTD.—See GEA Group Aktiengesellschaft; *Int'l*, pg. 2902
GEA PROCESS ENGINEERING S.A.S.—See GEA Group Aktiengesellschaft; *Int'l*, pg. 2902
GEA PROCESS ENGINEERING S.R.O.—See GEA Group Aktiengesellschaft; *Int'l*, pg. 2902
GEA REFRIGERATION NORTH AMERICA INC.—See GEA Group Aktiengesellschaft; *Int'l*, pg. 2902
GEBERIT KFT—See Geberit AG; *Int'l*, pg. 2904
GECI ENGINEERING SERVICES SRL—See GECI International SA; *Int'l*, pg. 2909
GECI INTERNATIONAL SA; *Int'l*, pg. 2909
GEC, INC.; *U.S. Private*, pg. 1655
GEEKAY WIRES LTD.; *Int'l*, pg. 2911
GE ENGINE SERVICES DISTRIBUTION, LLC—See General Electric Company; *U.S. Public*, pg. 916
THE GEL GROUP, INC.; *U.S. Private*, pg. 4032
GEMCO ENGINEERS B.V.; *Int'l*, pg. 2915
GEMINI CORPORATION; *Int'l*, pg. 2916
GEMINI ENGINEERED SOLUTIONS LP—See Gemini Corporation; *Int'l*, pg. 2916
GEMINI ENGINEERING LIMITED—See Gemini Corporation; *Int'l*, pg. 2916
GEMINI FIELD SOLUTIONS LP—See Gemini Corporation; *Int'l*, pg. 2916

GEMINI MANAGEMENT LTD.—See Avio Global, Inc.; *U.S. Private*, pg. 407
GEMINYS S.L.—See Construcciones y Auxiliar de Ferrocarriles S.A.; *Int'l*, pg. 1777
GEMMA PLANT OPERATIONS, LLC—See Argan, Inc.; *U.S. Public*, pg. 191
GE MOZAMBIQUE LIMITADA—See Westinghouse Air Brake Technologies Corporation; *U.S. Public*, pg. 2358
GENERAL DYNAMICS MISSION SYSTEMS, INC.—See General Dynamics Corporation; *U.S. Public*, pg. 915
GENESIS GROUP INC.; *U.S. Private*, pg. 1669
GENESYS ENGINEERING, P.C.—See Willdan Group, Inc.; *U.S. Private*, pg. 2370
GENMECH ENGINEERING (S) PTE. LTD.—See Embelton Limited; *Int'l*, pg. 2375
GENSOL ENGINEERING LTD.; *Int'l*, pg. 2928
GENTEX GMBH—See Gentex Corporation; *U.S. Public*, pg. 931
GEOCAPITOL ENGINEERING LLC—See Terracon Consultants, Inc.; *U.S. Private*, pg. 3971
GEODESIGN, INC.—See NV5 Global, Inc.; *U.S. Public*, pg. 1557
GEO-MARINE, INC.—See Kingswood Capital Management LLC; *U.S. Private*, pg. 2312
GEOMET S.R.O.—See European Metals Holdings Limited; *Int'l*, pg. 2557
GEOPIER FOUNDATION COMPANY—See Commercial Metals Company; *U.S. Public*, pg. 547
GEOPOINT SURVEYING, INC.; *U.S. Private*, pg. 1681
GEORG FISCHER GIESSEREITECHNOLOGIE GMBH—See Georg Fischer AG; *Int'l*, pg. 2935
GEOSOLUTIONS, LLC—See Peak Rock Capital LLC; *U.S. Private*, pg. 3124
GEOST LLC—See ATL Partners, LLC; *U.S. Private*, pg. 369
GEOTECH HOLDINGS LTD.; *Int'l*, pg. 2941
GEOTECH PTY LTD.—See Acciona, S.A.; *Int'l*, pg. 90
GER2I—See Eiffage S.A.; *Int'l*, pg. 2331
GETC ASIA PRIVATE LIMITED—See CNA Group Ltd.; *Int'l*, pg. 1673
GET SOLUTIONS, INC.; *U.S. Private*, pg. 1688
GEYSER HPC, S.A.U.—See HPC AG; *Int'l*, pg. 3500
GFA INTERNATIONAL, INC.—See Universal Engineering Sciences, LLC; *U.S. Private*, pg. 4304
GHAFARI ASSOCIATES, L.L.C.; *U.S. Private*, pg. 1690
GHD LIMITED—See GHD Group Pty Ltd.; *Int'l*, pg. 2959
GHD S.A.—See GHD Group Pty Ltd.; *Int'l*, pg. 2959
GIBBS & COX INC.—See Leidos Holdings, Inc.; *U.S. Public*, pg. 1304
GIBSON ENGINEERING COMPANY, INC.—See Applied Industrial Technologies, Inc.; *U.S. Public*, pg. 171
GIBUNCO MECHANICAL LTD—See Gibunco Group Limited; *Int'l*, pg. 2963
GI ENGINEERING SOLUTIONS LIMITED; *Int'l*, pg. 2960
GIKEN HOLDINGS CO., LTD.; *Int'l*, pg. 2972
GIKEN KOGYO CO., LTD.; *Int'l*, pg. 2972
GILMORE & ASSOCIATES INC.; *U.S. Private*, pg. 1701
GIMHAE TECHNO VALLEY CO., LTD.—See Hanwha Group; *Int'l*, pg. 3264
GIPPSLAND ASPHALT PTY. LTD.—See Downer EDI Limited; *Int'l*, pg. 2186
GIRIRAJ CIVIL DEVELOPERS LTD.; *Int'l*, pg. 2979
GIS SURVEYORS, INC.; *U.S. Private*, pg. 1702
GITEC CONSULT GMBH; *Int'l*, pg. 2979
G.K. ASSEMBLY CO., LTD.—See Gunkul Engineering Co., Ltd.; *Int'l*, pg. 3183
GKN SINTER METALS ENGINEERING GMBH—See GKN plc; *Int'l*, pg. 2985
GKW LIMITED; *Int'l*, pg. 2986
GLASSTECH INC.; *U.S. Private*, pg. 1707
GLENCORE TECHNOLOGY PTY. LTD.—See Glencore plc; *Int'l*, pg. 2991
GLENMOUNT GLOBAL SOLUTIONS, INC.—See The Graham Group, Inc.; *U.S. Private*, pg. 4036
GLOBAL CATHODIC PROTECTION, INC.—See Hancom, Inc.; *Int'l*, pg. 3242
GLOBAL ECONOMIC ADVANTAGE PVT LTD; *Int'l*, pg. 2995
GLOBAL ENERGY SERVICES LIMITED—See Global Energy (Holdings) Ltd.; *Int'l*, pg. 2995
GLOBAL ENGINEERING SERVICE CO., LTD.—See Chugoku Marine Paints, Ltd.; *Int'l*, pg. 1595
GLOBAL ENGINEERING SOLUTIONS, INC.; *U.S. Private*, pg. 1713
GLOBAL INFRASTRUCTURE SOLUTIONS, INC.; *U.S. Private*, pg. 1714
GLOBAL MARINE CABLE SYSTEMS PTE, LTD—See INNOVATE Corp.; *U.S. Public*, pg. 1126
GLOBAL PORT SERVICES LIMITED—See Global Energy (Holdings) Ltd.; *Int'l*, pg. 2995
GLOBAL PROJECT (SERVICES) LTD—See Blue Water Energy LLP; *Int'l*, pg. 1070
GLOBAL SCIENCE & TECHNOLOGY INC.; *U.S. Private*, pg. 1717
GLOBAL SCS LTD—See Global Energy (Holdings) Ltd.; *Int'l*, pg. 2995
GLOBAL SURFACES LIMITED; *Int'l*, pg. 3001
GLOBAL SYSTEMS TECHNOLOGIES, INC.—See Broadtree Partners, LLC; *U.S. Private*, pg. 659

GLOBAL TCC—See Global Energy (Holdings) Ltd.; *Int'l*, pg. 2995
GLOBAL TECHNOLOGY ASSOCIATES, LLC—See Kelly Services, Inc.; *U.S. Public*, pg. 1218
GLOBAL TECHNOLOGY ASSOCIATES, LTD.; *U.S. Private*, pg. 1718
GLOBAL TOKEN LIMITED; *Int'l*, pg. 3001
GLORIETA GEOSCIENCE, INC.—See GZA GeoEnvironmental Inc.; *U.S. Private*, pg. 1822
GLOSTEN, INC.; *U.S. Private*, pg. 1720
GLOW NETWORKS, INC.; *U.S. Private*, pg. 1721
GLOW NETWORKS PVT LTD—See Glow Networks, Inc.; *U.S. Private*, pg. 1721
GLUCOTRACK, INC.; *Int'l*, pg. 3011
GMB ENGINEERS & PLANNERS INC.—See Vanasse Hangen Brustlin, Inc.; *U.S. Private*, pg. 4342
GMUNDNERBERG HOLDING GMBH—See Fresenius SE & Co. KGaA; *Int'l*, pg. 2778
GNOSTECH, INC. - SAN DIEGO—See Gnostech, Inc.; *U.S. Private*, pg. 1723
GNOSTECH, INC.; *U.S. Private*, pg. 1723
GOAL VERWALTUNGSGESELLSCHAFT MBH & CO. PROJEKT NR. 5 KG I.L.—See Deutsche Lufthansa AG; *Int'l*, pg. 2066
GOELLNER, INC.; *U.S. Private*, pg. 1726
GOLDBELT ORCA, LLC—See Gold Belt Incorporated; *U.S. Private*, pg. 1727
GOLDTEK TECHNOLOGY (SHENZHENG) CO., LTD.—See Ennoconn Corporation; *Int'l*, pg. 2443
GONZALEZ DESIGN ENGINEERING COMPANY INC.; *U.S. Private*, pg. 1737
GONZALEZ MANUFACTURING TECHNOLOGIES; *U.S. Private*, pg. 1737
GOODTECH ASA; *Int'l*, pg. 3041
GOODTECH PROJECTS & SERVICES AB—See Goodtech ASA; *Int'l*, pg. 3041
GOODTECH SOLUTIONS AS—See Goodtech ASA; *Int'l*, pg. 3041
GOODTECH SOLUTIONS KARLSTAD AB—See Goodtech ASA; *Int'l*, pg. 3041
GOODWIN REFRACTORY SERVICES LIMITED—See Goodwin PLC; *Int'l*, pg. 3041
GOVIND DEVELOPMENT, LLC; *U.S. Private*, pg. 1746
GPA TECHNOLOGIES, INC.; *U.S. Private*, pg. 1747
GPE-PLAST ENGINEERING GMBH—See capiton AG; *Int'l*, pg. 1314
GPT CONCRETE PRODUCTS SOUTH AFRICA (PTY.) LIMITED—See GPT Infraprojects Limited; *Int'l*, pg. 3047
GPT INFRAPROJECTS LIMITED; *Int'l*, pg. 3047
GRAEF-USA, INC.; *U.S. Private*, pg. 1750
GRAND ISLE SHIPYARD INC. - FABRICATION FACILITY—See Nana Regional Corporation, Inc.; *U.S. Private*, pg. 2832
GRANHERNE PTY LTD—See KBR, Inc.; *U.S. Public*, pg. 1215
GRAYCLIFF ENTERPRISES, INC.; *U.S. Private*, pg. 1760
GRAYCLIFF ENTERPRISES, INC. - TUCSON OFFICE—See Graycliff Enterprises, Inc.; *U.S. Private*, pg. 1760
GRAY & OSBORNE, INC.; *U.S. Private*, pg. 1759
GREAVES COTTON LTD; *Int'l*, pg. 3068
GREELEY & HANSEN LLC, FT. MYERS—See T.Y. Lin International Group Ltd.; *U.S. Private*, pg. 3913
GREELEY & HANSEN LLC, GARY—See T.Y. Lin International Group Ltd.; *U.S. Private*, pg. 3913
GREELEY & HANSEN LLC, INDIANAPOLIS—See T.Y. Lin International Group Ltd.; *U.S. Private*, pg. 3913
GREELEY & HANSEN LLC, LAS VEGAS—See T.Y. Lin International Group Ltd.; *U.S. Private*, pg. 3913
GREELEY & HANSEN LLC, NEW YORK—See T.Y. Lin International Group Ltd.; *U.S. Private*, pg. 3913
GREELEY & HANSEN LLC, PHILADELPHIA—See T.Y. Lin International Group Ltd.; *U.S. Private*, pg. 3913
GREELEY & HANSEN LLC, PHOENIX—See T.Y. Lin International Group Ltd.; *U.S. Private*, pg. 3913
GREELEY & HANSEN LLC, RICHMOND—See T.Y. Lin International Group Ltd.; *U.S. Private*, pg. 3913
GREELEY & HANSEN LLC, SARASOTA—See T.Y. Lin International Group Ltd.; *U.S. Private*, pg. 3913
GREELEY & HANSEN LLC—See T.Y. Lin International Group Ltd.; *U.S. Private*, pg. 3913
GREENBERG FARROW ARCHITECTURE INCORPORATED; *U.S. Private*, pg. 1775
GREENLEAF CAPITAL LLC—See HCI Group, Inc.; *U.S. Public*, pg. 1014
GREENMAN-PEDERSEN, INC.; *U.S. Private*, pg. 1779
GREEN MOUNTAIN DEVELOPMENT CORP.; *U.S. Public*, pg. 963
GREENOVATION POWER CO., LTD.—See Gunkul Engineering Co., Ltd.; *Int'l*, pg. 3183
GREKA ENGINEERING & TECHNOLOGY LTD.—See G3 Exploration Limited; *Int'l*, pg. 2866
GRICHTING & VALTERIO ELECTRO SA—See Burkhalter Holding AG; *Int'l*, pg. 1225
GRID SOLUTIONS (U.S.) LLC—See General Electric Company; *U.S. Public*, pg. 920
GRINAKER-LTA ENGINEERING AND MINING SERVICES LIMITED—See Aveng Limited; *Int'l*, pg. 738

N.A.I.C.S. INDEX

541330 — ENGINEERING SERVICE...

GRINAKER-LTA (NAMIBIA) (PTY) LIMITED—See Aveng Limited; *Int'l*, pg. 738
GROOM ENERGY SOLUTIONS, LLC—See Electricite de France S.A.; *Int'l*, pg. 2350
GROUPE AECON QUEBEC LTEE—See Aecon Group Inc.; *Int'l*, pg. 172
GROUPE AXOR INC.; *Int'l*, pg. 3091
GROUPE STAVIBEL INC.—See AtkinsRealis Group Inc.; *Int'l*, pg. 671
GROUPE TECHSOL MARINE INC.—See Electricite de France S.A.; *Int'l*, pg. 2351
GROUPE THIRAN SA.—See Ackermans & van Haaren NV; *Int'l*, pg. 106
GROUP FIVE CIVIL ENGINEERING (PROPRIETARY) LIMITED—See Group Five Limited; *Int'l*, pg. 3089
GRT, INC.—See ConocoPhillips; pg. 569
GRUNDER INGENIEURE AG—See BKW AG; *Int'l*, pg. 1055
GRUPA AZOTY PROREM SP. Z O.O.—See Grupa Azoty S.A.; *Int'l*, pg. 3115
GRUPO ANTOLIN INGENIERIE SIEGES, S.A.S.—See Grupo Antolin-Irausa, S.A.; *Int'l*, pg. 3119
G&S ENGINEERING SERVICES PTY. LTD.; *Int'l*, pg. 2862
GSTEK, INC.; *U.S. Private*, pg. 1801
GST GRUPPO SOLUZIONI TECNOLOGICHE S R L—See Exprivia SpA; *Int'l*, pg. 2591
GTTP—See FAYAT SAS; *Int'l*, pg. 2625
GUANGDONG BOLUO JIUNENG HIGH-NEW TECHNOLOGY ENGINEERING CO., LTD.—See China New Energy Limited; *Int'l*, pg. 1535
GUANGDONG SHILIUYE CONSTRUCTION CO., LTD—See Guangdong Rising Assets Management Co., Ltd.; *Int'l*, pg. 3159
GUANGXI BO HUAN ENVIRONMENTAL CONSULTING COMPANY—See Guangxi Bossco Environmental Protection Technology Co., Ltd.; *Int'l*, pg. 3163
GUANGZHOU METRO DESIGN & RESEARCH INSTITUTE CO., LTD.; *Int'l*, pg. 3167
GUANGZHOU S.P.I DESIGN CO., LTD.; *Int'l*, pg. 3167
GUIMAR ENGENHARIA LTDA.—See Jacobs Engineering Group, Inc.; *U.S. Public*, pg. 1184
GUIZHOU EAST CHINA ENGINEERING CO., LTD.—See East China Engineering Science & Technology Co., Ltd.; *Int'l*, pg. 2269
GULF POWER INTERNATIONAL LTD.—See Dabbagh Group Holding Company Ltd.; *Int'l*, pg. 1902
GULF TECHNICAL CONSTRUCTION COMPANY L.L.C—See Drake & Scull International PJSC; *Int'l*, pg. 2200
GUNDA CORPORATION, LLC—See Littlejohn & Co., LLC; *U.S. Private*, pg. 2469
GUNKUL ENGINEERING CO., LTD.; *Int'l*, pg. 3183
GUNZE ENGINEERING CO., LTD.—See Gunze Limited; *Int'l*, pg. 3185
GURIT (UK) LTD—See Gurit Holding AG; *Int'l*, pg. 3188
GUSTOMSC B.V.—See NOV, Inc.; *U.S. Public*, pg. 1545
GUTHRIE ENGINEERING (S) PTE LTD—See Guthrie GTS Limited; *Int'l*, pg. 3188
GUY F. ATKINSON CONSTRUCTION, LLC - SOUTHERN CALIFORNIA DIVISION—See Clark Enterprises, Inc.; *U.S. Private*, pg. 913
GVA CONSULTANTS AB—See KBR, Inc.; *U.S. Public*, pg. 1216
GWE WARME- UND ENERGIETECHNIK GMBH & CO. KG—See CEZ, a.s.; *Int'l*, pg. 1428
GWIN DOBSON & FOREMAN INC.; *U.S. Private*, pg. 1821
GX TECHNOLOGY TRINIDAD, LTD.—See ION Geophysical Corporation; *U.S. Public*, pg. 1166
GYXIS CORPORATION—See Idemitsu Kosan Co., Ltd.; *Int'l*, pg. 3590
GZA GEOENVIRONMENTAL INC.; *U.S. Private*, pg. 1821
HAFSLUND DRIFTSSENTRAL AS—See Hafslund ASA; *Int'l*, pg. 3206
HAGLER BAILLY PAKISTAN (PRIVATE) LIMITED—See Tetra Tech, Inc.; *U.S. Public*, pg. 2023
HAI LECK ENGINEERING PTE LTD—See Hai Leck Holdings Limited; *Int'l*, pg. 3208
HAIMO SUBSEA TECHNOLOLY (SHANGHAI) CO., LTD.—See Haimo Technologies Group Corp.; *Int'l*, pg. 3211
HAISAN SDN. BHD.—See Haisan Resources Berhad; *Int'l*, pg. 3217
HALCROW CHINA LIMITED—See Jacobs Engineering Group, Inc.; *U.S. Public*, pg. 1184
HALCROW GROUP IRELAND LIMITED—See Jacobs Engineering Group, Inc.; *U.S. Public*, pg. 1184
HALCROW, INC.—See Jacobs Engineering Group, Inc.; *U.S. Public*, pg. 1184
HALEY & ALDRICH CONSTRUCTION SERVICES, INC.—See Haley & Aldrich Inc.; *U.S. Private*, pg. 1842
HALEY & ALDRICH INC.; *U.S. Private*, pg. 1842
HALEY & WARD, INC.—See CES, Inc.; *U.S. Private*, pg. 842
HALFF ASSOCIATES, INC.; *U.S. Private*, pg. 1842
HAL HAYS CONSTRUCTION, INC.; *U.S. Private*, pg. 1841
HALLIBURTON AS—See Halliburton Company; *U.S. Public*, pg. 980
HAL OFFSHORE LIMITED; *Int'l*, pg. 3223
HAMMEL, GREEN & ABRAHAMSON, INC.; *U.S. Private*, pg. 1849

HAMPSON INDUSTRIES PLC; *Int'l*, pg. 3239
HANGAR 8 ENGINEERING LIMITED—See Gama Aviation plc; *Int'l*, pg. 2876
HANGJI GLOBAL LIMITED; *Int'l*, pg. 3246
HANKOOK ENGINEERING WORKS CO., LTD.—See Hankook Tire & Technology Co.,Ltd.; *Int'l*, pg. 3253
HANKYU KENSOU CO., LTD.—See H2O Retailing Corp.; *Int'l*, pg. 3200
HANMIGLOBAL CONSULTING (SHANGHAI) CO., LTD.—See HanmiGlobal Co., LTD.; *Int'l*, pg. 3257
HANMIGLOBAL SAUDI (LLC)—See HanmiGlobal Co., LTD.; *Int'l*, pg. 3257
HANMIGLOBAL VIETNAM CO., LTD.—See HanmiGlobal Co., LTD.; *Int'l*, pg. 3257
HANOVER ENGINEERS PC INC.; *U.S. Private*, pg. 1855
HANOVER LAND SERVICES, INC.; *U.S. Private*, pg. 1855
HANSHIN CONSTRUCTION CO., LTD.; *Int'l*, pg. 3260
HANSON ALASKA LLC—See Hanson Professional Services, Inc.; *U.S. Private*, pg. 1856
HANWHA ENGINEERING & CONSTRUCTION CORP.—See Hanwha Group; *Int'l*, pg. 3265
HANYANG CONSTRUCTION(DALIAN) CO., LTD.—See Hanyang Eng Co., Ltd.; *Int'l*, pg. 3267
HANYANG (XIAN) ENGINEERING CO., LTD.—See Hanyang Eng Co., Ltd.; *Int'l*, pg. 3267
HAPPOLD INGENIEURBURO GMBH—See Buro Happold Engineers Limited; *Int'l*, pg. 1226
HARCO MANUFACTURING COMPANY INC.; *U.S. Private*, pg. 1862
HARDESTY & HANOVER, LLC; *U.S. Private*, pg. 1863
HARGROVE ENGINEERS & CONSTRUCTORS; *U.S. Private*, pg. 1864
HARGROVE ENGINEERS + CONSTRUCTORS; *U.S. Private*, pg. 1864
HARLAND & WOLFF (APPLEDORE) LIMITED—See Harland & Wolff Group Holdings plc; *Int'l*, pg. 3277
HARLAND & WOLFF (BELFAST) LIMITED—See Harland & Wolff Group Holdings plc; *Int'l*, pg. 3277
HARLAND & WOLFF (METHIL) LIMITED—See Harland & Wolff Group Holdings plc; *Int'l*, pg. 3277
HARNDEN GROUP, LLC—See Haines & Kibblehouse Inc.; *U.S. Private*, pg. 1841
HARRIS COMPANIES - HARRIS MECHANICAL SOUTHWEST DIVISION—See Harris Companies; *U.S. Private*, pg. 1869
HARRIS GROUP INC.; *U.S. Private*, pg. 1869
HARRIS MECHANICAL SERVICE, LLC—See Harris Companies; *U.S. Private*, pg. 1869
HARRY O. HEFTER ASSOCIATES, INC.—See The HOH Group; *U.S. Private*, pg. 4054
HARRY PEPPER & ASSOCIATES, INC.—See EMCOR Group, Inc.; *U.S. Public*, pg. 738
HARSCO INFRASTRUCTURE GROUP LIMITED—See Brand Industrial Services, Inc.; *U.S. Private*, pg. 636
HARTCHROM TEIKURO AUTOMOTIVE GMBH.—See Arbonia AG; *Int'l*, pg. 538
HART ENGINEERING CORPORATION; *U.S. Private*, pg. 1872
HASLINGER ACELSZERKEZETEPITO KFT—See Hutter & Schrantz PMS Ges.m.b.H; *Int'l*, pg. 3540
HASLINGER PROJEKT GMBH—See Hutter & Schrantz PMS Ges.m.b.H; *Int'l*, pg. 3540
HASLINGER STAHLBAU GMBH—See Hutter & Schrantz PMS Ges.m.b.H; *Int'l*, pg. 3540
HATCH ASSOCIATES PTY. LTD.—See Hatch Ltd.; *Int'l*, pg. 3284
HATCH LTD.; *Int'l*, pg. 3284
HAWBAKER ENGINEERING, LLC.—See Glenn O. Hawbaker, Inc.; *U.S. Private*, pg. 1710
HAYDARI CONSTRUCTION COMPANY LIMITED; *Int'l*, pg. 3290
HAYLEYS ENGINEERING LTD—See Hayleys PLC; *Int'l*, pg. 3292
HAZAMA ANDO CORPORATION; *Int'l*, pg. 3294
HAZAMA CORPORATION—See Hazama Ando Corporation; *Int'l*, pg. 3294
HAZAMA CORPORATION—See Hazama Ando Corporation; *Int'l*, pg. 3294
HAZAMA PHILIPPINES, INC.—See Hazama Ando Corporation; *Int'l*, pg. 3295
HAZEN & SAWYER; *U.S. Private*, pg. 1886
HAZET BAUUNTERNEHMUNG GMBH—See ALPINE Bau GmbH; *Int'l*, pg. 371
HBK ENGINEERING, LLC—See Quanta Services, Inc.; *U.S. Public*, pg. 1751
HB NETWORK SOLUTIONS, INC.—See The Innovation Institute; *U.S. Private*, pg. 4056
HCC INDUSTRIES INTERNATIONAL—See Windward Capital Partners LP; *U.S. Private*, pg. 4539
HC ENERGIA—See EDP - Energias de Portugal, S.A.; *Int'l*, pg. 2314
H.C. HOSPITAL CONSULTING S.P.A—See Fresenius SE & Co. KGaA; *Int'l*, pg. 2778
H.C. STARCK INC—See Advent International Corporation; *U.S. Private*, pg. 102
H.C. STARCK INC—See The Carlyle Group Inc.; *U.S. Public*, pg. 2047
HDC HOLDINGS CO., LTD.; *Int'l*, pg. 3300

HDC HYUNDAI DEVELOPMENT COMPANY; *Int'l*, pg. 3300
HDC WASSERBAU NORD GMBH—See HAL Trust N.V.; *Int'l*, pg. 3226
HD GLOBAL (HK) ENGINEERING SERVICES LTD. (HONG KONG)—See Hyundai Group; *Int'l*, pg. 3557
HD-GLOBAL (HK) ENGINEERING SERVICES LTD. - SHENZHEN—See Hyundai Group; *Int'l*, pg. 3557
HDJ DESIGN GROUP—See PBS Engineering & Envrnmntl; *U.S. Private*, pg. 3119
HDR ARCHITECTURE INC.—See HDR, Inc.; *U.S. Private*, pg. 1890
HDR CONSTRUCTION CONTROL CORPORATION—See HDR, Inc.; *U.S. Private*, pg. 1890
HDR ENGINEERING INC.—See HDR, Inc.; *U.S. Private*, pg. 1890
HDR ENGINEERING INC.—See HDR, Inc.; *U.S. Private*, pg. 1890
HDT ENGINEERED TECHNOLOGIES, INC.—See Metalmark Capital Holdings LLC; *U.S. Private*, pg. 2681
HDT GLOBAL EUROPE LTD—See Metalmark Capital Holdings LLC; *U.S. Private*, pg. 2681
HEALY TIBBITTS BUILDERS, INC.—See Kiewit Corp.; *U.S. Private*, pg. 2304
HEATH & ASSOCIATES INC.—See Warren Equity Partners, LLC; *U.S. Private*, pg. 4443
HEATH CONSULTANTS INCORPORATED; *U.S. Private*, pg. 1902
HEBEI CONSTRUCTION GROUP CORPORATION LIMITED; *Int'l*, pg. 3305
HEIDT DESIGN LLC; *U.S. Private*, pg. 1904
HEIJMANS INFRA GEINTEGREERDE PROJECTEN B.V.—See Heijmans N.V.; *Int'l*, pg. 3322
THE HEIMBURG GROUP, INC.—See Hardesty & Hanover, LLC; *U.S. Private*, pg. 1863
HEINRICH HIRDES KAMPFMITTELRAUMUNG GMBH—See HAL Trust N.V.; *Int'l*, pg. 3226
HENAN GAOJIAN PROJECT MANAGEMENT CO., LTD.—See Henan Communications Planning and Design Institute Co., Ltd; *Int'l*, pg. 3342
HENAN PROVINCE ACADEMY OF ENGINEERING DETECT CROSS REINFORCEMENT LTD.—See Henan Communications Planning and Design Institute Co., Ltd; *Int'l*, pg. 3342
HENDERSON ENGINEERS INC.; *U.S. Private*, pg. 1913
HENGFENG INFORMATION TECHNOLOGY CO. LTD.; *Int'l*, pg. 3346
HENKELS & MCCOY CANADA, INC.—See MasTec, Inc.; *U.S. Public*, pg. 1393
HENRY VON OESEN & ASSOCIATES, INC.—See Littlejohn & Co., LLC; *U.S. Private*, pg. 2469
HENSEL AG ELEKTROTECHNISCHE UNTERNEHMUNGEN—See BKW AG; *Int'l*, pg. 1055
HENSOLDT SPACE CONSULTING S.A.S.—See HENSOLDT AG; *Int'l*, pg. 3356
HERALD ENGINEERING SERVICES INC.—See Herald Holdings Limited; *Int'l*, pg. 3358
HE SERVICES CO. INC.; *U.S. Private*, pg. 1890
HESS ROUNTREE INC—See Bowman Consulting Group Ltd.; *U.S. Public*, pg. 376
HEWLAND ENGINEERING LTD; *Int'l*, pg. 3367
HEXAGON HOLDINGS BERHAD; *Int'l*, pg. 3370
HEXAGON MIDCO INDIA PVT. LTD.—See Hexagon Holdings Berhad; *Int'l*, pg. 3370
HEXAGON TOWER PHILIPPINES INC.—See Hexagon Holdings Berhad; *Int'l*, pg. 3370
HEXAGON TOWER (TIANJIN) ENGINEERING CO., LTD.—See Hexagon Holdings Berhad; *Int'l*, pg. 3370
HEXCEL COMPOSITES GMBH & CO. KG—See Hexcel Corporation; *U.S. Public*, pg. 1032
HEXCEL COMPOSITES LIMITED—See Hexcel Corporation; *U.S. Public*, pg. 1032
HEXCEL COMPOSITES S.A.—See Hexcel Corporation; *U.S. Public*, pg. 1032
HEXCEL COMPOSITES S.P.R.L.—See Hexcel Corporation; *U.S. Public*, pg. 1032
HEXCEL REINFORCEMENTS—See Hexcel Corporation; *U.S. Public*, pg. 1033
HEZHOU BOSSCO ENVIRONMENTAL INVESTMENT & CONSTRUCTION CO., LTD.—See Guangxi Bossco Environmental Protection Technology Co., Ltd.; *Int'l*, pg. 3163
HGC HAMBURG GAS CONSULT GMBH—See E.ON SE; *Int'l*, pg. 2254
HHMI CORP.; *U.S. Private*, pg. 1931
HIAP SENG ENGINEERING LIMITED; *Int'l*, pg. 3382
HIAP SENG ENGINEERING (M) SDN. BHD.—See Hiap Seng Engineering Limited; *Int'l*, pg. 3382
HIAP SENG-SANKO TPM PTE. LTD.—See Hiap Seng Engineering Limited; *Int'l*, pg. 3382
HIDRAULICA DEL CHIRIQUI, S.A.—See ACS, Actividades de Construccion y Servicios, S.A.; *Int'l*, pg. 114
HIDROELEKTRA NISKOGRADNJA D.D.; *Int'l*, pg. 3384
HIDROGRADNJA D.D. SARAJEVO; *Int'l*, pg. 3384
HI-FI ENGINEERING INC.—See Enbridge Inc.; *Int'l*, pg. 2397
HIGHLIGHT S.R.L.—See Gek Terna Societe Anonyme Holdings Real Estate Constructions; *Int'l*, pg. 2913
HILL INTERNATIONAL (COLOMBIA) SAS—See Global In-

541330 — ENGINEERING SERVICE...

frastructure Solutions, Inc.; *U.S. Private,* pg. 1715
HILL INTERNATIONAL ENGINEERING CONSULTANCY, LLC—See Global Infrastructure Solutions, Inc.; *U.S. Private,* pg. 1715
HILL INTERNATIONAL INC.—See Global Infrastructure Solutions, Inc.; *U.S. Private,* pg. 1715
HILL INTERNATIONAL (LIBYA) LTD.—See Global Infrastructure Solutions, Inc.; *U.S. Private,* pg. 1715
HILL INTERNATIONAL (NORTH AFRICA) LTD.—See Global Infrastructure Solutions, Inc.; *U.S. Private,* pg. 1715
HILL INTERNATIONAL PROJECT MANAGEMENT (INDIA) PRIVATE LIMITED—See Global Infrastructure Solutions, Inc.; *U.S. Private,* pg. 1715
HILL INTERNATIONAL PROJE YONETIMI VE DANISMANLIK A.S.—See Global Infrastructure Solutions, Inc.; *U.S. Private,* pg. 1715
HILL INTERNATIONAL VIETNAM CO. LIMITED—See Global Infrastructure Solutions, Inc.; *U.S. Private,* pg. 1715
HILLIS-CARNES ENGINEERING ASSOCIATES, INC.; *U.S. Private,* pg. 1946
HILL TECHNICAL SOLUTIONS, INC.—See D.C. Capital Partners, LLC; *U.S. Private,* pg. 1141
HILTI ALBANIA SHPK—See Hilti AG; *Int'l,* pg. 3394
HILTI BAHRAIN W.L.L—See Hilti AG; *Int'l,* pg. 3394
HILTI BY FLLC—See Hilti AG; *Int'l,* pg. 3394
HILTI CONSTRUCTION EQUIPMENTS EURL—See Hilti AG; *Int'l,* pg. 3394
HILTI MAROC S.A.—See Hilti AG; *Int'l,* pg. 3395
HILTI MIDDLE EAST FZE—See Hilti AG; *Int'l,* pg. 3395
HILTI QATAR W.L.L.—See Hilti AG; *Int'l,* pg. 3395
HILTI ROMANIA S.R.L.—See Hilti AG; *Int'l,* pg. 3395
HILTI SMN DOO—See Hilti AG; *Int'l,* pg. 3395
HILTI-SYRIA L.L.C.—See Hilti AG; *Int'l,* pg. 3395
HILTI SYSTEMS BH SARAJEVO D.O.O.—See Hilti AG; *Int'l,* pg. 3395
HILTI VIETNAM CO. LTD—See Hilti AG; *Int'l,* pg. 3395
HINDUSTAN DORR-OLIVER LTD; *Int'l,* pg. 3399
HIOLLE TECHNOLOGIES SAS—See Hiolle Industries S.A.; *Int'l,* pg. 3401
HI-P NORTH AMERICA, INC.—See Hi-P International Limited; *Int'l,* pg. 3381
HIRATA CORPORATION OF AMERICA—See Hirata Corporation; *Int'l,* pg. 3403
HIRTENBERGER HOLDING GMBH; *Int'l,* pg. 3406
HITACHI ARCHITECTS & ENGINEERS CO., LTD.—See Hitachi, Ltd.; *Int'l,* pg. 3414
HITACHI ARCHITECTS & ENGINEERS (SHANGHAI) CO., LTD.—See Hitachi, Ltd.; *Int'l,* pg. 3414
HITACHI CRITICAL FACILITIES PROTECTION PTE. LTD.—See Hitachi, Ltd.; *Int'l,* pg. 3416
HITACHI INFRASTRUCTURE SYSTEMS (ASIA) PTE. LTD.—See Hitachi, Ltd.; *Int'l,* pg. 3419
HITACHI ZOSEN INOVA AG - SWEDEN BRANCH—See Hitachi Zosen Corporation; *Int'l,* pg. 3411
HITACHI ZOSEN INOVA U.S.A. LLC—See Hitachi Zosen Corporation; *Int'l,* pg. 3411
HI-TECH SERVICES & SUPPLIES LLC—See Al Hassan Engineering Company S.A.O.G.; *Int'l,* pg. 279
HIWIN S.R.O.—See Hiwin Technologies Corp.; *Int'l,* pg. 3427
HKC INTERNATIONAL HOLDINGS LIMITED; *Int'l,* pg. 3428
HKM INC.; *U.S. Private,* pg. 1953
HLH AGRICULTURE (CAMBODIA) CO., LTD.—See Hong Lai Huat Group Limited; *Int'l,* pg. 3467
HMI CONSTRUCTION INC.—See ANDRITZ AG; *Int'l,* pg. 455
H&M INDUSTRIAL SERVICE INC.—See H&M Company Inc.; *U.S. Private,* pg. 1823
HMK AUTOMATION GROUP LIMITED; *Int'l,* pg. 3431
HNTB-ATLANTA—See HNTB Corporation; *U.S. Private,* pg. 1956
HNTB-AUSTIN—See HNTB Corporation; *U.S. Private,* pg. 1956
HNTB-BATON ROUGE—See HNTB Corporation; *U.S. Private,* pg. 1956
HNTB-BOSTON—See HNTB Corporation; *U.S. Private,* pg. 1956
HNTB-CHARLOTTE—See HNTB Corporation; *U.S. Private,* pg. 1956
HNTB-COLUMBIA—See HNTB Corporation; *U.S. Private,* pg. 1957
HNTB CORPORATION - PARSIPPANY—See HNTB Corporation; *U.S. Private,* pg. 1956
HNTB CORPORATION, SANTA ANA BRANCH—See HNTB Corporation; *U.S. Private,* pg. 1956
HNTB CORPORATION; *U.S. Private,* pg. 1955
HNTB CORPORATION—See HNTB Corporation; *U.S. Private,* pg. 1956
HNTB CORPORATION—See HNTB Corporation; *U.S. Private,* pg. 1956
HNTB CORPORATION—See HNTB Corporation; *U.S. Private,* pg. 1956
HNTB-DALLAS—See HNTB Corporation; *U.S. Private,* pg. 1957
HNTB-DENVER—See HNTB Corporation; *U.S. Private,* pg. 1957

HNTB-DETROIT—See HNTB Corporation; *U.S. Private,* pg. 1957
HNTB-HARTFORD—See HNTB Corporation; *U.S. Private,* pg. 1957
HNTB-INDIANA—See HNTB Corporation; *U.S. Private,* pg. 1957
HNTB-JACKSONVILLE—See HNTB Corporation; *U.S. Private,* pg. 1957
HNTB-LOS ANGELES—See HNTB Corporation; *U.S. Private,* pg. 1957
HNTB-MADISON—See HNTB Corporation; *U.S. Private,* pg. 1957
HNTB-MIAMI—See HNTB Corporation; *U.S. Private,* pg. 1957
HNTB MICHIGAN INC—See HNTB Corporation; *U.S. Private,* pg. 1956
HNTB-MILWAUKEE—See HNTB Corporation; *U.S. Private,* pg. 1957
HNTB-MINNEAPOLIS—See HNTB Corporation; *U.S. Private,* pg. 1957
HNTB-MORGANTOWN—See HNTB Corporation; *U.S. Private,* pg. 1957
HNTB-NEW YORK—See HNTB Corporation; *U.S. Private,* pg. 1957
HNTB-OAKLAND—See HNTB Corporation; *U.S. Private,* pg. 1957
HNTB-OHIO,INC—See HNTB Corporation; *U.S. Private,* pg. 1957
HNTB-OHIO INC—See HNTB Corporation; *U.S. Private,* pg. 1957
HNTB-OVERLAND PARK—See HNTB Corporation; *U.S. Private,* pg. 1957
HNTB-PLANO—See HNTB Corporation; *U.S. Private,* pg. 1957
HNTB-PORTLAND—See HNTB Corporation; *U.S. Private,* pg. 1957
HNTB-RALEIGH—See HNTB Corporation; *U.S. Private,* pg. 1957
HNTB-SAINT LOUIS—See HNTB Corporation; *U.S. Private,* pg. 1957
HNTB-SALT LAKE CITY—See HNTB Corporation; *U.S. Private,* pg. 1957
HNTB-SAN ANTONIO—See HNTB Corporation; *U.S. Private,* pg. 1957
HNTB-SAN BERNARDINO—See HNTB Corporation; *U.S. Private,* pg. 1957
HNTB-SAN JOSE—See HNTB Corporation; *U.S. Private,* pg. 1957
HNTB-SANTA ANA—See HNTB Corporation; *U.S. Private,* pg. 1957
HNTB-SEATTLE—See HNTB Corporation; *U.S. Private,* pg. 1957
HNTB—See HNTB Corporation; *U.S. Private,* pg. 1956
HNTB-TAMPA—See HNTB Corporation; *U.S. Private,* pg. 1957
HNTB-TOLEDO—See HNTB Corporation; *U.S. Private,* pg. 1957
HOA BINH MECHANICAL ELECTRICAL (HBE) JSC—See Hoa Binh Construction Group JSC; *Int'l,* pg. 3435
HOCHTIEF CONCESSIONS AG—See ACS, Actividades de Construccion y Servicios, S.A.; *Int'l,* pg. 113
HOCHTIEF CZ A.S.—See ACS, Actividades de Construccion y Servicios, S.A.; *Int'l,* pg. 113
HOCHTIEF ENGINEERING GMBH—See ACS, Actividades de Construccion y Servicios, S.A.; *Int'l,* pg. 114
HOCHTIEF SOLUTIONS AG—See ACS, Actividades de Construccion y Servicios, S.A.; *Int'l,* pg. 114
HOCK LIAN SENG CONTRACTORS PTE LTD—See Hock Lian Seng Holdings Limited; *Int'l,* pg. 3438
HOCK LIAN SENG HOLDINGS LIMITED; *Int'l,* pg. 3438
HOCK LIAN SENG INFRASTRUCTURE PTE LTD—See Hock Lian Seng Holdings Limited; *Int'l,* pg. 3438
HOCK LIAN SENG PROPERTIES PTE. LTD.—See Hock Lian Seng Holdings Limited; *Int'l,* pg. 3438
HOCK SENG LEE BERHAD; *Int'l,* pg. 3438
HOFFMAN MECHANICAL CORPORATION—See Hoffman Corporation; *U.S. Private,* pg. 1960
HOFFMAN SPECIALTY—See Xylem Inc.; *U.S. Public,* pg. 2396
HOGANAS BELGIUM S.A.—See Hoganas AB; *Int'l,* pg. 3441
HOGANAS EAST EUROPE LLC—See Hoganas AB; *Int'l,* pg. 3441
HOGANAS FRANCE S.A.S.—See Hoganas AB; *Int'l,* pg. 3441
HOGANAS GMBH—See Hoganas AB; *Int'l,* pg. 3441
HOGANAS IBERICA S.A.—See Hoganas AB; *Int'l,* pg. 3441
HOGANAS JAPAN K.K.—See Hoganas AB; *Int'l,* pg. 3441
HOGANAS SWEDEN AB—See Hoganas AB; *Int'l,* pg. 3441
HOH ENGINEERS, INC.—See The HOH Group; *U.S. Private,* pg. 4053
THE HOH GROUP; *U.S. Private,* pg. 4053
HO HUP CONSTRUCTION COMPANY BERHAD; *Int'l,* pg. 3434
HO HUP (MYANMAR) E&C CO., LTD.—See Ho Hup Construction Company Berhad; *Int'l,* pg. 3434
HOKUDEN SOGO SEKKEI—See Hokkaido Electric Power Co., Inc.; *Int'l,* pg. 3443

CORPORATE AFFILIATIONS

HOKURIKU DENWA KOUJI CO., LTD.—See COMSYS Holdings Corporation; *Int'l,* pg. 1761
HOKURIKU ELECTRICAL CONSTRUCTION CO., LTD.; *Int'l,* pg. 3445
HOLBEN, MARTIN & WHITE, INC.—See John A. Martin & Associates, Incorporated; *U.S. Private,* pg. 2219
HOLE MONTES, INC.—See Bowman Consulting Group Ltd.; *U.S. Public,* pg. 376
HOLTEC INTERNATIONAL; *U.S. Private,* pg. 1969
HOMERUN ELECTRONICS, INC.—See Vangeo Technology Group, LLC; *U.S. Private,* pg. 4343
HOMEX-ATIZAPAN, S.A. DE C.V.—See Desarrolladora Homex, S.A. de C.V.; *Int'l,* pg. 2044
HOMEX INFRAESTRUCTURA OBRAS, S.A. DE C.V.—See Desarrolladora Homex, S.A. de C.V.; *Int'l,* pg. 2044
HOMEX INFRAESTRUCTURA, S.A. DE C.V.—See Desarrolladora Homex, S.A. de C.V.; *Int'l,* pg. 2044
HORIBA INDIA PRIVATE LTD.—See HORIBA Ltd; *Int'l,* pg. 3476
HORIBA INSTRUMENTS (SINGAPORE) PTE. LTD.—See HORIBA Ltd; *Int'l,* pg. 3476
HORIZON ENGINEERING GROUP, INC.—See Greenman-Pedersen, Inc.; *U.S. Private,* pg. 1779
HORIZON MARINE, INC.—See Collecte Localisation Satellites; *Int'l,* pg. 1699
HORMANN AUTOMATIONSSERVICE GMBH—See Hormann Holding GmbH & Co. KG; *Int'l,* pg. 3480
HORMANN INDUSTRIESERVICE GMBH—See Hormann Holding GmbH & Co. KG; *Int'l,* pg. 3480
HORMANN KOMMUNIKATINSNETZTE GMBH—See Hormann Holding GmbH & Co. KG; *Int'l,* pg. 3480
HORMANN RAWEMA ENGINEERING & CONSULTING GMBH—See Hormann Holding GmbH & Co. KG; *Int'l,* pg. 3480
HORNBACH BAUSTOFF UNION GMBH—See Hornbach Holding AG & Co. KGaA; *Int'l,* pg. 3481
HORNE INTERNATIONAL, INC.; *U.S. Private,* pg. 1983
HORN INDUSTRIAL SERVICES—See Charlesbank Capital Partners, LLC; *U.S. Public,* pg. 855
HORROCKS ENGINEERS, INC.; *U.S. Private,* pg. 1984
HOSOKAWA SOLIDS CHILE SPA—See Hosokawa Micron Corporation; *Int'l,* pg. 3486
HOSOKAWA SOLIDS MEXICO S.A. DE C.V.—See Hosokawa Micron Corporation; *Int'l,* pg. 3486
HOSOKAWA SOLIDS S.L.—See Hosokawa Micron Corporation; *Int'l,* pg. 3486
HOSOKAWA SOLIDS SOLUTIONS GMBH—See Hosokawa Micron Corporation; *Int'l,* pg. 3486
HOSPITALIA INTERNATIONAL GMBH—See Fresenius SE & Co. KGaA; *Int'l,* pg. 2780
HOUSTON OFFSHORE ENGINEERING, LLC—See Atkins-Realis Group Inc.; *Int'l,* pg. 673
HPC AUSTRIA GMBH—See HPC AG; *Int'l,* pg. 3500
HPC BULGARIA EOOD—See HPC AG; *Int'l,* pg. 3500
HPC DIERING ROMANIA SRL—See HPC AG; *Int'l,* pg. 3500
HPC ENGINEERING (THAILAND) CO., LTD.—See Hitachi, Ltd.; *Int'l,* pg. 3413
HPC ENVIROTEC S.A.—See HPC AG; *Int'l,* pg. 3500
HPC ITALIA S.R.L.—See HPC AG; *Int'l,* pg. 3500
HPC PASECO SP LTD.—See HPC AG; *Int'l,* pg. 3500
HPC POLSKA SP.Z.O.O.—See HPC AG; *Int'l,* pg. 3500
HPC VENEZUELA C.A.—See Hitachi, Ltd.; *Int'l,* pg. 3413
HRL LABORATORIES, LLC—See General Motors Company; *U.S. Public,* pg. 926
HRL LABORATORIES, LLC—See The Boeing Company; *U.S. Public,* pg. 2041
HRST, INC.; *U.S. Private,* pg. 1998
HS COMPRESSION & PROCESS PTE LTD—See Hiap Seng Engineering Limited; *Int'l,* pg. 3382
HTE NORTHEAST—See Charterhouse Capital Partners LLP; *Int'l,* pg. 1456
H.T. LYONS, INC.—See ENGIE SA; *Int'l,* pg. 2429
HTS ENGINEERING LTD.; *Int'l,* pg. 3509
HUALAN GROUP CO., LTD.; *Int'l,* pg. 3512
HUALU ENGINEERING & TECHNOLOGY CO., LTD.—See China National Chemical Engineering Co., Ltd.; *Int'l,* pg. 1531
HUI LYU ECOLOGICAL TECHNOLOGY GROUPS CO., LTD.; *Int'l,* pg. 3526
HUITT-ZOLLARS, INC.; *U.S. Private,* pg. 2004
HUIZHOU HENGYI WUJIN ZHIPIN LIMITED—See Hang Yick Holdings Company Limited; *Int'l,* pg. 3245
HULL & ASSOCIATES, INC. - BROWNFIELDS DIVISION—See Sterling Investment Partners, L.P.; *U.S. Private,* pg. 3806
HULLEY & KIRKWOOD CONSULTING ENGINEERS LTD; *Int'l,* pg. 3528
HUMANTECH, INC.—See CVC Capital Partners SICAV-FIS S.A.; *Int'l,* pg. 1885
HUMICLIMA VALLADOLID, S.L.—See ACS, Actividades de Construccion y Servicios, S.A.; *Int'l,* pg. 114
HUNAN BAILI ENGINEERING SCI & TECH CO.,LTD; *Int'l,* pg. 3531
HUNAN BOSSCO HUAYI ENVIRONMENT ENGINEERING CO., LTD—See Guangxi Bossco Environmental Protection Technology Co., Ltd.; *Int'l,* pg. 3163
HUNT, GUILLOT & ASSOCIATES, LLC; *U.S. Private,* pg. 2009

HUNTINGTON INGALLS INCORPORATED—See Huntington Ingalls Industries, Inc.; *U.S. Public*, pg. 1072
HUSCOMPAGNIET A/S; *Int'l*, pg. 3538
HWASUNG INDUSTRIAL CO., LTD.; *Int'l*, pg. 3543
HWP CAIRO PLANNING & ENGINEERING CONSULTANT LTD.—See HWP Planungs GmbH; *Int'l*, pg. 3543
HWP ISTANBUL MIMARLIK MUHENDISLIK VE DANISMANLIK LTD. SIRKETI—See HWP Planungs GmbH; *Int'l*, pg. 3543
HYDROCONSULT GMBH—See BKW AG; *Int'l*, pg. 1055
HYDROMOTION, INC.—See Dover Corporation; *U.S. Public*, pg. 681
HYDRONAMIC B.V.—See HAL Trust N.V.; *Int'l*, pg. 3226
HYDRONEXT SAS—See BKW AG; *Int'l*, pg. 1055
HYDRO SOLUTIONS CONSULTING LLC—See The Dewberry Companies Inc.; *U.S. Private*, pg. 4021
HYFLUX NEWSPRING CONSTRUCTION ENGINEERING (SHANGHAI) CO., LTD.—See Hyflux Ltd; *Int'l*, pg. 3548
HYUNDAI ASAN CORPORATION—See Hyundai Group; *Int'l*, pg. 3557
HYUNDAI ENGINEERING CO., LTD.—See Hyundai Engineering & Construction Co., Ltd.; *Int'l*, pg. 3556
HYUNDAI ENGINEERING & CONSTRUCTION CO., LTD.; *Int'l*, pg. 3556
HYUNDAI ENGINEERING & STEEL INDUSTRIES CO., LTD.—See Hyundai Engineering & Construction Co., Ltd.; *Int'l*, pg. 3556
I4B SP. Z O.O.—See LKQ Corporation; *U.S. Public*, pg. 1336
IAI INDUSTRIAL SYSTEMS B.V.—See ASSA ABLOY AB; *Int'l*, pg. 636
IBBERSON ENGINEERING, INC.—See Peter Kiewit Sons', Inc.; *U.S. Private*, pg. 3158
IBERDROLA ENGINEERING AND CONSTRUCTION BULGARIA—See Iberdrola, S.A.; *Int'l*, pg. 3572
IBERDROLA ENGINEERING AND CONSTRUCTION POLAND, SP. Z. O. O.—See Iberdrola, S.A.; *Int'l*, pg. 3572
IBERDROLA ENGINEERING AND CONSTRUCTION UK, LTD.—See Iberdrola, S.A.; *Int'l*, pg. 3572
IBERDROLA INGENIERIA Y CONSTRUCCION, S.A.—See Iberdrola, S.A.; *Int'l*, pg. 3572
IBI-MAAK INC.—See ARCADIS N.V.; *Int'l*, pg. 542
IBS—See FAYAT SAS; *Int'l*, pg. 2625
ICA SERVICIOS DE DIRECCION CORPORATIVA, S.A. DE C.V.—See Empresas ICA S.A.B. de C.V.; *Int'l*, pg. 2391
ICD (ASIA PACIFIC) PTY LIMITED—See Apollo Global Management, Inc.; *U.S. Public*, pg. 167
ICHIKEN CO., LTD.; *Int'l*, pg. 3580
IC MECHANICAL, INC.; *U.S. Private*, pg. 2029
ICON VENUE GROUP, LLC—See TPG Capital, L.P.; *U.S. Public*, pg. 2170
I.C. THOMASSON ASSOCIATES, INC.—See Salas O'Brien Engineers, Inc.; *U.S. Private*, pg. 3530
I.C. THOMASSON ASSOCIATES—See Salas O'Brien Engineers, Inc.; *U.S. Private*, pg. 3530
I.C. THOMASSON ASSOCIATES—See Salas O'Brien Engineers, Inc.; *U.S. Private*, pg. 3530
I.C. THOMASSON ASSOCIATES—See Salas O'Brien Engineers, Inc.; *U.S. Private*, pg. 3530
IDEAL HEIGHTS PROPERTIES SDN. BHD.—See Bina Puri Holdings Bhd; *Int'l*, pg. 1032
IDEMITSU CHEMICALS (SHANGHAI) CO., LTD.—See Idemitsu Kosan Co., Ltd.; *Int'l*, pg. 3590
IDEMITSU CHEMICALS TAIWAN CORP.—See Idemitsu Kosan Co., Ltd.; *Int'l*, pg. 3590
IDEMITSU COAL MARKETING AUSTRALIA PTY. LTD.—See Idemitsu Kosan Co., Ltd.; *Int'l*, pg. 3590
IDEMITSU ELECTRONIC MATERIALS (CHINA) CO., LTD.—See Idemitsu Kosan Co., Ltd.; *Int'l*, pg. 3590
IDEMITSU ELECTRONIC MATERIALS KOREA CO., LTD.—See Idemitsu Kosan Co., Ltd.; *Int'l*, pg. 3590
IDEMITSU ELECTRONIC MATERIALS (SHANGHAI) CO., LTD.—See Idemitsu Kosan Co., Ltd.; *Int'l*, pg. 3590
IDEMITSU ENGINEERING VIETNAM CO., LTD.—See Idemitsu Kosan Co., Ltd.; *Int'l*, pg. 3591
IDEMITSU FINE COMPOSITES CO., LTD.—See Idemitsu Kosan Co., Ltd.; *Int'l*, pg. 3591
IDEMITSU GAS PRODUCTION (VIETNAM) CO., LTD.—See Idemitsu Kosan Co., Ltd.; *Int'l*, pg. 3591
IDEMITSU LUBE ASIA PACIFIC PTE. LTD.—See Idemitsu Kosan Co., Ltd.; *Int'l*, pg. 3591
IDEMITSU LUBE (MALAYSIA) SDN. BHD.—See Idemitsu Kosan Co., Ltd.; *Int'l*, pg. 3591
IDEMITSU LUBE PAKISTAN (PRIVATE) LIMITED—See Idemitsu Kosan Co., Ltd.; *Int'l*, pg. 3591
IDEMITSU LUBE VIETNAM CO., LTD.—See Idemitsu Kosan Co., Ltd.; *Int'l*, pg. 3591
IDEMITSU LUBRICANTS MEXICO S.A. DE C.V.—See Idemitsu Kosan Co., Ltd.; *Int'l*, pg. 3591
IDEMITSU LUBRICANTS PHILIPPINES INC.—See Idemitsu Kosan Co., Ltd.; *Int'l*, pg. 3591
IDEMITSU LUBRICANTS (THAILAND) CO., LTD.—See Idemitsu Kosan Co., Ltd.; *Int'l*, pg. 3591
IDEMITSU OLED MATERIALS EUROPE AG—See Idemitsu Kosan Co., Ltd.; *Int'l*, pg. 3591
IDIADA AUTOMOTIVE TECHNOLOGY, S.A.—See I Squared Capital Advisors (US) LLC; *U.S. Private*, pg. 2022

IDIADA CZ, A.S.—See I Squared Capital Advisors (US) LLC; *U.S. Private*, pg. 2022
IDS INGEGNERIA DEI SISTEMI (UK) LTD.—See Fincantieri S.p.A.; *Int'l*, pg. 2671
IDS NORTH AMERICA LTD.—See Fincantieri S.p.A.; *Int'l*, pg. 2671
IFEC INGEGNERIA SA—See AFRY AB; *Int'l*, pg. 194
IFFLAND KAVANAGH WATERBURY, P.L.L.C.—See Jacobs Engineering Group, Inc.; *U.S. Public*, pg. 1184
IHI CONSTRUCTION SERVICE CO., LTD.—See IHI Corporation; *Int'l*, pg. 3604
IHI E&C INTERNATIONAL CORPORATION—See IHI Corporation; *Int'l*, pg. 3604
IHI FUSO ENGINEERING CO., LTD.—See IHI Corporation; *Int'l*, pg. 3605
IHI (HK) LTD.—See IHI Corporation; *Int'l*, pg. 3604
IHI-ICR, LLC.—See IHI Corporation; *Int'l*, pg. 3605
IHI INFRASTRUCTURE SYSTEMS CO., LTD.—See IHI Corporation; *Int'l*, pg. 3605
IHI LOGISTICS & MACHINERY CORPORATION—See IHI Corporation; *Int'l*, pg. 3605
IHI PACKAGED BOILER CO., LTD.—See IHI Corporation; *Int'l*, pg. 3605
IHI PHILIPPINES, INC.—See IHI Corporation; *Int'l*, pg. 3604
IHI PLANT SERVICES CORPORATION—See IHI Corporation; *Int'l*, pg. 3605
IHI POWER SYSTEM MALAYSIA SDN. BHD.—See IHI Corporation; *Int'l*, pg. 3604
IHI SCUBE CO., LTD.—See IHI Corporation; *Int'l*, pg. 3605
IHI SOUTHWEST TECHNOLOGIES INC.—See IHI Corporation; *Int'l*, pg. 3604
IHLAS YAPI TURIZM VE SAGLIK A.S.—See Ihlas Holding A.S.; *Int'l*, pg. 3606
IJM CONSTRUCTION (MIDDLE EAST) LIMITED LIABILITY COMPANY—See IJM Corporation Berhad; *Int'l*, pg. 3608
IJM CONSTRUCTION SDN BHD—See IJM Corporation Berhad; *Int'l*, pg. 3608
IJUS, LLC—See TRC Companies, Inc.; *U.S. Private*, pg. 4215
IKK ENGINEERING GMBH—See BKW AG; *Int'l*, pg. 1055
I. KLOUKINAS - I. LAPPAS CONSTRUCTION & COMMERCE S.A.; *Int'l*, pg. 3565
IKM DSC ENGINEERING AS—See IKM Gruppen AS; *Int'l*, pg. 3611
IKM INDUSTRIGRAVOREN AS—See IKM Gruppen AS; *Int'l*, pg. 3611
IKM MASKINERING AS—See IKM Gruppen AS; *Int'l*, pg. 3611
IKM OCEAN DESIGN AS—See IKM Gruppen AS; *Int'l*, pg. 3611
IKM RONTGENKONTROLLEN AS—See IKM Gruppen AS; *Int'l*, pg. 3611
IKM TECHNIQUE AS—See IKM Gruppen AS; *Int'l*, pg. 3612
ILIASI LTD.—See Elco Limited; *Int'l*, pg. 2345
ILIOHORA S.A.—See Gek Terna Societe Anonyme Holdings Real Estate Constructions; *Int'l*, pg. 2913
ILS SUPPLY TECHNOLOGIES SA DE CV—See Park-Ohio Holdings Corp.; *U.S. Public*, pg. 1639
ILSUNG CONSTRUCTION CO., LTD.; *Int'l*, pg. 3616
IMAGE ENGINEERING GROUP, LTD.—See Godspeed Capital Management LP; *U.S. Private*, pg. 1725
IMAGICA TOTAL SERVICE CORP.—See Imagica Group Inc.; *Int'l*, pg. 3618
IMAT AUTOMOTIVE TECHNOLOGY SERVICES INC.—See Centre Testing International Corporation; *Int'l*, pg. 1411
IMAT AUTOMOTIVE TECHNOLOGY SERVICES MEXICO S. DE R.L. DE C.V.—See Centre Testing International Corporation; *Int'l*, pg. 1411
IMAT (SHENYANG) AUTOMOTIVE TECHNOLOGY CO., LTD.—See Centre Testing International Corporation; *Int'l*, pg. 1411
IMAT-UVE AUTOMOTIVE TESTING CENTER (PTY.) LTD.—See Centre Testing International Corporation; *Int'l*, pg. 1411
IM ELECTRIC, INC.—See Quanta Services, Inc.; *U.S. Public*, pg. 1751
IMERYS USA, INC.—See Groupe Bruxelles Lambert SA; *Int'l*, pg. 3100
IMES PTE. LTD.—See IHI Corporation; *Int'l*, pg. 3606
IMPACT ENGINEERING, INC.—See urban-gro, Inc.; *U.S. Public*, pg. 2266
IMPACT TECHNOLOGIES, LLC; *U.S. Private*, pg. 2048
IMPELSYS INC.; *U.S. Private*, pg. 2049
I.M.P. GROUP INTERNATIONAL INC. - IMP AEROSPACE & DEFENCE UNIT—See I.M.P. Group International Inc.; *Int'l*, pg. 3566
IMP POLAND SP. Z O.O.—See Alten S.A.; *Int'l*, pg. 390
IMTECH AQUA LTD.—See Electricite de France S.A.; *Int'l*, pg. 2351
IMTECH BELGIUM N V—See Electricite de France S.A.; *Int'l*, pg. 2351
IMTECH ENGINEERING SERVICES LONDON AND SOUTH LTD.—See Electricite de France S.A.; *Int'l*, pg. 2351
IMTECH ENGINEERING SERVICES LTD.—See Electricite de France S.A.; *Int'l*, pg. 2351
IMTECH HUNGARY KFT—See Electricite de France S.A.; *Int'l*, pg. 2351

IMTECH MAINTENANCE N.V.—See Electricite de France S.A.; *Int'l*, pg. 2351
IMTECH PROJECTS N.V.—See Electricite de France S.A.; *Int'l*, pg. 2351
IMTECH PROJECTS N.V.—See Electricite de France S.A.; *Int'l*, pg. 2351
INACUI S.A.—See Air Products & Chemicals, Inc.; *U.S. Public*, pg. 66
INDECK ENERGY SERVICES OF SILVER SPRINGS INC.—See Indeck Power Equipment Company; *U.S. Private*, pg. 2055
INDIKAR - INDIVIDUAL KAROSSERIEBAU GMBH—See Farmingtons Holding GmbH; *Int'l*, pg. 2619
INDUS SURVEYORS (PVT.) LTD.—See First Elite Capital Modaraba; *Int'l*, pg. 2683
INDUSTRIAL ENGINEERING SYSTEMS PTE. LTD.—See Annica Holdings Limited; *Int'l*, pg. 474
INDUSTRIAL SOLUTIONS, INC.—See The Helm Group; *U.S. Private*, pg. 4051
INEC ENGINEERING CO. LTD.—See Energoprojekt Holding a.d.; *Int'l*, pg. 2422
INFINITY OFFSHORE MARINE, LLC—See J.F. Lehman & Company, Inc.; *U.S. Private*, pg. 2164
INFORMATION MANAGEMENT RESOURCES, INC.; *U.S. Private*, pg. 2073
INFORM PRODUCT DEVELOPMENT, INC.; *U.S. Private*, pg. 2072
INFOTECH ENTERPRISES AMERICA INC.—See Cyient Limited; *Int'l*, pg. 1896
INFOTERRA MAGYARORSZAG KFT.—See Airbus SE; *Int'l*, pg. 245
INFOTREE SERVICE INC.; *U.S. Private*, pg. 2074
INFOVISION CONSULTANTS, INC.; *U.S. Private*, pg. 2074
INFRASTRUCTURE ENGINEERING CORP.—See Littlejohn & Co., LLC; *U.S. Private*, pg. 2469
INGENICOMM, LLC—See Parsons Corporation; *U.S. Public*, pg. 1651
INGENIERIA, ESTUDIOS Y CONSTRUCCIONES, S.A.—See Iberdrola, S.A.; *Int'l*, pg. 3573
INGENIUM PROFESSIONAL SERVICES INC; *U.S. Private*, pg. 2075
INGERSOLL-RAND BEST-MATIC AB—See Ingersoll Rand Inc.; *U.S. Public*, pg. 1121
ING. TOMAS FRIED—See Doppelmayr Group; *Int'l*, pg. 2175
INMATION UK LTD.—See Emerson Electric Co.; *U.S. Public*, pg. 752
INNOVATIVE TECHNICAL SOLUTIONS, INC.—See Gilbane, Inc.; *U.S. Private*, pg. 1698
INNOVION CORPORATION—See Coherent Corp.; *U.S. Public*, pg. 528
INOVA GROUPE—See Altawest Group; *Int'l*, pg. 388
INPARK DETACHERINGEN B.V.—See Fugro N.V.; *Int'l*, pg. 2807
IN PRACTICE SYSTEMS LTD.—See Cegedim S.A.; *Int'l*, pg. 1390
IN PROJEKT LOUNY ENGINEERING S.R.O.—See CEZ, a.s.; *Int'l*, pg. 1426
INSELKO AS—See Bilfinger SE; *Int'l*, pg. 1028
INSER-TRANSFIELD SERVICES S.A.—See Apollo Global Management, Inc.; *U.S. Public*, pg. 167
INSPIRE DEFENCE LTD—See Jacobs Engineering Group, Inc.; *U.S. Public*, pg. 1186
INSTALLIT AS—See Endur ASA; *Int'l*, pg. 2410
INSULATION PLUS, LLC—See MacArthur Co.; *U.S. Private*, pg. 2534
INTECH, INC.—See Electricite de France S.A.; *Int'l*, pg. 2351
INTECH INTERNATIONAL INC.—See BWX Technologies, Inc.; *U.S. Public*, pg. 413
INTECSA-INARSA, S.A.—See AtkinsRealis Group Inc.; *Int'l*, pg. 673
INTECSA INGENIERIA INDUSTRIAL, S.A.—See ACS, Actividades de Construccion y Servicios, S.A.; *Int'l*, pg. 115
INTEGRAL GROUP, INC.; *U.S. Private*, pg. 2098
INTEGRATED DESIGN GROUP, INC.—See Harley Ellis Devereaux Corporation; *U.S. Private*, pg. 1865
INTEGRATED ENGINEERING SERVICES—See SSOE Group; *U.S. Private*, pg. 3769
INTEGRATED PROCESS TECHNOLOGIES, INC.; *U.S. Private*, pg. 2100
INTEGRATED PROCESS TECHNOLOGIES, INC.—See Integrated Process Technologies, Inc.; *U.S. Private*, pg. 2100
INTEGRATION INNOVATION, INC.; *U.S. Private*, pg. 2101
INTEGRITY ENGINEERING & DESIGN SOLUTIONS; *U.S. Private*, pg. 2102
INTELECT CORPORATION; *U.S. Private*, pg. 2104
INTELLISERV NORWAY AS—See NOV, Inc.; *U.S. Public*, pg. 1545
INTERNATIONAL STEEL SERVICES, INC.; *U.S. Private*, pg. 2121
INTERSTATES ENGINEERING—See Harbor Group Inc; *U.S. Private*, pg. 1859
INTOUCH AUTOMATION, INC.—See Lear Corporation; *U.S. Public*, pg. 1297
INVERSE GROUP PTY. LTD.—See Hiremii Limited; *Int'l*, pg. 3404

541330 — ENGINEERING SERVICE...

IOOO ERICPOL BREST—See Ericpol Sp. z o.o.; *Int'l*, pg. 2493
IPSI L.L.C.—See Bechtel Group, Inc.; *U.S. Private*, pg. 510
IRWIN ENGINEERS INC.—See Pennoni Associates Inc.; *U.S. Private*, pg. 3136
I & S GROUP, INC.; *U.S. Private*, pg. 2020
ISLEBURN LTD.—See Global Energy (Holdings) Ltd.; *Int'l*, pg. 2995
ISRA SURFACE VISION GMBH—See Atlas Copco AB; *Int'l*, pg. 682
ISYS, INC.; *U.S. Private*, pg. 2147
ITALCEMENTI INGEGNERIA S.R.L.—See Heidelberg Materials AG; *Int'l*, pg. 3317
ITALFERR S.P.A.—See Ferrovie dello Stato Italiane S.p.A.; *Int'l*, pg. 2645
ITASCA TECHNOLOGY INC.—See AcBel Polytech Inc.; *Int'l*, pg. 78
ITECO NEPAL (PVT.) LTD.—See AFRY AB; *Int'l*, pg. 194
ITEK PL—See Addtech AB; *Int'l*, pg. 133
ITEUVE CANARIAS, S.L.—See I Squared Capital Advisors (US) LLC; *U.S. Private*, pg. 2023
ITS INGENIEURGESELLSCHAFT MBH—See BKW AG; *Int'l*, pg. 1055
IZGRADNJA D.O.O.—See Bain Capital, LP; *U.S. Private*, pg. 443
IZGRADNJA D.O.O.—See Cinven Limited; *Int'l*, pg. 1613
JACOBI, TOOMBS & LANZ, INC.—See NewHold Enterprises LLC; *U.S. Private*, pg. 2915
JACOBS ADVISERS INC.—See Jacobs Engineering Group, Inc.; *U.S. Public*, pg. 1184
JACOBS AUSTRALIA PTY. LIMITED—See Jacobs Engineering Group, Inc.; *U.S. Public*, pg. 1185
JACOBS BELGIE NV—See Jacobs Engineering Group, Inc.; *U.S. Public*, pg. 1184
JACOBS CHINA LIMITED—See Jacobs Engineering Group, Inc.; *U.S. Public*, pg. 1185
JACOBS COLOMBIA S.A.S.—See Jacobs Engineering Group, Inc.; *U.S. Public*, pg. 1184
JACOBS CONSULTANTS, INC.—See Jacobs Engineering Group, Inc.; *U.S. Public*, pg. 1184
JACOBS EAGLETON LLC—See Jacobs Engineering Group, Inc.; *U.S. Public*, pg. 1184
JACOBS E&C AUSTRALIA PTY. LTD.—See Jacobs Engineering Group, Inc.; *U.S. Public*, pg. 1185
JACOBS E&C LIMITED—See Jacobs Engineering Group, Inc.; *U.S. Public*, pg. 1186
JACOBS ENGINEERING AND CONSTRUCTION (THAILAND) LIMITED—See Jacobs Engineering Group, Inc.; *U.S. Public*, pg. 1184
JACOBS ENGINEERING DEUTSCHLAND GMBH—See Jacobs Engineering Group, Inc.; *U.S. Public*, pg. 1184
JACOBS ENGINEERING GROUP, INC. - ARLINGTON (NORTH GLEBE ROAD), VA—See Jacobs Engineering Group, Inc.; *U.S. Public*, pg. 1184
JACOBS ENGINEERING GROUP, INC. - BATON ROUGE, LA—See Jacobs Engineering Group, Inc.; *U.S. Public*, pg. 1184
JACOBS ENGINEERING GROUP, INC. - BOSTON, MA—See Jacobs Engineering Group, Inc.; *U.S. Public*, pg. 1184
JACOBS ENGINEERING GROUP, INC. - CINCINNATI, OH—See Jacobs Engineering Group, Inc.; *U.S. Public*, pg. 1184
JACOBS ENGINEERING GROUP, INC. - DENVER, CO—See Jacobs Engineering Group, Inc.; *U.S. Public*, pg. 1184
JACOBS ENGINEERING GROUP, INC. - GREENVILLE, SC—See Jacobs Engineering Group, Inc.; *U.S. Public*, pg. 1184
JACOBS ENGINEERING GROUP, INC. - MORRISTOWN, NJ—See Jacobs Engineering Group, Inc.; *U.S. Public*, pg. 1184
JACOBS ENGINEERING GROUP, INC. - NEW YORK, NY—See Jacobs Engineering Group, Inc.; *U.S. Public*, pg. 1184
JACOBS ENGINEERING GROUP, INC.; *U.S. Public*, pg. 1183
JACOBS ENGINEERING GROUP MALAYSIA SDN BHD—See Jacobs Engineering Group, Inc.; *U.S. Public*, pg. 1184
JACOBS ENGINEERING IRELAND LIMITED - BLACKROCK—See Jacobs Engineering Group, Inc.; *U.S. Public*, pg. 1184
JACOBS ENGINEERING IRELAND LIMITED—See Jacobs Engineering Group, Inc.; *U.S. Public*, pg. 1184
JACOBS ENGINEERING NEW YORK INC.—See Jacobs Engineering Group, Inc.; *U.S. Public*, pg. 1184
JACOBS ENGINEERING (SUZHOU) CO., LTD—See Jacobs Engineering Group, Inc.; *U.S. Public*, pg. 1185
JACOBS ENGINEERING UK LIMITED—See Jacobs Engineering Group, Inc.; *U.S. Public*, pg. 1185
JACOBS FIELD SERVICES AMERICAS INC.—See Jacobs Engineering Group, Inc.; *U.S. Public*, pg. 1185
JACOBS INTERNATIONAL LIMITED—See Jacobs Engineering Group, Inc.; *U.S. Public*, pg. 1185
JACOBS ITALIA SPA—See Jacobs Engineering Group, Inc.; *U.S. Public*, pg. 1185
JACOBS MINERALS, INC.—See Jacobs Engineering Group, Inc.; *U.S. Public*, pg. 1185
JACOBS NEDERLAND BV—See Jacobs Engineering Group, Inc.; *U.S. Public*, pg. 1185
JACOBS NEW ZEALAND LIMITED—See Jacobs Engineering Group, Inc.; *U.S. Public*, pg. 1186
JACOBS NORWAY AS—See Jacobs Engineering Group, Inc.; *U.S. Public*, pg. 1185
JACOBS ONE LIMITED—See Jacobs Engineering Group, Inc.; *U.S. Public*, pg. 1185
JACOBS PROCESS B.V.—See Jacobs Engineering Group, Inc.; *U.S. Public*, pg. 1185
JACOBS PROCESS LIMITED—See Jacobs Engineering Group, Inc.; *U.S. Public*, pg. 1186
JACOBS PROJECTS (PHILIPPINES) INC.—See Jacobs Engineering Group, Inc.; *U.S. Public*, pg. 1185
JACOBS PROJECTS (SHANGHAI) CO., LTD.—See Jacobs Engineering Group, Inc.; *U.S. Public*, pg. 1185
JACOBS RUSSIA LLC.—See Jacobs Engineering Group, Inc.; *U.S. Public*, pg. 1185
JACOBS SKM LTD—See Jacobs Engineering Group, Inc.; *U.S. Public*, pg. 1186
JACOBS STOBBARTS LTD—See Jacobs Engineering Group, Inc.; *U.S. Public*, pg. 1186
JACOBS SVERIGE AB—See Jacobs Engineering Group, Inc.; *U.S. Public*, pg. 1185
JACOBS TECHNOLOGY, INC.—See Jacobs Engineering Group, Inc.; *U.S. Public*, pg. 1185
JACOBS U.K. LIMITED—See Jacobs Engineering Group, Inc.; *U.S. Public*, pg. 1185
JANSEN STRAWN CONSULTING ENGINEERS, INC.—See Ware Malcomb; *U.S. Private*, pg. 4441
JAPAN JURONG ENGINEERING CO., LTD.—See IHI Corporation; *Int'l*, pg. 3605
JBA CONSULTING ENGINEERS (ASIA) LIMITED—See NV5 Global, Inc.; *U.S. Public*, pg. 1557
JBA CONSULTING ENGINEERS—See NV5 Global, Inc.; *U.S. Public*, pg. 1557
JBL RESOURCES; *U.S. Private*, pg. 2194
J. DANIEL & COMPANY, INC.—See The Danella Companies Inc.; *U.S. Private*, pg. 4018
J. D. STEVENSON AND ASSOCIATES, INC.—See Gryphon Investors, LLC; *U.S. Private*, pg. 1798
JE ARCHITECTS/ENGINEERS, P.C.—See Jacobs Engineering Group, Inc.; *U.S. Public*, pg. 1184
JEG ARCHITECTURE NEVADA, INC.—See Jacobs Engineering Group, Inc.; *U.S. Public*, pg. 1184
JENNINGS AERONAUTICS INC.—See AE Industrial Partners, LP; *U.S. Private*, pg. 112
JENSEN HUGHES, INC. - MIDWEST—See Gryphon Investors, LLC; *U.S. Private*, pg. 1798
JERA CO., LTD.—See Chubu Electric Power Co., Inc.; *Int'l*, pg. 1593
JERMANN INGENIEURE UND GEOMETER AG—See BKW AG; *Int'l*, pg. 1055
JET EAST CORPORATE AVIATION, LLC—See The Sterling Group, L.P.; *U.S. Private*, pg. 4123
JEYCO (1992) PTY. LTD.—See Enerpac Tool Group Corp.; *U.S. Public*, pg. 766
J.F. SHEA CONSTRUCTION, INC.—See J.F. Shea Co., Inc.; *U.S. Private*, pg. 2164
JGC FLUOR BC JOINT VENTURE—See Fluor Corporation; *U.S. Public*, pg. 858
JGD ASSOCIATES INC.—See Fiedler Group; *U.S. Private*, pg. 1503
JG MANAGEMENT SYSTEMS, INC.; *U.S. Private*, pg. 2207
JG SERVICE COMPANY; *U.S. Private*, pg. 2207
J.H. BERRA CONSTRUCTION CO., INC. - GRADING DIVISION—See J.H. Berra Holding Co., Inc.; *U.S. Private*, pg. 2165
J.H. BERRA CONSTRUCTION CO., INC. - LAND DEVELOPMENT DIVISION—See J.H. Berra Holding Co., Inc.; *U.S. Private*, pg. 2165
J.H. BERRA CONSTRUCTION CO., INC. - UTILITY DIVISION—See J.H. Berra Holding Co., Inc.; *U.S. Private*, pg. 2165
J.H. BERRA ENGINEERING & SURVEYING CO., INC.—See J.H. Berra Holding Co., Inc.; *U.S. Private*, pg. 2165
JIANGSU ALMADEN POWER INVESTMENT CO., LTD.—See Changzhou Almaden Stock Co., Ltd.; *Int'l*, pg. 1445
JINGDING ENGINEERING & CONSTRUCTION CO., LTD.—See CTCI Corporation; *Int'l*, pg. 1870
J. KOSKI COMPANY—See APi Group Corporation; *Int'l*, pg. 514
J&L HOLDING COMPANY—See ITE Management L.P.; *U.S. Private*, pg. 2149
JOBES, HENDERSON & ASSOCIATES, INC.—See Sterling Investment Partners, L.P.; *U.S. Private*, pg. 3806
JOBFAIR GMBH—See Bertrandt AG; *Int'l*, pg. 998
JOHN A MARTIN AND ASSOCIATES OF NEVADA—See John A. Martin & Associates, Incorporated; *U.S. Private*, pg. 2220
JOHN A. MARTIN & ASSOCIATES, INCORPORATED; *U.S. Private*, pg. 2219
JOHN A. MARTIN & ASSOCIATES, LTD.—See John A. Martin & Associates, Incorporated; *U.S. Private*, pg. 2220
JOHN H. ROBINSON TESTING INC.—See Urban Engineers Inc.; *U.S. Private*, pg. 4314
JOHNSON ENGINEERING, INC.—See Apex Companies, LLC; *U.S. Private*, pg. 292
JOHNSON, MIRMIRAN & THOMPSON, INC.; *U.S. Private*, pg. 2229
JONES EDMUNDS & ASSOCIATES, INC.; *U.S. Private*, pg. 2233
JONES-STUCKEY LTD., INC.—See Pennoni Associates Inc.; *U.S. Private*, pg. 3136
JORDAN, JONES AND GOULDING, INC.—See Jacobs Engineering Group, Inc.; *U.S. Public*, pg. 1186
JOSEPH NETO & ASSOCIATES INC.—See Lerch Bates Inc.; *U.S. Private*, pg. 2431
JOSEPH PARIS—See FAYAT SAS; *Int'l*, pg. 2625
JOSLIN LESSER & ASSOCIATES, INC.—See NV5 Global, Inc.; *U.S. Public*, pg. 1557
JPC GROUP, INC.; *U.S. Private*, pg. 2239
JPL PROJECT SP. Z O. O.—See Jacobs Engineering Group, Inc.; *U.S. Public*, pg. 1184
J-POWER ENTECH, INC.—See Electric Power Development Co., Ltd.; *Int'l*, pg. 2349
JR ANLEGG AS—See AF Gruppen ASA; *Int'l*, pg. 184
J. RAY MCDERMOTT DE MEXICO, S.A. DE C.V.—See McDermott International, Inc.; *U.S. Public*, pg. 1405
J.S. REDPATH CORPORATION—See ATON GmbH; *Int'l*, pg. 688
JUFFALI AIR CONDITIONING, MECHANICAL & ELECTRICAL COMPANY—See E.A. Juffali & Brothers Company; *Int'l*, pg. 2250
JURONG ENGINEERING LIMITED—See IHI Corporation; *Int'l*, pg. 3606
J. VAN VLIET B.V.—See HAL Trust N.V.; *Int'l*, pg. 3226
JWK INTERNATIONAL CORP.; *U.S. Private*, pg. 2247
JX NIPPON PROCUREMENT CORPORATION—See ENEOS Holdings, Inc.; *Int'l*, pg. 2417
J.Y. LEGNER ASSOCIATES INC; *U.S. Private*, pg. 2172
KAFI BV—See ARCADIS N.V.; *Int'l*, pg. 541
KAMAN ENGINEERING SERVICES, INC.—See Arcline Investment Management LP; *U.S. Private*, pg. 314
KANEY AEROSPACE, INC.; *U.S. Private*, pg. 2260
KANNAPOLIS ENERGY PARTNERS LLC—See Peregrine Energy Corp.; *U.S. Private*, pg. 3147
KARAK LAND SDN. BHD.—See Bina Puri Holdings Bhd; *Int'l*, pg. 1032
KARINS ENGINEERING GROUP, INC.; *U.S. Private*, pg. 2262
KARINS ENGINEERING GROUP, INC. - ST. PETERSBURG OFFICE—See Karins Engineering Group, Inc.; *U.S. Private*, pg. 2262
KARMAR SA—See Bouygues S.A.; *Int'l*, pg. 1123
KASKTAS KAYAR KALIP ALTYAPI SONDAJ KAZIK VE TECRIT ANONIM SIRKETI—See Enka Insaat ve Sanayi A.S.; *Int'l*, pg. 2440
KAY & ASSOCIATES INC.; *U.S. Private*, pg. 2266
KBD TECHNIC—See CECO Environmental Corp.; *U.S. Public*, pg. 463
KB ENGINEERING, PC; *U.S. Private*, pg. 2268
KBR ENGINEERING COMPANY, LLC—See KBR, Inc.; *U.S. Public*, pg. 1216
KBR OVERSEAS, INC.—See KBR, Inc.; *U.S. Public*, pg. 1216
KCI ASSOCIATES OF NORTH CAROLINA, P.A.—See KCI Holdings Inc.; *U.S. Private*, pg. 2269
KCI ASSOCIATES OF OHIO, P.A.—See KCI Holdings Inc.; *U.S. Private*, pg. 2269
KCI ASSOCIATES OF THE DISTRICT OF COLUMBIA, P.C.—See KCI Holdings Inc.; *U.S. Private*, pg. 2269
KCI COMMUNICATIONS INFRASTRUCTURE—See KCI Holdings Inc.; *U.S. Private*, pg. 2270
KCI HOLDINGS INC.; *U.S. Private*, pg. 2269
KCI PROTECTION TECHNOLOGIES LLC—See KCI Holdings Inc.; *U.S. Private*, pg. 2270
KCI TECHNOLOGIES INC.—See KCI Holdings Inc.; *U.S. Private*, pg. 2269
KDW SALAS O'BRIEN, LLC—See Salas O'Brien Engineers, Inc.; *U.S. Private*, pg. 3530
KELLOGG BROWN & ROOT (GREENFORD) LIMITED—See KBR, Inc.; *U.S. Public*, pg. 1216
KELLOGG BROWN & ROOT LLC—See KBR, Inc.; *U.S. Public*, pg. 1216
KELYNIAM GLOBAL, INC.; *U.S. Public*, pg. 1220
KENNEDY/JENKS CONSULTANTS INC.; *U.S. Private*, pg. 2285
KESTREL CORP.; *U.S. Private*, pg. 2291
KEYSTONE CONSULTING ENGINEERS, INC.—See Keystone Consulting Engineers, Inc.; *U.S. Private*, pg. 2296
K-FIVE CONSTRUCTION CORPORATION - CHICAGO PLANT—See K-Five Construction Corporation; *U.S. Private*, pg. 2251
K-FIVE CONSTRUCTION CORPORATION - ELMHURST PLANT—See K-Five Construction Corporation; *U.S. Private*, pg. 2251
K-FIVE CONSTRUCTION CORPORATION - MARKHAM PLANT—See K-Five Construction Corporation; *U.S. Private*, pg. 2251
K-FIVE CONSTRUCTION CORPORATION - NAPERVILLE PLANT—See K-Five Construction Corporation; *U.S. Private*, pg. 2251

541330 — ENGINEERING SERVICE...

KFP INGENIEURE GMBH—See BKW AG; *Int'l*, pg. 1055
K FRIESE & ASSOCIATES, INC.—See H.W. Lochner, Inc.; *U.S. Private*, pg. 1836
KIEFNER & ASSOCIATES INC.—See I Squared Capital Advisors (US) LLC; *U.S. Private*, pg. 2023
KIMLEY-HORN AND ASSOCIATES, INC.; *U.S. Private*, pg. 2305
KIMLEY-HORN AND ASSOCIATES, INC.—See Kimley-Horn and Associates, Inc.; *U.S. Private*, pg. 2305
KIMLEY-HORN AND ASSOCIATES, INC.—See Kimley-Horn and Associates, Inc.; *U.S. Private*, pg. 2305
KINETIC PROJECTS INC—See Gemini Corporation; *Int'l*, pg. 2916
KING ENGINEERING ASSOCIATES, INC.—See Littlejohn & Co., LLC; *U.S. Private*, pg. 2469
KINSEY TECHNICAL SERVICES, INC.—See Science Applications International Corporation; *U.S. Public*, pg. 1848
THE KIRKMAN OLIVER COMPANY—See Madison Dearborn Partners, LLC; *U.S. Private*, pg. 2541
KISINGER CAMPO & ASSOCIATES CORP.; *U.S. Private*, pg. 2315
KISO-JIBAN CONSULTANTS CO., LTD.—See Chodai Co., Ltd.; *Int'l*, pg. 1577
KIU LOK SERVICE MANAGEMENT COMPANY LIMITED—See FSE Services Group Limited; *Int'l*, pg. 2798
KLEINFELDER AUSTRALIA PTY LTD—See Goldberg Lindsay & Co., LLC; *U.S. Private*, pg. 1729
KLEINFELDER CENTRAL, INC.—See Goldberg Lindsay & Co., LLC; *U.S. Private*, pg. 1729
THE KLEINFELDER GROUP, INC.—See Goldberg Lindsay & Co., LLC; *U.S. Private*, pg. 1729
KLEINFELDER GUAM, LLC—See Goldberg Lindsay & Co., LLC; *U.S. Private*, pg. 1729
KLEINFELDER INTERNATIONAL, INC.-CALGARY—See Goldberg Lindsay & Co., LLC; *U.S. Private*, pg. 1729
KLEINFELDER NORTHEAST, INC.—See Goldberg Lindsay & Co., LLC; *U.S. Private*, pg. 1729
KLEINFELDER SOUTHEAST, INC.—See Goldberg Lindsay & Co., LLC; *U.S. Private*, pg. 1729
KLEINFELDER WEST, INC.—See Goldberg Lindsay & Co., LLC; *U.S. Private*, pg. 1730
KLOCHER BAUGESELLSCHAFT M.B.H.—See ALPINE Bau GmbH; *Int'l*, pg. 371
KMS SOLUTIONS, LLC—See Subsystem Technologies, Inc.; *U.S. Private*, pg. 3847
KMT PLANUNGSGESELLSCHAFT MBH—See BKW AG; *Int'l*, pg. 1055
KNEIPP-HOF DUSSNANG AG—See Fresenius SE & Co. KGaA; *Int'l*, pg. 2780
KNIGHT WENDLING GMBH—See GEMCO Engineers B.V.; *Int'l*, pg. 2915
K.N.P. SUPPLY CO., LTD.—See Gunkul Engineering Co., Ltd.; *Int'l*, pg. 3183
KOA CORPORATION—See H.W. Lochner, Inc.; *U.S. Private*, pg. 1836
KOHT'AENE ENTERPRISES COMPANY, LLC—See Ahtna Incorporated; *U.S. Private*, pg. 131
KOKUSAI KOGYO CO., LTD.—See The Carlyle Group Inc.; *U.S. Private*, pg. 2055
KONCEPO SCIENTECH INTERNATIONAL PVT. LTD.—See Kewaunee Scientific Corporation; *U.S. Public*, pg. 1225
KONRAD BEYER & CO SPEZIALBAU GMBH—See ALPINE Bau GmbH; *Int'l*, pg. 371
KOREA DEVELOPMENT CORPORATION—See Daelim Industrial Co., Ltd.; *Int'l*, pg. 1908
KORMAK PRAHA A.S.—See EnBW Energie Baden-Wurttemberg AG; *Int'l*, pg. 2399
KPFF INC.; *U.S. Private*, pg. 2346
KP SHAW, LLC—See The Shaw Group Inc.; *U.S. Private*, pg. 4117
KRATOS DEFENSE & ROCKET SUPPORT SERVICES, INC.—See Kratos Defense & Security Solutions, Inc.; *U.S. Public*, pg. 1276
KREUZ INTERNATIONAL PTE LTD—See Headland Capital Partners Limited; *Int'l*, pg. 3301
KREUZ OFFSHORE CONTRACTORS LTD.—See Headland Capital Partners Limited; *Int'l*, pg. 3301
KREUZ OFFSHORE MARINE PTE LTD—See Headland Capital Partners Limited; *Int'l*, pg. 3301
KROESCHELL OPERATIONS INC.—See Kroeschell, Inc.; *U.S. Private*, pg. 2352
K. SCHWEIZER AG—See Burkhalter Holding AG; *Int'l*, pg. 1225
KS ENERGY SERVICES, LLC—See Clayton, Dubilier & Rice, LLC; *U.S. Private*, pg. 919
KSH SOLUTIONS INC.—See AFRY AB; *Int'l*, pg. 194
K.S TRADING (PVT) LTD.—See Daikin Industries, Ltd.; *Int'l*, pg. 1935
KTA GROUP INC.—See Bowman Consulting Group Ltd.; *U.S. Public*, pg. 376
K-TRON (SHANGHAI) CO. LTD.—See Hillenbrand, Inc.; *U.S. Public*, pg. 1036
THE KULJIAN CORPORATION; *U.S. Private*, pg. 4066
KVAERNER CANADA LTD.—See Aker Solutions ASA; *Int'l*, pg. 263
KVAERNER LLC—See Aker Solutions ASA; *Int'l*, pg. 263

KWJ ENGINEERING INC.—See Interlink Electronics, Inc.; *U.S. Public*, pg. 1144
KYZEN BVBA—See Kyzen Corporation; *U.S. Private*, pg. 2361
KYZEN SDN. BHD.—See Kyzen Corporation; *U.S. Private*, pg. 2361
L-3 UNIDYNE—See L3Harris Technologies, Inc.; *U.S. Public*, pg. 1283
LABELLA ASSOCIATES, D.P.C.; *U.S. Private*, pg. 2370
LACHAUX PAYSAGES—See FAYAT SAS; *Int'l*, pg. 2625
LACO ASSOCIATES, INC.; *U.S. Private*, pg. 2394
LA JOLLA LOGIC—See Enlightenment Capital LLC; *U.S. Private*, pg. 1400
LANDAIR SURVEYING COMPANY OF GEORGIA—See KCI Holdings Inc.; *U.S. Private*, pg. 2270
LANGAN ENGINEERING & ENVIRONMENTAL SERVICES INC.; *U.S. Private*, pg. 2388
LANGAN ENGINEERING & ENVIRONMENTAL SERVICES, INC.—See Langan Engineering & Environmental Services, Inc.; *U.S. Private*, pg. 2389
LANGAN ENGINEERING & ENVIRONMENTAL SERVICES, INC.—See Langan Engineering & Environmental Services, Inc.; *U.S. Private*, pg. 2389
LANGAN ENGINEERING & ENVIRONMENTAL SERVICES, INC.—See Langan Engineering & Environmental Services, Inc.; *U.S. Private*, pg. 2389
LANGAN ENGINEERING & ENVIRONMENTAL SERVICES, INC.—See Langan Engineering & Environmental Services, Inc.; *U.S. Private*, pg. 2389
LANGAN INTERNATIONAL, LLC - ABU DHABI—See Langan Engineering & Environmental Services, Inc.; *U.S. Private*, pg. 2389
LARSON DESIGN GROUP—See Larson Design Group; *U.S. Private*, pg. 2394
LARSON DESIGN GROUP—See Larson Design Group; *U.S. Private*, pg. 2394
LARSON DESIGN GROUP—See Larson Design Group; *U.S. Private*, pg. 2394
LATA-MERRICK ENGINEERING & ENVIRONMENT, LLC—See Los Alamos Technical Associates, Inc.; *U.S. Private*, pg. 2496
LATECIS CANADA INC.—See Searchlight Capital Partners, L.P.; *U.S. Private*, pg. 3588
LATECIS UK LIMITED—See Searchlight Capital Partners, L.P.; *U.S. Private*, pg. 3588
LATECOERE INC.—See Searchlight Capital Partners, L.P.; *U.S. Private*, pg. 3588
LATECOERE SERVICES GMBH—See Searchlight Capital Partners, L.P.; *U.S. Private*, pg. 3588
LAUREN BHARAT ENGINEERING PRIVATE LIMITED—See Lauren Holdings Inc.; *U.S. Private*, pg. 2399
LAUREN ENGINEERS & CONSTRUCTORS INC.—See Lauren Holdings Inc.; *U.S. Private*, pg. 2399
LAUREN ENGINEERS & CONSTRUCTORS, ULC—See Lauren Holdings Inc.; *U.S. Private*, pg. 2399
LAYNE GEOCONSTRUCTION—See Granite Construction Incorporated; *U.S. Public*, pg. 958
L-CON CONSTRUCTORS COMPANY—See Lexicon, Inc.; *U.S. Private*, pg. 2440
LDG - TRANSPORTATION ENGINEERING—See Larson Design Group; *U.S. Private*, pg. 2393
LDIS, LLC—See Tetra Tech, Inc.; *U.S. Public*, pg. 2023
LEADER MARINE CONT. L.L.C.—See Build King Holdings Limited; *Int'l*, pg. 1212
LEADING EDGE ENGINEERING, PC—See Adaptive Corp.; *U.S. Private*, pg. 76
LEE-SIMPSON ASSOCIATES, INC.—See Comvest Group Holdings LLC; *U.S. Private*, pg. 1007
LEHIGH ENGINEERING ASSOCIATES, INC.; *U.S. Private*, pg. 2418
LEHIGH ENGINEERING LLC—See Reading Anthracite Company; *U.S. Private*, pg. 3366
LEIDOS CANADA—See Leidos Holdings, Inc.; *U.S. Public*, pg. 1304
LEIDOS ENGINEERING OF NORTH CAROLINA, INC.—See Leidos Holdings, Inc.; *U.S. Public*, pg. 1304
LEIDOS ENGINEERING—See Leidos Holdings, Inc.; *U.S. Public*, pg. 1304
LEIGHFISHER LTD.—See Jacobs Engineering Group, Inc.; *U.S. Public*, pg. 1186
LELOUP ENTREPRISE GENERALE SPRL—See Ackermans & van Haaren NV; *Int'l*, pg. 104
LENG AIK ENGINEERING PTE. LTD.—See EXEO Group Inc.; *Int'l*, pg. 2583
LEO A. DALY COMPANY; *U.S. Private*, pg. 2422
LESJOFORS BANDDETALJER AB—See Beijer Alma AB; *Int'l*, pg. 943
LEVIAT PTY LIMITED—See CRH plc; *Int'l*, pg. 1845
LEWANDOWSKI ENGINEERS—See Sterling Investment Partners, L.P.; *U.S. Private*, pg. 3806
LEWIS INNOVATIVE TECHNOLOGIES, INC.—See Mercury Systems, Inc.; *U.S. Public*, pg. 1122
LEYBOLD HISPÁNICA, S.A.—See Atlas Copco AB; *Int'l*, pg. 683
LHC STRUCTURAL ENGINEERS, PC—See Bennett & Pless, Inc.; *U.S. Private*, pg. 526
LIGHTING SCIENCES INC.—See Underwriters Laboratories Inc.; *U.S. Private*, pg. 4280
LILKER ASSOCIATES CONSULTING ENGINEERS, PC; *U.S. Private*, pg. 2455

LIMBACH ENGINEERING & DESIGN SERVICES (LEDS)—See Limbach Holdings, Inc.; *U.S. Public*, pg. 1316
LINAIR ENGINEERING PTE. LTD.—See Acesian Partners Limited; *Int'l*, pg. 102
LINDBERGH & ASSOCIATES, LLC—See T.Y. Lin International Group Ltd.; *U.S. Private*, pg. 3913
LINDSCHULTE + GGL INGENIEURGESELLSCHAFT MBH—See BKW AG; *Int'l*, pg. 1055
LINDSCHULTE INGENIEURGESELLSCHAFT MBH—See BKW AG; *Int'l*, pg. 1055
LINK TECHNOLOGIES; *U.S. Private*, pg. 2461
LINTON ENGINEERING LLC—See Bennett & Pless, Inc.; *U.S. Private*, pg. 527
LIONBRIDGE MIDWEST, LLC—See H.I.G. Capital, LLC; *U.S. Private*, pg. 1830
LIONSBRIDGE CONTRACTOR GROUP—See CCA Global Partners, Inc.; *U.S. Private*, pg. 799
LIQUID GAS EQUIPMENT LIMITED—See Babcock International Group PLC; *Int'l*, pg. 793
LIQUID ROBOTICS, INC.—See The Boeing Company; *U.S. Public*, pg. 2041
LISEGA SOUTH INC.—See US Tech Services Inc.; *U.S. Private*, pg. 4320
LITEPOINT CORP.—See Teradyne, Inc.; *U.S. Public*, pg. 2018
LIVELINE TECHNOLOGIES INC.—See Cooper-Standard Holdings Inc.; *U.S. Public*, pg. 574
LJA ENGINEERING, INC.; *U.S. Private*, pg. 2474
L. KEELEY CONSTRUCTION CO.—See The Keeley Companies; *U.S. Private*, pg. 4064
LKE HAUSTECHNIK AG—See Burkhalter Holding AG; *Int'l*, pg. 1225
LN MAURICE—See FAYAT SAS; *Int'l*, pg. 2625
LOCATING, INC.—See Dycom Industries, Inc.; *U.S. Public*, pg. 698
LOCHRANE ENGINEERING, INC.—See NV5 Global, Inc.; *U.S. Public*, pg. 1557
LOCKWOOD ANDREWS & NEWNAM, INC.—See Leo A. Daly Company; *U.S. Private*, pg. 2422
LOCKWOOD KESSLER & BARTLETT, INC.—See Wind Point Advisors LLC; *U.S. Private*, pg. 4536
LOENBRO, INC.—See Braemont Capital Management LLC; *U.S. Private*, pg. 633
LOGICAL SYSTEMS, LLC.; *U.S. Private*, pg. 2481
LOGOS ENGENHARIA S.A.—See ARCADIS N.V.; *Int'l*, pg. 542
LONG ENGINEERING, LLC—See GI Manager L.P.; *U.S. Private*, pg. 1691
LOS ALAMOS TECHNICAL ASSOCIATES, INC.; *U.S. Private*, pg. 2496
LOSINGER MARAZZI AG—See Bouygues S.A.; *Int'l*, pg. 1122
THE LOUIS BERGER GROUP, INC. - PROVIDENCE—See The Louis Berger Group, Inc.; *U.S. Private*, pg. 4073
THE LOUIS BERGER GROUP, INC.; *U.S. Private*, pg. 4073
LOUREIRO ENGINEERING ASSOCIATES INC.; *U.S. Private*, pg. 2501
LOW VOLTAGE CONTRACTORS, INC.; *U.S. Private*, pg. 2504
LPI, INC.; *U.S. Private*, pg. 2507
LRM—See FAYAT SAS; *Int'l*, pg. 2625
LSE SPACE MIDDLE EAST JLT—See GomSpace Group AB; *Int'l*, pg. 3037
LSI ADAPT INC.—See LSI Industries Inc.; *U.S. Public*, pg. 1344
LTC ENGINEERING ASSOCIATES, INC.—See CACI International Inc.; *U.S. Public*, pg. 418
LUBRIZOL SPECIALTY PRODUCTS LLC—See Berkshire Hathaway Inc.; *U.S. Public*, pg. 319
LUCHUAN BOSSCO BIOTECH CO., LTD.—See Guangxi Bossco Environmental Protection Technology Co., Ltd.; *Int'l*, pg. 3163
LUDGATE ENGINEERING CORP.; *U.S. Private*, pg. 2512
LUMASENSE SENSOR GMBH—See Advanced Energy Industries, Inc.; *U.S. Public*, pg. 47
LUMASENSE TECHNOLOGIES GMBH—See Advanced Energy Industries, Inc.; *U.S. Public*, pg. 47
LUMASENSE TECHNOLOGIES LIMITED—See Advanced Energy Industries, Inc.; *U.S. Public*, pg. 47
LUMMUS NOVOLEN TECHNOLOGY GMBH—See McDermott International, Inc.; *U.S. Public*, pg. 1405
LUMMUS TECHNOLOGY - HEAT TRANSFER—See McDermott International, Inc.; *U.S. Public*, pg. 1405
LUMMUS TECHNOLOGY, INC.—See McDermott International, Inc.; *U.S. Public*, pg. 1405
LUXENERGIE S.A.—See Enovos International S.A.; *Int'l*, pg. 2444
LVB LAWOG VAMED BAUPLANUNGS- UND ERRICHTUNGS-GMBH—See Fresenius SE & Co. KGaA; *Int'l*, pg. 2780
LYDALL INDUSTRIAL FILTRATION (EMEA) LIMITED—See Lydall, Inc.; *U.S. Public*, pg. 1349
LYDALL PERFORMANCE MATERIALS B.V.—See Lydall, Inc.; *U.S. Public*, pg. 1349
LYDALL PERFORMANCE MATERIALS, INC.—See Lydall, Inc.; *U.S. Public*, pg. 1350

LYDALL PERFORMANCE MATERIALS S.A.S.—See Lydall, Inc.; *U.S. Public*, pg. 1349
LYDALL THERMAL/ACOUSTICAL (TAICANG) COMPANY LIMITED—See Lydall, Inc.; *U.S. Public*, pg. 1350
M2E LLC; *U.S. Private*, pg. 2530
MABBETT & ASSOCIATES, INC.; *U.S. Private*, pg. 2531
MACDERMID CANNING LTD—See Element Solutions Inc.; *U.S. Public*, pg. 727
MACDERMID INVESTMENT CORP.—See Element Solutions Inc.; *U.S. Public*, pg. 727
MACDERMID OVERSEAS ASIA LTD—See Element Solutions Inc.; *U.S. Public*, pg. 727
MACKAY & SPOSITO, INC., *U.S. Private*, pg. 2536
MADAGASCAR DAIHO COMPANY LIMITED—See DAIHO CORPORATION; *Int'l*, pg. 1927
MAGNOLIA RIVER SERVICES, INC.—See Warren Equity Partners, LLC; *U.S. Private*, pg. 4443
MAGNUM TECHNICAL SERVICES, INC.—See Southland Industries; *U.S. Private*, pg. 3737
MAJESTIC ENGINEERING COMPANY LIMITED—See FSE Services Group Limited; *Int'l*, pg. 2798
MAJESTIC ENGINEERING (MACAO) COMPANY LIMITED—See FSE Services Group Limited; *Int'l*, pg. 2798
MALONE FINKLE ECKHARDT & COLLINS, INC.—See RTM & Associates, Inc.; *U.S. Private*, pg. 3498
MANAGEMENT RESOURCES GROUP, INC.—See Emerson Electric Co.; *U.S. Public*, pg. 748
MANNINGS (ASIA) CONSULTANTS LIMITED—See Boltek Holdings Limited; *Int'l*, pg. 1103
MANPOWER FRAMNAES INSTALLASJON AS—See ManpowerGroup Inc.; *U.S. Public*, pg. 1358
MANTECH ADVANCED SYSTEMS INTERNATIONAL INC.—See The Carlyle Group Inc.; *U.S. Public*, pg. 2048
MANTECH EUROPE SYSTEMS CORPORATION—See The Carlyle Group Inc.; *U.S. Public*, pg. 2048
MANTECH SENSOR TECHNOLOGIES, INC.—See The Carlyle Group Inc.; *U.S. Public*, pg. 2048
MANTECH TELECOMMUNICATIONS & INFORMATION SYSTEMS CORPORATION—See The Carlyle Group Inc.; *U.S. Public*, pg. 2049
MANTECH TELECOMMUNICATIONS—See The Carlyle Group Inc.; *U.S. Public*, pg. 2049
MANUFACTURAS SHAW SOUTH AMERICA, C.A.—See The Shaw Group Inc.; *U.S. Private*, pg. 4117
MAQUINARIA AMECO GUATEMALA, LIMITADA—See OEP Capital Advisors, L.P.; *U.S. Private*, pg. 2998
MARCEL HUFSCHMID AG—See Burkhalter Holding AG; *Int'l*, pg. 1225
MARCEL RIEBEN INGENIEURE AG—See BKW AG; *Int'l*, pg. 1055
MARINE ENGINEERING GALATI—See Damen Shipyards Group; *Int'l*, pg. 1956
MARINE INDUSTRIAL DESIGN LIMITED—See Babcock International Group PLC; *Int'l*, pg. 793
MARINI-ERMONT—See FAYAT SAS; *Int'l*, pg. 2625
MARIS SUBSEA LTD—See Global Energy (Holdings) Ltd.; *Int'l*, pg. 2995
MARKETCOUNSEL; *U.S. Private*, pg. 2579
MARSHAL SYSTEMS PTE. LTD.—See 9R Limited; *Int'l*, pg. 17
MARTIN & CHOCK, INC.—See John A. Martin & Associates, Incorporated; *U.S. Private*, pg. 2220
MARTINIC ENGINEERING, INC.—See TriMas Corporation; *U.S. Public*, pg. 2189
MARTIN/MARTIN INC.—See John A. Martin & Associates, Incorporated; *U.S. Private*, pg. 2220
MARTIN / MARTIN WYOMING, INC.—See John A. Martin & Associates, Incorporated; *U.S. Private*, pg. 2220
MARTIN PEVZNER ENGINEERING—See I & S Group, Inc.; *U.S. Private*, pg. 2020
MARX/OKUBO ASSOCIATES, INC.; *U.S. Private*, pg. 2598
MAS AUSTRALASIA PTY LTD—See AusGroup Limited; *Int'l*, pg. 716
MASSIVE DYNAMICS, INC.; *U.S. Private*, pg. 2606
MATERIALS SCIENCES CORPORATION—See Seemann Composites, Inc.; *U.S. Private*, pg. 3598
MAT MASCHINENTECHNIK GMBH—See Hormann Maschinenbau GmbH & Co. KG; *Int'l*, pg. 3480
MATRIX PDM ENGINEERING, INC.—See Matrix Service Company; *U.S. Public*, pg. 1397
MATRIX TECHNOLOGIES INCORPORATED; *U.S. Private*, pg. 2612
MATRIX TECHNOLOGIES, INC.—See Matrix Technologies Incorporated; *U.S. Private*, pg. 2612
MATTHEWS DESIGN GROUP, LLC—See White Wolf Capital LLC; *U.S. Private*, pg. 4510
MAXWELL-REDDICK & ASSOCIATES, INC.—See Palm Beach Capital Partners LLC; *U.S. Private*, pg. 3079
MAYES TESTING ENGINEERS, INC.—See Terracon Consultants, Inc.; *U.S. Private*, pg. 3971
MBG BRUGGE—See Ackermans & van Haaren NV; *Int'l*, pg. 105
MBG WILRIJK—See Ackermans & van Haaren NV; *Int'l*, pg. 105
MBTECH BOHEMIA S.R.O.—See Adecco Group AG; *Int'l*, pg. 140

MBTECH GROUP GMBH & CO. KGAA—See Adecco Group AG; *Int'l*, pg. 140
MB-TECHNOLOGY NA LLC—See Adecco Group AG; *Int'l*, pg. 140
MBTECH POLSKA SP. Z O.O.—See Adecco Group AG; *Int'l*, pg. 140
MCAFEE HENDERSON SOLUTIONS, INC.—See Alfred Benesch & Company; *U.S. Private*, pg. 165
MCCAULEY PROPELLER SYSTEMS—See Textron Inc.; *U.S. Public*, pg. 2028
MCCLURE ENGINEERING CO.; *U.S. Private*, pg. 2629
MCC MECHANICAL OF THE CAROLINAS, L.L.C. - BENNER & FIELDS DIVISION—See The MCC Group, LLC; *U.S. Private*, pg. 4076
MCC MECHANICAL OF THE CAROLINAS, L.L.C.—See The MCC Group, LLC; *U.S. Private*, pg. 4076
MCCONNELL DOWELL CONSTRUCTORS LIMITED—See Aveng Limited; *Int'l*, pg. 738
MCCONNELL DOWELL PHILIPPINES INC.—See Aveng Limited; *Int'l*, pg. 738
MCCORMICK STEVENSON CORP.; *U.S. Private*, pg. 2630
MCC SERVICES, L.L.C.—See The MCC Group, LLC; *U.S. Private*, pg. 4076
MCDONOUGH BOLYARD PECK, INC.; *U.S. Private*, pg. 2632
M&C ENGINEERING & TRADING SDN. BHD.—See AWC Berhad; *Int'l*, pg. 752
MCFARLAND-DYER & ASSOCIATES INC.—See Bowman Consulting Group Ltd.; *U.S. Public*, pg. 376
MCFARLAND JOHNSON INC.; *U.S. Private*, pg. 2633
MCGILL AIRPRESSURE CORP.—See The McGill Corporation; *U.S. Private*, pg. 4076
MCGILL AIRSILENCE LLC—See The McGill Corporation; *U.S. Private*, pg. 4076
MCKEAN DEFENSE GROUP LLC; *U.S. Private*, pg. 2637
MCKENNEY'S INC.; *U.S. Private*, pg. 2638
MCKIM & CREED, INC.; *U.S. Private*, pg. 2638
MCLAUGHLIN RESEARCH CORPORATION; *U.S. Private*, pg. 2640
MCLEAN ENGINEERING COMPANY, INC.—See EQT AB; *Int'l*, pg. 2479
MCTISH KUNKEL & ASSOCIATES INC.—See CDR Maguire Inc.; *U.S. Private*, pg. 803
MDA SYSTEMS INC.—See Advent International Corporation; *U.S. Private*, pg. 103
MEDITERRA S.R.O.—See Fresenius SE & Co. KGaA; *Int'l*, pg. 2780
MEDNET S.R.O.—See Fresenius SE & Co. KGaA; *Int'l*, pg. 2780
M/E ENGINEERING, P.C.; *U.S. Private*, pg. 2529
M-E ENGINEERS, INC.; *U.S. Private*, pg. 2525
MEGTEC TURBOSONIC, INC.—See Durr AG; *Int'l*, pg. 2231
MEI TECHNOLOGIES, INC.; *U.S. Private*, pg. 2660
MELNICKA ZDRAVOTNI, A.S.—See Fresenius SE & Co. KGaA; *Int'l*, pg. 2780
MEND CONSULTING PTY. LTD.—See Duratec Limited; *Int'l*, pg. 2228
MERAS ENGINEERING, INC.; *U.S. Private*, pg. 2668
MERINAT S.A.—See Burkhalter Holding AG; *Int'l*, pg. 1225
MERITAGE HOMES OF FLORIDA REALTY LLC—See Meritage Homes Corporation; *U.S. Public*, pg. 1425
MERITAGE HOMES OF THE CAROLINAS, INC.—See Meritage Homes Corporation; *U.S. Public*, pg. 1425
MERLIN ADVISORS, LLC—See BGC Group, Inc.; *U.S. Public*, pg. 329
MERRICK & COMPANY INC. - DECATUR—See Merrick & Company Inc.; *U.S. Private*, pg. 2675
MERRICK & COMPANY INC.; *U.S. Private*, pg. 2675
MES ENVIRONMENTAL LTD.—See CNIM Constructions Industrielles de la Mediterranee SA; *Int'l*, pg. 1677
METALLIC BUILDING SYSTEMS, LLC; *U.S. Private*, pg. 2681
METAL TECHNOLOGIES, INC.; *U.S. Private*, pg. 2680
METCALFE PLANT HIRE LIMITED—See CorpAcq Holdings Limited; *Int'l*, pg. 1802
METRIC ENGINEERING, INC.; *U.S. Private*, pg. 2684
METROCORP CORPORATION—See Metrocorp Holdings Inc.; *U.S. Private*, pg. 2687
METROCORP HOLDINGS INC.; *U.S. Private*, pg. 2687
METROPOLITAN MECHANICAL CONTRACTORS, INC.—See APi Group Corporation; *Int'l*, pg. 514
METZ AND ASSOCIATES, LLC—See Comvest Group Holdings LLC; *U.S. Private*, pg. 1007
METZGER & WILLARD, INC.—See V & A Consulting Engineers, Inc.; *U.S. Private*, pg. 4327
MGVV PROJEKTENTWICKLUNG DAIMLERSTRASSE GMBH & CO. KG—See GEA Group Aktiengesellschaft; *Int'l*, pg. 2904
MGVV PROJEKTENTWICKLUNG DAIMLERSTRASSE VERWALTUNGS GMBH—See GEA Group Aktiengesellschaft; *Int'l*, pg. 2904
MHA-STOPFORD LIMITED—See L3Harris Technologies, Inc.; *U.S. Public*, pg. 1284
MICHAEL BAKER INTERNATIONAL, LLC—See D.C. Capital Partners, LLC; *U.S. Private*, pg. 1141
MICHEL RIME SA—See BKW AG; *Int'l*, pg. 1055
MICRO CRAFT INC.; *U.S. Private*, pg. 2702
MICROFITS (BEIJING) TECHNOLOGY CO., LTD.—See Advanced Systems Automation Limited; *Int'l*, pg. 162

MID-ATLANTIC TECHNOLOGY, RESEARCH & INNOVATION CENTER, INC.—See AVN Corporation; *U.S. Private*, pg. 409
MIDDLEBY INDIA ENGINEERING PVT LTD—See The Middleby Corporation; *U.S. Public*, pg. 2114
MIDDOUGH CONSULTING, ILLINIOS—See Middough, Inc.; *U.S. Private*, pg. 2714
MIDDOUGH CONSULTING, INC—See Middough, Inc.; *U.S. Private*, pg. 2714
MIDDOUGH CONSULTING, KENTUCKY—See Middough, Inc.; *U.S. Private*, pg. 2714
MIDDOUGH, INC.; *U.S. Private*, pg. 2714
MIDLAND DESIGN SERVICE INC.—See American Tooling Center, Inc.; *U.S. Private*, pg. 257
MIDORI INDUSTRIES CO., LTD.—See Aso Co., Ltd.; *Int'l*, pg. 628
MID-SOUTH INDUSTRIES, INC.; *U.S. Private*, pg. 2708
MID-SOUTH PRODUCTS ENGINEERING, INC.—See Mid-South Industries, Inc.; *U.S. Private*, pg. 2708
MILAN RESOURCES SDN. BHD.—See Ekovest Berhad; *Int'l*, pg. 2339
MILHOUSE ENGINEERING & CONSTRUCTION, INC.; *U.S. Private*, pg. 2729
MILLENNIUM ENGINEERING & INTEGRATION COMPANY; *U.S. Private*, pg. 2731
MILLENNIUM ENGINEERING & INTEGRATION COMPANY—See Millennium Engineering & Integration Company; *U.S. Private*, pg. 2731
MILLS & ASSOCIATES, INC.—See Pennoni Associates Inc.; *U.S. Private*, pg. 3136
MILONE & MAC BROOM—See Charterhouse Capital Partners LLP; *Int'l*, pg. 1456
MINDFLOW DESIGN LLC—See Midwest Products & Engineering, Inc.; *U.S. Private*, pg. 2722
MINERA ANTUCOYA SCM—See Antofagasta plc; *Int'l*, pg. 484
MINERA LOS PELAMBRES SCM—See Antofagasta plc; *Int'l*, pg. 484
MING SURVEYORS, INC.—See Hoffman Corporation; *U.S. Private*, pg. 1960
MINTECH—See Momar, Inc.; *U.S. Private*, pg. 2768
MISSION SOLUTIONS, LLC—See Arctic Slope Regional Corporation; *U.S. Private*, pg. 316
M. KUNZ AG—See Burkhalter Holding AG; *Int'l*, pg. 1225
MMC MECHANICAL CONTRACTORS NORTH CENTRAL, INC.—See MMC Corp.; *U.S. Private*, pg. 2754
MMR CANADA, LIMITED—See MMR Group Inc.; *U.S. Private*, pg. 2755
MMR CARIBBEAN, LIMITED—See MMR Group Inc.; *U.S. Private*, pg. 2755
MMR COLOMBIA, S.A.S.—See MMR Group Inc.; *U.S. Private*, pg. 2755
MMR PROCOM, LLC—See MMR Group Inc.; *U.S. Private*, pg. 2755
MMR TECHNICAL SERVICES, INC.—See MMR Group Inc.; *U.S. Private*, pg. 2755
MMR VENEZUELA, S.A.—See MMR Group Inc.; *U.S. Private*, pg. 2755
MOD21 GMBH—See Erbud S.A.; *Int'l*, pg. 2489
MODUS CONSULT AG—See Bechtle AG; *Int'l*, pg. 938
MODUSLINK INTERNATIONAL B.V. APELDOORN SOLUTION CENTER—See Steel Connect, Inc.; *U.S. Public*, pg. 1941
MOOG CSA ENGINEERING—See Moog Inc.; *U.S. Public*, pg. 1470
MOREAS S.A.—See ELLAKTOR S.A.; *Int'l*, pg. 2365
MORELAND ALTOBELLI ASSOCIATES, INC.—See GI Manager L.P.; *U.S. Private*, pg. 1691
MORRISON GEOTECHNIC PTY LTD—See HRL Holdings Limited; *Int'l*, pg. 3501
MOSER & PARTNER INGENIEURBURO GMBH—See CEZ, a.s.; *Int'l*, pg. 1428
MOTHERWELL BRIDGE INDUSTRIES LIMITED—See Hili Ventures Ltd; *Int'l*, pg. 3391
MOTIVE OFFSHORE GROUP LTD—See H2 Equity Partners B.V.; *Int'l*, pg. 3199
MOYLAN ENGINEERING LIMITED—See CTI Engineering Co., Ltd.; *Int'l*, pg. 1871
M.P. COLINET S.P.R.L.U.—See Park-Ohio Holdings Corp.; *U.S. Public*, pg. 1639
MSE GROUP, LLC—See Montrose Environmental Group, Inc.; *U.S. Public*, pg. 1466
M&S ENGINEERING, LLC; *U.S. Private*, pg. 2525
MS TECHNOLOGY, INC.; *U.S. Private*, pg. 2806
MT HOJGAARD GRONLAND A.P.S.—See Hojgaard Holding A/S; *Int'l*, pg. 3442
MTS3 INC.; *U.S. Private*, pg. 2810
MT TEXAS LLC.—See Meyer Tool Inc.; *U.S. Private*, pg. 2693
MUNICIPAL DESIGN GROUP, LLC—See Tetra Tech, Inc.; *U.S. Public*, pg. 2023
MUSGROVE CONSTRUCTION, INC.—See Asplundh Tree Expert Co.; *U.S. Private*, pg. 353
MYR GROUP CONSTRUCTION CANADA, LTD.—See MYR Group Inc.; *U.S. Public*, pg. 1489
NAGOYA STATION AREA DEVELOPMENT

541330 — ENGINEERING SERVICE...

CORPORATION—See Central Japan Railway Company; *Int'l*, pg. 1408
NAIAD DYNAMICS US, INC.—See Naiad Maritime Group, Inc.; *U.S. Private*, pg. 2831
NAKUURUQ SOLUTIONS, LLC—See Nana Regional Corporation, Inc.; *U.S. Private*, pg. 2832
NANDI INFRASTRUCTURE CORRIDOR ENTERPRISES LTD.—See BF Utilities Ltd.; *Int'l*, pg. 1006
NANJING YANGZI PETROCHEMICAL DESIGN & ENGINEERING CO., LTD.—See China International Marine Containers (Group) Co., Ltd.; *Int'l*, pg. 1512
NANNO CONSTRUCTION CO., LTD.—See Fantasista Co., Ltd.; *Int'l*, pg. 2614
N. ARGYROPOULOS & SIA E.E.—See Doppelmayr Group; *Int'l*, pg. 2175
NASON CONTRACTING GROUP LTD.—See Bird Construction Inc.; *Int'l*, pg. 1046
NASS MECHANICAL—See Abdulla Ahmed Nass Group WLL; *Int'l*, pg. 58
NATIONAL PETROLEUM CONSTRUCTION CO. (SAUDI) LTD.—See Alpha Dhabi Holding PJSC; *Int'l*, pg. 367
NATIONAL TECHNICAL SYSTEMS, INC. - ACTON—See Aurora Capital Group, LLC; *U.S. Private*, pg. 393
NATRON RESOURCES, INC.—See Willcrest Partners; *U.S. Private*, pg. 4521
NAVATEK, LTD.—See Pacific Marine & Supply Co. Ltd. Inc.; *U.S. Private*, pg. 3068
ND SATCOM SATELLITE COMMUNICATION SYSTEMS (BEIJING) CO. LTD.—See Airbus SE; *Int'l*, pg. 245
NEHTRUH-EBA CONSULTING LTD.—See Tetra Tech, Inc.; *U.S. Public*, pg. 2023
NEMOCNICE SV. ZDISLAVY, A.S.—See Fresenius SE & Co. KGaA; *Int'l*, pg. 2780
NEPAL ROPEWAY SYSTEMS (P) LTD—See Doppelmayr Group; *Int'l*, pg. 2175
NES GLOBAL TALENT LIMITED—See AEA Investors LP; *U.S. Private*, pg. 115
NESMA & PARTNERS CONTRACTING LTD.—See Costain Group PLC; *Int'l*, pg. 1815
NE TECHNO CO., LTD.—See DN HOLDINGS CO.,LTD; *Int'l*, pg. 2147
NET ELEMENT SERVICES, LLC—See Mullen Automotive, Inc.; *U.S. Public*, pg. 1486
NETWORK ENGINEERING SERVICES—See Amphenol Corporation; *U.S. Public*, pg. 132
NEVADA CONSTRUCTION SERVICES—See Partner Engineering & Science, Inc; *U.S. Private*, pg. 3101
NEVA RIDGE TECHNOLOGIES, INC.—See General Atomics; *U.S. Private*, pg. 1663
NEW JOULES ENGINEERING NORTH AMERICA INC.—See ARGENT INDUSTRIAL LIMITED; *Int'l*, pg. 561
NEWMARK CONSTRUCTION SERVICES, LLC—See BGC Group, Inc.; *U.S. Public*, pg. 329
NEWPARK DRILLING FLUIDS INDIA PRIVATE LIMITED—See Newpark Resources, Inc.; *U.S. Public*, pg. 1517
NEW STATES CONTRACTING—See Irex Corporation; *U.S. Private*, pg. 2138
NEWTRON MECHANICAL, L.L.C.—See The Newtron Group Inc.; *U.S. Private*, pg. 4084
NEXUS ENGINEERING—See Gryphon Investors, LLC; *U.S. Private*, pg. 1798
NGI NATIONAL CONSTRUCTORS, L.L.C.—See The Newtron Group Inc.; *U.S. Private*, pg. 4084
NGI TECHNICAL SERVICES, L.L.C.—See The Newtron Group Inc.; *U.S. Private*, pg. 4084
NICHOLAS CONSULTING GROUP, INC.—See Independence Capital Partners, LLC; *U.S. Private*, pg. 2057
NICKERSON STREET ASSOCIATES, LLC—See Banner Corporation; *U.S. Public*, pg. 275
NIEDEROSTERREICHISCHE FACILITY MANAGEMENT GMBH—See Fresenius SE & Co. KGaA; *Int'l*, pg. 2780
NIKA TECHNOLOGIES, INC.; *U.S. Private*, pg. 2927
NIPPON ENGINEERING CONSULTANTS CO., LTD.—See DN HOLDINGS CO.,LTD; *Int'l*, pg. 2147
NIPPON ENGINEERING-VIETNAM CO., LTD.—See DN HOLDINGS CO.,LTD; *Int'l*, pg. 2147
NITTOC CONSTRUCTION CO., LTD.—See Aso Co., Ltd.; *Int'l*, pg. 628
NITTO ENGINEERING CO., LTD.—See Dai Nippon Toryo Co., Ltd.; *Int'l*, pg. 1916
NK POWER SOLA CO., LTD.—See Gunkul Engineering Co., Ltd.; *Int'l*, pg. 3183
NLOGIC; *U.S. Private*, pg. 2931
NOBLE CONSULTANTS, INC.—See GEC, Inc.; *U.S. Private*, pg. 1655
NOISE CONTROL ENGINEERING, LLC—See Glosten, Inc.; *U.S. Private*, pg. 1720
NOMAD TECH, LDA.—See Alstom S.A.; *Int'l*, pg. 383
NOOR AL KHALEEJ LLC—See Al Hassan Engineering Company S.A.O.G.; *Int'l*, pg. 279
NORD FRANCE CONSTRUCTIONS COMPIEGNE—See FAYAT SAS; *Int'l*, pg. 2626
NORD FRANCE CONSTRUCTIONS—See FAYAT SAS; *Int'l*, pg. 2626
NORESCO, LLC—See Carrier Global Corporation; *U.S. Public*, pg. 442
NORESCO, LLC—See Carrier Global Corporation; *U.S. Public*, pg. 442
NORESCO—See Carrier Global Corporation; *U.S. Public*, pg. 442
NORESCO—See Carrier Global Corporation; *U.S. Public*, pg. 442
NORTHLAND CONSTRUCTORS OF DULUTH, INC.—See APi Group Corporation; *Int'l*, pg. 514
NORTH TOWN ESTATES PRIVATE LIMITED—See Arihant Foundations & Housing Limited; *Int'l*, pg. 564
NORTHWEST LOGIC, INC.—See Rambus Inc.; *U.S. Public*, pg. 1762
NORTH WIND SERVICES, LLC330420—See Cook Inlet Region, Inc.; *U.S. Public*, pg. 1038
NORWELL ENGINEERING LIMITED—See Elemental Energies Holdings Limited; *Int'l*, pg. 2358
NOVA CONSTRUCTORS LLC—See Quanta Services, Inc.; *U.S. Public*, pg. 1752
NOVA CONSTRUCTORS LTD—See Quanta Services, Inc.; *U.S. Public*, pg. 1752
NOVATECH ENGINEERING & CONSTRUCTION PTE., LTD.—See Acter Co., Ltd.; *Int'l*, pg. 117
NOVA-TECH ENGINEERING, LP—See Advanced Integration Technology, LP; *U.S. Private*, pg. 90
NOVATRONICS, INC.—See Curtiss-Wright Corporation; *U.S. Public*, pg. 611
NOVUS ENGINEERING PC—See LaBella Associates, D.P.C.; *U.S. Private*, pg. 2370
NPCC ENGINEERING LIMITED—See Alpha Dhabi Holding PJSC; *Int'l*, pg. 367
NRB (USA), INC.—See Dexterra Group Inc.; *Int'l*, pg. 2093
NTA, LLC—See International Code Council, Inc.; *U.S. Private*, pg. 2115
NT ENERGIES LLC—See Alpha Dhabi Holding PJSC; *Int'l*, pg. 367
NTE SOLUTIONS; *U.S. Private*, pg. 2970
NTH CONSULTANTS, LTD.; *U.S. Private*, pg. 2970
NTH CONSULTANTS, LTD.—See NTH Consultants, Ltd.; *U.S. Private*, pg. 2970
NTH CONSULTANTS, LTD.—See NTH Consultants, Ltd.; *U.S. Private*, pg. 2970
NTH CONSULTANTS, LTD.—See NTH Consultants, Ltd.; *U.S. Private*, pg. 2971
NTH CONSULTANTS, LTD.—See NTH Consultants, Ltd.; *U.S. Private*, pg. 2971
NTS TECHNICAL SYSTEMS—See Aurora Capital Group, LLC; *U.S. Private*, pg. 393
NTZ INTERNATIONAL HOLDING B.V.—See Frencken Group Limited; *Int'l*, pg. 2773
NUCLEO DE COMUNICACIONES Y CONTROL, S.L.—See Amper, S.A.; *Int'l*, pg. 433
NUCLETUDES—See Airbus SE; *Int'l*, pg. 246
NU-CON SYSTEMS SDN. BHD.—See GEA Group Aktiengesellschaft; *Int'l*, pg. 2903
NUMFLO SA—See Cadence Design Systems, Inc.; *U.S. Public*, pg. 419
NUTRONICS, INC.—See nLIGHT, Inc.; *U.S. Public*, pg. 1530
NUVISION ENGINEERING, INC.—See Carr's Group PLC; *Int'l*, pg. 1343
NV5 GLOBAL, INC.; *U.S. Public*, pg. 1557
NV5, INC.—See NV5 Global, Inc.; *U.S. Public*, pg. 1557
NV5 LTD.—See NV5 Global, Inc.; *U.S. Public*, pg. 1557
NV5 MALAYSIA, SDN, BHD—See NV5 Global, Inc.; *U.S. Public*, pg. 1557
NV5 NORTHEAST, INC.—See NV5 Global, Inc.; *U.S. Public*, pg. 1557
NV5 WEST, INC.—See NV5 Global, Inc.; *U.S. Public*, pg. 1557
NYTEC INC.—See Accenture plc; *Int'l*, pg. 87
OBERMILLER NELSON ENGINEERING, INC.; *U.S. Private*, pg. 2987
THE O'BRIEN & GERE COMPANIES; *U.S. Private*, pg. 4087
OCEAN CITY RESEARCH CORPORATION—See New Mountain Capital, LLC; *U.S. Private*, pg. 2900
OCEANEERING AS—See Oceaneering International, Inc.; *U.S. Public*, pg. 1562
OCEANEERING AUSTRALIA PTY, LIMITED—See Oceaneering International, Inc.; *U.S. Public*, pg. 1562
OCEANEERING CANADA LIMITED—See Oceaneering International, Inc.; *U.S. Public*, pg. 1562
OCEANEERING INTERNATIONAL GMBH—See Oceaneering International, Inc.; *U.S. Public*, pg. 1562
OCEANEERING INTERVENTION ENGINEERING—See Oceaneering International, Inc.; *U.S. Public*, pg. 1563
OCI ASSOCIATES, INC.—See Blackstone Inc.; *U.S. Public*, pg. 355
THE O'CONNELL COMPANIES, INCORPORATED - UTILITIES DIVISION—See The O'Connell Companies, Incorporated; *U.S. Private*, pg 4087
O'CONNOR ENGINEERING—See The Carlyle Group Inc.; *U.S. Public*, pg. 2054
ODEBRECHT-CASSIDIAN DEFESA S.A—See Airbus SE; *Int'l*, pg. 242
OEVERMANN INGENIEURBAU GMBH—See Heijmans N.V.; *Int'l*, pg. 3323
OEVERMANN VERKEHRSWEGEBAU GMBH—See Heijmans N.V.; *Int'l*, pg. 3323
OFICINA TECNICA DE ESTUDIOS Y CONTROL DE OBRAS, S.A.—See ACS, Actividades de Construccion y Servicios, S.A.; *Int'l*, pg. 115
OHL INDUSTRIAL CHILE, S.A.—See Grupo Villar Mir, S.A.U.; *Int'l*, pg. 3139
OHL INDUSTRIAL USA, INC.—See Grupo Villar Mir, S.A.U.; *Int'l*, pg. 3139
OILFIELDS SUPPLY CENTRE LLC—See Bhatia Brothers Group; *Int'l*, pg. 1014
OIL & GAS SOLUTIONS PTE LTD—See BH Global Corporation Limited; *Int'l*, pg. 1009
OIL STATES—See Oil States International, Inc.; *U.S. Public*, pg. 1565
OKOTECHNA ENTSORGUNGS- UND UMWELTTECHNIK GMBH—See ALPINE Bau GmbH; *Int'l*, pg. 371
OLSSON ASSOCIATES, INC.; *U.S. Private*, pg. 3012
OLYMPUS CONTROLS CORP.—See Applied Industrial Technologies, Inc.; *U.S. Public*, pg. 171
OMAN SHARPOORJI CONSTRUCTION CO. LLC—See Al Yousef Group; *Int'l*, pg. 283
OMLAND ENGINEERING ASSOCIATES, INC.—See Bowman Consulting Group Ltd.; *U.S. Public*, pg. 376
OMINSTAL ELECTRICIDADE, S.A.—See Elecnor, S.A.; *Int'l*, pg. 2347
OMNITEC SOLUTIONS, INC.—See AE Industrial Partners, LP; *U.S. Private*, pg. 112
ONEIDA TOTAL INTEGRATED ENTERPRISES (OTIE); *U.S. Private*, pg. 3025
ONM ENVIRONMENTAL, INC.—See BioLargo, Inc.; *U.S. Public*, pg. 337
ONQUEST CANADA, ULC—See Primoris Services Corporation; *U.S. Public*, pg. 1718
OOO DOPPELMAYR RUSSIA—See Doppelmayr Group; *Int'l*, pg. 2175
OOO SIEMPELKAMP—See G. Siempelkamp GmbH & Co. KG; *Int'l*, pg. 2864
OOO VAMED—See Fresenius SE & Co. KGaA; *Int'l*, pg. 2780
OPAL SOFTWARE—See General Electric Company; *U.S. Public*, pg. 919
OPENCAPE CORPORATION; *U.S. Private*, pg. 3030
OPERATIONAL INTELLIGENCE LLC—See NewSpring Capital LLC; *U.S. Private*, pg. 2918
OPSENS SOLUTIONS INC.—See Haemonetics Corporation; *U.S. Public*, pg. 979
OPTIMAL DESIGN CO.—See Deloitte LLP; *U.S. Private*, pg. 1198
OPTIMAL DESIGN CO.—See Deloitte Touche Tohmatsu Limited; *Int'l*, pg. 2015
OPTIMAL GEO INC.—See Woolpert Inc.; *U.S. Private*, pg. 4562
OPTIMECH, LLC—See Ivey Mechanical Company LLC; *U.S. Private*, pg. 2151
OPTIMETRICS, INC.—See DCS Corporation; *U.S. Private*, pg. 1180
OPTIMIZED PROCESS DESIGNS INC.—See Koch Industries, Inc.; *U.S. Private*, pg. 2332
ORANGE SUPPORT SERVICES LIMITED—See Aramark; *U.S. Public*, pg. 178
ORANJEWOUD N.V.—See Centric Holding B.V.; *Int'l*, pg. 1412
ORION ENGINEERING BV—See Alten S.A.; *Int'l*, pg. 390
ORI SERVICES CORPORATION; *U.S. Private*, pg. 3041
ORTLOFF ENGINEERS, LTD.—See Torgo, Ltd.; *U.S. Private*, pg. 4189
ORT TOOL & DIE CORPORATION; *U.S. Private*, pg. 3045
OSDC CO., LTD.—See Bain Capital, LP; *U.S. Private*, pg. 435
OSD GMBH—See BKW AG; *Int'l*, pg. 1055
OSIATIS INGENIERIE S.A.S—See Econocom Group SA; *Int'l*, pg. 2298
OSTEC ENTERPRISE LTD.—See ESPEC Corp.; *Int'l*, pg. 2505
OTRACO INTERNATIONAL PTY LIMITED—See Bridgestone Corporation; *Int'l*, pg. 1159
OTTO WORK FORCE CZECH S.R.O.—See Bain Capital, LP; *U.S. Private*, pg. 435
OTTO WORK FORCE ROM S.R.L.—See Bain Capital, LP; *U.S. Private*, pg. 435
OVE ARUP & PARTNERS DANMARK A/S—See Arup Group Ltd.; *Int'l*, pg. 587
OVE ARUP & PARTNERS HONG KONG LIMITED—See Arup Group Ltd.; *Int'l*, pg. 587
OVE ARUP & PARTNERS INTERNATIONAL LIMITED—See Arup Group Ltd.; *Int'l*, pg. 587
OVE ARUP & PARTNERS IRELAND LIMITED—See Arup Group Ltd.; *Int'l*, pg. 587
OVE ARUP & PARTNERS POLAND SP. ZO.O—See Arup Group Ltd.; *Int'l*, pg. 587
OVE ARUP & PARTNERS SCOTLAND LIMITED—See Arup Group Ltd.; *Int'l*, pg. 587
OVE ARUP (THAILAND) LIMITED—See Arup Group Ltd.; *Int'l*, pg. 587
OVERSEAS TECHNICAL ENGINEERING AND CONSTRUCTION PTE. LTD.—See Dialog Group Berhad; *Int'l*, pg. 2104
OWEN AYRES & ASSOCIATES, INC.; *U.S. Private*, pg. 3054

541330 — ENGINEERING SERVICE...

OWENS-CORNING COMPOSITE SOLUTIONS—See Owens Corning; *U.S. Public*, pg. 1628
OWL ENERGY RESOURCES, INC.—See Owl Companies; *U.S. Private*, pg. 3055
P2 PLANT & PIPELINE ENGINEERING GMBH—See EnBW Energie Baden-Württemberg AG; *Int'l*, pg. 2399
P2S INC.—See Blackstone Inc.; *U.S. Public*, pg. 355
PAA RIVER CONSTRUCTION, LLC—See Nana Regional Corporation, Inc.; *U.S. Private*, pg. 2833
PACE CONTRACTING, LLC—See LPX, Inc.; *U.S. Private*, pg. 2507
PACE ENGINEERS, INC.; *U.S. Private*, pg. 3063
PACE RESOURCES, INC.; *U.S. Private*, pg. 3064
PACIFIC ARCHITECTS & ENGINEERS, INC.—See Amentum Services, Inc.; *U.S. Private*, pg. 219
PACIFICA SERVICES, INC.; *U.S. Private*, pg. 3072
PACIFIC ENGINEERS & CONSTRUCTORS, LTD.—See Bechtel Group, Inc.; *U.S. Private*, pg. 510
PACIFIC SHIPYARDS INTERNATIONAL, LLC—See Pacific Marine & Supply Co. Ltd. Inc.; *U.S. Private*, pg. 3068
THE PACKER GROUP INC.; *U.S. Private*, pg. 4090
PAGE ONE CONSULTANTS, INC.—See NV5 Global, Inc.; *U.S. Public*, pg. 1557
PAL GENERAL ENGINEERING INC.; *U.S. Private*, pg. 3076
PALMER GOTHEIM SKIFERBRUDD AS—See AF Gruppen ASA; *Int'l*, pg. 184
PANTECNIKI SA—See ELLAKTOR S.A.; *Int'l*, pg. 2365
PAPE-DAWSON ENGINEERS, LLC—See Palm Beach Capital Partners LLC; *U.S. Private*, pg. 3079
PARAGON SPACE DEVELOPMENT CORPORATION; *U.S. Private*, pg. 3091
PARAMETRIC SOLUTIONS, INC.; *U.S. Private*, pg. 3092
PARKWAY INTERNATIONAL CONTRACTING L.L.C.—See Al Shafar Group; *Int'l*, pg. 282
PARRISH & PARTNERS, LLC; *U.S. Private*, pg. 3100
PARSONS GROUP INTERNATIONAL LIMITED—See Parsons Corporation; *U.S. Public*, pg. 1651
PARSONS INFRASTRUCTURE & TECHNOLOGY GROUP INC.—See Parsons Corporation; *U.S. Public*, pg. 1651
PARSONS TRANSPORTATION GROUP INC.—See Parsons Corporation; *U.S. Public*, pg. 1651
PASSERO ASSOCIATES; *U.S. Private*, pg. 3104
PATTERSON POWER ENGINEERS LLC—See New Mountain Capital, LLC; *U.S. Private*, pg. 2903
PAULI ELEKTRO AG—See Burkhalter Holding AG; *Int'l*, pg. 1225
PAUL KELLER INGENIEURE AG—See AFRY AB; *Int'l*, pg. 195
PCA-ECHOLOGICS PTY LTD.—See Mueller Water Products, Inc.; *U.S. Public*, pg. 1485
P&C CONSTRUCTION INC.; *U.S. Private*, pg. 3058
PCD ENGINEERING SERVICES, INC.—See Bowman Consulting Group Ltd.; *U.S. Public*, pg. 376
PC&E INC.—See Emerson Electric Co.; *U.S. Public*, pg. 750
PCI INSUL-ENERGY INC.—See Performance Contracting Group; *U.S. Private*, pg. 3148
PCI SKANSKA INC.—See Salas O'Brien Engineers, Inc.; *U.S. Private*, pg. 3530
PDC ENGINEERING, INC.—See RESPEC Inc.; *U.S. Private*, pg. 3407
P.D.C. TECHNICAL SERVICES INC.—See Peoria Disposal Company/Area Disposal Service, Inc.; *U.S. Private*, pg. 3143
PDS TECHNICAL SERVICES, SEATTLE BRANCH—See Adecco Group AG; *Int'l*, pg. 140
PEAK CIVIL CONSULTANTS INC.—See Atwell, LLC; *U.S. Private*, pg. 384
PEAK POWER ENGINEERING, INC.—See Atwell, LLC; *U.S. Private*, pg. 384
PEDCO E&A SERVICES, INC.; *U.S. Private*, pg. 3127
PEGASUSTSI, INC.; *U.S. Private*, pg. 3130
PEG, LLC—See Installed Building Products, Inc.; *U.S. Public*, pg. 1133
PELICAN ENGINEERING CONSULTANTS LLC; *U.S. Private*, pg. 3130
PENDANT AUTOMATION, INC.; *U.S. Private*, pg. 3132
PENNONI ASSOCIATES INC. - NEW YORK—See Pennoni Associates Inc.; *U.S. Private*, pg. 3136
PENNONI ASSOCIATES INC.; *U.S. Private*, pg. 3136
PENSAR DEVELOPMENT INC; *U.S. Private*, pg. 3138
PENTLAND LIMITED—See Galliford Try Holdings plc; *Int'l*, pg. 2874
PEOPLETEC, INC.; *U.S. Private*, pg. 3142
PERFORMANCE ENERGY SERVICES, L.L.C.—See Quanta Services, Inc.; *U.S. Public*, pg. 1752
PERL-POOL AG—See Burkhalter Holding AG; *Int'l*, pg. 1225
PERMASTEELISA NORTH AMERICA CORP. - MIAMI—See Atlas Holdings, LLC; *U.S. Private*, pg. 377
PERMASTEELISA NORTH AMERICA CORP.—See Atlas Holdings, LLC; *U.S. Private*, pg. 377
PES ENVIRONMENTAL, INC.—See NV5 Global, Inc.; *U.S. Public*, pg. 1557
P.E. STRUCTURAL CONSULTANTS, INC.—See Hardesty & Hanover, LLC; *U.S. Private*, pg. 1863
PETER & BARBISCH AG—See Burkhalter Holding AG; *Int'l*, pg. 1225
PETERS ENGINEERING AG—See Bilfinger SE; *Int'l*, pg. 1026

PETROLOG AUTOMATION, INC.; *U.S. Private*, pg. 3162
PFEILER & ASSOCIATES ENGINEER INC.—See Psomas; *U.S. Private*, pg. 3297
PGAM ADVANCED TECHNOLOGIES LTD.—See Farmingtons Holding GmbH; *Int'l*, pg. 2620
PHANTOM TECHNICAL SERVICES, INC.—See Hamilton Robinson LLC; *U.S. Private*, pg. 1848
PHILOTECH FRANCE S.A.S.—See Bertrandt AG; *Int'l*, pg. 998
PHILOTECH IBERICA SISTEMAS Y LOGISTICA S.L.—See Bertrandt AG; *Int'l*, pg. 998
PIE CONSULTING & ENGINEERING, INC.—See Lerch Bates Inc.; *U.S. Private*, pg. 2431
PILET INTERSISTEMAS S.R.L.—See Doppelmayr Group; *Int'l*, pg. 2175
PINNACLE SOLUTIONS, INC.—See Nana Regional Corporation, Inc.; *U.S. Private*, pg. 2832
PJB BETEILIGUNGS-GMBH—See Bilfinger SE; *Int'l*, pg. 1028
PLALOC ASIA (THAILAND) CO., LTD.—See Idemitsu Kosan Co., Ltd.; *Int'l*, pg. 3592
PLAN GROUP INC.—See Bouygues S.A.; *Int'l*, pg. 1122
PLASMA TECHNOLOGY, INCORPORATED - EAST COAST FACILITY—See Plasma Technology, Incorporated; *U.S. Private*, pg. 3198
PLEXUS AEROSPACE, DEFENSE & SECURITY SERVICES, LLC—See Plexus Corp.; *U.S. Public*, pg. 1698
PLEXUS SCIENTIFIC CORPORATION; *U.S. Private*, pg. 3214
PLT. CONSTRUCTION CO., INC.—See Construction Partners, Inc.; *U.S. Public*, pg. 572
PMS ELEKTRO- UND AUTOMATIONSTECHNIK GMBH—See Christof Holding AG; *Int'l*, pg. 1587
PODUFAL-WIEHOFSKY GENERALPLANUNG GMBH—See BKW AG; *Int'l*, pg. 1056
POLLUTION MANAGEMENT, INC.—See Terracon Consultants, Inc.; *U.S. Private*, pg. 3971
POLY BUILDING CORPORATION—See China Poly Group Corporation; *Int'l*, pg. 1541
POLYMER FUSION EDUCATION PTY LTD—See Fletcher Building Limited; *Int'l*, pg. 2701
POLYSONICS CORPORATION; *U.S. Private*, pg. 3226
PORTAGE, INC.—See Cook Inlet Region, Inc.; *U.S. Private*, pg. 1038
POSITECH SRL—See Alten S.A.; *Int'l*, pg. 390
POSTWORTH LTD—See Carillion plc; *Int'l*, pg. 1330
POWER CONTROLS, INC.—See Braemont Capital Management LLC; *U.S. Private*, pg. 633
POWER ENGINEERING, INC.; *U.S. Private*, pg. 3238
POWER PARTNERS PTE. LTD.—See Air Water Inc.; *Int'l*, pg. 240
POWERPOINT ELECTRICAL & MECHANICAL WORKS L.L.C.—See Al Shafar Group; *Int'l*, pg. 282
POWERSCREEN INTERNATIONAL (U.K.) LIMITED—See Terex Corporation; *U.S. Public*, pg. 2020
POYRY (APPLETON) LLC—See AFRY AB; *Int'l*, pg. 195
POYRY & COMPANY LLC—See AFRY AB; *Int'l*, pg. 195
POYRY DEUTSCHLAND GMBH—See AFRY AB; *Int'l*, pg. 195
POYRY DEUTSCHLAND GMBH—See AFRY AB; *Int'l*, pg. 195
POYRY ENERGY INC.—See AFRY AB; *Int'l*, pg. 195
POYRY ENERGY LIMITED—See AFRY AB; *Int'l*, pg. 195
POYRY ENERGY LTD.—See AFRY AB; *Int'l*, pg. 195
POYRY ENERGY OY—See AFRY AB; *Int'l*, pg. 195
POYRY ENERGY SDN. BHD.—See AFRY AB; *Int'l*, pg. 195
POYRY FINLAND OY—See AFRY AB; *Int'l*, pg. 195
POYRY INFRA AG—See AFRY AB; *Int'l*, pg. 195
POYRY INFRA GMBH—See AFRY AB; *Int'l*, pg. 195
POYRY INFRA LTD.—See AFRY AB; *Int'l*, pg. 195
POYRY INFRA S.A.—See AFRY AB; *Int'l*, pg. 195
POYRY INFRA SP. Z O.O.—See AFRY AB; *Int'l*, pg. 195
POYRY MANAGEMENT CONSULTING (AUSTRALIA) PTY. LTD.—See AFRY AB; *Int'l*, pg. 196
POYRY MANAGEMENT CONSULTING (DEUTSCHLAND) GMBH—See AFRY AB; *Int'l*, pg. 196
POYRY MANAGEMENT CONSULTING (DUSSELDORF) GMBH—See AFRY AB; *Int'l*, pg. 196
POYRY MANAGEMENT CONSULTING (ITALIA) S.R.L.—See AFRY AB; *Int'l*, pg. 196
POYRY MANAGEMENT CONSULTING (NORWAY) AS—See AFRY AB; *Int'l*, pg. 196
POYRY MANAGEMENT CONSULTING (NZ) LIMITED—See AFRY AB; *Int'l*, pg. 196
POYRY MANAGEMENT CONSULTING OY—See AFRY AB; *Int'l*, pg. 195
POYRY MANAGEMENT CONSULTING (SCHWEIZ) AG—See AFRY AB; *Int'l*, pg. 196
POYRY MANAGEMENT CONSULTING (SINGAPORE) PTE. LTD.—See AFRY AB; *Int'l*, pg. 196
POYRY MANAGEMENT CONSULTING (SWEDEN) AB—See AFRY AB; *Int'l*, pg. 196
POYRY MANAGEMENT CONSULTING (UK) LIMITED—See AFRY AB; *Int'l*, pg. 196
POYRY MANAGEMENT CONSULTING (USA) INC.—See AFRY AB; *Int'l*, pg. 196
POYRY (MEXICO) S.A., DE C.V.—See AFRY AB; *Int'l*, pg. 195

CORPORATE AFFILIATIONS

POYRY (MONTREAL) INC.—See AFRY AB; *Int'l*, pg. 195
POYRY (PERU) S.A.C.—See AFRY AB; *Int'l*, pg. 195
POYRY POLAND SP. Z O.O.—See AFRY AB; *Int'l*, pg. 196
POYRY SHANDONG ENGINEERING CONSULTING CO., LTD.—See AFRY AB; *Int'l*, pg. 196
POYRY (VANCOUVER) INC.—See AFRY AB; *Int'l*, pg. 195
PPP SCHULEN HALLE GMBH—See Bilfinger SE; *Int'l*, pg. 1028
PPP SCHULEN LANDKREIS HOF GMBH—See Bilfinger SE; *Int'l*, pg. 1028
PRADERLOSINGER SA—See Bouygues S.A.; *Int'l*, pg. 1122
PRATT & MILLER ENGINEERING & FABRICATION, INC.—See Oshkosh Corporation; *U.S. Public*, pg. 1621
PRECISION CONTROL SDN BHD—See CHINO Corporation; *Int'l*, pg. 1571
PRIBUSS ENGINEERING, INC.; *U.S. Private*, pg. 3258
PRIMORIS DESIGN & CONSTRUCTION, INC.—See Primoris Services Corporation; *U.S. Public*, pg. 1719
PRIMORIS ENERGY SERVICES CORPORATION—See Primoris Services Corporation; *U.S. Public*, pg. 1719
PRIMORIS T&D SERVICES, LLC—See Primoris Services Corporation; *U.S. Public*, pg. 1719
PRIMUS LIMITED—See UGI Corporation; *U.S. Public*, pg. 2222
PRINCIPLE POWER, INC.; *U.S. Private*, pg. 3265
PRINSAMED - PROJECTOS INTERNACIONAIS DE SAUDE UNIPESSOAL LDA.—See Fresenius SE & Co. KGaA; *Int'l*, pg. 2780
PRIVATE ENERGY SYSTEMS, INC.; *U.S. Private*, pg. 3268
PRO-ACTIVE ENGINEERING, INC.—See Tide Rock Holdings, LLC; *U.S. Private*, pg. 4168
PROCESS PLUS LLC; *U.S. Private*, pg. 3272
PROCRANE ENGINEERING—See Berkshire Hathaway Inc.; *U.S. Public*, pg. 309
PRODUCTION ROBOTICS, INC.; *U.S. Private*, pg. 3273
PRODUCTIVE RESOURCES, LLC—See H.I.G. Capital, LLC; *U.S. Private*, pg. 1830
PROFESSIONAL ENGINEERING CONSULTANTS, P.A.; *U.S. Private*, pg. 3275
PROFESSIONAL PROJECT SERVICES, INC.; *U.S. Private*, pg. 3276
PROFIL-BAU INDUSTRIAL OY—See AFRY AB; *Int'l*, pg. 196
PROGRESSIVE ENGINEERING & CONSTRUCTION, INC.; *U.S. Private*, pg. 3279
PROJEKTGESELLSCHAFT JUSTIZVOLLZUG BURG GMBH & CO. KG—See Bilfinger SE; *Int'l*, pg. 1028
PROJEKT- UND BETRIEBSGESLLSCHAFT JUSTIZZENTRUM CHEMNITZ GMBH—See Bilfinger SE; *Int'l*, pg. 1028
PROMOCIONES MUNICH, C.A.—See Doppelmayr Group; *Int'l*, pg. 2175
PROTEK MEDICAL PRODUCTS, INC.—See Audax Group, Limited Partnership; *U.S. Private*, pg. 386
PROTEUS ENGINEERS PTY LTD.—See Tetra Tech, Inc.; *U.S. Public*, pg. 2023
PROTOPHARMA GESELLSCHAFT FUR ENGINEERING UND CONSULTING MBH—See Bain Capital, LP; *U.S. Private*, pg. 443
PROTOPHARMA GESELLSCHAFT FUR ENGINEERING UND CONSULTING MBH—See Cinven Limited; *Int'l*, pg. 1613
THE PROUD COMPANY; *U.S. Private*, pg. 4101
PROVENANCE CONSULTING LLC—See Keystone Group, L.P.; *U.S. Private*, pg. 2299
PROYECTOS ESPECIALES PACIFICO S.A.—See AECOM; *U.S. Public*, pg. 51
PROZAP SP. Z O.O.—See Grupa Azoty S.A.; *Int'l*, pg. 3116
PRZEDSIEBIORSTWO ROBOT INZYNIERYJNYCH POL-AQUA S.A.—See ACS, Actividades de Construccion y Servicios, S.A.; *Int'l*, pg. 111
PSA DEWBERRY—See Dewberry LLC; *U.S. Private*, pg. 1219
PSOMAS; *U.S. Private*, pg. 3297
PT ALSTOM TRANSPORT INDONESIA—See Alstom S.A.; *Int'l*, pg. 383
PT. ASAHI SYNCHROTECH INDONESIA—See Chubu Electric Power Co., Inc.; *Int'l*, pg. 1593
P.T. BCI ASIA—See Byggfakta Group Nordic HoldCo AB; *Int'l*, pg. 1235
PT BIMATEKNO KARYATAMA KONSULTAN—See Beca Group Limited; *Int'l*, pg. 936
P.T. BOSKALIS INTERNATIONAL INDONESIA—See HAL Trust N.V.; *Int'l*, pg. 3226
P.T. BRAEMAR TECHNICAL SERVICES OFFSHORE—See Braemar PLC; *Int'l*, pg. 1136
PT. CHIYODA INTERNATIONAL INDONESIA—See Chiyoda Corporation; *Int'l*, pg. 1575
PT DAELIM UTAMA CONSTRUCTION—See Daelim Industrial Co., Ltd.; *Int'l*, pg. 1908
PT DURO FELGUERA INDONESIA—See Duro Felguera, S.A.; *Int'l*, pg. 2229
PT. EPIROC SOUTHERN ASIA—See Epiroc AB; *Int'l*, pg. 2463
PT. FUJI FURUKAWA E&C INDONESIA—See Fuji Furukawa Engineering & Construction Co., Ltd.; *Int'l*, pg. 2813
P.T. HILTI NUSANTARA—See Hilti AG; *Int'l*, pg. 3395

N.A.I.C.S. INDEX

541330 — ENGINEERING SERVICE...

PT. HITACHI SUNWAY INFORMATION SYSTEMS INDONESIA—See Hitachi, Ltd.; *Int'l*, pg. 3424
P.T. IDEMITSU ENERGY INDONESIA—See Idemitsu Kosan Co., Ltd.; *Int'l*, pg. 3592
P.T. IDEMITSU LUBE INDONESIA—See Idemitsu Kosan Co., Ltd.; *Int'l*, pg. 3592
P.T. IDEMITSU LUBE TECHNO INDONESIA—See Idemitsu Kosan Co., Ltd.; *Int'l*, pg. 3592
PT JACOBS GROUP INDONESIA—See Jacobs Engineering Group, Inc.; *U.S. Public*, pg. 1186
PT MASTER INDONESIA—See Beng Kuang Marine Limited; *Int'l*, pg. 973
PT. NOVAMEX INDONESIA—See Acter Co., Ltd.; *Int'l*, pg. 117
PT OTRACO INDONESIA—See Downer EDI Limited; *Int'l*, pg. 2186
P.T REDPATH INDONESIA—See ATON GmbH; *Int'l*, pg. 688
P.T. SNC-LAVALIN TPS—See AtkinsRealis Group Inc.; *Int'l*, pg. 671
PT TECHNIC ENGINEERING SDN. BHD.—See APFT Berhad; *Int'l*, pg. 512
PT. THERMAX—See Chart Industries, Inc.; *U.S. Public*, pg. 482
PURBOND AG—See Henkel AG & Co. KGaA; *Int'l*, pg. 3354
PUSCH BAU GMBH & CO. KG—See H. Geiger GmbH; *Int'l*, pg. 3194
P. VAN EERD BEHEERSMAATSCHAPPIJ B.V—See Gammon India Limited; *Int'l*, pg. 2879
PVE SHEFFLER, LLC; *U.S. Private*, pg. 3308
QATAR BOOM ELECTRICAL ENGINEERING W.L.L.—See Aiphone Co., Ltd.; *Int'l*, pg. 235
QUALIS, CORPORATION; *U.S. Private*, pg. 3317
QUALITY COMPANIES USA, LLC.; *U.S. Private*, pg. 3318
QUALITY ENGINEERING SOLUTIONS, INC.; *U.S. Private*, pg. 3318
QUALITY INNOVATIVE SOLUTIONS INC.; *U.S. Private*, pg. 3319
QUALUS CORPORATION; *U.S. Private*, pg. 3322
QUANTA INFRASTRUCTURE SOLUTIONS GROUP, LLC—See Quanta Services, Inc.; *U.S. Public*, pg. 1752
QUANTA MARINE SERVICES, LLC—See Quanta Services, Inc.; *U.S. Public*, pg. 1752
QUANTA TELECOMMUNICATION SOLUTIONS, LLC—See Quanta Services, Inc.; *U.S. Public*, pg. 1752
QUANTUM TECHNOLOGY SCIENCES, INC.—See GEOSPACE TECHNOLOGIES CORPORATION; *U.S. Public*, pg. 934
QUEST INTEGRITY NLD B.V.—See Team, Inc.; *U.S. Public*, pg. 1988
QUEST INTEGRITY NZL LIMITED—See Baker Hughes Company; *U.S. Public*, pg. 265
QUESTIONS & SOLUTIONS ENGINEERING, INC.; *U.S. Private*, pg. 3326
QUICK RELEASE AUTOMOTIVE LTD.—See Alten S.A.; *Int'l*, pg. 390
QUILLE SA—See Bouygues S.A.; *Int'l*, pg. 1123
QWK INTEGRATED SOLUTIONS, LLC—See Veritas Capital Fund Management, LLC; *U.S. Private*, pg. 4364
RADIUS HONG KONG LTD—See Jabil Inc.; *U.S. Public*, pg. 1182
RADOS EQUIPMENT CORPORATION—See The Rados Companies; *U.S. Private*, pg. 4102
RAILPROS, INC.—See Court Square Capital Partners, L.P.; *U.S. Private*, pg. 1070
RAILWORKS TRANSIT, INC.—See Wind Point Advisors LLC; *U.S. Private*, pg. 4535
RAPID GLOBAL BUSINESS SOLUTIONS, INC.; *U.S. Private*, pg. 3355
RAPTOR MINING LLC—See T-REX Acquisition Corp.; *U.S. Public*, pg. 1978
RAST ELEKTRO AG—See Burkhalter Holding AG; *Int'l*, pg. 1225
RAYTHEON TECHNICAL SERVICES COMPANY LLC - MISSION SUPPORT OPERATIONS—See RTX Corporation; *U.S. Public*, pg. 1825
RAZEL ALGERIE SARL—See FAYAT SAS; *Int'l*, pg. 2626
RAZEL ANGOLA—See FAYAT SAS; *Int'l*, pg. 2626
RAZEL-BEC COTE-D'AZUR—See FAYAT SAS; *Int'l*, pg. 2626
RAZEL CAMEROUN—See FAYAT SAS; *Int'l*, pg. 2626
RAZEL GUINEE EQUATORIALE—See FAYAT SAS; *Int'l*, pg. 2626
RAZEL MALAISIE—See FAYAT SAS; *Int'l*, pg. 2626
RAZEL MAURITANIE—See FAYAT SAS; *Int'l*, pg. 2626
RAZEL NIGER—See FAYAT SAS; *Int'l*, pg. 2626
RBS WAVE GMBH—See EnBW Energie Baden-Wurttemberg AG; *Int'l*, pg. 2399
RCC BUILDERS & DEVELOPERS, INC.—See Railroad Construction Company, Inc.; *U.S. Private*, pg. 3346
RCC FABRICATORS, INC.—See Railroad Construction Company, Inc.; *U.S. Private*, pg. 3346
RCH COMPANY, INC.; *U.S. Private*, pg. 3362
REDLINE ENGINEERING SERVICES LTD—See Active Energy Group plc; *Int'l*, pg. 120
REDNISS & MEAD, INC., *U.S. Private*, pg. 3379
REDPATH ARGENTINA CONSTRUCCIONES S.A.—See ATON GmbH; *Int'l*, pg. 688

REDPATH AUSTRALIA PTY LIMITED—See ATON GmbH; *Int'l*, pg. 688
REDPATH CHILENA CONSTRUCCIONES Y CIA. LIMITADA—See ATON GmbH; *Int'l*, pg. 688
REDPATH MINING (S.A.) (PTY.) LTD.—See ATON GmbH; *Int'l*, pg. 688
REDPATH MINING ZAMBIA LIMITED—See ATON GmbH; *Int'l*, pg. 688
REDPATH MONGOLIA LLC—See ATON GmbH; *Int'l*, pg. 688
REEL GROUP INC—See Global Energy (Holdings) Ltd.; *Int'l*, pg. 2995
REHABILITATIONSZENTRUM ST. VEIT IM PONGAU BETRIEBS-GMBH—See Fresenius SE & Co. KGaA; *Int'l*, pg. 2780
REI AUTOMATION, INC.—See HAHN Group GmbH; *Int'l*, pg. 3208
REID MIDDLETON INC.; *U.S. Private*, pg. 3391
REI HI-TECH SDN BHD—See Chasen Holdings Limited; *Int'l*, pg. 1457
REI TECHNOLOGIES PTE LTD—See Chasen Holdings Limited; *Int'l*, pg. 1457
RELAY & POWER SYSTEMS—See Rumsey Electric Company; *U.S. Private*, pg. 3504
REMZAP SP. Z O.O.—See Grupa Azoty S.A.; *Int'l*, pg. 3116
RENOVATE NEIGHBORHOODS, INC.; *U.S. Public*, pg. 1783
RESEARCH ENGINEERS INTERNATIONAL—See Bentley Systems, Inc.; *U.S. Public*, pg. 297
RESEARCH SITES RESTORATION LIMITED—See Babcock International Group PLC; *Int'l*, pg. 793
RESOURCE MANAGEMENT ASSOCIATES, INC—See Global Infrastructure Solutions, Inc.; *U.S. Private*, pg. 1715
RESPEC INC.; *U.S. Private*, pg. 3407
RETTEW ASSOCIATES INC.; *U.S. Private*, pg. 3412
REX ENGINEERING GROUP, INC.; *U.S. Private*, pg. 3417
RICE DAUBNEY PTY LTD—See HDR, Inc.; *U.S. Private*, pg. 1890
RICHARD BRADY & ASSOCIATES, INC.; *U.S. Private*, pg. 3427
RICHARD COSTAIN LTD—See Costain Group PLC; *Int'l*, pg. 1815
RICK ENGINEERING COMPANY; *U.S. Private*, pg. 3431
RIDDLEBERGER BROTHERS, INC.—See Comfort Systems USA, Inc.; *U.S. Public*, pg. 544
RIGFIT OFFSHORE LTD—See Global Energy (Holdings) Ltd.; *Int'l*, pg. 2995
RI.ISA D.O.O.—See Atlas Holdings, LLC; *U.S. Private*, pg. 378
RINGSTED ENTREPRENORFORRETNING A.P.S.—See Hojgaard Holding A/S; *Int'l*, pg. 3442
RINGWAY BABTIE LIMITED—See Jacobs Engineering Group, Inc.; *U.S. Public*, pg. 1186
RITOCH-POWELL & ASSOC RPA INC.—See Littlejohn & Co., LLC; *U.S. Private*, pg. 2469
RIVES-MONTEIRO ENGINEERING, LLC—See InterCloud Systems, Inc.; *U.S. Public*, pg. 1141
RJB ENGINEERING (UK) LIMITED—See Schlumberger Limited; *U.S. Public*, pg. 1844
RJM CONSTRUCTION LLC; *U.S. Private*, pg. 3449
RKR HESS ASSOCIATES, INC.—See Universal Technical Resource Services, Inc.; *U.S. Private*, pg. 4306
R L H ENGINEERING, INC.—See Accenture plc; *Int'l*, pg. 86
RMA GROUP, INC.—See OceanSound Partners, LP; *U.S. Private*, pg. 2991
R&M AUSBAU LEIPZIG GMBH—See Bilfinger SE; *Int'l*, pg. 1028
R&M BAUDIENSTLEISTUNGEN GMBH—See Bilfinger SE; *Int'l*, pg. 1028
R&M KUHLLAGERBAU BIELEFELD GMBH—See Bilfinger SE; *Int'l*, pg. 1028
R.M. THORNTON, INC.—See Harris Companies; *U.S. Private*, pg. 1869
ROADCRETE AFRICA (PTY) LIMITED—See Basil Read Holdings Limited; *Int'l*, pg. 887
ROBERT E. LEE & ASSOCIATES, INC.; *U.S. Private*, pg. 3457
ROBERT H. VOGEL ENGINEERING, INC.—See Timmons Group; *U.S. Private*, pg. 4173
THE ROBERTS COMPANY FABRICATION SERVICES, INC.—See Argan, Inc.; *U.S. Public*, pg. 191
ROBERTS & SCHAEFER COMPANY—See KBR, Inc.; *U.S. Public*, pg. 1216
ROBERTS & SCHAEFER COMPANY—See KBR, Inc.; *U.S. Public*, pg. 1216
ROBUR PROTOTYPING & MATERIALS GMBH—See Clayton, Dubilier & Rice, LLC; *U.S. Private*, pg. 926
ROCCOR LLC—See Redwire Corporation; *U.S. Public*, pg. 1771
ROCHE CONTRACTORS PTY LTD—See Downer EDI Limited; *Int'l*, pg. 2186
ROCHE MINING (MT) INDIA PVT LTD.—See Downer EDI Limited; *Int'l*, pg. 2186
ROCKET SUPPORT SERVICES, LLC—See Kratos Defense & Security Solutions, Inc.; *U.S. Public*, pg. 1276
ROCK ISLAND INTEGRATED SERVICES—See Fluor Corporation; *U.S. Public*, pg. 859

ROCKWELL AUTOMATION CARIBBEAN LLP—See Rockwell Automation, Inc.; *U.S. Public*, pg. 1805
ROCKWELL COLLINS UK LTD. - INFORMATION MANAGEMENT SERVICES—See RTX Corporation; *U.S. Public*, pg. 1823
RODDEY ENGINEERING SERVICES, INC.—See Martin Resource Management Corporation; *U.S. Private*, pg. 2596
ROETO LTD.—See Gefen International A.I Ltd.; *Int'l*, pg. 2911
ROSS & BARUZZINI, INC.; *U.S. Private*, pg. 3485
ROSS-SHIRE ENGINEERING LTD—See Global Energy (Holdings) Ltd.; *Int'l*, pg. 2995
ROTATING MACHINERY SERVICES, INC.—See Cortec Group Management Services, LLC; *U.S. Private*, pg. 1060
ROY ET TREMBLAY INC.—See Avison Young (Canada) Inc.; *Int'l*, pg. 745
RPT BYGGFAKTA OY—See Byggfakta Group Nordic HoldCo AB; *Int'l*, pg. 1235
R&R ASSOCIATES LLC - CANADA—See R&R Associates LLC; *U.S. Private*, pg. 3332
R&R ASSOCIATES LLC; *U.S. Private*, pg. 3332
R-S-H ENGINEERING, INC.; *U.S. Private*, pg. 3333
R.S. MEANS COMPANY LLC—See Fortive Corporation; *U.S. Public*, pg. 871
RST RALF SCHMIDT TIEFBAU, KABEL & KABEL-ROHRVERLEGUNG GMBH—See Heidelberg Materials AG; *Int'l*, pg. 3319
RTM & ASSOCIATES, INC.; *U.S. Private*, pg. 3498
RUBY ASSOCIATES, PC—See Degenkolb Engineers; *U.S. Private*, pg. 1191
RUMMEL, KLEPPER & KAHL; *U.S. Private*, pg. 3503
RUNTIME DESIGN AUTOMATION—See Altair Engineering, Inc.; *U.S. Public*, pg. 86
RUSSELL CORROSION CONSULTANTS, INC.—See General Atlantic Service Company, L.P.; *U.S. Private*, pg. 1662
R.W. ARMSTRONG & ASSOCIATES LLC—See H.I.G. Capital, LLC; *U.S. Private*, pg. 1827
RWG I ABBRUCH UND TIEFBAU GMBH—See Heidelberg Materials AG; *Int'l*, pg. 3319
RYAN BIGGS CLARK DAVIS, ENGINEERING & SURVEYING, P.C.; *U.S. Private*, pg. 3509
SAALEX CORP; *U.S. Private*, pg. 3520
SAE (INDIA) LTD.—See SAE International; *U.S. Private*, pg. 3523
SAE INTERNATIONAL; *U.S. Private*, pg. 3523
SAEXPLORATION (BRASIL) SERVICOS SISMICOS LTDA.—See SAExploration Holdings, Inc.; *U.S. Private*, pg. 3523
SAFE AIR LIMITED—See Airbus SE; *Int'l*, pg. 247
SAFETEC ENTSORGUNGS- UND SICHERHEITSTECHNIK GMBH—See E.ON SE; *Int'l*, pg. 2259
SAFWAY ATLANTIC LLC—See Brand Industrial Services, Inc.; *U.S. Private*, pg. 636
SAIPEM AMERICA, INC.—See Eni S.p.A.; *Int'l*, pg. 2438
SAIPEM S.P.A.—See Eni S.p.A.; *Int'l*, pg. 2438
SAIPEM UK LTD—See Eni S.p.A.; *Int'l*, pg. 2438
SALAS O'BRIEN ENGINEERS, INC.; *U.S. Private*, pg. 3530
SALAS O'BRIEN SOUTH, LLC—See Salas O'Brien Engineers, Inc.; *U.S. Private*, pg. 3530
S. A. MIRO, INC.; *U.S. Private*, pg. 3514
SAM SCHWARTZ ENGINEERING D.P.C.; *U.S. Private*, pg. 3536
SAMUEL ENGINEERING, INC.; *U.S. Private*, pg. 3538
SAN ANTONIO DESIGN GROUP INC.—See M&S Engineering, LLC; *U.S. Private*, pg. 2525
SANDERSON BELLECCI, INC.; *U.S. Private*, pg. 3543
SANDERSON STEWART—See Sanderson Bellecci, Inc.; *U.S. Private*, pg. 3543
SAN DIEGO COMPOSITES, INC.—See AE Industrial Partners, LP; *U.S. Private*, pg. 111
SANJOSE ENERGIA Y MEDIO AMBIENTE S A.—See Grupo Empresarial San Jose, S.A.; *Int'l*, pg. 3128
SAN MARTIN CONTRATISTAS GENERALES S.A.—See Empresas ICA S.A.B. de C.V.; *Int'l*, pg. 2391
SANSHIN CORPORATION—See Aktio Holdings Corporation; *Int'l*, pg. 267
SANTA BARBARA APPLIED RESEARCH INC.; *U.S. Private*, pg. 3546
SANWA COMSYS ENGINEERING CORPORATION—See COMSYS Holdings Corporation; *Int'l*, pg. 1762
SANWA DENSHI INC.—See COMSYS Holdings Corporation; *Int'l*, pg. 1762
SAPB—See FAYAT SAS; *Int'l*, pg. 2626
SAREC TOULOUSE—See FAYAT SAS; *Int'l*, pg. 2626
SARGENT & LUNDY LLC; *U.S. Private*, pg. 3550
SAT (SURFACE ALUMINIUM TECHNOLOGIES) S.R.L.—See Graco, Inc.; *U.S. Public*, pg. 954
SAUER BIBUS GMBH—See Daikin Industries, Ltd.; *Int'l*, pg. 1936
SAXORE BERGBAU GMBH—See First Tin Plc; *Int'l*, pg. 2688
SBB BEUTLER & LANG GMBH & CO—See Beutler & Lang Schalungs- und Behalter-Bau GmbH; *Int'l*, pg. 1004
S&B INFRASTRUCTURE, LTD.—See S&B Engineers & Constructors, Ltd.; *U.S. Private*, pg. 3512

4579

541330 — ENGINEERING SERVICE...

S&B PLANT SERVICES, LTD.—See S&B Engineers & Constructors, Ltd.; *U.S. Private*, pg. 3512
SBSA, INC.—See Lovell Minnick Partners LLC; *U.S. Private*, pg. 2502
SCAMP MARINE SL—See Gibunco Group Limited; *Int'l*, pg. 2963
SCANMATIC ENVIRONMENTAL TECHNOLOGY AB—See Arendals Fossekompani ASA; *Int'l*, pg. 559
SCANSCOT TECHNOLOGY AB—See Addnode Group AB; *Int'l*, pg. 130
SCHACHTBAU NORDHAUSEN GMBH - CIVIL ENGINEERING DIVISION—See BAUER Aktiengesellschaft; *Int'l*, pg. 894
SCHACHTBAU NORDHAUSEN GMBH.—See BAUER Aktiengesellschaft; *Int'l*, pg. 893
SCHACHTBAU NORDHAUSEN GMBH - UNDERGROUND CONSTRUCTION DIVISION—See BAUER Aktiengesellschaft; *Int'l*, pg. 894
SCHACHTBAU NORDHAUSEN STAHLBAU GMBH—See BAUER Aktiengesellschaft; *Int'l*, pg. 894
SCHILD ELEKTRO AG—See Burkhalter Holding AG; *Int'l*, pg. 1225
SCHMITTER ELEKTRO, ZNL DER ELEKTRO-BAU AG—See Burkhalter Holding AG; *Int'l*, pg. 1225
SCHNABEL ENGINEERING, INC.; *U.S. Private*, pg. 3566
SCHULTHEIS-MOCKLI AG—See Burkhalter Holding AG; *Int'l*, pg. 1225
SCHULTZ SURVEYING & ENGINEERING, INC.; *U.S. Private*, pg. 3570
SCM CONSULTANTS, INC.—See Tetra Tech, Inc.; *U.S. Public*, pg. 2023
SCS ENGINEERS; *U.S. Private*, pg. 3580
SCS ENGINEERS - TAMPA—See SCS Engineers; *U.S. Private*, pg. 3580
SCS FIELD SERVICES—See SCS Engineers; *U.S. Private*, pg. 3580
SCST, INC.; *U.S. Private*, pg. 3580
S.D. DEACON CORP. OF WASHINGTON—See S.D. Deacon Corporation; *U.S. Private*, pg. 3517
SDII GLOBAL CORPORATION; *U.S. Private*, pg. 3581
SEA FORREST TECHNOLOGIES PTE. LTD.—See BH Global Corporation Limited; *Int'l*, pg. 1009
SEAMECH INTERNATIONAL, INC.—See Bascom Hunter Technologies Inc.; *U.S. Private*, pg. 484
SEBESTA, INC.—See NV5 Global, Inc.; *U.S. Public*, pg. 1557
SECAUTO S.A—See Eiffage S.A.; *Int'l*, pg. 2331
SECURON AG—See BKW AG; *Int'l*, pg. 1056
SEDELEC JURA BERNOIS, SUCCURSALE DE SEDELEC S.A.—See Burkhalter Holding AG; *Int'l*, pg. 1225
SEDELEC LA VALLEE, SUCCURSALE DE SEDELEC S.A.—See Burkhalter Holding AG; *Int'l*, pg. 1225
SEDELEC SAIGNELEGIER, SUCCURSALE DE SEDELEC S.A.—See Burkhalter Holding AG; *Int'l*, pg. 1225
SEDELEC SA LAUSANNE—See Burkhalter Holding AG; *Int'l*, pg. 1225
SEDELEC SA—See Burkhalter Holding AG; *Int'l*, pg. 1225
SEDELEC VEVEY, SUCCURSALE DE SEDELEC S.A.—See Burkhalter Holding AG; *Int'l*, pg. 1225
SEDELEC YVERDON, SUCCURSALE DE SEDELEC S.A.—See Burkhalter Holding AG; *Int'l*, pg. 1225
SEDGMAN PTY LIMITED—See ACS, Actividades de Construccion y Servicios, S.A.; *Int'l*, pg. 113
SEDIN ENGINEERING CO., LTD.—See China National Chemical Engineering Co., Ltd.; *Int'l*, pg. 1531
SEEYOND ARCHITECTURAL SOLUTIONS—See Liberty Diversified International Inc.; *U.S. Private*, pg. 2444
SEFI FONTEC—See FAYAT SAS; *Int'l*, pg. 2626
SEFNCO COMMUNICATIONS, INC.—See MasTec, Inc.; *U.S. Public*, pg. 1393
SEH OF INDIANA, LLC—See Short Elliott Hendrickson Inc.; *U.S. Private*, pg. 3642
SEIBERLING ASSOCIATES, INC.—See The Haskell Company; *U.S. Private*, pg. 4043
SEI GROUP, INC.; *U.S. Private*, pg. 3599
SELECT ENGINEERING, INC.; *U.S. Private*, pg. 3600
SELINSKY FORCE, LLC—See KLH Capital L.P.; *U.S. Private*, pg. 2319
SEMBCORP DESIGN AND CONSTRUCTION PTE LTD—See Chip Eng Seng Corporation Ltd.; *Int'l*, pg. 1572
SEMCON ENGINEERING UK LTD—See ASM Technologies Limited; *Int'l*, pg. 627
SENEOS GMBH—See Hitachi, Ltd.; *Int'l*, pg. 3424
SENSOR TECHNOLOGY ENGINEERING, LLC—See HEICO Corporation; *U.S. Public*, pg. 1020
SEPI ENGINEERING & CONSTRUCTION, INC.—See OceanSound Partners, LP; *U.S. Private*, pg. 2991
SEREMBAN ENGINEERING BERHAD—See CTCI Corporation; *Int'l*, pg. 1870
SERRANO AZNAR OBRAS PUBLICAS S.L—See Eiffage S.A.; *Int'l*, pg. 2331
SERVEONE CONSTRUCTION (NANJING) CO., LTD—See Affinity Equity Partners (HK) Ltd.; *Int'l*, pg. 186
SERVIDYNE, INC.—See SClenergy, Inc.; *U.S. Private*, pg. 3573
SESPE CONSULTING, INC.—See Keystone Group, L.P.; *U.S. Private*, pg. 2299

SEWER SYSTEMS EVALUATIONS, INC.—See Carylon Corporation; *U.S. Private*, pg. 777
SHAH & ASSOCIATES, INC.; *U.S. Private*, pg. 3623
SHAMA TECHNOLOGIES (S) PTE LTD.—See HUB Cyber Security Ltd.; *Int'l*, pg. 3516
SHANGHAI CCECC ENTERPRISES COMPANY LTD.—See China Railway Construction Corporation Limited; *Int'l*, pg. 1543
SHANGHAI EBARA ENGINEERING AND SERVICES CO., LTD.—See Ebara Corporation; *Int'l*, pg. 2284
SHANGHAI IDEMITSU LUBE TRADING CO., LTD.—See Idemitsu Kosan Co., Ltd.; *Int'l*, pg. 3592
SHANGHAI IMAT AUTOMOTIVE TECHNOLOGY SERVICE CO., LTD.—See Centre Testing International Corporation; *Int'l*, pg. 1411
SHANNON & WILSON, INC.; *U.S. Private*, pg. 3625
SHAPE FIDELITY, INC.—See Aerobotix, Inc; *U.S. Private*, pg. 118
SHARMA & ASSOCIATES, INC.—See TOPS Software, LLC; *U.S. Private*, pg. 4188
SHAW LANCAS, C.A.—See The Shaw Group Inc.; *U.S. Private*, pg. 4117
SHEAR ENGINEERING CORP.—See Chayah Consulting Group LLC; *U.S. Private*, pg. 868
SHENG HUEI (SHENZHEN) ENGINEERING CO., LTD.—See Acter Co., Ltd.; *Int'l*, pg. 117
SHENYANG XUANTAN AUTOMOBILE PARTS CO.—See Aisan Industry Co., Ltd.; *Int'l*, pg. 251
SHENZHEN CMEC INDUSTRY CO., LTD.—See China Machinery Engineering Corporation; *Int'l*, pg. 1516
SHEPHARD-WESNITZER, INC.—See Littlejohn & Co., LLC; *U.S. Private*, pg. 2470
SHERMCO INDUSTRIES, INC.—See Gryphon Investors, LLC; *U.S. Private*, pg. 1799
SH GROUP A/S—See BWB Partners P/S; *Int'l*, pg. 1232
SHIBATA INDUSTRY CO., LTD.—See Ashimori Industry Co., Ltd.; *Int'l*, pg. 607
SHIMMICK CORPORATION; *U.S. Public*, pg. 1875
SHIN CHANG INTERNATIONAL INC.—See Doppelmayr Group; *Int'l*, pg. 2175
SHIRLEY CONTRACTING COMPANY LLC—See Clark Enterprises, Inc.; *U.S. Private*, pg. 913
SHORT ELLIOTT HENDRICKSON INC.; *U.S. Private*, pg. 3642
SI2CHIP TECHNOLOGIES PRIVATE LTD.—See Alten S.A.; *Int'l*, pg. 391
SIA MERKS—See AS Merko Ehitus; *Int'l*, pg. 590
SICE HELLAS SISTEMAS TECNOLOGICOS SOCIEDAD UNIPERSONAL DE RESPONSABILIDAD LIMITADA—See ACS, Actividades de Construccion y Servicios, S.A.; *Int'l*, pg. 116
SICE, INC.—See ACS, Actividades de Construccion y Servicios, S.A.; *Int'l*, pg. 116
SICOPLAN N.V—See G. Siempelkamp GmbH & Co. KG; *Int'l*, pg. 2864
SIEMPELKAMP (QINGDAO) MACHINERY & EQUIPMENT CO. LTD.—See G. Siempelkamp GmbH & Co. KG; *Int'l*, pg. 2864
SI FACTOR LLC—See Agenzia Nazionale per l'Attrazione degli Investimenti e lo Sviluppo d'Impresa SpA; *Int'l*, pg. 206
SIGMA DEFENSE SYSTEMS LLC—See Sagewind Capital LLC; *U.S. Private*, pg. 3527
SIGMA SIX SOLUTIONS, INC.—See Gryphon Investors, LLC; *U.S. Private*, pg. 1799
SIGNA ENGINEERING CORP.—See Weatherford International plc; *U.S. Public*, pg. 2339
SIGNAL INNOVATIONS GROUP INC.—See BAE Systems plc; *U.S. Public*, pg. 798
SIGNET TECHNOLOGY INC—See Fluor Corporation; *U.S. Public*, pg. 859
SIHONG BOSSCO WATER CO., LTD—See Guangxi Bossco Environmental Protection Technology Co., Ltd.; *Int'l*, pg. 3163
SILICA VERFAHRENSTECHNIK GMBH—See Berndorf AG; *Int'l*, pg. 987
SIMBEX LLC—See Fenway Partners, LLC; *U.S. Private*, pg. 1495
SIMEC GROUP LIMITED—See GFG Alliance Limited; *Int'l*, pg. 2956
SIMFLEXI SDN. BHD.—See Handal Energy Berhad; *Int'l*, pg. 3243
SIMPSON GUMPERTZ & HEGER INC.; *U.S. Private*, pg. 3668
SIMPSON STRONG-TIE (BEIJING) COMPANY LIMITED—See Simpson Manufacturing Company, Inc.; *U.S. Public*, pg. 1883
SIMUTECH GROUP, INC.—See Amphenol Corporation; *U.S. Public*, pg. 131
SIMUTECH GROUP - TORONTO—See Amphenol Corporation; *U.S. Public*, pg. 131
SINGA DEVELOPMENT PTE LTD—See BBR Holdings (S) Ltd.; *Int'l*, pg. 921
SINGAPORE ENGINEERING & CONSTRUCTION PTE. LTD.—See BBR Holdings (S) Ltd.; *Int'l*, pg. 921
SINGAPORE PILING & CIVIL ENGINEERING PRIVATE LIMITED—See BBR Holdings (S) Ltd.; *Int'l*, pg. 921

SINGHOFEN & ASSOCIATES, INC.—See Halff Associates, Inc.; *U.S. Private*, pg. 1842
SINGLANDE—See FAYAT SAS; *Int'l*, pg. 2626
SINOMA YANZHOU MINING ENGINEERING CO., LTD.—See China National Materials; *Int'l*, pg. 1532
SINOPEC ENGINEERING (GROUP) CO. LTD.—See China Petrochemical Corporation; *Int'l*, pg. 1540
SINOPHARM UNITED ENGINEERING COMPANY LTD.—See China National Pharmaceutical Group Corporation; *Int'l*, pg. 1534
SIRFIA—See FAYAT SAS; *Int'l*, pg. 2626
SITE CONSULTANTS INC.—See Westwood Professional Services, Inc.; *U.S. Private*, pg. 4502
SKAELSKOR ANLAEGSGARTNERE A/S—See Det Danske Hedeselskab; *Int'l*, pg. 2047
S.K. ENGINEERING CO., LTD.—See Hanwa Co., Ltd.; *Int'l*, pg. 3263
SKM (SINGAPORE) PTE LTD—See Jacobs Engineering Group, Inc.; *U.S. Public*, pg. 1186
SKODA PRAHA, A.S.—See CEZ, a.s.; *Int'l*, pg. 1428
SMART ROBOTICS CO.LTD.—See Bain Capital, LP; *U.S. Private*, pg. 435
SMART SA—See CNTEE TRANSELECTRICA SA; *Int'l*, pg. 1678
S&ME, INC.; *U.S. Private*, pg. 3513
SMITH SECKMAN REID INC.; *U.S. Private*, pg. 3695
SMPE GROUP—See Airbus SE; *Int'l*, pg. 246
SNC-LAVALIN AGRO—See AtkinsRealis Group Inc.; *Int'l*, pg. 671
SNC-LAVALIN ALGERIE EURL—See AtkinsRealis Group Inc.; *Int'l*, pg. 672
SNC-LAVALIN AMERICA, INC.—See AtkinsRealis Group Inc.; *Int'l*, pg. 672
SNC-LAVALIN ARABIA ENGINEERING CONSULTANCY—See AtkinsRealis Group Inc.; *Int'l*, pg. 672
SNC-LAVALIN ARABIA, LLC—See AtkinsRealis Group Inc.; *Int'l*, pg. 672
SNC-LAVALIN AUSTRALIA PTY. LTD.—See AtkinsRealis Group Inc.; *Int'l*, pg. 672
SNC-LAVALIN CAPITAL ENGINEERING LLC—See AtkinsRealis Group Inc.; *Int'l*, pg. 672
SNC-LAVALIN CHILE S.A.—See AtkinsRealis Group Inc.; *Int'l*, pg. 672
SNC-LAVALIN CONSTRUCTION (ATLANTIC) INC.—See AtkinsRealis Group Inc.; *Int'l*, pg. 671
SNC-LAVALIN CONSTRUCTION INTERNATIONAL SAS—See AtkinsRealis Group Inc.; *Int'l*, pg. 672
SNC-LAVALIN CONSTRUCTION (ONTARIO) INC.—See AtkinsRealis Group Inc.; *Int'l*, pg. 671
SNC-LAVALIN EGYPT LLC—See AtkinsRealis Group Inc.; *Int'l*, pg. 672
SNC-LAVALIN ENGINEERING INDIA PRIVATE LIMITED—See AtkinsRealis Group Inc.; *Int'l*, pg. 672
SNC-LAVALIN ENGINEERING & TECHNOLOGY PVT LIMITED—See AtkinsRealis Group Inc.; *Int'l*, pg. 672
SNC-LAVALIN ENGINEERS & CONSTRUCTORS, INC.—See AtkinsRealis Group Inc.; *Int'l*, pg. 672
SNC-LAVALIN EURASIA OOO—See AtkinsRealis Group Inc.; *Int'l*, pg. 672
SNC-LAVALIN GULF CONTRACTORS LLC—See AtkinsRealis Group Inc.; *Int'l*, pg. 672
SNC-LAVALIN INC. - CALGARY—See AtkinsRealis Group Inc.; *Int'l*, pg. 671
SNC-LAVALIN INC. - EDMONTON—See AtkinsRealis Group Inc.; *Int'l*, pg. 671
SNC-LAVALIN INC. - HALIFAX—See AtkinsRealis Group Inc.; *Int'l*, pg. 671
SNC-LAVALIN INC. - LEVIS—See AtkinsRealis Group Inc.; *Int'l*, pg. 671
SNC-LAVALIN INC. - LONGUEUIL—See AtkinsRealis Group Inc.; *Int'l*, pg. 671
SNC LAVALIN INC. - OTTAWA—See AtkinsRealis Group Inc.; *Int'l*, pg. 671
SNC-LAVALIN INC. - RIMOUSKI—See AtkinsRealis Group Inc.; *Int'l*, pg. 671
SNC-LAVALIN INC. - SARNIA—See AtkinsRealis Group Inc.; *Int'l*, pg. 671
SNC-LAVALIN INC.—See AtkinsRealis Group Inc.; *Int'l*, pg. 671
SNC-LAVALIN INC. - THETFORD MINES—See AtkinsRealis Group Inc.; *Int'l*, pg. 671
SNC-LAVALIN INC. - TORONTO—See AtkinsRealis Group Inc.; *Int'l*, pg. 671
SNC-LAVALIN INC. - VANCOUVER—See AtkinsRealis Group Inc.; *Int'l*, pg. 671
SNC-LAVALIN INC. - WINNIPEG—See AtkinsRealis Group Inc.; *Int'l*, pg. 671
SNC-LAVALIN INFRASTRUCTURE PVT. LTD.—See AtkinsRealis Group Inc.; *Int'l*, pg. 672
SNC-LAVALIN INTERNATIONAL CO. INC.—See AtkinsRealis Group Inc.; *Int'l*, pg. 672
SNC LAVALIN INTERNATIONAL INC. - BEIJING REPRESENTATIVE OFFICE—See AtkinsRealis Group Inc.; *Int'l*, pg. 671
SNC-LAVALIN INTERNATIONAL INC. - CAMEROON—See AtkinsRealis Group Inc.; *Int'l*, pg. 672
SNC-LAVALIN INTERNATIONAL INC. - HONDURAS—See

N.A.I.C.S. INDEX

541330 — ENGINEERING SERVICE...

AtkinsRealis Group Inc.; *Int'l*, pg. 672
SNC-LAVALIN INTERNATIONAL INC. - KAZAKHSTAN—See AtkinsRealis Group Inc.; *Int'l*, pg. 672
SNC-LAVALIN INTERNATIONAL INC. - LIBYA—See AtkinsRealis Group Inc.; *Int'l*, pg. 672
SNC LAVALIN INTERNATIONAL INC. - RUSSIA—See AtkinsRealis Group Inc.; *Int'l*, pg. 671
SNC-LAVALIN INTERNATIONAL INC. - THAILAND—See AtkinsRealis Group Inc.; *Int'l*, pg. 672
SNC-LAVALIN INTERNATIONAL INC. - VIETNAM—See AtkinsRealis Group Inc.; *Int'l*, pg. 672
SNC-LAVALIN KOREA LIMITED—See AtkinsRealis Group Inc.; *Int'l*, pg. 672
SNC-LAVALIN (MALAYSIA) SDN. BHD.—See AtkinsRealis Group Inc.; *Int'l*, pg. 672
SNC-LAVALIN MUHENDISLIK VE TAAHHUT LIMITED SIRKETI—See AtkinsRealis Group Inc.; *Int'l*, pg. 673
SNC-LAVALIN NUCLEAR INC.—See AtkinsRealis Group Inc.; *Int'l*, pg. 673
SNC-LAVALIN PHARMA S.A.—See AtkinsRealis Group Inc.; *Int'l*, pg. 673
SNC-LAVALIN PROJECT SERVICES, INC.—See AtkinsRealis Group Inc.; *Int'l*, pg. 672
SNC-LAVALIN S.A.S.—See AtkinsRealis Group Inc.; *Int'l*, pg. 672
SNC-LAVALIN (SHANGHAI) INTERNATIONAL TRADING CO. LTD.—See AtkinsRealis Group Inc.; *Int'l*, pg. 672
SNC-LAVALIN SOUTH AFRICA (PTY) LTD.—See AtkinsRealis Group Inc.; *Int'l*, pg. 673
SNC-LAVALIN SPAIN SL—See AtkinsRealis Group Inc.; *Int'l*, pg. 673
SNOWDEN MINING INDUSTRY CONSULTANTS LIMITED—See Downer EDI Limited; *Int'l*, pg. 2186
SOCAMIP—See Eiffage S.A.; *Int'l*, pg. 2330
SOCIEDAD ASTURIANA DE DIVERSIFICACION MINERA S.A.—See Hulleras del Norte, S.A.; *Int'l*, pg. 3528
SOCIEDAD NACIONAL DE OLEODUCTOS S.A.—See AntarChile S.A.; *Int'l*, pg. 482
SOCIETE D'ENERGIE DE LA BAIE JAMES—See Hydro-Quebec; *Int'l*, pg. 3547
SOCIETE D'EXPERTISE ET D'INGENIERIE LGL S.A.—See AtkinsRealis Group Inc.; *Int'l*, pg. 673
SOCOTEC, INC.—See Cobepa S.A.; *Int'l*, pg. 1683
SODECLIM—See FAYAT SAS; *Int'l*, pg. 2626
SOFINEL—See Electricite de France S.A.; *Int'l*, pg. 2352
SOGETI HIGH TECH GMBH—See Capgemini SE; *Int'l*, pg. 1307
SOLAR POWER MANAGEMENT (THAILAND) COMPANY LIMITED—See BG Container Glass Public Company Limited; *Int'l*, pg. 1007
SOLIDS COMPONENTS MIGSA S.L.—See Hosokawa Micron Corporation; *Int'l*, pg. 3486
SOLIDYN SOLUTIONS, LLC—See Parsons Corporation; *U.S. Public*, pg. 1651
SOLS ET FONDATIONS—See FAYAT SAS; *Int'l*, pg. 2626
SOMATRA—See FAYAT SAS; *Int'l*, pg. 2626
SOMIFA—See FAYAT SAS; *Int'l*, pg. 2626
SONALYSTS, INC.; *U.S. Private*, pg. 3712
SONOCO AT WHIRLPOOL—See Sonoco Products Company; *U.S. Public*, pg. 1908
SONOMA TECHNICAL SERVICE, INC.—See ABM Industries, Inc.; *U.S. Public*, pg. 26
SONOPRESS GMBH—See Bertelsmann SE & Co. KGaA; *Int'l*, pg. 996
SOUND SOLUTIONS AUSTRIA GMBH—See Hon Hai Precision Industry Co., Ltd.; *Int'l*, pg. 3459
THE SOURCE GROUP INC.—See Apex Companies, LLC; *U.S. Private*, pg. 292
SOUTHERN DIVERSIFIED TECHNOLOGIES, INC.—See Littlejohn & Co., LLC; *U.S. Private*, pg. 2472
SOUTHERN DIVERSIFIED TECHNOLOGIES, INC.—See New Mountain Capital, LLC; *U.S. Private*, pg. 2903
SOUTHERN MARYLAND CABLE, INC.—See Argan, Inc.; *U.S. Public*, pg. 191
SOUTHWEST STEEL CASTING COMPANY—See The Greenbrier Companies, Inc.; *U.S. Public*, pg. 2086
SPACE GROUND SYSTEM SOLUTIONS, INC.—See The O'Neil Group Company, LLC; *U.S. Private*, pg. 4087
SPACEWORKS ENTERPRISES, INC.; *U.S. Private*, pg. 3744
SPALDING DEDECKER ASSOCIATES, INC.; *U.S. Private*, pg. 3744
SPECIAL AEROSPACE SERVICES LLC—See Godspeed Capital Management LP; *U.S. Private*, pg. 1725
SPECTRA SCAFFOLDING LTD—See Altrad Investment Authority SAS; *Int'l*, pg. 398
SPEECE LEWIS ENGINEERS, INC.—See Bowman Consulting Group Ltd.; *U.S. Public*, pg. 376
SPEEDWELL ENGINEERS PVT. LTD.—See Ace Software Exports Ltd.; *Int'l*, pg. 95
SPEEDY ENGINEERING & TRADING COMPANY LIMITED—See Dimmi Life Holdings Limited; *Int'l*, pg. 2126
SPESA SPEZIALBAU UND SANIERUNG GMBH.—See BAUER Aktiengesellschaft; *Int'l*, pg. 894
SPHEREA TEST & SERVICES LTD.—See Andera Partners SCA; *Int'l*, pg. 450
SPHEREA TEST & SERVICES LTD.—See Coller Capital Ltd.; *Int'l*, pg. 1699
SPLU EXPERTS GMBH—See ManpowerGroup Inc.; *U.S. Public*, pg. 1362
SPOT IMAGE CORPORATION, INC.—See Airbus SE; *Int'l*, pg. 243
SPOTLESS DEFENCE SERVICES PTY. LTD.—See Downer EDI Limited; *Int'l*, pg. 2185
SPRECHER AG—See Burkhalter Holding AG; *Int'l*, pg. 1225
SPRING ENGINEERS OF HOUSTON LTD.—See SEI MetalTek; *U.S. Private*, pg. 3599
SPX FLOW TECHNOLOGY (THAILAND) LIMITED—See Lone Star Funds; *U.S. Private*, pg. 2486
SQUAN CONSTRUCTION SERVICES LLC; *U.S. Private*, pg. 3766
SSN CUBE GMBH—See Consus Real Estate AG; *Int'l*, pg. 1778
SSP INDUSTRIES—See TransDigm Group Incorporated; *U.S. Public*, pg. 2183
STACKHOUSE BENSINGER INC.; *U.S. Private*, pg. 3774
STAHL + VERBUNDBAU GMBH—See Hutter & Schrantz PMS Ges.m.b.H; *Int'l*, pg. 3540
STANLEY CONSULTANTS (ENGINEERS), P.S.C.—See Stanley Consultants Co.; *U.S. Private*, pg. 3783
STANLEY CONSULTANTS INDIA PRIVATE LIMITED—See Stanley Consultants Co.; *U.S. Private*, pg. 3783
STATE BUILDING GROUP, INC.—See State Utility Contractors Inc.; *U.S. Private*, pg. 3793
STATHMOI PANTECHNIKI SA—See ELLAKTOR S.A.; *Int'l*, pg. 2365
STATS ASIA PACIFIC PTE. LTD.—See Eurofins Scientific S.E.; *Int'l*, pg. 2552
STAVANGER MEKANISKE AS—See IKM Gruppen AS; *Int'l*, pg. 3612
STEAG ENERGY SERVICES DO BRASIL LTDA.—See Asterion Industrial Partners SGEIC SA; *Int'l*, pg. 654
STEAG ENERGY SERVICES GMBH—See Asterion Industrial Partners SGEIC SA; *Int'l*, pg. 654
STEAG ENERGY SERVICES (INDIA) PVT. LTD.—See Asterion Industrial Partners SGEIC SA; *Int'l*, pg. 654
STEAG TECHNISCHER SERVICE GMBH—See Asterion Industrial Partners SGEIC SA; *Int'l*, pg. 654
STEAM ENGINEERING, INC.—See BHS Specialty Chemicals; *Int'l*, pg. 549
STEINMULLER ENGINEERING SERVICES (PTY) LTD.—See Bilfinger SE; *Int'l*, pg. 1029
STELLAR ENERGY AMERICAS INC.—See The Stellar Group Inc.; *U.S. Private*, pg. 4121
STELLARIS, LLC—See Primoris Services Corporation; *U.S. Public*, pg. 1719
STELLAR SOLUTIONS INC.; *U.S. Private*, pg. 3799
STENCOR COMPANY, LLC; *U.S. Private*, pg. 3801
STETSON ENGINEERING, INC.—See HDR, Inc.; *U.S. Private*, pg. 1890
STEVEN FELLER P.E., PL—See Yenni Capital, Inc.; *U.S. Private*, pg. 4588
STINGER GHAFFARIAN TECHNOLOGIES INC.—See KBR, Inc.; *U.S. Public*, pg. 1216
STINKAL—See Eiffage S.A.; *Int'l*, pg. 2331
STK DEKRA RYCHNOV S.R.O.—See DEKRA e.V.; *Int'l*, pg. 2009
STOBART RAIL LIMITED—See BAVARIA Industries Group AG; *Int'l*, pg. 899
THE STOKE ON TRENT & STAFFORDSHIRE SAFER COMMUNITIES COMMUNITY INTEREST COMPANY—See Bilfinger SE; *Int'l*, pg. 1029
STORK GERMAN HOLDING GMBH—See Fluor Corporation; *U.S. Public*, pg. 860
STORK POWER SERVICES & TECHNOLOGY BEIJING LIMITED—See Fluor Corporation; *U.S. Public*, pg. 860
STORK TECHNICAL SERVICES BELGIUM N.V.—See Fluor Corporation; *U.S. Public*, pg. 860
STORK TECHNICAL SERVICES (STS) LTD—See Fluor Corporation; *U.S. Public*, pg. 860
STORK TURBO SERVICE B V.—See Fluor Corporation; *U.S. Public*, pg. 860
STRAND ASSOCIATES, INC.; *U.S. Private*, pg. 3833
STREAMSETS, INC.—See Silver Lake Group, LLC; *U.S. Private*, pg. 3660
STRIKOWESTOFEN GMBH—See BPE Unternehmensbeteiligungen GmbH; *Int'l*, pg. 1131
STRUCTURA, INC.; *U.S. Private*, pg. 3841
STRUCTURAL ENGINEERING ASSOCIATES, INC.—See Johnson, Mirmiran & Thompson, Inc.; *U.S. Private*, pg. 2229
STRUKTON INTEGRALE PROJECTEN B.V.—See Centric Holding B.V.; *Int'l*, pg. 1412
STRUKTON SYSTEMS B.V.—See Centric Holding B.V.; *Int'l*, pg. 1413
STRUKTON WORKSPHERE B.V.—See Centric Holding B.V.; *Int'l*, pg. 1413
STS HOLDINGS, INC.; *U.S. Private*, pg. 3842
STUYVESANT ENVIRONMENTAL CONTRACTING, LLC—See HAL Trust N.V.; *Int'l*, pg. 3227
STV ARCHITECTS, INC.—See STV Group, Inc.; *U.S. Private*, pg. 3845
STV CONSTRUCTION SERVICES, INC.—See STV Group, Inc.; *U.S. Private*, pg. 3846
STV ENERGY SERVICES—See STV Group, Inc.; *U.S. Private*, pg. 3845
STV ENVIRONMENTAL, INC.—See STV Group, Inc.; *U.S. Private*, pg. 3846
STV GROUP, INC.; *U.S. Private*, pg. 3845
STV INC.—See STV Group, Inc.; *U.S. Private*, pg. 3845
STV/RALPH WHITEHEAD ASSOCIATES—See STV Group, Inc.; *U.S. Private*, pg. 3846
STV/RALPH WHITEHEAD ASSOCIATES—See STV Group, Inc.; *U.S. Private*, pg. 3846
S. TYGESEN ENERGI A/S—See Addtech AB; *Int'l*, pg. 135
SUBSYSTEM TECHNOLOGIES, INC.; *U.S. Private*, pg. 3847
SUIR ENGINEERING LTD.—See Duke Street Capital Limited; *Int'l*, pg. 2224
SULA SYSTEMS LTD.—See Jacobs Engineering Group, Inc.; *U.S. Public*, pg. 1186
SULLIVAN INTERNATIONAL GROUP, INC.; *U.S. Private*, pg. 3851
SUMMIT ENGINEERING, LABORATORY & TESTING, P.C.—See Universal Engineering Sciences, LLC; *U.S. Private*, pg. 4304
SUMO SERVICES LTD—See Franchise Concepts Limited; *Int'l*, pg. 2760
SUNCOM TECHNOLOGY CORPORATION—See COMSYS Holdings Corporation; *Int'l*, pg. 1762
SUPERIOR RESOURCE GROUP, INC.—See NSC Technologies, Inc.; *U.S. Private*, pg. 2970
SUPERIOR-WILD WELL ENERGY SERVICES LIMITED—See Superior Energy Services, Inc.; *U.S. Private*, pg. 3877
SUPPORT SYSTEMS ASSOCIATES, INC.; *U.S. Private*, pg. 3882
SUSTAINABLE ENERGY SOLUTIONS, INC.—See Chart Industries, Inc.; *U.S. Public*, pg. 482
SUSTAINED QUALITY LLC—See Groupe Crit, S.A.; *Int'l*, pg. 3101
SUT GLOBAL COMPANY LIMITED—See Hydrotek Public Company Limited; *Int'l*, pg. 3548
SUZHOU WINMAX TECHNOLOGY CORP.—See Acter Co., Ltd.; *Int'l*, pg. 117
SWANILLON, INC.; *U.S. Private*, pg. 3890
SYMVIONICS, INC.; *U.S. Private*, pg. 3902
SYNAPSE PRODUCT DEVELOPMENT, INC.—See Capgemini SE; *Int'l*, pg. 1305
SYNCRONESS, INC.; *U.S. Private*, pg. 3903
SYNECO TEC GMBH—See CEZ, a.s.; *Int'l*, pg. 1428
SYNTROL CORP.; *U.S. Public*, pg. 1972
SYSKA HENNESSY GROUP INC.; *U.S. Private*, pg. 3906
SYSTAG, SYSTEM TECHNIK AG—See Dottikon ES Holding AG; *Int'l*, pg. 2180
SYSTEM DYNAMICS INTERNATIONAL INC.; *U.S. Private*, pg. 3906
SYSTEMS DESIGN ENGINEERING, INC. (SDE); *U.S. Private*, pg. 3907
SYSTEMS ENGINEERING & ASSESSMENT LTD.—See Cohort plc; *Int'l*, pg. 1696
SYSTEMS ENGINEERING GROUP, INC.—See Griffon Corporation; *U.S. Public*, pg. 969
SYSTEMS & SOFTWARE SERVICE INC.—See Mullins & Associates Inc.; *U.S. Private*, pg. 2812
TABIMED GESTION DE PROYECTOS, S.L—See Banco de Sabadell, S.A.; *Int'l*, pg. 821
TAE AVIATION PTY LIMITED—See Air New Zealand Limited; *Int'l*, pg. 238
TAE GAS TURBINES PTY LIMITED—See Air New Zealand Limited; *Int'l*, pg. 238
TAE PTY LIMITED—See Air New Zealand Limited; *Int'l*, pg. 238
TAM CONSULTANTS, INC.—See Terracon Consultants, Inc.; *U.S. Private*, pg. 3971
TANDEL SYSTEMS, INC.—See AE Industrial Partners, LP; *U.S. Private*, pg. 111
TANGENT ENERGY SOLUTIONS, INC.—See Caterpillar, Inc.; *U.S. Public*, pg. 454
TANKNOLOGY INC; *U.S. Private*, pg. 3931
TANKNOLOGY/NDE CORPORATION—See Tanknology Inc; *U.S. Private*, pg. 3931
TANKNOLOGY OHIO VALLEY REGION—See Tanknology Inc; *U.S. Private*, pg. 3931
TARGET ENGINEERING CONSTRUCTION COMPANY LLC—See Arabtec Holding PJSC; *Int'l*, pg. 534
TBO-HAGLINDS AB—See Balco Group AB; *Int'l*, pg. 807
TEAM INDUSTRIAL SERVICES ASIA PRIVATE LTD.—See Team, Inc.; *U.S. Public*, pg. 1988
TEAM INDUSTRIAL SERVICES (UK) LIMITED—See Team, Inc.; *U.S. Public*, pg. 1988
TEAM TECHNICAL SCHOOL, LLC—See Team, Inc.; *U.S. Public*, pg. 1988
TEBODIN PETERS ENGINEERING FRANCE SARL—See Bilfinger SE; *Int'l*, pg. 1029
TEBODIN PETERS ENGINEERING GMBH—See Bilfinger SE; *Int'l*, pg. 1029
TECHNICAL PARTS COMPANY INDIA PVT LTD.—See Bhatia Brothers Group; *Int'l*, pg. 1014
TECHNICAL PARTS COMPANY LLC—See Bhatia Brothers Group; *Int'l*, pg. 1014
TECHNO LIKE US CO., LTD.—See Alten S.A.; *Int'l*, pg. 391

541330 — ENGINEERING SERVICE...

THE TECHNOLOGIES ALLIANCE, INC.—See Dril-Quip, Inc.; *U.S. Public*, pg. 688
TECHNOLOGY SECURITY ASSOCIATES, INC.—See JHNA, Inc.; *U.S. Private*, pg. 2208
TECHNOLOGY SERVICE CORPORATION; *U.S. Private*, pg. 3955
TECHNOPRO ENGINEERING INC.—See CVC Capital Partners SICAV-FIS S.A.; *Int'l*, pg. 1885
TECHNO SOLUTIONS PRIVATE LIMITED—See Endress+Hauser (International) Holding AG; *Int'l*, pg. 2409
TECHNUM-TRACTEBEL ENGINEERING N.V.—See ENGIE SA; *Int'l*, pg. 2432
TECH ORD—See National Presto Industries, Inc; *U.S. Public*, pg. 1497
TECHSKILLS RESOURCES LIMITED—See Bain Capital, LP; *U.S. Private*, pg. 434
TECHUM-TRACTABEL ENGINEERING N.V.—See ENGIE SA; *Int'l*, pg. 2432
TECHWELL ENGINEERING LTD.—See China CGame, Inc.; *Int'l*, pg. 1488
TEC, INC.; *U.S. Private*, pg. 3951
TEC-MASTERS INC.; *U.S. Private*, pg. 3951
TECMOTIVE GMBH—See Hella GmbH & Co. KGaA; *Int'l*, pg. 3332
TECNOSAGOT S.A.—See Endress+Hauser (International) Holding AG; *Int'l*, pg. 2409
TECTONIC ENGINEERING AND SURVEYING CONSULTANTS P.C.; *U.S. Private*, pg. 3957
TECVOX OEM SOLUTIONS, LLC—See Amphenol Corporation; *U.S. Public*, pg. 132
TEHNOUNION 1 D.O.O.—See Doppelmayr Group; *Int'l*, pg. 2175
TEI CONSTRUCTION SERVICES INC.—See Babcock Power, Inc.; *U.S. Private*, pg. 422
TEKNIK MUHENDISLIK VE MUSAVIRLIK A.S.—See Dogus Holding AS; *Int'l*, pg. 2155
TELE-CONSULTANTS, INC.; *U.S. Private*, pg. 3959
TELEDYNE CARIS USA, INC.—See Teledyne Technologies Incorporated; *U.S. Public*, pg. 1993
TELEDYNE CONTROLS—See Teledyne Technologies Incorporated; *U.S. Public*, pg. 1993
TELEDYNE OPTECH INCORPORATED—See Teledyne Technologies Incorporated; *U.S. Public*, pg. 1994
TELEDYNE SIGNAL PROCESSING DEVICES SWEDEN AB—See Teledyne Technologies Incorporated; *U.S. Public*, pg. 1995
TELEDYNE TECHNOLOGIES INCORPORATED; *U.S. Public*, pg. 1992
TELEFERICOS DOPPELMAYR BOLIVIA S.A.—See Doppelmayr Group; *Int'l*, pg. 2175
TENSAR CORPORATION, LLC—See Commercial Metals Company; *U.S. Public*, pg. 547
TENSAR GEOSYNTHETICS (CHINA) LIMITED—See Commercial Metals Company; *U.S. Public*, pg. 547
TENSAR INTERNATIONAL GMBH—See Commercial Metals Company; *U.S. Public*, pg. 547
TENSAR INTERNATIONAL LIMITED—See Commercial Metals Company; *U.S. Public*, pg. 547
TERNA BAHRAIN HOLDING W.L.L.—See Gek Terna Societe Anonyme Holdings Real Estate Constructions; *Int'l*, pg. 2913
TERRACON CONSULTANTS, INC; *U.S. Private*, pg. 3970
TERRADYNE ENGINEERING, INC.; *U.S. Private*, pg. 3971
TERRASOURCE GLOBAL CIS LIMITED LIABILITY COMPANY—See Hillenbrand, Inc.; *U.S. Public*, pg. 1037
TERRATECH ENGINEERS, INC.—See NV5 Global, Inc.; *U.S. Public*, pg. 1558
TES ENGINEERING; *U.S. Private*, pg. 3973
TESINC LLC—See Dycom Industries, Inc.; *U.S. Public*, pg. 699
TESLA GROHMANN AUTOMATION GMBH—See Tesla, Inc.; *U.S. Public*, pg. 2021
TETRA TECH BAS, INC.—See Tetra Tech, Inc.; *U.S. Public*, pg. 2023
TETRA TECH CANADA INC.—See Tetra Tech, Inc.; *U.S. Public*, pg. 2023
TETRA TECH CAPE CANAVERAL, LLC—See Tetra Tech, Inc.; *U.S. Public*, pg. 2023
TETRA TECH COFFEY PTY. LTD.—See Tetra Tech, Inc.; *U.S. Public*, pg. 2023
TETRA TECH CONSULTORIA LTDA—See Tetra Tech, Inc.; *U.S. Public*, pg. 2023
TETRA TECH EMC, INC.—See Tetra Tech, Inc.; *U.S. Public*, pg. 2023
TETRA TECH ENGINEERING & ARCHITECTURE SERVICES—See Tetra Tech, Inc.; *U.S. Public*, pg. 2023
TETRA TECH FHC, INC.—See Tetra Tech, Inc.; *U.S. Public*, pg. 2023
TETRA TECH HEI, INC.—See Tetra Tech, Inc.; *U.S. Public*, pg. 2023
TETRA TECH, INC. - ANN ARBOR—See Tetra Tech, Inc.; *U.S. Public*, pg. 2024
TETRA TECH, INC. - BRECKENRIDGE—See Tetra Tech, Inc.; *U.S. Public*, pg. 2024
TETRA TECH, INC. - FRAMINGHAM—See Tetra Tech, Inc.; *U.S. Public*, pg. 2024

TETRA TECH, INC. - MADISON—See Tetra Tech, Inc.; *U.S. Public*, pg. 2024
TETRA TECH, INC.; *U.S. Public*, pg. 2021
TETRA TECH INDIA LIMITED—See Tetra Tech, Inc.; *U.S. Public*, pg. 2023
TETRA TECH/KCM, INC.—See Tetra Tech, Inc.; *U.S. Public*, pg. 2024
TETRA TECH NUCLEAR—See Tetra Tech, Inc.; *U.S. Public*, pg. 2023
TETRA TECH OGD INC.—See Tetra Tech, Inc.; *U.S. Public*, pg. 2024
TETRA TECH RMC, INC.—See Tetra Tech, Inc.; *U.S. Public*, pg. 2024
TEXAS ENGINEERING & MAPPING CO.—See McKim & Creed, Inc.; *U.S. Private*, pg. 2638
TEXMACO RAIL & ENGINEERING LTD.—See Adventz Group; *Int'l*, pg. 167
TEXPLOR OF DALLAS, INC.—See Terracon Consultants, Inc; *U.S. Private*, pg. 3970
TEXTRON SYSTEMS CANADA INC.—See Textron Inc.; *U.S. Public*, pg. 2029
TGE GAS ENGINEERING GMBH—See China International Marine Containers (Group) Co., Ltd.; *Int'l*, pg. 1512
TGM GROUP PTY LTD—See Cardno Limited; *Int'l*, pg. 1323
THERMAL ENGINEERING INTERNATIONAL (USA) INC. - STRUTHERS WELLS DIVISION—See Babcock Power, Inc.; *U.S. Private*, pg. 422
THERME SEEWINKEL BETRIEBSGESELLSCHAFT M.B.H.—See Fresenius SE & Co. KGaA; *Int'l*, pg. 2781
THERMIVAL JSC—See Hiolle Industries S.A.; *Int'l*, pg. 3401
THERMON BENELUX B.V.—See Thermon Group Holdings, Inc.; *U.S. Public*, pg. 2155
THERMON DEUTSCHLAND GMBH—See Thermon Group Holdings, Inc.; *U.S. Public*, pg. 2155
THERMON HEATING SYSTEMS, INC.—See Thermon Group Holdings, Inc.; *U.S. Public*, pg. 2155
THERMON KOREA, LTD.—See Thermon Group Holdings, Inc.; *U.S. Public*, pg. 2155
THIELSCH ENGINEERING, INC.; *U.S. Private*, pg. 4144
THINKPATH INC.; *U.S. Private*, pg. 4144
THIN-WALL, LLC—See Owens Corning; *U.S. Public*, pg. 1628
THOMAS BOW LIMITED—See Breedon Group plc; *Int'l*, pg. 1144
THORBURN ASSOCIATES INC; *U.S. Private*, pg. 4162
THORPE CANADA CORPORATION—See Terra Millenium Corporation; *U.S. Private*, pg. 3970
TIAX LLC; *U.S. Private*, pg. 4166
TIERRA, INC; *U.S. Private*, pg. 4169
TIGHE & BOND, INC.; *U.S. Private*, pg. 4170
TIMKEN ENGINEERING AND RESEARCH-INDIA PRIVATE LIMITED—See The Timken Company; *U.S. Public*, pg. 2133
TIMMERMAN GEOTECHNICAL GROUP INC—See GPD Group; *U.S. Private*, pg. 1748
TIMMONS GROUP, INC.; *U.S. Private*, pg. 4173
TITAN FOUNDATION LIMITED—See Build King Holdings Limited; *Int'l*, pg. 1212
TJIKO GMBH—See BayWa AG; *Int'l*, pg. 919
TK KONTOR FREITAG GMBH—See Hexatronic Group AB; *Int'l*, pg. 3371
TKW CONSULTING ENGINEERS INC.—See Keystone Capital, Inc.; *U.S. Private*, pg. 2295
TLC ENGINEERING FOR ARCHITECTURE, INC.; *U.S. Private*, pg. 4178
TLG SERVICES, INC—See Entergy Corporation; *U.S. Public*, pg. 777
T&M ASSOCIATES—See T&M Associates; *U.S. Private*, pg. 3909
TMC DESIGN CORPORATION—See KBR, Inc.; *U.S. Public*, pg. 1216
TOC INTERNATIONAL—See Doppelmayr Group; *Int'l*, pg. 2175
T-O ENGINEERS, INC.—See Littlejohn & Co., LLC; *U.S. Private*, pg. 2470
TOLL ARCHITECTURE, INC.—See Toll Brothers, Inc.; *U.S. Public*, pg. 2162
TOLUNAY-WONG ENGINEERS, INC.; *U.S. Private*, pg. 4182
TOMI SA—See ELLAKTOR S.A.; *Int'l*, pg. 2365
TOPO PLANIFICATION INC.—See Tetra Tech, Inc.; *U.S. Public*, pg. 2024
TOTAL ENGINEERING INC.; *U.S. Private*, pg. 4191
TOT GROUP CYPRUS—See Mullen Automotive, Inc.; *U.S. Public*, pg. 1486
TOT GROUP KAZAKHSTAN LLC—See Mullen Automotive, Inc.; *U.S. Public*, pg. 1486
TOTUS ENERGY TRADING LLC—See Dron & Dickson Ltd.; *Int'l*, pg. 2205
TOV VAMED UKRAINE—See Fresenius SE & Co. KGaA; *Int'l*, pg. 2781
TOWER ENGINEERING PROFESSIONALS, INC.—See H.I.G. Capital, LLC; *U.S. Private*, pg. 1834
TOYAMA TELEPHONE CONSTRUCTION CORPORATION—See COMSYS Holdings Corporation; *Int'l*, pg. 1761
TRACTEBEL DEVELOPMENT ENGINEERING S.A.—See ENGIE SA; *Int'l*, pg. 2432

TRACTEBEL ENGINEERING—See ENGIE SA; *Int'l*, pg. 2432
TRAFFIC PLANNING & DESIGN, INC.; *U.S. Private*, pg. 4203
TRAFFIC PLANNING & DESIGN INC.—See Traffic Planning & Design, Inc.; *U.S. Private*, pg. 4203
TRAFIURBE—See ACS, Actividades de Construccion y Servicios, S.A.; *Int'l*, pg. 116
TRANSDIGM TECHNOLOGIES INDIA PRIVATE LIMITED—See TransDigm Group Incorporated; *U.S. Public*, pg. 2183
TRANSMART TECHNOLOGIES, INC.—See GI Manager L.P.; *U.S. Private*, pg. 1691
TRANSPORTES POR CABLE S.A.—See Doppelmayr Group; *Int'l*, pg. 2175
TRANSPORT TERTIAIRE INDUSTRIE SAS—See FAYAT SAS; *Int'l*, pg. 2626
TRANSTEL ENGINEERING ARABIA LIMITED CO—See CSE Global Ltd.; *Int'l*, pg. 1864
TRC COMPANIES, INC. - MOUNT LAUREL—See TRC Companies, Inc.; *U.S. Private*, pg. 4215
TRC ENGINEERS INC.—See TRC Companies, Inc.; *U.S. Private*, pg. 4215
TRC ENGINEERS LLC—See TRC Companies, Inc.; *U.S. Private*, pg. 4215
TRC SOFTWARE—See TRC Companies, Inc.; *U.S. Private*, pg. 4215
TRC WORLDWIDE ENGINEERING, INC.; *U.S. Private*, pg. 4215
TRIAD ENVIRONMENTAL CONSULTANT—See Montrose Environmental Group, Inc.; *U.S. Public*, pg. 1466
TRIANGEL FRANKFURT IMMOBILIEN GMBH & CO. KG—See Aroundtown SA; *Int'l*, pg. 578
TRIANGULAR FORCE CONSTRUCTION ENGINEERING LIMITED—See Beaver Group (HOLDING) Company Limited; *Int'l*, pg. 935
TRIDEUM CORP.; *U.S. Private*, pg. 4230
TRIMARK ROBERTCLARK—See Warburg Pincus LLC; *U.S. Private*, pg. 4440
TRIMBLE SOLUTIONS GOTHENBURG AB—See Trimble, Inc.; *U.S. Public*, pg. 2193
TRIMBLE SOLUTIONS KOREA CO., LTD.—See Trimble, Inc.; *U.S. Public*, pg. 2193
TRINITY ARGENTINA S.R.L.—See Trinity Industries, Inc.; *U.S. Public*, pg. 2193
TRIPLE M MECHANICAL SERVICES PTY LTD—See BSA Limited; *Int'l*, pg. 1201
TRIPLE M MECHANICAL SERVICES PTY LTD—See BSA Limited; *Int'l*, pg. 1202
TRI SAGE CONSULTING—See Qualus Corporation; *U.S. Private*, pg. 3322
TRISON CONSTRUCTION, INC.—See LSB Industries, Inc.; *U.S. Public*, pg. 1344
TRI-STAR ENGINEERING, INC.; *U.S. Private*, pg. 4223
TRI-STATE ENGINEERING, INC.—See Olsson Associates, Inc.; *U.S. Private*, pg. 3012
TRIULZI AG—See Burkhalter Holding AG; *Int'l*, pg. 1226
TRIUMPH INTERIORS, LLC—See Triumph Group, Inc.; *U.S. Public*, pg. 2196
TRIUMPH ON-DEMAND, INC.—See Genpact Limited; *Int'l*, pg. 2927
TRIUNITY ENGINEERING & MANAGEMENT, INC.—See H.W. Lochner, Inc.; *U.S. Private*, pg. 1836
TRUDELL CONSULTING ENGINEERS, INC.—See Bowman Consulting Group Ltd.; *U.S. Public*, pg. 377
TRUE NORTH CONSULTING LLC—See GSE Systems, Inc.; *U.S. Public*, pg. 973
TSO INDUSTRIEANLAGEN PLANUNG UND VERTRIEB GMBH—See ATON GmbH; *Int'l*, pg. 689
TSUSHIN DENSETSU CO., LTD.—See COMSYS Holdings Corporation; *Int'l*, pg. 1762
TUNG FENG INC.—See Chailease Holding Company Limited; *Int'l*, pg. 1437
TURNER HOCHTIEF CONSTRUCTION MANAGEMENT GMBH—See ACS, Actividades de Construccion y Servicios, S.A.; *Int'l*, pg. 114
TUTOR MICRONESIA CONSTRUCTION, LLC—See Tutor Perini Corporation; *U.S. Public*, pg. 2206
TWEEDS LIMITED—See Tetra Tech, Inc.; *U.S. Public*, pg. 2024
TWENTY FIRST CENTURY ENGINEERING CORP.—See Kelso & Company, L.P.; *U.S. Private*, pg. 2278
TWIG TECHNOLOGIES, LLC—See The Will Group, Inc.; *U.S. Private*, pg. 4136
T.Y. LIN INTERNATIONAL GROUP LTD.; *U.S. Private*, pg. 3912
T.Y. LIN INTERNATIONAL - MEDINA—See T.Y. Lin International Group Ltd.; *U.S. Private*, pg. 3913
TZ STROMAG—See Burkhalter Holding AG; *Int'l*, pg. 1226
UAB BOSKALIS BALTIC—See HAL Trust N.V.; *Int'l*, pg. 3227
UE NOVO (MALAYSIA) SDN. BHD.—See CITIC Group Corporation; *Int'l*, pg. 1620
UGL CANADA INC.—See ACS, Actividades de Construccion y Servicios, S.A.; *Int'l*, pg. 113
UGL (NZ) LIMITED—See ACS, Actividades de Construccion y Servicios, S.A.; *Int'l*, pg. 113
UGL RAIL PTY LTD—See ACS, Actividades de Construccion y Servicios, S.A.; *Int'l*, pg. 113

N.A.I.C.S. INDEX 541330 — ENGINEERING SERVICE...

UJV REZ, A. S.—See CEZ, a.s.; *Int'l*, pg. 1429
UKRON—See ARCADIS N.V.; *Int'l*, pg. 542
ULTIMATE POWERLINE CONTRACTING LTD.—See Quanta Services, Inc.; *U.S. Public*, pg. 1753
UMB COMMUNICATION AG—See BKW AG; *Int'l*, pg. 1056
UNDERGROUND IMAGING TECHNOLOGIES LLC—See Caterpillar, Inc.; *U.S. Public*, pg. 454
UNDERGROUND SERVICE LOCATORS—See Downer EDI Limited; *Int'l*, pg. 2186
UNICONS INVESTMENT CONSTRUCTION CO., LTD.—See Coteccons Construction Joint Stock Company; *Int'l*, pg. 1815
UNISERVICE SA—See Bouygues S.A.; *Int'l*, pg. 1123
UNISTRESS CORPORATION—See Petricca Industries, Inc.; *U.S. Private*, pg. 3161
UNITED ALUMINUM & METAL COATING CO. W.L.L—See Fouad Alghanim & Sons Group of Companies; *Int'l*, pg. 2753
UNITED INDUSTRIAL CORPORATION—See Textron Inc.; *U.S. Public*, pg. 2029
UNITED LIVING GROUP—See Elysian Capital LLP; *Int'l*, pg. 2372
UNITED STATES STEEL CORPORATION RESEARCH AND TECHNOLOGY CENTER—See United States Steel Corporation; *U.S. Public*, pg. 2237
UNIVERSAL ENGINEERING SCIENCES, LLC; *U.S. Private*, pg. 4304
UNIVERSAL ENGINEERING SCIENCES—See Universal Engineering Sciences, LLC; *U.S. Private*, pg. 4305
UNIVERSALPEGASUS INTERNATIONAL CANADA, INC.—See Huntington Ingalls Industries, Inc.; *U.S. Public*, pg. 1072
UNIVERSALPEGASUS INTERNATIONAL, INC.—See PMC Capital Partners, LLC; *U.S. Private*, pg. 3218
UNIVERSALPEGASUS INTERNATIONAL TRINIDAD AND TOBAGO LIMITED—See Huntington Ingalls Industries, Inc.; *U.S. Public*, pg. 1072
UNIVERSAL PIPING INDUSTRIES, LLC—See Gallagher-Kaiser Corporation; *U.S. Private*, pg. 1639
UNOSQUARE LLC—See Trivest Partners, LP; *U.S. Private*, pg. 4241
UOP RUSSELL LLC—See Honeywell International Inc.; *U.S. Public*, pg. 1052
UPDOWN INGENIEURTECHNIK FUR FORDERTECHNIK GMBH—See DEKRA e.V.; *Int'l*, pg. 2010
UPONOR AS—See Georg Fischer AG; *Int'l*, pg. 2937
URBAN ENGINEERS INC.; *U.S. Private*, pg. 4314
URBAN ENGINEERS OF NEW YORK, P.C.—See Urban Engineers Inc.; *U.S. Private*, pg. 4314
URSANAV; *U.S. Private*, pg. 4316
URS CARIBE, LLP—See AECOM; *U.S. Public*, pg. 51
URS CONSULTING (SHANGHAI) LTD.—See AECOM; *U.S. Public*, pg. 51
URS CORPORATION BOLIVIA SA—See AECOM; *U.S. Public*, pg. 51
URS CORPORATION DE MEXICO S DE RL DE CV—See AECOM; *U.S. Public*, pg. 51
URS CORPORATION S.A.—See AECOM; *U.S. Public*, pg. 51
URS CORPORATION—See AECOM; *U.S. Public*, pg. 51
URS CORPORATION—See AECOM; *U.S. Public*, pg. 51
URS CORP. - RIYADH—See AECOM; *U.S. Public*, pg. 51
URS NEW ZEALAND LTD.—See AECOM; *U.S. Public*, pg. 51
USA DEBUSK LLC—See H.I.G. Capital, LLC; *U.S. Private*, pg. 1834
USIC, LLC; *U.S. Private*, pg. 4323
U.S. PETROLEUM EQUIPMENT—See U.S. Venture, Inc.; *U.S. Private*, pg. 4272
UTC ENGINEERING SDN. BHD.—See Dancomech Holdings Berhad; *Int'l*, pg. 1959
U-TECH ENGINEERING COMPANY LIMITED—See Henderson Land Development Co. Ltd.; *Int'l*, pg. 3344
UTILITY SERVICES GROUP LIMITED—See Downer EDI Limited; *Int'l*, pg. 2185
UTILITY SUPPORT SYSTEMS INC.—See TRC Companies, Inc.; *U.S. Private*, pg. 4215
V & A CONSULTING ENGINEERS, INC.; *U.S. Private*, pg. 4327
VA CONSULTING, INC.; *U.S. Private*, pg. 4328
VADNAIS TRENCHLESS SERVICES, INC.—See Primoris Services Corporation; *U.S. Public*, pg. 1719
VALKYRIE ENTERPRISES, LLC—See D.C. Capital Partners, LLC; *U.S. Private*, pg. 1141
VALLEY BUILDING PRODUCTS COMPANY—See The Sowles Company; *U.S. Private*, pg. 4120
VALUETEC ENGINEERING SOLUTIONS LIMITED—See Endress+Hauser (International) Holding AG; *Int'l*, pg. 2409
VAMED CZ S.R.O.—See Fresenius SE & Co. KGaA; *Int'l*, pg. 2781
VAMED HEALTHCARE CO. LTD.—See Fresenius SE & Co. KGaA; *Int'l*, pg. 2781
VAMED HEALTHCARE SERVICES SDN. BHD.—See Fresenius SE & Co. KGaA; *Int'l*, pg. 2781
VAMED HEALTH PROJECTS CZ S.R.O.—See Fresenius SE & Co. KGaA; *Int'l*, pg. 2781
VAMED HEALTH PROJECTS UK LIMITED—See Fresenius SE & Co. KGaA; *Int'l*, pg. 2781
VAMED-HUNGARIA HEALTH CARE LTD.—See Fresenius SE & Co. KGaA; *Int'l*, pg. 2781
VAMED INTERNATIONAL HOSPITAL MANAGEMENT & CONSULTING (BEIJING) CO., LTD.—See Fresenius SE & Co. KGaA; *Int'l*, pg. 2781
VAMED MEDIZINTECHNIK GMBH—See Fresenius SE & Co. KGaA; *Int'l*, pg. 2781
VAMED NEDERLAND B.V.—See Fresenius SE & Co. KGaA; *Int'l*, pg. 2781
VAMED POLSKA SP. Z O.O.—See Fresenius SE & Co. KGaA; *Int'l*, pg. 2781
VAMED PROJETS HOSPITALIERS INTERNATIONAUX FRANCE S.A.S—See Fresenius SE & Co. KGaA; *Int'l*, pg. 2781
VAMED ROMANIA S.R.L.—See Fresenius SE & Co. KGaA; *Int'l*, pg. 2781
VAMED STANDORTENTWICKLUNG UND ENGINEERING GMBH—See Fresenius SE & Co. KGaA; *Int'l*, pg. 2781
VAMED TURKEY MUHENDISLIK INSAAT TAAHHUT MEDIKAL SAGLIK HIZMETLERI LIMITED SIRKETI—See Fresenius SE & Co. KGaA; *Int'l*, pg. 2781
VAN CLEEF ENGINEERING ASSOCIATES, INC.; *U.S. Private*, pg. 4339
VAN CLEEF ENGINEERING ASSOCIATES LLC—See Van Cleef Engineering Associates, Inc.; *U.S. Private*, pg. 4339
VAN LOOY GROUP B.V.—See Electricite de France S.A.; *Int'l*, pg. 2351
VAN LOOY GROUP N.V.—See Electricite de France S.A.; *Int'l*, pg. 2351
VARD AQUA CHILE SA—See Fincantieri S.p.A.; *Int'l*, pg. 2671
VARD AQUA SCOTLAND LTD.—See Fincantieri S.p.A.; *Int'l*, pg. 2671
VARD AQUA SUNNDAL AS—See Fincantieri S.p.A.; *Int'l*, pg. 2671
VARD DESIGN LIBURNA LTD.—See Fincantieri S.p.A.; *Int'l*, pg. 2671
VARD ELECTRO US INC.—See Cassa Depositi e Prestiti S.p.A.; *Int'l*, pg. 1355
VARD ENGINEERING BREVIK AS—See Fincantieri S.p.A.; *Int'l*, pg. 2672
V&C GMBH—See EVN AG; *Int'l*, pg. 2571
VEC CIVIL ENGINEERING PTY. LTD.—See Downer EDI Limited; *Int'l*, pg. 2186
VECTOR PLANNING & SERVICES, INC.—See Chugach Alaska Corporation; *U.S. Public*, pg. 893
VECTRUS MISSION SOLUTIONS CORPORATION—See V2X, Inc.; *U.S. Public*, pg. 2270
THE VELOCITY GROUP, INC.; *U.S. Private*, pg. 4130
VELOSI (GHANA) LTD.—See I Squared Capital Advisors (US) LLC; *U.S. Private*, pg. 2023
VELOSI SAUDI ARABIA CO LTD.—See I Squared Capital Advisors (US) LLC; *U.S. Private*, pg. 2024
VENEZCO, INC—See Fluor Corporation; *U.S. Public*, pg. 859
VENTECH INC.; *U.S. Private*, pg. 4357
VENTECH INVESTMENT CO., INC.—See Ventech Inc.; *U.S. Private*, pg. 4357
VENTIA PTY LTD—See Apollo Global Management, Inc.; *U.S. Public*, pg. 166
VENTURE AUTOMATION & ENGINEERING PTE. LTD.—See Beng Kuang Marine Limited; *Int'l*, pg. 973
VENTURE ENGINEERING & CONSTRUCTION; *U.S. Private*, pg. 4357
VERACITY ENGINEERING; *U.S. Private*, pg. 4359
VERAXX ENGINEERING CORP.—See Sagewind Capital LLC; *U.S. Private*, pg. 3527
VERDANTAS LLC—See Sterling Investment Partners, L.P.; *U.S. Private*, pg. 3806
VERIFONE ISRAEL LTD.—See British Columbia Investment Management Corp.; *Int'l*, pg. 1170
VERIFONE ISRAEL LTD.—See Francisco Partners Management, LP; *U.S. Private*, pg. 1592
VERKOL S.A.—See Quaker Chemical Corporation; *U.S. Public*, pg. 1747
VERSAR-DENVER—See Kingswood Capital Management LLC; *U.S. Private*, pg. 2313
VERSAR, INC.—See Kingswood Capital Management LLC; *U.S. Private*, pg. 2312
VERSATECH AUTOMATION SERVICES, LLC – HARVEY—See VersaTech Automation Services, LLC; *U.S. Private*, pg. 4369
VERSATECH AUTOMATION SERVICES, LLC; *U.S. Private*, pg. 4369
VERTASEFLI LIMITED—See FLI International Limited; *Int'l*, pg. 2705
VERTECH GROUP PTY LTD—See Global Energy (Holdings) Ltd.; *Int'l*, pg. 2995
VERTECH UK—See Global Energy (Holdings) Ltd.; *Int'l*, pg. 2995
THE VERTEX COMPANIES, INC.—See Wind Point Advisors LLC; *U.S. Private*, pg. 4536
VETH RESEARCH ASSOCIATES LLC—See AEVEX Aerospace; *U.S. Private*, pg. 121
VIANINI LAVORI S.P.A.—See Caltagirone Editore S.p.A.; *Int'l*, pg. 1266
VIENNA AIRPORT TECHNIK GMBH—See Flughafen Wien Aktiengesellschaft; *Int'l*, pg. 2713
VIGOR MARINE LLC—See Stellex Capital Management LP; *U.S. Private*, pg. 3800
VIGOR MARINE LLC—See The Carlyle Group Inc.; *U.S. Public*, pg. 2056
VILLA AUREA, S.L.—See ACS, Actividades de Construccion y Servicios, S.A.; *Int'l*, pg. 117
VILLANOVA, S.A.—See ACS, Actividades de Construccion y Servicios, S.A.; *Int'l*, pg. 117
VINCULUMS SERVICES, INC.—See QualTek Services Inc.; *U.S. Private*, pg. 1748
VIRENT ENERGY SYSTEMS, INC; *U.S. Private*, pg. 4387
VIRGINIA SYSTEMS & TECHNOLOGY, INC.—See Altamira Technologies Corporation; *U.S. Private*, pg. 204
VISIONARY PRODUCTS, INC.; *U.S. Private*, pg. 4392
VISION ENERGY CORPORATION; *U.S. Public*, pg. 2304
VISION LAND CONSULTANTS, INC.; *U.S. Private*, pg. 4391
VMA NV—See Ackermans & van Haaren NV; *Int'l*, pg. 105
VNG VIERTELENERGIE GMBH—See EnBW Energie Baden-Wurttemberg AG; *Int'l*, pg. 2400
VOF STATIONSEILAND—See ARCADIS N.V.; *Int'l*, pg. 541
VOLKERT, INC. - GEORGIA—See Volkert, Inc.; *U.S. Private*, pg. 4410
VOLKERT, INC.; *U.S. Private*, pg. 4410
VOLKERT, INC.—See Volkert, Inc.; *U.S. Private*, pg. 4410
VOLKERT, INC.—See Volkert, Inc.; *U.S. Private*, pg. 4410
VOLKERT, INC.—See Volkert, Inc.; *U.S. Private*, pg. 4410
VOLKERT, INC.—See Volkert, Inc.; *U.S. Private*, pg. 4410
VOLKERT, INC. - TAMPA—See Volkert, Inc.; *U.S. Private*, pg. 4410
VOLTAIR CONSULTING ENGINEERS, INC.; *U.S. Private*, pg. 4411
VOLVO CE EUROPE S.A.S.—See AB Volvo; *Int'l*, pg. 44
VSE SERVICES INTERNATIONAL, INC.—See VSE Corporation; *U.S. Public*, pg. 2313
VSL INTERNATIONAL LTD—See Bouygues S.A.; *Int'l*, pg. 1123
VT SERVICES, INC. - ALPHARETTA DIVISION—See Alvarez & Marsal, Inc.; *U.S. Private*, pg. 213
VT SERVICES, INC. - CHARLESTON DIVISION—See Alvarez & Marsal, Inc.; *U.S. Private*, pg. 213
VT SERVICES, INC. - CHESAPEAKE DIVISION—See Alvarez & Marsal, Inc.; *U.S. Private*, pg. 213
VT SERVICES, INC. - GROTON DIVISION—See Alvarez & Marsal, Inc.; *U.S. Private*, pg. 213
VT SERVICES, INC. - HAWAII DIVISION—See Alvarez & Marsal, Inc.; *U.S. Private*, pg. 213
VT SERVICES, INC. - SAN DIEGO DIVISION—See Alvarez & Marsal, Inc.; *U.S. Private*, pg. 213
VT SERVICES, INC.—See Alvarez & Marsal, Inc.; *U.S. Private*, pg. 213
VT SERVICES, INC. - STERLING DIVISION—See Alvarez & Marsal, Inc.; *U.S. Private*, pg. 213
VT SERVICES, INC. - VIRGINIA BEACH DIVISION—See Alvarez & Marsal, Inc.; *U.S. Private*, pg. 213
VUADENS CONTROLES SA—See Burkhalter Holding AG; *Int'l*, pg. 1226
VYZKUMNY A ZKUSEBNI USTAV PLZEN S.R.O.—See CEZ, a.s.; *Int'l*, pg. 1429
WAB TECHNIQUE S.A.R.L.—See BKW AG; *Int'l*, pg. 1056
WADE-TRIM ASSOCIATES INC.—See Wade-Trim Group Inc.; *U.S. Private*, pg. 4424
WADE-TRIM GROUP INC.; *U.S. Private*, pg. 4424
WADE-TRIM INC. (MICHIGAN)—See Wade-Trim Group Inc.; *U.S. Private*, pg. 4424
WADE-TRIM INC.—See Wade-Trim Group Inc.; *U.S. Private*, pg. 4424
WAID CORP.—See Keystone Group, L.P.; *U.S. Private*, pg. 2299
WALD + CORBE CONSULTING GMBH—See BKW AG; *Int'l*, pg. 1056
WALKER PARKING CONSULTANTS & ENGINEERS, INC.; *U.S. Private*, pg. 4429
WALTER P MOORE AND ASSOCIATES, INC.; *U.S. Private*, pg. 4434
WALTER P MOORE & ASSOCIATES, INC.—See Walter P Moore and Associates, Inc.; *U.S. Private*, pg. 4434
WALTER P MOORE & ASSOCIATES, INC.—See Walter P Moore and Associates, Inc.; *U.S. Private*, pg. 4434
WANTMAN GROUP, INC.; *U.S. Private*, pg. 4436
THE WASHINGTON CONSULTING GROUP INC.; *U.S. Private*, pg. 4133
WATER CONSULTING SPECIALISTS, INC.—See Xylem Inc.; *U.S. Public*, pg. 2394
WATERMAN AHW PTY LIMITED—See CTI Engineering Co., Ltd.; *Int'l*, pg. 1871
WATERMAN ASPEN LIMITED—See CTI Engineering Co., Ltd.; *Int'l*, pg. 1871
WATERMAN BUILDING SERVICES LIMITED—See CTI Engineering Co., Ltd.; *Int'l*, pg. 1871
WATERMAN ENERGY, ENVIRONMENT & DESIGN LIMITED—See CTI Engineering Co., Ltd.; *Int'l*, pg. 1871
WATERMAN GROUP (AUS) PTY LIMITED—See CTI Engineering Co., Ltd.; *Int'l*, pg. 1871
WATERMAN INTERNATIONAL (ASIA) PTY LIMITED—See CTI Engineering Co., Ltd.; *Int'l*, pg. 1871

541330 — ENGINEERING SERVICE...

WATERMARK ENVIRONMENTAL, INC.; *U.S. Private*, pg. 4454
WATER SYSTEMS OPTIMIZATION, INC.—See Align Capital Partners, LLC; *U.S. Private*, pg. 167
WAVESPEC LIMITED—See Braemar PLC; *Int'l*, pg. 1136
WAVIN B.V.—See Bharti Enterprises Limited; *Int'l*, pg. 1012
WBM PTY. LTD.—See BMT Group Limited; *Int'l*, pg. 1078
WBM - SYDNEY—See BMT Group Limited; *Int'l*, pg. 1078
WEBB, MURRAY & ASSOCIATES, INC.—See Littlejohn & Co., LLC; *U.S. Private*, pg. 2472
WEFIMA N.V—See Ackermans & van Haaren NV; *Int'l*, pg. 106
WEIDLINGER ASSOCIATES INC.—See Thornton-Tomasetti, Inc.; *U.S. Private*, pg. 4163
WELDIN CONSTRUCTION LLC—See Cook Inlet Region, Inc.; *U.S. Private*, pg. 1038
WELLS ENGINEERING, PSC—See Davis H. Elliot Company Inc.; *U.S. Private*, pg. 1173
WELSH COMMISSIONING GROUP, INC.—See Performance Validation, Inc.; *U.S. Private*, pg. 3150
W.E. MONKS & CO.—See TEC, Inc.; *U.S. Private*, pg. 3951
WENDLER ENGINEERING SERVICE INC.—See Willett Hofmann & Assoc Inc.; *U.S. Private*, pg. 4522
WESTECH INTERNATIONAL, INC.; *U.S. Private*, pg. 4489
WESTERMEYER INDUSTRIES, INC.; *U.S. Private*, pg. 4490
WESTERN UTILITY LLC—See Hylan Datacom & Electrical, LLC; *U.S. Private*, pg. 2018
WESTEST, LLC—See GI Manager L.P.; *U.S. Private*, pg. 1691
WESTLAND RESOURCES, INC.—See Keystone Group, L.P.; *U.S. Private*, pg. 2299
WESTON & SAMPSON, INC.; *U.S. Private*, pg. 4500
WESTWOOD PROFESSIONAL SERVICES, INC.; *U.S. Private*, pg. 4501
WEST YOST ASSOCIATES, INC.; *U.S. Private*, pg. 4488
WHITEOAK GROUP; *U.S. Private*, pg. 4511
WHITE RIVER ENGINEERING INC.—See Allgeier, Martin & Associates, Inc.; *U.S. Private*, pg. 181
W&H PACIFIC INC.; *U.S. Private*, pg. 4417
WIER & ASSOCIATES, INC.; *U.S. Private*, pg. 4516
WILDISH BUILDING CO.—See Wildish Land Company; *U.S. Private*, pg. 4519
WILLDAN ENERGY SOLUTIONS—See Willdan Group, Inc.; *U.S. Public*, pg. 2371
WILLDAN ENGINEERING—See Willdan Group, Inc.; *U.S. Public*, pg. 2371
WILLETT HOFMANN & ASSOC INC.; *U.S. Private*, pg. 4522
WILSON & COMPANY, INC.; *U.S. Private*, pg. 4529
WILSON STRUCTURAL CONSULTANTS, INC.; *U.S. Private*, pg. 4531
WIND ENERGY TRADING WET AG—See BKW AG; *Int'l*, pg. 1056
WINDMILL INTERNATIONAL, INC.; *U.S. Private*, pg. 4538
WINEMAN TECHNOLOGY, INC.—See CertTech, L.L.C.; *U.S. Private*, pg. 842
WINMAX TECHNOLOGY CORP.—See Acter Co., Ltd.; *Int'l*, pg. 117
WISE CONNECT, INC.—See Hastings Equity Partners, LLC; *U.S. Private*, pg. 1879
WISEROCK AG—See BKW AG; *Int'l*, pg. 1056
WISLER ELEKTRO AG—See Burkhalter Holding AG; *Int'l*, pg. 1226
WISS, JANNEY, ELSTNER ASSOCIATES, INC.; *U.S. Private*, pg. 4550
WOODARD & CURRAN INC.; *U.S. Private*, pg. 4557
WOODSON ENGINEERING & SURVEYING, INC.—See Littlejohn & Co., LLC; *U.S. Private*, pg. 2470
WOOLPERT INC.; *U.S. Private*, pg. 4562
WOOLPERT LLP; *U.S. Private*, pg. 4562
WORKBOAT INTERNATIONAL DMCCO—See Alam Maritim Resources Berhad; *Int'l*, pg. 290
WPCS INCORPORATED—See AYRO, Inc.; *U.S. Public*, pg. 256
WPM PROJEKTMANAGEMENT GMBH—See Airbus SE; *Int'l*, pg. 242
WRA; *U.S. Private*, pg. 4571
WS ATKINS IRELAND LIMITED—See AtkinsRealis Group Inc.; *Int'l*, pg. 673
WSB & ASSOCIATES, INC.—See GHK Capital Partners LP; *U.S. Private*, pg. 1690
WS CONSTRUCTION INC—See Gray Inc.; *U.S. Private*, pg. 1759
WUHUAN ENGINEERING CO., LTD.—See China National Chemical Engineering Co., Ltd.; *Int'l*, pg. 1531
WUNDERLICH-MALEC ENGINEERING, INC.; *U.S. Private*, pg. 4575
W.W. CLYDE AND COMPANY—See Clyde Companies Inc.; *U.S. Private*, pg. 949
WYG ENVIRONMENTAL (IRELAND) LIMITED—See Tetra Tech, Inc.; *U.S. Public*, pg. 2024
WYG [IRE]LAND LIMITED—See Tetra Tech, Inc.; *U.S. Public*, pg. 2024
WYG [R]YAN TWEEDS LIMITED—See Tetra Tech, Inc.; *U.S. Public*, pg. 2024
WZS BINARAYA SDN BHD—See Citaglobal Berhad; *Int'l*, pg. 1619
X8E, INC; *U.S. Private*, pg. 4579
XCANA PETROLEUM CORP.; *U.S. Public*, pg. 2385
X-DIN INC.—See Alten S.A.; *Int'l*, pg. 391
XINCHENG CONSTRUCTION SUPERVISION & CONSULTING CO., LTD.—See China Nonferrous Metal Mining (Group) Co., Ltd.; *Int'l*, pg. 1535
YAHYA COSTAIN LLC—See Costain Group PLC; *Int'l*, pg. 1815
YANCEY ENGINEERED SOLUTIONS—See Yancey Bros. Co.; *U.S. Private*, pg. 4585
YERBA BUENA ENGINEERING & CONSTRUCTION; *U.S. Private*, pg. 4588
YESMARITIME AS—See Egersund Group AS; *Int'l*, pg. 2324
YOLOBUS PRIVATE LIMITED—See Easy Trip Planners Limited; *Int'l*, pg. 2276
ZACHRY ENGINEERING CORPORATION—See Zachry Holdings, Inc.; *U.S. Private*, pg. 4596
ZACHRY NUCLEAR ENGINEERING, INC.—See Zachry Holdings, Inc.; *U.S. Private*, pg. 4596
ZAO EXACT SYSTEMS—See CVI Dom Maklerski sp. z o.o.; *Int'l*, pg. 1889
ZAO "ALPINE-GAZ"—See ALPINE Bau GmbH; *Int'l*, pg. 371
ZAPATA ENGINEERING; *U.S. Private*, pg. 4598
ZAP ENGINEERING & CONSTRUCTION SERVICES, INC.; *U.S. Private*, pg. 4598
ZEAG ENGINEERING GMBH—See EnBW Energie Baden-Wurttemberg AG; *Int'l*, pg. 2401
ZEPNICK SOLUTIONS, INC.—See Salas O'Brien Engineers, Inc.; *U.S. Private*, pg. 3531
ZHONG XU ARCHITECTURE DESIGN CO., LTD.—See China Architecture Design & Research Group; *Int'l*, pg. 1483
ZHONGYE CHANGTIAN INTERNATIONAL ENGINEERING CO., LTD.—See China Rare Earth Resources And Technology Co., Ltd.; *Int'l*, pg. 1545
ZINKCON INTERNATIONAL B.V.—See HAL Trust N.V.; *Int'l*, pg. 3227
ZINKCON MARINE SINGAPORE PTE. LTD.—See HAL Trust N.V.; *Int'l*, pg. 3225
ZNS ENGINEERING, L.C.; *U.S. Private*, pg. 4607

541340 — DRAFTING SERVICES

CAD SERVICES LTD.—See Facilities by ADF Plc; *Int'l*, pg. 2600
CANDRAFT DETAILING, INC.; *Int'l*, pg. 1289
HITACHI ZOSEN VIETNAM CO., LTD.—See Hitachi Zosen Corporation; *Int'l*, pg. 3411
ITC SERVICE GROUP, INC.—See Fujikura Ltd.; *Int'l*, pg. 2827

541350 — BUILDING INSPECTION SERVICES

A2Z FIELD SERVICES; *U.S. Private*, pg. 29
ACTEL POWER CO., LTD.—See AcBel Polytech Inc.; *Int'l*, pg. 78
AJ LUCAS TESTING PTY LIMITED—See A.J. Lucas Group Limited; *Int'l*, pg. 24
AMERISPEC LLC—See Roark Capital Group Inc.; *U.S. Private*, pg. 3456
ANESCO LIMITED—See Ara Partners Group; *U.S. Private*, pg. 306
APPLUS RTD—See I Squared Capital Advisors (US) LLC; *U.S. Private*, pg. 2022
APPLUS UK LTD—See I Squared Capital Advisors (US) LLC; *U.S. Private*, pg. 2022
AUSTAL CAIRNS PTY. LTD.—See Austal Limited; *Int'l*, pg. 716
AXIUM INSPECTIONS, LLC—See RFE Investment Partners; *U.S. Private*, pg. 3419
AZBIL KOREA CO., LTD.—See Azbil Corporation; *Int'l*, pg. 777
AZBIL MALAYSIA SDN. BHD.—See Azbil Corporation; *Int'l*, pg. 777
AZBIL (THAILAND) CO., LTD.—See Azbil Corporation; *Int'l*, pg. 776
BEIJING BUILDING MATERIALS TESTING ACADEMY CO., LTD.—See BBMG Corporation; *Int'l*, pg. 920
BELL TECHNICAL SERVICES INC.—See Textron Inc.; *U.S. Public*, pg. 2028
BMM, INC.—See Ingersoll Rand Inc.; *U.S. Public*, pg. 1120
BRCS (BUILDING CONTROL) LIMITED—See CEPS PLC; *Int'l*, pg. 1420
CANDEAL CO., LTD.; *Int'l*, pg. 1289
CARILLION SPECIALIST SERVICES—See Carillion plc; *Int'l*, pg. 1330
CLARE INSTRUMENTS US, INC.—See Littelfuse, Inc.; *U.S. Public*, pg. 1327
CODE MASTER INSPECTION SERVICES—See Barry Isett & Associates Inc.; *U.S. Private*, pg. 481
DEKRA INDUSTRIAL AB—See DEKRA e.V.; *Int'l*, pg. 2008
DEKRA INDUSTRIAL GMBH—See DEKRA e.V.; *Int'l*, pg. 2008
ENERGIX US LLC—See Energix Renewable Energies Ltd.; *Int'l*, pg. 2420
ENERTIS CHILE, SPA—See I Squared Capital Advisors (US) LLC; *U.S. Private*, pg. 2022
ENVIRONMENTAL SERVICE PROFESSIONALS, INC.; *U.S. Public*, pg. 781
EUROFINS DR. SPECHT EXPRESS TESTING & INSPECTION GMBH—See Eurofins Scientific S.E.; *Int'l*, pg. 2540
EUROFINS ELECTRIC & ELECTRONICS FINLAND OY—See Eurofins Scientific S.E.; *Int'l*, pg. 2540
FUTURE TECH CONSULTANTS OF NEW YORK, INC.—See Cobepa S.A.; *Int'l*, pg. 1683
GREENERU, INC.—See Casella Waste Systems, Inc.; *U.S. Public*, pg. 446
GREEN VALLEY GROUP, LLC—See Zoned Properties, Inc.; *U.S. Public*, pg. 2411
HAKUSEISHA CO., LTD.—See AEON Co., Ltd.; *Int'l*, pg. 177
HANCOCK CLAIMS CONSULTANTS, LLC; *U.S. Private*, pg. 1852
HANKYU COMMUNITY SERVICE CO., LTD.—See Hankyu Hanshin Holdings Inc.; *Int'l*, pg. 3255
IKM INSPECTION AS—See IKM Gruppen AS; *Int'l*, pg. 3611
IKM TESTING KOREA LLC—See IKM Gruppen AS; *Int'l*, pg. 3612
JAPAN ERI CO., LTD.—See ERI Holdings Co., Ltd.; *Int'l*, pg. 2491
LANGLE & STAUB SANITARPLANUNG GMBH—See Burkhalter Holding AG; *Int'l*, pg. 1225
LAUNCHPAD HOME GROUP—See RFE Investment Partners; *U.S. Private*, pg. 3419
LENDERS INSPECTION COMPANY—See Old Republic International Corporation; *U.S. Public*, pg. 1569
LERCH BATES INC.; *U.S. Private*, pg. 2431
NORTHWEST ENERGY EFFICIENCY ALLIANCE; *U.S. Private*, pg. 2960
QUALITY BUILT, LLC—See Gallant Capital Partners, LLC; *U.S. Private*, pg. 1639
QUALITY INSPECTION SERVICES, INC.—See I Squared Capital Advisors (US) LLC; *U.S. Private*, pg. 2022
QUALSPEC, INC.—See Team, Inc.; *U.S. Public*, pg. 1988
RUSSI HEIZUNG-SANITAR AG—See Burkhalter Holding AG; *Int'l*, pg. 1225
SIEMPELKAMP PRUF-UND GUTACHTER GESELLSCHAFT MBH—See G. Siempelkamp GmbH & Co. KG; *Int'l*, pg. 2865
SOCIETE INTERNATIONALE DE CONTROLE ET APPROVISIONNEMENT SASU—See Cobepa S.A.; *Int'l*, pg. 1683
SOCOTEC SA—See Cobepa S.A.; *Int'l*, pg. 1683
STANLEY INSPECTION SOUTH AFRICA (PTY) LIMITED—See Stanley Black & Decker, Inc.; *U.S. Public*, pg. 1935
TOWERSENTRY LLC—See Hughey & Phillips, LLC; *U.S. Private*, pg. 2004
TRINITY REAL ESTATE SOLUTIONS, INC.; *U.S. Private*, pg. 4235
WRIGHT ENERGY PARTNERS, LLC; *U.S. Private*, pg. 4573
WULSER LOSTORF AG—See Burkhalter Holding AG; *Int'l*, pg. 1226
WULSER ZOFINGEN AG—See Burkhalter Holding AG; *Int'l*, pg. 1226

541360 — GEOPHYSICAL SURVEYING AND MAPPING SERVICES

3001, INC.—See Northrop Grumman Corporation; *U.S. Public*, pg. 1540
AEROMETREX LTD.—See Aerometrex Limited; *Int'l*, pg. 181
AEROQUEST AIRBORNE—See Geotech Ltd.; *Int'l*, pg. 2941
AEROQUEST INTERNATIONAL LIMITED—See Geotech Ltd.; *Int'l*, pg. 2941
AEROQUEST LIMITED—See Geotech Ltd.; *Int'l*, pg. 2941
AEROQUEST MAPCON LTD.—See Geotech Ltd.; *Int'l*, pg. 2941
AIR MARINE SA; *Int'l*, pg. 238
ALPHAGEO INDIA LTD; *Int'l*, pg. 370
ALTUS GEOMATICS L.P.—See Altus Group Limited; *Int'l*, pg. 399
ASIA AIR SURVEY MYANMAR CO., LTD—See Asia Air Survey Co., Ltd.; *Int'l*, pg. 609
BAE SYSTEMS-ADR—See BAE Systems plc; *Int'l*, pg. 797
BEIJING URBAN CONSTRUCTION EXPLORATION & SURVEYING DESIGN RESEARCH INSTITUTE CO., LTD.—See Beijing Urban Construction Design & Development Group Co., Ltd.; *Int'l*, pg. 959
BKS SURVEYS LTD—See Amalgamated Metal Corporation PLC; *Int'l*, pg. 408
BLOM AEROFILMS LTD.—See Cyient Limited; *Int'l*, pg. 1895
BLUESKY INTERNATIONAL LTD.; *Int'l*, pg. 1074
THE BURKE GROUP, INC.; *U.S. Private*, pg. 4003
BURREN ENERGY—See Eni S.p.A.; *Int'l*, pg. 2437
CALIFORNIA SURVEYING & DRAFTING SUPPLY, INC.—See Cansel Survey Equipment, Ltd.; *Int'l*, pg. 1298

N.A.I.C.S. INDEX

541370 — SURVEYING AND MAPPI...

CGG AIRBORNE SURVEYS (PTY) LTD.—See CGG; *Int'l*, pg. 1431
CGG - ARGENTINA—See CGG; *Int'l*, pg. 1431
CGG AVIATION (AUSTRALIA) PTY LTD.—See CGG; *Int'l*, pg. 1431
CGG DO BRASIL LTDA.—See CGG; *Int'l*, pg. 1431
CGG GEOPHYSICAL (CANADA) CORPORATION—See CGG; *Int'l*, pg. 1431
CGG GEOPHYSICAL (CHILE) SA—See CGG; *Int'l*, pg. 1431
CGG NPA SATELLITE MAPPING LTD.—See CGG; *Int'l*, pg. 1432
CGG - PERU—See CGG; *Int'l*, pg. 1431
CGG SERVICES (AUSTRALIA) PTY. LTD.—See CGG; *Int'l*, pg. 1431
CGG SERVICES (CANADA) INC.—See CGG; *Int'l*, pg. 1431
CGG SERVICES DE MEXICO SA DE CV—See CGG; *Int'l*, pg. 1432
CGG SERVICES (NORWAY) AS—See CGG; *Int'l*, pg. 1431
CHI-KEN SOGO CONSULTANTS CO., LTD.—See CTI Engineering Co., Ltd.; *Int'l*, pg. 1871
CLEAN HARBORS ENERGY & INDUSTRIAL SERVICES CORP.—See Clean Harbors, Inc.; *U.S. Public*, pg. 509
CLEAN HARBORS EXPLORATION SERVICES LTD.—See Clean Harbors, Inc.; *U.S. Public*, pg. 509
COMTECH MOBILE DATACOM CORP.—See Comtech Telecommunications Corp.; *U.S. Public*, pg. 563
DAIWA LANTEC CO., LTD.—See Daiwa House Industry Co., Ltd.; *Int'l*, pg. 1945
DIGITALGLOBE, INC.—See Advent International Corporation; *U.S. Private*, pg. 103
EARTH-PANDA (BAOTOU) CO., LTD.—See Earth-Panda Advance Magnetic Material Co., Ltd.; *Int'l*, pg. 2268
EARTH-PANDA CO., LTD.—See Earth-Panda Advance Magnetic Material Co., Ltd.; *Int'l*, pg. 2268
EMGS AMERICAS INC.—See Electromagnetic Geoservices ASA; *Int'l*, pg. 2353
EMGS ASIA PACIFIC SDN BHD—See Electromagnetic Geoservices ASA; *Int'l*, pg. 2353
EMGS AS—See Electromagnetic Geoservices ASA; *Int'l*, pg. 2353
EMGS DO BRASIL LTDA.—See Electromagnetic Geoservices ASA; *Int'l*, pg. 2353
EXPLORATION SURVEYS, INC.—See Wilks Brothers LLC; *U.S. Private*, pg. 4521
FUGRO AERIAL MAPPING A/S—See Fugro N.V.; *Int'l*, pg. 2805
FUGRO AERIAL MAPPING B.V.—See Fugro N.V.; *Int'l*, pg. 2807
FUGRO AIRBORNE SURVEYS, CORP.—See Fugro N.V.; *Int'l*, pg. 2805
FUGRO ALBANIA SH.P.K.—See Fugro N.V.; *Int'l*, pg. 2805
FUGRO ALLUVIAL OFFSHORE LTD.—See Fugro N.V.; *Int'l*, pg. 2805
FUGRO APERIO LTD.—See Fugro N.V.; *Int'l*, pg. 2805
FUGRO AUSTRIA GMBH—See Fugro N.V.; *Int'l*, pg. 2805
FUGRO BELGIQUE/BELGIE S.A./N.V.—See Fugro N.V.; *Int'l*, pg. 2805
FUGRO BELGIUM SRL—See Fugro N.V.; *Int'l*, pg. 2805
FUGRO BRASIL LEVANTAMENTOS LTDA.—See Fugro N.V.; *Int'l*, pg. 2805
FUGRO BTW LTD.—See Fugro N.V.; *Int'l*, pg. 2805
FUGRO (CANADA), INC.—See Fugro N.V.; *Int'l*, pg. 2805
FUGRO C.I.S. B.V.—See Fugro N.V.; *Int'l*, pg. 2807
FUGRO CONSULT GMBH—See Fugro N.V.; *Int'l*, pg. 2805
FUGRO ECO CONSULT GMBH—See Fugro N.V.; *Int'l*, pg. 2806
FUGRO GEODETIC AG—See Fugro N.V.; *Int'l*, pg. 2806
FUGRO GEOSERVICES B.V.—See Fugro N.V.; *Int'l*, pg. 2807
FUGRO GEOSERVICES, INC.—See Fugro N.V.; *Int'l*, pg. 2805
FUGRO GEOSERVICES LTD.—See Fugro N.V.; *Int'l*, pg. 2806
FUGRO-GEOS, INC.—See Fugro N.V.; *Int'l*, pg. 2805
FUGRO GEOSURVEYS, INC.—See Fugro N.V.; *Int'l*, pg. 2806
FUGRO GEOTECHNICAL SERVICES LTD.—See Fugro N.V.; *Int'l*, pg. 2806
FUGRO GEOTECHNICS AS—See Fugro N.V.; *Int'l*, pg. 2806
FUGRO GEOTECHNICS VIETNAM LLC—See Fugro N.V.; *Int'l*, pg. 2806
FUGRO GERMANY LAND GMBH—See Fugro N.V.; *Int'l*, pg. 2806
FUGRO GERMANY MARINE GMBH—See Fugro N.V.; *Int'l*, pg. 2806
FUGRO HOLDING FRANCE S.A.S.—See Fugro N.V.; *Int'l*, pg. 2806
FUGRO IN SITU GEOTECNIA LTDA.—See Fugro N.V.; *Int'l*, pg. 2806
FUGRO INTERRA S.A.—See Fugro N.V.; *Int'l*, pg. 2806
FUGRO MALAYSIA LAND SDN BHD—See Fugro N.V.; *Int'l*, pg. 2806
FUGRO-MAPS S.A.R.L.—See Fugro N.V.; *Int'l*, pg. 2808
FUGRO-MAPS (UAE)—See Fugro N.V.; *Int'l*, pg. 2808
FUGRO MAURITIUS LTD.—See Fugro N.V.; *Int'l*, pg. 2806
FUGRO MEXICO S.A. DE C.V.—See Fugro N.V.; *Int'l*, pg. 2806

FUGRO MIDDLE EAST & PARTNERS LLC—See Fugro N.V.; *Int'l*, pg. 2806
FUGRO MULTI CLIENT SERVICES, INC.—See Fugro N.V.; *Int'l*, pg. 2805
FUGRO NEDERLAND B.V.—See Fugro N.V.; *Int'l*, pg. 2806
FUGRO NEW ZEALAND LTD.—See Fugro N.V.; *Int'l*, pg. 2807
FUGRO NIGERIA LIMITED—See Fugro N.V.; *Int'l*, pg. 2807
FUGRO NL LAND B.V.—See Fugro N.V.; *Int'l*, pg. 2807
FUGRO NORWAY AS—See Fugro N.V.; *Int'l*, pg. 2807
FUGRO N.V.; *Int'l*, pg. 2805
FUGRO OSAE GMBH—See Fugro N.V.; *Int'l*, pg. 2807
FUGRO PACIFICA QINHUANGDAO CO. LTD.—See Fugro N.V.; *Int'l*, pg. 2807
FUGRO PANAMA SA—See Fugro N.V.; *Int'l*, pg. 2807
FUGRO PELAGROS, INC.—See Fugro N.V.; *Int'l*, pg. 2805
FUGRO PERU S.A.—See Fugro N.V.; *Int'l*, pg. 2807
FUGRO PHILIPPINES INC.—See Fugro N.V.; *Int'l*, pg. 2807
FUGRO ROAMES PTY LTD—See Fugro N.V.; *Int'l*, pg. 2807
FUGRO S.A.E.—See Fugro N.V.; *Int'l*, pg. 2807
FUGRO SEACORE (AUSTRALIA) PTY LTD—See Fugro N.V.; *Int'l*, pg. 2807
FUGRO SEA LTD.—See Fugro N.V.; *Int'l*, pg. 2807
FUGRO SEASTAR MAURITIUS LTD.—See Fugro N.V.; *Int'l*, pg. 2807
FUGRO SIAL LTD.—See Fugro N.V.; *Int'l*, pg. 2807
FUGRO SINGAPORE MARINE PTE. LTD.—See Fugro N.V.; *Int'l*, pg. 2807
FUGRO SOUTH AMERICA GMBH—See Fugro N.V.; *Int'l*, pg. 2807
FUGRO SUBSEA TECHNOLOGIES PTE LTD—See Fugro N.V.; *Int'l*, pg. 2807
FUGRO SURVEY AFRICA (PTY) LTD.—See Fugro N.V.; *Int'l*, pg. 2808
FUGRO SURVEY AS—See Fugro N.V.; *Int'l*, pg. 2807
FUGRO SURVEY (BRUNEI) SDN BHD.—See Fugro N.V.; *Int'l*, pg. 2807
FUGRO SURVEY B.V.—See Fugro N.V.; *Int'l*, pg. 2807
FUGRO SURVEY CARIBBEAN N.V.—See Fugro N.V.; *Int'l*, pg. 2808
FUGRO SURVEY INTERNATIONAL LTD.—See Fugro N.V.; *Int'l*, pg. 2808
FUGRO SURVEY LTD.—See Fugro N.V.; *Int'l*, pg. 2808
FUGRO SURVEY MEXICO S.A. DE C.V.—See Fugro N.V.; *Int'l*, pg. 2808
FUGRO SURVEY (MIDDLE EAST) LTD.—See Fugro N.V.; *Int'l*, pg. 2807
FUGRO SURVEY PTY LTD.—See Fugro N.V.; *Int'l*, pg. 2808
FUGRO TECHNICAL SERVICES (MACAU) LTD.—See Fugro N.V.; *Int'l*, pg. 2808
GEOCONCEPT CHINA LTD—See GeoConcept SA; *Int'l*, pg. 2932
GEOCONCEPT INDIA PRIVATE LIMITED—See GeoConcept SA; *Int'l*, pg. 2933
GEOCONCEPT INTERNATIONAL SOFTWARE (SUISSE) SA—See GeoConcept SA; *Int'l*, pg. 2932
GEOCONCEPT JAPAN KK—See GeoConcept SA; *Int'l*, pg. 2932
GEOJUNXION B.V.—See GeoJunxion NV; *Int'l*, pg. 2933
GEOPHYSICAL EXPLORATION TECHNOLOGY INC.—See Getech Group plc; *Int'l*, pg. 2947
GEOSTRATA RESOURCES INC.; *Int'l*, pg. 2941
GEOTECH AVIATION LTD.—See Geotech Ltd.; *Int'l*, pg. 2941
GEOTECH LTD.; *Int'l*, pg. 2941
GEOTECHNICAL INSTRUMENTS (HONG KONG) LTD.—See Fugro N.V.; *Int'l*, pg. 2808
GEOVIEW, INC.—See Ambient Technologies, Inc.; *U.S. Private*, pg. 217
GETMAPPING PLC; *Int'l*, pg. 2953
GLOBAL SERVICOS GEOFISICOS, LTDA.—See Global Geophysical Services, Inc.; *U.S. Private*, pg. 1714
GREENTREE GAS & OIL LTD.; *Int'l*, pg. 3077
GX TECHNOLOGY CANADA, LTD.—See ION Geophysical Corporation; *U.S. Public*, pg. 1166
GX TECHNOLOGY CORPORATION—See ION Geophysical Corporation; *U.S. Public*, pg. 1166
GX TECHNOLOGY EAME LIMITED—See ION Geophysical Corporation; *U.S. Public*, pg. 1166
GX TECHNOLOGY PROCESSAMENTO DE DADOS LTDA.—See ION Geophysical Corporation; *U.S. Public*, pg. 1166
HALIS LLC—See Peak Rock Capital LLC; *U.S. Private*, pg. 3124
HANOVER LAND SERVICES, INC.-PENNSYLVANIA OFFICE—See Hanover Land Services, Inc.; *U.S. Private*, pg. 1855
HYDRO CONSULTANTS INC.—See Atwell, LLC; *U.S. Private*, pg. 384
IDENTIFIED TECHNOLOGIES, CORP—See Alpine 4 Holdings, Inc.; *U.S. Public*, pg. 85
INCREMENT P CORP—See EQT AB; *Int'l*, pg. 2470
INCREMENT P SHANGHAI CO.,LTD—See EQT AB; *Int'l*, pg. 2470
INTERGRAPH CR SPOL S.R.O.—See Hexagon AB; *Int'l*, pg. 3368
INTERMAP TECHNOLOGIES CORPORATION; *U.S. Public*, pg. 1144

INTERMAP TECHNOLOGIES INC.—See Intermap Technologies Corporation; *U.S. Public*, pg. 1145
I/O MARINE SYSTEMS, INC.—See ION Geophysical Corporation; *U.S. Public*, pg. 1166
JX NIPPON EXPLORATION & DEVELOPMENT CO., LTD.—See ENEOS Holdings, Inc.; *Int'l*, pg. 2416
LAUREL TECHNOLOGIES CO. LTD.—See Beijing Highlander Digital Technology Co., Ltd.; *Int'l*, pg. 951
LEICA GEOSYSTEMS AG—See Hexagon AB; *Int'l*, pg. 3367
LEICA GEOSYSTEMS GR, LLC—See Hexagon AB; *Int'l*, pg. 3368
MALTAIS GEOMATICS INC.—See Altus Group Limited; *Int'l*, pg. 399
MAPANYTHING, INC.—See Salesforce, Inc.; *U.S. Public*, pg. 1837
MAPMYFITNESS, INC—See Outside Interactive, Inc.; *U.S. Private*, pg. 3051
MENSI, S.A.—See Trimble, Inc.; *U.S. Public*, pg. 2190
MICROSEISMIC, INC.; *U.S. Private*, pg. 2704
MIND TECHNOLOGY, INC.; *U.S. Public*, pg. 1448
MITCHAM CANADA LTD.—See MIND Technology, Inc.; *U.S. Public*, pg. 1448
MITCHAM CANADA ULC—See MIND Technology, Inc.; *U.S. Public*, pg. 1448
MITCHAM SEISMIC EURASIA, LLC—See MIND Technology, Inc.; *U.S. Public*, pg. 1448
MSA PROFESSIONAL SERVICES, INC.; *U.S. Private*, pg. 2806
MULTIFIELD GEOPHYSICS AS—See CGG; *Int'l*, pg. 1432
MULTIMAP AUSTRALASIA—See Microsoft Corporation; *U.S. Public*, pg. 1440
NEARMAP LTD.—See Thoma Bravo, L.P.; *U.S. Private*, pg. 4150
NOVAGOLD RESOURCES USA—See Novagold Resources Inc.; *U.S. Public*, pg. 1547
ON ENERGY INC.—See CGX Energy Inc.; *Int'l*, pg. 1435
OPTIMAL GEOMATICS INC.—See Geotech Ltd.; *Int'l*, pg. 2941
PERIDIAN ASIA PTE LTD.—See Downer EDI Limited; *Int'l*, pg. 2186
P.T. FUGRO INDONESIA—See Fugro N.V.; *Int'l*, pg. 2808
QUANTUM SPATIAL, INC.—See Arlington Capital Partners LLC; *U.S. Private*, pg. 328
REGOS S.R.O.—See Minerals Technologies, Inc.; *U.S. Public*, pg. 1449
RUETTIGER, TONELLI & ASSOCIATES, INC.—See The Will Group, Inc.; *U.S. Private*, pg. 4136
SAEXPLORATION (AUSTRALIA) PTY. LTD.—See SAExploration Holdings, Inc.; *U.S. Private*, pg. 3523
SAEXPLORATION HOLDINGS, INC.; *U.S. Private*, pg. 3523
SAEXPLORATION, INC.—See SAExploration Holdings, Inc.; *U.S. Private*, pg. 3523
SAEXPLORATION SUB, INC.—See SAExploration Holdings, Inc.; *U.S. Private*, pg. 3523
SAM, INC.; *U.S. Private*, pg. 3536
SEAMAP LIMITED—See MIND Technology, Inc.; *U.S. Public*, pg. 1448
SEAMAP PTE. LTD.—See MIND Technology, Inc.; *U.S. Public*, pg. 1448
SEAMAP (UK) LTD.—See MIND Technology, Inc.; *U.S. Public*, pg. 1448
SEISMIC ASIA PACIFIC PTY. LTD.—See MIND Technology, Inc.; *U.S. Public*, pg. 1448
SEITEL, INC.—See ValueAct Capital Management, L.P.; *U.S. Private*, pg. 4338
SENSOR NEDERLAND B.V.—See ION Geophysical Corporation; *U.S. Public*, pg. 1166
SERCEL - LES ULIS—See CGG; *Int'l*, pg. 1432
SOCON SONAR CONTROL KAVERNENVERMESSUNG GMBH—See EWE Aktiengesellschaft; *Int'l*, pg. 2575
STEREOCARTO, S.L.—See Airtificial Intelligence Structures SA; *Int'l*, pg. 249
SURDEX CORP.—See Bowman Consulting Group Ltd.; *U.S. Public*, pg. 377
TAT-ARKA LLP—See Caspian Services, Inc.; *U.S. Public*, pg. 446
TERRA ENERGY & RESOURCE TECHNOLOGIES, INC.; *U.S. Public*, pg. 2020
UAB FUGRO BALTIC—See Fugro N.V.; *Int'l*, pg. 2808
UELS, LLC—See Wells Fargo & Company; *U.S. Public*, pg. 2345
WESTERNGECO A/S—See Schlumberger Limited; *U.S. Public*, pg. 1846
WESTERNGECO LIMITED—See Schlumberger Limited; *U.S. Public*, pg. 1846
WESTERNGECO LLC—See Schlumberger Limited; *U.S. Public*, pg. 1846
WOOLWICH SURVEYING SERVICES LIMITED—See Barclays PLC; *Int'l*, pg. 863

541370 — SURVEYING AND MAPPING (EXCEPT GEOPHYSICAL) SERVICES

1 ALLIANCE GEOMATICS, LLC—See GI Manager L.P.; *U.S. Private*, pg. 1691
40SEVEN LTD—See IDEX Corp; *U.S. Public*, pg. 1089

541370 — SURVEYING AND MAPPI...

AHNEMAN KIRBY LLC—See The Fibersmith Company; *U.S. Private*, pg. 4028
ALLTERRA OSTERREICH GMBH—See Trimble, Inc.; *U.S. Public*, pg. 2190
ALPINE OCEAN SEISMIC SURVEY, INC.—See HAL Trust N.V.; *Int'l*, pg. 3226
APPLY CAPNOR POLAND SP. Z O.O.—See Apply ASA; *Int'l*, pg. 521
APPLY CAPNOR US, INC.—See Apply ASA; *Int'l*, pg. 521
ASIA AIR SURVEY CO., LTD.; *Int'l*, pg. 609
AXIM GEOSPATIAL, LLC—See NV5 Global, Inc.; *U.S. Public*, pg. 1557
BEARTOOTH MAPPING INC—See Trimble, Inc.; *U.S. Public*, pg. 2190
BLOOD HOUND, LLC—See USIC, LLC; *U.S. Private*, pg. 4323
BOCK & CLARK CORPORATION—See NV5 Global, Inc.; *U.S. Public*, pg. 1557
BOLTON & MENK, INC.; *U.S. Private*, pg. 611
CALTECH SURVEYS LTD.; *Int'l*, pg. 1266
CARDNO SPECTRUM SURVEY PTY. LTD.—See Cardno Limited; *Int'l*, pg. 1322
CAROLINA SURVEYING SERVICES INC.—See Peak Rock Capital LLC; *U.S. Private*, pg. 3124
CARTOGRAFIA GENERAL, S.A.—See Airtificial Intelligence Structures SA; *Int'l*, pg. 249
CARTWRIGHT AERIAL SURVEYS, INC.; *U.S. Private*, pg. 776
CDS BUSINESS MAPPING, LLC—See Insight Venture Management, LLC; *U.S. Private*, pg. 2088
CDS BUSINESS MAPPING, LLC—See Stone Point Capital LLC; *U.S. Private*, pg. 3822
CHALLENGER GEOMATICS LTD.; *Int'l*, pg. 1438
C.H. FENSTERMAKER & ASSOCIATES, INC.; *U.S. Private*, pg. 707
CITEC INC.—See GIKEN Ltd.; *Int'l*, pg. 2972
C-MAP USA, INC.—See Altor Equity Partners AB; *Int'l*, pg. 394
COL-EAST, INC.—See Bluesky International Ltd.; *Int'l*, pg. 1074
DGT ASSOCIATES, INC.; *U.S. Private*, pg. 1221
DIGITALGLOBE INTERNATIONAL ASIA PACIFIC PTE. LTD.—See Advent International Corporation; *U.S. Private*, pg. 103
DIGITALGLOBE INTERNATIONAL, INC.—See Advent International Corporation; *U.S. Private*, pg. 103
DUNCAN-PARNELL—See Duncan-Parnell, Inc.; *U.S. Private*, pg. 1288
DYNAMIC RESOURCES, INC.; *U.S. Private*, pg. 1299
EAGLEVIEW TECHNOLOGIES, INC.—See Vista Equity Partners, LLC; *U.S. Private*, pg. 4396
E & E SOLUTIONS INC.—See Dowa Holdings Co., Ltd.; *Int'l*, pg. 2184
ENDURANCE EXPLORATION GROUP, INC.; *U.S. Public*, pg. 760
FUGRO BKS LTD.—See Fugro N.V.; *Int'l*, pg. 2805
FUGRO EARTHDATA, INC. - AVIATION—See Fugro N.V.; *Int'l*, pg. 2805
FUGRO EARTHDATA, INC.—See Fugro N.V.; *Int'l*, pg. 2805
FUGRO HOLDINGS (NZ) LTD.—See Fugro N.V.; *Int'l*, pg. 2806
FUGRO ITALY S.P.A.—See Fugro N.V.; *Int'l*, pg. 2806
FUGRO-MAPS GMBH—See Fugro N.V.; *Int'l*, pg. 2808
FUGRO SPATIAL SOLUTIONS PTY LTD.—See Fugro N.V.; *Int'l*, pg. 2807
FUGRO TRINIDAD LTD.—See Fugro N.V.; *Int'l*, pg. 2808
GANNETT FLEMING, INC. - GEODECISIONS DIVISION—See OceanSound Partners, LP; *U.S. Private*, pg. 2991
GEOD CORPORATION—See MFS Consulting Engineers & Surveyor Corporation; *U.S. Private*, pg. 2693
GEOMATICS DATA SOLUTIONS, LLC—See Woolpert Inc.; *U.S. Private*, pg. 4562
GUIZHOU TRANSPORTATION PLANNING SURVEY & DESIGN ACADEME CO., LTD.; *Int'l*, pg. 3175
I-CUBED, LLC—See Airbus SE; *Int'l*, pg. 243
INFOTERRA SERVICIOS DE GEOINFORMACION SA—See Airbus SE; *Int'l*, pg. 245
INSTITUT GAUER GMBH—See BKW AG; *Int'l*, pg. 1055
JOHN CHANCE LAND SURVEYS, INC.—See Fugro N.V.; *Int'l*, pg. 2805
LANDMARK ENGINEERING AND SURVEYING CORP.; *U.S. Private*, pg. 2385
LANDPOINT INC.; *U.S. Private*, pg. 2386
LANKELMA LTD.—See HAL Trust N.V.; *Int'l*, pg. 3226
LEMKE LAND SURVEYING, LLC—See Parkhill, Smith & Cooper, Inc.; *U.S. Private*, pg. 3098
MAPCITY.COM CHILE S.A—See Equifax Inc.; *U.S. Public*, pg. 786
MAPCITY PERU S.A.C.—See Equifax Inc.; *U.S. Public*, pg. 787
MAXAR TECHNOLOGIES INC.—See Advent International Corporation; *U.S. Private*, pg. 103
MAX DEVELOPMENT LLC—See Englander Knabe & Allen; *U.S. Private*, pg. 1399
MDA INFORMATIONS SYSTEMS LLC—See Advent International Corporation; *U.S. Private*, pg. 103

MEAD GILMAN & ASSOCIATES—See Atwell, LLC; *U.S. Private*, pg. 384
MIDLAND MAP COMPANY, LLC—See Hellman & Friedman LLC; *U.S. Private*, pg. 1908
MILLMAN SURVEYING, INC.; *U.S. Private*, pg. 2737
MODERN SURVEY, INC.—See Alight, Inc.; *U.S. Public*, pg. 76
NEARMAP PTY. LTD.—See Thoma Bravo, L.P.; *U.S. Private*, pg. 4150
NV5 GEOSPATIAL SOLUTIONS B.V.—See NV5 Global, Inc.; *U.S. Public*, pg. 1557
NV5 GEOSPATIAL SOLUTIONS FRANCE SARL—See NV5 Global, Inc.; *U.S. Public*, pg. 1557
NV5 GEOSPATIAL SOLUTIONS GMBH—See NV5 Global, Inc.; *U.S. Public*, pg. 1557
NV5 GEOSPATIAL SOLUTIONS, INC.—See NV5 Global, Inc.; *U.S. Public*, pg. 1557
NV5 GEOSPATIAL SOLUTIONS ITALIA S.R.L.—See NV5 Global, Inc.; *U.S. Public*, pg. 1557
NV5 GEOSPATIAL SOLUTIONS KK—See NV5 Global, Inc.; *U.S. Public*, pg. 1557
NV5 GEOSPATIAL SOLUTIONS UK LIMITED—See NV5 Global, Inc.; *U.S. Public*, pg. 1557
OGM LAND, LLC—See Percheron, LLC; *U.S. Private*, pg. 3146
OTT CONSULTING INC.—See Ott Consulting Inc.; *U.S. Private*, pg. 3049
PERCHERON, LLC; *U.S. Private*, pg. 3146
PICTOMETRY INTERNATIONAL CORP.; *U.S. Private*, pg. 3176
PRECISIONPOINT INC.—See Surveying And Mapping, LLC; *U.S. Private*, pg. 3885
RCP DEVELOPMENT INC.—See Rock Creek Pharmaceuticals, Inc.; *U.S. Public*, pg. 1804
REPLOGLE GLOBES PARTNERS LLC; *U.S. Private*, pg. 3401
RYAN & FAULDS LLC—See Redniss & Mead, Inc.; *U.S. Private*, pg. 3379
SETECH (GEOTECHNICAL ENGINEERS) LTD—See HAL Trust N.V.; *Int'l*, pg. 3226
SEVAN MULTI-SITE SOLUTIONS, INC.; *U.S. Private*, pg. 3618
STABIPLAN BVBA—See Trimble, Inc.; *U.S. Public*, pg. 2191
SUBSURFACE UTILITY IMAGING, LLC—See USIC, LLC; *U.S. Private*, pg. 4323
SURVEYING & MAPPING, LLC—See Peak Rock Capital LLC; *U.S. Private*, pg. 3124
TITAN ENVIRONMENTAL SURVEYS LTD—See HAL Trust N.V.; *Int'l*, pg. 3226
WELLSTON ASSOCIATES LAND SURVEYORS, LLC—See Peak Rock Capital LLC; *U.S. Private*, pg. 3124
WESTRIAN GROUP, INC.; *U.S. Private*, pg. 4500
WISESCAN ENGINEERING SERVICES PTE. LTD.—See CSC Holdings Limited; *Int'l*, pg. 1862
YOTTA LIMITED—See Causeway Technologies Limited; *Int'l*, pg. 1361

541380 — TESTING LABORATORIES

3C TEST LIMITED—See I Squared Capital Advisors (US) LLC; *U.S. Private*, pg. 2021
3DX-RAY LTD.—See Image Scan Holdings plc; *Int'l*, pg. 3618
A2M INDUSTRIES, SAS—See I Squared Capital Advisors (US) LLC; *U.S. Private*, pg. 2021
A3GEO, INC.—See OceanSound Partners, LP; *U.S. Private*, pg. 2991
ABBOTT ANALYTICAL LIMITED—See Neogen Corporation; *U.S. Public*, pg. 1505
ABBOTT TOXICOLOGY LIMITED—See Abbott Laboratories; *U.S. Public*, pg. 18
ABBOTT TOXICOLOGY LIMITED—See Abbott Laboratories; *U.S. Public*, pg. 18
AB SCIEX NETHERLANDS B.V.—See Danaher Corporation; *U.S. Public*, pg. 623
ACCESS GENETICS, LLC; *U.S. Private*, pg. 51
ACME BIOSCIENCE, INC.—See Hangzhou Tigermed Consulting Co., Ltd.; *Int'l*, pg. 3250
ADT, LLC—See Q-Lab Corp.; *U.S. Private*, pg. 3312
ADVANCED CELL DIAGNOSTICS, INC.—See Bio-Techne Corporation; *U.S. Public*, pg. 334
ADVANCED MICRO DEVICES EXPORT SDN. BHD.—See Advanced Micro Devices, Inc.; *U.S. Public*, pg. 48
ADVANCED TESTING LABORATORY, INC.—See Bureau Veritas S.A.; *Int'l*, pg. 1221
ADVIK LABORATORIES LTD.; *Int'l*, pg. 168
AEGIS TOXICOLOGY SCIENCES CORPORATION—See ABRY Partners, LLC; *U.S. Private*, pg. 40
AEROFLEX AVCOMM-RESEARCH & DEVELOPMENT CENTER—See Advent International Corporation; *U.S. Private*, pg. 99
AEROFLEX IRELAND LIMITED—See Viavi Solutions Inc.; *U.S. Public*, pg. 2295
AEROTEST OPERATIONS, INC.—See Autoliv, Inc.; *Int'l*, pg. 729
AGILENT TECHNOLOGIES, INC.; *U.S. Public*, pg. 60

AGRARTEST GMBH—See Eurofins Scientific S.E.; *Int'l*, pg. 2535
AGRIFOOD TECHNOLOGY PTY LTD.—See Australian Wool Testing Authority Ltd.; *Int'l*, pg. 723
AGROHUARPES - EUROFINS AGROSCIENCES SERVICES S.A.—See Eurofins Scientific S.E.; *Int'l*, pg. 2535
AIDAN NORWAY AS—See Axcel Management A/S; *Int'l*, pg. 762
AIDIAN SWEDEN AB—See Axcel Management A/S; *Int'l*, pg. 762
AIR WATER & SOIL LABORATORIES, INC.—See Montrose Environmental Group, Inc.; *U.S. Public*, pg. 1466
A-LAB CORP.—See Gray America Corp.; *U.S. Private*, pg. 1759
ALDINGER COMPANY; *U.S. Private*, pg. 160
ALERE GMBH—See Abbott Laboratories; *U.S. Public*, pg. 18
ALERE TOXICOLOGY SERVICES, INC.—See Abbott Laboratories; *U.S. Public*, pg. 19
ALLIANCE ONCOLOGY, LLC—See Akumin, Inc.; *U.S. Public*, pg. 70
ALMEDIO, INC.; *Int'l*, pg. 363
ALPABIO SAS—See Eurofins Scientific S.E.; *Int'l*, pg. 2535
ALPA CHIMIE ALIMENTAIRE SAS—See Eurofins Scientific S.E.; *Int'l*, pg. 2535
ALPA HYGIENE ALIMENTAIRE SAS—See Eurofins Scientific S.E.; *Int'l*, pg. 2535
ALPA MICROBIOLOGIE ALIMENTAIRE SAS—See Eurofins Scientific S.E.; *Int'l*, pg. 2535
ALPE METROLOGIA INDUSTRIAL, S.L.U.—See I Squared Capital Advisors (US) LLC; *U.S. Private*, pg. 2021
ALS BURKINA SARL—See ALS Limited; *Int'l*, pg. 377
ALS CANADA LTD—See ALS Limited; *Int'l*, pg. 378
ALS CHEMEX DE MEXICO S.A. DE C.V.—See ALS Limited; *Int'l*, pg. 378
ALS CHEMEX (GUANGZHOU) LTD.—See ALS Limited; *Int'l*, pg. 378
ALS CHEMEX SOUTH AFRICA (PROPRIETARY) LTD—See ALS Limited; *Int'l*, pg. 378
ALS CHITA LABORATORY LLC—See ALS Limited; *Int'l*, pg. 377
ALS CZECH REPUBLIC S.R.O—See ALS Limited; *Int'l*, pg. 378
ALS DENMARK AS—See ALS Limited; *Int'l*, pg. 377
ALS DOMINICAN REPUBLIC SAS—See ALS Limited; *Int'l*, pg. 377
ALS ENVIRONMENTAL—See ALS Limited; *Int'l*, pg. 378
ALS FINLAND OY—See ALS Limited; *Int'l*, pg. 378
ALS FOOD & PHARMACEUTICAL POLSKA SP. Z O.O.—See ALS Limited; *Int'l*, pg. 377
ALS GHANA LIMITED—See ALS Limited; *Int'l*, pg. 377
ALS GROUP USA, CORP—See ALS Limited; *Int'l*, pg. 378
ALS INSPECTION MOZAMBIQUE SERVICE, LDA.—See ALS Limited; *Int'l*, pg. 377
ALS INSPECTION NETHERLANDS BV—See ALS Limited; *Int'l*, pg. 377
ALS INSPECTION SOUTH KOREA LIMITED—See ALS Limited; *Int'l*, pg. 377
ALS INSPECTION UK LIMITED—See ALS Limited; *Int'l*, pg. 377
ALS ITALIA S.R.L.—See ALS Limited; *Int'l*, pg. 377
ALS LABORATORIES (UK) LTD.—See ALS Limited; *Int'l*, pg. 377
ALS LABORATORY GROUP NORWAY AS—See ALS Limited; *Int'l*, pg. 377
ALS LABORATORY GROUP (THAILAND) CO. LTD—See ALS Limited; *Int'l*, pg. 378
ALS METALLURGY - BURNIE—See ALS Limited; *Int'l*, pg. 378
ALS PATAGONIA S.A—See ALS Limited; *Int'l*, pg. 378
ALS PERU S.A.—See ALS Limited; *Int'l*, pg. 378
ALS POLAND SP. Z.O.O—See ALS Limited; *Int'l*, pg. 378
ALS SCANDINAVIA AB—See ALS Limited; *Int'l*, pg. 377
ALS SERVICES PLC—See ALS Limited; *Int'l*, pg. 377
ALS SK, S.R.O.—See ALS Limited; *Int'l*, pg. 377
ALS TAIWAN CO. LTD—See ALS Limited; *Int'l*, pg. 378
ALS TECHNICHEM (HK) PTY LTD—See ALS Limited; *Int'l*, pg. 378
ALS TECHNICHEM (SINGAPORE) PTE LTD—See ALS Limited; *Int'l*, pg. 378
ALS TESTING SERVICES NZ LIMITED—See ALS Limited; *Int'l*, pg. 377
ALS TESTING SERVICES (THAILAND) CO. LTD—See ALS Limited; *Int'l*, pg. 378
AMAR IMMUNODIAGNOSTICS PVT LTD—See Eurofins Scientific S.E.; *Int'l*, pg. 2535
AMATSIAQUITAINE SAS—See Eurofins Scientific S.E.; *Int'l*, pg. 2535
AMERICAN BIO MEDICA CORPORATION; *U.S. Public*, pg. 98
AMERICAN ELECTRICAL TESTING CO,, INC.—See Asplundh Tree Expert Co.; *U.S. Private*, pg. 353
AMERICAN GLASS RESEARCH—See Clayton, Dubilier & Rice, LLC; *U.S. Private*, pg. 924
AMERICAN METAL TESTING INC.—See Aero Metals Inc.; *U.S. Private*, pg. 118
AMERICAN STANDARD TESTING BUREAU; *U.S. Private*, pg. 255

541380 — TESTING LABORATORIE...

AMLAB SERVICES PTE. LTD.—See Blackstone Inc.; *U.S. Public*, pg. 354
AMPRO LABORATORIES, INC.—See American Proteins Inc.; *U.S. Private*, pg. 244
ANALYTICA INC.—See The Aleut Corporation; *U.S. Private*, pg. 3984
ANALYTICAL ENVIRONMENTAL SERVICES—See Montrose Environmental Group, Inc.; *U.S. Public*, pg. 1466
ANALYTICO BV—See Eurofins Scientific S.E.; *Int'l*, pg. 2535
ANALYTICO MILIEU NV—See Eurofins Scientific S.E.; *Int'l*, pg. 2535
ANMAR METROLOGY, INC.—See Transcat, Inc.; *U.S. Public*, pg. 2179
ANST, CHINA RESOURCES MICRO-ASSEMBLY TECHNOLOGY CO., LTD.—See China Resources (Holdings) Co., Ltd.; *Int'l*, pg. 1548
ANTARES VISION SPA; *Int'l*, pg. 482
APPLIED TECHNICAL SERVICES, INC.—See Odyssey Investment Partners, LLC; *U.S. Private*, pg. 2994
APPLUS COSTA RICA, S.A.—See I Squared Capital Advisors (US) LLC; *U.S. Private*, pg. 2021
APPLUS CZECH REPUBLIC, S.R.O.—See I Squared Capital Advisors (US) LLC; *U.S. Private*, pg. 2021
APPLUS FOMENTO DE CONTROL, S.A.—See I Squared Capital Advisors (US) LLC; *U.S. Private*, pg. 2021
APPLUS K2 AMERICA, LLC—See I Squared Capital Advisors (US) LLC; *U.S. Private*, pg. 2022
APPLUS LABORATORIES, AS—See I Squared Capital Advisors (US) LLC; *U.S. Private*, pg. 2022
APPLUS NORCONTROL PERU, S.A.C.—See I Squared Capital Advisors (US) LLC; *U.S. Private*, pg. 2022
APPLUS NORCONTROL, S.L.—See I Squared Capital Advisors (US) LLC; *U.S. Private*, pg. 2022
APPLUS PORTUGAL, LDA.—See I Squared Capital Advisors (US) LLC; *U.S. Private*, pg. 2022
APPLUS PTY, LTD.—See I Squared Capital Advisors (US) LLC; *U.S. Private*, pg. 2022
APPLUS QUALITEC SERVICOS DE ENGENHARIA, LTDA.—See I Squared Capital Advisors (US) LLC; *U.S. Private*, pg. 2022
APPLUS (SHANGAI) QUALITY INSPECTION CO, LTD.—See I Squared Capital Advisors (US) LLC; *U.S. Private*, pg. 2021
APPLUS SINGAPORE PTE LTD.—See I Squared Capital Advisors (US) LLC; *U.S. Private*, pg. 2022
APPLUS STEEL TEST (PTY.) LTD.—See I Squared Capital Advisors (US) LLC; *U.S. Private*, pg. 2022
AQL EMC LIMITED—See Eurofins Scientific S.E.; *Int'l*, pg. 2535
AQM VIETNAM LIMITED—See Eurofins Scientific S.E.; *Int'l*, pg. 2535
ARCADIA AEROSPACE INDUSTRIES LLC—See X-Ray Industries Inc.; *U.S. Private*, pg. 4579
ARIES OPTICAL LTD.—See EssilorLuxottica SA; *Int'l*, pg. 2512
ARS PROBATA GMBH—See Eurofins Scientific S.E.; *Int'l*, pg. 2535
ASCOM NETWORK TESTING AB—See Ascom Holding AG; *Int'l*, pg. 603
ASE TEST, INC.—See ASE Technology Holding Co., Ltd.; *Int'l*, pg. 604
ASHWOOD UK LIMITED—See Eurofins Scientific S.E.; *Int'l*, pg. 2535
ASPIRA LABS, INC.—See Aspira Women's Health Inc.; *U.S. Public*, pg. 213
ASSYSTEM ROMANIA SRL—See Assystem S.A.; *Int'l*, pg. 651
ATLANTIC ENGINEERING LABORATORIES INC.—See GI Manager L.P.; *U.S. Private*, pg. 1691
ATLAS MATERIAL TESTING TECHNOLOGY GMBH—See AMETEK, Inc.; *U.S. Public*, pg. 117
ATLAS WEATHERING DSET LABORATORIES—See AMETEK, Inc.; *U.S. Public*, pg. 117
ATP AUTOMOTIVE TESTING PAPENBURG GMBH—See Adecco Group AG; *Int'l*, pg. 140
ATS TEST INC.—See ATS Corporation; *Int'l*, pg. 695
AUSTRALIAN LABORATORY GROUP (ZAMBIA) LIMITED—See ALS Limited; *Int'l*, pg. 377
AUSTRALIAN LABORATORY SERVICES (ALS) (CAMBODIA) CO., LTD.—See ALS Limited; *Int'l*, pg. 377
AUSTRALIAN LABORATORY SERVICES PTY. LTD.—See ALS Limited; *Int'l*, pg. 378
AUSTRALIAN LABORATORY SERVICES SURINAME N.V.—See ALS Limited; *Int'l*, pg. 378
AUSTRALIAN WOOL TESTING AUTHORITY LTD. - AWTA PRODUCT TESTING DIVISION—See Australian Wool Testing Authority Ltd.; *Int'l*, pg. 723
AUSTRALIAN WOOL TESTING AUTHORITY LTD. - AWTA RAW WOOL DIVISION—See Australian Wool Testing Authority Ltd.; *Int'l*, pg. 723
AUSTRALIAN WOOL TESTING AUTHORITY LTD.; *Int'l*, pg. 723
AUTOLIV ASP, INC.—See Autoliv, Inc.; *Int'l*, pg. 729
AUTOLIV INFLATORS—See Autoliv, Inc.; *Int'l*, pg. 729
AUTOLIV NORTH AMERICA AIRBAG INFLATOR FACILITY—See Autoliv, Inc.; *Int'l*, pg. 729
AVL NORTH AMERICA INC.—See AVL List GmbH; *Int'l*, pg. 748

BAS EVANSVILLE, INC.—See Inotiv, Inc.; *U.S. Public*, pg. 1128
BASF CORP. - CHARLOTTE (CHESAPEAKE) SITE—See BASF SE; *Int'l*, pg. 876
BAYPO II LLC—See Bayer Aktiengesellschaft; *Int'l*, pg. 902
BEIJING LANDAUER RADIATION MONITORING TECHNOLOGY CO., LTD.—See Fortive Corporation; *U.S. Public*, pg. 871
BETA INSTITUT FOR SOZIAIMEDIZINISCHE FORSCHUNG AND ENTWICKLUNG GMBH—See Dr. Reddy's Laboratories Limited; *Int'l*, pg. 2195
BETOTECH, S.R.O.—See Heidelberg Materials AG; *Int'l*, pg. 3308
BIOAGILYTIX LABS, LLC—See Cobepa S.A.; *Int'l*, pg. 1683
BIOBRIDGES LLC—See Adecco Group AG; *Int'l*, pg. 141
BIOMNIS EMPREINTES GENETIQUES SAS—See Eurofins Scientific S.E.; *Int'l*, pg. 2535
BIOPOLIS, S.L.—See Archer-Daniels-Midland Company; *U.S. Public*, pg. 184
BIOPORTO DIAGNOSTICS INC—See BioPorto A/S; *Int'l*, pg. 1041
BIO SEARCH (N.I.) LIMITED—See Eurofins Scientific S.E.; *Int'l*, pg. 2535
BIOTAGE KOREA CO., LTD.—See Biotage AB; *Int'l*, pg. 1042
BIOTAGE TRADING (SHANGHAI) CO., LTD.—See Biotage AB; *Int'l*, pg. 1042
BK WERSTOFFTECHNIKPRUFSTELLE FUR WERKSTOFFE, GMBH.—See I Squared Capital Advisors (US) LLC; *U.S. Private*, pg. 2022
BML FUKUSHIMA, INC.—See BML, Inc.; *Int'l*, pg. 1076
BML, INC.; *Int'l*, pg. 1076
BODYCOTE SLOVAKIA S.R.O.—See Bodycote plc; *Int'l*, pg. 1098
BODYCOTE SURFACE TECHNOLOGY WARTBURG, INC.—See Bodycote plc; *Int'l*, pg. 1098
BRICKSTREET INSURANCE; *U.S. Private*, pg. 648
BRIDGESTONE AMERICAS TIRE OPERATIONS, LLC - TEXAS PROVING GROUND DIVISION—See Cox Enterprises, Inc.; *U.S. Public*, pg. 1075
BROWN INTEGRITY, LLC—See Cypress Environmental Partners, L.P.; *U.S. Public*, pg. 618
BUCKMAN LABORATORIES (ASIA) PTE LTD.—See Bulab Holdings, Inc.; *U.S. Private*, pg. 683
BUCKMAN LABORATORIES (INDIA) PRIVATE LIMITED—See Bulab Holdings, Inc.; *U.S. Private*, pg. 683
BUCKMAN LABORATORIES OF CANADA, LTD.—See Bulab Holdings, Inc.; *U.S. Private*, pg. 683
BUCKMAN LABORATORIES, S.A. DE C.V.—See Bulab Holdings, Inc.; *U.S. Private*, pg. 684
BUCKMAN LABORATORIES (SHANGHAI) CHEMICALS CO., LTD.—See Bulab Holdings, Inc.; *U.S. Private*, pg. 683
BUCKMAN LABORATORIOS CHILE LTDA.—See Bulab Holdings, Inc.; *U.S. Private*, pg. 684
BUREAU DE WIT BV—See Eurofins Scientific S.E.; *Int'l*, pg. 2535
BUREAU VERITAS CONSUMER PRODUCTS SERVICES, INC.—See Bureau Veritas S.A.; *Int'l*, pg. 1221
BUREAU VERITAS NORTH AMERICA, INC.—See Bureau Veritas S.A.; *Int'l*, pg. 1221
CALIBRATION TECHNOLOGIES—See Transcat, Inc.; *U.S. Public*, pg. 2179
CALSPAN CORP.—See TransDigm Group Incorporated; *U.S. Public*, pg. 2180
CAL TEC LABS, INC.—See Medical Technology Associates, LLC; *U.S. Private*, pg. 2656
CAMBI GROUP AS—See Cambi ASA; *Int'l*, pg. 1268
CAMIN CARGO CONTROL INC.—See Metalmark Capital Holdings LLC; *U.S. Private*, pg. 2681
CANADIAN STANDARDS ASSOCIATION—See CSA Group; *Int'l*, pg. 1861
CAPARO TESTING TECHNOLOGIES LTD - MIDDLE EAST FACILITY—See Caparo Group Ltd.; *Int'l*, pg. 1302
CAPARO TESTING TECHNOLOGIES LTD—See Caparo Group Ltd.; *Int'l*, pg. 1302
CD LABORATORIES, INC.—See Zimmer Biomet Holdings, Inc.; *U.S. Public*, pg. 2406
CENTRE TESTING INTERNATIONAL (BEIJING) CO., LTD.—See Centre Testing International Corporation; *Int'l*, pg. 1411
CENTRE TESTING INTERNATIONAL CORPORATION; *Int'l*, pg. 1411
CENTRE TESTING INTERNATIONAL GROUP (SHANDONG) CO., LTD.—See Centre Testing International Corporation; *Int'l*, pg. 1411
CENTRE TESTING INTERNATIONAL (HONG KONG) CO., LTD.—See Centre Testing International Corporation; *Int'l*, pg. 1411
CENTRO DE ANALISE E TIPAGEM DE GENOMAS LTDA.—See Eurofins Scientific S.E.; *Int'l*, pg. 2535
CEPHEID AB—See Danaher Corporation; *U.S. Public*, pg. 625
CERIUM LABORATORIES, LLC—See Cerium Holdings, Inc.; *U.S. Public*, pg. 841
CERTIFICATION ENGINEERS INTERNATIONAL LIMITED—See Engineers India Ltd.; *Int'l*, pg. 2435

CERTIFIED LABORATORIES, INC.; *U.S. Private*, pg. 841
CETERO RESEARCH—See Cetero Research; *U.S. Private*, pg. 843
CHANTEST CORPORATION—See Charles River Laboratories International, Inc.; *U.S. Public*, pg. 479
CHARLES RIVER FRANCE S.A.—See Charles River Laboratories International, Inc.; *U.S. Public*, pg. 479
CHARLES RIVER LABORATORIES-MI—See Charles River Laboratories International, Inc.; *U.S. Public*, pg. 480
CHARLES RIVER LABORATORIES—See Charles River Laboratories International, Inc.; *U.S. Public*, pg. 480
CHEMON INC.—See Corestem Inc.; *Int'l*, pg. 1800
CHEMTEST LIMITED—See Eurofins Scientific S.E.; *Int'l*, pg. 2535
CHEMTOX SAS—See Eurofins Scientific S.E.; *Int'l*, pg. 2542
CHORI ANALYSIS & TECHNOLOGY SERVICE (SUZHOU)CO., LTD.—See Chori Co., Ltd.; *Int'l*, pg. 1583
CIS COMMODITY INSPECTION SERVICES B.V.—See Catering International & Services S.A.; *Int'l*, pg. 1360
CITY ANALYSTS LIMITED—See Eurofins Scientific S.E.; *Int'l*, pg. 2535
CLEAN WATER TESTING—See A. O. Smith Corporation; *U.S. Public*, pg. 11
CLINISYS DEUTSCHLAND GMBH—See Roper Technologies, Inc.; *U.S. Public*, pg. 1810
CLINISYS N.V.—See Roper Technologies, Inc.; *U.S. Public*, pg. 1810
C-MARK BV—See Eurofins Scientific S.E.; *Int'l*, pg. 2541
CMIC, INC.—See CMIC Holdings Co., Ltd.; *Int'l*, pg. 1670
COBHAM RAD, INC.—See Radiation Test Solutions, Inc.; *U.S. Public*, pg. 3343
COLLARD ROSE—See EssilorLuxottica SA; *Int'l*, pg. 2513
COLT PRUF UND TEST GMBH—See FACC AG; *Int'l*, pg. 2600
COMMUNICATION GLOBAL CERTIFICATION INC.—See HTC Corporation; *Int'l*, pg. 3508
COMPASS WATER SOLUTIONS, INC—See CECO Environmental Corp.; *U.S. Public*, pg. 463
THE CONCENTRATE MANUFACTURING COMPANY OF IRELAND—See PepsiCo, Inc.; *U.S. Public*, pg. 1672
CONSTELLATION POWERLABS, LLC—See Constellation Energy Corporation; *U.S. Public*, pg. 572
CON-TEST ANALYTICAL LABORATORY—See Leonard Green & Partners, L.P.; *U.S. Private*, pg. 2426
CONTROLVET - SEGURANCA ALIMENTAR, SA—See ALS Limited; *Int'l*, pg. 378
COOL ENGINEERING AB—See Etteplan Oyj; *Int'l*, pg. 2524
COOPERGENOMICS INC.—See The Cooper Companies, Inc.; *U.S. Public*, pg. 2066
CORRELAGEN DIAGNOSTICS, INC.—See Laboratory Corporation of America Holdings; *U.S. Public*, pg. 1285
COTTON ELECTRIC SERVICES, INC.—See Cotton Electric Cooperative, Inc.; *U.S. Private*, pg. 1064
CREATIVE TESTING SOLUTIONS; *U.S. Private*, pg. 1090
CSA GROUP NETHERLANDS—See CSA Group; *Int'l*, pg. 1861
CSA INTERNATIONAL - ASIA—See CSA Group; *Int'l*, pg. 1861
CSA INTERNATIONAL—See CSA Group; *Int'l*, pg. 1861
CTRM TESTING LABORATORY SDN. BHD.—See DRB-HICOM Berhad; *Int'l*, pg. 2201
DAICEL CHIRAL TECHNOLOGIES (INDIA) PVT LTD.—See Daicel Corporation; *Int'l*, pg. 1918
DAINAN TECH (S) PTE LTD—See ESPEC Corp.; *Int'l*, pg. 2505
DATAPOINTLABS; *U.S. Private*, pg. 1166
DDL, INC.—See Integreon Global; *U.S. Private*, pg. 2102
DEKRA HASAR SERVISI LTD. STI.—See DEKRA e.V.; *Int'l*, pg. 2006
DENSO ABASHIRI TEST CENTER CORPORATION—See Denso Corporation; *Int'l*, pg. 2029
DENSO EMC ENGINEERING SERVICE CORPORATION—See Denso Corporation; *Int'l*, pg. 2029
DERMSCAN POLAND SP. Z.O.O.—See Eurofins Scientific S.E.; *Int'l*, pg. 2536
DHALIWAL LABS; *U.S. Private*, pg. 1221
DHL ANALYTICAL, INC—See Sentinel Capital Partners, L.L.C.; *U.S. Private*, pg. 3609
DICKSON TESTING COMPANY, INC.—See Berkshire Hathaway Inc.; *U.S. Public*, pg. 314
DISPOSABLE LAB SAS—See Eurofins Scientific S.E.; *Int'l*, pg. 2536
DNA DIAGNOSTICS CENTER, INC.—See GHO Capital Partners LLP; *Int'l*, pg. 2959
DOMINION DIAGNOSTICS, LLC—See Riverside Partners, LLC; *U.S. Private*, pg. 3446
DOOSAN TESNA INC; *Int'l*, pg. 2174
DR. LAUK & DR. BREITLING GMBH—See Eurofins Scientific S.E.; *Int'l*, pg. 2536
DT&C CO., LTD.; *Int'l*, pg. 2216
DVA LABORATORY SERVICES, INC.—See DaVita Inc.; *U.S. Public*, pg. 637
EAG LABORATORIES GMBH—See Eurofins Scientific S.E.; *Int'l*, pg. 2549
EAGLE APPLIED SCIENCES, LLC.—See Bristol Bay Native Corporation; *U.S. Private*, pg. 656

N.A.I.C.S. Index

541380 — TESTING LABORATORIE... CORPORATE AFFILIATIONS

EARTH SCIENCE ANALYTICS AS—See Equinor ASA; *Int'l*, pg. 2484
ECRI; *U.S. Private*, pg. 1330
EMERSON RESOURCES, INC.—See Leonard Green & Partners, L.P.; *U.S. Private*, pg. 2426
EMLAB P&K LLC—See Eurofins Scientific S.E.; *Int'l*, pg. 2536
EMPOWERDX UMWELTANALYTIK DEUTSCHLAND GMBH—See Eurofins Scientific S.E.; *Int'l*, pg. 2536
EMTEK (DONGGUAN) CO., LTD.—See EMTEK (Shenzhen) Co., Ltd.; *Int'l*, pg. 2394
EMTEK (GUANGZHOU) CO., LTD.—See EMTEK (Shenzhen) Co., Ltd.; *Int'l*, pg. 2394
EMTEK (NINGBO) CO., LTD.—See EMTEK (Shenzhen) Co., Ltd.; *Int'l*, pg. 2394
EMTEK (SHENZHEN) CO., LTD.; *Int'l*, pg. 2394
EMTEK (SUZHOU) CO., LTD.—See EMTEK (Shenzhen) Co., Ltd.; *Int'l*, pg. 2394
EMTEK (WUHAN) CO., LTD.—See EMTEK (Shenzhen) Co., Ltd.; *Int'l*, pg. 2394
ENERLABS, INC.; *U.S. Private*, pg. 1396
ENTHALPY ANALYTICAL, INC.—See Montrose Environmental Corp.; *U.S. Private*, pg. 2777
ENVIRA INGENIEROS ASESORES SL—See Eurofins Scientific S.E.; *Int'l*, pg. 2536
ENVIRONMENTAL CHEMISTRY CONSULTING SERVICES, INC.—See Leonard Green & Partners, L.P.; *U.S. Private*, pg. 2426
ENVIRONMENTAL CHEMISTRY, INC.—See Montrose Environmental Group, Inc.; *U.S. Public*, pg. 1466
ENVIRONMENTAL LABORATORIES BV—See Eurofins Scientific S.E.; *Int'l*, pg. 2536
ENVIRONMENTAL LABORATORY SERVICES LIMITED—See Eurofins Scientific S.E.; *Int'l*, pg. 2536
ENVIRONMENTAL SAMPLING SUPPLY, INC.—See Eurofins Scientific S.E.; *Int'l*, pg. 2536
ENVIRONMENTAL SCIENTIFICS GROUP LTD.—See 3i Group plc; *Int'l*, pg. 8
ENVIRONMENTAL SERVICE LABORATORIES INC.; *U.S. Private*, pg. 1408
EPIGENOMICS AG; *Int'l*, pg. 2460
EPMEDICAL CO., LTD.—See EPS Holdings, Inc.; *Int'l*, pg. 2465
ESL PRELEVEMENT SAS—See Eurofins Scientific S.E.; *Int'l*, pg. 2536
ESOTERIX, INC.—See Laboratory Corporation of America Holdings; *U.S. Public*, pg. 1286
ETON BIOSCIENCE INC.—See Telesis Bio, Inc.; *U.S. Public*, pg. 1998
EUROFINS 1. VERWALTUNGSGESELLSCHAFT MBH—See Eurofins Scientific S.E.; *Int'l*, pg. 2536
EUROFINS 3 OHMS SAS—See Eurofins Scientific S.E.; *Int'l*, pg. 2536
EUROFINS ACMAA INSPECTIE B.V.—See Eurofins Scientific S.E.; *Int'l*, pg. 2536
EUROFINS ACMAA LABORATORIA B.V.—See Eurofins Scientific S.E.; *Int'l*, pg. 2536
EUROFINS ADVINUS AGROSCIENCES SERVICES INDIA PRIVATE LIMITED—See Eurofins Scientific S.E.; *Int'l*, pg. 2536
EUROFINS ADVINUS BIOPHARMA SERVICES INDIA PVT LTD—See Eurofins Scientific S.E.; *Int'l*, pg. 2536
EUROFINS ADVINUS DISCOVERY SERVICES PRIVATE LIMITED—See Eurofins Scientific S.E.; *Int'l*, pg. 2536
EUROFINS AGRARANALYTIK DEUTSCHLAND GMBH—See Eurofins Scientific S.E.; *Int'l*, pg. 2536
EUROFINS AGROAMBIENTAL SA—See Eurofins Scientific S.E.; *Int'l*, pg. 2536
EUROFINS AGRO-ANALYSES S.A.S.—See Eurofins Scientific S.E.; *Int'l*, pg. 2536
EUROFINS AGROSCIENCE SERVICES AUSTRIA GMBH—See Eurofins Scientific S.E.; *Int'l*, pg. 2536
EUROFINS AGROSCIENCE SERVICES CHEM GMBH—See Eurofins Scientific S.E.; *Int'l*, pg. 2536
EUROFINS AGROSCIENCE SERVICES CHEM SAS—See Eurofins Scientific S.E.; *Int'l*, pg. 2536
EUROFINS AGROSCIENCE SERVICES CHILE S.A—See Eurofins Scientific S.E.; *Int'l*, pg. 2536
EUROFINS AGROSCIENCE SERVICES ECOCHEM GMBH—See Eurofins Scientific S.E.; *Int'l*, pg. 2536
EUROFINS AGROSCIENCE SERVICES ECOTOX GMBH—See Eurofins Scientific S.E.; *Int'l*, pg. 2536
EUROFINS AGROSCIENCE SERVICES GMBH—See Eurofins Scientific S.E.; *Int'l*, pg. 2536
EUROFINS AGROSCIENCE SERVICES INC.—See Eurofins Scientific S.E.; *Int'l*, pg. 2548
EUROFINS AGROSCIENCE SERVICES KFT—See Eurofins Scientific S.E.; *Int'l*, pg. 2537
EUROFINS AGROSCIENCE SERVICES LTD.—See Eurofins Scientific S.E.; *Int'l*, pg. 2536
EUROFINS AGROSCIENCE SERVICES MAROC SARL—See Eurofins Scientific S.E.; *Int'l*, pg. 2537
EUROFINS AGROSCIENCE SERVICES NZ LIMITED—See Eurofins Scientific S.E.; *Int'l*, pg. 2537
EUROFINS AGROSCIENCE SERVICES REGULATORY FRANCE SAS—See Eurofins Scientific S.E.; *Int'l*, pg. 2537
EUROFINS AGROSCIENCE SERVICES REGULATORY GERMANY GMBH—See Eurofins Scientific S.E.; *Int'l*, pg. 2537
EUROFINS AGROSCIENCE SERVICES REGULATORY SPAIN SL—See Eurofins Scientific S.E.; *Int'l*, pg. 2537
EUROFINS AGROSCIENCE SERVICES SEEDS FRANCE SAS—See Eurofins Scientific S.E.; *Int'l*, pg. 2537
EUROFINS AGROSCIENCE SERVICES SL—See Eurofins Scientific S.E.; *Int'l*, pg. 2537
EUROFINS AGROSCIENCE SERVICES SP. Z.O.O.—See Eurofins Scientific S.E.; *Int'l*, pg. 2536
EUROFINS AGROSCIENCE SERVICES SRL—See Eurofins Scientific S.E.; *Int'l*, pg. 2537
EUROFINS AGROSCIENCE SERVICES THAILAND CO. LTD.—See Eurofins Scientific S.E.; *Int'l*, pg. 2537
EUROFINS AGROSCIENCES SERVICES SAS—See Eurofins Scientific S.E.; *Int'l*, pg. 2542
EUROFINS AGROSCIENCE TESTING NZ LIMITED—See Eurofins Scientific S.E.; *Int'l*, pg. 2537
EUROFINS AGROSCIENCE TESTING PTY LTD—See Eurofins Scientific S.E.; *Int'l*, pg. 2537
EUROFINS AGRO TESTING BELGIUM NV—See Eurofins Scientific S.E.; *Int'l*, pg. 2536
EUROFINS AGRO TESTING DENMARK A/S—See Eurofins Scientific S.E.; *Int'l*, pg. 2536
EUROFINS AGRO TESTING NORWAY AS—See Eurofins Scientific S.E.; *Int'l*, pg. 2536
EUROFINS AGRO TESTING SWEDEN AB—See Eurofins Scientific S.E.; *Int'l*, pg. 2536
EUROFINS AGRO TESTING WAGENINGEN BV—See Eurofins Scientific S.E.; *Int'l*, pg. 2536
EUROFINS AHMA OY—See Eurofins Scientific S.E.; *Int'l*, pg. 2537
EUROFINS AIR A L'EMISSION FRANCE SAS—See Eurofins Scientific S.E.; *Int'l*, pg. 2542
EUROFINS AIR MONITORING BELGIUM N.V.—See Eurofins Scientific S.E.; *Int'l*, pg. 2537
EUROFINS AIR TOXICS, LLC—See Eurofins Scientific S.E.; *Int'l*, pg. 2548
EUROFINS AMATSI ANALYTICS SAS—See Eurofins Scientific S.E.; *Int'l*, pg. 2537
EUROFINS AMATSIGROUP NV—See Eurofins Scientific S.E.; *Int'l*, pg. 2537
EUROFINS AMS LABORATORIES PTY. LTD.—See Eurofins Scientific S.E.; *Int'l*, pg. 2550
EUROFINS ANALISIS ALIMENTARIO NORDESTE SL—See Eurofins Scientific S.E.; *Int'l*, pg. 2537
EUROFINS ANALISIS ALIMENTARIO SL—See Eurofins Scientific S.E.; *Int'l*, pg. 2537
EUROFINS ANALISIS CLINICOS CANARIAS, SL—See Eurofins Scientific S.E.; *Int'l*, pg. 2537
EUROFINS ANALYSES DES MATERIAUX ET COMBUSTIBLES FRANCE SAS—See Eurofins Scientific S.E.; *Int'l*, pg. 2537
EUROFINS ANALYSES NUTRITIONNELLES FRANCE S.A.S.—See Eurofins Scientific S.E.; *Int'l*, pg. 2537
EUROFINS ANALYSES POUR LE BATIMENT ILE DE FRANCE—See Eurofins Scientific S.E.; *Int'l*, pg. 2542
EUROFINS ANALYSES POUR LE BATIMENT NORD SAS—See Eurofins Scientific S.E.; *Int'l*, pg. 2537
EUROFINS ANALYSES POUR LE BATIMENT OUEST SAS—See Eurofins Scientific S.E.; *Int'l*, pg. 2537
EUROFINS ANALYSES POUR LE BATIMENT SUD EST SAS—See Eurofins Scientific S.E.; *Int'l*, pg. 2537
EUROFINS ANALYSES POUR LE BATIMENT SUD-OUEST SAS—See Eurofins Scientific S.E.; *Int'l*, pg. 2537
EUROFINS ANALYSES POUR LE BATIMENT SUD SAS—See Eurofins Scientific S.E.; *Int'l*, pg. 2537
EUROFINS ANALYSES POUR L'ENVIRONNEMENT FRANCE SAS—See Eurofins Scientific S.E.; *Int'l*, pg. 2542
EUROFINS ANALYTICAL LABORATORIES, INC.—See Eurofins Scientific S.E.; *Int'l*, pg. 2537
EUROFINS ANALYTICAL SERVICES HUNGARY KFT.—See Eurofins Scientific S.E.; *Int'l*, pg. 2537
EUROFINS ANALYTICAL SERVICES INDIA PVT LTD—See Eurofins Scientific S.E.; *Int'l*, pg. 2537
EUROFINS ANALYTICAL TESTING CENTER INC.—See Eurofins Scientific S.E.; *Int'l*, pg. 2548
EUROFINS ANALYTICS FRANCE SAS—See Eurofins Scientific S.E.; *Int'l*, pg. 2542
EUROFINS ANALYTICS & SERVICES AUSTRIA GMBH—See Eurofins Scientific S.E.; *Int'l*, pg. 2537
EUROFINS ANALYTIK GMBH—See Eurofins Scientific S.E.; *Int'l*, pg. 2537
EUROFINS ANIMAL HEALTH AUSTRALIA PTY LTD—See Eurofins Scientific S.E.; *Int'l*, pg. 2537
EUROFINS APAL PTY. LTD.—See Eurofins Scientific S.E.; *Int'l*, pg. 2537
EUROFINS AQUATIC ECOTOXICOLOGY GMBH—See Eurofins Scientific S.E.; *Int'l*, pg. 2537
EUROFINS ASBESTOS TESTING BELGIUM NV—See Eurofins Scientific S.E.; *Int'l*, pg. 2537
EUROFINS ASBESTOS TESTING EUROPE SAS—See Eurofins Scientific S.E.; *Int'l*, pg. 2537
EUROFINS ASCAL BATIMENT NORD SAS—See Eurofins Scientific S.E.; *Int'l*, pg. 2542
EUROFINS ASCAL BATIMENT SUD EST SAS—See Eurofins Scientific S.E.; *Int'l*, pg. 2542
EUROFINS ASCAL ENVIRONNEMENT SAS—See Eurofins Scientific S.E.; *Int'l*, pg. 2542
EUROFINS ASSURANCE CHINA CO., LTD.—See Eurofins Scientific S.E.; *Int'l*, pg. 2538
EUROFINS ASSURANCE INDIA PVT LTD.—See Eurofins Scientific S.E.; *Int'l*, pg. 2538
EUROFINS ATS SAS—See Eurofins Scientific S.E.; *Int'l*, pg. 2542
EUROFINS AVD. MOSS—See Eurofins Scientific S.E.; *Int'l*, pg. 2550
EUROFINS BACTERIOLOGISCH ADVIESBURO BV—See Eurofins Scientific S.E.; *Int'l*, pg. 2538
EUROFINS BAY OF PLENTY LIMITED—See Eurofins Scientific S.E.; *Int'l*, pg. 2538
EUROFINS BELGIUM NV—See Eurofins Scientific S.E.; *Int'l*, pg. 2538
EUROFINS BEL/NOVAMANN S.R.O.—See Eurofins Scientific S.E.; *Int'l*, pg. 2538
EUROFINS BESTLAB OY—See Eurofins Scientific S.E.; *Int'l*, pg. 2550
EUROFINS BIODIAGNOSTICS, INC.—See Eurofins Scientific S.E.; *Int'l*, pg. 2548
EUROFINS BIOFFICE SELAS—See Eurofins Scientific S.E.; *Int'l*, pg. 2538
EUROFINS BIOFUEL & ENERGY TESTING SWEDEN AB—See Eurofins Scientific S.E.; *Int'l*, pg. 2538
EUROFINS BIOLAB SRL—See Eurofins Scientific S.E.; *Int'l*, pg. 2548
EUROFINS BIOLOGIE MEDICALE ILE DE FRANCE SAS—See Eurofins Scientific S.E.; *Int'l*, pg. 2538
EUROFINS BIOLOGIE MOLECULAIRE FRANCE SAS—See Eurofins Scientific S.E.; *Int'l*, pg. 2538
EUROFINS BIOMNIS IRELAND LIMITED—See Eurofins Scientific S.E.; *Int'l*, pg. 2538
EUROFINS BIOMNIS SELAS—See Eurofins Scientific S.E.; *Int'l*, pg. 2538
EUROFINS BIOPHARMA PRODUCT TESTING DENMARK A/S—See Eurofins Scientific S.E.; *Int'l*, pg. 2538
EUROFINS BIOPHARMA PRODUCT TESTING HAMBURG GMBH—See Eurofins Scientific S.E.; *Int'l*, pg. 2538
EUROFINS BIOPHARMA PRODUCT TESTING INDIA PRIVATE LIMITED—See Eurofins Scientific S.E.; *Int'l*, pg. 2538
EUROFINS BIOPHARMA PRODUCT TESTING MUNICH GMBH—See Eurofins Scientific S.E.; *Int'l*, pg. 2538
EUROFINS BIOPHARMA PRODUCT TESTING NZ LIMITED—See Eurofins Scientific S.E.; *Int'l*, pg. 2538
EUROFINS BIOPHARMA PRODUCT TESTING SPAIN SLU—See Eurofins Scientific S.E.; *Int'l*, pg. 2538
EUROFINS BIOPHARMA PRODUCT TESTING SWEDEN AB—See Eurofins Scientific S.E.; *Int'l*, pg. 2538
EUROFINS BIOPHARMA PRODUCT TESTING SWITZERLAND AG—See Eurofins Scientific S.E.; *Int'l*, pg. 2538
EUROFINS BIOPHARMA PRODUCT TESTING UK LIMITED—See Eurofins Scientific S.E.; *Int'l*, pg. 2538
EUROFINS BIOTALDE, S.L.U.—See Eurofins Scientific S.E.; *Int'l*, pg. 2538
EUROFINS BIOTESTING SERVICES NORD GMBH—See Eurofins Scientific S.E.; *Int'l*, pg. 2538
EUROFINS BIOTESTING SERVICES OST GMBH—See Eurofins Scientific S.E.; *Int'l*, pg. 2538
EUROFINS BLC LEATHER TECHNOLOGY CENTRE LIMITED—See Eurofins Scientific S.E.; *Int'l*, pg. 2538
EUROFINS BUREAU DE WIT B.V.—See Eurofins Scientific S.E.; *Int'l*, pg. 2538
EUROFINS CALSCIENCE, LLC—See Eurofins Scientific S.E.; *Int'l*, pg. 2548
EUROFINS CAVENDISH, S.L.U.—See Eurofins Scientific S.E.; *Int'l*, pg. 2539
EUROFINS CBM69 SELAS—See Eurofins Scientific S.E.; *Int'l*, pg. 2538
EUROFINS CEBAT SAS—See Eurofins Scientific S.E.; *Int'l*, pg. 2538
EUROFINS CEF SELAS—See Eurofins Scientific S.E.; *Int'l*, pg. 2538
EUROFINS CEI, INC.—See Eurofins Scientific S.E.; *Int'l*, pg. 2548
EUROFINS CENTRAL ANALYTICAL LABORATORIES INC.—See Eurofins Scientific S.E.; *Int'l*, pg. 2548
EUROFINS CENTRAL LABORATORY CHINA CO., LTD.—See Eurofins Scientific S.E.; *Int'l*, pg. 2539
EUROFINS CENTRAL LABORATORY LLC—See Eurofins Scientific S.E.; *Int'l*, pg. 2539
EUROFINS CENTRAL LABORATORY PTE. LTD.—See Eurofins Scientific S.E.; *Int'l*, pg. 2539
EUROFINS CENTRAL LABORATORY—See Eurofins Scientific S.E.; *Int'l*, pg. 2539
EUROFINS CERTIFICATION SARL—See Eurofins Scientific S.E.; *Int'l*, pg. 2542
EUROFINS CERVAC SUD SAS—See Eurofins Scientific S.E.; *Int'l*, pg. 2542
EUROFINS CHIMIE ALIMENTAIRE ROUEN S.A.S.—See Eurofins Scientific S.E.; *Int'l*, pg. 2539
EUROFINS CIDESAL, S.L.U.—See Eurofins Scientific S.E.; *Int'l*, pg. 2539
EUROFINS CLF SPECIALISED NUTRITION TESTING SERVICES GMBH—See Eurofins Scientific S.E.; *Int'l*, pg. 2538

541380 — TESTING LABORATORIE...

EUROFINS CLINICAL DIAGNOSTICS BANGALORE PRIVATE LIMITED—See Eurofins Scientific S.E.; *Int'l*, pg. 2539
EUROFINS CLINICAL DIAGNOSTICS PTE. LTD.—See Eurofins Scientific S.E.; *Int'l*, pg. 2539
EUROFINS CLINICAL GENETICS KK—See Eurofins Scientific S.E.; *Int'l*, pg. 2539
EUROFINS CLINICAL TESTING SWEDEN AB—See Eurofins Scientific S.E.; *Int'l*, pg. 2539
EUROFINS CONSULTING ITALIA SRL—See Eurofins Scientific S.E.; *Int'l*, pg. 2548
EUROFINS CONSUMER PRODUCT TESTING GMBH—See Eurofins Scientific S.E.; *Int'l*, pg. 2547
EUROFINS CONSUMER PRODUCT TESTING (GUANGZHOU) CO., LTD.—See Eurofins Scientific S.E.; *Int'l*, pg. 2539
EUROFINS CONSUMER PRODUCT TESTING VIETNAM CO. LTD.—See Eurofins Scientific S.E.; *Int'l*, pg. 2539
EUROFINS CONTROL AMBIENTAL Y ECOGESTOR, S.L.U.—See Eurofins Scientific S.E.; *Int'l*, pg. 2539
EUROFINS CONVET, S.L.U.—See Eurofins Scientific S.E.; *Int'l*, pg. 2539
EUROFINS COSMETIC & PERSONAL CARE ITALY SRL—See Eurofins Scientific S.E.; *Int'l*, pg. 2539
EUROFINS COSMETICS & PERSONAL CARE TESTING CANADA, INC.—See Eurofins Scientific S.E.; *Int'l*, pg. 2539
EUROFINS CROATIAKONTROLA D.O.O.—See Eurofins Scientific S.E.; *Int'l*, pg. 2539
EUROFINS DERMATEST PTY LTD—See Eurofins Scientific S.E.; *Int'l*, pg. 2539
EUROFINS DERMSCAN TUNISIE S.A.R.L.—See Eurofins Scientific S.E.; *Int'l*, pg. 2539
EUROFINS DEUTSCHES INSTITUT FUR LEBENSMITTELUNTERSUCHUNG GMBH—See Eurofins Scientific S.E.; *Int'l*, pg. 2548
EUROFINS DIGITAL PRODUCT TESTING UK LIMITED—See Eurofins Scientific S.E.; *Int'l*, pg. 2539
EUROFINS DIGITAL TESTING BELGIUM NV—See Eurofins Scientific S.E.; *Int'l*, pg. 2540
EUROFINS DIGITAL TESTING SWEDEN AB—See Eurofins Scientific S.E.; *Int'l*, pg. 2540
EUROFINS DISPOSITIFS AU CONTACT DE L'EAU FRANCE SAS—See Eurofins Scientific S.E.; *Int'l*, pg. 2540
EUROFINS DO BRASIL ANALISE DE ALIMENTOS LTDA—See Eurofins Scientific S.E.; *Int'l*, pg. 2550
EUROFINS DONOR & PRODUCT TESTING, INC.—See Eurofins Scientific S.E.; *Int'l*, pg. 2540
EUROFINS DQCI—See Eurofins Scientific S.E.; *Int'l*, pg. 2548
EUROFINS DR. SPECHT INTERNATIONAL GMBH—See Eurofins Scientific S.E.; *Int'l*, pg. 2540
EUROFINS DR. SPECHT LABORATORIEN GMBH—See Eurofins Scientific S.E.; *Int'l*, pg. 2548
EUROFINS DSC FORENSICS SAS—See Eurofins Scientific S.E.; *Int'l*, pg. 2539
EUROFINS EAG AGROSCIENCE, LLC—See Eurofins Scientific S.E.; *Int'l*, pg. 2540
EUROFINS EAG EASTON—See Eurofins Scientific S.E.; *Int'l*, pg. 2549
EUROFINS EAG MATERIALS SCIENCE CHINA LTD.—See Eurofins Scientific S.E.; *Int'l*, pg. 2540
EUROFINS EAG MATERIALS SCIENCE SINGAPORE, PTE. LTD.—See Eurofins Scientific S.E.; *Int'l*, pg. 2540
EUROFINS EAG MATERIALS SCIENCE TOKYO CORPORATION KK—See Eurofins Scientific S.E.; *Int'l*, pg. 2540
EUROFINS EAG PRINCETON—See Eurofins Scientific S.E.; *Int'l*, pg. 2549
EUROFINS EAG SHANGHAI—See Eurofins Scientific S.E.; *Int'l*, pg. 2549
EUROFINS EAG SINGAPORE—See Eurofins Scientific S.E.; *Int'l*, pg. 2549
EUROFINS EAG ST LOUIS—See Eurofins Scientific S.E.; *Int'l*, pg. 2549
EUROFINS EAG SUNNYVALE—See Eurofins Scientific S.E.; *Int'l*, pg. 2549
EUROFINS EAG TAIWAN—See Eurofins Scientific S.E.; *Int'l*, pg. 2549
EUROFINS EAG TOKYO—See Eurofins Scientific S.E.; *Int'l*, pg. 2549
EUROFINS EAG TOULOUSE—See Eurofins Scientific S.E.; *Int'l*, pg. 2549
EUROFINS EATON ANALYTICAL, LLC—See Eurofins Scientific S.E.; *Int'l*, pg. 2548
EUROFINS EAUX RESIDUAIRES SAS—See Eurofins Scientific S.E.; *Int'l*, pg. 2540
EUROFINS ECCA BTX B.V.—See Eurofins Scientific S.E.; *Int'l*, pg. 2540
EUROFINS ECCA N.V.—See Eurofins Scientific S.E.; *Int'l*, pg. 2540
EUROFINS ECOSUR SA—See Eurofins Scientific S.E.; *Int'l*, pg. 2540
EUROFINS ECOTOXICOLOGIE FRANCE S.A.S.—See Eurofins Scientific S.E.; *Int'l*, pg. 2540
EUROFINS E&E ETC LIMITED—See Eurofins Scientific S.E.; *Int'l*, pg. 2540

EUROFINS E&E HURSLEY LIMITED—See Eurofins Scientific S.E.; *Int'l*, pg. 2540
EUROFINS E&E TAIWAN, LTD.—See Eurofins Scientific S.E.; *Int'l*, pg. 2540
EUROFINS EICHROM RADIOACTIVITE SAS—See Eurofins Scientific S.E.; *Int'l*, pg. 2540
EUROFINS ELECTRICAL & ELECTRONICS FRANCE S.A.S.—See Eurofins Scientific S.E.; *Int'l*, pg. 2540
EUROFINS ELECTRICAL TESTING SERVICE (SHENZHEN) CO., LTD.—See Eurofins Scientific S.E.; *Int'l*, pg. 2540
EUROFINS ELECTRIC & ELECTRONIC PRODUCT TESTING AG—See Eurofins Scientific S.E.; *Int'l*, pg. 2540
EUROFINS ELS LIMITED—See Eurofins Scientific S.E.; *Int'l*, pg. 2540
EUROFINS ENVIRON-LAB S.R.L.—See Eurofins Scientific S.E.; *Int'l*, pg. 2540
EUROFINS ENVIRONMENT TESTING AUSTRALIA PTY LTD—See Eurofins Scientific S.E.; *Int'l*, pg. 2540
EUROFINS ENVIRONMENT TESTING ESTONIA OU—See Eurofins Scientific S.E.; *Int'l*, pg. 2540
EUROFINS ENVIRONMENT TESTING FINLAND OY—See Eurofins Scientific S.E.; *Int'l*, pg. 2540
EUROFINS ENVIRONMENT TESTING IRELAND LIMITED—See Eurofins Scientific S.E.; *Int'l*, pg. 2540
EUROFINS ENVIRONMENT TESTING ITALY SRL—See Eurofins Scientific S.E.; *Int'l*, pg. 2548
EUROFINS ENVIRONMENT TESTING NORWAY AS—See Eurofins Scientific S.E.; *Int'l*, pg. 2540
EUROFINS ENVIRONMENT TESTING NZ LIMITED—See Eurofins Scientific S.E.; *Int'l*, pg. 2540
EUROFINS ENVIRONMENT TESTING SOUTHEAST, LLC—See Eurofins Scientific S.E.; *Int'l*, pg. 2540
EUROFINS ENVIRONMENT TESTING SWEDEN AB—See Eurofins Scientific S.E.; *Int'l*, pg. 2541
EUROFINS ENVIRONNEMENT FORMATION ET CONSEIL S.A.S.—See Eurofins Scientific S.E.; *Int'l*, pg. 2541
EUROFINS ENVIRONNEMENT & SANTE SAS—See Eurofins Scientific S.E.; *Int'l*, pg. 2542
EUROFINS ENVIRONNEMENT SAS—See Eurofins Scientific S.E.; *Int'l*, pg. 2542
EUROFINS EURACETA N.V.—See Eurofins Scientific S.E.; *Int'l*, pg. 2541
EUROFINS EVIC PRODUCT TESTING FRANCE SAS—See Eurofins Scientific S.E.; *Int'l*, pg. 2541
EUROFINS EVIC PRODUCT TESTING ROMANIA SRL—See Eurofins Scientific S.E.; *Int'l*, pg. 2541
EUROFINS EXPERTISE MICROBIOLOGIQUE FRANCE SAS—See Eurofins Scientific S.E.; *Int'l*, pg. 2541
EUROFINS EXPERTISES ENVIRONNEMENTALES SAS—See Eurofins Scientific S.E.; *Int'l*, pg. 2541
EUROFINS EXPERT SERVICES OY—See Eurofins Scientific S.E.; *Int'l*, pg. 2541
EUROFINS FINTELMANN UND MEYER GMP GMBH—See Eurofins Scientific S.E.; *Int'l*, pg. 2541
EUROFINS FOOD & AGRO TESTING SWEDEN AB—See Eurofins Scientific S.E.; *Int'l*, pg. 2541
EUROFINS FOOD ANALYTICA KFT.—See Eurofins Scientific S.E.; *Int'l*, pg. 2541
EUROFINS FOOD ASSURANCE CERTIFICATION US, LLC—See Eurofins Scientific S.E.; *Int'l*, pg. 2541
EUROFINS FOOD ASSURANCE ITALIA SRL—See Eurofins Scientific S.E.; *Int'l*, pg. 2541
EUROFINS FOOD ASSURANCE US, LLC—See Eurofins Scientific S.E.; *Int'l*, pg. 2541
EUROFINS FOOD CHEMISTRY TESTING DES MOINES, INC.—See Eurofins Scientific S.E.; *Int'l*, pg. 2541
EUROFINS FOOD CHEMISTRY TESTING MADISON, INC.—See Eurofins Scientific S.E.; *Int'l*, pg. 2541
EUROFINS FOOD & FEED TESTING NORWAY AS—See Eurofins Scientific S.E.; *Int'l*, pg. 2541
EUROFINS FOOD & FEED TESTING SWEDEN AB—See Eurofins Scientific S.E.; *Int'l*, pg. 2541
EUROFINS FOOD GMBH—See Eurofins Scientific S.E.; *Int'l*, pg. 2541
EUROFINS FOOD INTEGRITY CONTROL SERVICES GMBH—See Eurofins Scientific S.E.; *Int'l*, pg. 2541
EUROFINS FOOD INTEGRITY TESTING UK LIMITED—See Eurofins Scientific S.E.; *Int'l*, pg. 2541
EUROFINS FOOD NETHERLANDS BV—See Eurofins Scientific S.E.; *Int'l*, pg. 2541
EUROFINS FOOD & PRODUCT TESTING JAPAN KK—See Eurofins Scientific S.E.; *Int'l*, pg. 2541
EUROFINS FOOD SAFETY SOLUTIONS BV—See Eurofins Scientific S.E.; *Int'l*, pg. 2541
EUROFINS FOOD SAFETY SOLUTIONS LIMITED—See Eurofins Scientific S.E.; *Int'l*, pg. 2541
EUROFINS FOOD TESTING BELGIUM NV—See Eurofins Scientific S.E.; *Int'l*, pg. 2541
EUROFINS FOOD TESTING IRELAND LIMITED—See Eurofins Scientific S.E.; *Int'l*, pg. 2541
EUROFINS FOOD TESTING JAPAN KK LTD.—See Eurofins Scientific S.E.; *Int'l*, pg. 2541
EUROFINS FOOD TESTING LISBOA, UNIPESSOAL, LTDA.—See Eurofins Scientific S.E.; *Int'l*, pg. 2541
EUROFINS FOOD TESTING SERVICE (DALIAN) CO., LTD.—See Eurofins Scientific S.E.; *Int'l*, pg. 2541
EUROFINS FOOD TESTING SINGAPORE PTE. LTD.—See Eurofins Scientific S.E.; *Int'l*, pg. 2541

EUROFINS FOOD TESTING SLOVAKIA S.R.O.—See Eurofins Scientific S.E.; *Int'l*, pg. 2541
EUROFINS FOOD TESTING SRL—See Eurofins Scientific S.E.; *Int'l*, pg. 2541
EUROFINS FOOD TESTING TAIWAN, LTD.—See Eurofins Scientific S.E.; *Int'l*, pg. 2541
EUROFINS FOOD TESTING THAILAND CO. LTD.—See Eurofins Scientific S.E.; *Int'l*, pg. 2541
EUROFINS FOOD TESTING UK LIMITED—See Eurofins Scientific S.E.; *Int'l*, pg. 2542
EUROFINS FORENSICS BELGIUM - BRUGGE—See Eurofins Scientific S.E.; *Int'l*, pg. 2542
EUROFINS FORENSIC SERVICES LIMITED—See Eurofins Scientific S.E.; *Int'l*, pg. 2542
EUROFINS FQL LTD.—See Eurofins Scientific S.E.; *Int'l*, pg. 2541
EUROFINS GALYS SAS—See Eurofins Scientific S.E.; *Int'l*, pg. 2543
EUROFINS GENESCAN GMBH—See Eurofins Scientific S.E.; *Int'l*, pg. 2543
EUROFINS GENESCAN TECHNOLOGIES GMBH—See Eurofins Scientific S.E.; *Int'l*, pg. 2543
EUROFINS GENESCAN USA INC.—See Eurofins Scientific S.E.; *Int'l*, pg. 2543
EUROFINS GENOMA GROUP SRL—See Eurofins Scientific S.E.; *Int'l*, pg. 2543
EUROFINS GENOME VALLEY HYDERABAD RESOURCES PRIVATE LIMITED—See Eurofins Scientific S.E.; *Int'l*, pg. 2543
EUROFINS GENOMICS AUSTRIA GMBH—See Eurofins Scientific S.E.; *Int'l*, pg. 2543
EUROFINS GENOMICS EUROPE GENOTYPING A/S—See Eurofins Scientific S.E.; *Int'l*, pg. 2543
EUROFINS GENOMICS EUROPE PHARMA & DIAGNOSTICS PRODUCTS & SERVICES SANGER/PCR GMBH—See Eurofins Scientific S.E.; *Int'l*, pg. 2543
EUROFINS GENOMICS EUROPE SEQUENCING GMBH—See Eurofins Scientific S.E.; *Int'l*, pg. 2543
EUROFINS GENOMICS FRANCE S.A.S.—See Eurofins Scientific S.E.; *Int'l*, pg. 2543
EUROFINS GENOMICS INC.—See Eurofins Scientific S.E.; *Int'l*, pg. 2539
EUROFINS GENOMICS KK—See Eurofins Scientific S.E.; *Int'l*, pg. 2543
EUROFINS GENOMICS SWEDEN AB—See Eurofins Scientific S.E.; *Int'l*, pg. 2543
EUROFINS GENOMICS UK LIMITED—See Eurofins Scientific S.E.; *Int'l*, pg. 2543
EUROFINS GFA LAB SERVICE GMBH—See Eurofins Scientific S.E.; *Int'l*, pg. 2548
EUROFINS GLOBAL CENTRAL LABORATORY—See Eurofins Scientific S.E.; *Int'l*, pg. 2543
EUROFINS GLOBAL CONTROL GMBH—See Eurofins Scientific S.E.; *Int'l*, pg. 2541
EUROFINS GSC LUX SARL—See Eurofins Scientific S.E.; *Int'l*, pg. 2544
EUROFINS HT-ANALYTIK GMBH—See Eurofins Scientific S.E.; *Int'l*, pg. 2543
EUROFINS HYDROBIOLOGIE FRANCE S.A.S.—See Eurofins Scientific S.E.; *Int'l*, pg. 2544
EUROFINS HYDROLOGIE CENTRE EST SAS—See Eurofins Scientific S.E.; *Int'l*, pg. 2544
EUROFINS HYDROLOGIE EST SAS—See Eurofins Scientific S.E.; *Int'l*, pg. 2544
EUROFINS HYDROLOGIE ILE DE FRANCE SAS—See Eurofins Scientific S.E.; *Int'l*, pg. 2544
EUROFINS HYDROLOGIE NORD SAS—See Eurofins Scientific S.E.; *Int'l*, pg. 2544
EUROFINS HYDROLOGIE NORMANDIE SAS—See Eurofins Scientific S.E.; *Int'l*, pg. 2544
EUROFINS HYDROLOGIE OUEST SAS—See Eurofins Scientific S.E.; *Int'l*, pg. 2544
EUROFINS HYDROLOGIE SUD OUEST SAS—See Eurofins Scientific S.E.; *Int'l*, pg. 2544
EUROFINS HYDROLOGIE SUD SAS—See Eurofins Scientific S.E.; *Int'l*, pg. 2544
EUROFINS HYGIENE ALIMENTAIRE ILE-DE-FRANCE SAS—See Eurofins Scientific S.E.; *Int'l*, pg. 2544
EUROFINS HYGIENE ALIMENTAIRE NORD-EST SAS—See Eurofins Scientific S.E.; *Int'l*, pg. 2544
EUROFINS HYGIENE ALIMENTAIRE NORD-OUEST SAS—See Eurofins Scientific S.E.; *Int'l*, pg. 2544
EUROFINS HYGIENE ALIMENTAIRE SAS—See Eurofins Scientific S.E.; *Int'l*, pg. 2544
EUROFINS HYGIENE ALIMENTAIRE SUD-OUEST SAS—See Eurofins Scientific S.E.; *Int'l*, pg. 2544
EUROFINS HYGIENE DES LIEUX DE TRAVAIL SAS—See Eurofins Scientific S.E.; *Int'l*, pg. 2542
EUROFINS HYGIENE HOSPITALIERE NORD S.A.S.—See Eurofins Scientific S.E.; *Int'l*, pg. 2544
EUROFINS HYGIENE HOSPITALIERE OUEST S.A.S.—See Eurofins Scientific S.E.; *Int'l*, pg. 2544
EUROFINS HYGIENE HOSPITALIERE SUD SAS—See Eurofins Scientific S.E.; *Int'l*, pg. 2544
EUROFINS HYGIENE INSTITUT BERG GMBH—See Eurofins Scientific S.E.; *Int'l*, pg. 2544

541380 — TESTING LABORATORIE...

EUROFINS IDMYK SAS—See Eurofins Scientific S.E.; *Int'l*, pg. 2544
EUROFINS INDUSTRIAL TESTING LUX SARL—See Eurofins Scientific S.E.; *Int'l*, pg. 2544
EUROFINS INLAB GMBH—See Eurofins Scientific S.E.; *Int'l*, pg. 2544
EUROFINS INSTITUT DR. APPELT LEIPZIG GMBH—See Eurofins Scientific S.E.; *Int'l*, pg. 2544
EUROFINS INSTITUT DR. ROTHE GMBH—See Eurofins Scientific S.E.; *Int'l*, pg. 2544
EUROFINS INSTITUT JAGER GMBH—See Eurofins Scientific S.E.; *Int'l*, pg. 2544
EUROFINS INSTITUT NEHRING GMBH—See Eurofins Scientific S.E.; *Int'l*, pg. 2544
EUROFINS INTERLAB SELAS S.A.S—See Eurofins Scientific S.E.; *Int'l*, pg. 2544
EUROFINS IPL ILE DE FRANCE SAS—See Eurofins Scientific S.E.; *Int'l*, pg. 2542
EUROFINS IPL SUD SAS—See Eurofins Scientific S.E.; *Int'l*, pg. 2542
EUROFINS IT SOLUTIONS INDIA PVT LTD—See Eurofins Scientific S.E.; *Int'l*, pg. 2544
EUROFINS IZMIR GIDA ANALIZ LABORATUVARLARI LIMITED SIRKETI—See Eurofins Scientific S.E.; *Int'l*, pg. 2544
EUROFINS J3 RESOURCES, INC.—See Eurofins Scientific S.E.; *Int'l*, pg. 2544
EUROFINS JAPAN ANALYTICAL CHEMISTRY CONSULTANTS CO., LTD.—See Eurofins Scientific S.E.; *Int'l*, pg. 2544
EUROFINS JAPAN KK—See Eurofins Scientific S.E.; *Int'l*, pg. 2544
EUROFINS KOREA ANALYTIC SERVICE CO., LTD.—See Eurofins Scientific S.E.; *Int'l*, pg. 2544
EUROFINS KVI-PLUSZ KORNYEZETVEDELMI VIZSGALO IRODA KFT.—See Eurofins Scientific S.E.; *Int'l*, pg. 2544
EUROFINS LABAZUR BRETAGNE SELAS—See Eurofins Scientific S.E.; *Int'l*, pg. 2545
EUROFINS LABAZUR PROVENCE SELAS—See Eurofins Scientific S.E.; *Int'l*, pg. 2545
EUROFINS LABAZUR RHONE-ALPES SELAS—See Eurofins Scientific S.E.; *Int'l*, pg. 2545
EUROFINS LAB ENVIRONMENT TESTING PORTUGAL, UNIPESSOAL LDA.—See Eurofins Scientific S.E.; *Int'l*, pg. 2545
EUROFINS LABORATOIRE CENTRE SAS—See Eurofins Scientific S.E.; *Int'l*, pg. 2542
EUROFINS LABORATOIRE CONTAMINANTS SUD SAS—See Eurofins Scientific S.E.; *Int'l*, pg. 2545
EUROFINS LABORATOIRE DE BROMATOLOGIE OUEST ET BRETAGNE SAS—See Eurofins Scientific S.E.; *Int'l*, pg. 2545
EUROFINS LABORATOIRE DE MICROBIOLOGIE EST SAS—See Eurofins Scientific S.E.; *Int'l*, pg. 2542
EUROFINS LABORATOIRE DE MICROBIOLOGIE SUD SAS—See Eurofins Scientific S.E.; *Int'l*, pg. 2545
EUROFINS LABORATOIRE DE PATHOLOGIE VEGETALE SAS—See Eurofins Scientific S.E.; *Int'l*, pg. 2545
EUROFINS LABORATOIRE DERMSCAN SAS—See Eurofins Scientific S.E.; *Int'l*, pg. 2545
EUROFINS LABORATOIRE MICROBIOLOGIE RHONE-ALPES S.A.S.—See Eurofins Scientific S.E.; *Int'l*, pg. 2545
EUROFINS LABORATOIRE NORD SAS—See Eurofins Scientific S.E.; *Int'l*, pg. 2542
EUROFINS LABORATOIRES DE MICROBIOLOGIE OUEST SAS—See Eurofins Scientific S.E.; *Int'l*, pg. 2542
EUROFINS LABORATORIO ALFALAB INTERNACIONAL, SL—See Eurofins Scientific S.E.; *Int'l*, pg. 2545
EUROFINS LABORATORIO ANGEL MENDEZ, SL—See Eurofins Scientific S.E.; *Int'l*, pg. 2545
EUROFINS LABORATORIO BERNAD-MUNOZ, SL—See Eurofins Scientific S.E.; *Int'l*, pg. 2545
EUROFINS LABORATORIO CALBO, SL—See Eurofins Scientific S.E.; *Int'l*, pg. 2545
EUROFINS LABORATORIO CLINICO SANITARIO, SL—See Eurofins Scientific S.E.; *Int'l*, pg. 2545
EUROFINS LABORATORIO DRES. CERMENO, SL—See Eurofins Scientific S.E.; *Int'l*, pg. 2545
EUROFINS LABORATORIO DR. VALENZUELA, SL—See Eurofins Scientific S.E.; *Int'l*, pg. 2545
EUROFINS LABORATORIO PILAR LARRAZ, SL—See Eurofins Scientific S.E.; *Int'l*, pg. 2545
EUROFINS LABORATORIO RECIO, SL—See Eurofins Scientific S.E.; *Int'l*, pg. 2545
EUROFINS LABORATORIO SARRO SL—See Eurofins Scientific S.E.; *Int'l*, pg. 2545
EUROFINS LABORATORIO SURLAB, SL—See Eurofins Scientific S.E.; *Int'l*, pg. 2545
EUROFINS LABORATORIO VIRTUDES SL—See Eurofins Scientific S.E.; *Int'l*, pg. 2545
EUROFINS LABORSERVICES GMBH—See Eurofins Scientific S.E.; *Int'l*, pg. 2545
EUROFINS LABO VAN POUCKE BVBA—See Eurofins Scientific S.E.; *Int'l*, pg. 2545
EUROFINS LAB SOLUTION SRL—See Eurofins Scientific S.E.; *Int'l*, pg. 2545
EUROFINS LABTARNA LIETUVA UAB—See Eurofins Scientific S.E.; *Int'l*, pg. 2545
EUROFINS LABTIUM OY—See Eurofins Scientific S.E.; *Int'l*, pg. 2545
EUROFINS LAB ZEEUWS-VLAANDEREN (LZV) BV—See Eurofins Scientific S.E.; *Int'l*, pg. 2545
EUROFINS LANAGRAM SAS—See Eurofins Scientific S.E.; *Int'l*, pg. 2545
EUROFINS LANCASTER LABORATORIES, INC. PORTAGE—See Eurofins Scientific S.E.; *Int'l*, pg. 2548
EUROFINS LARA SA—See Eurofins Scientific S.E.; *Int'l*, pg. 2542
EUROFINS LCDI SAS—See Eurofins Scientific S.E.; *Int'l*, pg. 2544
EUROFINS LCPL BV—See Eurofins Scientific S.E.; *Int'l*, pg. 2545
EUROFINS LEA SAS—See Eurofins Scientific S.E.; *Int'l*, pg. 2545
EUROFINS MAS CONTROL SLU—See Eurofins Scientific S.E.; *Int'l*, pg. 2545
EUROFINS MECHEM PTE. LTD.—See Eurofins Scientific S.E.; *Int'l*, pg. 2545
EUROFINS MEDIGENOMIX FORENSIK GMBH—See Eurofins Scientific S.E.; *Int'l*, pg. 2546
EUROFINS MEDINET PTE. LTD.—See Eurofins Scientific S.E.; *Int'l*, pg. 2546
EUROFINS MEDISCAN LABORATORIES SDN. BHD.—See Eurofins Scientific S.E.; *Int'l*, pg. 2546
EUROFINS METODOS SERVICIOS AGRICOLAS, S.L.U.—See Eurofins Scientific S.E.; *Int'l*, pg. 2546
EUROFINS MGS LABORATORIES LIMITED—See Eurofins Scientific S.E.; *Int'l*, pg. 2545
EUROFINS MICROBIOLOGIE DES EAUX OUEST SAS—See Eurofins Scientific S.E.; *Int'l*, pg. 2546
EUROFINS MICROBIOLOGY LABORATORIES INC.—See Eurofins Scientific S.E.; *Int'l*, pg. 2546
EUROFINS MICROSCAN S.A.—See Eurofins Scientific S.E.; *Int'l*, pg. 2546
EUROFINS MIKRO KEMI AB—See Eurofins Scientific S.E.; *Int'l*, pg. 2546
EUROFINS MILJO (GALTEN)—See Eurofins Scientific S.E.; *Int'l*, pg. 2546
EUROFINS MILK TESTING DENMARK A/S—See Eurofins Scientific S.E.; *Int'l*, pg. 2546
EUROFINS MILK TESTING SWEDEN AB—See Eurofins Scientific S.E.; *Int'l*, pg. 2546
EUROFINS MINERAG KFT.—See Eurofins Scientific S.E.; *Int'l*, pg. 2546
EUROFINS MITOX BV—See Eurofins Scientific S.E.; *Int'l*, pg. 2546
EUROFINS MODERN TESTING SERVICE TAIWAN, LTD.—See Eurofins Scientific S.E.; *Int'l*, pg. 2546
EUROFINS MODULO UNO SPA—See Eurofins Scientific S.E.; *Int'l*, pg. 2548
EUROFINS MTS CONSUMER PRODUCT TESTING CAMBODIA LTD.—See Eurofins Scientific S.E.; *Int'l*, pg. 2545
EUROFINS MTS CONSUMER PRODUCT TESTING GERMANY GMBH—See Eurofins Scientific S.E.; *Int'l*, pg. 2545
EUROFINS MTS CONSUMER PRODUCT TESTING (SHANGHAI) CO., LTD.—See Eurofins Scientific S.E.; *Int'l*, pg. 2545
EUROFINS MTS CONSUMER PRODUCT TESTING UK LIMITED—See Eurofins Scientific S.E.; *Int'l*, pg. 2545
EUROFINS MWG BIOTECH FRANCE S.A.—See Eurofins Scientific S.E.; *Int'l*, pg. 2543
EUROFINS MWG GMBH—See Eurofins Scientific S.E.; *Int'l*, pg. 2551
EUROFINS MWG OPERON INC.—See Eurofins Scientific S.E.; *Int'l*, pg. 2548
EUROFINS NAB LABS OY—See Eurofins Scientific S.E.; *Int'l*, pg. 2546
EUROFINS NDSC FOOD FRANCE SAS—See Eurofins Scientific S.E.; *Int'l*, pg. 2543
EUROFINS NDSC FOOD TESTING GERMANY GMBH—See Eurofins Scientific S.E.; *Int'l*, pg. 2546
EUROFINS NDSC UMWELTANALYTIK GMBH—See Eurofins Scientific S.E.; *Int'l*, pg. 2546
EUROFINS NDSM LIMITED—See Eurofins Scientific S.E.; *Int'l*, pg. 2546
EUROFINS NM LABORATORY SDN BHD—See Eurofins Scientific S.E.; *Int'l*, pg. 2546
EUROFINS NORSK MATANALYSE AS—See Eurofins Scientific S.E.; *Int'l*, pg. 2546
EUROFINS NORSK MILJOANALYSE AS—See Eurofins Scientific S.E.; *Int'l*, pg. 2546
EUROFINS NORTH MALAYA LABORATORY SDN BHD—See Eurofins Scientific S.E.; *Int'l*, pg. 2546
EUROFINS NSC NETHERLANDS BV—See Eurofins Scientific S.E.; *Int'l*, pg. 2546
EUROFINS NSC UK & IRELAND LTD—See Eurofins Scientific S.E.; *Int'l*, pg. 2546
EUROFINS NTD, INC.—See Eurofins Scientific S.E.; *Int'l*, pg. 2546
EUROFINS OBIKS POLSKA SP. Z.O.O.—See Eurofins Scientific S.E.; *Int'l*, pg. 2546
EUROFINS - OFI LEBENSMITTELANALYTIK GMBH—See Eurofins Scientific S.E.; *Int'l*, pg. 2536
EUROFINS OKOLABOR KFT.—See Eurofins Scientific S.E.; *Int'l*, pg. 2546
EUROFINS OMEGAM BV—See Eurofins Scientific S.E.; *Int'l*, pg. 2546
EUROFINS OPTIMED SAS—See Eurofins Scientific S.E.; *Int'l*, pg. 2543
EUROFINS PANLABS DISCOVERY SERVICES TAIWAN, LTD.—See Eurofins Scientific S.E.; *Int'l*, pg. 2546
EUROFINS PATHOLOGIE SELAS—See Eurofins Scientific S.E.; *Int'l*, pg. 2547
EUROFINS PEGASUSLAB AB—See Eurofins Scientific S.E.; *Int'l*, pg. 2547
EUROFINS PHARMA CONTROL SAS—See Eurofins Scientific S.E.; *Int'l*, pg. 2543
EUROFINS PHARMA QUALITY CONTROL SAS—See Eurofins Scientific S.E.; *Int'l*, pg. 2543
EUROFINS PHARMA SERVICES INDIA PVT LTD—See Eurofins Scientific S.E.; *Int'l*, pg. 2547
EUROFINS PHAST DEVELOPMENT GMBH & CO. KG—See Eurofins Scientific S.E.; *Int'l*, pg. 2546
EUROFINS PIVETTI SRL—See Eurofins Scientific S.E.; *Int'l*, pg. 2547
EUROFINS POLSKA SP. Z.O.O.—See Eurofins Scientific S.E.; *Int'l*, pg. 2547
EUROFINS PRELEVEMENT POUR LE BATIMENT EST SAS—See Eurofins Scientific S.E.; *Int'l*, pg. 2547
EUROFINS PRELEVEMENT POUR LE BATIMENT FRANCE SAS—See Eurofins Scientific S.E.; *Int'l*, pg. 2550
EUROFINS PRELEVEMENT POUR LE BATIMENT ILE-DE-FRANCE SAS—See Eurofins Scientific S.E.; *Int'l*, pg. 2547
EUROFINS PRELEVEMENT POUR LE BATIMENT NORD SAS—See Eurofins Scientific S.E.; *Int'l*, pg. 2550
EUROFINS PRELEVEMENT POUR LE BATIMENT OUEST SAS—See Eurofins Scientific S.E.; *Int'l*, pg. 2550
EUROFINS PRELEVEMENT POUR LE BATIMENT SUD-EST SAS—See Eurofins Scientific S.E.; *Int'l*, pg. 2550
EUROFINS PRELEVEMENT POUR LE BATIMENT SUD-OUEST SAS—See Eurofins Scientific S.E.; *Int'l*, pg. 2547
EUROFINS PRODUCT SAFETY LABS INC.—See Eurofins Scientific S.E.; *Int'l*, pg. 2548
EUROFINS PRODUCT SERVICE GMBH—See Eurofins Scientific S.E.; *Int'l*, pg. 2547
EUROFINS PRODUCT SERVICE (THAILAND) CO., LTD—See Eurofins Scientific S.E.; *Int'l*, pg. 2547
EUROFINS PRODUCT TESTING DENMARK A/S—See Eurofins Scientific S.E.; *Int'l*, pg. 2547
EUROFINS PRODUCT TESTING INDIA PVT LTD—See Eurofins Scientific S.E.; *Int'l*, pg. 2547
EUROFINS PRODUCT TESTING ITALY SRL—See Eurofins Scientific S.E.; *Int'l*, pg. 2547
EUROFINS PRODUCT TESTING JAPAN KK—See Eurofins Scientific S.E.; *Int'l*, pg. 2547
EUROFINS PRODUCT TESTING SERVICE (SHANGHAI) CO., LTD—See Eurofins Scientific S.E.; *Int'l*, pg. 2547
EUROFINS PRODUCT TESTING SERVICES LTD—See Eurofins Scientific S.E.; *Int'l*, pg. 2547
EUROFINS PRODUCT TESTING US INC.—See Eurofins Scientific S.E.; *Int'l*, pg. 2547
EUROFINS PRODUCT TESTING VERWALTUNGS GMBH—See Eurofins Scientific S.E.; *Int'l*, pg. 2547
EUROFINS PROFESSIONAL SCIENTIFIC SERVICES BELGIUM NV—See Eurofins Scientific S.E.; *Int'l*, pg. 2547
EUROFINS PROMICRO PTY LTD.—See Eurofins Scientific S.E.; *Int'l*, pg. 2547
EUROFINS Q-BIOANALYTIC GMBH—See Eurofins Scientific S.E.; *Int'l*, pg. 2547
EUROFINS QTA INC.—See Eurofins Scientific S.E.; *Int'l*, pg. 2547
EUROFINS QUALITECH AG—See Eurofins Scientific S.E.; *Int'l*, pg. 2547
EUROFINS RADONLAB AS—See Eurofins Scientific S.E.; *Int'l*, pg. 2547
EUROFINS RADON TESTING SWEDEN AB—See Eurofins Scientific S.E.; *Int'l*, pg. 2547
EUROFINS REGULATORY AG—See Eurofins Scientific S.E.; *Int'l*, pg. 2547
EUROFINS SAC KY HAI DANG COMPANY LTD.—See Eurofins Scientific S.E.; *Int'l*, pg. 2547
EUROFINS SAM SENSORY & MARKETING ITALY SRL—See Eurofins Scientific S.E.; *Int'l*, pg. 2547
EUROFINS SANITAS INSPECTIONS BV—See Eurofins Scientific S.E.; *Int'l*, pg. 2547
EUROFINS SCIENTIFIC BIOSCIENCES SAS—See Eurofins Scientific S.E.; *Int'l*, pg. 2543
EUROFINS SCIENTIFIC BV—See Eurofins Scientific S.E.; *Int'l*, pg. 2547
EUROFINS SCIENTIFIC CZ S.R.O.—See Eurofins Scientific S.E.; *Int'l*, pg. 2548
EUROFINS SCIENTIFIC FINLAND OY—See Eurofins Scientific S.E.; *Int'l*, pg. 2548
EUROFINS SCIENTIFIC GMBH—See Eurofins Scientific S.E.; *Int'l*, pg. 2548
EUROFINS SCIENTIFIC (IRELAND) LIMITED—See Eurofins Scientific S.E.; *Int'l*, pg. 2547

541380 — TESTING LABORATORIE...

EUROFINS SCIENTIFIC ITALIA SRL—See Eurofins Scientific S.E.; *Int'l*, pg. 2548
EUROFINS SCIENTIFIC SERVICES S.A.—See Eurofins Scientific S.E.; *Int'l*, pg. 2548
EUROFINS SCIENTIFIC TEST CENTER SAS—See Eurofins Scientific S.E.; *Int'l*, pg. 2543
EUROFINS SCITEC S.A.—See Eurofins Scientific S.E.; *Int'l*, pg. 2548
EUROFINS SENSORY CONSUMER & PRODUCT RESEARCH (SHANGHAI), LTD.—See Eurofins Scientific S.E.; *Int'l*, pg. 2548
EUROFINS SF ANALYTICAL LABORATORIES, INC.—See Eurofins Scientific S.E.; *Int'l*, pg. 2548
EUROFINS SICA AGRIQ SL—See Eurofins Scientific S.E.; *Int'l*, pg. 2548
EUROFINS SISTHEMA S.R.L.—See Eurofins Scientific S.E.; *Int'l*, pg. 2548
EUROFINS SOFIA GMBH—See Eurofins Scientific S.E.; *Int'l*, pg. 2547
EUROFINS SPECTRUM ANALYTICAL, LLC—See Eurofins Scientific S.E.; *Int'l*, pg. 2548
EUROFINS SPINNOVATION ANALYTICAL BV—See Eurofins Scientific S.E.; *Int'l*, pg. 2548
EUROFINS STEINS LABORATORIUM A/S—See Eurofins Scientific S.E.; *Int'l*, pg. 2541
EUROFINS STEINS LABORATORIUM SP. Z.O.O.—See Eurofins Scientific S.E.; *Int'l*, pg. 2540
EUROFINS SUMMIT TSIANDE ENVIRONMENTAL CO., LTD.—See Eurofins Scientific S.E.; *Int'l*, pg. 2548
EUROFINS TAIYO TECHNO RESEARCH KK—See Eurofins Scientific S.E.; *Int'l*, pg. 2548
EUROFINS TECHNOLOGIES AUSTRALIA PTY LTD—See Eurofins Scientific S.E.; *Int'l*, pg. 2549
EUROFINS TECHNOLOGY SERVICE (GUANGZHOU) CO., LTD.—See Eurofins Scientific S.E.; *Int'l*, pg. 2549
EUROFINS TECHNOLOGY SERVICE (QINGDAO) CO., LTD.—See Eurofins Scientific S.E.; *Int'l*, pg. 2549
EUROFINS TECHNOLOGY SERVICES (SUZHOU) CO., LTD—See Eurofins Scientific S.E.; *Int'l*, pg. 2549
EUROFINS TEST CENTER SAS—See Eurofins Scientific S.E.; *Int'l*, pg. 2543
EUROFINS TESTING CHILE S.A.—See Eurofins Scientific S.E.; *Int'l*, pg. 2549
EUROFINS TESTING INSPECTION CERTIFICATION (CHENGDU) CO., LTD.—See Eurofins Scientific S.E.; *Int'l*, pg. 2549
EUROFINS TESTING INSPECTION CERTIFICATION (XIAMEN) CO., LTD.—See Eurofins Scientific S.E.; *Int'l*, pg. 2549
EUROFINS TESTING TECHNOLOGY (SHENZHEN) CO., LTD—See Eurofins Scientific S.E.; *Int'l*, pg. 2549
EUROFINS TESTIRANJA IN RAZISKAVE OKOLJA SLOVENIJA D.O.O.—See Eurofins Scientific S.E.; *Int'l*, pg. 2550
EUROFINS TESTOIL, INC.—See Eurofins Scientific S.E.; *Int'l*, pg. 2549
EUROFINS TEXTILE TESTING SPAIN SL—See Eurofins Scientific S.E.; *Int'l*, pg. 2549
EUROFINS TRIALCAMP, S.L.U.—See Eurofins Scientific S.E.; *Int'l*, pg. 2549
EUROFINS TSING HUA ENVIRONMENT TESTING CO., LTD.—See Eurofins Scientific S.E.; *Int'l*, pg. 2549
EUROFINS TUKETICI URUNLERI TEST HIZMETLERI A.S.—See Eurofins Scientific S.E.; *Int'l*, pg. 2549
EUROFINS TURKEY ANALIZ HIZMETLERI LIMITED SIRKETI—See Eurofins Scientific S.E.; *Int'l*, pg. 2549
EUROFINS UMWELT WEST GMBH—See Eurofins Scientific S.E.; *Int'l*, pg. 2537
EUROFINS VBM LABORATORIET A/S—See Eurofins Scientific S.E.; *Int'l*, pg. 2549
EUROFINS VETCONTROL KFT.—See Eurofins Scientific S.E.; *Int'l*, pg. 2549
EUROFINS VILJAVUUSPALVELU OY—See Eurofins Scientific S.E.; *Int'l*, pg. 2549
EUROFINS VILLAPHARMA RESEARCH SL—See Eurofins Scientific S.E.; *Int'l*, pg. 2549
EUROFINS WATER TESTING SWEDEN AB—See Eurofins Scientific S.E.; *Int'l*, pg. 2550
EUROFINS WATER&WASTE GMBH—See Eurofins Scientific S.E.; *Int'l*, pg. 2550
EUROFINS WEJ CONTAMINANTS GMBH—See Eurofins Scientific S.E.; *Int'l*, pg. 2549
EUROFINS WFC ANALYTICS B.V.—See Eurofins Scientific S.E.; *Int'l*, pg. 2549
EUROFINS WFC-FOOD SAFETY B.V.—See Eurofins Scientific S.E.; *Int'l*, pg. 2549
EUROFINS WKS LABSERVICE GMBH—See Eurofins Scientific S.E.; *Int'l*, pg. 2549
EUROFINS WOOSOL CO., LTD.—See Eurofins Scientific S.E.; *Int'l*, pg. 2550
EUROFINS YORK LIMITED—See Eurofins Scientific S.E.; *Int'l*, pg. 2550
EVANS ANALYTICAL GROUP, INC.—See Eurofins Scientific S.E.; *Int'l*, pg. 2549
EXPERTOX INC—See Cytogen Co., Ltd; *Int'l*, pg. 1897
FENGRAIN LTD.; *Int'l*, pg. 2634
FIELD SERVICES, INC.—See The Shaw Group Inc.; *U.S. Private*, pg. 4117
FIRMENICH DIS TIC. LTD. STI—See Firmenich International SA; *Int'l*, pg. 2680
FLUID TECHNOLOGIES, INC.—See Madison Industries Holdings LLC; *U.S. Private*, pg. 2543
FLUROTECH LTD.; *Int'l*, pg. 2715
FORMFACTOR BEAVERTON, INC.—See FormFactor, Inc.; *U.S. Public*, pg. 868
FORMULATION TECHNOLOGIES, LLC—See Akela Pharma, Inc.; *U.S. Private*, pg. 144
FREE-COL LABORATORIES—See Modern Industries Inc.; *U.S. Private*, pg. 2761
FRONTIER LABS, INC.—See Greencastle Resources Ltd.; *Int'l*, pg. 3073
FRUTAROM (SWITZERLAND) AG—See International Flavors & Fragrances Inc.; *U.S. Public*, pg. 1152
FRX POLYMERS INC.—See FRX Innovations Inc.; *U.S. Public*, pg. 888
FUGRO CHILE S.A.—See Fugro N.V.; *Int'l*, pg. 2805
FUGRO MOZAMBIQUE LDA.—See Fugro N.V.; *Int'l*, pg. 2806
FUJI ELECTRIC KOREA CO., LTD.—See Fuji Electric Co., Ltd.; *Int'l*, pg. 2811
FUJITSU LABORATORIES OF EUROPE LTD.—See Fujitsu Limited; *Int'l*, pg. 2835
FUJITSU QUALITY LABORATORY (SUZHOU) LTD.—See Fujitsu Limited; *Int'l*, pg. 2835
GALAXY CERTIFICATION SERVICES PRIVATE LIMITED—See EKI Energy Services Limited; *Int'l*, pg. 2338
GALBRAITH LABORATORIES, INC.—See Bureau Veritas S.A.; *Int'l*, pg. 1222
GARDIEN JAPAN CO., LTD.—See ESO Partners L.P.; *Int'l*, pg. 2504
GARDIEN PACIFIC LTD.—See ESO Partners L.P.; *Int'l*, pg. 2504
GARDIEN—See ESO Partners L.P.; *Int'l*, pg. 2504
GATEWAY ANALYTICAL LLC—See AptarGroup, Inc.; *U.S. Public*, pg. 174
GENEDX, INC.—See GeneDx Holdings Corp.; *U.S. Public*, pg. 911
GENISPHERE INC.—See Getinge AB; *Int'l*, pg. 2951
GENOLUX CO., LTD; *Int'l*, pg. 2925
GENON LABORATORIES LIMITED—See Cinven Limited; *Int'l*, pg. 1614
GENOSKAN A/S—See Eurofins Scientific S.E.; *Int'l*, pg. 2550
GEOSPHERE CONSULTANTS, INC.—See GI Manager L.P.; *U.S. Private*, pg. 1691
GFA GMBH—See Eurofins Scientific S.E.; *Int'l*, pg. 2550
GFBB PRUFTECHNIK GMBH & CO. KG—See Buzzi SpA; *Int'l*, pg. 1230
GLAXOSMITHKLINE—See GSK plc; *Int'l*, pg. 3146
GLOBAL BUSINESS SUPPORT SYSTEMS, INC.; *U.S. Private*, pg. 1712
GOLD STANDARD DIAGNOSTICS FREIBURG GMBH—See Eurofins Scientific S.E.; *Int'l*, pg. 2550
GOLD STANDARD DIAGNOSTICS SHANGHAI CO., LTD.—See Eurofins Scientific S.E.; *Int'l*, pg. 2550
GOLD STANDARD DIAGNOSTICS SINGAPORE PTE. LTD.—See Eurofins Scientific S.E.; *Int'l*, pg. 2550
GOLD STANDARD DIAGNOSTICS TRIESTE S.R.L.—See Eurofins Scientific S.E.; *Int'l*, pg. 2550
GROUP DE LABORATOIRE ALS MAIL SARL—See ALS Limited; *Int'l*, pg. 378
GUANGZHOU KINGMED DIAGNOSTICS CENTER CO., LTD.; *Int'l*, pg. 3166
GYNAE-SCREEN LIMITED—See Eurofins Scientific S.E.; *Int'l*, pg. 2550
HANGZHOU HUAAN TESTING TECHNOLOGY CO., LTD.—See Centre Testing International Corporation; *Int'l*, pg. 1411
HCT AMERICA LLC—See HCT Co., Ltd.; *Int'l*, pg. 3299
HEALTH MANAGEMENT CORPORATION OF AMERICA—See FONAR Corporation; *U.S. Public*, pg. 863
HEALTH TESTING CENTERS, INC.—See Laboratory Corporation of America Holdings; *U.S. Public*, pg. 1287
HERON SYSTEMS, INC.—See Shield AI Inc.; *U.S. Private*, pg. 3635
HIADVANCE (KOREA) CO., LTD.—See HiAdvance Inc.; *U.S. Private*, pg. 1932
HIADVANCE PHILIPPINES INC.—See HiAdvance Inc.; *U.S. Private*, pg. 1932
HILL TOP RESEARCH INC.; *U.S. Private*, pg. 1945
HOME HEALTHCARE LABORATORY OF AMERICA, LLC—See Laboratory Corporation of America Holdings; *U.S. Public*, pg. 1287
HORIBA EUROPE GMBH—See HORIBA Ltd; *Int'l*, pg. 3477
HORMEL HEALTHLABS, INC.—See Hormel Foods Corporation; *U.S. Public*, pg. 1054
HOUSE FOOD ANALYTICAL LABORATORY INC.—See House Foods Group Inc.; *Int'l*, pg. 3490
HOWMET RESEARCH CORPORATION—See Howmet Aerospace Inc.; *U.S. Public*, pg. 1061
H&R LUBETECH GMBH—See H&R KGaA; *Int'l*, pg. 3193
HTV GMBH; *Int'l*, pg. 3509
IBETA QUALITY ASSURANCE LLC; *U.S. Private*, pg. 2028
IBS FILTRAN KUNSTOFF-/METALLERZEUGNISSE GMBH—See Madison Industries Holdings LLC; *U.S. Private*, pg. 2543
IDEX HEALTH & SCIENCE LLC—See IDEX Corp; *U.S. Public*, pg. 1090
IDEXX REFERENCE LABORATORIES - DALLAS—See IDEXX Laboratories, Inc.; *U.S. Public*, pg. 1093
IDEXX REFERENCE LABORATORIES - DENVER—See IDEXX Laboratories, Inc.; *U.S. Public*, pg. 1093
IDEXX REFERENCE LABORATORIES - ELMHURST—See IDEXX Laboratories, Inc.; *U.S. Public*, pg. 1093
IDEXX REFERENCE LABORATORIES - IRVINE—See IDEXX Laboratories, Inc.; *U.S. Public*, pg. 1093
IDEXX REFERENCE LABORATORIES - PHOENIX—See IDEXX Laboratories, Inc.; *U.S. Public*, pg. 1093
IDEXX REFERENCE LABORATORIES - SACRAMENTO—See IDEXX Laboratories, Inc.; *U.S. Public*, pg. 1093
IDEXX REFERENCE LABORATORIES - TOTOWA—See IDEXX Laboratories, Inc.; *U.S. Public*, pg. 1093
IDEXX TECHNOLOGIES LIMITED—See IDEXX Laboratories, Inc.; *U.S. Public*, pg. 1093
I-DNA BIOTECHNOLOGY (M) SDN BHD—See BioLASCO Taiwan Co., Ltd.; *Int'l*, pg. 1038
IFB INSTITUT FUR BLUTGRUPPENFORSCHUNG GMBH—See Eurofins Scientific S.E.; *Int'l*, pg. 2550
IHSM B.V.—See Merck & Co., Inc.; *U.S. Public*, pg. 1416
IMR TEST LABS INC.—See Curtiss-Wright Corporation; *U.S. Public*, pg. 612
INDEPENDENT PETROLEUM LABORATORY LIMITED—See Channel Infrastructure NZ Limited; *Int'l*, pg. 1446
INDIANA ENGINEERING AND TEST CENTER—See Resilience Capital Partners, LLC; *U.S. Private*, pg. 3405
INFINITY LABORATORIES INC.—See Eurofins Scientific S.E.; *Int'l*, pg. 2550
INFOGARD LABORATORIES—See Underwriters Laboratories Inc.; *U.S. Private*, pg. 4280
INGRAIN, INC.—See Halliburton Company; *U.S. Public*, pg. 981
INIFY LABORATORIES AB—See Contextvision AB; *Int'l*, pg. 1780
INLAB GMBH INSTITUT FUR LEBENSMITTELMIKROBIOLOGIE—See Eurofins Scientific S.E.; *Int'l*, pg. 2550
INNOLAB DO BRASIL LTDA.—See Eurofins Scientific S.E.; *Int'l*, pg. 2550
INSTITUT DR. APPELT HILTER GMBH & CO. KG—See Eurofins Scientific S.E.; *Int'l*, pg. 2546
INSTITUT DR. APPELT THURINGEN GMBH & CO. KG—See Eurofins Scientific S.E.; *Int'l*, pg. 2546
INSTITUT DR. ROTHE GMBH—See Eurofins Scientific S.E.; *Int'l*, pg. 2550
INSTITUT FUR LEBENSMITTEL-, WASSER- UND UMWELTANALYTIK NURNBERG GMBH—See Eurofins Scientific S.E.; *Int'l*, pg. 2544
INTEGRATED PETROLEUM EXPERTISE COMPANY - SERVICOS EM PETROLEO LTDA.—See Eurofins Scientific S.E.; *Int'l*, pg. 2550
INTERCONTROLE SA—See Electricite de France S.A.; *Int'l*, pg. 2351
INTERNATIONAL FLAVORS & FRAGRANCES I.F.F. (NEDERLAND) B.V.—See International Flavors & Fragrances Inc.; *U.S. Public*, pg. 1153
INTERNATIONAL PAPER COMPANY - LOVELAND—See International Paper Company; *U.S. Public*, pg. 1157
INVETECH, LLC; *U.S. Private*, pg. 2132
IN VITRO-LABOR FUR VETERINARMEDIZINISCHE DIAGNOSTIK UND HYGIENE GMBH—See IDEXX Laboratories, Inc.; *U.S. Public*, pg. 1093
IPL SANTE ENVIRONNEMENT DURABLE ATLANTIQUE SAS—See Eurofins Scientific S.E.; *Int'l*, pg. 2542
ISOTECH LABORATORIES, INC.; *U.S. Private*, pg. 2146
IUVO BIOSCIENCE, LLC; *U.S. Private*, pg. 2150
IVEY-COOPER SERVICES LLC—See Electricite de France S.A.; *Int'l*, pg. 2351
JAPAN CLINICAL SERVICE, INC.—See BML, Inc.; *Int'l*, pg. 1076
KANO LABORATORIES INC.—See Gryphon Investors, LLC; *U.S. Private*, pg. 1798
KB HOME/SHAW LOUISIANA LLC—See KB Home; *U.S. Public*, pg. 1215
KETT ENGINEERING CORPORATION; *U.S. Private*, pg. 2292
KOLDT & RYO EL A/S—See AddLife AB; *Int'l*, pg. 129
LABCONNECT LLC; *U.S. Private*, pg. 2370
LABCOR, INC.—See Morgan Stanley; *U.S. Public*, pg. 1474
LAB M LIMITED—See Neogen Corporation; *U.S. Public*, pg. 1505
LABOMOSAN S.A.—See Fugro N.V.; *Int'l*, pg. 2808
LABORATORI CAT-GAIRIN, S.L.U.—See Eurofins Scientific S.E.; *Int'l*, pg. 2550
LABORATORIO ALAC LTDA.—See Eurofins Scientific S.E.; *Int'l*, pg. 2550
LABORATORIO DE ENSAYOS METROLOGICOS, S.L.—See I Squared Capital Advisors (US) LLC; *U.S. Private*, pg. 2023
LABORATORIO GESSYMA GALEA, S.L.—See Eurofins Scientific S.E.; *Int'l*, pg. 2550

541380 — TESTING LABORATORIE...

LABORATORIO PASTEUR DE ANALISES CLINICAS LTDA.—See Eurofins Scientific S.E.; *Int'l*, pg. 2550
LABORATORIOS BUCKMAN S.A.—See Bulab Holdings, Inc.; *U.S. Private*, pg. 684
LABORATORIOS GRIFOLS, S.A.—See Grifols, S.A.; *Int'l*, pg. 3085
LABORATORIOS VITAL, S.L.U.—See Eurofins Scientific S.E.; *Int'l*, pg. 2551
LABORATORY SERVICES MSO LLC; *U.S. Private*, pg. 2370
LABOTECH INTERNATIONAL CO., LTD.—See Furuno Electric Co., Ltd.; *Int'l*, pg. 2848
LANDAUER EUROPE SAS—See Fortive Corporation; *U.S. Public*, pg. 871
LCAM SAS—See Eurofins Scientific S.E.; *Int'l*, pg. 2542
LCN SAS—See Eurofins Scientific S.E.; *Int'l*, pg. 2543
LEON OVERSEAS PTE. LTD—See China Leon Inspection Holding Limited; *Int'l*, pg. 1514
LGAI CHILE, S.A.—See I Squared Capital Advisors (US) LLC; *U.S. Private*, pg. 2023
LGAI TECHNOLOGICAL, CENTER, S.A.—See I Squared Capital Advisors (US) LLC; *U.S. Private*, pg. 2023
LITHOLINK CORPORATION—See Laboratory Corporation of America Holdings; *U.S. Public*, pg. 1287
LIUZHOU RELIABLE AUTO ANALYSIS TESTING LTD.—See I Squared Capital Advisors (US) LLC; *U.S. Private*, pg. 2023
LOGAN LABORATORIES, LLC—See Bain Capital, LP; *U.S. Private*, pg. 445
LORENTZEN & WETTRE INTERNATIONAL AB—See ABB Ltd.; *Int'l*, pg. 50
LOWEN CORPORATION - LOWEN CERTIFIED DIVISION—See Lowen Corporation; *U.S. Private*, pg. 2505
LUMASENSE TECHNOLOGIES GMBH MERKEZI—See Advanced Energy Industries, Inc.; *U.S. Public*, pg. 47
LUMINEX (AUSTRALIA) PTY. LTD—See DiaSorin S.p.A.; *Int'l*, pg. 2106
MAGNETIC ANALYSIS AUSTRALIA, PTY. LTD.—See Magnetic Analysis Corporation; *U.S. Private*, pg. 2547
MAGNETIC ANALYSIS ITALIA, S.R.L.—See Magnetic Analysis Corporation; *U.S. Private*, pg. 2547
MAGNETIC ANALYSIS LTD—See Magnetic Analysis Corporation; *U.S. Private*, pg. 2547
MAGNETIC ANALYSIS NORDIC AB—See Magnetic Analysis Corporation; *U.S. Private*, pg. 2547
M.A.H. FOOD CONTROL KFT.—See Eurofins Scientific S.E.; *Int'l*, pg. 2551
MBTECH AUTO TESTING PROPERTIES LLC—See Adecco Group AG; *Int'l*, pg. 140
MEDION GRIFOLS DIAGNOSTIC AG—See Grifols, S.A.; *Int'l*, pg. 3085
MEDTEST DX, INC.; *U.S. Private*, pg. 2659
MEDTOX LABORATORIES, INC.—See Laboratory Corporation of America Holdings; *U.S. Public*, pg. 1287
MEDUSA LABS—See Viavi Solutions Inc.; *U.S. Public*, pg. 2295
MEDYTOX DIAGNOSTICS, INC.—See Rennova Health, Inc.; *U.S. Public*, pg. 1783
METALEACH LIMITED—See eEnergy Group Plc; *Int'l*, pg. 2317
METALLURGICAL & ENVIRONMENTAL TESTING LABORATORIES INC.—See Miller Consolidated Industries Inc.; *U.S. Private*, pg. 2733
METAL PROVING SERVICES LIMITED—See Goodwin PLC; *Int'l*, pg. 3042
METCO ENVIRONMENTAL, INC.—See H.I.G. Capital, LLC; *U.S. Private*, pg. 1831
MET KOREA, LTD.—See Eurofins Scientific S.E.; *Int'l*, pg. 2551
METRIC INDUSTRIAL A/S—See Addtech AB; *Int'l*, pg. 134
METSS LTD.—See Cakovecki Mlinovi d.d.; *Int'l*, pg. 1260
MICHIGAN ENGINEERING AND TEST CENTER—See Resilience Capital Partners, LLC; *U.S. Private*, pg. 3405
MICROBIOLOGY & QUALITY ASSOCIATES, INC.—See Microbiology Research Associates, Inc.; *U.S. Private*, pg. 2702
MICROBIOLOGY RESEARCH ASSOCIATES, INC.; *U.S. Private*, pg. 2702
MICRO-CLEAN INC.; *U.S. Private*, pg. 2702
MICROCONSULT INC.—See Certified Laboratories, Inc.; *U.S. Private*, pg. 841
MIDLAND OPTICAL CHICAGO LABS, INC.—See EssilorLuxottica SA; *Int'l*, pg. 2513
MIDWEST UNCUTS, INC.—See Bain Capital, LP; *U.S. Private*, pg. 445
MISTRAS GROUP LIMITED—See Mistras Group, Inc.; *U.S. Public*, pg. 1451
MNT HEALTHCARE SERVICES AND TRADE INC.—See Bozlu Holding; *Int'l*, pg. 1125
MOBILEX—See X-Ray Industries Inc.; *U.S. Private*, pg. 4579
MOCON EUROPE A/S—See AMETEK, Inc.; *U.S. Public*, pg. 120
MODERN TESTING SERVICES (DONGGUAN) CO., LTD.—See Eurofins Scientific S.E.; *Int'l*, pg. 2551
MODERN TESTING SERVICES LANKA PRIVATE LIMITED—See Eurofins Scientific S.E.; *Int'l*, pg. 2551

MONSANTO CO. - REMINGTON—See Bayer Aktiengesellschaft; *Int'l*, pg. 909
MORGAN SCHAFFER LTD.—See ESCO Technologies, Inc.; *U.S. Public*, pg. 794
MYRIAD RBM, INC.—See Myriad Genetics, Inc.; *U.S. Public*, pg. 1489
NAGASE-LANDAUER, LTD.—See Fortive Corporation; *U.S. Public*, pg. 871
NANOLAB TECHNOLOGIES, INC.; *U.S. Private*, pg. 2833
NATIONAL ANALYSIS CENTER, INC.—See Underwriters Laboratories Inc.; *U.S. Private*, pg. 4280
THE NATIONAL FOOD LAB, INC.—See Eurofins Scientific S.E.; *Int'l*, pg. 2552
NATIONAL FORENSIC SCIENCE TECHNOLOGY CENTER, INC.; *U.S. Private*, pg. 2854
NATIONAL GENETICS INSTITUTE—See Laboratory Corporation of America Holdings; *U.S. Public*, pg. 1287
NATIONAL MEDICAL SERVICES, INC.; *U.S. Private*, pg. 2859
NATIONAL TECHNICAL SYSTEMS, INC - WICHITA—See Aurora Capital Group, LLC; *U.S. Private*, pg. 393
NCALABS CO., LTD.—See H.I.G. Capital, LLC; *U.S. Private*, pg. 1831
NDSM LIMITED—See Eurofins Scientific S.E.; *Int'l*, pg. 2551
NELSON LABORATORIES, LLC—See Sotera Health Company; *U.S. Public*, pg. 1909
NELSON LABS NV—See Sotera Health Company; *U.S. Public*, pg. 1909
NEW ZEALAND LABORATORY SERVICES LTD—See Eurofins Scientific S.E.; *Int'l*, pg. 2551
NG4T GMBH—See Viavi Solutions Inc.; *U.S. Public*, pg. 2295
NORTH AMERICAN TESTING COMPANY, INC.—See National Association for Stock Car Auto Racing, Inc.; *U.S. Private*, pg. 2846
NORTHERN FOODS PLC-TECHNICAL SERVICES—See Boparan Holdings Limited; *Int'l*, pg. 1111
NORTHUMBRIAN WATER SCIENTIFIC SERVICES (NWSS)—See CK Hutchison Holdings Limited; *Int'l*, pg. 1637
NRAY SERVICES, INC.—See I Squared Capital Advisors (US) LLC; *U.S. Private*, pg. 2023
NTH CONSULTANTS, LTD.—See NTH Consultants, Ltd.; *U.S. Private*, pg. 2970
NTS SILICON VALLEY—See Aurora Capital Group, LLC; *U.S. Private*, pg. 393
NUTRILAB, S.L.—See Eurofins Scientific S.E.; *Int'l*, pg. 2551
NUVISAN PHARMA SERVICES GMBH & CO KG—See ADCURAM Group AG; *Int'l*, pg. 128
NZWTA LTD—See Australian Wool Testing Authority Ltd.; *Int'l*, pg. 723
OEKOMETRIC GMBH—See Eurofins Scientific S.E.; *Int'l*, pg. 2551
OIL ANALYZERS, INC.—See Amsoil Inc.; *U.S. Private*, pg. 267
OIL STATES INDUSTRIES (UK) LTD.—See Oil States International, Inc.; *U.S. Public*, pg. 1565
OMAC LABORATORIES LIMITED—See ALS Limited; *Int'l*, pg. 378
ONSPEX—See CSA Group; *Int'l*, pg. 1861
OPTICAL LABORATORIES LTD.—See EssilorLuxottica SA; *Int'l*, pg. 2516
OPTIMED S.A.—See Eurofins Scientific S.E.; *Int'l*, pg. 2543
OPTIVIA BIOTECHNOLOGY INC.—See BioIVT, LLC; *U.S. Private*, pg. 562
PACE ANALYTICAL SERVICES, INC. - ASHEVILLE ENVIRONMENTAL LABORATORY—See Leonard Green & Partners, L.P.; *U.S. Private*, pg. 2427
PACE ANALYTICAL SERVICES, INC. - GREEN BAY ENVIRONMENTAL LABORATORY—See Leonard Green & Partners, L.P.; *U.S. Private*, pg. 2427
PACE ANALYTICAL SERVICES, INC. - GREENSBURG ENVIRONMENTAL LABORATORY—See Leonard Green & Partners, L.P.; *U.S. Private*, pg. 2427
PACE ANALYTICAL SERVICES, INC. - HOUSTON LABOPS/SERVICE CENTER—See Leonard Green & Partners, L.P.; *U.S. Private*, pg. 2427
PACE ANALYTICAL SERVICES, INC. - HUNTERSVILLE ENVIRONMENTAL LABORATORY—See Leonard Green & Partners, L.P.; *U.S. Private*, pg. 2427
PACE ANALYTICAL SERVICES, INC. - INDIANAPOLIS ENVIRONMENTAL LABORATORY—See Leonard Green & Partners, L.P.; *U.S. Private*, pg. 2427
PACE ANALYTICAL SERVICES, INC. - LENEXA ENVIRONMENTAL LABORATORY—See Leonard Green & Partners, L.P.; *U.S. Private*, pg. 2427
PACE ANALYTICAL SERVICES, INC. - MINNEAPOLIS ENVIRONMENTAL LABORATORY—See Leonard Green & Partners, L.P.; *U.S. Private*, pg. 2427
PACE ANALYTICAL SERVICES, LLC—See Leonard Green & Partners, L.P.; *U.S. Private*, pg. 2426
PENN NON-DESTRUCTIVE TESTING, LLC—See Mistras Group, Inc.; *U.S. Public*, pg. 1451
PHARMACEUTICAL PRODUCT DEVELOPMENT SOUTH AFRICA (PROPRIETARY) LTD.—See Thermo Fisher Scientific Inc.; *U.S. Public*, pg. 2151
PLATO BIO PHARMA INC.—See Inotiv, Inc.; *U.S. Public*, pg. 1128

POLARIS LABORATORIES; *U.S. Private*, pg. 3223
POLYMER SOLUTIONS (PSI); *U.S. Private*, pg. 3226
POLY NDT PTE. LTD.—See Centre Testing International Corporation; *Int'l*, pg. 1411
POPLAR HEALTHCARE, PLLC; *U.S. Private*, pg. 3228
POWERTECH LABS, INC.—See B.C. Hydro; *Int'l*, pg. 789
PPD BULGARIA EOOD—See Thermo Fisher Scientific Inc.; *U.S. Public*, pg. 2150
PPD CZECH REPUBLIC S.R.O.—See Thermo Fisher Scientific Inc.; *U.S. Public*, pg. 2150
PPD DEVELOPMENT (HK) LIMITED—See Thermo Fisher Scientific Inc.; *U.S. Public*, pg. 2150
PPD DEVELOPMENT IRELAND LIMITED—See Thermo Fisher Scientific Inc.; *U.S. Public*, pg. 2150
PPD DEVELOPMENT (S) PTE. LTD.—See Thermo Fisher Scientific Inc.; *U.S. Public*, pg. 2150
PPD DEVELOPMENT (THAILAND) CO., LTD.—See Thermo Fisher Scientific Inc.; *U.S. Public*, pg. 2150
PPD GLOBAL CENTRAL LABS, LLC—See Thermo Fisher Scientific Inc.; *U.S. Public*, pg. 2150
PPD GLOBAL CENTRAL LABS (S) PTE. LTD.—See Thermo Fisher Scientific Inc.; *U.S. Public*, pg. 2150
PPD INTERNATIONAL HOLDINGS, INC.—See Thermo Fisher Scientific Inc.; *U.S. Public*, pg. 2150
PPD PERU S.A.C.—See Thermo Fisher Scientific Inc.; *U.S. Public*, pg. 2150
PPD ROMANIA S.R.L.—See Thermo Fisher Scientific Inc.; *U.S. Public*, pg. 2150
PPD SERVICES, INC.—See Thermo Fisher Scientific Inc.; *U.S. Public*, pg. 2150
PPD SLOVAK REPUBLIC S.R.O.—See Thermo Fisher Scientific Inc.; *U.S. Public*, pg. 2150
PREANALYTIX GMBH—See Becton, Dickinson & Company; *U.S. Public*, pg. 288
PRECISION DIAGNOSTICS, INC.—See Bruker Corporation; *U.S. Public*, pg. 407
PRECISION THERAPEUTICS, INC.; *U.S. Private*, pg. 3247
PREMIER INTEGRITY SOLUTIONS; *U.S. Private*, pg. 3250
PREMIER RESEARCH GROUP INTERNATIONAL LTD.—See Metalmark Capital Holdings LLC; *U.S. Private*, pg. 2681
PREMIER RESEARCH INTERNATIONAL LLC—See Metalmark Capital Holdings LLC; *U.S. Private*, pg. 2681
PROCAT TESTING LLC—See BASF SE; *Int'l*, pg. 876
PRODUCT PERCEPTIONS LIMITED—See Eurofins Scientific S.E.; *Int'l*, pg. 2551
PROPHASE DIAGNOSTICS, INC.—See ProPhase Labs, Inc.; *U.S. Public*, pg. 1727
PTI INDUSTRIES, INC—See Wynnchurch Capital, L.P.; *U.S. Private*, pg. 4577
PUBLIC ANALYST SCIENTIFIC SERVICES LTD—See Eurofins Scientific S.E.; *Int'l*, pg. 2551
PUBLIC ANALYST SCIENTIFIC SERVICES (NI) LTD—See Eurofins Scientific S.E.; *Int'l*, pg. 2551
PYROSEQUENCING, INC.—See Biotage AB; *Int'l*, pg. 1042
QPS AMERICA, INC.—See I Squared Capital Advisors (US) LLC; *U.S. Private*, pg. 2023
QPS EUROPE B.V.—See I Squared Capital Advisors (US) LLC; *U.S. Private*, pg. 2023
QPS EVALUATION SERVICES INC.—See I Squared Capital Advisors (US) LLC; *U.S. Private*, pg. 2023
QUAD CITY TESTING LABORATORY—See Premium Inspection & Testing, Inc.; *U.S. Private*, pg. 3252
QUADRANTS SCIENTIFIC, INC.—See Eurofins Scientific S.E.; *Int'l*, pg. 2550
QUALCODUNA PROFICIENCY TESTING HUNGARY NONPROFIT KFT.—See Eurofins Scientific S.E.; *Int'l*, pg. 2551
QUALITY CONTROL CONSULTANTS LIMITED—See China Resources Building Materials Technology Holdings Limited; *Int'l*, pg. 1549
QUALITY INSPECTION SERVICES BVBA—See Team, Inc.; *U.S. Public*, pg. 1988
QUALITY INSPECTION SERVICES B.V.—See Team, Inc.; *U.S. Public*, pg. 1988
QUALITYLABS BT GMBH—See Bio-Gate AG; *Int'l*, pg. 1035
QUALTEX LABORATORIES; *U.S. Private*, pg. 3322
RADATA, INC.—See RockBridge Growth Equity, LLC; *U.S. Private*, pg. 3465
RADIATION TEST SOLUTIONS, INC.; *U.S. Private*, pg. 3343
RAYTHEON ANALYSIS & TEST LABORATORY—See RTX Corporation; *U.S. Public*, pg. 1825
REACTION BIOLOGY CORPORATION; *U.S. Private*, pg. 3366
RELIABLE ANALYSIS (SHANGHAI) INC.—See I Squared Capital Advisors (US) LLC; *U.S. Private*, pg. 2023
REPROGENETICS, LLC—See The Cooper Companies, Inc.; *U.S. Public*, pg. 2066
REPROSOURCE, INC.—See Quest Diagnostics, Inc.; *U.S. Public*, pg. 1756
RIGA ANALYTICAL LAB INC.—See Covalent Metrology Services, Inc.; *U.S. Private*, pg. 1071
RIVAL LABS, INC.—See Live Nation Entertainment, Inc.; *U.S. Public*, pg. 1330
RTD QUALITY SERVICES NIGERIA LTD.—See I Squared Capital Advisors (US) LLC; *U.S. Private*, pg. 2023
RTI LABORATORIES, INC.; *U.S. Private*, pg. 3498

N.A.I.C.S. INDEX

541410 — INTERIOR DESIGN SER...

SAINT-GOBAIN CENTRE DE RECHERCHE ET D'ETUDES EUROPEENNES—See Compagnie de Saint-Gobain SA; *Int'l*, pg. 1732
SAM SENSORY & MARKETING ITALY S.R.L.—See Eurofins Scientific S.E.; *Int'l*, pg. 2551
SAPRA-LANDAUER, LTDA.—See Fortive Corporation; *U.S. Public*, pg. 871
SCIENTIFIC CERTIFICATION SYSTEMS, INC.; *U.S. Private*, pg. 3574
SEMSYSCO GMBH—See Lam Research Corporation; *U.S. Public*, pg. 1290
SEMSYSCO SINGAPORE PTE. LTD.—See Lam Research Corporation; *U.S. Public*, pg. 1290
SENSORY & MARKETING SPAIN, S.L.U.—See Eurofins Scientific S.E.; *Int'l*, pg. 2551
SEOUL CRO INC.—See CHA Biotech Co., Ltd.; *Int'l*, pg. 1436
S.G.M. S.R.L.—See CAD IT S.p.A.; *Int'l*, pg. 1247
SHANGHAI IDIADA AUTOMOTIVE TECHNOLOGY SERVICES CO., LTD.—See I Squared Capital Advisors (US) LLC; *U.S. Private*, pg. 2023
SHENZHEN ZHONGHAN TECHNOLOGY CO., LTD.—See FSP Technology Inc.; *Int'l*, pg. 2800
SIEMIC INC.—See Bureau Veritas S.A.; *Int'l*, pg. 1222
SIGNODE SINGAPORE PTE. LTD.—See Crown Holdings, Inc.; *U.S. Public*, pg. 600
SIMCO ELECTRONICS; *U.S. Private*, pg. 3665
SIRA TEST AND CERTIFICATION LIMITED—See CSA Group; *Int'l*, pg. 1861
SMARTTIP BV—See Bruker Corporation; *U.S. Public*, pg. 407
SMITHERS SCIENTIFIC SERVICES, INC.—See The Smithers Group; *U.S. Private*, pg. 4119
SOFIA GMBH—See Eurofins Scientific S.E.; *Int'l*, pg. 2541
SOFT LANDING LABS LTD; *U.S. Private*, pg. 3704
SOIL INVESTIGATION PTE. LTD.—See CSC Holdings Limited; *Int'l*, pg. 1862
SOLUS SCIENTIFIC SOLUTIONS, INC.—See Revvity, Inc.; *U.S. Public*, pg. 1795
SOLUS SCIENTIFIC SOLUTIONS LTD.—See Revvity, Inc.; *U.S. Public*, pg. 1795
SORA LABORATORIES, LLC—See Archer-Daniels-Midland Company; *U.S. Public*, pg. 185
SPECTRO ANALYTICAL LABS LTD.—See Eurofins Scientific S.E.; *Int'l*, pg. 2551
SPECTRO RESEARCH LAB VENTURES PRIVATE LIMITED—See Eurofins Scientific S.E.; *Int'l*, pg. 2551
SPECTRO SSA LABS PRIVATE LIMITED—See Eurofins Scientific S.E.; *Int'l*, pg. 2551
SPECTRUM LABORATORIES (JOHORE) SDN. BERHAD—See Brite-Tech Berhad; *Int'l*, pg. 1165
SPECTRUM LABORATORIES (PENANG) SDN. BERHAD—See Brite-Tech Berhad; *Int'l*, pg. 1165
STANLEY INSPECTION, L. L. C.—See Stanley Black & Decker, Inc.; *U.S. Public*, pg. 1935
STANLEY INSPECTION US, L.L.C.—See Stanley Black & Decker, Inc.; *U.S. Public*, pg. 1935
STANLEY PIPELINE INSPECTION, L.L.C.—See Stanley Black & Decker, Inc.; *U.S. Public*, pg. 1935
STEEL TESTING LABORATORY; *U.S. Private*, pg. 3796
ST. JOHN'S REGIONAL IMAGING CENTER, LLC—See Catholic Health Initiatives; *U.S. Private*, pg. 790
STR INC.—See STR Holdings, Inc.; *U.S. Public*, pg. 1953
STR LABORATUAR HIZMETLERI A.S.—See STR Holdings, Inc.; *U.S. Public*, pg. 1953
STR TESTING & INSPECTION AG—See STR Holdings, Inc.; *U.S. Public*, pg. 1953
SUMMIT ENVIRONMENTAL TECHNOLOGIES, INC.—See Morgan Stanley; *U.S. Public*, pg. 1474
SUNCAST SOLAR ENERGY, INC.; *U.S. Public*, pg. 1963
SUZHOU CTI TESTING TECHNOLOGY CO., LTD.—See Centre Testing International Corporation; *Int'l*, pg. 1411
SYNSPEC B.V.—See Focused Photonics (Hangzhou), Inc.; *Int'l*, pg. 2720
SYSTEST LABORATORIES INC.; *U.S. Private*, pg. 3908
TAIYO TECHNO RESEARCH LTD.—See Eurofins Scientific S.E.; *Int'l*, pg. 2552
TALON TEST LABORATORIES INCORPORATED—See I Squared Capital Advisors (US) LLC; *U.S. Private*, pg. 2023
TALON TEST LABORATORIES (PHOENIX) INC.—See I Squared Capital Advisors (US) LLC; *U.S. Private*, pg. 2023
TANDEM LABS, INC.—See Laboratory Corporation of America Holdings; *U.S. Public*, pg. 1287
TA TECHNOLOGY (SHANGHAI) CO., LTD.—See Eurofins Scientific S.E.; *Int'l*, pg. 2552
TECHNICAL SAFETY SERVICES, LLC—See Levine Leichtman Capital Partners, LLC; *U.S. Private*, pg. 2436
TECHNIC FRANCE—See Technic Incorporated; *U.S. Private*, pg. 3953
TERADYNE, K.K.—See Teradyne, Inc.; *U.S. Public*, pg. 2018
TERMICA COLLEFERRO SPA—See Enel S.p.A.; *Int'l*, pg. 2414
TESIS BIOSCIENCES, INC.; *U.S. Private*, pg. 3973
TESTAMERICA BUFFALO—See H.I.G. Capital, LLC; *U.S. Private*, pg. 1831

TESTAMERICA LABORATORIES, INC.—See H.I.G. Capital, LLC; *U.S. Private*, pg. 1831
TEVET, LLC; *U.S. Private*, pg. 3974
THAI ENVIRONMENTAL TECHNIC CO., LTD.—See Eurofins Scientific S.E.; *Int'l*, pg. 2552
TOXIKON CORPORATION—See Laboratory Corporation of America Holdings; *U.S. Public*, pg. 1287
TOXLAB SAS—See Eurofins Scientific S.E.; *Int'l*, pg. 2543
TRACE LABORATORIES EAST—See Methode Electronics, Inc.; *U.S. Public*, pg. 1429
TRAC EMC & SAFETY LTD—See Ecolab Inc.; *U.S. Public*, pg. 712
TRAC ENVIRONMENTAL & ANALYSIS LTD.—See Ecolab Inc.; *U.S. Public*, pg. 712
TRANSLAB NV—See ABO-Group NV/SA; *Int'l*, pg. 66
TRANSNETYX, INC.—See Thompson Street Capital Manager LLC; *U.S. Private*, pg. 4161
TRIALON CORPORATION—See Resilience Capital Partners, LLC; *U.S. Private*, pg. 3405
TRIESTA SCIENCES, INC.—See Healthcare Global Enterprises Limited; *Int'l*, pg. 3304
TRIMGEN CORPORATION; *U.S. Private*, pg. 4232
TRINITY SCIENTIFIC LTD—See DDD Ltd.; *Int'l*, pg. 1993
TRITON SYSTEMS INC.; *U.S. Private*, pg. 4239
TRL COMPLIANCE SERVICES LIMITED—See Ecolab Inc.; *U.S. Public*, pg. 712
TTE LABORATORIES INC.—See Transcat, Inc.; *U.S. Public*, pg. 2179
TULSA INSPECTION RESOURCES - CANADA, ULC—See Cypress Environmental Partners, L.P.; *U.S. Public*, pg. 618
TUMORGENESIS INC.—See Predictive Oncology Inc.; *U.S. Public*, pg. 1713
TURNER LABORATORIES, INC.; *U.S. Private*, pg. 4261
UBIC NORTH AMERICA, INC. HONG KONG—See Fronteo, Inc.; *Int'l*, pg. 2794
UBIC NORTH AMERICA, INC. SOUTH KOREA—See Fronteo, Inc.; *Int'l*, pg. 2794
UL DE MEXICO, S.A. DE C.V.—See Underwriters Laboratories Inc.; *U.S. Private*, pg. 4280
UL INDIA PRIVATE LTD.—See Underwriters Laboratories Inc.; *U.S. Private*, pg. 4280
UL INTERNATIONAL DEMKO A/S—See Underwriters Laboratories Inc.; *U.S. Private*, pg. 4280
UL INTERNATIONAL FRANCE S.A.—See Underwriters Laboratories Inc.; *U.S. Private*, pg. 4280
UL INTERNATIONAL GERMANY GMBH—See Underwriters Laboratories Inc.; *U.S. Private*, pg. 4280
UL INTERNATIONAL ITALIA S.R.L.—See Underwriters Laboratories Inc.; *U.S. Private*, pg. 4280
UL INTERNATIONAL ITALIA S.R.L.—See Underwriters Laboratories Inc.; *U.S. Private*, pg. 4280
UL INTERNATIONAL LTD.—See Underwriters Laboratories Inc.; *U.S. Private*, pg. 4280
UL INTERNATIONAL (NETHERLANDS) B.V.—See Underwriters Laboratories Inc.; *U.S. Private*, pg. 4280
UL INTERNATIONAL NEW ZEALAND LIMITED—See Underwriters Laboratories Inc.; *U.S. Private*, pg. 4280
UL INTERNATIONAL NEW ZEALAND LTD—See Underwriters Laboratories Inc.; *U.S. Private*, pg. 4280
UL INTERNATIONAL (SWEDEN) AB—See Underwriters Laboratories Inc.; *U.S. Private*, pg. 4280
UL INTERNATIONAL (UK) LTD.—See Underwriters Laboratories Inc.; *U.S. Private*, pg. 4280
UL JAPAN, INC.—See Underwriters Laboratories Inc.; *U.S. Private*, pg. 4280
UL KOREA LTD.—See Underwriters Laboratories Inc.; *U.S. Private*, pg. 4280
UL SERVICES (MALAYSIA) SDN. BHD.—See Underwriters Laboratories Inc.; *U.S. Private*, pg. 4280
UNDERWRITERS LABORATORIES INC.; *U.S. Private*, pg. 4280
UNDERWRITERS LABORATORIES OF CANADA—See Underwriters Laboratories Inc.; *U.S. Private*, pg. 4280
UNDERWRITERS LABORATORIES OF CANADA - VANCOUVER BRANCH—See Underwriters Laboratories Inc.; *U.S. Private*, pg. 4280
UNITED STATES STEEL CORP.—See United States Steel Corporation; *U.S. Public*, pg. 2237
UNIVERSAL ROBOTS A/S—See Teradyne, Inc.; *U.S. Public*, pg. 2018
UNIVERSAL ROBOTS GMBH—See Teradyne, Inc.; *U.S. Public*, pg. 2018
UNIVERSAL ROBOTS (INDIA) PTE. LTD.—See Teradyne, Inc.; *U.S. Public*, pg. 2018
UNIVERSAL ROBOTS (SHANGHAI) CO. LTD.—See Teradyne, Inc.; *U.S. Public*, pg. 2018
UNIVERSAL ROBOTS (SINGAPORE) PTE. LTD.—See Teradyne, Inc.; *U.S. Public*, pg. 2018
UNIVERSAL ROBOTS (SPAIN) S.L.—See Teradyne, Inc.; *U.S. Public*, pg. 2018
UNIVERSAL ROBOTS (USA), INC.—See Teradyne, Inc.; *U.S. Public*, pg. 2018
U.S. INSPECT, INC.; *U.S. Private*, pg. 4271
U.S. OILCHEK—See U.S. Venture, Inc.; *U.S. Private*, pg. 4272
VALIDUS VERIFICATION SERVICES—See Where Food Comes From, Inc.; *U.S. Public*, pg. 2366

VECTURA FERTIN PHARMA RESEARCH LABORATORIES PTE. LTD.—See Philip Morris International Inc.; *U.S. Public*, pg. 1688
VELOSI CBL (M) SDN BHD—See I Squared Capital Advisors (US) LLC; *U.S. Private*, pg. 2024
VELOSI CERTIFICATION SERVICES L.L.C—See I Squared Capital Advisors (US) LLC; *U.S. Private*, pg. 2024
VERITAS PETROLEUM SERVICES—See IK Investment Partners Limited; *Int'l*, pg. 3610
VICOM LTD.—See ComfortDelGro Corporation Limited; *Int'l*, pg. 1713
VIRO-MED LABORATORIES, INC.—See Laboratory Corporation of America Holdings; *U.S. Public*, pg. 1287
VWR INTERNATIONAL AB—See Avantor, Inc.; *U.S. Public*, pg. 241
VWR INTERNATIONAL KFT.—See Avantor, Inc.; *U.S. Public*, pg. 242
VWR INTERNATIONAL - MATERIAL DE LABORATORIO, LDA.—See Avantor, Inc.; *U.S. Public*, pg. 241
VWR INTERNATIONAL PBI S.R.L.—See Avantor, Inc.; *U.S. Public*, pg. 242
VWR INTERNATIONAL S. DE R.L. DE C.V.—See Avantor, Inc.; *U.S. Public*, pg. 242
VWR INTERNATIONAL SP. Z O.O.—See Avantor, Inc.; *U.S. Public*, pg. 242
VWR INTERNATIONAL S. R. O.—See Avantor, Inc.; *U.S. Public*, pg. 242
WANG ENGINEERING, INC.—See Terracon Consultants, Inc.; *U.S. Private*, pg. 3971
WASHINGTON LABORATORIES, LTD.—See Mace Security International, Inc.; *U.S. Public*, pg. 1352
WEATHERFORD LABORATORIES (CANADA) LTD.—See Weatherford International plc; *U.S. Public*, pg. 2340
WEATHERFORD LABORATORIES, INC.—See Weatherford International plc; *U.S. Public*, pg. 2340
WEATHERFORD LABORATORIES (MUSCAT) L.L.C.—See Weatherford International plc; *U.S. Public*, pg. 2340
WEATHERFORD LABORATORIES (UK) LIMITED—See Weatherford International plc; *U.S. Public*, pg. 2340
XCELOM LIMITED—See Berry Genomics Co., Ltd.; *Int'l*, pg. 989
X-RAY INDUSTRIES INC.; *U.S. Private*, pg. 4579
X-R-I TESTING—See X-Ray Industries Inc.; *U.S. Private*, pg. 4579
YXLON INTERNATIONAL A/S—See Comet Holding AG; *Int'l*, pg. 1711
YXLON INTERNATIONAL CT DEVELOPMENT GMBH—See Comet Holding AG; *Int'l*, pg. 1711
YXLON INTERNATIONAL FEINFOCUS GMBH—See Comet Holding AG; *Int'l*, pg. 1711
YXLON INTERNATIONAL INC.—See Comet Holding AG; *Int'l*, pg. 1711
YXLON INTERNATIONAL K.K.—See Comet Holding AG; *Int'l*, pg. 1711

541410 — INTERIOR DESIGN SERVICES

605 STUDIOS, LLC—See Broadridge Financial Solutions, Inc.; *U.S. Public*, pg. 391
AHB HOLDINGS BERHAD; *Int'l*, pg. 222
AL GROUP LIMITED; *Int'l*, pg. 278
APLEONA R&M AUSBAU FRANKFURT GMBH—See Bilfinger SE; *Int'l*, pg. 1024
APLEONA R&M AUSBAU GMBH—See Bilfinger SE; *Int'l*, pg. 1024
APLEONA R&M AUSBAU MUNCHEN GMBH—See Bilfinger SE; *Int'l*, pg. 1024
ARBONIA FRANCE S.A.R.L.—See Arbonia AG; *Int'l*, pg. 537
ARCHIDPLY DECOR LIMITED; *Int'l*, pg. 548
AREA 3 EQUIPAMIENTO Y DISENO INTERIORISMO, S.L.U.—See Elecnor, S.A.; *Int'l*, pg. 2347
AREA ZERO CONSULTING DE ARQUITECTURA E INTERIORISMO, S.L.—See Jones Lang LaSalle Incorporated; *U.S. Public*, pg. 1201
ARTHUR SHUSTER INC.; *U.S. Private*, pg. 342
ARTISAN DESIGN GROUP; *U.S. Private*, pg. 343
AXO LIGHT S.R.L.—See Dexelance S.p.A.; *Int'l*, pg. 2092
BALS CORPORATION; *Int'l*, pg. 811
BANKO DESIGN LLC; *U.S. Private*, pg. 468
BAYSIDE VILLAS, LLC—See INSPIRATO INCORPORATED; *U.S. Public*, pg. 1131
BELHASA INTERNATIONAL COMPANY—See Belhasa Group of Companies; *Int'l*, pg. 964
BELHASA JOINERY & DECORATION COMPANY LLC—See Belhasa Group of Companies; *Int'l*, pg. 964
BRAYTON & HUGHES DESIGN STUDIO—See DLR Holding, LLC; *U.S. Public*, pg. 1247
BUILDERS DESIGN & LEASING INC.; *U.S. Private*, pg. 682
BURKETTEUA—See Eppstein Uhen Architects, Inc.; *U.S. Private*, pg. 1414
C2DESIGN; *U.S. Private*, pg. 709
CANNON SLINE INC.—See The Halifax Group LLC; *U.S. Private*, pg. 4042
CARLSBAD ISI, INC.—See Kratos Defense & Security Solutions, Inc.; *U.S. Public*, pg. 1276
CENACCHI INT.I S.R.L.—See Dexelance S.p.A.; *Int'l*, pg. 2092

541410 — INTERIOR DESIGN SER...

CENTURY LIVING, LLC—See Century Communities, Inc.; *U.S. Public*, pg. 475
CHUN WO ELEGANT DECORATION ENGINEERING COMPANY LIMITED—See Asia Allied Infrastructure Holdings Limited; *Int'l*, pg. 610
CITYNEON DAG INDIA PRIVATE LIMITED—See Cityneon Holdings Limited; *Int'l*, pg. 1630
CLOSETS UNLIMITED, INC.; *U.S. Private*, pg. 946
COLLINS & DUPONT INTERIORS, INC.; *U.S. Private*, pg. 969
CONTRACT DECOR, INC.—See Qurate Retail, Inc.; *U.S. Public*, pg. 1758
COTTAGES & CASTLES, INC.; *U.S. Private*, pg. 1063
CREATIVE BUSINESS INTERIORS, INC.—See Interior Workplace Solutions LLC; *U.S. Private*, pg. 2111
CROSSTEC GROUP HOLDINGS LIMITED; *Int'l*, pg. 1856
CT AUTOMOTIVE JAPAN KK—See CT Automotive Group Plc; *Int'l*, pg. 1868
CUBE PLANNING CORPORATION—See Crest Investments Co., Ltd.; *Int'l*, pg. 1840
CUBO DESIGN S.R.L.—See Dexelance S.p.A.; *Int'l*, pg. 2092
CUSTOM DECORATORS, INC.; *U.S. Private*, pg. 1128
CYPRESS DESIGN LIMITED—See E. Bon Holdings Ltd; *Int'l*, pg. 2250
DANWOOD S.A.—See Enterprise Investors Sp. z o.o.; *Int'l*, pg. 2452
DECKER ROSS INTERIORS, INC.; *U.S. Private*, pg. 1187
DECO EMIRATES COMPANY LLC—See Depa PLC; *Int'l*, pg. 2040
THE DECORATORS UNLIMITED INC.; *U.S. Private*, pg. 4019
DECOR PRODUCTS INTERNATIONAL, INC.; *Int'l*, pg. 2001
DEPA AL BARAKAH L.L.C.—See Depa PLC; *Int'l*, pg. 2040
DEPA EGYPT—See Depa PLC; *Int'l*, pg. 2040
DEPA INDIA PVT. LTD.—See Depa PLC; *Int'l*, pg. 2040
DEPA INTERIORS L.L.C.—See Depa PLC; *Int'l*, pg. 2040
DEPA JORDAN—See Depa PLC; *Int'l*, pg. 2040
DEPA PLC; *Int'l*, pg. 2040
DEPA QATAR CO. W.L.L.—See Depa PLC; *Int'l*, pg. 2040
DEPA SAUDI ARABIA—See Depa PLC; *Int'l*, pg. 2040
DEPA UK LIMITED—See Depa PLC; *Int'l*, pg. 2040
DESIGN FORCE CORPORATION—See Valiant Products Corp.; *U.S. Private*, pg. 4332
DESIGN LINES, INC.—See TRIO, Inc.; *U.S. Private*, pg. 4236
DESIGN WITHIN REACH, INC.—See MillerKnoll, Inc.; *U.S. Public*, pg. 1447
DICKSON INTERIOR DESIGN LIMITED—See Dickson Concepts (International) Limited; *Int'l*, pg. 2112
DIVERSIFIED DESIGN INC.—See Beers & Hoffman, Ltd.; *U.S. Private*, pg. 514
ELEMENTS, LLC; *U.S. Private*, pg. 1357
ELITE BUILDER SERVICES, INC.—See Live Ventures Incorporated; *U.S. Public*, pg. 1332
ELKAY INTERIOR SYSTEMS—See Zurn Elkay Water Solutions Corporation; *U.S. Public*, pg. 2412
EMBELLENCE GROUP AB; *Int'l*, pg. 2374
ENERTECH SPECIALTY CONTRACTING—See Irex Corporation; *U.S. Private*, pg. 2138
EUROPA WORKSPACE SOLUTIONS LIMITED—See EQT AB; *Int'l*, pg. 2468
EXA E&C INC.; *Int'l*, pg. 2576
FACETS INTERIORS (PTY) LIMITED—See Basil Read Holdings Limited; *Int'l*, pg. 887
FACILITIES CONNECTION, INC.; *U.S. Private*, pg. 1459
FEDERAL FURNITURE INDUSTRIES SDN BHD—See Federal International Holdings Berhad; *Int'l*, pg. 2630
FEDERAL FURNITURE LIFESTYLE SDN BHD—See Federal International Holdings Berhad; *Int'l*, pg. 2630
FIBO-TRESPO AS—See FSN Capital Partners AS; *Int'l*, pg. 2799
FIREFLY POINT OF VIEW LTD.; *Int'l*, pg. 2679
FISKARS COMMERCIAL (SHANGHAI) CO., LTD.—See Fiskars Oyj Abp; *Int'l*, pg. 2694
FISKARS LIVING US, LLC—See Fiskars Oyj Abp; *Int'l*, pg. 2694
FISKARS POLSKA SP. Z.O.O.—See Fiskars Oyj Abp; *Int'l*, pg. 2694
GULF DYNAMIC SERVICES LLC (GDS)—See Dubai Investments PJSC; *Int'l*, pg. 2219
HASEKO ANESIS CORPORATION—See Haseko Corporation; *Int'l*, pg. 3283
HAUS AM BRUSSELER PLATZ GMBH & CO. KG—See Helaba Landesbank Hessen-Thuringen; *Int'l*, pg. 3328
HAVELOCK EUROPA PLC; *Int'l*, pg. 3287
HENREDON DESIGNER SHOWROOMS, INC.—See Heritage Home Group, LLC; *U.S. Private*, pg. 1924
HEXAGON SHOP SYSTEM SDN. BHD.—See Hexagon Holdings Berhad; *Int'l*, pg. 3370
HOME PRODUCT CENTER (MALAYSIA) SDN. BHD.—See Home Product Center Public Company Limited; *Int'l*, pg. 3455
IMAGE DESIGN, INC.; *U.S. Private*, pg. 2044
INTERIOR ARCHITECTS, INC .—See Interior Architects, Inc.; *U.S. Private*, pg. 2111

INTERIOR LOGIC GROUP, INC.—See Littlejohn & Co., LLC; *U.S. Private*, pg. 2470
INTERIOR LOGIC GROUP, INC.—See Platinum Equity, LLC; *U.S. Private*, pg. 2470
INTERIORS OF WINTER PARK, INC.; *U.S. Private*, pg. 2111
INTERIOR SPECIALISTS, INC.—See Littlejohn & Co., LLC; *U.S. Private*, pg. 2470
INTERIOR SPECIALISTS, INC.—See Platinum Equity, LLC; *U.S. Private*, pg. 3205
INTERIOR SYSTEMS INC.; *U.S. Private*, pg. 2111
INTERIOR WORKPLACE SOLUTIONS LLC; *U.S. Private*, pg. 2111
INTERPRISE/SOUTHWEST INTERIOR & SPACE DESIGN, INC.; *U.S. Private*, pg. 2123
JAMIE GIBBS & ASSOCIATES; *U.S. Private*, pg. 2186
JKAISER WORKSPACES, LLC; *U.S. Private*, pg. 2211
JOSEPH MINTON INC.; *U.S. Private*, pg. 2237
KDS INTERIORS, INC.; *U.S. Private*, pg. 2270
LMP INTERNATIONAL LIMITED—See Harbour Equine Holdings Limited; *Int'l*, pg. 3272
LUNEHJEM.NO AS—See Europris ASA; *Int'l*, pg. 2557
MAIS INTERIOR DESIGN LLC—See Alpha Dhabi Holding PJSC; *Int'l*, pg. 367
MARINE INTERIORS CABINS S.P.A.—See Cassa Depositi e Prestiti S.p.A.; *Int'l*, pg. 1355
MARINE INTERIORS S.P.A.—See Fincantieri S.p.A.; *Int'l*, pg. 2671
MEGA HOME CENTER COMPANY LIMITED—See Home Product Center Public Company Limited; *Int'l*, pg. 3455
MICHAELKATE INTERIORS AND GALLERY; *U.S. Private*, pg. 2699
MICO DMC S.R.L.—See Fiera Milano SpA; *Int'l*, pg. 2660
MICRON CLEANROOM (PHILIPPINES) INC.—See Channel Micron Holdings Company Limited; *Int'l*, pg. 1446
MIVAN DEPA CONTRACTING L.L.C.—See Depa PLC; *Int'l*, pg. 2040
MMM STUDIO LIMITED—See Live Nation Entertainment, Inc.; *U.S. Public*, pg. 1330
MODAR S.P.A.—See Dexelance S.p.A.; *Int'l*, pg. 2092
NATIONAL BUSINESS SUPPLY INC.; *U.S. Private*, pg. 2849
NATIONAL DESIGN & TRADE NETWORK; *U.S. Private*, pg. 2852
NBS-BAY CITY—See National Business Supply Inc.; *U.S. Private*, pg. 2849
NBS-TOLEDO—See National Business Supply Inc.; *U.S. Private*, pg. 2849
PACIFIC OFFICE INTERIORS; *U.S. Private*, pg. 3069
PCI ARDMAC—See Performance Contracting Group; *U.S. Private*, pg. 3148
PDM INTERNATIONAL (BEIJING) LIMITED—See Jones Lang LaSalle Incorporated; *U.S. Public*, pg. 1205
PDM INTERNATIONAL (CHENGDU) LIMITED—See Jones Lang LaSalle Incorporated; *U.S. Public*, pg. 1205
PDM INTERNATIONAL CHINA LIMITED—See Jones Lang LaSalle Incorporated; *U.S. Public*, pg. 1205
PERKINS + WILL - WASHINGTON, DC—See The Perkins + Will Group, Ltd.; *U.S. Private*, pg. 4093
PIER 1 SERVICES COMPANY—See Pier 1 Imports, Inc.; *U.S. Public*, pg. 1690
RESIDENTIAL DESIGN SERVICES, LLC—See Sun Capital Partners, Inc.; *U.S. Private*, pg. 3861
RH F&B MINNESOTA, LLC—See RH; *U.S. Public*, pg. 1796
RH F&B OPERATIONS CANADA, INC.—See RH; *U.S. Public*, pg. 1796
RH SAN FRANCISCO F&B, LLC—See RH; *U.S. Public*, pg. 1796
RH YOUNTVILLE F&B, LLC—See RH; *U.S. Public*, pg. 1796
RJE BUSINESS INTERIORS INC.; *U.S. Private*, pg. 3449
RMW ARCHITECTURE & INTERIORS; *U.S. Private*, pg. 3452
ROBB & STUCKY INTERNATIONAL; *U.S. Private*, pg. 3456
ROBIN'S NEST INTERIORS (MAURITIUS) LTD.—See ENL Limited; *Int'l*, pg. 2441
ROYER & SCHUTTS INC.; *U.S. Private*, pg. 3494
SAGE AUTOMOTIVE INTERIORS, LTD.—See Asahi Kasei Corporation; *Int'l*, pg. 597
SFA DESIGN; *U.S. Private*, pg. 3621
SPELLMAN BRADY & COMPANY; *U.S. Private*, pg. 3754
STAGE SYSTEMS LIMITED—See Havelock Europa PLC; *Int'l*, pg. 3287
STORE OPENING SOLUTIONS, INC.—See Berkshire Hathaway Inc.; *U.S. Public*, pg. 311
STYLMARK, INC.; *U.S. Private*, pg. 3846
SUMIKAWA ADD CO., LTD.—See A.D.Works Group Co., Ltd.; *Int'l*, pg. 23
SWANKE HAYDEN CONNELL LTD; *U.S. Private*, pg. 3890
THAI GALLERY SRL—See Graphex Group Limited; *Int'l*, pg. 3060
THEO KALOMIRAKIS THEATERS; *U.S. Private*, pg. 4141
TRIO, INC.; *U.S. Private*, pg. 4236
TUI LIFESTYLE, LLC; *U.S. Public*, pg. 4257
VARD ACCOMMODATION TULCEA S.R.L.—See Cassa Depositi e Prestiti S.p.A.; *Int'l*, pg. 1355
VEDDER GMBH—See Depa PLC; *Int'l*, pg. 2041
VEENENDAALCAVE, INC.; *U.S. Private*, pg. 4353
VERHALEN INC.; *U.S. Private*, pg. 4360

VOCON DESIGN, INC.; *U.S. Private*, pg. 4409
WARNER DESIGN ASSOCIATES, INC.—See Banko Design LLC; *U.S. Private*, pg. 468
WISEMAN GROUP INTERIOR DESIGN INC.; *U.S. Private*, pg. 4550
WOLCOTT ARCHITECTURE INTERIORS; *U.S. Private*, pg. 4553

541420 — INDUSTRIAL DESIGN SERVICES

AECOM—See AECOM; *U.S. Public*, pg. 50
ALLIANCE OFFSHORE DRILLING PTE LIMITED—See CM Energy Tech Co., Ltd.; *Int'l*, pg. 1666
ALLTERCO EUROPE GMBH—See Allterco JSCo; *Int'l*, pg. 360
ANTENNA RESEARCH ASSOCIATES, INCORPORATED; *U.S. Private*, pg. 287
BESTWORTH-ROMMEL, INC.—See OneAccord Capital LLC; *U.S. Private*, pg. 3024
BIG RED ROOSTER, INC.—See Jones Lang LaSalle Incorporated; *U.S. Public*, pg. 1201
BINZAGR INDUSTRIAL CLEANING SERVICES—See Binzagr Company; *Int'l*, pg. 1035
BLATT INDUSTRIAL SERVICES INC.—See Blatt Group; *U.S. Private*, pg. 580
BRACE INDUSTRIAL GROUP, INC.—See Brand Industrial Services, Inc.; *U.S. Private*, pg. 636
BRAMBLES LIMITED; *Int'l*, pg. 1138
CALLISONRTKL—See ARCADIS N.V.; *Int'l*, pg. 541
CATARC AUTOMOTIVE PROVING GROUND CO., LTD.; *Int'l*, pg. 1358
CROWN UK LIMITED—See Avingtrans plc; *Int'l*, pg. 743
DARKTRACE IRELAND LIMITED—See Thoma Bravo, L.P.; *U.S. Private*, pg. 4147
DENSO TEN TECHNOLOGY LIMITED—See Denso Corporation; *Int'l*, pg. 2030
DESIGNAFFAIRS BUSINESS CONSULTING (SHANGHAI) CO. LTD.—See Accenture plc; *Int'l*, pg. 87
DESIGNAFFAIRS GMBH—See Accenture plc; *Int'l*, pg. 87
EFFICIENT LIGHTING CONSULTANTS, INC.; *U.S. Private*, pg. 1343
FERROSTAAL CHRISTOF ROMANIA SRL—See Christof Holding AG; *Int'l*, pg. 1587
FIRE SYSTEMS WEST INC.; *U.S. Private*, pg. 1511
FRAMESTORE INC.—See Cultural Investment Holdings Co., Ltd.; *Int'l*, pg. 1877
FREEMAN EXHIBIT FABRICATION & GRAPHICS—See Freeman Decorating Co.; *U.S. Private*, pg. 1605
FT STUDIOS GMBH—See Bertelsmann SE & Co. KGaA; *Int'l*, pg. 992
GOMAX ELECTRONICS, INC.; *Int'l*, pg. 3037
HENSCHEL STEINAU INC.; *U.S. Private*, pg. 1919
HERITAGE GROUP; *U.S. Private*, pg. 1923
J. CHRISTOF GESELLSCHAFT M.B.H.—See Christof Holding AG; *Int'l*, pg. 1587
JCR-CHRISTOF CONSULTING S.R.L.—See Christof Holding AG; *Int'l*, pg. 1587
MIDDOUGH CONSULTING, WEST VIRGINIA—See Middough, Inc.; *U.S. Private*, pg. 2714
ORIGO SOLUTIONS AS—See HitecVision AS; *Int'l*, pg. 3426
O & S DESIGNS INC.—See MGS Manufacturing Group, Inc.; *U.S. Private*, pg. 2695
PETUNIA PICKLE BOTTOM CORPORATION; *U.S. Private*, pg. 3163
PRIMUS DESIGN SERVICES—See Primus Builders, Inc.; *U.S. Private*, pg. 3263
QUAD PLUS LLC; *U.S. Private*, pg. 3315
RABBIT PROTOTYPE CO., LTD.—See Applicad Public Company Limited; *Int'l*, pg. 521
REAL DATA MANAGEMENT INC.—See Building Engines, Inc.; *U.S. Private*, pg. 682
RENEWABLE ENERGY PRODUCTS GMBH—See Christof Holding AG; *Int'l*, pg. 1587
ROBRADY, INC.; *U.S. Private*, pg. 3462
SAMPIERANA S.P.A.—See CNH Industrial N.V.; *Int'l*, pg. 1676
SHAKLEE CANADA, INC.—See Activated Holdings LLC; *U.S. Private*, pg. 68
SHAKLEE CANADA, INC.—See Ripplewood Holdings LLC; *U.S. Private*, pg. 3439
SHANGAI SHUANGJE TECHNOLOGY CO., LTD.—See Alten S.A.; *Int'l*, pg. 391
SONNEMAN DESIGN GROUP, INC—See Dunes Point Capital, LLC; *U.S. Private*, pg. 1289
SPADONE-HYPEX INC.—See HyPex Inc.; *U.S. Private*, pg. 2020
STABIPLAN S.A.S.—See Trimble, Inc.; *U.S. Public*, pg. 2191
STERLING CONTROLS, INC.—See DNS Capital, LLC; *U.S. Private*, pg. 1249
T&T HONDA LTD—See Aga Khan Development Network; *Int'l*, pg. 199
WALTER DORWIN TEAGUE ASSOCIATES INC.; *U.S. Private*, pg. 4433

541430 — GRAPHIC DESIGN SERVICES

N.A.I.C.S. INDEX

541430 — GRAPHIC DESIGN SERV...

24 HOUR COMPANY; *U.S. Private*, pg. 6
3NORTH; *U.S. Private*, pg. 13
AB REPRONIK—See Carl Bennet AB; *Int'l*, pg. 1331
ACCENT GRAPHIC S.L.—See Fluidra SA; *Int'l*, pg. 2713
ACCOLADE FINLAND OY—See Apollo Global Management, Inc.; *U.S. Public*, pg. 165
ADGRAPHICS (US), INC.—See Taylor Corporation; *U.S. Private*, pg. 3938
ALI BIN ALI TECHNOLOGY SOLUTIONS—See Ali Bin Ali Establishment; *Int'l*, pg. 320
ALLIANCE CREATIVE GROUP, INC.; *U.S. Public*, pg. 79
AMANACLIQ SHANGHAI LIMITED—See Amana Inc.; *Int'l*, pg. 409
AMANA INC.; *Int'l*, pg. 409
AMC RO STUDIOS S.R.L.—See Canada Pension Plan Investment Board; *Int'l*, pg. 1280
AMC RO STUDIOS S.R.L.—See EQT AB; *Int'l*, pg. 2482
THE AMGRAPH GROUP; *U.S. Private*, pg. 3986
AMUSE INC.; *Int'l*, pg. 442
ANTHEM! DESIGN PTY. LTD.—See Matthews International Corporation; *U.S. Public*, pg. 1400
ANTHEM WORLDWIDE - TORONTO—See Matthews International Corporation; *U.S. Public*, pg. 1401
ARC DOCUMENT SOLUTIONS - TEXAS—See ARC DOCUMENT SOLUTIONS, INC.; *U.S. Public*, pg. 178
ARGO GRAPHICS INC.; *Int'l*, pg. 562
BENTO BOX ENTERTAINMENT, LLC—See Fox Corporation; *U.S. Public*, pg. 875
BIG MACHINE DESIGN LLC—See Roger TV; *U.S. Private*, pg. 3471
BRANDIMAGE DESGRIPPES AND LAGA SAS—See Matthews International Corporation; *U.S. Public*, pg. 1400
BRANDPACK CONSULTING GMBH—See Graphic Packaging Holding Company; *U.S. Public*, pg. 958
BRUCE MAU DESIGN INC.—See Stagwell, Inc.; *U.S. Public*, pg. 1926
BRUCE MAU HOLDINGS LTD.—See Stagwell, Inc.; *U.S. Public*, pg. 1926
BULLNOSE LIMITED—See Providence Equity Partners L.L.C.; *U.S. Private*, pg. 3291
CHARACTER SF, LLC—See Dentsu Group Inc.; *Int'l*, pg. 2035
CLASSIC GRAPHICS, LLC—See Keystone Group, L.P.; *U.S. Private*, pg. 2298
COLOR EDGE LLC - NEW JERSEY PRODUCTION OFFICE—See Saints Capital, LLC; *U.S. Private*, pg. 3530
COLOR EDGE LLC—See Saints Capital, LLC; *U.S. Private*, pg. 3530
COMP 24 LLC—See Saints Capital, LLC; *U.S. Private*, pg. 3530
COMPUTER GRAPHICS WORLD—See COP Communications; *U.S. Private*, pg. 1044
CONTINUUM INNOVATION LLC—See EPAM Systems, Inc.; *U.S. Public*, pg. 783
CONTINUUM SRL—See EPAM Systems, Inc.; *U.S. Public*, pg. 783
CUBICLE NINJAS LLC; *U.S. Private*, pg. 1120
CURIOSITY INC.—See Future Corporation; *Int'l*, pg. 2853
DATACHAMBERS LLC—See EQT AB; *Int'l*, pg. 2480
DB STUDIOS, INC.—See HH Global Group Limited; *Int'l*, pg. 3378
DENTSU CREATIVE X INC.—See Dentsu Group Inc.; *Int'l*, pg. 2034
DENTSU ON-DEMAND GRAPHICS INC.—See Dentsu Group Inc.; *Int'l*, pg. 2038
DESIGN GROUP ITALIA CORP.—See Alkemy SpA; *Int'l*, pg. 331
DESIGN GROUP ITALIA I.D. S.R.L.—See Alkemy SpA; *Int'l*, pg. 331
DESIGN PICKLE, LLC; *U.S. Private*, pg. 1214
DIALOGCONCEPTS, INC.—See Agital Holdings, LLC; *U.S. Private*, pg. 128
DIC COLOR DESIGN, INC.—See DIC Corporation; *Int'l*, pg. 2107
DIVERSIFIED LABELING SOLUTIONS, INC.; *U.S. Private*, pg. 1243
DNP ART COMMUNICATIONS CO., LTD.—See Dai Nippon Printing Co., Ltd.; *Int'l*, pg. 1914
DOT GF CO., LTD.—See FreakOut Holdings, Inc.; *U.S. Private*, pg. 2767
DR. GRAPHX—See Tukaiz LLC; *U.S. Private*, pg. 4257
DUARTE, INC.; *U.S. Private*, pg. 1283
DUNN BLUE PRINT COMPANY; *U.S. Private*, pg. 1290
EAGLE ENTERPRISE, INC.—See General Dynamics Corporation; *U.S. Public*, pg. 913
ECRM IMAGING SYSTEMS-CHINA—See ECRM Imaging Systems, Inc.; *U.S. Private*, pg. 1330
ECRM IMAGING SYSTEMS-HONG KONG—See ECRM Imaging Systems, Inc.; *U.S. Private*, pg. 1330
EDDING AG; *Int'l*, pg. 2304
EDMONTON JOURNAL GROUP INC.—See Chatham Asset Management, LLC; *U.S. Private*, pg. 861
ELANDERS DIGITALTRYCK AB—See Carl Bennet AB; *Int'l*, pg. 1331
ELANDERS GUMMESSONS AB—See Carl Bennet AB; *Int'l*, pg. 1331

ELANDERS HINDSON LTD.—See Carl Bennet AB; *Int'l*, pg. 1331
ELANDERS NOVUM AB, STOCKHOLM—See Carl Bennet AB; *Int'l*, pg. 1331
ELANDERS POLSKA SP. Z.O.O.—See Carl Bennet AB; *Int'l*, pg. 1331
ELANDERS—See Carl Bennet AB; *Int'l*, pg. 1331
ELANDERS STOCKHOLM—See Carl Bennet AB; *Int'l*, pg. 1331
ELANDERS SVENSKT TRYCK AB—See Carl Bennet AB; *Int'l*, pg. 1331
ELANDERS SVERIGE AB—See Carl Bennet AB; *Int'l*, pg. 1331
ELANDERS UK LTD.—See Carl Bennet AB; *Int'l*, pg. 1331
EMERA S.R.L.—See BayWa AG; *Int'l*, pg. 917
EMN ACQUISITION CORPORATION—See RMG Networks Holding Corporation; *U.S. Private*, pg. 3451
EMU DESIGN (QLD) PTY. LTD.—See GBST Holdings Limited; *Int'l*, pg. 2893
ENTAMEDIA LTD.—See Entatech UK Ltd.; *Int'l*, pg. 2450
ENVISIONIT MEDIA, INC.; *U.S. Private*, pg. 1410
EUROBANK DIREKTNA A.D—See Eurobank Ergasias Services and Holdings S.A.; *Int'l*, pg. 2532
EVOLUTION BUREAU; *U.S. Private*, pg. 1442
FAKE LOVE LLC—See The New York Times Company; *U.S. Public*, pg. 2116
FARHEAP SOLUTIONS, INC.; *U.S. Private*, pg. 1473
FILMOLUX DEUTSCHLAND GMBH—See Blue Cap AG; *Int'l*, pg. 1067
FILMOLUX SWISS AG—See Blue Cap AG; *Int'l*, pg. 1067
FORGE MEDIA GROUP LIMITED; *Int'l*, pg. 2733
FREEDOM OF CREATION B.V.—See 3D Systems Corporation; *U.S. Public*, pg. 4
FUJI CREATIVE CORPORATION—See Fuji Media Holdings, Inc.; *Int'l*, pg. 2813
FUJIFILM CANDA INC.-GRAPHIC SYSTEMS DIVISION—See FUJIFILM Holdings Corporation; *Int'l*, pg. 2821
FUJIFILM GRAPHIC SYSTEMS CO., LTD.—See FUJIFILM Holdings Corporation; *Int'l*, pg. 2824
FUSEFX, INC.—See EagleTree Capital, LP; *U.S. Private*, pg. 1311
GALILEO GLOBAL BRANDING GROUP INC.—See Bain Capital, LP; *U.S. Private*, pg. 439
GANNETT FLEMING, INC. - GANCOM DIVISION—See OceanSound Partners, LP; *U.S. Private*, pg. 2991
GDD POLET; *Int'l*, pg. 2896
GERARD DESIGN; *U.S. Private*, pg. 1686
GERBER SCIENTIFIC (SHANGHAI) CO., LTD.—See Vector Capital Management, L.P.; *U.S. Private*, pg. 4350
GIK OKO D.D.; *Int'l*, pg. 2972
GLOBALWIDE M&E PTE. LTD.—See Air Water Inc.; *Int'l*, pg. 240
GRAPHIC MATTER, INC.—See Baldwin & Obenauf, Inc.; *U.S. Private*, pg. 458
GRASSROOTS INC.; *Int'l*, pg. 3061
HAPPY FORSMAN & BODENFORS AB—See Stagwell, Inc.; *U.S. Public*, pg. 1927
HAROLD M. PITMAN COMPANY, INC.—See Agfa-Gevaert N.V.; *Int'l*, pg. 208
H. BRUNNER GMBH—See Chequers SA; *Int'l*, pg. 1471
HEARTWOOD STUDIOS, INC.; *U.S. Private*, pg. 1901
HELLO DESIGN, LLC—See Stagwell, Inc.; *U.S. Public*, pg. 1927
HINGE, INCORPORATED; *U.S. Private*, pg. 1949
HOLIDAY IMAGE, INC.; *U.S. Private*, pg. 1963
HORIZON DOWNING LLC—See Downing Displays Inc.; *U.S. Private*, pg. 1269
HOT STUDIO, INC.; *U.S. Private*, pg. 1989
HUNAN HUAKAI CULTURAL AND CREATIVE CO., LTD; *Int'l*, pg. 3532
IDEASTREAM CONSUMER PRODUCTS, LLC; *U.S. Private*, pg. 2037
IDESIGN INC.—See Phase 3 Media, LLC; *U.S. Private*, pg. 3166
IIMAGEMORE CO., LTD.—See Fullerton Technology Co., Ltd.; *Int'l*, pg. 2842
IMAGEBOX GROUP PTY LIMITED—See Enero Group Limited; *Int'l*, pg. 2424
IMAGELINX MILTON KEYNES LTD—See Imagelinx Plc; *Int'l*, pg. 3618
IMAGELINX SCOTLAND LTD—See Imagelinx Plc; *Int'l*, pg. 3618
IMAGELINX USA INC—See Imagelinx Plc; *Int'l*, pg. 3618
IMAGINE COMMUNICATIONS CORP. - GERMANY—See L3Harris Technologies, Inc.; *U.S. Public*, pg. 1280
INFLUENCE GRAPHICS; *U.S. Private*, pg. 2072
INREALITY, LLC—See The Jordan Company, L.P.; *U.S. Private*, pg. 4062
INTEGRATED PRINT & GRAPHICS—See Ennis, Inc.; *U.S. Public*, pg. 769
THE INTOUCH GROUP LTD—See Matthews International Corporation; *U.S. Public*, pg. 1401
IO MEDIA, INC.—See Live Nation Entertainment, Inc.; *U.S. Public*, pg. 1329
KAY PREMIUM MARKING FILMS, LTD.—See Kay Screen Printing, Inc.; *U.S. Private*, pg. 2266

KELMSCOTT COMMUNICATIONS, INC.; *U.S. Private*, pg. 2277
KIRKWOOD DIGITAL LLC—See Kirkwood Holding, Inc.; *U.S. Private*, pg. 2315
KPMF USA INC—See Kay Screen Printing, Inc.; *U.S. Private*, pg. 2266
LAUNCH CREATIVE MARKETING; *U.S. Private*, pg. 2398
LOGOWORKS—See HP Inc.; *U.S. Public*, pg. 1063
MACCHINGRAF SRL—See Sycamore Partners Management, LP; *U.S. Private*, pg. 3897
MADISON/GRAHAM COLORGRAPHICS INTERSTATE SERVICES, INC.—See Cenveo, Inc.; *U.S. Private*, pg. 835
MAGNAPLAN CORPORATION; *U.S. Private*, pg. 2546
MAQUINARIA ARTES GRAFICAS HARTMANN SA—See Sycamore Partners Management, LP; *U.S. Private*, pg. 3897
MARKETING BY DESIGN, LLC—See Matthews International Corporation; *U.S. Public*, pg. 1401
MARKETING CONCEPTS OF MINNESOTA, INC.; *U.S. Private*, pg. 2580
MARKETING PARTNERS INC.; *U.S. Private*, pg. 2580
MCLOONE METAL GRAPHICS, INC.—See JSJ Corporation; *U.S. Private*, pg. 2241
MDG—See Freeman Decorating Co.; *U.S. Private*, pg. 1605
MIDNIGHT OIL CREATIVE; *U.S. Private*, pg. 2716
MIRROR PLUS TECHNOLOGIES, INC.—See ARC DOCUMENT SOLUTIONS, INC.; *U.S. Public*, pg. 179
MONDO MEDIA CORPORATION; *U.S. Private*, pg. 2769
MOTIVATIONAL SYSTEMS INC.; *U.S. Private*, pg. 2796
MOXIE MEDIA MN, LLC—See Daggett Ventures, LLC; *U.S. Private*, pg. 1144
NATIONAL HEALTHCARE RESOURCES, INC—See Greenbriar Equity Group, L.P.; *U.S. Private*, pg. 1776
NATIONAL HEALTHCARE RESOURCES, INC—See Revolent Capital Solutions; *U.S. Private*, pg. 3416
NATIONAL INSTRUMENTS GERMANY GMBH—See National Instruments Corporation; *U.S. Public*, pg. 2857
NATIONAL INSTRUMENTS SINGAPORE (PTE) LTD.—See National Instruments Corporation; *U.S. Public*, pg. 2857
NATIONAL INSTRUMENTS (THAILAND) CO., LTD.—See National Instruments Corporation; *U.S. Public*, pg. 2857
NEUGELB STUDIOS GMBH—See Commerzbank AG; *Int'l*, pg. 1719
NEW YORK TIMES LIMITED—See The New York Times Company; *U.S. Public*, pg. 2117
NEXSYS TECHNOLOGIES LLC—See Rocket Companies, Inc.; *U.S. Public*, pg. 1804
OFFICE BEACON LLC; *U.S. Private*, pg. 3001
OMNISTUDIO, INC.; *U.S. Private*, pg. 3017
OPTIMA GRAPHICS, INC.—See Taylor Corporation; *U.S. Private*, pg. 3938
ORGANIC FOOD BROKERS, LLC—See Innovative Food Holdings, Inc.; *U.S. Public*, pg. 1127
PAPERG; *U.S. Private*, pg. 3088
PENTAGRAM DESIGN, INC.; *U.S. Private*, pg. 3140
PERFORMANCE DESIGNED PRODUCTS, LLC—See Diversis Capital, LLC; *U.S. Private*, pg. 1244
PHASE 3 MEDIA, LLC; *U.S. Private*, pg. 3166
PIPITONE GROUP; *U.S. Private*, pg. 3190
PRIMARY DESIGN INC.—See Cloud Mellow Consulting Ltd. Co.; *U.S. Private*, pg. 946
PRODUCTIONS GRAPHICS AGENCEMENT ET VOLUME—See HH Global Group Limited; *Int'l*, pg. 3379
PROSPERITY WELLNESS CENTER—See Discovery Behavioral Health, Inc; *U.S. Private*, pg. 1238
PT. NATIONAL INSTRUMENTS INDONESIA—See National Instruments Corporation; *U.S. Public*, pg. 2858
RICHARD LAYNE; *U.S. Private*, pg. 3428
ROCK CREEK STRATEGIC MARKETING; *U.S. Private*, pg. 3464
ROCKET COMMUNICATIONS INC.; *U.S. Private*, pg. 3466
ROSSO AMARANTO S.R.L.—See High Fashion International Limited; *Int'l*, pg. 3385
SALT BRANDING, LLC—See Tailwind Capital Group, LLC; *U.S. Private*, pg. 3924
SCHAFER CONDON CARTER; *U.S. Private*, pg. 3563
SCHAWK CANADA INC.—See Matthews International Corporation; *U.S. Public*, pg. 1401
SCHAWK DE MEXICO SRL DE CV—See Matthews International Corporation; *U.S. Public*, pg. 1401
SCHAWK IMAGING SDN. BHD.—See Matthews International Corporation; *U.S. Public*, pg. 1401
SCHAWK IMAGING (SHANGHAI) CO. LTD.—See Matthews International Corporation; *U.S. Public*, pg. 1401
SCHAWK JAPAN, LTD.—See Matthews International Corporation; *U.S. Public*, pg. 1401
SCHAWK RETAIL MARKETING—See Matthews International Corporation; *U.S. Public*, pg. 1401
SME, INC.—See Atairos Group, Inc.; *U.S. Private*, pg. 364
SOCIEDAD QUIMICA ALEMANA S.A.—See Avient Corporation; *U.S. Public*, pg. 248
SOULSIGHT, LLC—See Bruins Sports Capital, LLC; *U.S. Private*, pg. 672
SOUTHERN GRAPHIC SYSTEMS, LLC—See HPS Investment Partners, LLC; *U.S. Private*, pg. 1997
SPANDEX AG—See Chequers SA; *Int'l*, pg. 1471
SPECTRA GROUP LTD.; *U.S. Private*, pg. 3751

541430 — GRAPHIC DESIGN SERV...

STAN ADLER ASSOCIATES, INC.—See CHR Group LLC; *U.S. Private*, pg. 889
STRUCTURAL GRAPHICS, LLC; *U.S. Private*, pg. 3841
SUMMIT MANUFACTURING LLC—See Array Marketing Group Inc.; *Int'l*, pg. 578
SUN BELLE INC.; *U.S. Private*, pg. 3858
SUN GRAPHIC TECHNOLOGIES, INC.; *U.S. Private*, pg. 3863
SUOMALAINEN LEHTITAINO OY—See Alma Media Corporation; *Int'l*, pg. 362
SVENSKA MEDIA I LJUSDAL AB—See Byggfakta Group Nordic HoldCo AB; *Int'l*, pg. 1235
SYMPLICIT PTY LTD—See DWS Limited; *Int'l*, pg. 2236
TAG PAC LIMITED—See Deutsche Post AG; *Int'l*, pg. 2082
TAG PRINT SERVICES LIMITED—See Dentsu Group Inc.; *Int'l*, pg. 2039
TAG SAO PAULO SERVICO DE CONSULTORIA LTDA.—See Dentsu Group Inc.; *Int'l*, pg. 2039
TAPHANDLES INC.; *U.S. Private*, pg. 3932
TARGET OMAHA MARKETING, INC.; *U.S. Private*, pg. 3933
TEAM FITZ GRAPHICS, LLC; *U.S. Private*, pg. 3949
TERRES AGENTUR GMBH—See AGRAVIS Raiffeisen AG; *Int'l*, pg. 215
THEOREM CREATIONS—See Theorem Inc.; *U.S. Private*, pg. 4141
THEPRINTERS.COM; *U.S. Private*, pg. 4142
TREALITY SVS LLC—See TransDigm Group Incorporated; *U.S. Public*, pg. 2181
VALURATE CO., LTD.—See Grcs Inc.; *Int'l*, pg. 3063
VCG (HOLDINGS) LIMITED—See Matthews International Corporation; *U.S. Public*, pg. 1401
THE VERNON COMPANY - VERNON DISPLAY GRAPHICS DIVISION—See The Vernon Company; *U.S. Private*, pg. 4130
VIVID PRINT SOLUTIONS INC.—See Securian Financial Group, Inc.; *U.S. Private*, pg. 3594
WALKER DESIGN GROUP, LLC; *U.S. Private*, pg. 4429
THE WATKINS COMPANY INC.; *U.S. Private*, pg. 4133
WORKS ZEBRA CO., LTD.—See Amana Inc.; *Int'l*, pg. 409
XPD INC.—See AOI TYO Holdings Inc.; *Int'l*, pg. 488
XPLANE CORP.; *U.S. Private*, pg. 4582
XPRESSDOCS PARTNERS, LTD.—See The Reynolds & Reynolds Company; *U.S. Private*, pg. 4106
XPRESS MEDIA PHILIPPINES INC.—See A-Smart Holdings Ltd.; *Int'l*, pg. 20
YORKTEL FRANCE SAS—See Yorktel, Inc.; *U.S. Private*, pg. 4591

541490 — OTHER SPECIALIZED DESIGN SERVICES

ABINGDON FURNITURE GALLERY LIMITED; *Int'l*, pg. 61
AFG INTERNATIONAL AG—See Arbonia AG; *Int'l*, pg. 537
AKT ENTERPRISES; *U.S. Private*, pg. 146
AMMUNITION LLC; *U.S. Private*, pg. 264
ANSEM BV—See Cyient Limited; *Int'l*, pg. 1895
ANSEM NV—See Cyient Limited; *Int'l*, pg. 1895
AOKI HOLDINGS INC.; *Int'l*, pg. 488
AOKI INC.—See AOKI Holdings Inc.; *Int'l*, pg. 488
ARTEFACT; *U.S. Private*, pg. 340
AV PROMOTIONS HOLDINGS LIMITED; *Int'l*, pg. 733
THE BECKER GROUP, LTD.—See Viad Corp.; *U.S. Public*, pg. 2291
BOG'ART FASHION SRL—See Bog'Art S.R.L.; *Int'l*, pg. 1100
BRIERLEY+PARTNERS JAPAN, INC.—See Capillary Technologies International Pte Ltd.; *Int'l*, pg. 1308
BURTON ENERGY GROUP; *U.S. Private*, pg. 693
CALGARY TENT & AWNING LTD.; *Int'l*, pg. 1263
CAREER TECHNOLOGIES USA—See Arsenal Capital Management LP; *U.S. Private*, pg. 338
CG MOTORS PRIVATE LTD—See Avantha Group; *Int'l*, pg. 735
CHIA HER INDUSTRIAL CO., LTD. - TAINAN MILL—See Chia Her Industrial Co., Ltd.; *Int'l*, pg. 1475
CHOW TAI SENG JEWELLERY COMPANY LIMITED; *Int'l*, pg. 1585
COFELY EPULETGEPESZETI KFT.—See ENGIE SA; *Int'l*, pg. 2429
CONCEPTBAIT, INC.; *U.S. Private*, pg. 1009
CONRAN & PARTNERS LTD.—See Conran Holdings Limited; *Int'l*, pg. 1769
CPG CONSULTANTS INDIA PVT LTD—See China Architecture Design & Research Group; *Int'l*, pg. 1483
CREATIVE BRANCH; *U.S. Private*, pg. 1087
CREATIVE TENT INTERNATIONAL, INC.—See XFS Global LLC; *U.S. Private*, pg. 4581
CUBIC TECHNOLOGIES SINGAPORE PTE. LTD.—See Elliott Management Corporation; *U.S. Private*, pg. 1367
CUBIC TECHNOLOGIES SINGAPORE PTE. LTD.—See Veritas Capital Fund Management, LLC; *U.S. Private*, pg. 4361
DAIHEN CORPORATION; *Int'l*, pg. 1926
DARRELL'S SIGN COMPANY; *U.S. Private*, pg. 1159
DAVIDE GROPPI S.R.L.—See Dexelance S.p.A.; *Int'l*, pg. 2092

D&B INTERIORS (PTY) LTD.—See Draexlmaier Gruppe; *Int'l*, pg. 2198
DECOROUS INVESTMENT & TRADING CO. LTD.; *Int'l*, pg. 2001
DISTORTIONS UNLIMITED CORP.; *U.S. Private*, pg. 1239
DYNA CONTRACTING; *U.S. Private*, pg. 1297
EAC PRODUCT DEVELOPMENT SOLUTIONS; *U.S. Private*, pg. 1308
E.C. BARTON & CO. DESIGN CENTER—See E.C. Barton & Company; *U.S. Private*, pg. 1304
ENTIRE PRODUCTIONS, INC.; *U.S. Private*, pg. 1405
ENVOY TEXTILES LTD.; *Int'l*, pg. 2456
ESCADA UK LTD.—See Regent, L.P.; *U.S. Private*, pg. 3387
ESPRIT GLOBAL IMAGE GMBH—See Esprit Holdings Limited; *Int'l*, pg. 2507
FASBEE INC.—See BEENOS Inc.; *Int'l*, pg. 939
FASHOFF UK LTD—See Aeffe SpA; *Int'l*, pg. 173
FEV EUROPE GMBH—See E.ON SE; *Int'l*, pg. 2257
FISHMAN & ASSOCIATES, INC.; *U.S. Private*, pg. 1535
FLEXALIGHTING S.R.L.—See Dexelance S.p.A.; *Int'l*, pg. 2092
FOCUS LIGHTING CORP.—See Focus Lighting & Fixtures Limited; *Int'l*, pg. 2719
FRENCH CONNECTION LIMITED—See French Connection Group plc; *Int'l*, pg. 2772
FUSION OPTIX, INC.; *U.S. Private*, pg. 1625
GPD, PC; *U.S. Private*, pg. 1748
GREG NORMAN GOLF COURSE DESIGN COMPANY—See Great White Shark Enterprises, Inc.; *U.S. Private*, pg. 1768
GROUNDS FOR PLAY INC.—See Pfingsten Partners, LLC; *U.S. Private*, pg. 3164
HARMONIX MUSIC SYSTEMS, INC.—See National Amusements, Inc.; *U.S. Private*, pg. 2841
HAYAMIZUDENKI CO., LTD.—See Chudenko Corporation; *Int'l*, pg. 1594
HOLDING TEXTILE HERMES SAS—See Hermes International SCA; *Int'l*, pg. 3363
HONCO INC.; *Int'l*, pg. 3459
HYDER CONSULTING GMBH DEUTSCHLAND—See ARCADIS N.V.; *Int'l*, pg. 541
HYDER CONSULTING INDIA PVT LTD—See ARCADIS N.V.; *Int'l*, pg. 541
HYFN; *U.S. Private*, pg. 2018
IDL WORLDWIDE, INC.—See Matthews International Corporation; *U.S. Public*, pg. 1399
INTELLIGENT PRODUCT SOLUTIONS, INC.—See Forward Industries, Inc.; *U.S. Public*, pg. 874
ITE MODA LTD.—See Providence Equity Partners L.L.C.; *U.S. Private*, pg. 3293
ITE MODA LTD.—See Searchlight Capital Partners, L.P.; *U.S. Private*, pg. 3588
JACK WILLS LTD.—See Frasers Group plc; *Int'l*, pg. 2765
JADE DESIGN, INC.; *U.S. Private*, pg. 2181
L.A.R.K. INDUSTRIES, INC.—See Littlejohn & Co., LLC; *U.S. Private*, pg. 2470
L.A.R.K. INDUSTRIES, INC.—See Platinum Equity, LLC; *U.S. Private*, pg. 3205
LIGHT BUREAU LIMITED—See AFRY AB; *Int'l*, pg. 194
LIGHT PLUS DESIGN LIMITED—See Allied Sustainability & Environmental Consultants Group Limited; *Int'l*, pg. 358
LUNA TEXTILES—See Camira Fabrics Ltd.; *Int'l*, pg. 1273
LUXE LIGHTS LIMITED—See Eneraqua Technologies Plc; *Int'l*, pg. 2418
MACRO ENERGY; *U.S. Private*, pg. 2538
MAHARAM FABRIC CORPORATION—See MillerKnoll, Inc.; *U.S. Private*, pg. 1447
MARCHEX, INC.; *U.S. Public*, pg. 1364
MEDEX-MEDIA—See Clayton, Dubilier & Rice, LLC; *U.S. Private*, pg. 928
MICHAEL KORS, LLC—See Capri Holdings Limited; *Int'l*, pg. 1316
MOJOTECH, LLC; *U.S. Private*, pg. 2766
NEXT TOWER S.A.S.—See Carmila SA; *Int'l*, pg. 1342
NPI SOLUTIONS, INC.—See Amphenol Corporation; *U.S. Public*, pg. 131
ON DESIGN CZECH S.R.O.—See ON Semiconductor Corporation; *U.S. Public*, pg. 1600
ORIHICA INC.—See AOKI Holdings Inc.; *Int'l*, pg. 488
ORIZZONTE SISTEMI NAVALI S.P.A.—See Fincantieri S.p.A.; *Int'l*, pg. 2671
P2 LED CUBE—See Heerim Architects & Planners Co., Ltd.; *Int'l*, pg. 3307
PAN ASIA TECHNICAL AUTOMOTIVE CENTER CO., LTD.—See General Motors Company; *U.S. Public*, pg. 928
PANTONE, INC.—See Danaher Corporation; *U.S. Public*, pg. 632
PARKER WILLIAMS DESIGN LTD.—See DIC Corporation; *Int'l*, pg. 2109
PLANETART, LLC—See Claranova SA; *Int'l*, pg. 1642
POINT OF VIEW DESIGN PTY LIMITED—See Firefly Point of View Ltd.; *Int'l*, pg. 2679
POLLINI SPA—See Aeffe SpA; *Int'l*, pg. 173
PRETEX TEXTILHANDELS GMBH—See French Connection Group plc; *Int'l*, pg. 2772
RIETVELD SERIGRAFIE B.V.—See Avery Dennison Corporation; *U.S. Public*, pg. 245

CORPORATE AFFILIATIONS

RUHL-PARR/MORAN ARCHITECTS LLC; *U.S. Private*, pg. 3502
SANDSTORM DESIGN, INC.; *U.S. Private*, pg. 3545
SAVAGE RANGE SYSTEMS, INC.—See Vista Outdoor Inc.; *U.S. Public*, pg. 2305
SED S.R.L.—See A2A S.p.A.; *Int'l*, pg. 29
SHARKNINJA APPLIANCE LLC—See SharkNinja, Inc.; *U.S. Public*, pg. 1873
SHOWORKS INC.; *U.S. Private*, pg. 3643
SIENNA ECAD TECHNOLOGIES PVT. LTD.—See Sienna Corporation Inc.; *U.S. Private*, pg. 3646
SKETCHDECK INC.—See 24 Seven, LLC; *U.S. Private*, pg. 6
SOLUTIONSET LLC; *U.S. Private*, pg. 3711
SQBG, INC.—See Sequential Brands Group, Inc.; *U.S. Public*, pg. 1868
STAR ALLIANCE INTERNATIONAL CORP.; *U.S. Public*, pg. 1936
STV/GWD—See STV Group, Inc.; *U.S. Private*, pg. 3846
SUNDOG INTERACTIVE, INC.—See EQT AB; *Int'l*, pg. 2483
SUNRISE BRANDS, LLC—See Sunrise Acquisition Corp.; *U.S. Private*, pg. 3869
SYMMETRY CREATIVE PRODUCTION; *U.S. Private*, pg. 3899
TAG EUROPE LIMITED—See Dentsu Group Inc.; *Int'l*, pg. 2039
TAG RESPONSE LIMITED—See Dentsu Group Inc.; *Int'l*, pg. 2039
TAG WORLDWIDE (USA) INC.—See Dentsu Group Inc.; *Int'l*, pg. 2039
TANGO SYSTEM LLC—See Applied Materials, Inc.; *U.S. Public*, pg. 172
TECSOUND (QLD) PTY. LTD.—See Azure Healthcare Limited; *Int'l*, pg. 782
TECSOUND (VIC) PTY. LTD.—See Azure Healthcare Limited; *Int'l*, pg. 782
TECSOUND (WEST AUSTRALIA) PTY. LTD.—See Azure Healthcare Limited; *Int'l*, pg. 782
TENNESSEE RAND, INC.—See Lincoln Electric Holdings, Inc.; *U.S. Public*, pg. 1318
THERMOPATCH B.V.—See Avery Dennison Corporation; *U.S. Public*, pg. 245
THERMOPATCH (CANADA) INC.—See Avery Dennison Corporation; *U.S. Public*, pg. 245
THERMOPATCH DEUTSCHLAND GMBH—See Avery Dennison Corporation; *U.S. Public*, pg. 245
THERMOPATCH UK LTD.—See Avery Dennison Corporation; *U.S. Public*, pg. 245
THINKWELL GROUP, INC.—See Tait Towers Inc; *U.S. Private*, pg. 3925
TRICORBRAUN DESIGN & ENGINEERING—See Ares Management Corporation; *U.S. Public*, pg. 191
VARD DESIGN AS—See Fincantieri S.p.A.; *Int'l*, pg. 2671
VINCENT CAMUTO LLC—See Schottenstein Stores Corporation; *U.S. Private*, pg. 3569
WEBFIRM PTY LTD—See Adslot Ltd.; *Int'l*, pg. 154
WOMEN IN BUSINESS/FABRIQUE; *U.S. Private*, pg. 4556
WUXI CHINA RESOURCES SEMICO CO., LTD.—See China Resources (Holdings) Co., Ltd.; *Int'l*, pg. 1548
ZEBULON SOLUTIONS LLC; *U.S. Private*, pg. 4599

541511 — CUSTOM COMPUTER PROGRAMMING SERVICES

11 BIT STUDIOS SA; *Int'l*, pg. 1
12 RETECH CORPORATION; *U.S. Public*, pg. 1
1871—See Chicagoland Entrepreneurial Center; *U.S. Private*, pg. 879
1SPATIAL AUSTRALIA PTY LIMITED—See 1Spatial Plc; *Int'l*, pg. 3
1SPATIAL INC.—See 1Spatial Plc; *Int'l*, pg. 3
22ND CENTURY TECHNOLOGIES, INC.; *U.S. Private*, pg. 5
24I MEDIA USA LLC—See Aferian plc; *Int'l*, pg. 185
250K INC.—See Silversmith Management, L.P.; *U.S. Private*, pg. 3664
2CRSI SA; *Int'l*, pg. 4
2HB SOFTWARE DESIGNS, INC.; *U.S. Private*, pg. 6
2KS CLOUD SERVICES GMBH; *Int'l*, pg. 5
360SCIENCE, INC.—See Bridge Growth Partners, LLC; *U.S. Private*, pg. 648
3D INCORPORATED—See Denso Corporation; *Int'l*, pg. 2028
3D PIONEER SYSTEMS, INC.; *U.S. Public*, pg. 4
3POINTS, LLC—See Southfield Capital Advisors, LLC; *U.S. Private*, pg. 3736
3 STORY SOFTWARE LLC—See Hays PLC; *Int'l*, pg. 3293
THE 41ST PARAMETER, INC.—See Experian plc; *Int'l*, pg. 2587
4C GROUP AB; *Int'l*, pg. 11
4CITE MARKETING, LLC—See Dentsu Group Inc.; *Int'l*, pg. 2036
4C STRATEGIES AB—See 4C Group AB; *Int'l*, pg. 11
4DMEDICAL LIMITED; *Int'l*, pg. 11
4 GLOBAL PLC; *Int'l*, pg. 10
4U APPLICATIONS, INC—See FUJISOFT INCORPORATED; *Int'l*, pg. 2830

N.A.I.C.S. INDEX

541511 — CUSTOM COMPUTER PRO...

63 MOONS TECHNOLOGIES LIMITED; *Int'l*, pg. 14
6K SYSTEMS, INC.; *U.S. Private*, pg. 16
9274-5322 QUEBEC INC.—See Viavi Solutions Inc.; *U.S. Public*, pg. 2295
9SLIDES, INC.—See KKR & Co. Inc.; *U.S. Public*, pg. 1254
A10 NETWORKS INC.—See A10 Networks, Inc.; *U.S. Public*, pg. 12
A10 NETWORKS, INC.—See A10 Networks, Inc.; *U.S. Public*, pg. 12
A 2 CUSTOMER CARE SP. Z O.O.—See Atende S.A.; *Int'l*, pg. 668
A2IA SAS—See Mitek Systems, Inc.; *U.S. Public*, pg. 1452
A2Z, INC.; *U.S. Private*, pg. 29
A3 COMMUNICATIONS INC.—See Platinum Equity, LLC; *U.S. Private*, pg. 3208
AAA TECHNOLOGIES LIMITED; *Int'l*, pg. 30
AAMRA TECHNOLOGIES LIMITED; *Int'l*, pg. 36
AAREAL FIRST FINANCIAL SOLUTIONS AG—See Advent International Corporation; *U.S. Private*, pg. 96
AAREAL FIRST FINANCIAL SOLUTIONS AG—See Centerbridge Partners, L.P.; *U.S. Private*, pg. 812
AAREON FINLAND OY—See Advent International Corporation; *U.S. Private*, pg. 96
AAREON FINLAND OY—See Centerbridge Partners, L.P.; *U.S. Private*, pg. 812
AAREON NEDERLAND B.V.—See Advent International Corporation; *U.S. Private*, pg. 96
AAREON NEDERLAND B.V.—See Centerbridge Partners, L.P.; *U.S. Private*, pg. 812
AAREON NORGE AS—See Advent International Corporation; *U.S. Private*, pg. 96
AAREON NORGE AS—See Centerbridge Partners, L.P.; *U.S. Private*, pg. 812
AAREON SVERIGE AB—See Advent International Corporation; *U.S. Private*, pg. 96
AAREON SVERIGE AB—See Centerbridge Partners, L.P.; *U.S. Private*, pg. 812
AAREON UK LTD.—See Advent International Corporation; *U.S. Private*, pg. 96
AAREON UK LTD.—See Centerbridge Partners, L.P.; *U.S. Private*, pg. 812
AARHUSGEOSOFTWARE APS—See Bentley Systems, Inc.; *U.S. Public*, pg. 296
AATECH S.P.A.; *Int'l*, pg. 38
ABACAST, INC.; *U.S. Private*, pg. 33
ABACUS DATA SYSTEMS, INC.—See Thomas H. Lee Partners, L.P.; *U.S. Private*, pg. 4155
ABACUS SOFTWARE LIMITED—See Vista Equity Partners, LLC; *U.S. Private*, pg. 4398
ABATE AS INDUSTRIES LTD.; *Int'l*, pg. 48
ABC MULTIACTIVE LIMITED; *Int'l*, pg. 57
ABCS CO., LTD.—See Country Group Development Public Company Limited; *Int'l*, pg. 1818
ABEL SOLUTIONS, INC.; *U.S. Private*, pg. 37
ABLOY CANADA INC.—See ASSA ABLOY AB; *Int'l*, pg. 637
ABSOLUTE SOFTWARE EMEA LIMITED—See Crosspoint Capital Partners LP; *U.S. Private*, pg. 1107
ACADEMICWORKS, LLC—See Blackbaud, Inc.; *U.S. Public*, pg. 341
ACCELERATEBS INDIA LIMITED; *Int'l*, pg. 80
ACCELEWARE LTD.; *Int'l*, pg. 80
ACCELYA SOLUTIONS INDIA LIMITED—See Warburg Pincus LLC; *U.S. Private*, pg. 4436
ACCENTURE AUTOMACAO E TI INDUSTRIAL LTDA—See Accenture plc; *Int'l*, pg. 82
ACCENTURE PTE. LTD.—See Accenture plc; *Int'l*, pg. 84
ACCENTURE TANACSADO KORLATOLT FELELOSSEGU TARSASAG KFT—See Accenture plc; *Int'l*, pg. 84
ACCENTURE TECHNOLOGY SOLUTIONS BV—See Accenture plc; *Int'l*, pg. 84
ACCERTIFY, INC.—See Accel Partners L.P.; *U.S. Private*, pg. 47
ACCERTIFY, INC.—See KKR & Co. Inc.; *U.S. Public*, pg. 1237
ACCESS AP TAIWAN CO., LTD.—See Access Co., Ltd.; *Int'l*, pg. 88
ACCESS DATA CONSULTING CORPORATION—See GEE Group Inc.; *U.S. Public*, pg. 909
ACCESS EUROPE GMBH—See Access Co., Ltd.; *Int'l*, pg. 88
ACCESS SOLUTIONS BELGIUM B.V.—See Carrier Global Corporation; *U.S. Public*, pg. 440
ACCESS SYSTEMS FRANCE SARL—See Access Co., Ltd.; *Int'l*, pg. 88
ACCESS SYSTEMS USA, INC.—See Access Co., Ltd.; *Int'l*, pg. 88
ACCOLITE, INC.—See New Mountain Capital, LLC; *U.S. Private*, pg. 2899
ACCSYS LLC—See PAR Technology Corporation; *U.S. Public*, pg. 1636
ACCSYS (PROPRIETARY) LIMITED—See Business Connexion Group Limited; *Int'l*, pg. 1228
ACCUCODE, INC.; *U.S. Private*, pg. 54
ACCURATE COMPUTER SOLUTIONS, LLC—See The 20 Msp Group LLC; *U.S. Private*, pg. 3980
ACCUVAR, INC.—See Datix, Inc.; *U.S. Private*, pg. 1167
ACD SYSTEMS INTERNATIONAL INC.; *Int'l*, pg. 94

ACER EUROPE SERVICES S.R.L.—See Acer Incorporated; *Int'l*, pg. 99
ACESS TAIWAN LAB. CO., LTD.—See Access Co., Ltd.; *Int'l*, pg. 88
ACE TECHNOLOGIES INC.; *U.S. Private*, pg. 57
ACI AUSTRALIA PTY. LTD—See ACI Worldwide, Inc.; *U.S. Public*, pg. 34
ACI DO BRASIL S.A.—See Corporacion America Airports S.A.; *Int'l*, pg. 1803
ACIERNET SA—See Econocom Group SA; *Int'l*, pg. 2297
ACI GLOBAL LIMITED—See ACI Worldwide, Inc.; *U.S. Public*, pg. 34
ACI GLOBAL LIMITED—See ACI Worldwide, Inc.; *U.S. Public*, pg. 34
ACI WORLDWIDE COLOMBIA S.A.S.—See ACI Worldwide, Inc.; *U.S. Public*, pg. 34
ACI WORLDWIDE DE ARGENTINA S.A.—See ACI Worldwide, Inc.; *U.S. Public*, pg. 35
ACI WORLDWIDE (GERMANY) GMBH—See ACI Worldwide, Inc.; *U.S. Public*, pg. 34
ACLARION, INC.; *U.S. Public*, pg. 35
ACOMMIT AG—See Bechtle AG; *Int'l*, pg. 937
ACOUSTIGUIDE ASIA LTD.—See Espro Information Technologies Ltd.; *Int'l*, pg. 2507
ACOUSTIGUIDE JAPAN LTD.—See Espro Information Technologies Ltd.; *Int'l*, pg. 2507
ACOUSTIGUIDE OF AUSTRALIA PTY., LTD.—See Espro Information Technologies Ltd.; *Int'l*, pg. 2507
ACOUSTIGUIDE SAS—See Espro Information Technologies Ltd.; *Int'l*, pg. 2507
ACRELEC APS—See GLORY Ltd.; *Int'l*, pg. 3009
ACRELEC FINLAND OY—See GLORY Ltd.; *Int'l*, pg. 3009
ACRELEC GMBH—See GLORY Ltd.; *Int'l*, pg. 3009
ACRELEC GROUP BVBA—See GLORY Ltd.; *Int'l*, pg. 3009
ACRELEC INFORMATICA GROUP SL.—See GLORY Ltd.; *Int'l*, pg. 3009
ACRELEC SWEDEN AB—See GLORY Ltd.; *Int'l*, pg. 3009
ACRELEC UK LIMITED—See GLORY Ltd.; *Int'l*, pg. 3009
ACROTECH CO., LTD—See Encourage Technologies Co., Ltd.; *Int'l*, pg. 2402
ACTEOS GMBH & CO. KG—See Acteos S.A.; *Int'l*, pg. 117
ACTIVE BRAINS & TRUST CO., LTD.—See Core Corporation; *Int'l*, pg. 1797
ACTIVECAMPAIGN, LLC—See Silversmith Management, L.P.; *U.S. Private*, pg. 3663
ACTIVE INTERNET TECHNOLOGIES, INC.—See Bridge Growth Partners, LLC; *U.S. Private*, pg. 648
ACTIVEOPS LTD.; *Int'l*, pg. 120
ACTIVEPDF, INC.—See Thoma Bravo, L.P.; *U.S. Private*, pg. 4146
ACTIVEPORT GROUP LIMITED; *Int'l*, pg. 120
ACTIVE VOICES LIMITED—See Comcast Corporation; *U.S. Public*, pg. 537
ACTIVISION BLIZZARD, INC.—See Microsoft Corporation; *U.S. Public*, pg. 1438
ACTIVISION BLIZZARD PTY LIMITED—See Microsoft Corporation; *U.S. Public*, pg. 1438
ACTIX LIMITED—See Amdocs Limited; *Int'l*, pg. 419
ACUITYADS INC.; *Int'l*, pg. 121
ACUMIUM LLC—See Omega Laboratories, Inc.; *U.S. Private*, pg. 3015
ACUSENSUS LIMITED; *Int'l*, pg. 121
ADACEL INC.—See Adacel Technologies Limited; *Int'l*, pg. 123
ADAGE TECHNOLOGIES; *U.S. Private*, pg. 72
ADAPT IT AUSTRALASIA (PTY) LTD—See Constellation Software Inc.; *Int'l*, pg. 1775
ADAPT IT BOTSWANA (PTY) LTD—See Constellation Software Inc.; *Int'l*, pg. 1775
ADAPT IT INTERNATIONAL LIMITED—See Constellation Software Inc.; *Int'l*, pg. 1775
ADAPT IT NIGERIA LIMITED—See Constellation Software Inc.; *Int'l*, pg. 1775
ADAPT IT SOLUTIONS LIMITED—See Constellation Software Inc.; *Int'l*, pg. 1775
ADAPT IT SOLUTIONS PTE LIMITED—See Constellation Software Inc.; *Int'l*, pg. 1775
ADAPTIVE INSIGHTS LIMITED—See Workday, Inc.; *U.S. Public*, pg. 2378
ADAPTIVE INSIGHTS, LTD.—See Workday, Inc.; *U.S. Public*, pg. 2378
ADAPTIVE INSIGHTS PTY. LTD.—See Workday, Inc.; *U.S. Public*, pg. 2378
ADAPTIVEMOBILE SECURITY LTD.—See Enea AB; *Int'l*, pg. 2410
ADAPTIVE SOLUTIONS, INC.—See Morae Global Corp.; *U.S. Private*, pg. 2781
ADAQUEST, INC.; *U.S. Private*, pg. 76
ADCAP NETWORK SYSTEMS, INC.; *U.S. Private*, pg. 76
ADDRESSABLE NETWORKS, INC.; *U.S. Private*, pg. 77
ADDRESSDOCTOR GMBH—See Canada Pension Plan Investment Board; *Int'l*, pg. 1279
ADERANT LEGAL HOLDINGS (AUS) PTY LTD—See Roper Technologies, Inc.; *U.S. Public*, pg. 1810
ADERANT NORTH AMERICA, INC.—See Roper Technologies, Inc.; *U.S. Public*, pg. 1810

ADESAL TELECOM S.L.—See Cellnex Telecom, S.A.; *Int'l*, pg. 1394
ADESSO AUSTRIA GMBH—See adesso SE; *Int'l*, pg. 144
ADESSO HEALTH SOLUTIONS GMBH—See adesso SE; *Int'l*, pg. 144
ADESSO INSURANCE SOLUTIONS GMBH—See adesso SE; *Int'l*, pg. 144
ADESSO SCHWEIZ AG—See adesso SE; *Int'l*, pg. 144
ADESSO SPAIN CONSULTORIA Y SOLUCIONES TECNOLOGICAS S. L.—See adesso SE; *Int'l*, pg. 144
ADESSO TURKEY BILGI TEKNOLOJILERI LTD. STI.—See adesso SE; *Int'l*, pg. 144
ADEXUS S.A.—See Aenza S.A.A.; *Int'l*, pg. 176
ADGATE MEDIA LLC—See Great Hill Partners, L.P.; *U.S. Private*, pg. 1763
ADH SOFT SP. Z.O.O.—See Asseco Poland S.A.; *Int'l*, pg. 641
ADISH CO., LTD.; *Int'l*, pg. 149
ADLON INTELLIGENT SOLUTIONS GMBH; *Int'l*, pg. 151
ADMICOM OYJ; *Int'l*, pg. 151
ADNET SYSTEMS, INC.; *U.S. Private*, pg. 81
ADNOVUM INFORMATIK AG—See IHAG Holding AG; *Int'l*, pg. 3603
ADOBE SYSTEMS CANADA—See Adobe Inc.; *U.S. Public*, pg. 42
ADOBE SYSTEMS IBERICA SL—See Adobe Inc.; *U.S. Public*, pg. 42
ADOBE SYSTEMS INCORPORATED - SEATTLE—See Adobe Inc.; *U.S. Public*, pg. 42
ADP SECURITIES INDUSTRY SOFTWARE—See Automatic Data Processing, Inc.; *U.S. Public*, pg. 230
ADURO CLEAN TECHNOLOGIES INC.; *Int'l*, pg. 154
ADVANCED BLOCKCHAIN AG; *Int'l*, pg. 157
ADVANCED BUSINESS EQUIPMENT LIMITED—See Xerox Holdings Corporation; *U.S. Public*, pg. 2386
ADVANCED COMPUTER SOLUTIONS GROUP LLC—See BAE Systems Applied Intelligence US Corp; *U.S. Private*, pg. 425
ADVANCED CONCEPTS, INC.—See BAE Systems plc; *Int'l*, pg. 797
ADVANCED DIGITAL DATA INC.; *U.S. Private*, pg. 89
ADVANCED MANUFACTURING CONTROL SYSTEMS LTD.; *Int'l*, pg. 160
ADVANCED MEASUREMENTS INC.—See First Reserve Management, L.P.; *U.S. Private*, pg. 1525
ADVANCED PUBLIC SAFETY, INC.—See TA Associates, Inc.; *U.S. Private*, pg. 3914
ADVANCED SOFTWARE TALENT, LLC; *U.S. Private*, pg. 92
ADVANCED SOLUTIONS INTERNATIONAL INC.; *U.S. Private*, pg. 92
ADVANCED SYSTEM DESIGN INC.; *U.S. Private*, pg. 92
ADVANCED SYSTEMS CONCEPTS, INC.—See Redwood Software, Inc.; *U.S. Private*, pg. 3381
ADVANCED TECHNOLOGIES GROUP, INC.—See Jones Lang LaSalle Incorporated; *U.S. Public*, pg. 1201
ADVANCERETAIL TECHNOLOGY ASIA SDN BHD—See 3Q Holdings Limited; *Int'l*, pg. 9
ADVANCERETAIL TECHNOLOGY LIMITED—See 3Q Holdings Limited; *Int'l*, pg. 9
ADVANSOFT DEVELOPMENT CORPORATION—See Advantest Corporation; *Int'l*, pg. 165
ADVENT HEALTH PARTNERS, INC.—See Trend Health Partners LLC; *U.S. Private*, pg. 4218
ADVENT SOFTWARE, INC.—See SS&C Technologies Holdings, Inc.; *U.S. Public*, pg. 1922
ADYEN (CHINA) SOFTWARE TECHNOLOGY CO. LTD.—See Adyen N.V.; *Int'l*, pg. 169
AEMOS SDN BHD; *Int'l*, pg. 175
AEQUOR TECHNOLOGIES, LLC; *U.S. Private*, pg. 117
AERIA INC.; *Int'l*, pg. 179
AEROHIVE NETWORKS EUROPE LTD—See Extreme Networks, Inc.; *U.S. Public*, pg. 813
AEROINFO SYSTEMS, INC.—See The Boeing Company; *U.S. Public*, pg. 2040
AEROMETREX LIMITED; *Int'l*, pg. 181
AEROSCOUT JAPAN, CO., LTD.—See Stanley Black & Decker, Inc.; *U.S. Public*, pg. 1931
AEROSCOUT LTD.—See Stanley Black & Decker, Inc.; *U.S. Public*, pg. 1931
AEROSCOUT (SINGAPORE) PTE. LTD.—See Stanley Black & Decker, Inc.; *U.S. Public*, pg. 1931
AESCU DATA GESELLSCHAFT FUR DATENVERARBEITUNG MBH—See CompuGroup Medical SE & Co. KGaA; *Int'l*, pg. 1755
AESCUDATA GMBH—See CompuGroup Medical SE & Co. KGaA; *Int'l*, pg. 1755
AESPULA TECHNOLOGY INC.—See Alpha Networks Inc.; *Int'l*, pg. 369
AEVI CZ S.R.O—See Diebold Nixdorf, Inc.; *U.S. Public*, pg. 659
AEVI INTERNATIONAL GMBH—See Diebold Nixdorf, Inc.; *U.S. Public*, pg. 659
AEVI UK LIMITED—See Diebold Nixdorf, Inc.; *U.S. Public*, pg. 659
AEYE, INC.; *U.S. Public*, pg. 53
AFAS INC.—See BIPROGY Inc.; *Int'l*, pg. 1045
AFFECTO NORWAY AS—See CGI Inc.; *Int'l*, pg. 1433

AFFECTO SWEDEN AB—See CGI Inc.; *Int'l*, pg. 1433
AFFERO LAB PARTICIPACOES S.A.—See Bertelsmann SE & Co. KGaA; *Int'l*, pg. 989
AFRY APS—See AFRY Inc.; *Int'l*, pg. 194
AGC NETWORKS & CYBER SOLUTIONS LIMITED—See Black Box Limited; *Int'l*, pg. 1056
AGENCY MATRIX LLC—See Clearlake Capital Group, L.P.; *U.S. Private*, pg. 938
AGENCYPORT INSURANCE SERVICES, INC.—See Thomas H. Lee Partners, L.P.; *U.S. Private*, pg. 4155
AGENT, INC.; *Int'l*, pg. 205
AGFA-GEVAERT S.A.U.—See Agfa-Gevaert N.V.; *Int'l*, pg. 208
AGFA HEALTHCARE ARGENTINA S.A.—See Agfa-Gevaert N.V.; *Int'l*, pg. 207
AGFA HEALTHCARE COLOMBIA LTDA.—See Agfa-Gevaert N.V.; *Int'l*, pg. 207
AGFA HEALTHCARE DENMARK A/S—See Agfa-Gevaert N.V.; *Int'l*, pg. 207
AGFA HEALTHCARE FINLAND OY AB—See Agfa-Gevaert N.V.; *Int'l*, pg. 207
AGFA HEALTHCARE GMBH—See Ardian SAS; *Int'l*, pg. 555
AGFA HEALTHCARE INC.—See Agfa-Gevaert N.V.; *Int'l*, pg. 207
AGFA HEALTHCARE - KNIGHTSBRIDGE GMBH—See Ardian SAS; *Int'l*, pg. 555
AGFA HEALTHCARE LUXEMBOURG S.A.—See Agfa-Gevaert N.V.; *Int'l*, pg. 207
AGFA HEALTHCARE SHANGHAI LTD.—See Agfa-Gevaert N.V.; *Int'l*, pg. 207
AGILEASSETS, INC.; *U.S. Private*, pg. 128
AGILENCE, INC.; *U.S. Private*, pg. 128
AGILITY APPLICATIONS PTY LTD—See HUB24 Limited; *Int'l*, pg. 3516
AGILYSYS HK LIMITED—See Agilysys, Inc.; *U.S. Public*, pg. 62
AGILYSYS SINGAPORE PTE. LTD.—See Agilysys, Inc.; *U.S. Public*, pg. 62
AGILYSYS TECHNOLOGIES INDIA PRIVATE LIMITED—See Agilysys, Inc.; *U.S. Public*, pg. 62
AGILYSYS UK LTD.—See Agilysys, Inc.; *U.S. Public*, pg. 62
AGR (AUSTRALIA) PTY LTD—See Akastor ASA; *Int'l*, pg. 260
AGR GROUP AMERICAS, INC.—See Akastor ASA; *Int'l*, pg. 260
AHGAR INTERNATIONAL CO.—See Fouad Alghanim & Sons Group of Companies; *Int'l*, pg. 2753
AHSAY BACKUP SOFTWARE DEVELOPMENT COMPANY LIMITED; *Int'l*, pg. 226
AHSAY SYSTEMS CORPORATION LIMITED—See Ahsay Backup Software Development Company Limited; *Int'l*, pg. 226
AICHI INFORMATION SYSTEM CORPORATION—See Aichi Steel Corporation; *Int'l*, pg. 230
AI CROSS, INC.; *Int'l*, pg. 226
AIFORIA TECHNOLOGIES OYJ; *Int'l*, pg. 231
AI INSIDE, INC.; *Int'l*, pg. 227
AILLERON SA; *Int'l*, pg. 232
AIR2MP3 GMBH—See freenet AG; *Int'l*, pg. 2770
AIRITSYSTEMS HANNOVER GMBH—See Fraport AG; *Int'l*, pg. 2764
AIRMAGNET, INC.—See NetScout Systems, Inc.; *U.S. Public*, pg. 1509
AIROPS SOFTWARE LIMITED—See Gama Aviation plc; *Int'l*, pg. 2876
AIRPAS AVIATION GMBH—See Sabre Corporation; *U.S. Public*, pg. 1833
AIRSHIP AI HOLDINGS, INC.; *U.S. Public*, pg. 68
AIRSHIP, LLC—See Trivest Partners, LP; *U.S. Private*, pg. 4241
AIRSIS, INC.—See Oceaneering International, Inc.; *U.S. Public*, pg. 1562
AIRTASKER LIMITED; *Int'l*, pg. 249
AIRWATCH LLC—See Dell Technologies Inc.; *U.S. Public*, pg. 649
AISIN COMCRUISE CO., LTD.—See AISIN Corporation; *Int'l*, pg. 252
AITKEN SPENCE TECHNOLOGIES (PVT) LTD.—See Aitken Spence PLC; *Int'l*, pg. 254
AJEL TECHNOLOGIES INC—See Ajel Ltd.; *Int'l*, pg. 256
AJWAN INTERNATIONAL CO. WLL—See Caesars Group; *Int'l*, pg. 1249
AKA ENTERPRISE SOLUTIONS, INC.—See HSO Group BV; *Int'l*, pg. 3507
AKAMAI TECHNOLOGIES INTERNATIONAL AG—See Akamai Technologies, Inc.; *U.S. Public*, pg. 69
AKAMAI TECHNOLOGIES S.R.I.—See Akamai Technologies, Inc.; *U.S. Public*, pg. 69
AKATSUKI, INC.; *Int'l*, pg. 260
AKER CARBON CAPTURE ASA; *Int'l*, pg. 262
A LA CARTE CHARTS CORPORATION; *U.S. Private*, pg. 18
ALBATROS DATENSERVICE GMBH—See Comcast Corporation; *U.S. Public*, pg. 537
ALBAT+WIRSAM SOFTWARE GMBH—See Constellation Software Inc.; *Int'l*, pg. 1773
ALBECK FINANCIAL SERVICE INC.—See Calabrese Consulting, LLC; *U.S. Private*, pg. 715

ALBIS ARZTESERVICE PRODUCT GMBH & CO KG—See CompuGroup Medical SE & Co. KGaA; *Int'l*, pg. 1755
ALCHEMIST CODES SDN. BHD.—See AIQ Limited; *Int'l*, pg. 236
ALCHERA INC.; *Int'l*, pg. 300
ALCHIP TECHNOLOGIES, (CHONGQING) INC.—See Alchip Technologies, Limited; *Int'l*, pg. 301
ALCHIP TECHNOLOGIES, (GUANGZHOU) INC.—See Alchip Technologies, Limited; *Int'l*, pg. 301
ALCHIP TECHNOLOGIES (SHANGHAI) LIMITED—See Alchip Technologies, Limited; *Int'l*, pg. 301
ALCIDION NZ LIMITED—See Alcidion Group Limited; *Int'l*, pg. 301
ALCIDION UK LIMITED—See Alcidion Group Limited; *Int'l*, pg. 301
ALDEN SYSTEMS, INC.; *U.S. Private*, pg. 159
ALERT LOGIC, INC.—See HGGC, LLC; *U.S. Private*, pg. 1929
ALFABET, INC.; *U.S. Private*, pg. 164
ALFA FINANCIAL SOFTWARE HOLDINGS PLC; *Int'l*, pg. 308
ALFA FINANCIAL SOFTWARE LIMITED—See Alfa Financial Software Holdings PLC; *Int'l*, pg. 308
ALFI, INC.; *U.S. Public*, pg. 75
ALFY, INC.; *U.S. Private*, pg. 166
ALGOREX INC.—See Texas Instruments Incorporated; *U.S. Public*, pg. 2025
ALIGNMENT HEALTHCARE, INC.; *U.S. Public*, pg. 77
ALITECH INDIA LLP—See ALi Corporation; *Int'l*, pg. 320
ALITHYA CANADA INC.—See Alithya Group, Inc.; *Int'l*, pg. 329
ALITHYA USA, INC.—See Alithya Group, Inc.; *Int'l*, pg. 329
ALK TECHNOLOGIES, INC.—See Trimble, Inc.; *U.S. Public*, pg. 2190
ALLATA, LLC; *U.S. Private*, pg. 175
ALLEGIANT SYSTEMS, INC.—See Allegiant Travel Company; *U.S. Public*, pg. 78
ALLEN CORPORATION OF AMERICA, INC.; *U.S. Private*, pg. 178
ALLGEIER CORE GMBH—See Allgeier SE; *Int'l*, pg. 336
ALLGEIER GRC GMBH—See Allgeier SE; *Int'l*, pg. 337
ALLGO EMBEDDED SYSTEMS PVT. LTD.—See Visteon Corporation; *U.S. Public*, pg. 2305
ALLGO SYSTEMS, INC.—See Visteon Corporation; *U.S. Public*, pg. 2305
ALLIANCE MEDIA HOLDINGS, INC.; *U.S. Public*, pg. 79
ALLIANCE TECHNOLOGY SOLUTIONS, LLC.; *U.S. Private*, pg. 184
ALLIED TELESIS INTERNATIONAL SERVICES LTD.—See ALLIED TELESIS HOLDINGS K.K.; *Int'l*, pg. 358
ALLIED TELESIS INTERNATIONAL S.L.U—See ALLIED TELESIS HOLDINGS K.K.; *Int'l*, pg. 358
ALLIED TELESIS LABS (PHILIPPINES) INC.—See ALLIED TELESIS HOLDINGS K.K.; *Int'l*, pg. 358
ALLIED TELESYN SOUTH ASIA PTE. LTD.—See ALLIED TELESIS HOLDINGS K.K.; *Int'l*, pg. 359
ALLIGATOR COMPUTER SYSTEMS, INC.—See Health-Champion Partners LLC; *U.S. Private*, pg. 1895
ALL IN GAMES SA; *Int'l*, pg. 332
ALLSCRIPTS (UNITED KINGDOM) LIMITED—See Veradigm Inc.; *U.S. Public*, pg. 2279
ALLSTATE INDIA PRIVATE LIMITED—See The Allstate Corporation; *U.S. Public*, pg. 2032
ALLYIS, INC.; *U.S. Private*, pg. 194
ALNA SOFTWARE UAB—See Alna AB; *Int'l*, pg. 364
ALOGENT CORPORATION—See Battery Ventures, L.P.; *U.S. Private*, pg. 488
ALPAGRAPH TEAM GMBH—See Siris Capital Group, LLC; *U.S. Private*, pg. 3673
ALPHAGEN INTELLIGENCE CORP.; *Int'l*, pg. 370
ALPHA II, LLC; *U.S. Private*, pg. 197
ALPHALOGIC TECHSYS LTD.; *Int'l*, pg. 370
ALPHA MESS-STEUER-REGELTECHNIK GMBH—See Bilfinger SE; *Int'l*, pg. 1023
ALPHASOFT SERVICES CORPORATION—See Agnite Education Limited; *Int'l*, pg. 212
ALPHAX FOOD SYSTEM CO., LTD.; *Int'l*, pg. 370
ALPHINAT INC.; *Int'l*, pg. 370
ALSO CLOUD OY—See Droege Group AG; *Int'l*, pg. 2205
ALSO ENERGY INC.; *U.S. Private*, pg. 202
ALTABOX S.A.—See Econocom Group SA; *Int'l*, pg. 2297
ALTA VIA CONSULTING, LLC—See Bluestone Investment Partners, LLC; *U.S. Private*, pg. 598
ALTA VISTA TECHNOLOGY LLC; *U.S. Private*, pg. 203
ALT CO., LTD.; *Int'l*, pg. 383
ALTEXSOFT, INC.; *U.S. Private*, pg. 208
ALTIMATE BELGIUM BVBA—See Arrow Electronics, Inc.; *U.S. Public*, pg. 195
ALTIUSPAR, INC.—See Grupo Posadas S.A.B. de C.V.; *Int'l*, pg. 3134
ALTRAN AG—See Capgemini SE; *Int'l*, pg. 1304
ALTRAN PRAXIS LIMITED—See Capgemini SE; *Int'l*, pg. 1305
ALTRAN PRAXIS SAS—See Capgemini SE; *Int'l*, pg. 1305
ALTUS BILISIM HIZMETLERI ANONIM SIRKETI—See Diebold Nixdorf, Inc.; *U.S. Public*, pg. 659
ALVAREZ TECHNOLOGY GROUP, INC.; *U.S. Private*, pg. 214

ALVARIA, INC.—See Vector Capital Management, L.P.; *U.S. Private*, pg. 4350
AMA CORPORATION PLC; *Int'l*, pg. 402
AMADA ENGINEERING EUROPE S.P.A.—See Amada Holdings Co., Ltd.; *Int'l*, pg. 404
AMADA EUROPE SOFTWARE CENTER, S.A.S—See Amada Holdings Co., Ltd.; *Int'l*, pg. 403
AMADA SOFT (INDIA) PVT. LTD.—See Amada Holdings Co., Ltd.; *Int'l*, pg. 403
AMADEUS AIRPORT IT GMBH—See Amadeus IT Group, S.A.; *Int'l*, pg. 405
AMADEUS ALBANIA SH.P.K.—See Amadeus IT Group, S.A.; *Int'l*, pg. 405
AMADEUS AUSTRIA MARKETING GMBH—See Amadeus IT Group, S.A.; *Int'l*, pg. 405
AMADEUS (BEIJING) INFORMATION TECHNOLOGY CO., LTD.—See Amadeus IT Group, S.A.; *Int'l*, pg. 405
AMADEUS BENELUX N.V.—See Amadeus IT Group, S.A.; *Int'l*, pg. 405
AMADEUS BILGI TEKNOLOJISI HIZMETLERI A.S—See Amadeus IT Group, S.A.; *Int'l*, pg. 405
AMADEUS BOSNA D.O.O. ZA MARKETING SARAJEVO—See Amadeus IT Group, S.A.; *Int'l*, pg. 405
AMADEUS BRASIL LTDA.—See Amadeus IT Group, S.A.; *Int'l*, pg. 405
AMADEUS CENTRAL AND WEST AFRICA S.A.—See Amadeus IT Group, S.A.; *Int'l*, pg. 405
AMADEUS CZECH REPUBLIC & SLOVAKIA S.R.O.—See Amadeus IT Group, S.A.; *Int'l*, pg. 405
AMADEUS DENMARK A/S—See Amadeus IT Group, S.A.; *Int'l*, pg. 405
AMADEUS EESTI AS—See Amadeus IT Group, S.A.; *Int'l*, pg. 405
AMADEUS EGYPT COMPUTERIZED RESERVATION SERVICES S.A.E.—See Amadeus IT Group, S.A.; *Int'l*, pg. 405
AMADEUS GDS LLP—See Amadeus IT Group, S.A.; *Int'l*, pg. 405
AMADEUS GDS (MALAYSIA) SDN. BHD.—See Amadeus IT Group, S.A.; *Int'l*, pg. 405
AMADEUS GLOBAL TRAVEL DISTRIBUTION LTD.—See Amadeus IT Group, S.A.; *Int'l*, pg. 405
AMADEUS HOSPITALITY AMERICAS, INC.—See Amadeus IT Group, S.A.; *Int'l*, pg. 405
AMADEUS HOSPITALITY ASIA PACIFIC PTE. LTD.—See Amadeus IT Group, S.A.; *Int'l*, pg. 405
AMADEUS HOSPITALITY NETHERLANDS B.V.—See Amadeus IT Group, S.A.; *Int'l*, pg. 405
AMADEUS INFORMATION TECHNOLOGY LLC—See Amadeus IT Group, S.A.; *Int'l*, pg. 407
AMADEUS INTEGRATED SOLUTIONS PTY LTD—See Amadeus IT Group, S.A.; *Int'l*, pg. 405
AMADEUS IT GROUP COLOMBIA S.A.S.—See Amadeus IT Group, S.A.; *Int'l*, pg. 405
AMADEUS IT PACIFIC PTY. LTD.—See Amadeus IT Group, S.A.; *Int'l*, pg. 406
AMADEUS IT SERVICES UK LIMITED—See Amadeus IT Group, S.A.; *Int'l*, pg. 407
AMADEUS JAPAN K.K.—See Amadeus IT Group, S.A.; *Int'l*, pg. 406
AMADEUS KOREA, LTD.—See Amadeus IT Group, S.A.; *Int'l*, pg. 407
AMADEUS LEBANON S.A.R.L.—See Amadeus IT Group, S.A.; *Int'l*, pg. 407
AMADEUS LEISURE IT GMBH—See Amadeus IT Group, S.A.; *Int'l*, pg. 407
AMADEUS MACEDONIA DOOEL—See Amadeus IT Group, S.A.; *Int'l*, pg. 407
AMADEUS MAGYARORSZAG KFT—See Amadeus IT Group, S.A.; *Int'l*, pg. 406
AMADEUS MARKETING (GHANA) LTD.—See Amadeus IT Group, S.A.; *Int'l*, pg. 407
AMADEUS MARKETING IRELAND LTD.—See Amadeus IT Group, S.A.; *Int'l*, pg. 406
AMADEUS MARKETING NIGERIA LTD.—See Amadeus IT Group, S.A.; *Int'l*, pg. 407
AMADEUS MARKETING PHILS INC.—See Amadeus IT Group, S.A.; *Int'l*, pg. 406
AMADEUS MARKETING ROMANIA S.R.L.—See Amadeus IT Group, S.A.; *Int'l*, pg. 406
AMADEUS MEXICO, S.A. DE C.V.—See Amadeus IT Group, S.A.; *Int'l*, pg. 407
AMADEUS POLSKA SP. Z O.O.—See Amadeus IT Group, S.A.; *Int'l*, pg. 406
AMADEUS PURCHASE DEBT, S.A.—See Amadeus IT Group, S.A.; *Int'l*, pg. 406
AMADEUS REVENUE INTEGRITY INC.—See Amadeus IT Group, S.A.; *Int'l*, pg. 406
AMADEUS REZERVASYON DAGITIM SISTEMLERI A.S.—See Amadeus IT Group, S.A.; *Int'l*, pg. 406
AMADEUS S.A.S.—See Amadeus IT Group, S.A.; *Int'l*, pg. 407
AMADEUS SAUDI ARABIA LIMITED—See Amadeus IT Group, S.A.; *Int'l*, pg. 407
AMADEUS SLOVENIJA, D.O.O.—See Amadeus IT Group, S.A.; *Int'l*, pg. 407
AMADEUS SOFIA LABS EOOD—See Amadeus IT Group, S.A.; *Int'l*, pg. 407

N.A.I.C.S. INDEX

541511 — CUSTOM COMPUTER PRO...

AMADEUS SOFTWARE LABS INDIA PRIVATE LIMITED—See Amadeus IT Group, S.A.; *Int'l*, pg. 407
AMADEUS SOFTWARE TECHNOLOGY (SHANGAI) CO., LTD.—See Amadeus IT Group, S.A.; *Int'l*, pg. 407
AMADEUS SOLUCIONES TECNOLOGICAS, S.A—See Amadeus IT Group, S.A.; *Int'l*, pg. 406
AMADEUS SWEDEN AB—See Amadeus IT Group, S.A.; *Int'l*, pg. 406
AMADEUS SYRIA LIMITED LIABILITY—See Amadeus IT Group, S.A.; *Int'l*, pg. 407
AMADEUS TAIWAN COMPANY LIMITED—See Amadeus IT Group, S.A.; *Int'l*, pg. 407
AMANO CORPORATION-YOKOHAMA FACILITY—See Amano Corporation; *Int'l*, pg. 410
AMANO UK LTD. - PARKING DIVISION—See Amano Corporation; *Int'l*, pg. 410
AMAYA (INTERNATIONAL) LTD.—See Flutter Entertainment plc; *Int'l*, pg. 2715
AMAZIA, INC.; *Int'l*, pg. 413
AMBER ROAD, INC.—See Insight Venture Management, LLC; *U.S. Private*, pg. 2087
AMBER ROAD LIMITED—See Insight Venture Management, LLC; *U.S. Private*, pg. 2087
AMC TECHNOLOGY, L.L.C.; *U.S. Private*, pg. 218
AMDARIS BULGARIA EOOD—See Insight Enterprises, Inc.; *U.S. Public*, pg. 1129
AMDARIS GROUP LTD.—See Insight Enterprises, Inc.; *U.S. Public*, pg. 1129
AMDARIS ROMANIA S.R.L.—See Insight Enterprises, Inc.; *U.S. Public*, pg. 1129
AMDARIS S.R.L.—See Insight Enterprises, Inc.; *U.S. Public*, pg. 1129
AMDOCS AUSTRALIA PROPRIETARY LIMITED—See Amdocs Limited; *Int'l*, pg. 419
AMDOCS BRAZIL LIMITADA—See Amdocs Limited; *Int'l*, pg. 419
AMDOCS (CR) S.R.O.—See Amdocs Limited; *Int'l*, pg. 419
AMDOCS DEVELOPMENT CENTRE INDIA PRIVATE LIMITED—See Amdocs Limited; *Int'l*, pg. 419
AMDOCS DEVELOPMENT LIMITED—See Amdocs Limited; *Int'l*, pg. 419
AMDOCS DIGITAL COMMERCE DIVISION—See Amdocs Limited; *Int'l*, pg. 419
AMDOCS INC. - CALIFORNIA—See Amdocs Limited; *Int'l*, pg. 419
AMDOCS INTERNATIONAL GMBH—See Amdocs Limited; *Int'l*, pg. 419
AMDOCS (ISRAEL) LIMITED—See Amdocs Limited; *Int'l*, pg. 419
AMDOCS JAPAN—See Amdocs Limited; *Int'l*, pg. 419
AMDOCS MANAGEMENT LIMITED—See Amdocs Limited; *Int'l*, pg. 419
AMDOCS SOFTWARE GMBH—See Amdocs Limited; *Int'l*, pg. 419
AMDOCS SOFTWARE SYSTEMS LTD.—See Amdocs Limited; *Int'l*, pg. 419
AMDOCS (UK) LIMITED—See Amdocs Limited; *Int'l*, pg. 419
AMEEX TECHNOLOGIES CORPORATION—See EQT AB; *Int'l*, pg. 2483
AMELIA'S, LLC—See Grocery Outlet Holding Corp.; *U.S. Public*, pg. 970
AMERICANEAGLE.COM, INC.; *U.S. Private*, pg. 258
AMERICAN EXPRESS GLOBAL INFORMATION SERVICES—See American Express Company; *U.S. Public*, pg. 100
AMERICAN INTERNATIONAL MANAGEMENT—See New York Fragrance Inc.; *U.S. Private*, pg. 2909
AMERICAN IT SOLUTIONS, INC. (AIT); *U.S. Private*, pg. 238
AMERICAN TELECARE, INC.; *U.S. Private*, pg. 257
AMERISTAR NETWORK, INC.; *U.S. Public*, pg. 115
AMESITE INC.; *U.S. Public*, pg. 116
AMGENTECH INC.—See Telco Cuba, Inc.; *U.S. Public*, pg. 1992
AMOAD, INC.—See CyberAgent, Inc.; *Int'l*, pg. 1892
AMPAC SCIENTIFIC INC.; *U.S. Private*, pg. 264
AMPLIDATA N.V.—See Western Digital Corporation; *U.S. Public*, pg. 2355
AMPLITUDE, INC.; *U.S. Public*, pg. 133
AMPRO ADLINK TECHNOLOGY, INC.—See ADLINK Technology, Inc.; *Int'l*, pg. 151
AMSI PROPERTY MANAGEMENT - HOUSTON OFFICE—See Koch Industries, Inc.; *U.S. Private*, pg. 2330
AMSTERDAM SOFTWARE B.V.—See World Kinect Corporation; *U.S. Public*, pg. 2380
AMTECH GROUP LIMITED—See Trimble, Inc.; *U.S. Public*, pg. 2190
AMTEL, INC.—See StoneCalibre, LLC; *U.S. Private*, pg. 3828
ANACLE SYSTEMS LIMITED; *Int'l*, pg. 445
ANACLE SYSTEMS SDN BHD—See Anacle Systems Limited; *Int'l*, pg. 445
ANADOLU BILISIM HIZMETLERI A.S.—See AG Anadolu Grubu Holding A.S.; *Int'l*, pg. 197
ANALYSTS INTERNATIONAL-LAWSON PRACTICE—See American CyberSystems, Inc.; *U.S. Private*, pg. 229
ANALYSTS INTERNATIONAL-MANAGED SERVICES GROUP—See American CyberSystems, Inc.; *U.S. Private*, pg. 229
ANALYTICAL GRAPHICS INC.—See ANSYS, Inc.; *U.S. Public*, pg. 138
ANAPLAN, INC.; *U.S. Public*, pg. 136
ANCHOR (SHANGHAI) SEMICONDUCTOR INC.—See KLA Corporation; *U.S. Public*, pg. 1267
AND FACTORY, INC.; *Int'l*, pg. 449
ANEXINET CORP.—See Guggenheim Partners, LLC; *U.S. Private*, pg. 1811
ANEXIO, INC.; *U.S. Private*, pg. 281
ANGELPOINTS, LLC—See Blackbaud, Inc.; *U.S. Public*, pg. 341
ANIMANA B.V.—See IDEXX Laboratories, Inc.; *U.S. Public*, pg. 1092
ANIPARK CO., LTD.—See CJ Corporation; *Int'l*, pg. 1631
ANNKISSAM LLC—See Homecare Software Solutions LLC; *U.S. Private*, pg. 1973
ANSARADA GROUP LIMITED; *Int'l*, pg. 478
ANSARADA HONG KONG LIMITED—See Ansarada Group Limited; *Int'l*, pg. 478
ANSARADA PTE. LIMITED—See Ansarada Group Limited; *Int'l*, pg. 478
ANSARADA UK LIMITED—See Ansarada Group Limited; *Int'l*, pg. 478
ANSWER AND CONSULTING CO., LTD—See Core Corporation; *Int'l*, pg. 1797
ANSYS CHINA—See ANSYS, Inc.; *U.S. Public*, pg. 138
ANSYS HORSHAM—See ANSYS, Inc.; *U.S. Public*, pg. 138
ANSYS ICEM CFD INC.—See ANSYS, Inc.; *U.S. Public*, pg. 138
ANSYS, INC.—See ANSYS, Inc.; *U.S. Public*, pg. 138
ANSYS JAPAN K.K.—See ANSYS, Inc.; *U.S. Public*, pg. 138
ANSYS KOREA LLC—See ANSYS, Inc.; *U.S. Public*, pg. 138
ANSYS SWITZERLAND GMBH—See ANSYS, Inc.; *U.S. Public*, pg. 138
ANSYS TECHNOLOGY (SHANGHAI) CO., LTD.—See ANSYS, Inc.; *U.S. Public*, pg. 138
ANSYS UK, LTD.—See ANSYS, Inc.; *U.S. Public*, pg. 138
ANTENNA HOUSE, INC.—See Antenna House, Inc.; *Int'l*, pg. 482
ANTUIT, INC.; *U.S. Private*, pg. 289
ANTZ CO., LTD.; *Int'l*, pg. 485
ANYMIND GROUP, INC.; *Int'l*, pg. 487
A-ONLINE CAPITAL LTD.; *Int'l*, pg. 20
APACHE DESIGN SOLUTIONS INC.—See ANSYS, Inc.; *U.S. Public*, pg. 139
APACHE DESIGN SOLUTIONS, INC.—See ANSYS, Inc.; *U.S. Public*, pg. 139
APACHE DESIGN SOLUTIONS YUHAN HOESA—See ANSYS, Inc.; *U.S. Public*, pg. 139
APACHETA CORPORATION—See ResMed Inc.; *U.S. Public*, pg. 1790
APAK BEAM LTD—See Axway Software SA; *Int'l*, pg. 772
APAK GROUP LTD.—See Axway Software SA; *Int'l*, pg. 772
APCO SYSTEMS LIMITED—See Harvest Technology PLC; *Int'l*, pg. 3281
APE PTACEK ENGINEERING GMBH; *Int'l*, pg. 508
APEX SOFTWARE TECHNOLOGIES, LLC—See HgCapital Trust plc; *Int'l*, pg. 3376
APLICACIONES Y TRATAMIENTOS DE SISTEMAS S.A.; *Int'l*, pg. 515
APN DIGITAL PTY. LTD.—See ARN Media Limited; *Int'l*, pg. 576
APPARATUS, INC.—See EQT AB; *Int'l*, pg. 2471
APPASIA BERHAD; *Int'l*, pg. 519
APPDYNAMICS, LLC—See Cisco Systems, Inc.; *U.S. Public*, pg. 497
APPEN JAPAN PTY LTD.—See Appen Limited; *Int'l*, pg. 519
APPFIRST, INC.—See ScienceLogic LLC; *U.S. Private*, pg. 3573
APPIAN CORPORATION; *U.S. Public*, pg. 168
APPIAN EUROPE LTD.—See Appian Corporation; *U.S. Public*, pg. 169
APPIAN FRANCE SARL—See Appian Corporation; *U.S. Public*, pg. 169
APPIAN NETHERLANDS BV—See Appian Corporation; *U.S. Public*, pg. 169
APPIAN SINGAPORE PTE. LTD.—See Appian Corporation; *U.S. Public*, pg. 169
APPIAN SOFTWARE GERMANY GMBH—See Appian Corporation; *U.S. Public*, pg. 169
APPIAN SOFTWARE INTERNATIONAL GMBH—See Appian Corporation; *U.S. Public*, pg. 169
APPIAN SOFTWARE SWITZERLAND LLC—See Appian Corporation; *U.S. Public*, pg. 169
APPIAN SPAIN, S.L.—See Appian Corporation; *U.S. Public*, pg. 169
APPIER GROUP, INC.; *Int'l*, pg. 520
APPIRITS, INC.; *Int'l*, pg. 520
APPLAUSE APP QUALITY, INC.—See Vista Equity Partners, LLC; *U.S. Private*, pg. 4395
APPLE GREEN HOLDING, INC.; *Int'l*, pg. 520
APPLICAD PUBLIC COMPANY LIMITED; *Int'l*, pg. 521
APPLICATION DEVELOPMENT CONSULTANTS, LLC; *U.S. Private*, pg. 298
APPLICATION DEVELOPMENT RESOURCES, INC.; *U.S. Private*, pg. 298
APPLICATIONS SOFTWARE TECHNOLOGY LLC; *U.S. Private*, pg. 298
APPLIED CONTROL ENGINEERING, INC.; *U.S. Private*, pg. 298
APPLIED DEFENSE SOLUTIONS, INC.—See L3Harris Technologies, Inc.; *U.S. Public*, pg. 1280
APPLIED DIGITAL CORPORATION; *U.S. Public*, pg. 170
APPLIED GEOGRAPHICS, INC.—See The Sanborn Map Company, Inc.; *U.S. Private*, pg. 4114
APPLIFE DIGITAL SOLUTIONS, INC.; *U.S. Public*, pg. 173
APPLIKE GROUP GMBH—See Bertelsmann SE & Co. KGaA; *Int'l*, pg. 990
APPOGEE, LLC; *U.S. Private*, pg. 300
APPRISE SOFTWARE, INC.—See TA Associates, Inc.; *U.S. Private*, pg. 3914
APPSCATTER GROUP PLC; *Int'l*, pg. 522
APPSFLYER INC.; *U.S. Private*, pg. 300
APPSOFT TECHNOLOGIES, INC.; *U.S. Public*, pg. 173
APPSWARM, INC.; *U.S. Public*, pg. 174
APPTIO EUROPE LIMITED—See International Business Machines Corporation; *U.S. Public*, pg. 1145
APPTIO FRANCE SAS—See International Business Machines Corporation; *U.S. Public*, pg. 1145
APPTIO ITALY S.R.L.—See International Business Machines Corporation; *U.S. Public*, pg. 1145
APPTIO PTY LTD.—See International Business Machines Corporation; *U.S. Public*, pg. 1145
APRIORI TECHNOLOGIES, INC.; *U.S. Private*, pg. 302
APRISMA MANAGEMENT TECHNOLOGIES—See The Gores Group, LLC; *U.S. Private*, pg. 4034
APRYSE SOFTWARE INC.—See Thoma Bravo, L.P.; *U.S. Private*, pg. 4146
APSYS RISK ENGINEERING UK LIMITED—See Airbus SE; *Int'l*, pg. 246
APTEAN - GOMEMBERS AMS—See TA Associates, Inc.; *U.S. Private*, pg. 3914
APTUS HEALTH INTERNATIONAL FRANCE—See Merck & Co., Inc.; *U.S. Public*, pg. 1415
AQUA EYE LTD—See H2O Creative; *Int'l*, pg. 3200
ARARA, INC.; *Int'l*, pg. 536
ARCHANA SOFTWARE LIMITED; *Int'l*, pg. 547
ARCHERMIND TECHNOLOGY (NANJING) CO., LTD.; *Int'l*, pg. 548
ARCHIBUS, INC.—See Eptura, Inc.; *U.S. Private*, pg. 1414
ARCHIVEX S.A.—See Iron Mountain Incorporated; *U.S. Public*, pg. 1172
ARCHLYNK, LLC; *U.S. Private*, pg. 311
ARCHONIX SYSTEMS, LLC—See ABRY Partners, LLC; *U.S. Private*, pg. 41
ARCHOSAUR GAMES INC.; *Int'l*, pg. 549
ARCHTIS EU GMBH—See archTIS Limited; *Int'l*, pg. 549
ARCHTIS UK LIMITED—See archTIS Limited; *Int'l*, pg. 549
ARCHTIS US, INC.—See archTIS Limited; *Int'l*, pg. 549
ARCO PLATFORM LIMITED—See Dragoneer Investment Group, LLC; *U.S. Private*, pg. 1271
ARCO PLATFORM LIMITED—See General Atlantic Service Company, L.P.; *U.S. Private*, pg. 1662
ARCOS LLC—See The Riverside Company; *U.S. Private*, pg. 4107
ARCOT SYSTEMS INC.—See Broadcom Inc.; *U.S. Public*, pg. 388
ARCSOFT CORP., LTD.; *Int'l*, pg. 551
ARCSOFT, INC.; *U.S. Private*, pg. 315
ARC SOLUTIONS (INTERNATIONAL) LIMITED—See Enghouse Systems Limited; *Int'l*, pg. 2427
AREA 21 SOFTWARE GMBH—See ELMOS Semiconductor AG; *Int'l*, pg. 2368
ARENA SOLUTIONS, INC.—See PTC Inc.; *U.S. Public*, pg. 1734
ARGO DATA RESOURCE CORPORATION; *U.S. Private*, pg. 320
ARIAS INTEL CORP.; *U.S. Private*, pg. 322
ARISTA NETWORKS AUSTRALIA PTY LTD—See Arista Networks, Inc.; *U.S. Public*, pg. 192
ARISTA NETWORKS EURL—See Arista Networks, Inc.; *U.S. Public*, pg. 192
ARISTA NETWORKS GMBH—See Arista Networks, Inc.; *U.S. Public*, pg. 192
ARISTA NETWORKS INDIA PRIVATE LIMITED—See Arista Networks, Inc.; *U.S. Public*, pg. 192
ARISTA NETWORKS SINGAPORE PRIVATE LTD.—See Arista Networks, Inc.; *U.S. Public*, pg. 192
ARIUS SA—See BNP Paribas SA; *Int'l*, pg. 1079
ARKIVA AB—See Addnode Group AB; *Int'l*, pg. 130
ARMEDIA LLC; *U.S. Private*, pg. 330
ARPEGE SAS—See Fosun International Limited; *Int'l*, pg. 2751
ARQIT QUANTUM INC.; *Int'l*, pg. 578
ARRIBATEC HOSPITALITY AS—See Arribatec Group ASA; *Int'l*, pg. 579
ARRIVER US, INC.—See QUALCOMM Incorporated; *U.S. Public*, pg. 1747
ARROW ECS AG—See Arrow Electronics, Inc.; *U.S. Public*, pg. 195
ARROW ECS A.S.—See Arrow Electronics, Inc.; *U.S. Public*, pg. 196

4599

ARROW ECS BALTIC OU—See Arrow Electronics, Inc.; *U.S. Public*, pg. 196
ARROW ECS B.V.—See Arrow Electronics, Inc.; *U.S. Public*, pg. 196
ARROW ECS DENMARK A/S—See Arrow Electronics, Inc.; *U.S. Public*, pg. 196
ARROW ECS (IRELAND) LIMITED—See Arrow Electronics, Inc.; *U.S. Public*, pg. 195
ARROW ECS SARL—See Arrow Electronics, Inc.; *U.S. Public*, pg. 196
ARROW ENTERPRISE COMPUTING SOLUTIONS LTD. - NOTTINGHAM OFFICE—See Arrow Electronics, Inc.; *U.S. Public*, pg. 198
ARROW ENTERPRISE COMPUTING SOLUTIONS, S.A.—See Arrow Electronics, Inc.; *U.S. Public*, pg. 198
ARSIN CORP.—See SemanticSpace Technologies; *U.S. Private*, pg. 3603
ARTECH INFORMATION SYSTEMS LLC; *U.S. Private*, pg. 340
ARTERYEX INC.—See Eisai Co., Ltd.; *Int'l*, pg. 2334
ARTIFEX MUNDI S.A.; *Int'l*, pg. 584
ARTIFICIAL ELECTRONICS INTELLIGENT MATERIAL LIMITED; *Int'l*, pg. 584
ARTILIUM N.V.—See Pareteum Corporation; *U.S. Public*, pg. 1637
ARTQUEST INTERNATIONAL ALLIANCES, INC.; *Int'l*, pg. 585
ARTRONIQ INNOVATION SDN BHD—See ARTRONIQ BERHAD; *Int'l*, pg. 585
ARTRYA LIMITED; *Int'l*, pg. 585
ARTS ALLIANCE VENTURES; *Int'l*, pg. 585
ARVATO SYSTEMS PERDATA GMBH—See Bertelsmann SE & Co. KGaA; *Int'l*, pg. 997
ARVATO SYSTEMS S4M GMBH—See Bertelsmann SE & Co. KGaA; *Int'l*, pg. 997
ARWAY CORPORATION; *Int'l*, pg. 588
ARXAN TECHNOLOGIES, INC.—See TPG Capital, L.P.; *U.S. Public*, pg. 2173
ASANA, INC.; *U.S. Public*, pg. 209
ASAP SDN. BHD.—See Aldrich Resources Bhd; *Int'l*, pg. 305
ASARFI HOSPITAL LIMITED; *Int'l*, pg. 599
ASC AMERICAS L.P.—See ASC telecom AG; *Int'l*, pg. 600
ASCENDIA S.A.; *Int'l*, pg. 601
ASCEND LABORATORIES SDN. BHD.—See Alkem Laboratories Ltd.; *Int'l*, pg. 330
ASCEND SOLUTIONS SDN BHD—See Genting Berhad; *Int'l*, pg. 2928
ASCENT CLOUD LLC—See The Ascent Group LLC; *U.S. Private*, pg. 3988
ASCENT INNOVATIONS LLC; *U.S. Private*, pg. 348
ASC JAPAN INC.—See ASC telecom AG; *Int'l*, pg. 600
ASC SCHWEIZ AG—See ASC telecom AG; *Int'l*, pg. 600
ASC TECHNOLOGIES AG—See ASC telecom AG; *Int'l*, pg. 600
ASC TECHNOLOGIES GMBH—See ASC telecom AG; *Int'l*, pg. 601
ASC TECHNOLOGIES S.A.S.—See ASC telecom AG; *Int'l*, pg. 601
ASC TELECOM AG; *Int'l*, pg. 600
ASC TELECOM SINGAPORE PTE. LTD.—See ASC telecom AG; *Int'l*, pg. 601
ASC UK TECHNOLOGIES LTD—See ASC telecom AG; *Int'l*, pg. 601
ASC WFO SOLUTIONS DO BRASIL LTDA.—See ASC telecom AG; *Int'l*, pg. 601
ASERA INC.; *U.S. Private*, pg. 348
ASI BUSINESS SOLUTIONS INC.; *U.S. Private*, pg. 350
ASI PROPERTIES, INC.—See American Software, Inc.; *U.S. Public*, pg. 109
ASIT C.MEHTA FINANCIAL SERVICES LTD.; *Int'l*, pg. 621
ASJADE TECHNOLOGY INC.—See ASRock Inc.; *Int'l*, pg. 632
ASKME CORPORATION—See Abalance Corporation Ltd.; *Int'l*, pg. 48
ASL HOLDINGS LIMITED—See Halma plc; *Int'l*, pg. 3230
ASN TECHNOLOGIES, INC.—See Equity Residential; *U.S. Public*, pg. 791
ASOLVA, INC.—See Constellation Software Inc.; *Int'l*, pg. 1773
ASPAC INC.—See Canon Inc.; *Int'l*, pg. 1292
ASPECT CONSULTING, INC.; *U.S. Private*, pg. 351
ASPECT SOFTWARE ASIA PACIFIC PTE LTD.—See Vector Capital Management, L.P.; *U.S. Private*, pg. 4350
ASPENTECH ARGENTINA S.R.L.—See Emerson Electric Co.; *U.S. Public*, pg. 741
ASPENTECH (BEIJING) CO., LTD.—See Emerson Electric Co.; *U.S. Public*, pg. 741
ASPENTECH CANADA LTD.—See Emerson Electric Co.; *U.S. Public*, pg. 741
ASPENTECH CORPORATION—See Emerson Electric Co.; *U.S. Public*, pg. 741
ASPENTECH DE MEXICO S. DE R.L. DE C.V.—See Emerson Electric Co.; *U.S. Public*, pg. 741
ASPENTECH EUROPE B.V.—See Emerson Electric Co.; *U.S. Public*, pg. 741
ASPENTECH EUROPE SA/NV—See Emerson Electric Co.; *U.S. Public*, pg. 741

ASPENTECH, INC.—See Emerson Electric Co.; *U.S. Public*, pg. 741
ASPENTECH INDIA PVT. LTD.—See Emerson Electric Co.; *U.S. Public*, pg. 741
ASPENTECH JAPAN CO., LTD.—See Emerson Electric Co.; *U.S. Public*, pg. 741
ASPENTECH LTD.—See Emerson Electric Co.; *U.S. Public*, pg. 741
ASPEN TECHNOLOGY AUSTRALIA PTY LTD.—See Emerson Electric Co.; *U.S. Public*, pg. 741
ASPEN TECHNOLOGY LLC—See Emerson Electric Co.; *U.S. Public*, pg. 741
ASPEN TECHNOLOGY S.A.S.—See Emerson Electric Co.; *U.S. Public*, pg. 741
ASPEN TECHNOLOGY S.L.—See Emerson Electric Co.; *U.S. Public*, pg. 741
ASPEN TECHNOLOGY S.R.L.—See Emerson Electric Co.; *U.S. Public*, pg. 741
ASPENTECH NORWAY AS—See Emerson Electric Co.; *U.S. Public*, pg. 742
ASPENTECH PTE. LTD.—See Emerson Electric Co.; *U.S. Public*, pg. 741
ASPENTECH SOFTWARE BRAZIL LTDA.—See Emerson Electric Co.; *U.S. Public*, pg. 741
ASPENTECH SOLUTIONS SDN. BHD.—See Emerson Electric Co.; *U.S. Public*, pg. 741
ASPENTECH S.R.L.—See Emerson Electric Co.; *U.S. Public*, pg. 741
ASPEN TECH (THAILAND) LTD.—See Emerson Electric Co.; *U.S. Public*, pg. 741
ASPENTECH VENEZUELA, C.A.—See Emerson Electric Co.; *U.S. Public*, pg. 741
ASP SERVEUR SAS—See Econocom Group SA; *Int'l*, pg. 2297
ASSECO GERMANY AG—See Asseco Poland S.A.; *Int'l*, pg. 641
ASSECO SEE D.O.O.E.L.—See Asseco Poland S.A.; *Int'l*, pg. 641
ASSECO SEE D.O.O.—See Asseco Poland S.A.; *Int'l*, pg. 641
ASSECO SEE D.O.O.—See Asseco Poland S.A.; *Int'l*, pg. 641
ASSECO SEE D.O.O.—See Asseco Poland S.A.; *Int'l*, pg. 641
ASSECO SEE D.O.O.—See Asseco Poland S.A.; *Int'l*, pg. 641
ASSECO SEE D.O.O.—See Asseco Poland S.A.; *Int'l*, pg. 641
ASSECO SEE SH.P.K.—See Asseco Poland S.A.; *Int'l*, pg. 641
ASSECO SEE TEKNOLOJI A.S.—See Asseco Poland S.A.; *Int'l*, pg. 641
ASSIMA A/S—See Fonds de Solidarite des Travailleurs du Quebec; *Int'l*, pg. 2725
ASSIMA FRANCE SAS—See Fonds de Solidarite des Travailleurs du Quebec; *Int'l*, pg. 2725
ASSIMA SOFTWARE ESPAFIA, S.L.—See Fonds de Solidarite des Travailleurs du Quebec; *Int'l*, pg. 2725
ASSIMA SWITZERLAND SA—See Fonds de Solidarite des Travailleurs du Quebec; *Int'l*, pg. 2725
ASSISTEC CO. LTD.—See FUJIFILM Holdings Corporation; *Int'l*, pg. 2821
ASTA DEVELOPMENT PLC—See Eleco Plc; *Int'l*, pg. 2348
ASTROCAST SA; *Int'l*, pg. 662
ASURE SOFTWARE UK LTD.—See KKR & Co. Inc.; *U.S. Public*, pg. 1239
ASYA INFOSOFT LTD.; *Int'l*, pg. 664
ASYMMETRIK, LTD.—See Arlington Capital Partners LLC; *U.S. Private*, pg. 327
ATCOM INTERNET & MULTIMEDIA LTD.—See Dionic Industrial & Trading S.A; *Int'l*, pg. 2127
ATEA BALTIC UAB—See Atea ASA; *Int'l*, pg. 667
ATEA FINLAND OY—See Atea ASA; *Int'l*, pg. 667
ATEA GLOBAL SERVICES SIA—See Atea ASA; *Int'l*, pg. 667
ATEA SIA—See Atea ASA; *Int'l*, pg. 667
ATEMPO S.A.; *Int'l*, pg. 668
ATENDE MEDICA SP. Z O.O.—See Atende S.A.; *Int'l*, pg. 668
ATENDE SOFTWARE SP. Z O.O.—See Atende S.A.; *Int'l*, pg. 668
ATEX MEDIA INC.—See Vista Equity Partners, LLC; *U.S. Private*, pg. 4398
ATHEEB INTERGRAPH SAUDI COMPANY - RIYADH—See Hexagon AB; *Int'l*, pg. 3368
ATHENA DYNAMICS PTE. LTD.—See BH Global Corporation Limited; *Int'l*, pg. 1009
ATILZE DIGITAL SDN. BHD.—See G3 Global Berhad; *Int'l*, pg. 2866
ATIMO PERSONEELSTECHNIEK B.V.—See dormakaba Holding AG; *Int'l*, pg. 2177
ATLANTIC DATA SERVICES, INC.; *U.S. Private*, pg. 373
ATLANTIS INTERNET GROUP CORP.; *U.S. Public*, pg. 223
ATLAS HEALTHCARE SOFTWARE INDIA PRIVATE LIMITED—See Roper Technologies, Inc.; *U.S. Public*, pg. 1810
ATLASSIAN CORPORATION; *Int'l*, pg. 686
ATMOKY GMBH; *Int'l*, pg. 687

AT-NET SERVICES-GREENVILLE, INC.—See At-Net Services, Inc.; *U.S. Private*, pg. 363
ATODIA AB—See Platinum Equity, LLC; *U.S. Private*, pg. 3201
ATOMIC OBJECT LLC; *U.S. Private*, pg. 381
ATOMSYSTEM CO., LTD.; *Int'l*, pg. 688
ATOS INFORMATION TECHNOLOGY GMBH—See Atos SE; *Int'l*, pg. 690
ATOS IT SERVICES PRIVATE LTD—See Atos SE; *Int'l*, pg. 690
ATOS IT SERVICIOS DO BRAZIL LTDA—See Atos SE; *Int'l*, pg. 690
ATOS IT SOLUTIONS AND SERVICES GMBH—See Atos SE; *Int'l*, pg. 690
ATOS ORIGIN FZ LLC—See Atos SE; *Int'l*, pg. 691
ATOSS CSD SOFTWARE GMBH—See ATOSS Software AG; *Int'l*, pg. 692
ATOSS SOFTWARE AG—See ATOSS Software AG; *Int'l*, pg. 693
ATOSS SOFTWARE GESELLSCHAFT M.B.H.—See ATOSS Software AG; *Int'l*, pg. 693
ATOSS SOFTWARE S.R.L.—See ATOSS Software AG; *Int'l*, pg. 693
ATOS UK IT LIMITED—See Atos SE; *Int'l*, pg. 691
ATRAE, INC.; *Int'l*, pg. 693
ATRENTA INC.—See Synopsys, Inc.; *U.S. Public*, pg. 1970
ATRIUM SOFTWARE LTD—See Trimble, Inc.; *U.S. Public*, pg. 2190
ATR-TREK CO., LTD.—See AI Co., Ltd.; *Int'l*, pg. 226
ATS ENGINEERING LTD.; *Int'l*, pg. 696
ATSIGN, INC.; *U.S. Private*, pg. 382
ATTENDEE INTERACTIVE, LLC—See Insight Venture Management, LLC; *U.S. Private*, pg. 2088
ATTERO TECH, LLC.—See QSC, LLC; *U.S. Private*, pg. 3314
ATTUNITY ISRAEL (1992) LTD—See Thoma Bravo, L.P.; *U.S. Private*, pg. 4152
AUBASS CO., LTD.—See Denso Corporation; *Int'l*, pg. 2028
AUCNET IBS INC.—See Aucnet Inc.; *Int'l*, pg. 700
AUCTANE LLC—See Thoma Bravo, L.P.; *U.S. Private*, pg. 4153
AUCTION FRONTIER, LLC—See OPENLANE, Inc.; *U.S. Public*, pg. 1607
AUDACIA SA; *Int'l*, pg. 700
AUDINATE GROUP LIMITED; *Int'l*, pg. 701
AUDINATE, INC.—See Audinate Group Limited; *Int'l*, pg. 701
AUDINATE LIMITED—See Audinate Group Limited; *Int'l*, pg. 701
AUDINATE LIMITED—See Audinate Group Limited; *Int'l*, pg. 701
AUDINATE PTY LIMITED—See Audinate Group Limited; *Int'l*, pg. 701
AU LAC SOFTWARE DEVELOPMENT COMPANY LIMITED—See ALTA Company; *Int'l*, pg. 384
AU LAC TECHNOLOGY APPLICATIONS PLASTICS COMPANY LIMITED—See ALTA Company; *Int'l*, pg. 384
AUMO, INC.—See Gree Inc.; *Int'l*, pg. 3069
AURIA WIRELESS PTY LIMITED—See Etherstack PLC; *Int'l*, pg. 2523
AURIGO SOFTWARE TECHNOLOGIES INC.; *U.S. Private*, pg. 393
AURIONPRO SCM PTE LTD.—See Aurionpro Solutions Limited; *Int'l*, pg. 711
AURIONPRO SOLUTIONS LIMITED; *Int'l*, pg. 711
AURORA INNOVATIONS, LLC—See Hydrofarm Holdings Group, Inc.; *U.S. Public*, pg. 1079
AURORA SYSTEMS CORPORATION—See Aurora Corporation; *Int'l*, pg. 713
AURUM PACIFIC (CHINA) GROUP LIMITED; *Int'l*, pg. 715
AUSHANG.ONLINE GMBH—See FORTEC Elektronik AG; *Int'l*, pg. 2738
AUSTRIA CARD TURKEY KART OPERASYONLARI AS—See Austriacard Holdings AG; *Int'l*, pg. 724
AUTHENTIFY, INC.—See Wells Fargo & Company; *U.S. Public*, pg. 2343
AUTOCLERK, INC.—See Best Western International, Inc.; *U.S. Private*, pg. 544
AUTOCOUNT DOTCOM BERHAD; *Int'l*, pg. 726
AUTODESK B.V.—See Autodesk, Inc.; *U.S. Public*, pg. 229
AUTODESK (CHINA) SOFTWARE RESEARCH AND DEVELOPMENT CO., LTD.—See Autodesk, Inc.; *U.S. Public*, pg. 228
AUTODESK DO BRASIL LTDA.—See Autodesk, Inc.; *U.S. Public*, pg. 229
AUTODESK LTD. JAPAN—See Autodesk, Inc.; *U.S. Public*, pg. 229
AUTODESK SA—See Autodesk, Inc.; *U.S. Public*, pg. 229
AUTOMATED BENEFITS INC.—See Insight Venture Management, LLC; *U.S. Private*, pg. 2089
AUTOMATED BENEFITS INC.—See Stone Point Capital LLC; *U.S. Private*, pg. 3823
AUTOMATED LOGIC AUSTRALIA PTY. LIMITED—See Carrier Global Corporation; *U.S. Public*, pg. 440
AUTOMATEDQA CORP.; *U.S. Private*, pg. 399
AUTOMATION GROUP INC.; *U.S. Private*, pg. 399
AUTOONLINE B.V.—See Vista Equity Partners, LLC; *U.S. Private*, pg. 4399

541511 — CUSTOM COMPUTER PRO...

AUTOONLINE ITALIA S.R.L.—See Vista Equity Partners, LLC; *U.S. Private*, pg. 4399
AUTOONLINE MAGYARORSZAG KFT.—See Vista Equity Partners, LLC; *U.S. Private*, pg. 4399
AUTOQUOTES LLC—See TA Associates, Inc.; *U.S. Private*, pg. 3914
AVAAP INC.; *U.S. Private*, pg. 403
AVAILPRO SAS—See Accor S.A.; *Int'l*, pg. 91
AVALON SOLUTIONS INC.—See Devoteam SA; *Int'l*, pg. 2089
AVANADE ASIA PTE LTD.—See Accenture plc; *Int'l*, pg. 85
AVANADE AUSTRALIA PTY LTD.—See Accenture plc; *Int'l*, pg. 85
AVANADE BELGIUM SPRL—See Accenture plc; *Int'l*, pg. 85
AVANADE CANADA INC.—See Accenture plc; *Int'l*, pg. 85
AVANADE DEUTSCHLAND GMBH—See Accenture plc; *Int'l*, pg. 85
AVANADE DO BRASIL LTDA—See Accenture plc; *Int'l*, pg. 85
AVANADE FINLAND OY—See Accenture plc; *Int'l*, pg. 85
AVANADE GUANGZHOU—See Accenture plc; *Int'l*, pg. 85
AVANADE ITALY SRL—See Accenture plc; *Int'l*, pg. 85
AVANADE JAPAN KK—See Accenture plc; *Int'l*, pg. 85
AVANADE MALAYSIA SDN BHD—See Accenture plc; *Int'l*, pg. 85
AVANADE NETHERLANDS BV—See Accenture plc; *Int'l*, pg. 85
AVANADE NORWAY AS—See Accenture plc; *Int'l*, pg. 85
AVANADE SCHWEIZ GMBH—See Accenture plc; *Int'l*, pg. 85
AVANADE SPAIN SL—See Accenture plc; *Int'l*, pg. 85
AVANADE SWEDEN AB—See Accenture plc; *Int'l*, pg. 85
AVAYA CANADA CORP.—See Silver Lake Group, LLC; *U.S. Private*, pg. 3655
AVAYA CANADA CORP.—See TPG Capital, L.P.; *U.S. Public*, pg. 2169
AVAYA GOVERNMENT SOLUTIONS INC.—See Silver Lake Group, LLC; *U.S. Private*, pg. 3656
AVAYA GOVERNMENT SOLUTIONS INC.—See TPG Capital, L.P.; *U.S. Public*, pg. 2169
AVECTO LIMITED—See Francisco Partners Management, LP; *U.S. Private*, pg. 1589
AVEMIO AG; *Int'l*, pg. 737
AVENSIA AB; *Int'l*, pg. 738
AVENTRI, INC.—See HGGC, LLC; *U.S. Private*, pg. 1929
AVEROX (PVT.) LTD.—See AVEROX INC.; *Int'l*, pg. 739
AVID DEVELOPMENT GMBH—See Symphony Technology Group, LLC; *U.S. Private*, pg. 3901
AVID GENERAL PARTNER B.V.—See Symphony Technology Group, LLC; *U.S. Private*, pg. 3901
AVID TECHNOLOGIES, INC.—See Avnet, Inc.; *U.S. Public*, pg. 249
AVID TECHNOLOGY CANADA CORP.—See Symphony Technology Group, LLC; *U.S. Private*, pg. 3901
AVID TECHNOLOGY, INC. - MADISON—See Symphony Technology Group, LLC; *U.S. Private*, pg. 3901
AVID TECHNOLOGY INTERNATIONAL B.V.—See Symphony Technology Group, LLC; *U.S. Private*, pg. 3901
AVILEN, INC.; *Int'l*, pg. 743
AVI NETWORKS B.V.—See Dell Technologies Inc.; *U.S. Public*, pg. 649
AVI NETWORKS GERMANY GMBH—See Dell Technologies Inc.; *U.S. Public*, pg. 649
AVI NETWORKS INDIA PRIVATE LIMITED—See Dell Technologies Inc.; *U.S. Public*, pg. 649
AVINODE AKTIEBOLAG—See World Kinect Corporation; *U.S. Public*, pg. 2380
AVINODE, INC.—See World Kinect Corporation; *U.S. Public*, pg. 2380
AVIONTE; *U.S. Private*, pg. 407
AVIONYX, S.A.—See Joby Aviation, Inc.; *U.S. Public*, pg. 1190
AVISEN BV—See 1Spatial Plc; *Int'l*, pg. 3
AVNET ABACUS MADRID—See TD Synnex Corp; *U.S. Public*, pg. 1985
AWARE, INC.; *U.S. Public*, pg. 254
AWARENESS TECHNOLOGIES, INC.—See TZP Group LLC; *U.S. Private*, pg. 4269
AWE ACQUISITION, INC.—See Blackstreet Capital Management, LLC; *U.S. Private*, pg. 577
AWEK MICRODATA GMBH—See Fujitsu Limited; *Int'l*, pg. 2837
AWR-APLAC OY—See National Instruments Corporation; *U.S. Private*, pg. 2856
AWR JAPAN KK—See National Instruments Corporation; *U.S. Private*, pg. 2856
AXETURE CORP; *U.S. Private*, pg. 412
AXIATA DIGITAL LABS (PRIVATE) LIMITED—See Axiata Group Berhad; *Int'l*, pg. 768
AXIATA DIGITAL LABS SDN. BHD.—See Axiata Group Berhad; *Int'l*, pg. 768
AXIOMA, INC.—See Deutsche Borse AG; *Int'l*, pg. 2064
AXIOM EPM—See Vizient, Inc.; *U.S. Private*, pg. 4407
AXION HEALTH INC.—See Thoma Bravo, L.P.; *U.S. Private*, pg. 4146
AXIS41, INC.—See Dentsu Group Inc.; *Int'l*, pg. 2036
AXIZ BOTSWANA PROPRIETARY LIMITED—See Alviva Holdings Limited; *Int'l*, pg. 401

AXONOM, INC.—See TA Associates, Inc.; *U.S. Private*, pg. 3914
AXON VENTURES LIMITED; *Int'l*, pg. 771
AXWAY ASIA PACIFIC PTE LTD—See Axway Software SA; *Int'l*, pg. 772
AXWAY PTY LTD—See Axway Software SA; *Int'l*, pg. 772
AXWAY SRL—See Axway Software SA; *Int'l*, pg. 772
AYFIE GROUP AS; *Int'l*, pg. 775
AYO TECHNOLOGY SOLUTIONS LTD.; *Int'l*, pg. 775
AZERION GROUP N.V.; *Int'l*, pg. 778
AZTECA SYSTEMS, LLC—See Trimble, Inc.; *U.S. Public*, pg. 2190
B2B SOFTECH INC.—See B2B Software Technologies Limited; *Int'l*, pg. 790
B2B SOFTWARE TECHNOLOGIES KASSEL GMBH—See B2B Software Technologies Limited; *Int'l*, pg. 790
B2B SOFTWARE TECHNOLOGIES LIMITED; *Int'l*, pg. 790
BABCN LLC—See Accenture plc; *Int'l*, pg. 86
BACKOFFICE ASSOCIATES, LLC—See Bridge Growth Partners, LLC; *U.S. Private*, pg. 648
BACKSTOP SOLUTIONS GROUP, LLC; *U.S. Private*, pg. 423
BAE SYSTEMS INFORMATION TECHNOLOGY—See BAE Systems plc; *Int'l*, pg. 797
BAE SYSTEMS (OPERATIONS) LIMITED—See BAE Systems plc; *Int'l*, pg. 796
BAILEY SOUTHWELL & CO.; *U.S. Private*, pg. 426
BAIRESDEV LLC; *U.S. Private*, pg. 454
BAIRONG INC.; *Int'l*, pg. 803
BAKBONE SOFTWARE INCORPORATED—See Francisco Partners Management, LP; *U.S. Private*, pg. 1591
BAKED GAMES S.A.; *Int'l*, pg. 805
BALCO GROUP AB; *Int'l*, pg. 807
BANDAI VISUAL CO., LTD.—See BANDAI NAMCO Holdings Inc.; *Int'l*, pg. 828
BANGO PLC; *Int'l*, pg. 836
BANKADATI SERVIZI INFORMATICI S.P.A.—See Credito Valtellinese Societa Cooperativa; *Int'l*, pg. 1837
BANK OF INNOVATION, INC.; *Int'l*, pg. 843
BANKSOFT KFT—See 4iG Nyrt.; *Int'l*, pg. 12
BANNO, LLC—See Jack Henry & Associates, Inc.; *U.S. Public*, pg. 1182
BAOFENG GROUP CO., LTD.; *Int'l*, pg. 856
BAOKU ONLINE TECHNOLOGY LTD.—See Beijing Shiji Information Technology Co., Ltd.; *Int'l*, pg. 956
BARCO COORDINATION CENTER NV—See Barco N.V.; *Int'l*, pg. 863
BARCO VISUAL SOLUTIONS, LLC—See Barco N.V.; *Int'l*, pg. 864
BARE BONES SOFTWARE, INC.; *U.S. Private*, pg. 474
BARON INFOTECH LIMITED; *Int'l*, pg. 867
BARRACHD LTD.; *Int'l*, pg. 867
BARRACONSULT, LTDA.—See MSCI Inc.; *U.S. Public*, pg. 1483
BARRACUDA NETWORKS AG—See KKR & Co. Inc.; *U.S. Public*, pg. 1241
BARRA JAPAN K.K.—See MSCI Inc.; *U.S. Public*, pg. 1483
BARRA, LLC—See MSCI Inc.; *U.S. Public*, pg. 1483
BART & ASSOCIATES INC.; *U.S. Private*, pg. 482
BARUNSON ENTERTAINMENT & ARTS CORPORATION; *Int'l*, pg. 870
BASILIC FLY STUDIO LIMITED; *Int'l*, pg. 887
BASWARE AB—See Accel Partners L.P.; *U.S. Private*, pg. 48
BASWARE AB—See KKR & Co. Inc.; *U.S. Public*, pg. 1237
BASWARE AB—See Long Path Partners, LP; *U.S. Private*, pg. 2491
BASWARE A/S—See Accel Partners L.P.; *U.S. Private*, pg. 47
BASWARE AS—See Accel Partners L.P.; *U.S. Private*, pg. 48
BASWARE AS—See KKR & Co. Inc.; *U.S. Public*, pg. 1237
BASWARE A/S—See KKR & Co. Inc.; *U.S. Public*, pg. 1237
BASWARE AS—See Long Path Partners, LP; *U.S. Private*, pg. 2491
BASWARE A/S—See Long Path Partners, LP; *U.S. Private*, pg. 2491
BASWARE BELGIUM NV—See Accel Partners L.P.; *U.S. Private*, pg. 48
BASWARE BELGIUM NV—See KKR & Co. Inc.; *U.S. Public*, pg. 1237
BASWARE BELGIUM NV—See Long Path Partners, LP; *U.S. Private*, pg. 2491
BASWARE B.V.—See Accel Partners L.P.; *U.S. Private*, pg. 48
BASWARE B.V.—See KKR & Co. Inc.; *U.S. Public*, pg. 1237
BASWARE B.V.—See Long Path Partners, LP; *U.S. Private*, pg. 2491
BASWARE CORPORATION—See Accel Partners L.P.; *U.S. Private*, pg. 48
BASWARE CORPORATION—See KKR & Co. Inc.; *U.S. Public*, pg. 1237
BASWARE CORPORATION—See Long Path Partners, LP; *U.S. Private*, pg. 2491
BASWARE GMBH—See Accel Partners L.P.; *U.S. Private*, pg. 48
BASWARE GMBH—See KKR & Co. Inc.; *U.S. Public*, pg. 1237

BASWARE GMBH—See Long Path Partners, LP; *U.S. Private*, pg. 2491
BASWARE HOLDINGS LTD.—See Accel Partners L.P.; *U.S. Private*, pg. 48
BASWARE HOLDINGS LTD.—See KKR & Co. Inc.; *U.S. Public*, pg. 1237
BASWARE HOLDINGS LTD.—See Long Path Partners, LP; *U.S. Private*, pg. 2491
BASWARE, INC.—See Accel Partners L.P.; *U.S. Private*, pg. 48
BASWARE, INC.—See KKR & Co. Inc.; *U.S. Public*, pg. 1238
BASWARE, INC.—See Long Path Partners, LP; *U.S. Private*, pg. 2491
BASWARE INDIA PRIVATE LIMITED—See Accel Partners L.P.; *U.S. Private*, pg. 48
BASWARE INDIA PRIVATE LIMITED—See KKR & Co. Inc.; *U.S. Public*, pg. 1237
BASWARE INDIA PRIVATE LIMITED—See Long Path Partners, LP; *U.S. Private*, pg. 2491
BASWARE PTY LTD—See Accel Partners L.P.; *U.S. Private*, pg. 48
BASWARE PTY LTD—See KKR & Co. Inc.; *U.S. Public*, pg. 1238
BASWARE PTY LTD—See Long Path Partners, LP; *U.S. Private*, pg. 2491
BASWARE RUSSIA—See Accel Partners L.P.; *U.S. Private*, pg. 48
BASWARE RUSSIA—See KKR & Co. Inc.; *U.S. Public*, pg. 1238
BASWARE RUSSIA—See Long Path Partners, LP; *U.S. Private*, pg. 2491
BASWARE SAS—See Accel Partners L.P.; *U.S. Private*, pg. 48
BASWARE SAS—See KKR & Co. Inc.; *U.S. Public*, pg. 1238
BASWARE SAS—See Long Path Partners, LP; *U.S. Private*, pg. 2491
BASWARE UK LTD.—See Accel Partners L.P.; *U.S. Private*, pg. 48
BASWARE UK LTD.—See KKR & Co. Inc.; *U.S. Public*, pg. 1238
BASWARE UK LTD.—See Long Path Partners, LP; *U.S. Private*, pg. 2491
BAYVIEW TECHNOLOGIES, INC—See AsianLogic Limited; *Int'l*, pg. 619
B. B. STUDIO CO., LTD.—See BANDAI NAMCO Holdings Inc.; *Int'l*, pg. 828
BBVA INFORMATION TECHNOLOGY ESPANA, S.L.—See Banco Bilbao Vizcaya Argentaria, S.A.; *Int'l*, pg. 817
BCA TECHNOLOGIES INC.—See TA Associates, Inc.; *U.S. Private*, pg. 3918
BCL TECHNOLOGIES—See Thoma Bravo, L.P.; *U.S. Private*, pg. 4146
BCM ONE, INC.—See Thompson Street Capital Manager LLC; *U.S. Private*, pg. 4160
BDF SPA—See Econocom Group SA; *Int'l*, pg. 2297
BEACON MOBILE, LLC—See Vontier Corporation; *U.S. Public*, pg. 2308
BEACONSMIND AG; *Int'l*, pg. 932
BEAMR IMAGING LTD.; *Int'l*, pg. 932
BEANSTALK NETWORKS, LLC—See Thoma Bravo, L.P.; *U.S. Private*, pg. 4150
BECHTLE CLOUDS GMBH—See Bechtle AG; *Int'l*, pg. 937
BECHTLE STEFFEN SCHWEIZ AG—See Bechtle AG; *Int'l*, pg. 937
BEELINE—See Adecco Group AG; *Int'l*, pg. 141
BEFOREPAY GROUP LIMITED; *Int'l*, pg. 940
BEIJING ABT NETWORKS CO., LTD.; *Int'l*, pg. 945
BEIJING ADVANCED DIGITAL TECHNOLOGY CO., LTD.—See Green Leader Holdings Group Limited; *Int'l*, pg. 3071
BEIJING BAOLANDE SOFTWARE CORP.; *Int'l*, pg. 946
BEIJING BOE ENERGY TECHNOLOGY CO., LTD.—See BOE Technology Group Co., Ltd.; *Int'l*, pg. 1099
BEIJING BOHUI SCIENCE & TECHNOLOGY CO., LTD.; *Int'l*, pg. 946
BEIJING E-TECHSTAR CO LTD; *Int'l*, pg. 949
BEIJING FUJITSU SYSTEM ENGINEERING CO., LTD.—See Fujitsu Limited; *Int'l*, pg. 2832
BEIJING GAOCHENG SCIENCE & TECHNOLOGY DEVELOPMENT CO., LTD.—See Beijing E-Hualu Information Technology Co., Ltd.; *Int'l*, pg. 948
BEIJING GS TECHNOLOGY CO., LTD; *Int'l*, pg. 951
BEIJING HANYI INNOVATION TECHNOLOGY CO., LTD.; *Int'l*, pg. 951
BEIJING HUARU TECHNOLOGY CO., LTD.; *Int'l*, pg. 952
BEIJING HYF SOFTWARE CO., LTD—See Antenna House, Inc.; *Int'l*, pg. 482
BEIJING INFOSEC TECHNOLOGIES CO., LTD.; *Int'l*, pg. 952
BEIJING INTERACT TECHNOLOGY CO., LTD.; *Int'l*, pg. 952
BEIJING JDA TECHNOLOGIES COMPANY LTD.—See New Mountain Capital, LLC; *U.S. Private*, pg. 2902
BEIJING JIAODA SIGNAL TECHNOLOGY CO., LTD.; *Int'l*, pg. 952
BEIJING JOIN-CHEER SOFTWARE CO., LTD.; *Int'l*, pg. 953

BEIJING JOYFUL JOURNEY TECHNOLOGIES CO., LTD.—See Hainan Traffic Administration Holding Co., Ltd.; *Int'l*, pg. 3213
BEIJING KINGSOFT OFFICE SOFTWARE, INC.; *Int'l*, pg. 954
BEIJING LONGRUAN TECHNOLOGIES, INC., *Int'l*, pg. 954
BEIJING MAPPS-SERI TECHNOLOGY COMPANY LTD.—See L3Harris Technologies, Inc.; *U.S. Public*, pg. 1281
BEIJING ORIENT NATIONAL COMMUNICATION SCIENCE & TECHNOLOGY CO., LTD.; *Int'l*, pg. 954
BEIJING ROBOROCK TECHNOLOGY CO., LTD.; *Int'l*, pg. 955
BEIJING SEEYON INTERNET SOFTWARE CORP.; *Int'l*, pg. 955
BEIJING SHIJI KUNLUN SOFTWARE CO., LTD.—See Beijing Shiji Information Technology Co., Ltd.; *Int'l*, pg. 956
BEIJING SINOHYTEC CO., LTD.; *Int'l*, pg. 957
BEIJING SUNRISING TECHNOLOGY CO., LTD.—See Beijing E-Hualu Information Technology Co., Ltd.; *Int'l*, pg. 948
BEIJING TELESOUND ELECTRONICS CO., LTD.; *Int'l*, pg. 958
BEIJING TESTOR TECHNOLOGY CO., LTD.—See Beijing Tongtech Company Limited; *Int'l*, pg. 959
BEIJING TRANSTRUE TECHNOLOGY INC.; *Int'l*, pg. 959
BEIJING TRUSTFAR TECHNOLOGY CO., LTD.; *Int'l*, pg. 959
BEIJING YJK BUILDING SOFTWARE CO., LTD.; *Int'l*, pg. 961
BEIJING ZZNODE TECHNOLOGIES CO., LTD.; *Int'l*, pg. 961
BEIT GMBH—See Gauselmann AG; *Int'l*, pg. 2890
BEKKOAME INTERNET INC.—See FreeBit Co., Ltd.; *Int'l*, pg. 2769
BELLSOFT, INC.—See Enveric Biosciences, Inc.; *U.S. Public*, pg. 780
BELMONT SOFTWARE SERVICES; *U.S. Private*, pg. 521
BELUGGAWEB LTD.—See Francoudi & Stephanou Ltd.; *Int'l*, pg. 2761
BENCHMARK SYSTEMS, INC.—See AntWorks Pte. Ltd.; *Int'l*, pg. 485
BENEFIT EXPRESS SERVICES, LLC—See WEX, Inc.; *U.S. Public*, pg. 2364
BENESSE INFOSHELL CO., LTD.—See EQT AB; *Int'l*, pg. 2467
BENEVOLENTAI SA; *Int'l*, pg. 973
BENTLEY CANADA, INC.—See Bentley Systems, Inc.; *U.S. Public*, pg. 296
BENTLEY SYSTEMS (BEIJING) CO., LTD.—See Bentley Systems, Inc.; *U.S. Public*, pg. 296
BENTLEY SYSTEMS CO., LTD.—See Bentley Systems, Inc.; *U.S. Public*, pg. 296
BENTLEY SYSTEMS CR S.R.O.—See Bentley Systems, Inc.; *U.S. Public*, pg. 296
BENTLEY SYSTEMS DE MEXICO SA DE CV—See Bentley Systems, Inc.; *U.S. Public*, pg. 296
BENTLEY SYSTEMS FINLAND OY—See Bentley Systems, Inc.; *U.S. Public*, pg. 296
BENTLEY SYSTEMS GERMANY GMBH—See Bentley Systems, Inc.; *U.S. Public*, pg. 296
BENTLEY SYSTEMS HONG KONG LTD.—See Bentley Systems, Inc.; *U.S. Public*, pg. 296
BENTLEY SYSTEMS IBERICA, S.A.—See Bentley Systems, Inc.; *U.S. Public*, pg. 296
BENTLEY SYSTEMS, INCORPORATED—See Bentley Systems, Inc.; *U.S. Public*, pg. 297
BENTLEY SYSTEMS INDIA PVT. LTD.—See Bentley Systems, Inc.; *U.S. Public*, pg. 296
BENTLEY SYSTEMS INTERNATIONAL LTD.—See Bentley Systems, Inc.; *U.S. Public*, pg. 296
BENTLEY SYSTEMS ITALIA SRL—See Bentley Systems, Inc.; *U.S. Public*, pg. 296
BENTLEY SYSTEMS PAKISTAN (PVT.) LIMITED—See Bentley Systems, Inc.; *U.S. Public*, pg. 296
BENTLEY SYSTEMS POLSKA SP. Z O.O.—See Bentley Systems, Inc.; *U.S. Public*, pg. 296
BENTLEY SYSTEMS RUSSIA (OOO)—See Bentley Systems, Inc.; *U.S. Public*, pg. 296
BENTLEY SYSTEMS SCANDINAVIA A/S—See Bentley Systems, Inc.; *U.S. Public*, pg. 296
BENTLEY SYSTEMS SCANDINAVIA NUF—See Bentley Systems, Inc.; *U.S. Public*, pg. 296
BENTLEY SYSTEMS SDN. BHD.—See Bentley Systems, Inc.; *U.S. Public*, pg. 296
BENTLEY SYSTEMS SINGAPORE PTE. LTD.—See Bentley Systems, Inc.; *U.S. Public*, pg. 296
BENTLEY SYSTEMS SOUTH AFRICA (PTY) LTD.—See Bentley Systems, Inc.; *U.S. Public*, pg. 296
BENTLEY SYSTEMS SWEDEN AB—See Bentley Systems, Inc.; *U.S. Public*, pg. 296
BENTLEY SYSTEMS (UK) LTD.—See Bentley Systems, Inc.; *U.S. Public*, pg. 296
BENTLEY SYSTEMS YAZILIM COZUMLERI LTD.—See Bentley Systems, Inc.; *U.S. Public*, pg. 296
BERICO TECHNOLOGIES LLC; *U.S. Private*, pg. 531
BERTIN TECHNOLOGIES SAS—See CNIM Constructions Industrielles de la Mediterranee SA; *Int'l*, pg. 1677
BEST2SERVE B.V.—See Hainan Traffic Administration Holding Co., Ltd.; *Int'l*, pg. 3214
BETDIGITAL LTD.—See Light & Wonder, Inc.; *U.S. Public*, pg. 1314
BETHESDA SOFTWORKS, LLC—See Microsoft Corporation; *U.S. Public*, pg. 1443
BETREND CORPORATION; *Int'l*, pg. 1003
BETSSON AB; *Int'l*, pg. 1003
BEVILACQUA RESEARCH CORPORATION; *U.S. Private*, pg. 548
BEYOND4 SDN. BHD.—See Censof Holdings Berhad; *Int'l*, pg. 1401
BEYONDPAY INC.—See CBIZ, Inc.; *U.S. Public*, pg. 456
BEYONDSOFT JAPAN CO., LTD.—See Beyondsoft Corporation; *Int'l*, pg. 1005
BEYONDSOFT SOLUTIONS CORP—See Beyondsoft Corporation; *Int'l*, pg. 1005
BFFT GESELLSCHAFT FUR FAHRZEUGTECHNIK MBH—See ATON GmbH; *Int'l*, pg. 688
BIANOR HOLDING AD; *Int'l*, pg. 1017
BID2WIN SOFTWARE, INC.—See Trimble, Inc.; *U.S. Public*, pg. 2190
BIGEON CORP.; *Int'l*, pg. 1022
BIGHAND LTD.—See Levine Leichtman Capital Partners, LLC; *U.S. Private*, pg. 2435
BIG SWITCH NETWORKS, INC.—See Arista Networks, Inc.; *U.S. Public*, pg. 192
BIG TECHNOLOGIES PLC; *Int'l*, pg. 1021
BIGTECH SOFTWARE PRIVATE LIMITED—See Enveric Biosciences, Inc.; *U.S. Public*, pg. 780
B.I. INCORPORATED (CO)—See The GEO Group, Inc.; *U.S. Public*, pg. 2075
BILLEO, INC; *U.S. Private*, pg. 559
BIM ITALIA S.R.L.—See GPI S.p.A.; *Int'l*, pg. 3046
BIM SHARK APS—See Byggfakta Group Nordic HoldCo AB; *Int'l*, pg. 1234
BINARY TREE, INC.; *U.S. Private*, pg. 560
BINOVI TECHNOLOGIES CORP.; *Int'l*, pg. 1034
BIOCERES CROP SOLUTIONS CORP.—See Bioceres S.A.; *Int'l*, pg. 1036
BIO-ITECH B.V.—See Eppendorf AG; *Int'l*, pg. 2464
BIO-KEY HONG KONG LIMITED—See BIO-key International, Inc.; *U.S. Public*, pg. 332
BIONIC PRODUCTION GMBH—See Hamburger Hafen und Logistik AG; *Int'l*, pg. 3236
BIRDDOG TECHNOLOGY LIMITED; *Int'l*, pg. 1047
BIRDEYE, INC.; *U.S. Private*, pg. 564
BIRLASOFT LTD.; *Int'l*, pg. 1048
BIRLASOFT SOLUTIONS FRANCE SAS—See Birlasoft Ltd.; *Int'l*, pg. 1048
BIRLASOFT SOLUTIONS GMBH—See Birlasoft Ltd.; *Int'l*, pg. 1048
BIRLASOFT SOLUTIONS LIMITED—See Birlasoft Ltd.; *Int'l*, pg. 1048
BIRLASOFT SOLUTIONS LTDA.—See Birlasoft Ltd.; *Int'l*, pg. 1048
BIRLASOFT SOLUTIONS ME FZE—See Birlasoft Ltd.; *Int'l*, pg. 1048
BIT FLOW INC.—See Advantech Co., Ltd.; *Int'l*, pg. 165
BITSQUID AB—See Autodesk, Inc.; *U.S. Public*, pg. 229
BIZIT SYSTEMS & SOLUTIONS PTE. LTD.—See Aimflex Berhad; *Int'l*, pg. 233
BIZRIGHT TECHNOLOGY, INC.—See Ecomic Co Ltd; *Int'l*, pg. 2296
BIZSTREAM, INC.; *U.S. Private*, pg. 567
BIZZUKA, INC.; *U.S. Private*, pg. 568
BLACKBAUD CANADA, INC.—See Blackbaud, Inc.; *U.S. Public*, pg. 341
BLACKBAUD EUROPE LTD.—See Blackbaud, Inc.; *U.S. Public*, pg. 341
BLACKBIRD TECHNOLOGIES, INC.—See RTX Corporation; *U.S. Public*, pg. 1824
BLACKFORD ANALYSIS LIMITED—See Bayer Aktiengesellschaft; *Int'l*, pg. 907
BLACKLINE, INC.; *U.S. Public*, pg. 341
BLACKLINE SYSTEMS GERMANY GMBH—See BlackLine, Inc.; *U.S. Public*, pg. 341
BLACKLINE SYSTEMS LIMITED—See BlackLine, Inc.; *U.S. Public*, pg. 342
BLACKLINE SYSTEMS, LTD.—See BlackLine, Inc.; *U.S. Public*, pg. 342
BLACKLINE SYSTEMS PTE. LTD.—See BlackLine, Inc.; *U.S. Public*, pg. 342
BLACKLINE SYSTEMS S.A R.L.—See BlackLine, Inc.; *U.S. Public*, pg. 342
BLACK MOUNTAIN SOFTWARE, LLC; *U.S. Private*, pg. 572
BLACKSKY TECHNOLOGY INC.; *U.S. Public*, pg. 347
BLANCCO AUSTRALASIA PTY LTD—See Francisco Partners Management, LP; *U.S. Private*, pg. 1588
BLANCCO CENTRAL EUROPE GMBH—See Francisco Partners Management, LP; *U.S. Private*, pg. 1588
BLANCCO FRANCE SAS—See Francisco Partners Management, LP; *U.S. Private*, pg. 1588
BLANCCO JAPAN INC.—See Francisco Partners Management, LP; *U.S. Private*, pg. 1588
BLANCCO LLC—See Francisco Partners Management, LP; *U.S. Private*, pg. 1588
BLANCCO OY LTD—See Francisco Partners Management, LP; *U.S. Private*, pg. 1588
BLANCCO SEA SDN BHD—See Francisco Partners Management, LP; *U.S. Private*, pg. 1588
BLANCCO SWEDEN SFO—See Francisco Partners Management, LP; *U.S. Private*, pg. 1588
BLANCCO UK LTD—See Francisco Partners Management, LP; *U.S. Private*, pg. 1588
BLINK INTERACTIVE, INC.—See Blackstone Inc.; *U.S. Public*, pg. 356
BLIP SYSTEMS A/S—See Gentrack Group Limited; *Int'l*, pg. 2929
BLISS INTELLIGENCE PUBLIC COMPANY LIMITED; *Int'l*, pg. 1063
BLIZZARD ENTERTAINMENT S.A.S.—See Microsoft Corporation; *U.S. Public*, pg. 1438
BLK SISTEMAS FINANCEIROS LTDA.—See B3 S.A.; *Int'l*, pg. 791
BLOCKCHAIN OF THINGS, INC.; *U.S. Private*, pg. 583
BLOCKCHAINS, LLC; *U.S. Private*, pg. 583
BLOOMBERG CONSULTING, INC.—See YOUNG & Associates; *U.S. Private*, pg. 4592
BLOOMNATION, INC.; *U.S. Private*, pg. 584
BLS INFOTECH LIMITED; *Int'l*, pg. 1066
BLUE4IT PROFESSIONALS B.V.—See adesso SE; *Int'l*, pg. 144
BLUECIELO ECM SOLUTIONS B.V.—See Fortive Corporation; *U.S. Public*, pg. 870
BLUE COD TECHNOLOGIES, INC.; *U.S. Private*, pg. 586
BLUEFACE ITALIA S.R.L.—See Comcast Corporation; *U.S. Public*, pg. 537
BLUEFRONT B.V.—See adesso SE; *Int'l*, pg. 144
BLUE HAT INTERACTIVE ENTERTAINMENT TECHNOLOGY; *Int'l*, pg. 1068
BLUE INNOVATION CO., LTD.; *Int'l*, pg. 1068
BLUENICA CORPORATION—See Digi International Inc.; *U.S. Public*, pg. 662
BLUE OCEAN TECHNOLOGIES, LLC—See Beyond, Inc.; *U.S. Public*, pg. 327
BLUEPHOENIX SOLUTIONS ITALIA—See Advanced Business Software & Solutions Ltd.; *Int'l*, pg. 157
BLUEPHOENIX SOLUTIONS NORDIC APS—See Advanced Business Software & Solutions Ltd.; *Int'l*, pg. 157
BLUEPRINT GAMING LTD.—See Gauselmann AG; *Int'l*, pg. 2890
BLUE PRISM AB—See SS&C Technologies Holdings, Inc.; *U.S. Public*, pg. 1923
BLUE PRISM GMBH—See SS&C Technologies Holdings, Inc.; *U.S. Public*, pg. 1923
BLUE PRISM GROUP PLC—See SS&C Technologies Holdings, Inc.; *U.S. Public*, pg. 1922
BLUE PRISM INDIA PVT. LTD.—See SS&C Technologies Holdings, Inc.; *U.S. Public*, pg. 1923
BLUE PRISM K.K.—See SS&C Technologies Holdings, Inc.; *U.S. Public*, pg. 1923
BLUE PRISM LIMITED—See SS&C Technologies Holdings, Inc.; *U.S. Public*, pg. 1923
BLUE PRISM PTE. LTD.—See SS&C Technologies Holdings, Inc.; *U.S. Public*, pg. 1923
BLUE PRISM PTY. LTD.—See SS&C Technologies Holdings, Inc.; *U.S. Public*, pg. 1923
BLUE PRISM SARL—See SS&C Technologies Holdings, Inc.; *U.S. Public*, pg. 1923
BLUE PRISM SOFTWARE INC.—See SS&C Technologies Holdings, Inc.; *U.S. Public*, pg. 1923
BLUESNAP, INC.; *U.S. Private*, pg. 597
BLUE SOFTWARE LLC—See Danaher Corporation; *U.S. Public*, pg. 625
BLUE SOMBRERO, LLC—See Genstar Capital, LLC; *U.S. Private*, pg. 1678
BLUEWAVE COMPUTING LLC; *U.S. Private*, pg. 599
BLUEWORX—See Waterfield Technologies, Inc.; *U.S. Private*, pg. 4453
BLUWARE, INC.—See Computer Modelling Group Ltd.; *Int'l*, pg. 1760
BMC SOFTWARE DE MEXICO, S.A. DE C.V.—See KKR & Co. Inc.; *U.S. Public*, pg. 1240
BMC SOFTWARE INDIA PRIVATE LIMITED—See KKR & Co. Inc.; *U.S. Public*, pg. 1240
BMC SOFTWARE INVESTMENT, L.L.C.—See KKR & Co. Inc.; *U.S. Public*, pg. 1240
BMC SOFTWARE IRELAND LIMITED—See KKR & Co. Inc.; *U.S. Public*, pg. 1240
BMC SOFTWARE ISRAEL LTD.—See KKR & Co. Inc.; *U.S. Public*, pg. 1240
BMC SOFTWARE SALES (POLAND) SP. O.O.—See KKR & Co. Inc.; *U.S. Public*, pg. 1240
BMC SOFTWARE (THAILAND) LIMITED—See KKR & Co. Inc.; *U.S. Public*, pg. 1239
B+M INFORMATIK AG—See Allgeier SE; *Int'l*, pg. 338
BMK UAB—See Atea ASA; *Int'l*, pg. 667
BODYNET LTD—See HeiTech Padu Berhad; *Int'l*, pg. 3326
BODYSHOPBIDS, INC.; *U.S. Private*, pg. 608
BOEING ADVANCED INFORMATION SYSTEMS-MARYLAND OPERATIONS—See The Boeing Company; *U.S. Public*, pg. 2039
BOE OPTICAL SCIENCE & TECHNOLOGY CO., LTD.—See BOE Technology Group Co., Ltd.; *Int'l*, pg. 1099

N.A.I.C.S. INDEX 541511 — CUSTOM COMPUTER PRO...

BOHEMIA INTERACTIVE SIMULATIONS K.S.—See BAE Systems plc; *Int'l*, pg. 798
BOICE ENTERPRISES, INC.; *U.S. Private*, pg. 609
BOLT ON TECHNOLOGY, LLC—See Performant Management Company, LLC; *U.S. Private*, pg. 3150
BOND INTERNATIONAL JAPAN K.K.—See Symphony Technology Group, LLC; *U.S. Private*, pg. 3900
BOND INTERNATIONAL SOFTWARE CHINA LIMITED—See Symphony Technology Group, LLC; *U.S. Private*, pg. 3900
BOND INTERNATIONAL SOFTWARE, INC. - MINNEAPOLIS OFFICE—See Symphony Technology Group, LLC; *U.S. Private*, pg. 3900
BOND INTERNATIONAL SOFTWARE (UK) LIMITED—See Symphony Technology Group, LLC; *U.S. Private*, pg. 3900
BONREE DATA TECHNOLOGY CO., LTD.; *Int'l*, pg. 1109
BOOKS24X7.COM, INC.—See Charterhouse Capital Partners LLP; *Int'l*, pg. 1456
BOOMBIT S. A.; *Int'l*, pg. 1110
BOOMSET, INC.—See Bending Spoons S.p.A.; *Int'l*, pg. 971
BOOTSTRAP SOFTWARE PARTNERS, LLC; *U.S. Private*, pg. 617
BOOZT BALTICS UAB—See Boozt AB; *Int'l*, pg. 1111
BORN INC.; *U.S. Public*, pg. 371
BORQS INTERNATIONAL HOLDING CORP.—See BORQS Technologies, Inc.; *Int'l*, pg. 1114
BOTTLECUBE INC.—See CYBIRD Holdings Co., Ltd.; *Int'l*, pg. 1894
BOTTOM-LINE PERFORMANCE, INC.—See Tier 1 Performance Solutions, LLC; *U.S. Private*, pg. 4168
BOUVET SVERIGE AB—See Bouvet ASA; *Int'l*, pg. 1121
BOUYGUES E&S PROZESSAUTOMATION AG—See Bouygues S.A.; *Int'l*, pg. 1123
BOX.COM (UK) LTD—See Box, Inc.; *U.S. Public*, pg. 377
BP LOGIX, INC.—See Finrock Growth Partners, LLC; *U.S. Private*, pg. 1511
BRAGG GAMING GROUP INC.; *Int'l*, pg. 1136
BRAINGRID LTD.; *Int'l*, pg. 1137
BRAINSHARK, INC.—See Bigtincan Holdings Limited; *U.S. Public*, pg. 331
BRAINS TECHNOLOGY, INC.; *Int'l*, pg. 1137
BRAINZCOMPANY CO., LTD.; *Int'l*, pg. 1137
BRANDED ENTERTAINMENT NETWORK, INC.; *U.S. Private*, pg. 637
BRANDS ON FIRE, LLC—See Level Equity Management, LLC; *U.S. Private*, pg. 2434
BRAVOBUS S.R.L.—See Accel Partners L.P.; *U.S. Private*, pg. 48
BRAVOBUS S.R.L.—See KKR & Co. Inc.; *U.S. Public*, pg. 1238
BRAVOSOLUTION BENELUX B.V.—See Accel Partners L.P.; *U.S. Private*, pg. 48
BRAVOSOLUTION BENELUX B.V.—See KKR & Co. Inc.; *U.S. Public*, pg. 1238
BRAVOSOLUTION CHINA CO. LTD—See Accel Partners L.P.; *U.S. Private*, pg. 48
BRAVOSOLUTION CHINA CO. LTD—See KKR & Co. Inc.; *U.S. Public*, pg. 1238
BRAVOSOLUTION ESPANA S.A.—See Accel Partners L.P.; *U.S. Private*, pg. 48
BRAVOSOLUTION ESPANA S.A.—See KKR & Co. Inc.; *U.S. Public*, pg. 1238
BRAVOSOLUTION FRANCE S.A.S.—See Accel Partners L.P.; *U.S. Private*, pg. 48
BRAVOSOLUTION FRANCE S.A.S.—See KKR & Co. Inc.; *U.S. Public*, pg. 1238
BRAVOSOLUTION GMBH—See Accel Partners L.P.; *U.S. Private*, pg. 48
BRAVOSOLUTION GMBH—See KKR & Co. Inc.; *U.S. Public*, pg. 1238
BRAVOSOLUTION MEXICO S.R.L. DE C.V.—See Accel Partners L.P.; *U.S. Private*, pg. 48
BRAVOSOLUTION MEXICO S.R.L. DE C.V.—See KKR & Co. Inc.; *U.S. Public*, pg. 1238
BRAVOSOLUTION SOFTWARE, INC.—See Accel Partners L.P.; *U.S. Private*, pg. 48
BRAVOSOLUTION SOFTWARE, INC.—See KKR & Co. Inc.; *U.S. Public*, pg. 1238
BRAVOSOLUTION TECHNOLOGIES LTD—See Accel Partners L.P.; *U.S. Private*, pg. 48
BRAVOSOLUTION TECHNOLOGIES LTD—See KKR & Co. Inc.; *U.S. Public*, pg. 1238
BRAVOSOLUTION UK LTD—See Accel Partners L.P.; *U.S. Private*, pg. 48
BRAVOSOLUTION UK LTD—See KKR & Co. Inc.; *U.S. Public*, pg. 1238
BRAVURA SECURITY, INC.—See Constellation Software Inc.; *Int'l*, pg. 1775
BRAXTON TECHNOLOGIES, LLC—See Parsons Corporation; *U.S. Public*, pg. 1650
BRAZE, INC.; *U.S. Public*, pg. 380
BRIDGE SAAS LIMITED; *Int'l*, pg. 1152
BRIDGESTONE AMERICAS, INC. - BUSINESS TECHNOLOGY GROUP DIVISION—See Cox Enterprises, Inc.; *U.S. Private*, pg. 1075
BRIDGETEC CORP.; *Int'l*, pg. 1160

BRIGHTERION, INC.—See Mastercard Incorporated; *U.S. Public*, pg. 1394
BRIGHT OCEANS INTER-TELECOM CO., LTD.; *Int'l*, pg. 1161
BRIGHTSOLID—See D.C. Thomson & Co. Ltd.; *Int'l*, pg. 1900
BRIGHTSTAR PARTNERS, INC.—See Avnet, Inc.; *U.S. Public*, pg. 252
BRILLIANT FUTURE AB; *Int'l*, pg. 1163
BRIOX AB; *Int'l*, pg. 1164
BRIT MEDIA, INC.; *U.S. Private*, pg. 657
BROADBAND TOWER, INC.; *Int'l*, pg. 1172
BROADPOINT TECHNOLOGIES, INC.—See Velosio, LLC; *U.S. Private*, pg. 4355
BROADVISION DEUTSCHLAND GMBH—See ESW Capital, LLC; *U.S. Private*, pg. 1429
BROADVISION, INC.—See ESW Capital, LLC; *U.S. Private*, pg. 1430
BROKER GENIUS, INC.; *U.S. Private*, pg. 661
BROMIDE TECHNOLOGIES (PTY) LTD—See EOH HOLDINGS LIMITED; *Int'l*, pg. 2457
BROMIUM UK LIMITED—See HP Inc.; *U.S. Public*, pg. 1062
BROTHER MOBILE SOLUTIONS, INC.—See Brother Industries, Ltd.; *Int'l*, pg. 1197
BROTHER SOFTWARE DEVELOPMENT (HANGZHOU) LTD.—See Brother Industries, Ltd.; *Int'l*, pg. 1196
B+S BANKSYSTEME AKTIENGESELLSCHAFT—See B+S Banksysteme AG; *Int'l*, pg. 784
B+S BANKSYSTEME AKTIENGESELLSCHAFT—See B+S Banksysteme AG; *Int'l*, pg. 784
B+S BANKSYSTEME DEUTSCHLAND GMBH—See B+S Banksysteme AG; *Int'l*, pg. 784
B+S BANKSYSTEME SCHWEIZ AG—See B+S Banksysteme AG; *Int'l*, pg. 784
BSOFT S.R.L.—See Biesse S.p.A.; *Int'l*, pg. 1020
BSP SOFTWARE LLC; *U.S. Private*, pg. 675
BSV SARL—See Cegedim S.A.; *Int'l*, pg. 1390
BSWIFT LLC—See Francisco Partners Management, LP; *U.S. Private*, pg. 1593
BSWIFT RESOURCES LLC—See CVS Health Corporation; *U.S. Public*, pg. 616
BTC EMBEDDED SYSTEMS AG—See EWE Aktiengesellschaft; *Int'l*, pg. 2575
BTC SOLUTIONS LIMITED—See Snap-on Incorporated; *U.S. Public*, pg. 1897
BT (GERMANY) GMBH & CO. OHG—See BT Group plc; *Int'l*, pg. 1203
BT IT SERVICES LIMITED—See BT Group plc; *Int'l*, pg. 1203
BUBBLEUP, LTD; *U.S. Private*, pg. 676
BUDSOFT SP. Z O.O.—See Addnode Group AB; *Int'l*, pg. 130
BUGSENSE INC.—See Cisco Systems, Inc.; *U.S. Public*, pg. 500
BUILDASIGN.COM; *U.S. Private*, pg. 681
BUILDIUM, LLC—See Thoma Bravo, L.P.; *U.S. Private*, pg. 4152
BULLHORN, INC.—See Insight Venture Management, LLC; *U.S. Private*, pg. 2087
BULL INDIAN OCEAN LTD.—See Atos SE; *Int'l*, pg. 692
BULL INFORMATION SYSTEMS IRELAND—See Atos SE; *Int'l*, pg. 692
BULL POLSKA SP. Z.O.O.—See Atos SE; *Int'l*, pg. 692
BUMBLE, INC.; *U.S. Public*, pg. 410
BUOY LABS, INC.—See Resideo Technologies, Inc.; *U.S. Public*, pg. 1789
BUREAU VAN DIJK EDITIONS ELECTRONIQUES S.A.—See Moody's Corporation; *U.S. Public*, pg. 1467
BUREAU VAN DIJK ELECTRONIC PUBLISHING GMBH—See Moody's Corporation; *U.S. Public*, pg. 1467
THE BURGESS GROUP, LLC—See Blackstone Inc.; *U.S. Public*, pg. 354
THE BURGISS GROUP, LLC—See MSCI Inc.; *U.S. Public*, pg. 1483
BUSHIROAD, INC.; *Int'l*, pg. 1227
BUSINESS CONNEXION LIMITED—See Business Connexion Group Limited; *Int'l*, pg. 1228
BUSINESS CONNEXION MOZAMBIQUE LIMITADA—See Business Connexion Group Limited; *Int'l*, pg. 1228
BUSINESS CONNEXION NETWORKS (NIGERIA) LIMITED—See Business Connexion Group Limited; *Int'l*, pg. 1228
BUSINESS CONNEXION (PTY) LIMITED—See Business Connexion Group Limited; *Int'l*, pg. 1228
BUSINESS CONNEXION TANZANIA LIMITED—See Business Connexion Group Limited; *Int'l*, pg. 1228
BUSINESS CONNEXION TECHNOLOGY HOLDINGS (PTY) LIMITED—See Business Connexion Group Limited; *Int'l*, pg. 1228
BUSINESSON COMMUNICATION CO., LTD.; *Int'l*, pg. 1229
BUSINESS SOFT SERVICE CO., LTD.—See Computer Institute of Japan Ltd.; *Int'l*, pg. 1759
BUSYBUSY, INC.—See Toolwatch Corp.; *U.S. Private*, pg. 4186
BUT'ONE INFORMATION CORPORATION; *Int'l*, pg. 1229
BWAY.NET, INC.; *U.S. Private*, pg. 700
BWISE B.V.—See EQT AB; *Int'l*, pg. 2471

BYGGFAKTA GROUP NORDIC HOLDCO AB; *Int'l*, pg. 1234
BYLOG GROUP CORP.; *Int'l*, pg. 1235
BYTE SOFTWARE HOUSE S.P.A.; *Int'l*, pg. 1237
C3.AI, INC.; *U.S. Public*, pg. 415
C3 CO., LTD.—See Cresco, Ltd.; *Int'l*, pg. 1840
C3, LLC—See Constellation Energy Corporation; *U.S. Public*, pg. 571
CA BELGIUM BVBA—See Broadcom Inc.; *U.S. Public*, pg. 388
CABLE PRINT B.V.B.A.—See Diebold Nixdorf, Inc.; *U.S. Public*, pg. 659
CACCO, INC.; *Int'l*, pg. 1247
CACI-ISS, INC.—See CACI International Inc.; *U.S. Public*, pg. 417
CACI LIMITED—See CACI International Inc.; *U.S. Public*, pg. 417
CA CONSULTING SA—See ComArch S.A.; *Int'l*, pg. 1707
CAC ORBIS CORPORATION—See CAC Corporation; *Int'l*, pg. 1247
CA DEUTSCHLAND GMBH—See Broadcom Inc.; *U.S. Public*, pg. 389
CAFE24 CORP.; *Int'l*, pg. 1250
CALABRIO, INC.—See Thoma Bravo, L.P.; *U.S. Private*, pg. 4146
CALIAN LTD. - TORONTO—See Calian Group Ltd.; *Int'l*, pg. 1264
CALIFORNIA SOFTWARE COMPANY LTD.; *Int'l*, pg. 1264
CAMBRICON TECHNOLOGIES CORPORATION LIMITED; *Int'l*, pg. 1269
CAMBRIDGE BIZSERVE INC.—See Cambridge Technology Enterprises Ltd.; *Int'l*, pg. 1269
CAMBRIDGE INDUSTRIES GROUP, LTD.—See CIG Shanghai Co., Ltd.; *Int'l*, pg. 1606
CAMBRIDGE INDUSTRIES USA, INC.—See CIG Shanghai Co., Ltd.; *Int'l*, pg. 1607
CAMBRIDGE TECHNOLOGY ENTERPRISES LTD.; *Int'l*, pg. 1269
CAMBRIDGE TECHNOLOGY INC.—See Cambridge Technology Enterprises Ltd.; *Int'l*, pg. 1269
CAMBRIDGE TECHNOLOGY INVESTMENTS PTE. LTD.—See Cambridge Technology Enterprises Ltd.; *Int'l*, pg. 1269
CAMBRIDGE TECHNOLOGY PARTNERS, LTD.—See BIPROGY Inc.; *Int'l*, pg. 1045
CAMELEON SOFTWARE USA, INC.—See PROS Holdings, Inc.; *U.S. Public*, pg. 1728
CAMELOT MANAGEMENT CONSULTANTS INC.—See Camelot Management Consultants AG; *Int'l*, pg. 1271
CAMELOT MANAGEMENT CONSULTANTS MIDDLE EAST DMCC—See Camelot Management Consultants AG; *Int'l*, pg. 1271
CAMLINE DRESDEN GMBH—See Elisa Corporation; *Int'l*, pg. 2362
CAMLINE GMBH—See Elisa Corporation; *Int'l*, pg. 2362
CAMLINE PTE. LTD.—See Elisa Corporation; *Int'l*, pg. 2362
CAMLINE USA INC.—See Elisa Corporation; *Int'l*, pg. 2362
CAMPFIRE INTERACTIVE, INC.; *U.S. Private*, pg. 731
CAM SYSTEMS GMBH—See Certina Holding AG; *Int'l*, pg. 1423
CANAL GLOBE, LTD.—See BIPROGY Inc.; *Int'l*, pg. 1045
CANAL PAYMENT SERVICE, LTD.—See BIPROGY Inc.; *Int'l*, pg. 1045
CANARYS AUTOMATIONS LIMITED; *Int'l*, pg. 1288
CANBANK COMPUTER SERVICES LIMITED—See Canara Bank; *Int'l*, pg. 1287
CANCOM PUBLIC GMBH—See CANCOM SE; *Int'l*, pg. 1289
CANCOM SYSDAT GMBH—See CANCOM SE; *Int'l*, pg. 1289
CANDERA GMBH—See CELSYS, Inc.; *Int'l*, pg. 1396
CANNIS, INC.; *U.S. Private*, pg. 734
CANONICAL USA INC.—See Canonical Group Limited; *Int'l*, pg. 1298
CANON IMAGING SYSTEMS INC.—See Canon Inc.; *Int'l*, pg. 1295
CANON INFORMATION TECHNOLOGIES PHILIPPINES, INC.—See Canon Inc.; *Int'l*, pg. 1295
CANON SOFTWARE AMERICA, INC.—See Canon Inc.; *Int'l*, pg. 1296
CANON SOFTWARE INFORMATION SYSTEMS INC.—See Canon Inc.; *Int'l*, pg. 1296
CAPAX GLOBAL, LLC—See Hitachi, Ltd.; *Int'l*, pg. 3421
CAPCARGO AG; *Int'l*, pg. 1302
CAPCOM ENTERTAINMENT FRANCE, SAS—See Capcom Co., Ltd.; *Int'l*, pg. 1302
CAPCOM ENTERTAINMENT GERMANY GMBH—See Capcom Co., Ltd.; *Int'l*, pg. 1302
CAPELLA TECHNOLOGIES, INC.—See Levi, Ray & Shoup, Inc.; *U.S. Private*, pg. 2435
CAPGEMINI LTD—See Capgemini SE; *Int'l*, pg. 1305
CAPITAL COMPUTER ASSOCIATES, INC.—See Constellation Software Inc.; *Int'l*, pg. 1774
THE CAPITAL MARKETS COMPANY GMBH—See Clayton, Dubilier & Rice, LLC; *U.S. Private*, pg. 927
CAPITALONLINE DATA SERVICE CO., LTD.; *Int'l*, pg. 1314
CAPITA MORTGAGE SOFTWARE SOLUTIONS LTD.—See Capita plc; *Int'l*, pg. 1308

CAPITA SECURE INFORMATION SYSTEMS LIMITED—See Capita plc; *Int'l*, pg. 1308
CA PLUS LIMITED—See Gentrack Group Limited; *Int'l*, pg. 2929
CAPRICORN SYSTEMS GLOBAL SOLUTIONS LIMITED; *Int'l*, pg. 1317
CAPRICORN SYSTEMS, INC.—See Smart IMS; *U.S. Private*, pg. 3691
CARAVEL INFO SYSTEM PRIVATE LIMITED—See Cranes Software International Limited; *Int'l*, pg. 1828
CARBON REVOLUTION LIMITED; *Int'l*, pg. 1320
CARDTREND SYSTEMS SDN. BHD.—See Edenred S.A.; *Int'l*, pg. 2307
CAREBOOK TECHNOLOGIES INC.; *Int'l*, pg. 1323
CARELABS CO., LTD.; *Int'l*, pg. 1324
CAREMEDIC SYSTEMS, INC.—See UnitedHealth Group Incorporated; *U.S. Public*, pg. 2248
CAREPAYMENT TECHNOLOGIES, INC.—See Cedar Spring Capital LLC; *U.S. Private*, pg. 805
CAREPAYMENT TECHNOLOGIES, INC.—See Crestline Investors, Inc.; *U.S. Private*, pg. 1097
CAREPORT HEALTH, LLC—See Veradigm Inc.; *U.S. Public*, pg. 2280
CARINA SYSTEM CO., LTD.—See EIZO Corporation; *Int'l*, pg. 2337
CARINK, INC.—See Automatic Data Processing, Inc.; *U.S. Public*, pg. 230
CARL ZEISS MES SOLUTIONS GMBH—See Carl-Zeiss-Stiftung; *Int'l*, pg. 1334
CARRIEREQ, INC.; *U.S. Private*, pg. 772
CARRIER-SERVICES.DE GMBH—See ecotel communication ag; *Int'l*, pg. 2300
CARROT, LLC; *U.S. Private*, pg. 774
CARTESIAN LTD.—See Blackstreet Capital Holdings LLC; *U.S. Private*, pg. 576
CA (SINGAPORE) PTE LTD—See Broadcom Inc.; *U.S. Public*, pg. 388
CA SOFTWARE FINLAND OY—See Broadcom Inc.; *U.S. Public*, pg. 389
CA SOUTHERN AFRICA (PTY) LIMITED—See EOH HOLDINGS LIMITED; *Int'l*, pg. 2457
CASPIO, INC.; *U.S. Private*, pg. 783
CA SP. Z.O.O.—See Broadcom Inc.; *U.S. Public*, pg. 389
CASTLEROCK INNOVATIONS, LLC—See Bain Capital, LP; *U.S. Private*, pg. 439
CAST S.A.; *Int'l*, pg. 1355
CAST SOFTWARE INC.—See CAST S.A.; *Int'l*, pg. 1355
CASZYME, UAB—See Corteva, Inc.; *U.S. Public*, pg. 580
CATALYSIS LLC—See Catalysis Holding Corporation; *U.S. Private*, pg. 786
CATALYSTUX HOLDINGS, INC.—See Trivest Partners, LP; *U.S. Private*, pg. 4241
CATALYTE, INC.; *U.S. Private*, pg. 787
CATENAE INNOVATION PLC; *Int'l*, pg. 1359
CATO SOFTWARE SOLUTIONS GMBH—See Becton, Dickinson & Company; *U.S. Public*, pg. 292
CAT TECHNOLOGIES LIMITED; *Int'l*, pg. 1358
CATT LTD.—See CAT Technologies Limited; *Int'l*, pg. 1358
CATYLIST, INC.—See Moody's Corporation; *U.S. Public*, pg. 1468
CATYLIST REAL ESTATE SOFTWARE, INC.—See Moody's Corporation; *U.S. Public*, pg. 1468
CA WASHINGTON, LLC—See Insight Venture Management, LLC; *U.S. Private*, pg. 2087
CAYENNE ENTERTAINMENT TECHNOLOGY CO., LTD.; *Int'l*, pg. 1363
CBRAIN A/S; *Int'l*, pg. 1366
CCC INFORMATION SERVICES, INC.—See Advent International Corporation; *U.S. Private*, pg. 98
CCK FINANCIAL SOLUTIONS (CONSULTING) PTY. LTD.—See CCK Financial Solutions Pty Limited; *Int'l*, pg. 1367
CCP GLOBAL INC.; *U.S. Private*, pg. 801
CDP TECHNOLOGIES AS—See Cassa Depositi e Prestiti S.p.A.; *Int'l*, pg. 1354
CDS VISUAL, INC.—See Dover Corporation; *U.S. Public*, pg. 678
CEDEXIS INC.—See Elliott Management Corporation; *U.S. Private*, pg. 1366
CEDEXIS INC.—See Vista Equity Partners, LLC; *U.S. Private*, pg. 4395
CEGEDIM CLOUD SASU—See Cegedim S.A.; *Int'l*, pg. 1390
CEGID CORPORATION—See Silver Lake Group, LLC; *U.S. Private*, pg. 3656
C.E. INFO SYSTEMS LTD.; *Int'l*, pg. 1240
CELEBRATIONS.COM, LLC—See 1-800-FLOWERS.COM, Inc.; *U.S. Public*, pg. 1
CELERIT CORPORATION; *U.S. Private*, pg. 806
CELFINET - CONSULTORIA EM TELECOMUNICACOES, S.A.—See Cyient Limited; *Int'l*, pg. 1895
CELLGENTEK CO., LTD.; *Int'l*, pg. 1393
CELSYS, INC.—See CELSYS, Inc.; *Int'l*, pg. 1396
CELTIC SYSTEMS PRIVATE LIMITED—See i3 Verticals, Inc.; *U.S. Public*, pg. 1081
CENDEE SDN. BHD.—See Censof Holdings Berhad; *Int'l*, pg. 1401
CENTERGISTIC SOLUTIONS, INC.; *U.S. Private*, pg. 816

CENTRA 2000, INC.—See Auto-trol Technology Corporation; *U.S. Private*, pg. 398
CENTRALREACH, LLC; *U.S. Private*, pg. 826
CENTRAPAL S.R.L.—See Aramark; *U.S. Public*, pg. 177
CENTRA WORLDWIDE, INC.—See The Suddath Companies; *U.S. Private*, pg. 4124
CENTRIC BELGIUM NV—See Centric Holding B.V.; *Int'l*, pg. 1412
CENTRIC GERMANY GMBH—See Centric Holding B.V.; *Int'l*, pg. 1412
CENTRIC IT SOLUTIONS ROMANIA—See Centric Holding B.V.; *Int'l*, pg. 1412
CENTRIC IT SOLUTIONS SWITZERLAND AG—See Centric Holding B.V.; *Int'l*, pg. 1412
CENTRIC NORWAY—See Centric Holding B.V.; *Int'l*, pg. 1412
CENTRIC SWEDEN AB—See Centric Holding B.V.; *Int'l*, pg. 1412
CERENCE GMBH—See Microsoft Corporation; *U.S. Public*, pg. 1442
CERENCE INC.—See Microsoft Corporation; *U.S. Public*, pg. 1442
CERIDIAN DAYFORCE GERMANY GMBH—See Dayforce, Inc.; *U.S. Public*, pg. 645
CERMATE SOFTWARE INC.—See Advantech Co., Ltd.; *Int'l*, pg. 165
CERM N.V.—See Heidelberger Druckmaschinen AG; *Int'l*, pg. 3321
CERNER CORPORATION - CLAIRVIA—See Oracle Corporation; *U.S. Public*, pg. 1610
CERNER HEALTHCARE SOLUTIONS INDIA PRIVATE LIMITED—See Oracle Corporation; *U.S. Public*, pg. 1610
CERNER HEALTH SERVICES, INC.—See Oracle Corporation; *U.S. Public*, pg. 1610
CERTIFY DATA SYSTEMS, INC.—See Humana, Inc.; *U.S. Public*, pg. 1069
CERTON SOFTWARE, INC.—See Cyient Limited; *Int'l*, pg. 1895
CERTTECH, L.L.C.; *U.S. Private*, pg. 842
CERTUSVIEW TECHNOLOGIES, LLC—See Dycom Industries, Inc.; *U.S. Public*, pg. 698
CES TECHNOLOGY SERVICES PRIVATE LIMITED—See CES Limited; *Int'l*, pg. 1423
CETAN CORPORATION; *U.S. Private*, pg. 842
CEYONIQ TECHNOLOGY GMBH; *Int'l*, pg. 1426
C/F DATA SYSTEMS INC.; *U.S. Private*, pg. 709
CFD RESEARCH CORPORATION; *U.S. Private*, pg. 843
CFT CONSULTING GMBH—See Easy Software AG; *Int'l*, pg. 2275
CGC TECHNOLOGY LIMITED—See Comtech Telecommunications Corp.; *U.S. Public*, pg. 562
CGG SERVICES INDIA PRIVATE LTD.—See CGG; *Int'l*, pg. 1432
CGI FRANCE S.A.S. - AIX-EN-PROVENCE—See CGI Inc.; *Int'l*, pg. 1433
CGI FRANCE S.A.S. - BORDEAUX—See CGI Inc.; *Int'l*, pg. 1433
CGI FRANCE S.A.S. - BREST—See CGI Inc.; *Int'l*, pg. 1433
CGI FRANCE S.A.S. - LILLE—See CGI Inc.; *Int'l*, pg. 1433
CGI FRANCE S.A.S. - LYON—See CGI Inc.; *Int'l*, pg. 1433
CGI FRANCE S.A.S. - MONTPELLIER—See CGI Inc.; *Int'l*, pg. 1433
CGI FRANCE S.A.S. - NANTES—See CGI Inc.; *Int'l*, pg. 1433
CGI FRANCE S.A.S. - NIORT—See CGI Inc.; *Int'l*, pg. 1433
CGI FRANCE S.A.S. - PAU—See CGI Inc.; *Int'l*, pg. 1433
CGI FRANCE S.A.S. - RENNES—See CGI Inc.; *Int'l*, pg. 1433
CGI FRANCE S.A.S.—See CGI Inc.; *Int'l*, pg. 1433
CGI FRANCE S.A.S. - STRASBOURG—See CGI Inc.; *Int'l*, pg. 1433
CGI FRANCE S.A.S. - TOULOUSE—See CGI Inc.; *Int'l*, pg. 1433
CGI INFORMATION SYSTEMS & MANAGEMENT CONSULTANTS POLSKA—See CGI Inc.; *Int'l*, pg. 1433
CGI NEDERLAND B.V. - GRONINGEN—See CGI Inc.; *Int'l*, pg. 1434
CGI—See CGI Inc.; *Int'l*, pg. 1433
C&G SYSTEMS INC.; *Int'l*, pg. 1238
CG-VAK SOFTWARE & EXPORTS LTD.; *Int'l*, pg. 1430
CG-VAK SOFTWARE USA INC.—See CG-VAK Software & Exports Ltd.; *Int'l*, pg. 1430
CHAIONE; *U.S. Private*, pg. 845
CHAMS ACCESS LIMITED—See Chams Holding Company; *Int'l*, pg. 1440
CHAMS SWITCH LIMITED—See Chams Holding Company; *Int'l*, pg. 1440
CHANGE HEALTHCARE INC.—See UnitedHealth Group Incorporated; *U.S. Public*, pg. 2248
CHANGE HEALTHCARE NEW ZEALAND—See UnitedHealth Group Incorporated; *U.S. Public*, pg. 2248
CHANNELADVISOR (AU) PTY LIMITED—See Insight Venture Management, LLC; *U.S. Private*, pg. 2088
CHANNELADVISOR BRASIL TECNOLOGIA LTDA.—See Insight Venture Management, LLC; *U.S. Private*, pg. 2088
CHANNELADVISOR FRANCE—See Insight Venture Management, LLC; *U.S. Private*, pg. 2088

CHANNELADVISOR IRELAND LIMITED—See Insight Venture Management, LLC; *U.S. Private*, pg. 2088
CHANNELADVISOR (SHANGHAI) INFORMATION TECHNOLOGY CO., LIMITED—See Insight Venture Management, LLC; *U.S. Private*, pg. 2088
CHANNELADVISOR SPAIN S.L.—See Insight Venture Management, LLC; *U.S. Private*, pg. 2088
CHANNELADVISOR UK LIMITED—See Insight Venture Management, LLC; *U.S. Private*, pg. 2088
CHARGE ENTERPRISES, INC.; *U.S. Public*, pg. 478
CHARGEPANEL AB; *Int'l*, pg. 1448
CHARMT, INC.; *Int'l*, pg. 1451
CHARTER SOFTWARE, INC.—See Constellation Software Inc.; *Int'l*, pg. 1772
CHATEAUX SOFTWARE DEVELOPMENT—See Wells Fargo & Company; *U.S. Public*, pg. 2344
CHATTARY AJWAN INFOTECH PVT. LTD.—See Caesars Group; *Int'l*, pg. 1249
CHECKMARKET BV—See Thoma Bravo, L.P.; *U.S. Private*, pg. 4149
CHECK POINT SOFTWARE TECHNOLOGIES (BELGIUM) S.A.—See Check Point Software Technologies Ltd.; *Int'l*, pg. 1458
CHECK POINT SOFTWARE TECHNOLOGIES (BRAZIL) LTDA.—See Check Point Software Technologies Ltd.; *Int'l*, pg. 1458
CHECK POINT SOFTWARE TECHNOLOGIES (CZECH REPUBLIC) S.R.O.—See Check Point Software Technologies Ltd.; *Int'l*, pg. 1458
CHECK POINT SOFTWARE TECHNOLOGIES (GREECE) SA—See Check Point Software Technologies Ltd.; *Int'l*, pg. 1458
CHECK POINT SOFTWARE TECHNOLOGIES (HONG KONG) LTD.—See Check Point Software Technologies Ltd.; *Int'l*, pg. 1458
CHECK POINT SOFTWARE TECHNOLOGIES (HUNGARY) LTD.—See Check Point Software Technologies Ltd.; *Int'l*, pg. 1458
CHECK POINT SOFTWARE TECHNOLOGIES (KOREA) LTD.—See Check Point Software Technologies Ltd.; *Int'l*, pg. 1458
CHECK POINT SOFTWARE TECHNOLOGIES MEXICO S.A. DE C.V.—See Check Point Software Technologies Ltd.; *Int'l*, pg. 1458
CHECK POINT SOFTWARE TECHNOLOGIES NORWAY A.S.—See Check Point Software Technologies Ltd.; *Int'l*, pg. 1459
CHECK POINT SOFTWARE TECHNOLOGIES (POLAND) SP. Z O. O.—See Check Point Software Technologies Ltd.; *Int'l*, pg. 1458
CHECK POINT SOFTWARE TECHNOLOGIES (RMN) SRL.—See Check Point Software Technologies Ltd.; *Int'l*, pg. 1458
CHEMOCATO LLC—See Becton, Dickinson & Company; *U.S. Public*, pg. 292
CHENGDU GLOBAL INFOTECH INFORMATION TECHNOLOGY CO., LTD.—See Global Infotech Co., Ltd.; *Int'l*, pg. 2997
CHERBONNIER, MAYER & ASSOCIATES INC.; *U.S. Private*, pg. 873
CHERRYPICK GAMES SA; *Int'l*, pg. 1472
CHESAPEAKE TECHNOLOGY INTERNATIONAL CORP.—See Bluestone Investment Partners, LLC; *U.S. Private*, pg. 598
CHIASSO LLC; *U.S. Private*, pg. 876
CHIERU CO., LTD.; *Int'l*, pg. 1477
CHIME INC.; *U.S. Private*, pg. 885
CHINA CLEAN ENERGY TECHNOLOGY GROUP LIMITED; *Int'l*, pg. 1489
CHINA INFORMATION TECHNOLOGY DEVELOPMENT LIMITED—See Beijing Enterprises Holdings Limited; *Int'l*, pg. 950
CHINA INVESTMENT INFORMATION SERVICES CO., LTD.—See Hangzhou MDK Opto Electronic Corp., Ltd.; *Int'l*, pg. 3249
CHINA MULANS NANO TECHNOLOGY CORP. LTD.; *U.S. Public*, pg. 489
CHINA SOAR INFORMATION TECHNOLOGY, INC.; *Int'l*, pg. 1552
CHINESE GAMER INTERNATIONAL CORP.; *Int'l*, pg. 1569
CHINO SOFTEX CORPORATION—See CHINO Corporation; *Int'l*, pg. 1570
CHIPTOPIA (SHANGHAI) TECHNOLOGY CO., LTD.—See Alchip Technologies, Limited; *Int'l*, pg. 301
CHIROTOUCH; *U.S. Private*, pg. 887
CHOWGULE MEDICONSULT PRIVATE LIMITED—See Chowgule & Company Pvt. Ltd.; *Int'l*, pg. 1585
CHP CONSULTING INC—See Alfa Financial Software Holdings PLC; *Int'l*, pg. 308
CHRYSOS CORPORATION LIMITED; *Int'l*, pg. 1589
CHUTIAN DRAGON CO., LTD.; *Int'l*, pg. 1600
CIBAR, INC.—See Constellation Software Inc.; *Int'l*, pg. 1775
CIBER FRANCE SAS—See HTC Global Services Inc.; *U.S. Private*, pg. 1999
CIBER PTY LTD.—See HTC Global Services Inc.; *U.S. Private*, pg. 1999

N.A.I.C.S. INDEX 541511 — CUSTOM COMPUTER PRO...

CIBER UK—See HTC Global Services Inc.; *U.S. Private*, pg. 1999
CICLET HOLDINGS INC.; *Int'l*, pg. 1603
CIENA COMMUNICATIONS SINGAPORE PTE. LTD.—See Ciena Corporation; *U.S. Public*, pg. 494
CIGNEX DATAMATICS PTE. LIMITED—See Datamatics Global Services Ltd.; *Int'l*, pg. 1978
CIGNEX DATAMATICS TECHNOLOGIES LIMITED—See Datamatics Global Services Ltd.; *Int'l*, pg. 1978
CIGNITI TECHNOLOGIES CANADA INC.—See Cigniti Technologies Ltd.; *Int'l*, pg. 1607
CIGNITI TECHNOLOGIES INC.—See Cigniti Technologies Ltd.; *Int'l*, pg. 1607
CIG PHOTONICS JAPAN LIMITED—See CIG Shanghai Co., Ltd.; *Int'l*, pg. 1606
CIGTECH JAPAN LIMITED—See CIG Shanghai Co., Ltd.; *Int'l*, pg. 1606
CIJ SOLUTIONS, LTD.—See Computer Institute of Japan Ltd.; *Int'l*, pg. 1759
CIMARRON INC.; *U.S. Private*, pg. 897
CINERGY TECHNOLOGY, INC.—See Duke Energy Corporation; *U.S. Public*, pg. 690
CINIONIC BVBA—See Barco N.V.; *Int'l*, pg. 864
CINIONIC INC.—See Barco N.V.; *Int'l*, pg. 864
CINT GROUP AB; *Int'l*, pg. 1611
CIPIA VISION LTD.; *Int'l*, pg. 1616
CIRCLE COMPUTER RESOURCES, INC.; *U.S. Private*, pg. 899
CISION GLOBAL SOLUTIONS AB—See Platinum Equity, LLC; *U.S. Private*, pg. 3201
CITIZANT INC.; *U.S. Private*, pg. 902
CITRIX R&D LIMITED—See Elliott Management Corporation; *U.S. Private*, pg. 1366
CITRIX R&D LIMITED—See Vista Equity Partners, LLC; *U.S. Private*, pg. 4395
CITRIX SYSTEMS BELGIUM S.P.R.L.—See Elliott Management Corporation; *U.S. Private*, pg. 1366
CITRIX SYSTEMS BELGIUM S.P.R.L.—See Vista Equity Partners, LLC; *U.S. Private*, pg. 4396
CITRIX SYSTEMS POLAND SP. Z O.O—See Elliott Management Corporation; *U.S. Private*, pg. 1367
CITRIX SYSTEMS POLAND SP. Z O.O—See Vista Equity Partners, LLC; *U.S. Private*, pg. 4396
CIVICPLUS, LLC—See Insight Venture Management, LLC; *U.S. Private*, pg. 2087
CIVIQ SMARTSCAPES LLC—See JMC Capital Partners LLC; *U.S. Private*, pg. 2215
CJ OLIVENETWORKS VINA CO., LTD.—See CJ Corporation; *Int'l*, pg. 1633
CLAAS AGROSYSTEMS KGAA MBH & CO KG—See Claas KGaA mbH; *Int'l*, pg. 1640
CLARE CONTROLS LLC; *U.S. Private*, pg. 910
CLARISOFT TECHNOLOGIES, LLC—See Modus Create, LLC; *U.S. Private*, pg. 2764
CLARITY SOFTWARE SOLUTIONS, INC.; *U.S. Private*, pg. 912
CLAYTEX SERVICES LTD.—See Addnode Group AB; *Int'l*, pg. 130
CLAYTEX USA INC.—See Addnode Group AB; *Int'l*, pg. 130
CLEAN COMMUNICATION LIMITED—See Alphabet Inc.; *U.S. Public*, pg. 84
CLEANSPARK, LLC—See CleanSpark, Inc.; *U.S. Public*, pg. 511
CLEAR2PAY APAC PTY LTD.—See Fidelity National Infor.; *U.S. Public*, pg. 832
CLEAR2PAY BELGIUM NV—See Fidelity National Infor.; *U.S. Public*, pg. 832
CLEAR2PAY SERVICES NV—See Fidelity National Infor.; *U.S. Public*, pg. 832
CLEAR GOLD RESOURCES, INC.; *Int'l*, pg. 1656
CLEAR INTEC SP. Z O.O—See Alten S.A.; *Int'l*, pg. 390
CLEARLYBUSINESS.COM LIMITED—See Barclays PLC; *Int'l*, pg. 862
CLEAROBJECT, INC.—See ABS Capital Partners, L.P.; *U.S. Private*, pg. 44
CLEAROBJECT, INC.—See Egis Capital Partners LLC; *U.S. Private*, pg. 1344
CLEAR SECURE, INC.; *U.S. Public*, pg. 512
CLEAR TOUCH INTERACTIVE, INC.; *U.S. Private*, pg. 932
CLEARVIEW BUSINESS INTELLIGENCE, LLC; *U.S. Private*, pg. 938
CLIENT SERVICE INTERNATIONAL, INC.; *Int'l*, pg. 1658
CLIMB CHANNEL SOLUTIONS, INC.—See Climb Global Solutions, Inc.; *U.S. Public*, pg. 514
CLINAPPS, INC.—See Genstar Capital, LLC; *U.S. Private*, pg. 1675
CLINICAL COMPUTING, INC.—See Clinical Computing Plc; *Int'l*, pg. 1659
CLINICIENT, INC—See Warburg Pincus LLC; *U.S. Private*, pg. 4440
C-LINK SQUARED LIMITED; *Int'l*, pg. 1239
CLIQZ GMBH—See Hubert Burda Media Holding Kommanditgesellschaft; *Int'l*, pg. 3520
CLOCKSHARK, LLC; *U.S. Private*, pg. 945
CLOUD9, INC.—See CROOZ, Inc.; *Int'l*, pg. 1855
CLOUDCALL LIMITED—See CloudCall Group Limited; *Int'l*, pg. 1662

CLOUDCONNECT, LLC—See Salesforce, Inc.; *U.S. Public*, pg. 1837
CLOUDERA GMBH—See Clayton, Dubilier & Rice, LLC; *U.S. Private*, pg. 920
CLOUDERA GMBH—See KKR & Co. Inc.; *U.S. Public*, pg. 1243
CLOUDERA HUNGARY KFT.—See Clayton, Dubilier & Rice, LLC; *U.S. Private*, pg. 920
CLOUDERA HUNGARY KFT.—See KKR & Co. Inc.; *U.S. Public*, pg. 1243
CLOUDERA, INC.—See Clayton, Dubilier & Rice, LLC; *U.S. Private*, pg. 920
CLOUDERA, INC.—See KKR & Co. Inc.; *U.S. Public*, pg. 1243
CLOUDERA KOREA, INC.—See Clayton, Dubilier & Rice, LLC; *U.S. Private*, pg. 920
CLOUDERA KOREA, INC.—See KKR & Co. Inc.; *U.S. Public*, pg. 1243
CLOUDERA (SHANGHAI) SOFTWARE CO. LTD.—See Clayton, Dubilier & Rice, LLC; *U.S. Private*, pg. 920
CLOUDERA (SHANGHAI) SOFTWARE CO. LTD.—See KKR & Co. Inc.; *U.S. Public*, pg. 1243
CLOUDERA (UK) LIMITED—See Clayton, Dubilier & Rice, LLC; *U.S. Private*, pg. 920
CLOUDERA (UK) LIMITED—See KKR & Co. Inc.; *U.S. Public*, pg. 1243
CLOUDHEALTH TECHNOLOGIES AUSTRALIA PTY. LTD.—See Dell Technologies Inc.; *U.S. Public*, pg. 649
CLOUDLOCK CO.—See Cisco Systems, Inc.; *U.S. Public*, pg. 499
CLOUDMATRIX CO., LTD.—See Giga-Byte Technology Co., Ltd.; *Int'l*, pg. 2971
CLOUDMD SOFTWARE & SERVICES, INC.—See CPS Capital; *Int'l*, pg. 1826
CLOUDPOINT TECHNOLOGY BERHAD; *Int'l*, pg. 1662
CLOUDREPUBLIC AB; *Int'l*, pg. 1662
CLOUDTICITY, LLC; *U.S. Private*, pg. 947
CLOUDVISORY LLC—See Alphabet Inc.; *U.S. Public*, pg. 84
CLOVER HEALTH INVESTMENTS, CORP.; *U.S. Public*, pg. 515
CLPS INCORPORATION; *Int'l*, pg. 1663
CLUBESSENTIAL HOLDINGS, LLC; *U.S. Private*, pg. 948
CM.COM BELGIUM N.V.—See CM.com N.V.; *Int'l*, pg. 1666
CM.COM GERMANY GMBH—See CM.com N.V.; *Int'l*, pg. 1666
CME DIGITAL LIMITED—See CME Group, Inc.; *U.S. Public*, pg. 516
CMG (EUROPE) LIMITED—See Computer Modelling Group Ltd.; *Int'l*, pg. 1760
CMG MIDDLE EAST FZ LLC—See Computer Modelling Group Ltd.; *Int'l*, pg. 1760
CMMS DATA GROUP, INC.; *U.S. Private*, pg. 951
CMON LIMITED; *Int'l*, pg. 1671
CMORE AUTOMOTIVE GMBH—See DXC Technology Company; *U.S. Public*, pg. 694
CM TELECOM SINGAPORE PRIVATE LTD.—See CM.com N.V.; *Int'l*, pg. 1666
CM TELECOM SOUTH AFRICA LTD.—See CM.com N.V.; *Int'l*, pg. 1666
CMTSU LIQUIDATION, INC.—See HTC Global Services Inc.; *U.S. Private*, pg. 1999
CNS-SOLUTIONS & SUPPORT GMBH—See Frequentis AG; *Int'l*, pg. 2773
COCONSTRUCT, LLC—See Buildertrend Solutions Inc.; *U.S. Private*, pg. 682
CODE AUTHORITY, LLC—See Trinity Hunt Management, L.P.; *U.S. Private*, pg. 4234
CODEMASTERS GROUP HOLDINGS PLC—See Electronic Arts Inc.; *U.S. Public*, pg. 723
CODEMASTERS LIMITED—See Electronic Arts Inc.; *U.S. Public*, pg. 724
CODEMETTLE, LLC—See J.F. Lehman & Company, Inc.; *U.S. Private*, pg. 2163
CODESQUAD B.V.—See adesso SE; *Int'l*, pg. 144
CODICES S.R.L.—See Ardian SAS; *Int'l*, pg. 555
COFORGE ADVANTAGEGO LIMITED—See Coforge Ltd.; *Int'l*, pg. 1693
COFORGE AIRLINE TECHNOLOGIES GMBH—See Coforge Ltd.; *Int'l*, pg. 1693
COFORGE BV—See Coforge Ltd.; *Int'l*, pg. 1693
COFORGE DPA IRELAND LIMITED—See Coforge Ltd.; *Int'l*, pg. 1693
COFORGE DPA PRIVATE LTD.—See Coforge Ltd.; *Int'l*, pg. 1693
COFORGE GMBH—See Coforge Ltd.; *Int'l*, pg. 1693
COFORGE INC.—See Coforge Ltd.; *Int'l*, pg. 1693
COFORGE LIMITED—See Coforge Ltd.; *Int'l*, pg. 1693
COFORGE LTD.; *Int'l*, pg. 1693
COFORGE SA—See Coforge Ltd.; *Int'l*, pg. 1693
COFORGE SMARTSERVE LTD.—See Coforge Ltd.; *Int'l*, pg. 1693
COFORGE U.K. LIMITED—See Coforge Ltd.; *Int'l*, pg. 1693
COGENCY SOFTWARE, INC.—See Backstop Solutions Group, LLC; *U.S. Private*, pg. 423
COGENT (BEIJING) TECHNOLOGY COMPANY LIMITED—See Century Sage Scientific Holdings Limited; *Int'l*, pg. 1419
COGENT INDUSTRIAL TECHNOLOGIES LTD.—See Kad-

ant Inc.; *U.S. Public*, pg. 1212
COGNIZANT EL SALVADOR, SOCIEDAD ANONIMA DE CAPITAL VARIABLE—See Cognizant Technology Solutions Corporation; *U.S. Public*, pg. 523
COGNIZANT TECHNOLOGY SOLUTIONS ASIA PACIFIC PTE LTD.—See Cognizant Technology Solutions Corporation; *U.S. Public*, pg. 524
COGNIZANT TECHNOLOGY SOLUTIONS BELGIUM S.A.—See Cognizant Technology Solutions Corporation; *U.S. Public*, pg. 524
COGNIZANT TECHNOLOGY SOLUTIONS DE ARGENTINA S.R.L.—See Cognizant Technology Solutions Corporation; *U.S. Public*, pg. 524
COGNIZANT TECHNOLOGY SOLUTIONS DENMARK APS—See Cognizant Technology Solutions Corporation; *U.S. Public*, pg. 524
COGNIZANT TECHNOLOGY SOLUTIONS FRANCE S.A.—See Cognizant Technology Solutions Corporation; *U.S. Public*, pg. 524
COGNIZANT TECHNOLOGY SOLUTIONS GMBH—See Cognizant Technology Solutions Corporation; *U.S. Public*, pg. 524
COGNIZANT TECHNOLOGY SOLUTIONS HUNGARY KFT—See Cognizant Technology Solutions Corporation; *U.S. Public*, pg. 524
COGNIZANT TECHNOLOGY SOLUTIONS LITHUANIA, UAB—See Cognizant Technology Solutions Corporation; *U.S. Public*, pg. 524
COGNIZANT TECHNOLOGY SOLUTIONS NORWAY A.S.—See Cognizant Technology Solutions Corporation; *U.S. Public*, pg. 524
COGNIZANT TECHNOLOGY SOLUTIONS PHILIPPINES, INC.—See Cognizant Technology Solutions Corporation; *U.S. Public*, pg. 524
COGNIZANT TECHNOLOGY SOLUTIONS (SHANGHAI) CO., LTD.—See Cognizant Technology Solutions Corporation; *U.S. Public*, pg. 523
COGNIZANT TECHNOLOGY SOLUTIONS—See Cognizant Technology Solutions Corporation; *U.S. Public*, pg. 523
COGNIZANT TECHNOLOGY SOLUTIONS UK LIMITED—See Cognizant Technology Solutions Corporation; *U.S. Public*, pg. 524
COGNIZANT TECHNOLOGY SOLUTIONS U.S. CORPORATION—See Cognizant Technology Solutions Corporation; *U.S. Public*, pg. 524
COGNYTE SOFTWARE LTD.; *Int'l*, pg. 1695
COHERENT PATH INC.—See Movable, Inc.; *U.S. Private*, pg. 2801
COHERENT SOLUTIONS, INC.; *U.S. Private*, pg. 963
COILDNA GMBH—See AMAG Austria Metall AG; *Int'l*, pg. 408
COLLABORATIVE SOLUTIONS, LLC—See WestView Capital Partners, L.P.; *U.S. Private*, pg. 4501
COLLATERAL ANALYTICS, LLC—See Intercontinental Exchange, Inc.; *U.S. Public*, pg. 1141
COLUMBUS DEUTSCHLAND GMBH—See Columbus A/S; *Int'l*, pg. 1706
COLUMBUS EESTI AS—See Columbus A/S; *Int'l*, pg. 1706
COLUMBUS GLOBAL (UK) LTD.—See Columbus A/S; *Int'l*, pg. 1706
COLUMBUS M3 DANMARK APS—See Columbus A/S; *Int'l*, pg. 1706
COLUMBUS NORWAY AS—See Columbus A/S; *Int'l*, pg. 1706
COLUMBUS SWEDEN AB—See Columbus A/S; *Int'l*, pg. 1706
COLY, INC.; *Int'l*, pg. 1706
COM2000, INC.; *U.S. Private*, pg. 980
COM2M GMBH—See adesso SE; *Int'l*, pg. 144
COMANCHE INTERNATIONAL MALAYSIA SDN. BHD.—See Comanche International PCL; *Int'l*, pg. 1707
COMANCHE INTERNATIONAL VIETNAM CO., LTD.—See Comanche International PCL; *Int'l*, pg. 1707
COMARCH OOO—See ComArch S.A.; *Int'l*, pg. 1707
COMARCH R&D S.A.R.L.—See ComArch S.A.; *Int'l*, pg. 1707
COMARCH SCHILLING GMBH—See ComArch S.A.; *Int'l*, pg. 1707
COMARCH SOFTWARE S.A.R.L.—See ComArch S.A.; *Int'l*, pg. 1707
COMARCH SOFTWARE UND BERATUNG—See ComArch S.A.; *Int'l*, pg. 1707
COMARCH SOLUTIONS GMBH—See ComArch S.A.; *Int'l*, pg. 1707
COMARCH SOLUTIONS GMBH—See ComArch S.A.; *Int'l*, pg. 1707
COMARCH SWISS AG—See ComArch S.A.; *Int'l*, pg. 1707
COMARCH VIETNAM CO. LTD.—See ComArch S.A.; *Int'l*, pg. 1707
COMBIDATA POLAND SP. Z.O.O.—See Asseco Poland S.A.; *Int'l*, pg. 642
COME TO AGREEMENT LTD.; *Int'l*, pg. 1710
COMET SOLUTIONS, INC.—See Aras Corp; *U.S. Private*, pg. 308
COMGRAPH CO., LTD.—See FEV GmbH; *Int'l*, pg. 2648
COM-GUARD.COM, INC.; *U.S. Public*, pg. 536
COMINTELLI AB; *Int'l*, pg. 1714
COMIQ OY—See Alten S.A.; *Int'l*, pg. 390

4605

541511 — CUSTOM COMPUTER PRO...

COMMAND ALKON CORP—See Thoma Bravo, L.P.; *U.S. Private*, pg. 4146
COMMEX TECHNOLOGY LTD.; *Int'l*, pg. 1719
COMMONWEALTH COMPUTER RESEARCH INC.—See General Atomics; *U.S. Private*, pg. 1663
COMMSEED CORP; *Int'l*, pg. 1720
COMMS GROUP LTD; *Int'l*, pg. 1720
COMMUNITY INVESTORS, INC.; *U.S. Private*, pg. 995
COMMUNITY TECHKNOWLEDGE, INC.—See Social Solutions Global Inc.; *U.S. Private*, pg. 3703
COMMVAULT SYSTEMS (SOUTH AFRICA) (PTY) LTD.—See CommVault Systems, Inc.; *U.S. Public*, pg. 559
COMPANY MARGIN PURPOSE LTD.; *Int'l*, pg. 1749
COMPETITIVE COMPUTING, INC.—See Xerox Holdings Corporation; *U.S. Public*, pg. 2386
COMPETITIVE HEALTH, INC.—See WEX, Inc.; *U.S. Public*, pg. 2364
COMPLIA HEALTH, LLC—See Axxess Technology Solutions, Inc; *U.S. Private*, pg. 414
COMPLIANCEQUEST INC.; *U.S. Private*, pg. 1001
COMPONENTONE LLC; *U.S. Private*, pg. 1002
COMPOSITION RESEARCH TECHNOLOGIES, INC.—See Crawford Technologies, Inc.; *Int'l*, pg. 1829
COMPQSOFT, INC.; *U.S. Private*, pg. 1002
COMPREHENSIVE SOFTWARE SYSTEMS; *U.S. Private*, pg. 1003
COMPUCOM SOFTWARE LTD; *Int'l*, pg. 1754
COMPUCON S.A.; *Int'l*, pg. 1754
COMPUGAIN, INC.; *U.S. Private*, pg. 1003
COMPUGEN INC.; *Int'l*, pg. 1755
COMPUGROUP MEDICAL CEE GMBH—See CompuGroup Medical SE & Co. KGaA; *Int'l*, pg. 1755
COMPUGROUP MEDICAL DENTALSYSTEME GMBH—See CompuGroup Medical SE & Co. KGaA; *Int'l*, pg. 1755
COMPUGROUP MEDICAL HELLAS S.A.—See CompuGroup Medical SE & Co. KGaA; *Int'l*, pg. 1756
COMPUGROUP MEDICAL NORWAY AS—See CompuGroup Medical SE & Co. KGaA; *Int'l*, pg. 1756
COMPUGROUP MEDICAL SOFTWARE GMBH—See CompuGroup Medical SE & Co. KGaA; *Int'l*, pg. 1756
COMPUGROUP SERVICES GMBH—See CompuGroup Medical SE & Co. KGaA; *Int'l*, pg. 1756
COMPULAB LTD.; *Int'l*, pg. 1757
COMPUNNEL SOFTWARE GROUP; *U.S. Private*, pg. 1004
COMPUPROS LTD; *U.S. Private*, pg. 1004
COMPU-QUOTE INC.; *Int'l*, pg. 1754
COMPUTAPOLE—See Quanta Services, Inc.; *U.S. Public*, pg. 1752
COMPUTECH CORPORATION; *U.S. Private*, pg. 1004
COMPUTER AID, INC.; *U.S. Private*, pg. 1004
COMPUTER ASSOCIATES AFRICA (PTY.) LTD.—See Broadcom Inc.; *U.S. Public*, pg. 389
COMPUTER ASSOCIATES AG—See Broadcom Inc.; *U.S. Public*, pg. 389
COMPUTER ASSOCIATES (CAI) DE VENEZUELA, C.A.—See Broadcom Inc.; *U.S. Public*, pg. 389
COMPUTER ASSOCIATES DE ARGENTINA S.A.—See Broadcom Inc.; *U.S. Public*, pg. 389
COMPUTER ASSOCIATES DE CHILE S.A.—See Broadcom Inc.; *U.S. Public*, pg. 390
COMPUTER ASSOCIATES DE COLOMBIA S.A.—See Broadcom Inc.; *U.S. Public*, pg. 390
COMPUTER ASSOCIATES DEL PERU—See Broadcom Inc.; *U.S. Public*, pg. 390
COMPUTER ASSOCIATES DO BRASIL LTDA.—See Broadcom Inc.; *U.S. Public*, pg. 390
COMPUTER ASSOCIATES HUNGARY—See Broadcom Inc.; *U.S. Public*, pg. 389
COMPUTER ASSOCIATES INTERNATIONAL, INC.—See Broadcom Inc.; *U.S. Public*, pg. 389
COMPUTER ASSOCIATES NETHERLANDS—See Broadcom Inc.; *U.S. Public*, pg. 390
COMPUTER ASSOCIATES NORWAY A/S—See Broadcom Inc.; *U.S. Public*, pg. 390
COMPUTER ASSOCIATES PLC—See Broadcom Inc.; *U.S. Public*, pg. 390
COMPUTER ASSOCIATES PTE. LTD.—See Broadcom Inc.; *U.S. Public*, pg. 390
COMPUTER ASSOCIATES S.A.—See Broadcom Inc.; *U.S. Public*, pg. 390
COMPUTER ASSOCIATES SCANDINAVIA A/S—See Broadcom Inc.; *U.S. Public*, pg. 390
COMPUTER ASSOCIATES S.P.A.—See Broadcom Inc.; *U.S. Public*, pg. 390
COMPUTER ASSOCIATES SWEDEN AB—See Broadcom Inc.; *U.S. Public*, pg. 390
COMPUTER ASSOCIATES TAIWAN LTD.—See Broadcom Inc.; *U.S. Public*, pg. 390
COMPUTER CONFIGURATION SERVICES; *U.S. Private*, pg. 1004
COMPUTER DESIGN & INTEGRATION, LLC—See Berkshire Partners LLC; *U.S. Private*, pg. 534
COMPUTER ENGINEERING & CONSULTING LTD.; *Int'l*, pg. 1759
COMPUTER ENGINEERING & CONSULTING (SHANGHAI), LTD.—See Computer Engineering & Consulting Ltd.; *Int'l*, pg. 1759
COMPUTER EXPRESS INC.; *U.S. Private*, pg. 1004
COMPUTER FACTORY (INDIA) PRIVATE LIMITED—See Accel Limited; *Int'l*, pg. 79
COMPUTER GUIDANCE CORPORATION; *U.S. Private*, pg. 1005
COMPUTER MAINTENANCE AGENCY, INC.—See WESCO International, Inc.; *U.S. Public*, pg. 2351
COMPUTER MODELLING GROUP INC.—See Computer Modelling Group Ltd.; *Int'l*, pg. 1760
COMPUTER PACKAGES INCORPORATED; *U.S. Private*, pg. 1005
COMPUTER SERVICES CONSULTANTS (UK) LTD.—See Trimble, Inc.; *U.S. Public*, pg. 2190
COMPUTER SERVICES, INC—See Computer Services, Inc.; *U.S. Public*, pg. 561
COMPUTER SOFTWARE INNOVATIONS, INC.—See Constellation Software Inc.; *Int'l*, pg. 1775
COMPUTER SOLUTIONS & SOFTWARE INTERNATIONAL, INC.; *U.S. Private*, pg. 1005
COMPUTER TASK GROUP BELGIUM N.V.—See Cegeka Groep NV; *Int'l*, pg. 1391
COMPUTER TASK GROUP, INC.—See Cegeka Groep NV; *Int'l*, pg. 1391
COMPUTER TASK GROUP OF CANADA, INC.—See Cegeka Groep NV; *Int'l*, pg. 1391
COMPUTER TASK GROUP OF DELAWARE, INC.—See Cegeka Groep NV; *Int'l*, pg. 1391
COMPUTER TASK GROUP OF LUXEMBOURG PSF—See Cegeka Groep NV; *Int'l*, pg. 1391
COMPUTER & TECHNOLOGIES SOLUTIONS LIMITED—See Computer & Technologies Holdings Limited; *Int'l*, pg. 1758
COMPUTER TECHNOLOGY SOLUTIONS, INC.—See CGI Inc.; *Int'l*, pg. 1434
COMPUTING SYSTEM INNOCATIONS, LLC—See Tyler Technologies, Inc.; *U.S. Public*, pg. 2208
COMPUTRITION, INC.—See Constellation Software Inc.; *Int'l*, pg. 1773
COMPUWARE S.A.—See KKR & Co. Inc.; *U.S. Public*, pg. 1240
COMPUWARE SOFTWARE GROUP PTY. LTD.—See KKR & Co. Inc.; *U.S. Public*, pg. 1240
COMSOFT DIRECT AG—See Bechtle AG; *Int'l*, pg. 937
COMSYS TOHOKU TECHNO CO., LTD.—See COMSYS Holdings Corporation; *Int'l*, pg. 1762
COMTRADE INC.—See ComTrade Group B.V.; *Int'l*, pg. 1762
COMTRADE SOFTWARE SOLUTIONS GMBH—See ComTrade Group B.V.; *Int'l*, pg. 1762
CONCURRENT COMPUTER CORP. PTY. LTD—See CCUR Holdings Inc.; *U.S. Public*, pg. 461
CONCURRENT COMPUTER FRANCE S.A.—See CCUR Holdings Inc.; *U.S. Public*, pg. 461
CONCURRENT COMPUTER FRANCE S.A.—See CCUR Holdings Inc.; *U.S. Public*, pg. 461
CONCURRENT COMPUTER HONG KONG LIMITED—See CCUR Holdings Inc.; *U.S. Public*, pg. 461
CONDUENT HEALTHCARE KNOWLEDGE SOLUTIONS, LLC—See Conduent Incorporated; *U.S. Public*, pg. 566
CONDUENT SECURITIES SERVICES, INC.—See Conduent Incorporated; *U.S. Public*, pg. 566
CONDUENT STATE & LOCAL SOLUTIONS, INC.—See Conduent Incorporated; *U.S. Public*, pg. 566
CONECTISYS CORP.; *U.S. Public*, pg. 566
CONFERIZE A/S; *Int'l*, pg. 1767
CONFLUENT, INC.; *U.S. Public*, pg. 567
CONKOR SYSTEMS LTD.—See Amanet Management & Systems Ltd.; *Int'l*, pg. 410
CONNECTION TECHNOLOGY LTD.—See Superior Energy Services, Inc.; *U.S. Private*, pg. 3877
CONNEXION POINT LLC—See Integrity Marketing Group LLC; *U.S. Private*, pg. 2103
CONNEXTA, LLC—See Arlington Capital Partners LLC; *U.S. Private*, pg. 328
CONNEXXALIFE S.R.L.—See Ardian SAS; *Int'l*, pg. 555
CONNX SOLUTIONS INC.—See Silver Lake Group, LLC; *U.S. Private*, pg. 3658
CONSCIOUS CONTENT MEDIA, INC.; *U.S. Private*, pg. 1019
CONSEILLERS EN GESTION ET INFORMATIQUE CGI INC.—See CGI Inc.; *Int'l*, pg. 1434
CONSENSUS CLOUD SOLUTIONS, INC.; *U.S. Public*, pg. 569
CONSIST SOFTWARE SOLUTIONS, INC.; *U.S. Private*, pg. 1020
CONSOFT, S.A.U.—See Glintt - Global Intelligent Technologies, S.A.; *Int'l*, pg. 2992
CONSOLE AUSTRALIA PTY LTD—See Accel Partners L.P.; *U.S. Private*, pg. 48
CONSOLE AUSTRALIA PTY LTD—See KKR & Co. Inc.; *U.S. Public*, pg. 1238
CONSOLE LABS S.A.; *Int'l*, pg. 1770
CONSOLE NEW ZEALAND LIMITED—See Accel Partners L.P.; *U.S. Private*, pg. 48
CONSOLE NEW ZEALAND LIMITED—See KKR & Co. Inc.; *U.S. Public*, pg. 1238
CONSULTEC BYGGPROGRAM AB—See Eleco Plc; *Int'l*, pg. 2347
CONSULTEC GROUP AB—See Eleco Plc; *Int'l*, pg. 2347
CONSULTEC SYSTEM AB—See Eleco Plc; *Int'l*, pg. 2347
CONTAINE TECHNOLOGIES LTD.; *Int'l*, pg. 1778
CONTAKT WORLD TECHNOLOGIES CORP.; *Int'l*, pg. 1779
CONTEC SOLUTION CHINA CORPORATION—See Daifuku Co., Ltd.; *Int'l*, pg. 1925
CONTENT CONNECT AFRICA (PROPRIETARY) LIMITED—See Blue Label Telecoms Limited; *Int'l*, pg. 1068
CONTENTGUARD, INC.—See Pendrell Corporation; *U.S. Public*, pg. 1661
CONTEXTMEDIA HEALTH, LLC—See Catterton Management Company, LLC; *U.S. Private*, pg. 793
CONTEXTMEDIA, INC.—See Catterton Management Company, LLC; *U.S. Private*, pg. 794
CONTEXTVISION AB; *Int'l*, pg. 1780
CONTIGO SOFTWARE LIMITED—See Energy One Limited; *Int'l*, pg. 2423
CONTINUUM APPLIED TECHNOLOGY, INC.—See The Hearst Corporation; *U.S. Private*, pg. 4044
CONTROLEXPERT GMBH—See Allianz SE; *Int'l*, pg. 351
CONTROLSCAN, INC.—See Thompson Street Capital Manager LLC; *U.S. Private*, pg. 4161
CONVENE INDIA PRIVATE LIMITED—See Azeus Systems Holdings Ltd.; *Int'l*, pg. 778
CONVENE PTY LTD—See Azeus Systems Holdings Ltd.; *Int'l*, pg. 778
CONVENE SG PTE LTD—See Azeus Systems Holdings Ltd.; *Int'l*, pg. 778
CONVERGA PTY LIMITED—See Canon Inc.; *Int'l*, pg. 1293
CONVERGE CONSULTING INC.—See Ruffalo Noel Levitz, LLC; *U.S. Private*, pg. 3502
CONVERSIA IT, S.L.U.—See COCA-COLA EUROPACIFIC PARTNERS PLC; *Int'l*, pg. 1685
COOLADATA LTD.—See Thoma Bravo, L.P.; *U.S. Private*, pg. 4149
COOLFIRE SOLUTIONS LLC—See Coolfire Media, LLC; *U.S. Private*, pg. 1040
COOPERATIE ACTIVISION BLIZZARD INTERNATIONAL U.A.—See Microsoft Corporation; *U.S. Public*, pg. 1439
COORDINATED SYSTEMS INC.; *U.S. Private*, pg. 1043
COOTEK (CAYMAN) INC.; *Int'l*, pg. 1792
CORADIANT (CANADA) INC.—See KKR & Co. Inc.; *U.S. Public*, pg. 1241
CORDEL GROUP PLC; *Int'l*, pg. 1796
CORECARD SOFTWARE, INC.—See CoreCard Corporation; *U.S. Public*, pg. 577
CORE EDUCATION AND TECHNOLOGIES LTD.; *Int'l*, pg. 1797
CORE MEDICAL SOLUTIONS PTY LTD—See Veradigm Inc.; *U.S. Public*, pg. 2280
CORENTE, INC. - ENGINEERING CENTER—See Oracle Corporation; *U.S. Public*, pg. 1611
CORE PROJECTS & TECHNOLOGIES FZC—See Core Education and Technologies Ltd.; *Int'l*, pg. 1797
CORETEX USA INC.—See EROAD Limited; *Int'l*, pg. 2496
CORIANT, AMERICA, INC.—See Marlin Equity Partners, LLC; *U.S. Private*, pg. 2584
CORIANT JAPAN K.K.—See Marlin Equity Partners, LLC; *U.S. Private*, pg. 2584
CORIANT NETWORKS (SHANGHAI) CO., LTD.—See Marlin Equity Partners, LLC; *U.S. Private*, pg. 2584
CORITEL S.A.—See Accenture plc; *Int'l*, pg. 86
CORNERSTONE INFORMATION SYSTEM, INC.; *U.S. Private*, pg. 1052
CORTEX BUSINESS SOLUTIONS LTD.—See Hellman & Friedman LLC; *U.S. Private*, pg. 1908
CORTEX SOFTWARE GMBH—See Asklepios Kliniken GmbH & Co. KGaA; *Int'l*, pg. 623
CORUM GROUP LIMITED; *Int'l*, pg. 1808
CORUM HEALTH PTY LTD—See Corum Group Limited; *Int'l*, pg. 1808
COSMO COMPUTER CENTER CO., LTD.—See Cosmo Energy Holdings Co., Ltd.; *Int'l*, pg. 1811
COSMOS CONSULTANTS SA—See Clasquin S.A.; *Int'l*, pg. 1652
COSMOS I-TECH SOLUTIONS LTD.—See Cosmos Machinery Enterprises Limited; *Int'l*, pg. 1813
COSTAR ESPANA, S.L.—See CoStar Group, Inc.; *U.S. Public*, pg. 585
COSYN LIMITED; *Int'l*, pg. 1815
COULEE TECH, INC.; *U.S. Private*, pg. 1065
COUPA DEUTSCHLAND GMBH—See Thoma Bravo, L.P.; *U.S. Private*, pg. 4147
COUPA SOFTWARE INDIA PRIVATE LIMITED—See Thoma Bravo, L.P.; *U.S. Private*, pg. 4147
COUPA SOFTWARE SWITZERLAND AG—See Thoma Bravo, L.P.; *U.S. Private*, pg. 4147
COURTVIEW JUSTICE SOLUTIONS INC.—See Constellation Software Inc.; *Int'l*, pg. 1775
COVER CORPORATION; *Int'l*, pg. 1821
COVEROS, INC.; *U.S. Private*, pg. 1072
COVER YOUR ASSETS, LLC—See RollKall Technologies LLC; *U.S. Private*, pg. 3475
COVIDH TECHNOLOGIES LIMITED; *Int'l*, pg. 1821

N.A.I.C.S. INDEX

541511 — CUSTOM COMPUTER PRO...

COWON PLAY CO., LTD.; *Int'l*, pg. 1822
COZI GROUP INC.—See Meredith Corporation; *U.S. Public*, pg. 1422
CP-DBS, LLC—See i3 Verticals, Inc.; *U.S. Public*, pg. 1081
CPF IT CENTER CO., LTD.—See Charoen Pokphand Foods Public Company Limited; *Int'l*, pg. 1452
CP SOFTWARE GROUP, INC.; *U.S. Private*, pg. 1079
CQUB INFOSYSTEM PRIVATE LIMITED—See AIRAN Limited; *Int'l*, pg. 241
CRANES SOFTWARE INTERNATIONAL LIMITED; *Int'l*, pg. 1828
CRANEWARE INSIGHT, INC.—See Craneware plc; *Int'l*, pg. 1828
CRANK SOFTWARE ULC—See AMETEK, Inc.; *U.S. Public*, pg. 120
CRAYON AB—See Crayon Group AS; *Int'l*, pg. 1829
CRAYON A/S—See Crayon Group AS; *Int'l*, pg. 1829
CRAYON AUSTRIA GMBH—See Crayon Group AS; *Int'l*, pg. 1829
CRAYON B.V.—See Crayon Group AS; *Int'l*, pg. 1829
CRAYON CHANNEL APAC—See Crayon Group AS; *Int'l*, pg. 1829
CRAYON FRANCE SAS—See Crayon Group AS; *Int'l*, pg. 1829
CRAYON GLOBAL SERVICES GMBH—See Crayon Group AS; *Int'l*, pg. 1829
CRAYON ICELAND—See Crayon Group AS; *Int'l*, pg. 1829
CRAYON INDIA—See Crayon Group AS; *Int'l*, pg. 1829
CRAYON LTD—See Crayon Group AS; *Int'l*, pg. 1829
CRAYON MIDDLE EAST—See Crayon Group AS; *Int'l*, pg. 1829
CRAYON OY—See Crayon Group AS; *Int'l*, pg. 1829
CRAYON PORTUGAL—See Crayon Group AS; *Int'l*, pg. 1829
CRAYON PTE LTD—See Crayon Group AS; *Int'l*, pg. 1829
CRAYON SOFTWARE EXPERTS MALAYSIA SDN. BHD.—See Crayon Group AS; *Int'l*, pg. 1829
CRAYON SPAIN—See Crayon Group AS; *Int'l*, pg. 1829
CREACTIVES GROUP SPA; *Int'l*, pg. 1830
CREALOGIX HOLDING AG—See Constellation Software Inc.; *Int'l*, pg. 1772
CREATIVEFORGE GAMES S.A.; *Int'l*, pg. 1834
CREATIVE JAPAN CO, LTD.—See Cresco, Ltd.; *Int'l*, pg. 1840
CREATIVE LABS, INC.—See Creative Technology Ltd.; *Int'l*, pg. 1833
CREATIVE MARKET LABS, INC.—See Autodesk, Inc.; *U.S. Public*, pg. 229
CREATOR CAPITAL LTD.; *Int'l*, pg. 1834
CREEHAN & COMPANY CORPORATION—See Inovalon Holdings, Inc.; *U.S. Public*, pg. 1128
CREEK SYSTEMS, INC.; *U.S. Private*, pg. 1092
CREEPY JAR S.A.; *Int'l*, pg. 1837
CREO CO., LTD.; *Int'l*, pg. 1838
CREO MARKETING CO., LTD.—See CREO CO., LTD.; *Int'l*, pg. 1838
CREO NETWORKS CO., LTD.—See CREO CO., LTD.; *Int'l*, pg. 1838
CREO SOLUTION CO., LTD.—See CREO CO., LTD.; *Int'l*, pg. 1838
CRESCO DIGITAL TECHNOLOGIES LTD.—See Cresco, Ltd.; *Int'l*, pg. 1840
CRESCO J CUBE CO., LTD.—See Cresco, Ltd.; *Int'l*, pg. 1840
CRESCO VIETNAM CO., LTD.—See Cresco, Ltd.; *Int'l*, pg. 1840
CRIF CORPORATION—See CRIF S.p.A.; *Int'l*, pg. 1849
CRIF DECISION SOLUTIONS LTD.—See CRIF S.p.A.; *Int'l*, pg. 1849
CRIF GULF DWC LLC—See CRIF S.p.A.; *Int'l*, pg. 1849
CRIF S.A. DE S.V.—See CRIF S.p.A.; *Int'l*, pg. 1849
CRIF SP. Z O. O.—See CRIF S.p.A.; *Int'l*, pg. 1849
CRIMSONLOGIC BAHRAIN S.P.C—See CRIMSONLOGIC PTE LTD; *Int'l*, pg. 1850
CRIMSONLOGIC CHILE SPA—See CRIMSONLOGIC PTE LTD; *Int'l*, pg. 1850
CRIMSONLOGIC EMIRATES INFORMATION TECHNOLOGY LLC—See CRIMSONLOGIC PTE LTD; *Int'l*, pg. 1850
CRIMSONLOGIC INDIA PRIVATE LIMITED—See CRIMSONLOGIC PTE LTD; *Int'l*, pg. 1850
CRIMSONLOGIC IT SOLUTIONS PRIVATE LIMITED—See CRIMSONLOGIC PTE LTD; *Int'l*, pg. 1850
CRIMSONLOGIC (NORTH AMERICA) INC.—See CRIMSONLOGIC PTE LTD; *Int'l*, pg. 1850
CRIMSONLOGIC PANAMA INC.—See CRIMSONLOGIC PTE LTD; *Int'l*, pg. 1850
CRIMSONLOGIC SOFTWARE TECHNOLOGY (SHANGHAI) CO., LTD.—See CRIMSONLOGIC PTE LTD; *Int'l*, pg. 1850
CRIMSONLOGIC (TRINIDAD AND TOBAGO) LTD.—See CRIMSONLOGIC PTE LTD; *Int'l*, pg. 1850
CRIMSONLOGIC USA, INC.—See CRIMSONLOGIC PTE LTD; *Int'l*, pg. 1850
CRIMSON TIDE (IE) LIMITED—See Crimson Tide plc; *Int'l*, pg. 1850
CRITICAL INFRASTRUCTURE TECHNOLOGIES LTD.; *Int'l*, pg. 1851

CRITIQUEIT, INC.—See 2U, Inc.; *U.S. Public*, pg. 3
CROSS COUNTRY INFOTECH, PVT. LTD.—See Cross Country Healthcare, Inc.; *U.S. Public*, pg. 595
CROSS J TECH INC.—See Cross Marketing Group Inc.; *Int'l*, pg. 1856
CROSS-STRAIT INFORMATION CONSUMPTION INSTITUTE (XIAMEN) CO., LTD.—See Beijing E-Hualu Information Technology Co., Ltd.; *Int'l*, pg. 1452
CROWDICITY LIMITED—See Thoma Bravo, L.P.; *U.S. Private*, pg. 4149
CRUNCHFISH AB; *Int'l*, pg. 1859
CRYPTOBLOX TECHNOLOGIES INC.; *Int'l*, pg. 1860
CS DISCO, INC.; *U.S. Public*, pg. 600
CSG INTERNATIONAL PTY LIMITED—See CSG Systems International, Inc.; *U.S. Public*, pg. 601
CSG SMART ROBOT TECHNOLOGY CO., LTD.—See CSG Smart Science & Technology Co., Ltd.; *Int'l*, pg. 1864
CSG SYSTEMS—See CSG Systems International, Inc.; *U.S. Public*, pg. 601
CSI SOFTWARE—See GI Manager L.P.; *U.S. Private*, pg. 1692
CSP INC. SECURITIES CORP.—See CSP Inc.; *U.S. Public*, pg. 601
CTCI ADVANCED SYSTEMS SHANGHAI INC.—See CTCI Corporation; *Int'l*, pg. 1870
CTI REED CO., LTD.—See CTI Engineering Co., Ltd.; *Int'l*, pg. 1871
CTI U.S. INC.—See Centre Testing International Corporation; *Int'l*, pg. 1411
CTO 24/7 (PRIVATE) LIMITED—See Stewart Information Services Corporation; *U.S. Public*, pg. 1947
CTRACK BENELUX BV—See Inseego Corp.; *U.S. Public*, pg. 1129
CTRACK DEUTSCHLAND GMBH—See Inseego Corp.; *U.S. Public*, pg. 1129
CTS EVENTIM SOLUTIONS GMBH—See CTS Eventim AG & Co. KGAA; *Int'l*, pg. 1872
CTS EVENTIM SPORTS GMBH—See CTS Eventim AG & Co. KGAA; *Int'l*, pg. 1872
CUATTRO SOFTWARE, LLC—See Cuattro, LLC; *U.S. Private*, pg. 1119
CUBOX CO., LTD.; *Int'l*, pg. 1875
CULTURA TECHNOLOGIES INC.—See Constellation Software Inc.; *Int'l*, pg. 1775
CUMULUS NETWORKS, INC.—See NVIDIA Corporation; *U.S. Public*, pg. 1558
CUMULUS SYSTEMS PRIVATE LIMITED—See Hitachi, Ltd.; *Int'l*, pg. 3412
CURA RISK MANAGEMENT SOFTWARE (PTY) LIMITED—See Cura Technologies Ltd.; *Int'l*, pg. 1878
CURA SOFTWARE SOLUTIONS UK LIMITED—See Cura Technologies Ltd.; *Int'l*, pg. 1878
CURA TECHNOLOGIES LTD.; *Int'l*, pg. 1878
CURIOSITYVILLE, INC.—See Veritas Capital Fund Management, LLC; *U.S. Private*, pg. 4363
CURRIER MCCABE & ASSOCIATES; *U.S. Private*, pg. 1125
CUSTANET CO., LTD.—See Computer Institute of Japan Ltd.; *Int'l*, pg. 1759
CUSTOM CREDIT SYSTEMS LP—See Vista Equity Partners, LLC; *U.S. Private*, pg. 4397
CUSTOMWEATHER, INC.; *U.S. Private*, pg. 1130
CVENT HOLDING CORP.—See Blackstone Inc.; *U.S. Public*, pg. 353
CYBERAGENT VENTURES (BEIJING) CO., LTD—See CyberAgent, Inc.; *Int'l*, pg. 1892
CYBER COM CO., LTD.—See FUJISOFT INCORPORATED; *Int'l*, pg. 2830
CYBER DIGITAL, INC.; *U.S. Private*, pg. 1133
CYBER ENVIRO-TECH, INC.; *U.S. Public*, pg. 617
CYBERLINK INC.—See CyberLink Corp.; *Int'l*, pg. 1893
CYBERNET SYSTEMS MALAYSIA SDN BHD—See FUJISOFT INCORPORATED; *Int'l*, pg. 2830
CYBERNET SYSTEMS TAIWAN CO., LTD.—See FUJISOFT INCORPORATED; *Int'l*, pg. 2830
CYBERONE CO., LTD.; *Int'l*, pg. 1893
CYBEROO S.P.A.; *Int'l*, pg. 1893
CYBER RESOURCE GROUP; *U.S. Private*, pg. 1133
CYBERSCAPE MULTIMEDIA LTD.; *Int'l*, pg. 1894
CYBER SECURITY CLOUD, INC.; *Int'l*, pg. 1892
CYBERTECH SYSTEMS & SOFTWARE LTD.—See CyberTech Systems Inc.; *U.S. Private*, pg. 1133
CYBERTHINK, INC.; *U.S. Private*, pg. 1134
CYBOZU IT SHANGHAI INC.—See Cybozu Inc.; *Int'l*, pg. 1894
CYBOZU VIETNAM CO., LTD.—See Cybozu Inc.; *Int'l*, pg. 1894
CYBRA CORPORATION; *U.S. Public*, pg. 617
THE CYDIO GROUP—See 24 Seven, LLC; *U.S. Private*, pg. 6
CYFIR, LLC—See eSentire, Inc.; *Int'l*, pg. 2503
CYGNACOM SOLUTIONS, INC.—See DataCard Corporation; *U.S. Private*, pg. 1165
CYGNA ENERGY SERVICES, INC.—See Gryphon Investors, LLC; *U.S. Private*, pg. 1798
CYIENT LIMITED; *Int'l*, pg. 1895
CYNGN INC.; *U.S. Public*, pg. 617
CYQUATOR TECHNOLOGIES LIMITED—See Essel Corporate Resources Pvt. Ltd.; *Int'l*, pg. 2509
CYTEL INC.—See New Mountain Capital, LLC; *U.S. Private*, pg. 2900
CYVIZ PTE. LTD.—See Cyviz AS; *Int'l*, pg. 1898
D2M3 LTD.—See Addnode Group AB; *Int'l*, pg. 131
D4T4 SOLUTIONS INC.—See D4t4 Solutions Plc; *Int'l*, pg. 1901
DADO, INC.—See Stanley Black & Decker, Inc.; *U.S. Public*, pg. 1932
DAFFODIL COMPUTERS LIMITED; *Int'l*, pg. 1912
DAGANG NET TECHNOLOGIES SDN. BHD.—See Dagang NeXchange Berhad; *Int'l*, pg. 1912
DA GROUP; *Int'l*, pg. 1901
DAIDO IT SOLUTIONS CO., LTD.—See Daido Steel Co., Ltd.; *Int'l*, pg. 1922
DAIFUKU SOFTWARE DEVELOPMENT CO., LTD.—See Daifuku Co., Ltd.; *Int'l*, pg. 1925
DAIRY, LLC; *U.S. Private*, pg. 1146
THE DAISHI COMPUTER SERVICE CO., LTD.—See Daishi Hokuetsu Financial Group, Inc.; *Int'l*, pg. 1941
DAISHIN INFORMATION & COMMUNICATIONS CO.,LTD.; *Int'l*, pg. 1941
DAITRON (KOREA) CO., LTD.—See Daitron Co., Ltd.; *Int'l*, pg. 1944
DAIWA COMPUTER CO., LTD.; *Int'l*, pg. 1944
DALENYS S.A.—See Groupe BPCE; *Int'l*, pg. 3094
DALET AUSTRALIA PTY. LTD.—See Long Path Partners, LP; *U.S. Private*, pg. 2491
DALET DIGITAL MEDIA SYSTEMS ME—See Long Path Partners, LP; *U.S. Private*, pg. 2491
DALET DIGITAL MEDIA SYSTEMS MEXICO—See Long Path Partners, LP; *U.S. Private*, pg. 2491
DALET DIGITAL MEDIA SYSTEMS USA, INC.—See Long Path Partners, LP; *U.S. Private*, pg. 2491
DALET GMBH—See Long Path Partners, LP; *U.S. Private*, pg. 2491
DALET ITALIA SRL—See Long Path Partners, LP; *U.S. Private*, pg. 2491
DALET LTD.—See Long Path Partners, LP; *U.S. Private*, pg. 2491
DALET S.A.—See Long Path Partners, LP; *U.S. Private*, pg. 2491
DALET SISTEMAS S.A.—See Long Path Partners, LP; *U.S. Private*, pg. 2491
DALET SYSTEMS ASIA PTE LTD.—See Long Path Partners, LP; *U.S. Private*, pg. 2491
DALIAN SUPERELECTRONICS CO., LTD.—See DTS Corporation; *Int'l*, pg. 2217
DALLMEIER ELECTRONIC GMBH & CO. KG; *Int'l*, pg. 1954
DALTON+ANODE—See The Dalton Agency, Inc.; *U.S. Private*, pg. 4018
DAMANSARA TECHNOLOGY SDN. BHD.—See Damansara Realty Berhad; *Int'l*, pg. 1955
DANCHARIA RESEARCH & TRADE EAST AB—See Broadridge Financial Solutions, Inc.; *U.S. Public*, pg. 392
DAOU JAPAN KK—See Daou Data Corp.; *Int'l*, pg. 1970
DARC CORPORATION; *U.S. Private*, pg. 1158
DAREWAY SOFTWARE CO., LTD.; *Int'l*, pg. 1972
DARKTRACE GMBH—See Thoma Bravo, L.P.; *U.S. Private*, pg. 4147
DARKTRACE S.A.S.—See Thoma Bravo, L.P.; *U.S. Private*, pg. 4147
DARWIN TECHNOLOGIES SG PTE. LTD.—See Marsh & McLennan Companies, Inc.; *U.S. Public*, pg. 1374
DARWIN TECHNOLOGIES S.R.L.—See Marsh & McLennan Companies, Inc.; *U.S. Public*, pg. 1374
DARWIN ZONE S.A.—See H.I.G. Capital, LLC; *U.S. Private*, pg. 1830
DASSAULT SYSTEMES 3DEXCITE GMBH—See Dassault Systemes S.A.; *Int'l*, pg. 1974
DASSAULT SYSTEMES AB—See Dassault Systemes S.A.; *Int'l*, pg. 1974
DASSAULT SYSTEMES AMERICAS - WOODLAND HILLS—See Dassault Systemes S.A.; *Int'l*, pg. 1974
DASSAULT SYSTEMES APS—See Dassault Systemes S.A.; *Int'l*, pg. 1974
DASSAULT SYSTEMES AUSTRALIA PTY LTD—See Dassault Systemes S.A.; *Int'l*, pg. 1974
DASSAULT SYSTEMES BV—See Dassault Systemes S.A.; *Int'l*, pg. 1974
DASSAULT SYSTEMES CHINA—See Dassault Systemes S.A.; *Int'l*, pg. 1974
DASSAULT SYSTEMES CZ S.R.O.—See Dassault Systemes S.A.; *Int'l*, pg. 1974
DASSAULT SYSTEMES DEUTSCHLAND GMBH—See Dassault Systemes S.A.; *Int'l*, pg. 1974
DASSAULT SYSTEMES INC.—See Dassault Systemes S.A.; *Int'l*, pg. 1974
DASSAULT SYSTEMES INDIA PVT. LTD—See Dassault Systemes S.A.; *Int'l*, pg. 1974
DASSAULT SYSTEMES ISRAEL LTD.—See Dassault Systemes S.A.; *Int'l*, pg. 1975
DASSAULT SYSTEMES ITALIA SRL—See Dassault Systemes S.A.; *Int'l*, pg. 1975
DASSAULT SYSTEMES JAPAN—See Dassault Systemes S.A.; *Int'l*, pg. 1975
DASSAULT SYSTEMES KOREA CORP.—See Dassault

541511 — CUSTOM COMPUTER PRO...

Systemes S.A.; *Int'l*, pg. 1975
DASSAULT SYSTEMES MEXICO—See Dassault Systemes S.A.; *Int'l*, pg. 1975
DASSAULT SYSTEMES OY—See Dassault Systemes S.A.; *Int'l*, pg. 1975
DASSAULT SYSTEMES RUSSIA CORP.—See Dassault Systemes S.A.; *Int'l*, pg. 1975
DASSAULT SYSTEMES SCHWEIZ AG—See Dassault Systemes S.A.; *Int'l*, pg. 1975
DASSAULT SYSTEMES SIMULIA CORP.—See Dassault Systemes S.A.; *Int'l*, pg. 1974
DASSAULT SYSTEMES SINGAPORE PTE. LTD.—See Dassault Systemes S.A.; *Int'l*, pg. 1975
DASSAULT SYSTEMES SOLIDWORKS CORPORATION—See Dassault Systemes S.A.; *Int'l*, pg. 1975
DASSAULT SYSTEMES SP. Z O.O.—See Dassault Systemes S.A.; *Int'l*, pg. 1975
DASSAULT SYSTEMES (SUISSE) S.A.—See Dassault Systemes S.A.; *Int'l*, pg. 1974
DASSAULT SYSTEMES TAIWAN—See Dassault Systemes S.A.; *Int'l*, pg. 1975
DASSAULT SYTEMES AUSTRALIA PTY LTD—See Dassault Systemes S.A.; *Int'l*, pg. 1975
DATA#3 LIMITED; *Int'l*, pg. 1977
DATA41; *U.S. Private*, pg. 1164
DATA4VALUE, SRL—See CRIF S.p.A.; *Int'l*, pg. 1849
DATA ARCHITECTURE & TECHNOLOGY S.L.—See Banco Bilbao Vizcaya Argentaria, S.A.; *Int'l*, pg. 817
DATAART SOLUTIONS, INC.; *U.S. Private*, pg. 1164
DATABLE TECHNOLOGY CORP.; *Int'l*, pg. 1977
DATACENTRIX (PROPRIETARY) LIMITED—See Alviva Holdings Limited; *Int'l*, pg. 402
DATACENTRIX SOLUTIONS (PROPRIETARY) LIMITED—See Alviva Holdings Limited; *Int'l*, pg. 402
DATA CORE SYSTEMS INC.; *U.S. Private*, pg. 1162
DATACOR, INC.; *U.S. Private*, pg. 1165
DATA DESIGN S.A.—See AXON Holdings S.A.; *Int'l*, pg. 770
DATADOG, INC.; *U.S. Public*, pg. 635
DATAGRAVITY, INC.—See DataCard Corporation; *U.S. Private*, pg. 1165
DATA INTERCONNECT LTD.—See BlackLine, Inc.; *U.S. Public*, pg. 342
DATALEX NETHERLANDS B.V.—See Datalex plc; *Int'l*, pg. 1978
DATALEX SOLUTIONS (UK) LIMITED—See Datalex plc; *Int'l*, pg. 1978
DATALEX USA INC.—See Datalex plc; *Int'l*, pg. 1978
DATAMATICS GLOBAL SERVICES CORP.—See Datamatics Global Services Ltd.; *Int'l*, pg. 1979
DATAMATICS GLOBAL SERVICES FZ-LLC—See Datamatics Global Services Ltd.; *Int'l*, pg. 1979
DATAMATICS STAFFING SERVICES LIMITED—See Datamatics Global Services Ltd.; *Int'l*, pg. 1979
DATA PATTERNS (INDIA) LTD.; *Int'l*, pg. 1976
DATAPRISE, INC—See Trinity Hunt Management, L.P.; *U.S. Private*, pg. 4234
DATA QUALITY MANAGEMENT GROUP LIMITED—See Bloom Equity Partners Management, LLC; *U.S. Private*, pg. 583
DATASENTICS A.S.—See Atos SE; *Int'l*, pg. 692
DATASOLUTION, INC.; *Int'l*, pg. 1979
DATASONIC INNOVATION SDN. BHD.—See Datasonic Group Berhad; *Int'l*, pg. 1979
DATA SYSTEMS INTERNATIONAL, INC.—See Nextworld, LLC; *U.S. Private*, pg. 2921
DATATERN, INC.—See Amphion Innovations plc; *Int'l*, pg. 433
DATA VISION, INC.; *U.S. Private*, pg. 1164
DATAVIZ, INC.; *U.S. Private*, pg. 1166
DATAWALK S.A.; *Int'l*, pg. 1981
DATAWING SOFTWARE, LLC—See Great Point Partners, LLC; *U.S. Private*, pg. 1767
D&A TECHNOLOGY (SHANGHAI) CO., LTD.—See Argo Graphics Inc.; *Int'l*, pg. 562
DATENTECHNIK D.O.O.—See Datentechnik AG; *Int'l*, pg. 1982
DATEV.AT GMBH—See DATEV eG; *Int'l*, pg. 1982
DATEV.CZ S.R.O.—See DATEV eG; *Int'l*, pg. 1982
DATEV HUNGARY—See DATEV eG; *Int'l*, pg. 1982
DATEV KOINOS S.R.L.—See DATEV eG; *Int'l*, pg. 1982
DATEV.PL SP. Z O.O.—See DATEV eG; *Int'l*, pg. 1982
DATRIX S.P.A.; *Int'l*, pg. 1982
DAUF SA—See CSL Limited; *Int'l*, pg. 1866
DAVID LEWIS & ASSOCIATES INC.; *U.S. Private*, pg. 1170
DAWN CORPORATION; *Int'l*, pg. 1984
DAY ONLINE SOLUTIONS, LLC; *U.S. Private*, pg. 1176
DAZA PRODUCTIONS INC.—See National Amusements, Inc.; *U.S. Private*, pg. 2841
DAZ SYSTEMS, INC.—See Accenture plc; *Int'l*, pg. 87
DBAPP SECURITY CO., LTD.; *Int'l*, pg. 1986
D&B SALES & MARKETING SOLUTIONS—See Cannae Holdings, Inc.; *U.S. Public*, pg. 429
D&B SALES & MARKETING SOLUTIONS—See CC Capital Partners, LLC; *U.S. Private*, pg. 798
D&B SALES & MARKETING SOLUTIONS—See Intercontinental Exchange, Inc.; *U.S. Public*, pg. 1141
DCM ADVANCED TECHNOLOGIES CO., LTD.—See DCM Holdings Co., Ltd.; *Int'l*, pg. 1992
DCM INFOTECH LIMITED—See DCM Limited; *Int'l*, pg. 1992
DCML LIMITED—See Accident Exchange Group Plc; *Int'l*, pg. 90
DCS CONSULTING, INC.—See Bluestone Investment Partners, LLC; *U.S. Private*, pg. 598
DDS EFLEET SERVICES INC—See DDS Wireless International Inc.; *Int'l*, pg. 1994
DEALER-FX GROUP—See Snap-on Incorporated; *U.S. Public*, pg. 1897
DEALER INFO SYSTEMS CORP.; *U.S. Private*, pg. 1182
DEALER INSPIRE INC.—See Cars.com Inc.; *U.S. Public*, pg. 444
DECARE SYSTEMS IRELAND, LIMITED—See Elevance Health, Inc.; *U.S. Public*, pg. 729
DECIPHER, INC.—See decipher, inc.; *U.S. Private*, pg. 1187
DECISION RESEARCH CORP.—See Thoma Bravo, L.P.; *U.S. Private*, pg. 4149
DEEPNOID INC.; *Int'l*, pg. 2003
DEEPVERGE IRELAND LIMITED—See Deepverge PLC; *Int'l*, pg. 2003
DEFINITIVE HEALTHCARE LLC—See Definitive Healthcare Corp.; *U.S. Public*, pg. 648
DEFINITIVE LOGIC CORPORATION—See The Carlyle Group Inc.; *U.S. Public*, pg. 2048
DEGAMA SOFTWARE SOLUTIONS, INC.; *Int'l*, pg. 2004
DEGETEL BENELUX—See Degetel; *Int'l*, pg. 2004
DEGETEL PORTUGAL - SOCIEDADE UNIPESSOAL LDA.—See Degetel; *Int'l*, pg. 2004
DEGETEL; *Int'l*, pg. 2004
DELCAM PARTMAKER LIMITED—See Autodesk, Inc.; *U.S. Public*, pg. 229
DELOITTE DEVELOPMENT LLC—See Deloitte LLP; *U.S. Private*, pg. 1198
DELOITTE DEVELOPMENT LLC—See Deloitte Touche Tohmatsu Limited; *Int'l*, pg. 2014
DELTA CORPORATE SERVICES INC.; *U.S. Private*, pg. 1199
DELTA DATA SOFTWARE, INC.—See Terminus Capital Partners, LLC; *U.S. Private*, pg. 3969
DELTADNA LIMITED—See Unity Software Inc.; *U.S. Public*, pg. 2254
DELTEK, INC.—See Roper Technologies, Inc.; *U.S. Public*, pg. 1811
DELTEK PHILIPPINES LLC—See Roper Technologies, Inc.; *U.S. Public*, pg. 1811
DEMANDWARE GMBH—See Salesforce, Inc.; *U.S. Public*, pg. 1837
DEMANT TECHNOLOGY CENTRE SP. Z O. O.—See Demant A/S; *Int'l*, pg. 2023
DEMOCRASOFT HOLDINGS, INC.; *U.S. Public*, pg. 653
DENIM GROUP, LTD.—See Apax Partners LLP; *Int'l*, pg. 503
DENSO CREATE INC..—See Denso Corporation; *Int'l*, pg. 2031
DENSO SOFTWARE SHANGHAI CO., LTD.—See Denso Corporation; *Int'l*, pg. 2030
DENSO TECHNO CO., LTD.—See Denso Corporation; *Int'l*, pg. 2030
DENSO TECHNO PHILIPPINES, INC.—See Denso Corporation; *Int'l*, pg. 2030
DENSO TEN RESEARCH AND DEVELOPMENT (TIANJIN) LIMITED—See Denso Corporation; *Int'l*, pg. 2030
DEQUE SYSTEMS, INC.; *U.S. Public*, pg. 1209
DESERT CONTROL AS; *Int'l*, pg. 2044
DESIGNGEN, COMUNICACAO VISUAL, UNIPESSOAL LDA.—See CSG Systems International, Inc.; *U.S. Public*, pg. 601
DESIGNING SUCCESS, INC.—See MPACT Strategic Consulting LLC; *U.S. Private*, pg. 2803
DESIGN SYSTEMS INC.; *U.S. Private*, pg. 1214
DETERMINE SAS—See Corcentric, Inc.; *U.S. Private*, pg. 1047
DET NORSKE VERITAS HOLDING USA INC.—See DNV GL Group AS; *Int'l*, pg. 2151
DET NORSKE VERITAS USA INC—See DNV GL Group AS; *Int'l*, pg. 2151
DEUTSCHE POST GEMEINNUTZIGE GESELLSCHAFT FUR SICHERE UND VERTRAULICHE KOMMUNIKATION IM INTERNET MBH—See Deutsche Post AG; *Int'l*, pg. 2079
DEVBRIDGE CANADA ULC—See Cognizant Technology Solutions Corporation; *U.S. Public*, pg. 524
DEVBRIDGE UK LTD.—See Cognizant Technology Solutions Corporation; *U.S. Public*, pg. 524
DEVERO, INC.—See GI Manager L.P.; *U.S. Private*, pg. 1693
DEVERO, INC.—See TA Associates, Inc.; *U.S. Private*, pg. 3916
DEVERSIFY HEALTH AB; *Int'l*, pg. 2088
DEVESYS TECHNOLOGIES, INC.—See Bragg Gaming Group Inc.; *Int'l*, pg. 1136
DEV INFO-TECH NORTH AMERICA LIMITED—See DEV Information Technology Pvt. Ltd.; *Int'l*, pg. 2086
DEVOTEAM QUAINT AB—See Devoteam SA; *Int'l*, pg. 2090
DEVPORT AB; *Int'l*, pg. 2090
DEXMA SENSORS S.L.—See Herbalife Nutrition Ltd.; *Int'l*, pg. 3359

DFNN, INC.; *Int'l*, pg. 2096
DGIT SYSTEMS PTY. LTD.—See CSG Systems International, Inc.; *U.S. Public*, pg. 601
DG MOBILE, INC.—See Digital Garage, Inc.; *Int'l*, pg. 2122
DGTL HOLDINGS INC.; *Int'l*, pg. 2097
DHH SPA; *Int'l*, pg. 2099
DHL INFORMATION SERVICES (EUROPE) S.R.O.—See Deutsche Post AG; *Int'l*, pg. 2076
DIADROM HOLDING AB; *Int'l*, pg. 2101
DIAGNOTES, INC.—See DrFirst.com, Inc.; *U.S. Private*, pg. 1277
DIA-GO B.V.—See Eurofins Scientific S.E.; *Int'l*, pg. 2536
DIAMOND SOFTWARE, INC.; *U.S. Private*, pg. 1224
DIASPARK INC.; *U.S. Private*, pg. 1224
DIDI GLOBAL INC.; *Int'l*, pg. 2112
DIEBOLD NIXDORF AUSTRALIA PTY. LTD.—See Diebold Nixdorf, Inc.; *U.S. Public*, pg. 660
DIEBOLD NIXDORF BUSINESS ADMINISTRATION CENTER GMBH—See Diebold Nixdorf, Inc.; *U.S. Public*, pg. 661
DIEBOLD NIXDORF B.V.B.A—See Diebold Nixdorf, Inc.; *U.S. Public*, pg. 660
DIEBOLD NIXDORF EURL—See Diebold Nixdorf, Inc.; *U.S. Public*, pg. 661
DIEBOLD NIXDORF GLOBAL SOLUTIONS B.V.—See Diebold Nixdorf, Inc.; *U.S. Public*, pg. 660
DIEBOLD NIXDORF (HONG KONG) LTD.—See Diebold Nixdorf, Inc.; *U.S. Public*, pg. 661
DIEBOLD NIXDORF INDIA PRIVATE LIMITED—See Diebold Nixdorf, Inc.; *U.S. Public*, pg. 660
DIEBOLD NIXDORF INFORMATION SYSTEMS (SHANGHAI) CO. LTD.—See Diebold Nixdorf, Inc.; *U.S. Public*, pg. 661
DIEBOLD NIXDORF KFT.—See Diebold Nixdorf, Inc.; *U.S. Public*, pg. 661
DIEBOLD NIXDORF MIDDLE EAST FZ-LLC—See Diebold Nixdorf, Inc.; *U.S. Public*, pg. 661
DIEBOLD NIXDORF MYANMAR LIMITED—See Diebold Nixdorf, Inc.; *U.S. Public*, pg. 660
DIEBOLD NIXDORF PORTUGAL UNIPESSOAL, LDA.—See Diebold Nixdorf, Inc.; *U.S. Public*, pg. 660
DIEBOLD NIXDORF RETAIL SOLUTIONS S.R.O.—See Diebold Nixdorf, Inc.; *U.S. Public*, pg. 660
DIEBOLD NIXDORF S.A.—See Diebold Nixdorf, Inc.; *U.S. Public*, pg. 661
DIEBOLD NIXDORF SOUTH AFRICA (PTY) LTD.—See Diebold Nixdorf, Inc.; *U.S. Public*, pg. 660
DIEBOLD NIXDORF SP. Z.O.O.—See Diebold Nixdorf, Inc.; *U.S. Public*, pg. 661
DIEBOLD NIXDORF S.R.O. (CZECH REPUBLIC)—See Diebold Nixdorf, Inc.; *U.S. Public*, pg. 661
DIEBOLD NIXDORF S.R.O. (SLOVAKIA)—See Diebold Nixdorf, Inc.; *U.S. Public*, pg. 661
DIEBOLD NIXDORF S.R.O.—See Diebold Nixdorf, Inc.; *U.S. Public*, pg. 661
DIEBOLD NIXDORF TAIWAN LTD.—See Diebold Nixdorf, Inc.; *U.S. Public*, pg. 660
DIEBOLD NIXDORF TECHNOLOGY GMBH—See Diebold Nixdorf, Inc.; *U.S. Public*, pg. 661
DIEBOLD NIXDORF TEKNOLOJI A.S.—See Diebold Nixdorf, Inc.; *U.S. Public*, pg. 661
DIEBOLD NIXDORF (THAILAND) COMPANY LIMITED—See Diebold Nixdorf, Inc.; *U.S. Public*, pg. 660
DIEBOLD NIXDORF (UK) LIMITED—See Diebold Nixdorf, Inc.; *U.S. Public*, pg. 661
DIEBOLD NIXDORF VIETNAM COMPANY LIMITED—See Diebold Nixdorf, Inc.; *U.S. Public*, pg. 660
DIGIA SWEDEN AB—See Digia Plc; *Int'l*, pg. 2118
DIGICON CORPORATION; *U.S. Private*, pg. 1229
DIGIHAUL LIMITED—See Deutsche Post AG; *Int'l*, pg. 2080
DIGIHOST TECHNOLOGY, INC.; *Int'l*, pg. 2119
DIGIMARC GMBH—See Digimarc Corporation; *U.S. Public*, pg. 662
DIGISTAR HOLDINGS SDN. BHD.—See Digistar Corporation Berhad; *Int'l*, pg. 2120
DIGITAL DISPATCH LIMITED PARTNERSHIP—See DDS Wireless International Inc.; *Int'l*, pg. 1994
DIGITAL FUSION INC.—See Kratos Defense & Security Solutions, Inc.; *U.S. Public*, pg. 1276
DIGITALGLOBE INTELLIGENCE SOLUTIONS, INC.—See Advent International Corporation; *U.S. Private*, pg. 103
DIGITAL GOLF SOLUTIONS SAS—See Comcast Corporation; *U.S. Public*, pg. 538
DIGITALIST CANADA LTD.—See Digitalist Group Oyj; *Int'l*, pg. 2123
DIGITAL MANAGEMENT, INC.—See OceanSound Partners, LP; *U.S. Public*, pg. 2990
DIGITAL MATTER (PTY) LTD—See African Equity Empowerment Investmts Limited; *Int'l*, pg. 191
DIGITAL PROSPECTORS CORP.; *U.S. Private*, pg. 1231
DIGITAL RESULT GMBH—See Bertrandt AG; *Int'l*, pg. 998
DIGITAL SANDBOX, INC.—See Edgewater Services, LLC; *U.S. Public*, pg. 1335
DIGITAL SCANNING CORPORATION PTE LTD—See DGB Asia Berhad; *Int'l*, pg. 2096
DIGITAL SPICE CORPORATION—See Altech Corporation; *Int'l*, pg. 389

N.A.I.C.S. INDEX

541511 — CUSTOM COMPUTER PRO...

DIGITAL TURBINE (EMEA) LTD.—See Digital Turbine, Inc.; *U.S. Public*, pg. 664
DIGITAL VALUE S.P.A.; *Int'l*, pg. 2123
DIGIWIN SOFTWARE (VIETNAM) CO., LTD.—See Digiwin Software Co., Ltd.; *Int'l*, pg. 2124
DILLISTONE SOLUTIONS LIMITED—See Dillistone Group Plc; *Int'l*, pg. 2125
DILLISTONE SYSTEMS (AUSTRALIA) PTY LTD—See Dillistone Group Plc; *Int'l*, pg. 2125
DILLISTONE SYSTEMS (US) INC.—See Dillistone Group Plc; *Int'l*, pg. 2125
DIMAGI, INC.; *U.S. Private*, pg. 1232
DIMERCO DATA SYSTEM CORP.; *Int'l*, pg. 2126
DION GLOBAL SOLUTIONS (ASIA PACIFIC) PTY LTD.—See Dion Global Solutions Limited; *Int'l*, pg. 2127
DIRECT INFORMATION FZC—See Directi Group; *Int'l*, pg. 2130
DIRECT IT CANADA INC.; *Int'l*, pg. 2129
DIR INFORMATION SYSTEMS CO., LTD.—See Daiwa Securities Group Inc.; *Int'l*, pg. 1947
DISCOVERY TECHNOLOGY PTY LTD—See Data#3 Limited; *Int'l*, pg. 1977
DISEC CO., LTD.—See Core Corporation; *Int'l*, pg. 1797
DIS SOLUTION CO., LTD.—See Daiwabo Holdings Co., Ltd.; *Int'l*, pg. 1949
DISTEK INTEGRATION, INC.; *U.S. Private*, pg. 1239
D.I. SYSTEM CO., LTD.; *Int'l*, pg. 1900
DIVA CORPORATION OF AMERICA—See Avant Corporation; *Int'l*, pg. 735
DIVA CORPORATION OF UK—See Avant Corporation; *Int'l*, pg. 735
DIXID—See Alten S.A.; *Int'l*, pg. 390
DKB CODE FACTORY GMBH—See BayernLB Holding AG; *Int'l*, pg. 913
D.L.G.L. LTD.; *Int'l*, pg. 1901
D-LINK (DEUTSCHLAND) GMBH—See D-Link Corporation, Inc.; *Int'l*, pg. 1900
D-MARKET ELECTRONIC SERVICES & TRADING; *Int'l*, pg. 1900
DMBGROUP, LLC—See Data443 Risk Mitigation, Inc.; *U.S. Public*, pg. 635
DMX TECHNOLOGIES GROUP LIMITED; *Int'l*, pg. 2147
DNAKE XIAMEN INTELLIGENT TECHNOLOGY CO., LTD.; *Int'l*, pg. 2147
DNP AV CENTER CO., LTD.—See Dai Nippon Printing Co., Ltd.; *Int'l*, pg. 1914
DNP INFORMATION SYSTEMS CO., LTD.—See Dai Nippon Printing Co., Ltd.; *Int'l*, pg. 1914
DNV INC.—See DNV GL Group AS; *Int'l*, pg. 2151
DNV SOFTWARE USA—See DNV GL Group AS; *Int'l*, pg. 2151
DOAPP, INC.—See Vista Equity Partners, LLC; *U.S. Private*, pg. 4399
DOCEBO FRANCE S.A.S.—See Docebo, Inc.; *Int'l*, pg. 2153
DOCEBO, INC.; *Int'l*, pg. 2153
DOCLOGIX JSC—See Alna AB; *Int'l*, pg. 364
DOCSCORP PTY. LIMITED—See Freedom Solutions Group, L.L.C.; *U.S. Private*, pg. 1604
DOCUFY GMBH—See Heidelberger Druckmaschinen AG; *Int'l*, pg. 3321
DOCUMED LTD.—See CSL Limited; *Int'l*, pg. 1866
DOCUSIGN BRASIL PARTICIPACOES LTDA.—See DocuSign, Inc.; *U.S. Public*, pg. 672
DOCUSIGN FRANCE SAS—See DocuSign, Inc.; *U.S. Public*, pg. 672
DOCUSIGN, INC.; *U.S. Public*, pg. 672
DOCUSIGN INTERNATIONAL (ASIA-PACIFIC) PRIVATE LIMITED—See DocuSign, Inc.; *U.S. Public*, pg. 672
DOCUSIGN UK LIMITED—See DocuSign, Inc.; *U.S. Public*, pg. 672
DOCUTAP INC.—See Warburg Pincus LLC; *U.S. Private*, pg. 4438
DOLPHIN INTERCONNECT SOLUTIONS AS; *Int'l*, pg. 2159
DOMINO DATA LAB, INC.; *U.S. Private*, pg. 1256
DONATECH CORPORATION; *U.S. Private*, pg. 1260
DONAT IT GMBH—See Adecco Group AG; *Int'l*, pg. 140
DONGGUAN EDENSOFT LIMITED—See Edensoft Holdings Limited; *Int'l*, pg. 2308
DONNELL SYSTEMS INC.; *U.S. Private*, pg. 1260
DONNERWOOD MEDIA, INC.; *U.S. Private*, pg. 1261
DONT NOD ENTERTAINMENT SA; *Int'l*, pg. 2172
DOOSAN GRIDTECH LLC—See Doosan Corporation; *Int'l*, pg. 2173
DOOSAN LOGISTICS SOLUTION CO., LTD.—See Doosan Corporation; *Int'l*, pg. 2173
DOOSAN MOBILITY INNOVATION INC.—See Doosan Corporation; *Int'l*, pg. 2173
DOOSAN ROBOTICS INC.—See Doosan Corporation; *Int'l*, pg. 2173
DOSEME LLC—See Nautic Partners, LLC; *U.S. Private*, pg. 2871
DOTPHOTO, INC.; *U.S. Private*, pg. 1265
DOTWALK, INC.—See ServiceNow, Inc.; *U.S. Public*, pg. 1872
DOUZONE BIZON CO., LTD.; *Int'l*, pg. 2182
DOVARRI, INC.; *U.S. Private*, pg. 1268
DOVRE GROUP PLC; *Int'l*, pg. 2182

DOW JONES BUSINESS & RELATIONSHIP INTELLIGENCE CANADA—See News Corporation; *U.S. Public*, pg. 1518
DOW JONES BUSINESS & RELATIONSHIP INTELLIGENCE—See News Corporation; *U.S. Public*, pg. 1518
DOXEE S.P.A; *Int'l*, pg. 2187
DOXIM INC.—See GI Manager L.P.; *U.S. Private*, pg. 1692
DRAEGER HELLAS A.E.—See Draegerwerk AG & Co. KGaA; *Int'l*, pg. 2196
DRAGO ENTERTAINMENT SA; *Int'l*, pg. 2199
DRAGONTAIL SYSTEMS LIMITED; *Int'l*, pg. 2200
DRAW DISTANCE S.A.; *Int'l*, pg. 2200
DRECOM CO., LTD.; *Int'l*, pg. 2203
DREW TECHNOLOGIES INC.—See Searchlight Capital Partners, L.P.; *U.S. Private*, pg. 3590
DRISHTICON INC.; *U.S. Private*, pg. 1278
DSA-SOFTWARE, INC.—See Distribution Services of America, Inc.; *U.S. Private*, pg. 1239
DSE DEVELOPMENT LTD.—See Caledonia Investments plc; *Int'l*, pg. 1262
DSI ASIA/PACIFIC—See Nextworld, LLC; *U.S. Private*, pg. 2921
DSI EMEA LTD.—See Nextworld, LLC; *U.S. Private*, pg. 2921
DSOFT TECHNOLOGY COMPANY—See Chiulista Services, Inc.; *U.S. Private*, pg. 887
D.T.C. ENTERPRISE PUBLIC COMPANY LIMITED; *Int'l*, pg. 1901
DTS INSIGHT CORPORATION—See DTS Corporation; *Int'l*, pg. 2217
DTS SOFTWARE VIETNAM CO., LTD.—See DTS Corporation; *Int'l*, pg. 2217
DUALIS GMBH—See Durr AG; *Int'l*, pg. 2230
DUG TECHNOLOGY LTD.; *Int'l*, pg. 2223
DUIBA GROUP LIMITED; *Int'l*, pg. 2224
DUOLINGO, INC.; *U.S. Public*, pg. 691
DUO WORLD, INC.; *U.S. Public*, pg. 691
DUSTIN NORWAY AS—See Dustin Group AB; *Int'l*, pg. 2235
DUXWARE, LLC—See i3 Verticals, Inc.; *U.S. Public*, pg. 1081
DXC ECLIPSE PTY LTD—See DXC Technology Company; *U.S. Public*, pg. 695
DXC TECHNOLOGY SARL—See DXC Technology Company; *U.S. Public*, pg. 696
DYE & DURHAM LIMITED; *Int'l*, pg. 2238
DYNAMIC COMPUTING SERVICES CORP.; *U.S. Private*, pg. 1297
DYNAMIC CONCEPTS, INC.—See Millennium Engineering & Integration Company; *U.S. Private*, pg. 2731
DYNARDO AUSTRIA GMBH—See ANSYS, Inc.; *U.S. Public*, pg. 139
DYNARDO (DYNAMIC SOFTWARE & ENGINEERING) GMBH—See ANSYS, Inc.; *U.S. Public*, pg. 139
DYNATRACE ASIA PACIFIC LIMITED—See Dynatrace, Inc.; *U.S. Public*, pg. 700
DYNATRACE ASIA-PACIFIC PTY. LTD—See Dynatrace, Inc.; *U.S. Public*, pg. 700
DYNATRACE A/S—See KKR & Co. Inc.; *U.S. Public*, pg. 1240
DYNATRACE BV—See KKR & Co. Inc.; *U.S. Public*, pg. 1240
DYNATRACE DE MEXICO—See Dynatrace, Inc.; *U.S. Public*, pg. 700
DYNATRACE FINLAND OY—See KKR & Co. Inc.; *U.S. Public*, pg. 1240
DYNATRACE, INC.; *U.S. Public*, pg. 699
DYNATRACE INDIA SOFTWARE OPERATIONS PVT. LTD.—See Dynatrace, Inc.; *U.S. Public*, pg. 700
DYNATRACE IRELAND LIMITED—See Dynatrace, Inc.; *U.S. Public*, pg. 700
DYNATRACE LIMITED—See KKR & Co. Inc.; *U.S. Public*, pg. 1240
DYNATRACE SARL—See KKR & Co. Inc.; *U.S. Public*, pg. 1240
DYNATRACE SP. Z.O.O—See Dynatrace, Inc.; *U.S. Public*, pg. 700
DYNAWARE ASIA PACIFIC PTE. LTD.—See Dynatrace, Inc.; *U.S. Public*, pg. 700
DYNAXYS LLC; *U.S. Private*, pg. 1300
DYNNIQ PEEK TRAFFIC B.V.—See Egeria Capital Management B.V.; *Int'l*, pg. 2323
DYNTEK, INC.; *U.S. Public*, pg. 700
DYNTEK INC.—See DynTek, Inc.; *U.S. Public*, pg. 700
DZ SOLUTIONS; *U.S. Private*, pg. 1300
E2MAX CENTRE PTE LTD—See Cathay Organisation Holdings Ltd; *Int'l*, pg. 1360
E7 PTY LTD—See Bentley Systems, Inc.; *U.S. Public*, pg. 297
EA.COM—See Electronic Arts Inc.; *U.S. Public*, pg. 724
EAGLE POINT SOFTWARE CORPORATION; *U.S. Private*, pg. 1310
EAGLE TECHNOLOGY, INC.—See Silversmith Management, L.P.; *U.S. Private*, pg. 3664
EARNIX LTD.; *Int'l*, pg. 2267
EARTH911, INC.—See Quest Resource Holding Corporation; *U.S. Public*, pg. 1756
EARTH LIFE SCIENCES, INC.; *U.S. Public*, pg. 703

EASTERN COMMUNICATIONS CO., LTD.; *Int'l*, pg. 2272
EASTERN COMPUTER SERVICE INC.—See Cooperative Holdings Inc.; *U.S. Private*, pg. 1042
EASY SOFTWARE GMBH—See Easy Software AG; *Int'l*, pg. 2276
EASY SOFTWARE INC.—See Easy Software AG; *Int'l*, pg. 2276
EASY SOFTWARE (UK) PLC—See Easy Software AG; *Int'l*, pg. 2275
EBAY GMBH—See eBay Inc.; *U.S. Public*, pg. 709
EBET, INC.; *U.S. Public*, pg. 709
EBIX EUROPE LIMITED—See Ebix Inc.; *U.S. Public*, pg. 710
EBIXEXCHANGE—See Ebix Inc.; *U.S. Public*, pg. 710
EBRAHIM K. KANOO COMPANY B.S.C - KANOO IT DIVISION—See Ebrahim K. Kanoo Company B.S.C.; *Int'l*, pg. 2286
EBREVIA, INC.—See Donnelley Financial Solutions, Inc.; *U.S. Public*, pg. 677
EBRIDGE, INC.; *U.S. Private*, pg. 1324
EBROKER GROUP LTD.; *Int'l*, pg. 2287
EBS DEALING RESOURCES JAPAN LIMITED—See CME Group, Inc.; *U.S. Public*, pg. 516
ECCO AUTO WORLD CORPORATION; *Int'l*, pg. 2288
E-CENTIVES, INC.—See Invenda Corporation; *U.S. Private*, pg. 2131
ECHO DATA GROUP INC.—See Fort Point Capital, LLC; *U.S. Private*, pg. 1574
ECIT SOLUTIONS PRO AB—See TowerBrook Capital Partners, L.P.; *U.S. Private*, pg. 4195
ECOENERGY INSIGHTS LIMITED—See Carrier Global Corporation; *U.S. Public*, pg. 443
ECOINTERACTIVE, LLC—See KKR & Co. Inc.; *U.S. Public*, pg. 1267
ECOMOTT, INC.; *Int'l*, pg. 2296
ECONOCOM AUSTRIA GMBH—See Econocom Group SA; *Int'l*, pg. 2297
ECONOCOM BRASIL S.A.—See Econocom Group SA; *Int'l*, pg. 2297
ECONOCOM DEUTSCHLAND GMBH—See Econocom Group SA; *Int'l*, pg. 2297
ECONOCOM DIGITAL FINANCE LIMITED—See Econocom Group SA; *Int'l*, pg. 2297
ECONOCOM FINANCE SNC—See Econocom Group SA; *Int'l*, pg. 2297
ECONOCOM INTERNATIONAL ITALIA SPA—See Econocom Group SA; *Int'l*, pg. 2297
ECONOCOM LTD.—See Econocom Group SA; *Int'l*, pg. 2297
ECONOCOM POLSKA SP Z.O.O—See Econocom Group SA; *Int'l*, pg. 2297
ECONOCOM PUBLIC BV—See Econocom Group SA; *Int'l*, pg. 2298
ECONOCOM SERVICIOS SA—See Econocom Group SA; *Int'l*, pg. 2298
ECOPLAN CO., LTD.—See Founder's Consultants Holdings, Inc.; *Int'l*, pg. 2753
ECORA SOFTWARE CORPORATION—See ESW Capital, LLC; *U.S. Private*, pg. 1430
EC SOURCING GROUP INC.—See Simfoni, Inc.; *U.S. Private*, pg. 3665
EDAPTIVE SYSTEMS, LLC—See The Carlyle Group Inc.; *U.S. Public*, pg. 2048
EDARAN IT SERVICES SDN. BHD.—See Edran Berhad; *Int'l*, pg. 2315
EDENBRIDGE HEALTHCARE LIMITED—See EMIS Group plc; *Int'l*, pg. 2383
EDEN SERVICES, INC.—See Hilton Grand Vacations Inc.; *U.S. Public*, pg. 1040
EDGESOURCE CORPORATION; *U.S. Private*, pg. 1334
EDGE TESTING SOLUTIONS LIMITED—See Eurofins Scientific S.E.; *Int'l*, pg. 2539
EDGIO, INC.; *U.S. Public*, pg. 718
EDICT EGAMING GMBH—See Gauselmann AG; *Int'l*, pg. 2891
EDIFECS, INC.; *U.S. Private*, pg. 1336
EDION X VENTURES CORPORATION—See EDION Corporation; *Int'l*, pg. 2310
EDM AMERICAS; *U.S. Private*, pg. 1337
EDUCATION ADVANCED, INC.—See Serent Capital Management Company, LLC; *U.S. Private*, pg. 3613
EDUCATION MANAGEMENT SOLUTIONS, INC—See Collegis LLC; *U.S. Private*, pg. 968
EDUTECH LAB AP PRIVATE LIMITED—See EduLab, Inc.; *Int'l*, pg. 2316
EDUTECH LAB, INC.—See EduLab, Inc.; *Int'l*, pg. 2316
EDVANCE INTERNATIONAL HOLDINGS LIMITED; *Int'l*, pg. 2316
EDYNAMICS SOLUTIONS LTD; *Int'l*, pg. 2317
EFI BELGIUM BVBA—See Siris Capital Group, LLC; *U.S. Private*, pg. 3672
EFRONT D.O.O.—See BlackRock, Inc.; *U.S. Public*, pg. 347
EFRONT GMBH—See BlackRock, Inc.; *U.S. Public*, pg. 347
EFRONT HONG KONG LIMITED—See BlackRock, Inc.; *U.S. Public*, pg. 347
EFRONT (JERSEY) LIMITED—See BlackRock, Inc.; *U.S. Public*, pg. 347

EFRONT KABUSHIKI KAISHA—See BlackRock, Inc.; *U.S. Public,* pg. 347
EFRONT LTD.—See BlackRock, Inc.; *U.S. Public,* pg. 347
EFRONT SINGAPORE PTE. LTD.—See BlackRock, Inc.; *U.S. Public,* pg. 347
EFRONT SOFTWARE LUXEMBOURG S.A R.L.—See BlackRock, Inc.; *U.S. Public,* pg. 347
EFRONT SOLUTIONS FINANCEIERES INC.—See BlackRock, Inc.; *U.S. Public,* pg. 347
EFUSION CO., LTD.—See ASJ Inc.; *Int'l,* pg. 621
EGAIN COMMUNICATIONS BV—See eGain Corporation; *U.S. Public,* pg. 721
EGAIN COMMUNICATIONS LTD.—See eGain Corporation; *U.S. Public,* pg. 721
EGAIN COMMUNICATIONS SRL—See eGain Corporation; *U.S. Public,* pg. 721
EGIS PARKING SERVICES B.V.—See Groupe Egis S.A.; *Int'l,* pg. 3102
EGROUP, INC.; *U.S. Private,* pg. 1345
EG SOLUTIONS LTD.—See Verint Systems Inc.; *U.S. Public,* pg. 2281
EGTON MEDICAL INFORMATION SYSTEMS LTD. EGTON DIVISION—See EMIS Group plc; *Int'l,* pg. 2382
EHAVE, INC.; *U.S. Public,* pg. 721
E-HUALU (FUJIAN) INFORMATION TECHNOLOGY CO., LTD.—See Beijing E-Hualu Information Technology Co., Ltd.; *Int'l,* pg. 949
E-HUALU INTEGRATION TECHNOLOGY CO., LTD.—See Beijing E-Hualu Information Technology Co., Ltd.; *Int'l,* pg. 949
E-HUALU (JILIN) INFORMATION TECHNOLOGY CO., LTD.—See Beijing E-Hualu Information Technology Co., Ltd.; *Int'l,* pg. 949
E-HUALU (LESHAN) INVESTMENT DEVELOPMENT CO., LTD.—See Beijing E-Hualu Information Technology Co., Ltd.; *Int'l,* pg. 949
E-HUALU (QUANZHOU) INVESTMENT DEVELOPMENT CO., LTD.—See Beijing E-Hualu Information Technology Co., Ltd.; *Int'l,* pg. 949
E-HUALU (SHANDONG) INFORMATION TECHNOLOGY CO., LTD.—See Beijing E-Hualu Information Technology Co., Ltd.; *Int'l,* pg. 949
E-HUALU (TIANJIN) INFORMATION TECHNOLOGY CO., LTD.—See Beijing E-Hualu Information Technology Co., Ltd.; *Int'l,* pg. 949
E-HUALU (TIANJIN) INTERNATIONAL TRADE COMPANY—See Beijing E-Hualu Information Technology Co., Ltd.; *Int'l,* pg. 949
THE EIGHTEENTH SOFTWARE CO., LTD.—See Fukuoka Financial Group, Inc.; *Int'l,* pg. 2840
EIT SPRENDIMAI UAB—See Atea ASA; *Int'l,* pg. 667
EKAHAU, INC.; *U.S. Private,* pg. 1348
EKENNIS SOFTWARE SERVICE LTD.; *Int'l,* pg. 2338
EKM GLOBAL LIMITED—See TD Synnex Corp; *U.S. Public,* pg. 1985
ELARA LEITSTELLENTECHNIK GMBH—See Frequentis AG; *Int'l,* pg. 2773
ELASTIC N.V.; *U.S. Public,* pg. 723
ELASTICSEARCH (BEIJING) INFORMATION TECHNOLOGY CO., LTD.—See Elastic N.V.; *U.S. Public,* pg. 723
ELASTICSEARCH B.V.—See Elastic N.V.; *U.S. Public,* pg. 723
ELASTICSEARCH KK—See Elastic N.V.; *U.S. Public,* pg. 723
ELASTICSEARCH KOREA LIMITED—See Elastic N.V.; *U.S. Public,* pg. 723
ELASTICSEARCH PTY. LTD.—See Elastic N.V.; *U.S. Public,* pg. 723
ELCA TECHNOLOGIES S.R.L.—See Cefla S.C.; *Int'l,* pg. 1390
ELCOM PLUS JSC—See ELCOM Technology Communications Corporation; *Int'l,* pg. 2345
ELCOM TECHNOLOGY COMMUNICATIONS CORPORATION; *Int'l,* pg. 2345
ELECOSOFT BV—See Eleco Plc; *Int'l,* pg. 2348
ELECTRA INFORMATION SYSTEMS, INC.—See Symphony Technology Group, LLC; *U.S. Private,* pg. 3900
ELECTRONIC ARTS INC.; *U.S. Public,* pg. 723
ELECTRONIC ENVIRONMENTS CORP.; *U.S. Private,* pg. 1355
ELECTRONIC REGISTRY SYSTEMS, INC.—See Health Catalyst, Inc.; *U.S. Public,* pg. 1014
ELECTRONICS FOR IMAGING, INC. - GEORGIA—See Siris Capital Group, LLC; *U.S. Private,* pg. 3672
ELEKTROBIT AUSTRIA GMBH—See Continental Aktiengesellschaft; *Int'l,* pg. 1783
ELEKTROBIT AUTOMOTIVE AMERICAS INC—See Continental Aktiengesellschaft; *Int'l,* pg. 1783
ELEKTROBIT AUTOMOTIVE GMBH—See Continental Aktiengesellschaft; *Int'l,* pg. 1783
ELEKTROBIT FRANCE SAS—See Continental Aktiengesellschaft; *Int'l,* pg. 1783
ELEKTRO-TECHNIK-PFISTERER-GMBH—See CEZ, a.s.; *Int'l,* pg. 1427
ELEMICA INTERNATIONAL INC.—See Eurazeo SE; *Int'l,* pg. 2528
ELEVATIVE NETWORKS LLC—See Rimstorm, Inc.; *U.S. Private,* pg. 3437

ELIAN SOLUTIONS SRL—See Bittnet Systems SA Bucuresti; *Int'l,* pg. 1050
ELISA SANTA MONICA OY—See Elisa Corporation; *Int'l,* pg. 2361
ELITE COMPUTER CONSULTANTS LP; *U.S. Private,* pg. 1360
ELLIPTIC LABORATORIES ASA; *Int'l,* pg. 2366
ELMOS CENTRAL IT SERVICES GMBH & CO. KG—See ELMOS Semiconductor AG; *Int'l,* pg. 2368
ELMO SOFTWARE LIMITED—See K1 Investment Management, LLC; *U.S. Private,* pg. 2252
ELSPEC LTD.—See Elspec Engineering Ltd.; *Int'l,* pg. 2370
ELUON CORPORATION; *Int'l,* pg. 2371
ELUSOFT GMBH—See Cifin S.r.l.; *Int'l,* pg. 1606
EMAKINA AB—See EPAM Systems, Inc.; *U.S. Public,* pg. 783
EMAKINA.CH LABEL.CH S.A.—See EPAM Systems, Inc.; *U.S. Public,* pg. 783
EMAN A.S.; *Int'l,* pg. 2374
EMAN SOLUTIONS LLC—See eMan A.S.; *Int'l,* pg. 2374
EMBRACER GROUP AB; *Int'l,* pg. 2375
EMC COMPUTER SYSTEMS POLAND SP. Z O.O.—See Dell Technologies Inc.; *U.S. Public,* pg. 650
EMEDAPPS INC.—See Med Tech Solutions; *U.S. Private,* pg. 2650
EMEDGENE TECHNOLOGIES LTD.—See Illumina, Inc.; *U.S. Public,* pg. 1112
EMENTUM, INC.; *U.S. Private,* pg. 1379
EMERGEO SOLUTIONS WORLDWIDE INC.; *Int'l,* pg. 2378
EMIS HEALTH—See EMIS Group plc; *Int'l,* pg. 2382
EML PAYMENT SOLUTIONS LIMITED—See EML Payments Limited; *Int'l,* pg. 2383
EMMEGISOFT SRL.—See Cifin S.r.l.; *Int'l,* pg. 1606
EMOLECULES, INC.—See Avista Capital Partners, L.P.; *U.S. Private,* pg. 409
EMPERIA INFO SP. Z O.O.—See Emperia Holding S.A; *Int'l,* pg. 2385
EMPHASYS COMPUTER SOLUTIONS, INC.—See Constellation Software Inc.; *Int'l,* pg. 1772
EMPLOCITY S.A.; *Int'l,* pg. 2387
EMPLOYER MANAGEMENT SOLUTIONS, INC.; *U.S. Private,* pg. 1386
EMPYREAN TECHNOLOGY CO., LTD.; *Int'l,* pg. 2392
EMRO CO. LTD.; *Int'l,* pg. 2392
EMS BRUEL & KJAER IBERICA S.A.—See EnviroSuite Limited; *Int'l,* pg. 2455
EMS BRUEL & KJAER TAIWAN LTD.—See EnviroSuite Limited; *Int'l,* pg. 2455
EMS TECHNOLOGY SOLUTIONS, LLC; *U.S. Private,* pg. 1388
EMUNDO GMBH—See Gofore PLC; *Int'l,* pg. 3022
ENABLING ASIA, INC.; *U.S. Public,* pg. 754
ENALYZER A/S; *Int'l,* pg. 2396
ENCODA SYSTEMS INC.—See Quad/Graphics, Inc.; *U.S. Public,* pg. 1744
ENDAT OY—See Clyde Blowers Capital IM LLP; *Int'l,* pg. 1665
ENDAVA DOOEL SKOPJE—See Endava plc; *Int'l,* pg. 2402
ENDAVA GMBH—See Endava plc; *Int'l,* pg. 2402
ENDAVA ROMANIA SRL—See Endava plc; *Int'l,* pg. 2402
ENDAVA (US) LLC—See Endava plc; *Int'l,* pg. 2402
ENDEAVOR COMMERCE, INC.—See Francisco Partners Management, LP; *U.S. Private,* pg. 1592
ENDEAVOUR SOFTWARE TECHNOLOGIES INC.—See Genpact Limited; *Int'l,* pg. 2926
ENDEAVOUR SOFTWARE TECHNOLOGIES PRIVATE LIMITED—See Genpact Limited; *Int'l,* pg. 2926
ENDPOINT EXCHANGE, LLC—See Fidelity National Information Services, Inc.; *U.S. Public,* pg. 832
END RESULT COMPANY LLC—See Genstar Capital, LLC; *U.S. Private,* pg. 1678
ENEA GMBH—See Enea AB; *Int'l,* pg. 2410
ENEA KK—See Enea AB; *Int'l,* pg. 2410
ENEA NETBRICKS SAS—See Enea AB; *Int'l,* pg. 2410
ENEA POLYHEDRA LTD—See Enea AB; *Int'l,* pg. 2410
ENEA SOFTWARE (BEIJING) CO., LTD.—See Enea AB; *Int'l,* pg. 2410
ENEA SOFTWARE & SERVICES, INC—See Enea AB; *Int'l,* pg. 2410
ENEA SOFTWARE SRL—See Enea AB; *Int'l,* pg. 2410
ENEA TEKSCI INC.—See Enea AB; *Int'l,* pg. 2410
ENERAQUA TECHNOLOGIES PLC; *Int'l,* pg. 2418
ENERGIES S.A.; *Int'l,* pg. 2420
ENERGOPROJEKT ENERGODATA A.D.—See Energoprojekt Holding a.d.; *Int'l,* pg. 2421
ENERGY DATA LAB SP. Z O.O.—See Atende S.A.; *Int'l,* pg. 668
ENERGY NET GMBH—See Econocom Group SA; *Int'l,* pg. 2298
ENERGY ONE LIMITED; *Int'l,* pg. 2423
ENERGY SOLUTIONS INTERNATIONAL PRIVATE LIMITED—See Emerson Electric Co.; *U.S. Public,* pg. 749
ENERSIZE OYJ; *Int'l,* pg. 2424
ENERTIS SOLAR, S.L.U.—See I Squared Capital Advisors (US) LLC; *U.S. Private,* pg. 2022
ENGAGE IT SERVICES, INC.—See Providence St. Joseph Health; *U.S. Private,* pg. 3294

ENGAGEMENT LABS INC.—See DGTL Holdings Inc.; *Int'l,* pg. 2097
ENGAGE MOBILITY, INC.; *Int'l,* pg. 2426
ENGAGEPOINT; *U.S. Private,* pg. 1397
ENGAGE PTY LTD.—See LivePerson, Inc.; *U.S. Public,* pg. 1332
ENGAGESMART, INC.—See Vista Equity Partners, LLC; *U.S. Private,* pg. 4402
ENGAGE XR HOLDINGS PLC; *Int'l,* pg. 2426
ENGHOUSE TRANSPORTATION LLC—See Enghouse Systems Limited; *Int'l,* pg. 2427
ENGHOUSE (U.K.) LIMITED—See Enghouse Systems Limited; *Int'l,* pg. 2427
ENGINEERING SYSTEM INTERNATIONAL GMBH—See Keysight Technologies, Inc.; *U.S. Public,* pg. 1226
ENGINEERING SYSTEM INTERNATIONAL SAS—See Keysight Technologies, Inc.; *U.S. Public,* pg. 1227
ENGIS TECHNOLOGIES, INC; *Int'l,* pg. 2435
ENHANCE TECHNOLOGIES (PVT) LTD.—See Daikin Industries, Ltd.; *Int'l,* pg. 1935
ENHERENT CORP.; *U.S. Public,* pg. 768
ENHOPS SOLUTIONS PRIVATE LIMITED—See ProArch IT Solutions, Inc.; *U.S. Private,* pg. 3271
ENIBLOCK S.A.; *Int'l,* pg. 2439
ENISIAS CO., LTD.—See Cresco, Ltd.; *Int'l,* pg. 1840
ENRICH CONSULTING, INC.—See TA Associates, Inc.; *U.S. Private,* pg. 3917
ENRICH CONSULTING, INC.—See TPG Capital, L.P.; *U.S. Public,* pg. 2175
ENSENTA CORPORATION—See Jack Henry & Associates, Inc.; *U.S. Public,* pg. 1182
ENSERVIO, INC.—See Vista Equity Partners, LLC; *U.S. Private,* pg. 4400
ENSPERT INC.; *Int'l,* pg. 2448
ENTERPRIME FINANCE SRL—See Capgemini SE; *Int'l,* pg. 1306
ENTERPRISE COMPUTING SOLUTIONS INC.; *U.S. Private,* pg. 1403
ENTERPRISE INTEGRATION CORPORATION; *U.S. Private,* pg. 1404
ENTERPRISE RESOURCE PERFORMANCE, INC.—See ASGN Incorporated; *U.S. Public,* pg. 210
ENTERSOFT BULGARIA EOOD—See Entersoft S.A.; *Int'l,* pg. 2452
ENTERSOFT MIDDLE EAST FZ LLC—See Entersoft S.A.; *Int'l,* pg. 2452
ENTERSOFT ROMANIA SOFTWARE SRL—See Entersoft S.A.; *Int'l,* pg. 2452
ENTERSOFT S,A.; *Int'l,* pg. 2452
ENTHUSIAST GAMING (TSR) INC.—See Enthusiast Gaming Holdings, Inc.; *Int'l,* pg. 2452
ENTIGO CORPORATION; *U.S. Private,* pg. 1405
ENTRANCE SOFTWARE; *U.S. Private,* pg. 1405
ENTROPYSOFT S.A.S.—See Salesforce, Inc.; *U.S. Public,* pg. 1837
ENVESTNET RETIREMENT SOLUTIONS, LLC—See Bain Capital, LP; *U.S. Private,* pg. 439
ENVIROSUITE DENMARK APS—See EnviroSuite Limited; *Int'l,* pg. 2455
ENVISAGE INFORMATION SYSTEMS, LLC; *U.S. Private,* pg. 1409
ENVISAGE TECHNOLOGIES, LLC; *U.S. Private,* pg. 1410
ENVISION TELEPHONY INC.; *U.S. Private,* pg. 1410
ENVISIONWARE, INC.—See Constellation Software Inc.; *Int'l,* pg. 1775
ENVOY TECHNOLOGIES, INC.—See Blink Charging Co.; *U.S. Public,* pg. 361
ENVY LABS, LLC; *U.S. Private,* pg. 1410
ENVYSION, INC.—See Motorola Solutions, Inc.; *U.S. Public,* pg. 1477
EOLE, INC.; *Int'l,* pg. 2457
E-ON SOFTWARE SARL—See Bentley Systems, Inc.; *U.S. Public,* pg. 297
EONTARR IT SOLUTIONS SDN. BHD.—See Eonmetall Group Berhad; *Int'l,* pg. 2458
EOS INTERNATIONAL—See SirsiDynix Corporation; *U.S. Private,* pg. 3675
EPAM SOLUTIONS, LLC—See EPAM Systems, Inc.; *U.S. Public,* pg. 783
EPAM SYSTEMS BULGARIA EOOD—See EPAM Systems, Inc.; *U.S. Public,* pg. 783
EPAM SYSTEMS (CZECH REPUBLIC) S.R.O.—See EPAM Systems, Inc.; *U.S. Public,* pg. 783
EPAM SYSTEMS (HONG KONG) LIMITED—See EPAM Systems, Inc.; *U.S. Public,* pg. 783
EPAM SYSTEMS NETHERLANDS B.V.—See EPAM Systems, Inc.; *U.S. Public,* pg. 783
EPAM SYSTEMS PLLC—See EPAM Systems, Inc.; *U.S. Public,* pg. 783
EPAM SYSTEMS PORTUGAL, UNIPESSOAL LDA.—See EPAM Systems, Inc.; *U.S. Public,* pg. 783
EPHIBIAN INC; *U.S. Private,* pg. 1412
EPHOX; *U.S. Private,* pg. 1412
EPITEC GROUP INC.; *U.S. Private,* pg. 1413
EPLUS TECHNOLOGY, INC—See ePlus Inc.; *U.S. Public,* pg. 784
EPOS CAT GMBH—See Adecco Group AG; *Int'l,* pg. 140

EPS DIGITAL-SHARE CO., LTD.—See EPS Holdings, Inc.; *Int'l*, pg. 2465
EPSIIA CORPORATION—See Fiserv, Inc.; *U.S. Public*, pg. 850
EPSILON EUROPE PLC—See Epsilon Net S.A.; *Int'l*, pg. 2466
EPSILON NET S.A.; *Int'l*, pg. 2466
EP&T GLOBAL LIMITED; *Int'l*, pg. 2458
EQ LABS, INC.; *U.S. Public*, pg. 784
EQUAL EXPERTS DEVICES INC—See Equal Experts UK Ltd.; *Int'l*, pg. 2483
EQUAL EXPERTS INDIA PRIVATE LTD—See Equal Experts UK Ltd.; *Int'l*, pg. 2483
EQUAL EXPERTS UK LTD.; *Int'l*, pg. 2483
EQUIFAX WORKFORCE SOLUTIONS—See Equifax Inc.; *U.S. Public*, pg. 786
EQUINITI DATA LIMITED—See Siris Capital Group, LLC; *U.S. Private*, pg. 3673
EQUINITI GATEWAY LIMITED—See Siris Capital Group, LLC; *U.S. Private*, pg. 3673
EQUINITI INDIA (PRIVATE) LIMITED—See Siris Capital Group, LLC; *U.S. Private*, pg. 3673
EQUINITI KYC SOLUTIONS B.V.—See Siris Capital Group, LLC; *U.S. Private*, pg. 3673
EQUITY ANALYTICS, LLC—See Bank of America Corporation; *U.S. Public*, pg. 272
ERAD, INC.—See RadNet, Inc.; *U.S. Public*, pg. 1761
E-RAPTOR TECHNOLOGIES INC.—See Ilustrato Pictures International Inc.; *Int'l*, pg. 3616
ERAS—See Checkalt, LLC; *U.S. Private*, pg. 869
ERS GENOMICS LTD.—See CRISPR Therapeutics AG; *Int'l*, pg. 1850
ERSTE DIGITAL GMBH—See Erste Group Bank AG; *Int'l*, pg. 2498
ESAKON ITALIA S.R.L.—See GPI S.p.A.; *Int'l*, pg. 3046
ESECTOR, LTD.—See Computer Engineering & Consulting Ltd.; *Int'l*, pg. 1759
E-SECURE (PTY) LIMITED—See EOH HOLDINGS LIMITED; *Int'l*, pg. 2457
ESE ENTERTAINMENT, INC.; *Int'l*, pg. 2502
ESHARES, INC.; *U.S. Private*, pg. 1425
ESH (HONG KONG) LIMITED—See Edvance International Holdings Limited; *Int'l*, pg. 2316
ESHIPPERS MANAGEMENT LTD.; *Int'l*, pg. 2503
ESI CFD SERVICES—See Keysight Technologies, Inc.; *U.S. Public*, pg. 1226
ESI CHINA—See Keysight Technologies, Inc.; *U.S. Public*, pg. 1226
ESI FRANCE SARL—See Keysight Technologies, Inc.; *U.S. Public*, pg. 1226
ESI GERMANY GMBH—See Keysight Technologies, Inc.; *U.S. Public*, pg. 1226
ESI GROUP HISPANIA, S.L.—See Keysight Technologies, Inc.; *U.S. Public*, pg. 1226
ESI ITALIA SRL—See Keysight Technologies, Inc.; *U.S. Public*, pg. 1226
ESI ITI GMBH—See Keysight Technologies, Inc.; *U.S. Public*, pg. 1226
ESI JAPAN LTD—See Keysight Technologies, Inc.; *U.S. Public*, pg. 1226
ESI NORDICS AB—See Keysight Technologies, Inc.; *U.S. Public*, pg. 1226
ESI SERVICES TUNISIA SARL—See Keysight Technologies, Inc.; *U.S. Public*, pg. 1226
ESI SERVICES VIETNAM CO., LTD.—See Keysight Technologies, Inc.; *U.S. Public*, pg. 1226
ESI SOUTH AMERICA COMERCIO E SERVICOS DE INFORMATICA LTDA—See Keysight Technologies, Inc.; *U.S. Public*, pg. 1227
ESI US R&D, INC.—See Keysight Technologies, Inc.; *U.S. Public*, pg. 1227
ESKER AUSTRALIA PTY. LTD.—See Esker S.A.; *Int'l*, pg. 2503
ESKER GMBH—See Esker S.A.; *Int'l*, pg. 2503
ESKER IBERICA—See Esker S.A.; *Int'l*, pg. 2503
ESKER, INC.—See Esker S.A.; *Int'l*, pg. 2503
ESKER ITALIA S.R.L.—See Esker S.A.; *Int'l*, pg. 2503
ESKER LTD.—See Esker S.A.; *Int'l*, pg. 2503
ESKO-GRAPHICS INC.—See Danaher Corporation; *U.S. Public*, pg. 626
ESOL CO., LTD.; *Int'l*, pg. 2504
ESOL EUROPE S.A.S.—See Esol Co., Ltd.; *Int'l*, pg. 2504
ESOLUTIONS, INC.—See Canada Pension Plan Investment Board; *Int'l*, pg. 1282
ESOLUTIONS, INC.—See EQT AB; *Int'l*, pg. 2481
THE ESPY CORP.—See Dover Corporation; *U.S. Public*, pg. 683
ESRI SINGAPORE PTE LTD—See Boustead Singapore Limited; *Int'l*, pg. 1120
ESS ASIA LTD; *Int'l*, pg. 2508
ESSENSYS PLC; *Int'l*, pg. 2510
ESSEX TECHNOLOGY GROUP, INC.—See Converge Technology Solutions Corp.; *Int'l*, pg. 1787
ESTECH CORP.—See Dentsu Group Inc.; *Int'l*, pg. 2039
ETC SIMULATION ADMS INNOVATION CENTER—See Environmental Tectonics Corporation; *U.S. Public*, pg. 781
ETECH SYSTEMS, INC.—See Hebert Kannegiesser GmbH; *Int'l*, pg. 3306

ETHERSTACK INC.—See Etherstack PLC; *Int'l*, pg. 2523
ETHERSTACK JAPAN LIMITED—See Etherstack PLC; *Int'l*, pg. 2523
ETHERSTACK LIMITED—See Etherstack PLC; *Int'l*, pg. 2523
E-TIC SISTEMES S.L.U.—See Alten S.A.; *Int'l*, pg. 390
ETISON LLC; *U.S. Private*, pg. 1432
ETRURIA INFORMATICA SRL—See Banca Popolare dell'Etruria e del Lazio S.C.; *Int'l*, pg. 815
ET SOFTWARE DEVELOPMENTS GMBH—See Fresenius Medical Care AG; *Int'l*, pg. 2774
ETTEPLAN DENMARK A/S—See Etteplan Oyj; *Int'l*, pg. 2524
ETTEPLAN GERMANY GMBH—See Etteplan Oyj; *Int'l*, pg. 2524
ET TRADE LIMITED—See Hong Kong Economic Times Holdings Ltd; *Int'l*, pg. 3465
ET WEALTH LIMITED—See Hong Kong Economic Times Holdings Ltd; *Int'l*, pg. 3465
EUROFINS IT INFRASTRUCTURE GSC S.A.—See Eurofins Scientific S.E.; *Int'l*, pg. 2544
EUROGROUP LAMINATIONS S.P.A.; *Int'l*, pg. 2552
EUROPEAN SUPPORT LIMITED—See Amdocs Limited; *Int'l*, pg. 419
EUROPRIS ASA; *Int'l*, pg. 2557
EUROSOFTWARE S.R.O—See Fujitsu Limited; *Int'l*, pg. 2837
EV8 TECHNOLOGIES LIMITED; *Int'l*, pg. 2560
EVANA AUTOMATION SPECIALISTS—See Phillips Service Industries, Inc. (PSI); *U.S. Private*, pg. 3171
EVE DESIGN AUTOMATION PVT. LTD.—See Synopsys, Inc.; *U.S. Public*, pg. 1970
EVERBRIDGE ASIA PTE. LTD.—See Thoma Bravo, L.P.; *U.S. Private*, pg. 4147
EVERBRIDGE FINLAND OY—See Thoma Bravo, L.P.; *U.S. Private*, pg. 4147
EVERBRIDGE FRANCE SAS—See Thoma Bravo, L.P.; *U.S. Private*, pg. 4147
EVERBRIDGE NORWAY AS—See Thoma Bravo, L.P.; *U.S. Private*, pg. 4147
EVERCOMMERCE INC.; *U.S. Public*, pg. 799
EVEREST CONSULTING GROUP; *U.S. Private*, pg. 1437
EVERYACTION, INC.—See Insight Venture Management, LLC; *U.S. Private*, pg. 2090
EVIDIAN SA—See Atos SE; *Int'l*, pg. 692
EVIDIAN SYSTEMS INC.—See Atos SE; *Int'l*, pg. 692
EVIDON, INC.—See CrownPeak Technology, Inc.; *U.S. Private*, pg. 1113
EVIMERIA EMR AB—See Carasent ASA; *Int'l*, pg. 1319
EVISO S.P.A.; *Int'l*, pg. 2570
EVITBE AB—See Addnode Group AB; *Int'l*, pg. 130
EVIXAR INC.; *Int'l*, pg. 2570
EVMO, INC.; *U.S. Public*, pg. 803
EVOLINK AD—See DHH SpA; *Int'l*, pg. 2099
EVOLUTION AB; *Int'l*, pg. 2572
EVOLUTION FINANCIAL TECHNOLOGIES, LLC; *U.S. Private*, pg. 1443
EVORA IT SOLUTIONS GMBH—See Allgeier SE; *Int'l*, pg. 337
EVORA IT SOLUTIONS GROUP GMBH—See Allgeier SE; *Int'l*, pg. 337
EVORA IT SOLUTIONS PVT. LTD.—See Allgeier SE; *Int'l*, pg. 337
EVSA, INC.—See Equitable Holdings, Inc.; *U.S. Public*, pg. 789
EXACTA CORP.; *U.S. Private*, pg. 1445
EXACT GROUP B.V.—See KKR & Co. Inc.; *U.S. Public*, pg. 1250
EXACT MANUFACTURING SYSTEMS (UK) LTD—See KKR & Co. Inc.; *U.S. Public*, pg. 1250
EXACT ONLINE B.V.—See KKR & Co. Inc.; *U.S. Public*, pg. 1250
EXACTRAK LIMITED—See Illinois Tool Works Inc.; *U.S. Public*, pg. 1103
EXACT SOFTWARE (ANTILLES) N.V.—See KKR & Co. Inc.; *U.S. Public*, pg. 1250
EXACT SOFTWARE AUSTRALIA PTY LTD—See KKR & Co. Inc.; *U.S. Public*, pg. 1251
EXACT SOFTWARE CZECH REPUBLIC, S.R.O.—See KKR & Co. Inc.; *U.S. Public*, pg. 1250
EXACT SOFTWARE DE MEXICO S.A. DE C.V.—See KKR & Co. Inc.; *U.S. Public*, pg. 1251
EXACT SOFTWARE (INTERNATIONAL) N.V.—See KKR & Co. Inc.; *U.S. Public*, pg. 1251
EXACT SOFTWARE (SHANGHAI) CO., LTD.—See KKR & Co. Inc.; *U.S. Public*, pg. 1250
EXACT SOFTWARE SINGAPORE PTE LTD.—See KKR & Co. Inc.; *U.S. Public*, pg. 1251
EXACT SOUTHEAST ASIA SDN. BHD.—See KKR & Co. Inc.; *U.S. Public*, pg. 1251
EXACTTARGET A.B.—See Salesforce, Inc.; *U.S. Public*, pg. 1837
EXACTTARGET GMBH—See Salesforce, Inc.; *U.S. Public*, pg. 1837
EXACTTARGET PTE. LTD.—See Salesforce, Inc.; *U.S. Public*, pg. 1837
EXACTTARGET S.A.S.—See Salesforce, Inc.; *U.S. Public*, pg. 1837

EXACTTARGET TECNOLOGIA, LTDA.—See Salesforce, Inc.; *U.S. Public*, pg. 1837
EXAMOBILE SA; *Int'l*, pg. 2577
EXASOL AG; *Int'l*, pg. 2577
EXCELIAN LUXOFT FINANCIAL SERVICES (SWITZERLAND) AG—See DXC Technology Company; *U.S. Public*, pg. 696
EXCELITY AUSTRALIA PTY LTD—See Dayforce, Inc.; *U.S. Public*, pg. 645
EXCELITY HCM SOLUTIONS SDN. BHD.—See Dayforce, Inc.; *U.S. Public*, pg. 645
EXCELITY PHILIPPINES, INC.—See Dayforce, Inc.; *U.S. Public*, pg. 645
EXCEL MICRO, LLC—See Ziff Davis, Inc.; *U.S. Public*, pg. 2403
EXCENT CORPORATION—See Roper Technologies, Inc.; *U.S. Public*, pg. 1811
EXEBLOCK TECHNOLOGY CORP.; *Int'l*, pg. 2580
EXELA TECHNOLOGIES BV—See Exela Technologies, Inc.; *U.S. Public*, pg. 806
EXELA TECHNOLOGIES GMBH—See Exela Technologies, Inc.; *U.S. Public*, pg. 806
EXELA TECHNOLOGIES IBERCIA S.A.—See Exela Technologies, Inc.; *U.S. Public*, pg. 806
EXELA TECHNOLOGIES LIMITED—See Exela Technologies, Inc.; *U.S. Public*, pg. 806
EXELA TECHNOLOGIES S.P. Z O.O.—See Exela Technologies, Inc.; *U.S. Public*, pg. 806
EXEM CHINA CO., LTD.—See EXEM Co., Ltd.; *Int'l*, pg. 2583
EXEM JAPAN CO., LTD.—See EXEM Co., Ltd.; *Int'l*, pg. 2583
EXEM USA, INC.—See EXEM Co., Ltd.; *Int'l*, pg. 2583
EXERTIS HAMMER LIMITED—See DCC plc; *Int'l*, pg. 1990
EXIGEN INC.; *U.S. Private*, pg. 1449
EX-LABO CO., LTD.—See extreme Co., Ltd.; *Int'l*, pg. 2592
EXMO, INC.—See Live Nation Entertainment, Inc.; *U.S. Public*, pg. 1328
EXOR CORPORATION—See Bentley Systems, Inc.; *U.S. Public*, pg. 297
EXPENSE WIRE LLC—See Paychex, Inc.; *U.S. Public*, pg. 1655
EXPENSIFY, INC.; *U.S. Public*, pg. 812
EXPERIAN DECISION ANALYTICS—See Experian plc; *Int'l*, pg. 2586
EXPERIAN ESPANA S.L.U.—See Experian plc; *Int'l*, pg. 2586
EXPERIAN-SCOREX S.R.L. ITALIA—See Experian plc; *Int'l*, pg. 2587
EXPERIS SOFTWARE—See ManpowerGroup Inc.; *U.S. Public*, pg. 1358
EXPERT SYSTEM USA INC.—See Expert.ai S.p.A.; *Int'l*, pg. 2588
EXPLEO GROUP LIMITED—See Assystem S.A.; *Int'l*, pg. 650
EXPLEO NETHERLANDS BV—See Assystem S.A.; *Int'l*, pg. 650
EXPLEO NORDIC AB—See Assystem S.A.; *Int'l*, pg. 650
EXPLEO TECHNOLOGY IRELAND LIMITED—See Assystem S.A.; *Int'l*, pg. 650
EXSCRIBE, INC.—See Modernizing Medicine, Inc.; *U.S. Private*, pg. 2763
EXTOL CORPORATION SDN BHD.—See AppAsia Berhad; *Int'l*, pg. 519
EXTREME NETWORKS MEXICO, SA DE CV—See Extreme Networks, Inc.; *U.S. Public*, pg. 813
EXTREME VIETNAM CO., LTD—See extreme Co., Ltd.; *Int'l*, pg. 2592
EYEON SOFTWARE, INC.—See Blackmagic Design Pty. Ltd.; *Int'l*, pg. 1061
EZCARETECH CO., LTD.; *Int'l*, pg. 2593
EZCARETECH JAPAN CO., LTD.—See ezCaretech Co., Ltd.; *Int'l*, pg. 2593
EZE SOFTWARE GROUP, LLC—See SS&C Technologies Holdings, Inc.; *U.S. Public*, pg. 1923
EZ SYSTEMS POLSKA SP. Z O.O.—See eZ Systems AS; *Int'l*, pg. 2593
EZ SYSTEMS US INC.—See eZ Systems AS; *Int'l*, pg. 2593
F24 UNITED STATES, INC.—See HgCapital Trust plc; *Int'l*, pg. 3376
F5 NETWORKS AUSTRALIA PTY. LIMITED—See F5, Inc.; *U.S. Public*, pg. 819
F5 NETWORKS COLOMBIA S.A.S.—See F5, Inc.; *U.S. Public*, pg. 819
F5 NETWORKS HONG KONG LIMITED—See F5, Inc.; *U.S. Public*, pg. 819
F5 NETWORKS (ISRAEL) LTD.—See F5, Inc.; *U.S. Public*, pg. 819
F5 NETWORKS JAPAN K.K.—See F5, Inc.; *U.S. Public*, pg. 819
F5 NETWORKS KOREA LTD.—See F5, Inc.; *U.S. Public*, pg. 819
F5 NETWORKS LLC—See F5, Inc.; *U.S. Public*, pg. 819
F5 NETWORKS NEW ZEALAND LTD.—See F5, Inc.; *U.S. Public*, pg. 819
F5 NETWORKS POLAND SP Z O.O—See F5, Inc.; *U.S. Public*, pg. 819

F5 NETWORKS SINGAPORE PTE LTD.—See F5, Inc.; *U.S. Public*, pg. 819
FABASOFT AG; *Int'l*, pg. 2598
FABASOFT AUSTRIA GMBH—See Fabasoft AG; *Int'l*, pg. 2598
FABASOFT DEUTSCHLAND GMBH—See Fabasoft AG; *Int'l*, pg. 2598
FACEPHI APAC, LTD.—See Facephi Biometrica SA; *Int'l*, pg. 2600
FACT INFORMATIONSSYSTEME UND CONSULTING AG—See Silver Lake Group, LLC; *U.S. Private*, pg. 3658
FACTLINES AS—See Arendals Fossekompani ASA; *Int'l*, pg. 559
FACTSET PHILIPPINES, INC.—See FactSet Research Systems Inc.; *U.S. Public*, pg. 819
FACTSET SWITZERLAND AG—See FactSet Research Systems Inc.; *U.S. Public*, pg. 820
FACTSET SYSTEMS INDIA PRIVATE LIMITED—See FactSet Research Systems Inc.; *U.S. Public*, pg. 820
FAIRDINKUM CONSULTING, LLC; *U.S. Private*, pg. 1462
FAIRFAX DATA SYSTEMS, INC.; *U.S. Private*, pg. 1462
FAIR ISAAC (AUSTRALIA) PTY LTD—See Fair Isaac Corporation; *U.S. Public*, pg. 820
FAIR ISAAC UK GROUP LIMITED—See Fair Isaac Corporation; *U.S. Public*, pg. 820
FAIRWAY PAYMENTS, LLC—See i3 Verticals, Inc.; *U.S. Public*, pg. 1081
FAIRWAY TECHNOLOGIES, INC.—See Accenture plc; *Int'l*, pg. 87
FAMILIAR, INC.—See Axon Enterprise, Inc.; *U.S. Public*, pg. 256
FANCY CHAP, INC.—See WPEngine, Inc.; *U.S. Private*, pg. 4571
FANTASMA GAMES AB—See EveryMatrix Ltd.; *Int'l*, pg. 2570
FANTASY ACES DAILY FANTASY SPORTS CORP.; *U.S. Public*, pg. 821
FAO BULGARIA EOOD—See Amadeus IT Group, S.A.; *Int'l*, pg. 407
FAO GROUP GMBH—See Amadeus IT Group, S.A.; *Int'l*, pg. 407
FARELOGIX INC.—See Vista Equity Partners, LLC; *U.S. Private*, pg. 4394
FARO TECHNOLOGIES DO BRASIL LTDA—See FARO Technologies, Inc.; *U.S. Public*, pg. 823
FARO TECH POLSKA—See FARO Technologies, Inc.; *U.S. Public*, pg. 823
FAR SIGHTED MEDIA INC.; *U.S. Private*, pg. 1473
FASCOR, INC.—See Dunes Point Capital, LLC; *U.S. Private*, pg. 1288
FASTBOOKING S.A.—See Accor S.A.; *Int'l*, pg. 91
FASTLY, INC.; *U.S. Public*, pg. 824
FATHER TIME, INC.; *U.S. Private*, pg. 1483
FATHOM DIGITAL MANUFACTURING CORPORATION—See CORE Industrial Partners, LLC; *U.S. Private*, pg. 1048
FAYE BUSINESS SYSTEMS GROUP INC.; *U.S. Private*, pg. 1484
FCG, INC.; *U.S. Public*, pg. 824
FCS SOFTWARE SOLUTIONS LTD; *Int'l*, pg. 2628
FELICA POCKET MARKETING INC.—See AEON Co., Ltd.; *Int'l*, pg. 177
FEMTO TECHNOLOGIES INC.; *Int'l*, pg. 2633
FENDX TECHNOLOGIES, INC.; *Int'l*, pg. 2633
FENIX SOLUTIONS OY—See Elisa Corporation; *Int'l*, pg. 2361
FERGUSON CONSULTING INC.—See Stone Point Capital LLC; *U.S. Private*, pg. 3823
FERMAT PRIVATE LTD.—See Moody's Corporation; *U.S. Public*, pg. 1467
FIBER NETWORK SOLUTIONS, INC.—See QualTek Services Inc.; *U.S. Public*, pg. 1748
FICHA, INC.; *Int'l*, pg. 2653
FIDELIS CYBERSECURITY SOLUTIONS, INC.—See Fonds de Solidarite des Travailleurs du Quebec; *Int'l*, pg. 2725
FIGR CANNABIS INC.—See Pyxus International, Inc.; *U.S. Public*, pg. 1740
FINACCEL PTE LTD.; *Int'l*, pg. 2664
FINANCIAL MODELS COMPANY LTD.—See SS&C Technologies Holdings, Inc.; *U.S. Public*, pg. 1923
FINANCIAL NAVIGATOR, INC.—See Asset Vantage Systems Pvt. Ltd.; *Int'l*, pg. 642
FINDMYPAST LIMITED—See D.C. Thomson & Co. Ltd.; *Int'l*, pg. 1900
FINEOS CORP. LTD.; *Int'l*, pg. 2674
FINGER FOOD STUDIOS INC.—See Unity Software Inc.; *U.S. Public*, pg. 2254
FINGER INC.; *Int'l*, pg. 2675
FINGERTANGO, INC.; *Int'l*, pg. 2675
THE FINIT GROUP LLC; *U.S. Private*, pg. 4028
FINLOGIK INC.—See Canaccord Genuity Group Inc.; *Int'l*, pg. 1277
FINSOFT FINANCIAL INVESTMENT HOLDINGS LIMITED; *Int'l*, pg. 2677
FINZSOFT SOLUTIONS LIMITED; *Int'l*, pg. 2677
FIRE ROCK HOLDINGS LIMITED; *Int'l*, pg. 2678

FIRM II, LLC—See Fidelity National Infor; *U.S. Public*, pg. 832
FIRSTBEST SYSTEMS, INC.—See Guidewire Software, Inc.; *U.S. Public*, pg. 974
FIRST DERIVATIVES CANADA INC.—See FD Technologies PLC; *Int'l*, pg. 2628
FIRST DERIVATIVES PTY LIMITED—See FD Technologies PLC; *Int'l*, pg. 2628
FIRST EDGE SOLUTIONS, INC.; *U.S. Private*, pg. 1517
FIRSTOBJECT TECHNOLOGIES LTD.; *Int'l*, pg. 2689
FIS APPLICATION SERVICE PROVIDING UND IT-OUTSOURCING GMBH—See FIS Informationssysteme und Consulting GmbH; *Int'l*, pg. 2691
FISERV ASPAC PTE. LTD.—See Fiserv, Inc.; *U.S. Public*, pg. 851
FISERV (EUROPE) LTD.—See Fiserv, Inc.; *U.S. Public*, pg. 851
FISERV LEMANS, INC.—See Fiserv, Inc.; *U.S. Public*, pg. 851
FIS INFORMATIONSSYSTEME UND CONSULTING GMBH; *Int'l*, pg. 2691
FIS INFORMATION SYSTEMS INC.—See FIS Informationssysteme und Consulting GmbH; *Int'l*, pg. 2692
FIS INFORMATION SYSTEMS UK LIMITED—See FIS Informationssysteme und Consulting GmbH; *Int'l*, pg. 2692
FIS TECHNOLOGY SERVICES (POLAND) SP. Z.O.O.—See Fidelity National Infor; *U.S. Public*, pg. 832
FIS TECHNOLOGY SERVICES SINGAPORE PTE. LTD.—See Fidelity National Infor; *U.S. Public*, pg. 832
FIS VIETNAM LLC—See Fidelity National Infor; *U.S. Public*, pg. 832
FITEK, LLC; *U.S. Private*, pg. 1535
FIXSTARS SOLUTIONS INC.—See Fixstars Corporation; *Int'l*, pg. 2696
FJORD OY—See Accenture plc; *Int'l*, pg. 87
FLASHAPP INC.; *Int'l*, pg. 2698
FLASHZERO CORP.; *U.S. Public*, pg. 852
FLEET ADVANTAGE, LLC.; *U.S. Private*, pg. 1541
FLEXTECH, INC.—See emids Technologies Pvt. Ltd. Corp.; *Int'l*, pg. 2380
FLOW MANAGEMENT TECHNOLOGIES, INC.; *U.S. Private*, pg. 1551
FLUID, INC.—See Astound Commerce Corp.; *U.S. Private*, pg. 361
FLUXX LABS, INC.—See ABS Capital Partners, L.P.; *U.S. Private*, pg. 44
FLYHT INC—See Firan Technology Group Corporation; *Int'l*, pg. 2699
FLYWIRE CORPORATION; *U.S. Public*, pg. 861
FNZ (UK) LTD—See Caisse de Depot et Placement du Quebec; *Int'l*, pg. 1254
FNZ (UK) LTD—See Generation Investment Management LLP; *Int'l*, pg. 2920
FOCUS BUSINESS SOLUTION LTD.; *Int'l*, pg. 2719
FOCUS DIGITAL MEDIA—See Focus 4U Ltd.; *Int'l*, pg. 2718
FOCUS TECHNOLOGY GROUP, INC.—See Levine Leichtman Capital Partners, LLC; *U.S. Private*, pg. 2435
FORCE BY DESIGN, INC.; *U.S. Private*, pg. 1563
FORCEX INC.—See L3Harris Technologies, Inc.; *U.S. Public*, pg. 1281
FORCIVITY, INC.—See Quad-C Management, Inc.; *U.S. Private*, pg. 3315
FORECROSS CORPORATION; *U.S. Public*, pg. 867
FORESCOUT TECHNOLOGIES, INC.—See Advent International Corporation; *U.S. Private*, pg. 101
FORESCOUT TECHNOLOGIES ISRAEL LTD.—See Advent International Corporation; *U.S. Private*, pg. 101
FORESIGHT SYSTEM CO., LTD.—See Computer Engineering & Consulting Ltd.; *Int'l*, pg. 1759
FORESITE TECHNOLOGIES, INC; *U.S. Private*, pg. 1566
FOREVER ENTERTAINMENT S.A.; *Int'l*, pg. 2732
FORGEROCK, INC.—See Thoma Bravo, L.P.; *U.S. Private*, pg. 4148
FORMFIRE, LLC—See Resurgens Technology Partners, LLC; *U.S. Private*, pg. 3410
FORMPIPE INC—See FormPipe Software AB; *Int'l*, pg. 2736
FORMPIPE SOFTWARE COPENHAGEN A/S—See FormPipe Software AB; *Int'l*, pg. 2736
FORNEBU CONSULTING AS—See Devoteam SA; *Int'l*, pg. 2090
FORRESTER SINGAPORE PTE. LTD.—See Forrester Research, Inc.; *U.S. Public*, pg. 868
FORTE RESEARCH SYSTEMS, INC.; *U.S. Private*, pg. 1575
FORTEX, INC.; *U.S. Public*, pg. 869
FORTINET AUSTRIA GMBH—See Fortinet, Inc.; *U.S. Public*, pg. 869
FORTINET BELGIUM BV—See Fortinet, Inc.; *U.S. Public*, pg. 869
FORTINET DENMARK APS—See Fortinet, Inc.; *U.S. Public*, pg. 869
FORTINET FINLAND OY—See Fortinet, Inc.; *U.S. Public*, pg. 869
FORTINET, INC.; *U.S. Public*, pg. 869
FORTINET SECURITY NETWORK (THAILAND) LTD.—See Fortinet, Inc.; *U.S. Public*, pg. 869

FORTINET SECURITY PHILIPPINES, INC.—See Fortinet, Inc.; *U.S. Public*, pg. 869
FORTINET SWITZERLAND GMBH—See Fortinet, Inc.; *U.S. Public*, pg. 869
FORTIUSONE, INC.—See Environmental Systems Research Institute Inc.; *U.S. Private*, pg. 1409
FORTNOX AB; *Int'l*, pg. 2740
FORWARD SLOPE, INC.—See Trive Capital Inc.; *U.S. Private*, pg. 4239
FOS S.P.A.; *Int'l*, pg. 2748
FOUNDER HOLDINGS LIMITED; *Int'l*, pg. 2753
FOURSQUARE LABS, INC.; *U.S. Private*, pg. 1583
FOURTH GENERATION INFORMATION SYSTEMS LIMITED; *Int'l*, pg. 2755
FOURTH TECHNOLOGIES INC.; *U.S. Private*, pg. 1583
FP NEOMONITOR GMBH—See Francotyp-Postalia Holding AG; *Int'l*, pg. 2761
FPT CANADA CO., LTD.—See FPT Corporation; *Int'l*, pg. 2757
FPT COMPANY FOR INFORMATION TECHNOLOGY WLL—See FPT Corporation; *Int'l*, pg. 2757
FPT CORPORATION; *Int'l*, pg. 2757
FPT DEUTSCHLAND GMBH—See FPT Corporation; *Int'l*, pg. 2757
FPT INDIA PRIVATE LIMITED—See FPT Corporation; *Int'l*, pg. 2757
FPT INFORMATION SYSTEM COMPANY LIMITED—See FPT Corporation; *Int'l*, pg. 2757
FPT SMART CLOUD COMPANY LIMITED—See FPT Corporation; *Int'l*, pg. 2757
FPT SOFTWARE CENTRAL REGION COMPANY LIMITED—See FPT Corporation; *Int'l*, pg. 2757
FPT SOFTWARE COMPANY LIMITED—See FPT Corporation; *Int'l*, pg. 2757
FPT SOFTWARE HO CHI MINH COMPANY LIMITED—See FPT Corporation; *Int'l*, pg. 2757
FPT SOFTWARE MALAYSIA SDN. BHD.—See FPT Corporation; *Int'l*, pg. 2758
FPT SOFTWARE PHILIPPINES CORP.—See FPT Corporation; *Int'l*, pg. 2758
FPT TAIWAN CO., LTD.—See FPT Corporation; *Int'l*, pg. 2758
FPT TECHNOLOGY DMCC—See FPT Corporation; *Int'l*, pg. 2758
FRAGBITE GROUP AB; *Int'l*, pg. 2758
FRAME.IO, INC.—See Adobe Inc.; *U.S. Public*, pg. 42
FRANCHETTI S.P.A.; *Int'l*, pg. 2759
FRANPOS, INC.; *U.S. Private*, pg. 1598
FREDHOPPER BV—See CrownPeak Technology, Inc.; *U.S. Private*, pg. 1113
FREEBEES B.V.—See BP plc; *Int'l*, pg. 1131
FREEBORDERS, INC.—See Symbio, LLC; *U.S. Private*, pg. 3899
FREEDOM CONSULTING GROUP LLC; *U.S. Private*, pg. 1603
FREEDOM DATA SYSTEMS INC.—See UnitedHealth Group Incorporated; *U.S. Public*, pg. 2248
FREEDOM SCIENTIFIC GMBH—See Freedom Scientific Inc.; *U.S. Private*, pg. 1604
FREEDOM SCIENTIFIC INC.; *U.S. Private*, pg. 1604
FREEDOM SOLUTIONS GROUP, L.L.C.; *U.S. Private*, pg. 1604
FREEE K.K.; *Int'l*, pg. 2769
FREENET CITYLINE GMBH—See freenet AG; *Int'l*, pg. 2770
FREEWILL SOLUTIONS COMPANY LIMITED—See Charoen Pokphand Group Co., Ltd.; *Int'l*, pg. 1453
FRELII, INC.; *U.S. Public*, pg. 885
FREQUENTIS DEUTSCHLAND GMBH—See Frequentis AG; *Int'l*, pg. 2773
FREQUENTIS ORTHOGON GMBH—See Frequentis AG; *Int'l*, pg. 2773
FREQUENTIS USA INC.—See Frequentis AG; *Int'l*, pg. 2773
FRESHWORKS AUSTRALIA PTY. LTD.—See Freshworks Inc.; *U.S. Public*, pg. 886
FRESHWORKS GMBH—See Freshworks Inc.; *U.S. Public*, pg. 886
FRESHWORKS INC.; *U.S. Public*, pg. 886
FRESHWORKS SAS—See Freshworks Inc.; *U.S. Public*, pg. 886
FRESHWORKS TECHNOLOGIES B.V.—See Freshworks Inc.; *U.S. Public*, pg. 886
FRESHWORKS TECHNOLOGIES PRIVATE LIMITED—See Freshworks Inc.; *U.S. Public*, pg. 886
FRESHWORKS TECHNOLOGIES UK LIMITED—See Freshworks Inc.; *U.S. Public*, pg. 886
FRICTIONLESS SOLUTIONS, INC.; *U.S. Private*, pg. 1610
FRIEDMAN CORPORATION—See Constellation Software Inc.; *Int'l*, pg. 1773
FRIEDOMTECH LLC; *U.S. Private*, pg. 1611
FRIENDFINDER VENTURES, INC.—See FriendFinder Networks Inc.; *U.S. Private*, pg. 1611
FRIENDTIMES, INC.; *Int'l*, pg. 2792
FRILO SOFTWARE GMBH—See Herbalife Nutrition Ltd.; *Int'l*, pg. 3359
FRINX S.R.O.—See Elisa Corporation; *Int'l*, pg. 2361
FRONTLINE TEST EQUIPMENT, INC.—See Teledyne Technologies Incorporated; *U.S. Public*, pg. 1994

N.A.I.C.S. INDEX

541511 — CUSTOM COMPUTER PRO...

FRS SOFTWARE; *U.S. Private*, pg. 1617
FSBM CTECH SDN. BHD.—See FSBM Holdings Berhad; *Int'l*, pg. 2798
FSPORT AB; *Int'l*, pg. 2800
FUETREK CO., LTD.—See AI Co., Ltd.; *Int'l*, pg. 226
FUGRO ROADWARE, INC.—See Fugro N.V.; *Int'l*, pg. 2807
FUJIAN FOXIT SOFTWARE DEVELOPMENT JOINT STOCK CO., LTD.; *Int'l*, pg. 2817
FUJIAN FUJITSU COMMUNICATION SOFTWARE CO., LTD.—See Fujitsu Limited; *Int'l*, pg. 2817
FUJI ELECTRIC (HANGZHOU) SOFTWARE CO., LTD.—See Fuji Electric Co., Ltd.; *Int'l*, pg. 2811
FUJIFILM SOFTWARE CO., LTD.—See FUJIFILM Holdings Corporation; *Int'l*, pg. 2825
FUJIFILM SYSTEMS CORPORATION—See FUJIFILM Holdings Corporation; *Int'l*, pg. 2825
FUJIFILM TERAMEDICA, INC.—See FUJIFILM Holdings Corporation; *Int'l*, pg. 2823
FUJI IT CO., LTD.—See Fuji Electric Co., Ltd.; *Int'l*, pg. 2812
FUJISOFT AMERICA INC.—See FUJISOFT INCORPORATED; *Int'l*, pg. 2830
FUJISOFT KIKAKU LTD.—See FUJISOFT INCORPORATED; *Int'l*, pg. 2830
FUJISOFT SERVICE BUREAU INCORPORATED—See FUJISOFT INCORPORATED; *Int'l*, pg. 2830
FUJISOFT SSS, INC.—See FUJISOFT INCORPORATED; *Int'l*, pg. 2830
FUJI TECHNO SOLUTIONS CO., INC.; *Int'l*, pg. 2817
FUJITSU BROAD SOLUTION & CONSULTING INC.—See Fujitsu Limited; *Int'l*, pg. 2833
FUJITSU CARIBBEAN (BARBADOS) LIMITED—See Fujitsu Limited; *Int'l*, pg. 2834
FUJITSU CARIBBEAN (TRINIDAD) LIMITED—See Fujitsu Limited; *Int'l*, pg. 2834
FUJITSU CONSULTING—See Fujitsu Limited; *Int'l*, pg. 2833
FUJITSU DMR CONSULTING—See Fujitsu Limited; *Int'l*, pg. 2834
FUJITSU ENABLING SOFTWARE TECHNOLOGY GMBH—See Fujitsu Limited; *Int'l*, pg. 2834
FUJITSU EUROPE LIMITED—See Fujitsu Limited; *Int'l*, pg. 2834
FUJITSU FRONTECH CANADA INC.—See Fujitsu Limited; *Int'l*, pg. 2834
FUJITSU FRONTECH SYSTEMS LIMITED—See Fujitsu Limited; *Int'l*, pg. 2834
FUJITSU MARKETING LIMITED—See Fujitsu Limited; *Int'l*, pg. 2835
FUJITSU SOFTWARE CORPORATION—See Fujitsu Limited; *Int'l*, pg. 2833
FUJITSU SOUTH CHINA TECHNOLOGY SERVICES LIMITED—See Fujitsu Limited; *Int'l*, pg. 2835
FUJITSU SYSTEMS EAST LIMITED—See Fujitsu Limited; *Int'l*, pg. 2836
FUJITSU SYSTEMS WEST LIMITED—See Fujitsu Limited; *Int'l*, pg. 2836
FUJITSU TECHNOLOGY SOLUTIONS FZ LLC—See Fujitsu Limited; *Int'l*, pg. 2836
FUJITSU TECHNOLOGY SOLUTIONS LTD.—See Fujitsu Limited; *Int'l*, pg. 2837
FUJITSU (XI'AN) SYSTEM ENGINEERING CO., LTD.—See Fujitsu Limited; *Int'l*, pg. 2833
FUKUOKA COMPUTER SERVICE CO., LTD.—See Fukuoka Financial Group, Inc.; *Int'l*, pg. 2840
FULCRUM TECHNOLOGIES INC.; *U.S. Private*, pg. 1620
FULL TRUCK ALLIANCE CO. LTD.; *Int'l*, pg. 2842
FUNTOWN HONG KONG LIMITED—See GigaMedia Limited; *Int'l*, pg. 2971
FURUNO EURUS LLC—See Furuno Electric Co., Ltd.; *Int'l*, pg. 2848
FURUNO SHANGHAI CO., LTD.—See Furuno Electric Co., Ltd.; *Int'l*, pg. 2848
FURUNO SOFTECH CO., LTD.—See Furuno Electric Co., Ltd.; *Int'l*, pg. 2848
FURUNO SOFTECH (DALIAN) CO., LTD.—See Furuno Electric Co., Ltd.; *Int'l*, pg. 2848
FUSION DATA CO., LTD.; *Int'l*, pg. 2849
FUSIONEX CORP. SDN. BHD.—See Fusionex International Plc; *Int'l*, pg. 2849
FUSIONSTORM, INC.—See Computacenter plc; *Int'l*, pg. 1758
FUSIONWARE CORP.; *U.S. Private*, pg. 1626
FUTURE APPLIED COMPUTER TECHNOLOGY COMPANY—See Al Baraka Banking Group B.S.C.; *Int'l*, pg. 276
FUTURE ARCHITECT, INC.—See Future Corporation; *Int'l*, pg. 2853
FUTURE ENERGY CORPORATION CO., LTD.—See Gunkul Engineering Co., Ltd.; *Int'l*, pg. 3183
G4S TECHNOLOGY LTD.—See Allied Universal Manager LLC; *Int'l*, pg. 190
GAAP POINT-OF-SALE (PROPRIETARY) LIMITED—See Capital Eye Investments Limited; *Int'l*, pg. 1310
GADIV GMBH—See adesso SE; *Int'l*, pg. 144
GAIAX CO., LTD.; *Int'l*, pg. 2869
GAINSIGHT, INC.—See Vista Equity Partners, LLC; *U.S. Private*, pg. 4397
GALASYS GLOBAL (SUZHOU) CO. LTD.—See Beijing Shiji Information Technology Co., Ltd.; *Int'l*, pg. 956

GALE FORCE SOFTWARE CORPORATION; *U.S. Private*, pg. 1636
GAMA PARTICIPACOES S.A.; *Int'l*, pg. 2876
GAMEHOUSE EUROPE B.V.—See RealNetworks, Inc.; *U.S. Private*, pg. 3369
GAMEONE HOLDINGS LTD.; *Int'l*, pg. 2877
GAMES OPERATORS S.A.; *Int'l*, pg. 2877
GAMESYS GROUP PLC—See Bally's Corporation; *U.S. Public*, pg. 268
GAMING TECHNOLOGIES, INC.; *U.S. Public*, pg. 896
GAMIVO S.A.; *Int'l*, pg. 2878
GAXOS.AI INC.; *U.S. Public*, pg. 908
GBG (AUSTRALIA) PTY. LTD.—See GB Group plc; *Int'l*, pg. 2892
GBG (MALAYSIA) SDN BHD—See GB Group plc; *Int'l*, pg. 2892
G-BITS NETWORK TECHNOLOGY (XIAMEN) CO., LTD.; *Int'l*, pg. 2862
GBS EUROPA GMBH—See BULPROS Consulting AD; *Int'l*, pg. 1214
GCOM SOFTWARE LLC—See Sagewind Capital LLC; *U.S. Private*, pg. 3527
GDEV INC.; *Int'l*, pg. 2896
GEAR DESIGN SOLUTIONS, INC.—See ANSYS, Inc.; *U.S. Public*, pg. 139
GE ENERGY—See General Electric Company; *U.S. Public*, pg. 917
GEFEN INTERNATIONAL A.I LTD.; *Int'l*, pg. 2911
GEHRY TECHNOLOGIES MIDDLE EAST LLC—See Trimble, Inc.; *U.S. Public*, pg. 2190
GEKKO SAS—See Accenture plc; *Int'l*, pg. 87
GE MEDICAL SYSTEMS, INC.—See GE HealthCare Technologies Inc.; *U.S. Public*, pg. 909
GENABILITY, INC.—See Enel S.p.A.; *Int'l*, pg. 2414
GENARTS, INC.—See Boris FX, Inc.; *U.S. Private*, pg. 618
GEN DIGITAL INC.; *U.S. Public*, pg. 910
GENERAL DYNAMICS INFORMATION TECHNOLOGY COMMERCIAL SOLUTIONS, LLC—See General Dynamics Corporation; *U.S. Public*, pg. 915
GENERAL INFORMATICS; *U.S. Private*, pg. 1665
GENERATIVE AI SOLUTIONS CORP.; *Int'l*, pg. 2920
GENETEC ASIA PACIFIC PTE LTD—See Genetec Inc.; *Int'l*, pg. 2922
GENETEC CORPORATION; *Int'l*, pg. 2922
GENETEC INC.; *Int'l*, pg. 2922
GENIANS INC; *Int'l*, pg. 2923
GENIE SCANDINAVIA AB—See Terex Corporation; *U.S. Public*, pg. 2019
GENKI CO., LTD.—See Daikoku Denki Co., Ltd.; *Int'l*, pg. 1937
GENOMATIX, INC.—See Precigen, Inc.; *U.S. Public*, pg. 1713
GENROBOTIC INNOVATIONS PRIVATE LIMITED; *Int'l*, pg. 2927
GENTLE GIANT STUDIOS, INC.—See 3D Systems Corporation; *U.S. Public*, pg. 4
GENTRACK UK LIMITED—See Gentrack Group Limited; *Int'l*, pg. 2929
GENUENT USA, LLC—See Willis Group LLC; *U.S. Private*, pg. 4528
GEOJUNXION NV; *Int'l*, pg. 2933
GEOLOGICS CORP.; *U.S. Private*, pg. 1680
GEOMAGIC GMBH—See 3D Systems Corporation; *U.S. Public*, pg. 4
GEOMAGIC, INC.—See 3D Systems Corporation; *U.S. Public*, pg. 4
GEOMETRIC SRL—See HCL Technologies Ltd.; *Int'l*, pg. 3298
GEOTRONICS SOUTHERN EUROPE S.L—See Trimble, Inc.; *U.S. Public*, pg. 2190
GEOVIS TECHNOLOGY CO., LTD.; *Int'l*, pg. 2942
GEO WEB SERVICE CO., LTD—See GEO Holdings Corporation; *Int'l*, pg. 2932
GERBER TECHNOLOGY LLC—See AIP, LLC; *U.S. Private*, pg. 134
GETBUSY PLC; *Int'l*, pg. 2947
GETUSROI LLC—See Softeon, Inc.; *U.S. Private*, pg. 3705
GFINITY PLC; *Int'l*, pg. 2957
GFT BRASIL CONSULTORIA INFORMATICA LTDA.—See GFT Technologies SE; *Int'l*, pg. 2957
GFT IBERIA SOLUTIONS S.A.—See GFT Technologies SE; *Int'l*, pg. 2957
GFT IT CONSULTING, S.L.U.—See GFT Technologies SE; *Int'l*, pg. 2957
GFT TECHNOLOGIES (SCHWEIZ) AG.—See GFT Technologies SE; *Int'l*, pg. 2957
GFT UK LIMITED—See GFT Technologies SE; *Int'l*, pg. 2957
GFT USA INC—See GFT Technologies SE; *Int'l*, pg. 2957
GHOST STUDIO LTD.; *Int'l*, pg. 2959
GHP FAR EAST CO. LTD.—See Die Schweizerische Post AG; *Int'l*, pg. 2113
GIGA CO., LTD—See Core Corporation; *Int'l*, pg. 1797
GIJIMAAST AMERICAS INCORPORATED—See FirstRand Limited; *Int'l*, pg. 2690
GIJIMAAST AMERICAS INCORPORATED—See Hasso Plattner Ventures Africa (Pty) Ltd.; *Int'l*, pg. 3283

GIN INTERNATIONAL LTD.—See GINSMS Inc.; *Int'l*, pg. 2977
GIS WORKSHOP, LLC; *U.S. Private*, pg. 1702
GITLAB INC.; *U.S. Public*, pg. 938
GIVEMEPOWER CORP.; *U.S. Private*, pg. 2982
GK SOFTWARE AFRICA (PTY) LTD.—See Fujitsu Limited; *Int'l*, pg. 2837
GK SOFTWARE USA, INC.—See Fujitsu Limited; *Int'l*, pg. 2837
GLANCE NETWORKS, INC.; *U.S. Private*, pg. 1706
GLASER ISB CAD PROGRAMMSYSTEME GMBH; *Int'l*, pg. 2988
GLASSBOX LTD.; *Int'l*, pg. 2989
GLASSBOX US INC.—See Glassbox Ltd.; *Int'l*, pg. 2989
GLASTON SWITZERLAND AG—See Glaston Oyj Abp; *Int'l*, pg. 2989
GLIDEFAST CONSULTING LLC—See ASGN Incorporated; *U.S. Public*, pg. 210
THE GLIMPSE GROUP, INC.; *U.S. Public*, pg. 2075
GLOBAL DATA VAULT, LLC; *U.S. Private*, pg. 1713
GLOBAL E-BUSINESS SERVICES LIMITED—See Computer & Technologies Holdings Limited; *Int'l*, pg. 1758
GLOBAL GRAPHICS SOFTWARE INC.—See Hybrid Software Group PLC; *Int'l*, pg. 3544
GLOBAL GRAPHICS SOFTWARE LTD—See Hybrid Software Group PLC; *Int'l*, pg. 3544
GLOBAL MARKET INSITE, INC.—See Bain Capital, LP; *U.S. Private*, pg. 448
GLOBALMED GROUP, LLC.; *U.S. Private*, pg. 1719
GLOBALMOTION MEDIA, INC.—See TripAdvisor, Inc.; *U.S. Public*, pg. 2195
GLOBALSIGN CHINA CO., LTD—See GMO GlobalSign Holdings K.K.; *Int'l*, pg. 3013
GLOBALSIGN NV—See GMO GlobalSign Holdings K.K.; *Int'l*, pg. 3013
GLOBAL TECHNOLOGIES, LTD.; *U.S. Public*, pg. 945
GLOBAL TECHNOLOGY GROUP PTY LTD—See Golden Matrix Group, Inc.; *U.S. Public*, pg. 950
GLOBEOSS (BRUNEI) SDN. BHD.—See Captii Limited; *Int'l*, pg. 1317
GLOCZUS, INC.—See Fujitsu Limited; *Int'l*, pg. 2837
GLORY GLOBAL SOLUTIONS (AUSTRALIA) PTY. LTD.—See GLORY Ltd.; *Int'l*, pg. 3009
GLORY GLOBAL SOLUTIONS (BELGIUM) N. V./S. A.—See GLORY Ltd.; *Int'l*, pg. 3009
GLORY GLOBAL SOLUTIONS (COLOMBIA) S.A.—See GLORY Ltd.; *Int'l*, pg. 3009
GLORY GLOBAL SOLUTIONS (IRELAND) LTD.—See GLORY Ltd.; *Int'l*, pg. 3010
GLORY GLOBAL SOLUTIONS (MALAYSIA) SDN. BHD.—See GLORY Ltd.; *Int'l*, pg. 3010
GLORY GLOBAL SOLUTIONS MEXICO, S.A. DE C.V.—See GLORY Ltd.; *Int'l*, pg. 3010
GLORY GLOBAL SOLUTIONS NAKIT OTOMASYON TEKNOLOJILERI LTD. STI.—See GLORY Ltd.; *Int'l*, pg. 3010
GLORY GLOBAL SOLUTIONS (NEW ZEALAND) LTD.—See GLORY Ltd.; *Int'l*, pg. 3010
GLORY GLOBAL SOLUTIONS (PORTUGAL) S. A.—See GLORY Ltd.; *Int'l*, pg. 3010
GLORY GLOBAL SOLUTIONS RUS, LLC—See GLORY Ltd.; *Int'l*, pg. 3010
GLORY GLOBAL SOLUTIONS (SHANGHAI) CO., LTD.—See GLORY Ltd.; *Int'l*, pg. 3010
GLORY GLOBAL SOLUTIONS (SINGAPORE) PTE. LTD.—See GLORY Ltd.; *Int'l*, pg. 3010
GLORY GLOBAL SOLUTIONS (SOUTH ASIA) PVT. LTD.—See GLORY Ltd.; *Int'l*, pg. 3010
GLORY GLOBAL SOLUTIONS (SWITZERLAND) A. G.—See GLORY Ltd.; *Int'l*, pg. 3010
GLORY IPO ASIA LTD.—See GLORY Ltd.; *Int'l*, pg. 3010
GLORY IST CO., LTD.—See GLORY Ltd.; *Int'l*, pg. 3010
GLORY VIEW TECHNOLOGY CO., LTD.; *Int'l*, pg. 3011
GLOSTREAM, INC.; *U.S. Private*, pg. 1720
GLOVIA INTERNATIONAL, INC.—See Fujitsu Limited; *Int'l*, pg. 2833
GLOWWORM INC.; *U.S. Private*, pg. 1721
GLU MOBILE INC.—See Electronic Arts Inc.; *U.S. Public*, pg. 724
GMA NEW MEDIA, INC.—See GMA Holdings, Inc.; *Int'l*, pg. 3012
GMG/AXIS, INC.—See ION Geophysical Corporation; *U.S. Public*, pg. 1166
GMH SYSTEMS GMBH—See Georgsmarienhutte Holding GmbH; *Int'l*, pg. 2940
GMO CONNECT INC.—See GMO Internet Group, Inc.; *Int'l*, pg. 3013
GMO DIGITAL LAB K.K.—See GMO GlobalSign Holdings K.K.; *Int'l*, pg. 3013
GMO GLOBALSIGN CERTIFICATE SERVICES PRIVATE LIMITED—See GMO GlobalSign Holdings K.K.; *Int'l*, pg. 3013
GMO GLOBALSIGN, INC.—See GMO GlobalSign Holdings K.K.; *Int'l*, pg. 3013
GMO GLOBALSIGN LTD.—See GMO GlobalSign Holdings K.K.; *Int'l*, pg. 3013
GMO GLOBALSIGN PTE. LTD.—See GMO GlobalSign Holdings K.K.; *Int'l*, pg. 3013

GMO GLOBALSIGN RUSSIA LLC—See GMO GlobalSign Holdings K.K.; *Int'l*, pg. 3013
GMO MOBILE, INC.—See GMO Internet Group, Inc.; *Int'l*, pg. 3014
GMO REGISTRY, INC.—See GMO Internet Group, Inc.; *Int'l*, pg. 3014
GMO RUNSYSTEM INC.—See GMO Internet Group, Inc.; *Int'l*, pg. 3014
G-NEXT, INC.; *Int'l*, pg. 2862
GOAT INDUSTRIES LTD.; *Int'l*, pg. 3018
GODREJ INFOTECH LTD.—See Godrej & Boyce Mfg. Co. Ltd.; *Int'l*, pg. 3021
GOETECH LLC—See Becton, Dickinson & Company; *U.S. Public*, pg. 292
GOFORE PLC; *Int'l*, pg. 3022
GOGOLOOK CO., LTD.; *Int'l*, pg. 3022
GOLDEN MATRIX GROUP, INC.; *U.S. Public*, pg. 950
GOLDEN SOURCE CORPORATION; *U.S. Private*, pg. 1733
GOLDLEAF TECHNOLOGIES, LLC—See Jack Henry & Associates, Inc.; *U.S. Public*, pg. 1182
GOLFBOX A/S—See FirstRand Limited; *Int'l*, pg. 2690
GOLOGIQ, INC.; *U.S. Public*, pg. 951
GOODBYE KANSAS GROUP AB; *Int'l*, pg. 3039
GOOD + GEEK, LLC—See Blackbaud, Inc.; *U.S. Public*, pg. 341
GOODPATCH, INC.; *Int'l*, pg. 3041
GORILLA COMMERCE; *U.S. Private*, pg. 1743
GORILLA LOGIC, INC.; *U.S. Private*, pg. 1743
GOSUNCN TECHNOLOGY GROUP CO., LTD.; *Int'l*, pg. 3043
GOVPLACE, INC.; *U.S. Private*, pg. 1746
GPI USA INC.—See GPI S.p.A.; *Int'l*, pg. 3046
GRADIENT.SYSTEMINTEGRATION GMBH—See IQVIA Holdings Inc.; *U.S. Public*, pg. 1171
GRAFOPROJEKT A.D.; *Int'l*, pg. 3050
GRAITEC GMBH—See Autodesk, Inc.; *U.S. Public*, pg. 229
GRAITEC SAS—See Autodesk, Inc.; *U.S. Public*, pg. 229
GRANTA DESIGN LIMITED—See ANSYS, Inc.; *U.S. Public*, pg. 139
GRAPHISOFT ITALIA S.R.L.—See Herbalife Nutrition Ltd.; *Int'l*, pg. 3359
GRAVITY NEOCYON INC.—See Gravity Co., Ltd.; *Int'l*, pg. 3062
GRCS INC.; *Int'l*, pg. 3063
GREAT FRIDAYS INC.—See EPAM Systems, Inc.; *U.S. Public*, pg. 783
GREENBYTES, INC.—See Oracle Corporation; *U.S. Public*, pg. 1611
GREEN CALL SERVICE S.R.L.—See Gruppo MutuiOnline S.p.A; *Int'l*, pg. 3141
GREEN HILLS SOFTWARE INC.; *U.S. Private*, pg. 1773
GREEN HILLS SOFTWARE (ISRAEL) LTD—See Green Hills Software Inc.; *U.S. Private*, pg. 1773
GREEN HILLS SOFTWARE, LAGUNA HILLS—See Green Hills Software Inc.; *U.S. Private*, pg. 1773
GREEN HILLS SOFTWARE LTD.—See Green Hills Software Inc.; *U.S. Private*, pg. 1773
GREENHOUSE SOFTWARE, INC.; *U.S. Private*, pg. 1778
GREENLINE SYNERGY CO., LTD.—See Bangkok Dusit Medical Services Public Company Limited; *Int'l*, pg. 834
GREEN PACKET, INC.—See Green Packet Berhad; *Int'l*, pg. 3072
GRESHAM FINANCIAL SYSTEMS LIMITED—See Symphony Technology Group, LLC; *U.S. Private*, pg. 3901
GRESHAM TECHNOLOGIES (US) INC.—See Symphony Technology Group, LLC; *U.S. Private*, pg. 3901
GREY MATTER (EMEA) LIMITED—See Climb Global Solutions, Inc.; *U.S. Public*, pg. 515
GRIDSUM HOLDING INC.; *Int'l*, pg. 3083
GRINNELL INFOSYSTEMS INC.—See Grinnell Mutual Reinsurance Company Inc.; *U.S. Private*, pg. 1790
GROOVE LABS, INC.—See Clari, Inc.; *U.S. Private*, pg. 911
GROUPE CT INC.—See Xerox Holdings Corporation; *U.S. Public*, pg. 2386
GROVER GAMING, INC.; *U.S. Private*, pg. 1795
GROWTH ACCELERATION PARTNERS, LLC; *U.S. Private*, pg. 1795
GRUNLAND GMBH—See Hochland SE; *Int'l*, pg. 3437
GRYPHON TECHNOLOGIES, LC—See AE Industrial Partners, LP; *U.S. Private*, pg. 112
GT NEXUS, INC. - NEW YORK OFFICE—See Koch Industries, Inc.; *U.S. Private*, pg. 2330
GT NEXUS, INC.—See Koch Industries, Inc.; *U.S. Private*, pg. 2330
GTX SEF, LLC—See StoneX Group Inc.; *U.S. Public*, pg. 1952
GUANGXI FPT SOFTWARE CO., LTD.—See FPT Corporation; *Int'l*, pg. 2758
GUANGXI XINXUNDA TECHNOLOGY GROUP CO., LTD.; *Int'l*, pg. 3164
GUANGZHOU ARMITAGE COMPUTER SOFTWARE CO., LTD.—See Beijing Shiji Information Technology Co., Ltd.; *Int'l*, pg. 956
GUANGZHOU ARMITAGE TECHNOLOGIES LTD.—See Beijing Shiji Information Technology Co., Ltd.; *Int'l*, pg. 956
GUANGZHOU JET BIO-FILTRATION CO., LTD.; *Int'l*, pg. 3166

GUANGZHOU SKYTONE SMART TECHNOLOGIES CO., LTD.—See Anhui Tatfook Technology Co., Ltd; *Int'l*, pg. 469
GUIDEWIRE CANADA LTD.—See Guidewire Software, Inc.; *U.S. Public*, pg. 974
GUIDEWIRE SOFTWARE (BEIJING) CO., LTD.—See Guidewire Software, Inc.; *U.S. Public*, pg. 974
GUIDEWIRE SOFTWARE (SWITZERLAND) GMBH—See Guidewire Software, Inc.; *U.S. Public*, pg. 974
GUJ INFO PETRO LIMITED—See Gujarat State Petroleum Corporation Limited; *Int'l*, pg. 3177
GUOCHUANG SOFTWARE CO., LTD; *Int'l*, pg. 3186
GURU APP FACTORY CORP.; *Int'l*, pg. 3188
GUYOT-WALSER INFORMATIQUE S.A.R.L.—See GPI S.p.A.; *Int'l*, pg. 3046
GVL RECHENZENTRUM GMBH—See Arzneiwerk AG VIDA; *Int'l*, pg. 589
GVS S.P.A.; *Int'l*, pg. 3190
HACKETT GROUP (INDIA) LTD.—See The Hackett Group, Inc.; *U.S. Public*, pg. 2086
THE HAGERMAN GROUP—See Hagerman Construction Corporation; *U.S. Private*, pg. 1839
HAINAN EKING TECHNOLOGY CO., LTD.—See Hainan Traffic Administration Holding Co., Ltd.; *Int'l*, pg. 3215
HAMPSON RUSSEL LIMITED PARTNERSHIP—See CGG; *Int'l*, pg. 1431
HAMPSON-RUSSELL SOFTWARE SERVICES LP—See CGG; *Int'l*, pg. 1431
HANCOM MDS (SHENZHEN) TECHNOLOGY LTD. CO.—See Hancom, Inc.; *Int'l*, pg. 3243
HANDS-ON LEARNING SOLUTIONS LLC; *U.S. Private*, pg. 1853
HANGZHOU DPTECH TECHNOLOGIES CO., LTD.; *Int'l*, pg. 3247
HANGZHOU HOPECHART IOT TECHNOLOGY CO., LTD.; *Int'l*, pg. 3248
HANGZHOU ONECHANCE TECHNOLOGY CORP.; *Int'l*, pg. 3249
HANGZHOU PINMING SOFTWARE CO., LTD.; *Int'l*, pg. 3249
HANGZHOU RAYCLOUD TECHNOLOGY CO., LTD.; *Int'l*, pg. 3250
HANGZHOU SECK INTELLIGENT TECHNOLOGY CO., LTD.; *Int'l*, pg. 3250
HANKOOK ESI—See Keysight Technologies, Inc.; *U.S. Public*, pg. 1227
HANSEN TECHNOLOGIES CDE LIMITED—See Hansen Technologies Limited; *Int'l*, pg. 3260
HANSSAK CO., LTD.; *Int'l*, pg. 3261
HANU SOFTWARE SOLUTIONS, INC.—See Insight Enterprises, Inc.; *U.S. Public*, pg. 1129
HAOYUN TECHNOLOGIES CO., LTD.; *Int'l*, pg. 3268
HARBOR BUSINESS COMPLIANCE CORPORATION; *U.S. Private*, pg. 1858
HARMONIA, INC; *U.S. Private*, pg. 1866
HARMONYCHAIN AS; *Int'l*, pg. 3278
HARRIS CANADA HOLDINGS INC.—See L3Harris Technologies, Inc.; *U.S. Public*, pg. 1280
HARRIS ORTHOGON GMBH—See L3Harris Technologies, Inc.; *U.S. Public*, pg. 1280
HARSCO INDIA SERVICES PRIVATE LTD.—See Enviri Corporation; *U.S. Public*, pg. 780
HASHICORP, INC.; *U.S. Public*, pg. 988
HAVA PTY LTD.—See World Kinect Corporation; *U.S. Public*, pg. 2380
HAWK SEARCH, INC.—See Bridgeline Digital, Inc.; *U.S. Public*, pg. 382
HAYES SOFTWARE SYSTEMS, INC.—See Roper Technologies, Inc.; *U.S. Public*, pg. 1811
HCI SOLUTIONS LTD.—See CSL Limited; *Int'l*, pg. 1866
HCL ARGENTINA S.A.—See HCL Technologies Ltd.; *Int'l*, pg. 3298
HCL AXON (PTY) LTD.—See HCL Technologies Ltd.; *Int'l*, pg. 3298
HCL BERMUDA LIMITED—See HCL Technologies Ltd.; *Int'l*, pg. 3298
HCL POLAND SP.Z.O.O.—See HCL Technologies Ltd.; *Int'l*, pg. 3299
HCL TECHNOLOGIES DENMARK APS.—See HCL Technologies Ltd.; *Int'l*, pg. 3299
HCL TECHNOLOGIES NORWAY AS—See HCL Technologies Ltd.; *Int'l*, pg. 3299
HCL TECHNOLOGIES (SHANGHAI) LIMITED—See HCL Technologies Ltd.; *Int'l*, pg. 3299
HCT2 CO.—See HealthStream, Inc.; *U.S. Public*, pg. 1017
HEADSTART (PRIVATE) LIMITED—See Axiata Group Berhad; *Int'l*, pg. 768
HEADWATERS CO., LTD.; *Int'l*, pg. 3302
HEALTHBEACON PLC; *Int'l*, pg. 3303
HEALTHCARE COMMUNICATIONS UK LTD.—See Cisco Systems, Inc.; *U.S. Public*, pg. 499
HEALTHCARE SYSTEMS & TECHNOLOGIES, LLC; *U.S. Private*, pg. 1895
HEALTH CATALYST, INC.; *U.S. Public*, pg. 1014
HEALTH COMMUNICATION NETWORK PTY LIMITED—See Affinity Equity Partners (HK) Ltd.; *Int'l*, pg. 186
HEALTH DATA & MANAGEMENT SOLUTIONS, INC.—See CVS Health Corporation; *U.S. Public*, pg. 614
HEALTHFINCH, LLC—See Health Catalyst, Inc.; *U.S. Public*, pg. 1014
HEALTHLINK NEW ZEALAND GROUP LIMITED—See HFBG Holding B.V.; *Int'l*, pg. 3375
HEALTHSPARQ, INC.—See Cambia Health Solutions, Inc.; *U.S. Private*, pg. 726
HEALTH TECHNOLOGY SOLUTIONS, INC.—See Rennova Health, Inc.; *U.S. Public*, pg. 1783
HEALTHWARE SOLUTIONS, LLC—See MD On-Line Inc.; *U.S. Private*, pg. 2646
HEALTHY SOFTWARE LTD.—See Vista Equity Partners, LLC; *U.S. Private*, pg. 4394
HEALWELL AI INC.; *Int'l*, pg. 3304
HEARTLAND SCHOOL SOLUTIONS—See Global Payments Inc.; *U.S. Public*, pg. 944
HEARTSOFT, INC.; *U.S. Public*, pg. 1018
HEBEI GONGDA KEYA ENERGY TECHNOLOGY CO., LTD.; *Int'l*, pg. 3305
HELIOS AND MATHESON ANALYTICS INC.; *U.S. Public*, pg. 1023
HELIOS & MATHESON INFORMATION TECHNOLOGY LIMITED; *Int'l*, pg. 3330
HELLA AGLAIA MOBILE VISION GMBH—See Hella GmbH & Co. KGaA; *Int'l*, pg. 3331
HEMASOFT AMERICA CORP.—See GPI S.p.A.; *Int'l*, pg. 3046
HENGGELER COMPUTER CONSULTANTS, INC.—See RTX Corporation; *U.S. Public*, pg. 1824
HENNEBERRY HILL TECHNOLOGIES; *U.S. Private*, pg. 1916
HENNGE K.K.; *Int'l*, pg. 3354
HENRY SCHEIN ONE AUSTRALIA—See Henry Schein, Inc.; *U.S. Public*, pg. 1025
HENRY SCHEIN ONE, LLC—See Henry Schein, Inc.; *U.S. Public*, pg. 1025
HENSOLDT CYBER GMBH—See HENSOLDT AG; *Int'l*, pg. 3355
HERALD TECHNOLOGY INC.—See Herald Holdings Limited; *Int'l*, pg. 3358
HERAMED LIMITED; *Int'l*, pg. 3358
HERMOS AG—See CEZ, a.s.; *Int'l*, pg. 1428
HERMOS SP. Z O.O.—See CEZ, a.s.; *Int'l*, pg. 1428
HERMOS SYSTEMS GMBH—See CEZ, a.s.; *Int'l*, pg. 1428
HEROZ, INC.; *Int'l*, pg. 3364
HERTZ SYSTEMTECHNIK GMBH—See CEWE Stiftung & Co. KGaA; *Int'l*, pg. 1425
HESAI GROUP; *Int'l*, pg. 3365
HETRAS DEUTSCHLAND GMBH—See Beijing Shiji Information Technology Co., Ltd.; *Int'l*, pg. 956
HETRONIC ITALY S.R.L.—See Methode Electronics, Inc.; *U.S. Public*, pg. 1428
HETRONIC MIDWEST, LLC—See Methode Electronics, Inc.; *U.S. Public*, pg. 1428
HEYBRYAN MEDIA, INC.; *Int'l*, pg. 3374
HHK DATEBTECHNIK GMBH—See Trimble, Inc.; *U.S. Public*, pg. 2190
HIDEEP INC.; *Int'l*, pg. 3384
HIGHPOINT SERVICE NETWORK CORPORATION—See Acer Incorporated; *Int'l*, pg. 99
HIMACS, LTD.; *Int'l*, pg. 3396
HINDUJA TECH GMBH—See Hinduja Group Ltd.; *Int'l*, pg. 3398
HINDUJA TECH, INC.—See Hinduja Group Ltd.; *Int'l*, pg. 3398
HINDUJA TECH LIMITED—See Hinduja Group Ltd.; *Int'l*, pg. 3398
HIQ ACCELERATED CONCEPT EVALUATION AB—See HiQ International AB; *Int'l*, pg. 3402
HIQ APPROVE AB—See HiQ International AB; *Int'l*, pg. 3402
HIQ GOTEBORG AB—See HiQ International AB; *Int'l*, pg. 3402
HIQ KARLSKRONA AB—See HiQ International AB; *Int'l*, pg. 3402
HIQ MOBILEYES AB—See HiQ International AB; *Int'l*, pg. 3402
HIQ SKANE AB—See HiQ International AB; *Int'l*, pg. 3402
HIQ SOFTPLAN OY—See HiQ International AB; *Int'l*, pg. 3402
HIQ STOCKHOLM AB—See HiQ International AB; *Int'l*, pg. 3402
HIRATA SOFTWARE TECHNOLOGY CO.—See Hirata Corporation; *Int'l*, pg. 3404
HIREVUE, INC.—See The Carlyle Group Inc.; *U.S. Public*, pg. 2047
HITACHI CONSULTING ASIA PACIFIC PTE. LTD.—See Hitachi, Ltd.; *Int'l*, pg. 3416
HITACHI CONSULTING AUSTRALIA PTY. LTD.—See Hitachi, Ltd.; *Int'l*, pg. 3416
HITACHI EAST ASIA LTD.—See Hitachi, Ltd.; *Int'l*, pg. 3416
HITACHI FOODS & LOGISTICS SYSTEMS INC.—See Hitachi, Ltd.; *Int'l*, pg. 3417
HITACHI ICT BUSINESS SERVICES, LTD.—See Hitachi, Ltd.; *Int'l*, pg. 3419
HITACHI INFORMATION & CONTROL SOLUTIONS, LTD.—See Hitachi, Ltd.; *Int'l*, pg. 3419
HITACHI INFORMATION ENGINEERING, LTD.—See Hitachi, Ltd.; *Int'l*, pg. 3419

HITACHI SC, LTD.—See Hitachi, Ltd.; *Int'l*, pg. 3421
HITACHI SOLUTIONS ASIA PACIFIC PTE. LTD.—See Hitachi, Ltd.; *Int'l*, pg. 3421
HITACHI SOLUTIONS CREATE, LTD.—See Hitachi, Ltd.; *Int'l*, pg. 3421
HITACHI SOLUTIONS EAST JAPAN, LTD.—See Hitachi, Ltd.; *Int'l*, pg. 3421
HITACHI SOLUTIONS GERMANY GMBH—See Hitachi, Ltd.; *Int'l*, pg. 3421
HITACHI SOLUTIONS INDIA PRIVATE LIMITED—See Hitachi, Ltd.; *Int'l*, pg. 3421
HITACHI SOLUTIONS, LTD.—See Hitachi, Ltd.; *Int'l*, pg. 3421
HITACHI SOLUTIONS PHILIPPINES CORPORATION—See Hitachi, Ltd.; *Int'l*, pg. 3421
HITACHI SOLUTIONS TECHNOLOGY, LTD.—See Hitachi, Ltd.; *Int'l*, pg. 3421
HITACHI SOLUTIONS (THAILAND) LTD.—See Hitachi, Ltd.; *Int'l*, pg. 3421
HITACHI SOLUTIONS WEST JAPAN, LTD.—See Hitachi, Ltd.; *Int'l*, pg. 3421
HITACHI SUNWAY DATA CENTRE SERVICES SDN. BHD.—See Hitachi, Ltd.; *Int'l*, pg. 3421
HITACHI SUNWAY INFORMATION SYSTEMS SDN. BHD.—See Hitachi, Ltd.; *Int'l*, pg. 3421
HITACHI SUNWAY INFORMATION SYSTEMS (SINGAPORE) PTE. LTD.—See Hitachi, Ltd.; *Int'l*, pg. 3421
HITACHI SUNWAY INFORMATION SYSTEMS (THAILAND), LTD.—See Hitachi, Ltd.; *Int'l*, pg. 3421
HITACHI SYSTEMS DIGITAL SERVICES (MALAYSIA) SDN. BHD.—See Hitachi, Ltd.; *Int'l*, pg. 3421
HITACHI SYSTEMS DIGITAL SERVICES (SINGAPORE) PTE. LTD.—See Hitachi, Ltd.; *Int'l*, pg. 3421
HITACHI SYSTEMS ENGINEERING SERVICES, LTD.—See Hitachi, Ltd.; *Int'l*, pg. 3421
HITACHI SYSTEMS FIELD SERVICES, LTD.—See Hitachi, Ltd.; *Int'l*, pg. 3421
HITACHI SYSTEMS MICRO CLINIC PVT. LTD.—See Hitachi, Ltd.; *Int'l*, pg. 3421
HITACHI SYSTEMS POWER SERVICIES, LTD.—See Hitachi, Ltd.; *Int'l*, pg. 3421
HITACHI SYSTEMS VIETNAM COMPANY LIMITED—See Hitachi, Ltd.; *Int'l*, pg. 3422
HITACHI VANTARA A/S—See Hitachi, Ltd.; *Int'l*, pg. 3422
HITACHI VANTARA A/S—See Hitachi, Ltd.; *Int'l*, pg. 3422
HITACHI VANTARA (CHILE) LIMITADA—See Hitachi, Ltd.; *Int'l*, pg. 3422
HITACHI VANTARA (CHINA) CO., LTD.—See Hitachi, Ltd.; *Int'l*, pg. 3422
HITACHI VANTARA DIGITAL SOLUTIONS JAPAN, K.K.—See Hitachi, Ltd.; *Int'l*, pg. 3422
HITACHI VANTARA GMBH—See Hitachi, Ltd.; *Int'l*, pg. 3422
HITACHI VANTARA (IRELAND) LIMITED—See Hitachi, Ltd.; *Int'l*, pg. 3422
HITACHI VANTARA ISRAEL LTD.—See Hitachi, Ltd.; *Int'l*, pg. 3422
HITACHI VANTARA KENYA LIMITED—See Hitachi, Ltd.; *Int'l*, pg. 3422
HITACHI VANTARA KOREA LIMITED—See Hitachi, Ltd.; *Int'l*, pg. 3422
HITACHI VANTARA LLC—See Hitachi, Ltd.; *Int'l*, pg. 3422
HITACHI VANTARA LTD.—See Hitachi, Ltd.; *Int'l*, pg. 3422
HITACHI VANTARA NIGERIA LIMITED—See Hitachi, Ltd.; *Int'l*, pg. 3422
HITACHI VANTARA OOO—See Hitachi, Ltd.; *Int'l*, pg. 3422
HITACHI VANTARA OY—See Hitachi, Ltd.; *Int'l*, pg. 3422
HITACHI VANTARA (POLSKA) SP. Z O.O.—See Hitachi, Ltd.; *Int'l*, pg. 3422
HITACHI VANTARA S.A.—See Hitachi, Ltd.; *Int'l*, pg. 3422
HIVE BLOCKCHAIN TECHNOLOGIES LTD.; *Int'l*, pg. 3427
HLB THERAPEUTICS CO., LTD.; *Int'l*, pg. 3431
HMS INDUSTRIAL NETWORKS AB—See HMS Networks AB; *Int'l*, pg. 3432
HOBSONS, INC.—See Daily Mail & General Trust plc; *Int'l*, pg. 1938
HOFNETZ UND IT SERVICES GMBH—See CPI Property Group, S.A.; *Int'l*, pg. 1825
HOGIA FERRY SYSTEMS OY—See Hogia AB; *Int'l*, pg. 3441
HOGIA LONN AS—See Hogia AB; *Int'l*, pg. 3441
HOGIA TRANSPORT SYSTEMS LTD.—See Hogia AB; *Int'l*, pg. 3441
HOKENSO SDN, BHD.—See Hitachi, Ltd.; *Int'l*, pg. 3422
HOKKAIDO CUBE SYSTEM INC.—See Cube System Inc.; *Int'l*, pg. 1875
HOKKAIDO HITACHI SYSTEMS, LTD.—See Hitachi, Ltd.; *Int'l*, pg. 3422
HOKUDEN INFORMATION SYSTEM SERVICE COMPANY, INC.—See Hokuriku Electric Power Co.; *Int'l*, pg. 3445
HOKUGIN SOFTWARE CO., LTD.—See Hokuhoku Financial Group, Inc.; *Int'l*, pg. 3444
HOLD ME LTD.; *Int'l*, pg. 3449
H ONE (PRIVATE) LIMITED—See Axiata Group Berhad; *Int'l*, pg. 768
HORIZON SOFTWARE INTERNATIONAL LLC—See Roper Technologies, Inc.; *U.S. Public*, pg. 1813
HORIZONTAL SOFTWARE SAS; *Int'l*, pg. 3479
HOROQUARTZ S.A.—See Amano Corporation; *Int'l*, pg. 411

HOTEL EQUIPMENT & DESIGN GMBH—See H World Group Limited; *Int'l*, pg. 3191
HOWARD SYSTEMS INTERNATIONAL INC.; *U.S. Private*, pg. 1995
HOWTELEVISION, INC.; *Int'l*, pg. 3494
HOYA MICROELECTRONICS (SUZHOU) LTD.—See Hoya Corporation; *Int'l*, pg. 3496
HOYLU AB; *Int'l*, pg. 3499
HPC AMERICA LLC—See Cognizant Technology Solutions Corporation; *U.S. Public*, pg. 525
HP EXSTREAM SOFTWARE—See HP Inc.; *U.S. Public*, pg. 1063
HPN HOLDINGS, INC.; *U.S. Public*, pg. 1065
HPSI PURCHASING SERVICES, LLC—See Aramark; *U.S. Public*, pg. 177
H&R BLOCK TAX RESOLUTION SERVICES, INC.—See H&R Block, Inc.; *U.S. Public*, pg. 976
HRI IT-CONSULTING GMBH—See H&R KGaA; *Int'l*, pg. 3193
H&R INFOTECH GMBH—See H&R KGaA; *Int'l*, pg. 3193
HSO GROUP BV; *Int'l*, pg. 3507
HUALU OPTICAL STORAGE INSTITUTE (DALIAN) CO., LTD.—See Beijing E-Hualu Information Technology Co., Ltd.; *Int'l*, pg. 949
HUALU SENIOR CARE & HEALTH DEVELOPMENT CO., LTD.—See Beijing E-Hualu Information Technology Co., Ltd.; *Int'l*, pg. 949
HUBB, INC.—See Apollo Global Management, Inc.; *U.S. Public*, pg. 152
HUBCONNECT PTY LTD—See HUB24 Limited; *Int'l*, pg. 3517
HUDDLESTOCK FINTECH AS; *Int'l*, pg. 3521
HUDDLY AS; *Int'l*, pg. 3522
HUITONGDA NETWORK CO., LTD.; *Int'l*, pg. 3527
HULINKS INC.—See Argo Graphics Inc.; *Int'l*, pg. 562
HUMANICA PUBLIC COMPANY LIMITED; *Int'l*, pg. 3530
HUMANICA SDN. BHD.—See Humanica Public Company Limited; *Int'l*, pg. 3530
HUMANSOFT KFT.—See 4iG Nyrt.; *Int'l*, pg. 12
HUMAN XTENSIONS LTD.; *Int'l*, pg. 3529
HUNDSUN TECHNOLOGIES INC.; *Int'l*, pg. 3534
HUNESION CO., LTD.; *Int'l*, pg. 3535
HURCO COMPANIES, INC.; *U.S. Public*, pg. 1075
HYBRID ANALYSIS GMBH—See CrowdStrike Holdings, Inc.; *U.S. Public*, pg. 596
HYDRA MANAGEMENT LIMITED—See eTask Technologies Limited; *Int'l*, pg. 2520
HYLAND SOFTWARE GERMANY GMBH—See Thoma Bravo, L.P.; *U.S. Private*, pg. 4148
HYPEFACTORS A/S; *Int'l*, pg. 3552
HYPERACTIVE TECHNOLOGIES, INC.—See GLORY Ltd.; *Int'l*, pg. 3009
HYPERBLOCK, INC.; *Int'l*, pg. 3553
HYSON INTERNATIONAL CORP.—See Edge Centres Pty Ltd; *Int'l*, pg. 2309
I3-INFIN, LLC—See i3 Verticals, Inc.; *U.S. Public*, pg. 1081
I3LOGIC; *U.S. Private*, pg. 2027
I3-ONE, LLC—See i3 Verticals, Inc.; *U.S. Public*, pg. 1081
I3-PBS, LLC—See i3 Verticals, Inc.; *U.S. Public*, pg. 1081
I3-SOFTWARE & SERVICES, LLC—See i3 Verticals, Inc.; *U.S. Public*, pg. 1081
I3 SYSTEMS, INC.; *Int'l*, pg. 3566
IAR SYSTEMS GMBH—See IAR Systems Group AB; *Int'l*, pg. 3569
IBABS B.V.—See Euronext N.V.; *Int'l*, pg. 2554
IBI GROUP INC.—See ARCADIS N.V.; *Int'l*, pg. 541
IBIZ CONSULTANCY SERVICES INDIA PVT. LTD.—See Blackstone Inc.; *U.S. Public*, pg. 357
IBIZ CONSULTING SERVICES (SHANGHAI) CO., LTD.—See Blackstone Inc.; *U.S. Public*, pg. 357
IBL UNISYS LIMITED—See IBL HealthCare Limited; *Int'l*, pg. 3576
IBM BUSINESS CONTINUITY & RESILIENCY SERVICES—See International Business Machines Corporation; *U.S. Public*, pg. 1147
IBM KUWAIT SPC—See International Business Machines Corporation; *U.S. Public*, pg. 1147
IBM LUXEMBOURG SARL—See International Business Machines Corporation; *U.S. Public*, pg. 1147
I-BRIDGE SYSTEMS PHILIPPINES INC.—See Computer Institute of Japan Ltd.; *Int'l*, pg. 1759
IBYKUS AG; *Int'l*, pg. 3577
ICAR VISION SYSTEMS, S.L.—See Mitek Systems, Inc.; *U.S. Public*, pg. 1452
ICE EDGE BUSINESS SOLUTIONS LTD.—See DIRTT Environmental Solutions Ltd.; *Int'l*, pg. 2130
ICESOFT TECHNOLOGIES, INC.; *Int'l*, pg. 3579
ICETANA LIMITED; *Int'l*, pg. 3579
ICLINIC DESENVOLVIMENTO DE SOFTWARE LTDA.—See Afya Limited; *Int'l*, pg. 196
ICO LIMITED—See ICO Group Limited; *Int'l*, pg. 3582
ICON CENTRAL LABORATORIES INC.—See ICON plc; *Int'l*, pg. 3584
ICON GROUP LTD.; *Int'l*, pg. 3583
ICONSOFT INC.; *U.S. Private*, pg. 2033
ICSA (INDIA) LTD.; *Int'l*, pg. 3586
ICS ENDAVA SRL—See Endava plc; *Int'l*, pg. 2402
ICSYNERGY INTERNATIONAL, LLC—See iC Consult

Group GmbH; *Int'l*, pg. 3577
ID4 AG—See Anemoi International Ltd; *Int'l*, pg. 458
IDEA COUTURE LATIN AMERICA, S.A.P.I. DE C.V.—See Cognizant Technology Solutions Corporation; *U.S. Public*, pg. 524
IDEAGEN CAPTURE LIMITED—See HgCapital Trust plc; *Int'l*, pg. 3377
IDEALWORKS GMBH—See Bayerische Motoren Werke Aktiengesellschaft; *Int'l*, pg. 912
IDEENION AUTOMOBIL AG—See Apollo Future Mobility Group Limited; *Int'l*, pg. 517
IDENTILLECT TECHNOLOGIES CORP.; *U.S. Public*, pg. 1088
IDENTIV AUSTRALIA PTY LTD—See Identiv, Inc.; *U.S. Public*, pg. 1089
IDENTIV PTE. LTD.—See Identiv, Inc.; *U.S. Public*, pg. 1089
IDENTIV PVT. LTD.—See Identiv, Inc.; *U.S. Public*, pg. 1089
IDERA, INC.—See HGGC, LLC; *U.S. Private*, pg. 1929
I.D.I. INFORMATICA DATA INTEGRATION LTD.—See Canada Pension Plan Investment Board; *Int'l*, pg. 1279
IDIMENSION MSC SDN. BHD.—See Evd Berhad; *Int'l*, pg. 2561
IDOX PLC - SOFTWARE DIVISION—See IDOX PLC; *Int'l*, pg. 3595
IDOX SOFTWARE LIMITED—See IDOX PLC; *Int'l*, pg. 3595
IDS INGEGNERIA DEI SISTEMI S.P.A.—See Fincantieri S.p.A.; *Int'l*, pg. 2671
ID SOFTWARE, INC.—See Microsoft Corporation; *U.S. Public*, pg. 1443
IDS SCHEER AMERICAS, INC.—See Silver Lake Group, LLC; *U.S. Private*, pg. 3658
IDS SCHEER CHINA LTD.—See Silver Lake Group, LLC; *U.S. Private*, pg. 3658
IDS SCHEER, D.O.O.—See Silver Lake Group, LLC; *U.S. Private*, pg. 3658
IDS SCHEER RUSSIA—See Silver Lake Group, LLC; *U.S. Private*, pg. 3658
IDS SCHEER SAUDI ARABIA LLC—See Silver Lake Group, LLC; *U.S. Private*, pg. 3658
IDS SCHEER SDC S.R.O.—See Silver Lake Group, LLC; *U.S. Private*, pg. 3658
IDS SCHEER SISTEMAS DE PROCESSAMENTO DE DADOS LTDA.—See Silver Lake Group, LLC; *U.S. Private*, pg. 3658
IENTERPRISE ONLINE SDN. BHD.—See Ancom Nylex Berhad; *Int'l*, pg. 449
IFCA CONSULTING PRIVATE LIMITED—See IFCA MSC Berhad; *Int'l*, pg. 3598
IFCA CONSULTING (SABAH) SDN BHD—See IFCA MSC Berhad; *Int'l*, pg. 3598
IFCA CONSULTING (SARAWAK) SDN BHD—See IFCA MSC Berhad; *Int'l*, pg. 3598
IFCA (GUANGZHOU) TECHNOLOGY COMPANY LIMITED—See IFCA MSC Berhad; *Int'l*, pg. 3598
IFCA MSC BERHAD; *Int'l*, pg. 3598
IFCA SOFTWARE (GUANGZHOU) CO., LTD.—See IFCA MSC Berhad; *Int'l*, pg. 3598
IFCA SYSTEMS (JB) SDN BHD—See IFCA MSC Berhad; *Int'l*, pg. 3598
IFCA SYSTEMS (PENANG) SDN BHD—See IFCA MSC Berhad; *Int'l*, pg. 3598
IFCA (WUHAN) TECHNOLOGY COMPANY LIMITED—See IFCA MSC Berhad; *Int'l*, pg. 3598
IFLYTEK CO., LTD.; *Int'l*, pg. 3599
IFS APPLICATIONS IBERICA, S.A.—See EQT AB; *Int'l*, pg. 2477
IFSAR S.A.—See EQT AB; *Int'l*, pg. 2478
IFS DEUTSCHLAND GMBH & CO KG—See EQT AB; *Int'l*, pg. 2477
IFS FINLAND OY AB—See EQT AB; *Int'l*, pg. 2477
IFS HUNGARY KFT.—See EQT AB; *Int'l*, pg. 2477
IFS SOLUTIONS (SHANGHAI) CO LTD—See EQT AB; *Int'l*, pg. 2478
IFS SRI LANKA LTD—See EQT AB; *Int'l*, pg. 2478
IFS SVERIGE AB—See EQT AB; *Int'l*, pg. 2478
IFS UK LTD.—See EQT AB; *Int'l*, pg. 2478
IGATE COMPUTER SYSTEMS (SUZHOU) CO., LTD.—See Capgemini SE; *Int'l*, pg. 1306
IGATE SINGAPORE PTE LTD.—See Capgemini SE; *Int'l*, pg. 1306
IGB DIGITAL SDN. BHD.—See IGB Berhad; *Int'l*, pg. 3601
IGLUE, INC.; *Int'l*, pg. 3602
IHOMEFINDER, INC.—See Community Investors, Inc.; *U.S. Private*, pg. 995
IKEGPS INC.—See ikeGPS Group Limited; *Int'l*, pg. 3610
ILAB SOLUTIONS, LLC—See Agilent Technologies, Inc.; *U.S. Public*, pg. 62
ILB PTY LTD.—See The Experience Co Limited; *Int'l*, pg. 2588
ILINK SYSTEMS, INC.; *U.S. Private*, pg. 2041
ILLUSTRO SYSTEMS INTERNATIONAL, LLC—See UNICOM Global, Inc.; *U.S. Private*, pg. 4282
ILYDA SA; *Int'l*, pg. 3617
IMAGE POWER S.A.; *Int'l*, pg. 3617
IMAGE SYSTEMS NORDIC AB—See Image Systems AB; *Int'l*, pg. 3618
IMAGETECH SYSTEMS INC.—See Black Belt Solutions LLC; *U.S. Private*, pg. 569
IMAGETREND, INC.; *U.S. Private*, pg. 2045

IMAGICA ALOBASE CO., LTD.—See Imagica Group Inc.; *Int'l*, pg. 3618
IMAGINE LEARNING, LLC—See Silver Lake Group, LLC; *U.S. Private*, pg. 3661
IMAGINE SOFTWARE INC.; *U.S. Private*, pg. 2045
IMA MATERIALFORSCHUNG UND ANWENDUNGSTECHNIK GMBH—See I Squared Capital Advisors (US) LLC; *U.S. Private*, pg. 2022
IMARC LLC; *U.S. Private*, pg. 2046
IMD SOFT—See Constellation Software Inc.; *Int'l*, pg. 1774
IMMERSION MEDIA, INC.—See Clubessential Holdings, LLC; *U.S. Private*, pg. 949
IMPORT-IO CORPORATION; *U.S. Private*, pg. 2050
IMPRIVATA, INC.—See Thoma Bravo, L.P.; *U.S. Private*, pg. 4148
IMS HEALTH KOREA LTD—See IQVIA Holdings Inc.; *U.S. Public*, pg. 1168
INDEX ASIA LTD—See HS Holdings Co., Ltd.; *Int'l*, pg. 3503
INDIE SEMICONDUCTOR, INC.; *U.S. Public*, pg. 1116
INDIGIO GROUP, INC.—See Bridgeline Digital, Inc.; *U.S. Public*, pg. 382
INDRASOFT INC.—See ASGN Incorporated; *U.S. Public*, pg. 210
INDUS CORPORATION—See Tetra Tech, Inc.; *U.S. Public*, pg. 2023
INDUS TECHNOLOGY, INC.; *U.S. Private*, pg. 2064
INEFI INCORPORATION—See Flytech Technology Co., Ltd.; *Int'l*, pg. 2716
INERGIZE DIGITAL MEDIA—See Nexstar Media Group, Inc.; *U.S. Public*, pg. 1522
I-NET DATA SERVICE CORP.—See I-Net Corporation; *Int'l*, pg. 3563
INETXPERTS, CORP.—See TruBridge, Inc.; *U.S. Public*, pg. 2198
I-NEXUS (AMERICA) INC.—See i-nexus Global plc; *Int'l*, pg. 3563
I-NEXUS GLOBAL PLC; *Int'l*, pg. 3563
INFEENY S.A.S.—See Econocom Group SA; *Int'l*, pg. 2298
INFINIGATE FRANCE SAS—See H.I.G. Capital, LLC; *U.S. Private*, pg. 1833
INFINIGATE OSTERREICH GMBH—See H.I.G. Capital, LLC; *U.S. Private*, pg. 1833
INFINIGATE UK LTD.—See H.I.G. Capital, LLC; *U.S. Private*, pg. 1833
INFINITE BLUE PLATFORM LLC; *U.S. Private*, pg. 2070
INFINITE TECHNOLOGY GROUP LTD.; *U.S. Private*, pg. 2071
INFINITY SYSTEMS ENGINEERING, LLC; *U.S. Private*, pg. 2072
INFINITY WARD, INC.—See Microsoft Corporation; *U.S. Public*, pg. 1439
INFITECH, LLC—See Pro-Copy Technologies, Inc.; *U.S. Private*, pg. 3270
INFLECTION POINT SYSTEMS INC.—See EQT AB; *Int'l*, pg. 2483
INFLUENCE HEALTH, INC.—See Vestar Capital Partners, LLC; *U.S. Private*, pg. 4372
INFOBLU SPA—See Edizione S.r.l.; *Int'l*, pg. 2312
INFOCROSSING HEALTHCARE, INC.—See Verizon Communications Inc.; *U.S. Public*, pg. 2286
INFOLOGIC PTE LTD—See Beijing E-Hualu Information Technology Co., Ltd.; *Int'l*, pg. 949
INFOMED SOFTWARE, S.L.—See Henry Schein, Inc.; *U.S. Public*, pg. 1027
INFOR GLOBAL SOLUTIONS, INC. - CHICAGO—See Koch Industries, Inc.; *U.S. Private*, pg. 2330
INFOR GLOBAL SOLUTIONS, INC. - EAST GREENWICH—See Koch Industries, Inc.; *U.S. Private*, pg. 2330
INFOR GLOBAL SOLUTIONS, INC. - GRAND RAPIDS—See Koch Industries, Inc.; *U.S. Private*, pg. 2331
INFOR GLOBAL SOLUTIONS, INC. - HAMPTON—See Koch Industries, Inc.; *U.S. Private*, pg. 2331
INFOR GLOBAL SOLUTIONS, INC. - OPERATIONS CENTER—See Koch Industries, Inc.; *U.S. Private*, pg. 2331
INFOR GLOBAL SOLUTIONS - MELBOURNE—See Koch Industries, Inc.; *U.S. Private*, pg. 2330
INFOR GLOBAL SOLUTIONS - PETALING JAYA—See Koch Industries, Inc.; *U.S. Private*, pg. 2330
INFOR GLOBAL SOLUTIONS - SAO PAOLO—See Koch Industries, Inc.; *U.S. Private*, pg. 2330
INFOR GLOBAL SOLUTIONS - TORONTO—See Koch Industries, Inc.; *U.S. Private*, pg. 2330
INFOR, INC.—See Koch Industries, Inc.; *U.S. Private*, pg. 2330
INFOR JAPAN K.K.—See Koch Industries, Inc.; *U.S. Private*, pg. 2331
INFOR LIBRARY & INFORMATION SOLUTIONS—See Koch Industries, Inc.; *U.S. Private*, pg. 2331
INFORMATICA INC.; *U.S. Public*, pg. 1117
INFORMATICA RESEARCH AND DEVELOPMENT CENTER LLC—See Canada Pension Plan Investment Board; *Int'l*, pg. 1280
INFORMATICA SOFTWARE DE MEXICO S. DE R.L. DE C.V.—See Canada Pension Plan Investment Board; *Int'l*, pg. 1280

INFORMATICA SOFTWARE LIMITED—See Canada Pension Plan Investment Board; *Int'l*, pg. 1280
INFORMATION & COMPUTING SERVICES, INC.; *U.S. Private*, pg. 2073
INFORMATION DEVELOPMENT SINGAPORE PTE. LTD.—See ID Holdings Corporation; *Int'l*, pg. 3587
INFORMATION DEVELOPMENT WUHAN CO., LTD.—See ID Holdings Corporation; *Int'l*, pg. 3587
INFORMATION TECHNOLOGY GROUP COMPANY LIMITED—See Bliss Intelligence Public Company Limited; *Int'l*, pg. 1064
INFORMATIQUE BANQUES POPULAIRES SA—See Groupe BPCE; *Int'l*, pg. 3098
INFOSEMANTICS; *U.S. Private*, pg. 2074
INFOSOURCE INC.—See Gauge Capital LLC; *U.S. Private*, pg. 1652
INFOVISTA CORPORATION—See Apax Partners LLP; *Int'l*, pg. 504
INFOVISTA GMBH—See Apax Partners LLP; *Int'l*, pg. 504
INFOVISTA IBE SA—See Apax Partners LLP; *Int'l*, pg. 504
INFOVISTA PTE LTD—See Apax Partners LLP; *Int'l*, pg. 504
INFOVISTA S.A.S.—See Apax Partners LLP; *Int'l*, pg. 504
INFOVISTA UK LIMITED—See Apax Partners LLP; *Int'l*, pg. 504
INFOZEN, LLC—See The Carlyle Group Inc.; *U.S. Public*, pg. 2048
INFRASYS (BEIJING) LTD.—See Beijing Shiji Information Technology Co., Ltd.; *Int'l*, pg. 956
INFRASYS INTERNATIONAL LIMITED—See Beijing Shiji Information Technology Co., Ltd.; *Int'l*, pg. 956
INFRASYS MALAYSIA SDN. BHD.—See Beijing Shiji Information Technology Co., Ltd.; *Int'l*, pg. 956
INFUSION DEVELOPMENT CORPORATION; *U.S. Private*, pg. 2075
INGENIERIA DE SOFTWARE BANCARIO, S.L.—See Banco Santander, S.A.; *Int'l*, pg. 826
INGENIOUS MED, INC.—See Constellation Software Inc.; *Int'l*, pg. 1774
INGRAM MICRO CFS COMMERCE B.V.—See Hainan Traffic Administration Holding Co., Ltd.; *Int'l*, pg. 3214
INGRAM MICRO CFS E-BUSINESS GMBH—See Hainan Traffic Administration Holding Co., Ltd.; *Int'l*, pg. 3214
INGRAM MICRO CFS FULFILMENT GMBH—See Hainan Traffic Administration Holding Co., Ltd.; *Int'l*, pg. 3214
INGRAM MICRO CFS FULFILMENT LTD—See Hainan Traffic Administration Holding Co., Ltd.; *Int'l*, pg. 3214
INIT.VOICE GMBH—See ecotel communication ag; *Int'l*, pg. 2300
INMATION SOFTWARE GMBH—See Emerson Electric Co.; *U.S. Public*, pg. 752
INMEDEA GMBH—See CompuGroup Medical SE & Co. KGaA; *Int'l*, pg. 1757
INMOMENT, INC.—See Madison Dearborn Partners, LLC; *U.S. Private*, pg. 2541
INNOCV SOLUTIONS S.L.—See Alkemy SpA; *Int'l*, pg. 331
INNORIID GMBH—See AMETEK, Inc.; *U.S. Public*, pg. 122
INNOTAS, INC.—See TA Associates, Inc.; *U.S. Private*, pg. 3917
INNOTAS, INC.—See TPG Capital, L.P.; *U.S. Public*, pg. 2175
INNOVATIVE SOLUTION SYSTEMS; *U.S. Private*, pg. 2083
INNOVATIVE SYSTEMS GROUP INC.; *U.S. Private*, pg. 2083
INNOVATUM, INC.—See Banyan Software, Inc.; *U.S. Private*, pg. 470
INNOVEST SYSTEMS, LLC—See SS&C Technologies Holdings, Inc.; *U.S. Public*, pg. 1923
INNOVIZANT, LLC—See Blackstone Inc.; *U.S. Public*, pg. 357
INNOVO CLOUD GMBH—See Friedhelm Loh Stiftung & Co. KG; *Int'l*, pg. 2792
INNOVYZE, INC.—See Autodesk, Inc.; *U.S. Public*, pg. 229
INNOWACYJNA PLATFORMA HANDLU SP. Z O.O.—See Eurocash S.A.; *Int'l*, pg. 2533
INPHOSOFT MALAYSIA SDN BHD—See GINSMS Inc.; *Int'l*, pg. 2977
INPHOSOFT SINGAPORE PTE LTD—See GINSMS Inc.; *Int'l*, pg. 2977
INQVENTURES GMBH—See adesso SE; *Int'l*, pg. 144
INSEEGO BELGIUM B.V.—See Inseego Corp.; *U.S. Public*, pg. 1129
INSEEGO BENELUX B.V.—See Inseego Corp.; *U.S. Public*, pg. 1129
INSEEGO CORP.; *U.S. Public*, pg. 1129
INSEEGO DEUTSCHLAND GMBH—See Inseego Corp.; *U.S. Public*, pg. 1129
INSEEGO IRELAND LIMITED—See Inseego Corp.; *U.S. Public*, pg. 1129
INSERSO CORPORATION; *U.S. Private*, pg. 2085
INSIEL MERCATO S.P.A.—See GPI S.p.A.; *Int'l*, pg. 3046
INSIGHT AGENTS FRANCE S.R.L.—See Agfa-Gevaert N.V.; *Int'l*, pg. 208
INSPEARIT S.R.L.—See Ardian SAS; *Int'l*, pg. 555
INSPERITY PAYROLL SERVICES, L.L.C.—See Insperity, Inc.; *U.S. Public*, pg. 1131
INSPIRAGE, LLC—See Accenture plc; *Int'l*, pg. 87
INSPIRATION SOFTWARE, INC.; *U.S. Private*, pg. 2092
INSPIRIX TECHNOLOGIES LLC; *U.S. Private*, pg. 2092

INSPRO TECHNOLOGIES, LLC—See Thoma Bravo, L.P.; *U.S. Private*, pg. 4149
INSTASAFE INC.—See ABM Knowledgeware Ltd; *Int'l*, pg. 63
INSTREAM, LLC; *U.S. Private*, pg. 2094
INSTRUCTURE, INC.—See Thoma Bravo, L.P.; *U.S. Private*, pg. 4148
INSURAGUEST TECHNOLOGIES, INC.; *U.S. Public*, pg. 1134
INTACT TECHNOLOGY, INC.; *U.S. Private*, pg. 2097
INTEGRA CONSULTING & COMPUTER SERVICES; *U.S. Private*, pg. 2098
INTEGRAL ANALYTICS, INC.—See Willdan Group, Inc.; *U.S. Public*, pg. 2371
INTEGRANT, INC.; *U.S. Private*, pg. 2098
INTEGRATED DATA SERVICES, INC.—See Arlington Capital Partners LLC; *U.S. Private*, pg. 328
INTEGRATED DEALER SYSTEMS, INC.—See Constellation Software Inc.; *Int'l*, pg. 1772
INTEGRATED DESIGN, INC.; *U.S. Private*, pg. 2099
INTEGRATED ENTERPRISE SOLUTIONS, INC.—See Cloud Equity Group, LLC; *U.S. Private*, pg. 946
INTEGRATED FINANCE & ACCOUNTING SOLUTIONS, LLC.; *U.S. Private*, pg. 2099
INTEGRATED SYSTEMS CO. LTD.—See Ali Zaid Al-Quraishi & Brothers Co.; *Int'l*, pg. 323
INTEGRATED TELEMANAGEMENT SERVICES, INC.; *U.S. Private*, pg. 2101
INTEGRATION MANAGEMENT, INC.—See ABRY Partners, LLC; *U.S. Private*, pg. 41
INTEGRATIVE SYSTEMS, INC.; *U.S. Private*, pg. 2101
INTEGRATOUCH, LLC; *U.S. Private*, pg. 2101
INTEGRITY DATA SOLUTIONS INC.; *U.S. Private*, pg. 2102
INTEGRO TECHNOLOGIES PTE LTD.—See Aurionpro Solutions Limited; *Int'l*, pg. 711
INTEGWARE, INC.; *U.S. Private*, pg. 2104
INTEL DEUTSCHLAND GMBH—See Intel Corporation; *U.S. Public*, pg. 1138
INTELECOM DANMARK AS—See Herkules Capital AS; *Int'l*, pg. 3362
INTELECOM SWEDEN AB—See Herkules Capital AS; *Int'l*, pg. 3362
INTELIE TECHNOLOGY LLC—See ViaSat, Inc.; *U.S. Public*, pg. 2292
INTELLECT TECHNICAL SOLUTIONS, INC.; *U.S. Private*, pg. 2105
INTELLICORP, INC.; *U.S. Private*, pg. 2105
INTELLIENT (PTY) LIMITED—See EOH HOLDINGS LIMITED; *Int'l*, pg. 2457
INTELLIGENT DEVICES, LLC—See HEICO Corporation; *U.S. Public*, pg. 1021
INTELLIGENT RETAIL UK LIMITED—See 3Q Holdings Limited; *Int'l*, pg. 9
INTELLIGRAPHICS INC.; *U.S. Private*, pg. 2106
INTELLIPHARM PTY LTD—See EBOS Group Limited; *Int'l*, pg. 2285
INTELLIQUIP, INC.—See FPX, LLC; *U.S. Private*, pg. 1586
INTENTIONAL SOFTWARE CORPORATION—See Microsoft Corporation; *U.S. Public*, pg. 1439
INTERACTIVE COMMUNICATIONS SOLUTIONS GROUP, INC.—See Strattam Capital, LLC; *U.S. Private*, pg. 3837
INTERACTIVE DATA, LLC—See Red Violet, Inc.; *U.S. Public*, pg. 1770
INTERACTIVE DATA VISUALIZATION, INC.—See Unity Software Inc.; *U.S. Public*, pg. 2254
INTERACTIVE STRENGTH INC.; *U.S. Public*, pg. 1140
INTERBIT DATA, INC.; *U.S. Private*, pg. 2109
INTER CENTRAL, INC.—See ARE Holdings, Inc.; *Int'l*, pg. 557
INTERFACE SYSTECH CO., LTD.—See Daido Kogyo Co., Ltd.; *Int'l*, pg. 1921
INTERFAX COMMUNICATIONS LIMITED—See Upland Software, Inc.; *U.S. Public*, pg. 2264
INTERGRAPH CORP. (NZ) LIMITED—See Hexagon AB; *Int'l*, pg. 3368
INTERGRAPH CORP. PTY. LTD.—See Hexagon AB; *Int'l*, pg. 3368
INTERGRAPH CORP. PTY. LTD.—See Hexagon AB; *Int'l*, pg. 3368
INTERGRAPH DE MEXICO S.A. DE C.V.—See Hexagon AB; *Int'l*, pg. 3369
INTERGRAPH SERVICIOS DE VENEZUELA, C.A.—See Hexagon AB; *Int'l*, pg. 3369
INTERICA, INC.—See ALS Limited; *Int'l*, pg. 378
INTERICA LIMITED—See ALS Limited; *Int'l*, pg. 378
INTERLINK INSURED SWEEP LLC—See Webster Financial Corporation; *U.S. Public*, pg. 2341
INTERMEDIX FRANCE S.A.R.L.—See CompuGroup Medical SE & Co. KGaA; *Int'l*, pg. 1757
INTERMEDIX OSTERREICH GMBH—See CompuGroup Medical SE & Co. KGaA; *Int'l*, pg. 1755
INTERNATIONAL BUSINESS MACHINES CORPORATION; *U.S. Public*, pg. 1145
INTERNATIONAL FINANCIAL DATA SERVICES (CANADA) LIMITED—See SS&C Technologies Holdings, Inc.; *U.S. Public*, pg. 1923
INTERNATIONAL SYSTEMS DEVELOPMENT CO., LTD.—See BIPROGY Inc.; *Int'l*, pg. 1045

THE INTERNET BUSINESS LIMITED—See News Corporation; *U.S. Public*, pg. 1520
INTEROUTE MANAGED SERVICES SWITZERLAND SARL—See GTT Communications, Inc.; *U.S. Private*, pg. 1808
INTERSECT—See Insight Venture Management, LLC; *U.S. Private*, pg. 2089
INTERSECT—See Stone Point Capital LLC; *U.S. Private*, pg. 3822
INTERSYSTEMS (ASIA PACIFIC) PTY. LTD.—See Daifuku Co., Ltd.; *Int'l*, pg. 1926
INTERTRADE SYSTEMS INC.—See KKR & Co. Inc.; *U.S. Public*, pg. 1267
INTERVAL SOFTWARE SERVICES, LLC—See Marriott Vacations Worldwide Corporation; *U.S. Public*, pg. 1373
INTERWARE DEVELOPMENT COMPANY, INC.—See Arlington Capital Partners LLC; *U.S. Private*, pg. 327
INTETICS CO.; *U.S. Private*, pg. 2128
INTIFIC, INC—See Elliott Management Corporation; *U.S. Private*, pg. 1368
INTIFIC, INC—See Veritas Capital Fund Management, LLC; *U.S. Private*, pg. 4362
INTRAHEALTH SYSTEMS LIMITED—See HEALWELL AI Inc.; *Int'l*, pg. 3304
INTRAPHONE SOLUTIONS AB—See Addnode Group AB; *Int'l*, pg. 130
INTREXON BIOINFORMATICS GERMANY GMBH—See Precigen, Inc.; *U.S. Public*, pg. 1713
INTRIGO SYSTEMS, INC.—See Accenture plc; *Int'l*, pg. 87
INVESTMENT PROPERTY DATABANK LIMITED—See MSCI Inc.; *U.S. Public*, pg. 1483
INVESTORTOOLS INC.; *U.S. Private*, pg. 2132
INVOLVIO LLC—See Cisco Systems, Inc.; *U.S. Public*, pg. 499
INWHATLANGUAGE, LLC—See TrustPoint International, LLC; *U.S. Private*, pg. 4251
IOFFICE, LLC; *U.S. Private*, pg. 2133
IOLAP, INC.—See Elixirr International plc; *Int'l*, pg. 2363
ION WAVE TECHNOLOGIES, INC.—See GI Manager L.P.; *U.S. Private*, pg. 1692
IOS CO., LTD.—See Cresco, Ltd.; *Int'l*, pg. 1840
IO-TAHOE LLC—See NRG Energy, Inc.; *U.S. Public*, pg. 1550
IOVATION INC.—See TransUnion; *U.S. Public*, pg. 2185
IOWA INTERACTIVE, LLC—See Tyler Technologies, Inc.; *U.S. Public*, pg. 2208
IPFOLIO CORPORATION; *U.S. Private*, pg. 2136
IPG; *U.S. Private*, pg. 2136
IP INFUSION SOFTWARE INDIA PVT. LTD.—See Access Co., Ltd.; *Int'l*, pg. 88
IP LABS GMBH—See FUJIFILM Holdings Corporation; *Int'l*, pg. 2822
IPMOTION INC.—See Imagica Group Inc.; *Int'l*, pg. 3618
I-POWER SOLUTIONS INDIA LTD.; *Int'l*, pg. 3564
IQBLADE LIMITED—See TD Synnex Corp; *U.S. Public*, pg. 1986
IQMS INC.—See Dassault Systemes S.A.; *Int'l*, pg. 1975
IQUEST SCHWEIZ AG—See Allgeier SE; *Int'l*, pg. 338
IQUEST TECHNOLOGIES KFT—See Allgeier SE; *Int'l*, pg. 338
IQUEST TECHNOLOGIES SRL—See Allgeier SE; *Int'l*, pg. 338
IQVIA COMMERCIAL SOFTWARE GMBH—See IQVIA Holdings Inc.; *U.S. Public*, pg. 1169
IQVIA CONSULTING AND INFORMATION SERVICES INDIA PVT. LTD.—See IQVIA Holdings Inc.; *U.S. Public*, pg. 1168
IQVIA SOLUTIONS ARGENTINA S.A.—See IQVIA Holdings Inc.; *U.S. Public*, pg. 1168
IQVIA SOLUTIONS BANGLADESH LIMITED—See IQVIA Holdings Inc.; *U.S. Public*, pg. 1168
IRISE; *U.S. Private*, pg. 2138
IRON BOW TECHNOLOGIES LLC; *U.S. Private*, pg. 2139
IRON MOUNTAIN BAHRAIN CO., LTD.—See Iron Mountain Incorporated; *U.S. Public*, pg. 1172
IRON MOUNTAIN DATA MANAGEMENT CONSULTING (BEIJING) CO., LTD.—See Iron Mountain Incorporated; *U.S. Public*, pg. 1172
IRON MOUNTAIN FOR INFORMATION DOCUMENTS STORING PSC—See Iron Mountain Incorporated; *U.S. Public*, pg. 1173
IRON MOUNTAIN KUWAIT FOR DOCUMENTS PRESERVATION AND DESTRUCTION SERVICES—See Iron Mountain Incorporated; *U.S. Public*, pg. 1173
IRON MOUNTAIN (THAILAND) LIMITED—See Iron Mountain Incorporated; *U.S. Public*, pg. 1172
IROOFING, LLC—See Porch Group, Inc.; *U.S. Public*, pg. 1702
ISAM AUTOMATION CANADA CORP.—See Hamburger Hafen und Logistik AG; *Int'l*, pg. 3237
ISAM NORTH AMERICA CORP.—See Hamburger Hafen und Logistik AG; *Int'l*, pg. 3237
ISCAN ONLINE, INC.; *U.S. Private*, pg. 2143
ISI-DENTSU OF EUROPE, LTD.—See Dentsu Group Inc.; *Int'l*, pg. 2038
ISID INTERTECHNOLOGIES, LTD.—See Dentsu Group Inc.; *Int'l*, pg. 2038
IS INFORMATICA SOFTWARE LTDA.—See Canada Pension Plan Investment Board; *Int'l*, pg. 1279
ISITE DESIGN INC.; *U.S. Private*, pg. 2144
ISM INFORMATION SYSTEMS MANAGEMENT CORPORATION—See International Business Machines Corporation; *U.S. Public*, pg. 1146
ISOFT EHEALTH PTY LTD—See DXC Technology Company; *U.S. Public*, pg. 696
ISOLVED HCM LLC; *U.S. Private*, pg. 2146
ISOTRAK, INC.—See Horizon Capital LLP; *Int'l*, pg. 3479
ISOTRAK LIMITED—See Horizon Capital LLP; *Int'l*, pg. 3479
ISRA PARSYTEC GMBH—See Atlas Copco AB; *Int'l*, pg. 682
ISRA VISION BRASIL—See Atlas Copco AB; *Int'l*, pg. 682
ISRA VISION FRANCE S.A.—See Atlas Copco AB; *Int'l*, pg. 682
ISRA VISION ITALY—See Atlas Copco AB; *Int'l*, pg. 682
ISRA VISION (SHANGHAI) CORP LTD—See Atlas Copco AB; *Int'l*, pg. 682
ISRA VISION TURKEY—See Atlas Copco AB; *Int'l*, pg. 682
ISR INFORMATION PRODUCTS AG—See CENIT AG; *Int'l*, pg. 1401
IST-SOFTWARE CO., LTD.—See I-Net Corporation; *Int'l*, pg. 3563
ITAAS, INC.—See Cognizant Technology Solutions Corporation; *U.S. Public*, pg. 524
ITAAS INDIA PRIVATE LIMITED—See Cognizant Technology Solutions Corporation; *U.S. Public*, pg. 524
ITAC SOFTWARE AG—See Durr AG; *Int'l*, pg. 2233
ITAGROUP, INC.-DALLAS—See ITAGroup, Inc.; *U.S. Private*, pg. 2148
ITALWARE S.R.L.—See Digital Value S.p.A.; *Int'l*, pg. 2123
ITAPP INC.—See ServiceNow, Inc.; *U.S. Public*, pg. 1872
ITASCA RETAIL INFORMATION SYSTEMS, INC.—See Application Development Consultants, LLC; *U.S. Private*, pg. 298
ITCAMPUS SOFTWARE UND SYSTEMHAUS GMBH—See Silver Lake Group, LLC; *U.S. Private*, pg. 3660
ITCAMPUS (UK) LIMITED—See Silver Lake Group, LLC; *U.S. Private*, pg. 3660
ITD SOLUTIONS S.P.A.—See Digital Value S.p.A.; *Int'l*, pg. 2123
ITECHART GROUP, INC.; *U.S. Private*, pg. 2149
I-TER/INFORMATICA & TERRITORIO S.P.A.—See Advanced Business Software & Solutions Ltd.; *Int'l*, pg. 157
ITEXICO LLC—See Trinity Hunt Management, L.P.; *U.S. Private*, pg. 4235
ITEXT SOFTWARE ASIA PTE. LTD.—See Hancom, Inc.; *Int'l*, pg. 3243
ITEXT SOFTWARE BVBA—See Hancom, Inc.; *Int'l*, pg. 3243
ITEXT SOFTWARE CORP.—See Hancom, Inc.; *Int'l*, pg. 3243
ITG PLATFORMS INC.—See Virtu Financial, Inc.; *U.S. Public*, pg. 2300
ITRACS CORP.—See CommScope Holding Company, Inc.; *U.S. Public*, pg. 549
ITSCOPE GMBH—See 3U Holding AG; *Int'l*, pg. 10
IT SOLUTIONS, INC.; *U.S. Private*, pg. 2148
IT SONIX CUSTOM DEVELOPMENT GMBH—See Adecco Group AG; *Int'l*, pg. 140
IT WORKS S.A.—See Enterprise Investors Sp. z o.o.; *Int'l*, pg. 2452
IVARA CORPORATION—See Bentley Systems, Inc.; *U.S. Private*, pg. 297
IVDESK HOLDINGS, INC.; *U.S. Private*, pg. 2151
IVY COMPTECH PRIVATE LIMITED—See Entain PLC; *Int'l*, pg. 2450
IVY GLOBAL SHARED SERVICES PRIVATE LIMITED—See Entain PLC; *Int'l*, pg. 2450
IVY SOFTWARE DEVELOPMENT SERVICES PRIVATE LIMITED—See Entain PLC; *Int'l*, pg. 2450
IWORK SOFTWARE LLC—See Falk Integrated Technologies; *U.S. Private*, pg. 1467
IXONOS DENMARK APS—See Digitalist Group Oyj; *Int'l*, pg. 2123
IXONOS FINLAND MTSW LTD.—See Digitalist Group Oyj; *Int'l*, pg. 2123
IXONOS GERMANY GMBH—See Digitalist Group Oyj; *Int'l*, pg. 2123
IXONOS TESTHOUSE LTD.—See Digitalist Group Oyj; *Int'l*, pg. 2123
IXONOS USA LTD.—See Digitalist Group Oyj; *Int'l*, pg. 2123
IZENO PRIVATE LIMITED—See Datatec Limited; *Int'l*, pg. 1981
JABIL GLOBAL SERVICES POLAND SP Z.O.O.—See Jabil Inc.; *U.S. Public*, pg. 1181
JACC STUDIOS INC.; *U.S. Private*, pg. 2173
JAMF JAPAN KK—See Jamf Holding Corp.; *U.S. Public*, pg. 1187
JAMF SOFTWARE PACIFIC LIMITED—See Jamf Holding Corp.; *U.S. Public*, pg. 1187
JAMF SOFTWARE UK LIMITED—See Jamf Holding Corp.; *U.S. Public*, pg. 1187
JAMF SWEDEN AB—See Jamf Holding Corp.; *U.S. Public*, pg. 1187
JAPAN HUNDSUN SOFTWARE INC.—See Hundsun Technologies, Inc.; *Int'l*, pg. 3534
JAPAN INTERNET NEWS CO., LTD.—See FUJISOFT INCORPORATED; *Int'l*, pg. 2830
JAPAN LOGISTICS DEVELOPMENT CO., LTD.—See AZ-COM MARUWA Holdings Inc.; *Int'l*, pg. 776
JAPAN SETTLEMENT INFORMATION CENTER LTD.—See GLORY LTD; *Int'l*, pg. 3010
JAPAN SOFTWARE DESIGN CO.,LTD.—See Cresco, Ltd.; *Int'l*, pg. 1840
JAPAN SYSTEMS ENGINEERING CORPORATION—See DTS Corporation; *Int'l*, pg. 2217
JARDON & HOWARD TECHNOLOGIES; *U.S. Private*, pg. 2188
JAYWAY APS—See Devoteam SA; *Int'l*, pg. 2090
JAYWAY HALMSTAD AB—See Devoteam SA; *Int'l*, pg. 2090
JAYWAY INC.—See Devoteam SA; *Int'l*, pg. 2090
JAYWAY MALMO AB—See Devoteam SA; *Int'l*, pg. 2090
JAYWAY STOCKHOLM AB—See Devoteam SA; *Int'l*, pg. 2090
JBI TECHNOLOGIES INC; *U.S. Private*, pg. 2193
JDA CHILE S.A.—See New Mountain Capital, LLC; *U.S. Private*, pg. 2902
JDA INTERNATIONAL LTD.—See New Mountain Capital, LLC; *U.S. Private*, pg. 2902
JDA SOFTWARE AUSTRALIA PTY. LTD.—See New Mountain Capital, LLC; *U.S. Private*, pg. 2902
JDA SOFTWARE BELGIUM—See New Mountain Capital, LLC; *U.S. Private*, pg. 2902
JDA SOFTWARE CANADA LTD.—See New Mountain Capital, LLC; *U.S. Private*, pg. 2902
JDA SOFTWARE FRANCE S.A.—See New Mountain Capital, LLC; *U.S. Private*, pg. 2902
JDA SOFTWARE INDIA PRIVATE LIMITED—See New Mountain Capital, LLC; *U.S. Private*, pg. 2902
JDA SOFTWARE JAPAN CO., LTD.—See New Mountain Capital, LLC; *U.S. Private*, pg. 2902
JDA SOFTWARE KOREA, LTD.—See New Mountain Capital, LLC; *U.S. Private*, pg. 2902
JDA SOFTWARE NETHERLANDS B.V.—See New Mountain Capital, LLC; *U.S. Private*, pg. 2902
JDA SOFTWARE RUSSIA HOLDINGS, INC.—See New Mountain Capital, LLC; *U.S. Private*, pg. 2902
JDA SOFTWARE SHANGHAI CO. LTD.—See New Mountain Capital, LLC; *U.S. Private*, pg. 2902
JDA SOFTWARE (TAIWAN), INC.—See New Mountain Capital, LLC; *U.S. Private*, pg. 2902
JDA SOLUTIONS DO BRASIL LTDA.—See New Mountain Capital, LLC; *U.S. Private*, pg. 2903
JDA TECHNOLOGIES FINLAND OY LTD.—See New Mountain Capital, LLC; *U.S. Private*, pg. 2903
JDA TECHNOLOGIES, GMBH—See New Mountain Capital, LLC; *U.S. Private*, pg. 2903
JEEVES DEUTSCHLAND GMBH—See Battery Ventures, L.P.; *U.S. Private*, pg. 489
JEEVES FRANCE SAS—See Battery Ventures, L.P.; *U.S. Private*, pg. 489
JEEVES INFORMATION SYSTEMS NORWAY—See Battery Ventures, L.P.; *U.S. Private*, pg. 489
JETIT CORPORATION—See Azion Corp.; *Int'l*, pg. 780
JFROG LTD.; *U.S. Public*, pg. 1190
JHA PAYMENT PROCESSING SOLUTIONS, INC.—See Jack Henry & Associates, Inc.; *U.S. Public*, pg. 1182
JIANGSU YINGDA INFORMATION TECHNOLOGY CO., LTD.—See Global Infotech Co., Ltd.; *Int'l*, pg. 2997
JINGYOU INFORMATION TECHNOLOGY (SHANGHAI) CO., LTD—See IFCA MSC Berhad; *Int'l*, pg. 3599
JINNY SOFTWARE LTD.—See Enghouse Systems Limited; *Int'l*, pg. 2427
JITTERBIT, INC.—See KKR & Co. Inc.; *U.S. Public*, pg. 1254
JIVE SOFTWARE AUSTRALIA PTY LTD.—See ESW Capital, LLC; *U.S. Private*, pg. 1430
JLT INTERACTIVE PTE LTD—See Marsh & McLennan Companies, Inc.; *U.S. Public*, pg. 1377
J.M. SMITH CORPORATION; *U.S. Private*, pg. 2169
JOBFOX, INC.; *U.S. Private*, pg. 2217
JOBSCIENCE, INC.—See Insight Venture Management, LLC; *U.S. Private*, pg. 2087
JOBVITE, INC.—See K1 Investment Management, LLC; *U.S. Private*, pg. 2252
JOHN WILEY & SONS COMMERCIAL SERVICE (BEIJING) CO., LTD.—See John Wiley & Sons, Inc.; *U.S. Public*, pg. 1192
JOTA GMBH—See ATON GmbH; *Int'l*, pg. 689
JOULE MICROSYSTEMS INC.—See Banneker Partners, LLC; *U.S. Private*, pg. 469
JOYWORKS INC.—See Business Brain Showa-Ota Inc.; *Int'l*, pg. 1228
JRL ENTERPRISES, INC.; *U.S. Private*, pg. 2240
JS ADWAYS MEDIA INC.—See Adways Inc.; *Int'l*, pg. 169
JSCAPE LLC—See Redwood Software, Inc.; *U.S. Private*, pg. 3381
JUMPFORWARD LLC—See Global Payments Inc.; *U.S. Public*, pg. 943
JUNO TECHNOLOGIES, INC.—See Sagewind Capital LLC; *U.S. Private*, pg. 3528
JUSTDICE GMBH—See Bertelsmann SE & Co. KGaA; *Int'l*, pg. 992
JUSTICETRAX, INC.—See Banneker Partners, LLC; *U.S. Private*, pg. 469

541511 — CUSTOM COMPUTER PRO...

JUSTTRACK GMBH—See Bertelsmann SE & Co. KGaA; *Int'l*, pg. 993
JUSTWORKS, INC.; *U.S. Public*, pg. 1211
JX NIPPON INFORMATION TECHNOLOGY CO., LTD.—See ENEOS Holdings, Inc.; *Int'l*, pg. 2416
JZZ TECHNOLOGIES, INC.; *U.S. Private*, pg. 2247
K2 CO., LTD—See Capcom Co., Ltd.; *Int'l*, pg. 1302
K2L GMBH—See Microchip Technology Incorporated; *U.S. Public*, pg. 1436
K2 SOLUTIONS, INC.; *U.S. Private*, pg. 2253
KABA ACCESS SYSTEMS (SHANGHAI) CO., LTD.—See dormakaba Holding AG; *Int'l*, pg. 2178
KABAM, INC.; *U.S. Private*, pg. 2253
KABA WORKFORCE SOLUTIONS, LLC—See dormakaba Holding AG; *Int'l*, pg. 2177
KABUSHIKI KAISHA BRILLIANT SERVICE—See Cognizant Technology Solutions Corporation; *U.S. Public*, pg. 524
KALIDO INC.—See TA Associates, Inc.; *U.S. Private*, pg. 3915
KALSHOVEN AUTOMATION B.V.—See Advent International Corporation; *U.S. Private*, pg. 97
KALSHOVEN AUTOMATION B.V.—See Centerbridge Partners, L.P.; *U.S. Private*, pg. 813
KALTURA, INC.; *U.S. Public*, pg. 1213
KALTURA LTD.—See Kaltura, Inc.; *U.S. Public*, pg. 1213
KAMAKURA CORPORATION—See SAS Institute Inc.; *U.S. Private*, pg. 3551
KANA SOFTWARE INC. - CHICAGO—See Verint Systems Inc.; *U.S. Public*, pg. 2281
KANA SOFTWARE, INC.—See Verint Systems Inc.; *U.S. Public*, pg. 2281
KANA SOFTWARE KK—See Verint Systems Inc.; *U.S. Public*, pg. 2281
KANA SOFTWARE PTY LIMITED—See Verint Systems Inc.; *U.S. Public*, pg. 2281
KANA SOFTWARE—See Verint Systems Inc.; *U.S. Public*, pg. 2281
KANAZAWA SOFTWARE CO., LTD.—See Computer Institute of Japan Ltd.; *Int'l*, pg. 1759
KANHAN TECHNOLOGIES LIMITED—See Aurum Pacific (China) Group Limited; *Int'l*, pg. 715
KAREO, INC.; *U.S. Private*, pg. 2262
KASEYA LLC—See Insight Venture Management, LLC; *U.S. Private*, pg. 2090
KBACE TECHNOLOGIES, INC.—See Cognizant Technology Solutions Corporation; *U.S. Public*, pg. 524
KBR AL-YUSR LIMITED COMPANY—See KBR, Inc.; *U.S. Public*, pg. 1215
KEIHIN ELECTRONICS TECHNOLOGY INC—See Hitachi Astemo, Ltd.; *Int'l*, pg. 3409
KEMP TECHNOLOGIES INDIA PRIVATE LIMITED—See Progress Software Corporation; *U.S. Public*, pg. 1725
KEMP TECHNOLOGIES LIMITED—See Progress Software Corporation; *U.S. Public*, pg. 1725
KEMP TECHNOLOGIES PTE. LTD.—See Progress Software Corporation; *U.S. Public*, pg. 1725
KENZAN MEDIA, LLC—See Amdocs Limited; *Int'l*, pg. 420
KEPIT SYSTEMS OY—See Elisa Corporation; *Int'l*, pg. 2361
KEPLER ROMINFO SA—See Alten S.A.; *Int'l*, pg. 390
KERLIFE S.R.L.—See Ardian SAS; *Int'l*, pg. 555
KERRIDGE COMMERCIAL SYSTEMS LIMITED—See KKR & Co. Inc.; *U.S. Public*, pg. 1256
KESTE, LLC—See Trinity Hunt Management, L.P.; *U.S. Private*, pg. 4235
KEWILL—See Francisco Partners Management, LP; *U.S. Private*, pg. 1589
KEYBASE LLC—See Zoom Video Communications, Inc.; *U.S. Public*, pg. 2411
KEYCENTRIX—See CGF Industries, Inc.; *U.S. Private*, pg. 844
KEYEDIN SOLUTIONS LIMITED—See KeyedIn Solutions, Inc.; *U.S. Private*, pg. 2294
KEYLIMETIE, LLC.; *U.S. Private*, pg. 2294
KEYNETICS, INC.; *U.S. Private*, pg. 2294
KEYSTAR CORP.; *U.S. Public*, pg. 1227
KIGO, INC.—See Thoma Bravo, L.P.; *U.S. Private*, pg. 4153
KIGO RENTAL SYSTEMS, S.L.—See Thoma Bravo, L.P.; *U.S. Private*, pg. 4153
KIMURA INFORMATION TECHNOLOGY CO., LTD.—See CMC Corporation; *Int'l*, pg. 1669
KINGSMEN SOFTWARE LLC; *U.S. Private*, pg. 2312
KINTIPS LIMITED—See Ahsay Backup Software Development Company Limited; *Int'l*, pg. 226
KINVEY LLC—See Progress Software Corporation; *U.S. Public*, pg. 1725
KIONA SP. Z O.O.—See Carel Industries S.p.A.; *Int'l*, pg. 1324
KIPSU, INC.; *U.S. Private*, pg. 2314
KIRIWORKS, LLC—See i3 Verticals, Inc.; *U.S. Public*, pg. 1081
KIS INFORMATIK AG—See Cognizant Technology Solutions Corporation; *U.S. Public*, pg. 524
KIS INFORMATION SERVICES GMBH—See Cognizant Technology Solutions Corporation; *U.S. Public*, pg. 524
KIWIPLAN GMBH—See Illinois Tool Works Inc.; *U.S. Public*, pg. 1108
KIWIPLAN INC.—See Illinois Tool Works Inc.; *U.S. Public*, pg. 1109

KLDISCOVERY, INC.—See Pivotal Acquisition Corp.; *U.S. Private*, pg. 3192
KLIGER-WEISS INFOSYSTEMS, INC.; *U.S. Private*, pg. 2320
K LOGIX, LLC; *U.S. Private*, pg. 2249
KMS VERTRIEB UND SERVICES GMBH—See CompuGroup Medical SE & Co. KGaA; *Int'l*, pg. 1757
KNOWBE4, INC.—See Vista Equity Partners, LLC; *U.S. Private*, pg. 4398
KNOWLEDGE FACTOR, INC.—See Polaris Growth Management, LLC; *U.S. Private*, pg. 3223
KNOWLEDGEFOX GMBH—See Fabasoft AG; *Int'l*, pg. 2598
KOPFWERK DATENSYSTEME GMBH—See Henry Schein, Inc.; *U.S. Public*, pg. 1027
KORD TECHNOLOGIES, INC.—See KBR, Inc.; *U.S. Public*, pg. 1216
KORRIO, INC.—See Waud Capital Partners LLC; *U.S. Private*, pg. 4457
KOTEM HUNGARY LTD.—See Quality Vision International Inc.; *U.S. Private*, pg. 3321
KOTEM TECHNOLOGIES INC.—See Quality Vision International Inc.; *U.S. Private*, pg. 3321
KRATOS NETWORKS, INC.—See Kratos Defense & Security Solutions, Inc.; *U.S. Public*, pg. 1276
KRATOS TECHNOLOGY & TRAINING SOLUTIONS, INC.—See Kratos Defense & Security Solutions, Inc.; *U.S. Public*, pg. 1276
KRATOS UNMANNED SYSTEMS SOLUTIONS, INC.—See Kratos Defense & Security Solutions, Inc.; *U.S. Public*, pg. 1276
KREG CORPORATION—See Vizient, Inc.; *U.S. Private*, pg. 4407
KROLL ONTRACK BELGIUM—See Pivotal Acquisition Corp.; *U.S. Private*, pg. 3192
KROLL ONTRACK SP. Z O.O.—See Pivotal Acquisition Corp.; *U.S. Private*, pg. 3192
KRYPT INC.—See ArchLynk, Inc.; *U.S. Private*, pg. 311
KRYPTOS NETWORKS PVT LTD—See Crayon Group AS; *Int'l*, pg. 1829
KTL SOLUTIONS, INC.; *U.S. Private*, pg. 2355
KUBIENT, INC.; *U.S. Public*, pg. 1277
KURZWEIL/INTELLITOOLS, INC.—See Veritas, Capital Fund Management, LLC; *U.S. Public*, pg. 4361
KWIKCLICK, INC.; *U.S. Public*, pg. 1278
KYNECTIS SA—See Atos SE; *Int'l*, pg. 692
KYUSHU DTS CORPORATION—See DTS Corporation; *Int'l*, pg. 2217
KYUSHU HITACHI SYSTEMS, LTD.—See Hitachi, Ltd.; *Int'l*, pg. 3423
KYYBA, INC.; *U.S. Private*, pg. 2361
L-3 COMMUNICATIONS COMCEPT—See L3Harris Technologies, Inc.; *U.S. Public*, pg. 1282
L-3 COMMUNICATIONS—See L3Harris Technologies, Inc.; *U.S. Public*, pg. 1281
LABSTYLE INNOVATION LTD.—See DarioHealth Corp.; *U.S. Public*, pg. 633
LABVANTAGE SOLUTIONS INC.; *U.S. Private*, pg. 2371
LABYRINTH INC.—See Harbor Business Compliance Corporation; *U.S. Private*, pg. 1858
LAMY; *U.S. Private*, pg. 2381
LANCESOFT INC.; *U.S. Private*, pg. 2382
LANCET TECHNOLOGY INC—See ESO Solutions, Inc.; *U.S. Private*, pg. 1426
LANYON SOLUTIONS, INC.—See Blackstone Inc.; *U.S. Public*, pg. 353
LAPLINK SOFTWARE, INC.; *U.S. Private*, pg. 2391
LASER APP SOFTWARE, INC.—See Roper Technologies, Inc.; *U.S. Public*, pg. 1812
LASTLINE G.K.—See Dell Technologies Inc.; *U.S. Public*, pg. 651
LASTLINE INC.; *U.S. Private*, pg. 2395
LAVANTE INC.—See PRGX Global, Inc.; *U.S. Private*, pg. 3257
LAW ENFORCEMENT TECHNOLOGY GROUP—See Vista Equity Partners, LLC; *U.S. Private*, pg. 4395
LCA CONSULTING OY—See Etteplan Oyj; *Int'l*, pg. 2525
LEADING EDGE CO., LTD.—See CREEK & RIVER Co., Ltd.; *Int'l*, pg. 1837
LEADNOMICS; *U.S. Private*, pg. 2407
LEADSCOPE, INC.—See ArchiMed SAS; *Int'l*, pg. 548
LEAD TECHNOLOGIES, INC.—See Thoma Bravo, L.P.; *U.S. Private*, pg. 4146
LEAF GROUP LTD.—See Graham Holdings Company; *U.S. Public*, pg. 956
LEANTEQ LLC—See Enpro Inc.; *U.S. Public*, pg. 775
LEASEACCELERATOR INC.; *U.S. Private*, pg. 2408
LEEYO SOFTWARE INC.—See Zuora, Inc.; *U.S. Public*, pg. 2412
LEIDOS CYBER, INC.—See Capgemini SE; *Int'l*, pg. 1307
LEIDOS HOLDINGS, INC.; *U.S. Public*, pg. 1304
LEIDOS, INC.—See Leidos Holdings, Inc.; *U.S. Public*, pg. 1304
LENDING SPACE INC.; *U.S. Private*, pg. 2421
LENEL SYSTEMS INTERNATIONAL INC.—See Carrier Global Corporation; *U.S. Public*, pg. 441
LESS ANNOYING SOFTWARE, LLC; *U.S. Private*, pg. 2432
LEVEL ELEVEN, LLC—See The Ascent Group LLC; *U.S. Private*, pg. 3988

LEVER GLOBAL CORPORATION; *U.S. Private*, pg. 2434
LEVI, RAY & SHOUP, INC.; *U.S. Private*, pg. 2435
LEVVEL, LLC—See Endava plc; *Int'l*, pg. 2402
LEXALYTICS, INC.—See Madison Dearborn Partners, LLC; *U.S. Private*, pg. 2541
LIBERA INC.; *U.S. Private*, pg. 2442
THE LIBRARY CORPORATION; *U.S. Private*, pg. 4069
LIFE360, INC.; *U.S. Public*, pg. 1312
LIFESHARE TECHNOLOGIES LLC—See The Jordan Company, L.P.; *U.S. Private*, pg. 4062
LIFEWHERE, LLC—See Resideo Technologies, Inc.; *U.S. Public*, pg. 1789
LIGHTHOUSE TECHNOLOGIES, INC.; *U.S. Private*, pg. 2453
LIGHTSTEP, INC.—See ServiceNow, Inc.; *U.S. Public*, pg. 1872
LIGHT & WONDER, INC.; *U.S. Public*, pg. 1314
LIL PROJECTS PRIVATE LIMITED—See Brightcom Group Ltd.; *Int'l*, pg. 1162
LIMELIGHT NETWORKS FRANCE SARL—See EDGIO, INC.; *U.S. Public*, pg. 718
LIMELIGHT NETWORKS KOREA LTD.—See EDGIO, INC.; *U.S. Public*, pg. 719
LIMITLESS PROJECTS INC.; *U.S. Private*, pg. 2456
LINGUAMATICS LIMITED—See IQVIA Holdings Inc.; *U.S. Public*, pg. 1169
LINK SYSTEMS, INC.—See GI Manager L.P.; *U.S. Private*, pg. 1693
LIQUIDFRAMEWORKS, INC.—See Silver Lake Group, LLC; *U.S. Private*, pg. 3658
LIQUID MOTORS INC.; *U.S. Private*, pg. 2466
LIQUIDPLANNER, INC.—See Tempo Software, Inc.; *U.S. Private*, pg. 3964
LIVEAREALABS, INC.—See GXO Logistics, Inc.; *U.S. Public*, pg. 975
LIVEBLOCK AUCTIONS INTERNATIONAL INC—See OPENLANE, INC.; *U.S. Public*, pg. 1607
LIVEPERSON NETHERLANDS B.V.—See LivePerson, Inc.; *U.S. Public*, pg. 1332
LIVERMORE SOFTWARE TECHNOLOGY CORP.—See ANSYS, INC.; *U.S. Public*, pg. 139
LIVEWIRE, LLC—See Xerox Holdings Corporation; *U.S. Public*, pg. 2388
LIVING LENS ENTERPRISE LIMITED—See Thoma Bravo, L.P.; *U.S. Private*, pg. 4149
LIVONGO HEALTH, INC.—See Teladoc Health, Inc.; *U.S. Public*, pg. 1992
LIXOFT SAS—See Simulations Plus, Inc.; *U.S. Public*, pg. 1884
LK TECHNOLOGY IMPORTACAO E EXPORTACAO LTDA—See Gadsden Properties, Inc.; *U.S. Public*, pg. 894
LLC WINCOR NIXDORF—See Diebold Nixdorf, Inc.; *U.S. Public*, pg. 661
LMACP SA—See Alten S.A.; *Int'l*, pg. 390
LOANSOURCE INC.; *U.S. Private*, pg. 2477
LOCAL MARKETING SOLUTIONS GROUP, INC.; *U.S. Private*, pg. 2477
LOCATION INC. GROUP CORPORATION—See Insight Venture Management, LLC; *U.S. Private*, pg. 2089
LOCATION INC. GROUP CORPORATION—See Stone Point Capital LLC; *U.S. Private*, pg. 3822
LOCKHEED MARTIN BUSINESS TECHNOLOGY SOLUTIONS LIMITED—See Lockheed Martin Corporation; *U.S. Public*, pg. 1338
LOCKHEED MARTIN DESKTOP SOLUTIONS, INC.—See Lockheed Martin Corporation; *U.S. Public*, pg. 1338
LOCOMOTE TECHNOLOGIES TRADING PTY. LTD.—See Elliott Management Corporation; *U.S. Private*, pg. 1373
LOCOMOTE TECHNOLOGIES TRADING PTY. LTD.—See Siris Capital Group, LLC; *U.S. Private*, pg. 3674
LOFT INC.; *U.S. Private*, pg. 2480
LOGIC INFORMATION SYSTEMS, INC.—See Accenture plc; *Int'l*, pg. 87
LOGIC WAY B.V.—See Trimble, Inc.; *U.S. Public*, pg. 2190
LOGIGEAR CORPORATION; *U.S. Private*, pg. 2481
LOGIGEAR JAPAN CORPORATION—See Digital Hearts Holdings Co., Ltd.; *Int'l*, pg. 2122
LOGILITY NZ (UC)—See American Software, Inc.; *U.S. Public*, pg. 109
LOGISOFT COMPUTER PRODUCTS, LLC—See RMK Holdings Corp.; *U.S. Public*, pg. 3452
LOGISOLVE, LLC.; *U.S. Private*, pg. 2481
LOGISTIC SOLUTIONS INC.; *U.S. Private*, pg. 2482
LOGMEIN SYSTEMS INDIA PRIVATE LIMITED—See Elliott Management Corporation; *U.S. Private*, pg. 1368
LOGMEIN SYSTEMS INDIA PRIVATE LIMITED—See Francisco Partners Management, LP; *U.S. Private*, pg. 1590
LOQATE LIMITED—See GB Group plc; *Int'l*, pg. 2892
LORD TECHNOL, INC.—See Parker Hannifin Corporation; *U.S. Public*, pg. 1641
LORE IO, INC.—See Clearlake Capital Group, L.P.; *U.S. Private*, pg. 933
LORE IO, INC.—See Insight Venture Management, LLC; *U.S. Private*, pg. 2087
LOYALTY PARTNER SOLUTIONS GMBH—See American Express Company; *U.S. Public*, pg. 102
LTM INC.; *U.S. Private*, pg. 2509

N.A.I.C.S. INDEX

541511 — CUSTOM COMPUTER PRO...

LUBEKONSULT AB—See Eleco Plc; *Int'l*, pg. 2348
LUFTHANSA SYSTEMS AMERICAS, INC.—See Deutsche Lufthansa AG; *Int'l*, pg. 2069
LUMEDX CORP.—See HgCapital Trust plc; *Int'l*, pg. 3376
LUMESIS, INC.—See Solve Advisors Inc.; *U.S. Private*, pg. 3711
LUMINA DATAMATICS, INC.—See Datamatics Global Services Ltd.; *Int'l*, pg. 1979
LUMINA DATAMATICS LIMITED—See Datamatics Global Services Ltd.; *Int'l*, pg. 1979
LUXOFT GMBH—See DXC Technology Company; *U.S. Public*, pg. 696
LUXOFT INDIA LLP—See DXC Technology Company; *U.S. Public*, pg. 696
LUXOFT ITALY S.R.L.—See DXC Technology Company; *U.S. Public*, pg. 696
LUXOFT KOREA LLC—See DXC Technology Company; *U.S. Public*, pg. 696
LUXOFT MALAYSIA SDN. BHD.—See DXC Technology Company; *U.S. Public*, pg. 696
LUXOFT MEXICO S.A. DE C.V.—See DXC Technology Company; *U.S. Public*, pg. 696
LUXOFT SWEDEN AB—See DXC Technology Company; *U.S. Public*, pg. 696
LUXOFT VIETNAM COMPANY LIMITED—See DXC Technology Company; *U.S. Public*, pg. 696
MAASDOTS SDN. BHD.—See G3 Global Berhad; *Int'l*, pg. 2866
MADISON RESEARCH CORPORATION—See Kratos Defense & Security Solutions, Inc.; *U.S. Public*, pg. 1276
MADIVA SOLUCIONES, S.L.—See Banco Bilbao Vizcaya Argentaria, S.A.; *Int'l*, pg. 818
MA FEDERAL INC.; *U.S. Private*, pg. 2530
MAGICAD GROUP OY—See Glodon Co., Ltd.; *Int'l*, pg. 3008
MAGIRUS UK LTD—See Avnet, Inc.; *U.S. Public*, pg. 253
MAGNA5 LLC—See NewSpring Capital LLC; *U.S. Private*, pg. 2918
MAGPIE SOFTWARE SERVICES CORP.—See Syncroness, Inc.; *U.S. Private*, pg. 3903
MAGPLUS INC.—See Bonnier AB; *Int'l*, pg. 1108
MAILUP INC.—See Growens S.p.A.; *Int'l*, pg. 3112
MAINCONCEPT GMBH—See William Morris Endeavor Entertainment, LLC; *U.S. Private*, pg. 4523
MAINCONCEPT JAPAN, INC.—See William Morris Endeavor Entertainment, LLC; *U.S. Private*, pg. 4523
MAINCONCEPT LLC—See William Morris Endeavor Entertainment, LLC; *U.S. Private*, pg. 4523
MAINNERVE FEDERAL SERVICES, INC.—See Castellum, Inc.; *U.S. Public*, pg. 447
MAINSTREAM TECHNOLOGIES, INC; *U.S. Private*, pg. 2553
MAINTECH EUROPE LIMITED—See American CyberSystems, Inc.; *U.S. Private*, pg. 230
MAJESCO—See Thoma Bravo, L.P.; *U.S. Private*, pg. 4149
MAKUAKE, INC.—See CyberAgent, Inc.; *Int'l*, pg. 1892
MAM SOFTWARE, INC.—See KKR & Co. Inc.; *U.S. Public*, pg. 1257
MANHATTAN ASSOCIATES (INDIA) DEVELOPMENT CENTRE PRIVATE LIMITED—See Manhattan Associates, Inc.; *U.S. Public*, pg. 1356
MANHATTAN ASSOCIATES KK—See Manhattan Associates, Inc.; *U.S. Public*, pg. 1356
MANHATTAN ASSOCIATES SOFTWARE (SHANGHAI), CO. LTD.—See Manhattan Associates, Inc.; *U.S. Public*, pg. 1356
MANHATTAN CENTERSTONE, INC.—See Trimble, Inc.; *U.S. Public*, pg. 2190
MANHATTAN DATACRAFT LTD—See Trimble, Inc.; *U.S. Public*, pg. 2190
MANHATTANTECHSUPPORT.COM LLC—See Acrisure, LLC; *U.S. Private*, pg. 65
MANNIX MARKETING, INC.; *U.S. Private*, pg. 2566
MANPOWER BUSINESS SOLUTIONS -RETAIL AS—See ManpowerGroup Inc.; *U.S. Public*, pg. 1360
MANPOWER SERVICES CANADA LIMITED—See ManpowerGroup Inc.; *U.S. Public*, pg. 1359
MANPOWER SLOVAKIA SRO—See ManpowerGroup Inc.; *U.S. Public*, pg. 1359
MANTECH INTERNATIONAL CORPORATION—See The Carlyle Group Inc.; *U.S. Public*, pg. 2048
MANUFACTURING AUTOMATION & SOFTWARE SYSTEM, INC.—See The Brydon Group LLC; *U.S. Private*, pg. 4001
MANZANITA SYSTEMS, LLC—See Xperi Inc.; *U.S. Public*, pg. 2392
MAPDATA SERVICES PTY LTD—See Boustead Singapore Limited; *Int'l*, pg. 1120
MAPLESOFT EUROPE GMBH—See FUJISOFT INCORPORATED; *Int'l*, pg. 2830
MAP LICENSE AS—See Crayon Group AS; *Int'l*, pg. 1829
MAPTEXT, INC.—See Deutsche Lufthansa AG; *Int'l*, pg. 2069
MAQSIMA GMBH—See BASSETTI GROUP SAS; *Int'l*, pg. 888
MARATHON DATA SYSTEMS, INC.—See Chicago Growth Partners, LLC; *U.S. Private*, pg. 877
MARCH NETWORKS (AUSTRALIA) PTY LIMITED—See Delta Electronics, Inc.; *Int'l*, pg. 2018
MARCH NETWORKS (FRANCE) SAS—See Delta Electronics, Inc.; *Int'l*, pg. 2018
MARIADB PLC—See K1 Investment Management, LLC; *U.S. Private*, pg. 2252
MARINE CYBERNETICS AS—See DNV GL Group AS; *Int'l*, pg. 2151
MARIN SOFTWARE GMBH—See Marin Software Inc.; *U.S. Public*, pg. 1366
MARIN SOFTWARE K.K.—See Marin Software Inc.; *U.S. Public*, pg. 1366
MARIN SOFTWARE LIMITED(UK)—See Marin Software Inc.; *U.S. Public*, pg. 1366
MARIN SOFTWARE (SHANGHAI) CO., LTD.—See Marin Software Inc.; *U.S. Public*, pg. 1366
MARITECH DYNAMICS LIMITED—See Symphony Technology Group, LLC; *U.S. Private*, pg. 3902
MARIX TECHNOLOGIES, INC.—See US Internet Corporation; *U.S. Private*, pg. 4319
MARK BOULTON DESIGN LIMITED—See HGGC, LLC; *U.S. Private*, pg. 1930
MARKEM-IMAJE SDN BHD—See Dover Corporation; *U.S. Public*, pg. 680
MARKET DATA SERVICE LLC—See Gridiron Capital, LLC; *U.S. Private*, pg. 1786
MARKETING EVOLUTION, INC.; *U.S. Private*, pg. 2580
MARKETNET, INC.—See Bridgeline Digital, Inc.; *U.S. Public*, pg. 382
MARKLOGIC CORPORATION—See Vector Capital Management, L.P.; *U.S. Private*, pg. 4351
MARKMONITOR INC.—See Clearlake Capital Group, L.P.; *U.S. Private*, pg. 934
MARKMONITOR INC.—See Siris Capital Group, LLC; *U.S. Private*, pg. 3673
MARLABS SOFTWARE PRIVATE LTD.—See Marlabs, Inc.; *U.S. Private*, pg. 2582
MARQUIS SOFTWARE SOLUTIONS, INC.—See Falfurrias Capital Partners, LP; *U.S. Private*, pg. 1467
MARTECH MEDIA—See Waud Capital Partners LLC; *U.S. Private*, pg. 4457
MASSIVE INTERACTIVE, INC.—See Bruins Sports Capital, LLC; *U.S. Private*, pg. 671
MASTERNAUT GMBH—See Compagnie Generale des Etablissements Michelin SCA; *Int'l*, pg. 1743
MATEREALITY, LLC—See I Squared Capital Advisors (US) LLC; *U.S. Private*, pg. 2023
THE MATHWORKS AUSTRALIA PTY LTD—See The Mathworks, Inc.; *U.S. Private*, pg. 4075
THE MATHWORKS KOREA, LLC—See The Mathworks, Inc.; *U.S. Private*, pg. 4076
THE MATHWORKS S.A.S.—See The Mathworks, Inc.; *U.S. Private*, pg. 4076
MATRIKON INC.—See Honeywell International Inc.; *U.S. Public*, pg. 1051
MATTERPORT OPERATING, LLC—See Matterport, Inc.; *U.S. Public*, pg. 1399
MAUTILUS S.R.O.—See Aferian plc; *Int'l*, pg. 185
MAVENIR AUSTRALASIA PTY LTD.—See Siris Capital Group, LLC; *U.S. Private*, pg. 3673
MAVENIR (NZ) LIMITED—See Siris Capital Group, LLC; *U.S. Private*, pg. 3673
MAVENIR SPAIN SL—See Siris Capital Group, LLC; *U.S. Private*, pg. 3673
MAXCOM SERVICES DIVISION—See Platinum Equity, LLC; *U.S. Private*, pg. 3210
MAXIL TECHNOLOGY SOLUTIONS, INC.; *U.S. Private*, pg. 2618
MAX INTERACTIVE PTY LTD.—See Brightcom Group Ltd.; *Int'l*, pg. 1162
MAXSEC GROUP LIMITED—See Ava Risk Group Limited; *Int'l*, pg. 733
MAXXTON B.V.—See Choice Hotels International, Inc.; *U.S. Public*, pg. 490
MAXXTON US CORP.—See Choice Hotels International, Inc.; *U.S. Public*, pg. 490
MBS SYSTEMS, LLC—See Sealaska Corporation; *U.S. Private*, pg. 3585
MCALISTER DESIGN, INC.—See Wauseon Machine and Manufacturing, Inc.; *U.S. Private*, pg. 4457
MCA SOLUTIONS BVBA—See PTC Inc.; *U.S. Public*, pg. 1734
MCCALLIE ASSOCIATES INC.—See Afognak Native Corporation; *U.S. Private*, pg. 124
MCG HEALTH, LLC—See The Hearst Corporation; *U.S. Private*, pg. 4045
MCKESSON PHARMACY SYSTEMS—See McKesson Corporation; *U.S. Public*, pg. 1408
MCLABS, LLC—See The Riverside Company; *U.S. Private*, pg. 4108
MCLOUD D.O.O.—See DHH SpA; *Int'l*, pg. 2099
MCM INTEGRATED TECHNOLOGIES, LTD.—See Occidental Development Group, Inc.; *U.S. Private*, pg. 2988
MCS EUROPE GROUP B.V.—See Addtech AB; *Int'l*, pg. 134
M.D.C. LTD—See Africa Israel Investments Ltd.; *Int'l*, pg. 190
MDS CHINA HOLDING CO., LTD.—See Hancom, Inc.; *Int'l*, pg. 3243
MDS PACIFIC INDIA PVT., LTD.—See Hancom, Inc.; *Int'l*, pg. 3243

MDWERKS, INC.; *U.S. Public*, pg. 1411
MEALSUITE, INC.; *U.S. Private*, pg. 2647
MEAL TICKET; *U.S. Private*, pg. 2647
MED3000 GROUP, INC. - SCOTTSDALE—See McKesson Corporation; *U.S. Public*, pg. 1408
MEDALLIA SPAIN S.L.U.—See Thoma Bravo, L.P.; *U.S. Private*, pg. 4149
MEDECISION, INC.—See Health Care Service Corporation; *U.S. Private*, pg. 1892
MEDEFIS, INC.—See AMN Healthcare Services, Inc.; *U.S. Public*, pg. 125
MEDGINEERING GMBH—See adesso SE; *Int'l*, pg. 144
MEDIACURRENT INTERACTIVE SOLUTIONS LLC—See Stagwell, Inc.; *U.S. Public*, pg. 1927
MEDIAG3, INC.; *U.S. Public*, pg. 1411
MEDIAMATH, INC.—See PaeDae, Inc.; *U.S. Private*, pg. 3074
MEDIAMISER LTD.—See Innodata, Inc.; *U.S. Public*, pg. 1125
MEDIANT COMMUNICATIONS LLC—See Clearlake Capital Group, L.P.; *U.S. Private*, pg. 936
MEDIAOCEAN LLC - LOS ANGELES—See Vista Equity Partners, LLC; *U.S. Private*, pg. 4398
MEDIAOCEAN LLC—See Vista Equity Partners, LLC; *U.S. Private*, pg. 4398
MEDIFOX GMBH—See ECM Equity Capital Management GmbH; *Int'l*, pg. 2291
MEDISTAR PRAXISCOMPUTER GMBH—See CompuGroup Medical SE & Co. KGaA; *Int'l*, pg. 1757
MEDMATICA CONSULTING ASSOCIATES, INC.—See CareCloud, Inc.; *U.S. Public*, pg. 435
MEDPAGES INTERNATIONAL PROPRIETARY LIMITED—See IQVIA Holdings Inc.; *U.S. Public*, pg. 1170
MEDSYNERGIES, INC.—See UnitedHealth Group Incorporated; *U.S. Public*, pg. 2248
MED TECH SOLUTIONS; *U.S. Private*, pg. 2650
MEDUS TECHNOLOGY INC.—See ASUSTeK Computer Inc.; *Int'l*, pg. 664
MELILLO CONSULTING INC.; *U.S. Private*, pg. 2662
MELISSA CORPORATION; *U.S. Private*, pg. 2662
MELTMEDIA; *U.S. Private*, pg. 2663
MERCAREON GMBH—See Trimble, Inc.; *U.S. Public*, pg. 2193
MERCOM CORPORATION; *U.S. Private*, pg. 2670
MERCURY TECHNOLOGIES, INC.; *U.S. Private*, pg. 2671
MERIDIANLINK, INC.—See Thoma Bravo, L.P.; *U.S. Private*, pg. 4150
MERIDIUM, INC.—See General Electric Company; *U.S. Public*, pg. 920
MERSIVE TECHNOLOGIES, INC.—See OpenGate Capital Management, LLC; *U.S. Private*, pg. 3031
MESSAGEGEARS, LLC—See Long Ridge Equity Partners, LLC; *U.S. Private*, pg. 2492
MESTRELAB RESEARCH S.L.—See Bruker Corporation; *U.S. Public*, pg. 404
METAPACK FAR EAST LIMITED—See Thoma Bravo, L.P.; *U.S. Private*, pg. 4154
METAPACK GERMANY GMBH—See Thoma Bravo, L.P.; *U.S. Private*, pg. 4154
METAPACK HOLDINGS USA, INC.—See Thoma Bravo, L.P.; *U.S. Private*, pg. 4154
METAPACK POLAND SP. Z O.O.—See Thoma Bravo, L.P.; *U.S. Private*, pg. 4154
METAPACK SOFTWARE SAS—See Thoma Bravo, L.P.; *U.S. Private*, pg. 4154
METATRON APPS, INC.; *U.S. Public*, pg. 1427
METEOR INKJET LIMITED—See Hybrid Software Group PLC; *Int'l*, pg. 3544
METRONOM AUTOMATION GMBH—See Atlas Copco AB; *Int'l*, pg. 683
METROPOLIS TECHNOLOGIES, INC.—See Eldridge Industries, LLC; *U.S. Private*, pg. 1351
METROPOLITAN INTERACTIVE, LTD.; *U.S. Private*, pg. 2688
METROSTAR SYSTEMS; *U.S. Private*, pg. 2691
MEXESS CO., LTD.—See Cresco, Ltd.; *Int'l*, pg. 1840
MGM INTEGRATION PARTNERS GMBH—See Allgeier SE; *Int'l*, pg. 338
MGM SECURITY PARTNERS GMBH—See Allgeier SE; *Int'l*, pg. 337
MGM TECHNOLOGY PARTNERS EURL—See Allgeier SE; *Int'l*, pg. 337
MGM TECHNOLOGY PARTNERS GMBH—See Allgeier SE; *Int'l*, pg. 338
MGM TECHNOLOGY PARTNERS SCHWEIZ AG—See Allgeier SE; *Int'l*, pg. 337
MGM TECHNOLOGY PARTNERS S.R.O.—See Allgeier SE; *Int'l*, pg. 338
MGM TECHNOLOGY PARTNERS USA CORP.—See Allgeier SE; *Int'l*, pg. 337
MGM TECHNOLOGY PARTNERS VIETNAM CO., LTD.—See Allgeier SE; *Int'l*, pg. 337
MIAMI INTERNATIONAL HOLDINGS, INC.; *U.S. Private*, pg. 2697
M&I CO., LTD.—See CL Holdings Inc.; *Int'l*, pg. 1640
MICROCODE SARL—See Groupe Industriel Marcel Dassault S.A.; *Int'l*, pg. 3105

4619

MICRODESK LLC—See Addnode Group AB; *Int'l*, pg. 130
MICRODOC COMPUTERSYSTEME GMBH—See Adecco Group AG; *Int'l*, pg. 140
MICRO DRAINAGE LIMITED—See Cardno Limited; *Int'l*, pg. 1322
MICROGAME S.P.A.—See Monitor Clipper Partners, LLC; *U.S. Private*, pg. 2770
MICROGEN BANKING SYSTEMS LIMITED—See Aptitude Software Group Plc; *Int'l*, pg. 523
MICROGEN POLAND SP. Z.O.O.—See Aptitude Software Group Plc; *Int'l*, pg. 524
MICROSOFT CORP. - BOISE OFFICE—See Microsoft Corporation; *U.S. Public*, pg. 1439
MICROS SOUTH AFRICA (PTY) LTD—See Constellation Software Inc.; *Int'l*, pg. 1775
MICRO STRATEGIES INC.; *U.S. Private*, pg. 2702
MICROSTRATEGY AUSTRIA GMBH—See MicroStrategy, Inc.; *U.S. Public*, pg. 1443
MICROSTRATEGY BELGIUM BVBA—See MicroStrategy, Inc.; *U.S. Public*, pg. 1443
MICROSTRATEGY BRASIL LTDA.—See MicroStrategy, Inc.; *U.S. Public*, pg. 1443
MICROSTRATEGY IBERICA, S.L.U.—See MicroStrategy, Inc.; *U.S. Public*, pg. 1443
MICROSTRATEGY INDIA PRIVATE LIMITED—See MicroStrategy, Inc.; *U.S. Public*, pg. 1443
MICROSTRATEGY LIMITED—See MicroStrategy, Inc.; *U.S. Public*, pg. 1444
MICROSTRATEGY MIDDLE EAST FZ-LLC—See MicroStrategy, Inc.; *U.S. Public*, pg. 1444
MICROSTRATEGY POLAND SP. Z. O. O.—See MicroStrategy, Inc.; *U.S. Public*, pg. 1444
MICROSTRATEGY SWITZERLAND GMBH—See MicroStrategy, Inc.; *U.S. Public*, pg. 1444
MICROSTRATEGY YAZILIM HIZMETLERI VE URUNLERI LIMITED SIRKETI—See MicroStrategy, Inc.; *U.S. Public*, pg. 1444
MICROSYSTEMS AUTOMATION GROUP; *U.S. Private*, pg. 2704
MICROSYSTEM SRL—See 3D Systems Corporation; *U.S. Public*, pg. 4
MIDDLETON TECHNOLOGY LIMITED—See Thoma Bravo, L.P.; *U.S. Private*, pg. 4149
MIL CORPORATION; *U.S. Private*, pg. 2726
MILES 33 INTERNATIONAL LTD—See Vista Equity Partners, LLC; *U.S. Private*, pg. 4399
MILES 33 SERVICOS EM INFORMATICA LTDA—See Vista Equity Partners, LLC; *U.S. Private*, pg. 4399
MILES 33—See Vista Equity Partners, LLC; *U.S. Private*, pg. 4399
MILES SOFTWARE SOLUTIONS FZ - LLC—See Ebix Inc.; *U.S. Public*, pg. 710
MILES SOFTWARE SOLUTIONS INC.—See Ebix Inc.; *U.S. Public*, pg. 710
MILES SOFTWARE SOLUTIONS UK LIMITED—See Ebix Inc.; *U.S. Public*, pg. 710
MILESTONE TECHNOLOGIES INC.—See H.I.G. Capital, LLC; *U.S. Private*, pg. 1831
MILLENNIUM SOFTWARE DEVELOPERS, INC.—See AccuTitle LLC; *U.S. Private*, pg. 55
MIMO TECH COMPANY LIMITED—See Advanced Info Service Plc; *Int'l*, pg. 160
MIM SOFTWARE INC.—See GE HealthCare Technologies Inc.; *U.S. Public*, pg. 909
MINAMIOSAKA COMPUTING CENTER CO., LTD.—See Cyberlinks Co., Ltd.; *Int'l*, pg. 1893
MIND OVER MACHINES, INC.; *U.S. Private*, pg. 2740
MINDWAY APS—See Better Collective A/S; *Int'l*, pg. 1003
MINERP CANADA LIMITED—See Epiroc AB; *Int'l*, pg. 2463
MINERP—See FirstRand Limited; *Int'l*, pg. 2690
MINERP—See Hasso Plattner Ventures Africa (Pty) Ltd.; *Int'l*, pg. 3283
MINERVA ASSOCIATES, INC.—See Connell Limited Partnership; *U.S. Private*, pg. 1017
MINING INFORMATION SYSTEMS, INC.—See Trimble, Inc.; *U.S. Public*, pg. 2190
MINUS5 D.O.O.—See Entain PLC; *Int'l*, pg. 2450
MIRABEAU B.V.—See Cognizant Technology Solutions Corporation; *U.S. Public*, pg. 524
MIRACLE SOFTWARE SYSTEMS INC.; *U.S. Private*, pg. 2745
MISSION CLOUD SERVICES INC.—See CDW Corporation; *U.S. Public*, pg. 462
MISYS INTERNATIONAL BANKING SYSTEMS (CIS) LIMITED—See Vista Equity Partners, LLC; *U.S. Private*, pg. 4397
MISYS INTERNATIONAL BANKING SYSTEMS GMBH—See Vista Equity Partners, LLC; *U.S. Private*, pg. 4397
MISYS INTERNATIONAL BANKING SYSTEMS INC.—See Vista Equity Partners, LLC; *U.S. Private*, pg. 4397
MISYS INTERNATIONAL BANKING SYSTEMS K.K—See Vista Equity Partners, LLC; *U.S. Private*, pg. 4397
MISYS INTERNATIONAL BANKING SYSTEMS LIMITED—See Vista Equity Partners, LLC; *U.S. Private*, pg. 4397
MISYS INTERNATIONAL BANKING SYSTEMS LIMITED—See Vista Equity Partners, LLC; *U.S. Private*, pg. 4397
MISYS INTERNATIONAL BANKING SYSTEMS MEXICO S.A. DE CV—See Vista Equity Partners, LLC; *U.S. Private*, pg. 4397
MISYS INTERNATIONAL BANKING SYSTEMS PTY LIMITED—See Vista Equity Partners, LLC; *U.S. Private*, pg. 4397
MISYS INTERNATIONAL BANKING SYSTEMS SA—See Vista Equity Partners, LLC; *U.S. Private*, pg. 4397
MISYS INTERNATIONAL BANKING SYSTEMS SA—See Vista Equity Partners, LLC; *U.S. Private*, pg. 4397
MISYS INTERNATIONAL FINANCIAL SYSTEMS PTE LIMITED—See Vista Equity Partners, LLC; *U.S. Private*, pg. 4397
MISYS INTERNATIONAL FINANCIAL SYSTEMS (PTY) LIMITED—See Vista Equity Partners, LLC; *U.S. Private*, pg. 4397
MISYS INTERNATIONAL FINANCIAL SYSTEMS S.L.—See Vista Equity Partners, LLC; *U.S. Private*, pg. 4397
MISYS INTERNATIONAL SYSTEMS SDN BHD—See Vista Equity Partners, LLC; *U.S. Private*, pg. 4397
MISYS IQ LLC—See Vista Equity Partners, LLC; *U.S. Private*, pg. 4397
MISYS NETHERLANDS BV—See Vista Equity Partners, LLC; *U.S. Private*, pg. 4397
MISYS PHILIPPINES INC—See Vista Equity Partners, LLC; *U.S. Private*, pg. 4397
MISYS SERVICES LIMITED—See Vista Equity Partners, LLC; *U.S. Private*, pg. 4397
MISYS SOFTWARE SOLUTIONS (INDIA) PRIVATE LIMITED—See Vista Equity Partners, LLC; *U.S. Private*, pg. 4397
MISYS WHOLESALE BANKING SYSTEMS—See Vista Equity Partners, LLC; *U.S. Private*, pg. 4397
MITCHELL ONE—See Snap-on Incorporated; *U.S. Public*, pg. 1897
MITEK SYSTEMS B.V.—See Mitek Systems, Inc.; *U.S. Public*, pg. 1452
MITEK SYSTEMS PRIVATE LIMITED—See Mitek Systems, Inc.; *U.S. Public*, pg. 1452
MITEL NETWORKS LTD.—See Searchlight Capital Partners, L.P.; *U.S. Private*, pg. 3589
MITEL SOUTH AFRICA—See Searchlight Capital Partners, L.P.; *U.S. Private*, pg. 3589
MITEM CORPORATION; *U.S. Private*, pg. 2751
MITRAIS PTE. LTD.—See CAC Holdings Corporation; *Int'l*, pg. 1247
MIVA MERCHANT, INC.; *U.S. Private*, pg. 2752
MIXAMO, INC.—See Adobe Inc.; *U.S. Public*, pg. 42
MIXBOOK INC.; *U.S. Private*, pg. 2752
MIXT SOLUTIONS LLC; *U.S. Private*, pg. 2752
MMIX BISCOM INC.; *U.S. Private*, pg. 2755
MMO TECH CO., LTD.—See Advanced Info Service Plc; *Int'l*, pg. 160
MOBESTREAM MEDIA, INC.—See inMarket Media LLC; *U.S. Private*, pg. 2079
MOBICA LIMITED SP. Z O.O.—See Cognizant Technology Solutions Corporation; *U.S. Public*, pg. 525
MOBICA US INC.—See Cognizant Technology Solutions Corporation; *U.S. Public*, pg. 525
MOBIENTS INC.; *U.S. Private*, pg. 2756
MOBILEAXEPT NORTH AMERICA, INC.—See i3 Verticals, Inc.; *U.S. Public*, pg. 1081
MOBILECAUSE, INC.—See Insight Venture Management, LLC; *U.S. Private*, pg. 2088
MOBILE CREATE USA, INC.—See Future Innovation Group, Inc.; *Int'l*, pg. 2856
MOBILE DATA TECHNOLOGIES LTD.—See Patterson-UTI Energy, Inc.; *U.S. Public*, pg. 1654
MOBILE DEFENSE, INC.—See Assurant, Inc.; *U.S. Public*, pg. 215
MOBILE GLOBAL EXPORTS INC.; *U.S. Private*, pg. 2757
MOBILEYE GLOBAL INC.—See Intel Corporation; *U.S. Public*, pg. 1139
MOBISOFT OY—See DDS Wireless International Inc.; *Int'l*, pg. 1994
MOBLICO SOLUTIONS, LLC—See SS&C Technologies Holdings, Inc.; *U.S. Public*, pg. 1923
MODEL N INDIA SOFTWARE PRIVATE LIMITED—See Model N, Inc.; *U.S. Public*, pg. 1454
MODEL N UK LIMITED—See Model N, Inc.; *U.S. Public*, pg. 1454
MODERN MESSAGE, INC.—See Thoma Bravo, L.P.; *U.S. Private*, pg. 4153
MODSYS INTERNATIONAL LTD.—See Advanced Business Software & Solutions Ltd.; *Int'l*, pg. 157
MODUS CREATE, LLC; *U.S. Private*, pg. 2764
MOLI GROUP LIMITED—See Celestial Asia Securities Holdings Limited; *Int'l*, pg. 1392
MOMENTIVE GLOBAL INC.—See Symphony Technology Group, LLC; *U.S. Private*, pg. 3901
MONETATE, INC.—See Centre Lane Partners, LLC; *U.S. Private*, pg. 827
MONGODB LIMITED—See MongoDB, Inc.; *U.S. Public*, pg. 1464
MONKEDIA LLC; *U.S. Private*, pg. 2771
MONOTYPE HONG KONG LIMITED—See HGGC, LLC; *U.S. Private*, pg. 1930
MONOTYPE IMAGING HOLDINGS, INC.—See HGGC, LLC; *U.S. Private*, pg. 1930
MONOTYPE IMAGING, INC.—See HGGC, LLC; *U.S. Private*, pg. 1930
MONOTYPE KK—See HGGC, LLC; *U.S. Private*, pg. 1930
MONOTYPE LIMITED—See HGGC, LLC; *U.S. Private*, pg. 1930
MONSOON COMPANY—See Capital One Financial Corporation; *U.S. Public*, pg. 431
MONTA GORINCHEM EDISONWEG B.V.—See Deutsche Post AG; *Int'l*, pg. 2082
MOODY'S ANALYTICS (DIFC) LIMITED—See Moody's Corporation; *U.S. Public*, pg. 1468
MOORE RESOURCE SYSTEMS (ONTARIO) LIMITED—See Enghouse Systems Limited; *Int'l*, pg. 2427
MOOVIT SOFTWARE PRODUCTS GMBH—See Avemio AG; *Int'l*, pg. 738
MOQDIGITAL PTY LTD—See Brennan IT Pty. Limited; *Int'l*, pg. 1145
MOQ LTD.—See Brennan IT Pty. Limited; *Int'l*, pg. 1145
MOREDIRECT, INC.—See PC Connection, Inc.; *U.S. Public*, pg. 1658
MORE I.T. RESOURCES LTD.—See Dell Technologies Inc.; *U.S. Public*, pg. 651
MORE MAGIC SOLUTIONS, INC.—See Advent International Corporation; *U.S. Private*, pg. 102
MORTGAGEFLEX SYSTEMS INC.; *U.S. Private*, pg. 2791
MOTIFWORKS, INC.; *U.S. Private*, pg. 2795
MOTIONDSP, INC.—See Elliott Management Corporation; *U.S. Private*, pg. 1368
MOTIONDSP, INC.—See Veritas Capital Fund Management, LLC; *U.S. Private*, pg. 4362
MOTIONSOFT, INC.—See GI Manager L.P.; *U.S. Private*, pg. 1692
MOTORIT AB—See Bilia AB; *Int'l*, pg. 1029
MOTOROLA SOLUTIONS SYSTEMS POLSKA SP. Z O.O.—See Motorola Solutions, Inc.; *U.S. Public*, pg. 1478
MOYO GROUP, INC.—See Kalio, Inc.; *U.S. Private*, pg. 2257
M-PATHY GMBH—See Verint Systems Inc.; *U.S. Public*, pg. 2281
MPP GLOBAL SOLUTIONS LIMITED—See Aptitude Software Group Plc; *Int'l*, pg. 523
MPS DEVELOPMENT INC—See Trimble, Inc.; *U.S. Public*, pg. 2190
MQSOFTWARE GMBH MIDDLEWARE SOLUTIONS—See KKR & Co. Inc.; *U.S. Public*, pg. 1241
M S A SYSTEMS, INC.—See Odyssey Investment Partners, LLC; *U.S. Private*, pg. 2994
MSCI CANADA INC.—See MSCI Inc.; *U.S. Public*, pg. 1483
MSC.SOFTWARE AB—See Hexagon AB; *Int'l*, pg. 3369
MSE AUGSBURG GMBH—See Advent International Corporation; *U.S. Private*, pg. 97
MSE AUGSBURG GMBH—See Centerbridge Partners, L.P.; *U.S. Private*, pg. 813
MSE IMMOBILIENSOFTWARE GMBH—See Advent International Corporation; *U.S. Private*, pg. 97
MSE IMMOBILIENSOFTWARE GMBH—See Centerbridge Partners, L.P.; *U.S. Private*, pg. 813
MSL ENTERPRISES, INC.—See Enterprise Onsite Services Co.; *U.S. Private*, pg. 1404
MTS KOREA, INC.—See Amphenol Corporation; *U.S. Public*, pg. 131
MTS SYSTEMS (HONG KONG) INC.—See Amphenol Corporation; *U.S. Public*, pg. 131
MTT-PRO S.R.L.—See Ardian SAS; *Int'l*, pg. 555
MULTIMODAL TECHNOLOGIES, LLC—See Solventum Corporation; *U.S. Public*, pg. 1902
MULTI SERVICE PTY LIMITED—See World Kinect Corporation; *U.S. Public*, pg. 2381
MURASAKI TECHNOLOGY SDN. BHD.—See EA Holdings Berhad; *Int'l*, pg. 2261
MVTRAC, LLC; *U.S. Private*, pg. 2822
MYDIGITALOFFICE.COM, LLC—See myDigitalOffice Holdings Inc.; *U.S. Private*, pg. 2824
MYMIC LLC; *U.S. Private*, pg. 2825
MYPHOTOBOOK GMBH—See Carl Bennet AB; *Int'l*, pg. 1332
MYVEST CORPORATION—See Teachers Insurance Association - College Retirement Fund; *U.S. Private*, pg. 3945
N2PLAY CO., LTD.—See CJ Corporation; *Int'l*, pg. 1634
NADHI INFORMATION TECHNOLOGIES PRIVATE LIMITED—See Bentley Systems, Inc.; *U.S. Public*, pg. 297
NAGARRO AS—See Allgeier SE; *Int'l*, pg. 337
NAGARRO GMBH—See Allgeier SE; *Int'l*, pg. 337
NAGARRO INC.—See Allgeier SE; *Int'l*, pg. 337
NAGARRO K.K.—See Allgeier SE; *Int'l*, pg. 337
NAGARRO PTY. LTD.—See Allgeier SE; *Int'l*, pg. 337
NAGARRO SDN. BHD.—See Allgeier SE; *Int'l*, pg. 337
NAGARRO SOFTWARE AB—See Allgeier SE; *Int'l*, pg. 337
NAGARRO SOFTWARE A/S—See Allgeier SE; *Int'l*, pg. 337
NAGARRO SOFTWARE GMBH—See Allgeier SE; *Int'l*, pg. 337

541511 — CUSTOM COMPUTER PRO...

NAGARRO SOFTWARE PVT. LTD.—See Allgeier SE; *Int'l*, pg. 337
NAGARRO SOFTWARE S.A.—See Allgeier SE; *Int'l*, pg. 337
NAGARRO SOFTWARE SAS—See Allgeier SE; *Int'l*, pg. 337
NAGARRO SOFTWARE SRL—See Allgeier SE; *Int'l*, pg. 337
NANJING SILVERSTONE COMPUTER SYSTEM CO., LTD.—See Beijing Shiji Information Technology Co., Ltd.; *Int'l*, pg. 956
NASDAQ OMX (SOUTH EAST ASIA & PACIFIC) PTE. LTD.—See Nasdaq, Inc.; *U.S. Public*, pg. 1492
NATIONAL CENTER FOR SAFETY INITIATIVES, LLC—See Comcast Corporation; *U.S. Public*, pg. 541
NATIONAL COMPUTER SERVICES; *U.S. Private*, pg. 2851
NATIONAL INSTRUMENTS AM LLC—See National Instruments Corporation; *U.S. Private*, pg. 2857
NATIONAL INSTRUMENTS BRAZIL LTDA.—See National Instruments Corporation; *U.S. Private*, pg. 2857
NATIONAL INSTRUMENTS CHILE SPA.—See National Instruments Corporation; *U.S. Private*, pg. 2857
NATIONAL INSTRUMENTS COLOMBIA SAS—See National Instruments Corporation; *U.S. Private*, pg. 2857
NATIONAL INSTRUMENTS DENMARK APS—See National Instruments Corporation; *U.S. Private*, pg. 2857
NATIONAL INSTRUMENTS EGYPT LLC—See National Instruments Corporation; *U.S. Private*, pg. 2857
NATIONAL INSTRUMENTS FRANCE SAS—See National Instruments Corporation; *U.S. Private*, pg. 2857
NATIONAL INSTRUMENTS ITALY S.R.L.—See National Instruments Corporation; *U.S. Private*, pg. 2857
NATIONAL INSTRUMENTS JAPAN KK—See National Instruments Corporation; *U.S. Private*, pg. 2857
NATIONAL INSTRUMENTS LEBANON SARL—See National Instruments Corporation; *U.S. Private*, pg. 2857
NATIONAL INSTRUMENTS POLAND SP. Z.O.O.—See National Instruments Corporation; *U.S. Private*, pg. 2857
NATIONAL INSTRUMENTS PORTUGAL UNIPESSOAL LDA.—See National Instruments Corporation; *U.S. Private*, pg. 2857
NATIONAL INSTRUMENTS RUS LLC—See National Instruments Corporation; *U.S. Private*, pg. 2857
NATIONAL INSTRUMENTS SAUDI ARABIA, LLC—See National Instruments Corporation; *U.S. Private*, pg. 2857
NATIONAL INSTRUMENTS SPAIN, S.L.—See National Instruments Corporation; *U.S. Private*, pg. 2857
NAVIGANCE GMBH—See Clariant AG; *Int'l*, pg. 1648
NCINO APAC PTY LTD—See nCino, Inc.; *U.S. Public*, pg. 1501
NCINO CANADA, INC.—See nCino, Inc.; *U.S. Public*, pg. 1501
NCINO GLOBAL LTD.—See nCino, Inc.; *U.S. Public*, pg. 1501
NCINO, INC.; *U.S. Public*, pg. 1501
NCINO K.K.—See nCino, Inc.; *U.S. Public*, pg. 1501
N-DESIGN GESELLSCHAFT FUR SYSTEMATISCHE GESTALTUNGEN MBH—See CompuGroup Medical SE & Co. KGaA; *Int'l*, pg. 1757
NDS INFORMATION SYSTEM CO., LTD—See COMSYS Holdings Corporation; *Int'l*, pg. 1761
NEARSHORE TECHNOLOGY COMPANY, LLC; *U.S. Private*, pg. 2877
NEDGEX GMBH—See Erich Netzsch GmbH & Co. Holding KG; *Int'l*, pg. 2492
NEDSENSE LOFT B.V.—See LOFT Inc.; *U.S. Private*, pg. 2480
NELITO SYTEMS LIMITED—See DTS Corporation; *Int'l*, pg. 2217
NEOSPEECH, INC.—See Hoya Corporation; *Int'l*, pg. 3497
NEOSYSTEMS INC.—See AppDirect Inc.; *U.S. Private*, pg. 296
NERVOGRID NETHERLANDS—See Droege Group AG; *Int'l*, pg. 2205
NESS TECHNOLOGIES, INC.—See KKR & Co. Inc.; *U.S. Public*, pg. 1261
NETCAPITAL INC.; *U.S. Public*, pg. 1507
NETCENTRIC AG—See Cognizant Technology Solutions Corporation; *U.S. Public*, pg. 525
NETCENTRIC BENELUX BV—See Cognizant Technology Solutions Corporation; *U.S. Public*, pg. 525
NETCENTRIC DEUTSCHLAND GMBH—See Cognizant Technology Solutions Corporation; *U.S. Public*, pg. 525
NETCENTRIC EASTERN EUROPE S.R.L.—See Cognizant Technology Solutions Corporation; *U.S. Public*, pg. 525
NETCENTRIC IBERICA SLU—See Cognizant Technology Solutions Corporation; *U.S. Public*, pg. 525
NETCLIME-BULGARIA EOOD—See Deluxe Corporation; *U.S. Public*, pg. 653
NETEDI LTD.—See Cegedim S.A.; *Int'l*, pg. 1390
NETGAIN TECHNOLOGY INC.; *U.S. Private*, pg. 2887
NET HEALTH SYSTEMS, INC.—See Level Equity Management, LLC; *U.S. Private*, pg. 2434
NET HEALTH SYSTEMS, INC.—See Silversmith Management, L.P.; *U.S. Private*, pg. 3664
NET HEALTH SYSTEMS, INC.—See The Carlyle Group Inc.; *U.S. Public*, pg. 2050
NET-INSPECT; *U.S. Private*, pg. 2886
NETMOTION SOFTWARE CANADA, INC.—See Crosspoint Capital Partners LP; *U.S. Private*, pg. 1107
NETSCOUT SYSTEMS TEXAS, LLC—See NetScout Systems, Inc.; *U.S. Public*, pg. 1509
NETSENSE BUSINES SOLUTIONS PTE. LTD.—See Censof Holdings Berhad; *Int'l*, pg. 1402
NETSOFT HOLDINGS, LLC; *U.S. Private*, pg. 2888
NETSOL OMNI (PRIVATE) LTD.—See NetSol Technologies, Inc.; *U.S. Public*, pg. 1509
NETSOL TECHNOLOGIES AUSTRALIA PTY LIMITED—See NetSol Technologies, Inc.; *U.S. Public*, pg. 1509
NETSOL TECHNOLOGIES THAILAND LIMITED—See NetSol Technologies, Inc.; *U.S. Public*, pg. 1509
NETSUITE CANADA INC.—See Oracle Corporation; *U.S. Public*, pg. 1611
NETTIME SOLUTIONS LLC—See Paychex, Inc.; *U.S. Public*, pg. 1655
NETWORK-1 TECHNOLOGIES, INC.; *U.S. Public*, pg. 1509
NETWORKED INSIGHTS, INC.—See American Family Mutual Insurance Company; *U.S. Private*, pg. 233
NETWORKERS TELECOMMUNICATIONS INC—See Gattaca plc; *Int'l*, pg. 2890
NETWRIX CORPORATION—See TA Associates, Inc.; *U.S. Private*, pg. 3916
NETXPOSURE, INC.; *U.S. Private*, pg. 2890
NEURAL TECHNOLOGY LIMITED—See Thoma Bravo, L.P.; *U.S. Private*, pg. 4149
NEUSTAR COSTA RICA LIMITADA—See TransUnion; *U.S. Public*, pg. 2184
NEUSTAR DATA INFOTECH (INDIA) PRIVATE LIMITED—See TransUnion; *U.S. Public*, pg. 2184
NEVERBOUNCE, LLC—See ZoomInfo Technologies Inc.; *U.S. Public*, pg. 2411
NEWAGESYS, INC.; *U.S. Private*, pg. 2913
NEW DIRECTIONS GMBH—See freenet AG; *Int'l*, pg. 2771
NEW ENGLAND SYSTEMS INC.—See Micro Strategies Inc.; *U.S. Private*, pg. 2702
NEWNET COMMUNICATION TECHNOLOGIES, LLC—See Skyview Capital, LLC; *U.S. Private*, pg. 3686
NEW PROIMAGE AMERICA INC.—See Agfa-Gevaert N.V.; *Int'l*, pg. 209
NEW PROIMAGE LTD.—See Agfa-Gevaert N.V.; *Int'l*, pg. 209
NEW SIGNATURE US, INC.—See Cognizant Technology Solutions Corporation; *U.S. Public*, pg. 525
NEXANTIS CORPORATION—See Dai Nippon Printing Co., Ltd.; *Int'l*, pg. 1916
NEXG CO., LTD.—See Hansol Group; *Int'l*, pg. 3261
NEXPRISE, INC.; *U.S. Private*, pg. 2919
NEXSCIENT, INC.; *U.S. Public*, pg. 1522
NEXTANCE, INC.—See ESW Capital, LLC; *U.S. Private*, pg. 1430
NEXTBIO—See Illumina, Inc.; *U.S. Public*, pg. 1112
NEXT CENTURY CORPORATION; *U.S. Private*, pg. 2919
NEXT GALAXY CORP.; *U.S. Private*, pg. 2919
NEXTGEN INFORMATION SERVICES, INC.; *U.S. Private*, pg. 2921
NEXTLOT, INC; *U.S. Private*, pg. 2921
NEXTONLINE LIMITED—See Compass Group PLC; *Int'l*, pg. 1752
NEXTWORLD, LLC; *U.S. Private*, pg. 2921
NEXUS SYSTEMS, INC.—See Thoma Bravo, L.P.; *U.S. Private*, pg. 4146
NEXXTEP TECHNOLOGY SERVICES, INC.—See Spire Capital Partners, LLC; *U.S. Private*, pg. 3757
NICIRA, INC.—See Broadcom Inc.; *U.S. Public*, pg. 390
NIC TECHNOLOGIES, LLC—See Tyler Technologies, Inc.; *U.S. Public*, pg. 2208
NIGHTINGALE INTELLIGENT SYSTEMS INC.; *U.S. Private*, pg. 1528
NIHAKI SYSTEMS, INC.; *U.S. Private*, pg. 2927
NIHON BUSINESS SOFT CO., LTD.—See FUJISOFT INCORPORATED; *Int'l*, pg. 2830
NIIT MALAYSIA SDN BHD.—See Coforge Ltd.; *Int'l*, pg. 1693
NIIT TECHNOLOGIES INC.—See Coforge Ltd.; *Int'l*, pg. 1693
NIKSOFT SYSTEMS CORPORATION; *U.S. Private*, pg. 2927
NINTEX GLOBAL LTD.—See TPG Capital, L.P.; *U.S. Public*, pg. 2175
NIONEX GMBH—See Bertelsmann SE & Co. KGaA; *Int'l*, pg. 995
NIPPON COLUMBIA CO., LTD.—See Faith, Inc.; *Int'l*, pg. 2609
NIPPON INFORMATION & COMMUNICATION CORPORATION—See International Business Machines Corporation; *U.S. Public*, pg. 1147
NISHITELE INFORMATION & SCIENCE CO., LTD—See Computer Engineering & Consulting Ltd.; *Int'l*, pg. 1759
NI TAIWAN CORPORATION—See National Instruments Corporation; *U.S. Private*, pg. 2857
NJEVITY, INC.; *U.S. Private*, pg. 2930
NMR CONSULTING; *U.S. Private*, pg. 2931
NODUS TECHNOLOGIES, INC.—See Global Payments Inc.; *U.S. Public*, pg. 943
NOEMALIFE ARGENTINA SRL—See Ardian SAS; *Int'l*, pg. 555
NOEMALIFE CHILE—See Ardian SAS; *Int'l*, pg. 555
NOEMALIFE GMBH—See Ardian SAS; *Int'l*, pg. 555
NOEMALIFE MENA FZ-LLC—See Ardian SAS; *Int'l*, pg. 555
NOEMALIFE MEXICO DE RL DE CV—See Ardian SAS; *Int'l*, pg. 555
NOEMALIFE S.P.A.—See Ardian SAS; *Int'l*, pg. 555
NOEMALIFE UK LTD—See Ardian SAS; *Int'l*, pg. 555
NOEO, GMBH—See The Healing Company Inc.; *U.S. Public*, pg. 2088
NOESIS SOLUTIONS NV—See FUJISOFT INCORPORATED; *Int'l*, pg. 2830
NOLOCK SOFTWARELOSUNGEN GMBH—See CTS Eventim AG & Co. KGaA; *Int'l*, pg. 1874
NOMAD DIGITAL FRANCE SARL—See Alstom S.A.; *Int'l*, pg. 383
NOMAD DIGITAL ITALIA S.R.L.—See Alstom S.A.; *Int'l*, pg. 383
NO MAGIC INC.—See Dassault Systemes S.A.; *Int'l*, pg. 1975
NOMIS SOLUTIONS, INC.—See Symphony Technology Group, LLC; *U.S. Private*, pg. 3901
NOOSH INC.; *U.S. Private*, pg. 2935
NORDIC INSURANCE SOFTWARE A/S—See Acturis Ltd.; *Int'l*, pg. 121
NORMOND INFO SAS—See Danaher Corporation; *U.S. Public*, pg. 629
THE NORTHEAST TEXAS DATA CORP.—See i3 Verticals, Inc.; *U.S. Public*, pg. 1081
NOTHING BUT NET, LLC—See PLJ Information Systems, Inc.; *U.S. Private*, pg. 3214
NOUVELLES SOLUTIONS INFORMATIQUES-N.S.I.—See Cegeka Groep NV; *Int'l*, pg. 1391
NOVA DEVELOPMENT CORP.—See Claranova SA; *Int'l*, pg. 1642
NOVA LIBRA, INC.—See GrubMarket, Inc.; *U.S. Private*, pg. 1797
NOWDOCS INTERNATIONAL, INC.—See Taylor Corporation; *U.S. Private*, pg. 3938
NOWFORCE LIMITED—See Verint Systems Inc.; *U.S. Public*, pg. 2281
NPG HEALTH LLC; *U.S. Private*, pg. 2969
NRI SYSTEM TECHNO, LTD.—See Ajinomoto Company, Inc.; *Int'l*, pg. 257
NSI S.A.—See Capgemini SE; *Int'l*, pg. 1305
N-SYSTEM CORPORATION—See Cresco, Ltd.; *Int'l*, pg. 1840
NTS TECHNOLOGY SERVICES PRIVATE LIMITED—See News Corporation; *U.S. Public*, pg. 1520
NTT SECURITY APPSEC SOLUTIONS INC.—See Synopsys, Inc.; *U.S. Public*, pg. 1970
NUANCE COMMUNICATIONS AUSTRALIA PTY LTD.—See Microsoft Corporation; *U.S. Public*, pg. 1442
NUANCE COMMUNICATIONS AUSTRIA GMBH—See Microsoft Corporation; *U.S. Public*, pg. 1442
NUANCE COMMUNICATIONS CANADA, INC.—See Microsoft Corporation; *U.S. Public*, pg. 1442
NUANCE COMMUNICATIONS JAPAN K.K.—See Microsoft Corporation; *U.S. Public*, pg. 1442
NUANCE COMMUNICATIONS KOREA LTD.—See Microsoft Corporation; *U.S. Public*, pg. 1442
NUANCE DOCUMENT IMAGING SOLUTIONS—See Microsoft Corporation; *U.S. Public*, pg. 1442
NUANCE ENTERPRISE SOLUTIONS & SERVICES CORPORATION—See Microsoft Corporation; *U.S. Public*, pg. 1442
NUANCE INDIA PVT. LTD.—See Microsoft Corporation; *U.S. Public*, pg. 1443
NUANCE SOFTWARE TECHNOLOGY (BEIJING) CO., LTD.—See Microsoft Corporation; *U.S. Public*, pg. 1443
NUBEVA TECHNOLOGIES LTD.; *U.S. Public*, pg. 1553
NUL ACCESSIBILITY, LTD.—See BIPROGY Inc.; *Int'l*, pg. 1045
NUMARA SOFTWARE (FRANCE) SAS—See KKR & Co. Inc.; *U.S. Public*, pg. 1241
NUMARA SOFTWARE LIMITED—See KKR & Co. Inc.; *U.S. Public*, pg. 1241
NUMSP LLC—See Tonka Bay Equity Partners LLC; *U.S. Private*, pg. 4185
NWC SERVICES GMBH—See CANCOM SE; *Int'l*, pg. 1289
NWN CORPORATION—See American Securities LLC; *U.S. Private*, pg. 250
NWORK CO., LTD.—See EDION Corporation; *Int'l*, pg. 2310
NXCHAIN, INC.; *U.S. Private*, pg. 2975
OASYS AUSTRALIA PTY LTD—See Arup Group Ltd.; *Int'l*, pg. 587
OASYS LIMITED—See Arup Group Ltd.; *Int'l*, pg. 587
OASYS MOBILE, INC.; *U.S. Private*, pg. 2986
OBJECTIF LUNE ASIA PTY. LTD.—See Upland Software, Inc.; *U.S. Public*, pg. 2264
OBJECTIF LUNE CAPTURE INC.—See Upland Software, Inc.; *U.S. Public*, pg. 2264
OBJECTIF LUNE GMBH—See Upland Software, Inc.; *U.S. Public*, pg. 2264
OBJECTIVA SOFTWARE SOLUTIONS (BEIJING) CO., LTD.—See Allgeier SE; *Int'l*, pg. 337
OBJECTIVA SOFTWARE SOLUTIONS, INC.—See Allgeier SE; *Int'l*, pg. 337
OBJECTIVA SOFTWARE SOLUTIONS (XI'AN) CO.,

LTD.—See Allgeier SE; *Int'l*, pg. 337
OBJECTIVITY INC.; *U.S. Private*, pg. 2987
OBJECT SYSTEMS GROUP INC.; *U.S. Private*, pg. 2987
OBJECTVIDEO LABS, LLC—See ABS Capital Partners, L.P.; *U.S. Private*, pg. 44
OBJECTWIN TECHNOLOGY, INC.; *U.S. Private*, pg. 2987
OBLONG INDUSTRIES, INC.—See Oblong, Inc.; *U.S. Public*, pg. 1560
OBSCURE TECHNOLOGY PROPRIETARY LIMITED—See Alviva Holdings Limited; *Int'l*, pg. 402
OBSERVEPOINT LLC; *U.S. Private*, pg. 2987
OBSIDIAN ENTERTAINMENT, INC.—See Microsoft Corporation; *U.S. Public*, pg. 1440
OCEAN CLOUD TECHNOLOGY CO., LIMITED—See MicroCloud Hologram Inc.; *U.S. Public*, pg. 1437
OCEAN NEXUS SDN. BHD.—See I Synergy Group Limited; *Int'l*, pg. 3562
OCEANWIDE EUROPE LIMITED—See GI Manager L.P.; *U.S. Private*, pg. 1692
OCE-FINLAND OY—See Canon Inc.; *Int'l*, pg. 1294
OCHRESOFT TECHNOLOGIES LTD.—See Daily Mail & General Trust plc; *Int'l*, pg. 1938
OCTFOLIO PTY LTD—See HRL Holdings Limited; *Int'l*, pg. 3501
ODECEE PTY LIMITED—See Cognizant Technology Solutions Corporation; *U.S. Public*, pg. 525
ODS TECHNOLOGIES LP—See Flutter Entertainment plc; *Int'l*, pg. 2715
OFFICEMATE SOFTWARE SOLUTIONS—See Vision Service Plan; *U.S. Private*, pg. 4391
OFF MARKET DATA, INC.; *U.S. Private*, pg. 3001
OFFSPRING SOLUTIONS; *U.S. Private*, pg. 3003
OHB DIGITAL SERVICES GMBH—See Hiscox Ltd.; *Int'l*, pg. 3407
OIDON CO., LTD.; *U.S. Public*, pg. 1565
OKINAWA HITACHI NETWORK SYSTEMS, LTD.—See Hitachi, Ltd.; *Int'l*, pg. 3423
OKTA AUSTRALIA PTY LIMITED—See Okta, Inc.; *U.S. Public*, pg. 1566
OKTA, INC.; *U.S. Public*, pg. 1566
OLAS SOFTWARE TRAINING AND DEVELOPMENT LIMITED—See Fonds de Solidarite des Travailleurs du Quebec; *Int'l*, pg. 2725
OLO INC.; *U.S. Public*, pg. 1570
OMELIA LIMITED—See Acsion Limited; *Int'l*, pg. 117
OMNICOMM EUROPE GMBH.—See ABRY Partners, LLC; *U.S. Private*, pg. 41
OMNICOMM SYSTEMS B.V—See ABRY Partners, LLC; *U.S. Private*, pg. 41
OMNI RESOURCES INC—See Saggezza Inc.; *U.S. Private*, pg. 3528
OMNYON LLC—See Alpine Investors; *U.S. Private*, pg. 201
ON CENTER SOFTWARE, INC.—See Roper Technologies, Inc.; *U.S. Public*, pg. 1812
ONEBRIDGE SOLUTIONS, INC.—See Blackstone Inc.; *U.S. Public*, pg. 355
ONEBRIDGE SOLUTIONS INC.—See Blackstone Inc.; *U.S. Public*, pg. 355
ONEEVENT TECHNOLOGIES, INC.—See National Presto Industries, Inc; *U.S. Public*, pg. 1497
THE ONE-PAGE COMPANY INC.; *U.S. Private*, pg. 4088
ONERAIL GLOBAL HOLDINGS PTY, LTD.—See Amadeus IT Group, S.A.; *Int'l*, pg. 407
ONEREPORT, INC.—See Nasdaq, Inc.; *U.S. Public*, pg. 1492
ONESPAN CANADA INC.—See OneSpan Inc.; *U.S. Public*, pg. 1603
ONIONTECH CO. LIMITED—See Edition Ltd.; *Int'l*, pg. 2311
ONLINE MEDIA SOLUTIONS LIMITED—See Brightcom Group Ltd.; *Int'l*, pg. 1162
ONMOBILE SYSTEMS, INC.; *U.S. Private*, pg. 3027
ON-NET SURVEILLANCE SYSTEMS INC.—See Hexagon AB; *Int'l*, pg. 3369
ONRAD, INC.; *U.S. Private*, pg. 3028
ONSHAPE INC.—See PTC Inc.; *U.S. Public*, pg. 1734
ONSITE COMPUTER SERVICES—See Enterprise Onsite Services Co.; *U.S. Private*, pg. 1404
ONTODIA, INC.—See Cox Enterprises, Inc.; *U.S. Private*, pg. 1078
ONTRACKS EAM CONSULTING LTD.—See Bentley Systems, Inc.; *U.S. Public*, pg. 297
OOO CRIF—See CRIF S.p.A.; *Int'l*, pg. 1849
OOO DALET MEDIA SYSTEMY—See Long Path Partners, LP; *U.S. Private*, pg. 2491
OOO GK SOFTWARE RUS—See Fujitsu Limited; *Int'l*, pg. 2837
OOO LNR—See Elisa Corporation; *Int'l*, pg. 2361
OOO SAVCOR ART RUS—See Trimble, Inc.; *U.S. Public*, pg. 2191
OPEN ACCESS TECHNOLOGY INTERNATIONAL, INC.; *U.S. Private*, pg. 3028
OPEN ADVENTURE SDN. BHD.—See Harvest Miracle Capital Berhad; *Int'l*, pg. 3281
OPENAI, L.L.C.—See OpenAI, Inc.; *U.S. Private*, pg. 3030
OPEN APPLICATIONS CONSULTING LIMITED—See IQVIA Holdings Inc.; *U.S. Public*, pg. 1170
OPENCFD LTD.—See Keysight Technologies, Inc.; *U.S. Public*, pg. 1227

OPEN DENTAL SOFTWARE; *U.S. Private*, pg. 3029
OPENET TELECOM LTD.—See Amdocs Limited; *Int'l*, pg. 420
OPENET TELECOM SALES LIMITED—See Amdocs Limited; *Int'l*, pg. 420
OPENGEAR LIMITED—See Digi International Inc.; *U.S. Public*, pg. 662
OPENGEAR PTY. LTD.—See Digi International Inc.; *U.S. Public*, pg. 662
OPEN KERNEL LABS, INC.—See General Dynamics Corporation; *U.S. Public*, pg. 916
OPEN KERNEL LABS PTY LTD—See General Dynamics Corporation; *U.S. Public*, pg. 916
OPENMAIL LLC; *U.S. Private*, pg. 3031
OPEN RULE SYSTEMS INC.—See defi SOLUTIONS, Inc.; *U.S. Private*, pg. 1191
OPEN SOLUTIONS GROUP, INC.—See AE Industrial Partners, LP; *U.S. Private*, pg. 112
OPEN SYSTEMS INTEGRATORS, INC.—See The Carlyle Group Inc.; *U.S. Public*, pg. 2053
OPEN SYSTEMS INTERNATIONAL AUSTRALIA PTY LTD—See Emerson Electric Co.; *U.S. Public*, pg. 750
OPEN SYSTEMS INTERNATIONAL EUROPE SL—See Emerson Electric Co.; *U.S. Public*, pg. 750
OPEN SYSTEMS INTERNATIONAL, INC.; *U.S. Private*, pg. 3029
OPTIFACTS INC.—See EssilorLuxottica SA; *Int'l*, pg. 2514
OPTIMIZED ENERGY SOLUTIONS, LLC—See Chevron Corporation; *U.S. Public*, pg. 487
OPTIONS & CHOICES, INC.—See Stone Point Capital LLC; *U.S. Private*, pg. 3824
OPTIONS INFORMATION TECHNOLOGY LLC—See ABRY Partners, LLC; *U.S. Private*, pg. 42
OPTIS CN LIMITED—See ANSYS, Inc.; *U.S. Public*, pg. 139
OPTIS JAPAN K.K.—See ANSYS, Inc.; *U.S. Public*, pg. 139
OPTIS KOREA CO., LTD—See ANSYS, Inc.; *U.S. Public*, pg. 139
OPTIS PRISTINE LIMITED—See ANSYS, Inc.; *U.S. Public*, pg. 139
OPTIS SAS—See ANSYS, Inc.; *U.S. Public*, pg. 139
OPTIZMO TECHNOLOGIES, LLC; *U.S. Private*, pg. 3035
ORACLE CANADA ULC - MONTREAL—See Oracle Corporation; *U.S. Public*, pg. 1611
ORACLE INDIA PRIVATE LIMITED—See Oracle Corporation; *U.S. Public*, pg. 1612
ORACLE SOFTWARE TECHNOLOGY GMBH—See Oracle Corporation; *U.S. Public*, pg. 1613
ORASI SOFTWARE, INC.; *U.S. Private*, pg. 3038
ORBOTECH JAPAN CO., LTD.—See KLA Corporation; *U.S. Public*, pg. 1268
ORCHESTRO INC.—See Insight Venture Management, LLC; *U.S. Private*, pg. 2090
ORCKESTRA TECHNOLOGIES INC.—See KKR & Co. Inc.; *U.S. Public*, pg. 1267
OREDEV AB—See Devoteam SA; *Int'l*, pg. 2090
ORGANOTIKI S.A.—See Brookfield Corporation; *Int'l*, pg. 1180
ORGANOTIKI S.A.—See Elliott Management Corporation; *U.S. Private*, pg. 1372
ORGOSOFT CO., LTD.—See Digital Hearts Holdings Co., Ltd.; *Int'l*, pg. 2122
ORGSYNC, INC.—See Leeds Equity Partners, LLC; *U.S. Private*, pg. 2414
ORGSYNC, INC.—See Veritas Capital Fund Management, LLC; *U.S. Private*, pg. 4361
ORIGAMI FRONTIERS—See Hakuhodo DY Holdings Incorporated; *Int'l*, pg. 3222
ORIGINATE LABS; *U.S. Private*, pg. 3042
ORIGIN SOLUTIONS, LTD.—See KKR & Co. Inc.; *U.S. Public*, pg. 1257
ORION SYSTEMS INTEGRATORS, INC.—See OEP Capital Advisors, L.P.; *U.S. Private*, pg. 2999
ORISLINE ESPANA S.L.—See Henry Schein, Inc.; *U.S. Public*, pg. 1027
ORPAK LATINA S.P.A.—See Vontier Corporation; *U.S. Public*, pg. 2309
ORPAK ROMANIA S.R.L.—See Vontier Corporation; *U.S. Public*, pg. 2309
ORPAK SOLUTION CO., LTD.—See Vontier Corporation; *U.S. Public*, pg. 2309
OSCAR TECHNOLOGY CORPORATION—See Fixstars Corporation; *Int'l*, pg. 2696
OSI AUTOMATION SOFTWARE SYSTEMS (BEIJING) CO., LTD.—See Emerson Electric Co.; *U.S. Public*, pg. 750
OSI DU CANADA INC.—See Emerson Electric Co.; *U.S. Public*, pg. 750
OSI ENERGY AUTOMATION INDIA PRIVATE LIMITED—See Emerson Electric Co.; *U.S. Public*, pg. 750
OSIRIUM LIMITED—See Thoma Bravo, L.P.; *U.S. Private*, pg. 4153
OSIRIUM TECHNOLOGIES PLC—See Thoma Bravo, L.P.; *U.S. Private*, pg. 4153
OS SOLUTIONS SDN. BHD.—See Evd Berhad; *Int'l*, pg. 2561
OT MOBILITY, INC.—See General Motors Company; *U.S. Public*, pg. 926

OTONOMO TECHNOLOGIES LTD.—See Urgent.ly, Inc.; *U.S. Public*, pg. 2266
OTRACOM PTY LTD.—See Downer EDI Limited; *Int'l*, pg. 2186
OUTERBOX LLC—See WILsquare Capital LLC; *U.S. Private*, pg. 4532
OVATIONS MANAGEMENT SOLUTIONS, LLC—See Cendyn Corp.; *U.S. Private*, pg. 808
OVERIIT S.P.A.—See Bain Capital, LP; *U.S. Private*, pg. 442
OVERIIT S.P.A.—See Neuberger Berman Group LLC; *U.S. Private*, pg. 2890
OVERSIGHT SYSTEMS, INC.—See TCMI, Inc.; *U.S. Private*, pg. 3943
OWLS, INC.—See en-japan Inc.; *Int'l*, pg. 2395
OXFORD NORTHEAST, LTD.; *U.S. Private*, pg. 3057
OXLO SYSTEMS, INC.—See Dura Software Series A Qof LLC; *U.S. Private*, pg. 1292
OXYGEN BUSINESS SOLUTIONS PTY. LTD—See DXC Technology Company; *U.S. Public*, pg. 695
PACOM SYSTEMS (NORTH AMERICA) INC.—See Stanley Black & Decker, Inc.; *U.S. Public*, pg. 1933
PACTERA TECHNOLOGY NA, INC.—See China Electronics Corporation; *Int'l*, pg. 1499
PAGAYA TECHNOLOGIES LTD.; *U.S. Public*, pg. 1634
PALANTIR TECHNOLOGIES INC.; *U.S. Public*, pg. 1634
PALMETTO GBA, LLC—See Blue Cross & Blue Shield of South Carolina; *U.S. Private*, pg. 587
PALTALK, INC.; *U.S. Public*, pg. 3082
PANDERA SYSTEMS, LLC—See Sunstone Partners Management LLC; *U.S. Private*, pg. 3873
PAPERWISE, INC.—See Dura Software Series A Qof LLC; *U.S. Private*, pg. 1292
PARADIGM B.V.—See Apax Partners LLP; *Int'l*, pg. 505
PARADIGM B.V.—See JMI Services, Inc.; *U.S. Private*, pg. 2216
PARADIGM INFOTECH, INC.; *U.S. Private*, pg. 3089
PARAGON DYNAMICS INC.—See Mercury Systems, Inc.; *U.S. Private*, pg. 1422
PARAGON SOFTWARE SYSTEMS INC—See TA Associates, Inc.; *U.S. Private*, pg. 3914
PARAGON TECHNOLOGY GROUP, INC.—See Independence Capital Partners, LLC; *U.S. Private*, pg. 2056
PARAMETRIC TECHNOLOGY (DENMARK) A/S—See PTC Inc.; *U.S. Public*, pg. 1734
PARATURE, INC.—See Microsoft Corporation; *U.S. Public*, pg. 1443
PARISHSOFT LLC—See Site Organic, LLC; *U.S. Private*, pg. 3676
PARIS SECURITIES CORP—See Paris Foods Corporation; *U.S. Private*, pg. 3095
PARKMOTIVE GMBH—See ATON GmbH; *Int'l*, pg. 689
PARSELY, INC.—See Automattic Inc.; *U.S. Private*, pg. 400
PARSEPORT APS—See Workiva Inc.; *U.S. Public*, pg. 2379
PASSAGE CO., LTD.—See Crestec Inc.; *Int'l*, pg. 1841
PASSPORT HEALTH COMMUNICATIONS, INC.—See Experian plc; *Int'l*, pg. 2587
PATIENTCO HOLDINGS, INC.; *U.S. Private*, pg. 3109
PAULETTE CARTER DESIGN INC.; *U.S. Private*, pg. 3114
PAYDAY LLC—See Hilan Ltd.; *Int'l*, pg. 3390
PAYDIANT, INC.—See PayPal Holdings, Inc.; *U.S. Public*, pg. 1657
PAYER COMPASS, LLC—See PCP Enterprise, L.P.; *U.S. Private*, pg. 3121
PAYK12, LLC—See Raptor Technologies, Inc; *U.S. Private*, pg. 3356
PAYLOCITY CORPORATION—See Paylocity Holding Corporation; *U.S. Public*, pg. 1656
PAYMENTSPRING, LLC—See Nelnet, Inc.; *U.S. Public*, pg. 1504
PAYPROS LLC—See Global Payments Inc.; *U.S. Public*, pg. 944
PAYTABS—See EFG Holding; *Int'l*, pg. 2319
PCAMERICA, LLC—See Global Payments Inc.; *U.S. Public*, pg. 944
PCF FRONTEO INC.—See Fronteo, Inc.; *Int'l*, pg. 2794
PC SCALE, INC.—See Advanced Manufacturing Control Systems Ltd.; *Int'l*, pg. 160
PCS PROFESSIONAL CLINICAL SOFTWARE GMBH—See GPI S.p.A.; *Int'l*, pg. 3046
PC SYNERGY, INC.—See A.P. Moller-Maersk A/S; *Int'l*, pg. 28
PDF SOLUTIONS, INC.; *U.S. Public*, pg. 1658
PDX INC.—See UnitedHealth Group Incorporated; *U.S. Public*, pg. 2248
PEAXY, INC.; *U.S. Private*, pg. 3126
PEDIGREE TECHNOLOGIES L.L.C.; *U.S. Private*, pg. 3128
PEGASUS TRANSTECH, LLC; *U.S. Private*, pg. 3129
PEKAT S.R.O.—See Datalogic S.p.A.; *Int'l*, pg. 1978
PENDO.IO, INC.; *U.S. Private*, pg. 3132
PEN-LINK, LTD.; *U.S. Private*, pg. 3132
PEOPLEFINDERS.COM; *U.S. Private*, pg. 3141
PEOPLELINX, LLC; *U.S. Private*, pg. 3141
PEOPLENET COMMUNICATIONS CORPORATION—See Trimble, Inc.; *U.S. Public*, pg. 2190
PEPPERDASH TECHNOLOGY CORP.; *U.S. Private*, pg. 3145
PEPR INC.—See Caterpillar, Inc.; *U.S. Public*, pg. 453
PERCEPTIVE ENGINEERING LIMITED—See Applied Ma-

N.A.I.C.S. INDEX

541511 — CUSTOM COMPUTER PRO...

terials, Inc.; *U.S. Public*, pg. 172
PERCEPTIVE ENGINEERING PTE. LTD.—See Applied Materials, Inc.; *U.S. Public*, pg. 172
PERCEPTIVE RECRUITING, LLC; *U.S. Private*, pg. 3146
PERCH SOLUTIONS OY—See Bruker Corporation; *U.S. Public*, pg. 407
PERCISION SERVICES GMBH—See adesso SE; *Int'l*, pg. 144
PERCONA LLC.; *U.S. Private*, pg. 3146
PERFICIENT, INC. - DENVER—See EQT AB; *Int'l*, pg. 2483
PERFORMANCE LIVESTOCK ANALYTICS, INC.—See Zoetis, Inc.; *U.S. Public*, pg. 2409
PERISCOPE (ASIA) LIMITED—See Quad/Graphics, Inc.; *U.S. Public*, pg. 1744
PERKINELMER INFORMATICS, INC.—See Revvity, Inc.; *U.S. Public*, pg. 1795
PETRIS TECHNOLOGY, INC.—See Halliburton Company; *U.S. Public*, pg. 980
PETROWEB, INC.—See Thoma Bravo, L.P.; *U.S. Private*, pg. 4152
PEX SOFTWARE AUSTRALIA PTY. LTD.—See Thoma Bravo, L.P.; *U.S. Private*, pg. 4153
PEX SOFTWARE LIMITED—See Thoma Bravo, L.P.; *U.S. Private*, pg. 4153
PHASE FORWARD EUROPE LIMITED—See Oracle Corporation; *U.S. Public*, pg. 1613
PHASE FORWARD PTY LIMITED—See Oracle Corporation; *U.S. Public*, pg. 1613
PHENIXID AB—See Clavister Holding AB; *Int'l*, pg. 1653
PHOBIO, LLC; *U.S. Private*, pg. 3172
PHOENIX AMERICAN SALESFOCUS SOLUTIONS, INC.—See Phoenix American Incorporated; *U.S. Private*, pg. 3172
PHOENIX SYSTEMS SP. Z O.O.—See Atende S.A.; *Int'l*, pg. 668
PHOTON-TECH INSTRUMENTS CO., LTD.—See Basler AG; *Int'l*, pg. 887
PHREESIA, INC.; *U.S. Public*, pg. 1689
PHUNWARE OPCO, INC.—See Phunware, Inc.; *U.S. Public*, pg. 1689
PHYN LLC—See Hon Hai Precision Industry Co., Ltd.; *Int'l*, pg. 3457
PHYSICIANS INTERACTIVE INDIA PRIVATE LIMITED—See Merck & Co., Inc.; *U.S. Public*, pg. 1421
PICABOO CORPORATION—See Reischling Press, Inc.; *U.S. Private*, pg. 3392
PIGCHAMP INC.—See Farms.com Ltd.; *Int'l*, pg. 2620
PILLAR TECHNOLOGY GROUP, LLC—See Accenture plc; *Int'l*, pg. 87
PINFENG (SHANGHAI) INFORMATION TECHNOLOGY CO., LTD.—See Dayforce, Inc.; *U.S. Public*, pg. 645
PING IDENTITY CANADA INC.—See Thoma Bravo, L.P.; *U.S. Private*, pg. 4150
PING IDENTITY FRANCE, SAS—See Thoma Bravo, L.P.; *U.S. Private*, pg. 4150
PING IDENTITY ISRAEL, LTD.—See Thoma Bravo, L.P.; *U.S. Private*, pg. 4150
PING IDENTITY UK LIMITED—See Thoma Bravo, L.P.; *U.S. Private*, pg. 4150
PINNACLE HEALTH PARTNERSHIP LLP—See EMIS Group plc; *Int'l*, pg. 2383
PISTOLSTAR, INC.—See BIO-key International, Inc.; *U.S. Public*, pg. 332
PITCH TECHNOLOGIES AB—See BAE Systems plc; *Int'l*, pg. 798
PITCH TECHNOLOGIES LIMITED—See BAE Systems plc; *Int'l*, pg. 798
PIVOTAL SOFTWARE, INC.—See Broadcom Inc.; *U.S. Public*, pg. 390
PIVOT COMPANIES, LLC—See GEE Group Inc.; *U.S. Public*, pg. 910
PIVOT REMESYS LIMITED—See K1 Investment Management, LLC; *U.S. Public*, pg. 2252
PIVOT REMESYS PTY. LIMITED—See K1 Investment Management, LLC; *U.S. Public*, pg. 2252
PIXAFY, INC.—See Net@Work, Inc.; *U.S. Private*, pg. 2886
PIXELPUSHERS, INC.—See Events.com, Inc.; *U.S. Private*, pg. 1437
PKWARE, INC.—See Thompson Street Capital Manager LLC; *U.S. Private*, pg. 4161
PLAID INC.; *U.S. Private*, pg. 3194
PLANB TECHNOLOGIES, INC.—See Berkshire Partners LLC; *U.S. Private*, pg. 534
PLANCAL GMBH—See Trimble, Inc.; *U.S. Public*, pg. 2190
PLANET SIGNAL, INC.; *U.S. Private*, pg. 1697
PLANETSOFTWARE GMBH—See Bechtle AG; *Int'l*, pg. 938
PLANGRID, INC.—See Autodesk, Inc.; *U.S. Public*, pg. 229
PLANPRESCRIBER, INC.—See eHealth, Inc.; *U.S. Public*, pg. 721
PLATFORM 9 CORPORATION—See PlayAGS, Inc.; *U.S. Public*, pg. 1697
PLAYSTUDIOS, INC.—See PlayStudios, Inc.; *U.S. Public*, pg. 1698
PLCS PLUS INTERNATIONAL, INC.; *U.S. Private*, pg. 3213
PLEX SYSTEMS, INC.—See Francisco Partners Management, LP; *U.S. Private*, pg. 1591
PLIXER INTERNATIONAL, INC.—See Battery Ventures, L.P.; *U.S. Private*, pg. 489

PLM JAPAN INC.—See Business Brain Showa-Ota Inc.; *Int'l*, pg. 1228
PLUSFORTA GMBH—See Advent International Corporation; *U.S. Private*, pg. 97
PLUSFORTA GMBH—See Centerbridge Partners, L.P.; *U.S. Private*, pg. 813
PLUTORA, INC.—See TA Associates, Inc.; *U.S. Private*, pg. 3917
PLUTORA, INC.—See TPG Capital, L.P.; *U.S. Public*, pg. 2175
PMG WORLDWIDE LLC; *U.S. Private*, pg. 3218
PMOD TECHNOLOGIES LLC—See Bruker Corporation; *U.S. Public*, pg. 407
PNI DIGITAL MEDIA ULC—See Sycamore Partners Management, LP; *U.S. Private*, pg. 3897
PNMSOFT LTD.—See Genpact Limited; *Int'l*, pg. 2927
PNMSOFT PORTUGAL SOC UNIPESSOAL, LDA.—See Genpact Limited; *Int'l*, pg. 2927
PNMSOFT UK LIMITED—See Genpact Limited; *Int'l*, pg. 2927
PNMSOFT USA INC.INC...—See Genpact Limited; *Int'l*, pg. 2927
PODIO APS—See Elliott Management Corporation; *U.S. Private*, pg. 1367
PODIO APS—See Vista Equity Partners, LLC; *U.S. Private*, pg. 4396
POGOTEC, INC.; *U.S. Private*, pg. 3220
POINTILLIST, INC.—See Altisource Portfolio Solutions S.A.; *Int'l*, pg. 393
POINT TO POINT METHODICS, INC.; *U.S. Public*, pg. 1700
POINTWISE, INC.—See Cadence Design Systems, Inc.; *U.S. Public*, pg. 419
POLARIS CONSULTING & SERVICES IRELAND LTD.—See EQT AB; *Int'l*, pg. 2472
POLARIS CONSULTING & SERVICES LIMITED—See EQT AB; *Int'l*, pg. 2472
POLARIS CONSULTING & SERVICES LTD—See EQT AB; *Int'l*, pg. 2472
POLARIS WIRELESS; *U.S. Private*, pg. 3223
POLICY ADM SOLUTIONS INC.; *U.S. Private*, pg. 3224
POLYCOM UNIFIED COMMUNICATIONS SOLUTIONS PVT. LTD.—See HP Inc.; *U.S. Public*, pg. 1065
POMS CORP.—See Constellation Software Inc.; *Int'l*, pg. 1772
PORTAL DE DOCUMENTOS S.A.—See B3 S.A.; *Int'l*, pg. 791
PORTER VALLEY SOFTWARE, INC.—See Environmental Service Professionals, Inc.; *U.S. Public*, pg. 781
POSABIT SYSTEMS CORP.; *U.S. Public*, pg. 1703
THE POSEIDON GROUP, INC.—See Thoma Bravo, L.P.; *U.S. Private*, pg. 4150
POUNCE TECHNOLOGIES INC.—See Anzu Partners, LLC; *U.S. Private*, pg. 289
POWEL AG—See Arendals Fossekompani ASA; *Int'l*, pg. 559
POWEL ASA—See Arendals Fossekompani ASA; *Int'l*, pg. 559
POWERHOUSE DYNAMICS INC.—See The Middleby Corporation; *U.S. Public*, pg. 2115
POWER LINE SYSTEMS, INC.—See TA Associates, Inc.; *U.S. Private*, pg. 3917
POWER SYSTEMS OPERATIONS, INC.—See Babcock & Wilcox Enterprises, Inc.; *U.S. Public*, pg. 263
PQR HOLDING B.V.—See Bechtle AG; *Int'l*, pg. 938
PRACTICAL COMPUTER APPLICATIONS, INC.; *U.S. Private*, pg. 3241
PRACTICE INSIGHT, LLC—See Canada Pension Plan Investment Board; *Int'l*, pg. 1282
PRACTICE INSIGHT, LLC—See EQT AB; *Int'l*, pg. 2481
PRAEZISION LIFE S.R.L.—See Ardian SAS; *Int'l*, pg. 555
PRAGMATIX SA—See G7 Entreprises; *Int'l*, pg. 2867
PRAIRIE SYSTEMS, LLC—See Dairy, LLC; *U.S. Private*, pg. 1146
PRAXIS ENGINEERING; *U.S. Private*, pg. 3243
PRECISION DEVELOPMENT; *U.S. Private*, pg. 3244
PREFERRED MEDICAL MARKETING CORPORATION; *U.S. Private*, pg. 3248
PREMIER LOGIC INDIA PRIVATE LTD.—See Alten S.A.; *Int'l*, pg. 390
PREMINET OY—See Elisa Corporation; *Int'l*, pg. 2361
PRESAGIS EUROPE (S.A.)—See CAE Inc.; *Int'l*, pg. 1249
PRESAGIS USA INC.—See CAE Inc.; *Int'l*, pg. 1249
PRESCRIBEWELLNESS—See BlackRock, Inc.; *U.S. Public*, pg. 347
PRESTOSPORTS, INC.—See Clubessential Holdings, LLC; *U.S. Private*, pg. 949
PREVISTAR PRIVATE LIMITED—See Thoma Bravo, L.P.; *U.S. Private*, pg. 4147
PRIMARY INTELLIGENCE INC.—See The Riverside Company; *U.S. Private*, pg. 4108
PRIMA SOLUTIONS BELGIUM SA—See Simulations Plus, Inc.; *U.S. Public*, pg. 1885
PRIMECARE SYSTEMS, INC.; *U.S. Public*, pg. 1717
PRIME INNOVATIONS FOR TRADE S.A.E.—See ADES International Holding PLC; *Int'l*, pg. 144
PRIME KI SOFTWARE SOLUTIONS PVT LTD.—See Frontenac Company LLC; *U.S. Private*, pg. 1614
PRIORITY SOFTWARE LTD.—See Fortissimo Capital Management Ltd.; *Int'l*, pg. 2740

PRISMA TECHNOLOGIES PTE LTD—See Forise International Ltd.; *Int'l*, pg. 2733
PRISM TECHNOLOGIES, LLC—See Prism Technologies Group, Inc.; *U.S. Public*, pg. 1722
PRIVACY & VALUE INC.; *U.S. Private*, pg. 3268
PRIVY, INC.; *U.S. Private*, pg. 3269
PROCERA NETWORKS AB—See Francisco Partners Management, LP; *U.S. Private*, pg. 1591
PROCERA NETWORKS, INC.—See Francisco Partners Management, LP; *U.S. Private*, pg. 1591
PROCORE TECHNOLOGIES, INC.; *U.S. Public*, pg. 1724
PROCOUNTOR INTERNATIONAL OY—See Dovre Group Plc; *Int'l*, pg. 2182
PROCURRI GMBH—See EXEO Group Inc.; *Int'l*, pg. 2583
PROCURRI INDIA PRIVATE LIMITED—See EXEO Group Inc.; *Int'l*, pg. 2583
PROCURRI MALAYSIA SDN. BHD.—See EXEO Group Inc.; *Int'l*, pg. 2583
PROCURRI S. DE R.L. DE C.V.—See EXEO Group Inc.; *Int'l*, pg. 2583
PRODUCTIVE DATA SOLUTIONS INC.; *U.S. Private*, pg. 3273
PRODUCTIVITY LEAP OY—See Digia Plc; *Int'l*, pg. 2118
PROFDOC ASA—See CompuGroup Medical SE & Co. KGaA; *Int'l*, pg. 1757
PROFESSIONAL IMPLEMENTATION CONSULTING SERVICES, INC.; *U.S. Private*, pg. 3275
PROFITECT, INC.—See Zebra Technologies Corporation; *U.S. Public*, pg. 2401
PROFUND SOLUTIONS LIMITED—See Marsh & McLennan Companies, Inc.; *U.S. Public*, pg. 1377
PROGEA DEUTSCHLAND GMBH—See Emerson Electric Co.; *U.S. Public*, pg. 751
PROGEA INTERNATIONAL, S.A.—See Emerson Electric Co.; *U.S. Public*, pg. 751
PROGEA NORTH AMERICA, CORP.—See Emerson Electric Co.; *U.S. Public*, pg. 751
PROGEA S.R.L.—See Emerson Electric Co.; *U.S. Public*, pg. 751
PROGRESS OPENEDGE—See Progress Software Corporation; *U.S. Public*, pg. 1725
PROGRESS SOFTWARE GESMBH—See Progress Software Corporation; *U.S. Public*, pg. 1725
PROIV TECHNOLOGY INC—See Alight, Inc.; *U.S. Public*, pg. 77
PROJECT LEADERSHIP ASSOCIATES, INC.; *U.S. Private*, pg. 3280
PROJECTMANAGER.COM, INC.; *U.S. Private*, pg. 3281
PROJECTOR PSA, INC.—See Vista Equity Partners, LLC; *U.S. Private*, pg. 4395
PROJEKT-PARTNER-ONLINE GMBH—See Bilfinger SE; *Int'l*, pg. 1029
PROMODEL CORPORATION—See AE Industrial Partners, LP; *U.S. Private*, pg. 112
PROMOSERVE BUSINESS SYSTEMS LIMITED—See Altitude Group plc; *Int'l*, pg. 393
PROMOTER.IO INC.—See Thoma Bravo, L.P.; *U.S. Private*, pg. 4149
PROMPTWORKS LLC—See Modus Create, LLC; *U.S. Private*, pg. 2764
PROPLANNER, INC—See Advantive LLC; *U.S. Private*, pg. 95
PROS BULGARIA EOOD—See PROS Holdings, Inc.; *U.S. Public*, pg. 1728
PROSITES, INC.—See RockBridge Growth Equity, LLC; *U.S. Private*, pg. 3465
PROS REVENUE MANAGEMENT, L.P.—See PROS Holdings, Inc.; *U.S. Public*, pg. 1728
PROSYSTEMS IT GMBH—See Diebold Nixdorf, Inc.; *U.S. Public*, pg. 661
PROTAK SYSTEMS AB—See AFRY AB; *Int'l*, pg. 196
PROTECH SOLUTIONS, INC.; *U.S. Private*, pg. 3289
PROTOSOURCE CORP.; *U.S. Public*, pg. 1730
PROVIDGE CONSULTING, LLC; *U.S. Private*, pg. 3295
PROXIMA SOLUTIONS GMBH—See BKW AG; *Int'l*, pg. 1056
PRUDSYS AG—See Fujitsu Limited; *Int'l*, pg. 2837
PSD CODAX LIMITED—See Dover Corporation; *U.S. Public*, pg. 682
PSIGEN SOFTWARE, INC.—See Clearlake Capital Group, L.P.; *U.S. Private*, pg. 936
PSIGEN SOFTWARE, INC.—See TA Associates, Inc.; *U.S. Private*, pg. 3916
PS PLUS PORTFOLIO SOFTWARE + CONSULTING GMBH—See Deutsche Bank Aktiengesellschaft; *Int'l*, pg. 2061
PT AMADEUS TECHNOLOGY INDONESIA—See Amadeus IT Group, S.A.; *Int'l*, pg. 407
PT AXIATA DIGITAL LABS INDONESIA—See Axiata Group Berhad; *Int'l*, pg. 768
PTC INC. - FORT COLLINS—See PTC Inc.; *U.S. Public*, pg. 1734
PTC INC. - NEEDHAM—See PTC Inc.; *U.S. Public*, pg. 1734
PTC (SSI) LIMITED—See PTC Inc.; *U.S. Public*, pg. 1734
PT. DIEBOLD NIXDORF INDONESIA—See Diebold Nixdorf, Inc.; *U.S. Public*, pg. 661

PT FINACCEL TEKNOLOGI INDONESIA—See FinAccel Pte Ltd.; *Int'l*, pg. 2664
PT FORTINET INDONESIA SECURITY—See Fortinet, Inc.; *U.S. Public*, pg. 869
P.T. FPT SOFTWARE INDONESIA—See FPT Corporation; *Int'l*, pg. 2758
P.T. GIFTEE INTERNATIONAL INDONESIA—See Giftee, Inc.; *Int'l*, pg. 2970
P.T. GLORY GLOBAL SOLUTIONS INDONESIA—See GLORY Ltd.; *Int'l*, pg. 3010
PT HIPERNET INDODATA—See Axiata Group Berhad; *Int'l*, pg. 768
PT IFCA PROPERTY365 INDONESIA—See IFCA MSC Berhad; *Int'l*, pg. 3599
PT IFCA PROPERTY365 INDONESIA—See IFCA MSC Berhad; *Int'l*, pg. 3599
PT INDONESIA APPLICAD CO., LTD.—See Applicad Public Company Limited; *Int'l*, pg. 521
PT INPHOSOFT INDONESIA—See GINSMS Inc.; *Int'l*, pg. 2977
PT IZENO TEKNOLOGI INDONESIA—See Datatec Limited; *Int'l*, pg. 1981
PT MISYS INTERNATIONAL FINANCIAL SYSTEMS—See Vista Equity Partners, LLC; *U.S. Private*, pg. 4397
PT PAYASIA KONSULTANSI INDONESIA—See Deel, Inc.; *U.S. Private*, pg. 1189
PT PRAISINDO TEKNOLOGI—See Censof Holdings Berhad; *Int'l*, pg. 1402
THE PTR GROUP, LLC—See Huntington Ingalls Industries, Inc.; *U.S. Public*, pg. 1072
PT. R SYSTEMS IBIZCS INTERNATIONAL—See Blackstone Inc.; *U.S. Public*, pg. 357
PT TECH DATA ADVANCED SOLUTIONS INDONESIA—See Avnet, Inc.; *U.S. Public*, pg. 253
PUBLICPLAN GMBH—See Allgeier SE; *Int'l*, pg. 338
PULSANT LIMITED—See Keystone Group, L.P.; *U.S. Private*, pg. 2299
PULSE VOICE INC—See Enghouse Systems Limited; *Int'l*, pg. 2427
PULSO INFORMATICA, S.L.U.—See Glintt - Global Intelligent Technologies, S.A.; *Int'l*, pg. 2992
PUNCH TELEMATIX FRANCE S.A.S—See Trimble, Inc.; *U.S. Public*, pg. 2191
PUNCH TELEMATIX IBERICA S.L—See Trimble, Inc.; *U.S. Public*, pg. 2191
PURE STORAGE HK LTD.—See Pure Storage, Inc.; *U.S. Public*, pg. 1738
PURE STORAGE LTD.—See Pure Storage, Inc.; *U.S. Public*, pg. 1738
PURE-SYSTEMS GMBH—See PTC Inc.; *U.S. Public*, pg. 1735
PURISMA, INC.—See Cannae Holdings, Inc.; *U.S. Public*, pg. 430
PURISMA, INC.—See CC Capital Partners, LLC; *U.S. Private*, pg. 798
PURISMA, INC.—See Intercontinental Exchange, Inc.; *U.S. Public*, pg. 1142
PUSHPAY HOLDINGS LIMITED—See BGH Capital Pty Ltd; *Int'l*, pg. 1008
PUSHPAY HOLDINGS LIMITED—See Sixth Street Partners LLC; *U.S. Private*, pg. 3677
PYPE LLC—See Autodesk, Inc.; *U.S. Public*, pg. 229
PYRAMID PLATFORM, LLC—See Radian Group, Inc.; *U.S. Public*, pg. 1759
PYRAMID SOLUTIONS, INC.; *U.S. Private*, pg. 3310
PYTON COMMUNICATION SERVICES B.V.—See Amadeus IT Group, S.A.; *Int'l*, pg. 407
PYXIS SOLUTIONS, LLC—See Bain & Company, Inc.; *U.S. Private*, pg. 428
Q4 INC.—See Sumeru Equity Partners LLC; *U.S. Private*, pg. 3852
Q9 TECHNOLOGY COMPANY LIMITED—See Cloud Investment Holdings Limited; *Int'l*, pg. 1662
QAD SISTEMAS INTEGRADOS CASA DE SOFTWARE, S.A. DE C.V.—See Thoma Bravo, L.P.; *U.S. Private*, pg. 4152
QATALYS INCORPORATED; *U.S. Private*, pg. 3312
QELP B.V.—See Creadev SAS; *Int'l*, pg. 1831
QELP DO BRASIL SOFTWARE E CONTUEDO DIGITAL LTDA—See Creadev SAS; *Int'l*, pg. 1831
Q-FREE NETHERLANDS B.V.—See Guardian Capital Group Limited; *Int'l*, pg. 1831
QLARION, INC.—See Sagewind Capital LLC; *U.S. Private*, pg. 3527
QLIKTECH ITALY S.R.L.—See Thoma Bravo, L.P.; *U.S. Private*, pg. 4152
QSI MANAGEMENT, LLC—See Thoma Bravo, L.P.; *U.S. Private*, pg. 4150
QS QUARTERHOUSE SOFTWARE, INC.—See Sycamore Partners Management, LP; *U.S. Private*, pg. 3897
QTS FINANCE CORPORATION—See Blackstone Inc.; *U.S. Public*, pg. 351
QUADIGI UAB—See Draegerwerk AG & Co. KGaA; *Int'l*, pg. 2198
QUADRAMED CORPORATION—See Constellation Software Inc.; *Int'l*, pg. 1774
QUADSTONE PARAMICS LTD—See Pitney Bowes Inc.; *U.S. Public*, pg. 1695

QUALITY INVESTMENT PROPERTIES RICHMOND, LLC—See Blackstone Inc.; *U.S. Public*, pg. 351
QUALITY LIFE ENTERPRISE (INDIA) PVT. LTD.—See Hitachi, Ltd.; *Int'l*, pg. 3424
QUALYSITE TECHNOLOGIES INC.—See Canon Inc.; *Int'l*, pg. 1296
QUANTITATIVE MEDICAL SYSTEMS, INC.—See Constellation Software Inc.; *Int'l*, pg. 1772
QUANTROS, INC.; *U.S. Private*, pg. 3322
QUEST INTEGRITY DEUTSCHLAND GMBH—See Team, Inc.; *U.S. Public*, pg. 1988
QUEST INTEGRITY MYS SDN BHD—See Baker Hughes Company; *U.S. Public*, pg. 265
QUESTIONMARK CORPORATION—See Learnosity Ltd.; *U.S. Private*, pg. 2408
QUEST NATIONAL SERVICES LLC; *U.S. Private*, pg. 3326
QUICK CHECK LIMITED—See Beijing Shiji Information Technology Co., Ltd.; *Int'l*, pg. 956
QUINSTREET EUROPE LTD.—See QuinStreet, Inc.; *U.S. Public*, pg. 1757
QUMU JAPAN CO., LTD.—See Enghouse Systems Limited; *Int'l*, pg. 2427
QUMU (SINGAPORE) PTE. LTD—See Enghouse Systems Limited; *Int'l*, pg. 2427
QUOTIENT, INC.—See Jacmel Growth Partners Management LLC; *U.S. Private*, pg. 2179
QUOTIT CORPORATION—See The Allstate Corporation; *U.S. Public*, pg. 2034
QWINIX TECHNOLOGIES, INC.; *U.S. Private*, pg. 3331
RACKSPACE TECHNOLOGY, INC.; *U.S. Public*, pg. 1759
RA COMPUTER S.P.A.—See Cassa Depositi e Prestiti S.p.A.; *Int'l*, pg. 1354
RADIANT RFID; *U.S. Private*, pg. 3343
RADIOPULSE, INC.—See Littelfuse, Inc.; *U.S. Public*, pg. 1327
RADIUMONE, INC.; *U.S. Private*, pg. 3344
RAF TECHNOLOGY INC.—See Constellation Software Inc.; *Int'l*, pg. 1775
RAILINC CORP.—See Association of American Railroads; *Int'l*, pg. 358
RAINTREE SYSTEMS, INC.; *U.S. Private*, pg. 3348
RAMQUEST SOFTWARE, INC.—See Old Republic International Corporation; *U.S. Public*, pg. 1569
RAM SOFTWARE SYSTEMS INC.—See ComTec Solutions; *U.S. Private*, pg. 1006
RAM TECH SYSTEMS, INC.; *U.S. Private*, pg. 3351
RAPID7 SINGAPORE PTE. LTD.—See Rapid7, Inc.; *U.S. Public*, pg. 1763
RAVE MOBILE SAFETY, INC.—See Motorola Solutions, Inc.; *U.S. Public*, pg. 1479
RAXCO SOFTWARE, INC.; *U.S. Private*, pg. 3358
RAYMARK ASIA LIMITED—See Mi9 Retail, Inc.; *U.S. Private*, pg. 2696
RAYMARK EUROPE—See Mi9 Retail, Inc.; *U.S. Private*, pg. 2696
RAYTHEON BBN TECHNOLOGIES—See RTX Corporation; *U.S. Public*, pg. 1824
RAYTHEON UNITED KINGDOM—See RTX Corporation; *U.S. Public*, pg. 1825
RBC DEVELOPMENT, LLC—See Ampersand Management LLC; *U.S. Private*, pg. 266
R.C. OLMSTEAD, INC.—See Nymbus, Inc.; *U.S. Private*, pg. 2976
RDA CORPORATION; *U.S. Private*, pg. 3363
READY AT DAWN STUDIOS, LLC—See Meta Platforms, Inc.; *U.S. Public*, pg. 1427
REALCOM TECHNOLOGY INDIA PVT LTD—See Abalance Corporation Ltd.; *Int'l*, pg. 48
REALDEFENSE LLC; *U.S. Private*, pg. 3368
REALEC TECHNOLOGIES, INC.—See Fidelity National Financial, Inc.; *U.S. Public*, pg. 831
REALITY BY DESIGN INC.—See Advanced Interactive Systems; *U.S. Private*, pg. 90
REALLY STRATEGIES, INC.; *U.S. Private*, pg. 3368
REALNETWORKS GMBH—See RealNetworks, Inc.; *U.S. Private*, pg. 3369
REALNETWORKS, INC.; *U.S. Private*, pg. 3368
REALNETWORKS, LTD.—See RealNetworks, Inc.; *U.S. Private*, pg. 3369
REAL TIME COMPANIES, LLC.; *U.S. Private*, pg. 3368
REALVOLVE, INC.; *U.S. Private*, pg. 3369
REBASE CONSULTING OY—See Gofore PLC; *Int'l*, pg. 3022
RECONDO TECHNOLOGY, INC.—See Canada Pension Plan Investment Board; *Int'l*, pg. 1282
RECONDO TECHNOLOGY, INC.—See EQT AB; *Int'l*, pg. 2481
RECOVERY DATABASE NETWORK, INC.—See OPENLANE, Inc.; *U.S. Public*, pg. 1607
REDBLACK SOFTWARE PRIVATE LIMITED—See Invesco Ltd.; *U.S. Public*, pg. 1163
RED BOOK CONNECT, LLC—See Marlin Equity Partners, LLC; *U.S. Private*, pg. 2585
REDFISH HOLDINGS, INC.; *U.S. Private*, pg. 3378
RED HAT SOFTWARE SERVICES (INDIA) PVT. LTD.—See International Business Machines Corporation; *U.S. Public*, pg. 1150
RED HAT (THAILAND) LIMITED—See International Business Machines Corporation; *U.S. Public*, pg. 1150
RED MILE ENTERTAINMENT, INC.; *U.S. Public*, pg. 1769
REDSPIN—See Altaris Capital Partners, LLC; *U.S. Private*, pg. 206
REDTAIL TECHNOLOGY, INC.—See Orion Advisor Solutions, LLC; *U.S. Private*, pg. 3042
REFLEXIS SYSTEMS, INC.—See Zebra Technologies Corporation; *U.S. Public*, pg. 2401
REGENCY TECHNOLOGIES, INC.; *U.S. Private*, pg. 3386
REGGIANI MACCHINE S.P.A.—See Siris Capital Group, LLC; *U.S. Private*, pg. 3673
REGOLA S.R.L.—See Frequentis AG; *Int'l*, pg. 2773
RELATIONAL NETWORKS, INC.—See Silver Lake Group, LLC; *U.S. Private*, pg. 3660
RELIABLE SOFTWARE RESOURCES, INC; *U.S. Private*, pg. 3394
REMEDY INFORMATICS; *U.S. Private*, pg. 3396
REMEDY INTERACTIVE, INC.—See Thoma Bravo, L.P.; *U.S. Private*, pg. 4146
RENTALUTIONS, INC.—See News Corporation; *U.S. Public*, pg. 1519
RENTLYTICS, INC.—See Thoma Bravo, L.P.; *U.S. Private*, pg. 4153
REPLICON AUSTRALIA PTY LTD—See Roper Technologies, Inc.; *U.S. Public*, pg. 1811
REPLICON EUROPE LTD—See Roper Technologies, Inc.; *U.S. Public*, pg. 1811
REPUTATION.COM, INC.; *U.S. Private*, pg. 3403
RESEARCH, DEVELOPMENT & MANUFACTURING CORPORATION—See Deluxe Corporation; *U.S. Public*, pg. 653
RESIDENTIAL MANAGEMENT SYSTEMS—See Starrez Inc.; *U.S. Private*, pg. 3788
RESI MEDIA LLC—See BGH Capital Pty Ltd; *Int'l*, pg. 1008
RESI MEDIA LLC—See Sixth Street Partners LLC; *U.S. Private*, pg. 3678
RESOLVIT RESOURCES, LLC—See Aditi Consulting LLC; *U.S. Private*, pg. 79
RESPOND BEHEER B.V.—See Thoma Bravo, L.P.; *U.S. Private*, pg. 4147
RESPONSYS, INC.—See Oracle Corporation; *U.S. Public*, pg. 1613
RESTAURANT TECHNOLOGY SERVICES UK LIMITED—See Xerox Holdings Corporation; *U.S. Public*, pg. 2388
RETAIL CLOUD TECHNOLOGIES, LLC; *U.S. Private*, pg. 3411
RETROFICIENCY, INC.—See ENGIE SA; *Int'l*, pg. 2431
REVENUE WELL SYSTEMS, LLC—See Marlin Equity Partners, LLC; *U.S. Private*, pg. 2585
REV.IO, LLC; *U.S. Private*, pg. 3413
REV SOLUTIONS INC.—See GXO Logistics, Inc.; *U.S. Public*, pg. 975
REVTECH SOLUTIONS INDIA PRIVATE LIMITED—See GXO Logistics, Inc.; *U.S. Public*, pg. 976
REYNOLDS AND REYNOLDS B.V.—See The Reynolds & Reynolds Company; *U.S. Private*, pg. 4106
RIBBON COMMUNICATIONS GERMANY GMBH—See Ribbon Communications Inc.; *U.S. Public*, pg. 1797
RIBBON COMMUNICATIONS HONG KONG LIMITED—See Ribbon Communications Inc.; *U.S. Public*, pg. 1797
RIBBON COMMUNICATIONS SWITZERLAND GMBH—See Ribbon Communications Inc.; *U.S. Public*, pg. 1797
RICSTON LIMITED—See EPAM Systems, Inc.; *U.S. Public*, pg. 783
RICSTON UK LIMITED—See EPAM Systems, Inc.; *U.S. Public*, pg. 783
RIDGELINE INTERNATIONAL INC.; *U.S. Private*, pg. 3432
RIGETTI COMPUTING, INC.; *U.S. Public*, pg. 1798
RIGHT MANAGEMENT DENMARK A/S—See ManpowerGroup Inc.; *U.S. Public*, pg. 1361
RIGOR, INC.—See Cisco Systems, Inc.; *U.S. Public*, pg. 500
RIMILIA CANADA LTD.—See BlackLine, Inc.; *U.S. Public*, pg. 342
RIMILIA EUROPE LTD.—See BlackLine, Inc.; *U.S. Public*, pg. 342
RIMINI STREET CANADA INC.—See Rimini Street, Inc.; *U.S. Public*, pg. 1799
RIPPE & KINGSTON SYSTEMS, INC.—See Rippe & Kingston, LLC; *U.S. Private*, pg. 3439
RI-SOLUTION GMBH—See BayWa AG; *Int'l*, pg. 918
ROBEX LLC—See Angeles Equity Partners, LLC; *U.S. Private*, pg. 282
ROBLOX CORPORATION; *U.S. Public*, pg. 1804
ROCKETFUEL BLOCKCHAIN, INC.; *U.S. Public*, pg. 1805
ROCKIT PTY. LTD.—See FirstRand Limited; *Int'l*, pg. 2690
RODHE SECURITY, S.A. DE C.V.—See Aiphone Co., Ltd.; *Int'l*, pg. 235
ROGUE WAVE SOFTWARE, INC.—See Clearlake Capital Group, L.P.; *U.S. Private*, pg. 936
ROGUE WAVE SOFTWARE, INC.—See Francisco Partners Management, L.P.; *U.S. Private*, pg. 1591
ROMLOGIC TECHNOLOGY S.A.—See BRK Financial Group S.A.; *Int'l*, pg. 1171
ROOK SECURITY, LLC—See Apax Partners LLP; *Int'l*, pg. 506

541511 — CUSTOM COMPUTER PRO...

ROSS SYSTEMS IBERICA S.L.—See TA Associates, Inc.; *U.S. Private*, pg. 3914

ROSTRVM SOLUTIONS LIMITED—See Cisco Systems, Inc.; *U.S. Public*, pg. 500

RR DONNELLEY ITALY S.R.L.—See Chatham Asset Management, LLC; *U.S. Private*, pg. 865

RSOFT DESIGN GROUP, INC.—See Synopsys, Inc.; *U.S. Public*, pg. 1970

RSYS TECHNOLOGIES LTD.—See Blackstone Inc.; *U.S. Public*, pg. 357

R SYSTEMS COMPUTARIS EUROPE SRL—See Blackstone Inc.; *U.S. Public*, pg. 357

R SYSTEMS COMPUTARIS MALAYSIA SDN. BHD.—See Blackstone Inc.; *U.S. Public*, pg. 357

R SYSTEMS COMPUTARIS PHILIPPINES PTE. LTD. INC.—See Blackstone Inc.; *U.S. Public*, pg. 357

R SYSTEMS COMPUTARIS POLAND SP Z O.O.—See Blackstone Inc.; *U.S. Public*, pg. 357

R SYSTEMS COMPUTARIS S.R.L.—See Blackstone Inc.; *U.S. Public*, pg. 357

R SYSTEMS CONSULTING SERVICES (SHANGHAI) CO., LTD.—See Blackstone Inc.; *U.S. Public*, pg. 357

R SYSTEMS IBIZCS SDN. BHD.—See Blackstone Inc.; *U.S. Public*, pg. 357

R SYSTEMS SOLUTIONS, INC.—See Blackstone Inc.; *U.S. Public*, pg. 357

RTDS TECHNOLOGIES INC.—See AMETEK, Inc.; *U.S. Public*, pg. 121

RTM REALTIME MONITORING GMBH—See Silver Lake Group, LLC; *U.S. Private*, pg. 3658

RTP KOREA CO. LTD.—See RTP Corp.; *U.S. Private*, pg. 3498

RUCKUS WIRELESS PRIVATE LTD.—See CommScope Holding Company, Inc.; *U.S. Public*, pg. 548

RURO INCORPORATED—See Azenta, Inc.; *U.S. Public*, pg. 258

RWS HOLDING, LLC; *U.S. Private*, pg. 3509

S2TECH; *U.S. Private*, pg. 3519

SAASMAX CORP.; *U.S. Public*, pg. 1832

SAASOPTICS, LLC—See Battery Ventures, L.P.; *U.S. Private*, pg. 489

SABAND SOFTWARE TECHNOLOGIES PRIVATE LIMITED—See Cognizant Technology Solutions Corporation; *U.S. Public*, pg. 525

SABA SOFTWARE SP. Z O.O.—See Clearlake Capital Group, L.P.; *U.S. Private*, pg. 934

SABIO MOBILE, INC.; *U.S. Private*, pg. 3521

SABRE UKRAINE LLC—See Sabre Corporation; *U.S. Public*, pg. 1834

SACC INC.—See Alten S.A.; *Int'l*, pg. 390

SAFECOM GMBH—See Microsoft Corporation; *U.S. Public*, pg. 1443

SAFEGUARD SERVICES LLC—See Veritas Capital Fund Management, LLC; *U.S. Private*, pg. 4364

SAFEIT SECURITY SWEDEN AB—See Francisco Partners Management, LP; *U.S. Private*, pg. 1588

SAFENET CONSULTING, LLC—See Stone Point Capital LLC; *U.S. Private*, pg. 3823

SAFER SYSTEMS LLC—See Fortive Corporation; *U.S. Public*, pg. 871

SAFETEC COMPLIANCE SYSTEMS—See The Riverside Company; *U.S. Private*, pg. 4110

SAFFRON TECHNOLOGY, INC.—See Intel Corporation; *U.S. Public*, pg. 1139

SAG DEUTSCHLAND GMBH—See Silver Lake Group, LLC; *U.S. Private*, pg. 3658

SAGE DATA SECURITY, LLC—See Tyler Technologies, Inc.; *U.S. Public*, pg. 2209

SAGENT AUTO, LLC; *U.S. Private*, pg. 3527

SAGGEZZA INC.; *U.S. Private*, pg. 3528

SAG SYSTEMS RUS LIMITED LIABILITY COMPANY—See Silver Lake Group, LLC; *U.S. Private*, pg. 3659

SAISON INFORMATION SYSTEMS CO., LTD.—See Credit Saison Co., Ltd.; *Int'l*, pg. 1836

SAKATA SAS CO., LTD.—See extreme Co., Ltd.; *Int'l*, pg. 2592

SAKUSAKU CO., LTD.—See Cominix Co., Ltd.; *Int'l*, pg. 1714

SALEPOINT INC.; *U.S. Private*, pg. 3531

SALESFORCE ARGENTINA S.R.L.—See Salesforce, Inc.; *U.S. Public*, pg. 1837

SALESFORCE.COM DANMARK, FILIAL AF SFDC SWEDEN AB—See Salesforce, Inc.; *U.S. Public*, pg. 1837

SALESFORCE.COM KOREA LIMITED—See Salesforce, Inc.; *U.S. Public*, pg. 1837

SAL, JOHNSON & ASSOCIATES, INC.—See Tyler Technologies, Inc.; *U.S. Public*, pg. 2209

SAMBA TV, INC.; *U.S. Private*, pg. 3536

SAMEDI GMBH—See Asklepios Kliniken GmbH & Co. KGaA; *Int'l*, pg. 624

SAMEPAGE LABS INC.—See Paylocity Holding Corporation; *U.S. Public*, pg. 1656

SAMI SHOP S.A.C.—See Credicorp Ltd.; *Int'l*, pg. 1834

SAMSARA INC.; *U.S. Public*, pg. 1839

SAMSARA NETWORKS LIMITED—See Samsara Inc.; *U.S. Public*, pg. 1839

SANCHEZ COMPUTER ASSOCIATES, LLC—See Fidelity National Infor; *U.S. Public*, pg. 833

SANDWIRE CORP.—See Circle Computer Resources, Inc.; *U.S. Private*, pg. 899

SAPERIUM, INC.—See OPENLANE, Inc.; *U.S. Public*, pg. 1607

SARATOGA SOFTWARE (PTY) LTD—See African Equity Empowerment Investmts Limited; *Int'l*, pg. 191

SASA APAC PTE. LTD.—See BH Global Corporation Limited; *Int'l*, pg. 1009

SAS INSTITUTE INC.—See SAS Institute Inc.; *U.S. Private*, pg. 3551

SA TECHNOLOGIES, INC.; *U.S. Private*, pg. 3519

SATELLOGIC INC.; *U.S. Public*, pg. 1841

SATORI SOFTWARE INC.—See Platinum Equity, LLC; *U.S. Private*, pg. 3202

SATURN SYSTEMS, INC.—See RBA, Inc.; *U.S. Private*, pg. 3360

SAUDI AMERICAN HOLDINGS CORP.; *U.S. Private*, pg. 3554

SAVCOR FOREST INC.—See Trimble, Inc.; *U.S. Public*, pg. 2191

SAVCOR FOREST LIMITADA—See Trimble, Inc.; *U.S. Public*, pg. 2191

SAVIYNT, INC.; *U.S. Private*, pg. 3557

SAVVIS, INC—See Lumen Technologies, Inc.; *U.S. Public*, pg. 1347

SAXON GLOBAL INC.; *U.S. Private*, pg. 3558

SAYLENT TECHNOLOGIES, INC.; *U.S. Private*, pg. 3558

SBAS (HK) LTD.—See Fortune Information Systems Corp.; *Int'l*, pg. 2743

SCALABLE NETWORK TECHNOLOGIES, INC.—See Keysight Technologies, Inc.; *U.S. Public*, pg. 1227

SCALA, INC.—See Stratacache Inc.; *U.S. Public*, pg. 3834

SCALEBASE, INC.—See ESW Capital, LLC; *U.S. Private*, pg. 1430

SCALE-UP SYSTEMS LIMITED—See Mettler-Toledo International, Inc.; *U.S. Public*, pg. 1433

SC CONTINENTAL AUTOMOTIVE ROMANIA S.R.L.—See Continental Aktiengesellschaft; *Int'l*, pg. 1783

SCEPTRE HOSPITALITY RESOURCES, LLC—See Access Technology Group Limited; *Int'l*, pg. 89

SCHRODINGER, INC.; *U.S. Public*, pg. 1848

SCHULER BUSINESS SOLUTIONS S.L.—See Durr AG; *Int'l*, pg. 2232

SCHWAB PERFORMANCE TECHNOLOGIES INC.—See The Charles Schwab Corporation; *U.S. Public*, pg. 2058

SCIA NV—See Herbalife Nutrition Ltd.; *Int'l*, pg. 3360

SCIENCE APPLICATIONS INTERNATIONAL CORPORATION - HUNTSVILLE—See Science Applications International Corporation; *U.S. Public*, pg. 1848

SCIENT, INC.; *U.S. Public*, pg. 1848

SCIPLAY CORPORATION—See Light & Wonder, Inc.; *U.S. Public*, pg. 1314

SCM MICROSYSTEMS INDIA PVT. LTD.—See Identiv, Inc.; *U.S. Public*, pg. 1089

SCOREX SCANDINAVIA—See Experian plc; *Int'l*, pg. 2587

SCOREX (UK) LIMITED—See Experian plc; *Int'l*, pg. 2587

THE SCREENING PROS, LLC—See CoStar Group, Inc.; *U.S. Public*, pg. 586

SCRIPTSENDER, LLC—See RadNet, Inc.; *U.S. Public*, pg. 1761

SEAGULL SCIENTIFIC, INC.—See Peak Rock Capital LLC; *U.S. Private*, pg. 3124

SEAL INFOTECH PRIVATE LIMITED—See Lumen Technologies, Inc.; *U.S. Public*, pg. 1348

SEALNET SDN. BHD.—See Dagang NeXchange Berhad; *Int'l*, pg. 1912

SEAL SOFTWARE INC.—See DocuSign, Inc.; *U.S. Public*, pg. 672

SEARCE, INC.; *U.S. Private*, pg. 3586

SEATADVISOR, INC.—See Providence Equity Partners L.L.C.; *U.S. Private*, pg. 3293

SEC SELECTA ENERGY CONSULTING GMBH—See EWE Aktiengesellschaft; *Int'l*, pg. 2575

SECURBORATION, INC.; *U.S. Private*, pg. 3593

SECURCASH B.V.—See Allied Universal Manager LLC; *U.S. Private*, pg. 190

SEDARU, INC.—See Danaher Corporation; *U.S. Public*, pg. 631

SEDE CENTRAL SOFTWARE AG ESPANA S.A.—See Silver Lake Group, LLC; *U.S. Private*, pg. 3659

SEECONTROL, INC.—See Autodesk, Inc.; *U.S. Public*, pg. 229

SEEQUENT AUSTRALIA PTY LIMITED—See Bentley Systems, Inc.; *U.S. Public*, pg. 297

SEEQUENT CHILE SPA—See Bentley Systems, Inc.; *U.S. Public*, pg. 297

SEEQUENT PERU S.A.C—See Bentley Systems, Inc.; *U.S. Public*, pg. 297

SEEQUENT SOUTH AFRICA PTY LIMITED—See Bentley Systems, Inc.; *U.S. Public*, pg. 297

SEEQUENT UK LIMITED—See Bentley Systems, Inc.; *U.S. Public*, pg. 297

SEEQUENT USA INC.—See Bentley Systems, Inc.; *U.S. Public*, pg. 297

SEEUNITY INC.—See Insight Venture Management, LLC; *U.S. Private*, pg. 2087

THE SEGAL COMPANY, LTD.—See The Segal Group, Inc.; *U.S. Private*, pg. 4116

SEGUE TECHNOLOGIES, INC.—See Tetra Tech, Inc.; *U.S. Public*, pg. 2023

SEINE GMBH—See Allianz SE; *Int'l*, pg. 355

SELLING SIMPLIFIED GROUP, INC.—See Eagle Publishing Inc.; *U.S. Private*, pg. 1310

SEMPCHECK SERVICES LLC—See Energy Overwatch LLC; *U.S. Private*, pg. 1395

SENSEMETRICS, INC.—See Bentley Systems, Inc.; *U.S. Public*, pg. 297

SENSIML CORPORATION—See QuickLogic Corporation; *U.S. Public*, pg. 1756

SENSUS CHILE SA—See Xylem Inc.; *U.S. Public*, pg. 2395

SENSUS ESPANA SA—See Xylem Inc.; *U.S. Public*, pg. 2395

SENSUS FRANCE SAS—See Xylem Inc.; *U.S. Public*, pg. 2395

SENSUS ITALIA SRL—See Xylem Inc.; *U.S. Public*, pg. 2395

SENSUS MAROC S.A.—See Xylem Inc.; *U.S. Public*, pg. 2395

SENSUS METERING SYSTEMS (FUZHOU) CO., LTD.—See Xylem Inc.; *U.S. Public*, pg. 2395

SENSUS POLSKA SP. ZOO—See Xylem Inc.; *U.S. Public*, pg. 2395

SENSUS SOUTH AFRICA (PROPRIETARY) LTD.—See Xylem Inc.; *U.S. Public*, pg. 2395

SENTINELONE, INC.; *U.S. Public*, pg. 1868

SENTRANA INC.; *U.S. Private*, pg. 3610

SEPIALINE, INC.; *U.S. Private*, pg. 3611

SERENDEBYTE INC.—See TTEC Holdings, Inc.; *U.S. Public*, pg. 2203

SERVERIAI VERSLUI UAB—See Atea ASA; *Int'l*, pg. 667

SERVIAN PTY LTD—See Cognizant Technology Solutions Corporation; *U.S. Public*, pg. 525

SERVICE LIFE S.R.L.—See Ardian SAS; *Int'l*, pg. 555

SERVICEMAX AUSTRALIA PTY. LTD.—See PTC Inc.; *U.S. Public*, pg. 1735

SERVICENOW A.B. ISRAEL LTD—See ServiceNow, Inc.; *U.S. Public*, pg. 1872

SERVICENOW AUSTRALIA PTY LTD—See ServiceNow, Inc.; *U.S. Public*, pg. 1872

SERVICENOW BELGIUM BVBA—See ServiceNow, Inc.; *U.S. Public*, pg. 1872

SERVICENOW BRASIL GERENCIAMENTO DE SERVICOS LTDA.—See ServiceNow, Inc.; *U.S. Public*, pg. 1872

SERVICENOW FINLAND OY—See ServiceNow, Inc.; *U.S. Public*, pg. 1872

SERVICENOW FRANCE SAS—See ServiceNow, Inc.; *U.S. Public*, pg. 1872

SERVICENOW HONG KONG LIMITED—See ServiceNow, Inc.; *U.S. Public*, pg. 1872

SERVICENOW, INC.; *U.S. Public*, pg. 1872

SERVICENOW ITALY—See ServiceNow, Inc.; *U.S. Public*, pg. 1872

SERVICENOW JAPAN KK—See ServiceNow, Inc.; *U.S. Public*, pg. 1872

SERVICENOW NEDERLAND BV—See ServiceNow, Inc.; *U.S. Public*, pg. 1872

SERVICENOW NORWAY AS—See ServiceNow, Inc.; *U.S. Public*, pg. 1872

SERVICENOW OPERATIONS MEXICO—See ServiceNow, Inc.; *U.S. Public*, pg. 1872

SERVICENOW PTE. LTD.—See ServiceNow, Inc.; *U.S. Public*, pg. 1872

SERVICENOW SOUTH AFRICA (PTY) LTD.—See ServiceNow, Inc.; *U.S. Public*, pg. 1872

SERVICENOW SPAIN S.L.—See ServiceNow, Inc.; *U.S. Public*, pg. 1872

SERVICENOW SWEDEN AB—See ServiceNow, Inc.; *U.S. Public*, pg. 1872

SERVICENOW SWITZERLAND GMBH—See ServiceNow, Inc.; *U.S. Public*, pg. 1872

SERVICENOW TURKEY BILISIM SANAYIVE TICARET LTD—See ServiceNow, Inc.; *U.S. Public*, pg. 1872

SERVICENOW UK LTD.—See ServiceNow, Inc.; *U.S. Public*, pg. 1872

SERVICE PLUS GMBH—See E.ON SE; *Int'l*, pg. 2259

SERVICEPOWER BUSINESS SOLUTIONS LIMITED—See Diversis Capital, LLC; *U.S. Private*, pg. 1244

SERVICEPOWER, INC—See Diversis Capital, LLC; *U.S. Private*, pg. 1244

SERVICETITAN, INC.; *U.S. Private*, pg. 3616

SERVICE WORKS GLOBAL NORDIC AB—See Addnode Group AB; *Int'l*, pg. 130

SERVICE WORKS GLOBAL PTY. LTD.—See Addnode Group AB; *Int'l*, pg. 130

SERVICEXPERT GESELLSCHAFT FUR SERVICE INFORMATIONSSYSTEME MBH—See Cognizant Technology Solutions Corporation; *U.S. Public*, pg. 525

SESSIONCAM LTD.—See Glassbox Ltd.; *Int'l*, pg. 2989

SFDC NORWAY AS—See Salesforce, Inc.; *U.S. Public*, pg. 1837

SF SOFTWARE & FRIENDS GMBH—See Allgeier SE; *Int'l*, pg. 338

SG GAMING ASIA LIMITED—See Light & Wonder, Inc.; *U.S. Public*, pg. 1314

SG GAMING AUSTRALIA HOLDINGS I PTY LTD—See Light & Wonder, Inc.; *U.S. Public*, pg. 1314

SG PROFESSIONAL SERVICES B.V.—See Advent International Corporation; *U.S. Private*, pg. 97
SG PROFESSIONAL SERVICES B.V.—See Centerbridge Partners, L.P.; *U.S. Private*, pg. 813
S-GROUP SOLUTIONS AB—See Addnode Group AB; *Int'l*, pg. 130
SHANGHAI BESTECH SOFTWARE CO., LTD.—See Beijing Shiji Information Technology Co., Ltd.; *Int'l*, pg. 956
SHANGHAI CORE CO., LTD—See Core Corporation; *Int'l*, pg. 1797
SHANGHAI HUATENG SOFTWARE SYSTEMS CO., LTD.—See Chinasoft International Ltd; *Int'l*, pg. 1569
SHANGHAI SHANGLUO SOFTWARE CO., LTD.—See Computer & Technologies Holdings Limited; *Int'l*, pg. 1758
SHANGHAI XIZHEN INFORMATION TECHNOLOGY CO., LTD.—See Global Infotech Co., Ltd.; *Int'l*, pg. 2997
SHAPE SECURITY, INC.—See F5, Inc.; *U.S. Public*, pg. 819
SHARK COMPUTERS INK.; *U.S. Private*, pg. 3626
SHARP BANCSYSTEMS, INC.—See Nymbus, Inc.; *U.S. Private*, pg. 2976
SHARPEN TECHNOLOGIES INC.—See Teleo Capital Management, LLC; *U.S. Private*, pg. 3961
SHARP SOFTWARE DEVELOPMENT INDIA PVT LTD.—See Hon Hai Precision Industry Co., Ltd.; *Int'l*, pg. 3459
SHAW SYSTEMS ASSOCIATES INC.; *U.S. Private*, pg. 3628
SHENZHEN GENIUS INFORMATION TECHNOLOGY CO., LTD.—See China Finance Online Co. Limited; *Int'l*, pg. 1502
SHENZHEN SOLUSOFT SOFTWARE CO., LTD.—See Beijing Shiji Information Technology Co., Ltd.; *Int'l*, pg. 956
SHIELD AI INC.; *U.S. Private*, pg. 3635
SHIFT4 CORPORATION—See Shift4 Payments, Inc.; *U.S. Public*, pg. 1875
SHIFT ADMINISTRATORS, LLC—See QGenda, LLC; *U.S. Private*, pg. 3313
SHIFTPIXY, INC.; *U.S. Public*, pg. 1875
SHIFTWIZARD, INC.—See HealthStream, Inc.; *U.S. Public*, pg. 1017
SHIJI (AUSTRALIA) PTY LTD—See Beijing Shiji Information Technology Co., Ltd.; *Int'l*, pg. 956
SHIJI DEUTSCHLAND GMBH—See Beijing Shiji Information Technology Co., Ltd.; *Int'l*, pg. 956
SHIJI GMBH—See Beijing Shiji Information Technology Co., Ltd.; *Int'l*, pg. 956
SHIJI (HONG KONG) LTD.—See Beijing Shiji Information Technology Co., Ltd.; *Int'l*, pg. 956
SHIJI INFORMATION TECHNOLOGY (HONG KONG) LIMITED—See Beijing Shiji Information Technology Co., Ltd.; *Int'l*, pg. 956
SHIJI INFORMATION TECHNOLOGY (PHILIPPINES), INC.—See Beijing Shiji Information Technology Co., Ltd.; *Int'l*, pg. 956
SHIJI JAPAN CO., LTD.—See Beijing Shiji Information Technology Co., Ltd.; *Int'l*, pg. 956
SHIJI MALAYSIA SDN. BHD.—See Beijing Shiji Information Technology Co., Ltd.; *Int'l*, pg. 956
SHIJI MIDDLE EAST FZ-LLC—See Beijing Shiji Information Technology Co., Ltd.; *Int'l*, pg. 956
SHIJI POLAND SP. Z O.O.—See Beijing Shiji Information Technology Co., Ltd.; *Int'l*, pg. 956
SHIJI PORTUGAL - CONCEPTEK SISTEMAS DE INFORMACAO S.A.—See Beijing Shiji Information Technology Co., Ltd.; *Int'l*, pg. 956
SHIJI SINGAPORE PTE. LTD.—See Beijing Shiji Information Technology Co., Ltd.; *Int'l*, pg. 956
SHIJI SLOVAKIA S.R.O.—See Beijing Shiji Information Technology Co., Ltd.; *Int'l*, pg. 956
SHIJI THAILAND LIMITED—See Beijing Shiji Information Technology Co., Ltd.; *Int'l*, pg. 956
SHIJI (UK) LIMITED—See Beijing Shiji Information Technology Co., Ltd.; *Int'l*, pg. 956
SHIJI (US) INC.—See Beijing Shiji Information Technology Co., Ltd.; *Int'l*, pg. 956
SHIKOKU HITACHI SYSTEMS, LTD.—See Hitachi, Ltd.; *Int'l*, pg. 3424
SHINBA-EDARAN SDN. BHD.—See Edran Berhad; *Int'l*, pg. 2315
SHINETECH SOFTWARE; *U.S. Private*, pg. 3637
SHINEWAVE INTERNATIONAL INC.—See ASUSTeK Computer Inc.; *Int'l*, pg. 664
SHINYOPTICS CORP.—See ASUSTeK Computer Inc.; *Int'l*, pg. 664
SHIPBOB, INC.; *U.S. Private*, pg. 3637
SHIPENGINE INC.—See Thoma Bravo, L.P.; *U.S. Private*, pg. 4154
SHIPSTATION LIMITED—See Thoma Bravo, L.P.; *U.S. Private*, pg. 4154
SHIZUOKA HITACHI CO., LTD.—See Hitachi, Ltd.; *Int'l*, pg. 3424
SHOPADVISOR, INC.—See Targetable Marketing Services LLC; *U.S. Private*, pg. 3933
SHORELINE GROUP LLC; *U.S. Private*, pg. 3641
S&I CO., LTD.—See BIPROGY Inc.; *Int'l*, pg. 1045
SIERRA BRAVO, CORPORATION; *U.S. Private*, pg. 3646
SIERRA TECHNOLOGY CORPORATION—See American CyberSystems, Inc.; *U.S. Private*, pg. 230
SIGFIG WEALTH MANAGEMENT, LLC—See Nvest, Inc.; *U.S. Private*, pg. 2975
SIGHTPLAN, INC.—See SmartRent, Inc.; *U.S. Public*, pg. 1896
SIGMA BRAVO PTY LTD—See KBR, Inc.; *U.S. Public*, pg. 1216
SIGMA SEVEN LIMITED—See Capita plc; *Int'l*, pg. 1309
SIGMA SYSTEMS JAPAN K.K.—See Hansen Technologies Limited; *Int'l*, pg. 3260
SIGNALDEMAND, INC.—See PROS Holdings, Inc.; *U.S. Public*, pg. 1728
SIGNIANT INC.; *U.S. Private*, pg. 3650
SILABS INDIA PRIVATE LIMITED—See Silicon Laboratories Inc.; *U.S. Public*, pg. 1879
SILICON LABORATORIES DENMARK APS—See Silicon Laboratories Inc.; *U.S. Public*, pg. 1880
SILICON LABORATORIES FINLAND OY—See Silicon Laboratories Inc.; *U.S. Public*, pg. 1880
SILK ROAD ENTERTAINMENT, INC.; *U.S. Public*, pg. 1880
SILKROUTE; *U.S. Private*, pg. 3653
SILVER BULLET TECHNOLOGY, INC.—See COMSovereign Holding Corp.; *U.S. Public*, pg. 562
SILVON SOFTWARE INC.; *U.S. Private*, pg. 3664
SILVON SOFTWARE, LTD.—See Silvon Software Inc.; *U.S. Private*, pg. 3665
SIMCORP BENELUX SA/NV—See Deutsche Borse AG; *Int'l*, pg. 2064
SIMCORP CANADA INC.—See Deutsche Borse AG; *Int'l*, pg. 2064
SIMCORP DEVELOPMENT CENTRE UK LIMITED—See Deutsche Borse AG; *Int'l*, pg. 2064
SIMCORP HONG KONG LTD.—See Deutsche Borse AG; *Int'l*, pg. 2064
SIMCORP ITALIANA S.R.L.—See Deutsche Borse AG; *Int'l*, pg. 2064
SIMCORP JAPAN KK—See Deutsche Borse AG; *Int'l*, pg. 2064
SIMCORP LTD.—See Deutsche Borse AG; *Int'l*, pg. 2064
SIMCORP OSTERREICH GMBH—See Deutsche Borse AG; *Int'l*, pg. 2064
SIMCORP SCHWEIZ AG—See Deutsche Borse AG; *Int'l*, pg. 2064
SIMCORP SINGAPORE PTE. LTD—See Deutsche Borse AG; *Int'l*, pg. 2064
SIMCORP SP Z O.O.—See Deutsche Borse AG; *Int'l*, pg. 2064
SIMCORP UKRAINE LLC—See Deutsche Borse AG; *Int'l*, pg. 2064
SIMCORP USA INC—See Deutsche Borse AG; *Int'l*, pg. 2064
SIMENO HOLDING AG—See Thoma Bravo, L.P.; *U.S. Private*, pg. 4147
SIMIGON LTD.—See Maxify Solutions Inc.; *U.S. Private*, pg. 2618
SIMONCOMPUTING, INC.; *U.S. Private*, pg. 3666
SIMPLICITY GROUP; *U.S. Private*, pg. 3667
SIMPLICITY V8 HONG KONG LTD.—See Bally's Corporation; *U.S. Public*, pg. 268
SIMPLIFY DIGITAL LIMITED—See Currys plc; *Int'l*, pg. 1879
SIMULUS LIMITED—See KKR & Co. Inc.; *U.S. Public*, pg. 1241
SIMVENTIONSM INC.; *U.S. Private*, pg. 3669
SINGLEPOINT INC.; *U.S. Public*, pg. 1888
SINO STRIDE TECHNOLOGY CO., LTD—See HNA International Investment Holdings Limited; *Int'l*, pg. 3433
SINQIA S.A.—See EVERTEC, Inc.; *U.S. Public*, pg. 802
SINTECMEDIA AMS B.V.—See Francisco Partners Management, LP; *U.S. Private*, pg. 1591
SINTECMEDIA GLOBAL LTD.—See Francisco Partners Management, LP; *U.S. Private*, pg. 1591
SIRSIDYNIX CORPORATION; *U.S. Private*, pg. 3675
SIRSIDYNIX—See SirsiDynix Corporation; *U.S. Private*, pg. 3675
SITECH DEUTSCHLAND GMBH—See Trimble, Inc.; *U.S. Public*, pg. 2191
SITECH SOUTHERN AFRICA (PTY) LTD—See Trimble, Inc.; *U.S. Public*, pg. 2191
SITECORE AUSTRALIA PTY LTD—See EQT AB; *Int'l*, pg. 2480
SITECORE CANADA LTD—See EQT AB; *Int'l*, pg. 2480
SITECORE DEUTSCHLAND GMBH—See EQT AB; *Int'l*, pg. 2480
SITECORE JAPAN—See EQT AB; *Int'l*, pg. 2480
SITECORE NEDERLAND BV—See EQT AB; *Int'l*, pg. 2480
SITECORE NEW ZEALAND—See EQT AB; *Int'l*, pg. 2480
SITECORE SVERIGE AB—See EQT AB; *Int'l*, pg. 2480
SITECORE UK LTD.—See EQT AB; *Int'l*, pg. 2480
SITEL FRANCE SAS—See Creadev SAS; *Int'l*, pg. 1830
SITEL GMBH—See Creadev SAS; *Int'l*, pg. 1830
SITEL IBERICA TELESERVICES, S.A.—See Creadev SAS; *Int'l*, pg. 1831
SITEL NETHERLANDS—See Creadev SAS; *Int'l*, pg. 1831
SITEL NEW ZEALAND LIMITED—See Creadev SAS; *Int'l*, pg. 1831
SITEL UK LTD.—See Creadev SAS; *Int'l*, pg. 1831
SITESTUFF, INC.—See Yardi Systems, Inc.; *U.S. Private*, pg. 4586
SIXNET WIRELESS PRODUCT GROUP CANADA—See HMS Networks AB; *Int'l*, pg. 3433
SKAN, INC.; *U.S. Private*, pg. 3681
SKUID, INC.—See TPG Capital, L.P.; *U.S. Public*, pg. 2175
SKYHOOK WIRELESS, INC.—See Liberty Broadband Corporation; *U.S. Public*, pg. 1311
SKYLAND ANALYTICS INC.—See Danaher Corporation; *U.S. Public*, pg. 631
SKYSCAPE.COM INC.—See KKR & Co. Inc.; *U.S. Public*, pg. 1253
SKYWARD INC.; *U.S. Private*, pg. 3686
SLACK TECHNOLOGIES, INC.—See Salesforce, Inc.; *U.S. Public*, pg. 1838
SLINGO, INC.—See RealNetworks, Inc.; *U.S. Private*, pg. 3369
SLINGSHOT SEO; *U.S. Private*, pg. 3688
SMA ALLIANCE, INC.; *U.S. Public*, pg. 1895
SMALLPONDS, LLC—See Gale Force Software Corporation; *U.S. Private*, pg. 1636
SMART BEAR SOFTWARE, INC.; *U.S. Private*, pg. 3691
SMART BUTTON ASSOCIATES, INC.—See Aimia Inc.; *Int'l*, pg. 234
SMARTCLIXX, LLC—See TA Associates, Inc.; *U.S. Private*, pg. 3917
SMART FACTORY & SERVICES HOLDINGS (THAILAND) CO., LTD.—See Hitachi, Ltd.; *Int'l*, pg. 3424
SMARTFUN DIGITAL CO., LTD.—See Chunghwa Telecom Co., Ltd.; *Int'l*, pg. 1598
SMART I.T. SYSTEMS BV—See IQVIA Holdings Inc.; *U.S. Public*, pg. 1170
SMART LINE S.R.L.—See CAD IT S.p.A.; *Int'l*, pg. 1247
SMARTLING, INC.; *U.S. Private*, pg. 3692
SMART MODULAR TECHNOLOGIES SDN. BHD.—See Penguin Solutions, Inc.; *U.S. Public*, pg. 1661
SMART RX SAS—See Cegedim S.A.; *Int'l*, pg. 1390
SMART SOURCING CO., LTD.—See Aucfan Co., Ltd.; *Int'l*, pg. 699
SMART TECHNOLOGIES (GERMANY) GMBH—See Hon Hai Precision Industry Co., Ltd.; *Int'l*, pg. 3457
SMART TECHNOLOGIES (SEATTLE) INC.—See Hon Hai Precision Industry Co., Ltd.; *Int'l*, pg. 3457
SMA SOLUTIONS; *U.S. Private*, pg. 3690
SMITH MICRO SOFTWARE UK LIMITED—See Smith Micro Software, Inc.; *U.S. Public*, pg. 1896
SMOOBU GMBH—See HomeToGo SE; *Int'l*, pg. 3456
SMS ALTERNATIVES INC.; *U.S. Public*, pg. 1896
SNAPCOMMS, INC.—See Thoma Bravo, L.P.; *U.S. Private*, pg. 4148
SNAPCOMMS LIMITED—See Thoma Bravo, L.P.; *U.S. Private*, pg. 4147
SNAPCOMMS UK LIMITED—See Thoma Bravo, L.P.; *U.S. Private*, pg. 4147
SNAPSHOT GMBH—See Beijing Shiji Information Technology Co., Ltd.; *Int'l*, pg. 956
SNAPTRACK, INC.—See QUALCOMM Incorporated; *U.S. Public*, pg. 1747
SNOWBOUND SOFTWARE CORP.—See Pegasus Imaging Corporation; *U.S. Private*, pg. 3129
SNOWFLAKE COMPUTING PTY. LTD.—See Snowflake Inc.; *U.S. Public*, pg. 1899
SNOWFLAKE INC.; *U.S. Public*, pg. 1899
SOCIALCHORUS, INC.—See Sumeru Equity Partners LLC; *U.S. Private*, pg. 3852
SOCIAL & SCIENTIFIC SYSTEMS, INC.—See DLH Holdings Corp.; *U.S. Public*, pg. 670
SOFTCON IT SERVICE S.R.L.—See Allgeier SE; *Int'l*, pg. 337
SOFTERWARE, INC.; *U.S. Private*, pg. 3705
SOFTGARDEN E-RECRUITING GMBH—See Grupa Pracuj S.A.; *Int'l*, pg. 3117
SOFTLANDING SYSTEMS, INC.—See UNICOM Global, Inc.; *U.S. Private*, pg. 4281
SOFTSOL RESOURCES; *U.S. Private*, pg. 3705
SOFTTECH SOLUTIONS, INC.—See Falfurrias Capital Partners, LP; *U.S. Private*, pg. 1467
SOFTURA, INC; *U.S. Private*, pg. 3705
SOFTWARE AG ARGENTINA S.R.L.—See Silver Lake Group, LLC; *U.S. Private*, pg. 3659
SOFTWARE AG (ASIA PACIFIC/SINGAPORE) LTD.—See Silver Lake Group, LLC; *U.S. Private*, pg. 3659
SOFTWARE AG BANGALORE TECHNOLOGIES PRIVATE LTD—See Silver Lake Group, LLC; *U.S. Private*, pg. 3659
SOFTWARE AG CANADA CORPORATION—See Silver Lake Group, LLC; *U.S. Private*, pg. 3659
SOFTWARE AG CHENNAI DEVELOPMENT CENTER INDIA PVT LTD—See Silver Lake Group, LLC; *U.S. Private*, pg. 3659
SOFTWARE AG DEVELOPMENT CENTER INDIA PRIVATE LIMITED—See Silver Lake Group, LLC; *U.S. Private*, pg. 3659
SOFTWARE AG DEVELOPMENT CENTRE BULGARIA EOOD—See Silver Lake Group, LLC; *U.S. Private*, pg. 3659
SOFTWARE AG ESPANA S.A.—See Silver Lake Group, LLC; *U.S. Private*, pg. 3659
SOFTWARE AG ESPANA SYSTEMHAUS S.L.—See Silver Lake Group, LLC; *U.S. Private*, pg. 3659

SOFTWARE AG FRANCE S.A.R.L.—See Silver Lake Group, LLC; *U.S. Private*, pg. 3659
SOFTWARE AG GOVERNMENT SOLUTIONS, INC.—See Silver Lake Group, LLC; *U.S. Private*, pg. 3660
SOFTWARE AG HONG KONG—See Silver Lake Group, LLC; *U.S. Private*, pg. 3659
SOFTWARE AG KOREA CO., LTD.—See Silver Lake Group, LLC; *U.S. Private*, pg. 3660
SOFTWARE AG LATINOAMERICA S.L.—See Silver Lake Group, LLC; *U.S. Private*, pg. 3660
SOFTWARE AG, LTD.—See Silver Lake Group, LLC; *U.S. Private*, pg. 3660
SOFTWARE AG NORDIC AB—See Silver Lake Group, LLC; *U.S. Private*, pg. 3660
SOFTWARE AG NORDIC A/S—See Silver Lake Group, LLC; *U.S. Private*, pg. 3660
SOFTWARE AG OPERATIONS MALAYSIA SDN BHD—See Silver Lake Group, LLC; *U.S. Private*, pg. 3660
SOFTWARE AG (PHILIPPINES) INC.—See Silver Lake Group, LLC; *U.S. Private*, pg. 3659
SOFTWARE AG POLSKA SP. Z O.O.—See Silver Lake Group, LLC; *U.S. Private*, pg. 3660
SOFTWARE AG—See Silver Lake Group, LLC; *U.S. Private*, pg. 3658
SOFTWARE AG S.R.O.—See Silver Lake Group, LLC; *U.S. Private*, pg. 3660
SOFTWARE AG UK LTD.—See Silver Lake Group, LLC; *U.S. Private*, pg. 3660
SOFTWARE AG USA, INC.—See Silver Lake Group, LLC; *U.S. Private*, pg. 3660
SOFTWARE CO-WORK LLC—See DraftKings Inc.; *U.S. Public*, pg. 687
SOFTWARE EXPRESS INFORMATICA LTDA—See Fiserv, Inc.; *U.S. Public*, pg. 851
SOFTWARE FOLKS, INC.; *U.S. Private*, pg. 3705
SOFTWARE OF EXCELLENCE UNITED KINGDOM LIMITED—See Henry Schein, Inc.; *U.S. Public*, pg. 1027
SOFTWARE PROFESSIONALS INCORPORATED; *U.S. Private*, pg. 3705
SOFTWARE TRANSFORMATIONS, INC.; *U.S. Private*, pg. 3705
SOGETI IRELAND LTD.—See Capgemini SE; *Int'l*, pg. 1307
SOGETI USA LLC—See Capgemini SE; *Int'l*, pg. 1307
SOGETI USA LLC—See Capgemini SE; *Int'l*, pg. 1307
SOKOWEB TECHNOLOGIES, S.L.—See Axel Springer SE; *Int'l*, pg. 766
SOLAI & CAMERON INC.; *U.S. Private*, pg. 3706
SOLIBRI BENELUX B.V.—See Herbalife Nutrition Ltd.; *Int'l*, pg. 3360
SOLID INSTANCE, INC.—See Elliott Management Corporation; *U.S. Private*, pg. 1367
SOLID INSTANCE, INC.—See Vista Equity Partners, LLC; *U.S. Private*, pg. 4396
SOLID LINE AG—See Bechtle AG; *Int'l*, pg. 938
SOLID SAS—See Trimble, Inc.; *U.S. Public*, pg. 2191
SOLIDSIM ENGINEERING GMBH—See Emerson Electric Co.; *U.S. Public*, pg. 742
SOLINFO S.R.L.—See Ardian SAS; *Int'l*, pg. 555
SOLUTIONS 4 MOBILITY LLC—See Allgeier SE; *Int'l*, pg. 337
THE SOLUTIONSDEVELOPERS CORPORATION; *U.S. Private*, pg. 4119
SOLVER UAB—See Atea ASA; *Int'l*, pg. 667
SOMETHINGDIGITAL.COM LLC—See Genpact Limited; *Int'l*, pg. 2927
SONAK S.A.—See AXON Holdings S.A.; *Int'l*, pg. 770
SONA MOBILE HOLDINGS, CORP.; *U.S. Private*, pg. 3712
SONATYPE, INC—See Hummer Winblad Operating Co., LLC; *U.S. Private*, pg. 2007
SONATYPE, INC—See In-Q-Tel, Inc.; *U.S. Private*, pg. 2052
SONENDO, INC.; *U.S. Public*, pg. 1902
SONTIQ, INC.—See TransUnion; *U.S. Public*, pg. 2184
SOPHEON GMBH—See Wellspring Worldwide, LLC; *U.S. Private*, pg. 4478
SOPHEON UK LTD.—See Wellspring Worldwide, LLC; *U.S. Private*, pg. 4478
SOPRA BANKING SOFTWARE BELGIUM—See Axway Software SA; *Int'l*, pg. 772
SOSYAL YAZILIM VE DANISMANLIK HIZMETLERI AS—See Wynn Resorts Limited; *U.S. Public*, pg. 2384
SOU 300 GROUP HOLDING CO.; *U.S. Public*, pg. 1910
SOUNDTHINKING, INC.; *U.S. Public*, pg. 1910
SOURCE MEDICAL SOLUTIONS, INC.—See Wells Fargo & Company; *U.S. Public*, pg. 2344
SOURCETOAD, LLC; *U.S. Private*, pg. 3719
SOURCIFY GMBH—See H World Group Limited; *Int'l*, pg. 3191
SOUTH CAROLINA INTERACTIVE, LLC—See Tyler Technologies, Inc.; *U.S. Public*, pg. 2209
SOUTHEASTERN COMPUTER CONSULTANTS, INC.; *U.S. Private*, pg. 3727
SOVOS COMPLIANCE, LLC—See HgCapital Trust plc; *Int'l*, pg. 3377
SPACE AGE SERVICES, INC.; *U.S. Private*, pg. 3743
SPACECLAIM CORPORATION—See ANSYS, Inc.; *U.S. Public*, pg. 139
SPACECLAIM JAPAN, K.K.—See ANSYS, Inc.; *U.S. Public*, pg. 139

SPACEWELL INTERNATIONAL NV.—See Herbalife Nutrition Ltd.; *Int'l*, pg. 3360
SPARC, LLC; *U.S. Private*, pg. 3745
SPATIAL BUSINESS SYSTEMS, INC.—See Peak Rock Capital LLC; *U.S. Private*, pg. 3124
SPATIAL CORP.—See Dassault Systemes S.A.; *Int'l*, pg. 1974
SPECIALTY SYSTEMS, INC.—See Castellum, Inc.; *U.S. Public*, pg. 447
SPECTRAL AI, INC.; *U.S. Public*, pg. 1915
SPECTRA SYSTEMS CORPORATION; *U.S. Public*, pg. 1915
SPEECHLY OY—See Roblox Corporation; *U.S. Public*, pg. 1804
SPERIDIAN TECHNOLOGIES, LLC; *U.S. Private*, pg. 3756
SPIDAWEB LLC—See Bentley Systems, Inc.; *U.S. Public*, pg. 297
SPINDANCE, INC.—See Century Technology Group; *U.S. Private*, pg. 834
SPIRE GLOBAL CANADA SUBSIDIARY CORP.—See Spire Global, Inc.; *U.S. Public*, pg. 1918
SPIRE GLOBAL LUXEMBOURG S.A.R.L.—See Spire Global, Inc.; *U.S. Public*, pg. 1918
SPIRE GLOBAL SINGAPORE PTE LTD—See Spire Global, Inc.; *U.S. Public*, pg. 1918
SPIRE GLOBAL SUBSIDIARY, INC.—See Spire Global, Inc.; *U.S. Public*, pg. 1918
SPIRE GLOBAL UK LTD.—See Spire Global, Inc.; *U.S. Public*, pg. 1918
SPL SOFTWARE ALLIANCE LLC—See Caterpillar, Inc.; *U.S. Public*, pg. 453
SPLUNK SERVICES GERMANY GMBH—See Cisco Systems, Inc.; *U.S. Public*, pg. 500
SPORTSMEDIA TECHNOLOGY CORP.; *U.S. Private*, pg. 3761
SPOTINST LLC—See NetApp, Inc.; *U.S. Public*, pg. 1507
SPOTINST LLC—See NetApp, Inc.; *U.S. Public*, pg. 1507
SPOTLIGHT TICKET MANAGEMENT, INC.; *U.S. Private*, pg. 3762
SPRINGCM INC.—See DocuSign, Inc.; *U.S. Public*, pg. 672
SPRING HOUSE ENTERTAINMENT TECH. INC.—See Chunghwa Telecom Co., Ltd.; *Int'l*, pg. 1598
SPRINKLR, INC.; *U.S. Public*, pg. 1920
SPROUT SOCIAL, INC.; *U.S. Public*, pg. 1920
SQLI BELGIUM SA—See DBAY Advisors Limited; *Int'l*, pg. 1987
SQLI LUXEMBOURG SA—See DBAY Advisors Limited; *Int'l*, pg. 1987
SQUARE ROOT, INC.; *U.S. Private*, pg. 3766
SRL TECHNOSYSTEM, INC.—See H.U. Group Holdings, Inc.; *Int'l*, pg. 3197
SRO SOLUTIONS LIMITED—See Bentley Systems, Inc.; *U.S. Public*, pg. 297
SRSSOFT; *U.S. Private*, pg. 3768
SS&C SOLUTIONS PTY LIMITED—See SS&C Technologies Holdings, Inc.; *U.S. Public*, pg. 1924
SS&C TECHNOLOGIES AUSTRALIA PTY LTD.—See SS&C Technologies Holdings, Inc.; *U.S. Public*, pg. 1924
SS&C TECHNOLOGIES BV—See SS&C Technologies Holdings, Inc.; *U.S. Public*, pg. 1924
SS&C TECHNOLOGIES LTD.—See SS&C Technologies Holdings, Inc.; *U.S. Public*, pg. 1924
SS&C TECHNOLOGIES SDN. BHD.—See SS&C Technologies Holdings, Inc.; *U.S. Public*, pg. 1924
THE SSI GROUP, INC.; *U.S. Private*, pg. 4120
SSS BIOMEDICAL RESEARCH SUPPORT DIVISION—See DLH Holdings Corp.; *U.S. Public*, pg. 670
SSS COMPUTER SYSTEMS AND DATA ANALYSIS DIVISION—See DLH Holdings Corp.; *U.S. Public*, pg. 670
STACKIFY, LLC—See Netreo, Inc.; *U.S. Private*, pg. 2887
STADIUM TECHNOLOGY GROUP, LLC—See Entain PLC; *Int'l*, pg. 2450
STAMFORD STOCKHOLM AB—See Addnode Group AB; *Int'l*, pg. 130
STARLIMS FRANCE S.A.S.—See Abbott Laboratories; *U.S. Public*, pg. 20
STARLIMS IBERICA, S.A.—See Abbott Laboratories; *U.S. Public*, pg. 20
STARLIMS NETHERLANDS B.V.—See Abbott Laboratories; *U.S. Public*, pg. 20
STARLIMS (SEA) PTE. LTD.—See Abbott Laboratories; *U.S. Public*, pg. 21
STATPRO AUSTRALIA PTY LTD.—See TA Associates, Inc.; *U.S. Private*, pg. 3915
STELLAR IT SOLUTIONS, INC.; *U.S. Private*, pg. 3799
STELLASERVICE, INC.—See Thoma Bravo, L.P.; *U.S. Private*, pg. 4149
STERLING SOFTWARE (NETHERLANDS) IV B.V.—See Broadcom Inc.; *U.S. Public*, pg. 390
STERLING SOFTWARE PRIVATE LIMITED—See Computer Age Management Services Limited; *Int'l*, pg. 1759
STERLING TRADER, INC.—See Professional Trading Solutions, Inc.; *U.S. Private*, pg. 3276
STOCK & INFO LTDA.—See EVERTEC, Inc.; *U.S. Public*, pg. 802
STOCKVANTAGE INC.—See Morgan Stanley; *U.S. Public*, pg. 1475

STONE APPLE SOLUTIONS PTE. LTD.—See Hitachi, Ltd.; *Int'l*, pg. 3424
STOPLIFT, INC.—See NCR Voyix Corporation.; *U.S. Public*, pg. 1503
STOREWEAVER GMBH—See Fujitsu Limited; *Int'l*, pg. 2837
STORIS INC.; *U.S. Private*, pg. 3831
STRATA DECISION TECHNOLOGY INDIA PRIVATE LIMITED—See Roper Technologies, Inc.; *U.S. Public*, pg. 1813
STRATA DECISION TECHNOLOGY LLC—See Roper Technologies, Inc.; *U.S. Public*, pg. 1813
STRATASAN, LLC—See Roper Technologies, Inc.; *U.S. Public*, pg. 1813
STRATEGIC HEALTHCARE PROGRAMS, LLC—See Roper Technologies, Inc.; *U.S. Public*, pg. 1813
STRATEGIC RESOURCES INTERNATIONAL, INC.—See Peraton Government Communications, Inc.; *U.S. Private*, pg. 3146
STRATEGIC SYSTEMS, INC.; *U.S. Private*, pg. 3835
STRATEGIC SYSTEMS & TECHNOLOGY CORPORATION; *U.S. Private*, pg. 3835
STRATIX CORPORATION—See Independence Capital Partners, LLC; *U.S. Private*, pg. 2056
STRATUS TECHNOLOGIES IRELAND LIMITED—See Penguin Solutions, Inc.; *U.S. Public*, pg. 1661
STRIDE CONSULTING LLC; *U.S. Private*, pg. 3840
STRIKEDECK, INC.—See Thoma Bravo, L.P.; *U.S. Private*, pg. 4149
SUBMITTABLE HOLDINGS, INC.; *U.S. Private*, pg. 3847
SUMINISTROS, IMPORTACIONES Y MANTENIMIENTOS ELECTRONICOS, S.A.—See ACS, Actividades de Construccion y Servicios, S.A.; *Int'l*, pg. 116
SUMMIT2SEA CONSULTING, LLC—See Bluestone Investment Partners, LLC; *U.S. Private*, pg. 598
SUMMIT SOFTWARE, INC.—See F.W. Davison & Company, Inc.; *U.S. Private*, pg. 1457
SUMMIT SYSTEMS, INC.—See Vista Equity Partners, LLC; *U.S. Private*, pg. 4397
SUMMIT SYSTEMS SA—See Vista Equity Partners, LLC; *U.S. Private*, pg. 4397
SUNBLOCK SYSTEMS, INC.; *U.S. Private*, pg. 3865
SUNGAME CORPORATION; *U.S. Private*, pg. 3867
SUNHILLO CORPORATION; *U.S. Private*, pg. 3867
SUNMERGE SYSTEMS INC.; *U.S. Private*, pg. 3868
SUNQUEST INFORMATION SYSTEMS (EUROPE) LIMITED—See Roper Technologies, Inc.; *U.S. Public*, pg. 1813
SUNQUEST INFORMATION SYSTEMS (INDIA) PRIVATE LIMITED—See Roper Technologies, Inc.; *U.S. Public*, pg. 1813
SUPERIOR DATA SOLUTIONS INC.—See Recast Software Inc.; *U.S. Private*, pg. 3370
SUPERONE CO., LTD.—See AI Co., Ltd.; *Int'l*, pg. 226
SUPERSTREAM INC.—See Canon Inc.; *Int'l*, pg. 1296
SUPPORT SYSTEMS INTERNATIONAL INC.; *U.S. Private*, pg. 3882
SUREHARVEST SERVICES, LLC—See Where Food Comes From, Inc.; *U.S. Public*, pg. 2366
SURETEC; *U.S. Private*, pg. 3883
SURE TRACE SECURITY CORP.; *U.S. Private*, pg. 3883
SUSE S.A.—See EQT AB; *Int'l*, pg. 2479
SUTARIA SERVICES INC.—See Elisa Corporation; *Int'l*, pg. 2361
SWEDA INTERNATIONAL LTD.—See Sweda Corporation; *U.S. Private*, pg. 3891
SWISS AVIATION SOFTWARE AG—See Deutsche Lufthansa AG; *Int'l*, pg. 2070
SWISSSIGN AG—See Die Schweizerische Post AG; *Int'l*, pg. 2113
SWORD GRC LTD.—See TA Associates, Inc.; *U.S. Private*, pg. 3918
SWYPE, INC.—See Microsoft Corporation; *U.S. Public*, pg. 1443
SYCLE, LLC—See Cochlear Limited; *Int'l*, pg. 1687
SYFADIS SAS—See ManpowerGroup Inc.; *U.S. Public*, pg. 1360
SYG INC.—See AOYAMA TRADING Co. Ltd.; *Int'l*, pg. 499
SYLOG SYSTEMS AB—See Adecco Group AG; *Int'l*, pg. 140
SYMANTEC LIMITED—See Gen Digital Inc.; *U.S. Public*, pg. 911
SYMANTEC SECURITY (UK) LIMITED—See Gen Digital Inc.; *U.S. Public*, pg. 911
SYMBEO, INC.—See CorVel Corporation; *U.S. Public*, pg. 585
SYMBILITY SOLUTIONS CORP.—See Insight Venture Management, LLC; *U.S. Private*, pg. 2089
SYMBILITY SOLUTIONS CORP.—See Stone Point Capital LLC; *U.S. Private*, pg. 3823
SYMBILITY SOLUTIONS GMBH—See Insight Venture Management, LLC; *U.S. Private*, pg. 2089
SYMBILITY SOLUTIONS GMBH—See Stone Point Capital LLC; *U.S. Private*, pg. 3823
SYMBILITY SOLUTIONS INC.—See Insight Venture Management, LLC; *U.S. Private*, pg. 2089
SYMBILITY SOLUTIONS INC.—See Stone Point Capital LLC; *U.S. Private*, pg. 3823
SYMBILITY SOLUTIONS LIMITED—See Insight Venture Management, LLC; *U.S. Private*, pg. 2089

SYMBILITY SOLUTIONS LIMITED—See Stone Point Capital LLC; *U.S. Private*, pg. 3823
SYMBIO (APAC) CO., LTD.—See Symbio, LLC; *U.S. Private*, pg. 3899
SYMBIO FINLAND OY - OULU—See Bain Capital, LP; *U.S. Private*, pg. 451
SYMBIO FINLAND OY—See Bain Capital, LP; *U.S. Private*, pg. 451
SYMBIO, LLC; *U.S. Private*, pg. 3898
SY.MED DEVELOPMENT, INC.—See HealthStream, Inc.; *U.S. Public*, pg. 1017
SYMETRI AB—See Addnode Group AB; *Int'l*, pg. 130
SYMETRI A/S—See Addnode Group AB; *Int'l*, pg. 130
SYMETRI AS—See Addnode Group AB; *Int'l*, pg. 131
SYMETRI LTD.—See Addnode Group AB; *Int'l*, pg. 131
SYMETRI OY—See Addnode Group AB; *Int'l*, pg. 131
SYMITAR SYSTEMS, INC.—See Jack Henry & Associates, Inc.; *U.S. Public*, pg. 1183
SYMPHONIC SOFTWARE LIMITED—See Thoma Bravo, L.P.; *U.S. Private*, pg. 4150
SYMPHONY CORP.; *U.S. Private*, pg. 3899
SYNABIZ CO., LTD.—See Aucfan Co., Ltd.; *Int'l*, pg. 699
SYNAPSENSE CORPORATION—See Vigilent Corporation; *U.S. Private*, pg. 4382
SYNAPSE STUDIOS, LLC; *U.S. Private*, pg. 3902
SYNAPTICS INTERNATIONAL INC.—See Synaptics Incorporated; *U.S. Public*, pg. 1969
SYNAPTIC SOLUTIONS, INC.—See Carl Marks & Co., Inc.; *U.S. Private*, pg. 763
SYNCFUSION, INC; *U.S. Private*, pg. 3902
SYNCORE TECHNOLOGIES AB—See Etteplan Oyj; *Int'l*, pg. 2525
SYNERGERP LIMITED - DWC LCC—See Alviva Holdings Limited; *Int'l*, pg. 402
SYNERGETIC INFORMATION SYSTEMS INC.; *U.S. Private*, pg. 3903
SYNERGISTIX, INC.; *U.S. Private*, pg. 3903
SYNERGY ECP, LLC—See Falfurrias Capital Partners, LP; *U.S. Private*, pg. 1467
SYNERGY LTD.—See Cyberlinks Co., Ltd.; *Int'l*, pg. 1893
SYNER TRADE S.A.—See Econocom Group SA; *Int'l*, pg. 2298
SYNETRIX LIMITED—See Capita plc; *Int'l*, pg. 1309
SYNOPSYS ARMENIA CJSC—See Synopsys, Inc.; *U.S. Public*, pg. 1971
SYNOPSYS GLOBAL KFT.—See Synopsys, Inc.; *U.S. Public*, pg. 1971
SYNOPSYS HARDWARE PLATFORMS GROUP AB—See Synopsys, Inc.; *U.S. Public*, pg. 1971
SYNOPSYS (INDIA) PRIVATE LIMITED—See Synopsys, Inc.; *U.S. Public*, pg. 1970
SYNOPSYS LLC—See Synopsys, Inc.; *U.S. Public*, pg. 1971
SYNOPSYS SARL—See Synopsys, Inc.; *U.S. Public*, pg. 1971
SYNOPSYS SPB LLC—See Synopsys, Inc.; *U.S. Public*, pg. 1971
SYNTEL EUROPE LTD.—See Atos SE; *Int'l*, pg. 692
SYNTEL, INC.—See Atos SE; *Int'l*, pg. 692
SYNTEL INTERNATIONAL PVT. LTD.—See Atos SE; *Int'l*, pg. 692
SYNTEL LTD.—See Atos SE; *Int'l*, pg. 692
SYNTEL PRIVATE LIMITED—See Atos SE; *Int'l*, pg. 692
SYNTHESIS SOFTWARE TECHNOLOGIES PROPRIETARY LIMITED—See Capital Appreciation Ltd.; *Int'l*, pg. 1309
SYNTHESIS TECHNOLOGY CORP.—See Blue Horizon Software Holdings LLC; *U.S. Private*, pg. 589
SYNXIS CORPORATION; *U.S. Private*, pg. 3905
SYRA HEALTH CORP.; *U.S. Public*, pg. 1972
SYRAINFOTEK LLC; *U.S. Private*, pg. 3905
SYSTAT SOFTWARE GMBH—See Cranes Software International Limited; *Int'l*, pg. 1828
SYSTEMA HIS HUMAN INFORMATION SYSTEMS GESELLSCHAFT MBH—See CompuGroup Medical SE & Co. KGaA; *Int'l*, pg. 1755
SYSTEMA S.R.L.—See Cellularline SpA; *Int'l*, pg. 1395
SYSTEM CREATIVE CO., LTD—See Core Corporation; *Int'l*, pg. 1797
SYSTEM DESIGN DEVELOPMENT CO., LTD.—See Broadmedia Corporation; *Int'l*, pg. 1172
SYSTEM DYNAMIX CORPORATION—See GSS Infotech Limited; *Int'l*, pg. 3150
SYSTEM IC CO., LTD.—See Densan System Co., Ltd.; *Int'l*, pg. 2028
SYSTEMS ALLIANCE, INC.; *U.S. Private*, pg. 3907
SYSTEMS INTEGRATION AND DEVELOPMENT, INC.; *U.S. Private*, pg. 3907
SYSTEMS MADE SIMPLE, INC.—See Lockheed Martin Corporation; *U.S. Public*, pg. 1339
SYSTEMS TECHNOLOGY ASSOCIATES, INC.—See Sagewind Capital LLC; *U.S. Private*, pg. 3528
SYSTEMWARE, INC.; *U.S. Private*, pg. 3908
T 2 SOFTWARE S.A.—See Antares Vision SpA; *Int'l*, pg. 482
T3 CORPORATION; *U.S. Private*, pg. 3913
TABERNUS EUROPE LIMITED—See Francisco Partners Management, LP; *U.S. Private*, pg. 1589

TABERNUS LLC—See Francisco Partners Management, LP; *U.S. Private*, pg. 1588
TABLEAU ASIA PACIFIC PTE. LTD.—See Salesforce, Inc.; *U.S. Public*, pg. 1838
TABLEAU (CHINA) CO., LTD.—See Salesforce, Inc.; *U.S. Public*, pg. 1838
TABLEAU FRANCE S.A.S.—See Salesforce, Inc.; *U.S. Public*, pg. 1838
TABLEAU GERMANY GMBH—See Salesforce, Inc.; *U.S. Public*, pg. 1838
TABLEAU JAPAN K.K.—See Salesforce, Inc.; *U.S. Public*, pg. 1838
TABLE TRAC, INC.; *U.S. Public*, pg. 1978
TAG WORLDWIDE GROUP LIMITED—See Dentsu Group Inc.; *Int'l*, pg. 2039
TAIHEI COMPUTER CO., LTD.—See Hirata Corporation; *Int'l*, pg. 3404
TAIWAN VMWARE INFORMATION TECHNOLOGY LLC—See Broadcom Inc.; *U.S. Public*, pg. 390
TAIWAN WEB SERVICE CORPORATION—See ASUSTeK Computer Inc.; *Int'l*, pg. 664
TAKE-TWO INTERACTIVE SOFTWARE, INC.; *U.S. Public*, pg. 1979
TAKT SYSTEMS, INC.—See Comture Corporation; *Int'l*, pg. 1763
TALESIS LIMITED—See HM International Holdings Limited; *Int'l*, pg. 3431
TALIX, INC.—See Edifecs, Inc.; *U.S. Private*, pg. 1336
TALLAN INC.; *U.S. Private*, pg. 3927
TAMARAC, INC.—See Bain Capital, LP; *U.S. Private*, pg. 439
TANAGER, INC.; *U.S. Private*, pg. 3930
TANGO TECHNOLOGY PTY. LTD.—See Comms Group Ltd; *Int'l*, pg. 1720
TAPPLE, INC.—See CyberAgent, Inc.; *Int'l*, pg. 1892
TARSIN MOBILE, INC.; *U.S. Public*, pg. 1982
TAVANT TECHNOLOGIES, INC.; *U.S. Private*, pg. 3936
TAVVE SOFTWARE COMPANY—See Defiance Ventures LLC; *U.S. Private*, pg. 1191
TBD NETWORKS, INC.—See MetricStream, Inc.; *U.S. Private*, pg. 2685
TBG SECURITY INC.—See Kelso & Company, L.P.; *U.S. Private*, pg. 2278
TDK TECHNOLOGIES, LLC; *U.S. Private*, pg. 3944
TEAM INFORMATION SERVICES; *U.S. Private*, pg. 3949
TEAMSNAP, INC.—See Waud Capital Partners LLC; *U.S. Private*, pg. 4457
TEAMUP TECHNOLOGIES, INC.—See Autodesk, Inc.; *U.S. Public*, pg. 229
TECALLIANCE GMBH—See Aptiv PLC; *Int'l*, pg. 525
TECHCHEFS SOFTWARE PRIVATE LIMITED—See EQT AB; *Int'l*, pg. 2472
TECH DATA CANADA CORPORATION—See TD Synnex Corp; *U.S. Public*, pg. 1986
TECH DATA DISTRIBUTION CROATIA D.O.O.—See TD Synnex Corp; *U.S. Public*, pg. 1986
TECHDEMOCRACY LLC; *U.S. Private*, pg. 3952
TECHHEALTH, INC.—See Apax Partners LLP; *Int'l*, pg. 505
TECHNESIS, INC.—See Sepialine, Inc.; *U.S. Private*, pg. 3611
TECHNIA B.V.—See Addnode Group AB; *Int'l*, pg. 131
TECHNIA INC.—See Addnode Group AB; *Int'l*, pg. 131
TECHNIA K.K.—See Addnode Group AB; *Int'l*, pg. 131
TECHNIA LTD.—See Addnode Group AB; *Int'l*, pg. 131
TECHNIA S.A.S.—See Addnode Group AB; *Int'l*, pg. 131
TECHNIA SLOVAKIA S.R.O.—See Addnode Group AB; *Int'l*, pg. 131
TECHNOLOGY FOR BUSINESS CORP.—See Fusion Connect, Inc.; *U.S. Private*, pg. 1625
TECHNOLOGY PARTNERS, INC.; *U.S. Private*, pg. 3955
TECHNOLOGY PARTNERS INC.; *U.S. Private*, pg. 3955
TECHNOMILE LLC; *U.S. Private*, pg. 3956
TECHNO-STEP GMBH—See Durr AG; *Int'l*, pg. 2233
TECHSPIRE CO., LTD.—See Argo Graphics Inc.; *Int'l*, pg. 562
TECHTURN, INC.—See Arrow Electronics, Inc.; *U.S. Public*, pg. 200
TECHWAN SA—See Thoma Bravo, L.P.; *U.S. Private*, pg. 4148
TECNA SRL—See Eurofins Scientific S.E.; *Int'l*, pg. 2552
TECPLOT, INC.—See Constellation Software Inc.; *Int'l*, pg. 1774
TEGO CYBER INC.; *U.S. Public*, pg. 1991
TEICHIKU ENTERTAINMENT, INC.—See Brother Industries, Ltd.; *Int'l*, pg. 1198
TEKLA CORPORATION—See Trimble, Inc.; *U.S. Public*, pg. 2191
TELCO DATA SYSTEMS, INC.—See Chickasaw Holding Company; *U.S. Private*, pg. 880
TELEDYNE COLLABORX, INC.—See Teledyne Technologies Incorporated; *U.S. Public*, pg. 1993
TELENAV GMBH—See Telenav, Inc.; *U.S. Private*, pg. 3960
TELESIS CORPORATION; *U.S. Public*, pg. 3961
TELLENGER, INC.—See WaveDancer, Inc.; *U.S. Public*, pg. 2338
TELRITE CORPORATION—See Telrite Holdings, Inc.; *U.S. Private*, pg. 3962
TEMETRA LIMITED—See Itron, Inc.; *U.S. Public*, pg. 1176

TENABLE NETWORK SECURITY, INC.; *U.S. Private*, pg. 3964
TENMAST SOFTWARE CO.; *U.S. Private*, pg. 3967
TERADATA CESKA REPUBLIKA SPOL. S R.O.—See Teradata Corporation; *U.S. Public*, pg. 2017
TERADICI CORPORATION—See HP Inc.; *U.S. Public*, pg. 1065
TERA D.P. S.R.L.—See Vista Equity Partners, LLC; *U.S. Private*, pg. 4399
TERALOGICS LLC—See Elliott Management Corporation; *U.S. Private*, pg. 1368
TERALOGICS LLC—See Veritas Capital Fund Management, LLC; *U.S. Private*, pg. 4362
TERMINUS SOFTWARE, INC.—See Demand Science Group, LLC; *U.S. Private*, pg. 1203
TERRASIM, INC.—See BAE Systems plc; *Int'l*, pg. 798
TESCHGLOBAL LLC; *U.S. Private*, pg. 3973
TESNET SOFTWARE TESTING, LTD.—See Amanet Management & Systems Ltd.; *Int'l*, pg. 410
TEST IO GMBH—See EPAM Systems, Inc.; *U.S. Public*, pg. 783
TEST IO, INC.—See EPAM Systems, Inc.; *U.S. Public*, pg. 783
TETEL SA DE CV—See Concentrix Corporation; *U.S. Public*, pg. 565
TETRA CONCEPTS LLC—See Carl Marks & Co., Inc.; *U.S. Private*, pg. 763
THEMAVEN NETWORK, INC.—See The Arena Group Holdings, Inc; *U.S. Public*, pg. 2035
THEORIS INC.—See Asseco Poland S.A.; *Int'l*, pg. 642
THERADOC, INC.—See Premier, Inc.; *U.S. Public*, pg. 1715
THINK BIG ANALYTICS, INC.—See Teradata Corporation; *U.S. Public*, pg. 2017
THINK FINANCE, INC.; *U.S. Private*, pg. 4144
THINK RESEARCH CORPORATION—See Beedie Capital Partners; *Int'l*, pg. 939
THINK SILICON SINGLE MEMBER P.C.—See Applied Materials, Inc.; *U.S. Public*, pg. 172
THINMANAGER—See Rockwell Automation, Inc.; *U.S. Public*, pg. 1807
THINSOLUTIONS; *U.S. Private*, pg. 4144
THOROUGHBRED SOFTWARE INTERNATIONAL; *U.S. Private*, pg. 4163
THREE X COMMUNICATION LIMITED—See Compagnie Generale des Etablissements Michelin SCA; *Int'l*, pg. 1743
THRIVE WORLD WIDE, INC.; *U.S. Private*, pg. 4165
THUMZUP MEDIA CORPORATION; *U.S. Public*, pg. 2157
THYCOTIC SOFTWARE LIMITED—See TPG Capital, L.P.; *U.S. Public*, pg. 2169
TIANJIN HUAYI ZHICHENG TECHNOLOGY DEVELOPMENT CO., LTD.—See Beijing E-Hualu Information Technology Co., Ltd.; *Int'l*, pg. 949
TIBCO SOFTWARE INC. - BOSTON—See Vista Equity Partners, LLC; *U.S. Private*, pg. 4402
TICONTRACT GMBH—See The Riverside Company; *U.S. Private*, pg. 4110
TIES; *U.S. Private*, pg. 4169
TIGER ANALYTICS LLC; *U.S. Private*, pg. 4169
TIGER CORRECTIONAL SERVICES; *U.S. Private*, pg. 4169
TIGER SOFT (1998) COMPANY LIMITED—See Humanica Public Company Limited; *Int'l*, pg. 3530
TIGERSPIKE FZ-LLC—See TD Synnex Corp; *U.S. Public*, pg. 1987
TIGERSPIKE, INC.—See TD Synnex Corp; *U.S. Public*, pg. 1987
TIGERSPIKE KK—See TD Synnex Corp; *U.S. Public*, pg. 1987
TIGERSPIKE LTD—See TD Synnex Corp; *U.S. Public*, pg. 1987
TIGERSPIKE PTE. LTD.—See TD Synnex Corp; *U.S. Public*, pg. 1987
TIGERSPIKE PTY LTD—See TD Synnex Corp; *U.S. Public*, pg. 1987
TIKIT GROUP PLC—See Vista Equity Partners, LLC; *U.S. Private*, pg. 4395
TIME CARE AB—See TA Associates, Inc.; *U.S. Private*, pg. 3917
TIN ROOF SOFTWARE LLC; *U.S. Private*, pg. 4173
TINTRI INC.—See DataDirect Networks Inc.; *U.S. Private*, pg. 1165
TIPDATA MEDICAL SOFTWARE—See CompuGroup Medical SE & Co. KGaA; *Int'l*, pg. 1757
TIP TECHNOLOGIES, INC.—See Roper Technologies, Inc.; *U.S. Public*, pg. 1811
TITAN WIRELESS LLC—See ISP Supplies LLC; *U.S. Private*, pg. 2146
TIVERSA, INC.; *U.S. Private*, pg. 4177
TIVO KK—See Adeia Inc.; *U.S. Public*, pg. 41
TIVO KOREA CO. LTD.—See Adeia Inc.; *U.S. Public*, pg. 41
TIVO POLAND SP. Z O. O.—See Adeia Inc.; *U.S. Public*, pg. 41
TIVO SINGAPORE PTE. LTD.—See Adeia Inc.; *U.S. Public*, pg. 41
TIVO TECH PRIVATE LIMITED—See Adeia Inc.; *U.S. Public*, pg. 41
TLC TECHNOLOGIES, INC.; *U.S. Private*, pg. 4178

N.A.I.C.S. INDEX

541511 — CUSTOM COMPUTER PRO...

TMI SOLUTIONS, LLC—See Stone Point Capital LLC; *U.S. Private*, pg. 3821
TOKENEX, LLC; *U.S. Private*, pg. 4181
TOMORROW NETWORKS, LLC—See KKR & Co. Inc.; *U.S. Public*, pg. 1253
TONIC DESIGN CO.—See Printfly Corp.; *U.S. Private*, pg. 3266
TOOLWATCH CORP.; *U.S. Private*, pg. 4186
TOPICUS.COM INC.—See Constellation Software Inc.; *Int'l*, pg. 1774
TOPLEVEL COMPUTING LIMITED—See Siris Capital Group, LLC; *U.S. Private*, pg. 3673
TORITON, INC—See GMO GlobalSign Holdings K.K.; *Int'l*, pg. 3013
TOTAL EXPERT INC; *U.S. Private*, pg. 4191
TOTAL MULTIMEDIA INCORPORATED; *U.S. Public*, pg. 2165
TOUCH CLOUD INC.—See Chroma ATE Inc.; *Int'l*, pg. 1588
TOV EUROSOFTWARE-UA—See Fujitsu Limited; *Int'l*, pg. 2837
TPG RESEARCH PTY LTD—See CK Hutchison Holdings Limited; *Int'l*, pg. 1638
TPG TELEMANAGEMENT INC.; *U.S. Private*, pg. 4200
TQS INTEGRATION AG—See Cognizant Technology Solutions Corporation; *U.S. Public*, pg. 525
TRACEGUARD TECHNOLOGIES, INC.; *U.S. Private*, pg. 4200
TRACEN TECHNOLOGIES, INC.; *U.S. Private*, pg. 4200
TRADE ALERT, LLC—See Cboe Global Markets, Inc.; *U.S. Public*, pg. 459
TRADE AREA SYSTEMS INC.—See Hanover Investors Management LLP; *Int'l*, pg. 3258
TRADEGECKO PTE LTD—See Intuit Inc.; *U.S. Public*, pg. 1160
TRADE ONLY INC.—See Altitude Group plc; *Int'l*, pg. 393
TRADETICITY D.O.O.—See Antares Vision SpA; *Int'l*, pg. 482
TRAJECTOR, INC.; *U.S. Private*, pg. 4204
TRAMADA SYSTEMS PTY. LTD.—See Corporate Travel Management Limited; *Int'l*, pg. 1806
TRANCOS, INC.; *U.S. Private*, pg. 4205
TRANDES CORPORATION; *U.S. Private*, pg. 4205
TRANSACTION ASSOCIATES, INC.; *U.S. Private*, pg. 4206
TRANSACTION DATA SYSTEMS INC.—See BlackRock, Inc.; *U.S. Public*, pg. 347
TRANSACTION WIRELESS, INC.—See Fiserv, Inc.; *U.S. Public*, pg. 851
TRANSACT TECHNOLOGIES (MACAU) LIMITED—See TransAct Technologies Incorporated; *U.S. Public*, pg. 2179
TRANSCEND INSIGHTS, INC.—See Humana, Inc.; *U.S. Public*, pg. 1070
TRANSCENTRA FTS PRIVATE LTD.—See Exela Technologies, Inc.; *U.S. Public*, pg. 806
TRANSEND CORPORATION—See ACI Worldwide, Inc.; *U.S. Public*, pg. 35
TRANSLOC INC.—See Constellation Software Inc.; *Int'l*, pg. 1775
TRANSON MEDIA LLC; *U.S. Private*, pg. 4210
TRANSPOREON GMBH—See Trimble, Inc.; *U.S. Public*, pg. 2193
TRANSPOREON SP. Z O. O.—See Trimble, Inc.; *U.S. Public*, pg. 2193
TRANSUNION BRASIL SISTEMAS EM INFORMATICA LTDA.—See TransUnion; *U.S. Public*, pg. 2184
TRANSUNION CIBIL LIMITED—See TransUnion; *U.S. Public*, pg. 2184
TRANSUNION INFORMATION SOLUTIONS, INC.—See TransUnion; *U.S. Public*, pg. 2184
TRANS UNION OF CANADA, INC.—See TransUnion; *U.S. Public*, pg. 2184
TRANSWORKS COMPANY—See Norfolk Southern Corporation; *U.S. Public*, pg. 1536
TRANSZAP, INC.—See Hellman & Friedman LLC; *U.S. Private*, pg. 1908
TRAPEZE GROUP DEUTSCHLAND GMBH—See Constellation Software Inc.; *Int'l*, pg. 1775
TRAPEZE GROUP EUROPE A/S—See Constellation Software Inc.; *Int'l*, pg. 1775
TRAPEZE GROUP (UK) LIMITED—See Constellation Software Inc.; *Int'l*, pg. 1775
TRAPEZE ITS GERMANY GMBH—See Constellation Software Inc.; *Int'l*, pg. 1775
TRAPEZE ITS SWITZERLAND GMBH—See Constellation Software Inc.; *Int'l*, pg. 1775
TRAPEZE POLAND SP. Z O.O.—See Constellation Software Inc.; *Int'l*, pg. 1775
TRAPEZE SOFTWARE GROUP, INC.—See Constellation Software Inc.; *Int'l*, pg. 1775
TRAPEZE SOFTWARE INC.—See Constellation Software Inc.; *Int'l*, pg. 1775
TRASYS CHARLEROI—See Ackermans & van Haaren NV; *Int'l*, pg. 106
TRASYS CHARLEROI—See BNP Paribas SA; *Int'l*, pg. 1090
TRASYS CHARLEROI—See Frere-Bourgeois; *Int'l*, pg. 2774
TRASYS GREECE—See Ackermans & van Haaren NV; *Int'l*, pg. 106
TRASYS GREECE—See BNP Paribas SA; *Int'l*, pg. 1090

TRASYS GREECE—See Frere-Bourgeois; *Int'l*, pg. 2774
TRASYS LUXEMBOURG—See Ackermans & van Haaren NV; *Int'l*, pg. 106
TRASYS LUXEMBOURG—See BNP Paribas SA; *Int'l*, pg. 1090
TRASYS LUXEMBOURG—See Frere-Bourgeois; *Int'l*, pg. 2774
TRASYS S.A—See Ackermans & van Haaren NV; *Int'l*, pg. 106
TRASYS S.A—See BNP Paribas SA; *Int'l*, pg. 1090
TRASYS S.A—See Frere-Bourgeois; *Int'l*, pg. 2774
TRAVTECH INC.—See Omega World Travel, Inc.; *U.S. Private*, pg. 3015
TRAX TECHNOLOGIES, INC.; *U.S. Private*, pg. 4215
TREATMENT.COM INTERNATIONAL INC.; *U.S. Public*, pg. 2186
TREBI GENERALCONSULT S.R.L.—See Gruppo MutuiOnline S.p.A; *Int'l*, pg. 3141
TRESYS TECHNOLOGY LLC—See Behrman Brothers Management Corp.; *U.S. Private*, pg. 515
TRIAD INTERACTIVE, INC.—See Platinum Equity, LLC; *U.S. Private*, pg. 3206
TRIAMUN AG—See CSL Limited; *Int'l*, pg. 1866
TRIBIA AB—See Addnode Group AB; *Int'l*, pg. 131
TRICENTIS USA CORP.; *U.S. Private*, pg. 4229
TRIDIUM, INC.—See Honeywell International Inc.; *U.S. Public*, pg. 1052
TRIFACTA GMBH—See Clearlake Capital Group, L.P.; *U.S. Private*, pg. 933
TRIFACTA GMBH—See Insight Venture Management, LLC; *U.S. Private*, pg. 2087
TRIFECTA TECHNOLOGIES, INC.; *U.S. Private*, pg. 4230
TRI-FORCE CONSULTING SERVICES, INC.; *U.S. Private*, pg. 4222
TRIHEDRAL UK LIMITED—See Delta Electronics, Inc.; *Int'l*, pg. 2018
TRILAB ADVANCED SOLUTIONS B.V.—See IEX Group N.V.; *Int'l*, pg. 3598
TRIMBLE GERMANY GMBH—See Trimble, Inc.; *U.S. Public*, pg. 2192
TRIMBLE LOADRITE AUCKLAND LIMITED—See Trimble, Inc.; *U.S. Public*, pg. 2192
TRIMBLE NANTES S.A.S—See Trimble, Inc.; *U.S. Public*, pg. 2192
TRIMBLE SOLUTIONS AARHUS A/S—See Trimble, Inc.; *U.S. Public*, pg. 2192
TRINITY INSIGHT, LLC—See WILsquare Capital LLC; *U.S. Private*, pg. 4532
TRIO DANMARK A/S—See Enghouse Systems Limited; *Int'l*, pg. 2428
TRIO ENTERPRISE AB—See Enghouse Systems Limited; *Int'l*, pg. 2428
TRIO NORGE AS—See Enghouse Systems Limited; *Int'l*, pg. 2428
TRIPLINGO, LLC—See Travel & Transport Inc.; *U.S. Private*, pg. 4212
TRI PLUS GRUPA D.O.O—See SmartRent, Inc.; *U.S. Public*, pg. 1896
TRISTAR WEB SOLUTIONS, INC.—See Tristar Holdings Inc.; *U.S. Private*, pg. 4238
TRI-VALLEY RESELLER, LLC—See Workday, Inc.; *U.S. Public*, pg. 2378
TROPICS SOFTWARE TECHNOLOGIES, INC.—See GI Manager L.P.; *U.S. Private*, pg. 1692
TRUBRIDGE, INC.; *U.S. Public*, pg. 2198
TRUENORTHLOGIC; *U.S. Private*, pg. 4249
TRULIA, LLC—See Zillow Group, Inc.; *U.S. Public*, pg. 2405
TRUPAL MEDIA, INC.; *U.S. Private*, pg. 4250
TRUST IT SP. Z O.O.—See Atende S.A.; *Int'l*, pg. 668
TRUVISO LLC—See Cisco Systems, Inc.; *U.S. Public*, pg. 500
TSG NORWAY AS—See Austriacard Holdings AG; *Int'l*, pg. 724
TSG SOLUTIONS, INC.—See Bluestone Investment Partners, LLC; *U.S. Private*, pg. 598
TSR, INC.; *U.S. Public*, pg. 2202
T STAMP, INC.; *U.S. Public*, pg. 1977
TUFIN SOFTWARE TECHNOLOGIES LTD.—See Turn/River Management LLC; *U.S. Private*, pg. 4259
TURBOSQUID, INC.—See Shutterstock, Inc.; *U.S. Public*, pg. 1876
TURNER CONSULTING GROUP, INC.; *U.S. Private*, pg. 4260
TWILIO INC.; *U.S. Public*, pg. 2206
TWITCH INTERACTIVE, INC.—See Amazon.com, Inc.; *U.S. Public*, pg. 91
TWNKLS B.V.—See PTC Inc.; *U.S. Public*, pg. 1735
TX3 SERVICES, LLC—See Tricentis USA Corp.; *U.S. Private*, pg. 4229
TXTLOCAL LTD.—See Cisco Systems, Inc.; *U.S. Public*, pg. 499
TYBRIN CORPORATION—See Jacobs Engineering Group, Inc.; *U.S. Public*, pg. 1185
TYLER TECHNOLOGIES: FUNDBALANCE SOLUTIONS—See Tyler Technologies, Inc.; *U.S. Public*, pg. 2209
UAB BULL BALTIJA—See Atos SE; *Int'l*, pg. 692

UAB COLUMBUS LIETUVA—See Columbus A/S; *Int'l*, pg. 1706
UAB S-GROUP LIETUVA—See Addnode Group AB; *Int'l*, pg. 131
UA MULTIMEDIA, INC.; *U.S. Public*, pg. 2217
UBCARE CO., LTD.—See GC Biopharma Corp.; *Int'l*, pg. 2894
UBISENSE AMERICA LLC—See KKR & Co. Inc.; *U.S. Public*, pg. 1253
UBISENSE GMBH—See KKR & Co. Inc.; *U.S. Public*, pg. 1253
UBISENSE JAPAN K.K.—See KKR & Co. Inc.; *U.S. Public*, pg. 1253
UBISENSE SAS—See KKR & Co. Inc.; *U.S. Public*, pg. 1253
UCS SOFTWARE MANUFACTURING (PROPRIETARY) LIMITED—See Capital Eye Investments Limited; *Int'l*, pg. 1311
UES, INC.; *U.S. Private*, pg. 4274
UGENIUS TECHNOLOGY, LLC.; *U.S. Private*, pg. 4274
UIPATH, INC.; *U.S. Public*, pg. 2223
UKG INC.; *U.S. Public*, pg. 4275
ULEAD SYSTEMS, INC.—See KKR & Co. Inc.; *U.S. Public*, pg. 1243
THE ULTIMATE SOFTWARE GROUP OF CANADA, INC.—See Hellman & Friedman LLC; *U.S. Private*, pg. 1911
ULTIMO SOFTWARE SOLUTIONS, INC.; *U.S. Private*, pg. 4277
ULTISALES RETAIL SOFTWARE (PROPRIETARY) LIMITED—See Capital Eye Investments Limited; *Int'l*, pg. 1311
ULTRAMATICS, INC.; *U.S. Private*, pg. 4278
UMETRICS, INC.—See MKS Instruments, Inc.; *U.S. Public*, pg. 1453
UMS APS—See Thoma Bravo, L.P.; *U.S. Private*, pg. 4148
UMS OY—See Thoma Bravo, L.P.; *U.S. Private*, pg. 4148
UNBOUNDID CORP.—See Vista Equity Partners, LLC; *U.S. Private*, pg. 4399
UNIADEX, LTD.—See BIPROGY Inc.; *Int'l*, pg. 1045
UNIAID CO., LTD.—See BIPROGY Inc.; *Int'l*, pg. 1045
UNIBAR, INC.—See Nextworld, LLC; *U.S. Private*, pg. 2921
UNICOM SYSTEMS INC.—See UNICOM Global, Inc.; *U.S. Private*, pg. 4282
UNIFIED COMMUNICATIONS (OHQ) SDN. BHD.—See Advance Synergy Berhad; *Int'l*, pg. 157
UNIFIED MESSAGING SYSTEMS AS—See Thoma Bravo, L.P.; *U.S. Private*, pg. 4148
UNIFY SQUARE, INC.—See Unisys Corporation; *U.S. Public*, pg. 2228
UNIHORN, INC.—See Unison Pacific Corporation; *U.S. Private*, pg. 4286
UNI IT SRL—See GPI S.p.A.; *Int'l*, pg. 3046
UNION SQUARE DEVELOPMENTS LIMITED—See Hammerson plc; *Int'l*, pg. 3238
UNITY SOFTWARE INC.; *U.S. Public*, pg. 2254
UNIVERSAL KNOWLEDGE SOFTWARE (PROPRIETARY) LIMITED—See Capital Eye Investments Limited; *Int'l*, pg. 1311
UNIVERSAL POWER INDUSTRY CORPORATION; *U.S. Public*, pg. 2262
U.N.P.-HRSOLUTIONS GMBH—See Allgeier SE; *Int'l*, pg. 338
UNTANGLE, INC.—See Providence Equity Partners L.L.C.; *U.S. Private*, pg. 3294
UPAY, INC.; *U.S. Public*, pg. 2263
U-PAYMENT LTD.—See DGB Financial Group Co., Ltd.; *Int'l*, pg. 2096
UPLAND SOFTWARE II, INC.—See Upland Software, Inc.; *U.S. Public*, pg. 2264
UPLAND SOFTWARE IV, INC.—See Upland Software, Inc.; *U.S. Public*, pg. 2264
UPLIGHT, INC.—See The AES Corporation; *U.S. Public*, pg. 2032
UPWORK INC.—See Upwork Global Inc.; *U.S. Private*, pg. 4313
US EDIRECT INC.—See Tyler Technologies, Inc.; *U.S. Public*, pg. 2209
USERADGENTS SAS—See HighCo S.A.; *Int'l*, pg. 3387
USERFUL CORPORATION; *U.S. Private*, pg. 4322
USERTESTING, INC.—See Sunstone Partners Management LLC; *U.S. Private*, pg. 3873
USERTESTING, INC.—See Thoma Bravo, L.P.; *U.S. Private*, pg. 4154
USHER INCORPORATED—See MicroStrategy, Inc.; *U.S. Public*, pg. 1444
US INFORMATION TECHNOLOGIES CORPORATION; *U.S. Private*, pg. 4319
USI TECHNOLOGIES, INC.; *U.S. Private*, pg. 4323
USOL VIETNAM CO., LTD.—See BIPROGY Inc.; *Int'l*, pg. 1045
UTEGRATION, LLC—See Cognizant Technology Solutions Corporation; *U.S. Public*, pg. 525
UTILITY SOFTWARE SERVICES PTY. LTD.—See AD1 Holdings Limited; *Int'l*, pg. 123
UTOPIA, INC.; *U.S. Private*, pg. 4327
V2SOFT, INC.; *U.S. Private*, pg. 4328
VAARI DIGITAL CO., LTD.—See AP (Thailand) Public Company Limited; *Int'l*, pg. 499

VAE INC.; *U.S. Private,* pg. 4329
VALEXCONSULTING; *U.S. Private,* pg. 4331
VALOR IT; *U.S. Private,* pg. 4336
VALOR WATER ANALYTICS, INC.—See Xylem Inc.; *U.S. Public,* pg. 2395
VALUEPHONE GMBH—See Fujitsu Limited; *Int'l,* pg. 2837
VALUESOURCE TECHNOLOGIES PRIVATE LIMITED—See Cognizant Technology Solutions Corporation; *U.S. Public,* pg. 525
VALUGUARD SOLUTIONS, LLC—See Stewart Information Services Corporation; *U.S. Public,* pg. 1948
VANGUARD SYSTEMS, INC.—See Strattam Capital, LLC; *U.S. Private,* pg. 3837
VAREN TECHNOLOGIES, INC.—See Godspeed Capital Management LP; *U.S. Private,* pg. 1725
VARITE, INC.; *U.S. Private,* pg. 4347
VARONIS SYSTEMS (AUSTRALIA) PTY LTD—See Varonis Systems Inc.; *U.S. Public,* pg. 2275
VARONIS SYSTEMS (IRELAND) LIMITED—See Varonis Systems Inc.; *U.S. Public,* pg. 2276
VARSITY LOGISTICS, INC.—See Constellation Software Inc.; *Int'l,* pg. 1773
VASCO DATA SECURITY AUSTRIA GMBH—See OneSpan Inc.; *U.S. Public,* pg. 1603
VASCO DATA SECURITY INTERNATIONAL, GMBH—See OneSpan Inc.; *U.S. Public,* pg. 1603
VAULT IQ NZ LTD.—See Damstra Holdings Ltd.; *Int'l,* pg. 1957
VCARGO CLOUD PTE. LTD.—See EXEO Group Inc.; *Int'l,* pg. 2584
VECTOR CHOICE TECHNOLOGY SOLUTIONS, CORP.; *U.S. Private,* pg. 4353
VECTOR MEDIA GROUP INC.; *U.S. Private,* pg. 4353
VEDALEON TECHNOLOGIES PTY. LTD.—See Amadeus IT Group, S.A.; *Int'l,* pg. 407
VEEDER-ROOT FUELQUEST, LLC—See Vontier Corporation; *U.S. Public,* pg. 2309
VEEUZE GMBH—See Eleco Plc; *Int'l,* pg. 2348
VELA SOFTWARE INTERNATIONAL INC.—See Constellation Software Inc.; *Int'l,* pg. 1775
VELIR; *U.S. Private,* pg. 4354
VELOCIFY, INC.—See Intercontinental Exchange, Inc.; *U.S. Public,* pg. 1142
V-EMPOWER SOLUTIONS PVT., LTD.—See V-Empower, Inc.; *U.S. Private,* pg. 4328
VENDA LIMITED—See Oracle Corporation; *U.S. Public,* pg. 1611
VENDING MANAGEMENT SERVICES LTD—See COCA-COLA EUROPACIFIC PARTNERS PLC; *Int'l,* pg. 1684
VENDORIN, INC.—See Corcentric, Inc.; *U.S. Private,* pg. 1047
VENNERS SYSTEMS & SERVICES CORPORATION—See Christie Group plc; *Int'l,* pg. 1587
VENTERA CORPORATION—See CI Capital Partners LLC; *U.S. Private,* pg. 896
VENTRAQ CORPORATION—See StoneCalibre, LLC; *U.S. Private,* pg. 3828
VENTYX ASIA INC.—See ABB Ltd.; *Int'l,* pg. 52
VENTYX MANAGED SERVICES, INC.—See ABB Ltd.; *Int'l,* pg. 52
VERACITY CONSULTING, INC.; *U.S. Private,* pg. 4359
VERAFIN SOLUTIONS ULC—See Nasdaq, Inc.; *U.S. Public,* pg. 1492
VERATTA TECHNOLOGIES INC.—See ARCpoint Inc.; *U.S. Public,* pg. 186
VERB TECHNOLOGY COMPANY, INC.; *U.S. Public,* pg. 2280
VERIATO, INC.; *U.S. Private,* pg. 4360
VERIFONE SYSTEMS AUSTRALIA PTY. LTD.—See British Columbia Investment Management Corp.; *Int'l,* pg. 1170
VERIFONE SYSTEMS AUSTRALIA PTY. LTD.—See Francisco Partners Management, LP; *U.S. Private,* pg. 1592
VERIFONE URUGUAY—See British Columbia Investment Management Corp.; *Int'l,* pg. 1170
VERIFONE URUGUAY—See Francisco Partners Management, LP; *U.S. Private,* pg. 1593
VERIFY SMART CORP.; *U.S. Public,* pg. 2280
VERINT WITNESS SYSTEMS LLC - SANTA CLARA—See Verint Systems Inc.; *U.S. Public,* pg. 2281
VERISIGN, INC.; *U.S. Public,* pg. 2282
VERISIGN, INC.—See VeriSign, Inc.; *U.S. Public,* pg. 2282
VERITONE, INC.; *U.S. Public,* pg. 2283
VERITY SOLUTIONS GROUP, INC.—See The Cigna Group; *U.S. Public,* pg. 2061
VERMONT SYSTEMS, INC.—See Clubessential Holdings, LLC; *U.S. Private,* pg. 949
THE VERNDALE CORPORATION; *U.S. Private,* pg. 4130
VERO CHINA—See Hexagon AB; *Int'l,* pg. 3367
VERO FRANCE—See Hexagon AB; *Int'l,* pg. 3367
VERO ITALIA SRL—See Hexagon AB; *Int'l,* pg. 3367
VERO ITALIA SRL—See Hexagon AB; *Int'l,* pg. 3367
VERO ITALIA SRL—See Hexagon AB; *Int'l,* pg. 3367
VERO JAPAN K.K.—See Hexagon AB; *Int'l,* pg. 3367
VERO USA INC.—See Hexagon AB; *Int'l,* pg. 3367
VERSIONONE, INC.—See TPG Capital, L.P.; *U.S. Public,* pg. 2173
VERTICAL MANAGEMENT SYSTEMS, INC.—See NewSpring Capital LLC; *U.S. Private,* pg. 2918

VERTIV FRANCE—See Vertiv Holdings Co; *U.S. Public,* pg. 2289
VERYS, LLC—See West Monroe Partners, LLC; *U.S. Private,* pg. 4486
VESPA GROUP, LLC; *U.S. Private,* pg. 4371
VESTMARK, INC.; *U.S. Private,* pg. 4373
V GROUP INC.; *U.S. Private,* pg. 4327
VIAFINTECH GMBH—See GLORY Ltd.; *Int'l,* pg. 3010
VIATRACK SYSTEMS, LLC—See Thoma Bravo, L.P.; *U.S. Private,* pg. 4150
VICARIOUS VISIONS, INC.—See Microsoft Corporation; *U.S. Public,* pg. 1439
VIDEO DESIGN SOFTWARE (USA), INC.—See LTN Global Communications, Inc.; *U.S. Private,* pg. 2510
VIEWPOINT, INC.—See Trimble, Inc.; *U.S. Public,* pg. 2193
VIGILANT SOFTWARE LTD.—See Bloom Equity Partners Management, LLC; *U.S. Private,* pg. 583
VILLAWAY, INC.; *U.S. Private,* pg. 4384
VIOO COMPANY LIMITED—See Bexcellent Group Holdings Limited; *Int'l,* pg. 1005
VIRGIN PULSE, INC.—See Marlin Equity Partners, LLC; *U.S. Private,* pg. 2585
VIRTUAL ED LINK, INC.; *U.S. Private,* pg. 4388
VIRTUAL INFORMATION SYSTEMS CORP.—See Print Reach, Inc.; *U.S. Private,* pg. 3265
VIRTUAL INSTRUMENTS, INC.; *U.S. Private,* pg. 4389
VIRTUOSO LLC—See Enveric Biosciences, Inc.; *U.S. Public,* pg. 780
VISIBLE EQUITY, LLC—See nCino, Inc.; *U.S. Public,* pg. 1501
VISIBLE MEASURES CORPORATION—See AcuityAds Inc.; *Int'l,* pg. 121
VISIODENT S.A.—See Cegedim S.A.; *Int'l,* pg. 1390
VISION4CE LIMITED—See Cohort plc; *Int'l,* pg. 1696
VISIONSOFT INTERNATIONAL INC.; *U.S. Private,* pg. 4392
VISION TECHNOLOGY CORP.; *U.S. Private,* pg. 4391
VISIQUATE, INC.—See Accel Partners L.P.; *U.S. Private,* pg. 49
VISIQUATE, INC.—See KKR & Co. Inc.; *U.S. Public,* pg. 1239
VISITALK CAPITAL CORPORATION; *U.S. Private,* pg. 4392
VISLAB S.R.L.—See Ambarella, Inc.; *U.S. Public,* pg. 92
VISTASOURCE INC.—See Parallax Capital Partners, LLC; *U.S. Private,* pg. 3092
VISTRONIX, INC.; *U.S. Private,* pg. 4403
VISUAL CONCEPTS, LLC; *U.S. Private,* pg. 4404
VISUALJAPAN INC.—See Dai Nippon Printing Co., Ltd.; *Int'l,* pg. 1916
VITALWARE, LLC—See Health Catalyst, Inc.; *U.S. Public,* pg. 1014
VITA MOBILE SYSTEMS, INC.; *U.S. Public,* pg. 2306
VIVID LEARNING SYSTEMS, INC.—See Waud Capital Partners LLC; *U.S. Private,* pg. 4457
VIVOX, INC.; *U.S. Private,* pg. 4406
VIZTU TECHNOLOGIES, INC.—See 3D Systems Corporation; *U.S. Public,* pg. 4
VLOCITY AR SRL—See Salesforce, Inc.; *U.S. Public,* pg. 1838
VLOCITY AUSTRALIA PTY LTD—See Salesforce, Inc.; *U.S. Public,* pg. 1838
VLOCITY CLOUD APPLICATIONS INDIA PRIVATE LIMITED—See Salesforce, Inc.; *U.S. Public,* pg. 1838
VLOCITY CLOUD APPLICATIONS MEXICO S. DE R.L. DE C.V.—See Salesforce, Inc.; *U.S. Public,* pg. 1838
VLOCITY CLOUD COMPUTING ISRAEL LTD.—See Salesforce, Inc.; *U.S. Public,* pg. 1838
VLOCITY JAPAN K.K.—See Salesforce, Inc.; *U.S. Public,* pg. 1838
VLOCITY SINGAPORE PTE. LTD.—See Salesforce, Inc.; *U.S. Public,* pg. 1838
VMC CONSULTING EUROPE LIMITED—See American CyberSystems, Inc.; *U.S. Private,* pg. 230
VMWARE ARGENTINA S.R.L.—See Dell Technologies Inc.; *U.S. Public,* pg. 651
VMWARE BULGARIA EOOD—See Broadcom Inc.; *U.S. Public,* pg. 390
VMWARE CANADA INC.—See Broadcom Inc.; *U.S. Public,* pg. 390
VMWARE DENMARK APS.—See Broadcom Inc.; *U.S. Public,* pg. 390
VMWARE EASTERN EUROPE—See Broadcom Inc.; *U.S. Public,* pg. 390
VMWARE INTERNATIONAL LIMITED—See Broadcom Inc.; *U.S. Public,* pg. 390
VMWARE INTERNATIONAL SPAIN, S.L.—See Dell Technologies Inc.; *U.S. Public,* pg. 651
VMWARE ISRAEL LTD.—See Broadcom Inc.; *U.S. Public,* pg. 391
VMWARE ITALY S.R.L.—See Broadcom Inc.; *U.S. Public,* pg. 391
VMWARE LLC—See Broadcom Inc.; *U.S. Public,* pg. 390
VMWARE SWITZERLAND S.A.R.L.—See Broadcom Inc.; *U.S. Public,* pg. 391
VNOMICS CORP.; *U.S. Private,* pg. 4408
VOBILE GROUP LIMITED; *U.S. Private,* pg. 4408

VOCI TECHNOLOGIES, INC.—See Thoma Bravo, L.P.; *U.S. Private,* pg. 4149
VOCODIA HOLDINGS CORP.; *U.S. Public,* pg. 2308
VOICEINTEROP, INC.; *U.S. Private,* pg. 4409
VOICE SIGNAL K.K.—See Microsoft Corporation; *U.S. Public,* pg. 1443
VOLA S.R.L.—See Corporacion America Airports S.A.; *Int'l,* pg. 1803
VOLT DELTA INTERNATIONAL B.V.—See ESW Capital, LLC; *U.S. Private,* pg. 1431
VOLT DELTA INTERNATIONAL GMBH—See ESW Capital, LLC; *U.S. Private,* pg. 1431
VOLT EUROPE (BELGIUM) SPRL—See American CyberSystems, Inc.; *U.S. Private,* pg. 230
VOLUE GERMANY GMBH—See Arendals Fossekompani ASA; *Int'l,* pg. 559
VOLUE GMBH—See Arendals Fossekompani ASA; *Int'l,* pg. 559
VOLUNTIS SA—See AptarGroup, Inc.; *U.S. Public,* pg. 175
VORTX INC.—See Constellation Software Inc.; *Int'l,* pg. 1773
VOYAGE BB INC—See CyberAgent, Inc.; *Int'l,* pg. 1892
VPI SYSTEMS; *U.S. Private,* pg. 4414
VPI SYSTEMS—See VPI Systems; *U.S. Private,* pg. 4414
VR KREDITSERVICE GMBH—See DZ BANK AG Deutsche Zentral-Genossenschaftsbank; *Int'l,* pg. 2245
VROMAN SYSTEMS INC.—See PSG Equity L.L.C.; *U.S. Private,* pg. 3297
VROMAN SYSTEMS INC.—See Silversmith Management, L.P.; *U.S. Private,* pg. 3663
VSS, LLC—See Converge Technology Solutions Corp.; *Int'l,* pg. 1787
VSS MONITORING, INC.—See Danaher Corporation; *U.S. Public,* pg. 560
VS VISUAL STATEMENTS INC.—See Trimble, Inc.; *U.S. Public,* pg. 2193
VULNERABILITY RESEARCH LABS, LLC—See General Dynamics Corporation; *U.S. Public,* pg. 916
V-VALLEY ADVANCED SOLUTIONS ESPANA, S.A.—See Esprinet S.p.A.; *Int'l,* pg. 2506
VYOPTA INCORPORATED; *U.S. Private,* pg. 4416
WALL STREET SYSTEMS INC.; *U.S. Private,* pg. 4430
WALTECH INC.; *U.S. Private,* pg. 4433
WANDISCO, INC.—See Cirata PLC; *Int'l,* pg. 1617
WARDY IT SOLUTIONS PTY LIMITED—See Brennan IT Pty. Limited; *Int'l,* pg. 1145
WARREN SYSTEMS GROUP, INC.—See Fairdinkum Consulting, LLC; *U.S. Private,* pg. 1462
WASP BARCODE TECHNOLOGIES LTD.—See Datalogic S.p.A.; *U.S. Private,* pg. 1978
WATERLOO MAPLE INC.—See FUJISOFT INCORPORATED; *Int'l,* pg. 2831
WAVE SOFTWARE, LLC; *U.S. Private,* pg. 4458
WAVICLE DATA SOLUTIONS LLC; *U.S. Private,* pg. 4458
WAYSTAR, INC.—See Canada Pension Plan Investment Board; *Int'l,* pg. 1282
WAYSTAR, INC.—See EQT AB; *Int'l,* pg. 2481
WBT SYSTEMS, INC.—See Avnet, Inc.; *U.S. Public,* pg. 254
WDEV SOLUCOES EM TECNOLOGIA S.A.—See Ebix Inc.; *U.S. Public,* pg. 710
WE ARE CLOUD SAS—See Hellman & Friedman LLC; *U.S. Private,* pg. 1911
WEAVE COMMUNICATIONS, INC.; *U.S. Public,* pg. 2341
WEB ADVANCED; *U.S. Private,* pg. 4463
WEBMETHODS AUSTRALIA PTY LTD.—See Silver Lake Group, LLC; *U.S. Private,* pg. 3660
WEBSTAR TECHNOLOGY GROUP, INC.; *U.S. Public,* pg. 2341
WECLAPP SE—See 3U Holding AG; *Int'l,* pg. 10
WEGOLOOK, LLC—See Crawford & Company; *U.S. Public,* pg. 592
THE WEIDT GROUP, INC.—See Willdan Group, Inc.; *U.S. Public,* pg. 2371
WELL IN TECHNOLOGY DEVELOPMENT LIMITED—See Finsoft Financial Investment Holdings Limited; *Int'l,* pg. 2677
WELLNESSFX, INC.—See Catterton Management Company, LLC; *U.S. Private,* pg. 794
WELLNESS MATRIX GROUP, INC.; *U.S. Private,* pg. 4476
WELLSOFT CORP.—See Medsphere Systems Corp.; *U.S. Private,* pg. 2658
WELLSTAR WORLDWIDE, LLC; *U.S. Private,* pg. 4478
WEMLO, LLC—See RE/MAX Holdings, Inc.; *U.S. Public,* pg. 1768
WENNSOFT INC.—See Constellation Software Inc.; *Int'l,* pg. 1776
WESTCON GROUP NETHERLANDS B.V.—See Datatec Limited; *Int'l,* pg. 1981
WESTCON MIDDLE EAST BAHRAIN WLL—See Datatec Limited; *Int'l,* pg. 1981
WESTCON SAUDI COMPANY LLC—See Datatec Limited; *Int'l,* pg. 1981
WESTDEUTSCHE IMMOBILIEN SERVICING AG—See Advent International Corporation; *U.S. Private,* pg. 97
WESTDEUTSCHE IMMOBILIEN SERVICING AG—See Centerbridge Partners, L.P.; *U.S. Private,* pg. 813
WEST HIGHLAND SUPPORT SERVICES, LLC—See Koch Industries, Inc.; *U.S. Private,* pg. 2333

N.A.I.C.S. INDEX

541512 — COMPUTER SYSTEMS DE...

WESUPPLY LIMITED—See Accellos, Inc.; *U.S. Private*, pg. 50
WEVIDEO, INC.—See Thompson Street Capital Manager LLC; *U.S. Private*, pg. 4162
WHATSAPP INC.—See Meta Platforms, Inc.; *U.S. Public*, pg. 1427
WHISHWORKS IT CONSULTING PRIVATE LIMITED—See Coforge Ltd.; *Int'l*, pg. 1693
WHITEBOARD LABS LLC; *U.S. Private*, pg. 4511
WHITE CUP SE, INC.—See Eden Capital Management LLC; *U.S. Private*, pg. 1333
WIAM GMBH—See I Squared Capital Advisors (US) LLC; *U.S. Private*, pg. 2024
WINCAN DEUTSCHLAND GMBH—See IDEX Corp; *U.S. Public*, pg. 1092
WINCOR NIXDORF INTERNATIONAL GMBH—See Diebold Nixdorf, Inc.; *U.S. Public*, pg. 661
WINDWARD STUDIOS, INC.—See Thoma Bravo, L.P.; *U.S. Private*, pg. 4146
WINGARC DALIAN INC.—See The Carlyle Group Inc.; *U.S. Public*, pg. 2057
WINGARC SHANGHAI INC.—See The Carlyle Group Inc.; *U.S. Public*, pg. 2057
WINGARC SINGAPORE PTE. LTD.—See The Carlyle Group Inc.; *U.S. Public*, pg. 2057
WIREDRIVE; *U.S. Private*, pg. 4546
WISDOM INFOTECH; *U.S. Private*, pg. 4549
WISE LAUSNIR EHF—See Centara ehf; *Int'l*, pg. 1402
WISERTOGETHER, INC.—See Evive Health, LLC; *U.S. Private*, pg. 1442
WITHIN TECHNOLOGIES LIMITED—See Autodesk, Inc.; *U.S. Public*, pg. 229
WITHPHOTO INC.—See Canon Inc.; *Int'l*, pg. 1296
WIZCORP INC.—See Canada Pension Plan Investment Board; *Int'l*, pg. 1281
WIZCORP INC.—See EQT AB; *Int'l*, pg. 2483
WIZEHIVE, INC.; *U.S. Private*, pg. 4551
WM LOGISTICS INDIA PRIVATE LIMITED—See Waste Management, Inc.; *U.S. Public*, pg. 2333
WM LOGISTICS, LLC—See Waste Management, Inc.; *U.S. Public*, pg. 2333
WOLFRAM RESEARCH INC.; *U.S. Private*, pg. 4554
WONDO MOBILITY, S.L.U.—See Ferrovial S.A.; *Int'l*, pg. 2645
WOODRIDGE ADVISORS LLC—See Frontenac Company LLC; *U.S. Private*, pg. 1614
WOOFOUND, INC.; *U.S. Private*, pg. 4561
WORDSTREAM, INC.—See Gannett Co., Inc.; *U.S. Public*, pg. 901
WORK & CO—See Accenture plc; *Int'l*, pg. 88
WORKDAY ASIA PACIFIC LIMITED—See Workday, Inc.; *U.S. Public*, pg. 2379
WORKDAY AUSTRALIA PTY. LTD.—See Workday, Inc.; *U.S. Public*, pg. 2379
WORKDAY AUSTRIA GMBH—See Workday, Inc.; *U.S. Public*, pg. 2379
WORKDAY B.V.—See Workday, Inc.; *U.S. Public*, pg. 2379
WORKDAY DENMARK APS—See Workday, Inc.; *U.S. Public*, pg. 2379
WORKDAY FINLAND OY—See Workday, Inc.; *U.S. Public*, pg. 2379
WORKDAY FRANCE—See Workday, Inc.; *U.S. Public*, pg. 2379
WORKDAY GMBH—See Workday, Inc.; *U.S. Public*, pg. 2379
WORKDAY INTERNATIONAL LIMITED—See Workday, Inc.; *U.S. Public*, pg. 2379
WORKDAY ITALY S.R.L.—See Workday, Inc.; *U.S. Public*, pg. 2379
WORKDAY K.K.—See Workday, Inc.; *U.S. Public*, pg. 2379
WORKDAY NORWAY AS—See Workday, Inc.; *U.S. Public*, pg. 2379
WORKDAY SOUTH AFRICA (PTY.) LTD.—See Workday, Inc.; *U.S. Public*, pg. 2379
WORKDAY SWEDEN AKTIEBOLAG—See Workday, Inc.; *U.S. Public*, pg. 2379
WORKDAY (UK) LIMITED—See Workday, Inc.; *U.S. Public*, pg. 2378
WORKFORCE SOFTWARE LTD—See Insight Venture Management, LLC; *U.S. Private*, pg. 2091
WORKLETE, INC.—See The Stage Fund, LLC; *U.S. Private*, pg. 4120
WORK MARKET INC.—See Automatic Data Processing, Inc.; *U.S. Public*, pg. 230
WORK TECHNOLOGY CORPORATION—See Genstar Capital, LLC; *U.S. Private*, pg. 1678
WORXTIME LLC—See Equifax Inc.; *U.S. Public*, pg. 787
WOVENWARE INC.—See Advent International Corporation; *U.S. Private*, pg. 104
WPVIP INC.—See Automattic Inc.; *U.S. Private*, pg. 400
WTS PARADIGM LLC—See Builders FirstSource, Inc.; *U.S. Public*, pg. 410
WU BA SUPERIOR PRODUCTS HOLDING GROUP, INC.; *U.S. Private*, pg. 4574
WUNDERKIND, LLC; *U.S. Private*, pg. 4575
WYSE TECHNOLOGY INC.—See Dell Technologies Inc.; *U.S. Public*, pg. 650

X2 DEVELOPMENT CORPORATION—See Follett Corporation; *U.S. Private*, pg. 1559
XACTWARE INC.; *U.S. Private*, pg. 4579
XACTWARE SOLUTIONS, INC.—See Verisk Analytics, Inc.; *U.S. Public*, pg. 2283
XAP CORPORATION; *U.S. Private*, pg. 4580
XCHANGING SOLUTIONS LIMITED—See DXC Technology Company; *U.S. Public*, pg. 695
XEROX (EUROPE) LIMITED—See Xerox Holdings Corporation; *U.S. Public*, pg. 2387
XEROX LUXEMBOURG SA—See Xerox Holdings Corporation; *U.S. Public*, pg. 2390
XERVICES GMBH—See flatexDEGIRO AG; *Int'l*, pg. 2698
XEVO INC.—See Lear Corporation; *U.S. Public*, pg. 1298
XEXEC INC.—See ABRY Partners, LLC; *U.S. Private*, pg. 43
XEXEC INC.—See Castik Capital S.a.r.l.; *Int'l*, pg. 1356
XEXEC LIMITED—See ABRY Partners, LLC; *U.S. Private*, pg. 43
XEXEC LIMITED—See Castik Capital S.a.r.l.; *Int'l*, pg. 1356
XIDERA S.R.L.—See GPI S.p.A.; *Int'l*, pg. 3046
XILINX AB—See Advanced Micro Devices, Inc.; *U.S. Public*, pg. 49
XILINX INTERNATIONAL, INC.—See Advanced Micro Devices, Inc.; *U.S. Public*, pg. 49
XILINX ISRAEL LIMITED—See Advanced Micro Devices, Inc.; *U.S. Public*, pg. 49
XINNOVATION, INC.—See Bigtincan Holdings Limited; *U.S. Public*, pg. 331
XMATTERS, INC.—See Thoma Bravo, L.P.; *U.S. Private*, pg. 4148
XMPIE, INC.—See Xerox Holdings Corporation; *U.S. Public*, pg. 2388
XORIANT CANADA—See ChrysCapital Management Co.; *Int'l*, pg. 1589
XORIANT INDIA—See ChrysCapital Management Co.; *Int'l*, pg. 1589
XOR SECURITY LLC—See Enlightenment Capital LLC; *U.S. Private*, pg. 1400
XP SOFTWARE PTY. LTD.—See Cardno Limited; *Int'l*, pg. 1323
XPURE GMBH—See Adecco Group AG; *Int'l*, pg. 140
XYLEME, INC.—See Battery Ventures, L.P.; *U.S. Private*, pg. 489
XYPRO TECHNOLOGY CORPORATION; *U.S. Private*, pg. 4584
XY - THE PERSISTENT COMPANY; *U.S. Private*, pg. 4583
YANG ENTERPRISES, INC.; *U.S. Private*, pg. 4585
YANTAI KEDA ZHENGXIN ELECTRIC CO., LTD.—See CSG Smart Science & Technology Co., Ltd.; *Int'l*, pg. 1865
YAPPA WORLD INCORPORATED; *U.S. Private*, pg. 4586
YARDI CANADA LTD.—See Yardi Systems, Inc.; *U.S. Private*, pg. 4586
YARDI SINGAPORE PTE LTD—See Yardi Systems, Inc.; *U.S. Private*, pg. 4586
YARDI SOFTWARE INDIA PVT LTD—See Yardi Systems, Inc.; *U.S. Private*, pg. 4586
YARDI SYDNEY LTD—See Yardi Systems, Inc.; *U.S. Private*, pg. 4586
YARDI SYSTEMS BV—See Yardi Systems, Inc.; *U.S. Private*, pg. 4586
YARDI SYSTEMS GMBH—See Yardi Systems, Inc.; *U.S. Private*, pg. 4586
YARDI SYSTEMS (HK) LTD.—See Yardi Systems, Inc.; *U.S. Private*, pg. 4586
YARDI SYSTEMS LTD—See Yardi Systems, Inc.; *U.S. Private*, pg. 4586
YDILO ADVANCED VOICE SOLUTIONS S.A.—See Espiga Capital Gestion S.G.E.C.R., S.A.; *Int'l*, pg. 2506
YMIRLINK INC.—See Cybozu Inc.; *Int'l*, pg. 1894
YOKOGAWA MEDICAL SOLUTIONS CORPORATION—See FUJIFILM Holdings Corporation; *Int'l*, pg. 2823
YOSPACE TECHNOLOGIES LIMITED—See Bertelsmann SE & Co. KGaA; *Int'l*, pg. 996
YOTTA280, INC.—See Ziff Davis, Inc.; *U.S. Public*, pg. 2404
YOTTA GLOBAL, INC.; *U.S. Private*, pg. 2399
YOUMEMIRU INC.—See EDION Corporation; *Int'l*, pg. 2310
YUMMLY, INC.—See Whirlpool Corporation; *U.S. Public*, pg. 2368
ZAMURAI CORPORATION—See Elliott Management Corporation; *U.S. Private*, pg. 1369
ZAMURAI CORPORATION—See Francisco Partners Management, LP; *U.S. Private*, pg. 1590
ZAO MOBILEYES—See HiQ International AB; *Int'l*, pg. 3402
ZAPPROVED LLC—See Leeds Equity Partners, LLC; *U.S. Private*, pg. 2414
ZAYO FRANCE SAS—See DigitalBridge Group, Inc.; *U.S. Public*, pg. 665
ZAYO FRANCE SAS—See EQT AB; *Int'l*, pg. 2482
ZEDGE, INC.; *U.S. Public*, pg. 2402
ZEL TECHNOLOGIES, LLC; *U.S. Private*, pg. 4600
ZEMENTIS, INC.—See Silver Lake Group, LLC; *U.S. Private*, pg. 3660
ZENDESK KOREA LLC—See Hellman & Friedman LLC; *U.S. Private*, pg. 1911
ZENDESK SINGAPORE PTE. LTD—See Hellman & Friedman LLC; *U.S. Private*, pg. 1911
ZEND TECHNOLOGIES, INC.—See Clearlake Capital Group, L.P.; *U.S. Private*, pg. 936
ZEND TECHNOLOGIES, INC.—See Francisco Partners Management, LP; *U.S. Private*, pg. 1591
ZENOSS, INC.; *U.S. Private*, pg. 4601
ZETA ASSOCIATES, INC.—See Lockheed Martin Corporation; *U.S. Public*, pg. 1339
ZETTASCALE TECHNOLOGY B.V.—See ADLINK Technology, Inc.; *Int'l*, pg. 151
ZEVA INC.; *U.S. Private*, pg. 4603
ZFERRAL, INC.; *U.S. Private*, pg. 4603
ZHEJIANG HUAHE WANRUN INFORMATION TECHNOLOGY CO., LTD.—See China Security Co., Ltd.; *Int'l*, pg. 1550
ZILLIOUS SOLUTIONS PRIVATE LIMITED—See Ebix Inc.; *U.S. Public*, pg. 710
ZINGLE, INC.—See Thoma Bravo, L.P.; *U.S. Private*, pg. 4149
ZIP FULFILLMENT LLC—See Pyxus International, Inc.; *U.S. Public*, pg. 1741
ZIPWHIP, INC.—See Twilio Inc.; *U.S. Public*, pg. 2206
ZOCDOC, INC.; *U.S. Private*, pg. 4607
ZOLON TECH SOLUTIONS INC.; *U.S. Private*, pg. 4607
ZOMBIE, INC.; *U.S. Private*, pg. 4607
ZONE LABS LLC—See Check Point Software Technologies Ltd.; *Int'l*, pg. 1459
ZOOM VIDEO COMMUNICATIONS, INC.; *U.S. Public*, pg. 2411
ZUI NOVUM SP. Z.O.O.—See Asseco Poland S.A.; *Int'l*, pg. 642
ZUI OTAGO SP. Z O.O.—See Asseco Poland S.A.; *Int'l*, pg. 642
ZUMASYS, INC; *U.S. Private*, pg. 4610
ZVC AUSTRALIA PTY. LTD.—See Zoom Video Communications, Inc.; *U.S. Public*, pg. 2411
ZVC FRANCE SAS—See Zoom Video Communications, Inc.; *U.S. Public*, pg. 2411
ZVC JAPAN KK—See Zoom Video Communications, Inc.; *U.S. Public*, pg. 2411
ZVC UK LTD.—See Zoom Video Communications, Inc.; *U.S. Public*, pg. 2411
ZYNGA GAME NETWORK INDIA PRIVATE LIMITED—See Zynga Inc.; *U.S. Private*, pg. 4611
ZYNGA ISRAEL LTD.—See Take-Two Interactive Software, Inc.; *U.S. Public*, pg. 1979
ZYNX HEALTH INCORPORATED—See The Hearst Corporation; *U.S. Private*, pg. 4045
ZYROBOTICS LLC; *U.S. Private*, pg. 4611

541512 — COMPUTER SYSTEMS DESIGN SERVICES

10PEARLS LLC; *U.S. Private*, pg. 2
1399 INTERNET TECHNOLOGY APPLICATION GROUP, INC.; *U.S. Public*, pg. 2
21ST CENTURY SYSTEMS, INC.; *U.S. Private*, pg. 5
365 OPERATING COMPANY LLC; *U.S. Private*, pg. 8
3AM TECHNOLOGIES, INC.; *Int'l*, pg. 7
3GTMS, INC.—See Sumeru Equity Partners LLC; *U.S. Private*, pg. 3852
3 KV GMBH—See HPI AG; *Int'l*, pg. 3500
3M HEALTH INFORMATION SYSTEMS—See Solventum Corporation; *U.S. Public*, pg. 1901
3 PHOENIX, INC.—See Advent International Corporation; *U.S. Private*, pg. 100
3T SYSTEMS, INC.; *U.S. Private*, pg. 14
5FLOW GMBH—See Matthews International Corporation; *U.S. Public*, pg. 1399
7DELTA, INC.—See The Carlyle Group Inc.; *U.S. Public*, pg. 2048
7SAFE LIMITED—See The Carlyle Group Inc.; *U.S. Public*, pg. 2051
9164-4187 QUEBEC INC.; *Int'l*, pg. 16
AAC CLYDE SPACE AB; *Int'l*, pg. 31
AAJ TECHNOLOGIES; *U.S. Private*, pg. 31
AASYS GROUP, INC.; *U.S. Private*, pg. 33
ABACUS DISTRIBUTION SYSTEMS TAIWAN LTD.—See China Airlines Ltd.; *Int'l*, pg. 1481
ABACUS SOLUTIONS LLC—See American Pacific Group, LLC; *U.S. Private*, pg. 242
ABB INFORMATION SYSTEMS LTD.—See ABB Ltd.; *Int'l*, pg. 47
ABB ROBOTICS AB—See ABB Ltd.; *Int'l*, pg. 49
ABCO ADVISORY SERVICES INDIA PRIVATE LIMITED—See UnitedHealth Group Incorporated; *U.S. Public*, pg. 2248
ACADIANA COMPUTER SYSTEMS INC.; *U.S. Private*, pg. 47
ACADIA TECHNOLOGY GROUP; *U.S. Private*, pg. 47
ACCEDERE LIMITED; *Int'l*, pg. 79
ACCELERA SOLUTIONS, INC.; *U.S. Private*, pg. 49
ACCEL LIMITED; *Int'l*, pg. 79
ACCELL IT SERVICES B.V.—See Accell Group N.V.; *Int'l*, pg. 80
ACCENTURE AUSTRALIA LTD.—See Accenture plc; *Int'l*, pg. 82
ACCENTURE BULGARIA EOOD—See Accenture plc; *Int'l*, pg. 82

541512 — COMPUTER SYSTEMS DE... CORPORATE AFFILIATIONS

ACCENTURE BV—See Accenture plc; *Int'l*, pg. 82
ACCENTURE INTERNATIONAL SARL—See Accenture plc; *Int'l*, pg. 83
ACCENTURE NZ LIMITED—See Accenture plc; *Int'l*, pg. 86
ACCENTURE SAUDI ARABIA LTD—See Accenture plc; *Int'l*, pg. 86
ACCENTURE SRL—See Accenture plc; *Int'l*, pg. 86
ACCENTURE TECHNOLGY SOLUTIONS (THAILAND) LTD.—See Accenture plc; *Int'l*, pg. 84
ACCENTURE TECHNOLOGY SOLUTIONS (ATS) NV—See Accenture plc; *Int'l*, pg. 82
ACCENTURE TECHNOLOGY SOLUTIONS PTE LTD.—See Accenture plc; *Int'l*, pg. 84
ACCENTURE TECHNOLOGY SOLUTIONS S.A.—See Accenture plc; *Int'l*, pg. 84
ACCENTURE TECHNOLOGY SOLUTIONS SDN BHD—See Accenture plc; *Int'l*, pg. 85
ACCENTURE TECHNOLOGY SOLUTIONS-SLOVAKIA S.R.O.—See Accenture plc; *Int'l*, pg. 85
ACCENTURE TECHNOLOGY SOLUTIONS SRL—See Accenture plc; *Int'l*, pg. 84
ACCENTURE TECHNOLOGY VENTURES S.P.R.L.—See Accenture plc; *Int'l*, pg. 85
ACCEO SOLUTIONS, INC.—See Constellation Software Inc.; *Int'l*, pg. 1773
ACCESS TAIWAN LAB CO., LTD.—See Access Co., Ltd.; *Int'l*, pg. 88
ACCION LABS US, INC.—See TA Associates, Inc.; *U.S. Private*, pg. 3914
ACCLAIM GAMES, INC.—See The Walt Disney Company; *U.S. Public*, pg. 2139
ACCORD SYSTEM CO., LTD.—See Core Corporation; *Int'l*, pg. 1797
ACCRETE, INC.; *Int'l*, pg. 93
ACCTTWO SHARED SERVICES, LLC; *U.S. Private*, pg. 54
ACE AUTOMATION (TIANJIN) CO. LTD.—See ATS Corporation; *Int'l*, pg. 694
ACE INFO SOLUTIONS, INC.—See Veritas Capital Fund Management, LLC; *U.S. Private*, pg. 4362
ACE INTEGRATED SOLUTIONS LTD.; *Int'l*, pg. 94
ACE NETWORK ZRT. PLC.—See 4iG Nyrt.; *Int'l*, pg. 12
ACENTRIX GMBH—See CANCOM SE; *Int'l*, pg. 1288
ACER INFORMATION PRODUCTS GROUP—See Acer Incorporated; *Int'l*, pg. 99
ACF SOLUTIONS, LLC—See Attain, LLC; *U.S. Private*, pg. 383
ACHIKO AG; *Int'l*, pg. 103
ACHILLES GUARD, INC.—See HGGC, LLC; *U.S. Private*, pg. 1929
ACI INFOCOM LIMITED; *Int'l*, pg. 104
ACMOS SOURCING SERVICE INC.—See ACMOS INC.; *Int'l*, pg. 107
ACOM SOLUTIONS INC. -ISERIES AS/400 DIVISION—See ACOM Solutions Inc.; *U.S. Private*, pg. 62
ACS DATALINE, LP—See Black Box Limited; *Int'l*, pg. 1056
ACS INTERNATIONAL RESOURCES INC.; *U.S. Private*, pg. 66
ACSIS, INC.—See Saints Capital, LLC; *U.S. Private*, pg. 3530
ACS SERVICES, INC.; *U.S. Private*, pg. 66
ACS SYSTEMS UK LIMITED—See Bechtle AG; *Int'l*, pg. 936
AC TECHNOLOGY, INC.; *U.S. Private*, pg. 46
ACTIVEWORLDS, INC.; *U.S. Private*, pg. 70
ACUMATICA, INC.—See EQT AB; *Int'l*, pg. 2467
ACXIOM JAPAN K. K.—See The Interpublic Group of Companies, Inc.; *U.S. Public*, pg. 2090
ADACEL TECHNOLOGIES LIMITED; *Int'l*, pg. 123
ADEO BILISIM DANISMANLIK HIZMETLERI SAN. VE TIC, A.S.—See Arena Bilgisayar Sanayi ve Ticaret A.S.; *Int'l*, pg. 558
ADEPT4 MANAGED IT LIMITED—See CloudCoCo Group plc; *Int'l*, pg. 1662
ADERAS, INC.; *U.S. Private*, pg. 78
ADESSO AS A SERVICE GMBH—See adesso SE; *Int'l*, pg. 144
ADESSO BENEFIT SOLUTIONS GMBH—See adesso SE; *Int'l*, pg. 144
ADESSO U.K. LIMITED—See adesso SE; *Int'l*, pg. 144
ADEXA INC.; *U.S. Private*, pg. 78
ADFLOW NETWORKS, INC.—See Daktronics, Inc.; *U.S. Public*, pg. 620
ADI, LLC—See Bread Financial Holdings Inc.; *U.S. Public*, pg. 380
ADISYN LTD; *Int'l*, pg. 149
ADJIA TECHNOLOGIES LIMITED; *Int'l*, pg. 150
ADL SOFTWARE PTY LTD—See Insight Venture Management, LLC; *U.S. Private*, pg. 2088
ADL SOFTWARE PTY LTD—See Stone Point Capital LLC; *U.S. Private*, pg. 3822
ADP BELGIUM CVA—See Automatic Data Processing, Inc.; *U.S. Public*, pg. 229
ADP GSI FRANCE SAS—See Automatic Data Processing, Inc.; *U.S. Public*, pg. 229
ADSWIZZ INC.—See Liberty Media Corporation; *U.S. Public*, pg. 1311
ADTRAN NETWORKS CANADA, INC.—See ADTRAN Holdings, Inc.; *U.S. Public*, pg. 43
ADVANCED CLINICAL SERVICES—See The Advanced Group of Companies; *U.S. Private*, pg. 3982
ADVANCED CONCEPTS & TECHNOLOGIES INTERNATIONAL, LLC; *U.S. Private*, pg. 88
ADVANCED CORE TECHNOLOGY CO., LTD.—See Aucnet Inc.; *Int'l*, pg. 699
ADVANCED HI-TECH CORPORATION; *U.S. Private*, pg. 90
ADVANCED INFORMATION TECHNOLOGY PCL; *Int'l*, pg. 160
ADVANCED INTEGRATION TECHNOLOGY, LP; *U.S. Private*, pg. 90
ADVANCED INTERACTIVE SOLUTIONS LTD.—See Advanced Interactive Systems; *U.S. Private*, pg. 90
ADVANCED NETWORK MANAGEMENT, INC.; *U.S. Private*, pg. 91
ADVANCED PROGRAMMING RESOURCES; *U.S. Private*, pg. 92
ADVANCED RESOURCES INC.—See The Advanced Group of Companies; *U.S. Private*, pg. 3982
ADVANCED RESOURCE TECHNOLOGIES, INC.; *U.S. Private*, pg. 92
ADVANCED SOFTWARE SYSTEMS, INC.; *U.S. Private*, pg. 92
ADVANCED SYSTEMS GROUP INC.; *U.S. Private*, pg. 92
ADVANCED SYSTEMS TECHNOLOGY, INC.; *U.S. Private*, pg. 92
ADVANCED TECHNICAL SOLUTIONS, LLC; *U.S. Private*, pg. 93
ADVANCED TECHNOLOGY SOLUTIONS, INC.; *U.S. Private*, pg. 93
ADVANCED TECHNOLOGY & SYSTEMS CO., LTD.; *Int'l*, pg. 162
ADVANCE INFORMATION MARKETING BERHAD; *Int'l*, pg. 156
ADVANCE TECHNOLOGY, INC.—See Comfort Systems USA, Inc.; *U.S. Public*, pg. 543
ADVANIXS CORPORATION—See Advantech Co., Ltd.; *Int'l*, pg. 164
ADVANSOFT INTERNATIONAL INC.; *U.S. Private*, pg. 93
ADVANTECH CO. MALAYSIA SDN. BHD.—See Advantech Co., Ltd.; *Int'l*, pg. 164
ADVANTECH TECHNOLOGIES LTD.; *Int'l*, pg. 165
ADVENT COMPUTER SERVICES LTD.; *Int'l*, pg. 167
ADVENT GLOBAL SOLUTIONS, INC.; *U.S. Private*, pg. 95
ADYEN AUSTRALIA PTY LIMITED—See Adyen N.V.; *Int'l*, pg. 169
AERO GROUP, INC.—See Furst-McNess Company; *U.S. Private*, pg. 1624
AETEA INFORMATION TECHNOLOGY INC.—See Great Mill Rock LLC; *U.S. Private*, pg. 1766
AEXIS FRANCE—See Aexis N.V.; *Int'l*, pg. 183
AEXIS N.V.; *Int'l*, pg. 183
AGC AMENITECH CO., LTD.—See AGC Inc.; *Int'l*, pg. 200
AGC NETWORKS, INC.—See Black Box Limited; *Int'l*, pg. 1058
AG CONNECTIONS, LLC—See China National Chemical Corporation; *Int'l*, pg. 1529
AGFA HEALTHCARE GERMANY GMBH—See Ardian SAS; *Int'l*, pg. 555
AGILE DECISIONPOINT CORPORATION; *U.S. Private*, pg. 127
AGILEPATH CORPORATION; *U.S. Private*, pg. 128
AGOSTO, INC.; *U.S. Private*, pg. 128
AGS BUSINESS COMPUTER CO., LTD.—See AGS Corporation; *Int'l*, pg. 221
AGSI; *U.S. Private*, pg. 130
AGS SYSTEM ADVISORY CO., LTD.—See AGS Corporation; *Int'l*, pg. 221
AHEAD, LLC—See Berkshire Partners LLC; *U.S. Private*, pg. 534
A-HOST CO., LTD.—See Country Group Development Public Company Limited; *Int'l*, pg. 1818
AION-TECH SOLUTIONS LIMITED; *Int'l*, pg. 234
AIRCRAFT SYSTEMS DIVISION, LOS ANGELES—See The Heico Companies, L.L.C.; *U.S. Private*, pg. 4050
AIRIT SERVICES AG—See Fraport AG; *Int'l*, pg. 2764
AIRTIFICIAL INTELLIGENCE STRUCTURES SA; *Int'l*, pg. 249
AISIN INFOTEX CO., LTD.—See AISIN Corporation; *Int'l*, pg. 252
AISINO CORPORATION; *Int'l*, pg. 254
AIVEBS SPA—See Capgemini SE; *Int'l*, pg. 1303
AIVE SPA—See Capgemini SE; *Int'l*, pg. 1303
AJEL LTD.; *Int'l*, pg. 255
AJILLUS INC.; *U.S. Private*, pg. 144
AJILON NORTH AMERICA, LLC—See Adecco Group AG; *Int'l*, pg. 138
AJM TECHNOLOGY (SHANGHAI) CO., LTD.—See Argo Graphics Inc.; *Int'l*, pg. 562
AKAMAI TECHNOLOGIES NETHERLANDS B.V.—See Akamai Technologies, Inc.; *U.S. Public*, pg. 69
AKAMAI TECHNOLOGIES POLAND SP. Z O.O.—See Akamai Technologies, Inc.; *U.S. Public*, pg. 69
AKILI INC.—See UnitedHealth Group Incorporated; *U.S. Public*, pg. 2252
AKIMA GLOBAL SERVICES, LLC—See Nana Regional Corporation, Inc.; *U.S. Private*, pg. 2832
AKIMA, LLC—See Nana Regional Corporation, Inc.; *U.S. Private*, pg. 2832
AKZO NOBEL WILTON APPLIED RESEARCH GROUP—See Akzo Nobel N.V.; *Int'l*, pg. 273
ALCHIP INVESTMENT INC.—See Alchip Technologies, Limited; *Int'l*, pg. 301
ALCHIP TECHNOLOGIES, (HEFEI) INC.—See Alchip Technologies, Limited; *Int'l*, pg. 301
ALCHIP TECHNOLOGIES, INC.—See Alchip Technologies, Limited; *Int'l*, pg. 301
ALCHIP TECHNOLOGIES, (JINAN) INC.—See Alchip Technologies, Limited; *Int'l*, pg. 301
ALCHIP TECHNOLOGIES, LIMITED—See Alchip Technologies, Limited; *Int'l*, pg. 301
ALCHIP TECHNOLOGIES, (WUXI) INC.—See Alchip Technologies, Limited; *Int'l*, pg. 301
ALDER TECHNOLOGY, INC.—See Blue Delta Capital Partners LLC; *U.S. Private*, pg. 588
ALDRICH RESOURCES BHD; *Int'l*, pg. 305
ALEUT COMMUNICATIONS SERVICES, LLC—See The Aleut Corporation; *U.S. Private*, pg. 3984
ALEXSSA ENTERPRISES LTD.—See River Run Computers, Inc.; *U.S. Private*, pg. 3444
ALFABET SAUDI ARABIA LLC—See Silver Lake Group, LLC; *U.S. Private*, pg. 3658
AL-FARIS NATIONAL COMPANY FOR INVESTMENT & EXPORT PLC; *Int'l*, pg. 285
ALFONSINO S.P.A.; *Int'l*, pg. 316
ALFRESA SYSTEM CORPORATION—See Alfresa Holdings Corporation; *Int'l*, pg. 317
AL-FUTTAIM TECHNOLOGIES LLC—See Al-Futtaim Private Company LLC; *Int'l*, pg. 285
ALITHYA GROUP, INC.; *Int'l*, pg. 329
ALKAMI TECHNOLOGY, INC.; *U.S. Public*, pg. 78
ALL BASES COVERED INC.; *U.S. Private*, pg. 170
ALLEGIENT LLC; *U.S. Private*, pg. 176
ALLEGRO WIRELESS CANADA INC.; *Int'l*, pg. 336
ALLEN SYSTEMS GROUP—See Allen Systems Group, Inc.; *U.S. Private*, pg. 180
ALLGEIER DMS SOLUTIONS—See Allgeier SE; *Int'l*, pg. 336
ALLGEIER IT SOLUTIONS AG—See Allgeier SE; *Int'l*, pg. 337
ALLGEIER IT SOLUTIONS GMBH—See Allgeier SE; *Int'l*, pg. 337
ALLGEIER LTD.—See Allgeier SE; *Int'l*, pg. 337
ALLGEIER S.A.—See Allgeier SE; *Int'l*, pg. 337
ALLGEIER (SCHWEIZ) AG—See Allgeier SE; *Int'l*, pg. 336
ALLIANCE TECHNOLOGY GROUP, LLC; *U.S. Private*, pg. 184
ALLIANZ CORNHILL INFORMATION SERVICES PRIVATE LTD.—See Allianz SE; *Int'l*, pg. 348
ALLIANZ MANAGED OPERATIONS & SERVICES SE—See Allianz SE; *Int'l*, pg. 349
ALLIED COMPUTERS INTERNATIONAL ASIA LTD.; *Int'l*, pg. 357
ALLIED TECHNOLOGY GROUP INC.—See The Carlyle Group Inc.; *U.S. Public*, pg. 2048
ALLIED TELESIS LABS S.R.L.—See ALLIED TELESIS HOLDINGS K.K.; *Int'l*, pg. 358
ALLIED TELESYN INTERNATIONAL (ASIA) PTE. LTD.—See ALLIED TELESIS HOLDINGS K.K.; *Int'l*, pg. 358
ALLIED TELESYN INTERNATIONAL GMBH—See ALLIED TELESIS HOLDINGS K.K.; *Int'l*, pg. 358
ALLIN CORPORATION; *U.S. Public*, pg. 81
ALLIN INTERACTIVE CORPORATION—See Allin Corporation; *U.S. Public*, pg. 81
ALL-IN-ONE NETWORK SOLUTIONS, INC.; *U.S. Private*, pg. 173
ALLIXO TECHNOLOGIES, LLC; *U.S. Private*, pg. 192
ALLSCRIPTS—See Veradigm Inc.; *U.S. Public*, pg. 2279
ALL STAR CONSULTING INC.; *U.S. Private*, pg. 172
ALL SYSTEMS INSTALLATION INC.; *U.S. Private*, pg. 173
ALLTERRA IBERICA, S.L.U.—See Trimble, Inc.; *U.S. Public*, pg. 2190
ALMANA NETWORKS SOLUTIONS; *Int'l*, pg. 363
ALMAWAVE S.P.A.; *Int'l*, pg. 363
ALNA AB; *Int'l*, pg. 364
ALNA INTELLIGENCE UAB—See Alna AB; *Int'l*, pg. 364
ALNOVA TECHNOLOGIES CORPORATION S.L.—See Accenture plc; *Int'l*, pg. 86
ALPHANUMERIC SYSTEMS INC.; *U.S. Private*, pg. 200
ALPHA OMEGA INTEGRATION, LLC; *U.S. Private*, pg. 199
ALPHASERVE TECHNOLOGIES, LLC; *U.S. Private*, pg. 200
ALPHA TECHNOLOGY GROUP LIMITED; *Int'l*, pg. 370
ALTEN ITALIA—See Alten S.A.; *Int'l*, pg. 390
ALTEN SI-TECHNO ROMANIA SRL—See Alten S.A.; *Int'l*, pg. 389
ALTIUSPAR SOLUTIONS S.A. DE C.V.—See Grupo Posadas S.A.B. de C.V.; *Int'l*, pg. 3134
ALTRAN CIS FRANCE—See Capgemini SE; *Int'l*, pg. 1304
ALTRAN INNOVACION S.L.U.—See Capgemini SE; *Int'l*, pg. 1304
ALTRAN INTERNATIONAL B.V.—See Capgemini SE; *Int'l*, pg. 1304
ALTRAN OSTERREICH GMBH—See Capgemini SE; *Int'l*, pg. 1304

N.A.I.C.S. INDEX

541512 — COMPUTER SYSTEMS DE...

ALTRAN PORTUGAL S.A.—See Capgemini SE; *Int'l*, pg. 1305
ALTRAN SVERIGE AB—See Capgemini SE; *Int'l*, pg. 1305
ALTRAN (SWITZERLAND) S.A.—See Capgemini SE; *Int'l*, pg. 1304
ALTRAN TECHNOLOGIES SWEDEN AB—See Capgemini SE; *Int'l*, pg. 1305
ALTRAN TECHNOLOGIES UK LTD.—See Capgemini SE; *Int'l*, pg. 1305
ALTRAN UK LIMITED—See Capgemini SE; *Int'l*, pg. 1305
ALTURNA INTEGRATION SERVICES N.V.—See Amphenol Corporation; *U.S. Public*, pg. 126
AMADEUS ARGENTINA S.A.—See Amadeus IT Group, S.A.; *Int'l*, pg. 405
AMADEUS BULGARIA OOD—See Amadeus IT Group, S.A.; *Int'l*, pg. 405
AMADEUS GDS SINGAPORE PTE. LTD.—See Amadeus IT Group, S.A.; *Int'l*, pg. 406
AMADEUSGLOBAL ECUADOR S.A.—See Amadeus IT Group, S.A.; *Int'l*, pg. 405
AMADEUS GLOBAL TRAVEL ISRAEL LTD.—See Amadeus IT Group, S.A.; *Int'l*, pg. 406
AMADEUS GTD (MALTA) LIMITED—See Amadeus IT Group, S.A.; *Int'l*, pg. 406
AMADEUS GTD SOUTHERN AFRICA PTY. LTD.—See Amadeus IT Group, S.A.; *Int'l*, pg. 406
AMADEUS HELLAS S.A.—See Amadeus IT Group, S.A.; *Int'l*, pg. 406
AMADEUS HONG KONG LIMITED—See Amadeus IT Group, S.A.; *Int'l*, pg. 406
AMADEUS ITALIA S.P.A.—See Amadeus IT Group, S.A.; *Int'l*, pg. 406
AMADEUS MARKETING (SCHWEIZ) A.G.—See Amadeus IT Group, S.A.; *Int'l*, pg. 406
AMADEUS MARKETING (UK) LTD.—See Amadeus IT Group, S.A.; *Int'l*, pg. 406
AMADEUS NORWAY AS—See Amadeus IT Group, S.A.; *Int'l*, pg. 406
AMADEUS PARAGUAY S.R.L.—See Amadeus IT Group, S.A.; *Int'l*, pg. 406
AMADEUS PERU S.A.—See Amadeus IT Group, S.A.; *Int'l*, pg. 406
AMADEUS SCANDINAVIA AB.—See Amadeus IT Group, S.A.; *Int'l*, pg. 406
AMADEUS SERVICES LTD.—See Amadeus IT Group, S.A.; *Int'l*, pg. 406
AMANO MCGANN, INC.—See Amano Corporation; *Int'l*, pg. 411
AMBASSADOR INC.; *U.S. Private*, pg. 217
AMBIENT CONSULTING, LLC; *U.S. Private*, pg. 217
AMDOCS (FINLAND) OY—See Amdocs Limited; *Int'l*, pg. 419
AMDOCS HELLAS LTD.—See Amdocs Limited; *Int'l*, pg. 419
AMDOCS TETHYS LIMITED—See Amdocs Limited; *Int'l*, pg. 420
AMERICAN MEGATRENDS, INC.—See HGGC, LLC; *U.S. Private*, pg. 1928
AMERICAN MEGATRENDS INFORMATION TECHNOLOGY (KUNSHAN) CO., LTD.—See HGGC, LLC; *U.S. Private*, pg. 1929
AMESYS S.A.—See Atos SE; *Int'l*, pg. 691
AMHERST SYSTEMS, INC.—See Northrop Grumman Corporation; *U.S. Public*, pg. 1540
AMOS AUSTRIA GMBH—See Allianz SE; *Int'l*, pg. 342
AMPCUS INC.; *U.S. Private*, pg. 265
AMPD VENTURES, INC.; *Int'l*, pg. 433
AMPVOLTS LIMITED; *Int'l*, pg. 437
AMTEX SYSTEMS INC.; *U.S. Private*, pg. 268
ANALYSIS, DESIGN & DIAGNOSTICS, INC.—See SEACORP, LLC; *U.S. Private*, pg. 3584
ANALYSYS MASON GROUP LIMITED—See Datatec Limited; *Int'l*, pg. 1980
ANALYTICS PARTNERS, LLC—See HealthAxis Group, LLC; *U.S. Private*, pg. 1895
ANALYTIXINSIGHT INC.; *Int'l*, pg. 446
ANGELALIGN TECHNOLOGY INC.; *Int'l*, pg. 459
ANHUI WANTONG TECHNOLOGY CO., LTD.; *Int'l*, pg. 470
ANNAGEN, LLC; *U.S. Private*, pg. 284
ANNAMS SYSTEMS, CORP.—See CGI Inc.; *Int'l*, pg. 1432
ANOVA MICROSYSTEMS INC.; *U.S. Private*, pg. 285
ANSYS GOVERNMENT INITIATIVES, INC. AGI.—See ANSYS, Inc.; *U.S. Public*, pg. 138
ANTARES-DESENVOLVIMENTO DE SOFTWARE, LDA.—See FARO Technologies, Inc.; *U.S. Public*, pg. 823
ANTARES TECHNOLOGY SOLUTIONS, INC.—See Guggenheim Partners, LLC; *U.S. Private*, pg. 1812
ANTERIX INC.; *U.S. Public*, pg. 139
ANTHOLOGY INC.—See Leeds Equity Partners, LLC; *U.S. Private*, pg. 2414
ANTHOLOGY INC.—See Veritas Capital Fund Management, LLC; *U.S. Private*, pg. 4360
ANTN CO., LTD.; *Int'l*, pg. 484
ANVICOM-COMMAND FEDERAL, INC.—See Bridge Growth Partners, LLC; *U.S. Private*, pg. 649
ANVICOM-COMMAND FEDERAL, INC.—See Frontenac Company LLC; *U.S. Private*, pg. 1614
APEX INTERNATIONAL FINANCIAL ENGINEERING RESEARCH & TECHNOLOGY CO., LIMITED; *Int'l*, pg. 511
APEX TECHNOLOGY GROUP, INC.; *U.S. Private*, pg. 293
APOLLO CONSULTING SERVICES CORPORATION—See Indotronix International Corporation; *U.S. Private*, pg. 2064
APPLIED GLOBAL TECHNOLOGIES; *U.S. Private*, pg. 298
APPLIED INFORMATION SCIENCES, INC.; *U.S. Private*, pg. 298
APPLIED INTERNATIONAL INFORMATICS GMBH—See Atos SE; *Int'l*, pg. 690
APPLIED MATERIALS CANADA, INC.—See Applied Materials, Inc.; *U.S. Public*, pg. 172
APPLIED TECHNOLOGIES INC.—See French Gerleman Electric Co., Inc.; *U.S. Private*, pg. 1608
APPLIED TECHNOLOGY CO., LTD.; *Int'l*, pg. 521
APPLIED TECHNOLOGY SERVICES, INC.; *U.S. Private*, pg. 299
APPLIED TRUST ENGINEERING, INC.—See GI Manager L.P.; *U.S. Private*, pg. 1693
APPLIED VISIONS, INC.; *U.S. Private*, pg. 300
APPRIO INC.; *U.S. Private*, pg. 300
APPTECH INC.; *U.S. Private*, pg. 300
APPTIS, INC.—See New Mountain Capital, LLC; *U.S. Private*, pg. 2900
AQIWO; *U.S. Private*, pg. 302
AQUENT GMBH & CO. KG—See Aquent Inc.; *U.S. Private*, pg. 303
ARAB INFORMATION MANAGEMENT SERVICES; *Int'l*, pg. 530
ARAD-OPHIR LTD.; *Int'l*, pg. 534
ARB IOT GROUP LIMITED; *Int'l*, pg. 537
ARBOR CONSULTING RESOURCES INC.; *U.S. Private*, pg. 308
ARBOR NETWORKS UK LTD—See Danaher Corporation; *U.S. Public*, pg. 624
ARCHERPOINT, L.L.C.—See Cherry Bekaert LLP; *U.S. Private*, pg. 874
ARCONTECH GROUP PLC; *Int'l*, pg. 550
ARCSOURCE GROUP, INC.; *U.S. Private*, pg. 315
ARCUS S.A.; *Int'l*, pg. 553
ARD GRUP BILISIM TEKNOLOJILERI A.S.; *Int'l*, pg. 553
ARETE M PTE. LTD.—See 8Telecom International Holdings Co. Ltd.; *Int'l*, pg. 16
ARGO BUSINESS SERVICES INC.—See Argo Graphics Inc.; *Int'l*, pg. 562
ARK SYSTEMS CO., LTD.—See CAC Holdings Corporation; *Int'l*, pg. 1247
ARP EUROPE AG—See Bechtle AG; *Int'l*, pg. 937
ARP GMBH—See Bechtle AG; *Int'l*, pg. 937
ARP NEDERLAND B.V.—See Bechtle AG; *Int'l*, pg. 937
ARP NV—See Bechtle AG; *Int'l*, pg. 937
ARP SAS—See Bechtle AG; *Int'l*, pg. 937
ARP SCHWEIZ AG—See Bechtle AG; *Int'l*, pg. 937
ARRAY INFORMATION TECHNOLOGY, INC.; *U.S. Private*, pg. 334
ARRIBATEC GROUP ASA; *Int'l*, pg. 578
ARRIS GROUP, INC. - GLOBAL STRATEGIES—See CommScope Holding Company, Inc.; *U.S. Public*, pg. 547
ARROW ECS AG—See Arrow Electronics, Inc.; *U.S. Public*, pg. 195
ARROWPOINT CORPORATION; *U.S. Private*, pg. 336
ARTELCOM GRAND SUD SAS—See Artelcom S.A.; *Int'l*, pg. 581
ARTELCOM S.A.; *Int'l*, pg. 581
ARTEMIS FINLAND OY—See ESW Capital, LLC; *U.S. Private*, pg. 1430
ARTEMIS INTERNATIONAL FRANCE—See ESW Capital, LLC; *U.S. Private*, pg. 1430
ARTEMIS INTERNATIONAL GMBH—See ESW Capital, LLC; *U.S. Private*, pg. 1430
ARTEMIS INTERNATIONAL SOLUTIONS CORPORATION—See ESW Capital, LLC; *U.S. Private*, pg. 1430
ARTEMIS INTERNATIONAL SRL—See ESW Capital, LLC; *U.S. Private*, pg. 1430
ARTERIAN, INC.—See The Aldridge Company; *U.S. Private*, pg. 3983
ARTESYS SA—See Capgemini SE; *Int'l*, pg. 1303
ART & LOGIC, INC.; *U.S. Private*, pg. 339
ARYAKA NETWORKS INC.; *U.S. Private*, pg. 345
ARYAKA NETWORKS INDIA PVT. LTD.—See Aryaka Networks Inc.; *U.S. Private*, pg. 345
ASAHI KASEI MICROSYSTEMS CO., LTD.—See Asahi Kasei Corporation; *Int'l*, pg. 596
ASA INTERNATIONAL LTD.; *U.S. Private*, pg. 345
ASCENS SERVICES SAS—See Financiere de L'Odet; *Int'l*, pg. 2665
ASCENTECH, K.K.; *Int'l*, pg. 602
THE ASCENT SERVICES GROUP; *U.S. Private*, pg. 3989
AS FUJITSU ESTONIA—See Fujitsu Limited; *Int'l*, pg. 2835
ASG SOFTWARE SOLUTIONS—See Allen Systems Group, Inc.; *U.S. Private*, pg. 180
ASG SOFTWARE SOLUTIONS—See Allen Systems Group, Inc.; *U.S. Private*, pg. 180
ASHBURN CONSULTING LLC—See IMB Partners, U.S. Private, pg. 2046
ASIAINFO INTERNATIONAL PTE. LTD.—See CITIC Group Corporation; *Int'l*, pg. 1619
AS INPRO GMBH—See Deutsche Lufthansa AG; *Int'l*, pg. 2066
ASITE SOLUTIONS PRIVATE LIMITED—See Asite Solutions Ltd.; *Int'l*, pg. 621
ASM DIGITAL TECHNOLOGIES INC.—See ASM Technologies Limited; *Int'l*, pg. 627
ASM DIGITAL TECHNOLOGIES PTE LTD.—See ASM Technologies Limited; *Int'l*, pg. 627
ASPONE LTD—See Ekwienox Limited; *Int'l*, pg. 2340
ASPYRA, INC.; *U.S. Public*, pg. 213
ASSECO AUSTRIA GMBH—See Asseco Poland S.A.; *Int'l*, pg. 641
ASSECO CENTRAL EUROPE, A.S.—See Asseco Poland S.A.; *Int'l*, pg. 641
ASSECO DENMARK A/S—See Asseco Poland S.A.; *Int'l*, pg. 641
ASSECO SOUTH EASTERN EUROPE S.A.—See Asseco Poland S.A.; *Int'l*, pg. 641
ASSECO SPAIN SA—See Asseco Poland S.A.; *Int'l*, pg. 641
ASSETT, INC.; *U.S. Private*, pg. 354
ASTARO GMBH & CO. KG—See Apax Partners LLP; *Int'l*, pg. 506
ASTRIUM NORTH AMERICA, INC.—See Airbus SE; *Int'l*, pg. 245
ASURE SOFTWARE, INC.; *U.S. Public*, pg. 218
ASYSTEL ITALIA SPA—See Econocom Group SA; *Int'l*, pg. 2297
ATCO I-TEK AUSTRALIA—See ATCO Ltd.; *Int'l*, pg. 666
ATEAM CONNECT INC.—See Ateam Inc.; *Int'l*, pg. 667
ATEB, INC.—See Omnicell, Inc.; *U.S. Public*, pg. 1572
ATHENA GLOBAL TECHNOLOGIES LTD.; *Int'l*, pg. 669
ATHON SA; *Int'l*, pg. 670
ATK AEROSPACE SYSTEMS—See Northrop Grumman Corporation; *U.S. Public*, pg. 1540
ATLANTIC BUSINESS TECHNOLOGIES, INC.; *U.S. Private*, pg. 372
ATLAS COMMUNICATIONS, INC.—See North 6th Agency, Inc.; *U.S. Private*, pg. 2939
ATLAS ELEKTRONIK FINLAND OY—See Airbus SE; *Int'l*, pg. 242
ATLAS TECHNOLOGIES CORPORATION; *Int'l*, pg. 686
ATMIRA ESPACIO DE CONSULTORIA S.L.; *Int'l*, pg. 687
ATOMIC DATA, LLC.; *U.S. Private*, pg. 381
ATOS (AUSTRALIA) PTY. LTD.—See Atos SE; *Int'l*, pg. 690
ATOS BELGIUM SA—See Atos SE; *Int'l*, pg. 690
ATOS BILISIM DANISMANLIK VE MUSTERI HIZMETLERI SANAYI VE TICARET A/S—See Atos SE; *Int'l*, pg. 690
ATOS CONSLUTING CANAROIAS, SA—See Atos SE; *Int'l*, pg. 690
ATOS COVICS BUSINESS SOLUTIONS CO., LTD.—See Atos SE; *Int'l*, pg. 690
ATOS GLOBAL DELIVERY CENTER MEXICO, S. DE R.L. DE C.V.—See Atos SE; *Int'l*, pg. 690
ATOS GLOBAL DELIVERY CENTER PHILIPPINES, INC.—See Atos SE; *Int'l*, pg. 690
ATOS INDIA PRIVATE LIMITED—See Atos SE; *Int'l*, pg. 690
ATOS INFORMATION TECHNOLOGY (CHINA) CO., LTD.—See Atos SE; *Int'l*, pg. 690
ATOS INFORMATION TECHNOLOGY HK LTD.—See Atos SE; *Int'l*, pg. 691
ATOS INFORMATION TECHNOLOGY INC.—See Atos SE; *Int'l*, pg. 691
ATOS INFORMATION TECHNOLOGY (NANJING) CO., LTD.—See Atos SE; *Int'l*, pg. 690
ATOS IT SERVICES SARL—See Atos SE; *Int'l*, pg. 690
ATOS IT SOLUTIONS & SERVICES A/S—See Atos SE; *Int'l*, pg. 690
ATOS IT SOLUTIONS & SERVICES LLC—See Atos SE; *Int'l*, pg. 690
ATOS IT SOLUTIONS & SERVICES LTD.—See Atos SE; *Int'l*, pg. 690
ATOS IT SOLUTIONS & SERVICES OY—See Atos SE; *Int'l*, pg. 690
ATOS IT SOLUTIONS & SERVICES S.A.S.—See Atos SE; *Int'l*, pg. 690
ATOS IT SOLUTIONS & SERVICES S.R.O—See Atos SE; *Int'l*, pg. 690
ATOS KK—See Atos SE; *Int'l*, pg. 691
ATOS LUXEMBOURG PSF S.A.—See Atos SE; *Int'l*, pg. 691
ATOS MAGYARORSZAG KFT.—See Atos SE; *Int'l*, pg. 691
ATOS NEDERLAND B.V.—See Atos SE; *Int'l*, pg. 691
ATOS ORIGIN SERVICOS DE TECNOLOGIA DA INFORMACAO DO BRASIL LTDA—See Atos SE; *Int'l*, pg. 691
ATOS POLAND GLOBAL SERVICE SP ZOO—See Atos SE; *Int'l*, pg. 691
ATOS POLSKA SA—See Atos SE; *Int'l*, pg. 691
ATOS PTY. LTD.—See Atos SE; *Int'l*, pg. 691
ATOS SE; *Int'l*, pg. 691
ATOS SOLUCOES E SERIVCOS PARA TECNOLOGIAS DE INFORMACAO, UNIPESSOAL, LTDA.—See Atos SE; *Int'l*, pg. 691
ATOS SPAIN SA—See Atos SE; *Int'l*, pg. 691
ATOSS SOFTWARE AG; *Int'l*, pg. 692
ATS ADVANCED MANUFACTURING DIVISION—See ATS Corporation; *Int'l*, pg. 694
ATS AUTOMATION ASIA PTE LTD—See ATS Corporation; *Int'l*, pg. 695
ATS AUTOMATION—See ATS Corporation; *Int'l*, pg. 695

541512 — COMPUTER SYSTEMS DE...

ATS AUTOMATION TOOLING SYSTEMS GMBH—See ATS Corporation; *Int'l*, pg. 695
ATS CORPORATION; *Int'l*, pg. 694
ATS PRECISION METAL COMPONENTS—See ATS Corporation; *Int'l*, pg. 695
ATS PRECISION PLASTIC COMPONENTS—See ATS Corporation; *Int'l*, pg. 695
ATS WICKEL-UND MONTAGETECHNIK AG—See ATS Corporation; *Int'l*, pg. 695
ATTAINED PTY. LTD.—See Adisyn Ltd; *Int'l*, pg. 149
AT&T GOVERNMENT SOLUTIONS—See AT&T Inc.; *U.S. Public*, pg. 219
ATTRONICA COMPUTERS INC.; *U.S. Private*, pg. 383
AUN CONSULTING, INC.; *Int'l*, pg. 705
AUN GLOBAL MARKETING PTE. LTD.—See AUN Consulting, Inc.; *Int'l*, pg. 705
AUN HONG KONG MARKETING CO., LTD.—See AUN Consulting, Inc.; *Int'l*, pg. 705
AUN THAI LABORATORIES CO., LTD.—See AUN Consulting, Inc.; *Int'l*, pg. 705
AURIONPRO SOLUTIONS PTY LTD.—See Aurionpro Solutions Limited; *Int'l*, pg. 711
AURIONPRO SOLUTIONS, SPC—See Aurionpro Solutions Limited; *Int'l*, pg. 711
AURORA INNOVATION, INC.; *U.S. Public*, pg. 227
AUROTEK CORPORATION; *Int'l*, pg. 714
AUTHENTEC (SHANGHAI) CO., LTD—See Apple Inc.; *U.S. Public*, pg. 169
AUTODESK SOFTWARE, UNIPESSOAL, LDA.—See Autodesk, Inc.; *U.S. Public*, pg. 229
AUTODESK S.R.L.—See Autodesk, Inc.; *U.S. Public*, pg. 229
AUTOEVER SYSTEMS EUROPE GMBH—See Hyundai Motor Company; *Int'l*, pg. 3558
AUTOMATIC DATA PROCESSING LIMITED—See Automatic Data Processing, Inc.; *U.S. Public*, pg. 230
AUTOSERVER CO., LTD; *Int'l*, pg. 732
AUTOSTRADE TEC SPA—See Edizione S.r.l.; *Int'l*, pg. 2312
AUTO-TROL TECHNOLOGY AUSTRALIA—See Auto-trol Technology Corporation; *U.S. Private*, pg. 398
AUTO-TROL TECHNOLOGY CANADA LTD.—See Auto-trol Technology Corporation; *U.S. Private*, pg. 398
AUTO-TROL TECHNOLOGY CORPORATION; *U.S. Private*, pg. 398
AUTO-TROL TECHNOLOGY GMBH—See Auto-trol Technology Corporation; *U.S. Private*, pg. 398
AUTOWEB, INC.—See One Planet Group LLC; *U.S. Private*, pg. 3020
AVANADE INC.—See Accenture plc; *Int'l*, pg. 85
AVANADE SOUTH AFRICA—See Accenture plc; *Int'l*, pg. 85
AVANT NORTH AMERICA—See ACI Group; *U.S. Private*, pg. 59
AVELEAD CONSULTING, LLC—See Streamline Health Solutions, Inc.; *U.S. Public*, pg. 1954
AVERY DENNISON PRINTER SYSTEMS DIVISION—See Avery Dennison Corporation; *U.S. Public*, pg. 243
AVESTA COMPUTER SERVICES LTD.; *U.S. Private*, pg. 405
AVI-TECH, INC.—See Avi-Tech Holdings Limited; *Int'l*, pg. 741
AVNET D.O.O., BEOGRAD—See Avnet, Inc.; *U.S. Public*, pg. 252
AVNET D. O. O.—See Avnet, Inc.; *U.S. Public*, pg. 252
AXA GROUP OPERATIONS SWITZERLAND AG—See AXA S.A.; *Int'l*, pg. 756
AXA SERVICES SAS—See AXA S.A.; *Int'l*, pg. 758
AXA TECHNOLOGY SERVICES AMERICA INC—See Equitable Holdings, Inc.; *U.S. Public*, pg. 788
AXA TECHNOLOGY SERVICES AUSTRALIA—See AXA S.A.; *Int'l*, pg. 758
AXA TECHNOLOGY SERVICES GERMANY GMBH—See AXA S.A.; *Int'l*, pg. 758
AXA TECHNOLOGY SERVICES JAPAN K.K—See AXA S.A.; *Int'l*, pg. 758
AXA TECHNOLOGY SERVICES PORTUGAL—See AXA S.A.; *Int'l*, pg. 758
AXA TECHNOLOGY SERVICES SOUTH EAST ASIA—See AXA S.A.; *Int'l*, pg. 758
AXA TECHNOLOGY SERVICES UK PLC—See AXA S.A.; *Int'l*, pg. 758
AXEDA SYSTEMS INC.; *U.S. Private*, pg. 412
AXELON SERVICES CORPORATION; *U.S. Private*, pg. 412
AXEL SEMRAU GMBH & CO. KG—See Abbott Laboratories; *U.S. Public*, pg. 20
AXFOOD IT AB—See Axel Johnson Gruppen AB; *Int'l*, pg. 764
AXIANS INFOMA (SCHWEIZ) A.G.—See Electricite de France S.A.; *Int'l*, pg. 2351
AXIATA BUSINESS SERVICES SDN BHD—See Axiata Group Berhad; *Int'l*, pg. 768
AXIOM CORPORATION; *U.S. Private*, pg. 413
AXIOS SYSTEMS PLC.—See EQT AB; *Int'l*, pg. 2477
AXIS CONSULTING 2000 LTD—See 4iG Nyrt.; *Int'l*, pg. 12
AXIS GROUP, LLC; *U.S. Private*, pg. 413
AXLBIT, INC.—See Equinix, Inc.; *U.S. Public*, pg. 787
AXPO INFORMATIK AG—See Axpo Holding AG; *Int'l*, pg. 771
AXWAY BV—See Axway Software SA; *Int'l*, pg. 772

AXWAY INC.—See Axway Software SA; *Int'l*, pg. 772
AXWAY UK LTD—See Axway Software SA; *Int'l*, pg. 772
AXXIOME AG; *Int'l*, pg. 772
AXXIOME AMERICAS, INC.—See Axxiome AG; *Int'l*, pg. 772
AXXIOME ASIA PACIFIC PTE. LTD.—See Axxiome AG; *Int'l*, pg. 772
AXXIOME BENELUX BV—See Axxiome AG; *Int'l*, pg. 772
AXXIOME BRASIL LTDA.—See Axxiome AG; *Int'l*, pg. 773
AXXIOME CANADA LTD.—See Axxiome AG; *Int'l*, pg. 773
AXXIOME CIS LLC.—See Axxiome AG; *Int'l*, pg. 773
AXXIOME COLOMBIA S.A.S.—See Axxiome AG; *Int'l*, pg. 773
AXXIOME DEUTSCHLAND GMBH—See Axxiome AG; *Int'l*, pg. 773
AXXIOME POLSKA SP. Z O.O—See Axxiome AG; *Int'l*, pg. 773
AXXIOME S.A.—See Axxiome AG; *Int'l*, pg. 773
AXXIOME UK LTD.—See Axxiome AG; *Int'l*, pg. 773
AXXIOME URUGUAY S.A.—See Axxiome AG; *Int'l*, pg. 773
AXXIOME USA LLC—See Axxiome AG; *Int'l*, pg. 773
AZENTIO SOFTWARE PTE. LTD.—See Apax Partners LLP; *Int'l*, pg. 502
AZIENDA INFORMATICA ITALIANA S.R.L.—See CY4Gate S.p.A.; *Int'l*, pg. 1891
AZION CORP.; *Int'l*, pg. 780
B2B INDUSTRIES LLC.; *U.S. Private*, pg. 421
B2EN CO., LTD.; *Int'l*, pg. 790
B3 CONSULTING GROUP AB; *Int'l*, pg. 791
BABY CALENDAR, INC.; *Int'l*, pg. 793
BAE SYSTEMS APPLIED INTELLIGENCE—See BAE Systems plc; *Int'l*, pg. 796
BAE SYSTEMS-TECHNOLOGY SOLUTIONS & SERVICES SECTOR—See BAE Systems plc; *Int'l*, pg. 797
BAIDU JAPAN INC.—See Baidu, Inc.; *Int'l*, pg. 801
BAKER COMMUNICATIONS, INC.—See Windstream Holdings, Inc.; *U.S. Public*, pg. 2373
BALKAN SERVICES LTD.—See Bulgarian Stock Exchange - Sofia AD; *Int'l*, pg. 1213
BALU FORGE INDUSTRIES LTD.; *Int'l*, pg. 812
BAND OF CODERS, LP; *U.S. Private*, pg. 464
BASF IT SERVICES CONSULT GMBH—See BASF SE; *Int'l*, pg. 879
BASF IT SERVICES S.A.—See BASF SE; *Int'l*, pg. 879
BAUER CORPORATE SERVICES PRIVATE LIMITED—See BAUER Aktiengesellschaft; *Int'l*, pg. 891
BAY COMPUTING GROUP; *U.S. Private*, pg. 492
BAYRAK EBT TABAN SANAYI VE TICARET A.S.; *Int'l*, pg. 915
BAYSHORE NETWORKS, LLC—See OPSWAT, Inc.; *U.S. Private*, pg. 3034
B B H SOLUTIONS, INC.; *U.S. Private*, pg. 417
BBREAK SYSTEMS CO., LTD.; *Int'l*, pg. 921
BBS TECHNOLOGIES, INC.; *U.S. Private*, pg. 498
BCC BUSINESS COMMUNICATION COMPANY GMBH—See EWE Aktiengesellschaft; *Int'l*, pg. 2575
BCC SISTEMI INFORMATICI SPA—See Iccrea Holding S.p.A.; *Int'l*, pg. 3578
BEARINGPOINT SRL—See BearingPoint, Inc.; *U.S. Private*, pg. 507
BECHTLE BRUSSELS NV—See Bechtle AG; *Int'l*, pg. 937
BECHTLE DIRECT AG—See Bechtle AG; *Int'l*, pg. 937
BECHTLE DIRECT B.V.—See Bechtle AG; *Int'l*, pg. 937
BECHTLE DIRECT GMBH—See Bechtle AG; *Int'l*, pg. 937
BECHTLE DIRECT GMBH—See Bechtle AG; *Int'l*, pg. 937
BECHTLE DIRECT KFT.—See Bechtle AG; *Int'l*, pg. 937
BECHTLE DIRECT LIMITED—See Bechtle AG; *Int'l*, pg. 937
BECHTLE DIRECT LTD.—See Bechtle AG; *Int'l*, pg. 937
BECHTLE DIRECT POLSKA SP.Z.OO.—See Bechtle AG; *Int'l*, pg. 937
BECHTLE DIRECT PORTUGAL UNIPESSOAL LDA—See Bechtle AG; *Int'l*, pg. 937
BECHTLE DIRECT SAS—See Bechtle AG; *Int'l*, pg. 937
BECHTLE DIRECT S.L.—See Bechtle AG; *Int'l*, pg. 937
BECHTLE DIRECT SRL-GMBH—See Bechtle AG; *Int'l*, pg. 937
BECHTLE DIRECT S.R.O.—See Bechtle AG; *Int'l*, pg. 937
BECHTLE FINANZ- & MARKETINGSERVICES GMBH—See Bechtle AG; *Int'l*, pg. 937
BECHTLE GMBH & CO. KG—See Bechtle AG; *Int'l*, pg. 937
BECHTLE GMBH & CO. KG—See Bechtle AG; *Int'l*, pg. 937
BECHTLE GMBH—See Bechtle AG; *Int'l*, pg. 937
BECHTLE GMBH—See Bechtle AG; *Int'l*, pg. 937
BECHTLE IT-SYSTEMHAUS GMBH—See Bechtle AG; *Int'l*, pg. 937
BECHTLE PRINTING SOLUTIONS AG—See Bechtle AG; *Int'l*, pg. 937
BECHTLE REGENSDORF AG—See Bechtle AG; *Int'l*, pg. 937
BECHTLE REMARKETING GMBH—See Bechtle AG; *Int'l*, pg. 937
BECHTLE ST. GALLEN AG—See Bechtle AG; *Int'l*, pg. 937
BEECUBE, INC.—See National Instruments Corporation; *U.S. Private*, pg. 2856
BEIJING 58 DAOJIA INFORMATION TECHNOLOGY CO., LTD.—See 58.com Inc.; *Int'l*, pg. 13
BEIJING AIRDOC TECHNOLOGY CO., LTD.; *Int'l*, pg. 945
BEIJING ASIACOM INFORMATION TECHNOLOGY CO., LTD.; *Int'l*, pg. 945

BEIJING BEIDA JADE BIRD UNIVERSAL SCI-TECH LIMITED; *Int'l*, pg. 946
BEIJING CHANGYI INFORMATION TECHNOLOGIES CO., LTD.—See Beijing Shiji Information Technology Co., Ltd.; *Int'l*, pg. 956
BEIJING CTJ INFORMATION TECHNO CO., LTD.; *Int'l*, pg. 948
BEIJING DATAWAY HORIZON CO., LTD.; *Int'l*, pg. 948
BEIJING LUZHU BIOTECHNOLOGY CO., LTD.; *Int'l*, pg. 954
BEIJING NEW SPACE TECHNOLOGY CO., LTD.; *Int'l*, pg. 954
BEIJING QUANSHI WORLD ONLINE NETWORK INFORMATION CO., LTD.; *Int'l*, pg. 955
BEIJING SUNWAYWORLD SCIENCE AND TECHNOLOGY CO., LTD—See Abbott Laboratories; *U.S. Public*, pg. 20
BEIJING TEAMSUN TECHNOLOGY CO., LTD.; *Int'l*, pg. 958
BEIJING TOPNEW INFORMATION & TECHNOLOGY CO., LTD.; *Int'l*, pg. 959
BEIJING UNITED INFORMATION TECHNOLOGY CO., LTD.; *Int'l*, pg. 959
BEIJING WALUER INFORMATION TECHNOLOGY CO., LTD.; *Int'l*, pg. 960
BEIT SYSTEMSHAUS GMBH—See Gauselmann AG; *Int'l*, pg. 2890
BELMONT TECHNOLOGY REMARKETING—See Belmont Trading Company; *U.S. Private*, pg. 521
BELMONT TECHNOLOGY REMARKETING—See SiPi Metals Corp.; *U.S. Private*, pg. 3671
BESTIT CORP.; *U.S. Private*, pg. 544
BETACOM S.A.; *Int'l*, pg. 1002
BETA SOFT SYSTEMS, INC.; *U.S. Private*, pg. 545
BEXAR VENTURES, INC.; *Int'l*, pg. 1004
BHARAT IT SERVICES LIMITED—See Digilife Technologies Limited; *Int'l*, pg. 2119
BIAS CORPORATION—See Deloitte LLP; *U.S. Private*, pg. 1198
BIAS CORPORATION—See Deloitte Touche Tohmatsu Limited; *Int'l*, pg. 2014
BIG IDEA TECHNOLOGY, LLC; *U.S. Private*, pg. 553
BILENDI SA; *Int'l*, pg. 1023
BINTERSISTEMAS—See Binter Canarias, S.A.; *Int'l*, pg. 1034
BIO-OPTRONICS, INC.—See Genstar Capital, LLC; *U.S. Private*, pg. 1673
BITHEADS, INC.; *Int'l*, pg. 1050
BIT-WIZARDS INFORMATION TECHNOLOGY SOLUTIONS, INC.; *U.S. Private*, pg. 566
BIZIM HESAP A.S.—See Fibabanka A.S.; *Int'l*, pg. 2651
BIZNESS APPS, INC.—See Buildfire, Inc.; *U.S. Private*, pg. 682
BLACK BOOK MARKET RESEARCH LLC; *U.S. Private*, pg. 569
BLACK BOX NETWORK PRODUCTS NV—See Black Box Limited; *Int'l*, pg. 1057
BLACK BOX NETWORK SERVICES NEW ZEALAND LIMITED—See Black Box Limited; *Int'l*, pg. 1058
BLADE NETWORK TECHNOLOGIES, INC.—See International Business Machines Corporation; *U.S. Public*, pg. 1148
BLOCKMINT TECHNOLOGIES, INC.; *Int'l*, pg. 1064
BLOCK SOLUTIONS LTD.; *Int'l*, pg. 1064
BLUE CANOPY GROUP, LLC—See Jacobs Engineering Group, Inc.; *U.S. Public*, pg. 1183
BLUECAT JAPAN CO., LTD.—See Madison Dearborn Partners, LLC; *U.S. Private*, pg. 2540
BLUEGRANITE, INC.—See Gryphon Investors, LLC; *U.S. Private*, pg. 1798
BLUEPEAK TECHNOLOGY SOLUTIONS, LLC; *U.S. Private*, pg. 597
BLUE SKY IT PARTNERS CORPORATION; *U.S. Private*, pg. 593
BLUESOURCE LTD.; *Int'l*, pg. 1074
BLUESTAR OPTIONS INC.—See Microsoft Corporation; *U.S. Public*, pg. 1442
BLUEWAVE TECHNOLOGY GROUP, LLC; *U.S. Private*, pg. 599
BLYTHECO, LLC; *U.S. Private*, pg. 600
BMC SOFTWARE EUROPE—See KKR & Co. Inc.; *U.S. Public*, pg. 1240
BOARDWARE INTELLIGENCE TECHNOLOGY LIMITED; *Int'l*, pg. 1094
BOC BUSINESS OBJECTIVES CONSULTING IBERICA S.L.U.—See BOC Information Technologies Consulting AG; *Int'l*, pg. 1096
BOC INFORMATION SYSTEMS GMBH—See BOC Information Technologies Consulting AG; *Int'l*, pg. 1096
BOC INFORMATION TECHNOLOGIES CONSULTING AG; *Int'l*, pg. 1096
BOC INFORMATION TECHNOLOGIES CONSULTING GMBH—See BOC Information Technologies Consulting AG; *Int'l*, pg. 1096
BOC INFORMATION TECHNOLOGIES CONSULTING LTD.—See BOC Information Technologies Consulting AG; *Int'l*, pg. 1096
BOC INFORMATION TECHNOLOGIES CONSULTING SP.

Z O.O.—See BOC Information Technologies Consulting AG; *Int'l*, pg. 1096
BOC UNTERNEHMENSBERATUNG GMBH—See BOC Information Technologies Consulting AG; *Int'l*, pg. 1096
BODHTREE CONSULTING LTD.; *Int'l*, pg. 1097
BOEING INTELLIGENCE & ANALYTICS, INC.—See The Boeing Company; *U.S. Public*, pg. 2039
BOUNTEOUS, INC.; *U.S. Private*, pg. 624
BOUSTEAD INFORMATION TECHNOLOGY PTE LTD—See Boustead Singapore Limited; *Int'l*, pg. 1120
BPCE INFOGERANCE & TECHNOLOGIES EIG—See Groupe BPCE; *Int'l*, pg. 3092
BPER SERVICES S.C.P.A.—See BPER BANCA S.p.A; *Int'l*, pg. 1132
BRADY/TISCOR, INC.—See Brady Corporation; *U.S. Public*, pg. 379
BRANDING ENGINEER CO., LTD.; *Int'l*, pg. 1140
BRAVENETMEDIA.COM; *Int'l*, pg. 1141
BRENNAN IT PTY. LIMITED; *Int'l*, pg. 1145
BRIDGEPOINT TECHNOLOGIES; *U.S. Private*, pg. 649
BRIDGEQUEST, INC.—See Advanced Business Software & Solutions Ltd.; *Int'l*, pg. 157
BRIGHTBOX, INC.; *U.S. Private*, pg. 651
BRIGHTONE GMBH—See Aurelius Equity Opportunities SE & Co. KGaA; *Int'l*, pg. 710
BROADBAND ACCESS NETWORKING GROUP, INC.; *U.S. Private*, pg. 658
BROADSOFT TECHNOLOGIES PRIVATE LIMITED—See Cisco Systems, Inc.; *U.S. Public*, pg. 497
BROGENT TECHNOLOGIES, INC.; *Int'l*, pg. 1173
BROKER TECHNOLOGY SOLUTIONS LLC—See Anywhere Real Estate Inc.; *U.S. Public*, pg. 142
BROTHER INDUSTRIES TECHNOLOGY (M) SDN. BHD.—See Brother Industries, Ltd.; *Int'l*, pg. 1197
BRUKER FRANCE S.A.S.—See Bruker Corporation; *U.S. Public*, pg. 405
BRUNEL BELGIUM N.V.—See Brunel International N.V.; *Int'l*, pg. 1199
BRUNEL CZ S.R.O.—See Brunel International N.V.; *Int'l*, pg. 1199
BRUNEL ENERGY JAPAN KK—See Brunel International N.V.; *Int'l*, pg. 1199
BRUNEL ENERGY KUWAIT W.L.L.—See Brunel International N.V.; *Int'l*, pg. 1199
BRUNEL SURINAME N.V.—See Brunel International N.V.; *Int'l*, pg. 1200
B+S BANKSYSTEME AG; *Int'l*, pg. 784
BS SYSTEM INFORMATION CO., LTD.—See BNK Financial Group Inc.; *Int'l*, pg. 1079
BTC BUSINESS TECHNOLOGY CONSULTING AG—See EWE Aktiengesellschaft; *Int'l*, pg. 2575
BTC IT SERVICES GMBH—See EWE Aktiengesellschaft; *Int'l*, pg. 2575
BUCHANAN TECHNOLOGIES, INC.—See Lightview Capital LLC; *U.S. Private*, pg. 2453
BUILDINGIQ, INC.; *Int'l*, pg. 1212
BUILDPAY LLC—See Marsh & McLennan Companies, Inc.; *U.S. Public*, pg. 1374
BULL COTE D'IVOIRE SA—See Atos SE; *Int'l*, pg. 691
BULL CYPRUS LTD—See Atos SE; *Int'l*, pg. 691
BULL DO BRASIL SISTEMAS DE INFORMACAO LTDA—See Atos SE; *Int'l*, pg. 692
BULL S.A.—See Atos SE; *Int'l*, pg. 691
BULL SENEGAL SARL—See Atos SE; *Int'l*, pg. 692
BUNDESDRUCKEREI GMBH; *Int'l*, pg. 1215
BUSINESS CENTRIC SERVICES GROUP; *Int'l*, pg. 1228
BUSINESS CONTROL SYSTEMS LP; *U.S. Private*, pg. 694
BUSINESS IT SOURCE, INC.—See Computacenter plc; *Int'l*, pg. 1758
BUSINESSNOW COPENHAGEN APS—See DXC Technology Company; *U.S. Public*, pg. 694
BUSINESS SYSTEMS HOLDINGS GROUP PLC—See Vista Equity Partners, LLC; *U.S. Private*, pg. 4394
BUYERQUEST HOLDINGS INC.—See The ODP Corporation; *U.S. Public*, pg. 2117
BYTE COMPUTER SA—See Ideal Group S.A.; *Int'l*, pg. 3589
C2 SOFTWARE LIMITED—See BGF Group PLC; *Int'l*, pg. 1007
C3 COMPUTER CORPORATION; *U.S. Private*, pg. 710
C3I, INC.—See HCL Technologies Ltd.; *Int'l*, pg. 3299
C3 INTEGRATED SOLUTIONS INC.; *U.S. Private*, pg. 710
CAANES, LLC.; *U.S. Private*, pg. 710
CABLEUROPA, S.A.U.—See Banco Santander, S.A.; *Int'l*, pg. 825
CABLEVISION LIGHTPATH, LLC—See Altice USA, Inc.; *U.S. Public*, pg. 87
CAC EUROPE LIMITED—See CAC Corporation; *Int'l*, pg. 1247
CACI DYNAMIC SYSTEMS, INC.—See CACI International Inc.; *U.S. Public*, pg. 417
CACI, INC.-FEDERAL—See CACI International Inc.; *U.S. Public*, pg. 417
CACI INTERNATIONAL INC.; *U.S. Public*, pg. 417
CACI PREMIER TECHNOLOGY, INC.—See CACI International Inc.; *U.S. Public*, pg. 417
CACI TECHNOLOGIES, INC—See CACI International Inc.; *U.S. Public*, pg. 417

CAC MARUHA NICHIRO SYSTEMS CORPORATION—See CAC Corporation; *Int'l*, pg. 1247
CADDPLUS INC.—See MGS Manufacturing Group, Inc.; *U.S. Private*, pg. 2695
CADENCE AMS DESIGN INDIA PRIVATE LIMITED—See Cadence Design Systems, Inc.; *U.S. Public*, pg. 418
CADENCE DESIGN SERVICES TYK—See Cadence Design Systems, Inc.; *U.S. Public*, pg. 418
CADENCE DESIGN SYSTEMS DO BRASIL MICROELETRONICA LTDA.—See Cadence Design Systems, Inc.; *U.S. Public*, pg. 418
CADENCE DESIGN SYSTEMS (INDIA) PRIVATE LTD.—See Cadence Design Systems, Inc.; *U.S. Public*, pg. 418
CADENCE DESIGN SYSTEMS KFT.—See Cadence Design Systems, Inc.; *U.S. Public*, pg. 418
CADENCE DESIGN SYSTEMS LIMITED—See Cadence Design Systems, Inc.; *U.S. Public*, pg. 418
CADENCE DESIGN SYSTEMS MANAGEMENT (SHANGHAI) CO., LTD.—See Cadence Design Systems, Inc.; *U.S. Public*, pg. 418
CAD IT S.P.A.; *Int'l*, pg. 1247
CAD QUALITY A/S—See Addnode Group AB; *Int'l*, pg. 130
CAD-QUALITY SVERIGE AB—See Addnode Group AB; *Int'l*, pg. 130
CADSYS (INDIA) LTD.; *Int'l*, pg. 1248
CAD TECHNOLOGY CENTER—See Addnode Group AB; *Int'l*, pg. 130
CAI CANADA INC—See Computer Aid, Inc.; *U.S. Private*, pg. 1004
CALANCE CORPORATION; *Int'l*, pg. 1261
CALIBRE SYSTEMS INC.; *U.S. Public*, pg. 717
CALLDRIP LLC; *U.S. Private*, pg. 722
CAL NET TECHNOLOGY GROUP; *U.S. Private*, pg. 715
CAMGIAN MICROSYSTEMS, INC.; *U.S. Private*, pg. 729
CAMO SOFTWARE, INC.; *U.S. Private*, pg. 729
CAN2 TERMIK A.S.; *Int'l*, pg. 1277
CANCOM A+D IT SOLUTIONS GMBH—See CANCOM SE; *Int'l*, pg. 1289
CANCOM IT SOLUTIONS GMBH—See CANCOM SE; *Int'l*, pg. 1288
CANCOM NSG GMBH—See CANCOM SE; *Int'l*, pg. 1289
CANDELIS - INDIA—See Candle Acquisition Corporation; *U.S. Private*, pg. 733
CANON ELECTRONIC BUSINESS MACHINES (H.K.) CO., LTD.—See Canon Inc.; *Int'l*, pg. 1295
CANON INFORMATION AND IMAGING SOLUTIONS, INC.—See Canon Inc.; *Int'l*, pg. 1297
CANON IT SOLUTIONS INC.—See Canon Inc.; *Int'l*, pg. 1296
CANON RESEARCH CENTRE FRANCE S.A.S.—See Canon Inc.; *Int'l*, pg. 1294
CANTABRIA - MUNDIVIA S.A—See Atos SE; *Int'l*, pg. 691
CAPGEMINI ASIA PACIFIC PTE. LTD.—See Capgemini SE; *Int'l*, pg. 1304
CAPGEMINI BUSINESS SERVICES AUSTRALIA PTY LTD.—See Capgemini SE; *Int'l*, pg. 1304
CAPGEMINI CANADA INC.—See Capgemini SE; *Int'l*, pg. 1304
CAPGEMINI CONSULTING S.A.S.—See Capgemini SE; *Int'l*, pg. 1304
CAPGEMINI DANMARK A/S—See Capgemini SE; *Int'l*, pg. 1304
CAPGEMINI DO BRASIL, SERVICOS DE CONSULTORIA E INFORMATICA LTDA.—See Capgemini SE; *Int'l*, pg. 1306
CAPGEMINI FINANCIAL SERVICES INTERNATIONAL INC.—See Capgemini SE; *Int'l*, pg. 1305
CAPGEMINI FINLAND OY—See Capgemini SE; *Int'l*, pg. 1305
CAPGEMINI INDIA PRIVATE LTD.—See Capgemini SE; *Int'l*, pg. 1305
CAPGEMINI MAGYARORSZAG KFT—See Capgemini SE; *Int'l*, pg. 1305
CAPGEMINI MIDDLE EAST FZ LLC—See Capgemini SE; *Int'l*, pg. 1306
CAPGEMINI NORGE AS—See Capgemini SE; *Int'l*, pg. 1306
CAPGEMINI NORTH AMERICA INC.—See Capgemini SE; *Int'l*, pg. 1306
CAPGEMINI PHILLIPINES SBOS—See Capgemini SE; *Int'l*, pg. 1306
CAPGEMINI POLSKA SP. Z O. O—See Capgemini SE; *Int'l*, pg. 1306
CAPGEMINI RETAIL SOLUTIONS B.V.—See Capgemini SE; *Int'l*, pg. 1306
CAPGEMINI SERVICE S.A.S—See Capgemini SE; *Int'l*, pg. 1306
CAPGEMINI SERVICES MALAYSIA SDN BHD—See Capgemini SE; *Int'l*, pg. 1306
CAPGEMINI SERVICES ROMANIA S.R.L.—See Capgemini SE; *Int'l*, pg. 1306
CAPGEMINI SLOVENSKO, S.R.O.—See Capgemini SE; *Int'l*, pg. 1306
CAPGEMINI SOLUTIONS PRIVATE LIMITED—See Capgemini SE; *Int'l*, pg. 1306
CAPGEMINI TECHNOLOGIES LLC—See Capgemini SE; *Int'l*, pg. 1306

CAPGEMINI TECHNOLOGY SERVICES INDIA LIMITED—See Capgemini SE; *Int'l*, pg. 1306
CAPGEMINI TECHNOLOGY SERVICES MAROC S.A.—See Capgemini SE; *Int'l*, pg. 1306
CAPGEMINI TECHNOLOGY SERVICES S.A.S.—See Capgemini SE; *Int'l*, pg. 1306
CAPINFO COMPANY LIMITED; *Int'l*, pg. 1308
CAPITAL ASSET PLANNING, INC.; *Int'l*, pg. 1309
CAPTECH VENTURES, INC.; *U.S. Private*, pg. 746
CAPULA LIMITED; *Int'l*, pg. 1318
CAPULA NUCLEAR—See Capula Limited; *Int'l*, pg. 1318
THE CARA GROUP, INC.; *U.S. Private*, pg. 4005
CARDINAL SOLUTIONS GROUP, INC.; *U.S. Private*, pg. 751
CARD PROCESSING RESELLER, INC.—See Bank of America Corporation; *U.S. Public*, pg. 271
CARETEQ LIMITED; *Int'l*, pg. 1325
CAROLINAS IT, LLC—See The Riverside Company; *U.S. Private*, pg. 4109
CASD SOLUTIONS SDN. BHD.—See Hong Seng Consolidated Berhad; *Int'l*, pg. 3469
CASTLE COMPUTER SERVICES LTD.—See BGF Group PLC; *Int'l*, pg. 1007
CATERPILLAR MARINE ASSET INTELLIGENCE LLC—See Caterpillar, Inc.; *U.S. Public*, pg. 451
CAVU CORP PTE. LTD.—See Digilife Technologies Limited; *Int'l*, pg. 2119
CBM OF AMERICA, INC.; *U.S. Private*, pg. 797
CCA FOR SOCIAL GOOD—See CCA Global Partners, Inc.; *U.S. Private*, pg. 799
CCA GLOBAL PARTNERS, INC. - BIZUNITE DIVISION—See CCA Global Partners, Inc.; *U.S. Private*, pg. 799
C-CAM GMBH—See Bechtle AG; *Int'l*, pg. 938
CDC SOFTWARE OY—See TA Associates, Inc.; *U.S. Private*, pg. 3914
CDC SOFTWARE SINGAPORE PTE. LTD.—See TA Associates, Inc.; *U.S. Private*, pg. 3914
CDLX GMBH—See DBAY Advisors Limited; *Int'l*, pg. 1987
CDO TECHNOLOGIES INC.; *U.S. Private*, pg. 803
CDW TECHNOLOGIES, INC.—See CDW Corporation; *U.S. Public*, pg. 462
CEB MAINTENANCE AFRICA (PROPRIETARY) LIMITED—See Business Connexion Group Limited; *Int'l*, pg. 1228
CELARTEM TECHNOLOGY INC.; *Int'l*, pg. 1391
CELOXICA HOLDINGS PLC; *Int'l*, pg. 1395
CENIT AG; *Int'l*, pg. 1401
CENIT FRANCE SARL—See CENIT AG; *Int'l*, pg. 1401
CENIT JAPAN K. K.—See CENIT AG; *Int'l*, pg. 1401
CENIT NORTH AMERICA INC.—See CENIT AG; *Int'l*, pg. 1401
CENIT SCHWEIZ AG—See CENIT AG; *Int'l*, pg. 1401
CENIT S.R.L.—See CENIT AG; *Int'l*, pg. 1401
CEN SOLUTIONS CORP.—See CAC Holdings Corporation; *Int'l*, pg. 1247
CENTARE GROUP, LTD.; *U.S. Private*, pg. 809
CENTER FOR COMPUTER RESOURCES, LLC; *U.S. Private*, pg. 810
CENTRAL SERVICE ASSOCIATION; *U.S. Private*, pg. 824
CENTRIFUGE SYSTEMS, INC.—See Hale Capital Partners, L.P.; *U.S. Private*, pg. 1842
CENTRIX INNOVATIONS (PTY) LTD.—See IQVIA Holdings Inc.; *U.S. Public*, pg. 1168
CENTURYLINK AUSTRALIA PTY. LTD.—See Lumen Technologies, Inc.; *U.S. Public*, pg. 1345
CENTURYLINK JAPAN, LTD—See Lumen Technologies, Inc.; *U.S. Public*, pg. 1345
CENTURYLINK SINGAPORE PTE. LTD.—See Lumen Technologies, Inc.; *U.S. Public*, pg. 1346
CENTURYLINK TECHNOLOGIES INDIA PRIVATE LIMITED—See Lumen Technologies, Inc.; *U.S. Public*, pg. 1346
CENTURYLINK TECHNOLOGY HONG KONG LIMITED—See Lumen Technologies, Inc.; *U.S. Public*, pg. 1346
CENTURYLINK TECHNOLOGY UK LIMITED—See Lumen Technologies, Inc.; *U.S. Public*, pg. 1346
CERNA SOLUTIONS, LLC—See Sunstone Partners Management LLC; *U.S. Private*, pg. 3873
CERNER CANADA ULC—See Oracle Corporation; *U.S. Public*, pg. 1610
CERNER CORPORATION—See Oracle Corporation; *U.S. Public*, pg. 1610
CERNER HEALTH SERVICES DEUTSCHLAND GMBH—See Oracle Corporation; *U.S. Public*, pg. 1610
CERNER (MALAYSIA) SDN BHD—See Oracle Corporation; *U.S. Public*, pg. 1610
CERNER NEDERLAND B.V.—See Oracle Corporation; *U.S. Public*, pg. 1610
CERNER OSTERREICH GMBH—See Oracle Corporation; *U.S. Public*, pg. 1610
CERTICOM CORP.—See BlackBerry Limited; *Int'l*, pg. 1060
CERVELLO INC.—See A.T. Kearney, Inc.; *U.S. Private*, pg. 28
CETC DIGITAL TECHNOLOGY CO., LTD; *Int'l*, pg. 1424
CETISA, S.A.—See Atos SE; *Int'l*, pg. 691
CEXEC, INC.; *U.S. Private*, pg. 843

CFM—See OceanSound Partners, LP; U.S. Private, pg. 2990
CGI INFORMATION SYSTEMS & MANAGEMENT CONSULTANTS AUSTRALIA PTY LTD—See CGI Inc.; Int'l, pg. 1432
CGI INFORMATION SYSTEMS & MANAGEMENT CONSULTANTS DEUTSCHLAND GMBH—See CGI Inc.; Int'l, pg. 1432
CGI INFORMATION SYSTEMS & MANAGEMENT CONSULTANTS ESPANA S.A.—See CGI Inc.; Int'l, pg. 1432
CGI INFORMATION SYSTEMS & MANAGEMENT CONSULTANTS INC.—See CGI Inc.; Int'l, pg. 1433
CGI INFORMATION SYSTEMS & MANAGEMENT CONSULTANTS, INC.—See CGI Inc.; Int'l, pg. 1433
CGI INFORMATION SYSTEMS & MANAGEMENT CONSULTANTS NETHERLANDS B.V.—See CGI Inc.; Int'l, pg. 1433
CGI INFORMATION SYSTEMS & MANAGEMENT CONSULTANTS PORTUGAL—See CGI Inc.; Int'l, pg. 1433
CGI INFORMATION SYSTEMS & MANAGEMENT CONSULTANTS SA/NV—See CGI Inc.; Int'l, pg. 1433
CGI INFORMATION SYSTEMS & MANAGEMENT CONSULTANTS SWITZERLAND SA—See CGI Inc.; Int'l, pg. 1433
CGI INFORMATION SYSTEMS & MANAGEMENT CONSULTANTS UK LTD.—See CGI Inc.; Int'l, pg. 1433
CGI INFORMATION SYSTEMS—See CGI Inc.; Int'l, pg. 1433
CGI INFORMATION SYSTEMS—See CGI Inc.; Int'l, pg. 1433
CGI SVERIGE AB—See CGI Inc.; Int'l, pg. 1434
CGI TECHNOLOGIES & SOLUTIONS INC.—See CGI Inc.; Int'l, pg. 1434
CGI UK LTD. - ABERDEEN—See CGI Inc.; Int'l, pg. 1434
CGI UK LTD. - BRIDGEND—See CGI Inc.; Int'l, pg. 1434
CGI UK LTD. - BRISTOL—See CGI Inc.; Int'l, pg. 1434
CGI UK LTD. - CARDIFF—See CGI Inc.; Int'l, pg. 1434
CGI UK LTD. - EDINBURGH—See CGI Inc.; Int'l, pg. 1434
CGI UK LTD. - LEATHERHEAD—See CGI Inc.; Int'l, pg. 1434
CGI UK LTD. - MANCHESTER—See CGI Inc.; Int'l, pg. 1434
CGI UK LTD.—See CGI Inc.; Int'l, pg. 1434
CG SERVICE SYSTEMS CURACAO NV—See Avantha Group; Int'l, pg. 736
CGS TECHNOLOGY ASSOCIATES, INC.; U.S. Private, pg. 844
CHAMS HOLDING COMPANY; Int'l, pg. 1440
CHANGCHUN JILIN UNIVERSITY ZHENGYUAN INFORMATION TECHNOLOGIES CO., LTD.; Int'l, pg. 1442
CHANGE, INC.; Int'l, pg. 1443
CHASE SCIENCE CO., LTD.; Int'l, pg. 1456
CHECK POINT HOLDING (SINGAPORE) PTE LTD.—See Check Point Software Technologies Ltd.; Int'l, pg. 1458
CHECK POINT SOFTWARE TECHNOLOGIES (AUSTRIA) GMBH—See Check Point Software Technologies Ltd.; Int'l, pg. 1458
CHECK POINT SOFTWARE TECHNOLOGIES (FINLAND) OY—See Check Point Software Technologies Ltd.; Int'l, pg. 1458
CHECK POINT SOFTWARE TECHNOLOGIES (INDIA) PRIVATE LIMITED—See Check Point Software Technologies Ltd.; Int'l, pg. 1458
CHERISH SUNSHINE INTERNATIONAL LIMITED; Int'l, pg. 1471
CHEROKEE INFORMATION SERVICES, INC.; U.S. Private, pg. 873
CHERRYROAD TECHNOLOGIES INC.; U.S. Private, pg. 874
CHEVALIER (NETWORK SOLUTIONS) LIMITED—See Chevalier International Holdings Limited; Int'l, pg. 1473
CHEVRON INFORMATION TECHNOLOGY COMPANY—See Chevron Corporation; U.S. Public, pg. 486
CHINA CRESCENT ENTERPRISES, INC.; U.S. Private, pg. 885
CHINAETEK SERVICE & TECHNOLOGY CO., LTD.; Int'l, pg. 1568
CHINA ITS (HOLDINGS) CO., LTD.; Int'l, pg. 1513
CHINA MARINE INFORMATION ELECTRONICS COMPANY LIMITED; Int'l, pg. 1517
CHIYODA U-TECH CO., LTD.—See Chiyoda Corporation; Int'l, pg. 1575
CHOICE SOLUTIONS LLC; U.S. Private, pg. 888
CHR SOLUTIONS INC. - DALLAS—See CHR Solutions, Inc.; U.S. Private, pg. 889
CHR SOLUTIONS, INC. - HOUSTON—See CHR Solutions, Inc.; U.S. Private, pg. 889
CHR SOLUTIONS, INC. - LUBBOCK—See CHR Solutions, Inc.; U.S. Private, pg. 889
CHR SOLUTIONS, INC.; U.S. Private, pg. 889
CHS DATA SYSTEMS GESELLSCHAFT FUR SYSTEMENTWICKLUNG UND BERATUNG GMBH—See Capgemini SE; Int'l, pg. 1305
CHUNGHWA SYSTEM INTEGRATION CO., LTD.—See Chunghwa Telecom Co., Ltd.; Int'l, pg. 1598
CIBER DANMARK A/S—See HTC Global Services Inc.; U.S. Private, pg. 1999

CIBER LLC—See HTC Global Services Inc.; U.S. Private, pg. 1999
CIBER MANAGED SERVICES GMBH—See HTC Global Services Inc.; U.S. Private, pg. 1999
CIBER NORGE AS—See ManpowerGroup Inc.; U.S. Public, pg. 1360
CIBER UK LTD.—See HTC Global Services Inc.; U.S. Private, pg. 1999
CIENA CANADA, INC.—See Ciena Corporation; U.S. Public, pg. 494
CIENA CORPORATION; U.S. Public, pg. 494
CIENA LIMITED—See Ciena Corporation; U.S. Public, pg. 494
CIGNEX DATAMATICS CORPORATION—See Datamatics Global Services Ltd.; Int'l, pg. 1978
CIGNITI, INC.—See Cigniti Technologies Ltd.; Int'l, pg. 1607
CIGNITI TECHNOLOGIES LTD.; Int'l, pg. 1607
CIJ MANAGE SYSTEM, INC.—See Computer Institute of Japan Ltd.; Int'l, pg. 1759
CIMEX CORP.—See Arden Software Ltd.; Int'l, pg. 554
CIO SOLUTIONS; U.S. Private, pg. 899
CIPHERTECHS, INC.—See Periscope Equity LLC; U.S. Private, pg. 3151
CIRQUE CORPORATION—See Alps Alpine Co., Ltd.; Int'l, pg. 376
CIRRASCALE CORPORATION—See Craftsman Capital Partners, LLC; U.S. Private, pg. 1082
CISCO PHOTONICS ITALY S.R.L.—See Cisco Systems, Inc.; U.S. Public, pg. 497
CISCO SYSTEMS (ARGENTINA) S.A.—See Cisco Systems, Inc.; U.S. Public, pg. 497
CISCO SYSTEMS AUSTRALIA PTY., LTD.—See Cisco Systems, Inc.; U.S. Public, pg. 497
CISCO SYSTEMS BELGIUM S.P.R.L.—See Cisco Systems, Inc.; U.S. Public, pg. 498
CISCO SYSTEMS BULGARIA EOOD—See Cisco Systems, Inc.; U.S. Public, pg. 498
CISCO SYSTEMS CANADA CO.—See Cisco Systems, Inc.; U.S. Public, pg. 498
CISCO SYSTEMS CARIBE—See Cisco Systems, Inc.; U.S. Public, pg. 498
CISCO SYSTEMS CHILE S.A.—See Cisco Systems, Inc.; U.S. Public, pg. 498
CISCO SYSTEMS (COLOMBIA) LIMITADA—See Cisco Systems, Inc.; U.S. Public, pg. 497
CISCO SYSTEMS COSTA RICA SA—See Cisco Systems, Inc.; U.S. Public, pg. 498
CISCO SYSTEMS CYPRUS LTD.—See Cisco Systems, Inc.; U.S. Public, pg. 498
CISCO SYSTEMS (CZECH REPUBLIC) S.R.O—See Cisco Systems, Inc.; U.S. Public, pg. 497
CISCO SYSTEMS DANMARK A/S—See Cisco Systems, Inc.; U.S. Public, pg. 498
CISCO SYSTEMS DE MEXICO, S.A. DE C.V.—See Cisco Systems, Inc.; U.S. Public, pg. 499
CISCO SYSTEMS DO BRASIL LTDA.—See Cisco Systems, Inc.; U.S. Public, pg. 499
CISCO SYSTEMS EGYPT LTD.—See Cisco Systems, Inc.; U.S. Public, pg. 498
CISCO SYSTEMS FINLAND OY—See Cisco Systems, Inc.; U.S. Public, pg. 498
CISCO SYSTEMS FRANCE SARL—See Cisco Systems, Inc.; U.S. Public, pg. 498
CISCO SYSTEMS G.K. TOKYO—See Cisco Systems, Inc.; U.S. Public, pg. 498
CISCO SYSTEMS GMBH—See Cisco Systems, Inc.; U.S. Public, pg. 498
CISCO SYSTEMS HELLAS S.A.—See Cisco Systems, Inc.; U.S. Public, pg. 498
CISCO SYSTEMS (HK), LTD.—See Cisco Systems, Inc.; U.S. Public, pg. 497
CISCO SYSTEMS HOLDING GMBH & CO. KG—See Cisco Systems, Inc.; U.S. Public, pg. 498
CISCO SYSTEMS (INDIA) PVT. LTD.—See Cisco Systems, Inc.; U.S. Public, pg. 497
CISCO SYSTEMS ISRAEL LTD.—See Cisco Systems, Inc.; U.S. Public, pg. 498
CISCO SYSTEMS (ITALY) S.R.L.—See Cisco Systems, Inc.; U.S. Public, pg. 497
CISCO SYSTEMS LIMITED—See Cisco Systems, Inc.; U.S. Public, pg. 498
CISCO SYSTEMS LTD.—See Cisco Systems, Inc.; U.S. Public, pg. 498
CISCO SYSTEMS LUXEMBOURG S.A.R.L.—See Cisco Systems, Inc.; U.S. Public, pg. 498
CISCO SYSTEMS MAGYARORSZG KFT.—See Cisco Systems, Inc.; U.S. Public, pg. 498
CISCO SYSTEMS MALAYSIA SDN, BHD—See Cisco Systems, Inc.; U.S. Public, pg. 498
CISCO SYSTEMS NETHERLANDS HOLDINGS B.V—See Cisco Systems, Inc.; U.S. Public, pg. 498
CISCO SYSTEMS NEW ZEALAND LIMITED—See Cisco Systems, Inc.; U.S. Public, pg. 498
CISCO SYSTEMS NORWAY AS—See Cisco Systems, Inc.; U.S. Public, pg. 498
CISCO SYSTEMS PERU S.A.—See Cisco Systems, Inc.; U.S. Public, pg. 498
CISCO SYSTEMS POLAND SP. Z O.O.—See Cisco Systems, Inc.; U.S. Public, pg. 498

CISCO SYSTEMS PORTUGAL SISTEMAS INFORMATICOS SOCIEDADE UNIPESSOAL LTDA.—See Cisco Systems, Inc.; U.S. Public, pg. 498
CISCO SYSTEMS ROMANIA S.R.L.—See Cisco Systems, Inc.; U.S. Public, pg. 498
CISCO SYSTEMS (SCOTLAND) LIMITED—See Cisco Systems, Inc.; U.S. Public, pg. 497
CISCO SYSTEMS SLOVAKIA, SPOL. S R.O.—See Cisco Systems, Inc.; U.S. Public, pg. 498
CISCO SYSTEMS SOUTH KOREA—See Cisco Systems, Inc.; U.S. Public, pg. 499
CISCO SYSTEMS (SPAIN) S.L.—See Cisco Systems, Inc.; U.S. Public, pg. 497
CISCO SYSTEMS (SWEDEN) AB—See Cisco Systems, Inc.; U.S. Public, pg. 497
CISCO SYSTEMS (SWITZERLAND) GMBH—See Cisco Systems, Inc.; U.S. Public, pg. 497
CISCO SYSTEMS TAIWAN LTD.—See Cisco Systems, Inc.; U.S. Public, pg. 499
CISCO SYSTEMS (THAILAND) LTD.—See Cisco Systems, Inc.; U.S. Public, pg. 497
CISCO SYSTEMS VENEZUELA—See Cisco Systems, Inc.; U.S. Public, pg. 499
CISCO SYSTEMS VIETNAM LIMITED—See Cisco Systems, Inc.; U.S. Public, pg. 499
CISO GLOBAL, INC.; U.S. Public, pg. 501
CITECH CO., LTD.; Int'l, pg. 1619
CITIC NETWORKS CO., LTD.—See CITIC Group Corporation; Int'l, pg. 1621
CITI FUND SERVICES OHIO, INC.—See Citigroup Inc.; U.S. Public, pg. 502
CITILABS, INC.—See Bentley Systems, Inc.; U.S. Public, pg. 297
CLARANET LIMITED; Int'l, pg. 1642
CLEAREDGE IT SOLUTIONS, LLC.; U.S. Private, pg. 932
CLEARSHARK LLC—See KKR & Co. Inc.; U.S. Public, pg. 1262
CLEARSTREAM SERVICES S.A.—See Deutsche Borse AG; Int'l, pg. 2063
CLEARTECH BRASIL LTDA—See DXC Technology Company; U.S. Public, pg. 695
CLEARWATER COMPLIANCE LLC—See Altaris Capital Partners, LLC; U.S. Private, pg. 205
CLERITY SOLUTIONS, INC.—See Dell Technologies Inc.; U.S. Public, pg. 649
CLEVERMETHOD, INC.; U.S. Private, pg. 942
CLIENT RESOURCES, INC; U.S. Private, pg. 943
CLOUDCOCO GROUP PLC; Int'l, pg. 1662
CLOUD CREEK SYSTEMS, INC.; U.S. Private, pg. 946
CLOUDFLARE, INC.; U.S. Public, pg. 515
CLOUDIT, LLC; U.S. Private, pg. 947
CLOUDMARK, INC.—See Thoma Bravo, L.P.; U.S. Private, pg. 4151
CLOUDMARK LABS SARL—See Thoma Bravo, L.P.; U.S. Private, pg. 4151
CLOUD SHERPAS, INC.—See Accenture plc; Int'l, pg. 86
CLUB NETS CORPORATION—See Crest Investments Co., Ltd.; Int'l, pg. 1840
CLYDESTONE (GHANA) LIMITED; Int'l, pg. 1665
CMA CONSULTING SERVICES; U.S. Private, pg. 949
CMC SOLUTIONS INC.—See CMC Corporation; Int'l, pg. 1669
CMS COMPUTERS LIMITED—See CMS Computers Ltd.; Int'l, pg. 1672
COALFIRE SYSTEMS, INC.—See Apax Partners LLP; Int'l, pg. 503
CODEWORKS, INC.; U.S. Private, pg. 960
COFELY INEO - INEO ENGINEERING & SYSTEMS DIVISION—See ENGIE SA; Int'l, pg. 2430
COFINITY, INC.—See CVS Health Corporation; U.S. Public, pg. 614
COGDEV MALAYSIA SDN BHD—See Cognizant Technology Solutions Corporation; U.S. Public, pg. 523
COGNEX FRANCE—See Cognex Corporation; U.S. Public, pg. 523
COGNEX GERMANY, INC.—See Cognex Corporation; U.S. Public, pg. 523
COGNEX K.K.—See Cognex Corporation; U.S. Public, pg. 523
COGNITRAN INC.—See Snap-on Incorporated; U.S. Public, pg. 1897
COGNITRAN LIMITED—See Snap-on Incorporated; U.S. Public, pg. 1897
COGNITRAN SP. Z O.O.—See Snap-on Incorporated; U.S. Public, pg. 1897
COGNIX GROUP LTD.—See Datamatics Consultants Inc.; U.S. Private, pg. 1166
COGNIZANT CONSULTING AND SERVICES GMBH—See Cognizant Technology Solutions Corporation; U.S. Public, pg. 523
COGNIZANT JAPAN KK—See Cognizant Technology Solutions Corporation; U.S. Public, pg. 523
COGNIZANT MOBILITY GMBH—See Cognizant Technology Solutions Corporation; U.S. Public, pg. 523
COGNIZANT MORTGAGE SERVICES CORPORATION—See Cognizant Technology Solutions Corporation; U.S. Public, pg. 523

N.A.I.C.S. INDEX

541512 — COMPUTER SYSTEMS DE...

COGNIZANT TECHNOLOGY SOLUTIONS A.G.—See Cognizant Technology Solutions Corporation; *U.S. Public*, pg. 524
COGNIZANT TECHNOLOGY SOLUTIONS BENELUX B.V.—See Cognizant Technology Solutions Corporation; *U.S. Public*, pg. 524
COGNIZANT TECHNOLOGY SOLUTIONS INDIA PVT. LIMITED—See Cognizant Technology Solutions Corporation; *U.S. Public*, pg. 524
COGNIZANT TECHNOLOGY SOLUTIONS INDIA PVT. LTD.—See Cognizant Technology Solutions Corporation; *U.S. Public*, pg. 524
COGNIZANT TECHNOLOGY SOLUTIONS NEW ZEALAND LIMITED—See Cognizant Technology Solutions Corporation; *U.S. Public*, pg. 524
COHESIVE INFORMATION SOLUTIONS, INC.; *U.S. Private*, pg. 963
COHORT PLC; *Int'l*, pg. 1695
COLEMAN & ASSOCIATES ENTERPRISES, INC.; *U.S. Private*, pg. 966
COLLECT ARTIFICIAL INTELLIGENCE GMBH—See Advent International Corporation; *U.S. Private*, pg. 96
COLLECT ARTIFICIAL INTELLIGENCE GMBH—See Centerbridge Partners, L.P.; *U.S. Private*, pg. 812
THE COLLECTIVE GROUP, LLC; *U.S. Private*, pg. 4011
COLOPLAST BUSINESS CENTRE SP. Z O.O.—See Coloplast A/S; *Int'l*, pg. 1703
COLORADO INTERACTIVE, LLC—See Tyler Technologies, Inc.; *U.S. Public*, pg. 2208
COLSA CORPORATION; *U.S. Private*, pg. 975
COMA SERVICES AG—See Bechtle AG; *Int'l*, pg. 937
COMBINEDX AB; *Int'l*, pg. 1709
COMCAVE AG—See Gilde Buy Out Partners B.V.; *Int'l*, pg. 2974
COMF5 INTERNATIONAL, INC.; *U.S. Public*, pg. 542
COMMAND INFORMATION, INC.—See Bridge Growth Partners, LLC; *U.S. Private*, pg. 649
COMMAND INFORMATION, INC.—See Frontenac Company LLC; *U.S. Private*, pg. 1614
COMMERZ GLOBAL SERVICE SOLUTIONS SDN. BHD.—See Commerzbank AG; *Int'l*, pg. 1716
COMMERZ SYSTEMS GMBH—See Commerzbank AG; *Int'l*, pg. 1716
COMM NET INTERNATIONAL INC.; *U.S. Private*, pg. 982
COMMON ANGLE, INC.; *U.S. Private*, pg. 985
COMMUNICATIONS ENGINEERING CO.; *U.S. Private*, pg. 988
COMMUNITY COMPUTER SERVICE; *U.S. Private*, pg. 991
COMPACT SOLUTIONS LLC—See Canada Pension Plan Investment Board; *Int'l*, pg. 1279
COMPETITIVE INNOVATIONS, LLC; *U.S. Private*, pg. 1000
COMPETITIVE RANGE SOLUTIONS, LLC; *U.S. Private*, pg. 1000
COMPLETE DISCOVERY SOURCE, INC.; *U.S. Private*, pg. 1000
COMPLIANCE SCIENCE, INC.; *U.S. Private*, pg. 1001
COMPLY365, LLC—See Liberty Hall Capital Partners, L.P.; *U.S. Private*, pg. 2444
COMPREHENSIVE COMPUTER CONSULTING, INC.; *U.S. Private*, pg. 1003
COMPROBASE, INC.; *U.S. Private*, pg. 1003
COMPTA - EQUIPAMENTOS E SERVICOS DE INFORMATICA, S.A.; *Int'l*, pg. 1754
COMPUTACENTER FRANCE S.A.—See Computacenter plc; *Int'l*, pg. 1758
COMPUTACENTER GMBH—See Computacenter plc; *Int'l*, pg. 1758
COMPUTACENTER HOLDING GMBH—See Computacenter plc; *Int'l*, pg. 1758
COMPUTACENTER NV/SA—See Computacenter plc; *Int'l*, pg. 1758
COMPUTACENTER PSF SA—See Computacenter plc; *Int'l*, pg. 1758
COMPUTACENTER (UK) LTD.—See Computacenter plc; *Int'l*, pg. 1758
COMPUTER AND TECHNOLOGIES INTERNATIONAL LIMITED—See Computer & Technologies Holdings Limited; *Int'l*, pg. 1758
COMPUTER CONCEPTS OF IOWA, INC.—See ICE Technologies, Inc.; *U.S. Private*, pg. 2031
COMPUTER DIRECT GROUP LTD.; *Int'l*, pg. 1759
COMPUTER ENTERPRISES INC.; *U.S. Private*, pg. 1004
COMPUTER GENERATED SOLUTIONS CANADA LTD.—See Computer Generated Solutions Inc.; *U.S. Private*, pg. 1005
COMPUTER GENERATED SOLUTIONS INC.; *U.S. Private*, pg. 1004
COMPUTER GENERATED SOLUTIONS INDIA PVT LTD—See Computer Generated Solutions Inc.; *U.S. Private*, pg. 1005
COMPUTER GENERATED SOLUTIONS ROMANIA—See Computer Generated Solutions Inc.; *U.S. Private*, pg. 1005
COMPUTER INSTITUTE OF JAPAN LTD.; *Int'l*, pg. 1759
COMPUTERLAND UK LTD.—See Capita plc; *Int'l*, pg. 1309
COMPUTER MANAGEMENT CO., LTD.; *Int'l*, pg. 1759
THE COMPUTER MERCHANT LTD.; *U.S. Private*, pg. 4013
COMPUTER MIND CO., LTD.; *Int'l*, pg. 1759

COMPUTER OPTIONS INC.; *U.S. Private*, pg. 1005
COMPUTER POINT LIMITED; *Int'l*, pg. 1760
COMPUTER SCIENCES CORPORATION SERVICES (PTY) LIMITED—See DXC Technology Company; *U.S. Public*, pg. 695
COMPUTER SCIENCES CORPORATION—See DXC Technology Company; *U.S. Public*, pg. 695
COMPUTER SCIENCES CORPORATION—See DXC Technology Company; *U.S. Public*, pg. 695
COMPUTER & TECHNOLOGIES HOLDINGS LIMITED; *Int'l*, pg. 1758
COMPUTER & TECHNOLOGIES INTEGRATION LIMITED—See Computer & Technologies Holdings Limited; *Int'l*, pg. 1758
COMPUTER & TECHNOLOGIES (SHANGHAI) CO., LTD—See Computer & Technologies Holdings Limited; *Int'l*, pg. 1758
COMPUTER TROUBLESHOOTERS W.L.L.—See Gulf Franchising Holding Company K.S.C.C.; *Int'l*, pg. 3180
COMPUTING TECHNOLOGIES INC.; *U.S. Private*, pg. 1006
COMPUWAVE INC.; *U.S. Private*, pg. 1006
COMSOFT DIRECT B.V—See Bechtle AG; *Int'l*, pg. 938
COMSOFT DIRECT GMBH—See Bechtle AG; *Int'l*, pg. 938
COMSOFT DIRECT S.L.U.—See Bechtle AG; *Int'l*, pg. 938
COMSOFT DIRECT S.R.L—See Bechtle AG; *Int'l*, pg. 938
COMSOFT SOS DEVELOPERS SAS—See Bechtle AG; *Int'l*, pg. 937
COMTEC SYSTEMS CO., LTD.; *Int'l*, pg. 1762
COMTRADE D.O.O.—See ComTrade Group B.V.; *Int'l*, pg. 1762
COMTREX SYSTEMS CORPORATION—See Zonal Hospitality Systems Inc.; *U.S. Private*, pg. 4608
COMTURE CORPORATION; *Int'l*, pg. 1762
COMYMEDIA PROYECTOS Y SERVICIOS SL—See Gamma Communications PLC; *Int'l*, pg. 2878
CONCENTRIX SREV, INC.—See Concentrix Corporation; *U.S. Public*, pg. 564
CONCEPT TECHNOLOGY INC.; *U.S. Private*, pg. 1009
CONCURRENT FEDERAL SYSTEMS, INC.—See CCUR Holdings Inc.; *U.S. Public*, pg. 461
CONFIDENTIA - TECNOLOGIAS INFORMATICAS APLICADAS, LTDA.—See Eurofins Scientific S.E.; *Int'l*, pg. 2535
CONFIGURA SVERIGE AB; *Int'l*, pg. 1768
CONNECTENS B.V.; *Int'l*, pg. 1769
CONNECTIS ICT SERVICES S.A.—See Aurelius Equity Opportunities SE & Co. KGaA; *Int'l*, pg. 708
CONNECTIS ICT SERVICES S.A.U.—See Aurelius Equity Opportunities SE & Co. KGaA; *Int'l*, pg. 708
CONNECTIVE TECHNOLOGIES, INC.—See Ebix Inc.; *U.S. Public*, pg. 710
CONNECTIVITY TECHNOLOGIES—See Methode Electronics, Inc.; *U.S. Public*, pg. 1428
CONNECTSHIP, INC.—See United Parcel Service, Inc.; *U.S. Public*, pg. 2233
CONNECT THE KNOWLEDGE NETWORK CORP.—See Asseco Poland S.A.; *Int'l*, pg. 642
CONQUEST SYSTEMS, INC.; *U.S. Private*, pg. 1018
CONSTELLATION SOFTWARE ENGINEERING, CORP.; *U.S. Private*, pg. 1023
CONSULTANTS IN BUSINESS ENGINEERING AND RESEARCH SWEDEN AB—See Bouvet ASA; *Int'l*, pg. 1121
CONTEC DTX INC.—See Daifuku Co., Ltd.; *Int'l*, pg. 1924
CONTENT MANAGEMENT CONSULTING APS; *Int'l*, pg. 1779
CONTINUUM MANAGED SERVICES LLC—See Thoma Bravo, L.P.; *U.S. Private*, pg. 4146
CONTINUUM WORLDWIDE CORPORATION—See CDW Corporation; *U.S. Public*, pg. 462
CONTROLCIRCLE LTD.; *Int'l*, pg. 1786
CONTROL GROUP, INC.—See Titan; *U.S. Private*, pg. 4176
CONTROL SOLUTIONS, INC.; *U.S. Private*, pg. 1034
CONVERGENCE TECHNOLOGY CONSULTING, LLC; *U.S. Private*, pg. 1035
CONVERGENZ, LLC; *U.S. Private*, pg. 1035
CONVERGYS NETHERLANDS LLC—See Concentrix Corporation; *U.S. Public*, pg. 565
CORE BTS, INC.—See Tailwind Capital Group, LLC; *U.S. Private*, pg. 3924
CORE BTS INC.—See Tailwind Capital Group, LLC; *U.S. Private*, pg. 3924
CORELOGIC SARL—See Insight Venture Management, LLC; *U.S. Private*, pg. 2089
CORELOGIC SARL—See Stone Point Capital LLC; *U.S. Private*, pg. 3822
CORENET INTERNATIONAL CO., LTD.—See Core Corporation; *Int'l*, pg. 1797
CORE PROJECTS AND TECHNOLOGIES LTD.—See Core Education and Technologies Ltd.; *Int'l*, pg. 1798
CORETELLIGENT LLC—See Wells Fargo & Company; *U.S. Public*, pg. 2344
CORLIANT, INC.—See Accenture plc; *Int'l*, pg. 86
CORNERSTONE INFORMATION TECHNOLOGIES, LLC; *U.S. Private*, pg. 1052
CORNING DATA SERVICES INC.; *U.S. Private*, pg. 1053
COROUS360 SDN. BHD.—See EXEO Group Inc.; *Int'l*, pg. 2583
CORPORACION TECNOLOGA GLOBAL 21, C.A.—See Abbott Laboratories; *U.S. Public*, pg. 20
CORPORATE TECHNOLOGIES LLC—See Tonka Bay Equity Partners LLC; *U.S. Private*, pg. 4184
CORPUS MEDIA LABS, INC.; *U.S. Private*, pg. 1058
COURIER TECHNOLOGIA EM SERVICOS GRAFICOS LTDA—See Chatham Asset Management, LLC; *U.S. Private*, pg. 863
COURT SQUARE GROUP; *U.S. Public*, pg. 1070
COVANSYS S.L.—See DXC Technology Company; *U.S. Public*, pg. 695
COVESTIC, INC.—See H.I.G. Capital, LLC; *U.S. Private*, pg. 1831
COYOTE TECHNOLOGIES INC.—See Gefen International A.I Ltd.; *Int'l*, pg. 2911
CPM BRAXIS ERP TECNOLOGIA DA INFORMACAO LTDA.—See Capgemini SE; *Int'l*, pg. 1303
CPM BRAXIS USA CORP.—See Capgemini SE; *Int'l*, pg. 1303
CPT NETWORK SOLUTIONS; *U.S. Private*, pg. 1081
CRAIG TECHNOLOGIES; *U.S. Private*, pg. 1083
CRC INTERNATIONAL INC.; *U.S. Private*, pg. 1087
CREATE LAB CO., LTD.—See CREO CO., LTD.; *Int'l*, pg. 1838
CREATIVE INFORMATION TECHNOLOGY, INC.; *U.S. Private*, pg. 1089
CREATIVE LABS, INC. - LATIN AMERICA—See Creative Technology Ltd.; *Int'l*, pg. 1833
CREATIVE REALITIES, INC.; *U.S. Public*, pg. 593
CREDATIV GMBH—See NetApp, Inc.; *U.S. Public*, pg. 1507
CREDERA; *U.S. Private*, pg. 1091
CRESCO E-SOLUTION CO. LTD.—See Cresco, Ltd.; *Int'l*, pg. 1840
CRESSANDA SOLUTIONS LIMITED; *Int'l*, pg. 1840
CRESTEC INFORMATION TECHNOLOGY (SHENZHEN) LIMITED—See Crestec Inc.; *Int'l*, pg. 1841
CRG INC.; *U.S. Private*, pg. 1100
CROSS CAT CO., LTD.; *Int'l*, pg. 1855
CROSS MATCH TECHNOLOGIES GMBH—See ASSA ABLOY AB; *Int'l*, pg. 637
CROSS MATCH TECHNOLOGIES, INC. - REDWOOD CITY—See ASSA ABLOY AB; *Int'l*, pg. 637
CROSS MATCH TECHNOLOGIES, INC.—See ASSA ABLOY AB; *Int'l*, pg. 637
CROSSUSA, INC.—See American CyberSystems, Inc.; *U.S. Private*, pg. 229
CR SOFTWARE LLC—See Fair Isaac Corporation; *U.S. Public*, pg. 820
CRYPTOGRAPHY RESEARCH, INC.—See Rambus Inc.; *U.S. Public*, pg. 1762
CRYSTAL GROUP, INC.—See Dexter Apache Holdings, Inc.; *U.S. Private*, pg. 1220
CSB-AUTOMATION AG—See CSB-System AG; *Int'l*, pg. 1862
CSB SERVICES ASIA PACIFIC PVT. LTD—See CSB-System AG; *Int'l*, pg. 1862
CSB-SYSTEM AG; *Int'l*, pg. 1861
CSB-SYSTEM AUSTRIA GMBH—See CSB-System AG; *Int'l*, pg. 1862
CSB-SYSTEM BENELUX BV—See CSB-System AG; *Int'l*, pg. 1862
CSB-SYSTEM BULGARIA EGMBH—See CSB-System AG; *Int'l*, pg. 1862
CSB-SYSTEM D.O.O.—See CSB-System AG; *Int'l*, pg. 1862
CSB-SYSTEM ESPANA S.L.—See CSB-System AG; *Int'l*, pg. 1862
CSB-SYSTEM HUNGARY KFT.—See CSB-System AG; *Int'l*, pg. 1862
CSB-SYSTEM INTERNATIONAL, INC.—See CSB-System AG; *Int'l*, pg. 1862
CSB-SYSTEM INTERNATIONAL, INC.—See CSB-System AG; *Int'l*, pg. 1862
CSB-SYSTEM POLSKA SP.Z.O.O.—See CSB-System AG; *Int'l*, pg. 1862
CSB-SYSTEM ROMANIA SRL—See CSB-System AG; *Int'l*, pg. 1862
CSB-SYSTEM S.R.L.—See CSB-System AG; *Int'l*, pg. 1862
CSC COMPUTER SCIENCES BRASIL S/A—See DXC Technology Company; *U.S. Public*, pg. 695
CSC COMPUTER SCIENCES LIMITED—See DXC Technology Company; *U.S. Public*, pg. 695
CSC COMPUTER SCIENCES S.A.—See DXC Technology Company; *U.S. Public*, pg. 695
CSC JAPAN, LTD.—See DXC Technology Company; *U.S. Public*, pg. 695
CS CONSULTING GMBH—See Capgemini SE; *Int'l*, pg. 1303
CSE COMMUNICATIONS & SECURITY SDN BHD—See CSE Global Ltd.; *Int'l*, pg. 1863
CSE-EIS (MALAYSIA) SDN BHD—See CSE Global Ltd.; *Int'l*, pg. 1863
CSE-GLOBAL (AUSTRALIA), LTD.—See CSE Global Ltd.; *Int'l*, pg. 1863
CSE GLOBAL LTD.; *Int'l*, pg. 1863
CSE-HANKIN (CHINA) CO., LTD.—See CSE Global Ltd.; *Int'l*, pg. 1863
CSE ICON, INC.—See CSE Global Ltd.; *Int'l*, pg. 1863
CSE-SERVELEC LIMITED—See CSE Global Ltd.; *Int'l*, pg. 1863

CSE-UNISERVE PTY LIMITED—See CSE Global Ltd.; *Int'l*, pg. 1863
CSE W-INDUSTRIES NIGERIA LTD.—See CSE Global Ltd.; *Int'l*, pg. 1863
CSF, INC.—See Iconectiv, LLC; *U.S. Private*, pg. 2032
CSP INC.; *U.S. Public*, pg. 601
CSSI INC.; *U.S. Private*, pg. 1118
CSSS.NET; *U.S. Private*, pg. 1118
CSW SUPERIOR IT SOLUTIONS, INC.—See Summit 7 Systems, LLC; *U.S. Private*, pg. 3853
CTAC BELGIE N.V.—See Ctac N.V.; *Int'l*, pg. 1869
CTAC BELGIUM BVBA—See Ctac N.V.; *Int'l*, pg. 1869
CTAC DEUTSCHLAND GMBH—See Ctac N.V.; *Int'l*, pg. 1869
CTAC FRANCE SAS—See Ctac N.V.; *Int'l*, pg. 1869
C&T CONSULTING SERVICES LLP; *U.S. Private*, pg. 704
CTI SUPPLY, INC.—See Yunhong Green CTI Ltd.; *U.S. Public*, pg. 2400
CTP SYSTEM SRL—See Adecco Group AG; *Int'l*, pg. 139
CUBE LABS S.P.A.; *Int'l*, pg. 1875
CUBE MANAGEMENT GMBH—See Allgeier SE; *Int'l*, pg. 337
CUBE SYSTEM INC.; *Int'l*, pg. 1875
CUBE SYSTEM VIETNAM CO., LTD.—See Cube System Inc.; *Int'l*, pg. 1875
CUBIC APPLICATIONS, INC.—See Elliott Management Corporation; *U.S. Private*, pg. 1367
CUBIC APPLICATIONS, INC.—See Veritas Capital Fund Management, LLC; *U.S. Private*, pg. 4361
CUBIC TRANSPORTATION SYSTEMS (INDIA) PVT. LIMITED—See Elliott Management Corporation; *U.S. Private*, pg. 1368
CUBIC TRANSPORTATION SYSTEMS (INDIA) PVT. LIMITED—See Veritas Capital Fund Management, LLC; *U.S. Private*, pg. 4362
CUCULUS GMBH—See E.ON SE; *Int'l*, pg. 2251
CUMULUS IT AS—See Hafslund ASA; *Int'l*, pg. 3206
CURTISS-WRIGHT CONTROLS DEFENSE SOLUTIONS - OTTAWA—See Curtiss-Wright Corporation; *U.S. Public*, pg. 611
CUSTOM COMPUTER SPECIALISTS, LLC; *U.S. Private*, pg. 1128
CWPS, INC.; *U.S. Private*, pg. 1132
CXD NEXT CO., LTD.—See Casio Computer Co., Ltd.; *Int'l*, pg. 1353
CY4GATE S.P.A.; *Int'l*, pg. 1891
CYBERCOM FINLAND—See Formica Capital Holding AB; *Int'l*, pg. 2734
CYBERCOM POLAND SP.ZO.O.—See Formica Capital Holding AB; *Int'l*, pg. 2734
CYBERCOM SWEDEN - GOTHENBURG—See Formica Capital Holding AB; *Int'l*, pg. 2734
CYBERCORE TECHNOLOGIES LLC—See Moelis Asset Management LP; *U.S. Private*, pg. 2764
CYBERNET SYSTEMS CO., LTD.—See FUJISOFT INCORPORATED; *Int'l*, pg. 2830
CYBER OPERATIONS, INC.; *U.S. Private*, pg. 1133
CYBERTECH INFORMATION SERVICES LTD. UK—See CyberTech Systems Inc.; *U.S. Private*, pg. 1133
CYBERTECH SYSTEMS INC.; *U.S. Private*, pg. 1133
CYBERTECH SYSTEMS & SOFTWARE INC.—See CyberTech Systems Inc.; *U.S. Private*, pg. 1133
CYBERTROL ENGINEERING, LLC; *U.S. Private*, pg. 1134
THE CYBRIX GROUP, INC.; *U.S. Private*, pg. 4017
CYIOS CORPORATION; *U.S. Public*, pg. 617
CYQUENT, INC.; *U.S. Private*, pg. 1135
CYRADAR JOINT STOCK COMPANY LTD.—See FPT Corporation; *Int'l*, pg. 2757
CYVIZ AS; *Int'l*, pg. 1898
DAELIM I&S CO., LTD.—See Daelim Industrial Co., Ltd.; *Int'l*, pg. 1908
DAGANG NEXCHANGE BERHAD; *Int'l*, pg. 1912
DA INFORMATION CO., LTD.—See Dong-A Socio Holdings Co., Ltd.; *Int'l*, pg. 2164
DAIWA INSTITUTE OF RESEARCH LTD.—See Daiwa Securities Group Inc.; *Int'l*, pg. 1948
DANAOS PERIPHERALS S.A.—See Danaos Corporation; *Int'l*, pg. 1958
DAOU TECHNOLOGY, INC.; *Int'l*, pg. 1970
DARKTRACE HOLDINGS LIMITED—See Thoma Bravo, L.P.; *U.S. Private*, pg. 4147
DARKTRACE PLC—See Thoma Bravo, L.P.; *U.S. Private*, pg. 4147
DARTNELL ENTERPRISES INC.; *U.S. Private*, pg. 1160
DASI SOLUTIONS, LLC; *U.S. Private*, pg. 1162
DASSAULT SYSTEMES CANADA INNOVATION TECHNOLOGIES INC.—See Dassault Systemes S.A.; *Int'l*, pg. 1974
DATA BLUE LLC—See Court Square Capital Partners, L.P.; *U.S. Private*, pg. 1068
DATA CANOPY COLOCATION LLC—See Intelishift Technologies; *U.S. Private*, pg. 2104
DATACENTRIX HOLDINGS LIMITED—See Alviva Holdings Limited; *Int'l*, pg. 402
DATACEP SA—See Capgemini SE; *Int'l*, pg. 1305
DATACOLOR AG; *Int'l*, pg. 1977
DATACOMM NETWORKS, INC.; *U.S. Private*, pg. 1165

DATA COMPUTER CORPORATION OF AMERICA; *U.S. Private*, pg. 1162
DATA CONNECT CORP.—See Predictive Safety LLC; *U.S. Private*, pg. 3247
DATAGILITY, INC.—See Industry Data Exchange Association, Inc.; *U.S. Private*, pg. 2069
DATA INDUSTRIES LTD.; *U.S. Private*, pg. 1163
DATA INTEGRITY INC.; *Int'l*, pg. 1976
DATALAB AL SH.P.K.—See Datalab Tehnologije d.d.; *Int'l*, pg. 1977
DATALINK CORPORATION—See Insight Enterprises, Inc.; *U.S. Public*, pg. 1129
DATALOGIC JAPAN CO., LTD.—See Datalogic S.p.A.; *Int'l*, pg. 1978
DATAMATICS CONSULTANTS INC.; *U.S. Private*, pg. 1166
DATAMIRROR CORPORATION—See International Business Machines Corporation; *U.S. Public*, pg. 1148
DATA MODUL LTD.—See Data Modul AG; *Int'l*, pg. 1976
DATA NETWORKS OF AMERICA INC.; *U.S. Private*, pg. 1163
DATANOMICS INC.; *U.S. Private*, pg. 1166
DATA PATH; *U.S. Private*, pg. 1163
DATAPROCES GROUP A/S; *Int'l*, pg. 1979
DATA PROCESSING SCIENCES CORPORATION; *U.S. Private*, pg. 1163
DATAPRO, INC.—See Constellation Software Inc.; *Int'l*, pg. 1775
DATAPULSE LIMITED—See Enghouse Systems Limited; *Int'l*, pg. 2427
DATA RESPONS SYREN AB—See Adecco Group AG; *Int'l*, pg. 140
DATASTRONG, LLC—See OceanSound Partners, LP; *U.S. Private*, pg. 2992
DATATEC MANAGEMENT SERVICES (PTY) LIMITED—See Datatec Limited; *Int'l*, pg. 1980
DATATREND TECHNOLOGIES, INC.—See Converge Technology Solutions Corp.; *Int'l*, pg. 1787
DATAWIZ CORPORATION; *U.S. Private*, pg. 1167
DATAXU, INC.—See Roku, Inc.; *U.S. Public*, pg. 1808
DATEC TECHNOLOGIES, LTD.—See Belmont Trading Company; *U.S. Private*, pg. 521
DATEC TECHNOLOGIES, LTD.—See SiPi Metals Corp.; *U.S. Private*, pg. 3671
DAUGHERTY SYSTEMS INC.; *U.S. Private*, pg. 1167
DBA KNOWLEDGE, INC.; *U.S. Private*, pg. 1178
DB KOMMUNIKATIONSTECHNIK GMBH—See Deutsche Bahn AG; *Int'l*, pg. 2050
DB MOBILITY SERVICES AUSTRIA GMBH—See Deutsche Bahn AG; *Int'l*, pg. 2050
DBMOTION, INC.—See Veradigm Inc.; *U.S. Public*, pg. 2280
DB PROFESSIONALS, INC.; *U.S. Private*, pg. 1178
DB TECHNOLOGY, INC.—See Dura Software Series A Qof LLC; *U.S. Private*, pg. 1292
DCM DATA SYSTEMS LIMITED—See DCM Limited; *Int'l*, pg. 1992
DCOM CO., LTD.—See Bain Capital, LP; *U.S. Private*, pg. 434
DCS CORPORATION; *U.S. Private*, pg. 1180
DCS GROUP PLC—See The Reynolds & Reynolds Company; *U.S. Private*, pg. 4106
DC VALUE ADDED SERVICE TECHNOLOGY; *U.S. Private*, pg. 1179
DECENTRAL LIFE, INC.; *U.S. Public*, pg. 645
DECIBEL RESEARCH, INC.; *U.S. Private*, pg. 1187
DECISIONPOINT SYSTEMS CA, INC.—See The Graham Group, Inc.; *U.S. Private*, pg. 4036
DECISIONPOINT SYSTEMS CT, INC.—See The Graham Group, Inc.; *U.S. Private*, pg. 4036
DECISIONPOINT SYSTEMS, INC.—See The Graham Group, Inc.; *U.S. Private*, pg. 4036
DELCAM FRANCE—See Autodesk, Inc.; *U.S. Public*, pg. 229
DELCAM ITALIA S.R.L.—See Autodesk, Inc.; *U.S. Public*, pg. 229
DELCAM JAPAN KABUSHIKI KAISYA—See Autodesk, Inc.; *U.S. Public*, pg. 229
DELL INC. - FREMONT—See Dell Technologies Inc.; *U.S. Public*, pg. 649
DELTA CLEANTECH INC.; *Int'l*, pg. 2015
DELTA PROJECTS GMBH—See Azerion Group N.V.; *Int'l*, pg. 778
DELTA TECHNOLOGY INC.—See Delta Air Lines, Inc.; *U.S. Public*, pg. 651
DELTEQ SYSTEMS (M) SDN BHD—See Digilife Technologies Limited; *Int'l*, pg. 2119
DEMAE-CAN CO., LTD.; *Int'l*, pg. 2022
DENALI ADVANCED INTEGRATION, INC.; *U.S. Private*, pg. 1204
DENSAN SYSTEM CO., LTD.; *Int'l*, pg. 2028
DENSO IT SOLUTIONS, INC.—See Denso Corporation; *Int'l*, pg. 2029
DENSO SI CORPORATION—See Denso Corporation; *Int'l*, pg. 2030
DENTSU SOKEN INC—See Dentsu Group Inc.; *Int'l*, pg. 2038
DESAI SYSTEMS INC.; *U.S. Private*, pg. 1210
DESARROLLO INFORMATICO, S.A.—See ACS, Actividades de Construccion y Servicios, S.A.; *Int'l*, pg. 111

DEUTSCHE POST DHL INHOUSE CONSULTING GMBH—See Deutsche Post AG; *Int'l*, pg. 2079
DEUTSCHE POST IT BRIEF GMBH—See Deutsche Post AG; *Int'l*, pg. 2079
DEUTSCHE POST IT SERVICES GMBH—See Deutsche Post AG; *Int'l*, pg. 2079
DEV DIGITAL LLC; *U.S. Private*, pg. 1217
DEVOTEAM CONSULTING GMBH—See Devoteam SA; *Int'l*, pg. 2089
DEVOTEAM DAVINCI AS—See Devoteam SA; *Int'l*, pg. 2089
DEVOTEAM GENESIS AG—See Devoteam SA; *Int'l*, pg. 2089
DEVOTEAM GUIDANCE S.A.—See Devoteam SA; *Int'l*, pg. 2090
DEVOTEAM INTEGRA—See Devoteam SA; *Int'l*, pg. 2090
DEVOTEAM MIDDLE EAST—See Devoteam SA; *Int'l*, pg. 2090
DEVOTEAM MOROCCO—See Devoteam SA; *Int'l*, pg. 2090
DEVOTEAM NEDERLAND BV—See Devoteam SA; *Int'l*, pg. 2090
DEVOTEAM SECURA—See Devoteam SA; *Int'l*, pg. 2090
DEVOTEAM SPAIN—See Devoteam SA; *Int'l*, pg. 2090
DEVOTEAM S.R.O.—See Devoteam SA; *Int'l*, pg. 2090
DEVOTEAM TELIGENT—See Devoteam SA; *Int'l*, pg. 2090
DEVOTEAM UK LTD.—See Devoteam SA; *Int'l*, pg. 2090
DEWPOINT, INC.; *U.S. Private*, pg. 1220
DHI COMPUTING SERVICE INCORPORATED; *U.S. Private*, pg. 1221
DIALMARK, LLC—See The Beekman Group, LLC; *U.S. Private*, pg. 3993
DIAMOND INFOSYSTEMS LTD; *Int'l*, pg. 2105
DIGIA FINLAND OY—See Digia Plc; *Int'l*, pg. 2118
DIGI INTERNATIONAL GMBH—See Digi International Inc.; *U.S. Public*, pg. 662
DIGI INTERNATIONAL (HK) LTD.—See Digi International Inc.; *U.S. Public*, pg. 662
DIGI INTERNATIONAL KABUSHIKIKAISHA—See Digi International Inc.; *U.S. Public*, pg. 662
DIGI INTERNATIONAL SARL—See Digi International Inc.; *U.S. Public*, pg. 662
DIGI M2M SOLUTIONS INDIA PVT. LTD.—See Digi International Inc.; *U.S. Public*, pg. 662
DIGISTAR CORPORATION BERHAD; *Int'l*, pg. 2120
DIGITAL CHINA LIMITED—See Digital China Holdings Limited; *Int'l*, pg. 2121
DIGITAL CHINA MACAO COMMERCIAL OFFSHORE LIMITED—See Digital China Holdings Limited; *Int'l*, pg. 2121
DIGITAL CONNECTIONS, INC.; *U.S. Private*, pg. 1230
DIGITAL HANDS, LLC; *U.S. Private*, pg. 1230
DIGITAL VIDEO NETWORKS LLC—See Marlin Equity Partners, LLC; *U.S. Private*, pg. 2583
DIGITAL WEST NETWORKS, INC.—See Stonepeak Partners L.P.; *U.S. Private*, pg. 3829
DIGITAL WORKFORCE SERVICES PLC; *Int'l*, pg. 2123
DIRECT COMMUNICATION SOLUTIONS, INC.; *U.S. Public*, pg. 667
DISPATCH TECHNOLOGIES, INC.; *U.S. Private*, pg. 1238
DIS SERVICE & SOLUTION CO., LTD.—See Daiwabo Holdings Co., Ltd.; *Int'l*, pg. 1949
DIVERSE LYNX, LLC; *U.S. Private*, pg. 1240
DIVERSIFIED SPECIALTIES, INC.; *U.S. Private*, pg. 1243
DIZBI PRIVATE LIMITED; *Int'l*, pg. 2138
DKSH CORPORATE SHARED SERVICES CENTER SDN. BHD.—See Diethelm Keller Holding Limited; *Int'l*, pg. 2116
DK UNC CO., LTD.—See Dongkuk Steel Mill Co., Ltd.; *Int'l*, pg. 2169
DKW COMMUNICATIONS INC.; *U.S. Private*, pg. 1247
DLT SOLUTIONS, LLC—See TD Synnex Corp; *U.S. Public*, pg. 1985
DNP DIGITALCOM CO., LTD.—See Dai Nippon Printing Co., Ltd.; *Int'l*, pg. 1914
DOMAIN TECHNOLOGY PARTNERS, INC.—See Frontenac Company LLC; *U.S. Private*, pg. 1613
DOMINION DIGITAL, INC.; *U.S. Private*, pg. 1256
DONGBU HITEK FABRICATION 1—See Dongbu Group; *Int'l*, pg. 2166
DONGBU INC.—See Dongbu Group; *Int'l*, pg. 2166
DOWNUNDER GEOSOLUTIONS (AMERICA) LLC—See DUG Technology Ltd.; *Int'l*, pg. 2223
DOWNUNDER GEOSOLUTIONS (ASIA) SDN. BHD.—See DUG Technology Ltd.; *Int'l*, pg. 2223
DOWNUNDER GEOSOLUTIONS (LONDON) PTY LTD.—See DUG Technology Ltd.; *Int'l*, pg. 2223
DRAGONFLY TECHNOLOGIES PTY. LTD.—See Black Box Limited; *Int'l*, pg. 1058
DRAGONPLAY LTD—See Light & Wonder, Inc.; *U.S. Public*, pg. 1314
DRB SYSTEMS, LLC—See New Mountain Capital, LLC; *U.S. Private*, pg. 2900
DREAMSCAPE NETWORKS LIMITED; *Int'l*, pg. 2203
DR. FOODS, INC.; *Int'l*, pg. 2191
DRIVEN, INC.; *U.S. Private*, pg. 1278
DRONEACHARYA AERIAL INNOVATIONS LIMITED; *Int'l*, pg. 2206

541512 — COMPUTER SYSTEMS DE...

DROPMYSITE PTE. LTD.—See Dropsuite Limited; *Int'l*, pg. 2206
DSS, INC.; *U.S. Public*, pg. 689
DST GLOBAL SOLUTIONS S.A. (PROPRIETARY) LTD—See SS&C Technologies Holdings, Inc.; *U.S. Public*, pg. 1923
DST GLOBAL SOLUTIONS SHANGHAI LIMITED—See SS&C Technologies Holdings, Inc.; *U.S. Public*, pg. 1923
DTS CORPORATION; *Int'l*, pg. 2217
DTS (SHANGHAI) CORPORATION—See DTS Corporation; *Int'l*, pg. 2217
DUDIGITAL GLOBAL LIMITED; *Int'l*, pg. 2223
DURR IT SERVICE GMBH—See Durr AG; *Int'l*, pg. 2231
DUSTIN FINLAND OY—See Dustin Group AB; *Int'l*, pg. 2235
DWS LIMITED; *Int'l*, pg. 2236
DXC CONNECT PTY LTD—See DXC Technology Company; *U.S. Public*, pg. 695
DXC TECHNOLOGY BULGARIA E.O.O.D.—See DXC Technology Company; *U.S. Public*, pg. 695
DXC TECHNOLOGY DEUTSCHLAND GMBH—See DXC Technology Company; *U.S. Public*, pg. 695
DXC TECHNOLOGY SERVICES VIETNAM COMPANY LIMITED—See DXC Technology Company; *U.S. Public*, pg. 696
DXC TECHONOLOGY INFORMATION SERVICES SLOVAKIA S.R.O.—See DXC Technology Company; *U.S. Public*, pg. 696
DYNACONS SYSTEMS & SOLUTIONS LTD.; *Int'l*, pg. 2239
DYNAMIC DISPLAYS, INC.; *U.S. Private*, pg. 1298
DYNAMICSIGNALS LLC; *U.S. Private*, pg. 1299
DYNAMICS RESOURCES INC.—See Sverica Capital Management LP; *U.S. Private*, pg. 3889
DYNAMIX GROUP INC.; *U.S. Private*, pg. 1299
DYNAMORE NORDIC AB—See ANSYS, Inc.; *U.S. Public*, pg. 139
E2E NETWORKS LIMITED; *Int'l*, pg. 2260
E2OPEN PARENT HOLDINGS, INC.—See Insight Venture Management, LLC; *U.S. Private*, pg. 2090
EABI CONSULTING SAS—See ManpowerGroup Inc.; *U.S. Public*, pg. 1360
EAGLE CREEK SOFTWARE SERVICES, INC.—See Atos SE; *Int'l*, pg. 692
EAI DESIGN SERVICES, LLC—See ViaSat, Inc.; *U.S. Public*, pg. 2291
EAI TECHNOLOGIES, LLC; *U.S. Private*, pg. 1312
EALIXIR, INC.; *U.S. Public*, pg. 703
EA MSC SDN. BHD.—See EA Holdings Berhad; *Int'l*, pg. 2261
EARLYWORKS CO., LTD.; *Int'l*, pg. 2267
EASTRIDGE TECHNOLOGY, INC.—See SHI International Corp.; *U.S. Private*, pg. 3635
EASY INTERNATIONAL CONSULTING GMBH—See Easy Software AG; *Int'l*, pg. 2275
EASYVISTA INC.—See Eurazeo SE; *Int'l*, pg. 2528
EASYVISTA ITALY—See Eurazeo SE; *Int'l*, pg. 2528
EASYVISTA PORTUGAL S.A.—See Eurazeo SE; *Int'l*, pg. 2528
EASYVISTA S.A.—See Eurazeo SE; *Int'l*, pg. 2528
EASYVISTA SPAIN—See Eurazeo SE; *Int'l*, pg. 2528
EASYVISTA UNITED KINGDOM—See Eurazeo SE; *Int'l*, pg. 2528
EBASE CO., LTD.; *Int'l*, pg. 2284
EBECS LIMITED—See Blackstone Inc.; *U.S. Public*, pg. 356
EBIXCASH WORLD MONEY LTD.—See Ebix Inc.; *U.S. Public*, pg. 710
EBIX CONSULTING—See Ebix Inc.; *U.S. Public*, pg. 710
EBIX INC.; *U.S. Public*, pg. 709
ECIT ACCOUNT A/S—See TowerBrook Capital Partners, L.P.; *U.S. Private*, pg. 4194
ECIT ADVISORY AB—See TowerBrook Capital Partners, L.P.; *U.S. Private*, pg. 4194
ECIT AKTIVAPLUSS AS—See TowerBrook Capital Partners, L.P.; *U.S. Private*, pg. 4195
ECIT AS—See TowerBrook Capital Partners, L.P.; *U.S. Private*, pg. 4194
ECIT AUTOGEAR AS—See TowerBrook Capital Partners, L.P.; *U.S. Private*, pg. 4194
ECIT CAPSTONE AS—See TowerBrook Capital Partners, L.P.; *U.S. Private*, pg. 4194
ECIT CONSULTA AS—See TowerBrook Capital Partners, L.P.; *U.S. Private*, pg. 4194
ECI TELECOM AMERICAS INC.—See Ribbon Communications Inc.; *U.S. Public*, pg. 1797
ECIT LILLEHAMMER AS—See TowerBrook Capital Partners, L.P.; *U.S. Private*, pg. 4194
ECIT NORMANN & OYGARDEN AS—See TowerBrook Capital Partners, L.P.; *U.S. Private*, pg. 4194
ECIT PERITUS AS—See TowerBrook Capital Partners, L.P.; *U.S. Private*, pg. 4194
ECIT SERVICES AB—See TowerBrook Capital Partners, L.P.; *U.S. Private*, pg. 4195
ECIT SOLUTIONS A/S—See TowerBrook Capital Partners, L.P.; *U.S. Private*, pg. 4195
ECIT SOLUTIONS DI AS—See TowerBrook Capital Partners, L.P.; *U.S. Private*, pg. 4195
ECIT SOLUTIONS ITS AS—See TowerBrook Capital Partners, L.P.; *U.S. Private*, pg. 4195
ECIT SOLUTIONS ONE AS—See TowerBrook Capital Partners, L.P.; *U.S. Private*, pg. 4195
ECIT STORD AS—See TowerBrook Capital Partners, L.P.; *U.S. Private*, pg. 4195
ECIT TRONDHEIM AS—See TowerBrook Capital Partners, L.P.; *U.S. Private*, pg. 4195
ECIT VEIBY AKONTO AS—See TowerBrook Capital Partners, L.P.; *U.S. Private*, pg. 4195
ECOMITIZE LLC; *U.S. Private*, pg. 1329
ECONOCOM GROUP SA; *Int'l*, pg. 2297
ECONOCOM LEASE SA/NV—See Econocom Group SA; *Int'l*, pg. 2297
ECONOCOM LUXEMBOURG SA—See Econocom Group SA; *Int'l*, pg. 2297
ECONOCOM MANAGED SERVICES SA/NV—See Econocom Group SA; *Int'l*, pg. 2298
ECONOCOM MAROC SARL—See Econocom Group SA; *Int'l*, pg. 2297
ECONOCOM PRODUCTS & SOLUTIONS BELUX SA/NV—See Econocom Group SA; *Int'l*, pg. 2297
ECONOCOM PSF SA—See Econocom Group SA; *Int'l*, pg. 2297
ECOREXPERIENCE, INC.; *U.S. Private*, pg. 1330
ECOSISTEMAS DIGITALES S.A.S.—See Bancolombia S.A.; *Int'l*, pg. 828
E-CREDIBLE CO., LTD.; *Int'l*, pg. 2247
ECSC GROUP PLC—See Daisy Group Limited; *Int'l*, pg. 1943
E.C.S. D.O.O.—See Illinois Tool Works Inc.; *U.S. Public*, pg. 1102
ECS FEDERAL, LLC—See ASGN Incorporated; *U.S. Public*, pg. 210
EDGEAQ, LLC—See Summit Partners, L.P.; *U.S. Private*, pg. 3856
EDGEAQ, LLC—See The Jordan Company, L.P.; *U.S. Private*, pg. 4062
EDGE SYSTEMS, LLC; *U.S. Private*, pg. 1334
EDGE TECHNOLOGY GROUP, LLC—See Court Square Capital Partners, L.P.; *U.S. Private*, pg. 1070
EDI, LTD.—See Ross & Baruzzini, Inc.; *U.S. Private*, pg. 3485
EDTS, LLC—See WDIT, Incorporated; *U.S. Private*, pg. 4462
EDUSPEC HOLDINGS BERHAD; *Int'l*, pg. 2316
EDX INFORMATION SYSTEMS, INC.; *U.S. Private*, pg. 1342
EFRAME, LLC; *U.S. Private*, pg. 1344
EFT SOLUTIONS PTY LTD—See ComfortDelGro Corporation Limited; *Int'l*, pg. 1712
EFUSION SOLUTIONS PTE. LTD.; *Int'l*, pg. 2322
EGNYTE INC.; *U.S. Private*, pg. 1344
E-INFOCHIPS KK—See Arrow Electronics, Inc.; *U.S. Public*, pg. 199
ELAN I.T. RESOURCE SAS—See ManpowerGroup Inc.; *U.S. Public*, pg. 1357
ELCA INFORMATION TECHNOLOGY LTD.—See ELCA Holding SA; *Int'l*, pg. 2345
ELECTRIC CONTROL SYSTEMS AUTOMATION AS—See Addtech AB; *Int'l*, pg. 133
THE ELECTRIC MAIL COMPANY—See Ziff Davis, Inc.; *U.S. Public*, pg. 2404
ELECTRONIC DATA, LLC—See Arora Engineers, Inc.; *U.S. Private*, pg. 334
ELECTRONIC KNOWLEDGE INTERCHANGE CO.; *U.S. Private*, pg. 1355
ELECTRONIC WARFARE ASSOCIATES, INC.—See Sagewind Capital LLC; *U.S. Private*, pg. 3527
ELECTROSOFT SERVICES INC; *U.S. Private*, pg. 1356
ELITEGROUP COMPUTER SYSTEMS CO., LTD.; *Int'l*, pg. 2363
ELITESOFT GLOBAL INC.; *U.S. Private*, pg. 1362
ELLUCIAN COMPANY L.P. - MALVERN—See Vista Equity Partners, LLC; *U.S. Private*, pg. 4396
ELLUMEN INC.; *U.S. Private*, pg. 1375
ELTES CO., LTD.; *Int'l*, pg. 2371
ELUMICOR; *U.S. Private*, pg. 1377
EMA DESIGN AUTOMATION, INC.; *U.S. Private*, pg. 1377
EMAGINE IT, INC.; *U.S. Private*, pg. 1378
EMBARCADERO TECHNOLOGIES EUROPE LTD.—See HGGC, LLC; *U.S. Private*, pg. 1929
EMBARCADERO TECHNOLOGIES, INC.—See HGGC, LLC; *U.S. Private*, pg. 1929
EMC COMPUTER SYSTEMS ITALIA S.P.A—See Dell Technologies Inc.; *U.S. Public*, pg. 650
E&M COMPUTING LTD.—See First Israel Mezzanine Investors Ltd.; *Int'l*, pg. 2685
EMERGENCY VISIONS, INC.; *U.S. Private*, pg. 1380
EMERGINGSOFT CORP.—See Dean Evans & Associates, Inc.; *U.S. Private*, pg. 1183
E-MERGING TECHNOLOGIES GROUP, INC.; *U.S. Private*, pg. 1302
EMERGINT TECHNOLOGIES, INC.—See CACI International Inc.; *U.S. Public*, pg. 417
EMFRONTIER INC.; *Int'l*, pg. 2380
EMOVIS OPERATIONS IRELAND LIMITED—See ACS, Actividades de Construccion y Servicios, S.A.; *Int'l*, pg. 112
EMPIRIX INC.—See Apax Partners LLP; *Int'l*, pg. 504
EMPLOYEASE, INC.—See Automatic Data Processing, Inc.; *U.S. Public*, pg. 230
EMPOWER INDIA LIMITED; *Int'l*, pg. 2388
EMS-PATVAG S.R.O.—See Hirtenberger Holding GmbH; *Int'l*, pg. 3406
EMS SOFTWARE, LLC—See Fortive Corporation; *U.S. Public*, pg. 870
EM SYSTEMS CO., LTD.; *Int'l*, pg. 2372
EMUDHRA, INC.—See eMudhra Limited; *Int'l*, pg. 2394
EMUDHRA LIMITED; *Int'l*, pg. 2394
ENABLES IT GROUP LIMITED; *Int'l*, pg. 2395
ENCHOICE, INC.; *U.S. Private*, pg. 1390
ENCRISP, LLC; *U.S. Private*, pg. 1391
ENDAVA LIMITED—See Endava plc; *Int'l*, pg. 2402
ENDAVA LIMITED—See Endava plc; *Int'l*, pg. 2402
ENDAVA PLC; *Int'l*, pg. 2402
ENDAVA ROMANIA SRL—See Endava plc; *Int'l*, pg. 2402
ENDOR EHF.—See Hexatronic Group AB; *Int'l*, pg. 3370
ENEA SERVICES ROMANIA SRL—See AROBS Transilvania Software S.A.; *Int'l*, pg. 577
ENFO ENJOYIT INTERGRATION AB—See Enfo Oyj; *Int'l*, pg. 2425
ENFO OYJ; *Int'l*, pg. 2425
E.NFRASTRUCTURE TECHNOLOGIES, INC.—See Zones, Inc.; *U.S. Private*, pg. 4608
ENGAGEDLY, INC.; *U.S. Private*, pg. 1397
ENGHOUSE SYSTEMS LIMITED; *Int'l*, pg. 2427
ENGINEERING INTERNATIONAL BELGIUM SA—See Apax Partners LLP; *Int'l*, pg. 504
ENGINEERING.MO S.P.A—See Apax Partners LLP; *Int'l*, pg. 504
ENGINEERING SYSTEMS SOLUTIONS INC.; *U.S. Private*, pg. 1399
ENJOYOR TECHNOLOGY CO., LTD.; *Int'l*, pg. 2439
ENKLERESTART.NO AS—See TowerBrook Capital Partners, L.P.; *U.S. Private*, pg. 4195
ENLACE OPERATIVO S.A.—See Grupo de Inversiones Suramericana S.A.; *Int'l*, pg. 3125
ENLIGHTED, INC.—See The Carlyle Group Inc.; *U.S. Public*, pg. 2046
ENNOCONN (SUZHOU) TECHNOLOGY CO., LTD.—See Ennoconn Corporation; *Int'l*, pg. 2443
EN POINTE GOV, INC.—See Din Global Corp.; *U.S. Private*, pg. 1233
EN POINTE TECHNOLOGIES SALES, INC.—See Insight Enterprises, Inc.; *U.S. Public*, pg. 1130
ENQUIZIT INC.—See CDW Corporation; *U.S. Public*, pg. 462
ENTEGRIS TAIWAN TECHNOLOGIES CO., LTD.—See Entegris, Inc.; *U.S. Public*, pg. 777
ENTERPRISE CARE TELECONFERENCING (ASIA) PTY LTD.—See Siris Capital Group, LLC; *U.S. Private*, pg. 3673
ENTERPRISE INFORMATION SERVICES, INC.—See Accenture plc; *Int'l*, pg. 85
ENTERPRISE SERVICES NEDERLAND B.V.—See DXC Technology Company; *U.S. Public*, pg. 696
ENTERPRISE SOFTWORKS (PTY) LIMITED—See EOH HOLDINGS LIMITED; *Int'l*, pg. 2457
ENTERPRISE TECHNOLOGY SERVICES LLC—See WestView Capital Partners, L.P.; *U.S. Private*, pg. 4501
ENTERWEB (PTY) LIMITED—See EOH HOLDINGS LIMITED; *Int'l*, pg. 2457
ENTSERV SCHWEIZ GMBH—See DXC Technology Company; *U.S. Public*, pg. 696
ENVATO PTY LTD.—See Shutterstock, Inc.; *U.S. Public*, pg. 1876
ENVIRONMENTAL SYSTEMS CORPORATION—See Fidelity Engineering LLC; *U.S. Private*, pg. 1502
EOH CONSULTING SERVICES (EASTERN CAPE) (PTY) LIMITED—See EOH HOLDINGS LIMITED; *Int'l*, pg. 2457
EOH CONSULTING SERVICES (WESTERN CAPE) (PTY) LIMITED—See EOH HOLDINGS LIMITED; *Int'l*, pg. 2457
EOH MTHOMBO (PTY) LIMITED—See EOH HOLDINGS LIMITED; *Int'l*, pg. 2457
E.ON IT BULGARIA EOOD—See E.ON SE; *Int'l*, pg. 2254
E.ON IT HUNGARY KFT.—See E.ON SE; *Int'l*, pg. 2254
E.ON IT NETHERLANDS B.V.—See E.ON SE; *Int'l*, pg. 2254
EPAM SISTEMOS—See EPAM Systems, Inc.; *U.S. Public*, pg. 783
EPAM SYSTEMS ARMENIA—See EPAM Systems, Inc.; *U.S. Public*, pg. 783
EPARTNERS, INC.; *U.S. Private*, pg. 1411
EPI-USE AMERICA; *U.S. Private*, pg. 1412
EQUATERRA, INC.; *U.S. Private*, pg. 1415
EQUIFAX WORKFORCE SOLUTIONS—See Equifax Inc.; *U.S. Public*, pg. 786
ERNEX—See Bank of Montreal; *Int'l*, pg. 847
ERPSOFT SYSTEMS LTD.; *Int'l*, pg. 2497
ERPSOFT SYSTEMS LTD.; *Int'l*, pg. 2497
ESG CONSULTING INC.; *U.S. Private*, pg. 1425
ESIT ADVANCED SOLUTIONS INC.—See DXC Technology Company; *U.S. Public*, pg. 696
ESP SYSTEX LTD.; *Int'l*, pg. 2505
ESR ASSOCIATES INC—See ASM Technologies Limited; *Int'l*, pg. 627
ESRI SOUTH ASIA PTE LTD—See Boustead Singapore Limited; *Int'l*, pg. 1120

541512 — COMPUTER SYSTEMS DE...

ESSENCE INFORMATION TECHNOLOGY CO., LTD.; *Int'l,* pg. 2510
E-SYSTEM CORPORATION—See Canon Inc.; *Int'l,* pg. 1293
ETRANSERVICES, LLC; *U.S. Private,* pg. 1432
E-TRINITY N.V.—See Cegeka Groep NV; *Int'l,* pg. 1391
ETTEPLAN DEUTSCHLAND GMBH—See Etteplan Oyj; *Int'l,* pg. 2524
ETTEPLAN OYJ; *Int'l,* pg. 2524
ETTEPLAN TECHNOLOGY CENTER LTD.—See Etteplan Oyj; *Int'l,* pg. 2525
ETTEPLAN USA INC.—See Etteplan Oyj; *Int'l,* pg. 2525
EUROFINS IT-INFRASTRUCTURE GMBH—See Eurofins Scientific S.E.; *Int'l,* pg. 2548
EURONET USA INC.—See Euronet Worldwide, Inc.; *U.S. Public,* pg. 798
EURO SOLUTIONS GROUP INC.; *U.S. Private,* pg. 1433
EVALUATOR GROUP, INC.—See Futurum, LLC; *U.S. Private,* pg. 1627
THE EVANSTON GROUP, LLC—See Stone Point Capital LLC; *U.S. Private,* pg. 3823
EVERGREEN SYSTEMS, INC.—See Sunstone Partners Management LLC; *U.S. Private,* pg. 3873
EVIDIAN-BULL JAPAN KK—See Atos SE; *Int'l,* pg. 692
EVOLVING SYSTEMS NETWORKS INDIA PVT. LTD.—See CCUR Holdings Inc.; *U.S. Public,* pg. 461
EWA TECHNOLOGIES—See Sagewind Capital LLC; *U.S. Private,* pg. 3528
EXACT DATA, LLC; *U.S. Private,* pg. 1445
EXACT INTERNATIONAL DEVELOPMENT B.V.—See KKR & Co. Inc.; *U.S. Public,* pg. 1250
EXALT INTEGRATED TECHNOLOGIES; *U.S. Private,* pg. 1445
EXAPROBE SAS—See Econocom Group SA; *Int'l,* pg. 2298
EXATECH SOLUTIONS, INC.—See Vistronix, Inc.; *U.S. Private,* pg. 4403
EXCALIBUR TECHNOLOGY CORP.; *U.S. Private,* pg. 1445
EXCELFORCE MSC BERHAD; *Int'l,* pg. 2578
EXCELLA CONSULTING; *U.S. Private,* pg. 1445
EXCENTUS CORP.—See TA Associates, Inc.; *U.S. Private,* pg. 3917
EXCIVITY, INC.—See Arlington Capital Partners LLC; *U.S. Private,* pg. 327
EXCLUSIVE GROUP SASU; *Int'l,* pg. 2580
EXECUTECH UTAH, LLC; *U.S. Private,* pg. 1447
EXOSTAR LLC—See Arlington Capital Partners LLC; *U.S. Private,* pg. 327
EXPERIS AG—See ManpowerGroup Inc.; *U.S. Public,* pg. 1357
EXPERIS CYBER LTD.—See ManpowerGroup Inc.; *U.S. Public,* pg. 1357
EXPERT SYSTEMS HOLDINGS LIMITED; *Int'l,* pg. 2588
EXPERT SYSTEMS (MACAU) LIMITED—See Expert Systems Holdings Limited; *Int'l,* pg. 2588
EXPLORE CONSULTING; *U.S. Private,* pg. 1450
EXPONENT FAILURE ANALYSIS ASSOCIATES—See Exponent, Inc.; *U.S. Public,* pg. 812
EXPONENTIAL-E LIMITED; *Int'l,* pg. 2590
EXPONENT, INC.- ALEXANDRIA, VIRGINIA—See Exponent, Inc.; *U.S. Public,* pg. 812
EXPONENT, INC.-CHICAGO—See Exponent, Inc.; *U.S. Public,* pg. 812
EXPONENT, INC.-DENVER AREA—See Exponent, Inc.; *U.S. Public,* pg. 812
EXPONENT, INC.-PHOENIX—See Exponent, Inc.; *U.S. Public,* pg. 812
EXPONENT INC—See Exponent, Inc.; *U.S. Public,* pg. 812
EXPRESS DATA HOLDINGS PTY LTD—See Dicker Data Limited; *Int'l,* pg. 2111
EXPRESSION NETWORKS, LLC; *U.S. Private,* pg. 1451
EXTERNETWORKS, INC.; *U.S. Private,* pg. 1452
EXTRADEV, INC.—See DSS, Inc.; *U.S. Public,* pg. 689
EXTRAMED LIMITED—See Alcidion Group Limited; *Int'l,* pg. 301
EXTREME NETWORKS B.V.—See Extreme Networks, Inc.; *U.S. Public,* pg. 813
EXTREME NETWORKS CHINA LTD.—See Extreme Networks, Inc.; *U.S. Public,* pg. 813
EXTREME NETWORKS GMBH—See Extreme Networks, Inc.; *U.S. Public,* pg. 813
EYP MISSION CRITICAL FACILITIES, INC.—See Hewlett Packard Enterprise Company; *U.S. Public,* pg. 1031
F1 COMPUTER SOLUTIONS, INC.; *U.S. Private,* pg. 1457
F5 NETWORKS GMBH—See F5, Inc.; *U.S. Public,* pg. 819
F5 NETWORKS LIMITED—See F5, Inc.; *U.S. Public,* pg. 819
F5 NETWORKS SARL—See F5, Inc.; *U.S. Public,* pg. 819
FACILITY GATEWAY CORPORATION; *U.S. Private,* pg. 1459
FACILITYONE TECHNOLOGIES, LLC—See RainMaker Capital, LLC; *U.S. Private,* pg. 3348
FAITHFUL+GOULD INC.—See AtkinsRealis Group Inc.; *Int'l,* pg. 673
FALCONSTOR ASIA PACIFIC—See FalconStor Software, Inc.; *U.S. Public,* pg. 821
FALCONSTOR CHINA—See FalconStor Software, Inc.; *U.S. Public,* pg. 821

FALCONSTOR FRANCE—See FalconStor Software, Inc.; *U.S. Public,* pg. 821
FALCONSTOR JAPAN—See FalconStor Software, Inc.; *U.S. Public,* pg. 821
FALK INTEGRATED TECHNOLOGIES; *U.S. Private,* pg. 1467
FAR AD; *Int'l,* pg. 2615
FARO INTERNATIONAL (SHANGHAI) CO., LTD—See FARO Technologies, Inc.; *U.S. Public,* pg. 823
FARO TECHNOLOGIES UK LTD.—See FARO Technologies, Inc.; *U.S. Public,* pg. 823
FAST SWITCH, LTD.; *U.S. Private,* pg. 1482
FAST TRACK COMPUTER SOLUTIONS, INC.; *U.S. Private,* pg. 1482
FASTVVIEWER GMBH—See Atos SE; *Int'l,* pg. 692
FEDERATED IT, INC.; *U.S. Private,* pg. 1491
FEDVAR CORP.; *U.S. Private,* pg. 1492
FEED DYNAMIX GMBH—See Equistone Partners Europe Limited; *Int'l,* pg. 2487
FEITIAN TECHNOLOGIES CO., LTD.; *Int'l,* pg. 2632
FFT INDIA PVT. LTD.—See Ava Risk Group Limited; *Int'l,* pg. 733
FIBERHOME TECHNOLOGIES GROUP; *Int'l,* pg. 2652
FIDELITY INFORMATION SERVICES GMBH—See Fidelity National Infor; *U.S. Public,* pg. 832
FIFTH GEAR LLC; *U.S. Private,* pg. 1505
FIG LEAF SOFTWARE INC; *U.S. Private,* pg. 1505
FINOTEK CO., LTD.; *Int'l,* pg. 2676
FINSETA PLC; *Int'l,* pg. 2676
FINTELLIGENCE PTY. LTD.—See Australia Finance Group Ltd; *Int'l,* pg. 720
FIRESTREAM WORLDWIDE, INC.; *U.S. Private,* pg. 1512
FIRST LEVEL TECHNOLOGY LLC—See NCR Voyix Corporation.; *U.S. Public,* pg. 1502
FIRST RATE, INC.; *U.S. Private,* pg. 1524
FIS BUSINESS SYSTEMS LLC—See Fidelity National Infor; *U.S. Public,* pg. 832
FISHER UNITECH LLC—See Court Square Capital Partners, L.P.; *U.S. Private,* pg. 1069
FIT.COM CO., LTD.—See Daiwa Computer Co., Ltd.; *Int'l,* pg. 1944
FIT INSTITUTO DE TECNOLOGIA DA AMAZONIA—See Flex Ltd.; *Int'l,* pg. 2702
FIVE9, INC. UK LIMITED—See Five9, Inc.; *U.S. Public,* pg. 852
FIVE9 PHILIPPINES INC.—See Five9, Inc.; *U.S. Public,* pg. 852
FIVE9.RU—See Five9, Inc.; *U.S. Public,* pg. 852
FLEXIBLE BUSINESS SYSTEMS; *U.S. Private,* pg. 1544
FLEXOS FRANCE—See FleXos S.A.; *Int'l,* pg. 2705
FLEX SUPPORT GROUP, INC.—See Key Family of Companies; *U.S. Private,* pg. 2293
FLEXWARE INNOVATION, INC.—See Hitachi, Ltd.; *Int'l,* pg. 3412
FLOWING CLOUD TECHNOLOGY LTD.; *Int'l,* pg. 2709
FOBI AI INC.; *Int'l,* pg. 2718
FOCUS TECHNOLOGY CO., LTD.; *Int'l,* pg. 2720
FOCUS TECHNOLOGY SOLUTIONS, INC.; *U.S. Private,* pg. 1556
FONET BILGI TEKNOLOJILERI AS; *Int'l,* pg. 2726
FONIX MOBILE PLC; *Int'l,* pg. 2726
FORENSICS CONSULTING SOLUTIONS, LLC; *U.S. Private,* pg. 1566
FORMTEK, INC.—See Marsh & McLennan Companies, Inc.; *U.S. Public,* pg. 1386
FORSYTHE SOLUTIONS GROUP, INC.—See CDW Corporation; *U.S. Public,* pg. 463
FORSYTHE TECHNOLOGY CANADA, INC.—See CDW Corporation; *U.S. Public,* pg. 463
FORTE DESIGN SYSTEMS, K.K.—See Cadence Design Systems, Inc.; *U.S. Public,* pg. 418
FOUNDATIONTV, INC.—See Cineverse Corp.; *U.S. Public,* pg. 495
FOUR SOFT USA, INC.—See Francisco Partners Management, LP; *U.S. Private,* pg. 1589
FPT AUSTRALASIA PTY., LTD.—See FPT Corporation; *Int'l,* pg. 2757
FPT INFORMATICS SERVICES COMPANY LIMITED—See FPT Corporation; *Int'l,* pg. 2757
FPT JAPAN HOLDINGS CO., LTD.—See FPT Corporation; *Int'l,* pg. 2757
FPT SERVICE CO., LTD—See FPT Corporation; *Int'l,* pg. 2757
FPT SOFTWARE EUROPE S.A.R.L—See FPT Corporation; *Int'l,* pg. 2757
FPT SOFTWARE HUE CO., LTD.—See FPT Corporation; *Int'l,* pg. 2757
FPT SOFTWARE JAPAN CO., LTD.—See FPT Corporation; *Int'l,* pg. 2758
FPT SOFTWARE UNITED KINGDOM LTD.—See FPT Corporation; *Int'l,* pg. 2758
FRANCESOIR GROUPE SA; *Int'l,* pg. 2759
FREIGHTWAYS INFORMATION SERVICES LIMITED—See Freightways Group Limited; *Int'l,* pg. 2771
FRESCHE SOLUTIONS INC.—See American Pacific Group, LLC; *U.S. Private,* pg. 242
FRESENIUS NETCARE GMBH—See Fresenius SE & Co. KGaA; *Int'l,* pg. 2778

CORPORATE AFFILIATIONS

FREUDENBERG IT LP—See Freudenberg SE; *Int'l,* pg. 2787
FREUDENBERG IT (SUZHOU) CO., LTD.—See Freudenberg SE; *Int'l,* pg. 2787
FRONTIER TECHNOLOGY LLC; *U.S. Private,* pg. 1615
FRUITION PARTNERS B.V.—See DXC Technology Company; *U.S. Public,* pg. 696
FRUITION PARTNERS; *U.S. Private,* pg. 1617
FUJIFILM COMPUTER SYSTEM CO., LTD.—See FUJIFILM Holdings Corporation; *Int'l,* pg. 2821
FUJISOFT INCORPORATED; *Int'l,* pg. 2830
FUJITSU ASIA PTE. LTD.—See Fujitsu Limited; *Int'l,* pg. 2833
FUJITSU (CHINA) CO., LTD.—See Fujitsu Limited; *Int'l,* pg. 2833
FUJITSU CONSEIL (CANADA) INC.—See Fujitsu Limited; *Int'l,* pg. 2834
FUJITSU CONSULTING INDIA PVT LTD.—See Fujitsu Limited; *Int'l,* pg. 2836
FUJITSU CONSULTING—See Fujitsu Limited; *Int'l,* pg. 2833
FUJITSU CONSULTING—See Fujitsu Limited; *Int'l,* pg. 2833
FUJITSU CONSULTING—See Fujitsu Limited; *Int'l,* pg. 2834
FUJITSU HONG KONG LIMITED—See Fujitsu Limited; *Int'l,* pg. 2834
FUJITSU (IRELAND) LIMITED—See Fujitsu Limited; *Int'l,* pg. 2833
FUJITSU KOREA LTD.—See Fujitsu Limited; *Int'l,* pg. 2835
FUJITSU LIMITED—See Fujitsu Limited; *Int'l,* pg. 2833
FUJITSU NETWORK SOLUTIONS LTD.—See Fujitsu Limited; *Int'l,* pg. 2835
FUJITSU SERVICES LIMITED—See Fujitsu Limited; *Int'l,* pg. 2836
FUJITSU SERVICES LTD—See Fujitsu Limited; *Int'l,* pg. 2836
FUJITSU SERVICES SOUTH AFRICA—See Fujitsu Limited; *Int'l,* pg. 2836
FUJITSU SERVICES SP. Z.O.O.—See Fujitsu Limited; *Int'l,* pg. 2836
FUJITSU SOUTH CHINA LIMITED—See Fujitsu Limited; *Int'l,* pg. 2836
FUJITSU SYSTEMS BUSINESS (THAILAND) LTD.—See Fujitsu Limited; *Int'l,* pg. 2836
FUJITSU TECHNOLOGY SOLUTIONS AB—See Fujitsu Limited; *Int'l,* pg. 2836
FUJITSU TECHNOLOGY SOLUTIONS A.E.—See Fujitsu Limited; *Int'l,* pg. 2836
FUJITSU TECHNOLOGY SOLUTIONS AG—See Fujitsu Limited; *Int'l,* pg. 2836
FUJITSU TECHNOLOGY SOLUTIONS AS—See Fujitsu Limited; *Int'l,* pg. 2836
FUJITSU TECHNOLOGY SOLUTIONS BILISIM LTD. STI.—See Fujitsu Limited; *Int'l,* pg. 2836
FUJITSU TECHNOLOGY SOLUTIONS D.O.O.—See Fujitsu Limited; *Int'l,* pg. 2837
FUJITSU TECHNOLOGY SOLUTIONS GESMBH—See Fujitsu Limited; *Int'l,* pg. 2836
FUJITSU TECHNOLOGY SOLUTIONS GMBH—See Fujitsu Limited; *Int'l,* pg. 2836
FUJITSU TECHNOLOGY SOLUTIONS (LUXEMBOURG) SA—See Fujitsu Limited; *Int'l,* pg. 2836
FUJITSU TECHNOLOGY SOLUTIONS NV—See Fujitsu Limited; *Int'l,* pg. 2837
FUJITSU TECHNOLOGY SOLUTIONS (PTY) LTD.—See Fujitsu Limited; *Int'l,* pg. 2836
FUJITSU TECHNOLOGY SOLUTIONS S.A.R.L.—See Fujitsu Limited; *Int'l,* pg. 2837
FUJITSU TECHNOLOGY SOLUTIONS S.A—See Fujitsu Limited; *Int'l,* pg. 2837
FUJITSU TECHNOLOGY SOLUTIONS SL—See Fujitsu Limited; *Int'l,* pg. 2837
FUJITSU TECHNOLOGY SOLUTIONS S.P.A.—See Fujitsu Limited; *Int'l,* pg. 2837
FUJITSU TECHNOLOGY SOLUTIONS S.R.O—See Fujitsu Limited; *Int'l,* pg. 2837
FUJITSU TELECOM SYSTEMS PHILIPPINES, INC.—See Fujitsu Limited; *Int'l,* pg. 2837
FUJITSU TRANSACTION SOLUTIONS CANADA INC.—See Fujitsu Limited; *Int'l,* pg. 2837
FUJITSU VIETNAM LIMITED—See Fujitsu Limited; *Int'l,* pg. 2837
FULCRUM DIGITAL INC.; *U.S. Private,* pg. 1620
FULCRUM IT SERVICES, LLC—See Huntington Ingalls Industries, Inc.; *U.S. Public,* pg. 1072
FUSIC CO., LTD.; *Int'l,* pg. 2849
FUSIONAPPS, LLC; *U.S. Private,* pg. 1626
FUSIONARY MEDIA; *U.S. Private,* pg. 1626
FUSIONWORKS, INC.; *U.S. Private,* pg. 1626
FUTURE COM DISTRIBUTORS INC.—See ePlus Inc.; *U.S. Public,* pg. 784
FUTURE COM LTD.—See ePlus Inc.; *U.S. Public,* pg. 784
FUTURE CORPORATION; *Int'l,* pg. 2853
FUTURE DATA GROUP LIMITED; *Int'l,* pg. 2853
FUTUREWORLD TECHNOLOGIES, INC.—See Blackwatch International Corp.; *U.S. Public,* pg. 577
G2 WEB SERVICES, INC.—See Stellex Capital Management LP; *U.S. Private,* pg. 3800
GADBERRY GROUP, LLC—See RE/MAX Holdings, Inc.; *U.S. Public,* pg. 1768

N.A.I.C.S. INDEX

541512 — COMPUTER SYSTEMS DE...

GADELLNET CONSULTING SERVICES, LLC; *U.S. Private*, pg. 1633
GALILEO INTERNATIONAL, LLC—See Elliott Management Corporation; *U.S. Private*, pg. 1373
GALILEO INTERNATIONAL, LLC—See Siris Capital Group, LLC; *U.S. Private*, pg. 3674
GALILEO IRELAND LTD.—See Elliott Management Corporation; *U.S. Private*, pg. 1373
GALILEO IRELAND LTD.—See Siris Capital Group, LLC; *U.S. Private*, pg. 3674
GAMESVILLE, INC.—See Brightcom Group Ltd.; *Int'l*, pg. 1162
GAMMA PROJECTS LTD.—See Enghouse Systems Limited; *Int'l*, pg. 2427
GAMSUNG CORPORATION CO., LTD.; *Int'l*, pg. 2879
GARTNER CZECH REPUBLIC S.R.O.—See Gartner, Inc.; *U.S. Public*, pg. 907
GATE INFORMATIC AG—See Bechtle AG; *Int'l*, pg. 938
GATEWAY TICKETING SYSTEMS, INC.; *U.S. Private*, pg. 1651
GBL SYSTEMS CORPORATION; *U.S. Private*, pg. 1653
GBM PAKISTAN PVT. LTD.—See Gulf Business Machines EC; *Int'l*, pg. 3179
GDG INFO ET GESTION INC.—See Alan Allman Associates SA; *Int'l*, pg. 290
GEA IT SERVICES GMBH—See GEA Group Aktiengesellschaft; *Int'l*, pg. 2899
GEDAS AG—See Deutsche Telekom AG; *Int'l*, pg. 2084
GEDAS ARGENTINA, S.A.—See Deutsche Telekom AG; *Int'l*, pg. 2084
GEDAS MEXICO, S.A. DE C.V.—See Deutsche Telekom AG; *Int'l*, pg. 2084
GEDAS UNITED KINGDOM LTD.—See Deutsche Telekom AG; *Int'l*, pg. 2084
GED GARTNER ELECTRONIC DESIGN GMBH—See ELMOS Semiconductor AG; *Int'l*, pg. 2368
GE ENERGY—See General Electric Company; *U.S. Public*, pg. 917
GE ENERGY—See General Electric Company; *U.S. Public*, pg. 917
GEFEN TECHNOLOGIES A.I. LTD.—See Gefen International A.I Ltd.; *Int'l*, pg. 2911
GE HEALTHCARE AS—See GE HealthCare Technologies Inc.; *U.S. Public*, pg. 909
GENERAL DYNAMICS INFORMATION TECHNOLOGY CANADA, LIMITED—See General Dynamics Corporation; *U.S. Public*, pg. 915
GENERAL DYNAMICS INFORMATION TECHNOLOGY, INC.—See General Dynamics Corporation; *U.S. Public*, pg. 914
GENERAL DYNAMICS INFORMATION TECHNOLOGY LIMITED—See General Dynamics Corporation; *U.S. Public*, pg. 915
GENERAL DYNAMICS INFORMATION TECHNOLOGY—See General Dynamics Corporation; *U.S. Public*, pg. 914
GENERAL DYNAMICS INFORMATION TECHNOLOGY—See General Dynamics Corporation; *U.S. Public*, pg. 914
GENERAL DYNAMICS INFORMATION TECHNOLOGY—See General Dynamics Corporation; *U.S. Public*, pg. 914
GENERAL DYNAMICS MISSION SYSTEMS - CANADA—See General Dynamics Corporation; *U.S. Public*, pg. 915
GENERAL DYNAMICS MISSION SYSTEMS, INC.—See General Dynamics Corporation; *U.S. Public*, pg. 915
GENERAL DYNAMICS UK LTD.—See General Dynamics Corporation; *U.S. Public*, pg. 915
GENERALI DEVELOPMENT SPOL SRO—See Assicurazioni Generali S.p.A.; *Int'l*, pg. 646
GENERALI IT-SOLUTIONS GMBH—See Assicurazioni Generali S.p.A; *Int'l*, pg. 645
GENESIS CORP.; *U.S. Private*, pg. 1669
GENESYS ENTERPRISES INC.—See GI Engineering Solutions Limited; *Int'l*, pg. 2960
GENESYS INTERNATIONAL CORPORATION LTD; *Int'l*, pg. 2922
GENEVA CONSULTING GROUP, INC.—See TSR, Inc.; *U.S. Public*, pg. 2202
GENIANT, LLC; *U.S. Private*, pg. 1671
GENTRACK GROUP LIMITED; *Int'l*, pg. 2929
GENUENT, LLC—See Willis Group LLC; *U.S. Private*, pg. 4528
GEOCENT, LLC—See DFW Capital Partners; *U.S. Private*, pg. 1221
GEOCENT, LLC—See Enlightenment Capital LLC; *U.S. Private*, pg. 1400
GEOJIT TECHNOLOGIES PRIVATE LIMITED—See Geojit Financial Services Limited; *Int'l*, pg. 2933
GEOVANTAGE, INC.—See Jacobs Engineering Group, Inc.; *U.S. Public*, pg. 1186
GERMANE SYSTEMS LC; *U.S. Private*, pg. 1687
GETRONICS DEUTSCHLAND GMBH—See Aurelius Equity Opportunities SE & Co. KGaA; *Int'l*, pg. 708
GETRONICS HUNGARY KFT—See Aurelius Equity Opportunities SE & Co. KGaA; *Int'l*, pg. 708
GETRONICS (SCHWEIZ) AG—See Aurelius Equity Opportunities SE & Co. KGaA; *Int'l*, pg. 708
GETRONICS SOLUTIONS (S) PTE LTD—See Aurelius Equity Opportunities SE & Co. KGaA; *Int'l*, pg. 708
GFT CANADA INC.—See GFT Technologies SE; *Int'l*, pg. 2957
GFT COSTA RICA S.A.—See GFT Technologies SE; *Int'l*, pg. 2957
GFT FINANCIAL LIMITED—See GFT Technologies SE; *Int'l*, pg. 2957
GFT ITALIA S.R.L.—See GFT Technologies SE; *Int'l*, pg. 2957
GFT MEXICO S.A. DE C.V.—See GFT Technologies SE; *Int'l*, pg. 2957
GFT POLAND SP. Z O.O—See GFT Technologies SE; *Int'l*, pg. 2957
GFT SWITZERLAND AG—See GFT Technologies SE; *Int'l*, pg. 2957
GFT TECHNOLOGIES CANADA INC.—See GFT Technologies SE; *Int'l*, pg. 2957
GFT TECHNOLOGIES SE; *Int'l*, pg. 2957
GIJIMAAST HOLDINGS (PTY) LIMITED—See Guma Group; *Int'l*, pg. 3183
GIJIMAAST INFORMATION TECHNOLOGY SERVICES (PTY) LIMITED—See Guma Group; *Int'l*, pg. 3183
GIJIMAAST (PTY) LIMITED—See FirstRand Limited; *Int'l*, pg. 2690
GIJIMAAST (PTY) LIMITED—See Hasso Plattner Ventures Africa (Pty) Ltd.; *Int'l*, pg. 3284
GLASSHOUSE TECHNOLOGIES, INC.; *U.S. Private*, pg. 1706
GLASSHOUSE TECHNOLOGIES LTD.—See GLASSHOUSE TECHNOLOGIES, INC.; *U.S. Private*, pg. 1706
GLASSHOUSE TECHNOLOGIES (UK) LIMITED—See GLASSHOUSE TECHNOLOGIES, INC.; *U.S. Private*, pg. 1706
GLOBAL CONVERGENCE SOLUTIONS, INC.; *U.S. Private*, pg. 1713
GLOBAL DATA SYSTEMS INC.; *U.S. Private*, pg. 1713
GLOBAL INFORMATION, INC.; *Int'l*, pg. 2997
GLOBAL MANAGEMENT SYSTEMS INC.—See Dinocrates Group LLC; *U.S. Private*, pg. 1233
GLOBAL MOFY METAVERSE LIMITED; *Int'l*, pg. 2999
GLOBAL NETWORK SYSTEMS, INC.; *U.S. Private*, pg. 1716
GLOBALSERVE, INC.—See PC Connection, Inc.; *U.S. Public*, pg. 1658
GLOBAL STRATEGIC GROUP LIMITED; *Int'l*, pg. 3001
GLOBAL SUPPLY CHAIN SOLUTIONS INC.; *U.S. Private*, pg. 1718
GLOBAL TECHNICAL SYSTEMS; *U.S. Private*, pg. 1718
GLOBAL UNICHIP CORP. EUROPE B.V.—See Global Unichip Corp.; *Int'l*, pg. 3002
GLOBAL UNICHIP CORP.—See Global Unichip Corp.; *Int'l*, pg. 3002
GLOBAL UNICHIP CORP.—See Global Unichip Corp.; *Int'l*, pg. 3002
GLOBAL UNICHIP JAPAN CO., LTD.—See Global Unichip Corp.; *Int'l*, pg. 3002
GLOBAL UNICHIP (NANJING) LTD.—See Global Unichip Corp.; *Int'l*, pg. 3002
GLOBAL UNICHIP (SHANGHAI) COMPANY, LIMITED—See Global Unichip Corp.; *Int'l*, pg. 3002
GLOBANET CONSULTING SERVICES, INC.—See The Carlyle Group Inc.; *U.S. Public*, pg. 2056
GLOBEOP FINANCIAL SERVICES (CAYMAN) LIMITED—See SS&C Technologies Holdings, Inc.; *U.S. Public*, pg. 1923
GL TRADE S.A.—See Fidelity National Infor; *U.S. Public*, pg. 832
GMO GLOBALSIGN FZ-LLC—See GMO GlobalSign Holdings K.K.; *Int'l*, pg. 3013
GMO GLOBALSIGN HOLDINGS K.K.; *Int'l*, pg. 3013
GMO GLOBALSIGN, INC.—See GMO GlobalSign Holdings K.K.; *Int'l*, pg. 3013
GMO GLOBALSIGN K.K.—See GMO GlobalSign Holdings K.K.; *Int'l*, pg. 3013
GO CONCEPTS, INC.—See VC3, Inc.; *U.S. Private*, pg. 4349
GOLDBELT HAWK, LLC—See Gold Belt Incorporated; *U.S. Private*, pg. 1727
GOLDBELT RAVEN, LLC—See Gold Belt Incorporated; *U.S. Private*, pg. 1727
GOPRO GMBH—See GoPro, Inc.; *U.S. Public*, pg. 952
GRAPHICS SYSTEMS CORP. (GXSC); *U.S. Private*, pg. 1758
GRATEX INTERNATIONAL, A.S.; *Int'l*, pg. 3061
GRATEX INTERNATIONAL AUST PTY LTD.—See Gratex International, a.s.; *Int'l*, pg. 3061
GRAVITY COMMUNICATIONS CO., LTD.—See Gravity Co., Ltd.; *Int'l*, pg. 3062
GRAVITY GAME HUB (GGH) PTE., LTD.—See Gravity Co., Ltd.; *Int'l*, pg. 3062
GRAVITY GAME VISION LIMITED—See Gravity Co., Ltd.; *Int'l*, pg. 3062
GRAVITY INTERACTIVE LLC—See Gravity Co., Ltd.; *Int'l*, pg. 3062
GRC INTERNATIONAL GROUP PLC—See Bloom Equity Partners Management, LLC; *U.S. Private*, pg. 583
GREATECH TECHNOLOGY BERHAD; *Int'l*, pg. 3067
GREAT WALL TERROIR HOLDINGS LIMITED; *Int'l*, pg. 3066
GREAVES TECHNOLOGIES LIMITED—See Greaves Cotton Ltd; *Int'l*, pg. 3068
GREENPAGES, INC.; *U.S. Private*, pg. 1779
GRENZEBACH - INOS AUTOMATION SOFTWARE INC.—See Grenzebach Maschinenbau GmbH; *Int'l*, pg. 3081
GRESHAM ENTERPRISE STORAGE INC—See Symphony Technology Group, LLC; *U.S. Private*, pg. 3900
GREYLOGIX GMBH—See E.ON SE; *Int'l*, pg. 2258
GROQ, INC.; *U.S. Private*, pg. 1792
GROUNDWORK OPEN SOURCE, INC.—See HGGC, LLC; *U.S. Private*, pg. 1929
GROUPE CONSEIL DMR, INC.—See Fujitsu Limited; *Int'l*, pg. 2834
GROUPWARE TECHNOLOGY, INC.—See American Securities LLC; *U.S. Private*, pg. 250
GROWTHOPS LIMITED; *Int'l*, pg. 3113
GRT CORPORATION; *U.S. Private*, pg. 1796
GSE POWER SYSTEMS AB—See GSE Systems, Inc.; *U.S. Public*, pg. 973
GSM CONSULTING INC.—See Carl Marks & Co., Inc.; *U.S. Private*, pg. 763
G-TECH INFO-TRAINING LTD.; *Int'l*, pg. 2863
GUANGDONG AOFEI DATA TECHNOLOGY CO., LTD.; *Int'l*, pg. 3152
GUANGDONG TIANYIMA INFORMATION INDUSTRY CO., LTD.; *Int'l*, pg. 3161
GUANGZHOU GRG METROLOGY & TEST CO., LTD.; *Int'l*, pg. 3165
GUANGZHOU HONGFAN TECHNOLOGY CO., LTD.—See CSSC Offshore & Marine Engineering Company Ltd.; *Int'l*, pg. 1868
GUANGZHOU SIE CONSULTING CO., LTD.; *Int'l*, pg. 3168
GULF BUSINESS MACHINES B.S.C. (C)—See Gulf Business Machines EC; *Int'l*, pg. 3179
GULF BUSINESS MACHINES EC; *Int'l*, pg. 3179
GULF BUSINESS MACHINES W.L.L.—See Gulf Business Machines EC; *Int'l*, pg. 3179
G&U SYSTEM SERVICE, LTD.—See BIPROGY Inc.; *Int'l*, pg. 1045
G&U SYSTEM SERVICE, LTD.—See Gunze Limited; *Int'l*, pg. 3185
GWANDA, LLC—See iVenture Solutions, Inc.; *U.S. Private*, pg. 2151
HAITEX CO., LTD.—See Hayashi Telempu Co., Ltd.; *Int'l*, pg. 3289
HALCYON CREEK INC.; *U.S. Private*, pg. 1842
THE HALO GROUP, LLC—See Global Employment Holdings, Inc.; *U.S. Private*, pg. 1713
HALSKI SYSTEMS, LLC—See The Riverside Company; *U.S. Private*, pg. 4109
HALVIK CORP.; *U.S. Private*, pg. 1846
HANA I&S—See Hana Financial Group, Inc.; *Int'l*, pg. 3240
HANGZHOU ARCVIDEO TECHNOLOGY CO., LTD.; *Int'l*, pg. 3246
HANGZHOU DIGITAL CHINA LIMITED—See Digital China Holdings Limited; *Int'l*, pg. 2121
HANGZHOU IECHO SCIENCE & TECHNOLOGY CO., LTD.; *Int'l*, pg. 3248
HANGZHOU SHUNWANG TECHNOLOGY CO., LTD.; *Int'l*, pg. 3250
HANMI IT CO., LTD.—See Hanmi Pharmaceutical Co., Ltd.; *Int'l*, pg. 3256
HANSEN TECHNOLOGIES (SHANGHAI) COMPANY LIMITED—See Hansen Technologies Limited; *Int'l*, pg. 3260
HANSEVISION GMBH—See Bechtle AG; *Int'l*, pg. 938
HANWHA S&C CO., LTD.—See Hanwha Group; *Int'l*, pg. 3266
HAREL MALLAC OUTSOURCING LTD—See Harel Mallac & Co. Ltd.; *Int'l*, pg. 3274
HARITA-NTI LIMITED—See Northern Technologies International Corporation; *U.S. Public*, pg. 1538
HARRIS CORP. - WASHINGTON OPERATIONS—See L3Harris Technologies, Inc.; *U.S. Public*, pg. 1280
HARTCO INC.; *Int'l*, pg. 3280
HARVEST MIRACLE CAPITAL BERHAD; *Int'l*, pg. 3280
HARVEST TECHNOLOGY PLC; *Int'l*, pg. 3281
HARVEY NASH GMBH—See DBAY Advisors Limited; *Int'l*, pg. 1987
HASIBAT INFORMATION TECHNOLOGIST COMPANY—See Arabi Holding Group Company K.S.C.C.; *Int'l*, pg. 532
HATCH IAS—See Hatch Ltd.; *Int'l*, pg. 3284
HAVERSTICK CONSULTING, INC.—See Kratos Defense & Security Solutions, Inc.; *U.S. Public*, pg. 1276
HAYES E-GOVERNMENT RESOURCES, INC.; *U.S. Private*, pg. 1884
HAYES MANAGEMENT CONSULTING; *U.S. Private*, pg. 1884
HCL AUSTRALIA SERVICES PTY. LTD.—See HCL Technologies Ltd.; *Int'l*, pg. 3298
HCL AUSTRALIA SERVICES PTY. LTD.—See HCL Technologies Ltd.; *Int'l*, pg. 3298

HCL AVITAS PRIVATE LIMITED—See HCL Infosystems Limited; *Int'l*, pg. 3297
HCL CLIENT/SERVER APPLICATIONS DIVISION—See HCL Technologies Ltd.; *Int'l*, pg. 3298
HCL COMNET LIMITED—See HCL Infosystems Limited; *Int'l*, pg. 3297
HCL COMNET SYSTEMS AND SERVICES LIMITED—See HCL Infosystems Limited; *Int'l*, pg. 3297
HCL CORE TECHNOLOGIES DIVISION—See HCL Technologies Ltd.; *Int'l*, pg. 3298
HCL EAS LIMITED—See HCL Technologies Ltd.; *Int'l*, pg. 3298
HCL GREAT BRITAIN LTD.—See HCL Technologies Ltd.; *Int'l*, pg. 3298
HCL HONG KONG SAR LTD—See HCL Technologies Ltd.; *Int'l*, pg. 3298
HCL JAPAN LTD.—See HCL Technologies Ltd.; *Int'l*, pg. 3299
HCL LEARNING LIMITED—See HCL Infosystems Limited; *Int'l*, pg. 3297
HCL NETHERLANDS B.V.—See HCL Technologies Ltd.; *Int'l*, pg. 3299
HCL NETWORKING PRODUCTS DIVISION—See HCL Technologies Ltd.; *Int'l*, pg. 3299
HCL NEW ZEALAND LTD.—See HCL Technologies Ltd.; *Int'l*, pg. 3298
HCL NEW ZEALAND LTD.—See HCL Technologies Ltd.; *Int'l*, pg. 3298
HCL SERVICES LIMITED—See HCL Infosystems Limited; *Int'l*, pg. 3297
HCL TALENT CARE PRIVATE LIMITED—See HCL Infosystems Limited; *Int'l*, pg. 3297
HCL TECHNOLOGIES BELGIUM SA/NV—See HCL Technologies Ltd.; *Int'l*, pg. 3299
HCL TECHNOLOGIES EUROPE LTD.—See HCL Technologies Ltd.; *Int'l*, pg. 3299
HCL TECHNOLOGIES GMBH—See HCL Technologies Ltd.; *Int'l*, pg. 3299
HCL TECHNOLOGIES (SINGAPORE) LTD.—See HCL Technologies Ltd.; *Int'l*, pg. 3299
HCL TECHNOLOGIES SWEDEN AB—See HCL Technologies Ltd.; *Int'l*, pg. 3299
HCL TOUCH INC.—See HCL Infosystems Limited; *Int'l*, pg. 3297
HCR CO., LTD.; *Int'l*, pg. 3299
HCV DATA MANAGEMENT GMBH—See Bechtle AG; *Int'l*, pg. 938
HEALTHSTREAM, INC.; *U.S. Public*, pg. 1016
HEALTH SYSTEM TECHNOLOGIES (PTY) LTD—See African Equity Empowerment Investmts Limited; *Int'l*, pg. 191
HEALTHTRIO, LLC; *U.S. Private*, pg. 1898
HEALTHX, INC.—See Frontier Capital LLC; *U.S. Private*, pg. 1615
HEARTLAND BUSINESS SYSTEMS; *U.S. Private*, pg. 1899
HEARTLAND LABEL PRINTERS, INC.; *U.S. Private*, pg. 1900
HEDBERG DATA SYSTEMS INC.—See Steelcase Inc.; *U.S. Public*, pg. 1944
HEITECH MANAGED SERVICES SDN. BHD—See HeiTech Padu Berhad; *Int'l*, pg. 3326
HEITECH SERVICES, INC.; *U.S. Private*, pg. 1905
HENGBAO INTERNATIONAL PTE LTD.—See Hengbao Co., Ltd.; *Int'l*, pg. 3346
HENRY BROS. ELECTRONICS, INC.—See Kratos Defense & Security Solutions, Inc.; *U.S. Public*, pg. 1276
HENRY BROS. ELECTRONICS, INC.—See Kratos Defense & Security Solutions, Inc.; *U.S. Public*, pg. 1276
HENRY BROS. ELECTRONICS, INC.—See Kratos Defense & Security Solutions, Inc.; *U.S. Public*, pg. 1276
HENRY SCHEIN PRACTICE SOLUTIONS INC.—See Henry Schein, Inc.; *U.S. Public*, pg. 1026
HERMAN INTEGRATION SERVICES LLC—See Resideo Technologies, Inc.; *Int'l*, pg. 1789
HEWLETT PACKARD ENTERPRISE COMPANY; *U.S. Public*, pg. 1030
HEWLETT-PACKARD INDIA SALES PVT. LTD.—See HP Inc.; *U.S. Public*, pg. 1063
HEWLETT-PACKARD PHILIPPINES CORPORATION—See Hewlett Packard Enterprise Company; *U.S. Public*, pg. 1032
HEWLETT PACKARD TAIWAN LTD.—See Hewlett Packard Enterprise Company; *U.S. Public*, pg. 1031
HEWLETT-PACKARD TEKNOLOJI COZUMLERI LIMITED SIRKETI—See Hewlett Packard Enterprise Company; *U.S. Public*, pg. 1032
HG TECHNOLOGIES CO., LTD.; *Int'l*, pg. 3375
HIBLEAD INC.; *Int'l*, pg. 3383
HIGHPOINT SERVICE NETWORK SDN BHD—See Acer Incorporated; *Int'l*, pg. 99
HIGH POINT SOLUTIONS, INC.; *U.S. Private*, pg. 1936
HILLSTONE NETWORKS CO., LTD.; *Int'l*, pg. 3393
HINTTECH BV—See Tahzoo LLC; *U.S. Private*, pg. 3923
HIQ FINLAND OY—See HiQ International AB; *Int'l*, pg. 3402
HIQ KOBENHAVN A/S—See HiQ International AB; *Int'l*, pg. 3402

HIQ MALARDALEN AB—See HiQ International AB; *Int'l*, pg. 3402
HIRE TECHNOLOGIES, INC.; *Int'l*, pg. 3404
HIROGIN IT SOLUTIONS CO., LTD.—See Hirogin Holdings, Inc.; *Int'l*, pg. 3404
HI SUN TECHNOLOGY (CHINA) LIMITED; *Int'l*, pg. 3379
HITACHI CONSULTING (CHINA) CO., LTD.—See Hitachi, Ltd.; *Int'l*, pg. 3413
HITACHI CONSULTING INDIA PRIVATE LIMITED—See Hitachi, Ltd.; *Int'l*, pg. 3413
HITACHI CONSULTING PORTUGAL S.A.—See Hitachi, Ltd.; *Int'l*, pg. 3413
HITACHI CONSULTING SINGAPORE PTE LTD.—See Hitachi, Ltd.; *Int'l*, pg. 3413
HITACHI CONSULTING UK LIMITED—See Hitachi, Ltd.; *Int'l*, pg. 3413
HITACHI DATA SYSTEMS AB (GOTHENBURG)—See Hitachi, Ltd.; *Int'l*, pg. 3413
HITACHI DATA SYSTEMS A/S—See Hitachi, Ltd.; *Int'l*, pg. 3413
HITACHI DATA SYSTEMS A/S—See Hitachi, Ltd.; *Int'l*, pg. 3413
HITACHI DATA SYSTEMS AUSTRALIA PTY LTD—See Hitachi, Ltd.; *Int'l*, pg. 3413
HITACHI DATA SYSTEMS BELGIUM NV/SA—See Hitachi, Ltd.; *Int'l*, pg. 3414
HITACHI DATA SYSTEMS B.V.—See Hitachi, Ltd.; *Int'l*, pg. 3414
HITACHI DATA SYSTEMS (CHILE) LIMITADA—See Hitachi, Ltd.; *Int'l*, pg. 3413
HITACHI DATA SYSTEMS GMBH—See Hitachi, Ltd.; *Int'l*, pg. 3414
HITACHI DATA SYSTEMS INDIA PVT. LTD.—See Hitachi, Ltd.; *Int'l*, pg. 3414
HITACHI DATA SYSTEMS ITALIA S.R.L.—See Hitachi, Ltd.; *Int'l*, pg. 3414
HITACHI DATA SYSTEMS KOREA LIMITED—See Hitachi, Ltd.; *Int'l*, pg. 3414
HITACHI DATA SYSTEMS LIMITED—See Hitachi, Ltd.; *Int'l*, pg. 3414
HITACHI DATA SYSTEMS LTD.—See Hitachi, Ltd.; *Int'l*, pg. 3414
HITACHI DATA SYSTEMS LTD.—See Hitachi, Ltd.; *Int'l*, pg. 3414
HITACHI DATA SYSTEMS NEDERLAND BV—See Hitachi, Ltd.; *Int'l*, pg. 3414
HITACHI DATA SYSTEMS OY—See Hitachi, Ltd.; *Int'l*, pg. 3414
HITACHI DATA SYSTEMS (POLSKA) SP. Z.O.O.—See Hitachi, Ltd.; *Int'l*, pg. 3413
HITACHI DATA SYSTEMS PTE. LTD.—See Hitachi, Ltd.; *Int'l*, pg. 3414
HITACHI DATA SYSTEMS S.A. (BARCELONA)—See Hitachi, Ltd.; *Int'l*, pg. 3414
HITACHI DATA SYSTEMS S.A.S—See Hitachi, Ltd.; *Int'l*, pg. 3414
HITACHI DATA SYSTEMS SDN BHD—See Hitachi, Ltd.; *Int'l*, pg. 3414
HITACHI DATA SYSTEMS (SPAIN)—See Hitachi, Ltd.; *Int'l*, pg. 3413
HITACHI DIGITAL HOST SDN. BHD.—See Hitachi, Ltd.; *Int'l*, pg. 3416
HITACHI EBWORX (INDO-CHINA) CO. LTD.—See Hitachi, Ltd.; *Int'l*, pg. 3422
HITACHI EBWORX INTERNATIONAL PTE. LTD.—See Hitachi, Ltd.; *Int'l*, pg. 3422
HITACHI EBWORX SDN. BHD.—See Hitachi, Ltd.; *Int'l*, pg. 3422
HITACHI EBWORX TECHNOLOGY (CHENGDU) CO. LTD.—See Hitachi, Ltd.; *Int'l*, pg. 3422
HITACHI EUROPE LTD. - INFORMATION SYSTEMS GROUP DIVISION—See Hitachi, Ltd.; *Int'l*, pg. 3417
HITACHI INFORMATION SYSTEMS (SHANGHAI), LTD—See Hitachi, Ltd.; *Int'l*, pg. 3419
HITACHI KE SYSTEMS, LTD.—See Hitachi, Ltd.; *Int'l*, pg. 3419
HITACHI SOLUTIONS AMERICA, LTD.—See Hitachi, Ltd.; *Int'l*, pg. 3421
HITACHI SOLUTIONS (CHINA) CO., LTD.—See Hitachi, Ltd.; *Int'l*, pg. 3421
HITACHI SOLUTIONS EUROPE A.G.—See Hitachi, Ltd.; *Int'l*, pg. 3421
HITACHI SOLUTIONS EUROPE LTD.—See Hitachi, Ltd.; *Int'l*, pg. 3421
HITACHI SOLUTIONS EUROPE S.A.S—See Hitachi, Ltd.; *Int'l*, pg. 3421
HITECH ASSETS LLC—See Caretta Partners, LLC; *U.S. Private*, pg. 754
HITECHPROS S.A.; *Int'l*, pg. 3425
HITEK GLOBAL, INC.; *Int'l*, pg. 3426
HIXARDT TECHNOLOGIES, INC.; *U.S. Private*, pg. 1953
HMS IT S.P.A.—See Cassa Depositi e Prestiti S.p.A.; *Int'l*, pg. 1355
HMS TECHNOLOGIES, INC.; *U.S. Private*, pg. 1955
HNAC TECHNOLOGY CO., LTD.; *Int'l*, pg. 3433
HOLCOMB ENTERPRISES; *U.S. Private*, pg. 1961
HOMECARE SOFTWARE SOLUTIONS LLC; *U.S. Private*, pg. 1973

HOMELAND INTERACTIVE TECHNOLOGY LTD.; *Int'l*, pg. 3455
HONEYWELL AUTOMATION INDIA LTD.—See Honeywell International Inc.; *U.S. Public*, pg. 1051
HONGCHENG ENVIRONMENTAL TECHNOLOGY CO., LTD.; *Int'l*, pg. 3470
HONG KONG IT ALLIANCE LIMITED—See Champion Technology Holdings Ltd; *Int'l*, pg. 1440
THE HOTH CORP.; *U.S. Private*, pg. 4054
HOTLINE TO HR INC.; *Int'l*, pg. 3489
HOUSE OF BRICK TECHNOLOGIES LLC—See OpsCompass, LLC; *U.S. Private*, pg. 3034
HOYOS CONSULTING LLC; *U.S. Private*, pg. 1996
HPS EUROPE—See Hightech Payment Systems S A; *Int'l*, pg. 3388
HRH NEXT SERVICES LIMITED; *Int'l*, pg. 3501
HS GOVTECH SOLUTIONS INC.—See Banneker Partners, LLC; *U.S. Private*, pg. 468
HTC GLOBAL SERVICES INC.; *U.S. Private*, pg. 1999
HTEC LTD—See TA Associates, Inc.; *U.S. Private*, pg. 3917
HUBBELL BUILDING AUTOMATION—See Hubbell Incorporated; *U.S. Public*, pg. 1066
HUBER & ASSOCIATES INC.; *U.S. Private*, pg. 2000
HUB TECHNICAL SERVICES; *U.S. Private*, pg. 2000
HUF SECURE MOBILE GMBH—See Huf Hulsbeck & Furst GmbH & Co. KG; *Int'l*, pg. 3523
HUMAN FACTORS INTERNATIONAL, INC.; *U.S. Private*, pg. 2005
HUMANIFY, INC.—See TTEC Holdings, Inc.; *U.S. Public*, pg. 2202
HUNTINGTON BUSINESS SYSTEMS INC.; *U.S. Private*, pg. 2010
HURCO EUROPE LIMITED—See Hurco Companies, Inc.; *U.S. Public*, pg. 1076
HURCO INDIA PTE. LTD.—See Hurco Companies, Inc.; *U.S. Public*, pg. 1076
HURCO S.A.R.L.—See Hurco Companies, Inc.; *U.S. Public*, pg. 1076
HURCO (S.E. ASIA) PTE LTD.—See Hurco Companies, Inc.; *U.S. Public*, pg. 1075
HURCO S.R.L.—See Hurco Companies, Inc.; *U.S. Public*, pg. 1076
HVH PRECISION ANALYTICS LLC—See JLL Partners, LLC; *U.S. Private*, pg. 2212
HVH PRECISION ANALYTICS LLC—See Water Street Healthcare Partners, LLC; *U.S. Private*, pg. 4452
HWA CREATE CORPORATION LTD.; *Int'l*, pg. 3541
HYDSOFT TECHNOLOGY CO., LTD.; *Int'l*, pg. 3548
HYPERSOFT TECHNOLOGIES LIMITED; *Int'l*, pg. 3553
HYUNDAI AUTOEVER CORP.—See Hyundai Motor Company; *Int'l*, pg. 3559
I2 ENTERPRISE PUBLIC COMPANY LIMITED; *Int'l*, pg. 3566
IBERDROLA SISTEMAS, S.A.U.—See Iberdrola, S.A.; *Int'l*, pg. 3573
IBEX LIMITED—See The Resource Group International Ltd.; *U.S. Private*, pg. 4105
IBM INTERNATIONAL GROUP CAPITAL LLC—See International Business Machines Corporation; *U.S. Public*, pg. 1147
IBM MAGYARORSZAGI KFT—See International Business Machines Corporation; *U.S. Public*, pg. 1147
IBM MALTA LIMITED—See International Business Machines Corporation; *U.S. Public*, pg. 1147
IBM UKRAINE—See International Business Machines Corporation; *U.S. Public*, pg. 1148
IBOL CO., LTD.—See Business Online Public Company Limited; *Int'l*, pg. 1229
IC CO., LTD.; *Int'l*, pg. 3577
ICE PORTAL, INC.—See Beijing Shiji Information Technology Co., Ltd.; *Int'l*, pg. 956
ICE TECHNOLOGIES, INC.; *U.S. Private*, pg. 2031
ICP INC.—See Island Computer Products, Inc.; *U.S. Private*, pg. 2145
ICRAFT CO., LTD.; *Int'l*, pg. 3586
IDEA CONSULTING INC.—See FUJISOFT INCORPORATED; *Int'l*, pg. 2831
IDEAL INTEGRATIONS, INC.; *U.S. Private*, pg. 2036
IDEMIA IDENTITY & SECURITY USA, LLC—See Advent International Corporation; *U.S. Private*, pg. 102
IDISCOVERY SOLUTIONS, INC.; *U.S. Private*, pg. 2038
IDL SOLUTIONS, INC.—See CACI International Inc.; *U.S. Public*, pg. 418
IDOX BELGIUM NV—See IDOX PLC; *Int'l*, pg. 3595
IDOX FRANCE SARL—See IDOX PLC; *Int'l*, pg. 3595
IDOX PLC; *Int'l*, pg. 3595
IDS SA; *Int'l*, pg. 3596
IDS SCHEER D.O.O.—See Silver Lake Group, LLC; *U.S. Private*, pg. 3658
IDS SCHEER INDIA PVT. LTD.—See Silver Lake Group, LLC; *U.S. Private*, pg. 3658
IFLAG CO., LTD.; *Int'l*, pg. 3599
IFS CZECH S.R.O.—See EQT AB; *Int'l*, pg. 2477
IFS DANMARK A/S—See EQT AB; *Int'l*, pg. 2477
IFS NEW ZEALAND PTY LTD—See EQT AB; *Int'l*, pg. 2478
IFS SLOVAKIA, SPOL. S.R.O.—See EQT AB; *Int'l*, pg. 2477
IFS SOLUTION INDIA PVT LTD—See EQT AB; *Int'l*, pg. 2478

N.A.I.C.S. INDEX

541512 — COMPUTER SYSTEMS DE...

IGXGLOBAL UK, LIMITED—See ePlus Inc.; *U.S. Public*, pg. 784
I&I GROUP PUBLIC COMPANY LIMITED; *Int'l*, pg. 3562
IKON SCIENCE LIMITED; *Int'l*, pg. 3612
ILOOP MOBILE, INC.—See LENCO MOBILE INC.; *U.S. Private*, pg. 2421
IMAGESOFT, INC.—See i3 Verticals, Inc.; *U.S. Public*, pg. 1081
IMAGINIT TECHNOLOGIES—See Rand Worldwide, Inc.; *U.S. Public*, pg. 1762
IMC GLOBAL SERVICES—See Calibre Systems Inc.; *U.S. Private*, pg. 717
IMMEDIENT CORPORATION; *U.S. Private*, pg. 2047
IMMEDIENT CORPORATION—See Immedient Corporation; *U.S. Private*, pg. 2047
IMODULES SOFTWARE, INC.—See Leeds Equity Partners, LLC; *U.S. Private*, pg. 2414
IMODULES SOFTWARE, INC.—See Veritas Capital Fund Management, LLC; *U.S. Private*, pg. 4360
IMPRES TECHNOLOGY SOLUTIONS, INC.; *U.S. Private*, pg. 2050
IMP SOLUTIONS INC.—See I.M.P. Group International Inc.; *Int'l*, pg. 3566
INAWISDOM LTD.—See Cognizant Technology Solutions Corporation; *U.S. Public*, pg. 524
INBENTA TECHNOLOGIES INC.; *U.S. Private*, pg. 2052
INCAPSULATE, LLC—See Accenture plc; *Int'l*, pg. 87
INCENTRA SOLUTIONS NW—See Presilient, LLC; *U.S. Private*, pg. 3255
INCEPTUS MEDIA GP INC.—See GVIC Communications Corp.; *Int'l*, pg. 3189
INCOMM CANADA LLC—See Interactive Communications Inc; *U.S. Private*, pg. 2108
INCOMM EUROPE LIMITED—See Interactive Communications Inc; *U.S. Private*, pg. 2108
INCOMM JAPAN KK—See Interactive Communications Inc; *U.S. Private*, pg. 2108
INCOMM LTD.—See Interactive Communications Inc; *U.S. Private*, pg. 2108
INCOMM MEXICO, LLC—See Interactive Communications Inc; *U.S. Private*, pg. 2108
INCOMM PUERTO RICO LLC—See Interactive Communications Inc; *U.S. Private*, pg. 2108
INDEPENDENT TELECOM SYSTEMS; *U.S. Private*, pg. 2061
INDIANA INTERACTIVE, LLC—See Tyler Technologies, Inc.; *U.S. Public*, pg. 2208
INDIGOVISION LIMITED—See Motorola Solutions, Inc.; *U.S. Public*, pg. 1477
INDOTRONIX INTERNATIONAL CORPORATION; *U.S. Private*, pg. 2064
INDUSTRIAS W DE MEXICO, SA DE C.V.—See CSE Global Ltd.; *Int'l*, pg. 1864
INDUSTRI-MATEMATIK, LIMITED—See TA Associates, Inc.; *U.S. Private*, pg. 3914
INDUSTRI-MATEMATIK NEDERLAND B.V.—See TA Associates, Inc.; *U.S. Private*, pg. 3914
INDYNE INC.; *U.S. Private*, pg. 2069
INERGEX INC.; *U.S. Private*, pg. 2069
I-NET CORPORATION; *Int'l*, pg. 3563
INFINERA JAPAN K.K.—See Infinera Corporation; *U.S. Public*, pg. 1117
INFINIGATE DANMARK A/S—See H.I.G. Capital, LLC; *U.S. Private*, pg. 1833
INFINIGATE DEUTSCHLAND GMBH—See H.I.G. Capital, LLC; *U.S. Private*, pg. 1833
INFINIGATE HOLDING AG—See H.I.G. Capital, LLC; *U.S. Private*, pg. 1833
INFINIGATE NORGE AS—See H.I.G. Capital, LLC; *U.S. Private*, pg. 1833
INFINIGATE SVERIGE AB—See H.I.G. Capital, LLC; *U.S. Private*, pg. 1833
INFINIGY ENGINEERING; *U.S. Private*, pg. 2070
INFINITE LEAP, INC.—See Halma plc; *Int'l*, pg. 3232
INFINITE SP.Z.O.O—See DialCom24 Sp. z o.o.; *Int'l*, pg. 2104
INFINITY COMPUTER SYSTEMS, INC.—See Sourcepass, Inc.; *U.S. Private*, pg. 3719
INFINITY NETWORK SOLUTIONS, INC.; *U.S. Private*, pg. 2071
INFOCHAMP SYSTEMS CORPORATION—See China Steel Corporation; *Int'l*, pg. 1556
INFOGAIN CORPORATION—See ChrysCapital Investment Advisors (India) Private Limited; *Int'l*, pg. 1588
INFOGRESSIVE, INC.—See Ascend Technologies, LLC; *U.S. Private*, pg. 346
INFO-LINK TECHNOLOGIES, INC.—See Tonka Bay Equity Partners LLC; *U.S. Public*, pg. 4185
INFOLOB SOLUTIONS, INC.; *U.S. Private*, pg. 2072
INFORELAY ONLINE SYSTEMS, INC.—See Stonecourt Capital LP; *U.S. Private*, pg. 3828
INFORMACNI SLUZBY - ENERGETIKA, A.S.—See E.ON SE; *Int'l*, pg. 2258
INFORMATION BUILDERS BELGIUM—See Vista Equity Partners, LLC; *U.S. Private*, pg. 4401
INFORMATION BUILDERS (CANADA) - CALGARY—See Vista Equity Partners, LLC; *U.S. Public*, pg. 4401
INFORMATION BUILDERS (CANADA) INC.—See Vista Equity Partners, LLC; *U.S. Private*, pg. 4401
INFORMATION BUILDERS (CANADA) VANCOUVER—See Vista Equity Partners, LLC; *U.S. Private*, pg. 4401
INFORMATION BUILDERS (DEUTSCHLAND) GMBH—See Vista Equity Partners, LLC; *U.S. Private*, pg. 4401
INFORMATION BUILDERS FRANCE—See Vista Equity Partners, LLC; *U.S. Private*, pg. 4401
INFORMATION BUILDERS INC.—See Vista Equity Partners, LLC; *U.S. Private*, pg. 4401
INFORMATION BUILDERS MEXICO—See Vista Equity Partners, LLC; *U.S. Private*, pg. 4401
INFORMATION BUILDERS NETHERLANDS—See Vista Equity Partners, LLC; *U.S. Private*, pg. 4401
INFORMATION BUILDERS PORTUGAL—See Vista Equity Partners, LLC; *U.S. Private*, pg. 4401
INFORMATION BUILDERS PTY., LTD.—See Vista Equity Partners, LLC; *U.S. Private*, pg. 4402
INFORMATION BUILDERS SPAIN—See Vista Equity Partners, LLC; *U.S. Private*, pg. 4402
INFORMATION BUILDERS SWITZERLAND—See Vista Equity Partners, LLC; *U.S. Private*, pg. 4402
INFORMATION BUILDERS UK—See Vista Equity Partners, LLC; *U.S. Private*, pg. 4402
INFORMATION CONTROL CORPORATION; *U.S. Private*, pg. 2073
INFORMATION MANAGEMENT SERVICES; *U.S. Private*, pg. 2073
INFORMATION SYSTEMS EXPERTS, LLC; *U.S. Private*, pg. 2073
INFORMATION SYSTEMS SOLUTIONS, INC.; *U.S. Private*, pg. 2073
INFORMATION TECHNOLOGY EXPERTS, INC.; *U.S. Private*, pg. 2073
INFORMATION TECHNOLOGY PROFESSIONALS, LLC—See Gordon Flesch Company, Inc.; *U.S. Private*, pg. 1743
INFORONICS, LLC; *U.S. Private*, pg. 2074
INFOSPECTRUM CONSULTING INC.—See GSS Infotech Limited; *Int'l*, pg. 3150
INFOSTRETCH CORPORATION; *U.S. Private*, pg. 2074
INFOTECH ENTERPRISES LTD—See Cyient Limited; *Int'l*, pg. 1896
INFOTECH PRISM, LLC; *U.S. Private*, pg. 2074
INFOTERRA GMBH—See Airbus SE; *Int'l*, pg. 245
INFOYOGI LLC; *U.S. Private*, pg. 2074
INFRANET TECHNOLOGIES GROUP, INC.; *U.S. Private*, pg. 2074
INFRONT CONSULTING GROUP (S) PTE LTD.—See Axiata Group Berhad; *Int'l*, pg. 768
INGAGE NETWORKS, INC.; *U.S. Private*, pg. 2075
INGENUITY, INC.; *U.S. Private*, pg. 2075
INGRAM MICRO AMERICAS INC.—See Hainan Traffic Administration Holding Co., Ltd.; *Int'l*, pg. 3214
INGRAM MICRO ISRAEL LTD—See Hainan Traffic Administration Holding Co., Ltd.; *Int'l*, pg. 3214
INGRAM MICRO OY—See Hainan Traffic Administration Holding Co., Ltd.; *Int'l*, pg. 3215
INGRAM MICRO SRL—See Hainan Traffic Administration Holding Co., Ltd.; *Int'l*, pg. 3215
INNOVASIC, INC.—See Analog Devices, Inc.; *U.S. Public*, pg. 135
INNOVATEK INNOVATION TECHNOLGIES LTDA—See Abbott Laboratories; *U.S. Public*, pg. 20
INNOVATIVE COMPUTING & APPLIED TECHNOLOGY LLC; *U.S. Private*, pg. 2082
INNOVATIVE COMPUTING SYSTEMS, INC.; *U.S. Private*, pg. 2082
INNOVATIVE PICKING TECHNOLOGIES, INC.; *U.S. Private*, pg. 2083
INNOVATIVE TECHNOLOGY PARTNERSHIPS, LLC; *U.S. Private*, pg. 2083
INNOVATIVE TECHNOLOGY SYSTEMS & SOLUTIONS INC.—See ePlus Inc.; *U.S. Public*, pg. 784
INOS AUTOMATIONSSOFTWARE GMBH—See Grenzebach Maschinenbau GmbH; *Int'l*, pg. 3082
INOS HELLAS S.A.—See Grenzebach Maschinenbau GmbH; *Int'l*, pg. 3082
INOVEC INC.—See USNR; *U.S. Public*, pg. 4323
INOVEX INFORMATION SYSTEMS, INC.; *U.S. Private*, pg. 2084
INOVITY, INC.—See Sole Source Capital LLC; *U.S. Private*, pg. 3708
INSIGHT ENTERPRISES HONG KONG—See Insight Enterprises, Inc.; *U.S. Public*, pg. 1130
INSIGHT ENTERPRISES, INC.; *U.S. Public*, pg. 1129
INSIGHT TECHNOLOGY SOLUTIONS AB—See Insight Enterprises, Inc.; *U.S. Public*, pg. 1130
INSIGHT TECHNOLOGY SOLUTIONS AG—See Insight Enterprises, Inc.; *U.S. Public*, pg. 1130
INSIGHT TECHNOLOGY SOLUTIONS N.U.F.—See Insight Enterprises, Inc.; *U.S. Public*, pg. 1130
INSIGHT TECHNOLOGY SOLUTIONS SAS—See Insight Enterprises, Inc.; *U.S. Public*, pg. 1130
INSIGHT TECHNOLOGY SOLUTIONS, S.L.—See Insight Enterprises, Inc.; *U.S. Public*, pg. 1130
INSYSCO, INC.—See MAXIMUS, Inc.; *U.S. Public*, pg. 1402
INTEC SYSTEMS, INC.; *U.S. Private*, pg. 2097
INTEG QUEENSLAND PTY LTD—See DXC Technology Company; *U.S. Public*, pg. 696
INTEGRAL SOLUTIONS, LLC—See J.M. Smith Corporation; *U.S. Private*, pg. 2169
INTEGRA TECHNOLOGY CONSULTING CORPORATION; *U.S. Private*, pg. 2098
INTEGRATED ARCHIVE SYSTEMS INC.; *U.S. Private*, pg. 2098
INTEGRATED BROADCAST SERVICES LIMITED (IBIS)—See Symphony Technology Group, LLC; *U.S. Private*, pg. 3901
INTEGRATED DATA STORAGE, LLC; *U.S. Private*, pg. 2099
INTEGRATED PARTNERS, INC.; *U.S. Private*, pg. 2100
INTEGRATED SYSTEMS ANALYSTS, INC.; *U.S. Private*, pg. 2101
INTEGRATION PARTNERS CORP.—See InterCloud Systems, Inc.; *U.S. Public*, pg. 1141
INTEGRATION TECHNOLOGIES, INC.; *U.S. Private*, pg. 2101
INTEGRITY GLOBAL SECURITY, LLC—See Green Hills Software Inc.; *U.S. Private*, pg. 1773
INTEGRITY NETWORKING SYSTEMS; *U.S. Private*, pg. 2104
INTEKRAS, INC.; *U.S. Private*, pg. 2104
INTELESYS CORPORATION—See Arlington Capital Partners LLC; *U.S. Private*, pg. 328
INTELEX TECHNOLOGIES, ULC—See Fortive Corporation; *U.S. Public*, pg. 871
INTEL ITALIA, S.P.A.—See Intel Corporation; *U.S. Public*, pg. 1138
INTELLIBRIDGE, LLC—See Enlightenment Capital LLC; *U.S. Private*, pg. 1400
INTELLIGENT INSITES, INC.—See Koch Industries, Inc.; *U.S. Private*, pg. 2331
INTELLIHR LIMITED—See Accel Partners L.P.; *U.S. Public*, pg. 49
INTELLIHR LIMITED—See KKR & Co. Inc.; *U.S. Public*, pg. 1239
INTELLISWIFT SOFTWARE INC.; *U.S. Private*, pg. 2106
INTERACTIVE BUSINESS SYSTEMS, INC.—See Odyssey Investment Partners, LLC; *U.S. Private*, pg. 2996
INTERACTIVE LIQUID, LLC; *U.S. Private*, pg. 2108
INTERAQT CORP.—See Aluf Holdings, Inc.; *U.S. Public*, pg. 89
INTERCARE DX, INC.; *U.S. Public*, pg. 1141
INTERCOSMOS MEDIA GROUP, INC.; *U.S. Private*, pg. 2110
INTERGRAPH HONG KONG LIMITED—See Hexagon AB; *Int'l*, pg. 3369
INTERLOGICS, INC.—See Dentsu Group Inc.; *Int'l*, pg. 2039
INTERNATIONAL COMPUTER MARKETING CORPORATION (ICM); *U.S. Private*, pg. 2116
INTERNATIONAL COMPUTER SOLUTIONS INC.; *U.S. Private*, pg. 2116
INTERNATIONAL MANAGEMENT CONSULTING INC.; *U.S. Private*, pg. 2118
INTERNATIONAL SHARED SERVICES, INC.—See Geisinger Health System; *U.S. Private*, pg. 1656
INTERNATIONAL SOFTWARE SYSTEMS, INC.; *U.S. Private*, pg. 2120
INTERNET CORPORATION FOR ASSIGNED NAMES & NUMBERS; *U.S. Private*, pg. 2122
INTERNET SCIENCES, INC.; *U.S. Private*, pg. 2122
INTERNETWORK ENGINEERING—See BC Partners LLP; *Int'l*, pg. 925
INTERSYS CONSULTING, INC.—See ASGN Incorporated; *U.S. Public*, pg. 210
INTERVISE CONSULTANTS INC.; *U.S. Private*, pg. 2128
INTERVISION SYSTEMS, LLC—See Huron Capital Partners LLC; *U.S. Private*, pg. 2012
INTERVISION SYSTEMS, LLC—See MidOcean Partners, LLP; *U.S. Private*, pg. 2716
INTERWORKS, INC.; *U.S. Private*, pg. 2128
INTRINIUM, INC.; *U.S. Private*, pg. 2129
INTRIX TECHNOLOGIES INC.—See SunChase Holdings, Inc.; *U.S. Private*, pg. 3865
INVENIO BUSINESS SOLUTIONS DWC LLC—See BGF Group PLC; *Int'l*, pg. 1007
INVENIO BUSINESS SOLUTIONS GMBH—See BGF Group PLC; *Int'l*, pg. 1007
INVENIO BUSINESS SOLUTIONS INC.—See BGF Group PLC; *Int'l*, pg. 1007
INVENIO BUSINESS SOLUTIONS LIMITED—See BGF Group PLC; *Int'l*, pg. 1007
INVENIO BUSINESS SOLUTIONS LTD—See BGF Group PLC; *Int'l*, pg. 1007
INVENIO BUSINESS SOLUTIONS PVT LTD—See BGF Group PLC; *Int'l*, pg. 1007
INVENTA TECHNOLOGIES INC.—See ANTs Software Inc.; *U.S. Private*, pg. 289
INVENTCOMMERCE LTD.—See DBAY Advisors Limited; *Int'l*, pg. 1987
INVENTCOMMERCE PROPRIETARY LTD.—See DBAY Advisors Limited; *Int'l*, pg. 1987
INVIVO BIOTECH SVS GMBH—See Bruker Corporation; *U.S. Public*, pg. 405
IONIDEA, INC.; *U.S. Private*, pg. 2134

N.A.I.C.S. Index
541512 — COMPUTER SYSTEMS DE... CORPORATE AFFILIATIONS

IOT DEUTSCHLAND GMBH—See adesso SE; *Int'l*, pg. 144
IPCAS GMBH—See Adecco Group AG; *Int'l*, pg. 140
IPC INFORMATION SYSTEMS LTD.—See Strategic Value Partners, LLC; *U.S. Private*, pg. 3836
IPCOS (UK) LTD.—See ATS Corporation; *Int'l*, pg. 695
IPC SYSTEMS, INC.—See Strategic Value Partners, LLC; *U.S. Private*, pg. 3836
IPIPELINE LIMITED—See Roper Technologies, Inc.; *U.S. Public*, pg. 1814
IREWARD24 SA—See ComArch S.A.; *Int'l*, pg. 1707
IRIDIUM TECHNOLOGY OPCO, LLC—See Levine Leichtman Capital Partners, LLC; *U.S. Private*, pg. 2435
I.R.I.S. FRANCE S.A.—See Canon Inc.; *Int'l*, pg. 1295
I.R.I.S. GROUP S.A.—See Canon Inc.; *Int'l*, pg. 1295
I.R.I.S. LUXEMBOURG S.A.—See Canon Inc.; *Int'l*, pg. 1295
IRIS SOFTWARE, INC.; *U.S. Private*, pg. 2138
IRONARCH TECHNOLOGY, LLC; *U.S. Private*, pg. 2140
ISA INFORMATION SYSTEMS SERVICES—See Integrated Systems Analysts, Inc.; *U.S. Private*, pg. 2101
ISA INSTALLATION & DEPLOYMENT CENTER—See Integrated Systems Analysts, Inc.; *U.S. Private*, pg. 2101
ISC CORP.; *U.S. Private*, pg. 2143
ISEATZ INC.; *U.S. Private*, pg. 2143
ISG TECHNOLOGY, INC.; *U.S. Private*, pg. 2143
ISI-DENTSU SOUTH EAST ASIA PTE. LTD.—See Dentsu Group Inc.; *Int'l*, pg. 2038
I&S IT-BERATUNG & SERVICE GMBH—See Capgemini SE; *Int'l*, pg. 1306
ISKOOT TECHNOLOGIES, INC.—See QUALCOMM Incorporated; *U.S. Public*, pg. 1747
ISOFT SOLUTIONS (INTERNATIONAL) PTY LTD.—See DXC Technology Company; *U.S. Public*, pg. 696
ISONOR IT AS—See TowerBrook Capital Partners, L.P.; *U.S. Private*, pg. 4195
ISS GROUP, INC.; *U.S. Private*, pg. 2147
ISSQUARED INC.; *U.S. Private*, pg. 2147
ISTONISH INC.—See Istonish Holding Company, Inc.; *U.S. Private*, pg. 2147
IT AUTHORITIES, INC.—See WidePoint Corporation; *U.S. Public*, pg. 2370
IT-CE EIG—See Groupe BPCE; *Int'l*, pg. 3098
ITEC HANKYU HANSHIN CO., LTD.—See Hankyu Hanshin Holdings Inc.; *Int'l*, pg. 3256
ITEGRIA, LLC—See RIA in a Box LLC; *U.S. Private*, pg. 3424
ITG SOFTWARE INC.—See Insight Venture Management, LLC; *U.S. Private*, pg. 2091
THE IT GUYS, LLC—See BMI Systems Corporation; *U.S. Private*, pg. 601
ITID CONSULTING, LTD.—See Dentsu Group Inc.; *Int'l*, pg. 2038
ITM COMMUNICATIONS LTD.—See Aliter Capital LLP; *Int'l*, pg. 329
IT PEOPLE CORPORATION, INC.; *U.S. Private*, pg. 2148
IT PROPHETS, LLC; *U.S. Private*, pg. 2148
IT SOLUTIONS CONSULTING LLC; *U.S. Private*, pg. 2148
ITSOURCE TECHNOLOGY INC.; *U.S. Private*, pg. 2150
ITWAY VAD—See Esprinet S.p.A.; *Int'l*, pg. 2506
ITZ INFORMATIONSTECHNOLOGIE GMBH—See Bechtle AG; *Int'l*, pg. 938
IVENTURE SOLUTIONS, INC.; *U.S. Private*, pg. 2151
IWISE AB—See Adecco Group AG; *Int'l*, pg. 140
J4B SOFTWARE & PUBLISHING LIMITED—See IDOX PLC; *Int'l*, pg. 3596
JABIL CIRCUIT, LLC—See Jabil Inc.; *U.S. Public*, pg. 1181
JABIL SDN BHD LTD.—See Jabil Inc.; *U.S. Public*, pg. 1181
JACK HENRY & ASSOCIATES, INC.; *U.S. Public*, pg. 1182
JACK HENRY BANKING—See Jack Henry & Associates, Inc.; *U.S. Public*, pg. 1182
JACK HENRY, LLC—See Jack Henry & Associates, Inc.; *U.S. Public*, pg. 1182
JACK HENRY SERVICES, LP—See Jack Henry & Associates, Inc.; *U.S. Public*, pg. 1182
JACK HENRY SYSTEMS, LP—See Jack Henry & Associates, Inc.; *U.S. Public*, pg. 1182
JACKSON & TULL; *U.S. Private*, pg. 2175
JACOBS STRATEGIC SOLUTIONS GROUP, INC.—See Jacobs Engineering Group, Inc.; *U.S. Public*, pg. 1185
JADARD TECHNOLOGY LIMITED—See Fitipower Integrated Technology, Inc.; *Int'l*, pg. 2695
JADE GLOBAL, INC.; *U.S. Private*, pg. 2181
JAPAN SYSTEMS CO., LTD.—See DXC Technology Company; *U.S. Public*, pg. 696
JASPER DESIGN AUTOMATION, A.B.—See Cadence Design Systems, Inc.; *U.S. Public*, pg. 418
JASPER DESIGN AUTOMATION DO BRASIL INFORMATICA E MICROELECTRONICA LTDA.—See Cadence Design Systems, Inc.; *U.S. Public*, pg. 418
JASPER DESIGN AUTOMATION, INC.—See Cadence Design Systems, Inc.; *U.S. Public*, pg. 419
JASPER DESIGN AUTOMATION - ISRAEL, LTD.—See Cadence Design Systems, Inc.; *U.S. Public*, pg. 418
JAT SOFTWARE, INC.—See Greatland Corporation; *U.S. Private*, pg. 1770
JBS SHANGHAI, INC.—See Amiya Corporation; *Int'l*, pg. 428
JC TECHNOLOGY, INC.; *U.S. Private*, pg. 2194
JEDAT INC.—See Argo Graphics Inc.; *Int'l*, pg. 562
JIM KRANTZ ASSOCIATES INC.; *U.S. Private*, pg. 2209
JJR SOLUTIONS, LLC.—See Logistics Management Institute; *U.S. Private*, pg. 2482
JMA INFORMATION TECHNOLOGY; *U.S. Private*, pg. 2214
JUST DYNAMICS SOFTWARE SOLUTIONS (PTY) LTD—See Capital Eye Investments Limited; *Int'l*, pg. 1311
KAIZEN TECHNOLOGIES, INC.; *U.S. Private*, pg. 2256
KAMIND IT INC.; *U.S. Private*, pg. 2258
KARMAK INC.; *U.S. Private*, pg. 2263
KARTENA AB—See Addnode Group AB; *Int'l*, pg. 130
KBM GROUP, INC.; *U.S. Private*, pg. 2268
KEDRIOS S.P.A.—See Cassa Depositi e Prestiti S.p.A.; *Int'l*, pg. 1354
KENILWORTH SYSTEMS CORP.; *U.S. Public*, pg. 1221
KENTUCKY INTERACTIVE, LLC—See Tyler Technologies, Inc.; *U.S. Public*, pg. 2208
KEY INFORMATION SYSTEMS, INC.; *U.S. Private*, pg. 2293
KEYLOGIC SYSTEMS, LLC—See System One Holdings, LLC; *U.S. Private*, pg. 3907
KEYSTONE DIGITAL IMAGING, INCORPORATED; *U.S. Private*, pg. 2296
THE KEYW HOLDING CORPORATION—See Jacobs Engineering Group, Inc.; *U.S. Public*, pg. 1186
KFORCE GOVERNMENT SOLUTIONS, INC.—See The Carlyle Group Inc.; *U.S. Public*, pg. 2048
KINEX INC.—See Planned Systems International, Inc.; *U.S. Private*, pg. 3196
KIWI CONSULTING EDV-BERATUNG GMBH—See adesso SE; *Int'l*, pg. 144
KIZAN TECHNOLOGIES; *U.S. Private*, pg. 2317
KJ TECHNOLOGY CONSULTING, INC.; *U.S. Private*, pg. 2317
K.K. PURAIDO—See ID Holdings Corporation; *Int'l*, pg. 3587
KLA-TENCOR SOFTWARE INDIA PRIVATE LIMITED—See KLA Corporation; *U.S. Public*, pg. 1268
KLD LABS, INC.—See Ensco Inc.; *U.S. Private*, pg. 1402
KLEINSCHMIDT INC.; *U.S. Private*, pg. 2319
KLSS INC; *U.S. Private*, pg. 2320
K MICRO INC.; *U.S. Private*, pg. 2249
KNACK SYSTEMS, LLC—See LKCM Headwater Investments; *U.S. Private*, pg. 2475
KNOVATION, INC.; *U.S. Private*, pg. 2323
KNOWLEDGE INFORMATION SOLUTIONS, INC.; *U.S. Private*, pg. 2323
KNOWLEDGELAKE INC.; *U.S. Private*, pg. 2324
KOAM ENGINEERING SYSTEMS INC.; *U.S. Private*, pg. 2325
KOGA-CITY INFORMATION CENTER CO., LTD.—See Core Corporation; *Int'l*, pg. 1797
KOVARUS, INC.; *U.S. Private*, pg. 2345
KPI PARTNERS, INC.; *U.S. Private*, pg. 2346
KRAFT & KENNEDY, INC.; *U.S. Private*, pg. 2348
KRATOS DEFENSE ENGINEERING SOLUTIONS, INC.—See Kratos Defense & Security Solutions, Inc.; *U.S. Public*, pg. 1276
KUTIR, CORP.; *U.S. Private*, pg. 2358
KYUSYU DTS CORPORATION—See DTS Corporation; *Int'l*, pg. 2217
L-3 COMMUNICATIONS NOVA ENGINEERING, INC.—See L3Harris Technologies, Inc.; *U.S. Public*, pg. 1282
L-3 MARINE SYSTEMS—See L3Harris Technologies, Inc.; *U.S. Public*, pg. 1283
LADYBUG RESOURCE GROUP, INC.; *U.S. Public*, pg. 1288
LANCET DATA SCIENCES; *U.S. Private*, pg. 2382
LANLOGIC, INC.—See Brown Brothers Harriman & Co.; *U.S. Private*, pg. 667
LANTRONIX HONG KONG LTD.—See Lantronix, Inc.; *U.S. Public*, pg. 1293
LATITUDE 34 TECHNOLOGIES, LLC—See Team Solutions Group, Inc.; *U.S. Private*, pg. 3950
LAURUS TECHNOLOGIES, INC.; *U.S. Private*, pg. 2400
LCG TECHNOLOGIES CORPORATION; *U.S. Private*, pg. 2403
LCI, INC.—See Verisk Analytics, Inc.; *U.S. Public*, pg. 2283
LEAD IT CORPORATION; *U.S. Private*, pg. 2405
LEADS.COM—See Siris Capital Group, LLC; *U.S. Private*, pg. 3675
LEAPFROG INTERACTIVE; *U.S. Private*, pg. 2407
LEASEDIMENSIONS, INC.—See Genpact Limited; *Int'l*, pg. 2927
LEIDOS ENGINEERING—See Leidos Holdings, Inc.; *U.S. Public*, pg. 1304
LEVEL 8 TECHNOLOGIES, INC.—See SMS Alternatives Inc.; *U.S. Public*, pg. 1896
LEVERAGED TECHNOLOGY INC.; *U.S. Private*, pg. 2435
LG HITACHI LTD.—See Hitachi, Ltd.; *Int'l*, pg. 3423
LGS INNOVATIONS LLC—See CACI International Inc.; *U.S. Public*, pg. 418
LIACOM SYSTEMS LTD.—See Advanced Business Software & Solutions Ltd.; *Int'l*, pg. 157
LIBERTYCOM LLC—See ERPSOFT Systems Ltd.; *Int'l*, pg. 2497
LIETZ DEVELOPMENT, INC.; *U.S. Private*, pg. 2448
LIFESCAPE MARKETING CORPORATION—See Dai Nippon Printing Co., Ltd.; *Int'l*, pg. 1915
LIGHTHOUSE COMPUTER SERVICES, INC.—See Converge Technology Solutions Corp.; *Int'l*, pg. 1787
LIGHTSPEED SYSTEMS INC.; *U.S. Private*, pg. 2453
LINDENBERG TECHNOLOGIES LLC—See Stockell Consulting Inc.; *U.S. Private*, pg. 3815
LINKSOURCE TECHNOLOGIES, LLC.—See UPSTACK, Inc.; *U.S. Private*, pg. 4312
LIQUID DEVELOPMENT LLC—See Canada Pension Plan Investment Board; *Int'l*, pg. 1280
LIQUID DEVELOPMENT LLC—See EQT AB; *Int'l*, pg. 2483
LIQUIDHUB, INC.; *U.S. Private*, pg. 2466
LIVEPROCESS CORP.; *U.S. Private*, pg. 2473
LIVERAMP, INC.—See LiveRamp Holdings, Inc.; *U.S. Public*, pg. 1333
LIVEWIRE KIOSK, INC.—See REDYREF Interactive Kiosks; *U.S. Private*, pg. 3381
LLC KELLY SERVICES IT SOLUTIONS—See Kelly Services, Inc.; *U.S. Public*, pg. 1219
LOCAL BOUNTI CORPORATION; *U.S. Public*, pg. 1337
LOCKHEED MARTIN CANADA INC.—See Lockheed Martin Corporation; *U.S. Public*, pg. 1338
LOCKHEED MARTIN UK LTD.—See Lockheed Martin Corporation; *U.S. Public*, pg. 1338
LOGICAL DESIGN SOLUTIONS INC.; *U.S. Private*, pg. 2481
LOGICALIS AUSTRALIA PTY LIMITED—See Datatec Limited; *Int'l*, pg. 1980
LOGICALIS DEUTSCHLAND GMBH—See Datatec Limited; *Int'l*, pg. 1980
LOGICALIS GROUP LTD.—See Datatec Limited; *Int'l*, pg. 1980
LOGICALIS, INC.—See Datatec Limited; *Int'l*, pg. 1980
LOGICALIS-MINTERS GMBH—See Datatec Limited; *Int'l*, pg. 1980
LOGICIELS EASYVISTA INC—See Eurazeo SE; *Int'l*, pg. 2528
LOGICOM SYSTEMS INC.; *U.S. Private*, pg. 2481
LOGIC SOLUTIONS, INC.; *U.S. Private*, pg. 2481
LOGISTER, S.A.—See Grifols, S.A.; *Int'l*, pg. 3084
LOGITECH NORDIC AB—See Logitech International S.A.; *U.S. Public*, pg. 1341
LONGITUDE LLC—See Nasdaq, Inc.; *U.S. Public*, pg. 1491
LOWEN CORPORATION - LOWEN IT DIVISION—See Lowen Corporation; *U.S. Private*, pg. 2505
LOXEO GMBH—See Durr AG; *Int'l*, pg. 2233
LOYALTYONE, INC.—See Bread Financial Holdings Inc.; *U.S. Public*, pg. 381
LPS INTEGRATION INC.—See Court Square Capital Partners, L.P.; *U.S. Private*, pg. 1068
LTS CORPORATION—See Sentrillion Corporation; *U.S. Private*, pg. 3610
LUCID GLOBAL, INC.—See Altaris Capital Partners, LLC; *U.S. Private*, pg. 206
LUCID TECHNOLOGY; *U.S. Private*, pg. 2511
LUFTHANSA SYSTEMS AS GMBH—See Deutsche Lufthansa AG; *Int'l*, pg. 2069
LUFTHANSA SYSTEMS ASIA PACIFIC PTE. LTD.—See Deutsche Lufthansa AG; *Int'l*, pg. 2069
LUFTHANSA SYSTEMS BUSINESS SOLUTIONS GMBH—See Deutsche Lufthansa AG; *Int'l*, pg. 2069
LUFTHANSA SYSTEMS FLIGHTNAV AG—See Deutsche Lufthansa AG; *Int'l*, pg. 2069
LUFTHANSA SYSTEMS HUNGARIA KFT—See Deutsche Lufthansa AG; *Int'l*, pg. 2069
LUFTHANSA SYSTEMS IS CONSULTING GMBH—See Deutsche Lufthansa AG; *Int'l*, pg. 2069
LUFTHANSA SYSTEMS NETWORK GMBH—See Deutsche Lufthansa AG; *Int'l*, pg. 2069
LUFTHANSA SYSTEMS NETWORK SERVICES GMBH—See Deutsche Lufthansa AG; *Int'l*, pg. 2069
LUFTHANSA SYSTEMS POLAND SP. Z O.O.—See Deutsche Lufthansa AG; *Int'l*, pg. 2069
LUIDIA, INC.; *U.S. Private*, pg. 2512
LUMENATE.COM; *U.S. Private*, pg. 2514
LUTECH SPA—See Apax Partners LLP; *Int'l*, pg. 501
LUXENDO GMBH—See Bruker Corporation; *U.S. Public*, pg. 407
LYNK USA, INC.—See B.O.S. Better OnLine Solutions Ltd.; *Int'l*, pg. 790
M2 TECHNOLOGY, INC.; *U.S. Private*, pg. 2530
M7 SERVICES, LLC; *U.S. Private*, pg. 2530
THE MACALUSO GROUP; *U.S. Private*, pg. 4073
MACH 4 AUTOMATISIERUNGS TECHNIK, GMBH.—See Omnicell, Inc.; *U.S. Public*, pg. 1572
MACHINELOGIC, LLC—See Sourcepass, Inc.; *U.S. Private*, pg. 3719
MACROLOGIC S.A.—See Asseco Poland S.A.; *Int'l*, pg. 641
MADEN TECH CONSULTING INC.; *U.S. Private*, pg. 2539
MADRONA SOLUTIONS GROUP; *U.S. Private*, pg. 2544
MAGEX CORPORATION; *U.S. Private*, pg. 2545
MAGIC SOFTWARE ENTERPRISES FRANCE—See Asseco Poland S.A.; *Int'l*, pg. 642
MAGIC SOFTWARE ENTERPRISES HUNGARY LTD.—See Asseco Poland S.A.; *Int'l*, pg. 642
MAGIC SOFTWARE ENTERPRISES INDIA PVT. LTD.—See Asseco Poland S.A.; *Int'l*, pg. 642
MAGIC SOFTWARE ENTERPRISES NEDERLAND B.V.—See Asseco Poland S.A.; *Int'l*, pg. 642

N.A.I.C.S. INDEX

541512 — COMPUTER SYSTEMS DE...

MAGIC SOFTWARE ENTERPRISES UK LTD.—See Asseco Poland S.A.; *Int'l*, pg. 642
MAGIC SOFTWARE JAPAN KK—See Asseco Poland S.A.; *Int'l*, pg. 642
MAINGEAR INC.; *U.S. Private*, pg. 2553
MAINLINE SYSTEMS DO BRASIL LTDA.—See H.I.G. Capital, LLC; *U.S. Private*, pg. 1833
MAINSPRING, INC.; *U.S. Private*, pg. 2553
MAINSTAY TECHNOLOGIES; *U.S. Private*, pg. 2553
MAINSTREAM DATA, INC.; *U.S. Private*, pg. 2553
MAINSTREET COMPUTERS, INC.—See The Beekman Group, LLC; *U.S. Private*, pg. 3992
MAINTECH, INCORPORATED—See Oak Lane Partners, LLC; *U.S. Private*, pg. 2983
MALAPUR CAPTIVE POWER LTD—See Avantha Group; *Int'l*, pg. 736
MANAGED BUSINESS SOLUTIONS LLC; *U.S. Private*, pg. 2559
MANGROVE SOFTWARE, INC.—See Asure Software, Inc.; *U.S. Public*, pg. 218
MANPOWERGROUP SOLUTIONS SRL—See ManpowerGroup Inc.; *U.S. Public*, pg. 1361
MANTECH SECURITY & MISSION ASSURANCE—See The Carlyle Group Inc.; *U.S. Public*, pg. 2048
MANTECH SRS TECHNOLOGIES, INC.—See The Carlyle Group Inc.; *U.S. Public*, pg. 2048
MANTECH TECHNICAL SERVICES INC.—See The Carlyle Group Inc.; *U.S. Public*, pg. 2049
MARCO TECHNOLOGIES, LLC—See Wells Fargo & Company; *U.S. Public*, pg. 2344
THE MARCUS BUCKINGHAM COMPANY, LLC.—See Automatic Data Processing, Inc.; *U.S. Public*, pg. 230
MARKET6, INC.—See The Kroger Co.; *U.S. Public*, pg. 2108
MARKETPLACE TECHNOLOGIES PVT LTD.—See Bombay Stock Exchange Limited; *Int'l*, pg. 1104
MARKETRON BROADCAST SOLUTIONS, LLC—See Diversis Capital, LLC; *U.S. Private*, pg. 1244
MARQETA, INC.; *U.S. Public*, pg. 1370
MARQUAM GROUP; *U.S. Private*, pg. 2586
MARSHALL RESOURCES INC.; *U.S. Private*, pg. 2593
MARVEL TECHNOLOGIES, INC.; *U.S. Private*, pg. 2597
MARYVILLE DATA SYSTEMS INC.; *U.S. Private*, pg. 2600
MASTECH DIGITAL, INC.; *U.S. Public*, pg. 1393
MATERIAL AUTOMATION (THAILAND) CO., LTD.—See Amiya Corporation; *Int'l*, pg. 428
MATRIKON DEUTSCHLAND AG—See Honeywell International Inc.; *U.S. Public*, pg. 1051
MATRIKON INTERNATIONAL INC.—See Honeywell International Inc.; *U.S. Public*, pg. 1051
MATRIKON MIDDLE EAST CO WLL—See Honeywell International Inc.; *U.S. Public*, pg. 1051
MATRIX CONSULTING, LLC.—See The Climatic Corporation; *U.S. Private*, pg. 4010
MATRIX INTEGRATION LLC; *U.S. Private*, pg. 2612
MATRIX IT LTD.—See Asseco Poland S.A.; *Int'l*, pg. 642
MATRIX SYSTEMS, INC.; *U.S. Private*, pg. 2612
MAVENIR SYSTEMS, INC.—See Siris Capital Group, LLC; *U.S. Private*, pg. 3673
MAVENS CONSULTING SERVICES, INC.—See Komodo Health, Inc.; *U.S. Private*, pg. 2342
MAX DIGITAL, LLC—See ACV Auctions Inc.; *U.S. Public*, pg. 37
MAXIMUS ASIA PTE. LTD.—See MAXIMUS, Inc.; *U.S. Public*, pg. 1402
MBL TECHNOLOGIES; *U.S. Private*, pg. 2624
MCCRACKEN FINANCIAL SOLUTIONS CORP.; *U.S. Private*, pg. 2630
MCKESSON PROVIDER TECHNOLOGIES—See McKesson Corporation; *U.S. Public*, pg. 1408
MCOR CO., LTD.—See CDS Co., Ltd.; *Int'l*, pg. 1371
MCR, LLC—See Arlington Capital Partners LLC; *U.S. Private*, pg. 328
MCS OF TAMPA, INC.; *U.S. Private*, pg. 2644
MDI ENTERTAINMENT LLC—See Light & Wonder, Inc.; *U.S. Public*, pg. 1314
MDSOL EUROPE LTD.—See Dassault Systemes S.A.; *Int'l*, pg. 1975
MEDIDATA SOLUTIONS, INC.—See Dassault Systemes S.A.; *Int'l*, pg. 1975
MEDIDATA SOLUTIONS K.K.—See Dassault Systemes S.A.; *Int'l*, pg. 1975
MEDPRO TECHNOLOGIES, LLC—See Bristol Bay Native Corporation; *U.S. Private*, pg. 656
MED TRENDS, INC.; *U.S. Private*, pg. 2650
MEDULLAN, INC.—See ZS Associates, Inc.; *U.S. Private*, pg. 4609
MED-USE S.R.L.—See GFT Technologies SE; *Int'l*, pg. 2957
MELLANOX FEDERAL SYSTEMS, LLC—See NVIDIA Corporation; *U.S. Public*, pg. 1558
MELROSEMAC, INC.; *U.S. Private*, pg. 2663
MERGE HEALTHCARE INCORPORATED—See International Business Machines Corporation; *U.S. Public*, pg. 1149
MERIDIAN IT LIMITED—See Meridian Group International, Inc.; *U.S. Private*, pg. 2673
MERIDIAN IT PTY LTD.—See Meridian Group International, Inc.; *U.S. Private*, pg. 2673
MERIDIAN IT SINGAPORE—See Meridian Group International, Inc.; *U.S. Private*, pg. 2673
MERIDIAN MEDICAL MANAGEMENT—See The Gores Group, LLC; *U.S. Private*, pg. 4035
MERIDIAN TECHNOLOGY GROUP; *U.S. Private*, pg. 2673
MERIZON GROUP INCORPORATED—See Xerox Holdings Corporation; *U.S. Public*, pg. 2389
MERLIN DIAGNOSTIKA GMBH—See Bruker Corporation; *U.S. Public*, pg. 405
METALKRAFT INDUSTRIES, INC.; *U.S. Private*, pg. 2681
METHODICAL INC.; *U.S. Private*, pg. 2683
METRICA INC.; *U.S. Private*, pg. 2685
METTERS INDUSTRIES, INC.; *U.S. Private*, pg. 2691
MGA SYSTEMS, INC.—See Roper Technologies, Inc.; *U.S. Public*, pg. 1814
MICROAGE, INC.—See Frontier Technology LLC; *U.S. Private*, pg. 1616
MICROEXCEL, INC.; *U.S. Private*, pg. 2703
MICROLOGIC BUSINESS SYSTEMS, INC.; *U.S. Private*, pg. 2703
MICROMENDERS INC.; *U.S. Private*, pg. 2703
MICRON CONSUMER PRODUCTS GROUP—See Micron Technology, Inc.; *U.S. Public*, pg. 1437
MICRON CONSUMER PRODUCTS—See Micron Technology, Inc.; *U.S. Public*, pg. 1437
MICRON EUROPE LIMITED—See Micron Technology, Inc.; *U.S. Public*, pg. 1437
MICRONNEXUS GMBH—See Canada Pension Plan Investment Board; *Int'l*, pg. 1279
MICRONNEXUS GMBH—See Cinven Limited; *Int'l*, pg. 1612
MICROSEP (PTY) LTD—See Waters Corporation; *U.S. Public*, pg. 2334
MICROTECHNOLOGIES LLC; *U.S. Private*, pg. 2704
MICRO-WORLD, INC.; *U.S. Private*, pg. 2702
MID DEL CONSULTING NETWORK; *U.S. Private*, pg. 2706
MIDDLEGROUND TECHNOLOGIES LLC—See Southfield Capital Advisors, LLC; *U.S. Private*, pg. 3736
MIDTECH PARTNERS, INC.—See PipelineRx; *U.S. Private*, pg. 3189
MILES DATA TECHNOLOGIES, LLC—See Sole Source Capital LLC; *U.S. Private*, pg. 3708
MILES TECHNOLOGIES, INC.; *U.S. Private*, pg. 2727
MILLENNIUM TECHNOLOGY GROUP LLC—See Rosen Hotels & Resorts, Inc.; *U.S. Private*, pg. 3483
MINDBANK CONSULTING GROUP OF VIRGINIA, INC.; *U.S. Private*, pg. 2740
MIPRO CONSULTING, LLC.; *U.S. Private*, pg. 2745
MISHA CONSULTING GROUP INC.; *U.S. Private*, pg. 2746
MKS UMETRICS AB—See MKS Instruments, Inc.; *U.S. Public*, pg. 1453
MOBICA LTD.—See Cognizant Technology Solutions Corporation; *U.S. Public*, pg. 524
MOBILECOMM PROFESSIONALS, INC.—See UST Global Inc.; *U.S. Private*, pg. 4324
MOBILEIRON AUSTRALIA—See MobileIron, Inc.; *U.S. Private*, pg. 2758
MOBILEIRON CENTRAL & EASTERN EUROPE—See MobileIron, Inc.; *U.S. Private*, pg. 2758
MOBILEIRON EMEA—See MobileIron, Inc.; *U.S. Private*, pg. 2758
MOBILEIRON FRANCE—See MobileIron, Inc.; *U.S. Private*, pg. 2758
MOBILEIRON HONG KONG—See MobileIron, Inc.; *U.S. Private*, pg. 2758
MOBILEIRON, INC.; *U.S. Private*, pg. 2758
MOBILEIRON JAPAN—See MobileIron, Inc.; *U.S. Private*, pg. 2758
MOBILEIRON SINGAPORE—See MobileIron, Inc.; *U.S. Private*, pg. 2758
MOBILEIRON UK & IRELAND—See MobileIron, Inc.; *U.S. Private*, pg. 2758
MOBIUS MANAGEMENT SYSTEMS BENELUX B.V.—See Allen Systems Group, Inc.; *U.S. Private*, pg. 180
MODCOMP, INC.—See CSP Inc.; *U.S. Public*, pg. 601
MODCOMP, LTD.—See CSP Inc.; *U.S. Public*, pg. 601
MODIS, INC.-NATIONAL ENTERPRISE PRACTICE—See Adecco Group AG; *Int'l*, pg. 140
MODUS CONSULT GMBH—See Bechtle AG; *Int'l*, pg. 938
MOMENT DESIGN—See Verizon Communications Inc.; *U.S. Public*, pg. 2285
MOMENTUM SOLUTIONZ, LLC—See BGSF, Inc.; *U.S. Public*, pg. 330
MOOVIT GMBH—See Avemio AG; *Int'l*, pg. 738
MORGANFRANKLIN CORPORATION; *U.S. Private*, pg. 2784
MORRIS DIGITAL WORKS, LLC—See Shivers Trading & Operating Company; *U.S. Private*, pg. 3638
MOVEMENT INDUSTRIES CORP.; *U.S. Public*, pg. 1480
MRESULT CORP; *U.S. Private*, pg. 2805
MSC.SOFTWARE LTD.—See Hexagon AB; *Int'l*, pg. 3369
MSC.SOFTWARE S.R.L.—See Hexagon AB; *Int'l*, pg. 3369
MSC.SOFTWARE S.R.O.—See Hexagon AB; *Int'l*, pg. 3369
MSL VERTEDA LIMITED—See FirstRand Limited; *Int'l*, pg. 2690
MSS TECHNOLOGIES INC.; *U.S. Private*, pg. 2808
MTAB LLC—See Poplar Capital Partners LLC; *U.S. Private*, pg. 3228
MTM TECHNOLOGIES, INC.; *U.S. Private*, pg. 2809
MULLIGAN TECHNOLOGIES, INC.; *U.S. Private*, pg. 2811
MULTIVISON INC.; *U.S. Private*, pg. 2813
MUNICIPIA S.P.A.—See Apax Partners LLP; *Int'l*, pg. 504
MUTUAL TELECOM SERVICES INC.—See Black Box Limited; *Int'l*, pg. 1058
MXOTECH, INC.—See Southfield Capital Advisors, LLC; *U.S. Private*, pg. 3736
MYCROFT INC.; *U.S. Private*, pg. 2824
N2GRATE GOVERNMENT TECHNOLOGY SOLUTIONS, LLC—See Source Capital, LLC; *U.S. Private*, pg. 3718
NAKOMA GROUP; *U.S. Private*, pg. 2831
NAMTEK CORP; *U.S. Private*, pg. 2832
NAMTRA BUSINESS SOLUTIONS, INC.; *U.S. Private*, pg. 2832
NANJING DIGITAL CHINA LIMITED—See Digital China Holdings Limited; *Int'l*, pg. 2121
NANTHEALTH, INC.—See NantWorks, LLC; *U.S. Private*, pg. 2834
NATIONAL COMPUTER SYSTEM CO. LTD.—See Haji Husein Alireza & Co. Ltd.; *Int'l*, pg. 3219
NATIONAL MEDICAL BILLING SERVICES LLC—See Aquiline Capital Partners LLC; *U.S. Private*, pg. 304
NATIONAL PRESORT, LP—See Warburg Pincus LLC; *U.S. Private*, pg. 4438
NATIONAL SYSTEMS CONSULTING L.P.; *U.S. Private*, pg. 2863
NAVEX, INC.—See Vista Equity Partners, LLC; *U.S. Private*, pg. 4400
NAVIMENTUM INFORMATION SYSTEM LIMITED—See Digital China Holdings Limited; *Int'l*, pg. 2121
NCOMPUTING, INC.—See ZeroDesktop, Inc.; *U.S. Private*, pg. 4602
NCR A/O—See NCR Voyix Corporation.; *U.S. Public*, pg. 1502
NCR AUSTRALIA PTY. LIMITED—See NCR Voyix Corporation.; *U.S. Public*, pg. 1502
NCR (BAHRAIN) W.L.L.—See NCR Voyix Corporation.; *U.S. Public*, pg. 1502
NCR BELGIUM & CO. SNC—See NCR Voyix Corporation.; *U.S. Public*, pg. 1502
NCR BILISIM SISTEMLERI LS—See NCR Voyix Corporation.; *U.S. Public*, pg. 1502
NCR BRASIL LTDA.—See NCR Voyix Corporation.; *U.S. Public*, pg. 1502
NCR CANADA LTD.—See NCR Voyix Corporation.; *U.S. Public*, pg. 1503
NCR CORPORATION (PHILIPPINES)—See NCR Voyix Corporation.; *U.S. Public*, pg. 1503
NCR CORP. - UAE BRANCH—See NCR Voyix Corporation.; *U.S. Public*, pg. 1502
NCR (CYPRUS) LIMITED—See NCR Voyix Corporation.; *U.S. Public*, pg. 1502
NCR CZESKA REPUBLIKA SPOL. S.R.O.—See NCR Voyix Corporation.; *U.S. Public*, pg. 1503
NCR DANMARK A/S—See NCR Voyix Corporation.; *U.S. Public*, pg. 1503
NCR DE CHILE, S.A.—See NCR Voyix Corporation.; *U.S. Public*, pg. 1503
NCR DOMINICANA C. POR A.—See NCR Voyix Corporation.; *U.S. Public*, pg. 1503
NCR ESPANA, S.A.—See NCR Voyix Corporation.; *U.S. Public*, pg. 1503
NCR FINLAND OY—See NCR Voyix Corporation.; *U.S. Public*, pg. 1503
NCR GHANA LIMITED—See NCR Voyix Corporation.; *U.S. Public*, pg. 1503
NCR GLOBAL SOLUTIONS LIMITED—See NCR Voyix Corporation.; *U.S. Public*, pg. 1503
NCR (HONG KONG) LIMITED—See NCR Voyix Corporation.; *U.S. Public*, pg. 1502
NCR (IRI) LTD.—See NCR Voyix Corporation.; *U.S. Public*, pg. 1502
NCR KENYA LTD.—See NCR Voyix Corporation.; *U.S. Public*, pg. 1503
NCR MAGYARORSZAG KFT.—See NCR Voyix Corporation.; *U.S. Public*, pg. 1503
NCR (MALAYSIA) SDN. BHD.—See NCR Voyix Corporation.; *U.S. Public*, pg. 1502
NCR (MIDDLE EAST) LIMITED—See NCR Voyix Corporation.; *U.S. Public*, pg. 1502
NCR NEDERLAND N.V.—See NCR Voyix Corporation.; *U.S. Public*, pg. 1503
NCR (NORTH AFRICA) LIMITED—See NCR Voyix Corporation.; *U.S. Public*, pg. 1502
NCR OSTERREICH GES.M.B.H.—See NCR Voyix Corporation.; *U.S. Public*, pg. 1503
NCR POLSKA SP.Z.O.O.—See NCR Voyix Corporation.; *U.S. Public*, pg. 1503
NCR SINGAPORE PTE LTD.—See NCR Voyix Corporation.; *U.S. Public*, pg. 1503
NCR SYSTEMS TAIWAN LIMITED—See NCR Voyix Corporation.; *U.S. Public*, pg. 1503
NCR TAIWAN SOFTWARE LTD—See NCR Voyix Corporation.; *U.S. Public*, pg. 1503
NCR (THAILAND) LIMITED—See NCR Voyix Corporation.; *U.S. Public*, pg. 1502
NCR UK GROUP LIMITED—See NCR Voyix Corporation.; *U.S. Public*, pg. 1503

541512 — COMPUTER SYSTEMS DE...

NCSI (PHILIPPINES) INC.—See Globe Telecom, Inc.; *Int'l*, pg. 3006
NDIVISION, INC.; *U.S. Public*, pg. 1504
NER HOLDINGS INC. - TORONTO FACILITY—See NER Holdings Inc.; *U.S. Private*, pg. 2885
NESS CANADA INC—See KKR & Co. Inc.; *U.S. Public*, pg. 1261
NESS CZECH S.R.O. - BRNO—See KKR & Co. Inc.; *U.S. Public*, pg. 1261
NESS CZECH S.R.O. - OSTRAVA—See KKR & Co. Inc.; *U.S. Public*, pg. 1261
NESS CZECH S.R.O—See KKR & Co. Inc.; *U.S. Public*, pg. 1261
NESS GLOBAL SERVICES LTD.—See KKR & Co. Inc.; *U.S. Public*, pg. 1261
NESS HUNGARY LTD.—See KKR & Co. Inc.; *U.S. Public*, pg. 1261
NESS KDC S.R.O.—See KKR & Co. Inc.; *U.S. Public*, pg. 1261
NESSPRO ITALY S.P.A. - MILAN—See Advantech Technologies Ltd.; *Int'l*, pg. 165
NESSPRO ITALY S.P.A. - ROME—See Advantech Technologies Ltd.; *Int'l*, pg. 165
NESSPRO PORTUGAL—See Advantech Technologies Ltd.; *Int'l*, pg. 165
NESSPRO SPAIN S.A.—See Advantech Technologies Ltd.; *Int'l*, pg. 165
NESS ROMANIA—See KKR & Co. Inc.; *U.S. Public*, pg. 1261
NESS SLOVENSKO A.S.—See KKR & Co. Inc.; *U.S. Public*, pg. 1261
NESS TECHNOLOGIES (INDIA) PVT. LTD. - HYDERABAD—See KKR & Co. Inc.; *U.S. Public*, pg. 1262
NESS TECHNOLOGIES (INDIA) PVT. LTD.—See KKR & Co. Inc.; *U.S. Public*, pg. 1261
NESS TECHNOLOGIES ISRAEL LTD—See Hilan Ltd.; *Int'l*, pg. 3390
NESS USA, INC.—See KKR & Co. Inc.; *U.S. Public*, pg. 1262
NET2EZ INC.; *U.S. Private*, pg. 2886
NET 2 TECHNOLOGY GROUP INC.; *U.S. Private*, pg. 2886
NETAPP AUSTRALIA PTY. LTD.—See NetApp, Inc.; *U.S. Public*, pg. 1507
NETAPP BRASIL SGAD LTDA—See NetApp, Inc.; *U.S. Public*, pg. 1507
NETAPP B.V.—See NetApp, Inc.; *U.S. Public*, pg. 1507
NETAPP CHILE LIMITADA—See NetApp, Inc.; *U.S. Public*, pg. 1507
NETAPP DENMARK APS—See NetApp, Inc.; *U.S. Public*, pg. 1507
NETAPP FRANCE SAS—See NetApp, Inc.; *U.S. Public*, pg. 1507
NETAPP G.K.—See NetApp, Inc.; *U.S. Public*, pg. 1507
NETAPP (HONG KONG) LIMITED—See NetApp, Inc.; *U.S. Public*, pg. 1507
NETAPP RTP—See NetApp, Inc.; *U.S. Public*, pg. 1507
NETAPP SINGAPORE PTE. LTD.—See NetApp, Inc.; *U.S. Public*, pg. 1507
NETAPP SOUTH AFRICA (PTY) LIMITED—See NetApp, Inc.; *U.S. Public*, pg. 1507
NETAPP SWEDEN AB—See NetApp, Inc.; *U.S. Public*, pg. 1507
NETAPP TEKNOLOJI LIMITED SIRKETI—See NetApp, Inc.; *U.S. Public*, pg. 1507
NETAPP (THAILAND) LIMITED—See NetApp, Inc.; *U.S. Public*, pg. 1507
NETCENTRICS CORP.—See Edgewater Services, LLC; *U.S. Private*, pg. 1335
NETCENTRIC TECHNOLOGY INC.—See Vistronix, Inc.; *U.S. Private*, pg. 4403
NETGAIN INFORMATION SYSTEMS CO. LLC—See Aunalytics, Inc.; *U.S. Private*, pg. 393
NETGEAR AUSTRALIA PTY. LTD.—See NETGEAR, Inc.; *U.S. Public*, pg. 1508
NETGEAR (BEIJING) NETWORK TECHNOLOGY CO., LTD.—See NETGEAR, Inc.; *U.S. Public*, pg. 1508
NETGEAR DEUTSCHLAND GMBH—See NETGEAR, Inc.; *U.S. Public*, pg. 1508
NETGEAR DO BRASIL PRODUTOS ELECTRONICOS LTDA.—See NETGEAR, Inc.; *U.S. Public*, pg. 1508
NETGEAR FILIAL SWEDEN—See NETGEAR, Inc.; *U.S. Public*, pg. 1508
NETGEAR FRANCE SAS—See NETGEAR, Inc.; *U.S. Public*, pg. 1508
NETGEAR INTERNATIONAL, INC. - ITALY—See NETGEAR, Inc.; *U.S. Public*, pg. 1508
NETGEAR INTERNATIONAL, INC. - KOREA—See NETGEAR, Inc.; *U.S. Public*, pg. 1508
NETGEAR INTERNATIONAL, INC. - MIDDLE EAST—See NETGEAR, Inc.; *U.S. Public*, pg. 1508
NETGEAR INTERNATIONAL, INC. - RUSSIA—See NETGEAR, Inc.; *U.S. Public*, pg. 1508
NETGEAR JAPAN GK—See NETGEAR, Inc.; *U.S. Public*, pg. 1508
NETGEAR NETHERLANDS B.V.—See NETGEAR, Inc.; *U.S. Public*, pg. 1508
NETGEAR POLAND SP. Z O.O.—See NETGEAR, Inc.; *U.S. Public*, pg. 1508
NETGEAR TECHNOLOGIES INDIA PTE. LTD.—See NETGEAR, Inc.; *U.S. Public*, pg. 1508
NETGEAR UK LIMITED—See NETGEAR, Inc.; *U.S. Public*, pg. 1508
NETLINK; *U.S. Private*, pg. 2887
NET MATRIX SOLUTIONS; *U.S. Private*, pg. 2886
NETPACE, INC.; *U.S. Private*, pg. 2887
NETRANOM COMMUNICATIONS, INC.—See Alpine Investors; *U.S. Private*, pg. 201
NETRATE SYSTEMS, INC.—See Roper Technologies, Inc.; *U.S. Public*, pg. 1814
NETREO, INC.; *U.S. Private*, pg. 2887
NETSCOUT BERLIN GMBH & CO. KG—See NetScout Systems, Inc.; *U.S. Public*, pg. 1509
NETSCOUT SYSTEMS CANADA, INC.—See NetScout Systems, Inc.; *U.S. Public*, pg. 1509
NETSCOUT SYSTEMS, INC.; *U.S. Public*, pg. 1509
NETSCOUT SYSTEMS JAPAN K.K.—See NetScout Systems, Inc.; *U.S. Public*, pg. 1509
NETSCOUT SYSTEMS MEXICO, S.A. DE C.V.—See NetScout Systems, Inc.; *U.S. Public*, pg. 1509
NETSOL CONNECT (PRIVATE), LTD.—See NetSol Technologies, Inc.; *U.S. Public*, pg. 1509
NETSTARLOGICALIS MALAYSIA SDN BHD—See Datatec Limited; *Int'l*, pg. 1980
NETSURION, LLC—See Providence Equity Partners L.L.C.; *U.S. Private*, pg. 3293
NETVISION RESOURCES, INC.; *U.S. Private*, pg. 2888
NETWOLVES, LLC—See Vaso Corporation; *U.S. Public*, pg. 2276
NETWORK21 CO., LTD.—See Digital Hearts Holdings Co., Ltd.; *Int'l*, pg. 2122
NETWORK ALLIANCE, INC.—See Southfield Capital Advisors, LLC; *U.S. Private*, pg. 3736
NETWORK APPLIANCE SAUDI ARABIA LTD—See NetApp, Inc.; *U.S. Public*, pg. 1507
NETWORK COMPUTING ARCHITECTS, INC.—See IS-SQUARED Inc.; *U.S. Private*, pg. 2147
NETWORK COMPUTING TECHNOLOGY & SERVICES SARL—See ManpowerGroup Inc.; *U.S. Public*, pg. 1362
NETWORK DATA SYSTEMS INC.; *U.S. Private*, pg. 2889
NETWORKD CORP.—See Signal Peak Venture Partners, LLC; *U.S. Private*, pg. 3649
NETWORK DESIGN & INTEGRATION, INC.—See Novacoast, Inc.; *U.S. Private*, pg. 2966
NET@WORK, INC.; *U.S. Private*, pg. 2886
NETWORKING TECHNOLOGIES & SUPPORT, INC.; *U.S. Private*, pg. 2889
NETWORK MAPPING LIMITED—See Trimble, Inc.; *U.S. Public*, pg. 2190
NETWORK OUTSOURCE, INC.; *U.S. Private*, pg. 2889
THE NETWORK PRO, INC.—See IT Solutions Consulting LLC; *U.S. Private*, pg. 2148
NETWORK SERVICES GROUP, LLC—See Windstream Holdings, Inc.; *U.S. Public*, pg. 2373
NETWORKS UNLIMITED, INC.; *U.S. Private*, pg. 2889
NETWOVEN INC.; *U.S. Private*, pg. 2889
NET XPERTS LLC; *U.S. Private*, pg. 2886
NETXUSA, INC.—See Hainan Traffic Administration Holding Co., Ltd.; *Int'l*, pg. 3215
NEURIO TECHNOLOGY ULC—See Generac Holdings Inc.; *U.S. Public*, pg. 912
NEW DAWN TECHNOLOGIES, INC.—See Daily Journal Corporation; *U.S. Public*, pg. 620
NEWFIELD INFORMATION TECHNOLOGY LIMITED—See Xerox Holdings Corporation; *U.S. Public*, pg. 2388
NEWTON CONSULTING, LLC; *U.S. Private*, pg. 2918
NEXIUS SOLUTIONS INC.; *U.S. Private*, pg. 2919
N. HARRIS COMPUTER CORPORATION—See Constellation Software Inc.; *Int'l*, pg. 1773
NIANDC NETSYSTEM INC.—See International Business Machines Corporation; *U.S. Public*, pg. 1147
NICE-BUSINESS SOLUTIONS FINLAND OY—See Fujitsu Limited; *Int'l*, pg. 2837
NIIT AIRLINE TECHNOLOGIES GMBH—See Coforge Ltd.; *Int'l*, pg. 1693
NIIT TECHNOLOGIES AG—See Coforge Ltd.; *Int'l*, pg. 1693
NIIT TECHNOLOGIES GMBH—See Coforge Ltd.; *Int'l*, pg. 1693
NIIT TECHNOLOGIES GMBH—See Coforge Ltd.; *Int'l*, pg. 1693
NIPPON DENTSU CO., LTD.—See EXEO Group Inc.; *Int'l*, pg. 2253
NIPPON GPS DATA SERVICE CORPORATION—See Hitachi Zosen Corporation; *Int'l*, pg. 3412
NI SOUTHEAST ASIA SDN. BHD.—See National Instruments Corporation; *U.S. Private*, pg. 2857
NITYO INFOTECH CORPORATION; *U.S. Private*, pg. 2930
NIVIS LLC; *U.S. Private*, pg. 2930
NIXIL PTY. LTD.—See Axxiome AG; *Int'l*, pg. 773
NIXSOL INC.; *U.S. Private*, pg. 2930
NOBLE SYSTEMS AUSTRALIA PTY LIMITED—See Vector Capital Management, L.P.; *U.S. Private*, pg. 4350
NOBLE SYSTEMS FRANCE S.A.R.L.—See Vector Capital Management, L.P.; *U.S. Private*, pg. 4350
NOBLE SYSTEMS INDIA PVT. LTD.—See Vector Capital Management, L.P.; *U.S. Private*, pg. 4350
NOBLE SYSTEMS PHILIPPINES CORPORATION—See Vector Capital Management, L.P.; *U.S. Private*, pg. 4350
NORDCOM S.P.A.—See FNM S.p.A.; *Int'l*, pg. 2718
NORTHFORGE INNOVATIONS INC.—See Access Co., Ltd.; *Int'l*, pg. 88
NORTHPORT NETWORK SYSTEMS, INC.; *U.S. Private*, pg. 2957
NORTHROP GRUMMAN AEROSPACE SYSTEMS-EL SEGUNDO—See Northrop Grumman Corporation; *U.S. Public*, pg. 1540
NORTHROP GRUMMAN AEROSPACE SYSTEMS-SAINT AUGUSTINE—See Northrop Grumman Corporation; *U.S. Public*, pg. 1540
NORTHROP GRUMMAN DEFENSIVE SYSTEMS—See Northrop Grumman Corporation; *U.S. Public*, pg. 1540
NORTHROP GRUMMAN INFORMATION TECHNOLOGY, INC.—See Northrop Grumman Corporation; *U.S. Public*, pg. 1540
NORTHROP GRUMMAN TECHNICAL SERVICES-KANSAS CITY—See Northrop Grumman Corporation; *U.S. Public*, pg. 1541
NORTHSTAR.IO, INC.; *U.S. Private*, pg. 2958
NOVACOAST, INC.; *U.S. Private*, pg. 2966
NOVERKA CONSEIL INC.—See Alan Allman Associates SA; *Int'l*, pg. 290
NOWCOM CORPORATION; *U.S. Private*, pg. 2969
NSR SOLUTIONS INC.; *U.S. Private*, pg. 2970
NTH GENERATION COMPUTING, INCORPORATED; *U.S. Private*, pg. 2971
N-TIERACTIVE INCORPORATED; *U.S. Private*, pg. 2827
NUANCE COMMUNICATIONS GMBH—See Microsoft Corporation; *U.S. Public*, pg. 1442
NUANCE COMMUNICATIONS HEALTHCARE GERMANY GMBH—See Microsoft Corporation; *U.S. Public*, pg. 1442
NUANCE COMMUNICATIONS HONG KONG LIMITED—See Microsoft Corporation; *U.S. Public*, pg. 1442
NUANCE COMMUNICATIONS IBERICA SA—See Microsoft Corporation; *U.S. Public*, pg. 1442
NUL SYSTEM SERVICES CORPORATION—See BIPROGY Inc.; *Int'l*, pg. 1045
NUMERA SISTEMI E INFORMATICA S.P.A.—See BPER BANCA S.p.A; *Int'l*, pg. 1132
NUTRAVEL TECHNOLOGY SOLUTIONS, LLC—See Airlines Reporting Corporation; *U.S. Private*, pg. 141
NUVEK LLC—See Varsity Contractors, Inc.; *U.S. Private*, pg. 4347
NWN CORPORATION—See American Securities LLC; *U.S. Private*, pg. 250
OAKLAND CONSULTING GROUP; *U.S. Private*, pg. 2984
OASIS SYSTEMS, LLC; *U.S. Private*, pg. 2986
OBERMAN TIVOLI MILLER PICKERT; *U.S. Private*, pg. 2987
OBERTHUR CARD SYSTEMS ROMANIA S.R.L—See Advent International Corporation; *U.S. Private*, pg. 102
OBJECT PARTNERS, INC.—See Trinity Hunt Management, L.P.; *U.S. Private*, pg. 4234
OBJECTWAVE CORPORATION—See AEA Investors LP; *U.S. Private*, pg. 114
OBVIENT STRATEGIES, INC.—See ABB Ltd.; *Int'l*, pg. 52
OBXTEK INC.; *U.S. Private*, pg. 2988
OCTO TECHNOLOGY SA—See Accenture plc; *Int'l*, pg. 84
ODIN TECHNOLOGIES—See Quake Global, Inc.; *U.S. Private*, pg. 3316
OHO INTERACTIVE; *U.S. Private*, pg. 3006
OITA COMPUTER ENGINEERING & CONSULTING, LTD.—See Computer Engineering & Consulting Ltd.; *Int'l*, pg. 1759
OLD TOWN IT, LLC; *U.S. Private*, pg. 3009
OMNIGO SOFTWARE LLC—See The Riverside Company; *U.S. Private*, pg. 4109
OMNITI; *U.S. Private*, pg. 3017
ONEPATH SYSTEMS, LLC—See Trivest Partners, LP; *U.S. Private*, pg. 4241
ONESOURCE VIRTUAL; *U.S. Private*, pg. 3025
ONESPAN INC.; *U.S. Public*, pg. 1603
ONESPRING LLC; *U.S. Private*, pg. 3025
ONSTREAM MEDIA CORPORATION; *U.S. Private*, pg. 3028
OOO CSB-SYSTEM—See CSB-System AG; *Int'l*, pg. 1862
OPENLOGIX CORP.—See K2 Partnering Solutions, Inc.; *U.S. Private*, pg. 2253
OPEN SYSTEMS TECHNOLOGIES, INC.; *U.S. Private*, pg. 3029
OPERATIONAL RESEARCH CONSULTANTS, INC.—See WidePoint Corporation; *U.S. Public*, pg. 2370
OPTECH, LLC; *U.S. Private*, pg. 3034
OPTIMUM TECHNOLOGY SOLUTIONS INC.; *U.S. Private*, pg. 3035
OPTIMUS CORPORATION; *U.S. Private*, pg. 3035
ORACLE CORPORATION UK LTD.-LONDON—See Oracle Corporation; *U.S. Public*, pg. 1612
ORACLE HARDWARE RUSSIA—See Oracle Corporation; *U.S. Public*, pg. 1611
ORION COMMUNICATIONS, INC.—See Fieldware, LLC; *U.S. Private*, pg. 1504

N.A.I.C.S. INDEX

541512 — COMPUTER SYSTEMS DE...

ORION GLOBAL SOLUTIONS, LLC; *U.S. Private*, pg. 3043
ORION SOLUTIONS, INC.—See Ayalaland Logistics Holdings Corp.; *Int'l*, pg. 774
OSIATIS BELGIUM NV—See Econocom Group SA; *Int'l*, pg. 2298
OSIATIS COMPUTER SERVICES GMBH—See Econocom Group SA; *Int'l*, pg. 2298
OSIATIS SA—See Econocom Group SA; *Int'l*, pg. 2298
OSS IM VIEW INC.—See Creative Vistas Inc.; *Int'l*, pg. 1834
OS SUPPORT, INC.; *U.S. Private*, pg. 3046
OTAVA, LLC—See Schurz Communications, Inc.; *U.S. Private*, pg. 3571
OUTLINE SYSTEMS LLC—See Vista Equity Partners, LLC; *U.S. Private*, pg. 4396
OUTSCALE SAS—See Dassault Systemes S.A.; *Int'l*, pg. 1975
OUTSOURCE IT CORP; *U.S. Private*, pg. 3052
OVERTURE PARTNERS, LLC; *U.S. Private*, pg. 3054
OXFORD CONSULTING GROUP, INC.; *U.S. Private*, pg. 3057
OYO RMS CORPORATION—See Moody's Corporation; *U.S. Public*, pg. 1469
PACE SYSTEMS, INC.; *U.S. Private*, pg. 3064
PACIFIC MICRO-TECH; *U.S. Private*, pg. 3068
PACIFIC SOFTWARE PUBLISHING, INC.; *U.S. Private*, pg. 3070
PACIFIC STAR COMMUNICATIONS, INC.; *U.S. Private*, pg. 3071
PA CONSULTING GROUP AB—See The Carlyle Group Inc.; *U.S. Public*, pg. 2051
PA CONSULTING GROUP A/S—See The Carlyle Group Inc.; *U.S. Public*, pg. 2051
PA CONSULTING GROUP AS—See The Carlyle Group Inc.; *U.S. Public*, pg. 2051
PA CONSULTING GROUP GMBH—See The Carlyle Group Inc.; *U.S. Public*, pg. 2051
PA CONSULTING GROUP INC—See The Carlyle Group Inc.; *U.S. Public*, pg. 2051
PA CONSULTING SERVICES (INDIA) PRIVATE LIMITED—See The Carlyle Group Inc.; *U.S. Public*, pg. 2052
PA CONSULTING SERVICES LIMITED—See The Carlyle Group Inc.; *U.S. Public*, pg. 2052
PACTERA TECHNOLOGY JAPAN CO., LTD.—See China Electronics Corporation; *Int'l*, pg. 1499
PAGERDUTY, INC.; *U.S. Public*, pg. 1634
PAKEDGE DEVICE & SOFTWARE INC.—See Resideo Technologies, Inc.; *U.S. Public*, pg. 1790
PARACON SA (PTY) LIMITED—See Adcorp Holdings Limited; *Int'l*, pg. 127
PARADATA FINANCIAL SYSTEMS—See World Acceptance Corporation; *U.S. Public*, pg. 2379
PARAGON COMPUTER PROFESSIONALS INC.—See CGI Inc.; *Int'l*, pg. 1434
PARAGUS STRATEGIC IT; *U.S. Private*, pg. 3092
PARAMETRIC TECHNOLOGY (CANADA) LTD. - WATERLOO—See PTC Inc.; *U.S. Public*, pg. 1734
PARSE, LLC—See Meta Platforms, Inc.; *U.S. Public*, pg. 1427
PARTMAKER, INC.—See Autodesk, Inc.; *U.S. Public*, pg. 229
PARTNER'S CONSULTING, INC.; *U.S. Private*, pg. 3101
PARTNERS CONSULTING SERVICES, INC.—See Calance Corporation; *Int'l*, pg. 1261
PASSAGEWAYS, LLC; *U.S. Private*, pg. 3104
PATIENTBOND, LLC—See Upfront Healthcare Services, Inc.; *U.S. Private*, pg. 4311
PAVION CORP.—See Wind Point Advisors LLC; *U.S. Private*, pg. 4535
PAWAA SOFTWARE PRIVATE LIMITED—See Cisco Systems, Inc.; *U.S. Public*, pg. 500
PAYBOX CORP—See Aquiline Capital Partners LLC; *U.S. Private*, pg. 305
PCC SYSTEMS LLC—See Professional Control Corporation; *U.S. Private*, pg. 3274
PC MALL GOV, INC.—See Insight Enterprises, Inc.; *U.S. Public*, pg. 1130
PC SPECIALISTS, INC.—See Converge Technology Solutions Corp.; *Int'l*, pg. 1787
PDF SOLUTIONS GMBH—See PDF Solutions, Inc.; *U.S. Public*, pg. 1658
P. DUSSMANN EOOD—See Dussmann Stiftung & Co. KGaA; *Int'l*, pg. 2234
P. DUSSMANN KFT.—See Dussmann Stiftung & Co. KGaA; *Int'l*, pg. 2234
P. DUSSMANN ROMANIA S.R.L.—See Dussmann Stiftung & Co. KGaA; *Int'l*, pg. 2234
P. DUSSMANN SPOL. S.R.O.—See Dussmann Stiftung & Co. KGaA; *Int'l*, pg. 2235
PEAK RESOURCES, INC.; *U.S. Private*, pg. 3123
PEAKSWARE, LLC; *U.S. Private*, pg. 3125
PEERLESS TECHNOLOGIES CORPORATION; *U.S. Private*, pg. 3129
PEGASUS TECHNOLOGY SOLUTIONS, LLC; *U.S. Private*, pg. 3129
PENGUIN COMPUTING INC.—See Penguin Solutions, Inc.; *U.S. Public*, pg. 1661
PENTANA INC.—See HgCapital Trust plc; *Int'l*, pg. 3377

PENTANA LIMITED—See HgCapital Trust plc; *Int'l*, pg. 3377
PERAGO FINANCIAL SYSTEMS ENABLERS (PTY) LTD—See Cassa Depositi e Prestiti S.p.A.; *Int'l*, pg. 1354
PERATON CORP.—See Veritas Capital Fund Management, LLC; *U.S. Private*, pg. 4363
PERFICIENT, INC. - NEW ORLEANS—See EQT AB; *Int'l*, pg. 2483
PERFICIENT, INC. - PLANO—See EQT AB; *Int'l*, pg. 2483
PERFICIENT, INC.—See EQT AB; *Int'l*, pg. 2483
PERTH INTERNATIONAL EXCHANGE PTY LTD—See Aware Super Pty Ltd; *Int'l*, pg. 752
PERVIGIL, INC.—See Mobius Partners Enterprise Solutions; *U.S. Private*, pg. 2758
PETRO-CYBERWORKS INFORMATION TECHNOLOGY CO., LTD.—See China Petrochemical Corporation; *Int'l*, pg. 1539
PFSWEB, INC.—See GXO Logistics, Inc.; *U.S. Public*, pg. 975
PG CALC, INC.—See GTCR LLC; *U.S. Private*, pg. 1805
PHOENIX INTEGRATION, INC. - NORTH AMERICA—See ANSYS, Inc.; *U.S. Public*, pg. 139
PHOENIX INTEGRATION, INC.—See ANSYS, Inc.; *U.S. Public*, pg. 139
PICIS CLINICAL SOLUTIONS, INC.—See Constellation Software Inc.; *Int'l*, pg. 1774
PICIS CLINICAL SOLUTIONS, LTD.—See Constellation Software Inc.; *Int'l*, pg. 1774
PICIS CLINICAL SOLUTIONS S.A.—See Constellation Software Inc.; *Int'l*, pg. 1774
PING HD LLC—See The Jordan Company, L.P.; *U.S. Private*, pg. 4062
PINNACLE MICRO (PTY) LIMITED—See Alviva Holdings Limited; *Int'l*, pg. 402
PINNACLE TECHNICAL RESOURCES, INC.; *U.S. Private*, pg. 3185
PINNACLE TEK, INC.—See Scienture Holdings, Inc.; *U.S. Public*, pg. 1849
PIRAEUS DATA LLC.; *U.S. Private*, pg. 3190
PIREAN LTD.—See Arlington Capital Partners LLC; *U.S. Private*, pg. 327
PIVOTAL CORPORATION—See TA Associates, Inc.; *U.S. Private*, pg. 3914
PIXELCREEK TECHNOLOGY INC.—See Adams Remco Inc.; *U.S. Private*, pg. 75
PLANNED SYSTEMS INTERNATIONAL, INC.; *U.S. Private*, pg. 3196
PLASCO, LLC—See Odyssey Investment Partners, LLC; *U.S. Private*, pg. 2994
PLATTE RIVER NETWORKS INC.; *U.S. Private*, pg. 3211
P&L TECHNOLOGY, INC.—See Transom Capital Group, LLC; *U.S. Private*, pg. 4210
PLUMTREE GROUP LIMITED—See HgCapital Trust plc; *Int'l*, pg. 3378
POLARIS ALPHA ADVANCED SYSTEMS, INC.—See Parsons Corporation; *U.S. Public*, pg. 1651
POLI COMPUTER PC KFT. LTD.—See 4iG Nyrt.; *Int'l*, pg. 12
POMEROY IT SOLUTIONS SALES COMPANY, INC.—See Aurelius Equity Opportunities SE & Co. KGaA; *Int'l*, pg. 708
PORTAL SOLUTIONS, LLC; *U.S. Private*, pg. 3231
POSMATIC GMBH—See Shift4 Payments, Inc.; *U.S. Public*, pg. 1875
POWERLAND ,COMPUTERS LTD.—See Xerox Holdings Corporation; *U.S. Public*, pg. 2386
POWERSPORTS NETWORK, INC.—See Irish Times; *U.S. Private*, pg. 2138
POWERTEAM, INC.—See HCL Technologies Ltd.; *Int'l*, pg. 3298
PP 2000 BUSINESS INTEGRATION AG—See Bechtle AG; *Int'l*, pg. 938
PQR B.V.—See Bechtle AG; *Int'l*, pg. 938
PRACTICE VELOCITY, LLC—See Warburg Pincus LLC; *U.S. Private*, pg. 4438
PRAGMATICS INC.; *U.S. Private*, pg. 3242
PRAGMATIX, INC.—See Anexio, Inc.; *U.S. Private*, pg. 281
PRAMO EKONOMI & DATA AB—See TowerBrook Capital Partners, L.P.; *U.S. Private*, pg. 4195
PRAXIS TECHNOLOGY CO. LTD.—See Capgemini SE; *Int'l*, pg. 1304
PRECISE SYSTEMS, INC.—See Tucson Embedded Systems, Inc.; *U.S. Private*, pg. 4256
PREFERRED DATA SYSTEMS LLC; *U.S. Private*, pg. 3247
PREGO S.A.—See Computer Generated Solutions Inc.; *U.S. Private*, pg. 1005
PRELUDE SYSTEMS, INC.; *U.S. Private*, pg. 3249
PREMIERE CONFERENCING PTY LIMITED—See Siris Capital Group, LLC; *U.S. Private*, pg. 3674
PREMIER ELECTION SOLUTIONS, INC.—See Lee Enterprises, Incorporated; *U.S. Public*, pg. 1298
PREMIER ELECTION SOLUTIONS, INC.—See McCarthy Group, LLC; *U.S. Private*, pg. 2626
PRESIDIO - CALEDONIA—See BC Partners LLP; *Int'l*, pg. 925
PRESIDIO - LEWISVILLE—See BC Partners LLP; *Int'l*, pg. 925
PRESIDIO - NORCROSS—See BC Partners LLP; *Int'l*, pg. 925
PRIVATEERIT, LLC; *U.S. Private*, pg. 3268

PROACTIVE TECHNOLOGIES, LLC—See WestView Capital Partners, L.P.; *U.S. Private*, pg. 4501
PROCURIAN INDIA PRIVATE LIMITED—See Accenture plc; *Int'l*, pg. 87
PROCURIAN LLC—See Accenture plc; *Int'l*, pg. 87
PRODLIB OY—See Byggfakta Group Nordic HoldCo AB; *Int'l*, pg. 1235
PROFESSIONAL SUPPORT INC.; *U.S. Private*, pg. 3276
PROGENY SYSTEMS CORPORATION; *U.S. Private*, pg. 3277
PROJECT INFORMATICA SRL—See H.I.G. Capital, LLC; *U.S. Private*, pg. 1831
PROJECT ONE INC.—See Stone Point Capital LLC; *U.S. Private*, pg. 3823
PROMAKS YAZILIM SANAYI VE TICARET A.S.—See Vontier Corporation; *U.S. Public*, pg. 2309
PROMEDIA TECHNOLOGY SERVICES INC.—See Advanced AV, LLC; *U.S. Private*, pg. 88
PROOFPOINT GMBH—See Thoma Bravo, L.P.; *U.S. Private*, pg. 4151
PROPELLER MEDIA WORKS, LLC; *U.S. Private*, pg. 3285
PROSERVIA SA—See ManpowerGroup Inc.; *U.S. Public*, pg. 1360
PROS FRANCE SAS—See PROS Holdings, Inc.; *U.S. Public*, pg. 1728
PROSODIE FRANCE S.A.—See Capgemini SE; *Int'l*, pg. 1307
PROSODIE IBERICA S.L.U.—See Capgemini SE; *Int'l*, pg. 1307
PROSOFT TECHNOLOGY GROUP INC.; *U.S. Private*, pg. 3287
PROSYNC TECHNOLOGY GROUP LLC; *U.S. Private*, pg. 3289
PROTRAK INTERNATIONAL, INC.—See Backstop Solutions Group, LLC; *U.S. Public*, pg. 423
PROVADE, INC.—See Pinnacle Technical Resources, Inc.; *U.S. Private*, pg. 3185
PROVIDYN INC.—See Frontenac Company LLC; *U.S. Private*, pg. 1614
PSB GMBH—See Bechtle AG; *Int'l*, pg. 938
PSC GROUP, LLC—See Netrix LLC; *U.S. Private*, pg. 2888
PSR ENGINEERING SOLUTIONS D.O.O.—See RCM Technologies, Inc.; *U.S. Public*, pg. 1767
PSYCHOLOGICAL SERVICES, INC.—See ABRY Partners, LLC; *U.S. Private*, pg. 43
PSYCHSOFT; *U.S. Private*, pg. 3298
PT CISCO SYSTEMS INDONESIA—See Cisco Systems, Inc.; *U.S. Public*, pg. 500
PT DGIT INDONESIA—See CSG Systems International, Inc.; *U.S. Public*, pg. 601
PT DST GLOBAL SOLUTIONS INDONESIA—See SS&C Technologies Holdings, Inc.; *U.S. Public*, pg. 1923
PT. HITACHI EBWORX INDONESIA—See Hitachi, Ltd.; *Int'l*, pg. 3422
PT SOFTWARE AG INDONESIA OPERATIONS—See Silver Lake Group, LLC; *U.S. Private*, pg. 3658
PUZZLEPART AS—See Crayon Group Holding ASA; *Int'l*, pg. 1829
Q1 LABS INC.—See International Business Machines Corporation; *U.S. Public*, pg. 1149
Q ANALYSTS LLC—See Bridgepoint Group Plc; *Int'l*, pg. 1154
QA SYSTEMS INC.; *U.S. Private*, pg. 3312
QOGNIFY, INC.—See Hexagon AB; *Int'l*, pg. 3369
QOS NETWORKS LLC—See DigitalBridge Group, Inc.; *U.S. Public*, pg. 665
QOS NETWORKS LLC—See EQT AB; *Int'l*, pg. 2481
QUAKE GLOBAL, INC.; *U.S. Private*, pg. 3316
QUALIFACTS SYSTEMS, INC.—See Warburg Pincus LLC; *U.S. Private*, pg. 4439
QUALITY SOFTWARE SERVICES, INC.—See UnitedHealth Group Incorporated; *U.S. Public*, pg. 2250
QUANTUMKORE INC.; *U.S. Public*, pg. 1754
QUANTUM RESEARCH INTERNATIONAL, INC.; *U.S. Private*, pg. 3323
QUANTUM SECURE, INC.—See ASSA ABLOY AB; *Int'l*, pg. 637
QUARK SECURITY INC.—See Parsons Corporation; *U.S. Public*, pg. 1651
QUEBIT CONSULTING, LLC; *U.S. Private*, pg. 3325
QUEST MEDIA & SUPPLIES INC.—See Brown Brothers Harriman & Co.; *U.S. Private*, pg. 667
QUICKPIVOT CORPORATION—See MacAndrews & Forbes Incorporated; *U.S. Private*, pg. 2532
QUICK SOLUTIONS INC.; *U.S. Private*, pg. 3326
QUINNOX, INC.; *U.S. Private*, pg. 3328
RADIANT SYSTEMS, INC.—See NCR Voyix Corporation; *U.S. Public*, pg. 1503
RAIN KING SOFTWARE, INC.—See TA Associates, Inc.; *U.S. Private*, pg. 3915
RAMBUS K.K.—See Rambus Inc.; *U.S. Public*, pg. 1762
RAMP TECHNOLOGY GROUP, LLC; *U.S. Private*, pg. 3351
RAND A TECHNOLOGY CORPORATION—See Ampersand Management LLC; *U.S. Private*, pg. 265
RANGAM CONSULTANTS INC.; *U.S. Private*, pg. 3354
RAPID TECHNOLOGIES INC.—See Sverica Capital Management LP; *U.S. Private*, pg. 3889
RAPIER SOLUTIONS, INC.; *U.S. Private*, pg. 3356

541512 — COMPUTER SYSTEMS DE...

RAPTOR TECHNOLOGIES, INC; *U.S. Private*, pg. 3356
RAYTHEON SI GOVERNMENT SOLUTIONS—See RTX Corporation; *U.S. Public*, pg. 1824
RCG GLOBAL SERVICES, INC.—See Frontenac Company LLC; *U.S. Private*, pg. 1614
RCN COMMUNICATIONS LLC—See Renodis, Inc.; *U.S. Private*, pg. 3399
RDR INC; *U.S. Private*, pg. 3364
RDSK, INC.; *U.S. Private*, pg. 3364
REALPHA TECH CORP; *U.S. Public*, pg. 1768
REALTA' INFORMATCA SRL—See Capgemini SE; *Int'l*, pg. 1307
REALTECH, INC.; *U.S. Private*, pg. 3369
RED GROUP (M) SDN. BHD.—See NV5 Global, Inc.; *U.S. Public*, pg. 1557
RED LEVEL NETWORKS; *U.S. Private*, pg. 3375
REDMOND INTEGRATORS GMBH—See Bechtle AG; *Int'l*, pg. 938
REDSALSA TECHNOLOGIES INC.; *U.S. Private*, pg. 3379
RED TECHNOLOGIES (S) PTE. LTD.—See NV5 Global, Inc.; *U.S. Public*, pg. 1557
REDYREF INTERACTIVE KIOSKS; *U.S. Private*, pg. 3381
REEHER LLC—See Blackbaud, Inc.; *U.S. Public*, pg. 341
REGAN TECHNOLOGIES CORPORATION; *U.S. Private*, pg. 3386
RELACOM AB—See Altor Equity Partners AB; *Int'l*, pg. 396
RELATIONAL TECHNOLOGY SOLUTIONS—See Relational LLC; *U.S. Private*, pg. 3392
RELAYHEALTH—See McKesson Corporation; *U.S. Public*, pg. 1408
RELM HOLDINGS, INC.; *U.S. Public*, pg. 1782
RELWARE; *U.S. Private*, pg. 3395
RENAISSANCE SYSTEMS, INC.; *U.S. Private*, pg. 3397
RESOLUTE TECHNOLOGIES LLC; *U.S. Private*, pg. 3406
RESOLVIT, LLC—See Aditi Consulting LLC; *U.S. Private*, pg. 79
RESONATE NETWORKS, INC.; *U.S. Private*, pg. 3406
REVACOMM, INC—See Enlightenment Capital LLC; *U.S. Private*, pg. 1400
REVITUP ENTERPRISES LLC; *U.S. Private*, pg. 3416
THE REYNOLDS & REYNOLDS COMPANY; *U.S. Private*, pg. 4106
RHINOCORPS LTD. CO.; *U.S. Private*, pg. 3421
RIBBON COMMUNICATIONS CZECH REPUBLIC S.R.O.—See Ribbon Communications Inc.; *U.S. Public*, pg. 1797
RIBBON COMMUNICATIONS FRANCE EURL—See Ribbon Communications Inc.; *U.S. Public*, pg. 1797
RIMSTORM, INC.; *U.S. Private*, pg. 3437
RINGCENTRAL FRANCE—See RingCentral, Inc.; *U.S. Public*, pg. 1799
RISIKOMANAGEMENT UND SOFTWAREENTWICKLUNG GMBH—See Allianz SE; *Int'l*, pg. 355
RISKONNECT CLEARSIGHT LLC—See TA Associates, Inc.; *U.S. Private*, pg. 3918
RI-SOLUTION GMBH GESELLSCHAFT FUR RETAIL-INFORMATIONSSYSTEME, SERVICES UND LOSUNGEN MBH—See BayWa AG; *Int'l*, pg. 918
RI-SOLUTION SERVICE GMBH—See BayWa AG; *Int'l*, pg. 918
RIVERBED TECHNOLOGY FZ-LLC—See Vector Capital Management, L.P.; *U.S. Private*, pg. 4352
RIVERBED TECHNOLOGY LLC—See Vector Capital Management, L.P.; *U.S. Private*, pg. 4352
RIVERBED TECHNOLOGY LTD.—See Vector Capital Management, L.P.; *U.S. Private*, pg. 4352
RIVERBED TECHNOLOGY S. DE R.L. DE C.V.—See Vector Capital Management, L.P.; *U.S. Private*, pg. 4352
RIVERPOINT KANSAS, L.L.C.—See Lyon & Dittrich Holding Company; *U.S. Private*, pg. 2522
RIVER RUN COMPUTERS, INC.; *U.S. Private*, pg. 3444
RJT COMPUQUEST, INC.; *U.S. Private*, pg. 3449
RMSI PRIVATE LIMITED—See Moody's Corporation; *U.S. Public*, pg. 1469
RMS LTD.—See Moody's Corporation; *U.S. Public*, pg. 1469
RM SOURCE, INC.—See Check Point Software Technologies Ltd.; *Int'l*, pg. 1459
RNA, INC.; *U.S. Private*, pg. 3452
THE ROBOT REPORT—See WTWH Media, LLC; *U.S. Private*, pg. 4574
ROCKET OSS—See Bain Capital, LP; *U.S. Private*, pg. 442
ROCKIT SOLUTIONS, LLC—See Fitek, LLC; *U.S. Private*, pg. 1536
ROCKWELL AUTOMATION SERVICES S.R.O.—See Rockwell Automation, Inc.; *U.S. Public*, pg. 1806
ROCKWELL AUTOMATION SOLUTIONS GMBH—See Rockwell Automation, Inc.; *U.S. Public*, pg. 1806
ROHN ROGERS ASSOCIATES INC.; *U.S. Private*, pg. 3473
ROLTA AMERICAS—See Rolta Americas; *U.S. Private*, pg. 3475
ROSOKA SOFTWARE, INC.—See Constellation Software Inc.; *Int'l*, pg. 1774
ROUND ROCK SOLUTIONS, INC.—See ADVANTEX; *U.S. Private*, pg. 95
ROUNDTOWER TECHNOLOGIES, LLC; *U.S. Private*, pg. 3489
RR DONNELLEY (SHANGHAI) INFORMATION TECHNOLOGY CO., LTD.—See Chatham Asset Management, LLC; *U.S. Private*, pg. 865
RSA SECURITY, GMBH—See Symphony Technology Group, LLC; *U.S. Private*, pg. 3901
RSA SECURITY GMBH—See The Carlyle Group Inc.; *U.S. Public*, pg. 2044
RSA SECURITY UK LIMITED—See Symphony Technology Group, LLC; *U.S. Private*, pg. 3901
RSA SECURITY UK LIMITED—See The Carlyle Group Inc.; *U.S. Public*, pg. 2045
R SYSTEMS INC.—See Blackstone Inc.; *U.S. Public*, pg. 357
R SYSTEMS INTERNATIONAL LIMITED—See Blackstone Inc.; *U.S. Public*, pg. 357
R SYSTEMS S.A.S.—See Blackstone Inc.; *U.S. Public*, pg. 357
R SYSTEMS SINGAPORE LTD.—See Blackstone Inc.; *U.S. Public*, pg. 357
RTL NETWORKS, INC.; *U.S. Private*, pg. 3498
RTM CONSULTING, INC.—See AE Industrial Partners, LP; *U.S. Private*, pg. 111
RTS UNIFIED COMMUNICATIONS; *U.S. Private*, pg. 3498
RTUNET (AUSTRALIA) PTY LTD.—See CSE Global Ltd.; *Int'l*, pg. 1864
RUMOS S.A.—See Enka Insaat ve Sanayi A.S.; *Int'l*, pg. 2440
RWD TECHNOLOGIES LLC; *U.S. Private*, pg. 3509
RXP SERVICES LIMITED—See Capgemini SE; *Int'l*, pg. 1303
RXSIGHT, INC.; *U.S. Public*, pg. 1827
S4 INC.; *U.S. Private*, pg. 3519
SADA SYSTEMS, INC.—See Insight Enterprises, Inc.; *U.S. Public*, pg. 1130
SAFECOM A/S—See Microsoft Corporation; *U.S. Public*, pg. 1443
SAG CONSULTING SERVICES GMBH—See Silver Lake Group, LLC; *U.S. Private*, pg. 3658
SAGENET LLC—See Woodard Technology & Investments LLC; *U.S. Private*, pg. 4557
SAG SALES CENTRE IRELAND LIMITED—See Silver Lake Group, LLC; *U.S. Private*, pg. 3659
SAG SOFTWARE AG LUXEMBOURG S.A.—See Silver Lake Group, LLC; *U.S. Private*, pg. 3659
SAILPOINT TECHNOLOGIES HOLDINGS, INC.—See Thoma Bravo, L.P.; *U.S. Private*, pg. 4153
SAI SYSTEMS INTERNATIONAL, INC.; *U.S. Private*, pg. 3528
SALDAB IT AB—See Dustin Group AB; *Int'l*, pg. 2235
SALESLOFT, INC.; *U.S. Private*, pg. 3532
SALIENT FEDERAL SOLUTIONS, INC.—See Bridge Growth Partners, LLC; *U.S. Private*, pg. 648
SALIENT FEDERAL SOLUTIONS, INC.—See Frontenac Company LLC; *U.S. Private*, pg. 1614
SALIENT IT INC.—See Tonka Bay Equity Partners LLC; *U.S. Private*, pg. 4185
SANDVINE INCORPORATED ULC—See Francisco Partners Management, LP; *U.S. Private*, pg. 1591
SARATOGA TECHNOLOGIES, INC.—See Hon Hai Precision Industry Co., Ltd.; *Int'l*, pg. 3458
SAS EGYPT LLC—See SAS Institute Inc.; *U.S. Private*, pg. 3551
SAS INSTITUTE CR, S.R.O.—See SAS Institute Inc.; *U.S. Private*, pg. 3551
SAS INSTITUTE INC.—See SAS Institute Inc.; *U.S. Private*, pg. 3551
SAS INSTITUTE (INDIA) PVT. LTD.—See SAS Institute Inc.; *U.S. Private*, pg. 3551
SAS INSTITUTE KFT.—See SAS Institute Inc.; *U.S. Private*, pg. 3551
SAS INSTITUTE LTD.—See SAS Institute Inc.; *U.S. Private*, pg. 3551
SAS INSTITUTE OU—See SAS Institute Inc.; *U.S. Private*, pg. 3551
SAS INSTITUTE SARL—See SAS Institute Inc.; *U.S. Private*, pg. 3552
SAS INSTITUTE SA—See SAS Institute Inc.; *U.S. Private*, pg. 3552
SAS RESEARCH & DEVELOPMENT (INDIA) PVT. LTD.—See SAS Institute Inc.; *U.S. Private*, pg. 3552
SAS SLOVAKIA, S.R.O.—See SAS Institute Inc.; *U.S. Private*, pg. 3552
SAS SOFTWARE (THAILAND) COMPANY LIMITED.—See SAS Institute Inc.; *U.S. Private*, pg. 3552
SATURN BUSINESS SYSTEMS INC.; *U.S. Private*, pg. 3553
SATURN INFOTECH, INC.—See Jade Global, Inc.; *U.S. Private*, pg. 2181
SAVANTAGE SOLUTIONS INC.; *U.S. Private*, pg. 3556
SAVVIS SINGAPORE COMPANY PTE. LTD.—See Lumen Technologies, Inc.; *U.S. Public*, pg. 1347
SAYERS GROUP LLC; *U.S. Private*, pg. 3558
SCANSOURCE DE MEXICO S DE RL DE CV—See ScanSource, Inc.; *U.S. Public*, pg. 1843
SCANSOURCE EUROPE LIMITED—See ScanSource, Inc.; *U.S. Public*, pg. 1843
SCANSOURCE EUROPE SPRL—See ScanSource, Inc.; *U.S. Public*, pg. 1843
SCHARFSTEIN S.A.—See Aiphone Co., Ltd.; *Int'l*, pg. 235

CORPORATE AFFILIATIONS

SCHLUMBERGER OILFIELD CORP.—See Schlumberger Limited; *U.S. Public*, pg. 1845
SCHOWALTER & JABOURI COMPUTER SOLUTIONS, INC.—See Honkamp Krueger & Co., PC; *U.S. Private*, pg. 1977
SCI CONSULTING SERVICES, INC.; *U.S. Private*, pg. 3573
SCIENCE APPLICATIONS INTERNATIONAL CORPORATION - HUNTSVILLE—See Science Applications International Corporation; *U.S. Public*, pg. 1848
SCIENCE APPLICATIONS INTERNATIONAL CORPORATION; *U.S. Public*, pg. 1848
SCIENCE + COMPUTING AG—See Atos SE; *Int'l*, pg. 690
SCIENTIFIC GAMES KFT.—See Light & Wonder, Inc.; *U.S. Public*, pg. 1315
SCIENTIFIC GAMES NEW JERSEY, LLC—See Light & Wonder, Inc.; *U.S. Public*, pg. 1315
SCISYS DEUTSCHLAND GMBH—See CGI Inc.; *Int'l*, pg. 1434
SCM DATA INC.; *U.S. Private*, pg. 3574
S.C. NESS ROMANIA S.R.L—See KKR & Co. Inc.; *U.S. Public*, pg. 1261
SCOOT—See BT Group plc; *Int'l*, pg. 1203
SCOPUS TECNOLOGIA LTDA—See Banco Bradesco S.A.; *Int'l*, pg. 819
SCORPION DESIGN LLC; *U.S. Private*, pg. 3575
SD PARTNERS LIMITED—See Alten S.A.; *Int'l*, pg. 390
SEASTEMA S.P.A.—See Fincantieri S.p.A.; *Int'l*, pg. 2671
SECTOR7 USA INC.; *U.S. Private*, pg. 3593
SECUNET SECURITY NETWORKS AG—See Giesecke & Devrient GmbH; *Int'l*, pg. 2970
SECURE DATA, INC.—See Kelso & Company, L.P.; *U.S. Private*, pg. 2278
SECURED SERVICES, INC.; *U.S. Public*, pg. 1855
SECURITYMETRICS, INC.; *U.S. Private*, pg. 3597
SEECLICKFIX, INC.—See Insight Venture Management, LLC; *U.S. Private*, pg. 2087
SEI INFORMATION TECHNOLOGY INC.; *U.S. Private*, pg. 3599
SEKUNJALO TECHNOLOGY SOLUTIONS GROUP (PTY) LTD—See African Equity Empowerment Investmts Limited; *Int'l*, pg. 191
SENECA RESOURCES, LLC—See Caymus Equity Partners LLC; *U.S. Private*, pg. 795
SENSA EHF.—See Crayon Group Holding ASA; *Int'l*, pg. 1830
SENSE CORP.; *U.S. Private*, pg. 3607
SEQUEL DATA SYSTEMS, INC.; *U.S. Private*, pg. 3612
SEQUENT CHINA/HONG KONG LIMITED—See Green Leader Holdings Group Limited; *Int'l*, pg. 3071
SEQUOIA RETAIL SYSTEMS, INC.—See Class Technologies Inc.; *U.S. Private*, pg. 915
SERCEL BEIJING TECHNOLOGICAL SERVICES CO LTD.—See CGG; *Int'l*, pg. 1432
SERMICRO, S.A.—See ACS, Actividades de Construccion y Servicios, S.A.; *Int'l*, pg. 116
SERVERWARE CORPORATION—See FUJISOFT INCORPORATED; *Int'l*, pg. 2830
SERVICENOW POLAND SP. Z.O.O.—See ServiceNow, Inc.; *U.S. Public*, pg. 1872
SERVICEONE AG—See Comdat Datasystems AG; *Int'l*, pg. 1709
SERVICESOURCE INTERNATIONAL SINGAPORE PTE. LTD.—See Concentrix Corporation; *U.S. Public*, pg. 564
SESAME COMMUNICATIONS, INC.—See KKR & Co. Inc.; *U.S. Public*, pg. 1253
SG AUTOMATISERING B.V.—See Advent International Corporation; *U.S. Private*, pg. 97
SG AUTOMATISERING B.V.—See Centerbridge Partners, L.P.; *U.S. Private*, pg. 813
SG FACILITOR B.V.—See Advent International Corporation; *U.S. Private*, pg. 97
SG FACILITOR B.V.—See Centerbridge Partners, L.P.; *U.S. Private*, pg. 813
SHANGHAI QINGTIAN ELECTRONIC TECHNOLOGY CO., LTD.—See China Security Co., Ltd.; *Int'l*, pg. 1550
SHANGHAI TECHNODIA SYSTEM INTEGRATION CO., LTD.—See Computer Institute of Japan Ltd.; *Int'l*, pg. 1759
SHARP DECISIONS INC.; *U.S. Private*, pg. 3626
SHARP DECISIONS—See Sharp Decisions Inc.; *U.S. Private*, pg. 3626
SHENYANG DIGITAL CHINA LIMITED—See Digital China Holdings Limited; *Int'l*, pg. 2121
SHERLOCK SERVICES, INC.—See Harvest Partners L.P.; *U.S. Private*, pg. 1877
SHFL ENTERTAINMENT (ARGENTINA) S.R.L.—See Light & Wonder, Inc.; *U.S. Public*, pg. 1314
SHIFTRIGHT, INC.—See Zscaler, Inc.; *U.S. Public*, pg. 2411
SHIRAZI TRADING COMPANY PRIVATE LIMITED—See Atlas Group of Companies; *Int'l*, pg. 685
SHR CONSULTING GROUP, LLC; *U.S. Private*, pg. 3643
SIA CENTRAL EUROPE ZRT.—See Cassa Depositi e Prestiti S.p.A.; *Int'l*, pg. 1354
SIA UNITREE—See Alna AB; *Int'l*, pg. 364
THE SIERRA-CEDAR GROUP, INC.—See Golden Gate Capital Management II, LLC; *U.S. Private*, pg. 1732
SIGMA SURVEILLANCE, INC.; *U.S. Private*, pg. 3649

N.A.I.C.S. INDEX

541512 — COMPUTER SYSTEMS DE...

SIGNAL SCIENCES, LLC—See Fastly, Inc.; *U.S. Public*, pg. 824
SIGNATURE BUSINESS SYSTEMS, INC.; *U.S. Private*, pg. 3650
SIGNATURE DEVICES, INC.; *U.S. Public*, pg. 1878
SILKEBORG DATA A/S—See Francisco Partners Management, LP; *U.S. Private*, pg. 1589
SILVERADO SYSTEMS, INC.; *U.S. Private*, pg. 3662
SILVERBULLET A/S—See IQVIA Holdings Inc.; *U.S. Public*, pg. 1170
SILVERLINK PCS SOFTWARE LIMITED—See Alcidion Group Limited; *Int'l*, pg. 301
SILVERWARE, INC.—See Velosio, LLC; *U.S. Private*, pg. 4355
SILVEY INFORMATION SYSTEMS INC.—See Aubrey Silvey Enterprises Inc.; *U.S. Private*, pg. 385
SIMCORP ASIA PTY. LTD.—See Deutsche Borse AG; *Int'l*, pg. 2064
SIMCORP FRANCE S.A.S.—See Deutsche Borse AG; *Int'l*, pg. 2064
SIMCORP GMBH—See Deutsche Borse AG; *Int'l*, pg. 2064
SIMCORP SVERIGE AB—See Deutsche Borse AG; *Int'l*, pg. 2064
SIMFONI, INC.; *U.S. Private*, pg. 3665
SIMULATIONS PLUS, INC.; *U.S. Public*, pg. 1884
SINGLEPLATFORM, LLC—See TripAdvisor, Inc.; *U.S. Public*, pg. 2195
SINGULAR GENOMICS SYSTEMS, INC.; *U.S. Public*, pg. 1888
SINU, INC.; *U.S. Private*, pg. 3670
SIPERA SYSTEMS, INC.—See Silver Lake Group, LLC; *U.S. Private*, pg. 3656
SIPERA SYSTEMS, INC.—See TPG Capital, L.P.; *U.S. Public*, pg. 2169
SIRIUS COMPUTER SOLUTIONS, INC.—See CDW Corporation; *U.S. Public*, pg. 462
SIRSIDYNIX CORPORATION—See SirsiDynix Corporation; *U.S. Private*, pg. 3675
SISGE MEDICAL SRL—See Apax Partners LLP; *Int'l*, pg. 501
SISTEMAS DE RESERVACIONES CRS DE VENEZUELA, C.A.—See Amadeus IT Group, S.A.; *Int'l*, pg. 407
S IT SOLUTIONS CZ, S.R.O.—See Erste Group Bank AG; *Int'l*, pg. 2499
S IT SOLUTIONS HR DRUSTVO S OGRANICENOM ODGOVORNOSCU ZA USLUGE INFORMACIJSKIH TEHNOLOGIJA—See Erste Group Bank AG; *Int'l*, pg. 2499
SIWEL CONSULTING INC.; *U.S. Private*, pg. 3677
SKIPTON GROUP INC.—See Data Integrity Inc.; *Int'l*, pg. 1976
SKYLINE ULTD, INC.—See Central Research, Inc.; *U.S. Private*, pg. 824
SKYTEC AG—See Allgeier SE; *Int'l*, pg. 337
SLAIT CONSULTING, LLC—See ePlus Inc.; *U.S. Private*, pg. 784
SLS CORPORATION—See FLSmidth & Co. A/S; *Int'l*, pg. 2712
SM2 BALEARES SA—See Atos SE; *Int'l*, pg. 691
SMARTDRIVE SYSTEMS, INC.; *U.S. Private*, pg. 3692
SMARTOPTICS AS—See Coherent Corp.; *U.S. Public*, pg. 528
SMART VISION WORKS, LLC—See Union Park Capital; *U.S. Private*, pg. 4285
SMILE SAS—See Eurazeo SE; *Int'l*, pg. 2528
SMR HOLDINGS, LLC; *U.S. Private*, pg. 3698
SMT SOFTWARE S.A.—See Grupa SMT S.A.; *Int'l*, pg. 3117
SNAP, INC.; *U.S. Private*, pg. 3700
SNAP INSTALL, INC.; *U.S. Private*, pg. 3700
SNC SQUARED; *U.S. Private*, pg. 3700
SNS TECHNOLOGY CO., LTD.—See ADTechnology Co., Ltd.; *Int'l*, pg. 154
SNVC, L.C.; *U.S. Private*, pg. 3701
SOAR TECHNOLOGY, INC.—See Trive Capital Inc.; *U.S. Private*, pg. 4240
SOCIETY PASS INCORPORATED; *U.S. Public*, pg. 1899
SOFTCHOICE CORPORATION—See Birch Hill Equity Partners Management Inc.; *Int'l*, pg. 1046
SOFT COMPUTER CONSULTANTS INC.; *U.S. Private*, pg. 3704
SOFTCON AG—See Allgeier SE; *Int'l*, pg. 337
SOFTWARE AG CHINA LTD.—See Silver Lake Group, LLC; *U.S. Private*, pg. 3659
SOFTWARE AG DE PANAMA, S.A—See Silver Lake Group, LLC; *U.S. Private*, pg. 3660
SOFTWARE AG DE PUERTO RICO, INC.—See Silver Lake Group, LLC; *U.S. Private*, pg. 3659
SOFTWARE AG DEVELOPMENT CENTRE SLOVAKIA S.R.O.—See Silver Lake Group, LLC; *U.S. Private*, pg. 3659
SOFTWARE AG (GULF) S.P.C.—See Silver Lake Group, LLC; *U.S. Private*, pg. 3659
SOFTWARE AG INTERNATIONAL FZ-LLC—See Silver Lake Group, LLC; *U.S. Private*, pg. 3660
SOFTWARE AG (SINGAPORE) PTE LTD—See Silver Lake Group, LLC; *U.S. Private*, pg. 3659
SOFTWARE AG SWEDEN AB—See Silver Lake Group, LLC; *U.S. Private*, pg. 3660

SOFTWARE DEVELOPMENT EUROPE, INC.—See 3Pillar Global, Inc.; *U.S. Private*, pg. 14
SOFTWARE MANAGEMENT CONSULTANTS INC.; *U.S. Private*, pg. 3705
SOFTWARE PARADIGMS INTERNATIONAL GROUP LLC; *U.S. Private*, pg. 3705
SOFTWAREPUNDITS, INC.; *U.S. Private*, pg. 3706
SOFTWARE TECHNICAL SERVICES; *U.S. Private*, pg. 3705
SOGETI BELGIUM—See Capgemini SE; *Int'l*, pg. 1307
SOGETI CORPORATE SERVICES SAS—See Capgemini SE; *Int'l*, pg. 1307
SOGETI DEUTSCHLAND GMBH—See Capgemini SE; *Int'l*, pg. 1307
SOGETI ESPANA SL—See Capgemini SE; *Int'l*, pg. 1307
SOGETI FINLAND OY—See Capgemini SE; *Int'l*, pg. 1307
SOGETI FRANCE S.A.S.—See Capgemini SE; *Int'l*, pg. 1307
SOGETI HIGH TECH S.A.S.—See Capgemini SE; *Int'l*, pg. 1307
SOGETI LUXEMBOURG S.A.—See Capgemini SE; *Int'l*, pg. 1307
SOGETI NEDERLAND B.V.—See Capgemini SE; *Int'l*, pg. 1307
SOGETI NORGE AS—See Capgemini SE; *Int'l*, pg. 1307
SOGETI N.V./S.A.—See Capgemini SE; *Int'l*, pg. 1307
SOGETI PSF S.A.—See Capgemini SE; *Int'l*, pg. 1307
SOGETI—See Capgemini SE; *Int'l*, pg. 1307
SOGETI SVERIGE AB—See Capgemini SE; *Int'l*, pg. 1307
SOGETI UK LTD.—See Capgemini SE; *Int'l*, pg. 1307
SOGETI USA LLC—See Capgemini SE; *Int'l*, pg. 1307
SOGETI USA LLC—See Capgemini SE; *Int'l*, pg. 1307
SOGETI USA LLC—See Capgemini SE; *Int'l*, pg. 1307
SOGETI USA LLC—See Capgemini SE; *Int'l*, pg. 1307
SOGETI USA LLC—See Capgemini SE; *Int'l*, pg. 1307
SOGETI USA LLC—See Capgemini SE; *Int'l*, pg. 1307
SOLIDPRO INFORMATIONSSYSTEME GMBH—See Bechtle AG; *Int'l*, pg. 938
SOLID SOLUTIONS AG—See Bechtle AG; *Int'l*, pg. 938
SOLIGEN TECHNOLOGIES, INC.; *U.S. Public*, pg. 1901
SOLSTICE SAS—See Cognizant Technology Solutions Corporation; *U.S. Public*, pg. 525
SOLUGENIX CORP.; *U.S. Private*, pg. 3710
SOLUTION BEACON LLC; *U.S. Private*, pg. 3710
SOLUTIONS BY DESIGN II, LLC—See Converged Security Solutions LLC; *U.S. Private*, pg. 1035
SOLUTIONS-II INCORPORATED; *U.S. Private*, pg. 3711
SOLUTION STREET, LLC; *U.S. Private*, pg. 3711
SOLVEGY, INC.; *U.S. Private*, pg. 3711
SONOMA PARTNERS, LLC; *U.S. Private*, pg. 3714
SOONR, INC.—See Vista Equity Partners, LLC; *U.S. Private*, pg. 4395
SOPHISTICATED SYSTEMS INC.—See IP Pathways, LLC; *U.S. Private*, pg. 2136
SOS SECURITY INC—See CDW Corporation; *U.S. Public*, pg. 463
SOURCE EVOLUTION INC.—See Alan Allman Associates SA; *Int'l*, pg. 290
SOURCEMANTRA INC; *U.S. Private*, pg. 3718
SOURCE RECOVERY COMPANY INC.; *U.S. Private*, pg. 3718
SPACE FITTERS INC.; *U.S. Private*, pg. 3744
SPACENET, INC.—See Woodard Technology & Investments LLC; *U.S. Private*, pg. 4557
SPARKHOUND, INC.; *U.S. Private*, pg. 3746
SPARXENT, INC.—See Signal Peak Venture Partners, LLC; *U.S. Private*, pg. 3649
SPECTRAFORCE TECHNOLOGIES INC.; *U.S. Private*, pg. 3751
SPECTRUM SYSTEMS, INC.; *U.S. Private*, pg. 3753
SPIE ICS AG—See Clayton, Dubilier & Rice, LLC; *U.S. Private*, pg. 926
SPIKES CAVELL ANALYTIC INC.—See DXC Technology Company; *U.S. Public*, pg. 697
SPLUNK SERVICES FRANCE SAS—See Cisco Systems, Inc.; *U.S. Public*, pg. 500
SPLUNK SERVICES FZ-LLC—See Cisco Systems, Inc.; *U.S. Public*, pg. 500
SPLUNK SERVICES HONG KONG LTD.—See Cisco Systems, Inc.; *U.S. Public*, pg. 500
SPLUNK SERVICES JAPAN GK—See Cisco Systems, Inc.; *U.S. Public*, pg. 500
SPLUNK SERVICES KOREA—See Cisco Systems, Inc.; *U.S. Public*, pg. 500
SPLUNK SERVICES SWEDEN AB—See Cisco Systems, Inc.; *U.S. Public*, pg. 500
SPLUNK SERVICES UK LIMITED—See Cisco Systems, Inc.; *U.S. Public*, pg. 500
SPR INC.; *U.S. Private*, pg. 3762
SPRINGPOINT TECHNOLOGIES; *U.S. Private*, pg. 3764
SPS COMMERCE, INC.; *U.S. Public*, pg. 1920
SQLI SA—See DBAY Advisors Limited; *Int'l*, pg. 1987
SQS SOFTWARE QUALITY SYSTEMS (SCHWEIZ) AG, ZURICH—See Assystem S.A.; *Int'l*, pg. 650
THE SQUIRES GROUP INC; *U.S. Private*, pg. 4120
SRIVEN SYSTEMS, INC.; *U.S. Private*, pg. 3768
STAFFING TECHNOLOGIES, LLC; *U.S. Private*, pg. 3775
STAFFLOGIX CORPORATION; *U.S. Private*, pg. 3775

STANDARD TECHNOLOGY INC.; *U.S. Private*, pg. 3781
STANLEY SECURITY ITALIA S.R.L.—See Stanley Black & Decker, Inc.; *U.S. Public*, pg. 1935
STARFIELD TECHNOLOGIES, INC.—See KKR & Co. Inc.; *U.S. Public*, pg. 1252
STARFIELD TECHNOLOGIES, INC.—See Silver Lake Group, LLC; *U.S. Private*, pg. 3657
STARFIELD TECHNOLOGIES, INC.—See TCMI, Inc.; *U.S. Private*, pg. 3943
STARLIMS ASIA PACIFIC LIMITED—See Abbott Laboratories; *U.S. Public*, pg. 20
STARLIMS CORPORATION—See Abbott Laboratories; *U.S. Public*, pg. 20
STARLIMS GERMANY GMBH—See Abbott Laboratories; *U.S. Public*, pg. 20
STARLIMS ISRAEL LTD.—See Abbott Laboratories; *U.S. Public*, pg. 20
STARLIMS TECHNOLOGIES LTD.—See Abbott Laboratories; *U.S. Public*, pg. 20
STARLIMS THAILAND CO., LTD.—See Abbott Laboratories; *U.S. Public*, pg. 20
STAR REPUBLIC AB—See DBAY Advisors Limited; *Int'l*, pg. 1987
STARREZ INC.; *U.S. Private*, pg. 3787
STATERA, INC.—See Boathouse Capital Management, LLC; *U.S. Private*, pg. 603
STAYTOP SYSTEMS INC—See AION-TECH Solutions Limited; *Int'l*, pg. 234
STEMMER GMBH—See Bechtle AG; *Int'l*, pg. 938
STEPHEN GOULD OF ROCHESTER—See Stephen Gould Corporation; *U.S. Private*, pg. 3802
STERILUMEN, INC.—See Applied UV, Inc.; *U.S. Public*, pg. 173
STI GROUP; *U.S. Public*, pg. 1949
STOCKELL CONSULTING INC.; *U.S. Private*, pg. 3814
STOLTENBERG CONSULTING, INC.; *U.S. Private*, pg. 3816
STONE APPLE CONSULTING CO., LTD.—See Hitachi, Ltd.; *Int'l*, pg. 3424
STONE APPLE MALAYSIA SDN BHD.—See Hitachi, Ltd.; *Int'l*, pg. 3424
STONEBRIDGE; *U.S. Private*, pg. 3827
THE STONE GROUP, INC.; *U.S. Private*, pg. 4123
STONEWORKS TECHNOLOGIES, INC.—See Fulcrum IT Partners; *Int'l*, pg. 2841
STORIX INC.—See Cristie Software Limited; *Int'l*, pg. 1850
STRATACACHE INC.; *U.S. Private*, pg. 3833
STRATEGIC BCP, INC.—See EQT AB; *Int'l*, pg. 2471
STRATEGIC BUSINESS SYSTEMS, INC.; *U.S. Private*, pg. 3834
STRATEGIC FOCUS; *U.S. Private*, pg. 3835
STRATEGIC MICRO SYSTEMS OF NJ, LLC.; *U.S. Private*, pg. 3835
STRATEGIC STAFFING SOLUTIONS INC.; *U.S. Private*, pg. 3835
STRATOS MANAGEMENT SYSTEMS, INC.—See Calian Group Ltd.; *Int'l*, pg. 1264
STREAMLINE HEALTH SOLUTIONS, INC.; *U.S. Public*, pg. 1954
STRIKEIRON, LLC—See Canada Pension Plan Investment Board; *Int'l*, pg. 1280
STRONGBRIDGE CORPORATION; *U.S. Private*, pg. 3841
STRUCTURED COMMUNICATION SYSTEMS, INC.; *U.S. Private*, pg. 3842
STRUCTUREDWEB, INC.; *U.S. Private*, pg. 3842
STS EVERMEDIA CORP.; *U.S. Public*, pg. 1958
STS INTERNATIONAL, INC.; *U.S. Private*, pg. 3842
SULAAN SOLUTIONS INC.; *U.S. Private*, pg. 3850
SULLIVAN DATA MANAGEMENT, INC.—See The Riverside Company; *U.S. Private*, pg. 4109
SUMMIT 7 SYSTEMS, LLC; *U.S. Private*, pg. 3853
SUMMIT SOLUTIONS, INC.—See FedCap Partners, LLC; *U.S. Public*, pg. 1486
SUMMIT TECHNOLOGY, INC.; *U.S. Private*, pg. 3857
SUMO LOGIC, INC.—See Francisco Partners Management, LP; *U.S. Public*, pg. 1592
SUNQUEST INFORMATION SYSTEMS, INC.—See Roper Technologies, Inc.; *U.S. Public*, pg. 1813
SUNRAY ENTERPRISE INC.; *U.S. Private*, pg. 3869
SUNSOFT TECHNOLOGIES, INC.; *U.S. Private*, pg. 3872
SUPERIOR SUPPORT RESOURCES, INC.; *U.S. Private*, pg. 3880
SUPPLY CHAIN SERVICES, LLC—See Sole Source Capital LLC; *U.S. Private*, pg. 3708
SUSE LINUX GMBH—See EQT AB; *Int'l*, pg. 2481
SUTHERLAND CONSULTING LIMITED—See Capgemini SE; *Int'l*, pg. 1305
SUVITECH CO., LTD.—See Axiata Group Berhad; *Int'l*, pg. 768
SVOX AG—See Microsoft Corporation; *U.S. Public*, pg. 1442
SWITCHFAST TECHNOLOGIES LLC; *U.S. Private*, pg. 3894
SYCOM TECHNOLOGIES, L.L.C.—See Huron Capital Partners LLC; *U.S. Private*, pg. 2012
SYCOM TECHNOLOGIES, L.L.C.—See MidOcean Partners, LLP; *U.S. Private*, pg. 2716
SYGNITY S.A.—See Constellation Software Inc.; *Int'l*, pg. 1774

541512 — COMPUTER SYSTEMS DE...

SYKES ASIA, INC.—See Creadev SAS; *Int'l*, pg. 1831
SYKES ENTERPRISES, INCORPORATED—See Creadev SAS; *Int'l*, pg. 1831
SYLOG OST AB—See Adecco Group AG; *Int'l*, pg. 140
SYLOG SVERIGE AB—See Adecco Group AG; *Int'l*, pg. 140
SYMBIONT, INC.; *U.S. Private*, pg. 3899
SYNACOR, INC.—See Centre Lane Partners, LLC; *U.S. Private*, pg. 827
SYNAPSIS ARGENTINA LTDA—See Enel S.p.A.; *Int'l*, pg. 2412
SYNAPSYS LIMITED—See DFCC Bank PLC; *Int'l*, pg. 2094
SYNAPTICS HONG KONG LTD.—See Synaptics Incorporated; *U.S. Public*, pg. 1969
SYNECTIVE LABS AB—See Addtech AB; *Int'l*, pg. 135
SYNERGY ASSOCIATES LLC; *U.S. Private*, pg. 3904
SYNNEFO TECHNOLOGY SOLUTIONS, INC.—See CDW Corporation; *U.S. Public*, pg. 463
SYNOPSE SAS—See Econocom Group SA; *Int'l*, pg. 2298
SYNOPSYS, INC.; *U.S. Public*, pg. 1970
SYNOPTEK, LLC—See Sverica Capital Management LP; *U.S. Private*, pg. 3888
SYNTAX SOFT-TECH PVT. LTD.—See UCA Group Component Specialty Inc.; *U.S. Private*, pg. 4273
SYNTHES INDUSTRIA E COMERCIO LTDA.—See Johnson & Johnson; *U.S. Public*, pg. 1200
SYSCOM INC.; *U.S. Private*, pg. 3906
SYSNET TECHNOLOGY SOLUTIONS, INC.—See ASTIR IT Solutions, Inc.; *U.S. Private*, pg. 360
SYS TECHNOLOGIES, INC.—See Kratos Defense & Security Solutions, Inc.; *U.S. Public*, pg. 1277
SYSTEM C HEALTHCARE LTD.—See Symphony Technology Group, LLC; *U.S. Private*, pg. 3902
SYSTEMS ENGINEERING SERVICES; *U.S. Private*, pg. 3907
SYSTEMS INTEGRATION SOLUTIONS INC.; *U.S. Private*, pg. 3907
SYSTEMS TECHNOLOGY ASSOCIATES INC.; *U.S. Private*, pg. 3908
SYSTIMA TECHNOLOGIES, INC.—See Trive Capital Inc.; *U.S. Private*, pg. 4240
SYSTIME COMPUTER SYSTEMS (I) LTD.—See CMS Computers Ltd.; *Int'l*, pg. 1672
SYVANTIS TECHNOLOGIES, INC.; *U.S. Private*, pg. 3908
TACIT KNOWLEDGE, INC.—See Grid Dynamics Holdings, Inc.; *U.S. Public*, pg. 969
TACTILE LIMITED—See Advent International Corporation; *U.S. Private*, pg. 97
TACTILE LIMITED—See Centerbridge Partners, L.P.; *U.S. Private*, pg. 813
TAG SOLUTIONS, LLC—See Charge Enterprises, Inc.; *U.S. Public*, pg. 479
TAJ TECHNOLOGIES INC.; *U.S. Private*, pg. 3925
TAMALPAIS GROUP INC.; *U.S. Private*, pg. 3928
TANGO MANAGEMENT CONSULTING, LLC; *U.S. Private*, pg. 3931
TANJUNG DIGITAL SDN BHD—See Axiata Group Berhad; *Int'l*, pg. 768
TANTRA INFOSOLUTIONS PVT. LTD.—See UCA Group Component Specialty Inc.; *U.S. Private*, pg. 4273
TANTUS TECHNOLOGIES, INC.; *U.S. Private*, pg. 3932
TASC TECHNICAL SERVICES LLC; *U.S. Private*, pg. 3934
TAYLOR ASSOCIATES/COMMUNICATIONS, INC.—See Clearlake Capital Group, L.P.; *U.S. Private*, pg. 934
TBL NETWORKS, INC.; *U.S. Private*, pg. 3941
TCG; *U.S. Private*, pg. 3942
TCS INTERNATIONAL, INC.—See Guardian Capital Group Limited; *Int'l*, pg. 3170
TD SYNNEX AS CZECH S.R.O.—See TD Synnex Corp; *U.S. Public*, pg. 1984
TD SYNNEX AUSTRIA GMBH—See TD Synnex Corp; *U.S. Public*, pg. 1984
TD SYNNEX CANADA ULC—See TD Synnex Corp; *U.S. Public*, pg. 1984
TD SYNNEX CROATIA D.O.O.—See TD Synnex Corp; *U.S. Public*, pg. 1984
TD SYNNEX CZECH S.R.O.—See TD Synnex Corp; *U.S. Public*, pg. 1984
TD SYNNEX EUROPE GMBH—See TD Synnex Corp; *U.S. Public*, pg. 1984
TD SYNNEX FINLAND OY—See TD Synnex Corp; *U.S. Public*, pg. 1984
TD SYNNEX FRANCE S.A.S.—See TD Synnex Corp; *U.S. Public*, pg. 1984
TD SYNNEX GERMANY GMBH & CO. OHG—See TD Synnex Corp; *U.S. Public*, pg. 1984
TD SYNNEX HUNGARY KFT—See TD Synnex Corp; *U.S. Public*, pg. 1984
TD SYNNEX IRELAND LIMITED—See TD Synnex Corp; *U.S. Public*, pg. 1984
TD SYNNEX ITALY S.R.L.—See TD Synnex Corp; *U.S. Public*, pg. 1984
TD SYNNEX KFT—See TD Synnex Corp; *U.S. Public*, pg. 1984
TD SYNNEX NETHERLANDS B.V.—See TD Synnex Corp; *U.S. Public*, pg. 1984
TD SYNNEX NORWAY AS—See TD Synnex Corp; *U.S. Public*, pg. 1985

TD SYNNEX POLAND SP. Z O.O.—See TD Synnex Corp; *U.S. Public*, pg. 1985
TD SYNNEX PORTUGAL, LDA—See TD Synnex Corp; *U.S. Public*, pg. 1985
TD SYNNEX SPAIN, S.L.U.—See TD Synnex Corp; *U.S. Public*, pg. 1985
TD SYNNEX SWEDEN AB—See TD Synnex Corp; *U.S. Public*, pg. 1985
TD SYNNEX SWITZERLAND GMBH—See TD Synnex Corp; *U.S. Public*, pg. 1985
TD SYNNEX UK LIMITED—See TD Synnex Corp; *U.S. Public*, pg. 1985
TEAL; *U.S. Public*, pg. 3948
TEC D DISTRIBUTION (MALAYSIA) SDN. BHD.—See TD Synnex Corp; *U.S. Public*, pg. 1985
TECH 21 ENGINEERING SOLUTIONS LIMITED—See Weatherford International plc; *U.S. Public*, pg. 2339
TECH AMERICAS USA, INC.; *U.S. Private*, pg. 3951
TECH DATA BILGISAYAR SISTEMLERI A.S.—See TD Synnex Corp; *U.S. Public*, pg. 1985
TECHEX—See INNOVARO, INC.; *U.S. Private*, pg. 2081
TECHFINO LLC; *U.S. Private*, pg. 3952
TECHNICA CORPORATION; *U.S. Private*, pg. 3953
TECHNICAL DESIGN SERVICES, INC—See NV5 Global, Inc.; *U.S. Public*, pg. 1558
TECHNICAL RESOURCES INTERNATIONAL, INC.; *U.S. Private*, pg. 3954
TECHNICAL YOUTH LLC; *U.S. Private*, pg. 3954
TECHNOLOGY ONE; *U.S. Private*, pg. 3955
TECHNOLOGY SERVICES CORP.; *U.S. Private*, pg. 3955
TECH PEOPLE AS—See Adecco Group AG; *Int'l*, pg. 140
TECHPOWER SOLUTIONS INC.; *U.S. Private*, pg. 3956
TECH-PRO INC.; *U.S. Private*, pg. 3952
TECHSOUP GLOBAL; *U.S. Private*, pg. 3956
TECHSOURCE LLC—See Dubai Investments PJSC; *Int'l*, pg. 2219
TECHSTAR GROUP, INC.; *U.S. Private*, pg. 3956
TECNO DIAGNOSTICA—See Abbott Laboratories; *U.S. Public*, pg. 20
TEKIS AB—See Addnode Group AB; *Int'l*, pg. 131
TEKLA OYJ—See Trimble, Inc.; *U.S. Public*, pg. 2191
TEKMARK GLOBAL SOLUTIONS LLC—See OEP Capital Advisors, L.P.; *U.S. Private*, pg. 2999
TEKMATE, LLC—See ATN International, Inc.; *U.S. Public*, pg. 224
TEKMATE, LLC—See Freedom 3 Capital, LLC; *U.S. Private*, pg. 1603
TEKNOLUXION CONSULTING LLC—See NewSpring Capital LLC; *U.S. Private*, pg. 2917
TEKONTROL INC.; *U.S. Private*, pg. 3959
TELEDYNE DALSA, INC.—See Teledyne Technologies Incorporated; *U.S. Public*, pg. 1993
TELEION CONSULTING LLC; *U.S. Private*, pg. 3960
TELOS CORPORATION; *U.S. Public*, pg. 1999
TEMPOS21 S.A—See Atos SE; *Int'l*, pg. 691
TEMPUS INC.; *U.S. Private*, pg. 3964
TEOCO CORPORATION; *U.S. Private*, pg. 3968
TESM LIMITED—See DXC Technology Company; *U.S. Public*, pg. 697
TESM/NL B.V.—See DXC Technology Company; *U.S. Public*, pg. 697
THAILAND WEI AN CO., LTD.—See China Security Co. Ltd.; *Int'l*, pg. 1550
THEIPGUYS.NET LLC; *U.S. Public*, pg. 4141
THESIA S.P.A.—See Cassa Depositi e Prestiti S.p.A.; *Int'l*, pg. 1354
THINK ANALYTICS INDIA PRIVATE LIMITED—See Computer Age Management Services Limited; *Int'l*, pg. 1759
THOMAS GLOVER ASSOCIATES, INC.; *U.S. Private*, pg. 4155
THOUGHTWORKS, INC.—See Apax Partners LLP; *Int'l*, pg. 507
THREE WIRE SYSTEMS, LLC; *U.S. Private*, pg. 4164
TIGER COMMISSARY SERVICES, INC.; *U.S. Private*, pg. 4169
TIMBERHORN, LLC.—See ManpowerGroup Inc.; *U.S. Public*, pg. 1362
TIVIT TERCEIRIZACAO DE PROCESSOS, SERVICOS E TECNOLOGIA S.A.—See Apax Partners LLP; *Int'l*, pg. 507
TMA SYSTEMS, LLC—See Silversmith Management, L.P.; *U.S. Private*, pg. 3664
TM SYSTEMS, LLC; *U.S. Private*, pg. 4179
TODAY'S GROWTH CONSULTANT, INC.; *U.S. Private*, pg. 4180
TOHOKU INFORMATION CENTER CO., LTD.—See Core Corporation; *Int'l*, pg. 1797
TOMAR COMPUTER INTEGRATION, INC.—See Trinity Hunt Management, L.P.; *U.S. Private*, pg. 4234
TOOLBOX NO. 9 INC.—See Band of Coders, LP; *U.S. Private*, pg. 464
TOOLWORX INFORMATION PRODUCTS, INC.—See Raco Industries, Inc.; *U.S. Private*, pg. 3342
TOONTEC SOLUTIONS CO., LTD.—See Amiya Corporation; *Int'l*, pg. 428
TOPCONTRACTS GMBH—See HTC Global Services Inc.; *U.S. Public*, pg. 1999
TOP INFORMATION TECHNOLOGIES CO., LTD.—See Brookfield Corporation; *Int'l*, pg. 1181
TOPJECTS GMBH—See Allgeier SE; *Int'l*, pg. 337
TOPTECH SYSTEMS, INC.—See IDEX Corp; *U.S. Public*, pg. 1092
TOPTECH SYSTEMS N.V.—See IDEX Corp; *U.S. Public*, pg. 1092
TORPEDO FACTORY GROUP LIMITED—See Aukett Swanke Group Plc; *Int'l*, pg. 704
TOTAL BUSINESS SOLUTIONS LIMITED—See Belize Telecommunications Limited; *Int'l*, pg. 965
TOTAL OUTSOURCE, INC.—See UCA Group Component Specialty Inc.; *U.S. Private*, pg. 4273
TOUCHTURNS LLC—See CN Innovations Holdings Limited; *Int'l*, pg. 1673
TPG NETWORK PTY LTD—See CK Hutchison Holdings Limited; *Int'l*, pg. 1638
TRACE3, INC.—See American Securities LLC; *U.S. Private*, pg. 250
TRAFFICCAST INTERNATIONAL, INC—See Almaviva S.p.A.; *Int'l*, pg. 363
TRANSACTION NETWORK SERVICES (INDIA) PRIVATE LTD—See Koch Industries, Inc.; *U.S. Private*, pg. 2333
TRANSACTION NETWORK SERVICES PTY LIMITED—See Koch Industries, Inc.; *U.S. Private*, pg. 2333
TRANSACTION NETWORK SERVICES SG PTE LIMITED—See Koch Industries, Inc.; *U.S. Private*, pg. 2333
TRANSACTION NETWORK SERVICES (UK) LIMITED—See Koch Industries, Inc.; *U.S. Private*, pg. 2333
TRANSACTION PROCESSING SPECIALISTS, INC.—See Xerox Holdings Corporation; *U.S. Public*, pg. 2388
TRANSTEL ENGINEERING ARABIAN LIMITED CO.—See CSE Global Ltd.; *Int'l*, pg. 1864
TRANSTEL ENGINEERING (NIGERIA) LTD.—See CSE Global Ltd.; *Int'l*, pg. 1864
TRANSTEL ENGINEERING PTE LTD.—See CSE Global Ltd.; *Int'l*, pg. 1864
TRANZION, LLC—See National HealthCare Corporation; *U.S. Public*, pg. 1497
TRAVCO INC.; *U.S. Private*, pg. 4212
TRAVELTAINMENT AG—See Amadeus IT Group, S.A.; *Int'l*, pg. 407
TRAX USA, CORP.—See AAR Corp.; *U.S. Public*, pg. 13
TREENO SOFTWARE, INC.—See LoneTree Capital LLC; *U.S. Private*, pg. 2490
TRENDMINER NV—See Silver Lake Group, LLC; *U.S. Private*, pg. 3660
T-REX SOLUTIONS, LLC; *U.S. Private*, pg. 3910
TREXTEL, LLC; *U.S. Private*, pg. 4219
TRIAD WEB DESIGN; *U.S. Private*, pg. 4225
TRIDEA PARTNERS, LLC.—See Columbus A/S; *Int'l*, pg. 1706
TRIDENT COMPUTER RESOURCES, INC.—See Harvest Partners L.P.; *U.S. Private*, pg. 1877
TRIDENT INFOSOL PVT. LTD.—See HUB Cyber Security Ltd.; *Int'l*, pg. 3516
TRIDENT SYSTEMS INCORPORATED—See ATL Partners, LLC; *U.S. Private*, pg. 369
TRIFUSION, LP; *U.S. Private*, pg. 4230
TRIMBLE SOLUTIONS UK LTD—See Trimble, Inc.; *U.S. Public*, pg. 2193
TRIMIN SYSTEMS INC.; *U.S. Private*, pg. 4232
TRINET SYSTEMS, INC.—See American Securities LLC; *U.S. Private*, pg. 250
TRINITY CONSULTING, INC.; *U.S. Private*, pg. 4233
TRIZETTO INDIA PRIVATE LIMITED—See Cognizant Technology Solutions Corporation; *U.S. Public*, pg. 525
TRIZETTO SERVICES INDIA PRIVATE LIMITED—See Cognizant Technology Solutions Corporation; *U.S. Public*, pg. 525
TROFHOLZ TECHNOLOGIES, INC.; *U.S. Private*, pg. 4241
TROY GROUP INC.; *U.S. Private*, pg. 4243
TROY GROUP, INC.—See Troy Group Inc.; *U.S. Private*, pg. 4243
TRUESTONE, LLC—See Nana Regional Corporation, Inc.; *U.S. Private*, pg. 2832
TRUMETHODS, LLC—See Insight Venture Management, LLC; *U.S. Private*, pg. 2091
TRUSANT TECHNOLOGIES, LLC.; *U.S. Private*, pg. 4250
TSR CONSULTING SERVICES, INC.—See TSR, Inc.; *U.S. Public*, pg. 2202
TSR CONSULTING SERVICES, INC.—See TSR, Inc.; *U.S. Public*, pg. 2202
TSR CONSULTING SERVICES, INC.—See TSR, Inc.; *U.S. Public*, pg. 2202
TSS REDMOND LLC—See 360training.com, Inc.; *U.S. Private*, pg. 8
TSYMMETRY, INC.; *U.S. Private*, pg. 4254
T-SYSTEMS—See Deutsche Telekom AG; *Int'l*, pg. 2084
TTC ANALYTICAL SERVICE CORP.—See Abbott Laboratories; *U.S. Public*, pg. 20
TURNINGPOINT GLOBAL SOLUTIONS; *U.S. Private*, pg. 4261
TWD & ASSOCIATES INC.; *U.S. Private*, pg. 4263
TWO SHEA CONSULTING, INC.—See ChrysCapital Investment Advisors (India) Private Limited; *Int'l*, pg. 1588

TYLER TECHNOLOGIES - EAGLE DIVISION—See Tyler Technologies, Inc.; *U.S. Public*, pg. 2209
TYLER TECHNOLOGIES INCODE SOLUTIONS—See Tyler Technologies, Inc.; *U.S. Public*, pg. 2209
TYLER TECHNOLOGIES, INC.; *U.S. Public*, pg. 2208
TYTO ATHENE, LLC—See Arlington Capital Partners LLC; *U.S. Private*, pg. 328
UAB AMADEUS LIETUVA—See Amadeus IT Group, S.A.; *Int'l*, pg. 407
UCS SOLUTIONS—See Business Connexion Group Limited; *Int'l*, pg. 1228
UEL CORPORATION—See BIPROGY Inc.; *Int'l*, pg. 1045
UI2 CORPORATION—See FUJISOFT INCORPORATED; *Int'l*, pg. 2830
ULTRAGENDA N.V—See DXC Technology Company; *U.S. Public*, pg. 696
ULTRA TECHNOLOGIES INC.; *U.S. Private*, pg. 4277
UNICOMP INC.; *U.S. Private*, pg. 4282
UNICON INTERNATIONAL; *U.S. Private*, pg. 4282
UNICORN HRO—See The Unicorn Group; *U.S. Private*, pg. 4129
UNIFIED INDUSTRIES INC.; *U.S. Private*, pg. 4282
UNION IT-SERVICES GMBH—See DZ BANK AG Deutsche Zentral-Genossenschaftsbank; *Int'l*, pg. 2245
UNIQUE DIGITAL TECHNOLOGY; *U.S. Private*, pg. 4286
UNITEK INFORMATION SYSTEMS; *U.S. Private*, pg. 4302
UNITIV, INC.—See Ludvik Holdings, Inc.; *U.S. Private*, pg. 2512
UNIVERSAL E-BUSINESS SOLUTIONS; *U.S. Private*, pg. 4304
U.N.P. - SOFTWARE GMBH—See Allgeier SE; *Int'l*, pg. 338
URSA INFORMATION SYSTEMS INC.; *U.S. Private*, pg. 4316
URUK FOR COMPUTER SERVICES & OFFICE EQUIPMENT CO. LTD.—See Eng. Shabah Al-Shammery & Partners Co.; *Int'l*, pg. 2426
USA DIRECT COMPUTER SYSTEMS—See USA Direct Holdings; *U.S. Private*, pg. 4321
USA DIRECT HOLDINGS; *U.S. Private*, pg. 4321
USER INSIGHT, INC.; *U.S. Private*, pg. 4322
USFALCON, INC.; *U.S. Private*, pg. 4323
US INTERACTIVE INC.; *U.S. Private*, pg. 4319
USM BUSINESS SYSTEMS, INC.; *U.S. Private*, pg. 4323
U.S. MICRO CORPORATION - DALLAS FACILITY—See Mountville Mills Inc.; *U.S. Private*, pg. 2801
U.S. MICRO CORPORATION - TORONTO FACILITY—See Mountville Mills Inc.; *U.S. Private*, pg. 2801
UST GLOBAL INC.; *U.S. Private*, pg. 4324
USWIRED INCORPORATED—See Trivest Partners, LP; *U.S. Private*, pg. 4241
UTILANT LLC—See Thoma Bravo, L.P.; *U.S. Private*, pg. 4149
UXC CONSULTING PTE LTD—See DXC Technology Company; *U.S. Public*, pg. 697
UXC ECLIPSE SOLUTIONS (CANADA) LTD—See DXC Technology Company; *U.S. Public*, pg. 697
UXC ECLIPSE (USA) INC.—See DXC Technology Company; *U.S. Public*, pg. 695
UXC PROFESSIONAL SOLUTIONS HOLDINGS PTY LTD—See DXC Technology Company; *U.S. Public*, pg. 695
VALITON GMBH—See Hubert Burda Media Holding Kommanditgesellschaft; *Int'l*, pg. 3520
VALLEY NETWORK SOLUTIONS, INC.; *U.S. Private*, pg. 4334
VALUESOURCE NV—See Cognizant Technology Solutions Corporation; *U.S. Public*, pg. 525
THE VAN DYKE TECHNOLOGY GROUP, INC.—See Jacobs Engineering Group, Inc.; *U.S. Public*, pg. 1186
VANGUARD INTEGRATION INTERNATIONAL PTY LTD—See Capgemini SE; *Int'l*, pg. 1303
VANTEON CORPORATION; *U.S. Private*, pg. 4345
VASCO DATA SECURITY, INC.—See OneSpan Inc.; *U.S. Public*, pg. 1604
VASCO DATA SECURITY MIDDLE EAST FZE—See OneSpan Inc.; *U.S. Public*, pg. 1603
VC3, INC.; *U.S. Private*, pg. 4348
VCOM; *U.S. Private*, pg. 4349
VECTOR SOLUTIONS, INC.—See Genstar Capital, LLC; *U.S. Private*, pg. 1679
VECTRON SYSTEMS AG—See Shift4 Payments, Inc.; *U.S. Public*, pg. 1875
VENTECH SOLUTIONS INC.; *U.S. Private*, pg. 4357
VERACITY SOLUTIONS, INC.; *U.S. Private*, pg. 4359
VERINT VIDEO SOLUTIONS INC—See Verint Systems Inc.; *U.S. Public*, pg. 2281
VERIZON DIGITAL MEDIA SERVICES INC.—See Apollo Global Management, Inc.; *U.S. Public*, pg. 167
VERSANT GMBH—See HCL Technologies Ltd.; *Int'l*, pg. 3298
VERTIGIS HOLDINGS LTD.—See Battery Ventures, L.P.; *U.S. Private*, pg. 489
VERUS TECHNOLOGY GROUP, INC.—See Arlington Capital Partners LLC; *U.S. Private*, pg. 327
VETSAMERICA BUSINESS CONSULTING, INC.; *U.S. Private*, pg. 4374
VIALINK SAS—See Groupe BPCE; *Int'l*, pg. 3099

VIDEOPROPULSION INTERACTIVE TELEVISION, INC.; *U.S. Public*, pg. 2297
VINCENT & VINCENT MICROSYSTEMS—See Vincent & Vincent Companies, Inc.; *U.S. Private*, pg. 4385
VIPDESK, INC.; *U.S. Private*, pg. 4387
VIPS INC.—See General Dynamics Corporation; *U.S. Public*, pg. 914
VIRE TECHNOLOGIES, LLC; *U.S. Private*, pg. 4387
VIRTELLIGENCE; *U.S. Private*, pg. 4388
VIRTUAL TECH GURUS INC.; *U.S. Private*, pg. 4389
VIRTUSA CONSULTING & SERVICES LIMITED—See EQT AB; *Int'l*, pg. 2472
VIRTUSA MEXICO S DE RL DE CV—See EQT AB; *Int'l*, pg. 2472
VIRTUSA QFC IT CONSULTING LLC—See EQT AB; *Int'l*, pg. 2472
VISALIGN LLC; *U.S. Private*, pg. 4389
VISTA INTERNATIONAL OPERATIONS, INC.—See Bristol Bay Native Corporation; *U.S. Private*, pg. 656
VISTA TECHNOLOGY SERVICES, INC.; *U.S. Private*, pg. 4403
VISTAUXX LTD.; *U.S. Private*, pg. 4403
VISTRACKS, INC.—See Vista Equity Partners, LLC; *U.S. Private*, pg. 4399
VIZSTONE PTY. LTD.—See ActivePort Group Limited; *Int'l*, pg. 120
VMD SYSTEMS INTEGRATORS, INC.; *U.S. Private*, pg. 4408
VOCOLLECT INTERNATIONAL LIMITED—See Honeywell International Inc.; *U.S. Public*, pg. 1050
VOLT DELTA RESOURCES, LLC—See ESW Capital, LLC; *U.S. Private*, pg. 1431
VOLVO INFORMATION TECHNOLOGY FRANCE—See AB Volvo; *Int'l*, pg. 45
VOLVO INFORMATION TECHNOLOGY MALAYSIA—See AB Volvo; *Int'l*, pg. 45
VOLVO INFORMATION TECHNOLOGY MEXICO—See AB Volvo; *Int'l*, pg. 45
VOLVO INFORMATION TECHNOLOGY NORTH AMERICA INC.—See AB Volvo; *Int'l*, pg. 45
VOLVO INFORMATION TECHNOLOGY POLAND—See AB Volvo; *Int'l*, pg. 45
VOLVO INFORMATION TECHNOLOGY ROCKLEIGH—See AB Volvo; *Int'l*, pg. 45
VOLVO INFORMATION TECHNOLOGY (TIANJIN) CO., LTD—See AB Volvo; *Int'l*, pg. 45
VOLVO IT BELGIUM—See AB Volvo; *Int'l*, pg. 45
VOLVO IT CANADA—See AB Volvo; *Int'l*, pg. 45
VOLVO IT ESKILSTUNA—See AB Volvo; *Int'l*, pg. 45
VOLVO IT KOPING—See AB Volvo; *Int'l*, pg. 45
VOLVO IT KOREA—See AB Volvo; *Int'l*, pg. 45
VOLVO IT SOUTH AFRICA—See AB Volvo; *Int'l*, pg. 45
VOLVO IT THAILAND—See AB Volvo; *Int'l*, pg. 45
VOXWARE, INC.; *U.S. Private*, pg. 4414
VPIPHOTONICS GMBH—See VPI Systems; *U.S. Private*, pg. 4414
V-SOFT CONSULTING GROUP, INC.; *U.S. Private*, pg. 4328
VST CONSULTING, INC.; *U.S. Private*, pg. 4415
W82, LLC—See Camping World Holdings, Inc.; *U.S. Public*, pg. 428
WAGGL, INC.—See Perceptyx, Inc.; *U.S. Private*, pg. 3146
WALL STREET NETWORK SOLUTIONS; *U.S. Private*, pg. 4430
WARNER CONNECT, INC.; *U.S. Private*, pg. 4442
WAUSAU FINANCIAL SYSTEMS, INC.—See Augeo Affinity Marketing, Inc.; *U.S. Private*, pg. 392
WAVEFRONT TECHNOLOGIES, INC.—See Ball Corporation; *U.S. Public*, pg. 266
WAYPOINT SOLUTIONS GROUP, LLC; *U.S. Private*, pg. 4460
WDIT, INCORPORATED; *U.S. Private*, pg. 4462
WEATHERFORD PETROLEUM CONSULTANTS AS—See Weatherford International plc; *U.S. Public*, pg. 2340
WEBIT SERVICES, INC.; *U.S. Private*, pg. 4466
WEBLINK INTERNATIONAL, INC.—See Acer Incorporated; *Int'l*, pg. 100
WEBSITE PIPELINE, INC.; *U.S. Private*, pg. 4466
WESTCON CALA, INC.—See TD Synnex Corp; *U.S. Public*, pg. 1987
WESTCON GROUP AFRICA OPERATIONS LIMITED—See TD Synnex Corp; *U.S. Public*, pg. 1987
WESTCON GROUP PTY LIMITED—See TD Synnex Corp; *U.S. Public*, pg. 1987
WESTCON MEXICO S.A. DE C.V.—See TD Synnex Corp; *U.S. Public*, pg. 1987
WESTCON SA (PTY) LIMITED—See TD Synnex Corp; *U.S. Public*, pg. 1987
WESTERN DIGITAL CANADA—See Western Digital Corporation; *U.S. Public*, pg. 2355
WESTERN DIGITAL DEUTSCHLAND GMBH—See Western Digital Corporation; *U.S. Public*, pg. 2355
WESTERN DIGITAL JAPAN, LTD.—See Western Digital Corporation; *U.S. Public*, pg. 2355
WESTERN DIGITAL KOREA INC.—See Western Digital Corporation; *U.S. Public*, pg. 2355
WESTERN DIGITAL NETHERLANDS B.V.—See Western Digital Corporation; *U.S. Public*, pg. 2355

WESTERN DIGITAL (UK) LTD.—See Western Digital Corporation; *U.S. Public*, pg. 2355
WESTERNTECHSYSTEMS INC.; *U.S. Private*, pg. 4498
WIDEN ENTERPRISES INC.—See Vista Equity Partners, LLC; *U.S. Private*, pg. 4394
WIDEPOINT CORPORATION; *U.S. Public*, pg. 2370
WIDEPOINT INTEGRATED SOLUTIONS CORP.—See WidePoint Corporation; *U.S. Public*, pg. 2370
WILLBROOK SOLUTIONS, INC.—See Godspeed Capital Management LP; *U.S. Private*, pg. 1725
WILLOUGHBY'S INC.; *U.S. Private*, pg. 4528
WIMMER SOLUTIONS; *U.S. Private*, pg. 4532
W-INDUSTRIES, INC.—See CSE Global Ltd.; *Int'l*, pg. 1864
WINGSPAN TECHNOLOGY, INC.; *U.S. Private*, pg. 4541
WINMILL SOFTWARE COMPANY; *U.S. Private*, pg. 4542
WIREDCOMMUTE, LLC.—See Edenred S.A.; *Int'l*, pg. 2308
WISCNET; *U.S. Private*, pg. 4547
WORDEN BROTHERS, INC.; *U.S. Private*, pg. 4563
WORKGROUP TECHNOLOGY PARTNERS; *U.S. Private*, pg. 4563
WORKSIGHTED; *U.S. Private*, pg. 4564
WORLDCOM EXCHANGE, INC.; *U.S. Private*, pg. 4568
WOT.IO, INC.—See InterDigital, Inc.; *U.S. Public*, pg. 1144
WRAP MEDIA, LLC—See DXC Technology Company; *U.S. Public*, pg. 697
WUHAN INFOCHAMP I.T. CO., LTD.—See China Steel Corporation; *Int'l*, pg. 1556
WYDE CORPORATION—See Blackstone Inc.; *U.S. Public*, pg. 356
XANDROS INC.; *U.S. Private*, pg. 4580
XANGATI, INC.—See Virtual Instruments, Inc.; *U.S. Private*, pg. 4389
XCELIGENT, INC.; *U.S. Private*, pg. 4580
XCEND GROUP, INC.; *U.S. Private*, pg. 4580
XCHANGING GLOBAL INSURANCE SOLUTIONS LIMITED—See DXC Technology Company; *U.S. Public*, pg. 697
XEROX BUSINESS SOLUTIONS NORTHEAST, INC.—See Xerox Holdings Corporation; *U.S. Public*, pg. 2387
XEROX IT SERVICES LIMITED—See Xerox Holdings Corporation; *U.S. Public*, pg. 2390
XORIANT CORPORATION—See ChrysCapital Management Co.; *Int'l*, pg. 1588
XPLORE TECHNOLOGIES CORP.—See Zebra Technologies Corporation; *U.S. Public*, pg. 2402
XP SYSTEMS CORPORATION—See Fiserv, Inc.; *U.S. Public*, pg. 851
XTIVIA, INC.—See Asseco Poland S.A.; *Int'l*, pg. 642
XTRACON A/S—See TowerBrook Capital Partners, L.P.; *U.S. Private*, pg. 4195
XWAVE—See BCE Inc.; *Int'l*, pg. 926
YASH TECHNOLOGIES, INC.; *U.S. Private*, pg. 4586
Y.M.P.-INTERNATIONAL CORPORATION—See Fair Friend Group; *Int'l*, pg. 2605
YORK SOLUTIONS, LLC.; *U.S. Private*, pg. 4591
ZANTECH IT SERVICES, INC.; *U.S. Private*, pg. 4598
ZAVDA TECHNOLOGIES, LLC—See CACI International Inc.; *U.S. Public*, pg. 417
ZDI IMAGES & MOTION INC.—See Stirista, LLC; *U.S. Private*, pg. 3813
ZELTECH TRAINING SOLUTIONS, LLC—See Zel Technologies, LLC; *U.S. Public*, pg. 4600
ZEMAX EUROPE LIMITED—See ANSYS, Inc.; *U.S. Public*, pg. 139
ZEMAX JAPAN K.K.—See ANSYS, Inc.; *U.S. Public*, pg. 139
ZEMAX OPTICAL TECHNOLOGY CONSULTING (SHANGHAI) CO., LTD.—See ANSYS, Inc.; *U.S. Public*, pg. 139
ZENMONICS INC.—See Fidelity National Infor; *U.S. Public*, pg. 833
ZIATH B.V.—See Azenta, Inc.; *U.S. Public*, pg. 258
ZIATH LTD.—See Azenta, Inc.; *U.S. Public*, pg. 258
ZILKER TECHNOLOGY LLC; *U.S. Private*, pg. 4604
ZILLION TECHNOLOGIES; *U.S. Private*, pg. 4605
ZOT, INC.—See T-Rex Solutions, LLC; *U.S. Private*, pg. 3911
ZQUARED LLC; *U.S. Private*, pg. 4609
ZYMPHONY TECHNOLOGY SOLUTIONS; *U.S. Private*, pg. 4611

541513 — COMPUTER FACILITIES MANAGEMENT SERVICES

ABS INFOLINK INC.—See American Bureau of Shipping; *U.S. Public*, pg. 225
ACORIO LLC; *U.S. Private*, pg. 63
ACRODEX INC.—See Insight Enterprises, Inc.; *U.S. Public*, pg. 1130
ADASTRA CORPORATION; *Int'l*, pg. 125
ADESSO LAKES GMBH—See adesso SE; *Int'l*, pg. 144
ADYEN CANADA LTD.—See Adyen N.V.; *Int'l*, pg. 169
AEDIAN SA—See Aubay SA; *Int'l*, pg. 698
AGILITY RECOVERY SOLUTIONS, INC.—See New State Capital Partners LLC; *U.S. Private*, pg. 2906
ALARUM TECHNOLOGIES LTD.; *Int'l*, pg. 291
ALIGNED TECHNOLOGY SOLUTIONS, LLC—See Teal; *U.S. Private*, pg. 3948
ALLIED TELESYN (CHINA) LTD.—See ALLIED TELESIS

541513 — COMPUTER FACILITIES...

HOLDINGS K.K.; *Int'l*, pg. 358
ANOVO NORDIC AB—See Francisco Partners Management, LP; *U.S. Private*, pg. 1588
AN POST BILLPOST PROCESSING SERVICES LIMITED—See An Post LLC; *Int'l*, pg. 443
ARITHNEA GMBH—See adesso SE; *Int'l*, pg. 144
ARROW CENTRAL EUROPE GMBH—See Arrow Electronics, Inc.; *U.S. Public*, pg. 195
ATLAS CSF SDN BHD—See CSF Group plc; *Int'l*, pg. 1864
ATOS IT-DIENSTLEISTUNG UND BERATUNG GMBH—See Atos SE; *Int'l*, pg. 690
AUTHENTICOM, INC.; *U.S. Private*, pg. 396
AXIOLOGIC SOLUTIONS, LLC; *U.S. Private*, pg. 412
AZLAN GROUP PLC—See TD Synnex Corp; *U.S. Public*, pg. 1986
BASF IT SERVICES GMBH—See BASF SE; *Int'l*, pg. 879
BASF IT SERVICES LTD.—See BASF SE; *Int'l*, pg. 879
BASF IT SERVICES N.V./S.A. - FRANCE—See BASF SE; *Int'l*, pg. 879
BASF IT SERVICES N.V./S.A.—See BASF SE; *Int'l*, pg. 879
BASF IT SERVICES S.P.A.—See BASF SE; *Int'l*, pg. 879
BLUE CANOPY INC.; *U.S. Private*, pg. 585
BROADSOFT HOSPITALITY, INC.—See Cisco Systems, Inc.; *U.S. Public*, pg. 497
CARREFOUR SYSTEMES D'INFORMATIONS FRANCE—See Carrefour SA; *Int'l*, pg. 1344
CASPIDA, INC.—See Cisco Systems, Inc.; *U.S. Public*, pg. 500
CHALLENGER BANK LIMITED—See Heartland Group Holdings Limited; *Int'l*, pg. 3304
CHINABANK PROPERTIES & COMPUTER CENTER, INC.—See China Banking Corporation; *Int'l*, pg. 1484
CLARITY SOLUTION GROUP, LLC—See Accenture plc; *Int'l*, pg. 87
CLEARPOINTE, INC.—See WestView Capital Partners, L.P.; *U.S. Private*, pg. 4501
CLIENT NETWORK SERVICES INC.—See The Carlyle Group Inc.; *U.S. Public*, pg. 2045
CLOUD DATA CORPORATION—See Microelectronics Technology Company; *U.S. Private*, pg. 2703
COGNIZANT TECHNOLOGY SOLUTIONS CORPORATION; *U.S. Public*, pg. 523
COI GMBH—See Certina Holding AG; *Int'l*, pg. 1423
COMCAST ENTERPRISE SERVICES, LLC—See Comcast Corporation; *U.S. Public*, pg. 537
COMPUTERIZED FACILITY INTEGRATION, L.L.C.—See BGC Group, Inc.; *U.S. Public*, pg. 329
COMPUTER SYSTEMS COMPANY, INC. - HEALTHCARE CONSULTING SERVICES DIVISION—See Thoma Bravo, L.P.; *U.S. Private*, pg. 4148
CORESHED PTY. LTD.—See Epiroc AB; *Int'l*, pg. 2461
CROPLOGIC LIMITED; *Int'l*, pg. 1855
CYNTERGY SERVICES LIMITED—See Heritage Group Ltd.; *Int'l*, pg. 3361
CYRUSONE LLC—See BlackRock, Inc.; *U.S. Public*, pg. 346
CYRUSONE LLC—See KKR & Co. Inc.; *U.S. Public*, pg. 1244
DATACORE SOFTWARE CORP.; *U.S. Private*, pg. 1165
DATAMATICS GLOBAL SERVICES LTD.; *Int'l*, pg. 1978
DELL INC. - NASHUA—See Dell Technologies Inc.; *U.S. Public*, pg. 649
DIGITAL REALTY AUSTRIA GMBH—See Digital Realty Trust, Inc.; *U.S. Public*, pg. 663
DIGITAL REALTY SWITZERLAND GMBH—See Digital Realty Trust, Inc.; *U.S. Public*, pg. 663
DOCUGROUP PAPIR SZOLGALTATO KORLATOLT FELELOSSEGU TARSASAG—See Iron Mountain Incorporated; *U.S. Public*, pg. 1172
DXC TECHNOLOGY DANMARK A/S—See DXC Technology Company; *U.S. Public*, pg. 695
DXC TECHNOLOGY HONG KONG LIMITED—See DXC Technology Company; *U.S. Public*, pg. 695
DXC TECHNOLOGY SCANDIHEALTH A/S—See DXC Technology Company; *U.S. Public*, pg. 695
DXC TECHONOLOGY NORGE AS—See DXC Technology Company; *U.S. Public*, pg. 695
EC CONCIERGE CORPORATION—See Canon Inc.; *Int'l*, pg. 1293
EP CONSULTING SERVICES CORPORATION—See Business Brain Showa-Ota Inc.; *Int'l*, pg. 1228
E-PERFECT IT LIMITED—See GET Holdings Limited; *Int'l*, pg. 2946
EQUINIX, INC. - RESTON—See Equinix, Inc.; *U.S. Public*, pg. 788
ESCENDENT, LLC; *U.S. Private*, pg. 1425
E-SPIRIT AG—See adesso SE; *Int'l*, pg. 144
FINOCOM AG—See Cisco Systems, Inc.; *U.S. Public*, pg. 497
FLOWJO LLC—See Becton, Dickinson & Company; *U.S. Public*, pg. 292
FSA TECHNOLOGY, LLC—See Fort Sill Apache Tribe of Oklahoma; *U.S. Private*, pg. 1575
FUJITSU CANADA LIMITED—See Fujitsu Limited; *Int'l*, pg. 2834
GLASSEN CONSULTING & AUTOMATION, LLC—See T.J. Haggerty, Inc.; *U.S. Private*, pg. 3912
GLOBAL EMERGENCY RESOURCES, LLC—See Central Research, Inc.; *U.S. Private*, pg. 824
GREAT WALL COMPUTER SOFTWARE & SYSTEMS CO., LTD.—See China Electronics Corporation; *Int'l*, pg. 1499
HALFAKER & ASSOCIATES, LLC—See Science Applications International Corporation; *U.S. Public*, pg. 1848
HATENA CO., LTD.; *Int'l*, pg. 3284
HITACHI SYSTEMS, LTD.—See Hitachi, Ltd.; *Int'l*, pg. 3422
HMS HEALTHCARE MANAGEMENT SOLUTIONS, INC.—See HealthEdge Investment Partners, LLC; *U.S. Private*, pg. 1896
IBM GLOBAL TECHNOLOGY SERVICES—See International Business Machines Corporation; *U.S. Public*, pg. 1147
ICOMARCH24 SA—See ComArch S.A.; *Int'l*, pg. 1707
ICS NETT INC.; *U.S. Private*, pg. 2033
ID HOLDINGS CORPORATION; *Int'l*, pg. 3587
IMPACT TECHNOLOGY SOLUTIONS—See Impact Logistics, Inc.; *U.S. Private*, pg. 2048
INNODATA KNOWLEDGE SERVICES, INC.—See Innodata, Inc.; *U.S. Public*, pg. 1125
INNOVISE LTD.—See Accel Partners L.P.; *U.S. Private*, pg. 49
INNOVISE LTD.—See KKR & Co. Inc.; *U.S. Public*, pg. 1238
INSIGHT TECHNOLOGY SOLUTIONS S.R.L.—See Insight Enterprises, Inc.; *U.S. Public*, pg. 1130
INSPIRISYS SOLUTIONS LIMITED—See CAC Corporation; *Int'l*, pg. 1247
INTERNATIONAL PAPER COMPANY - MEMPHIS SOUTHWIND INFORMATION TECHNOLOGY CENTER—See International Paper Company; *U.S. Public*, pg. 1157
IRON MOUNTAIN FINLAND OY—See Iron Mountain Incorporated; *U.S. Public*, pg. 1173
J9 TECHNOLOGIES, INC.—See Axxiome AG; *Int'l*, pg. 773
JHM RESEARCH & DEVELOPMENT INC.; *U.S. Private*, pg. 2207
KEYLOGIC ASSOCIATES, INC.—See System One Holdings, LLC; *U.S. Private*, pg. 3907
KINETIC GROUP INC.; *U.S. Public*, pg. 1234
LINKVERSE S.R.L.—See Cosmo Pharmaceuticals N.V.; *Int'l*, pg. 1813
LOGISTICS & ENVIRONMENTAL SUPPORT SERVICES CORPORATION; *U.S. Private*, pg. 2482
MANAGEMENT TECHNOLOGY, INC.; *U.S. Private*, pg. 2561
MANUS DEI, INC.—See The 20 Msp Group LLC; *U.S. Private*, pg. 3980
MASTECH INFOTRELLIS, INC.—See Mastech Digital, Inc.; *U.S. Public*, pg. 1394
MASTERCONTROL, INC.; *U.S. Private*, pg. 2608
MEDICUS SOLUTIONS, LLC; *U.S. Private*, pg. 2656
MOTORDATA RESEARCH CONSORTIUM SDN. BHD—See HeiTech Padu Berhad; *Int'l*, pg. 3326
MPS CAPITAL SERVICES BANCA PER LE IMPRESE S.P.A.—See Banca Monte dei Paschi di Siena S.p.A.; *Int'l*, pg. 815
MY COMPUTER WORKS, INC; *U.S. Private*, pg. 2823
NETSTAR-1, INC.; *U.S. Private*, pg. 2888
NI INFORMATION SYSTEM CO., LTD.—See International Business Machines Corporation; *U.S. Public*, pg. 1147
OETKER DATEN- UND INFORMATIONSVERARBEITUNG KG—See Dr. August Oetker KG; *Int'l*, pg. 2190
OSCILLATE PLC—See Gunsynd plc; *Int'l*, pg. 3185
PARK PLACE TECHNOLOGIES, LLC—See Charlesbank Capital Partners, LLC; *U.S. Private*, pg. 856
PARK PLACE TECHNOLOGIES, LLC—See GTCR LLC; *U.S. Private*, pg. 1806
PARSEC INNOVATION LABS LLC—See Golden Agri-Resources Ltd.; *Int'l*, pg. 3028
PENBAY SOLUTIONS LLC—See Pamlico Capital Management, L.P.; *U.S. Private*, pg. 3083
PERFECT EVENT SERVICES LIMITED—See FSE Services Group Limited; *U.S. Private*, pg. 2798
PLATFORM COMPUTING INC.—See International Business Machines Corporation; *U.S. Public*, pg. 1148
PROMETHEUS RESEARCH, LLC; *U.S. Private*, pg. 3283
PRUDENTIAL GENERAL SERVICES OF JAPAN Y.K.—See Prudential Financial, Inc.; *U.S. Public*, pg. 1734
PUREAPPS LIMITED—See Accenture plc; *Int'l*, pg. 87
RAE & LIPSKIE INVESTMENT COUNSEL INC.—See Guardian Capital Group Limited; *Int'l*, pg. 3170
RAPID7 CANADA, INC.—See Rapid7, Inc.; *U.S. Public*, pg. 1763
RCM SOLUTIONS, INC.; *U.S. Private*, pg. 3362
RISK SCIENCES GROUP, INC.—See Crawford & Company; *U.S. Public*, pg. 592
ROCKWELL AUTOMATION SAS—See Rockwell Automation, Inc.; *U.S. Public*, pg. 1806
SAAMA TECHNOLOGIES, INC.; *U.S. Private*, pg. 3520
SAFE HOUSE INFORMATION MANAGEMENT SOLUTIONS PRIVATE LIMITED—See Iron Mountain Incorporated; *U.S. Public*, pg. 1174
SAINT-GOBAIN WEBER NETSERVICES—See Compagnie de Saint-Gobain SA; *Int'l*, pg. 1727
SANITY SOLUTIONS INC.; *U.S. Private*, pg. 3546
SATORY GLOBAL, LLC; *U.S. Private*, pg. 3553
SAVVIS HONG KONG LIMITED—See Lumen Technologies, Inc.; *U.S. Public*, pg. 1347
SAVVIS SINGAPORE—See Lumen Technologies, Inc.; *U.S. Public*, pg. 1347
SAVVIS UNITED KINGDOM—See Lumen Technologies, Inc.; *U.S. Public*, pg. 1347
SCIO HEALTH ANALYTICS (UK) LIMITED—See ExlService Holdings, Inc.; *U.S. Public*, pg. 808
SECUREWORKS CORP.—See Dell Technologies Inc.; *U.S. Public*, pg. 650
SECURINFOR SA—See Compagnie Lebon SA; *U.S. Private*, pg. 1745
SERVERLIFT CORP.; *U.S. Private*, pg. 3614
SERVICE COMMUNICATIONS INC.; *U.S. Private*, pg. 3615
SHYFT ANALYTICS, INC.—See Dassault Systèmes S.A.; *Int'l*, pg. 1975
SINGAPORE-RE MANAGEMENT SERVICES PTE. LTD.—See Fairfax Financial Holdings Limited; *Int'l*, pg. 2608
SMARTENCRYPT PTY. LTD.—See Crayon Group Holding ASA; *Int'l*, pg. 1830
STRATA INFORMATION TECHNOLOGY INC.—See GoodSuite; *U.S. Private*, pg. 1740
SUN MICROSYSTEMS LUXEMBOURG SARL—See Oracle Corporation; *U.S. Public*, pg. 1611
SWANKTEK, INC.; *U.S. Private*, pg. 3890
TBC NET INC.; *U.S. Private*, pg. 3941
TELEPLAN POLSKA SP. Z O.O.—See Clover Wireless; *U.S. Private*, pg. 948
UDACITY, INC.—See Asas Capital Ltd; *Int'l*, pg. 599
VIVID AUTOMOTIVE DATA (UK) LTD—See Apax Partners LLP; *Int'l*, pg. 502
VIVID AUTOMOTIVE DATA (UK) LTD—See TowerBrook Capital Partners, L.P.; *U.S. Private*, pg. 4195
VIVID ITALIA SRL—See Apax Partners LLP; *Int'l*, pg. 502
VIVID ITALIA SRL—See TowerBrook Capital Partners, L.P.; *U.S. Private*, pg. 4195
WESTBROOK TECHNOLOGIES, INC.; *U.S. Private*, pg. 4488
WORLDWIDE TECHSERVICES, INC; *U.S. Private*, pg. 4570
W.T. CHEN & CO., INC.; *U.S. Private*, pg. 4423
ZEBRA TECHNOLOGIES NETHERLANDS B.V.—See Zebra Technologies Corporation; *U.S. Public*, pg. 2402

541519 — OTHER COMPUTER RELATED SERVICES

10TH MAGNITUDE INC.—See Pamlico Capital Management, L.P.; *U.S. Private*, pg. 3083
4DS MEMORY LIMITED; *Int'l*, pg. 11
5TH GEAR TECHNOLOGIES CONCEPTS, INC.; *U.S. Private*, pg. 16
6FUSION USA, INC.; *U.S. Private*, pg. 16
A8 NEW MEDIA GROUP LTD.; *Int'l*, pg. 30
ABACO SYSTEMS INC.—See AMETEK, Inc.; *U.S. Public*, pg. 119
ABILITY NETWORK INC.—See Inovalon Holdings, Inc.; *U.S. Public*, pg. 1128
ABM KNOWLEDGEWARE LTD; *Int'l*, pg. 63
ABTECH TECHNOLOGIES, INC.; *U.S. Private*, pg. 45
ACCELALPHA INC.—See Century Park Capital Partners, LLC; *U.S. Private*, pg. 833
ACCENTIA TECHNOLOGIES LIMITED; *Int'l*, pg. 81
ACCUDATA TECHNOLOGIES; *U.S. Private*, pg. 54
ACCUNET SOLUTIONS—See Red River Computer Co., Inc.; *U.S. Private*, pg. 3375
ACENTIA, LLC—See MAXIMUS, Inc.; *U.S. Public*, pg. 1402
ACER AUSTRIA GMBH—See Acer Incorporated; *Int'l*, pg. 98
ACER COMPUTER POLAND—See Acer Incorporated; *Int'l*, pg. 99
ACER CZECH REPUBLIC S.R.O.—See Acer Incorporated; *Int'l*, pg. 99
ACER MAGYARORSZAG—See Acer Incorporated; *Int'l*, pg. 99
ACER SWEDEN AB—See Acer Incorporated; *Int'l*, pg. 99
ACTCALL INC.; *Int'l*, pg. 117
ACTIVEOUTDOORS—See Vista Equity Partners, LLC; *U.S. Private*, pg. 4394
ACTUAL I.T., D.D.—See DBA Group SRL; *Int'l*, pg. 1986
ACUATIVE CORP.; *U.S. Private*, pg. 71
ADC INTEGRATED SYSTEMS, INC.—See Sole Source Capital LLC; *U.S. Private*, pg. 3708
ADDNODE GROUP AB; *Int'l*, pg. 130
ADDPRO AB—See Adelis Equity Partners AB; *Int'l*, pg. 142
ADMELD INC.—See Alphabet Inc.; *U.S. Public*, pg. 83
ADTRAN NETWORKS HONG KONG LIMITED—See ADTRAN Holdings, Inc.; *U.S. Public*, pg. 43
ADTRAN NETWORKS, PTY. LTD.—See ADTRAN Holdings, Inc.; *U.S. Public*, pg. 44
ADVANCED AV, LLC; *U.S. Private*, pg. 88
ADVANCED CONTROL & SYSTEMS INC.—See CTCI Corporation; *Int'l*, pg. 1870
ADVANCED DUPLICATION SERVICES INC.; *U.S. Private*, pg. 89
ADVANCED GRAPHIC PRODUCTS INC.—See Follett Corporation; *U.S. Private*, pg. 1559
ADVANCED MICRO - ELECTRONICS, INC.; *U.S. Private*, pg. 91

N.A.I.C.S. INDEX

541519 — OTHER COMPUTER RELA...

ADVANIA HOLDING HF—See Enterprise Investment Fund slhf.; *Int'l*, pg. 2451
ADVANTECH AUSTRALIA PTY. LIMITED—See Advantech Co., Ltd.; *Int'l*, pg. 164
ADVICE MEDIA LLC; *U.S. Private*, pg. 110
AEERIS LIMITED; *Int'l*, pg. 173
AFFECTO PLC—See CGI Inc.; *Int'l*, pg. 1433
AFP GMBH—See Agence France-Presse; *Int'l*, pg. 205
AFP-SERVICES SA—See Agence France-Presse; *Int'l*, pg. 205
AGEST, INC.—See Digital Hearts Holdings Co., Ltd.; *Int'l*, pg. 2122
AGFA HEALTHCARE NV—See Agfa-Gevaert N.V.; *Int'l*, pg. 208
AGILYSYS, INC.; *U.S. Public*, pg. 62
AGS CORPORATION; *Int'l*, pg. 221
AIGIN COMPUTER SERVICE CO., LTD.—See Aichi Financial Group Co., Ltd.; *Int'l*, pg. 229
AIR-TRANSPORT IT SERVICES, INC.—See Amadeus IT Group, S.A.; *Int'l*, pg. 406
AKIMEKA LLC—See VSE Corporation; *U.S. Public*, pg. 2313
AKTA WEB STUDIO; *U.S. Private*, pg. 147
ALCYONIX—See DBAY Advisors Limited; *Int'l*, pg. 1987
THE ALDRIDGE COMPANY - DALLAS OFFICE—See The Aldridge Company; *U.S. Private*, pg. 3983
THE ALDRIDGE COMPANY; *U.S. Private*, pg. 3983
ALEUT GLOBAL SOLUTIONS—See The Aleut Corporation; *U.S. Private*, pg. 3984
AL FAISALIAH ELECTRONICS SERVICES—See Al Faisaliah Group; *Int'l*, pg. 277
ALLEGIENT DEFENSE INC.—See BCS, LLC; *U.S. Private*, pg. 500
ALLGEIER CYRIS GMBH—See Allgeier SE; *Int'l*, pg. 336
ALLGEIER ENTERPRISE SERVICES SE—See Allgeier SE; *Int'l*, pg. 336
ALLGEIER EXPERTS GO GMBH—See Allgeier SE; *Int'l*, pg. 336
ALLGEIER EXPERTS HOLDING GMBH—See Allgeier SE; *Int'l*, pg. 336
ALLGEIER EXPERTS PRO GMBH—See Allgeier SE; *Int'l*, pg. 336
ALLGEIER INOVAR GMBH—See Allgeier SE; *Int'l*, pg. 337
ALLGEIER IT SERVICES GMBH—See Allgeier SE; *Int'l*, pg. 337
ALLGEIER PUBLIC SE—See Allgeier SE; *Int'l*, pg. 337
ALLIED DIGITAL SERVICES LIMITED; *Int'l*, pg. 357
ALLSCRIPTS CANADA CORPORATION—See Veradigm Inc.; *U.S. Public*, pg. 2279
ALLSCRIPTS INDIA—See Veradigm Inc.; *U.S. Public*, pg. 2280
ALPINE SECURITY, LLC—See CISO Global, Inc.; *U.S. Public*, pg. 501
ALTA IT SERVICES LLC—See System One Holdings, LLC; *U.S. Private*, pg. 3906
ALTEN CALSOFT LABS, INC.—See Alten S.A.; *Int'l*, pg. 389
ALTIA CONSULTORES SA; *Int'l*, pg. 392
AMADEUS GERMANY GMBH—See Amadeus IT Group, S.A.; *Int'l*, pg. 406
AMAZON WEB SERVICES, INC.—See Amazon.com, Inc.; *U.S. Public*, pg. 90
AMERI & PARTNERS INC.—See Enveric Biosciences, Inc.; *U.S. Public*, pg. 780
AM PM SYSTEMS; *Int'l*, pg. 402
AM PM USA SERVICE, LLC—See AM PM Systems; *Int'l*, pg. 402
ANOTO GROUP AB; *Int'l*, pg. 474
ANOTO INC.—See Anoto Group AB; *Int'l*, pg. 474
ANOTO K.K—See Anoto Group AB; *Int'l*, pg. 474
APEX PRINT TECHNOLOGIES, LLC—See GTCR LLC; *U.S. Private*, pg. 1806
APPENTURE D.O.O—See Adveritas Limited; *Int'l*, pg. 167
APPLIED COMPUTER SOLUTIONS—See Pivot Technology Solutions, Inc.; *U.S. Public*, pg. 1695
APPLIED SOFTWARE TECHNOLOGY, INC.; *U.S. Private*, pg. 299
APPS ASSOCIATES GMBH—See Quad-C Management, Inc.; *U.S. Private*, pg. 3315
APPS ASSOCIATES LLC—See Quad-C Management, Inc.; *U.S. Private*, pg. 3315
APPS ASSOCIATES PVT. LTD.—See Quad-C Management, Inc.; *U.S. Private*, pg. 3315
A-P-T RESEARCH, INC.; *U.S. Private*, pg. 22
ARAG AUSTRALIA PTY LTD.—See Nordson Corporation; *U.S. Public*, pg. 1532
ARAG DO BRASIL S.A.—See Nordson Corporation; *U.S. Public*, pg. 1532
ARCHEO, INC.—See Marchex, Inc.; *U.S. Public*, pg. 1364
ARCOT DEUTSCHLAND GMBH—See Broadcom Inc.; *U.S. Public*, pg. 388
ARCUS SYSTEMY INFORMATYCZNE SP. Z O.O.—See Arcus S.A.; *Int'l*, pg. 553
ARDENT SUPPORT TECHNOLOGIES, LLC—See Charlesbank Capital Partners, LLC; *U.S. Private*, pg. 856
ARDENT SUPPORT TECHNOLOGIES, LLC—See GTCR LLC; *U.S. Private*, pg. 1806
ARGUS HEALTH SYSTEMS, INC.—See SS&C Technologies Holdings, Inc.; *U.S. Public*, pg. 1923

ARMORBLOX LLC—See Cisco Systems, Inc.; *U.S. Public*, pg. 497
ARROW ECS BELGIUM—See Arrow Electronics, Inc.; *U.S. Public*, pg. 196
ARROW ECS INTERNET SECURITY AG - BRUTTISELLEN—See Arrow Electronics, Inc.; *U.S. Public*, pg. 196
ARTIFICIAL LABS LTD.—See Capita plc; *Int'l*, pg. 1308
ASCENDUM SOLUTIONS LLC—See Vora Ventures LLC; *U.S. Private*, pg. 4412
ASCOM DANMARK A/S—See Ascom Holding AG; *Int'l*, pg. 603
ASCOM (MALAYSIA) SDN BHD—See Ascom Holding AG; *Int'l*, pg. 602
ASCOM SOLUTIONS (SINGAPORE) PTE LTD—See Ascom Holding AG; *Int'l*, pg. 603
ASCOM UMS S.R.L.—See Ascom Holding AG; *Int'l*, pg. 603
AS IRON MOUNTAIN LATVIA AS—See Iron Mountain Incorporated; *U.S. Public*, pg. 1172
ASPYRA-EAST COAST OFFICE—See ASPYRA, INC.; *U.S. Public*, pg. 214
ASSETCORE LTD.—See Aquila Services Group PLC; *Int'l*, pg. 528
ASSURED INFORMATION SECURITY, INC.; *U.S. Private*, pg. 359
ASTOUND COMMERCE CORP.; *U.S. Private*, pg. 361
ATA TESTING AUTHORITY (BEIJING) LIMITED—See ATA Creativity Global; *Int'l*, pg. 665
ATEA UAB—See Atea ASA; *Int'l*, pg. 667
ATEN ADVANCE CO.,LTD—See Aten International Co., Ltd.; *Int'l*, pg. 668
ATENDE S.A.; *Int'l*, pg. 668
ATEN JAPAN CO., LTD—See Aten International Co., Ltd.; *Int'l*, pg. 668
ATEN NEW JERSEY INC—See Aten International Co., Ltd.; *Int'l*, pg. 668
ATEN U.K. LIMITED—See Aten International Co., Ltd.; *Int'l*, pg. 668
ATOS IT SERVICES UK LIMITED—See Atos SE; *Int'l*, pg. 690
ATOS SERVICES (MALAYSIA) SDN BHD—See Atos SE; *Int'l*, pg. 691
ATOS SINGAPORE—See Atos SE; *Int'l*, pg. 691
ATRENEW INC.; *Int'l*, pg. 693
ATRILOGY SOLUTIONS GROUP, INC.—See DIVERSANT, LLC; *U.S. Private*, pg. 1240
AUCTION TECHNOLOGY GROUP PLC; *Int'l*, pg. 700
AUDIUS SE—See audius AG; *Int'l*, pg. 702
AUGUSTA SYSTEMS, INC.—See Hexagon AB; *Int'l*, pg. 3368
AUSTIN GEOMODELING, INC.; *U.S. Private*, pg. 395
AUTOMATED RESOURCE MANAGEMENT ASSOCIATES, INC.; *U.S. Private*, pg. 399
AVERTIUM TENNESSEE, INC.—See Sunstone Partners Management LLC; *U.S. Private*, pg. 3873
AVINEON INDIA PRIVATE LIMITED—See Avineon, Inc.; *U.S. Private*, pg. 407
AVIX TECHNOLOGIES, INC.; *U.S. Private*, pg. 249
AVNET S.R.O.—See Avnet, Inc.; *U.S. Public*, pg. 252
AXCELL TECHNOLOGIES, INC.—See Switchfast Technologies LLC; *U.S. Private*, pg. 3894
AXIANS AB—See Electricite de France S.A.; *Int'l*, pg. 2351
AXIS TECHNOLOGY, LLC—See Clearlake Capital Group, L.P.; *U.S. Private*, pg. 936
AXIS TECHNOLOGY, LLC—See Francisco Partners Management, LP; *U.S. Private*, pg. 1591
AXON SOLUTIONS LIMITED—See HCL Technologies Ltd.; *Int'l*, pg. 3298
AXWAY IRELAND LIMITED—See Axway Software SA; *Int'l*, pg. 772
AXWAY LTD.—See Axway Software SA; *Int'l*, pg. 772
AXWAY ROMANIA SRL—See Axway Software SA; *Int'l*, pg. 772
AXWAY SOFTWARE DO BRASIL LTDA.—See Axway Software SA; *Int'l*, pg. 772
AXWAY SOFTWARE IBERIA—See Axway Software SA; *Int'l*, pg. 772
AZ-COM DATA SECURITY CO., LTD.—See AZ-COM MARUWA Holdings Co., Ltd.; *Int'l*, pg. 776
AZOLVER ITALY S.R.L.—See Francotyp-Postalia Holding AG; *Int'l*, pg. 2760
B2B TECHNOLOGIES, LLC—See Source Capital, LLC; *U.S. Private*, pg. 3718
B2 INTERACTIVE; *U.S. Private*, pg. 421
BAE SYSTEMS APPLIED INTELLIGENCE US CORP; *U.S. Private*, pg. 424
BARRISTER GLOBAL SERVICES NETWORK, INC.; *U.S. Private*, pg. 480
BEAMR LTD.; *Int'l*, pg. 932
BEARSKIN SERVICES—See Wyandotte Tribal Corporation; *U.S. Private*, pg. 4575
BEIJING LIONBRIDGE GLOBAL SOLUTIONS TECHNOLOGIES, INC.—See H.I.G. Capital, LLC; *U.S. Private*, pg. 1830
BEIJING WATERTEK INFORMATION TECHNOLOGY CO., LTD.; *Int'l*, pg. 960
BELL TECHLOGIX—See Bell Industries, Inc.; *U.S. Public*, pg. 295

BE-TERNA GMBH—See DPE Deutsche Private Equity GmbH; *Int'l*, pg. 2187
BEYONDEXPECT S.L.—See Beyondsoft Corporation; *Int'l*, pg. 1005
BEYONDSOFT CORPORATION; *Int'l*, pg. 1005
BEYONDSOFT CORPORATION—See Beyondsoft Corporation; *Int'l*, pg. 1005
BEYONDSOFT CORPORATION—See Beyondsoft Corporation; *Int'l*, pg. 1005
BEYONDSOFT CORPORATION—See Beyondsoft Corporation; *Int'l*, pg. 1005
BEYONDSOFT CORPORATION—See Beyondsoft Corporation; *Int'l*, pg. 1005
BEYONDSOFT CORPORATION—See Beyondsoft Corporation; *Int'l*, pg. 1005
BEYONDSOFT CORPORATION—See Beyondsoft Corporation; *Int'l*, pg. 1005
BEYONDSOFT CORPORATION—See Beyondsoft Corporation; *Int'l*, pg. 1005
BEYONDSOFT CORPORATION—See Beyondsoft Corporation; *Int'l*, pg. 1005
BEYONDSOFT CORPORATION—See Beyondsoft Corporation; *Int'l*, pg. 1005
BEYONDSOFT CORPORATION—See Beyondsoft Corporation; *Int'l*, pg. 1005
BEYONDSOFT CORPORATION—See Beyondsoft Corporation; *Int'l*, pg. 1005
BEYONDSOFT CORPORATION—See Beyondsoft Corporation; *Int'l*, pg. 1005
BEYONDSOFT CORPORATION—See Beyondsoft Corporation; *Int'l*, pg. 1005
BEYONDSOFT JIZHI TECH CO., LTD.—See Beyondsoft Corporation; *Int'l*, pg. 1005
BHARATIYA GLOBAL INFOMEDIA LTD.; *Int'l*, pg. 1011
BIDDINGFORGOOD INC.; *U.S. Private*, pg. 551
BIG SUR TECHNOLOGIES, INC.; *U.S. Private*, pg. 554
BIZCOM WEB SERVICES, INC.; *U.S. Private*, pg. 567
BIZLINK ELOCAB GMBH—See BizLink Holding Inc.; *Int'l*, pg. 1053
BIZLINK INDUSTRY SLOVAKIA SPOL. S.R.O.—See BizLink Holding Inc.; *Int'l*, pg. 1053
BIZLINK INTL CORP.—See BizLink Holding Inc.; *Int'l*, pg. 1053
BIZLINK ROBOTIC SOLUTIONS GERMANY GMBH—See BizLink Holding Inc.; *Int'l*, pg. 1053
BIZLINK SPECIAL CABLES (CHANGZHOU) CO., LTD.—See BizLink Holding Inc.; *Int'l*, pg. 1053
BLACK BIRD BIOTECH, INC.; *U.S. Public*, pg. 340
BLACKBIRD PLC; *Int'l*, pg. 1056
BLACK BOX A/S—See Black Box Limited; *Int'l*, pg. 1056
BLACK BOX CHILE S.A.—See Black Box Limited; *Int'l*, pg. 1056
BLACK BOX DE MEXICO S.A. DE C.V.—See Black Box Limited; *Int'l*, pg. 1058
BLACK BOX DEUTSCHLAND GMBH—See Black Box Limited; *Int'l*, pg. 1057
BLACK BOX DO BRASIL INDUSTRIA E COMERCIO LTDA—See Black Box Limited; *Int'l*, pg. 1058
BLACK BOX FINLAND OY—See Black Box Limited; *Int'l*, pg. 1057
BLACK BOX FRANCE—See Black Box Limited; *Int'l*, pg. 1057
BLACK BOX ITALIA S.R.L.—See Black Box Limited; *Int'l*, pg. 1057
BLACK BOX NETWORK SERVICES AB—See Black Box Limited; *Int'l*, pg. 1057
BLACK BOX NETWORK SERVICES AG—See Black Box Limited; *Int'l*, pg. 1057
BLACK BOX NETWORK SERVICES AUSTRALIA PTY LTD—See Black Box Limited; *Int'l*, pg. 1057
BLACK BOX NETWORK SERVICES B.V.—See Black Box Limited; *Int'l*, pg. 1058
BLACK BOX NETWORK SERVICES - GOVERNMENT SOLUTIONS—See Black Box Limited; *Int'l*, pg. 1058
BLACK BOX NETWORK SERVICES HONG KONG LIMITED—See Black Box Limited; *Int'l*, pg. 1058
BLACK BOX NETWORK SERVICES, INC. - GOVERNMENT SOLUTIONS—See Black Box Limited; *Int'l*, pg. 1058
BLACK BOX NETWORK SERVICES SINGAPORE PTE LTD—See Black Box Limited; *Int'l*, pg. 1058
BLACK BOX NETWORK SERVICES—See Black Box Limited; *Int'l*, pg. 1057
BLACK BOX NETWORK SERVICES—See Black Box Limited; *Int'l*, pg. 1057
BLACK BOX NETWORK SERVICES—See Black Box Limited; *Int'l*, pg. 1057
BLACK BOX NETWORK SERVICES—See Black Box Limited; *Int'l*, pg. 1057
BLACK BOX NETWORK SERVICES—See Black Box Limited; *Int'l*, pg. 1057
BLACK BOX NETWORK SERVICES—See Black Box Limited; *Int'l*, pg. 1057
BLACK BOX NETWORK SERVICES—See Black Box Limited; *Int'l*, pg. 1057
BLACK BOX NETWORK SERVICES—See Black Box Limited; *Int'l*, pg. 1057
BLACK BOX NETWORK SERVICES—See Black Box Limited; *Int'l*, pg. 1057
BLACK BOX NETWORK SERVICES—See Black Box Limited; *Int'l*, pg. 1057

541519 — OTHER COMPUTER RELA...

BLACK BOX NETWORK SERVICES—See Black Box Limited; *Int'l*, pg. 1057
BLACK BOX NETWORK SERVICES—See Black Box Limited; *Int'l*, pg. 1057
BLACK BOX NETWORK SERVICES—See Black Box Limited; *Int'l*, pg. 1057
BLACK BOX NETWORK SERVICES—See Black Box Limited; *Int'l*, pg. 1057
BLACK BOX NETWORK SERVICES—See Black Box Limited; *Int'l*, pg. 1057
BLACK BOX NETWORK SERVICES—See Black Box Limited; *Int'l*, pg. 1057
BLACK BOX NETWORK SERVICES—See Black Box Limited; *Int'l*, pg. 1057
BLACK BOX NETWORK SERVICES—See Black Box Limited; *Int'l*, pg. 1057
BLACK BOX NETWORK SERVICES—See Black Box Limited; *Int'l*, pg. 1057
BLACK BOX NETWORK SERVICES (UK) LTD.—See Black Box Limited; *Int'l*, pg. 1057
BLACK BOX NORGE AS—See Black Box Limited; *Int'l*, pg. 1058
BLACK BOX PHILADELPHIA—See Black Box Limited; *Int'l*, pg. 1058
BLACK BOX P.R. CORP.—See Black Box Limited; *Int'l*, pg. 1058
BLACK DUCK SOFTWARE, INC.—See Synopsys, Inc.; *U.S. Public*, pg. 1970
BLACK LOTUS COMMUNICATIONS; *U.S. Private*, pg. 572
BLACKWOOD SEVEN A/S; *Int'l*, pg. 1062
BLOCK CAPITAL CORP; *U.S. Public*, pg. 361
BLOOMREACH B.V.—See BloomReach, Inc.; *U.S. Private*, pg. 584
BLOOMREACH, INC.; *U.S. Private*, pg. 584
BLUE GECKO, LLC; *U.S. Private*, pg. 588
BLUEGOLF, LLC—See Clubessential Holdings, LLC; *U.S. Private*, pg. 949
BLUEPAY PROCESSING, LLC—See Fiserv, Inc.; *U.S. Public*, pg. 850
BOARDWARE INFORMATION SYSTEM LIMITED—See BoardWare Intelligence Technology Limited; *Int'l*, pg. 1094
BOOYAH NETWORKS, INC.; *U.S. Private*, pg. 617
BORGWARNER IT SERVICES GROUP GMBH—See BorgWarner Inc.; *U.S. Public*, pg. 369
BOUVET ASA; *Int'l*, pg. 1121
BOWMAN SYSTEMS, L.L.C.—See Leonard Green & Partners, L.P.; *U.S. Private*, pg. 2430
BOWMAN SYSTEMS, L.L.C.—See TPG Capital, L.P.; *U.S. Public*, pg. 2177
BRACKET GLOBAL LLC—See Genstar Capital, LLC; *U.S. Private*, pg. 1675
BRACKET GLOBAL, S.R.O.—See Genstar Capital, LLC; *U.S. Private*, pg. 1675
BRAIN FORCE B.V.—See Cegeka Groep NV; *Int'l*, pg. 1390
BRANDIFY, INC.—See SOCi, Inc.; *U.S. Private*, pg. 3702
BRAND NETWORKS, LLC—See Augeo Affinity Marketing, Inc.; *U.S. Private*, pg. 391
BRIDGENEXT, INC.—See Kelso & Company, L.P.; *U.S. Private*, pg. 2277
BRIDGE TECHNOLOGY INC; *U.S. Private*, pg. 649
BRIGHTONE HEALTHCARE SOLUTIONS B.V.—See Aurelius Equity Opportunities SE & Co. KGaA; *Int'l*, pg. 710
BRIGHTWHISTLE, INC.—See Vestar Capital Partners, LLC; *U.S. Private*, pg. 4372
BRINGSPRING SCIENCE & TECHNOLOGY CO., LTD.; *Int'l*, pg. 1164
BSH IT SOLUTIONS GMBH—See Allgeier SE; *Int'l*, pg. 337
BUBBLR, INC.; *Int'l*, pg. 1206
BUDDY PLATFORM LTD.; *Int'l*, pg. 1210
BUILDERTREND SOLUTIONS INC.; *U.S. Private*, pg. 682
BULL GABON—See Atos SE; *Int'l*, pg. 691
BULL GMBH—See Atos SE; *Int'l*, pg. 691
BURTEK ENTERPRISES, INC.—See Stone River Capital Partners, LLC; *U.S. Private*, pg. 3826
BURTEK ENTERPRISES, INC.—See Wynnchurch Capital, L.P.; *U.S. Private*, pg. 4577
BUSINESS COMMUNICATIONS, INC.; *U.S. Private*, pg. 694
BUSINESS INFORMATION SYSTEMS, INC.—See i3 Verticals, Inc.; *U.S. Public*, pg. 1081
BUSINESS INFORMATION TECHNOLOGY SOLUTIONS, INC.—See Accenture plc; *Int'l*, pg. 85
BWISE BEHEER B.V.—See EQT AB; *Int'l*, pg. 2471
BWISE DEVELOPMENT B.V.—See EQT AB; *Int'l*, pg. 2471
BWISE INTERNAL CONTROL INC.—See EQT AB; *Int'l*, pg. 2471
BYTE BULGARIA LTD.—See Ideal Group S.A.; *Int'l*, pg. 3589
BYTE IT SRL—See Ideal Group S.A.; *Int'l*, pg. 3589
CAASE GROUP BV—See Insight Enterprises, Inc.; *U.S. Public*, pg. 1129
CAC AMERICA CORPORATION—See CAC Corporation; *Int'l*, pg. 1247
CAC CORPORATION; *Int'l*, pg. 1246
CACI N.V.—See CACI International Inc.; *U.S. Public*, pg. 417
CAC SHANGHAI CORPORATION—See CAC Corporation; *Int'l*, pg. 1247

CAD-QUALITY FINLAND OY—See Addnode Group AB; *Int'l*, pg. 130
CAE TECHNOLOGY INDIA PRIVATE LIMITED—See CAE Inc.; *Int'l*, pg. 1249
CALLPOINTE.COM, INC.—See Apollo Global Management, Inc.; *U.S. Public*, pg. 152
CAMELOT INFORMATION SYSTEMS INC.; *Int'l*, pg. 1271
CANDESCENT SOFTBASE, LLC—See Brooke Private Equity Associates Management LLC; *U.S. Private*, pg. 663
CANDESCENT SOFTBASE, LLC—See Candescent Partners, LLC; *U.S. Private*, pg. 733
CANDESCENT SOFTBASE, LLC—See Harbert Management Corporation; *U.S. Private*, pg. 1858
CAPITA CUSTOMER SERVICES AG—See Capita plc; *Int'l*, pg. 1308
CAPITA CUSTOMER SERVICES (GERMANY) GMBH—See Capita plc; *Int'l*, pg. 1308
CARAHSOFT TECHNOLOGY CORP.; *U.S. Private*, pg. 748
CARELON GLOBAL SOLUTIONS INDIA LLP—See Elevance Health, Inc.; *U.S. Public*, pg. 729
CARELON GLOBAL SOLUTIONS IRELAND LIMITED—See Elevance Health, Inc.; *U.S. Public*, pg. 729
CAROLINA COMPUTERS, INC.; *U.S. Private*, pg. 767
CARTESIA GIS AB—See Addnode Group AB; *Int'l*, pg. 130
CASHSTAR, INC.—See P2 Capital Partners, LLC; *U.S. Private*, pg. 3061
CASHSTAR, INC.—See Silver Lake Group, LLC; *U.S. Private*, pg. 3656
CAST BENELUX SA—See CAST S.A.; *Int'l*, pg. 1355
CAST ITALIA S.R.L.—See CAST S.A.; *Int'l*, pg. 1355
CASTLETON TECHNOLOGY PLC—See GI Manager L.P.; *U.S. Private*, pg. 1693
CAST SOFTWARE ESPANA SL—See CAST S.A.; *Int'l*, pg. 1355
CAST SOFTWARE INDIA PRIVATE LIMITED—See CAST S.A.; *Int'l*, pg. 1355
CAST SOFTWARE LTD.—See CAST S.A.; *Int'l*, pg. 1355
CATALYST MEDIA GROUP PLC; *Int'l*, pg. 1358
CATAPULT TECHNOLOGY, LTD.—See D.C. Capital Partners, LLC; *U.S. Private*, pg. 1141
CBC PROPERTIES & COMPUTER CENTER, INC.—See China Banking Corporation; *Int'l*, pg. 1484
CCS LOUISIANA—See AEA Investors LP; *U.S. Private*, pg. 116
CDS CO., LTD.; *Int'l*, pg. 1371
CEGEDIM OUTSOURCING SAS—See Cegedim S.A.; *Int'l*, pg. 1390
CEGEKA NV—See Cegeka Groep NV; *Int'l*, pg. 1390
CENTRACOMM COMMUNICATIONS, LTD.; *U.S. Private*, pg. 818
CENTRIC BUSINESS SYSTEMS, INC.; *U.S. Private*, pg. 829
CEZDATA, S.R.O.—See CEZ, a.s.; *Int'l*, pg. 1427
CFORIA SOFTWARE, LLC—See Highradius Corporation; *U.S. Private*, pg. 1941
THE CHANNEL COMPANY LLC—See EagleTree Capital, LP; *U.S. Private*, pg. 1312
CHECKPOINT TECHNOLOGIES INC.; *U.S. Private*, pg. 869
CHENGDU DIGITAL CHINA LIMITED—See Digital China Holdings Limited; *Int'l*, pg. 2121
CHENGDU XINHAI CHUANGXIN TECHNOLOGY CO., LTD.—See Chipsea Technologies (Shenzhen) Corp.; *Int'l*, pg. 1573
CHEOPS TECHNOLOGY FRANCE SA; *Int'l*, pg. 1471
CHERN YIH ELECTRONICS ENT.CO., LTD.—See Advanced Analog Technology, Inc.; *Int'l*, pg. 157
CHEROKEE DATA SOLUTIONS; *U.S. Private*, pg. 873
CHINASOFT INTERNATIONAL LTD.; *Int'l*, pg. 1568
CHONGQIONG YIBOHUTONG TECH CO., LTD.—See Beyondsoft Corporation; *Int'l*, pg. 1005
CHUDEN CTI CO., LTD.—See Chubu Electric Power Co., Inc.; *Int'l*, pg. 1593
CIBER AG—See HTC Global Services Inc.; *U.S. Private*, pg. 1999
CILNET - COMUNICACOES E PROJECTOS ESPECIAIS S.A.—See Datatec Limited; *Int'l*, pg. 1980
CINNOBER FINANCIAL TECHNOLOGY AB—See Nasdaq, Inc.; *U.S. Public*, pg. 1491
CIRRUS NETWORKS HOLDINGS LIMITED; *Int'l*, pg. 1618
CITIC NETWORKS MANAGEMENT CO., LTD.—See CITIC Group Corporation; *Int'l*, pg. 1621
CITRA HEALTH SOLUTIONS, INC.—See Great Point Partners, LLC; *U.S. Private*, pg. 1767
CJ OLIVE NETWORKS CO., LTD.—See CJ Freshway Corporation; *Int'l*, pg. 1634
CLARKS COMPANIES - IT DIVISION—See C&J Clark Limited; *Int'l*, pg. 1239
CLEARCOMMERCE CORPORATION—See Fidelity National Infor; *U.S. Public*, pg. 832
CLOUDBACKO CORPORATION—See Ahsay Backup Software Development Company Limited; *Int'l*, pg. 226
CMC XMANICOM CO., LTD.—See CMC Corporation; *Int'l*, pg. 1669
CMH SOLUTIONS LLC—See Ardian SAS; *U.S. Private*, pg. 554
CMS COMPUTERS LTD.; *Int'l*, pg. 1672
CNI GLOBAL SOLUTIONS, LLC—See The Chickasaw Nation; *U.S. Private*, pg. 4008
CNSHANGQUAN E-COMMERCE CO., LTD.; *Int'l*, pg. 1678

COASIN CHILE S.A.—See Datatec Limited; *Int'l*, pg. 1980
COGNITIV, INC.; *U.S. Public*, pg. 523
COKEVA, INC.—See TD Synnex Corp; *U.S. Public*, pg. 1984
COLRUYT IT CONSULTANCY INDIA PRIVATE LIMITED—See Colruyt Group N.V.; *Int'l*, pg. 1705
COLUMBIA SERVICES GROUP INC.; *U.S. Private*, pg. 977
COMANCHE INTERNATIONAL PCL; *Int'l*, pg. 1707
COMARCO, INC.; *U.S. Private*, pg. 980
COMDAT DATASYSTEMS AG; *Int'l*, pg. 1709
COMITEM S.A.S.—See Alan Allman Associates SA; *Int'l*, pg. 290
COMMERCIAL PROGRAMMING SYSTEMS, INC.—See Drishticon Inc.; *U.S. Private*, pg. 1278
COMMUNITY NETWORK CENTER INC.—See Chubu Electric Power Co., Inc.; *Int'l*, pg. 1593
COMPEAT, INC.—See DYN365, Inc.; *U.S. Private*, pg. 1296
COMPROMISE DOMINO B.V.—See Dustin Group AB; *Int'l*, pg. 2235
COMPUAGE INFOCOM LTD.; *Int'l*, pg. 1754
COMPUCOM CANADA CO.—See Variant Equity Advisors, LLC; *U.S. Private*, pg. 4346
COMPUCOM SYSTEMS, INC. - BELLEVUE—See Variant Equity Advisors, LLC; *U.S. Private*, pg. 4346
COMPUCOM SYSTEMS, INC.—See Variant Equity Advisors, LLC; *U.S. Private*, pg. 4346
COMPUQUIP TECHNOLOGIES, LLC—See Dosal Capital, LLC; *U.S. Private*, pg. 1264
COMPUTER GALLERY, INC.—See VC3, Inc.; *U.S. Private*, pg. 4349
COMPUTER INTEGRATED SERVICES COMPANY OF NEW YORK, LLC—See Baymark Partners; *U.S. Private*, pg. 496
COMPUTER SCIENCES CORPORATION INDIA PRIVATE LIMITED—See DXC Technology Company; *U.S. Public*, pg. 695
COMPUTER SCIENCES CORPORATION—See DXC Technology Company; *U.S. Public*, pg. 695
COMPUTER SECURITY SOLUTIONS, LLC—See D.C. Capital Partners, LLC; *U.S. Private*, pg. 1141
COMPUTER SYSTEMS INTEGRATION LIMITED—See Blackhawk Capital LLP; *Int'l*, pg. 1061
COMPUVISION SYSTEMS INC; *Int'l*, pg. 1761
COMRISE TECHNOLOGY, INC.; *U.S. Private*, pg. 1006
COMSOFT DIRECT NV—See Bechtle AG; *Int'l*, pg. 938
COMSYS JOHO SYSTEM CORPORATION—See COMSYS Holdings Corporation; *Int'l*, pg. 1761
COMTEC INC.; *Int'l*, pg. 1762
CONDUCTOR, INC.; *U.S. Private*, pg. 1012
CONGRUITY, LLC.—See EXEO Group Inc.; *Int'l*, pg. 2583
CONGSTER GMBH—See Deutsche Telekom AG; *Int'l*, pg. 2085
CONNECTIVE COMPUTING INC.—See Modern Office Methods Inc.; *U.S. Private*, pg. 2762
CONNECTRIA LLC—See GI Manager L.P.; *U.S. Private*, pg. 1692
CONTEGIX, LLC; *U.S. Private*, pg. 1027
CONTEMPORARY COMPUTER SERVICES, INC.; *U.S. Private*, pg. 1027
CONTINENTAL RESOURCES, INC.; *U.S. Public*, pg. 573
CONVENE, INC.; *U.S. Private*, pg. 1035
CONVERTERTECHNOLOGY INC.—See CPS Group Investments Pty. Ltd.; *Int'l*, pg. 1826
CORCENTRIC, LLC—See Corcentric, Inc.; *U.S. Private*, pg. 1047
CORE CORPORATION; *Int'l*, pg. 1797
CORE SOFTWARE CORPORATION; *Int'l*, pg. 1798
CORISTO GMBH—See CENIT AG; *Int'l*, pg. 1401
CORPORATE DISK COMPANY; *U.S. Private*, pg. 1054
CORPORATE MOBILE RECYCLING ESPANA S.L.—See TD Synnex Corp; *U.S. Public*, pg. 1984
CORPORATE MOBILE RECYCLING LTD.—See TD Synnex Corp; *U.S. Public*, pg. 1984
COSMOTE GLOBAL SOLUTIONS S.A.—See Hellenic Telecommunications Organization S.A.; *Int'l*, pg. 3333
COURIER PLUS, INC.; *U.S. Private*, pg. 1068
COVERITY, INC.—See Synopsys, Inc.; *U.S. Public*, pg. 1970
COYNI, INC.; *U.S. Public*, pg. 588
CPSG PARTNERS LLC—See Marsh & McLennan Companies, Inc.; *U.S. Public*, pg. 1385
CRAYON AFRICA S.A.—See Crayon Group Holding ASA; *Int'l*, pg. 1829
CRAYON, CELOVITE IT RESITVE, D.O.O.—See Crayon Group Holding ASA; *Int'l*, pg. 1829
CRAYON CZECH REPUBLIC AND SLOVAKIA S.R.O.—See Crayon Group Holding ASA; *Int'l*, pg. 1829
CRAYON MAURITIUS LTD.—See Crayon Group Holding ASA; *Int'l*, pg. 1829
CRAYON SOFTWARE EXPERTS INDIA PVT. LTD.—See Crayon Group Holding ASA; *Int'l*, pg. 1829
CRAYON SOFTWARE EXPERTS PHILIPPINES INC.—See Crayon Group Holding ASA; *Int'l*, pg. 1829
CRAYON SOFTWARE EXPERTS ROMANIA S.R.L.—See Crayon Group Holding ASA; *Int'l*, pg. 1829
CRAYON SOFTWARE EXPERTS SPAIN S.L.—See Crayon Group Holding ASA; *Int'l*, pg. 1829
CRAYON UK LTD.—See Crayon Group Holding ASA; *Int'l*, pg. 1829
CSC COMPUTER SCIENCES (SOUTH AFRICA) (PTY)

LIMITED—See DXC Technology Company; *U.S. Public*, pg. 695
C TECHNOLOGIES—See Anoto Group AB; *Int'l*, pg. 474
CUBE.ITG SA; *Int'l*, pg. 1875
CUBIC CORPORATION—See Elliott Management Corporation; *U.S. Private*, pg. 1367
CUBIC CORPORATION—See Veritas Capital Fund Management, LLC; *U.S. Private*, pg. 4361
CURTISS-WRIGHT CONTROLS EMBEDDED COMPUTING-HIGH WYCOMBE—See Curtiss-Wright Corporation; *U.S. Public*, pg. 611
CUSTOMCALL DATA SYSTEMS, INC.—See Enghouse Systems Limited; *Int'l*, pg. 2427
CYBER SCIENCES INC.—See Trystar, LLC; *U.S. Private*, pg. 4252
CYIENT KK—See Cyient Limited; *Int'l*, pg. 1896
CYIENT N.V.—See Cyient Limited; *Int'l*, pg. 1896
D7 ENTERPRISES, INC.; *U.S. Public*, pg. 620
DALIAN PACTERA TECHNOLOGY INTERNATIONAL CO., LTD.—See China Electronics Corporation; *Int'l*, pg. 1499
DALTIX NV—See Colruyt Group N.V.; *Int'l*, pg. 1705
DANAL, INC.—See Twilio Inc.; *U.S. Public*, pg. 2206
DANLAW TECHNOLOGIES, INC.—See Danlaw, Inc.; *U.S. Private*, pg. 1157
DATALAB AUTOMOTIVE, D.O.O.—See Datalab Tehnologije d.d.; *Int'l*, pg. 1977
DATALAB BH, D.O.O.—See Datalab Tehnologije d.d.; *Int'l*, pg. 1977
DATALAB BULGARIA, LTD.—See Datalab Tehnologije d.d.; *Int'l*, pg. 1977
DATALAB HR D.O.O.—See Datalab Tehnologije d.d.; *Int'l*, pg. 1977
DATALAB MK, D.O.O.—See Datalab Tehnologije d.d.; *Int'l*, pg. 1977
DATALAB.MN, D.O.O.—See Datalab Tehnologije d.d.; *Int'l*, pg. 1978
DATALAB SI D.O.O.—See Datalab Tehnologije d.d.; *Int'l*, pg. 1978
DATALAB SR, D.O.O.—See Datalab Tehnologije d.d.; *Int'l*, pg. 1978
DATALAB TEHNOLOGIJE D.O.O.—See Datalab Tehnologije d.d.; *Int'l*, pg. 1978
DATA PROCESSING SOLUTIONS, INC.; *U.S. Private*, pg. 1163
DATA RESPONS GMBH—See Adecco Group AG; *Int'l*, pg. 139
DATASERV LLC; *U.S. Private*, pg. 1166
DATASONIC GROUP BERHAD; *Int'l*, pg. 1979
DATA SYSTEMS TECHNOLOGY SOLUTIONS—See Data Systems of Texas, Inc.; *U.S. Private*, pg. 1163
DATA TRANSFER SOLUTIONS, LLC—See AtkinsRealis Group Inc.; *Int'l*, pg. 671
DATATRON DOCUMENT IMAGE ARCHIVING LIMITED—See HP Inc.; *U.S. Public*, pg. 1062
DATAVAIL CORPORATION—See CIVC Partners LLC; *U.S. Private*, pg. 907
DATTO ASIAPAC PTY. LTD.—See Insight Venture Management, LLC; *U.S. Private*, pg. 2090
DATTO CANADA ENTERPRISES, INC.—See Insight Venture Management, LLC; *U.S. Private*, pg. 2090
DATTO GMBH—See Insight Venture Management, LLC; *U.S. Private*, pg. 2090
DATTO NEDERLAND B.V.—See Insight Venture Management, LLC; *U.S. Private*, pg. 2091
DATTO SINGAPORE PTE. LTD.—See Insight Venture Management, LLC; *U.S. Private*, pg. 2091
DB INVESTMENT SERVICES GMBH—See Deutsche Bank Aktiengesellschaft; *Int'l*, pg. 2056
DCC SERCOM—See DCC plc; *Int'l*, pg. 1990
DCC TECHNOLOGY LIMITED—See DCC plc; *Int'l*, pg. 1990
DDC ELECTRONICS K.K.—See TransDigm Group Incorporated; *U.S. Public*, pg. 2182
DEALER.COM, INC.; *U.S. Private*, pg. 1182
DEALER DOT COM, INC.—See Cox Enterprises, Inc.; *U.S. Private*, pg. 1074
DECERNO VAST AB—See Addnode Group AB; *Int'l*, pg. 130
DECLOUT LIMITED—See EXEO Group Inc.; *Int'l*, pg. 2583
DEFENSE SYSTEMS, INC.—See Kratos Defense & Security Solutions, Inc.; *U.S. Public*, pg. 1276
DEFINITIVE RESULTS, LLC; *U.S. Private*, pg. 1191
DELPHIX CORP.—See Clearlake Capital Group, L.P.; *U.S. Private*, pg. 936
DELPHIX CORP.—See Francisco Partners Management, LP; *U.S. Private*, pg. 1591
DENOVO VENTURES LLC—See TAC Partners, Inc.; *U.S. Private*, pg. 3920
DENSO IT LABORATORY, INC.—See Denso Corporation; *Int'l*, pg. 2031
DEVOTEAM BELGIUM SA/NV—See Devoteam SA; *Int'l*, pg. 2089
DIGITAL BOARDWALK, INC.; *U.S. Private*, pg. 1230
DIGITALBRAINZ INC.; *U.S. Private*, pg. 1231
DIGITAL GARAGE, INC.; *Int'l*, pg. 2121
DIGITAL GUARDIAN, INC.—See Fairhaven Capital Management, LLC; *U.S. Private*, pg. 1464
DIGITAL HEARTS CO., LTD.—See Digital Hearts Holdings Co., Ltd.; *Int'l*, pg. 2122
DIGITAL HEARTS KOREA CO., LTD.—See Digital Hearts Holdings Co., Ltd.; *Int'l*, pg. 2122
DIGITAL HEARTS (THAILAND) CO., LTD.—See Digital Hearts Holdings Co., Ltd.; *Int'l*, pg. 2122
DIGITAL HEARTS USA INC.—See Digital Hearts Holdings Co., Ltd.; *Int'l*, pg. 2122
DIGITALIST GROUP OYJ; *Int'l*, pg. 2123
DIGITAL STORM, INC.; *U.S. Private*, pg. 1231
DIGITEK SOFTWARE, INC.; *U.S. Private*, pg. 1231
DION GLOBAL SOLUTIONS (NZ) LTD.—See Dion Global Solutions Limited; *Int'l*, pg. 2127
DIRECT DATA CORPORATION; *U.S. Private*, pg. 1235
DIRECT EDI, INC.—See SPS Commerce, Inc.; *U.S. Public*, pg. 1920
DIVERTCO USA INC.—See Divestco Inc.; *Int'l*, pg. 2137
DIVESTCO INC.; *Int'l*, pg. 2137
DMDCONNECTS SERVICES INC.; *Int'l*, pg. 2143
DMG BLOCKCHAIN SOLUTIONS INC.; *Int'l*, pg. 2143
DNP DIGITAL SOLUTIONS CO., LTD.—See Dai Nippon Printing Co., Ltd.; *Int'l*, pg. 1914
DOCULEGAL, LLC—See Adecco Group AG; *Int'l*, pg. 141
THE DODSON GROUP, INC.; *U.S. Private*, pg. 4022
DOMAINS BY PROXY, LLC—See KKR & Co. Inc.; *U.S. Public*, pg. 1252
DOMAINS BY PROXY, LLC—See Silver Lake Group, LLC; *U.S. Private*, pg. 3657
DOMAINS BY PROXY, LLC—See TCMI, Inc.; *U.S. Private*, pg. 3943
DOSSIER SYSTEMS, INC.—See Advanced Manufacturing Control Systems Ltd.; *Int'l*, pg. 160
DPRA INC.—See OakLeaf Software, Inc.; *U.S. Private*, pg. 2985
DRAKONTAS LLC; *U.S. Private*, pg. 1272
DROPSUITE LIMITED; *Int'l*, pg. 2206
DSG, INC.—See Signant Health MGT LLP; *U.S. Private*, pg. 3649
DSIT SOLUTIONS LTD.—See Acorn Energy, Inc.; *U.S. Public*, pg. 36
DTB DEUTSCHE TECHNIKBERATUNG GMBH—See Ceconomy AG; *Int'l*, pg. 1373
DUESENBERG TECHNOLOGIES INC.; *Int'l*, pg. 2223
DUNCAN SOLUTIONS, INC.—See Navient Corporation; *U.S. Public*, pg. 1500
DUSTIN A/S—See Dustin Group AB; *Int'l*, pg. 2235
DWARF TECHNOLOGY HOLDINGS, INC.; *Int'l*, pg. 2236
DXC TECHNOLOGY AUSTRALIA HOLDINGS PTY LIMITED—See DXC Technology Company; *U.S. Public*, pg. 695
DXC TECHNOLOGY AUSTRALIA PTY. LIMITED—See DXC Technology Company; *U.S. Public*, pg. 695
DXC TECHNOLOGY SLOVAKIA S.R.O—See DXC Technology Company; *U.S. Public*, pg. 695
DXC TECHNOLOGY SWITZERLAND GMBH—See DXC Technology Company; *U.S. Public*, pg. 695
DXC UNITED PTY. LIMITED—See DXC Technology Company; *U.S. Public*, pg. 695
DYNAMIC COMPUTER CORPORATION; *U.S. Private*, pg. 1297
DYNAMIC SOLUTIONS GROUP INC.; *U.S. Private*, pg. 1299
DYONYX, L.P.; *U.S. Private*, pg. 1300
EAF COMPUTER SERVICE SUPPLIES GMBH—See eaf Holding GmbH; *Int'l*, pg. 2262
EARLY BIRDS S.A.S.—See CrownPeak Technology, Inc.; *U.S. Private*, pg. 1113
EASE INC.—See Luminate Capital Management, Inc.; *U.S. Private*, pg. 2514
EASTCOMPEACE TECHNOLOGY CO., LTD.; *Int'l*, pg. 2271
EASTERN SOFTWARE SYSTEMS PVT. LTD.—See Beyondsoft Corporation; *Int'l*, pg. 1005
EASTERN SOFTWARE SYSTEMS PVT. LTD.—See Beyondsoft Corporation; *Int'l*, pg. 1006
EASTERN SOFTWARE SYSTEMS PVT. LTD.—See Beyondsoft Corporation; *Int'l*, pg. 1006
EASTERN SOFTWARE SYSTEMS PVT. LTD.—See Beyondsoft Corporation; *Int'l*, pg. 1006
EASYMEDMOBILE INDIA PRIVATE LTD.—See Easy Technologies Inc.; *Int'l*, pg. 2276
EASYMED TECHNOLOGIES, INC.—See Easy Technologies Inc.; *Int'l*, pg. 2276
EASY TECHNOLOGIES INC.; *Int'l*, pg. 2276
EBROKER SYSTEMS LIMITED—See eBroker Group Ltd.; *Int'l*, pg. 2287
ECLIPSE SP LLC—See Danir Resources AB; *Int'l*, pg. 1963
ECOMNETS, INC.; *U.S. Private*, pg. 1329
ECONOCOM NEDERLAND BV—See Econocom Group SA; *Int'l*, pg. 2297
EDGEWISE NETWORKS INC.—See Zscaler, Inc.; *U.S. Public*, pg. 2411
EDOTFOODS, INC.—See Dot Foods, Inc.; *U.S. Private*, pg. 1265
EFFORTLESS IT LLC; *U.S. Private*, pg. 1343
EG KOMMUNEINFORMATION A/S—See Francisco Partners Management, LP; *U.S. Private*, pg. 1589
EG RETAIL & MEDIE—See Francisco Partners Management, LP; *U.S. Private*, pg. 1589
EG UTILITY A/S—See Francisco Partners Management, LP; *U.S. Private*, pg. 1589

EKOMI INC.; *U.S. Private*, pg. 1348
EKOMI, LTD.—See The Goldman Sachs Group, Inc.; *U.S. Public*, pg. 2081
ELAN MICROELECTRONICS (SHANGHAI) CO., LTD.—See ELAN Microelectronic Corp.; *Int'l*, pg. 2342
ELAN MICROELECTRONICS (SHENZHEN) CO., LTD.—See ELAN Microelectronic Corp.; *Int'l*, pg. 2342
EL CORTE INGLES, S.A. COMPUTERS—See El Corte Ingles, S.A.; *Int'l*, pg. 2340
ELC TECHNOLOGIES; *U.S. Private*, pg. 1350
ELECTRONIC NETWORK SYSTEMS, INC.—See UnitedHealth Group Incorporated; *U.S. Public*, pg. 2248
ELEMICA, INC.—See Eurazeo SE; *Int'l*, pg. 2528
ELEMICA INTERNATIONAL B.V.—See Eurazeo SE; *Int'l*, pg. 2528
ELISA CAMLINE HOLDING GMBH—See Elisa Corporation; *Int'l*, pg. 2361
ELISA VIDERA NORGE AS—See Elisa Corporation; *Int'l*, pg. 2361
ELISA VIDERA OY—See Elisa Corporation; *Int'l*, pg. 2361
ELISA VIDERA SPAIN S.L—See Elisa Corporation; *Int'l*, pg. 2361
ELISA VIDERA UK LTD.—See Elisa Corporation; *Int'l*, pg. 2361
ELTA TECHNOLOGY CO., LTD; *Int'l*, pg. 2370
ELYSIUM DIGITAL LLC—See Aon plc; *Int'l*, pg. 493
EMC SALES & MARKETING—See Dell Technologies Inc.; *U.S. Public*, pg. 651
EMERALD DATA SOLUTIONS, INC.; *U.S. Private*, pg. 1379
EMIDS TECHNOLOGIES PVT. LTD. CORP. - HEADQUARTERS—See emids Technologies Pvt. Ltd. Corp.; *Int'l*, pg. 2380
EMIDS TECHNOLOGIES PVT. LTD. CORP.; *Int'l*, pg. 2380
EMTEC FEDERAL, INC.—See Kelso & Company, L.P.; *U.S. Private*, pg. 2278
EMTEC FEDERAL, INC.—See Kelso & Company, L.P.; *U.S. Private*, pg. 2278
EMX COMPANY LTD.—See Ameriprise Financial, Inc.; *U.S. Public*, pg. 114
ENABLEWISE, LLC; *U.S. Private*, pg. 1389
THE ENDURANCE INTERNATIONAL GROUP, INC.—See Clearlake Capital Group, L.P.; *U.S. Private*, pg. 934
THE ENDURANCE INTERNATIONAL GROUP, INC.—See Siris Capital Group, LLC; *U.S. Private*, pg. 3673
ENEL X WAY ROMANIA S.R.L.—See Enel S.p.A.; *Int'l*, pg. 2414
ENERGY4U GMBH—See Atos SE; *Int'l*, pg. 692
ENFO ZYSTEMS—See Enfo Oyj; *Int'l*, pg. 2425
ENGINEERING INGEGNERIA INFORMATICA S.P.A. - OSIMO—See Apax Partners LLP; *Int'l*, pg. 504
THE ENGLE GROUP; *U.S. Private*, pg. 4026
ENLIGHTEN IT CONSULTING INC.—See Veritas Capital Fund Management, LLC; *U.S. Private*, pg. 4360
ENLIGHTEN IT CONSULTING LLC—See Huntington Ingalls Industries, Inc.; *U.S. Public*, pg. 1072
ENSONO, INC.—See KKR & Co. Inc.; *U.S. Public*, pg. 1244
ENTERPRISEDB CORPORATION—See Great Hill Partners, L.P.; *U.S. Private*, pg. 1763
ENTERPRISE INTEGRATION, INC.; *U.S. Private*, pg. 1404
ENTSORGA WEST VIRGINIA LLC—See Renovare Environmental, Inc.; *U.S. Public*, pg. 1783
ENVERUS, INC.—See Hellman & Friedman LLC; *U.S. Private*, pg. 1908
ENVIRONMENT FRIENDLY HOLDINGS CORP.; *Int'l*, pg. 2454
E.ON IS GMBH—See E.ON SE; *Int'l*, pg. 2253
E.ON IS HUNGARY KFT.—See E.ON SE; *Int'l*, pg. 2253
EPAM SYSTEMS JAPAN G.K.—See EPAM Systems, Inc.; *U.S. Public*, pg. 783
EPIC BROADBAND SOLUTIONS; *U.S. Private*, pg. 1412
EPLUS INC.; *U.S. Public*, pg. 783
EQUINIX PERU S.R.L.—See Equinix, Inc.; *U.S. Public*, pg. 788
EQUINIX SECURITY (CU1) LLC—See Equinix, Inc.; *U.S. Public*, pg. 788
ESCAPE TECHNOLOGY GMBH—See 2Crsi SA; *Int'l*, pg. 4
ESCAPE TECHNOLOGY LTD.—See 2Crsi SA; *Int'l*, pg. 4
ESCHER ASIA PACIFIC PRIVATE LIMITED—See Escher Group Limited; *U.S. Private*, pg. 1425
ESCHER EUROPE LIMITED—See Escher Group Limited; *U.S. Private*, pg. 1425
ESCHER UK LIMITED—See Escher Group Limited; *U.S. Private*, pg. 1425
ESLINK CLOUD COMPUTING CO., LTD.—See Goldcard Smart Group Co., Ltd.; *Int'l*, pg. 3027
E-SPIRIT INC.—See adesso SE; *Int'l*, pg. 144
E-SPIRIT SCHWEIZ AG—See adesso SE; *Int'l*, pg. 144
E-SPIRIT UK LTD.—See adesso SE; *Int'l*, pg. 144
ESSINTIAL ENTERPRISE SOLUTIONS—See Global Equity Capital, LLC; *U.S. Private*, pg. 1714
ESTSECURITY CORP.—See EStsoft Corp; *Int'l*, pg. 2519
ETS INGENIERIA SAS—See Hydac International GmbH; *Int'l*, pg. 3544
EUROFINS CYBER SECURITY NETHERLANDS HOLDING BV—See Eurofins Scientific S.E.; *Int'l*, pg. 2539
EUROTECH S.P.A.; *Int'l*, pg. 2558
EVENTS.COM, INC.; *U.S. Private*, pg. 1437
EVOLVE IT AUSTRALIA PTY. LTD.; *Int'l*, pg. 2573

541519 — OTHER COMPUTER RELA...   CORPORATE AFFILIATIONS

EVOLVER, INC.—See Converged Security Solutions LLC; *U.S. Private*, pg. 1035
EXADEL, INC.—See Sun Capital Partners, Inc.; *U.S. Private*, pg. 3859
EXCEL DE MEXICO S DE R.L. DE C.V.—See BizLink Holding Inc.; *Int'l*, pg. 1053
EXCLUSIVE CONCEPTS, INC; *U.S. Private*, pg. 1446
EXTOL INTERNATIONAL INC.—See CLEO Communications, Inc.; *U.S. Private*, pg. 940
F12..NET, INC.; *Int'l*, pg. 2597
FALCON TECHNOLOGIES, INC.; *U.S. Public*, pg. 820
FATHOM, LLC; *U.S. Private*, pg. 1483
FBS CO., LTD.—See Daiwa House Industry Co., Ltd.; *Int'l*, pg. 1946
FGV PRODATA SYSTEMS SDN. BHD.—See FGV Holdings Bhd; *Int'l*, pg. 2649
FIDELITY NATIONAL INFORMATION SERVICES, INC. - ORLANDO—See Fidelity National Infor; *U.S. Public*, pg. 832
FISHER SCIENTIFIC UK LTD.—See Thermo Fisher Scientific Inc.; *U.S. Public*, pg. 2148
FLAME HEARTS CO., LTD.—See Digital Hearts Holdings Co., Ltd.; *Int'l*, pg. 2122
FLATIRONS SOLUTIONS, INC.—See InfoTrust Group, Inc.; *U.S. Private*, pg. 2074
FLECTION UNITED KINGDOM LTD.—See Arrow Electronics, Inc.; *U.S. Public*, pg. 199
FLEETCROSS HOLDINGS, INC.—See The Hearst Corporation; *U.S. Private*, pg. 4045
FLEXOS S.A; *Int'l*, pg. 2705
FLOOIDCX CORP.; *Int'l*, pg. 2707
FLUIDMESH NETWORKS S.R.L.—See Cisco Systems, Inc.; *U.S. Public*, pg. 499
FMPP VERWALTUNGSGESELLSCHAFT MBH—See Hellman & Friedman LLC; *U.S. Private*, pg. 1907
FORCE 3, INC.—See CDW Corporation; *U.S. Public*, pg. 462
FORTINET FEDERAL, INC.—See Fortinet, Inc.; *U.S. Public*, pg. 869
FORTINET INFORMATION TECHNOLOGY (TIANJIN) CO., LTD.—See Fortinet, Inc.; *U.S. Public*, pg. 869
FORTRESS ITX LLC; *U.S. Private*, pg. 1576
FORTUNE TECHNOLOGY SYSTEM CORP.—See Fortune Information Systems Corp.; *Int'l*, pg. 2743
FOS GREEN TECH SRL—See FOS S.p.A.; *Int'l*, pg. 2748
FOUR LEAF TECHNOLOGIES A/S—See Arrow Electronics, Inc.; *U.S. Public*, pg. 199
FOX SPORTS DIGITAL MEDIA, INC.—See Fox Corporation; *U.S. Public*, pg. 876
FPT ASIA PACIFIC PTE. LTD.—See FPT Corporation; *Int'l*, pg. 2757
FPT SLOVAKIA S.R.O.—See FPT Corporation; *Int'l*, pg. 2757
FPT SOFTWARE KOREA CO., LTD.—See FPT Corporation; *Int'l*, pg. 2758
FPT SOFTWARE SOLUTIONS ASIA PACIFIC PTE. LTD.—See FPT Corporation; *Int'l*, pg. 2758
FSN, INC.—See Modern Office Methods Inc.; *U.S. Private*, pg. 2762
FTE NETWORKS, INC.; *U.S. Public*, pg. 889
FUJIFILM MEDICAL IT SOLUTIONS CO., LTD.—See FUJIFILM Holdings Corporation; *Int'l*, pg. 2824
FUJITSU COMPUTER SYSTEMS CORPORATION—See Fujitsu Limited; *Int'l*, pg. 2833
FUJITSU FINLAND OY—See Fujitsu Limited; *Int'l*, pg. 2834
FUJITSU TECHNOLOGY SOLUTIONS LDA—See Fujitsu Limited; *Int'l*, pg. 2836
FUTURE FIRST TECHNOLOGIES LTD.; *Int'l*, pg. 2856
FUTURE INSPACE, INC.—See Future Corporation; *Int'l*, pg. 2853
G4S SECURE INTEGRATION LLC—See Allied Universal Manager LLC; *U.S. Private*, pg. 189
GALEN HEALTHCARE SOLUTIONS—See TA Associates, Inc.; *U.S. Private*, pg. 3918
GARTNER DANMARK APS—See Gartner, Inc.; *U.S. Public*, pg. 907
GCI SYSTEMS; *U.S. Private*, pg. 1653
GCREST, INC.—See CyberAgent, Inc.; *Int'l*, pg. 1892
GEEKS ON CALL HOLDINGS, INC.; *U.S. Private*, pg. 1655
GENECA, LLC; *U.S. Private*, pg. 1660
GENERAL DYNAMICS INFORMATION TECHNOLOGY—See General Dynamics Corporation; *U.S. Public*, pg. 914
GENERAL MEDICAL APPLICATIONS, INC.—See Modernizing Medicine, Inc.; *U.S. Private*, pg. 2763
GEODESIC LIMITED; *Int'l*, pg. 2933
GINZAMARKETS, INC.; *U.S. Private*, pg. 1702
GIX MARTECH INNOVATION; *Int'l*, pg. 2982
GLADIATOR TECHNOLOGY SERVICES, INC.—See Jack Henry & Associates, Inc.; *U.S. Public*, pg. 1182
GLADSTONE MRM AUSTRALIA PTY LTD—See Gladstone PLC; *Int'l*, pg. 2987
GLADSTONE MRM LIMITED—See Gladstone PLC; *Int'l*, pg. 2987
GLADSTONE PLC; *Int'l*, pg. 2987
GLOBAL BUSINESS SOLUTIONS, INC.; *U.S. Private*, pg. 1712

GLOBAL SAFETY SURVEILLANCE, INC.—See HCL Technologies Ltd.; *Int'l*, pg. 3299
GLOBALWARE SOLUTIONS INC.; *U.S. Private*, pg. 1719
GLOBAL WARE SOLUTIONS—See Globalware Solutions Inc.; *U.S. Private*, pg. 1719
GLOBALWARE SOLUTIONS—See Globalware Solutions Inc.; *U.S. Private*, pg. 1719
GLOWTOUCH TECHNOLOGIES; *U.S. Private*, pg. 1721
GMO NETSHOP SUPPORT, INC.—See GMO Internet Group, Inc.; *Int'l*, pg. 3014
GOLDKEY CORPORATION; *U.S. Public*, pg. 951
GOODDATA CORPORATION; *U.S. Private*, pg. 1738
GOODDATA PTY LTD—See GoodData Corporation; *U.S. Private*, pg. 1739
GOOLD HEALTH SYSTEMS—See McKesson Corporation; *U.S. Public*, pg. 1407
GOVERNMENT ACQUISITIONS, INC.; *U.S. Private*, pg. 1746
GRACENOTE, INC.—See Brookfield Corporation; *Int'l*, pg. 1178
GRACENOTE, INC.—See Elliott Management Corporation; *U.S. Private*, pg. 1370
GRAPEVINE LOGIC, INC.—See FNL Technologies, Inc.; *U.S. Private*, pg. 1555
GRAVITY GAME TECH CO., LTD.—See Gravity Co., Ltd.; *Int'l*, pg. 3062
GREE INC.; *Int'l*, pg. 3069
GREE INTERNATIONAL INC.—See RockYou, Inc.; *U.S. Private*, pg. 3469
GREEN CLOUD TECHNOLOGIES, LLC; *U.S. Private*, pg. 1772
GREEN HILLS SOFTWARE S.A.R.L.—See Green Hills Software Inc.; *U.S. Private*, pg. 1773
GRONEMEYER IT GMBH; *Int'l*, pg. 3088
GSI LEASING GMBH—See 7C Solarparken AG; *Int'l*, pg. 15
GSW PEGASUS GMBH—See Deutsche Wohnen SE; *Int'l*, pg. 2085
GTI SOFTWARE & NETWORKING SARLAU—See Esprinet S.p.A.; *Int'l*, pg. 2506
GUARDIAN SMART INFRASTRUCTURE MANAGEMENT INC—See Guardian Capital Group Limited; *Int'l*, pg. 3170
GUARDSIGHT, INC.—See Iron Bow Technologies LLC; *U.S. Private*, pg. 2139
GUIYANG LONGMASTER INFORMATION & TECHNOLOGY CO., LTD.; *Int'l*, pg. 3174
GZ6G TECHNOLOGIES CORP.; *U.S. Public*, pg. 976
HAB, INC.—See GI Manager L.P.; *U.S. Private*, pg. 1693
HAIKU LEARNING SYSTEMS, INC.—See Vista Equity Partners, LLC; *U.S. Private*, pg. 4398
HALO GROUP, INC.—See Halo Companies, Inc.; *U.S. Public*, pg. 981
HAND ENTERPRISE SOLUTIONS CO., LTD.; *Int'l*, pg. 3243
HANU SOFTWARE SOLUTIONS (INDIA) PRIVATE LTD.—See Insight Enterprises, Inc.; *U.S. Public*, pg. 1129
HAREL HAMISHMAR COMPUTERS LTD.—See Harel Insurance Investments & Financial Services Ltd.; *Int'l*, pg. 3274
HAYSTACKID LLC—See Quad-C Management, Inc.; *U.S. Private*, pg. 3315
HCTEC PARTNERS LLC—See TruArc Partners, L.P.; *U.S. Private*, pg. 4245
HEALTH SYSTEMS INTERNATIONAL, LLC—See Great Point Partners, LLC; *U.S. Private*, pg. 1767
HEFEI XINHAI ELECTRONIC TECHNOLOGY CO., LTD.—See Chipsea Technologies (Shenzhen) Corp.; *Int'l*, pg. 1573
HEHEIST CO., LTD.; *Int'l*, pg. 3308
HEWLETT PACKARD ENTERPRISE CANADA CO.—See Hewlett Packard Enterprise Company; *U.S. Public*, pg. 1031
HEWLETT-PACKARD KOREA LTD.—See Hewlett Packard Enterprise Company; *U.S. Public*, pg. 1031
HEWLETT-PACKARD LIMITED—See Hewlett Packard Enterprise Company; *U.S. Public*, pg. 1032
HITACHI SYSTEMS SECURITY EUROPE SA—See Hitachi, Ltd.; *Int'l*, pg. 3421
HITACHI SYSTEMS SECURITY INC.—See Hitachi, Ltd.; *Int'l*, pg. 3421
HITCENTS—See Houchens Industries, Inc.; *U.S. Private*, pg. 1990
HL TECH SP. Z O.O.—See Hargreaves Lansdown PLC; *Int'l*, pg. 3274
HONG KONG WEI—See China Security Co., Ltd.; *Int'l*, pg. 1550
HONGZHI TECHNOLOGY CO., LTD.—See Beyondsoft Corporation; *Int'l*, pg. 1006
HUBWOO S.A.—See Perfect Commerce Holdings, LLC.; *U.S. Private*, pg. 3148
HUDSON HORIZONS, INC.; *U.S. Private*, pg. 2002
HUMAN SOFT HOLDING K.S.C.C.; *Int'l*, pg. 3529
HYVE WORLDWIDE B.V.—See Providence Equity Partners L.L.C.; *U.S. Private*, pg. 3292
HYVE WORLDWIDE B.V.—See Searchlight Capital Partners, L.P.; *U.S. Private*, pg. 3587
IAPPSYS; *U.S. Private*, pg. 2028
IBASE TECHNOLOGY INTERNATIONAL PTE. LTD.—See

IBase Technology Pte. Ltd.; *Int'l*, pg. 3569
IBITECH CO., LTD.—See Ibiden Co., Ltd.; *Int'l*, pg. 3576
IB MAROC; *Int'l*, pg. 3569
IBM GLOBAL BUSINESS SERVICES—See International Business Machines Corporation; *U.S. Public*, pg. 1147
IBM GLOBAL SERVICES—See International Business Machines Corporation; *U.S. Public*, pg. 1147
ICF SYSTEMS AG—See ICF Kursmakler AG; *Int'l*, pg. 3579
ICONSUMER CORP.; *U.S. Public*, pg. 1086
IDA INFRONT AB—See Addnode Group AB; *Int'l*, pg. 130
IDATA TECHNOLOGIES INC; *U.S. Private*, pg. 2035
IDEAOVERTEN, LLC; *U.S. Private*, pg. 2037
ID GROUP, INC.; *U.S. Private*, pg. 2034
ID INSIGHT, INC.; *U.S. Private*, pg. 2034
ID TECHNOLOGIES, LLC—See Acacia Capital NL LLC; *U.S. Public*, pg. 46
IET SOLUTIONS, LLC—See UNICOM Global, Inc.; *U.S. Private*, pg. 4282
IGXGLOBAL, INC; *U.S. Private*, pg. 2040
IHM SERVICES COMPANY—See Persivia, Inc.; *U.S. Private*, pg. 3155
IMAGE METRICS, INC.; *U.S. Public*, pg. 1112
IMAGE PROJECT, INC.; *U.S. Private*, pg. 2044
IM ASSOCIATES BV—See IQVIA Holdings Inc.; *U.S. Public*, pg. 1168
IMMEDION LLC; *U.S. Private*, pg. 2047
IMMUNITY, INC.—See Cyxtera Technologies, Inc.; *U.S. Public*, pg. 619
INACOMP TECHNICAL SERVICES GROUP; *U.S. Private*, pg. 2052
INDUSTRIAL DEFENDER, INC.—See Teleo Capital Management, LLC; *U.S. Private*, pg. 3961
INEOQUEST TECHNOLOGIES, INC.—See Genstar Capital, LLC; *U.S. Private*, pg. 1679
INFERENCE TECHNOLOGIES GROUP, INC.—See Five9, Inc.; *U.S. Public*, pg. 852
INFINITY COMPUTER SOLUTIONS LLC; *U.S. Private*, pg. 2071
INFOCRAFT LTD.—See Hayleys PLC; *Int'l*, pg. 3292
INFOLYNX SERVICES, INC.; *U.S. Private*, pg. 2072
INGALLS INFORMATION SECURITY LLC—See C3 Integrated Solutions Inc.; *U.S. Private*, pg. 710
INGRAM MICRO AB—See Hainan Traffic Administration Holding Co., Ltd.; *Int'l*, pg. 3214
INSIGHT DIRECT WORLDWIDE, INC.—See Insight Enterprises, Inc.; *U.S. Public*, pg. 1130
INSIGHT ENTERPRISES UK, LTD.—See Insight Enterprises, Inc.; *U.S. Public*, pg. 1130
INSITE ONE, INC.—See Dell Technologies Inc.; *U.S. Public*, pg. 650
THE INSTANT WEB COMPANIES - MAIL-GARD DIVISION—See The Instant Web Companies; *U.S. Private*, pg. 4056
INTEGRACORE, LLC—See A.P. Moller-Maersk A/S; *Int'l*, pg. 28
INTEGRO TECHNOLOGIES CO. LTD.—See Aurionpro Solutions Limited; *Int'l*, pg. 711
INTEGRO TECHNOLOGIES SDN. BHD.—See Aurionpro Solutions Limited; *Int'l*, pg. 711
INTEGRO TECHNOLOGIES (VIETNAM) LLC—See Aurionpro Solutions Limited; *Int'l*, pg. 711
INTELLIFUEL SYSTEMS INC.—See TA Associates, Inc.; *U.S. Private*, pg. 3917
INTELLIFY TALENT SOLUTIONS, LLC—See Cross Country Healthcare, Inc.; *U.S. Public*, pg. 595
INTELLIGENT DIGITAL AVATARS, INC.; *U.S. Private*, pg. 2105
INTELLIGENT MEDICAL OBJECTS, INC.—See Thomas H. Lee Partners, L.P.; *U.S. Private*, pg. 4156
INTERACTIVE BROADBAND CONSULTING GROUP LLC—See Accenture plc; *Int'l*, pg. 87
INTERACTIVE INNOVATION GROUP, INC.; *U.S. Private*, pg. 2108
INTERCHANGE TECHNOLOGIES, INC.—See ePlus Inc.; *U.S. Public*, pg. 784
INTERDYN BMI—See Columbus A/S; *Int'l*, pg. 1706
INTERNATIONAL INTEGRATED SOLUTIONS, LTD.; *U.S. Private*, pg. 2118
INTERNATIONAL SOLUTIONS GROUP, INC.; *U.S. Private*, pg. 2121
INTERNET BROADCASTING SYSTEMS—See Nexstar Media Group, Inc.; *U.S. Public*, pg. 1522
INTERTECH SECURITY, LLC; *U.S. Private*, pg. 2127
INTONE NETWORKS INC.; *U.S. Private*, pg. 2129
INTUITIVE TECHNOLOGY GROUP LLC; *U.S. Private*, pg. 2130
INVENTIO IT A/S—See Dustin Group AB; *Int'l*, pg. 2235
INVENT VENTURES, INC.; *U.S. Private*, pg. 2131
INWARE TECHNOLOGIES, INC.; *U.S. Private*, pg. 2133
IOXP GMBH—See PTC Inc.; *U.S. Public*, pg. 1734
IPCOS BV—See ATS Corporation; *Int'l*, pg. 695
IPCOS ENGINEERING SOLUTIONS PVT. LTD.—See ATS Corporation; *Int'l*, pg. 695
I.R.I.S. ECOMMUNICATION—See Canon Inc.; *Int'l*, pg. 1295
I.R.I.S. INC.—See Canon Inc.; *Int'l*, pg. 1295
IRIS SOLUTIONS, LLC—See Anatomy IT, LLC; *U.S. Private*, pg. 272

N.A.I.C.S. INDEX

541519 — OTHER COMPUTER RELA...

IRON MOUNTAIN ANAMNIS GDM SAS—See Iron Mountain Incorporated; *U.S. Public*, pg. 1173
IRON MOUNTAIN AUSTRALIA PTY. LTD.—See Iron Mountain Incorporated; *U.S. Public*, pg. 1172
IRON MOUNTAIN CANADA CORPORATION—See Iron Mountain Incorporated; *U.S. Public*, pg. 1172
IRON MOUNTAIN CESKA REPUBLIKA S.R.O.—See Iron Mountain Incorporated; *U.S. Public*, pg. 1173
IRON MOUNTAIN DEUTSCHLAND GMBH—See Iron Mountain Incorporated; *U.S. Public*, pg. 1173
IRON MOUNTAIN FRANCE S.A.S.—See Iron Mountain Incorporated; *U.S. Public*, pg. 1173
IRON MOUNTAIN HONG KONG LIMITED—See Iron Mountain Incorporated; *U.S. Public*, pg. 1173
IRON MOUNTAIN (INDIA) PVT LTD.—See Iron Mountain Incorporated; *U.S. Public*, pg. 1172
IRON MOUNTAIN ITALIA S.P.A.—See Iron Mountain Incorporated; *U.S. Public*, pg. 1173
IRON MOUNTAIN MUSCAT SPC—See Iron Mountain Incorporated; *U.S. Public*, pg. 1173
IRON MOUNTAIN NEDERLAND B.V.—See Iron Mountain Incorporated; *U.S. Public*, pg. 1173
IRON MOUNTAIN NORGE AS—See Iron Mountain Incorporated; *U.S. Public*, pg. 1173
IRON MOUNTAIN POLSKA SP. Z O.O.—See Iron Mountain Incorporated; *U.S. Public*, pg. 1173
IRON MOUNTAIN SLOVAKIA S.R.O.—See Iron Mountain Incorporated; *U.S. Public*, pg. 1173
IRON MOUNTAIN (UK) LTD.—See Iron Mountain Incorporated; *U.S. Public*, pg. 1172
ISN SOFTWARE CORP.; *U.S. Private*, pg. 2146
ISP WEST S.R.O.—See CEZ, a.s.; *Int'l*, pg. 1428
ISSYS ICT B.V.—See Dustin Group AB; *Int'l*, pg. 2235
ISYS LLC—See WidePoint Corporation; *U.S. Public*, pg. 2370
ITAITO OY—See Dustin Group AB; *Int'l*, pg. 2235
ITALENT INC.; *U.S. Private*, pg. 2149
ITECH SOLUTIONS, INC.—See Ampcus Inc.; *U.S. Private*, pg. 265
ITECH US, INC.—See SharedLABS, Inc.; *U.S. Private*, pg. 3626
ITN INTERNATIONAL INC.—See HGGC, LLC; *U.S. Private*, pg. 1929
IT-NOVUM GMBH—See Allgeier SE; *Int'l*, pg. 338
ITRON-AUSTRALASIA PTY LIMITED—See Itron, Inc.; *U.S. Public*, pg. 1176
ITS PARTNERS, LLC; *U.S. Private*, pg. 2150
ITUMA GMBH—See Datatec Limited; *Int'l*, pg. 1980
ITVANTAGE, INC.—See Digerati Technologies, Inc.; *U.S. Public*, pg. 661
ITWIN TECHNOLOGY SDN. BHD.—See Cabnet Holding Berhad; *Int'l*, pg. 1246
ITZ CASH CARD LIMITED—See Ebix Inc.; *U.S. Public*, pg. 710
IV4, INC.—See ProArch IT Solutions, Inc.; *U.S. Private*, pg. 3271
IXIA - AUSTIN—See Keysight Technologies, Inc.; *U.S. Public*, pg. 1227
IXIA PTE. LTD.—See Keysight Technologies, Inc.; *U.S. Public*, pg. 1227
IXIA TECHNOLOGIES EUROPE LIMITED—See Keysight Technologies, Inc.; *U.S. Public*, pg. 1227
JACER CORPORATION; *U.S. Private*, pg. 2173
JACOBSRIMELL—See Amdocs Limited; *Int'l*, pg. 419
JAM FILLED ENTERTAINMENT, INC.—See Boat Rocker Media; *Int'l*, pg. 1095
JAPAN PHOTOCATALYST CENTER CO., LTD.—See Abalance Corporation Ltd.; *Int'l*, pg. 48
JR TOKAI INFORMATION SYSTEMS COMPANY—See Central Japan Railway Company; *Int'l*, pg. 1408
JUNO TECHNOLOGY CORPORATION; *U.S. Private*, pg. 2244
JUS-COM INC.—See FTE Networks, Inc.; *U.S. Public*, pg. 889
K4 SOLUTIONS, INC.; *U.S. Private*, pg. 2253
KALIO, INC.; *U.S. Private*, pg. 2257
KAURI BUSINESS SYSTEMS LIMITED—See TA Associates, Inc.; *U.S. Private*, pg. 3914
KEEPITSAFE, INC.—See Ziff Davis, Inc.; *U.S. Private*, pg. 2403
THE KEMTAH GROUP INC.—See AE Industrial Partners, LP; *U.S. Private*, pg. 111
KEONYS BELGIQUE SPRL—See CENIT AG; *Int'l*, pg. 1401
KEONYS NL BV—See CENIT AG; *Int'l*, pg. 1401
KEONYS SAS—See CENIT AG; *Int'l*, pg. 1401
KEYNOTE LLC—See Dynatrace, Inc.; *U.S. Public*, pg. 700
KEYSTONE SOLUTIONS INC.—See Rekor Systems, Inc.; *U.S. Public*, pg. 1778
KIT DIGITAL LIMITED—See Piksel, Inc.; *U.S. Private*, pg. 3180
KOLLEX GMBH—See COCA-COLA EUROPACIFIC PARTNERS PLC; *Int'l*, pg. 1685
KONDOSERVIS MANAGEMENT SDN. BHD.—See IGB Berhad; *Int'l*, pg. 3601
KROLL ONTRACK LIMITED—See Pivotal Acquisition Corp.; *U.S. Public*, pg. 3192
L-3 COMMAND & CONTROL SYSTEMS AND SOFTWARE—See L3Harris Technologies, Inc.; *U.S. Public*, pg. 1281
LABOTEC INC.; *U.S. Private*, pg. 2370
LAW TRUSTED THIRD PARTY SERVICES (PTY) LTD—See Etion Limited; *Int'l*, pg. 2523
LGS GROUP INC—See International Business Machines Corporation; *U.S. Public*, pg. 1146
LIFESPAN; *U.S. Private*, pg. 2451
LIGATT SECURITY INTERNATIONAL, INC.; *U.S. Public*, pg. 1314
LINKEDGE TECHNOLOGIES, INC.; *U.S. Private*, pg. 2462
LINKEDGE TECHNOLOGIES, INC.—See LinkEdge Technologies, Inc.; *U.S. Private*, pg. 2462
LINKED TECHNOLOGIES, INC.—See SureTec; *U.S. Private*, pg. 3883
LINQUEST CORPORATION—See KBR, Inc.; *U.S. Public*, pg. 1216
LIONBRIDGE (CANADA) INC.—See H.I.G. Capital, LLC; *U.S. Private*, pg. 1830
LIONBRIDGE DENMARK A/S—See H.I.G. Capital, LLC; *U.S. Private*, pg. 1830
LIONBRIDGE DEUTSCHLAND GMBH—See H.I.G. Capital, LLC; *U.S. Private*, pg. 1830
LIONBRIDGE ESPANA S.L.—See H.I.G. Capital, LLC; *U.S. Private*, pg. 1830
LIONBRIDGE FRANCE SAS—See H.I.G. Capital, LLC; *U.S. Private*, pg. 1830
LIONBRIDGE HOLDING GMBH—See H.I.G. Capital, LLC; *U.S. Private*, pg. 1830
LIONBRIDGE IRELAND LIMITED—See H.I.G. Capital, LLC; *U.S. Private*, pg. 1830
LIONBRIDGE JAPAN III K.K.—See H.I.G. Capital, LLC; *U.S. Private*, pg. 1830
LIONBRIDGE JAPAN KK—See H.I.G. Capital, LLC; *U.S. Private*, pg. 1830
LIONBRIDGE KOREA CO. LTD.—See H.I.G. Capital, LLC; *U.S. Private*, pg. 1830
LIONBRIDGE NEDERLAND B.V.—See H.I.G. Capital, LLC; *U.S. Private*, pg. 1830
LIONBRIDGE OY—See H.I.G. Capital, LLC; *U.S. Private*, pg. 1830
LIONBRIDGE POLAND SP. Z O.O.—See H.I.G. Capital, LLC; *U.S. Private*, pg. 1830
LIONBRIDGE SINGAPORE PTE LTD.—See H.I.G. Capital, LLC; *U.S. Private*, pg. 1830
LIONBRIDGE (SLOVAKIA) S.R.O.—See H.I.G. Capital, LLC; *U.S. Private*, pg. 1830
LIONBRIDGE SWEDEN AKTIEBOLAG—See H.I.G. Capital, LLC; *U.S. Private*, pg. 1830
LIONBRIDGE TECHNOLOGIES, INC.—See H.I.G. Capital, LLC; *U.S. Private*, pg. 1830
LIONBRIDGE TECHNOLOGIES PRIVATE LIMITED—See H.I.G. Capital, LLC; *U.S. Private*, pg. 1830
LIONBRIDGE (THAILAND) LIMITED—See H.I.G. Capital, LLC; *U.S. Private*, pg. 1830
LIONBRIDGE (UK) LTD.—See H.I.G. Capital, LLC; *U.S. Private*, pg. 1830
LIQUIDM TECHNOLOGY GMBH—See Bertelsmann SE & Co. KGaA; *Int'l*, pg. 993
LIST ENGAGE, INC.—See Broadtree Partners, LLC; *U.S. Private*, pg. 659
LLC IT-PARK UNIVERSITY—See EPAM Systems, Inc.; *U.S. Public*, pg. 783
LOGICALIS ARGENTINA S.A.—See Datatec Limited; *Int'l*, pg. 1980
LOGICALIS CHILE S.A.—See Datatec Limited; *Int'l*, pg. 1980
LOGICALIS ECUADOR S.A.—See Datatec Limited; *Int'l*, pg. 1980
LOGICALIS GUERNSEY LIMITED—See Datatec Limited; *Int'l*, pg. 1980
LOGICALIS IRELAND LIMITED—See Datatec Limited; *Int'l*, pg. 1980
LOGICALIS JERSEY LIMITED—See Datatec Limited; *Int'l*, pg. 1980
LOGICALIS MALAYSIA SDN. BHD.—See Datatec Limited; *Int'l*, pg. 1980
LOGICALIS MEXICO, S. DE R.L. DE C.V.—See Datatec Limited; *Int'l*, pg. 1980
LOGICALIS PARAGUAY S.A.—See Datatec Limited; *Int'l*, pg. 1980
LOGICALIS PTE. LIMITED—See Datatec Limited; *Int'l*, pg. 1980
LOGICALIS PUERTO RICO INC.—See Datatec Limited; *Int'l*, pg. 1980
LOGICALIS SA (PTY) LTD—See Datatec Limited; *Int'l*, pg. 1981
LOGICALIS SHANGHAI LIMITED—See Datatec Limited; *Int'l*, pg. 1981
LOGICALIS SINGAPORE PTE. LIMITED—See Datatec Limited; *Int'l*, pg. 1981
LOGICALIS SPAIN SL—See Datatec Limited; *Int'l*, pg. 1980
LOGICALIS UK LIMITED—See Datatec Limited; *Int'l*, pg. 1980
LOGICALIS US—See Datatec Limited; *Int'l*, pg. 1980
LOGISTICS MANAGEMENT RESOURCES INC.; *U.S. Private*, pg. 2482
LOGIX S.A.—See Arrow Electronics, Inc.; *U.S. Public*, pg. 199
LOGIXTECH SOLUTIONS, LLC—See TSR, Inc.; *U.S. Public*, pg. 2202
LOGMEIN, INC.—See Elliott Management Corporation; *U.S. Private*, pg. 1368
LOGMEIN, INC.—See Francisco Partners Management, LP; *U.S. Private*, pg. 1590
LUFTHANSA SYSTEMS AG—See Deutsche Lufthansa AG; *Int'l*, pg. 2069
LUMETA CORP.—See Insight Venture Management, LLC; *U.S. Private*, pg. 2090
LYCOS, INC.—See Brightcom Group Ltd.; *Int'l*, pg. 1162
M2M DATA CORP.—See Caterpillar, Inc.; *U.S. Public*, pg. 452
MACAU WEI AN CO., LTD.—See China Security Co., Ltd.; *Int'l*, pg. 1550
MAD MOBILE, INC.; *U.S. Private*, pg. 2539
MAESTROSOFT, INC.—See Arreva LLC; *U.S. Private*, pg. 335
MAINTHIA TECHNOLOGIES, INC.; *U.S. Private*, pg. 2554
MARKET AMERICA WORLDWIDE, INC.; *U.S. Private*, pg. 2578
MARTI ILERI TEKNOLOJI A.S.—See Marti Technologies, Inc.; *U.S. Public*, pg. 1389
MARTINI MEDIA NETWORK, INC.—See Evolve Media, LLC; *U.S. Private*, pg. 1443
MATRIX INFORMATION CONSULTING, INC.; *U.S. Private*, pg. 2612
MATRIX VEHICLE TRACKING—See PowerFleet, Inc.; *U.S. Public*, pg. 1706
MDTVISION—See International Business Machines Corporation; *U.S. Public*, pg. 1149
MECHANICNET GROUP, INC.—See Clayton, Dubilier & Rice, LLC; *U.S. Private*, pg. 923
MEDACIST SOLUTION GROUP, LLC—See Thoma Bravo, L.P.; *U.S. Private*, pg. 4146
MEDEANALYTICS, INC.—See Thoma Bravo, L.P.; *U.S. Private*, pg. 4149
MEDIA TECH INC.—See Daiwa House Industry Co., Ltd.; *Int'l*, pg. 1947
MEDISIGN GMBH—See Deutsche Apotheker- und Arztebank eG; *Int'l*, pg. 2049
MEDWING.COM INC.; *U.S. Private*, pg. 2659
MERLIN TECHNICAL SOLUTIONS, INC.; *U.S. Private*, pg. 2675
MGM TECHNOLOGY PARTNERS PORTUGAL, UNIPESSOAL LDA.—See Allgeier SE; *Int'l*, pg. 337
MICRO CAD CO., LTD.—See Future Corporation; *Int'l*, pg. 2853
MICROPACT, INC.—See Tyler Technologies, Inc.; *U.S. Public*, pg. 2208
MICROSOFT ONLINE, INC.—See Microsoft Corporation; *U.S. Public*, pg. 1441
MIG & CO.; *U.S. Private*, pg. 2724
MILES CONSULTING CORP.; *U.S. Private*, pg. 2727
MINDLEAF TECHNOLOGIES, INC.; *U.S. Private*, pg. 2740
MINDSPARK INTERNATIONAL INC.; *U.S. Private*, pg. 2741
MIRANTIS, INC.; *U.S. Private*, pg. 2746
MISSION DATA LLC—See Growth Acceleration Partners, LLC; *U.S. Private*, pg. 1796
MISTRAS ROPEWORKS TRAINING CORP.—See Mistras Group, Inc.; *U.S. Public*, pg. 1451
MIX TELEMATICS INTERNATIONAL (PTY) LTD.—See PowerFleet, Inc.; *U.S. Public*, pg. 1706
MODUSLINK CORP.—See Steel Connect, Inc.; *U.S. Public*, pg. 1941
MODUSLINK INTERNATIONAL B.V.—See Steel Connect, Inc.; *U.S. Public*, pg. 1941
MOGUL AB—See Addnode Group AB; *Int'l*, pg. 130
MONIKER ONLINE SERVICES, LLC—See Oversee.net; *U.S. Private*, pg. 3053
MONOLITH CORPORATION—See Constellation Software Inc.; *Int'l*, pg. 1772
MONOTYPE GMBH—See HGGC, LLC; *U.S. Private*, pg. 1930
MONOTYPE SOLUTIONS INDIA PRIVATE LIMITED—See HGGC, LLC; *U.S. Private*, pg. 1930
MOVERO, INC. - COLUMBUS—See Movero, Inc.; *U.S. Private*, pg. 2802
MPHASIS LIMITED—See Blackstone Inc.; *U.S. Public*, pg. 356
MUSICNET—See Baker Capital Partners, LLC; *U.S. Private*, pg. 455
MY EYE MEDIA, LLC—See Eurofins Scientific S.E.; *Int'l*, pg. 2549
NAMEMEDIA, INC.; *U.S. Private*, pg. 2832
NANHAI JO YEH ELECTRONICS CO., LTD.—See BizLink Holding Inc.; *Int'l*, pg. 1053
NANSEN INC.—See CapMan PLC; *Int'l*, pg. 1315
NAP DE LAS AMERICAS-MADRID, S.A.—See Verizon Communications Inc.; *U.S. Public*, pg. 2285
NAP OF THE AMERICAS/WEST INC.—See Verizon Communications Inc.; *U.S. Public*, pg. 2285
NATIONAL COMPUTER SERVICES—See Al-Babtain Group; *Int'l*, pg. 284
NATIONAL ELECTRONIC ATTACHMENT, INC.—See Accel Partners L.P.; *U.S. Private*, pg. 48

541519 — OTHER COMPUTER RELA...

NATIONAL ELECTRONIC ATTACHMENT, INC.—See KKR & Co. Inc.; *U.S. Public*, pg. 1238
NATIONAL PAYMENT CARD ASSOCIATION—See TA Associates, Inc.; *U.S. Private*, pg. 3917
NAVANTIS INC.—See CIVC Partners LLC; *U.S. Private*, pg. 907
NAVICLE PTY. LTD.—See Crayon Group Holding ASA; *Int'l*, pg. 1829
NAVIGY INC.—See GuideWell Mutual Holding Corporation; *U.S. Private*, pg. 1814
NCR COMMERCE JAPAN LTD.—See NCR Voyix Corporation.; *U.S. Public*, pg. 1503
NDP, LLC; *U.S. Private*, pg. 2876
NESS S.A.—See KKR & Co. Inc.; *U.S. Public*, pg. 1261
NESS TECHNOLOGIES, INC. - TECHNOLOGY INNOVATION CENTER—See KKR & Co. Inc.; *U.S. Public*, pg. 1262
NET ENFORCERS, INC.—See General Catalyst Partners; *U.S. Private*, pg. 1664
NET ENFORCERS, INC.—See iSubscribed Inc.; *U.S. Private*, pg. 2147
NET ENFORCERS, INC.—See WndrCo Holdings, LLC; *U.S. Private*, pg. 4552
NETE; *U.S. Private*, pg. 2887
NET OPTICS, INC.—See Keysight Technologies, Inc.; *U.S. Public*, pg. 1227
NETPUBLICATOR APPS AB—See Addnode Group AB; *Int'l*, pg. 130
NETWORK CABLING SERVICES, INC.; *U.S. Private*, pg. 2888
NETWORK PEOPLE, INC.—See Frontenac Company LLC; *U.S. Private*, pg. 1614
THE NEWBERRY GROUP, INC.; *U.S. Private*, pg. 4083
NEWBROOK SOLUTIONS, INC.—See Edgesource Corporation; *U.S. Private*, pg. 1334
NEXSTGO COMPANY LIMITED—See Alco Holdings Limited; *Int'l*, pg. 301
NEXTAG, INC.—See Regent, L.P.; *U.S. Private*, pg. 3388
NEXTINPUT, INC.—See Qorvo, Inc.; *U.S. Public*, pg. 1743
THE NEXUS GROUP, INC.—See EverWatch Capital; *U.S. Private*, pg. 1441
THE NIELSEN NORMAN GROUP; *U.S. Private*, pg. 4084
NIMBUSNOW, INC.; *U.S. Private*, pg. 2927
N-LINK CORPORATION; *U.S. Private*, pg. 2827
NOBLE SYSTEMS CORPORATION—See Vector Capital Management, L.P.; *U.S. Private*, pg. 4350
NOBLE SYSTEMS UK—See Vector Capital Management, L.P.; *U.S. Private*, pg. 4350
NORISK IT GROEP B.V.—See Dustin Group AB; *Int'l*, pg. 2235
NOVIS SOFTWARE GMBH—See ICF Kursmakler AG; *Int'l*, pg. 3579
NSK & ASSOCIATES, INC.; *U.S. Private*, pg. 2970
NSSLGLOBAL GMBH—See Arendals Fossekompani ASA; *Int'l*, pg. 559
NWN CORPORATION—See American Securities LLC; *U.S. Private*, pg. 250
OBEO, INC.; *U.S. Private*, pg. 2986
OBERTHUR CARD SYSTEMS SP. Z O.O.—See Advent International Corporation; *U.S. Private*, pg. 102
OBJECTIVE INTEGRITY, INC.; *U.S. Private*, pg. 2987
OBJECT TECHNOLOGY SOLUTIONS, INC.; *U.S. Private*, pg. 2987
OCENTURE LLC; *U.S. Private*, pg. 2992
ODYSSEY TECHNICAL SOLUTIONS, LLC; *U.S. Private*, pg. 2996
OMICRON CONSULTING, LLC; *U.S. Private*, pg. 3016
OMNEON, INC.—See Harmonic, Inc.; *U.S. Public*, pg. 986
OMNIM2M INC.—See TraQiQ, Inc.; *U.S. Public*, pg. 2185
OMX TECHNOLOGY AB—See Nasdaq, Inc.; *U.S. Public*, pg. 1492
OMX TECHNOLOGY ITALY SRL—See Nasdaq, Inc.; *U.S. Public*, pg. 1492
OMX TECHNOLOGY LTD.—See Nasdaq, Inc.; *U.S. Public*, pg. 1492
ONCIDIUM INC.—See CPS Capital; *Int'l*, pg. 1826
ONENECK IT SERVICES CORPORATION—See Telephone & Data Systems, Inc.; *U.S. Public*, pg. 1997
ONEZERO COMPANY LTD.—See Commercial Bank of Ceylon PLC; *Int'l*, pg. 1715
OPENTECH ALLIANCE, INC.; *U.S. Private*, pg. 3031
OPTIMATION TECHNOLOGY, INC.—See Owner Resource Group, LLC; *U.S. Private*, pg. 3055
OPTIMOS LLC—See MAXIMUS, Inc.; *U.S. Public*, pg. 1402
OPTIV SECURITY, INC.—See KKR & Co. Inc.; *U.S. Public*, pg. 1262
ORANGE NETWORKS GMBH—See Datatec Limited; *Int'l*, pg. 1981
OVERGROUP CONSULTING LLC; *U.S. Private*, pg. 3052
OY GAMECLUSTER LTD.—See G-cluster Global Corporation; *Int'l*, pg. 2862
PANOPTA LLC—See Fortinet, Inc.; *U.S. Public*, pg. 869
PARAGON MICRO, INC.; *U.S. Private*, pg. 3091
PARALLO LIMITED—See Crayon Group Holding ASA; *Int'l*, pg. 1829
PATIENT ACCESS SOLUTIONS, INC.; *U.S. Public*, pg. 1652
PAY TEL COMMUNICATIONS, INC.; *U.S. Private*, pg. 3116

PCB APPS, LLC; *U.S. Private*, pg. 3119
PCPC DIRECT, LTD.; *U.S. Private*, pg. 3121
PERFORMANT FINANCIAL CORPORATION; *U.S. Public*, pg. 1676
PIESYNC NV—See HubSpot, Inc.; *U.S. Public*, pg. 1068
PIKETEC GMBH—See Synopsys, Inc.; *U.S. Public*, pg. 1970
PIKSEL, INC.; *U.S. Private*, pg. 3180
PINNACLE 21, LLC—See Certara, Inc.; *U.S. Public*, pg. 476
PINNACLE DATA SYSTEMS, LLC—See GI Manager L.P.; *U.S. Private*, pg. 1692
PLASMA COMPUTING GROUP, INC.; *U.S. Private*, pg. 3198
PLUMCHOICE, INC.—See The Allstate Corporation; *U.S. Public*, pg. 2032
PLUS CONSULTING LLC—See iVision Scale, LLC; *U.S. Private*, pg. 2151
PMDSOFT INC.; *U.S. Private*, pg. 3218
PMSQUARE LLC; *U.S. Private*, pg. 3218
POOLE & ASSOCIATES, INC.—See Jacobs Engineering Group, Inc.; *U.S. Public*, pg. 1186
PRECISION COMPUTER SERVICES, INC.; *U.S. Private*, pg. 3244
PREFERRED SYSTEMS SOLUTIONS, INC.—See Carl Marks & Co., Inc.; *U.S. Private*, pg. 763
PRELERT INC.—See Elastic N.V.; *U.S. Public*, pg. 723
PRIME TECHNOLOGY GROUP, INC.—See Frontenac Company LLC; *U.S. Private*, pg. 1614
PRIVATUM N.V.—See Alan Allman Associates SA; *Int'l*, pg. 290
PROFESSIONAL SOFTWARE ENGINEERING INC.; *U.S. Private*, pg. 3276
PROJECT LEADERSHIP ASSOCIATES, INC.—See Project Leadership Associates, Inc.; *U.S. Private*, pg. 3280
PROLEXIC TECHNOLOGIES INC.—See Akamai Technologies, Inc.; *U.S. Public*, pg. 69
PROSILIA SOFTWARE AB—See Addnode Group AB; *Int'l*, pg. 130
PROTECTOR AS—See AF Gruppen ASA; *Int'l*, pg. 184
PROTECTOR KKS GMBH—See AF Gruppen ASA; *Int'l*, pg. 184
PRYSM, INC.; *U.S. Private*, pg. 3296
PSI INTERNATIONAL, INC.; *U.S. Private*, pg. 3297
P.T. AWAN TEKNOLOGI GLOBAL—See Amiya Corporation; *Int'l*, pg. 428
P.T. KRAYON KONSULTAN INDONESIA—See Crayon Group Holding ASA; *Int'l*, pg. 1829
PT. PACKET SYSTEMS INDONESIA—See Datatec Limited; *Int'l*, pg. 1981
PT WESTCON INTERNATIONAL INDONESIA—See Datatec Limited; *Int'l*, pg. 1981
PULAU CORPORATION; *U.S. Private*, pg. 3303
PYRAMID CONSULTING, INC.; *U.S. Private*, pg. 3310
Q9 NETWORKS INC.—See BCE Inc.; *Int'l*, pg. 928
QUALCOMM INNOVATION CENTER, INC.—See QUALCOMM Incorporated; *U.S. Public*, pg. 1747
QUANTIC SA—See Aubay SA; *Int'l*, pg. 698
QUANTUM GROUP, INC.; *U.S. Private*, pg. 3323
R2C ONLINE LIMITED—See Corpay, Inc.; *U.S. Public*, pg. 580
THE RADIANT GROUP, LLC—See Advent International Corporation; *U.S. Private*, pg. 103
RAHI SYSTEMS AUSTRALIA PTY. LTD.—See WESCO International, Inc.; *U.S. Public*, pg. 2351
RAHI SYSTEMS GMBH—See WESCO International, Inc.; *U.S. Public*, pg. 2351
RAHI SYSTEMS INC.—See WESCO International, Inc.; *U.S. Public*, pg. 2351
RAHI SYSTEMS JAPAN LLC—See WESCO International, Inc.; *U.S. Public*, pg. 2351
RAHI SYSTEMS LIMITED—See WESCO International, Inc.; *U.S. Public*, pg. 2351
RAHI TECHNOLOGIES LIMITED—See WESCO International, Inc.; *U.S. Public*, pg. 2351
RALLY4, INC.—See GRYYT, LLC; *U.S. Private*, pg. 1800
RANDA SOLUTIONS; *U.S. Private*, pg. 3353
RAYTHEON AUSTRALIA INTEGRATED SOLUTIONS—See RTX Corporation; *U.S. Public*, pg. 1824
RAYTHEON CIVIL COMMUNICATIONS SOLUTIONS—See RTX Corporation; *U.S. Public*, pg. 1824
RAYTHEON COMBAT SYSTEMS—See RTX Corporation; *U.S. Public*, pg. 1824
RE2, INC.—See Palladyne AI Corp.; *U.S. Public*, pg. 1634
READYOP COMMUNICATIONS, INC.—See Cleartronic, Inc.; *U.S. Public*, pg. 513
REALEFLOW, LLC; *U.S. Private*, pg. 3368
RED HAT GMBH—See International Business Machines Corporation; *U.S. Public*, pg. 1150
RED RIVER COMPUTER CO., INC.; *U.S. Private*, pg. 3375
REFLEXIS SYSTEMS GMBH—See Zebra Technologies Corporation; *U.S. Public*, pg. 2401
REFLEXIS SYSTEMS INDIA PRIVATE LIMITED—See Zebra Technologies Corporation; *U.S. Public*, pg. 2401
REFLEXIS SYSTEMS (UK) LIMITED—See Zebra Technologies Corporation; *U.S. Public*, pg. 2401
REGENT SYSTEMS, INC.; *U.S. Private*, pg. 3387
REI SYSTEMS, INC.; *U.S. Private*, pg. 3390
RELIAQUEST LLC; *U.S. Private*, pg. 3395

RENOVARE ENVIRONMENTAL, INC.; *U.S. Public*, pg. 1783
RESAPP HEALTH LIMITED—See Pfizer Inc.; *U.S. Public*, pg. 1680
RESONA INC.—See Core Corporation; *Int'l*, pg. 1797
RIGHTPOINT CONSULTING LLC—See Genpact Limited; *Int'l*, pg. 2926
RIGHTPOINT INDIA DIGITAL PRIVATE LIMITED—See Genpact Limited; *Int'l*, pg. 2927
RIMINI STREET AUSTRALIA PTY. LIMITED—See Rimini Street, Inc.; *U.S. Public*, pg. 1799
RIMINI STREET BRAZILS SERVICOS DE TECNOLOGIA LTDA.—See Rimini Street, Inc.; *U.S. Public*, pg. 1799
RIMINI STREET FZ, LLC—See Rimini Street, Inc.; *U.S. Public*, pg. 1799
RIMINI STREET GMBH—See Rimini Street, Inc.; *U.S. Public*, pg. 1799
RIMINI STREET, INC.; *U.S. Public*, pg. 1798
RIMINI STREET, LTD.—See Rimini Street, Inc.; *U.S. Public*, pg. 1799
RINOCLOUD LIMITED—See Deepverge PLC; *Int'l*, pg. 2003
ROCKYOU, INC.; *U.S. Private*, pg. 3469
ROCTEC TECHNOLOGY LIMITED—See BTS Group Holdings Public Company Limited; *Int'l*, pg. 1206
ROLTA AMERICAS; *U.S. Private*, pg. 3475
ROOM 77, INC.—See Lexyl Travel Technologies LLC; *U.S. Private*, pg. 2441
ROSE INTERNATIONAL INC.; *U.S. Private*, pg. 3481
ROXIO UK LTD.—See Vector Capital Management, L.P.; *U.S. Private*, pg. 4352
RRGP SERVICES, INC.; *U.S. Private*, pg. 3496
RS-UNIX; *U.S. Private*, pg. 3496
RYZEX INC.—See Sole Source Capital LLC; *U.S. Private*, pg. 3708
SABRE CORPORATION; *U.S. Public*, pg. 1833
SABRE HOSPITALITY SOLUTIONS—See Sabre Corporation; *U.S. Public*, pg. 1833
SAFEDX S.R.O.—See Hon Hai Precision Industry Co., Ltd.; *Int'l*, pg. 3457
SAGENTIC WEB DESIGN; *U.S. Private*, pg. 3527
SAGE TECHNOLOGIES CO.—See Ferrer Freeman & Company, LLC; *U.S. Private*, pg. 1498
SAUDI EGYPTIAN LOGISTICS AND ELECTRONICS COMPANY, S.A.E.—See Dabbagh Group Holding Company Ltd.; *Int'l*, pg. 1903
SCD INFORMATION TECHNOLOGY, LLC; *U.S. Private*, pg. 3562
SCISYS DEUTSCHLAND GMBH—See CGI Inc.; *Int'l*, pg. 1434
SC SOFT AMERICAS LLC—See Aurionpro Solutions Limited; *Int'l*, pg. 711
SEARCH DISCOVERY, INC.; *U.S. Private*, pg. 3586
SECURELEMENT INFRASTRUCTURE SOLUTIONS LLC—See IT Solutions Consulting LLC; *U.S. Private*, pg. 2148
SECURITIES INDUSTRY AUTOMATION CORPORATION—See Intercontinental Exchange, Inc.; *U.S. Public*, pg. 1143
SECURITY COMPLIANCE ASSOCIATES LLC; *U.S. Private*, pg. 3595
SEDAO LIMITED—See Boxlight Corporation; *U.S. Public*, pg. 377
SEGMENT.IO, INC.—See Twilio Inc.; *U.S. Public*, pg. 2206
SEMANTICBITS, LLC—See ICF International, Inc.; *U.S. Public*, pg. 1086
SERVICEAIDE, INC.; *U.S. Private*, pg. 3616
SESMAT SRL—See FOS S.p.A.; *Int'l*, pg. 2748
SHANGHAI CHIPSEA INNOVATION TECHNOLOGY CO., LTD.—See Chipsea Technologies (Shenzhen) Corp.; *Int'l*, pg. 1573
SHARPTEXT LIMITED—See DCC plc; *Int'l*, pg. 1991
SHD AG—See COFRA Holding AG; *Int'l*, pg. 1693
SHMITT TECHNOLOGIES LLC—See Baymark Partners; *U.S. Private*, pg. 496
SIGMA ADACTUM AB—See Danir Resources AB; *Int'l*, pg. 1963
SIGMA CONSULTING SOLUTIONS LTD—See Danir Resources AB; *Int'l*, pg. 1963
SIGMA EMPROVE AB—See Danir Resources AB; *Int'l*, pg. 1963
SIGMA IMAL PROJEKTLEDNING AB—See Danir Resources AB; *Int'l*, pg. 1963
SIGMA MAXIFLEX OY—See Danir Resources AB; *Int'l*, pg. 1963
SIGMA SOLUTIONS AB—See Danir Resources AB; *Int'l*, pg. 1963
SIGMA TECHNOLOGY HUNGARY LTD.—See Danir Resources AB; *Int'l*, pg. 1963
SILITHERM IMMOBILIARE S.R.L.—See BizLink Holding Inc.; *Int'l*, pg. 1053
SILVERRAIL TECHNOLOGIES, INC.—See Expedia Group, Inc.; *U.S. Public*, pg. 810
SILVERRAIL TECHNOLOGIES UK LIMITED—See Expedia Group, Inc.; *U.S. Public*, pg. 810
SINCERUS B.V.—See Dustin Group AB; *Int'l*, pg. 2235
SIRONAHEALTH, INC.—See Great Point Partners, LLC; *U.S. Private*, pg. 1767
SITEWORX, INC.; *U.S. Private*, pg. 3676

N.A.I.C.S. INDEX

541519 — OTHER COMPUTER RELA...

SMART DCC LIMITED—See Capita plc; *Int'l*, pg. 1309
SMART TECHNICS NV—See Colruyt Group N.V.; *Int'l*, pg. 1705
SMOKESCREEN TECHNOLOGIES PRIVATE LIMITED—See Zscaler, Inc.; *U.S. Public*, pg. 2411
SOFTWARE AG BELGIUM S.A.—See Silver Lake Group, LLC; *U.S. Private*, pg. 3659
SOFTWARE AG (ISRAEL) LTD—See Silver Lake Group, LLC; *U.S. Private*, pg. 3659
SOFTWARE GMBH OSTERREICH—See Silver Lake Group, LLC; *U.S. Private*, pg. 3660
SOFTWINK, INC.—See Worklyn Partners; *U.S. Private*, pg. 4564
SOGETI USA LLC—See Capgemini SE; *Int'l*, pg. 1307
SOGETI USA LLC—See Capgemini SE; *Int'l*, pg. 1307
SOGO JIMU SERVICE CO., LTD.—See Honda Motor Co., Ltd.; *Int'l*, pg. 3464
SOKIGO AB—See Addnode Group AB; *Int'l*, pg. 130
SOLARWINDS, INC.—See Silver Lake Group, LLC; *U.S. Private*, pg. 3661
SOLARWINDS, INC.—See Thoma Bravo, L.P.; *U.S. Private*, pg. 4153
SOLID CACTUS INC.—See Siris Capital Group, LLC; *U.S. Private*, pg. 3675
SOLIUM CAPITAL UK LIMITED—See Morgan Stanley; *U.S. Public*, pg. 1475
SOLMAC INC.; *U.S. Private*, pg. 3709
SOLSTICE MOBILE; *U.S. Private*, pg. 3710
SPARKWARE TECHNOLOGIES SRL—See evoke plc; *Int'l*, pg. 2572
SPECIAL DOMAINS SERVICES, INC.—See KKR & Co. Inc.; *U.S. Public*, pg. 1252
SPECIAL DOMAINS SERVICES, INC.—See Silver Lake Group, LLC; *U.S. Private*, pg. 3657
SPECIAL DOMAINS SERVICES, INC.—See TCMI, Inc.; *U.S. Private*, pg. 3943
SPECTRUM TECHNOLOGY, INC.; *U.S. Private*, pg. 3753
SPINDUSTRY INTERACTIVE, INC.; *U.S. Private*, pg. 3757
SPINETEX AG—See BNP Paribas SA; *Int'l*, pg. 1089
SPINNAKER SUPPORT, LLC—See Spinnaker Management Group, LLC; *U.S. Private*, pg. 3757
SPIREON, INC.—See Greenbriar Equity Group, L.P.; *U.S. Private*, pg. 1776
SPIRE PAYMENTS LTD.—See KleinPartners Capital Corp.; *U.S. Private*, pg. 2319
SPRASIA, INC.—See Hakuten Corporation; *Int'l*, pg. 3222
SQLI AGENCY—See DBAY Advisors Limited; *Int'l*, pg. 1987
SQLI CONSEIL IT—See DBAY Advisors Limited; *Int'l*, pg. 1987
SQLI INSTITUT—See DBAY Advisors Limited; *Int'l*, pg. 1987
SQLI NEWBI—See DBAY Advisors Limited; *Int'l*, pg. 1987
STARBOARD IT PTY. LTD.—See ActivePort Group Limited; *Int'l*, pg. 120
STAR GROUP PVT. LTD.—See Atlantic China Welding Consumables, Inc.; *Int'l*, pg. 674
STG GROUP, INC.; *U.S. Public*, pg. 1948
STONEEAGLE F&I, INC.; *U.S. Private*, pg. 3828
STRADAVERSE SDN. BHD.—See Chin Hin Group Berhad; *Int'l*, pg. 1480
STREETACCOUNT LLC—See FactSet Research Systems Inc.; *U.S. Public*, pg. 820
STROZ FRIEDBERG, LLC—See Aon plc; *Int'l*, pg. 493
SUNESYS, LLC—See Quanta Services, Inc.; *U.S. Public*, pg. 1751
SUNGARD AVAILABILITY SERVICES (FRANCE) SA—See SunGard Availability Services Capital, Inc.; *U.S. Private*, pg. 3867
SUPERIOR DOCUMENT SERVICE INC.—See Pivotal Acquisition Corp.; *U.S. Private*, pg. 3192
SURF INVESTMENTS, LTD.—See E-Waste Systems, Inc.; *U.S. Private*, pg. 1303
SUTHERLAND GLOBAL SERVICES, INC.; *U.S. Private*, pg. 3886
SVAM INTERNATIONAL, INC.; *U.S. Private*, pg. 3888
SWEDELTACO AB—See DistIT AB; *Int'l*, pg. 2136
SWITCH IT SOLUTIONS B.V.—See Dustin Group AB; *Int'l*, pg. 2235
SYMETA HYBRID NV—See Colruyt Group N.V.; *Int'l*, pg. 1705
SYNECHRON INC.; *U.S. Private*, pg. 3903
SYNERGIS; *U.S. Private*, pg. 3903
SYNERGY COMPUTERS & COMMUNICATIONS LIMITED—See BoardWare Intelligence Technology Limited; *Int'l*, pg. 1094
SYNERGY CORE LLC; *U.S. Private*, pg. 3904
SYNOPSYS SOFTWARE SCIENCE AND TECHNOLOGY (SHANGHAI) CO., LTD.—See Synopsys, Inc.; *U.S. Public*, pg. 1971
SYNOPSYS TAIWAN CO., LTD.—See Synopsys, Inc.; *U.S. Public*, pg. 1971
SYSCO LABS TECHNOLOGIES (PRIVATE) LIMITED—See Sysco Corporation; *U.S. Public*, pg. 1976
SYSCOM (USA) INC.; *U.S. Private*, pg. 3905
SYSTEMS TECHNOLOGY GROUP, INC.; *U.S. Private*, pg. 3908
SYSTIME—See CMS Computers Ltd.; *Int'l*, pg. 1672
TAIWAN NEXSTGO LIMITED—See Alco Holdings Limited; *Int'l*, pg. 301

TALENTED IT INC.; *U.S. Private*, pg. 3926
TASK TECHNOLOGIES, INC.; *U.S. Private*, pg. 3935
TC3 HEALTH, INC.—See McKesson Corporation; *U.S. Public*, pg. 1407
TCS, INC.—See L3Harris Technologies, Inc.; *U.S. Public*, pg. 1284
TCT COMPUTING GROUP, INC.—See 10Pearls LLC; *U.S. Private*, pg. 2
TD SYNNEX CORP; *U.S. Public*, pg. 1983
TEALIUM INC.; *U.S. Private*, pg. 3948
TEAM SOFTWARE, INC.—See Accel Partners L.P.; *U.S. Private*, pg. 49
TEAM SOFTWARE, INC.—See KKR & Co. Inc.; *U.S. Public*, pg. 1238
TECCWEB INC.—See Alan Allman Associates SA; *Int'l*, pg. 290
TECH DATA AS CZECH S.R.O.—See TD Synnex Corp; *U.S. Public*, pg. 1985
TECH DATA LATIN AMERICA, INC.—See TD Synnex Corp; *U.S. Public*, pg. 1986
TECHGEN CONSULTING, INC.—See Teal; *U.S. Private*, pg. 3948
TECH IMPACT; *U.S. Private*, pg. 3951
TECHNIA AB—See Addnode Group AB; *Int'l*, pg. 131
TECHNIA AS—See Addnode Group AB; *Int'l*, pg. 131
TECHNIA PLM OY—See Addnode Group AB; *Int'l*, pg. 131
TECHNIGRAPHICS, INC—See CACI International Inc.; *U.S. Public*, pg. 418
TECNOLOGIA MARITIMA, S.A.—See Emera, Inc.; *Int'l*, pg. 2377
TEKNIK I MEDIA DATACENTER STOCKHOLM AB—See Addnode Group AB; *Int'l*, pg. 131
TELETRONICS TECHNOLOGY CORP.—See Curtiss-Wright Corporation; *U.S. Public*, pg. 612
TERAKEET, LLC; *U.S. Private*, pg. 3969
TESI DE MEXICO S.A. DE C.V.—See GPI S.p.A.; *Int'l*, pg. 3046
T&G SRL—See FOS S.p.A.; *Int'l*, pg. 2748
THERMOPYLAE SCIENCES + TECHNOLOGY—See Hexagon AB; *Int'l*, pg. 3369
THINK360 AI, INC.—See Computer Age Management Services Limited; *Int'l*, pg. 1759
THOMAS DURYEA LOGICALIS ASIA PACIFIC MSC SDN. BHD.—See Datatec Limited; *Int'l*, pg. 1981
TICKETFLY, LLC—See Eventbrite, Inc.; *U.S. Public*, pg. 799
TICKETSWEST.COM, INC.—See The RMR Group Inc.; *U.S. Public*, pg. 2126
TICOMIX, INC.; *U.S. Private*, pg. 4167
TIGERJET NETWORK, INC.—See B. Riley Financial, Inc.; *U.S. Public*, pg. 262
TIME ZONE MULTIMEDIA; *U.S. Private*, pg. 4172
TLDS, LLC—See Siris Capital Group, LLC; *U.S. Private*, pg. 3675
TOLEDO WEB SHOP; *U.S. Private*, pg. 4181
TRANSFORM-X, INC.; *U.S. Private*, pg. 4208
TRANSOURCE SERVICES CORP; *U.S. Private*, pg. 4210
TRAQIQ SOLUTIONS, PVT. LTD.—See TraQiQ, Inc.; *U.S. Public*, pg. 2185
TRILLIUM SOLUTIONS GROUP, INC.—See Element 78 LLC; *U.S. Private*, pg. 1357
TRIMECH SOLUTIONS, LLC—See Sentinel Capital Partners, L.L.C.; *U.S. Private*, pg. 3609
TRIPLAY, INC.; *U.S. Private*, pg. 4236
TRUEPATH TECHNOLOGIES, INC.—See Antin Infrastructure Partners SAS; *Int'l*, pg. 483
TRUSTE; *U.S. Private*, pg. 4251
TSG EDV-TERMINAL SERVICE GMBH—See Atos SE; *Int'l*, pg. 692
TSSLINK, INC.—See Avnet, Inc.; *U.S. Public*, pg. 254
TUCSON EMBEDDED SYSTEMS, INC.; *U.S. Private*, pg. 4256
UAB CGI LITHUANIA—See CGI Inc.; *Int'l*, pg. 1433
UMANIS S.A.—See CGI Inc.; *Int'l*, pg. 1434
UNICOM ENGINEERING, INC.—See UNICOM Global, Inc.; *U.S. Private*, pg. 4281
UNILOGIC B.V.—See Dustin Group AB; *Int'l*, pg. 2235
UNITED BIOSOURCE CORPORATION LLC—See Avista Capital Partners, L.P.; *U.S. Private*, pg. 409
UNITED BIOSOURCE (GERMANY) GMBH—See Avista Capital Partners, L.P.; *U.S. Private*, pg. 409
UNITED BIOSOURCE (SUISSE) SA—See Avista Capital Partners, L.P.; *U.S. Private*, pg. 409
UNITED PEOPLE POWER, INC.; *U.S. Private*, pg. 4295
UNITRENDS, INC.—See Insight Venture Management, LLC; *U.S. Private*, pg. 2091
UPSIGHT, INC.; *U.S. Private*, pg. 4312
URBANYS—See DBAY Advisors Limited; *Int'l*, pg. 1987
US-ANALYTICS SOLUTIONS GROUP, LLC; *U.S. Private*, pg. 4320
UTEST INC.; *U.S. Private*, pg. 4325
UXC BSG HOLDINGS PTY. LTD.—See DXC Technology Company; *U.S. Public*, pg. 695
VANGUARD VIDEO LLC—See Beamr Ltd.; *Int'l*, pg. 932
VCORE TECHNOLOGY PARTNERS LLC—See Berkshire Partners LLC; *U.S. Private*, pg. 534
VENNERSYS LTD.—See Christie Group plc; *Int'l*, pg. 1587
VENTURENET, INC.; *U.S. Private*, pg. 4358
VERACITY CONSULTING GROUP, LLC—See Resources Connection, Inc.; *U.S. Public*, pg. 1792
VERIFONE AFRICA (PTY) LTD—See British Columbia Investment Management Corp.; *Int'l*, pg. 1170
VERIFONE AFRICA (PTY) LTD—See Francisco Partners Management, LP; *U.S. Private*, pg. 1592
VERIFONE DENMARK A/S—See British Columbia Investment Management Corp.; *Int'l*, pg. 1170
VERIFONE DENMARK A/S—See Francisco Partners Management, LP; *U.S. Private*, pg. 1592
VERIFONE FINLAND OY—See British Columbia Investment Management Corp.; *Int'l*, pg. 1170
VERIFONE FINLAND OY—See Francisco Partners Management, LP; *U.S. Private*, pg. 1592
VERIFONE ITALIA S.R.L.—See British Columbia Investment Management Corp.; *Int'l*, pg. 1170
VERIFONE ITALIA S.R.L.—See Francisco Partners Management, LP; *U.S. Private*, pg. 1592
VERIFONE SINGAPORE PTE. LTD.—See British Columbia Investment Management Corp.; *Int'l*, pg. 1170
VERIFONE SINGAPORE PTE. LTD.—See Francisco Partners Management, LP; *U.S. Private*, pg. 1592
VERIFONE SYSTEMS SPAIN SLU—See British Columbia Investment Management Corp.; *Int'l*, pg. 1170
VERIFONE SYSTEMS SPAIN SLU—See Francisco Partners Management, LP; *U.S. Private*, pg. 1593
VERISYS CORP.—See Cressey & Company, LP; *U.S. Private*, pg. 1095
VERISYS CORP.—See Spectrum Equity Investors, L.P.; *U.S. Private*, pg. 3752
VERITEC, INC.; *U.S. Public*, pg. 2283
VERITRANS INC.—See Digital Garage, Inc.; *Int'l*, pg. 2122
VIGET LABS LLC; *U.S. Private*, pg. 4381
VIGILANZ CORPORATION—See Inovalon Holdings, Inc.; *U.S. Public*, pg. 1128
VINCERE GROUP B.V.—See Dustin Group AB; *Int'l*, pg. 2235
VINX VIETNAM CO.,LTD.—See FUJISOFT INCORPORATED; *Int'l*, pg. 2830
VIRIDITY ENERGY, INC.—See Ormat Technologies, Inc.; *U.S. Public*, pg. 1618
VIRTUAL HOLD TECHNOLOGY, LLC—See Thoma Bravo, L.P.; *U.S. Private*, pg. 4149
VIRTUSA CONSULTING SERVICES PRIVATE LIMITED—See EQT AB; *Int'l*, pg. 2472
VIRTUSA MIDDLE EAST FZ LLC—See EQT AB; *Int'l*, pg. 2472
VIRTUSA (PRIVATE) LIMITED—See EQT AB; *Int'l*, pg. 2472
VIRTUSA UK LIMITED—See EQT AB; *Int'l*, pg. 2472
VISIONARY INTEGRATION PROFESSIONALS; *U.S. Private*, pg. 4392
VISION TECHNOLOGIES, INC.; *U.S. Private*, pg. 4391
VITAL PATH, INC.—See Xybion Corporation; *U.S. Private*, pg. 4583
VITIL SOLUTIONS; *U.S. Private*, pg. 4405
VIXIMO, INC.—See Pocket Games, Inc.; *U.S. Private*, pg. 3219
VIZCONNECT, INC.; *U.S. Private*, pg. 4406
VMWARE BELGIUM—See Broadcom Inc.; *U.S. Public*, pg. 390
VMWARE KOREA CO., LTD.—See Broadcom Inc.; *U.S. Public*, pg. 391
VOICE PROVIDER SWEDEN AB—See Addnode Group AB; *Int'l*, pg. 131
VORTAL COMERCIO ELECTRONICO, CONSULTADORIAE MULTIMEDIA, S.A.—See Byggfakta Group Nordic HoldCo LP; *Int'l*, pg. 1235
WEBCOLLAGE, INC.—See Apax Partners LLP; *Int'l*, pg. 501
WEB.COM CANADA, INC.—See Siris Capital Group, LLC; *U.S. Private*, pg. 3675
WEB.COM GROUP, INC.—See Siris Capital Group, LLC; *U.S. Private*, pg. 3675
WEB.COM HOLDING COMPANY, INC.—See Siris Capital Group, LLC; *U.S. Private*, pg. 3675
WEBEX COMMUNICATIONS DEUTSCHLAND GMBH—See Cisco Systems, Inc.; *U.S. Public*, pg. 501
WEBEX COMMUNICATIONS FRANCE SARL—See Cisco Systems, Inc.; *U.S. Public*, pg. 501
WEBEXONE—See Cisco Systems, Inc.; *U.S. Public*, pg. 501
WEBHOUSE, INC.; *U.S. Private*, pg. 4466
WEBLOYALTY.COM—See Tenerity, Inc.; *U.S. Private*, pg. 3966
WEBOLUTIONS, INC.; *U.S. Private*, pg. 4466
WEBSTARTS; *U.S. Private*, pg. 4466
WESTCON AFRICA ANGOLA LIMITED—See Datatec Limited; *Int'l*, pg. 1981
WESTCON AFRICA DISTRIBUTION (NIGERIA) LIMITED—See Datatec Limited; *Int'l*, pg. 1981
WESTCON AFRICA (KENYA) LIMITED—See Datatec Limited; *Int'l*, pg. 1981
WESTCON AFRICA (MAURITIUS) LIMITED—See Datatec Limited; *Int'l*, pg. 1981
WESTCON AFRICA (MOROCCO) SARL—See Datatec Limited; *Int'l*, pg. 1981
WESTCON DENMARK APS—See Datatec Limited; *Int'l*, pg. 1981
WESTCON GROUP AUSTRIA GMBH—See Datatec Limited; *Int'l*, pg. 1981

541519 — OTHER COMPUTER RELA...

WESTCON GROUP GERMANY GMBH—See Datatec Limited; *Int'l*, pg. 1981
WESTCON GROUP ITALIA S.R.L.—See Datatec Limited; *Int'l*, pg. 1981
WESTCON GROUP POLAND SP. Z.O.O.—See Datatec Limited; *Int'l*, pg. 1981
WESTCON GROUP PORTUGAL, SOCIEDADE UNIPESSOAL, LIMITADA—See Datatec Limited; *Int'l*, pg. 1981
WESTCON GROUP PTE. LIMITED—See Datatec Limited; *Int'l*, pg. 1981
WESTCON GROUP (THAILAND) CO. LIMITED—See Datatec Limited; *Int'l*, pg. 1981
WESTCON GROUP (VIETNAM) CO. LIMITED—See Datatec Limited; *Int'l*, pg. 1981
WESTCON INTERNATIONAL, LIMITED—See Datatec Limited; *Int'l*, pg. 1981
WESTCON LLC—See Datatec Limited; *Int'l*, pg. 1981
WESTCON SOLUTIONS (HK) LIMITED—See Datatec Limited; *Int'l*, pg. 1981
WESTCON SOLUTIONS (M) SDN. BHD.—See Datatec Limited; *Int'l*, pg. 1981
WESTCON SOLUTIONS PHILIPPINES, INC.—See Datatec Limited; *Int'l*, pg. 1981
WESTERN COMPUTER, LLC—See Alpine Investors; *U.S. Private*, pg. 201
WGEO SWITZERLAND GMBH—See Datatec Limited; *Int'l*, pg. 1981
WHEEL, INC.—See Digital Garage, Inc.; *Int'l*, pg. 2122
WILD WEST DOMAINS, INC.—See KKR & Co. Inc.; *U.S. Public*, pg. 1252
WILD WEST DOMAINS, INC.—See Silver Lake Group, LLC; *U.S. Private*, pg. 3657
WILD WEST DOMAINS, INC.—See TCMI, Inc.; *U.S. Private*, pg. 3943
WINKING TECHNOLOGY CO., LTD.—See Advanced Analog Technology, Inc.; *Int'l*, pg. 157
WINTELLECT LLC—See Atmosera, Inc.; *U.S. Private*, pg. 381
WINTERHAWK CONSULTING LLC—See PentaFour Solutions, LLC; *U.S. Private*, pg. 3139
WURL, INC.—See AppLovin Corp.; *U.S. Public*, pg. 173
XCELLENT AUTOMATISERING B.V.—See Dustin Group AB; *Int'l*, pg. 2235
XING INTERNATIONAL HOLDING GMBH—See Hubert Burda Media Holding Kommanditgesellschaft; *Int'l*, pg. 3520
YEO & YEO COMPUTER CONSULTING, LLC—See Yeo & Yeo, P.C.; *U.S. Private*, pg. 4588
ZHONG'AN XIAOXULONG ELECTRONIC TECHNOLOGY CO., LTD.—See China Security Co., Ltd.; *Int'l*, pg. 1550
ZINGLE BY ENFO AB—See Enfo Oyj; *Int'l*, pg. 2425
ZINOPY LIMITED—See BC Partners LLP; *Int'l*, pg. 925
ZIVARO, INC.—See AG Acquisition Group, Inc.; *U.S. Private*, pg. 124
ZONES CANADA, INC.—See Zones, Inc.; *U.S. Private*, pg. 4608
ZONES EUROPE, INC.—See Zones, Inc.; *U.S. Private*, pg. 4608
ZONES, INC.; *U.S. Private*, pg. 4608
ZR SYSTEMS GROUP LLC—See Evocative, Inc.; *U.S. Private*, pg. 1442
ZSCALER, INC.; *U.S. Public*, pg. 2411
ZVELO, INC.; *U.S. Private*, pg. 4610

541611 — ADMINISTRATIVE MANAGEMENT AND GENERAL MANAGEMENT CONSULTING SERVICES

13I CAPITAL CORPORATION; *U.S. Private*, pg. 3
24/7 CUSTOMER INC.; *U.S. Private*, pg. 6
24/7 CUSTOMER PHILIPPINES INC.—See 24/7 Customer Inc.; *U.S. Private*, pg. 6
24/7 CUSTOMER PVT. LTD.—See 24/7 Customer Inc.; *U.S. Private*, pg. 6
3C CONSULTANTS LTD.—See Aquila Services Group PLC; *Int'l*, pg. 528
3M FINANCIAL MANAGEMENT COMPANY—See 3M Company; *U.S. Public*, pg. 6
3S/TRACERE—See Cegedim S.A.; *Int'l*, pg. 1390
7IM INVESTMENT & RETIREMENT SOLUTIONS LTD.—See Caledonia Investments plc; *Int'l*, pg. 1262
9GAUGE PARTNERS, LLC—See Element 78 LLC; *U.S. Private*, pg. 1357
9G PRODUCTS, INC.—See Compass Diversified Holdings, *U.S. Public*, pg. 559
A2Z INFRASERVICES PRIVATE LIMITED—See A2Z Infra Engineering Limited; *Int'l*, pg. 30
A3A STRATEGY CONSULTING GMBH—See adesso SE; *Int'l*, pg. 144
AALLON GROUP OY; *Int'l*, pg. 36
AAREAL-FINANCIAL SERVICE, SPOL. S R.O.—See Advent International Corporation; *U.S. Private*, pg. 96
AAREAL-FINANCIAL SERVICE, SPOL. S R.O.—See Centerbridge Partners, L.P.; *U.S. Private*, pg. 812
AASGARD SUMMIT MANAGEMENT SERVICES INC.—See Lovell Minnick Partners LLC; *U.S. Private*, pg. 2502
AAVAS FINANCIERS LTD.; *Int'l*, pg. 38

ABACUS TECHNOLOGY CORP.; *U.S. Private*, pg. 34
ABA STEPHENSON & BROOK—See Anchin, Block & Anchin LLP; *U.S. Private*, pg. 272
ABBOTT FINANCE B.V.—See Abbott Laboratories; *U.S. Public*, pg. 14
ABBOTT LOGISTICS B.V.—See Abbott Laboratories; *U.S. Public*, pg. 14
ABERDEEN STANDARD EUROPEAN LOGISTICS INCOME PLC; *Int'l*, pg. 60
ABHISHEK INTEGRATIONS LIMITED; *Int'l*, pg. 61
ABSENCE.IO GMBH—See Grupa Pracuj S.A.; *Int'l*, pg. 3117
AB TRACTION—See Duroc AB; *Int'l*, pg. 2229
ABV CONSULTING, INC.; *Int'l*, pg. 74
ACAL MANAGEMENT SERVICES LTD.—See discoverIE Group plc; *Int'l*, pg. 2133
ACANDO AB; *Int'l*, pg. 77
ACANDO AS—See Acando AB; *Int'l*, pg. 77
ACANDO BUSINESS INTELLIGENCE AB—See Acando AB; *Int'l*, pg. 77
ACANDO CONSULTING AB—See Acando AB; *Int'l*, pg. 77
ACANDO DENMARK A/S—See Acando AB; *Int'l*, pg. 78
ACANDO INCENTIVE AB—See Acando AB; *Int'l*, pg. 78
ACANDO LTD—See Acando AB; *Int'l*, pg. 78
ACANDO MANAGEMENT CONSULTING AB—See Acando AB; *Int'l*, pg. 78
ACANDO SVERIGE AB—See Acando AB; *Int'l*, pg. 78
ACCENTURE C.A.—See Accenture plc; *Int'l*, pg. 82
ACCENTURE CENTRAL EUROPE B.V.—See Accenture plc; *Int'l*, pg. 83
ACCENTURE (CHINA) CO., LTD.—See Accenture plc; *Int'l*, pg. 82
ACCENTURE CONSULTORES DE GESTAO S.A.—See Accenture plc; *Int'l*, pg. 83
ACCENTURE DANISMANLIK LIMITED SIRKETI—See Accenture plc; *Int'l*, pg. 83
ACCENTURE GMBH—See Accenture plc; *Int'l*, pg. 83
ACCENTURE INC.—See Accenture plc; *Int'l*, pg. 83
ACCENTURE INC.—See Accenture plc; *Int'l*, pg. 83
ACCENTURE, INC.—See Accenture plc; *Int'l*, pg. 85
ACCENTURE SERVICE CENTER SRL—See Accenture plc; *Int'l*, pg. 84
ACCENTURE SERVICES (MAURITIUS) LTD.—See Accenture plc; *Int'l*, pg. 84
ACCENTURE SERVICES S.R.L.—See Accenture plc; *Int'l*, pg. 84
ACCENTURE SOLUTIONS SDN BHD—See Accenture plc; *Int'l*, pg. 84
ACCENTURE TECHNOLOGY SOLUTIONS LTD.—See Accenture plc; *Int'l*, pg. 84
ACCENTURE TECHNOLOGY SOLUTIONS PTY LTD.—See Accenture plc; *Int'l*, pg. 84
ACCENTURE TECHNOLOGY SOLUTIONS SAS—See Accenture plc; *Int'l*, pg. 84
ACCENTURE TECHNOLOGY SOLUTIONS S.C.—See Accenture plc; *Int'l*, pg. 84
ACCENTURE TECHNOLOGY SOLUTIONS S.R.O.—See Accenture plc; *Int'l*, pg. 85
ACCENTURE TECHNOLOGY VENTURES BV—See Accenture plc; *Int'l*, pg. 85
ACCENTURE (UK) LTD.—See Accenture plc; *Int'l*, pg. 82
ACHILLES DEVELOPMENT SERVICES AS—See Bridgepoint Group Plc; *Int'l*, pg. 1153
ACHILLES DO BRASIL LTDA.—See Bridgepoint Group Plc; *Int'l*, pg. 1154
ACHILLES FIRST POINT ASSESSMENT LIMITED—See Bridgepoint Group Plc; *Int'l*, pg. 1153
ACHILLES INFORMATION APS—See Bridgepoint Group Plc; *Int'l*, pg. 1153
ACHILLES INFORMATION (AUSTRALIA) PTY LTD—See Bridgepoint Group Plc; *Int'l*, pg. 1153
ACHILLES INFORMATION CENTRE AS—See Bridgepoint Group Plc; *Int'l*, pg. 1153
ACHILLES INFORMATION GMBH—See Bridgepoint Group Plc; *Int'l*, pg. 1153
ACHILLES INFORMATION HONG KONG LTD—See Bridgepoint Group Plc; *Int'l*, pg. 1153
ACHILLES INFORMATION INC—See Bridgepoint Group Plc; *Int'l*, pg. 1153
ACHILLES INFORMATION (INDIA) PRIVATE LIMITED—See Bridgepoint Group Plc; *Int'l*, pg. 1153
ACHILLES INFORMATION LIMITED—See Bridgepoint Group Plc; *Int'l*, pg. 1153
ACHILLES INFORMATION LIMITED—See Bridgepoint Group Plc; *Int'l*, pg. 1153
ACHILLES INFORMATION SLOVAKIA S.R.O.—See Bridgepoint Group Plc; *Int'l*, pg. 1153
ACHILLES PROCUREMENT SERVICES LIMITED—See Bridgepoint Group Plc; *Int'l*, pg. 1153
ACHILLES SOUTH EUROPE, S.L.U.—See Bridgepoint Group Plc; *Int'l*, pg. 1154
ACHILLES SOUTH EUROPE S.L.U.—See Bridgepoint Group Plc; *Int'l*, pg. 1154
ACHILLES SOUTH EUROPE S.L.U.—See Bridgepoint Group Plc; *Int'l*, pg. 1154
ACHILLEVS INFORMATION AB—See Bridgepoint Group Plc; *Int'l*, pg. 1154
ACME RESOURCES LIMITED; *Int'l*, pg. 107
ACQUIS CONSULTING GROUP, LLC; *U.S. Private*, pg. 65

ACS SOLUTIONS POLAND SP. Z.O.O.—See Conduent Incorporated; *U.S. Public*, pg. 566
ACTIMO APS—See The Goldman Sachs Group, Inc.; *U.S. Public*, pg. 2082
ACTIVE INTERNATIONAL AUSTRALIA PTY LTD.—See Active Media Services, Inc.; *U.S. Private*, pg. 69
ACTIVE INTERNATIONAL DO BRASIL S.A.—See Active Media Services, Inc.; *U.S. Private*, pg. 69
ACTIVE INTERNATIONAL (EUROPE) S.A.R.L.—See Active Media Services, Inc.; *U.S. Private*, pg. 69
ACTIVE INTERNATIONAL GMBH—See Active Media Services, Inc.; *U.S. Private*, pg. 69
ACTIVE INTERNATIONAL LTD.—See Active Media Services, Inc.; *U.S. Private*, pg. 69
ACTIVE INTERNATIONAL (MEXICO) S.A. DE C.V.—See Active Media Services, Inc.; *U.S. Private*, pg. 69
ACTIVE INTERNATIONAL NORTHERN EUROPE—See Active Media Services, Inc.; *U.S. Private*, pg. 69
ACTIVE MEDIA SERVICES CANADA, INC.—See Active Media Services, Inc.; *U.S. Private*, pg. 69
ACTIVE MEDIA SERVICES- CENTRAL EUROPE GROUP—See Active Media Services, Inc.; *U.S. Private*, pg. 69
ACTIVE MEDIA SERVICES, INC.; *U.S. Private*, pg. 69
ACTS 29 CONSULTING, LLC—See CMTA Inc.; *U.S. Private*, pg. 951
ACUMEN BUILDING ENTERPRISE, INC.; *U.S. Private*, pg. 71
ACUMEN, LLC—See Alpine Investors; *U.S. Private*, pg. 201
ADAMS KEEGAN, INC.; *U.S. Private*, pg. 74
ADCB ASSET MANAGEMENT LIMITED—See Abu Dhabi Commercial Bank PJSC; *Int'l*, pg. 70
ADD ONE GMBH & CO. KG—See Deutsche Bank Aktiengesellschaft; *Int'l*, pg. 2055
ADECCO COORDINATION CENTER NV—See Adecco Group AG; *Int'l*, pg. 136
ADEPTRA LIMITED—See Fair Isaac Corporation; *U.S. Public*, pg. 820
ADESSO ORANGE AG—See adesso SE; *Int'l*, pg. 144
ADIUV INVESTMENTS SA; *Int'l*, pg. 150
ADMINISTRADORA DE FONDOS DE PENSIONES ARGENTUM S.A.—See Principal Financial Group, Inc.; *U.S. Public*, pg. 1720
ADMINISTRADORA PICSA, S.A. DE C.V.—See Desarrolladora Homex, S.A. de C.V.; *Int'l*, pg. 2043
ADO PROFESSIONAL SOLUTIONS, INC.—See Adecco Group AG; *Int'l*, pg. 136
ADP DEALER SERVICES ITALIA S.R.L.—See Automatic Data Processing, Inc.; *U.S. Public*, pg. 229
ADP GSI ITALIA SPA—See Automatic Data Processing, Inc.; *U.S. Public*, pg. 230
ADP TOTALSOURCE—See Automatic Data Processing, Inc.; *U.S. Public*, pg. 230
ADS VENTURES, INC.; *U.S. Private*, pg. 82
ADVANCE AMERICA, CASH ADVANCE CENTERS OF SOUTH CAROLINA, INC.—See Grupo Salinas, S.A. de C.V.; *Int'l*, pg. 3135
ADVANCED PLANNING SERVICES, INC.; *U.S. Private*, pg. 92
ADVANCED RELIABILITY TECHNOLOGIES, LLC—See PinnacleART International, LLC; *U.S. Private*, pg. 3186
ADVANCED WORKPLACE STRATEGIES, INC.; *U.S. Private*, pg. 93
ADVANSIA AS—See AFRY AB; *Int'l*, pg. 194
ADVANTAGE LOGISTICS - SOUTHWEST—See United Natural Foods, Inc.; *U.S. Public*, pg. 2231
ADVANTAGE L.P.; *U.S. Private*, pg. 94
ADVANTAGE SALES & MARKETING, LLC; *U.S. Private*, pg. 95
THE ADVISORY BOARD COMPANY—See UnitedHealth Group Incorporated; *U.S. Public*, pg. 2248
ADVISORYCLOUD, INC.; *U.S. Private*, pg. 110
ADVOCAT FINANCE, INC.—See Diversicare Healthcare Services, Inc.; *U.S. Public*, pg. 669
AEGIS BPO SERVICES AUSTRALIA HOLDINGS PTY. LTD.—See StarTek, Inc.; *U.S. Private*, pg. 3788
AEGIS PERU S.A.C—See StarTek, Inc.; *U.S. Private*, pg. 3788
AEGIS SERVICES LANKA PRIVATE LIMITED—See StarTek, Inc.; *U.S. Private*, pg. 3788
AEONX DIGITAL SOLUTIONS PRIVATE LIMITED—See ASHOK ALCO CHEM LIMITED; *Int'l*, pg. 608
AEQUITAS CAPITAL MANAGEMENT; *U.S. Private*, pg. 117
AEROPLAN CANADA INC—See Aimia Inc.; *Int'l*, pg. 233
AES MERIDA OPERACIONES SRL DE CV—See The AES Corporation; *U.S. Public*, pg. 2031
AETNA MEDICAID ADMINISTRATORS LLC—See CVS Health Corporation; *U.S. Public*, pg. 614
AF CONSULT DO BRASIL LTDA.—See AFRY AB; *Int'l*, pg. 193
AFFECTO POLAND SP.Z. O.O.—See CGI Inc.; *Int'l*, pg. 1433
AFFIRMATIVE INVESTMENT MANAGEMENT PARTNERS LTD.—See MetLife, Inc.; *U.S. Public*, pg. 1429
AFFLUENT INSIGHTS; *U.S. Private*, pg. 123
AFORTI HOLDING SA; *Int'l*, pg. 189
AFS IT SERVICES ESTONIA OU—See Bertelsmann SE & Co. KGaA; *Int'l*, pg. 989

N.A.I.C.S. INDEX 541611 — ADMINISTRATIVE MANA...

AGKNOWLEDGE, LLC—See KCoe Isom, LLP; *U.S. Private*, pg. 2270
AGREEYA SOLUTIONS LLC; *U.S. Private*, pg. 129
AHEADCOM BETEILIGUNGS-GMBH—See Deutsche Bank Aktiengesellschaft; *Int'l*, pg. 2055
AIB INTERNATIONAL CONSULTANTS LTD.—See AIB Group plc; *Int'l*, pg. 228
AIB-VINCOTTE BELGIUM VZW; *Int'l*, pg. 228
AIG MANAGEMENT FRANCE S.A.—See American International Group, Inc.; *U.S. Public*, pg. 104
AIMCO EQUITY SERVICES, LLC—See Apartment Investment and Management Company; *U.S. Private*, pg. 143
AIR MILES MIDDLE EAST—See Aimia Inc.; *Int'l*, pg. 233
AJN RESOURCES, INC.; *Int'l*, pg. 258
ALADDIN BLOCKCHAIN TECHNOLOGIES; *Int'l*, pg. 289
ALAM HZEM SDN. BHD.—See Hitachi Zosen Corporation; *Int'l*, pg. 3410
ALARIC COMPLIANCE SERVICES LLC—See Genstar Capital, LLC; *U.S. Private*, pg. 1677
ALARIS GROUP, INC.—See Summit Partners, L.P.; *U.S. Private*, pg. 3856
ALBION STAFFING SOLUTIONS INC.—See Hoosier Investment LLC; *U.S. Private*, pg. 1978
ALCION GROUP—See Insight Venture Management, LLC; *U.S. Private*, pg. 2091
ALEXANDRIA TRUST CORPORATION—See Guardian Capital Group Limited; *Int'l*, pg. 3169
ALGOE; *Int'l*, pg. 318
ALIBABA.COM, INC.—See Alibaba Group Holding Limited; *Int'l*, pg. 326
ALIGHT SOLUTIONS LLC—See Alight, Inc.; *U.S. Public*, pg. 76
ALJAZIRA CAPITAL COMPANY—See Bank Aljazira; *Int'l*, pg. 837
ALLIANT STAFFING, LLC—See McLarty Capital Partners UK LLP; *U.S. Private*, pg. 2640
ALLIED ENERGY CORPORATION—See CAMAC International Corporation; *U.S. Private*, pg. 725
ALLIED TECHNOLOGIES HOLDINGS PTE. LTD.—See Allied Technologies Ltd.; *Int'l*, pg. 358
ALLSTATE CORPORATE SERVICES CORP.—See Apax Partners LLP; *Int'l*, pg. 503
ALLWORLD PROJECT MANAGEMENT, LLC; *U.S. Private*, pg. 194
ALLWORTH FINANCIAL GROUP LP—See Lightyear Capital LLC; *U.S. Private*, pg. 2454
ALLWORTH FINANCIAL HOLDINGS, LLC—See Lightyear Capital LLC; *U.S. Private*, pg. 2454
ALLWORTH FINANCIAL, LP—See Lightyear Capital LLC; *U.S. Private*, pg. 2454
ALPHA CARD S.C.R.L./C.V.B.A.—See American Express Company; *U.S. Public*, pg. 100
ALPHA GROWTH MANAGEMENT INC.—See Alpha Growth PLC; *Int'l*, pg. 368
ALPHA GROWTH PLC; *Int'l*, pg. 368
ALPIQ MANAGEMENT LTD.—See Alpiq Holding AG; *Int'l*, pg. 373
ALPIQ PRODUCTION FRANCE MANAGEMENT S.A.S.—See Alpiq Holding AG; *Int'l*, pg. 372
ALP LIQUIDATING TRUST; *U.S. Private*, pg. 196
ALP MANAGEMENT CORP.—See ALP Industries, Inc.; *U.S. Private*, pg. 196
ALTIMETER GROUP, LLC—See Prophet Brand Strategy, Inc.; *U.S. Private*, pg. 3285
ALTODIGITAL NETWORKS LIMITED—See Xerox Holdings Corporation; *U.S. Public*, pg. 2386
ALTRAN B.V.—See Capgemini SE; *Int'l*, pg. 1304
ALTRAN ITALIA S.P.A.—See Capgemini SE; *Int'l*, pg. 1304
ALUBAR A/S—See ManpowerGroup Inc.; *U.S. Public*, pg. 1360
ALVAREZ & MARSAL BUSINESS CONSULTING, LLC—See Alvarez & Marsal, Inc.; *U.S. Private*, pg. 213
ALVAREZ & MARSAL HEALTHCARE INDUSTRY GROUP, LLC—See Alvarez & Marsal, Inc.; *U.S. Private*, pg. 213
ALVAREZ & MARSAL PUBLIC SECTOR SERVICES, LLC—See Alvarez & Marsal, Inc.; *U.S. Private*, pg. 213
AMADEUS HOSPITALITY UK LIMITED—See Amadeus IT Group, S.A.; *Int'l*, pg. 405
AMAN COTTON FIBROUS LIMITED; *Int'l*, pg. 409
AMANRESORTS INTERNATIONAL PRIVATE LIMITED—See DLF Limited; *Int'l*, pg. 2141
AMDEX CORPORATION; *U.S. Private*, pg. 218
AMERICAN CANNABIS COMPANY, INC.; *U.S. Public*, pg. 98
AMERICAN HEALTH HOLDING INC.—See CVS Health Corporation; *U.S. Public*, pg. 615
AMERICAN POOL ENTERPRISES INC.—See FirstService Corporation; *Int'l*, pg. 2690
AMERICAN RENAISSANCE CAPITAL, INC.; *U.S. Private*, pg. 245
AMERICAN SEAFOODS COMPANY—See American Seafoods, LP; *U.S. Private*, pg. 246
AMIND SOLUTIONS, LLC.—See Trinity Hunt Management, L.P.; *U.S. Private*, pg. 4234
AMPRO INC.; *U.S. Private*, pg. 266
ANALIZY ONLINE S.A; *Int'l*, pg. 446
ANALYSIS GROUP, INC.; *U.S. Private*, pg. 271

ANALYSIS-ONE—See Financial Index Australia Pty Ltd.; *Int'l*, pg. 2665
ANALYSYS MASON PTE LIMITED—See Datatec Limited; *Int'l*, pg. 1980
ANALYSYS MASON VENTURES FUND NORDIC 1 AS—See Datatec Limited; *Int'l*, pg. 1980
ANALYTICAL WIZARDS, INC.—See Definitive Healthcare Corp.; *U.S. Public*, pg. 2665
ANDERSCH AG—See FTI Consulting, Inc.; *U.S. Public*, pg. 890
ANDERSON PERFORMANCE IMPROVEMENT COMPANY, INC.—See Business Impact Group LLC; *U.S. Private*, pg. 694
ANDLINGER & COMPANY CVBA—See Andlinger & Company, Inc.; *U.S. Private*, pg. 278
ANDY BUSINESS CONGLOMERATE, USA; *U.S. Private*, pg. 281
ANGELOU ECONOMIC ADVISORS INC.; *U.S. Private*, pg. 282
ANGELOU ECONOMIC ADVISORS INC.—See Angelou Economic Advisors Inc.; *U.S. Private*, pg. 282
ANGLE PLC; *Int'l*, pg. 460
ANGLE TECHNOLOGY LIMITED—See ANGLE plc; *Int'l*, pg. 461
ANGLE TECHNOLOGY LLC—See ANGLE plc; *Int'l*, pg. 460
ANGLIN REICHMANN SNELLGROVE & ARMSTRONG, P.C.; *U.S. Private*, pg. 283
ANHEUSER-BUSCH COS., INC.—See Anheuser-Busch InBev SA/NV; *Int'l*, pg. 465
ANIMA ALTERNATIVE S.P.A.—See ANIMA Holding S.p.A.; *Int'l*, pg. 471
ANKURA CONSULTING GROUP, LLC; *U.S. Private*, pg. 284
ANNEX CONSULTING GROUP INC.—See Cornell Capital LLC; *U.S. Private*, pg. 1051
ANSER ADVISORY LLC—See Accenture plc; *Int'l*, pg. 86
ANTARES HOMES, LTD.—See Landsea Homes Corp.; *U.S. Public*, pg. 1292
ANY-G B.V.—See World Kinect Corporation; *U.S. Public*, pg. 2380
AOC SOLUTIONS, INC.; *U.S. Private*, pg. 289
AON CAPTIVE SERVICES GROUP—See Aon plc; *Int'l*, pg. 490
AON CONSULTING NEW ZEALAND LTD.—See Aon plc; *Int'l*, pg. 490
AON CONSULTING—See Aon plc; *Int'l*, pg. 490
AON CORPORATION AUSTRALIA—See Aon plc; *Int'l*, pg. 490
AON GLOBAL RISK CONSULTING AB—See Aon plc; *Int'l*, pg. 491
AON HEWITT GMBH—See Alight, Inc.; *U.S. Public*, pg. 76
AON HEWITT - MONTREAL—See Aon plc; *Int'l*, pg. 490
AON INVESTMENTS USA INC.—See Aon plc; *Int'l*, pg. 492
AON RISK SERVICES INC.—See Aon plc; *Int'l*, pg. 493
AON RISK SERVICES, JAPAN, LTD.—See Aon plc; *Int'l*, pg. 493
AOYAMA ZAISAN NETWORKS CO., LTD.; *Int'l*, pg. 499
APEX CREDIT SOLUTIONS INC.—See Chailease Holding Company Limited; *Int'l*, pg. 1436
APEX MEDICAL COMMUNICATIONS, INC.; *U.S. Private*, pg. 293
APPLEBEE'S SERVICES, INC.—See Dine Brands Global, Inc.; *U.S. Public*, pg. 667
APPLIED CLINICAL INTELLIGENCE, LLC—See Leonard Green & Partners, L.P.; *U.S. Private*, pg. 2429
APPLIED RESEARCH ASSOCIATES NORTH FLORIDA DIVISION—See Applied Research Associates, Inc.; *U.S. Private*, pg. 299
APPLUS II MEIO AMBIENTE PORTUGAL, LDA.—See I Squared Capital Advisors (US) LLC; *U.S. Private*, pg. 2021
APPLUS ITALY, S.R.L.—See I Squared Capital Advisors (US) LLC; *U.S. Private*, pg. 2021
APTITUDE SOFTWARE (CANADA) LIMITED—See Aptitude Software Group Plc; *Int'l*, pg. 523
APTO SOLUTIONS, INC.; *U.S. Private*, pg. 302
AQS MANAGEMENT SYSTEMS, INC.—See DEKRA e.V.; *Int'l*, pg. 2007
AQUENTA CONSULTING PTY LTD—See Jacobs Engineering Group, Inc.; *U.S. Public*, pg. 1183
AQUILA SERVICES GROUP PLC; *Int'l*, pg. 528
AQUILES CHILE SPA.—See Bridgepoint Group Plc; *Int'l*, pg. 1154
ARAB JORDAN INVESTMENT BANK (QATAR) L.L.C.—See Arab Jordan Investment Bank; *Int'l*, pg. 530
ARAMARK ENTERTAINMENT, LLC—See Aramark; *U.S. Public*, pg. 177
ARAMARK FACILITY SERVICES, LLC—See Aramark; *U.S. Public*, pg. 176
ARAMARK REFRESHMENT SERVICES OF TAMPA, LLC—See Aramark; *U.S. Public*, pg. 176
ARAVANIS INSOLVENCY PTY LTD—See FSA Group Limited; *Int'l*, pg. 2798
ARBELLA INSURANCE GROUP; *U.S. Private*, pg. 308
ARCHSTONE FINANCIAL SERVICES LLC—See AvalonBay Communities, Inc.; *U.S. Public*, pg. 240
ARENA GROUP LIMITED—See Xerox Holdings Corporation; *U.S. Public*, pg. 2386

ARETUM HOLDINGS, LLC—See Renovus Capital Partners; *U.S. Private*, pg. 3399
ARGENT FIDUCIARY CONSULTING SERVICES, LLC—See Argent Financial Group, Inc.; *U.S. Private*, pg. 320
ARGENTUM 47, INC.; *Int'l*, pg. 561
ARGONAUT MANAGEMENT SERVICES, INC.—See Brookfield Reinsurance Ltd.; *Int'l*, pg. 1194
ARGO TURBOSERVE CORPORATION; *U.S. Private*, pg. 320
ARIS SOLUTIONS INC.; *U.S. Private*, pg. 323
ARMA GLOBAL CORP.; *U.S. Private*, pg. 329
ARMED FORCES SERVICES CORPORATION—See Centene Corporation; *U.S. Public*, pg. 469
ARSENAL SECURITY GROUP, INC.; *U.S. Private*, pg. 339
ARTEX RISK SOLUTIONS, INC.—See Arthur J. Gallagher & Co.; *U.S. Public*, pg. 203
ARTHUR D. LITTLE AB—See Arthur D. Little SAS; *Int'l*, pg. 583
ARTHUR D. LITTLE AB—See Arthur D. Little SAS; *Int'l*, pg. 583
ARTHUR D. LITTLE ASIA PACIFIC LTD.—See Arthur D. Little SAS; *Int'l*, pg. 583
ARTHUR D. LITTLE ASIA PTD. LTD.—See Arthur D. Little SAS; *Int'l*, pg. 583
ARTHUR D. LITTLE AUSTRIA GMBH—See Arthur D. Little SAS; *Int'l*, pg. 583
ARTHUR D. LITTLE BENELUX S.A.—See Arthur D. Little SAS; *Int'l*, pg. 583
ARTHUR D. LITTLE GMBH—See Arthur D. Little SAS; *Int'l*, pg. 583
ARTHUR D. LITTLE GMBH—See Arthur D. Little SAS; *Int'l*, pg. 583
ARTHUR D. LITTLE, INC.—See Arthur D. Little SAS; *Int'l*, pg. 584
ARTHUR D. LITTLE JAPAN, INC.—See Arthur D. Little SAS; *Int'l*, pg. 583
ARTHUR D. LITTLE KOREA—See Arthur D. Little SAS; *Int'l*, pg. 583
ARTHUR D. LITTLE LIMITED—See Arthur D. Little SAS; *Int'l*, pg. 583
ARTHUR D. LITTLE MIDDLE EAST FZ LLC—See Arthur D. Little SAS; *Int'l*, pg. 583
ARTHUR D. LITTLE (M) SDN BHD—See Arthur D. Little SAS; *Int'l*, pg. 583
ARTHUR D. LITTLE SAS; *Int'l*, pg. 583
ARTHUR D. LITTLE SAUDI ARABIA—See Arthur D. Little SAS; *Int'l*, pg. 583
ARTHUR D. LITTLE (SCHWEIZ) AG—See Arthur D. Little SAS; *Int'l*, pg. 583
ARTHUR D. LITTLE S.L.—See Arthur D. Little SAS; *Int'l*, pg. 584
ARTHUR D. LITTLE—See Arthur D. Little SAS; *Int'l*, pg. 583
ARTHUR D. LITTLE—See Arthur D. Little SAS; *Int'l*, pg. 584
ARTHUR D. LITTLE S.P.A.—See Arthur D. Little SAS; *Int'l*, pg. 584
ARTHUR F. BELL, JR. & ASSOCIATES, LLC—See Cohen & Company; *U.S. Private*, pg. 962
ARTRA GROUP CORPORATION; *Int'l*, pg. 585
ARYA RESOURCES LTD.; *Int'l*, pg. 588
ASCENDANT COMPLIANCE MANAGEMENT; *U.S. Private*, pg. 346
ASCOLTA, LLC—See Management Science & Innovation LLC; *U.S. Private*, pg. 2561
ASCOM (FRANCE) SA—See Ascom Holding AG; *Int'l*, pg. 602
ASCOM LEASING & INVESTMENTS LTD.; *Int'l*, pg. 603
ASCON CO., LTD.—See AOYAMA TRADING Co. Ltd.; *Int'l*, pg. 498
ASESORIA TECNICA Y GESTION ADMINISTRATIVA, S.A. DE C.V.—See Empresas ICA S.A.B. de C.V.; *Int'l*, pg. 2390
ASHTEAD FINANCING LIMITED—See Ashtead Group Plc; *Int'l*, pg. 609
ASIA PACK LIMITED; *Int'l*, pg. 614
ASR INTERNATIONAL CORPORATION; *U.S. Private*, pg. 353
ASSET ACCEPTANCE, LLC—See Encore Capital Group, Inc.; *U.S. Public*, pg. 759
ASSET DATA SOLUTIONS, LLC—See Emerson Electric Co.; *U.S. Public*, pg. 748
ASSOCIATED RISK CONSULTANTS LIMITED—See Epiris Managers LLP; *Int'l*, pg. 2461
ASSOCIATED; *U.S. Private*, pg. 354
ASSOCIATION HEADQUARTERS, LLC—See Corridor Capital, LLC; *U.S. Private*, pg. 1058
ASSURANT CONSULTING COMPANY, LIMITED.—See Assurant, Inc.; *U.S. Public*, pg. 215
ASTERIKS INC.—See DTS Corporation; *Int'l*, pg. 2217
ASTRAPE CONSULTING LLC—See TA Associates, Inc.; *U.S. Private*, pg. 3917
ASTRO STUDIOS, INC.—See The Carlyle Group Inc.; *U.S. Public*, pg. 2051
A.T. CLAYTON & COMPANY, INC.; *U.S. Private*, pg. 28
ATC REALTY SIXTEEN, INC.—See Wells Fargo & Company; *U.S. Public*, pg. 2343
ATEA ASA; *Int'l*, pg. 667
ATEVIA AG; *Int'l*, pg. 669

541611 — ADMINISTRATIVE MANA...

ATHENA CONSEIL LUX S.A.; *Int'l*, pg. 669
ATH POWER CONSULTING CORPORATION; *U.S. Private*, pg. 367
A.T. KEARNEY, INC.; *U.S. Private*, pg. 28
ATLANTIX PARTNERS LLC; *U.S. Private*, pg. 375
ATOM EMPREENDIMENTOS E PARTICIPACOES S.A.; *Int'l*, pg. 687
ATOS CONSULTING FRANCE—See Atos SE; *Int'l*, pg. 690
ATOS ORIGIN CONSULTING CANARIAS, SA—See Atos SE; *Int'l*, pg. 691
ATOS ORIGIN INTEGRATION SAS—See Atos SE; *Int'l*, pg. 691
ATOS ORIGIN MANAGEMENT FRANCE SAS—See Atos SE; *Int'l*, pg. 691
ATP LONDON—See ATP Tour, Inc.; *U.S. Private*, pg. 381
AT&T SOUTHEAST—See AT&T Inc.; *U.S. Public*, pg. 219
AURIEMMA CONSULTING GROUP, INC.; *U.S. Private*, pg. 393
AUTOMATION & CONTROL CONCEPTS, INC.—See Hamilton Robinson LLC; *U.S. Private*, pg. 1848
AUTOMOTIVE TRAINING INSTITUTE, LLC—See Driven Brands Holdings Inc.; *U.S. Public*, pg. 688
AVANADE DENMARK APS—See Accenture plc; *Int'l*, pg. 85
AVANADE FRANCE—See Accenture plc; *Int'l*, pg. 85
AVANTAX WEALTH MANAGEMENT, INC.—See Genstar Capital, LLC; *U.S. Private*, pg. 1676
AVASCENT GROUP—See Marsh & McLennan Companies, Inc.; *U.S. Public*, pg. 1386
AVENICA—See University Ventures Funds Management LLC; *U.S. Private*, pg. 4310
AVERY DENNISON MANAGEMENT GMBH—See Avery Dennison Corporation; *U.S. Public*, pg. 244
AVISEN UK LIMITED—See 1Spatial Plc; *Int'l*, pg. 3
AVNET EUROPE EXECUTIVE BVBA—See Avnet, Inc.; *U.S. Public*, pg. 251
AVTECH CORPORATION—See TransDigm Group Incorporated; *U.S. Public*, pg. 2182
AWWAL MODARABA MANAGEMENT LIMITED; *Int'l*, pg. 753
AXANCE SA—See Devoteam SA; *Int'l*, pg. 2089
AXIA STRATEGIES, INC.—See Aquiline Capital Partners LLC; *U.S. Private*, pg. 304
AXIOM CAPITAL ADVISORS, INC.; *Int'l*, pg. 768
AXIOM CONSULTING PARTNERS, LLC; *U.S. Private*, pg. 413
AXIS CONSULTING CORPORATION; *Int'l*, pg. 770
AXON SOLUTIONS SDN BHD—See HCL Technologies Ltd.; *Int'l*, pg. 3298
AZIMA DLI, LLC—See Fortive Corporation; *U.S. Public*, pg. 870
AZIMUT (DIFC) LIMITED—See Azimut Holding SpA; *Int'l*, pg. 779
AZIMUT EGYPT ASSET MANAGEMENT S.A.E.—See Azimut Holding SpA; *Int'l*, pg. 779
AZIMUT INVESTMENTS SA—See Azimut Holding SpA; *Int'l*, pg. 779
AZIMUT (ME) LIMITED—See Azimut Holding SpA; *Int'l*, pg. 779
AZIMUT PORTFOY YONETIMI A.S.—See Azimut Holding SpA; *Int'l*, pg. 779
B2A, LLC.; *U.S. Private*, pg. 421
B2B SALUD S.L.U.—See Centene Corporation; *U.S. Public*, pg. 468
B 2 BUSINESS SYSTEMS LIMITED—See Xerox Holdings Corporation; *U.S. Public*, pg. 2386
B3 SOLUTIONS, INC.; *U.S. Private*, pg. 421
BAC IP BV—See Thermo Fisher Scientific Inc.; *U.S. Public*, pg. 2145
BADGER METER INTERNATIONAL, INC.—See Badger Meter, Inc.; *U.S. Public*, pg. 263
BAE SYSTEMS INFORMATION TECHNOLOGY—See BAE Systems plc; *Int'l*, pg. 796
BAE SYSTEMS-ORDNANCE SYSTEMS—See BAE Systems plc; *Int'l*, pg. 797
BAIN & COMPANY BELGIUM, INC.—See Bain & Company, Inc.; *U.S. Private*, pg. 427
BAIN & COMPANY FINLAND, INC.—See Bain & Company, Inc.; *U.S. Private*, pg. 427
BAIN & COMPANY GERMANY, INC.—See Bain & Company, Inc.; *U.S. Private*, pg. 427
BAIN & COMPANY IBERICA, INC.—See Bain & Company, Inc.; *U.S. Private*, pg. 427
BAIN & COMPANY, INC. - NEW YORK—See Bain & Company, Inc.; *U.S. Private*, pg. 427
BAIN & COMPANY, INC. - SAN FRANCISCO—See Bain & Company, Inc.; *U.S. Private*, pg. 428
BAIN & COMPANY, INC.; *U.S. Private*, pg. 426
BAIN & COMPANY INDIA PVT. LTD.—See Bain & Company, Inc.; *U.S. Private*, pg. 427
BAIN & COMPANY ITALY, INC.—See Bain & Company, Inc.; *U.S. Private*, pg. 427
BAIN & COMPANY MEXICO, INC.—See Bain & Company, Inc.; *U.S. Private*, pg. 427
BAIN & COMPANY MIDDLE EAST, INC.—See Bain & Company, Inc.; *U.S. Private*, pg. 427
BAIN & COMPANY NETHERLANDS, LLC—See Bain & Company, Inc.; *U.S. Private*, pg. 427

BAIN & COMPANY RUSSIA, LLC—See Bain & Company, Inc.; *U.S. Private*, pg. 427
BAIN & COMPANY SE ASIA, INC.—See Bain & Company, Inc.; *U.S. Private*, pg. 427
BAIN & COMPANY SOUTH AFRICA, INC.—See Bain & Company, Inc.; *U.S. Private*, pg. 427
BAIN & COMPANY SWITZERLAND, INC.—See Bain & Company, Inc.; *U.S. Private*, pg. 427
BAIN & COMPANY THAILAND, INC.—See Bain & Company, Inc.; *U.S. Private*, pg. 427
BAIN ET COMPAGNIE SNC—See Bain & Company, Inc.; *U.S. Private*, pg. 428
BAIN INTERNATIONAL INC. - AUSTRALIA, MAIN OFFICE—See Bain & Company, Inc.; *U.S. Private*, pg. 428
BALANCE AGROTECH CO.—See Balance Labs, Inc.; *U.S. Public*, pg. 265
BALANCE LABS, INC.; *U.S. Public*, pg. 265
BALASA DINVERNO FOLTZ LLC—See CI Financial Corporation; *Int'l*, pg. 1600
BALTIC INTERNATIONAL USA, INC.; *U.S. Public*, pg. 268
BANCA CREDIFARMA S.P.A.—See Banca IFIS S.p.A.; *Int'l*, pg. 815
BANCO CATERPILLAR S.A.—See Caterpillar, Inc.; *U.S. Public*, pg. 449
BANC OF AMERICA CREDIT PRODUCTS, INC.—See Bank of America Corporation; *U.S. Public*, pg. 270
BANCO J.P. MORGAN S.A., INSTITUCION DE BANCA MULTIPLE, J.P. MORGAN GRUPO FINANCIERO—See JPMorgan Chase & Co.; *U.S. Public*, pg. 1208
BANCO MONTEPIO GERAL - CABO VERDE, SOCIEDADE UNIPESSOAL, S.A.—See Caixa Economica Montepio Geral; *Int'l*, pg. 1259
BANKBERATUNG ORGANISATIONSU IT-BERATUNGFUR BANKEN AG—See Diebold Nixdorf, Inc.; *U.S. Public*, pg. 661
BANK OF AMERICA MERRILL LYNCH INTERNATIONAL LIMITED—See Bank of America Corporation; *U.S. Public*, pg. 270
BANKPOWER GMBH PERSONALDIENSTLEISTUNGEN—See ManpowerGroup Inc.; *U.S. Public*, pg. 1357
BANTA GLOBAL TURNKEY LTD. - LIMERICK—See Chatham Asset Management, LLC; *U.S. Private*, pg. 862
BANTA GLOBAL TURNKEY LTD.—See Chatham Asset Management, LLC; *U.S. Private*, pg. 862
BARBER FINANCIAL GROUP—See Crestview Partners, L.P.; *U.S. Private*, pg. 1098
BARCLAY HEDGE, LTD.—See Backstop Solutions Group, LLC; *U.S. Private*, pg. 423
BARKAWI MANAGEMENT CONSULTANTS GMBH—See Barkawi Holding GmbH; *Int'l*, pg. 865
BARKAWI MANAGEMENT CONSULTING (SHANGHAI) CO., LTD.—See Barkawi Holding GmbH; *Int'l*, pg. 865
BARRIE & HIBBERT LTD.—See Moody's Corporation; *U.S. Public*, pg. 1466
BAS BUROSYSTEME GMBH—See HP Inc.; *U.S. Public*, pg. 1062
BASF AGRO TRADEMARKS GMBH—See BASF SE; *Int'l*, pg. 872
BASF AKQUISITIONS- UND OBJEKTVERWERTUNGSGESELLSCHAFT MBH—See BASF SE; *Int'l*, pg. 872
BASF ASIA-PACIFIC SERVICE CENTRE SDN BHD—See BASF SE; *Int'l*, pg. 878
BASF INTERSERVICIOS S.A. DE C.V.—See BASF SE; *Int'l*, pg. 879
B-ASSIST, INC.—See Bookoff Group Holdings Ltd.; *Int'l*, pg. 1110
BATES WHITE, LLC.; *U.S. Private*, pg. 486
BAYCURRENT CONSULTING, INC.; *Int'l*, pg. 901
BAYER BUSINESS SERVICES GMBH—See Bayer Aktiengesellschaft; *Int'l*, pg. 902
BAYFIRST SOLUTIONS, LLC—See Kingswood Capital Management LLC; *U.S. Private*, pg. 2312
BCC FINLAND OY—See Atea ASA; *Int'l*, pg. 667
BCFORWARD; *U.S. Private*, pg. 499
BCS, LLC; *U.S. Private*, pg. 500
BDO REMIT LIMITED—See BDO Unibank, Inc.; *Int'l*, pg. 930
BDP TRANSPORT, LLC—See BDP International Inc.; *U.S. Private*, pg. 502
THE BEAIRD GROUP; *U.S. Private*, pg. 3992
BEARINGPOINT (ASIA PACIFIC) PTE. LTD.—See BearingPoint, Inc.; *U.S. Private*, pg. 507
BEARINGPOINT BELGIUM S.P.R.L.—See BearingPoint Holdings Europe B.V.; *Int'l*, pg. 933
BEARINGPOINT CONSULTING INC.—See BearingPoint Holdings Europe B.V.; *Int'l*, pg. 933
BEARINGPOINT DENMARK AS—See BearingPoint Holdings Europe B.V.; *Int'l*, pg. 933
BEARINGPOINT FINLAND OY—See BearingPoint Holdings Europe B.V.; *Int'l*, pg. 933
BEARINGPOINT FRANCE SAS—See BearingPoint Holdings Europe B.V.; *Int'l*, pg. 933
BEARINGPOINT GMBH—See BearingPoint Holdings Europe B.V.; *Int'l*, pg. 933
BEARINGPOINT GMBH—See BearingPoint Holdings Europe B.V.; *Int'l*, pg. 933
BEARINGPOINT, INC.; *U.S. Private*, pg. 507

CORPORATE AFFILIATIONS

BEARINGPOINT INFONOVA GMBH—See BearingPoint Holdings Europe B.V.; *Int'l*, pg. 933
BEARINGPOINT INFORMATION TECHNOLOGIES (SHANGHAI) LTD.—See BearingPoint, Inc.; *U.S. Private*, pg. 507
BEARINGPOINT INFORMATION TECHNOLOGY N.V.—See BearingPoint, Inc.; *U.S. Private*, pg. 507
BEARINGPOINT IRELAND LIMITED—See BearingPoint Holdings Europe B.V.; *Int'l*, pg. 933
BEARINGPOINT ITALY SRL—See BearingPoint Holdings Europe B.V.; *Int'l*, pg. 933
BEARINGPOINT LIMITED—See BearingPoint Holdings Europe B.V.; *Int'l*, pg. 933
BEARINGPOINT MANAGEMENT CONSULTING N.V.—See BearingPoint, Inc.; *U.S. Private*, pg. 507
BEARINGPOINT MAROC—See BearingPoint Holdings Europe B.V.; *Int'l*, pg. 933
BEARING POINT MIDDLE EAST FZ LLC—See BearingPoint Holdings Europe B.V.; *Int'l*, pg. 933
BEARINGPOINT NORWAY A/S—See BearingPoint Holdings Europe B.V.; *Int'l*, pg. 933
BEARINGPOINT OOO—See BearingPoint, Inc.; *U.S. Private*, pg. 507
BEARINGPOINT PTE. LTD.—See BearingPoint, Inc.; *U.S. Private*, pg. 507
BEARINGPOINT (SHANGHAI) ENTERPRISE MANAGEMENT CONSULTING CO. LTD.—See BearingPoint Holdings Europe B.V.; *Int'l*, pg. 933
BEARINGPOINT SOUTH EAST ASIA LLC—See BearingPoint, Inc.; *U.S. Private*, pg. 507
BEARINGPOINT SWEDEN AB—See BearingPoint Holdings Europe B.V.; *Int'l*, pg. 933
BEARINGPOINT SWITZERLAND AG—See BearingPoint Holdings Europe B.V.; *Int'l*, pg. 933
BEAZLEY USA SERVICES, INC.—See Beazley plc; *Int'l*, pg. 936
BEEZLEY MANAGEMENT, LLC—See CBRE Group, Inc.; *U.S. Public*, pg. 459
BEIJING POLY FORBIDDEN CITY THEATRE MANAGEMENT CO., LTD.—See China Poly Group Corporation; *Int'l*, pg. 1540
BELLSYSTEM24 HOLDINGS, INC.; *Int'l*, pg. 967
BENCHMARK HOSPITALITY INTERNATIONAL INC.; *U.S. Private*, pg. 523
BENEFIT ADVISORS, INC.; *U.S. Private*, pg. 525
BENEFIT PLANS ADMINISTRATIVE SERVICES, INC.—See Community Bank System, Inc.; *U.S. Public*, pg. 549
BENEFITS NETWORK INC.; *U.S. Private*, pg. 525
BENTELER MANAGEMENT CONSULTING (SHANGHAI) CO., LTD.—See Benteler International AG; *Int'l*, pg. 977
BERKELEY RESEARCH GROUP LLC; *U.S. Private*, pg. 532
BERKSHIRE ASSOCIATES, LLC.—See Levine Leichtman Capital Partners, LLC; *U.S. Private*, pg. 2436
BEST-BLU CONSULTING WITH ENERGY GMBH—See EWE Aktiengesellschaft; *Int'l*, pg. 2576
BEST DOCTORS, INC.—See Teladoc Health, Inc.; *U.S. Public*, pg. 1992
BEST TFI S.A—See BEST S.A.; *Int'l*, pg. 999
BETOTECH MUNCHEN VERWALTUNGS GMBH—See Heidelberg Materials AG; *Int'l*, pg. 3321
BETOTECH VERWALTUNGS-GMBH—See Heidelberg Materials AG; *Int'l*, pg. 3309
BEVESTOR GMBH—See DekaBank; *Int'l*, pg. 2005
B&F CAPITAL MARKETS, LLC—See Stifel Financial Corp.; *U.S. Public*, pg. 1949
BFS ABRECHNUNGS GMBH—See ECM Equity Capital Management GmbH; *Int'l*, pg. 2291
BFS FINANCE GMBH—See Bertelsmann SE & Co. KGaA; *Int'l*, pg. 993
BFS FINANCE MUNSTER GMBH—See Bertelsmann SE & Co. KGaA; *Int'l*, pg. 993
BILD & COMPANY; *U.S. Private*, pg. 556
BIMSA ULUSLARARASI IS, BILGI VE YONETIM SISTEMLERI A.S.—See Haci Omer Sabanci Holding A.S.; *Int'l*, pg. 3203
BIONIC SOLUTION LLC—See Accenture plc; *Int'l*, pg. 86
BIOSTAR ANGEL STEM CELL CORPORATION; *U.S. Private*, pg. 563
BIOSTRATEGIES GROUP, INC.—See CRA International, Inc.; *U.S. Public*, pg. 588
BITMIS CORP.; *Int'l*, pg. 1050
BKD CORPORATE FINANCE, LLC—See BKD, LLP; *U.S. Private*, pg. 568
BKEP MANAGEMENT, INC.—See Ergon, Inc.; *U.S. Private*, pg. 1418
BKM MANAGEMENT LIMITED; *Int'l*, pg. 1054
BLACK DIAMOND ASSOCIATES, LLC; *U.S. Private*, pg. 570
BLACKROCK ENERGY & RESOURCES—See BlackRock, Inc.; *U.S. Public*, pg. 345
BLACKROCK INVESTMENT MANAGEMENT INTERNATIONAL LIMITED—See BlackRock, Inc.; *U.S. Public*, pg. 345
BLACKROCK MUNICIPAL INCOME TRUST; *U.S. Public*, pg. 343
BLACKROCK SERVICES INDIA PRIVATE LIMITED—See

BlackRock, Inc.; *U.S. Public*, pg. 345
BLACKWELL GLOBAL CONSULTING LLC—See CGN & Associates Inc.; *U.S. Private*, pg. 844
BLACKWOOD ADVISORY PTY. LTD.—See Azimut Holding SpA; *Int'l*, pg. 779
BLAUPUNKT INTERNATIONAL SERVICES AG—See Aurelius Equity Opportunities SE & Co. KGaA; *Int'l*, pg. 708
BLC FINANCE SAL—See BLC Bank SAL; *Int'l*, pg. 1063
BLC INVEST SAL—See BLC Bank SAL; *Int'l*, pg. 1063
B-LOT SINGAPORE PTE., LTD.—See b-lot Co., Ltd.; *Int'l*, pg. 785
BLUEBAND FINANCING LIMITED; *Int'l*, pg. 1070
BLUE CANYON PARTNERS, INC.; *U.S. Private*, pg. 585
BLUE ENGINE MESSAGE & MEDIA, LLC; *U.S. Private*, pg. 588
BMT DEFENCE SERVICES LTD.—See BMT Group Limited; *Int'l*, pg. 1077
BMT HI-Q SIGMA LTD—See BMT Group Limited; *Int'l*, pg. 1078
BOARDROOM.COM SDN. BHD.—See Aldrich Resources Bhd; *Int'l*, pg. 305
BOLD ORANGE COMPANY, LLC; *U.S. Private*, pg. 610
BOMBARDIER-WIEN SCHIENENFAHRZEUGE AG—See Alstom S.A.; *Int'l*, pg. 383
BOOKKEEPERS.COM, LLC; *U.S. Private*, pg. 615
BOOM FREESPORTS LIMITED—See Boomerang Plus plc; *Int'l*, pg. 1110
BOOZ ALLEN HAMILTON INC.—See Booz Allen Hamilton Holding Corporation; *U.S. Public*, pg. 369
BORE TECH UTILITIES & MAINTENANCE INC.; *U.S. Private*, pg. 618
THE BOSTON CONSULTING GROUP GMBH—See The Boston Consulting Group, Inc.; *U.S. Private*, pg. 3997
THE BOSTON CONSULTING GROUP, INC. - WASHINGTON, D.C.—See The Boston Consulting Group, Inc.; *U.S. Private*, pg. 3998
BOSTON HEALTHCARE ASSOCIATES, INC.—See Veranex; *U.S. Private*, pg. 4359
BOUNTY BRANDS PTY LTD.; *Int'l*, pg. 1119
BOUTIQUE HOTEL MANAGEMENT GROUP, LLC; *U.S. Private*, pg. 624
BPER FACTOR S.P.A.—See BPER BANCA S.p.A; *Int'l*, pg. 1132
BPI OPERATIONS MANAGEMENT CORPORATION—See Bank of the Philippine Islands; *Int'l*, pg. 848
BRABANK ASA; *Int'l*, pg. 1133
BRAEMAR FALCONER VIETNAM CO LIMITED—See Braemar PLC; *Int'l*, pg. 1135
BRANCH & ASSOCIATES, INC. - RICHMOND DIVISION—See The Branch Group, Inc.; *U.S. Private*, pg. 3999
BRANDEX EUROPE C.V.—See Abbott Laboratories; *U.S. Public*, pg. 19
BRAND INTEGRITY, INC.—See Edenred S.A.; *Int'l*, pg. 2308
BRANDYWINE AUTO PARTS INC.; *U.S. Private*, pg. 639
BRB BANCO DE BRASILIA SA; *Int'l*, pg. 1143
BREAKTHROUGH MANAGEMENT GROUP, INC.; *U.S. Private*, pg. 642
BRIDGES CONSULTING, INC.—See CACI International Inc.; *U.S. Public*, pg. 417
BRILLIANT ENVIRONMENTAL SERVICES, LLC; *U.S. Private*, pg. 654
BRISTOL BAY RESOURCE SOLUTIONS, LLC—See Bristol Bay Native Corporation; *U.S. Private*, pg. 655
BRITAM ASSET MANAGERS (KENYA) LIMITED—See Britam Holdings Plc; *Int'l*, pg. 1164
BROADSPIRE SERVICES, INC.—See Crawford & Company; *U.S. Public*, pg. 592
BROKERSXPRESS, LLC—See The Charles Schwab Corporation; *U.S. Public*, pg. 2058
BROOK STREET BUREAU PLC—See ManpowerGroup Inc.; *U.S. Public*, pg. 1359
BSB SA; *Int'l*, pg. 1202
BSC AMERICA; *U.S. Private*, pg. 674
BTS ASIA PACIFIC PTE. LTD.—See BTS Group AB; *Int'l*, pg. 1205
BTS LIMITED—See Abengoa S.A.; *Int'l*, pg. 59
BTS LIMITED—See Algonquin Power & Utilities Corp.; *Int'l*, pg. 319
BUCHER MANAGEMENT AG—See Bucher Industries AG; *Int'l*, pg. 1207
BUNGE N.A. FINANCE L.P.—See Bunge Limited; *U.S. Public*, pg. 411
BUSINESS ASPECT (ACT) PTY LTD—See Data#3 Limited; *Int'l*, pg. 1977
BUSINESS ASPECT PTY LTD—See Data#3 Limited; *Int'l*, pg. 1977
BUSINESS DEVELOPMENT ASIA LLC; *U.S. Private*, pg. 694
BUSINESS IMPACT GROUP LLC; *U.S. Private*, pg. 694
BUSINESS RESOURCE SOLUTIONS LLC—See Bristol Bay Native Corporation; *U.S. Private*, pg. 656
BUSINESS SENSE SOLUTIONS; *U.S. Private*, pg. 695
BUSINESS TALENT GROUP, LLC—See Heidrick & Struggles International, Inc.; *U.S. Public*, pg. 1022
BUSLINK MEDIA; *U.S. Private*, pg. 695
BWT-BETEILIGUNGSGESELLSCHAFT FUR DEN WIRTSCHAFTSAUFBAU THURINGENS MBH—See Helaba Landesbank Hessen-Thuringen; *Int'l*, pg. 3327
BYALLACCOUNTS, INC.—See Morningstar, Inc.; *U.S. Public*, pg. 1476
BY APPOINTMENT ONLY, INC.; *U.S. Private*, pg. 700
BYMANPOWER, S.L.U.—See ManpowerGroup Inc.; *U.S. Public*, pg. 1357
BYPASS POWER COMPANY—See Enel S.p.A.; *Int'l*, pg. 2411
BYRNES CONSULTING, LLC; *U.S. Private*, pg. 701
C3 CONSULTING LLC; *U.S. Private*, pg. 710
CACI-WGI, INC.—See CACI International Inc.; *U.S. Public*, pg. 417
CA FINANCIAL APPOINTMENTS (PTY) LTD.—See ADvTECH Limited; *Int'l*, pg. 168
CALIBER POINT BUSINESS SOLUTIONS—See EQT AB; *Int'l*, pg. 2470
CALLSOURCE, INC.; *U.S. Private*, pg. 723
CAMBRIA CONSULTING INC.—See SSI (U.S.) Inc.; *U.S. Private*, pg. 3769
CAMBRIDGE CONSTRUCTION MANAGEMENT, INC.—See Accenture plc; *Int'l*, pg. 86
CAMBRIDGE CONSULTANTS, INC.—See Capgemini SE; *Int'l*, pg. 1305
CAMELOT MANAGEMENT CONSULTANTS AG; *Int'l*, pg. 1271
CANADA POST INTERNATIONAL LTD.—See Canada Post Corporation; *Int'l*, pg. 1282
CANAL CAPITAL MANAGEMENT LLC; *U.S. Private*, pg. 732
CANDID PARTNERS, LLC—See McKinsey & Company, Inc.; *U.S. Private*, pg. 2639
CANTONVALLEY MACAU COMPANY LIMITED—See AsianLogic Limited; *Int'l*, pg. 620
CAPGEMINI AUSTRALIA PTY LTD—See Capgemini SE; *Int'l*, pg. 1303
CAPGEMINI BELGIUM N.V/S.A—See Capgemini SE; *Int'l*, pg. 1306
CAPGEMINI BUSINESS SERVICES ASIA LTD.—See Capgemini SE; *Int'l*, pg. 1303
CAPGEMINI CHINA—See Capgemini SE; *Int'l*, pg. 1303
CAPGEMINI CONSULTING INDIA PVT. LTD.—See Capgemini SE; *Int'l*, pg. 1304
CAPGEMINI CONSULTING OSTERREICH AG—See Capgemini SE; *Int'l*, pg. 1304
CAPGEMINI CONSULTING SLOVAKIA D.O.O—See Capgemini SE; *Int'l*, pg. 1304
CAPGEMINI CZECH REPUBLIC S.R.O—See Capgemini SE; *Int'l*, pg. 1304
CAPGEMINI DEUTSCHLAND GMBH - COLOGNE—See Capgemini SE; *Int'l*, pg. 1304
CAPGEMINI DEUTSCHLAND GMBH - HAMBURG—See Capgemini SE; *Int'l*, pg. 1304
CAPGEMINI DEUTSCHLAND GMBH - MUNICH—See Capgemini SE; *Int'l*, pg. 1304
CAPGEMINI DEUTSCHLAND GMBH - OFFENBACH—See Capgemini SE; *Int'l*, pg. 1304
CAPGEMINI DEUTSCHLAND GMBH—See Capgemini SE; *Int'l*, pg. 1304
CAPGEMINI DEUTSCHLAND GMBH - STUTTGART—See Capgemini SE; *Int'l*, pg. 1304
CAPGEMINI ESPANA S.L. - BARCELONA—See Capgemini SE; *Int'l*, pg. 1305
CAPGEMINI ESPANA S.L.—See Capgemini SE; *Int'l*, pg. 1305
CAPGEMINI GOUVIEUX S.A.S.—See Capgemini SE; *Int'l*, pg. 1305
CAPGEMINI ITALIA—See Capgemini SE; *Int'l*, pg. 1305
CAPGEMINI ITALIA—See Capgemini SE; *Int'l*, pg. 1305
CAPGEMINI ITALIA—See Capgemini SE; *Int'l*, pg. 1305
CAPGEMINI ITALIA SPA—See Capgemini SE; *Int'l*, pg. 1305
CAPGEMINI ITALIA SPA—See Capgemini SE; *Int'l*, pg. 1305
CAPGEMINI OUTSOURCING B.V—See Capgemini SE; *Int'l*, pg. 1306
CAPGEMINI PORTUGAL, SERVICOS DE CONSULTORIA E INFORMATICA, SA—See Capgemini SE; *Int'l*, pg. 1306
CAPGEMINI SCHWEIZ AG (BASEL)—See Capgemini SE; *Int'l*, pg. 1306
CAPGEMINI SCHWEIZ AG (GENF)—See Capgemini SE; *Int'l*, pg. 1306
CAPGEMINI SCHWEIZ AG—See Capgemini SE; *Int'l*, pg. 1306
CAPGEMINI SINGAPORE PTE. LTD.—See Capgemini SE; *Int'l*, pg. 1306
CAPGEMINI SUISSE SA—See Capgemini SE; *Int'l*, pg. 1306
CAPGEMINI SVERIGE AB—See Capgemini SE; *Int'l*, pg. 1306
CAPGEMINI UK—See Capgemini SE; *Int'l*, pg. 1306
CAPITAL AVIATION PTE LTD—See AT Capital Pte Limited; *Int'l*, pg. 664
CAPITAL CITY PETROLEUM, INC.—See Capital City Energy Group, Inc.; *U.S. Private*, pg. 739
CAPITAL DYNAMICS ASSET MANAGEMENT SDN. BHD.—See icapital.biz Berhad; *Int'l*, pg. 3578
CAPITAL PARTNERS MORTGAGE, LLC—See Rithm Capital Corp.; *U.S. Private*, pg. 1800
CAPITA PLC; *Int'l*, pg. 1308
CAPITA RESOURCING LIMITED—See Capita plc; *Int'l*, pg. 1308
CAPITOL CONSULTANTS INC.; *U.S. Private*, pg. 743
CAPTIVE RESOURCES, LLC; *U.S. Private*, pg. 747
CARANA CORP.; *U.S. Private*, pg. 748
CAREERENGINE NETWORK—See Classified Solutions Group, Inc.; *U.S. Private*, pg. 917
CAREER HARMONY, LTD—See ManpowerGroup Inc.; *U.S. Public*, pg. 1357
CAREER MANAGEMENT PARTNERS; *U.S. Private*, pg. 752
CARLSON MARKETING GROUP—See Aimia Inc.; *Int'l*, pg. 233
CARPEDATUM LLC—See Converge Technology Solutions Corp.; *Int'l*, pg. 1787
CARTESIAN, INC.—See Blackstreet Capital Holdings LLC; *U.S. Private*, pg. 576
CARTUS BRASIL SERVICOS DE RELOCACAO LTDA.—See Anywhere Real Estate Inc.; *U.S. Public*, pg. 142
CASA BAHIA CONTACT CENTER LTDA—See Companhia Brasileira de Distribuicao; *Int'l*, pg. 1746
CASEY QUIRK BY DELOITTE—See Deloitte LLP; *U.S. Private*, pg. 1198
CASEY QUIRK BY DELOITTE—See Deloitte Touche Tohmatsu Limited; *Int'l*, pg. 2014
CASEY'S SERVICES COMPANY—See Casey's General Stores, Inc.; *U.S. Public*, pg. 446
CASH FREDERICK TAYLOR LIMITED—See CASH Financial Services Group Limited; *Int'l*, pg. 1352
CASH QUANT-FINANCE LAB LIMITED—See Celestial Asia Securities Holdings Limited; *Int'l*, pg. 1392
CASPIAN CAPITAL B.V.—See Baring Vostok Capital Partners; *Int'l*, pg. 865
CASTELLANA PHYSICIAN SERVICES, LLC—See Elevance Health, Inc.; *U.S. Public*, pg. 729
CASTELLAN SOLUTIONS LLC—See Resurgens Technology Partners, LLC; *U.S. Private*, pg. 3410
CASTELLO SGR S.P.A.—See ANIMA Holding S.p.A.; *Int'l*, pg. 471
CASTLELINE HOLDINGS, LLC—See Altisource Portfolio Solutions S.A.; *Int'l*, pg. 393
CATALYSIS GROUP, INC.; *U.S. Private*, pg. 786
CATERPILLAR FINANCIAL COMMERCIAL ACCOUNT CORPORATION—See Caterpillar, Inc.; *U.S. Public*, pg. 450
CATERPILLAR LUXEMBOURG LLC—See Caterpillar, Inc.; *U.S. Public*, pg. 451
CBIZ CMF, LLC—See CBIZ, Inc.; *U.S. Public*, pg. 456
CBIZ LIFE INSURANCE SOLUTIONS, INC.—See CBIZ, Inc.; *U.S. Public*, pg. 456
CB RENAISSANCE CREDIT LLC; *Int'l*, pg. 1364
CCA ENGINEERING SIMULATION SOFTWARE (SHANGHAI) CO., LTD.—See FUJISOFT INCORPORATED; *Int'l*, pg. 2830
CCID CONSULTING COMPANY LIMITED; *Int'l*, pg. 1366
CC SERVICES, INC.—See COUNTRY Financial; *U.S. Private*, pg. 1066
CDA FINANCEMENT SNC—See Compagnie des Alpes S.A.; *Int'l*, pg. 1737
CDI CHINA, INC.—See CD International Enterprises, Inc.; *U.S. Public*, pg. 461
CDI SHANGHAI MANAGEMENT CO., LTD.—See CD International Enterprises, Inc.; *U.S. Public*, pg. 461
CDK GLOBAL GROUP BV—See Brookfield Corporation; *Int'l*, pg. 1175
CDK GLOBAL (UK) LIMITED—See Brookfield Corporation; *Int'l*, pg. 1175
CEB LLC.—See Gartner, Inc.; *U.S. Public*, pg. 906
CEBOS, LTD.—See Thoma Bravo, L.P.; *U.S. Private*, pg. 4151
CEGEDIM S.A.; *Int'l*, pg. 1390
CEMEPE INVESTIMENTOS S.A.; *Int'l*, pg. 1398
THE CENTENNIAL GROUP, LLC—See Genstar Capital, LLC; *U.S. Private*, pg. 1675
CENTER FOR INTERNATIONAL PRIVATE ENTERPRISE; *U.S. Private*, pg. 810
CENTRAL IQ, INC.; *U.S. Private*, pg. 822
CENTRAL MEDICAL SOLUTIONS, LLC—See Nobilis Health Corp.; *U.S. Private*, pg. 2932
CENTRAL RESEARCH, INC.; *U.S. Private*, pg. 824
CENTRI BUSINESS CONSULTING, LLC; *U.S. Private*, pg. 829
CENTRIC FINANCIAL PROFESSIONALS B.V.—See Centric Holding B.V.; *Int'l*, pg. 1412
CENTURIA CORPORATION; *U.S. Private*, pg. 830
CENTURY BUSINESS SOLUTIONS, INC.; *U.S. Private*, pg. 832
CENTURY GAMING, INC.—See Accel Entertainment, Inc.; *U.S. Public*, pg. 32
CERTE WEALTH PROTECTION PTY. LTD.—See Azimut Holding SpA; *Int'l*, pg. 779
CETELEM SERVICIOS SA DE CV—See BNP Paribas SA; *Int'l*, pg. 1090
CETROM INFORMATION TECHNOLOGY, INC.; *U.S. Private*, pg. 843

541611 — ADMINISTRATIVE MANA...

CGI DEUTSCHLAND GMBH & CO. KG—See CGI Inc.; *Int'l*, pg. 1433
CGI INC.—See CGI Inc.; *Int'l*, pg. 1433
CGI IT UK LIMITED—See CGI Inc.; *Int'l*, pg. 1432
CGN & ASSOCIATES INC.; *U.S. Private*, pg. 844
CHAILEASE AUTO RENTAL CO., LTD.—See Chailease Holding Company Limited; *Int'l*, pg. 1436
CHAILEASE BERJAYA CREDIT SDN. BHD.—See Chailease Holding Company Limited; *Int'l*, pg. 1436
CHAILEASE BERJAYA FINANCE CORPORATION—See Chailease Holding Company Limited; *Int'l*, pg. 1436
CHAILEASE INSURANCE BROKERS CO., LTD.—See Chailease Holding Company Limited; *Int'l*, pg. 1436
CHAILEASE ROYAL FINANCE PLC—See Chailease Holding Company Limited; *Int'l*, pg. 1437
CHAILEASE ROYAL LEASING PLC—See Chailease Holding Company Limited; *Int'l*, pg. 1437
CHARLES F. DAY & ASSOCIATES, INC.; *U.S. Private*, pg. 852
CHARLES RIVER GERMANY VERWALTUNGS GMBH—See Charles River Laboratories International, Inc.; *U.S. Public*, pg. 480
CHARTER ONE HOTELS & RESORTS, INC.; *U.S. Private*, pg. 858
CHARTIS CLINICAL QUALITY SOLUTIONS—See Audax Group, Limited Partnership; *U.S. Private*, pg. 390
THE CHARTIS GROUP, LLC—See Audax Group, Limited Partnership; *U.S. Private*, pg. 390
CHASE ENTERPRISES, INC.; *U.S. Private*, pg. 859
CHAUCER SYNDICATES LIMITED—See China Reinsurance (Group) Corporation; *Int'l*, pg. 1547
CHEMONICS INTERNATIONAL, INC.; *U.S. Private*, pg. 872
CHESKIN ADDED VALUE; *U.S. Private*, pg. 875
CHEVRON OVERSEAS PETROLEUM LIMITED—See Chevron Corporation; *U.S. Public*, pg. 486
C.H. GUERNSEY & COMPANY, INC.; *U.S. Private*, pg. 707
CHINA BULL MANAGEMENT INC.; *U.S. Private*, pg. 885
CHINA HUARONG (MACAU) INTERNATIONAL COMPANY LIMITED—See China CITIC Financial Asset Management Co., Ltd.; *Int'l*, pg. 1489
CHINA TIAN YUAN HEALTHCARE GROUP LIMITED; *Int'l*, pg. 1559
CHODAI & KISO - JIBAN VIETNAM CO., LTD.—See Chodai Co., Ltd.; *Int'l*, pg. 1577
CHODAI-TEC CO., LTD.—See Chodai Co., Ltd.; *Int'l*, pg. 1577
CHOICE CONSULTANCY SERVICES PVT. LTD.—See Choice International Limited; *Int'l*, pg. 1577
CHONGQING POLY INTERNATIONAL CINEMA—See China Poly Group Corporation; *Int'l*, pg. 1541
CHONGQING POLY WANHE CINEMA CHAIN CO., LTD.—See China Poly Group Corporation; *Int'l*, pg. 1541
CHUGACH MANAGEMENT SERVICES INC.—See Chugach Alaska Corporation; *U.S. Private*, pg. 894
CHURCH INTERNATIONAL LTD; *Int'l*, pg. 1600
CIGPF LTDA EN LIQUIDACION—See Citigroup Inc.; *U.S. Public*, pg. 501
CIMC FINANCE COMPANY LIMITED—See China International Marine Containers (Group) Co., Ltd.; *Int'l*, pg. 1511
CIMC FINANCING & LEASING CO., LTD.—See China International Marine Containers (Group) Co., Ltd.; *Int'l*, pg. 1511
CINDA - DB NPL SECURITIZATION TRUST 2003-1—See Deutsche Bank Aktiengesellschaft; *Int'l*, pg. 2056
CIS FINANCE LTD—See Co-operative Group Limited; *Int'l*, pg. 1679
CIS TCHAD S.A.R.L.—See Catering International & Services S.A.; *Int'l*, pg. 1360
CITIGROUP MANAGEMENT CORP.—See Citigroup Inc.; *U.S. Public*, pg. 504
CITY SERVICE POLSKA SP. Z O.O.—See City Service SE; *Int'l*, pg. 1627
CLAIMS FULFILMENT COMPANY (PTY) LTD.—See Aon plc; *Int'l*, pg. 494
CLASSIC LEASING & FINANCE LTD.; *Int'l*, pg. 1653
CLASSIC RESIDENCE BY HYATT—See Hyatt Hotels Corporation; *U.S. Public*, pg. 1076
CLEAREDGE PARTNERS, INC.—See Accenture plc; *Int'l*, pg. 87
CLEARXCHANGE, LLC—See Bank of America Corporation; *U.S. Public*, pg. 272
CLEARXCHANGE, LLC—See Capital One Financial Corporation; *U.S. Public*, pg. 431
CLEARXCHANGE, LLC—See JPMorgan Chase & Co.; *U.S. Public*, pg. 1210
CLEARXCHANGE, LLC—See Wells Fargo & Company; *U.S. Public*, pg. 2343
CLIFTON CONSULTING LTD—See Clifton Asset Management Plc; *Int'l*, pg. 1659
CLINE RESOURCE & DEVELOPMENT CO.; *U.S. Private*, pg. 943
CLINLOGIX, LLC—See ArchiMed SAS; *Int'l*, pg. 549
CLINOVATIONS, LLC.; *U.S. Private*, pg. 944
CLIS CO., LTD.—See Prudential Financial, Inc.; *U.S. Public*, pg. 1733
CLOSEOUT DISTRIBUTION, INC.—See Big Lots, Inc.; *U.S. Public*, pg. 330

CLOUDBURST CONSULTING GROUP, INC.; *U.S. Private*, pg. 947
CLOUDMED, LLC—See R1 RCM Inc.; *U.S. Public*, pg. 1758
CLUB 24 LIMITED—See Capita plc; *Int'l*, pg. 1308
CMGRP, INC.—See The Interpublic Group of Companies, Inc.; *U.S. Public*, pg. 2090
CMTI, INC.; *U.S. Private*, pg. 951
COADY DIEMAR PARTNERS, LLC; *U.S. Private*, pg. 953
COALITION DEVELOPMENT LTD.—See S&P Global Inc.; *U.S. Public*, pg. 1830
COALITION DEVELOPMENT SYSTEMS (INDIA) PRIVATE LIMITED—See S&P Global Inc.; *U.S. Public*, pg. 1830
COALSOLV, LLC—See Alpha Natural Resources, Inc.; *U.S. Private*, pg. 198
COASTAL STRATEGIES, INC.; *U.S. Private*, pg. 957
COAST HOLDING CORPORATION—See Coast Investment & Development Company K.S.C.C.; *Int'l*, pg. 1681
COBREW N.V.—See Anheuser-Busch InBev SA/NV; *Int'l*, pg. 466
CODA RESOURCES, LTD.; *U.S. Private*, pg. 959
COFFEY INTERNATIONAL DEVELOPMENT LIMITED—See Tetra Tech, Inc.; *U.S. Public*, pg. 2022
COFFEY INTERNATIONAL DEVELOPMENT SP. Z.O.O.—See Tetra Tech, Inc.; *U.S. Public*, pg. 2022
COFFEY PROJECTS (AUSTRALIA) PTY. LTD.—See Tetra Tech, Inc.; *U.S. Public*, pg. 2022
COGENT B2B LTD.; *Int'l*, pg. 1694
COHEN PARTNERS CO. LTD.; *Int'l*, pg. 1695
COLLABORATIVE SOLUTIONS EUROPE LIMITED—See Cognizant Technology Solutions Corporation; *U.S. Public*, pg. 524
COLLIGENT INKASSO AB—See Collector AB; *Int'l*, pg. 1699
COLONY MANAGEMENT SERVICES—See Brookfield Reinsurance Ltd.; *Int'l*, pg. 1194
COLORADO MILLS LP—See Simon Property Group, Inc.; *U.S. Public*, pg. 1882
COLWEN MANAGEMENT INC.; *U.S. Private*, pg. 980
COMARCH AG—See ComArch S.A.; *Int'l*, pg. 1707
COMAT EUROPE—See Comat Technologies (P) Ltd.; *Int'l*, pg. 1708
COMAT TECHNOLOGIES, INC.—See Comat Technologies (P) Ltd.; *Int'l*, pg. 1708
COMAT TECHNOLOGIES (P) LTD.; *Int'l*, pg. 1708
COMENSURA LTD.—See HFBG Holding B.V.; *Int'l*, pg. 3374
COMMERCE ASSET VENTURES SDN BHD—See CIMB Group Holdings Berhad; *Int'l*, pg. 1608
COMMUNITY HEALTH SOLUTIONS OF AMERICA, INC.; *U.S. Private*, pg. 994
COMMUNITY TIES OF AMERICA, INC.; *U.S. Private*, pg. 997
COMPEX CORPORATION; *U.S. Private*, pg. 1000
COMPEX LEGAL SERVICES INC.—See Windjammer Capital Investors, LLC; *U.S. Private*, pg. 4537
COMPOTECH PROVIDER AB—See Addtech AB; *Int'l*, pg. 132
COMPREHENSIVE HEALTH MANAGEMENT, INC.—See Centene Corporation; *U.S. Public*, pg. 471
COMPUTARIS INTERNATIONAL LIMITED—See Blackstone Inc.; *U.S. Public*, pg. 357
CONCENTRIX EUROPE LIMITED—See TD Synnex Corp; *U.S. Public*, pg. 1984
CONCENTRIX SERVICES (POLAND) SPOLLKA Z O.O.—See TD Synnex Corp; *U.S. Public*, pg. 1984
CONCENTRIX SERVICES PORTUGAL, SOCIEDADE UNIPESSOAL, LDA—See TD Synnex Corp; *U.S. Public*, pg. 1984
CONCENTRIX SERVICES PTY LTD—See TD Synnex Corp; *U.S. Public*, pg. 1984
CONCRETE ITALIA S.R.L.—See Heidelberg Materials AG; *Int'l*, pg. 3310
CONDOMINIUM MANAGMENT GROUP, INC.; *U.S. Private*, pg. 1012
CONEXUS CPA GROUP LLC—See Cherry Bekaert LLP; *U.S. Private*, pg. 874
THE CONFERENCE BOARD, INC.; *U.S. Private*, pg. 4013
CONFIDIO, LLC—See RxBenefits, Inc.; *U.S. Private*, pg. 3509
CONIFER CARE CONTINUUM SOLUTIONS, LLC—See Tenet Healthcare Corporation; *U.S. Public*, pg. 2002
CONOCOPHILLIPS ASIA VENTURES PTE. LTD.—See ConocoPhillips; *U.S. Public*, pg. 568
CONSENEC LTD—See ABB Ltd.; *Int'l*, pg. 54
CONSOLIDATED MARKETING SERVICES, INC. OF MA; *U.S. Private*, pg. 1021
CONSTRUCTORA CABLEMAS, S.A. DE C.V.—See Grupo Televisa, S.A.B.; *Int'l*, pg. 3136
CONSUMERS 2014 SECURITIZATION FUNDING LLC—See CMS Energy Corporation; *U.S. Public*, pg. 518
CONTACT CENTER COMPANY—See StarTek, Inc.; *U.S. Private*, pg. 3788
CONTINENTAL CONSULTING LIMITED COMPANY—See Continental Holdings Corp.; *Int'l*, pg. 1784
CONTRACTOR MANAGEMENT SERVICES, LLC—See Riverside Partners, LLC; *U.S. Private*, pg. 3445
CONTROL RISKS EAST AFRICA—See Control Risks Group Holdings Ltd.; *Int'l*, pg. 1785
CONWAY FINANCIAL SERVICES, LLC—See Rithm Capital

Corp.; *U.S. Public*, pg. 1800
CONWAY MACKENZIE ATLANTA, LLC—See Conway MacKenzie, Inc.; *U.S. Private*, pg. 1036
CONWAY MACKENZIE CHICAGO, LLC—See Conway MacKenzie, Inc.; *U.S. Private*, pg. 1036
CONWAY MACKENZIE HOUSTON, LLC—See Conway MacKenzie, Inc.; *U.S. Private*, pg. 1036
CONWAY MACKENZIE, INC.; *U.S. Private*, pg. 1036
CONWAY MACKENZIE LOS ANGELES, LLC—See Conway MacKenzie, Inc.; *U.S. Private*, pg. 1036
CONWAY MACKENZIE NEW YORK, LLC—See Conway MacKenzie, Inc.; *U.S. Private*, pg. 1036
COOK M&A ADVISORY SERVICES—See Cook Associates, Inc.; *U.S. Private*, pg. 1037
CO-OPERATIVE PURCHASING SERVICES LTD.; *Int'l*, pg. 1679
COPAL PARTNERS UK LIMITED—See Moody's Corporation; *U.S. Public*, pg. 1467
COPAL PARTNERS (US) INC.—See Moody's Corporation; *U.S. Public*, pg. 1467
COPAL RESEARCH INDIA PRIVATE LIMITED—See Moody's Corporation; *U.S. Public*, pg. 1467
COPAL RESEARCH LTD. (MAURITIUS)—See Moody's Corporation; *U.S. Public*, pg. 1467
COPC INC.—See Black Box Limited; *Int'l*, pg. 1058
COPYRITE BUSINESS SOLUTIONS LIMITED—See Xerox Holdings Corporation; *U.S. Public*, pg. 2386
CORAL HOSPITALITY, LLC; *U.S. Private*, pg. 1046
CORNERSTONE ADVISORS, INC.; *U.S. Private*, pg. 1051
CORNERSTONE ADVISORS, INC.—See Lovell Minnick Partners LLC; *U.S. Private*, pg. 2503
CORPBRASIL COMUNICACAO CORPORATIVA LTDA.—See Grupo MZ; *Int'l*, pg. 3133
CORPERACION GENERAL DE SERVICIOS S.A.—See Grupo Romero; *Int'l*, pg. 3134
CORPORACION VENEZOLANA DE GUAYANA; *Int'l*, pg. 1805
CORPORATE ALLOCATION SERVICES, INC.; *U.S. Private*, pg. 1054
CORPORATE BENEFIT ADVISORS, INC.—See Aon plc; *Int'l*, pg. 495
CORPORATE CITIZENSHIP LIMITED—See Charterhouse Capital Partners LLP; *Int'l*, pg. 1455
CORPORATE COACHES, INC.; *U.S. Private*, pg. 1054
CORPORATE FITNESS WORKS, INC.; *U.S. Private*, pg. 1055
CORPORATE HEALTH GROUP, LLC; *U.S. Private*, pg. 1055
CORPORATEL, S.A. DE C.V.—See Grupo Televisa, S.A.B.; *Int'l*, pg. 3136
CORPORATE RESULTS INC; *U.S. Private*, pg. 1056
CORPORATION FINANCIERE L'EXCELLENCE LTEE (CFE)—See iA Financial Corporation Inc.; *Int'l*, pg. 3567
CORREA HOLDING LTD—See ELLAKTOR S.A.; *Int'l*, pg. 2365
COSMO VENTURES INC.; *U.S. Private*, pg. 1062
COUNTRY SERVICES INC.—See National Amusements, Inc.; *U.S. Private*, pg. 2841
COVERPOINT CATERING CONSULTANCY LIMITED—See Jones Lang LaSalle Incorporated; *U.S. Public*, pg. 1201
C.P. BAKER & COMPANY, LTD; *U.S. Private*, pg. 708
CRA INTERNATIONAL, INC.; *U.S. Public*, pg. 588
CRA INTERNATIONAL LTD.—See CRA International, Inc.; *U.S. Public*, pg. 588
CRA INTERNATIONAL (NETHERLANDS) BV—See CRA International, Inc.; *U.S. Public*, pg. 588
CRA INTERNATIONAL UK LTD.—See CRA International, Inc.; *U.S. Public*, pg. 588
CRANAGE FINANCIAL GROUP PTY. LTD.—See Azimut Holding SpA; *Int'l*, pg. 779
CRA; *U.S. Private*, pg. 1081
THE CRAWFORD GROUP INC.; *U.S. Private*, pg. 4016
CREATIVE DINING SERVICES, INC.; *U.S. Private*, pg. 1088
CREDENCE MANAGEMENT SOLUTIONS; *U.S. Private*, pg. 1090
CREDIT AGRICOLE ALPES PROVENCE; *Int'l*, pg. 1834
THE CREDIT COUNSELLING AND DEBT MANAGEMENT AGENCY—See Bank Negara Malaysia; *Int'l*, pg. 839
CREDIT INTELLIGENCE LIMITED; *Int'l*, pg. 1835
CREDIT SERVICE INT'L CORP.; *U.S. Private*, pg. 1091
CRESAPARTNERS LLC; *U.S. Private*, pg. 1093
CRESA; *U.S. Private*, pg. 1093
CRESCO HOKURIKU LTD.—See Cresco, Ltd.; *Int'l*, pg. 1840
CRIBIS D&B S.R.L.—See CRIF S.p.A.; *Int'l*, pg. 1849
CRIF - CZECH CREDIT BUREAU, A. S.—See CRIF S.p.A.; *Int'l*, pg. 1849
CRISIL IREVNA UK LIMITED—See S&P Global Inc.; *U.S. Public*, pg. 1830
CRISIL IREVNA US LLC—See S&P Global Inc.; *U.S. Public*, pg. 1830
CROMWELL DENMARK A/S—See Cromwell Property Group; *Int'l*, pg. 1854
CROMWELL FINLAND O/Y—See Cromwell Property Group; *Int'l*, pg. 1854
CROSSVIEW, INC.—See GXO Logistics, Inc.; *U.S. Public*, pg. 975

N.A.I.C.S. INDEX

541611 — ADMINISTRATIVE MANA...

CROWN VERPAKKING BELGIE NV—See Crown Holdings, Inc.; *U.S. Public*, pg. 598
CROWN VERPAKKING NEDERLAND N.V.—See Crown Holdings, Inc.; *U.S. Public*, pg. 598
CROZER-KEYSTONE HEALTH SYSTEM INC.; *U.S. Private*, pg. 1113
CSC COMPUTER SCIENCES CONSULTING AUSTRIA GMBH—See DXC Technology Company; *U.S. Public*, pg. 695
CSC DISTRIBUTION, INC.—See Big Lots, Inc.; *U.S. Public*, pg. 330
CSR, INC.—See CVS Health Corporation; *U.S. Public*, pg. 616
CSUBS; *U.S. Private*, pg. 1118
CTY GROUP AS; *Int'l*, pg. 1874
CULTURE PARTNERS—See Hammond, Kennedy, Whitney & Company, Inc.; *U.S. Private*, pg. 1850
CUSTOMER PORTFOLIOS, LLC—See Stirista, LLC; *U.S. Private*, pg. 3813
CUSTOMERWORKS EUROPE SL—See Accenture plc; *Int'l*, pg. 86
CYBERLOGISTICS CORPORATION—See TD Synnex Corp; *U.S. Public*, pg. 1984
DAIWA INSTITUTE OF RESEARCH EUROPE LTD.—See Daiwa Securities Group Inc.; *Int'l*, pg. 1948
DANAOS MANAGEMENT CONSULTANTS SA—See Danaos Corporation; *Int'l*, pg. 1958
DANAOS SHIPPING CO., LTD.—See Danaos Corporation; *Int'l*, pg. 1958
DANE STREET; *U.S. Private*, pg. 1153
DANFORTH ADVISORS, LLC—See Avesi Partners, LLC; *U.S. Private*, pg. 405
THE DANIEL GROUP, LTD.; *U.S. Private*, pg. 4018
DANMARE GROUP INC.—See Ag Growth International Inc.; *Int'l*, pg. 198
DANSKE COMMODITIES US LLC—See Equinor ASA; *Int'l*, pg. 2484
DANYA INTERNATIONAL, LLC—See DLH Holdings Corp.; *U.S. Public*, pg. 670
DAOU DATA CORP.; *Int'l*, pg. 1970
DARK HORSE CONSULTING; *U.S. Private*, pg. 1159
DARK HORSE TECHNOLOGY GROUP CO., LTD.; *Int'l*, pg. 1973
DASHPAY PROPRIETARY LIMITED—See Capital Appreciation Ltd.; *Int'l*, pg. 1309
DATUM CORPORATION; *U.S. Private*, pg. 1167
DAVIES CONSULTING INC.—See Accenture plc; *Int'l*, pg. 86
DAVIES GROUP LIMITED—See HGGC, LLC; *U.S. Private*, pg. 1929
DAVISLOGIC INC—See Jogan, Inc.; *U.S. Private*, pg. 2219
THE D&B COMPANIES OF CANADA LTD.—See Cannae Holdings, Inc.; *U.S. Public*, pg. 430
THE D&B COMPANIES OF CANADA LTD.—See CC Capital Partners, LLC; *U.S. Private*, pg. 799
THE D&B COMPANIES OF CANADA LTD.—See Intercontinental Exchange, Inc.; *U.S. Public*, pg. 1142
DB HR SOLUTIONS GMBH—See Deutsche Bank Aktiengesellschaft; *Int'l*, pg. 2056
DB INVESTMENT MANAGEMENT, INC.—See Deutsche Bank Aktiengesellschaft; *Int'l*, pg. 2056
DBJ LIMITED—See Iron Mountain Incorporated; *U.S. Public*, pg. 1172
DB MAIA LLC—See Deutsche Bank Aktiengesellschaft; *Int'l*, pg. 2056
DB MANAGEMENT SUPPORT GMBH—See Deutsche Bank Aktiengesellschaft; *Int'l*, pg. 2056
DBOI GLOBAL SERVICES (UK) LIMITED—See Deutsche Bank Aktiengesellschaft; *Int'l*, pg. 2057
DB PARTNERSHIP MANAGEMENT II, LLC—See Deutsche Bank Aktiengesellschaft; *Int'l*, pg. 2056
DB PERRY INVESTMENTS LIMITED—See Deutsche Bank Aktiengesellschaft; *Int'l*, pg. 2056
DB PETRI LLC—See Deutsche Bank Aktiengesellschaft; *Int'l*, pg. 2056
DBRS RATINGS GMBH—See Morningstar, Inc.; *U.S. Public*, pg. 1476
DBRS RATINGS LIMITED—See Morningstar, Inc.; *U.S. Public*, pg. 1476
DBS FINANCIAL MANAGEMENT PLC—See Vista Equity Partners, LLC; *U.S. Private*, pg. 4397
DC FINANCIAL, LLC—See Dollar General Corporation; *U.S. Public*, pg. 672
DCH MANAGEMENT SERVICES INC.—See Lithia Motors, Inc.; *U.S. Public*, pg. 1322
DCI CONSULTING GROUP, INC.; *U.S. Private*, pg. 1180
DEAN & COMPANY; *U.S. Private*, pg. 1183
DECIMAL TECHNOLOGIES INC.; *Int'l*, pg. 2001
DECISION INTELLECT PTY. LTD.—See Archer Capital Pty. Ltd.; *Int'l*, pg. 547
DEEP WATER POINT LLC; *U.S. Private*, pg. 1189
DEFACTOSTANDARD, LTD.—See BEENOS Inc.; *Int'l*, pg. 939
DEKRA AGENCIJA D.O.O.—See DEKRA e.V.; *Int'l*, pg. 2010
DELEK FINANCE, INC.—See Delek Group Ltd.; *Int'l*, pg. 2011
DELPHOS INTERNATIONAL, LTD.—See APQ Global Limited; *Int'l*, pg. 522

DELTEK GB LIMITED—See Roper Technologies, Inc.; *U.S. Public*, pg. 1811
DELTEK NETHERLANDS B.V.—See Roper Technologies, Inc.; *U.S. Public*, pg. 1811
DELTEK NORGE AS—See Roper Technologies, Inc.; *U.S. Public*, pg. 1811
DELTEK SVERIGE AB—See Roper Technologies, Inc.; *U.S. Public*, pg. 1811
DENDRIO SOLUTIONS SRL—See Bittnet Systems SA Bucuresti; *Int'l*, pg. 1050
DENTAL NETWORK OF AMERICA INC.; *U.S. Private*, pg. 1206
DENVER MINING FINANCE COMPANY, INC.—See Royal Gold, Inc.; *U.S. Public*, pg. 1815
DEPOSIT INSURANCE CORPORATION OF JAPAN; *Int'l*, pg. 2041
DESANE GROUP HOLDINGS LTD; *Int'l*, pg. 2043
DESIGN LABORATORY, INC.; *U.S. Private*, pg. 1213
DESTEK FAKTORING A.S.; *Int'l*, pg. 2046
DETWILER FENTON GROUP, INC.; *U.S. Public*, pg. 657
DEUTSCHE STRUCTURED FINANCE GMBH & CO. ALPHARD KG—See Advent International Corporation; *U.S. Private*, pg. 96
DEUTSCHE STRUCTURED FINANCE GMBH & CO. ALPHARD KG—See Centerbridge Partners, L.P.; *U.S. Private*, pg. 812
DEUTSCHE STRUCTURED FINANCE GMBH & CO. DENEB KG—See Advent International Corporation; *U.S. Private*, pg. 96
DEUTSCHE STRUCTURED FINANCE GMBH & CO. DENEB KG—See Centerbridge Partners, L.P.; *U.S. Private*, pg. 812
DEUTSCHE STRUCTURED FINANCE GMBH & CO. TITAN KG—See Advent International Corporation; *U.S. Private*, pg. 96
DEUTSCHE STRUCTURED FINANCE GMBH & CO. TITAN KG—See Centerbridge Partners, L.P.; *U.S. Private*, pg. 812
DEUTSCHE STRUCTURED FINANCE GMBH—See Advent International Corporation; *U.S. Private*, pg. 96
DEUTSCHE STRUCTURED FINANCE GMBH—See Centerbridge Partners, L.P.; *U.S. Private*, pg. 812
DEVOTEAM MANAGEMENT CONSULTING NV—See Devoteam SA; *Int'l*, pg. 2090
DEWOLFF, BOBERG & ASSOCIATES INC.; *U.S. Private*, pg. 1220
DEX ONE SERVICE, INC.—See Thryv Holdings, Inc.; *U.S. Public*, pg. 2157
DFCC CONSULTING (PVT) LIMITED—See DFCC Bank PLC; *Int'l*, pg. 2094
DF DEUTSCHE FORFAIT AG; *Int'l*, pg. 2094
DHA GROUP INC.—See ASGN Incorporated; *U.S. Public*, pg. 210
DHL CORPORATE SERVICES SC MEXICO—See Deutsche Post AG; *Int'l*, pg. 2072
DHS CONSULTING, LLC—See Accenture plc; *Int'l*, pg. 86
DIALOG FINANCE PLC; *Int'l*, pg. 2104
DIAMOND SOLUTIONS, INC.; *U.S. Private*, pg. 1224
DIA TIANTIAN (SHANGHAI) MANAGEMENT CONSULTING SERVICE CO. LTD—See Carrefour SA; *Int'l*, pg. 1344
DIEBOLD NIXDORF SINGAPORE PTE. LTD.—See Diebold Nixdorf, Inc.; *U.S. Public*, pg. 661
DIEHL VENTURES GMBH—See Diehl Stiftung & Co. KG; *Int'l*, pg. 2115
DISCERN, LLC—See New Mountain Capital, LLC; *U.S. Private*, pg. 2904
DISNEY MAGIC COMPANY LIMITED—See The Walt Disney Company; *U.S. Public*, pg. 2139
DIVERSICARE LEASING CORP.—See Diversicare Healthcare Services, Inc.; *U.S. Public*, pg. 669
DIVERSIFIED EXECUTIVE SYSTEMS, INC.; *U.S. Private*, pg. 1242
DJI OPCO LLC—See S&P Global Inc.; *U.S. Public*, pg. 1830
DLC INC.—See Odyssey Investment Partners, LLC; *U.S. Private*, pg. 2994
DNXCORP SE; *Int'l*, pg. 2151
DOCTORS ADMINISTRATIVE SOLUTIONS, LLC; *U.S. Private*, pg. 1251
DOCTORS RESOURCE SPECIALISTS, LLC—See Riverside Partners, LLC; *U.S. Private*, pg. 3446
DOE & INGALLS OF FLORIDA OPERATING LLC—See Thermo Fisher Scientific Inc.; *U.S. Public*, pg. 2146
DOLLAR TREE MANAGEMENT, INC.—See Dollar Tree, Inc.; *U.S. Public*, pg. 2162
DOMINION CAPITAL, INC.—See Dominion Energy, Inc.; *U.S. Public*, pg. 673
DONATOR BERATUNGS GMBH—See Allianz SE; *Int'l*, pg. 352
DONNELLEY TRANSLATION SERVICES (SHANGHAI) CO., LTD.—See Donnelley Financial Solutions, Inc.; *U.S. Public*, pg. 677
DORUK FINANSMAN A.S.—See Adil Bey Holding A.S.; *Int'l*, pg. 148
DOUBLE LINE, INC.; *U.S. Private*, pg. 1265
DOUGLAS EMMETT MANAGEMENT, INC.—See Douglas Emmett, Inc.; *U.S. Public*, pg. 678
DOUG RILEY ENTERPRISES INC.; *U.S. Private*, pg. 1266

DOVRE CANADA LTD.—See Dovre Group Plc; *Int'l*, pg. 2182
DOVRE GROUP ENERGY AS—See Dovre Group Plc; *Int'l*, pg. 2182
DRAGON JADE INTERNATIONAL LIMITED; *Int'l*, pg. 2199
DREFA IMMOBILIEN MANAGEMENT GMBH—See DREFA Media Holding GmbH; *Int'l*, pg. 2204
DR FINSTERER UND KONIGS INKASSO GMBH—See Altor Equity Partners AB; *Int'l*, pg. 396
D.R. HORTON/CONTINENTAL SERIES—See D.R. Horton, Inc.; *U.S. Public*, pg. 619
DROEGE GROUP AG; *Int'l*, pg. 2204
DSP BLACKROCK INVESTMENT MANAGERS PRIVATE LIMITED—See BlackRock, Inc.; *U.S. Public*, pg. 345
DSP BLACKROCK INVESTMENT MANAGERS PRIVATE LIMITED—See Synaptics Incorporated; *U.S. Public*, pg. 1969
DST HEALTH SOLUTIONS, INC.—See SS&C Technologies Holdings, Inc.; *U.S. Public*, pg. 1923
DUN & BRADSTREET CANADA BV—See Cannae Holdings, Inc.; *U.S. Public*, pg. 429
DUN & BRADSTREET CANADA BV—See CC Capital Partners, LLC; *U.S. Private*, pg. 798
DUN & BRADSTREET CANADA BV—See Intercontinental Exchange, Inc.; *U.S. Public*, pg. 1142
DUN & BRADSTREET EUROPE, LTD.—See Cannae Holdings, Inc.; *U.S. Public*, pg. 429
DUN & BRADSTREET EUROPE, LTD.—See CC Capital Partners, LLC; *U.S. Private*, pg. 798
DUN & BRADSTREET EUROPE, LTD.—See Intercontinental Exchange, Inc.; *U.S. Public*, pg. 1142
DUN & BRADSTREET (VIETNAM) LLC—See Cannae Holdings, Inc.; *U.S. Public*, pg. 429
DUN & BRADSTREET (VIETNAM) LLC—See CC Capital Partners, LLC; *U.S. Private*, pg. 798
DUN & BRADSTREET (VIETNAM) LLC—See Intercontinental Exchange, Inc.; *U.S. Public*, pg. 1142
DUNLOP GRUND UND SERVICE VERWALTUNGS GMBH—See The Goodyear Tire & Rubber Company; *U.S. Public*, pg. 2083
DUNSFORD FINANCE PLANNING PTY. LTD.—See Azimut Holding SpA; *Int'l*, pg. 779
DUNSFORD FINANCIAL PLANNING PTY. LTD.—See Azimut Holding SpA; *Int'l*, pg. 779
DUPONT IBERICA, S.L.—See Corteva, Inc.; *U.S. Public*, pg. 584
DUPONT (THAILAND) LIMITED—See Corteva, Inc.; *U.S. Public*, pg. 582
DYNALENE INC.; *U.S. Private*, pg. 1297
DYNALINQ BV—See bpost NV/SA; *Int'l*, pg. 1133
DYNAMIC RISK ASSESSMENT SYSTEMS, INC.—See Eddyfi NDT, Inc.; *Int'l*, pg. 2304
DYNAMIC WORKFORCE SOLUTIONS, LLC—See Madison Dearborn Partners, LLC; *U.S. Private*, pg. 2540
DYNAMIC WORKFORCE SOLUTIONS - TEXAS, LLC—See Madison Dearborn Partners, LLC; *U.S. Private*, pg. 2540
DYNAM JAPAN HOLDINGS, CO., LTD.; *Int'l*, pg. 2239
DZ COMPLIANCEPARTNER GMBH—See DZ BANK AG Deutsche Zentral-Genossenschaftsbank; *Int'l*, pg. 2243
E3 FEDERAL SOLUTIONS, LLC—See NewSpring Capital LLC; *U.S. Private*, pg. 2918
EAGLE RAY TECHNOLOGIES GROUP—See Carl Marks & Co., Inc.; *U.S. Private*, pg. 763
EARL G. GRAVES LTD.; *U.S. Private*, pg. 1312
EASTERN DRAGON FILM CO., LTD—See China Poly Group Corporation; *Int'l*, pg. 1541
EASYACCESS FINANCIAL SERVICES LIMITED; *Int'l*, pg. 2276
ECAPITAL ADVISORS, LLC.; *U.S. Private*, pg. 1326
ECNET (HONG KONG) LIMITED—See Blackstone Inc.; *U.S. Public*, pg. 357
ECNET KABUSHIKI KAISHA—See Blackstone Inc.; *U.S. Public*, pg. 357
ECNET LIMITED—See Blackstone Inc.; *U.S. Public*, pg. 357
ECNET (M) SDN. BHD.—See Blackstone Inc.; *U.S. Public*, pg. 357
ECNET (SHANGHAI) CO. LTD.—See Blackstone Inc.; *U.S. Public*, pg. 357
ECNET SYSTEMS (THAILAND) COMPANY LIMITED—See Blackstone Inc.; *U.S. Public*, pg. 357
ECOFYS GERMANY GMBH—See Bain Capital, LP; *U.S. Private*, pg. 432
ECOFYS INVESTMENTS B.V.—See Bain Capital, LP; *U.S. Private*, pg. 432
ECOFYS UK LIMITED—See Bain Capital, LP; *U.S. Private*, pg. 432
ECOMANAGE CORPORATION—See Hitachi Zosen Corporation; *Int'l*, pg. 3410
ECONOSERVE SOLUTIONS, LLC—See Riverside Partners, LLC; *U.S. Private*, pg. 3446
ECVISION (SHENZHEN) CO. LTD.—See Insight Venture Management, LLC; *U.S. Private*, pg. 2087
ECZACIBASI INVESTMENT HOLDING CO.—See Eczacibasi Holding A.S.; *Int'l*, pg. 2301
EDENRED AUSTRIA GMBH—See Edenred S.A.; *Int'l*, pg. 2307
EDENRED INCENTIVES & MOTIVATION LTD—See Edenred S.A.; *Int'l*, pg. 2307

541611 — ADMINISTRATIVE MANA...   CORPORATE AFFILIATIONS

EDGAR, DUNN & COMPANY (EDC)—See Auriemma Consulting Group, Inc.; *U.S. Private*, pg. 393
EDP SERVICOS - SISTEMAS PARA A QUALIDADE E EFICIENCIA ENERGETICA, S.A.—See EDP - Energias de Portugal, S.A.; *Int'l*, pg. 2314
EDP SERVINER - SERVICOS DE ENERGIA, S.A.—See EDP - Energias de Portugal, S.A.; *Int'l*, pg. 2314
EDUCATIONAL COMMISSION FOR FOREIGN MEDICAL GRADUATES; *U.S. Private*, pg. 1339
EFG ASSET MANAGEMENT (SWITZERLAND) S.A.—See EFG International AG; *Int'l*, pg. 2320
EFORT FRANCE S.A.S—See EFORT Intelligent Equipment Co., Ltd.; *Int'l*, pg. 2321
EIMC, LLC—See Engle Martin & Associates, LLC; *U.S. Private*, pg. 1399
EKO FAKTORING A.S.; *Int'l*, pg. 2339
ELAND ENGINEERING, INC.—See Comvest Group Holdings LLC; *U.S. Private*, pg. 1007
ELAN IT RESOURCE A/S—See ManpowerGroup Inc.; *U.S. Public*, pg. 1357
ELAN IT SERVICES GMBH—See ManpowerGroup Inc.; *U.S. Public*, pg. 1357
ELEVAATE LIMITED—See Charlesbank Capital Partners, LLC; *U.S. Private*, pg. 855
ELEVATE TECHNOLOGY SOLUTIONS; *U.S. Private*, pg. 1358
ELIXIRR, INC.—See Elixirr International plc; *Int'l*, pg. 2363
ELIZA CORPORATION—See Veritas Capital Fund Management, LLC; *U.S. Private*, pg. 4362
THE ELOCEN GROUP LLC; *U.S. Private*, pg. 4025
ELPOOL I UMEA AB—See Addnode Group AB; *Int'l*, pg. 130
ELVICTOR GROUP, INC.; *Int'l*, pg. 2371
EMCOM ENTERTAINMENT CO., LTD.—See EMCOM Holdings Co., Ltd.; *Int'l*, pg. 2376
EMEDIA GROUP INC; *U.S. Private*, pg. 1379
EMERGENT METHOD, LLC; *U.S. Private*, pg. 1381
EMERSON ELECTRIC OVERSEAS FINANCE CORP.—See Emerson Electric Co.; *U.S. Public*, pg. 742
EMERSON PROCESS MANAGEMENT—See Emerson Electric Co.; *U.S. Public*, pg. 746
EMEX LLC—See O2 Investment Partners, LLC; *U.S. Private*, pg. 2982
EMGS INTERNATIONAL BV—See Electromagnetic Geoservices ASA; *Int'l*, pg. 2353
EMPIRIS LLC—See Bain Capital, LP; *U.S. Private*, pg. 432
EMPLOYMENT TECHNOLOGIES CORPORATION; *U.S. Private*, pg. 1387
EMPYREAN SERVICES LLC; *U.S. Private*, pg. 1388
ENCAP INVESTMENTS L.P.; *U.S. Private*, pg. 1389
ENDERLE GROUP, INC.; *U.S. Private*, pg. 1391
ENDESA SERVICIOS SL—See Enel S.p.A.; *Int'l*, pg. 2412
ENENTO GROUP PLC; *Int'l*, pg. 2415
ENERGETICS INCORPORATED-WASHINGTON—See TPG Capital, L.P.; *U.S. Public*, pg. 2176
ENERSYS CORPORATION; *U.S. Private*, pg. 1396
ENI OIL & GAS INC—See Eni S.p.A.; *Int'l*, pg. 2438
ENSHU (QINGDAO) MACHINE CO., LTD.—See Enshu Limited; *Int'l*, pg. 2446
ENTRUST WEALTH MANAGEMENT PTY LTD—See Euroz Hartleys Group Limited; *Int'l*, pg. 2559
ENVIRITE, INC.—See Republic Services, Inc.; *U.S. Public*, pg. 1788
ENVIRONMENTAL HEALTH TESTING; *U.S. Private*, pg. 1408
ENVISION BUSINESS CONSULTING, LLC.; *U.S. Private*, pg. 1410
EOH CONSULTING (PTY) LIMITED—See EOH HOLDINGS LIMITED; *Int'l*, pg. 2457
E.ON BETEILIGUNGSVERWALTUNGS GMBH—See E.ON SE; *Int'l*, pg. 2252
E.ON GRUGA GESCHAFTSFUHRUNGSGESELLSCHAFT MBH—See E.ON SE; *Int'l*, pg. 2254
E.ON INHOUSE CONSULTING GMBH—See E.ON SE; *Int'l*, pg. 2254
E.ON WESTFALEN WESER 2. VERMOGENSVERWALTUNGS-GMBH—See E.ON SE; *Int'l*, pg. 2256
EPBF SA—See Groupe BPCE; *Int'l*, pg. 3094
EPIC ADVISORS, INC.—See NBT Bancorp Inc.; *U.S. Public*, pg. 1501
EPIC RETIREMENT PLAN SERVICES, PORTLAND—See NBT Bancorp Inc.; *U.S. Public*, pg. 1501
EPM SOLUTIONS, INC.; *U.S. Private*, pg. 1414
EPONYMOUS ASSOCIATES LLC—See Steiner Equities Group LLC; *U.S. Private*, pg. 3798
EP-SOGO CO., LTD.—See EPS Holdings, Inc.; *Int'l*, pg. 2465
EPUREX FILMS GESCHAFTSFUHRUNGS-GMBH—See Bayer Aktiengesellschaft; *Int'l*, pg. 907
EQUIPMENT RESEARCH GROUP PTY. LTD.—See carsales.com Limited; *Int'l*, pg. 1347
ESCORTS SECURITIES LIMITED—See Escorts Kubota Limited; *Int'l*, pg. 2502
ESPACIO DE VINCULACION, A.C.—See Grupo Televisa, S.A.B.; *Int'l*, pg. 3136
ETASK TECHNOLOGIES LIMITED; *Int'l*, pg. 2520
EUREKA FINANCIAL GROUP PTY. LTD.—See Azimut Holding SpA; *Int'l*, pg. 779

EUROFINS AGROSCIENCE SERVICES EAG LABORATORIES GMBH—See Eurofins Scientific S.E.; *Int'l*, pg. 2536
EUROFINS AGROSCIENCE SERVICES ITALY S.R.L.—See Eurofins Scientific S.E.; *Int'l*, pg. 2536
EUROFINS AGROSCIENCE SERVICES S.A.S.—See Eurofins Scientific S.E.; *Int'l*, pg. 2537
EUROFINS AGRO TESTING UK LIMITED—See Eurofins Scientific S.E.; *Int'l*, pg. 2536
EUROFINS ALBA SCIENCE LIMITED—See Eurofins Scientific S.E.; *Int'l*, pg. 2537
EUROFINS AMATSIAQUITAINE S.A.S.—See Eurofins Scientific S.E.; *Int'l*, pg. 2537
EUROFINS AMATSIGROUP S.A.S.—See Eurofins Scientific S.E.; *Int'l*, pg. 2537
EUROFINS ANALYTICS LLC—See Eurofins Scientific S.E.; *Int'l*, pg. 2537
EUROFINS ASSURANCE MYANMAR LTD.—See Eurofins Scientific S.E.; *Int'l*, pg. 2538
EUROFINS ASSURANCE TURKEY KALITE VE DENETIM HIZMETLERI LIMITED SIRKETI—See Eurofins Scientific S.E.; *Int'l*, pg. 2538
EUROFINS BEACON DISCOVERY, INC.—See Eurofins Scientific S.E.; *Int'l*, pg. 2538
EUROFINS BIOPHARMA PRODUCT TESTING ENCO, INC.—See Eurofins Scientific S.E.; *Int'l*, pg. 2538
EUROFINS BIOPHARMA PRODUCT TESTING HUNGARY KFT.—See Eurofins Scientific S.E.; *Int'l*, pg. 2538
EUROFINS BIOSKIN GMBH—See Eurofins Scientific S.E.; *Int'l*, pg. 2538
EUROFINS CDMO ALPHORA, INC.—See Eurofins Scientific S.E.; *Int'l*, pg. 2538
EUROFINS CELLTX, INC.—See Eurofins Scientific S.E.; *Int'l*, pg. 2539
EUROFINS CENTRO ANALITICO MIGUEZ MUINOS, S.L.U.—See Eurofins Scientific S.E.; *Int'l*, pg. 2539
EUROFINS CIMERA ESTUDIOS APLICADOS, S.L.U.—See Eurofins Scientific S.E.; *Int'l*, pg. 2539
EUROFINS CLINICAL DIAGNOSTICS UK LIMITED—See Eurofins Scientific S.E.; *Int'l*, pg. 2539
EUROFINS CONSUMER PRODUCT TESTING IBLSC US, INC.—See Eurofins Scientific S.E.; *Int'l*, pg. 2539
EUROFINS COSMETICS & PERSONAL CARE ITALY S.R.L.—See Eurofins Scientific S.E.; *Int'l*, pg. 2539
EUROFINS CRA CO., LTD.—See Eurofins Scientific S.E.; *Int'l*, pg. 2538
EUROFINS DERMA TRONNIER GMBH—See Eurofins Scientific S.E.; *Int'l*, pg. 2539
EUROFINS DERMSCAN POLAND SP. Z O.O.—See Eurofins Scientific S.E.; *Int'l*, pg. 2539
EUROFINS DISPOSABLE LAB S.A.S.—See Eurofins Scientific S.E.; *Int'l*, pg. 2540
EUROFINS EAG MATERIALS SCIENCE TAIWAN, LTD.—See Eurofins Scientific S.E.; *Int'l*, pg. 2540
EUROFINS EARTH CONSUL KK—See Eurofins Scientific S.E.; *Int'l*, pg. 2540
EUROFINS ENVIRONMENT TESTING NORTHEAST, LLC—See Eurofins Scientific S.E.; *Int'l*, pg. 2540
EUROFINS ENVIRONMENT TESTING NORTHWEST, LLC—See Eurofins Scientific S.E.; *Int'l*, pg. 2540
EUROFINS ENVIRONMENT TESTING PHILADELPHIA, LLC—See Eurofins Scientific S.E.; *Int'l*, pg. 2540
EUROFINS ENVIRONMENT TESTING SOUTH CENTRAL, LLC—See Eurofins Scientific S.E.; *Int'l*, pg. 2540
EUROFINS FOOD BARCELONA, S.L.U.—See Eurofins Scientific S.E.; *Int'l*, pg. 2541
EUROFINS FOOD TESTING ROTTERDAM B.V.—See Eurofins Scientific S.E.; *Int'l*, pg. 2541
EUROFINS FOOD TESTING SUD GMBH—See Eurofins Scientific S.E.; *Int'l*, pg. 2541
EUROFINS GYNAE-SCREEN LIMITED—See Eurofins Scientific S.E.; *Int'l*, pg. 2543
EUROFINS I VERWALTUNGSGESELLSCHAFT GMBH—See Eurofins Scientific S.E.; *Int'l*, pg. 2544
EUROFINS KCTL CO., LTD.—See Eurofins Scientific S.E.; *Int'l*, pg. 2544
EUROFINS LANCASTER LABORATORIES ENVIRONMENT TESTING, LLC—See Eurofins Scientific S.E.; *Int'l*, pg. 2545
EUROFINS MEDISCHE MICROBIOLOGIE B.V.—See Eurofins Scientific S.E.; *Int'l*, pg. 2546
EUROFINS NANOLAB TECHNOLOGIES, INC.—See Eurofins Scientific S.E.; *Int'l*, pg. 2546
EUROFINS NBLSC ENVIRONMENT TESTING SPAIN, S.L.U.—See Eurofins Scientific S.E.; *Int'l*, pg. 2546
EUROFINS NSC FINANCE GERMANY GMBH—See Eurofins Scientific S.E.; *Int'l*, pg. 2546
EUROFINS PHYLIAE S.A.S.—See Eurofins Scientific S.E.; *Int'l*, pg. 2547
EUROFINS PRODUCT TESTING, COSMETICS & PERSONAL CARE SPAIN, S.L.U.—See Eurofins Scientific S.E.; *Int'l*, pg. 2547
EUROFINS REGULATORY & CONSULTANCY SERVICES ITALY S.R.L.—See Eurofins Scientific S.E.; *Int'l*, pg. 2547
EUROFINS SALUX B.V.—See Eurofins Scientific S.E.; *Int'l*, pg. 2547
EUROFINS SAUDI AJAL LABORATORIES LTD.—See Eurofins Scientific S.E.; *Int'l*, pg. 2547
EUROFINS VIRACOR BIOPHARMA SERVICES, INC.—See Eurofins Scientific S.E.; *Int'l*, pg. 2549

EVANS INCORPORATED; *U.S. Private*, pg. 1435
EVANTA VENTURES, INC.—See Gartner, Inc.; *U.S. Public*, pg. 906
EVERBRIGHT PRAMERICA FUND MANAGEMENT CO., LTD.—See Prudential Financial, Inc.; *U.S. Public*, pg. 1732
EVEREST NATIONAL—See Everest Group, Ltd.; *Int'l*, pg. 2564
EVERGREEN REMEDIATION SERVICES, LLC—See Energy Transfer LP; *U.S. Public*, pg. 764
EVERKEY GLOBAL FUND, L.P.—See Wells Fargo & Company; *U.S. Public*, pg. 2343
EVERON TECHNOLOGY SERVICES, LLC—See The Allstate Corporation; *U.S. Public*, pg. 2033
EVIO, INC.; *U.S. Public*, pg. 803
EWORK DANMARK APS—See eWork Group AB; *Int'l*, pg. 2576
EWORK NORDIC OY—See eWork Group AB; *Int'l*, pg. 2576
EWORK NORGE AS—See eWork Group AB; *Int'l*, pg. 2576
EXCALIBUR MANAGEMENT CONSULTING (SHANGHAI) CO., LTD.—See Fiskars Oyj Abp; *Int'l*, pg. 2694
EXCELLENCE IN MOTIVATION, INC.—See Aimia Inc.; *Int'l*, pg. 233
EXCELLERANT, INC.; *Int'l*, pg. 2578
EXCEPTIONAL SOFTWARE STRATEGIES, INC.—See Godspeed Capital Management LP; *U.S. Private*, pg. 1725
EXCHANGE SERVICES L.L.C.—See Zions Bancorporation, National Association; *U.S. Public*, pg. 2408
EXIGER LLC; *U.S. Private*, pg. 1449
EXPANSION STRATEGIES INC.; *U.S. Private*, pg. 1449
EXPERIS CIBER B.V.—See ManpowerGroup Inc.; *U.S. Public*, pg. 1357
EXPLEO GERMANY GMBH - MUNICH—See Assystem S.A.; *Int'l*, pg. 650
EXPRIVIA PROJECTS S.R.L.—See Exprivia SpA; *Int'l*, pg. 2591
EXUSIA INC.—See Globant S.A.; *Int'l*, pg. 3005
EXXONMOBIL FINANCE COMPANY LIMITED—See Exxon Mobil Corporation; *U.S. Public*, pg. 815
EXZAC, INC.—See Asseco Poland S.A.; *Int'l*, pg. 642
EZ HK, LTD.—See Global Payments Inc.; *U.S. Public*, pg. 943
EZIDEBIT PTY LTD.—See Global Payments Inc.; *U.S. Public*, pg. 943
EZI MANAGEMENT PTY LTD.—See Global Payments Inc.; *U.S. Public*, pg. 943
FACTORIA Y MANUFACTURA S.A. DE C.V.—See ManpowerGroup Inc.; *U.S. Public*, pg. 1358
FACT UNTERNEHMENSBERATUNG SCHWEIZ AG—See Silver Lake Group, LLC; *U.S. Private*, pg. 3658
FAIRFIELD MAXWELL LTD.; *U.S. Private*, pg. 1463
FAIRWINDS PARTNERS, LLC; *U.S. Private*, pg. 1465
THE FAMILY BUSINESS INSTITUTE LLC—See The Travelers Companies, Inc.; *U.S. Public*, pg. 2136
FAMILY WEALTH ALLIANCE, LLC—See The Charles Schwab Corporation; *U.S. Public*, pg. 2058
FAO OFFICE GMBH—See ManpowerGroup Inc.; *U.S. Public*, pg. 1358
FARITEC HOLDINGS LIMITED; *Int'l*, pg. 2618
FAS CAPITAL MANAGEMENT LTD.—See FAS Finance & Investment Limited; *Int'l*, pg. 2620
FASSFORWARD CONSULTING GROUP; *U.S. Private*, pg. 1481
FASTIGHETS AB KLADESHANDLAREN—See Lone Star Funds; *U.S. Private*, pg. 2485
FAZZI ASSOCIATES, INC.—See Leonard Green & Partners, L.P.; *U.S. Private*, pg. 2430
FAZZI ASSOCIATES, INC.—See TPG Capital, L.P.; *U.S. Public*, pg. 2177
FBG GROUP PTY LTD.—See Madison Dearborn Partners, LLC; *U.S. Private*, pg. 2540
FBMC BENEFITS MANAGEMENT, INC.; *U.S. Private*, pg. 1485
FCI FEDERAL, INC.—See Amentum Services, Inc.; *U.S. Private*, pg. 219
FEDERAL CONTRACTING GROUP—See M.A. Mortenson Company; *U.S. Private*, pg. 2527
FEDEX CUSTOMER INFORMATION SERVICES, INC.—See FedEx Corporation; *U.S. Public*, pg. 827
FERNRIDGE CONSULTING (PROPRIETARY) LIMITED—See Capital Eye Investments Limited; *Int'l*, pg. 1310
FERRARI MANAGEMENT CONSULTING (SHANGHAI) CO., LTD.—See Ferrari N.V.; *Int'l*, pg. 2639
FFG BUSINESS CONSULTING CO., LTD.—See Fukuoka Financial Group, Inc.; *Int'l*, pg. 2840
FGL GROUP BUSINESS SERVICE CO., LTD.—See Fuyo General Lease Co., Ltd.; *Int'l*, pg. 2859
FHL PROPERTIES PTE LIMITED—See Fijian Holdings Limited; *Int'l*, pg. 2662
FHM INSURANCE COMPANY—See LUBA Mutual Holding Company; *U.S. Public*, pg. 2510
FI CONSULTING; *U.S. Private*, pg. 1501
FIDELIS GROUP LLC—See Emerson Electric Co.; *U.S. Public*, pg. 741
FIDUCIAL; *Int'l*, pg. 2655

4666

N.A.I.C.S. INDEX

541611 — ADMINISTRATIVE MANA...

FIDUCIARY CAPITAL MANAGEMENT, INC.—See Public Financial Management, Inc.; *U.S. Private*, pg. 3299
FIERTE CORPORATION—See Avant Corporation; *Int'l*, pg. 735
FILMOLUX ITALIA S.R.L.—See Blue Cap AG; *Int'l*, pg. 1067
FINANCIAL.SERVICE.PLUS GMBH—See flatexDEGIRO AG; *Int'l*, pg. 2698
FINANCIERA EL CORTE INGLES E.F.C., S.A.—See Banco Santander, S.A.; *Int'l*, pg. 827
FINN PARTNERS, INC.; *U.S. Private*, pg. 1510
FINTECH ASSET MANAGEMENT INCORPORATED—See FinTech Global Incorporated; *Int'l*, pg. 2677
FINTEL PLC; *Int'l*, pg. 2677
FIRESTORM SOLUTIONS, LLC—See Rekor Systems, Inc.; *U.S. Public*, pg. 1778
THE FIRM ADVISORS, LLC; *U.S. Private*, pg. 4029
FIRST CHOICE PURCHASING LIMITED—See Aramark; *U.S. Public*, pg. 178
FIRST DEALER RESOURCES, INC.—See iA Financial Corporation Inc.; *Int'l*, pg. 3568
FIRST DERIVATIVES (HONG KONG) LIMITED—See FD Technologies PLC; *Int'l*, pg. 2628
FIRST DERIVATIVES (IRELAND) LIMITED—See FD Technologies PLC; *Int'l*, pg. 2628
FIRST DERIVATIVES JAPAN CO. LIMITED—See FD Technologies PLC; *Int'l*, pg. 2628
FIRST DERIVATIVES PTE LIMITED—See FD Technologies PLC; *Int'l*, pg. 2628
FIRST FINANCIAL EQUIPMENT FINANCE, LLC—See First Financial Bancorp.; *U.S. Public*, pg. 843
FIRST FINANCIAL PREFERRED CAPITAL, INC.—See First Financial Bancorp.; *U.S. Public*, pg. 843
FIRST FRANCHISE CAPITAL CORPORATION—See First Financial Bancorp.; *U.S. Public*, pg. 843
FIRST MANHATTAN CONSULTING GROUP, LLC—See Deluxe Corporation; *U.S. Public*, pg. 653
FIRST NAMES CORPORATE SERVICES LIMITED—See AnaCap Financial Partners LLP; *Int'l*, pg. 445
FIRST NAMES (CYPRUS) LIMITED—See AnaCap Financial Partners LLP; *Int'l*, pg. 445
FIRST NAMES (ISLE OF MAN) LIMITED—See AnaCap Financial Partners LLP; *Int'l*, pg. 445
FIRSTSOURCE ADVANTAGE LLC—See Firstsource Solutions Limited; *Int'l*, pg. 2691
FIRSTSOURCE ADVANTAGE LLC—See Firstsource Solutions Limited; *Int'l*, pg. 2691
FISHER INTERNATIONAL, INC.—See Battery Ventures, L.P.; *U.S. Private*, pg. 489
FISHKIND & ASSOCIATES, INC.—See Public Financial Management, Inc.; *U.S. Private*, pg. 3299
FITAS VERWALTUNG GMBH & CO. REGIUM-OBJEKTE KG—See E.ON SE; *Int'l*, pg. 2257
FIVE BRIDGES ADVISORS LLC—See Radian Group, Inc.; *U.S. Public*, pg. 1759
FIVE STAR DEVELOPMENT, INC.; *U.S. Private*, pg. 1537
FLEETPRO RIVER LTD.; *Int'l*, pg. 2699
FLETCHER JONES MANAGEMENT GROUP, INC.; *U.S. Private*, pg. 1542
FLEXSERVICE SOLUTIONS BV—See ManpowerGroup Inc.; *U.S. Public*, pg. 1358
FLEXSHOPPER, INC.; *U.S. Public*, pg. 853
FLORAGO SA—See Floridienne SA; *Int'l*, pg. 2708
FLUIDEDGE CONSULTING, INC.—See CitiusTech Inc.; *U.S. Private*, pg. 902
FOAMHAND LIMITED—See OSI Systems, Inc.; *U.S. Public*, pg. 1621
FOCUM BELGIUM BVBA—See Arrow Global Group PLC; *Int'l*, pg. 579
FOCUM GROEP B.V.—See Arrow Global Group PLC; *Int'l*, pg. 579
FOCUS MANAGEMENT GROUP USA, INC.; *U.S. Private*, pg. 1556
FOOTE PARTNERS LLC; *U.S. Private*, pg. 1562
FORAM GROUP, INC.; *U.S. Private*, pg. 1562
FORCE MANAGEMENT, LLC—See GrowthPlay LLC; *U.S. Private*, pg. 1796
FOREST SUPPORT SERVICES PLC; *Int'l*, pg. 2732
FORRESTER RESEARCH GMBH & CO. KG—See Forrester Research, Inc.; *U.S. Public*, pg. 868
FORRESTER RESEARCH LTD.—See Forrester Research, Inc.; *U.S. Public*, pg. 868
FORTIS PRIVATE EQUITY EXPANSION BELGIUM NV—See BNP Paribas SA; *Int'l*, pg. 1084
FORTRESS FINANCIAL SOLUTIONS PTY. LTD.—See Arthur J. Gallagher & Co.; *U.S. Public*, pg. 205
FORWARD DIMENSION CAPITAL 1 LLP—See Forward Internet Group Ltd.; *Int'l*, pg. 2747
FORZA LIEN, INC.—See Patriot National, Inc.; *U.S. Private*, pg. 3110
FOSTER RAFFAN IPLAN PTY. LTD.—See Azimut Holding SpA; *Int'l*, pg. 779
FOTEXNET KFT.—See Fotex Holding SE; *Int'l*, pg. 2752
FOUNDATION SOURCE PHILANTHROPIC SERVICES INC.—See GTCR LLC; *U.S. Private*, pg. 1805
FRANCORP, INC.; *U.S. Private*, pg. 1593
FRANKLIN ADVISERS, INC.—See Franklin Resources, Inc.; *U.S. Public*, pg. 880
FRANKLIN COVEY COMPANY; *U.S. Public*, pg. 877

FRANKLIN TEMPLETON INVESTIMENTOS (BRASIL) LTDA.—See Franklin Resources, Inc.; *U.S. Public*, pg. 880
FRANKLIN TEMPLETON INVESTMENTS JAPAN LIMITED—See Franklin Resources, Inc.; *U.S. Public*, pg. 880
FREEDOM TECHNOLOGIES, INC.; *U.S. Private*, pg. 1604
FREEMAN & CO., LLC.—See Houlihan Lokey, Inc.; *U.S. Public*, pg. 1055
FRMO CORP.; *U.S. Public*, pg. 886
FRONTEC AB—See Acando AB; *Int'l*, pg. 78
FRONTEC AFFARSSYSTEM AB—See Acando AB; *Int'l*, pg. 78
FRONTEC BUSINESS INTEGRATION AB—See Acando AB; *Int'l*, pg. 78
FRONTEC BUSINESS SOLUTIONS AB—See Acando AB; *Int'l*, pg. 78
FRONTEC MULTIDESIGN AB—See Acando AB; *Int'l*, pg. 78
FRONTERA GROUP INC.; *U.S. Public*, pg. 887
FTI CAPITAL ADVISORS, LLC—See FTI Consulting, Inc.; *U.S. Public*, pg. 890
FTI COMMERCIAL CONSULTING (SHANGHAI) CO. LTD.—See FTI Consulting, Inc.; *U.S. Public*, pg. 890
FTI CONSULTING (ASIA) LTD—See FTI Consulting, Inc.; *U.S. Public*, pg. 890
FTI CONSULTING BELGIUM SA—See FTI Consulting, Inc.; *U.S. Public*, pg. 890
FTI CONSULTING (CHINA) LTD.—See FTI Consulting, Inc.; *U.S. Public*, pg. 890
FTI CONSULTING COLOMBIA S.A.S.—See FTI Consulting, Inc.; *U.S. Public*, pg. 890
FTI CONSULTING, INC.; *U.S. Public*, pg. 889
FTI CONSULTING PANAMA, SDAD. LTDA.—See FTI Consulting, Inc.; *U.S. Public*, pg. 890
FTI CONSULTING S.A.—See FTI Consulting, Inc.; *U.S. Public*, pg. 890
FTI CONSULTING (SINGAPORE) PTE. LTD.—See FTI Consulting, Inc.; *U.S. Public*, pg. 890
FTI CONSULTING SOLUTIONS LIMITED—See FTI Consulting, Inc.; *U.S. Public*, pg. 891
FTI CONSULTING SPAIN, S.R.L.—See FTI Consulting, Inc.; *U.S. Public*, pg. 891
FTI CONSULTING TECHNOLOGY (SYDNEY) PTY LTD—See FTI Consulting, Inc.; *U.S. Public*, pg. 891
FTI CONSULTORIA LTDA.—See FTI Consulting, Inc.; *U.S. Public*, pg. 891
FUJITSU AMERICA, INC.—See Fujitsu Limited; *Int'l*, pg. 2833
FUJITSU MANAGEMENT SERVICES OF AMERICA, INC.—See Fujitsu Limited; *Int'l*, pg. 2833
FUJI XEROX KOREA COMPANY LIMITED—See FUJIFILM Holdings Corporation; *Int'l*, pg. 2825
FUKUYAMA BUSINESS NETWORK CO., LTD.—See Founder's Consultants Holdings, Inc.; *Int'l*, pg. 2753
FULFILMENT PLUS GMBH—See Droege Group AG; *Int'l*, pg. 2205
FUNAI CONSULTING, INC.—See Funai Soken Holdings Incorporated; *Int'l*, pg. 2845
FUNAI CONSULTING SHANGHAI, INC.—See Funai Soken Holdings Incorporated; *Int'l*, pg. 2845
FUNDACAO PORTUGAL TELECOM—See Altice Europe N.V.; *Int'l*, pg. 392
FUNDADMINISTRATION, INC.—See Apex Fund Services Holdings Ltd.; *Int'l*, pg. 510
FX GLOBAL INC.—See FUJIFILM Holdings Corporation; *Int'l*, pg. 2825
G4S RISK MANAGEMENT LIMITED—See Allied Universal Manager LLC; *U.S. Private*, pg. 189
GAGEN MACDONALD, LLC.—See APCO Worldwide; *U.S. Private*, pg. 291
GALAXY FUTURES COMPANY LIMITED—See China Galaxy Securities Company Limited; *Int'l*, pg. 1503
GALLAGHER BENEFIT SERVICES, INC.—See Arthur J. Gallagher & Co.; *U.S. Public*, pg. 205
GALLAGHER COMMUNICATION—See Arthur J. Gallagher & Co.; *U.S. Public*, pg. 202
GALLUP CONSULTING—See The Gallup Organization; *U.S. Private*, pg. 4031
GAMA CONSULTORES ASSOCIADOS LTDA.—See Marsh & McLennan Companies, Inc.; *U.S. Public*, pg. 1375
GAMBRO DIALISIS DE MEXICO, SA. DE R.L.—See Baxter International Inc.; *U.S. Public*, pg. 282
GANNETT FLEMING VALUATION & RATE CONSULTANTS, LLC—See OceanSound Partners, LP; *U.S. Private*, pg. 2991
GARTNER AUSTRIA GMBH—See Gartner, Inc.; *U.S. Public*, pg. 907
GARTNER BELGIUM BVBA—See Gartner, Inc.; *U.S. Public*, pg. 907
GARTNER CANADA CO.—See Gartner, Inc.; *U.S. Public*, pg. 907
GARTNER ESPANA, S.L.—See Gartner, Inc.; *U.S. Public*, pg. 907
GARTNER FRANCE S.A.R.L.—See Gartner, Inc.; *U.S. Public*, pg. 907
GARTNER ISRAEL ADVISORY LTD.—See Gartner, Inc.; *U.S. Public*, pg. 907

GARTNER ITALIA, S.R.L.—See Gartner, Inc.; *U.S. Public*, pg. 907
GARTNER NEDERLAND B.V.—See Gartner, Inc.; *U.S. Public*, pg. 907
GARTNER RESEARCH & ADVISORY KOREA CO., LTD.—See Gartner, Inc.; *U.S. Public*, pg. 907
GARTNER SVERIGE AB—See Gartner, Inc.; *U.S. Public*, pg. 907
GATX GLOBAL FINANCE B.V.—See GATX Corporation; *U.S. Public*, pg. 907
GAVEL INTERNATIONAL CORPORATION; *U.S. Private*, pg. 1652
GB GROUP PLC; *Int'l*, pg. 2892
GCM CAPITAL ADVISORS LTD; *Int'l*, pg. 2895
GEEKDOM; *U.S. Private*, pg. 1655
GELLER & CO.; *U.S. Private*, pg. 1656
GELSENBERG VERWALTUNGS GMBH—See E.ON SE; *Int'l*, pg. 2257
GEMINI GROUP, INC.; *U.S. Private*, pg. 1657
GENAXIS GROUP SDN. BHD.—See Dagang NeXchange Berhad; *Int'l*, pg. 1912
GENERAL ELECTRIC HEALTHCARE PORTUGAL, SOCIEDADE UNIPESSOAL, LDA.—See GE HealthCare Technologies Inc.; *U.S. Public*, pg. 909
GENERATIONAL CAPITAL, LLC—See Generational Equity Group, Inc.; *U.S. Private*, pg. 1668
GENERATIONAL EQUITY, LLC—See Generational Equity Group, Inc.; *U.S. Private*, pg. 1668
GENERIC ENGINEERING CONSTRUCTION AND PROJECTS LIMITED; *Int'l*, pg. 2920
GENEX INFOSYS LTD.—See China Baoan Group Co., Ltd.; *Int'l*, pg. 1485
GENEX SERVICES, LLC—See Stone Point Capital LLC; *U.S. Private*, pg. 3823
GENPACT AUSTRALIA PTY LTD—See Genpact Limited; *Int'l*, pg. 2926
GENPACT CONSULTING KK—See Genpact Limited; *Int'l*, pg. 2926
GENPACT ENTERPRISE RISK CONSULTING LLP—See Genpact Limited; *Int'l*, pg. 2926
GENPACT KENYA LIMITED—See Genpact Limited; *Int'l*, pg. 2926
GENPACT LATVIA SIA—See Genpact Limited; *Int'l*, pg. 2926
GENPACT SERVICES CZECH S.R.O.—See Genpact Limited; *Int'l*, pg. 2927
GENQUEST, INC.; *U.S. Private*, pg. 1673
GENWORTH CONSULTING SERVICES (BEIJING) LIMITED—See Genworth Financial, Inc.; *U.S. Public*, pg. 933
GEO BUSINESS SUPPORT CO., LTD.—See GEO Holdings Corporation; *Int'l*, pg. 2932
GEO SYSTEM SOLUTIONS VIETNAM CO., LTD.—See GEO Holdings Corporation; *Int'l*, pg. 2932
GES ENERJI A.S—See Global Yatirim Holding A.S.; *Int'l*, pg. 3002
GHK HOLDINGS LTD.—See ICF International, Inc.; *U.S. Public*, pg. 1086
GILARDI & CO , LLC—See Computershare Limited; *Int'l*, pg. 1760
GIULIANI PARTNERS LLC; *U.S. Private*, pg. 1703
GLASSRATNER ADVISORY & CAPITAL GROUP, LLC—See B. Riley Financial, Inc.; *U.S. Public*, pg. 261
GLENN G GEIGER COMPANY INC—See LTC Global, Inc.; *U.S. Private*, pg. 2509
GLOBAL LEADERS CORP.; *Int'l*, pg. 2998
GLOBAL PAYMENTS, INC.; *U.S. Public*, pg. 945
GLOBALSTREAMS, INC.; *U.S. Private*, pg. 1719
GLOBAL TECH, INC.—See Tetra Tech, Inc.; *U.S. Public*, pg. 2023
GLOBELEQ INC.—See General Atlantic Service Company, L.P.; *U.S. Private*, pg. 1661
GLOCAL CO., LTD.—See Bain Capital, LP; *U.S. Private*, pg. 434
GLOME MANAGEMENT, INC.—See Glome Holding, Inc.; *Int'l*, pg. 3008
G.M.A.C. FINANCIERA DE COLOMBIA S.A. COMPANIA DE FINANCIAMIENTO COMERCIAL—See General Motors Company; *U.S. Public*, pg. 925
GNARUS ADVISORS LLC—See Nathan Associates Inc.; *U.S. Private*, pg. 2838
GOERTEK ELECTRONICS,INC.—See GoerTek Inc.; *Int'l*, pg. 3021
GOLDBELT EAGLE, LLC—See Gold Belt Incorporated; *U.S. Private*, pg. 1727
GOLDEN STATE FOODS-OAK BROOK—See Golden State Foods Corp.; *U.S. Private*, pg. 1733
GOLDIN ASSOCIATES, LLC—See CVC Capital Partners SICAV-FIS S.A.; *Int'l*, pg. 1888
GOLD STANDARD DIAGNOSIS FRANKFURT GMBH—See Eurofins Scientific S.E.; *Int'l*, pg. 2550
GONZALES CONSULTING SERVICES, INC.; *U.S. Private*, pg. 1737
GOPA CONSULTANTS; *Int'l*, pg. 3042
GOPHERCENTRAL.COM—See NextEra Media, LLC; *U.S. Private*, pg. 2921
GORDON BROTHERS INTERNATIONAL, LLC—See Gordon Brothers Group, LLC; *U.S. Private*, pg. 1742

GORDON BROTHERS RETAIL PARTNERS, LLC—See Gordon Brothers Group, LLC; *U.S. Private*, pg. 1742
GOULD & ASSOCIATES GLOBAL SERVICES, INC.; *U.S. Private*, pg. 1745
GOVCO, LLC—See Citigroup Inc.; *U.S. Public*, pg. 504
GOVERNMENT LOAN SOLUTIONS, INC.—See Live Oak Bancshares, Inc.; *U.S. Public*, pg. 1331
GRANT SAMUEL GROUP; *Int'l*, pg. 3059
GRAYS LEASING LIMITED; *Int'l*, pg. 3063
GREATER CHINA APPRAISAL LIMITED—See Asia-Pac Financial Investment Company Limited; *Int'l*, pg. 616
GREAT GAME OF BUSINESS INC.—See SRC Holdings Corporation; *U.S. Private*, pg. 3767
GREAT PLACE TO WORK INSTITUTE, INC.—See Hellman & Friedman LLC; *U.S. Private*, pg. 1910
GREAT PLAINS HEALTH ALLIANCE INC.; *U.S. Private*, pg. 1767
GREENPRO CAPITAL CORP.; *Int'l*, pg. 3076
GREENWOODS (ST IVES) LIMITED—See Heidelberg Materials AG; *Int'l*, pg. 3310
GREENZONE SOLUTIONS, INC.—See OceanSound Partners, LP; *U.S. Private*, pg. 2991
GRESHAM HOUSE PLC—See Searchlight Capital Partners, L.P.; *U.S. Private*, pg. 3587
GROUP BENEFITS LLC—See Genstar Capital, LLC; *U.S. Private*, pg. 1674
GROUPE LGS INC.—See International Business Machines Corporation; *U.S. Public*, pg. 1146
GROW AB—See Digitalist Group Oyj; *Int'l*, pg. 2123
GROWTHINK, INC.; *U.S. Private*, pg. 1796
GROWTHPLAY LLC; *U.S. Private*, pg. 1796
GUIDANT GROUP, INC.—See HFBG Holding B.V.; *Int'l*, pg. 3375
GUIDEHOUSE INC.—See Bain Capital, LP; *U.S. Private*, pg. 432
GUIDELINE GROUP INFORMATION TECHNOLOGIES LTD.; *Int'l*, pg. 3173
GUTHRIE CONSULTANCY SERVICES PTE LTD—See Guthrie GTS Limited; *Int'l*, pg. 3188
HACCP JAPAN CO., LTD.—See 4Cs Holdings Co., Ltd.; *Int'l*, pg. 11
THE HACKETT GROUP GMBH—See The Hackett Group, Inc.; *U.S. Public*, pg. 2086
THE HACKETT GROUP, INC.; *U.S. Public*, pg. 2086
HACKETT-REL LIMITED—See The Hackett Group, Inc.; *U.S. Public*, pg. 2086
HALDEX GMBH—See Haldex AB; *Int'l*, pg. 3228
HALLMARK BUSINESS CONNECTIONS, INC.—See Interactive Communications Inc; *U.S. Private*, pg. 2108
HAMAGIN RESEARCH INSTITUTE LTD—See Concordia Financial Group, Ltd.; *Int'l*, pg. 1765
HAMILTON BOND LIMITED—See Marsh & McLennan Companies, Inc.; *U.S. Public*, pg. 1376
HAMILTON LANE (JAPAN) GK—See Hamilton Lane Incorporated; *U.S. Public*, pg. 982
HANA INSTITUTE OF FINANCE—See Hana Financial Group, Inc.; *Int'l*, pg. 3240
HANKYU QUALITY SUPPORT—See H2O Retailing Corp.; *Int'l*, pg. 3200
HANNON ARMSTRONG SECURITIES, LLC—See Hannon Armstrong Sustainable Infrastructure Capital, Inc.; *U.S. Public*, pg. 983
HANSON CREWING SERVICES LIMITED—See Heidelberg Materials AG; *Int'l*, pg. 3312
HAN TANG TECHNOLOGY, INC.; *U.S. Public*, pg. 982
HARDIN COMPLIANCE CONSULTING, LLC—See Genstar Capital, LLC; *U.S. Private*, pg. 1677
HARIMA CHEMICALS (SHANGHAI) CO., LTD.—See Harima Chemicals Group, Inc.; *Int'l*, pg. 3276
HARKCON INC.; *U.S. Private*, pg. 1864
HARMA-BIO SERV PR, INC.—See PHARMA-BIO SERV, INC.; *U.S. Public*, pg. 1684
HARRISON RESOURCES, LLC—See Oxford Mining Company, LLC; *U.S. Private*, pg. 3057
HARTE-HANKS CRM SERVICES BELGIUM N.V.—See Harte Hanks, Inc.; *U.S. Public*, pg. 986
HARTE-HANKS DIRECT MARKETING—See Harte Hanks, Inc.; *U.S. Public*, pg. 986
HART HOTELS, INC.—See WPH Airport Associates; *U.S. Private*, pg. 4571
HARVEST WEALTHPTY. LTD.—See Azimut Holding SpA; *Int'l*, pg. 779
HARWOOD WEALTH MANAGEMENT GROUP PLC—See The Carlyle Group Inc.; *U.S. Public*, pg. 2047
HATSTAND LTD.—See Synechron Inc.; *U.S. Private*, pg. 3903
HAWAII HUMAN RESOURCES, INC.—See ProService Hawaii; *U.S. Private*, pg. 3287
HAWK MANAGEMENT & FINANCIAL SERVICES INC.; *U.S. Private*, pg. 1882
HAY GROUP LIMITADA—See Korn Ferry; *U.S. Public*, pg. 1274
HBR CONSULTING LLC; *U.S. Private*, pg. 1888
HCA SWITZERLAND FINANCE GMBH—See HCA Healthcare, Inc.; *U.S. Public*, pg. 998
HCI HANSEATISCHE SCHIFFSCONSULT GMBH—See Ernst Russ AG; *Int'l*, pg. 2495
HCL TECHNOLOGIES LTD.; *Int'l*, pg. 3298

HDFC SALES—See Housing Development Finance Corporation Limited; *Int'l*, pg. 3492
HEADSENT AB; *Int'l*, pg. 3301
HEALTHCARE PERFORMANCE PARTNERS—See Vizient, Inc.; *U.S. Private*, pg. 4407
HEALTH DATA MANAGEMENT PARTNERS SA—See Cegedim S.A.; *Int'l*, pg. 1390
HEALTH DIALOG SERVICES CORP.—See New Rite Aid, LLC; *U.S. Private*, pg. 2905
HEALTH DIMENSIONS GROUP; *U.S. Private*, pg. 1893
HEALTH INTEGRATED, INC.—See ExlService Holdings, Inc.; *U.S. Public*, pg. 807
HEALTH RISK RESOURCE GROUP INC—See Principal Financial Group, Inc.; *U.S. Public*, pg. 1720
HEALTHTRUST - EUROPE LLP—See HCA Healthcare, Inc.; *U.S. Public*, pg. 998
HEALTHTRUST, L.L.C.—See Sabra Health Care REIT, Inc.; *U.S. Public*, pg. 1833
HEARST BALTIMORE RADIO MANAGEMENT—See The Hearst Corporation; *U.S. Private*, pg. 4048
THE HEBETS COMPANY—See Aon plc; *Int'l*, pg. 497
HEELING SPORTS LIMITED—See Sequential Brands Group, Inc.; *U.S. Private*, pg. 1868
HEITECH I-SOLUTIONS SDN. BHD.—See HeiTech Padu Berhad; *Int'l*, pg. 3326
HELMSBRISCOE INC; *U.S. Private*, pg. 1912
HELVETIA CONSULTA GESELLSCHAFT FUR VORSORGEBERATUNG AG—See Helvetia Holding AG; *Int'l*, pg. 3339
HELVETIA CONSULTING AG—See Helvetia Holding AG; *Int'l*, pg. 3339
HENGTAI CAPITAL INVESTMENT CO., LTD.—See HengTai Securities CO., LTD; *Int'l*, pg. 3347
HENKEL MANAGEMENT AG—See Henkel AG & Co. KGaA; *Int'l*, pg. 3351
HENNESSEE GROUP LLC—See Terrapin Partners LLC; *U.S. Private*, pg. 3972
THE HESSEL GROUP LIMITED—See News Corporation; *U.S. Public*, pg. 1519
HEWLETT-PACKARD - BUSINESS INTELLIGENCE—See HP Inc.; *U.S. Public*, pg. 1063
HICAPS, INC.; *U.S. Private*, pg. 1933
HICKEY & ASSOCIATES, LLC.; *U.S. Private*, pg. 1933
HIGHLAND ASSOCIATES, INC.—See Regions Financial Corporation; *U.S. Public*, pg. 1776
HIGHPOINT GLOBAL, LLC; *U.S. Private*, pg. 1941
HIGHPOINT SOLUTIONS, LLC; *U.S. Private*, pg. 1941
HILL INTERNATIONAL INC.- ABU DHABI, U.A.E.—See Global Infrastructure Solutions, Inc.; *U.S. Private*, pg. 1715
HILL INTERNATIONAL INC.-GREECE—See Global Infrastructure Solutions, Inc.; *U.S. Private*, pg. 1715
HILL INTERNATIONAL INC.-PENNSYLVANIA—See Global Infrastructure Solutions, Inc.; *U.S. Private*, pg. 1715
HILL INTERNATIONAL (UK), LTD.—See Global Infrastructure Solutions, Inc.; *U.S. Private*, pg. 1715
HILLROSS ALLIANCES LIMITED—See AMP Limited; *Int'l*, pg. 432
HILLROSS INNISFAIL PTY LIMITED—See AMP Limited; *Int'l*, pg. 432
HIPOTECARIA CRUZ DEL SUR PRINCIPAL, S.A.—See Principal Financial Group, Inc.; *U.S. Public*, pg. 1720
HIQ INTERNATIONAL AB; *Int'l*, pg. 3402
HIRAYAMA CO., LTD.—See Hirayama Holdings Co., Ltd.; *Int'l*, pg. 3404
HIRAYAMA (THAILAND) CO., LTD.—See Hirayama Holdings Co., Ltd.; *Int'l*, pg. 3404
HIROGIN AREA DESIGN CO., LTD.—See Hirogin Holdings, Inc.; *Int'l*, pg. 3404
HITCHCOCK AUTOMOTIVE RESOURCES; *U.S. Private*, pg. 1952
HKL (PRINCE'S BUILDING) LTD.—See Hong Kong Land Holdings Ltd.; *Int'l*, pg. 3466
HK RESOURCES, LLC—See Battalion Oil Corp.; *U.S. Public*, pg. 279
HM INTERNATIONAL; *U.S. Private*, pg. 1954
HNB ASSURANCE PLC; *Int'l*, pg. 3433
HOERBIGER INTERNATIONAL MANAGEMENT SERVICES GMBH—See Hoerbiger Holding AG; *Int'l*, pg. 3440
HOLLEY HOLLAND LIMITED; *Int'l*, pg. 3451
HOLLIDAY GROUP, LLC; *U.S. Private*, pg. 1965
HOLLSTADT & ASSOCIATES, INC.; *U.S. Private*, pg. 1966
HOOKER & HOLCOMBE, INC.—See Caisse de Depot et Placement du Quebec; *Int'l*, pg. 1257
HOOKER & HOLCOMBE, INC.—See KKR & Co. Inc.; *U.S. Public*, pg. 1265
HORIZON CONSULTANTS, INC.—See Mangan, Inc.; *U.S. Private*, pg. 2563
HORIZON MENTAL HEALTH MANAGEMENT, LLC—See Universal Health Services, Inc.; *U.S. Public*, pg. 2258
HOSPITAL CENTRAL SERVICES, INC.; *U.S. Private*, pg. 1987
HOTELIGA INT. SP. Z O.O.—See Epsilon Net S.A.; *Int'l*, pg. 2466
HOULIHAN LOKEY CAPITAL, INC.—See Houlihan Lokey, Inc.; *U.S. Public*, pg. 1055
HOULIHAN LOKEY FINANCIAL ADVISORS, INC.—See Houlihan Lokey, Inc.; *U.S. Public*, pg. 1055

HOWA BANK LTD.; *Int'l*, pg. 3492
HPC HAMBURG PORT CONSULTING GMBH—See Hamburger Hafen und Logistik AG; *Int'l*, pg. 3236
HPM CORP.—See Workcare, Inc.; *U.S. Private*, pg. 4563
HRG DEBTCO LIMITED—See Global Business Travel Group, Inc.; *U.S. Public*, pg. 941
HSBC CORPORATE FINANCE LIMITED—See HSBC Holdings plc; *Int'l*, pg. 3506
HUA NAN MANAGEMENT & CONSULTING CO., LTD.—See Hua Nan Financial Holdings Co., Ltd.; *Int'l*, pg. 3509
HUARONG CAPITAL MANAGEMENT CO., LTD.—See China CITIC Financial Asset Management Co., Ltd.; *Int'l*, pg. 1489
HUARONG CONSUMER FINANCE CO., LTD.—See Bank of Ningbo Co., Ltd.; *Int'l*, pg. 847
HUARONG HUITONG ASSET MANAGEMENT CO., LTD.—See China CITIC Financial Asset Management Co., Ltd.; *Int'l*, pg. 1489
HUARONG INDUSTRIAL INVESTMENT & MANAGEMENT CO., LTD.—See China CITIC Financial Asset Management Co., Ltd.; *Int'l*, pg. 1489
HUARONG INTERNATIONAL TRUST CO., LTD.—See China CITIC Financial Asset Management Co., Ltd.; *Int'l*, pg. 1489
HUARONG RONGTONG (BEIJING) TECHNOLOGY CO., LTD.—See China CITIC Financial Asset Management Co., Ltd.; *Int'l*, pg. 1489
HUARONG RUITONG EQUITY INVESTMENT MANAGEMENT CO., LTD.—See China CITIC Financial Asset Management Co., Ltd.; *Int'l*, pg. 1489
HUARONG TIANZE INVESTMENT CO., LTD.—See China CITIC Financial Asset Management Co., Ltd.; *Int'l*, pg. 1489
HUARONG YUFU EQUITY INVESTMENT FUND MANAGEMENT CO., LTD.—See China CITIC Financial Asset Management Co., Ltd.; *Int'l*, pg. 1489
HUARONG ZHIYUAN INVESTMENT & MANAGEMENT CO., LTD.—See China CITIC Financial Asset Management Co., Ltd.; *Int'l*, pg. 1489
HUARONG ZHONGGUANCUN DISTRESSED ASSET EXCHANGE CO., LTD.—See China CITIC Financial Asset Management Co., Ltd.; *Int'l*, pg. 1489
HUCO CONSULTING INC.—See Montrose Environmental Group, Inc.; *U.S. Public*, pg. 1466
THE HUMAN CAPITAL GROUP, INC.—See Arthur J. Gallagher & Co.; *U.S. Public*, pg. 207
HUMANICA ASIA PTE. LTD.—See Humanica Public Company Limited; *Int'l*, pg. 3530
HUMAN RESOURCE SPECIALTIES INC.—See DCI Consulting Group, Inc.; *U.S. Private*, pg. 1180
HUMAN RESOURCE STAFFING, LLC; *U.S. Private*, pg. 2005
HUMAN UNITEC INTERNATIONAL INC.; *U.S. Public*, pg. 1069
HUNDSUN.COM CO., LTD.—See Hundsun Technologies Inc.; *Int'l*, pg. 3534
HURON CONSULTING SERVICES LLC—See Huron Consulting Group Inc.; *U.S. Public*, pg. 1076
HUSYS CONSULTING LTD.—See TPG Capital, L.P.; *U.S. Public*, pg. 2177
HUZUR FAKTORING A.S.; *Int'l*, pg. 3541
HYBRIGENICS SERVICES—See Diagnostic Medical Systems S.A.; *Int'l*, pg. 2103
IBC MANAGEMENT, LLC; *U.S. Private*, pg. 2028
IBM APPLICATION SERVICES—See International Business Machines Corporation; *U.S. Public*, pg. 1146
IBM CREDIT LLC—See International Business Machines Corporation; *U.S. Public*, pg. 1146
IC CONSULT GROUP GMBH; *Int'l*, pg. 3577
ICF CONSULTING CANADA, INC.—See ICF International, Inc.; *U.S. Public*, pg. 1086
ICF CONSULTING INDIA PRIVATE, LTD.—See ICF International, Inc.; *U.S. Public*, pg. 1086
ICF CONSULTING LIMITED—See ICF International, Inc.; *U.S. Public*, pg. 1086
ICF CONSULTING SERVICES, LTD.—See ICF International, Inc.; *U.S. Public*, pg. 1086
ICF CONSULTING—See ICF International, Inc.; *U.S. Public*, pg. 1086
ICF INTERNATIONAL CONSULTING (BEIJING) COMPANY, LTD.—See ICF International, Inc.; *U.S. Public*, pg. 1086
ICF JONES & STOKES, INC.—See ICF International, Inc.; *U.S. Public*, pg. 1086
ICF MACRO, INC.—See ICF International, Inc.; *U.S. Public*, pg. 1086
ICF SH&E, INC.—See ICF International, Inc.; *U.S. Public*, pg. 1086
ICF SH&E LIMITED—See ICF International, Inc.; *U.S. Public*, pg. 1086
ICONTRACTS, INC.—See TA Associates, Inc.; *U.S. Private*, pg. 3918
ICSGLOBAL LIMITED - CYBRAND—See ICSGlobal Limited; *Int'l*, pg. 3586
IDCON INCORPORATED—See Total Resource Management, Inc.; *U.S. Private*, pg. 4191
IDC WORLDSOURCE INSURANCE NETWORK INC.—See

N.A.I.C.S. INDEX

541611 — ADMINISTRATIVE MANA...

Guardian Capital Group Limited; *Int'l*, pg. 3170
IDS MANAGEMENT CORPORATION—See Ameriprise Financial, Inc.; *U.S. Public*, pg. 114
IFIS FINANCE I.F.N. S.A.—See Banca IFIS S.p.A.; *Int'l*, pg. 815
IGD INDUSTRIES INC.; *U.S. Private*, pg. 2039
IJJ CORP.; *U.S. Public*, pg. 1100
IKM ACONA AS—See IKM Gruppen AS; *Int'l*, pg. 3611
IKM CONSULTANTS UK LTD.—See IKM Gruppen AS; *Int'l*, pg. 3611
ILLINOIS VALLEY COMMUNITY HOSPITAL; *U.S. Private*, pg. 2042
IMC CONSULTING; *U.S. Private*, pg. 2046
IMMO CONSULTING S.P.A.—See Advent International Corporation; *U.S. Private*, pg. 96
IMMO CONSULTING S.P.A.—See Centerbridge Partners, L.P.; *U.S. Private*, pg. 813
IMPACT HUMAN RESOURCES—See Impact Logistics, Inc.; *U.S. Private*, pg. 2048
IMPERIAL FINANCE & TRADING LLC—See Emergent Capital, Inc.; *U.S. Private*, pg. 1381
THE IMPEX GROUP OF COMPANIES; *U.S. Private*, pg. 4055
IMPROTECH LTD.—See Ag Growth International Inc.; *Int'l*, pg. 198
INDUPIPE AB—See Bravida Holding AB; *Int'l*, pg. 1142
INEWA SRL—See CEZ, a.s.; *Int'l*, pg. 1428
INFINITY INFO SYSTEMS CORP.—See Genesis Corp.; *U.S. Private*, pg. 1669
INFINITY SUPPORT SERVICES, INC.—See Sedulous Consulting Services, LLC; *U.S. Private*, pg. 3597
INFLEXXION, INC.—See Integrated Behavioral Health, Inc.; *U.S. Private*, pg. 2099
INFONOVA GMBH—See BearingPoint, Inc.; *U.S. Private*, pg. 507
INFORMATION MANAGEMENT SOLUTIONS, LLC—See Usio Inc.; *U.S. Public*, pg. 2267
INFORMATION PLANNING & MANAGEMENT SERVICE, INC.—See Court Square Capital Partners, L.P.; *U.S. Private*, pg. 1069
INFOSCORE NEDERLAND B.V.—See Bertelsmann SE & Co. KGaA; *Int'l*, pg. 992
INFOSERVICIOS S.A—See Atos SE; *Int'l*, pg. 691
INGROUP ASSOCIATES, LLC—See Genstar Capital, LLC; *U.S. Private*, pg. 1674
INJURY NET AUSTRALIA PTY LTD—See MAXIMUS, Inc.; *U.S. Public*, pg. 1402
INLINE CONSULTING, LLC—See YOUNG & Associates; *U.S. Private*, pg. 4592
INMED GROUP, INC.—See All Things Mobile Analytic, Inc.; *U.S. Public*, pg. 78
INNCO MANAGEMENT CORP.—See Family Inns of America, Inc.; *U.S. Private*, pg. 1470
INNOSIGHT CONSULTING ASIA PACIFIC PTE. LTD.—See Huron Consulting Group Inc.; *U.S. Public*, pg. 1076
INNOSIGHT CONSULTING, LLC—See Huron Consulting Group Inc.; *U.S. Public*, pg. 1076
INNOVAL TECHNOLOGY LTD.—See Danieli & C. Officine Meccaniche S.p.A.; *Int'l*, pg. 1963
INNOVATIA INC.—See BCE Inc.; *Int'l*, pg. 926
INNOVATION NETWORK, INC.—See eTRANSERVICES, LLC; *U.S. Private*, pg. 1432
INNOVATIVE DISCOVERY, LLC—See Silver Oak Services Partners, LLC; *U.S. Private*, pg. 3661
INNOVATIVE SYSTEMS, LLC—See TA Associates, Inc.; *U.S. Private*, pg. 3914
INNOVATIX, LLC—See Premier, Inc.; *U.S. Public*, pg. 1715
INNOVIA COMMUNITY MANAGEMENT COOPERATIVE—See CCA Global Partners, Inc.; *U.S. Private*, pg. 799
INO.COM; *U.S. Private*, pg. 2084
INPUT PROJEKTENTWICKLUNGS GMBH—See Doppelmayr Group; *Int'l*, pg. 2175
INSIGHT PERFORMANCE, INC.—See New Mountain Capital, LLC; *U.S. Private*, pg. 2901
INSPERITY BUSINESS SERVICES, L.P.—See Insperity, Inc.; *U.S. Public*, pg. 1131
INSPERITY EXPENSE MANAGEMENT, INC.—See Insperity, Inc.; *U.S. Public*, pg. 1131
INSPERITY, INC.; *U.S. Public*, pg. 1131
INSTITUT FRANCAIS DES EMPREINTES GENETIQUES S.A.S.—See Eurofins Scientific S.E.; *Int'l*, pg. 2550
INTEGRATED MANAGEMENT RESOURCES GROUP INC.; *U.S. Private*, pg. 2100
INTEGRATE IT—See Sterling Investment Partners, L.P.; *U.S. Private*, pg. 3806
INTEGRIGUARD, LLC—See Veritas Capital Fund Management, LLC; *U.S. Private*, pg. 4362
INTELLINET CONSULTING, LLC—See FPT Corporation; *Int'l*, pg. 2758
INTERNATIONAL DEVELOPMENT GROUP LIMITED—See XWELL, Inc.; *U.S. Public*, pg. 2393
INTERNATIONAL FINANCE COMPANY - SAL—See Arzan Financial Group for Financing & Investment K.S.P.C.; *Int'l*, pg. 589
INTERSYSTEMS CORPORATION - NEW YORK—See InterSystems Corporation; *U.S. Private*, pg. 2126

INTERVAL MANAGEMENT INC.—See QM Corporation; *U.S. Private*, pg. 3313
INTL FCSTONE EUROPE S.A.—See StoneX Group Inc.; *U.S. Public*, pg. 1952
INTL FCSTONE PTY. LTD.—See StoneX Group Inc.; *U.S. Public*, pg. 1952
INTREPID SOLUTIONS AND SERVICES, LLC—See Hammond, Kennedy, Whitney & Company, Inc.; *U.S. Private*, pg. 1850
INVESTORS TRUST COMPANY—See Investors Title Company; *U.S. Public*, pg. 1165
INVITA KUWAIT K.S.C.C—See BBK B.S.C.; *Int'l*, pg. 920
INVIZION, INC.; *U.S. Private*, pg. 2133
IOWA MANAGEMENT SYSTEMS INC.; *U.S. Private*, pg. 2135
IPM INTEGRATED PRESCRIPTION MANAGEMENT; *U.S. Private*, pg. 2136
IPT ASSOCIATES LLC.; *U.S. Private*, pg. 2137
IRON MOUNTAIN HELLAS SA—See Iron Mountain Incorporated; *U.S. Public*, pg. 1173
ISS HOSPITAL SERVICES B.V.—See EQT AB; *Int'l*, pg. 2477
ISS HOSPITAL SERVICES B.V.—See The Goldman Sachs Group, Inc.; *U.S. Public*, pg. 2078
ISS INTEGRATED FACILITY SERVICES B.V.—See EQT AB; *Int'l*, pg. 2477
ISS INTEGRATED FACILITY SERVICES B.V.—See The Goldman Sachs Group, Inc.; *U.S. Public*, pg. 2078
ITAGROUP, INC.-MINNEAPOLIS—See ITAGroup, Inc.; *U.S. Private*, pg. 2148
ITEC CONNECT LIMITED—See Xerox Holdings Corporation; *U.S. Public*, pg. 2386
THE IT PROS; *U.S. Private*, pg. 4057
ITSOLUTIONS NET INC.—See MAXIMUS, Inc.; *U.S. Public*, pg. 1402
ITW CANADA MANAGEMENT COMPANY—See Illinois Tool Works Inc.; *U.S. Public*, pg. 1105
JABIL ADVANCED MECHANICAL SOLUTIONS DE MEXICO, S DE RL DE C.V.—See Jabil Inc.; *U.S. Public*, pg. 1180
JACKSON AND ASSOCIATES, INC.—See Forward Solutions; *U.S. Private*, pg. 1578
JAKE SWEENEY AUTOMOTIVE INC.; *U.S. Private*, pg. 2182
JAPAN CONCENTRIX K.K—See TD Synnex Corp; *U.S. Public*, pg. 1984
JAPAN ECVISION CO., LTD.—See Insight Venture Management, LLC; *U.S. Private*, pg. 2087
JBTV, INC.—See Aucnet Inc.; *Int'l*, pg. 700
JEFFERIES FINANCE, LLC—See Jefferies Financial Group Inc.; *U.S. Public*, pg. 1188
JELF FINANCIAL PLANNING LIMITED—See Marsh & McLennan Companies, Inc.; *U.S. Public*, pg. 1378
JELF FINANCIAL PLANNING LIMITED—See Marsh & McLennan Companies, Inc.; *U.S. Public*, pg. 1378
JEP MANAGEMENT, INC.; *U.S. Private*, pg. 2201
JF APEX NOMINEES (ASING) SDN. BHD.—See Apex Equity Holdings Berhad; *Int'l*, pg. 509
J-FEEL INC.—See Amuse Inc.; *Int'l*, pg. 442
JIH SUN FINANCIAL HOLDINGS CO., LTD.—See Fubon Financial Holding Co. Ltd.; *Int'l*, pg. 2802
JIRONG REAL ESTATE CO., LTD.—See Chailease Holding Company Limited; *Int'l*, pg. 1437
JJF MANAGEMENT SERVICES, INC.; *U.S. Private*, pg. 2211
JMJ ASSOCIATES, LLC—See 3i Group plc; *Int'l*, pg. 9
JOHN DEERE FINANCIAL INC.—See Deere & Company; *U.S. Public*, pg. 646
JOHN DEERE TECHNOLOGIES CENTER—See Deere & Company; *U.S. Public*, pg. 647
JOHN M. FLOYD & ASSOCIATES, INC.—See Hammond, Kennedy, Whitney & Company, Inc.; *U.S. Private*, pg. 1850
JOHN MUIR HEALTH; *U.S. Private*, pg. 2223
JOHN SNOW, INC.; *U.S. Private*, pg. 2224
JOHNSON & JOHNSON FINANCE CORPORATION—See Johnson & Johnson; *U.S. Public*, pg. 1198
JOHNSON STEPHENS CONSULTING, INC.—See Dunes Point Capital, LLC; *U.S. Private*, pg. 1288
JOINT VENTURE PIPING INC.; *U.S. Private*, pg. 2230
JONES MANAGEMENT SERVICES, LLC—See Check Into Cash Inc.; *U.S. Private*, pg. 869
JOORNEY LLC; *U.S. Private*, pg. 2234
J.P. MORGAN BANK LUXEMBOURG S.A.—See JPMorgan Chase & Co.; *U.S. Public*, pg. 1208
J.P. MORGAN LIMITED—See JPMorgan Chase & Co.; *U.S. Public*, pg. 1209
J.P. MORGAN SERVICES INDIA PRIVATE LIMITED—See JPMorgan Chase & Co.; *U.S. Public*, pg. 1208
J.P. MORGAN SERVICES (MALAYSIA) SDN. BHD.—See JPMorgan Chase & Co.; *U.S. Public*, pg. 1208
JPMP CAPITAL CORP.—See JPMorgan Chase & Co.; *U.S. Public*, pg. 1208
JURINNOV LTD.—See Technology Concepts & Design, Inc.; *U.S. Private*, pg. 3955
K2 CONSULTANCY GROUP LIMITED—See HanmiGlobal Co., LTD.; *Int'l*, pg. 3257
KA.DE.GE KG—See Baader Bank AG; *Int'l*, pg. 791

KAHNAWAKE MANAGEMENT SERVICES INC.—See Entain PLC; *Int'l*, pg. 2450
KAI POLU SERVICES LLC; *U.S. Private*, pg. 2254
THE KAIZEN COMPANY, LLC.—See Tetra Tech, Inc.; *U.S. Public*, pg. 2024
KALMAR INDUSTRIES SOUTH AFRICA (PTY) LTD—See Cargotec Corporation; *Int'l*, pg. 1327
KALYPSO, LP—See Rockwell Automation, Inc.; *U.S. Public*, pg. 1805
KARTEREDA HOLDING LTD—See ELLAKTOR S.A.; *Int'l*, pg. 2365
KAUFMAN, HALL & ASSOCIATES, LLC—See Vizient, Inc.; *U.S. Private*, pg. 4407
KAYA ASSOCIATES INC.; *U.S. Private*, pg. 2266
KCPAG FINANCIAL ADVISORS LLC—See Kemper CPA Group LLP; *U.S. Private*, pg. 2282
KELLER FAY GROUP—See DGTL Holdings Inc.; *Int'l*, pg. 2097
KEMPER CAPITAL MANAGEMENT LLC—See Kemper CPA Group LLP; *U.S. Private*, pg. 2282
KEN TECHNOLOGY CO., LTD.—See Bain Capital, LP; *U.S. Private*, pg. 434
KENT RELIANCE BUILDING SOCIETY—See J.C. Flowers & Co. LLC; *U.S. Private*, pg. 2160
KEPLER ASSOCIATES LIMITED—See Marsh & McLennan Companies, Inc.; *U.S. Public*, pg. 1377
KEPNER-TREGOE, INC.; *U.S. Private*, pg. 2290
KILEY ADVISORS LLC—See FMI Corporation; *U.S. Private*, pg. 1554
KILEY GROUP, INC.; *U.S. Public*, pg. 1228
KINETIC ENERGY, LLC—See EagleTree Capital, LP; *U.S. Private*, pg. 1311
KINGSBRIDGE PRIVATE PTY. LTD.—See Azimut Holding SpA; *Int'l*, pg. 779
KINGSLEY ASSOCIATES, INC.—See Stone Point Capital LLC; *U.S. Private*, pg. 3825
KIRBY BATES ASSOCIATES, INC.—See Jackson Healthcare, LLC; *U.S. Private*, pg. 2177
K-LINE PRAXISLOSUNGEN GMBH—See CompuGroup Medical SE & Co. KGaA; *Int'l*, pg. 1756
KMK CONSULTING COMPANY, LLC—See Keating, Muething & Klekamp PLL; *U.S. Private*, pg. 2271
KMS ENTERPRISES, INC.; *U.S. Private*, pg. 2321
KNOWLEDGE CAPITAL GROUP LLC—See Vizient, Inc.; *U.S. Private*, pg. 4407
KNOWLEDGE WORKS, INC.—See Equifax Inc.; *U.S. Public*, pg. 786
KONSORTIUM LOGISTIK BERHAD—See DRB-HICOM Berhad; *Int'l*, pg. 2201
KRELLER GROUP INC.; *U.S. Private*, pg. 2351
KRONOS, INCORPORATED - ISERIES SOLUTIONS GROUP—See Hellman & Friedman LLC; *U.S. Private*, pg. 1911
KRONOS SYSTEMS BVBA—See Hellman & Friedman LLC; *U.S. Private*, pg. 1910
KSJ & ASSOCIATES; *U.S. Private*, pg. 2354
KSL RESORTS—See KSL Capital Partners, LLC; *U.S. Private*, pg. 2355
KURT SALMON ASSOCIATES, INC.—See Accenture plc; *Int'l*, pg. 86
KYRIBA CORPORATION—See Bridgepoint Group Plc; *Int'l*, pg. 1155
KYUSHU SANGYO KOTSU HOLDINGS CO., LTD.—See H.I.S. Co., Ltd.; *Int'l*, pg. 3195
LABORATORIO DE ANALISES CLINICAS J. PINTO DE BARROS, S.A.—See Eurofins Scientific S.E.; *Int'l*, pg. 2551
L'AGEFI—See Financiere Pinault SCA; *Int'l*, pg. 2668
LAKES AREA NONPROFIT SUPPORT FOUNDATION; *U.S. Private*, pg. 2376
LAM RESEARCH MANAGEMENT GMBH—See Lam Research Corporation; *U.S. Public*, pg. 1289
LBA HAYNES STRAND, PLLC—See Aprio, LLP; *U.S. Private*, pg. 301
LEEDOM & ASSOCIATES, LLC—See Leedom Management Group, Inc.; *U.S. Private*, pg. 2414
LEEDOM MANAGEMENT GROUP, INC.; *U.S. Private*, pg. 2414
LEE HECHT HARRISON, INC.—See Adecco Group AG; *Int'l*, pg. 138
LEE HECHT HARRISON—See Adecco Group AG; *Int'l*, pg. 138
LEE HECHT HARRISON—See Adecco Group AG; *Int'l*, pg. 138
LEIGHFISHER INC.—See Jacobs Engineering Group, Inc.; *U.S. Public*, pg. 1186
LENDER'S CONSULTING GROUP, INC.; *U.S. Private*, pg. 2421
LERNER REAL ESTATE ADVISORS, INC.; *U.S. Private*, pg. 2431
LE SOLUZIONI SCARL—See ACEA S.p.A.; *Int'l*, pg. 95
LIBERTY STREET ADVISORS, LLC; *U.S. Private*, pg. 2447
LIFE DESIGN STATION INTERNATIONAL, INC.; *U.S. Public*, pg. 1312
LIFEPOINT CORPORATE SERVICES, GENERAL PARTNERSHIP—See Apollo Global Management, Inc.; *U.S. Public*, pg. 158

541611 — ADMINISTRATIVE MANA...

LINCOLN ROAD MANAGEMENT LLC—See Vornado Realty Trust; *U.S. Public*, pg. 2310
LINKAGE INC.—See Prospect Partners, LLC; *U.S. Private*, pg. 3288
LINKVISUM CONSULTING GROUP; *U.S. Private*, pg. 2462
LION FINANCE PTY LTD—See Collection House Limited; *Int'l*, pg. 1699
LIPPINCOTT - SAN FRANCISCO—See Marsh & McLennan Companies, Inc.; *U.S. Public*, pg. 1387
LIST AMERICA—See Market Development Group, Inc.; *U.S. Private*, pg. 2579
LN PARTICIPACOES LTDA.—See W.W. Grainger, Inc.; *U.S. Public*, pg. 2320
LOBUE & MAJDALANY MANAGEMENT GROUP, INC.; *U.S. Private*, pg. 2477
LOCKHEED MARTIN TACTICAL DEFENSE SYSTEMS—See Lockheed Martin Corporation; *U.S. Public*, pg. 1338
LOCUZ ENTERPRISE SOLUTIONS LTD.—See SHI International Corp.; *U.S. Private*, pg. 3635
LOMBARD INTERNATIONAL ASSURANCE SA—See Blackstone Inc.; *U.S. Public*, pg. 360
THE LONDON GENERAL PRACTICE LIMITED—See HCA Healthcare, Inc.; *U.S. Public*, pg. 1012
LONG KANG MEDICAL INVESTMENT MANAGEMENT HEBEI CO., LTD.—See Hebei Changshan Biochemical Pharmaceutical Co. Ltd.; *Int'l*, pg. 3305
LORD GREEN REAL ESTATE STRATEGIES, INC.—See Blackstone Inc.; *U.S. Public*, pg. 355
LP MANAGEMENT VERWALTUNG GMBH—See American Express Company; *U.S. Public*, pg. 102
LRA WORLDWIDE, INC.—See Deloitte LLP; *U.S. Private*, pg. 1198
LSC GROUP LIMITED—See Babcock International Group PLC; *Int'l*, pg. 792
LSW LANDE-STADTWERKE WOLFSBURG VERWALTUNGS-GMBH—See E.ON SE; *Int'l*, pg. 2258
LUCERA FINANCIAL INFRASTRUCTURES, LLC—See BGC Group, Inc.; *U.S. Public*, pg. 329
LUCIDITY CONSULTING GROUP LP—See Kelso & Company, L.P.; *U.S. Private*, pg. 2278
LUTHIN ASSOCIATES, INC.—See L5E LLC; *U.S. Private*, pg. 2367
MACCOUNTING, LLC—See InDinero Inc.; *U.S. Private*, pg. 2064
MACDERMID ACUMEN INC.—See Element Solutions Inc.; *U.S. Public*, pg. 726
MACDERMID NETHERLANDS COOPERATIEF W.A.—See Element Solutions Inc.; *U.S. Public*, pg. 727
MACFADDEN & ASSOCIATES, INC.—See Amentum Services, Inc.; *U.S. Private*, pg. 219
MACKINAW ADMINISTRATORS, LLC—See Fosun International Limited; *Int'l*, pg. 2752
MACMUNNIS, INC.—See GI Manager L.P.; *U.S. Private*, pg. 1693
MACNEILL GROUP, INC.; *U.S. Private*, pg. 2538
MACROSCOPE INFORMATIQUE, INC.—See Fujitsu Limited; *Int'l*, pg. 2834
MACTUS GROUP; *U.S. Private*, pg. 2538
MADISON CONSULTING GROUP, INC.—See FTI Consulting, Inc.; *U.S. Public*, pg. 891
MAGNUS MANAGEMENT GROUP, LLC—See NXTKey Corporation; *U.S. Private*, pg. 2976
MAIL A DOC LIMITED—See Xerox Holdings Corporation; *U.S. Public*, pg. 2386
MAINEHEALTH; *U.S. Private*, pg. 2552
MAINSTREAM FUND SERVICES (CAYMAN) LIMITED—See Apex Fund Services Holdings Ltd.; *Int'l*, pg. 510
MAINSTREAM FUND SERVICES (HK) LIMITED—See Apex Fund Services Holdings Ltd.; *Int'l*, pg. 510
MAINSTREAM FUND SERVICES (IOM) LIMITED—See Apex Fund Services Holdings Ltd.; *Int'l*, pg. 510
MAINSTREAM FUND SERVICES (IRELAND) LIMITED—See Apex Fund Services Holdings Ltd.; *Int'l*, pg. 510
MAINSTREAM FUND SERVICES (MALTA) LIMITED—See Apex Fund Services Holdings Ltd.; *Int'l*, pg. 510
MAINSTREAM FUND SERVICES PTE LTD—See Apex Fund Services Holdings Ltd.; *Int'l*, pg. 510
MAINSTREAM PE SERVICES, INC.—See Apex Fund Services Holdings Ltd.; *Int'l*, pg. 510
MAINSTREAM PE SERVICES, INC.—See Apex Fund Services Holdings Ltd.; *Int'l*, pg. 510
MAINTENANCE DESIGN GROUP LLC—See HDR, Inc.; *U.S. Private*, pg. 1890
MANAGED CARE ADVISORS, INC.—See The Carlyle Group Inc.; *U.S. Public*, pg. 2053
MANAGEMENT ALLIANCE PROGRAMS, INC.; *U.S. Private*, pg. 2560
MANAGEMENT PARTNERS, INC.—See Baker Tilly US, LLP; *U.S. Private*, pg. 457
MANAGEMENT SCIENCE & INNOVATION LLC; *U.S. Private*, pg. 2560
MANAGEMENT SOLUTIONS, LLC; *U.S. Private*, pg. 2561
MANPOWER A/S (DENMARK)—See ManpowerGroup Inc.; *U.S. Public*, pg. 1358

MANPOWER A/S—See ManpowerGroup Inc.; *U.S. Public*, pg. 1360
MANPOWER BULGARIA OOD—See ManpowerGroup Inc.; *U.S. Public*, pg. 1358
MANPOWER BUSINESS SOLUTIONS GMBH—See ManpowerGroup Inc.; *U.S. Public*, pg. 1358
MANPOWER BUSINESS SOLUTIONS KFT—See ManpowerGroup Inc.; *U.S. Public*, pg. 1358
MANPOWER BUSINESS SOLUTIONS SA—See ManpowerGroup Inc.; *U.S. Public*, pg. 1358
MANPOWER BUSINESS SOLUTIONS SERVICE CENTER AB—See ManpowerGroup Inc.; *U.S. Public*, pg. 1360
MANPOWER BUSINESS SOLUTIONS, S.L.U—See ManpowerGroup Inc.; *U.S. Public*, pg. 1358
MANPOWER CADEN CHINA CO LTD—See ManpowerGroup Inc.; *U.S. Public*, pg. 1358
MANPOWER EUROPE HOLDINGS, APS—See ManpowerGroup Inc.; *U.S. Public*, pg. 1358
MANPOWER GMBH & CO. KG PERSONALDIENSTLEISTUNGEN—See ManpowerGroup Inc.; *U.S. Public*, pg. 1358
MANPOWER HOLDING AG—See ManpowerGroup Inc.; *U.S. Public*, pg. 1358
MANPOWER HR MANAGEMENT S.A.—See ManpowerGroup Inc.; *U.S. Public*, pg. 1358
MANPOWER LIT UAB—See ManpowerGroup Inc.; *U.S. Public*, pg. 1359
MANPOWER MENSAJERIA, S.A. DE C.V.—See ManpowerGroup Inc.; *U.S. Public*, pg. 1359
MANPOWER NORWAY HOLDINGS AS—See ManpowerGroup Inc.; *U.S. Public*, pg. 1359
MANPOWER OUTSOURCING SERVICES INC.—See ManpowerGroup Inc.; *U.S. Public*, pg. 1359
MANPOWER PERU S.A.—See ManpowerGroup Inc.; *U.S. Public*, pg. 1359
MANPOWER POLSKA SP. ZO. O—See ManpowerGroup Inc.; *U.S. Public*, pg. 1359
MANPOWER PROFESSIONAL ENGINEERING AS—See ManpowerGroup Inc.; *U.S. Public*, pg. 1360
MANPOWER SERVICE INC.—See ManpowerGroup Inc.; *U.S. Public*, pg. 1359
MANPOWER SERVICES (MACAU) LIMITED—See ManpowerGroup Inc.; *U.S. Public*, pg. 1359
MANPOWER STAFFING SERVICES AS—See ManpowerGroup Inc.; *U.S. Public*, pg. 1360
MANPOWER STAFFING SERVICES (MALAYSIA) SDN BHD—See ManpowerGroup Inc.; *U.S. Public*, pg. 1359
MANPOWER TUNISIE INTERNATIONAL SARL—See ManpowerGroup Inc.; *U.S. Public*, pg. 1359
MANPOWER UK LIMITED—See ManpowerGroup Inc.; *U.S. Public*, pg. 1359
MANSON GULF LLC—See Manson Construction Co., Inc.; *U.S. Private*, pg. 2566
MANZELLA MARKETING GROUP, INC—See 360 PSG, Inc.; *U.S. Public*, pg. 8
MARAKON ASSOCIATES, INC.—See CRA International, Inc.; *U.S. Public*, pg. 588
MARITZ RESEARCH—See Maritz Holdings Inc.; *U.S. Private*, pg. 2577
MARKETING SUPPORT SOLUTIONS, INC.—See Integrated Distribution & Logistics Direct LLC; *U.S. Private*, pg. 2099
MARKETING TECHNOLOGY CONCEPTS, INC.; *U.S. Private*, pg. 2580
MARKON, INC.—See Sterling Investment Partners, L.P.; *U.S. Private*, pg. 3805
MARLIN & ASSOCIATES NEW YORK LLC; *U.S. Private*, pg. 2583
MARS CAPITAL FINANCE IRELAND DAC—See Arrow Global Group PLC; *Int'l*, pg. 579
MARSH, BERRY & COMPANY, INC. - NEW YORK—See Marsh, Berry & Company, Inc.; *U.S. Private*, pg. 2592
MARSH, BERRY & COMPANY, INC.; *U.S. Private*, pg. 2591
MARSH BROKER JAPAN, INC.—See Marsh & McLennan Companies, Inc.; *U.S. Public*, pg. 1379
MARSH IAS MANAGEMENT SERVICES (BERMUDA) LTD.—See Marsh & McLennan Companies, Inc.; *U.S. Public*, pg. 1378
MARSH MANAGEMENT SERVICES (DUBAI) LIMITED—See Marsh & McLennan Companies, Inc.; *U.S. Public*, pg. 1383
MARSH MANAGEMENT SERVICES (DUBLIN) LIMITED—See Marsh & McLennan Companies, Inc.; *U.S. Public*, pg. 1383
MARSH MANAGEMENT SERVICES (LUXEMBOURG) SA—See Marsh & McLennan Companies, Inc.; *U.S. Public*, pg. 1379
MARTS & LUNDY, INC.; *U.S. Private*, pg. 2597
THE MATRIX COMPANIES; *U.S. Private*, pg. 4076
MATRIX DATA LTD—See FactSet Research Systems Inc.; *U.S. Public*, pg. 820
MATRIX RESOURCES, INC.—See Littlejohn & Co., LLC; *U.S. Private*, pg. 2471
MATRIX TECHNOLOGIES, INC.—See Matrix Technologies Incorporated; *U.S. Private*, pg. 2612
MATTHEWS STEER PTY. LTD.—See Azimut Holding SpA; *Int'l*, pg. 779
MAXIM INTEGRATED PRODUCTS INTERNATIONAL

CORPORATE AFFILIATIONS

SALES LIMITED—See Analog Devices, Inc.; *U.S. Public*, pg. 135
MAXIMUS CANADA, INC.—See MAXIMUS, Inc.; *U.S. Public*, pg. 1402
MAXIMUS HEALTH SERVICES, INC.—See MAXIMUS, Inc.; *U.S. Public*, pg. 1402
MAX RECOVERY LIMITED—See JPMorgan Chase & Co.; *U.S. Public*, pg. 1210
MBA HEALTHGROUP; *U.S. Private*, pg. 2624
MBS (MANPOWER BUSINESS SOLUTIONS) LTD.—See ManpowerGroup Inc.; *U.S. Public*, pg. 1358
MC2 DESIGN GROUP, INC.—See Lone Fir Consulting, LLC; *U.S. Private*, pg. 2484
MCCI, LLC—See Century Park Capital Partners, LLC; *U.S. Private*, pg. 834
MCCUSKER & COMPANY, INC.—See MHHC Enterprises Inc; *U.S. Public*, pg. 1436
MCGRAW-HILL FINANCIAL JAPAN K.K.—See S&P Global Inc.; *U.S. Public*, pg. 1830
MCGRAW-HILL FINANCIAL SINGAPORE PTE. LIMITED—See S&P Global Inc.; *U.S. Public*, pg. 1830
MCGRAW-HILL INDICES U.K. LIMITED—See S&P Global Inc.; *U.S. Public*, pg. 1830
MCGRAW WENTWORTH, INC.; *U.S. Private*, pg. 2635
MCI-EXPERIAN CO., LTD.—See Experian plc; *Int'l*, pg. 2588
MCKENZIE CHECK ADVANCE OF OHIO, LLC—See Grupo Salinas, S.A. de C.V.; *Int'l*, pg. 3135
MCKINSEY & COMPANY, INC. - MIDWEST—See McKinsey & Company, Inc.; *U.S. Private*, pg. 2639
MCKINSEY & COMPANY, INC.; *U.S. Private*, pg. 2639
MCLAGAN PARTNERS INC.—See Aon plc; *Int'l*, pg. 491
MCLANE GROUP LP; *U.S. Private*, pg. 2640
M CORP; *U.S. Private*, pg. 2523
MEDIA MARKT SATURN ADMINISTRACION ESPANA, S.A.U.—See Ceconomy AG; *Int'l*, pg. 1374
MEDIA SATURN HELLAS COMPANY ADMINISTRATION ANONYMI ETERIA—See Ceconomy AG; *Int'l*, pg. 1385
MEDICAL MUTUAL SERVICES, LLC—See Medical Mutual of Ohio; *U.S. Private*, pg. 2655
MEDICAL RECORD ASSOCIATES INC—See ChrysCapital Management Co.; *Int'l*, pg. 1588
MEDICAL RESEARCH CONSULTANTS, INC.; *U.S. Private*, pg. 2655
MEDICAL RESOURCE ASSOCIATION, INC.; *U.S. Private*, pg. 2655
MEDIFIT CORPORATE SERVICES, INC.—See Athletes' Performance, Inc.; *U.S. Private*, pg. 368
MEDIOLANUM GESTIONE FONDI SGRPA—See Banca Mediolanum S.p.A.; *Int'l*, pg. 815
MEDMARC CASUALTY INSURANCE COMPANY—See ProAssurance Corporation; *U.S. Public*, pg. 1723
MEDSERV KFT.—See Eurofins Scientific S.E.; *Int'l*, pg. 2551
MEDVAL, LLC—See Brown & Brown, Inc.; *U.S. Public*, pg. 397
MEETING PROFESSIONALS INTERNATIONAL (MPI); *U.S. Private*, pg. 2660
MEETING PROFESSIONALS INTERNATIONAL (MPI)—See Meeting Professionals International (MPI); *U.S. Private*, pg. 2660
MEETINGS & EVENTS INTERNATIONAL INC.; *U.S. Private*, pg. 2660
MEGAL VERWALTUNGS-GMBH—See E.ON SE; *Int'l*, pg. 2258
MENICO TUCK PARRISH FINANCIAL SERVICES PTY. LTD.—See Azimut Holding SpA; *Int'l*, pg. 779
MENONO, INC.; *U.S. Private*, pg. 2666
MENTOR PARTNERS LLC; *U.S. Private*, pg. 2667
MEON VERWALTUNGS GMBH—See E.ON SE; *Int'l*, pg. 2258
MERCER (AUSTRALIA) PTY LTD—See Marsh & McLennan Companies, Inc.; *U.S. Public*, pg. 1384
MERCER (AUSTRIA) GMBH—See Marsh & McLennan Companies, Inc.; *U.S. Public*, pg. 1384
MERCER BENEFIT SERVICES PTY LTD—See Marsh & McLennan Companies, Inc.; *U.S. Public*, pg. 1385
MERCER CERTIFICERING B.V.—See Marsh & McLennan Companies, Inc.; *U.S. Public*, pg. 1385
MERCER CONSULTING (AUSTRALIA) PTY LTD—See Marsh & McLennan Companies, Inc.; *U.S. Public*, pg. 1385
MERCER CONSULTING B.V.—See Marsh & McLennan Companies, Inc.; *U.S. Public*, pg. 1385
MERCER CONSULTING (CHINA) LTD.—See Marsh & McLennan Companies, Inc.; *U.S. Public*, pg. 1385
MERCER CONSULTING (FRANCE) SAS—See Marsh & McLennan Companies, Inc.; *U.S. Public*, pg. 1385
MERCER CONSULTING (INDIA) PRIVATE LTD.—See Marsh & McLennan Companies, Inc.; *U.S. Public*, pg. 1385
MERCER (DANMARK) A/S—See Marsh & McLennan Companies, Inc.; *U.S. Public*, pg. 1384
MERCER EMPLOYEE BENEFITS - MEDIACAO DE SEGUROS, LDA.—See Marsh & McLennan Companies, Inc.; *U.S. Public*, pg. 1385
MERCER EMPLOYEE BENEFITS OY—See Marsh & McLennan Companies, Inc.; *U.S. Public*, pg. 1385
MERCER (FRANCE) SAS—See Marsh & McLennan Companies, Inc.; *U.S. Public*, pg. 1384

MERCER (HONG KONG) LIMITED—See Marsh & McLennan Companies, Inc.; *U.S. Public*, pg. 1384
MERCER (IRELAND) LIMITED—See Marsh & McLennan Companies, Inc.; *U.S. Public*, pg. 1384
MERCER (MALAYSIA) SDN. BHD.—See Marsh & McLennan Companies, Inc.; *U.S. Public*, pg. 1384
MERCER (NORGE) AS—See Marsh & McLennan Companies, Inc.; *U.S. Public*, pg. 1384
MERCER (N.Z.) LIMITED—See Marsh & McLennan Companies, Inc.; *U.S. Public*, pg. 1384
MERCER (POLSKA) SP.Z O.O.—See Marsh & McLennan Companies, Inc.; *U.S. Public*, pg. 1384
MERCER (SINGAPORE) PTE LTD—See Marsh & McLennan Companies, Inc.; *U.S. Public*, pg. 1384
MERCER (SWEDEN) AB—See Marsh & McLennan Companies, Inc.; *U.S. Public*, pg. 1384
MERCER (TAIWAN) LTD.—See Marsh & McLennan Companies, Inc.; *U.S. Public*, pg. 1385
MERIDIAN FINANCIAL SERVICES, INC.—See Marriott Vacations Worldwide Corporation; *U.S. Public*, pg. 1373
MERIDIAN FINANCIAL SERVICES, INC.—See Marriott Vacations Worldwide Corporation; *U.S. Public*, pg. 1373
MERIDIAN FINANCIAL SERVICES, INC.—See Marriott Vacations Worldwide Corporation; *U.S. Public*, pg. 1373
MERIDIAN FINANCIAL SERVICES, INC.—See Marriott Vacations Worldwide Corporation; *U.S. Public*, pg. 1374
MERIDIAN LEASING—See Meridian Group International, Inc.; *U.S. Private*, pg. 2673
MERIT INSURANCE SERVICES, INC.—See Integrity Marketing Group LLC; *U.S. Private*, pg. 2103
MERIT RESOURCES, INC. - MERIT SENIOR LIVING DIVISION—See Iowa Network Services Inc.; *U.S. Private*, pg. 2135
MESERCO, S.L.—See Banco de Sabadell, S.A.; *Int'l*, pg. 821
MESIROW FINANCIAL ADMINISTRATIVE CORPORATION—See Mesirow Financial Holdings, Inc.; *U.S. Private*, pg. 2678
MESIROW FINANCIAL CONSULTING, LLC—See Mesirow Financial Holdings, Inc.; *U.S. Private*, pg. 2678
MESIROW FINANCIAL INTERIM MANAGEMENT, LLC—See Mesirow Financial Holdings, Inc.; *U.S. Private*, pg. 2678
MESIROW FINANCIAL INTERNATIONAL UK, LIMITED—See Mesirow Financial Holdings, Inc.; *U.S. Private*, pg. 2678
MESIROW FINANCIAL INVESTMENT MANAGEMENT, INC.—See Mesirow Financial Holdings, Inc.; *U.S. Private*, pg. 2678
MESSENGER ASSOCIATES, INC.—See Adecco Group AG; *Int'l*, pg. 139
METEC ASSET MANAGEMENT, LC; *U.S. Private*, pg. 2683
METHOD3, INC.; *U.S. Private*, pg. 2683
METIS SOLUTIONS LLC—See Amentum Services, Inc.; *U.S. Private*, pg. 219
METRIKA BUSINESS INTELLIGENCE CONSULTING, INC.—See IQVIA Holdings Inc.; *U.S. Public*, pg. 1170
MEXICO SALES MADE EASY, INC.; *U.S. Private*, pg. 2692
MGG INVESTMENT GROUP, LP; *U.S. Private*, pg. 2694
MGM INTERNATIONAL, LLC—See MGM Resorts International; *U.S. Public*, pg. 1435
MHM INNOVATIONS, INC.—See Integrity Management Consulting, Inc.; *U.S. Private*, pg. 2103
MICROALLOYING INTERNATIONAL, INC.—See Stanley Black & Decker, Inc.; *U.S. Public*, pg. 1933
MICROBILT CORPORATION—See Bristol Investments, Ltd.; *U.S. Private*, pg. 657
MICROGEN SOLUTIONS INC—See Aptitude Software Group Plc; *Int'l*, pg. 524
MICROSTAR KEG MANAGEMENT LLC—See Freeman Spogli & Co. Incorporated; *U.S. Private*, pg. 1606
MIDTOWN CONSULTING GROUP, INC.; *U.S. Private*, pg. 2718
MIDWAY PRODUCTS GROUP, INC.; *U.S. Private*, pg. 2719
MI FULFILLMENT SERVICES, LLC—See Marriott International, Inc.; *U.S. Public*, pg. 1371
MILLAR & BRYCE LIMITED—See Daily Mail & General Trust plc; *Int'l*, pg. 1937
MILLENNIUM, CORP.; *U.S. Private*, pg. 2732
MILLENNIUM RISK MANAGEMENT LLC—See Bilfinger SE; *Int'l*, pg. 1028
MILLER ADVISORS INC.—See MFG Partners LLC; *U.S. Private*, pg. 2693
MILLER ADVISORS INC.—See The PNC Financial Services Group, Inc.; *U.S. Public*, pg. 2119
MILLER BUCKFIRE & CO., LLC; *U.S. Private*, pg. 2733
MILLSTEIN & CO., L.P.—See Guggenheim Partners, LLC; *U.S. Private*, pg. 1811
MINSHENG FINANCIAL LEASING CO., LTD.—See China Minsheng Banking Corporation Ltd.; *Int'l*, pg. 1524
MINSHENG ROYAL FUND MANAGEMENT CO., LTD.—See China Minsheng Banking Corporation Ltd.; *Int'l*, pg. 1524
MIS QUALITY MANAGEMENT CORP.—See Moody's Corporation; *U.S. Public*, pg. 1468
MISSOURI TOOLING & AUTOMATION, LLC; *U.S. Private*, pg. 2749
MMA FINANCIAL TC, LLC—See Fundamental Advisors LP; *U.S. Private*, pg. 1622

MOBILE MATCHMAKING, INC.; *U.S. Public*, pg. 1454
MOBILEPAY DENMARK A/S—See Danske Bank A/S; *Int'l*, pg. 1969
MODERN MEDIA ACQUISITION CORP.; *U.S. Public*, pg. 1454
MODERN TESTING SERVICES (HONG KONG) CO., LTD.—See Eurofins Scientific S.E.; *Int'l*, pg. 2551
MODIS INTERNATIONAL CO.—See Adecco Group AG; *Int'l*, pg. 140
MONEYWISE GLOBAL PTY. LTD.—See Flight Centre Travel Group Limited; *Int'l*, pg. 2706
MONROE CAPITAL CORPORATION; *U.S. Public*, pg. 1465
MOODY'S INVESTMENT CO. INDIA PVT. LTD.—See Moody's Corporation; *U.S. Public*, pg. 1468
MORGAN LLOYD ADMINISTRATION LTD—See Clifton Asset Management Plc; *Int'l*, pg. 1659
MORROW SODALI INTERNATIONAL LLC—See TPG Capital, L.P.; *U.S. Public*, pg. 2176
MOSIER & COMPANY, INC.; *U.S. Private*, pg. 2793
MOUNTAIN ONE FINANCIAL PARTNERS; *U.S. Private*, pg. 2799
MPACT STRATEGIC CONSULTING LLC; *U.S. Private*, pg. 2803
M-POWER SOLUTIONS PTY LTD—See DXC Technology Company; *U.S. Public*, pg. 696
MRE CONSULTING, INC.; *U.S. Private*, pg. 2805
MSCI BARRA (SUISSE) SARL—See MSCI Inc.; *U.S. Public*, pg. 1483
M'S COMMUNICATE CO., LTD—See Dai Nippon Printing Co., Ltd.; *Int'l*, pg. 1915
MS EUROPE B.V.—See World Kinect Corporation; *U.S. Public*, pg. 2380
MULTIMEDIA TELECOM, S.A. DE C.V.—See Grupo Televisa, S.A.B.; *Int'l*, pg. 3136
MURTECH CONSULTING; *U.S. Private*, pg. 2817
MUSIC REPORTS, INC.—See MidOcean Partners, LLP; *U.S. Private*, pg. 2717
MVW INTERNATIONAL FINANCE COMPANY LLC—See Marriott Vacations Worldwide Corporation; *U.S. Public*, pg. 1374
MYERS-HOLUM, INC.; *U.S. Private*, pg. 2824
MYRTLE CONSULTING GROUP LLC—See Accenture plc; *Int'l*, pg. 87
MZ ASIA-PACIFIC LTD.—See Grupo MZ; *Int'l*, pg. 3133
MZ CONSULT NY LLC—See Grupo MZ; *Int'l*, pg. 3133
MZ CONSULT PARTICIPACOES S.A.—See Grupo MZ; *Int'l*, pg. 3133
MZ TAIWAN—See Grupo MZ; *Int'l*, pg. 3133
NAKOMA GROUP—See Nakoma Group; *U.S. Private*, pg. 2831
NAMRA FINANCE LIMITED—See Arman Financial Services Ltd.; *Int'l*, pg. 574
NATIONAL ASSOCIATES, INC.—See Farmers National Banc Corp.; *U.S. Public*, pg. 822
NATIONAL COMMERCE BANK SERVICES, INC.—See Lincoln Property Company; *U.S. Private*, pg. 2458
NATIONAL ECONOMIC RESEARCH ASSOCIATES KK—See Marsh & McLennan Companies, Inc.; *U.S. Public*, pg. 1387
NATIONAL IMAGING ASSOCIATES INC.—See Centene Corporation; *U.S. Public*, pg. 470
NATIONALL RESPONSE CORPORATION OF PUERTO RICO—See AIP, LLC; *U.S. Public*, pg. 136
NATIONAL MUTUAL FUNDS MANAGEMENT LTD.—See AMP Limited; *Int'l*, pg. 432
NATIONAL PROFESSIONAL SERVICES, INC.—See Environmental Service Professionals, Inc.; *U.S. Public*, pg. 781
NATIONAL REGULATORY SERVICES—See Compliance Science, Inc.; *U.S. Private*, pg. 1001
NATIONAL SEMICONDUCTOR INTERNATIONAL B.V.—See Texas Instruments Incorporated; *U.S. Public*, pg. 2026
NATIONAL UTILITY SERVICE (CANADA) LTD.—See National Utility Service, Inc.; *U.S. Private*, pg. 2864
NATIONAL WHOLESALE LIQUIDATORS INC.; *U.S. Private*, pg. 2865
NATURAL CO., LTD.—See Bain Capital, LP; *U.S. Private*, pg. 434
NAVIGANT BPM (INDIA) PRIVATE LIMITED—See Bain Capital, LP; *U.S. Private*, pg. 432
NAVIGANT CONSULTING (APAC) PTE. LTD.—See Bain Capital, LP; *U.S. Private*, pg. 432
NAVIGANT CONSULTING ASIA LIMITED—See Bain Capital, LP; *U.S. Private*, pg. 432
NAVIGANT CONSULTING LTD.—See Bain Capital, LP; *U.S. Private*, pg. 432
NAVIGANT ECONOMICS, LLC - NEW YORK—See Bain Capital, LP; *U.S. Private*, pg. 432
NAVIGANT GERMANY GMBH—See Bain Capital, LP; *U.S. Private*, pg. 432
NAVIGATOR MANAGEMENT PARTNERS LLC—See Avaap Inc.; *U.S. Private*, pg. 403
NAVIN, HAFFTY & ASSOCIATES LLC—See Providence St. Joseph Health; *U.S. Private*, pg. 3294
NAVINT PARTNERS, LLC—See Boathouse Capital Management, LLC; *U.S. Private*, pg. 603
NAVITUS HEALTH SOLUTIONS, LLC—See SSM Health Care Corporation; *U.S. Private*, pg. 3769
NAVVIS HEALTHCARE, LLC; *U.S. Public*, pg. 2873
NBL INTERNATIONAL FINANCE B.V.—See Chevron Corporation; *U.S. Public*, pg. 487
NCH MANAGEMENT SYSTMES, INC.—See Evolent Health, Inc.; *U.S. Public*, pg. 804
NCR COLOMBIA LTDA—See NCR Voyix Corporation.; *U.S. Public*, pg. 1503
NELLIS MANAGEMENT CORPORATION; *U.S. Private*, pg. 2882
NELNET FINANCE CORP.—See Nelnet, Inc.; *U.S. Public*, pg. 1504
NELNET TRANSACTION SERVICES, LLC—See Nelnet, Inc.; *U.S. Public*, pg. 1504
NEOSFER GMBH—See Commerzbank AG; *Int'l*, pg. 1719
NEOSYSTEMS CORP.; *U.S. Private*, pg. 2885
NERA AUSTRALIA PTY LIMITED—See Marsh & McLennan Companies, Inc.; *U.S. Public*, pg. 1387
NERA S.R.L.—See Marsh & McLennan Companies, Inc.; *U.S. Public*, pg. 1387
NERA UK LIMITED—See Marsh & McLennan Companies, Inc.; *U.S. Public*, pg. 1387
NESTWORTH FINANCIAL STRATEGISTS PTY. LTD.—See Azimut Holding SpA; *Int'l*, pg. 779
NET POSITIVE BUSINESS ANALYTICS PRIVATE LIMITED—See Equifax Inc.; *U.S. Public*, pg. 787
NETWEAVE SOCIAL NETWORKING LLC; *U.S. Private*, pg. 2888
NETWORKERS FUNDING, LLC; *U.S. Private*, pg. 2889
NETWORK MEDICAL MANAGEMENT, INC.—See Astrana Health Inc.; *U.S. Public*, pg. 217
NEW10 B.V.—See ABN AMRO Group N.V.; *Int'l*, pg. 65
NEWCOMB ANDERSON MCCORMICK, INC.—See Willdan Group, Inc.; *U.S. Public*, pg. 2371
NEW EDITIONS CONSULTING, INC.; *U.S. Private*, pg. 2893
NEW ENGLAND ACCEPTANCE CORPORATION—See Citizens Financial Group, Inc.; *U.S. Public*, pg. 506
NEW HORIZON EQUITY GROUP, INC.; *U.S. Private*, pg. 2897
NEW RESOURCES CONSULTING, LLC; *U.S. Private*, pg. 2905
NEW WORQ, LLC; *U.S. Private*, pg. 2908
NEXEN S.P.A—See Apax Partners LLP; *Int'l*, pg. 504
NEXT-CHEMX CORPORATION; *U.S. Public*, pg. 1525
NFP CORPORATE SERVICES (NY), LLC.—See Aon plc; *Int'l*, pg. 496
NFP MOSSE & MOSSE ASSOCIATES, INC.—See Aon plc; *Int'l*, pg. 497
NISGA'A DATA SYSTEMS, LLC—See Gold Belt Incorporated; *U.S. Private*, pg. 1727
NOBLE BROADBAND LLC—See Guggenheim Partners, LLC; *U.S. Private*, pg. 1812
NOBLE FINANCE CORPORATION—See Gentry Finance Corporation; *U.S. Public*, pg. 1680
NODECHAIN, INC.; *U.S. Public*, pg. 1531
NOMAD DIGITAL BELGIUM S.A.—See Alstom S.A.; *Int'l*, pg. 383
NOR-AM SERVICE CORPORATION—See NASB Financial, Inc.; *U.S. Public*, pg. 1491
NORDIC GROUP OF COMPANIES, LTD.; *U.S. Private*, pg. 2936
NORTH AMERICAN PARTNERS IN ANESTHESIA LLP; *U.S. Private*, pg. 2941
NORTHEAST ASSOCIATION MANAGEMENT, INC.—See The Carlyle Group Inc.; *U.S. Public*, pg. 2054
NORTHEAST UTILITIES SERVICE COMPANY—See Eversource Energy; *U.S. Public*, pg. 802
THE NORTHERN TRUST COMPANY OF DELAWARE—See Northern Trust Corporation; *U.S. Public*, pg. 1539
THE NORTHERN TRUST COMPANY OF SAUDI ARABIA—See Northern Trust Corporation; *U.S. Public*, pg. 1539
THE NORTH HIGHLAND COMPANY; *U.S. Private*, pg. 4084
NORTHWEST PIPELINE CORPORATION—See The Williams Companies, Inc.; *U.S. Public*, pg. 2144
NORTHWEST PIPELINE CORPORATION—See The Williams Companies, Inc.; *U.S. Public*, pg. 2144
NOTUS AVIATION, INC.—See The ODP Corporation; *U.S. Public*, pg. 2117
NOVAGOLD USA, INC.—See Novagold Resources Inc.; *U.S. Public*, pg. 1547
NOVITEX ENTERPRISE SOLUTIONS CANADA, INC.—See Exela Technologies, Inc.; *U.S. Public*, pg. 806
NOVOLOGIX INC.; *U.S. Private*, pg. 2968
NTA LIFE BUSINESS SERVICES GROUP, INC.—See Horace Mann Educators Corporation; *U.S. Public*, pg. 1053
NTA LIFE INSURANCE COMPANY OF NEW YORK—See Horace Mann Educators Corporation; *U.S. Public*, pg. 1053
NTC GROUP; *U.S. Private*, pg. 2970
NUS CONSULTING GROUP PTY LIMITED—See National Utility Service, Inc.; *U.S. Private*, pg. 2864
NU SKIN ASIA INVESTMENT, INC.—See Nu Skin Enterprises, Inc.; *U.S. Public*, pg. 1552
NUS-SOUTH AFRICA—See National Utility Service, Inc.; *U.S. Private*, pg. 2864

541611 — ADMINISTRATIVE MANA... CORPORATE AFFILIATIONS

OAO CITY SERVICE—See City Service SE; *Int'l*, pg. 1627
O'BRIEN & GERE INC. OF NORTH AMERICA—See The O'Brien & Gere Companies; *U.S. Private*, pg. 4087
OCWEN MORTGAGE SERVICING, INC.—See Onity Group Inc.; *U.S. Public*, pg. 1604
OFFICE SUITES PLUS; *U.S. Private*, pg. 3002
OHSU FACULTY PRACTICE PLAN; *U.S. Private*, pg. 3006
OLGOONIK MANAGEMENT SERVICES, LLC—See Olgoonik Corporation;. *U.S. Private*, pg. 3010
THE OLIVER GROUP, INC.; *U.S. Private*, pg. 4088
OLIVER WYMAN ACTUARIAL CONSULTING, INC.—See Marsh & McLennan Companies, Inc.; *U.S. Public*, pg. 1387
OLIVER WYMAN AG—See Marsh & McLennan Companies, Inc.; *U.S. Public*, pg. 1387
OLIVER WYMAN CONSULTING GMBH—See Marsh & McLennan Companies, Inc.; *U.S. Public*, pg. 1387
OLIVER WYMAN CONSULTING LIMITED—See Marsh & McLennan Companies, Inc.; *U.S. Public*, pg. 1387
OLIVER WYMAN CONSULTING SARL—See Marsh & McLennan Companies, Inc.; *U.S. Public*, pg. 1387
OLIVER WYMAN CONSULTING (SHANGHAI) LTD—See Marsh & McLennan Companies, Inc.; *U.S. Public*, pg. 1386
OLIVER WYMAN CONSULTING SL—See Marsh & McLennan Companies, Inc.; *U.S. Public*, pg. 1387
OLIVER WYMAN ENERGY CONSULTING LIMITED—See Marsh & McLennan Companies, Inc.; *U.S. Public*, pg. 1387
OLIVER WYMAN GERMANY GMBH—See Marsh & McLennan Companies, Inc.; *U.S. Public*, pg. 1387
OLIVER WYMAN GROUP, KK—See Marsh & McLennan Companies, Inc.; *U.S. Public*, pg. 1387
OLIVER WYMAN (HONG KONG) LIMITED—See Marsh & McLennan Companies, Inc.; *U.S. Public*, pg. 1386
OLIVER WYMAN, INC.—See Marsh & McLennan Companies, Inc.; *U.S. Public*, pg. 1386
OLIVER WYMAN LIMITED—See Marsh & McLennan Companies, Inc.; *U.S. Public*, pg. 1387
OLIVER WYMAN PTE. LTD.—See Marsh & McLennan Companies, Inc.; *U.S. Public*, pg. 1387
OLIVER WYMAN PTY. LTD.—See Marsh & McLennan Companies, Inc.; *U.S. Public*, pg. 1387
OLIVER WYMAN PTY. LTD.—See Marsh & McLennan Companies, Inc.; *U.S. Public*, pg. 1387
OLIVER WYMAN SAS—See Marsh & McLennan Companies, Inc.; *U.S. Public*, pg. 1386
OLIVER WYMAN, S. DE R.L. DE C.V.—See Marsh & McLennan Companies, Inc.; *U.S. Public*, pg. 1388
OMNICHANNEL SOLUTIONS, LLC—See Thoma Bravo, L.P.; *U.S. Private*, pg. 4149
OMNI MANAGEMENT ACQUISITION CORP.; *U.S. Private*, pg. 3016
ONCO360; *U.S. Private*, pg. 3019
ONEACCORD CAPITAL LLC; *U.S. Private*, pg. 3024
O'NEAL INC.; *U.S. Private*, pg. 2979
O'NEILL AND ASSOCIATES, LLC—See Blue Engine Message & Media, LLC; *U.S. Private*, pg. 588
ONE RING NETWORKS, INC.—See Trive Capital Inc.; *U.S. Private*, pg. 4239
ONE SIXTY OVER NINETY, INC.—See William Morris Endeavor Entertainment, LLC; *U.S. Private*, pg. 4523
ONE STEP VENDING CORP.; *U.S. Public*, pg. 1602
ON-TRACK FINANCIAL SOLUTIONS PTY. LTD.—See Azimut Holding SpA; *Int'l*, pg. 779
OPPENHEIMER EUROPE LTD.—See Oppenheimer Holdings Inc.; *U.S. Public*, pg. 1608
OPTIMA GROUP, INC.; *U.S. Private*, pg. 3034
OPTUMINSIGHT, INC.—See UnitedHealth Group Incorporated; *U.S. Public*, pg. 2248
OPVANTEK, INC.—See Off Market Data, Inc.; *U.S. Private*, pg. 3001
ORBIS TECHNOLOGIES, INC.; *U.S. Private*, pg. 3038
OREGON RAIL MARKETING CO.—See Radius Recycling, Inc.; *U.S. Public*, pg. 1760
ORHUB, INC.; *U.S. Public*, pg. 1617
ORION ASSOCIATES; *U.S. Private*, pg. 3042
ORION MOBILITY; *U.S. Private*, pg. 3043
ORSCHELN MANAGEMENT CO.—See Orscheln Group; *U.S. Private*, pg. 3045
OS CAPITAL PARTNERS INC.—See Bain Capital, LP; *U.S. Private*, pg. 434
OS HRS INDIA PRIVATE LIMITED—See Bain Capital, LP; *U.S. Private*, pg. 434
OS HRS JAPAN INC.—See Bain Capital, LP; *U.S. Private*, pg. 434
OS HRS SDN BHD—See Bain Capital, LP; *U.S. Private*, pg. 434
OS LOGITEC CO., LTD.—See Bain Capital, LP; *U.S. Private*, pg. 434
OSLO ITALIA S.R.L.—See GPI S.p.A.; *Int'l*, pg. 3046
OS PLATINUM CO., LTD.—See Bain Capital, LP; *U.S. Private*, pg. 434
OS SUPPORT CO., LTD.—See Bain Capital, LP; *U.S. Private*, pg. 434
OUT OF THE BOXTECHNOLOGY; *U.S. Private*, pg. 3050
OUTSOURCING COMMUNICATIONS CO., LTD.—See Bain Capital, LP; *U.S. Private*, pg. 435

OY SAMLINK AB—See Cognizant Technology Solutions Corporation; *U.S. Public*, pg. 525
P2BINVESTOR INC.; *U.S. Private*, pg. 3062
P3I INC.; *U.S. Private*, pg. 3062
PACE HARMON, LLC—See West Monroe Partners, LLC; *U.S. Private*, pg. 4486
PACESETTER CAPITAL GROUP; *U.S. Private*, pg. 3064
PACIFIC HEALTH CARE ORGANIZATION, INC.; *U.S. Public*, pg. 1632
PACIFIC THEATRES CORPORATION—See Decurion Corp.; *U.S. Private*, pg. 1188
PACIFIC WESTERN TRAINING COMPANY—See Oppenheimer Companies, Inc.; *U.S. Private*, pg. 3033
PA CONSULTING HOLDINGS LIMITED—See The Carlyle Group Inc.; *U.S. Public*, pg. 2051
PACWEST EQUITIES, INC.; *U.S. Public*, pg. 1634
PALLADIUM GROUP, INC.; *U.S. Private*, pg. 3079
PANUM TELECOMMUNICATIONS, LLC—See Renovus Capital Partners; *U.S. Private*, pg. 3399
THE PARQUET GROUP; *U.S. Private*, pg. 4091
PARR CREDIT S.R.L.—See Arrow Global Group PLC; *Int'l*, pg. 579
PARSLEY FINANCE CORP.—See Pioneer Natural Resources Company; *U.S. Public*, pg. 1693
PARTNERPATH, LLC; *U.S. Private*, pg. 3101
PARTNERS IN ASSOCIATION MANAGEMENT, INC.; *U.S. Private*, pg. 3102
PATINA GROUP—See Delaware North Companies, Inc.; *U.S. Private*, pg. 1195
PATRIOT SERVICES, INC.—See Patriot National, Inc.; *U.S. Private*, pg. 3110
PAYMERANG, LLC—See Aldrich Capital Partners, LLC; *U.S. Private*, pg. 160
PB FACTORING GMBH—See Deutsche Bank Aktiengesellschaft; *Int'l*, pg. 2061
PBL MANAGEMENT PTY LIMITED—See News Corporation; *U.S. Public*, pg. 1521
PCH GROUP PTY LTD.—See Altrad Investment Authority SAS; *Int'l*, pg. 398
PCI STRATEGIC MANAGEMENT, LLC; *U.S. Private*, pg. 3120
PEC SAFETY OPERATIONS LLC—See Thoma Bravo, L.P.; *U.S. Private*, pg. 4150
PEKAO INVESTMENT MANAGEMENT S.A.—See Bank Polska Kasa Opieki Spolka Akcyjna; *Int'l*, pg. 850
PENINSULA FINANCE LLC—See Elliott Management Corporation; *U.S. Private*, pg. 1367
PENINSULA FINANCE LLC—See Vista Equity Partners, LLC; *U.S. Private*, pg. 4396
PENNYMAC LOAN SERVICES, LLC—See PennyMac Financial Services, Inc.; *U.S. Public*, pg. 1664
PEOPLE & PARTNERS PTY. LTD.—See Azimut Holding SpA; *Int'l*, pg. 779
PEOPLE & PARTNERS WEALTH MANAGEMENT PTY. LTD.—See Azimut Holding SpA; *Int'l*, pg. 779
THE PERDUCO GROUP, INC.—See KBR, Inc.; *U.S. Public*, pg. 1216
PERFICIENT D.O.O.—See EQT AB; *Int'l*, pg. 2483
PERFORMANCE INCORPORATED—See Automatic Data Processing, Inc.; *U.S. Public*, pg. 230
PERLMART MANAGEMENT CO. INC.—See Perlmart Inc.; *U.S. Private*, pg. 3152
PERMEDION INC.—See Veritas Capital Fund Management, LLC; *U.S. Private*, pg. 4362
PETSKY PRUNIER, LLC—See Canaccord Genuity Group Inc.; *Int'l*, pg. 1277
PHACIL FORT MONMOUTH (CECOM) OFFICE—See Sagewind Capital LLC; *U.S. Private*, pg. 3527
PHACIL-WASHINGTON, DC—See Sagewind Capital LLC; *U.S. Private*, pg. 3527
PHACIL-WEST COAST—See Sagewind Capital LLC; *U.S. Private*, pg. 3527
PHARMA-BIO SERV US, INC.—See PHARMA-BIO SERV, INC.; *U.S. Public*, pg. 1684
PHARMALINK CONSULTING INC.—See Genpact Limited; *Int'l*, pg. 2927
PHARMALINK CONSULTING LTD.—See Genpact Limited; *Int'l*, pg. 2927
PHARMANEX, LLC—See Nu Skin Enterprises, Inc.; *U.S. Public*, pg. 1552
PHARMASTOCK—See Cegedim S.A.; *Int'l*, pg. 1390
PHEASANT LANE MALL MANAGEMENT—See S.R. Weiner & Associates Inc.; *U.S. Private*, pg. 3518
PHILOSOPHY IB, LLP—See Heidrick & Struggles International, Inc.; *U.S. Public*, pg. 1023
PHOENIX PARTNERS INC.; *U.S. Private*, pg. 3173
PHOENIX SYNERGISTICS—See Phoenix Marketing International, Inc.; *U.S. Private*, pg. 3173
PI COMPANY; *U.S. Private*, pg. 3175
PIRS CAPITAL, LLC; *U.S. Private*, pg. 3190
PIXID S.N.C.—See ManpowerGroup Inc.; *U.S. Public*, pg. 1360
PLAN ADMINISTRATORS, INC.—See Aquiline Capital Partners LLC; *U.S. Public*, pg. 304
PLAN ADMINISTRATORS, INC.—See Genstar Capital, LLC; *U.S. Private*, pg. 1675
PLANVISTA CORPORATION; *U.S. Private*, pg. 3198
THE PLASENCIA GROUP, INC.; *U.S. Private*, pg. 4096

PLATFORM SPECIALISTS, LLC—See Accordion Partners LLC; *U.S. Private*, pg. 53
PLUM LOGIC, LLC; *U.S. Private*, pg. 3214
PMALLIANCE, INC.; *U.S. Private*, pg. 3217
PNEO LLC; *U.S. Private*, pg. 3219
POINT GUARD PARTNERS LLC; *U.S. Private*, pg. 3222
POLY (CHONGQING) GOLF MANAGEMENT CO., LTD.—See China Poly Group Corporation; *Int'l*, pg. 1541
PONDER & CO.—See Vizient, Inc.; *U.S. Private*, pg. 4407
POOLIESTUDIOS GMBH—See Allgeier SE; *Int'l*, pg. 337
POPE WOODHEAD AND ASSOCIATES—See Huron Consulting Group Inc.; *U.S. Public*, pg. 1076
POPPER AND COMPANY LLC; *U.S. Private*, pg. 3228
POSTBANK LEASING GMBH—See Deutsche Bank Aktiengesellschaft; *Int'l*, pg. 2061
POWER MANAGEMENT, INC.—See Tetra Tech, Inc.; *U.S. Public*, pg. 2022
PPI BENEFITS SOLUTIONS—See Principal Financial Group, Inc.; *U.S. Public*, pg. 1721
PQMS LTD.—See Hexatronic Group AB; *Int'l*, pg. 3371
PRAIRIE QUEST, INC.; *U.S. Private*, pg. 3243
PRECISIONSCIENTIA, INC.—See Precision Medicine Group, Inc.; *U.S. Private*, pg. 3245
PREMIER, INC.; *U.S. Public*, pg. 1715
PREMIER WORKCOMP MANAGEMENT, L.L.C.—See Blue Cross & Blue Shield of Kansas City, Inc.; *U.S. Private*, pg. 586
PREMIUM RETAIL SERVICES INC.; *U.S. Private*, pg. 3252
PRESTADORA DE SERVICIOS INDUSTRIALES DE PERSONAL, S.A. DE R.L. DE C.V.—See Avient Corporation; *U.S. Public*, pg. 248
PRIDE ADVICE PTY. LTD.—See Azimut Holding SpA; *Int'l*, pg. 779
PRIMARILY CARE, INC.; *U.S. Private*, pg. 3260
PRIMATICS FINANCIAL LLC—See SS&C Technologies Holdings, Inc.; *U.S. Public*, pg. 1923
PRIMED MANAGEMENT CONSULTING SERVICES INC.; *U.S. Private*, pg. 3262
PRIME MANAGEMENT LIMITED—See SS&C Technologies Holdings, Inc.; *U.S. Public*, pg. 1923
PRIME THERAPEUTICS, LLC—See GuideWell Mutual Holding Corporation; *U.S. Private*, pg. 1814
PRINCIPAL CHILE LIMITADA—See Principal Financial Group, Inc.; *U.S. Public*, pg. 1720
PRINCIPAL INSURANCE COMPANY (HONG KONG) LIMITED—See Principal Financial Group, Inc.; *U.S. Public*, pg. 1721
PRISTINE CAPITAL HOLDINGS, INC.—See T3 Live LLC; *U.S. Private*, pg. 3913
PRIVATES INSTITUT FUR QUANTITATIVE KAPITALMARKTFORSCHUNG DER DEKABANK GMBH—See DekaBank; *Int'l*, pg. 2005
PROCEDURELINK, LLC—See The Rudolph/Libbe Companies; *U.S. Private*, pg. 4113
PRO CONSULT MANAGEMENT- UND SYSTEMBERATUNG GMBH—See EWE Aktiengesellschaft; *Int'l*, pg. 2575
PROGRAM PLANNING PROFESSIONALS; *U.S. Private*, pg. 3278
PRO INSURANCE SOLUTIONS LIMITED—See Financiere Pinault SCA; *Int'l*, pg. 2668
PROJECTMATRIX CORP.—See Configura Sverige AB; *Int'l*, pg. 1768
PROJECT ONE INTEGRATED SERVICES LLC—See Cumming Construction Management, Inc.; *U.S. Private*, pg. 1123
PROJECT SOLUTIONS S.A.—See ManpowerGroup Inc.; *U.S. Public*, pg. 1361
PROMO WORKS, LLC—See Acosta, Inc.; *U.S. Private*, pg. 64
PROPERTY DEVELOPMENT LTD—See Bank of Ceylon; *Int'l*, pg. 841
PROSERVIA GMBH—See ManpowerGroup Inc.; *U.S. Public*, pg. 1361
PRO-TELLIGENT, LLC—See Tetra Tech, Inc.; *U.S. Public*, pg. 2023
PROTIVITI BVBA—See Robert Half Inc.; *U.S. Public*, pg. 1803
PROTIVITI B.V.—See Robert Half Inc.; *U.S. Public*, pg. 1803
PROTIVITI CONSULTING PRIVATE LIMITED—See Robert Half Inc.; *U.S. Public*, pg. 1803
PROTIVITI GOVERNMENT SERVICES, INC.—See Robert Half Inc.; *U.S. Public*, pg. 1803
PROTIVITI PTE. LTD.—See Robert Half Inc.; *U.S. Public*, pg. 1803
PROTIVITI PTY. LIMITED—See Robert Half Inc.; *U.S. Public*, pg. 1803
PROTIVITI SAS—See Robert Half Inc.; *U.S. Public*, pg. 1803
PROTIVITI S.R.L.—See Robert Half Inc.; *U.S. Public*, pg. 1803
PROTIVITI SWITZERLAND GMBH—See Robert Half Inc.; *U.S. Public*, pg. 1803
PRS INTERNATIONAL CONSULTING INC—See EFG International AG; *Int'l*, pg. 2321
PRUDENCE CRANDALL FUND III, LLC—See Wells Fargo & Company; *U.S. Public*, pg. 2345
PT. CLS SYSTEM—See Advance Information Marketing Berhad; *Int'l*, pg. 156

N.A.I.C.S. INDEX

541611 — ADMINISTRATIVE MANA...

PT DAIWA HOUSE INDONESIA—See Daiwa House Industry Co., Ltd.; *Int'l*, pg. 1947
PT. FTI CONSULTING INDONESIA—See FTI Consulting, Inc.; *U.S. Public*, pg. 891
PT. HAIDA AGRICULTURE INDONESIA—See Guangdong Haid Group Co., Ltd.; *Int'l*, pg. 3155
PT. POYRY INDONESIA—See AFRY AB; *Int'l*, pg. 195
P.T. RHIPE INTERNATIONAL INDONESIA—See Crayon Group Holding ASA; *Int'l*, pg. 1829
PT SAI GLOBAL INDONESIA—See EQT AB; *Int'l*, pg. 2471
PUBLIC COMPANY MANAGEMENT CORPORATION; *U.S. Public*, pg. 1735
PUBLIC INTEREST DATA, LLC—See Blackbaud, Inc.; *U.S. Public*, pg. 341
PUBLIC KNOWLEDGE, LLC—See Gaming Laboratories International LLC; *U.S. Private*, pg. 1640
PULSEPOINT GROUP, LLC—See ICF International, Inc.; *U.S. Public*, pg. 1086
PULTE GEORGIA—See PulteGroup, Inc.; *U.S. Public*, pg. 1737
PUROSYSTEMS, INC.; *U.S. Private*, pg. 3306
PWC STRATEGY& (US) INC.—See PricewaterhouseCoopers LLP (USA); *U.S. Private*, pg. 3259
PYXERA GLOBAL; *U.S. Private*, pg. 3311
QA MANAGEMENT SERVICES PTY LTD.—See I Squared Capital Advisors (US) LLC; *U.S. Private*, pg. 2023
QIPRO SOLUCIONES S.L.—See Banco Bilbao Vizcaya Argentaria, S.A.; *Int'l*, pg. 818
QMC SYSTEMS, INC.; *U.S. Private*, pg. 3313
QORVAL, L.L.C.; *U.S. Private*, pg. 3313
Q-PARTNERS CONSULTING & MANAGEMENT GMBH—See Devoteam SA; *Int'l*, pg. 2090
QTEC SOLUTIONS, INC.; *U.S. Private*, pg. 3314
QUALCHOICE OF ARKANSAS, INC.—See Centene Corporation; *U.S. Public*, pg. 470
QUALITY HEALTH LIMITED—See IQVIA Holdings Inc.; *U.S. Public*, pg. 1170
QUANTECH SERVICES, INC.; *U.S. Private*, pg. 3322
QUANTITECH LLC—See Millennium Engineering & Integration Company; *U.S. Private*, pg. 2731
QUANTUM BUSINESS STRATEGIES, INC.; *U.S. Private*, pg. 3322
QUEST INTEGRITY CAN LTD.—See Team, Inc.; *U.S. Public*, pg. 1988
QUEST MANAGEMENT CONSULTANTS, INC—See Career Management Partners; *U.S. Private*, pg. 752
QUESTOR MANAGEMENT COMPANY, LLC; *U.S. Private*, pg. 3326
QUEZON MANAGEMENT SERVICE INC.—See Electricity Generating Public Co., Ltd.; *Int'l*, pg. 2352
QUORUM HOTELS & RESORTS, LTD.—See Somera Capital Management, LLC; *U.S. Public*, pg. 3711
QUSQU INTELLIGENCE GMBH—See Axxiome AG; *Int'l*, pg. 773
R1 RCM INC.; *U.S. Public*, pg. 1758
RADAR SERVICIOUS CELAYA S. DE R.L. DE C.V.—See Shiloh Industries, Inc.; *U.S. Private*, pg. 3636
RADDON FINANCIAL GROUP—See Fiserv, Inc.; *U.S. Public*, pg. 851
RADIATION ONCOLOGY SERVICES, INC.; *U.S. Private*, pg. 3343
RAVIX FINANCIAL, INC.—See Kingsway Financial Services Inc.; *U.S. Public*, pg. 1235
RCB INVESTIMENTOS S.A.—See Banco Bradesco S.A.; *Int'l*, pg. 819
RECURSOS CORPORATIVOS ALAMEDA, S.C.—See Grupo Televisa, S.A.B.; *Int'l*, pg. 3136
RED24 LIMITED—See iJET International, Inc.; *U.S. Private*, pg. 2040
REDBERRY CONTACT CENTER SDN. BHD.—See Ancom Nylex Berhad; *Int'l*, pg. 449
REDCLOUD CONSULTING INC.; *U.S. Private*, pg. 3377
RED ROCK CONSULTING PTY LTD—See DXC Technology Company; *U.S. Public*, pg. 695
RED ROSE COMMONS ASSOCIATES, L.P.—See Pennsylvania Real Estate Investment Trust; *U.S. Public*, pg. 1664
REDSTONE STRATEGY GROUP, LLC—See Arabella Advisors, LLC; *U.S. Private*, pg. 307
REDWOOD SHORES OWNERS ASSOCIATION—See Equity Residential; *U.S. Public*, pg. 792
REDW STANLEY FINANCIAL ADVISORS LLC; *U.S. Private*, pg. 3380
REED GROUP MANAGEMENT LLC—See Alight, Inc.; *U.S. Public*, pg. 77
REFERENCE DATA FACTORY LLC—See FD Technologies PLC; *Int'l*, pg. 2628
REFICOR S.R.O.—See Assicurazioni Generali S.p.A.; *Int'l*, pg. 647
REGIONS COMMERCIAL EQUIPMENT FINANCE, LLC—See Regions Financial Corporation; *U.S. Public*, pg. 1776
REGISTERED AGENT SOLUTIONS, INC.—See Apax Partners LLP; *Int'l*, pg. 503
REGISTRAR CORP—See Paine Schwartz Partners, LLC; *U.S. Private*, pg. 3076
REGROUP THERAPY, INC.—See Harbour Point Management LLC; *U.S. Private*, pg. 1861

REGULATORY ASSISTANCE PROJECT; *U.S. Private*, pg. 3389
REHACARE GMBH—See Allianz SE; *Int'l*, pg. 356
RE HARRINGTON UNEMPLOYMENT TAX SERVICE—See PlanVista Corporation; *U.S. Private*, pg. 3198
RELIABLE INSURANCE SERVICES CORP.—See Wells Fargo & Company; *U.S. Public*, pg. 2345
RELIANCE FIRST CAPITAL, LLC—See Tiptree Inc.; *U.S. Public*, pg. 2159
THE REMINGTON GROUP INC—See Avison Young (Canada) Inc.; *Int'l*, pg. 745
RENSON ENTERPRISES—See Benson Motors Corporation; *U.S. Private*, pg. 528
RESCUE SOCIAL CHANGE GROUP, LLC.; *U.S. Private*, pg. 3403
THE RESEARCH BOARD, INC.—See Gartner, Inc.; *U.S. Public*, pg. 907
RESIP—See Cegedim S.A.; *Int'l*, pg. 1390
RESORT FUNDING LLC—See Bank of America Corporation; *U.S. Public*, pg. 272
RESOURCE CONSULTING GROUP, INC.; *U.S. Private*, pg. 3406
RESOURCES CONNECTION MEXICO S DE RL DE CV—See Resources Connection, Inc.; *U.S. Public*, pg. 1791
RESOURCES GLOBAL PROFESSIONALS (EUROPE) BV—See Resources Connection, Inc.; *U.S. Public*, pg. 1791
RESOURCES GLOBAL PROFESSIONALS (FRANCE) SAS—See Resources Connection, Inc.; *U.S. Public*, pg. 1791
RESOURCES GLOBAL PROFESSIONALS (GERMANY) GMBH—See Resources Connection, Inc.; *U.S. Public*, pg. 1791
RESOURCES GLOBAL PROFESSIONALS (HONG KONG) LIMITED—See Resources Connection, Inc.; *U.S. Public*, pg. 1791
RESOURCES GLOBAL PROFESSIONALS (INDIA) PRIVATE LTD.—See Resources Connection, Inc.; *U.S. Public*, pg. 1791
RESOURCES GLOBAL PROFESSIONALS (IRELAND) LTD.—See Resources Connection, Inc.; *U.S. Public*, pg. 1792
RESOURCES GLOBAL PROFESSIONALS (JAPAN) K.K.—See Resources Connection, Inc.; *U.S. Public*, pg. 1792
RESOURCES GLOBAL PROFESSIONALS (KOREA) LTD.—See Resources Connection, Inc.; *U.S. Public*, pg. 1792
RESOURCES GLOBAL PROFESSIONALS (NORWAY) AS—See Resources Connection, Inc.; *U.S. Public*, pg. 1792
RESOURCES GLOBAL PROFESSIONALS (SINGAPORE) PTE. LTD.—See Resources Connection, Inc.; *U.S. Public*, pg. 1792
RESOURCES GLOBAL PROFESSIONALS SWEDEN AB—See Resources Connection, Inc.; *U.S. Public*, pg. 1792
RESOURCES GLOBAL PROFESSIONALS (TAIWAN) CO. LTD.—See Resources Connection, Inc.; *U.S. Public*, pg. 1792
RETIREMENT COMMUNITY SPECIALISTS, INC.; *U.S. Private*, pg. 3412
RETIREMENT PLAN SERVICES, LLC—See NBT Bancorp Inc.; *U.S. Public*, pg. 1501
REVEL CONSULTING INC.—See ChrysCapital Investment Advisors (India) Private Limited; *Int'l*, pg. 1588
REVENUE MANAGEMENT SYSTEMS INC.—See Warburg Pincus LLC; *U.S. Private*, pg. 4439
REVITALIZATION PARTNERS, LLC—See Formula Brewing, LLC; *U.S. Private*, pg. 1572
RFC FINANCIAL SERVICES HOLDING LLC—See Regions Financial Corporation; *U.S. Public*, pg. 1776
RGS ASSOCIATES, INC.—See Carl Marks & Co., Inc.; *U.S. Private*, pg. 763
RHG GROUP, INC.; *U.S. Private*, pg. 3421
RHIPE JAPAN KK—See Crayon Group Holding ASA; *Int'l*, pg. 1829
RHIPE LANKA (PVT.) LIMITED—See Crayon Group Holding ASA; *Int'l*, pg. 1830
RHIPE TECHNOLOGY PHILIPPINES, INC.—See Crayon Group Holding ASA; *Int'l*, pg. 1830
RHIPE TECHNOLOGY (THAILAND) CO., LTD.—See Crayon Group Holding ASA; *Int'l*, pg. 1830
THE RICCIARDI GROUP CORP.; *U.S. Public*, pg. 4106
THE RIESE ORGANIZATION; *U.S. Private*, pg. 4107
RIGHT DO BRASIL LTDA—See ManpowerGroup Inc.; *U.S. Public*, pg. 1361
RIGHT MANAGEMENT CHINA—See ManpowerGroup Inc.; *U.S. Public*, pg. 1361
RIGHT MANAGEMENT CONSULTANTS INTERNATIONAL PTY LTD—See ManpowerGroup Inc.; *U.S. Public*, pg. 1361
RIGHT MANAGEMENT CONSULTANTS PTY LTD—See ManpowerGroup Inc.; *U.S. Public*, pg. 1361
RIGHT MANAGEMENT NORDIC HOLDING A/S—See ManpowerGroup Inc.; *U.S. Public*, pg. 1361
RIGHT MANAGEMENT NORWAY A/S—See ManpowerGroup Inc.; *U.S. Public*, pg. 1361
RIGHT MANAGEMENT PERU S.A.C.—See ManpowerGroup Inc.; *U.S. Public*, pg. 1361
RIGHT MANAGEMENT SWITZERLAND AG—See ManpowerGroup Inc.; *U.S. Public*, pg. 1361
RIGHT SINOVA AB—See ManpowerGroup Inc.; *U.S. Public*, pg. 1361
RISKSOL CONSULTING LTD.—See Coller Capital Ltd.; *Int'l*, pg. 1699
RISK & STRATEGIC MANAGEMENT, CORP.—See Growth Catalyst Partners, LLC; *U.S. Private*, pg. 1796
RITENET CORPORATION; *U.S. Private*, pg. 3442
RIVER & MERCANTILE LLC—See Agilis Holding Company LLC; *U.S. Private*, pg. 128
RIVERSIDE MANAGEMENT SERVICES INC.—See Health Quest Systems, Inc.; *U.S. Private*, pg. 1894
RIVERSOURCE DISTRIBUTORS, INC.—See Ameriprise Financial, Inc.; *U.S. Public*, pg. 114
RIZZETTA & COMPANY, INC.—See FirstService Corporation; *Int'l*, pg. 2691
THE RK LOGISTICS GROUP, INC.; *U.S. Private*, pg. 4110
RNR CONSULTING; *U.S. Private*, pg. 3453
ROBERT FERRILLI; *U.S. Private*, pg. 3457
ROBERT HALF S.R.L.—See Robert Half Inc.; *U.S. Public*, pg. 1804
THE ROBERTSON GROUP, INC.; *U.S. Private*, pg. 4111
ROBINSONS BANK CORPORATION—See Bank of the Philippine Islands; *Int'l*, pg. 849
ROCK CREEK FUND (E) LTD.—See Wells Fargo & Company; *U.S. Public*, pg. 2345
ROGENSI LTD—See TTEC Holdings, Inc.; *U.S. Public*, pg. 2203
ROGENSI PTY LTD.—See TTEC Holdings, Inc.; *U.S. Public*, pg. 2203
ROGENSI SERVICES PTY LTD.—See TTEC Holdings, Inc.; *U.S. Public*, pg. 2203
RONGDE ASSET MANAGEMENT CO., LTD.—See China CITIC Financial Asset Management Co., Ltd.; *Int'l*, pg. 1489
ROOT DESIGN COMPANY; *U.S. Private*, pg. 3480
ROY JORGENSEN ASSOCIATES, INC.; *U.S. Private*, pg. 3490
RPI PROFESSIONAL ALTERNATIVES—See Response Personnel, Inc.; *U.S. Private*, pg. 3408
RPM MANAGEMENT INC; *U.S. Private*, pg. 3495
RR DONNELLEY JAPAN, INC.—See Chatham Asset Management, LLC; *U.S. Private*, pg. 865
RR DONNELLEY SINGAPORE PTE LTD.—See Chatham Asset Management, LLC; *U.S. Private*, pg. 865
RUNPATH REGULATED SERVICES LIMITED—See Experian plc; *Int'l*, pg. 2588
RUNZHEIMER INTERNATIONAL LLC—See Thoma Bravo, L.P.; *U.S. Private*, pg. 4150
RUSH ADMINISTRATIVE SERVICES, INC.—See Rush Enterprises, Inc.; *U.S. Public*, pg. 1826
RVM ENTERPRISES, INC.—See JLL Partners, LLC; *U.S. Private*, pg. 2213
RW BLOCK CONSULTING, INC.—See Accenture plc; *Int'l*, pg. 86
RXC ACQUISITION COMPANY—See McKesson Corporation; *U.S. Public*, pg. 1408
RX OPTIONS, LLC—See New Rite Aid, LLC; *U.S. Private*, pg. 2906
RYAN TRANSPORTATION GROUP, INC.—See Auto Expediting Inc.; *U.S. Private*, pg. 397
RYUGIN RESEARCH INSTITUTE., LTD.—See Bank of The Ryukyus, Ltd.; *Int'l*, pg. 849
SAFETY CONTROLS TECHNOLOGY, INC.—See ScaleCo Management LLC; *U.S. Private*, pg. 3560
SAGE BUSINESS GROUP PTY. LTD.—See Azimut Holding SpA; *Int'l*, pg. 779
SAIA LOGISTICS SERVICES, LLC—See Saia, Inc.; *U.S. Public*, pg. 1835
SAI GLOBAL JAPAN CO LTD—See EQT AB; *Int'l*, pg. 2471
SAINT-GOBAIN CONSULTING INFORMATION AND ORGANIZATION—See Compagnie de Saint-Gobain SA; *Int'l*, pg. 1727
SAISON PARTNERS CO., LTD.—See Credit Saison Co., Ltd.; *Int'l*, pg. 1836
SAMMONS RETIREMENT SOLUTIONS, INC.—See Sammons Enterprises, Inc.; *U.S. Private*, pg. 3537
SAM SENSORY INTERNATIONAL FRANCE S.A.S.—See Eurofins Scientific S.E.; *Int'l*, pg. 2551
SANCTUARY WEALTH GROUP LLC—See Azimut Holding SpA; *Int'l*, pg. 779
SANDLER SYSTEMS, INC.; *U.S. Private*, pg. 3544
SANEI COLLECTION SERVICE CO., LTD.—See Prudential Financial, Inc.; *U.S. Public*, pg. 1733
SAPERE CONSULTING, INC.; *U.S. Private*, pg. 3548
SAS INSTITUTE INC. - SHERMAN OAKS—See SAS Institute Inc.; *U.S. Private*, pg. 3551
SASKATCHEWAN OPPORTUNITIES CORPORATION—See Crown Investments Corporation of Saskatchewan; *Int'l*, pg. 1857
SATUIT TECHNOLOGIES, INC.—See Dura Software Series A Qof LLC; *U.S. Private*, pg. 1292
SAUDI ARABIAN INTEGRATED LOGISTIC SYSTEMS—See Al-Hejailan Group; *Int'l*, pg. 286

SAUDI KOREAN HEALTH INFORMATICS COMPANY—See ezCaretech Co., Ltd.; *Int'l*, pg. 2593
SAUGATUCK TECHNOLOGY INC.—See Information Services Group, Inc.; *U.S. Private*, pg. 1118
SAXONY PARTNERS LLC; *U.S. Private*, pg. 3558
SCHERING CHINA LIMITED—See Bayer Aktiengesellschaft; *Int'l*, pg. 904
SCHROEDER MEASUREMENT TECHNOLOGIES, INC.—See Educational Testing Service Inc.; *U.S. Private*, pg. 1340
SCHWARZKOPF & HENKEL PRODUCTION MANAGEMENT GMBH—See Henkel AG & Co. KGaA; *Int'l*, pg. 3354
SCIENTIFIC ADVANTAGE LLC—See Acquis Consulting Group, LLC; *U.S. Private*, pg. 65
SCM FINANCIAL GROUP PTY. LTD.—See Azimut Holding SpA; *Int'l*, pg. 779
SCORPIO PARTNERSHIP LIMITED—See Aon plc; *Int'l*, pg. 495
SCOTT CITRUS MANAGEMENT, INC.; *U.S. Private*, pg. 3576
SCS SOFTWARE, INC.—See CrossCountry Consulting LLC; *U.S. Private*, pg. 1106
SEABREEZE MANAGEMENT COMPANY, INC.; *U.S. Private*, pg. 3583
SEACHANGE NLG B.V.—See SeaChange International, Inc.; *U.S. Public*, pg. 1851
SEAFORD CONSULTING, LLC—See Godspeed Capital Management LP; *U.S. Private*, pg. 1725
SEALY & SMITH FOUNDATION; *U.S. Private*, pg. 3585
SEICHOU SENRYAKU INC.—See Funai Soken Holdings Incorporated; *Int'l*, pg. 2845
SEI FINANCIAL MANAGEMENT CORPORATION—See SEI Investments Company; *U.S. Public*, pg. 1856
SEI INVESTMENTS EUROPE LIMITED—See SEI Investments Company; *U.S. Public*, pg. 1857
SEJ SERVICES LLC; *U.S. Private*, pg. 3600
SEMA GMBH—See Atos SE; *Int'l*, pg. 692
SEMINOLE HARD ROCK ENTERTAINMENT, INC.—See Seminole Tribe of Florida, Inc.; *U.S. Private*, pg. 3604
SEM YAYINCILIK A.S—See Global Yatirim Holding A.S.; *Int'l*, pg. 3003
SENDERO BUSINESS SERVICES LP; *U.S. Private*, pg. 3606
SENSA SOLUTIONS, INC.—See Korn Ferry; *U.S. Public*, pg. 1273
SERENISYS SARL—See DigitalBridge Group, Inc.; *U.S. Public*, pg. 665
SERENISYS SARL—See EQT AB; *Int'l*, pg. 2482
SERVICESOURCE INTERNATIONAL BULGARIA EOOD—See Concentrix Corporation; *U.S. Public*, pg. 564
SERVICIOS ADMINISTRATIVOS AMERICA S. DE RL DE C.V.—See National Amusements, Inc.; *U.S. Private*, pg. 2843
SERVICIOS ADMINISTRATIVOS API ACAPULCO, S.A. DE C.V.—See Grupo TMM, S.A.B.; *Int'l*, pg. 3137
SERVICIOS ADMINISTRATIVOS CABLEMAS, S.A. DE C.V.—See Grupo Televisa, S.A.B.; *Int'l*, pg. 3136
SERVICIOS EJECUTIVOS PROGRESS S. DE R.L. DE C.V.—See Caterpillar, Inc.; *U.S. Public*, pg. 453
SERVICIOS LOGISTICOS BENAVIDES, S.A. DE C.V.—See Walgreens Boots Alliance, Inc.; *U.S. Public*, pg. 2323
SERVITAS CALIDAD SA DE CV—See Apollo Global Management, Inc.; *U.S. Public*, pg. 165
SEV1TECH, LLC—See DFW Capital Partners; *U.S. Private*, pg. 1221
SEV1TECH, LLC—See Enlightenment Capital LLC; *U.S. Private*, pg. 1400
THE SEXTANT GROUP, INC.—See NV5 Global, Inc.; *U.S. Public*, pg. 1558
SFM, LLC—See Sprouts Farmers Markets, Inc.; *U.S. Public*, pg. 1920
SHANGHAI DONGZHENG AUTOMOTIVE FINANCE CO., LTD.—See China ZhengTong Auto Services Holdings Limited; *Int'l*, pg. 1566
SHANGHAI FRANKFURT AIRPORT CONSULTING SERVICES CO., LTD. (SFACS)—See Fraport AG; *Int'l*, pg. 2764
SHANGHAI HUAXIA DUN & BRADSTREET BUSINESS INFORMATION CONSULTING CO., LIMITED—See Cannae Holdings, Inc.; *U.S. Public*, pg. 430
SHANGHAI HUAXIA DUN & BRADSTREET BUSINESS INFORMATION CONSULTING CO., LIMITED—See CC Capital Partners, LLC; *U.S. Private*, pg. 798
SHANGHAI HUAXIA DUN & BRADSTREET BUSINESS INFORMATION CONSULTING CO., LIMITED—See Intercontinental Exchange, Inc.; *U.S. Public*, pg. 1142
SHANGHAI JUYUAN DATA CO., LTD.—See Hundsun Technologies Inc.; *Int'l*, pg. 3534
SHANGHAI KORN/FERRY HUMAN CAPITAL CONSULTING CO., LTD.—See Korn Ferry; *U.S. Public*, pg. 1275
SHAREBPO PTY LTD—See Apex Fund Services Holdings Ltd.; *Int'l*, pg. 510
SHENZHEN POLY CULTURE PLAZA CO., LTD—See China Poly Group Corporation; *Int'l*, pg. 1541
SHENZHEN YIDIAN DOUBLE WAY OF INNOVATION CULTURE MEDIA CORP.; *U.S. Public*, pg. 1874

THE SHERWOOD GROUP, INC.; *U.S. Private*, pg. 4117
SHIPLEY ASSOCIATES; *U.S. Private*, pg. 3637
SHIPLEY LIMITED—See Shipley Associates; *U.S. Private*, pg. 3637
SHIPLEY (UK) GMBH—See Shipley Associates; *U.S. Private*, pg. 3637
SIA CENTRAL EUROPE. A.S.—See Cassa Depositi e Prestiti S.p.A.; *Int'l*, pg. 1355
SIA CITY SERVICE ENGINEERING—See City Service SE; *Int'l*, pg. 1355
SIA CROATIA D.O.O.—See Cassa Depositi e Prestiti S.p.A.; *Int'l*, pg. 1355
SIA CZECH REPUBLIC. S.R.O.—See Cassa Depositi e Prestiti S.p.A.; *Int'l*, pg. 1355
SIA ROMANIA PAYMENT TECHNOLOGIES S.R.L.—See Cassa Depositi e Prestiti S.p.A.; *Int'l*, pg. 1355
SIA RS D.O.O.—See Cassa Depositi e Prestiti S.p.A.; *Int'l*, pg. 1355
SIDD SARL—See ADLPartner SA; *Int'l*, pg. 151
SIGNATURE LEISURE, INC.; *U.S. Public*, pg. 1878
SILOSMASHERS, INC.; *U.S. Private*, pg. 3653
SILVER MANAGEMENT GROUP, INC.—See Apex Fintech Solutions LLC; *U.S. Private*, pg. 292
SIMULEON B.V.—See Addnode Group AB; *Int'l*, pg. 130
SIRIUSDECISIONS, INC.—See Forrester Research, Inc.; *U.S. Public*, pg. 869
SIROTA CONSULTING LLC—See Marsh & McLennan Companies, Inc.; *U.S. Public*, pg. 1385
SITUSAMC HOLDINGS CORPORATION—See Stone Point Capital LLC; *U.S. Private*, pg. 3825
SITUS GROUP LLC—See Stone Point Capital LLC; *U.S. Private*, pg. 3825
SKILLPOWER SERVICES (THAILAND) CO. LTD.—See ManpowerGroup Inc.; *U.S. Public*, pg. 1504
SLG 16 COURT STREET LLC—See SL Green Realty Corp.; *U.S. Public*, pg. 1894
SLG 711 THIRD LLC—See SL Green Realty Corp.; *U.S. Public*, pg. 1894
SM&A—See SM&A Corporation; *U.S. Private*, pg. 3690
SM&A-WEST—See SM&A Corporation; *U.S. Private*, pg. 3690
SMITHS CONSULTING LTD.—See Capita plc; *Int'l*, pg. 1309
SOCIAL DETENTION, INC.; *U.S. Public*, pg. 1899
SOCIAL FINANCE, INC.—See SoFi Technologies, Inc.; *U.S. Public*, pg. 1899
SOCIETA INIZIATIVE AUTOSTRADALI E SERVIZI S.P.A.—See Argo Finanziaria S.p.A.; *Int'l*, pg. 562
SOELLINGEN ADVISORY GROUP, INC.; *U.S. Private*, pg. 3704
SOLIUM CAPITAL INC.—See Morgan Stanley; *U.S. Public*, pg. 1475
SOUTH CAROLINA MANUFACTURING EXTENSION PARTNERSHIP; *U.S. Private*, pg. 3720
SOUTHERN MEDICAL HEALTH SYSTEMS INC.; *U.S. Private*, pg. 3733
SPARK.ORANGE, LLC; *U.S. Private*, pg. 3745
SPARKROOM, LLC—See Nelnet, Inc.; *U.S. Public*, pg. 1504
SPECIAL DISTRICT SERVICES, INC.; *U.S. Private*, pg. 3748
SPINCONTROL S.A.S—See Eurofins Scientific S.E.; *Int'l*, pg. 2551
SPINNAKER CONSULTING GROUP LLC; *U.S. Private*, pg. 3757
SPINNAKER MANAGEMENT GROUP, LLC; *U.S. Private*, pg. 3757
SPIRIT SEARCH SAS—See ManpowerGroup Inc.; *U.S. Public*, pg. 1360
SPORTS TOTO VIETNAM JOINT STOCK COMPANY—See Development Investment Construction JSC; *Int'l*, pg. 2088
SPRINGHILL MEDICAL COMPLEX INC.—See Southern Medical Health Systems Inc.; *U.S. Private*, pg. 3733
SPS COMMERCE CANADA, LTD.—See SPS Commerce, Inc.; *U.S. Public*, pg. 1920
SPX VALLEY FORGE TECHNICAL INFORMATION SERVICES, INC.—See SPX Technologies, Inc.; *U.S. Public*, pg. 1921
SQUADHELP, INC.; *U.S. Private*, pg. 3765
SQUARETRADE, INC.—See The Allstate Corporation; *U.S. Public*, pg. 2032
SRD INC.—See Dos Gringos Inc.; *U.S. Private*, pg. 1264
SS&C TECHNOLOGIES IRELAND LIMITED—See SS&C Technologies Holdings, Inc.; *U.S. Public*, pg. 1924
SSI STRATEGY—See Acquis Consulting Group, LLC; *U.S. Private*, pg. 65
SST BENEFITS CONSULTING & INSURANCE SERVICES INC.—See Aon plc; *U.S. Private*, pg. 497
STA BENEFITS, LTD.—See Aon plc; *Int'l*, pg. 497
STAFF SOLUTIONS AUSTRALIA PTY LTD—See Bain Capital, LP; *U.S. Private*, pg. 435
STANLEY BENEFIT SERVICES, INC.—See Mid Atlantic Capital Group, Inc.; *U.S. Private*, pg. 2705
STANLEY CONSULTANTS INC—See Stanley Consultants Co.; *U.S. Private*, pg. 3783
STANLEY, HUNT, DUPREE & RHINE, INC.—See Truist Financial Corporation; *U.S. Public*, pg. 2201
STANSON HEALTH, INC.—See Premier, Inc.; *U.S. Public*, pg. 1715

STARTEK AUSTRALIA PTY LTD—See StarTek, Inc.; *U.S. Private*, pg. 3788
STARWOOD ITALIA S.R.L.—See Marriott International, Inc.; *U.S. Public*, pg. 1372
STAT TECH SERVICES, LLC.—See CMC Consulting Boston, Inc.; *U.S. Private*, pg. 950
STERLING GLOBAL OPERATIONS, INC.; *U.S. Private*, pg. 3805
STERLING PLANNERS PTY. LTD.—See Azimut Holding SpA; *Int'l*, pg. 779
STIFEL INDEPENDENT ADVISORS, LLC—See Stifel Financial Corp.; *U.S. Public*, pg. 1950
ST JAMES CORPORATE SERVICES LIMITED—See Gold Fields Limited; *Int'l*, pg. 3024
ST. LOUIS MUNICIPAL FINANCE CORPORATION; *U.S. Private*, pg. 3770
STOCK & OPTION SOLUTIONS, INC.; *U.S. Private*, pg. 3814
STORA FASAD AB—See Balco Group AB; *Int'l*, pg. 807
STORM INDUSTRIES, INC.; *U.S. Private*, pg. 3831
STRATEGEX, INC.; *U.S. Private*, pg. 3834
STRATEGIC ASSET MANAGEMENT, INC.; *U.S. Private*, pg. 3834
STRATEGIC INSIGHT, INC.—See Genstar Capital, LLC; *U.S. Private*, pg. 1675
STRATEGIC INTELLIGENCE GROUP LLC—See D.C. Capital Partners, LLC; *U.S. Private*, pg. 1141
STRATEGIC INVESTMENTS & HOLDING INC.; *U.S. Private*, pg. 3835
STRATEGIC MANAGEMENT & OPPORTUNITY CORP.; *U.S. Public*, pg. 1954
STRATEGIC RISK SOLUTIONS INC.; *U.S. Private*, pg. 3835
STRATEGY TO REVENUE INC.—See LevelBlox, Inc.; *U.S. Public*, pg. 1308
STRATEGYWISE, LLC—See Align Capital Partners, LLC; *U.S. Private*, pg. 167
STRATIVA, INC.—See Avasant LLC; *U.S. Private*, pg. 404
STREET RESOURCE GROUP, INC.—See Stone Point Capital LLC; *U.S. Private*, pg. 3825
STRONG-BRIDGE CONSULTING LLC.; *U.S. Private*, pg. 3840
SUCHERMAN CONSULTING GROUP, INC.—See RFE Investment Partners; *U.S. Private*, pg. 3420
SUDDEUTSCHE VERMOGENSVERWALTUNG GESELLSCHAFT MIT BESCHRANKTER HAFTUNG—See Deutsche Bank Aktiengesellschaft; *Int'l*, pg. 2062
SUI TAI & ASSOCIATES LIMITED—See Heng Tai Consumables Group Limited; *Int'l*, pg. 3345
SULLIVAN, INC.; *U.S. Private*, pg. 3852
SUMMIT FINANCE GROUP, LLC—See Summit Materials, Inc.; *U.S. Public*, pg. 1959
SUNERA LLC; *U.S. Private*, pg. 3867
SUNORA ENERGY SOLUTIONS LIMITED PARTNERSHIP—See NRG Energy, Inc.; *U.S. Public*, pg. 1551
SUNTIVA, LLC; *U.S. Private*, pg. 3873
SUNWIN SERVICES GROUP, LIMITED—See NCR Voyix Corporation.; *U.S. Public*, pg. 1501
SUPPLAY SAS—See ManpowerGroup Inc.; *U.S. Public*, pg. 1360
SUSTAINSERV, INC.; *U.S. Private*, pg. 3886
SVM, LP—See P2 Capital Partners, LLC; *U.S. Private*, pg. 3061
SVM, LP—See Silver Lake Group, LLC; *U.S. Private*, pg. 3656
SVO MANAGEMENT, INC.—See Marriott International, Inc.; *U.S. Public*, pg. 1372
SWT HOLDINGS B.V.—See Illinois Tool Works Inc.; *U.S. Public*, pg. 1110
SYNDICATION, INC.; *U.S. Private*, pg. 3903
SYNEOS HEALTH GERMANY GMBH—See Elliott Management Corporation; *U.S. Private*, pg. 1365
SYNEOS HEALTH GERMANY GMBH—See Patient Square Capital, L.P.; *U.S. Private*, pg. 3108
SYNEOS HEALTH GERMANY GMBH—See Veritas Capital Fund Management, LLC; *U.S. Private*, pg. 4365
SYNEOS HEALTH ITALY S.R.L.—See Elliott Management Corporation; *U.S. Private*, pg. 1365
SYNEOS HEALTH ITALY S.R.L.—See Patient Square Capital, L.P.; *U.S. Private*, pg. 3108
SYNEOS HEALTH ITALY S.R.L.—See Veritas Capital Fund Management, LLC; *U.S. Private*, pg. 4365
SYNEOS HEALTH IVH UK LIMITED—See Elliott Management Corporation; *U.S. Private*, pg. 1365
SYNEOS HEALTH IVH UK LIMITED—See Patient Square Capital, L.P.; *U.S. Private*, pg. 3108
SYNEOS HEALTH IVH UK LIMITED—See Veritas Capital Fund Management, LLC; *U.S. Private*, pg. 4365
SYNEOS HEALTH NETHERLANDS B.V.—See Elliott Management Corporation; *U.S. Private*, pg. 1365
SYNEOS HEALTH NETHERLANDS B.V.—See Patient Square Capital, L.P.; *U.S. Private*, pg. 3108
SYNEOS HEALTH NETHERLANDS B.V.—See Veritas Capital Fund Management, LLC; *U.S. Private*, pg. 4365
SYNYGY, INC.; *U.S. Private*, pg. 3905
SYSCOM AS—See DXC Technology Company; *U.S. Public*, pg. 697

541611 — ADMINISTRATIVE MANA...

N.A.I.C.S. INDEX

SYS - ENTERPRISE SOLUTIONS DIVISION—See Kratos Defense & Security Solutions, Inc.; *U.S. Public*, pg. 1277
SYS - INTEGRATED & INFORMATION SOLUTIONS GROUP—See Kratos Defense & Security Solutions, Inc.; *U.S. Public*, pg. 1277
SYS - SYSTEMS ENGINEERING & MANAGEMENT DIVISION—See Kratos Defense & Security Solutions, Inc.; *U.S. Public*, pg. 1277
SYSTEMS INTEGRATION, INC.—See Rimhub, Inc.; *U.S. Private*, pg. 3437
TABREWER CONSULTING, INC.—See General Atlantic Service Company, L.P.; *U.S. Private*, pg. 1662
TABREWER CONSULTING, INC.—See HgCapital Trust plc; *Int'l*, pg. 3376
TALENT CURVE SOLUTIONS LLC; *U.S. Private*, pg. 3926
TAMPA BAY INNOVATION CENTER; *U.S. Private*, pg. 3928
TANKE, INC.; *U.S. Public*, pg. 1981
TAPFIN LLC—See ManpowerGroup Inc.; *U.S. Public*, pg. 1362
TARGET CORPORATION INDIA PRIVATE LIMITED—See Target Corporation; *U.S. Public*, pg. 1982
TARRAGUE A.G.—See Grupo Televisa, S.A.B.; *Int'l*, pg. 3136
TASKUS, INC.; *U.S. Public*, pg. 1982
TAX PLANNING SEMINARS INC—See Allianz SE; *Int'l*, pg. 347
T.C. MANAGEMENT, INC.—See Yadav Enterprises, Inc.; *U.S. Private*, pg. 4584
TD AMERITRADE FUTURES & FOREX LLC—See The Charles Schwab Corporation; *U.S. Public*, pg. 2058
TDCI, INC.—See Koch Industries, Inc.; *U.S. Private*, pg. 2331
TDX GROUP LIMITED—See Equifax Inc.; *U.S. Public*, pg. 786
TEAM HEALTH, LLC—See Blackstone Inc.; *U.S. Public*, pg. 359
TECHLAW SOLUTIONS, INC.—See Fronteo, Inc.; *Int'l*, pg. 2794
TECHNICAL AND PROJECT ENGINEERING, LLC; *U.S. Private*, pg. 3953
TECHNICAL RESOURCE GROUP, INC.—See White Wolf Capital LLC; *U.S. Private*, pg. 4510
TECHNOLOGY & BUSINESS INTEGRATORS INC.; *U.S. Private*, pg. 3955
TECHNOLOGY FINANCE PARTNERS INC.; *U.S. Private*, pg. 3955
TECMA GROUP, LLC; *U.S. Private*, pg. 3956
TELCO EXPERTS LLC—See Alpine Investors; *U.S. Private*, pg. 201
TEMPUS WEALTH GROUP PTY. LTD.—See Azimut Holding SpA; *Int'l*, pg. 779
TENEO SAS—See Sealed Air Corporation; *U.S. Public*, pg. 1855
TERATHINK CORPORATION; *U.S. Private*, pg. 3969
TERRAHEALTH INC.; *U.S. Private*, pg. 3971
THE TERRALIGN GROUP, INC.—See Salesforce, Inc.; *U.S. Public*, pg. 1837
TETRA TECH EM INC.—See Tetra Tech, Inc.; *U.S. Public*, pg. 2023
TETRA TECH, INC. - BURLINGTON—See Tetra Tech, Inc.; *U.S. Public*, pg. 2024
TEXAS ENERGY AGGREGATION—See O2 Investment Partners, LLC; *U.S. Private*, pg. 2982
TGAS ADVISORS, LLC—See Kohlberg & Company, LLC; *U.S. Private*, pg. 2339
THERMO FISHER SCIENTIFIC FINANCE COMPANY BV—See Thermo Fisher Scientific Inc.; *U.S. Public*, pg. 2154
THE THRESHOLD GROUP, LLC—See AlTi Global, Inc.; *U.S. Public*, pg. 87
THURMAN HOTEL CONSULTANTS; *U.S. Private*, pg. 4166
TIDAL BASIN GOVERNMENT CONSULTING, LLC—See D.C. Capital Partners, LLC; *U.S. Private*, pg. 1141
TIER 1 PERFORMANCE SOLUTIONS, LLC; *U.S. Private*, pg. 4168
TILSON HR, INC.; *U.S. Private*, pg. 4171
TIS CHIYODA SYSTEMS INC.—See Chiyoda Corporation; *Int'l*, pg. 1575
TMF GROUP—See CVC Capital Partners SICAV-FIS S.A.; *Int'l*, pg. 1886
TMG CONSULTING LLC—See Avance Investment Management, LLC; *U.S. Private*, pg. 403
TODAY CARD, LLC—See Continental Finance; *U.S. Private*, pg. 1029
TOTAL TRIAL MANAGEMENT CONSULTING CO., LTD.—See EPS Holdings, Inc.; *Int'l*, pg. 2466
TPG DEVELOPMENT MANAGEMENT CONSULTANTS—See The Plasencia Group, Inc.; *U.S. Private*, pg. 4096
TRACESECURITY INC.; *U.S. Private*, pg. 4200
TRADEONE; *U.S. Private*, pg. 4202
TRADETECH CONSULTING SCANDINAVIA AB—See EQT AB; *Int'l*, pg. 2472
TRADEWEB COMMERCIAL INFORMATION CONSULTING (SHANGHAI) CO., LTD.—See Tradeweb Markets Inc.; *U.S. Public*, pg. 2178
TRADEWEB EU B.V.—See Tradeweb Markets Inc.; *U.S. Public*, pg. 2178

TRADEWEB EUROPE LIMITED—See Tradeweb Markets Inc.; *U.S. Public*, pg. 2178
TRADEWEB JAPAN K.K.—See Tradeweb Markets Inc.; *U.S. Public*, pg. 2178
TRAFFIC SERVICES, INC.—See Jacobs Engineering Group, Inc.; *U.S. Public*, pg. 1186
TRANSWORLD BUSINESS ADVISORS OF COLORADO LLC; *U.S. Private*, pg. 4212
TREACY & COMPANY, INC.—See Cherry Bekaert LLP; *U.S. Private*, pg. 874
TRICHOME FINANCIAL CORP.—See IM Cannabis Corp.; *Int'l*, pg. 3617
TRINITY CAPITAL, LLC—See Citizens Financial Group, Inc.; *U.S. Public*, pg. 506
TRINITY HEALTH PLANS—See Trinity Health Corporation; *U.S. Public*, pg. 4234
TRINITY HEALTH SYSTEM INC.; *U.S. Private*, pg. 4234
TRINITY PARTNERS, LLC—See Kohlberg & Company, LLC; *U.S. Private*, pg. 2339
TRIPLE-I INVESTMENTS INC.; *U.S. Private*, pg. 4237
TRISSENTIAL, LLC—See Assystem S.A.; *Int'l*, pg. 650
TROON GOLF L.L.C.; *U.S. Private*, pg. 4242
TRS STAFFING SOLUTIONS (CANADA), INC.—See Fluor Corporation; *U.S. Public*, pg. 859
TRUIST LEADERSHIP INSTITUTE, INC.—See Truist Financial Corporation; *U.S. Public*, pg. 2201
TSA CONSULTING GROUP, INC.; *U.S. Private*, pg. 4252
TUC AMU CENTER TUC MIDTJYLLAND APS—See DEKRA e.V.; *Int'l*, pg. 2009
TUNSTALL CONSULTING, INC.; *U.S. Private*, pg. 4258
TUPPERWARE GLOBAL CENTER SARL—See Tupperware Brands Corporation; *U.S. Public*, pg. 2204
TURNER & TOWNSEND LTD.—See CBRE Group, Inc.; *U.S. Public*, pg. 460
TWELVE POINTS WEALTH MANAGEMENT, LLC; *U.S. Private*, pg. 4264
TWENTY/TWENTY WORLDWIDE HOSPITALITY, LLC; *U.S. Private*, pg. 4264
TWIN MEDICAL TRANSACTION SERVICES, INC—See Firstsource Solutions Limited; *Int'l*, pg. 2691
UAB PASTATU VALDYMAS—See City Service SE; *Int'l*, pg. 1628
UGL PTY LIMITED—See ACS, Actividades de Construccion y Servicios, S.A.; *Int'l*, pg. 113
UHS OF DELAWARE, INC.—See Universal Health Services, Inc.; *U.S. Public*, pg. 2260
ULTRAMAR ENERGY INC.—See Valero Energy Corporation; *U.S. Public*, pg. 2272
UMS GROUP, INC.—See Align Capital Partners, LLC; *U.S. Private*, pg. 167
UNAMIC/HCN B.V.—See Conduent Incorporated; *U.S. Public*, pg. 566
UNDERCURRENT LLC—See Quirky Inc.; *U.S. Private*, pg. 3329
UNILINK DATA SYSTEMS PTY LTD—See Nelnet, Inc.; *U.S. Public*, pg. 1504
UNISON CONSULTING, INC.; *U.S. Private*, pg. 4286
UNITED BEHAVIORAL HEALTH—See UnitedHealth Group Incorporated; *U.S. Public*, pg. 2252
UNITED BIOSOURCE PATIENT SOLUTIONS, INC.—See The Cigna Group; *U.S. Public*, pg. 2062
UNITED CAPITAL CONSULTANTS, INC.; *U.S. Private*, pg. 4288
UNITED DEVELOPMENT SYSTEMS, INC.—See Brown & Brown, Inc.; *U.S. Public*, pg. 399
UNITEDHEALTHCARE OF WASHINGTON, INC.—See UnitedHealth Group Incorporated; *U.S. Public*, pg. 2252
UNITED PARADYNE CORPORATION; *U.S. Private*, pg. 4295
UNITED PIG PLACEMENT SERVICES—See United Animal Health, Inc.; *U.S. Private*, pg. 4287
UNIVERSAL CONSULTING SERVICES, INC.; *U.S. Private*, pg. 4304
UNIVERSITY CITY SCIENCE CENTER; *U.S. Private*, pg. 4307
UPPER RANCH COMPANY LLC; *U.S. Private*, pg. 4312
USAGENCIES MANAGEMENT SERVICES, INC.—See J.C. Flowers & Co. LLC; *U.S. Private*, pg. 2159
US CABLE GROUP; *U.S. Private*, pg. 4318
USCC SERVICES, LLC—See Telephone & Data Systems, Inc.; *U.S. Public*, pg. 1998
U.S. FINANCIAL ADVISORS LLC—See Great Valley Advisor Group, Inc.; *U.S. Private*, pg. 1768
US-REPORTS, INC.—See HGGC, LLC; *U.S. Private*, pg. 1929
US VR GLOBAL.COM INC.; *U.S. Private*, pg. 4320
UTILITY CONCIERGE, LLC; *U.S. Private*, pg. 4326
VALADOR, INC.; *U.S. Private*, pg. 4330
VALE GENERAL, S.A.—See Banco General, S.A.; *Int'l*, pg. 822
VALENCE HEALTH, LLC—See Evolent Health, Inc.; *U.S. Public*, pg. 804
VALENTINE MARK CORPORATION; *U.S. Public*, pg. 2272
VALIFY, INC.—See HCA Healthcare, Inc.; *U.S. Public*, pg. 1013
VANTAGE KNOWLEDGE ACADEMY LTD.—See Anupam Finserv Ltd.; *Int'l*, pg. 486

VCHECK GLOBAL LLC; *U.S. Private*, pg. 4349
VC UK LP—See Freudenberg SE; *Int'l*, pg. 2790
VECTOR CONSULTANTS LIMITED—See Freudenberg SE; *Int'l*, pg. 2790
VECTOR DATA SERVICES, INC.—See Freudenberg SE; *Int'l*, pg. 2791
VECTOR ENVIRONMENTAL SERVICES LIMITED—See Aramark; *U.S. Public*, pg. 178
VECTOR GROUP INC.—See Freudenberg SE; *Int'l*, pg. 2790
VECTOR WORKPLACE AND FACILITY MANAGEMENT LIMITED—See Aramark; *U.S. Public*, pg. 178
VEGAGEST SGR SPA—See Arrow Global Group PLC; *Int'l*, pg. 579
VEI INC.—See Jacobs Engineering Group, Inc.; *U.S. Public*, pg. 1186
VELOSI ENGINEERING MANAGEMENT CONSULTANCY (SHANGAI) LTD CO.—See I Squared Capital Advisors (US) LLC; *U.S. Private*, pg. 2023
VENNERSYS LIMITED—See Christie Group plc; *Int'l*, pg. 1587
VERACITY MANAGEMENT GLOBAL, INC.; *U.S. Private*, pg. 4359
VERIFI, INC.—See Visa, Inc.; *U.S. Public*, pg. 2301
VERIS CONSULTING, INC.—See Bow River Asset Management Corp.; *U.S. Private*, pg. 625
VERITAS CONSULTING KFT.—See 4iG Nyrt.; *Int'l*, pg. 12
VERITAS TOTAL SOLUTIONS, LLC—See Marsh & McLennan Companies, Inc.; *U.S. Public*, pg. 1388
VERIZON BUSINESS SECURITY SOLUTIONS—See Verizon Communications Inc.; *U.S. Public*, pg. 2285
VERIZON SERVICES GROUP INC.—See Verizon Communications Inc.; *U.S. Public*, pg. 2286
VERTICAL APPLICATIONS, INC.—See MindPetal Software Solutions, Inc.; *U.S. Private*, pg. 2741
VETERAN INFRASTRUCTURE PRODUCTS LLC; *U.S. Private*, pg. 4373
VICKIE MILAZZO INSTITUTE; *U.S. Private*, pg. 4377
VICTOR O. SCHINNERER & COMPANY, INC.—See Marsh & McLennan Companies, Inc.; *U.S. Public*, pg. 1383
VIRTUAL CLARITY LIMITED—See DXC Technology Company; *U.S. Public*, pg. 697
VIRTUAL, INC; *U.S. Private*, pg. 4389
VIRTUAL SOURCING, LLC; *U.S. Private*, pg. 4389
VIRTUSA AUSTRIA GMBH—See EQT AB; *Int'l*, pg. 2472
VIRTUSA CORPORATION - CONNECTICUT—See EQT AB; *Int'l*, pg. 2472
VIRTUSA MALAYSIA PRIVATE LIMITED—See EQT AB; *Int'l*, pg. 2472
VIRTUSA PHILIPPINES, INC.—See EQT AB; *Int'l*, pg. 2472
VIRTUSA SWITZERLAND GMBH—See EQT AB; *Int'l*, pg. 2472
VISUALVEST GMBH—See DZ BANK AG Deutsche Zentral-Genossenschaftsbank; *Int'l*, pg. 2245
VITIELLO COMMUNICATIONS GROUP, LLC—See Clayton, Dubilier & Rice, LLC; *U.S. Public*, pg. 925
VIVE FINANCIAL, LLC—See Aaron's Company, Inc.; *U.S. Public*, pg. 13
VIVENTO INTERIM SERVICES GMBH—See ManpowerGroup Inc.; *U.S. Public*, pg. 1362
VOLT TELECOMMUNICATIONS GROUP—See American CyberSystems, Inc.; *U.S. Private*, pg. 230
VOLVO GROUP NORTH AMERICA, LLC—See AB Volvo; *Int'l*, pg. 44
VONLEHMAN & CO. INC.—See Dean Dorton Allen Ford, PLLC; *U.S. Private*, pg. 1183
VOTRAINT NO 1537 PTY LTD—See ICM Limited; *Int'l*, pg. 3582
VRTUAL, INC.—See XWELL, Inc.; *U.S. Public*, pg. 2393
VYSNOVA PARTNERS, INC.—See Hale Capital Partners, L.P.; *U.S. Private*, pg. 1842
WADEWARE LLC—See Hands-On Learning Solutions LLC; *U.S. Public*, pg. 1853
WADLEY-DONOVAN GROUP; *U.S. Private*, pg. 4425
WADLEY-DONOVAN-GUTSHAW CONSULTING, LLC—See Wadley-Donovan Group; *U.S. Private*, pg. 4425
WATER MANAGEMENT SERVICES DIVISION—See Thielsch Engineering, Inc.; *U.S. Private*, pg. 4144
WATERMAN GROUP PLC—See CTI Engineering Co., Ltd.; *Int'l*, pg. 1871
WEALTHMED AUSTRALIA PTY. LTD.—See Azimut Holding SpA; *Int'l*, pg. 779
WEALTHWISE PTY. LTD.—See Azimut Holding SpA; *Int'l*, pg. 780
WEBYES LLC; *U.S. Private*, pg. 4468
WEEKES & CALLAWAY, INC.—See CBIZ, Inc.; *U.S. Public*, pg. 457
WEEKES & CALLOWAY—See CBIZ, Inc.; *U.S. Public*, pg. 457
WELLEN CAPITAL, LLC; *U.S. Private*, pg. 4475
WELLEZ INFORMATION MANAGEMENT, LLC—See Thoma Bravo, L.P.; *U.S. Private*, pg. 4152
WELLINGTON DIAGNOSTIC SERVICES; *U.S. Private*, pg. 4475
WELLNESS CORPORATE SOLUTIONS, LLC; *U.S. Private*, pg. 4476
WELLS FARGO AUTO RECEIVABLES, LLC—See Wells Fargo & Company; *U.S. Public*, pg. 2345

541611 — ADMINISTRATIVE MANA...

WELLS FARGO FINANCIAL OREGON, INC.—See Wells Fargo & Company; *U.S. Public*, pg. 2346
WELLS FARGO GLOBAL FUND SERVICES (ASIA) PTE LTD.—See Wells Fargo & Company; *U.S. Public*, pg. 2346
WELLS FARGO GLOBAL FUND SERVICES (UK) LIMITED—See Wells Fargo & Company; *U.S. Public*, pg. 2346
WELLS FARGO SECURITIES INTERNATIONAL LIMITED—See Wells Fargo & Company; *U.S. Public*, pg. 2347
WELLS FARGO SECURITIES (JAPAN) CO., LTD.—See Wells Fargo & Company; *U.S. Public*, pg. 2347
WELLS FARGO SOPORTE GLOBAL LIMITADA—See Wells Fargo & Company; *U.S. Public*, pg. 2347
WENTWORTH FINANCIAL PARTNERS, LLC; *U.S. Private*, pg. 4481
WENTWORTH RESEARCH LIMITED—See Gartner, Inc.; *U.S. Public*, pg. 907
WEST MONROE PARTNERS, LLC; *U.S. Private*, pg. 4486
WEXCO INCORPORATED FSC—See Wexco Incorporated; *U.S. Private*, pg. 4502
WEXFORD HEALTH SOURCES INC.; *U.S. Private*, pg. 4502
WHEATON FRANCISCAN SERVICES INC.; *U.S. Private*, pg. 4504
WHIRLPOOL CANADA CO.—See Whirlpool Corporation; *U.S. Public*, pg. 2367
WHITETAIL ROCK QUANTITATIVE STRATEGIES I, LP—See Nelnet, Inc.; *U.S. Public*, pg. 1504
WHITEWATER, INC.—See R.H. White Companies Inc.; *U.S. Private*, pg. 3336
WHITNEY & WHITNEY, INC.—See Itronics Inc.; *U.S. Public*, pg. 1176
WHO'S CALLING, INC.—See Vista Equity Partners, LLC; *U.S. Private*, pg. 4402
WILDER DEEM, INC.; *U.S. Private*, pg. 4519
WILLIAMS LEA LIMITED—See Advent International Corporation; *U.S. Private*, pg. 107
WILLIAMSMARSTON LLC—See Kelso & Company, L.P.; *U.S. Private*, pg. 2281
WILLIAMSON INTERNATIONAL CORP.—See T.D. Williamson, Inc.; *U.S. Private*, pg. 3912
WILLIS ASSET MANAGEMENT LIMITED—See Willis Lease Finance Corporation; *U.S. Public*, pg. 2372
THE WILLOW GROUP, INC.—See Trinity Hunt Management, L.P.; *U.S. Private*, pg. 4235
WITTENBERG WEINER CONSULTING, LLC; *U.S. Private*, pg. 4551
WNC CORPORATION; *U.S. Private*, pg. 4552
WOD RETAIL SOLUTIONS, INC.; *U.S. Public*, pg. 2376
WORKFORCE DELTA PTY. LTD.—See Cyient Limited; *Int'l*, pg. 1896
WORKWELL SYSTEMS, INC.—See Chrysalis Ventures; *U.S. Private*, pg. 893
WORLD-DIRECT EBUSINESS SOLUTIONS GMBH—See America Movil, S.A.B. de C.V.; *Int'l*, pg. 421
WPMI, LLC—See Elevance Health, Inc.; *U.S. Public*, pg. 730
WSOS COMMUNITY ACTION COMMISSION, INC.; *U.S. Private*, pg. 4574
XELLERATION, LLC—See Speridian Technologies, LLC; *U.S. Private*, pg. 3756
XEROX BUSINESS SERVICES—See Xerox Holdings Corporation; *U.S. Public*, pg. 2390
XEROX BUSINESS SOLUTIONS SOUTHEAST, LLC—See Xerox Holdings Corporation; *U.S. Public*, pg. 2387
XLA, INC.; *U.S. Private*, pg. 4581
XPO LOGISTICS SUPPLY CHAIN, INC.—See XPO, Inc.; *U.S. Public*, pg. 2392
XTREME CONSULTING GROUP, INC.; *U.S. Private*, pg. 4583
YALE TRANSACTION FINDERS, INC.; *U.S. Public*, pg. 2398
THE YOUNG ENTREPRENEURS ACADEMY INC.; *U.S. Private*, pg. 4139
YSTRATEGIES CORP.; *U.S. Public*, pg. 2399
ZA GROUP, INC.; *U.S. Public*, pg. 2400
ZAO CITY SERVICE—See City Service SE; *Int'l*, pg. 1628
ZAPATA ENGINEERING - BLACKHAWK DIVISION—See Zapata Engineering; *U.S. Private*, pg. 4598
ZENETEX LLC—See V2X, Inc.; *U.S. Public*, pg. 2270
ZENITH SERVICE S.P.A.—See Arrow Global Group PLC; *Int'l*, pg. 579
ZERO NOMINEES PTY. LTD.—See Euroz Hartleys Group Limited; *Int'l*, pg. 2559
ZEUUS, INC.; *U.S. Public*, pg. 2403
ZHENGZHOU POLY INTERNATIONAL CINEMA—See China Poly Group Corporation; *Int'l*, pg. 1541
ZIONS PUBLIC FINANCE, INC.—See Zions Bancorporation, National Association; *U.S. Public*, pg. 2408

541612 — HUMAN RESOURCES CONSULTING SERVICES

12 INTERACTIVE, LLC; *U.S. Private*, pg. 2
1-CALL STAFFING LLC; *U.S. Private*, pg. 1
1LINK TECHNOLOGY, LLC; *U.S. Private*, pg. 3
1 SOURCE BUSINESS SOLUTIONS, LLC—See PCF Insurance Services of The West, LLC; *U.S. Private*, pg. 3120
21 LADY CO., LTD.; *Int'l*, pg. 4
51JOB, INC.; *Int'l*, pg. 12
AAVALAR CONSULTING, INC.; *U.S. Private*, pg. 33
ABBA STAFFING & CONSULTING SERVICES; *U.S. Private*, pg. 34
ABBEY HR SERVICES—See Markel Group Inc.; *U.S. Public*, pg. 1367
ABSOLUTE CONSULTING, INC.—See GSE Systems, Inc.; *U.S. Public*, pg. 973
ACCESS KELLYOCG GMBH—See Kelly Services, Inc.; *U.S. Public*, pg. 1219
ACLOCHE - EXECUTIVE SEARCH DIVISION—See Acloche; *U.S. Private*, pg. 60
ADCORP HOLDINGS LIMITED; *Int'l*, pg. 127
ADDISON PROFESSIONAL FINANCIAL SEARCH LLC—See Odyssey Investment Partners, LLC; *U.S. Private*, pg. 2994
ADECCO ARGENTINA S.A.—See Adecco Group AG; *Int'l*, pg. 136
ADECCO BETEILIGUNGS GMBH—See Adecco Group AG; *Int'l*, pg. 136
ADECCO DETACHERING BV—See Adecco Group AG; *Int'l*, pg. 136
ADECCO GROUP NORWAY AS—See Adecco Group AG; *Int'l*, pg. 137
ADECCO INDIA PRIVATE LIMITED—See Adecco Group AG; *Int'l*, pg. 137
ADECCO INDUSTRIAL PTY LTD—See Adecco Group AG; *Int'l*, pg. 137
ADECCO ITALIA S.P.A.—See Adecco Group AG; *Int'l*, pg. 137
ADECCO MANAGEMENT & CONSULTING S.A.—See Adecco Group AG; *Int'l*, pg. 137
ADECCO RAMA IV RECRUITMENT LTD.—See Adecco Group AG; *Int'l*, pg. 137
ADECCO TT SA—See Adecco Group AG; *Int'l*, pg. 138
ADP, INC. - ALPHARETTA (WESTSIDE) OFFICE—See Automatic Data Processing, Inc.; *U.S. Public*, pg. 230
ADP INTERNATIONAL SERVICES BV—See Automatic Data Processing, Inc.; *U.S. Public*, pg. 230
ADP TOTALSOURCE GROUP, INC.—See Automatic Data Processing, Inc.; *U.S. Public*, pg. 230
ADP TOTALSOURCE I, INC.—See Automatic Data Processing, Inc.; *U.S. Public*, pg. 230
ADVANCED INTERACTIVE SYSTEMS; *U.S. Private*, pg. 90
ADVANCEONLINE SOLUTIONS, INC.—See 360training.com, Inc.; *U.S. Private*, pg. 8
ADVANTAGE PERSONNEL CONSULTANTS, INC.; *U.S. Private*, pg. 95
ADVTECH HOUSE—See ADvTECH Limited; *Int'l*, pg. 168
ADVTECH RESOURCING (PTY) LTD—See ADvTECH Limited; *Int'l*, pg. 168
ADVTECH RESOURCING (PTY) LTD - TECH-PRO PERSONNEL DIVISION—See ADvTECH Limited; *Int'l*, pg. 168
AGENSI PEKERJAAN KORN FERRY SDN. BHD.—See Korn Ferry; *U.S. Public*, pg. 1272
AISIN COLLABO CO., LTD.—See AISIN Corporation; *Int'l*, pg. 252
ALCHEMY SEARCH PARTNERS, INC.—See SOAProjects, Inc.; *U.S. Private*, pg. 3702
ALCOTT HR; *U.S. Private*, pg. 154
ALEXANDER BENEFITS CONSULTING, LLC—See Aon plc; *Int'l*, pg. 495
ALEXI TRAINING & CONSULTING COMPANY LIMITED—See Do Day Dream PCL; *Int'l*, pg. 2152
ALL ABOUT PEOPLE, INC.; *U.S. Private*, pg. 169
ALLEGIS GROUP GMBH—See Allegis Group, Inc.; *U.S. Private*, pg. 177
ALLGEIER EXPERTS SE—See Allgeier SE; *Int'l*, pg. 336
ALLIED PERSONNEL SERVICES, INC.; *U.S. Private*, pg. 187
ALLIS PARTICIPACOES S.A.; *Int'l*, pg. 359
AL MAWARID MANPOWER CO.; *Int'l*, pg. 281
ALPHA RAE PERSONNEL INC.; *U.S. Private*, pg. 199
ALTEDIA SAS—See Adecco Group AG; *Int'l*, pg. 141
ALTERNATTIVA EMPRESA DE SERVICIOS TRANSITORIOS LIMITADA—See Empresaria Group Plc; *Int'l*, pg. 2388
ALUMNI AB—See DBAY Advisors Limited; *Int'l*, pg. 1987
AMEDES BELGIUM N.V.—See DEKRA e.V.; *Int'l*, pg. 2007
AMERICAN CYBERSYSTEMS, INC.; *U.S. Private*, pg. 229
AMOTEC, INC.; *U.S. Private*, pg. 264
ANYHELP BRASIL ASSESSORIA E SERVICOS EM SISTEMAS DE INFORMACAO LTDA.—See ManpowerGroup Inc.; *U.S. Public*, pg. 1357
AON CONSULTING - CHICAGO—See Aon plc; *Int'l*, pg. 490
AON CONSULTING, INC.—See Aon plc; *Int'l*, pg. 490
AON CONSULTING—See Aon plc; *Int'l*, pg. 490
AON CONSULTING—See Aon plc; *Int'l*, pg. 490
AON HEWITT BELGIUM—See Alight, Inc.; *U.S. Public*, pg. 76
AON HEWITT GMBH—See Alight, Inc.; *U.S. Public*, pg. 76
AON HEWITT HR ONE CORPORATION—See Alight, Inc.; *U.S. Public*, pg. 76
AON HEWITT KOREA—See Alight, Inc.; *U.S. Public*, pg. 76
AON HEWITT S.A.—See Alight, Inc.; *U.S. Public*, pg. 76
AON HEWITT SAUDI ARABIA LLC—See Aon plc; *Int'l*, pg. 491
AON HEWITT SINGAPORE PTE. LTD.—See Alight, Inc.; *U.S. Public*, pg. 76
AON HEWITT SP. Z O.O.—See Alight, Inc.; *U.S. Public*, pg. 76
AON HEWITT (THAILAND) LTD.—See Alight, Inc.; *U.S. Public*, pg. 76
AON HEWITT - TORONTO—See Alight, Inc.; *U.S. Public*, pg. 76
AON HONG KONG LIMITED—See Alight, Inc.; *U.S. Public*, pg. 76
AON POLAND SP. Z.O.O.—See Alight, Inc.; *U.S. Public*, pg. 76
AON SOLUTIONS MIDDLE EAST LIMITED—See Alight, Inc.; *U.S. Public*, pg. 76
AON TUNISIE S.A.—See Aon plc; *Int'l*, pg. 494
AP ARBEITPARTNER GMBH & CO. KG—See DEKRA e.V.; *Int'l*, pg. 2007
ARAGON-ERH, SAS—See Econocom Group SA; *Int'l*, pg. 2297
ARCTERN CONSULTING PRIVATE LIMITED—See American CyberSystems, Inc.; *U.S. Private*, pg. 229
ARCTERN, INC.—See American CyberSystems, Inc.; *U.S. Private*, pg. 229
ASAHI KASEI AMIDAS CO., LTD.—See Asahi Kasei Corporation; *Int'l*, pg. 595
ASPEN RISK MANAGEMENT GROUP—See Tristar Insurance Group, Inc.; *U.S. Private*, pg. 4238
ASSOCIATED THIRD PARTY ADMINISTRATORS; *U.S. Private*, pg. 357
ATMOS CO., LTD.—See Copro Holdings Co., Ltd.; *Int'l*, pg. 1794
ATRIA CONSULTING, LLC; *U.S. Private*, pg. 382
AVALON STAFFING, LLC—See Corecivic, Inc.; *U.S. Public*, pg. 577
AVID TECHNICAL RESOURCES, INC.; *U.S. Private*, pg. 407
B4S SOLUTIONS PVT LTD.; *Int'l*, pg. 791
BABCOCK WEST SUSSEX CAREERS LIMITED—See Babcock International Group PLC; *Int'l*, pg. 792
BASF SERVICES EUROPE GMBH—See BASF SE; *Int'l*, pg. 881
BATTALIA WINSTON INTERNATIONAL; *U.S. Private*, pg. 487
BAWLA CONSULTING INC.; *U.S. Private*, pg. 491
BCA BETEILIGUNGS GMBH—See Aurelius Equity Opportunities SE & Co. KGaA; *Int'l*, pg. 707
BEACON HILL ASSOCIATES—See Beacon Hill Staffing Group LLC; *U.S. Private*, pg. 504
BEACON HILL FINANCIAL—See Beacon Hill Staffing Group LLC; *U.S. Private*, pg. 504
BEACON HILL FINANCIAL—See Beacon Hill Staffing Group LLC; *U.S. Private*, pg. 504
BEACON HILL HR—See Beacon Hill Staffing Group LLC; *U.S. Private*, pg. 504
BEACON HILL LEGAL—See Beacon Hill Staffing Group LLC; *U.S. Private*, pg. 504
BEACON HILL TECHNOLOGIES—See Beacon Hill Staffing Group LLC; *U.S. Private*, pg. 504
THE BEDDISON GROUP PTY. LTD.—See Bain Capital, LP; *U.S. Private*, pg. 435
BEIJING CAREER INTERNATIONAL CO., LTD.; *Int'l*, pg. 947
BEIJING HEIDRICK & STRUGGLES INTERNATIONAL MANAGEMENT CONSULTING COMPANY LIMITED—See Heidrick & Struggles International, Inc.; *U.S. Public*, pg. 1022
BELAY, INC.; *U.S. Private*, pg. 516
BELVEDERE PACIFIC LLC—See Aquiline Capital Partners LLC; *U.S. Private*, pg. 305
THE BENECON GROUP; *U.S. Private*, pg. 3993
BENECO SYSTEMS, INC.—See Aquiline Capital Partners LLC; *U.S. Private*, pg. 303
BENECO SYSTEMS, INC.—See Genstar Capital, LLC; *U.S. Private*, pg. 1675
BENEFIT ADMINISTRATION COMPANY LLC; *U.S. Private*, pg. 525
BENEFIT CONSULTING ALLIANCE, LLC—See Hylant Group Inc.; *U.S. Private*, pg. 2019
BENEFITS ADVISORY GROUP LLC—See Marsh & McLennan Companies, Inc.; *U.S. Public*, pg. 1380
BENEFITS & INCENTIVES GROUP, INC.—See Mesirow Financial Holdings, Inc.; *U.S. Private*, pg. 2678
THE BERKELEY ASSOCIATES CORPORATION—See The Judge Group, Inc.; *U.S. Private*, pg. 4064
BERNHARD SCHULTE SHIPMANAGEMENT (POLAND) LTD.—See Bernhard Schulte Shipmanagement (Cyprus) Ltd.; *Int'l*, pg. 988
BERSIN BY DELOITTE—See Deloitte LLP; *U.S. Private*, pg. 1198
BERSIN BY DELOITTE—See Deloitte Touche Tohmatsu Limited; *Int'l*, pg. 2014
BETOP STAFF, LTD.—See Brother Industries, Ltd.; *Int'l*, pg. 1196
BIS SHARED SERVICES B.V.—See Bilfinger SE; *Int'l*, pg. 1026

N.A.I.C.S. INDEX

541612 — HUMAN RESOURCES CON...

BIS SHARED SERVICES OSTERREICH GMBH—See Bilfinger SE; *Int'l*, pg. 1026
BIZTECH SOLUTIONS; *U.S. Private*, pg. 567
BJERKE & LUTHER AS—See DBAY Advisors Limited; *Int'l*, pg. 1987
BLACK & VEATCH CORPORATION—See Black & Veatch Holding Company; *U.S. Private*, pg. 569
BLUE ARROW LTD.—See HFBG Holding B.V.; *Int'l*, pg. 3374
BLUE PRAIRIE GROUP LLC—See Genstar Capital, LLC; *U.S. Private*, pg. 1676
BLUESKY RESOURCE SOLUTIONS, LLC; *U.S. Private*, pg. 597
BON ARTISAN CO., LTD.—See Di-Nikko Engineering Co., Ltd.; *Int'l*, pg. 2101
BOSTON BENEFIT PARTNERS, LLC; *U.S. Private*, pg. 621
BOYDEN WORLD CORPORATION; *U.S. Private*, pg. 627
BRADFORD & GALT INC.—See ManpowerGroup Inc.; *U.S. Public*, pg. 1362
BRADLEY MORRIS INC.—See Thompson Street Capital Manager LLC; *U.S. Private*, pg. 4160
BRIDGE CONSULTING GROUP INC.; *Int'l*, pg. 1152
BRIGHTWING; *U.S. Private*, pg. 653
BRING UP CO.,LTD.—See Cybozu Inc.; *Int'l*, pg. 1894
BRUNEL ENERGY NIGERIA LTD—See Brunel International N.V.; *Int'l*, pg. 1199
BRUNEL INTERNATIONAL FRANCE SARL—See Brunel International N.V.; *Int'l*, pg. 1200
BRYAN, PENDLETON, SWATS & MCALLISTER, LLC—See Wells Fargo & Company; *U.S. Public*, pg. 2343
BSM CREW SERVICE CENTRE (CROATIA) LTD.—See Bernhard Schulte Shipmanagement (Cyprus) Ltd.; *Int'l*, pg. 988
BSM CREW SERVICE CENTRE (LATVIA) LTD.—See Bernhard Schulte Shipmanagement (Cyprus) Ltd.; *Int'l*, pg. 988
BSM CREW SERVICE CENTRE (MYANMAR) LTD.—See Bernhard Schulte Shipmanagement (Cyprus) Ltd.; *Int'l*, pg. 988
BSM CREW SERVICE CENTRE (ROMANIA) SRL—See Bernhard Schulte Shipmanagement (Cyprus) Ltd.; *Int'l*, pg. 988
BSM CREW SERVICE CENTRE (VENEZUELA) C.A.—See Bernhard Schulte Shipmanagement (Cyprus) Ltd.; *Int'l*, pg. 988
BUCK CONSULTANTS BV—See Arthur J. Gallagher & Co.; *U.S. Public*, pg. 204
BUCK CONSULTANTS (HEALTHCARE) LIMITED—See Arthur J. Gallagher & Co.; *U.S. Public*, pg. 204
BUCK CONSULTANTS LIMITED—See Arthur J. Gallagher & Co.; *U.S. Public*, pg. 204
BUCK CONSULTANTS NV/SA—See Arthur J. Gallagher & Co.; *U.S. Public*, pg. 204
BULLFROG MINES LLC—See Augusta Gold Corp.; *Int'l*, pg. 703
THE BURCHFIELD GROUP, INC.—See Aon plc; *Int'l*, pg. 495
BUTLER TECHNICAL SERVICES INDIA PRIVATE LIMITED—See Butler America, Inc.; *U.S. Private*, pg. 696
CALIPER CORPORATION—See Educational Testing Service Inc.; *U.S. Private*, pg. 1340
CAREER CO., LTD.; *Int'l*, pg. 1323
CAREER GROUP INC.; *U.S. Private*, pg. 752
CAREERS IN TRANSITION, INC.; *U.S. Private*, pg. 752
CAREERS REGISTER LIMITED—See Bain Capital, LP; *U.S. Private*, pg. 433
CARTERBALDWIN; *U.S. Private*, pg. 776
CECOR STAFFING INC.—See Essential Personnel, Inc.; *U.S. Private*, pg. 1427
CENERGY CORPORATION; *U.S. Private*, pg. 808
THE CENTER FOR EXECUTIVE OPTIONS—See Adecco Group AG; *Int'l*, pg. 139
CENTURY II STAFFING TN, INC.—See Paychex, Inc.; *U.S. Public*, pg. 1655
CEO SERVICE DEVELOPMENT JOINT STOCK COMPANY—See C.E.O Group Joint Stock Company; *Int'l*, pg. 1240
CHAIN GROWTH CO., LTD.—See Autobacs Seven Co., Ltd.; *Int'l*, pg. 726
CHARON PLANNING CORPORATION—See Aon plc; *Int'l*, pg. 495
CHER A BUMPS & ASSOCIATES, INC.—See The Plexus Groupe, Inc.; *U.S. Private*, pg. 4096
CHERNOFF DIAMOND & CO, LLC—See Caisse de Depot et Placement du Quebec; *Int'l*, pg. 1256
CHERNOFF DIAMOND & CO, LLC—See KKR & Co. Inc.; *U.S. Public*, pg. 1265
CHURCHILL LEADERSHIP GROUP, INC.; *U.S. Private*, pg. 895
CIO PARTNERS, INC.; *U.S. Private*, pg. 898
CISIVE INC.; *U.S. Private*, pg. 900
CLEARCOMPANY, INC.—See Gemspring Capital Management, LLC; *U.S. Private*, pg. 1658
CLIMATE HUMAN CAPITAL PLC; *Int'l*, pg. 1659
CLP RESOURCES, INC.—See TrueBlue, Inc.; *U.S. Public*, pg. 2198
COADVANTAGE CORPORATION—See Aquiline Capital Partners LLC; *U.S. Private*, pg. 304
COBALT ASTRA LLC; *U.S. Private*, pg. 957
COCUBES TECHNOLOGIES PRIVATE LIMITED—See Aon plc; *Int'l*, pg. 494
COMPHEALTH ASSOCIATES, INC.—See Ares Management Corporation; *U.S. Public*, pg. 188
COMPHEALTH ASSOCIATES, INC.—See Leonard Green & Partners, L.P.; *U.S. Private*, pg. 2425
CONCENTRIC HEALTHCARE STAFFING; *U.S. Private*, pg. 1008
CONGRUITY HR, LLC; *U.S. Private*, pg. 1014
CONTEMPORARY BENEFITS DESIGN, INC.—See Aon plc; *Int'l*, pg. 495
COOK ASSOCIATES, INC.; *U.S. Private*, pg. 1037
COOKBIZ CO., LTD.; *Int'l*, pg. 1788
CORE ASIA HUMAN RESOURCES MANAGEMENT CO., LTD.—See BES Engineering Corporation; *Int'l*, pg. 998
CORNERSTONE STAFFING SOLUTIONS, INC.; *U.S. Private*, pg. 1053
CORPORATE BENEFITS, INC.—See Aon plc; *Int'l*, pg. 495
CORPORATE BROKERS LLC; *U.S. Private*, pg. 1054
CORPORATE SYNERGIES GROUP, LLC; *U.S. Private*, pg. 1056
CPL JOBS KFT—See Bain Capital, LP; *U.S. Private*, pg. 433
CPL JOBS SP Z.O.O—See Bain Capital, LP; *U.S. Private*, pg. 433
CPL JOBS S.R.O.—See Bain Capital, LP; *U.S. Private*, pg. 433
CPL JOBS S.R.O.—See Bain Capital, LP; *U.S. Private*, pg. 433
CPL (NORTHERN IRELAND) LIMITED—See Bain Capital, LP; *U.S. Private*, pg. 433
CPL RESOURCES PLC.—See Bain Capital, LP; *U.S. Private*, pg. 433
CPL TRAINING LIMITED—See Bain Capital, LP; *U.S. Private*, pg. 433
CREATIVE GROUP, INC.; *U.S. Private*, pg. 1089
C.T.A. S.A.R.L.—See DEKRA e.V.; *Int'l*, pg. 2008
CTC AVIATION GROUP LIMITED—See L3Harris Technologies, Inc.; *U.S. Public*, pg. 1281
CYBERCODERS INC.—See ASGN Incorporated; *U.S. Public*, pg. 210
D2L GROUP SA; *Int'l*, pg. 1901
DALEY & ASSOCIATES, LLC.; *U.S. Private*, pg. 1149
DANEL (ADIR YEHOSHUA) LTD.; *Int'l*, pg. 1959
DAVASO HOLDING GMBH—See IQVIA Holdings Inc.; *U.S. Public*, pg. 1168
DAVID BARRETT PARTNERS LLC.—See BraddockMatthewsBarrett, LLC; *U.S. Private*, pg. 631
DB GRANT ASSOCIATES INC.—See Madison Dearborn Partners, LLC; *U.S. Private*, pg. 2540
DEDALE S.A.—See Apollo Global Management, Inc.; *U.S. Public*, pg. 147
DEKRA AKADEMIE KFT.—See DEKRA e.V.; *Int'l*, pg. 2008
DEKRA ARBEIT BULGARIA EOOD—See DEKRA e.V.; *Int'l*, pg. 2006
DEKRA ARBEIT ISGUCU SECME VE YERLESTIRME HIZMETLERI LTD.—See DEKRA e.V.; *Int'l*, pg. 2007
DEKRA ARBEIT MAGYAROSZAG SZOLGALTATO KFT.—See DEKRA e.V.; *Int'l*, pg. 2008
DEKRA EMPLEO ETT S.L.—See DEKRA e.V.; *Int'l*, pg. 2008
DEKRA EMPLOYMENT LTD.—See DEKRA e.V.; *Int'l*, pg. 2008
DEKRA ENDUSTRI YATIRIMLARI A.S.—See DEKRA e.V.; *Int'l*, pg. 2008
DEKRA-FORMARE PROFESIONALA SRL—See DEKRA e.V.; *Int'l*, pg. 2009
DEKRA KVALIFIKACIA A PORADENSTVO S.R.O.—See DEKRA e.V.; *Int'l*, pg. 2009
DEKRA PERSONALDIENSTE GMBH—See DEKRA e.V.; *Int'l*, pg. 2008
DEKRA PRACA SP. Z O.O—See DEKRA e.V.; *Int'l*, pg. 2009
DEKRA SAVJETOVANJE DOO—See DEKRA e.V.; *Int'l*, pg. 2009
DEKRA SERVICIOS RECURSOS HUMANO S.L.—See DEKRA e.V.; *Int'l*, pg. 2009
DEKRA SOLUTIONS SP. Z O.O.—See DEKRA e.V.; *Int'l*, pg. 2009
DEKRA VRABOTUVANJE DOOEL—See DEKRA e.V.; *Int'l*, pg. 2009
DEKRA ZAPOSLITEV D.O.O.—See DEKRA e.V.; *Int'l*, pg. 2009
DEKRA ZAPOSLJAVANJE D.O.O.—See DEKRA e.V.; *Int'l*, pg. 2009
DEKRA ZAPOSLJAVANJE D.O.O.—See DEKRA e.V.; *Int'l*, pg. 2009
DEKRA ZA PRIVREMENO ZAPOSLJAVANJE D.O.O.—See DEKRA e.V.; *Int'l*, pg. 2009
DELUXE FINANCIAL SERVICES, INC.—See Augeo Affinity Marketing, Inc.; *U.S. Private*, pg. 391
DENSO TEN STAFF LIMITED—See Denso Corporation; *Int'l*, pg. 2030
DENSO TEN STAFF LIMITED—See Denso Corporation; *Int'l*, pg. 2030
DENTAL POST, INC.—See 424 Capital, LLC; *U.S. Private*, pg. 15
DENTAL POST, INC.—See HealthEdge Investment Partners, LLC; *U.S. Private*, pg. 1896
DEUTSCHES INSTITUT FUR BETRIEBSWIRTSCHAFT GMBH—See DEKRA e.V.; *Int'l*, pg. 2009
DEVELOPMENT DIMENSIONS INTERNATIONAL INC.; *U.S. Private*, pg. 1217
THE DEVINE GROUP, INC.; *U.S. Private*, pg. 4020
DEVONSHIRE GMBH—See Chatham Asset Management, LLC; *U.S. Private*, pg. 863
DEVONSHIRE SP. Z O.O—See Chatham Asset Management, LLC; *U.S. Private*, pg. 863
DIVERSIFIED HUMAN RESOURCES, INC.—See Paychex, Inc.; *U.S. Public*, pg. 1655
DIVERSIFIED INDUSTRIAL STAFFING; *U.S. Private*, pg. 1242
DOCS GLOBAL INC.—See ICON plc; *Int'l*, pg. 3584
DR EGON ZEHNDER & PARTNER AG—See Egon Zehnder International Inc.; *U.S. Private*, pg. 1344
D.S. WOLF GROUP INTERNATIONAL, LLC; *U.S. Private*, pg. 1142
EARTHSTAFF GMBH—See Cordant Group PLC; *Int'l*, pg. 1795
ECCO SERVICIOS DE PERSONAL SA DE CV—See Adecco Group AG; *Int'l*, pg. 141
ECI—See Electronic Commerce Inc.; *U.S. Private*, pg. 1355
EDENRED ITALIA SRL—See Edenred S.A.; *Int'l*, pg. 2308
EDENRED NORTH AMERICA INC.—See Edenred S.A.; *Int'l*, pg. 2308
EDGELINK, LLC; *U.S. Private*, pg. 1334
EDUCATION CENTRE OF THE SLOVENIAN ELECTRIC POWER AUTHORITY—See Elektro Slovenia d.o.o.; *Int'l*, pg. 2357
EDUCATIONDYNAMICS, LLC—See Renovus Capital Partners; *U.S. Private*, pg. 3399
EGON ZEHNDER ASSOCIES S.A.—See Egon Zehnder International Inc.; *U.S. Private*, pg. 1344
EGON ZEHNDER INTERNACIONAL DE MEXICO S.A. DE C.V.—See Egon Zehnder International Inc.; *U.S. Private*, pg. 1344
EGON ZEHNDER INTERNATIONAL B.V.—See Egon Zehnder International Inc.; *U.S. Private*, pg. 1344
EGON ZEHNDER INTERNATIONAL CHILE S.A.—See Egon Zehnder International Inc.; *U.S. Private*, pg. 1345
EGON ZEHNDER INTERNATIONAL CO., LTD.—See Egon Zehnder International Inc.; *U.S. Private*, pg. 1345
EGON ZEHNDER INTERNATIONAL CONSULTORES LDA.—See Egon Zehnder International Inc.; *U.S. Private*, pg. 1345
EGON ZEHNDER INTERNATIONAL GES.M.B.H.—See Egon Zehnder International Inc.; *U.S. Private*, pg. 1345
EGON ZEHNDER INTERNATIONAL GMBH—See Egon Zehnder International Inc.; *U.S. Private*, pg. 1345
EGON ZEHNDER INTERNATIONAL GMBH—See Egon Zehnder International Inc.; *U.S. Private*, pg. 1345
EGON ZEHNDER INTERNATIONAL GMBH—See Egon Zehnder International Inc.; *U.S. Private*, pg. 1345
EGON ZEHNDER INTERNATIONAL GMBH—See Egon Zehnder International Inc.; *U.S. Private*, pg. 1345
EGON ZEHNDER INTERNATIONAL GMBH—See Egon Zehnder International Inc.; *U.S. Private*, pg. 1345
EGON ZEHNDER INTERNATIONAL GMBH—See Egon Zehnder International Inc.; *U.S. Private*, pg. 1345
EGON ZEHNDER INTERNATIONAL INC.; *U.S. Private*, pg. 1344
EGON ZEHNDER INTERNATIONAL (ISRAEL) LTD.—See Egon Zehnder International Inc.; *U.S. Private*, pg. 1344
EGON ZEHNDER INTERNATIONAL KFT.—See Egon Zehnder International Inc.; *U.S. Private*, pg. 1345
EGON ZEHNDER INTERNATIONAL LTDA.—See Egon Zehnder International Inc.; *U.S. Private*, pg. 1345
EGON ZEHNDER INTERNATIONAL LTDA.—See Egon Zehnder International Inc.; *U.S. Private*, pg. 1345
EGON ZEHNDER INTERNATIONAL LTD.—See Egon Zehnder International Inc.; *U.S. Private*, pg. 1345
EGON ZEHNDER INTERNATIONAL (M) SDN BHD—See Egon Zehnder International Inc.; *U.S. Private*, pg. 1344
EGON ZEHNDER INTERNATIONAL OY—See Egon Zehnder International Inc.; *U.S. Private*, pg. 1345
EGON ZEHNDER INTERNATIONAL PTE LTD.—See Egon Zehnder International Inc.; *U.S. Private*, pg. 1345
EGON ZEHNDER INTERNATIONAL PTY LTD.—See Egon Zehnder International Inc.; *U.S. Private*, pg. 1345
EGON ZEHNDER INTERNATIONAL PTY LTD.—See Egon Zehnder International Inc.; *U.S. Private*, pg. 1345
EGON ZEHNDER INTERNATIONAL PVT. LTD.—See Egon Zehnder International Inc.; *U.S. Private*, pg. 1345
EGON ZEHNDER INTERNATIONAL PVT. LTD.—See Egon Zehnder International Inc.; *U.S. Private*, pg. 1345
EGON ZEHNDER INTERNATIONAL S.A.—See Egon Zehnder International Inc.; *U.S. Private*, pg. 1345
EGON ZEHNDER INTERNATIONAL S.A.—See Egon Zehnder International Inc.; *U.S. Private*, pg. 1345
EGON ZEHNDER INTERNATIONAL S.A.—See Egon Zehnder International Inc.; *U.S. Private*, pg. 1345
EGON ZEHNDER INTERNATIONAL S.A.—See Egon Zehnder International Inc.; *U.S. Private*, pg. 1345
EGON ZEHNDER INTERNATIONAL S.A.—See Egon Zehnder International Inc.; *U.S. Private*, pg. 1345
EGON ZEHNDER INTERNATIONAL (SHANGHAI) COM-

541612 — HUMAN RESOURCES CON...

PANY LIMITED—See Egon Zehnder International Inc.; *U.S. Private*, pg. 1344
EGON ZEHNDER INTERNATIONAL S.L.—See Egon Zehnder International Inc.; *U.S. Private*, pg. 1345
EGON ZEHNDER INTERNATIONAL S.L.—See Egon Zehnder International Inc.; *U.S. Private*, pg. 1345
EGON ZEHNDER INTERNATIONAL S.P.A.—See Egon Zehnder International Inc.; *U.S. Private*, pg. 1345
EGON ZEHNDER INTERNATIONAL SP. Z O.O.—See Egon Zehnder International Inc.; *U.S. Private*, pg. 1345
EGON ZEHNDER LUXEMBOURG S.A.—See Egon Zehnder International Inc.; *U.S. Private*, pg. 1345
EI COMPANIES; *U.S. Private*, pg. 1346
ELEVATE STAFFING, INC.; *U.S. Private*, pg. 1358
ELG FZE—See UnitedHealth Group Incorporated; *U.S. Public*, pg. 2240
ELITE HUMAN CAPITAL GROUP; *U.S. Private*, pg. 1361
ELITE HUMAN RESOURCE MANAGEMENT CO., LTD.—See BES Engineering Corporation; *Int'l*, pg. 998
ELITE WORLD S.A.; *Int'l*, pg. 2362
ELIZABETH HALL & ASSOCIATES, INC.; *U.S. Private*, pg. 1362
EMPLICITY; *U.S. Private*, pg. 1386
EMPRESARIA GROUP PLC; *Int'l*, pg. 2388
EMPYREAN BENEFIT SOLUTIONS, INC.; *U.S. Private*, pg. 1388
ENGAGE2EXCEL, INC.; *U.S. Private*, pg. 1397
ENGAGE2EXCEL RECRUITMENT SOLUTIONS—See Engage2Excel, Inc.; *U.S. Private*, pg. 1397
ENGAGE PEO, LLC—See Kohlberg & Company, LLC; *U.S. Private*, pg. 2338
ENI CORPORATE UNIVERSITY SPA—See Eni S.p.A.; *Int'l*, pg. 2437
ENI INTERNATIONAL RESOURCES LTD—See Eni S.p.A.; *Int'l*, pg. 2437
E.ON HUMAN RESOURCES INTERNATIONAL GMBH—See E.ON SE; *Int'l*, pg. 2254
E.ON SERVICE GMBH—See E.ON SE; *Int'l*, pg. 2255
ERP INTERNATIONAL, LLC.; *U.S. Private*, pg. 1423
ESAVVY PTY LTD—See Empired Ltd; *Int'l*, pg. 2387
ESWATINI INSURANCE BROKERS (PTY) LIMITED—See Aon plc; *Int'l*, pg. 494
ESW, INC.; *U.S. Private*, pg. 1431
EUROMEDICA EXECUTIVE SEARCH GMBH—See Barclays PLC; *Int'l*, pg. 862
EUROMEDICA INTERNATIONAL LTD.—See Barclays PLC; *Int'l*, pg. 862
EUROMEDICA LTD.—See Barclays PLC; *Int'l*, pg. 862
EUROMEDICA SARL—See Barclays PLC; *Int'l*, pg. 862
EUROPEAN ROAD STARS ACADEMY (ERSA) SPRL—See DEKRA e.V.; *Int'l*, pg. 2009
EUROSTAFF FINANCE GMBH—See Cordant Group PLC; *Int'l*, pg. 1796
EUROSTAFF GROUP GMBH—See Cordant Group PLC; *Int'l*, pg. 1796
EVAN THOMAS GLOBAL LLC; *U.S. Private*, pg. 1434
EVERGLADES DIRECT INC—See Taylor Corporation; *U.S. Private*, pg. 3938
EXCEL STAFFING COMPANIES; *U.S. Private*, pg. 1445
EXECUTIVE DIRECTION INC.; *U.S. Private*, pg. 1447
EXECUTIVE PLACEMENTS, LLC; *U.S. Private*, pg. 1448
EXECUTIVE SEARCH DIVISION—See Cook Associates, Inc.; *U.S. Private*, pg. 1037
EXPERIS AB—See ManpowerGroup Inc.; *U.S. Public*, pg. 1357
EXPERIS AS—See ManpowerGroup Inc.; *U.S. Public*, pg. 1357
EXPERIS A/S—See ManpowerGroup Inc.; *U.S. Public*, pg. 1357
EXPERIS EXECUTIVE FRANCE SAS—See ManpowerGroup Inc.; *U.S. Public*, pg. 1358
EXPERIS GMBH—See ManpowerGroup Inc.; *U.S. Public*, pg. 1358
EXPERIS IT PRIVATE LIMITED—See ManpowerGroup Inc.; *U.S. Public*, pg. 1358
EXPERIS LIMITED—See ManpowerGroup Inc.; *U.S. Public*, pg. 1358
EXPERIS LIMITED—See ManpowerGroup Inc.; *U.S. Public*, pg. 1358
EXPERIS NEDERLAND B.V.—See ManpowerGroup Inc.; *U.S. Public*, pg. 1358
FDM ASTRA IRELAND LIMITED—See FDM Group (Holdings) plc; *Int'l*, pg. 2629
FDM GROUP AUSTRALIA PTY LTD.—See FDM Group (Holdings) plc; *Int'l*, pg. 2629
FDM GROUP CANADA INC.—See FDM Group (Holdings) plc; *Int'l*, pg. 2629
FDM GROUP HK LIMITED—See FDM Group (Holdings) plc; *Int'l*, pg. 2629
FDM GROUP (HOLDINGS) PLC; *Int'l*, pg. 2629
FDM GROUP NV—See FDM Group (Holdings) plc; *Int'l*, pg. 2629
FDM SINGAPORE CONSULTING PTE LIMITED—See FDM Group (Holdings) plc; *Int'l*, pg. 2629
FDM SOUTH AFRICA (PTY) LIMITED—See FDM Group (Holdings) plc; *Int'l*, pg. 2629
FDM SWITZERLAND GMBH—See FDM Group (Holdings) plc; *Int'l*, pg. 2629

FDM TECHNOLOGY (SHANGHAI) CO. LIMITED—See FDM Group (Holdings) plc; *Int'l*, pg. 2629
FINANCIAL CONCEPTS OF THE TWIN CITIES, INC.—See Aon plc; *Int'l*, pg. 496
FIRST ADVANTAGE RECRUITING SOLUTIONS—See Silver Lake Group, LLC; *U.S. Private*, pg. 3654
FIRST PERSON, INC.—See Aon plc; *Int'l*, pg. 496
FIRSTPRO, INC.—See Staffing 360 Solutions, Inc.; *U.S. Public*, pg. 1925
FIRST TENNESSEE HUMAN RESOURCE AGENCY; *U.S. Private*, pg. 1529
FLEX HR, INC.; *U.S. Private*, pg. 1543
FLEXIBLE STAFFING OF GEORGIA, INC.; *U.S. Private*, pg. 1544
FLEXSOURCE LIMITED—See Bain Capital, LP; *U.S. Private*, pg. 433
FLORES & ASSOCIATES, LLC—See CNO Financial Group, Inc.; *U.S. Public*, pg. 520
FLSMIDTH (JERSEY) LIMITED—See FLSmidth & Co. A/S; *Int'l*, pg. 2710
THE FOOTBRIDGE COMPANIES; *U.S. Private*, pg. 4029
FORFEITURE SUPPORT ASSOCIATES LLC—See L3Harris Technologies, Inc.; *U.S. Public*, pg. 1281
FRANKLIN COVEY CLIENT SALES, INC.—See Franklin Covey Company; *U.S. Public*, pg. 877
FROST HR CONSULTING—See Cullen/Frost Bankers, Inc.; *U.S. Public*, pg. 604
FUJIFILM EUROPE BUSINESS SERVICE SP.ZO.O.—See FUJIFILM Holdings Corporation; *Int'l*, pg. 2824
FUJITSU MARKETING AGENT LTD.—See Fujitsu Limited; *Int'l*, pg. 2835
FULLCAST HOLDINGS CO., LTD.; *Int'l*, pg. 2842
FURST GROUP—See Management Partners, Inc.; *U.S. Private*, pg. 2560
FUSE3 SOLUTIONS LLC; *U.S. Private*, pg. 1625
FUSION RECRUITING LABS, INC.; *U.S. Private*, pg. 1625
FUTURE STATE CONSULTING LLC—See Odyssey Investment Partners, LLC; *U.S. Private*, pg. 2996
FUTURESTEP (ESPANA), S.L.—See Korn Ferry; *U.S. Public*, pg. 1274
FUTURESTEP RECRUITMENT SERVICES PRIVATE LTD.—See Korn Ferry; *U.S. Public*, pg. 1274
FUTURESTEP (SHANGHAI) TALENT CONSULTING COMPANY LIMITED—See Korn Ferry; *U.S. Public*, pg. 1272
FUTURESTEP (UK) LIMITED—See Korn Ferry; *U.S. Public*, pg. 1274
FUTURIS TECHNOLOGY SERVICES, INC.—See Futuris Company; *U.S. Public*, pg. 893
GALATA MINERAL MADENCILIK SAN. VE TIC. A.S.—See Ariana Resources plc; *Int'l*, pg. 564
GENERALI EMPLOYEE BENEFITS BRUXELLES—See Assicurazioni Generali S.p.A.; *Int'l*, pg. 644
GENPACT (DALIAN) INFORMATION & TECHNOLOGY SERVICE CO., LTD.—See Genpact Limited; *Int'l*, pg. 2926
GENPACT (FOSHAN) INFORMATION & TECHNOLOGY SERVICE CO., LTD.—See Genpact Limited; *Int'l*, pg. 2926
GENPACT (QINGDAO) INFORMATION & TECHNOLOGY SERVICE CO., LTD.—See Genpact Limited; *Int'l*, pg. 2926
GENPACT (SUZHOU) INFORMATION & TECHNOLOGY SERVICE CO., LTD.—See Genpact Limited; *Int'l*, pg. 2926
GLOBALBRIDGE RESOURCES CORPORATION—See Globe Telecom, Inc.; *Int'l*, pg. 3006
GLOBAL EXECUTIVE SOLUTIONS GROUP, LLC; *U.S. Private*, pg. 1714
GLOBAL NETWORKERS, INC.—See BCforward; *U.S. Private*, pg. 499
GLOBAL RADAR ACQUISITION LLC—See Audax Group, Limited Partnership; *U.S. Private*, pg. 387
GLOBAL RECRUITERS NETWORK, INC.; *U.S. Private*, pg. 1717
GLOBAL RESOURCE MANAGEMENT INC.; *U.S. Private*, pg. 1717
GLOBIS ASIA PACIFIC PTE. LTD.—See Globis Corporation; *Int'l*, pg. 3007
GLOBIS CHINA CO., LTD.—See Globis Corporation; *Int'l*, pg. 3007
GOLDBELT WOLF, LLC—See Gold Belt Incorporated; *U.S. Private*, pg. 1727
GOLDEN KEY GROUP, LLC; *U.S. Private*, pg. 1732
GOOROO VENTURES LIMITED; *Int'l*, pg. 3042
GRA, INC.; *U.S. Private*, pg. 1748
GRANT COOPER & ASSOCIATES, LLC—See Diversified Search, LLC; *U.S. Private*, pg. 1243
GREAT HIRE INC.; *U.S. Private*, pg. 1764
GREAT LAKES BEHAVIORAL RESEARCH INSTITUTE; *U.S. Private*, pg. 1764
GREENWELL GLEESON GMBH—See Amadeus Fire AG; *Int'l*, pg. 405
GREENWELL GLEESON LTD.—See Amadeus Fire AG; *Int'l*, pg. 405
GREENWOOD/ASHER & ASSOCIATES, LLC—See Kelly Services, Inc.; *U.S. Public*, pg. 1218
GREYTHORN PTY LTD.—See ManpowerGroup Inc.; *U.S. Public*, pg. 1358

GROWTH GEAR CO. LTD—See Digital Holdings, Inc.; *Int'l*, pg. 2122
GUANGZHOU KORN/FERRY HUMAN CAPITAL COMPANY LTD.—See Korn Ferry; *U.S. Public*, pg. 1272
HAKUHODO DY TOTAL SUPPORT INC.—See Hakuhodo DY Holdings Incorporated; *Int'l*, pg. 3221
HARBRIDGE CONSULTING GROUP, LLC—See Community Bank System, Inc.; *U.S. Public*, pg. 549
HARMONY HEALTHCARE, LLC—See Odyssey Investment Partners, LLC; *U.S. Private*, pg. 2994
HARVEY NASH (IRELAND) LTD—See DBAY Advisors Limited; *Int'l*, pg. 1987
HAY GROUP LLC—See Korn Ferry; *U.S. Public*, pg. 1272
HAY GROUP OY—See Korn Ferry; *U.S. Public*, pg. 1274
HAY GROUP S.A.—See Korn Ferry; *U.S. Public*, pg. 1274
HAY GROUP S.R.O.—See Korn Ferry; *U.S. Public*, pg. 1272
HAY GROUP UAB—See Korn Ferry; *U.S. Public*, pg. 1272
HAYS BELGIUM NV—See Hays PLC; *Int'l*, pg. 3293
HAYS BV—See Hays PLC; *Int'l*, pg. 3293
HAYS EXECUTIVE SASU—See Hays PLC; *Int'l*, pg. 3293
HAYS FZ-LLC—See Hays PLC; *Int'l*, pg. 3293
HAYS HEALTHCARE LIMITED—See Hays PLC; *Int'l*, pg. 3293
HAYS HONG KONG LIMITED—See Hays PLC; *Int'l*, pg. 3293
HAYS HUNGARY KFT—See Hays PLC; *Int'l*, pg. 3293
HAYS LIFE SCIENCES UK—See Hays PLC; *Int'l*, pg. 3293
HAYS NORD EST SASU—See Hays PLC; *Int'l*, pg. 3293
HAYS OUEST SASU—See Hays PLC; *Int'l*, pg. 3293
HAYS OVERSEAS (PORTUGAL) SGPS LDA—See Hays PLC; *Int'l*, pg. 3293
HAYS PERSONNEL ESPANA EMPRESA DE TRABOJO TEMPORAL SA—See Hays PLC; *Int'l*, pg. 3293
HAYS PERSONNEL SERVICES ESPANA SA—See Hays PLC; *Int'l*, pg. 3293
HAYS POLAND SP Z.O.O—See Hays PLC; *Int'l*, pg. 3293
HAYSP - RECRUTAMENTO, SELECCAO E EMPRESA DE TRABALHO TEMPORARIO, UNIPESSOAL, LDA—See Hays PLC; *Int'l*, pg. 3294
HAYS RESOURCE MANAGEMENT JAPAN K.K.—See Hays PLC; *Int'l*, pg. 3293
HAYS S.A. DE C.V.—See Hays PLC; *Int'l*, pg. 3293
HAYS S.A.R.L—See Hays PLC; *Int'l*, pg. 3293
HAYS SERVICES NV—See Hays PLC; *Int'l*, pg. 3293
HAYS SPECIALIST RECRUITMENT LIMITED—See Hays PLC; *Int'l*, pg. 3294
HAYS SPECIALIST RECRUITMENT PRIVATE LIMITED—See Hays PLC; *Int'l*, pg. 3294
HAYS SPECIALIST RECRUITMENT (SHANGHAI) CO. LIMITED—See Hays PLC; *Int'l*, pg. 3294
HAYS S.R.L—See Hays PLC; *Int'l*, pg. 3293
HAYS SUD OUEST SASU—See Hays PLC; *Int'l*, pg. 3294
HAYS TALENT SOLUTIONS GMBH—See Hays PLC; *Int'l*, pg. 3294
HC GROUP SEARCH LTD.—See HC Group, Inc.; *Int'l*, pg. 3297
HC GROUP SEARCH PTE. LTD.—See HC Group, Inc.; *Int'l*, pg. 3297
HCTEC PARTNERS—See TruArc Partners, L.P.; *U.S. Private*, pg. 4245
HEADWAY WORKFORCE SOLUTIONS, INC.—See Staffing 360 Solutions, Inc.; *U.S. Public*, pg. 1925
HEALTHCARE STAFFING INC; *U.S. Private*, pg. 1895
HEC RESOURCES LIMITED—See Empresaria Group Plc; *Int'l*, pg. 2389
HEIDRICK & STRUGGLES AB—See Heidrick & Struggles International, Inc.; *U.S. Public*, pg. 1022
HEIDRICK & STRUGGLES AG—See Heidrick & Struggles International, Inc.; *U.S. Public*, pg. 1022
HEIDRICK & STRUGGLES A/S—See Heidrick & Struggles International, Inc.; *U.S. Public*, pg. 1022
HEIDRICK & STRUGGLES AUSTRALIA, LTD.—See Heidrick & Struggles International, Inc.; *U.S. Public*, pg. 1022
HEIDRICK & STRUGGLES BV—See Heidrick & Struggles International, Inc.; *U.S. Public*, pg. 1022
HEIDRICK & STRUGGLES CANADA, INC.—See Heidrick & Struggles International, Inc.; *U.S. Public*, pg. 1022
HEIDRICK & STRUGGLES DE CHILE LIMITADA—See Heidrick & Struggles International, Inc.; *U.S. Public*, pg. 1023
HEIDRICK & STRUGGLES DO BRASIL LTDA.—See Heidrick & Struggles International, Inc.; *U.S. Public*, pg. 1023
HEIDRICK & STRUGGLES ESPANA, INC.—See Heidrick & Struggles International, Inc.; *U.S. Public*, pg. 1022
HEIDRICK & STRUGGLES HONG KONG LTD.—See Heidrick & Struggles International, Inc.; *U.S. Public*, pg. 1022
HEIDRICK & STRUGGLES (INDIA) PRIVATE LIMITED—See Heidrick & Struggles International, Inc.; *U.S. Public*, pg. 1022
HEIDRICK & STRUGGLES INTERIM EXECUTIVE GMBH—See Heidrick & Struggles International, Inc.; *U.S. Public*, pg. 1022
HEIDRICK & STRUGGLES INTERNATIONAL SRL—See Heidrick & Struggles International, Inc.; *U.S. Public*, pg. 1022

541612 — HUMAN RESOURCES CON...

HEIDRICK & STRUGGLES IRELAND, LIMITED—See Heidrick & Struggles International, Inc.; *U.S. Public*, pg. 1022
HEIDRICK & STRUGGLES JAPAN, LTD.—See Heidrick & Struggles International, Inc.; *U.S. Public*, pg. 1022
HEIDRICK & STRUGGLES KOREA, INC.—See Heidrick & Struggles International, Inc.; *U.S. Public*, pg. 1022
HEIDRICK & STRUGGLES (MIDDLE EAST) LLC—See Heidrick & Struggles International, Inc.; *U.S. Public*, pg. 1022
HEIDRICK & STRUGGLES (NZ) LIMITED—See Heidrick & Struggles International, Inc.; *U.S. Public*, pg. 1022
HEIDRICK & STRUGGLES RECRUITMENT THAILAND CO., LTD.—See Heidrick & Struggles International, Inc.; *U.S. Public*, pg. 1022
HEIDRICK & STRUGGLES RUSSIA LLC—See Heidrick & Struggles International, Inc.; *U.S. Public*, pg. 1023
HEIDRICK & STRUGGLES S.A. DE C.V.—See Heidrick & Struggles International, Inc.; *U.S. Public*, pg. 1023
HEIDRICK & STRUGGLES (SHP) LIMITED—See Heidrick & Struggles International, Inc.; *U.S. Public*, pg. 1022
HEIDRICK & STRUGGLES SINGAPORE PTE LTD.—See Heidrick & Struggles International, Inc.; *U.S. Public*, pg. 1023
HEIDRICK & STRUGGLES SP. Z O.O.—See Heidrick & Struggles International, Inc.; *U.S. Public*, pg. 1023
HEIDRICK & STRUGGLES UK LTD.—See Heidrick & Struggles International, Inc.; *U.S. Public*, pg. 1023
HEIDRICK & STRUGGLES UNTERNEHMENSBERATUNG GMBH—See Heidrick & Struggles International, Inc.; *U.S. Public*, pg. 1023
HEIDRICK & STRUGGLES UNTERNEHMENSBERATUNG VERWALTUNG- GMBH—See Heidrick & Struggles International, Inc.; *U.S. Public*, pg. 1022
HELIOS HR, LLC; *U.S. Private*, pg. 1906
HELPNET INGENIERIA Y SERVICIOS DE RECURSOS HUMANOS S.A.—See Bain Capital, LP; *U.S. Private*, pg. 434
HEUREKA-GAMMA AG—See E.ON SE; *Int'l*, pg. 2258
HEWITT ASSOCIATES (CHILE) LTDA.—See Alight, Inc.; *U.S. Public*, pg. 76
HEWITT ASSOCIATES GMBH—See Alight, Inc.; *U.S. Public*, pg. 76
HEWITT ASSOCIATES KABUSHIKI GAISYA—See Alight, Inc.; *U.S. Public*, pg. 76
HEWITT ASSOCIATES SARL—See Alight, Inc.; *U.S. Public*, pg. 76
HEWITT ASSOCIATES S.A.—See Alight, Inc.; *U.S. Public*, pg. 76
HEWITT ASSOCIATES SDN BHD—See Alight, Inc.; *U.S. Public*, pg. 76
HEWITT ASSOCIATES SRL—See Alight, Inc.; *U.S. Public*, pg. 76
HIRE DYNAMICS, LLC.—See Apollo Global Management, Inc.; *U.S. Public*, pg. 151
HIREMETHODS; *U.S. Private*, pg. 1950
HIRERIGHT BACKGROUND SCREENING INDIA LLP—See General Atlantic Service Company, L.P.; *U.S. Private*, pg. 1663
HIRERIGHT BACKGROUND SCREENING INDIA LLP—See Stone Point Capital LLC; *U.S. Private*, pg. 3825
HIRERIGHT, INC.—See Corporate Risk Holdings LLC; *U.S. Private*, pg. 1056
HIRERIGHT PTE LTD—See Corporate Risk Holdings LLC; *U.S. Private*, pg. 1056
HIRERIGHT UK HOLDING LIMITED—See General Atlantic Service Company, L.P.; *U.S. Private*, pg. 1663
HIRERIGHT UK HOLDING LIMITED—See Stone Point Capital LLC; *U.S. Private*, pg. 3825
HIREWELL; *U.S. Private*, pg. 1950
HIROGIN HUMAN RESOURCES CO., LTD.—See Hirogin Holdings, Inc.; *Int'l*, pg. 3404
HITECH GROUP AUSTRALIA LIMITED - HITECH PERSONNEL DIVISION—See HiTech Group Australia Limited; *Int'l*, pg. 3425
HITECS B.V.—See Fluor Corporation; *U.S. Public*, pg. 860
HMS EMPLOYER SOLUTIONS—See Veritas Capital Fund Management, LLC; *U.S. Private*, pg. 4362
HNM SYSTEMS, INC.; *U.S. Private*, pg. 1955
HOWARD FISCHER ASSOCIATES INTERNATIONAL; *U.S. Private*, pg. 1994
HR CERTIFICATION INSTITUTE; *U.S. Private*, pg. 1997
HR PATH SAS; *Int'l*, pg. 3501
HR WORKS, INC.; *U.S. Private*, pg. 1998
HUMAN RESOURCES PLUS INC—See JER HR Group LLC; *U.S. Private*, pg. 2201
HUMAN SOLUTIONS, INC.—See Oasis Systems, LLC; *U.S. Private*, pg. 2986
HUMAN TECHNOLOGIES, INC.; *U.S. Private*, pg. 2006
HYDROGEN GROUP PLC; *Int'l*, pg. 3547
ICON INFORMATION CONSULTANTS, L.P.; *U.S. Private*, pg. 2032
IKM RADA AS—See IKM Gruppen AS; *Int'l*, pg. 3611
IMAGINE STAFFING TECHNOLOGY, INC.; *U.S. Private*, pg. 2045
IMPACT GROUP INTERNATIONAL, LLC; *U.S. Private*, pg. 2048

IMPACT MANAGEMENT SERVICES LLC; *U.S. Private*, pg. 2048
INFINISOURCE; *U.S. Private*, pg. 2070
INFINITI HR, LLC.; *U.S. Private*, pg. 2071
INFORMATION DEVELOPMENT AMERICA INC.—See ID Holdings Corporation; *Int'l*, pg. 3587
INGEUS AB—See ModivCare, Inc.; *U.S. Public*, pg. 1455
INGEUS AG—See ModivCare, Inc.; *U.S. Public*, pg. 1455
INGEUS GMBH—See ModivCare, Inc.; *U.S. Public*, pg. 1455
INGEUS LLC—See ModivCare, Inc.; *U.S. Public*, pg. 1455
INGEUS SP Z.O.O.—See ModivCare, Inc.; *U.S. Public*, pg. 1455
INGEUS UK LIMITED—See ModivCare, Inc.; *U.S. Public*, pg. 1455
INNOVATIVE STAFFING, INC.; *U.S. Private*, pg. 2083
INSEARCH WORLDWIDE CORPORATION; *U.S. Private*, pg. 2085
INTAC ACTUARIAL SERVICES, INC.—See Aquiline Capital Partners LLC; *U.S. Private*, pg. 303
INTAC ACTUARIAL SERVICES, INC.—See Genstar Capital, LLC; *U.S. Private*, pg. 1675
INTEGRATED HEALTHCARE STRATEGIES, LLC—See Arthur J. Gallagher & Co.; *U.S. Public*, pg. 205
INTEGRITY HR INC.—See Fifth Third Bancorp; *U.S. Public*, pg. 833
INTEGRITY HR, INC.—See Marsh & McLennan Companies, Inc.; *U.S. Public*, pg. 1381
INTERACTIVE MANPOWER SOLUTIONS PRIVATE LIMITED—See Empresaria Group Plc; *Int'l*, pg. 2389
INT TECHNOLOGIES LLC—See ManpowerGroup Inc.; *U.S. Public*, pg. 1362
ISENSE & B.V.—See ManpowerGroup Inc.; *U.S. Public*, pg. 1362
ISENSE EINDHOVEN B.V.—See ManpowerGroup Inc.; *U.S. Public*, pg. 1362
ITAC SOLUTIONS; *U.S. Private*, pg. 2148
ITAGROUP, INC.; *U.S. Private*, pg. 2148
ITC APT SP. Z.O.O.—See Empresaria Group Plc; *Int'l*, pg. 2389
ITC CS SP. Z.O.O.—See Empresaria Group Plc; *Int'l*, pg. 2389
ITT INDUSTRIES INC.—See ITT Inc.; *U.S. Public*, pg. 1178
I.T. WORKS RECRUITMENT INC.; *U.S. Private*, pg. 2027
JACKSON HEALTHCARE, LLC; *U.S. Private*, pg. 2177
JACOBS PROFESSIONAL SERVICES INC.—See Jacobs Engineering Group, Inc.; *U.S. Public*, pg. 1185
JAMESBECK GLOBAL PARTNERS, LLC—See RFE Investment Partners; *U.S. Private*, pg. 3420
JBK ASSOCIATES INTERNATIONAL, INC.; *U.S. Private*, pg. 2193
JCW SEARCH LTD.; *U.S. Private*, pg. 2195
JDC GROUP, LLC—See White Wolf Capital LLC; *U.S. Private*, pg. 4510
JENOVATION GMBH—See ManpowerGroup Inc.; *U.S. Public*, pg. 1362
JER HR GROUP LLC; *U.S. Private*, pg. 2201
JOBING.COM, INC.; *U.S. Private*, pg. 2217
JOBSITE UK (WORLDWIDE) LIMITED—See Axel Springer SE; *Int'l*, pg. 767
JOBSTUDIO PTE. LTD.—See BELLUNA CO. LTD.; *Int'l*, pg. 967
JUDGE.COM, INC.—See The Judge Group, Inc.; *U.S. Private*, pg. 4063
THE JUDGE GROUP, INC.; *U.S. Private*, pg. 4063
JUDGE TECHNICAL SERVICES INC.—See The Judge Group, Inc.; *U.S. Private*, pg. 4063
JUICE RESOURCE SOLUTIONS LIMITED—See ManpowerGroup Inc.; *U.S. Public*, pg. 1359
JUNO SEARCH PARTNERS, LLC—See Aon plc; *Int'l*, pg. 496
KAIN MANAGEMENT GROUP; *U.S. Private*, pg. 2254
KAPELE APPOINTMENTS (PTY) LTD - VERTEX-KAPELE DIVISION—See ADvTECH Limited; *Int'l*, pg. 168
KAUFMANN & GOBLE ASSOCIATES, INC.—See Northwest Plan Services, Inc.; *U.S. Private*, pg. 2961
KAWADER SERVICES—See Abu Dhabi Islamic Bank PJSC; *Int'l*, pg. 72
KAZAN INTERNATIONAL, INC.; *U.S. Private*, pg. 2267
KAZAN INTERNATIONAL—See Kazan International, Inc.; *U.S. Private*, pg. 2267
KELLY GROUP LIMITED - RENWICK TALENT—See Adcorp Holdings Limited; *Int'l*, pg. 127
KELLY SERVICES (AUSTRALIA), LTD.—See Kelly Services, Inc.; *U.S. Public*, pg. 1218
KELLY SERVICES HEALTHCARE UNIPESSOAL, LDA.—See Kelly Services, Inc.; *U.S. Public*, pg. 1219
KELLY SERVICES HUNGARY STAFFING, KFT.—See Kelly Services, Inc.; *U.S. Public*, pg. 1218
KEN CLARK INTERNATIONAL; *U.S. Private*, pg. 2282
KENEXA CORPORATION—See International Business Machines Corporation; *U.S. Public*, pg. 1148
KIMMEL & ASSOCIATES; *U.S. Private*, pg. 2305
KONA HR CONSULTING GROUP LLC; *U.S. Private*, pg. 2342
KORN FERRY A/S—See Korn Ferry; *U.S. Public*, pg. 1273
KORN FERRY (AT) GMBH—See Korn Ferry; *U.S. Public*, pg. 1272

KORN FERRY (AU) PTY. LTD. - MELBOURNE—See Korn Ferry; *U.S. Public*, pg. 1272
KORN FERRY (AU) PTY. LTD.—See Korn Ferry; *U.S. Public*, pg. 1272
KORN FERRY (BE) BVBA—See Korn Ferry; *U.S. Public*, pg. 1272
KORN FERRY (BR) CONSULTORES LTDA. - RIO DE JANEIRO—See Korn Ferry; *U.S. Public*, pg. 1272
KORN FERRY (BR) CONSULTORES LTDA.—See Korn Ferry; *U.S. Public*, pg. 1272
KORN FERRY (CA) LTD. - CALGARY—See Korn Ferry; *U.S. Public*, pg. 1273
KORN FERRY (CA) LTD.—See Korn Ferry; *U.S. Public*, pg. 1273
KORN FERRY (CA) LTD. - VANCOUVER—See Korn Ferry; *U.S. Public*, pg. 1273
KORN FERRY (DE) GMBH—See Korn Ferry; *U.S. Public*, pg. 1273
KORN FERRY (DK) A/S—See Korn Ferry; *U.S. Public*, pg. 1273
KORN FERRY (FR) SARL—See Korn Ferry; *U.S. Public*, pg. 1273
KORN FERRY (HK) LIMITED—See Korn Ferry; *U.S. Public*, pg. 1273
KORN/FERRY INTERNATIONAL AB - GOTHENBURG—See Korn Ferry; *U.S. Public*, pg. 1274
KORN/FERRY INTERNATIONAL AB—See Korn Ferry; *U.S. Public*, pg. 1274
KORN/FERRY INTERNATIONAL BELNORDE S.A. DE C.V.—See Korn Ferry; *U.S. Public*, pg. 1274
KORN/FERRY INTERNATIONAL BUDAPEST INDIVIDUAL CONSULTING & SERVICE LTD.—See Korn Ferry; *U.S. Public*, pg. 1274
KORN/FERRY INTERNATIONAL - COLOMBIA—See Korn Ferry; *U.S. Public*, pg. 1274
KORN/FERRY INTERNATIONAL CONSULTORES ASOCIADOS, C.A.—See Korn Ferry; *U.S. Public*, pg. 1274
KORN/FERRY INTERNATIONAL (KOREA) LIMITED—See Korn Ferry; *U.S. Public*, pg. 1274
KORN/FERRY INTERNATIONAL LIMITED—See Korn Ferry; *U.S. Public*, pg. 1274
KORN/FERRY INTERNATIONAL MUSAVIRILIK LIMITED SIRKETI—See Korn Ferry; *U.S. Public*, pg. 1274
KORN/FERRY INTERNATIONAL OY—See Korn Ferry; *U.S. Public*, pg. 1274
KORN/FERRY INTERNATIONAL-PERU SOCIEDAD ANONIMA—See Korn Ferry; *U.S. Public*, pg. 1274
KORN/FERRY INTERNATIONAL PRIVATE LIMITED—See Korn Ferry; *U.S. Public*, pg. 1274
KORN/FERRY INTERNATIONAL S.A. DE C.V.—See Korn Ferry; *U.S. Public*, pg. 1274
KORN FERRY INTERNATIONAL S.A.—See Korn Ferry; *U.S. Public*, pg. 1273
KORN FERRY INTERNATIONAL S.A.—See Korn Ferry; *U.S. Public*, pg. 1273
KORN FERRY INTERNATIONAL S.A.—See Korn Ferry; *U.S. Public*, pg. 1274
KORN/FERRY INTERNATIONAL S.A.—See Korn Ferry; *U.S. Public*, pg. 1274
KORN/FERRY INTERNATIONAL (TAIWAN) CO. LIMITED—See Korn Ferry; *U.S. Public*, pg. 1274
KORN FERRY (IT) S.R.L. - ROME—See Korn Ferry; *U.S. Public*, pg. 1273
KORN FERRY (IT) S.R.L.—See Korn Ferry; *U.S. Public*, pg. 1273
KORN FERRY (JAPAN) LTD.—See Korn Ferry; *U.S. Public*, pg. 1273
KORN FERRY LIMITED—See Korn Ferry; *U.S. Public*, pg. 1274
KORN FERRY (LUXEMBOURG) S.A.R.L.—See Korn Ferry; *U.S. Public*, pg. 1273
KORN FERRY (NL) B.V.—See Korn Ferry; *U.S. Public*, pg. 1273
KORN FERRY (NZ)—See Korn Ferry; *U.S. Public*, pg. 1273
KORN FERRY (PL) SP. Z O.O.—See Korn Ferry; *U.S. Public*, pg. 1273
KORN FERRY RPOPS (HONG KONG) LTD.—See Korn Ferry; *U.S. Public*, pg. 1273
KORN FERRY RPOPS (SG) PTE. LTD.—See Korn Ferry; *U.S. Public*, pg. 1273
KORN FERRY S.A.—See Korn Ferry; *U.S. Public*, pg. 1274
KORN FERRY (SCHWEIZ) GMBH—See Korn Ferry; *U.S. Public*, pg. 1273
KORN FERRY (SG) PTE. LTD.—See Korn Ferry; *U.S. Public*, pg. 1273
KORN/FERRY (SHANGHAI) HUMAN CAPITAL CONSULTING CO., LTD.—See Korn Ferry; *U.S. Public*, pg. 1274
KORN FERRY SP LLC—See Korn Ferry; *U.S. Public*, pg. 1274
KORN FERRY S.R.O.—See Korn Ferry; *U.S. Public*, pg. 1274
KORN/FERRY (THAILAND) LIMITED—See Korn Ferry; *U.S. Public*, pg. 1274
KORN FERRY (US)—See Korn Ferry; *U.S. Public*, pg. 1273
LAB SUPPORT, LLC—See ASGN Incorporated; *U.S. Public*, pg. 211
LANDRUM CONSULTING, INC.—See Landrum Human Resource Companies, Inc.; *U.S. Private*, pg. 2386

541612 — HUMAN RESOURCES CON...

LANDRUM HUMAN RESOURCE COMPANIES, INC.; *U.S. Private*, pg. 2386
LATITUDE 36, INC.—See DBAY Advisors Limited; *Int'l*, pg. 1987
LEAN STAFFING SOLUTIONS, INC.; *U.S. Private*, pg. 2407
LEAVELOGIC, INC.—See Unum Group; *U.S. Public*, pg. 2263
LEE HECHT HARRISON LIMITED—See Adecco Group AG; *Int'l*, pg. 139
LEE HECHT HARRISON, LLC—See Adecco Group AG; *Int'l*, pg. 139
LEE HECHT HARRISON—See Adecco Group AG; *Int'l*, pg. 138
LEWIS-PRICE & ASSOCIATES, INC.; *U.S. Private*, pg. 2440
LEXOLUTION, LLC—See JLL Partners, LLC; *U.S. Private*, pg. 2213
LINCOLN BENEFITS GROUP, INC.—See Aon plc; *Int'l*, pg. 496
LINDSAY MORGAN ASSOCIATES LTD.—See Empresaria Group Plc; *Int'l*, pg. 2389
LLOYD STAFFING INC. - NEW YORK CITY—See Lloyd Staffing Inc.; *U.S. Private*, pg. 2476
LMA RECRUITMENT LIMITED—See Empresaria Group Plc; *Int'l*, pg. 2389
LONGNECKER & ASSOCIATES INC.—See Aon plc; *Int'l*, pg. 496
LTC PERFORMANCE STRATEGIES, INC.—See IMA Financial Group, Inc.; *U.S. Private*, pg. 2043
LUNA DATA SOLUTIONS, INC.; *U.S. Private*, pg. 2515
LUTECH RESOURCES LTD—See ABB Ltd.; *Int'l*, pg. 53
MAGELLAN SEARCH GROUP, INC.; *U.S. Private*, pg. 2545
MANAGEMENT RECRUITERS INC. BOSTON; *U.S. Private*, pg. 2560
MANAGEMENT RECRUITERS OF TAMPA-NORTH, INC.; *U.S. Private*, pg. 2560
MANDEX INC.—See MTS3 Inc.; *U.S. Private*, pg. 2810
MANPOWER AB—See ManpowerGroup Inc.; *U.S. Public*, pg. 1360
MANPOWER B.V.—See ManpowerGroup Inc.; *U.S. Public*, pg. 1360
MANPOWER DE VENEZUELA C.A.—See ManpowerGroup Inc.; *U.S. Public*, pg. 1360
MANPOWER D.O.O.—See ManpowerGroup Inc.; *U.S. Public*, pg. 1360
MANPOWERGROUP AB—See ManpowerGroup Inc.; *U.S. Public*, pg. 1360
MANPOWERGROUP AS—See ManpowerGroup Inc.; *U.S. Public*, pg. 1360
MANPOWERGROUP DEUTSCHLAND GMBH—See ManpowerGroup Inc.; *U.S. Public*, pg. 1360
MANPOWERGROUP FRANCE SAS—See ManpowerGroup Inc.; *U.S. Public*, pg. 1360
MANPOWERGROUP NETHERLANDS B.V.—See ManpowerGroup Inc.; *U.S. Public*, pg. 1360
MANPOWERGROUP OY—See ManpowerGroup Inc.; *U.S. Public*, pg. 1360
MANPOWERGROUP POLSKA SP. Z O.O.—See ManpowerGroup Inc.; *U.S. Public*, pg. 1360
MANPOWERGROUP PORTUGAL - SGPS, S.A.—See ManpowerGroup Inc.; *U.S. Public*, pg. 1360
MANPOWERGROUP SLOVENSKO S.R.O.—See ManpowerGroup Inc.; *U.S. Public*, pg. 1361
MANPOWERGROUP SOLUTIONS AS—See ManpowerGroup Inc.; *U.S. Public*, pg. 1361
MANPOWERGROUP SOLUTIONS BELGIUM SA—See ManpowerGroup Inc.; *U.S. Public*, pg. 1362
MANPOWERGROUP SOLUTIONS IT AB—See ManpowerGroup Inc.; *U.S. Public*, pg. 1360
MANPOWERGROUP SOLUTIONS LDA—See ManpowerGroup Inc.; *U.S. Public*, pg. 1360
MANPOWERGROUP SOLUTIONS, S.L.U—See ManpowerGroup Inc.; *U.S. Public*, pg. 1361
MANPOWER INSAN KAYNAKLARI LIMITED SIRKETI—See ManpowerGroup Inc.; *U.S. Public*, pg. 1359
MANPOWER MIDDLE EAST FZ-LLC—See ManpowerGroup Inc.; *U.S. Public*, pg. 1359
MANPOWER PANAMA S.A.—See ManpowerGroup Inc.; *U.S. Public*, pg. 1359
MANPOWER SA (PTY) LTD.—See ManpowerGroup Inc.; *U.S. Public*, pg. 1359
MANSION HOUSE RECRUITMENT LTD.—See Empresaria Group Plc; *Int'l*, pg. 2389
MARDER BENEFITS, INC.—See New Mountain Capital, LLC; *U.S. Private*, pg. 2901
MARKETING INNOVATORS INTERNATIONAL, INC.; *U.S. Private*, pg. 2580
MARSH & MCLENNAN AGENCY A/S—See Marsh & McLennan Companies, Inc.; *U.S. Public*, pg. 1381
MASTECH STAFFING SERVICES PVT. LTD.—See Mastech Digital, Inc.; *U.S. Public*, pg. 1394
MCGRATH SYSTEMS; *U.S. Private*, pg. 2635
MD&E CLARITY; *U.S. Private*, pg. 2646
MEDICAL CONNECTIONS HOLDINGS, INC.; *U.S. Private*, pg. 1411
MEDITERRANEAN CARRIERS, INC.—See Heidelberg Materials AG; *Int'l*, pg. 3318

MERCER (ARGENTINA) S.A.—See Marsh & McLennan Companies, Inc.; *U.S. Public*, pg. 1384
MERCER CONSULTING (CHILE) LTDA.—See Marsh & McLennan Companies, Inc.; *U.S. Public*, pg. 1385
MERCER CONSULTING LIMITED—See Marsh & McLennan Companies, Inc.; *U.S. Public*, pg. 1385
MERCER CORREDORES DE SEGUROS LTDA.—See Marsh & McLennan Companies, Inc.; *U.S. Public*, pg. 1385
MERCER DEUTSCHLAND GMBH—See Marsh & McLennan Companies, Inc.; *U.S. Public*, pg. 1385
MERCER FINLAND—See Marsh & McLennan Companies, Inc.; *U.S. Public*, pg. 1385
MERCER HUMAN RESOURCE CONSULTING AND INSURANCE BROKERS LIMITED—See Marsh & McLennan Companies, Inc.; *U.S. Public*, pg. 1385
MERCER HUMAN RESOURCE CONSULTING A/S—See Marsh & McLennan Companies, Inc.; *U.S. Public*, pg. 1385
MERCER HUMAN RESOURCE CONSULTING AS—See Marsh & McLennan Companies, Inc.; *U.S. Public*, pg. 1385
MERCER HUMAN RESOURCE CONSULTING LIMITED—See Marsh & McLennan Companies, Inc.; *U.S. Public*, pg. 1385
MERCER HUMAN RESOURCE CONSULTING LTDA—See Marsh & McLennan Companies, Inc.; *U.S. Public*, pg. 1385
MERCER HUMAN RESOURCE CONSULTING OF KENTUCKY, INC.—See Marsh & McLennan Companies, Inc.; *U.S. Public*, pg. 1385
MERCER HUMAN RESOURCE CONSULTING OF MASSACHUSETTS, INC.—See Marsh & McLennan Companies, Inc.; *U.S. Public*, pg. 1385
MERCER HUMAN RESOURCE CONSULTING OF TEXAS, INC.—See Marsh & McLennan Companies, Inc.; *U.S. Public*, pg. 1385
MERCER HUMAN RESOURCE CONSULTING OF VIRGINIA, INC.—See Marsh & McLennan Companies, Inc.; *U.S. Public*, pg. 1385
MERCER HUMAN RESOURCE CONSULTING PTY LTD—See Marsh & McLennan Companies, Inc.; *U.S. Public*, pg. 1385
MERCER HUMAN RESOURCE CONSULTING S.A. DE C.V.—See Marsh & McLennan Companies, Inc.; *U.S. Public*, pg. 1385
MERCER HUMAN RESOURCE CONSULTING S.A.—See Marsh & McLennan Companies, Inc.; *U.S. Public*, pg. 1385
MERCER HUMAN RESOURCE CONSULTING SA—See Marsh & McLennan Companies, Inc.; *U.S. Public*, pg. 1385
MERCER HUMAN RESOURCE CONSULTING—See Marsh & McLennan Companies, Inc.; *U.S. Public*, pg. 1385
MERCER HUMAN RESOURCE CONSULTING (S) PTE LTD—See Marsh & McLennan Companies, Inc.; *U.S. Public*, pg. 1385
MERCER LLC—See Marsh & McLennan Companies, Inc.; *U.S. Public*, pg. 1384
MERCER LLC—See Marsh & McLennan Companies, Inc.; *U.S. Public*, pg. 1386
MERCER—See Marsh & McLennan Companies, Inc.; *U.S. Public*, pg. 1384
MERCER (US) INC.—See Marsh & McLennan Companies, Inc.; *U.S. Public*, pg. 1385
MIDWAY STAFFING, INC.; *U.S. Private*, pg. 2719
MILLIMAN, INC.; *U.S. Private*, pg. 2737
MIND YOUR BUSINESS, INC.; *U.S. Private*, pg. 2740
MOMENTUM, A VOLT INFORMATION SCIENCES COMPANY, INC.—See American CyberSystems, Inc.; *U.S. Private*, pg. 230
MONROE CONSULTING GROUP—See Empresaria Group Plc; *Int'l*, pg. 2389
MORGAN SAMUELS COMPANY; *U.S. Private*, pg. 2784
MOTIVACTION LLC—See Augeo Affinity Marketing, Inc.; *U.S. Private*, pg. 392
MOUNTAIN STATES EMPLOYERS COUNCIL, INC.; *U.S. Private*, pg. 2800
MP SERVICES SP. Z O.O.—See ManpowerGroup Inc.; *U.S. Public*, pg. 1358
M SQUARED CONSULTING, INC.—See SolomonEdwards Group, LLC; *U.S. Private*, pg. 3710
MULLINS & ASSOCIATES INC.; *U.S. Private*, pg. 2811
NATIONAL COLLEGIATE SCOUTING ASSOCIATION; *U.S. Private*, pg. 2850
NATIONAL PERSONNEL ASSOCIATES COOPERATIVE, INC.; *U.S. Private*, pg. 2860
NEW ENGLAND CONSERVATION SERVICES LLC—See PosiGen LLC; *U.S. Private*, pg. 3233
NEW LIFE SOLUTION, INC.; *U.S. Private*, pg. 2898
NEXT BATTER'S CIRCLE INC.—See Allied Architects, Inc.; *Int'l*, pg. 356
NGA HR SP. Z O.O.—See Alight, Inc.; *U.S. Public*, pg. 76
NICHOLAS ANDREWS LIMITED—See ManpowerGroup Inc.; *U.S. Public*, pg. 1359
NORTHGATEARINSO AUSTRIA GMBH—See Alight, Inc.; *U.S. Public*, pg. 77

CORPORATE AFFILIATIONS

NORTHGATEARINSO SWITZERLAND LTD.—See Alight, Inc.; *U.S. Public*, pg. 77
NOW SOLUTIONS, INC.—See Vertical Computer Systems, Inc.; *U.S. Public*, pg. 4370
NRT TECHNOLOGIES INC.; *U.S. Private*, pg. 2969
NWI DE MEXICO S. DE R.L. DE C.V—See Gattaca plc; *Int'l*, pg. 2890
OAE SOFTWARE LLC—See Toast, Inc.; *U.S. Public*, pg. 2161
OASIS STAFFING, INC.—See Performance Personnel Partners, LLC; *U.S. Private*, pg. 3149
THE O'CONNOR GROUP; *U.S. Private*, pg. 4087
OLIVER WYMAN GMBH—See Marsh & McLennan Companies, Inc.; *U.S. Public*, pg. 1387
ONECLICKHR PLC—See Automatic Data Processing, Inc.; *U.S. Public*, pg. 230
ONEIDA WEALTH MANAGEMENT, INC.—See Community Bank System, Inc.; *U.S. Public*, pg. 550
ONE, INC.—See Great Hill Partners, L.P.; *U.S. Private*, pg. 1763
ONTARGETJOBS, INC.—See Ziff Davis, Inc.; *U.S. Public*, pg. 2404
OOO HAY GROUP—See Korn Ferry; *U.S. Public*, pg. 1275
OPALSTAFF; *U.S. Private*, pg. 3028
ORANGE TREE STAFFING, LLC; *U.S. Private*, pg. 3037
OS FACILITIES CO., LTD.—See Bain Capital, LP; *U.S. Private*, pg. 434
OTS INC.—See Bain Capital, LP; *U.S. Private*, pg. 435
OTTERBASE TECHNICAL SERVICES, INC.; *U.S. Private*, pg. 3049
PADES PERSONALSERVICE GMBH—See E.ON SE; *Int'l*, pg. 2258
PARALLON WORKFORCE MANAGEMENT SOLUTIONS, LLC—See HCA Healthcare, Inc.; *U.S. Public*, pg. 1006
PAXUS AUSTRALIA PTY. LIMITED—See Adcorp Holdings Limited; *Int'l*, pg. 127
PAYGROUP LIMITED—See Deel, Inc.; *U.S. Private*, pg. 1189
PEARL MEYER & PARTNERS, LLC; *U.S. Private*, pg. 3125
PENNA CONSULTING LIMITED—See Adecco Group AG; *Int'l*, pg. 139
PEOPLEG2; *U.S. Private*, pg. 3141
PEOPLE SCOUT INC.—See TrueBlue, Inc.; *U.S. Public*, pg. 2198
PEOPLESEARCH PTE. LTD.—See HRnetGroup Limited; *Int'l*, pg. 3501
PERCEPTYX, INC.; *U.S. Private*, pg. 3146
PERPETUAL INSIGHTS LLC; *U.S. Private*, pg. 3153
PERSITY RESOURCING B.V.—See Ctac N.V.; *Int'l*, pg. 1869
PERSONNEL MANAGEMENT SYSTEMS, INC.—See Asure Software, Inc.; *U.S. Public*, pg. 218
PERSONNEL SERVICES; *U.S. Private*, pg. 3156
POINT RECOGNITION; *U.S. Private*, pg. 3222
PREFERRED BENEFITS GROUP, INC.—See Aon plc; *Int'l*, pg. 497
PRIDESTAFF, INC.; *U.S. Private*, pg. 3260
THE PRIMARY GROUP, INC.; *U.S. Private*, pg. 4098
PRIMESKILL STAFFING SERVICES; *U.S. Private*, pg. 3263
PRINCETONONE ASIA—See My Job Matcher, Inc.; *U.S. Private*, pg. 2823
PRINCETONONE LLC—See My Job Matcher, Inc.; *U.S. Private*, pg. 2823
PROCUREABILITY, INC.—See Jabil Inc.; *U.S. Public*, pg. 1182
PROFESSIONAL BENEFITS SOLUTIONS, INC.—See Aon plc; *Int'l*, pg. 497
PROLINK STAFFING LLC; *U.S. Private*, pg. 3282
PRO-LOG IV GMBH—See DEKRA e.V.; *Int'l*, pg. 2009
PRO-LOG NIEDERRHEIN GMBH—See DEKRA e.V.; *Int'l*, pg. 2009
PRO-LOG ROSENHEIM GMBH—See DEKRA e.V.; *Int'l*, pg. 2009
PRO-LOG RUHR GMBH—See DEKRA e.V.; *Int'l*, pg. 2009
PROSERVICE HAWAII; *U.S. Private*, pg. 3287
PROVEN INC.; *U.S. Private*, pg. 3291
PT. BSM CREW SERVICE CENTRE INDONESIA—See Bernhard Schulte Shipmanagement (Cyprus) Ltd.; *Int'l*, pg. 989
PT EGON ZEHNDER INTERNATIONAL—See Egon Zehnder International Inc.; *U.S. Private*, pg. 1345
PT KORN/FERRY INTERNATIONAL—See Korn Ferry; *U.S. Public*, pg. 1275
PTS ADVANCE; *U.S. Private*, pg. 3298
PURSUIT OF EXCELLENCE, INC.; *U.S. Private*, pg. 3307
QUAD, A SOLOMONEDWARDS COMPANY—See SolomonEdwardsGroup, LLC; *U.S. Private*, pg. 3710
QUANTUM MARKET RESEARCH, INC.; *U.S. Private*, pg. 3323
RECOURSE COMMUNICATIONS, INC.; *U.S. Private*, pg. 3371
RECRUITICS, LLC; *U.S. Private*, pg. 3372
THE RECRUITMENT BUSINESS LIMITED—See Empresaria Group Plc; *Int'l*, pg. 2389
RECRUITWISE; *U.S. Private*, pg. 3372
RESOURCE ALLIANCE LLC; *U.S. Private*, pg. 3406
RESOURCEFUL HR LLC—See New Mountain Capital, LLC; *U.S. Private*, pg. 2901

N.A.I.C.S. INDEX

541613 — MARKETING CONSULTIN...

RESOURCE OPTIONS, INC.; *U.S. Private,* pg. 3407
RESPONSE PERSONNEL, INC.; *U.S. Private,* pg. 3408
RHODES ASSOCIATES; *U.S. Private,* pg. 3422
   RICHMOND RECRUITMENT LIMITED—See Bain Capital, LP; *U.S. Private,* pg. 434
   RIGHT CZECH REPUBLIC—See ManpowerGroup Inc.; *U.S. Public,* pg. 1361
   RIGHT MANAGEMENT CANADA—See ManpowerGroup Inc.; *U.S. Public,* pg. 1361
   RIGHT MANAGEMENT SINGAPORE PTE. LTD.—See ManpowerGroup Inc.; *U.S. Public,* pg. 1361
   RIGHT MANAGEMENT SPAIN, S.L.U.—See Manpower-Group Inc.; *U.S. Public,* pg. 1361
RIGHTSTAFF, INC.; *U.S. Private,* pg. 3436
ROCS, INC.; *U.S. Private,* pg. 3469
   RUSSELL REYNOLDS ASSOCIATES, CHICAGO—See Russell Reynolds Associates Inc.; *U.S. Private,* pg. 3506
RUSSELL REYNOLDS ASSOCIATES INC.; *U.S. Private,* pg. 3506
   RUSSELL REYNOLDS ASSOCIATES INC.—See Russell Reynolds Associates Inc.; *U.S. Private,* pg. 3506
   RUSSELL REYNOLDS ASSOCIATES, MENLO PARK—See Russell Reynolds Associates Inc.; *U.S. Private,* pg. 3507
RWR ENTERPRISES INC.; *U.S. Private,* pg. 3509
RXBENEFITS, INC.; *U.S. Private,* pg. 3509
   SABA SOFTWARE GMBH—See Clearlake Capital Group, L.P.; *U.S. Private,* pg. 934
   SABA SOFTWARE (UK) LTD.—See Clearlake Capital Group, L.P.; *U.S. Private,* pg. 934
   S.A. EGON ZEHNDER ASSOCIATES (INTERNATIONAL) N.V.—See Egon Zehnder International Inc.; *U.S. Private,* pg. 1345
   SAINT-GOBAIN SERVICES RH FRANCE—See Compagnie de Saint-Gobain SA; *Int'l,* pg. 1728
SAI PEOPLE SOLUTIONS, INC.; *U.S. Private,* pg. 3528
SALES PERFORMANCE INTERNATIONAL, LLC; *U.S. Private,* pg. 3532
   SAVITZ ORGANIZATION, INCORPORATED—See CBIZ, Inc.; *U.S. Public,* pg. 457
   SAXON HUMAN RESOURCES PVT. LTD.—See Saxon Global Inc.; *U.S. Private,* pg. 3558
SAYVA SOLUTIONS INC.; *U.S. Private,* pg. 3558
SCHOENECKERS INC.; *U.S. Private,* pg. 3567
   SC MANPOWER ROMANIA SRL—See ManpowerGroup Inc.; *U.S. Public,* pg. 1362
   SEGAL BENZ—See The Segal Group, Inc.; *U.S. Private,* pg. 4116
   THE SEGAL COMPANY (EASTERN STATES), INC.—See The Segal Group, Inc.; *U.S. Private,* pg. 4116
   SENN-DELANEY LEADERSHIP CONSULTING GROUP, LLC—See Heidrick & Struggles International, Inc.; *U.S. Public,* pg. 1023
   SERVISOURCE RECRUITMENT LIMITED—See Bain Capital, LP; *U.S. Private,* pg. 434
   SHANGHAI INTERNATIONAL TRADE PROMOTION CO., LTD.—See DLG Exhibitions & Events Corp Ltd.; *Int'l,* pg. 2141
   SHAREDHR—See ABD Insurance & Financial Services, Inc.; *U.S. Private,* pg. 37
THE SHEAKLEY GROUP; *U.S. Private,* pg. 4117
   SHONAN HI-TECH PLANNING CO., LTD.—See Imagica Group Inc.; *Int'l,* pg. 3619
   SIBSON CONSULTING, LLC - LOS ANGELES—See The Segal Group, Inc.; *U.S. Private,* pg. 4116
   SIBSON CONSULTING, LLC - PRINCETON—See The Segal Group, Inc.; *U.S. Private,* pg. 4116
   SIBSON CONSULTING, LLC - RALEIGH—See The Segal Group, Inc.; *U.S. Private,* pg. 4116
   SIBSON CONSULTING, LLC—See The Segal Group, Inc.; *U.S. Private,* pg. 4116
   SILTA OY—See Administer Oy; *Int'l,* pg. 151
   SJB SERVICES UK LIMITED—See ManpowerGroup Inc.; *U.S. Public,* pg. 1360
SM&A CORPORATION; *U.S. Private,* pg. 3690
SMITH HANLEY ASSOCIATES INC.; *U.S. Private,* pg. 3695
   SOLID BENEFIT GUIDANCE LLC—See Arthur J. Gallagher & Co.; *U.S. Public,* pg. 205
   SOURCEPOINTE, LLC—See Aquiline Capital Partners LLC; *U.S. Private,* pg. 304
   SPARTAN STAFFING, LLC—See TrueBlue, Inc.; *U.S. Public,* pg. 2198
SSI (U.S.) INC.; *U.S. Private,* pg. 3769
   SSS CONSULTING, INC.—See GrowthPlay LLC; *U.S. Private,* pg. 1796
   STAFFGROUP LTD.—See Cordant Group PLC; *Int'l,* pg. 1795
   STAFF ONE, INC.—See Paychex, Inc.; *U.S. Public,* pg. 1655
STEVEN DOUGLAS ASSOCIATES, INC.; *U.S. Private,* pg. 3808
   SURGE RESOURCES INC.—See GPB Capital Holdings, LLC; *U.S. Private,* pg. 1748
   TALENT2 INTERNATIONAL LIMITED—See Allegis Group, Inc.; *U.S. Private,* pg. 177
   TALENT2 NZ LIMITED—See Allegis Group, Inc.; *U.S. Private,* pg. 177
   TALENT2 PTY LIMITED—See Allegis Group, Inc.; *U.S. Private,* pg. 177

   TALENT2 SINGAPORE PTE. LTD.—See Allegis Group, Inc.; *U.S. Private,* pg. 177
   TALENT2 WORKS LIMITED—See Allegis Group, Inc.; *U.S. Private,* pg. 177
   TALENT2 WORKS PTY. LTD.—See Allegis Group, Inc.; *U.S. Private,* pg. 177
TALENTBURST, INC.; *U.S. Private,* pg. 3926
TALENT CONNECTIONS, LLC; *U.S. Private,* pg. 3926
   TALENTMINE LLC—See Webster Equity Partners, LLC; *U.S. Private,* pg. 4467
   TALENT PARTNERS (DUBAI) LLC—See Allegis Group, Inc.; *U.S. Private,* pg. 177
TALENTQUEST INC.; *U.S. Private,* pg. 3926
TANDEM HR, INC.; *U.S. Private,* pg. 3930
TANDEM; *U.S. Private,* pg. 3930
   TANDYM GROUP, LLC—See Great Mill Rock LLC; *U.S. Private,* pg. 1766
   TAPFIN SARL—See ManpowerGroup Inc.; *U.S. Public,* pg. 1360
   TAYLOR HOPKINSON PTE. LTD.—See Brunel International N.V.; *Int'l,* pg. 1200
   TCFCW, LLC—See Aquiline Capital Partners LLC; *U.S. Private,* pg. 304
   TCFCW, LLC—See Genstar Capital, LLC; *U.S. Private,* pg. 1675
   TEAM24 LIMITED—See Capita plc; *Int'l,* pg. 1309
TEAM BUILDERS PLUS; *U.S. Private,* pg. 3949
   TECHNOLOGY RESOURCE COMPANY LIMITED—See Aleator Energy Limited; *Int'l,* pg. 305
   TECOLOCO EL SALVADOR S.A. DE C.V.—See Axel Springer SE; *Int'l,* pg. 767
TEXAS ENGINEERING EXT SERVICE; *U.S. Private,* pg. 3975
TGRP SOLUTIONS LLC; *U.S. Private,* pg. 3979
   THORBAHN AND ASSOCIATES INSURANCE AGENCY, INC.—See Aon plc; *Int'l,* pg. 497
   TIVA HEALTHCARE, INC.—See KKR & Co. Inc.; *U.S. Public,* pg. 1249
   TONER GRAHAM LIMITED—See Kelly Services, Inc.; *U.S. Public,* pg. 1219
TRADEMARK RECRUITING INC.; *U.S. Private,* pg. 4202
   TRESTLETREE, INC.—See Harvard Pilgrim Health Care, Inc.; *U.S. Private,* pg. 1875
TRICORE INC.; *U.S. Private,* pg. 4229
   TRIPLE CREEK ASSOCIATES, INC.—See MentorcliQ, Inc.; *U.S. Private,* pg. 2667
   TRS STAFFING SOLUTIONS BV—See Fluor Corporation; *U.S. Public,* pg. 858
   TRS STAFFING SOLUTIONS LIMITED—See Fluor Corporation; *U.S. Public,* pg. 860
   TUC AMU CENTER TUC SYD A/S—See DEKRA e.V.; *Int'l,* pg. 2010
   TUC DANSK VOGNMANDSSKOLE A/S—See DEKRA e.V.; *Int'l,* pg. 2010
   TUC DUCAS APS—See DEKRA e.V.; *Int'l,* pg. 2010
   TUJA ZEITARBEIT GMBH—See Adecco Group AG; *Int'l,* pg. 141
   TURNKEY BENEFITS INC.—See Key Family of Companies; *U.S. Private,* pg. 2293
UNITED STATES HOMELAND INVESTIGATIONS INC; *U.S. Private,* pg. 4299
   UNITED TECHNOLOGIES INTERNATIONAL CORPORATION-ASIA PRIVATE LIMITED—See RTX Corporation; *U.S. Public,* pg. 1825
URBAN AFFAIRS COALITION; *U.S. Private,* pg. 4313
   USI CONSULTING GROUP—See Caisse de Depot et Placement du Quebec; *Int'l,* pg. 1257
   USI CONSULTING GROUP—See KKR & Co. Inc.; *U.S. Public,* pg. 1265
   VALUE ARK CONSULTING CO., LTD.—See Copro Holdings Co., Ltd.; *Int'l,* pg. 1794
   VAUGHN HOUSE, INC.—See Easter Seals Central Texas; *U.S. Private,* pg. 1319
VENSURE EMPLOYER SERVICES, INC.; *U.S. Private,* pg. 4357
VENTEON HOLDINGS, LLC.; *U.S. Private,* pg. 4357
   VENUTI & ASSOCIATES—See Northwest Plan Services, Inc.; *U.S. Private,* pg. 2961
VERTEX RESOURCE GROUP, INC.; *U.S. Private,* pg. 4370
VESA HEALTH & TECHNOLOGY, INC.; *U.S. Private,* pg. 4371
   VIA TECHNICAL, LLC—See Stone Point Capital LLC; *U.S. Private,* pg. 3823
VISIUM RESOURCES, INC.; *U.S. Private,* pg. 4393
   VISTA STAFFING SERVICES, INC.—See ASGN Incorporated; *U.S. Public,* pg. 211
   VOLT ASIA ENTERPRISES (TAIWAN) CO. LTD.—See American CyberSystems, Inc.; *U.S. Private,* pg. 230
   VOLT CONSULTING GROUP LIMITED—See American CyberSystems, Inc.; *U.S. Private,* pg. 230
   VOLT EUROPE (GERMANY) GMBH—See American CyberSystems, Inc.; *U.S. Private,* pg. 230
   VOLT EUROPE LIMITED—See American CyberSystems, Inc.; *U.S. Private,* pg. 230
   VOLT MANAGEMENT CORP.—See American CyberSystems, Inc.; *U.S. Private,* pg. 230
   VOLT SERVICE CORPORATION PTE. LTD.—See American CyberSystems, Inc.; *U.S. Private,* pg. 230

   VOLT WORKFORCE SOLUTIONS, INC.—See American CyberSystems, Inc.; *U.S. Private,* pg. 230
WALDRON & COMPANY; *U.S. Private,* pg. 4428
   WERKSTOFFPRUFUNG PETERS GMBH—See DEKRA e.V.; *Int'l,* pg. 2010
WHITNEY PARTNERS INC.; *U.S. Private,* pg. 4513
WINSLOW TECHNOLOGY GROUP, LLC; *U.S. Private,* pg. 4543
WITT, KIEFFER, HADELMAN, LLOYD & FORD CO. INC.; *U.S. Private,* pg. 4551
   WOFE KORN/FERRY INTERNATIONAL HUMAN CAPITAL CONSULTING (BEIJING) LIMITED—See Korn Ferry; *U.S. Public,* pg. 1275
   WORKFORCE INSIGHT LLC—See Accenture plc; *Int'l,* pg. 88
WORKFORCE INVESTMENT BOARD OF HERKIMER, MADISON & ONEIDA COUNTIES; *U.S. Private,* pg. 4563
   WORKFORCE SOLUTIONS GROUP, INCORPORATED—See Cross Country Healthcare, Inc.; *U.S. Public,* pg. 595
   WORKFORCETACTIX, INC.—See GTCR LLC; *U.S. Private,* pg. 1804
   WORKPLACE OPTIONS, LLC—See Accor S.A.; *Int'l,* pg. 91
   WORKSHOP BEMANNING OG KOMPETANSE AS—See ManpowerGroup Inc.; *U.S. Public,* pg. 1362
   YOH SERVICES, LLC—See The Day & Zimmermann Group, Inc.; *U.S. Private,* pg. 4019
   YOURENCORE, INC.—See Genstar Capital, LLC; *U.S. Private,* pg. 1673
ZAMPHR, INC.; *U.S. Private,* pg. 4597
   ZRG PARTNERS, LLC—See RFE Investment Partners; *U.S. Private,* pg. 3419

541613 — MARKETING CONSULTING SERVICES

   THE 10 GROUP LIMITED—See Cromwell Property Group; *Int'l,* pg. 1854
206INC.; *U.S. Private,* pg. 5
3DSHOPPING.COM INC.; *U.S. Public,* pg. 4
4 FORCES GROUP LLC; *U.S. Private,* pg. 14
   919 MARKETING COMPANY—See Greens Farms Capital LLC; *U.S. Private,* pg. 1779
   919 MARKETING COMPANY—See Landon Capital Partners, LLC; *U.S. Private,* pg. 1362
ABACUS PLANNING GROUP, INC.; *U.S. Private,* pg. 34
   ABERDEEN MARKET INTELLIGENCE U.S., LLC—See Ziff Davis, Inc.; *U.S. Public,* pg. 2404
ABSOLUTDATA RESEARCH & ANALYTICS (P) LTD.; *U.S. Private,* pg. 44
ACADEMIXDIRECT INC.; *U.S. Private,* pg. 46
   ACCENTIV BRESIL MIMETICA—See Edenred S.A.; *Int'l,* pg. 2307
   ACCENTIV SHANGHAI COMPANY—See Edenred S.A.; *Int'l,* pg. 2307
   ACCESS WORLDWIDE COMMUNICATIONS, INC. - AUGUSTA—See Access Worldwide Communications, Inc.; *U.S. Public,* pg. 32
   ACCUMARK PARTNERS INC—See Stagwell, Inc.; *U.S. Public,* pg. 1925
   A.C. NIELSEN CHILE LIMITADA—See Brookfield Corporation; *Int'l,* pg. 1177
   A.C. NIELSEN CHILE LIMITADA—See Elliott Management Corporation; *U.S. Private,* pg. 1369
   AC NIELSEN COTE D'IVOIRE LIMITED—See Brookfield Corporation; *Int'l,* pg. 1177
   AC NIELSEN COTE D'IVOIRE LIMITED—See Elliott Management Corporation; *U.S. Private,* pg. 1369
   ACNIELSEN PAKISTAN (PRIVATE) LIMITED—See Brookfield Corporation; *Int'l,* pg. 1177
   ACNIELSEN PAKISTAN (PRIVATE) LIMITED—See Elliott Management Corporation; *U.S. Private,* pg. 1369
   ACORN DIRECT MARKETING LIMITED—See Bread Financial Holdings Inc.; *U.S. Public,* pg. 381
ACORN INTERNATIONAL, INC.; *Int'l,* pg. 108
   ACOUSTIC, L.P.—See International Business Machines Corporation; *U.S. Public,* pg. 1148
ACROBATANT, LLC; *U.S. Private,* pg. 65
ACTION SPORTS MEDIA, INC.; *U.S. Private,* pg. 68
   ACTITO S.A.—See Altor Equity Partners AB; *Int'l,* pg. 395
   ACTIVA MEDIA (S) PTE. LTD.—See AM Group Holdings Limited; *Int'l,* pg. 402
   ACTIVE INTERNATIONAL INC.—See Active Media Services, Inc.; *U.S. Private,* pg. 69
ACTIVENGAGE, INC.; *U.S. Private,* pg. 70
   ACTON DIREKT-MARKETING GMBH—See ACTON International Ltd.; *U.S. Private,* pg. 70
   ACXIOM AUSTRALIA PTY LTD—See The Interpublic Group of Companies, Inc.; *U.S. Public,* pg. 2090
   ACXIOM CH, INC.—See The Interpublic Group of Companies, Inc.; *U.S. Public,* pg. 2090
   ACXIOM FRANCE SAS—See The Interpublic Group of Companies, Inc.; *U.S. Public,* pg. 2090
   ACXIOM GOVERNMENT SERVICES, INC.—See The Interpublic Group of Companies, Inc.; *U.S. Public,* pg. 2090
   ADAPTLY, INC.—See Accenture plc; *Int'l,* pg. 86

541613 — MARKETING CONSULTIN...

ADD3, LLC.; *U.S. Private*, pg. 77
AD DIALETO AGENCIA DE PUBLICIDADE SA—See Accenture plc; *Int'l*, pg. 82
ADDISON; *U.S. Private*, pg. 77
ADEKA BRASIL LTDA.—See Adeka Corporation; *Int'l*, pg. 141
ADEPT MARKETING OUTSOURCED LLC—See Ascentium Corporation; *U.S. Private*, pg. 348
ADEVINTA ASA; *Int'l*, pg. 145
ADFLEX COMMUNICATIONS INC.—See Bain Capital, LP; *U.S. Private*, pg. 449
ADISH PLUS CO., LTD.—See Adish Co., Ltd.; *Int'l*, pg. 149
ADLPARTNER SA; *Int'l*, pg. 151
ADLUCENT, LLC; *U.S. Private*, pg. 80
ADOBE SYSTEMS EUROPE LIMITED.—See Adobe Inc.; *U.S. Public*, pg. 42
ADTAILY SP. Z O.O—See Agora S.A.; *Int'l*, pg. 212
ADVANCED ENTERPRISES INC.; *U.S. Private*, pg. 89
ADVANTAGE SALES & MARKETING, LLC - GRAND RAPIDS—See Leonard Green & Partners, L.P.; *U.S. Private*, pg. 2423
ADVANTAGE SALES & MARKETING, LLC - RENTON—See Leonard Green & Partners, L.P.; *U.S. Private*, pg. 2423
ADVANTAGE SALES & MARKETING, LLC - WOODCLIFF LAKE—See Leonard Green & Partners, L.P.; *U.S. Private*, pg. 2423
ADVANTAGE SALES & MARKETING - SAN ANTONIO—See Leonard Green & Partners, L.P.; *U.S. Private*, pg. 2423
ADVANTAGE WAYPOINT LLC—See Prospect Hill Growth Partners, L.P.; *U.S. Private*, pg. 3288
ADVANTEX DINING CORPORATION—See Advantex Marketing International Inc.; *Int'l*, pg. 166
ADVANTEX MARKETING CORPORATION—See Advantex Marketing International Inc.; *Int'l*, pg. 166
AD VENTURE PUBLIC COMPANY LIMITED—See Advanced Info Service Plc; *Int'l*, pg. 159
ADVENTURES IN ADVERTISING FRANCHISE INC—See The Riverside Company; *U.S. Private*, pg. 4107
ADW ACOSTA, LLC—See Acosta, Inc.; *U.S. Private*, pg. 64
ADWAYS CHINA CO., LTD.—See Adways Inc.; *Int'l*, pg. 169
AFFILIATE SALES & MARKETING, INC—See Qurate Retail, Inc.; *U.S. Public*, pg. 1758
AFFILIATE TRACTION—See eBay Inc.; *U.S. Public*, pg. 709
AFFINITAS CORPORATION; *U.S. Private*, pg. 122
AFFINITIV; *U.S. Private*, pg. 122
AFFLINK, INC.—See Performance Food Group Company; *U.S. Public*, pg. 1674
AGB NIELSEN MEDIA RESEARCH (THAILAND) LTD.—See Brookfield Corporation; *Int'l*, pg. 1178
AGB NIELSEN MEDIA RESEARCH (THAILAND) LTD.—See Elliott Management Corporation; *U.S. Private*, pg. 1370
AGEHA INC.; *Int'l*, pg. 205
AGENDA CORPORATION; *Int'l*, pg. 205
AGENT LINK; *U.S. Private*, pg. 127
AGILLIC A/S; *Int'l*, pg. 210
AIDMA MARKETING COMMUNICATION CORPORATION; *Int'l*, pg. 231
AIIR CONSULTING, LLC; *U.S. Private*, pg. 132
AIMCLEAR BLOG; *U.S. Private*, pg. 133
AIMIA ACQUISITION UK LIMITED—See Aimia Inc.; *Int'l*, pg. 233
AJAX UNION; *U.S. Private*, pg. 143
AJINOMOTO COMMUNICATIONS CO., INC.—See Ajinomoto Company, Inc.; *Int'l*, pg. 256
AJIS MERCHANDISING SERVICE CO., LTD.—See AJIS Co., Ltd.; *Int'l*, pg. 258
AJIS USA, INC.—See AJIS Co., Ltd.; *Int'l*, pg. 258
ALBERT TECHNOLOGIES LIMITED; *Int'l*, pg. 297
ALCHEMY WORX INC.—See SellUp Inc.; *U.S. Private*, pg. 3603
ALCHEMY WORX—See SellUp Inc.; *U.S. Private*, pg. 3603
ALFA LAVAL, INC.—See Alfa Laval AB; *Int'l*, pg. 309
ALFA LAVAL SHARPLES—See Alfa Laval AB; *Int'l*, pg. 309
ALKEMY SPA; *Int'l*, pg. 331
ALLEGIANCE MARKETING GROUP LLC—See Allianz SE; *Int'l*, pg. 343
ALLIED ARCHITECTS, INC.; *Int'l*, pg. 356
ALLIED TECH BASE CO., LTD.—See Allied Architects, Inc.; *Int'l*, pg. 356
ALL TERRAIN; *U.S. Private*, pg. 173
ALPHADETAIL, INC.—See IQVIA Holdings Inc.; *U.S. Public*, pg. 1169
ALPHA FINANCIAL MARKETS CONSULTING INC.—See Bridgepoint Group Plc; *Int'l*, pg. 1153
ALPHA FINANCIAL MARKETS CONSULTING S.A.S.—See Bridgepoint Group Plc; *Int'l*, pg. 1153
ALPHA FINANCIAL MARKETS CONSULTING SWITZERLAND S.A.—See Bridgepoint Group Plc; *Int'l*, pg. 1153
ALPHAGILITY LLC; *U.S. Private*, pg. 200
ALPHA MARKETING, INC.; *U.S. Private*, pg. 198
ALTAVIA BELGIUM SA—See Altavia S.A.; *Int'l*, pg. 387
ALTAVIA CESKA SRO—See Altavia S.A.; *Int'l*, pg. 387
ALTAVIA DEUTSCHLAND GMBH—See Altavia S.A.; *Int'l*, pg. 387
ALTAVIA HELLAS AE—See Altavia S.A.; *Int'l*, pg. 387
ALTAVIA HTT LTD—See Altavia S.A.; *Int'l*, pg. 387
ALTAVIA HUNGARIA KFT—See Altavia S.A.; *Int'l*, pg. 387

ALTAVIA IBERICA CFA—See Altavia S.A.; *Int'l*, pg. 387
ALTAVIA ILETISIM AS—See Altavia S.A.; *Int'l*, pg. 387
ALTAVIA ITALIA SRL—See Altavia S.A.; *Int'l*, pg. 387
ALTAVIA LILLE SAS—See Altavia S.A.; *Int'l*, pg. 387
ALTAVIA POLSKA SP. Z.O.O.—See Altavia S.A.; *Int'l*, pg. 388
ALTAVIA ROMANIA COMMUNICATION SRL—See Altavia S.A.; *Int'l*, pg. 388
ALTAVIA RUS, OOO—See Altavia S.A.; *Int'l*, pg. 388
ALTAVIA S.A.; *Int'l*, pg. 387
ALTAVIA SWISS SA—See Altavia S.A.; *Int'l*, pg. 388
ALTITUDE MARKETING; *U.S. Private*, pg. 209
ALTITUDE MARKETING—See Altitude Marketing; *U.S. Private*, pg. 209
ALTOVISION INC.—See Experian plc; *Int'l*, pg. 2586
ALTRIA CONSUMER ENGAGEMENT SERVICES INC.—See Altria Group, Inc.; *U.S. Public*, pg. 89
AMERICAN FIDELITY SECURITIES, INC.—See American Fidelity Corporation; *U.S. Public*, pg. 233
AMER TUNISIA SARL—See Brookfield Corporation; *Int'l*, pg. 1178
AMER TUNISIA SARL—See Elliott Management Corporation; *U.S. Private*, pg. 1370
AMPLIFIED DIGITAL, LLC—See Lee Enterprises, Incorporated; *U.S. Public*, pg. 1298
ANADOLU ENDUSTRI HOLDING UND CO. KG—See AG Anadolu Grubu Holding A.S.; *Int'l*, pg. 197
ANC SPORTS ENTERPRISES, LLC—See Atairos Group, Inc.; *U.S. Private*, pg. 363
ANGKARA SETIA DEVELOPMENT SDN. BHD.—See Advance Information Marketing Berhad; *Int'l*, pg. 156
ANOMALY B.V—See Stagwell, Inc.; *U.S. Public*, pg. 1925
ANOMALY LONDON LLP—See Stagwell, Inc.; *U.S. Public*, pg. 1926
ANOMALY PARTNERS LLC—See Stagwell, Inc.; *U.S. Public*, pg. 1926
ANTHEM MARKETING, LLC—See Quad/Graphics, Inc.; *U.S. Public*, pg. 1744
ANTHILL BV—See bpost NV/SA; *Int'l*, pg. 1133
ANTWERPES AG—See DocCheck AG; *Int'l*, pg. 2153
AOC KEY SOLUTIONS, INC.; *U.S. Private*, pg. 289
APPLIQATE, INC.; *U.S. Public*, pg. 173
APT, INC.; *U.S. Private*, pg. 302
AQUARIUS AI, INC.; *Int'l*, pg. 528
ARCELORMITTAL-KISWIRE LLC—See ArcelorMittal S.A.; *Int'l*, pg. 545
ARKEMA KOREA HOLDING CO., LTD.—See Arkema S.A.; *Int'l*, pg. 569
ARMED FORCES COMMUNICATIONS, INC. - CRANBURY—See Armed Forces Communications, Inc.; *U.S. Private*, pg. 330
ARRAY ASIA LTD.—See Array Marketing Group Inc.; *Int'l*, pg. 578
ARRAY NEW YORK—See Array Marketing Group Inc.; *Int'l*, pg. 578
ARTCRAFT PROMOTIONAL CONCEPTS; *U.S. Private*, pg. 340
ARTEC GLOBAL MEDIA, INC.; *U.S. Public*, pg. 201
ARTEFACT S.A.—See Ardian SAS; *Int'l*, pg. 554
ASHFIELD HEALTHCARE GMBH—See Clayton, Dubilier & Rice, LLC; *U.S. Private*, pg. 927
ASHMORE INVESTMENT MANAGEMENT INDIA LLP—See Ashmore Group plc; *Int'l*, pg. 608
ASM SALES FORCE AGENCY SP. Z O.O.—See ASM Group S.A.; *Int'l*, pg. 625
THE ASPIRE GROUP, INC.—See Playfly Sports Properties, LLC; *U.S. Private*, pg. 3212
AS TARTU KESKKATLAMAJA—See Fortum Oyj; *Int'l*, pg. 2740
ASTONISH; *U.S. Private*, pg. 360
ATCOM SA—See Dionic Industrial & Trading S.A; *Int'l*, pg. 2128
ATLANTIS CO., LTD.—See Gree Inc.; *Int'l*, pg. 3069
AUGEO AFFINITY MARKETING, INC.; *U.S. Private*, pg. 391
AUTOBYTEL DEALER SERVICES, INC.—See One Planet Group LLC; *U.S. Private*, pg. 3020
AUTOBYTEL FLORIDA, INC.—See One Planet Group LLC; *U.S. Private*, pg. 3020
AVERY DENNISON RIS DOMINICAN REPUBLIC—See Avery Dennison Corporation; *U.S. Public*, pg. 243
AVIS FINANCIAL CORP.; *Int'l*, pg. 744
AVISION SALES GROUP—See Osceola Capital Management, LLC; *U.S. Private*, pg. 3046
THE AVOCA GROUP, INC.—See Leonard Green & Partners, L.P.; *U.S. Private*, pg. 2430
AVTEX SOLUTIONS, LLC—See TTEC Holdings, Inc.; *U.S. Public*, pg. 2203
AXIATA DIGITAL SERVICES SDN BHD—See Axiata Group Berhad; *Int'l*, pg. 768
AZ DIRECT AG—See Bertelsmann SE & Co. KGaA; *Int'l*, pg. 989
AZ DIRECT GMBH—See Bertelsmann SE & Co. KGaA; *Int'l*, pg. 993
AZ DIRECT OSTERREICH GMBH—See Bertelsmann SE & Co. KGaA; *Int'l*, pg. 989
AZUL PARTNERS, INC.; *U.S. Private*, pg. 416
BAIDU INTERNATIONAL TECHNOLOGY (SHENZHEN) CO., LTD.—See Baidu, Inc.; *Int'l*, pg. 801

BALLYWHOSOCIAL; *U.S. Private*, pg. 461
BAUER MEDIA APS—See Heinrich Bauer Verlag KG; *Int'l*, pg. 3323
BBEX INC.; *U.S. Private*, pg. 498
BC TECHNOLOGY GROUP LIMITED; *Int'l*, pg. 925
BCV SOCIAL LLC—See RateGain Technologies Inc.; *U.S. Private*, pg. 3357
BEANSTALK—See Omnicom Group Inc.; *U.S. Public*, pg. 1577
BEAUTYCOM SAS—See FemTec Health, Inc.; *U.S. Private*, pg. 1494
BEEBY CLARK + MEYLER; *U.S. Private*, pg. 513
BEE-LINE COMMUNICATIONS; *U.S. Private*, pg. 513
BE FOUND ONLINE; *U.S. Private*, pg. 503
BEIJING YUANZHIMENG ADVERTISING CO., LTD—See HS Ad Inc.; *Int'l*, pg. 3502
BELLSYSTEM24, INC.—See Bain Capital, LP; *U.S. Private*, pg. 436
BENCHMARK INTERNET GROUP, LLC; *U.S. Private*, pg. 524
THE BERRY COMPANY LLC - CINCINNATI—See The Berry Company LLC; *U.S. Private*, pg. 3994
THE BERRY COMPANY LLC - INGLEWOOD—See The Berry Company LLC; *U.S. Private*, pg. 3994
THE BERRY COMPANY LLC; *U.S. Private*, pg. 3994
BEST RATE REFERRALS—See Digital Media Solutions, Inc.; *U.S. Private*, pg. 663
BEYONDROI, LLC; *U.S. Private*, pg. 548
B!FERRAZ; *Int'l*, pg. 783
BIG SEA, INC.; *U.S. Private*, pg. 554
BILENDI SA—See Bilendi SA; *Int'l*, pg. 1023
BINTAN RESORTS INTERNATIONAL PTE. LTD.—See Gallant Venture Ltd.; *Int'l*, pg. 2874
BIOFUELS MARKETING, INC.—See Aemetis, Inc.; *U.S. Public*, pg. 52
BITAUTO HOLDINGS LIMITED; *Int'l*, pg. 1049
BJC MARKETING COMPANY LIMITED—See Berli Jucker Public Co. Ltd.; *Int'l*, pg. 985
BLACK RETAIL; *U.S. Private*, pg. 572
BLITZ AGENCY; *U.S. Private*, pg. 582
BLUEBIRD INTERACTIVE; *U.S. Private*, pg. 596
BLUE CORONA; *U.S. Private*, pg. 586
BLUE MOON WORKS, INC.; *U.S. Private*, pg. 589
BLUERUSH DIGITAL MEDIA CORP—See BlueRush Inc.; *Int'l*, pg. 1072
BLUERUSH INC.; *Int'l*, pg. 1072
BOLA WEBINFORMATION GMBH—See Better Collective A/S; *Int'l*, pg. 1003
BOND BRAND LOYALTY INC.; *Int'l*, pg. 1105
BONDSPOT S.A.—See Gielda Papierow Wartosciowych w Warszawie S.A.; *Int'l*, pg. 2968
BONFIRE MARKETING COMPANY—See Thesis, Inc.; *U.S. Private*, pg. 4143
BONNIER ANNONS AB—See Bonnier AB; *Int'l*, pg. 1108
BOOST REWARDS—See Boost Technologies, LLC; *U.S. Private*, pg. 616
THE BOSTON CONSULTING GROUP - ATHENS—See The Boston Consulting Group, Inc.; *U.S. Private*, pg. 3997
THE BOSTON GROUP, INC.—See Isovera, LLC; *U.S. Private*, pg. 2146
BOSTON LIMITED—See Cerberus Capital Management, L.P.; *U.S. Private*, pg. 839
BPATT LLC—See Agital Holdings, LLC; *U.S. Private*, pg. 128
BRADLEY DIRECT SERVICES—See W.C. Bradley Co.; *U.S. Private*, pg. 4419
BRADY MARKETING COMPANY; *U.S. Private*, pg. 633
BRAFTON, INCORPORATED; *U.S. Private*, pg. 633
BRANDBEE HOLDING AB; *Int'l*, pg. 1139
BRAND CONNECTIONS, LLC—See Advantage Sales & Marketing, LLC; *U.S. Private*, pg. 95
BRANDEXTRACT, LLC; *U.S. Private*, pg. 637
BRAND LEARNING LLC—See Accenture plc; *Int'l*, pg. 87
BRAND LOYALTY BV—See Bread Financial Holdings Inc.; *U.S. Public*, pg. 381
BRAND LOYALTY FRANCE SARL—See Bread Financial Holdings Inc.; *U.S. Public*, pg. 381
BRAND LOYALTY JAPAN KK—See Bread Financial Holdings Inc.; *U.S. Public*, pg. 381
BRAND LOYALTY LIMITED—See Bread Financial Holdings Inc.; *U.S. Public*, pg. 381
BRAND UP, LLC; *U.S. Private*, pg. 637
BREAKAWAY HOLDINGS, LLC—See Insight Venture Management, LLC; *U.S. Private*, pg. 2088
BREAKAWAY HOLDINGS, LLC—See Stone Point Capital LLC; *U.S. Private*, pg. 3822
BREAKTHROUGH PHYSICAL THERAPY MARKETING LLC; *U.S. Private*, pg. 643
BREWER DIRECT, INC.; *U.S. Private*, pg. 647
BRIDGE INTERNATIONAL CORP.; *Int'l*, pg. 1152
BRIGHTPOOL LIMITED—See IG Group Holdings plc; *Int'l*, pg. 3601
BRIGHTSOURCE LIMITED—See Arsenal Capital Management LP; *U.S. Private*, pg. 338
BRIGHTWAVE MARKETING, LLC—See Ansira Partners, Inc.; *U.S. Private*, pg. 285
BTU ANALYTICS, LLC—See FactSet Research Systems Inc.; *U.S. Public*, pg. 819

N.A.I.C.S. INDEX
541613 — MARKETING CONSULTIN...

BUFFALO GROUPE LLC—See Troon Golf L.L.C.; *U.S. Private*, pg. 4242
BUILDER HOMESITE, INC.; *U.S. Private*, pg. 681
BULLDOG MEDIA GROUP, INC.; *U.S. Private*, pg. 684
BULLDOG SOLUTIONS EUROPE—See AEA Investors LP; *U.S. Private*, pg. 114
BULLDOG SOLUTIONS, INC.—See AEA Investors LP; *U.S. Private*, pg. 114
BURTON MCCALL LIMITED—See Bollin Group Ltd.; *Int'l*, pg. 1103
BYMAX CORP.; *Int'l*, pg. 1235
CABIC CO., LTD.—See Bain Capital, LP; *U.S. Private*, pg. 433
CADOOZ REWARDS GMBH—See Euronet Worldwide, Inc.; *U.S. Public*, pg. 798
CALIFORNIA MARKETING ASSOCIATES, INC.—See Ivystone Group, LLC; *U.S. Private*, pg. 2152
THE CAMBRIDGE GROUP, INC.—See Brookfield Corporation; *Int'l*, pg. 1180
THE CAMBRIDGE GROUP, INC.—See Elliott Management Corporation; *U.S. Private*, pg. 1372
THE CAMPUS SPECIAL, LLC—See Chegg Inc.; *U.S. Public*, pg. 483
CANFOR GEORGIA-PACIFIC JAPAN CORPORATION—See Canfor Corporation; *Int'l*, pg. 1291
CANFOR GEORGIA-PACIFIC JAPAN CORPORATION—See Koch Industries, Inc.; *U.S. Private*, pg. 2327
CANIDIUM, LLC; *U.S. Private*, pg. 734
CAPACITYGRID UK LTD.—See Bain Capital, LP; *U.S. Private*, pg. 433
CAPITAL CITY CONSULTING, LLC; *U.S. Private*, pg. 739
CAPTURE; *Int'l*, pg. 1318
CARLSON MARKETING CANADA—See Aimia Inc.; *Int'l*, pg. 233
CARLSON MARKETING GROUP (AUST.) PTY. LIMITED—See Aimia Inc.; *Int'l*, pg. 233
CARLSON MARKETING GROUP HK LTD.—See Aimia Inc.; *Int'l*, pg. 233
CARLSON MARKETING GROUP INTERACT—See Aimia Inc.; *Int'l*, pg. 233
CARLSON MARKETING GROUP LTD.—See Aimia Inc.; *Int'l*, pg. 233
CARLSON MARKETING GROUP SDN. BHD.—See Aimia Inc.; *Int'l*, pg. 233
CARLSON MARKETING GROUP—See Aimia Inc.; *Int'l*, pg. 233
CARLSON MARKETING GROUP—See Aimia Inc.; *Int'l*, pg. 233
CARLSON MARKETING GROUP—See Aimia Inc.; *Int'l*, pg. 233
CARLSON MARKETING GROUP—See Aimia Inc.; *Int'l*, pg. 233
CARLSON MARKETING—See Aimia Inc.; *Int'l*, pg. 233
CARNEGIE DARTLET LLC; *U.S. Private*, pg. 766
CASEY'S MARKETING COMPANY—See Casey's General Stores, Inc.; *U.S. Public*, pg. 446
CATALINA MARKETING DEUTSCHLAND GMBH—See Berkshire Partners LLC; *U.S. Private*, pg. 534
CATALINA UK LTD.—See Berkshire Partners LLC; *U.S. Private*, pg. 534
CB NEPTUNE HOLDINGS, LLC—See Charlesbank Capital Partners, LLC; *U.S. Private*, pg. 854
CBS COLLEGIATE SPORTS PROPERTIES INC.—See National Amusements, Inc.; *U.S. Private*, pg. 2840
CBS TELEVISION DISTRIBUTION—See National Amusements, Inc.; *U.S. Private*, pg. 2840
CDG CO., LTD.; *Int'l*, pg. 1370
CDN COMUNICACAO CORPORATIVA LTDA.—See Omnicom Group Inc.; *U.S. Public*, pg. 1585
CELEMIAB GROUP AB—See Bure Equity AB; *Int'l*, pg. 1221
CELLTRUST CORPORATION; *U.S. Private*, pg. 807
CERES INC.; *Int'l*, pg. 1422
CFI HOSPITALITY GROUP, INC.—See Central Florida Investments Inc.; *U.S. Private*, pg. 820
CFN ENTERPRISES INC.; *U.S. Public*, pg. 477
CGM MARKETING INC.—See Digital Garage, Inc.; *Int'l*, pg. 2121
CHALET LIFESTYLES, INC.; *U.S. Private*, pg. 845
CHANDLER GROUP, INC.; *U.S. Private*, pg. 848
CHANGING OUR WORLD—See Omnicom Group Inc.; *U.S. Public*, pg. 1579
CHANNELNET; *U.S. Private*, pg. 849
CHASE DESIGN, LLC—See The Interpublic Group of Companies, Inc.; *U.S. Public*, pg. 2102
CHEETAH DIGITAL, INC.—See Vector Capital Management, L.P.; *U.S. Private*, pg. 4350
CHESHIRES OF NOTTINGHAM—See Headlam Group plc; *Int'l*, pg. 3301
CHINA EMEDIA HOLDINGS CORPORATION; *Int'l*, pg. 1499
CHINA MEDIA (SHANGHAI) MANAGEMENT CONSULTING COMPANY LIMITED—See Ebiquity plc; *Int'l*, pg. 2285
CHINA PARENTING NETWORK HOLDINGS LIMITED; *Int'l*, pg. 1539
CHINASOFT INTERNATIONAL (GUANG ZHOU) INFORMATION TECHNOLOGY LIMITED—See Chinasoft International Ltd.; *Int'l*, pg. 1568
CHINASOFT INTERNATIONAL INC.—See Chinasoft International Ltd.; *Int'l*, pg. 1568
CHINASOFT RESOURCE (INTERNATIONAL) LIMITED—See Chinasoft International Ltd.; *Int'l*, pg. 1569
CHIRPIFY, INC.; *U.S. Private*, pg. 887
CHIZCOMM LTD.—See Kartoon Studios, Inc.; *U.S. Public*, pg. 1214
CIOCIOLA COMMUNICATIONS, INC.; *U.S. Private*, pg. 899
CIRQIT S.A.—See HH Global Group Limited; *Int'l*, pg. 3378
CITIGATE GUNPOWDER S.R.L.—See Clayton, Dubilier & Rice, LLC; *U.S. Private*, pg. 924
CITIZEN, INC.; *U.S. Private*, pg. 902
CITIZENS RESOURCE DEVELOPMENT CORPORATION, INC.—See Citizens Energy Group; *U.S. Private*, pg. 903
CJ MARKETING PROPRIETARY LIMITED—See Dis-Chem Pharmacies Ltd.; *Int'l*, pg. 2130
CLARUS COMMERCE LLC—See Marlin Equity Partners, LLC; *U.S. Private*, pg. 2584
CLASSYAUTO.COM; *U.S. Private*, pg. 917
CLAY MORE INNOVATION LAB CO., LTD.—See AP (Thailand) Public Company Limited; *Int'l*, pg. 499
CLEAR NIGHT GROUP—See Evening Post Publishing Co.; *U.S. Private*, pg. 1436
CL HOLDINGS INC.; *Int'l*, pg. 1640
CLICK SALES INC.—See Keynetics, Inc.; *U.S. Private*, pg. 2294
CLICKSTOP INC.; *U.S. Private*, pg. 942
CLIENT ATTRACTION LLC; *U.S. Private*, pg. 943
CLM LLC—See Quad/Graphics, Inc.; *U.S. Public*, pg. 1744
CLOUD MELLOW CONSULTING LTD. CO.; *U.S. Private*, pg. 946
CMC ENERGY SERVICES, INC.; *U.S. Private*, pg. 950
CMG HOLDINGS GROUP, INC.; *U.S. Public*, pg. 518
CMIC ASHFIELD CO., LTD.—See CMIC Holdings Co., Ltd.; *Int'l*, pg. 1670
CNI RESEARCH LTD; *Int'l*, pg. 1676
COCREATIV CORP.—See Frontenac Company LLC; *U.S. Private*, pg. 1613
CODEMEDIA SA—See Grupa SMT S.A.; *Int'l*, pg. 3117
CODIGO LLC—See The Jordan Company, L.P.; *U.S. Private*, pg. 4062
COMENITY CAPITAL BANK—See Bread Financial Holdings, Inc.; *U.S. Public*, pg. 381
COMMOTION PROMOTIONS, LTD.; *U.S. Private*, pg. 987
COMMUNICATIONS STRATEGIES, INC.; *U.S. Private*, pg. 988
THE COMPLEX SALE, INC.—See Sales Performance International, LLC; *U.S. Private*, pg. 3532
COMSCORE, INC.; *U.S. Public*, pg. 561
COMUNICAD, LLC—See Ruder Finn Group, Inc.; *U.S. Private*, pg. 3501
CONCENTRIX INTERNATIONAL SERVICES EUROPE B.V.—See Concentrix Corporation; *U.S. Public*, pg. 564
CONE—See Omnicom Group Inc.; *U.S. Public*, pg. 1579
CONNECT MARKETING, INC.; *U.S. Private*, pg. 1014
CONSULTANTS2GO; *U.S. Private*, pg. 1025
CONSUMER CAPITAL GROUP INC.; *U.S. Private*, pg. 1025
CONVERSEEN, INC.; *U.S. Private*, pg. 1035
CONVERSEON NORDICS—See Converseon, Inc.; *U.S. Private*, pg. 1035
CONVERTEO SAS—See ADLPartner SA; *Int'l*, pg. 151
CORE FOODSERVICE—See Acosta, Inc.; *U.S. Private*, pg. 64
COREGMEDIA—See Trancos, Inc.; *U.S. Private*, pg. 4205
CORE STRATEGY GROUP; *U.S. Private*, pg. 1049
COSMIC COMMUNICATION SA—See Altavia S.A.; *Int'l*, pg. 388
COTTON INCORPORATED CONSUMER MARKETING HEADQUARTERS—See Cotton Incorporated; *U.S. Private*, pg. 1064
CPALEAD, LLC; *U.S. Private*, pg. 1080
CREATE GROUP NYC, LLC—See Clayton, Dubilier & Rice, LLC; *U.S. Private*, pg. 927
CREATING RESULTS, LLC-STRATEGIC MARKETING; *U.S. Private*, pg. 1087
CREATIVE COMMUNICATION LTD.—See Advanced Chemical Industries Limited; *Int'l*, pg. 158
CREATIVE SALES INC.; *U.S. Private*, pg. 1090
CRIMSON CONSULTING GROUP, INC.; *U.S. Private*, pg. 1100
CRISP MARKETING; *U.S. Private*, pg. 1101
CRM COMPANY GROUP SA; *Int'l*, pg. 1851
CROSS CLICK MEDIA INC.; *U.S. Private*, pg. 1104
CROSSMARK AUSTRALIA PTY. LTD. - MELBOURNE—See Acosta, Inc.; *U.S. Private*, pg. 64
CROSSMARK AUSTRALIA PTY. LTD.—See Acosta, Inc.; *U.S. Private*, pg. 64
CROSSMARK, INC.—See Acosta, Inc.; *U.S. Private*, pg. 64
CS&S CYBER RESOURCES SOFTWARE TECHNOLOGY (TIANJIN) CO., LTD.—See Chinasoft International Ltd.; *Int'l*, pg. 1568
CUSTOMER ACQUISITION SPECIALISTS OF AMERICA, INC.—See Energy Professionals, LLC; *U.S. Private*, pg. 1396
CUSTOMER COMMUNICATIONS GROUP, INC. (CCG); *U.S. Private*, pg. 1130
CUSTOMER CONNEXX, LLC—See ALT5 Sigma Corporation; *U.S. Public*, pg. 85
CUSTOMERSTREAM; *U.S. Private*, pg. 1130
CYDCOR, INC.; *U.S. Private*, pg. 1134
D3 LOGIC, INC.; *U.S. Private*, pg. 1143
DADI INTERNATIONAL GROUP LIMITED; *Int'l*, pg. 1905
DAILY INCHES, INC.—See Upland Software, Inc.; *U.S. Public*, pg. 2264
DAIRY MARKETING SERVICES, LLC—See Dairy Farmers of America, Inc.; *U.S. Private*, pg. 1146
DARKBLUE.COM PTY LIMITED—See Enero Group Limited; *Int'l*, pg. 2423
THE DATABASE MARKETING AGENCY LLC—See The Riverside Company; *U.S. Private*, pg. 4110
DATABASE MARKETING GROUP; *U.S. Private*, pg. 1164
DATACON NORTH AMERICA, INC.—See BE Semiconductor Industries N.V.; *Int'l*, pg. 931
DATAMYX LLC—See Deluxe Corporation; *U.S. Public*, pg. 652
DATANYZE, LLC—See ZoomInfo Technologies Inc.; *U.S. Public*, pg. 2411
DATORAMA GMBH—See Salesforce, Inc.; *U.S. Public*, pg. 1837
DAVID KURLAN & ASSOCIATES, INC.; *U.S. Private*, pg. 1170
DAYMON WORLDWIDE INC.—See Bain Capital, LP; *U.S. Private*, pg. 439
DAY VISION MARKETING; *U.S. Private*, pg. 1176
DBS ADMINISTRATION PTY LIMITED—See Enero Group Limited; *Int'l*, pg. 2423
DEALERON, INC.; *U.S. Private*, pg. 1182
DEANHOUSTON, INC.; *U.S. Private*, pg. 1185
DEBOCK SALES & MARKETING LTD.; *Int'l*, pg. 1998
DEG; *U.S. Private*, pg. 1191
DEI WORLDWIDE, INC.; *U.S. Private*, pg. 1191
DELIVER MEDIA; *U.S. Private*, pg. 1197
DELUXE MARKETING, INC. (DMI); *U.S. Private*, pg. 1202
DEMANDBASE, INC.; *U.S. Private*, pg. 1203
DEMANDDRIVE, LLC; *U.S. Private*, pg. 1203
DEMANDGEN AG—See BDO USA, LLP; *U.S. Private*, pg. 501
DEMANDGEN AUSTRALIA PTY LTD.—See BDO USA, LLP; *U.S. Private*, pg. 501
DEMANDGEN INTERNATIONAL, INC.—See BDO USA, LLP; *U.S. Private*, pg. 501
DEMANDGEN INTERNATIONAL—See BDO USA, LLP; *U.S. Private*, pg. 501
DEMANDGEN UK—See BDO USA, LLP; *U.S. Private*, pg. 501
DENNY MOUNTAIN MEDIA, LLC—See RedCloud Consulting Inc.; *U.S. Private*, pg. 3377
DENTSU AEGIS NETWORK (DEUTSCHLAND) GMBH—See Dentsu Group Inc.; *Int'l*, pg. 2036
DENTSU DIGITAL DRIVE INC.—See Dentsu Group Inc.; *Int'l*, pg. 2034
DENTSU DIGITAL INC—See Dentsu Group Inc.; *Int'l*, pg. 2034
DENTSU, SUDLER & HENNESSEY INC.—See Dentsu Group Inc.; *Int'l*, pg. 2039
DERFLAN INC; *U.S. Private*, pg. 1209
DERSE INC.; *U.S. Private*, pg. 1210
DESIGNONE JAPAN, INC.; *Int'l*, pg. 2045
DGM INDIA INTERNET MARKETING PRIVATE LIMITED—See Dentsu Group Inc.; *Int'l*, pg. 2038
DIAMANT ART CORP.; *Int'l*, pg. 2104
DICK JONES COMMUNICATIONS, LLC—See Renovus Capital Partners; *U.S. Private*, pg. 3399
DIETHELM & CO. LTD.—See Diethelm Keller Holding Limited; *Int'l*, pg. 2117
DIGITAL AIR STRIKE INC.; *U.S. Private*, pg. 1229
DIGITAL BALANCE AUSTRALIA PTY. LIMITED—See Ebiquity plc; *Int'l*, pg. 2285
DIGITAL EVOLUTION GROUP LLC—See Dentsu Group Inc.; *Int'l*, pg. 2037
DIGITAL FINANCIAL NETWORK INC.—See NewGround Resources; *U.S. Private*, pg. 2915
DIGITAL MEDIA ENTERPRISES LLC—See Chicken Soup for the Soul Entertainment, Inc.; *U.S. Public*, pg. 488
DIGITAL RIVER GMBH—See Siris Capital Group, LLC; *U.S. Private*, pg. 3672
DIGITAL RIVER, INC.—See Siris Capital Group, LLC; *U.S. Private*, pg. 3672
DIGITAL RIVER IRELAND LIMITED—See Siris Capital Group, LLC; *U.S. Private*, pg. 3672
DIGITREE GROUP S.A.; *Int'l*, pg. 2124
DIRECT AGENTS, INC.; *U.S. Private*, pg. 1234
DIRECT CHECK REDEMPTION CENTER, INC.; *U.S. Private*, pg. 1234
DIRECT MARKETING MIX, INC.; *Int'l*, pg. 2130
THE DIRECT RESPONSE GROUP, LLC; *U.S. Private*, pg. 4021
DIRECT SERVICES GUTERSLOH GMBH—See Bertelsmann SE & Co. KGaA; *Int'l*, pg. 992
DISCOVERORG, LLC—See TA Associates, Inc.; *U.S. Private*, pg. 3915

DIVERSIFIED MARKETING GROUP, INC.; *U.S. Private*, pg. 1243
DJM SALES & MARKETING; *U.S. Private*, pg. 1246
DKSH (CAMBODIA) LTD.—See Diethelm Keller Holding Limited; *Int'l*, pg. 2116
DKSH (FRANCE) S.A.—See Diethelm Keller Holding Limited; *Int'l*, pg. 2116
DKSH GMBH—See Diethelm Keller Holding Limited; *Int'l*, pg. 2116
DKSH GREAT BRITAIN LTD.—See Diethelm Keller Holding Limited; *Int'l*, pg. 2116
DKSH GUAM, INC.—See Diethelm Keller Holding Limited; *Int'l*, pg. 2116
DKSH HONG KONG LTD.—See Diethelm Keller Holding Limited; *Int'l*, pg. 2116
DKSH LOGISTICS LTD.—See Diethelm Keller Holding Limited; *Int'l*, pg. 2116
DKSH MANAGEMENT PTE LTD.—See Diethelm Keller Holding Limited; *Int'l*, pg. 2116
DKSH NEW ZEALAND LTD.—See Diethelm Keller Holding Limited; *Int'l*, pg. 2116
DKSH PHILIPPINES INC.—See Diethelm Keller Holding Limited; *Int'l*, pg. 2116
DKSH SINGAPORE PTE LTD.—See Diethelm Keller Holding Limited; *Int'l*, pg. 2117
DKSH VIETNAM CO. LTD.—See Diethelm Keller Holding Limited; *Int'l*, pg. 2117
DMA MEDIA LTD.; *Int'l*, pg. 2142
DMB DIRECT MAIL BIEL-BIENNE AG—See Die Schweizerische Post AG; *Int'l*, pg. 2112
DOCCHECK AG; *Int'l*, pg. 2153
DOMAIN ACTIVE PTY LIMITED—See Enero Group Limited; *Int'l*, pg. 2423
DO MY OWN PEST CONTROL; *U.S. Private*, pg. 1250
DOTDIGITAL EMEA LIMITED—See dotdigital Group PLC; *Int'l*, pg. 2180
DOTDIGITAL POLAND SP. Z O.O—See dotdigital Group PLC; *Int'l*, pg. 2180
DOUBLEPOSITIVE MARKETING GROUP, INC.—See Aquiline Capital Partners LLC; *U.S. Private*, pg. 304
DOUBLE-TEAM BUSINESS PLANS LLC; *U.S. Private*, pg. 1266
DOWA HD EUROPE GMBH—See Dowa Holdings Co., Ltd.; *Int'l*, pg. 2182
DOWA INTERNATIONAL CORPORATION—See Dowa Holdings Co., Ltd.; *Int'l*, pg. 2183
DREAM INCUBATOR (VIETNAM) JOINT STOCK COMPANY—See Dream Incubator Inc.; *Int'l*, pg. 2202
D&R LATHIAN LLC; *U.S. Private*, pg. 1138
DRUPAL CONNECT; *U.S. Private*, pg. 1280
DSTILLERY; *U.S. Private*, pg. 1282
DU-ART FILM LABS, INC.; *U.S. Public*, pg. 689
DVL SMITH LIMITED—See Enero Group Limited; *Int'l*, pg. 2423
DYNAMIT; *U.S. Private*, pg. 1299
EAB GLOBAL, INC.; *U.S. Private*, pg. 1308
EBIQUITY GERMANY GMBH—See Ebiquity plc; *Int'l*, pg. 2285
EBIQUITY ITALIA S.R.L.—See Ebiquity plc; *Int'l*, pg. 2285
EBIQUITY PTE. LIMITED—See Ebiquity plc; *Int'l*, pg. 2285
EBIQUITY RUSSIA OOO—See Ebiquity plc; *Int'l*, pg. 2285
EBIQUITY SAS—See Ebiquity plc; *Int'l*, pg. 2285
EBQUICKSTART, LLC; *U.S. Private*, pg. 1324
EBSCO INDUSTRIES, INC. - PUBLISHER PROMOTION AND FULFILLMENT DIVISION—See EBSCO Industries, Inc.; *U.S. Private*, pg. 1325
ECA MARKETING, INC.—See Aon plc; *Int'l*, pg. 496
ECOCASH HOLDINGS ZIMBABWE LIMITED; *Int'l*, pg. 2294
ECOMMERCE PARTNERS; *U.S. Private*, pg. 1329
E-CONSULTANCY.COM LIMITED—See Centaur Media plc; *Int'l*, pg. 1402
ECO WORLD INTERNATIONAL MARKETING SDN BHD—See Eco World International Berhad; *Int'l*, pg. 2293
E.DIALOG GMBH—See E.ON SE; *Int'l*, pg. 2260
EDOT LLC—See CyberAdvisors, Inc.; *U.S. Private*, pg. 1133
EDUTUTOR OY—See BHG Group AB; *Int'l*, pg. 1014
EDWARD KELLER (PHILIPPINES) INC.—See Diethelm Keller Holding Limited; *Int'l*, pg. 2116
EFFICIENT FRONTIER TECHNOLOGY INDIA PRIVATE LIMITED—See Adobe Inc.; *U.S. Public*, pg. 42
EGUMBALL, INC.; *U.S. Private*, pg. 1346
THE EISEN AGENCY; *U.S. Private*, pg. 4025
EI-TECHNOLOGIES FRANCE SAS—See Cognizant Technology Solutions Corporation; *U.S. Public*, pg. 524
EJECTA MARKETING LTD.; *Int'l*, pg. 2337
ELECTRIC ARTISTS, INC.; *U.S. Private*, pg. 1352
ELECTRONIC ENTERTAINMENT DESIGN & RESEARCH—See The NPD Group, Inc.; *U.S. Private*, pg. 4085
ELEPRENEURS U.S., LLC—See Sharing Services Global Corporation; *U.S. Public*, pg. 1873
ELITE MEETINGS INTERNATIONAL, LLC—See Blackstone Inc.; *U.S. Public*, pg. 353
ELIXIRR INTERNATIONAL PLC; *Int'l*, pg. 2363
ELM STREET TECHNOLOGY LLC; *U.S. Private*, pg. 1376
EMI STRATEGIC MARKETING, INC.; *U.S. Private*, pg. 1382

EMMA, INC.; *U.S. Private*, pg. 1383
EMNOS GMBH—See Clayton, Dubilier & Rice, LLC; *U.S. Private*, pg. 926
EMNOS IBERIA S.L—See American Express Company; *U.S. Public*, pg. 102
EMNOS S.A.R.L—See American Express Company; *U.S. Public*, pg. 102
EMNOS UK LTD.—See American Express Company; *U.S. Public*, pg. 102
EMNOS USA CORP.—See American Express Company; *U.S. Public*, pg. 102
ENCORE ASSOCIATES INC.; *U.S. Private*, pg. 1390
ENERGO GROUP LIMITED—See Enero Group Limited; *Int'l*, pg. 2424
ENGIE ENERGY MARKETING NA, INC.—See ENGIE SA; *Int'l*, pg. 2428
E-NOR EMEA—See Dentsu Group Inc.; *Int'l*, pg. 2037
E-NOR LLC—See Dentsu Group Inc.; *Int'l*, pg. 2037
ENSTAR HOLDINGS (US) LLC—See Enstar Group Limited; *Int'l*, pg. 2448
ENVIROSELL JAPAN INC.—See Cross Marketing Group Inc.; *Int'l*, pg. 1856
ENVISION TECHNOLOGY MARKETING GROUP, INC.; *U.S. Private*, pg. 1410
E.ON KUNDSUPPORT SVERIGE AB—See E.ON SE; *Int'l*, pg. 2255
EPROFESSIONAL GMBH—See Axel Springer SE; *Int'l*, pg. 766
ERUPTR LLC—See H.I.G. Capital, LLC; *U.S. Private*, pg. 1829
ES NETWORKS CO., LTD.; *Int'l*, pg. 2500
ESOLUTIONS GROUP—See GHD Group Pty Ltd.; *Int'l*, pg. 2959
THE E-TAILING GROUP, INC.—See Astound Commerce Corp.; *U.S. Private*, pg. 361
EULER HERMES RATING DEUTSCHLAND GMBH—See Allianz SE; *Int'l*, pg. 353
EUROPEAN INVESTOR RELATIONS SA; *Int'l*, pg. 2556
EVENT ELITE PRODUCTION AND PROMOTION LIMITED—See ManpowerGroup Inc.; *U.S. Public*, pg. 1357
EVERYDAYFAMILY, INC.; *U.S. Private*, pg. 1441
EVERYMUNDO LLC—See PROS Holdings, Inc.; *U.S. Public*, pg. 1728
EVERYTHING BLOCKCHAIN, INC.; *U.S. Public*, pg. 802
EVIEW 360; *U.S. Private*, pg. 1441
EVIEW 360—See Eview 360; *U.S. Private*, pg. 1441
EVN UMWELTHOLDING UND BETRIEBS-GMBH—See EVN AG; *Int'l*, pg. 2571
EVOLUTION ROAD, LLC—See Clayton, Dubilier & Rice, LLC; *U.S. Private*, pg. 924
EXACT DATA CONSUMERBASE LLC—See Exact Data, LLC; *U.S. Private*, pg. 1445
EXCELSIOR INTEGRATED, LLC.—See Excelsior Printing Company; *U.S. Private*, pg. 1446
EXECUTIVE COMMUNICATIONS, INC.; *U.S. Private*, pg. 1447
EXPERIAN AS—See Experian plc; *Int'l*, pg. 2586
EXPRESS MARKETS, INC.—See Eli Lilly & Company; *U.S. Public*, pg. 733
EXTOLE INC.; *U.S. Private*, pg. 1452
EYELEVEL, INC.—See HH Global Group Limited; *Int'l*, pg. 3378
EYELEVEL RETAIL SOLUTIONS CONSULTORIA LTDA—See HH Global Group Limited; *Int'l*, pg. 3378
EYELEVEL SOLUTIONS LTD.—See HH Global Group Limited; *Int'l*, pg. 3378
EYELEVEL S.R.O.—See HH Global Group Limited; *Int'l*, pg. 3378
FABULOUS.COM PTY LIMITED—See Enero Group Limited; *Int'l*, pg. 2423
FACILITATE DIGITAL HOLDINGS LIMITED—See Adslot Ltd.; *Int'l*, pg. 154
FACTORY 360; *U.S. Private*, pg. 1460
FANTEX, INC.; *U.S. Private*, pg. 1473
FARADAY RESEARCH LLP—See StoneX Group Inc.; *U.S. Public*, pg. 1952
FAST APPROACH INC.—See Planet Green Holdings Corp.; *U.S. Public*, pg. 1697
FAST TRACK SAILING LIMITED—See Wasserman Media Group, LLC; *U.S. Private*, pg. 4450
F.E. BORDING A/S; *Int'l*, pg. 2596
THE FENTON GROUP; *U.S. Private*, pg. 4028
FINDMYCOMPANY.COM LLC; *U.S. Private*, pg. 1509
FINGERPAINT MARKETING, INC.—See Knox Lane LP; *U.S. Private*, pg. 2324
FINIBANCO ANGOLA, S.A.—See Access Corporation; *Int'l*, pg. 89
FIRST FOODS GROUP, INC.; *U.S. Public*, pg. 844
FIRST GENERATION; *U.S. Private*, pg. 1519
FIRST GENERATION—See First Generation; *U.S. Private*, pg. 1519
FIRST GENERATION—See First Generation; *U.S. Private*, pg. 1519
FIRST IMAGE MARKETING, INC.—See PetMed Express, Inc.; *U.S. Public*, pg. 1678
FIRST IMPRESSION INTERACTIVE, LLC; *U.S. Private*, pg. 1520

FISCHERAPPELT AG; *Int'l*, pg. 2692
FISHBOWL MARKETING; *U.S. Private*, pg. 1533
FISHER & PAYKEL DO BRASIL LTDA—See Fisher & Paykel Healthcare Corporation Limited; *Int'l*, pg. 2693
FLEXIUM INTERCONNECT AMERICA, LLC—See Flexium Interconnect, Inc.; *Int'l*, pg. 2705
FONTIS SOLUTIONS, INC.—See Deluxe Corporation; *U.S. Public*, pg. 652
FOSINA MARKETING GROUP—See Digital Media Solutions, Inc.; *U.S. Public*, pg. 663
FRANCHISE BANCORP CONSULTING LTD.—See Franchise Bancorp Inc.; *Int'l*, pg. 2760
FRANKLIN INVESTMENT ADVISORY SERVICES, LLC—See Franklin Resources, Inc.; *U.S. Public*, pg. 880
FREEXMEDIA GMBH—See freenet AG; *Int'l*, pg. 2770
FRESH CONSULTING LLC; *U.S. Private*, pg. 1609
FRONTIER DIGITAL MARKETING CO., LTD.—See Hakuhodo DY Holdings Incorporated; *Int'l*, pg. 3221
FRONTLINE SELLING, LLC; *U.S. Private*, pg. 1616
FRUITION.NET; *U.S. Private*, pg. 1617
FS DEVELOPMENT INVESTMENT HOLDINGS; *Int'l*, pg. 2797
FUELFX, LLC; *U.S. Private*, pg. 1619
FULLSIX S.P.A.; *Int'l*, pg. 2843
FUSE8 DELETE—See Fuse 8 Group Ltd; *Int'l*, pg. 2848
FUSE8 RUSSIA—See Fuse 8 Group Ltd; *Int'l*, pg. 2848
FUSION92; *U.S. Private*, pg. 1626
FUTUREDONTICS, INC.; *U.S. Private*, pg. 1627
GAINCLIENTS, INC.; *U.S. Public*, pg. 894
GAP INTELLIGENCE; *U.S. Private*, pg. 1641
GEDEON RICHTER (SCHWEIZ) AG—See Gedeon Richter Plc.; *Int'l*, pg. 2909
GEN3 MARKETING LLC—See Comvest Group Holdings LLC; *U.S. Private*, pg. 1007
GENERALI SALES PROMOTION GMBH—See Assicurazioni Generali S.p.A.; *Int'l*, pg. 646
GENERATE, INC.—See News Corporation; *U.S. Public*, pg. 1518
GENEVA SUPPLY, INC.; *U.S. Private*, pg. 1670
GEN MEDIA PARTNERS LLC; *U.S. Private*, pg. 1660
GEORESULTS, INC.—See ShareTracker, LLC; *U.S. Private*, pg. 3626
GEORGE P. JOHNSON BRASIL LTDA.—See Project: Worldwide, Inc.; *U.S. Private*, pg. 3281
GEORGE P. JOHNSON (UK) LTD—See Project: Worldwide, Inc.; *U.S. Private*, pg. 3281
GIANT PARTNERS; *U.S. Private*, pg. 1695
GIESECKE+DEVRIENT ADVANCE52 GMBH—See Giesecke & Devrient GmbH; *Int'l*, pg. 2970
GIGGLE, INC.; *U.S. Private*, pg. 1697
GIG WORKS INC.; *Int'l*, pg. 2971
GIIR AMERICA INC.—See HS Ad Inc.; *Int'l*, pg. 3502
GIIR GERMANY GMBH—See HS Ad Inc.; *Int'l*, pg. 3502
GISTAR INNOVATION INC.—See FTGroup Co Ltd.; *Int'l*, pg. 2800
GLAZER-KENNEDY INSIDER'S CIRCLE, LLC; *U.S. Private*, pg. 1708
GLOBRANDS GROUP LTD.; *Int'l*, pg. 3008
GLOSSOM, INC.—See Gree Inc.; *Int'l*, pg. 3069
GO INSPIRE GROUP LIMITED—See Xerox Holdings Corporation; *U.S. Public*, pg. 2386
GOLOG HOLDING S.A.; *Int'l*, pg. 3036
GOOD SOLUTIONS GROUP; *U.S. Private*, pg. 1738
GREENLIGHT DIGITAL LIMITED—See Brave Bison Group plc; *Int'l*, pg. 1141
GREEN ZEBRA MEDIA; *U.S. Private*, pg. 1774
GRIFFIN INTERNATIONAL COMPANIES; *U.S. Private*, pg. 1788
GROWENS S.P.A.; *Int'l*, pg. 3112
THE GROWTH PARTNERSHIP—See Engineered Tax Services, Inc; *U.S. Private*, pg. 1398
GS NETVISION CO., LTD.—See GS Holdings Corp.; *Int'l*, pg. 3142
GUOEN HOLDINGS LIMITED; *Int'l*, pg. 3186
HAINES & COMPANY, INC. - AMERICALIST DIVISION—See Haines & Company, Inc.; *U.S. Private*, pg. 1840
HAI-O MARKETING. SDN. BHD.—See Hai-O Enterprise Berhad; *Int'l*, pg. 3209
HAMPTON ROADS ECONOMIC DEVELOPMENT ALLIANCE; *U.S. Private*, pg. 1851
HANAPIN MARKETING, LLC—See Brain Labs Digital Ltd.; *Int'l*, pg. 1137
HANLEY WOOD MEDIA, INC.—See MidOcean Partners, LLP; *U.S. Private*, pg. 2717
HARLOW-HRK, LLC—See CI Capital Partners LLC; *U.S. Private*, pg. 895
HARTE-HANKS SHOPPERS INC.—See Harte Hanks, Inc.; *U.S. Public*, pg. 986
HDS MARKETING, INC.; *U.S. Private*, pg. 1890
HEALTHCARE CONSULTANCY GROUP.—See Omnicom Group Inc.; *U.S. Public*, pg. 1586
HEALTHCARE REGIONAL MARKETING (HRM); *U.S. Private*, pg. 1895
HEBS DIGITAL; *U.S. Private*, pg. 1903
HELLOWORLD, INC.—See Dentsu Group Inc.; *Int'l*, pg. 2036
THE HERITAGE CO.; *U.S. Private*, pg. 4052

N.A.I.C.S. INDEX

541613 — MARKETING CONSULTIN...

HIGHCO BENELUX—See HighCo S.A.; *Int'l*, pg. 3387
HIGHCO BOX, S.A.S.—See HighCo S.A.; *Int'l*, pg. 3387
HIGHCO DATA, S.A.S.—See HighCo S.A.; *Int'l*, pg. 3387
HIGHCO MRM—See HighCo S.A.; *Int'l*, pg. 3387
HIGHCO S.A.; *Int'l*, pg. 3386
HIGHCO SPAIN—See HighCo S.A.; *Int'l*, pg. 3387
HIGHER POWER MARKETING (HPM); *U.S. Private*, pg. 1937
HI-MEDIA PERFOMANCE GMBH—See AdUX SA; *Int'l*, pg. 155
HOPE, INC.; *Int'l*, pg. 3473
HORIZON DIRECT—See Horizon Media, Inc.; *U.S. Private*, pg. 1982
HOSPITALITY MARKETING CONCEPTS, INC.; *U.S. Private*, pg. 1987
HOUSECOM TECHNOLOGIES CO., LTD.—See Daito Trust Construction Co., Ltd.; *Int'l*, pg. 1944
HOUSE OF KAIZEN LLC; *U.S. Private*, pg. 1991
HS AD INC.; *Int'l*, pg. 3502
HUBSHOUT, LLC; *U.S. Private*, pg. 2001
H.U. FRONTIER, INC.—See H.U. Group Holdings, Inc.; *Int'l*, pg. 3197
HUMAN DIGITAL CONSULTANTS CO., LTD.—See Human Holdings Co., Ltd.; *Int'l*, pg. 3529
HUNTSWORTH LIMITED—See Clayton, Dubilier & Rice, LLC; *U.S. Private*, pg. 924
HW MEDIA, LLC; *U.S. Private*, pg. 2015
ICEMOBILE AGENCY BV—See Bread Financial Holdings Inc.; *U.S. Public*, pg. 381
ICON FINE WINE & SPIRITS LTD.; *Int'l*, pg. 3583
ICON—See Wasserman Media Group, LLC; *U.S. Private*, pg. 4450
ICROSSING SAN FRANCISCO—See The Hearst Corporation; *U.S. Private*, pg. 4049
IG ASIA PTE LIMITED—See IG Group Holdings plc; *Int'l*, pg. 3601
IG BANK S.A.—See IG Group Holdings plc; *Int'l*, pg. 3601
IG LIMITED—See IG Group Holdings plc; *Int'l*, pg. 3601
IG SECURITIES LIMITED—See IG Group Holdings plc; *Int'l*, pg. 3601
IG US HOLDINGS INC.—See IG Group Holdings plc; *Int'l*, pg. 3601
IKNOWTION, LLC—See TTEC Holdings, Inc.; *U.S. Public*, pg. 2203
I.LINK GROUP LIMITED—See HM International Holdings Limited; *Int'l*, pg. 3431
ILLUMINATI STUDIOS INC.; *U.S. Private*, pg. 2043
IMAGINATION SPECIALTIES, INC.; *U.S. Private*, pg. 2045
IMARKETEUROPE KFT.—See iMarketKorea, Inc.; *Int'l*, pg. 3620
IMASTE-IPS S.L.—See ON24, Inc.; *U.S. Public*, pg. 1601
IMJ CORPORATION—See Accenture plc; *Int'l*, pg. 86
IMPACT GROUP, LLC—See CI Capital Partners LLC; *U.S. Private*, pg. 895
IMPACT XM—See Riverside Partners, LLC; *U.S. Private*, pg. 3446
IMPALA DIGITAL LIMITED—See Entain PLC; *Int'l*, pg. 2450
IMPERIAL MARKETING CORPORATION—See The Allstate Corporation; *U.S. Public*, pg. 2033
IMS INTERNET MEDIA SERVICES, INC.; *U.S. Private*, pg. 2051
IMWAVE, INC.; *U.S. Private*, pg. 2052
INCENTIVE SOLUTIONS; *U.S. Private*, pg. 2053
INCISIVE MEDIA—See Apax Partners LLP; *Int'l*, pg. 504
INCREASE VISIBILITY, INC.; *U.S. Private*, pg. 2054
INFINITY RESOURCES, INC.; *U.S. Private*, pg. 2071
INGENICO MARKETING SOLUTIONS GMBH—See Apollo Global Management, Inc.; *U.S. Public*, pg. 151
INGENIOUS DESIGNS LLC—See Qurate Retail, Inc.; *U.S. Public*, pg. 1758
INLAND LABEL & MARKETING SERVICES, LLC - IN*TECH DIVISION—See Inland Label & Marketing Services, LLC; *U.S. Private*, pg. 2078
INLAND LABEL & MARKETING SERVICES, LLC - LA CROSSE FACILITY—See Inland Label & Marketing Services, LLC; *U.S. Private*, pg. 2078
INLAND LABEL & MARKETING SERVICES, LLC - WINONA FACILITY—See Inland Label & Marketing Services, LLC; *U.S. Private*, pg. 2078
INNERWORKINGS ANDINA S.A.S.—See HH Global Group Limited; *Int'l*, pg. 3378
INNERWORKINGS ASIA PACIFIC—See HH Global Group Limited; *Int'l*, pg. 3378
INNERWORKINGS COLOMBIA S.A.S.—See HH Global Group Limited; *Int'l*, pg. 3378
INNERWORKINGS DUBAI—See HH Global Group Limited; *Int'l*, pg. 3378
INNERWORKINGS EUROPE LIMITED—See HH Global Group Limited; *Int'l*, pg. 3378
INNERWORKINGS FRANCE—See HH Global Group Limited; *Int'l*, pg. 3378
INNERWORKINGS INDIA PRIVATE LIMITED—See HH Global Group Limited; *Int'l*, pg. 3378
INNERWORKINGS NEDERLAND BV—See HH Global Group Limited; *Int'l*, pg. 3378
INNERWORKINGS PERU S.A.C.—See HH Global Group Limited; *Int'l*, pg. 3378

INNERWORKINGS RUSSIA LLA—See HH Global Group Limited; *Int'l*, pg. 3378
INNERWORKINGS SINGAPORE PRIVATE LIMITED—See HH Global Group Limited; *Int'l*, pg. 3378
INNOTEQ, INC.—See Endo International plc; *Int'l*, pg. 2404
INQBRANDS, INC.—See Focus Technology Co., Ltd.; *Int'l*, pg. 2720
INSIDEVIEW TECHNOLOGIES, INC.—See Demandbase, Inc.; *U.S. Private*, pg. 1203
INSURANCE MARKETING GROUP, LLC—See Integrity Marketing Group LLC; *U.S. Private*, pg. 2103
INSYS GROUP, INC.—See DXC Technology Company; *U.S. Public*, pg. 696
INTEGRAL AD SCIENCE, INC.—See Vista Equity Partners, LLC; *U.S. Private*, pg. 4398
INTEGRAL MARKETING, INC.; *U.S. Private*, pg. 2098
INTEGRATED MARKETING GROUP; *U.S. Private*, pg. 2100
INTELLIGENT BEAUTY, LLC; *U.S. Private*, pg. 2105
INTERBRAND—See Omnicom Group Inc.; *U.S. Public*, pg. 1585
INTERMARKETS, INC.; *U.S. Private*, pg. 2112
INTERMEDIX SA (PTY) LTD.—See CompuGroup Medical SE & Co. KGaA; *Int'l*, pg. 1756
INTERNET MARKETING INC.—See Trinity Hunt Management, L.P.; *U.S. Private*, pg. 4235
INTERNET MARKETING INC.—See Trinity Hunt Management, L.P.; *U.S. Private*, pg. 4235
INTER-PACIFIC CAPITAL SDN BHD—See Berjaya Corporation Berhad; *Int'l*, pg. 982
INVENIO SOLUTIONS; *U.S. Private*, pg. 2131
INVENTA CPM S.R.L.—See Omnicom Group Inc.; *U.S. Public*, pg. 1578
INVISION COMMUNICATIONS, INC. - CHICAGO—See InVision Communications, Inc.; *U.S. Private*, pg. 2133
INVISION COMMUNICATIONS, INC.; *U.S. Private*, pg. 2133
INVISION COMMUNICATIONS, INC.—See InVision Communications, Inc.; *U.S. Private*, pg. 2133
INWK MEXICO S DE R.L. DE C.V.—See HH Global Group Limited; *Int'l*, pg. 3378
INWK PANAMA S.A.—See HH Global Group Limited; *Int'l*, pg. 3378
IPURE LABS, INC.; *U.S. Public*, pg. 1167
IQVIA LTD.—See IQVIA Holdings Inc.; *U.S. Public*, pg. 1169
IRIX DESIGN GROUP INC.—See Global Education Communities Corp; *Int'l*, pg. 2995
ISIM S.P.A.—See Assicurazioni Generali S.p.A.; *Int'l*, pg. 643
ISS MARKETING PTY LIMITED—See Enero Group Limited; *Int'l*, pg. 2424
I SYNERGY GROUP LIMITED; *Int'l*, pg. 3562
I SYNERGY HOLDINGS BERHAD; *Int'l*, pg. 3562
IVYSTONE GROUP, LLC - DALLAS—See Ivystone Group, LLC; *U.S. Private*, pg. 2152
IVYSTONE GROUP, LLC; *U.S. Private*, pg. 2152
JACK MORTON UK LIMITED—See The Interpublic Group of Companies, Inc.; *U.S. Public*, pg. 2096
JEBCOMMERCE LLC; *U.S. Private*, pg. 2196
JEFFREY M. CONSULTING LLC; *U.S. Private*, pg. 2198
J. KNIPPER & COMPANY, INC. - SOMERSET—See J. Knipper & Company, Inc.; *U.S. Private*, pg. 2156
J. KNIPPER & COMPANY, INC.; *U.S. Private*, pg. 2156
J. TARRAN MARKETING INC.; *U.S. Private*, pg. 2157
JUMBO CO., LTD.—See Encho Co., Ltd.; *Int'l*, pg. 2401
JUXT—See Project: Worldwide, Inc.; *U.S. Private*, pg. 3281
THE KANTAR GROUP—See Bain Capital, LP; *U.S. Private*, pg. 448
KANTORWASSINK; *U.S. Private*, pg. 2261
KATZ DIRECT—See iHeartMedia, Inc.; *U.S. Public*, pg. 1096
KATZ MARKETING SOLUTIONS—See iHeartMedia, Inc.; *U.S. Public*, pg. 1096
KAUTILYA INFOTECH LIMITED—See Alchemist Corporation Limited; *Int'l*, pg. 300
KBR WYLE SERVICES LLC—See KBR, Inc.; *U.S. Public*, pg. 1216
KELLY EDUCATIONAL STAFFING—See Kelly Services, Inc.; *U.S. Public*, pg. 1219
KELLY GROUP LIMITED—See Adcorp Holdings Limited; *Int'l*, pg. 127
KELTON RESEARCH, LLC—See Tailwind Capital Group, LLC; *U.S. Private*, pg. 3924
KENNA COMMUNICATIONS LP—See Stagwell, Inc.; *U.S. Public*, pg. 1927
KEPLER GROUP LLC—See Kyu Investment, Inc.; *U.S. Private*, pg. 2361
KESTONE CL ASIA HUB PTE. LTD.—See CL Educate Limited; *Int'l*, pg. 1640
KESTONE CL US LIMITED—See CL Educate Limited; *Int'l*, pg. 1640
KESTONE INTEGRATED MARKETING SERVICES PRIVATE LIMITED—See CL Educate Limited; *Int'l*, pg. 1640
KILLER INTERACTIVE, LLC; *U.S. Private*, pg. 2304
KINERGY MARKETING LLC—See Alto Ingredients, Inc.; *U.S. Public*, pg. 88
KLAVIYO, INC.; *U.S. Public*, pg. 1269
KNOWLEDGE SUPPORT SYSTEMS INC.—See Hanover Investors Management LLP; *Int'l*, pg. 3258
KNOWN GLOBAL LLC; *U.S. Private*, pg. 2324
KODA SPECIALTY PRODUCTS GROUP—See KODA En-

terprises Group, LLC; *U.S. Private*, pg. 2335
KOGNITIV SINGAPORE PTE. LTD.—See Aimia Inc.; *Int'l*, pg. 233
KOMPANI GROUP; *U.S. Private*, pg. 2342
KONTOR NEW MEDIA GMBH—See Edel SE & Co. KGaA; *Int'l*, pg. 2305
KORTX, LLC; *U.S. Private*, pg. 2344
KREATIVA NEW FORMULA D.O.O.—See Alkemy SpA; *Int'l*, pg. 331
KYU INVESTMENT, INC.; *U.S. Private*, pg. 2360
THE LASH GROUP, INC.—See Cencora, Inc.; *U.S. Public*, pg. 467
LAUNCH DIGITAL MARKETING LLC—See Cars.com Inc.; *U.S. Public*, pg. 444
LBEST INC.—See HS Ad Inc.; *Int'l*, pg. 3502
LEAD5 MEDIA, LLC; *U.S. Private*, pg. 2405
LEADCLOUD, LLC—See The Allstate Corporation; *U.S. Public*, pg. 2033
LEADCREATIONS.COM LLC; *U.S. Private*, pg. 2405
LEADJEN; *U.S. Private*, pg. 2406
LEADMD, INC.; *U.S. Private*, pg. 2407
LEGAL BRAND MARKETING, L.L.C.; *U.S. Private*, pg. 2417
LEISURE TRENDS GROUP, LLC—See The NPD Group, Inc.; *U.S. Private*, pg. 4085
LGI NETWORK—See The NPD Group, Inc.; *U.S. Private*, pg. 4085
LIGHTHOUSE DIGITAL INC.—See Aquarius AI, Inc.; *Int'l*, pg. 528
LIGHTHOUSE LIST COMPANY INC.; *U.S. Private*, pg. 2453
LINKS MARKETING GROUP INC.—See Grossman Marketing Group; *U.S. Private*, pg. 1792
LINKTECH WORLDWIDE; *U.S. Private*, pg. 2462
LIST MANAGEMENT SERVICES, INC.; *U.S. Private*, pg. 2466
LOCALEDGE MEDIA, INC.—See The Hearst Corporation; *U.S. Private*, pg. 4047
LOGISTICS SPECIALTIES, INC.; *U.S. Private*, pg. 2482
LONE FIR CONSULTING, LLC; *U.S. Private*, pg. 2483
LOYALTYEXPRESS INC.—See Williston Financial Group, LLC; *U.S. Private*, pg. 4528
LRG MARKETING COMMUNICATIONS, INC.; *U.S. Private*, pg. 2507
L-SOFT INTERNATIONAL, INC.; *U.S. Private*, pg. 2364
LUMATA AUSTRALASIA PTY. LTD.—See Francisco Partners Management, LP; *U.S. Private*, pg. 1590
LUMATA ITALIA S.R.L.—See Francisco Partners Management, LP; *U.S. Private*, pg. 1590
LUMATA NETHERLANDS B.V.—See Francisco Partners Management, LP; *U.S. Private*, pg. 1590
LUMATA UK LIMITED—See CCUR Holdings Inc.; *U.S. Public*, pg. 461
LUNCH COMMUNICATIONS LIMITED—See Enero Group Limited; *Int'l*, pg. 2424
M6 PUBLICITE SAS—See Bertelsmann SE & Co. KGaA; *Int'l*, pg. 993
MADISON LOGIC, INC.—See Clarion Capital Partners, LLC; *U.S. Private*, pg. 911
MAGIC LOGIX INC.; *U.S. Private*, pg. 2546
MANAGED MARKET RESOURCES LLC—See NPG Health LLC; *U.S. Private*, pg. 2969
MANIFEST DIGITAL; *U.S. Private*, pg. 2564
MAN MARKETING, INC.; *U.S. Private*, pg. 2559
MANSFIELD SALES PARTNERS, LLC—See JMC Capital Partners LLC; *U.S. Private*, pg. 2215
MAPP DIGITAL US, LLC—See Marlin Equity Partners, LLC; *U.S. Private*, pg. 2584
MARANDA ENTERPRISES, LLC; *U.S. Private*, pg. 2569
MARATHON PETROLEUM COMPANY CANADA LTD.—See Marathon Petroleum Corporation; *U.S. Public*, pg. 1364
MARCOM CO LTD.—See British American Investment Co. (Mtius) Ltd.; *Int'l*, pg. 1165
MARCOM GROUP; *U.S. Private*, pg. 2572
MARIN'S DEUTSCHLAND GMBH—See Quad/Graphics, Inc.; *U.S. Public*, pg. 1744
MARITZ DEALER SOLUTIONS—See Maritz Holdings Inc.; *U.S. Private*, pg. 2577
THE MARITZ INSTITUTE—See Maritz Holdings Inc.; *U.S. Private*, pg. 2577
MARITZ RESEARCH LTD.—See Maritz Holdings Inc.; *U.S. Private*, pg. 2577
MARKETECHING SOLUTIONS, LLC.—See New Mountain Capital, LLC; *U.S. Private*, pg. 2904
MARKETING & EVENTS GROUP—See Viad Corp.; *U.S. Public*, pg. 2291
MARKETING GENERAL INC.—See Taylor Corporation; *U.S. Private*, pg. 3938
MARKETING IN COLOR INC.; *U.S. Private*, pg. 2580
MARKETINGPROFS, LLC; *U.S. Private*, pg. 2581
MARKETING WERKS, INC.—See Acosta, Inc.; *U.S. Private*, pg. 64
MARKETPLACE STRATEGY, LLC—See Graham Holdings Company; *U.S. Public*, pg. 956
MARKETSHARE PARTNERS, LLC—See TransUnion; *U.S. Public*, pg. 2184
MARKETSMITH, INC.; *U.S. Private*, pg. 2581
MARKETSTAR CORPORATION—See Wasatch Advantage

541613 — MARKETING CONSULTIN...

Group, LLC; *U.S. Private*, pg. 4445
MARKET VANTAGE, LLC; *U.S. Private*, pg. 2579
MARQUET INTERNATIONAL LTD.—See Sunblock Systems, Inc.; *U.S. Private*, pg. 3865
THE MASTERLINK GROUP, INC.; *U.S. Private*, pg. 4075
MCKINLEY MARKETING PARTNERS, INC.—See 24 Seven, LLC; *U.S. Private*, pg. 6
MCNEIL CONSUMER NUTRITIONALS LTD.—See Kenvue Inc.; *U.S. Public*, pg. 1224
MEDEXACT SAS—See Cegedim S.A.; *Int'l*, pg. 1390
MEDFORCE LLC—See Eureka Equity Partners, L.P.; *U.S. Private*, pg. 1433
MEDIAADVANTAGE CONSULTING L.D.A—See Ebiquity plc; *Int'l*, pg. 2285
MEDIAFORGE; *U.S. Private*, pg. 2653
MEDIAPLEX SYSTEMS, INC.—See Bread Financial Holdings Inc.; *U.S. Public*, pg. 381
MEDIA SOLUTIONS—See Brookfield Corporation; *Int'l*, pg. 1178
MEDIA SOLUTIONS—See Elliott Management Corporation; *U.S. Private*, pg. 1371
MEDIATRUST; *U.S. Private*, pg. 2654
MEDICINE MAN TECHNOLOGIES, INC.; *U.S. Public*, pg. 1412
MEDTOUCH LLC—See EQT AB; *Int'l*, pg. 2483
MELBOURNE IT GP HOLDINGS PTY. LTD.—See 5G Networks Limited; *Int'l*, pg. 13
MERIDIAN CONSULTING GROUP, LLC—See HOV Services Limited; *Int'l*, pg. 3492
MERIDIAN ENTERPRISES CORPORATION; *U.S. Private*, pg. 2672
MESASIX, LLC; *U.S. Private*, pg. 2678
METHOD COMMUNICATIONS, INC.—See Providence Equity Partners L.L.C.; *U.S. Private*, pg. 3292
MICROMASS COMMUNICATIONS, INC.—See Clayton, Dubilier & Rice, LLC; *U.S. Private*, pg. 928
MILES MEDIA GROUP, LLLP; *U.S. Private*, pg. 2727
MILES SOUTH PACIFIC—See Miles Media Group, LLLP; *U.S. Private*, pg. 2727
MILESTONE MARKETING ASSOCIATES, INC.; *U.S. Private*, pg. 2728
MILLER HEIMAN EUROPE GMBH—See Korn Ferry; *U.S. Public*, pg. 1274
MILLER HEIMAN GROUP, INC.—See Korn Ferry; *U.S. Public*, pg. 1274
MILLER HEIMAN GROUP (UK) LIMITED—See Korn Ferry; *U.S. Public*, pg. 1274
MINDS CO., LTD.—See Crestec Inc.; *Int'l*, pg. 1841
MOBILE.DE GMBH—See eBay Inc.; *U.S. Public*, pg. 709
MODUSLINK B.V.—See Steel Connect, Inc.; *U.S. Public*, pg. 1941
MOGO MARKETING & MEDIA, INC.—See Atairos Group, Inc.; *U.S. Private*, pg. 364
MOM CENTRAL CONSULTING; *U.S. Private*, pg. 2767
MOOD MEDIA A/S—See Vector Capital Management, L.P.; *U.S. Private*, pg. 4351
MOOD MEDIA AS—See Vector Capital Management, L.P.; *U.S. Private*, pg. 4351
MOOD MEDIA AUSTRALIA PTY LTD—See Vector Capital Management, L.P.; *U.S. Private*, pg. 4351
MOOD MEDIA BELGIUM NV—See Vector Capital Management, L.P.; *U.S. Private*, pg. 4351
MOOD MEDIA FINLAND OY—See Vector Capital Management, L.P.; *U.S. Private*, pg. 4351
MOOD MEDIA GMBH—See Vector Capital Management, L.P.; *U.S. Private*, pg. 4351
MOOD MEDIA GMBH—See Vector Capital Management, L.P.; *U.S. Private*, pg. 4351
MOOD MEDIA GROUP CZ, S.R.O.—See Vector Capital Management, L.P.; *U.S. Private*, pg. 4351
MOOD MEDIA HUNGARY KFT—See Vector Capital Management, L.P.; *U.S. Private*, pg. 4351
MOOD MEDIA IRELAND LIMITED—See Vector Capital Management, L.P.; *U.S. Private*, pg. 4351
MOOD MEDIA JAPAN CO., LTD.—See Vector Capital Management, L.P.; *U.S. Private*, pg. 4351
MOOD MEDIA LIMITED—See Vector Capital Management, L.P.; *U.S. Private*, pg. 4351
MOOD MEDIA NETHERLANDS B.V.—See Vector Capital Management, L.P.; *U.S. Private*, pg. 4351
MOOD MEDIA POLSKA SP. Z O.O.—See Vector Capital Management, L.P.; *U.S. Private*, pg. 4351
MOOD MEDIA S.A.—See Vector Capital Management, L.P.; *U.S. Private*, pg. 4351
MOOD MEDIA S.A.—See Vector Capital Management, L.P.; *U.S. Private*, pg. 4351
MOOD MEDIA SAS—See Vector Capital Management, L.P.; *U.S. Private*, pg. 4351
MOOSYLVANIA MARKETING; *U.S. Private*, pg. 2781
M&O PARTNERS LTDA—See Daeyang Electric Co., Ltd.; *Int'l*, pg. 1911
MOTIVE—See Project: Worldwide, Inc.; *U.S. Private*, pg. 3281
MOTIV, INC.; *U.S. Private*, pg. 2796
MOVABLE, INC.; *U.S. Private*, pg. 2801
MUTESIX, LLC—See Dentsu Group Inc.; *Int'l*, pg. 2037
MYELIN HEALTH COMMUNICATIONS, INC.; *U.S. Private*, pg. 2824

NAKED COMMUNICATIONS AUSTRALIA PTY LIMITED—See Enero Group Limited; *Int'l*, pg. 2424
NASTYGOAT CORPORATION; *U.S. Private*, pg. 2837
NATIONAL MARKETING SOLUTIONS (NMS); *U.S. Private*, pg. 2859
NATIONAL PATIENT SERVICES CORPORATION; *U.S. Private*, pg. 2860
NATIONAL POSITIONS; *U.S. Private*, pg. 2860
NAVIPLUS CO., LTD.—See Digital Garage, Inc.; *Int'l*, pg. 2122
NAYAPAY (PRIVATE) LIMITED—See COLGATE-PALMOLIVE (PAKISTAN) LTD; *Int'l*, pg. 1698
NCH MARKETING SERVICES, INC.—See MacAndrews & Forbes Incorporated; *U.S. Private*, pg. 2532
NECTAR 360 LIMITED—See Aimia Inc.; *Int'l*, pg. 233
THE NET IMPACT—See Unified Development, Inc.; *U.S. Private*, pg. 4282
NETMARK.COM; *U.S. Private*, pg. 2887
NETPRESS GMBH—See Adelis Equity Partners AB; *Int'l*, pg. 142
NETSERTIVE, INC.; *U.S. Private*, pg. 2888
NETSTRATEGIES; *U.S. Private*, pg. 2888
NEUTRON INTERACTIVE; *U.S. Private*, pg. 2891
NEVERBLUE MEDIA INCORPORATED—See Vertrue Inc.; *U.S. Private*, pg. 4370
NEW ANGLE MEDIA LLC; *U.S. Private*, pg. 2892
NEWBRANDANALYTICS INC.—See Sprinklr, Inc.; *U.S. Public*, pg. 1920
NEWHALL LABORATORIES, INC.—See Brynwood Partners Management LLC; *U.S. Private*, pg. 674
NEWS MARKETING CANADA—See News Corporation; *U.S. Public*, pg. 1521
NEWS-PRESS DIGITAL—See News-Press & Gazette Company; *U.S. Private*, pg. 2917
NEWSTYLE—See Omnicom Group Inc.; *U.S. Public*, pg. 1585
NEXT MARKETING; *U.S. Private*, pg. 2920
NICOR ENERCHANGE, LLC—See The Southern Company; *U.S. Public*, pg. 2131
NIELSEN ARASTIRMA HIZMETLERI LIMITED SIRKET—See Brookfield Corporation; *Int'l*, pg. 1177
NIELSEN ARASTIRMA HIZMETLERI LIMITED SIRKET—See Elliott Management Corporation; *U.S. Private*, pg. 1370
THE NIELSEN COMPANY (BELGIUM) SPRL—See Brookfield Corporation; *Int'l*, pg. 1180
THE NIELSEN COMPANY (BELGIUM) SPRL—See Elliott Management Corporation; *U.S. Private*, pg. 1372
THE NIELSEN COMPANY (DENMARK) APS—See Brookfield Corporation; *Int'l*, pg. 1177
THE NIELSEN COMPANY (DENMARK) APS—See Elliott Management Corporation; *U.S. Private*, pg. 1370
THE NIELSEN COMPANY (GERMANY) GMBH—See Brookfield Corporation; *Int'l*, pg. 1180
THE NIELSEN COMPANY (GERMANY) GMBH—See Elliott Management Corporation; *U.S. Private*, pg. 1372
THE NIELSEN COMPANY LANKA (PRIVATE) LIMITED—See Brookfield Corporation; *Int'l*, pg. 1180
THE NIELSEN COMPANY LANKA (PRIVATE) LIMITED—See Elliott Management Corporation; *U.S. Private*, pg. 1373
THE NIELSEN COMPANY MEDYA YAYINCILIK VE TANITIM HIZMETLERI ANONIM SIRKETII—See Brookfield Corporation; *Int'l*, pg. 1180
THE NIELSEN COMPANY MEDYA YAYINCILIK VE TANITIM HIZMETLERI ANONIM SIRKETII—See Elliott Management Corporation; *U.S. Private*, pg. 1373
THE NIELSEN COMPANY (SHANGHAI) LTD.—See Brookfield Corporation; *Int'l*, pg. 1180
THE NIELSEN COMPANY (SHANGHAI) LTD.—See Elliott Management Corporation; *U.S. Private*, pg. 1373
NIELSEN EGYPT LLC—See Brookfield Corporation; *Int'l*, pg. 1179
NIELSEN EGYPT LLC—See Elliott Management Corporation; *U.S. Private*, pg. 1371
NIELSEN FOR MARKET RESEARCH LLC—See Brookfield Corporation; *Int'l*, pg. 1180
NIELSEN FOR MARKET RESEARCH LLC—See Elliott Management Corporation; *U.S. Private*, pg. 1372
NIELSEN MEDIA RESEARCH AS—See Brookfield Corporation; *Int'l*, pg. 1179
NIELSEN MEDIA RESEARCH AS—See Elliott Management Corporation; *U.S. Private*, pg. 1371
NIELSEN SERVICES GERMANY GMBH—See Brookfield Corporation; *Int'l*, pg. 1180
NIELSEN SERVICES GERMANY GMBH—See Elliott Management Corporation; *U.S. Private*, pg. 1372
NIELSEN SPORTS FRANCE SARL—See Brookfield Corporation; *Int'l*, pg. 1179
NIELSEN SPORTS FRANCE SARL—See Elliott Management Corporation; *U.S. Private*, pg. 1372
NIELSEN SPORTS INDIA PRIVATE LIMITED—See Brookfield Corporation; *Int'l*, pg. 1179
NIELSEN SPORTS INDIA PRIVATE LIMITED—See Elliott Management Corporation; *U.S. Private*, pg. 1372
NIELSEN TV AUDIENCE MEASUREMENT S.A.—See Brookfield Corporation; *Int'l*, pg. 1180
NIELSEN TV AUDIENCE MEASUREMENT S.A.—See Elliott

CORPORATE AFFILIATIONS

Management Corporation; *U.S. Private*, pg. 1372
NIGHT VISION ENTERTAINMENT; *U.S. Private*, pg. 2927
NOBLE MARKETING INC.; *U.S. Private*, pg. 2933
NORDIS DIRECT, INC.; *U.S. Private*, pg. 2937
NOVAETUS INC.—See SurveyVitals, Inc.; *U.S. Private*, pg. 3885
NOVOTEC CONSULTORES, S.A., SOCIEDAD UNIPERSONAL—See I Squared Capital Advisors (US) LLC; *U.S. Private*, pg. 2023
NPD DISPLAYSEARCH LLC—See The NPD Group, Inc.; *U.S. Private*, pg. 4085
NPDGROUP DEUTSCHLAND GMBH—See The NPD Group, Inc.; *U.S. Private*, pg. 4085
THE NPD GROUP LTD—See The NPD Group, Inc.; *U.S. Private*, pg. 4085
NPD INFORMATION CONSULTING (SHANGHAI) CO., LTD.—See The NPD Group, Inc.; *U.S. Private*, pg. 4085
NPD JAPAN LTD.—See The NPD Group, Inc.; *U.S. Private*, pg. 4085
NUS CONSULTING GROUP—See National Utility Service, Inc.; *U.S. Private*, pg. 2864
NUTRICIA BAGO S.A.—See Bago Group; *Int'l*, pg. 799
NUTRICIA BAGO S.A.—See Danone; *Int'l*, pg. 1966
OBATA DESIGN, INC.; *U.S. Private*, pg. 2986
OB MEDIA LLC—See Enero Group Limited; *Int'l*, pg. 2424
OLIVER MARKETING, INC.; *U.S. Private*, pg. 3011
OMG NATIONAL; *U.S. Private*, pg. 3016
OMNIBUS K.K.—See Credit Saison Co., Ltd.; *Int'l*, pg. 1836
ON BOARD ENTERTAINMENT, INC.; *U.S. Private*, pg. 3018
ONE ON ONE MARKETING INC.; *U.S. Private*, pg. 3020
ONLINE MEDIA COMMUNICATIONS DESIGN GMBH—See Berndorf AG; *Int'l*, pg. 987
ONLINE REWARDS; *U.S. Private*, pg. 3027
OPENSYMMETRY-UK—See OpenSymmetry, Inc.; *U.S. Private*, pg. 3031
OPTIMISSA CAPITAL MARKETS CONSULTING S.A. DE C.V.—See Alten S.A.; *Int'l*, pg. 390
OPTIMISSA LTD.—See Alten S.A.; *Int'l*, pg. 390
OPTIMISSA PORTUGAL UNIPESSOAL, LDA—See Alten S.A.; *Int'l*, pg. 390
OPTIMIZERX CORPORATION; *U.S. Public*, pg. 1609
OPTIMO IT; *U.S. Private*, pg. 3034
OPTS IDEAS; *U.S. Private*, pg. 3036
OPUS EVENTS AGENCY; *U.S. Private*, pg. 3036
ORANGESODA, INC.—See Deluxe Corporation; *U.S. Public*, pg. 653
ORCHID FIELD MARKETING LTD—See H2O Creative; *Int'l*, pg. 3200
ORGAN WORLDWIDE LLC; *U.S. Private*, pg. 3041
OTHELLO INC.—See Allied Architects, Inc.; *Int'l*, pg. 356
OUTFRONT MEDIA VW COMMUNICATIONS LLC—See OUTFRONT Media Inc.; *U.S. Public*, pg. 1625
OVERDRIVE INTERACTIVE; *U.S. Private*, pg. 3052
OVERSEES.NET; *U.S. Private*, pg. 3053
P97 NETWORKS INC.—See Corpay, Inc.; *U.S. Public*, pg. 580
PACIFIC AG. PRODUCTS, LLC—See Alto Ingredients, Inc.; *U.S. Public*, pg. 88
PACIFIC SHORE HOLDINGS, INC.—See Med-X, Inc.; *U.S. Private*, pg. 2650
PAKISTAN INDUSTRIAL AIDS (PRIVATE) LIMITED—See House of Habib; *Int'l*, pg. 3491
PARETO CORPORATION—See The Riverside Company; *U.S. Private*, pg. 4109
PARKER AEROSPACE CUSTOMER SUPPORT INC.—See Parker Hannifin Corporation; *U.S. Public*, pg. 1643
PARKER AEROSPACE, SAO PAULO CUSTOMER SERVICE CENTER—See Parker Hannifin Corporation; *U.S. Public*, pg. 1643
PARKER HANNIFIN CO., LTD.-AEROSPACE CUSTOMER SUPPORT—See Parker Hannifin Corporation; *U.S. Public*, pg. 1644
PASCH CONSULTING GROUP, LLC; *U.S. Private*, pg. 3103
THE PASSION GROUP; *U.S. Private*, pg. 4091
PAXAR CORPORATION PTY. LTD.—See Avery Dennison Corporation; *U.S. Public*, pg. 244
PAYBACK GMBH—See American Express Company; *U.S. Public*, pg. 102
PBS HOLDING, INC.; *U.S. Public*, pg. 1657
PDV LTD—See DM plc; *Int'l*, pg. 2142
PENNEBAKER LLC—See Comcast Corporation; *U.S. Public*, pg. 541
PENN GLOBAL MARKETING, LLC—See Integrity Marketing Group LLC; *U.S. Private*, pg. 2104
PEP DIRECT, LLC; *U.S. Private*, pg. 3143
PERFORMANCE INTERACTIVE ALLIANCE GMBH—See Equistone Partners Europe Limited; *Int'l*, pg. 2487
PERILS AG—See Marsh & McLennan Companies, Inc.; *U.S. Public*, pg. 1388
THE PERISHABLES GROUP, INC.—See Brookfield Corporation; *Int'l*, pg. 1180
THE PERISHABLES GROUP, INC.—See Elliott Management Corporation; *U.S. Private*, pg. 1373
PHARMEXX UK LTD.—See Clayton, Dubilier & Rice, LLC; *U.S. Private*, pg. 928
PHOENIX ONE SALES, MARKETING, MANAGEMENT + COMMUNICATIONS LLC; *U.S. Private*, pg. 3173

541613 — MARKETING CONSULTIN...

PHOTRON M&E SOLUTIONS INC.—See Imagica Group Inc.; *Int'l*, pg. 3618
PINT, INC.; *U.S. Private*, pg. 3186
PLAN 365, INC.—See BCD Holdings N.V.; *Int'l*, pg. 926
THE POINT-OF-SALE CENTRE (NEW ZEALAND) LTD—See Hancock & Gore Ltd.; *Int'l*, pg. 3242
POP2LIFE LLC; *U.S. Private*, pg. 3228
PORTU-SUNBERG & ASSOCIATES INC.—See Brass Ring Capital Inc.; *U.S. Private*, pg. 640
POSITION2, INC.—See thismoment, Inc.; *U.S. Private*, pg. 4145
PRACTICE BUILDERS—See Ascend Integrated Media, LLC; *U.S. Private*, pg. 346
PRAGMATIC INSTITUTE, LLC—See MidOcean Partners, LLP; *U.S. Private*, pg. 2717
PRECISION PUBLIC RELATIONS, INC.—See Peopletomysite.com, LLC; *U.S. Private*, pg. 3143
PREMIER CONCEPTS LLC—See Premium Retail Services Inc.; *U.S. Private*, pg. 3252
PREMIER PLACEMENT MEDIA, LTD; *U.S. Private*, pg. 3250
PRIMACY; *U.S. Private*, pg. 3260
PRIMAPHOT SPRL—See Activa Capital S.A.S.; *Int'l*, pg. 119
PRIMAVISTA GROUP—See Activa Capital S.A.S.; *Int'l*, pg. 119
PROFIT RANK, INC.; *U.S. Private*, pg. 3277
PROJECTLINE SERVICES, INC.; *U.S. Private*, pg. 3281
PRO MARKETING SALES INC.; *U.S. Private*, pg. 3270
PROMEDICA INC.—See Arsenal Capital Management LP; *U.S. Private*, pg. 338
PROMOTE FOR LESS—See Metro Printed Products, Inc.; *U.S. Private*, pg. 2686
PROPHASE DIGITAL MEDIA, INC.—See ProPhase Labs, Inc.; *U.S. Public*, pg. 1727
PROPHET BRAND STRATEGY, INC.; *U.S. Private*, pg. 3285
PROSPECT MEDIA GROUP LTD.—See Ciscom Corp.; *Int'l*, pg. 1618
THE PROSPER GROUP CORPORATION; *U.S. Private*, pg. 4101
PSKW, LLC—See Genstar Capital, LLC; *U.S. Private*, pg. 1678
PT DKSH INDONESIA—See Diethelm Keller Holding Limited; *Int'l*, pg. 2117
PT. HAI-O INDONESIA—See Hai-O Enterprise Berhad; *Int'l*, pg. 3209
PULSE 360 INC.—See Seevast Corporation; *U.S. Private*, pg. 3598
THE PURCHASING GROUP, LLC—See CHS INC.; *U.S. Public*, pg. 493
PURELY CREATIVE LTD—See DM plc; *Int'l*, pg. 2142
PURE MARKETING GROUP; *U.S. Private*, pg. 3305
QIIGO, INC.—See Listen360, Inc.; *U.S. Private*, pg. 2466
QUADRIS MEDICAL—See Taylor Corporation; *U.S. Private*, pg. 3939
QUINSTREET, INC.; *U.S. Public*, pg. 1757
RATESPECIAL INTERACTIVE; *U.S. Private*, pg. 3357
RAUMTECHNIK MESSEBAU & EVENT SERVICES GMBH—See Project: Worldwide, Inc.; *U.S. Private*, pg. 3281
RAWNET LIMITED—See Castelnau Group Limited; *Int'l*, pg. 1356
RAYTHEON COMPANY—See RTX Corporation; *U.S. Public*, pg. 1824
RB OPPENHEIM ASSOCIATES, INC.; *U.S. Private*, pg. 3360
REACHBIRD SOLUTIONS GMBH—See adesso SE; *Int'l*, pg. 144
REACHLOCAL SERVICES PVT. LTD.—See Gannett Co., Inc.; *U.S. Public*, pg. 899
REACT2MEDIA, LLC.; *U.S. Private*, pg. 3366
RED CLOUD PROMOTIONS; *U.S. Private*, pg. 3373
REDI-DIRECT MARKETING, INC.; *U.S. Private*, pg. 3378
RED SPOT INTERACTIVE; *U.S. Private*, pg. 3376
RED VENTURES, LLC; *U.S. Private*, pg. 3376
REESE INTEGRATED MARKETING; *U.S. Private*, pg. 3383
REINGOLD LINK, LLC; *U.S. Private*, pg. 3392
RELEVENT PARTNERS LLC—See Stagwell, Inc.; *U.S. Public*, pg. 1927
RESEARCH DATA SERVICES, INC.; *U.S. Private*, pg. 3403
RESONATE BLENDS, INC.; *U.S. Public*, pg. 1791
RESOURCES GLOBAL PROFESSIONALS; *U.S. Private*, pg. 3407
RESPONSE, LLC; *U.S. Private*, pg. 3408
REVLOCAL, LLC—See H.I.G. Capital, LLC; *U.S. Private*, pg. 1834
REVOLUTION; *U.S. Private*, pg. 3416
RIPPLEFFECT STUDIO LIMITED—See IDOX PLC; *Int'l*, pg. 3596
RISE INTERACTIVE MEDIA & ANALYTICS, LLC—See Quad/Graphics, Inc.; *U.S. Public*, pg. 1745
RISK PLACEMENT SERVICES, INC.—See Arthur J. Gallagher & Co.; *U.S. Public*, pg. 207
RITTMAN MEAD CONSULTING PRIVATE LIMITED—See Huron Consulting Group Inc.; *U.S. Public*, pg. 1076
RIVER SURPLUS AND SUPPLY, LLC—See Fastenal Company; *U.S. Public*, pg. 824

RKD GROUP, LLC—See Incline MGMT Corp.; *U.S. Private*, pg. 2054
ROAR.COM PTY LIMITED—See Enero Group Limited; *Int'l*, pg. 2424
ROCK CONTENT SERVICOS DE MIDIA LTDA.—See e.Bricks Ventures; *Int'l*, pg. 2251
ROCKET CLICKS—See BizLab, Inc.; *U.S. Private*, pg. 567
ROCKET FUEL LTD.—See Zeta Interactive Corporation; *U.S. Private*, pg. 4603
ROCKET MEDIA, INC.; *U.S. Private*, pg. 3466
ROYAL MEDIA GROUP, INC.; *U.S. Private*, pg. 3492
R.R. DONNELLEY—See Chatham Asset Management, LLC; *U.S. Private*, pg. 864
RS CONSULTING LIMITED—See Arsenal Capital Management LP; *U.S. Private*, pg. 338
SALEBUILD, INC.—See Ziff Davis, Inc.; *U.S. Public*, pg. 2403
SALELIFTER SP. Z O.O.—See Digitree Group S.A.; *Int'l*, pg. 2124
SALES EMPOWERMENT GROUP LLC—See RFE Investment Partners; *U.S. Private*, pg. 3419
SALES FOCUS INC.; *U.S. Private*, pg. 3532
SALESIFY INC.; *U.S. Private*, pg. 3532
SALES SUPPORT GROUP LIMITED—See Akzo Nobel N.V.; *Int'l*, pg. 275
SAS ALTAVIA SAINT-ETIENNE—See Altavia S.A.; *Int'l*, pg. 388
SAS RETAIL SERVICES, LLC—See Bain Capital, LP; *U.S. Private*, pg. 439
SCHOOL—See Project: Worldwide, Inc.; *U.S. Private*, pg. 3281
SCHWARZECK-VERLAG GMBH—See IQVIA Holdings Inc.; *U.S. Public*, pg. 1169
SCOUT MARKETING, INC.—See Stagwell, Inc.; *U.S. Public*, pg. 1928
SCREEN SERVICE AMERICA LLC—See DB Elettronica Telecomunicazioni SpA; *Int'l*, pg. 1986
SCUBIA GBR—See Axel Springer SE; *Int'l*, pg. 766
SEBRING SOFTWARE, INC.; *U.S. Private*, pg. 3593
SECTOR 5 DIGITAL, LLC—See The Glimpse Group, Inc.; *U.S. Public*, pg. 2075
SEEVAST CORPORATION; *U.S. Private*, pg. 3598
SELLER'S CHOICE, LLC—See Creatd, Inc.; *U.S. Public*, pg. 593
SELLING SOURCE, LLC—See London Bay Capital LLC; *U.S. Private*, pg. 2483
SEZ KOREA LTD.—See Lam Research Corporation; *U.S. Public*, pg. 1290
SG ACTIVAMEDIA (M) SDN. BHD.—See AM Group Holdings Limited; *Int'l*, pg. 402
S. GRAHAM & ASSOCIATES; *U.S. Private*, pg. 3515
SGRP MERIDIAN—See SPAR Group, Inc.; *U.S. Public*, pg. 1914
SHANGHAI GOOD COM BUSINESS CONSULTING CO., LTD.—See Good Com Asset Co., Ltd.; *Int'l*, pg. 3038
SHANGHAI POWER STREAM MOBILE MEDIA CO., LTD.—See BC Technology Group Limited; *Int'l*, pg. 925
SHANGHAI SMU WARNER INVESTMENT MANAGEMENT CO., LTD.—See BC Technology Group Limited; *Int'l*, pg. 925
SHARETRACKER, LLC; *U.S. Private*, pg. 3626
SHARK BRANDING; *U.S. Private*, pg. 3626
SHOC MEDIA AGENCY AB—See Bertelsmann SE & Co. KGaA; *Int'l*, pg. 996
SHOPTOLOGY, INC.—See Project: Worldwide, Inc.; *U.S. Private*, pg. 3281
SHOWTIME MARKETING INC.—See National Amusements, Inc.; *U.S. Private*, pg. 2843
SHUTTLEROCK JAPAN, INC.—See Digital Holdings, Inc.; *Int'l*, pg. 2122
SILVERTECH, INC.; *U.S. Private*, pg. 3664
THE SIMBLIST GROUP INC—See Ivystone Group, LLC; *U.S. Private*, pg. 2152
SINNERSCHRADER AKTIENGESELLSCHAFT—See Accenture plc; *Int'l*, pg. 88
SINNERSCHRADER COMMERCE GMBH—See Accenture plc; *Int'l*, pg. 88
SIREN INTERACTIVE, LLC—See Dohmen Co.; *U.S. Private*, pg. 1254
SIXTH MAN MARKETING—See JEBCommerce LLC; *U.S. Private*, pg. 2196
SKM MEDIA CORP.; *U.S. Private*, pg. 3683
SKYBRIDGE AMERICAS, INC.; *U.S. Private*, pg. 3684
SLACK AND COMPANY, LLC; *U.S. Private*, pg. 3687
SMARTBOX, LLC—See 424 Capital, LLC; *U.S. Private*, pg. 15
SMARTBOX, LLC—See HealthEdge Investment Partners, LLC; *U.S. Private*, pg. 1896
SMART CARD MARKETING SYSTEMS, INC.; *U.S. Public*, pg. 1895
SMARTERHQ, INC.—See Wunderkind, LLC; *U.S. Private*, pg. 4575
SNT DEUTSCHLAND AG—See E.ON SE; *Int'l*, pg. 2260
SOH MECHANICAL & ELECTRICAL ENGINEERS CORPORATION—See Ikeshita Sekkei Co. Ltd.; *Int'l*, pg. 3610
SOLDOUT, INC.—See Hakuhodo DY Holdings Incorporated; *Int'l*, pg. 3222

SOLID INTELLIGENCE INC.—See Datasection Inc.; *Int'l*, pg. 1979
SOLUTIONSET—See SolutionSet LLC; *U.S. Private*, pg. 3711
SOMNIO SOLUTIONS INC.; *U.S. Private*, pg. 3712
SOPRANO OYJ—See Eiffage S.A.; *Int'l*, pg. 2331
THE SOURCE (BELL) ELECTRONICS INC.—See BCE Inc.; *Int'l*, pg. 926
SPACE COAST BUSINESS, LLC; *U.S. Private*, pg. 3743
SPARFACTS AUSTRALIA PTY LTD.—See SPAR Group, Inc.; *U.S. Public*, pg. 1914
SPAR FM JAPAN—See SPAR Group, Inc.; *U.S. Public*, pg. 1914
SPAR GREECE—See SPAR Group, Inc.; *U.S. Public*, pg. 1914
SPAR KROGNOS MARKETING PRIVATE LIMITED—See SPAR Group, Inc.; *U.S. Public*, pg. 1914
SPAR MARKETING FORCE, INC.—See SPAR Group, Inc.; *U.S. Public*, pg. 1914
SPAR (SHANGHAI) MARKETING MANAGEMENT COMPANY LTD.—See SPAR Group, Inc.; *U.S. Public*, pg. 1914
SPAR TODOPROMO, SAPI, DE CV—See SPAR Group, Inc.; *U.S. Public*, pg. 1914
SPECTRUM MTF OPERATOR GMBH—See IG Group Holdings plc; *Int'l*, pg. 3601
SPINIFEX GROUP—See Project: Worldwide, Inc.; *U.S. Private*, pg. 3281
SPOON AS—See Bonnier AB; *Int'l*, pg. 1109
SPOON PUBLISHING AB—See Bonnier AB; *Int'l*, pg. 1109
SPORTS IMAGE INC.; *U.S. Private*, pg. 3761
SPRINGBIG, INC.—See SpringBig Holdings, Inc.; *U.S. Public*, pg. 1919
SQUARE 2 MARKETING, INC.—See RFE Investment Partners; *U.S. Private*, pg. 3419
SSP INNOVATIONS, LLC—See Warren Equity Partners, LLC; *U.S. Private*, pg. 4443
STAGE 4 SOLUTIONS, INC.; *U.S. Private*, pg. 3775
STEAK GROUP LTD.—See Dentsu Group Inc.; *Int'l*, pg. 2038
STEWART PAKISTAN (PRIVATE) LIMITED—See Stewart Information Services Corporation; *U.S. Public*, pg. 1948
STIFEL NICOLAUS EUROPE LIMITED—See Stifel Financial Corp.; *U.S. Public*, pg. 1950
STORY(ATION) PTY LIMITED—See News Corporation; *U.S. Public*, pg. 1521
STRAN & COMPANY, INC.; *U.S. Public*, pg. 1953
STRAN LOYALTY SOLUTIONS, LLC—See Stran & Company, Inc.; *U.S. Public*, pg. 1953
STRATEGIC EDGE COMMUNICATIONS, INC.—See MD On-Line Inc.; *U.S. Private*, pg. 2646
STRATEGIQUE SANTE—See IQVIA Holdings Inc.; *U.S. Public*, pg. 1170
STROTTMAN INTERNATIONAL INC.; *U.S. Private*, pg. 3841
STUDENT MARKETING GROUP, INC.—See Nelnet, Inc.; *U.S. Public*, pg. 1504
SUITE EXPERIENCE GROUP LLC; *U.S. Private*, pg. 3850
SUMMIT RESOURCES LLC; *U.S. Private*, pg. 3856
SUN BRANDING SOLUTIONS LTD.—See DIC Corporation; *Int'l*, pg. 2109
SUNKIST (FAR EAST) PROMOTION, LTD.—See Sunkist Growers, Inc.; *U.S. Private*, pg. 3867
SUNRISE IDENTITY; *U.S. Private*, pg. 3870
THE SUN US, INC.—See News Corporation; *U.S. Public*, pg. 1521
SUPERIOR INTERNET SOLUTIONS; *U.S. Private*, pg. 3878
SURETY SYSTEMS, INC.; *U.S. Private*, pg. 3883
SUSCRIPCIONES ESPANA—See ADLPartner SA; *Int'l*, pg. 151
SUUNNITTELUTOIMISTO TTNK HELSINKI OY—See Alma Media Corporation; *Int'l*, pg. 362
SWEET SPOT DIGITAL (MALAYSIA) SDN BHD—See Berjaya Corporation Berhad; *Int'l*, pg. 984
SWEP GERMANY GMBH—See Dover Corporation; *U.S. Public*, pg. 682
SYMMETRI MARKETING GROUP, LLC; *U.S. Private*, pg. 3899
T3MEDIA, INC.; *U.S. Private*, pg. 3913
TAJ MEDIA, LLC—See AAC Holdings, Inc.; *U.S. Private*, pg. 31
TAP-ON-IT, LLC—See Gannett Co., Inc.; *U.S. Public*, pg. 906
TARGA LIQUIDS MARKETING & TRADE LLC—See Targa Resources Corp.; *U.S. Public*, pg. 1982
TARGETBASE—See Omnicom Group Inc.; *U.S. Public*, pg. 1599
TEAM ENTERPRISES, INC.—See Stagwell, Inc.; *U.S. Public*, pg. 1928
TEAM MARKETING AG—See Highlight Communications AG; *Int'l*, pg. 3388
TECHLIGHTENMENT LIMITED—See Experian plc; *Int'l*, pg. 2588
TECH RESOURCES, INC.; *U.S. Private*, pg. 3952
TECMARKET SERVIZI S.P.A.—See Banco BPM S.p.A.; *Int'l*, pg. 819
TELECOMMUNICATIONS ON DEMAND, INC.; *U.S. Private*, pg. 3960

541613 — MARKETING CONSULTIN...

TELERX MARKETING, INC.—See HCL Technologies Ltd.; *Int'l*, pg. 3299
TELMETRICS CORPORATION—See Marchex, Inc.; *U.S. Public*, pg. 1365
TENTHWAVE DIGITAL, LLC—See Wire Stone, LLC; *U.S. Private*, pg. 4546
TERRITORY INFLUENCE GMBH—See Bertelsmann SE & Co. KGaA; *Int'l*, pg. 996
TGI SOLAR POWER GROUP INC.; *U.S. Public*, pg. 2030
THEOREM ESPANOL—See Theorem Inc.; *U.S. Private*, pg. 4142
THEOREM INC.; *U.S. Private*, pg. 4141
THEOREM INDIA PVT. LTD.—See Theorem Inc.; *U.S. Private*, pg. 4142
THESIS, INC.; *U.S. Private*, pg. 4143
THE THINC GROUP—See Hakuhodo DY Holdings Incorporated; *Int'l*, pg. 3222
THINK! INC.; *U.S. Private*, pg. 4144
THINK LIMITED—See EPAM Systems, Inc.; *U.S. Public*, pg. 783
THIRD DOOR MEDIA INC.; *U.S. Private*, pg. 4145
THIRTYTHREE APAC LIMITED—See Capita plc; *Int'l*, pg. 1308
THIRTYTHREE—See Capita plc; *Int'l*, pg. 1308
THIRTYTHREE USA INC.—See Capita plc; *Int'l*, pg. 1308
TIER10; *U.S. Private*, pg. 4169
TINUITI INC.—See New Mountain Capital, LLC; *U.S. Private*, pg. 2903
TITAN MARKETING SERVICES, INC.—See Titan International, Inc.; *U.S. Public*, pg. 2160
TNS LANDIS STRATEGY & INNOVATION—See Bain Capital, LP; *U.S. Private*, pg. 448
TOP GUN SALES PERFORMANCE; *U.S. Private*, pg. 4186
T.O.P. MARKETING GROUP INC.; *U.S. Private*, pg. 3912
TOPRANK ONLINE MARKETING; *U.S. Private*, pg. 4187
TOPSPOT INTERNET MARKETING; *U.S. Private*, pg. 4188
TRADEEASY HOLDINGS LIMITED—See CCT Fortis Holdings Limited; *Int'l*, pg. 1370
TRANSPORT RISK MANAGEMENT INC.—See Kelso & Company, L.P.; *U.S. Private*, pg. 2280
TRAVELZOO LOCAL (AUSTRALIA) PTY LIMITED—See Travelzoo; *U.S. Public*, pg. 2186
TRENDERS INC.—See CyberAgent, Inc.; *Int'l*, pg. 1892
TRGRP, INC.—See Vista Equity Partners, LLC; *U.S. Private*, pg. 4402
TRIDENT MARKETING; *U.S. Private*, pg. 4229
TRIER & COMPANY; *U.S. Private*, pg. 4230
TRIMARK DIGITAL, LLC; *U.S. Private*, pg. 4232
TRIPLEFIN LLC—See JLL Partners, LLC; *U.S. Private*, pg. 2212
TRIPLEFIN LLC—See Water Street Healthcare Partners, LLC; *U.S. Private*, pg. 4452
TRITON TECHNOLOGIES, INC.; *U.S. Private*, pg. 4239
TRND SARL—See Bertelsmann SE & Co. KGaA; *Int'l*, pg. 997
TURNER NETWORK SALES, INC.—See Warner Bros. Discovery, Inc.; *U.S. Public*, pg. 2328
UNDERGROUND ELEPHANT INC.; *U.S. Private*, pg. 4279
UNISONO FIELDMARKETING—See Omnicom Group Inc.; *U.S. Public*, pg. 1599
UNISONO FIELDMARKETING—See Omnicom Group Inc.; *U.S. Public*, pg. 1599
UNISONO FIELDMARKETING—See Omnicom Group Inc.; *U.S. Public*, pg. 1599
US HEALTH ADVISORS INC—See National Health Corporation; *U.S. Private*, pg. 2856
V3 BROADSUITE, LLC; *U.S. Private*, pg. 4328
VALUECENTRIC MARKETING GROUP, INC.—See Fidelity National Infor; *U.S. Public*, pg. 833
THE VALUE ENGINEERS LIMITED—See Arsenal Capital Management LP; *U.S. Private*, pg. 338
VANTAGE CLIMICAL SOLUTIONS, LLC—See Level Equity Management, LLC; *U.S. Private*, pg. 2434
VANTAGE CLIMICAL SOLUTIONS, LLC—See Silversmith Management, L.P.; *U.S. Private*, pg. 3664
VANTAGE CLIMICAL SOLUTIONS, LLC—See The Carlyle Group Inc.; *U.S. Public*, pg. 2050
VANTAGE PRODUCTION, LLC.—See United Communications Group; *U.S. Private*, pg. 4289
VECTRA, INC.—See Taylor Corporation; *U.S. Private*, pg. 3939
VELOCITY MARKETING CONCEPTS, INC—See Live Ventures Incorporated; *U.S. Public*, pg. 1332
VENDINI, INC.—See AudienceView Ticketing Corporation; *Int'l*, pg. 701
VENTURE SOLUTIONS INC.—See Taylor Corporation; *U.S. Private*, pg. 3939
VERACENTRA, INC.; *U.S. Private*, pg. 4359
VERINT SYSTEMS (PHILIPPINES) CORPORATION—See Verint Systems Inc.; *U.S. Public*, pg. 2281
VERINT SYSTEMS UK LTD.—See Verint Systems Inc.; *U.S. Public*, pg. 2281
VERTIKOM AUSTRIA GMBH—See ASM Group S.A.; *Int'l*, pg. 625
VERTIKOM SALES BERLIN GMBH—See ASM Group S.A.; *Int'l*, pg. 625
VERTIKOM SALES GMBH—See ASM Group S.A.; *Int'l*, pg. 625

VERTIKOM SWITZERLAND GMBH—See ASM Group S.A.; *Int'l*, pg. 625
VERTIVE, LLC; *U.S. Private*, pg. 4370
VHMNETWORK LLLC; *U.S. Private*, pg. 4375
VIA LUNA GROUP (VLG); *U.S. Private*, pg. 4375
VINCODO, LLC—See Brookfield Corporation; *Int'l*, pg. 1188
VIRID INTERATIVIDADE DIGITAL LTDA—See Experian plc; *Int'l*, pg. 2588
VISITURE, LLC—See ZelnickMedia Corp.; *U.S. Private*, pg. 4600
VISTEX, INC.; *U.S. Private*, pg. 4403
VISTRA COMMUNICATIONS; *U.S. Private*, pg. 4403
VISUAL IQ, INC.—See Brookfield Corporation; *Int'l*, pg. 1180
VISUAL IQ, INC.—See Brookfield Corporation; *Int'l*, pg. 1180
VISUAL IQ, INC.—See Elliott Management Corporation; *U.S. Private*, pg. 1373
VISUAL IQ, INC.—See Elliott Management Corporation; *U.S. Private*, pg. 1373
VITRADO GMBH—See freenet AG; *Int'l*, pg. 2770
VIVACITY HEALTH PTY. LTD.—See IQVIA Holdings Inc.; *U.S. Public*, pg. 1170
VIVA LIFE SCIENCE CORP—See Westar Nutrition Corp.; *U.S. Private*, pg. 4488
VOLUME 9 INC; *U.S. Private*, pg. 4411
VOSTOCHNAYA TECHNICA UK LTD—See Barloworld Ltd.; *Int'l*, pg. 866
VOTIGO, INC.; *U.S. Private*, pg. 4413
V P HOLDINGS, INC.—See Platinum Equity, LLC; *U.S. Private*, pg. 3209
VSA PARTNERS, INC.—See Innovatus Capital Partners LLC; *U.S. Private*, pg. 2083
VTD VAKUUMTECKNIK DRESDEN GMBH—See Icahn Enterprises L.P.; *U.S. Public*, pg. 1085
W3I, LLC; *U.S. Private*, pg. 4423
WALKERTEK INTERACTIVE MARKETING, INC.; *U.S. Private*, pg. 4429
WASSERMAN MEDIA GROUP, LLC; *U.S. Private*, pg. 4450
WE ARE SOCIAL LTD.—See Bluefocus Intelligent Communications Group Co., Ltd.; *Int'l*, pg. 1071
WEBIMAX; *U.S. Private*, pg. 4466
WEBIMAX—See WebiMax; *U.S. Private*, pg. 4466
WEBIMAX—See WebiMax; *U.S. Private*, pg. 4466
WEBIMAX—See WebiMax; *U.S. Private*, pg. 4466
WEBIMAX—See WebiMax; *U.S. Private*, pg. 4466
WEB RESERVATIONS INTERNATIONAL, LTD.—See Hellman & Friedman LLC; *U.S. Private*, pg. 1911
WEBTIVITY DESIGN SOLUTIONS; *U.S. Private*, pg. 4467
WHATCOUNTS, INC.—See Aquiline Capital Partners LLC; *U.S. Private*, pg. 305
WILEN NEW YORK; *U.S. Private*, pg. 4519
WILLIAMS INTERACTIVE LLC—See Light & Wonder, Inc.; *U.S. Public*, pg. 1315
WINN TECHNOLOGY GROUP, INC.; *U.S. Private*, pg. 4542
WINSOR LEARNING INC.—See Silver Lake Group, LLC; *U.S. Private*, pg. 3661
WINTERBERRY GROUP, LLC; *U.S. Private*, pg. 4545
WOMEN'S MARKETING, INC. - NEW YORK OFFICE—See SF Holding Corp.; *U.S. Private*, pg. 3621
WOMEN'S MARKETING, INC.—See SF Holding Corp.; *U.S. Private*, pg. 3621
WOODRUFF SWEITZER; *U.S. Private*, pg. 4560
WORDSMITH MEDIA, INC.; *U.S. Private*, pg. 2378
WORLD WEB PARTNERS, INC.; *U.S. Private*, pg. 4567
WPROMOTE, INC. - DALLAS—See ZelnickMedia Corp.; *U.S. Private*, pg. 4601
WTECH; *U.S. Private*, pg. 4574
WUNDERKNABEN KOMMUNIKATION GMBH—See ASM Group S.A.; *Int'l*, pg. 625
WUNDERMAN DENTSU INC.—See Dentsu Group Inc.; *Int'l*, pg. 2040
XCENDA, LLC—See Cencora, Inc.; *U.S. Public*, pg. 467
YING INTERACTIVE MARKETING SERVICES LTD.—See Grand Vision Media Holdings PLC; *Int'l*, pg. 3057
YOU & MR JONES INC.; *U.S. Private*, pg. 4591
YOUR SPEAKEASY LLC—See DallasNews Corporation; *U.S. Public*, pg. 621
ZEO CORPORATION—See AOI TYO Holdings Inc.; *Int'l*, pg. 488
ZETA INTERACTIVE CORPORATION; *U.S. Private*, pg. 4602
ZS ASSOCIATES, INC.; *U.S. Private*, pg. 4609
Z SQUARED MEDIA, LLC; *U.S. Private*, pg. 4596

541614 — PROCESS, PHYSICAL DISTRIBUTION, AND LOGISTICS CONSULTING SERVICES

7DAYS MEDIA SERVICES GMBH—See 7Days Group GmbH & Co. KG; *Int'l*, pg. 15
9R MANAGEMENT SDN. BHD.—See 9R Limited; *Int'l*, pg. 17
A2A LOGISTICA S.P.A.—See A2A S.p.A.; *Int'l*, pg. 29
A3 DISTRIB, SAS—See Brookfield Corporation; *Int'l*, pg. 1176
A3 DISTRIB SAS—See Elliott Management Corporation; *Int'l*, pg. 1369
AARDVARK EVENT LOGISTICS, INC.; *U.S. Private*, pg. 32

ABB LOGISTICS CENTER EUROPE GMBH—See ABB Ltd.; *Int'l*, pg. 50
ABC INDIA LTD.; *Int'l*, pg. 57
ABERTIS LOGISTICA CHILE—See ACS, Actividades de Construccion y Servicios, S.A.; *Int'l*, pg. 112
ABERTIS LOGISTICA, S.A.—See ACS, Actividades de Construccion y Servicios, S.A.; *Int'l*, pg. 112
ABF LOGISTICS II, INC.—See ArcBest Corporation; *U.S. Public*, pg. 180
ABF LOGISTICS, INC.—See ArcBest Corporation; *U.S. Public*, pg. 180
ABLE TRANSPORTE DE CARGA S. DE R.L. DE C.V.—See Able Freight Services Inc.; *U.S. Private*, pg. 39
ABU DHABI PORTS COMPANY PJSC—See Abu Dhabi Developmental Holding Company PJSC; *Int'l*, pg. 71
ACCA INTERNATIONAL CO., LTD.—See Daiwa House Industry Co., Ltd.; *Int'l*, pg. 1947
ACCESS DATA CORP.—See Broadridge Financial Solutions, Inc.; *U.S. Public*, pg. 391
ACCESS TECHNOLOGY SOLUTIONS, LC; *U.S. Private*, pg. 53
ACI LAST MILE NETWORK LLC; *U.S. Private*, pg. 59
ACTION LOGISTICS (WA) PTY LTD—See CTI Logistics Limited; *Int'l*, pg. 1871
ACTIVE ANTS BELGIUM BV—See bpost NV/SA; *Int'l*, pg. 1133
ADAM SYSTEMS—See Karmak Inc.; *U.S. Private*, pg. 2263
ADANI AGRI LOGISTICS LTD—See Adani Enterprises Limited; *Int'l*, pg. 124
ADANI LOGISTICS LTD—See Adani Enterprises Limited; *Int'l*, pg. 125
ADDICKS & KREYE CONTAINER LOGISTIK GMBH & CO—See Addicks & Kreye Holding GmbH; *Int'l*, pg. 128
ADEKA LOGISTICS CORP.—See Adeka Corporation; *Int'l*, pg. 142
THE ADVANCE GROUP; *U.S. Private*, pg. 3982
ADVANTAGE LOGISTICS USA, INC.—See United Natural Foods, Inc.; *U.S. Public*, pg. 2231
ADVANTIS INTASL BANGLADESH (PVT) LTD.—See Hayleys PLC; *Int'l*, pg. 3291
ADVANTIS KUSUHARA SEDATE MYANMAR (PVT) LTD.—See Hayleys PLC; *Int'l*, pg. 3291
ADVANTIS SABANG RAYA LINES PTE. LTD.—See Hayleys PLC; *Int'l*, pg. 3291
AEGIS LOGISTICS LTD.; *Int'l*, pg. 173
AEI DRAWBACK SERVICES INC.—See Deutsche Post AG; *Int'l*, pg. 2071
AENIX INFORMATIQUE S.A.; *Int'l*, pg. 176
AERO INVENTORY PLC; *Int'l*, pg. 180
AEROSIM TECHNOLOGIES, INC.—See L3Harris Technologies, Inc.; *U.S. Public*, pg. 1280
AFFLE (INDIA) LIMITED; *Int'l*, pg. 188
AFT CORPORATION LIMITED; *Int'l*, pg. 196
AGC LOGISTICS CO., LTD.—See AGC Inc.; *Int'l*, pg. 202
AGENCIA DE ADUANAS DHL EXPRESS COLOMBIA LTDA.—See Deutsche Post AG; *Int'l*, pg. 2071
AGENCIA DE ADUANAS DHL GLOBAL FORWARDING (COLOMBIA) S.A.—See Deutsche Post AG; *Int'l*, pg. 2071
AGHEERA GMBH—See Deutsche Post AG; *Int'l*, pg. 2071
AGILITY INTERNATIONAL LOGISTICS PTE. LTD.—See Agility; *Int'l*, pg. 209
AGILITY LOGISTICS CORP.—See Agility; *Int'l*, pg. 210
AGILITY LOGISTICS HOLDINGS PTE. LTD.—See Agility; *Int'l*, pg. 210
AGILITY LOGISTICS INTERNATIONAL B.V.—See Agility; *Int'l*, pg. 210
AGILITY LOGISTICS LIMITED—See Agility; *Int'l*, pg. 210
AGILITY LOGISTICS SARL—See DSV A/S; *Int'l*, pg. 2210
AGILITY PROJECT LOGISTICS INC.—See Agility; *Int'l*, pg. 210
AGS-SECUTRANS B.V.—See The Brink's Company; *U.S. Public*, pg. 2042
AIKYO SANGYO CO., LTD.—See Aisan Industry Co., Ltd.; *Int'l*, pg. 250
AI LOGISTICS COMPANY LIMITED—See AI Energy Public Company Limited; *Int'l*, pg. 226
AIR EXPRESS INTERNATIONAL USA, INC.—See Deutsche Post AG; *Int'l*, pg. 2071
AITC LOGISTICS (VIETNAM) CO., LTD.—See AIT Corporation; *Int'l*, pg. 254
AIT (HKG) LIMITED—See AIT Corporation; *Int'l*, pg. 254
AIT INTERNATIONAL LOGISTICS (SHANGHAI) CO., LTD.—See AIT Corporation; *Int'l*, pg. 254
AIT INTERNATIONAL LOGISTICS (TAIWAN) CO., LTD.—See AIT Corporation; *Int'l*, pg. 254
AJINOMOTO LOGISTICS CORPORATION—See Ajinomoto Company, Inc.; *Int'l*, pg. 256
AJIS PHILIPPINES, INC.—See AJIS Co., Ltd.; *Int'l*, pg. 258
AKAMAI TECHNOLOGIES, INC.; *U.S. Public*, pg. 68
AKIMA LOGISTICS SERVICES, LLC—See Nana Regional Corporation, Inc.; *U.S. Private*, pg. 2832
ALBATROS LOGISTIC, MAROC, S.A.—See ACS, Actividades de Construccion y Servicios, S.A.; *Int'l*, pg. 110
ALBATROS LOGISTIC, S.A.—See ACS, Actividades de Construccion y Servicios, S.A.; *Int'l*, pg. 110
ALBERT SCHEID GMBH—See Deutsche Post AG; *Int'l*, pg. 2071

AL JABER SHIPPING AGENCY & MARINE WORKS LLC—See Al Jaber Group; *Int'l*, pg. 279
ALLIANCE ADVISORS LLC; *U.S. Private*, pg. 181
ALLOGA AG—See CSL Limited; *Int'l*, pg. 1866
ALLOGA (NEDERLAND) B.V.—See Walgreens Boots Alliance, Inc.; *U.S. Public*, pg. 2322
ALLSEAS MARINE SERVICES PTE LTD—See AMOS Group Limited; *Int'l*, pg. 430
ALOCS CORPORATION—See Akebono Brake Industry Co., Ltd.; *Int'l*, pg. 262
ALPI LIVORNO SRL—See Albini & Pitigliani S.p.A.; *Int'l*, pg. 298
ALPI NETHERLANDS B.V.—See Albini & Pitigliani S.p.A.; *Int'l*, pg. 298
ALPI OLIMPIKA LTD—See Albini & Pitigliani S.p.A.; *Int'l*, pg. 298
ALRAINE SHIPPING AGENCIES LTD.—See Financiere de L'Odet; *Int'l*, pg. 2665
ALTA LOGISTICS, INC.—See Saltchuk Resources Inc.; *U.S. Private*, pg. 3534
ALTAVIA OPTITRANS S.A.S.—See Altavia S.A.; *Int'l*, pg. 387
ALTRAD ASIA LIMITED—See Altrad Investment Authority SAS; *Int'l*, pg. 397
ALVOCOL N.V.—See Colruyt Group N.V.; *Int'l*, pg. 1705
AMA MARINE PUBLIC COMPANY LIMITED; *Int'l*, pg. 403
AMARA BRASIL, LTDA.—See Iberdrola, S.A.; *Int'l*, pg. 3570
AMAZON ROBOTICS LLC—See Amazon.com, Inc.; *U.S. Public*, pg. 90
AMB/AFCO CARGO, LLC—See Prologis, Inc.; *U.S. Public*, pg. 1727
AMBER ROAD, INC.—See Insight Venture Management, LLC; *U.S. Private*, pg. 2087
AMBIPAR PARTICIPACOES E EMPREENDIMENTOS SA; *Int'l*, pg. 414
AMBIPAR RESPONSE LIMITED—See Ambipar Participacoes e Empreendimentos SA; *Int'l*, pg. 414
AMERICAN CARTAGE & DISTRIBUTION, LLC—See American Shipping Co. Inc.; *U.S. Private*, pg. 253
AMERICAN GLOBAL LOGISTICS, LLC—See Moelis Asset Management LP; *U.S. Private*, pg. 2764
AMERICAN INTERMODAL MANAGEMENT, LLC—See I Squared Capital Advisors (US) LLC; *U.S. Private*, pg. 2021
AMERICAN LABELMARK COMPANY INC.; *U.S. Private*, pg. 239
AMER SPORTS UK LOGISTICS CENTER—See ANTA Sports Products Limited; *Int'l*, pg. 480
AMI (TANZANIA) LTD.—See Financiere de L'Odet; *Int'l*, pg. 2665
AMWARE LOGISTICS SERVICES, INC.—See Rotunda Capital Partners LLC; *U.S. Private*, pg. 3487
ANA CARGO INC.—See ANA Holdings Inc.; *Int'l*, pg. 444
ANCRA ESPANA S.L.—See The Heico Companies, L.L.C.; *U.S. Private*, pg. 4050
ANDEAVOR LOGISTICS LP—See Marathon Petroleum Corporation; *U.S. Public*, pg. 1364
ANSA MCAL TRADING INC.—See ANSA McAL Limited; *Int'l*, pg. 476
ANTERIST + SCHNEIDER ZEEBRUGGE B.V.—See Deutsche Bahn AG; *Int'l*, pg. 2049
APM GROUP LTD.; *Int'l*, pg. 516
APM TERMINALS ELIZABETH, LLC—See A.P. Moller-Maersk A/S; *Int'l*, pg. 25
APM TERMINALS MOIN S.A.—See A.P. Moller-Maersk A/S; *Int'l*, pg. 25
APM TERMINALS PACIFIC LLC—See A.P. Moller-Maersk A/S; *Int'l*, pg. 25
APPROACH EXCELLENCE TRADING LTD.—See Apex International Co., Ltd.; *Int'l*, pg. 511
AQUA LOGISTICS LIMITED; *Int'l*, pg. 527
ARAI & CO., LTD.; *Int'l*, pg. 534
ARAMEX AMMAN—See Aramex PJSC; *Int'l*, pg. 535
ARAMEX INDIA PRIVATE LIMITED—See Aramex PJSC; *Int'l*, pg. 535
ARAMEX IRELAND—See Aramex PJSC; *Int'l*, pg. 535
ARCBEST LOGISTICS, INC.—See ArcBest Corporation; *U.S. Public*, pg. 180
ARCELORMITTAL DISTRIBUTION S.A.S.—See ArcelorMittal S.A.; *Int'l*, pg. 544
ARCH LOGISTICS, LLC—See Bunzl plc; *Int'l*, pg. 1217
ARCUS INSTALLATION N.V.—See Deufol SE; *Int'l*, pg. 2048
ARMOUR LOGISTICS SERVICES INC.—See Armour Transportation Systems; *Int'l*, pg. 575
ARMOUR TRANSPORT INC—See Armour Transportation Systems; *Int'l*, pg. 575
A&R PACKAGING & DISTRIBUTION SERVICES, INC.—See A&R Transport, Inc.; *U.S. Private*, pg. 20
ARRENDADORA KCSM, S. DE R.L. DE C.V.—See Canadian Pacific Kansas City Limited; *Int'l*, pg. 1285
ARRIVA EAST HERTS & ESSEX LTD—See I Squared Capital Advisors (US) LLC; *U.S. Private*, pg. 2024
ARRIVA HOLDING CESKA REPUBLIKA S.R.O.—See I Squared Capital Advisors (US) LLC; *U.S. Private*, pg. 2024
ARRIVA TAG AB—See I Squared Capital Advisors (US) LLC; *U.S. Private*, pg. 2025

ARROW FREIGHT CORPORATION—See Benguet Corporation; *Int'l*, pg. 974
ARSHIYA LIMITED; *Int'l*, pg. 580
ARS-UNIKAI GMBH—See Hamburger Hafen und Logistik AG; *Int'l*, pg. 3236
ARVATO SE—See Bertelsmann SE & Co. KGaA; *Int'l*, pg. 990
ARVATO SUPPLY CHAIN SOLUTIONS SE—See Bertelsmann SE & Co. KGaA; *Int'l*, pg. 990
ASCENT GLOBAL LOGISTICS, LLC—See Elliott Management Corporation; *U.S. Private*, pg. 1365
ASIMEX ANTERIST + SCHNEIDER IMPORT - EXPORT SAS—See Deutsche Bahn AG; *Int'l*, pg. 2049
ASJ COMMERCE INC.—See ASJ Inc.; *Int'l*, pg. 621
A-SONIC EXPRESS LOGISTICS (INDIA) PRIVATE LIMITED—See A-Sonic Aerospace Limited; *Int'l*, pg. 20
A-SONIC LOGISTICS (AUSTRALIA) PTY LTD—See A-Sonic Aerospace Limited; *Int'l*, pg. 20
A-SONIC LOGISTICS (H.K.) LIMITED—See A-Sonic Aerospace Limited; *Int'l*, pg. 21
A-SONIC LOGISTICS (KOREA) CO., LTD.—See A-Sonic Aerospace Limited; *Int'l*, pg. 21
A-SONIC LOGISTICS (NETHERLANDS) B.V.—See A-Sonic Aerospace Limited; *Int'l*, pg. 21
A-SONIC LOGISTICS PTE. LTD.—See A-Sonic Aerospace Limited; *Int'l*, pg. 20
A-SONIC LOGISTICS (USA), INC.—See A-Sonic Aerospace Limited; *Int'l*, pg. 21
A-SONIC LOGISTICS (VIETNAM) COMPANY LIMITED—See A-Sonic Aerospace Limited; *Int'l*, pg. 21
ASPEN TRANSPORTATION, LLC; *U.S. Private*, pg. 352
ASPINWALL & CO. LTD.,; *Int'l*, pg. 630
ASPIRE CONSULTING GROUP LLC; *U.S. Private*, pg. 352
ASRCO LOGISTICS LTD.—See Beijing Sports & Entertainment Industry Group Limited; *Int'l*, pg. 957
ASR EUROPE LOGISTICS LTD.—See Beijing Sports & Entertainment Industry Group Limited; *Int'l*, pg. 957
ASR LOGISTICS LTD.—See Beijing Sports & Entertainment Industry Group Limited; *Int'l*, pg. 957
AS SCHENKER—See Deutsche Bahn AG; *Int'l*, pg. 2052
ASSETCO FREIGHT BROKERS INC.; *U.S. Private*, pg. 354
ASSET KINETICS PTY. LTD.—See Engenco Limited; *Int'l*, pg. 2426
ATLAS LOGISTICS INC.—See Atlas World Group, Inc.; *U.S. Private*, pg. 380
ATS-TANNER BANDING SYSTEMS AG; *Int'l*, pg. 696
AUDELI, S.A.—See ACS, Actividades de Construccion y Servicios, S.A.; *Int'l*, pg. 110
AURIONPRO TRANSIT PTE. LTD.—See Aurionpro Solutions Limited; *Int'l*, pg. 711
AURIZON PORT SERVICES NSW PTY. LTD.—See Aurizon Holdings Limited; *Int'l*, pg. 711
AUSTRALIAN FULFILMENT SERVICES PTY LTD—See CTI Logistics Limited; *Int'l*, pg. 1871
AUTOLOGISTIC POLAND SP. Z O. O.—See Deutsche Bahn AG; *Int'l*, pg. 2050
AVASANT LLC; *U.S. Private*, pg. 404
AVION LOGISTICS LIMITED—See General Dynamics Corporation; *U.S. Public*, pg. 913
AVITEA INDUSTRIESERVICE GMBH—See Hella GmbH & Co. KGaA; *Int'l*, pg. 3333
AVNET LOGISTICS DO BRASIL LTDA.—See Avnet, Inc.; *U.S. Public*, pg. 251
AVNET LOGISTICS GMBH—See Avnet, Inc.; *U.S. Public*, pg. 251
AVNET LOGISTICS PMC STUTENSEE GMBH—See Avnet, Inc.; *U.S. Public*, pg. 251
AVNET LOGISTICS—See Avnet, Inc.; *U.S. Public*, pg. 251
AVNET LOGISTICS STUTENSEE GMBH—See Avnet, Inc.; *U.S. Public*, pg. 251
AVVASHYA CCI LOGISTICS PRIVATE LIMITED—See Allcargo Logistics Limited; *Int'l*, pg. 333
AZEGO COMPONENTS AG—See HPI AG; *Int'l*, pg. 3500
BACHLE LOGISTICS GMBH—See Die Schweizerische Post AG; *Int'l*, pg. 2112
BANDAI LOGIPAL INC.—See BANDAI NAMCO Holdings Inc.; *Int'l*, pg. 828
BANG & OLUFSEN OPERATIONS A/S—See Bang & Olufsen a/s; *Int'l*, pg. 831
BANG TAI INTERNATIONAL LOGISTICS CO., LIMITED—See Hon Hai Precision Industry Co., Ltd.; *Int'l*, pg. 3456
BANTA GLOBAL TURNKEY, LTD.—See Chatham Asset Management, LLC; *U.S. Private*, pg. 862
BARLOWORLD LOGISTICS (PTY) LIMITED—See Barloworld Ltd.; *Int'l*, pg. 866
BASF LOGISTICS GMBH—See BASF SE; *Int'l*, pg. 880
BAYER BITTERFELD GMBH—See Bayer Aktiengesellschaft; *Int'l*, pg. 902
BDP ASIA PACIFIC LIMITED—See BDP International Inc.; *U.S. Private*, pg. 501
BDP ASIA PACIFIC PTE LTD.—See BDP International Inc.; *U.S. Private*, pg. 501
BDP CANADA ULC—See BDP International Inc.; *U.S. Private*, pg. 501
BDP CHILE LTDA.—See BDP International Inc.; *U.S. Private*, pg. 501
BDP GLOBAL LOGISTICS (INDIA) PRIVATE LIMITED—See

BDP International Inc.; *U.S. Private*, pg. 501
BDP INTERNATIONAL BV—See BDP International Inc.; *U.S. Private*, pg. 501
BDP INTERNATIONAL LTD.—See BDP International Inc.; *U.S. Private*, pg. 501
BDP INTERNATIONAL MEXICO, S.A. DE C.V.—See BDP International Inc.; *U.S. Private*, pg. 501
BDP INTERNATIONAL NV - AIRFREIGHT DIVISION—See BDP International Inc.; *U.S. Private*, pg. 501
BDP INTERNATIONAL NV—See BDP International Inc.; *U.S. Private*, pg. 501
BDP INTERNATIONAL SPAIN, S.A—See BDP International Inc.; *U.S. Private*, pg. 501
BDP INTERNATIONAL UK LIMITED—See BDP International Inc.; *U.S. Private*, pg. 501
BDP ITALIA S.P.A—See BDP International Inc.; *U.S. Private*, pg. 501
BDP KANOO CHEMICAL LOGISTICS CO. LTD—See BDP International Inc.; *U.S. Private*, pg. 501
BDP LOGISTICS KOREA LIMITED—See BDP International Inc.; *U.S. Private*, pg. 501
BDP (MALAYSIA) SDN BHD—See BDP International Inc.; *U.S. Private*, pg. 501
BDP SOUTH AMERICA LTDA.—See BDP International Inc.; *U.S. Private*, pg. 502
BECK & POLLITZER CZECH S.R.O.—See Graphite Capital Management LLP; *Int'l*, pg. 3060
BECK & POLLITZER DEUTSCHLAND GMBH—See Graphite Capital Management LLP; *Int'l*, pg. 3060
BECK & POLLITZER ENGINEERING LTD—See Graphite Capital Management LLP; *Int'l*, pg. 3060
BECK & POLLITZER FRANCE SAS—See Graphite Capital Management LLP; *Int'l*, pg. 3060
BECK & POLLITZER HUNGARY KFT.—See Graphite Capital Management LLP; *Int'l*, pg. 3060
BECK & POLLITZER INDIA PVT. LTD.—See Graphite Capital Management LLP; *Int'l*, pg. 3060
BECK & POLLITZER ITALIA S.R.L.—See Graphite Capital Management LLP; *Int'l*, pg. 3060
BECK & POLLITZER POLSKA SP.Z.O.O—See Graphite Capital Management LLP; *Int'l*, pg. 3060
BECK & POLLITZER ROMANIA SRL—See Graphite Capital Management LLP; *Int'l*, pg. 3060
BECK & POLLITZER TICARET LTD. STI.—See Graphite Capital Management LLP; *Int'l*, pg. 3060
BEIJING CHANGJIU LOGISTICS CORP; *Int'l*, pg. 947
BEIJING INLAND PORT INTERNATIONAL LOGISTICS CO. LTD.—See Beijing Properties (Holdings) Limited; *Int'l*, pg. 955
BEIJING UMEONE DIGITAL TEC.CO., LTD.—See HUB Cyber Security Ltd.; *Int'l*, pg. 3516
BENIN TERMINAL S.A.—See Financiere de L'Odet; *Int'l*, pg. 2665
BENNETT DISTRIBUTION SERVICES, LLC—See Bennett International Group, Inc.; *U.S. Private*, pg. 527
BEST LOGISTICS GROUP, INC.; *U.S. Private*, pg. 543
BEST LOGISTICS TECHNOLOGIES (CHINA) CO., LTD.—See Best Inc.; *Int'l*, pg. 999
BEWHERE HOLDINGS INC.; *Int'l*, pg. 1004
BIBBY DISTRIBUTION LIMITED—See Endless LLP; *Int'l*, pg. 2403
BIEFFE CONTAINER LOGISTIC S.R.L.—See Deutsche Post AG; *Int'l*, pg. 2071
BIRDDOG SOLUTIONS, INC.; *U.S. Private*, pg. 564
BIRDS TRANSPORT & LOGISTICS LTD—See Ballyvesey Holdings Limited; *Int'l*, pg. 809
BLG AUTOTERMINAL BREMERHAVEN GMBH & CO. KG—See Bremer Lagerhaus-Gesellschaft; *Int'l*, pg. 1145
BLG LOGISTICS GROUP AG & CO. KG—See Bremer Lagerhaus-Gesellschaft; *Int'l*, pg. 1145
BLUE DART AVIATION LTD.—See Deutsche Post AG; *Int'l*, pg. 2071
BLUESCOPE STEEL LOGISTICS CO PTY LTD—See BlueScope Steel Limited; *Int'l*, pg. 1073
BLUESPED FRANCE SARL—See Die Schweizerische Post AG; *Int'l*, pg. 2112
BLUESPED LOGISTICS SARL—See Die Schweizerische Post AG; *Int'l*, pg. 2112
BLUESTAR DISTRIBUTION INC.—See Apollo Global Management, Inc.; *U.S. Public*, pg. 165
BLUESWORD INTELLIGENT TECHNOLOGY CO., LTD.; *Int'l*, pg. 1075
BLUEWATER FEDERAL SOLUTIONS, INC.—See Tetra Tech, Inc.; *U.S. Public*, pg. 2022
BMMI DJIBOUTI—See BMMI B.S.C.; *Int'l*, pg. 1076
BNSF LOGISTICS, LLC—See Berkshire Hathaway Inc.; *U.S. Public*, pg. 303
BNSF LOGISTICS, LLC—See Berkshire Hathaway Inc.; *U.S. Public*, pg. 303
BOLLORE AFRICA LOGISTICS ANGOLA LIMITADA—See Financiere de L'Odet; *Int'l*, pg. 2666
BOLLORE AFRICA LOGISTICS MAROC SA—See Financiere de L'Odet; *Int'l*, pg. 2666
BOLLORE AFRICA LOGISTICS (SL) LTD.—See Financiere de L'Odet; *Int'l*, pg. 2666
BOLLORE LOGISTICS ARGENTINA SA—See Financiere de L'Odet; *Int'l*, pg. 2666

541614 — PROCESS, PHYSICAL D...

BOLLORE LOGISTICS ASIA-PACIFIC CORPORATE PTE. LTD.—See Financiere de L'Odet; *Int'l*, pg. 2666
BOLLORE LOGISTICS AUSTRALIA PTY. LTD.—See Financiere de L'Odet; *Int'l*, pg. 2666
BOLLORE LOGISTICS BELGIUM NV—See Financiere de L'Odet; *Int'l*, pg. 2666
BOLLORE LOGISTICS BRAZIL LTDA—See Financiere de L'Odet; *Int'l*, pg. 2666
BOLLORE LOGISTICS (CAMBODIA) LTD.—See Financiere de L'Odet; *Int'l*, pg. 2666
BOLLORE LOGISTICS CANADA INC.—See Financiere de L'Odet; *Int'l*, pg. 2666
BOLLORE LOGISTICS CHILE SA—See Financiere de L'Odet; *Int'l*, pg. 2666
BOLLORE LOGISTICS CHINA CO. LTD.—See Financiere de L'Odet; *Int'l*, pg. 2666
BOLLORE LOGISTICS CZECH REPUBLIC S.R.O.—See Financiere de L'Odet; *Int'l*, pg. 2666
BOLLORE LOGISTICS GERMANY GMBH—See Financiere de L'Odet; *Int'l*, pg. 2666
BOLLORE LOGISTICS GUADELOUPE SAS—See Financiere de L'Odet; *Int'l*, pg. 2666
BOLLORE LOGISTICS HONG KONG LTD.—See Financiere de L'Odet; *Int'l*, pg. 2666
BOLLORE LOGISTICS INDIA LTD.—See Financiere de L'Odet; *Int'l*, pg. 2666
BOLLORE LOGISTICS JAPAN KK—See Financiere de L'Odet; *Int'l*, pg. 2666
BOLLORE LOGISTICS KOREA CO. LTD.—See Financiere de L'Odet; *Int'l*, pg. 2666
BOLLORE LOGISTICS LAO LTD.—See Financiere de L'Odet; *Int'l*, pg. 2666
BOLLORE LOGISTICS LUXEMBOURG SA—See Financiere de L'Odet; *Int'l*, pg. 2666
BOLLORE LOGISTICS MARTINIQUE SAS—See Financiere de L'Odet; *Int'l*, pg. 2666
BOLLORE LOGISTICS MAYOTTE SARL—See Financiere de L'Odet; *Int'l*, pg. 2666
BOLLORE LOGISTICS MEXICO, SA DE CV—See Financiere de L'Odet; *Int'l*, pg. 2666
BOLLORE LOGISTICS NETHERLANDS BV—See Financiere de L'Odet; *Int'l*, pg. 2666
BOLLORE LOGISTICS NEW ZEALAND LTD.—See Financiere de L'Odet; *Int'l*, pg. 2666
BOLLORE LOGISTICS NORWAY AS—See Financiere de L'Odet; *Int'l*, pg. 2666
BOLLORE LOGISTICS NOUVELLE-CALEDONIE SA—See Financiere de L'Odet; *Int'l*, pg. 2666
BOLLORE LOGISTICS POLAND SP. Z.O.O.—See Financiere de L'Odet; *Int'l*, pg. 2666
BOLLORE LOGISTICS POLYNESIE SAS—See Financiere de L'Odet; *Int'l*, pg. 2666
BOLLORE LOGISTICS PORTUGAL LDA—See Financiere de L'Odet; *Int'l*, pg. 2666
BOLLORE LOGISTICS REUNION SAS—See Financiere de L'Odet; *Int'l*, pg. 2666
BOLLORE LOGISTICS (SHANGHAI) CO. LTD.—See Financiere de L'Odet; *Int'l*, pg. 2666
BOLLORE LOGISTICS SINGAPORE PTE. LTD.—See Financiere de L'Odet; *Int'l*, pg. 2666
BOLLORE LOGISTICS TAIWAN LTD.—See Financiere de L'Odet; *Int'l*, pg. 2666
BOLLORE LOGISTICS TANGER MED SA—See Financiere de L'Odet; *Int'l*, pg. 2666
BOLLORE LOGISTICS UK LTD.—See Financiere de L'Odet; *Int'l*, pg. 2666
BOLLORE LOGISTICS VIETNAM CO. LTD.—See Financiere de L'Odet; *Int'l*, pg. 2666
BOLLORE TRANSPORT & LOGISTICS BOTSWANA (PTY) LTD.—See Financiere de L'Odet; *Int'l*, pg. 2667
BOLLORE TRANSPORT & LOGISTICS BURUNDI SA—See Financiere de L'Odet; *Int'l*, pg. 2667
BOLLORE TRANSPORT & LOGISTICS CAMEROUN SA—See Financiere de L'Odet; *Int'l*, pg. 2667
BOLLORE TRANSPORT & LOGISTICS CENTRAFRIQUE SA—See Financiere de L'Odet; *Int'l*, pg. 2667
BOLLORE TRANSPORT & LOGISTICS CONGO SA—See Financiere de L'Odet; *Int'l*, pg. 2667
BOLLORE TRANSPORT & LOGISTICS CORPORATE SAS—See Financiere de L'Odet; *Int'l*, pg. 2667
BOLLORE TRANSPORT & LOGISTICS COTE D'IVOIRE SA—See Financiere de L'Odet; *Int'l*, pg. 2667
BOLLORE TRANSPORT & LOGISTICS GAMBIA LTD.—See Financiere de L'Odet; *Int'l*, pg. 2667
BOLLORE TRANSPORT & LOGISTICS GUINEE SA—See Financiere de L'Odet; *Int'l*, pg. 2667
BOLLORE TRANSPORT & LOGISTICS KENYA LTD.—See Financiere de L'Odet; *Int'l*, pg. 2667
BOLLORE TRANSPORT & LOGISTICS LEKKI FZE—See Financiere de L'Odet; *Int'l*, pg. 2667
BOLLORE TRANSPORT & LOGISTICS MADAGASCAR—See Financiere de L'Odet; *Int'l*, pg. 2667
BOLLORE TRANSPORT & LOGISTICS MALAWI LTD.—See Financiere de L'Odet; *Int'l*, pg. 2667
BOLLORE TRANSPORT & LOGISTICS MALI—See Financiere de L'Odet; *Int'l*, pg. 2667
BOLLORE TRANSPORT & LOGISTICS MAROC SA—See Financiere de L'Odet; *Int'l*, pg. 2667
BOLLORE TRANSPORT & LOGISTICS MOCAMBIQUE SA—See Financiere de L'Odet; *Int'l*, pg. 2667
BOLLORE TRANSPORT & LOGISTICS NAMIBIA PROPRIETARY LTD.—See Financiere de L'Odet; *Int'l*, pg. 2667
BOLLORE TRANSPORT & LOGISTICS NIGERIA LTD.—See Financiere de L'Odet; *Int'l*, pg. 2667
BOLLORE TRANSPORT & LOGISTICS RDC SA—See Financiere de L'Odet; *Int'l*, pg. 2667
BOLLORE TRANSPORT & LOGISTICS RWANDA LTD.—See Financiere de L'Odet; *Int'l*, pg. 2667
BOLLORE TRANSPORT & LOGISTICS (SL) LTD.—See Financiere de L'Odet; *Int'l*, pg. 2667
BOLLORE TRANSPORT & LOGISTICS SOUTH AFRICA (PTY.) LTD.—See Financiere de L'Odet; *Int'l*, pg. 2667
BOLLORE TRANSPORT LOGISTICS SPAIN SA—See Financiere de L'Odet; *Int'l*, pg. 2667
BOLLORE TRANSPORT & LOGISTICS TANZANIA LTD.—See Financiere de L'Odet; *Int'l*, pg. 2667
BOLLORE TRANSPORT & LOGISTICS TOGO CO., LTD.—See Financiere de L'Odet; *Int'l*, pg. 2667
BOLLORE TRANSPORT & LOGISTICS TUNISIE SA—See Financiere de L'Odet; *Int'l*, pg. 2667
BOLLORE TRANSPORT & LOGISTICS UGANDA LTD.—See Financiere de L'Odet; *Int'l*, pg. 2667
BOLLORE TRANSPORT & LOGISTICS ZAMBIA LTD.—See Financiere de L'Odet; *Int'l*, pg. 2667
BOLLORE TRANSPORT & LOGISTICS ZIMBABWE (PRIVATE) LTD.—See Financiere de L'Odet; *Int'l*, pg. 2667
BOMBAY METRICS SUPPLY CHAIN LIMITED; *Int'l*, pg. 1104
BONDEX SUPPLY CHAIN MANAGEMENT CO., LTD.; *Int'l*, pg. 1105
BONVER AB; *Int'l*, pg. 1109
BOSSARD CANADA INC.—See Bossard Holding AG; *Int'l*, pg. 1117
BOSSARD CZ S.R.O.—See Bossard Holding AG; *Int'l*, pg. 1117
BOSSARD DENMARK A/S—See Bossard Holding AG; *Int'l*, pg. 1117
BOSSARD DEUTSCHLAND GMBH—See Bossard Holding AG; *Int'l*, pg. 1117
BOSSARD FRANCE SAS—See Bossard Holding AG; *Int'l*, pg. 1117
BOSSARD (KOREA) LTD.—See Bossard Holding AG; *Int'l*, pg. 1117
BOSSARD LTD.—See Bossard Holding AG; *Int'l*, pg. 1117
BOSSARD M SDN. BHD.—See Bossard Holding AG; *Int'l*, pg. 1117
BOSSARD POLAND SP. Z O.O.—See Bossard Holding AG; *Int'l*, pg. 1117
BOSSARD SOUTH AFRICA (PTY.) LTD.—See Bossard Holding AG; *Int'l*, pg. 1117
BOSSARD SPAIN SA—See Bossard Holding AG; *Int'l*, pg. 1117
BOSSARD SWEDEN AB—See Bossard Holding AG; *Int'l*, pg. 1117
BOSSARD THAILAND LTD.—See Bossard Holding AG; *Int'l*, pg. 1117
BOTEC BONCOURT S.A.—See Die Schweizerische Post AG; *Int'l*, pg. 2112
BOTEC SARL—See Die Schweizerische Post AG; *Int'l*, pg. 2112
BOWMAN LOGISTICS—See Bowman Group LLP; *U.S. Private*, pg. 626
B. PACORINI S.P.A.; *Int'l*, pg. 788
BPS SPEDITIONS-SERVICE AG—See Die Schweizerische Post AG; *Int'l*, pg. 2112
BPS SPEDITIONS-SERVICE BASEL AG—See Die Schweizerische Post AG; *Int'l*, pg. 2112
BRASADA CAPITAL MANAGEMENT LP; *U.S. Private*, pg. 640
BREMER LAGERHAUS-GESELLSCHAFT; *Int'l*, pg. 1145
BRENNTAG AUSTRALIA PTY. LTD.—See BRENNTAG SE; *Int'l*, pg. 1146
BRENNTAG TANZANIA LIMITED—See BRENNTAG SE; *Int'l*, pg. 1148
BRENNTAG TUNISIE S.A.R.L.—See BRENNTAG SE; *Int'l*, pg. 1148
BRENNTAG UGANDA LIMITED—See BRENNTAG SE; *Int'l*, pg. 1148
BRIDGE AGRI PARTNERS, INC.—See The Andersons Incorporated; *U.S. Public*, pg. 2034
BRIDGER, LLC; *U.S. Private*, pg. 649
BRIGHTSTAR CORP.—See Brightstar Capital Partners, L.P.; *U.S. Private*, pg. 653
BRIGHTSTAR LOGISTICS PTY. LTD.—See Brightstar Capital Partners, L.P.; *U.S. Private*, pg. 653
BRINK'S GLOBAL SERVICES DEUTSCHLAND GMBH—See The Brink's Company; *U.S. Public*, pg. 2042
BRINK'S GLOBAL SERVICES INTERNATIONAL, INC.—See The Brink's Company; *U.S. Public*, pg. 2042
BRINK'S GLOBAL SERVICES—See The Brink's Company; *U.S. Public*, pg. 2042
BROSTROM AB—See A.P. Moller-Maersk A/S; *Int'l*, pg. 26
BROSTROM HOLDING BV—See A.P. Moller-Maersk A/S; *Int'l*, pg. 26
BROSTROM TANKERS SAS—See A.P. Moller-Maersk A/S; *Int'l*, pg. 26
BROTHER LOGITEC LTD.—See Brother Industries, Ltd.; *Int'l*, pg. 1196
BRUNEL OIL & GAS SERVICES WLL—See Brunel International N.V.; *Int'l*, pg. 1200
BUSLINK ALICE SPRINGS PTY. LTD.—See ComfortDelGro Corporation Limited; *Int'l*, pg. 1712
BUSLINK BROKEN HILL PTY. LTD.—See ComfortDelGro Corporation Limited; *Int'l*, pg. 1712
BUSLINK GLADSTONE PTY. LTD.—See ComfortDelGro Corporation Limited; *Int'l*, pg. 1712
BUSLINK NT PTY. LTD.—See ComfortDelGro Corporation Limited; *Int'l*, pg. 1712
BUSLINK SUNRAYSIA PTY. LTD.—See ComfortDelGro Corporation Limited; *Int'l*, pg. 1712
BUSLINK SUNSHINE COAST PTY. LTD.—See ComfortDelGro Corporation Limited; *Int'l*, pg. 1712
BUTMAC PTY LTD—See Eagers Automotive Limited; *Int'l*, pg. 2263
CAI LOGISTICS INC.—See CAI International, Inc.; *U.S. Public*, pg. 421
CALNUTRI, INC.; *U.S. Private*, pg. 723
CAM LOGISTICS, LLC—See US 1 Industries, Inc.; *U.S. Private*, pg. 4317
CAM TRANSPORT, LLC—See US 1 Industries, Inc.; *U.S. Private*, pg. 4317
CAPITAL TRANSPORTATION SOLUTIONS LLC—See Odyssey Logistics & Technology Corp.; *U.S. Private*, pg. 2996
CAPSTONE LOGISTICS, LLC—See H.I.G. Capital, LLC; *U.S. Private*, pg. 1827
CARGOLUTION INC.—See Clasquin S.A.; *Int'l*, pg. 1652
CARGOSOL LOGISTICS LIMITED; *Int'l*, pg. 1326
CARIBEX WORLDWIDE INC. - CANCUN FACILITY—See CaribEx Worldwide Inc.; *U.S. Private*, pg. 761
CARIBEX WORLDWIDE INC. - GUATEMALA CITY FACILITY—See CaribEx Worldwide Inc.; *U.S. Private*, pg. 761
CARIBEX WORLDWIDE INC. - MANAGUA FACILITY—See CaribEx Worldwide Inc.; *U.S. Private*, pg. 761
CARIBEX WORLDWIDE INC. - OLOCUILTA FACILITY—See CaribEx Worldwide Inc.; *U.S. Private*, pg. 761
CARIBEX WORLDWIDE INC. - SAN PEDRO SULA FACILITY—See CaribEx Worldwide Inc.; *U.S. Private*, pg. 761
CARIBEX WORLDWIDE INC. - SANTO DOMINGO FACILITY—See CaribEx Worldwide Inc.; *U.S. Private*, pg. 761
CARTER LOGISTICS, LLC—See KKR & Co. Inc.; *U.S. Public*, pg. 1258
CASESTACK, INC.—See Hub Group, Inc.; *U.S. Public*, pg. 1065
CASIO (GUANGZHOU) CO., LTD.—See Casio Computer Co., Ltd.; *Int'l*, pg. 1353
CATENA AB; *Int'l*, pg. 1359
CATERPILLAR LOGISTICS SERVICES INDIA PRIVATE LIMITED—See Caterpillar, Inc.; *U.S. Public*, pg. 451
CAVALRY LOGISTICS INTERNATIONAL, INC.—See Universal Logistics Holdings, Inc.; *U.S. Public*, pg. 2261
CAVALRY LOGISTICS INTERNATIONAL OF CANADA, INC.—See Universal Logistics Holdings, Inc.; *U.S. Public*, pg. 2261
CAVALRY LOGISTICS, LLC—See Universal Logistics Holdings, Inc.; *U.S. Public*, pg. 2261
CCR LOGISTICS SYSTEMS AG—See Monitor Clipper Partners, LLC; *U.S. Private*, pg. 2771
CCTC FRIEND STEVEDORE CO., LTD.—See China Container Terminal Corp.; *Int'l*, pg. 1491
CDC BALLARAT PTY. LTD.—See ComfortDelGro Corporation Limited; *Int'l*, pg. 1712
CDC GEELONG PTY. LTD.—See ComfortDelGro Corporation Limited; *Int'l*, pg. 1712
CDC OAKLEIGH PTY. LTD.—See ComfortDelGro Corporation Limited; *Int'l*, pg. 1712
CDC SUNSHINE PTY. LTD.—See ComfortDelGro Corporation Limited; *Int'l*, pg. 1712
CDC TULLAMARINE PTY. LTD.—See ComfortDelGro Corporation Limited; *Int'l*, pg. 1712
CDC WYNDHAM PTY. LTD.—See ComfortDelGro Corporation Limited; *Int'l*, pg. 1712
CDI SERVICES INC.; *U.S. Private*, pg. 802
CELLMARK AB; *Int'l*, pg. 1393
CENTRAL WAREHOUSE OPERATIONS, INC.—See Peoples Services Inc.; *U.S. Private*, pg. 3142
CENTROTRANS A.D.; *Int'l*, pg. 1415
CENTURION TRANSPORT CO. PTY LTD—See CFC Group Pty. Ltd.; *Int'l*, pg. 1429
CENTURY LOGISTICS SDN. BHD.—See CJ Century Logistics Holdings Berhad; *Int'l*, pg. 1631
CEPL HOLDING SAS—See ID Logistics SAS; *Int'l*, pg. 3587
CEPL MICHELSTADT GMBH—See ID Logistics SAS; *Int'l*, pg. 3587
CERTEX OFFSHORE SERVICES AS—See Axel Johnson Gruppen AB; *Int'l*, pg. 764
CEVA LIMITED—See CEVA, Inc.; *U.S. Public*, pg. 476

N.A.I.C.S. INDEX

CFM LOGISTICS—See Golden State Foods Corp.; *U.S. Private*, pg. 1733
CHASEN ENGINEERING SDN. BHD.—See Chasen Holdings Limited; *Int'l*, pg. 1457
CHASEN HOLDINGS LIMITED; *Int'l*, pg. 1457
CHASEN TRANSPORT LOGISTICS CO., LTD.—See Chasen Holdings Limited; *Int'l*, pg. 1457
CHASEN (USA), INC.—See Chasen Holdings Limited; *Int'l*, pg. 1457
CHEETAH NET SUPPLY CHAIN SERVICE INC.; *U.S. Public*, pg. 483
CHEMCHINA LOGISTICS CO LTD—See China National Chemical Corporation; *Int'l*, pg. 1526
CHEMICAL MARKETING CONCEPTS LLC—See Odyssey Logistics & Technology Corp.; *U.S. Private*, pg. 2996
CHENNAI CONTAINER TERMINAL PRIVATE LIMITED—See Dubai World Corporation; *Int'l*, pg. 2220
CHEONG FATT HOLDINGS PTE. LTD.—See CFM Holdings Limited; *Int'l*, pg. 1430
CHEP PALLECON SOLUTIONS PTY LTD—See Brambles Limited; *Int'l*, pg. 1138
CHERBOURG MARITIME VOYAGES SARL—See Financiere de L'Odet; *Int'l*, pg. 2667
CHERIN TRANSPORTATION, INC.—See Purity Wholesale Grocers, Inc.; *U.S. Private*, pg. 3306
CHEYENNE LOGISTICS LLC—See HF Sinclair Corporation; *U.S. Public*, pg. 1033
CHIEF CARRIERS, INC.—See Chief Industries, Inc.; *U.S. Private*, pg. 881
CHINA CIFCO INVESTMENT CO., LTD.; *Int'l*, pg. 1488
CHINA COMMUNICATIONS IMPORT & EXPORT CORPORATION—See China Merchants Group Limited; *Int'l*, pg. 1521
CHINA LOGISTICS PROPERTY HOLDINGS COMPANY LIMITED; *Int'l*, pg. 1515
CHINA MASTER LOGISTICS CO., LTD.; *Int'l*, pg. 1517
CHINA METAL JAPAN CO., LTD.—See China Metal Products Co., Ltd.; *Int'l*, pg. 1523
CHINA RAILWAY SPECIAL CARGO LOGISTICS CO., LTD.; *Int'l*, pg. 1544
CHOROKBAEM COMPANY CO., LTD.; *Int'l*, pg. 1583
C.H. ROBINSON AUSTRIA GMBH—See C.H. Robinson Worldwide, Inc.; *U.S. Public*, pg. 414
C.H. ROBINSON CZECH REPUBLIC S.R.O.—See C.H. Robinson Worldwide, Inc.; *U.S. Public*, pg. 414
C.H. ROBINSON FREIGHT SERVICES (CHINA) LTD.—See C.H. Robinson Worldwide, Inc.; *U.S. Public*, pg. 415
C.H. ROBINSON FREIGHT SERVICES (SINGAPORE) PTE. LTD.—See C.H. Robinson Worldwide, Inc.; *U.S. Public*, pg. 415
C.H. ROBINSON FREIGHT SERVICES (TAIWAN) LTD.—See C.H. Robinson Worldwide, Inc.; *U.S. Public*, pg. 415
C.H. ROBINSON INTERNATIONAL, INC.—See C.H. Robinson Worldwide, Inc.; *U.S. Public*, pg. 415
C.H. ROBINSON INTERNATIONAL (INDIA) PRIVATE LTD.—See C.H. Robinson Worldwide, Inc.; *U.S. Public*, pg. 415
C.H. ROBINSON LUXEMBOURG FINANCE S.A R.L.—See C.H. Robinson Worldwide, Inc.; *U.S. Public*, pg. 415
C.H. ROBINSON POLSKA S.A.—See C.H. Robinson Worldwide, Inc.; *U.S. Public*, pg. 415
C.H. ROBINSON PROJECT LOGISTICS, INC.—See C.H. Robinson Worldwide, Inc.; *U.S. Public*, pg. 415
C.H. ROBINSON PROJECT LOGISTICS LTD.—See C.H. Robinson Worldwide, Inc.; *U.S. Public*, pg. 415
C.H. ROBINSON PROJECT LOGISTICS PTE. LTD.—See C.H. Robinson Worldwide, Inc.; *U.S. Public*, pg. 415
CH ROBINSON PROJECT LOGISTICS SDN. BHD.—See C.H. Robinson Worldwide, Inc.; *U.S. Public*, pg. 415
C.H. ROBINSON SLOVAKIA, S.R.O.—See C.H. Robinson Worldwide, Inc.; *U.S. Public*, pg. 415
C.H. ROBINSON SWITZERLAND GMBH—See C.H. Robinson Worldwide, Inc.; *U.S. Public*, pg. 415
C.H. ROBINSON WORLDWIDE (AUSTRALIA) PTY. LTD.—See C.H. Robinson Worldwide, Inc.; *U.S. Public*, pg. 415
C.H. ROBINSON WORLDWIDE (NZ) LTD.—See C.H. Robinson Worldwide, Inc.; *U.S. Public*, pg. 415
C.H ROBINSON WORLDWIDE (SHANGHAI) CO. LTD.—See C.H. Robinson Worldwide, Inc.; *U.S. Public*, pg. 415
CHUHATSU UNYU CO., LTD.—See Chuo Spring Co., Ltd.; *Int'l*, pg. 1599
CHUN YUAN STEEL INDUSTRY CO., LTD. - AUTOMATED STORAGE SYSTEM DIVISION—See Chun Yuan Steel Industry Co., Ltd.; *Int'l*, pg. 1596
CIMC MODERN LOGISTICS DEVELOPMENT CO., LTD.—See China International Marine Containers (Group) Co., Ltd.; *Int'l*, pg. 1511
CIRCLE S.P.A.; *Int'l*, pg. 1617
CITY ZONE EXPRESS (SHANGHAI) CO., LTD.—See Chasen Holdings Limited; *Int'l*, pg. 1457
CITY ZONE EXPRESS WORLDWIDE CO., LTD.—See Chasen Holdings Limited; *Int'l*, pg. 1457
CJ CENTURY TECHNOLOGY SDN. BHD.—See CJ Century Logistics Holdings Berhad; *Int'l*, pg. 1631
CJ DARCL LOGISTICS LIMITED; *Int'l*, pg. 1634

CJ GLS ASIA PTE. LTD.—See CJ Corporation; *Int'l*, pg. 1632
CJ GLS CENTRAL AMERICA, S.A. DE C.V.—See CJ Corporation; *Int'l*, pg. 1633
CJ GLS (HONG KONG) LTD.—See CJ Corporation; *Int'l*, pg. 1633
CJ GLS MALAYSIA SDN. BHD.—See CJ Corporation; *Int'l*, pg. 1633
CJ GLS PHILIPPINES INC.—See CJ Corporation; *Int'l*, pg. 1633
CJ GLS PHILIPPINES VMI WAREHOUSE INC.—See CJ Corporation; *Int'l*, pg. 1633
CJ GLS (SHENZHEN) CO., LTD.—See CJ Corporation; *Int'l*, pg. 1633
CJ GLS (S) INFOTECH PTE. LTD.—See CJ Corporation; *Int'l*, pg. 1633
CJ GLS (THAILAND) CO., LTD.—See CJ Corporation; *Int'l*, pg. 1633
CJ ICM AUSTRIA GMBH—See CJ Corporation; *Int'l*, pg. 1632
CJ ICM FZCO—See CJ Corporation; *Int'l*, pg. 1632
CJ ICM ITALIA S.R.L—See CJ Corporation; *Int'l*, pg. 1632
CJ ICM LOGISTICS ESPANA S.L.—See CJ Corporation; *Int'l*, pg. 1632
CJ ICM LOGISTICS GMBH—See CJ Corporation; *Int'l*, pg. 1632
CJ ICM LOGISTICS LLC—See CJ Corporation; *Int'l*, pg. 1632
CJ ICM TASHKENT MCHJ—See CJ Corporation; *Int'l*, pg. 1632
CJ ICM (UK) LTD.—See CJ Corporation; *Int'l*, pg. 1632
CJ INTERNATIONAL TRADING CO., LTD.—See CJ Corporation; *Int'l*, pg. 1632
CJ KOREA EXPRESS BUSAN CONTAINER TERMINAL CORPORATION—See CJ Corporation; *Int'l*, pg. 1633
CJ LOGISTICS ASIA PTE. LTD.—See CJ Corporation; *Int'l*, pg. 1632
CJ LOGISTICS CORPORATION—See CJ Corporation; *Int'l*, pg. 1632
CJ LOGISTICS JAPAN CORPORATION—See CJ Corporation; *Int'l*, pg. 1633
CJ LOGISTICS PH CORP.—See CJ Corporation; *Int'l*, pg. 1633
CJ LOGISTICS USA CORPORATION—See CJ Corporation; *Int'l*, pg. 1633
CLAAS SERVICE AND PARTS GMBH—See Claas KGaA mbH; *Int'l*, pg. 1640
CLARKSONS DEUTSCHLAND GMBH—See Clarkson PLC; *Int'l*, pg. 1651
CLARKSONS DMCC—See Clarkson PLC; *Int'l*, pg. 1651
CLARKSONS JAPAN K.K.—See Clarkson PLC; *Int'l*, pg. 1651
CLARKSONS KOREA LIMITED—See Clarkson PLC; *Int'l*, pg. 1651
CLARKSONS NETHERLANDS B.V.—See Clarkson PLC; *Int'l*, pg. 1651
CLARKSONS NORWAY AS—See Clarkson PLC; *Int'l*, pg. 1651
CLARKSONS SINGAPORE PTE. LIMITED—See Clarkson PLC; *Int'l*, pg. 1651
CLARKSONS SOUTH AFRICA (PTY.) LTD.—See Clarkson PLC; *Int'l*, pg. 1651
CLARKSONS SWEDEN AB—See Clarkson PLC; *Int'l*, pg. 1651
CLARKSONS SWITZERLAND S.A.—See Clarkson PLC; *Int'l*, pg. 1651
CLASQUIND INDIA PVT. LTD.—See Clasquin S.A.; *Int'l*, pg. 1652
CLASQUIN SHANGHAI LTD.—See Clasquin S.A.; *Int'l*, pg. 1652
CLIPPER LOGISTICS GROUP LTD.; *Int'l*, pg. 1660
CLIPPER LOGISTICS KG GMBH & CO.—See Clipper Logistics Group Ltd.; *Int'l*, pg. 1660
CLOUDBLUE TECHNOLOGIES, INC.—See Hainan Traffic Administration Holding Co., Ltd.; *Int'l*, pg. 3214
CME CHILE, SPA—See ACS, Actividades de Construccion y Servicios, S.A.; *Int'l*, pg. 110
CML AIRPORT INTERNATIONAL LOGISTICS CO., LTD.—See China Master Logistics Co., Ltd.; *Int'l*, pg. 1517
CML CHANGXING (TIANJIN) INTERNATIONAL LOGISTICS CO., LTD.—See China Master Logistics Co., Ltd.; *Int'l*, pg. 1517
CML (DALIAN) LOGISTICS CO., LTD.—See China Master Logistics Co., Ltd.; *Int'l*, pg. 1517
CML GLOBAL LOGISTICS CO., LTD.—See China Master Logistics Co., Ltd.; *Int'l*, pg. 1517
CML GRAND JOURNEY LOGISTICS SHANGHAI CO., LTD.—See China Master Logistics Co., Ltd.; *Int'l*, pg. 1517
CML GRANDRAIL INTERNATIONAL LOGISTICS CO., LTD.—See China Master Logistics Co., Ltd.; *Int'l*, pg. 1517
CML GRANDTRUST LOGISTICS CO., LTD.—See China Master Logistics Co., Ltd.; *Int'l*, pg. 1517
CML GRANDWILL LOGISTICS CO., LTD.—See China Master Logistics Co., Ltd.; *Int'l*, pg. 1517
CML (LIANYUNGANG) LOGISTICS CO., LTD.—See China Master Logistics Co., Ltd.; *Int'l*, pg. 1517

541614 — PROCESS, PHYSICAL D...

CML(LONGKOU)LOGISTICS CO., LTD.—See China Master Logistics Co., Ltd.; *Int'l*, pg. 1517
CML (NINBO) LOGISTICS CO., LTD.—See China Master Logistics Co., Ltd.; *Int'l*, pg. 1517
CML (NINGBO) LOGISTICS CO., LTD.—See China Master Logistics Co., Ltd.; *Int'l*, pg. 1517
CMLOG TIANCHI SMART COLD CHAIN (QINGDAO) CO., LTD.—See China Master Logistics Co., Ltd.; *Int'l*, pg. 1517
CML (QINGDAO) BONDED LOGISTICS CO., LTD.—See China Master Logistics Co., Ltd.; *Int'l*, pg. 1517
CML-REEFER (QINGDAO) CONTAINER TECHNICAL CO., LTD.—See China Master Logistics Co., Ltd.; *Int'l*, pg. 1517
CML (RIZHAO) LOGISTICS CO., LTD.—See China Master Logistics Co., Ltd.; *Int'l*, pg. 1517
CML (RONGCHENG) LOGISTICS CO., LTD.—See China Master Logistics Co., Ltd.; *Int'l*, pg. 1517
CML (SHAANXI) LOGISTICS CO., LTD.—See China Master Logistics Co., Ltd.; *Int'l*, pg. 1517
CML SUPPLY CHAIN MANAGEMENT CO., LTD.—See China Master Logistics Co., Ltd.; *Int'l*, pg. 1517
CML SUPPLY CHAIN MANAGEMENT (ZHENGZHOU) CO., LTD.—See China Master Logistics Co., Ltd.; *Int'l*, pg. 1517
CML (TIANJIN) BINHAI LOGISTICS CO., LTD.—See China Master Logistics Co., Ltd.; *Int'l*, pg. 1517
CML (TIANJIN) LOGISTICS CO., LTD.—See China Master Logistics Co., Ltd.; *Int'l*, pg. 1517
CML (TIANJIN) MARITIME CO., LTD.—See China Master Logistics Co., Ltd.; *Int'l*, pg. 1517
CML (WEIHAI) LOGISTICS CO., LTD.—See China Master Logistics Co., Ltd.; *Int'l*, pg. 1517
CML (YANTAI) LOGISTICS CO., LTD.—See China Master Logistics Co., Ltd.; *Int'l*, pg. 1517
CML ZHENGHAI LOGISTICS CO., LTD.—See China Master Logistics Co., Ltd.; *Int'l*, pg. 1517
CMST DEVELOPMENT CO., LTD.; *Int'l*, pg. 1672
CMST GUANGZHOU COMPANY—See CMST Development Co., Ltd.; *Int'l*, pg. 1672
C&N HOLDINGS LIMITED; *Int'l*, pg. 1239
COASTAL LOGISTICS GROUP, INC.; *U.S. Private*, pg. 956
COASTAL ROADWAYS LIMITED; *Int'l*, pg. 1681
COECLERICI LOGISTICS S.P.A.—See Coeclerici S.p.A.; *Int'l*, pg. 1689
COFELY AIRPORT & LOGISTICS SERVICES SA—See ENGIE SA; *Int'l*, pg. 2429
COMERCIAL SENSITECH SOUTH AMERICA LIMITADA—See Carrier Global Corporation; *U.S. Public*, pg. 443
COMPANIA LOGISTICA DE HIDROCARBUROS CLH, S.A.; *Int'l*, pg. 1749
COMPLIANCE SYSTEMS, INC.—See Colonial Group, Inc.; *U.S. Private*, pg. 971
COMPUTER CAB (ABERDEEN) LIMITED—See ComfortDelGro Corporation Limited; *Int'l*, pg. 1712
COMPUTER CAB (LIVERPOOL) LIMITED—See ComfortDelGro Corporation Limited; *Int'l*, pg. 1712
CONCOR AIR LTD.—See Container Corporation of India Ltd.; *Int'l*, pg. 1779
CONNECTED LOGISTICS, INC.; *U.S. Private*, pg. 1015
CONNETICS LIMITED—See Christchurch City Holdings Ltd.; *Int'l*, pg. 1586
CONPAC WAREHOUSING PTE. LTD.—See CJ Corporation; *Int'l*, pg. 1633
CONSTRUCTOR GROUP AS—See Corporacion Gestamp SL; *Int'l*, pg. 1804
CONTAINER APPLICATIONS INTERNATIONAL (AUSTRALIA) PTY LTD.—See CAI International, Inc.; *U.S. Public*, pg. 421
CONTAINER CORPORATION OF INDIA LTD.; *Int'l*, pg. 1779
CONTAINER RAIL ROAD SERVICES PRIVATE LIMITED—See Dubai World Corporation; *Int'l*, pg. 2220
CONTAINERWAY INTERNATIONAL LIMITED; *Int'l*, pg. 1779
CONTECH LOGISTICS SOLUTIONS PRIVATE LIMITED—See Allcargo Logistics Limited; *Int'l*, pg. 333
COPERSUCAR NORTH AMERICA LLC—See Copersucar S.A.; *Int'l*, pg. 1793
CORE-MARK INTERRELATED COMPANIES, INC.—See Core-Mark Holding Co. Inc.; *U.S. Public*, pg. 576
CORE-MARK MIDCONTINENT, INC.—See Core-Mark Holding Co. Inc.; *U.S. Public*, pg. 576
CORE-MARK—See Core-Mark Holding Co. Inc.; *U.S. Public*, pg. 576
COSCO SHIPPING INTERNATIONAL TRADING COMPANY LIMITED—See China COSCO Shipping Corporation Limited; *Int'l*, pg. 1493
COSCO SHIPPING LINES (DALIAN) CO.—See COSCO Shipping Holdings Co., Ltd.; *Int'l*, pg. 1810
CPF LOGISTICS CO., LTD.—See Charoen Pokphand Foods Public Company Limited; *Int'l*, pg. 1452
CROSSGLOBE EXPRESS, LLC—See Blue Wolf Capital Partners LLC; *U.S. Private*, pg. 595
CROSSLOG SA; *Int'l*, pg. 1856
CROWN WAREHOUSING & LOGISTICS INC—See Peoples Services Inc.; *U.S. Private*, pg. 3142

4691

541614 — PROCESS, PHYSICAL D...

CROZIER FINE ARTS, INC.—See Iron Mountain Incorporated; *U.S. Public*, pg. 1172
CRST MALONE INC.—See CRST International, Inc.; *U.S. Private*, pg. 1113
CRYOSITE DISTRIBUTION PTY LIMITED—See Cryosite Limited; *Int'l*, pg. 1860
C & S CARPET DISTRIBUTION, INC.—See Best Logistics Group, Inc.; *U.S. Public*, pg. 543
CSC ENTERPRISES L.P.—See DXC Technology Company; *U.S. Public*, pg. 695
CTI LOGISTICS LTD - FLEET MANAGEMENT DIVISION—See CTI Logistics Limited; *Int'l*, pg. 1871
CTI LOGISTICS LTD - GENERAL & CONTAINER TRANSPORT DIVISION—See CTI Logistics Limited; *Int'l*, pg. 1871
CTL LOGISTICS S.A.—See Compass Advisers Group LLC; *U.S. Private*, pg. 998
CTS GLOBAL SUPPLY CHAIN SOLUTIONS—See CTS International Logistics Corporation Limited; *Int'l*, pg. 1874
CTS INTERNATIONAL LOGISTICS CORPORATION LIMITED; *Int'l*, pg. 1874
CTS INTERNATIONAL LOGISTICS (GERMANY) GMBH—See CTS International Logistics Corporation Limited; *Int'l*, pg. 1874
CTS INTERNATIONAL LOGISTICS (HK) CO., LTD.—See CTS International Logistics Corporation Limited; *Int'l*, pg. 1874
CTS INTERNATIONAL LOGISTICS (NETHERLANDS) B.V.—See CTS International Logistics Corporation Limited; *Int'l*, pg. 1874
CTS INTERNATIONAL LOGISTICS (SINGAPORE) PTE LTD.—See CTS International Logistics Corporation Limited; *Int'l*, pg. 1874
CVL INTERNATIONAL SAS—See Clasquin S.A.; *Int'l*, pg. 1652
C. WEAVER PHYSICAL THERAPY, INC.—See Athletico Ltd.; *U.S. Private*, pg. 368
CWT INTERNATIONAL LIMITED; *Int'l*, pg. 1891
CWT LIMITED—See Hainan Traffic Administration Holding Co., Ltd.; *Int'l*, pg. 3213
CYTERRACE CO., LTD.—See Envipro Holdings Inc.; *Int'l*, pg. 2454
DACHSER (BANGLADESH) LTD.—See Dachser GmbH & Co.; *Int'l*, pg. 1903
DACHSER BELGIUM AIR & SEA LOGISTICS NV—See Dachser GmbH & Co.; *Int'l*, pg. 1903
DACHSER BELGIUM N.V.—See Dachser GmbH & Co.; *Int'l*, pg. 1903
DACHSER BRASIL LOGISTICA LTDA.—See Dachser GmbH & Co.; *Int'l*, pg. 1903
DACHSER CHILE S.A.—See Dachser GmbH & Co.; *Int'l*, pg. 1903
DACHSER CZECH REPUBLIC A.S.—See Dachser GmbH & Co.; *Int'l*, pg. 1903
DACHSER DE MEXICO S.A. DE C.V.—See Dachser GmbH & Co.; *Int'l*, pg. 1904
DACHSER DENMARK A/S—See Dachser GmbH & Co.; *Int'l*, pg. 1903
DACHSER FAR EAST LTD—See Dachser GmbH & Co.; *Int'l*, pg. 1903
DACHSER FRANCE S.A.S.—See Dachser GmbH & Co.; *Int'l*, pg. 1903
DACHSER HONG KONG LTD.—See Dachser GmbH & Co.; *Int'l*, pg. 1904
DACHSER INDIA PRIVATE LIMITED—See Dachser GmbH & Co.; *Int'l*, pg. 1904
DACHSER LTD.—See Dachser GmbH & Co.; *Int'l*, pg. 1904
DACHSER MALAYSIA SDN. BHD.—See Dachser GmbH & Co.; *Int'l*, pg. 1904
DACHSER NETHERLANDS B.V.—See Dachser GmbH & Co.; *Int'l*, pg. 1904
DACHSER NORWAY AS—See Dachser GmbH & Co.; *Int'l*, pg. 1904
DACHSER OOO—See Dachser GmbH & Co.; *Int'l*, pg. 1904
DACHSER ROMANIA SRL—See Dachser GmbH & Co.; *Int'l*, pg. 1904
DACHSER S.A.R.L.—See Dachser GmbH & Co.; *Int'l*, pg. 1904
DACHSER SHENZHEN CO. LTD.—See Dachser GmbH & Co.; *Int'l*, pg. 1904
DACHSER SINGAPORE PTE LTD.—See Dachser GmbH & Co.; *Int'l*, pg. 1904
DACHSER SOUTH AFRICA (PTY.) LTD.—See Dachser GmbH & Co.; *Int'l*, pg. 1904
DACHSER SPEDITION AG—See Dachser GmbH & Co.; *Int'l*, pg. 1904
DACHSER S.R.O.—See Dachser GmbH & Co.; *Int'l*, pg. 1904
DACHSER SWEDEN AB—See Dachser GmbH & Co.; *Int'l*, pg. 1904
DACHSER TAIWAN, INC.—See Dachser GmbH & Co.; *Int'l*, pg. 1904
DACHSER TANGER SARL—See Dachser GmbH & Co.; *Int'l*, pg. 1904
DACHSER (THAILAND) CO., LTD.—See Dachser GmbH & Co.; *Int'l*, pg. 1903
DACHSER VIETNAM CO., LTD.—See Dachser GmbH & Co.; *Int'l*, pg. 1904

DAEHAN NETWORKS CO., LTD—See Daehan Steel Co., Ltd.; *Int'l*, pg. 1907
DAHANG INTERNATIONAL TRANSPORTATION CO., LTD.—See KKR & Co. Inc.; *U.S. Public*, pg. 1258
DAITO KOUN CO., LTD.; *Int'l*, pg. 1943
DAIWA LOGISTICS CO., LTD.—See Daiwa House Industry Co., Ltd.; *Int'l*, pg. 1946
DAIWA LOGITECH INC.—See Daiwa House Industry Co., Ltd.; *Int'l*, pg. 1946
DALIAN PORT BULK LOGISTICS CENTER CO., LTD.—See China Master Logistics Co., Ltd.; *Int'l*, pg. 1517
DAMCO SWEDEN AB—See A.P. Moller-Maersk A/S; *Int'l*, pg. 26
DAMCO USA INC.—See A.P. Moller-Maersk A/S; *Int'l*, pg. 26
DANZAS FASHION NV—See Deutsche Post AG; *Int'l*, pg. 2079
DASH-IT LTD—See CitySprint (UK) Limited; *Int'l*, pg. 1630
DATA EXCHANGE EUROPE, LTD—See Data Exchange Corporation; *U.S. Private*, pg. 1163
DAVACO, INC.—See Crane Worldwide Logistics LLC; *U.S. Private*, pg. 1085
DAVIS TRANSFER LOGISTICS INC.—See Deutsche Bahn AG; *Int'l*, pg. 2054
DAWSON LOGISTICS; *U.S. Private*, pg. 1176
DB SCHENKER BTT GMBH—See Deutsche Bahn AG; *Int'l*, pg. 2050
DB SCHENKER (CAMBODIA) LIMITED—See Deutsche Bahn AG; *Int'l*, pg. 2052
DB SCHENKER FLLC—See Deutsche Bahn AG; *Int'l*, pg. 2052
DB SCHENKER NIETEN GMBH—See Deutsche Bahn AG; *Int'l*, pg. 2050
DB SCHENKER RAIL AUTOMOTIVE GMBH—See Deutsche Bahn AG; *Int'l*, pg. 2050
DB SCHENKER RAIL BULGARIA EOOD—See Deutsche Bahn AG; *Int'l*, pg. 2050
DB SCHENKER RAIL DANMARK SERVICES A/S—See Deutsche Bahn AG; *Int'l*, pg. 2050
DB SCHENKER RAIL HUNGARIA KFT.—See Deutsche Bahn AG; *Int'l*, pg. 2050
DB SCHENKER RAIL INFORMATION SERVICES LIMITED—See Deutsche Bahn AG; *Int'l*, pg. 2050
DB SYSTEL GMBH—See Deutsche Bahn AG; *Int'l*, pg. 2051
DDN—See Dohmen Co.; *U.S. Private*, pg. 1254
DEEWIN TIANXIA CO., LTD.; *Int'l*, pg. 2003
DELIXI XINJIANG TRANSPORTATION GROUP CO., LTD; *Int'l*, pg. 2013
DELMAR INTERNATIONAL, INC.; *Int'l*, pg. 2014
DELO-CENTER LLC—See Delo Group; *Int'l*, pg. 2014
DELTA COMPANIES GROUP—See Greif Inc.; *U.S. Public*, pg. 967
DELTA CORP HOLDINGS LIMITED; *Int'l*, pg. 2016
DELTON LOGISTICS SARL—See Delton AG; *Int'l*, pg. 2021
DEMA SERVICE S.P.A.—See C.H. Robinson Worldwide, Inc.; *U.S. Public*, pg. 415
DEMATIC LOGISTICS GMBH—See KKR & Co. Inc.; *U.S. Public*, pg. 1254
DEMATIC LOGISTICS GMBH—See KKR & Co. Inc.; *U.S. Public*, pg. 1254
DEMATIC LOGISTICS GMBH—See The Goldman Sachs Group, Inc.; *U.S. Public*, pg. 2078
DEMATIC LOGISTICS GMBH—See The Goldman Sachs Group, Inc.; *U.S. Public*, pg. 2078
DEMATIC LTD.—See KKR & Co. Inc.; *U.S. Public*, pg. 1254
DEMATIC LTD.—See The Goldman Sachs Group, Inc.; *U.S. Public*, pg. 2078
DEN HARTOGH DRY BULK LOGISTICS LIMITED—See Den Hartogh Holding BV; *Int'l*, pg. 2026
DEN HARTOGH LOGISTICS AB—See Den Hartogh Holding BV; *Int'l*, pg. 2026
DEPENDABLE LOGISTICS SOLUTIONS—See Dependable Highway Express Inc.; *U.S. Private*, pg. 1209
DEPPON LOGISTICS CO., LTD.; *Int'l*, pg. 2041
DERRIMON TRADING CO., LTD.; *Int'l*, pg. 2043
DESTINAS AG—See Die Schweizerische Post AG; *Int'l*, pg. 2112
DESTINY LOGISTICS & INFRA LIMITED; *Int'l*, pg. 2047
DEUFOL SLOVENSKO S.R.O.—See Deufol SE; *Int'l*, pg. 2048
DEUFOL WAREMME S.A.—See Deufol SE; *Int'l*, pg. 2048
DEUTSCHE POST ADRESS GMBH—See Deutsche Post AG; *Int'l*, pg. 2079
DEUTSCHE TRANSFESA GMBH—See Deutsche Bahn AG; *Int'l*, pg. 2051
DEUTSCHE UMSCHLAGGESELLSCHAFT SCHIENE-STRASSE (DUSS) MBH—See Deutsche Bahn AG; *Int'l*, pg. 2051
DEX SUPPLY CHAIN SERVICES COOPERATIE N.V.—See Data Exchange Corporation; *U.S. Private*, pg. 1163
DEX SUPPLY CHAIN SERVICES LIMITED—See Data Exchange Corporation; *U.S. Private*, pg. 1163
DEXTERRA GROUP INC.; *Int'l*, pg. 2093
DFDS KOLETRANSPORT A/S—See DFDS A/S; *Int'l*, pg. 2094
DFDS LOGISTICS LIMITED—See DFDS A/S; *Int'l*, pg. 2094
DFDS LOGISTICS OU—See DFDS A/S; *Int'l*, pg. 2094
DFDS LOGISTICS SARL—See DFDS A/S; *Int'l*, pg. 2094

DFDS LOGISTICS SERVICES NV—See DFDS A/S; *Int'l*, pg. 2094
DHL 2-MANN-HANDLING GMBH—See Deutsche Post AG; *Int'l*, pg. 2072
DHL AUTOMOTIVE GMBH—See Deutsche Post AG; *Int'l*, pg. 2073
DHL AVIATION (NETHERLANDS) B.V.—See Deutsche Post AG; *Int'l*, pg. 2073
DHL (BAHAMAS) LIMITED—See Deutsche Post AG; *Int'l*, pg. 2072
DHL (BOLIVIA) SRL—See Deutsche Post AG; *Int'l*, pg. 2072
DHL (BVI) LTD.—See Deutsche Post AG; *Int'l*, pg. 2072
DHL BWLOG GMBH—See Deutsche Post AG; *Int'l*, pg. 2072
DHL ECOMMERCE (MALAYSIA) SDN. BHD.—See Deutsche Post AG; *Int'l*, pg. 2078
DHL ECOMMERCE (SINGAPORE) PTE. LTD.—See Deutsche Post AG; *Int'l*, pg. 2078
DHL ELANCOURT SARL—See Deutsche Post AG; *Int'l*, pg. 2072
DHL EXEL SLOVAKIA, S.R.O.—See Deutsche Post AG; *Int'l*, pg. 2072
DHL EXEL SUPPLY CHAIN EUSKAL-LOG, S.L.U.—See Deutsche Post AG; *Int'l*, pg. 2073
DHL EXEL SUPPLY CHAIN HUNGARY LIMITED—See Deutsche Post AG; *Int'l*, pg. 2073
DHL EXEL SUPPLY CHAIN PHILS., INC.—See Deutsche Post AG; *Int'l*, pg. 2073
DHL EXEL SUPPLY CHAIN PORTUGAL, S.A.—See Deutsche Post AG; *Int'l*, pg. 2072
DHL EXEL SUPPLY CHAIN (SPAIN), S.L.U.—See Deutsche Post AG; *Int'l*, pg. 2073
DHL EXEL SUPPLY CHAIN (SWEDEN) AB—See Deutsche Post AG; *Int'l*, pg. 2073
DHL EXEL SUPPLY CHAIN TRADE (POLAND) SP.Z.O.O.—See Deutsche Post AG; *Int'l*, pg. 2073
DHL EXPRESS ADUANAS PERU S.A.C.—See Deutsche Post AG; *Int'l*, pg. 2073
DHL EXPRESS ADUANAS VENEZUELA C.A.—See Deutsche Post AG; *Int'l*, pg. 2074
DHL EXPRESS (ARGENTINA) S.A.—See Deutsche Post AG; *Int'l*, pg. 2073
DHL EXPRESS (AUSTRIA) GMBH—See Deutsche Post AG; *Int'l*, pg. 2073
DHL EXPRESS BARCELONA SPAIN S.L.—See Deutsche Post AG; *Int'l*, pg. 2074
DHL EXPRESS (BRAZIL) LTDA.—See Deutsche Post AG; *Int'l*, pg. 2074
DHL EXPRESS BULGARIA EOOD—See Deutsche Post AG; *Int'l*, pg. 2074
DHL EXPRESS (CAMBODIA) LTD.—See Deutsche Post AG; *Int'l*, pg. 2074
DHL EXPRESS (CANADA) LTD.—See Deutsche Post AG; *Int'l*, pg. 2072
DHL EXPRESS (CHILE) LTDA.—See Deutsche Post AG; *Int'l*, pg. 2072
DHL EXPRESS COLOMBIA LTDA.—See Deutsche Post AG; *Int'l*, pg. 2072
DHL EXPRESS (ECUADOR) S.A.—See Deutsche Post AG; *Int'l*, pg. 2072
DHL EXPRESS (EL SALVADOR) S.A.DE C.V.—See Deutsche Post AG; *Int'l*, pg. 2074
DHL EXPRESS ESTONIA AS—See Deutsche Post AG; *Int'l*, pg. 2072
DHL EXPRESS (FIJI) LTD.—See Deutsche Post AG; *Int'l*, pg. 2074
DHL EXPRESS (FINLAND) OY—See Deutsche Post AG; *Int'l*, pg. 2072
DHL EXPRESS (FRANCE) SAS—See Deutsche Post AG; *Int'l*, pg. 2074
DHL EXPRESS (HELLAS) S.A.—See Deutsche Post AG; *Int'l*, pg. 2074
DHL EXPRESS (ICELAND) EHF—See Deutsche Post AG; *Int'l*, pg. 2074
DHL EXPRESS (INDIA) PVT. LTD.—See Deutsche Post AG; *Int'l*, pg. 2074
DHL EXPRESS LAOS SOLE COMPANY LIMITED—See Deutsche Post AG; *Int'l*, pg. 2072
DHL EXPRESS LATVIA SIA—See Deutsche Post AG; *Int'l*, pg. 2072
DHL EXPRESS LDA—See Deutsche Post AG; *Int'l*, pg. 2074
DHL EXPRESS (MACAU) LTD.—See Deutsche Post AG; *Int'l*, pg. 2072
DHL EXPRESS MACEDONIA D.O.O.E.L.—See Deutsche Post AG; *Int'l*, pg. 2072
DHL EXPRESS (MALAYSIA) SDN. BHD.—See Deutsche Post AG; *Int'l*, pg. 2072
DHL EXPRESS MAROC S.A.—See Deutsche Post AG; *Int'l*, pg. 2074
DHL EXPRESS NAVARRA SPAIN, S.L.—See Deutsche Post AG; *Int'l*, pg. 2074
DHL EXPRESS NEPAL PVT. LTD.—See Deutsche Post AG; *Int'l*, pg. 2074
DHL EXPRESS (NETHERLANDS) B.V.—See Deutsche Post AG; *Int'l*, pg. 2074
DHL EXPRESS (NORWAY) AS—See Deutsche Post AG; *Int'l*, pg. 2074
DHL EXPRESS (PAPUA NEW GUINEA) LTD.—See Deutsche Post AG; *Int'l*, pg. 2072

N.A.I.C.S. INDEX

541614 — PROCESS, PHYSICAL D...

DHL EXPRESS PERU S.A.C.—See Deutsche Post AG; *Int'l*, pg. 2074
DHL EXPRESS PORTUGAL, LDA.—See Deutsche Post AG; *Int'l*, pg. 2074
DHL EXPRESS (RWANDA) LIMITED—See Deutsche Post AG; *Int'l*, pg. 2072
DHL EXPRESS SERVICES (FRANCE) SAS—See Deutsche Post AG; *Int'l*, pg. 2074
DHL EXPRESS (SLOVAKIA), SPOL. S R. O.—See Deutsche Post AG; *Int'l*, pg. 2074
DHL EXPRESS SPAIN S.L.—See Deutsche Post AG; *Int'l*, pg. 2072
DHL EXPRESS, UNIPESSOAL, LDA.—See Deutsche Post AG; *Int'l*, pg. 2072
DHL FOOD LOGISTICS EGYPT LTD.—See Deutsche Post AG; *Int'l*, pg. 2072
DHL FOODLOGISTICS GMBH—See Deutsche Post AG; *Int'l*, pg. 2072
DHL FOOD SERVICES GMBH—See Deutsche Post AG; *Int'l*, pg. 2075
DHL FREIGHT CZ S.R.O.—See Deutsche Post AG; *Int'l*, pg. 2072
DHL FREIGHT DENMARK A/S—See Deutsche Post AG; *Int'l*, pg. 2072
DHL FREIGHT D.O.O.—See Deutsche Post AG; *Int'l*, pg. 2072
DHL FREIGHT ESTONIA AS—See Deutsche Post AG; *Int'l*, pg. 2075
DHL FREIGHT (FRANCE) SAS—See Deutsche Post AG; *Int'l*, pg. 2072
DHL FREIGHT PORTUGAL, UNIPESSOAL LDA.—See Deutsche Post AG; *Int'l*, pg. 2072
DHL FREIGHT ROMANIA S.R.L.—See Deutsche Post AG; *Int'l*, pg. 2072
DHL FREIGHT SLOVAKIA, S.R.O.—See Deutsche Post AG; *Int'l*, pg. 2072
DHL FREIGHT TASIMACILIK VE LOJISTIK HIZMETLERI A.S.—See Deutsche Post AG; *Int'l*, pg. 2072
DHL GBS (UK) LIMITED—See Deutsche Post AG; *Int'l*, pg. 2075
DHL (GHANA) LIMITED—See Deutsche Post AG; *Int'l*, pg. 2073
DHL GLOBAL EVENT LOGISTICS GMBH—See Deutsche Post AG; *Int'l*, pg. 2072
DHL GLOBAL FORWARDING BAHRAIN WLL—See Deutsche Post AG; *Int'l*, pg. 2072
DHL GLOBAL FORWARDING CUSTOMS, LLC—Deutsche Post AG; *Int'l*, pg. 2072
DHL GLOBAL FORWARDING D.O.O. BELGRADE—See Deutsche Post AG; *Int'l*, pg. 2072
DHL GLOBAL FORWARDING MANAGEMENT GMBH—See Deutsche Post AG; *Int'l*, pg. 2072
DHL GLOBAL FORWARDING (MAURITIUS) LTD.—See Deutsche Post AG; *Int'l*, pg. 2072
DHL GLOBAL FORWARDING PORTUGAL, UNIPESSOAL, LDA.—See Deutsche Post AG; *Int'l*, pg. 2072
DHL GLOBAL FORWARDING ZIMBABWE LTD.—See Deutsche Post AG; *Int'l*, pg. 2072
DHL GLOBAL MATCH (BELGIUM) N.V.—See Deutsche Post AG; *Int'l*, pg. 2072
DHL GROUP SERVICES NV/SA—See Deutsche Post AG; *Int'l*, pg. 2073
DHL INTERNATIONAL ANTILLES SARL—See Deutsche Post AG; *Int'l*, pg. 2073
DHL INTERNATIONAL (BRUNEI) SDN BHD—See Deutsche Post AG; *Int'l*, pg. 2076
DHL INTERNATIONAL B.S.C. (C)—See Deutsche Post AG; *Int'l*, pg. 2076
DHL INTERNATIONAL CAMEROON SARL—See Deutsche Post AG; *Int'l*, pg. 2076
DHL INTERNATIONAL COTE D'IVOIRE SARL—See Deutsche Post AG; *Int'l*, pg. 2076
DHL INTERNATIONAL EXPRESS (FRANCE) SAS—See Deutsche Post AG; *Int'l*, pg. 2076
DHL INTERNATIONAL KAZAKHSTAN, TOO—See Deutsche Post AG; *Int'l*, pg. 2076
DHL INTERNATIONAL LTD.—See Deutsche Post AG; *Int'l*, pg. 2076
DHL INTERNATIONAL MADAGASCAR SA—See Deutsche Post AG; *Int'l*, pg. 2076
DHL INTERNATIONAL MALAWI LTD.—See Deutsche Post AG; *Int'l*, pg. 2076
DHL INTERNATIONAL-SARAJEVO D.O.O.—See Deutsche Post AG; *Int'l*, pg. 2077
DHL INTERNATIONAL (UGANDA) LTD.—See Deutsche Post AG; *Int'l*, pg. 2076
DHL ISC (HONG KONG) LIMITED—See Deutsche Post AG; *Int'l*, pg. 2076
DHL (ISRAEL) LTD.—See Deutsche Post AG; *Int'l*, pg. 2073
DHL (JAMAICA) LTD—See Deutsche Post AG; *Int'l*, pg. 2073
DHL LAO LIMITED—See Deutsche Post AG; *Int'l*, pg. 2077
DHL LOGISTICA D.O.O.—See Deutsche Post AG; *Int'l*, pg. 2077
DHL LOGISTICS GHANA LTD.—See Deutsche Post AG; *Int'l*, pg. 2078
DHL LOGISTICS OOO—See Deutsche Post AG; *Int'l*, pg. 2077
DHL LOGISTICS (SLOVAKIA), SPOL. S R. O.—See Deutsche Post AG; *Int'l*, pg. 2077
DHL LOGISTICS TANZANIA LIMITED—See Deutsche Post AG; *Int'l*, pg. 2077
DHL LOGISTICS (UKRAINE) LTD.—See Deutsche Post AG; *Int'l*, pg. 2077
DHL LOGISTIK SERVICE GMBH—See Deutsche Post AG; *Int'l*, pg. 2078
DHL LOJISTIK HIZMETLERI A.S.—See Deutsche Post AG; *Int'l*, pg. 2077
DHL METROPOLITAN LOGISTICS SC MEXICO S.A. DE C.V.—See Deutsche Post AG; *Int'l*, pg. 2078
DHL MOZAMBIQUE LDA.—See Deutsche Post AG; *Int'l*, pg. 2077
DHL NETWORK OPERATIONS (USA), INC.—See Deutsche Post AG; *Int'l*, pg. 2078
DHL PAKET GMBH—See Deutsche Post AG; *Int'l*, pg. 2078
DHL (PARAGUAY) S.R.L.—See Deutsche Post AG; *Int'l*, pg. 2073
DHL PIPELIFE LOGISTIK GMBH—See Deutsche Post AG; *Int'l*, pg. 2078
DHL RAIL AB—See Deutsche Post AG; *Int'l*, pg. 2077
DHL SAINGHIN SARL—See Deutsche Post AG; *Int'l*, pg. 2077
DHL SANDOUVILLE SARL—See Deutsche Post AG; *Int'l*, pg. 2078
DHL, S.A.—See Deutsche Post AG; *Int'l*, pg. 2076
DHL SC TRANSPORT SASU—See Deutsche Post AG; *Int'l*, pg. 2078
DHL SERVICES LIMITED—See Deutsche Post AG; *Int'l*, pg. 2077
DHL SERVICES LOGISTIQUES SAS—See Deutsche Post AG; *Int'l*, pg. 2077
DHL SOLUTIONS (BELGIUM) NV—See Deutsche Post AG; *Int'l*, pg. 2077
DHL SOLUTIONS GMBH—See Deutsche Post AG; *Int'l*, pg. 2077
DHL SOLUTIONS GROSSGUT GMBH—See Deutsche Post AG; *Int'l*, pg. 2077
DHL SOLUTIONS (USA), INC.—See Deutsche Post AG; *Int'l*, pg. 2077
DHL STOCK EXPRESS SAS—See Deutsche Post AG; *Int'l*, pg. 2078
DHL SUPPLY CHAIN (DENMARK) A / S—See Deutsche Post AG; *Int'l*, pg. 2078
DHL SUPPLY CHAIN (FINLAND) OY—See Deutsche Post AG; *Int'l*, pg. 2077
DHL SUPPLY CHAIN INC.—See Deutsche Post AG; *Int'l*, pg. 2078
DHL SUPPLY CHAIN (KOREA) LTD.—See Deutsche Post AG; *Int'l*, pg. 2077
DHL SUPPLY CHAIN MANAGEMENT GMBH—See Deutsche Post AG; *Int'l*, pg. 2078
DHL SUPPLY CHAIN (NEW ZEALAND) LIMITED—See Deutsche Post AG; *Int'l*, pg. 2078
DHL SUPPLY CHAIN (POLAND) SP. Z O.O.—See Deutsche Post AG; *Int'l*, pg. 2078
DHL SUPPLY CHAIN (SOUTH AFRICA) (PTY) LTD.—See Deutsche Post AG; *Int'l*, pg. 2078
DHL SUPPLY CHAIN (VIETNAM) LIMITED—See Deutsche Post AG; *Int'l*, pg. 2078
DHL TRADE FAIRS & EVENTS GMBH—See Deutsche Post AG; *Int'l*, pg. 2078
DHL (URUGUAY) S.R.L.—See Deutsche Post AG; *Int'l*, pg. 2073
DHL-VNPT EXPRESS LTD.—See Deutsche Post AG; *Int'l*, pg. 2078
DHL VOIGT INTERNATIONAL GMBH—See Deutsche Post AG; *Int'l*, pg. 2078
DHL WAHL INTERNATIONAL GMBH—See Deutsche Post AG; *Int'l*, pg. 2078
DHL WORLDWIDE EXPRESS CAMBODIA LTD—See Deutsche Post AG; *Int'l*, pg. 2078
DHL WORLDWIDE EXPRESS, INC—See Deutsche Post AG; *Int'l*, pg. 2078
DHL WORLDWIDE EXPRESS LOGISTICS NV /SA—See Deutsche Post AG; *Int'l*, pg. 2078
DIAKINISIS S.A.—See ELGEKA S.A.; *Int'l*, pg. 2359
DIETHELM KELLER LOGISTICS LTD.—See Diethelm Keller Holding Limited; *Int'l*, pg. 2117
DIMALSA LOGISTICS INC.—See Deutsche Post AG; *Int'l*, pg. 2080
DIRECT MAIL LOGISTIK AG—See Die Schweizerische Post AG; *Int'l*, pg. 2112
DISTRIBUTION SOLUTIONS INTERNATIONAL, INC.—See Thermo Fisher Scientific Inc.; *U.S. Public*, pg. 2146
DISTRIBUTOR RESOURCE MANAGEMENT, INC.—See Meal Ticket; *U.S. Private*, pg. 2647
DIVERSE SUPPLY CHAIN SDN. BHD.—See 9R Limited; *Int'l*, pg. 17
DIVERSIFIED DISTRIBUTION SYSTEMS, LLC—See Bunzl plc; *Int'l*, pg. 1218
DIVERSIFIED FREIGHT SYSTEM PHILIPPINES CORPORATION—See Dimerco Express Corporation; *Int'l*, pg. 2126
DIVERSIFIED INTERNATIONAL LOGISTICS PTE. LTD.—See Dimerco Express Corporation; *Int'l*, pg. 2126
DME ALMY SA—See Financiere de l'Odet; *Int'l*, pg. 2667
DM TRANS, LLC; *U.S. Private*, pg. 1248
DNKH LOGISTICS PTE LTD—See Chasen Holdings Limited; *Int'l*, pg. 1457
DOBBS BROTHERS MANAGEMENT; *U.S. Private*, pg. 1250
DOCCHECK MEDIZINBEDARF & LOGISTIK GMBH—See DocCheck AG; *Int'l*, pg. 2153
DONGBU CORP - LOGISTICS—See Dongbu Group; *Int'l*, pg. 2166
DONGBU EXPRESS CO., LTD.—See Dongwon Enterprise Co., Ltd.; *Int'l*, pg. 2170
DONGYANG PISTON USA INC.—See Dongyang Piston Co., Ltd.; *Int'l*, pg. 2172
DOT TRANSPORTATION, INC.—See Dot Foods, Inc.; *U.S. Private*, pg. 1264
DP SCHENKER—See Deutsche Bahn AG; *Int'l*, pg. 2052
DPWN HOLDINGS (USA), INC.—See Deutsche Post AG; *Int'l*, pg. 2079
DP WORLD ANTWERP N.V.—See Dubai World Corporation; *Int'l*, pg. 2220
DP WORLD CALLAO S.R.L.—See Dubai World Corporation; *Int'l*, pg. 2220
DP WORLD (CANADA) INC.—See Dubai World Corporation; *Int'l*, pg. 2220
DP WORLD CARGO SERVICES (PTY) LIMITED—See Dubai World Corporation; *Int'l*, pg. 2220
DP WORLD FUJAIRAH FZE—See Dubai World Corporation; *Int'l*, pg. 2220
DP WORLD FZE—See Dubai World Corporation; *Int'l*, pg. 2220
DP WORLD GERMERSHEIM, GMBH AND CO. KG—See Dubai World Corporation; *Int'l*, pg. 2220
DP WORLD MARITIME COOPERATIEVE U.A.—See Dubai World Corporation; *Int'l*, pg. 2221
DP WORLD—See Dubai World Corporation; *Int'l*, pg. 2220
DP WORLD TARRAGONA S.A.—See Dubai World Corporation; *Int'l*, pg. 2221
DP WORLD YARIMCA LIMAN ISLETMELERI ANONIM SIRKETI—See Dubai World Corporation; *Int'l*, pg. 2221
DRIVERS ALERT, LLC—See MidOcean Partners, LLP; *U.S. Private*, pg. 2717
DRT TRANSPORTATION; *U.S. Private*, pg. 1279
DSI/DATASOURCE, INC.—See The Graham Group, Inc.; *U.S. Private*, pg. 4037
DS SPEDITION GMBH; *Int'l*, pg. 2209
DSV AIR AND SEA FOR LOGISTICS SERVICES COMPANY W.L.L.—See DSV A/S; *Int'l*, pg. 2212
DSV AIR & SEA AG—See DSV A/S; *Int'l*, pg. 2211
DSV AIR & SEA DOMINICANA, S.R.L.—See DSV A/S; *Int'l*, pg. 2211
DSV AIR & SEA D.O.O.—See DSV A/S; *Int'l*, pg. 2212
DSV AIR & SEA INTERNATIONAL PRIVATE LIMITED—See DSV A/S; *Int'l*, pg. 2211
DSV AIR & SEA JSC—See DSV A/S; *Int'l*, pg. 2211
DSV AIR & SEA PA INC.—See DSV A/S; *Int'l*, pg. 2211
DSV AIR & SEA PORTUGAL, LDA—See DSV A/S; *Int'l*, pg. 2211
DSV AIR & SEA (PR) INC.—See DSV A/S; *Int'l*, pg. 2211
DSV AIR & SEA S.A.—See DSV A/S; *Int'l*, pg. 2211
DSV AIR & SEA S.A.—See DSV A/S; *Int'l*, pg. 2212
DSV AIR & SEA S.A.—See DSV A/S; *Int'l*, pg. 2212
DSV AIR & SEA S.A.—See DSV A/S; *Int'l*, pg. 2212
DSV AIR & SEA S.A.S.—See DSV A/S; *Int'l*, pg. 2212
DSV AIR & SEA—See DSV A/S; *Int'l*, pg. 2211
DSV AIR & SEA SRL—See DSV A/S; *Int'l*, pg. 2212
DSV AIR & SEA W.L.L.—See DSV A/S; *Int'l*, pg. 2211
DSV AIR SERVICES S.A.—See DSV A/S; *Int'l*, pg. 2212
DSV A/S; *Int'l*, pg. 2210
DSV HUNGARIA KFT—See DSV A/S; *Int'l*, pg. 2212
DSV INTERNATIONAL HAVA VE DENIZ TASIMACILIGI LTD.SIRKETI—See DSV A/S; *Int'l*, pg. 2212
DSV LOGISTICS LLC—See DSV A/S; *Int'l*, pg. 2212
DSV ROAD B.V.—See DSV A/S; *Int'l*, pg. 2213
DSV ROAD DOOEL SKOPJE—See DSV A/S; *Int'l*, pg. 2212
DSV ROAD D.O.O.—See DSV A/S; *Int'l*, pg. 2213
DSV ROAD OOO—See DSV A/S; *Int'l*, pg. 2212
DSV ROAD S.R.L.—See DSV A/S; *Int'l*, pg. 2212
DSV SAKHALIN, OOO—See DSV A/S; *Int'l*, pg. 2213
DSV SLOVAKIA, S.R.O.—See DSV A/S; *Int'l*, pg. 2213
DSV SOLUTIONS AS—See DSV A/S; *Int'l*, pg. 2213
DSV SOLUTIONS BRASIL SERVICOS DE LOGISTICA LTDA.—See DSV A/S; *Int'l*, pg. 2213
DSV SOLUTIONS B.V.—See DSV A/S; *Int'l*, pg. 2213
DSV SOLUTIONS (DORDRECHT) B.V.—See DSV A/S; *Int'l*, pg. 2213
DSV SOLUTIONS FOR LOGISTICS SERVICES COMPANY LLC—See DSV A/S; *Int'l*, pg. 2213
DSV SOLUTIONS GMBH—See DSV A/S; *Int'l*, pg. 2213
DSV SOLUTIONS INC.—See DSV A/S; *Int'l*, pg. 2213
DSV SOLUTIONS (MOERDIJK) B.V.—See DSV A/S; *Int'l*, pg. 2213
DSV SOLUTIONS NEDERLAND B.V.—See DSV A/S; *Int'l*, pg. 2213
DSV SOLUTIONS OY—See DSV A/S; *Int'l*, pg. 2213
DSV SOLUTIONS PTE. LTD.—See DSV A/S; *Int'l*, pg. 2213
DSV SOLUTIONS S.A.E.—See DSV A/S; *Int'l*, pg. 2213
DSV SOLUTIONS S.A.U.—See DSV A/S; *Int'l*, pg. 2213
DSV SOLUTIONS SRL—See DSV A/S; *Int'l*, pg. 2213

DSV S.P.A—See DSV A/S; *Int'l*, pg. 2213
D-TERRA SOLUTIONS LLC—See DeBartolo Holdings, LLC; *U.S. Private*, pg. 1186
DTG VERPACKUNGSLOGISTIK GMBH—See Deufol SE; *Int'l*, pg. 2048
DUBAI MARITIME CITY LLC—See Dubai World Corporation; *Int'l*, pg. 2221
DUBAI TRADE FZE—See Dubai World Corporation; *Int'l*, pg. 2221
DUNLOP CONVEYOR BELTING POLSKA SP.Z.O.O—See Compagnie Generale des Etablissements Michelin SCA; *Int'l*, pg. 1742
DUPRE LOGISTICS, LLC; *U.S. Private*, pg. 1291
DX (GROUP) PLC—See H.I.G. Capital, LLC; *U.S. Private*, pg. 1828
DYNAMIC LOGISTIX, LLC; *U.S. Private*, pg. 1298
DYNAMIC METHODS; *U.S. Private*, pg. 1298
DYNAMIC WORLDWIDE WEST, INC.—See Dynamic International USA, Inc.; *U.S. Private*, pg. 1298
EAGLE ENVIRONMENTAL CONSULTING, INC—See Sun Capital Partners, Inc.; *U.S. Private*, pg. 3859
EAGLE SUPPORT SERVICES CORPORATION; *U.S. Private*, pg. 1310
EARTHTRON LLC; *U.S. Private*, pg. 1314
EAST AFRICA COMMERCIAL & SHIPPING CO., LTD.—See Financiere de L'Odet; *Int'l*, pg. 2667
EAST WEST HOLDINGS LIMITED; *Int'l*, pg. 2270
ECHO GLOBAL LOGISTICS, INC.—See The Jordan Company, L.P.; *U.S. Private*, pg. 4060
ECONOMIC ZONES WORLD COMPANY—See Dubai World Corporation; *Int'l*, pg. 2222
ECORODOVIAS INFRAESTRUCTURA E LOGISTICA S.A.—See Argo Finanziaria S.p.A.; *Int'l*, pg. 562
ECU LINE JAPAN LTD.—See Allcargo Logistics Limited; *Int'l*, pg. 333
ECU-LINE PARAGUAY SA—See Allcargo Logistics Limited; *Int'l*, pg. 334
ECU-LINE SAUDI ARABIA LLC—See Allcargo Logistics Limited; *Int'l*, pg. 334
ECU WORLDWIDE CEE S.R.L.—See Allcargo Logistics Limited; *Int'l*, pg. 333
ECU WORLDWIDE (CYPRUS) LTD.—See Allcargo Logistics Limited; *Int'l*, pg. 334
ECU WORLDWIDE ITALY S.R.L.—See Allcargo Logistics Limited; *Int'l*, pg. 334
ECU WORLDWIDE (KENYA) LTD.—See Allcargo Logistics Limited; *Int'l*, pg. 334
ECU WORLDWIDE LANKA (PRIVATE) LTD.—See Allcargo Logistics Limited; *Int'l*, pg. 334
ECU WORLDWIDE LOGISTICS DO BRAZIL LTDA—See Allcargo Logistics Limited; *Int'l*, pg. 334
ECU WORLDWIDE (MAURITIUS) LTD.—See Allcargo Logistics Limited; *Int'l*, pg. 334
ECU WORLDWIDE MEXICO SA DE CV—See Allcargo Logistics Limited; *Int'l*, pg. 334
ECU WORLDWIDE NEW ZEALAND LTD.—See Allcargo Logistics Limited; *Int'l*, pg. 334
ECU WORLDWIDE (POLAND) SP ZOO—See Allcargo Logistics Limited; *Int'l*, pg. 334
ECU WORLDWIDE (SOUTH AFRICA) PTY LTD—See Allcargo Logistics Limited; *Int'l*, pg. 334
ECU WORLDWIDE TURKEY TASIMACILIK LIMITED SIRKETI—See Allcargo Logistics Limited; *Int'l*, pg. 334
EDS MEDIA AG—See Die Schweizerische Post AG; *Int'l*, pg. 2112
EGYPTIAN TRANSPORT & COMMERCIAL SERVICES COMPANY S.A.E.; *Int'l*, pg. 2327
EHB LOGISTICS CO., LTD.—See KKR & Co. Inc.; *U.S. Public*, pg. 1258
EIF SDN. BHD.—See Expeditors International of Washington, Inc.; *U.S. Public*, pg. 810
EKOL LOJISTIK AS—See Abu Dhabi Investment Company; *Int'l*, pg. 72
ELECTRIFICATION COALITION; *U.S. Private*, pg. 1353
ELEKTRO STILLER GMBH—See Alpiq Holding AG; *Int'l*, pg. 372
ELGEKA FERFELIS ROMANIA S.A.—See ELGEKA S.A.; *Int'l*, pg. 2359
E-LOGI CORPORATION—See EDION Corporation; *Int'l*, pg. 2310
E-LOGISTICS N.V.—See Colruyt Group N.V.; *Int'l*, pg. 1705
E-LOGIT CO., LTD.; *Int'l*, pg. 2249
EMCOR FACILITIES KNOWLEDGE CENTER—See EMCOR Group, Inc.; *U.S. Public*, pg. 737
EMERSON PROCESS MANAGEMENT SAS—See Emerson Electric Co.; *U.S. Public*, pg. 749
EMO AUSTRALASIA NZ LTD—See Emo-Trans Inc.; *U.S. Private*, pg. 1383
EMO TRANS (CANADA) FREIGHT LTD.—See Emo-Trans Inc.; *U.S. Private*, pg. 1383
EMO TRANS KOREA CO LTD.—See Emo-Trans Inc.; *U.S. Private*, pg. 1383
EMO TRANS PERU S.A.C.—See Emo-Trans Inc.; *U.S. Private*, pg. 1383
ENG KONG HOLDINGS PTE LTD.; *Int'l*, pg. 2425
ENTERPRISE LOGISTIC SERVICES LLC—See Enterprise Products Partners L.P.; *U.S. Public*, pg. 778
ENTERTAINMENT LOGISTIX PTY. LTD.—See Helloworld Travel Limited; *Int'l*, pg. 3337
ENVIPCO PICKUP & PROCESSING SERVICES INC.—See Envipco Holding N.V.; *Int'l*, pg. 2453
EPES FREIGHT MANAGEMENT—See EPES Carriers Inc.; *U.S. Private*, pg. 1412
EPIC LOGISTICS, INC.—See EPES Carriers Inc.; *U.S. Private*, pg. 1412
EPOQ LOGISTIC DC K.S.—See Currys plc; *Int'l*, pg. 1879
EQUINOXE SOLUTIONS LIMITED—See Compass Group PLC; *Int'l*, pg. 1751
ERNST & YOUNG J&M MANAGEMENT CONSULTING GMBH—See Ernst & Young GmbH Wirtschaftsprufungsgesellschaft; *Int'l*, pg. 2494
ERVIN EQUIPMENT, INC.; *U.S. Private*, pg. 1423
ESA CARGO & LOGISTICS GMBH—See Allianz SE; *Int'l*, pg. 352
ESA S.R.O.—See KKR & Co. Inc.; *U.S. Public*, pg. 1258
ESR GROUP LIMITED; *Int'l*, pg. 2507
ESSILOR LOGISTIK GMBH—See EssilorLuxottica SA; *Int'l*, pg. 2513
ESTES EXPRESS LINES, INC. - ESTES LEVEL2 LOGISTICS DIVISION—See Estes Express Lines, Inc.; *U.S. Private*, pg. 1429
ESTES EXPRESS LINES, INC. - ESTES SPECIALIZED TRUCKLOAD AND DELIVERY SERVICES DIVISION—See Estes Express Lines, Inc.; *U.S. Private*, pg. 1429
E-SUPPORTLINK, LTD.; *Int'l*, pg. 2249
ETERNITY GRAND LOGISTICS PUBLIC COMPANY LIMITED—See KKR & Co. Inc.; *U.S. Public*, pg. 1258
ETGA GROUP LTD.; *Int'l*, pg. 2523
EURO ASIA COLD CHAIN LOGISTIC CO., LTD.—See DFDS A/S; *Int'l*, pg. 2095
EUROGROUP SA—See Coop-Gruppe Genossenschaft; *Int'l*, pg. 1790
EURO NORDIC LOGISTICS B.V.—See China National Chemical Corporation; *Int'l*, pg. 1527
EUROPA MULTIPURPOSE TERMINALS S.P.A.—See Abu Dhabi Investment Company; *Int'l*, pg. 72
EUROPE CORPORATION—See Hyundai Glovis Co., Ltd.; *Int'l*, pg. 3556
EURO-TERMINAL AS—See Caiano AS; *Int'l*, pg. 1252
EURO TERMINAL SP Z O O—See Caiano AS; *Int'l*, pg. 1252
EUSU LOGISTICS SPAIN SA—See Financiere de L'Odet; *Int'l*, pg. 2667
EVAG EMDER VERKEHRS UND AUTOMOTIVE GESELLSCHAFT MBH—See Deutsche Bahn AG; *Int'l*, pg. 2051
EVERETT LOGISTICS, LLC—See Roadrunner Transportation Systems, Inc.; *U.S. Private*, pg. 1802
EVERGREEN INTERNATIONAL LOGISTICS (HK) LTD.—See Evergreen International Storage & Transport Corp.; *Int'l*, pg. 2565
EVERGREEN INTERNATIONAL LOGISTICS (KOREA) CO., LTD.—See Evergreen International Storage & Transport Corp.; *Int'l*, pg. 2566
EVERGREEN LOGISTICS (INDIA) PRIVATE LTD.—See Evergreen International Storage & Transport Corp.; *Int'l*, pg. 2566
EVERGREEN LOGISTICS PHILIPPINES CORP.—See Evergreen International Storage & Transport Corp.; *Int'l*, pg. 2566
EVERGREEN LOGISTICS VIETNAM CO., LTD.—See Evergreen International Storage & Transport Corp.; *Int'l*, pg. 2566
EXCELENCIA EN TRANSPORTE DE PERSONAL, S.A.P.I. DE C.V.—See Grupo Traxion, S. A. B. de C. V.; *Int'l*, pg. 3138
EXEDY LOGISTICS CO., LTD.—See Exedy Corporation; *Int'l*, pg. 2580
EXEL CANADA LTD.—See Deutsche Post AG; *Int'l*, pg. 2080
EXEL DISTRIBUTION (THAILAND) LTD.—See Deutsche Post AG; *Int'l*, pg. 2080
EXEL GLOBAL LOGISTICS DO BRASIL S.A.—See Deutsche Post AG; *Int'l*, pg. 2080
EXEL GROUP HOLDINGS (NEDERLAND) B.V.—See Deutsche Post AG; *Int'l*, pg. 2080
EXEL INTERNATIONAL HOLDINGS (NETHERLANDS 1) B.V.—See Deutsche Post AG; *Int'l*, pg. 2080
EXEL INTERNATIONAL HOLDINGS (NETHERLANDS 2) B.V.—See Deutsche Post AG; *Int'l*, pg. 2080
EXEL SUPPLY CHAIN SERVICES DE MEXICO, S.A. DE C.V.—See Deutsche Post AG; *Int'l*, pg. 2080
EXEL SUPPLY CHAIN SERVICES (SOUTH AFRICA) (PTY) LTD.—See Deutsche Post AG; *Int'l*, pg. 2080
EXERTIS IRELAND LIMITED—See DCC plc; *Int'l*, pg. 1990
EXERTIS SUPPLY CHAIN SERVICES LIMITED—See DCC plc; *Int'l*, pg. 1990
EXPEDITED SOLUTIONS, INC.—See ArcBest Corporation; *U.S. Public*, pg. 180
EXPEDITORS (BANGLADESH), LTD.—See Expeditors International of Washington, Inc.; *U.S. Public*, pg. 810
EXPEDITORS CHILE TRANSPORTES INTERNACIONALES LIMITADA—See Expeditors International of Washington, Inc.; *U.S. Public*, pg. 810
EXPEDITORS DENMARK APS—See Expeditors International of Washington, Inc.; *U.S. Public*, pg. 810
EXPEDITORS DOMINICANA SAS—See Expeditors International of Washington, Inc.; *U.S. Public*, pg. 810
EXPEDITORS EGYPT S.A.E.—See Expeditors International of Washington, Inc.; *U.S. Public*, pg. 810
EXPEDITORS FINLAND OY—See Expeditors International of Washington, Inc.; *U.S. Public*, pg. 810
EXPEDITORS HONG KONG LIMITED—See Expeditors International of Washington, Inc.; *U.S. Public*, pg. 810
EXPEDITORS INTERNATIONAL CR S.R.O.—See Expeditors International of Washington, Inc.; *U.S. Public*, pg. 811
EXPEDITORS INTERNATIONAL DE URUGUAY S.A.—See Expeditors International of Washington, Inc.; *U.S. Public*, pg. 811
EXPEDITORS INTERNATIONAL E.I. (SWITZERLAND) SAGL—See Expeditors International of Washington, Inc.; *U.S. Public*, pg. 811
EXPEDITORS INTERNATIONAL FORWARDING AND CLEARING (ABU DHABI) LLC—See Expeditors International of Washington, Inc.; *U.S. Public*, pg. 811
EXPEDITORS INTERNATIONAL HELLAS A.E.—See Expeditors International of Washington, Inc.; *U.S. Public*, pg. 811
EXPEDITORS INTERNATIONAL (INDIA) PVT. LTD.—See Expeditors International of Washington, Inc.; *U.S. Public*, pg. 810
EXPEDITORS INTERNATIONAL (KUWAIT) W.L.L.—See Expeditors International of Washington, Inc.; *U.S. Public*, pg. 810
EXPEDITORS INTERNATIONAL OCEAN, INC.—See Expeditors International of Washington, Inc.; *U.S. Public*, pg. 811
EXPEDITORS INTERNATIONAL SA (PROPRIETARY) LIMITED—See Expeditors International of Washington, Inc.; *U.S. Public*, pg. 811
EXPEDITORS INTERNATIONAL TASIMACILIK VE TICARET AS—See Expeditors International of Washington, Inc.; *U.S. Public*, pg. 811
EXPEDITORS KOREA LTD.—See Expeditors International of Washington, Inc.; *U.S. Public*, pg. 811
EXPEDITORS LITHUANIA, UAB—See Expeditors International of Washington, Inc.; *U.S. Public*, pg. 811
EXPEDITORS LLC—See Expeditors International of Washington, Inc.; *U.S. Public*, pg. 811
EXPEDITORS (MALAYSIA) SDN. BHD.—See Expeditors International of Washington, Inc.; *U.S. Public*, pg. 810
EXPEDITORS PANAMA LOGISTICS SERVICES, INC.—See Expeditors International of Washington, Inc.; *U.S. Public*, pg. 811
EXPEDITORS PHILIPPINES, INC.—See Expeditors International of Washington, Inc.; *U.S. Public*, pg. 811
EXPEDITORS QATAR LLC—See Expeditors International of Washington, Inc.; *U.S. Public*, pg. 811
EXPEDITORS (SINGAPORE) PRIVATE LIMITED—See Expeditors International of Washington, Inc.; *U.S. Public*, pg. 810
EXPEDITORS SPEDITIONSGES.M.B.H.—See Expeditors International of Washington, Inc.; *U.S. Public*, pg. 811
EXPEDITORS TAIWAN CO., LTD.—See Expeditors International of Washington, Inc.; *U.S. Public*, pg. 812
EXPEDITORS (THAILAND) LTD.—See Expeditors International of Washington, Inc.; *U.S. Public*, pg. 810
EXPEDITORS VIETNAM COMPANY LIMITED—See Expeditors International of Washington, Inc.; *U.S. Public*, pg. 812
EXPERT LOGISTICS LTD.—See AO World PLC; *Int'l*, pg. 487
EXPOLANKA HOLDINGS PLC; *Int'l*, pg. 2589
EXPONENT, INC.; *U.S. Public*, pg. 812
EXPONENT INTERNATIONAL LTD.—See Exponent, Inc.; *U.S. Public*, pg. 812
EXTRON LOGISTICS, LLC; *U.S. Private*, pg. 1452
FACT DENMARK A / S—See Deutsche Post AG; *Int'l*, pg. 2080
FAIRFIELD SOUTHERN COMPANY, INC.—See United States Steel Corporation; *U.S. Public*, pg. 2236
FAIRPLAY TOWAGE B.V.—See Fairplay Schleppdampfschiffs-Reederei Richard Borchard GmbH; *Int'l*, pg. 2609
FAIRPLAY TOWAGE POLSKA SP. Z.O.O. SP.K.—See Fairplay Schleppdampfschiffs-Reederei Richard Borchard GmbH; *Int'l*, pg. 2609
FASTFRATE HOLDINGS INC. MONTREAL DIVISION—See Fenway Partners, LLC; *U.S. Private*, pg. 1496
FASTFRATE HOLDINGS INC.—See Fenway Partners, LLC; *U.S. Private*, pg. 1495
FASTFRATE HOLDINGS INC. - TORONTO DIVISION—See Fenway Partners, LLC; *U.S. Private*, pg. 1496
FASTFRATE HOLDINGS INC. - VANCOUVER DIVISION—See Fenway Partners, LLC; *U.S. Private*, pg. 1496
FDI PLANNING CONSULTANTS, INC.—See Kitchell Corporation; *U.S. Private*, pg. 2316
FEDEX BRASIL LOGISTICA E TRANSPORTE S.A.—See FedEx Corporation; *U.S. Public*, pg. 827
FERROVIA CENTRO-ATLANTICA S.A.; *Int'l*, pg. 2643
FINAL MILE LOGISTICS, INC.—See Mercury Air Group Inc.; *U.S. Private*, pg. 2670
FINE CHEMICAL LOGISITICS CHINA COMPANY

LIMITED—See KKR & Co. Inc.; *U.S. Public*, pg. 1258
FINE CHEMICAL LOGISTICS HONG KONG CO., LTD.—See KKR & Co. Inc.; *U.S. Public*, pg. 1258
FIN MILE LOGISTICS LIMITED; *Int'l*, pg. 2664
FIRST STEAMSHIP S.A.—See First Steamship Co., Ltd.; *Int'l*, pg. 2688
FLEET ASSISTANCE LIMITED—See Arthur J. Gallagher & Co.; *U.S. Public*, pg. 204
FLEETWORTHY SOLUTIONS, INC.—See Bestpass, Inc.; *U.S. Private*, pg. 544
THE FLEXPRO GROUP, LLC—See Beecken Petty O'Keefe & Company, LLC; *U.S. Private*, pg. 514
FLEXQUBE AB; *Int'l*, pg. 2705
FLEXTRONICS LOGISTICS B.V.—See Flex Ltd.; *Int'l*, pg. 2703
FLEXTRONICS LOGISTICS POLAND SP. Z.O.O.—See Flex Ltd.; *Int'l*, pg. 2703
F-LOGISTIIKKA OY—See Atria Plc; *Int'l*, pg. 694
FLOUR MILLS OF GHANA LIMITED—See Seaboard Corporation; *U.S. Public*, pg. 1850
FLS TRANSPORTATION SERVICES, LTD—See ABRY Partners, LLC; *U.S. Private*, pg. 41
FLYJAC LOGISTICS PVT. LTD.—See KKR & Co. Inc.; *U.S. Public*, pg. 1258
FM GLOBAL CONSOLIDATION SERVICES PRIVATE LIMITED—See FM Global Logistics Holdings Berhad; *Int'l*, pg. 2717
FONTANA FASTENERS DE MEXICO S.A. C.V.—See Fontana Luigi S.p.A.; *Int'l*, pg. 2726
FONTANA FASTENERS DEUTSCHLAND GMBH—See Fontana Luigi S.p.A.; *Int'l*, pg. 2726
FONTANA FASTENERS DO BRASIL INDUSTRIA E COMERCIO DE FIXADORES LTDA—See Fontana Luigi S.p.A.; *Int'l*, pg. 2726
FONTANA FASTENERS FRANCE S.A.S.—See Fontana Luigi S.p.A.; *Int'l*, pg. 2726
FONTANA FASTENERS INC.—See Fontana Luigi S.p.A.; *Int'l*, pg. 2726
FONTANA FASTENERS INDIA PRIVATE LTD—See Fontana Luigi S.p.A.; *Int'l*, pg. 2726
FONTANA FASTENERS ITALIA S.P.A.—See Fontana Luigi S.p.A.; *Int'l*, pg. 2726
FONTANA FASTENERS POLAND SP. Z.O.O.—See Fontana Luigi S.p.A.; *Int'l*, pg. 2726
FONTANA FASTENERS S.A.—See Fontana Luigi S.p.A.; *Int'l*, pg. 2726
FONTANA FASTENERS SRL—See Fontana Luigi S.p.A.; *Int'l*, pg. 2726
FONTANA FASTENERS UK LTD—See Fontana Luigi S.p.A.; *Int'l*, pg. 2726
FOSTER BUSINESS SERVICE LTD.—See Foster Electric Co., Ltd.; *Int'l*, pg. 2749
FOUNDRY SERVICE GMBH—See Park-Ohio Holdings Corp.; *U.S. Public*, pg. 1638
FOUNDRY SERVICE GMBH—See Park-Ohio Holdings Corp.; *U.S. Public*, pg. 1639
FOUNDRY SERVICE GMBH—See Park-Ohio Holdings Corp.; *U.S. Public*, pg. 1639
FOUNDRY SERVICE GMBH—See Park-Ohio Holdings Corp.; *U.S. Public*, pg. 1639
FRAMEWORX INC.—See Daiwa House Industry Co., Ltd.; *Int'l*, pg. 1946
FRAUNHOFER AUSTRIA RESEARCH GMBH—See Fraunhofer-Gesellschaft zur Forderung der angewandten Forschung e.V.; *Int'l*, pg. 2767
FREIGHT CONNECTIONS, INC.—See Transportation and Logistics Systems, Inc.; *U.S. Public*, pg. 2184
FREIGHTVIEW, INC.—See C.H. Robinson Worldwide, Inc.; *U.S. Public*, pg. 415
FRESH & HEALTHY ENTERPRISES LTD.—See Container Corporation of India Ltd.; *Int'l*, pg. 1779
FRESH LOGISTICS, LLC—See Campbell Soup Company; *U.S. Public*, pg. 427
FRIEDRICH MULLER OMNIBUSUNTERNEHMEN GMBH—See Deutsche Bahn AG; *Int'l*, pg. 2051
FRIGOCONSULT S.L.—See Frigosped GmbH; *Int'l*, pg. 2792
FRIGOLOGISTICS CONSULTING LIMITED—See Frigosped GmbH; *Int'l*, pg. 2792
FRONTIER TRANSPORT HOLDINGS LIMITED; *Int'l*, pg. 2796
F&S DISTRIBUTING, LLC—See California Cartage Company LLC; *U.S. Private*, pg. 718
FUJIAN KEMEN PORT SUPPLY CHAIN MANAGEMENT CO., LTD.—See China Master Logistics Co., Ltd.; *Int'l*, pg. 1517
FUJIFILM LOGISTICS CO., LTD.—See FUJIFILM Holdings Corporation; *Int'l*, pg. 2824
FUJIFILM LOGISTICS SOLUTION (CHINA) LIMITED—See FUJIFILM Holdings Corporation; *Int'l*, pg. 2824
FUJIKURA LOGISTICS CO., LTD.—See Fujikura Ltd.; *Int'l*, pg. 2828
FUNAI SOKEN LOGISTICS, INC.—See Funai Soken Holdings Incorporated; *Int'l*, pg. 2845
FUSION TRANSPORT, LLC—See Hudson Hill Capital LLC; *U.S. Private*, pg. 2002
FUTURE SUPPLY CHAIN SOLUTIONS LTD.—See Future Corporate Resources Limited; *Int'l*, pg. 2853

FUTURE TRANSFER CO. INC.—See Apollo Global Management, Inc.; *U.S. Public*, pg. 165
GALEXIS AG—See CSL Limited; *Int'l*, pg. 1866
GAMPAC EXPRESS, INC.—See US Foods Holding Corp.; *U.S. Public*, pg. 2266
GANSU GOME LOGISTICS COMPANY LIMITED—See Gome Retail Holdings Limited; *Int'l*, pg. 3037
GATI HONG KONG LTD.—See Gati Ltd.; *Int'l*, pg. 2889
GD EXPRESS SDN BHD.; *Int'l*, pg. 2895
GEBERIT LOGISTIK GMBH—See Geberit AG; *Int'l*, pg. 2904
GEMADEPT LOGISTICS ONE MEMBER COMPANY LIMITED—See CJ Corporation; *Int'l*, pg. 1634
GENCO MARKETPLACE, INC.—See FedEx Corporation; *U.S. Public*, pg. 828
GENESIS LOGISTICS INC. - CHARLESTOWN FACILITY—See Deutsche Post AG; *Int'l*, pg. 2079
GENESIS LOGISTICS INC. - DAYTON FACILITY—See Deutsche Post AG; *Int'l*, pg. 2079
GENESIS LOGISTICS INC. - EAGAN FACILITY—See Deutsche Post AG; *Int'l*, pg. 2079
GENESIS LOGISTICS INC. - FOREST PARK FACILITY—See Deutsche Post AG; *Int'l*, pg. 2079
GERLACH AG—See Deutsche Post AG; *Int'l*, pg. 2080
GERLACH & CO INTERNATIONALE EXPEDITEURS B.V.—See Deutsche Post AG; *Int'l*, pg. 2080
GERLACH & CO. NV—See Deutsche Post AG; *Int'l*, pg. 2080
GERLACH CUSTOMS SERVICES EOOD—See Deutsche Post AG; *Int'l*, pg. 2080
GERLACH CUSTOMS SERVICES UK LIMITED—See Deutsche Post AG; *Int'l*, pg. 2080
GERLACH EUROPEAN CUSTOMS SERVICES, SPOL. S.R.O.—See Deutsche Post AG; *Int'l*, pg. 2080
GERLACH EUROPEAN SERVICES S.R.L.—See Deutsche Post AG; *Int'l*, pg. 2080
GERLACH SPOL S.R.O.—See Deutsche Post AG; *Int'l*, pg. 2080
GERLACH SWEDEN AB—See Deutsche Post AG; *Int'l*, pg. 2080
GERLACH ZOLLDIENSTE GMBH—See Deutsche Post AG; *Int'l*, pg. 2080
GH ELECTROTHERMIE, S.A.S.—See Park-Ohio Holdings Corp.; *U.S. Public*, pg. 1639
GH INDUCTION ATMOSPHERES, LLC—See Park-Ohio Holdings Corp.; *U.S. Public*, pg. 1639
GH INDUCTION DEUTSCHLAND GMBH—See Park-Ohio Holdings Corp.; *U.S. Public*, pg. 1639
GH INDUCTION EQUIPMENT SHANGHAI CO. LTD.—See Park-Ohio Holdings Corp.; *U.S. Public*, pg. 1639
GH INDUCTION INDIA PVT. LTD.—See Park-Ohio Holdings Corp.; *U.S. Public*, pg. 1639
GH MEXICANA, S.A. DE C.V.—See Park-Ohio Holdings Corp.; *U.S. Public*, pg. 1639
GIBB GROUP (NETHERLANDS) B.V.—See Clarkson PLC; *Int'l*, pg. 1651
THE GINN GROUP, INC.; *U.S. Private*, pg. 4033
GIORGIO GORI USA, INC.—See Deutsche Post AG; *Int'l*, pg. 2080
GKE CORPORATION LIMITED; *Int'l*, pg. 2983
GKE EXPRESS LOGISTICS PTE LTD—See GKE Corporation Limited; *Int'l*, pg. 2983
GKE PRIVATE LIMITED—See GKE Corporation Limited; *Int'l*, pg. 2983
GKE SERVICES PTE. LTD.—See GKE Corporation Limited; *Int'l*, pg. 2983
GLEN RAVEN LOGISTICS, INC.—See Glen Raven, Inc.; *U.S. Private*, pg. 1709
GLOBAL SYNERGY BUYING GROUP S.A.—See ELGEKA S.A.; *Int'l*, pg. 2359
GLOBE INTERNATIONAL CARRIERS LTD.; *Int'l*, pg. 3006
GLOVIS ALABAMA, LLC—See Hyundai Glovis Co., Ltd.; *Int'l*, pg. 3557
GLOVIS CHENNAI CORPORATION—See Hyundai Glovis Co., Ltd.; *Int'l*, pg. 3557
GOLDEN OCEAN SHIPPING CO PTE. LTD.—See Golden Ocean Group Ltd.; *Int'l*, pg. 3030
GOLD STAR FOODS INC.—See Alvarez & Marsal, Inc.; *U.S. Private*, pg. 213
GOLD STAR FOODS INC.—See Highview Capital, LLC; *U.S. Private*, pg. 1942
GOODMAN LOGISTICS DEVELOPMENTS (UK) LTD—See Goodman Limited; *Int'l*, pg. 3040
G. PETER REBER MOBEL-LOGISTIK GMBH; *Int'l*, pg. 2864
GRAND CHINA PROJECT LOGISTICS CO., LTD—See Hainan Traffic Administration Holding Co., Ltd.; *Int'l*, pg. 3213
GRAND POWER LOGISTICS GROUP LIMITED; *Int'l*, pg. 3056
GREGORY DISTRIBUTION LIMITED—See Gregory Distribution (Holdings) Limited; *Int'l*, pg. 3078
GROUP7 AG; *Int'l*, pg. 3090
GROUPE LOGISTICS IDL S.A.U.—See ID Logistics SAS; *Int'l*, pg. 3587
GROUPE ROBERT INC.—See Gestion Claude Robert Inc.; *Int'l*, pg. 2946
GROUP O INC.; *U.S. Private*, pg. 1793

GRUBER GMBH & CO. KG; *Int'l*, pg. 3114
GRUBER UK LTD.—See Gruber GmbH & Co. KG; *Int'l*, pg. 3114
GRUPO TRAXION, S. A. B. DE C. V.; *Int'l*, pg. 3138
G T EXHIBITIONS LIMITED—See DSV A/S; *Int'l*, pg. 2214
GTI TRANSPORT SOLUTIONS, INC.; *Int'l*, pg. 3151
GUANGDONG GENSHO LOGISTICS CO., LTD.; *Int'l*, pg. 3154
GUANGDONG GREAT RIVER SMARTER LOGISTICS CO., LTD.; *Int'l*, pg. 3154
GUANGDONG JUSHEN LOGISTICS COMPANY LIMITED; *Int'l*, pg. 3157
GUANGDONG YUEYUN TRANSPORTATION COMPANY LIMITED; *Int'l*, pg. 3162
GUANGZHOU JIACHENG INTERNATIONAL LOGISTICS CO., LTD.; *Int'l*, pg. 3166
GUANGZHOU UNIQUE LOGISTICS INTERNATIONAL LIMITED—See Unique Logistics International Inc.; *U.S. Public*, pg. 2227
GUDEL INTRALOGISTICS GMBH—See Gudel Group AG; *Int'l*, pg. 3171
GULF MARINE SERVICES PLC; *Int'l*, pg. 3181
GWC GLOBAL TRANSPORT LLC—See Gulf Warehousing Company QSC; *Int'l*, pg. 3182
GXO LOGISTICS, INC.; *U.S. Public*, pg. 975
GYARMATHY & PARTNERS LTD.; *Int'l*, pg. 3190
HAAF SPEDITION GMBH & CO. KG; *Int'l*, pg. 3201
HAI MINH LOGISTICS CO.,LTD.—See Hai Minh Corporation; *Int'l*, pg. 3208
HAINAN HAIQI TRANSPORTATION GROUP CO., LTD.; *Int'l*, pg. 3212
HALLA MEISTER SUZHOU LOGISTICS CO., LTD—See Halla Group; *Int'l*, pg. 3229
HALL ENTERPRISES, INC.—See Providence Equity Partners L.L.C.; *U.S. Private*, pg. 3292
HANEXPRESS CO., LTD.; *Int'l*, pg. 3244
HANEXPRESS LOGISTICS (NINGBO) CO., LTD—See HANEXPRESS CO., LTD.; *Int'l*, pg. 3244
HANGZHOU SF INTRA-CITY INDUSTRIAL CO., LTD.; *Int'l*, pg. 3250
HANKOOK NETWORKS AMERICA, INC.—See Hankook Tire & Technology Co.,Ltd.; *Int'l*, pg. 3253
HANKOOK NETWORKS CO., LTD.—See Hankook Tire & Technology Co.,Ltd.; *Int'l*, pg. 3253
HANSA LOGISTIK EG—See Arla Foods amba; *Int'l*, pg. 573
HANSA MARINE LOGISTICS GMBH—See Bremer Lagerhaus-Gesellschaft; *Int'l*, pg. 1145
HANSETANK SPEDITION GMBH; *Int'l*, pg. 3260
HAPPINET LOGISTICS SERVICE CORPORATION—See Happinet Corporation; *Int'l*, pg. 3269
HARSCO INFRASTRUCTURE LOGISTIC SERVICES B.V.—See Brand Industrial Services, Inc.; *U.S. Private*, pg. 636
HARSCO METALS LOGISTIQUE ET SERVICES SPECIALISES S.A.S.—See Enviri Corporation; *U.S. Public*, pg. 780
HAVELLS SYLVANIA SPAIN LOGISTICS S.L.—See Havell's India Ltd.; *Int'l*, pg. 3286
HD LOGISTICS, INC.—See Harmonic Drive Systems Inc.; *Int'l*, pg. 3277
HENGTONG LOGISTICS CO., LTD.; *Int'l*, pg. 3347
HENZETEAM GMBH; *Int'l*, pg. 3356
H.E.S. BEHEER N.V.; *Int'l*, pg. 3195
HESSENATIE LOGISTICS NV—See Compagnie Maritime Belge S.A.; *Int'l*, pg. 1746
HEUNG-A LOGISTICS CO., LTD; *Int'l*, pg. 3366
HEXTAR TECHNOLOGIES SOLUTIONS BHD—See Hextar Holdings Sdn. Bhd.; *Int'l*, pg. 3373
HEZHOU PINGGUI PGMA TRANSPORTATION CO. LTD—See China Nonferrous Metal Mining (Group) Co., Ltd.; *Int'l*, pg. 1535
HG LOGISTICS, LLC—See Hill & Griffith Company; *U.S. Private*, pg. 1944
HHE (USA) INC.—See Hankyu Hanshin Holdings Inc.; *Int'l*, pg. 3255
HHLA LOGISTICS ALTENWERDER GMBH & CO. KG—See Hamburger Hafen und Logistik AG; *Int'l*, pg. 3236
HHLA LOGISTICS ALTENWERDER VERWALTUNGSGESELLSCHAFT MBH—See Hamburger Hafen und Logistik AG; *Int'l*, pg. 3236
HHLA LOGISTICS GMBH—See Hamburger Hafen und Logistik AG; *Int'l*, pg. 3236
HHLA NEXT GMBH—See Hamburger Hafen und Logistik AG; *Int'l*, pg. 3236
HHLA PROJECT LOGISTICS LLC—See Hamburger Hafen und Logistik AG; *Int'l*, pg. 3236
HIDRIA LC D.O.O.—See Hidria d.o.o.; *Int'l*, pg. 3384
HIGASHI TWENTY ONE CO., LTD.; *Int'l*, pg. 3385
HIGGS INTERNATIONAL LIMITED—See Deutsche Post AG; *Int'l*, pg. 2080
HIRERIGHT, LLC; *U.S. Private*, pg. 1950
HITACHI COLLABONEXT TRANSPORT SYSTEM CO., LTD.—See KKR & Co. Inc.; *U.S. Public*, pg. 1258
HITACHI DISTRIBUTION SOFTWARE (SHANGHAI) CO., LTD.—See KKR & Co. Inc.; *U.S. Public*, pg. 1258
HITACHI SISTEMA DE TRANSPORTE MEXICO, S.A. DE C.V.—See KKR & Co. Inc.; *U.S. Public*, pg. 1258
HITACHI TRANSPORT SYSTEEM (NEDERLAND) BV—See

541614 — PROCESS, PHYSICAL D...

KKR & Co. Inc.; *U.S. Public*, pg. 1258
HITACHI TRANSPORT SYSTEM (ASIA) PTE. LTD.—See KKR & Co. Inc.; *U.S. Public*, pg. 1258
HITACHI TRANSPORT SYSTEM (AUSTRALIA) PTY. LTD.—See KKR & Co. Inc.; *U.S. Public*, pg. 1258
HITACHI TRANSPORT SYSTEM (EUROPE) B.V.—See KKR & Co. Inc.; *U.S. Public*, pg. 1258
HITACHI TRANSPORT SYSTEM (EUROPE) GMBH—See KKR & Co. Inc.; *U.S. Public*, pg. 1258
HITACHI TRANSPORT SYSTEM (HONG KONG) LTD.—See KKR & Co. Inc.; *U.S. Public*, pg. 1258
HITACHI TRANSPORT SYSTEM INDIA PVT. LTD.—See KKR & Co. Inc.; *U.S. Public*, pg. 1259
HITACHI TRANSPORT SYSTEM (KOREA), LTD.—See KKR & Co. Inc.; *U.S. Public*, pg. 1258
HITACHI TRANSPORT SYSTEM (M) SDN. BHD.—See KKR & Co. Inc.; *U.S. Public*, pg. 1258
HITACHI TRANSPORT SYSTEMS (FRANCE) S.A.R.L.—See KKR & Co. Inc.; *U.S. Public*, pg. 1259
HITACHI TRANSPORT SYSTEM (SHANGHAI), LTD—See KKR & Co. Inc.; *U.S. Public*, pg. 1259
HITACHI TRANSPORT SYSTEMS LTD.—See KKR & Co. Inc.; *U.S. Public*, pg. 1259
HITACHI TRANSPORT SYSTEMS S.A.R.L.—See KKR & Co. Inc.; *U.S. Public*, pg. 1259
HITACHI TRANSPORT SYSTEM (TAIWAN) LTD.—See KKR & Co. Inc.; *U.S. Public*, pg. 1259
HITACHI TRANSPORT SYSTEM (THAILAND), LTD.—See KKR & Co. Inc.; *U.S. Public*, pg. 1259
HITACHI TRANSPORT SYSTEM (UK) LTD.—See KKR & Co. Inc.; *U.S. Public*, pg. 1259
HITACHI TRAVEL BUREAU SHANGHAI CO., LTD.—See KKR & Co. Inc.; *U.S. Public*, pg. 1259
HITACHI XINXIN GLOBAL LOGISTICS (HENAN) CO., LTD—See KKR & Co. Inc.; *U.S. Public*, pg. 1259
HLE CONSTRUCTION & ENGINEERING SDN. BHD.—See Chasen Holdings Limited; *Int'l*, pg. 1457
HMD TRANSPORT, INC.; *U.S. Private*, pg. 1955
H & M HENNES & MAURITZ LOGISTICS AB CO. KG—See H&M Hennes & Mauritz AB; *Int'l*, pg. 3192
H & M HENNES & MAURITZ LOGISTICS GBC NV—See H&M Hennes & Mauritz AB; *Int'l*, pg. 3192
H & M HENNES & MAURITZ LOGISTICS GBC—See H&M Hennes & Mauritz AB; *Int'l*, pg. 3192
H & M HENNES & MAURITZ LOGISTICS SP. Z.O.O.—See H&M Hennes & Mauritz AB; *Int'l*, pg. 3192
HNA CARGO CO., LTD.—See Hainan Traffic Administration Holding Co., Ltd.; *Int'l*, pg. 3213
HN AUTOTRANSPORT N.V.—See Hoedlmayr International AG; *Int'l*, pg. 3439
HNRY LOGISTICS, INC.—See Yellow Corporation; *U.S. Public*, pg. 2398
H&N TRANSPORT—See Hartung Brothers Inc.; *U.S. Private*, pg. 1874
HODLMAYR LOGISTICS CZECH REPUBLIC A.S.—See Hoedlmayr International AG; *Int'l*, pg. 3439
HODLMAYR LOGISTICS GMBH—See Hoedlmayr International AG; *Int'l*, pg. 3439
HODLMAYR ZASTAVA D.O.O.—See Hoedlmayr International AG; *Int'l*, pg. 3439
HOEDLMAYR INTERNATIONAL AG; *Int'l*, pg. 3439
HOEDLMAYR-LAZAR ROMANIA S.R.L.—See Hoedlmayr International AG; *Int'l*, pg. 3439
HORIZON TERMINALS LIMITED—See Emirates National Oil Company Limited; *Int'l*, pg. 2381
HORMANN LOGISTIK GMBH—See Hormann Holding GmbH & Co. KG; *Int'l*, pg. 3480
HOUSE LOGISTICS SERVICE CORPORATION—See House Foods Group Inc.; *Int'l*, pg. 3490
HOYER GMBH; *Int'l*, pg. 3498
HOYER UK LTD.—See Hoyer Gmbh; *Int'l*, pg. 3499
HPI ASIA PACIFIC LTD.—See HPI AG; *Int'l*, pg. 3500
HPI LOGISTICS GMBH & CO. KG—See HPI AG; *Int'l*, pg. 3500
HSH MOVE+MORE GMBH—See Cerberus Capital Management, L.P.; *U.S. Private*, pg. 838
HSH MOVE+MORE GMBH—See GoldenTree Asset Management LP; *U.S. Private*, pg. 1734
HSH MOVE+MORE GMBH—See J.C. Flowers & Co. LLC; *U.S. Private*, pg. 2159
HTS FORWARDING MALAYSIA SDN. BHD.—See KKR & Co. Inc.; *U.S. Public*, pg. 1258
HUAIHE ENERGY (GROUP) CO., LTD.; *Int'l*, pg. 3512
HUANGSHAN PROCUREMENT AND DISTRIBUTION CENTER CO.—See Huangshan Tourism Development Co., Ltd.; *Int'l*, pg. 3513
HULL BLYTH NIGERIA LTD.—See Deutsche Post AG; *Int'l*, pg. 2080
HYUNDAI GLOVIS CO., LTD.; *Int'l*, pg. 3556
ICF CONSULTING SERVICES, INDIA PRIVATE, LTD.—See ICF International, Inc.; *U.S. Public*, pg. 1086
ICG LOGISTICS, LLC—See US 1 Industries, Inc.; *U.S. Private*, pg. 4317
ICT HOLDING A/S—See DFDS A/S; *Int'l*, pg. 2095
ICT LOGISTICS GMBH—See DFDS A/S; *Int'l*, pg. 2095
ID COMMERCE + LOGISTICS—See Inktel Direct Inc.; *U.S. Private*, pg. 2078

ID DO BRASIL LOGISTICA LTDA—See ID Logistics SAS; *Int'l*, pg. 3587
IDEAL SETECH SHARE-THE-SPARE LLC—See The Ideal Group, Inc.; *U.S. Private*, pg. 4055
IDEC LOGISTICS SERVICE CORPORATION—See IDEC Corporation; *Int'l*, pg. 3590
ID LOGISTICS BENELUX B.V.—See ID Logistics SAS; *Int'l*, pg. 3587
ID LOGISTICS ESPANA—See ID Logistics SAS; *Int'l*, pg. 3587
ID LOGISTICS POLSKA S.A.—See ID Logistics SAS; *Int'l*, pg. 3587
ID LOGISTICS RUS OOO—See ID Logistics SAS; *Int'l*, pg. 3587
ID LOGISTICS SAS; *Int'l*, pg. 3587
ID LOGISTICS TAIWAN CO., LTD.—See ID Logistics SAS; *Int'l*, pg. 3587
ID LOGISTICS US, INC.—See ID Logistics SAS; *Int'l*, pg. 3587
ID SUPPLY CHAIN S.A.—See ID Logistics SAS; *Int'l*, pg. 3587
IEMOLI TRASPORTI S.R.L.—See Die Schweizerische Post AG; *Int'l*, pg. 2113
IGLO (M) SDN. BHD.—See Haisan Resources Berhad; *Int'l*, pg. 3217
IHI LOGISTICS SYSTEM TECHNOLOGY SHANGHAI CO., LTD.—See IHI Corporation; *Int'l*, pg. 3604
ILB GROUP BERHAD; *Int'l*, pg. 3613
ILLINOIS DISTRIBUTING CO.—See Grey Eagle Distributors Inc.; *U.S. Private*, pg. 1784
I-LOGIC CO., LTD.—See FP Corporation; *Int'l*, pg. 2756
IMCD ALGERIA—See IMCD N.V.; *Int'l*, pg. 3621
IMCD IRELAND LTD—See IMCD N.V.; *Int'l*, pg. 3622
IMCD (SHANGHAI) TRADING CO. LTD.—See IMCD N.V.; *Int'l*, pg. 3621
IMPACT 21 GROUP LLC—See W. Capra Consulting Group, Inc.; *U.S. Private*, pg. 4417
IMPERIAL LOGISTICS INTERNATIONAL B.V. & CO. KG—See Dubai World Corporation; *Int'l*, pg. 2221
IMPERIAL LOGISTICS & TRANSPORT—See Dubai World Corporation; *Int'l*, pg. 2221
IMPERIAL MOBILITY INTERNATIONAL BV—See Dubai World Corporation; *Int'l*, pg. 2221
IMPERILOG LIMITED—See Dubai World Corporation; *Int'l*, pg. 2221
IMPORTLA, INC.—See Bunker Hill Capital LP; *U.S. Private*, pg. 685
INCOMM S.A.S.—See StoneX Group Inc.; *U.S. Public*, pg. 1952
INDIA GATEWAY TERMINAL PVT. LTD—See Dubai World Corporation; *Int'l*, pg. 2221
INGRAM MICRO AUSTRALIA PTY LTD—See Hainan Traffic Administration Holding Co., Ltd.; *Int'l*, pg. 3214
INGRAM MICRO LOGISTICS LP—See Hainan Traffic Administration Holding Co., Ltd.; *Int'l*, pg. 3214
INTEGER.PL S.A.—See Advent International Corporation; *U.S. Private*, pg. 103
INTEGRATED COMMERCIALIZATION SOLUTIONS—See Cencora, Inc.; *U.S. Public*, pg. 467
INTEGRATED LOGISTICS (H.K.) LIMITED—See Hovid Berhad; *Int'l*, pg. 3492
INTELLIGENT AUDIT; *U.S. Private*, pg. 2105
INTERAFRICA GRAINS (PROPRIETARY) LIMITED—See Seaboard Corporation; *U.S. Public*, pg. 1850
INTERDEAN RELOCATION SERVICES GMBH—See EAC Invest AS; *Int'l*, pg. 2262
INTERNATIONAL CARGO SERVICE CO., LTD.—See ANA Holdings Inc.; *Int'l*, pg. 444
INTERNATIONAL CLAIMS HANDLING SERVICES INC.—See DSV A/S; *Int'l*, pg. 2214
INTERNATIONAL CLAIMS HANDLING SERVICES LTD.—See DSV A/S; *Int'l*, pg. 2214
INTERNATIONAL FREIGHT LOGISTICS—See DSV A/S; *Int'l*, pg. 2214
INTERNATIONAL FREIGHT SERVICES, INC.—See Deutsche Bahn AG; *Int'l*, pg. 2054
INTERSERV GESELLSCHAFT FUR PERSONALUND BERATERDIENSTLEISTUNGEN MBH—See Deutsche Post AG; *Int'l*, pg. 2083
INTERSTATE LOGISTICS GROUP, INC.; *U.S. Private*, pg. 2125
INTERSTATE TRANSPORT, INC.—See Dupre Logistics, LLC; *U.S. Private*, pg. 1291
IQR CONSULTING, INC.—See ExlService Holdings, Inc.; *U.S. Public*, pg. 808
ISI LOGISTICS SOUTH, LLC—See Roadrunner Transportation Systems, Inc.; *U.S. Public*, pg. 1802
ISSEL NORD S.R.L.—See Fincantieri S.p.A.; *Int'l*, pg. 2671
IT4LOGISTICS AG—See Deutsche Post AG; *Int'l*, pg. 2083
ITG GLOBAL LOGISTICS B.V.—See Deutsche Post AG; *Int'l*, pg. 2081
ITG INTERNATIONAL TRANSPORTS, INC.—See Deutsche Post AG; *Int'l*, pg. 2081
I T K INTERNATIONALES TRANSPORT-KONTOR GMBH; *Int'l*, pg. 3562
JABIL CIRCUIT (SHANGHAI) CO. LTD.—See Jabil Inc.; *U.S. Public*, pg. 1181

JABIL CIRCUIT (SHENZHEN) CO. LTD.—See Jabil Inc.; *U.S. Public*, pg. 1181
JAPAN CARGO CO., LTD.—See Bain Capital, LP; *U.S. Private*, pg. 444
JARRETT LOGISTICS SYSTEMS, INC.; *U.S. Private*, pg. 2188
THE JAY GROUP; *U.S. Private*, pg. 4058
JMC VAN TRANS LIMITED—See An Post LLC; *Int'l*, pg. 443
JO-ANN STORES SUPPLY CHAIN MANAGEMENT, INC.—See Leonard Green & Partners, L.P.; *U.S. Private*, pg. 2426
JR TOKAI LOGISTICS CO., LTD.—See Central Japan Railway Company; *Int'l*, pg. 1408
JUSDA EUROPE S.R.O.—See Hon Hai Precision Industry Co., Ltd.; *Int'l*, pg. 3457
KALSTAR ENTERPRISES LLC—See Kane Is Able, Inc.; *U.S. Private*, pg. 2260
KANE 3PL, LLC—See The Kane Company; *U.S. Private*, pg. 4064
KANSAI SUPER PREMIUM CO.,LTD.—See H2O Retailing Corp.; *Int'l*, pg. 3200
KARPELES FLIGHT SERVICES GMBH—See Deutsche Bahn AG; *Int'l*, pg. 2052
KEWILL SERVICE LOGISTICS B.V.—See Francisco Partners Management, LP; *U.S. Private*, pg. 1589
KEYSTONE LOGISTICS, LLC—See US 1 Industries, Inc.; *U.S. Private*, pg. 4317
KM PROPPANTS, LLC—See Koch Industries, Inc.; *U.S. Private*, pg. 2333
KNW HOLDINGS, INC.; *U.S. Private*, pg. 2325
KPI LOGISTICS, INC.—See P&S Transportation, Inc.; *U.S. Private*, pg. 3059
KW TRANSPORTATION SERVICES, LLC—See Kennedy-Wilson Holdings, Inc.; *U.S. Public*, pg. 1223
L3 TECHNOLOGIES MAS INC.—See L3Harris Technologies, Inc.; *U.S. Public*, pg. 1284
LAFARGE LOGISTIQUE ALGERIE LLA—See Holcim Ltd.; *Int'l*, pg. 3448
LANDSTAR BLUE LLC—See Landstar System, Inc.; *U.S. Public*, pg. 1292
LANGHAM LOGISTICS INC.; *U.S. Private*, pg. 2389
LANGSTONE SUPPLIES LIMITED—See Park-Ohio Holdings Corp.; *U.S. Public*, pg. 1639
LAWRY FREIGHT SYSTEM, INC.; *U.S. Private*, pg. 2402
LCL LOGISTIX TANZANIA LTD.—See CMA CGM S.A.; *Int'l*, pg. 1668
LEAF RIVER ENERGY CENTER LLC—See New Jersey Resources Corporation; *U.S. Public*, pg. 1511
LEDD TECHNOLOGIES W.L.L.—See Gulf Warehousing Company QSC; *Int'l*, pg. 3182
LEEN MENKEN FOODSERVICE LOGISTICS BV—See bpost NV/SA; *Int'l*, pg. 1133
LEGACY SUPPLY CHAIN SERVICES - BRAMPTON—See LEGACY Supply Chain Services; *U.S. Private*, pg. 2417
LEGACY SUPPLY CHAIN SERVICES - FONTANA—See LEGACY Supply Chain Services; *U.S. Private*, pg. 2417
LEGACY SUPPLY CHAIN SERVICES - RENO—See LEGACY Supply Chain Services; *U.S. Private*, pg. 2417
LEGACY SUPPLY CHAIN SERVICES; *U.S. Private*, pg. 2417
LESAINT LOGISTICS LLC; *U.S. Private*, pg. 2432
LESAINT LOGISTICS—See LeSaint Logistics LLC; *U.S. Private*, pg. 2432
L-EX EQUIPMENTS TRANSPORTS LOGISTICS—See Axel Johnson Gruppen AB; *Int'l*, pg. 764
LIBERTY LOGISTICS SERVICES, INC.—See RPM Consolidated Services, Inc.; *U.S. Private*, pg. 3495
LIEGL & DÄCHSER SZALLITMANYOSZASI ES LOGISZTIKAI KFT.—See Dachser GmbH & Co.; *Int'l*, pg. 1904
LILY TRANSPORTATION CORP.—See ZS Fund L.P.; *U.S. Private*, pg. 4609
LIMITED LIABILITY COMPANY BRINK'S—See The Brink's Company; *U.S. Public*, pg. 2043
LIMOLINK, INC.; *U.S. Private*, pg. 2456
LINC LOGISTICS COMPANY—See Universal Logistics Holdings, Inc.; *U.S. Public*, pg. 2261
LINEAFRESCA LOGISTIC AG—See F. Murpf AG; *Int'l*, pg. 2596
LINEAGE LOGISTICS, LLC—See Bay Grove Capital LLC; *U.S. Private*, pg. 493
LINMARK INTERNATIONAL (HONG KONG) LIMITED—See Daohe Global Group Limited; *Int'l*, pg. 1970
LIVE CONSULTING, INC.—See Frontenac Company LLC; *U.S. Private*, pg. 1614
LLC DFDS—See DFDS A/S; *Int'l*, pg. 2095
LMS INTELLIBOUND, INC.; *U.S. Private*, pg. 2476
LOGENIX INTERNATIONAL; *U.S. Private*, pg. 2481
LOGICALIS ANDINA S.A.C.—See Datatec Limited; *Int'l*, pg. 1980
LOGICALIS BRASIL IMPORTACAO EXPORTACAO LTDA—See Datatec Limited; *Int'l*, pg. 1980
LOGICALIS HONG KONG LIMITED—See Datatec Limited; *Int'l*, pg. 1980
LOGICAL SOLUTION SERVICES INC.; *U.S. Private*, pg. 2481
LOGIN LOGISTICS LLC—See EPES Carriers Inc.; *U.S. Private*, pg. 1412

N.A.I.C.S. INDEX

541614 — PROCESS, PHYSICAL D...

LOGIPAL EXPRESS INC—See BANDAI NAMCO Holdings Inc.; *Int'l*, pg. 829
LOGIS INDUSTRIEDIENSTLEISTUNG GMBH—See Deufol SE; *Int'l*, pg. 2048
LOGIS PRUMYSLOVE OBALY A.S.—See Deufol SE; *Int'l*, pg. 2048
LOGISTEED, LTD.—See KKR & Co. Inc.; *U.S. Public*, pg. 1258
LOGISTICA GRIFOLS S.A DE C.V—See Grifols, S.A.; *Int'l*, pg. 3085
LOGISTICA SANMIVAL S.L.—See Deutsche Bahn AG; *Int'l*, pg. 2051
LOGISTICA TRANSPORTE Y SERVICIOS ASOCIADOS S.A.S.—See Companhia Brasileira de Distribuicao; *Int'l*, pg. 1746
LOGISTIC MAO DE MEXICO, S.A. DE C.V.—See Mid-America Overseas Inc.; *U.S. Private*, pg. 2707
LOGISTICS MANAGEMENT SERVICES LTD.—See McCollister's Transportation Group Inc.; *U.S. Private*, pg. 2629
LOGISTIC; *U.S. Private*, pg. 2481
LOGISTIK SERVICE CENTER S.R.O.—See Hubert Burda Media Holding Kommanditgesellschaft; *Int'l*, pg. 3520
LOGISTYX TECHNOLOGIES, LLC—See Insight Venture Management, LLC; *U.S. Private*, pg. 2091
LOGITERS PORTUGAL, S.A.—See Corpfin Capital SA; *Int'l*, pg. 1802
LOGOS LOGISTICS, INC.; *U.S. Private*, pg. 2482
LOME MULTIPURPOSE TERMINAL SA—See Financiere de L'Odet; *Int'l*, pg. 2667
LONDON GATEWAY PORT LIMITED—See Dubai World Corporation; *Int'l*, pg. 2220
LPS BOSSARD PVT. LTD.—See Bossard Holding AG; *Int'l*, pg. 1117
LYNDEN INTERNATIONAL LOGISTICS CO.—See Lynden Incorporated; *U.S. Private*, pg. 2521
MACGREGOR PARTNERS, LLC—See Accenture plc; *Int'l*, pg. 87
MACH1 GLOBAL SERVICES, INC.; *U.S. Private*, pg. 2535
MACY'S LOGISTICS & OPERATIONS—See Macy's, Inc.; *U.S. Public*, pg. 1353
MAERSK BANGLADESH LTD.—See A.P. Moller-Maersk A/S; *Int'l*, pg. 26
MAERSK GABON SA—See A.P. Moller-Maersk A/S; *Int'l*, pg. 27
MAERSK LOGISTICS & SERVICES INTERNATIONAL A/S—See A.P. Moller-Maersk A/S; *Int'l*, pg. 27
MAGNUM LOGISTICS, INC.—See Magnum, Ltd.; *U.S. Private*, pg. 2549
MAIN LINE AUDIOLOGY CONSULTANTS, PC—See Alpaca Audiology; *U.S. Private*, pg. 196
MAINSTREET 1878 (PTY.) LTD.—See A.P. Moller-Maersk A/S; *Int'l*, pg. 27
MAJESTIC TRANSPORTATION; *U.S. Private*, pg. 2554
MAKIBER, S.A.—See ACS, Actividades de Construccion y Servicios, S.A.; *Int'l*, pg. 115
MALOYTERMINALEN AS—See Caiano AS; *Int'l*, pg. 1252
MANHEIM ASIA PACIFIC LTD.—See Cox Enterprises, Inc.; *U.S. Private*, pg. 1076
MANILA INTERNATIONAL FREIGHT FORWARDERS, INC.—See KKR & Co. Inc.; *U.S. Public*, pg. 1259
MARINER CAPITAL LTD.—See First Steamship Co., Ltd.; *Int'l*, pg. 2688
MARITIME TRANSPORT SERVICES LIMITED—See CK Hutchison Holdings Limited; *Int'l*, pg. 1638
MARKET LOGISTICS SERVICES, LTD.—See Wilson Logistics, Inc.; *U.S. Private*, pg. 4531
MARMON DISTRIBUTION SERVICES—See Berkshire Hathaway Inc.; *U.S. Public*, pg. 309
MARMON RETAIL STORE FIXTURES—See Berkshire Hathaway Inc.; *U.S. Public*, pg. 311
MATERIAL CONNEXION, INC.—See Sandow Media LLC; *U.S. Private*, pg. 3544
MATRIX LOGISTICS SERVICES LTD.—See Deutsche Post AG; *Int'l*, pg. 2081
MAXIMUS FEDERAL SERVICES, INC.—See MAXIMUS, Inc.; *U.S. Public*, pg. 1402
MDS LOGISTICS LIMITED—See Dubai World Corporation; *Int'l*, pg. 2221
MED-STAT USA LLC; *U.S. Private*, pg. 2650
MEISTER LOGISTICS CORPORATION AMERICA—See Halla Group; *Int'l*, pg. 3229
MENASHA PACKAGING COMPANY, LLC - AURORA FACILITY—See Menasha Corporation; *U.S. Private*, pg. 2665
MENASHA PACKAGING COMPANY, LLC - BETHLEHEM FACILITY—See Menasha Corporation; *U.S. Private*, pg. 2665
MENASHA PACKAGING COMPANY, LLC - EDWARDSVILLE FACILITY—See Menasha Corporation; *U.S. Private*, pg. 2665
MENASHA PACKAGING COMPANY, LLC - HARTFORD PLANT—See Menasha Corporation; *U.S. Private*, pg. 2665
MENASHA PACKAGING COMPANY, LLC - HODGKINS FACILITY—See Menasha Corporation; *U.S. Private*, pg. 2665
MENASHA PACKAGING COMPANY, LLC - LAKEVILLE PLANT—See Menasha Corporation; *U.S. Private*, pg. 2665
MENASHA PACKAGING COMPANY, LLC - MINOOKA FACILITY—See Menasha Corporation; *U.S. Private*, pg. 2665
MENASHA PACKAGING COMPANY, LLC - MUSCATINE PLANT—See Menasha Corporation; *U.S. Private*, pg. 2665
MENASHA PACKAGING COMPANY, LLC - ONTARIO FACILITY—See Menasha Corporation; *U.S. Private*, pg. 2665
MENASHA PACKAGING COMPANY, LLC - ROCK ISLAND FACILITY—See Menasha Corporation; *U.S. Private*, pg. 2665
MENASHA PACKAGING COMPANY, LLC - ST. CLOUD PLANT—See Menasha Corporation; *U.S. Private*, pg. 2665
MENTOR MEDIA CBZ (CHONGQING) CO., LTD—See Carl Bennet AB; *Int'l*, pg. 1332
MENTOR MEDIA (CHONGQING) CO., LTD—See Carl Bennet AB; *Int'l*, pg. 1332
MENTOR MEDIA CZECH S.R.O—See Carl Bennet AB; *Int'l*, pg. 1332
MENTOR MEDIA JAPAN GODOGAISHA—See Carl Bennet AB; *Int'l*, pg. 1332
MENTOR MEDIA JUAREZ S.A. DE C.V—See Carl Bennet AB; *Int'l*, pg. 1332
MENTOR MEDIA (KUNSHAN) CO., LTD—See Carl Bennet AB; *Int'l*, pg. 1332
MENTOR MEDIA LTD—See Carl Bennet AB; *Int'l*, pg. 1332
MENTOR MEDIA (SHENZHEN) CO., LTD—See Carl Bennet AB; *Int'l*, pg. 1332
MENTOR MEDIA (SONGJIANG) CO., LTD—See Carl Bennet AB; *Int'l*, pg. 1332
MENTOR MEDIA (SUZHOU) CO., LTD—See Carl Bennet AB; *Int'l*, pg. 1332
MENTOR MEDIA (USA) SUPPLY CHAIN MANAGEMENT INC—See Carl Bennet AB; *Int'l*, pg. 1332
MENTOR MEDIA (XIAMEN) CO., LTD—See Carl Bennet AB; *Int'l*, pg. 1332
M.G.F. LOGISTIQUE S.A.—See G7 Entreprises; *Int'l*, pg. 2867
MGI & DACHSER, INC.—See Dachser GmbH & Co.; *Int'l*, pg. 1904
MHD ENTERPRISES; *U.S. Private*, pg. 2695
MHS DISTRIBUTION & FULFILLMENT, LLC—See Thomas H. Lee Partners, L.P.; *U.S. Private*, pg. 4156
MID-AMERICA OVERSEAS DO BRASIL LOGISTICA LTDA.—See Mid-America Overseas Inc.; *U.S. Private*, pg. 2707
MIDNITE AIR CORP.—See United Parcel Service, Inc.; *U.S. Public*, pg. 2233
MIDNITE EXPRESS INC.—See The Riverside Company; *U.S. Private*, pg. 4109
MIFFI LOGISTICS, CO. INC.—See KKR & Co. Inc.; *U.S. Public*, pg. 1259
MILLER INTERMODAL LOGISTICS SERVICES, INC.—See Dewey Corporation; *U.S. Private*, pg. 1219
MITRADIOPHARMA S.R.L.—See Deutsche Post AG; *Int'l*, pg. 2081
MNPM SOLUTIONS LTD—See ManpowerGroup Inc.; *U.S. Public*, pg. 1358
MODUSLINK KILDARE—See Steel Connect, Inc.; *U.S. Public*, pg. 1941
MODUSLINK PTS, INC.—See Steel Connect, Inc.; *U.S. Public*, pg. 1941
MODUSLINK SERVICES EUROPE—See Steel Connect, Inc.; *U.S. Public*, pg. 1941
MODUSLINK (SHANGHAI) CO. LTD.—See Steel Connect, Inc.; *U.S. Public*, pg. 1941
MODUSLINK SOLUTIONS SERVICE PTE. LTD.—See Steel Connect, Inc.; *U.S. Public*, pg. 1942
MOLDING BOX INC.; *U.S. Private*, pg. 2767
MONTA BREDA B.V.—See Deutsche Post AG; *Int'l*, pg. 2082
MONTA DEN BOSCH B.V.—See Deutsche Post AG; *Int'l*, pg. 2082
MONTA ENSCHEDE B.V.—See Deutsche Post AG; *Int'l*, pg. 2082
MONTA GORINCHEM PAPLAND B.V.—See Deutsche Post AG; *Int'l*, pg. 2082
MONTA GORINCHEM WEIDE B.V.—See Deutsche Post AG; *Int'l*, pg. 2082
MONTA KREFELD GMBH—See Deutsche Post AG; *Int'l*, pg. 2082
MONTA LELYSTAD B.V.—See Deutsche Post AG; *Int'l*, pg. 2082
MONTA MOLENAARSGRAAF B.V.—See Deutsche Post AG; *Int'l*, pg. 2082
MONTA NIEUWVEEN B.V.—See Deutsche Post AG; *Int'l*, pg. 2082
MONTA OOSTERHOUT B.V.—See Deutsche Post AG; *Int'l*, pg. 2082
MONTA OUD GASTEL B.V.—See Deutsche Post AG; *Int'l*, pg. 2082
MONTA PLATFORM B.V.—See Deutsche Post AG; *Int'l*, pg. 2082
MONTA SERVICES B.V.—See Deutsche Post AG; *Int'l*, pg. 2082
MONTA TWI B.V.—See Deutsche Post AG; *Int'l*, pg. 2082
MONTA WASPIK B.V.—See Deutsche Post AG; *Int'l*, pg. 2082
MOORE TRANSPORT; *U.S. Private*, pg. 2780
MORTON SECURITIES LTD.—See Da Yu Financial Holdings Ltd.; *Int'l*, pg. 1902
MOSTRA, SA—See ICF International, Inc.; *U.S. Public*, pg. 1086
M.O.T. INTERMODAL SHIPPING INC.—See C.H. Robinson Worldwide, Inc.; *U.S. Public*, pg. 415
MOVIANTO BELGIUM NV—See Owens & Minor, Inc.; *U.S. Public*, pg. 1626
MOVIANTO CESKA REPUBLIKA SRO—See Owens & Minor, Inc.; *U.S. Public*, pg. 1626
MOVIANTO FRANCE SAS—See Owens & Minor, Inc.; *U.S. Public*, pg. 1626
MOVING CONTENT SOLUTIONS PTE LTD.—See Hakuhodo DY Holdings Incorporated; *Int'l*, pg. 3222
MRL MANNESMANNROHREN LOGISTIK GMBH—See HPI AG; *Int'l*, pg. 3500
MUSKET CORPORATION—See Love's Travel Stops & Country Stores, Inc.; *U.S. Private*, pg. 2501
MYSUPPLYCHAINGROUP (MSCG); *U.S. Private*, pg. 2826
NAM PHAT LOGISTICS CO., LTD.—See Hai Minh Corporation; *Int'l*, pg. 3209
NAVEGATE LOGISTICS, LTD.—See Radiant Logistics, Inc.; *U.S. Public*, pg. 1759
NAVEGATE SUPPLY CHAIN (SHANGHAI) CO., LTD.—See Radiant Logistics, Inc.; *U.S. Public*, pg. 1759
NAVIS INDIA TECHNOLOGIES PRIVATE LIMITED—See Cargotec Corporation; *Int'l*, pg. 1329
NEO HUNGARY KFT.—See The Heico Companies, L.L.C.; *U.S. Private*, pg. 4050
NEO INDUSTRIES, INC.—See The Heico Companies, L.L.C.; *U.S. Private*, pg. 4050
NEO SLOVAKIA, S.R.O.—See The Heico Companies, L.L.C.; *U.S. Private*, pg. 4050
NEOVIA LOGISTICS GERMANY GMBH—See Rhone Group, LLC; *U.S. Private*, pg. 3424
NEOVIA LOGISTICS GERMANY GMBH—See The Goldman Sachs Group, Inc.; *U.S. Public*, pg. 2080
NEOVIA LOGISTICS SERVICES, LLC—See Rhone Group, LLC; *U.S. Private*, pg. 3424
NEOVIA LOGISTICS SERVICES, LLC—See The Goldman Sachs Group, Inc.; *U.S. Public*, pg. 2080
NETWORK GLOBAL LOGISTICS, LLC—See United Parcel Service, Inc.; *U.S. Public*, pg. 2233
NEW CITY MOVING LLC; *U.S. Private*, pg. 2893
NEW ENG KONG CONTAINER LOGISTIC SERVICES (M) SDN BHD—See Eng Kong Holdings Pte Ltd.; *Int'l*, pg. 2426
NFI CANADA—See NFI Industries, Inc.; *U.S. Private*, pg. 2923
NFI WAREHOUSING & DISTRIBUTION DIVISION - ARLINGTON FACILITY—See NFI Industries, Inc.; *U.S. Private*, pg. 2923
NFI WAREHOUSING & DISTRIBUTION DIVISION - BENSENVILLE FACILITY—See NFI Industries, Inc.; *U.S. Private*, pg. 2923
NFI WAREHOUSING & DISTRIBUTION DIVISION - BRAMPTON FACILITY—See NFI Industries, Inc.; *U.S. Private*, pg. 2923
NFI WAREHOUSING & DISTRIBUTION DIVISION - CHAMPLAIN FACILITY—See NFI Industries, Inc.; *U.S. Private*, pg. 2923
NFI WAREHOUSING & DISTRIBUTION DIVISION - CHINO FACILITY—See NFI Industries, Inc.; *U.S. Private*, pg. 2923
NFI WAREHOUSING & DISTRIBUTION DIVISION - DAYTON FACILITY—See NFI Industries, Inc.; *U.S. Private*, pg. 2923
NFI WAREHOUSING & DISTRIBUTION DIVISION - HEBRON FACILITY—See NFI Industries, Inc.; *U.S. Private*, pg. 2923
NFI WAREHOUSING & DISTRIBUTION DIVISION - LOGAN TOWNSHIP FACILITY—See NFI Industries, Inc.; *U.S. Private*, pg. 2923
NFI WAREHOUSING & DISTRIBUTION DIVISION - ONTARIO FACILITY—See NFI Industries, Inc.; *U.S. Private*, pg. 2923
NFI WAREHOUSING & DISTRIBUTION DIVISION - ORLANDO FACILITY—See NFI Industries, Inc.; *U.S. Private*, pg. 2923
NFI WAREHOUSING & DISTRIBUTION DIVISION - PENNSAUKEN FACILITY—See NFI Industries, Inc.; *U.S. Private*, pg. 2923
NHAVA SHEVA INTERNATIONAL CONTAINER TERMINAL PRIVATE LIMITED—See Dubai World Corporation; *Int'l*, pg. 2221
NICHINO SERVICE CO., LTD.—See Adeka Corporation; *Int'l*, pg. 142
NIC INC.—See Tyler Technologies, Inc.; *U.S. Public*, pg. 2208
NIGER TERMINAL SA—See Financiere de L'Odet; *Int'l*, pg. 2667
NIHON SENSITECH CORPORATION—See Carrier Global Corporation; *U.S. Public*, pg. 443
NINGBO CML GRANDCORP LOGISTICS CO., LTD.—See

China Master Logistics Co., Ltd.; *Int'l*, pg. 1517
NISSHIN TRANSPORTATION (QINGDAO) CO., LTD.—See KKR & Co. Inc.; *U.S. Public*, pg. 1259
NISSHIN TRANSPORTATION (SHANGHAI) CO., LTD.—See KKR & Co. Inc.; *U.S. Public*, pg. 1259
NISSHIN UNYU (SHANGHAI) CO., LTD.—See KKR & Co. Inc.; *U.S. Public*, pg. 1259
NORDEN SHIPPING ABIDJAN SARLU—See Dampskibsselskabet NORDEN A/S; *Int'l*, pg. 1957
NORDEN SHIPPING MIDDLE EAST DMCC—See Dampskibsselskabet NORDEN A/S; *Int'l*, pg. 1957
NORTH AMERICA PROCUREMENT COUNCIL, INC.—See Byggfakta Group Nordic HoldCo AB; *Int'l*, pg. 1235
NOV CANADA ULC—See NOV, Inc.; *U.S. Public*, pg. 1545
NPO SOLUTIONS—See Health Management Associates, Inc.; *U.S. Private*, pg. 1893
OIA GLOBAL LOGISTICS—See LDI Ltd., LLC; *U.S. Private*, pg. 2404
OLL LOGISTICS (MALAYSIA) SDN. BHD.—See China COSCO Shipping Corporation Limited; *Int'l*, pg. 1495
OMEGA SYSTEMS, LLC—See Pfingsten Partners, LLC; *U.S. Private*, pg. 3164
O&M-MOVIANTO NEDERLAND B.V.—See Owens & Minor, Inc.; *U.S. Public*, pg. 1626
OMNI LOGISTICS LLC—See Forward Air Corporation; *U.S. Public*, pg. 874
ONE WORLD LOGISTICS MALDIVES (PVT) LTD.—See Hayleys PLC; *Int'l*, pg. 3292
OOCL LOGISTICS (AUSTRALIA) PTY. LTD.—See China COSCO Shipping Corporation Limited; *Int'l*, pg. 1496
OOCL LOGISTICS (CHINA) LTD—See China COSCO Shipping Corporation Limited; *Int'l*, pg. 1496
OOCL LOGISTICS (EUROPE) LTD - BREMEN BRANCH—See China COSCO Shipping Corporation Limited; *Int'l*, pg. 1496
OOCL LOGISTICS (EUROPE) LTD - ROTTERDAM BRANCH—See China COSCO Shipping Corporation Limited; *Int'l*, pg. 1496
OOCL LOGISTICS (EUROPE) LTD—See China COSCO Shipping Corporation Limited; *Int'l*, pg. 1496
OOCL LOGISTICS (INDIA) PRIVATE LIMITED—See China COSCO Shipping Corporation Limited; *Int'l*, pg. 1496
OOCL LOGISTICS (JAPAN) LTD—See China COSCO Shipping Corporation Limited; *Int'l*, pg. 1496
OOCL LOGISTICS (KOREA) LTD—See China COSCO Shipping Corporation Limited; *Int'l*, pg. 1496
OOCL LOGISTICS LIMITED—See China COSCO Shipping Corporation Limited; *Int'l*, pg. 1495
OOCL LOGISTICS PHILIPPINES INC.—See China COSCO Shipping Corporation Limited; *Int'l*, pg. 1495
OOCL LOGISTICS (SINGAPORE) PTE. LTD.—See China COSCO Shipping Corporation Limited; *Int'l*, pg. 1496
OOCL LOGISTICS (TAIWAN) LTD—See China COSCO Shipping Corporation Limited; *Int'l*, pg. 1496
OOCL LOGISTICS (THAILAND) LTD—See China COSCO Shipping Corporation Limited; *Int'l*, pg. 1496
OOCL LOGISTICS (USA) INC.—See China COSCO Shipping Corporation Limited; *Int'l*, pg. 1496
OOCL (UAE) LLC—See China COSCO Shipping Corporation Limited; *Int'l*, pg. 1495
OOO OPTISCAN—See Amplex AB; *Int'l*, pg. 434
OPEN ROADS CONSULTING, INC.—See Guardian Capital Group Limited; *Int'l*, pg. 3170
OPTISCAN AB—See Amplex AB; *Int'l*, pg. 434
OPTISCAN DENMARK—See Amplex AB; *Int'l*, pg. 434
OPTISCAN OY—See Amplex AB; *Int'l*, pg. 434
OST-WEST CARGO BALTIC UAB—See Die Schweizerische Post AG; *Int'l*, pg. 2113
OST-WEST CARGO EUROPE GMBH—See Die Schweizerische Post AG; *Int'l*, pg. 2113
OST-WEST CARGO TRANSPORT UAB—See Die Schweizerische Post AG; *Int'l*, pg. 2113
OWENDO CONTAINER TERMINAL SARL—See Financiere de L'Odet; *Int'l*, pg. 2667
OWL LOGISTICS SHANGHAI LIMITED—See XPO, Inc.; *U.S. Public*, pg. 2392
OWL OCEAN WORLD LINES EUROPE GMBH—See XPO, Inc.; *U.S. Public*, pg. 2392
OY SCHENKER EAST AB—See Deutsche Bahn AG; *Int'l*, pg. 2053
PACORINI IBERICA SAU—See B. Pacorini S.p.A.; *Int'l*, pg. 789
PAKETERIA GMBH—See Acorn Energy, Inc.; *U.S. Public*, pg. 36
PALM COAST DATA HOLDCO, INC.—See AMREP Corporation; *U.S. Public*, pg. 133
PAN AFRICAN AIRLINES (NIGERIA) LIMITED—See Bristow Group, Inc.; *U.S. Public*, pg. 387
PANALPINA IAF (KOREA) LTD.—See DSV A/S; *Int'l*, pg. 2214
PANALPINA LOGISTICS (WUHAN) LTD.—See DSV A/S; *Int'l*, pg. 2214
PANALPINA LTD.—See DSV A/S; *Int'l*, pg. 2214
PANALPINA ROMANIA S.R.L.—See DSV A/S; *Int'l*, pg. 2215
PANDEE SERVICES PTY LTD—See ALS Limited; *Int'l*, pg. 378
PARCEL PRO, INC.—See United Parcel Service, Inc.; *U.S. Public*, pg. 2233

PARISI GRAND SMOOTH LOGISTICS LTD.—See Francesco Parisi S.p.A.; *Int'l*, pg. 2759
PASHA DISTRIBUTION SERVICES LLC—See The Pasha Group; *U.S. Private*, pg. 4091
THE PASHA GROUP - AUTOMOTIVE AND LOGISTICS DIVISION—See The Pasha Group; *U.S. Private*, pg. 4091
PATHFINDER AVIATION, LLC—See Dios Rios Partners, LP; *U.S. Private*, pg. 1234
PATRIOT LOGISTICS, INC.—See US 1 Industries, Inc.; *U.S. Private*, pg. 4317
PATRIOT LOGISTICS; *U.S. Private*, pg. 3110
PDC LOGISTICS—See Product Development Corporation; *U.S. Private*, pg. 3273
PELICAN PROCUREMENT SERVICES LIMITED—See Aramark; *U.S. Public*, pg. 178
PENSERSC—See The Suddath Companies; *U.S. Private*, pg. 4124
THE PERSIMMON GROUP LLC; *U.S. Private*, pg. 4093
PETRO-CHEMICAL TRANSPORT—See Rhone Group, LLC; *U.S. Private*, pg. 3424
PETRO-CHEMICAL TRANSPORT—See The Goldman Sachs Group, Inc.; *U.S. Public*, pg. 2080
PHARMA LOGISTICS NV—See Deutsche Post AG; *Int'l*, pg. 2082
PHU ELMAR SP. Z O.O.—See BRENNTAG SE; *Int'l*, pg. 1149
PHYZ HOLDINGS INC.—See AZ-COM MARUWA Holdings Inc.; *Int'l*, pg. 776
PILOT TRUCK BROKERAGE, LLC—See A.P. Moller-Maersk A/S; *Int'l*, pg. 27
PLAINS MARKETING, L.P.—See Plains GP Holdings, L.P.; *U.S. Public*, pg. 1697
PLAN4DEMAND SOLUTIONS, INC.—See Spinnaker Management Group, LLC; *U.S. Private*, pg. 3757
POLARIS LOGISTICS GROUP, INC.; *U.S. Private*, pg. 3223
POLY SAGAWA LOGISTIC CO., LTD.—See China Poly Group Corporation; *Int'l*, pg. 1541
P&O MARITIME FZE—See Dubai World Corporation; *Int'l*, pg. 2222
P&O MARITIME SERVICES PTY LTD—See Dubai World Corporation; *Int'l*, pg. 2222
PORT LOGISTICS GROUP, INC.; *U.S. Private*, pg. 3230
PORTUARIA CABO FROWARD SA—See Grupo Empresas Navieras S.A.; *Int'l*, pg. 3128
PORVOON KIRJAKESKUS OY—See Bonnier AB; *Int'l*, pg. 1109
POST CH NETWORK LTD.—See Die Schweizerische Post AG; *Int'l*, pg. 2113
POST IMMOBILIEN MANAGEMENT UND SERVICES AG—See Die Schweizerische Post AG; *Int'l*, pg. 2113
POSTLOGISTICS AG—See Die Schweizerische Post AG; *Int'l*, pg. 2113
POTI SEA PORT CORPORATION—See A.P. Moller-Maersk A/S; *Int'l*, pg. 27
PRECIS E-BUISNESS SYSTEMS—See PIN Business Network; *U.S. Private*, pg. 3181
PRGX COLOMBIA LTDA.—See PRGX Global, Inc.; *U.S. Private*, pg. 3257
PRIME DISTRIBUTION SERVICES, INC.—See C.H. Robinson Worldwide, Inc.; *U.S. Public*, pg. 415
PRIME SURFACTANTS LIMITED I.L.—See BRENNTAG SE; *Int'l*, pg. 1149
PRIORITY SOLUTIONS INTERNATIONAL, INC.—See Thermo Fisher Scientific Inc.; *U.S. Public*, pg. 2151
PROFESSIONAL CARE LOGISTICS, S.L.U.—See The Procter & Gamble Company; *U.S. Public*, pg. 2123
PSC GROUP LLC.—See Aurora Capital Group, LLC; *U.S. Private*, pg. 394
PSC GROUP LLC.—See The Jordan Company, L.P.; *U.S. Private*, pg. 4061
PS HOLDCO LLC—See OEP Capital Advisors, L.P.; *U.S. Private*, pg. 2999
PSI SEMICON SERVICES—See Phillips Service Industries, Inc. (PSI); *U.S. Private*, pg. 3171
PSS COMMODITIES, S. DE R.L. DE C.V.—See Seaboard Corporation; *U.S. Public*, pg. 1850
PT. BERDIRI MATAHARI LOGISTIK—See Hitachi, Ltd.; *Int'l*, pg. 3423
PT BOLLORE LOGISTICS INDONESIA—See Financiere de L'Odet; *Int'l*, pg. 2668
PT CJ GLS INDONESIA—See CJ Corporation; *Int'l*, pg. 1633
PT CJ LOGISTICS INDONESIA—See CJ Corporation; *Int'l*, pg. 1634
PT. DSV TRANSPORT INDONESIA—See DSV A/S; *Int'l*, pg. 2214
PT ECU WORLDWIDE INDONESIA—See Allcargo Logistics Limited; *Int'l*, pg. 334
P.T. EXPEDITORS INDONESIA—See Expeditors International of Washington, Inc.; *U.S. Public*, pg. 812
PT INTI DINAMIKA ID LOGITAMA INDONESIA—See ID Logistics SAS; *Int'l*, pg. 3588
PT. NISSHIN KUWAHARA INDONESIA—See KKR & Co. Inc.; *U.S. Public*, pg. 1259
PT. OOCL LOGISTICS INDONESIA—See China COSCO Shipping Corporation Limited; *Int'l*, pg. 1496

PT SANTA FE INDONUSA—See EAC Invest AS; *Int'l*, pg. 2262
PT. SCHENKER PETROLOG UTAMA—See Deutsche Bahn AG; *Int'l*, pg. 2053
PT SINARMAS DISTRIBUSI NUSANTARA—See Golden Agri-Resources Ltd.; *Int'l*, pg. 3028
PT. SINOTRANS CSC INDONESIA—See China Merchants Group Limited; *Int'l*, pg. 1522
QEF (GLOBAL) IRELAND LIMITED—See Park-Ohio Holdings Corp.; *U.S. Public*, pg. 1640
QINGDAO CJ GLS INC.—See CJ Corporation; *Int'l*, pg. 1633
QINGDAO GLX LOGISTICS CO., LTD.—See China Master Logistics Co., Ltd.; *Int'l*, pg. 1517
QINGDAO GRAND OCEAN MARITIME CO., LTD.—See China Master Logistics Co., Ltd.; *Int'l*, pg. 1517
QINGDAO KOOLL LOGISTICS CO., LTD.—See China International Marine Containers (Group) Co., Ltd.; *Int'l*, pg. 1512
QINGDAO PORT DONGJIAKOU BULK LOGISTICS CENTER CO., LTD.—See China Master Logistics Co., Ltd.; *Int'l*, pg. 1518
Q INTERNATIONAL COURIER, LLC; *U.S. Private*, pg. 3311
QUALITY IN REAL TIME—See TA Associates, Inc.; *U.S. Private*, pg. 3916
QUBIQA ESBJERG A/S—See BWB Partners P/S; *Int'l*, pg. 1232
QUICK COURIER SERVICES, INC.—See Dropoff, Inc.; *U.S. Private*, pg. 1279
QUIMILOG TRANSPORTES E LOGISTICA LTDA.—See BRENNTAG SE; *Int'l*, pg. 1149
RADIANT GLOBAL LOGISTICS (SHANGHAI) LTD.—See Radiant Logistics, Inc.; *U.S. Public*, pg. 1759
RADIANT LOGISTICS PARTNERS LLC—See Radiant Logistics, Inc.; *U.S. Public*, pg. 1759
RAIL & LOGISTIK CENTER WUSTERMARK GMBH & CO. KG—See Havellandische Eisenbahn AG; *Int'l*, pg. 3286
RAIL SERVICE CENTER ROTTERDAM B. V.—See Deutsche Bahn AG; *Int'l*, pg. 2051
RAND TRANSPORT (1986) PTY LTD—See Eagers Automotive Limited; *Int'l*, pg. 2263
RAND TRANSPORT PTY LTD—See Eagers Automotive Limited; *Int'l*, pg. 2263
RANGEN, INC. - RANGEN LOGISTICS DIVISION—See Wilbur-Ellis Company; *U.S. Private*, pg. 4518
RANSA COMERCIAL S.A.—See Grupo Romero; *Int'l*, pg. 3135
RBH LOGISTICS GMBH—See Deutsche Bahn AG; *Int'l*, pg. 2051
RBO REGIONALBUS OSTBAYERN GMBH—See Deutsche Bahn AG; *Int'l*, pg. 2052
RBW LOGISTICS CORPORATION; *U.S. Private*, pg. 3361
REACH SUBSEA ASA—See Caiano AS; *Int'l*, pg. 1252
RECYCLING ASSET HOLDINGS, INC.—See Nucor Corporation; *U.S. Public*, pg. 1554
REDWOOD LOGISTICS LLC—See AEA Investors LP; *U.S. Private*, pg. 115
REGAL LOGISTICS; *U.S. Private*, pg. 3385
REGENERSIS (DEUTSCHLAND) GMBH—See Francisco Partners Management, LP; *U.S. Private*, pg. 1588
REGENERSIS (HUNTINGDON) LTD.—See Francisco Partners Management, LP; *U.S. Private*, pg. 1588
REGIONALBUS BRAUNSCHWEIG GMBH—See Deutsche Bahn AG; *Int'l*, pg. 2052
REGIONAL BUS STUTTGART GMBH—See Deutsche Bahn AG; *Int'l*, pg. 2052
REGIONALVERKEHR ALLGAU GMBH—See Deutsche Bahn AG; *Int'l*, pg. 2052
REGIONALVERKEHR KURHESSEN GMBH—See Deutsche Bahn AG; *Int'l*, pg. 2052
REGIO VERKEHRSVERBUND LORRACH GMBH—See Deutsche Bahn AG; *Int'l*, pg. 2052
REICH ONLINE SERVICES GMBH—See Calida Holding AG; *Int'l*, pg. 1264
REINDEER AUTO RELOCATION; *U.S. Private*, pg. 3392
RELATRA AG—See Die Schweizerische Post AG; *Int'l*, pg. 2113
REMOLCADORES DE PUERTO Y ALTURA, S.A.—See Dubai World Corporation; *Int'l*, pg. 2222
RESOURCE SYSTEMS GROUP, INC.; *U.S. Private*, pg. 3407
RGT LOGISTICS, LLC.—See Red Gold Inc.; *U.S. Private*, pg. 3374
RHEINPFALZBUS GMBH—See Deutsche Bahn AG; *Int'l*, pg. 2052
RHEIN-WESTERWALD NAHVERKEHR GMBH—See Deutsche Bahn AG; *Int'l*, pg. 2052
RICHLAND LOGISTICS SERVICES PTE. LTD.—See Eneco Energy Limited; *Int'l*, pg. 2411
RIO LOPES TRANSPORTES LTD.—See Deutsche Post AG; *Int'l*, pg. 2082
RIVER METALS RECYCLING LLC—See Nucor Corporation; *U.S. Public*, pg. 1554
RIVERON CONSULTING, LLC—See Kohlberg & Company, LLC; *U.S. Private*, pg. 2339
RIVIERA TRASPORTI LINEA S.P.A.—See Deutsche Bahn AG; *Int'l*, pg. 2052
RIZHAO LANDBRIDGE PORT SUPPLY CHAIN MANAGE-

MENT CO., LTD.—See China Master Logistics Co., Ltd.; *Int'l*, pg. 1518
RMV RHEIN-MOSEL VERKEHRSGESELLSCHAFT MBH—See Deutsche Bahn AG; *Int'l*, pg. 2052
@ROAD, INC.—See Trimble, Inc.; *U.S. Public*, pg. 2192
ROADWAY REVERSE LOGISTICS, INC.—See Yellow Corporation; *U.S. Public*, pg. 2398
ROBERT'S HAWAII HOTELS INC.—See Robert's Hawaii Inc.; *U.S. Private*, pg. 3459
ROCKLIN PHYSICAL THERAPY, INC.—See Gryphon Investors, LLC; *U.S. Private*, pg. 1799
ROCKWELL AUTOMATION (XIAMEN) LTD.—See Rockwell Automation, Inc.; *U.S. Public*, pg. 1805
ROEHL LOGISTICS, INC.—See Roehl Transport, Inc.; *U.S. Private*, pg. 3470
ROGERS GERMANY GMBH—See Rogers Corporation; *U.S. Public*, pg. 1808
ROLAND TRANSPORT KG—See Dr. August Oetker KG; *Int'l*, pg. 2190
RO-RO INTERNATIONAL TM AB—See Axel Johnson Gruppen AB; *Int'l*, pg. 764
RPM HARBOR SERVICES, INC.—See RPM Consolidated Services, Inc.; *U.S. Private*, pg. 3495
R.R. DONNELLEY GLOBAL TURNKEY SOLUTIONS—See Chatham Asset Management, LLC; *U.S. Private*, pg. 865
RTT GROUP (PTY) LTD—See TRG Management LP; *U.S. Private*, pg. 4219
RUSH LOGISTICS, INC.—See Rush Enterprises, Inc.; *U.S. Public*, pg. 1826
RUSSIA CORPORATION—See Hyundai Glovis Co., Ltd.; *Int'l*, pg. 3557
RVE REGIONALVERKEHR EUREGIO MAAS-RHEIN GMBH—See Deutsche Bahn AG; *Int'l*, pg. 2052
RVN REGIONALVERKEHR NIEDERRHEIN GMBH—See Deutsche Bahn AG; *Int'l*, pg. 2052
RVS REGIONALBUSVERKEHR SUDWEST GMBH—See Deutsche Bahn AG; *Int'l*, pg. 2052
RWG I/SCHICHT BAUSTOFFAUFBEREITUNG, LOGISTIK + ENTSORGUNG GMBH—See Heidelberg Materials AG; *Int'l*, pg. 3319
RYDER-ASCENT LOGISTICS PTE LTD.—See Ryder System, Inc.; *U.S. Public*, pg. 1828
RYDER PUERTO RICO, INC.—See Ryder System, Inc.; *U.S. Public*, pg. 1828
RYDER (SHANGHAI) LOGISTICS, CO., LTD.—See Ryder System, Inc.; *U.S. Public*, pg. 1828
SAAR-PFALZ-BUS GMBH—See Deutsche Bahn AG; *Int'l*, pg. 2052
SAAR-PFALZ-MOBIL GMBH—See Deutsche Bahn AG; *Int'l*, pg. 2052
SAB PIEMONTE S.R.L.—See Deutsche Bahn AG; *Int'l*, pg. 2052
SAFE CHAIN SOLUTIONS, LLC—See Benchworks, Inc.; *U.S. Private*, pg. 524
SAFEWAY GLOBAL SOURCING LIMITED—See Cerberus Capital Management, L.P.; *U.S. Private*, pg. 836
SAGA GABON SA—See Financiere de L'Odet; *Int'l*, pg. 2668
SAGA REUNION SA—See Financiere de L'Odet; *Int'l*, pg. 2668
SAIA TRASPORTI S.P.A.—See Deutsche Bahn AG; *Int'l*, pg. 2052
SAINT-GOBAIN GLASS LOGISTICS S.A.S—See Compagnie de Saint-Gobain SA; *Int'l*, pg. 1733
SALOODO GMBH—See Deutsche Post AG; *Int'l*, pg. 2082
SANDBOX LOGISTICS, LLC—See Apollo Global Management, Inc.; *U.S. Public*, pg. 165
SANKYO LOGI ASSOCIATE. CO., LTD.—See Bain Capital, LP; *U.S. Private*, pg. 435
SAN TAI DISTRIBUTION CO., LTD.—See Global Brands Manufacture Ltd.; *Int'l*, pg. 2993
SANYO JIDOSHA UNSO CO., LTD.—See Hankyu Hanshin Holdings Inc.; *Int'l*, pg. 3256
SATELLITE LOGISTICS GROUP, INC.—See Deutsche Post AG; *Int'l*, pg. 2081
SATURN INTEGRATED LOGISTICS INC.—See Deutsche Post AG; *Int'l*, pg. 2082
SAUDI MAINTENANCE & SUPPLY CHAIN MANAGEMENT COMPANY LIMITED—See BAE Systems plc; *Int'l*, pg. 799
S-BAHN BERLIN GMBH—See Deutsche Bahn AG; *Int'l*, pg. 2052
S-BAHN HAMBURG GMBH—See Deutsche Bahn AG; *Int'l*, pg. 2052
SBG SUDBADENBUS GMBH—See Deutsche Bahn AG; *Int'l*, pg. 2052
SCANSHIP (GHANA) LTD.—See Financiere de L'Odet; *Int'l*, pg. 2668
SCHENKER-ARKAS NAKLIYAT VE TIC. A.S.—See Deutsche Bahn AG; *Int'l*, pg. 2054
SCHENKER A/S—See Deutsche Bahn AG; *Int'l*, pg. 2053
SCHENKER AS—See Deutsche Bahn AG; *Int'l*, pg. 2053
SCHENKER AUSTRALIA PTY. LTD.—See Deutsche Bahn AG; *Int'l*, pg. 2053
SCHENKER (BAX) HOLDING CORP.—See Deutsche Bahn AG; *Int'l*, pg. 2054
SCHENKER BITCC LOGISTICS (BEIJING) CO. LTD.—See Deutsche Bahn AG; *Int'l*, pg. 2053

SCHENKER-BTL LTD.—See Deutsche Bahn AG; *Int'l*, pg. 2054
SCHENKER B.V.—See Deutsche Bahn AG; *Int'l*, pg. 2053
SCHENKER CHILE S.A.—See Deutsche Bahn AG; *Int'l*, pg. 2053
SCHENKER CHINA LTD.—See Deutsche Bahn AG; *Int'l*, pg. 2053
SCHENKER CONSULTING AB—See Deutsche Bahn AG; *Int'l*, pg. 2053
SCHENKER CUSTOMS AGENCY B.V.—See Deutsche Bahn AG; *Int'l*, pg. 2053
SCHENKER DOOEL—See Deutsche Bahn AG; *Int'l*, pg. 2053
SCHENKER D.O.O.—See Deutsche Bahn AG; *Int'l*, pg. 2053
SCHENKER D.O.O—See Deutsche Bahn AG; *Int'l*, pg. 2054
SCHENKER D.O.O.—See Deutsche Bahn AG; *Int'l*, pg. 2054
SCHENKER EGYPT LTD.—See Deutsche Bahn AG; *Int'l*, pg. 2053
SCHENKER EOOD—See Deutsche Bahn AG; *Int'l*, pg. 2053
SCHENKER FRANCE SAS—See Deutsche Bahn AG; *Int'l*, pg. 2054
SCHENKER-GEMADEPT LOGISTICS VIETNAM COMPANY LIMITED—See Deutsche Bahn AG; *Int'l*, pg. 2053
SCHENKER HIGH TECH LOGISTICS B.V.—See Deutsche Bahn AG; *Int'l*, pg. 2053
SCHENKER INDIA PRIVATE LIMITED—See Deutsche Bahn AG; *Int'l*, pg. 2053
SCHENKER ITALIANA S.P.A.—See Deutsche Bahn AG; *Int'l*, pg. 2053
SCHENKER KHIMJI'S LLC—See Deutsche Bahn AG; *Int'l*, pg. 2053
SCHENKER KOREA LTD.—See Deutsche Bahn AG; *Int'l*, pg. 2053
SCHENKER (L.L.C)—See Deutsche Bahn AG; *Int'l*, pg. 2053
SCHENKER LOGISTICS AB—See Deutsche Bahn AG; *Int'l*, pg. 2053
SCHENKER LOGISTICS (GUANGZHOU) COMPANY LTD.—See Deutsche Bahn AG; *Int'l*, pg. 2053
SCHENKER LOGISTICS L.L.C.—See Deutsche Bahn AG; *Int'l*, pg. 2053
SCHENKER LOGISTICS (MALAYSIA) SDN BHD.—See Deutsche Bahn AG; *Int'l*, pg. 2053
SCHENKER LOGISTICS (SHANGHAI) CO., LTD.—See Deutsche Bahn AG; *Int'l*, pg. 2053
SCHENKER LOGISTICS (SUZHOU) COMPANY LTD.—See Deutsche Bahn AG; *Int'l*, pg. 2053
SCHENKER LOGISTICS VIETNAM CO. LTD.—See Deutsche Bahn AG; *Int'l*, pg. 2053
SCHENKER LOGISTICS (XIAMEN) CO. LTD.—See Deutsche Bahn AG; *Int'l*, pg. 2053
SCHENKER LTD.—See Deutsche Bahn AG; *Int'l*, pg. 2053
SCHENKER LUXEMBURG GMBH—See Deutsche Bahn AG; *Int'l*, pg. 2053
SCHENKER MIDDLE EAST FZE—See Deutsche Bahn AG; *Int'l*, pg. 2053
SCHENKER NAMIBIA (PTY) LTD.—See Deutsche Bahn AG; *Int'l*, pg. 2053
SCHENKER N.V.—See Deutsche Bahn AG; *Int'l*, pg. 2053
SCHENKER (NZ) LTD.—See Deutsche Bahn AG; *Int'l*, pg. 2053
SCHENKER OY—See Deutsche Bahn AG; *Int'l*, pg. 2054
SCHENKER PANAMA S.A.—See Deutsche Bahn AG; *Int'l*, pg. 2054
SCHENKER PERU S.R.L.—See Deutsche Bahn AG; *Int'l*, pg. 2054
SCHENKER SA—See Deutsche Bahn AG; *Int'l*, pg. 2054
SCHENKER SAUDI ARABIA LLC—See Deutsche Bahn AG; *Int'l*, pg. 2054
SCHENKER-SEINO CO. LTD.—See Deutsche Bahn AG; *Int'l*, pg. 2054
SCHENKER SOUTH AFRICA (PTY) LTD.—See Deutsche Bahn AG; *Int'l*, pg. 2054
SCHENKER SPOL. S R.O.—See Deutsche Bahn AG; *Int'l*, pg. 2053
SCHENKER S.R.O.—See Deutsche Bahn AG; *Int'l*, pg. 2053
SCHENKER SWITZERLAND AG—See Deutsche Bahn AG; *Int'l*, pg. 2054
SCHENKER (THAI) LTD.—See Deutsche Bahn AG; *Int'l*, pg. 2053
SCHILLI DISTRIBUTION SERVICES, INC.—See Daseke, Inc.; *U.S. Public*, pg. 1161
SCHNEIDER LOGISTICS TRANSLOADING AND DISTRIBUTION, INC.—See Schneider National, Inc.; *U.S. Public*, pg. 1847
SCOTTISH CITYLINK COACHES LIMITED—See ComfortDelGro Corporation Limited; *Int'l*, pg. 1713
SDDS HOLDINGS, INC.; *U.S. Private*, pg. 3581
SDI, INC.—See Independence Capital Partners, LLC; *U.S. Private*, pg. 2056
SDI, INC.—See Pouschine Cook Capital Management LLC; *U.S. Private*, pg. 3236
SDV INTERNATIONAL LOGISTICS—See Financiere de L'Odet; *Int'l*, pg. 2667
SEACOR ISLAND LINES LLC—See AIP, LLC; *U.S. Private*, pg. 136
SEACOR LIFTBOATS LLC—See AIP, LLC; *U.S. Private*, pg. 136

SEALAND MAERSK ASIA PTE. LTD.—See A.P. Moller-Maersk A/S; *Int'l*, pg. 27
SEALASKA GLOBAL LOGISTICS, LLC—See Sealaska Corporation; *U.S. Private*, pg. 3585
SEASSURANCE LIMITED—See AIP, LLC; *U.S. Private*, pg. 137
SELECT 1 TRANSPORT INC.; *U.S. Private*, pg. 3600
SENSITECH BRASIL LTDA.—See Carrier Global Corporation; *U.S. Public*, pg. 444
SENSITECH CANADA INC.—See Carrier Global Corporation; *U.S. Public*, pg. 444
SENSITECH EMEA B.V.—See Carrier Global Corporation; *U.S. Public*, pg. 444
SENSITECH PTY LIMITED—See Carrier Global Corporation; *U.S. Public*, pg. 444
SENTEC LIMITED—See Xylem Inc.; *U.S. Public*, pg. 2395
SEPETIBA TECON S.A.—See Companhia Siderurgica Nacional; *Int'l*, pg. 1748
SEVEN BRIDGES TRADING 14 (PTY) LTD—See Barrick Gold Corporation; *Int'l*, pg. 870
SHANGHAI BONDEX NISSHIN LOGISTICS CO., LTD.—See KKR & Co. Inc.; *U.S. Public*, pg. 1259
SHANGHAI INDUSTRY & COMMERCE EXHIBITION CO., LTD.—See DLG Exhibitions & Events Corp Ltd.; *Int'l*, pg. 2141
SHANGHAI POLY SAGAWA LOGISTIC CO., LTD.—See China Poly Group Corporation; *Int'l*, pg. 1541
SHANGHAI WELL-TRANS INTERNATIONAL LOGISTICS CO., LTD.—See China Merchants Group Limited; *Int'l*, pg. 1522
SHANGHAI XIEXIN CUSTOMS DECLARATION CO., LTD.—See KKR & Co. Inc.; *U.S. Public*, pg. 1259
SHARP JUSDA LOGISTICS CORP.—See Hon Hai Precision Industry Co., Ltd.; *Int'l*, pg. 3459
SHENZHEN UNIQUE LOGISTICS INTERNATIONAL LTD.—See Unique Logistics International Inc.; *U.S. Public*, pg. 2227
SHIN-NIHON HELICOPTER CO., LTD.—See Chubu Electric Power Co., Inc.; *Int'l*, pg. 1593
SHIPWIRE, INC.—See Hainan Traffic Administration Holding Co., Ltd.; *Int'l*, pg. 3215
SIA SCHENKER—See Deutsche Bahn AG; *Int'l*, pg. 2053
S.I.A. SOCIETA ITALIANA AUTOSERVIZI S.P.A.—See Deutsche Bahn AG; *Int'l*, pg. 2052
SIEMPELKAMP LOGISTICS & SERVICE GMBH—See G. Siempelkamp GmbH & Co. KG; *Int'l*, pg. 2865
SIGMA KUDOS FINLAND OY—See Danir Resources AB; *Int'l*, pg. 1963
SINOTRANS CHANGJIANG COMPANY LIMITED—See China Merchants Group Limited; *Int'l*, pg. 1522
SINOTRANS & CSC HOLDINGS CO., LTD.—See China Merchants Group Limited; *Int'l*, pg. 1521
SINOTRANS & CSC SHIPBUILDING INDUSTRY CORPORATION—See China Merchants Group Limited; *Int'l*, pg. 1521
SINOTRANS DONGGUAN LOGISTICS CO., LTD.—See China Merchants Group Limited; *Int'l*, pg. 1522
SINOTRANS EASTERN COMPANY LIMITED—See China Merchants Group Limited; *Int'l*, pg. 1522
SINOTRANS FOSHAN LOGISTICS CO., LTD.—See China Merchants Group Limited; *Int'l*, pg. 1523
SINOTRANS (HK) LOGISTICS LIMITED—See China Merchants Group Limited; *Int'l*, pg. 1522
SINOTRANS JAPAN CO., LTD.—See China Merchants Group Limited; *Int'l*, pg. 1522
SINOTRANS JIANGXI CO., LTD.—See China Merchants Group Limited; *Int'l*, pg. 1522
SINOTRANS LOGISTICS (CAMBODIA) CO. LTD.—See China Merchants Group Limited; *Int'l*, pg. 1522
SINOTRANS LOGISTICS (M) SDN. BHD.—See China Merchants Group Limited; *Int'l*, pg. 1522
SINOTRANS NANCHANG CO., LTD.—See China Merchants Group Limited; *Int'l*, pg. 1522
SINOTRANS NANJING EXPORT PROCESSING ZONE LOGISTICS CO., LTD.—See China Merchants Group Limited; *Int'l*, pg. 1522
SINOTRANS THAI LOGISTICS COMPANY LIMITED—See China Merchants Group Limited; *Int'l*, pg. 1522
SINOTRANS ZHONGSHAN LOGISTICS CO., LTD.—See China Merchants Group Limited; *Int'l*, pg. 1523
SINTAX LOGISTICA TRANSPORTES, S.A.—See ACS, Actividades de Construccion y Servicios, S.A.; *Int'l*, pg. 116
SINTAX NAVIGOMES, LTDA.—See ACS, Actividades de Construccion y Servicios, S.A.; *Int'l*, pg. 116
SINWA AUSTRALIA PTY LIMITED—See Financiere SYZ & CO SA; *Int'l*, pg. 2669
SKC ENGINEERING LTD.—See I Squared Capital Advisors (US) LLC; *U.S. Public*, pg. 2023
SKYBITZ, INC.—See AMETEK, Inc.; *U.S. Public*, pg. 122
SKY PARTNERS OU—See Deutsche Bahn AG; *Int'l*, pg. 2054
SNAS LEBANON SARL—See Deutsche Post AG; *Int'l*, pg. 2082
SOCIEDAD PORTUARIA PUERTO WILCHES MUTIPROPOSITO SA—See AIP, LLC; *U.S. Private*, pg. 137
SOCIETE DE MANUTENTION DU TERMINAL A CONTENEURS DE COTONOU—See Financiere de L'Odet; *Int'l*, pg. 2668

SOCIETE ECU-LINE TUNISIE SARL—See Allcargo Logistics Limited; *Int'l*, pg. 334
SOCOPAO RDC SA—See Financiere de L'Odet; *Int'l*, pg. 2668
SOGESTER - SOCIEDADE GESTORA DE TERMINAIS S.A.—See A.P. Moller-Maersk A/S; *Int'l*, pg. 27
SOUTHAMPTON CONTAINER TERMINALS LIMITED—See Dubai World Corporation; *Int'l*, pg. 2222
SPECIALIZED TRANSPORTATION, INC.—See CRST International, Inc.; *U.S. Private*, pg. 1113
SPENDIFFERENCE LLC—See Compass Group PLC; *Int'l*, pg. 1752
SPIRIANT GMBH—See Deutsche Lufthansa AG; *Int'l*, pg. 2067
SPORTS LOGISTICS CO., LTD.—See Alpen Co., Ltd.; *Int'l*, pg. 366
SPOT FREIGHT, INC.; *U.S. Private*, pg. 3761
SQUADRON MEDICAL LIMITED—See DCC plc; *Int'l*, pg. 1991
STANDARD FORWARDING LLC—See Deutsche Post AG; *Int'l*, pg. 2082
STANLEY BLACK & DECKER LOGISTICS BVBA—See Stanley Black & Decker, Inc.; *U.S. Public*, pg. 1934
STAR PACIFIC LOGISTICS LTD.—See Beijing Sports & Entertainment Industry Group Limited; *Int'l*, pg. 957
STEEL CONNECT, INC.; *U.S. Public*, pg. 1941
STERR & EDER INDUSTRIESERVICE GMBH—See Quaker Chemical Corporation; *U.S. Public*, pg. 1747
STINGER LOGISTICS, INC.—See Celadon Group, Inc.; *U.S. Public*, pg. 464
STOBART (IRELAND) LIMITED—See DBAY Advisors Limited; *Int'l*, pg. 1986
STRATEGIC DELIVERY SOLUTIONS LLC—See HCI Equity Management, L.P.; *U.S. Private*, pg. 1889
SUDDATH GLOBAL LOGISTICS, LLC—See The Suddath Companies; *U.S. Private*, pg. 4124
SUDDATH RELOCATION SYSTEMS OF ATLANTA, INC.—See The Suddath Companies; *U.S. Private*, pg. 4124
SUDDATH RELOCATION SYSTEMS OF CHARLOTTE, LLC—See The Suddath Companies; *U.S. Private*, pg. 4124
SUDDATH RELOCATION SYSTEMS OF HOUSTON, INC.—See The Suddath Companies; *U.S. Private*, pg. 4124
SUDDATH RELOCATION SYSTEMS OF MARYLAND, INC.—See The Suddath Companies; *U.S. Private*, pg. 4124
SUDDATH RELOCATION SYSTEMS OF MILWAUKEE, LLC—See The Suddath Companies; *U.S. Private*, pg. 4124
SUDDATH RELOCATION SYSTEMS OF MINNESOTA, LLC—See The Suddath Companies; *U.S. Private*, pg. 4124
SUDDATH RELOCATION SYSTEMS OF NORTHERN CALIFORNIA, INC.—See The Suddath Companies; *U.S. Private*, pg. 4124
SUDDATH RELOCATION SYSTEMS OF ORLANDO, INC.—See The Suddath Companies; *U.S. Private*, pg. 4124
SUDDATH RELOCATION SYSTEMS OF ST. PETERSBURG, INC.—See The Suddath Companies; *U.S. Private*, pg. 4124
SUDDATH RELOCATION SYSTEMS OF TEXAS, INC.—See The Suddath Companies; *U.S. Private*, pg. 4124
SUDWEST MOBIL GMBH—See Deutsche Bahn AG; *Int'l*, pg. 2054
SUEZ CANAL CONTAINER TERMINAL SAE—See A.P. Moller-Maersk A/S; *Int'l*, pg. 28
SUNCO CARRIERS, INC.—See Watkins Associated Industries Inc.; *U.S. Private*, pg. 4455
SUPERFRIO ARMAZENS GERIAS S.A.—See Americold Realty Trust, Inc.; *U.S. Public*, pg. 113
SUPERTRANSPORT - TRAFFIC CENTER KONTICH—See Carrefour SA; *Int'l*, pg. 1344
SUPERTRANSPORT - TRAFFIC CENTER NORD (KDC)—See Carrefour SA; *Int'l*, pg. 1344
SUPERTRANSPORT - TRAFFIC CENTER SUD—See Carrefour SA; *Int'l*, pg. 1344
SUPERTRANSPORT - TRAFFIC CENTER VILVOORDE—See Carrefour SA; *Int'l*, pg. 1344
SUPPLY CHAIN COACH, INC.—See AEA Investors LP; *U.S. Private*, pg. 115
SUPPLY CHAIN SERVICES INTERNATIONAL, INC—See Ardian SAS; *Int'l*, pg. 556
SUPPLY CHAIN SOLUTIONS, INC. - HOLLAND OFFICE—See Supply Chain Solutions, Inc.; *U.S. Private*, pg. 3882
SUPPLY CHAIN SOLUTIONS, INC.; *U.S. Private*, pg. 3882
SUPPLY CHAIN SOLUTIONS LLC—See *U.S. Private*, pg. 3882
SUPPLY FORCE INTERNATIONAL PTE LTD—See Capital Limited; *Int'l*, pg. 1311
SUPPLY TECHNOLOGIES COMPANY OF CANADA—See Park-Ohio Holdings Corp.; *U.S. Public*, pg. 1640
SUPPLY TECHNOLOGIES COMPANY OF PUERTO RICO—See Park-Ohio Holdings Corp.; *U.S. Public*, pg. 1640

SUPPLY TECHNOLOGIES (INDIA) PRIVATE LIMITED—See Park-Ohio Holdings Corp.; *U.S. Public*, pg. 1640
SUPPLY TECHNOLOGIES KFT—See Park-Ohio Holdings Corp.; *U.S. Public*, pg. 1640
SUPPLY TECHNOLOGIES LIMITED—See Park-Ohio Holdings Corp.; *U.S. Public*, pg. 1640
SUPPLY TECHNOLOGIES LIMITED—See Park-Ohio Holdings Corp.; *U.S. Public*, pg. 1640
SUPPLY TECHNOLOGIES PTE. LTD.—See Park-Ohio Holdings Corp.; *U.S. Public*, pg. 1640
SUZHOU BONDEX NISSHIN LOGISTIC CO., LTD.—See KKR & Co. Inc.; *U.S. Public*, pg. 1259
SVT FLEET, LLC—See Velocity Vehicle Group; *U.S. Private*, pg. 4355
SWISS POST INTERNATIONAL HOLDING AG—See Die Schweizerische Post AG; *Int'l*, pg. 2113
SWISS POST SOLUTIONS HOLDING PTE. LTD.—See Die Schweizerische Post AG; *Int'l*, pg. 2113
SWITZERLAND BOSSARD AG—See Bossard Holding AG; *Int'l*, pg. 1118
SW ZOLL-BERATUNG GMBH—See Deutsche Bahn AG; *Int'l*, pg. 2052
SYMBIA LOGISTICS; *U.S. Private*, pg. 3898
SYNCREON DUBLIN—See syncreon International Group; *U.S. Private*, pg. 3903
SYNCREON INTERNATIONAL GROUP; *U.S. Private*, pg. 3903
TACTICAL PRODUCTS GROUP, INC.; *U.S. Private*, pg. 3921
TAGG LOGISTICS, LLC—See Hub Group, Inc.; *U.S. Public*, pg. 1066
TAMARIND TRADING (SHANGHAI) LIMITED—See Daohe Global Group Limited; *Int'l*, pg. 1970
TANKLINK CORPORATION—See AMETEK, Inc.; *U.S. Public*, pg. 122
TCL SUPPLY CHAIN (CANADA) INC.—See Deutsche Post AG; *Int'l*, pg. 2082
TEAM GLASS ENGINEERING PTE. LTD.—See Chasen Holdings Limited; *Int'l*, pg. 1457
TECH DATA ADVANCED PRIVATE LIMITED—See TD Synnex Corp; *U.S. Public*, pg. 1985
TECH DATA DISTRIBUTION (HONG KONG) LIMITED—See TD Synnex Corp; *U.S. Public*, pg. 1987
TECH DATA DISTRIBUTION (SINGAPORE) PTE. LTD.—See TD Synnex Corp; *U.S. Public*, pg. 1987
TECH DATA MOBILE ACQUISITION LIMITED—See TD Synnex Corp; *U.S. Public*, pg. 1986
TECHNICAL TRAFFIC CONSULTANTS CORP.—See PKF O'Connor Davies, LLP; *U.S. Private*, pg. 3193
TECHNIPAK; *U.S. Private*, pg. 3954
TECHNOLOGY VENTURES, INC; *U.S. Private*, pg. 3956
TEE HAI CHEM PTE. LTD.—See BRENNTAG SE; *Int'l*, pg. 1150
TEGRO AG—See Deutsche Bahn AG; *Int'l*, pg. 2054
TEMA CONTENEUR TERMINAL LTD.—See Financiere de L'Odet; *Int'l*, pg. 2668
TERMINAL DE CARVAO—See Companhia Siderurgica Nacional; *Int'l*, pg. 1748
TERMINALES RIO DE LA PLATA SA—See Dubai World Corporation; *Int'l*, pg. 2222
TGF UNIQUE LTD—See Unique Logistics International Inc.; *U.S. Public*, pg. 2227
THENETHERLANDS622009 B. V.—See Deutsche Post AG; *Int'l*, pg. 2082
THOMSON LINEAR LLC—See Regal Rexnord Corporation; *U.S. Public*, pg. 1772
TIANJIN PORT MASTER LOGISTICS CO., LTD.—See China Master Logistics Co., Ltd.; *Int'l*, pg. 1518
TIANJIN TRANSWELL INTERNATIONAL LOGISTICS CO., LTD.—See Beijing Properties (Holdings) Limited; *Int'l*, pg. 955
TIDONENERGIE SRL—See A2A S.p.A.; *Int'l*, pg. 29
TIE KINETIX DACH GMBH—See SPS Commerce, Inc.; *U.S. Public*, pg. 1920
TIE TIE INTELLIGENCE LOGISTICS CO., LTD.—See HBIS Group Co., Ltd.; *Int'l*, pg. 3296
TIGERS LIMITED—See JAS Worldwide, Inc.; *U.S. Private*, pg. 2189
TIMOR PORT SA—See Financiere de L'Odet; *Int'l*, pg. 2668
TITAN GLOBAL DISTRIBUTION, INC.—See Atlas World Group, Inc.; *U.S. Private*, pg. 381
TNT EXPRESS GMBH—See FedEx Corporation; *U.S. Public*, pg. 828
TOSHOKAN RYUTSU CENTER CO., LTD.—See Dai Nippon Printing Co., Ltd.; *Int'l*, pg. 1916
TOTAL TRANSPORTATION TRUCKING, INC.—See RJW, Inc.; *U.S. Private*, pg. 3450
TOTAL TRANSPORT SOLUTIONS MALDIVES (PVT) LTD.—See Hayleys PLC; *Int'l*, pg. 3292
TOWARDS GREEN SDN. BHD.—See Chasen Holdings Limited; *Int'l*, pg. 1457
THE TPS HEALTHCARE GROUP LIMITED—See DCC plc; *Int'l*, pg. 1991
TRACELOGISTICS, S.A.—See Fluidra SA; *Int'l*, pg. 2714
TRACKER LOGISTICS INC.—See Deutsche Post AG; *Int'l*, pg. 2082

TRADETEAM LIMITED—See Deutsche Post AG; *Int'l*, pg. 2078
TRANSA SPEDITION GMBH—See Deutsche Bahn AG; *Int'l*, pg. 2054
TRANSFESA RAIL S.A.—See Deutsche Bahn AG; *Int'l*, pg. 2051
TRANS-GLOBAL SOLUTIONS INC.; *U.S. Private*, pg. 4206
TRANS-GLOBAL SOLUTIONS, INC.—See Trans-Global Solutions Inc.; *U.S. Private*, pg. 4206
TRANS INTER EUROPE, S.A.S—See ACS, Actividades de Construccion y Servicios, S.A.; *Int'l*, pg. 116
TRANSPORTATION IMPACT LLC—See The Jordan Company, L.P.; *U.S. Private*, pg. 4062
TRANSTECH CONSULTING, INC.—See Blue Horseshoe Solutions, Inc.; *U.S. Private*, pg. 589
TRANSYSTEMS—See Transystems LLC; *U.S. Private*, pg. 4212
TRATEL AIRVAULT—See E B Trans SA; *Int'l*, pg. 2246
TRATEL AIRVAULT—See Groupe GARNIER; *Int'l*, pg. 3103
TRATEL MOULT—See E B Trans SA; *Int'l*, pg. 2246
TRATEL MOULT—See Groupe GARNIER; *Int'l*, pg. 3103
TRATEL PESSAC—See E B Trans SA; *Int'l*, pg. 2246
TRATEL PESSAC—See Groupe GARNIER; *Int'l*, pg. 3103
TRAXION SOLUTIONS, S.A. DE C.V.—See Grupo Traxion, S. A. B. de C. V.; *Int'l*, pg. 3138
TRAXYS NORTH AMERICA LLC—See The Carlyle Group Inc.; *U.S. Public*, pg. 2056
TRAXYS S.A.—See The Carlyle Group Inc.; *U.S. Public*, pg. 2056
TRIMBLE MOBILE SOLUTIONS, INC.—See Trimble, Inc.; *U.S. Public*, pg. 2192
TRIMBLE MRM—See Trimble, Inc.; *U.S. Public*, pg. 2192
TRINITY AIR MEDICAL, INC.—See Blade Air Mobility, Inc.; *U.S. Public*, pg. 361
TRINITY LOGISTICS INC.; *U.S. Private*, pg. 4235
TRIOSE, INC.; *U.S. Private*, pg. 4236
TRISTAR TERMINALS GUAM INC.—See Agility; *Int'l*, pg. 210
TRUCKOMAN LLC—See Al Yousef Group; *Int'l*, pg. 283
TSN EAST, LLC—See Bunzl plc; *Int'l*, pg. 1219
TSS, INC.; *U.S. Public*, pg. 2202
TSSK LOGISTIC CO., LTD.—See AMA Marine Public Company Limited; *Int'l*, pg. 403
TST SUNRISE SERVICE, LTD.—See KKR & Co. Inc.; *U.S. Public*, pg. 1259
TURKEY CORPORATION—See Hyundai Glovis Co., Ltd.; *Int'l*, pg. 3557
UAB DHL LIETUVA—See Deutsche Post AG; *Int'l*, pg. 2078
UAB GREEN TERMINAL—See Caiano AS; *Int'l*, pg. 1252
UAB SCHENKER—See Deutsche Bahn AG; *Int'l*, pg. 2054
UBI LOGISTICS (HK) LIMITED—See A-Sonic Aerospace Limited; *Int'l*, pg. 21
ULTRA AIR CARGO, INC.—See A-Sonic Aerospace Limited; *Int'l*, pg. 21
UMZUGSAUKTION GMBH & CO. KG—See Axel Springer SE; *Int'l*, pg. 767
UNIGROUP WORLDWIDE LOGISTICS, LLC—See UniGroup, Inc.; *U.S. Private*, pg. 4283
UNIQUE LOGISTICS INTERNATIONAL (BOS), INC.—See Unique Logistics International Inc.; *U.S. Public*, pg. 2227
UNIQUE LOGISTICS INTERNATIONAL (CHICAGO), LLC—See Unique Logistics International Inc.; *U.S. Public*, pg. 2227
UNIQUE LOGISTICS INTERNATIONAL (FUZHOU) LTD.—See Unique Logistics International Inc.; *U.S. Public*, pg. 2227
UNIQUE LOGISTICS INTERNATIONAL INC.; *U.S. Public*, pg. 2227
UNIQUE LOGISTICS INTERNATIONAL (INDIA) PRIVATE LIMITED—See Unique Logistics International Inc.; *U.S. Public*, pg. 2227
UNIQUE LOGISTICS INTERNATIONAL (MACAU) LTD.—See Unique Logistics International Inc.; *U.S. Public*, pg. 2227
UNIQUE LOGISTICS INTERNATIONAL XIAMEN LIMITED—See Unique Logistics International Inc.; *U.S. Public*, pg. 2227
UNIQUE LOGISTICS INTERNATIONAL (ZHONGSHAN) LTD.—See Unique Logistics International Inc.; *U.S. Public*, pg. 2227
UNIQUE SCM (H.K) LIMITED—See Unique Logistics International Inc.; *U.S. Public*, pg. 2227
UNIR S.A.—See Grupo Clarin S.A.; *Int'l*, pg. 3124
UNITED EXPRESS, INC.; *U.S. Public*, pg. 2230
UNITED FREIGHT & LOGISTICS, LTD.; *U.S. Private*, pg. 4292
UNITED PARCEL SERVICE NEDERLAND BV—See United Parcel Service, Inc.; *U.S. Public*, pg. 2234
UNITED PARCEL SERVICE NEDERLANDS B.V.—See United Parcel Service, Inc.; *U.S. Public*, pg. 2234
UNIVERSAL CORPORATION LTD—See E.T. Browne Drug Company, Inc.; *U.S. Private*, pg. 1307
UNIVERSAL LOGISTICS SOLUTIONS CANADA, LTD.—See Universal Logistics Holdings, Inc.; *U.S. Public*, pg. 2261
UNIVERSAL LOGISTICS SOLUTIONS INTERNATIONAL, INC.—See Universal Logistics Holdings, Inc.; *U.S. Public*, pg. 2262

N.A.I.C.S. INDEX

541618 — OTHER MANAGEMENT CO...

UNIVERSAL SERVICE CENTER COMPANY—See Universal Logistics Holdings, Inc.; *U.S. Public*, pg. 2262
UPS INTERNATIONAL, INC.—See United Parcel Service, Inc.; *U.S. Public*, pg. 2233
UPS SCS (NEDERLAND) B.V.—See United Parcel Service, Inc.; *U.S. Public*, pg. 2233
URB-IT AB—See Fin Mile Logistics Limited; *Int'l*, pg. 2664
USC DISTRIBUTION SERVICES LLC—See Deutsche Post AG; *Int'l*, pg. 2083
U.S. MARINE MANAGEMENT, INCORPORATED—See A.P. Moller-Maersk A/S; *Int'l*, pg. 28
U.S. NETTING, INC.—See Mativ Holdings, Inc.; *U.S. Public*, pg. 1397
US PACK LOGISTICS LLC—See NewSpring Capital LLC; *U.S. Private*, pg. 2918
UTA BULGARIA OOD—See Edenred S.A.; *Int'l*, pg. 2308
UTA CZECH S.R.O.—See Edenred S.A.; *Int'l*, pg. 2308
UTA FRANCE S.A.R.L.—See Edenred S.A.; *Int'l*, pg. 2308
UTA ROMANIA SERVICES SRL—See Edenred S.A.; *Int'l*, pg. 2308
UTC ACCORD LOGISTICS AUSTRALIA PTY. LTD.—See UTC Overseas, Inc.; *U.S. Private*, pg. 4325
UTC INTERNATIONAL LOGISTICS LIMITED—See UTC Overseas, Inc.; *U.S. Private*, pg. 4325
UTC OVERSEAS, AB—See UTC Overseas, Inc.; *U.S. Private*, pg. 4325
UTC OVERSEAS BOLIVIA SRL—See UTC Overseas, Inc.; *U.S. Private*, pg. 4325
UTC OVERSEAS BRASIL LTDA.—See UTC Overseas, Inc.; *U.S. Private*, pg. 4325
UTC OVERSEAS COLOMBIA SAS—See UTC Overseas, Inc.; *U.S. Private*, pg. 4325
UTC OVERSEAS ECUADOR S.A.—See UTC Overseas, Inc.; *U.S. Private*, pg. 4325
UTC OVERSEAS GMBH—See UTC Overseas, Inc.; *U.S. Private*, pg. 4325
UTC OVERSEAS (HK) LIMITED—See UTC Overseas, Inc.; *U.S. Private*, pg. 4325
UTC OVERSEAS (INDIA) PVT. LTD.—See UTC Overseas, Inc.; *U.S. Private*, pg. 4325
UTC OVERSEAS IRELAND LTD—See UTC Overseas, Inc.; *U.S. Private*, pg. 4325
UTC OVERSEAS LOGISTICS LTD—See UTC Overseas, Inc.; *U.S. Private*, pg. 4325
UTC OVERSEAS LTD.—See UTC Overseas, Inc.; *U.S. Private*, pg. 4325
UTC OVERSEAS OY—See UTC Overseas, Inc.; *U.S. Private*, pg. 4325
UTC OVERSEAS (PERU) S.A.C.—See UTC Overseas, Inc.; *U.S. Private*, pg. 4325
UTC OVERSEAS S.A.—See UTC Overseas, Inc.; *U.S. Private*, pg. 4325
UTC OVERSEAS S DE RL DE CV—See UTC Overseas, Inc.; *U.S. Private*, pg. 4325
UTC OVERSEAS (TAIWAN) CO., LTD.—See UTC Overseas, Inc.; *U.S. Private*, pg. 4325
UTC UK LTD—See UTC Overseas, Inc.; *U.S. Private*, pg. 4325
UTEXAM LOGISTICS LTD.—See BNP Paribas SA; *Int'l*, pg. 1093
UTI INVENTORY MANAGEMENT SOLUTIONS INC.—See DSV A/S; *Int'l*, pg. 2216
UT WORLDWIDE (INDIA) PVT. LTD.—See DSV A/S; *Int'l*, pg. 2216
VASCOR, LTD.—See Fujitrans Corporation; *Int'l*, pg. 2832
VECTORA TRANSPORTATION; *U.S. Private*, pg. 4353
VECTORCSP, LLC; *U.S. Private*, pg. 4353
VECTURA AS—See Arcus ASA; *Int'l*, pg. 552
VEHICLE STORAGE & ENGINEERING PTY. LTD.—See Eagers Automotive Limited; *Int'l*, pg. 2264
VENTURE LOGISTICS S.A. DE C.V.—See Deutsche Post AG; *Int'l*, pg. 2083
VERITIV—See Clayton, Dubilier & Rice, LLC; *U.S. Private*, pg. 929
VICSA COMMERCE & TRADING (SHANGHAI) CO., LTD.—See Bunzl plc; *Int'l*, pg. 1219
VIEWPOINT CONSULTING, INC.—See Research America, Inc.; *U.S. Private*, pg. 3403
VINALINK LOGISTICS (CAMBODIA) CO., LTD.—See Cong ty Co Phan Logistics Vinalink; *Int'l*, pg. 1768
VISIBLE SUPPLY CHAIN MANAGEMENT, LLC—See A.P. Moller-Maersk A/S; *Int'l*, pg. 28
VIVANIUM GMBH—See Bilfinger SE; *Int'l*, pg. 1027
VMC CONSULTING CORPORATION—See Canada Pension Plan Investment Board; *Int'l*, pg. 1281
VMC CONSULTING CORPORATION—See EQT AB; *Int'l*, pg. 2483
V- MODAL MEXICANA, S.C.—See Grupo Traxion, S. A. B. de C. V.; *Int'l*, pg. 3138
VMTP PJSC—See Far Eastern Shipping Company OJSC; *Int'l*, pg. 2617
VOLVO LOGISTICS AB—See AB Volvo; *Int'l*, pg. 45
VOLVO LOGISTICS CORPORATION—See AB Volvo; *Int'l*, pg. 45
WAGIC INC; *U.S. Private*, pg. 4425
WALON B.V.—See DBAY Advisors Limited; *Int'l*, pg. 1986
WALON CZ S.R.O.—See DBAY Advisors Limited; *Int'l*, pg. 1986

WATCO SUPPLY CHAIN SERVICES, LLC—See Kinder Morgan, Inc.; *U.S. Public*, pg. 1233
WATERMAN LOGISTICS, INC.—See AIP, LLC; *U.S. Private*, pg. 137
WAVEPOINT 3PL EXPEDITE LLC; *U.S. Private*, pg. 4458
WAYPOINT GLOBAL LLC; *U.S. Private*, pg. 4460
WEICHERT WORKFORCE MOBILITY INC.—See Weichert Co.; *U.S. Private*, pg. 4470
WELL TRANSPORTATION MYANMAR CO., LTD.—See China Merchants Group Limited; *Int'l*, pg. 1522
WESTSTAR TRUCKING INC.—See J.D. Rush Company Inc.; *U.S. Private*, pg. 2161
WHIPLASH MERCHANDISING INC.—See Port Logistics Group, Inc.; *U.S. Private*, pg. 3230
WHITACRE LOGISTICS, LLC.; *U.S. Private*, pg. 4507
WHITAKER TAYLOR, INC.—See HR Path SAS; *Int'l*, pg. 3501
WICPACK MALAYSIA SDN BHD—See Western Industries Corporation; *U.S. Private*, pg. 4494
WICPACK SINGAPORE PTE LTD—See Western Industries Corporation; *U.S. Private*, pg. 4494
WILDCAT MINERALS LLC—See Eagle Materials Inc.; *U.S. Public*, pg. 702
WINDCAT WORKBOATS INTERNATIONAL LIMITED—See AIP, LLC; *U.S. Private*, pg. 137
WIN TOP SHIPPING COMPANY LIMITED—See Dafeng Port Heshun Technology Company Limited; *Int'l*, pg. 1911
WITT O'BRIEN'S, LLC—See Ambipar Participacoes e Empreendimentos SA; *Int'l*, pg. 414
WITT O'BRIEN'S LTD—See AIP, LLC; *U.S. Private*, pg. 137
WLX, LLC; *U.S. Private*, pg. 4552
THE WORK CENTER, INC.—See Athletico Ltd.; *U.S. Private*, pg. 368
WUHAN CML GRANDLINK LOGISTICS CO., LTD.—See China Master Logistics Co., Ltd.; *Int'l*, pg. 1518
XATOR CORPORATION—See Parsons Corporation; *U.S. Public*, pg. 1651
XPO LAST MILE CANADA INC.—See XPO, Inc.; *U.S. Public*, pg. 2392
XPO LAST MILE, INC.—See XPO, Inc.; *U.S. Public*, pg. 2392
XPO LOGISTICS CANADA INC.—See XPO, Inc.; *U.S. Public*, pg. 2392
YANKEE ALLIANCE; *U.S. Private*, pg. 4585
ZAO GREEN TERMINAL—See Caiano AS; *Int'l*, pg. 1252
ZAO SCHENKER—See Deutsche Bahn AG; *Int'l*, pg. 2054
ZAPF CREATION LOGISTICS GMBH & CO. KG—See MGA Entertainment, Inc.; *U.S. Private*, pg. 2694
ZENTRA LLC; *U.S. Private*, pg. 4601
ZHENGZHOU CTS INTERNATIONAL LOGISTICS CORPORATION LIMITED—See CTS International Logistics Corporation Limited; *Int'l*, pg. 1874
ZHENHUA LOGISTICS GROUP CO., LTD.—See China Communications Construction Company Limited; *Int'l*, pg. 1491
ZHONGCHUANG SHIPS MANAGEMENT CO., LTD.—See China Master Logistics Co., Ltd.; *Int'l*, pg. 1518

541618 — OTHER MANAGEMENT CONSULTING SERVICES

110 CONSULTING; *U.S. Private*, pg. 2
12 POINTS CONSULTING CORP.—See Renodis, Inc.; *U.S. Private*, pg. 3399
1798, LLC—See Knox Lane LP; *U.S. Private*, pg. 2324
2020 EXHIBITS, INC.; *U.S. Private*, pg. 5
225 UNLIMITED INCORPORATED; *U.S. Private*, pg. 5
360TRAINING.COM, INC.; *U.S. Private*, pg. 8
3 BRIDGE SOLUTIONS LLC; *U.S. Private*, pg. 7
3M HEALTH INFO SYSTEMS CONSULTING SERVICES—See Solventum Corporation; *U.S. Public*, pg. 1901
7PIXEL S.R.L.—See Gruppo MutuiOnline S.p.A; *Int'l*, pg. 3140
8WORKS LTD.—See Marsh & McLennan Companies, Inc.; *U.S. Public*, pg. 1374
AAI SERVICES CORPORATION—See Textron Inc.; *U.S. Public*, pg. 2029
AAREAL VALUATION GMBH—See Advent International Corporation; *U.S. Private*, pg. 96
AAREAL VALUATION GMBH—See Centerbridge Partners, L.P.; *U.S. Private*, pg. 812
ABBAKUS GMBH & CO. KG—See Bilfinger SE; *Int'l*, pg. 1024
ABB FZ-LLC—See ABB Ltd.; *Int'l*, pg. 50
ABBVIE BIOTECHNOLOGY GMBH—See AbbVie Inc.; *U.S. Public*, pg. 21
ABC ARBITRAGE ASSET MANAGEMENT—See ABC Arbitrage S.A.; *Int'l*, pg. 57
AB DRITTE FLUGZEUGVERMIETUNGS GMBH—See Air Berlin PLC & Co. Luftverkehrs KG; *Int'l*, pg. 236
A BENBOW HOLDING INC.; *U.S. Private*, pg. 17
AB ERSTE FLUGZEUGVERMIETUNGS GMBH—See Air Berlin PLC & Co. Luftverkehrs KG; *Int'l*, pg. 236
ABSA CAPITAL REPRESENTATIVE OFFICE NIGERIA LIMITED—See Absa Group Limited; *Int'l*, pg. 69

ABS CONSULTING LTD.—See American Bureau of Shipping; *U.S. Private*, pg. 225
ABSG CONSULTING DE VENEZUELA, C.A.—See American Bureau of Shipping; *U.S. Private*, pg. 226
ABSG CONSULTING INC.—See American Bureau of Shipping; *U.S. Private*, pg. 225
ABSG CONSULTING INC.—See American Bureau of Shipping; *U.S. Private*, pg. 225
ABSG CONSULTING - IRVINE—See American Bureau of Shipping; *U.S. Private*, pg. 225
ABSG CONSULTING - KNOXVILLE—See American Bureau of Shipping; *U.S. Private*, pg. 225
ABSG CONSULTING - LAKEWOOD—See American Bureau of Shipping; *U.S. Private*, pg. 225
ABSG CONSULTING - MIDDLE EAST—See American Bureau of Shipping; *U.S. Private*, pg. 225
ABSG CONSULTING - ROCKVILLE—See American Bureau of Shipping; *U.S. Private*, pg. 225
ABSG CONSULTING - SAINT LOUIS—See American Bureau of Shipping; *U.S. Private*, pg. 225
ABSG CONSULTING - SALT LAKE CITY—See American Bureau of Shipping; *U.S. Private*, pg. 225
ABSG CONSULTING - SAN ANTONIO—See American Bureau of Shipping; *U.S. Private*, pg. 225
ABSG CONSULTING - TAIWAN—See American Bureau of Shipping; *U.S. Private*, pg. 225
ABSG CONSULTING - WILMINGTON—See American Bureau of Shipping; *U.S. Private*, pg. 225
ABS GROUP SERVICES DE MEXICO, S.A. DE C.V.—See American Bureau of Shipping; *U.S. Private*, pg. 225
ABS GROUP SERVICES DO BRASIL LTDA.—See American Bureau of Shipping; *U.S. Private*, pg. 225
ABT ASSOCIATES INC.; *U.S. Private*, pg. 44
AB VIERTE FLUGZEUGVERMIETUNGS GMBH—See Air Berlin PLC & Co. Luftverkehrs KG; *Int'l*, pg. 236
AB ZWEITE FLUGZEUGVERMIETUNGS GMBH—See Air Berlin PLC & Co. Luftverkehrs KG; *Int'l*, pg. 236
ACCEL SERVICIOS, S. A. DE C. V.—See Accel, S.A.B. de C.V.; *Int'l*, pg. 79
ACCENTURE (CHINA) CO., LTD. - SHANGHAI—See Accenture plc; *Int'l*, pg. 82
ACCENTURE FEDERAL SERVICES LLC—See Accenture plc; *Int'l*, pg. 85
ACCENTURE LTD.—See Accenture plc; *Int'l*, pg. 83
ACCENTURE S.C.—See Accenture plc; *Int'l*, pg. 84
ACCENTURE SERVICES (SOUTH AFRICA) PTY LTD.—See Accenture plc; *Int'l*, pg. 84
ACENDA INTEGRATED HEALTH; *U.S. Private*, pg. 58
ACHIEVEGLOBAL INC.—See Korn Ferry; *U.S. Public*, pg. 1274
ACUITY INC.; *U.S. Private*, pg. 71
ADCB FINANCE (CAYMAN) LIMITED—See Abu Dhabi Commercial Bank PJSC; *Int'l*, pg. 71
ADESSO MOBILE SOLUTIONS GMBH—See adesso SE; *Int'l*, pg. 144
ADMINISTRATIVE RESOURCE OPTIONS, INC.; *U.S. Private*, pg. 80
AD MISSIONS; *Int'l*, pg. 122
ADM SOUTHERN CELLULOSE—See Archer-Daniels-Midland Company; *U.S. Public*, pg. 182
ADOBE SYSTEMS PTE. LTD.—See Adobe Inc.; *U.S. Public*, pg. 42
ADVANCE COMPUTER SERVICES LTD.—See ACS International Resources Inc.; *U.S. Public*, pg. 66
ADVANCED COMPOSITE PRODUCTS & TECHNOLOGY, INC.—See Charger Investment Partners LP; *U.S. Private*, pg. 850
ADVANCED LOGISTICS, LLC.; *U.S. Private*, pg. 90
ADVANCED MANAGEMENT TECHNOLOGY, INC.—See Tetra Tech, Inc.; *U.S. Public*, pg. 2022
ADVANCED SYSTEMS GROUP, LLC; *U.S. Private*, pg. 92
ADVANTAGE HEALTHCARE, INC.—See Arsenal Capital Management LP; *U.S. Private*, pg. 338
ADVANTAGE SCI; *U.S. Private*, pg. 95
ADVANTOR HOLDING CORPORATION; *U.S. Private*, pg. 95
ADVERTISING CHECKING BUREAU INCORPORATED; *U.S. Private*, pg. 109
THE ADVISORS RESOURCE, INC—See Bates Group LLC; *U.S. Private*, pg. 486
ADVOCATE BILLING LLC.; *U.S. Private*, pg. 110
AFFINITY, INC.; *U.S. Private*, pg. 123
AFFIRMA CONSULTING; *U.S. Private*, pg. 123
AFRICA RISK CONSULTING LTD.; *Int'l*, pg. 191
AGAVE CONSULTANTS LIMITED—See Accenture plc; *Int'l*, pg. 86
AGDNA TECHNOLOGIES PTY LTD.—See CNH Industrial N.V.; *Int'l*, pg. 1674
AGEATIA TECHNOLOGY CONSULTANCY SERVICES INC.; *U.S. Private*, pg. 126
AGRALYS SERVICES; *Int'l*, pg. 213
AGRI-EDGE DEVELOPMENT, LLC—See Dairy Farmers of America, Inc.; *U.S. Private*, pg. 1145
AIC-AARTECH SOLONICS PRIVATE LIMITED—See Aartech solonics Limited; *Int'l*, pg. 38
AIG MARKETS, INC.—See American International Group, Inc.; *U.S. Public*, pg. 105

541618 — OTHER MANAGEMENT CO...   CORPORATE AFFILIATIONS

AI METRIX, INC.—See Kratos Defense & Security Solutions, Inc.; *U.S. Public*, pg. 1276
AIMRITE HOLDINGS CORP.; *U.S. Public*, pg. 63
AIR BERLIN GMBH & CO. FUNFTE FLUGZEUGVERMIETUNGS OHG—See Air Berlin PLC & Co. Luftverkehrs KG; *Int'l*, pg. 236
AIR BERLIN LUFTFAHRTTECHNISCHER BETRIEB GMBH—See Air Berlin PLC & Co. Luftverkehrs KG; *Int'l*, pg. 236
AJINOMOTO TREASURY MANAGEMENT, INC.—See Ajinomoto Company, Inc.; *Int'l*, pg. 257
AKCELERANT ADVISORS LLC—See Akcelerant Holdings LLC; *U.S. Private*, pg. 144
AKHELA S.R.L.—See Angelo Moratti S.A.P.A.; *Int'l*, pg. 460
AKIMA INFRASTRUCTURE SERVICES, LLC—See Nana Regional Corporation, Inc.; *U.S. Private*, pg. 2832
AKKA CONSULTING GMBH—See Adecco Group AG; *Int'l*, pg. 139
ALAN ALLMAN ASSOCIATES SA; *Int'l*, pg. 290
ALBIO DATA S.A.—See Biokarpet S.A.; *Int'l*, pg. 1038
ALBOURNE AMERICA LLC—See Albourne Partners Limited; *Int'l*, pg. 299
ALBOURNE PARTNERS (ASIA) LIMITED—See Albourne Partners Limited; *Int'l*, pg. 299
ALBOURNE PARTNERS DEUTSCHLAND AG—See Albourne Partners Limited; *Int'l*, pg. 299
ALBOURNE PARTNERS JAPAN LIMITED—See Albourne Partners Limited; *Int'l*, pg. 299
ALBOURNE PARTNERS (SINGAPORE) PTE. LTD.—See Albourne Partners Limited; *Int'l*, pg. 299
ALEUT MANAGEMENT SERVICES—See The Aleut Corporation; *U.S. Private*, pg. 3984
ALEXANDRE LIMITED—See Heidelberg Materials AG; *Int'l*, pg. 3308
ALIGN COMMUNICATIONS INC.; *U.S. Private*, pg. 167
ALIXPARTNERS, LLP—See Caisse de Depot et Placement du Quebec; *Int'l*, pg. 1253
ALLCORE S.P.A.; *Int'l*, pg. 334
ALLEASING PTY LTD—See CHAMP Private Equity Pty. Ltd.; *Int'l*, pg. 1439
ALLEN LANE LIMITED—See Bain Capital, LP; *U.S. Private*, pg. 433
ALLIANCE OF PROFESSIONALS & CONSULTANTS, INC.; *U.S. Private*, pg. 183
ALLIED TELESIS, INC.—See ALLIED TELESIS HOLDINGS K.K.; *Int'l*, pg. 358
ALLIED TELESIS INC.—See ALLIED TELESIS HOLDINGS K.K.; *Int'l*, pg. 358
ALL STAR VACATION HOMES MANAGEMENT, INC.; *U.S. Private*, pg. 172
ALL TRAFFIC DATA SERVICES, LLC—See Rekor Systems, Inc.; *U.S. Public*, pg. 1778
ALON ASSETS, INC.—See Delek Group Ltd.; *Int'l*, pg. 2011
ALP CONSULTING LIMITED—See Bain Capital, LP; *U.S. Private*, pg. 433
AL.SYSTEMS GMBH—See Commerzbank AG; *Int'l*, pg. 1718
THE ALTA GROUP, LLC; *U.S. Private*, pg. 3984
ALTERNATIVE BILLING SOLUTIONS, INC.; *U.S. Private*, pg. 207
ALTERWAY GROUP SARL—See Econocom Group SA; *Int'l*, pg. 2297
ALTIA SWEDEN SERVICES AB—See Altia Oyj; *Int'l*, pg. 392
ALTITUDE INTERNATIONAL HOLDINGS, INC.; *U.S. Public*, pg. 88
ALTOS MANDOS DE NEGOCIOS, S.A. DE C.V.—See Desarrolladora Homex, S.A. de C.V.; *Int'l*, pg. 2044
ALTRAN NORWAY AS—See Capgemini SE; *Int'l*, pg. 1304
ALTRAN SHANGAI LTD.—See Capgemini SE; *Int'l*, pg. 1305
ALVAREZ & MARSAL DISPUTE ANALYSIS & FORENSIC SERVICES, LLC—See Alvarez & Marsal, Inc.; *U.S. Private*, pg. 213
ALVAREZ & MARSAL REAL ESTATE ADVISORY SERVICES, LLC—See Alvarez & Marsal, Inc.; *U.S. Private*, pg. 213
ALVAREZ & MARSAL TAXAND, LLC—See Alvarez & Marsal, Inc.; *U.S. Private*, pg. 213
ALVIN H. BUTZ, INC.—See Butz Enterprises, Inc.; *U.S. Private*, pg. 698
AMANO MANAGEMENT SERVICE CORP.—See Amano Corporation; *Int'l*, pg. 410
AMATA FACILITY SERVICE CO. LTD.—See Amata Corporation Public Company Limited; *Int'l*, pg. 412
AMBC INC.; *U.S. Private*, pg. 217
AMBER CAPITAL UK LLP; *Int'l*, pg. 414
AMDOCS SINGAPORE PTE. LTD.—See Amdocs Limited; *Int'l*, pg. 419
AMERICAN ENVIRONMENTAL CONSULTANTS, INC.—See TRC Companies, Inc.; *U.S. Private*, pg. 4215
AMERICAN MORTGAGE CONSULTANTS, INC.—See Stone Point Capital LLC; *U.S. Private*, pg. 3825
AMERICAN SYSTEMS CORPORATION; *U.S. Private*, pg. 256
AMERISOURCEBERGEN CONSULTING SERVICES, INC.—See Cencora, Inc.; *U.S. Public*, pg. 466
AMEY TPT LIMITED—See Ferrovial S.A.; *Int'l*, pg. 2644
AMGEN INC. - GOVERNMENT AFFAIRS OFFICE—See Amgen Inc.; *U.S. Public*, pg. 123

AMPCO SERVICES, LLC—See Chevron Corporation; *U.S. Public*, pg. 487
AMPCO SERVICES, LLC—See ConocoPhillips; *U.S. Public*, pg. 569
AMPHIL; *U.S. Private*, pg. 266
AMP SERVICES LIMITED—See AMP Limited; *Int'l*, pg. 432
AM TECHNICAL SOLUTIONS, INC.; *U.S. Private*, pg. 215
ANALYSYS MASON AS—See Datatec Limited; *Int'l*, pg. 1980
ANALYSYS MASON FZ LLC—See Datatec Limited; *Int'l*, pg. 1980
ANALYSYS MASON INDIA PVT. LIMITED—See Datatec Limited; *Int'l*, pg. 1980
ANALYSYS MASON LIMITED—See Bridgepoint Group Plc; *Int'l*, pg. 1154
ANALYSYS MASON LIMITED—See Datatec Limited; *Int'l*, pg. 1980
ANALYSYS MASON LIMITED—See Datatec Limited; *Int'l*, pg. 1980
ANALYSYS MASON SAS—See Datatec Limited; *Int'l*, pg. 1980
ANALYSYS MASON SPAIN S.L.—See Datatec Limited; *Int'l*, pg. 1980
ANALYSYS MASON S.R.L.—See Datatec Limited; *Int'l*, pg. 1980
ANDRES CONSTRUCTION SERVICES INC.; *U.S. Private*, pg. 279
ANGARAI INTERNATIONAL, INC.; *U.S. Private*, pg. 281
ANGLE TECHNOLOGY VENTURES LIMITED—See ANGLE plc; *Int'l*, pg. 461
ANTAEAN SOLUTIONS, LLC; *U.S. Private*, pg. 286
ANTHONY HODGES CONSULTING LIMITED—See Arthur J. Gallagher & Co.; *U.S. Public*, pg. 202
AON GLOBAL RISK CONSULTING—See Aon plc; *Int'l*, pg. 490
AON HEWITT (CYPRUS) LIMITED—See Alight, Inc.; *U.S. Public*, pg. 76
AON HEWITT LIMITED—See Alight, Inc.; *U.S. Public*, pg. 76
AON MANAGEMENT CONSULTING/RATH & STRONG INC.—See Aon plc; *Int'l*, pg. 491
AON RISKMINDER A/S—See Aon plc; *Int'l*, pg. 494
APM HUMAN SERVICES INTERNATIONAL LIMITED—See Madison Dearborn Partners, LLC; *U.S. Private*, pg. 2540
APONTIS PHARMA DEUTSCHLAND GMBH & CO. KG—See Advent International Corporation; *U.S. Private*, pg. 108
APPLIED ANALYTIX INC.—See QueBIT Consulting, LLC; *U.S. Private*, pg. 3325
APPROACH OPERATING, LLC—See Approach Resources Inc.; *U.S. Private*, pg. 300
AQUILA TREASURY & FINANCE SOLUTIONS LIMITED—See Aquila Services Group PLC; *Int'l*, pg. 528
ARABELLA ADVISORS, LLC; *U.S. Private*, pg. 306
ARAMARK SPORTS & ENTERTAINMENT SERVICES, LLC—See Aramark; *U.S. Public*, pg. 176
ARCADIA SOLUTIONS, LLC—See Ferrer Freeman & Company, LLC; *U.S. Private*, pg. 1498
ARCADIS AUSTRALIA PACIFIC HOLDINGS PTY. LTD.—See ARCADIS N.V.; *Int'l*, pg. 541
ARCADIS FRANCE S.A.S.—See ARCADIS N.V.; *Int'l*, pg. 541
ARC ASPICIO LLC; *U.S. Private*, pg. 309
ARDENT MANAGEMENT CONSULTING, INC; *U.S. Private*, pg. 317
ARGO CAPITAL MANAGEMENT (CYPRUS) LIMITED—See Argo Group Limited; *Int'l*, pg. 562
ARGO CAPITAL MANAGEMENT LIMITED—See Argo Group Limited; *Int'l*, pg. 562
ARGUS INFORMATION & ADVISORY SERVICES, LLC—See Verisk Analytics, Inc.; *U.S. Public*, pg. 2282
ARKANSAS INFORMATION CONSORTIUM, LLC—See Tyler Technologies, Inc.; *U.S. Public*, pg. 2208
ARONSON LLC; *U.S. Private*, pg. 334
ARROW ECS NETWORK & SECURITY SAS—See Arrow Electronics, Inc.; *U.S. Public*, pg. 196
ARROW PARTNERSHIP, LLC; *U.S. Private*, pg. 335
ARTHUR D. LITTLE BENELUX N.V.—See Arthur D. Little SAS; *Int'l*, pg. 583
ARTHUR D. LITTLE CHINA LIMITED—See Arthur D. Little SAS; *Int'l*, pg. 583
ARTHUR D. LITTLE HONG KONG—See Arthur D. Little SAS; *Int'l*, pg. 583
ARTIFEX TECHNOLOGY CONSULTING, INC.; *U.S. Private*, pg. 342
ARTISAN PARTNERS UK LLP—See Artisan Partners Asset Management Inc.; *U.S. Public*, pg. 208
ASAHI KASEI BUSINESS MANAGEMENT (SHANGHAI) CO., LTD.—See Asahi Kasei Corporation; *Int'l*, pg. 595
ASB CONSULT LLC—See Belarusbank; *Int'l*, pg. 963
ASCENDO ACADEMY PTE. LTD.—See Ascendo International Holdings Pte. Ltd.; *Int'l*, pg. 602
ASCER PTE. LTD.—See Ascendo International Holdings Pte. Ltd.; *Int'l*, pg. 602
ASCOT ASSET CONSULTING CORP.—See Ascot Corp.; *Int'l*, pg. 604
A.S. MANAGEMENT CORPORATION; *U.S. Private*, pg. 28
ASPEN DENTAL MANAGEMENT, INC.—See Ares Management Corporation; *U.S. Public*, pg. 188

ASPIREHR; *U.S. Private*, pg. 352
ASRC MANAGEMENT SERVICES, INC.—See Arctic Slope Regional Corporation; *U.S. Private*, pg. 316
ASRC SERVICE CENTER, INC.—See Arctic Slope Regional Corporation; *U.S. Private*, pg. 316
ASSMANN BERATEN + PLANEN GMBH; *Int'l*, pg. 648
ASSYSTEM INNOVATION—See Assystem S.A.; *Int'l*, pg. 651
ASTADIA, INC.-ATLANTA—See The Gores Group, LLC; *U.S. Private*, pg. 4034
ASTMAX TRADING, INC.; *Int'l*, pg. 655
ATCO ENERGYSENSE—See ATCO Ltd.; *Int'l*, pg. 666
ATLANCE FRANCE SAS—See Econocom Group SA; *Int'l*, pg. 2297
ATOS ORIGIN INFORMATION TECHNOLOGY (CHINA) CO. LTD—See Atos SE; *Int'l*, pg. 691
ATTUNIX CORPORATION; *U.S. Private*, pg. 383
AUBURN ENTERPRISES LLC—See Aptiv PLC; *Int'l*, pg. 524
AUCNET ADVANCE INC.—See Aucnet Inc.; *Int'l*, pg. 700
AUCTION SYSTEMS AUCTIONEERS & APPRAISERS, INC.; *U.S. Private*, pg. 385
AURELIUS BETEILIGUNGSBERATUNGS AG—See Aurelius Equity Opportunities SE & Co. KGaA; *Int'l*, pg. 707
AUSTINCSI, LLC—See Cognizant Technology Solutions Corporation; *U.S. Public*, pg. 523
AUSTRALIAN LEISURE & ENTERTAINMENT PROPERTY MANAGEMENT LIMITED—See Charter Hall Limited; *Int'l*, pg. 1454
AUSTRALIAN LEISURE & ENTERTAINMENT PROPERTY MANAGEMENT LIMITED—See Host-Plus Pty. Limited; *Int'l*, pg. 3486
AUSTRALIAN LEISURE & ENTERTAINMENT PROPERTY TRUST—See Charter Hall Limited; *Int'l*, pg. 1454
AUSTRALIAN LEISURE & ENTERTAINMENT PROPERTY TRUST—See Host-Plus Pty. Limited; *Int'l*, pg. 3486
AVALON CONSULTING, LLC; *U.S. Private*, pg. 403
AVENIR CONSEIL FORMATION SA—See Alten S.A.; *Int'l*, pg. 390
AVENIR FINANCE CORPORATE—See Advenis; *Int'l*, pg. 166
AVENIR FINANCE GESTION—See Advenis; *Int'l*, pg. 166
AVENIR FINANCE SECURITIES—See Advenis; *Int'l*, pg. 167
AVIATION QUALITY SERVICES GMBH—See Deutsche Lufthansa AG; *Int'l*, pg. 2068
AVITAS INC.; *U.S. Private*, pg. 409
AVIVA RISK MANAGEMENT SOLUTIONS UK LIMITED—See Aviva plc; *Int'l*, pg. 746
AVOCENT BELGIUM LIMITED BVBA/SPRL—See Vertiv Holdings Co; *U.S. Public*, pg. 2288
AVOCENT HUNTSVILLE, LLC—See Vertiv Holdings Co; *U.S. Public*, pg. 2288
AVOCENT INTERNATIONAL LIMITED—See Vertiv Holdings Co; *U.S. Public*, pg. 2288
AVOCENT SWEDEN AB—See Vertiv Holdings Co; *U.S. Public*, pg. 2288
AVTEC SYSTEMS, INC.—See Kratos Defense & Security Solutions, Inc.; *U.S. Public*, pg. 1276
AWK GROUP AG—See DPE Deutsche Private Equity GmbH; *Int'l*, pg. 2187
AXIA CONSULTING, LLC; *Int'l*, pg. 412
AXIOM SALES FORCE DEVELOPMENT LLC; *U.S. Private*, pg. 413
AXON PARTNERS GROUP SA; *Int'l*, pg. 771
AXXIS CONSULTING (S) PTE. LTD.—See BIPROGY Inc.; *Int'l*, pg. 1045
AXYON CONSULTING, LLC; *U.S. Private*, pg. 414
AYUJOY HERBALS LTD.; *U.S. Public*, pg. 257
AZIEL CORP.; *U.S. Private*, pg. 415
AZTECH TECHNOLOGIES, INC.—See LaBella Associates, D.P.C.; *U.S. Private*, pg. 2370
BACCO CONSTRUCTION CO.; *U.S. Private*, pg. 422
BACKGROUNDCHECKS.COM; *U.S. Private*, pg. 423
BALANCEPOINT, INC.; *U.S. Private*, pg. 458
BALDWIN RISK PARTNER'S LLC—See The Baldwin Insurance Group, Inc.; *U.S. Public*, pg. 2036
BALLARD PARTNERS, INC.; *U.S. Private*, pg. 460
BANK OF AMERICA BUSINESS CAPITAL—See Bank of America Corporation; *U.S. Public*, pg. 270
BARBARICUM; *U.S. Private*, pg. 472
BARINGS BDC, INC.; *U.S. Public*, pg. 276
BARKAWI MANAGEMENT CONSULTANTS, LLC—See Genpact Limited; *Int'l*, pg. 2926
BARTON MALOW COMPANY—See Barton Malow Enterprises, Inc.; *U.S. Private*, pg. 483
BASF AKQUISITIONS GMBH—See BASF SE; *Int'l*, pg. 872
BASF LUDWIGSHAFEN GRUNDBESITZ SE & CO. KG—See BASF SE; *Int'l*, pg. 880
BASIC REMEDIATION COMPANY LLC—See Contran Corporation; *U.S. Private*, pg. 1033
BCS CALLPROCESSING, INC.; *U.S. Private*, pg. 500
BCT CONSULTING, INC.; *U.S. Private*, pg. 500
BEACON ASSOCIATES, INC.; *U.S. Private*, pg. 504
BEACON CONSULTING GROUP, LLC—See Accenture plc; *Int'l*, pg. 86
BEHEERMAATSCHAPPIJ BURG B.V.—See China International Marine Containers (Group) Co., Ltd.; *Int'l*, pg. 1511

541618 — OTHER MANAGEMENT CO...

BEIJING GEOENVIRON ENGINEERING & TECHNOLOGY, INC.; *Int'l*, pg. 951
BEIJING NAVIGANT CONSULTING CO., LTD.—See Bain Capital, LP; *U.S. Private*, pg. 432
BEM SYSTEMS - PHOENIX—See Bernhard Capital Partners Management, LP; *U.S. Private*, pg. 537
BENEFEX LIMITED; *Int'l*, pg. 972
THE BENEFIT SERVICES GROUP, INC.; *U.S. Private*, pg. 3993
BEONE STUTTGART GMBH—See Alten S.A.; *Int'l*, pg. 390
BERING SEA ECCOTECH INC.—See Tanadgusix Corp.; *U.S. Private*, pg. 3930
BF&M (CANADA) LIMITED—See BF&M Limited; *Int'l*, pg. 1006
BIG SOFA TECHNOLOGIES GROUP PLC; *Int'l*, pg. 1021
BILFINGER INDUSTRIAL SERVICES NORWAY AS—See Bilfinger SE; *Int'l*, pg. 1026
BINARY FOUNTAIN INC.—See Ares Management Corporation; *U.S. Public*, pg. 190
BINARY FOUNTAIN INC.—See Leonard Green & Partners, L.P.; *U.S. Private*, pg. 2427
BIOMAX ENVIRONMENTAL TECHNOLOGY (SHANGHAI) COMPANY LIMITED—See Capital Environment Holdings Limited; *Int'l*, pg. 1310
BIRD ROCK SYSTEMS, INC.; *U.S. Private*, pg. 564
BIVARUS, INC.—See Ares Management Corporation; *U.S. Public*, pg. 190
BIVARUS, INC.—See Leonard Green & Partners, L.P.; *U.S. Private*, pg. 2427
BIZMATICA SPA—See Econocom Group SA; *Int'l*, pg. 2297
BLACKBAUD PACIFIC PTY. LTD.—See Blackbaud, Inc.; *U.S. Public*, pg. 341
BLACKROCK ASSET MANAGEMENT CANADA LIMITED—See BlackRock, Inc.; *U.S. Public*, pg. 344
BLACKROCK (NETHERLANDS) B.V.—See BlackRock, Inc.; *U.S. Public*, pg. 344
BLACKROCK (SINGAPORE HOLDCO) PTE. LIMITED—See BlackRock, Inc.; *U.S. Public*, pg. 344
BLADE ENERGY PARTNERS, LTD.; *U.S. Private*, pg. 577
BLOYALTY SDN BHD—See Berjaya Corporation Berhad; *Int'l*, pg. 982
BLUE ARROW RECRUITMENT SOLUTIONS LTD.—See HFBG Holding B.V.; *Int'l*, pg. 3374
BLUEFIN RESOURCES PTY. LIMITED—See Bain Capital, LP; *U.S. Private*, pg. 433
BLUEFIN UNDERWRITING LIMITED—See Marsh & McLennan Companies, Inc.; *U.S. Public*, pg. 1374
BLUE HORSESHOE SOLUTIONS, INC.; *U.S. Private*, pg. 589
BLUE SLATE SOLUTIONS, LLC—See ExlService Holdings, Inc.; *U.S. Public*, pg. 807
BLUE WATER ENERGY SOLUTIONS, LLC—See GreenHunter Resources, Inc.; *U.S. Private*, pg. 1778
BLUE WATER SHIELD LLC; *U.S. Private*, pg. 594
BLUM, SHAPIRO & COMPANY, P.C.; *U.S. Private*, pg. 599
BMO GLOBAL ASSET MANAGEMENT—See Bank of Montreal; *Int'l*, pg. 846
BNG CONSULTANCY SERVICES B.V.—See BNG Bank N.V.; *Int'l*, pg. 1078
BODONI SYSTEMS—See Agfa-Gevaert N.V.; *Int'l*, pg. 208
THE BOSTON CONSULTING GROUP AB—See The Boston Consulting Group, Inc.; *U.S. Private*, pg. 3997
THE BOSTON CONSULTING GROUP - ABU DHABI—See The Boston Consulting Group, Inc.; *U.S. Private*, pg. 3997
THE BOSTON CONSULTING GROUP - BANGKOK—See The Boston Consulting Group, Inc.; *U.S. Private*, pg. 3997
THE BOSTON CONSULTING GROUP - BARCELONA—See The Boston Consulting Group, Inc.; *U.S. Private*, pg. 3997
THE BOSTON CONSULTING GROUP - BEIJING—See The Boston Consulting Group, Inc.; *U.S. Private*, pg. 3997
THE BOSTON CONSULTING GROUP - BRUSSELS—See The Boston Consulting Group, Inc.; *U.S. Private*, pg. 3997
THE BOSTON CONSULTING GROUP - BUDAPEST—See The Boston Consulting Group, Inc.; *U.S. Private*, pg. 3997
THE BOSTON CONSULTING GROUP - BUENOS AIRES—See The Boston Consulting Group, Inc.; *U.S. Private*, pg. 3997
THE BOSTON CONSULTING GROUP B.V.—See The Boston Consulting Group, Inc.; *U.S. Private*, pg. 3997
THE BOSTON CONSULTING GROUP - CASABLANCA—See The Boston Consulting Group, Inc.; *U.S. Private*, pg. 3997
THE BOSTON CONSULTING GROUP - DUBAI—See The Boston Consulting Group, Inc.; *U.S. Private*, pg. 3997
THE BOSTON CONSULTING GROUP GMBH - BERLIN—See The Boston Consulting Group, Inc.; *U.S. Private*, pg. 3997
THE BOSTON CONSULTING GROUP GMBH - COLOGNE—See The Boston Consulting Group, Inc.; *U.S. Private*, pg. 3997
THE BOSTON CONSULTING GROUP - HONG KONG—See The Boston Consulting Group, Inc.; *U.S. Private*, pg. 3997

THE BOSTON CONSULTING GROUP, INC. - ATLANTA—See The Boston Consulting Group, Inc.; *U.S. Private*, pg. 3998
THE BOSTON CONSULTING GROUP, INC. - CHICAGO—See The Boston Consulting Group, Inc.; *U.S. Private*, pg. 3998
THE BOSTON CONSULTING GROUP, INC. - DALLAS—See The Boston Consulting Group, Inc.; *U.S. Private*, pg. 3998
THE BOSTON CONSULTING GROUP, INC. - HOUSTON—See The Boston Consulting Group, Inc.; *U.S. Private*, pg. 3998
THE BOSTON CONSULTING GROUP, INC.; *U.S. Private*, pg. 3997
THE BOSTON CONSULTING GROUP - JAKARTA—See The Boston Consulting Group, Inc.; *U.S. Private*, pg. 3997
THE BOSTON CONSULTING GROUP - KUALA LUMPUR—See The Boston Consulting Group, Inc.; *U.S. Private*, pg. 3997
THE BOSTON CONSULTING GROUP - MADRID—See The Boston Consulting Group, Inc.; *U.S. Private*, pg. 3997
THE BOSTON CONSULTING GROUP NORDIC AB - COPENHAGEN—See The Boston Consulting Group, Inc.; *U.S. Private*, pg. 3997
THE BOSTON CONSULTING GROUP NORDIC AB - HELSINKI—See The Boston Consulting Group, Inc.; *U.S. Private*, pg. 3997
THE BOSTON CONSULTING GROUP NORDIC AB - OSLO—See The Boston Consulting Group, Inc.; *U.S. Private*, pg. 3997
THE BOSTON CONSULTING GROUP PTY. LTD. - NEW ZEALAND—See The Boston Consulting Group, Inc.; *U.S. Private*, pg. 3998
THE BOSTON CONSULTING GROUP PTY. LTD.—See The Boston Consulting Group, Inc.; *U.S. Private*, pg. 3998
THE BOSTON CONSULTING GROUP PTY. LTD. - SYDNEY—See The Boston Consulting Group, Inc.; *U.S. Private*, pg. 3998
THE BOSTON CONSULTING GROUP RSA PTY. LTD.—See The Boston Consulting Group, Inc.; *U.S. Private*, pg. 3998
THE BOSTON CONSULTING GROUP - SHANGHAI—See The Boston Consulting Group, Inc.; *U.S. Private*, pg. 3997
THE BOSTON CONSULTING GROUP SINGAPORE PTE. LTD.—See The Boston Consulting Group, Inc.; *U.S. Private*, pg. 3998
THE BOSTON CONSULTING GROUP - TAIPEI—See The Boston Consulting Group, Inc.; *U.S. Private*, pg. 3997
THE BOSTON CONSULTING GROUP - TOKYO—See The Boston Consulting Group, Inc.; *U.S. Private*, pg. 3997
BO TECHNOLOGY INCORPORATED; *U.S. Private*, pg. 602
BPO COLLECTIONS LTD.—See Everyday People Financial Corp.; *Int'l*, pg. 2570
BRAILSFORD & DUNLAVEY; *U.S. Private*, pg. 634
BRAKE SYSTEMS, INC.—See Enstar Group Limited; *Int'l*, pg. 2448
BRCCA SERVICES PRIVATE LIMITED; *Int'l*, pg. 1143
BREW-BEV—See Neal H. Knapp, LLC; *U.S. Private*, pg. 2877
BRIDGE PARTNERS CONSULTING; *U.S. Private*, pg. 649
BRIDGEPOINT CONSULTING LLC—See Odyssey Investment Partners, LLC; *U.S. Private*, pg. 2994
BRIGHTWORKS SUSTAINABILITY LLC; *U.S. Private*, pg. 654
BROOKFIELD GLOBAL RELOCATION SERVICES—See Brookfield Corporation; *Int'l*, pg. 1181
BRUNEL INTERNATIONAL SOUTH EAST ASIA PTE LTD—See Brunel International N.V.; *Int'l*, pg. 1200
BTC BILISIM HIZMETLERI A.S.—See EWE Aktiengesellschaft; *Int'l*, pg. 2575
BTC SOFTWARE SYSTEMS SP. Z O.O.—See EWE Aktiengesellschaft; *Int'l*, pg. 2575
BTC SOFTWARE TECHNOLOGY (SHANGHAI) CO., LTD.—See EWE Aktiengesellschaft; *Int'l*, pg. 2575
BTI GROUP; *U.S. Private*, pg. 675
BTS AUSTRALASIA—See BTS Group AB; *Int'l*, pg. 1205
BTS LONDON—See BTS Group AB; *Int'l*, pg. 1205
BTS SOUTH AFRICA—See BTS Group AB; *Int'l*, pg. 1205
BUCHANAN & EDWARDS INC.; *U.S. Private*, pg. 676
BUCK GLOBAL LLC—See Arthur J. Gallagher & Co.; *U.S. Public*, pg. 204
BUILDING SECURITY SERVICES, INC.; *U.S. Private*, pg. 683
BURGEL WIRTSCHAFTSINFORMATIONEN VERWALTUNGS-GMBH—See Allianz SE; *Int'l*, pg. 351
BUSINESS BRAIN SHOWA-OTA INC.; *Int'l*, pg. 1228
BUSINESS COMMUNICATIONS MANAGEMENT, INC; *U.S. Private*, pg. 694
BUSINESS CONSULTING GROUP, INC.; *U.S. Private*, pg. 694
BUSINESS NETWORK CONSULTING, LTD.; *U.S. Private*, pg. 695
BUSINESS OFFICE SUITE SERVICES, INC.; *U.S. Private*, pg. 695
BUSINESS SECURITY CONSULTANTS, INC.; *U.S. Private*, pg. 695

BUSINESS TECHNOLOGY SERVICES, INC.; *U.S. Private*, pg. 695
BUXBAUM GROUP; *U.S. Private*, pg. 698
CADOOZ GMBH—See Euronet Worldwide, Inc.; *U.S. Public*, pg. 798
CAGE INC.—See Ross & Baruzzini, Inc.; *U.S. Private*, pg. 3485
CA IMMO ASSET MANAGEMENT GMBH—See Starwood Capital Group Global I, LLC; *U.S. Private*, pg. 3788
CA IMMOBILIEN ANLAGEN BETEILIGUNGS GMBH & CO FINANZIERUNGS OEG—See Starwood Capital Group Global I, LLC; *U.S. Private*, pg. 3789
CA IMMOBILIEN ANLAGEN BETEILIGUNGS GMBH—See Starwood Capital Group Global I, LLC; *U.S. Private*, pg. 3789
CA IMMO DEUTSCHLAND GMBH—See Starwood Capital Group Global I, LLC; *U.S. Private*, pg. 3789
CA IMMO RENNWEG 16 GMBH—See Starwood Capital Group Global I, LLC; *U.S. Private*, pg. 3789
CALABRESE CONSULTING, LLC; *U.S. Private*, pg. 715
CAL INVESTMENTS LIMITED—See CalBank PLC; *Int'l*, pg. 1261
CALLCREDIT MARKETING LIMITED—See GTCR LLC; *U.S. Private*, pg. 1804
CALVERT RESEARCH, LLC—See Calvert Holdings, Inc.; *U.S. Private*, pg. 724
CAMPAIGN CONSULTATION, INC.; *U.S. Private*, pg. 730
CAMPER & NICHOLSONS MARINAS LTD.—See Camper & Nicholsons Marina Invst. Ltd.; *Int'l*, pg. 1274
CANNON GROUP ENTERPRISES, LLC—See Charlesbank Capital Partners, LLC; *U.S. Private*, pg. 854
CANTALOUPE SYSTEMS INC.—See Cantaloupe, Inc.; *U.S. Public*, pg. 430
CAPGEMINI ARGENTINA S.A.—See Capgemini SE; *Int'l*, pg. 1303
CAPGEMINI GOVERNMENT SOLUTIONS LLC—See Capgemini SE; *Int'l*, pg. 1305
CAPGEMINI (SHANGHAI)—See Capgemini SE; *Int'l*, pg. 1303
CAPGEMINI U.S.—See Capgemini SE; *Int'l*, pg. 1306
THE CAPITAL MARKETS COMPANY—See Clayton, Dubilier & Rice, LLC; *U.S. Private*, pg. 927
CAPITOL VIEW, LLC—See E*TRADE Financial Corporation; *U.S. Private*, pg. 1302
CAPPADONNA ELECTRICAL MANAGEMENT CORPORATION; *U.S. Private*, pg. 745
CAP SOGETI 2005 S.A.S.—See Capgemini SE; *Int'l*, pg. 1303
CARDENAS PARTNERS, LLC; *U.S. Private*, pg. 749
CARDINAL HEALTH, INC. - WAYNE—See Cardinal Health, Inc.; *U.S. Public*, pg. 434
CARDINAL HEALTH SPECIALTY PHARMACEUTICAL SERVICES—See Cardinal Health, Inc.; *U.S. Public*, pg. 433
CARDINAL PEAK, LLC—See FPT Corporation; *Int'l*, pg. 2757
CARLO GAVAZZI AG—See Carlo Gavazzi Holding AG; *Int'l*, pg. 1338
CARLO GAVAZZI MARKETING AG—See Carlo Gavazzi Holding AG; *Int'l*, pg. 1339
CARLO GAVAZZI SERVICES AG—See Carlo Gavazzi Holding AG; *Int'l*, pg. 1339
CARRICK WILLIAMS HOLDINGS INC.; *U.S. Private*, pg. 772
CASH FLOW SOLUTIONS INC.; *U.S. Private*, pg. 782
CASK, LLC; *U.S. Private*, pg. 783
CATALYST TECHNOLOGY GROUP USA; *U.S. Private*, pg. 786
CATAPULT CONSULTANTS LLC; *U.S. Private*, pg. 787
CBIZ PRIVATE EQUITY ADVISORY, LLC—See CBIZ, Inc.; *U.S. Public*, pg. 457
C B R INTERNATIONAL CORP.—See TPG Capital, L.P.; *U.S. Public*, pg. 2175
CCA INC.—See Corecivic, Inc.; *U.S. Public*, pg. 577
CCB MANAGEMENT SERVICES GMBH—See Coca-Cola HBC AG; *Int'l*, pg. 1685
CCK FINANCIAL SOLUTIONS (MALAYSIA) SDN. BHD.—See CCK Financial Solutions Pty Limited; *Int'l*, pg. 1367
CD INTERNATIONAL ENTERPRISES, INC.; *U.S. Public*, pg. 461
CDR ADVANCE CAPITAL S.P.A.; *Int'l*, pg. 1371
CELERITY CONSULTING GROUP, INC.—See Hastings Equity Partners, LLC; *U.S. Private*, pg. 1879
CEMENT SERVICES COMPANY S.A.E.—See Camargo Correa S.A.; *Int'l*, pg. 1267
CEMIT INTERACTIVE MEDIA S.P.A.—See Fininvest S.p.A.; *Int'l*, pg. 2675
THE CENTER FOR INNOVATION, EXCELLENCE & LEADERSHIP; *U.S. Private*, pg. 4006
CENTRAMED, INC.—See Analytix On Demand, Inc.; *U.S. Private*, pg. 271
CENTRIC CONSULTING, LLC; *U.S. Private*, pg. 829
CEYLON TRADING CO. LTD.—See AAK AB; *Int'l*, pg. 32
CGA STRATEGY LIMITED—See Advent International Corporation; *U.S. Private*, pg. 105
CGMP CENTRO DE GESTAO DE MEIOS DE PAGAMENTOS LTDA.—See Corpay, Inc.; *U.S. Public*, pg. 579

541618 — OTHER MANAGEMENT CO...   CORPORATE AFFILIATIONS

CHALLENGER GROUP SERVICES PTY LTD—See Challenger Limited; *Int'l*, pg. 1438
CHALLENGER INTERNATIONAL NOMINEES LTD—See Challenger Limited; *Int'l*, pg. 1438
CHALLENGER PORTFOLIO MANAGEMENT LIMITED—See Challenger Limited; *Int'l*, pg. 1438
CHAMELEO GMBH—See Highlight Event & Entertainment AG; *Int'l*, pg. 3388
CHAMPION, INC.; *U.S. Private*, pg. 847
CHANGE MANAGEMENT CONSULTING, INC.; *U.S. Private*, pg. 848
CHARLES TAYLOR AVIATION (ASSET MANAGEMENT) LIMITED—See Lovell Minnick Partners LLC; *U.S. Private*, pg. 2502
CHARLES TAYLOR (HAMILTON) LTD—See Lovell Minnick Partners LLC; *U.S. Private*, pg. 2502
C&H COMMUNICATIONS; *Int'l*, pg. 1238
CHEMTECH CONSULTING GROUP, INC.—See Morgan Stanley; *U.S. Public*, pg. 1474
THE CHERTOFF GROUP, LLC; *U.S. Private*, pg. 4007
CHINA FORTUNE HOLDINGS LIMITED; *Int'l*, pg. 1503
CHINA INTERNATIONAL ECONOMIC CONSULTANTS CO., LTD.—See CITIC Group Corporation; *Int'l*, pg. 1621
CHINA MOBILE GROUP BEIJING COMPANY LIMITED—See China Mobile Communications Corporation; *Int'l*, pg. 1524
CHINA MOBILE GROUP HEBEI COMPANY LIMITED—See China Mobile Communications Corporation; *Int'l*, pg. 1524
CHINA MOBILE GROUP HEILONGJIANG COMPANY LIMITED—See China Mobile Communications Corporation; *Int'l*, pg. 1524
CHINA MOBILE GROUP NEIMENGGU COMPANY LIMITED—See China Mobile Communications Corporation; *Int'l*, pg. 1524
CHINA MOBILE GROUP NINGXIA COMPANY LIMITED—See China Mobile Communications Corporation; *Int'l*, pg. 1524
CHINA MOBILE GROUP TIANJIN COMPANY LIMITED—See China Mobile Communications Corporation; *Int'l*, pg. 1524
CHINASTEEL MANAGEMENT CONSULTING CORPORATION—See China Steel Corporation; *Int'l*, pg. 1555
THE CHRISTMAN COMPANY INC.; *U.S. Private*, pg. 4009
CHS CABIN AND HANDLING SERVICE GMBH—See Air Berlin PLC & Co. Luftverkehrs KG; *Int'l*, pg. 236
CIC GROUP, INC.; *U.S. Private*, pg. 896
CISCO OPTICAL GMBH—See Cisco Systems, Inc.; *U.S. Public*, pg. 497
CIVEO CANADA INC.—See Oil States International, Inc.; *U.S. Public*, pg. 1565
CIVITAS INTERNATIONAL MANAGEMENT CONSULTANTS GMBH; *Int'l*, pg. 1630
CLAIM TECHNOLOGIES INC.—See Brown & Brown, Inc.; *U.S. Public*, pg. 399
CLANCY CONSULTING LTD; *Int'l*, pg. 1641
CLAREITY CONSULTING LTD.; *U.S. Private*, pg. 910
CLARK THOMSON INSURANCE BROKERS LIMITED—See Marsh & McLennan Companies, Inc.; *U.S. Public*, pg. 1374
CLEAN HARBORS DEER PARK, LLC—See Clean Harbors, Inc.; *U.S. Public*, pg. 510
CLEANTECH NRW GMBH—See Bayer Aktiengesellschaft; *Int'l*, pg. 907
THE CLEARING, INC.; *U.S. Private*, pg. 4010
CLICKS RECRUIT (AUSTRALIA) PTY. LTD.—See Bain Capital, LP; *U.S. Private*, pg. 433
CLIENT STRATEGY GROUP, LLC—See Columbus A/S; *Int'l*, pg. 1706
CLOUDCHECKR LLC—See NetApp, Inc.; *U.S. Public*, pg. 1507
CMS OPERATIONS; *U.S. Private*, pg. 951
CNA TECHNOLOGY INC—See CNA Group Ltd.; *Int'l*, pg. 1673
COASTAL HEALTHCARE CONSULTING, INC.—See Dynamic Computing Services Corp.; *U.S. Private*, pg. 1297
COASTAL TRAINING TECHNOLOGIES CORP.—See DuPont de Nemours, Inc.; *U.S. Public*, pg. 692
CODESMART HOLDINGS, INC.; *U.S. Private*, pg. 960
CODY CONSULTING SERVICES, INC.; *U.S. Private*, pg. 960
COESTER VMS; *U.S. Private*, pg. 960
COFFEY INTERNATIONAL DEVELOPMENT PTY. LTD.—See Tetra Tech, Inc.; *U.S. Public*, pg. 2022
COFRETH (M) SDN BHD—See IJM Corporation Berhad; *Int'l*, pg. 3608
COGNIZANT TECHNOLOGY SOLUTIONS AUSTRALIA PTY. LTD.—See Cognizant Technology Solutions Corporation; *U.S. Public*, pg. 524
COHESION CORPORATION—See System One Holdings, LLC; *U.S. Private*, pg. 3906
COILLTE NORTH/WESTERN REGION—See Coillte Ltd.; *Int'l*, pg. 1696
COLONIAL COMMERCIAL DEVELOPMENT—See Colonial Company; *U.S. Private*, pg. 970
COLONIAL COMMERCIAL REALTY—See Colonial Company; *U.S. Private*, pg. 970
COLUMN TECHNOLOGIES, INC.; *U.S. Private*, pg. 979
COMMERCIAL ENERGY SERVICES PTY LTD—See EnviroSuite Limited; *Int'l*, pg. 2455
COMMERZ BUSINESS CONSULTING GMBH—See Commerzbank AG; *Int'l*, pg. 1716
COMMONWEALTH TELEPHONE ENTERPRISES, INC.—See Frontier Communications Parent, Inc.; *U.S. Public*, pg. 887
COMMUNICATION INFRASTRUCTURE CORPORATION; *U.S. Private*, pg. 988
COMPASS ANALYTICS, LLC—See Intercontinental Exchange, Inc.; *U.S. Public*, pg. 1141
COMPASS CONSULTING AB—See Information Services Group, Inc.; *U.S. Public*, pg. 1118
COMPASS MANAGEMENT CONSULTING IBERICA SA—See Information Services Group, Inc.; *U.S. Public*, pg. 1118
COMPASS MANAGEMENT CONSULTING S.A.—See Information Services Group, Inc.; *U.S. Public*, pg. 1118
THE COMPLIANCE DOCTOR, LLC; *U.S. Private*, pg. 4013
COMPREHENSIVE LOSS MANAGEMENT, INC.—See Waud Capital Partners LLC; *U.S. Private*, pg. 4457
COMPREHENSIVE PHARMACY SERVICES, INC.—See PPS, Inc.; *U.S. Private*, pg. 3240
CONCENTRA SOLUTIONS, INC.—See Select Medical Holdings Corporation; *U.S. Public*, pg. 1857
CONCENTRA SOLUTIONS, INC.—See Welsh, Carson, Anderson & Stowe; *U.S. Private*, pg. 4479
CONCEPTS & STRATEGIES INC; *U.S. Private*, pg. 1009
CONCEPT SYSTEMS INC.—See Head B.V.; *Int'l*, pg. 3300
CONDE GROUP, INC.; *U.S. Private*, pg. 1011
CONDUENT CREDIT BALANCE SOLUTIONS, LLC—See Conduent Incorporated; *U.S. Public*, pg. 566
CONSERO GLOBAL SOLUTIONS LLC; *U.S. Private*, pg. 1019
CONSORTA, INC.; *U.S. Private*, pg. 1023
CONSULTORIA EN GESTION DE RIESGOS IPS SURAMERICANA S.A.—See Grupo de Inversiones Suramericana S.A.; *Int'l*, pg. 3125
CONTOUR DATA SOLUTIONS; *U.S. Private*, pg. 1031
CONTROLEXPERT COLOMBIA SAS—See Allianz SE; *Int'l*, pg. 351
COOLEY GROUP, INC.; *U.S. Private*, pg. 1039
COPIJN UTRECHT HOLDING BV—See Hoek Hoveniers B.V.; *Int'l*, pg. 3439
CORCORAN & JOHNSTON; *U.S. Private*, pg. 1047
CORDEV INC.; *U.S. Private*, pg. 1047
CORE CONSTRUCTION INC.—See Otto Baum Company, Inc.; *U.S. Private*, pg. 3050
CORPORACION NOROESTE S.A.—See Camargo Correa S.A.; *Int'l*, pg. 1268
CORPORATE & RESOURCE CONSULTANTS PTY LTD; *Int'l*, pg. 1805
CORPORATE SERVICE SYSTEMS OAO; *Int'l*, pg. 1805
CORPORATE UNITED, INC.; *U.S. Private*, pg. 1056
CORPORATE VISIONS, INC.—See The Riverside Company; *U.S. Private*, pg. 4108
CORTINA SOLUTIONS, LLC; *U.S. Private*, pg. 1061
COSG—See Carrefour SA; *Int'l*, pg. 1344
COST CONTROL ASSOCIATES, INC.—See O2 Investment Partners, LLC; *U.S. Private*, pg. 2982
COURTEVILLE BUSINESS SOLUTIONS PLC.; *Int'l*, pg. 1819
COURY HEALTH SERVICES, LLC—See Genstar Capital, LLC; *U.S. Private*, pg. 1674
COVANCE HEALTH ECONOMICS & OUTCOME SERVICES, INC.—See Laboratory Corporation of America Holdings; *U.S. Public*, pg. 1286
CPS PROFESSIONAL SERVICES; *U.S. Private*, pg. 1081
CPT GLOBAL INC—See CPT Global Limited; *Int'l*, pg. 1826
CQUEST; *U.S. Private*, pg. 1081
CRAIN COMMUNICATIONS, INC. - STAFFING INDUSTRY ANALYSTS UNIT—See Crain Communications, Inc.; *U.S. Private*, pg. 1084
CREDENT TECHNOLOGIES LLC.; *U.S. Private*, pg. 1090
CREED CAPITAL MANAGEMENT AND RESEARCH, INC.—See CREED Corporation; *Int'l*, pg. 1837
CREED HOTEL MANAGEMENT CORPORATION—See CREED Corporation; *Int'l*, pg. 1837
CREEK & RIVER CO., LTD.; *Int'l*, pg. 1837
CREEK & RIVER SHANGHAI CO., LTD.—See CREEK & RIVER Co., Ltd.; *Int'l*, pg. 1837
CRENSHAW CONSULTING GROUP, LLC—See O2 Investment Partners, LLC; *U.S. Private*, pg. 2982
CRESA PARTNERS OF LOS ANGELES, INC.—See TPG Capital, L.P.; *U.S. Public*, pg. 2171
CRISPELL-SNYDER, INC.—See Comvest Group Holdings LLC; *U.S. Private*, pg. 1007
CRISPWAY LIMITED—See Heidelberg Materials AG; *Int'l*, pg. 3310
CRITICALCONTROL ENERGY SERVICES—See Critical Control Energy Services Corp.; *Int'l*, pg. 1851
CROS NT SRL—See CMC Consulting Boston, Inc.; *U.S. Private*, pg. 950
CSC DIGITAL BRAND SERVICES LIMITED—See Corporation Service Company; *U.S. Private*, pg. 1057
CSC DIGITAL BRAND SERVICES—See Corporation Service Company; *U.S. Private*, pg. 1057
CSM SPORT & ENTERTAINMENT NEW ZEALAND LIMITED—See Wasserman Media Group, LLC; *U.S. Private*, pg. 4450
CSRA BOLIVIA S.R.L.—See General Dynamics Corporation; *U.S. Public*, pg. 913
CTS EVENTIM SCHWEDEN AB—See CTS Eventim AG & Co. KGAA; *Int'l*, pg. 1872
CUBA BUSINESS DEVELOPMENT GROUP, INC.—See Fuego Enterprises, Inc.; *U.S. Public*, pg. 891
CULINAIRE INTERNATIONAL INC.; *U.S. Private*, pg. 1120
CUMBERLAND CONSULTING GROUP, LLC; *U.S. Private*, pg. 1122
CURA HOSPITALITY INC.—See Eat'n Park Hospitality Group, Inc.; *U.S. Private*, pg. 1323
CUSHMAN & WAKEFIELD (BAHRAIN) W.L.L.—See TPG Capital, L.P.; *U.S. Public*, pg. 2171
CUSTOMIZED ENERGY SOLUTIONS LTD.; *U.S. Private*, pg. 1130
CWI BENEFITS, INC.—See Patriot National, Inc.; *U.S. Private*, pg. 3110
CXLOYALTY, INC.—See JPMorgan Chase & Co.; *U.S. Public*, pg. 1210
CYMETRIX CORPORATION—See Bain Capital, LP; *U.S. Private*, pg. 432
CYRUS INNOVATION; *U.S. Private*, pg. 1135
DADI EARLY-CHILDHOOD EDUCATION GROUP LTD.; *Int'l*, pg. 1904
DAITO BUILDING MANAGEMENT CO LTD—See Daito Trust Construction Co., Ltd.; *Int'l*, pg. 1943
DAIWA INSTITUTE OF RESEARCH BUSINESS INNOVATION LTD.—See Daiwa Securities Group Inc.; *Int'l*, pg. 1948
DAMEN TRADING & CHARTERING—See Damen Shipyards Group; *Int'l*, pg. 1956
DAMSTRA TECHNOLOGY PTY LTD—See Damstra Holdings Ltd.; *Int'l*, pg. 1957
DANIEL P. O'REILLY & COMPANY; *U.S. Private*, pg. 1156
DATACORE TECHNOLOGIES PRIVATE LIMITED—See Bain Capital, LP; *U.S. Private*, pg. 433
DAT-SCHAUB (DEUTSCHLAND) GMBH—See Danish Crown AmbA; *Int'l*, pg. 1964
DAVINCI CONSULTING AS—See Devoteam SA; *Int'l*, pg. 2089
DB CONSULTING GROUP, INC.; *U.S. Private*, pg. 1178
D&B EUROPE LIMITED—See Cannae Holdings, Inc.; *U.S. Public*, pg. 429
D&B EUROPE LIMITED—See CC Capital Partners, LLC; *U.S. Private*, pg. 798
D&B EUROPE LIMITED—See Intercontinental Exchange, Inc.; *U.S. Public*, pg. 1141
DBXB NETHERLANDS B.V.—See Cannae Holdings, Inc.; *U.S. Public*, pg. 429
DBXB NETHERLANDS B.V.—See CC Capital Partners, LLC; *U.S. Private*, pg. 798
DBXB NETHERLANDS B.V.—See Intercontinental Exchange, Inc.; *U.S. Public*, pg. 1141
DBXB S.R.L.—See Cannae Holdings, Inc.; *U.S. Public*, pg. 429
DBXB S.R.L.—See CC Capital Partners, LLC; *U.S. Private*, pg. 798
DBXB S.R.L.—See Intercontinental Exchange, Inc.; *U.S. Public*, pg. 1141
DCCM, LLC—See White Wolf Capital LLC; *U.S. Private*, pg. 4510
DDSB (M) SDN. BHD.—See EA Holdings Berhad; *Int'l*, pg. 2261
DEALER ASSOCIATES, INC.—See Brown & Brown, Inc.; *U.S. Public*, pg. 399
DEBTSCAPE, INC.; *U.S. Private*, pg. 1186
DECISIONPATH CONSULTING; *U.S. Private*, pg. 1187
DEFINED HEALTH, INC.—See Arsenal Capital Management LP; *U.S. Private*, pg. 338
DEKRA ZAPOSLJAVANJE D.O.O.—See DEKRA e.V.; *Int'l*, pg. 2010
DELBERT CRAIG FOOD BROKERS; *U.S. Private*, pg. 1196
DELOITTE CONSULTING LLP—See Deloitte LLP; *U.S. Private*, pg. 1198
DELOITTE CONSULTING LLP—See Deloitte Touche Tohmatsu Limited; *Int'l*, pg. 2014
DELPHI PRIVATE ADVISORS—See Lourd Capital LLC; *U.S. Private*, pg. 2500
DELTA CONSULTING GROUP, INC.; *U.S. Private*, pg. 1199
DENTISTAT, INC.—See The Beekman Group, LLC; *U.S. Private*, pg. 3993
DENTSU CONSULTING INC.—See Dentsu Group Inc.; *Int'l*, pg. 2034
DENTSU CUSTOMER ACCESS CENTER INC—See Dentsu Group Inc.; *Int'l*, pg. 2034
DENTSU MACROMILL INSIGHT, INC.—See Dentsu Group Inc.; *Int'l*, pg. 2038
DENTSU RETAIL MARKETING INC.—See Dentsu Group Inc.; *Int'l*, pg. 2038
DENTSU SPORTS EUROPE, LTD.—See Dentsu Group Inc.; *Int'l*, pg. 2037
DETICA LIMITED—See BAE Systems plc; *Int'l*, pg. 798
DETICA SYSTEM INTEGRATION LIMITED—See BAE Systems plc; *Int'l*, pg. 798
DET NORSKE VERITAS EIENDOM AS - HARSTAD—See

541618 — OTHER MANAGEMENT CO...

DNV GL Group AS; *Int'l*, pg. 2151
DEUTSCHE INTERNATIONAL FINANCE (IRELAND) LIMITED—See Deutsche Bank Aktiengesellschaft; *Int'l*, pg. 2060
DEVOTEAM ITALIA S.R.L.—See Devoteam SA; *Int'l*, pg. 2090
DEVOTEAM OSICONSULT GMBH—See Devoteam SA; *Int'l*, pg. 2090
DEX MEDIA - ALBUQUERQUE—See Thryv Holdings, Inc.; *U.S. Public*, pg. 2157
DHL TRADE FAIRS AND EVENTS (UK) LIMITED—See Deutsche Post AG; *Int'l*, pg. 2078
DIGITAL ARTS AMERICA, INC.—See Digital Arts Inc.; *Int'l*, pg. 2120
DIGITAL ARTS ASIA PACIFIC PTE. LTD.—See Digital Arts Inc.; *Int'l*, pg. 2120
DIGITAL ARTS CONSULTING INC.—See Digital Arts Inc.; *Int'l*, pg. 2120
DINI SPHERIS; *U.S. Private*, pg. 1233
DIRECT EDGE CAMPAIGNS, LLC; *U.S. Private*, pg. 1235
DISCOVERY LEARNING INC.—See Multi-Health Systems, Inc.; *U.S. Private*, pg. 2812
DIVERSEY SWEDEN SERVICES AB—See Sealed Air Corporation; *U.S. Public*, pg. 1853
DIVERSIFIED PROJECT MANAGEMENT, INC.—See STV Group, Inc.; *U.S. Private*, pg. 3845
DJM ASSET MANAGEMENT, LLC—See Gordon Brothers Group, LLC; *U.S. Private*, pg. 1742
DK CONSULTING, LLC; *U.S. Private*, pg. 1247
DKS SYSTEMS, LLC; *U.S. Private*, pg. 1247
DMOS DRESDEN MOS DESIGN GMBH—See ELMOS Semiconductor AG; *Int'l*, pg. 2368
DOAR COMMUNICATIONS INC.; *U.S. Private*, pg. 1250
DOMINION ENERGY BRAYTON POINT, LLC—See Dominion Energy, Inc.; *U.S. Public*, pg. 673
DORI MEDIA DISTRIBUTION GMBH—See Dori Media Group Ltd.; *Int'l*, pg. 2176
DRAW CONNECT LIMITED—See Marsh & McLennan Companies, Inc.; *U.S. Public*, pg. 1374
DRAW CREATE LIMITED—See Marsh & McLennan Companies, Inc.; *U.S. Public*, pg. 1374
DRT STRATEGIES, INC.; *U.S. Private*, pg. 1279
DRUG SAFETY ALLIANCE, INC.—See Clayton, Dubilier & Rice, LLC; *U.S. Private*, pg. 927
DSS SUSTAINABLE SOLUTIONS SWITZERLAND SA; *Int'l*, pg. 2210
DYNPORT VACCINE COMPANY LLC—See General Dynamics Corporation; *U.S. Public*, pg. 913
EACCESS SOLUTIONS, INC.; *U.S. Private*, pg. 1308
EARL ENTERPRISES; *U.S. Private*, pg. 1312
EARLY WARNING SERVICES, LLC—See Wells Fargo & Company; *U.S. Public*, pg. 2343
EARTH SYSTEM SCIENCE CO., LTD.—See Founder's Consultants Holdings, Inc.; *Int'l*, pg. 2753
EASS SDN. BHD.—See EA Holdings Berhad; *Int'l*, pg. 2261
EAST GARRISON PARTNERS I, LLC—See Brookfield Corporation; *Int'l*, pg. 1183
EAV BETEILIGUNGS-GMBH—See E.ON SE; *Int'l*, pg. 2256
EBIQUITY MARSH LIMITED—See Ebiquity plc; *Int'l*, pg. 2285
EBRIDGE BUSINESS SOLUTIONS LLC; *U.S. Private*, pg. 1324
E-BUSINESS INTERNATIONAL INC (E-BI); *U.S. Private*, pg. 1302
EBUSINESS STRATEGIS, LLC; *U.S. Private*, pg. 1326
EBV ELEKTRONIK OU—See Avnet, Inc.; *U.S. Public*, pg. 252
EBY GEWERBEOBJEKT GMBH—See E.ON SE; *Int'l*, pg. 2256
EBY PORT 3 GMBH—See E.ON SE; *Int'l*, pg. 2256
EBY PORT 5 GMBH—See E.ON SE; *Int'l*, pg. 2256
EC AMERICA, INC.—See Arrow Electronics, Inc.; *U.S. Public*, pg. 200
ECG MANAGEMENT CONSULTANTS, INC.—See Gryphon Investors, LLC; *U.S. Private*, pg. 1798
ECOLUTIONS CARBON INDIA PVT. LTD.—See ecolutions GmbH & Co. KGaA; *Int'l*, pg. 2295
ECOLUTIONS NEW ENERGY INVESTMENT CO., LTD.—See ecolutions GmbH & Co. KGaA; *Int'l*, pg. 2295
ECOSCIENCES, INC.; *U.S. Public*, pg. 717
EC&R ENERGY MARKETING, LLC—See E.ON SE; *Int'l*, pg. 2252
ECS LIMITED; *Int'l*, pg. 2301
EDARA L.L.C.—See Emirates NBD PJSC; *Int'l*, pg. 2382
EDELWEISS FINANCIAL PRODUCTS AND SOLUTIONS LIMITED—See Edelweiss Financial Services Ltd.; *Int'l*, pg. 2306
EDGEWATER TECHNOLOGY (DELAWARE), INC.—See Alithya Group, Inc.; *Int'l*, pg. 329
EDGEWEBHOSTING, INC.; *U.S. Private*, pg. 1335
EDUCARE HUMAN CAPITAL PRIVATE LIMITED—See Ascendo International Holdings Pte. Ltd.; *Int'l*, pg. 602
EDWARDS INDUSTRIES, LLC; *U.S. Private*, pg. 1342
EFESO CONSULTING S.A.—See Eurazeo SE; *Int'l*, pg. 2528
EFFICIENT MARKET ADVISORS—See Cantor Fitzgerald, L.P.; *U.S. Private*, pg. 736
EKI ENERGY SERVICES LIMITED; *Int'l*, pg. 2338

ELEVATE ENTERTAINMENT, INC.; *U.S. Private*, pg. 1358
ELFTE BASF PROJEKTENTWICKLUNGSGESELLSCHAFT MBH—See BASF SE; *Int'l*, pg. 883
ELITE WORKWEAR UK LIMITED; *Int'l*, pg. 2362
ELUMINATE, LLC—See Healthcare Services Group, Inc.; *U.S. Public*, pg. 1015
EMERGE 180 INC.; *U.S. Private*, pg. 1380
EMIRATES NBD ASSET MANAGEMENT LTD—See Emirates NBD PJSC; *Int'l*, pg. 2382
EMPOWEREDBENEFITS, LLC—See Aflac Incorporated; *U.S. Public*, pg. 57
ENCOMPASS LATIN AMERICA—See Encompass Digital Media; *U.S. Private*, pg. 1390
ENDRESS+HAUSER CONSULT AG—See Endress+Hauser (International) Holding AG; *Int'l*, pg. 2407
ENDRESS+HAUSER D.O.O.—See Endress+Hauser (International) Holding AG; *Int'l*, pg. 2407
ENERGETICS INCORPORATED-ARLINGTON—See TPG Capital, L.P.; *U.S. Private*, pg. 2176
ENERGY ENTERPRISE SOLUTIONS, LLC—See 1 Source Consulting, Inc.; *U.S. Private*, pg. 1
ENERGYIQ LLC—See Thoma Bravo, L.P.; *U.S. Private*, pg. 4152
ENERGY TRANSFER DATA CENTER, LLC—See Energy Transfer LP; *U.S. Public*, pg. 763
ENERWISE GLOBAL TECHNOLOGIES, INC.—See LS Power Development, LLC; *U.S. Private*, pg. 2508
ENGIE INSIGHT SERVICES, INC.—See Avista Corporation; *U.S. Public*, pg. 249
ENHERENT CORP.—See enherent Corp.; *U.S. Public*, pg. 768
EN-JAPAN INC.; *Int'l*, pg. 2395
ENTARA CORPORATION; *U.S. Private*, pg. 1402
THE ENTERPRISE STRATEGY GROUP, INC.—See TechTarget, Inc.; *U.S. Public*, pg. 1989
ENVIRONMENTAL GOVERNANCE LTD—See Jones Lang LaSalle Incorporated; *U.S. Public*, pg. 1203
ENVIRONMENTAL PARTNERS, INC.—See TRC Companies, Inc.; *U.S. Private*, pg. 4215
E.ON BAYERN WARME 1. BETEILIGUNGS-GMBH—See E.ON SE; *Int'l*, pg. 2252
E.ON IT SVERIGE AB—See E.ON SE; *Int'l*, pg. 2254
E.ON IT UK LIMITED—See E.ON SE; *Int'l*, pg. 2254
E.ON UK ENERGY SOLUTIONS LIMITED—See E.ON SE; *Int'l*, pg. 2256
E.ON VARMEKRAFT SVERIGE AB—See E.ON SE; *Int'l*, pg. 2255
E.ON ZWANZIGSTE VERWALTUNGS GMBH—See E.ON SE; *Int'l*, pg. 2256
EPE, INC—See Enstar Group Limited; *Int'l*, pg. 2448
EPURON PTY LTD—See Kawa Capital Management, Inc.; *U.S. Private*, pg. 2266
EQECAT, INC.—See American Bureau of Shipping; *U.S. Private*, pg. 226
EQUITY METHODS, LLC—See Bank of America Corporation; *U.S. Public*, pg. 272
ERICPOL SP. Z O.O.; *Int'l*, pg. 2493
ERP ANALYSTS, INC.; *U.S. Private*, pg. 1423
ERP TECH S.P.A.—See BT Group plc; *Int'l*, pg. 1203
ESCO MARGINALEN AB; *Int'l*, pg. 2502
ESI INTERNATIONAL, INC.—See Providence Equity Partners L.L.C.; *U.S. Private*, pg. 3292
ETERA CONSULTING LLC—See Quad-C Management, Inc.; *U.S. Private*, pg. 3315
ETERNAL ASIA SUPPLY CHAIN MANAGEMENT LTD.; *Int'l*, pg. 2520
THE ETICA GROUP INC.; *U.S. Private*, pg. 4027
EUCONUS FLUGZEUGLEASINGGESELLSCHAFT MBH—See Air Berlin PLC & Co. Luftverkehrs KG; *Int'l*, pg. 236
EULER HERMES MANAGEMENT UK LIMITED—See Allianz SE; *Int'l*, pg. 352
EUROCONSULTANTS S.A.; *Int'l*, pg. 2534
EUROFINS 2. VERWALTUNGSGESELLSCHAFT MBH—See Eurofins Scientific S.E.; *Int'l*, pg. 2536
EUROFINS BIOSCIENCES CERVAC CONSULTING—See Eurofins Scientific S.E.; *Int'l*, pg. 2542
EUROFINS CONSULT GMBH—See Eurofins Scientific S.E.; *Int'l*, pg. 2539
EUROFINS-GAB GMBH—See Eurofins Scientific S.E.; *Int'l*, pg. 2550
EUROFINS LEM SAS—See Eurofins Scientific S.E.; *Int'l*, pg. 2543
EUROFINS NSC DENMARK A/S—See Eurofins Scientific S.E.; *Int'l*, pg. 2546
EUROFINS SCIENTIFIC JAPAN K.K.—See Eurofins Scientific S.E.; *Int'l*, pg. 2548
EUROGRAFICA SYSTEMPLANUNGS-GMBH—See Allianz SE; *Int'l*, pg. 352
EVENTIM SPORTS CONSULTING GMBH—See CTS Eventim AG & Co. KGAA; *Int'l*, pg. 1872
EVENTPRO STRATEGIES, LLC; *U.S. Private*, pg. 1437
EVERGLADES TECHNOLOGIES; *U.S. Private*, pg. 1438
EVERYSPORT.NET, INC.; *U.S. Private*, pg. 1441
EVOKE RESEARCH & CONSULTING LLC; *U.S. Private*, pg. 1442
EVOLUSYS SA—See Bechtle AG; *Int'l*, pg. 938

EVOLVE ANALYTICS LIMITED—See Gentrack Group Limited; *Int'l*, pg. 2929
EWA INFORMATION AND INFRASTRUCTURE TECHNOLOGIES, INC.—See Sagewind Capital LLC; *U.S. Private*, pg. 3528
EXECUS SPA; *Int'l*, pg. 2580
EXECUTIVE MANAGEMENT ASSOCIATES, INC.; *U.S. Private*, pg. 1447
EXHIBITION CONSULTANTS LTD.—See Angus Montgomery Ltd.; *Int'l*, pg. 463
EXPERIENT—See The Riverside Company; *U.S. Private*, pg. 4108
EXPONENT, INC - MENLO PARK—See Exponent, Inc.; *U.S. Public*, pg. 812
EYEFINITY, INC.—See Vision Service Plan; *U.S. Private*, pg. 4391
EZH-SEON B.V.—See E.ON SE; *Int'l*, pg. 2257
EZI GMBH; *Int'l*, pg. 2594
FAITH ROOT RECRUITMENT VIETNAM JOINT STOCK COMPANY—See Bain Capital, LP; *U.S. Private*, pg. 434
FAMILY OFFICE DER FRANKFURTER BANKGESELLSCHAFT AG—See Helaba Landesbank Hessen-Thuringen; *Int'l*, pg. 3327
FANUC THAI LIMITED—See FANUC Corporation; *Int'l*, pg. 2614
FARO RECRUITMENT (CHINA) CO., LTD.—See Bain Capital, LP; *U.S. Private*, pg. 434
FAXXON LEGAL INFORMATION SERVICES, INC.—See First American Financial Corporation; *U.S. Public*, pg. 836
FEDEX SUPPLYCHAIN SYSTEMS, INC.—See FedEx Corporation; *U.S. Public*, pg. 828
FIDUCIAN BUSINESS SERVICES PTY. LTD.—See Fiducian Group Limited; *Int'l*, pg. 2655
FINANCIAL MANAGEMENT SOLUTIONS, INC.—See Hellman & Friedman LLC; *U.S. Private*, pg. 1910
FINANZA.TECH S.P.A. SB; *Int'l*, pg. 2669
FINELINE TECHNOLOGIES, INC.—See Summit Partners, L.P.; *U.S. Private*, pg. 3855
FIRMDECISIONS ASJP GERMANY GMBH—See Ebiquity plc; *Int'l*, pg. 2285
FIRST ADVANTAGE TAX CONSULTING SERVICES, LLC—See Silver Lake Group, LLC; *U.S. Private*, pg. 3655
FIRST ANNAPOLIS CONSULTING, INC.—See Accenture plc; *Int'l*, pg. 86
FIRST EAGLE MANAGEMENT CORP.; *U.S. Private*, pg. 1517
FIRST FINANCIAL MANAGEMENT CONSULTING CO., LTD.—See First Financial Holding Co., Ltd.; *Int'l*, pg. 2683
FIRSTSERVICE RESIDENTIAL, NEVADA, LLC—See FirstService Corporation; *Int'l*, pg. 2691
FISCHER CONSULTING GMBH—See fischerwerke GmbH & Co. KG; *Int'l*, pg. 2692
FIVE NINES TECHNOLOGY GROUP; *U.S. Private*, pg. 1537
FLEET TEAM, INC.; *U.S. Private*, pg. 1542
FM ENGINEERING CONSULTING (SHANGHAI) CO. LTD—See Factory Mutual Insurance Company; *U.S. Private*, pg. 1460
FMI CORPORATION; *U.S. Private*, pg. 1554
THE FOCIS GROUP LLC—See The Reserves Network Inc.; *U.S. Private*, pg. 4105
FOLEY TIMBER & LAND COMPANY, LP; *U.S. Private*, pg. 1558
FOOTHILLS CONSULTING GROUP, INC.—See Stone Point Capital LLC; *U.S. Private*, pg. 3823
FORVAL REALSTRAIGHT INC.; *Int'l*, pg. 2745
FOS CO., LTD.—See Bain Capital, LP; *U.S. Private*, pg. 434
FOUR TWENTY SEVEN, INC.—See Moody's Corporation; *U.S. Public*, pg. 1467
FRANKLIN COVEY (SHENZHEN) LTD.—See Franklin Covey Company; *U.S. Public*, pg. 877
FRANNET LLC; *U.S. Private*, pg. 1598
FRASERS HOSPITALITY MANAGEMENT PTE LTD—See Frasers Property Limited; *Int'l*, pg. 2766
THE FRAYMAN GROUP, INC.—See IntApp, Inc.; *U.S. Public*, pg. 1134
FREDERICK P CLARK ASSOCIATES, INC.—See Hardesty & Hanover, LLC; *U.S. Private*, pg. 1863
FRONTIER MANAGEMENT INC.; *U.S. Private*, pg. 2795
FRONTIER MANAGEMENT (SHANGHAI) INC.—See Frontier Management Inc.; *Int'l*, pg. 2795
FSP ELDRIDGE GREEN LIMITED PARTNERSHIP—See Franklin Street Properties Corp.; *U.S. Public*, pg. 883
FSP GREENWOOD PLAZA CORP.—See Franklin Street Properties Corp.; *U.S. Public*, pg. 883
FUJISANKEI COMMUNICATIONS INTERNATIONAL, INC. - LOS ANGELES—See Fuji Media Holdings, Inc.; *Int'l*, pg. 2814
FUNFZEHNTE BASF PROJEKTENTWICKLUNGSGESELLSCHAFT MBH—See BASF SE; *Int'l*, pg. 883
FURUNO EUROPE BV—See Furuno Electric Co., Ltd.; *Int'l*, pg. 2848
FUSE PROJECT, LLC—See Bluefocus Intelligent Communications Group Co., Ltd.; *Int'l*, pg. 1071
FUTRON CORPORATION; *U.S. Private*, pg. 1626

541618 — OTHER MANAGEMENT CO...

GAFCON INC.; *U.S. Private*, pg. 1634
GAI CONSTRUCTION MONITORING SERVICES, INC.—See Comvest Group Holdings LLC; *U.S. Private*, pg. 1007.
GALI SERVICE INDUSTRIES, INC.; *U.S. Private*, pg. 1637
GAMECHANGER PRODUCTS LLC; *U.S. Private*, pg. 1640
GARDEN NETWORK, LTD.—See Densan System Co., Ltd.; *Int'l*, pg. 2028
GAZELLES INC.; *U.S. Private*, pg. 1652
GCA SAVVIAN CAPITAL LLC—See Houlihan Lokey, Inc.; *U.S. Public*, pg. 1055
GEBERIT INTERNATIONAL AG—See Geberit AG; *Int'l*, pg. 2904
GEBERIT VERWALTUNGS AG—See Geberit AG; *Int'l*, pg. 2905
GECI LTD—See GECI International SA; *Int'l*, pg. 2909
GEECHS, INC.; *Int'l*, pg. 2911
GEKE S.A; *Int'l*, pg. 2913
GENERALI CONSULTING SOLUTIONS LLC—See Assicurazioni Generali S.p.A.; *Int'l*, pg. 644
GENERAL PENSION PLANNING CORP.—See TWG Benefits, Inc.; *U.S. Private*, pg. 4264
GENESIS CONSULTING PARTNERS, LLC.; *U.S. Private*, pg. 1669
GENEX SERVICES OF CANADA, INC.—See Stone Point Capital LLC; *U.S. Private*, pg. 3823
GENSPRING FAMILY OFFICES, L.L.C.—See Truist Financial Corporation; *U.S. Public*, pg. 2199
GENTING MANAGEMENT AND CONSULTANCY SERVICES SDN BHD—See Genting Berhad; *Int'l*, pg. 2928
THE GEORGETOWN COMPANY, LLC; *U.S. Private*, pg. 4032
GEORGE W. AUCH COMPANY; *U.S. Private*, pg. 1683
GEORG FISCHER VERWALTUNGS GMBH—See Georg Fischer AG; *Int'l*, pg. 2937
GEOTEXT TRANSLATIONS, INC.—See Geotext Translations, Inc.; *U.S. Private*, pg. 1685
GESTALT, LLC—See Accenture plc; *Int'l*, pg. 86
GE-TE MEDIA AB; *Int'l*, pg. 2897
GEXEED CO., LTD.; *Int'l*, pg. 2955
GIBRALTAR IT, LLC; *U.S. Private*, pg. 1696
GIGGLE BROADBAND LIMITED—See Digital 9 Infrastructure Plc; *Int'l*, pg. 2120
GIIR GROUP LG—See HS Ad Inc.; *Int'l*, pg. 3502
GIVEANYTHING.COM, INC.—See The Riverside Company; *U.S. Private*, pg. 4108
GLOBAL BUSINESS CONSULTING SERVICES, INC.; *U.S. Private*, pg. 1712
GLOBAL COMMUNICATIONS GROUP, INC.; *U.S. Private*, pg. 1712
GLOBALDATA TRADING (SHANGHAI) CO., LIMITED—See GlobalData Plc; *Int'l*, pg. 3003
GLOBAL PORTFOY YONETIMI A.S—See Global Yatirim Holding A.S.; *Int'l*, pg. 3002
GLOBAL STRATEGIES, INCORPORATED; *U.S. Private*, pg. 1718
GOLD STANDARD RESOURCES, INC.—See The Ensign Group, Inc.; *U.S. Public*, pg. 2071
THE GORDIAN GROUP, INC.—See Fortive Corporation; *U.S. Public*, pg. 872
GOTUWIRED, INC.; *U.S. Private*, pg. 1745
GPSC UK LIMITED—See General Motors Company; *U.S. Public*, pg. 928
GRACEKENNEDY REMITTANCE SERVICES LIMITED—See GraceKennedy Limited; *Int'l*, pg. 3049
GRAND CITY PROPERTIES SA; *Int'l*, pg. 3054
GRAND HOTEL GROUP LIMITED—See Hang Lung Group Limited; *Int'l*, pg. 3245
GRASP SYSTEMS INTERNATIONAL INC.—See Koch Industries, Inc.; *U.S. Private*, pg. 2330
GRAY CONSULTING INC.—See Thoma Bravo, L.P.; *U.S. Private*, pg. 4148
GREGG COMMUNICATIONS SYSTEMS, INC.—See APLJ Capital Management LLC; *U.S. Private*, pg. 294
GREYSTONE HEALTHCARE MANAGEMENT CORP.; *U.S. Private*, pg. 1786
GROVE RESOURCE SOLUTIONS INCORPORATED—See DLH Holdings Corp.; *U.S. Public*, pg. 670
GUARDIAN GROUP, INC.—See YOUNG & Associates; *U.S. Private*, pg. 4592
THE GURNET GROUP LLC—See Praecipio Consulting LLC; *U.S. Private*, pg. 3241
H20 CREATIVE—See H2O Creative; *Int'l*, pg. 3200
THE HACKETT GROUP AUSTRALIA PTY. LTD.—See The Hackett Group, Inc.; *U.S. Public*, pg. 2086
THE HACKETT GROUP BV—See The Hackett Group, Inc.; *U.S. Public*, pg. 2086
HANG LUNG PROJECT MANAGEMENT LIMITED—See Hang Lung Group Limited; *Int'l*, pg. 3245
HANSON ISLAND MANAGEMENT LIMITED—See Heidelberg Materials AG; *Int'l*, pg. 3312
HANSON PROFESSIONAL SERVICES, INC.; *U.S. Private*, pg. 1856
HARBOUR CONTRACTORS, INC.; *U.S. Private*, pg. 1859
HARMONIC LIMITED—See KBR, Inc.; *U.S. Public*, pg. 1215
HARTE HANKS CONSULTING—See Harte Hanks, Inc.; *U.S. Public*, pg. 986

HARVEY NASH NV—See DBAY Advisors Limited; *Int'l*, pg. 1987
HCFS, INC.—See ABRY Partners, LLC; *U.S. Private*, pg. 41
HCL AMERICA, INC.—See HCL Technologies Ltd.; *Int'l*, pg. 3298
HEALTH CARE FUTURES, L.P.—See Northlane Capital Partners, LLC; *U.S. Private*, pg. 2956
HEALTHCARE RISK SPECIALISTS, LLC—See Captive Resources, LLC; *U.S. Private*, pg. 747
HEALTH DIRECTIONS INC.; *U.S. Private*, pg. 1893
HEALTH FACILITY SOLUTIONS CO., (HFS); *U.S. Private*, pg. 1893
HEALTH MANAGEMENT ASSOCIATES, INC.; *U.S. Private*, pg. 1893
HEALTH RESEARCH INC.; *U.S. Private*, pg. 1894
HEATH CONSULTANTS—See Heath Consultants Incorporated; *U.S. Private*, pg. 1902
HEDERA CONSULTING BVBA—See Cognizant Technology Solutions Corporation; *U.S. Public*, pg. 524
HELIS SAS—See Econocom Group SA; *Int'l*, pg. 2298
HERMANN SEIPPEL-UNTERSTUTZUNGSEINRICHTUNG GMBH—See E.ON SE; *Int'l*, pg. 2258
HERMES S.L.—See Assicurazioni Generali S.p.A.; *Int'l*, pg. 644
HERNANDEZ CONSULTING; *U.S. Private*, pg. 1925
HGS USA—See Hinduja Global Solutions Ltd.; *Int'l*, pg. 3398
HILL & ASSOCIATES LIMITED—See Allied Universal Manager LLC; *U.S. Private*, pg. 190
HILL INTERNATIONAL BH DO.O—See Global Infrastructure Solutions, Inc.; *U.S. Private*, pg. 1715
HILL INTERNATIONAL (BUCHAREST) S.R.L.—See Global Infrastructure Solutions, Inc.; *U.S. Private*, pg. 1715
HILL INTERNATIONAL DE MEXICO, S.A. DE C.V.—See Global Infrastructure Solutions, Inc.; *U.S. Private*, pg. 1715
HILL INTERNATIONAL (HELLAS) S.A.—See Global Infrastructure Solutions, Inc.; *U.S. Private*, pg. 1715
HILL INTERNATIONAL INC.-CALIFORNIA—See Global Infrastructure Solutions, Inc.; *U.S. Private*, pg. 1715
HILL INTERNATIONAL INC.-FLORIDA—See Global Infrastructure Solutions, Inc.; *U.S. Private*, pg. 1715
HILL INTERNATIONAL INC.-NEW YORK—See Global Infrastructure Solutions, Inc.; *U.S. Private*, pg. 1715
HILL INTERNATIONAL (SPAIN) S.A.—See Global Infrastructure Solutions, Inc.; *U.S. Private*, pg. 1715
HINDA, INC.; *U.S. Private*, pg. 1948
HIQ WISE A/S—See HiQ International AB; *Int'l*, pg. 3402
HIRE VELOCITY, LLC; *U.S. Private*, pg. 1950
HITACHI CONSULTING CORPORATION—See Hitachi, Ltd.; *Int'l*, pg. 3413
HMP PROPERTIES, INC.—See JPMorgan Chase & Co.; *U.S. Public*, pg. 1207
HOBAN RECRUITMENT PTY. LTD.—See Bain Capital, LP; *U.S. Private*, pg. 435
HOLLISTER & BLACKSMITH, INC.—See American Cannabis Company, Inc.; *U.S. Public*, pg. 98
HOME & CAPITAL TRUST LIMITED—See Grainger plc; *Int'l*, pg. 3052
HOMEX CENTRAL MARCARIA, S.A. DE C.V.—See Desarrolladora Homex, S.A. de C.V.; *Int'l*, pg. 2044
HONG KONG I.V.A. CONSULTANTS LIMITED—See Credit Intelligence Limited; *Int'l*, pg. 1835
HORIZON INVESTMENTS, LLC; *U.S. Private*, pg. 1981
HQ DIRECT AB—See HQ AB; *Int'l*, pg. 3501
HS BRANDS INTERNATIONAL; *U.S. Private*, pg. 1998
HUAAN ASSET MANAGEMENT (HONG KONG) LIMITED—See Guotai Junan Securities Co., Ltd.; *Int'l*, pg. 3187
HUDSON VALLEY ECONOMIC DEVELOPMENT CORPORATION; *U.S. Private*, pg. 2002
HUMAN HOLDINGS CO., LTD.; *Int'l*, pg. 3529
HUMAN RESOCIA CO., LTD.—See Human Holdings Co., Ltd.; *Int'l*, pg. 3529
HUMAN RESOURCE TRAINING, INC.—See ATAR Capital, LLC; *U.S. Private*, pg. 364
HUNT CONSTRUCTION GROUP, INC. - SAN FRANCISCO—See AECOM; *U.S. Public*, pg. 51
HYDRO CONSULTING & MAINTENANCE SERVICES, INC.; *U.S. Private*, pg. 2017
HYUNDAI INVESTMENTS CO., LTD.—See Hyundai Marine & Fire Insurance Co., Ltd.; *Int'l*, pg. 3558
IBS&D CORP.; *U.S. Private*, pg. 2028
ICNET CO., LTD.—See BELLUNA CO. LTD.; *Int'l*, pg. 967
ICOR PARTNERS, LLC; *U.S. Private*, pg. 2033
ICRA MANAGEMENT CONSULTING SERVICES LIMITED—See Moody's Corporation; *U.S. Public*, pg. 1467
IDC ISRAEL—See China Oceanwide Holdings Group Co., Ltd.; *Int'l*, pg. 1537
IDC ISRAEL—See IDG Capital; *Int'l*, pg. 3593
IDC UK LTD.—See China Oceanwide Holdings Group Co., Ltd.; *Int'l*, pg. 1537
IDC UK LTD.—See IDG Capital; *Int'l*, pg. 3594
IDFC PENSION FUND MANAGEMENT COMPANY LIMITED—See IDFC Limited; *Int'l*, pg. 3593
IDFC PROJECTS LIMITED—See IDFC Limited; *Int'l*, pg. 3593
IDOX GERMANY GMBH—See IDOX PLC; *Int'l*, pg. 3595

CORPORATE AFFILIATIONS

IFS ITALIA S.R.L.—See EQT AB; *Int'l*, pg. 2477
I&I SOFTWARE, INC.; *U.S. Private*, pg. 2026
IJET INTERNATIONAL, INC.; *U.S. Private*, pg. 2040
IJM MANAGEMENT SERVICES SDN BHD—See IJM Corporation Berhad; *Int'l*, pg. 3609
IKASYSTEMS CORPORATION; *U.S. Private*, pg. 2040
IMA KILIAN VERWALTUNGS GMBH—See I.M.A. Industria Macchine Automatiche S.p.A.; *Int'l*, pg. 3565
IMA OF TOPEKA INC.—See IMA Financial Group, Inc.; *U.S. Private*, pg. 2043
IMMIXGROUP, INC.—See Arrow Electronics, Inc.; *U.S. Public*, pg. 200
IMPACT ADVISORS LLC; *U.S. Private*, pg. 2048
IMPACT MAKERS, INC.; *U.S. Private*, pg. 2048
IMS TECHNOLOGY SERVICES; *U.S. Private*, pg. 2051
INDEX CONSULTANTS PTY. LTD.—See Bain Capital, LP; *U.S. Private*, pg. 435
INERGI LP—See Capgemini SE; *Int'l*, pg. 1306
INFOARMOR, INC.—See The Allstate Corporation; *U.S. Public*, pg. 2033
INFOMATICS, INC; *U.S. Private*, pg. 2072
INFORMATION EXPERTS, INC.; *U.S. Private*, pg. 2073
INFORMATION SERVICES GROUP DENMARK APS—See Information Services Group, Inc.; *U.S. Public*, pg. 1118
INFORMATION SERVICES GROUP GERMANY GMBH—See Information Services Group, Inc.; *U.S. Public*, pg. 1118
INFORMATION SERVICES GROUP, INC.; *U.S. Public*, pg. 1117
INFORMATION SERVICES GROUP NETHERLANDS B.V.—See Information Services Group, Inc.; *U.S. Public*, pg. 1118
INFORMATION SERVICES GROUP OY—See Information Services Group, Inc.; *U.S. Public*, pg. 1118
INFORMATION SERVICES GROUP SA—See Information Services Group, Inc.; *U.S. Public*, pg. 1118
INFORMATION SERVICES GROUP SWEDEN AB—See Information Services Group, Inc.; *U.S. Public*, pg. 1118
INFORMATION SERVICES GROUP SWITZERLAND GMBH—See Information Services Group, Inc.; *U.S. Public*, pg. 1118
INFORMED FAMILY FINANCIAL SERVICES, INC.; *U.S. Private*, pg. 2073
INGENUITY ASSOCIATES, LLC; *U.S. Private*, pg. 2075
INNOVAZIONE ITALIA S.P.A.—See Agenzia Nazionale per l'Attrazione degli Investimenti e lo Sviluppo d'Impresa SpA; *Int'l*, pg. 206
INOVIS EMPLOYMENT SERVICE; *U.S. Private*, pg. 2084
INSTITUTE FOR PROFESSIONAL DEVELOPMENT—See Apollo Global Management, Inc.; *U.S. Public*, pg. 146
INSTITUTE FOR PROFESSIONAL DEVELOPMENT—See The Vistria Group, LP; *U.S. Private*, pg. 4131
INSURANCE SERVICES OFFICE, LTD.—See Verisk Analytics, Inc.; *U.S. Public*, pg. 2283
THE INTEGRAL BUILDING GROUP LLC—See The Integral Group LLC; *U.S. Private*, pg. 4057
INTEGRATED ACCESS CORP.; *U.S. Private*, pg. 2098
INTEGRATED MEDIA TECHNOLOGIES, INC.; *U.S. Private*, pg. 2100
INTEGRATED PROJECT MANAGEMENT CO., INC.—See Integrated Project Management Company, Inc.; *U.S. Private*, pg. 2100
INTEGRATED PROJECT MANAGEMENT CO., INC.—See Integrated Project Management Company, Inc.; *U.S. Private*, pg. 2100
INTEGRATED PROJECT MANAGEMENT CO., INC.—See Integrated Project Management Company, Inc.; *U.S. Private*, pg. 2101
INTEGRATED PROJECT MANAGEMENT COMPANY, INC.; *U.S. Private*, pg. 2100
INTEGRO, INC.—See Silver Oak Services Partners, LLC; *U.S. Private*, pg. 3661
INTERCOM CONSULTING & FEDERAL SYSTEMS CORPORATION—See AE Industrial Partners, LP; *U.S. Private*, pg. 111
INTERNET NAMES WORDWIDE ESPANA SL—See Corporation Service Company; *U.S. Private*, pg. 1057
INTERSECT GROUP; *U.S. Private*, pg. 2123
INTUEOR CONSULTING INC.; *U.S. Private*, pg. 2130
INTUITIVE RESEARCH & TECHNOLOGY CORPORATION; *U.S. Private*, pg. 2130
INVESTMENT MANAGEMENT OF VIRGINIA, LLC.—See Pinnacle Associates, Ltd.; *U.S. Private*, pg. 3184
INVIGORS EMEA LLP—See The Alta Group, LLC; *U.S. Private*, pg. 3984
IPL RESEARCH LIMITED—See Computer & Technologies Holdings Limited; *Int'l*, pg. 1758
IQ RESEARCH LIMITED—See 1Spatial Plc; *Int'l*, pg. 3
ITELLIGENCE SLOVAKIA, S.R.O.—See Silver Lake Group, LLC; *U.S. Private*, pg. 3658
IT MANAGEMENT COMPANY LIMITED—See Bliss Intelligence Public Company Limited; *Int'l*, pg. 1064
ITRADENETWORK, INC.—See Roper Technologies, Inc.; *U.S. Public*, pg. 1814
ITRADENETWORK, LTD.—See Roper Technologies, Inc.; *U.S. Public*, pg. 1814
ITRON MANAGEMENT SERVICES IRELAND, LIMITED—See Itron, Inc.; *U.S. Public*, pg. 1176

N.A.I.C.S. INDEX

541618 — OTHER MANAGEMENT CO...

IWP INTERNATIONAL WEST PICTURES GMBH & CO. ERSTE PRODUKTIONS KG—See Commerzbank AG; *Int'l*, pg. 1718
IXONOS TECHNOLOGY CONSULTING LTD—See Digitalist Group Oyj; *Int'l*, pg. 2123
JABIAN; *U.S. Private*, pg. 2173
THE JACKSON GROUP INC.—See Ares Management Corporation; *U.S. Public*, pg. 190
THE JACKSON GROUP INC.—See Leonard Green & Partners, L.P.; *U.S. Private*, pg. 2427
JAKOB MARKETING PARTNERS; *U.S. Private*, pg. 2182
JAWOOD; *U.S. Private*, pg. 2191
JBW GROUP LIMITED—See Bain Capital, LP; *U.S. Private*, pg. 434
J. CHRISTOF ROMANIA S.R.L.—See Christof Holding AG; *Int'l*, pg. 1587
J. GOWDY CONSULTING, LLC—See Sustainserv, Inc.; *U.S. Private*, pg. 3886
J & J INDUSTRIES INC.; *U.S. Private*, pg. 2152
JLL TECHNOLOGY SOLUTIONS—See Jones Lang LaSalle Incorporated; *U.S. Public*, pg. 1202
JMM MANAGEMENT GROUP, LLC—See Titan Cloud Software, LLC; *U.S. Private*, pg. 4177
JOHN M. OLSON CORPORATION; *U.S. Private*, pg. 2223
JOHNSON & BLANTON; *U.S. Private*, pg. 2226
JONES LANG LASALLE GLOBAL SERVICES - RR, INC.—See Jones Lang LaSalle Incorporated; *U.S. Public*, pg. 1203
JPW CONSULTING; *U.S. Private*, pg. 2239
J RUSSELL & ASSOCIATES LLC; *U.S. Private*, pg. 2153
J.S. HELD LLC—See Kelso & Company, L.P.; *U.S. Private*, pg. 2278
JVKELLYGROUP, INC.; *U.S. Private*, pg. 2246
KAMEDDATA.COM, INC; *U.S. Private*, pg. 2258
KANTAR RETAIL—See Bain Capital, LP; *U.S. Private*, pg. 447
KASAMBA, INC.—See LivePerson, Inc.; *U.S. Public*, pg. 1332
KAUFMAN COMPANY INC.; *U.S. Private*, pg. 2265
KEEN INFOTEK INC.; *U.S. Private*, pg. 2272
KELPEN RESOURCES SDN BHD (KRSB)—See Ewein Berhad; *Int'l*, pg. 2576
KEMP TECHNOLOGIES INC.—See Progress Software Corporation; *U.S. Public*, pg. 1725
THE KENJYA GROUP, INC.; *U.S. Private*, pg. 4065
KENSINGTON CAPITAL ADVISORS, LLC—See Jones Lang LaSalle Incorporated; *U.S. Public*, pg. 1205
KEPNER-TREGOE AUSTRALASIA PTY LTD—See Kepner-Tregoe, Inc.; *U.S. Private*, pg. 2290
KEPNER-TREGOE DEUTSCHLAND, LLC—See Kepner-Tregoe, Inc.; *U.S. Private*, pg. 2290
KEPNER-TREGOE JAPAN, LLC—See Kepner-Tregoe, Inc.; *U.S. Private*, pg. 2290
KEPNER-TREGOE LTD.—See Kepner-Tregoe, Inc.; *U.S. Private*, pg. 2290
KEPNER-TREGOE (MALAYSIA) SDN. BHD.—See Kepner-Tregoe, Inc.; *U.S. Private*, pg. 2290
KEPNER-TREGOE SARL—See Kepner-Tregoe, Inc.; *U.S. Private*, pg. 2290
KEPNER-TREGOE, SA—See Kepner-Tregoe, Inc.; *U.S. Private*, pg. 2290
KEPNER-TREGOE SOUTHEAST ASIA LIMITED.—See Kepner-Tregoe, Inc.; *U.S. Private*, pg. 2290
KEPNER-TREGOE SOUTHEAST ASIA LTD—See Kepner-Tregoe, Inc.; *U.S. Private*, pg. 2290
KEPNER-TREGOE THAILAND, LLC—See Kepner-Tregoe, Inc.; *U.S. Private*, pg. 2290
KEYGENT LLC; *U.S. Private*, pg. 2294
KEYOT, LLC—See 3 Bridge Solutions LLC; *U.S. Private*, pg. 7
KEYSTONE CONSULTING ENGINEERS, INC.; *U.S. Private*, pg. 2295
KITCHELL CEM, INC.—See Kitchell Corporation; *U.S. Private*, pg. 2316
KLEINFELDER EAST, INC.—See Goldberg Lindsay & Co., LLC; *U.S. Private*, pg. 1729
KNIGHT POINT SYSTEMS, LLC—See Veritas Capital Fund Management, LLC; *U.S. Private*, pg. 4364
KOCH BUSINESS SOLUTIONS, LP.—See Koch Industries, Inc.; *U.S. Private*, pg. 2331
KOCHMAN CONSULTANTS LTD—See TA Associates, Inc.; *U.S. Private*, pg. 3918
KONEXUS CONSULTING GROUP GMBH—See Capgemini SE; *Int'l*, pg. 1307
KPI DIRECT LLC; *U.S. Private*, pg. 2346
KUZULUK KAPLICA INSAAT TURIZM SAGLIK VE PETROL URUNLERI TIC. A.S—See Ihlas Holding A.S.; *Int'l*, pg. 3606
KYODO ENGINEERING CORPORATION—See Bain Capital, LP; *U.S. Private*, pg. 434
KYPROU MUTUAL FUND MANAGEMENT COMPANY S.A.—See Bank of Cyprus Holdings Public Limited Company; *Int'l*, pg. 842
KYRA SOLUTIONS INC.; *U.S. Private*, pg. 2360
LABAT-ANDERSON INC.—See Corporate Risk Holdings LLC; *U.S. Private*, pg. 1056
LAC GROUP; *U.S. Private*, pg. 2371
LAFRANCE ASSOCIATES, LLC; *U.S. Private*, pg. 2373

LARIX AS—See Alten S.A.; *Int'l*, pg. 390
LARIX SWEDEN AB—See Alten S.A.; *Int'l*, pg. 390
LARRY J. OVERTON & ASSOCIATES INC.; *U.S. Private*, pg. 2393
LATHIAN SYSTEMS, INC.—See D&R Lathian LLC; *U.S. Private*, pg. 1138
LAZORPOINT, LLC; *U.S. Private*, pg. 2403
LCT GLOBAL RESOURCES, INC.; *U.S. Private*, pg. 2404
LEE HECHT HARRISON HK LIMITED—See Adecco Group AG; *Int'l*, pg. 141
LEE HECHT HARRISON—See Adecco Group AG; *Int'l*, pg. 138
LEE & MAN MANAGEMENT CO. LTD.—See Best Food Holding Company Limited; *Int'l*, pg. 999
LEGACY RESOURCE CORPORATION; *U.S. Private*, pg. 2417
LEGENDS HOSPITALITY, LLC—See Sixth Street Partners LLC; *U.S. Private*, pg. 3677
THE LESS PACKAGING COMPANY LTD—See DS Smith Plc; *Int'l*, pg. 2208
THE LEWIN GROUP—See UnitedHealth Group Incorporated; *U.S. Public*, pg. 2248
LIFECARE, INC.—See IAC Inc.; *U.S. Public*, pg. 1082
LIFEDOJO INC.—See Ontrak, Inc.; *U.S. Public*, pg. 1605
LIGHTHOUSE BUSINESS INFORMATION SOLUTIONS, LLC—See The Riverside Company; *U.S. Private*, pg. 4109
LINMARK (HK) LIMITED—See Daohe Global Group Limited; *Int'l*, pg. 1970
LITMUS SOLUTIONS PTY. LTD.—See HFBG Holding B.V.; *Int'l*, pg. 3375
LOGICAL VENTURES INC.; *U.S. Private*, pg. 2481
LONDON & CAPITAL GROUP LTD.—See Lovell Minnick Partners LLC; *U.S. Private*, pg. 2503
LONGFORD & COMPANY INC.—See Great Mill Rock LLC; *U.S. Private*, pg. 1766
LOUIS P. CIMINELLI CONSTRUCTION CO. INC.—See LPCiminelli Inc.; *U.S. Private*, pg. 2507
LOVETT, SILVERMAN CONSTRUCTION CONSULTANTS, INC.—See Kelso & Company, L.P.; *U.S. Private*, pg. 2278
LRN CORPORATION; *U.S. Private*, pg. 2508
LSE SPACE GMBH—See GomSpace Group AB; *Int'l*, pg. 3037
LUMENDATA, INC.; *U.S. Private*, pg. 2514
LYONS CONSULTING GROUP INC.—See Capgemini SE; *Int'l*, pg. 1307
MACH ENERGY—See Gainline Capital Partners LP; *U.S. Private*, pg. 1635
MAESTRO TECHNOLOGIES, INC.; *U.S. Private*, pg. 2545
MAGICAL CRUISE COMPANY, LIMITED—See The Walt Disney Company; *U.S. Public*, pg. 2139
MAKRO TECHNOLGIES, INC.; *U.S. Private*, pg. 2556
MALAYSIAN VENTURES MANAGEMENT INCORPORATED SDN BHD—See AMMB Holdings Berhad; *Int'l*, pg. 429
MANAGEMENT DIAGNOSTICS LIMITED—See The Arena Group Holdings, Inc; *U.S. Public*, pg. 2035
MANAGEMENT SCIENCES FOR HEALTH, INC.; *U.S. Private*, pg. 2561
MANAGEMENT SYSTEMS INTERNATIONAL INC.—See Tetra Tech, Inc.; *U.S. Public*, pg. 2023
MANHATTAN ASSOCIATES EUROPE B.V.—See Manhattan Associates, Inc.; *U.S. Public*, pg. 1356
MANHATTAN ASSOCIATES FRANCE SARL—See Manhattan Associates, Inc.; *U.S. Public*, pg. 1356
MANHATTAN ASSOCIATES LIMITED—See Manhattan Associates, Inc.; *U.S. Public*, pg. 1356
MANPOWERGROUP SOLUTIONS B.V.—See Manpower Group Inc.; *U.S. Public*, pg. 1360
MANPOWERGROUP UK LIMITED—See ManpowerGroup Inc.; *U.S. Public*, pg. 1361
MANPOWER SERVICES (TAIWAN) CO., LTD.—See ManpowerGroup Inc.; *U.S. Public*, pg. 1359
MANTRA DESIGN SDN. BHD.—See Berjaya Corporation Berhad; *Int'l*, pg. 984
MARATHON CONSULTING; *U.S. Private*, pg. 2570
MAREK LIEBERBERG KONZERTAGENTUR HOLDING GMBH—See CTS Eventim AG & Co. KGAA; *Int'l*, pg. 1873
THE MARKET CREATION GROUP, LLC; *U.S. Private*, pg. 4074
MARKET FORCE INFORMATION, INC.; *U.S. Private*, pg. 2579
MARKET METRICS, LLC—See FactSet Research Systems Inc.; *U.S. Public*, pg. 820
MARKETSPHERE CONSULTING, LLC; *U.S. Private*, pg. 2581
MARS & CO.; *U.S. Private*, pg. 2588
MARSHALL & STEVENS INC.; *U.S. Private*, pg. 2592
MARVIN F. POER & COMPANY; *U.S. Private*, pg. 2598
MAS ADVISORS, LLC; *U.S. Private*, pg. 2600
MATRIX RISK CONSULTANTS, INC.—See Equitable Holdings, Inc.; *U.S. Public*, pg. 790
MATT CONSTRUCTION CORPORATION; *U.S. Private*, pg. 2613
MAUI TACOS INTERNATIONAL, INC.—See Blimpie International, Inc.; *U.S. Private*, pg. 581

MAVEN WAVE PARTNERS, LLC—See Atos SE; *Int'l*, pg. 692
MAVERICK INFOTEC—See Bhoruka Aluminium Ltd.; *Int'l*, pg. 1015
THE MCCARRON GROUP; *U.S. Private*, pg. 4076
MCCLATCHY MANAGEMENT SERVICES, INC.—See Chatham Asset Management, LLC; *U.S. Public*, pg. 866
MCVEIGH ASSOCIATES LTD.—See InteleTravel.com; *U.S. Private*, pg. 2104
MDSTRATEGIES, INC.—See Aquiline Capital Partners LLC; *U.S. Private*, pg. 304
MEDIOLANUM INTERNATIONAL FUNDS LTD—See Banca Mediolanum S.p.A.; *Int'l*, pg. 815
MEDIREVV INC.; *U.S. Private*, pg. 2657
MEDISTAR, INC.; *U.S. Private*, pg. 2657
MEDSOURCE; *U.S. Private*, pg. 2658
MELIORCONSULTING SPA—See BPER BANCA S.p.A; *Int'l*, pg. 1132
MERCATOR ENERGY, LLC—See The Southern Company; *U.S. Public*, pg. 2131
MERCER (THAILAND) LTD.—See Marsh & McLennan Companies, Inc.; *U.S. Public*, pg. 1385
MERIT RESOURCES, INC.—See Iowa Network Services Inc.; *U.S. Private*, pg. 2135
META POWER INTERNATIONAL, INC.; *U.S. Public*, pg. 1427
METRONOME, INC.—See WAVE Technology Solutions Group; *U.S. Private*, pg. 4458
METRO PARKING (M) SDN. BHD.—See Damansara Realty Berhad; *Int'l*, pg. 1955
MGMTREE GMBH—See EnBW Energie Baden-Wurttemberg AG; *Int'l*, pg. 2400
MICROGEN (SOUTH AFRICA) LIMITED—See Aptitude Software Group Plc; *Int'l*, pg. 523
MID-STATE CONSULTANTS, INC.—See John Staurulakis, LLC; *U.S. Private*, pg. 2224
MI-GSO GMBH—See Alten S.A.; *Int'l*, pg. 390
MI-GSO SA—See Alten S.A.; *Int'l*, pg. 390
MILBRO, INC.—See Sycamore Partners Management, LP; *U.S. Private*, pg. 3897
MILLENNIUM BCP GESTAO DE ACTIVOS - SOCIEDADE GESTORA DE FUNDOS DE INVESTIMENTO, S.A.—See Banco Comercial Portugues, S.A.; *Int'l*, pg. 820
THE MILLENNIUM GROUP; *U.S. Private*, pg. 4079
MILLER-DAVIS COMPANY INC.; *U.S. Private*, pg. 2736
MILSAT SERVICES GMBH—See Airbus SE; *Int'l*, pg. 243
MMA ENERGY CAPITAL, LLC—See Fundamental Advisors LP; *U.S. Private*, pg. 1622
MM MAIN-MORTEL VERWALTUNGSGESELLSCHAFT MBH—See Heidelberg Materials AG; *Int'l*, pg. 3318
MOBILE COMMUNICATIONS CO., LTD.—See Bain Capital, LP; *U.S. Private*, pg. 434
MOBI WIRELESS MANAGEMENT, LLC—See Marlin Equity Partners, LLC; *U.S. Private*, pg. 2583
MODERN BIOMEDICAL SERVICES, INC.—See Cressey & Company, LP; *U.S. Private*, pg. 1095
MODERN BIOMEDICAL SERVICES, INC.—See Health Enterprise Partners LLC; *U.S. Private*, pg. 1893
MONARCH MANAGEMENT SERVICES, INC.—See UnitedHealth Group Incorporated; *U.S. Public*, pg. 2242
MOONLIGHT BPO; *U.S. Private*, pg. 2779
MORGAN BORSZCZ CONSULTING; *U.S. Private*, pg. 2783
MORTON CONSULTING LLC; *U.S. Private*, pg. 2792
MOSAIC TECHNOLOGIES GROUP, LLC; *U.S. Private*, pg. 2792
MPLUS TECHNOLOGY CO., LTD.—See Cipherlab Co., Ltd.; *Int'l*, pg. 1616
MSIGHTS INC.; *U.S. Private*, pg. 2807
MSX INTERNATIONAL, INC.—See Bain Capital, LP; *U.S. Private*, pg. 441
MTS (JAPAN) LTD.—See Amphenol Corporation; *U.S. Public*, pg. 131
MTS SYSTEMS (CHINA) LTD.—See Amphenol Corporation; *U.S. Public*, pg. 131
MTS SYSTEMS NORDEN AB—See Amphenol Corporation; *U.S. Public*, pg. 131
MTS SYSTEMS SA—See Amphenol Corporation; *U.S. Public*, pg. 131
MUNICIBID.COM LLC; *U.S. Private*, pg. 2813
MY DATA INTELLIGENCE INC.—See Dentsu Group Inc.; *Int'l*, pg. 2039
MYRIAD360, LLC; *U.S. Private*, pg. 2826
MZILIOS LLC—See Grupo MZ; *Int'l*, pg. 3133
NAKED NZ LIMITED—See Enero Group Limited; *Int'l*, pg. 2424
NATIONAL ASSET RECOVERY SERVICES; *U.S. Private*, pg. 2845
NATIONAL CHARITY SERVICES; *U.S. Private*, pg. 2850
NATIONAL QUALITY REVIEW, LLC—See Terminus Capital Partners, LLC; *U.S. Private*, pg. 3970
NATIONAL UTILITY SERVICE, INC.; *U.S. Private*, pg. 2864
NAVCOM TECHNOLOGY INC—See Deere & Company; *U.S. Public*, pg. 647
NAVEX GLOBAL, INC.—See BC Partners LLP; *Int'l*, pg. 925
NAVIGANT EUROPE LIMITED—See Bain Capital, LP; *U.S. Private*, pg. 432
NAVIGATE CORPORATION; *U.S. Private*, pg. 2873

541618 — OTHER MANAGEMENT CO...

NAZTEC INTERNATIONAL GROUP, LLC; *U.S. Private,* pg. 2874
NCM ASSOCIATES, INC.; *U.S. Private,* pg. 2876
NEBRASKA INTERACTIVE, LLC—See Tyler Technologies, Inc.; *U.S. Public,* pg. 2208
NELNET BUSINESS SOLUTIONS, INC.—See Nelnet, Inc.; *U.S. Public,* pg. 1504
NEOGOV; *U.S. Private,* pg. 2884
NEON CAPITAL LIMITED—See American Financial Group, Inc.; *U.S. Public,* pg. 103
NEOS LLC—See Clayton, Dubilier & Rice, LLC; *U.S. Private,* pg. 927
NERA ECONOMIC CONSULTING—See Marsh & McLennan Companies, Inc.; *U.S. Public,* pg. 1387
NESTER CONSULTING LLC—See Welsh, Carson, Anderson & Stowe; *U.S. Private,* pg. 4480
NETMAGIC II SARL—See ManpowerGroup Inc.; *U.S. Public,* pg. 1361
NETWORK CONSULTING SERVICES, INC.; *U.S. Private,* pg. 2889
NETWORK PACKAGING GROUP LLC—See Beecken Petty O'Keefe & Company, LLC; *U.S. Private,* pg. 514
NEUSTRATEGY, INC.—See Gryphon Investors, LLC; *U.S. Private,* pg. 1798
NEVADA CORPORATE HEADQUARTERS, INC.; *U.S. Private,* pg. 2891
NEW HARQUAHALA GENERATING CO, LLC—See Beal Financial Corporation; *U.S. Private,* pg. 505
NEWPORT NEWS NUCLEAR, INC.—See Huntington Ingalls Industries, Inc.; *U.S. Public,* pg. 1072
NEW RESOURCES CONSULTING—See New Resources Companies; *U.S. Private,* pg. 2905
NEW TECH GLOBAL VENTURES, LLC; *U.S. Private,* pg. 2907
NEW VENTURES GROUP LLC—See Jabil Inc.; *U.S. Public,* pg. 1181
NEXTGEN CONSULTING INC.; *U.S. Private,* pg. 2921
NEXTGEN GLOBAL RESOURCES, LLC—See Kelly Services, Inc.; *U.S. Public,* pg. 1220
NEXVORTEX INC.—See Thompson Street Capital Manager LLC; *U.S. Private,* pg. 4160
NINETY FIVE 5 LLC—See Franklin Covey Company; *U.S. Public,* pg. 878
NITYO INFOTECH INC.—See Nityo Infotech Corporation; *U.S. Private,* pg. 2930
NITYO INFOTECH LIMITED—See Nityo Infotech Corporation; *U.S. Private,* pg. 2930
NITYO INFOTECH SERVICES PTE LTD.—See Nityo Infotech Corporation; *U.S. Private,* pg. 2930
NITYO INFOTECH SERVICES PVT. LTD.—See Nityo Infotech Corporation; *U.S. Private,* pg. 2930
NITYO INFOTECH SERVICES SDN BHD—See Nityo Infotech Corporation; *U.S. Private,* pg. 2930
NITYO INFOTECH (THAILAND) LTD—See Nityo Infotech Corporation; *U.S. Private,* pg. 2930
NOC OUTSOURCING & CONSULTING INC.—See Fuyo General Lease Co., Ltd.; *Int'l,* pg. 2859
NORRIS TRAINING SYSTEMS, INC.—See Surge Private Equity LLC; *U.S. Private,* pg. 3884
NORTHPOINT SOLUTIONS LLC.; *U.S. Private,* pg. 2957
NORTH STAR GROUP, LLC.; *U.S. Private,* pg. 2947
NORTHWEST WEALTH ADVISORS LLC—See tru Independce LLC; *U.S. Private,* pg. 4244
NOVO PLM—See Sconce Solutions Pte. Ltd.; *U.S. Private,* pg. 3575
NSPM AG—See Cactus Communications, Inc.; *U.S. Private,* pg. 712
N-TECH SOLUTIONS INC.; *U.S. Private,* pg. 2827
NTRINSIC CONSULTING EUROPE LIMITED—See Bain Capital, LP; *U.S. Private,* pg. 434
NTRINSIC CONSULTING RESOURCES LIMITED—See Bain Capital, LP; *U.S. Private,* pg. 434
NUCOMPASS MOBILITY SERVICES INC.; *U.S. Private,* pg. 2972
NURSE AUDIT, LLC—See New Mountain Capital, LLC; *U.S. Private,* pg. 2902
NUSOFT SOLUTIONS INC.—See TTEC Holdings, Inc.; *U.S. Public,* pg. 2203
NUTECH SYSTEMS INC.; *U.S. Private,* pg. 2974
OAKBROOK SOLUTIONS, INC.—See Renovus Capital Partners; *U.S. Private,* pg. 3399
OAKS CONSULTANCY LTD.—See Aquila Services Group PLC; *Int'l,* pg. 528
O'BRIEN'S RESPONSE MANAGEMENT INC.—See AIP, LLC; *U.S. Private,* pg. 136
OCEANEERING ANGOLA, S.A.—See Oceaneering International, Inc.; *U.S. Public,* pg. 1562
OCEAN SPRAY INTERNATIONAL SERVICES, INC.—See Ocean Spray Cranberries, Inc.; *U.S. Private,* pg. 2990
OCTO CONSULTING GROUP, INC.—See Arlington Capital Partners LLC; *U.S. Private,* pg. 328
OFFICEWORKS, INC.; *U.S. Private,* pg. 3002
OI DEVELOPMENT CO LTD—See H2O Retailing Corp.; *Int'l,* pg. 3200
OLIVER WYMAN CONSULTORIA EM ESTRATEGIA DE NEGOCIOS LTDA.—See Marsh & McLennan Companies, Inc.; *U.S. Public,* pg. 1387
OLIVER WYMAN (PTY) LTD.—See Marsh & McLennan Companies, Inc.; *U.S. Public,* pg. 1386
OLIVER WYMAN S.A.S.—See Marsh & McLennan Companies, Inc.; *U.S. Public,* pg. 1386
OMEGA PERFORMANCE CORPORATION—See Moody's Corporation; *U.S. Public,* pg. 1469
THE OMNIA GROUP INC.; *U.S. Private,* pg. 4088
OMNIPRO GESELLSCHAFT FUR PROJEKTMANAGEMENT MBH—See Starwood Capital Group Global I, LLC; *U.S. Private,* pg. 3789
OMNIVUE BUSINESS SOLUTIONS; *U.S. Private,* pg. 3017
ONEGROUP WEALTH PARTNERS, INC.—See Community Bank System, Inc.; *U.S. Public,* pg. 550
ONE SOURCE TALENT; *U.S. Private,* pg. 3023
ONE WORLD INC; *U.S. Private,* pg. 3024
OOMURA INDUSTRIAL CO., LTD.—See Bain Capital, LP; *U.S. Private,* pg. 434
OPENSYMMETRY-AUSTRALIA—See OpenSymmetry, Inc.; *U.S. Private,* pg. 3031
OPENSYMMETRY-CANADA—See OpenSymmetry, Inc.; *U.S. Private,* pg. 3031
OPENSYMMETRY, INC.; *U.S. Private,* pg. 3031
OPENSYMMETRY-MALAYSIA—See OpenSymmetry, Inc.; *U.S. Private,* pg. 3031
OPENSYMMETRY-SOUTH AFRICA—See OpenSymmetry, Inc.; *U.S. Private,* pg. 3031
OPTIMAL STRATEGIX GROUP, INC.; *U.S. Private,* pg. 3034
OPTIMISSA SERVICIOS PROFESIONALES SL—See Alten S.A.; *Int'l,* pg. 390
OPTUMHEALTH ALLIES; *U.S. Private,* pg. 3036
OPTUMINSIGHT (SWEDEN) AB—See UnitedHealth Group Incorporated; *U.S. Public,* pg. 2248
OPTUMRX, INC.—See UnitedHealth Group Incorporated; *U.S. Public,* pg. 2247
OPU INC.; *U.S. Private,* pg. 3036
ORGANIZATIONAL DYNAMICS INC.; *U.S. Private,* pg. 3041
ORIN USA; *U.S. Private,* pg. 3042
ORJ INC.—See Bain Capital, LP; *U.S. Private,* pg. 434
ORRIDGE SA—See Blackstone Inc.; *U.S. Public,* pg. 357
OS RECRUITMENT (THAILAND) CO., LTD.—See Bain Capital, LP; *U.S. Private,* pg. 434
OSUDIO NORDICS APS—See DBAY Advisors Limited; *Int'l,* pg. 1987
OS VIETNAM CO., LTD.—See Bain Capital, LP; *U.S. Private,* pg. 435
OTTO WORK FORCE B.V.—See Bain Capital, LP; *U.S. Private,* pg. 435
OUTSOURCING BUSINESS SERVICE INC.—See Bain Capital, LP; *U.S. Private,* pg. 435
OUTSOURCING (CAMBODIA) INC.—See Bain Capital, LP; *U.S. Private,* pg. 435
OUTSOURCING TECHNOLOGY INC.—See Bain Capital, LP; *U.S. Private,* pg. 435
OVERSEAS ADJUSTERS AND SURVEYORS CO—See Lovell Minnick Partners LLC; *U.S. Private,* pg. 2502
OVIDIAN GROUP LLC—See Pendrell Corporation; *U.S. Public,* pg. 1661
OXYGEN CONSULTANCY—See Allgeier SE; *Int'l,* pg. 337
THE PACIELLO GROUP, LLC—See Freedom Scientific Inc.; *U.S. Private,* pg. 1604
PACIFIC MEDICAL MANAGEMENT SERVICES, INC—See Constellation Software Inc.; *Int'l,* pg. 1774
PAMS, INC.—See Key Impact & Sales Systems, Inc.; *U.S. Private,* pg. 2293
PARAMETRIC TECHNOLOGY CORPORATION (MALAYSIA) SDN. BHD.—See PTC Inc.; *U.S. Public,* pg. 1735
PARAMOUNT PROPERTY FUND LIMITED—See Growthpoint Properties Limited; *Int'l,* pg. 3113
PARANET SOLUTIONS, LLC.; *U.S. Private,* pg. 3093
PARIVEDA SOLUTIONS, INC.; *U.S. Private,* pg. 3095
PARTNERS HARVARD MEDICAL INTERNATIONAL—See Partners HealthCare System, Inc.; *U.S. Public,* pg. 3101
PARTNERS RX MANAGEMENT, LLC—See Centene Corporation; *U.S. Public,* pg. 470
PASSPORT GLOBAL INC.; *U.S. Private,* pg. 3104
PATHLINE, INC.—See Gwin Dobson & Foreman Inc.; *U.S. Private,* pg. 1821
PAYPAL POLSKA SP Z O.O.—See PayPal Holdings, Inc.; *U.S. Public,* pg. 1656
PAYPAL (UK) LIMITED—See PayPal Holdings, Inc.; *U.S. Public,* pg. 1656
PCUBED AUSTRALIA PTY LTD—See Alten S.A.; *Int'l,* pg. 390
PEGASUS ORGANIZATION INTERNATIONAL INC.; *U.S. Private,* pg. 3129
PENDRELL CORPORATION; *U.S. Public,* pg. 1661
PEO CO., LTD.—See Bain Capital, LP; *U.S. Private,* pg. 435
PERCEPTA LLC—See Ford Motor Company; *U.S. Public,* pg. 867
PERCEPTA LLC—See TTEC Holdings, Inc.; *U.S. Public,* pg. 2202
PERFICIENT CANADA CORP.—See EQT AB; *Int'l,* pg. 2483
PERFICIENT UK LTD.—See EQT AB; *Int'l,* pg. 2483
PERFORMANCE ARCHITECTS INC.; *U.S. Private,* pg. 3148
PETRA INVESTMENT COMPANY—See Severson Group Incorporated; *U.S. Private,* pg. 3619

CORPORATE AFFILIATIONS

PHARMACYCLICS (SHANGHAI) MANAGEMENT CONSULTING SERVICE LIMITED—See AbbVie Inc.; *U.S. Public,* pg. 24
PHOTIZO GROUP; *U.S. Private,* pg. 3174
PILAT INC.—See Galileo Tech Ltd.; *Int'l,* pg. 2873
PILAT ISRAEL—See Galileo Tech Ltd.; *Int'l,* pg. 2873
PINEAPPLE, INC.; *U.S. Private,* pg. 1691
PIRA INTERNATIONAL LIMITED—See The Smithers Group; *U.S. Private,* pg. 4118
PKF CONSULTING, INC.—See CBRE Group, Inc.; *U.S. Public,* pg. 460
PLUS DELTA CONSULTING, LLC; *U.S. Private,* pg. 3215
PM LINK PTE LTD—See China Architecture Design & Research Group; *Int'l,* pg. 1483
PMOA, INC.—See Stone Point Capital LLC; *U.S. Private,* pg. 3824
PMOLINK LLC; *U.S. Private,* pg. 3218
PM TECHNOLOGIES; *U.S. Private,* pg. 3217
PNEURON CORP.—See UST Global Inc.; *U.S. Private,* pg. 4324
POINT HEALTH TECH, INC.; *U.S. Private,* pg. 3222
POLARIS CONSULTING & SERVICES GMBH—See EQT AB; *Int'l,* pg. 2472
POLARIS CONSULTING & SERVICES SA—See EQT AB; *Int'l,* pg. 2472
POLYWIN COMPUTER LIMITED—See China Bester Group Telecom Co., Ltd.; *Int'l,* pg. 1486
PORTABLE CHURCH INDUSTRIES, INC.; *U.S. Private,* pg. 3231
PORT BROKERS INC.; *U.S. Private,* pg. 3229
POWER GROUP COMPANY, LLC—See CRETCHER HEARTLAND LLC; *U.S. Public,* pg. 1099
POWER OF THREE LLC—See Casella Waste Systems, Inc.; *U.S. Public,* pg. 446
POYRY ENERGY AG—See AFRY AB; *Int'l,* pg. 195
POYRY ENERGY CONSULTING (ITALIA) S.R.L.—See AFRY AB; *Int'l,* pg. 195
POYRY ENERGY CONSULTING (SCHWEIZ) AG—See AFRY AB; *Int'l,* pg. 195
POYRY ENERGY SRL—See AFRY AB; *Int'l,* pg. 195
PRAEMITTIAS GROUP INC.; *U.S. Private,* pg. 3241
PRAIRIE CAPITAL MANAGEMENT, LLC—See UMB Financial Corporation; *U.S. Public,* pg. 2224
PRECISION PACKAGING—See CRH plc; *Int'l,* pg. 1843
PREFERRED DISABILITY MANAGEMENT, LLC—See Rising Medical Solutions, LLC.; *U.S. Private,* pg. 3440
THE PRESIDIO GROUP, INC.—See Arthur J. Gallagher & Co.; *U.S. Public,* pg. 203
PREUSS GMBH—See CBRE Group, Inc.; *U.S. Public,* pg. 460
PRGX ASIA, INC. - THAILAND—See PRGX Global, Inc.; *U.S. Private,* pg. 3257
PRGX AUSTRALIA, INC.—See PRGX Global, Inc.; *U.S. Private,* pg. 3257
PRGX CANADA CORP.—See PRGX Global, Inc.; *U.S. Private,* pg. 3257
PRGX DEUTSCHLAND GMBH—See PRGX Global, Inc.; *U.S. Private,* pg. 3257
PRGX FRANCE, INC.—See PRGX Global, Inc.; *U.S. Private,* pg. 3257
PRGX INTERNATIONAL PTE. LTD. - HONG KONG—See PRGX Global, Inc.; *U.S. Private,* pg. 3257
PRGX INTERNATIONAL PTE. LTD.—See PRGX Global, Inc.; *U.S. Private,* pg. 3257
PRGX MEXICO S DE RL DE CV—See PRGX Global, Inc.; *U.S. Private,* pg. 3257
PRGX SPAIN, INC.—See PRGX Global, Inc.; *U.S. Private,* pg. 3257
PRGX SUZHOU CO., LTD.—See PRGX Global, Inc.; *U.S. Private,* pg. 3257
PRGX SVENSKA AB—See PRGX Global, Inc.; *U.S. Private,* pg. 3257
PRGX UK LTD.—See PRGX Global, Inc.; *U.S. Private,* pg. 3257
PRICOA RELOCATION FRANCE SAS—See Prudential Financial, Inc.; *U.S. Public,* pg. 1731
PRIME CAPITAL INVESTMENT ADVISORS, LLC; *U.S. Private,* pg. 3261
PRINCIPAL ASSET MANAGEMENT COMPANY PRIVATE LIMITED—See Principal Financial Group, Inc.; *U.S. Public,* pg. 1720
PRINCIPLES GROUP LLC; *U.S. Private,* pg. 3265
PRIORITY POWER MANAGEMENT, LLC—See I Squared Capital Advisors (US) LLC; *U.S. Private,* pg. 2026
PROARCH IT SOLUTIONS, INC.; *U.S. Private,* pg. 3271
PROCONCEPT MARKETING GROUP, INC.; *U.S. Private,* pg. 3272
PRODUCTIVE DENTIST ACADEMY; *U.S. Private,* pg. 3274
PROFECTUS, LLC; *U.S. Private,* pg. 3274
PROFESSIONAL DISABILITY ASSOCIATES, PA—See Brown & Brown, Inc.; *U.S. Public,* pg. 397
PROFESSIONAL WASTE CONSULTING, LLC—See O2 Investment Partners, LLC; *U.S. Private,* pg. 2982
PROFIT RECOVERY BRASIL LTDA.—See PRGX Global, Inc.; *U.S. Private,* pg. 3258
PROHA OY—See Dovre Group Plc; *Int'l,* pg. 2182
PROJECT DEVELOPMENT INTERNATIONAL, INC.; *U.S. Private,* pg. 3280

N.A.I.C.S. INDEX 541618 — OTHER MANAGEMENT CO...

PROJECT ENHANCEMENT CORPORATION; *U.S. Private*, pg. 3280
PROJECT MANAGEMENT GROUP, LLC—See Ashford Inc.; *U.S. Public*, pg. 211
PROJECT MANAGEMENT PARTNERS PTY. LTD.—See Bain Capital, LP; *U.S. Private*, pg. 435
PROJILITY; *U.S. Private*, pg. 3282
PROMONTORY FINANCIAL GROUP AUSTRALASIA, LLP—See International Business Machines Corporation; *U.S. Public*, pg. 1149
PROMONTORY FINANCIAL GROUP GLOBAL SERVICES - JAPAN, LLC—See International Business Machines Corporation; *U.S. Public*, pg. 1149
PROMONTORY FINANCIAL GROUP LLC—See International Business Machines Corporation; *U.S. Public*, pg. 1149
PROMONTORY FINANCIAL GROUP (UK) LIMITED—See International Business Machines Corporation; *U.S. Public*, pg. 1149
PROSPECT MEDICAL GROUP, INC.—See Leonard Green & Partners, L.P.; *U.S. Private*, pg. 2428
PROTANG TEKNIKINFORMATION AB—See Etteplan Oyj; *Int'l*, pg. 2525
PROTIVITI GMBH—See Robert Half Inc.; *U.S. Public*, pg. 1803
PROTIVITI INC.—See Robert Half Inc.; *U.S. Public*, pg. 1803
PROTRIALS RESEARCH, INC.; *U.S. Private*, pg. 3291
PRUDENTIAL CALIFORNIA REALTY—See Berkshire Hathaway Inc.; *U.S. Public*, pg. 315
P.T. COMBA TELECOM NETWORK INDONESIA—See Comba Telecom Systems Holdings Limited; *Int'l*, pg. 1708
PT. DENTSU CONSULTANTS INDONESIA—See Dentsu Group Inc.; *Int'l*, pg. 2037
PT MULTI BANGUN GALAXY—See Heidelberg Materials AG; *Int'l*, pg. 3318
PT. OS SELNAJAYA INDONESIA—See Bain Capital, LP; *U.S. Private*, pg. 435
PT TAPIAN NADENGGAN—See Golden Agri-Resources Ltd.; *Int'l*, pg. 3028
PT VIKING OFFSHORE—See 9R Limited; *Int'l*, pg. 17
PUBLIC CONSULTING GROUP, INC.; *U.S. Private*, pg. 3299
PUBLIC MANAGEMENT CONSULTING CORPORATION—See FinTech Global Incorporated; *Int'l*, pg. 2677
PULSO EUROPE BV—See Asklepios Kliniken GmbH & Co. KGaA; *Int'l*, pg. 624
PULSO EUROPE LDA—See Asklepios Kliniken GmbH & Co. KGaA; *Int'l*, pg. 624
PULSO SOUTH EAST EUROPE P.C.—See Asklepios Kliniken GmbH & Co. KGaA; *Int'l*, pg. 624
PURE INTEGRATION, LLC; *U.S. Private*, pg. 3305
QCI TECHNOLOGY; *U.S. Private*, pg. 3312
QNEXIS INC; *U.S. Private*, pg. 3313
QSACK & ASSOCIATES, INC.; *U.S. Private*, pg. 3313
QUADEL CONSULTING CORP.—See System One Holdings, LLC; *U.S. Private*, pg. 3906
QUALEX CONSULTING GROUP, INC.—See Cumberland Technologies, Inc.; *U.S. Private*, pg. 1123
QUALITY BAKERS OF AMERICA COOPERATIVE, INC.; *U.S. Private*, pg. 3317
QUOIN INC.; *U.S. Private*, pg. 3329
RADFORD—See Aon plc; *Int'l*, pg. 491
RADIANCE SAS—See Kadant Inc.; *U.S. Public*, pg. 1212
RAFTELIS FINANCIAL CONSULTANTS, INC.; *U.S. Private*, pg. 3345
RAGE ADMINISTRATIVE & MARKETING SERVICES, INC.; *U.S. Private*, pg. 3345
RAINMAKER SYSTEMS, INC.; *U.S. Public*, pg. 1761
RALAND TECHNOLOGIES LLC; *U.S. Private*, pg. 3349
RBA, INC.; *U.S. Private*, pg. 3360
RDE VERWALTUNGS-GMBH—See E.ON SE; *Int'l*, pg. 2259
RDS SOLUTIONS LLC—See UPSTACK, Inc.; *U.S. Private*, pg. 4313
RED24 CRM (PTY) LIMITED—See iJET International, Inc.; *U.S. Private*, pg. 2040
REDBOX CONSULTING SERVICES LIMITED—See Datatec Limited; *Int'l*, pg. 1981
RED SKY BLUE WATER, LLC; *U.S. Private*, pg. 3376
RELATIONAL LLC; *U.S. Private*, pg. 3392
RELIANCE MEDICAL GROUP, LLC—See Four Corners Property Trust, Inc.; *U.S. Public*, pg. 875
RENTAL HISTORY REPORTS—See GI Manager L.P.; *U.S. Private*, pg. 1693
RESOURCE PARTNERS GROUP, INC.; *U.S. Private*, pg. 3407
RESOURCE SOLUTIONS GROUP, INC.; *U.S. Public*, pg. 1791
RES-Q HEALTHCARE SYSTEMS, INC.—See Clearlake Capital Group, L.P.; *U.S. Private*, pg. 937
RES-Q HEALTHCARE SYSTEMS, INC.—See SkyKnight Capital LLC; *U.S. Private*, pg. 3685
RETAIL BUSINESS DEVELOPMENT, INC.; *U.S. Private*, pg. 3411
THE RETAIL OUTSOURCE; *U.S. Private*, pg. 4105
REVGEN PARTNERS, INC.; *U.S. Private*, pg. 3416

REVOLUTION TECHNOLOGIES, LLC; *U.S. Private*, pg. 3416
REZ 1, INC.—See Apollo Global Management, Inc.; *U.S. Public*, pg. 150
RIA ADVISORY LLC—See Avance Investment Management, LLC; *U.S. Private*, pg. 403
RICHARDSON GROUP INC.; *U.S. Private*, pg. 3429
RICHTER INTERNATIONAL CONSULTING, LLC—See Arthur J. Gallagher & Co.; *U.S. Public*, pg. 207
RIMKUS CONSULTING GROUP, INC.; *U.S. Private*, pg. 3437
RISK MANAGEMENT SOLUTIONS - EAST COAST US—See Moody's Corporation; *U.S. Public*, pg. 1469
RISK MANAGEMENT SOLUTIONS, INC.—See Moody's Corporation; *U.S. Public*, pg. 1469
ROCKWELL COLLINS DEUTSCHLAND HOLDINGS GMBH—See RTX Corporation; *U.S. Public*, pg. 1823
ROI COMMUNICATION; *U.S. Private*, pg. 3473
ROMBALDS RUN-OFF LIMITED—See Enstar Group Limited; *Int'l*, pg. 2449
ROOT LLC—See Accenture plc; *Int'l*, pg. 87
RPX ASIA CORPORATION—See HGGC, LLC; *U.S. Private*, pg. 1930
RPX CORPORATION—See HGGC, LLC; *U.S. Private*, pg. 1930
RST ROSTOCK SYSTEM-TECHNIK GMBH—See Airbus SE; *Int'l*, pg. 243
R T WESTERN MISSOURI FRANCHISE LLC; *U.S. Private*, pg. 3331
THE RUBIN GROUP, INC.; *U.S. Private*, pg. 4113
RUOTOLO ASSOCIATES, INC.—See Collegium Holdings, Inc.; *U.S. Private*, pg. 968
RUSS BLAKELY & ASSOCIATES, LLC—See The Baldwin Insurance Group, Inc.; *U.S. Public*, pg. 2036
RUST CONSULTING, INC.—See Gainline Capital Partners LP; *U.S. Private*, pg. 1635
RWA CONSULTING S.R.L.—See Edenred S.A.; *Int'l*, pg. 2308
SAFETY MANAGEMENT GROUP; *U.S. Private*, pg. 3524
SAGE SETTLEMENT CONSULTING, LLC; *U.S. Private*, pg. 3527
SAHARA INC.; *U.S. Private*, pg. 3528
SALES INTELLIGENCE SP. Z O.O.—See Digitree Group S.A.; *Int'l*, pg. 2124
SALES READINESS INC.—See Sales Benchmark Index LLC; *U.S. Private*, pg. 3531
SALZINGER LLC.; *U.S. Private*, pg. 3535
SBH ASSOCIATES, INC.; *U.S. Private*, pg. 3559
SCHEELITE MANAGEMENT PTY LTD—See Group 6 Metals Limited; *Int'l*, pg. 3088
SCHOOLEY MITCHELL TELECOM CONSULTANTS; *U.S. Private*, pg. 3568
SCIENTIFIC COMMERCIALIZATION, LLC—See The CM Group, LLC; *U.S. Private*, pg. 4011
SCOTWORK (NA); *U.S. Private*, pg. 3578
SDI PRESENCE LLC; *U.S. Private*, pg. 3581
SDLC PARTNERS, L.P.—See CitiusTech Inc.; *U.S. Private*, pg. 902
SD RETAIL CONSULTING—See Hilco Trading, LLC; *U.S. Private*, pg. 1944
SEABOARD SHIP MANAGEMENT INC.—See Seaboard Corporation; *U.S. Public*, pg. 1851
SEAMAR MANAGEMENT S.A.—See Pangaea Logistics Solutions Ltd.; *U.S. Public*, pg. 1635
SEC CONSULT AUSTRIA AG—See Atos SE; *Int'l*, pg. 692
SECURICON, LLC—See Risk Mitigation Consulting Inc.; *U.S. Private*, pg. 3441
SEDLAK MANAGEMENT CONSULTANTS, INC.; *U.S. Private*, pg. 3597
SEDULOUS CONSULTING SERVICES, LLC; *U.S. Private*, pg. 3597
SEGURIDAD PRIVADA ACTIVE SECURITY COMPANY A.S.C. CIA. LTDA.—See Bain Capital, LP; *U.S. Private*, pg. 435
SENTINEL ASSET MANAGEMENT, INC.—See National Life Insurance Company; *U.S. Public*, pg. 2859
SEPARTIS HOLDINGS AG—See Biotage AB; *Int'l*, pg. 1043
SERCOM SOLUTIONS LIMITED—See DCC plc; *Int'l*, pg. 1991
SERC RELIABILITY CORPORATION; *U.S. Private*, pg. 3613
SERVICIOS ADMINISTRATIVOS ACCEL, S.A. DE C.V.—See Accel, S.A.B. de C.V.; *Int'l*, pg. 79
SERVICIOS HOTELEROS POSADAS, S.A. DE C.V.—See Grupo Posadas S.A.B. de C.V.; *Int'l*, pg. 3134
SERVIZIO TITOLI S.P.A.—See Computershare Limited; *Int'l*, pg. 1760
SETSCO SERVICES PTE. LTD.—See ComfortDelGro Corporation Limited; *Int'l*, pg. 1713
SEVATEC, INC.—See Arlington Capital Partners LLC; *U.S. Private*, pg. 328
SG DETACHERING B.V.—See Advent International Corporation; *U.S. Private*, pg. 97
SG DETACHERING B.V.—See Centerbridge Partners, L.P.; *U.S. Private*, pg. 813
SHEARER & ASSOCIATES, INC.; *U.S. Private*, pg. 3629
SHENTEL MANAGEMENT COMPANY—See Shenandoah Telecommunications Co.; *U.S. Public*, pg. 1874

SHL AG—See Exponent Private Equity LLP; *Int'l*, pg. 2589
SHL DANMARK A/S—See Exponent Private Equity LLP; *Int'l*, pg. 2589
SHL HONG KONG LIMITED—See Exponent Private Equity LLP; *Int'l*, pg. 2589
SHL NEDERLAND BV—See Exponent Private Equity LLP; *Int'l*, pg. 2589
SHL PEOPLE SOLUTIONS LTD.—See Exponent Private Equity LLP; *Int'l*, pg. 2589
SHL POLSKA SP. Z.O.O.—See Exponent Private Equity LLP; *Int'l*, pg. 2589
SHL SAVILLE & HOLDSWORTH (DEUTSCHLAND) GMBH—See Exponent Private Equity LLP; *Int'l*, pg. 2589
SHOEMAKER CONSTRUCTION—See Butz Enterprises, Inc.; *U.S. Private*, pg. 698
SIB FIXED COST REDUCTION COMPANY, LLC—See O2 Investment Partners, LLC; *U.S. Private*, pg. 2982
SIGMA CIVIL AB—See Danir Resources AB; *Int'l*, pg. 1963
SIMPLICITY CONSULTING, INC; *U.S. Private*, pg. 3667
SIMPLYWELL INC.—See Marlin Equity Partners, LLC; *U.S. Private*, pg. 2585
SIROTA ASIA PACIFIC PTE. LTD.—See Marsh & McLennan Companies, Inc.; *U.S. Public*, pg. 1388
SIROTA CONSULTING UK LIMITED—See Marsh & McLennan Companies, Inc.; *U.S. Public*, pg. 1388
SIRSAI MULTI SOURCING; *U.S. Private*, pg. 3675
SKCG GROUP, INC.—See GTCR LLC; *U.S. Private*, pg. 1804
SKIDATA INC.—See ASSA ABLOY AB; *Int'l*, pg. 640
SKIL-TECH, INC.; *U.S. Private*, pg. 3682
SKIPPING STONE, INC.; *U.S. Private*, pg. 3682
SMARTANALYST INC.—See Clayton, Dubilier & Rice, LLC; *U.S. Private*, pg. 928
SMART IMS; *U.S. Private*, pg. 3691
SMARTPOINT IT CONSULTING GMBH—See Bechtle AG; *Int'l*, pg. 938
SME - SCIENCE MANAGEMENT & ENGINEERING AG—See DXC Technology Company; *U.S. Public*, pg. 696
SMITH, BRYAN & MYERS INC.; *U.S. Private*, pg. 3696
SNOWDEN MINING INDUSTRY CONSULTANTS PTY LTD.—See Downer EDI Limited; *Int'l*, pg. 2186
SOAPROJECTS, INC.; *U.S. Private*, pg. 3702
SOCIAL VALUE INCUBATION LAB CO., LTD.—See Founder's Consultants Holdings, Inc.; *Int'l*, pg. 2753
SOCIETY CONSULTING, LLC—See Ernst & Young LLP; *U.S. Private*, pg. 1423
SOFTWARE BY DESIGN, INC.—See H.I.G. Capital, LLC; *U.S. Private*, pg. 1833
SOGETI USA LLC—See Capgemini SE; *Int'l*, pg. 1307
SOGETI USA LLC—See Capgemini SE; *Int'l*, pg. 1307
SOLENTUS; *U.S. Private*, pg. 3708
SOUND INPATIENT PHYSICIANS, INC.—See Summit Partners, L.P.; *U.S. Private*, pg. 3856
SOUTHERN CORRECTIONS SYSTEM OF WYOMING, LLC—See Corecivic, Inc.; *U.S. Public*, pg. 577
SOYRING CONSULTING, INC.—See Ares Management Corporation; *U.S. Public*, pg. 190
SOYRING CONSULTING, INC.—See Leonard Green & Partners, L.P.; *U.S. Private*, pg. 2427
SPATIAL DIMENSION SOUTH AFRICA PTY LTD—See Trimble, Inc.; *U.S. Public*, pg. 2191
SPECTRUM GAMING GROUP; *U.S. Private*, pg. 3752
SPENDMEND LLC—See Morgan Stanley; *U.S. Public*, pg. 1474
SPINNAKER SCA—See Black Lake Capital, LLC; *U.S. Private*, pg. 572
THE SPORTS FACILITIES ADVISORY; *U.S. Private*, pg. 4120
SQUARE S HOLDING GMBH—See Starwood Capital Group Global I, LLC; *U.S. Private*, pg. 3789
SR TECHNICS MANAGEMENT AG—See Hainan Traffic Administration Holding Co., Ltd.; *Int'l*, pg. 3216
SS&C TECHNOLOGIES, INC.—See SS&C Technologies Holdings, Inc.; *U.S. Public*, pg. 1924
STANLEY DESIGN-BUILD, INC.—See Stanley Consultants Co.; *U.S. Private*, pg. 3783
STAPOR RESEARCH, INC.—See Kratos Defense & Security Solutions, Inc.; *U.S. Public*, pg. 1277
STARPOINT GENERAL CORPORATION; *U.S. Private*, pg. 3787
STARSTONE INSURANCE SERVICES LIMITED—See Enstar Group Limited; *Int'l*, pg. 2449
STRATEGIC DECISIONS GROUP INTERNATIONAL LLC; *U.S. Private*, pg. 3834
STRATIVIA LLC; *U.S. Private*, pg. 3837
THE STRAWHECKER GROUP, LLC; *U.S. Private*, pg. 4123
STREAMLINE DEFENSE, LLC; *U.S. Private*, pg. 3838
STRIA, INC.; *U.S. Private*, pg. 3839
THE STUDER GROUP, LLC—See Huron Consulting Group Inc.; *U.S. Public*, pg. 1076
SUGAR FARMS INC.—See Florida Crystals Corporation; *U.S. Private*, pg. 1548
SUMMIT AG INVESTORS, LLC—See Summit Agricultural Group, LLC; *U.S. Private*, pg. 3853
SUPER-SERVER, LLC—See Sourcepass, Inc.; *U.S. Private*, pg. 3719

541618 — OTHER MANAGEMENT CO...

SURCON, LTD.—See Helmerich & Payne, Inc.; *U.S. Public*, pg. 1024
SURGICAL DIRECTIONS, LLC—See MEDNAX, Inc.; *U.S. Public*, pg. 1413
SURVEYING AND MAPPING, LLC; *U.S. Private*, pg. 3885
SUZANNE EVANS COACHING LLC; *U.S. Private*, pg. 3887
SVILUPPO ITALIA CAMPANIA SPA—See Agenzia Nazionale per l'Attrazione degli Investimenti e lo Sviluppo d'Impresa SpA; *Int'l*, pg. 206
SVILUPPO ITALIA MARCHE SPA—See Agenzia Nazionale per l'Attrazione degli Investimenti e lo Sviluppo d'Impresa SpA; *Int'l*, pg. 206
SVILUPPO ITALIA MOLISE SPA—See Agenzia Nazionale per l'Attrazione degli Investimenti e lo Sviluppo d'Impresa SpA; *Int'l*, pg. 206
SVILUPPO ITALIA PUGLIA SPA—See Agenzia Nazionale per l'Attrazione degli Investimenti e lo Sviluppo d'Impresa SpA; *Int'l*, pg. 206
SYNAPSE GROUP, INC.—See Meredith Corporation; *U.S. Public*, pg. 1423
SYNAPTICORE; *U.S. Private*, pg. 3902
SYNEOS HEALTH CONSULTING, INC.—See Elliott Management Corporation; *U.S. Private*, pg. 1365
SYNEOS HEALTH CONSULTING, INC.—See Patient Square Capital, L.P.; *U.S. Private*, pg. 3108
SYNEOS HEALTH CONSULTING, INC.—See Veritas Capital Fund Management, LLC; *U.S. Private*, pg. 4365
SYNEOS HEALTH US, INC.—See Elliott Management Corporation; *U.S. Private*, pg. 1365
SYNEOS HEALTH US, INC.—See Patient Square Capital, L.P.; *U.S. Private*, pg. 3108
SYNEOS HEALTH US, INC.—See Veritas Capital Fund Management, LLC; *U.S. Private*, pg. 4365
SYNERGEN CONSULTING INTERNATIONAL LLC—See Cobepa S.A.; *Int'l*, pg. 1683
SYNERGY NETWORKS GMBH—See freenet AG; *Int'l*, pg. 2770
SYNTERAS, LLC—See Nana Regional Corporation, Inc.; *U.S. Private*, pg. 2832
T5 CORP.; *U.S. Private*, pg. 3913
TAG CONSULTING; *U.S. Private*, pg. 3922
TAHOE PARTNERS, LLC; *U.S. Private*, pg. 3923
TAIWAN TOTAL MANAGEMENT CONSULTING LTD.—See EPS Holdings, Inc.; *Int'l*, pg. 2465
TALENT, INC.; *U.S. Private*, pg. 3926
TANGOE EUROPE LIMITED—See Marlin Equity Partners, LLC; *U.S. Private*, pg. 2584
TAYGANPOINT CONSULTING GROUP, INC.—See Grant Thornton LLP - USA; *U.S. Private*, pg. 1757
TAYLOR CONSULTING INC.; *U.S. Public*, pg. 1983
TBG TRANSPORTBETON ELSTER-SPREE VERWALTUNGS-GMBH—See Heidelberg Materials AG; *Int'l*, pg. 3320
TCE, INCORPORATED; *U.S. Private*, pg. 3942
TECARENA+ GMBH—See Bayer Aktiengesellschaft; *Int'l*, pg. 910
TECH. FINANCE CO., LLC—See Kingsbridge Holdings LLC; *U.S. Private*, pg. 2311
TECHLAW INC.—See TechLaw Holdings, Inc.; *U.S. Private*, pg. 3952
TECHNOLOGY MANAGEMENT CORP.—See The Carlyle Group Inc.; *U.S. Public*, pg. 2049
TECHNOMAX LLC; *U.S. Private*, pg. 3956
TECNOCREDIT, S.A.—See Banco de Sabadell, S.A.; *Int'l*, pg. 822
TECNONET S.P.A.—See Ascom Holding AG; *Int'l*, pg. 603
TEKSCAPE; *U.S. Private*, pg. 3959
TELECOMODA, S.A. DE C.V.—See America Movil, S.A.B. de C.V.; *Int'l*, pg. 421
TELEPHONY PARTNERS LLC; *U.S. Private*, pg. 3961
TELEPLAN COMMUNICATIONS HOLDING B.V.—See Clover Wireless; *U.S. Private*, pg. 948
TERACORE, INC. (MID-ATLANTIC REGION)—See Teracore, Inc.; *U.S. Private*, pg. 3969
TERACORE, INC.; *U.S. Private*, pg. 3969
TERRES MARKETING- UND CONSULTING GMBH—See AGRAVIS Raiffeisen AG; *Int'l*, pg. 216
TERRY ENVIRONMENTAL SERVICES, INC.; *U.S. Private*, pg. 3972
TESTOUT CORP.—See Computing Technology Industry Association; *U.S. Private*, pg. 1006
TETRA TECH EC, INC.—See Tetra Tech, Inc.; *U.S. Public*, pg. 2023
T-FORCE GROUP; *U.S. Private*, pg. 3910
TITAN ITM HOLDING SPA—See Titan International, Inc.; *U.S. Public*, pg. 2160
TM IMMO D.O.O—See Starwood Capital Group Global I, LLC; *U.S. Private*, pg. 3789
TORCON, INC.; *U.S. Private*, pg. 4188
TORRENT TECHNOLOGIES, INC.—See Marsh & McLennan Companies, Inc.; *U.S. Public*, pg. 1388
TPI ADVISORY SERVICES INDIA PVT. LTD.—See Information Services Group, Inc.; *U.S. Public*, pg. 1118
TRANSUNION INFORMATION GROUP LIMITED—See TransUnion; *U.S. Public*, pg. 2184
TRC ALBUQUERQUE—See TRC Companies, Inc.; *U.S. Private*, pg. 4215
TRC COMPANIES, INC. - CINCINNATI—See TRC Companies, Inc.; *U.S. Private*, pg. 4215
T-REX ACQUISITION CORP.; *U.S. Public*, pg. 1977
TRICOR AXCELASIA SDN BHD—See Axington Inc.; *Int'l*, pg. 768
TRICOR AXCELASIA (SG) PTE LTD—See Axington Inc.; *Int'l*, pg. 768
TRICOR ROOTS SDN BHD—See Axington Inc.; *Int'l*, pg. 768
TRIDATA INC.—See System Planning Corporation; *U.S. Private*, pg. 3907
TRIMBLE POLAND SP. Z.O.O.—See Trimble, Inc.; *U.S. Public*, pg. 2192
TRIMBLE SOLUTIONS SEA PTE. LTD.—See Trimble, Inc.; *U.S. Public*, pg. 2193
TRIMBLE SOLUTIONS USA INC.—See Trimble, Inc.; *U.S. Public*, pg. 2193
TRIMEDX INDIA PVT. LTD.—See Ascension Health Alliance; *U.S. Private*, pg. 346
TRIPLE-I CORP—See Triple-I Investments Inc.; *U.S. Private*, pg. 4237
TRIPLE-I OF COLORADO INC.—See Triple-I Investments Inc.; *U.S. Private*, pg. 4237
TRITEN CORPORATION; *U.S. Private*, pg. 4238
TSAMOUTALES STRATEGIES; *U.S. Private*, pg. 4252
T-SYSTEM, INC.—See Fidelity National Financial, Inc.; *U.S. Public*, pg. 831
TURLEY RESIDENTIAL CENTER, LLC—See Corecivic, Inc.; *U.S. Public*, pg. 577
TXU WARM FRONT LIMITED—See E.ON SE; *Int'l*, pg. 2256
UNISSANT, INC.; *U.S. Private*, pg. 4286
UNISYS CORPORATION; *U.S. Public*, pg. 2228
UNITED HEALTH ACTUARIAL SERVICES, INC.—See Kelso & Company, L.P.; *U.S. Private*, pg. 2280
UNITED STATES STEEL CORP.—See United States Steel Corporation; *U.S. Public*, pg. 2237
UNIVERSAL MANAGEMENT SERVICES, INC.—See Universal Logistics Holdings, Inc.; *U.S. Public*, pg. 2262
UNLOCK HEALTH, INC.—See Amulet Capital Partners, L.P.; *U.S. Private*, pg. 268
URBAN SCIENCE, INC.; *U.S. Private*, pg. 4315
U-RIGHT (HK) LIMITED—See Fullsun International Holdings Group Co., Limited; *Int'l*, pg. 2843
URS SAFETY MANAGEMENT SOLUTIONS—See AECOM; *U.S. Public*, pg. 51
USC CONSULTING GROUP, LLC; *U.S. Private*, pg. 4322
US INVESTIGATIONS SERVICES PROFESSIONAL SERVICES DIVISION, INC.—See Corporate Risk Holdings LLC; *U.S. Private*, pg. 1056
USMD HOLDINGS, INC.—See UnitedHealth Group Incorporated; *U.S. Public*, pg. 2240
US MEDICAL MANAGEMENT LLC—See Centene Corporation; *U.S. Public*, pg. 471
UTILITY SALES ASSOCIATES, INC.—See Osceola Capital Management, LLC; *U.S. Private*, pg. 3047
UTILLIGENT LLC—See Align Capital Partners, LLC; *U.S. Private*, pg. 167
VALUE BASED SOLUTIONS, LLC; *U.S. Private*, pg. 4337
VERAVIS GMBH—See AGRAVIS Raiffeisen AG; *Int'l*, pg. 216
VERBALYS—See CNIM Constructions Industrielles de la Mediterranee SA; *Int'l*, pg. 1677
VERINON TECHNOLOGY SOLUTIONS LTD; *U.S. Private*, pg. 4360
VERISAE, INC.—See Fortive Corporation; *U.S. Public*, pg. 870
VERITIV EUROPE GMBH—See Clayton, Dubilier & Rice, LLC; *U.S. Private*, pg. 928
VERIZON AMERICAS INC.—See Verizon Communications Inc.; *U.S. Public*, pg. 2285
VERUS CONSULTING GROUP LLP; *U.S. Private*, pg. 4370
VERVE CLOUD, INC.—See Digerati Technologies, Inc.; *U.S. Public*, pg. 661
VFA, INC.—See Fortive Corporation; *U.S. Public*, pg. 870
VICTOR INSURANCE EUROPE B.V.—See Marsh & McLennan Companies, Inc.; *U.S. Public*, pg. 1388
VICTOR INSURANCE ITALIA S.R.L.—See Marsh & McLennan Companies, Inc.; *U.S. Public*, pg. 1388
VIDERITY INC.; *U.S. Private*, pg. 4381
VILLA WORLD GROUP—See AVID Property Group; *Int'l*, pg. 743
VINTAGE IT SERVICES; *U.S. Private*, pg. 4386
VIRIDOR ENVIROSCOT LIMITED—See KKR & Co. Inc.; *U.S. Public*, pg. 1266
VISTAGE WORLDWIDE, INC.—See Providence Equity Partners L.L.C.; *U.S. Private*, pg. 3294
VITEC VIENNA INFORMATION TECHNOLOGY CONSULTING GMBH—See adesso SE; *Int'l*, pg. 144
VOCERA CANADA, LTD.—See Stryker Corporation; *U.S. Public*, pg. 1958
VOLT CONSULTING GROUP, LTD.—See American Cyber-Systems, Inc.; *U.S. Private*, pg. 230
VOLVO TREASURY ASIA LTD.—See AB Volvo; *Int'l*, pg. 45
VREC, INC.—See Viad Corp.; *U.S. Public*, pg. 2291
V.SHIPS OFFSHORE (ASIA) PTE. LTD.—See Ackermans & van Haaren NV; *Int'l*, pg. 106
VYNAMIC LLC—See Clayton, Dubilier & Rice, LLC; *U.S. Private*, pg. 928
WALHALLA KALK VERWALTUNGSGESELLSCHAFT MBH—See Heidelberg Materials AG; *Int'l*, pg. 3320
WALTER SCOTT & PARTNERS LIMITED—See The Bank of New York Mellon Corporation; *U.S. Public*, pg. 2038
WAMBERG GENOMIC ADVISORS, INC.; *U.S. Private*, pg. 4435
WASHINGTON MANAGEMENT GROUP, INC.—See Aronson LLC; *U.S. Private*, pg. 334
WATERMAN INTERNATIONAL LIMITED—See CTI Engineering Co., Ltd.; *Int'l*, pg. 1871
WATERMARK GROUP SERVICES (UK) LIMITED—See Harwood Capital LLP; *Int'l*, pg. 3282
WAYPORT, INC.—See AT&T Inc.; *U.S. Public*, pg. 220
WEALTHENGINE.COM; *U.S. Private*, pg. 4462
WEC BUSINESS SERVICES LLC—See WEC Energy Group, Inc.; *U.S. Public*, pg. 2342
WEGENER ICT MEDIA BV—See DPG Media Group NV; *Int'l*, pg. 2189
WEHR CONSTRUCTORS, INC.; *U.S. Private*, pg. 4470
WEISER REALITY ADVISORS LLC; *U.S. Private*, pg. 4472
WELCH CONSULTING—See CRA International, Inc.; *U.S. Public*, pg. 588
WESTERN ELECTROCHEMICAL COMPANY—See H.I.G. Capital, LLC; *U.S. Private*, pg. 1829
WESTERN UNION FINANCIAL SERVICES (AUSTRALIA) PTY LTD.—See The Western Union Company; *U.S. Public*, pg. 2142
WESTERN UNION INTERNATIONAL BANK GMBH—See The Western Union Company; *U.S. Public*, pg. 2142
WESTERN UNION RETAIL SERVICES NORWAY AS—See The Western Union Company; *U.S. Public*, pg. 2142
WESTERN UNION SERVICES INDIA PRIVATE LIMITED—See The Western Union Company; *U.S. Public*, pg. 2142
THE WEXFORD GROUP INTERNATIONAL—See CACI International Inc.; *U.S. Public*, pg. 418
THE WHEELHOUSE GROUP, INC.—See CI Capital Partners LLC; *U.S. Private*, pg. 896
THE WHITE STONE GROUP INC.—See Accel Partners L.P.; *U.S. Private*, pg. 48
THE WHITE STONE GROUP INC.—See KKR & Co. Inc.; *U.S. Public*, pg. 1238
WHOLE SECURITY S.A.C.—See Bain Capital, LP; *U.S. Private*, pg. 435
WILLAMETTE MANAGEMENT ASSOCIATES; *U.S. Private*, pg. 4521
WILLDAN FINANCIAL SERVICES—See Willdan Group, Inc.; *U.S. Public*, pg. 2371
WILLIAMS LEA INC.—See Advent International Corporation; *U.S. Private*, pg. 107
WILMORITE INC.; *U.S. Private*, pg. 4529
WIRELESS ANALYTICS, LLC—See Thoma Bravo, L.P.; *U.S. Private*, pg. 4150
WOODBRIDGE INTERNATIONAL LLC—See Mariner Wealth Advisors, LLC; *U.S. Private*, pg. 2576
WORKCARE, INC.; *U.S. Private*, pg. 4563
WYG CONSULTING LIMITED—See Tetra Tech, Inc.; *U.S. Public*, pg. 2024
WYNGATE INTERNATIONAL, INC.; *U.S. Private*, pg. 4576
XCALIBRE RISK SERVICES, INC.—See Atlantic American Corporation; *U.S. Public*, pg. 222
XIO STRATEGIES, INC.—See Elliott Management Corporation; *U.S. Private*, pg. 1368
XIO STRATEGIES, INC.—See Veritas Capital Fund Management, LLC; *U.S. Private*, pg. 4362
X PERION CONSULTING AG—See Atos SE; *Int'l*, pg. 692
XTENSIBLE SOLUTIONS, INC.—See ESCO Technologies, Inc.; *U.S. Public*, pg. 794
Y&A PROFESSIONAL SERVICES LIMITED—See Computer & Technologies Holdings Limited; *Int'l*, pg. 1758
YOUNG & ASSOCIATES; *U.S. Private*, pg. 4592
YOUNG & ASSOCIATES; *U.S. Private*, pg. 4592
ZACHRY ENGINEERING CORP. - AMARILLO—See Zachry Holdings, Inc.; *U.S. Private*, pg. 4596
ZENCOS CONSULTING LLC—See Executive Information Systems, LLC; *U.S. Public*, pg. 1447
ZIBRANT LIMITED—See BCD Holdings N.V.; *Int'l*, pg. 926
ZIETA TECHNOLOGIES LLC; *U.S. Private*, pg. 4604
ZOLFO COOPER, LLC; *U.S. Private*, pg. 4607
ZUBATKIN OWNER REPRESENTATION, LLC—See Cumming Construction Management, Inc.; *U.S. Private*, pg. 1123
ZWEITE K-W-A BETEILIGUNGSGESELLSCHAFT MBH—See Bayer Aktiengesellschaft; *Int'l*, pg. 910

541620 — ENVIRONMENTAL CONSULTING SERVICES

A1-ENVIROSCIENCES GMBH—See Diploma PLC; *Int'l*, pg. 2129
A1-ENVIROSCIENCES LIMITED—See Diploma PLC; *Int'l*, pg. 2129
A2L TECHNOLOGIES, INC.; *U.S. Private*, pg. 29
ABEDNEGO ENVIRONMENTAL SERVICES, LLC—See Ecolab Inc.; *U.S. Public*, pg. 715
ABO MLLIEUCONSULT BV—See ABO-Group NV/SA; *Int'l*, pg. 66
ACEGASAPSAMGA S.P.A.—See Hera S.p.A.; *Int'l*, pg. 3356

N.A.I.C.S. INDEX

541620 — ENVIRONMENTAL CONSU...

ACQUE INDUSTRIALI S.R.L.—See ACEA S.p.A.; *Int'l*, pg. 95
A.C.R. DI REGGIANI ALBERTINO S.P.A—See Hera S.p.A.; *Int'l*, pg. 3356
ACS SERVICIOS Y CONCESIONES, S.L.—See ACS, Actividades de Construccion y Servicios, S.A.; *Int'l*, pg. 109
ADVANTEST GREEN CORPORATION—See Advantest Corporation; *Int'l*, pg. 166
AECOM BRASIL LTDA.—See AECOM; *U.S. Public*, pg. 50
AECOM C&E, INC.—See AECOM; *U.S. Public*, pg. 50
AECOM—See AECOM; *U.S. Public*, pg. 50
AECOM—See AECOM; *U.S. Public*, pg. 50
AECOM—See AECOM; *U.S. Public*, pg. 50
AECOM—See AECOM; *U.S. Public*, pg. 50
AECOM—See AECOM; *U.S. Public*, pg. 50
AECOM—See AECOM; *U.S. Public*, pg. 50
AECOM—See AECOM; *U.S. Public*, pg. 50
AECOM VENEZUELA—See AECOM; *U.S. Public*, pg. 51
AERIS ENVIRONMENTAL LTD; *Int'l*, pg. 179
AF-ESTIVO AS—See AFRY AB; *Int'l*, pg. 193
AGRICULTURA, TECNOLOGIA, PASION ATP S.A.—See HORIBA Ltd; *Int'l*, pg. 3474
AGRI-TECH, INC. OF OREGON—See Republic Services, Inc.; *U.S. Public*, pg. 1785
ALFRED BENESCH & COMPANY—See Alfred Benesch & Company; *U.S. Private*, pg. 165
ALFRED BENESCH & COMPANY—See Alfred Benesch & Company; *U.S. Private*, pg. 165
ALIRON INTERNATIONAL, INC.; *U.S. Private*, pg. 168
ALLIANCE SOURCE TESTING LLC—See Align Capital Partners, LLC; *U.S. Public*, pg. 167
ALLIANCE TECHNICAL GROUP, LLC—See Morgan Stanley; *U.S. Public*, pg. 1474
ALLIED INDUSTRIES, INC.; *U.S. Private*, pg. 186
ALLIED RESOURCE CORPORATION; *U.S. Private*, pg. 187
ALLIED SUSTAINABILITY & ENVIRONMENTAL CONSULTANTS GROUP LIMITED; *Int'l*, pg. 358
ALLIED WASTE ENVIRONMENTAL MANAGEMENT GROUP, LLC—See Republic Services, Inc.; *U.S. Public*, pg. 1785
ALLIED WASTE SERVICES OF FORT WORTH, LLC—See Republic Services, Inc.; *U.S. Public*, pg. 1785
ALLIED WASTE SERVICES OF MASSACHUSETTS, LLC—See Republic Services, Inc.; *U.S. Public*, pg. 1785
ALLIED WASTE SERVICES OF STILLWATER, INC.—See Republic Services, Inc.; *U.S. Public*, pg. 1785
ALLIED WASTE SYSTEMS OF ARIZONA, LLC—See Republic Services, Inc.; *U.S. Public*, pg. 1785
ALLWYN PRIORITIES, LLC—See NV5 Global, Inc.; *U.S. Public*, pg. 1557
ALTA ENVIRONMENTAL CORPORATION; *U.S. Private*, pg. 203
ALTEC ENVIRONMENTAL CONSULTING, LLC—See Martin Resource Management Corporation; *U.S. Private*, pg. 2595
AMBIPAR EMERGENCY RESPONSE; *Int'l*, pg. 414
AMERICAN DISPOSAL SERVICES OF WEST VIRGINIA, INC.—See Republic Services, Inc.; *U.S. Public*, pg. 1786
AMERICAN ENVIRONMENTAL GROUP LTD.—See Tetra Tech, Inc.; *U.S. Public*, pg. 2022
AMERICAN SANITATION, INC.—See Republic Services, Inc.; *U.S. Public*, pg. 1786
ANN JOO GREEN ENERGY SDN. BHD.—See Ann Joo Resources Berhad; *Int'l*, pg. 473
ANTEA BELGIUM N.V.—See Centric Holding B.V.; *Int'l*, pg. 1412
ANTEA S.A.S.—See Centric Holding B.V.; *Int'l*, pg. 1412
ANTEA USA, INC.—See Centric Holding B.V.; *Int'l*, pg. 1412
APACHE JUNCTION LANDFILL CORPORATION—See Republic Services, Inc.; *U.S. Public*, pg. 1786
APEX COMPANIES, LLC; *U.S. Private*, pg. 292
APPLIED ECOLOGICAL SERVICES, INC.—See KKR & Co. Inc.; *U.S. Public*, pg. 1263
AQUA GUARDIAN GROUP LIMITED; *Int'l*, pg. 527
AQUANEX, SERVICIO DOMICILIARIO DEL AGUA DE EXTREMADURA SA; *Int'l*, pg. 527
AQUA SERVICES, INC.—See Fort Point Capital, LLC; *U.S. Private*, pg. 1574
AQUATERRA ENVIRONMENTAL SOLUTIONS, INC.—See SCS Engineers; *U.S. Private*, pg. 3580
ARDENT ENVIRONMENTAL GROUP, INC.—See Brookfield Corporation; *Int'l*, pg. 1182
ARS INTERNATIONAL LLC—See The Aleut Corporation; *U.S. Private*, pg. 3984
ASESORIAS Y REPRESENTACIONES ANALITICAS S.R.L.—See HORIBA Ltd; *Int'l*, pg. 3475
ASIAN LIFT PTE LTD—See HAL Trust N.V.; *Int'l*, pg. 3227
ATACAMA RESOURCES INTERNATIONAL, INC.; *U.S. Public*, pg. 220
ATC GROUP SERVICES (CT) INC.—See GI Manager L.P.; *U.S. Private*, pg. 1691
ATC GROUP SERVICES LLC—See Bernhard Capital Partners Management, LP; *U.S. Private*, pg. 536
ATLAS TRANSPORT, INC.—See Republic Services, Inc.; *U.S. Public*, pg. 1786
AVANPRO, S.A.—See HORIBA Ltd; *Int'l*, pg. 3475

AWIN LEASING COMPANY, INC.—See Republic Services, Inc.; *U.S. Public*, pg. 1785
AXIUS WATER—See KKR & Co. Inc.; *U.S. Public*, pg. 1239
BABCOCK SERVICES, INC.—See CNIM Constructions Industrielles de la Mediterranee SA; *Int'l*, pg. 1676
BADGER TECHNICAL SERVICES, LLC—See Bristol Bay Native Corporation; *U.S. Private*, pg. 655
BAQUS GROUP - OXFORD—See Baqus Group Limited; *Int'l*, pg. 857
BAUER ENVIRO KFT.—See BAUER Aktiengesellschaft; *Int'l*, pg. 891
BAY AREA ECONOMICS; *U.S. Private*, pg. 491
BCG PUBLICIDAD & AGRONEGOCIOS S.A.C—See HORIBA Ltd; *Int'l*, pg. 3475
BEACON OCCUPATIONAL HEALTH & SAFETY SERVICES, INC.; *U.S. Private*, pg. 504
BEFESA ZINC US, INC.—See Befesa S.A.; *Int'l*, pg. 940
BEIJING NOVEL ENVIRONMENTAL PROTECTION CO LIMITED—See Dongjiang Environmental Company Limited; *Int'l*, pg. 2168
BEOND GROUP LIMITED—See eEnergy Group Plc; *Int'l*, pg. 2317
BERGERABAM—See The Louis Berger Group, Inc.; *U.S. Private*, pg. 4073
BFI TRANSFER SYSTEMS OF GEORGIA, LLC—See Republic Services, Inc.; *U.S. Public*, pg. 1786
BFI WASTE SYSTEMS OF GEORGIA, LLC—See Republic Services, Inc.; *U.S. Public*, pg. 1786
BFI WASTE SYSTEMS OF KENTUCKY, LLC—See Republic Services, Inc.; *U.S. Public*, pg. 1786
BILFINGER BERGER ENTSORGUNG GMBH—See Bilfinger SE; *Int'l*, pg. 1025
BIO CLEAN ENVIRONMENTAL SERVICES—See Lone Star Global Acquisitions, LLC; *U.S. Private*, pg. 2487
THE BIOENGINEERING GROUP, INC.; *U.S. Private*, pg. 3995
BIRKITT ENVIRONMENTAL SERVICES, INC.; *U.S. Private*, pg. 564
BLANKINSHIP & ASSOCIATES, INC.—See Bowman Consulting Group Ltd.; *U.S. Public*, pg. 376
BLUEPLANET ENVIRONMENTAL INC.; *Int'l*, pg. 1072
BMT CORDAH LIMITED—See BMT Group Limited; *Int'l*, pg. 1077
BMT ISIS LTD—See BMT Group Limited; *Int'l*, pg. 1078
BMT OCEANICA PTY LTD—See BMT Group Limited; *Int'l*, pg. 1078
BONTERRA CONSULTING; *U.S. Private*, pg. 615
THE CADMUS GROUP, INC. - PORTLAND—See CI Capital Partners LLC; *U.S. Public*, pg. 896
THE CADMUS GROUP, LLC—See CI Capital Partners LLC; *U.S. Private*, pg. 895
CAMELOT LANDFILL TX, LP—See Republic Services, Inc.; *U.S. Public*, pg. 1786
CAM PARTECIPAZIONI S.P.A.—See Camfin S.p.A.; *Int'l*, pg. 1272
CAN GEOTECHNICAL LTD—See CAN (Offshore) Ltd; *Int'l*, pg. 1276
CAPPCO TUBULAR PRODUCTS USA, LLC—See Icahn Enterprises L.P.; *U.S. Public*, pg. 1084
CARBON DELTA AG—See MSCI Inc.; *U.S. Public*, pg. 1483
CARDINAL RESOURCES, INC.; *U.S. Private*, pg. 750
CARDNO ENTRIX, INC.—See Cardno Limited; *Int'l*, pg. 1322
CARDNO ERI, INC.—See Cardno Limited; *Int'l*, pg. 1322
CCR ENVIRONMENTAL INC.—See Vanasse Hangen Brustlin, Inc.; *U.S. Private*, pg. 4342
CECOS INTERNATIONAL, INC.—See Republic Services, Inc.; *U.S. Public*, pg. 1786
CEHI ACQUISITION CORPORATION—See Compass Diversified Holdings; *U.S. Public*, pg. 559
CELINA LANDFILL, INC.—See Republic Services, Inc.; *U.S. Public*, pg. 1786
CENERGIST BV—See Eneraqua Technologies Plc; *Int'l*, pg. 2418
THE CENTER FOR TOXICOLOGY & ENVIRONMENTAL HEALTH, LLC—See Montrose Environmental Group, Inc.; *U.S. Public*, pg. 1466
C.F. BEAN, LLC; *U.S. Public*, pg. 706
CHARAH SOLUTIONS, INC.—See SER Capital Partners LLC; *U.S. Private*, pg. 3612
CHARTECH SOLUTIONS INC.—See CHAR Technologies Ltd.; *Int'l*, pg. 1448
CHEMSTAFF, INC.—See Ecolab Inc.; *U.S. Public*, pg. 712
CHEM-TEL INC.—See CVC Capital Partners SICAV-FIS S.A.; *Int'l*, pg. 1885
CHEROKEE ENTERPRISES, INC.; *U.S. Private*, pg. 873
CHESAPEAKE BAY FOUNDATION; *U.S. Private*, pg. 874
CITIZENS DISPOSAL, INC.—See Republic Services, Inc.; *U.S. Public*, pg. 1786
CIVIL & ENVIRONMENTAL CONSULTANTS, INC.; *U.S. Private*, pg. 908
CLARK ENVIRONMENTAL, INC.—See One Rock Capital Partners, LLC; *U.S. Public*, pg. 3022
CLEAN EARTH, INC.—See Enviri Corporation; *U.S. Public*, pg. 780
CLEARESULT CONSULTING, INC.—See TPG Capital, L.P.; *U.S. Public*, pg. 2175

CLOVER LEAF ENVIRONMENTAL SOLUTIONS, INC.; *U.S. Private*, pg. 947
COGGIN & FAIRCHILD ENVIRONMENTAL CONSULTANTS, INC.; *U.S. Private*, pg. 962
COMMTECH COMMISSIONING SERVICES S.A.—See Fagerhult Group AB; *Int'l*, pg. 2601
CONCURRENT GROUP LLC—See QualTek Services Inc.; *U.S. Private*, pg. 1748
CONFIANCE GROUP; *U.S. Private*, pg. 1013
CONSOLIDATED SAFETY SERVICES, INC.; *U.S. Private*, pg. 1022
CONSUMER ENERGY SOLUTIONS, INC.; *U.S. Private*, pg. 1025
CONTROL TECNICO Y REPRESENTACIONES SA DE CV—See HORIBA Ltd; *Int'l*, pg. 3475
COPPER ENVIRONMENTAL CONSULTING, LLC—See The White Oak Group, Inc.; *U.S. Private*, pg. 4135
COPPER MOUNTAIN LANDFILL, INC.—See Republic Services, Inc.; *U.S. Public*, pg. 1786
CORNERSTONE ENVIRONMENTAL GROUP, LLC—See Tetra Tech, Inc.; *U.S. Public*, pg. 2022
COURTNEY RIDGE LANDFILL, LLC—See Republic Services, Inc.; *U.S. Public*, pg. 1786
COWORKRS LLC; *U.S. Private*, pg. 1074
CP DESIGN CONSULTING CO., LTD.—See Dai Nippon Printing Co., Ltd.; *Int'l*, pg. 1914
C-POWER N.V.—See Ackermans & van Haaren NV; *Int'l*, pg. 105
CROP QUEST AGRONOMIC SERVICES; *U.S. Private*, pg. 1103
CRYSTAL CLEAR TECHNOLOGIES, INC.; *U.S. Private*, pg. 1115
CUBE BIO-ENERGY PVT LTD; *Int'l*, pg. 1875
DARCO ENVIRONMENTAL (PHILIPPINES) INC.—See Darco Water Technologies Limited; *Int'l*, pg. 1972
DEME BLUE ENERGY N.V.—See Ackermans & van Haaren NV; *Int'l*, pg. 105
DEME OFFSHORE BE NV—See Ackermans & van Haaren NV; *Int'l*, pg. 105
DENOX ENVIRONMENTAL & TECHNOLOGY HOLDINGS LIMITED; *Int'l*, pg. 2028
DE REGT GERMANY GMBH—See CGG; *Int'l*, pg. 1432
DERICHEBOURG AVIATION & ENERGY RESOURCES LTD.—See Derichebourg S.A.; *Int'l*, pg. 2042
DERICHEBOURG CANADA ENVIRONNEMENT INC.—See Derichebourg S.A.; *Int'l*, pg. 2041
DERICHEBOURG EVOLUTION FORMATION EURL—See Derichebourg S.A.; *Int'l*, pg. 2042
DERICHEBOURG MEDIO AMBIENTE SA—See Derichebourg S.A.; *Int'l*, pg. 2042
DERICHEBOURG RECYCLING MEXICO SA—See Derichebourg S.A.; *Int'l*, pg. 2042
DERICHEBOURG RECYCLING USA, INC.—See Derichebourg S.A.; *Int'l*, pg. 2042
DERICHEBOURG SNG SAS—See Derichebourg S.A.; *Int'l*, pg. 2042
DERICHEBOURG SOURCING AERO & ENERGY SAS—See Derichebourg S.A.; *Int'l*, pg. 2042
DERICHEBOURG TECHNOLOGIES SAS—See Derichebourg S.A.; *Int'l*, pg. 2042
DEXTER FIELD SERVICES; *U.S. Private*, pg. 1220
DIA CONSULTANTS CO., LTD.—See DN HOLDINGS CO.,LTD; *Int'l*, pg. 2147
DISCOVERY WETLANDS SDN. BHD.—See Gamuda Berhad; *Int'l*, pg. 2879
DOWA TECNO-RESEACH CO., LTD.—See Dowa Holdings Co., Ltd.; *Int'l*, pg. 2184
DRACE MEDIO AMBIENTE, S.A.—See ACS, Actividades de Construccion y Servicios, S.A.; *Int'l*, pg. 111
DRA CONSULTANTS LIMITED; *Int'l*, pg. 2196
E4E SOLUTIONS; *U.S. Private*, pg. 1308
EAGLE FORD ENVIRONMENTAL SERVICES, LLC—See Texcom, Inc.; *U.S. Public*, pg. 2027
EARTH CONSULTING GROUP, INC.; *U.S. Private*, pg. 1314
ECOACT S.A.S.—See Atos SE; *Int'l*, pg. 692
E CO CONSULTANTS, INC.—See Littlejohn & Co., LLC; *U.S. Private*, pg. 2469
ECOFLO FIELD SERVICES, LLC—See Republic Services, Inc.; *U.S. Public*, pg. 1786
ECOLUTIONS GMBH & CO. KGAA; *Int'l*, pg. 2295
ECO-PAN, INC.—See Concrete Pumping Holdings, Inc.; *U.S. Public*, pg. 566
ECOREC SRL—See Derichebourg S.A.; *Int'l*, pg. 2042
ECOSAVE HOLDINGS LIMITED; *Int'l*, pg. 2299
ECOSECURITIES GROUP PLC; *Int'l*, pg. 2299
ECOSECURITIES, LTD.—See EcoSecurities Group plc; *Int'l*, pg. 2299
ECOTERRES S.A.—See Ackermans & van Haaren NV; *Int'l*, pg. 105
ECOTONE, INC.—See L2 Capital Partners; *U.S. Private*, pg. 2367
ECOWISE ENVIRONMENTAL PTY LTD—See ALS Limited; *Int'l*, pg. 378
THE EDINBURGH CENTRE FOR CARBON MANAGEMENT LIMITED—See CVC Capital Partners SICAV-FIS S.A.; *Int'l*, pg. 1882
EDP GEOSCIENCES—See Soil & Materials Engineers, Inc.; *U.S. Private*, pg. 3706

541620 — ENVIRONMENTAL CONSU...

EDS-R GMBH; *Int'l*, pg. 2315
EDUCATIONAL DATA SYSTEMS, INC.; *U.S. Private*, pg. 1339
EE&G ENVIRONMENTAL SERVICES, LLC; *U.S. Private*, pg. 1342
EEVS INSIGHT LIMITED—See APC Technology Group plc; *Int'l*, pg. 508
ELEMENT MARKETS LLC—See TPG Capital, L.P.; *U.S. Public*, pg. 2177
ELLIS COUNTY LANDFILL TX, LP—See Republic Services, Inc.; *U.S. Public*, pg. 1786
ELOS ENVIRONMENTAL, LLC—See Bernhard Capital Partners Management, LP; *U.S. Private*, pg. 537
EM-ASSIST, INC.—See Cardno Limited; *Int'l*, pg. 1322
EMISSION ADVISORS, INC.—See AEGIS Hedging Solutions, LLC; *U.S. Private*, pg. 116
ENBIO ENGINEERING, INC.—See EnBio Holdings Inc.; *Int'l*, pg. 2396
ENBIO HOLDINGS INC.; *Int'l*, pg. 2396
ENCINO ENVIRONMENTAL SERVICES, LLC; *U.S. Private*, pg. 1390
ENCO INDUSTRIES, INC.; *U.S. Private*, pg. 1390
ENDRESS+HAUSER ITALIA S.P.A.—See Endress+Hauser (International) Holding AG; *Int'l*, pg. 2407
ENERNEX LLC—See Cesi S.p.A.; *Int'l*, pg. 1424
ENGLOBE CORP.—See Colliers International Group Inc.; *Int'l*, pg. 1701
ENTECH INDUSTRIES PTY. LIMITED—See KKR & Co. Inc.; *U.S. Public*, pg. 1263
ENTEC SERVICES, INC.; *U.S. Private*, pg. 1402
ENVIRO CLEAN SERVICES LLC; *U.S. Private*, pg. 1406
ENVIROCON, INC.—See Washington Corporations; *U.S. Private*, pg. 4446
ENVIROCON, INC.—See Washington Corporations; *U.S. Private*, pg. 4446
ENVIROCON, INC.—See Washington Corporations; *U.S. Private*, pg. 4446
ENVIROCON, INC.—See Washington Corporations; *U.S. Private*, pg. 4446
ENVIROCON, INC.—See Washington Corporations; *U.S. Private*, pg. 4446
ENVIROCON, INC.—See Washington Corporations; *U.S. Private*, pg. 4446
ENVIROCON, INC.—See Washington Corporations; *U.S. Private*, pg. 4446
ENVIROCON, INC.—See Washington Corporations; *U.S. Private*, pg. 4446
ENVIROCYCLE, INC.—See Republic Services, Inc.; *U.S. Public*, pg. 1786
ENVIRONMENTAL ALLIANCE, INC.—See Montrose Environmental Group, Inc.; *U.S. Public*, pg. 1466
ENVIRONMENTAL BIOTECH INTERNATIONAL, LLC; *U.S. Private*, pg. 1407
ENVIRONMENTAL CONSULTING & TECHNOLOGY, INC.; *U.S. Private*, pg. 1407
ENVIRONMENTAL CONTROL CENTER CO., LTD.; *Int'l*, pg. 2455
ENVIRONMENTAL HOLDINGS GROUP, LLC; *U.S. Private*, pg. 1408
ENVIRONMENTAL INTEGRATED SOLUTIONS LTD.—See CECO Environmental Corp.; *U.S. Public*, pg. 463
ENVIRONMENTAL MANAGEMENT RESOURCES, INC.; *U.S. Private*, pg. 1408
ENVIRONMENTAL MANAGEMENT SPECIALISTS, INC.—See Gryphon Investors, LLC; *U.S. Private*, pg. 1798
ENVIRONMENTAL PRODUCTS & SERVICES OF VERMONT, INC.—See GenNx360 Capital Partners, L.P.; *U.S. Private*, pg. 1672
ENVIRONMENTAL RESEARCH & SOLUTIONS CO., LTD.—See CTI Engineering Co., Ltd.; *Int'l*, pg. 1871
ENVIRONMENTAL RESOURCE ASSOC., INC.—See Waters Corporation; *U.S. Public*, pg. 2334
ENVIRONMENTAL RESOURCES MANAGEMENT LIMITED—See Alberta Investment Management Corporation; *Int'l*, pg. 297
ENVIRONMENTAL SERVICES GROUP LTD.—See 3i Group plc; *Int'l*, pg. 8
ENVIRONMENTAL TECHNOLOGY COMPANY—See Amano Corporation; *Int'l*, pg. 411
ENVIRONMENTAL WASTE MINIMIZATION INC.; *U.S. Private*, pg. 1409
ENVIRONMENTAL WASTE SOLUTIONS LLC; *U.S. Private*, pg. 1409
ENVIROPURE SYSTEMS, INC.—See T&S Brass & Bronze Works, Inc.; *U.S. Private*, pg. 3910
ENVIROS CONSULTING LTD.—See Jacobs Engineering Group, Inc.; *U.S. Public*, pg. 1185
ENVIROS, S. R. O.—See Jacobs Engineering Group, Inc.; *U.S. Public*, pg. 1185
ENVIROSUITE LIMITED; *Int'l*, pg. 2455
ENVIROSYS LTD.—See HORIBA Ltd; *Int'l*, pg. 3475
ENVIROTECH ENGINEERING & CONSULTING, INC.; *U.S. Private*, pg. 1409
ENVIROTEK ENVIRONMENTAL & CONSTRUCTION SERVICES; *U.S. Private*, pg. 1409
ENVIROTRAC LTD.; *U.S. Private*, pg. 1409

ENVIROWASTE SERVICES GROUP, INC.; *U.S. Private*, pg. 1409
ENVOTECH-ILLINOIS L.L.C.—See Republic Services, Inc.; *U.S. Public*, pg. 1786
EPROLAB SA—See HORIBA Ltd; *Int'l*, pg. 3475
EQUILAB, S.A. DE C.V.—See HORIBA Ltd; *Int'l*, pg. 3475
EQUISOL LLC—See Environmental Infrastructure Holdings Corp.; *U.S. Private*, pg. 1408
ERI SOLUTIONS, LLC; *U.S. Private*, pg. 1419
THE ERM GROUP, INC.—See Alberta Investment Management Corporation; *Int'l*, pg. 297
THE EROSION COMPANY; *U.S. Private*, pg. 4026
ESA ENVIRONMENTAL SPECIALISTS, INC.; *U.S. Private*, pg. 1424
ESIS ACADEMY PTE. LTD.—See Chubb Limited; *Int'l*, pg. 1591
ETHICALCHEM—See Ethical Solutions, LLC; *U.S. Private*, pg. 1431
ETHICAL SOLUTIONS, LLC; *U.S. Private*, pg. 1431
EURALIS ESPACES VERTS—See Euralis Coop; *Int'l*, pg. 2527
EUROFINS ANALISIS AGRO, S.A.—See Eurofins Scientific S.E.; *Int'l*, pg. 2537
EUROFINS EAC CORPORATION—See Eurofins Scientific S.E.; *Int'l*, pg. 2540
EUROFINS ENVIRONMENTAL SERVICES LTD—See Eurofins Scientific S.E.; *Int'l*, pg. 2544
EUROFINS ENVIRONMENT II DE GMBH—See Eurofins Scientific S.E.; *Int'l*, pg. 2544
EUROFINS ENVIRONMENT TESTING SWEDEN HOLDING AB—See Eurofins Scientific S.E.; *Int'l*, pg. 2540
EUROFINS IPL ENVIRONNEMENT SAS—See Eurofins Scientific S.E.; *Int'l*, pg. 2542
EUROFINS QUIMICO ONUBENSE, S.L.U.—See Eurofins Scientific S.E.; *Int'l*, pg. 2547
E.VIRONMENT, LLC—See Charterhouse Capital Partners LLP; *Int'l*, pg. 1455
EVN UMWELT BETEILIGUNGS UND SERVICE GMBH—See EVN AG; *Int'l*, pg. 2571
EVU.IT GMBH—See adesso SE; *Int'l*, pg. 144
FCC ENVIRONMENT (LINCOLNSHIRE) LTD.—See Fomento de Construcciones y Contratas, S.A.; *Int'l*, pg. 2722
FEDERAL ENVIRONMENTAL & ENERGY PTE. LTD.—See Federal International (2000) Ltd; *Int'l*, pg. 2630
FERTILIVITA S.R.L.—See A2A S.p.A.; *Int'l*, pg. 29
FERUS INC.; *Int'l*, pg. 2646
FLI FRANCE SAS—See FLI International Limited; *Int'l*, pg. 2705
FLI INTERNATIONAL LIMITED; *Int'l*, pg. 2705
FLOWEN S.A.C—See HORIBA Ltd; *Int'l*, pg. 3475
FONDASOL SA—See BNP Paribas SA; *Int'l*, pg. 1083
FORDIE ESTATES LIMITED—See Averon Park Limited; *Int'l*, pg. 739
FUGRO EMU LTD.—See Fugro N.V.; *Int'l*, pg. 2806
FUGRO NIGERIA LTD.—See Fugro N.V.; *Int'l*, pg. 2807
FUNDACION TRAXION, A. C.—See Grupo Traxion, S. A. B. de C. V.; *Int'l*, pg. 3138
GEOINGENIERIA S.A.—See Centric Holding B.V.; *Int'l*, pg. 1412
GEOSONDA BVBA—See ABO-Group NV/SA; *Int'l*, pg. 66
GEOSONDA ENVIRONMENT NV—See ABO-Group NV/SA; *Int'l*, pg. 66
GEOSYNTEC CONSULTANTS, INC. - ACTON—See Geosyntec Consultants, Inc.; *U.S. Private*, pg. 1685
GEOSYNTEC CONSULTANTS, INC. - COLORADO—See Geosyntec Consultants, Inc.; *U.S. Private*, pg. 1685
GEOSYNTEC CONSULTANTS, INC.; *U.S. Private*, pg. 1685
GEO-SYNTHETICS, INC.; *U.S. Private*, pg. 1680
GESELLSCHAFT FUR ENERGIE UND KLIMASCHUTZ SCHLESWIG- HOLSTEIN GMBH—See E.ON SE; *Int'l*, pg. 2258
GES GROUNDWATER & ENVIRONMENTAL SERVICES, INC.; *U.S. Private*, pg. 1688
G.K. FOUR TWENTY SEVEN JAPAN—See Moody's Corporation; *U.S. Public*, pg. 1467
GLE ASSOCIATES, INC.; *U.S. Private*, pg. 1708
GLOBAL ALERTS LLC—See Quest Resource Holding Corporation; *U.S. Public*, pg. 1756
GLOBAL WATER TECHNOLOGIES, INC.; *U.S. Public*, pg. 945
GRAY & PAPE, INC.; *U.S. Private*, pg. 1759
GREAT ECOLOGY, INC.; *U.S. Private*, pg. 1763
GREAT ECOLOGY, INC.—See Great Ecology, Inc.; *U.S. Private*, pg. 1763
GREAT ECOLOGY, INC.—See Great Ecology, Inc.; *U.S. Private*, pg. 1763
GREAT ECOLOGY, INC.—See Great Ecology, Inc.; *U.S. Private*, pg. 1763
GREEN BUILDING CERTIFICATION INSTITUTE; *U.S. Private*, pg. 1772
GREENIX LLC; *U.S. Private*, pg. 1778
GREENORDER, LLC—See Cleantech Group, Inc.; *U.S. Private*, pg. 931
GREENRIDGE WASTE SERVICES, LLC—See Republic Services, Inc.; *U.S. Public*, pg. 1786
GREENSOURCE CORPORATION; *U.S. Private*, pg. 1780
GRONN VEKST AS—See Cambi ASA; *Int'l*, pg. 1268

CORPORATE AFFILIATIONS

GSI ENVIRONNEMENT—See Colliers International Group Inc.; *Int'l*, pg. 1701
GULLBERG & JANSSON AB; *Int'l*, pg. 3182
HAMER ENVIRONMENTAL L.P.—See Environmental Enginuity Group LLC; *U.S. Private*, pg. 1407
HANDEX CONSULTING AND REMEDIATION, LLC; *U.S. Private*, pg. 1852
HFP ACOUSTICAL CONSULTANTS CORP.—See Charterhouse Capital Partners LLP; *Int'l*, pg. 1456
HILL'S ENVIRONMENTAL LIMITED—See Arthur J. Gallagher & Co.; *U.S. Public*, pg. 203
HOKKAIDO ECO RECYCLE SYSTEMS CO., LTD.—See Hitachi, Ltd.; *Int'l*, pg. 3422
HOV ENVIRONMENT SOLUTIONS PRIVATE LIMITED—See HOV Services Limited; *Int'l*, pg. 3492
HPC AG; *Int'l*, pg. 3500
HUIZHOU DONGJIANG ENVIRONMENT TECHNOLOGY CO. LIMITED—See Dongjiang Environmental Company Limited; *Int'l*, pg. 2168
HYDRO-LOGIC ASSOCIATES, INC.; *U.S. Private*, pg. 2017
HYDROMETRICS, INC.; *U.S. Private*, pg. 2018
IDEA CONSULTANTS, INC.; *Int'l*, pg. 3588
IESA INC.—See IESA Pty Ltd; *Int'l*, pg. 3598
IESA INC.—See IESA Pty Ltd; *Int'l*, pg. 3598
IESA PTY LTD; *Int'l*, pg. 3598
IETG LTD.; *Int'l*, pg. 3598
IHI ENVIRONMENTAL INC—See Terracon Consultants, Inc.; *U.S. Private*, pg. 3971
IL&FS ENVIRONMENTAL INFRASTRUCTURE & SERVICE LIMITED—See Everstone Capital Advisors Pvt. Ltd.; *Int'l*, pg. 2569
ILLIANA DISPOSAL PARTNERSHIP—See Republic Services, Inc.; *U.S. Public*, pg. 1786
ILLINOIS LANDFILL, INC.—See Republic Services, Inc.; *U.S. Public*, pg. 1786
IMAGE MICROSYSTEMS - COMMERCE—See Image Microsystems, Inc.; *U.S. Private*, pg. 2044
IMPERIAL LANDFILL, INC.—See Republic Services, Inc.; *U.S. Public*, pg. 1786
INSTRUMED PANAMA, S.A.—See HORIBA Ltd; *Int'l*, pg. 3477
INTEGRATED SCIENCE & TECHNOLOGY, INC.—See Hunan Yonker Investment Group Co., Ltd.; *Int'l*, pg. 3534
INTERCOVAMEX, S.A. DE C.V.—See HORIBA Ltd; *Int'l*, pg. 3477
ISI ENVIRONMENTAL; *U.S. Private*, pg. 2144
JACOBS CLEAN ENERGY S.R.O.—See Jacobs Engineering Group, Inc.; *U.S. Public*, pg. 1184
JAPAN FACILITY SOLUTIONS, INC.—See Azbil Corporation; *Int'l*, pg. 777
KASHIWA ENVIRONMENT TECHNOLOGY CO.,LTD—See Hitachi Zosen Corporation; *Int'l*, pg. 3411
K C HARVEY ENVIRONMENTAL LLC—See Bernhard Capital Partners Management, LP; *U.S. Private*, pg. 537
KEIKA VENTURES LLC; *U.S. Private*, pg. 2273
KEMRON ENVIRONMENTAL SERVICES, INC.; *U.S. Private*, pg. 2282
KESSLER CONSULTING, INC.—See Marsh & McLennan Companies, Inc.; *U.S. Public*, pg. 1377
KINGSTON ENVIRONMENTAL SERVICES, INC.; *U.S. Private*, pg. 2312
KOUKI CORP.—See Daiei Kankyo Co., Ltd.; *Int'l*, pg. 1924
KPA SERVICES, LLC—See Providence Equity Partners L.L.C.; *U.S. Private*, pg. 3293
KRANZ, INC.—See Bain Capital, LP; *U.S. Private*, pg. 440
KREIS WASSER AG—See Burkhalter Holding AG; *Int'l*, pg. 1225
LABORATORIO DE CONTROL ARJ, S. A. DE C. V.—See ALS Limited; *Int'l*, pg. 378
LAB TOP PERU S.R.L—See HORIBA Ltd; *Int'l*, pg. 3477
LAKE NORMAN LANDFILL, INC.—See Republic Services, Inc.; *U.S. Public*, pg. 1786
LAND MANAGEMENT GROUP, INC.—See The Davey Tree Expert Company; *U.S. Private*, pg. 4018
LANDMARK INFORMATION GROUP—See Daily Mail & General Trust plc; *Int'l*, pg. 1938
LANGAN ENGINEERING & ENVIRONMENTAL SERVICES, INC.; *U.S. Private*, pg. 2388
LANGAN ENGINEERING & ENVIRONMENTAL SERVICES, INC.—See Langan Engineering & Environmental Services, Inc.; *U.S. Private*, pg. 2388
LANGAN ENGINEERING & ENVIRONMENTAL SERVICES, INC.—See Langan Engineering & Environmental Services, Inc.; *U.S. Private*, pg. 2389
LANGAN ENGINEERING & ENVIRONMENTAL SERVICES, INC.—See Langan Engineering & Environmental Services, Inc.; *U.S. Private*, pg. 2389
LANGAN ENGINEERING & ENVIRONMENTAL SERVICES, INC.—See Langan Engineering & Environmental Services, Inc.; *U.S. Private*, pg. 2389
LANGAN ENGINEERING & ENVIRONMENTAL SERVICES, INC.—See Langan Engineering & Environmental Services, Inc.; *U.S. Private*, pg. 2389
LANGAN ENGINEERING & ENVIRONMENTAL SERVICES, INC.—See Langan Engineering & Environmental Services, Inc.; *U.S. Private*, pg. 2389
LANGAN ENGINEERING & ENVIRONMENTAL SERVICES, INC.—See Langan Engineering & Environmental Ser-

N.A.I.C.S. INDEX

541620 — ENVIRONMENTAL CONSU...

vices, Inc.; *U.S. Private*, pg. 2389
LANGAN ENGINEERING & ENVIRONMENTAL SERVICES, INC.—See Langan Engineering & Environmental Services, Inc.; *U.S. Private*, pg. 2389
LANGAN ENGINEERING & ENVIRONMENTAL SERVICES, INC.—See Langan Engineering & Environmental Services, Inc.; *U.S. Private*, pg. 2389
LANGAN ENGINEERING & ENVIRONMENTAL SERVICES, INC.—See Langan Engineering & Environmental Services, Inc.; *U.S. Private*, pg. 2389
LANGAN ENGINEERING & ENVIRONMENTAL SERVICES, INC.—See Langan Engineering & Environmental Services, Inc.; *U.S. Private*, pg. 2389
LANGAN ENGINEERING & ENVIRONMENTAL SERVICES, INC.—See Langan Engineering & Environmental Services, Inc.; *U.S. Private*, pg. 2389
LANGAN INTERNATIONAL, LLC - GREECE—See Langan Engineering & Environmental Services, Inc.; *U.S. Private*, pg. 2389
LANGAN INTERNATIONAL, LLC - QATAR—See Langan Engineering & Environmental Services, Inc.; *U.S. Private*, pg. 2389
LANGAN INTERNATIONAL, LLC - TURKEY—See Langan Engineering & Environmental Services, Inc.; *U.S. Private*, pg. 2389
LANGAN INTERNATIONAL, LLC - UNITED ARAB EMIRATES—See Langan Engineering & Environmental Services, Inc.; *U.S. Private*, pg. 2389
LANGAN TREADWELL ROLLO - OAKLAND—See Langan Engineering & Environmental Services, Inc.; *U.S. Private*, pg. 2389
LANGAN TREADWELL ROLLO - SACRAMENTO—See Langan Engineering & Environmental Services, Inc.; *U.S. Private*, pg. 2389
LANGAN TREADWELL ROLLO - SAN JOSE—See Langan Engineering & Environmental Services, Inc.; *U.S. Private*, pg. 2389
LANGAN TREADWELL ROLLO—See Langan Engineering & Environmental Services, Inc.; *U.S. Private*, pg. 2389
LASA PROSPECCOES SA—See CGG; *Int'l*, pg. 1432
LEE COUNTY LANDFILL, INC.—See Republic Services, Inc.; *U.S. Public*, pg. 1786
LEE COUNTY LANDFILL SC, LLC—See Republic Services, Inc.; *U.S. Public*, pg. 1786
LEGENCE HOLDINGS LLC—See Blackstone Inc.; *U.S. Public*, pg. 355
LEMOS LABS, LLC; *U.S. Private*, pg. 2421
LIESCH ASSOCIATES, INC.—See Terracon Consultants, Inc.; *U.S. Private*, pg. 3971
LONG HO SCIENCE CO., LTD.—See Hitachi Zosen Corporation; *Int'l*, pg. 3411
LOTSPEICH AND ASSOCIATES, INC.—See Comvest Group Holdings LLC; *U.S. Private*, pg. 1007
MADRID ENGINEERING GROUP, INC.; *U.S. Private*, pg. 2544
MARRON & ASSOCIATES, INC.—See NV5 Global, Inc.; *U.S. Public*, pg. 1557
MATERIALAB CONSULTANTS LTD.—See Fugro N.V.; *Int'l*, pg. 2808
M-CUBED INFORMATION SYSTEMS, INC.—See Transformation Advisors Group, LLC; *U.S. Private*, pg. 4208
MDH ENGINEERED SOLUTIONS CORP.—See AtkinsRealis Group Inc.; *Int'l*, pg. 671
MD ORTHOPAEDICS, INC.; *U.S. Private*, pg. 2646
METROPOLITAN ENVIRONMENTAL SERVICES, INC.—See Carylon Corporation; *U.S. Private*, pg. 777
MICAH GROUP ENERGY AND ENVIRONMENTAL; *U.S. Private*, pg. 2697
MINNOW ENVIRONMENTAL, INC.—See Keystone Group, L.P.; *U.S. Private*, pg. 2299
MONARCH SITE SERVICES; *U.S. Private*, pg. 2769
MONTROSE ENVIRONMENTAL GROUP, INC.; *U.S. Public*, pg. 1466
MORAN ENVIRONMENTAL RECOVERY, LLC—See Moran Towing Corporation; *U.S. Private*, pg. 2781
MOUNTAIN ENVIRONMENTAL SERVICES, INC.—See Palladium Equity Partners, LLC; *U.S. Private*, pg. 3078
NACE INTERNATIONAL; *U.S. Private*, pg. 2829
NAP ACOUSTICS FAR EAST LIMITED—See Embelton Limited; *Int'l*, pg. 2375
NATIVE ENVIRONMENTAL, LLC; *U.S. Private*, pg. 2866
NATURAL RESOURCES CONSULTING, INC.; *U.S. Private*, pg. 2867
NAUTILUS ENVIRONMENTAL, LLC.; *U.S. Private*, pg. 2872
NES ECOLOGICAL SERVICES—See Robert E. Lee & Associates, Inc.; *U.S. Private*, pg. 3457
NETWORK MAPPING INC.—See Trimble, Inc.; *U.S. Public*, pg. 2190
NEW ENGLAND ENVIROSTRATEGIES, INC.—See Terracon Consultants, Inc.; *U.S. Private*, pg. 3971
NEW MORGAN LANDFILL COMPANY, INC.—See Republic Services, Inc.; *U.S. Public*, pg. 1786
NEXT STEP LIVING, INC.; *U.S. Private*, pg. 2920
NORD-DIREKT GMBH—See E.ON SE; *Int'l*, pg. 2258
NORTH POINT GEOGRAPHIC SOLUTIONS—See Avineon, Inc.; *U.S. Private*, pg. 407
NORTHSTAR CONTRACTING GROUP, INC.—See J.F. Lehman & Company, Inc.; *U.S. Private*, pg. 2164
NORTHWEST TENNESSEE DISPOSAL CORPORATION—See Republic Services, Inc.; *U.S. Public*, pg. 1786
NUVERRA ENVIRONMENTAL SOLUTIONS, INC.—See Select Water Solutions, Inc.; *U.S. Public*, pg. 1862
NV5, LLC—See NV5 Global, Inc.; *U.S. Public*, pg. 1557
OCTIEF PTY LTD—See HRL Holdings Limited; *Int'l*, pg. 3501
OGM, LTD.; *U.S. Private*, pg. 3003
OMNI ENVIRONMENTAL LLC—See Goldberg Lindsay & Co., LLC; *U.S. Private*, pg. 1730
ONSITE ENERGY CORPORATION—See Willdan Group, Inc.; *U.S. Public*, pg. 2371
OPINION DYNAMICS CORPORATION; *U.S. Private*, pg. 3032
ORCHARD, HILTZ & MCCLIMENT INC.; *U.S. Private*, pg. 3039
PACIFIC AIR & ENVIRONMENT PTY LTD—See EnviroSuite Limited; *Int'l*, pg. 2455
PACIFIC MUNICIPAL CONSULTANTS; *U.S. Private*, pg. 3068
PARS ENVIRONMENTAL, INC.—See Montrose Environmental Group, Inc.; *U.S. Public*, pg. 1466
PARTNER ENGINEERING & SCIENCE, INC; *U.S. Private*, pg. 3101
PETROTECH SOUTHEAST, INC.; *U.S. Private*, pg. 3163
POLU KAI SERVICES LLC; *U.S. Private*, pg. 3225
POWERLINK LLC.; *U.S. Private*, pg. 3239
POWER@SEA N.V.—See Ackermans & van Haaren NV; *Int'l*, pg. 105
POYRY SILVICONSULT ENGENHARIA LTDA.—See AFRY AB; *Int'l*, pg. 196
PRUDENT TECHNOLOGIES INC.; *U.S. Private*, pg. 3295
PT CGG SERVICES INDONESIA—See CGG; *Int'l*, pg. 1432
PURE AIR CONTROL SERVICES, INC.—See RPM International Inc.; *U.S. Public*, pg. 1817
QUALITY ENVIRONMENTAL SERVICES, LLC—See Caymus Equity Partners LLC; *U.S. Private*, pg. 795
QUANTUM TECHNICAL SERVICES, LLC—See Ecolab Inc.; *U.S. Public*, pg. 716
QUEENSLAND ENVIRONMENT PTY LTD—See EnviroSuite Limited; *Int'l*, pg. 2455
QUEST RECYCLING SERVICES LLC; *U.S. Private*, pg. 3326
QUEST RESOURCE MANAGEMENT GROUP, LLC—See Quest Resource Holding Corporation; *U.S. Public*, pg. 1756
RABANCO COMPANIES—See Republic Services, Inc.; *U.S. Public*, pg. 1787
RAINBOW ENVIRONMENTAL SERVICES, LLC—See Republic Services, Inc.; *U.S. Public*, pg. 1787
REA DALMINE S.P.A.—See Green Holding S.p.A.; *Int'l*, pg. 3071
RECON ENVIRONMENTAL, INC.; *U.S. Private*, pg. 3371
REFINAL INDUSTRIES SAS—See Derichebourg S.A.; *Int'l*, pg. 2042
REPUBLIC SERVICES OF CANADA, INC.—See Republic Services, Inc.; *U.S. Public*, pg. 1787
REPUBLIC SERVICES OF COLORADO HAULING, LLC—See Republic Services, Inc.; *U.S. Public*, pg. 1787
REPUBLIC SERVICES OF GEORGIA, LIMITED PARTNERSHIP—See Republic Services, Inc.; *U.S. Public*, pg. 1787
REPUBLIC SERVICES OF INDIANA TRANSPORTATION, LLC—See Republic Services, Inc.; *U.S. Public*, pg. 1787
REPUBLIC SERVICES OF KENTUCKY, LLC—See Republic Services, Inc.; *U.S. Public*, pg. 1787
REPUBLIC SERVICES OF NEW JERSEY, LLC—See Republic Services, Inc.; *U.S. Public*, pg. 1787
REPUBLIC SERVICES OF NORTH CAROLINA, LLC—See Republic Services, Inc.; *U.S. Public*, pg. 1787
REPUBLIC SERVICES OF OHIO HAULING, LLC—See Republic Services, Inc.; *U.S. Public*, pg. 1787
REPUBLIC SERVICES OF SOUTH CAROLINA, LLC—See Republic Services, Inc.; *U.S. Public*, pg. 1787
REPUBLIC SERVICES VASCO ROAD, LLC—See Republic Services, Inc.; *U.S. Public*, pg. 1787
REPUBLIC WASTE SERVICES OF TEXAS, LTD.—See Republic Services, Inc.; *U.S. Public*, pg. 1787
RESOURCE INNOVATIONS, LLC—See BV Investment Partners, LLC; *U.S. Private*, pg. 699
RESOURCE SOLUTIONS GROUP LLC—See TPG Capital, L.P.; *U.S. Public*, pg. 2176
RESOURCEWISE—See Battery Ventures, L.P.; *U.S. Private*, pg. 489
RE SUSTAINABILITY INTERNATIONAL (SINGAPORE) PTE. LTD.—See KKR & Co. Inc.; *U.S. Public*, pg. 1263
RETRIEV TECHNOLOGIES, INC.—See Heritage Group; *U.S. Private*, pg. 1923
RICHMOND SANITARY SERVICE, INC.—See Republic Services, Inc.; *U.S. Public*, pg. 1787
RIGMAX H2O, LLC—See RigMax, LLC; *U.S. Private*, pg. 3436
RIGMAX, LLC; *U.S. Private*, pg. 3436
ROCKWATER ENERGY SOLUTIONS, INC.—See Select Water Solutions, Inc.; *U.S. Public*, pg. 1862
RONCO CONSULTING CORPORATION—See Allied Universal Manager LLC; *U.S. Private*, pg. 189
ROYAL HOLDINGS, INC.—See Republic Services, Inc.; *U.S. Public*, pg. 1787
RSB SOLUTIONS, LC; *U.S. Private*, pg. 3496
RUG RAIFFEISEN UMWELTGESELLSCHAFT M.B.H—See BayWa AG; *Int'l*, pg. 918
SAGE ATC ENVIRONMENTAL CONSULTING LLC—See Bernhard Capital Partners Management, LP; *U.S. Private*, pg. 536
SAIN ENGINEERING ASSOCIATES, INC.; *U.S. Private*, pg. 3529
SANEXEN ENVIRONMENTAL SERVICES INC.—See Blue Wolf Capital Partners LLC; *U.S. Private*, pg. 595
SANEXEN ENVIRONMENTAL SERVICES INC. TORONTO—See Blue Wolf Capital Partners LLC; *U.S. Private*, pg. 595
SCALDIS SALVAGE AND MARINE CONTRACTORS N.V.—See Ackermans & van Haaren NV; *Int'l*, pg. 105
SCENIC HUDSON, INC.; *U.S. Private*, pg. 3562
SCHEDA ECOLOGICAL ASSOCIATES, INC.; *U.S. Private*, pg. 3564
SCS ENGINEERS KOREA, LTD.—See SCS Engineers; *U.S. Private*, pg. 3580
SCS ENGINEERS OF NEW YORK, PC—See SCS Engineers; *U.S. Private*, pg. 3580
SCS ENGINEERS - SCS ENERGY DIVISION—See SCS Engineers; *U.S. Private*, pg. 3580
SCS ES CONSULTANTS—See SCS Engineers; *U.S. Private*, pg. 3580
SCS GLOBEX ENGINEERING—See SCS Engineers; *U.S. Private*, pg. 3580
SCS TRACER ENVIRONMENTAL—See SCS Engineers; *U.S. Private*, pg. 3580
SEC RADCON ALLIANCE, LLC—See Perma-Fix Environmental Services, Inc.; *U.S. Public*, pg. 1676
SELECT ENVIRONMENTAL SERVICES, INC.—See Carylon Corporation; *U.S. Private*, pg. 777
SIERRA RESEARCH, INC.—See Gryphon Investors, LLC; *U.S. Private*, pg. 1799
SIMAM S.P.A.—See ACEA S.p.A.; *Int'l*, pg. 95
SLR CONSULTING AUSTRALIA PTY LTD—See Charterhouse Capital Partners LLP; *Int'l*, pg. 1456
SLR CONSULTING (CANADA) LTD—See Charterhouse Capital Partners LLP; *Int'l*, pg. 1456
SLR CONSULTING (IRELAND) LTD—See Charterhouse Capital Partners LLP; *Int'l*, pg. 1456
SLR CONSULTING LTD.—See Charterhouse Capital Partners LLP; *Int'l*, pg. 1455
SLR CONSULTING (SOUTH AFRICA) PTY LTD—See Charterhouse Capital Partners LLP; *Int'l*, pg. 1456
SLR INTERNATIONAL CORPORATION—See Charterhouse Capital Partners LLP; *Int'l*, pg. 1456
SMITH MANAGEMENT GROUP, INC.—See All4 LLC; *U.S. Private*, pg. 174
SML ENTERPRISES INC.—See Angeles Equity Partners, LLC; *U.S. Private*, pg. 282
SNC-LAVALIN ENVIRONMENT INC—See AtkinsRealis Group Inc.; *Int'l*, pg. 671
SNC-LAVALIN MAGYARORSZAG KFT—See AtkinsRealis Group Inc.; *Int'l*, pg. 672
SNC-LAVALIN RURAL DEVELOPMENT—See AtkinsRealis Group Inc.; *Int'l*, pg. 673
SN ENVIRONMENT TECHNOLOGY CO., LTD—See Hitachi Zosen Corporation; *Int'l*, pg. 3412
SOIL & MATERIALS ENGINEERS, INC.; *U.S. Private*, pg. 3706
SOLANO GARBAGE COMPANY—See Republic Services, Inc.; *U.S. Public*, pg. 1787
SOLUTIONS-IES, INC.; *U.S. Private*, pg. 3711
SOUNDVIEW CONSULTANTS LLC—See Keystone Group, L.P.; *U.S. Private*, pg. 2299
SOVEREIGN CONSULTING INC.; *U.S. Private*, pg. 3743
SPECPRO ENVIRONMENTAL SERVICES LLC—See Bristol Bay Native Corporation; *U.S. Private*, pg. 656
SPECTRAL-AECOM—See AECOM; *U.S. Public*, pg. 51
STANDARD GOLD CORP.—See Augusta Gold Corp.; *Int'l*, pg. 704
STEINMULLER ENGINEERING GMBH—See IHI Corporation; *Int'l*, pg. 3606
STOLLER NEWPORT NEWS NUCLEAR, INC.—See Huntington Ingalls Industries, Inc.; *U.S. Public*, pg. 1072
STORMGEO AB—See Alfa Laval AB; *Int'l*, pg. 312
STORMGEO AS—See Alfa Laval AB; *Int'l*, pg. 312
STORMGEO AS—See EQT AB; *Int'l*, pg. 2481
STORMGEO DO BRASIL—See Alfa Laval AB; *Int'l*, pg. 312
STORMGEO FZ LLC—See Alfa Laval AB; *Int'l*, pg. 312
STORMGEO GERMANY—See Alfa Laval AB; *Int'l*, pg. 312
STORMGEO KOREA—See Alfa Laval AB; *Int'l*, pg. 312
STORMGEO LIMITED—See Alfa Laval AB; *Int'l*, pg. 312
STORMGEO SINGAPORE—See Alfa Laval AB; *Int'l*, pg. 312
STREAMLINE ENVIRONMENTAL, INC.; *U.S. Private*, pg. 3838
SUMILAB, S.A DE C.V.—See HORIBA Ltd; *Int'l*, pg. 3478
SUNRISE SANITATION SERVICE, INC.—See Republic Services, Inc.; *U.S. Public*, pg. 1787
SUSTAINABLE RESOURCES MANAGEMENT, LLC—See Quest Resource Holding Corporation; *U.S. Public*, pg. 1756

541620 — ENVIRONMENTAL CONSU...

SVENSK ARBETSHYGIEN AB—See Eurofins Scientific S.E.; *Int'l*, pg. 2552
SYCAMORE LANDFILL, INC.—See Republic Services, Inc.; *U.S. Public*, pg. 1787
TEAM INTEGRATED ENGINEERING, INC.; *U.S. Private*, pg. 3949
TECFRESH SAC—See HORIBA Ltd; *Int'l*, pg. 3478
TECHNOLOGIES FOR WATER SERVICES S.P.A.—See ACEA S.p.A.; *Int'l*, pg. 95
TEMPTRONIC CORPORATION—See inTEST Corporation; *U.S. Public*, pg. 1159
TERRACON CONSULTANTS, INC. - TAMPA—See Terracon Consultants, Inc.; *U.S. Private*, pg. 3971
TERRAPHASE ENGINEERING INC.; *U.S. Private*, pg. 3972
TEXCOM BENNETT ENVIRONMENTAL SERVICES, LLC—See Texcom, Inc.; *U.S. Public*, pg. 2027
TEXCOM ENVIRONMENTAL SERVICES, LLC—See Texcom, Inc.; *U.S. Public*, pg. 2027
TEXCOM, INC.; *U.S. Public*, pg. 2027
TEXCOM PEAK ENVIRONMENTAL SERVICES, LLC—See Texcom, Inc.; *U.S. Public*, pg. 2027
TIDEWATER ENVIRONMENTAL SERVICES, INC.—See Artesian Resources Corporation; *U.S. Public*, pg. 202
TOKYO ENVIRONMENTAL MEASUREMENT CENTER CO., LTD—See Adeka Corporation; *Int'l*, pg. 142
TORTEC GROUP CORP.; *U.S. Public*, pg. 2164
TOXIKOS PTY LTD—See EnviroSuite Limited; *Int'l*, pg. 2455
TRC COMPANIES, INC.; *U.S. Private*, pg. 4215
TRC COMPANIES, LTD.—See TRC Companies, Inc.; *U.S. Private*, pg. 4215
TRINITY CONSULTANTS, INC.—See Keystone Group, L.P.; *U.S. Private*, pg. 2299
TRIPLEPOINT ENVIRONMENTAL, LLC—See KKR & Co. Inc.; *U.S. Public*, pg. 1239
UMETCO MINERALS CORPORATION—See Dow Inc.; *U.S. Public*, pg. 686
UNITED STATES ENVIRONMENTAL SERVICES, LLC—See The Halifax Group LLC; *U.S. Private*, pg. 4042
UPPER ROCK ISLAND COUNTY LANDFILL, INC.—See Republic Services, Inc.; *U.S. Public*, pg. 1788
VALLEY RECYCLING; *U.S. Private*, pg. 4335
VANSOLIX S.A—See HORIBA Ltd; *Int'l*, pg. 3478
VERCO ADVISORY SERVICES LTD.—See CVC Capital Partners SICAV-FIS S.A.; *Int'l*, pg. 1882
VERTEX ENGINEERING SERVICES, INC.; *U.S. Private*, pg. 4370
VICTORIA LANDFILL TX, LP—See Republic Services, Inc.; *U.S. Public*, pg. 1788
VIGEO BELGIUM NV—See Moody's Corporation; *U.S. Public*, pg. 1469
VIGEO EIRIS CHILE SPA—See Moody's Corporation; *U.S. Public*, pg. 1469
VIGEO EIRIS HONG KONG LIMITED—See Moody's Corporation; *U.S. Public*, pg. 1469
VIGEO EIRIS USA, LLC—See Moody's Corporation; *U.S. Public*, pg. 1469
VIGEO—See Moody's Corporation; *U.S. Public*, pg. 1469
VIRONEX TECHNICAL SERVICES LLC—See TruArc Partners, L.P.; *U.S. Private*, pg. 4245
VMS PTY. LTD.—See Eagers Automotive Limited; *Int'l*, pg. 2264
VOLKERT ENVIRONMENTAL, INC.—See Volkert, Inc.; *U.S. Private*, pg. 4410
WASTREN ADVANTAGE, INC.—See Wastren Advantage, Inc.; *U.S. Private*, pg. 4451
WATERBORNE ENVIRONMENTAL INC.; *U.S. Private*, pg. 4452
WDTR, INC.—See Republic Services, Inc.; *U.S. Public*, pg. 1788
WEIR ENVIRONMENTAL LLC—See NV5 Global, Inc.; *U.S. Public*, pg. 1558
WEST CONTRA COSTA SANITARY LANDFILL, INC.—See Republic Services, Inc.; *U.S. Public*, pg. 1788
WHITE SHIELD, INC.; *U.S. Private*, pg. 4510
WILLAMETTE RESOURCES, INC.—See Republic Services, Inc.; *U.S. Public*, pg. 1789
WM LAMPTRACKER, INC.—See Waste Management, Inc.; *U.S. Public*, pg. 2333
WYG ENVIRONMENTAL LIMITED—See Tetra Tech, Inc.; *U.S. Public*, pg. 2024
WYG ENVIRONMENT PLANNING TRANSPORT LIMITED—See Tetra Tech, Inc.; *U.S. Public*, pg. 2024
ZEBRA ENVIRONMENTAL AND INDUSTRIAL SERVICES, INC.; *U.S. Private*, pg. 4599
ZIA ENGINEERING & ENVIRONMENTAL CONSULTANTS, LLC; *U.S. Private*, pg. 4603
ZWEIGWHITE LLC; *U.S. Private*, pg. 4610

541690 — OTHER SCIENTIFIC AND TECHNICAL CONSULTING SERVICES

159 SOLUTIONS, INC.—See IQVIA Holdings Inc.; *U.S. Public*, pg. 1168
1 SOURCE CONSULTING, INC.; *U.S. Private*, pg. 1
284 PARTNERS LLC—See Ankura Consulting Group, LLC; *U.S. Private*, pg. 284
3DEGREES GROUP, INC.; *U.S. Private*, pg. 9
3E COMPANY ENVIROMENTAL, ECOLOGICAL & ENGINEERING—See Verisk Analytics, Inc.; *U.S. Public*, pg. 2282
4IT, INC.—See Court Square Capital Partners, L.P.; *U.S. Private*, pg. 1070
ABBA TECHNOLOGIES INC.; *U.S. Private*, pg. 34
ABBISKO THERAPEUTICS CO., LTD.—See Abbisko Cayman Limited; *Int'l*, pg. 56
ABLE ANALYTICS CO., LTD.—See Green Cross WellBeing Corp.; *Int'l*, pg. 3070
ABT GLOBAL INC.—See Abt Associates Inc.; *U.S. Private*, pg. 45
ABT JTA PTY LTD.—See Abt Associates Inc.; *U.S. Private*, pg. 45
ACCENT COMPUTER SOLUTIONS, INC.—See VC3, Inc.; *U.S. Private*, pg. 4349
ACID SERVICES, LLC—See Basic Energy Services Inc.; *U.S. Public*, pg. 279
ACI GROUP; *U.S. Private*, pg. 59
ACI INFOTECH; *U.S. Private*, pg. 59
ACOUSTICS BY DESIGN, INC.; *U.S. Private*, pg. 64
ACOUSTIC TECHNOLOGIES, INC.—See Cirrus Logic, Inc.; *U.S. Public*, pg. 496
ACQUISITIONS RESEARCH & LOGISTICS LLC; *U.S. Private*, pg. 65
ACUMEN SCIENTIFIC SDN. BHD.—See Merieux NutriSciences Corp.; *U.S. Public*, pg. 2674
ADAYANA GOVERNMENT GROUP—See Comvest Group Holdings LLC; *U.S. Private*, pg. 1007
ADDX CORPORATION; *U.S. Private*, pg. 77
ADEPTPROS INC.; *U.S. Private*, pg. 78
ADITI CONSULTING LLC; *U.S. Private*, pg. 79
ADROIT ASSOCIATES INC.; *U.S. Private*, pg. 82
ADVANCED C4 SOLUTIONS, INC.—See Hui Huliau; *U.S. Private*, pg. 2004
ADVANCED DESIGN TECHNOLOGY LIMITED—See Ebara Corporation; *Int'l*, pg. 2282
ADVANCED MARKETPLACE INC.; *U.S. Private*, pg. 91
ADVANCER SMART TECHNOLOGY PTE. LTD.—See Advancer Global Limited; *Int'l*, pg. 163
ADVOCATE NETWORKS, INC.—See Accenture plc; *Int'l*, pg. 86
AEC GROUP, INC.; *U.S. Private*, pg. 116
AECOM ENVIRONMENT—See AECOM; *U.S. Public*, pg. 50
AECOM ENVIRONMENT—See AECOM; *U.S. Public*, pg. 51
AECOM—See AECOM; *U.S. Public*, pg. 50
AECOM—See AECOM; *U.S. Public*, pg. 50
A.E.P. ENVIRONMENTAL, L.L.C.; *U.S. Private*, pg. 25
A & E SECURITY NV—See Stanley Black & Decker, Inc.; *U.S. Public*, pg. 1931
AF ADVANSIA AS—See AFRY AB; *Int'l*, pg. 193
AF ADVANSIA NORDVEST AS—See AFRY AB; *Int'l*, pg. 193
AF A/S—See AFRY AB; *Int'l*, pg. 194
AF-AUTOMAATIKA OU—See AFRY AB; *Int'l*, pg. 193
AF-CONSULT AB—See AFRY AB; *Int'l*, pg. 193
AF-CONSULT CZECH REPUBLIC S.R.O.—See AFRY AB; *Int'l*, pg. 193
AF-CONSULT ENERGY DOO—See AFRY AB; *Int'l*, pg. 193
AF-CONSULT GMBH—See AFRY AB; *Int'l*, pg. 193
AF-CONSULT ITALY S.R.L.—See AFRY AB; *Int'l*, pg. 193
AF-CONSULT, LLC—See AFRY AB; *Int'l*, pg. 193
AF-CONSULT LTD.—See AFRY AB; *Int'l*, pg. 194
AF-CONSULT OY—See AFRY AB; *Int'l*, pg. 193
AF-CONSULT (THAILAND) LTD.—See AFRY AB; *Int'l*, pg. 193
AF ENGINEERING AS—See AFRY AB; *Int'l*, pg. 193
AF INDUSTRIER AS—See AFRY AB; *Int'l*, pg. 194
AF-INDUSTRY AB—See AFRY AB; *Int'l*, pg. 194
AF INFRASTRUCTURE POLSKA SP. Z O.O.—See AFRY AB; *Int'l*, pg. 193
AF-INGEMANSSON AB—See AFRY AB; *Int'l*, pg. 194
AF-MERCADOS EMI ENERJI MUHENDISLIGI AR-GE KONTROL VE TEST HIZMETLERI LTD. STI.—See AFRY AB; *Int'l*, pg. 193
AF MERCADOS ENERGY MARKETS INTERNATIONAL S.A.—See AFRY AB; *Int'l*, pg. 193
AF NORGE AS—See AFRY AB; *Int'l*, pg. 193
AGILE360, INC.—See Entisys Solutions, Inc.; *U.S. Private*, pg. 1405
AGILE TECHNOLOGIES, LLC—See Thoma Bravo, L.P.; *U.S. Private*, pg. 4149
AGL ENERGY SERVICES PTY LIMITED—See AGL Energy Limited; *Int'l*, pg. 211
AGRAM D.D.; *Int'l*, pg. 213
AGRIFORCE GROWING SYSTEMS, LTD.; *Int'l*, pg. 217
AGRIPOWER FRANCE SA; *Int'l*, pg. 217
AGRO INNOVATION LAB GMBH—See BayWa AG; *Int'l*, pg. 915
AHANA RENEWABLES, LLC—See ATN International, Inc.; *U.S. Public*, pg. 222
AHNLAB, INC.; *Int'l*, pg. 225
AIG CONSULTANTS, INC.—See American International Group, Inc.; *U.S. Public*, pg. 104
AIXIAL GMBH—See Alten S.A.; *Int'l*, pg. 389
AIXIAL SAS—See Alten S.A.; *Int'l*, pg. 389
AIXIAL SPRL—See Alten S.A.; *Int'l*, pg. 390
AIXIAL S.R.O.—See Alten S.A.; *Int'l*, pg. 389

AJE BEST-ON SDN. BHD.—See Ann Joo Resources Berhad; *Int'l*, pg. 473
AKKA BENELUX NV/SA—See Adecco Group AG; *Int'l*, pg. 139
AKKA TECHNOLOGIES SE—See Adecco Group AG; *Int'l*, pg. 139
AKUWA SOLUTIONS GROUP, INC.; *U.S. Public*, pg. 147
ALAGEN LLC—See General Microsystems, Inc.; *U.S. Private*, pg. 1666
ALCAN TECHNOLOGY & MANAGEMENT AG—See Amcor plc; *Int'l*, pg. 417
ALL4 LLC; *U.S. Private*, pg. 174
ALLARI SOLUTIONS, INC.; *U.S. Private*, pg. 175
ALLCONNEX; *U.S. Private*, pg. 175
ALLIED MINERAL TECHNICAL SERVICES, INC.—See Allied Mineral Products, Inc.; *U.S. Private*, pg. 187
ALMAC CLINICAL TECHNOLOGIES—See Almac Sciences Group Ltd.; *Int'l*, pg. 362
ALMEGA ENVIRONMENTAL & TECHNICAL SERVICES, INC.—See Align Capital Partners, LLC; *U.S. Private*, pg. 167
ALPHA SYNOPSYS INC; *U.S. Private*, pg. 200
ALPIQ ECOSERVICES LTD.—See Bouygues S.A.; *Int'l*, pg. 1123
ALPIQ NORWAY AS—See Alpiq Holding AG; *Int'l*, pg. 373
ALTAIR ENGINEERING (SINGAPORE) PTD. LTD.—See Altair Engineering, Inc.; *U.S. Public*, pg. 86
ALTEN CANADA INC.—See Alten S.A.; *Int'l*, pg. 389
ALTEN CHINA LTD.—See Alten S.A.; *Int'l*, pg. 389
ALTEN DELIVERY CENTER IASI SRL—See Alten S.A.; *Int'l*, pg. 389
ALTEN LUXEMBOURG SARL—See Alten S.A.; *Int'l*, pg. 389
ALTEN NEDERLAND BV—See Alten S.A.; *Int'l*, pg. 389
ALTEN PCS—See Alten S.A.; *Int'l*, pg. 390
ALTEN POLSKA SP. Z O.O.—See Alten S.A.; *Int'l*, pg. 389
ALTEN SPAIN SA—See Alten S.A.; *Int'l*, pg. 389
ALTE OY—See Alten S.A.; *Int'l*, pg. 390
ALTRAD BABCOCK LIMITED—See Altrad Investment Authority SAS; *Int'l*, pg. 397
ALTRAN S.A.N.V.—See Capgemini SE; *Int'l*, pg. 1305
ALTRAN TECHNOLOGIES INDIA LTD.—See Capgemini SE; *Int'l*, pg. 1305
ALTRAN XYPE DEUTSCHLAND GMBH—See Capgemini SE; *Int'l*, pg. 1304
AMBIENT TECHNOLOGIES, INC.; *U.S. Private*, pg. 217
AM COMMUNICATIONS; *U.S. Private*, pg. 214
AMERESCO DMHS LLC—See Ameresco, Inc.; *U.S. Public*, pg. 95
AMERESCO GEORGIA LLC—See Ameresco, Inc.; *U.S. Public*, pg. 95
AMEREX BROKERS LLC—See BGC Group, Inc.; *U.S. Public*, pg. 329
AMEREX ENERGY SERVICES—See BGC Group, Inc.; *U.S. Public*, pg. 329
AMERICAN EFFICIENT LLC; *U.S. Private*, pg. 231
AMERICAN ENVIRONMENTAL GROUP, INC.—See McLarens, Inc.; *U.S. Private*, pg. 2640
AMERICAN PARTNERS INC.; *U.S. Private*, pg. 243
AMERICAN PROCESS, INC.—See GranInvestimentos SA; *Int'l*, pg. 3059
AMESYS CANADA INC.—See Atos SE; *Int'l*, pg. 691
AMSPHERE LIMITED; *Int'l*, pg. 441
AMT-SYBEX LTD.—See Capita plc; *Int'l*, pg. 1308
ANA INFORMATION SYSTEMS PLANNING CO., LTD.—See ANA Holdings Inc.; *Int'l*, pg. 444
ANALYSTS INTERNATIONAL CORPORATION—See American CyberSystems, Inc.; *U.S. Private*, pg. 239
ANALYSYS MASON LIMITED—See Bridgepoint Group Plc; *Int'l*, pg. 1154
ANATOMY IT, LLC; *U.S. Private*, pg. 272
ANCHOR QEA, LLC; *U.S. Private*, pg. 273
ANDRADE & CANELLAS ENERGIA S.A.; *Int'l*, pg. 451
ANIMUS SOLUTIONS INC.; *U.S. Private*, pg. 283
ANITTEL PTY. LTD.—See 5G Networks Limited; *Int'l*, pg. 13
ANRIKA QUALITY SERVICES AB—See Anrika Group Scandinavia AB; *Int'l*, pg. 475
APEX COVANTAGE; *U.S. Private*, pg. 292
APEX INFINITE SOLUTIONS LLC; *U.S. Private*, pg. 292
APPLICATION CONSULTING GROUP; *U.S. Private*, pg. 298
APPLIED ENERGY GROUP, INC.—See Ameresco, Inc.; *U.S. Public*, pg. 95
AQUATERRA, LLC—See Terracon Consultants, Inc.; *U.S. Private*, pg. 3970
AQUATIS SPOL S.R.O.—See AFRY AB; *Int'l*, pg. 194
ARCADIS LLP—See ARCADIS N.V.; *Int'l*, pg. 541
ARCADIS U.S., INC. - AUSTIN—See ARCADIS N.V.; *Int'l*, pg. 541
ARCADIS U.S., INC.—See ARCADIS N.V.; *Int'l*, pg. 541
ARGUS PACIFIC, INC.—See Terracon Consultants, Inc.; *U.S. Private*, pg. 3970
ARI NETWORK SERVICES, INC.—See True Wind Capital Management, L.P.; *U.S. Private*, pg. 4248
ARMSTRONG FORENSIC ENGINEERS, INC.; *U.S. Private*, pg. 331
ARMSTRONG INTERNATIONAL ITALIANA S.R.L.—See Armstrong International, Inc.; *U.S. Private*, pg. 331
ARMSTRONG INTERNATIONAL SA—See Armstrong Inter-

N.A.I.C.S. INDEX
541690 — OTHER SCIENTIFIC AN...

national, Inc.; *U.S. Private*, pg. 331
ARRAYA SOLUTIONS, INC.; *U.S. Private*, pg. 334
ASCENTIUM CORPORATION; *U.S. Private*, pg. 348
ASECO INTEGRATED SYSTEMS LTD.; *Int'l*, pg. 605
ASO CO., LTD.; *Int'l*, pg. 628
ASRC FEDERAL HOLDING COMPANY—See Arctic Slope Regional Corporation; *U.S. Private*, pg. 316
ASTIR IT SOLUTIONS, INC.; *U.S. Private*, pg. 360
ATKINS NUCLEAR SOLUTIONS US, INC.—See AtkinsRealis Group Inc.; *Int'l*, pg. 673
ATLAS PROFESSIONAL SERVICES, INC.; *U.S. Private*, pg. 379
ATOS AG—See Atos SE; *Int'l*, pg. 690
ATOS ARGENTINA SA—See Atos SE; *Int'l*, pg. 690
ATOS INFORMATION TECHNOLOGY SAE—See Atos SE; *Int'l*, pg. 691
ATOS IT SOLUTIONS AND SERVICES D.O.O.—See Atos SE; *Int'l*, pg. 690
ATOS IT SOLUTIONS AND SERVICES, INC.—See Atos SE; *Int'l*, pg. 690
ATOS ORIGIN INDONESIA PT—See Atos SE; *Int'l*, pg. 691
ATOS QATAR LLC—See Atos SE; *Int'l*, pg. 691
ATOS SAUDI COMPANY—See Atos SE; *Int'l*, pg. 691
ATOS TAIWAN LTD—See Atos SE; *Int'l*, pg. 691
AT&T GOVERNMENT SOLUTIONS, INC.—See Arlington Capital Partners LLC; *U.S. Private*, pg. 328
AT&T TECHNICAL SERVICES COMPANY—See Arlington Capital Partners LLC; *U.S. Private*, pg. 328
AUTOMATION TECHNOLOGIES, INC.; *U.S. Private*, pg. 400
AVANKIA LLC; *U.S. Private*, pg. 404
AVEROX INC.; *Int'l*, pg. 739
AVIAN ENGINEERING, LLC; *U.S. Private*, pg. 406
AVISTA CAPITAL, INC.—See Avista Corporation; *U.S. Public*, pg. 249
AWARD SOLUTIONS, INC.—See Accenture plc; *Int'l*, pg. 86
AZZUR GROUP, LLC; *U.S. Private*, pg. 416
BAE SYSTEMS SPECTAL LLC—See BAE Systems plc; *Int'l*, pg. 797
BANELCO S.A.—See Banco Macro S.A.; *Int'l*, pg. 823
BASF ZAMBIA LIMITED—See BASF SE; *Int'l*, pg. 882
BAUPERFORMANCE GMBH—See Bilfinger SE; *Int'l*, pg. 1024
BAYER TECHNOLOGY & ENGINEERING (SHANGHAI) CO., LTD.—See Bayer Aktiengesellschaft; *Int'l*, pg. 907
BAYER TECHNOLOGY SERVICES AMERICAS—See Bayer Aktiengesellschaft; *Int'l*, pg. 906
BAYER TECHNOLOGY SERVICES GMBH—See Bayer Aktiengesellschaft; *Int'l*, pg. 906
BAYPO LIMITED PARTNERSHIP—See Bayer Aktiengesellschaft; *Int'l*, pg. 902
BBKO CONSULTING S.A.; *Int'l*, pg. 920
BCP TECHNICAL SERVICE, INC.; *U.S. Private*, pg. 499
BDO DIGITAL, LLC—See BDO USA, LLP; *U.S. Private*, pg. 501
BEACH STREET CONSULTING, INC.—See InfoTrust Group, Inc.; *U.S. Private*, pg. 2074
BEHAVIORAL SCIENCE TECHNOLOGY (BST) INC.—See DEKRA e.V.; *Int'l*, pg. 2007
BEHAVIORAL SCIENE TECHNOLOGY CONSULTORES DO BRASIL LTDA.—See DEKRA e.V.; *Int'l*, pg. 2007
BEIJING CERTIFICATE AUTHORITY CO., LTD.; *Int'l*, pg. 947
BEIJING TECNATOM NUCLEAR POWER SAFETY TECHNOLOGY SERVICES COMPANY LIMITED—See Enel S.p.A.; *Int'l*, pg. 2411
BEST PRACTICE ASSOCIATES, L.L.C.—See Sagewind Capital LLC; *U.S. Private*, pg. 3527
BEYONDSOFT CONSULTING INC.—See Beyondsoft Corporation; *Int'l*, pg. 1005
B&H CONSULTING SERVICES, INC.—See Voisin Consulting, Inc.; *U.S. Private*, pg. 4409
BHI ENERGY; *U.S. Private*, pg. 549
BIGBEAR.AI HOLDINGS LLC—See AE Industrial Partners, LP; *U.S. Private*, pg. 112
BILFINGER NUCLEAR & ENERGY TRANSITION GMBH—See Bilfinger SE; *Int'l*, pg. 1027
BINARY DEFENSE SYSTEMS, LLC; *U.S. Private*, pg. 560
BINARY GROUP, INC.—See Cybergy Holdings, Inc.; *U.S. Private*, pg. 1133
BIOCENTRIC ENERGY HOLDINGS, INC.; *U.S. Public*, pg. 335
BIOSEED RESEARCH INDIA PRIVATE LIMITED—See DCM Shriram Limited; *Int'l*, pg. 1992
BIOWISDOM LTD.—See ArchiMed SAS; *Int'l*, pg. 548
BIP - BUSINESS INTEGRATION PARTNERS S.P.A.—See CVC Capital Partners SICAV-FIS S.A.; *Int'l*, pg. 1882
BIS PROZESSTECHNIK GMBH—See Bilfinger SE; *Int'l*, pg. 1025
BITTWARE, INC.—See Koch Industries, Inc.; *U.S. Private*, pg. 2333
BJORNSEN BERATENDE INGENIEURE GMBH; *Int'l*, pg. 1054
BLACK BOX RESALE SERVICES—See Black Box Limited; *Int'l*, pg. 1058
BLACKPOINT IT SERVICES, INC.; *U.S. Private*, pg. 576
BLAKE WILLSON GROUP, LLC; *U.S. Private*, pg. 578

BLANTON & ASSOCIATES, INC.—See ICF International, Inc.; *U.S. Public*, pg. 1085
BLATTNER HOLDING COMPANY, LLC—See Quanta Services, Inc.; *U.S. Public*, pg. 1750
BLUECHIP STOCKSPIN LIMITED; *Int'l*, pg. 1070
BLUE TECH, INC.; *U.S. Private*, pg. 593
THE BOEING CO. - LONG BEACH—See The Boeing Company; *U.S. Public*, pg. 2041
BOMBARDIER TRANSIT CORPORATION—See Alstom S.A.; *Int'l*, pg. 382
BOUVET STOCKHOLM AB—See Bouvet ASA; *Int'l*, pg. 1121
BRAUN INTERTEC CORPORATION; *U.S. Private*, pg. 641
BRIDGE ENERGY GROUP, INC.—See Accenture plc; *Int'l*, pg. 86
BRIGADE CAPITAL MANAGEMENT, LLC; *U.S. Private*, pg. 650
BRIGHTFIELDS, INC.; *U.S. Private*, pg. 652
BRISTOL ENVIRONMENTAL ENGINEERING SERVICES CORPORATION—See Bristol Bay Native Corporation; *U.S. Private*, pg. 655
BRISTOL-MYERS SQUIBB TRUSTEES LTD.—See Bristol-Myers Squibb Company; *U.S. Public*, pg. 385
BRITISH AGRICULTURAL SERVICES LIMITED—See Heidelberg Materials AG; *Int'l*, pg. 3309
BRIXTON GROUP INC.; *U.S. Private*, pg. 658
BROADGATE INC; *U.S. Private*, pg. 659
BROKER ONLINE EXCHANGE LLC; *U.S. Private*, pg. 661
THE BROOKESIDE GROUP, INC.; *U.S. Private*, pg. 4001
BRUNEL TECHNICAL SERVICES PTE LTD—See Brunel International N.V.; *Int'l*, pg. 1200
BRUNEL TECHNICAL SERVICES PTY LTD—See Brunel International N.V.; *Int'l*, pg. 1200
BST CONSULTANTS PTE. LTD.—See DEKRA e.V.; *Int'l*, pg. 2007
BT FRONTLINE PTE. LTD.—See BT Group plc; *Int'l*, pg. 1203
BT IGNITE—See BT Group plc; *Int'l*, pg. 1203
BULL INFORMATION SYSTEMS CO. LIMITED (BEIJING)—See Atos SE; *Int'l*, pg. 692
BULL INFORMATION SYSTEMS (HONG KONG) LTD.—See Atos SE; *Int'l*, pg. 692
BULL MADAGASCAR S.A.—See Atos SE; *Int'l*, pg. 692
BULL MOROCCO—See Atos SE; *Int'l*, pg. 692
BULL SAL—See Atos SE; *Int'l*, pg. 692
BULL URUGUAY SA—See Atos SE; *Int'l*, pg. 692
BULPROS CONSULTING AD; *Int'l*, pg. 1214
BUREAU VERITAS NORTH AMERICA, INC. - COSTA MESA—See Bureau Veritas S.A.; *Int'l*, pg. 1221
BURLESON CONSULTING, INC.—See Terracon Consultants, Inc.; *U.S. Private*, pg. 3970
BURWOOD GROUP INC.; *U.S. Private*, pg. 693
BY LIGHT PROFESSIONAL IT SERVICES, LLC—See Sagewind Capital LLC; *U.S. Private*, pg. 3527
CACTUS COMMUNICATIONS, INC.; *U.S. Private*, pg. 712
CADENCE CAPITAL LIMITED; *Int'l*, pg. 1247
CALHOUN INTERNATIONAL, LLC; *U.S. Private*, pg. 717
CALIAN GROUP LTD.; *Int'l*, pg. 1263
CALNET, INC. OF SAN DIEGO—See CALNET, Inc.; *U.S. Private*, pg. 723
CALNET, INC.; *U.S. Private*, pg. 723
CAMBRIA SOLUTIONS, INC.; *U.S. Private*, pg. 726
CAMBRIDGE CONSULTANTS LTD—See Capgemini SE; *Int'l*, pg. 1305
CAMRIS INTERNATIONAL, LLC—See Henry M. Jackson Foundation for the Advance; *U.S. Private*, pg. 1919
CANADIAN SOLAR SOUTH AFRICA (PTY) LTD.—See Canadian Solar Inc.; *Int'l*, pg. 1286
CAPE EMPOWERMENT TRUST LIMITED; *Int'l*, pg. 1303
CAPGEMINI FRANCE - GRENOBLE—See Capgemini SE; *Int'l*, pg. 1305
CARDNO CHEMRISK, LLC—See Cardno Limited; *Int'l*, pg. 1322
CARDNO CHEMRISK - SAN FRANCISCO—See Cardno Limited; *Int'l*, pg. 1322
CARDNO EMERGING MARKETS (EAST AFRICA) LIMITED—See Cardno Limited; *Int'l*, pg. 1322
CARDNO EMERGING MARKETS (UK) LIMITED—See Cardno Limited; *Int'l*, pg. 1322
CARENET INC.; *Int'l*, pg. 1324
CARGAS SYSTEMS, INC; *U.S. Private*, pg. 754
CARRICK CAPITAL PARTNERS, LLC; *U.S. Private*, pg. 772
CASCADE TECHNOLOGIES, INC.; *U.S. Private*, pg. 781
CASCADIA PM, LLC—See Centerline Solutions LLC; *U.S. Private*, pg. 816
CASSIDIAN AIR SYSTEMS GMBH.—See Airbus SE; *Int'l*, pg. 242
CASSIDIAN DEFESA E SEGURANCA DO BRASIL LTDA.—See Airbus SE; *Int'l*, pg. 242
CATALYST SOLUTIONS; *U.S. Private*, pg. 786
C-BOND SYSTEMS, INC.; *U.S. Public*, pg. 414
CCS GLOBAL TECH; *U.S. Private*, pg. 801
CDI CORPORATION—See AE Industrial Partners, LP; *U.S. Private*, pg. 112
CDM SMITH CONSULT GMBH—See CDM Smith Inc.; *U.S. Private*, pg. 803

CE3, INC.—See NovaQuest Capital Management, LLC; *U.S. Private*, pg. 2967
CEC ENERGIECONSULTING GMBH—See E.ON SE; *Int'l*, pg. 2251
CELCITE MANAGEMENT SOLUTIONS, LLC—See Amdocs Limited; *Int'l*, pg. 420
CELESTAR CORPORATION; *U.S. Private*, pg. 806
CENTAURI SOLUTIONS, LLC; *U.S. Private*, pg. 809
CENTER FOR SUSTAINABLE ENERGY; *U.S. Private*, pg. 811
CENTRICS LLC; *U.S. Private*, pg. 830
CENTRUM PRE VEDU A VYSKUM S.R.O.—See Enel S.p.A.; *Int'l*, pg. 2411
CENTURIA RIT S.C.A.R.L.—See Hera S.p.A.; *Int'l*, pg. 3356
CERTARA, INC.; *U.S. Public*, pg. 476
CESI S.P.A.; *Int'l*, pg. 1424
CGI AB—See CGI Inc.; *Int'l*, pg. 1433
CGI AUSTRALIA PTY LTD.—See CGI Inc.; *Int'l*, pg. 1434
CGI BELGIUM NV/SA—See CGI Inc.; *Int'l*, pg. 1433
CGI CZECH REPUBLIC SRO—See CGI Inc.; *Int'l*, pg. 1433
CGI DANMARK AS—See CGI Inc.; *Int'l*, pg. 1433
CGI-DUBAI—See CGI Inc.; *Int'l*, pg. 1434
CGI FEDERAL, INC.—See CGI Inc.; *Int'l*, pg. 1432
CGI INC.; *Int'l*, pg. 1432
CGI INFORMATION SYSTEMS AND MANAGEMENT CONSULTANTS (AUSTRALIA) PTY LTD—See CGI Inc.; *Int'l*, pg. 1434
CGI LUXEMBOURG S.A.—See CGI Inc.; *Int'l*, pg. 1434
CGI MALAYSIA SDN. BHD.—See CGI Inc.; *Int'l*, pg. 1434
CGI NORGE AS—See CGI Inc.; *Int'l*, pg. 1434
CGI SOUTH AMERICA—See CGI Inc.; *Int'l*, pg. 1434
CGI SUOMI OY—See CGI Inc.; *Int'l*, pg. 1434
CGITI PORTUGAL SA—See CGI Inc.; *Int'l*, pg. 1434
CHC CONSULTING LLC—See Crestview Partners, L.P.; *U.S. Private*, pg. 1098
CHECK-6, INC.; *U.S. Private*, pg. 869
CHEMADVISOR, INC.—See Underwriters Laboratories Inc.; *U.S. Private*, pg. 4280
CHILWORTH AMALTHEA S.L.—See DEKRA e.V.; *Int'l*, pg. 2007
CHILWORTH FRANCE S.A.S.—See DEKRA e.V.; *Int'l*, pg. 2007
CHILWORTH PACIFIC FIRE LABORATORIES INC.—See DEKRA e.V.; *Int'l*, pg. 2007
CHILWORTH TECHNOLOGY INC.—See DEKRA e.V.; *Int'l*, pg. 2007
CHILWORTH TECHNOLOGY LTD.—See DEKRA e.V.; *Int'l*, pg. 2007
CHILWORTH TECHNOLOGY (PVT) LTD.—See DEKRA e.V.; *Int'l*, pg. 2008
CHILWORTH VASSALLO S.R.L.—See DEKRA e.V.; *Int'l*, pg. 2007
CHINA AUTOMOTIVE ENGINEERING RESEARCH INSTITUTE CO., LTD.; *Int'l*, pg. 1484
CHORUS COMMUNICATIONS, INC.; *U.S. Private*, pg. 889
CHRISTIE INTRUDER ALARMS LIMITED—See Stanley Black & Decker, Inc.; *U.S. Public*, pg. 1932
CHRYSALIS SOFTWARE, INC.—See Waterfield Technologies, Inc.; *U.S. Private*, pg. 4453
CI2I SERVICES, INC.; *U.S. Private*, pg. 896
CIS SECURE COMPUTING, INC.—See Hammond, Kennedy, Whitney & Company, Inc.; *U.S. Private*, pg. 1850
CITY LIGHT & POWER, INC.—See Hunt Companies, Inc.; *U.S. Private*, pg. 2008
CK ENVIRONMENTAL, INC.; *U.S. Private*, pg. 909
CLANCY ENVIRONMENTAL CONSULTANTS, INC.—See Tetra Tech, Inc.; *U.S. Public*, pg. 2022
CLARK ENERGY GROUP LLC—See Clark Enterprises, Inc.; *U.S. Private*, pg. 913
CLEAN FUEL CONNECTION INC.; *U.S. Private*, pg. 931
CLEANGOAL ENERGY, CORP.; *U.S. Private*, pg. 931
CLEAR CONSULT GMBH—See Alten S.A.; *Int'l*, pg. 390
CLEMONDO GROUP AB; *Int'l*, pg. 1657
CLIENT SOLUTIONS LTD.—See TD Synnex Corp; *U.S. Public*, pg. 1985
CLIMEON AB; *Int'l*, pg. 1659
CLOCKWORK SOLUTIONS LLC—See Logistics Management Institute; *U.S. Private*, pg. 2482
CMC CONSULTING BOSTON, INC.; *U.S. Private*, pg. 950
CMX TECHNOLOGIES; *U.S. Private*, pg. 951
COASTAL CLOUD LLC; *U.S. Private*, pg. 955
COGNIGEN CORPORATION—See Simulations Plus, Inc.; *U.S. Public*, pg. 1884
COGNOSANTE LLC—See Accenture plc; *Int'l*, pg. 85
COMLINE GMBH—See IQVIA Holdings Inc.; *U.S. Public*, pg. 1168
COMM3; *U.S. Private*, pg. 982
COMMUNICATIONS RESOURCE, INC.; *U.S. Private*, pg. 988
COMMUNITY REDEVELOPMENT INC.; *U.S. Public*, pg. 558
COMPASS LEXECON - CAMBRIDGE—See FTI Consulting, Inc.; *U.S. Public*, pg. 890
COMPASS LEXECON LLC—See FTI Consulting, Inc.; *U.S. Public*, pg. 890
COMPREHENSIVE ENVIRONMENTAL ASSESSMENTS, INC.; *U.S. Private*, pg. 1003

4715

541690 — OTHER SCIENTIFIC AN...   **CORPORATE AFFILIATIONS**

COMPUTEC SRL—See Bain Capital, LP; *U.S. Private*, pg. 452
CONATEL, S.A.; *Int'l*, pg. 1763
CONCENTRA CONSULTING LIMITED; *Int'l*, pg. 1763
CONCEPT AG—See Bertrandt AG; *Int'l*, pg. 998
CONCEPTSOLUTIONS, LLC; *U.S. Private*, pg. 1009
CONCOURSE FEDERAL GROUP, LLC; *U.S. Private*, pg. 1011
CONFIGURATION MANAGEMENT INC.; *U.S. Private*, pg. 1013
CONSERVATION SERVICES GROUP, INC.; *U.S. Private*, pg. 1019
CONSTRUCTIVE TECHNOLOGIES GROUP, INC.—See CI Capital Partners LLC; *U.S. Private*, pg. 895
CONSULTING SERVICES, INC.; *U.S. Private*, pg. 1025
THE CONSULTING SOURCE, INC.1990—See AutoNation, Inc.; *U.S. Public*, pg. 238
CONSULT PARAGON COMPUTER PROFESSIONALS LTD.—See CGI Inc.; *Int'l*, pg. 1434
CONVERGENCE CONSULTING GROUP, INC.; *U.S. Private*, pg. 1035
CORE CONSULTING LLC; *U.S. Private*, pg. 1048
CORETEK SERVICES; *U.S. Private*, pg. 1050
COREZO, LTD.—See Hokkoku Financial Holdings, Inc.; *Int'l*, pg. 3443
CORPUS MEDICAL, LLC—See TPG Capital, L.P.; *U.S. Public*, pg. 2169
COST MANAGEMENT SERVICES, INC.; *U.S. Private*, pg. 1062
COVANCE RESEARCH PRODUCTS INC.—See Laboratory Corporation of America Holdings; *U.S. Public*, pg. 1286
CPRIME INC.—See Alten S.A.; *Int'l*, pg. 391
CPT GLOBAL LIMITED; *Int'l*, pg. 1826
CRAYON DEUTSCHLAND GMBH—See Crayon Group Holding ASA; *Int'l*, pg. 1829
CRAYON SCHWEIZ AG—See Crayon Group Holding ASA; *Int'l*, pg. 1829
CRAYON SOFTWARE LICENSING UNIPESSOAL LDA—See Crayon Group Holding ASA; *Int'l*, pg. 1829
CREATIVE SOLUTIONS CONSULTING INC; *U.S. Private*, pg. 1090
CRITICAL PROJECT SERVICES, LLC; *U.S. Private*, pg. 1102
CROWN-BAELE NV/SA; *Int'l*, pg. 1858
CRUNCHY LOGISTICS; *U.S. Private*, pg. 1114
CRYO-CELL INTERNATIONAL, INC.; *U.S. Public*, pg. 600
CSG GLOBAL; *U.S. Private*, pg. 1117
CSI IT, LLC—See White Wolf Capital LLC; *U.S. Private*, pg. 4510
CS TECHNOLOGY, INC.; *U.S. Private*, pg. 1116
CTAC N.V.; *Int'l*, pg. 1869
CTEAM CONSULTING & ANLAGENBAU GMBH; *Int'l*, pg. 1870
CURAS, INC.; *U.S. Private*, pg. 1124
CURRENT TECHNOLOGY CORPORATION; *Int'l*, pg. 1879
CURRIE & BROWN (AUSTRALIA) PTY. LIMITED—See Currie & Brown Holdings Limited; *Int'l*, pg. 1879
CUTTER INFORMATION, LLC—See Arthur D. Little SAS; *Int'l*, pg. 584
CYBERCOM GROUP AB—See Formica Capital Holding AB; *Int'l*, pg. 2734
CYBERNOOR CORP—See Lightview Capital LLC; *U.S. Private*, pg. 2453
CYBERSPACE SOLUTIONS, LLC—See Godspeed Capital Management LP; *U.S. Private*, pg. 1725
CYPRESS ENERGY PARTNERS, LLC—See Cypress Environmental Partners, L.P.; *U.S. Private*, pg. 618
D4T4 SOLUTIONS PLC; *Int'l*, pg. 1901
DADC LUFT- UND RAUMFAHRT BETEILIGUNGS AG—See Airbus SE; *Int'l*, pg. 242
DAIWA INVESTOR RELATIONS CO. LTD.—See Daiwa Securities Group Inc.; *Int'l*, pg. 1948
DATAMANUSA, LLC; *U.S. Private*, pg. 1165
DATAMETRIX; *U.S. Private*, pg. 1166
DAVEY RESOURCE GROUP, INC.—See The Davey Tree Expert Company; *U.S. Private*, pg. 4018
DAVIDSON TECHNOLOGIES, INC.; *U.S. Private*, pg. 1172
DBA ENGINEERING LTD.—See AtkinsRealis Group Inc.; *Int'l*, pg. 671
DECERNIS LLC—See Berkshire Partners LLC; *U.S. Private*, pg. 534
DECISIONMETRICS LTD.—See GTCR LLC; *U.S. Private*, pg. 1804
DEEGIT INC.; *U.S. Private*, pg. 1189
DEERNS RAADGEVENDE INGENIEURS B.V; *Int'l*, pg. 2003
DEKRA INCOS GMBH—See DEKRA e.V.; *Int'l*, pg. 2008
DEKRA INDUSTRIAL (PTY) LTD.—See DEKRA e.V.; *Int'l*, pg. 2008
DEKRA INSIGHT AB—See DEKRA e.V.; *Int'l*, pg. 2009
DELTA MAX; *U.S. Private*, pg. 1201
DELTA PROJECT MANAGEMENT, INC.—See Lightview Capital LLC; *U.S. Private*, pg. 2454
DETICA CONSULTING LLC—See BAE Systems plc; *Int'l*, pg. 798
DETICA GROUP LIMITED—See BAE Systems plc; *Int'l*, pg. 798
DEUTZ SICHERHEIT GESELLSCHAFT FUR INDUSTRI-ESERVICE MBH—See DEUTZ AG; *Int'l*, pg. 2086
DEVBRIDGE GROUP LLC; *U.S. Private*, pg. 1217
DEVELOPMENT ALTERNATIVES, INC.; *U.S. Private*, pg. 1217
DEWITT & COMPANY INCORPORATED—See General Atlantic Service Company, L.P.; *U.S. Private*, pg. 1662
DEWITT & COMPANY INCORPORATED—See HgCapital Trust plc; *Int'l*, pg. 3376
DG TECHNOLOGY CONSULTING, LLC; *U.S. Private*, pg. 1221
DHPC TECHNOLOGIES, INC.—See Veritas Capital Fund Management, LLC; *U.S. Private*, pg. 4363
DIALES; *Int'l*, pg. 2104
DIALOG SERVICES PTY. LTD.—See Dialog Group Berhad; *Int'l*, pg. 2104
DIGINEER, INC.; *U.S. Private*, pg. 1229
DIGITAL INTELLIGENCE SYSTEMS, LLC; *U.S. Private*, pg. 1230
DIGITS LLC—See Avalon Documents Services; *U.S. Private*, pg. 403
DIMENSIIONS HEALTHCARE LLC—See IQVIA Holdings Inc.; *U.S. Public*, pg. 1168
DIRECLOGIX CORP—See CDW Corporation; *U.S. Public*, pg. 462
DIVERSIFIED INTERNATIONAL SCIENCES CORPORATION; *U.S. Private*, pg. 1242
DOBLER CONSULTING INC.; *U.S. Private*, pg. 1250
DOBOJINVEST A.D.; *Int'l*, pg. 2152
DRAGISA BRASOVAN TRUDBENIK A.D.; *Int'l*, pg. 2199
DRUG DEV INC.—See IQVIA Holdings Inc.; *U.S. Public*, pg. 1168
DSE DIREKT-SERVICE-ENERGIE GMBH—See ENGIE SA; *Int'l*, pg. 2429
DSE DIREKT-SERVICE-ENERGIE GMBH—See E.ON SE; *Int'l*, pg. 2257
DSM TECHNOLOGY CONSULTANTS LLC—See Court Square Capital Partners, L.P.; *U.S. Private*, pg. 1070
DSR MANAGEMENT, INC.; *U.S. Private*, pg. 1281
DUNSTAN THOMAS CONSULTING LIMITED—See Dunstan Thomas Group Limited; *Int'l*, pg. 2227
DURKIN GROUP & ASSOCIATES LLC—See Gordon Brothers Group, LLC; *U.S. Private*, pg. 1742
DUTA SECURITY SDN. BHD.—See Global Oriental Berhad; *Int'l*, pg. 3000
DWFRITZ AUTOMATION INC.—See Balmoral Funds LLC; *U.S. Private*, pg. 461
DYNAMAC CORPORATION—See Dynamac International Inc.; *U.S. Private*, pg. 1297
E4 HEALTH LLC—See GuideWell Mutual Holding Corporation; *U.S. Private*, pg. 1814
EADS TAIWAN CO., LTD.—See Airbus SE; *Int'l*, pg. 246
EA ENGINEERING, SCIENCE & TECHNOLOGY, INC.; *U.S. Private*, pg. 1308
EARLY GROWTH FINANCIAL SERVICES, LLC—See Escalon Services Inc.; *U.S. Private*, pg. 1424
EARNEST & ASSOCIATES, LLC; *U.S. Private*, pg. 1314
EARTHINTEGRATE—See Mittera Group, Inc.; *U.S. Private*, pg. 2751
EARTH NETWORKS, INC.—See Union Park Capital; *U.S. Private*, pg. 4284
EBIT INFORMATION SYSTEMS; *U.S. Private*, pg. 1324
ECIT AROS A/S—See TowerBrook Capital Partners, L.P.; *U.S. Private*, pg. 4194
ECIT RAD & REGNSKAP AS—See TowerBrook Capital Partners, L.P.; *U.S. Private*, pg. 4195
ECLAT HEALTH SOLUTIONS INC.—See Gulf Capital PJSC; *Int'l*, pg. 3180
E-CONCERT SOLUTIONS—See Apollo Global Management, Inc.; *U.S. Public*, pg. 151
ECONOMIC INSTITUTE AD BANJA LUKA; *Int'l*, pg. 2298
ECOVA, INC.—See ENGIE SA; *Int'l*, pg. 2431
ECSI, LLC—See SynTerra Corp.; *U.S. Private*, pg. 3905
EDGEROCK TECHNOLOGIES, LLC—See BGSF, Inc.; *U.S. Public*, pg. 330
EDMONDS ENGINEERING, INC.—See The Dewberry Companies Inc.; *U.S. Private*, pg. 4020
EFFECTIVE ENVIRONMENTAL, INC.; *U.S. Private*, pg. 1343
EF-ON INC.; *Int'l*, pg. 2318
EG A/S—See Francisco Partners Management, LP; *U.S. Private*, pg. 1589
EG NORGE AS—See Francisco Partners Management, LP; *U.S. Private*, pg. 1589
EGP INVEST, SPOL. S R.O.—See CEZ, a.s.; *Int'l*, pg. 1429
EG SVERIGE AB—See Francisco Partners Management, LP; *U.S. Private*, pg. 1589
EHARVEST—See Farms.com Ltd.; *Int'l*, pg. 2620
EHS TECHNOLOGIES CORP.; *U.S. Private*, pg. 1346
E-IT PROFESSIONALS INDIA PVT. LTD.—See eIT Professionals Corp.; *U.S. Private*, pg. 1348
ELCA HOLDING SA; *Int'l*, pg. 2345
ELECTRAWINDS SE; *Int'l*, pg. 2348
ELEGRITY, INC.—See iManage LLC; *U.S. Private*, pg. 2046
ELEMENTAL ENERGIES HOLDINGS LIMITED; *Int'l*, pg. 2358
ELEVION GROUP B.V.—See CEZ, a.s.; *Int'l*, pg. 1427
ELICERE INC; *U.S. Private*, pg. 1360
EMINENT TECHNOLOGY SOLUTIONS, INC.; *U.S. Private*, pg. 1382
EMO ENERGY SOLUTIONS, LLC.—See Lilker Associates Consulting Engineers, PC; *U.S. Private*, pg. 2455
EMS CONSULTING - INTELLIGENT CHAOS; *U.S. Private*, pg. 1388
ENABLEIT, LLC; *U.S. Private*, pg. 1389
ENBW BENELUX B.V.—See EnBW Energie Baden-Wurttemberg AG; *Int'l*, pg. 2398
ENBW OMEGA SIEBZEHNTE VERWALTUNGSGESELLSCHAFT MBH—See EnBW Energie Baden-Wurttemberg AG; *Int'l*, pg. 2398
ENBW SYSTEME INFRASTRUKTUR SUPPORT GMBH—See EnBW Energie Baden-Wurttemberg AG; *Int'l*, pg. 2398
ENCOMPASS ENERGY SERVICES, INC.; *U.S. Public*, pg. 754
ENERACTIVE SOLUTIONS, LLC.—See Edison International; *U.S. Public*, pg. 719
ENERFIN RENEWABLES, LLC—See Elecnor, S.A.; *Int'l*, pg. 2347
ENERGETICS INCORPORATED—See TPG Capital, L.P.; *U.S. Public*, pg. 2176
ENERGETYKA POZNANSKA PRZEDSIEBIORSTWO USLUG ENERGETYCZNYCH ENERGOBUD LESZNO SP. Z O.O.—See ENEA S.A.; *Int'l*, pg. 2410
ENERGIEDIENST NETZE GMBH—See EnBW Energie Baden-Wurttemberg AG; *Int'l*, pg. 2398
ENERGO CONSULT L.L.C.—See Energoprojekt Holding a.d.; *Int'l*, pg. 2421
ENERGOGREEN RENEWABLES S.R.L.—See Fintel Energia Group S.p.A.; *Int'l*, pg. 2677
ENERGY CONSULTING GROUP, LLC—See Quanta Services, Inc.; *U.S. Public*, pg. 1751
ENERGY CONSULTING SERVICES S.A.—See ENGIE SA; *Int'l*, pg. 2432
ENERGY & ENVIRONMENTAL ECONOMICS, INC.—See Willdan Group, Inc.; *U.S. Public*, pg. 2370
ENERGYICT N.V.—See Honeywell International Inc.; *U.S. Public*, pg. 1048
ENERGYLOGIC INC; *U.S. Private*, pg. 1396
ENERGY OVERWATCH LLC; *U.S. Private*, pg. 1395
ENERNOC NEW ZEALAND LIMITED—See Enel S.p.A.; *Int'l*, pg. 2413
ENERNOC PTY LTD—See Enel S.p.A.; *Int'l*, pg. 2413
ENETIQA A.S.—See Groupe BPCE; *Int'l*, pg. 3094
ENGINEERING/REMEDIATION RESOURCES GROUP, INC.; *U.S. Private*, pg. 1399
ENOSERV, LLC—See ESCO Technologies, Inc.; *U.S. Public*, pg. 794
ENSAFE INC.; *U.S. Private*, pg. 1401
ENS GROUP, INC.; *U.S. Private*, pg. 1401
ENSYNC SOLUTIONS, INC.—See Nextworld, LLC; *U.S. Private*, pg. 2921
ENTERPRISE ENERGY SERVICES INC.—See Enterprise Group, Inc.; *Int'l*, pg. 2451
ENTERPRISE SERVICES INFORMATION SECURITY UK LIMITED—See Veritas Capital Fund Management, LLC; *U.S. Private*, pg. 4364
ENTERPRISE SYSTEMS SOFTWARE LLC; *U.S. Private*, pg. 1404
ENVIRONMENTAL DATA RESOURCES, INC.—See Daily Mail & General Trust plc; *Int'l*, pg. 1937
ENVIRONMENTAL PLANNING GROUP, LLC—See Terracon Consultants, Inc.; *U.S. Private*, pg. 3971
ENVIRONMENTAL STANDARDS, INC.—See Montrose Environmental Group, Inc.; *U.S. Public*, pg. 1466
ENVIRO-SAFE CONSULTING, LLC; *U.S. Private*, pg. 1406
E.ON ENERGIE 39. BETEILIGUNGS-GMBH—See E.ON SE; *Int'l*, pg. 2252
E.ON GRID SOLUTIONS GMBH—See E.ON SE; *Int'l*, pg. 2254
E.ON KRAFTWERKE GMBH—See E.ON SE; *Int'l*, pg. 2253
EPLAN SOFTWARE & SERVICE GMBH & CO. KG—See Friedhelm Loh Stiftung & Co. KG; *Int'l*, pg. 2791
EPS CORP.; *U.S. Private*, pg. 1414
EPS CORP—See EPS Corp.; *U.S. Private*, pg. 1414
EQLIPSE TECHNOLOGIES—See Arlington Capital Partners LLC; *U.S. Private*, pg. 327
EQT FUND MANAGEMENT S.A.R.L.—See EQT AB; *Int'l*, pg. 2475
EQT PARTNERS SPAIN S.L.U.—See EQT AB; *Int'l*, pg. 2475
EQT SERVICES (UK) LIMITED—See EQT AB; *Int'l*, pg. 2475
EQUALIZERCM; *U.S. Private*, pg. 1415
EQUATION ENERGY PTE. LTD.—See DISA LIMITED; *Int'l*, pg. 2131
ERGOS TECHNOLOGY PARTNERS, INC.; *U.S. Private*, pg. 1418
ESOLUTION ARCHITECTS, INC.; *U.S. Private*, pg. 1426
E-SOLUTIONS INC.; *U.S. Private*, pg. 1303
E SOURCE COMPANIES, LLC—See Align Capital Partners, LLC; *U.S. Private*, pg. 167
ESSENTIA ADVISORY PARTNERS, LLC—See EPAM Systems, Inc.; *U.S. Public*, pg. 783
ESSESS INC.—See Exelon Corporation; *U.S. Public*, pg. 806
E-STAR ALTERNATIVE PLC.; *Int'l*, pg. 2249

N.A.I.C.S. INDEX

541690 — OTHER SCIENTIFIC AN...

EUROCOPTER KHDS LIMITED—See Airbus SE; *Int'l*, pg. 243
EUROFINS CONSULTING AGROALIMENTAIRE SAS—See Eurofins Scientific S.E.; *Int'l*, pg. 2539
EUROFINS DR. SPECHT EXPRESS GMBH—See Eurofins Scientific S.E.; *Int'l*, pg. 2540
EUROFINS GENOMICS INDIA PVT LTD—See Eurofins Scientific S.E.; *Int'l*, pg. 2543
EUROFINS SCIENTIFIC ANALYTICS SAS—See Eurofins Scientific S.E.; *Int'l*, pg. 2543
EUROFINS UMWELT OST GMBH—See Eurofins Scientific S.E.; *Int'l*, pg. 2549
EVANS ENVIRONMENTAL & GEOLOGICAL SCIENCE AND MANAGEMENT INC.; *U.S. Private*, pg. 1435
EVOLUTE CONSOLIDATED HOLDINGS, INC.—See PipelineRx; *U.S. Private*, pg. 3189
EWORK GROUP AB; *Int'l*, pg. 2576
EXCELIAN LIMITED—See DXC Technology Company; *U.S. Public*, pg. 696
EXCELSIOR SOLUTIONS, LLC—See The Lockton Companies, LLC; *U.S. Private*, pg. 4071
EXIGENT TECHNOLOGIES, LLC; *U.S. Private*, pg. 1449
EXMOTION CO., LTD.; *Int'l*, pg. 2586
THE EXPERTS, INC.; *U.S. Private*, pg. 4027
EXPLEO GERMANY HOLDING GMBH—See Assystem S.A.; *Int'l*, pg. 650
EXPONENT ENVIRONMENTAL GROUP—See Exponent, Inc.; *U.S. Public*, pg. 812
EXPONENT SCIENCE AND TECHNOLOGY CONSULTING (SHANGHAI) CO., LTD.—See Exponent, Inc.; *U.S. Public*, pg. 812
EXTENSYS, INC.; *U.S. Private*, pg. 1452
FAIRFIELD TECHNOLOGIES INC.; *U.S. Private*, pg. 1463
FARALLON CONSULTING, LLC; *U.S. Private*, pg. 1473
FD ADVISORY, LTD.—See Hokkoku Financial Holdings, Inc.; *Int'l*, pg. 3443
FEDTECH SERVICES, INC.; *U.S. Private*, pg. 1492
FINNAIR TECHNICAL SERVICES OY—See Finnair Plc; *Int'l*, pg. 2676
FIRST TECHNOLOGY CHINA LTD.—See Fuji Corporation; *Int'l*, pg. 2809
FITCH SOLUTIONS, INC.—See The Hearst Corporation; *U.S. Private*, pg. 4044
FLASHPARKING, INC.; *U.S. Private*, pg. 1540
FLEXIBLE BENEFITS SYSTEM INC.—See Genstar Capital, LLC; *U.S. Private*, pg. 1674
FLORIDA GROUNDWATER SERVICES, INC.; *U.S. Private*, pg. 1548
FORKLIFT TRAINING SYSTEMS, INC—See Fleet Team, Inc.; *U.S. Private*, pg. 1542
FORSYTHE TECHNOLOGY INC.—See CDW Corporation; *U.S. Public*, pg. 463
FORT POINT ASSOCIATES, INC.—See Tetra Tech, Inc.; *U.S. Public*, pg. 2023
FORTUM POWER AND HEAT OY—See Fortum Oyj; *Int'l*, pg. 2741
FRANKLIN ENERGY SERVICES LLC—See ABRY Partners, LLC; *U.S. Private*, pg. 41
FREEDOM INFORMATION SYSTEMS, INC.; *U.S. Private*, pg. 1603
FREE ENERGY S.R.L.—See A2A S.p.A.; *Int'l*, pg. 29
FRONTIER COMPUTER CORP. B.V.—See Frontier Computer Corp.; *U.S. Private*, pg. 1615
FRONTIER COMPUTER CORP.; *U.S. Private*, pg. 1615
FRONTIER COMPUTER CORP. UK LTD.—See Frontier Computer Corp.; *U.S. Private*, pg. 1615
FUGRO GEOCONSULTING LTD.—See Fugro N.V.; *Int'l*, pg. 2806
FUGRO GEOLAB NOR AS—See Fugro N.V.; *Int'l*, pg. 2806
FUGRO SATELLITE POSITIONING PTE. LTD.—See Fugro N.V.; *Int'l*, pg. 2807
FUJITA RESEARCH (ENCINO OFFICE)—See Daiwa House Industry Co., Ltd.; *Int'l*, pg. 1946
FUJITSU AMERICA, INC.—See Fujitsu Limited; *Int'l*, pg. 2833
FUJITSU CONSULTING—See Fujitsu Limited; *Int'l*, pg. 2833
FUJITSU CONSULTING—See Fujitsu Limited; *Int'l*, pg. 2833
FULL SPEED INC.—See FreeBit Co., Ltd.; *Int'l*, pg. 2769
FUSION RISK MANAGEMENT, INC.—See Great Hill Partners, L.P.; *U.S. Private*, pg. 1763
FUSION SOLUTIONS, INC.; *U.S. Private*, pg. 1626
FUTURE STATE—See Accenture plc; *Int'l*, pg. 87
G2 CONSULTING GROUP, LLC; *U.S. Private*, pg. 1632
GADGITKIDS, LLC; *U.S. Private*, pg. 1633
GARANTIZAR S.G.R.—See Banco Macro S.A.; *Int'l*, pg. 823
GARCIA & ASSOCIATES, INC.—See Goldberg Lindsay & Co., LLC; *U.S. Private*, pg. 1729
GB TECH, INC.; *U.S. Private*, pg. 1653
GCS TECHNOLOGIES, INC.; *U.S. Private*, pg. 1654
GEE CONSULTANTS, INC.; *U.S. Private*, pg. 1655
GEENIUS, INC.; *U.S. Private*, pg. 1655
GEI CONSULTANTS, INC.—See Global Infrastructure Solutions, Inc.; *U.S. Private*, pg. 1715
GEM ENERGY LLC—See The Rudolph/Libbe Companies; *U.S. Private*, pg. 4113
GEMINI COMMUNICATION LTD.; *Int'l*, pg. 2916
GENAGRICOLA 1851 S.P.A.—See Assicurazioni Generali S.p.A.; *Int'l*, pg. 644

GENOMICS BIOSCI & TECH CO., LTD.; *Int'l*, pg. 2925
GEOMET TECHNOLOGIES, LLC—See Kingswood Capital Management LLC; *U.S. Private*, pg. 2312
GIANT IMPACT, LLC—See LC Group LLC; *U.S. Private*, pg. 2403
GIBSON TECHNICAL SERVICES, INC.—See Streeterville Capital LLC; *U.S. Private*, pg. 3838
GLADSTEIN, NEANDROSS & ASSOCIATES LLC—See TRC Companies, Inc.; *U.S. Private*, pg. 4215
GLOBAL INFOTECH CORP.—See Intelliswift Software Inc.; *U.S. Private*, pg. 2106
GLOBAL SECURITY EXPERTS INC.—See Business Brain Showa-Ota Inc.; *Int'l*, pg. 1228
GLOBE-BAY AREA FORKLIFT—See The Pape Group, Inc.; *U.S. Private*, pg. 4090
GO2CALL.COM, INC.; *U.S. Private*, pg. 1724
GOODBEE AND ASSOCIATES, INC.; *U.S. Private*, pg. 1738
GORMAN HEALTH GROUP, LLC—See TPG Capital, L.P.; *U.S. Private*, pg. 2170
GOSOFT (THAILAND) COMPANY LIMITED—See C.P. All Public Company Limited; *Int'l*, pg. 1244
GRAIL INSIGHTS—See Symphony Technology Group, LLC; *U.S. Private*, pg. 3900
GRANUM COMMUNICATIONS; *U.S. Private*, pg. 1757
GRETTE ASSOCIATES, LLC—See Farallon Consulting, LLC; *U.S. Private*, pg. 1473
GRIDSMART TECHNOLOGIES, INC.—See Elliott Management Corporation; *U.S. Private*, pg. 1368
GRIDSMART TECHNOLOGIES, INC.—See Veritas Capital Fund Management, LLC; *U.S. Private*, pg. 4362
GROUPE ONEPOINT SAS; *Int'l*, pg. 3109
GROWTH ENERGY; *U.S. Private*, pg. 1796
GRYPHON SCIENTIFIC, LLC—See Deloitte LLP; *U.S. Private*, pg. 1198
GRYPHON SCIENTIFIC, LLC—See Deloitte Touche Tohmatsu Limited; *Int'l*, pg. 2015
GSL DARDAN LIMITED—See HAL Trust N.V.; *Int'l*, pg. 3226
GSS INFOTECH LIMITED; *Int'l*, pg. 3150
GUOTAI JUNAN SECURITIES (VIETNAM) CORPORATION—See Guotai Junan Securities Co., Ltd.; *Int'l*, pg. 3187
HAMILTON ENGINEERING, INC.—See Harlow Aerostructures, LLC; *U.S. Private*, pg. 1865
HAZMED INC.; *U.S. Private*, pg. 1886
HCL AMERICA, INC.—See HCL Technologies Ltd.; *Int'l*, pg. 3298
HCL SAFETY LIMITED—See MSA Safety Incorporated; *U.S. Public*, pg. 1481
HCMS GROUP, LLC—See UPMC WorkPartners; *U.S. Private*, pg. 4312
HEITECH PADU BERHAD; *Int'l*, pg. 3326
HENRY S. MILLER CONSULTING, LLC—See Henry S. Miller Management Co.; *U.S. Private*, pg. 1919
HEP-OBNOVLJIVI IZVORI ENERGIJE D.O.O.—See Hrvatska elektroprivreda d.d.; *Int'l*, pg. 3502
HERO DIGITAL LLC—See AEA Investors LP; *U.S. Private*, pg. 114
HESCHONG MAHONE GROUP, INC.; *U.S. Private*, pg. 1927
HEXAWARE TECHNOLOGIES INC.—See EQT AB; *Int'l*, pg. 2470
HEXAWARE TECHNOLOGIES LTD—See EQT AB; *Int'l*, pg. 2470
HIDROBIRO A.D.; *Int'l*, pg. 3384
HIGH TOUCH, INC.—See High Touch, Inc.; *U.S. Private*, pg. 1937
HILL INTERNATIONAL INC.-DISTRICT OF COLUMBIA—See Global Infrastructure Solutions, Inc.; *U.S. Private*, pg. 1715
HIPERSCAN GMBH—See Fagron NV; *Int'l*, pg. 2603
HIRERIGHT POLAND SP. Z. O.O.—See Corporate Risk Holdings LLC; *U.S. Private*, pg. 1056
HIRERIGHT SOLUTIONS, INC.—See Corporate Risk Holdings LLC; *U.S. Private*, pg. 1056
HIROGIN CAPITAL PARTNERS CO., LTD.—See Hirogin Holdings, Inc.; *Int'l*, pg. 3404
HITACHI ABB POWER GRIDS AG—See Hitachi, Ltd.; *Int'l*, pg. 3413
HLB LIFE SCIENCE CO.,LTD.; *Int'l*, pg. 3430
HORIZONTAL INTEGRATION; *U.S. Private*, pg. 1983
HOSTVENTURES.COM, INC.; *U.S. Private*, pg. 1988
HYDROGEOPHYSICS, INC.; *U.S. Private*, pg. 2017
IBEX IT BUSINESS EXPERTS, LLC; *U.S. Private*, pg. 2028
IBIDEN U.S.A. R&D INC.—See Ibiden Co., Ltd.; *Int'l*, pg. 3576
ICF CONSULTING—See ICF International, Inc.; *U.S. Public*, pg. 1086
ICF INTERNATIONAL, INC.; *U.S. Public*, pg. 1085
ICO GROUP LIMITED; *Int'l*, pg. 3582
ICON MEDIA HOLDINGS, INC.; *U.S. Public*, pg. 1086
ICORE HEALTHCARE LLC—See Centene Corporation; *U.S. Public*, pg. 469
ICPROA SA; *Int'l*, pg. 3586
ICPV SA; *Int'l*, pg. 3586
IDEA INTEGRATION CORP.—See The Gores Group, LLC; *U.S. Private*, pg. 4034
IDICO INVESTMENT CONSULTANT JSC; *Int'l*, pg. 3595

IKM CONSULTANTS A/S—See IKM Gruppen AS; *Int'l*, pg. 3611
IMAGENET CONSULTING, LLC—See BMI Systems Corporation; *U.S. Private*, pg. 601
IMETHODS, LLC; *U.S. Private*, pg. 2046
IMPEX TECH LAB INC.; *U.S. Private*, pg. 2050
IMPINJ RFID TECHNOLOGY (SHANGHAI) CO., LTD.—See Impinj, Inc.; *U.S. Public*, pg. 1113
IMPROVING HOLDINGS, LLC—See Trinity Hunt Management, L.P.; *U.S. Private*, pg. 4234
IMSERV EUROPE LIMITED—See Blue Water Energy LLP; *Int'l*, pg. 1070
INCODE TELECOM GROUP, INC.; *U.S. Private*, pg. 2054
INCODE TELECOM GROUP—See inCode Telecom Group, Inc.; *U.S. Private*, pg. 2054
INCONTROL TECHNOLOGIES, INC.—See Universal Engineering Sciences, LLC; *U.S. Private*, pg. 4304
INDEPENDENT PHARMACEUTICAL CONSULTANTS, INC.—See Aquiline Capital Partners LLC; *U.S. Private*, pg. 304
INDSOFT, INC.; *U.S. Private*, pg. 2064
INDUSTROPROJEKT A.D.—See Grupa Fortis d.o.o. Banja Luka; *Int'l*, pg. 3116
INFINITI SYSTEMS GROUP, INC.; *U.S. Private*, pg. 2071
INFOAXIS INC; *U.S. Private*, pg. 2072
INFOJINI INC; *U.S. Private*, pg. 2072
INFORMATION SYSTEMS MANAGEMENT, INC.; *U.S. Private*, pg. 2073
INFOTRUST GROUP, INC.; *U.S. Private*, pg. 2074
INGENUITY CONSULTING PARTNERS, INC.—See Speridian Technologies, LLC; *U.S. Private*, pg. 3756
INNOVA INTERNATIONAL CORP.—See Great Universal Incorporated; *U.S. Private*, pg. 1768
INNOVATION LABORATORY, INC.—See Future Corporation; *Int'l*, pg. 2853
INNOVATIVE SOLUTIONS UNLIMITED, LLC; *U.S. Private*, pg. 2083
INOVA VENTURE PTE. LTD.—See Green Packet Berhad; *Int'l*, pg. 3072
INRHYTHM; *U.S. Private*, pg. 2085
INTECHSTRA CO., LTD.—See BIPROGY Inc.; *Int'l*, pg. 1045
INTEGRA TELECOM OF WASHINGTON, INC.—See Warburg Pincus LLC; *U.S. Private*, pg. 4438
INTELLIGENT VAR TECHNOLOGY INC.; *U.S. Private*, pg. 2106
INTERNATIONAL INFORMATION SYSTEMS CONSORTIUM INC.; *U.S. Private*, pg. 2117
INTERSEQT, LLC—See Occidental Petroleum Corporation; *U.S. Public*, pg. 1561
INTERSTATE BIOLOGIC SERVICES, LLC—See Grifols, S.A.; *Int'l*, pg. 3085
INTEX ENVIRONMENTAL GROUP, INC.; *U.S. Private*, pg. 2128
IN THE KNOW, INC.; *U.S. Private*, pg. 2052
INTHINC TECHNOLOGY SOLUTIONS, INC; *U.S. Private*, pg. 2128
INTREORG SYSTEMS, INC.; *U.S. Private*, pg. 2129
INTUITIVE MACHINES, LLC—See Intuitive Machines, Inc.; *U.S. Private*, pg. 1160
INVICTUS INTERNATIONAL CONSULTING, LLC; *U.S. Private*, pg. 2132
INVOYENT, LLC—See West Monroe Partners, LLC; *U.S. Private*, pg. 4486
IRONWARE TECHNOLOGIES, LLC; *U.S. Private*, pg. 2140
IRVING BURTON ASSOCIATES, LLC—See DLH Holdings Corp.; *U.S. Public*, pg. 670
ISC2 ASIA-PACIFIC—See International Information Systems Consortium Inc.; *U.S. Private*, pg. 2118
ISC2 EMEA—See International Information Systems Consortium Inc.; *U.S. Private*, pg. 2118
ISC2 JAPAN—See International Information Systems Consortium Inc.; *U.S. Private*, pg. 2118
ISI TELEMANAGEMENT SOLUTIONS, LLC—See Valent Capital Partners LLC; *U.S. Private*, pg. 4331
ISPACE, INC.; *U.S. Private*, pg. 2146
JACOBS GROUP (AUSTRALIA) PTY LTD—See Jacobs Engineering Group, Inc.; *U.S. Public*, pg. 1185
JB MANAGEMENT INC.; *U.S. Private*, pg. 2193
JEEVY COMPUTING, LLC; *U.S. Private*, pg. 2196
JENSEN HUGHES, INC.—See Gryphon Investors, LLC; *U.S. Private*, pg. 1798
JETTAINER GMBH—See Deutsche Lufthansa AG; *Int'l*, pg. 2068
JHNA, INC.; *U.S. Private*, pg. 2208
JM SORGE, INC.—See Sterling Investment Partners, L.P.; *U.S. Private*, pg. 3806
JOBSON PUBLISHING CORPORATION—See The Wicks Group of Companies, LLC; *U.S. Private*, pg. 4135
JX NIPPON RESEARCH INSTITUTE, LTD.—See ENEOS Holdings, Inc.; *Int'l*, pg. 2417
KESHAV MANGLAM IMPEX PVT LTD.—See Impex Tech Lab Inc.; *U.S. Private*, pg. 2050
KEYEDIN SOLUTIONS, INC.; *U.S. Private*, pg. 2294
KEYEDIN (UK) LIMITED—See KeyedIn Solutions, Inc.; *U.S. Private*, pg. 2294
KEY RISK MANAGEMENT SERVICES, INC.—See W.R. Berkley Corporation; *U.S. Public*, pg. 2318
KEYSTONE PHYSICS LIMITED—See Associates in Medical

Physics, LLC; *U.S. Private*, pg. 358
KHI MANAGEMENT INTERNATIONAL LTD.—See Cobepa S.A.; *Int'l*, pg. 1683
KIESLING MASCHINENTECHNIK GMBH—See Friedhelm Loh Stiftung & Co. KG; *Int'l*, pg. 2791
KINECT CONSULTING, LLC—See World Kinect Corporation; *U.S. Private*, pg. 2380
KINETEK CONSULTING, LLC; *U.S. Private*, pg. 2308
KMA ONE, INC.—See Local Marketing Solutions Group, Inc.; *U.S. Private*, pg. 2477
KODIAK GAS SERVICES, LLC—See EQT AB; *Int'l*, pg. 2478
KORS ENGINEERING COMPANY, INC.—See Francisco Partners Management, LP; *U.S. Private*, pg. 1591
KORTEC, INC.; *U.S. Private*, pg. 2344
KSASHMTSSI GMBH—See Atlassian Corporation; *Int'l*, pg. 686
K T M, INC.—See World Kinect Corporation; *U.S. Public*, pg. 2380
L-3 D.P. ASSOCIATES INC.—See L3Harris Technologies, Inc.; *U.S. Public*, pg. 1283
L5E LLC; *U.S. Private*, pg. 2367
LANDRUM & BROWN, INCORPORATED; *U.S. Private*, pg. 2386
LANSPEED; *U.S. Private*, pg. 2391
LC GROUP LLC; *U.S. Private*, pg. 2403
LEADING EDJE; *U.S. Private*, pg. 2406
LEIGHTON ASSOCIATES, INC.—See Kelso & Company, L.P.; *U.S. Private*, pg. 2278
LEXIPOL, LLC—See Riverside Partners, LLC; *U.S. Private*, pg. 3446
LEXNET LLC—See Visual Edge Technology, Inc.; *U.S. Private*, pg. 4404
LIGHTSHIP SECURITY, INC.—See I Squared Capital Advisors (US) LLC; *U.S. Private*, pg. 2023
LIGHTSHIP SECURITY USA, INC.—See I Squared Capital Advisors (US) LLC; *U.S. Private*, pg. 2023
LINK2GOV CORP.—See Fidelity National Infor; *U.S. Public*, pg. 833
LIONBRIDGE TECHNOLOGIES (FRANCE) S.A.R.L.—See H.I.G. Capital, LLC; *U.S. Private*, pg. 1830
LIST INNOVATIVE SOLUTIONS, INC.—See Bridge Growth Partners, LLC; *U.S. Private*, pg. 649
LIST INNOVATIVE SOLUTIONS, INC.—See Frontenac Company LLC; *U.S. Private*, pg. 1614
LKH KUNSTSTOFFWERK HEILIGENROTH GMBH & CO. KG—See Friedhelm Loh Stiftung & Co. KG; *Int'l*, pg. 2791
THE LLOYD GROUP, INC.; *U.S. Private*, pg. 4071
LMC INTERNATIONAL LIMITED—See GlobalData Plc; *Int'l*, pg. 3003
LOGICALLY, INC.—See The Riverside Company; *U.S. Private*, pg. 4109
LOH SERVICES GMBH & CO. KG—See Friedhelm Loh Stiftung & Co. KG; *Int'l*, pg. 2791
LS TECHNOLOGIES, LLC.—See Tetra Tech, Inc; *U.S. Public*, pg. 2023
L&T-CHIYODA LIMITED—See Chiyoda Corporation; *Int'l*, pg. 1575
LUFTHANSA CONSULTING GMBH—See Deutsche Lufthansa AG; *Int'l*, pg. 2069
LUKE & ASSOCIATES, INC.; *U.S. Private*, pg. 2512
LUTAB AB—See Etteplan Oyj; *Int'l*, pg. 2525
LUTECH ADVANCED SOLUTIONS S.P.A.—See Apax Partners LLP; *Int'l*, pg. 501
LUX CONSULTING GROUP INC; *U.S. Private*, pg. 2518
LUX RESEARCH, INC.—See COFRA Holding AG; *Int'l*, pg. 1694
M9 SOLUTIONS; *U.S. Private*, pg. 2530
THE MAKO GROUP, LLC—See Centric Consulting, LLC; *U.S. Private*, pg. 829
MANUFACTURING TECHNICAL SOLUTIONS INC.; *U.S. Private*, pg. 2567
MARAKANA INC.; *U.S. Private*, pg. 2569
MARSTEL-DAY, LLC; *U.S. Private*, pg. 2593
MARTIA A.S.—See CEZ, a.s.; *Int'l*, pg. 1428
MAS GLOBAL CONSULTING, LLC; *U.S. Private*, pg. 2600
MASSTOCK ARABLE (UK) LTD—See ARYZTA AG; *Int'l*, pg. 589
MASTER CANADA INC. - FORT ST. JOHN—See MasTec, Inc.; *U.S. Public*, pg. 1393
MASTER KEY RESOURCES LLC; *U.S. Private*, pg. 2607
MATERIAL CONNEXION MILANO—See Sandow Media LLC; *U.S. Private*, pg. 3544
MATRIX ENERGY SERVICES INC.; *U.S. Private*, pg. 2612
MAVERICK TECHNOLOGIES, LLC—See Rockwell Automation, Inc.; *U.S. Public*, pg. 1805
MBTECH CONSULTING GMBH—See Adecco Group AG; *Int'l*, pg. 140
MCCLENDON, LLC—See BAE Systems plc; *Int'l*, pg. 797
MCFA LLC; *U.S. Private*, pg. 2633
MCH CORP.; *U.S. Private*, pg. 2636
MCKINLEY CONSULTING, INC.—See McKinley Group, Inc.; *U.S. Private*, pg. 2639
MEETIO AB—See Logitech International S.A.; *U.S. Public*, pg. 1341
MEETIO INC.—See Logitech International S.A.; *U.S. Public*, pg. 1341
MEMDATA, LLC—See Premier, Inc.; *U.S. Public*, pg. 1715

MERIEUX NUTRISCIENCES CORP.; *U.S. Private*, pg. 2674
MERMOZ BASTIE S.C.I.—See DEKRA e.V.; *Int'l*, pg. 2009
MERRITT & HARRIS, INC.—See Jones Lang LaSalle Incorporated; *U.S. Public*, pg. 1205
METRO FIRE SAFETY, INC.—See Paris Maintenance Co. Inc.; *U.S. Private*, pg. 3095
METRUM RESEARCH GROUP LLC; *U.S. Private*, pg. 2691
MGT OF AMERICA, LLC—See The Vistria Group, LP; *U.S. Private*, pg. 4132
MICHELSEN BENEFITS GROUP, INC.—See Aon plc; *Int'l*, pg. 496
MID-STATES ENERGY WORKS, INC.; *U.S. Private*, pg. 2709
MINDLANCE, INC.; *U.S. Private*, pg. 2740
MINERCONSULT ENGENHARIA LTDA—See AtkinsRealis Group Inc.; *Int'l*, pg. 672
MMY CONSULTING, INC.—See Global Commerce & Information, Inc.; *U.S. Private*, pg. 1712
MODERN TECHNOLOGY SOLUTIONS, INC.; *U.S. Private*, pg. 2762
MODIS BULGARIA EOOD—See Adecco Group AG; *Int'l*, pg. 141
MOMENTUM CONSULTING CORPORATION—See CGI Inc.; *Int'l*, pg. 1434
MONTAUK RENEWABLES, INC.; *U.S. Public*, pg. 1465
MOSAIC ATM, INC.; *U.S. Private*, pg. 2792
MOSS ADAMS LLP - ISSAQUAH—See Moss Adams LLP; *U.S. Private*, pg. 2794
MPHASIS CONSULTING LIMITED—See Blackstone Inc.; *U.S. Public*, pg. 356
MSA SAFETY SERVICES GMBH—See MSA Safety Incorporated; *U.S. Public*, pg. 1482
MTS EUROPE HOLDINGS LLC—See Illinois Tool Works Inc.; *U.S. Public*, pg. 1109
MULTISTATE ASSOCIATES INC.—See Public Policy Holding Company; *U.S. Public*, pg. 1735
MYTEK NETWORK SOLUTIONS; *U.S. Private*, pg. 2826
MZB TECHNOLOGIES, LLC—See South Dakota Wheat Growers Association; *U.S. Private*, pg. 3722
NANOTOX, INC.; *U.S. Private*, pg. 2833
NATIONAL INDUSTRIAL FUEL EFFICIENCY LIMITED—See Grovepoint Capital LLP; *Int'l*, pg. 3112
NATIONAL INSPECTION & CONSULTANTS, LLC—See Edgewater Services, LLC; *U.S. Private*, pg. 1335
NATIONAL STOCK YARDS CO.; *U.S. Public*, pg. 1497
NATURAL RESOURCE TECHNOLOGY, INC.—See The O'Brien & Gere Companies; *U.S. Private*, pg. 4087
NAVITAS BUSINESS CONSULTING INC; *U.S. Private*, pg. 2873
NAZDAR COMPANY - NAZDAR CONSULTING SERVICES DIVISION—See Thrall Enterprises, Inc.; *U.S. Private*, pg. 4163
NB VENTURES, INC.; *U.S. Private*, pg. 2874
NEOCOM SOLUTIONS, INC.—See Dycom Industries, Inc.; *U.S. Public*, pg. 698
NET D CONSULTING, INC.—See Gawk, Incorporated; *U.S. Private*, pg. 1652
NETRIX LLC; *U.S. Private*, pg. 2887
NETWORK ONE SOLUTIONS INC.—See UPSTACK, Inc.; *U.S. Private*, pg. 4313
NEWPORT PARTNERS, LLC; *U.S. Private*, pg. 2916
NEXTRACKER AUSTRALIA PTY. LTD.—See Flex Ltd.; *Int'l*, pg. 2704
NEXTRACKER MEXICO, S. DE R.L. DE C.V.—See Flex Ltd.; *Int'l*, pg. 2704
NEXT TIER CONCEPTS, INC.; *U.S. Private*, pg. 2920
NEXUSTEK, INC.—See ABRY Partners, LLC; *U.S. Private*, pg. 42
NFF, INC.; *U.S. Private*, pg. 2922
NICE-BUSINESS CONSULTING OY—See Fujitsu Limited; *Int'l*, pg. 2837
NOKAS SVERIGE—See Avarn Security Group Holding AS; *Int'l*, pg. 737
NORDBLADS VVS-KONSTRUKTIONER AB—See AFRY AB; *Int'l*, pg. 194
NORDISK ENERGIPARTNER A/S—See World Kinect Corporation; *U.S. Public*, pg. 2381
NORMANDEAU ASSOCIATES, INC.; *U.S. Private*, pg. 2938
NORTH 6TH AGENCY, INC.; *U.S. Private*, pg. 2939
NORTHERN TECHNOLOGIES GROUP INC.; *U.S. Private*, pg. 2954
NORTH HILL VETERINARY CLINIC PTY. LTD.—See Apiam Animal Health Limited; *Int'l*, pg. 515
NORTHROP GRUMMAN INTEGRATED DEFENCE SERVICES PTY. LTD.—See Northrop Grumman Corporation; *U.S. Public*, pg. 1541
NORTHSTAR SOLUTIONS GROUP; *U.S. Private*, pg. 2958
NOVAK GROUP LLC; *U.S. Private*, pg. 2966
NOVIGO INC.—See ArchLynk, LLC; *U.S. Private*, pg. 311
NTH CONSULTANTS, LTD.—See NTH Consultants, Ltd.; *U.S. Private*, pg. 2970
N-TIER SOLUTIONS INC.; *U.S. Private*, pg. 2827
NUVENTRA, INC.—See Cato SMS; *Int'l*, pg. 1361
NVISH SOLUTIONS INC.; *U.S. Private*, pg. 2975
OCEAN ACOUSTICAL SERVICES AND INSTRUMENTATION SYSTEMS, INC.—See ThayerMahan, Inc.; *U.S. Private*, pg. 3980
OCTANE ENERGY, LLC; *U.S. Private*, pg. 2992

ODYSSEY SYSTEMS; *U.S. Private*, pg. 2996
OMNIVERE, LLC—See Driven, Inc.; *U.S. Private*, pg. 1278
ONCOLIX INC.; *U.S. Public*, pg. 1601
ONCORE CONSULTING, LLC—See Sagewind Capital LLC; *U.S. Private*, pg. 3527
ONESTA; *U.S. Private*, pg. 3025
ONLINE-REDEFINED, INC.; *U.S. Private*, pg. 3027
ONLOCATION, INC.—See System One Holdings, LLC; *U.S. Private*, pg. 3907
OPERA SOLUTIONS, LLC; *U.S. Private*, pg. 3031
OPTIV INC.; *U.S. Private*, pg. 3035
ORBITEC AB—See AFRY AB; *Int'l*, pg. 194
ORION INTERNATIONAL CONSULTING GROUP, LLC - GEMINI ENERGY SERVICES DIVISION—See L2 Capital Partners; *U.S. Private*, pg. 2367
ORION INTERNATIONAL CONSULTING GROUP, LLC - GEMINI ENERGY SERVICES DIVISION—See Lakewood Capital, LLC; *U.S. Private*, pg. 2379
ORIZON, INC.; *U.S. Private*, pg. 3043
ORODAY, INC.; *U.S. Private*, pg. 3044
OTE PLUS TECHNICAL & BUSINESS SOLUTIONS S.A.—See Hellenic Telecommunications Organization S.A.; *Int'l*, pg. 3334
OUTSOURCING UNLIMITED, INC.—See ScanSource, Inc.; *U.S. Public*, pg. 1843
PACKET FUSION, INC.; *U.S. Private*, pg. 3073
PALLADIUS, INC.—See Rockwell Automation, Inc.; *U.S. Public*, pg. 1805
PANELCLAW, INC.—See Esdec BV; *Int'l*, pg. 2502
PARAMETRIX, INC.; *U.S. Private*, pg. 3092
PATHFINDER CONSULTANTS LLC; *U.S. Private*, pg. 3105
PATRIOT RENEWABLE FUELS, LLC—See CHS INC.; *U.S. Public*, pg. 492
PAUL C. RIZZO ASSOCIATES, INC.; *U.S. Private*, pg. 3112
PAYNODE AB—See World Kinect Corporation; *U.S. Public*, pg. 2381
PBG CONSULTING, LLC; *U.S. Private*, pg. 3118
PENN ENVIRONMENTAL & REMEDIATION, INC.—See Penn Color Inc.; *U.S. Private*, pg. 3133
PENTEC ENVIRONMENTAL—See Haley & Aldrich Inc.; *U.S. Private*, pg. 1842
PERFICIENT, INC. - ATLANTA—See EQT AB; *Int'l*, pg. 2483
PERFICIENT, INC. - CHICAGO—See EQT AB; *Int'l*, pg. 2483
PETRA GEOTECHNICAL, INC.; *U.S. Private*, pg. 3161
PFIZER HEALTH SOLUTIONS INC.—See Pfizer Inc.; *U.S. Public*, pg. 1681
PINNACLE COMMUNICATION SERVICES; *U.S. Private*, pg. 3184
PIONEER HI-BRED INTERNATIONAL—See Corteva, Inc.; *U.S. Public*, pg. 583
PITCHBOOK DATA INC.—See Morningstar, Inc.; *U.S. Public*, pg. 1476
PLANET METRIX—See Warranty Corporation America; *U.S. Private*, pg. 4443
PLANT IMPACT TECNOLOGIA EM NUTRICAO LTDA—See Croda International plc; *Int'l*, pg. 1852
PLASMA BIOLOGICAL SERVICES, LLC—See Grifols, S.A.; *Int'l*, pg. 3085
PLEDOC GESELLSCHAFT FUR DOKUMENTATIONSERSTELLUNG UND -PFLEGE MBH—See British Columbia Investment Management Corp.; *Int'l*, pg. 1169
POINT ONE, LLC—See FedCap Partners, LLC; *U.S. Private*, pg. 1486
POPULUS, LLC—See TPG Capital, L.P.; *U.S. Public*, pg. 2176
THE PORTAL GROUP CONSULTING LLC—See Beyondsoft Corporation; *Int'l*, pg. 1005
POWERGEM, LLC—See TA Associates, Inc.; *U.S. Private*, pg. 3917
POYRY ENERGY CONSULTING GROUP AG—See AFRY AB; *Int'l*, pg. 195
POYRY ENERGY LTD.—See AFRY AB; *Int'l*, pg. 195
POYRY SWEDEN AB—See AFRY AB; *Int'l*, pg. 196
PPM CONSULTANTS, INC.; *U.S. Private*, pg. 3240
PRAECIPIO CONSULTING LLC; *U.S. Private*, pg. 3241
PRIME SOLUTIONS LLC—See Altamira Technologies Corporation; *U.S. Private*, pg. 204
PRIME TECHNICAL SERVICES INC.; *U.S. Private*, pg. 3262
PRINCETON INFORMATION LTD.—See Digital Intelligence Systems, LLC; *U.S. Private*, pg. 1230
PRIVOWNY FRANCE SAS—See Assurant, Inc.; *U.S. Public*, pg. 215
PROALPHA SOFTWARE GMBH—See COFRA Holding AG; *Int'l*, pg. 1694
PRODUCTIVITY ASSOCIATES, INC.; *U.S. Private*, pg. 3274
PROMAR INTERNATIONAL LIMITED—See Genus Plc; *Int'l*, pg. 2931
PROMINIC.NET; *U.S. Private*, pg. 3283
PROSPECTIVE PAYMENT SPECIALISTS, INC.—See Cognizant Technology Solutions Corporation; *U.S. Public*, pg. 523
PRO-SPHERE TEK, INC.—See Planned Systems International, Inc.; *U.S. Private*, pg. 3196
PROSUM, INC.; *U.S. Private*, pg. 3289

N.A.I.C.S. INDEX 541690 — OTHER SCIENTIFIC AN...
N.A.I.C.S. Index

PROSYS INFORMATION SYSTEMS INC.—See TD Synnex Corp; *U.S. Public*, pg. 1985
PROTANG AB—See Etteplan Oyj; *Int'l*, pg. 2525
PROV INTERNATIONAL, INC.; *U.S. Private*, pg. 3291
PT CIBOODLE INDONESIA—See Verint Systems Inc.; *U.S. Public*, pg. 2281
PVR TECHNOLOGIES INC.—See Alten S.A.; *Int'l*, pg. 390
QUALITY IT PARTNERS INC.; *U.S. Private*, pg. 3319
QUALITY MANAGEMENT SOLUTIONS INC.; *U.S. Private*, pg. 3319
QUALITY SAFETY EDGE; *U.S. Private*, pg. 3321
QUALITY-SAFETY-ENGINEERING GMBH—See Christof Holding AG; *Int'l*, pg. 1587
QUARDEV, INC.; *U.S. Private*, pg. 3323
QUATRRO BUSINESS SUPPORT SERVICES, INC.—See Trivest Partners, LP; *U.S. Private*, pg. 4241
QUINTILES IMS INC. - PARSIPPANY—See IQVIA Holdings Inc.; *U.S. Public*, pg. 1169
QUIRINDI FEEDLOT SERVICES PTY. LTD.—See Apiam Animal Health Limited; *Int'l*, pg. 515
QUIRINDI VETERINARY CLINIC PTY. LTD.—See Apiam Animal Health Limited; *Int'l*, pg. 515
R3 ENERGY MANAGEMENT AUDIT & REVIEW LLC—See David Energy Systems, Inc.; *U.S. Private*, pg. 1170
RAB AGGREGATOR, LLC—See Gemspring Capital Management, LLC; *U.S. Private*, pg. 1659
RADIATION BILLING SOLUTIONS, INC.; *U.S. Private*, pg. 3343
RADIATION SAFETY & CONTROL SERVICES, INC.—See Bernhard Capital Partners Management, LP; *U.S. Private*, pg. 536
RAD-INFO, INC.; *U.S. Private*, pg. 3342
RALPH E. DAVIS ASSOCIATES LP—See Opportune LLP; *U.S. Private*, pg. 3033
RAMEY ENVIRONMENTAL COMPLIANCE INC.—See Consolidated Water Co. Ltd.; *Int'l*, pg. 1771
RCS ETM SICUREZZA S.P.A.—See CY4Gate S.p.A.; *Int'l*, pg. 1891
REAKTORTEST SRO—See Enel S.p.A.; *Int'l*, pg. 2414
REDAPTIVE, INC.; *U.S. Private*, pg. 3377
RELEVANTE CONSULTING (INDIA) PRIVATE LIMITED—See Relevante, Inc.; *U.S. Private*, pg. 3393
RELEVANTE, INC.; *U.S. Private*, pg. 3393
RELIABLE GOVERNMENT SOLUTIONS INC.; *U.S. Private*, pg. 3394
REMINGTON ASSOCIATES LTD.; *U.S. Private*, pg. 3396
REMOTE TIGER; *U.S. Private*, pg. 3396
RENODIS, INC.; *U.S. Private*, pg. 3399
REQROUTE INC.; *U.S. Private*, pg. 3403
RESOLUTION ECONOMICS, LLC—See Levine Leichtman Capital Partners, LLC; *U.S. Private*, pg. 2436
REVEREIT LLC; *U.S. Private*, pg. 3414
RIMROCK GROUP, INC.—See BCER Engineering, Inc.; *U.S. Private*, pg. 499
RINCON CONSULTANTS, INC.; *U.S. Private*, pg. 3437
RISE ENGINEERING, INC.—See Thielsch Engineering, Inc.; *U.S. Private*, pg. 4144
RISE INTERNATIONAL L.L.C.—See ARCADIS N.V.; *Int'l*, pg. 541
RISK BASED SECURITY, INC.—See EJ2 Communications, Inc.; *U.S. Private*, pg. 1348
RISK MITIGATION CONSULTING INC.; *U.S. Private*, pg. 3441
RITTAL GMBH & CO. KG—See Friedhelm Loh Stiftung & Co. KG; *Int'l*, pg. 2791
RIVERSIDE TECHNOLOGY, INC.; *U.S. Private*, pg. 3446
ROCHESTER RIVERSIDE CONVENTION CENTER; *U.S. Private*, pg. 3464
ROCKET SCIENCE CONSULTING CORP.; *U.S. Private*, pg. 3466
ROCKFARM SUPPLY CHAIN SOLUTIONS INC.—See AEA Investors LP; *U.S. Private*, pg. 115
ROKE MANOR RESEARCH LTD—See Chemring Group PLC; *Int'l*, pg. 1463
ROOT9B HOLDINGS, INC.; *U.S. Public*, pg. 1810
RXP SERVICES LTD.—See Capgemini SE; *Int'l*, pg. 1303
SAASFORCE CONSULTING PRIVATE LIMITED—See Cognizant Technology Solutions Corporation; *U.S. Public*, pg. 525
SABER PROTECTION SOLUTIONS, LLC—See Akal Security, Inc.; *U.S. Private*, pg. 144
SAGE RENEWABLE ENERGY CONSULTING, INC.—See NV5 Global, Inc.; *U.S. Public*, pg. 1557
SAICON CONSULTANTS, INC.; *U.S. Private*, pg. 3529
SALO SOLUTIONS, INC.; *U.S. Private*, pg. 3533
SANTILLANA DE SEGURIDAD VIGILANCIA PRIVADA LTDA.—See Bain Capital, LP; *U.S. Private*, pg. 435
SARTELL GROUP, INC.; *U.S. Private*, pg. 3550
SBG TECHNOLOGY SOLUTIONS INC.; *U.S. Private*, pg. 3559
SCE GROUP; *U.S. Private*, pg. 3562
SCEPTER TECHNOLOGIES INC.; *U.S. Private*, pg. 3562
SCIMETRIKA; *U.S. Private*, pg. 3574
SEBA BROS. FARMS, INC.; *U.S. Private*, pg. 3592
SECURESTATE LLC—See RSM US LLP; *U.S. Private*, pg. 3497
SEH TECHNOLOGY SOLUTIONS—See Short Elliott Hendrickson Inc.; *U.S. Private*, pg. 3642
SERVERCENTRAL; *U.S. Private*, pg. 3614
SERVICES AND PROMOTIONS MIAMI LLC—See Banco Santander, S.A.; *Int'l*, pg. 827
SERVICIOS DE DESARROLLO ORIENTADO A SOLUCIONES SL—See Alten S.A.; *Int'l*, pg. 391
SGI-AVIATION SERVICES B.V.—See FinTech Global Incorporated; *Int'l*, pg. 2677
SHANGHAI EASTMAN CONSULTING COMPANY LTD.—See Eastman Chemical Company; *U.S. Public*, pg. 705
SHAW ENVIRONMENTAL & INFRASTRUCTURE—See The Shaw Group Inc.; *U.S. Private*, pg. 4117
SIERRA W/O WIRES, INC.; *U.S. Private*, pg. 3648
SIGMA GROUP, INC.; *U.S. Private*, pg. 3648
SIGMAWAYS INC.; *U.S. Private*, pg. 3649
SIGNUM GROUP, LLC; *U.S. Private*, pg. 3651
SIMPLEX INC.—See The Carlyle Group Inc.; *U.S. Public*, pg. 2055
SINERGIA S.R.L.—See Hera S.p.A.; *Int'l*, pg. 3356
SISU HEALTHCARE IT SOLUTIONS, LLC; *U.S. Private*, pg. 3676
SKILLSTORM, INC.; *U.S. Private*, pg. 3682
SKYE ASSOCIATES LLC; *U.S. Private*, pg. 3684
SMART CITY SOLUTIONS, LLC—See US Cable Group; *U.S. Private*, pg. 4318
SMARTDOG SERVICES, LLC—See Quad-C Management, Inc.; *U.S. Private*, pg. 3315
SMARTSOFT INTERNATIONAL, INC.; *U.S. Private*, pg. 3692
SMARTWATT ENERGY, INC.—See Centrica plc; *Int'l*, pg. 1413
SNC-LAVALIN MINERCONSULT LTDA—See AtkinsRealis Group Inc.; *Int'l*, pg. 672
SOBRAN, INC.; *U.S. Private*, pg. 3702
SOFTRAMS LLC—See Sagewind Capital LLC; *U.S. Private*, pg. 3527
SOFTWARE GALAXY SYSTEMS, LLC; *U.S. Private*, pg. 3705
SOLIUM CAPITAL LLC—See Morgan Stanley; *U.S. Public*, pg. 1475
SOLUTION IT INC.; *U.S. Private*, pg. 3710
SOLVE IT, INC.; *U.S. Private*, pg. 3711
SOUFFLET AGRO POLSKA SP. Z O.O.—See Etablissements J. Soufflet; *Int'l*, pg. 2519
SOUFFLET AGRO S.R.O.—See Etablissements J. Soufflet; *Int'l*, pg. 2519
SOUND ENGINEERING, INC.; *U.S. Private*, pg. 3717
SOUTHEAST UNITED DAIRY INDUSTRY ASSOCIATION, INC.; *U.S. Private*, pg. 3726
SOUTHERN TRAFFIC SERVICES, INC.—See Rekor Systems, Inc.; *U.S. Public*, pg. 1778
SOUTHTECH SOLUTIONS INC.—See Court Square Capital Partners, L.P.; *U.S. Private*, pg. 1070
SOVEREIGN SYSTEMS LLC—See GreenPages, Inc.; *U.S. Private*, pg. 1779
SPAETH COMMUNICATIONS, INC.—See Sun West Communications, Inc.; *U.S. Private*, pg. 3864
SPALDING CONSULTING INC.—See Saalex Corp.; *U.S. Private*, pg. 3520
SPARTAN ACQUISITION CORP.; *U.S. Public*, pg. 1914
SPEARMC CONSULTING; *U.S. Private*, pg. 3748
SPECIAL OPERATIONS SOLUTIONS LLC; *U.S. Private*, pg. 3748
SPERIDIAN TECHNOLOGIES LLC—See Speridian Technologies, LLC; *U.S. Private*, pg. 3756
SPERIDIAN TECHNOLOGIES PVT LTD—See Speridian Technologies, LLC; *U.S. Private*, pg. 3756
SPERIDIAN TECHNOLOGIES PVT LTD—See Speridian Technologies, LLC; *U.S. Private*, pg. 3756
SPIE ENERGY SOLUTIONS GMBH—See Clayton, Dubilier & Rice, LLC; *U.S. Private*, pg. 926
SPITFIRE GROUP, LLC; *U.S. Private*, pg. 3758
SPORTS SYSTEMS SERVICES, INC.—See Spotlight Ticket Management, Inc.; *U.S. Private*, pg. 3762
SPRINGBOARD TELECOM, LLC—See Comporium Group; *U.S. Private*, pg. 1002
SPT LABTECH LIMITED; *U.S. Private*, pg. 3765
STACKS SERVICIOS TECHNOLOGICOS SL CHILE LTDA—See Cegedim S.A.; *Int'l*, pg. 1390
THE STAFFING GROUP LTD.; *U.S. Private*, pg. 4120
STAFFORD CONSULTING ENGINEERS, INC.—See Terracon Consultants, Inc.; *U.S. Private*, pg. 3971
STAHLO STAHLSERVICE GMBH & CO. KG—See Friedhelm Loh Stiftung & Co. KG; *Int'l*, pg. 2791
STANDARD & POOR'S FINANCIAL SERVICES LLC—See S&P Global Inc.; *U.S. Public*, pg. 1831
STANSOURCE INC.—See Stellar IT Solutions, Inc.; *U.S. Private*, pg. 3799
STATMINDS LLC—See Alten S.A.; *Int'l*, pg. 391
STEAG NEW ENERGIES GMBH—See Asterion Industrial Partners SGEIC SA; *Int'l*, pg. 654
STEALTH-ISS GROUP INC.; *U.S. Private*, pg. 3795
STELLAR ENERGY ASIA—See The Stellar Group Inc.; *U.S. Private*, pg. 4121
STELLAR ENERGY MENA—See The Stellar Group Inc.; *U.S. Private*, pg. 4121
STOLLER ENTERPRISES, INC.—See Corteva, Inc.; *U.S. Public*, pg. 584
STOLLER USA, INC.—See Corteva, Inc.; *U.S. Public*, pg. 585
STRATEGIC FEEDBACK INC.; *U.S. Private*, pg. 3835
STRATEGIC MOBILITY GROUP; *U.S. Private*, pg. 3835
STRATIVITY GROUP, LLC—See Tailwind Capital Group, LLC; *U.S. Private*, pg. 3924
STRATUS CONSULTING, INC.—See Abt Associates Inc.; *U.S. Private*, pg. 45
STRINGFELLOW TECHNOLOGY GROUP INC.; *U.S. Private*, pg. 3840
STRYVE ADVISORS—See Tectonic LLC; *U.S. Private*, pg. 3957
SUMMIT TECHNICAL SOLUTIONS, LLC; *U.S. Private*, pg. 3857
SURECLICK PROMOTIONS, LLC; *U.S. Private*, pg. 3883
SURESERVE GROUP PLC—See Cap10 Partners LLP; *Int'l*, pg. 1301
SWB SERVICES AG & CO. KG—See EWE Aktiengesellschaft; *Int'l*, pg. 2576
SYAPPS LLC; *U.S. Private*, pg. 3895
SYNCHROGENIX INFORMATION STRATEGIES INC.—See Certara, Inc.; *U.S. Public*, pg. 476
SYNERGETICS DCS INC.; *U.S. Private*, pg. 3903
SYNERGIC SOLUTIONS, INC.; *U.S. Private*, pg. 3903
SYNTELLIS PERFORMANCE SOLUTIONS, LLC—See Roper Technologies, Inc.; *U.S. Public*, pg. 1813
SYNTERRA CORP.; *U.S. Private*, pg. 3905
SYSTEM ONE HOLDINGS, LLC; *U.S. Private*, pg. 3906
SYSTEMS CONSULTANTS SERVICES LIMITED—See Cohort plc; *Int'l*, pg. 1696
TAKE2 CONSULTING, LLC; *U.S. Private*, pg. 3925
TALISMAN INTERNATIONAL, LLC—See Brookfield Corporation; *Int'l*, pg. 1182
TAMLYN SHIPPING LIMITED—See World Kinect Corporation; *U.S. Public*, pg. 2381
TASFIYE HALINDE ARAKLI DOGALGAZ URETIM SANAYI VE TICARET A.S.—See Ayen Enerji AS; *Int'l*, pg. 775
TBH INGENIEUR GMBH—See BKW AG; *Int'l*, pg. 1056
TEAMSOFT, INC.—See Groupe Crit, S.A.; *Int'l*, pg. 3101
TECHALTEN PORTUGAL, LDA—See Alten S.A.; *Int'l*, pg. 391
TECHCXO; *U.S. Private*, pg. 3952
TECHDIGITAL CORP.; *U.S. Private*, pg. 3952
TECHHOUSE INTEGRATED INFORMATION SYSTEM SOLUTIONS, INC.; *U.S. Private*, pg. 3952
TECHNET RESOURCES, INC.; *U.S. Private*, pg. 3953
TECHNICAL RESPONSE PLANNING CORP.—See Gryphon Investors, LLC; *U.S. Private*, pg. 1798
TECHNOLOGY SOLUTIONS PROVIDER INC.—See Abt Associates Inc.; *U.S. Private*, pg. 45
TECHSOURCE, INC.; *U.S. Private*, pg. 3956
TECHWAVE CONSULTING INC.; *U.S. Private*, pg. 3956
TECTURA CORPORATION; *U.S. Private*, pg. 3957
TEGRIA HOLDINGS LLC—See Providence St. Joseph Health; *U.S. Private*, pg. 3295
TEKMASTERS LLC—See Godspeed Capital Management LP; *U.S. Private*, pg. 1725
TEKNETEX INC.; *U.S. Private*, pg. 3958
TEKPRO SERVICES, LLC—See Bristol Bay Native Corporation; *U.S. Private*, pg. 656
TEKPROS INC.; *U.S. Private*, pg. 3959
TEKSYSTEMS GLOBAL SERVICES, LLC—See Allegis Group, Inc.; *U.S. Private*, pg. 177
TELECOMMUNICATIONS DEVELOPMENT CORPORATION; *U.S. Private*, pg. 3960
TELE-IMAGES INC.—See Gonzales Consulting Services, Inc.; *U.S. Private*, pg. 1737
TELEPROVIDERS INC.; *U.S. Private*, pg. 3961
TELLENNIUM, INC.; *U.S. Private*, pg. 3962
TERRACON CONSULTANTS, INC. - AMES—See Terracon Consultants, Inc.; *U.S. Private*, pg. 3971
TERRACON CONSULTANTS, INC. - BIRMINGHAM—See Terracon Consultants, Inc.; *U.S. Private*, pg. 3971
TERRACON CONSULTANTS, INC. - CINCINNATI—See Terracon Consultants, Inc.; *U.S. Private*, pg. 3971
TERRACON CONSULTANTS, INC. - DALLAS—See Terracon Consultants, Inc.; *U.S. Private*, pg. 3971
TERRACON CONSULTANTS, INC. - SIOUX CITY—See Terracon Consultants, Inc.; *U.S. Private*, pg. 3971
TERRACON CONSULTANTS, INC.; *U.S. Private*, pg. 3970
TERRACON CONSULTANTS, INC. - WEST FARGO—See Terracon Consultants, Inc.; *U.S. Private*, pg. 3971
TERRANEXT L.L.C.; *U.S. Private*, pg. 3971
TESSERACT CORPORATION WEATHERFORD LABORATORIES—See Weatherford International plc; *U.S. Public*, pg. 2339
TETRA TECH NUS, INC.—See Tetra Tech, Inc.; *U.S. Public*, pg. 2023
TEXTERITY INC.—See Godengo, Inc.; *U.S. Private*, pg. 1724
THUNDERCAT TECHNOLOGY, LLC; *U.S. Private*, pg. 4166
TIDELANDS GEOPHYSICAL CO., INC.—See Wilks Brothers LLC; *U.S. Private*, pg. 4521
TILSON TECHNOLOGY MANAGEMENT; *U.S. Private*, pg. 4171
TISTA SCIENCE AND TECHNOLOGY CORP; *U.S. Private*, pg. 4176
TITAN CONSULTING LLC; *U.S. Private*, pg. 4177

541690 — OTHER SCIENTIFIC AN...

TOTAL ADMINISTRATIVE SERVICES CORPORATION; *U.S. Private*, pg. 4190
TOXSTRATEGIES INC.—See Renovus Capital Partners; *U.S. Private*, pg. 3399
TRADE WINGS, INC.; *U.S. Private*, pg. 4202
TRAFFIC RESEARCH & ANALYSIS, INC.—See Rekor Systems, Inc.; *U.S. Public*, pg. 1778
TRANSNETBW GMBH—See EnBW Energie Baden-Wurttemberg AG; *Int'l*, pg. 2400
TRAPOLLO, LLC—See Validic, Inc.; *U.S. Private*, pg. 4332
TRC ENVIRONMENTAL CORPORATION—See TRC Companies, Inc.; *U.S. Private*, pg. 4215
TRC ENVIRONMENTAL - LARAMIE—See TRC Companies, Inc.; *U.S. Private*, pg. 4215
TREETOP TECHNOLOGIES, INC.—See MobileDataforce, Inc.; *U.S. Private*, pg. 2758
TREXIN CONSULTING LLC; *U.S. Private*, pg. 4219
TRIHYDRO CORPORATION; *U.S. Private*, pg. 4231
TRILOGY TECHNOLOGIES LIMITED—See BC Partners LLP; *Int'l*, pg. 925
TRUE DIGITAL SECURITY, INC.; *U.S. Private*, pg. 4247
TUNNELL CONSULTING; *U.S. Private*, pg. 4258
TUNNELL CONSULTING—See Tunnell Consulting; *U.S. Private*, pg. 4258
TWELVE CONSULTING GROUP, INC.; *U.S. Private*, pg. 4264
UNBOUNDED SOLUTIONS; *U.S. Private*, pg. 4279
UNDERWRITERS LABORATORIES AG—See Underwriters Laboratories Inc.; *U.S. Private*, pg. 4280
UNITED WHOLESALE MORTGAGE, LLC—See The Gores Group, LLC; *U.S. Private*, pg. 4035
UNIVERSAL ENGINEERING SCIENCES—See Universal Engineering Sciences, LLC; *U.S. Private*, pg. 4305
UNIVERSAL TECHNICAL RESOURCE SERVICES, INC.; *U.S. Private*, pg. 4306
UPTIME INSTITUTE, LLC—See 451 Group, LLC; *U.S. Private*, pg. 15
USER CENTRIC COMMUNICATIONS; *U.S. Private*, pg. 4322
USTAV APLIKOVANE MECHANIKY BRNO, S.R.O.—See CEZ, a.s.; *Int'l*, pg. 1429
US TECH SOLUTIONS INC.; *U.S. Private*, pg. 4320
UTX TECHNOLOGIES LIMITED—See Verint Systems Inc.; *U.S. Public*, pg. 2281
VALANTIC GMBH—See DPE Deutsche Private Equity GmbH; *Int'l*, pg. 2188
VALIDATEK INC.; *U.S. Private*, pg. 4332
VALUE LIGHTING, INC.—See Revolution Lighting Technologies, Inc.; *U.S. Public*, pg. 1793
VDART INC.; *U.S. Private*, pg. 4349
VENIO LLC—See Lovell Minnick Partners LLC; *U.S. Private*, pg. 2503
VENN PARTNERS LLP—See ESR Group Limited; *Int'l*, pg. 2508
VERIFYME, INC.; *U.S. Public*, pg. 2280
VERIZON SELECT SERVICES INC.—See Verizon Communications Inc.; *U.S. Public*, pg. 2286
VERMONT ENERGY INVESTMENT CORPORATION; *U.S. Private*, pg. 4367
VERSAR ESM OPERATIONS—See Kingswood Capital Management LLC; *U.S. Private*, pg. 2312
VERSAR RISK MANAGEMENT, INC.—See Kingswood Capital Management LLC; *U.S. Private*, pg. 2313
VICTOROPS, INC.—See Cisco Systems, Inc.; *U.S. Public*, pg. 500
VIFOR FRESENIUS KABI (BEIJING) PHARMACEUTICAL CONSULTING CO. LTD.—See CSL Limited; *Int'l*, pg. 1866
VIKING ENERGY MANAGEMENT LLC—See National Utility Service, Inc.; *U.S. Private*, pg. 2864
VIRTUAL-AGENT SERVICES; *U.S. Private*, pg. 4389
VIRTUALEX CONSULTING, INC.—See The Carlyle Group Inc.; *U.S. Public*, pg. 2055
VIRTUSA CORPORATION—See EQT AB; *Int'l*, pg. 2471
VISUAL LOGIC GROUP; *U.S. Private*, pg. 4404
VLS IT CONSULTING; *U.S. Private*, pg. 4408
VOISIN CONSULTING, INC.; *U.S. Private*, pg. 4409
VOLT TELECOMMUNICAITONS GROUP—See American CyberSystems, Inc.; *U.S. Private*, pg. 230
VOLT TEMPORARY SERVICES—See American CyberSystems, Inc.; *U.S. Private*, pg. 230
VREDESTEIN CONSULTING B.V.—See Apollo Tyres Ltd.; *Int'l*, pg. 519
VSE CORPORATION; *U.S. Public*, pg. 2312
WALTER'S WHOLESALE ELECTRIC COMPANY INC.; *U.S. Private*, pg. 4434
WATERFIELD TECHNOLOGIES, INC.; *U.S. Private*, pg. 4453
WATERHOUSE GROUP, INC.—See The Predictive Index LLC; *U.S. Private*, pg. 4097
WATERMAN STRUCTURES LIMITED—See CTI Engineering Co., Ltd.; *Int'l*, pg. 1871
WATT DEUTSCHLAND GMBH—See EnBW Energie Baden-Wurttemberg AG; *Int'l*, pg. 2400
WATT SYNERGIA GMBH—See EnBW Energie Baden-Wurttemberg AG; *Int'l*, pg. 2400
WAVEGARD, INC.; *U.S. Private*, pg. 4458

W. CAPRA CONSULTING GROUP, INC.; *U.S. Private*, pg. 4417
W DEXTER BENDER & ASSOCIATES, LLC—See Atwell, LLC; *U.S. Private*, pg. 384
WEATHERBANK, INC.—See AccuWeather, Inc.; *U.S. Private*, pg. 56
WEBRUNNERS, INC.; *U.S. Private*, pg. 4466
WEG ENGINEERING—See Weavertown Transport Leasing, Inc.; *U.S. Private*, pg. 4463
WFN STRATEGIES; *U.S. Private*, pg. 4503
WHITE ENVIRONMENTAL CONSULTANTS, INC.—See Bernhard Capital Partners Management, LP; *U.S. Private*, pg. 536
WHITELIGHT GROUP, LLC—See CVC Capital Partners SICAV-FIS S.A.; *Int'l*, pg. 1883
WIDENET CONSULTING GROUP; *U.S. Private*, pg. 4516
WILD BRUSH ENERGY, INC.; *U.S. Public*, pg. 2370
WIREVIBE; *U.S. Private*, pg. 4547
WOHLERS ASSOCIATES INC.—See American Society for Testing & Materials; *U.S. Private*, pg. 254
WORLD WIDE TECHNOLOGY, LLC—See World Wide Technology Holding Co., LLC; *U.S. Private*, pg. 4568
WPC, INC.—See Terracon Consultants, Inc.; *U.S. Private*, pg. 3971
WS ATKINS LIMITED—See AtkinsRealis Group Inc.; *Int'l*, pg. 673
WWT APJ-SINGAPORE PTE. LTD.—See World Wide Technology Holding Co., LLC; *U.S. Private*, pg. 4568
WWT BRASIL COMERCIO E SERVICOS LTDA.—See World Wide Technology Holding Co., LLC; *U.S. Private*, pg. 4568
WWT EMEA UK LTD.—See World Wide Technology Holding Co., LLC; *U.S. Private*, pg. 4568
WYNDHAM GROUP INC.; *U.S. Private*, pg. 4576
WYOMING BUSINESS COUNCIL - AGRIBUSINESS DIVISION—See Wyoming Business Council; *U.S. Private*, pg. 4578
XDUCE CORP.; *U.S. Private*, pg. 4581
XENOSOFT TECHNOLOGIES; *U.S. Private*, pg. 4581
XENSPIRE, INC.; *U.S. Private*, pg. 4581
XL, INC.; *U.S. Private*, pg. 4581
YAHSGS LLC; *U.S. Private*, pg. 4584
YIRONGZHAN FINTECH (SHENZHEN) LIMITED—See Allied Group Limited; *Int'l*, pg. 357
ZENITH TECHNOLOGIES BVBA—See Cognizant Technology Solutions Corporation; *U.S. Public*, pg. 525
ZENITH TECHNOLOGIES LIMITED—See Cognizant Technology Solutions Corporation; *U.S. Public*, pg. 525
ZENOSYS LLC; *U.S. Private*, pg. 4601
ZIK ENERGY POINTS INC.—See COFRA Holding AG; *Int'l*, pg. 1694
ZINNOV LLC; *U.S. Private*, pg. 4605
ZT AUTOMATION LIMITED—See Cognizant Technology Solutions Corporation; *U.S. Public*, pg. 525

541713 — RESEARCH AND DEVELOPMENT IN NANOTECHNOLOGY

ADGERO BIOPHARMACEUTICALS HOLDINGS, INC.—See Kintara Therapeutics, Inc.; *U.S. Public*, pg. 1235
AKCEA THERAPEUTICS, INC.—See Ionis Pharmaceuticals, Inc.; *U.S. Public*, pg. 1166
ALLPHASE CLINICAL RESEARCH SERVICES INC.—See Calian Group Ltd.; *Int'l*, pg. 1263
APPLIED NANOTECH, INC.; *U.S. Private*, pg. 299
AVENUE THERAPEUTICS, INC.; *U.S. Public*, pg. 242
BIO-SYNECTICS; *Int'l*, pg. 1035
BOSKALIS GERMANY HOLDING GMBH—See HAL Trust N.V.; *Int'l*, pg. 3225
CARDIOVASCULAR BIOTHERAPEUTICS, INC.; *U.S. Private*, pg. 751
CAVITATION TECHNOLOGIES, INC.; *U.S. Public*, pg. 455
CEA INDUSTRIES INC.; *U.S. Public*, pg. 463
CELCUITY INC.; *U.S. Public*, pg. 465
CELLULAR RESEARCH, INC.—See Becton, Dickinson & Company; *U.S. Public*, pg. 292
CHILTERN INTERNATIONAL SRO—See Laboratory Corporation of America Holdings; *U.S. Public*, pg. 1285
DENTSU SCIENCEJAM INC.—See Dentsu Group Inc.; *Int'l*, pg. 2038
EUROFINS IESPM S.A.S.—See Eurofins Scientific S.E.; *Int'l*, pg. 2544
GEMINI OPEN CLOUD COMPUTING, INC.—See Super Micro Computer, Inc.; *U.S. Public*, pg. 1966
GENCELL BIOSYSTEMS LTD.—See Becton, Dickinson & Company; *U.S. Public*, pg. 292
GENEDATA AG—See Danaher Corporation; *U.S. Public*, pg. 627
GLOBAL SPECIMEN SOLUTIONS INC—See Laboratory Corporation of America Holdings; *U.S. Public*, pg. 1287
HFACTOR, INC.; *U.S. Public*, pg. 1034
HUMAN LONGEVITY, INC.; *U.S. Private*, pg. 2005
IDORSIA PHARMACEUTICALS LTD.—See Idorsia Ltd.; *Int'l*, pg. 3595
IMAGION BIOSYSTEMS LIMITED; *Int'l*, pg. 3619
INNOVATIVE NEUROTRONICS, INC.—See Patient Square Capital, L.P.; *U.S. Private*, pg. 3107
KALA BIO, INC.; *U.S. Public*, pg. 1213
LUFTHANSA INNOVATION HUB GMBH—See Deutsche Lufthansa AG; *Int'l*, pg. 2069
MEDINEOS S.R.L.—See IQVIA Holdings Inc.; *U.S. Public*, pg. 1170
MERA PHARMACEUTICALS, INC.; *U.S. Private*, pg. 2667
MERSANA THERAPEUTICS, INC; *U.S. Public*, pg. 1425
NANOLOGIX, INC.; *U.S. Public*, pg. 1490
ONKODATAMED GMBH—See IQVIA Holdings Inc.; *U.S. Public*, pg. 1170
ORIGIN BIOSCIENCES, INC.—See BridgeBio Pharma, Inc.; *U.S. Public*, pg. 382
OVID THERAPEUTICS INC.; *U.S. Public*, pg. 1625
PENTIXAPHARM GMBH—See Eckert & Ziegler Strahlen- und Medizintechnik AG; *Int'l*, pg. 2290
PRECIPIO DIAGNOSTICS LLC—See Precipio, Inc.; *U.S. Public*, pg. 1713
QED THERAPEUTICS, INC.—See BridgeBio Pharma, Inc.; *U.S. Public*, pg. 382
QRONS INC.; *U.S. Public*, pg. 1743
SANGAMO THERAPEUTICS, INC.; *U.S. Public*, pg. 1840
SDC MATERIALS, INC.—See General Motors Company; *U.S. Public*, pg. 928
SOURCE SUPPORT SERVICES, INC.—See Logan Ridge Finance Corporation; *U.S. Public*, pg. 1340
SRI LANKA INSTITUTE OF NANOTECHNOLOGY (PVT) LTD.—See Hayleys PLC; *Int'l*, pg. 3292
STOLLER SOUTH AFRICA (PTY) LTD.—See Corteva, Inc.; *U.S. Public*, pg. 584
TELEDYNE MICRALYNE, INC.—See Teledyne Technologies Incorporated; *U.S. Public*, pg. 1994
TGR BIOSCIENCES PTY LTD.—See 2invest AG; *Int'l*, pg. 5
VIRATHERAPEUTICS GMBH—See C.H. Boehringer Sohn AG & Co. KG; *Int'l*, pg. 1243
ZIMMER TRABECULAR METAL TECHNOLOGY, INC.—See Zimmer Biomet Holdings, Inc.; *U.S. Public*, pg. 2407

541714 — RESEARCH AND DEVELOPMENT IN BIOTECHNOLOGY (EXCEPT NANOBIOTECHNOLOGY)

10X GENOMICS, INC.; *U.S. Public*, pg. 1
22ND CENTURY GROUP, INC.; *U.S. Public*, pg. 3
23ANDME HOLDING CO.; *U.S. Public*, pg. 3
23ANDME, INC.—See 23andMe Holding Co.; *U.S. Public*, pg. 3
2E CREATIVE, INC.; *U.S. Public*, pg. 6
2SEVENTY BIO, INC.; *U.S. Public*, pg. 3
3D MEDICINES INC.; *Int'l*, pg. 7
4BASEBIO PLC; *Int'l*, pg. 11
4D MOLECULAR THERAPEUTICS, INC.; *U.S. Public*, pg. 9
89BIO, INC.; *U.S. Public*, pg. 10
9 METERS BIOPHARMA, INC.; *U.S. Public*, pg. 10
A4F-ALGAE FOR FUTURE SA; *Int'l*, pg. 30
AADI BIOSCIENCE, INC.; *U.S. Public*, pg. 12
AAP IMPLANTATE AG; *Int'l*, pg. 36
ABBISKO CAYMAN LIMITED; *Int'l*, pg. 56
ABCAM AUSTRALIA PTY. LIMITED—See Danaher Corporation; *U.S. Public*, pg. 623
ABCELLERA BIOLOGICS INC.; *Int'l*, pg. 57
ABCLON, INC.; *Int'l*, pg. 57
ABERA BIOSCIENCE AB; *Int'l*, pg. 60
ABPRO CORPORATION—See Abpro Holdings, Inc.; *U.S. Public*, pg. 26
ABREOS BIOSCIENCES, INC.; *U.S. Private*, pg. 40
ABSCI CORP.; *U.S. Public*, pg. 27
AB SCIEX LLC—See Danaher Corporation; *U.S. Public*, pg. 623
ACCUSTEM SCIENCES, INC.; *Int'l*, pg. 94
ACEA BIOSCIENCES INC.—See Agilent Technologies, Inc.; *U.S. Public*, pg. 60
ACELYRIN, INC.; *U.S. Public*, pg. 33
ACER THERAPEUTICS, INC.—See Zevra Therapeutics, Inc.; *U.S. Public*, pg. 2403
ACROBIOSYSTEMS CO., LTD.; *Int'l*, pg. 109
ACTELION CLINICAL RESEARCH, INC.—See Johnson & Johnson; *U.S. Public*, pg. 1194
ACTELION PHARMACEUTICALS AUSTRALIA PTY. LIMITED—See Johnson & Johnson; *U.S. Public*, pg. 1193
ACTELION PHARMACEUTICALS JAPAN LTD.—See Johnson & Johnson; *U.S. Public*, pg. 1194
ACTICOR BIOTECH SA; *Int'l*, pg. 118
ACTINOGEN MEDICAL LIMITED; *Int'l*, pg. 118
ACTIVE BIOTECH AB; *Int'l*, pg. 120
ACUITY SPATIAL GENOMICS, INC.—See Bruker Corporation; *U.S. Public*, pg. 404
ACUMEN PHARMACEUTICAL, INC.; *U.S. Public*, pg. 37
ACURX PHARMACEUTICALS, INC.; *U.S. Public*, pg. 37
ADAGENE INC.; *Int'l*, pg. 123
ADAPTIVE BIOTECHNOLOGIES CORPORATION; *U.S. Public*, pg. 39
ADASTRA HOLDINGS LTD.; *Int'l*, pg. 125
ADC THERAPEUTICS SA; *Int'l*, pg. 126
ADESIS, INC.—See Universal Display Corporation; *U.S. Public*, pg. 2255

N.A.I.C.S. INDEX

541714 — RESEARCH AND DEVELO...

ADIAL PHARMACEUTICALS, INC.; *U.S. Public*, pg. 41
ADICET BIO, INC.; *U.S. Public*, pg. 41
ADITXT, INC.; *U.S. Public*, pg. 41
ADLAI NORTYE BIOPHARMA CO., LTD.—See Adlai Nortye Ltd.; *U.S. Public*, pg. 41
ADLAI NORTYE USA INC—See Adlai Nortye Ltd.; *U.S. Public*, pg. 41
ADMA BIO CENTERS GEORGIA INC.—See ADMA Biologics, Inc.; *U.S. Public*, pg. 42
ADOCIA SAS; *Int'l*, pg. 152
ADVANCED BIOLOGICAL LABORATORIES (ABL) S.A.; *Int'l*, pg. 157
ADVANCED BIOMATRIX INC.—See BICO Group AB; *Int'l*, pg. 1019
AEGIRBIO AB—See Abreos Biosciences, Inc.; *U.S. Private*, pg. 40
AELIS FARMA SA; *Int'l*, pg. 175
AEROVATE THERAPEUTICS, INC.; *U.S. Public*, pg. 52
AFFINIA THERAPEUTICS INC.; *U.S. Private*, pg. 122
AFG BIOSOLUTIONS, INC.; *U.S. Private*, pg. 123
AFYREN SA; *Int'l*, pg. 196
AGC BIOLOGICS GMBH—See AGC Inc.; *Int'l*, pg. 202
AGENT INFORMATION SOFTWARE, INC.; *U.S. Public*, pg. 60
AGILEX BIOLABS PTY. LTD.—See Healius Limited; *Int'l*, pg. 3302
AGILUX LABORATORIES, INC.—See Charles River Laboratories International, Inc.; *U.S. Public*, pg. 479
AGILYX ASA; *U.S. Public*, pg. 62
AG (SHANGHAI) AGRICULTURE TECHNOLOGY CO., LTD.—See Corteva, Inc.; *U.S. Public*, pg. 580
AIRWAY MEDIX SA; *Int'l*, pg. 250
AJAX ENVIRONMENTAL & SAFETY SUPPLY, INC.—See In-Situ, Inc.; *U.S. Private*, pg. 2052
AJINOMOTO GENEXINE CO., LTD.—See Ajinomoto Company, Inc.; *Int'l*, pg. 256
AKER BIOMARINE ASA—See Aker ASA; *Int'l*, pg. 262
AKERO THERAPEUTICS, INC.; *U.S. Public*, pg. 69
AKESOGEN, INC.—See Tempus AI, Inc.; *U.S. Public*, pg. 2000
AKOUOS, INC.—See Eli Lilly & Company; *U.S. Public*, pg. 731
AKOYA BIOSCIENCES, INC.; *U.S. Public*, pg. 69
ALCODES INTERNATIONAL LIMITED—See AIQ Limited; *Int'l*, pg. 236
ALDERYS SAS—See Givaudan S.A.; *Int'l*, pg. 2979
ALECTOR, INC.; *U.S. Public*, pg. 74
ALIGOS THERAPEUTICS, INC.; *U.S. Public*, pg. 77
ALIMERA SCIENCES OPTHAMOLOGIE GMBH—See ANI Pharmaceuticals, Inc.; *U.S. Public*, pg. 137
ALKAHEST, INC.—See Grifols, S.A.; *Int'l*, pg. 3084
ALLAKOS, INC.; *U.S. Public*, pg. 78
ALLARITY THERAPEUTICS, INC.; *U.S. Public*, pg. 78
ALLIGATOR BIOSCIENCE AB; *Int'l*, pg. 359
ALLOGENE THERAPEUTICS, INC.; *U.S. Public*, pg. 81
ALLOVIR, INC.; *U.S. Public*, pg. 81
ALOPEXX, INC.; *U.S. Private*, pg. 195
ALPHA COGNITION INC.; *Int'l*, pg. 367
ALX ONCOLOGY HOLDINGS INC.; *U.S. Public*, pg. 89
ALZHEON, INC.; *U.S. Private*, pg. 214
ALZINOVA AB; *Int'l*, pg. 402
AMBRX BIOPHARMA INC.—See Johnson & Johnson; *U.S. Public*, pg. 1194
AMCHI GENDYNAMY SCIENCE CORPORATION; *U.S. Private*, pg. 218
AMERICAN PRECLINICAL SERVICES LLC—See ArchiMed SAS; *Int'l*, pg. 549
AMICUS THERAPEUTICS UK OPERATIONS LIMITED—See Amicus Therapeutics, Inc.; *U.S. Public*, pg. 124
AMINOLOGICS CO., LTD.; *Int'l*, pg. 428
AMYLYX PHARMACEUTICALS, INC.; *U.S. Public*, pg. 134
AMYRIS, INC.; *U.S. Public*, pg. 134
AN2 THERAPEUTICS, INC.; *U.S. Public*, pg. 134
ANABIOS CORPORATION; *U.S. Private*, pg. 271
ANAGENICS LIMITED; *Int'l*, pg. 446
ANALYTICON DISCOVERY LLC—See BRAIN Biotech AG; *Int'l*, pg. 1137
ANAVEX LIFE SCIENCES CORP.; *U.S. Public*, pg. 136
ANEBULO PHARMACEUTICALS, INC.; *U.S. Public*, pg. 136
ANGIOLAB, INC.; *Int'l*, pg. 460
ANHUI HUAHENG BIOTECHNOLOGY CO., LTD.; *Int'l*, pg. 468
ANNEXON, INC.; *U.S. Public*, pg. 138
ANNOVIS BIO, INC.; *U.S. Public*, pg. 138
ANTAI-HEYUAN NUCLEAR ENERGY TECHNOLOGY & MATERIALS CO., LTD.—See Advanced Technology & Materials Co., Ltd.; *Int'l*, pg. 162
ANTEOTECH LTD; *Int'l*, pg. 482
APEXIGEN, INC.—See Pyxis Oncology, Inc.; *U.S. Public*, pg. 1740
APOGEE THERAPEUTICS, INC.; *U.S. Public*, pg. 145
APOLLOMICS (AUSTRALIA) PTY. LTD.—See Apollomics Inc.; *U.S. Public*, pg. 168
APOLLOMICS INC.; *U.S. Public*, pg. 168
APPLIED BIOSCIENCES CORP.; *U.S. Public*, pg. 170
APPLIED MOLECULAR TRANSPORT INC.—See Cyclo Therapeutics, Inc.; *U.S. Public*, pg. 617
APPLIED STEMCELL, INC.—See QHP Capital, L.P.; *U.S. Private*, pg. 3313
APPLIED THERAPEUTICS, INC.; *U.S. Public*, pg. 173
APREA THERAPEUTICS, INC.; *U.S. Public*, pg. 174
APTAMER GROUP PLC; *Int'l*, pg. 523
APTAMER SCIENCES INC.; *Int'l*, pg. 523
APURES CO LTD.; *Int'l*, pg. 526
AQUABOUNTY TECHNOLOGIES, INC.; *U.S. Public*, pg. 175
ARACLON BIOTECH, S.L.—See Grifols, S.A.; *Int'l*, pg. 3084
ARAGEN BIOSCIENCE, INC.—See GVK Power and Infrastructure Limited; *Int'l*, pg. 3190
ARCELLX, INC.; *U.S. Public*, pg. 180
ARCTIC BIOSCIENCE AS; *Int'l*, pg. 551
ARCUS BIOSCIENCES, INC.; *U.S. Public*, pg. 187
ARCUTIS BIOTHERAPEUTICS, INC.; *U.S. Public*, pg. 187
ARECOR THERAPEUTICS PLC; *Int'l*, pg. 557
ARMO BIOSCIENCES, INC.—See Eli Lilly & Company; *U.S. Public*, pg. 731
AROA BIOSURGERY LIMITED; *Int'l*, pg. 577
AROG PHARMACEUTICALS, INC.; *U.S. Private*, pg. 333
ARRIVENT BIOPHARMA INC.; *U.S. Public*, pg. 194
ARS PHARMACEUTICALS, INC.; *U.S. Public*, pg. 201
ARTERRA BIOSCIENCE SRL; *Int'l*, pg. 583
ARTGEN BIOTECH PJSC; *Int'l*, pg. 583
ARTHROGEN B.V.—See MeiraGTx Holdings plc; *U.S. Public*, pg. 1414
ARTIVA BIOTHERAPEUTICS, INC.; *U.S. Private*, pg. 343
ASAHI RESEARCH CENTER CO., LTD.—See Asahi Kasei Corporation; *Int'l*, pg. 596
ASCEND CLINICAL LLC—See Eurofins Scientific S.E.; *Int'l*, pg. 2535
ASCENDIS PHARMA ENDOCRINOLOGY, INC.—See Ascendis Pharma A/S; *Int'l*, pg. 602
ASCEND TECHNOLOGIES, LLC; *U.S. Private*, pg. 346
ASIA GREEN BIOTECHNOLOGY CORP.; *Int'l*, pg. 612
ASURAGEN, INC.—See Bio-Techne Corporation; *U.S. Public*, pg. 334
ATEA PHARMACEUTICALS, INC.; *U.S. Public*, pg. 220
ATHIRA PHARMA, INC.; *U.S. Public*, pg. 221
ATLANTIC INTERNATIONAL CORP.; *U.S. Public*, pg. 222
AT&M AMORPHOUS TECHNOLOGY CO., LTD.—See Advanced Technology & Materials Co., Ltd.; *Int'l*, pg. 162
AT&M BIOMATERIALS CO., LTD.—See Advanced Technology & Materials Co., Ltd.; *Int'l*, pg. 162
AT&M ENVIRONMENTAL ENGINEERING TECHNOLOGY CO., LTD.—See Advanced Technology & Materials Co., Ltd.; *Int'l*, pg. 162
AT&M VENTURE CAPITAL INVESTMENT (SHENZHEN) CO., LTD.—See Advanced Technology & Materials Co., Ltd.; *Int'l*, pg. 162
ATRECA, INC.; *U.S. Public*, pg. 225
AURA BIOSCIENCES, INC.; *U.S. Public*, pg. 227
AUSHON BIOSYSTEMS, INC.—See Quanterix Corporation; *U.S. Public*, pg. 1753
AUSTRALIS CAPITAL, INC.; *U.S. Public*, pg. 228
AUTOLUS THERAPEUTICS PLC; *Int'l*, pg. 730
AVACTA GROUP PLC; *Int'l*, pg. 733
AVALON GLOBOCARE CORP.; *U.S. Public*, pg. 239
AVIDITY BIOSCIENCES, INC.; *U.S. Public*, pg. 246
AVILA THERAPEUTICS, INC.—See Bristol-Myers Squibb Company; *U.S. Public*, pg. 386
AVITA MEDICAL, INC.; *U.S. Public*, pg. 249
AVITIDE, INC.; *U.S. Private*, pg. 409
AWAKN LIFE SCIENCES CORP.; *Int'l*, pg. 751
AXCELLA HEALTH INC.; *U.S. Public*, pg. 255
AXOGEN CORPORATION—See AxoGen, Inc.; *U.S. Public*, pg. 255
AZENTA BEIJING TECHNOLOGIES LIMITED—See Azenta, Inc.; *U.S. Public*, pg. 257
AZENTA GERMANY GMBH—See Azenta, Inc.; *U.S. Public*, pg. 257
AZENTA (GUANGZHOU) LIFE SCIENCE CO., LTD.—See Azenta, Inc.; *U.S. Public*, pg. 257
AZITRA INC.; *U.S. Public*, pg. 258
BACTECH ENVIRONMENTAL CORPORATION; *Int'l*, pg. 795
BACTIQUANT A/S; *Int'l*, pg. 795
BARINTHUS BIOTHERAPEUTICS PLC; *Int'l*, pg. 865
BATAVIA BIOSCIENCES B.V.—See CJ Corporation; *Int'l*, pg. 1631
BATAVIA BIOSCIENCES INC.—See CJ Corporation; *Int'l*, pg. 1631
BCAL DIAGNOSTICS LIMITED; *Int'l*, pg. 925
BEAM THERAPEUTICS INC.; *U.S. Public*, pg. 287
BEIGENE, LTD.; *Int'l*, pg. 942
BEIJING AT&M SIX NINE NEW MATERIALS CO., LTD.—See Advanced Technology & Materials Co., Ltd.; *Int'l*, pg. 162
BEIJING GANG YAN DIAMOND PRODUCTS CO., LTD.—See Advanced Technology & Materials Co., Ltd.; *Int'l*, pg. 162
BEIJING GLOBAL PHARMACEUTICAL RESEARCH CO., LTD.—See EPS Holdings, Inc.; *Int'l*, pg. 2465
BEIJING HARMOFINERY TECHNOLOGY CO., LTD.—See Advanced Technology & Materials Co., Ltd.; *Int'l*, pg. 162
BEIJING HUAAN MAGNECH BIO-TECH CO., LTD.—See Revvity, Inc.; *U.S. Public*, pg. 1793
BEIJING MEIZHENG BIO-TECH CO., LTD.—See Revvity, Inc.; *U.S. Public*, pg. 1793
BEIJING VITAL RIVER LABORATORY ANIMAL TECHNOLOGY CO. LTD.—See Charles River Laboratories International, Inc.; *U.S. Public*, pg. 479
BELITE BIO, INC.; *U.S. Public*, pg. 294
BENCHMARK GENETICS NORWAY AS—See Benchmark Holdings Plc; *Int'l*, pg. 970
BENEVIR BIOPHARM, INC.—See Johnson & Johnson; *U.S. Public*, pg. 1196
BENITEC BIOPHARMA INC.; *Int'l*, pg. 974
BERRY GENOMICS CO., LTD.; *Int'l*, pg. 989
BETHYL LABORATORIES, INC.—See Fortis Life Sciences; *U.S. Private*, pg. 1576
BGI GENOMICS CO., LTD.; *Int'l*, pg. 1008
BICYCLE THERAPEUTICS PLC; *Int'l*, pg. 1019
THE BINDING SITE BRASIL COMERCIO DE PRODUTOS PARA LABORATORIO LTDA.—See Thermo Fisher Scientific Inc.; *U.S. Public*, pg. 2152
BIOAFFINITY TECHNOLOGIES, INC.; *U.S. Public*, pg. 334
BIOARCTIC AB; *Int'l*, pg. 1036
BIOCELL TECHNOLOGY LIMITED—See China Regenerative Medicine International Co., Ltd.; *Int'l*, pg. 1547
BIOCELTIX S.A.; *Int'l*, pg. 1036
BIO-CONCEPT LABORATORIES, INC—See Leonard Green & Partners, L.P.; *U.S. Private*, pg. 2426
BIOCRATES LIFE SCIENCES AG; *Int'l*, pg. 1036
BIOCYTOGEN BOSTON CORP.—See Biocytogen Pharmaceuticals (Beijing) Co., Ltd.; *Int'l*, pg. 1037
BIOCYTOGEN PHARMACEUTICALS (BEIJING) CO., LTD.; *Int'l*, pg. 1037
BIODESIX, INC.; *U.S. Public*, pg. 335
BIODIRECT INC.—See Copia Scientific, Inc.; *U.S. Private*, pg. 1044
BIOEXTRAX AB; *Int'l*, pg. 1037
BIO FD&C CO., LTD.; *Int'l*, pg. 1035
BIOFORTIS, INC.—See IQVIA Holdings Inc.; *U.S. Public*, pg. 1168
BIOFRONTERA INC.; *U.S. Public*, pg. 335
BIOGAIA JAPAN INC.—See Biogaia AB; *Int'l*, pg. 1037
BIOGEN ESTONIA OU—See Biogen Inc.; *U.S. Public*, pg. 336
BIO-GENE TECHNOLOGY LIMITED; *Int'l*, pg. 1035
BIOGEN HONG KONG LIMITED—See Biogen Inc.; *U.S. Public*, pg. 336
BIOGEN IDEC MA INC.—See Biogen Inc.; *U.S. Public*, pg. 336
BIOGEN LATVIA SIA—See Biogen Inc.; *U.S. Public*, pg. 336
BIOGEN LITHUANIA UAB—See Biogen Inc.; *U.S. Public*, pg. 336
BIOGEN PHARMA D.O.O.—See Biogen Inc.; *U.S. Public*, pg. 336
BIOHARVEST SCIENCES INC.; *Int'l*, pg. 1038
BIOHAVEN LTD.; *U.S. Public*, pg. 337
BIOINFRA LIFE SCIENCE INC.; *Int'l*, pg. 1038
BIOKRAFT INTERNATIONAL AB; *Int'l*, pg. 1038
BIOMARIN PHARMACEUTICAL INC.; *U.S. Public*, pg. 337
BIOMATRICA, INC.—See Exact Sciences Corporation; *U.S. Public*, pg. 805
BIO-MATRIX SCIENTIFIC GROUP, INC.; *U.S. Public*, pg. 332
BIOMEA FUSION, INC.; *U.S. Public*, pg. 337
BIOME AUSTRALIA LIMITED; *Int'l*, pg. 1039
BIOME MAKERS INC.; *U.S. Private*, pg. 562
BIONEER CORPORATION; *Int'l*, pg. 1040
BIONET CORP.; *Int'l*, pg. 1040
BIONTECH DELIVERY TECHNOLOGIES GMBH—See BioNTech SE; *Int'l*, pg. 1041
BIONTECH EUROPE GMBH—See BioNTech SE; *Int'l*, pg. 1041
BIONTECH MANUFACTURING MARBURG GMBH—See BioNTech SE; *Int'l*, pg. 1041
BIONTECH SE; *Int'l*, pg. 1040
BIONTECH US INC.—See BioNTech SE; *Int'l*, pg. 1041
BIONXT SOLUTIONS INC.; *Int'l*, pg. 1041
BIOPHYTIS SA; *Int'l*, pg. 1041
BIOPROTECTION SYSTEMS CORPORATION—See Lumos Pharma, Inc.; *U.S. Public*, pg. 1348
BIOQUELL INC.—See Ecolab Inc.; *U.S. Public*, pg. 712
BIO-RAD LABORATORIES S.A.S.—See Bio-Rad Laboratories, Inc.; *U.S. Public*, pg. 332
BIOREGENX, INC.; *U.S. Public*, pg. 338
BIORETEC LTD.; *Int'l*, pg. 1041
BIOSERGEN AB; *Int'l*, pg. 1042
BIOSPACIFIC, INC.—See Bio-Techne Corporation; *U.S. Public*, pg. 334
BIOSTAT INTERNATIONAL, INC.; *U.S. Private*, pg. 563
BIOSTORAGE TECHNOLOGIES, INC—See Azenta, Inc.; *U.S. Public*, pg. 257
BIOTALYS NV; *Int'l*, pg. 1043
BIO-TECHNE LTD.—See Bio-Techne Corporation; *U.S. Public*, pg. 334
BIO-TECHNICAL RESOURCES—See Arkion Life Sciences L.L.C.; *U.S. Private*, pg. 326
BIOTE CORP.; *U.S. Public*, pg. 339
BIOTHERA, INC.—See Biothera Holding Corp.; *U.S. Private*, pg. 563

541714 — RESEARCH AND DEVELO... CORPORATE AFFILIATIONS

N.A.I.C.S. Index

BIOTOXTECH CO., LTD.; *Int'l*, pg. 1043

BIOVAXYS TECHNOLOGY CORP.; *Int'l*, pg. 1044

BIOVECTRA INC.—See Agilent Technologies, Inc.; *U.S. Public*, pg. 62

BIOVENTIX PLC; *Int'l*, pg. 1045

BIOVISION, INC.—See Danaher Corporation; *U.S. Public*, pg. 624

BIO-WORKS TECHNOLOGIES AB; *Int'l*, pg. 1036

BIOXCEL THERAPEUTICS, INC.; *U.S. Public*, pg. 339

BIVICTRIX THERAPEUTICS PLC; *Int'l*, pg. 1052

BLACK DIAMOND THERAPEUTICS, INC.; *U.S. Public*, pg. 340

BLOOMAGE BIOTECHNOLOGY CORPORATION LIMITED; *Int'l*, pg. 1065

BLUEBIRD BIO GREECE SINGLE MEMBER, L.L.C.—See bluebird bio, Inc.; *U.S. Public*, pg. 365

BLUEBIRD BIO, INC.; *U.S. Public*, pg. 365

BLUE HERON BIOTECH, LLC—See Eurofins Scientific S.E.; *Int'l*, pg. 2535

BLUE WATER VACCINES, INC.; *U.S. Public*, pg. 365

B-MOGEN BIOTECHNOLOGIES INC.—See Bio-Techne Corporation; *U.S. Public*, pg. 334

BOLT BIOTHERAPEUTICS, INC.; *U.S. Public*, pg. 368

BON CLINICAL LABORATORIES—See Schryver Medical Sales; *U.S. Private*, pg. 3570

BOOJ, LLC—See RE/MAX Holdings, Inc.; *U.S. Public*, pg. 1768

BRAIN BIOTECH AG; *Int'l*, pg. 1137

BRIACELL THERAPEUTICS CORP. - BERKELEY BRANCH—See BriaCell Therapeutics Corp.; *Int'l*, pg. 1151

BRIDGEBIO PHARMA, INC.; *U.S. Public*, pg. 381

BRIGHT MINDS BIOSCIENCES INC.; *U.S. Public*, pg. 383

BRII BIOSCIENCES LIMITED; *Int'l*, pg. 1163

BRISTOL-MYERS SQUIBB AKTIEBOLAG—See Bristol-Myers Squibb Company; *U.S. Public*, pg. 385

BRISTOL-MYERS SQUIBB GESMBH.—See Bristol-Myers Squibb Company; *U.S. Public*, pg. 385

BRISTOL-MYERS SQUIBB MARKETING SERVICES S.R.L.—See Bristol-Myers Squibb Company; *U.S. Public*, pg. 385

BRISTOL-MYERS SQUIBB MIDDLE EAST & AFRICA FZ-LLC—See Bristol-Myers Squibb Company; *U.S. Public*, pg. 385

BRISTOL-MYERS SQUIBB (NZ) LIMITED—See Bristol-Myers Squibb Company; *U.S. Public*, pg. 384

BRISTOL-MYERS SQUIBB SARL—See Bristol-Myers Squibb Company; *U.S. Public*, pg. 385

BRISTOL-MYERS SQUIBB SA—See Bristol-Myers Squibb Company; *U.S. Public*, pg. 385

BRITANNIA LIFE SCIENCES INC.; *Int'l*, pg. 1165

BROOKS LIFE SCIENCES—See Azenta, Inc.; *U.S. Public*, pg. 258

BRUKER CELLULAR ANALYSIS, INC.—See Bruker Corporation; *U.S. Public*, pg. 405

C4 THERAPEUTICS, INC.; *U.S. Public*, pg. 416

CABALETTA BIO, INC.; *U.S. Public*, pg. 416

CAC CROIT CORPORATION—See CAC Holdings Corporation; *Int'l*, pg. 1247

CADRENAL THERAPEUTICS, INC.; *U.S. Public*, pg. 419

CALCIMEDICA, INC.; *U.S. Public*, pg. 422

CALIBRE SCIENTIFIC, INC—See StoneCalibre, LLC; *U.S. Private*, pg. 3827

CALICO LLC—See Alphabet Inc.; *U.S. Public*, pg. 82

CAMBRIDGE BIOMEDICAL INC.—See Cobepa S.A.; *Int'l*, pg. 1683

CANDEL THERAPEUTICS, INC.; *U.S. Public*, pg. 428

CANNABIS BIOSCIENCE INTERNATIONAL HOLDINGS, INC.; *U.S. Public*, pg. 428

CAPTOR THERAPEUTICS S.A.; *Int'l*, pg. 1317

CARDIO DIAGNOSTICS HOLDINGS, INC.; *U.S. Public*, pg. 434

CARGO THERAPEUTICS, INC.; *U.S. Public*, pg. 435

CARIS LIFE SCIENCES, LTD.; *U.S. Private*, pg. 761

CARMEDA AB—See W.L. Gore & Associates, Inc.; *U.S. Private*, pg. 4421

CARMELL CORPORATION; *U.S. Public*, pg. 437

CASTLE BIOSCIENCES, INC.; *U.S. Public*, pg. 447

CATALYST CLINICAL RESEARCH LLC—See NovaQuest Capital Management, LLC; *U.S. Private*, pg. 2967

CELGENE ILAC PAZARLAMA VE TIC. LTD.—See Bristol-Myers Squibb Company; *U.S. Public*, pg. 386

CELGENE S.R.O—See Bristol-Myers Squibb Company; *U.S. Public*, pg. 386

CELGENE S.R.O.—See Bristol-Myers Squibb Company; *U.S. Public*, pg. 386

CELL CURE NEUROSCIENCES, LTD.—See Lineage Cell Therapeutics, Inc.; *U.S. Public*, pg. 1320

CELL MICROSYSTEMS, INC.; *U.S. Private*, pg. 807

CELL SYSTEMS LLC—See Anabios Corporation; *U.S. Private*, pg. 271

CELLULAR GOODS PLC; *Int'l*, pg. 1395

CELSIS INTERNATIONAL BV—See Charles River Laboratories International, Inc.; *U.S. Public*, pg. 479

...LARITY INC.; *U.S. Public*, pg. 466

...RY THERAPEUTICS, INC.; *U.S. Public*, pg. 475

... BENELUX—See Danaher Corporation; *U.S. Public*, pg. ...25

CEPHEID EUROPE SAS—See Danaher Corporation; *U.S. Public*, pg. 625

CEPHEID GK—See Danaher Corporation; *U.S. Public*, pg. 625

CEPHEID GMBH—See Danaher Corporation; *U.S. Public*, pg. 625

CEPHEID SOUTH AFRICA—See Danaher Corporation; *U.S. Public*, pg. 625

CETERO RESEARCH—See Cetero Research; *U.S. Private*, pg. 843

CEVA SANTE ANIMALE SA; *Int'l*, pg. 1425

CEYGEN BIOTECH (PVT) LTD.—See Durdans Hospital; *Int'l*, pg. 2228

CG ONCOLOGY, INC.; *U.S. Public*, pg. 477

CHARLES RIVER DISCOVERY RESEARCH SERVICES FINLAND—See Charles River Laboratories International, Inc.; *U.S. Public*, pg. 479

CHARLES RIVER ENDOTOXIN MICROBIAL DETECTION EUROPE SAS—See Charles River Laboratories International, Inc.; *U.S. Public*, pg. 479

CHARLES RIVER LABORATORIES ITALIA SRL—See Charles River Laboratories International, Inc.; *U.S. Public*, pg. 480

CHARLES RIVER LABORATORIES JAPAN, INC.—See Charles River Laboratories International, Inc.; *U.S. Public*, pg. 480

CHARLES RIVER LABORATORIES PRECLINICAL SERVICES MONTREAL, ULC—See Charles River Laboratories International, Inc.; *U.S. Public*, pg. 480

CHARLES RIVER LABORATORIES SAINT-CONSTANT S.A.—See Charles River Laboratories International, Inc.; *U.S. Public*, pg. 480

CHARLES RIVER LABORATORIES SA NETHERLANDS HOLDINGS BV—See Charles River Laboratories International, Inc.; *U.S. Public*, pg. 480

CHARLES RIVER UK LIMITED—See Charles River Laboratories International, Inc.; *U.S. Public*, pg. 480

CHECKMATE PHARMACEUTICALS, INC.—See Regeneron Pharmaceuticals, Inc.; *U.S. Public*, pg. 1775

CHEMOMAB THERAPEUTICS INC.—See Chemomab Therapeutics Ltd.; *Int'l*, pg. 1463

CHENGDU UNOVEL PHARMACEUTICAL CO., LTD.—See Chengdu Easton Biopharmaceuticals Co., Ltd.; *Int'l*, pg. 1467

CHILTERN INTERNATIONAL HOLDINGS LIMITED—See Laboratory Corporation of America Holdings; *U.S. Public*, pg. 1285

CHILTERN INTERNATIONAL INC.—See Laboratory Corporation of America Holdings; *U.S. Public*, pg. 1285

CHILTERN INTERNATIONAL KFT—See Laboratory Corporation of America Holdings; *U.S. Public*, pg. 1285

CHILTERN INTERNATIONAL PORTUGAL LDA—See Laboratory Corporation of America Holdings; *U.S. Public*, pg. 1285

CHIMERIC THERAPEUTICS LIMITED; *Int'l*, pg. 1479

CHOSA ONCOLOGY AB; *Int'l*, pg. 1584

CHROMOCELL THERAPEUTICS CORPORATION; *U.S. Public*, pg. 490

CIBUS CORP.—See Cibus, Inc.; *U.S. Public*, pg. 494

CIRCIO HOLDING ASA; *Int'l*, pg. 1617

CISRI DA HUI INVESTMENT CO., LTD.—See Advanced Technology & Materials Co., Ltd.; *Int'l*, pg. 162

CJ BIOSCIENCE, INC.; *Int'l*, pg. 1630

CJ (SHENYANG) BIOTECH CO., LTD.—See CJ Corporation; *Int'l*, pg. 1631

CLARITAS PHARMACEUTICALS, INC.; *U.S. Public*, pg. 507

CLENE INC.; *U.S. Public*, pg. 513

CLINICAL CONSULTANTS INTERNATIONAL LLC—See Novo Integrated Sciences, Inc.; *U.S. Public*, pg. 1549

CLINICAL ENTERPRISE, INC.—See Eurofins Scientific S.E.; *Int'l*, pg. 2535

CLINICAL RESEARCH MANAGEMENT, INC.—See ICON plc; *Int'l*, pg. 3584

CLINICAL TRIALS OF AMERICA, INC.—See IMA Group Management Company, LLC; *U.S. Private*, pg. 2044

CLINUVEL (UK) LTD.—See Clinuvel Pharmaceuticals Limited; *Int'l*, pg. 1660

CLOVER BIOPHARMACEUTICALS, LTD.; *Int'l*, pg. 1662

CMIC SHIFTZERO K.K.—See CMIC Holdings Co., Ltd.; *Int'l*, pg. 1670

CN INNOVATIONS HOLDINGS LIMITED; *Int'l*, pg. 1672

CNS PHARMACEUTICALS, INC.; *U.S. Public*, pg. 520

CO2 CAPSOL AS; *Int'l*, pg. 1680

CODEXIS LABORATORIES INDIA PVT. LTD.—See Codexis, Inc.; *U.S. Public*, pg. 521

CODIAK BIOSCIENCES, INC.; *U.S. Public*, pg. 521

CODIKOAT LTD.—See Greenbank Capital Inc.; *Int'l*, pg. 3073

COEGIN PHARMA AB; *Int'l*, pg. 1689

COGENT BIOSCIENCES, INC.; *U.S. Public*, pg. 522

COGNETIVITY NEUROSCIENCES LTD.; *Int'l*, pg. 1695

COGNITION THERAPEUTICS, INC.; *U.S. Public*, pg. 523

COGNITO THERAPEUTICS, INC.; *U.S. Private*, pg. 962

COMBIGENE AB; *Int'l*, pg. 1708

COMMONWEALTH INFORMATICS, INC.—See Genpact Limited; *Int'l*, pg. 2926

COMPASS THERAPEUTICS INC.; *U.S. Public*, pg. 561

COMPLEXA INC.; *U.S. Private*, pg. 1001

CONCENTRA BIOSCIENCES, LLC; *U.S. Private*, pg. 1008

CONCORD BIOTECH LIMITED; *Int'l*, pg. 1764

CONNECT BIOPHARMA HOLDINGS LIMITED; *Int'l*, pg. 1768

CONTEXT THERAPEUTICS INC.; *U.S. Public*, pg. 573

COOK MYOSITE INCORPORATED—See Cook Group Incorporated; *U.S. Private*, pg. 1037

COOK PHARMICA LLC—See Catalent, Inc.; *U.S. Public*, pg. 448

COOL PLANET ENERGY SYSTEMS, INC.—See Exelon Corporation; *U.S. Public*, pg. 806

COREVITAS, LLC—See Thermo Fisher Scientific Inc.; *U.S. Public*, pg. 2146

CORNERSTONE COMMISSIONING, INC.—See Levine Leichtman Capital Partners, LLC; *U.S. Private*, pg. 2436

COVANCE CLINICAL AND PERIAPPROVAL SERVICES LIMITED—See Laboratory Corporation of America Holdings; *U.S. Public*, pg. 1286

COVANCE CLINICAL RESEARCH UNIT LTD.—See Laboratory Corporation of America Holdings; *U.S. Public*, pg. 1286

COVANCE JAPAN CO. LTD.—See Laboratory Corporation of America Holdings; *U.S. Public*, pg. 1286

COVANCE LABORATORIES INC.—See Laboratory Corporation of America Holdings; *U.S. Public*, pg. 1286

COYA THERAPEUTICS, INC.; *U.S. Public*, pg. 588

CRESCENDO BIOSCIENCE, INC.—See Myriad Genetics, Inc.; *U.S. Public*, pg. 1489

CRIOESTAMINAL-SAUDE E TECNOLOGIA SA—See The Riverside Company; *U.S. Private*, pg. 4108

CRL DUTCH HOLDING COMPANY BV—See Charles River Laboratories International, Inc.; *U.S. Public*, pg. 479

CRONEX CO LTD; *Int'l*, pg. 1854

CRUCELL N.V.—See Johnson & Johnson; *U.S. Public*, pg. 1194

CSI LABORATORIES, INC.—See Fulgent Genetics, Inc.; *U.S. Public*, pg. 892

CSPC DOPHEN CORPORATION—See CSPC Pharmaceutical Group Limited; *Int'l*, pg. 1867

CUE BIOPHARMA, INC.; *U.S. Public*, pg. 604

CULLINAN THERAPEUTICS; *U.S. Public*, pg. 604

CURACHEM CO., LTD.; *Int'l*, pg. 1878

CURAGEN CORPORATION—See Celldex Therapeutics, Inc.; *U.S. Public*, pg. 465

CURATEQ BIOLOGICS PRIVATE LIMITED—See Aurobindo Pharma Ltd.; *Int'l*, pg. 713

CUREVO INC.—See Green Cross WellBeing Corp.; *Int'l*, pg. 3070

CURIA WASHINGTON, INC.—See GTCR LLC; *U.S. Private*, pg. 1805

CURIA WASHINGTON, INC.—See The Carlyle Group Inc.; *U.S. Public*, pg. 2046

CURIS SECURITIES CORPORATION—See Curis, Inc.; *U.S. Public*, pg. 610

CYCLERION THERAPEUTICS, INC.; *U.S. Public*, pg. 617

CYFUSE BIOMEDICAL K.K.; *Int'l*, pg. 1895

CYTEIR THERAPEUTICS, INC.; *U.S. Public*, pg. 618

CYTEK BIOSCIENCES, INC.; *U.S. Public*, pg. 618

DAC S.R.L.—See Genextra S.p.A.; *Int'l*, pg. 2923

DAESANG INFORMATION TECHNOLOGY CO., LTD.—See Daesang Holdings Co., Ltd.; *Int'l*, pg. 1909

DAESANG LIFE SCIENCE CORP.—See Daesang Holdings Co., Ltd.; *Int'l*, pg. 1909

DAIDO BUNSEKI RESEARCH INC.—See Daido Steel Co., Ltd.; *Int'l*, pg. 1922

DAY ONE BIOPHARMACEUTICALS, INC.; *U.S. Public*, pg. 644

DECIBEL THERAPEUTICS, INC.—See Regeneron Pharmaceuticals, Inc.; *U.S. Public*, pg. 1775

DEFENCE THERAPEUTICS INC.; *Int'l*, pg. 2004

DELTA 9 CANNABIS, INC.; *Int'l*, pg. 2015

DENALI THERAPEUTICS INC.; *U.S. Public*, pg. 653

DERMATA THERAPEUTICS, INC.; *U.S. Public*, pg. 656

DERMA TRONNIER INSTITUT FUR EXPERIMENTELLE DERMATOLOGIE GMBH & CO. KG—See Eurofins Scientific S.E.; *Int'l*, pg. 2536

DERMISONICS, INC.; *U.S. Public*, pg. 656

DESIGN THERAPEUTICS, INC.; *U.S. Public*, pg. 656

DEUTSCHE BIOTECH INNOVATIV AG; *Int'l*, pg. 2063

DEVYSER DIAGNOSTICS AB; *Int'l*, pg. 2091

DFINE, INC.—See Merit Medical Systems, Inc.; *U.S. Public*, pg. 1425

DIAGONAL BIO AB; *Int'l*, pg. 2103

DIANTHUS THERAPEUTICS, INC.; *U.S. Public*, pg. 659

DIASORIN AUSTRALIA (PTY) LTD.—See DiaSorin S.p.A.; *Int'l*, pg. 2106

DIASORIN CANADA INC.—See DiaSorin S.p.A.; *Int'l*, pg. 2106

DIASORIN CZECH S.R.O.—See DiaSorin S.p.A.; *Int'l*, pg. 2106

DIASORIN IBERIA S.A.—See DiaSorin S.p.A.; *Int'l*, pg. 2106

DIASORIN LTDA—See DiaSorin S.p.A.; *Int'l*, pg. 2106

DIASORIN MEXICO S.A DE C.V.—See DiaSorin S.p.A.; *Int'l*, pg. 2106

DIASORIN POLAND SP. Z O.O.—See DiaSorin S.p.A.; *Int'l*, pg. 2106

DIASORIN S.A/N.V.—See DiaSorin S.p.A.; *Int'l*, pg. 2106

N.A.I.C.S. INDEX 541714 — RESEARCH AND DEVELO...

DIASORIN S.A.—See DiaSorin S.p.A.; *Int'l*, pg. 2106
DIMERIX LIMITED; *Int'l*, pg. 2126
DISCOVER ECHO INC.—See BICO Group AB; *Int'l*, pg. 1019
DISCOVERY LIFE SCIENCES, LLC; *U.S. Private*, pg. 1238
DJS ANTIBODIES LTD.—See AbbVie Inc.; *U.S. Public*, pg. 24
DNA LINK INC.; *Int'l*, pg. 2147
DNA LINK USA, INC.—See DNA Link Inc.; *Int'l*, pg. 2147
DOMINION MINERALS LIMITED; *Int'l*, pg. 2161
DYADIC NEDERLAND B.V.—See Dyadic International, Inc.; *U.S. Public*, pg. 698
DYNACURE SA; *Int'l*, pg. 2239
DYNE THERAPEUTICS, INC.; *U.S. Public*, pg. 700
EASTWEST BIOSCIENCE, INC.; *Int'l*, pg. 2275
ECHELON BIOSCIENCES INC—See Avista Capital Partners, L.P.; *U.S. Private*, pg. 409
ECOANALYSTS, INC.; *U.S. Private*, pg. 1329
ECOATM, LLC—See Apollo Global Management, Inc.; *U.S. Public*, pg. 150
ECOFIBRE LIMITED; *Int'l*, pg. 2295
EDGEWISE THERAPEUTICS, INC.; *U.S. Public*, pg. 718
EIDOS THERAPEUTICS, INC.—See BridgeBio Pharma, Inc.; *U.S. Public*, pg. 381
ELEVATION ONCOLOGY, INC.; *U.S. Public*, pg. 731
ELICERA THERAPEUTICS AB; *Int'l*, pg. 2361
ELIEM THERAPEUTICS, INC.; *U.S. Public*, pg. 734
ELK ORTHOBIOLOGICS LIMITED; *Int'l*, pg. 2363
ELO LIFE SYSTEMS, INC.—See Precision BioSciences, Inc.; *U.S. Public*, pg. 1713
ELUTIA INC.; *U.S. Public*, pg. 735
EMERGENT BIODEFENSE OPERATIONS LANSING LLC—See Emergent BioSolutions Inc.; *U.S. Public*, pg. 739
EMERGENT BIOSOLUTIONS UK LTD.—See Emergent BioSolutions Inc.; *U.S. Public*, pg. 739
EMULATE THERAPEUTICS, INC.; *U.S. Public*, pg. 754
EMYRIA LIMITED; *Int'l*, pg. 2395
ENDRA LIFE SCIENCES INC.; *U.S. Public*, pg. 760
ENEVOLV, INC.—See Ginkgo Bioworks Holdings, Inc.; *U.S. Public*, pg. 938
ENGMAB SARL—See Bristol-Myers Squibb Company; *U.S. Public*, pg. 386
ENKO CHEM, INC.; *U.S. Private*, pg. 1400
ENLIGHTA INC.; *Int'l*, pg. 2442
ENLIVEN THERAPEUTICS, INC; *U.S. Public*, pg. 768
ENTERA BIO LTD; *Int'l*, pg. 2450
ENTERIX INC.—See Clinical Genomics Pty. Ltd.; *Int'l*, pg. 1659
ENTHEON BIOMEDICAL CORP.; *Int'l*, pg. 2452
ENTRADA THERAPEUTICS, INC.; *U.S. Public*, pg. 779
ENZA BIOTECH AB—See Croda International plc; *Int'l*, pg. 1852
EPI BIOTECH CO., LTD.; *Int'l*, pg. 2459
EPICORE BIONETWORKS INC.—See Archer-Daniels-Midland Company; *U.S. Public*, pg. 185
EPISTEM LIMITED—See Genedrive Plc; *Int'l*, pg. 2917
EPITOMICS HOLDINGS, INC.—See Danaher Corporation; *U.S. Public*, pg. 624
EPL ARCHIVES, SAS—See Avantor, Inc.; *U.S. Public*, pg. 242
EPL PATHOLOGY ARCHIVES, LLC—See Avantor, Inc.; *U.S. Public*, pg. 242
EP MEDIATE CO., LTD.—See EPS Holdings, Inc.; *Int'l*, pg. 2465
EPS AMERICAS CORP.—See EPS Holdings, Inc.; *Int'l*, pg. 2465
EPSI GLOBAL RESEARCH (TAIWAN) CO., LTD.—See EPS Holdings, Inc.; *Int'l*, pg. 2465
EPS INTERNATIONAL (CHINA) CO., LTD.—See EPS Holdings, Inc.; *Int'l*, pg. 2465
EPS INTERNATIONAL KOREA LIMITED—See EPS Holdings, Inc.; *Int'l*, pg. 2465
EQRX, INC.—See Revolution Medicines, Inc.; *U.S. Public*, pg. 1793
EQUILLIUM, INC.; *U.S. Public*, pg. 787
EQUIPPP SOCIAL IMPACT TECHNOLOGIES LTD; *Int'l*, pg. 2485
ERASCA, INC.; *U.S. Public*, pg. 792
ESTRELLA IMMUNOPHARMA, INC.; *U.S. Public*, pg. 796
ETERNA THERAPEUTICS INC.; *U.S. Public*, pg. 797
ETON PHARMACEUTICALS, INC.; *U.S. Public*, pg. 797
EUCODIS BIOSCIENCE GMBH; *Int'l*, pg. 2525
EUROFINS ADME BIOANALYSES SAS—See Eurofins Scientific S.E.; *Int'l*, pg. 2542
EUROFINS BACTUP SAS—See Eurofins Scientific S.E.; *Int'l*, pg. 2538
EUROFINS BECEWA NV—See Eurofins Scientific S.E.; *Int'l*, pg. 2538
EUROFINS BIOMI KFT.—See Eurofins Scientific S.E.; *Int'l*, pg. 2538
EUROFINS BIOPHARMA PRODUCT TESTING CZECH REPUBLIC S.R.O.—See Eurofins Scientific S.E.; *Int'l*, pg. 2538
EUROFINS BIOSCIENCES SAS—See Eurofins Scientific S.E.; *Int'l*, pg. 2542
EUROFINS CALIXAR S.A.S.—See Eurofins Scientific S.E.; *Int'l*, pg. 2539

EUROFINS DISCOVERX CORPORATION, INC.—See Eurofins Scientific S.E.; *Int'l*, pg. 2540
EUROFINS GENOMICS BLUE HERON LLC—See Eurofins Scientific S.E.; *Int'l*, pg. 2543
EUROFINS GENOMICS ENGINEERING, LLC—See Eurofins Scientific S.E.; *Int'l*, pg. 2543
EUROFINS GENOMICS GERMANY GMBH—See Eurofins Scientific S.E.; *Int'l*, pg. 2543
EUROFINS GENOMICS SRL—See Eurofins Scientific S.E.; *Int'l*, pg. 2543
EUROFINS NSC DEVELOPPEMENT FRANCE SAS—See Eurofins Scientific S.E.; *Int'l*, pg. 2543
EUROFINS OKOMETRIC GMBH—See Eurofins Scientific S.E.; *Int'l*, pg. 2546
EUROFINS OPTIMED LYON SAS—See Eurofins Scientific S.E.; *Int'l*, pg. 2543
EUROFINS PHARMA BIOANALYTICS SERVICES US, INC.—See Eurofins Scientific S.E.; *Int'l*, pg. 2547
EUTILEX CO., LTD.; *Int'l*, pg. 2560
EVAXION BIOTECH A/S; *Int'l*, pg. 2561
EVELO BIOSCIENCES, INC.; *U.S. Public*, pg. 799
EVER PROGRESSING SYSTEM PTE. LTD.—See EPS Holdings, Inc.; *Int'l*, pg. 2465
EVER SUPREME BIO TECHNOLOGY CO., LTD.; *Int'l*, pg. 2562
EVIDERA LTD.—See Thermo Fisher Scientific Inc.; *U.S. Public*, pg. 2146
EVOLUS, INC.—See ALPHAEON Corporation; *U.S. Private*, pg. 200
EVOXX TECHNOLOGIES GMBH—See Advanced Enzyme Technologies Limited; *Int'l*, pg. 159
EXACT THERAPEUTICS AS; *Int'l*, pg. 2576
EXAGEN INC.; *U.S. Public*, pg. 805
EXELGEN DISCOVERY; *Int'l*, pg. 2583
EXEMPLAR GENETICS, LLC—See Precigen, Inc.; *U.S. Public*, pg. 1713
EXICURE, INC.; *U.S. Public*, pg. 807
EXOCOBIO INC.; *Int'l*, pg. 2586
EXOSOME DIAGNOSTICS, INC.—See Bio-Techne Corporation; *U.S. Public*, pg. 334
EXOSOME SCIENCES, INC.—See Aethlon Medical, Inc.; *U.S. Public*, pg. 53
EXPLORA BIOLABS, INC.—See Charles River Laboratories International, Inc.; *U.S. Public*, pg. 480
EXPRES2ION BIOTECHNOLOGIES; *Int'l*, pg. 2590
EXSCIENTIA PLC; *Int'l*, pg. 2591
EYELOCK LLC—See VOXX International Corporation; *U.S. Public*, pg. 2311
EYENOVIA, INC.; *U.S. Public*, pg. 817
EZBIOME, INC.—See CJ Corporation; *Int'l*, pg. 1633
FACTORY CRO BV; *Int'l*, pg. 2601
FAI DO BRASIL CRIACAO ANIMAL LTDA—See Benchmark Holdings Plc; *Int'l*, pg. 970
FEDERAL FABRICS-FIBERS INC—See Charlesbank Capital Partners, LLC; *U.S. Private*, pg. 855
FERA SCIENCE LIMITED—See Bridgepoint Group Plc; *Int'l*, pg. 1155
FIBROBIOLOGICS, INC.; *U.S. Public*, pg. 830
FINCH THERAPEUTICS GROUP, INC.; *U.S. Public*, pg. 834
FLAGSHIP BIOSCIENCES, INC.; *U.S. Private*, pg. 1539
FLAMINGO THERAPEUTICS BV; *Int'l*, pg. 2698
FLERIE AB; *Int'l*, pg. 2699
FLORAGENEX, INC.—See Sedia Biosciences Corporation; *U.S. Private*, pg. 3597
FLUICELL AB; *Int'l*, pg. 2713
FLUIDIGM CANADA INC.—See Standard BioTools Inc.; *U.S. Public*, pg. 1928
FLUIDIGM GMBH—See Standard BioTools Inc.; *U.S. Public*, pg. 1928
FLUIDIGM SCIENCES INC.—See Standard BioTools Inc.; *U.S. Public*, pg. 1928
FLUOGUIDE A/S; *Int'l*, pg. 2715
FOGHORN THERAPEUTICS, INC.; *U.S. Public*, pg. 862
FORSCHUNGSINSTITUT FUR MOLEKULARE PATHOLOGIE GESELLSCHAFT MBH—See C.H. Boehringer Sohn AG & Co. KG; *Int'l*, pg. 1242
FORTE BIOSCIENCES, INC.; *U.S. Public*, pg. 869
FORTY SEVEN, INC.—See Gilead Sciences, Inc.; *U.S. Public*, pg. 936
FORU HOLDINGS, INC.; *U.S. Public*, pg. 873
FOXO TECHNOLOGIES INC.; *U.S. Public*, pg. 877
FREMONT ANALYTICAL INC.—See Morgan Stanley; *U.S. Public*, pg. 1474
FREQUENCY THERAPEUTICS, INC.; *U.S. Public*, pg. 885
FRESH2 GROUP LTD.; *Int'l*, pg. 2781
FRIULCHEM SPA; *Int'l*, pg. 2794
FULCRUM THERAPEUTICS, INC.; *U.S. Public*, pg. 891
FULGENT GENETICS, INC.; *U.S. Public*, pg. 892
FUSION PHARMACEUTICALS INC.—See AstraZeneca PLC; *Int'l*, pg. 661
GAIN THERAPEUTICS, INC.; *U.S. Public*, pg. 894
GALAPAGOS B.V.—See Galapagos N.V.; *Int'l*, pg. 2870
GALAPAGOS N.V.; *Int'l*, pg. 2870
GALECTO, INC.; *U.S. Public*, pg. 2872
GALERA THERAPEUTICS, INC.; *U.S. Public*, pg. 895
GAMIDA CELL LTD.—See Gamida for Life B.V.; *Int'l*, pg. 2878
GANZHOU JXTC SUMMIT AT&M NEW MATERIALS CO.,

LTD.—See Advanced Technology & Materials Co., Ltd.; *Int'l*, pg. 162
GC CELL CORP.—See Green Cross WellBeing Corp.; *Int'l*, pg. 3070
GC DO BRASIL CONSULTORIA DE NEGOCIOS LTDA.—See Green Cross WellBeing Corp.; *Int'l*, pg. 3070
GC GENOME CORPORATION—See Green Cross WellBeing Corp.; *Int'l*, pg. 3070
GC INVACFARM INC.—See Green Cross WellBeing Corp.; *Int'l*, pg. 3070
GEFFEN RESIDENCE & RENEWAL LTD; *Int'l*, pg. 2911
GE HEALTHCARE LIMITED—See GE HealthCare Technologies Inc.; *U.S. Public*, pg. 909
GEMINA LABORATORIES LTD.; *Int'l*, pg. 2916
GENARRAYTION INC.—See Nephros, Inc.; *U.S. Public*, pg. 1506
GENEDESIGN, INC.—See Ajinomoto Company, Inc.; *Int'l*, pg. 257
GENEDRIVE PLC; *Int'l*, pg. 2917
GENEFERM BIOTECHNOLOGY CO., LTD.; *Int'l*, pg. 2917
GENENTA SCIENCE S.P.A.; *Int'l*, pg. 2917
GENERATION BIO CO.; *U.S. Public*, pg. 929
GENEREACH BIOTECHNOLOGY CORP.; *Int'l*, pg. 2920
GENETETHER THERAPEUTICS INC.; *Int'l*, pg. 2922
GENETHERA, INC.; *U.S. Public*, pg. 930
GENETIC ANALYSIS AS; *Int'l*, pg. 2922
GENETICS GENERATION ASIA SDN. BHD.—See Genetics Generation Advancement Corp.; *Int'l*, pg. 2922
GENETYPE CORPORATION INC.—See Genetic Technologies Limited; *Int'l*, pg. 2922
GENEWIZ FRANCE, LTD.—See Azenta, Inc.; *U.S. Public*, pg. 258
GENEWIZ GMBH—See Azenta, Inc.; *U.S. Public*, pg. 258
GENEWIZ (GUANGZHOU), LTD.—See Azenta, Inc.; *U.S. Public*, pg. 258
GENEWIZ JAPAN—See Azenta, Inc.; *U.S. Public*, pg. 258
GENEWIZ (SUZHOU), LTD.—See Azenta, Inc.; *U.S. Public*, pg. 258
GENEWIZ TIANJIN, LTD.—See Azenta, Inc.; *U.S. Public*, pg. 258
GENFLOW BIOSCIENCES PLC; *Int'l*, pg. 2923
GENINCODE PLC; *Int'l*, pg. 2923
GENMAB A/S; *Int'l*, pg. 2924
GENMAB HOLDING B.V.—See Genmab A/S; *Int'l*, pg. 2924
GENMONT BIOTECH INCORPORATION; *Int'l*, pg. 2924
GENOLUTION INC.; *Int'l*, pg. 2925
GENOMIC VALLEY BIOTECH LIMITED; *Int'l*, pg. 2925
GENOMTEC SA; *Int'l*, pg. 2925
GENOVA INC.; *Int'l*, pg. 2926
GENOVIS AB; *Int'l*, pg. 2926
GENOVIS INC.—See Genovis AB; *Int'l*, pg. 2926
GENSCRIPT USA INCORPORATED—See GenScript Biotech Corporation; *Int'l*, pg. 2927
GENSIGHT BIOLOGICS S.A.; *Int'l*, pg. 2927
GENTEC INC.—See Hensall District Co-operative, Inc.; *Int'l*, pg. 3355
GERPANG HEALTHCARE GROUP; *Int'l*, pg. 2943
GETICA AB—See Gentian Diagnostics AS; *Int'l*, pg. 2928
GETSWIFT TECHNOLOGIES LIMITED; *U.S. Public*, pg. 935
GH RESEARCH PLC; *Int'l*, pg. 2958
GIANTCODE CORPORATION PLC; *Int'l*, pg. 2962
GI INNOVATION INC.; *Int'l*, pg. 2960
GILEAD SCIENCES FINLAND OY—See Gilead Sciences, Inc.; *U.S. Public*, pg. 937
GILEAD SCIENCES HONG KONG LIMITED—See Gilead Sciences, Inc.; *U.S. Public*, pg. 937
GILEAD SCIENCES, INC. - SEATTLE—See Gilead Sciences, Inc.; *U.S. Public*, pg. 937
GILEAD SCIENCES KK—See Gilead Sciences, Inc.; *U.S. Public*, pg. 937
GILEAD SCIENCES KOREA LIMITED—See Gilead Sciences, Inc.; *U.S. Public*, pg. 937
GILEAD SCIENCES MEXICO S. DE R.L. DE C.V.—See Gilead Sciences, Inc.; *U.S. Public*, pg. 937
GILEAD SCIENCES SINGAPORE PTE. LTD.—See Gilead Sciences, Inc.; *U.S. Public*, pg. 937
GILEAD SCIENCES SLOVAKIA S.R.O.—See Gilead Sciences, Inc.; *U.S. Public*, pg. 937
GILEAD SCIENCES SOUTH AFRICA (PTY) LTD—See Gilead Sciences, Inc.; *U.S. Public*, pg. 937
GINKGO BIOWORKS, INC.—See Ginkgo Bioworks Holdings, Inc.; *U.S. Public*, pg. 938
GLAXOSMITHKLINE BIOLOGICALS BIOTECH S.A.—See GSK plc; *Int'l*, pg. 3146
GLOBAL LIFE SCIENCES SOLUTIONS SINGAPORE PTE LTD—See Danaher Corporation; *U.S. Public*, pg. 627
GLOBAL LIFE SCIENCES SOLUTIONS USA LLC—See Danaher Corporation; *U.S. Public*, pg. 627
GLOBAL LIFE SCIENCES TECHNOLOGIES JAPAN KK—See Danaher Corporation; *U.S. Public*, pg. 627
GLOBESTAR THERAPEUTICS CORPORATION; *U.S. Public*, pg. 946
GOLDEN BIOTECHNOLOGY CORP.; *Int'l*, pg. 3028
GORDON RESEARCH CONFERENCES; *U.S. Private*, pg. 1743
GRACE BREEDING LTD.; *Int'l*, pg. 3048

541714 — RESEARCH AND DEVELO...

GRACELL BIOTECHNOLOGIES INC.—See AstraZeneca PLC; *Int'l*, pg. 661
GREEN CROSS MEDICAL SCIENCE CORP.—See Green Cross WellBeing Corp.; *Int'l*, pg. 3070
GREEN CROSS MEDIS CORP.—See Green Cross WellBeing Corp.; *Int'l*, pg. 3070
GREEN CROSS WELLBEING CORP.; *Int'l*, pg. 3070
GREENRISE GLOBAL BRANDS INC.; *Int'l*, pg. 3076
GREENSMART CORP.; *Int'l*, pg. 3076
GREENWICH LIFESCIENCES, INC.; *U.S. Public*, pg. 965
GRI BIO, INC.; *U.S. Public*, pg. 969
GRO ASIA AGRITECHNOLOGY SDN. BHD.—See Fintec Global Berhad; *Int'l*, pg. 2677
GROUNDWATER & ENVIRONMENTAL SERVICES, INC.; *U.S. Private*, pg. 1793
GSK PLC; *Int'l*, pg. 3145
GUARDANT HEALTH, INC.; *U.S. Public*, pg. 973
GUARD THERAPEUTICS INTERNATIONAL AB; *Int'l*, pg. 3169
GUBRA A/S; *Int'l*, pg. 3171
GUJARAT AKRUTI-TCG BIOTECH LIMITED—See Hubtown Limited; *Int'l*, pg. 3521
GVK BIOSCIENCES PVT. LTD.—See GVK Power and Infrastructure Limited; *Int'l*, pg. 3190
H3 BIOMEDICINE INC.—See Eisai Co., Ltd.; *Int'l*, pg. 2335
HARPOON THERAPEUTICS, INC.—See Merck & Co., Inc.; *U.S. Public*, pg. 1416
HAVN LIFE SCIENCES, INC.; *Int'l*, pg. 3287
HAYLEYS AGRO BIO-TECH (PVT) LTD.—See Hayleys PLC; *Int'l*, pg. 3292
HCW BIOLOGICS INC.; *U.S. Public*, pg. 1014
HEADLANDS RESEARCH, INC.—See KKR & Co. Inc.; *U.S. Public*, pg. 1252
HEMCHECK SWEDEN AB; *Int'l*, pg. 3341
HEMOSTEMIX INC.; *Int'l*, pg. 3341
HIBERCELL, INC.—See Arch Venture Partners; *U.S. Private*, pg. 310
HIGHPOINT SOLUTIONS, LLC—See IQVIA Holdings Inc.; *U.S. Public*, pg. 1168
HILLEVAX, INC.; *U.S. Public*, pg. 1037
HISTION LLC—See Inotiv, Inc.; *U.S. Public*, pg. 1128
HITEC, INC.—See CVC Capital Partners SICAV-FIS S.A.; *Int'l*, pg. 1885
HITGEN INC.; *Int'l*, pg. 3426
HOOKIPA PHARMA INC.; *U.S. Public*, pg. 1052
HOTH THERAPEUTICS, INC.; *U.S. Public*, pg. 1055
HSRL HOLDINGS LLC—See Ampersand Management LLC; *U.S. Private*, pg. 265
HXF SAW CO., LTD.—See Advanced Technology & Materials Co., Ltd.; *Int'l*, pg. 162
HYPGEN INC.; *U.S. Private*, pg. 2020
I3 PHARMACEUTICAL SERVICES, INC.—See Elliott Management Corporation; *U.S. Private*, pg. 1366
I3 PHARMACEUTICAL SERVICES, INC.—See Patient Square Capital, L.P.; *U.S. Private*, pg. 3108
I3 PHARMACEUTICAL SERVICES, INC.—See Veritas Capital Fund Management, LLC; *U.S. Private*, pg. 4365
IASO BIOMED, INC.; *U.S. Private*, pg. 2028
ICOSAVAX, INC.—See AstraZeneca PLC; *Int'l*, pg. 661
IDEAYA BIOSCIENCES, INC.; *U.S. Public*, pg. 1088
IDEX HEALTH & SCIENCE KK—See IDEX Corp; *U.S. Public*, pg. 1090
IGC PHARMA, INC.; *U.S. Public*, pg. 1095
IGM BIOSCIENCES, INC.; *U.S. Public*, pg. 1095
IKENA ONCOLOGY, INC.; *U.S. Public*, pg. 1101
ILIKA TECHNOLOGIES LIMITED—See Ilika PLC; *Int'l*, pg. 3614
ILLUMINA AUSTRALIA PTY. LTD.—See Illumina, Inc.; *U.S. Public*, pg. 1112
ILLUMINA BRASIL PRODUTOS DE BIOTECNOLOGIA LTDA.—See Illumina, Inc.; *U.S. Public*, pg. 1112
ILLUMINA CAMBRIDGE, LTD.—See Illumina, Inc.; *U.S. Public*, pg. 1112
ILLUMINA TRADING (SHANGHAI) CO., LTD.—See Illumina, Inc.; *U.S. Public*, pg. 1112
IMAGO BIOSCIENCES, INC.—See Merck & Co., Inc.; *U.S. Public*, pg. 1416
IMMIX BIOPHARMA, INC.; *U.S. Public*, pg. 1112
IMMUNEERING CORP.; *U.S. Public*, pg. 1113
IMMUNE PHARMACEUTICALS LTD.—See Immune Pharmaceuticals Inc.; *U.S. Public*, pg. 1113
IMMUNOGEN EUROPE LIMITED—See AbbVie Inc.; *U.S. Public*, pg. 24
IMMUNOGEN SECURITIES CORP.—See AbbVie Inc.; *U.S. Public*, pg. 24
IMMUNOME, INC.; *U.S. Public*, pg. 1113
IMMUNXPERTS BV—See IQVIA Holdings Inc.; *U.S. Public*, pg. 1169
IMPEL PHARMACEUTICALS INC.; *U.S. Public*, pg. 1113
IMS HEALTH ANALYTICS SERVICES PRIVATE LIMITED—See IQVIA Holdings Inc.; *U.S. Public*, pg. 1168
IMS HEALTH INFORMATION SOLUTIONS INDIA PRIVATE LTD.—See IQVIA Holdings Inc.; *U.S. Public*, pg. 1169
IMS HEALTH PAKISTAN (PRIVATE) LIMITED—See IQVIA Holdings Inc.; *U.S. Public*, pg. 1169
IMS HEALTH TECHNOLOGY SOLUTIONS INDIA PRIVATE LTD.—See IQVIA Holdings Inc.; *U.S. Public*, pg. 1169

IN8BIO, INC.; *U.S. Public*, pg. 1114
INDAPTUS THERAPEUTICS, INC.; *U.S. Public*, pg. 1115
INHIBIKASE THERAPEUTICS, INC.; *U.S. Public*, pg. 1124
INHIBRX, INC.; *U.S. Public*, pg. 2077
INMUNE BIO, INC.; *U.S. Public*, pg. 1125
INNOVATIVE ANALYTICS INC.; *U.S. Private*, pg. 2081
INOZYME PHARMA, INC.; *U.S. Public*, pg. 1128
INSCOPIX, INC.—See Bruker Corporation; *U.S. Public*, pg. 404
IN SILICO SOLUTIONS LLC—See Kiromic Biopharma, Inc.; *U.S. Public*, pg. 1236
INSPIRATA, INC.; *U.S. Private*, pg. 2092
INSPIRE MEDICAL SYSTEMS, INC.; *U.S. Public*, pg. 1131
INSTIL BIO, INC.; *U.S. Public*, pg. 1134
INTERNATIONAL STEM CELL CORPORATION; *U.S. Public*, pg. 1158
INTRINSIC MEDICINE, INC.; *U.S. Private*, pg. 2129
INVE AQUACULTURE, INC.—See Benchmark Holdings Plc; *Int'l*, pg. 970
INVE AQUACULTURE MEXICO, S.A. DE C.V.—See Benchmark Holdings Plc; *Int'l*, pg. 970
INVE ASIA SERVICES LTD.—See Benchmark Holdings Plc; *Int'l*, pg. 970
INVE DO BRASIL LTDA.—See Benchmark Holdings Plc; *Int'l*, pg. 970
INVE EURASIA SA—See Benchmark Holdings Plc; *Int'l*, pg. 970
INVE HELLAS S.A.—See Benchmark Holdings Plc; *Int'l*, pg. 970
INVESTORSHUB.COM INC.—See ADVFN PLC; *Int'l*, pg. 168
INVE TECHNOLOGIES NV—See Benchmark Holdings Plc; *Int'l*, pg. 970
INVE (THAILAND) LTD.—See Benchmark Holdings Plc; *Int'l*, pg. 970
INVE VIETNAM COMPANY LTD.—See Benchmark Holdings Plc; *Int'l*, pg. 970
INVITROGEN BIOSERVICES INDIA PRIVATE LIMITED—See Thermo Fisher Scientific Inc.; *U.S. Public*, pg. 2149
INVIVO BIOTECH SVX GMBH—See Bruker Corporation; *U.S. Public*, pg. 407
INVIVYD, INC.; *U.S. Public*, pg. 1166
IQVIA AG—See IQVIA Holdings Inc.; *U.S. Public*, pg. 1169
IQVIA COMMERCIAL GMBH & CO. OHG—See IQVIA Holdings Inc.; *U.S. Public*, pg. 1169
IQVIA COMMERCIAL SP. Z O.O.—See IQVIA Holdings Inc.; *U.S. Public*, pg. 1169
IQVIA COMMERICAL CONSULTING SP. Z O.O.—See IQVIA Holdings Inc.; *U.S. Public*, pg. 1169
IQVIA CONSULTING & INFORMATION SERVICES INDIA PRIVATE LIMITED—See IQVIA Holdings Inc.; *U.S. Public*, pg. 1169
IQVIA RDS AG—See IQVIA Holdings Inc.; *U.S. Public*, pg. 1169
IQVIA RDS D.O.O. BEOGRAD—See IQVIA Holdings Inc.; *U.S. Public*, pg. 1169
IQVIA RDS ESTONIA OU—See IQVIA Holdings Inc.; *U.S. Public*, pg. 1169
IQVIA RDS (INDIA) PRIVATE LIMITED—See IQVIA Holdings Inc.; *U.S. Public*, pg. 1169
IQVIA RDS LATVIA SIA—See IQVIA Holdings Inc.; *U.S. Public*, pg. 1169
IQVIA RDS SLOVAKIA S.R.O.—See IQVIA Holdings Inc.; *U.S. Public*, pg. 1169
IQVIA RDS SWITZERLAND SARL—See IQVIA Holdings Inc.; *U.S. Public*, pg. 1169
IQVIA SOLUTIONS GMBH—See IQVIA Holdings Inc.; *U.S. Public*, pg. 1169
IQVIA SOLUTIONS PHILIPINES, INC.—See IQVIA Holdings Inc.; *U.S. Public*, pg. 1169
IQVIA SOLUTIONS PHILIPPINES, INC.—See IQVIA Holdings Inc.; *U.S. Public*, pg. 1169
IQVIA TECHNOLOGY & SERVICES AG—See IQVIA Holdings Inc.; *U.S. Public*, pg. 1169
IQVIA (THAILAND) CO. LTD.—See IQVIA Holdings Inc.; *U.S. Public*, pg. 1169
ISD ITALIA S.R.L.—See HUB Cyber Security Ltd.; *Int'l*, pg. 3516
ISOPLEXIS CORPORATION—See Bruker Corporation; *U.S. Public*, pg. 405
ISPECIMEN INC.; *U.S. Public*, pg. 1174
ITEOS THERAPEUTICS, INC; *U.S. Public*, pg. 1175
J3 RESOURCES, INC.—See Eurofins Scientific S.E.; *Int'l*, pg. 2548
JANSSEN-CILAG (NEW ZEALAND) LIMITED—See Johnson & Johnson; *U.S. Public*, pg. 1197
JANUX THERAPEUTICS, INC.; *U.S. Public*, pg. 1187
JASPER THERAPEUTICS, INC.; *U.S. Public*, pg. 1187
JNANA THERAPEUTICS INC—See AbbVie Inc.; *U.S. Public*, pg. 24
JNANA THERAPEUTICS INC—See Bain Capital, LP; *U.S. Private*, pg. 441
JOHNSON & JOHNSON D.O.O.—See Johnson & Johnson; *U.S. Public*, pg. 1199
JOHNSON & JOHNSON MEDIKAL SANAYI VE TICARET LIMITED SIRKETI—See Johnson & Johnson; *U.S. Public*, pg. 1199

JOUNCE THERAPEUTICS, INC.—See Concentra Biosciences, LLC; *U.S. Private*, pg. 1008
JUPITER NEUROSCIENCES, INC.; *U.S. Public*, pg. 1211
KALEIDO BIOSCIENCES, INC.; *U.S. Public*, pg. 1213
KARUNA THERAPEUTICS, INC.—See Bristol-Myers Squibb Company; *U.S. Public*, pg. 386
KEROS THERAPEUTICS, INC.; *U.S. Public*, pg. 1224
KEZAR LIFE SCIENCES, INC.; *U.S. Public*, pg. 1227
KINAXO BIOTECHNOLOGIES GMBH—See Evotec SE; *Int'l*, pg. 2573
KINNATE BIOPHARMA INC.—See XOMA Corporation; *U.S. Public*, pg. 2391
KIRKSTALL LIMITED—See Braveheart Investment Group Plc; *Int'l*, pg. 1141
KIROMIC BIOPHARMA, INC.; *U.S. Public*, pg. 1236
KITE PHARMA EU B.V.—See Gilead Sciences, Inc.; *U.S. Public*, pg. 938
KITE PHARMA UK, LTD—See Gilead Sciences, Inc.; *U.S. Public*, pg. 938
KRONOS BIO, INC.; *U.S. Public*, pg. 1277
KUNSHAN AT&MIK CO., LTD.—See Advanced Technology & Materials Co., Ltd.; *Int'l*, pg. 162
KYMERA THERAPEUTICS, INC.; *U.S. Public*, pg. 1278
KYVERNA THERAPEUTICS, INC.; *U.S. Public*, pg. 1278
LA JOLLA PHARMACEUTICAL II B.V.—See Innoviva, Inc.; *U.S. Public*, pg. 1127
LAKEPHARMA, INC.; *U.S. Private*, pg. 2376
LANDOS BIOPHARMA, INC.—See AbbVie Inc.; *U.S. Public*, pg. 24
LANTERN PHARMA INC.; *U.S. Public*, pg. 1293
LASERGEN, INC.—See Agilent Technologies, Inc.; *U.S. Public*, pg. 62
LAVIE BIO LTD.—See Corteva, Inc.; *U.S. Public*, pg. 584
LEGEND BIOTECH CORPORATION; *U.S. Public*, pg. 1301
LENZ THERAPEUTICS, INC.; *U.S. Public*, pg. 1308
LENZ THERAPEUTICS OPERATIONS, INC.—See Lenz Therapeutics, Inc.; *U.S. Public*, pg. 1308
LEXEO THERAPEUTICS, INC.; *U.S. Public*, pg. 1309
LIANBIO; *U.S. Public*, pg. 1310
LIFE-SEQ, LLC; *U.S. Private*, pg. 2449
LIFE TECHNOLOGIES AUSTRALIA PTY LTD.—See Thermo Fisher Scientific Inc.; *U.S. Public*, pg. 2149
LILLY-NUS CENTRE FOR CLINICAL PHARMACOLOGY—See Eli Lilly & Company; *U.S. Public*, pg. 733
LIPELLA PHARMACEUTICALS INC.; *U.S. Public*, pg. 1320
LIPOGENE AB—See BASF SE; *Int'l*, pg. 884
LONGBOARD PHARMACEUTICALS, INC.; *U.S. Public*, pg. 1341
LONGEVERON INC.; *U.S. Public*, pg. 1342
LUMINEX CORPORATION—See DiaSorin S.p.A.; *Int'l*, pg. 2106
LYELL IMMUNOPHARMA, INC.; *U.S. Public*, pg. 1350
LYRA THERAPEUTICS, INC.; *U.S. Public*, pg. 1350
LZ LIFESCIENCE LIMITED—See Cognizant Technology Solutions Corporation; *U.S. Public*, pg. 524
LZ LIFESCIENCE US INC.—See Cognizant Technology Solutions Corporation; *U.S. Public*, pg. 524
MAIA BIOTECHNOLOGY, INC.; *U.S. Public*, pg. 1354
MASCOMA CORPORATION; *U.S. Private*, pg. 2601
MASTERFLEX LLC—See Avantor, Inc.; *U.S. Public*, pg. 242
MATICA BIOTECHNOLOGY, INC.—See Chabiotech Co., Ltd.; *Int'l*, pg. 1436
MATREYA LLC—See Cayman Chemical Company, Inc.; *U.S. Private*, pg. 795
MATTEK CORPORATION—See BICO Group AB; *Int'l*, pg. 1019
MBL INTERNATIONAL CORPORATION—See AESKU.Diagnostics GmbH & Co. KG; *Int'l*, pg. 182
MEDELIS, INC.—See Altasciences Company Inc.; *Int'l*, pg. 387
MEDPACE CLINICAL PHARMACOLOGY LLC—See Medpace Holdings, Inc.; *U.S. Public*, pg. 1414
MEDPACE HOLDINGS, INC.; *U.S. Public*, pg. 1414
MEMCINE PHARMACEUTICALS—See Spotlight Innovation Inc.; *U.S. Private*, pg. 3762
MERCK & CO. RESEARCH & DEVELOPMENT—See Merck & Co., Inc.; *U.S. Public*, pg. 1419
MERIDIAN CLINICAL RESEARCH, LLC—See GHO Capital Partners LLP; *Int'l*, pg. 2959
MERRIMACK PHARMACEUTICALS, INC.; *U.S. Public*, pg. 1425
MERYX, INC.; *U.S. Private*, pg. 2677
METABOLON, INC; *U.S. Private*, pg. 2679
METACRINE, INC.; *U.S. Public*, pg. 1427
METANOMICS GMBH—See BASF SE; *Int'l*, pg. 884
METASTAT, INC.; *U.S. Private*, pg. 2682
MICROBE INOTECH LABORATORIES—See Pluton Biosciences LLC; *U.S. Private*, pg. 3215
MICROFLUIDIC SYSTEMS—See PositiveID Corporation; *U.S. Public*, pg. 3233
MIMEDX TISSUE SERVICES, LLC—See MiMedx Group, Inc.; *U.S. Public*, pg. 1448
MINERALYS THERAPEUTICS, INC.; *U.S. Public*, pg. 1449
MINK THERAPEUTICS, INC.; *U.S. Public*, pg. 1449
MIRUM PHARMACEUTICALS, INC.; *U.S. Public*, pg. 1450
MLM MEDICAL LABS GMBH—See Great Point Partners, LLC; *U.S. Private*, pg. 1767

N.A.I.C.S. INDEX

541714 — RESEARCH AND DEVELO...

MOBILE TECHNOLOGIES INTERNATIONAL LLC—See ComfortDelGro Corporation Limited; *Int'l*, pg. 1712
MODERNA, INC.; *U.S. Public*, pg. 1454
MOLECULAR RESPONSE LLC—See Advent International Corporation; *U.S. Public*, pg. 98
MONOPAR THERAPEUTICS INC.; *U.S. Public*, pg. 1465
MONTE ROSA THERAPEUTICS, INC.; *U.S. Public*, pg. 1466
MYOKARDIA, INC.—See Bristol-Myers Squibb Company; *U.S. Public*, pg. 387
NANOMIX, INC.—See NANOMIX CORPORATION; *U.S. Public*, pg. 1490
NANOSTRING TECHNOLOGIES, INC.—See Bruker Corporation; *U.S. Public*, pg. 407
NAUTILUS BIOTECHNOLOGY, INC.; *U.S. Public*, pg. 1500
NEURAXIS, INC.; *U.S. Public*, pg. 1510
NEURONEXUS TECHNOLOGIES, INC.—See NEL Group, Inc.; *U.S. Private*, pg. 2882
NEXELIS—See Ampersand Management LLC; *U.S. Private*, pg. 265
NEXTCURE, INC.; *U.S. Public*, pg. 1526
NGM BIOPHARMACEUTICALS, INC.; *U.S. Public*, pg. 1527
NIGHTSTAR THERAPEUTICS PLC—See Biogen Inc.; *U.S. Public*, pg. 337
NIHON PREVENTIVE MEDICAL LABORATORY CO., LTD.—See AFC-HD AMS Life Science Co., Ltd.; *Int'l*, pg. 185
NIP'S SYSTEM CENTER CO., LTD.—See AJIS Co., Ltd.; *Int'l*, pg. 258
NKARTA, INC.; *U.S. Public*, pg. 1530
NOVAN, INC.; *U.S. Public*, pg. 1547
NOVOGY, INC.—See Ginkgo Bioworks Holdings, Inc.; *U.S. Public*, pg. 938
NOVOTECH HOLDINGS PTY LIMITED—See TPG Capital, L.P.; *U.S. Public*, pg. 2175
THE NOW CORPORATION; *U.S. Public*, pg. 2117
NUCLEUS BIOLOGICS LLC; *U.S. Private*, pg. 2972
NURIX THERAPEUTICS, INC.; *U.S. Public*, pg. 1555
NUVALENT, INC.; *U.S. Public*, pg. 1556
OAK THERAPEUTICS, INC.—See Avenir Wellness Solutions, Inc.; *U.S. Public*, pg. 242
OBJECT RESEARCH SYSTEMS (ORS) INC.—See Comet Holding AG; *Int'l*, pg. 1710
OCEAN BIOMEDICAL, INC.; *U.S. Public*, pg. 1562
OCEAN RIDGE BIOSCIENCES, INC.—See Hangzhou Tigermed Consulting Co., Ltd.; *Int'l*, pg. 3251
ODONATE THERAPEUTICS, INC.; *U.S. Public*, pg. 1564
OLD AYALA, INC.—See Ayala Pharmaceuticals, Inc.; *U.S. Public*, pg. 256
OLEMA PHARMACEUTICALS, INC.; *U.S. Public*, pg. 1570
OMEGA THERAPEUTICS, INC.; *U.S. Public*, pg. 1572
OMICIA, INC.; *U.S. Private*, pg. 3016
OMNIAB OPERATIONS, INC.—See OmniAb, Inc.; *U.S. Public*, pg. 1572
ONCOCYTE CORPORATION; *U.S. Public*, pg. 1601
ONCORUS, INC.; *U.S. Public*, pg. 1601
OPKO DO BRASIL COMERCIO DE PRODUTOS FARMACEUTICOS, LTDA—See OPKO Health, Inc.; *U.S. Public*, pg. 1608
OPTINOSE, INC.; *U.S. Public*, pg. 1609
OPX BIOTECHNOLOGIES INC—See Cargill, Inc.; *U.S. Private*, pg. 759
ORGHARVEST, INC.—See First Seed Farms Inc.; *U.S. Private*, pg. 1527
ORIG3N INC—See 180 Degree Capital Corp.; *U.S. Public*, pg. 2
OUTCOME SCIENCES, LLC—See IQVIA Holdings Inc.; *U.S. Public*, pg. 1170
OVULINE, INC.—See Laboratory Corporation of America Holdings; *U.S. Public*, pg. 1287
OXEIA BIOPHARMACEUTICALS, INC.; *U.S. Private*, pg. 3056
OYSTER POINT PHARMA, INC.—See Viatris Inc.; *U.S. Public*, pg. 2294
PANDION THERAPEUTICS, INC.—See Merck & Co., Inc.; *U.S. Public*, pg. 1420
PANOPTES PHARMA GES.M.B.H.—See Kiora Pharmaceuticals, Inc.; *U.S. Public*, pg. 1235
PARALLAX HEALTH SCIENCES, INC.; *U.S. Private*, pg. 3092
PARDES BIOSCIENCES, INC.—See Foresite Capital Management, LLC; *U.S. Private*, pg. 1566
PASITHEA THERAPEUTICS CORP.; *U.S. Public*, pg. 1651
PASSAGE BIO, INC.; *U.S. Public*, pg. 1651
PATHOS AI, INC.; *U.S. Private*, pg. 3106
PAXMEDICA, INC.; *U.S. Public*, pg. 1655
PBS ENGINEERING & ENVRNMNTL; *U.S. Private*, pg. 3119
PEAK BIO, INC.—See Akari Therapeutics, Plc; *Int'l*, pg. 259
PELOTON THERAPEUTICS, INC.; *U.S. Private*, pg. 3131
PEPGEN INC.; *U.S. Public*, pg. 1668
PERBIO SCIENCE AB—See Thermo Fisher Scientific Inc.; *U.S. Public*, pg. 2147
PERCIVIA LLC—See Johnson & Johnson; *U.S. Public*, pg. 1195
PERLEGEN SCIENCES, INC.; *U.S. Private*, pg. 3152
PERSONALIS, INC.; *U.S. Public*, pg. 1677

PERSONALIS (UK) LTD.—See Personalis, Inc.; *U.S. Public*, pg. 1677
PETROCHEM RECOVERY SERVICES, INC.—See Gryphon Investors, LLC; *U.S. Private*, pg. 1798
PHARMAREVIEW LIMITED—See IQVIA Holdings Inc.; *U.S. Public*, pg. 1170
PHARMATECH, INC.—See Caris Life Sciences, Ltd.; *U.S. Private*, pg. 761
PHARMOPTIMA, LLC—See Genesis Biotechnology Group, LLC; *U.S. Private*, pg. 1669
PHASERX, INC.; *U.S. Private*, pg. 3166
PHATHOM PHARMACEUTICALS, INC.; *U.S. Public*, pg. 1684
PLIANT THERAPEUTICS, INC.; *U.S. Public*, pg. 1699
PMV PHARMACEUTICALS, INC.; *U.S. Public*, pg. 1700
POINT BIOPHARMA GLOBAL INC.—See Eli Lilly & Company; *U.S. Public*, pg. 734
POLARITYTE, INC.; *U.S. Public*, pg. 1701
POLISH STEM CELL BANK S.A.—See Enterprise Investors Sp. z o.o.; *Int'l*, pg. 2452
POSEIDA THERAPEUTICS, INC.; *U.S. Public*, pg. 1703
PRAXIS PRECISION MEDICINES, INC.; *U.S. Public*, pg. 1712
PRECISION BIOSCIENCES, INC.; *U.S. Public*, pg. 1713
PRECISION FOR MEDICINE—See Precision Medicine Group, Inc.; *U.S. Private*, pg. 3245
PRECISION NANOSYSTEMS ULC—See Danaher Corporation; *U.S. Public*, pg. 630
PREDICTIVE ONCOLOGY INC.; *U.S. Public*, pg. 1713
PREDICTIVE TECHNOLOGY GROUP, INC.; *U.S. Public*, pg. 1713
PRELUDE THERAPEUTICS INCORPORATED; *U.S. Public*, pg. 1714
PRESCIENT MEDICINE HOLDINGS LLC; *U.S. Private*, pg. 3253
PREVAIL THERAPEUTICS INC.—See Eli Lilly & Company; *U.S. Public*, pg. 734
PRIME MEDICINE, INC.; *U.S. Public*, pg. 1716
PRIMITY BIO, INC.—See Arsenal Capital Management LP; *U.S. Private*, pg. 337
PROCHON BIOTECH, LTD.—See Ocugen, Inc.; *U.S. Public*, pg. 1563
PROKIDNEY CORP.; *U.S. Public*, pg. 1726
PROMETIC BIOSCIENCES LTD - ENABLING TECHNOLOGY—See Thomvest Ventures LLC; *U.S. Private*, pg. 4162
PROTAGENIC THERAPEUTICS, INC.; *U.S. Public*, pg. 1729
PROTAGENIC THERAPEUTICS, INC.—See Protagenic Therapeutics, Inc.; *U.S. Public*, pg. 1729
PROTEINTECH JAPAN CO., LTD.—See COSMO BIO Co., Ltd.; *Int'l*, pg. 1811
PROTEO BIOTECH AG—See Proteo, Inc.; *U.S. Public*, pg. 1729
PROTIVA BIOTHERAPEUTICS (USA), INC.—See Arbutus Biopharma Corporation; *U.S. Public*, pg. 178
PT GENTING PLANTATIONS NUSANTARA—See Genting Berhad; *Int'l*, pg. 2929
PT. INVE INDONESIA—See Benchmark Holdings Plc; *Int'l*, pg. 970
PYXIS ONCOLOGY, INC.; *U.S. Public*, pg. 1739
Q32 BIO INC.; *U.S. Public*, pg. 1741
Q BIOMED INC.; *U.S. Public*, pg. 1741
QINSTRUMENTS GMBH—See BICO Group AB; *Int'l*, pg. 1019
Q SQUARED SOLUTIONS EXPRESSION ANALYSIS LLC—See IQVIA Holdings Inc.; *U.S. Public*, pg. 1170
QUANTERIX CORPORATION; *U.S. Public*, pg. 1753
QUANTUM SIGNAL AI, LLC—See Ford Motor Company; *U.S. Public*, pg. 867
QUINCE THERAPEUTICS, INC.; *U.S. Public*, pg. 1757
QUINTILES TRANSNATIONAL CORP.—See IQVIA Holdings Inc.; *U.S. Public*, pg. 1170
RAIN ONCOLOGY INC.—See Pathos AI, Inc.; *U.S. Private*, pg. 3106
RALLYBIO CORPORATION; *U.S. Public*, pg. 1761
RAPT THERAPEUTICS, INC.; *U.S. Public*, pg. 1763
RAYZEBIO, INC.—See Bristol-Myers Squibb Company; *U.S. Public*, pg. 387
RDDT PTY, LTD.—See Vyant Bio, Inc.; *U.S. Public*, pg. 2315
R&D SYSTEMS EUROPE, LTD.—See Bio-Techne Corporation; *U.S. Public*, pg. 334
R&D SYSTEMS GMBH—See Bio-Techne Corporation; *U.S. Public*, pg. 334
REACH GENETICS, INC.; *U.S. Public*, pg. 3365
RECURSION PHARMACEUTICALS, INC.; *U.S. Public*, pg. 1769
RECYTE THERAPEUTICS, INC.—See Lineage Cell Therapeutics, Inc.; *U.S. Public*, pg. 1320
REDPOINT BIO CORPORATION; *U.S. Private*, pg. 3379
REDWING ECOLOGICAL SERVICE INC.—See KKR & Co. Inc.; *U.S. Public*, pg. 1263
RELAY THERAPEUTICS, INC.; *U.S. Public*, pg. 1778
RENOVORX, INC.; *U.S. Public*, pg. 1784
REPLIGEN ESTONIA OU—See Repligen Corporation; *U.S. Public*, pg. 1784
REPLIGEN INDIA PRIVATE LIMITED—See Repligen Corporation; *U.S. Public*, pg. 1784

REPLIGEN JAPAN LLC—See Repligen Corporation; *U.S. Public*, pg. 1784
REPLIGEN KOREA CO. LTD.—See Repligen Corporation; *U.S. Public*, pg. 1784
REPLIGEN (SHANGHAI) BIOTECHNOLOGY CO. LTD.—See Repligen Corporation; *U.S. Public*, pg. 1784
REPLIMUNE GROUP, INC.; *U.S. Public*, pg. 1785
RESEARCH AND DIAGNOSTIC SYSTEMS, INC.—See Bio-Techne Corporation; *U.S. Public*, pg. 334
REVEAL BIOSCIENCES, INC.—See Arsenal Capital Management LP; *U.S. Private*, pg. 337
RHYTHM PHARMACEUTICALS, INC.; *U.S. Public*, pg. 1796
ROBINSON NOBLE, INC.; *U.S. Private*, pg. 3462
RONE ENGINEERING SERVICES, LLC—See OceanSound Partners, LP; *U.S. Private*, pg. 2992
RTI HEALTH SOLUTIONS—See Research Triangle Institute; *U.S. Private*, pg. 3404
RTI ROCKVILLE—See Research Triangle Institute; *U.S. Private*, pg. 3404
RUBIUS THERAPEUTICS, INC.; *U.S. Public*, pg. 1825
SAGIMET BIOSCIENCES INC.; *U.S. Public*, pg. 1835
SALMOBREED SALTEN AS—See Benchmark Holdings Plc; *Int'l*, pg. 970
SAMSARA SCIENCES, INC.—See LifeNet Health, Inc.; *U.S. Private*, pg. 2450
SANA BIOTECHNOLOGY, INC.; *U.S. Public*, pg. 1839
SANDHILLS AREA LAND TRUST—See Three Rivers Land Trust, Inc.; *U.S. Private*, pg. 4164
SATIOGEN PHARMACEUTICALS, INC.—See Mirum Pharmaceuticals, Inc.; *U.S. Public*, pg. 1450
S*BIO PTE. LTD.—See EDB Investments Pte. Ltd.; *Int'l*, pg. 2304
SCHOLAR ROCK HOLDING CORPORATION; *U.S. Public*, pg. 1847
SCHOTT MINIFAB PTY LTD—See Carl-Zeiss-Stiftung; *Int'l*, pg. 1337
SCOPUS BIOPHARMA INC.; *U.S. Public*, pg. 1849
SCOUT BIO, INC.—See Ceva Sante Animale SA; *Int'l*, pg. 1425
SCPHARMACEUTICALS, INC.; *U.S. Public*, pg. 1849
SEAGEN B.V.—See Seagen Inc.; *U.S. Public*, pg. 1852
SEER, INC.; *U.S. Public*, pg. 1856
SELCIA LIMITED—See Eurofins Scientific S.E.; *Int'l*, pg. 2551
SEMMA THERAPEUTICS, INC.—See Vertex Pharmaceuticals Incorporated; *U.S. Public*, pg. 2287
SENESTECH, INC.; *U.S. Public*, pg. 1865
SENSEI BIOTHERAPEUTICS, INC.; *U.S. Public*, pg. 1866
SENTI BIOSCIENCES, INC.; *U.S. Public*, pg. 1868
SERINA THERAPEUTICS, INC.—See Serina Therapeutics, Inc.; *U.S. Public*, pg. 1869
SHANGHAI PERSONALIS BIOTECHNOLOGY CO., LTD.—See Personalis, Inc.; *U.S. Public*, pg. 1677
SHATTUCK LABS, INC.; *U.S. Public*, pg. 1874
SHRIRAM BIOSEED (THAILAND) LIMITED—See DCM Shriram Limited; *Int'l*, pg. 1992
SIGA DEVELOPMENT OPERATIONS—See MacAndrews & Forbes Incorporated; *U.S. Private*, pg. 2534
SIGILON THERAPEUTICS, INC.—See Eli Lilly & Company; *U.S. Public*, pg. 734
SIMWEB—See HUB Cyber Security Ltd.; *Int'l*, pg. 3516
SIRIGEN, INC.—See Becton, Dickinson & Company; *U.S. Public*, pg. 292
SOFIE BIOSCIENCES, INC.; *U.S. Private*, pg. 3704
SOFOTEC GMBH—See AstraZeneca PLC; *Int'l*, pg. 661
SOLID BIOSCIENCES, INC; *U.S. Public*, pg. 1900
SOLUBLE BIOTECH INC—See Predictive Oncology Inc.; *U.S. Public*, pg. 1713
SONNET BIOTHERAPEUTICS, INC.—See Sonnet Biotherapeutics Holdings, Inc.; *U.S. Public*, pg. 1904
SPERO THERAPEUTICS, INC.; *U.S. Public*, pg. 1917
SPRINGWORKS THERAPEUTICS, INC.; *U.S. Public*, pg. 1919
SPRUCE BIOSCIENCES, INC.; *U.S. Public*, pg. 1920
SQZ BIOTECHNOLOGIES COMPANY; *U.S. Public*, pg. 1922
STEMTECH INTERNATIONAL, INC.; *U.S. Private*, pg. 3801
STOFNFISKUR HF.—See Benchmark Holdings Plc; *Int'l*, pg. 970
STOKE THERAPEUTICS, INC.; *U.S. Public*, pg. 1951
STRUCTURE THERAPEUTICS INC.; *U.S. Public*, pg. 1955
SUNGENE GMBH—See BASF SE; *Int'l*, pg. 877
SURFACE ONCOLOGY, INC.—See Coherus BioSciences, Inc.; *U.S. Public*, pg. 529
SUTIMCO INTERNATIONAL, INC.—See AURI, Inc.; *U.S. Public*, pg. 227
SUTRO BIOPHARMA, INC.; *U.S. Public*, pg. 1968
SWIFT BIOSCIENCES, INC.—See Danaher Corporation; *U.S. Public*, pg. 627
SYBLEU INC.; *U.S. Public*, pg. 1968
SYMBORG CHILE, SPA—See Corteva, Inc.; *U.S. Public*, pg. 585
SYMBORG, INC.—See Corteva, Inc.; *U.S. Public*, pg. 585
SYMBORG PARTICIPACOES LTDA.—See Corteva, Inc.; *U.S. Public*, pg. 585
SYMBORG PERU S.A.C.—See Corteva, Inc.; *U.S. Public*, pg. 585

541714 — RESEARCH AND DEVELO...

SYMBORG (SHANGHAI) TRADING CO., LTD.—See Corteva, Inc.; *U.S. Public*, pg. 585
SYMBORG, S.L.U.—See Corteva, Inc.; *U.S. Public*, pg. 585
SYMBORG TURKEY TARIM A.S.—See Corteva, Inc.; *U.S. Public*, pg. 585
SYNAPTOGENIX, INC.; *U.S. Public*, pg. 1969
SYNEXUS CLINICAL RESEARCH SOUTH AFRICA (PTY.) LIMITED—See Thermo Fisher Scientific Inc.; *U.S. Public*, pg. 2152
SYNEXUS CZECH S.R.O.—See Thermo Fisher Scientific Inc.; *U.S. Public*, pg. 2152
SYNEXUS POLSKA SP. Z O.O.—See Thermo Fisher Scientific Inc.; *U.S. Public*, pg. 2152
SYNTHETIC GENOMICS, INC.; *U.S. Private*, pg. 3905
TALIS BIOMEDICAL CORPORATION; *U.S. Public*, pg. 1979
TARSUS PHARMACEUTICALS, INC.; *U.S. Public*, pg. 1982
TAYSHA GENE THERAPIES, INC.; *U.S. Public*, pg. 1983
TCR2 THERAPEUTICS, INC.; *U.S. Public*, pg. 1983
TECTONIC THERAPEUTIC, INC.; *U.S. Public*, pg. 1989
TEEWINOT LIFE SCIENCES CORPORATION; *U.S. Private*, pg. 3958
TELA BIO, INC.; *U.S. Public*, pg. 1991
TELESIS BIO, INC.; *U.S. Public*, pg. 1998
TELLURIDE HEALTH COMPANY—See American Cannabis Innovations Conglomerated; *U.S. Private*, pg. 226
TEMPUS AI, INC.; *U.S. Public*, pg. 2000
TENAYA THERAPEUTICS, INC.; *U.S. Public*, pg. 2001
TERNS PHARMACEUTICALS, INC.; *U.S. Public*, pg. 2020
TETHIS LABS INC.—See Genextra S.p.A.; *Int'l*, pg. 2923
TETHIS S.P.A.—See Genextra S.p.A.; *Int'l*, pg. 2923
TFF PHARMACEUTICALS, INC.; *U.S. Public*, pg. 2029
THEMIS BIOSCIENCE NV—See Merck & Co., Inc.; *U.S. Public*, pg. 1421
THERANOSTICS HEALTH—See Theralink Technologies, Inc.; *U.S. Public*, pg. 2144
THERAPEUTIC SOLUTIONS INTERNATIONAL, INC.; *U.S. Public*, pg. 2144
THERMO FISHER SCIENTIFIC KOREA LTD.—See Thermo Fisher Scientific Inc.; *U.S. Public*, pg. 2146
THESEUS PHARMACEUTICALS, INC.—See Concentra Biosciences, LLC; *U.S. Private*, pg. 1008
THIRD HARMONIC BIO, INC.; *U.S. Public*, pg. 2155
TIANJIN INVE AQUACULTURE CO., LTD.—See Benchmark Holdings Plc; *Int'l*, pg. 970
TIERRA AGROTECH PRIVATE LIMITED—See Grandeur Products Limited; *Int'l*, pg. 3058
TITAN WOOD INC.—See AccSys Technologies PLC; *Int'l*, pg. 93
TITAN WOOD LIMITED—See AccSys Technologies PLC; *Int'l*, pg. 93
TOURMALINE BIO, INC.; *U.S. Public*, pg. 2165
TRANSCODE THERAPEUTICS, INC.; *U.S. Public*, pg. 2180
TRANSPLANT GENOMICS, INC.—See Eurofins Scientific S.E.; *Int'l*, pg. 2552
TREVIGEN, INC.—See Bio-Techne Corporation; *U.S. Public*, pg. 334
TREVI THERAPEUTICS, INC.; *U.S. Public*, pg. 2188
TRU-FLOW LLC—See Wynnchurch Capital, L.P.; *U.S. Private*, pg. 4577
TRYANGLE CO., LTD.—See Bain Capital, LP; *U.S. Private*, pg. 435
TSCAN THERAPEUTICS, INC.; *U.S. Public*, pg. 2202
TURNING POINT THERAPEUTICS, INC.—See Bristol-Myers Squibb Company; *U.S. Public*, pg. 387
TURNSTONE BIOLOGICS CORP.; *U.S. Public*, pg. 2205
TWIST BIOSCIENCE CORPORATION; *U.S. Public*, pg. 2207
TYME TECHNOLOGIES, INC.—See Syros Pharmaceuticals, Inc.; *U.S. Public*, pg. 1972
TYRA BIOSCIENCES, INC.; *U.S. Public*, pg. 2209
UAB JOHNSON & JOHNSON—See Johnson & Johnson; *U.S. Public*, pg. 1200
UNICYCIVE THERAPEUTICS, INC.; *U.S. Public*, pg. 2226
UNITED THERAPEUTICS EUROPE, LTD.—See United Therapeutics Corporation; *U.S. Public*, pg. 2238
UNITY BIOTECHNOLOGY, INC.; *U.S. Public*, pg. 2253
US STEM CELL CLINIC, LLC—See U.S. Stem Cell, Inc.; *U.S. Public*, pg. 2217
U.S. STEM CELL, INC.; *U.S. Public*, pg. 2216
VACCINEX, LP; *U.S. Private*, pg. 4329
VANDA PHARMACEUTICALS LIMITED—See Vanda Pharmaceuticals Inc.; *U.S. Public*, pg. 2275
VAXCYTE, INC.; *U.S. Public*, pg. 2276
VAXXINITY, INC.; *U.S. Public*, pg. 2276
VELESCO PHARMACEUTICAL SERVICES LLC—See Leonard Green & Partners, L.P.; *U.S. Private*, pg. 2426
VELOCITY CLINICAL RESEARCH, INC.—See GHO Capital Partners LLP; *Int'l*, pg. 2959
VENTYX BIOSCIENCES, INC.; *U.S. Public*, pg. 2279
VERA THERAPEUTICS, INC.; *U.S. Public*, pg. 2279
VERTEX PHARMACEUTICALS (CANADA) INCORPORATED—See Vertex Pharmaceuticals Incorporated; *U.S. Public*, pg. 2287
VERVE THERAPEUTICS, INC.; *U.S. Public*, pg. 2290
VET THERAPEUTICS, INC.—See Elanco Animal Health Incorporated; *U.S. Public*, pg. 722
VG LIFE SCIENCES INC.; *U.S. Public*, pg. 2290

VGX ANIMAL HEALTH, INC.—See Inovio Pharmaceuticals, Inc.; *U.S. Public*, pg. 1128
VIACORD, LLC—See Revvity, Inc.; *U.S. Public*, pg. 1795
VIACYTE, INC.; *U.S. Private*, pg. 4375
VIAGEN, LC.—See Precigen, Inc.; *U.S. Public*, pg. 1713
VIELA BIO, INC.—See Amgen Inc.; *U.S. Public*, pg. 123
VIGENE BIOSCIENCES, INC.—See Charles River Laboratories International, Inc.; *U.S. Public*, pg. 480
VIGIL NEUROSCIENCE, INC.; *U.S. Public*, pg. 2297
VIIV HEALTHCARE BV—See GSK plc; *Int'l*, pg. 3149
VIIV HEALTHCARE COMPANY—See GSK plc; *Int'l*, pg. 3150
VINCERX PHARMA, INC.; *U.S. Public*, pg. 2298
VIRALYTICS LIMITED—See Merck & Co., Inc.; *U.S. Public*, pg. 1419
VIR BIOTECHNOLOGY, INC.; *U.S. Public*, pg. 2298
VIRIOS THERAPEUTICS, INC.; *U.S. Public*, pg. 2299
VISIKOL, INC.—See BICO Group AB; *Int'l*, pg. 1019
VIVIDION THERAPEUTICS, INC.; *U.S. Public*, pg. 2307
VIVOS THERAPEUTICS, INC.; *U.S. Public*, pg. 2307
VOLATILE ANALYSIS CORPORATION; *U.S. Private*, pg. 4410
VOR BIOPHARMA INC.; *U.S. Public*, pg. 2309
VYNE THERAPEUTICS, INC.; *U.S. Public*, pg. 2315
WCG CLINICAL, INC.; *U.S. Public*, pg. 2338
WEREWOLF THERAPEUTICS, INC.; *U.S. Public*, pg. 2349
WERTHENSTEIN BIOPHARMA GMBH—See Merck & Co., Inc.; *U.S. Public*, pg. 1416
WHATMAN LIMITED—See General Electric Company; *U.S. Public*, pg. 920
X4 PHARMACEUTICALS (AUSTRIA) GMBH—See X4 Pharmaceuticals, Inc.; *U.S. Public*, pg. 2385
X4 PHARMACEUTICALS, INC.; *U.S. Public*, pg. 2385
XADCERA BIOPHARMACEUTICAL (SUZHOU) CO., LTD.—See Biocytogen Pharmaceuticals (Beijing) Co., Ltd.; *Int'l*, pg. 1037
XCEDE TECHNOLOGIES, INC.—See Dynasil Corporation of America; *U.S. Private*, pg. 1300
XILIO THERAPEUTICS, INC.; *U.S. Public*, pg. 2391
YORK ANALYTICAL LABORATORIES, INC—See ALS Limited; *Int'l*, pg. 379
YUBO INTERNATIONAL BIOTECH LTD.; *U.S. Public*, pg. 2399
ZANDER THERAPEUTICS, INC.; *U.S. Public*, pg. 4597
ZAO AJINOMOTO-GENETIKA RESEARCH INSTITUTE—See Ajinomoto Company, Inc.; *Int'l*, pg. 257
ZENTALIS PHARMACEUTICALS, INC.; *U.S. Public*, pg. 2402
ZENTARIS IVF GMBH—See COSCIENS Biopharma Inc.; *U.S. Public*, pg. 585
ZERO GRAVITY SOLUTIONS, INC.; *U.S. Public*, pg. 2403
ZURA BIO LIMITED; *U.S. Public*, pg. 2412
ZYMERGEN INC.—See Ginkgo Bioworks Holdings, Inc.; *U.S. Public*, pg. 938

541715 — RESEARCH AND DEVELOPMENT IN THE PHYSICAL, ENGINEERING, AND LIFE SCIENCES (EXCEPT NANOTECHNOLOGY AND BIOTECHNOLOGY)

22ND CENTURY LIMITED, LLC—See 22nd Century Group, Inc.; *U.S. Public*, pg. 3
2G DRIVES GMBH—See 2G Energy AG; *Int'l*, pg. 5
3D LINE RESEARCH AND DEVELOPMENT S.R.L.—See Elekta AB; *Int'l*, pg. 2355
451 RESEARCH, LLC—See S&P Global Inc.; *U.S. Public*, pg. 1830
4SC AG; *Int'l*, pg. 12
AARTI INDUSTRIES LTD. - AARTI CRAMS DIVISION—See Aarti Industries Ltd.; *Int'l*, pg. 38
ABB SWITZERLAND LTD - CORPORATE RESEARCH—See ABB Ltd.; *Int'l*, pg. 54
ABBVIE BIORESEARCH CENTER INC.—See AbbVie Inc.; *U.S. Public*, pg. 21
ABOUNDBIO INC.—See Galapagos N.V.; *Int'l*, pg. 2870
ACACIA RESEARCH GROUP, LLC—See Acacia Research Corporation; *U.S. Public*, pg. 27
ACCELERATED PHARMA, INC.; *U.S. Private*, pg. 49
ACCELLACARE ESPANA S.L.—See ICON plc; *Int'l*, pg. 3583
ACCELLACARE OF BRISTOL, LLC—See ICON plc; *Int'l*, pg. 3583
ACCELLACARE OF CHARLESTON, LLC—See ICON plc; *Int'l*, pg. 3583
ACCELLACARE OF CHARLOTTE, LLC—See ICON plc; *Int'l*, pg. 3584
ACCELLACARE OF HICKORY, LLC—See ICON plc; *Int'l*, pg. 3584
ACCELLACARE OF RALEIGH, LLC—See ICON plc; *Int'l*, pg. 3584
ACCELLACARE OF ROCKY MOUNT, LLC—See ICON plc; *Int'l*, pg. 3584
ACCELLACARE OF SALISBURY, LLC—See ICON plc; *Int'l*, pg. 3584
ACCELLACARE OF WILMINGTON, LLC—See ICON plc; *Int'l*, pg. 3584

ACCELLACARE OF WINSTON-SALEM, LLC—See ICON plc; *Int'l*, pg. 3584
ACCELLACARE SOUTH AFRICA (PTY.) LTD.—See ICON plc; *Int'l*, pg. 3583
ACCELLACARE US INC.—See ICON plc; *Int'l*, pg. 3583
ACCELLECARE ESPANA S.L.—See ICON plc; *Int'l*, pg. 3584
ACCELLECARE OF RALEIGH, LLC—See ICON plc; *Int'l*, pg. 3584
ACCELLECARE OF WILMINGTON, LLC—See ICON plc; *Int'l*, pg. 3584
ACCELLECARE SOUTH AFRICA (PTY.) LTD.—See ICON plc; *Int'l*, pg. 3584
ACCESS ONCOLOGY INC.—See Akebia Therapeutics, Inc.; *U.S. Public*, pg. 69
ACGT SDN BHD—See Genting Berhad; *Int'l*, pg. 2928
ACTELION LTD.—See Johnson & Johnson; *U.S. Public*, pg. 1193
ACTELION PHARMACEUTICALS CANADA, INC.—See Johnson & Johnson; *U.S. Public*, pg. 1193
ACTELION PHARMACEUTICALS DO BRASIL LTDA.—See Johnson & Johnson; *U.S. Public*, pg. 1194
ACTELION PHARMACEUTICALS ESPANA, SL—See Johnson & Johnson; *U.S. Public*, pg. 1193
ACTELION PHARMACEUTICALS FRANCE SAS—See Johnson & Johnson; *U.S. Public*, pg. 1193
ACTELION PHARMACEUTICALS ITALIA SRL—See Johnson & Johnson; *U.S. Public*, pg. 1193
ACTELION PHARMACEUTICALS LTD.—See Johnson & Johnson; *U.S. Public*, pg. 1194
ACTELION PHARMACEUTICALS UK LTD.—See Johnson & Johnson; *U.S. Public*, pg. 1194
ACTELION PHARMACEUTICALS US, INC.—See Johnson & Johnson; *U.S. Public*, pg. 1194
ADDEX PHARMA S.A.—See Addex Therapeutics Ltd.; *Int'l*, pg. 128
ADDEX THERAPEUTICS LTD.; *Int'l*, pg. 128
ADDLIFE AB; *Int'l*, pg. 129
ADMA BIOLOGICS, INC.; *U.S. Public*, pg. 42
ADME BIOANALYSES SAS—See Eurofins Scientific S.E.; *Int'l*, pg. 2542
ADVANCE BIOFACTURES CORP.—See Endo International plc; *U.S. Public*, pg. 2403
ADVANCED BRAIN MONITORING, INC.; *U.S. Private*, pg. 88
ADVANCED COOLING TECHNOLOGIES, INC.; *U.S. Private*, pg. 88
ADVANCED DIGITAL HEALTH MEDICINA PREVENTIVA S.A.; *Int'l*, pg. 158
ADVANCED TECHNOLOGY INTERNATIONAL—See Analytic Services, Inc.; *U.S. Private*, pg. 271
ADVANCIA CORPORATION; *U.S. Private*, pg. 93
AERION CORPORATION—See Keystone Group, L.P.; *U.S. Private*, pg. 2296
THE AEROSPACE CORPORATION; *U.S. Private*, pg. 3982
AEROSPACE RESERCH & TRADING, INC.—See Eagle Industry Co., Ltd.; *Int'l*, pg. 2265
AEVI GENOMIC MEDICINE, LLC—See Avalo Therapeutics, Inc.; *U.S. Public*, pg. 239
AFFERENT PHARMACEUTICALS, INC.—See Merck & Co., Inc.; *U.S. Public*, pg. 1415
AFFINITY ENERGY AND HEALTH LIMITED; *Int'l*, pg. 186
AGAMATRIX, INC.—See i-SENS Inc.; *Int'l*, pg. 3564
AGC RESEARCH INSTITUTE, INC.—See AGC Inc.; *Int'l*, pg. 202
AGENNIX INC. - PRINCETON—See Agennix AG; *Int'l*, pg. 205
AGENSYS, INC.—See Astellas Pharma Inc.; *Int'l*, pg. 653
AGENUS SWITZERLAND INC.—See Agenus Inc.; *U.S. Public*, pg. 60
AGILITY CLINICAL, INC.—See Precision Medicine Group, Inc.; *U.S. Private*, pg. 3245
AGRICULTURE TECHNOLOGY RESEARCH INSTITUTE—See Dongbu Group; *Int'l*, pg. 2165
AGRIGENETICS, INC.—See Corteva, Inc.; *U.S. Public*, pg. 580
AICHI ELECTRIC DEVELOPMENT & ENVIRONMENT DIVISION—See Aichi Electric Co., Ltd.; *Int'l*, pg. 229
AI CO., LTD; *Int'l*, pg. 226
AILERON THERAPEUTICS, INC.; *U.S. Public*, pg. 63
AIRBUS PROSKY S.A.S.—See Airbus SE; *Int'l*, pg. 244
AIT BIOSCIENCE LLC—See Ampersand Management LLC; *U.S. Private*, pg. 265
AKEBONO R&D ENGINEERING CENTER—See Akebono Brake Industry Co., Ltd.; *Int'l*, pg. 261
ALEXION PHARMACEUTICALS AUSTRALASIA PTY LTD—See AstraZeneca PLC; *Int'l*, pg. 659
ALEXION PHARMA UK—See AstraZeneca PLC; *Int'l*, pg. 659
ALFA WASSERMANN (BEIJING) MARKET RESEARCH & MANAGEMENT CO., LTD.—See Alfa-Wassermann S.p.A.; *Int'l*, pg. 314
ALIOS BIOPHARMA, INC.—See Johnson & Johnson; *U.S. Public*, pg. 1196
ALLCELLS, LLC—See Discovery Life Sciences, LLC; *U.S. Private*, pg. 1238
ALLNEX USA, INC. - STAMFORD R&D FACILITY—See Advent International Corporation; *U.S. Private*, pg. 98

ALMAC SCIENCES GROUP LTD.; *Int'l*, pg. 362
ALMAC SCIENCES—See Almac Sciences Group Ltd.; *Int'l*, pg. 363
ALPHA LAB A.E.—See DIAGNOSTIC AND THERAPEUTIC CENTER OF ATHENS-HYGEIA S.A.; *Int'l*, pg. 2103
ALPHA TEKNOVA, INC.; *U.S. Public*, pg. 82
ALS ENVIRONMENTAL—See ALS Limited; *Int'l*, pg. 378
ALTAROCK ENERGY INC.; *U.S. Private*, pg. 206
ALTOR BIOSCIENCE, LLC—See NantWorks, LLC; *U.S. Private*, pg. 2833
AMANASU ENVIRONMENT CORPORATION; *U.S. Public*, pg. 90
AMD RESEARCH & DEVELOPMENT CENTER INDIA PRIVATE LIMITED—See Advanced Micro Devices, Inc.; *U.S. Public*, pg. 48
AMERICAN COLLEGE OF SPORTS MEDICINE; *U.S. Private*, pg. 227
AMERICAN FEDERATION FOR AGING RESEARCH; *U.S. Private*, pg. 233
AMGEN INC. - SAN FRANCISCO—See Amgen Inc.; *U.S. Public*, pg. 123
AMNIS THERAPEUTICS LTD.; *Int'l*, pg. 429
AMS ADVANCED MEDICAL SERVICES GMBH—See AMS Advanced Medical Services GmbH; *Int'l*, pg. 438
AMS ADVANCED MEDICAL SERVICES LTD.—See AMS Advanced Medical Services GmbH; *Int'l*, pg. 438
AMT DATASOUTH CORPORATION; *U.S. Private*, pg. 268
ANALYTICAL SERVICES, INC.—See Arctic Slope Regional Corporation; *U.S. Private*, pg. 316
ANALYTIC SERVICES, INC.; *U.S. Private*, pg. 271
ANC RESEARCH & DEVELOPMENT LLC—See Cook Inlet Region, Inc.; *U.S. Private*, pg. 1038
ANGES, INC.; *Int'l*, pg. 460
ANHUI JINXUAN TECHNOLOGICAL CO., LTD.—See Anhui Jinhe Industrial Co., Ltd.; *Int'l*, pg. 468
APM ENGINEERING & RESEARCH SDN. BHD.—See APM Automotive Holdings Berhad; *Int'l*, pg. 516
APOSENSE LTD.; *Int'l*, pg. 519
APOTEX CORP.—See SK Capital Partners, LP; *U.S. Private*, pg. 3678
APOTEX RESEARCH PRIVATE LIMITED.—See SK Capital Partners, LP; *U.S. Private*, pg. 3679
APPLIED BIOSYSTEMS INTERNATIONAL, INC. RUSSIA REP OFFICE—See Thermo Fisher Scientific Inc.; *U.S. Public*, pg. 2145
APPLIED BIOSYSTEMS, LLC—See Thermo Fisher Scientific Inc.; *U.S. Public*, pg. 2148
APPLIED FOOD TECHNOLOGIES, INC.; *U.S. Private*, pg. 298
APPLIED MATERIALS (XIAN), LTD.—See Applied Materials, Inc.; *U.S. Public*, pg. 172
APPLIED PHYSICAL SCIENCES CORP.—See General Dynamics Corporation; *U.S. Public*, pg. 913
APPLIED RESEARCH ASSOCIATES, INC.; *U.S. Private*, pg. 299
APPLIED RESEARCH ASSOCIATES MID-ATLANTIC DIVISION—See Applied Research Associates, Inc.; *U.S. Private*, pg. 299
APPLIED RESEARCH ASSOCIATES ROCKY MOUNTAIN DIVISION—See Applied Research Associates, Inc.; *U.S. Private*, pg. 299
APPLIED RESEARCH ASSOCIATES SOUTHWEST DIVISION—See Applied Research Associates, Inc.; *U.S. Private*, pg. 299
APPLIED SIGNAL TECHNOLOGY, INC.—See RTX Corporation; *U.S. Public*, pg. 1825
APP SYSTEMS SERVICES PTE. LTD.—See APP Systems Services Pte. Ltd.; *Int'l*, pg. 519
APTIMA, INC.; *U.S. Private*, pg. 302
APTIV INTERNATIONAL BV—See ICON plc; *Int'l*, pg. 3584
APTIV INTERNATIONAL SARL—See ICON plc; *Int'l*, pg. 3584
APTIV INTERNATIONAL SP. Z O.O.—See ICON plc; *Int'l*, pg. 3584
APTIV SOLUTIONS, INC. - MARYLAND—See ICON plc; *Int'l*, pg. 3584
APTIV SOLUTIONS, INC.—See ICON plc; *Int'l*, pg. 3584
APTUIT, LLC—See Evotec SE; *Int'l*, pg. 2573
AQUA PROTECH LABORATORIES, INC.—See Leonard Green & Partners, L.P.; *U.S. Private*, pg. 2426
ARAN RESEARCH & DEVELOPMENT (1982) LTD.; *Int'l*, pg. 535
ARATANA THERAPEUTICS NV—See Elanco Animal Health Incorporated; *U.S. Public*, pg. 722
ARBORGEN HOLDINGS LIMITED; *Int'l*, pg. 538
ARCELORMITTAL EAST CHICAGO—See Cleveland-Cliffs, Inc.; *U.S. Public*, pg. 514
ARETE ASSOCIATES; *U.S. Private*, pg. 318
ARGENX SE; *Int'l*, pg. 561
ARKEMA RESEARCH CENTER—See Arkema S.A.; *Int'l*, pg. 569
ARNO THERAPEUTICS, INC.; *U.S. Public*, pg. 194
ARQUEONAUTAS WORLDWIDE - ARQUEOLOGIA SUBAQUATICA S.A.; *Int'l*, pg. 578
ARRAYIT DIAGNOSTICS, INC.—See Arrayit Corp.; *U.S. Public*, pg. 194
ARROWHEAD MADISON, INC.—See Arrowhead Pharmaceuticals, Inc.; *U.S. Public*, pg. 201

ARUP LABORATORIES; *U.S. Private*, pg. 344
ASIA GLOBAL RESEARCH CO., LTD.—See Bumrungrad Hospital Public Company Limited; *Int'l*, pg. 1215
ASSUREX HEALTH, INC.—See Myriad Genetics, Inc.; *U.S. Public*, pg. 1489
ASTELLAS ANALYTICAL SCIENCE LABORATORIES, INC.—See Astellas Pharma Inc.; *Int'l*, pg. 651
ASTELLAS US TECHNOLOGIES, INC.—See Astellas Pharma Inc.; *Int'l*, pg. 653
ASTERAND INC.—See Stemgent, Inc.; *U.S. Private*, pg. 3801
ASTRAZENECA CLINICAL RESEARCH REGION CEE (HU)—See AstraZeneca PLC; *Int'l*, pg. 660
ASTRAZENECA R&D MOLNDAL—See AstraZeneca PLC; *Int'l*, pg. 659
ASTRAZENECA R&D SODERTALJE—See AstraZeneca PLC; *Int'l*, pg. 659
ASTRE CORPORATION; *U.S. Private*, pg. 361
ASUBIO PHAMACEUTICALS, INC.—See Daiichi Sankyo Co., Ltd.; *Int'l*, pg. 1930
ASUS TECHNOLOGY LICENSING INC.—See ASUSTeK Computer Inc.; *Int'l*, pg. 663
ATAI LIFE SCIENCES AG; *Int'l*, pg. 665
ATI TECHNOLOGIES (L) INC.—See Advanced Micro Devices, Inc.; *U.S. Public*, pg. 48
ATMOSPHERIC & ENVIRONMENTAL RESEARCH - AIR QUALITY—See Verisk Analytics, Inc.; *U.S. Public*, pg. 2283
ATTAIN, LLC; *U.S. Private*, pg. 383
AUDIOCODES EUROPE LIMITED—See AudioCodes Ltd.; *Int'l*, pg. 701
AURIGENE DISCOVERY TECHNOLOGIES LIMITED—See Dr. Reddy's Laboratories Limited; *Int'l*, pg. 2195
AURIS HEALTH, INC.—See Johnson & Johnson; *U.S. Public*, pg. 1194
AUSTRALIAN LUNG HEALTH INITIATIVE PTY LTD.—See 4DMedical Limited; *Int'l*, pg. 11
AUSTRIALS PTY LTD—See Healius Limited; *Int'l*, pg. 3302
AUTODESK DEVELOPMENT SARL—See Autodesk, Inc.; *U.S. Public*, pg. 228
AVENSYS UK LTD.—See Fresenius SE & Co. KGaA; *Int'l*, pg. 2777
AZURE SUMMIT TECHNOLOGY, INC.—See CACI International Inc.; *U.S. Public*, pg. 417
BACTERIOLOGISCH CONTROLE STATION BV—See Eurofins Scientific S.E.; *Int'l*, pg. 2535
BAE SYSTEMS-ANALYTICAL & ORDINANCE SOLUTIONS—See BAE Systems plc; *Int'l*, pg. 797
BAE SYSTEMS IAP RESEARCH, INC.—See BAE Systems plc; *Int'l*, pg. 798
BAE SYSTEMS—See BAE Systems plc; *Int'l*, pg. 797
BALLARD POWER SYSTEMS CORPORATION—See Ballard Power Systems, Inc.; *Int'l*, pg. 809
BALLISTIC RECOVERY SYSTEMS, INC.; *U.S. Public*, pg. 268
BANNER LIFE SCIENCES LLC—See Thermo Fisher Scientific Inc.; *U.S. Public*, pg. 2151
BARRIERMED INC.; *U.S. Private*, pg. 480
BASCOM HUNTER TECHNOLOGIES INC.; *U.S. Private*, pg. 484
BASF AGRICULTURAL RESEARCH FOUNDATION, INC.—See BASF SE; *Int'l*, pg. 877
BASF FUTURE BUSINESS GMBH—See BASF SE; *Int'l*, pg. 879
BASF INNOVATIONSFONDS GMBH—See BASF SE; *Int'l*, pg. 879
BASTIAN SOLUTIONS; *U.S. Private*, pg. 486
BATTELLE INDIA.—See Battelle Memorial Institute; *U.S. Private*, pg. 487
BATTELLE MEMORIAL INSTITUTE; *U.S. Private*, pg. 487
BATTELLE VENTURES, L.P.—See Battelle Memorial Institute; *U.S. Private*, pg. 487
BAYER ANIMAL HEALTH GMBH—See Elanco Animal Health Incorporated; *U.S. Public*, pg. 722
BAYER CORPORATION—See Bayer Aktiengesellschaft; *Int'l*, pg. 902
BBI LIFE SCIENCES CORPORATION; *Int'l*, pg. 920
BECKMAN COULTER LIFE SCIENCES—See Danaher Corporation; *U.S. Public*, pg. 624
BEIJING BOE SPECIAL DISPLAY TECHNOLOGY CO., LTD.—See BOE Technology Group Co., Ltd.; *Int'l*, pg. 1099
BEIJING MEDPACE MEDICAL SCIENCE & TECHNOLOGY LTD.—See Cinven Limited; *Int'l*, pg. 1612
BENAROYA RESEARCH INSTITUTE AT VIRGINIA MASON; *U.S. Private*, pg. 523
BERTIN PHARMA SAS—See CT Ingenieros AAISL; *Int'l*, pg. 1868
BE VACCINES SAS—See Biological E. Limited; *Int'l*, pg. 1039
BEYOND_I CO., LTD.—See Chemtronics Co., Ltd.; *Int'l*, pg. 1464
BEYONDSPRING INC.; *U.S. Public*, pg. 327
BGI AMERICAS CORPORATION—See BGI-Shenzhen; *Int'l*, pg. 1008
BGI CHINA—See BGI-Shenzhen; *Int'l*, pg. 1008
BGI HONG KONG CO. LIMITED—See BGI-Shenzhen; *Int'l*, pg. 1008

BGI JAPAN—See BGI-Shenzhen; *Int'l*, pg. 1008
BGI-SHENZHEN; *Int'l*, pg. 1008
BIGELOW LABORATORY FOR OCEAN SCIENCES; *U.S. Private*, pg. 555
BIOASIS TECHNOLOGIES INC.; *U.S. Public*, pg. 335
BIOBASE CORPORATION—See Incyte Corporation; *U.S. Public*, pg. 1115
BIOCAT GMBH—See AddLife AB; *Int'l*, pg. 129
BIOCON ACADEMY PVT. LTD.—See Biocon Ltd.; *Int'l*, pg. 1036
BIOCON BIOPHARMACEUTICALS PRIVATE LIMITED—See Biocon Ltd.; *Int'l*, pg. 1036
BIODIEM LIMITED; *Int'l*, pg. 1037
BIOFOCUS DPI—See Charles River Laboratories International, Inc.; *U.S. Public*, pg. 480
BIOGEMMA S.A.S.—See Avril SCA; *Int'l*, pg. 750
BIOGEMMA S.A.S.—See Euralis Coop; *Int'l*, pg. 2527
BIOGEMMA S.A.S.—See Groupe Limagrain Holding SA; *Int'l*, pg. 3107
BIOGEND THERAPEUTICS CO., LTD.; *Int'l*, pg. 1038
BIOLIGHT LIFE SCIENCES LTD.; *Int'l*, pg. 1039
BIOLINE INNOVATIONS JERUSALEM—See BioLineRX Ltd.; *Int'l*, pg. 1039
BIOLOGICS DEVELOPMENT SERVICES, LLC; *U.S. Private*, pg. 562
BIOMARIN BRASIL FARMACEUTICA LTDA.—See BioMarin Pharmaceutical Inc.; *U.S. Public*, pg. 337
BIOMAT, S.A.—See Grifols, S.A.; *Int'l*, pg. 3084
BIOMAT USA - ALTAMONTE SPRINGS—See Grifols, S.A.; *Int'l*, pg. 3084
BIOMAT USA - VAN NUYS—See Grifols, S.A.; *Int'l*, pg. 3084
BIOMEDICAL RESEARCH FOUNDATION OF NORTHWEST LOUISIANA; *U.S. Private*, pg. 562
BIOO SCIENTIFIC CORPORATION—See Revvity, Inc.; *U.S. Public*, pg. 1793
BIO-RAD FINLAND OY—See Bio-Rad Laboratories, Inc.; *U.S. Public*, pg. 332
BIO-RAD NEW ZEALAND—See Bio-Rad Laboratories, Inc.; *U.S. Public*, pg. 333
BIOSEEK LLC—See DiscoveRx Corp.; *U.S. Private*, pg. 1237
BIOSIGMA S.A.—See Corporacion Nacional del Cobre de Chile; *Int'l*, pg. 1804
BIOSIGMA S.A.—See ENEOS Holdings, Inc.; *Int'l*, pg. 2415
BIOSTEM TECHNOLOGIES, INC.; *U.S. Public*, pg. 338
BIOTAGE AB; *Int'l*, pg. 1042
BIOTAGE GB LTD.—See Biotage AB; *Int'l*, pg. 1042
BIOTAGE LLC—See Biotage AB; *Int'l*, pg. 1042
BIOTAGE SWEDEN AB—See Biotage AB; *Int'l*, pg. 1042
BIOTIX INC.; *U.S. Private*, pg. 563
BIOVENTURE CENTRE PTE. LTD.—See Becton, Dickinson & Company; *U.S. Public*, pg. 290
BIOVENTURE CENTRE PTE. LTD.—See Johns Hopkins University; *U.S. Private*, pg. 2226
BLUEINGREEN, LLC—See Chart Industries, Inc.; *U.S. Public*, pg. 481
BLUEROCK THERAPEUTICS LP—See Bayer Aktiengesellschaft; *Int'l*, pg. 907
BMT SYNTEK TECHNOLOGIES, INC.—See BMT Group Limited; *Int'l*, pg. 1078
BODE CELLMARK FORENSICS, INC.—See Laboratory Corporation of America Holdings; *U.S. Public*, pg. 1285
BOLDER BIOPATH, INC.—See Inotiv, Inc.; *U.S. Public*, pg. 1128
BONE BIOLOGICS, CORP.; *U.S. Public*, pg. 368
BOSTON BIOCHEM, INC.—See Bio-Techne Corporation; *U.S. Public*, pg. 334
BOSTON VA RESEARCH INSTITUTE, INC.; *U.S. Private*, pg. 622
BP ALTERNATIVE ENERGY NORTH AMERICA, INC.—See BP plc; *Int'l*, pg. 1126
BP BIOFUELS NORTH AMERICA LLC—See BP plc; *Int'l*, pg. 1126
BPH ENERGY LIMITED; *Int'l*, pg. 1132
BRAINSTORM CELL THERAPEUTICS INC.; *U.S. Public*, pg. 379
BRAINSTORM CELL THERAPEUTICS LTD.—See BrainStorm Cell Therapeutics Inc.; *U.S. Public*, pg. 380
BREEDING RESEARCH INSTITUTE—See Dongbu Group; *Int'l*, pg. 2165
BRENTWOOD BIOMEDICAL RESEARCH INSTITUTE, INC.; *U.S. Private*, pg. 646
BRI BIOPHARMACEUTICAL RESEARCH INC.—See Hangzhou Tigermed Consulting Co., Ltd.; *Int'l*, pg. 3251
BRIDGESTONE AMERICAS CENTER FOR RESEARCH AND TECHNOLOGY, LLC—See Cox Enterprises, Inc.; *U.S. Private*, pg. 1075
BRIDGESTONE AMERICAS, INC. - AKRON—See Cox Enterprises, Inc.; *U.S. Private*, pg. 1075
BRIDGESTONE AMERICAS, INC. - CENTER FOR RESEARCH & TECHNOLOGY—See Bridgestone Corporation; *Int'l*, pg. 1156
BRIDGESTONE AMERICAS TIRE OPERATIONS, LLC - AKRON TECHNICAL CENTER DIVISION—See Cox Enterprises, Inc.; *U.S. Private*, pg. 1075
BRINK CLIMATE SYSTEMS FRANCE S.A.S.—See CENTROTEC SE; *Int'l*, pg. 1414
BRISTOL-MYERS SQUIBB COMPANY - WALLINGFORD

541715 — RESEARCH AND DEVELO...   CORPORATE AFFILIATIONS

R&D FACILITY—See Bristol-Myers Squibb Company; *U.S. Public*, pg. 385
BRITISH AMERICAN TOBACCO RESEARCH & DEVELOPMENT—See British American Tobacco plc; *Int'l*, pg. 1167
BROADATA COMMUNICATIONS INC—See Mercury Systems, Inc.; *U.S. Public*, pg. 1422
BROADTEC TV R&D CENTER SDN. BHD.—See Funai Electric Co., Ltd.; *Int'l*, pg. 2844
BTG INTERNATIONAL LTD.—See Boston Scientific Corporation; *U.S. Public*, pg. 373
BUFFALO NIAGARA MEDICAL CAMPUS; *U.S. Private*, pg. 681
BURCON NUTRASCIENCE CORPORATION; *Int'l*, pg. 1221
BURCON NUTRASCIENCE (MB) CORP.—See Burcon NutraScience Corporation; *Int'l*, pg. 1221
BYSTRONIC (TIANJIN) MACHINERY CO. LTD.—See Bystronic AG; *Int'l*, pg. 1236
CABOT CORPORATION - BUSINESS & TECHNOLOGY CENTER—See Cabot Corporation; *U.S. Public*, pg. 416
CADENCE RESEARCH & CONSULTING; *U.S. Private*, pg. 713
CAELUM RESEARCH CORPORATION; *U.S. Private*, pg. 713
CALCIMEDICA SUBSIDIARY, INC.—See CalciMedica, Inc.; *U.S. Public*, pg. 422
CALLAGHAN INNOVATION RESEARCH LIMITED; *Int'l*, pg. 1265
CALVERT LABORATORIES, INC.—See Altasciences Company Inc.; *Int'l*, pg. 387
CAMECA GMBH—See AMETEK, Inc.; *U.S. Public*, pg. 117
CANNPAL ANIMAL THERAPEUTICS LIMITED—See AusCann Group Holdings Pty Ltd; *Int'l*, pg. 715
CANON SALES CO., INC.—See Canon Inc.; *Int'l*, pg. 1296
CANON TECHNOLOGY EUROPE LTD—See Canon Inc.; *Int'l*, pg. 1294
CANON U.S. LIFE SCIENCES, INC.—See Canon Inc.; *Int'l*, pg. 1297
CARGILL INC.—See Cargill, Inc.; *U.S. Private*, pg. 756
CARNEGIE INSTITUTION OF WASHINGTON; *U.S. Private*, pg. 766
CATO RESEARCH, LTD.—See Cato SMS; *Int'l*, pg. 1361
CBSET, INC.; *U.S. Private*, pg. 797
CDX, INC.—See MyDx, Inc.; *U.S. Public*, pg. 2824
CELANESE SWITZERLAND AG—See GIC Pte. Ltd.; *Int'l*, pg. 2968
CELANESE SWITZERLAND AG—See The Carlyle Group Inc.; *U.S. Public*, pg. 2051
CELLCARTA PRECISION MEDICINE INC.—See Arsenal Capital Management LP; *U.S. Private*, pg. 337
CELLECTIS S.A.; *Int'l*, pg. 1392
CELLULAR DYNAMICS INTERNATIONAL, INC.—See FUJIFILM Holdings Corporation; *Int'l*, pg. 2822
CENTER FOR GLOBAL DEVELOPMENT; *U.S. Private*, pg. 810
CENTER FOR ORGAN RECOVERY & EDUCATION; *U.S. Private*, pg. 811
CENTER FOR THE ADVANCEMENT OF SCIENCE IN SPACE, INC.; *U.S. Private*, pg. 811
CENTRAL INSTITUTE FOR EXPERIMENTAL ANIMALS; *Int'l*, pg. 1408
CENTRO DE PESQUISAS DE ENERGIA ELETRICA—See Centrais Eletricas Brasileiras S.A.; *Int'l*, pg. 1403
CENTRO DE TECNOLOGIA CANAVIEIRA S.A.—See Cosan S.A.; *Int'l*, pg. 1809
CENTRO PER GLI STUDI DI TECNICA NAVALE CETENA S.P.A.—See Fincantieri S.p.A.; *Int'l*, pg. 2671
CENTROTEC BUILDING TECHNOLOGY (JIAXING) CO. LTD.—See CENTROTEC SE; *Int'l*, pg. 1414
CENTROTEC SE; *Int'l*, pg. 1414
CENTRUM VYZKUMU REZ S.R.O.—See CEZ, a.s.; *Int'l*, pg. 1429
CEPROCIM S.A.; *Int'l*, pg. 1420
CEPTARIS THERAPEUTICS, INC.—See Johnson & Johnson; *U.S. Public*, pg. 1194
CERTARA USA, INC. - SAINT LOUIS—See Certara, Inc.; *U.S. Public*, pg. 476
CETERO RESEARCH; *U.S. Private*, pg. 843
CHARLES RIVER BIOPHARMACEUTICAL SERVICES GMBH—See Charles River Laboratories International, Inc.; *U.S. Public*, pg. 479
CHARLES RIVER LABORATORIES INDIA PRIVATE LIMITED—See Charles River Laboratories International, Inc.; *U.S. Public*, pg. 480
CHARLES RIVER LABORATORIES PRECLINICAL SERVICES IRELAND LIMITED—See Charles River Laboratories International, Inc.; *U.S. Public*, pg. 480
THE CHARLES STARK DRAPER LABORATORY, INC.; *U.S. Private*, pg. 4007
CHEMICAL CONTROL SRL—See Eurofins Scientific S.E.; *Int'l*, pg. 2535
THE CHEMISTRY RESEARCH SOLUTION LLC—See Welsh, Carson, Anderson & Stowe; *U.S. Private*, pg. 4479
CHEMOCENTRYX, INC.—See Amgen Inc.; *U.S. Public*, pg. 123
CHENGDU CHEMPARTNER CO., LTD.—See TPG Capital, L.P.; *U.S. Public*, pg. 2175

CHILTERN CLINICAL RESEARCH INDIA PRIVATE LTD.—See Laboratory Corporation of America Holdings; *U.S. Public*, pg. 1285
CHILTERN INTERNATIONAL LIMITED—See Laboratory Corporation of America Holdings; *U.S. Public*, pg. 1285
CHINA AEROSPACE SCIENCE AND INDUSTRY CORPORATION LIMITED; *Int'l*, pg. 1481
CHINA AEROSPACE SCIENCE AND TECHNOLOGY CORPORATION; *Int'l*, pg. 1481
CHINA BLUESTAR CHANGSHA CHEMICAL ENGINEERING CO LTD—See Bluestar Adisseo Company Limited; *Int'l*, pg. 1074
CHINA GATEWAY PHARMACEUTICAL DEVELOPMENT CO., LTD.—See TPG Capital, L.P.; *U.S. Public*, pg. 2175
CHINA MACHINERY INTERNATIONAL ENGINEERING DESIGN & RESEARCH INSTITUTE CO., LTD.—See China Machinery Engineering Corporation; *Int'l*, pg. 1516
CHMC ANESTHESIA FOUNDATION, INC.; *U.S. Private*, pg. 887
CHROMATIN, INC.—See S&W Seed Co.; *U.S. Public*, pg. 1832
CIBUS, INC.; *U.S. Public*, pg. 494
CIT-CITOXLAB FRANCE SAS—See Charles River Laboratories International, Inc.; *U.S. Public*, pg. 480
CITOXLAB HUNGARY LTD.—See Charles River Laboratories International, Inc.; *U.S. Public*, pg. 480
CITOXLAB NORTH AMERICA INC.—See Charles River Laboratories International, Inc.; *U.S. Public*, pg. 480
CJB INC.—See Laboratory Corporation of America Holdings; *U.S. Public*, pg. 1285
CLARION HEALTHCARE, LLC—See Arsenal Capital Management LP; *U.S. Private*, pg. 338
CLAUSE S.A.—See Groupe Limagrain Holding SA; *Int'l*, pg. 3108
CLAUSE-TEZIER S.A.—See Groupe Limagrain Holding SA; *Int'l*, pg. 3108
CLEA JAPAN, INC.—See Central Institute for Experimental Animals; *Int'l*, pg. 1408
CLEAN COAL POWER R&D CO., LTD.; *Int'l*, pg. 1654
CLEARABILITY, INC.; *U.S. Private*, pg. 932
CLINICAL TRIAL NETWORK; *U.S. Private*, pg. 944
CLINIGENE INTERNATIONAL LIMITED—See Biocon Ltd.; *Int'l*, pg. 1036
CLINIPACE, INC.—See dMed Biopharmaceutical Co. Ltd.; *Int'l*, pg. 2143
CMAI INDUSTRIES, INC.—See China Metal Products Co., Ltd.; *Int'l*, pg. 1523
CMIC CMO USA CORPORATION—See CMIC Holdings Co., Ltd.; *Int'l*, pg. 1670
CMK CORPORATION - TECHNICAL CENTER PLANT—See CMK Corporation; *Int'l*, pg. 1670
CN BIO INNOVATIONS LIMITED—See CN Innovations Holdings Limited; *Int'l*, pg. 1672
CN INNOVATIONS CO., LTD.—See CN Innovations Holdings Limited; *Int'l*, pg. 1672
CO2 GRO INC.; *Int'l*, pg. 1680
COFCO NUTRITION & HEALTH RESEARCH INSTITUTE CO. LTD.—See COFCO Limited; *Int'l*, pg. 1692
COLDQUANTA, INC.; *U.S. Private*, pg. 966
THE COLUMBIA GROUP, INC.; *U.S. Private*, pg. 4011
COMBUSTION TECHNOLOGIES CORP.—See Environmental Energy Services, Inc.; *U.S. Public*, pg. 1407
COMMUNICATION SERVICE FOR THE DEAF, INC.; *U.S. Private*, pg. 988
COMPENDIA BIOSCIENCE, INC.—See Thermo Fisher Scientific Inc.; *U.S. Public*, pg. 2148
COMPLETE GENOMICS, INC.—See BGI-Shenzhen; *Int'l*, pg. 1008
COMPUDENT PRAXISCOMPUTER GMBH & CO. KG—See CompuGroup Medical SE & Co. KGaA; *Int'l*, pg. 1755
COMPUTING RESEARCH ASSOCIATION; *U.S. Private*, pg. 1006
CONAGRA FOODS - INDIANAPOLIS—See Conagra Brands, Inc.; *U.S. Public*, pg. 563
CONCORD BIOSCIENCES LLC—See Hangzhou Tigermed Consulting Co., Ltd.; *Int'l*, pg. 3251
CONCURRENT TECHNOLOGIES CORPORATION; *U.S. Private*, pg. 1011
CONSOLIDATED ENGINEERING LABS; *U.S. Private*, pg. 1020
CONSORTIUM FOR OCEAN LEADERSHIP, INC.; *U.S. Private*, pg. 1023
CONSTRUCTION RESEARCH & TECHNOLOGY GMBH—See BASF SE; *Int'l*, pg. 883
CONSUMER TESTING LABORATORIES, INC.—See Underwriters Laboratories Inc.; *U.S. Private*, pg. 4280
CONTECH RESEARCH, INC.; *U.S. Private*, pg. 1027
CONTINENTAL ANALYTICAL SERVICES, INC.—See Leonard Green & Partners, L.P.; *U.S. Private*, pg. 2426
COOPERHEAT-MQS INC.—See Team, Inc.; *U.S. Public*, pg. 1987
COREBRACE, LLC—See SME Industries Inc.; *U.S. Private*, pg. 3693
CORESYS CONSULTING; *U.S. Private*, pg. 1050
CORNERSTONE RESEARCH & DEVELOPMENT, INC.—See Cornell Capital LLC; *U.S. Private*, pg. 1051
CORNERSTONE RESEARCH GROUP, INC.; *U.S. Private*, pg. 1052

COSMO BIO CO., LTD.; *Int'l*, pg. 1811
COVANCE (ASIA) PTE. LTD.—See Laboratory Corporation of America Holdings; *U.S. Public*, pg. 1285
COVANCE BIOANALYTICAL SERVICES LLC—See Laboratory Corporation of America Holdings; *U.S. Public*, pg. 1285
COVANCE CENTRAL LABORATORY SERVICES SA—See Laboratory Corporation of America Holdings; *U.S. Public*, pg. 1285
COVANCE CLINICAL AND PERIAPPROVAL SERVICES SARL—See Laboratory Corporation of America Holdings; *U.S. Public*, pg. 1286
COVANCE CLINICAL & PERIAPPROVAL SERVICES S.A.—See Laboratory Corporation of America Holdings; *U.S. Public*, pg. 1286
COVANCE GMBH—See Laboratory Corporation of America Holdings; *U.S. Public*, pg. 1286
COVANCE, INC.—See Laboratory Corporation of America Holdings; *U.S. Public*, pg. 1286
COVANCE LABORATORIES GMBH—See Laboratory Corporation of America Holdings; *U.S. Public*, pg. 1286
COVANCE LABORATORIES LIMITED—See Laboratory Corporation of America Holdings; *U.S. Public*, pg. 1286
COVANCE LIMITED—See Laboratory Corporation of America Holdings; *U.S. Public*, pg. 1286
COVANCE PTY. LTD.—See Laboratory Corporation of America Holdings; *U.S. Public*, pg. 1286
CREAFORM DEUTSCHLAND GMBH—See AMETEK, Inc.; *U.S. Public*, pg. 119
CREAFORM JAPAN K.K.—See AMETEK, Inc.; *U.S. Public*, pg. 120
CREAFORM USA, INC.—See AMETEK, Inc.; *U.S. Public*, pg. 120
CREATIVASC MEDICAL, LLC—See Brookhaven Medical, Inc.; *U.S. Private*, pg. 663
CRESTWOOD TECHNOLOGY GROUP; *U.S. Private*, pg. 1099
CRISPR THERAPEUTICS AG; *Int'l*, pg. 1850
CRISPR THERAPEUTICS, INC.—See CRISPR Therapeutics AG; *Int'l*, pg. 1850
CROMSOURCE INC.—See CROMSOURCE S.r.l.; *Int'l*, pg. 1853
CROMSOURCE LTD.—See CROMSOURCE S.r.l.; *Int'l*, pg. 1853
CROMSOURCE S.R.L.; *Int'l*, pg. 1853
CROPDESIGN N.V.—See BASF SE; *Int'l*, pg. 883
CRS (BEIJING) CLINICAL RESEARCH CO., LIMITED—See ICON plc; *Int'l*, pg. 3584
CRYOLIFE ASIA PACIFIC, PTE. LTD.—See Artivion, Inc.; *U.S. Public*, pg. 208
CULTIVA LLC; *U.S. Private*, pg. 1121
CURACLE CO., LTD.; *Int'l*, pg. 1878
CURIA HOLDINGS (UK) LIMITED—See GTCR LLC; *U.S. Private*, pg. 1805
CURIA HOLDINGS (UK) LIMITED—See The Carlyle Group Inc.; *U.S. Public*, pg. 2046
CURIA, INC.—See GTCR LLC; *U.S. Private*, pg. 1805
CURIA, INC.—See The Carlyle Group Inc.; *U.S. Public*, pg. 2046
CURIA INDIANA, LLC—See GTCR LLC; *U.S. Private*, pg. 1805
CURIA INDIANA, LLC—See The Carlyle Group Inc.; *U.S. Public*, pg. 2046
CURIA INDIA PRIVATE LIMITED—See GTCR LLC; *U.S. Private*, pg. 1805
CURIA INDIA PRIVATE LIMITED—See The Carlyle Group Inc.; *U.S. Public*, pg. 2046
CYCLONE POWER TECHNOLOGIES, INC.; *U.S. Public*, pg. 617
CYPROTEX DISCOVERY LIMITED—See Evotec SE; *Int'l*, pg. 2573
CYPROTEX LIMITED—See Evotec SE; *Int'l*, pg. 2573
CYTOGEN CO., LTD; *Int'l*, pg. 1897
CYTORI THERAPEUTICS K.K.; *Int'l*, pg. 1897
DAIFUKU INSTITUTE OF TECHNOLOGY & TRAINING CO., LTD.—See Daifuku Co., Ltd.; *Int'l*, pg. 1925
DAIWA INSTITUTE OF RESEARCH HONG KONG LTD.—See Daiwa Securities Group Inc.; *Int'l*, pg. 1948
DANA-FARBER CANCER INSTITUTE; *U.S. Private*, pg. 1152
DANDI BIOSCIENCE CO., LTD.—See HLB Global Co Ltd; *Int'l*, pg. 3430
DANONE RESEARCH B.V.—See Danone; *Int'l*, pg. 1966
DARKBLADE SYSTEMS CORPORATION—See Hammond, Kennedy, Whitney & Company, Inc.; *U.S. Private*, pg. 1850
DASAN INDIA PRIVATE LIMITED—See DZS Inc.; *U.S. Public*, pg. 701
DASAN VIETNAM COMPANY LIMITED—See DZS Inc.; *U.S. Public*, pg. 701
THE DATA APPEAL COMPANY S.P.A.—See Almawave S.p.A.; *Int'l*, pg. 363
DECODE GENETICS, INC.—See Amgen Inc.; *U.S. Public*, pg. 123
DELTAGEN, INC.; *U.S. Public*, pg. 652
DEPLOYABLE SPACE SYSTEMS, INC.—See Redwire Corporation; *U.S. Public*, pg. 1771
DESE RESEARCH INC.; *U.S. Private*, pg. 1211

N.A.I.C.S. INDEX

541715 — RESEARCH AND DEVELO...

D. E. SHAW RESEARCH, LLC—See D. E. Shaw & Co., L.P.; *U.S. Private*, pg. 1139
DESPATCH INDUSTRIES (SHANGHAI) TRADING CO., LTD.—See Illinois Tool Works Inc.; *U.S. Public*, pg. 1102
DESPATCH INDUSTRIES TAIWAN LTD.—See Illinois Tool Works Inc.; *U.S. Public*, pg. 1102
DEVICIX LLC—See Nortech Systems Incorporated; *U.S. Public*, pg. 1536
DIFFUSION PHARMACEUTICALS LLC—See CervoMed Inc.; *U.S. Public*, pg. 476
DIGITAL ARTEFACTS LLC—See GI Manager L.P.; *U.S. Private*, pg. 1692
DISCOVERX CORP.; *U.S. Private*, pg. 1237
DMED BIOPHARMACEUTICAL CO. LTD.; *Int'l*, pg. 2143
DNA CHIP RESEARCH INC.; *Int'l*, pg. 2147
DOCS INTERNATIONAL BELGIUM N.V.—See ICON plc; *Int'l*, pg. 3584
DOCS INTERNATIONAL POLAND SP. Z O.O.—See ICON plc; *Int'l*, pg. 3584
DOCS INTERNATIONAL SWEDEN AB—See ICON plc; *Int'l*, pg. 3584
DONALD DANFORTH PLANT SCIENCE CENTER; *U.S. Private*, pg. 1259
DOTTIKON EXCLUSIVE SYNTHESIS AG—See Dottikon ES Holding AG; *Int'l*, pg. 2180
DREAMCIS INC.—See Hangzhou Tigermed Consulting Co., Ltd.; *Int'l*, pg. 3251
DR. REDDY'S LABORATORIES NEW YORK, INC—See Dr. Reddy's Laboratories Limited; *Int'l*, pg. 2195
DTHERA SCIENCES; *U.S. Public*, pg. 689
DYNETICS INC.—See Leidos Holdings, Inc.; *U.S. Public*, pg. 1304
DZS JAPAN INC—See DZS Inc.; *U.S. Public*, pg. 701
EASTECH INNOVATIONS (TW) INC.—See Eastern Holding Limited; *Int'l*, pg. 2272
EASTECH (SG) PTE. LTD.—See Eastern Holding Limited; *Int'l*, pg. 2272
EAU TECHNOLOGIES, INC.; *U.S. Public*, pg. 709
ECOLAB ARGENTINA S.R.L.—See Ecolab Inc.; *U.S. Public*, pg. 713
ECOLAB ASIA PACIFIC PTE. LTD.—See Ecolab Inc.; *U.S. Public*, pg. 713
ECOLAB MAROC SOCIETE A RESPONSABILITÉ LIMITEE D'ASSOCIE UNIQUE—See Ecolab Inc.; *U.S. Public*, pg. 713
ECOLIVEGREEN CORP.; *U.S. Private*, pg. 1329
ECRI INSTITUTE; *U.S. Private*, pg. 1330
ECZACIBASI MONROL NUKLEER URUNLER SAN. VE TIC. A.S.—See Eczacibasi Holding A.S.; *Int'l*, pg. 2301
EDITAS MEDICINE INC; *U.S. Public*, pg. 719
EDWARDS LIFESCIENCES CORPORATION; *U.S. Public*, pg. 720
EHRFELD MIKROTECHNIK BTS GMBH—See Bayer Aktiengesellschaft; *Int'l*, pg. 906
EISAI CLINICAL RESEARCH SINGAPORE PTE LTD.—See Eisai Co., Ltd.; *Int'l*, pg. 2334
EISAI LTD.—See Eisai Co., Ltd.; *Int'l*, pg. 2335
EISAI R&D MANAGEMENT CO., LTD.—See Eisai Co., Ltd.; *Int'l*, pg. 2335
ELISHA TECHNOLOGIES INC—See Orscheln Group; *U.S. Private*, pg. 3045
ELITE LABORATORIES, INC.—See Elite Pharmaceuticals, Inc.; *U.S. Public*, pg. 734
ELITE RESEARCH, INC.—See Elite Pharmaceuticals, Inc.; *U.S. Public*, pg. 734
ELITISE LLC—See COMSovereign Holding Corp.; *U.S. Public*, pg. 562
ELOXX PHARMACEUTICALS, INC.; *U.S. Public*, pg. 735
EMBRYOME SCIENCES, INC.—See Lineage Cell Therapeutics, Inc.; *U.S. Public*, pg. 1320
EMERGENT PRODUCT DEVELOPMENT GAITHERSBURG INC.—See Emergent BioSolutions Inc.; *U.S. Public*, pg. 740
EMSL ANALYTICAL, INC.; *U.S. Private*, pg. 1388
ENGINEERING RESEARCH & CONSULTING INC.; *U.S. Private*, pg. 1398
ENSCO INC.; *U.S. Private*, pg. 1401
ENTELOS, INC.—See Clearlake Capital Group, L.P.; *U.S. Private*, pg. 934
ENVIRONMENTAL ENERGY SERVICES, INC.; *U.S. Private*, pg. 1407
ENVIRONMENTAL SCIENCE CORP.—See Leonard Green & Partners, L.P.; *U.S. Private*, pg. 2426
ENVIRONMENTAL STRATEGY CONSULTANTS, INC.—See All4 LLC; *U.S. Private*, pg. 174
ENZO LIFE SCIENCES (ELS) AG—See Enzo Biochem Inc.; *U.S. Public*, pg. 782
EP-CRSU CO., LTD.—See EPS Holdings, Inc.; *Int'l*, pg. 2465
EPHRAIM RESOURCES LIMITED; *Int'l*, pg. 2459
EPLAY DIGITAL INC.; *Int'l*, pg. 2463
EPS CHINA CO., LTD.—See EPS Holdings, Inc.; *Int'l*, pg. 2465
EPS TIGERMED (SUZHOU) CO., LTD.—See EPS Holdings, Inc.; *Int'l*, pg. 2465
EP YAMANASHI CO., LTD.—See EPS Holdings, Inc.; *Int'l*, pg. 2465
ESAC, INC.; *U.S. Private*, pg. 1424

ESPERITE N.V.; *Int'l*, pg. 2506
ETHLAB S.R.L.—See Eurotech S.p.A.; *Int'l*, pg. 2558
ETRA INVESTIGACION Y DESARROLLO, S.A.—See ACS, Actividades de Construccion y Servicios, S.A.; *Int'l*, pg. 112
ETR; *U.S. Private*, pg. 1432
EUROBRIDGE CONSULTING BV—See Dr. Reddy's Laboratories Limited; *Int'l*, pg. 2195
EUROFINS AGROSCIENCE SERVICES FRANCE SAS—See Eurofins Scientific S.E.; *Int'l*, pg. 2542
EUROFINS ANALYTICO FOOD BV—See Eurofins Scientific S.E.; *Int'l*, pg. 2537
EUROFINS ANALYTICO—See Eurofins Scientific S.E.; *Int'l*, pg. 2537
EUROFINS CHEMICAL CONTROL SRL—See Eurofins Scientific S.E.; *Int'l*, pg. 2548
EUROFINS CLINICAL GENETICS UK LIMITED—See Eurofins Scientific S.E.; *Int'l*, pg. 2539
EUROFINS C MARK BV—See Eurofins Scientific S.E.; *Int'l*, pg. 2538
EUROFINS EAG HERCULES—See Eurofins Scientific S.E.; *Int'l*, pg. 2549
EUROFINS GENOMICS SAS—See Eurofins Scientific S.E.; *Int'l*, pg. 2542
EUROFINS LANCASTER LABORATORIES, INC.—See Eurofins Scientific S.E.; *Int'l*, pg. 2548
EUROFINS MEDIGENOMIX GMBH—See Eurofins Scientific S.E.; *Int'l*, pg. 2546
EUROFINS MEDINET BV—See Eurofins Scientific S.E.; *Int'l*, pg. 2546
EUROFINS SCIENTIFIC AGROGENE SARL—See Eurofins Scientific S.E.; *Int'l*, pg. 2543
EUROFINS SCIENTIFIC AG—See Eurofins Scientific S.E.; *Int'l*, pg. 2547
EUROFINS SCIENTIFIC INC.—See Eurofins Scientific S.E.; *Int'l*, pg. 2548
EURONAVY - TINTAS MARITIMAS E INDUSTRIAIS S.A.—See The Sherwin-Williams Company; *U.S. Public*, pg. 2127
EUTHYMICS BIOSCIENCE, INC.; *U.S. Private*, pg. 1434
EVERWATCH CORP.—See Booz Allen Hamilton Holding Corporation; *U.S. Public*, pg. 369
EVOLVA BIOTECH PRIVATE LIMITED—See Evolva Holding SA; *Int'l*, pg. 2572
EWOS INNOVATION AS—See Cargill, Inc.; *U.S. Private*, pg. 759
EXACT SCIENCES CORPORATION; *U.S. Public*, pg. 805
EXMOVERE HOLDINGS, INC.; *U.S. Private*, pg. 1449
EXPLORATION & DEVELOPMENT RESEARCH INSTITUTE—See CPC Corporation; *Int'l*, pg. 1823
EXXONMOBIL CORPORATION—See Exxon Mobil Corporation; *U.S. Public*, pg. 815
EXXONMOBIL OIL CORPORATION RESEARCH AND ENGINEERING—See Exxon Mobil Corporation; *U.S. Public*, pg. 815
EXXONMOBIL RESEARCH & ENGINEERING—See Exxon Mobil Corporation; *U.S. Public*, pg. 816
EYETECH INC.—See Bausch Health Companies Inc.; *Int'l*, pg. 898
FAIR ISAAC CORPORATION; *U.S. Public*, pg. 820
FAURECIA GROJEC R&D CENTER SP. ZO.O—See FORVIA SE; *Int'l*, pg. 2746
FCG RESEARCH INSTITUTE, INC.—See Fuji Media Holdings, Inc.; *Int'l*, pg. 2813
FEDERAL-MOGUL TECHNICAL CENTER, LLC—See Apollo Global Management, Inc.; *U.S. Public*, pg. 162
FEDERATION OF AMERICAN SOCIETIES FOR EXPERIMENTAL BIOLOGY; *U.S. Private*, pg. 1492
FERRING RESEARCH INSTITUTE INC.—See Ferring Holding SA; *Int'l*, pg. 2642
FISH VET GROUP NORGE AS—See Zoetis, Inc.; *U.S. Public*, pg. 2409
FOOD ALLERGY RESEARCH & EDUCATION, INC.; *U.S. Private*, pg. 1560
FORTIS LIFE SCIENCES; *U.S. Private*, pg. 1576
FOUNDRY HEALTH, LLC—See IQVIA Holdings Inc.; *U.S. Public*, pg. 1168
FRAUNHOFER-GESELLSCHAFT ZUR FORDERUNG DER ANGEWANDTEN FORSCHUNG E.V.; *Int'l*, pg. 2767
FRAUNHOFER ITALIA RESEARCH KONSORTIALGESELLSCHAFT MBH—See Fraunhofer-Gesellschaft zur Forderung der angewandten Forschung e.V.; *Int'l*, pg. 2767
FRAUNHOFER UK RESEARCH LTD.—See Fraunhofer-Gesellschaft zur Forderung der angewandten Forschung e.V.; *Int'l*, pg. 2767
FRAUNHOFER USA, INC.—See Fraunhofer-Gesellschaft zur Forderung der angewandten Forschung e.V.; *Int'l*, pg. 2767
FREUND PHARMATEC, LTD.—See Freund Corporation; *Int'l*, pg. 2791
FROEHLING & ROBERTSON INC.; *U.S. Private*, pg. 1613
FRONTAGE LABORATORIES (SHANGHAI) CO., LTD.—See Hangzhou Tigermed Consulting Co., Ltd.; *Int'l*, pg. 3251
FRONTIER SCIENTIFIC INC.—See Avista Capital Partners, L.P.; *U.S. Public*, pg. 409
FSBM HOLDINGS BERHAD; *Int'l*, pg. 2798

FUJITSU LABORATORIES OF AMERICA, INC.—See Fujitsu Limited; *Int'l*, pg. 2835
FX PALO ALTO LABORATORY INC.—See FUJIFILM Holdings Corporation; *Int'l*, pg. 2825
GAB FRANCE SARL—See Eurofins Scientific S.E.; *Int'l*, pg. 2543
GALAPAGOS BIOPHARMA AUSTRIA GMBH—See Galapagos N.V.; *Int'l*, pg. 2870
GALAPAGOS BIOPHARMA NORWAY AS—See Galapagos N.V.; *Int'l*, pg. 2870
GALTRONICS CANADA CO., LTD.—See Baylin Technologies Inc.; *Int'l*, pg. 914
GAS TECHNOLOGY INSTITUTE; *U.S. Private*, pg. 1647
GCT RESEARCH, INC.—See GCT Semiconductor Holding, Inc.; *U.S. Public*, pg. 908
GDF GESELLSCHAFT FUR DENTALE FORSCHUNG UND INNOVATIONEN GMBH—See BayernLB Holding AG; *Int'l*, pg. 914
G.E.I.E. NICKERSON INTERNATIONAL RESEARCH—See Groupe Limagrain Holding SA; *Int'l*, pg. 3107
GEL-DEL TECHNOLOGIES INC.—See PetVivo Holdings, Inc.; *U.S. Public*, pg. 1679
GENEFIC—See Dalrada Financial Corporation; *U.S. Public*, pg. 621
GENERA ENERGY, LLC—See Ara Partners Group; *U.S. Private*, pg. 306
GENESEEK, INC.—See Neogen Corporation; *U.S. Public*, pg. 1505
GENE SHEARS—See Groupe Limagrain Holding SA; *Int'l*, pg. 3107
GENESIS RESEARCH & DEVELOPMENT CORPORATION LIMITED; *Int'l*, pg. 2921
GENETIC TECHNOLOGIES LIMITED; *Int'l*, pg. 2922
GENETIX GMBH—See Danaher Corporation; *U.S. Public*, pg. 627
THE GENEVA FOUNDATION; *U.S. Private*, pg. 4032
GENEWIZ, INC.—See Azenta, Inc.; *U.S. Public*, pg. 258
GENEZEN LABORATORIES INC.—See Ampersand Management LLC; *U.S. Private*, pg. 265
GENINCODE U.S. INC.—See GENinCode Plc; *Int'l*, pg. 2924
GENOMIC HEALTH, INC.—See Exact Sciences Corporation; *U.S. Public*, pg. 805
GENOPTIX, INC.—See NeoGenomics, Inc.; *U.S. Public*, pg. 1505
GEN-PROBE INCORPORATED—See Hologic, Inc.; *U.S. Public*, pg. 1044
GENSCRIPT BIOTECH CORPORATION; *Int'l*, pg. 2927
GENSCRIPT JAPAN INC.—See GenScript Biotech Corporation; *Int'l*, pg. 2927
GEORGIA-PACIFIC RESINS, INC.—See Koch Industries, Inc.; *U.S. Private*, pg. 2329
GIANT MAGELLAN TELESCOPE ORGANIZATION; *U.S. Private*, pg. 1695
GLAXOSMITHKLINE BIOLOGICALS MANUFACTURING S.A.—See GSK plc; *Int'l*, pg. 3146
GLAXOSMITHKLINE BIOLOGICALS S.A.—See GSK plc; *Int'l*, pg. 3146
GLAXOSMITHKLINE BIOLOGICALS (SHANGHAI) LTD—See GSK plc; *Int'l*, pg. 3146
GLAXOSMITHKLINE (CHINA) R&D CO., LTD.—See GSK plc; *Int'l*, pg. 3146
GLAXOSMITHKLINE RESEARCH & DEVELOPMENT LTD.—See GSK plc; *Int'l*, pg. 3148
GLENMARK PHARMACEUTICALS S.A.—See Glenmark Pharmaceuticals Limited; *Int'l*, pg. 2992
GLOBAL PHOTONIC ENERGY CORPORATION—See NanoFlex Power Corporation; *U.S. Public*, pg. 1490
GOLDEN WHEAT (NANJING) INTERNATIONAL TRADE CO., LTD.—See Anhui Jinhe Industrial Co., Ltd.; *Int'l*, pg. 468
GP INSPECT GMBH—See centrotherm photovoltaics AG; *Int'l*, pg. 1415
GREAT LAKES FISHERY COMMISSION; *U.S. Private*, pg. 1764
GREAVES TECHNOLOGIES INC.—See Greaves Cotton Ltd; *Int'l*, pg. 3068
GRIFOLS BIOLOGICALS, INC.—See Grifols, S.A.; *Int'l*, pg. 3084
GRIFOLS DEUTSCHLAND GMBH—See Grifols, S.A.; *Int'l*, pg. 3084
GRITSTONE BIO, INC.; *U.S. Public*, pg. 970
GROUPE LIMAGRAIN, PARIS OFFICE—See Groupe Limagrain Holding SA; *Int'l*, pg. 3107
GSK MACEDONIA—See GSK plc; *Int'l*, pg. 3145
GSK UZBEKISTAN—See GSK plc; *Int'l*, pg. 3145
GUANGDONG AUTOMOTIVE TEST CENTER CO., LTD.—See China Automotive Engineering Research Institute Co., Ltd.; *Int'l*, pg. 1484
THE HAMNER INSTITUTES FOR HEALTH SCIENCES; *U.S. Private*, pg. 4042
HANGZHOU SIMO CO., LTD.—See Hangzhou Tigermed Consulting Co., Ltd.; *Int'l*, pg. 3251
HANGZHOU TIGERMED CONSULTING CO., LTD.; *Int'l*, pg. 3250
HAOHUA CHEMICAL SCIENCE & TECHNOLOGY CORP.—See China National Chemical Corporation; *Int'l*, pg. 1526

541715 — RESEARCH AND DEVELO...

HAPPYNEURON SAS; *Int'l*, pg. 3269
HARBIN TIAN DI REN MEDICAL SCIENCE AND TECHNOLOGY COMPANY—See China Sky One Medical, Inc.; *Int'l*, pg. 1552
HAUPT PHARMA DEVELOPMENT GMBH—See BC Partners LLP; *Int'l*, pg. 922
HEALTH DIALOG ANALYTIC SOLUTIONS CORP.—See New Rite Aid, LLC; *U.S. Private*, pg. 2905
HEIDELBERG PHARMA AG; *Int'l*, pg. 3321
HEKTOEN INSTITUTE, LLC.; *U.S. Private*, pg. 1905
HELMHOLTZ-ZENTRUM HEREON; *Int'l*, pg. 3338
HELSINKI MEMORY TECHNOLOGIES OY—See Pendrell Corporation; *U.S. Public*, pg. 1661
HENAN JAKE NEW MATERIAL CO., LTD.—See Henan Shijia Photons Technology Co., Ltd.; *Int'l*, pg. 3343
HENAN SHIJIA COMMUNICATION TECHNOLOGY CO., LTD.—See Henan Shijia Photons Technology Co., Ltd.; *Int'l*, pg. 3343
HENAN SHIJIA ELECTRONIC TECHNOLOGY CO., LTD.—See Henan Shijia Photons Technology Co., Ltd.; *Int'l*, pg. 3343
HENAN SHIJIA OPTOELECTRONIC DEVICES CO., LTD.—See Henan Shijia Photons Technology Co., Ltd.; *Int'l*, pg. 3343
HENDRICKSON TRAILER COMMERCIAL VEHICLE SYSTEMS—See The Boler Company; *U.S. Private*, pg. 3996
HERMES-MICROVISION, INC.—See ASML Holding N.V.; *Int'l*, pg. 628
HEXCEL CORP. - DUBLIN—See Hexcel Corporation; *U.S. Public*, pg. 1033
HEXIMA LIMITED; *Int'l*, pg. 3371
HEXIS AG; *Int'l*, pg. 3371
HIGH VOLTAGE MAINTENANCE CORP.—See Emerson Electric Co.; *U.S. Public*, pg. 748
HISTOTOX LABS, INC.—See Inotiv, Inc.; *U.S. Public*, pg. 1128
HLB BIOSTEP CO., LTD.; *Int'l*, pg. 3430
HLH AGRI R&D PTE LTD—See Hong Lai Huat Group Limited; *Int'l*, pg. 3467
HM.CLAUSE ITALIA S.P.A.—See Groupe Limagrain Holding SA; *Int'l*, pg. 3108
HONDA R & D ASIA PACIFIC CO., LTD.—See Honda Motor Co., Ltd.; *Int'l*, pg. 3462
HONDA R & D EUROPE (U.K.) LTD.—See Honda Motor Co., Ltd.; *Int'l*, pg. 3462
HONDA R & D (INDIA) PVT. LTD.—See Honda Motor Co., Ltd.; *Int'l*, pg. 3462
HONDA R & D SOUTHEAST ASIA CO., LTD. (HRS)—See Honda Motor Co., Ltd.; *Int'l*, pg. 3462
HONDA RESEARCH INSTITUTE EUROPE G.M.B.H—See Honda Motor Co., Ltd.; *Int'l*, pg. 3462
HONDA RESEARCH INSTITUTE JAPAN CO., LTD.—See Honda Motor Co., Ltd.; *Int'l*, pg. 3462
HONDA RESEARCH INSTITUTE USA, INC.—See Honda Motor Co., Ltd.; *Int'l*, pg. 3462
H-PHAR SA—See Floridienne SA; *Int'l*, pg. 2708
HTE GMBH—See BASF SE; *Int'l*, pg. 886
HUALAN BIOLOGICAL ENGINEERING INC.; *Int'l*, pg. 3512
HUNAN COPOTE SCIENCE & TECHNOLOGY CO., LTD.; *Int'l*, pg. 3531
HUNTINGDON LIFE SCIENCES GROUP PLC—See Life Sciences Research, Inc.; *U.S. Private*, pg. 2449
HUP SOON GLOBAL CORPORATION LIMITED; *Int'l*, pg. 3538
HYBRIGENICS PHARMA—See Diagnostic Medical Systems S.A.; *Int'l*, pg. 2103
HYDROMER, INC.; *U.S. Public*, pg. 1079
HYUNDAI MOTOR JAPAN R&D CENTER INC.—See Hyundai Motor Company; *Int'l*, pg. 3559
IBEX PRECLINICAL RESEARCH, INC.—See JP Lawrence Biomedical, Inc.; *U.S. Private*, pg. 2239
ICON ANKARA KLINIK ARASTIRMA DIS TICARET ANONIM SIRKETI—See ICON plc; *Int'l*, pg. 3584
ICON BIOSCIENCE INC.—See EyePoint Pharmaceuticals, Inc.; *U.S. Public*, pg. 817
ICON CLINICAL RESEARCH AUSTRIA GMBH—See ICON plc; *Int'l*, pg. 3584
ICON CLINICAL RESEARCH (CANADA) INC.—See ICON plc; *Int'l*, pg. 3584
ICON CLINICAL RESEARCH D.O.O.—See ICON plc; *Int'l*, pg. 3585
ICON CLINICAL RESEARCH EOOD—See ICON plc; *Int'l*, pg. 3584
ICON CLINICAL RESEARCH ESPANA S.L—See ICON plc; *Int'l*, pg. 3584
ICON CLINICAL RESEARCH GMBH—See ICON plc; *Int'l*, pg. 3584
ICON CLINICAL RESEARCH INC—See ICON plc; *Int'l*, pg. 3584
ICON CLINICAL RESEARCH INDIA PRIVATE LIMITED—See ICON plc; *Int'l*, pg. 3584
ICON CLINICAL RESEARCH ISRAEL LIMITED—See ICON plc; *Int'l*, pg. 3585
ICON CLINICAL RESEARCH MEXICO, S.A. DE C.V.—See ICON plc; *Int'l*, pg. 3585
ICON CLINICAL RESEARCH (NEW ZEALAND) LIMITED—See ICON plc; *Int'l*, pg. 3584
ICON CLINICAL RESEARCH PERU S.A.—See ICON plc; *Int'l*, pg. 3585
ICON CLINICAL RESEARCH PTE LTD—See ICON plc; *Int'l*, pg. 3585
ICON CLINICAL RESEARCH PTY LIMITED—See ICON plc; *Int'l*, pg. 3585
ICON CLINICAL RESEARCH (RUS) LLC—See ICON plc; *Int'l*, pg. 3584
ICON CLINICAL RESEARCH RUSSIA OOO—See ICON plc; *Int'l*, pg. 3585
ICON CLINICAL RESEARCH SARL—See ICON plc; *Int'l*, pg. 3585
ICON CLINICAL RESEARCH S.A.—See ICON plc; *Int'l*, pg. 3585
ICON CLINICAL RESEARCH SERVICES PHILIPPINES, INC.—See ICON plc; *Int'l*, pg. 3585
ICON CLINICAL RESEARCH SLOVAKIA, S.R.O.—See ICON plc; *Int'l*, pg. 3585
ICON CLINICAL RESEARCH S.R.L.—See ICON plc; *Int'l*, pg. 3585
ICON CLINICAL RESEARCH S.R.O.—See ICON plc; *Int'l*, pg. 3585
ICON CLINICAL RESEARCH (SWITZERLAND) GMBH—See ICON plc; *Int'l*, pg. 3584
ICON CLINICAL RESEARCH TAIWAN LIMITED—See ICON plc; *Int'l*, pg. 3585
ICON CLINICAL RESEARCH (THAILAND) LIMITED—See ICON plc; *Int'l*, pg. 3584
ICON CLINICAL RESEARCH (UK) LIMITED—See ICON plc; *Int'l*, pg. 3584
ICON CONTRACTING SOLUTIONS HOLDINGS B.V.—See ICON plc; *Int'l*, pg. 3585
ICON DEVELOPMENT SOLUTIONS LIMITED—See ICON plc; *Int'l*, pg. 3585
ICON EARLY PHASE SERVICES, LLC—See ICON plc; *Int'l*, pg. 3585
ICON JAPAN K.K.—See ICON plc; *Int'l*, pg. 3585
ICON KLINIKAI KUTATO KORLATOLT FELELOSSEGU TARSASAG—See ICON plc; *Int'l*, pg. 3585
ICON LABORATORY SERVICES, INC.—See ICON plc; *Int'l*, pg. 3585
ICON LIFE SCIENCES CANADA INC.—See ICON plc; *Int'l*, pg. 3585
ICON PLC; *Int'l*, pg. 3583
IDEXX LABORATORIES NORGE AS—See IDEXX Laboratories, Inc.; *U.S. Public*, pg. 1092
IDEXX LABORATORIES SINGAPORE PTE, LTD.—See IDEXX Laboratories, Inc.; *U.S. Public*, pg. 1093
IDORSIA PHARMACEUTICALS JAPAN LTD.—See Idorsia Ltd.; *Int'l*, pg. 3595
IFEG SAS—See Eurofins Scientific S.E.; *Int'l*, pg. 2543
IFP ENERGIES NOUVELLES - LYON SITE—See IFP Energies Nouvelles; *Int'l*, pg. 3599
IFP ENERGIES NOUVELLES; *Int'l*, pg. 3599
IGEA PHARMA N.V.; *Int'l*, pg. 3602
II-VI ADVANCED MATERIALS DEVELOPMENT CENTER—See Coherent Corp.; *U.S. Public*, pg. 528
II-VI TECHNOLOGIES (BEIJING) CO., LTD.—See Coherent Corp.; *U.S. Public*, pg. 529
ILIKA PLC; *Int'l*, pg. 3614
IMMUNKEMI F&D AB—See Addtech AB; *Int'l*, pg. 133
IMMUNOCHEMISTRY TECHNOLOGIES, LLC—See Janel Corporation; *U.S. Public*, pg. 1187
IMMUNO DIAGNOSTIC OY—See Addtech AB; *Int'l*, pg. 134
IMPERIAL OIL LIMITED—See Exxon Mobil Corporation; *U.S. Public*, pg. 816
I.M.P. RESEARCH INSTITUTE OF MOLECULAR PATHOLOGY—See C.H. Boehringer Sohn AG & Co. KG; *Int'l*, pg. 1241
IMUGEN, INC.—See Revvity, Inc.; *U.S. Public*, pg. 1794
INC RESEARCH - GLOBAL CLINICAL DEVELOPMENT—See Elliott Management Corporation; *U.S. Private*, pg. 1365
INC RESEARCH - GLOBAL CLINICAL DEVELOPMENT—See Patient Square Capital, L.P.; *U.S. Private*, pg. 3108
INC RESEARCH - GLOBAL CLINICAL DEVELOPMENT—See Veritas Capital Fund Management, LLC; *U.S. Private*, pg. 4365
INC RESEARCH, LLC—See Elliott Management Corporation; *U.S. Private*, pg. 1365
INC RESEARCH, LLC—See Patient Square Capital, L.P.; *U.S. Private*, pg. 3108
INC RESEARCH, LLC—See Veritas Capital Fund Management, LLC; *U.S. Private*, pg. 4364
INC RESEARCH - MUNICH—See Elliott Management Corporation; *U.S. Private*, pg. 1365
INC RESEARCH - MUNICH—See Patient Square Capital, L.P.; *U.S. Private*, pg. 3108
INC RESEARCH - MUNICH—See Veritas Capital Fund Management, LLC; *U.S. Private*, pg. 4365
INC RESEARCH - SARONNO—See Elliott Management Corporation; *U.S. Private*, pg. 1365
INC RESEARCH - SARONNO—See Patient Square Capital, L.P.; *U.S. Private*, pg. 3108
INC RESEARCH - SARONNO—See Veritas Capital Fund Management, LLC; *U.S. Private*, pg. 4365
INC RESEARCH—See Elliott Management Corporation; *U.S. Private*, pg. 1365
INC RESEARCH—See Elliott Management Corporation; *U.S. Private*, pg. 1365
INC RESEARCH—See Elliott Management Corporation; *U.S. Private*, pg. 1365
INC RESEARCH—See Patient Square Capital, L.P.; *U.S. Private*, pg. 3108
INC RESEARCH—See Patient Square Capital, L.P.; *U.S. Private*, pg. 3108
INC RESEARCH—See Patient Square Capital, L.P.; *U.S. Private*, pg. 3108
INC RESEARCH—See Veritas Capital Fund Management, LLC; *U.S. Private*, pg. 4364
INC RESEARCH—See Veritas Capital Fund Management, LLC; *U.S. Private*, pg. 4365
INC RESEARCH—See Veritas Capital Fund Management, LLC; *U.S. Private*, pg. 4365
INCYTE CORPORATION; *U.S. Public*, pg. 1114
INFORMATION VISUALIZATION AND INNOVATIVE RESEARCH INC.; *U.S. Private*, pg. 2073
INGRAM MICRO LEVANT S.A.L.—See Hainan Traffic Administration Holding Co., Ltd.; *Int'l*, pg. 3214
INHIBITOR THERAPEUTICS, INC.; *U.S. Public*, pg. 1124
INOTIV, INC.; *U.S. Public*, pg. 1128
INSTITUTE FOR PHYSICAL SCIENCE, INC.; *U.S. Private*, pg. 2093
INSTITUTE FOR SYSTEMS BIOLOGY—See Providence St. Joseph Health; *U.S. Private*, pg. 3294
INSTITUTO GRIFOLS, S.A.—See Grifols, S.A.; *Int'l*, pg. 3085
INSTITUT PROF. DR. JAGER GMBH—See Eurofins Scientific S.E.; *Int'l*, pg. 2550
INTEGRATED DEVELOPMENT ASSOCIATES CO., LTD.—See Laboratory Corporation of America Holdings; *U.S. Public*, pg. 1287
INTEGRATED DEVELOPMENT ASSOCIATES PHILIPPINES, INC.—See Laboratory Corporation of America Holdings; *U.S. Public*, pg. 1287
INTEGRATED LAB SYSTEMS INC.; *U.S. Private*, pg. 2100
INTELLIA THERAPEUTICS, INC.; *U.S. Public*, pg. 1139
INTELLIGENT MICRO PATTERNING, LLC; *U.S. Private*, pg. 2106
INTER-COASTAL ELECTRONICS, LLC—See Greenbriar Equity Group, L.P.; *U.S. Private*, pg. 1775
INTERNATIONAL ONCOLOGY NETWORK, LLC—See Cencora, Inc.; *U.S. Public*, pg. 467
INTROTEK INTERNATIONAL—See AMETEK, Inc.; *U.S. Public*, pg. 121
INW MANUFACTURING LLC—See Cornell Capital LLC; *U.S. Private*, pg. 1051
ION TORRENT SYSTEMS, INC.—See Thermo Fisher Scientific Inc.; *U.S. Public*, pg. 2149
IPCREATE INC.; *U.S. Private*, pg. 2136
IPG (BEIJING) FIBER LASER TECHNOLOGY CO., LTD.—See IPG Photonics Corporation; *U.S. Public*, pg. 1167
IPSOTEK LTD.—See Atos SE; *Int'l*, pg. 692
IQVIA RDS AG—See IQVIA Holdings Inc.; *U.S. Public*, pg. 1170
IQVIA RDS AND INTEGRATED SERVICES BELGIUM NV—See IQVIA Holdings Inc.; *U.S. Public*, pg. 1170
IQVIA RDS ESTONIA OU—See IQVIA Holdings Inc.; *U.S. Public*, pg. 1170
IQVIA RDS FRANCE SAS—See IQVIA Holdings Inc.; *U.S. Public*, pg. 1170
IQVIA RDS GES.M.B.H—See IQVIA Holdings Inc.; *U.S. Public*, pg. 1170
IQVIA RDS IRELAND LIMITED—See IQVIA Holdings Inc.; *U.S. Public*, pg. 1170
IQVIA RDS MAGYARORSZAG GYOGYSZERFEJLESZTESI ES TANACSADO KFT.—See IQVIA Holdings Inc.; *U.S. Public*, pg. 1170
IQVIA RDS PTY. LIMITED—See IQVIA Holdings Inc.; *U.S. Public*, pg. 1170
IQVIA ROMANIA S.R.L.—See IQVIA Holdings Inc.; *U.S. Public*, pg. 1169
IQVIA TECHNOLOGY SOLUTIONS UKRAINE LLC—See IQVIA Holdings Inc.; *U.S. Public*, pg. 1170
IRON SOLUTIONS, INC.—See Trimble, Inc.; *U.S. Public*, pg. 2190
ISTO BIOLOGICS, INC.—See Thompson Street Capital Manager LLC; *U.S. Private*, pg. 4161
ITRONICS INC.; *U.S. Public*, pg. 1176
ITT CORP. - NEWTON—See ITT Inc.; *U.S. Public*, pg. 1178
THE JACKSON LABORATORY; *U.S. Private*, pg. 4058
JANX INTEGRITY GROUP, INC.—See I Squared Capital Advisors (US) LLC; *U.S. Private*, pg. 2022
JIAXING CLINFLASH COMPUTER TECHNOLOGY CO., LTD.—See Hangzhou Tigermed Consulting Co., Ltd.; *Int'l*, pg. 3251
JMAR RESEARCH, INC.—See JMAR, LLC; *U.S. Private*, pg. 2214
JOHNSON & JOHNSON PHARMACEUTICAL RESEARCH & DEVELOPMENT, LLC—See Johnson & Johnson; *U.S. Public*, pg. 1199
JOINT RESEARCH & DEVELOPMENT, INC.—See Broadtree Partners, LLC; *U.S. Private*, pg. 659

N.A.I.C.S. INDEX
541715 — RESEARCH AND DEVELO...

JSS MEDICAL RESEARCH, INC.—See Genesis Biotechnology Group, LLC; *U.S. Private*, pg. 1669
K2M, INC.—See Stryker Corporation; *U.S. Public*, pg. 1955
KAI PHARMACEUTICALS, INC.—See Amgen Inc.; *U.S. Public*, pg. 123
KAN RESEARCH INSTITUTE, INC.—See Eisai Co., Ltd.; *Int'l*, pg. 2335
KARADA LAB, INC.—See ARKRAY, Inc.; *Int'l*, pg. 572
KBM ENTERPRISES INC.; *U.S. Private*, pg. 2268
KDR BIOTECH CO LTD.—See Thermo Fisher Scientific Inc.; *U.S. Public*, pg. 2149
KEDDEM BIOSCIENCE LTD.—See Compugen Ltd.; *Int'l*, pg. 1755
KEMIS BH D.O.O.—See Hisense Co., Ltd.; *Int'l*, pg. 3407
KINEMED, INC.; *U.S. Private*, pg. 2307
KITASATO DAIICHI SANKYO VACCINE CO., LTD.—See Daiichi Sankyo Co., Ltd.; *Int'l*, pg. 1930
KJT GROUP, INC.; *U.S. Private*, pg. 2317
KNEXUS RESEARCH CORP.—See Lurie Investments, Inc; *U.S. Private*, pg. 2516
KORR MEDICAL TECHNOLOGIES INC.; *U.S. Private*, pg. 2344
KRAIG BIOCRAFT LABORATORIES, INC.; *U.S. Public*, pg. 1275
KYUDO CO., LTD.—See Central Institute for Experimental Animals; *Int'l*, pg. 1408
LABOPHARM EUROPE LIMITED—See Endo International plc; *Int'l*, pg. 2404
LABORATORIOS FARMACEUTICOS DE NICARAGUA, S.A.—See GSK plc; *Int'l*, pg. 3149
LABORELEC C.V.—See ENGIE SA; *Int'l*, pg. 2431
LABOR TRES LABORATORIOS E CONSULTORIA TECNICA LTDA.—See Eurofins Scientific S.E.; *Int'l*, pg. 2550
LAFARGE SERVICE GROUP - R&D CENTER LYON—See Holcim Ltd.; *Int'l*, pg. 3449
LAXAI PHARMA, LTD.; *U.S. Private*, pg. 2402
LEGEND BIOTECH USA INCORPORATED—See Legend Biotech Corporation; *U.S. Public*, pg. 1301
LEIDOS BIOMEDICAL RESEARCH, INC.—See Leidos Holdings, Inc.; *U.S. Public*, pg. 1304
LEIDOS ENGINEERING—See Leidos Holdings, Inc.; *U.S. Public*, pg. 1304
LEIDOS ENGINEERING—See Leidos Holdings, Inc.; *U.S. Public*, pg. 1304
LIFEBANKUSA—See Human Longevity, Inc.; *U.S. Private*, pg. 2005
LIFEMAP SCIENCES, LTD.—See Lineage Cell Therapeutics, Inc.; *U.S. Public*, pg. 1320
LIFE SCIENCES RESEARCH, INC.; *U.S. Private*, pg. 2449
LIFESOURCE BIOMEDICAL, LLC—See Gold Belt Incorporated; *U.S. Private*, pg. 1727
LIFE TECHNOLOGIES CHILE SPA—See Thermo Fisher Scientific Inc.; *U.S. Public*, pg. 2148
LIFE TECHNOLOGIES KOREA LLC—See Thermo Fisher Scientific Inc.; *U.S. Public*, pg. 2149
LIGHT SCIENCES ONCOLOGY, INC.; *U.S. Private*, pg. 2452
LIMAGRAIN GENETICS GRANDES CULTURES S.A.—See Groupe Limagrain Holding SA; *Int'l*, pg. 3107
LIONS EYE INSTITUTE FOR TRANSPLANT & RESEARCH, INC.; *U.S. Private*, pg. 2464
LIQUIDIA TECHNOLOGIES, INC.; *U.S. Public*, pg. 1320
LOADPATH, LLC—See Redwire Corporation; *U.S. Public*, pg. 1771
LOVELACE RESPIRATORY RESEARCH INSTITUTE; *U.S. Private*, pg. 2501
LUNA INNOVATIONS INCORPORATED; *U.S. Public*, pg. 1348
LUPUS FOUNDATION OF AMERICA, INC.; *U.S. Private*, pg. 2515
LYLLY CENTRE FOR CLINICAL PHARMACOLOGY PTE. LTD.—See Eli Lilly & Company; *U.S. Public*, pg. 734
LYPRO BIOSCIENCES, INC.—See Abionyx Pharma SA; *Int'l*, pg. 62
MACROSTAT (CHINA) CLINICAL RESEARCH CO., LTD.—See Hangzhou Tigermed Consulting Co., Ltd.; *Int'l*, pg. 3251
MANNKIND BIOPHARMACEUTICALS—See MannKind Corporation; *U.S. Public*, pg. 1357
MANTECH ENVIRONMENTAL RESEARCH SERVICES CORP.—See The Carlyle Group Inc.; *U.S. Public*, pg. 2048
MAPI LIFE SCIENCES SINGAPORE PTE. LTD.—See ICON plc; *Int'l*, pg. 3585
MARAVAI LIFESCIENCES, INC.; *U.S. Private*, pg. 2570
MARKET RESEARCH FOUNDATION; *U.S. Private*, pg. 2579
MARODYNE MEDICAL, LLC; *U.S. Public*, pg. 2586
MARSHALL UNIVERSITY RESEARCH CORP.; *U.S. Private*, pg. 2593
MASONITE CORP. - WEST CHICAGO—See Owens Corning; *U.S. Public*, pg. 1627
MASSACHUSETTS GREEN HIGH PERFORMANCE COMPUTING CENTER INC.; *U.S. Private*, pg. 2603
MAX PLANCK FLORIDA CORPORATION; *U.S. Private*, pg. 2617
MAYA DESIGN, INC.—See The Boston Consulting Group, Inc.; *U.S. Private*, pg. 3997

MD BIOSCIENCES, INC.—See Great Point Partners, LLC; *U.S. Private*, pg. 1767
MDECHEM, INC.; *U.S. Public*, pg. 1409
MEASUREMENT ANALYSIS CORP.; *U.S. Private*, pg. 2648
MECHALESS GMBH—See ELMOS Semiconductor AG; *Int'l*, pg. 2368
MEDGENICS MEDICAL (ISRAEL) LIMITED—See Avalo Therapeutics, Inc.; *U.S. Public*, pg. 239
MEDICAL ENGINEERING & DEVELOPMENT INSTITUTE, INC.—See Cook Group Incorporated; *U.S. Private*, pg. 1037
MEDINET INTERNATIONAL BV—See Eurofins Scientific S.E.; *Int'l*, pg. 2551
MEDISYS HEALTH COMMUNICATIONS, LLC; *U.S. Private*, pg. 2657
MEDPACE AUSTRALIA PTY. LTD.—See Cinven Limited; *Int'l*, pg. 1612
MEDPACE BELGIUM BVBA—See Cinven Limited; *Int'l*, pg. 1612
MEDPACE BRAZIL LTDA.—See Cinven Limited; *Int'l*, pg. 1612
MEDPACE CLINICAL RESEARCH INDIA PVT. LTD.—See Cinven Limited; *Int'l*, pg. 1612
MEDPACE EUROPE B.V.—See Cinven Limited; *Int'l*, pg. 1612
MEDPACE GERMANY GMBH—See Cinven Limited; *Int'l*, pg. 1612
MEDPACE HONG KONG LTD.—See Cinven Limited; *Int'l*, pg. 1612
MEDPACE HUNGARY KFT.—See Cinven Limited; *Int'l*, pg. 1612
MEDPACE, INC.—See Cinven Limited; *Int'l*, pg. 1612
MEDPACE ITALY SRL—See Cinven Limited; *Int'l*, pg. 1612
MEDPACE RUSSIA LLC—See Cinven Limited; *Int'l*, pg. 1612
MEDPACE SOUTH AFRICA PTY. LTD.—See Cinven Limited; *Int'l*, pg. 1612
MEDPACE TAIWAN LTD.—See Cinven Limited; *Int'l*, pg. 1612
MEDPASS INTERNATIONAL SAS—See ICON plc; *Int'l*, pg. 3585
MEMRB PULS PANEL TRGOVINA DOO—See Brookfield Corporation; *Int'l*, pg. 1178
MEMRB PULS PANEL TRGOVINA DOO—See Elliott Management Corporation; *U.S. Private*, pg. 1371
MERCK BIOLOGICS RESEARCH CENTER—See Merck & Co., Inc.; *U.S. Public*, pg. 1419
MERCK RESEARCH LABORATORIES—See Merck & Co., Inc.; *U.S. Public*, pg. 1419
MERCK SHARP & DOHME LIMITED—See Merck & Co., Inc.; *U.S. Public*, pg. 1420
MERRICK'S ANIMAL HEALTH, LLC—See Vets Plus, Inc.; *U.S. Private*, pg. 4374
MET LABORATORIES INC.; *U.S. Private*, pg. 2679
MICHELIN AMERICAS RESEARCH & DEVELOPMENT—See Compagnie Generale des Etablissements Michelin SCA; *Int'l*, pg. 1744
MICROBAC LABORATORIES, INC.; *U.S. Private*, pg. 2702
MICROBOT MEDICAL INC.; *U.S. Public*, pg. 1436
MICROMILL ELECTRONICS LIMITED—See Advent International Corporation; *U.S. Private*, pg. 100
MICROSOFT - HAIFA R&D CENTER—See Microsoft Corporation; *U.S. Public*, pg. 1440
MICROSOFT - HERZLIYYA R&D CENTER—See Microsoft Corporation; *U.S. Public*, pg. 1440
MICROTEL LLC—See Arlington Capital Partners LLC; *U.S. Private*, pg. 328
MID-AMERICA CAPITAL RESOURCES, INC.—See The AES Corporation; *U.S. Public*, pg. 2032
MINNEAPOLIS MEDICAL RESEARCH FOUNDATION, INC.—See Hennepin Healthcare System, Inc.; *U.S. Private*, pg. 1916
THE MITRE CORPORATION; *U.S. Private*, pg. 4080
THE MITRE CORPORATION; *U.S. Private*, pg. 4080
MODALITY SOLUTIONS, LLC—See Renovus Capital Partners; *U.S. Private*, pg. 3399
MOLECULAR IMAGING INDUSTRY AND TRADING CO. INC.—See Bozlu Holding; *Int'l*, pg. 1125
MOLECULAR TEMPLATES INC.; *U.S. Public*, pg. 1458
MOLECULIN BIOTECH, INC.; *U.S. Public*, pg. 1458
MOMENTA PHARMACEUTICALS, INC.—See Johnson & Johnson; *U.S. Public*, pg. 1197
MONSANTO CO. - DAYTON—See Bayer Aktiengesellschaft; *Int'l*, pg. 908
MONSANTO CO. - GLYNDON—See Bayer Aktiengesellschaft; *Int'l*, pg. 908
MONSANTO CO. - LOXLEY AGRONOMY CENTER—See Bayer Aktiengesellschaft; *Int'l*, pg. 908
MONSANTO CO. - MONMOUTH AGRONOMY CENTER—See Bayer Aktiengesellschaft; *Int'l*, pg. 908
MONSANTO CO. - OLIVIA—See Bayer Aktiengesellschaft; *Int'l*, pg. 909
MONSANTO CO. - PARKERSBURG FOUNDATION—See Bayer Aktiengesellschaft; *Int'l*, pg. 909
MONSANTO CO. - STUTTGART—See Bayer Aktiengesellschaft; *Int'l*, pg. 909
MONSANTO CO. - WATERMAN SEED TECHNOLOGY CENTER—See Bayer Aktiengesellschaft; *Int'l*, pg. 909

MONSANTO SAS—See Bayer Aktiengesellschaft; *Int'l*, pg. 909
MONTANA ECONOMIC REVITALIZATION & DEVELOPMENT INSTITUTE INC.; *U.S. Private*, pg. 2775
MORPHOTEK, INC.—See Eisai Co., Ltd.; *Int'l*, pg. 2335
MOUNT DESERT ISLAND BIOLOGICAL LABORATORY; *U.S. Private*, pg. 2798
MSD OSS—See Merck & Co., Inc.; *U.S. Public*, pg. 1420
MSD PHARMACEUTICALS PRIVATE LIMITED—See Merck & Co., Inc.; *U.S. Public*, pg. 1418
MSE TECHNOLOGY APPLICATIONS INC.—See Montana Economic Revitalization & Development Institute Inc.; *U.S. Private*, pg. 2775
MV GENETIX GMBH—See Eurofins Scientific S.E.; *Int'l*, pg. 2551
MYDX, INC.; *U.S. Private*, pg. 2824
MYRIAD GENETICS LTD—See Myriad Genetics, Inc.; *U.S. Public*, pg. 1489
NANJING BAOCHUN CHEMICAL INDUSTRY CO., LTD.—See Hongbaoli Group Co., Ltd; *Int'l*, pg. 3469
NANJING HBL INTERNATIONAL CO., LTD.—See Hongbaoli Group Co., Ltd; *Int'l*, pg. 3469
NANOAL LLC—See Unity Aluminum, Inc.; *U.S. Private*, pg. 4302
NANOTHERAPEUTICS, INC.; *U.S. Private*, pg. 2833
NATIONAL ACADEMY OF SCIENCES; *U.S. Private*, pg. 2839
NATIONAL CENTER FOR MANUFACTURING SCIENCES INC.; *U.S. Private*, pg. 2850
NATIONAL DEVELOPMENT & RESEARCH INSTITUTES, INC.; *U.S. Private*, pg. 2852
NATIONAL HEALTHCARE RESEARCH & EDUCATION FINANCE CORPORATION; *U.S. Private*, pg. 2856
NATIONAL INSTITUTE OF AEROSPACE; *U.S. Private*, pg. 2856
NATIONAL RESEARCH CORPORATION CANADA—See National Research Corporation; *U.S. Public*, pg. 1497
NATIONAL RESEARCH CORPORATION; *U.S. Public*, pg. 1497
NATIONAL SCIENCE TEACHERS ASSOCIATION; *U.S. Private*, pg. 2863
NATIONAL TECHNICAL SYSTEMS, INC. - DETROIT—See Aurora Capital Group, LLC; *U.S. Private*, pg. 393
NATIONAL TECHNICAL SYSTEMS, INC. - FULLERTON—See Aurora Capital Group, LLC; *U.S. Private*, pg. 393
NATIONAL TECHNICAL SYSTEMS, INC. - LOS ANGELES—See Aurora Capital Group, LLC; *U.S. Private*, pg. 393
NATURAL GAS TECHNOLOGY CENTRE—See Caisse de Depot et Placement du Quebec; *Int'l*, pg. 1256
ND COMPOUND BLENDING DIVISION/TEXAS—See H.B. Fuller Company; *U.S. Public*, pg. 978
NEAR EARTH AUTONOMY, INC.; *U.S. Private*, pg. 2877
NEBRASKA SOYBEAN BOARD; *U.S. Private*, pg. 2879
NEKTAR THERAPEUTICS (INDIA) PVT. LTD.—See Nektar Therapeutics; *U.S. Public*, pg. 1504
NELSON LABORATORIES FAIRFIELD, INC.—See Sotera Health Company; *U.S. Public*, pg. 1909
NEOMAGIC ISRAEL LTD.—See NeoMagic Corporation; *U.S. Public*, pg. 1506
NEUROFIT SAS—See Bionomics Limited; *Int'l*, pg. 1040
NEW SENSE RESEARCH LTD.—See Brookfield Corporation; *Int'l*, pg. 1180
NEW SENSE RESEARCH LTD.—See Elliott Management Corporation; *U.S. Private*, pg. 1372
THE NEW YORK GENOME CENTER; *U.S. Private*, pg. 4083
NEW YORK STATE ENERGY RESEARCH & DEVELOPMENT AUTHORITY; *U.S. Private*, pg. 2912
NEXTERA ENERGY RESOURCES, LLC—See NextEra Energy, Inc.; *U.S. Public*, pg. 1526
NEXT FUEL, INC.; *U.S. Private*, pg. 2919
NEYA SYSTEMS, LLC—See Applied Research Associates, Inc.; *U.S. Private*, pg. 299
NICKERSON ZWAAN B.V.—See Groupe Limagrain Holding SA; *Int'l*, pg. 3108
NIGHTSEA LLC—See Physical Sciences Inc.; *U.S. Private*, pg. 3175
NIPHIX KK—See ICON plc; *Int'l*, pg. 3584
NIPPON SOKEN, INC.—See Denso Corporation; *Int'l*, pg. 2032
NORDION INC.—See Warburg Pincus LLC; *U.S. Private*, pg. 4439
NORTH AMERICAN SCIENCE ASSOCIATES, INC.—See ArchiMed SAS; *Int'l*, pg. 549
NORTHERN CALIFORNIA INSTITUTE FOR RESEARCH AND EDUCATION; *U.S. Private*, pg. 2952
NOVADAN APS—See Illinois Tool Works Inc.; *U.S. Public*, pg. 1109
NULOGIX HEALTH, INC.—See RadNet, Inc.; *U.S. Public*, pg. 1761
NUMERICA CORPORATION; *U.S. Private*, pg. 2973
NUSEP, INC—See Dycent Biotech (Shanghai) Co. Ltd.; *Int'l*, pg. 2238
NUVECTRA CORPORATION; *U.S. Private*, pg. 2974
NUVERA FUEL CELLS EUROPE SRL—See Hyster-Yale Materials Handling, Inc.; *U.S. Public*, pg. 1080

541715 — RESEARCH AND DEVELO...   CORPORATE AFFILIATIONS

NUVERA FUEL CELLS, INC.—See Hyster-Yale Materials Handling, Inc.; *U.S. Public*, pg. 1080
OAKMAN AEROSPACE, INC.—See Redwire Corporation; *U.S. Public*, pg. 1771
O'BRIEN & GERE LABORATORIES, INC.—See The O'Brien & Gere Companies; *U.S. Private*, pg. 4087
OCEAN EXPLORATION TRUST; *U.S. Private*, pg. 2989
OMEGA LABORATORIES, INC.; *U.S. Private*, pg. 3015
ONEIDA RESEARCH SERVICES, INC.; *U.S. Private*, pg. 3025
OPERA CONTRACT RESEARCH ORGANIZATION SRL.—See Hangzhou Tigermed Consulting Co., Ltd.; *Int'l*, pg. 3251
OPTIC RIVER COMMUNICATION LTD.—See Henan Shijia Photons Technology Co., Ltd.; *Int'l*, pg. 3343
ORBITAL TECHNOLOGIES CORP.—See Sierra Nevada Corporation; *U.S. Private*, pg. 3647
ORCHID CELLMARK LTD.—See Laboratory Corporation of America Holdings; *U.S. Public*, pg. 1287
ORIGENE TECHNOLOGIES, INC.; *U.S. Private*, pg. 3042
PACCAR TECHNICAL CENTER—See PACCAR Inc.; *U.S. Public*, pg. 1631
PACIFIC GREEN MARINE TECHNOLOGIES INC.—See PACIFIC GREEN TECHNOLOGIES INC.; *U.S. Public*, pg. 1631
PACIFIC NORTHWEST NATIONAL LABORATORY—See Battelle Memorial Institute; *U.S. Private*, pg. 487
PALISADE BIO, INC.; *U.S. Public*, pg. 1634
PALMA BEE'Z RESEARCH INSTITUTE CO., LTD.—See Eisai Co., Ltd.; *Int'l*, pg. 2335
PALO ALTO RESEARCH CENTER INCORPORATED—See Xerox Holdings Corporation; *U.S. Public*, pg. 2388
PALOMA SYSTEMS, INC.; *U.S. Private*, pg. 3082
PARAGON TECHNICAL SERVICES, INC.—See Ergon, Inc.; *U.S. Private*, pg. 1418
PARKER HANNIFIN CORP., GAS TURBINE FUEL SYSTEMS DIV.—See Parker Hannifin Corporation; *U.S. Public*, pg. 1648
PATIENT PLUS LIMITED—See Crawford Healthcare Holdings Limited; *Int'l*, pg. 1829
PAVETEX ENGINEERING LLC—See GI Manager L.P.; *U.S. Private*, pg. 1691
P.D.C. LABORATORIES INC.—See Peoria Disposal Company/Area Disposal Service, Inc.; *U.S. Private*, pg. 3143
PERNIX THERAPEUTICS, LLC—See Pernix Therapeutics Holdings, Inc.; *U.S. Private*, pg. 3152
PERPETUAL INDUSTRIES INC.; *U.S. Public*, pg. 1677
PERSEID THERAPEUTICS LLC—See Astellas Pharma Inc.; *Int'l*, pg. 653
PETROLEUM INDUSTRY RESEARCH ASSOCIATES, INC.—See S&P Global Inc.; *U.S. Public*, pg. 1831
PFIZER RESEARCH & DEVELOPMENT—See Pfizer Inc.; *U.S. Public*, pg. 1682
PFIZER RESEARCH TECHNOLOGY CENTER—See Pfizer Inc.; *U.S. Public*, pg. 1682
P&G INNOVATION GODO KAISHA—See The Procter & Gamble Company; *U.S. Public*, pg. 2122
PHARMACEUTICAL PRODUCT DEVELOPMENT, LLC - AUSTIN—See Thermo Fisher Scientific Inc.; *U.S. Public*, pg. 2150
PHARMACEUTICAL PRODUCT DEVELOPMENT, LLC - BLUE BELL—See Thermo Fisher Scientific Inc.; *U.S. Public*, pg. 2151
PHARMACEUTICAL PRODUCT DEVELOPMENT, LLC - HAMILTON—See Thermo Fisher Scientific Inc.; *U.S. Public*, pg. 2151
PHARMACEUTICAL PRODUCT DEVELOPMENT, LLC - MIDDLETON—See Thermo Fisher Scientific Inc.; *U.S. Public*, pg. 2151
PHARMACEUTICAL PRODUCT DEVELOPMENT, LLC - MORRISVILLE—See Thermo Fisher Scientific Inc.; *U.S. Public*, pg. 2151
PHARMACEUTICAL PRODUCT DEVELOPMENT, LLC - RICHMOND BIOANALYTICAL LABORATORY—See Thermo Fisher Scientific Inc.; *U.S. Public*, pg. 2151
PHARMACEUTICAL PRODUCT DEVELOPMENT, LLC - SAN DIEGO—See Thermo Fisher Scientific Inc.; *U.S. Public*, pg. 2151
PHARMACEUTICAL PRODUCT DEVELOPMENT SPAIN SL—See Thermo Fisher Scientific Inc.; *U.S. Public*, pg. 2150
PHARMACEUTICAL RESEARCH ASSOCIATES ISRAEL LTD.—See ICON plc; *Int'l*, pg. 3585
PHARMACEUTICAL RESEARCH ASSOCIATES LTDA.—See ICON plc; *Int'l*, pg. 3586
PHARMACEUTICAL RESEARCH ASSOCIATES ROMANIA S.R.L.—See ICON plc; *Int'l*, pg. 3586
PHARMACEUTICAL RESEARCH ASSOCIATES TAIWAN, INC.—See ICON plc; *Int'l*, pg. 3586
PHARMALEX GMBH—See AUCTUS Capital Partners AG; *Int'l*, pg. 700
PHARMAQ ANALYTIQ AS—See Zoetis, Inc.; *U.S. Public*, pg. 2409
PHYSICAL OPTICS CORPORATION—See Mercury Systems, Inc.; *U.S. Public*, pg. 1422
PHYSICAL SCIENCES INC.; *U.S. Private*, pg. 3174

PHYTON BIOTECH GMBH—See DFB Pharmaceuticals, Inc.; *U.S. Private*, pg. 1220
PHYTON BIOTECH, INC.—See DFB Pharmaceuticals, Inc.; *U.S. Private*, pg. 1220
PIERCE BIOTECHNOLOGY, INC.—See Thermo Fisher Scientific Inc.; *U.S. Public*, pg. 2151
PIONEER HI-BRED INTERNATIONAL—See Corteva, Inc.; *U.S. Public*, pg. 583
PIONEER HI-BRED INTERNATIONAL—See Corteva, Inc.; *U.S. Public*, pg. 583
PIONEER HI-BRED LTD.—See Corteva, Inc.; *U.S. Public*, pg. 582
PIONEER HI-BRED RESEARCH CENTER—See Corteva, Inc.; *U.S. Public*, pg. 583
PIONEER RESEARCH CENTER USA INC—See EQT AB; *Int'l*, pg. 2470
PIPELINE RESEARCH COUNCIL INTERNATIONAL; *U.S. Private*, pg. 3189
PITNEY BOWES AUSTRALIA PTY LIMITED—See Pitney Bowes Inc.; *U.S. Public*, pg. 1694
PIVOTAL RESEARCH CENTERS LLC—See Metalmark Capital Holdings LLC; *U.S. Private*, pg. 2681
PLANT IMPACT PLC—See Croda International plc; *Int'l*, pg. 1852
PLASMET CORP.; *U.S. Private*, pg. 3198
POET RESEARCH, INC.—See POET, LLC; *U.S. Private*, pg. 3220
PORTOLA PHARMACEUTICALS, LLC—See AstraZeneca PLC; *Int'l*, pg. 659
PPD AUSTRALIA PTY. LTD.—See Thermo Fisher Scientific Inc.; *U.S. Public*, pg. 1220
PPD DO BRASIL-SUPORTE A PESQUISA CLINICA LTDA.—See Thermo Fisher Scientific Inc.; *U.S. Public*, pg. 2150
PPD GERMANY GMBH & CO KG—See Thermo Fisher Scientific Inc.; *U.S. Public*, pg. 2150
PPD GERMANY GMBH—See Thermo Fisher Scientific Inc.; *U.S. Public*, pg. 2150
PPD GLOBAL CENTRAL LABS BVBA—See Thermo Fisher Scientific Inc.; *U.S. Public*, pg. 2150
PPD GLOBAL LTD.—See Thermo Fisher Scientific Inc.; *U.S. Public*, pg. 2150
PPD HUNGARY RESEARCH & DEVELOPMENT LIMITED—See Thermo Fisher Scientific Inc.; *U.S. Public*, pg. 2150
PPD ITALY S.R.L.—See Thermo Fisher Scientific Inc.; *U.S. Public*, pg. 2150
PPD-LANARK—See Thermo Fisher Scientific Inc.; *U.S. Public*, pg. 2150
PPD PHASE I CLINIC - AUSTIN—See Thermo Fisher Scientific Inc.; *U.S. Public*, pg. 2151
PPD POLAND SP. Z O.O.—See Thermo Fisher Scientific Inc.; *U.S. Public*, pg. 2150
PPD SCANDINAVIA AB—See Thermo Fisher Scientific Inc.; *U.S. Public*, pg. 2150
PRA DEVELOPMENT CENTER KK—See ICON plc; *Int'l*, pg. 3585
PRA INTERNATIONAL INC.—See ICON plc; *Int'l*, pg. 3585
PRA INTERNATIONAL INC.—See ICON plc; *Int'l*, pg. 3585
PRA INTERNATIONAL OPERATIONS B.V.—See ICON plc; *Int'l*, pg. 3585
PRA PHARMACEUTICAL S A (PROPRIETARY) LIMITED—See ICON plc; *Int'l*, pg. 3585
PRA TURKEY SAGLIK ARASTIRMA VE GELISTIRME LIMITED SIRKETI—See ICON plc; *Int'l*, pg. 3586
PREDICTIVE MAINTENANCE SERVICES GROUP—See SES, LLC; *U.S. Private*, pg. 3617
PREMIER RESEARCH INSTITUTE, INC.—See Premier, Inc.; *U.S. Public*, pg. 1715
PRIORITY ONE SERVICES INC.; *U.S. Private*, pg. 3266
PROCOMM, INC.; *U.S. Private*, pg. 3272
PROCTER & GAMBLE - RESEARCH & DEVELOPMENT—See The Procter & Gamble Company; *U.S. Public*, pg. 2122
PROCTER & GAMBLE TECHNOLOGY (BEIJING) CO., LTD.—See The Procter & Gamble Company; *U.S. Public*, pg. 2123
PROEFBEDRIJF GEWASBESCHERMING DE BREDELAAR BV—See Eurofins Scientific S.E.; *Int'l*, pg. 2551
PROMERIC TECHNOLOGIES INC.—See First American Financial Corporation; *U.S. Public*, pg. 838
PROMIUS PHARMA LLC—See Dr. Reddy's Laboratories Limited; *Int'l*, pg. 2195
PROTAGONIST THERAPEUTICS, INC.; *U.S. Public*, pg. 1729
PROTEINONE; *U.S. Private*, pg. 3289
PROTOKINETIX, INC.; *U.S. Public*, pg. 1730
PROVEN PROCESS MEDICAL DEVICES, INC.—See Kidd & Company LLC; *U.S. Private*, pg. 2302
PSG CO., LTD.—See Honda Motor Co., Ltd.; *Int'l*, pg. 3464
PUBLIC HEALTH MANAGEMENT CORPORATION; *U.S. Private*, pg. 3299
PULSE BIOSCIENCES, INC.; *U.S. Public*, pg. 1737
PULSION BENELUX N.V.—See Getinge AB; *Int'l*, pg. 2952
PULSION FRANCE S.A.R.L.—See Getinge AB; *Int'l*, pg. 2952
PULSION SWITZERLAND GMBH—See Getinge AB; *Int'l*, pg. 2952

QC, INC.—See Land O'Lakes, Inc.; *U.S. Private*, pg. 2383
Q-PEAK—See Physical Sciences Inc.; *U.S. Private*, pg. 3175
QPHARMA, INC.; *U.S. Private*, pg. 3313
QUALCOMM SERVICES LABS, INC.—See QUALCOMM Incorporated; *U.S. Public*, pg. 1748
QUALITYMETRIC INCORPORATED—See UnitedHealth Group Incorporated; *U.S. Public*, pg. 2250
QUANTA, INC.; *U.S. Public*, pg. 1753
QUINCY BIOSCIENCE; *U.S. Private*, pg. 3327
QUINTILES B.V.—See IQVIA Holdings Inc.; *U.S. Public*, pg. 1170
QUINTILES ISRAEL LTD.—See IQVIA Holdings Inc.; *U.S. Public*, pg. 1170
QUINTILES LITHUANIA—See IQVIA Holdings Inc.; *U.S. Public*, pg. 1170
QUINTILES RUSSIA LLC—See IQVIA Holdings Inc.; *U.S. Public*, pg. 1170
RAININ INSTRUMENT LLC—See Mettler-Toledo International, Inc.; *U.S. Public*, pg. 1433
THE RAND CORPORATION; *U.S. Private*, pg. 4102
RANGE IMPACT, INC.; *U.S. Public*, pg. 1762
RAVEN EUROPE, B.V.—See CNH Industrial N.V.; *Int'l*, pg. 1676
RAYTHEON KTECH—See RTX Corporation; *U.S. Public*, pg. 1824
REDLATTICE, INC.—See AE Industrial Partners, LP; *U.S. Private*, pg. 112
REFINING & MANUFACTURING RESEARCH INSTITUTE—See CPC Corporation; *Int'l*, pg. 1824
REGENESYS BVBA—See Healios K.K.; *Int'l*, pg. 3302
REGULUS THERAPEUTICS, INC.; *U.S. Public*, pg. 1777
RESEARCH PHARMACEUTICAL SERVICES, INC.—See ICON plc; *Int'l*, pg. 3585
RESEARCH SUPPORT INSTRUMENTS, LANHAM OPERATIONS—See Physical Sciences Inc.; *U.S. Private*, pg. 3175
RESEARCH SUPPORT INSTRUMENTS, PRINCETON OPERATIONS—See Physical Sciences Inc.; *U.S. Private*, pg. 3175
RESEARCH TRIANGLE INSTITUTE; *U.S. Private*, pg. 3404
REV.1 ENGINEERING, INC.—See Asahi Intecc Co., Ltd.; *Int'l*, pg. 594
REVLON DEVELOPMENT CORP.—See MacAndrews & Forbes Incorporated; *U.S. Private*, pg. 2533
RINAT NEUROSCIENCE CORP.—See Pfizer Inc.; *U.S. Public*, pg. 1683
RJ LEE GROUP INC.; *U.S. Private*, pg. 3449
ROBOTICS TECHNOLOGY CONSORTIUM; *U.S. Private*, pg. 3462
ROMER LABS, INC.; *U.S. Private*, pg. 3476
ROSETTA GENOMICS INC.—See NeoGenomics, Inc.; *U.S. Public*, pg. 1506
ROSETTA GENOMICS LTD.—See NeoGenomics, Inc.; *U.S. Public*, pg. 1505
ROSKAMP INSTITUTE; *U.S. Private*, pg. 3485
RPS BEIJING, INC—See ICON plc; *Int'l*, pg. 3585
RPS CHILE LTDA.—See ICON plc; *Int'l*, pg. 3585
RPS COLOMBIA LTDA.—See ICON plc; *Int'l*, pg. 3585
RPS DO BRASIL SERVICOS DE PESQUISA LTDA.—See ICON plc; *Int'l*, pg. 3585
RPS LATVIA SIA—See ICON plc; *Int'l*, pg. 3586
RPS RESEARCH FRANCE, S.A.S.—See ICON plc; *Int'l*, pg. 3585
RPS RESEARCH IBERICA, S.L.U.—See ICON plc; *Int'l*, pg. 3585
RPS RESEARCH S.A.—See ICON plc; *Int'l*, pg. 3585
RPS RESEARCH SERVICIOS, S. DE RL DE CV—See ICON plc; *Int'l*, pg. 3585
RPS RESEARCH (THAILAND) CO., LTD.—See ICON plc; *Int'l*, pg. 3586
RPS SPAIN S.L.—See ICON plc; *Int'l*, pg. 3586
SAM SENSORY & MARKETING INTERNATIONAL GMBH—See Eurofins Scientific S.E.; *Int'l*, pg. 2551
SANDIA CORPORATION—See Lockheed Martin Corporation; *U.S. Public*, pg. 1339
SANERON CCEL THERAPEUTICS, INC.—See CRYO-CELL International, Inc.; *U.S. Public*, pg. 600
SANGAMO THERAPEUTICS FRANCE S.A.S.—See Sangamo Therapeutics, Inc.; *U.S. Public*, pg. 1840
SARAH CANNON RESEARCH UK LIMITED—See HCA Healthcare, Inc.; *U.S. Public*, pg. 1008
SARNOFF CORPORATION—See SRI International; *U.S. Private*, pg. 3768
SCALABLE SOFTWARE, INC.; *U.S. Private*, pg. 3560
SCALED COMPOSITES, LLC—See Northrop Grumman Corporation; *U.S. Public*, pg. 1540
SCHAFER CORPORATION—See AE Industrial Partners, LP; *U.S. Private*, pg. 112
SCHENCK TEST AUTOMATION LTD—See Durr AG; *Int'l*, pg. 2233
SCHLUMBERGER RESERVOIR COMPLETIONS CENTER—See Schlumberger Limited; *U.S. Public*, pg. 1846
SCIENCE AND TECHNOLOGY CORP.—See STC Group Inc.; *U.S. Private*, pg. 3794
SCIENCE & ENGINEERING SERVICES, INC.; *U.S. Private*, pg. 3573

N.A.I.C.S. INDEX

541720 — RESEARCH AND DEVELO...

SCIENCE SYSTEMS & APPLICATIONS, INC.; *U.S. Private*, pg. 3573
SCIENCE & TECHNOLOGY INTERNATIONAL; *U.S. Private*, pg. 3573
SCIENTIFIC AVIATION, INC.—See ChampionX Corporation; *U.S. Public*, pg. 478
SCREENCELL—See BNP Paribas SA; *Int'l*, pg. 1089
SDI EUROPE LIMITED—See OriGene Technologies, Inc.; *U.S. Private*, pg. 3042
S.D. MYERS, INC.; *U.S. Private*, pg. 3517
SEAWARD SERVICES INC.; *U.S. Private*, pg. 3592
SEMILLAS LIMAGRAIN DE CHILE LTDA.—See Groupe Limagrain Holding SA; *Int'l*, pg. 3108
SENASA—See Groupe Limagrain Holding SA; *Int'l*, pg. 3108
SENOMYX, INC.—See Firmenich International SA; *Int'l*, pg. 2680
SEVENTH WAVE LABORATORIES, LLC—See Inotiv, Inc.; *U.S. Public*, pg. 1128
SHANGHAI CHEMPARTNER CO., LTD.—See TPG Capital, L.P.; *U.S. Public*, pg. 2175
SHANGHAI HAOYUAN BIOTECH CO., LTD.—See Revvity, Inc.; *U.S. Public*, pg. 1795
SHARP ELECTRONICS (MALAYSIA) SDN. BHD.—See Hon Hai Precision Industry Co., Ltd.; *Int'l*, pg. 3458
SHARP LABORATORIES OF AMERICA, INC.—See Hon Hai Precision Industry Co., Ltd.; *Int'l*, pg. 3458
SHARP LABORATORIES OF EUROPE LIMITED—See Hon Hai Precision Industry Co., Ltd.; *Int'l*, pg. 3458
SICHUAN INDUSTRIAL INSTITUTE OF ANTIBIOTICS—See China National Pharmaceutical Group Corporation; *Int'l*, pg. 1534
SIEGE TECHNOLOGIES, LLC—See Braes Capital LLC; *U.S. Private*, pg. 633
SION POWER CORPORATION; *U.S. Private*, pg. 3670
SIRIGEN LIMITED—See Becton, Dickinson & Company; *U.S. Public*, pg. 292
SIRIUS XM INNOVATION CENTER—See Liberty Media Corporation; *U.S. Public*, pg. 1311
SISTEMI TERRITORIALI S.R.L.—See Almawave S.p.A.; *Int'l*, pg. 363
SMART RESEARCH CORP.—See HYUNDAI ADM BIO Inc; *Int'l*, pg. 3555
SMARTRONIX, LLC—See OceanSound Partners, LP; *U.S. Private*, pg. 2992
SMART TECHNOLOGIES (SINGAPORE) PRIVATE LIMITED—See Hon Hai Precision Industry Co., Ltd.; *Int'l*, pg. 3457
SMITH-EMERY COMPANY; *U.S. Private*, pg. 3696
SOCIETY FOR SCIENCE & THE PUBLIC; *U.S. Private*, pg. 3703
SOCIETY OF EXPLORATION GEOPHYSICISTS; *U.S. Private*, pg. 3704
SOLID POWER OPERATING, INC.—See Solid Power, Inc.; *U.S. Public*, pg. 1900
SOLITON, INC.—See AbbVie Inc.; *U.S. Public*, pg. 23
SOPHIRIS BIO INC.; *U.S. Private*, pg. 3715
SOUTHERN PETROLEUM LABORATORIES, INC.—See Sentinel Capital Partners, L.L.C.; *U.S. Private*, pg. 3609
SOUTHWEST POWER POOL INC.; *U.S. Private*, pg. 3740
SOUTHWEST RESEARCH INSTITUTE; *U.S. Private*, pg. 3740
SPECIALIZED TECHNOLOGY RESOURCES, INC.—See STR Holdings, Inc.; *U.S. Public*, pg. 1953
SPLUNK INFORMATION TECHNOLOGY (SHANGHAI) CO., LTD.—See Cisco Systems, Inc.; *U.S. Public*, pg. 500
SPRINGBORN SMITHERS LABS LLC—See Charles River Laboratories International, Inc.; *U.S. Public*, pg. 480
SRC, INC.; *U.S. Private*, pg. 3767
SRI INTERNATIONAL; *U.S. Private*, pg. 3767
SSANGYONG CEMENT INDUSTRIAL CO., LTD. - SSANGYONG TECHNOLOGY RESEARCH CENTER—See Hahn & Company; *Int'l*, pg. 3208
STANDARD LABORATORIES INC.; *U.S. Private*, pg. 3780
STATERA BIOPHARMA, INC.; *U.S. Public*, pg. 1941
STC GROUP INC.; *U.S. Private*, pg. 3794
STEMGENT, INC.; *U.S. Private*, pg. 3801
STI OPTRONICS, INC.; *U.S. Private*, pg. 3812
STONEHILL ENVIRONMENTAL, INC.—See Comprehensive Environmental Assessments, Inc.; *U.S. Private*, pg. 1003
STOWERS RESOURCE MANAGEMENT, INC.; *U.S. Private*, pg. 3832
STRATEGIC ANALYSIS INC.; *U.S. Private*, pg. 3834
SUREPURE, INC.; *U.S. Public*, pg. 1967
SURMODICS IVD, INC.—See SurModics, Inc.; *U.S. Public*, pg. 1967
SUSTAINABLE INNOVATIONS, LLC; *U.S. Private*, pg. 3886
SUZHOU CAERI AUTOMOBILE TEST & DEVELOPMENT CO., LTD.—See China Automotive Engineering Research Institute Co., Ltd.; *Int'l*, pg. 1484
SYGNIS BIOSCIENCE GMBH & CO. KG—See 2invest AG; *Int'l*, pg. 5
SYMPHONY CLINICAL RESEARCH SP. Z O.O.—See ICON plc; *Int'l*, pg. 3586
SYNEOS HEALTH CLINICAL, LLC—See Elliott Management Corporation; *U.S. Private*, pg. 1365
SYNEOS HEALTH CLINICAL, LLC—See Patient Square Capital, L.P.; *U.S. Private*, pg. 3108
SYNEOS HEALTH CLINICAL, LLC—See Veritas Capital Fund Management, LLC; *U.S. Private*, pg. 4365
SYNGENE INTERNATIONAL LIMITED—See Biocon Ltd.; *Int'l*, pg. 1036
SYNTECH RESEARCH, INC.; *U.S. Private*, pg. 3904
SYNTERACTHCR BENELUX NV—See Elliott Management Corporation; *U.S. Private*, pg. 1366
SYNTERACTHCR BENELUX NV—See Patient Square Capital, L.P.; *U.S. Private*, pg. 3108
SYNTERACTHCR BENELUX NV—See Veritas Capital Fund Management, LLC; *U.S. Private*, pg. 4365
SYNTERACTHCR DEUTSCHLAND GMBH—See Elliott Management Corporation; *U.S. Private*, pg. 1366
SYNTERACTHCR DEUTSCHLAND GMBH—See Patient Square Capital, L.P.; *U.S. Private*, pg. 3108
SYNTERACTHCR DEUTSCHLAND GMBH—See Veritas Capital Fund Management, LLC; *U.S. Private*, pg. 4365
SYNTERACTHCR EASTERN EUROPE FORSCHUNGSGESELLSCHAFT M.B.H.—See Elliott Management Corporation; *U.S. Private*, pg. 1366
SYNTERACTHCR EASTERN EUROPE FORSCHUNGSGESELLSCHAFT M.B.H.—See Patient Square Capital, L.P.; *U.S. Private*, pg. 3108
SYNTERACTHCR EASTERN EUROPE FORSCHUNGSGESELLSCHAFT M.B.H.—See Veritas Capital Fund Management, LLC; *U.S. Private*, pg. 4365
SYNTERACTHCR FRANCE SAS—See Elliott Management Corporation; *U.S. Private*, pg. 1366
SYNTERACTHCR FRANCE SAS—See Patient Square Capital, L.P.; *U.S. Private*, pg. 3108
SYNTERACTHCR FRANCE SAS—See Veritas Capital Fund Management, LLC; *U.S. Private*, pg. 4365
SYNTERACTHCR IBERICA, SL—See Elliott Management Corporation; *U.S. Private*, pg. 1366
SYNTERACTHCR IBERICA, SL—See Patient Square Capital, L.P.; *U.S. Private*, pg. 3108
SYNTERACTHCR IBERICA, SL—See Veritas Capital Fund Management, LLC; *U.S. Private*, pg. 4365
SYNTERACTHCR LIMITED—See Elliott Management Corporation; *U.S. Private*, pg. 1366
SYNTERACTHCR LIMITED—See Patient Square Capital, L.P.; *U.S. Private*, pg. 3109
SYNTERACTHCR LIMITED—See Veritas Capital Fund Management, LLC; *U.S. Private*, pg. 4365
SYNTERACTHCR S.R.L.—See Elliott Management Corporation; *U.S. Private*, pg. 1366
SYNTERACTHCR S.R.L.—See Patient Square Capital, L.P.; *U.S. Private*, pg. 3109
SYNTERACTHCR S.R.L.—See Veritas Capital Fund Management, LLC; *U.S. Private*, pg. 4365
SYNTERACTHCR SWEDEN AB—See Elliott Management Corporation; *U.S. Private*, pg. 1366
SYNTERACTHCR SWEDEN AB—See Patient Square Capital, L.P.; *U.S. Private*, pg. 3108
SYNTERACTHCR SWEDEN AB—See Veritas Capital Fund Management, LLC; *U.S. Private*, pg. 4365
TACONICARTEMIS GMBH—See Taconic Farms, Inc.; *U.S. Private*, pg. 3921
TAIZHOU TIGERMED-JYTON MEDICAL TECH. CO., LTD.—See Hangzhou Tigermed Consulting Co., Ltd.; *Int'l*, pg. 3251
TATSUTA ENVIRONMENTAL ANALYSIS CENTER CO., LTD.—See ENEOS Holdings, Inc.; *Int'l*, pg. 2416
TAURIGA SCIENCES, INC.; *U.S. Public*, pg. 1983
TECHNIC INCORPORATED - TECHNIC ADVANCED TECHNOLOGY DIVISION—See Technic Incorporated; *U.S. Private*, pg. 3953
TECHNOLOGIES RESEARCH CORPORATION—See National Center for Manufacturing Sciences Inc.; *U.S. Private*, pg. 2850
TECOLOTE RESEARCH INC.; *U.S. Private*, pg. 3957
TELEDYNE BROWN ENGINEERING, INC.—See Teledyne Technologies Incorporated; *U.S. Public*, pg. 1993
TELEDYNE RD TECHNOLOGIES (SHANGHAI) CO., LTD.—See Teledyne Technologies Incorporated; *U.S. Public*, pg. 1994
TELLUS INSTITUTE INC.; *U.S. Private*, pg. 3962
TEXAS BIOMEDICAL RESEARCH INSTITUTE; *U.S. Private*, pg. 3975
THERALINK TECHNOLOGIES, INC.; *U.S. Public*, pg. 2144
THERMO FISHER SCIENTIFIC MESSTECHNIK GMBH—See Thermo Fisher Scientific Inc.; *U.S. Public*, pg. 2154
THIONVILLE LABORATORIES INC.; *U.S. Private*, pg. 4144
TISSUE GENESIS, INC.—See Orgenesis Inc.; *U.S. Public*, pg. 1617
TORCH TECHNOLOGIES; *U.S. Private*, pg. 4188
TRACE LABORATORIES CHICAGO—See Methode Electronics, Inc.; *U.S. Public*, pg. 1429
TRAX INTERNATIONAL CORPORATION; *U.S. Private*, pg. 4215
TREATMENT RESEARCH INSTITUTE—See Public Health Management Corporation; *U.S. Private*, pg. 3299
TREX ENTERPRISES CORPORATION; *U.S. Private*, pg. 4219
TRIPATH ONCOLOGY, INC.—See Becton, Dickinson & Company; *U.S. Public*, pg. 288
TVAX BIOMEDICAL, INC.; *U.S. Private*, pg. 4263
U3 PHARMA GMBH—See Daiichi Sankyo Co., Ltd.; *Int'l*, pg. 1930
UMANDIAGNOSTICS AB—See Quanterix Corporation; *U.S. Public*, pg. 1753
UNICORN HRO—See The Unicorn Group; *U.S. Private*, pg. 4129
UNIQUE N.V.—See Ampersand Management LLC; *U.S. Private*, pg. 265
UNITHER TELMED, LTD.—See United Therapeutics Corporation; *U.S. Public*, pg. 2238
UPONOR INNOVATION AB—See Georg Fischer AG; *Int'l*, pg. 2938
UPTAKE MEDICAL CORP.—See Broncus Medical, Inc; *U.S. Private*, pg. 662
US MICRON LLC; *U.S. Private*, pg. 4319
VAN ANDEL INSTITUTE; *U.S. Private*, pg. 4338
VDOSOFT SDN. BHD.—See AWC Berhad; *Int'l*, pg. 752
VECNA TECHNOLOGIES, INC.; *U.S. Private*, pg. 4349
VERILY LIFE SCIENCES LLC—See Alphabet Inc.; *U.S. Public*, pg. 84
VERISTAT LLC—See MTS Health Partners, L.P.; *U.S. Private*, pg. 2810
VIECELI & FURLAN ASSOCIADOS INDUSTRIA E COMERCIO LTDA.—See Aiphone Co., Ltd.; *Int'l*, pg. 235
VIKING ENTERPRISE SOLUTIONS—See Sanmina Corporation; *U.S. Public*, pg. 1841
VILMORIN IBERICA S.A.—See Groupe Limagrain Holding SA; *Int'l*, pg. 3108
VILMORIN ITALIA S.R.L.—See Groupe Limagrain Holding SA; *Int'l*, pg. 3108
VILMORIN S.A.—See Groupe Limagrain Holding SA; *Int'l*, pg. 3108
VIRENT, INC.—See Marathon Petroleum Corporation; *U.S. Public*, pg. 1363
VIRGIN GALACTIC, LLC—See Virgin Galactic Holdings, Inc.; *U.S. Public*, pg. 2299
VIROSTAT, LLC—See DevCo Partners Oy; *Int'l*, pg. 2086
VIRTUSA HUNGARY KFT.—See EQT AB; *Int'l*, pg. 2472
VITAL HEALTH SCIENCES PTY LTD—See Avecho Biotechnology Ltd.; *Int'l*, pg. 737
VITRO BIOPHARMA, INC.; *U.S. Private*, pg. 4405
VIVEX BIOMEDICAL, INC.; *U.S. Private*, pg. 4406
VOLITIONRX LIMITED; *U.S. Public*, pg. 2308
WAIFE & ASSOCIATES, INC.—See Leonard Green & Partners, L.P.; *U.S. Private*, pg. 2430
WATLOW HEATER TECHNOLOGY CENTER—See Tinicum Enterprises, Inc.; *U.S. Private*, pg. 4174
WEST ANALYTICAL SERVICES, LLC—See West Pharmaceutical Services, Inc.; *U.S. Public*, pg. 2353
WESTBRIDGE FOODS (THAILAND) LTD.—See Charoen Pokphand Foods Public Company Limited; *Int'l*, pg. 1453
WESTED; *U.S. Private*, pg. 4489
WEX PHARMACEUTICALS INC.—See CK Hutchison Holdings Limited; *Int'l*, pg. 1638
WILLIAMS LABORATORIES SERVICES—See The Williams Companies, Inc.; *U.S. Public*, pg. 2144
WIRB-COPERNICUS GROUP, INC.—See Leonard Green & Partners, L.P.; *U.S. Private*, pg. 2429
WISCONSIN ALUMNI RESEARCH FOUNDATION; *U.S. Private*, pg. 4547
WORLD HEALTH ENERGY HOLDINGS, INC.; *U.S. Public*, pg. 2380
WRIGHT ASPHALT PRODUCTS COMPANY LLC—See Delek Group Ltd.; *Int'l*, pg. 2011
WUHAN SHIJIA PHOTOELECTRIC TECHNOLOGY CO., LTD.—See Henan Shijia Photons Technology Co., Ltd.; *Int'l*, pg. 3343
WUXI JAKE PLASTIC INDUSTRY CO., LTD.—See Henan Shijia Photons Technology Co., Ltd.; *Int'l*, pg. 3343
XEROX RESEARCH CENTER OF WEBSTER (XRCW)—See Xerox Holdings Corporation; *U.S. Public*, pg. 2390
XIMEDICA LLC—See SV Health Investors, LLP; *U.S. Private*, pg. 3888
YAHOO! RESEARCH—See Apollo Global Management, Inc.; *U.S. Public*, pg. 168
YAHOO! RESEARCH & STRATEGIC DATA SOLUTIONS—See Apollo Global Management, Inc.; *U.S. Public*, pg. 168
YOUNG GREEN ENERGY CO., LTD.—See Coretronic Corporation; *Int'l*, pg. 1800
YUKON DELTA FISHERIES DEVELOPMENT ASSOCIATION; *U.S. Private*, pg. 4595
ZBB ENERGY PTY. LTD.—See EnSync, Inc.; *U.S. Public*, pg. 776
ZERUST SPECIALTY TECH CO., LTD.—See Northern Technologies International Corporation; *U.S. Public*, pg. 1538
ZFX INNOVATION GMBH—See Zimmer Biomet Holdings, Inc.; *U.S. Public*, pg. 2406
ZIN TECHNOLOGIES INC.—See Voyager Space Holdings, Inc.; *U.S. Private*, pg. 4414
ZIVO BIOSCIENCE, INC.; *U.S. Public*, pg. 2409

541720 — RESEARCH AND DEVELOPMENT IN THE SOCIAL SCIENCES AND HUMANITIES

541720 — RESEARCH AND DEVELO...

ADVION, INC.—See Beijing Bohui Innovation Biotechnology Group Co., Ltd.; *Int'l*, pg. 946
AKEBONO RESEARCH & DEVELOPMENT CENTRE LTD.—See Akebono Brake Industry Co., Ltd.; *Int'l*, pg. 262
ALLIED INTERNATIONAL EMERGENCY SA—See Ambipar Participacoes e Empreendimentos SA; *Int'l*, pg. 414
ALLIED TELESIS R&D CENTER K.K.—See ALLIED TELESIS HOLDINGS K.K.; *Int'l*, pg. 358
AMANASU TECHNO HOLDINGS CORPORATION; *U.S. Public*, pg. 90
AMBU LTD.—See Ambu A/S; *Int'l*, pg. 416
AMERICAN ENTERPRISE INSTITUTE FOR PUBLIC POLICY RESEARCH; *U.S. Private*, pg. 232
AMERICAN INSTITUTE OF GASTRIC BANDING; *U.S. Private*, pg. 238
THE AMERICAN REGISTRY OF PATHOLOGY, INC.; *U.S. Private*, pg. 3986
ATMOSPHERIC & ENVIRONMENTAL RESEARCH, INC.—See Verisk Analytics, Inc.; *U.S. Public*, pg. 2282
AVN CORPORATION; *U.S. Private*, pg. 409
BAL LABORATORY—See Thielsch Engineering, Inc.; *U.S. Private*, pg. 4144
BC MANAGEMENT, INC.—See Resurgens Technology Partners, LLC; *U.S. Private*, pg. 3410
BD TECHNOLOGIES—See Becton, Dickinson & Company; *U.S. Public*, pg. 288
BECHTEL BETTIS INC.—See Bechtel Group, Inc.; *U.S. Private*, pg. 509
BIOLEGEND, INC.—See Revvity, Inc.; *U.S. Public*, pg. 1793
BIONEER, INC.—See Bioneer Corporation; *Int'l*, pg. 1040
BIONUMERIK PHARMACEUTICALS, INC.; *U.S. Private*, pg. 562
BIOQUAL INC.; *U.S. Public*, pg. 338
THE BOWEN CONSULTING GROUP, INC.; *U.S. Private*, pg. 3998
BRISTOL BAY ECONOMIC DEVELOPMENT CORPORATION; *U.S. Private*, pg. 655
THE BROOKINGS INSTITUTION; *U.S. Private*, pg. 4001
BURNING MAN PROJECT; *U.S. Private*, pg. 689
CARELON RESEARCH, INC.—See Elevance Health, Inc.; *U.S. Public*, pg. 729
CA RESEARCH, INC.—See Broadcom Inc.; *U.S. Public*, pg. 389
CENTER FOR INNOVATIVE TECHNOLOGY; *U.S. Private*, pg. 810
CETERO RESEARCH—See Cetero Research; *U.S. Private*, pg. 843
CHAMPLAIN VALLEY OFFICE OF ECONOMIC OPPORTUNITY, INC.; *U.S. Private*, pg. 847
CHARLOTTE REGIONAL PARTNERSHIP, INC.—See Charlotte Regional Business Alliance; *U.S. Private*, pg. 857
CIENTEC INSTRUMENTOS CIENTIFICOS SA—See HORIBA Ltd; *Int'l*, pg. 3475
CINTAS (GUANGZHOU) ENTERPRISE SERVICES CO., LTD.—See Cintas Corporation; *U.S. Public*, pg. 495
CNFA, INC.; *U.S. Private*, pg. 952
COASTAL ECONOMIC DEVELOPMENT CORPORATION; *U.S. Private*, pg. 956
COLD SPRING HARBOR LABORATORY; *U.S. Private*, pg. 966
COLOPLAST—See Coloplast A/S; *Int'l*, pg. 1703
COMSYS SHARED SERVICES CORPORATION—See COMSYS Holdings Corporation; *Int'l*, pg. 1761
CONCENTRA OCCUPATIONAL HEALTH RESEARCH INSTITUTE—See Select Medical Holdings Corporation; *U.S. Public*, pg. 1857
CONCENTRA OCCUPATIONAL HEALTH RESEARCH INSTITUTE—See Welsh, Carson, Anderson & Stowe; *U.S. Private*, pg. 4479
CONNECTICUT CENTER FOR ADVANCED TECHNOLOGY, INC.; *U.S. Private*, pg. 1015
COUNCIL ON FOREIGN RELATIONS; *U.S. Private*, pg. 1065
CREATE FOUNDATION; *U.S. Private*, pg. 1087
CUBRC, INC.; *U.S. Private*, pg. 1120
CULMEN INTERNATIONAL, LLC—See Hale Capital Partners, L.P.; *U.S. Private*, pg. 1842
CYBOZU RESEARCH INSTITUTE, INC.—See Cybozu Inc.; *Int'l*, pg. 1894
CYTOKINETICS, INC.; *U.S. Public*, pg. 618
DAIWA INSTITUTE OF RESEARCH HOLDINGS LTD.—See Daiwa Securities Group Inc.; *Int'l*, pg. 1948
DAVITA CLINICAL RESEARCH—See DaVita Inc.; *U.S. Public*, pg. 637
DECODE GENETICS, INC.—See Amgen Inc.; *U.S. Public*, pg. 124
DELTA AREA ECONOMIC OPPORTUNITY CORPORATION; *U.S. Private*, pg. 1199
DSP CLINICAL RESEARCH; *U.S. Private*, pg. 1281
THE ECONOMIC DEVELOPMENT CORPORATION OF KANSAS CITY, MISSOURI; *U.S. Private*, pg. 4025
ECONOMIC RESEARCH SERVICES INC.—See Exela Technologies, Inc.; *U.S. Public*, pg. 806
EDUCATION DEVELOPMENT CENTER INC.; *U.S. Private*, pg. 1338
EISAI INC. - ANDOVER RESEARCH LABORATORY—See Eisai Co., Ltd.; *Int'l*, pg. 2335
ENVIRONMENTAL SCIENCE ASSOCIATES; *U.S. Private*, pg. 1408
ENZO THERAPEUTICS INC.—See Enzo Biochem Inc.; *U.S. Public*, pg. 782
E-TECH TESTING SERVICES, INC.—See Trinity Industries, Inc.; *U.S. Public*, pg. 2193
EUROFINS DE BREDELAAR B.V.—See Eurofins Scientific S.E.; *Int'l*, pg. 2539
EVIDENT THERMOELECTRICS; *U.S. Private*, pg. 1441
FERDINAND BUILDING DEVELOPMENT CORPORATION; *U.S. Private*, pg. 1496
FHI 360; *U.S. Private*, pg. 1501
FISCO LTD—See Emerson Electric Co.; *U.S. Public*, pg. 749
FOCUS SUITES SOLUTIONS & SERVICES LIMITED; *Int'l*, pg. 2720
FORRESTER GERMANY GMBH—See Forrester Research, Inc.; *U.S. Public*, pg. 868
FORRESTER RESEARCH B.V.—See Forrester Research, Inc.; *U.S. Public*, pg. 868
FORRESTER RESEARCH, INC.—See Forrester Research, Inc.; *U.S. Public*, pg. 868
FORRESTER RESEARCH INDIA PRIVATE LIMITED—See Forrester Research, Inc.; *U.S. Public*, pg. 868
FORRESTER SWITZERLAND GMBH—See Forrester Research, Inc.; *U.S. Public*, pg. 869
FRONTIER SCIENCE & TECHNOLOGY RESEARCH FOUNDATION, INC.; *U.S. Private*, pg. 1615
GENMAB, INC.—See Genmab A/S; *Int'l*, pg. 2924
GENOVO, INC.—See Armata Pharmaceuticals, Inc.; *U.S. Public*, pg. 193
GLAXOSMITHKLINE—See GSK plc; *Int'l*, pg. 3146
GLAXOSMITHKLINE—See GSK plc; *Int'l*, pg. 3146
GLYCONEX, INC.; *Int'l*, pg. 3011
GRAND CENTRAL DISTRICT MANAGEMENT ASSOCIATION, INC.; *U.S. Private*, pg. 1752
GREAT WALL JAPAN MOTOR CO., LTD.—See Great Wall Motor Company Limited; *Int'l*, pg. 3066
GREENWOOD GENETIC CENTER INC.; *U.S. Private*, pg. 1781
HEALTH CORE, INC.—See Elevance Health, Inc.; *U.S. Public*, pg. 730
HELP - NEW MEXICO, INC.; *U.S. Private*, pg. 1912
HISTORIC PRESERVATION PARTNERS, INC.; *U.S. Private*, pg. 1951
HISTORY ASSOCIATES INC.; *U.S. Private*, pg. 1952
THE HOKUGIN ECONOMIC RESEARCH INSTITUTE LTD—See Daishi Hokuetsu Financial Group, Inc.; *Int'l*, pg. 1941
HOOSIER UPLANDS ECONOMIC DEVELOPMENT CORPORATION; *U.S. Private*, pg. 1978
HUMAN RESOURCES RESEARCH ORGANIZATION; *U.S. Private*, pg. 2006
HUMAN RIGHTS WATCH; *U.S. Private*, pg. 2006
ICHNOS SCIENCES INC.—See Glenmark Pharmaceuticals Limited; *Int'l*, pg. 2992
INTERNATIONAL ROBOTICS, INC.; *U.S. Private*, pg. 2120
JANSSEN BIOTECH, INC.—See Johnson & Johnson; *U.S. Public*, pg. 1196
JAPAN SOCIETY, INC.; *U.S. Private*, pg. 2188
LILLY RESEARCH CENTRE LIMITED—See Eli Lilly & Company; *U.S. Public*, pg. 733
LORD CORP. RESEARCH & DEVELOPMENT—See Parker Hannifin Corporation; *U.S. Public*, pg. 1641
MACON BIBB COUNTY ECONOMIC OPPORTUNITY COUNCIL, INC.; *U.S. Private*, pg. 2538
MAGIC HAT CONSULTING; *U.S. Private*, pg. 2546
MARSHFIELD CLINIC-MEDICAL RESEARCH FOUNDATION—See Marshfield Clinic; *U.S. Private*, pg. 2593
MATHEMATICA POLICY RESEARCH INC.—See Mathematica Inc.; *U.S. Private*, pg. 2610
MATHEMATICA POLICY RESEARCH, INC.—See Mathematica Inc.; *U.S. Private*, pg. 2610
MATHEMATICA POLICY RESEARCH, INC.—See Mathematica Inc.; *U.S. Private*, pg. 2610
MATHEMATICA POLICY RESEARCH, INC.—See Mathematica Inc.; *U.S. Private*, pg. 2610
MATHEMATICA POLICY RESEARCH, INC.—See Mathematica Inc.; *U.S. Private*, pg. 2610
MATHEMATICA POLICY RESEARCH, INC.—See Mathematica Inc.; *U.S. Private*, pg. 2610
MATHEMATICA POLICY RESEARCH, INC.—See Mathematica Inc.; *U.S. Private*, pg. 2610
MEASURED PROGRESS INC.; *U.S. Private*, pg. 2648
MEDIMMUNE LLC—See AstraZeneca PLC; *Int'l*, pg. 660
MEDIMMUNE PHARMA B.V.—See AstraZeneca PLC; *Int'l*, pg. 661
METROPLEX ECONOMIC DEVELOPMENT CORP.; *U.S. Private*, pg. 2687
MONSANTO CO. - MAUI—See Bayer Aktiengesellschaft; *Int'l*, pg. 908
MONSANTO CO. - REDWOOD FALLS-SOYBEAN RESEARCH—See Bayer Aktiengesellschaft; *Int'l*, pg. 909
MRIGLOBAL; *U.S. Private*, pg. 2805
MYRIAD GENETIC LABORATORIES, INC.—See Myriad Genetics, Inc.; *U.S. Public*, pg. 1489
NAGASAKI ECONOMIC RESEARCH INSTITUTE LTD—See Fukuoka Financial Group, Inc.; *Int'l*, pg. 2840
NAGASAKI RESEARCH INSTITUTE LIMITED—See Fukuoka Financial Group, Inc.; *Int'l*, pg. 2840
NATIONAL COUNCIL FOR AIR AND STREAM IMPROVEMENT, INC.; *U.S. Private*, pg. 2852
NATIONAL SOCIETY DAUGHTERS OF THE AMERICAN REVOLUTION; *U.S. Private*, pg. 2863
NEW ENGLAND RESEARCH INSTITUTES, INC.—See Elevance Health, Inc.; *U.S. Public*, pg. 730
NEW-YORK HISTORICAL SOCIETY; *U.S. Private*, pg. 2913
NEXTRIALS, INC.—See ICON plc; *Int'l*, pg. 3585
NIELSEN ADMOSPHERE SLOVAKIA, S.R.O.—See Brookfield Corporation; *Int'l*, pg. 1179
NIELSEN ADMOSPHERE SLOVAKIA, S.R.O.—See Elliott Management Corporation; *U.S. Private*, pg. 1371
THE NIELSEN COMPANY (THAILAND) LIMITED—See Brookfield Corporation; *Int'l*, pg. 1180
THE NIELSEN COMPANY (THAILAND) LIMITED—See Elliott Management Corporation; *U.S. Private*, pg. 1373
ORASURE TECHNOLOGIES, INC.; *U.S. Public*, pg. 1614
PACIFIC INSTITUTE FOR RESEARCH & EVALUATION; *U.S. Private*, pg. 3067
PACIRA - SAN DIEGO—See Pacira BioSciences, Inc.; *U.S. Public*, pg. 1632
PATHOLOGY ASSOCIATES—See Charles River Laboratories International, Inc.; *U.S. Public*, pg. 480
PERENNIAL ENVIRONMENTAL SERVICES—See Eagle Infrastructure Services, Inc.; *U.S. Private*, pg. 1309
PLANT SCIENCES INC.; *U.S. Private*, pg. 3197
PROSPECT RESEARCH & DEVELOPMENT STRATEGIES; *U.S. Private*, pg. 3288
REDA INTERNATIONAL, INC.—See Data Recognition Corporation; *U.S. Private*, pg. 1163
RED OAK SOURCING, LLC—See CVS Health Corporation; *U.S. Public*, pg. 615
THE REHANCEMENT GROUP, INC.; *U.S. Private*, pg. 4103
ROOTS OF PEACE; *U.S. Private*, pg. 3480
SEMATECH, INC.; *U.S. Private*, pg. 3603
SIL INTERNATIONAL; *U.S. Private*, pg. 3651
SOFTWARE AG DEVELOPMENT CENTER BULGARIA EOOD—See Silver Lake Group, LLC; *U.S. Private*, pg. 3659
SOUTH CAROLINA RESEARCH AUTHORITY; *U.S. Private*, pg. 3720
ST. JUDE CHILDREN'S RESEARCH HOSPITAL; *U.S. Private*, pg. 3772
STRUCTURED EMPLOYMENT ECONOMIC DEVELOPMENT CORPORATION; *U.S. Private*, pg. 3842
STRYKER BIOTECH LLC—See Stryker Corporation; *U.S. Public*, pg. 1956
SYNERGYST RESEARCH GROUP; *U.S. Private*, pg. 3904
SYSTEM PLANNING CORPORATION; *U.S. Private*, pg. 3907
THIRD LAW SOURCING; *U.S. Private*, pg. 4145
THE TRANSITION COMPANIES LLC; *U.S. Private*, pg. 4128
TRANSONIC COMBUSTION, INC.; *U.S. Private*, pg. 4210
UNITED GLOBAL TECHNOLOGIES, INC.; *U.S. Private*, pg. 4293
UNITED TECHNOLOGIES RESEARCH CENTER—See RTX Corporation; *U.S. Public*, pg. 1825
UNIVERSAL ENGINEERING SCIENCES—See Universal Engineering Sciences, LLC; *U.S. Private*, pg. 4305
UNIVERSITIES RESEARCH ASSOCIATION, INC.; *U.S. Private*, pg. 4307
VERALYTIC INC.; *U.S. Private*, pg. 4359
VERTEX PHARMACEUTICALS (SAN DIEGO) LLC—See Vertex Pharmaceuticals Incorporated; *U.S. Public*, pg. 2287
VOLUNTEERS FOR ECONOMIC GROWTH ALLIANCE; *U.S. Private*, pg. 4411
WATERMARK RESEARCH PARTNERS, INC.—See Genstar Capital, LLC; *U.S. Private*, pg. 1673
WORLDWIDE CLINICAL TRIALS EARLY PHASE SERVICES & BIOANALYTICAL SCIENCES—See The Jordan Company, L.P.; *U.S. Private*, pg. 4063

541810 — ADVERTISING AGENCIES

101, INC.—See TEGNA Inc.; *U.S. Public*, pg. 1989
11:24 DESIGN ADVERTISING, INC.; *U.S. Private*, pg. 2
1185 DESIGN; *U.S. Private*, pg. 2
140 BBDO—See Omnicom Group Inc.; *U.S. Public*, pg. 1573
180/AMSTERDAM; *Int'l*, pg. 3
180 LOS ANGELES—See 180/Amsterdam; *Int'l*, pg. 3
18 FEET & RISING LIMITED; *Int'l*, pg. 3
1TOUCH MARKETING; *U.S. Private*, pg. 4
22SQUARED, INC.; *U.S. Private*, pg. 5
22SQUARED - TAMPA—See 22squared, Inc.; *U.S. Private*, pg. 6
23RED LIMITED—See Capgemini SE; *Int'l*, pg. 1303
29 PRIME; *U.S. Private*, pg. 6
2ADVANCED STUDIOS, LLC; *U.S. Private*, pg. 6
2.GC, INC.; *U.S. Private*, pg. 4
2GEN NET; *Int'l*, pg. 5
303 MULLENLOWE—See The Interpublic Group of Companies, Inc.; *U.S. Public*, pg. 2089
303 MULLENLOWE - SYDNEY—See The Interpublic Group of Companies, Inc.; *U.S. Public*, pg. 2090

N.A.I.C.S. INDEX

541810 — ADVERTISING AGENCIE...

360 GROUP; *U.S. Private*, pg. 8
360 MARKETING COMMUNICATIONS & CONTACTS—See The Interpublic Group of Companies, Inc.; *U.S. Public*, pg. 2092
360PARTNERS, LP; *U.S. Private*, pg. 8
360 PSG, INC.; *U.S. Private*, pg. 8
3C TECHNOLOGY AS—See TowerBrook Capital Partners, L.P.; *U.S. Private*, pg. 4194
3 INTERACTIVE; *U.S. Private*, pg. 7
47CLUB INC.—See Dentsu Group Inc.; *Int'l*, pg. 2034
4 WALLS, INC.; *U.S. Private*, pg. 14
5BY5, LLC; *U.S. Private*, pg. 16
5METACOM; *U.S. Private*, pg. 16
5TH GEAR ADVERTISING; *U.S. Private*, pg. 16
72ANDSUNNY PARTNERS LLC—See Stagwell, Inc.; *U.S. Public*, pg. 1925
72ANDSUNNY—See Stagwell, Inc.; *U.S. Public*, pg. 1925
7SUMMITS, LLC—See International Business Machines Corporation; *U.S. Public*, pg. 1145
90OCTANE, LLC; *U.S. Private*, pg. 17
93 OCTANE; *U.S. Private*, pg. 17
999 DESIGN GROUP LTD.—See Matthews International Corporation; *U.S. Public*, pg. 1400
99 LOYALTY LIMITED; *Int'l*, pg. 16
A1C PARTNERS, LLC; *U.S. Private*, pg. 29
A1 OUTDOOR—See The Interpublic Group of Companies, Inc.; *U.S. Public*, pg. 2097
AAAZA, INC.—See Admerasia, Inc.; *U.S. Private*, pg. 80
AALP, INC. - ATLANTA—See AALP, Inc.; *U.S. Private*, pg. 31
AALP, INC. - CHICAGO—See AALP, Inc.; *U.S. Private*, pg. 31
AALP, INC. - CLEVELAND—See AALP, Inc.; *U.S. Private*, pg. 31
AALP, INC. - DENVER—See AALP, Inc.; *U.S. Private*, pg. 31
AALP, INC. - DETROIT—See AALP, Inc.; *U.S. Private*, pg. 31
AALP, INC. - KANSAS CITY—See AALP, Inc.; *U.S. Private*, pg. 31
AALP, INC. - LOS ANGELES—See AALP, Inc.; *U.S. Private*, pg. 31
AALP, INC. - MIAMI—See AALP, Inc.; *U.S. Private*, pg. 31
AALP, INC. - NEW YORK—See AALP, Inc.; *U.S. Private*, pg. 31
AALP, INC. - PHILADELPHIA—See AALP, Inc.; *U.S. Private*, pg. 31
AALP, INC. - PHOENIX—See AALP, Inc.; *U.S. Private*, pg. 32
AALP, INC. - SAN DIEGO—See AALP, Inc.; *U.S. Private*, pg. 32
AALP, INC. - SAN FRANCISCO—See AALP, Inc.; *U.S. Private*, pg. 32
AALP, INC. - SEATTLE—See AALP, Inc.; *U.S. Private*, pg. 32
AALP, INC.; *U.S. Private*, pg. 31
AALP, INC. - ST. LOUIS—See AALP, Inc.; *U.S. Private*, pg. 32
AALP, INC. - WASHINGTON, D.C.—See AALP, Inc.; *U.S. Private*, pg. 32
AARROW, INC.; *U.S. Private*, pg. 33
ABBOTT MEAD VICKERS BBDO—See Omnicom Group Inc.; *U.S. Public*, pg. 1573
ABBOTT MEAD VICKERS GROUP LIMITED—See Omnicom Group Inc.; *U.S. Public*, pg. 1573
AB+C PHILADELPHIA LLC—See Aloysius, Butler & Clark Associates, Inc.; *U.S. Private*, pg. 196
A.B. DATA, LTD. - WASHINGTON, D.C.—See A.B. Data, Ltd.; *U.S. Private*, pg. 24
ABELSONTAYLOR, INC.; *U.S. Private*, pg. 37
ABELSON-TAYLOR, INC.—See AbelsonTaylor, Inc.; *U.S. Private*, pg. 37
A. BROWN-OLMSTEAD ASSOCIATES; *U.S. Private*, pg. 22
ABSOLUTE MEDIA INC.; *U.S. Private*, pg. 44
ACADEMY COMMUNICATIONS INC.; *U.S. Private*, pg. 46
ACAST AB; *Int'l*, pg. 78
ACCELERATION COMMUNITY OF COMPANIES; *U.S. Private*, pg. 49
ACCELERATION PARTNERS LLC—See Mountaingate Capital Management, L.P.; *U.S. Private*, pg. 2801
ACCENTMARKETING—See The Interpublic Group of Companies, Inc.; *U.S. Public*, pg. 2090
ACCENTMARKETING—See The Interpublic Group of Companies, Inc.; *U.S. Public*, pg. 2090
ACCESS ADVERTISING, LLC; *U.S. Private*, pg. 50
ACCESS COMMUNICATIONS LLC—See Monitor Clipper Partners, LLC; *U.S. Private*, pg. 2770
ACCESSPOINT—See Brand Innovation Group; *U.S. Private*, pg. 637
ACCESS; *U.S. Private*, pg. 50
ACCUMARK COMMUNICATIONS, INC.—See Stagwell, Inc.; *U.S. Public*, pg. 1925
ACENTO ADVERTISING, INC.; *U.S. Private*, pg. 58
ACENTO ADVERTISING—See Acento Advertising, Inc.; *U.S. Private*, pg. 58
ACKERMAN MCQUEEN, INC. - COLORADO SPRINGS—See Ackerman McQueen, Inc.; *U.S. Private*, pg. 60
ACKERMAN MCQUEEN, INC.; *U.S. Private*, pg. 60
ACKERMAN MCQUEEN, INC.—See Ackerman McQueen, Inc.; *U.S. Private*, pg. 60

ACKERMAN MCQUEEN, INC.—See Ackerman McQueen, Inc.; *U.S. Private*, pg. 60
ACKLEY SWEENEY ADVERTISING; *U.S. Private*, pg. 60
A.C. NIELSEN DE COLOMBIA LTDA.—See Brookfield Corporation; *Int'l*, pg. 1177
A.C. NIELSEN DE COLOMBIA LTDA.—See Elliott Management Corporation; *U.S. Private*, pg. 1369
ACTION CLICK CO., LTD.—See Dentsu Group Inc.; *Int'l*, pg. 2034
ACTION PR CYPRUS—See The Interpublic Group of Companies, Inc.; *U.S. Public*, pg. 2094
ACTIVIS SAS—See ADLPartner SA; *Int'l*, pg. 151
ACTON AWKK (OSAKA)—See ACTON International Ltd.; *U.S. Private*, pg. 70
ACTON INTERNATIONAL LTD.; *U.S. Private*, pg. 70
ACTON WINS CO. LTD.—See ACTON International Ltd.; *U.S. Private*, pg. 70
ACXIOM DIGITAL; *U.S. Private*, pg. 71
AD 2-ONE; *Int'l*, pg. 122
AD AGENTS AG—See ad pepper media International NV; *Int'l*, pg. 122
AD AGENTS GMBH—See ad pepper media International NV; *Int'l*, pg. 122
ADAIR GREENE-MCCANN; *U.S. Private*, pg. 73
AD ALLIANCE GMBH—See Bertelsmann SE & Co. KGaA; *Int'l*, pg. 989
ADAM COMMUNICATIONS; *U.S. Private*, pg. 73
ADAM&CO.; *U.S. Private*, pg. 73
ADAM & EVE/DDB—See Omnicom Group Inc.; *U.S. Public*, pg. 1579
ADAM HOUSE; *U.S. Private*, pg. 73
THE ADAMS GROUP; *U.S. Private*, pg. 3981
ADAMS & KNIGHT ADVERTISING/PUBLIC RELATIONS; *U.S. Private*, pg. 73
AD AREA CO., LTD.—See Dentsu Group Inc.; *Int'l*, pg. 2034
ADASIA COMMUNICATIONS, INC.; *U.S. Private*, pg. 76
ADBIT'S ADVERTISING & PR; *U.S. Private*, pg. 76
ADCELLERANT, LLC; *U.S. Private*, pg. 76
ADCETERA GROUP; *U.S. Private*, pg. 76
ADCITYMEDIA AB; *Int'l*, pg. 126
ADCLOUD GMBH—See Deutsche Post AG; *Int'l*, pg. 2071
AD CLUB 2-SALES OFFICE—See Ad Club; *U.S. Private*, pg. 72
AD CLUB; *U.S. Private*, pg. 71
THE ADCOM GROUP, INC.; *U.S. Private*, pg. 3981
AD-COMM CO., LTD.; *Int'l*, pg. 122
ADCOMM GROUP, INC.; *U.S. Private*, pg. 76
AD-COMM GROUP INC.—See ad-comm Co., Ltd.; *Int'l*, pg. 122
ADCOMM LIMITED—See The Interpublic Group of Companies, Inc.; *U.S. Public*, pg. 2090
AD CONSULTANT GROUP INC.; *U.S. Private*, pg. 72
ADCORE, INC.; *Int'l*, pg. 127
ADCORP AUSTRALIA LIMITED; *Int'l*, pg. 127
ADCORP AUSTRALIA (QLD) PTY LTD—See Adcorp Australia Limited; *Int'l*, pg. 127
ADCORP AUSTRALIA (VIC) PTY LTD—See Adcorp Australia Limited; *Int'l*, pg. 127
ADCORP NEW ZEALAND LIMITED—See Adcorp Australia Limited; *Int'l*, pg. 127
AD DAIKO GIFU INC.—See Hakuhodo DY Holdings Incorporated; *Int'l*, pg. 3220
AD DAIKO NAGOYA INC.—See Hakuhodo DY Holdings Incorporated; *Int'l*, pg. 3220
ADDED VALUE, INC.; *U.S. Private*, pg. 77
AD DENTSU OSAKA INC.—See Dentsu Group Inc.; *Int'l*, pg. 2034
ADDIS CRESON; *U.S. Private*, pg. 77
(ADD)VENTURES; *U.S. Private*, pg. 1
ADELPHI EDEN HEALTH COMMUNICATIONS—See Omnicom Group Inc.; *U.S. Public*, pg. 1573
ADELPHI GROUP LIMITED—See Omnicom Group Inc.; *U.S. Public*, pg. 1573
AD-EVENT K.K.—See ad-comm Co., Ltd.; *Int'l*, pg. 123
AD EXCELLENCE; *U.S. Private*, pg. 72
ADFACTORS PR PVT. LTD.; *Int'l*, pg. 145
ADFERO GROUP; *U.S. Private*, pg. 79
ADFORMATIX, INC.; *Int'l*, pg. 145
A.D. HEMBROUGH ADVERTISING & MARKETING SERVICES; *U.S. Private*, pg. 25
ADINC/J. KAPLAN ADVERTISING; *U.S. Private*, pg. 79
ADJUST YOUR SET LIMITED—See You & Mr Jones Inc.; *U.S. Private*, pg. 4591
ADK AMERICA, INC. - NEW YORK OFFICE—See Bain Capital, LP; *U.S. Private*, pg. 428
ADK AMERICA, INC.—See Bain Capital, LP; *U.S. Private*, pg. 428
ADKINS DESIGN VISUAL COMMUNICATIONS LLC; *U.S. Private*, pg. 79
ADK INTERNATIONAL INC.—See Bain Capital, LP; *U.S. Private*, pg. 428
ADKNOWLEDGE UK LIMITED—See Adknowledge, Inc.; *U.S. Private*, pg. 80
ADLINK CABLE ADVERTISING, LLC; *U.S. Private*, pg. 80
A.D. LUBOW, LLC; *U.S. Private*, pg. 25
ADMARK ADVERTISING LIMITED; *Int'l*, pg. 151
THE ADMARK GROUP; *U.S. Private*, pg. 3982
ADMARSH, INC.; *U.S. Private*, pg. 80

AD-MEDIA K.K—See ad-comm Co., Ltd.; *Int'l*, pg. 123
ADMEDIA—See The Interpublic Group of Companies, Inc.; *U.S. Public*, pg. 2092
ADMERASIA, INC.; *U.S. Private*, pg. 80
ADMO, INC.; *U.S. Private*, pg. 81
ADMOOVE SWEDEN AB—See AdUX SA; *Int'l*, pg. 155
ADNET ADVERTISING AGENCY, INC.; *U.S. Private*, pg. 81
AD PARTNERS, INC.; *U.S. Private*, pg. 72
AD PEPPER MEDIA FRANCE S.A.R.L—See ad pepper media International NV; *Int'l*, pg. 122
AD PEPPER MEDIA GMBH—See ad pepper media International NV; *Int'l*, pg. 122
AD PEPPER MEDIA INTERNATIONAL NV; *Int'l*, pg. 122
AD PEPPER MEDIA SPAIN S.A.—See ad pepper media International NV; *Int'l*, pg. 122
AD PEPPER MEDIA UK LTD—See ad pepper media International NV; *Int'l*, pg. 122
AD PEPPER MEDIA USA LLC—See ad pepper media International NV; *Int'l*, pg. 122
ADPERIO; *U.S. Private*, pg. 82
ADPLEX INC.; *U.S. Private*, pg. 82
THE AD PROS GROUP; *U.S. Private*, pg. 3981
ADR ADVERTISING S.P.A.—See Edizione S.r.l.; *Int'l*, pg. 2312
ADREKA ADVERTISING; *U.S. Private*, pg. 82
ADRELEVANCE—See Brookfield Corporation; *Int'l*, pg. 1179
ADRELEVANCE—See Elliott Management Corporation; *U.S. Private*, pg. 1371
ADRENALINE, INC.—See NewGround Resources; *U.S. Private*, pg. 2915
AD RESULTS; *U.S. Private*, pg. 72
ADSLOT INC.—See Adslot Ltd.; *Int'l*, pg. 154
ADSLOT UK LIMITED—See Adslot Ltd.; *Int'l*, pg. 154
ADSOUTH PARTNERS, INC.; *U.S. Private*, pg. 82
ADS R US; *U.S. Private*, pg. 82
ADSTAFFING.COM; *U.S. Private*, pg. 83
THE AD STORE BRUSSELS—See The Ad Store, Inc.; *U.S. Private*, pg. 3981
THE AD STORE GMBH—See The Ad Store, Inc.; *U.S. Private*, pg. 3981
THE AD STORE, INC.; *U.S. Private*, pg. 3981
THE AD STORE ITALIA—See The Ad Store, Inc.; *U.S. Private*, pg. 3981
THE AD STORE PACIFIQUE—See The Ad Store, Inc.; *U.S. Private*, pg. 3981
THE AD STORE ROMANIA—See The Ad Store, Inc.; *U.S. Private*, pg. 3981
THE AD STORE WASHINGTON—See The Ad Store, Inc.; *U.S. Private*, pg. 3981
AD-SUCCESS MARKETING; *U.S. Private*, pg. 72
ADTEGRITY.COM INTERNATIONAL, INC.; *U.S. Public*, pg. 43
ADTEGRITY.COM; *U.S. Private*, pg. 83
ADTHENA LTD.; *Int'l*, pg. 154
ADTHINK MEDIA SA; *Int'l*, pg. 154
ADTRACTION GROUP AB; *Int'l*, pg. 154
ADUX BENELUX SPRL—See AdUX SA; *Int'l*, pg. 155
ADVANCED MARKETING STRATEGIES; *U.S. Private*, pg. 91
ADVANCED MARKETING STRATEGIES—See Advanced Marketing Strategies; *U.S. Private*, pg. 91
ADVANCED TELECOM SERVICES; *U.S. Private*, pg. 93
ADVANCE NOTICE, INC.; *U.S. Private*, pg. 83
AD-VANTAGE ADVERTISING; *U.S. Private*, pg. 72
ADVANTAGE CORPORATE COMMUNICATIONS GMBH—See Omnicom Group Inc.; *U.S. Public*, pg. 1583
ADVECOR, INC.; *U.S. Private*, pg. 95
ADVENTA LOWE—See The Interpublic Group of Companies, Inc.; *U.S. Public*, pg. 2090
ADVENTIVE MARKETING, INC.; *U.S. Private*, pg. 109
AD VENTURES, INC.; *U.S. Private*, pg. 72
ADVERTEX COMMUNICATIONS INC.—See Macy's, Inc.; *U.S. Public*, pg. 1353
ADVERTISEMENT EDI CENTER INC.—See Dentsu Group Inc.; *Int'l*, pg. 2034
ADVERTISE PURPLE, INC.; *U.S. Private*, pg. 109
ADVERTISING ASSOCIATES, INC.; *U.S. Private*, pg. 109
ADVERTISING ASSOCIATES INTERNATIONAL; *U.S. Private*, pg. 109
ADVERTISING CONNECTION INC.; *U.S. Private*, pg. 110
ADVERTISING SAVANTS, INC.; *U.S. Private*, pg. 110
ADVERTISING WORKS & PRODUCTION; *U.S. Private*, pg. 110
ADVICE A/S; *Int'l*, pg. 168
ADVICE, INC.; *U.S. Private*, pg. 110
ADVICE INTERACTIVE GROUP LLC; *U.S. Private*, pg. 110
ADVILLE/USA; *U.S. Private*, pg. 110
ADVOCATE COMMUNICATIONS INC.—See Schurz Communications, Inc.; *U.S. Private*, pg. 3571
ADWAYS FRONTIER INC.—See Adways Inc.; *Int'l*, pg. 169
ADWAYS INC.; *Int'l*, pg. 169
ADWAYS INTERACTIVE, INC.—See Adways Inc.; *Int'l*, pg. 169
ADWAYS KOREA, INC.—See Adways Inc.; *Int'l*, pg. 169
ADWAYS LABS (THAILAND) CO., LTD.—See Adways Inc.; *Int'l*, pg. 169
ADWAYS PHILIPPINES INC.—See Adways Inc.; *Int'l*, pg. 169

541810 — ADVERTISING AGENCIE... CORPORATE AFFILIATIONS

ADWAYS TECHNOLOGY CO., JSC.—See Adways Inc.; *Int'l*, pg. 169
ADWAYS VENTURES, INC.—See Adways Inc.; *Int'l*, pg. 169
AD WORKSHOP; *U.S. Private*, pg. 72
ADWORKS, INC; *U.S. Private*, pg. 111
AFFICHAGE ROMANIA SRL; *Int'l*, pg. 186
AFFILINET SCHWEIZ GMBH—See Axel Springer SE; *Int'l*, pg. 767
AFFINITIVE LLC—See Project: Worldwide, Inc.; *U.S. Private*, pg. 3280
AFIRMA—See The Interpublic Group of Companies, Inc.; *U.S. Public*, pg. 2092
AGENCE 154 S.A—See Hakuhodo DY Holdings Incorporated; *Int'l*, pg. 3220
AGENCE EURO SERVICES; *Int'l*, pg. 205
AGENCE MEESTERS; *Int'l*, pg. 205
AGENCY212, LLC; *U.S. Private*, pg. 126
AGENCY59 RESPONSE—See AGENCY59; *Int'l*, pg. 205
AGENCY59; *Int'l*, pg. 205
AGENCY.COM—See Omnicom Group Inc.; *U.S. Public*, pg. 1594
AGENCY.COM—See Omnicom Group Inc.; *U.S. Public*, pg. 1594
AGENCY.COM—See Omnicom Group Inc.; *U.S. Public*, pg. 1594
AGENCY EA, LLC; *U.S. Private*, pg. 126
AGENCY REPUBLIC—See Omnicom Group Inc.; *U.S. Public*, pg. 1573
AGENCYTWOFIFTEEN—See The Interpublic Group of Companies, Inc.; *U.S. Public*, pg. 2106
AGENT16; *U.S. Private*, pg. 127
AGENT X; *U.S. Private*, pg. 127
AGNES HUFF COMMUNICATIONS GROUP, LLC.; *U.S. Private*, pg. 128
AHA!; *U.S. Private*, pg. 130
AICHNER CLODI GGK—See GGK Zurich Werbeagentur AG; *Int'l*, pg. 2957
AID-ANALYSE INFORMATIQUE DE DONNEES—See Omnicom Group Inc.; *U.S. Public*, pg. 1592
AILLEURS EXACTEMENT; *Int'l*, pg. 232
AIM AGENCY; *U.S. Private*, pg. 132
AIM SMARTER LLC—See Altitude Group plc; *Int'l*, pg. 393
AKCENT MEDIA SP. Z O. O.—See Agora S.A.; *Int'l*, pg. 212
ALAN/ANTHONY, INC.; *U.S. Private*, pg. 150
A. LAVIN COMMUNICATIONS; *U.S. Private*, pg. 23
ALCONE MARKETING GROUP—See Omnicom Group Inc.; *U.S. Public*, pg. 1573
ALCONE MARKETING GROUP—See Omnicom Group Inc.; *U.S. Public*, pg. 1573
ALIANDA; *U.S. Private*, pg. 166
ALICE BBDO—See Omnicom Group Inc.; *U.S. Public*, pg. 1573
THE ALISON GROUP; *U.S. Private*, pg. 3984
ALL ABOUT, INC.; *Int'l*, pg. 331
ALLEGIANCE FUNDRAISING LLC; *U.S. Private*, pg. 176
ALLEN & GERRITSEN, INC.; *U.S. Private*, pg. 178
ALLEN INSURANCE ASSOCIATES, INC.—See Aon plc; *Int'l*, pg. 489
ALLER MEDIA AB—See Aller Holding A/S; *Int'l*, pg. 336
ALLER MEDIA OY—See Aller Holding A/S; *Int'l*, pg. 336
ALLIANCE PROMOTIONS, INC.; *U.S. Private*, pg. 184
ALLIED ADVERTISING PUBLIC RELATIONS OF CANADA, INC.—See AALP, Inc.; *U.S. Private*, pg. 32
ALLIED EXPERIENTIAL - LOS ANGELES—See AALP, Inc.; *U.S. Private*, pg. 32
ALLIED EXPERIENTIAL—See AALP, Inc.; *U.S. Private*, pg. 32
ALLIED LIVE—See AALP, Inc.; *U.S. Private*, pg. 32
ALL IN MEDIA PTY. LTD.—See Adeia Inc.; *U.S. Public*, pg. 40
ALLISON AND PARTNERS K.K.—See Allison & Partners LLC; *U.S. Private*, pg. 192
ALL RESPONSE MEDIA; *Int'l*, pg. 332
ALL STAR DIRECTORIES, INC.; *U.S. Private*, pg. 172
ALL STAR INCENTIVE MARKETING, INC.; *U.S. Private*, pg. 172
ALLTURNA, LLC—See Search Discovery, Inc.; *U.S. Private*, pg. 3586
ALL-WAYS ADVERTISING COMPANY; *U.S. Private*, pg. 174
ALMA AGENCY; *U.S. Private*, pg. 194
ALMA MEDIAPARTNERS OY—See Alma Media Corporation; *Int'l*, pg. 361
ALMAP BBDO—See Omnicom Group Inc.; *U.S. Public*, pg. 1573
ALMA TALENT AB; *Int'l*, pg. 362
ALMA TALENT MEDIA AB—See Alma Talent AB; *Int'l*, pg. 362
ALOFT GROUP, INC.; *U.S. Private*, pg. 195
ALOYSIUS, BUTLER & CLARK ASSOCIATES, INC.; *U.S. Private*, pg. 195
AL PUNTO ADVERTISING, INC.; *U.S. Private*, pg. 147
ALSTIN COMMUNICATIONS, INC.; *U.S. Private*, pg. 203
A.L.T. ADVERTISING & PROMOTION; *U.S. Private*, pg. 27
ALTAVIA ADVERTISING CO., LTD.—See Altavia S.A.; *Int'l*, pg. 387
ALTERNATE TRANSIT ADVERTISING; *U.S. Private*, pg. 207

ALTERNATIVE MARKETING SOLUTIONS, INC.; *U.S. Private*, pg. 207
ALTITUDE DIGITAL, INC.; *U.S. Private*, pg. 209
ALTO MARKETING; *Int'l*, pg. 394
ALT STUDIOS—See Sigler Companies, Inc.; *U.S. Private*, pg. 3648
AMALGAME; *Int'l*, pg. 409
AMAZON ADVERTISING; *U.S. Private*, pg. 216
AMCI—See Omnicom Group Inc.; *U.S. Public*, pg. 1573
AMCO SRL—See APG/SGA SA; *Int'l*, pg. 513
AMEREDIA INCORPORATED; *U.S. Private*, pg. 219
AMERICAN CLASSIFIED SERVICES, INC.; *U.S. Private*, pg. 227
AMES SCULLIN O'HAIRE; *U.S. Private*, pg. 262
AMP AGENCY; *U.S. Private*, pg. 264
AMPERAGE, LLC; *U.S. Private*, pg. 265
AMPERAGE MARKETING—See AMPERAGE, LLC; *U.S. Private*, pg. 265
AMPLIO DIGITAL, LLC; *U.S. Private*, pg. 266
AM/PM ADVERTISING INC.; *U.S. Private*, pg. 215
AMPM, INC. DETROIT—See AMPM, Inc.; *U.S. Private*, pg. 266
AMPM, INC.; *U.S. Private*, pg. 266
ANDERSON DDB HEALTH & LIFESTYLE—See Omnicom Group Inc.; *U.S. Public*, pg. 1579
ANDERSON DDB HEALTH & LIFESTYLE—See Omnicom Group Inc.; *U.S. Public*, pg. 1579
ANDERSON DDB SANTE.VIE.ESPRIT.—See Omnicom Group Inc.; *U.S. Public*, pg. 1579
THE ANDERSON GROUP; *U.S. Private*, pg. 3986
ANDERSON MARKETING GROUP; *U.S. Private*, pg. 277
ANDERSON PARTNERS; *U.S. Private*, pg. 277
ANDERSON SPRATT GROUP; *Int'l*, pg. 450
ANDERSSON & PARTNERS; *Int'l*, pg. 450
ANDIS ADVERTISING; *U.S. Private*, pg. 278
ANEW MARKETING GROUP; *U.S. Private*, pg. 281
ANEW MARKETING GROUP—See ANEW Marketing Group; *U.S. Private*, pg. 281
ANIMATED DESIGNS LLC; *U.S. Private*, pg. 283
ANIMATION COLLECTIVE; *U.S. Private*, pg. 283
ANOMALY INC.—See Stagwell, Inc.; *U.S. Public*, pg. 1925
ANR BBDO—See Omnicom Group Inc.; *U.S. Public*, pg. 1573
ANR BBDO—See Omnicom Group Inc.; *U.S. Public*, pg. 1573
ANSIRA PARTNERS, INC.; *U.S. Private*, pg. 285
ANSON-STONER INC.; *U.S. Private*, pg. 286
ANTARRA COMMUNICATIONS; *U.S. Private*, pg. 287
ANTARRA COMMUNICATIONS—See Antarra Communications; *U.S. Private*, pg. 287
ANTHEM WORLDWIDE - CINCINNATI—See Matthews International Corporation; *U.S. Public*, pg. 1401
ANTHEM WORLDWIDE - NEW YORK—See Matthews International Corporation; *U.S. Public*, pg. 1401
ANTHEM WORLDWIDE—See Matthews International Corporation; *U.S. Public*, pg. 1401
AOI PRO. INC.—See AOI TYO Holdings Inc.; *Int'l*, pg. 488
AOS ADS; *U.S. Private*, pg. 289
APCO WORLDWIDE; *U.S. Private*, pg. 290
APCO WORLDWIDE—See APCO Worldwide; *U.S. Private*, pg. 291
APCO WORLDWIDE—See APCO Worldwide; *U.S. Private*, pg. 291
APCO WORLDWIDE—See APCO Worldwide; *U.S. Private*, pg. 291
APEX BBDO PUBLICIDAD—See Omnicom Group Inc.; *U.S. Public*, pg. 1573
APG, ALLGEMEINE PLAKATGESELLSCHAFT APG—See APG/SGA SA; *Int'l*, pg. 513
APG-SGA TRAFFIC SA—See APG/SGA SA; *Int'l*, pg. 513
APOGEE RESULTS; *U.S. Private*, pg. 294
APOLLO INTERACTIVE, INC. - DALLAS—See Apollo Interactive, Inc.; *U.S. Private*, pg. 295
APOLLO INTERACTIVE, INC.; *U.S. Private*, pg. 294
APPLE ROCK; *U.S. Private*, pg. 297
AQUA ONLINE; *Int'l*, pg. 527
ARA DIRECT COMMUNICATIONS—See Omnicom Group Inc.; *U.S. Public*, pg. 1596
ARA GROEP B.V.—See Omnicom Group Inc.; *U.S. Public*, pg. 1596
ARA INTERACTIVE—See Omnicom Group Inc.; *U.S. Public*, pg. 1596
ARA M/V—See Omnicom Group Inc.; *U.S. Public*, pg. 1596
ARCHER COMMUNICATIONS, INC.; *U.S. Private*, pg. 310
THE ARCHER GROUP; *U.S. Private*, pg. 3987
ARCHER MALMO; *U.S. Private*, pg. 310
ARCHIBALD INGALL STRETTON; *Int'l*, pg. 548
ARCHRIVAL, INC.; *U.S. Private*, pg. 312
ARCOS COMMUNICATIONS; *U.S. Private*, pg. 315
ARENDS, INC.; *U.S. Private*, pg. 318
ARGONAUT CLAIMS SERVICES, LTD.—See Brookfield Reinsurance Ltd.; *Int'l*, pg. 1194
ARGUS; *U.S. Private*, pg. 322
ARIAD CUSTOM PUBLISHING LIMITED—See High Road Capital Partners, LLC; *U.S. Private*, pg. 1936
THE ARISTOS GROUP; *U.S. Private*, pg. 3988
ARKANSAS TELEVISION COMPANY—See TEGNA Inc.; *U.S. Public*, pg. 1990

ARMANDO TESTA BRUSSELS NV—See Armando Testa S.p.A.; *Int'l*, pg. 574
ARMANDO TESTA GMBH—See Armando Testa S.p.A.; *Int'l*, pg. 574
ARMANDO TESTA LTD.—See Armando Testa S.p.A.; *Int'l*, pg. 574
ARMANDO TESTA SL—See Armando Testa S.p.A.; *Int'l*, pg. 574
ARMANDO TESTA—See Armando Testa S.p.A.; *Int'l*, pg. 574
ARMANDO TESTA S.P.A.; *Int'l*, pg. 574
ARMANDO TESTA S.P.A.—See Armando Testa S.p.A.; *Int'l*, pg. 574
ARMANDO TESTA S.P.A.—See Armando Testa S.p.A.; *Int'l*, pg. 574
ARMANDO TESTA S.P.A.—See Armando Testa S.p.A.; *Int'l*, pg. 574
ARMANINO LLP; *U.S. Private*, pg. 330
ARMED FORCES COMMUNICATIONS, INC.; *U.S. Private*, pg. 330
AR MEDIA; *U.S. Private*, pg. 306
ARNELL—See Omnicom Group Inc.; *U.S. Public*, pg. 1573
THE ARRAS GROUP—See The Adcom Group, Inc.; *U.S. Private*, pg. 3981
ARRAS KEATHLEY ADVERTISING—See The Adcom Group, Inc.; *U.S. Private*, pg. 3981
ARROWHEAD ADVERTISING; *U.S. Private*, pg. 336
ARROW S.A.—See Omnicom Group Inc.; *U.S. Public*, pg. 1573
ARS ADVERTISING, LLC; *U.S. Private*, pg. 337
ARS ADVERTISING—See ARS Advertising, LLC; *U.S. Private*, pg. 337
ARS ADVERTISING—See ARS Advertising, LLC; *U.S. Private*, pg. 337
ARS PUBLICIDAD—See Omnicom Group Inc.; *U.S. Public*, pg. 1579
ARTICUS LTD. MARKETING COMMUNICATIONS; *U.S. Private*, pg. 342
ARTIFAX; *U.S. Private*, pg. 342
ARTILLERY MARKETING COMMUNICATIONS LLC; *U.S. Private*, pg. 343
THE ARTIME GROUP; *U.S. Private*, pg. 3988
ART MARKETING SYNDICATE SA—See Agora S.A.; *Int'l*, pg. 212
ARVO COMMUNICATIONS, INC.; *U.S. Private*, pg. 345
ASAHI AREA ADVERTISING INC.—See Hakuhodo DY Holdings Incorporated; *Int'l*, pg. 3220
ASAHI AREA ADVERTISING WAKAYAMA INC.—See Hakuhodo DY Holdings Incorporated; *Int'l*, pg. 3220
ASAHI AREA AVERTISING NARA INC.—See Hakuhodo DY Holdings Incorporated; *Int'l*, pg. 3220
ASA MARKETING; *U.S. Private*, pg. 345
ASATSU CENTURY (SHANGHAI) ADVERTISING CO.,LTD.—See Bain Capital, LP; *U.S. Private*, pg. 428
ASATSU-DK MALAYSIA SDN. BHD.—See Bain Capital, LP; *U.S. Private*, pg. 428
ASATSU-DK SINGAPORE PTE. LTD.—See Bain Capital, LP; *U.S. Private*, pg. 428
ASATSU (THAILAND) CO., LTD.—See Bain Capital, LP; *U.S. Private*, pg. 428
ASCENTIUM-MWR—See Ascentium Corporation; *U.S. Private*, pg. 348
ASG LTD—See Anderson Spratt Group; *Int'l*, pg. 450
ASHER AGENCY, INC. - LEXINGTON—See Asher Agency, Inc.; *U.S. Private*, pg. 349
ASHER AGENCY, INC.; *U.S. Private*, pg. 349
ASHER MEDIA, INC.; *U.S. Private*, pg. 349
ASPENCORE MEDIA GMBH—See Arrow Electronics, Inc.; *U.S. Public*, pg. 198
ASSEMBLY—See Stagwell, Inc.; *U.S. Public*, pg. 1926
ASSET ENTITIES INC.; *U.S. Public*, pg. 214
ASSOCIATED ADVERTISING AGENCY, INC.; *U.S. Private*, pg. 354
THE ASSOCIATED PRESS, INC.—See The Associated Press; *U.S. Private*, pg. 3989
ASSOCIATES IN ADVERTISING LIMITED—See Gemspring Capital Management, LLC; *U.S. Private*, pg. 1659
ASTOS DIZAINAS MCCANN ERICKSON VILNIUS—See The Interpublic Group of Companies, Inc.; *U.S. Public*, pg. 2097
ATCOMM PUBLISHING CORP.; *U.S. Private*, pg. 365
THE A TEAM, LLC; *U.S. Private*, pg. 3980
THE A TEAM PROMOTIONAL—See The A Team, LLC; *U.S. Private*, pg. 3980
ATLAN MEDIA INC.; *Int'l*, pg. 674
ATLANTIC MEDIA SERVICES; *U.S. Private*, pg. 373
ATLAS ADVERTISING, LLC; *U.S. Private*, pg. 375
ATOMIC DIRECT, LLC; *U.S. Private*, pg. 381
ATOMIC PLAYPEN; *U.S. Private*, pg. 381
ATOS FRANCE S.A.S.—See Atos SE; *Int'l*, pg. 690
ATOS INFORMATION TECHNOLOGY (SINGAPORE) PTE. LTD.—See Atos SE; *Int'l*, pg. 690
ATOS ITS NEARSHORE CENTER MAROC S.A.R.L.—See Atos SE; *Int'l*, pg. 690
ATOS SOLUCOES E SERVICOS PARA TECNOLOGIAS DE INFORMACAO, UNIPESSOAL, LTDA.—See Atos SE; *Int'l*, pg. 691
ATRAX MARKETING; *U.S. Private*, pg. 382
ATRES ADVERTISING S.L.U.—See Atresmedia Corporacion de Medios de Comunicacion, S.A.; *Int'l*, pg. 693

N.A.I.C.S. INDEX

541810 — ADVERTISING AGENCIE...

ATTIVO GROUP; *Int'l*, pg. 696
AUDIOBOOM LIMITED—See Audioboom Group plc; *Int'l*, pg. 701
AUDITOIRE—See Omnicom Group Inc.; *U.S. Public*, pg. 1596
AUGUST, LANG & HUSAK, INC.; *U.S. Private*, pg. 392
AUSTIN LAWRENCE GROUP; *U.S. Private*, pg. 396
AUSTIN & WILLIAMS; *U.S. Private*, pg. 395
AUSTRALIE SASU; *Int'l*, pg. 723
AVA ADVERTISING; *U.S. Private*, pg. 402
AVATRIA INC.; *U.S. Private*, pg. 404
AVC IMMEDIA LIMITED; *Int'l*, pg. 737
AVEX & HIROTSU BIO EMPOWER LLC—See Avex Inc.; *Int'l*, pg. 740
AVICOM MARKETING COMMUNICATIONS; *U.S. Private*, pg. 406
AVICOM MARKETING COMMUNICATIONS—See Avicom Marketing Communications; *U.S. Private*, pg. 406
AVIDLY OY—See Adelis Equity Partners AB; *Int'l*, pg. 142
AVIONOS, LLC—See AEA Investors LP; *U.S. Private*, pg. 114
AVREAFOSTER INC.—See Omnicom Group Inc.; *U.S. Public*, pg. 1573
AVRETT FREE GINSBERG—See The Interpublic Group of Companies, Inc.; *U.S. Public*, pg. 2097
AWARDIT AB; *Int'l*, pg. 752
AWESTRUCK MARKETING GROUP; *U.S. Private*, pg. 411
AWIN AB—See Axel Springer SE; *Int'l*, pg. 765
AWIN B.V.—See Axel Springer SE; *Int'l*, pg. 765
AWIN LTD.—See Axel Springer SE; *Int'l*, pg. 766
AWIN SAS—See Axel Springer SE; *Int'l*, pg. 765
AWIN SP. Z.O.O.—See Axel Springer SE; *Int'l*, pg. 765
AWIN SRL—See Axel Springer SE; *Int'l*, pg. 765
AWIN VEICULACAO DE PUBLICIDADE NA INTERNET LTDA.—See Axel Springer SE; *Int'l*, pg. 766
A WORK OF ART INC.; *U.S. Private*, pg. 19
AXIATA DIGITAL ADVERTISING SDN BHD—See Axiata Group Berhad; *Int'l*, pg. 768
AXIOM; *U.S. Private*, pg. 413
AXIS COMMUNICATIONS; *U.S. Private*, pg. 413
AXISS ADVERTISING; *U.S. Private*, pg. 414
AYLESWORTH FLEMING LIMITED—See You & Mr Jones Inc.; *U.S. Private*, pg. 4591
AYRES KAHLER + SACCO; *U.S. Private*, pg. 414
AYZENBERG GROUP, INC.; *U.S. Private*, pg. 415
AZERION PORTUGAL LDA.—See Azerion Group N.V.; *Int'l*, pg. 778
AZIMUTH FULL SCREEN PUBLICATIONS INC.; *U.S. Private*, pg. 415
AZZAM JORDAN; *U.S. Private*, pg. 416
BABCOCK & JENKINS, INC.; *U.S. Private*, pg. 421
BABYTREE GROUP; *Int'l*, pg. 793
BACKE DIGITAL BRAND MARKETING; *U.S. Private*, pg. 423
BACKUS TURNER INTERNATIONAL; *U.S. Private*, pg. 423
BADER RUTTER & ASSOCIATES, INC.; *U.S. Private*, pg. 424
BADER RUTTER & ASSOCIATES, INC.—See Bader Rutter & Associates, Inc.; *U.S. Private*, pg. 424
BADGER & PARTNERS, INC.; *U.S. Private*, pg. 424
BAILEY LAUERMAN; *U.S. Private*, pg. 425
BAILEY LAUERMAN—See Bailey Lauerman; *U.S. Private*, pg. 425
BAKER & ASSOCIATES ADVERTISING, INC.; *U.S. Private*, pg. 454
BAKER COMMUNICATIONS ADVERTISING, MARKETING & PUBLIC RELATIONS; *U.S. Private*, pg. 455
BAKER STREET PARTNERS; *U.S. Private*, pg. 456
THE BALCOM AGENCY; *U.S. Private*, pg. 3991
BALDRICA ADVERTISING & MARKETING; *U.S. Private*, pg. 458
BALDWIN & OBENAUF, INC.; *U.S. Private*, pg. 458
BAM STRATEGY; *Int'l*, pg. 813
BANDUJO DONKER & BROTHERS; *U.S. Private*, pg. 465
BANDY CARROLL HELLIGE ADVERTISING - INDIANAPOLIS—See Bandy Carroll Hellige Advertising; *U.S. Private*, pg. 465
BANDY CARROLL HELLIGE ADVERTISING; *U.S. Private*, pg. 465
BANGARANG ENTERPRISES, LLC—See Stran & Company, Inc.; *U.S. Public*, pg. 1953
BARANSKI & ASSOCIATES—See Barancorp, Ltd.; *U.S. Private*, pg. 471
BARBEAU-HUTCHINGS ADVERTISING, INC.; *U.S. Private*, pg. 472
BARBER MARTIN & ASSOCIATES; *U.S. Private*, pg. 472
BARKER/DZP; *U.S. Private*, pg. 475
BARKLEY HOLDING COMPANY, INC.; *U.S. Private*, pg. 475
BARKLEY REI—See Barkley; *U.S. Private*, pg. 475
BARKLEY; *U.S. Private*, pg. 475
BARKLEY—See Barkley; *U.S. Private*, pg. 475
BARNES, CATMUR & FRIENDS LIMITED—See Dentsu Group Inc.; *Int'l*, pg. 2034
BARNESMCINERNEY INC.; *Int'l*, pg. 866
BARNETT COX & ASSOCIATES—See Armanino LLP; *U.S. Private*, pg. 330
BARNETT & MURPHY, INC; *U.S. Private*, pg. 477

BARNHARDT, DAY & HINES; *U.S. Private*, pg. 478
BARNHART; *U.S. Private*, pg. 478
BAROLIN & SPENCER, INC.; *U.S. Private*, pg. 478
BARRELHOUSE CREATIVE—See Yaffe Group; *U.S. Private*, pg. 4584
&BARR; *U.S. Private*, pg. 1
BARTON GILANELLI & ASSOCIATES, INC.; *U.S. Private*, pg. 483
BASANITE, INC.; *U.S. Public*, pg. 278
BASE ONE INTEGRATED MARKETING SERVICES; *Int'l*, pg. 871
BATES/LEE ADVERTISING; *U.S. Private*, pg. 487
BAUZA & ASSOCIATES, LLC; *U.S. Private*, pg. 491
BAYARD ADVERTISING AGENCY, INC.—See Axel Springer SE; *Int'l*, pg. 766
BAYARD ADVERTISING AGENCY, INC.—See Axel Springer SE; *Int'l*, pg. 767
BAYARD ADVERTISING AGENCY, INC.—See Axel Springer SE; *Int'l*, pg. 767
BAYARD ADVERTISING AGENCY, INC.—See Axel Springer SE; *Int'l*, pg. 767
BAYARD ADVERTISING AGENCY, INC.—See Axel Springer SE; *Int'l*, pg. 767
BAYARD ADVERTISING AGENCY, INC.—See Axel Springer SE; *Int'l*, pg. 767
BAYARD ADVERTISING AGENCY, INC.—See Axel Springer SE; *Int'l*, pg. 767
BAYARD ADVERTISING AGENCY, INC.—See Axel Springer SE; *Int'l*, pg. 767
BAYARD ADVERTISING AGENCY, INC.—See Axel Springer SE; *Int'l*, pg. 767
BBCARLSON—See Aimia Inc.; *Int'l*, pg. 233
BBDO ARGENTINA—See Omnicom Group Inc.; *U.S. Public*, pg. 1573
BBDO ASIA/PACIFIC—See Omnicom Group Inc.; *U.S. Public*, pg. 1573
BBDO ATHENS—See Omnicom Group Inc.; *U.S. Public*, pg. 1573
BBDO ATLANTA—See Omnicom Group Inc.; *U.S. Public*, pg. 1573
BBDO BANGKOK—See Omnicom Group Inc.; *U.S. Public*, pg. 1573
BBDO BANGLADESH—See Omnicom Group Inc.; *U.S. Public*, pg. 1573
BBDO BUDAPEST—See Omnicom Group Inc.; *U.S. Public*, pg. 1573
BBDO CANADA CORP.—See Omnicom Group Inc.; *U.S. Public*, pg. 1573
BBDO CENTROAMERICA—See Omnicom Group Inc.; *U.S. Public*, pg. 1574
BBDO CHILE—See Omnicom Group Inc.; *U.S. Public*, pg. 1574
BBDO CHINA—See Omnicom Group Inc.; *U.S. Public*, pg. 1574
BBDO CHINA—See Omnicom Group Inc.; *U.S. Public*, pg. 1574
BBDO DUBLIN—See Omnicom Group Inc.; *U.S. Public*, pg. 1574
BBDO DUSSELDORF—See Omnicom Group Inc.; *U.S. Public*, pg. 1574
BBDO EMEA—See Omnicom Group Inc.; *U.S. Public*, pg. 1574
BBDO GUATEMALA—See Omnicom Group Inc.; *U.S. Public*, pg. 1574
BBDO GUERRERO—See Omnicom Group Inc.; *U.S. Public*, pg. 1574
BBDO HONDURAS—See Omnicom Group Inc.; *U.S. Public*, pg. 1574
BBDO INDIA—See Omnicom Group Inc.; *U.S. Public*, pg. 1574
BBDO JAPAN INC.—See Omnicom Group Inc.; *U.S. Public*, pg. 1575
BBDO/J WEST INC. HEADQUARTERS—See Omnicom Group Inc.; *U.S. Public*, pg. 1575
BBDO/J WEST INC. HIROSHIMA BRANCH—See Omnicom Group Inc.; *U.S. Public*, pg. 1575
BBDO/J WEST INC. KITA-KYUSHU BRANCH—See Omnicom Group Inc.; *U.S. Public*, pg. 1575
BBDO/J WEST INC. OKINAWA BRANCH—See Omnicom Group Inc.; *U.S. Public*, pg. 1575
BBDO KOMUNIKA—See Omnicom Group Inc.; *U.S. Public*, pg. 1574
BBDO KOREA—See Omnicom Group Inc.; *U.S. Public*, pg. 1574
BBDO MALAYSIA—See Omnicom Group Inc.; *U.S. Public*, pg. 1574
BBDO MEXICO—See Omnicom Group Inc.; *U.S. Public*, pg. 1574
BBDO MINNEAPOLIS—See Omnicom Group Inc.; *U.S. Public*, pg. 1574
BBDO MOSCOW—See Omnicom Group Inc.; *U.S. Public*, pg. 1574
BBDO NEW YORK—See Omnicom Group Inc.; *U.S. Public*, pg. 1574
BBDO NICARAGUA—See Omnicom Group Inc.; *U.S. Public*, pg. 1574

BBDO NORTH AMERICA—See Omnicom Group Inc.; *U.S. Public*, pg. 1574
BBDO PANAMA—See Omnicom Group Inc.; *U.S. Public*, pg. 1574
BBDO PORTUGAL—See Omnicom Group Inc.; *U.S. Public*, pg. 1574
BBDO/PROXIMITY SINGAPORE—See Omnicom Group Inc.; *U.S. Public*, pg. 1575
BBDO PUERTO RICO—See Omnicom Group Inc.; *U.S. Public*, pg. 1574
BBDO SAN FRANCISCO—See Omnicom Group Inc.; *U.S. Public*, pg. 1574
BBDO SINGAPORE—See Omnicom Group Inc.; *U.S. Public*, pg. 1574
BBDO—See Omnicom Group Inc.; *U.S. Public*, pg. 1573
BBDO STUTTGART—See Omnicom Group Inc.; *U.S. Public*, pg. 1575
BBDO TAIWAN—See Omnicom Group Inc.; *U.S. Public*, pg. 1575
BBDO TORONTO—See Omnicom Group Inc.; *U.S. Public*, pg. 1575
BBDO WEST—See Omnicom Group Inc.; *U.S. Public*, pg. 1575
BBDO WORLDWIDE INC.—See Omnicom Group Inc.; *U.S. Public*, pg. 1573
BBDO ZAGREB—See Omnicom Group Inc.; *U.S. Public*, pg. 1575
BB&M LOWE & PARTNERS—See The Interpublic Group of Companies, Inc.; *U.S. Public*, pg. 2090
BBTV HOLDINGS INC.; *Int'l*, pg. 921
BCA (BRIAN CRONIN & ASSOCIATES INC.); *U.S. Private*, pg. 498
THE BCB GROUP, INC.; *U.S. Private*, pg. 3992
BCF; *U.S. Private*, pg. 499
BCG COMMUNICATIONS; *Int'l*, pg. 928
BCP LTD.; *Int'l*, pg. 929
BCS BROADCAST SACHSEN GMBH & CO. KG—See Bertelsmann SE & Co. KGaA; *Int'l*, pg. 990
BDDP & FILS—See Omnicom Group Inc.; *U.S. Public*, pg. 1596
BD-NTWK LONDON; *Int'l*, pg. 929
BD-NTWK SCOTLAND—See BD-NTWK London; *Int'l*, pg. 929
BDS MARKETING, LLC; *U.S. Private*, pg. 502
BEACON MEDIA GROUP—See Kartoon Studios, Inc.; *U.S. Public*, pg. 1214
BEALS CUNNINGHAM STRATEGIC SERVICES; *U.S. Private*, pg. 505
BEATLEY GRAVITT COMMUNICATIONS; *U.S. Private*, pg. 507
BEATTIE COMMUNICATIONS GROUP; *Int'l*, pg. 933
BEATTIE COMMUNICATIONS GROUP—See Beattie Communications Group; *Int'l*, pg. 933
BEATTIE COMMUNICATIONS GROUP—See Beattie Communications Group; *Int'l*, pg. 933
BEATTIE MCGUINNESS BUNGAY; *Int'l*, pg. 933
BEBER SILVERSTEIN GROUP; *U.S. Private*, pg. 509
BECKETT & BECKETT, INC.; *U.S. Private*, pg. 511
BEDFORD ADVERTISING INC.; *U.S. Private*, pg. 512
BEECHWOOD CREATIVE, INC.; *U.S. Private*, pg. 513
BE HEARD GROUP PLC—See OEP Capital Advisors, L.P.; *U.S. Private*, pg. 2999
BEHIND THE SCENES MARKETING; *U.S. Private*, pg. 515
BEIJING ASIARAY ADVERTISING—See Asiaray Media Group Limited; *Int'l*, pg. 620
BEIJING DENTSU ADVERTISING CO., LTD.—See Dentsu Group Inc.; *Int'l*, pg. 2035
BEIJING DENTSU ADVERTISING CO., LTD.—See Dentsu Group Inc.; *Int'l*, pg. 2035
BEIJING DENTSU ADVERTISING CO., LTD.—See Dentsu Group Inc.; *Int'l*, pg. 2035
BEIJING DENTSU QINGDAO—See Dentsu Group Inc.; *Int'l*, pg. 2035
BEIJING GRAND-CHINA UNIVERSE MEDIA INC.—See Hainan Traffic Administration Holding Co., Ltd.; *Int'l*, pg. 3213
BEIJING HAKUHODO CO., LTD.—See Hakuhodo DY Holdings Incorporated; *Int'l*, pg. 3220
BEING—See Omnicom Group Inc.; *U.S. Public*, pg. 1596
BELGIOVANE WILLIAMS MACKAY PTY LTD - MELBOURNE—See Dentsu Group Inc.; *Int'l*, pg. 2035
BELGIOVANE WILLIAMS MACKAY PTY LTD—See Dentsu Group Inc.; *Int'l*, pg. 2035
BELL RECRUITMENT ADVERTISING; *U.S. Private*, pg. 519
THE BELLWETHER GROUP; *U.S. Private*, pg. 3993
BELTRAME LEFFLER ADVERTISING; *U.S. Private*, pg. 521
BEM (BURRELL ENGAGEMENT MARKETING)—See FVLCRUM PARTNERS LLC; *U.S. Private*, pg. 1628
BEN B. BLISS COMPANY, INC.; *U.S. Private*, pg. 522
BENCHMARK USA; *U.S. Private*, pg. 524
BENCHWORKS, INC.; *U.S. Private*, pg. 524
BENEDICT ADVERTISING; *U.S. Private*, pg. 525
BENNETT KUHN VARNER, INC.; *U.S. Private*, pg. 527
BENSUR CREATIVE MARKETING GROUP; *U.S. Private*, pg. 528

541810 — ADVERTISING AGENCIE...

BERCHER SA PUBLICITE GENERALE—See APG/SGA SA; *Int'l*, pg. 513
BERGMAN ASSOCIATES; *U.S. Private*, pg. 531
BERLINE; *U.S. Private*, pg. 535
BERNING MARKETING, LLC; *U.S. Private*, pg. 537
BERNSTEIN-REIN ADVERTISING, INC.; *U.S. Private*, pg. 538
BERRY NETWORK, INC.—See Thryv Holdings, Inc.; *U.S. Public*, pg. 2157
BEUERMAN MILLER FITZGERALD, INC.; *U.S. Private*, pg. 547
BEYOND SPOTS & DOTS INC.; *U.S. Private*, pg. 548
BEZIER LIMITED—See H.I.G. Capital, LLC; *U.S. Private*, pg. 1828
BFG MARKETING, LLC—See Eastport Holdings, Inc.; *U.S. Private*, pg. 1322
BGP CORP.—See BGP Corp.; *U.S. Private*, pg. 549
BIEDERMANN PUBLICIDAD S.A.—See The Interpublic Group of Companies, Inc.; *U.S. Public*, pg. 2099
BI.GARAGE, INC.—See Dentsu Group Inc.; *Int'l*, pg. 2034
BIG ARROW CONSULTING GROUP, LLC; *U.S. Private*, pg. 552
BIG CAT ADVERTISING; *U.S. Private*, pg. 552
BIG HONKIN' IDEAS (B.H.I.); *U.S. Private*, pg. 553
BIG IMAGINATION GROUP; *U.S. Private*, pg. 553
BIG SKY COMMUNICATIONS, INC.; *U.S. Private*, pg. 554
BIG VALLEY, INC.—See Chatham Asset Management, LLC; *U.S. Private*, pg. 866
BILLBOARD CENTRAL; *U.S. Private*, pg. 559
BILL FAIR & CO.; *U.S. Private*, pg. 557
BILL HUDSON & ASSOCIATES, INC., ADVERTISING & PUBLIC RELATIONS; *U.S. Private*, pg. 557
BILLINGTON CARTMELL; *Int'l*, pg. 1031
BIL MARKEDET APS—See eBay Inc.; *U.S. Public*, pg. 709
BIOPHARM COMMUNICATIONS, LLC—See Omnicom Group Inc.; *U.S. Public*, pg. 1577
BIOSECTOR 2; *U.S. Private*, pg. 563
BIRDSALL INTERACTIVE, INC.; *U.S. Private*, pg. 564
BIRDSONG GREGORY INC.; *U.S. Private*, pg. 564
BITMAMA S.R.L.—See Armando Testa S.p.A.; *Int'l*, pg. 574
BJL GROUP LIMITED—See Dentsu Group Inc.; *Int'l*, pg. 2035
BLACKFIN MARKETING GROUP; *U.S. Private*, pg. 573
BLACKTOP CREATIVE—See Barkley; *U.S. Private*, pg. 475
BLACK & WHITE ADVERTISING, INC.; *U.S. Private*, pg. 569
BLAINE WARREN ADVERTISING LLC; *U.S. Private*, pg. 578
BLAKESLEE ADVERTISING - PARK CITY—See Blakeslee Advertising; *U.S. Private*, pg. 578
BLAKESLEE ADVERTISING; *U.S. Private*, pg. 578
BLAMMO WORLDWIDE; *Int'l*, pg. 1062
BLANCHARD SCHAEFER ADVERTISING & PUBLIC RELATIONS; *U.S. Private*, pg. 579
BLASS MARKETING; *U.S. Private*, pg. 579
BLESS YOU INC.—See Dentsu Group Inc.; *Int'l*, pg. 2040
BLISS INTEGRATED COMMUNICATION; *U.S. Private*, pg. 582
BLITZ DDB—See Omnicom Group Inc.; *U.S. Public*, pg. 1579
BLOCK & DECORSO; *U.S. Private*, pg. 582
BLOGWATCHER INC.—See Dentsu Group Inc.; *Int'l*, pg. 2034
BLOMQUIST ANNONSBYRA AB; *Int'l*, pg. 1065
BLONDE DIGITAL LTD.—See Arsenal Capital Management LP; *U.S. Private*, pg. 338
BLR/FURTHER; *U.S. Private*, pg. 585
BLUE BELL ADVERTISING ASSOCIATES; *U.S. Private*, pg. 585
BLUE CLOVER; *U.S. Private*, pg. 586
BLUECURRENT HONG KONG—See Omnicom Group Inc.; *U.S. Public*, pg. 1583
BLUECURRENT JAPAN—See Omnicom Group Inc.; *U.S. Public*, pg. 1583
BLUE DAISY MEDIA; *U.S. Private*, pg. 588
BLUEDOT COMMUNICATIONS; *U.S. Private*, pg. 596
BLUEFIN IMAGING GROUP, LLC—See BVK, Inc.; *U.S. Private*, pg. 700
BLUE FLAME THINKING; *U.S. Private*, pg. 588
BLUEGLASS INTERACTIVE AG—See BlueGlass Interactive, Inc.; *U.S. Private*, pg. 596
BLUE ICEBERG; *U.S. Private*, pg. 589
BLUE LOTUS COMMUNICATIONS (BANGALORE)—See Blue Lotus Communications Consultancy; *Int'l*, pg. 1068
BLUE LOTUS COMMUNICATIONS (CHENNAI)—See Blue Lotus Communications Consultancy; *Int'l*, pg. 1068
BLUE LOTUS COMMUNICATIONS (HYDERBAD)—See Blue Lotus Communications Consultancy; *Int'l*, pg. 1068
BLUE LOTUS COMMUNICATIONS (KOLKATA)—See Blue Lotus Communications Consultancy; *Int'l*, pg. 1068
BLUE LOTUS COMMUNICATIONS (NEW DELHI)—See Blue Lotus Communications Consultancy; *Int'l*, pg. 1068
BLUE LOTUS COMMUNICATIONS (PUNE)—See Blue Lotus Communications Consultancy; *Int'l*, pg. 1069
BLUE MEDIUM, INC.; *U.S. Private*, pg. 589
BLUE SKY AGENCY; *U.S. Private*, pg. 593
BLUESPIRE, INC.—See High Road Capital Partners, LLC; *U.S. Private*, pg. 1936

BMC ADVERTISING; *U.S. Private*, pg. 600
BMF ADVERTISING PTY LIMITED—See Enero Group Limited; *Int'l*, pg. 2423
BMF—See Enero Group Limited; *Int'l*, pg. 2423
BMI ELITE, INC.; *U.S. Private*, pg. 600
BOATHOUSE GROUP INC.; *U.S. Private*, pg. 603
BOB FOWLER & ASSOCIATES; *U.S. Private*, pg. 604
BOB GOLD & ASSOCIATES; *U.S. Private*, pg. 604
BOCK COMMUNICATIONS, INC.; *U.S. Private*, pg. 607
BODDEN PARTNERS; *U.S. Private*, pg. 607
BODKIN ASSOCIATES, INC.; *U.S. Private*, pg. 608
BOELTER + LINCOLN MARKETING COMMUNICATIONS; *U.S. Private*, pg. 608
BOLGER ADVERTISING; *U.S. Private*, pg. 610
BOLIN MARKETING & ADVERTISING; *U.S. Private*, pg. 610
BOLLORE INTERMEDIA—See Financiere de L'Odet; *Int'l*, pg. 2667
BOLLORE MEDIA REGIE SA—See Financiere de L'Odet; *Int'l*, pg. 2666
THE BONER GROUP, INC./ANN K. SAVAGE—See The Boner Group, Inc.; *U.S. Private*, pg. 3996
THE BONER GROUP, INC.; *U.S. Private*, pg. 3996
BONNEVILLE COMMUNICATIONS; *U.S. Private*, pg. 615
BOOMING GMBH—See Blackwood Seven A/S; *Int'l*, pg. 1062
BOOMM MARKETING & COMMUNICATIONS; *U.S. Private*, pg. 616
BOOMWORKS PTY, LTD.; *Int'l*, pg. 1111
BOONE DELEON COMMUNICATIONS, INC.; *U.S. Private*, pg. 616
BOONEOAKLEY; *U.S. Private*, pg. 616
THE BOOYAH AGENCY—See Booyah Networks, Inc.; *U.S. Private*, pg. 617
THE BORDEN AGENCY; *U.S. Private*, pg. 3996
BORDERS PERRIN NORRANDER INC.; *U.S. Private*, pg. 618
THE BORENSTEIN GROUP, INC.; *U.S. Private*, pg. 3996
BORSENMEDIEN AG; *Int'l*, pg. 1115
THE BOUNCE AGENCY; *U.S. Private*, pg. 3998
BOVACO—See Omnicom Group Inc.; *U.S. Public*, pg. 1596
BOVIL DDB—See Omnicom Group Inc.; *U.S. Public*, pg. 1579
BOYDEN & YOUNGBLUTT ADVERTISING & MARKETING; *U.S. Private*, pg. 627
BOYD TAMNEY CROSS INC.; *U.S. Private*, pg. 627
BOZELL & JACOBS, LLC; *U.S. Private*, pg. 629
BRABENDERCOX, LLC - PITTSBURGH—See Brabender-Cox, LLC; *U.S. Private*, pg. 630
BRABENDERCOX, LLC; *U.S. Private*, pg. 630
BRADLEY & MONTGOMERY ADVERTISING; *U.S. Private*, pg. 632
BRADSHAW ADVERTISING; *U.S. Private*, pg. 633
BRAIN BOX—See Omnicom Group Inc.; *U.S. Public*, pg. 1596
BRAINERD COMMUNICATORS, INC.; *U.S. Private*, pg. 634
BRAINIUM INC.; *U.S. Private*, pg. 634
BRAIN LABS DIGITAL LTD.; *Int'l*, pg. 1137
BRAINS ON FIRE, INC. - LOS ANGELES—See Brains on Fire, Inc.; *U.S. Private*, pg. 634
BRAINS ON FIRE, INC.; *U.S. Private*, pg. 634
BRAND ARCHITECTURE INTERNATIONAL—See Omnicom Group Inc.; *U.S. Public*, pg. 1598
BRAND COOL MARKETING INC.—See Butler/Till Media Services, Inc.; *U.S. Private*, pg. 697
BRAND DEVELOPMENT COMPANY LIMITED; *Int'l*, pg. 1139
BRANDIA CENTRAL; *Int'l*, pg. 1139
BRANDIMAGE DESGRIPPES & LAGA; *U.S. Private*, pg. 637
BRANDING TECHNOLOGY, INC.; *Int'l*, pg. 1140
BRAND INNOVATION GROUP; *U.S. Private*, pg. 637
BRANDITO, LLC—See Monroe Street Partners LLC; *U.S. Private*, pg. 2774
BRAND LOUNGE; *Int'l*, pg. 1139
BRAND MARKETING TEAM LTD.—See Providence Equity Partners L.L.C.; *U.S. Private*, pg. 3291
BRANDMIND; *U.S. Private*, pg. 637
BRANDON ADVERTISING, INC.; *U.S. Private*, pg. 638
BRANDORCHARD; *U.S. Private*, pg. 638
BRANDSPA LLC; *U.S. Private*, pg. 638
BRANDSPRING SOLUTIONS LLC; *U.S. Private*, pg. 638
BRAND STORY EXPERTS INC.; *U.S. Private*, pg. 637
BRANDTRUST, INC.; *U.S. Private*, pg. 639
BRANDVISION K.K.—See ad-comm Co., Ltd.; *Int'l*, pg. 123
BRANDWIZARD—See Omnicom Group Inc.; *U.S. Public*, pg. 1577
BRASHE ADVERTISING, INC.; *U.S. Private*, pg. 640
BRASS AGENCY LTD.; *Int'l*, pg. 1140
BRAVO TANGO ADVERTISING FIRM INC.; *Int'l*, pg. 1142
BRAY MEDIA, LLC; *U.S. Private*, pg. 642
BREW; *U.S. Private*, pg. 646
BRIABE MEDIA INC.; *U.S. Private*, pg. 647
BRIDGE GLOBAL STRATEGIES, LLC—See Didit.com, Inc.; *U.S. Private*, pg. 1227
BRIECHLE-FERNANDEZ MARKETING SERVICES INC.; *U.S. Private*, pg. 650
BRIERLEY EUROPE LIMITED—See Capillary Technologies International Pte Ltd.; *Int'l*, pg. 1308
BRIERLEY & PARTNERS, INC.—See Capillary Technologies International Pte Ltd.; *Int'l*, pg. 1307
BRIERLEY & PARTNERS - LOS ANGELES—See Capillary Technologies International Pte Ltd.; *Int'l*, pg. 1308
BRIGANDI & ASSOCIATES, INC. MARKETING COMMUNICATIONS; *U.S. Private*, pg. 650
BRIGGS ADVERTISING, INC.—See CD&M Communications; *U.S. Private*, pg. 802
BRIGHTON AGENCY, INC.; *U.S. Private*, pg. 652
BRIGHT OUTDOOR MEDIA LIMITED; *Int'l*, pg. 1161
BRINDLEY ADVERTISING LTD.; *Int'l*, pg. 1164
BRISTOL GROUP - HALIFAX—See Bristol Group; *Int'l*, pg. 1164
BRISTOL GROUP; *Int'l*, pg. 1164
BROACH & COMPANY; *U.S. Private*, pg. 658
BROADCAST TIME, INC.; *U.S. Private*, pg. 659
BROADHEAD + CO., INC.; *U.S. Private*, pg. 659
BROGAN & PARTNERS CONVERGENCE MARKETING; *U.S. Private*, pg. 661
BROGAN & PARTNERS CONVERGENCE MARKETING—See Brogan & Partners Convergence Marketing; *U.S. Private*, pg. 661
BROGAN TENNYSON GROUP, INC.; *U.S. Private*, pg. 661
BROGAN TENNYSON—See Brogan Tennyson Group, Inc.; *U.S. Private*, pg. 661
THE BROOKLYN BROTHERS LIMITED—See The Interpublic Group of Companies, Inc.; *U.S. Public*, pg. 2094
BROTHERS & CO.; *U.S. Private*, pg. 665
BROWNBOOTS INTERACTIVE, INC.; *U.S. Private*, pg. 669
BROWN COMMUNICATIONS GROUP; *Int'l*, pg. 1198
BROWN COMMUNICATIONS GROUP—See Brown Communications Group; *Int'l*, pg. 1198
BROWN-FORMAN MEDIA SERVICES—See Brown-Forman Corporation; *U.S. Public*, pg. 403
BROWN PARKER & DEMARINIS ADVERTISING INC.; *U.S. Private*, pg. 668
BROWNSTEIN GROUP; *U.S. Private*, pg. 670
THE BROWNSTEIN GROUP—See Brownstein Group; *U.S. Private*, pg. 670
BRUMMEL KANEPI PIRITA—See Omnicom Group Inc.; *U.S. Public*, pg. 1592
BRUNET-GARCIA ADVERTISING, INC.—See Fors Marsh Group LLC.; *U.S. Private*, pg. 1573
BRUNNER; *U.S. Private*, pg. 672
BRUNNER—See Brunner; *U.S. Private*, pg. 672
BRUNSWICK GROUP—See Brunswick Group Limited; *Int'l*, pg. 1200
BRUNSWICK GROUP—See Brunswick Group Limited; *Int'l*, pg. 1201
BRUNSWICK MEDIA SERVICES LLC; *U.S. Private*, pg. 672
BRUSHFIRE, INC.—See Marketsmith, Inc.; *U.S. Private*, pg. 2581
BRYAN MILLS IRADESSO CORP.—See Stagwell, Inc.; *U.S. Public*, pg. 1926
B SCENE ADVERTISING AGENCY; *U.S. Private*, pg. 417
BUDCO CREATIVE SERVICES; *U.S. Private*, pg. 679
BUILD CREATIVEHAUS INC.—See Dentsu Group Inc.; *Int'l*, pg. 2034
BULLDOG DRUMMOND, INC.; *U.S. Private*, pg. 684
BULLSEYE DATABASE MARKETING LLC; *U.S. Private*, pg. 685
THE BUNTIN GROUP; *U.S. Private*, pg. 4002
BUNTIN OUT-OF-HOME MEDIA—See The Buntin Group; *U.S. Private*, pg. 4002
BURDITCH MARKETING COMMUNICATIONS; *U.S. Private*, pg. 686
BURK ADVERTISING & MARKETING; *U.S. Private*, pg. 687
BURKHARDT LTD.; *U.S. Private*, pg. 688
BURNHAM RICHARDS ADVERTISING; *U.S. Private*, pg. 689
BURNS MCCLELLAN, INC.; *U.S. Private*, pg. 691
BURN; *Int'l*, pg. 1226
BURRELL COMMUNICATIONS GROUP, LLC - ATLANTA—See FVLCRUM PARTNERS LLC; *U.S. Private*, pg. 1628
BURRELL COMMUNICATIONS GROUP, LLC—See FVLCRUM PARTNERS LLC; *U.S. Private*, pg. 1628
BUSH COMMUNICATIONS, LLC; *U.S. Private*, pg. 694
BUSINESS DATA LTD.—See The Interpublic Group of Companies, Inc.; *U.S. Public*, pg. 2092
BUSINESS-TO-BUSINESS MARKETING COMMUNICATIONS; *U.S. Private*, pg. 695
BUTLER, SHINE, STERN & PARTNERS; *U.S. Private*, pg. 697
BUYER ADVERTISING, INC.; *U.S. Private*, pg. 699
BUZZSAW ADVERTISING & DESIGN INC.; *U.S. Private*, pg. 699
BVK, INC.; *U.S. Private*, pg. 700
B-W ADVERTISING AGENCY, INC.—See Best Western International, Inc.; *U.S. Private*, pg. 544
BYDESIGN, INC.—See The BCB Group, Inc.; *U.S. Private*, pg. 3992
THE BYNE GROUP—See GMLV-Global Marketing With A Local Vision; *U.S. Private*, pg. 1722
C2C OUTDOOR; *U.S. Private*, pg. 709

N.A.I.C.S. INDEX

541810 — ADVERTISING AGENCIE...

C2 CREATIVE—See Omnicom Group Inc.; *U.S. Public*, pg. 1578
C2 IMAGING, LLC-CHICAGO—See Vomela Specialty Company; *U.S. Private*, pg. 4412
C2 IMAGING, LLC-ENGLEWOOD—See Vomela Specialty Company; *U.S. Private*, pg. 4412
C2 IMAGING, LLC - GAITHERSBURG—See Vomela Specialty Company; *U.S. Private*, pg. 4412
C2 IMAGING, LLC-HOUSTON—See Vomela Specialty Company; *U.S. Private*, pg. 4412
C2 IMAGING, LLC—See Vomela Specialty Company; *U.S. Private*, pg. 4412
C2SNOW; *U.S. Private*, pg. 709
CACTUS; *U.S. Private*, pg. 712
CADIENT, INC.—See Cognizant Technology Solutions Corporation; *U.S. Public*, pg. 523
CAFFEINE—See Mascola Advertising; *U.S. Private*, pg. 2601
CAIRO SPORT SRL—See Cairo Communication S.p.A.; *Int'l*, pg. 1253
CALIFORNIA OUTDOOR ADVERTISING; *U.S. Private*, pg. 720
CALISE PARTNERS, LLC; *U.S. Private*, pg. 721
CALISE & SEDEI; *U.S. Private*, pg. 721
CALLAHAN CREEK, INC.—See Barkley; *U.S. Private*, pg. 475
CALLAHAN CREEK—See Barkley; *U.S. Private*, pg. 475
CALLE & COMPANY; *U.S. Private*, pg. 722
CALYPSO COMMUNICATIONS LLC—See Matter Communications Inc.; *U.S. Private*, pg. 2613
CALYPSO COMMUNICATIONS—See Matter Communications Inc.; *U.S. Private*, pg. 2613
CAMARA/TBWA—See Omnicom Group Inc.; *U.S. Public*, pg. 1594
CAMARES COMMUNICATIONS INC.; *U.S. Private*, pg. 725
CAMBRIDGE BIOMARKETING GROUP, LLC—See Clayton, Dubilier & Rice, LLC; *U.S. Private*, pg. 927
CAMELOT COMMUNICATIONS LTD.—See PMG Worldwide LLC; *U.S. Private*, pg. 3218
CAM MEDIA CREATIVE WORKS SP. Z O.O.; *Int'l*, pg. 1266
CAMPAGNANI BBDO—See Omnicom Group Inc.; *U.S. Public*, pg. 1575
CAMPBELL-EWALD COMPANY—See The Interpublic Group of Companies, Inc.; *U.S. Public*, pg. 2090
CAMPBELL-EWALD DETROIT—See The Interpublic Group of Companies, Inc.; *U.S. Public*, pg. 2090
CAMPBELL-EWALD LOS ANGELES—See The Interpublic Group of Companies, Inc.; *U.S. Public*, pg. 2090
CAMPBELL-EWALD SAN ANTONIO—See The Interpublic Group of Companies, Inc.; *U.S. Public*, pg. 2090
CAMPBELL-EWALD—See The Interpublic Group of Companies, Inc.; *U.S. Public*, pg. 2090
CAMPBELL, HENRY & CALVIN, INC.; *U.S. Private*, pg. 731
CAMPFIRE; *U.S. Private*, pg. 731
CAMPOS CREATIVE WORKS, INC.; *U.S. Private*, pg. 731
CAMPUS MEDIA GROUP, LLC; *U.S. Private*, pg. 732
CANALWORKS ADVERTISING; *U.S. Private*, pg. 733
CANNONBALL; *U.S. Private*, pg. 735
CAP BRAND MARKETING; *U.S. Private*, pg. 737
CAPITAL C PARTNERS LP—See Stagwell, Inc.; *U.S. Public*, pg. 1926
CAPITALDATA SAS—See HighCo S.A.; *Int'l*, pg. 3386
CAPITAL IR K.K.—See ad-comm Co., Ltd.; *Int'l*, pg. 123
CAPITA TECHNOLOGIES, INC.; *U.S. Private*, pg. 738
CAPITOL MEDIA SOLUTIONS; *U.S. Private*, pg. 744
CAPPELLI MILES (SPRING); *U.S. Private*, pg. 745
CAPPELLI MILES (SPRING)—See Cappelli Miles (Spring); *U.S. Private*, pg. 745
CARAGAS AJL/PARK—See The Interpublic Group of Companies, Inc.; *U.S. Public*, pg. 2092
CARAT AUSTRIA GMBH—See Dentsu Group Inc.; *Int'l*, pg. 2035
CARAT BELGIUM—See Dentsu Group Inc.; *Int'l*, pg. 2035
CARAT BUSINESS LTD.—See Dentsu Group Inc.; *Int'l*, pg. 2035
CARAT CANADA—See Dentsu Group Inc.; *Int'l*, pg. 2036
CARAT EXPERT - MILAN—See Dentsu Group Inc.; *Int'l*, pg. 2035
CARAT FRANCE—See Dentsu Group Inc.; *Int'l*, pg. 2035
CARAT INTERNATIONAL HELLAS—See Dentsu Group Inc.; *Int'l*, pg. 2035
CARAT IRELAND—See Dentsu Group Inc.; *Int'l*, pg. 2035
CARAT ITALIA-FLORENCE—See Dentsu Group Inc.; *Int'l*, pg. 2035
CARAT ITALIA-ROME—See Dentsu Group Inc.; *Int'l*, pg. 2035
CARAT ITALIA-TURIN—See Dentsu Group Inc.; *Int'l*, pg. 2035
CARAT JAPAN CO., LTD.—See Dentsu Group Inc.; *Int'l*, pg. 2034
CARDATA, INC.; *U.S. Private*, pg. 749
CARGO, LLC; *U.S. Private*, pg. 760
CARIBCOM, INC.; *U.S. Private*, pg. 761
CARL BLOOM ASSOCIATES, INC.; *U.S. Private*, pg. 762
CARLSON MARKETING GROUP NZ LIMITED—See Aimia Inc.; *Int'l*, pg. 233
CARLSON MARKETING GROUP—See Aimia Inc.; *Int'l*, pg. 233
CARLSON MARKETING GROUP—See Aimia Inc.; *Int'l*, pg. 233
CARLSON MARKETING GROUP—See Aimia Inc.; *Int'l*, pg. 233
CARLSON MARKETING GROUP (UK) LTD.—See Aimia Inc.; *Int'l*, pg. 233
CARMICHAEL LYNCH, INC.—See The Interpublic Group of Companies, Inc.; *U.S. Public*, pg. 2090
CARMICHAEL LYNCH SPONG—See The Interpublic Group of Companies, Inc.; *U.S. Public*, pg. 2090
CAROL H. WILLIAMS ADVERTISING; *U.S. Public*, pg. 766
CAROL H. WILLIAMS ADVERTISING—See Carol H. Williams Advertising; *U.S. Private*, pg. 766
CAROL H. WILLIAMS ADVERTISING—See Carol H. Williams Advertising; *U.S. Private*, pg. 766
CARRAFIELLO-DIEHL & ASSOCIATES, INC.; *U.S. Private*, pg. 771
CARROLL/WHITE; *U.S. Private*, pg. 774
CARROT CREATIVE LLC—See Monroe Capital LLC; *U.S. Private*, pg. 2773
CARROT CREATIVE LLC—See Soros Fund Management LLC; *U.S. Private*, pg. 3716
THE CARSON GROUP; *U.S. Private*, pg. 4005
THE CARTEL GROUP; *U.S. Private*, pg. 4005
CASANOVA PENDRILL, LLC—See The Interpublic Group of Companies, Inc.; *U.S. Public*, pg. 2090
CASHMAN & KATZ INTEGRATED COMMUNICATIONS; *U.S. Private*, pg. 783
CASON NIGHTINGALE CREATIVE COMMUNICATIONS; *U.S. Private*, pg. 783
CASPARI MCCORMICK—See Aloysius, Butler & Clark Associates, Inc.; *U.S. Private*, pg. 196
CASTLE ADVERTISING; *U.S. Private*, pg. 784
THE CASTLE GROUP; *U.S. Private*, pg. 4006
CATALYST DIRECT INC.; *U.S. Private*, pg. 786
CATALYST EXPERIENTIAL, LLC; *U.S. Private*, pg. 786
CATALYST, INC.; *U.S. Private*, pg. 787
CATALYST, INC.; *U.S. Private*, pg. 787
CATALYST MARKETING COMMUNICATIONS INC.; *U.S. Private*, pg. 786
CATALYST MARKETING DESIGN; *U.S. Private*, pg. 786
CATALYST; *U.S. Private*, pg. 786
CATALYST STUDIOS; *U.S. Private*, pg. 786
CATAPULT DIRECT MARKETING LLC; *U.S. Private*, pg. 787
CATAPULT MARKETING—See Ryan Partnership, LLC; *U.S. Private*, pg. 3510
CATAPULT MARKETING—See Ryan Partnership, LLC; *U.S. Private*, pg. 3510
CATAPULT MARKETING—See Ryan Partnership, LLC; *U.S. Private*, pg. 3510
THE CAVALRY COMPANY; *U.S. Private*, pg. 4006
CAWOOD; *U.S. Private*, pg. 795
CAYENNE S.R.L.—See Dentsu Group Inc.; *Int'l*, pg. 2035
CAYENNE/TBWA—See Omnicom Group Inc.; *U.S. Public*, pg. 1594
CBK GROUP; *U.S. Private*, pg. 797
CB&S ADVERTISING AGENCY INC—See The Kroger Co.; *U.S. Public*, pg. 2107
CBS INTERACTIVE PTY. LTD.—See National Amusements, Inc.; *U.S. Public*, pg. 2840
CCI EUROPE A/S; *Int'l*, pg. 1366
CCM MARKETING COMMUNICATIONS; *U.S. Private*, pg. 800
CCM WEST—See CCM Marketing Communications; *U.S. Private*, pg. 800
CDHM COMMUNICATIONS; *U.S. Private*, pg. 802
CD&M COMMUNICATIONS; *U.S. Private*, pg. 802
CDP-TRAVISSULLY LTD.; *Int'l*, pg. 1371
CEDAR—See Omnicom Group Inc.; *U.S. Public*, pg. 1579
CELLO HEALTH PLC—See Arsenal Capital Management LP; *U.S. Private*, pg. 337
CELLO HEALTH—See Arsenal Capital Management LP; *U.S. Private*, pg. 338
CELLO SIGNAL—See Arsenal Capital Management LP; *U.S. Private*, pg. 338
CELLULAR GMBH; *Int'l*, pg. 1395
CELTIC, INC.—See Zizzo Group, Inc.; *U.S. Private*, pg. 4606
THE CEMENTWORKS, LLC; *U.S. Private*, pg. 4006
CENTER LINE; *U.S. Private*, pg. 811
CENTRA MARKETING & COMMUNICATIONS, LLC; *U.S. Private*, pg. 818
CENTRON—See HealthSTAR Communications, Inc.; *U.S. Private*, pg. 1898
CERCONE BROWN CURTIS; *U.S. Private*, pg. 840
C&G PARTNERS, LLC.; *U.S. Private*, pg. 703
CHAIR 10 MARKETING, INC.—See SmartBug Operating LLC; *U.S. Private*, pg. 3691
CHANDLER CHICCO AGENCY - LONDON—See Chandler Chicco Agency; *U.S. Private*, pg. 847
CHANDLER CHICCO AGENCY - LOS ANGELES—See Chandler Chicco Agency; *U.S. Private*, pg. 848
CHANDLER CHICCO AGENCY - PARIS—See Chandler Chicco Agency; *U.S. Private*, pg. 848
CHANDLER CHICCO AGENCY; *U.S. Private*, pg. 847
CHANDLER CHICCO AGENCY - WASHINGTON—See Chandler Chicco Agency; *U.S. Private*, pg. 848
CHANGE COMMUNICATIONS GMBH—See The Interpublic Group of Companies, Inc.; *U.S. Public*, pg. 2090
CHANNEL ISLANDS DESIGN; *U.S. Private*, pg. 848
CHANNEL KEY, LLC; *U.S. Private*, pg. 848
CHAOS CONCEPT MANUFACTURING—See McGarrah Jessee; *U.S. Private*, pg. 2634
CHAPPELLROBERTS INC.; *U.S. Private*, pg. 850
CHARLES RYAN ASSOCIATES INC.; *U.S. Private*, pg. 853
CHARLES RYAN ASSOCIATES—See Charles Ryan Associates Inc.; *U.S. Private*, pg. 853
CHARLES RYAN ASSOCIATES—See Charles Ryan Associates Inc.; *U.S. Private*, pg. 853
CHARLES TOMBRAS ADVERTISING, INC.; *U.S. Private*, pg. 854
CHARLESTON/ORWIG, INC.; *U.S. Private*, pg. 857
CHARM COMMUNICATIONS INC.; *Int'l*, pg. 1450
CHARTER DIGITAL MEDIA INC.—See Charter Direct Marketing; *U.S. Private*, pg. 858
CHARTER DIRECT MARKETING; *U.S. Private*, pg. 858
THE CHASE CREATIVE CONSULTANTS LIMITED—See Hasgrove plc; *Int'l*, pg. 3283
CHEMISTRY COMMUNICATIONS, INC.; *U.S. Private*, pg. 871
CHEMPETITIVE GROUP, LLC; *U.S. Private*, pg. 872
CHENGDU ASIARAY ADVERTISING—See Asiaray Media Group Limited; *Int'l*, pg. 620
CHERNOFF NEWMAN, LLC; *U.S. Private*, pg. 873
CHEROKEE COMMUNICATIONS INC.; *U.S. Private*, pg. 873
CHESS COMMUNICATIONS GROUP; *U.S. Private*, pg. 875
CHESTNUT COMMUNICATIONS, INC.; *U.S. Private*, pg. 875
CHESTON & GIBBENS INC.; *U.S. Private*, pg. 875
CHEVALIER ADVERTISING, INC.; *U.S. Private*, pg. 876
CHINA PHARMACEUTICAL ADVERTISING LIMITED COMPANY—See China National Pharmaceutical Group Corporation; *Int'l*, pg. 1533
CHI & PARTNERS LIMITED; *Int'l*, pg. 1474
CHISANO MARKETING GROUP, INC.; *U.S. Private*, pg. 887
CHITIKA, INC.; *U.S. Private*, pg. 887
CHITIKA, INC.—See Chitika, Inc.; *U.S. Private*, pg. 887
CHRISTENSON, BARCLAY & SHAW, INC.; *U.S. Private*, pg. 890
CHUGOKUSHIKOKU HAKUHODO INC.—See Hakuhodo DY Holdings Incorporated; *Int'l*, pg. 3220
CHUMNEY & ASSOCIATES; *U.S. Private*, pg. 894
CHUO SENKO ADVERTISING CO., LTD.; *Int'l*, pg. 1599
CHUO SENKO ADVERTISING CO., LTD.—See Chuo Senko Advertising Co., Ltd.; *Int'l*, pg. 1599
CHUO SENKO ADVERTISING CO., LTD.—See Chuo Senko Advertising Co., Ltd.; *Int'l*, pg. 1599
CHUO SENKO ADVERTISING CO., LTD.—See Chuo Senko Advertising Co., Ltd.; *Int'l*, pg. 1599
CHUO SENKO ADVERTISING CO., LTD.—See Chuo Senko Advertising Co., Ltd.; *Int'l*, pg. 1599
CHUO SENKO ADVERTISING CO., LTD.—See Chuo Senko Advertising Co., Ltd.; *Int'l*, pg. 1599
CHUO SENKO ADVERTISING CO., LTD.—See Chuo Senko Advertising Co., Ltd.; *Int'l*, pg. 1599
CHUO SENKO ADVERTISING CO., LTD.—See Chuo Senko Advertising Co., Ltd.; *Int'l*, pg. 1599
CHUO SENKO ADVERTISING CO., LTD.—See Chuo Senko Advertising Co., Ltd.; *Int'l*, pg. 1599
CHUO SENKO ADVERTISING (HK) LTD.—See Chuo Senko Advertising Co., Ltd.; *Int'l*, pg. 1599
CHUO SENKO ADVERTISING (S) PTE. LTD.—See Chuo Senko Advertising Co., Ltd.; *Int'l*, pg. 1599
CHUO SENKO ADVERTISING (TAIWAN) CO., LTD.—See Chuo Senko Advertising Co., Ltd.; *Int'l*, pg. 1599
CHUO SENKO (CAMBODIA) HOLDING CO., LTD.—See Chuo Senko Advertising Co., Ltd.; *Int'l*, pg. 1599
CHUO SENKO (THAILAND) PUBLIC CO., LTD.—See Chuo Senko Advertising Co., Ltd.; *Int'l*, pg. 1599
CHUO SENKO VIETNAM REPRESENTATIVE OFFICE—See Chuo Senko Advertising Co., Ltd.; *Int'l*, pg. 1599
CHURCH & MAIN ADVERTISING; *U.S. Private*, pg. 894
CINCO MEDIA COMMUNICATIONS; *U.S. Private*, pg. 898
CINETRANSFORMER INTERNATIONAL; *U.S. Private*, pg. 898
CIPLEX; *U.S. Private*, pg. 899
CIRCUIT—See The Interpublic Group of Companies, Inc.; *U.S. Public*, pg. 2092
THE CIRLOT AGENCY, INC.; *U.S. Private*, pg. 4010
CIRQIT DE COSTA RICA S.A.—See HH Global Group Limited; *Int'l*, pg. 3378
CISNEROS INTERACTIVE BOLIVIA, S.R.L.—See Entravision Communications Corporation; *U.S. Public*, pg. 779
CISNEROS INTERACTIVE ECUADOR CISTERACTEC, S.A.—See Entravision Communications Corporation; *U.S. Public*, pg. 779
CISNEROS INTERACTIVE GUATEMALA, S.A.—See Entravision Communications Corporation; *U.S. Public*, pg. 779
CISNEROS INTERACTIVE PUERTO RICO, S.A.—See Entravision Communications Corporation; *U.S. Public*, pg. 779
CISNEROS INTERACTIVE, S.A.—See Entravision Communications Corporation; *U.S. Public*, pg. 779

541810 — ADVERTISING AGENCIE...   CORPORATE AFFILIATIONS

CITIZENNET, INC.—See Advance Publications, Inc.; *U.S. Private*, pg. 85
CITY24 POLSKA SP. Z.O.O.—See Alma Media Corporation; *Int'l*, pg. 362
CJRW NORTHWEST—See Cranford Johnson Robinson Woods, Inc.; *U.S. Private*, pg. 1085
CK COMMUNICATIONS, INC.; *U.S. Private*, pg. 909
CKR INTERACTIVE, INC.—See Gemspring Capital Management, LLC; *U.S. Private*, pg. 1659
CKR INTERACTIVE—See Gemspring Capital Management, LLC; *U.S. Private*, pg. 1659
CLARITY COVERDALE FURY ADVERTISING, INC.; *U.S. Private*, pg. 911
CLARK & ASSOCIATES; *U.S. Private*, pg. 912
CLARK DESIGN; *U.S. Private*, pg. 912
CLARKE ADVERTISING & PUBLIC RELATIONS, INC.; *U.S. Private*, pg. 914
CLARK HUOT LLC—See CHR Group LLC; *U.S. Private*, pg. 889
CLARK/NIKDEL/POWELL INC.; *U.S. Private*, pg. 914
CLASSIFIED ADVERTISING PLUS, LLC; *U.S. Private*, pg. 917
CLAYMAN ADVERTISING; *U.S. Private*, pg. 918
CLAYTON-DAVIS & ASSOCIATES, INCORPORATED; *U.S. Private*, pg. 930
CLEAN DESIGN, INC.; *U.S. Private*, pg. 931
THE CLEAR AGENCY—See Highland Productions, LLC; *U.S. Private*, pg. 1939
CLEAR CHANNEL BELGIUM SPRL—See iHeartMedia, Inc.; *U.S. Public*, pg. 1095
CLEAR CHANNEL DANMARK A/S—See Clear Channel Outdoor Holdings, Inc.; *U.S. Public*, pg. 511
CLEAR CHANNEL NEDERLAND BV—See Clear Channel Outdoor Holdings, Inc.; *U.S. Public*, pg. 511
CLEAR LINK TECHNOLOGIES, LLC—See Creadev SAS; *Int'l*, pg. 1831
CLEARRIVER COMMUNICATIONS GROUP; *U.S. Private*, pg. 938
CLEMENGER BBDO ADELAIDE—See Omnicom Group Inc.; *U.S. Public*, pg. 1577
CLEMENGER BBDO BRISBANE—See Omnicom Group Inc.; *U.S. Public*, pg. 1577
CLEMENGER BBDO MELBOURNE—See Omnicom Group Inc.; *U.S. Public*, pg. 1577
CLEMENGER BBDO SYDNEY—See Omnicom Group Inc.; *U.S. Public*, pg. 1577
CLEMENGER BBDO WELLINGTON—See Omnicom Group Inc.; *U.S. Public*, pg. 1577
THE CLEMENGER GROUP LTD.—See Omnicom Group Inc.; *U.S. Public*, pg. 1577
CLEMENGER HARVIE EDGE; *Int'l*, pg. 1657
CLEVERWORKS; *U.S. Private*, pg. 942
CLICKCULTURE; *U.S. Private*, pg. 942
CLICKDEALER ASIA PTE LTD.; *Int'l*, pg. 1658
CLICK HERE, INC.; *U.S. Private*, pg. 942
CLICK HERE—See Click Here, Inc.; *U.S. Private*, pg. 942
CLICKMAIL MARKETING, INC.; *U.S. Private*, pg. 942
CLICKSPRING DESIGN; *U.S. Private*, pg. 942
CLINE, DAVIS & MANN, INC. - EUROPE—See Omnicom Group Inc.; *U.S. Public*, pg. 1579
CLINE, DAVIS & MANN, INC. - LOS ANGELES—See Omnicom Group Inc.; *U.S. Public*, pg. 1579
CLINE, DAVIS & MANN, INC. - PRINCETON—See Omnicom Group Inc.; *U.S. Public*, pg. 1579
CLINE, DAVIS & MANN, INC.—See Omnicom Group Inc.; *U.S. Public*, pg. 1579
CLIX MARKETING, LLC; *U.S. Private*, pg. 945
CLM BBDO—See Omnicom Group Inc.; *U.S. Public*, pg. 1575
CLOUDR GROUP LIMITED; *Int'l*, pg. 1662
CLX EUROPE MEDIA SOLUTION GMBH—See eClerx Services Ltd; *Int'l*, pg. 2291
CLX EUROPE S.P.A.—See eClerx Services Ltd; *Int'l*, pg. 2291
CMD INC.; *U.S. Private*, pg. 950
CMDS; *U.S. Private*, pg. 950
CMGRP UK LIMITED—See The Interpublic Group of Companies, Inc.; *U.S. Public*, pg. 2090
CMG WORLDWIDE, INC.; *U.S. Private*, pg. 951
CMSA ADVERTISING & PUBLIC RELATIONS; *U.S. Private*, pg. 951
COAST DIGITAL, LTD.; *Int'l*, pg. 1681
COGENT ELLIOT; *Int'l*, pg. 1695
COGNETIX, INC.; *U.S. Private*, pg. 962
COIL COUNTS FORD & CHENEY, INC.; *U.S. Private*, pg. 964
COLANGELO—See Omnicom Group Inc.; *U.S. Public*, pg. 1578
COLBEAR ADVERTISING LIMITED; *Int'l*, pg. 1697
COLENSO BBDO—See Omnicom Group Inc.; *U.S. Public*, pg. 1575
COLLECTIVE, INC.—See Zeta Interactive Corporation; *U.S. Private*, pg. 4603
COLLE & MCVOY LLC—See Stagwell, Inc.; *U.S. Public*, pg. 1926
COLLIDER LIMITED; *Int'l*, pg. 1700
COLMAN, BROHAN & DAVIS, INC.; *U.S. Private*, pg. 970

COLMAR BRUNTON—See Bain Capital, LP; *U.S. Private*, pg. 448
COLORPLAY STUDIO; *U.S. Private*, pg. 975
COLSKY MEDIA; *U.S. Private*, pg. 975
COMBS & COMPANY; *U.S. Private*, pg. 980
COMCAST VENTURE LLC—See Comcast Corporation; *U.S. Public*, pg. 538
COME&STAY DKH A/S—See Come and Stay S.A.; *Int'l*, pg. 1710
COME&STAY SPAIN SL.—See Come and Stay S.A.; *Int'l*, pg. 1710
.COM MARKETING; *U.S. Private*, pg. 1
COMMONWEALTH CREATIVE ASSOCIATES; *U.S. Private*, pg. 986
COMMUNICA, INC.; *U.S. Private*, pg. 987
COMMUNICATION ASSOCIATES; *U.S. Private*, pg. 988
COMMUNICATION SERVICES; *U.S. Private*, pg. 988
THE COMMUNICATIONS GROUP; *U.S. Private*, pg. 4012
COMMUNICREATIONS; *U.S. Private*, pg. 989
COMMUNIFX PARTNERS LLC—See Stagwell, Inc.; *U.S. Public*, pg. 1926
THE COMMUNIQUE GROUP, INC.; *U.S. Private*, pg. 4012
COMMUNITECH; *U.S. Private*, pg. 989
THE COMMUNITY PHONE BOOK, INC.—See American CyberSystems, Inc.; *U.S. Private*, pg. 230
THE COMPANY OF OTHERS; *U.S. Private*, pg. 4012
COMSCORE CANADA, INC.—See comScore, Inc.; *U.S. Public*, pg. 561
COMSCORE EUROPE, INC.—See comScore, Inc.; *U.S. Public*, pg. 562
CONCENTRIC MARKETING; *U.S. Private*, pg. 1008
CONCENTRIC PHARMA ADVERTISING; *U.S. Private*, pg. 1008
CONCEPT CHASER CO., INC.; *U.S. Private*, pg. 1008
CONCEPT THREE INC.; *U.S. Private*, pg. 1009
CONCRETE MEDIA; *U.S. Private*, pg. 1011
CONCUSSION, LLP; *U.S. Private*, pg. 1011
CONDON & ROOT; *U.S. Private*, pg. 1012
CONNECT2 COMMUNICATIONS; *U.S. Private*, pg. 1015
CONNECT DIRECT, INC.; *U.S. Private*, pg. 1014
CONNECT DIRECT, INC.—See Connect Direct, Inc.; *U.S. Private*, pg. 1014
CONNECT FKM—See The Company of Others; *U.S. Private*, pg. 4013
CONNECTIVITY MARKETING & MEDIA AGENCY, LLC; *U.S. Private*, pg. 1016
CONNELLY PARTNERS, LLC; *U.S. Private*, pg. 1017
CONOVER TUTTLE PACE; *U.S. Private*, pg. 1018
CONSELLGRUPPE; *Int'l*, pg. 1769
CONSORTE MEDIA, INC.—See AudienceScience Inc.; *U.S. Private*, pg. 391
CONSTRUCTION MARKETING ADVISORS; *U.S. Private*, pg. 1024
CONSULTECH—See Omnicom Group Inc.; *U.S. Public*, pg. 1579
CONSUMABLE, INC.; *U.S. Private*, pg. 1025
CONTACT IMPACT GMBH—See Axel Springer SE; *Int'l*, pg. 766
CONTEMPO ADVERTISING + DESIGN; *U.S. Private*, pg. 1027
CONTEXTA AG; *Int'l*, pg. 1780
CONTRAPUNTO—See Omnicom Group Inc.; *U.S. Public*, pg. 1575
CONVERSANT FRANCE—See IAC Inc.; *U.S. Public*, pg. 1082
CONVERSE MARKETING; *U.S. Private*, pg. 1035
CONVERSION INTERACTIVE AGENCY, LLC; *U.S. Private*, pg. 1035
CONVERSIONPOINT TECHNOLOGIES, INC.; *U.S. Private*, pg. 1035
COOPER COMMUNICATIONS; *U.S. Private*, pg. 1041
THE COOPER GROUP, LTD.—See Eastport Holdings, Inc.; *U.S. Private*, pg. 1322
CO-OP PROMOTIONS; *U.S. Private*, pg. 953
CO-OP PROMOTIONS—See CO-OP PROMOTIONS; *U.S. Private*, pg. 953
COPACINO + FUJIKADO, LLC; *U.S. Private*, pg. 1044
COPIA CREATIVE, INC.—See The Phelps Group; *U.S. Private*, pg. 4094
CORBIN COMMUNICATIONS LIMITED; *Int'l*, pg. 1795
CORBIN COMMUNICATIONS LIMITED—See Corbin Communications Limited; *Int'l*, pg. 1795
CORDERO & DAVENPORT ADVERTISING; *U.S. Private*, pg. 1047
COREBRAND, LLC; *U.S. Private*, pg. 1049
CORE-CREATE INC.; *U.S. Private*, pg. 1049
CORE-CREATE LTD.—See Core-Create Inc.; *U.S. Private*, pg. 1049
CORESCO, INC.; *U.S. Private*, pg. 1049
CORNERSTONE MEDIA; *U.S. Private*, pg. 1052
CORNETT INTEGRATED MARKETING SOLUTIONS; *U.S. Private*, pg. 1053
CORPORATE PROFILES DDB—See Omnicom Group Inc.; *U.S. Public*, pg. 1579
THE CORPORATE PROMOTIONS GROUP; *U.S. Private*, pg. 4015
COSMO COMMUNICATIONS INC.—See Hakuhodo DY Holdings Incorporated; *Int'l*, pg. 3220

COSSETTE COMMUNICATION INC.—See Bluefocus Intelligent Communications Group Co., Ltd.; *Int'l*, pg. 1071
COSSETTE COMMUNICATION INC. - TORONTO—See Bluefocus Intelligent Communications Group Co., Ltd.; *Int'l*, pg. 1071
COSSETTE COMMUNICATION INC. - VANCOUVER—See Bluefocus Intelligent Communications Group Co., Ltd.; *Int'l*, pg. 1071
COSSETTE COMMUNICATION-MARKETING (MONTREAL) INC.—See Bluefocus Intelligent Communications Group Co., Ltd.; *Int'l*, pg. 1071
COTETONIC—See The GAMS Group, Inc.; *U.S. Private*, pg. 4032
COTTMAN MCCANN ADVERTISING—See The Interpublic Group of Companies, Inc.; *U.S. Public*, pg. 2097
COUDAL PARTNERS; *U.S. Private*, pg. 1064
COVE-ITO ADVERTISING LTD.; *Int'l*, pg. 1820
COVE-ITO INTERACTIVE—See Cove-Ito Advertising Ltd.; *Int'l*, pg. 1820
COVE-ITO INTERNATIONAL LTD.—See Cove-Ito Advertising Ltd.; *Int'l*, pg. 1820
COVE-ITO (THAILAND) LTD.—See Cove-Ito Advertising Ltd.; *Int'l*, pg. 1820
COVEY-ODELL ADVERTISING LTD.; *U.S. Private*, pg. 1072
COWLEY ASSOCIATES, INC.; *U.S. Private*, pg. 1074
COYNE ADVERTISING & PUBLIC RELATIONS; *U.S. Private*, pg. 1079
CP+B BOULDER—See Stagwell, Inc.; *U.S. Public*, pg. 1926
CP+B CANADA—See Stagwell, Inc.; *U.S. Public*, pg. 1926
CP+B—See Stagwell, Inc.; *U.S. Public*, pg. 1926
CP+B—See Stagwell, Inc.; *U.S. Public*, pg. 1926
CP COMMUNICATION—See Omnicom Group Inc.; *U.S. Public*, pg. 1575
CPM AUSTRALIA—See Omnicom Group Inc.; *U.S. Public*, pg. 1578
CPM AUSTRALIA—See Omnicom Group Inc.; *U.S. Public*, pg. 1578
CPM AUSTRIA—See Omnicom Group Inc.; *U.S. Public*, pg. 1578
CPM BELGIUM—See Omnicom Group Inc.; *U.S. Public*, pg. 1578
CPMEDIA & MARKETING SERVICES, INC.; *U.S. Private*, pg. 1080
CPM FRANCE—See Omnicom Group Inc.; *U.S. Public*, pg. 1578
CPM GERMANY GMBH—See Omnicom Group Inc.; *U.S. Public*, pg. 1578
CPM IRELAND—See Omnicom Group Inc.; *U.S. Public*, pg. 1578
CPM NETHERLANDS—See Omnicom Group Inc.; *U.S. Public*, pg. 1578
CPM NETHERLANDS—See Omnicom Group Inc.; *U.S. Public*, pg. 1578
CPM—See Omnicom Group Inc.; *U.S. Public*, pg. 1578
CPM SPAIN—See Omnicom Group Inc.; *U.S. Public*, pg. 1578
CPM SWITZERLAND—See Omnicom Group Inc.; *U.S. Public*, pg. 1578
CRAFT MARKETING; *U.S. Private*, pg. 1081
THE CRAIG BUSINESS GROUP; *U.S. Private*, pg. 4015
THE CRAMER-KRASSELT CO. - MILWAUKEE—See The Cramer-Krasselt Co.; *U.S. Private*, pg. 4015
THE CRAMER-KRASSELT CO. - NEW YORK—See The Cramer-Krasselt Co.; *U.S. Private*, pg. 4015
THE CRAMER-KRASSELT CO. - PHOENIX—See The Cramer-Krasselt Co.; *U.S. Private*, pg. 4016
THE CRAMER-KRASSELT CO.; *U.S. Private*, pg. 4015
CRAMER PRODUCTIONS INC.; *U.S. Private*, pg. 1084
CRAMP & ASSOCIATES, INC.; *U.S. Private*, pg. 1085
CRANFORD JOHNSON ROBINSON WOODS, INC.; *U.S. Private*, pg. 1085
CRANKY SIGNS & ADVERTISING; *U.S. Private*, pg. 1085
CRAVEROLANIS; *Int'l*, pg. 1828
CRAWFORD ADVERTISING ASSOCIATES, LTD.; *U.S. Private*, pg. 1086
CRAWLEY & COMPANY INCORPORATED; *U.S. Private*, pg. 1086
CRAYON; *U.S. Private*, pg. 1086
CR BASEL; *Int'l*, pg. 1827
CRC MARKETING SOLUTIONS; *U.S. Private*, pg. 1087
CREAD—See The Interpublic Group of Companies, Inc.; *U.S. Public*, pg. 2092
CREA PUBLICIDAD—See The Interpublic Group of Companies, Inc.; *U.S. Public*, pg. 2092
CREA PUBLICIDAD—See The Interpublic Group of Companies, Inc.; *U.S. Public*, pg. 2092
CREATIVE BROADCAST CONCEPTS; *U.S. Private*, pg. 1088
CREATIVE CIVILIZATION AN AGUILAR/GIRARD AGENCY; *U.S. Private*, pg. 1088
CREATIVE COMMUNICATION ASSOCIATES; *U.S. Private*, pg. 1088
CREATIVE COMMUNICATIONS CONSULTANTS, INC.; *U.S. Private*, pg. 1088
THE CREATIVE DEPARTMENT; *U.S. Private*, pg. 4016
CREATIVE ENTERTAINMENT SERVICES; *U.S. Private*, pg. 1088

N.A.I.C.S. INDEX

541810 — ADVERTISING AGENCIE...

CREATIVE FEED; U.S. Private, pg. 1088
CREATIVE GARAGE; U.S. Private, pg. 1089
CREATIVEHUB; U.S. Private, pg. 1090
CREATIVE INSURANCE MARKETING CO.; U.S. Private, pg. 1089
CREATIVE JAR; Int'l, pg. 1832
CREATIVE JUICE G1—See Omnicom Group Inc.; U.S. Public, pg. 1595
CREATIVE LINK ADVERTISING; U.S. Private, pg. 1089
CREATIVE MARKETING ALLIANCE INC.; U.S. Private, pg. 1089
CREATIVE MARKETING RESOURCE, INC.; U.S. Private, pg. 1089
CREATIVE MARKETING RESOURCES; U.S. Private, pg. 1089
CREATIVE MARKETING SPECIALISTS, INC.; U.S. Private, pg. 1089
CREATIVE MEDIA SERVICES GMBH—See The Interpublic Group of Companies, Inc.; U.S. Public, pg. 2090
CREATIVE PARTNERS GROUP, INC.; U.S. Private, pg. 1089
CREATIVE PARTNERS; U.S. Private, pg. 1089
THE CREATIVE UNDERGROUND; U.S. Private, pg. 4016
CRENDO; U.S. Private, pg. 1092
CRESTON ADVERTISING & MARKETING INC.; U.S. Private, pg. 1097
CREW CREATIVE ADVERTISING, LLC.; U.S. Private, pg. 1099
CRISPIN PORTER & BOGUSKY EUROPE AB—See Stagwell, Inc.; U.S. Public, pg. 1926
CRISPIN PORTER & BOGUSKY LIMITED—See Stagwell, Inc.; U.S. Public, pg. 1926
CRISPIN PORTER & BOGUSKY—See Stagwell, Inc.; U.S. Public, pg. 1926
CRITEO ADVERTISING (BEIJING) CO., LTD.—See Criteo S.A.; Int'l, pg. 1850
CRITEO B.V.—See Criteo S.A.; Int'l, pg. 1850
CRITEO CANADA CORP.—See Criteo S.A.; Int'l, pg. 1850
CRITEO DO BRASIL DESENVOLVIMENTO DE SERVICOS DE INTERNET LTDA.—See Criteo S.A.; Int'l, pg. 1850
CRITEO ESPANA, S.L.—See Criteo S.A.; Int'l, pg. 1850
CRITEO FRANCE S.A.S.—See Criteo S.A.; Int'l, pg. 1850
CRITEO GMBH—See Criteo S.A.; Int'l, pg. 1850
CRITEO K.K.—See Criteo S.A.; Int'l, pg. 1850
CRITEO LLC—See Criteo S.A.; Int'l, pg. 1850
CRITEO SINGAPORE PTE. LTD.—See Criteo S.A.; Int'l, pg. 1850
CRITEO S.R.L.—See Criteo S.A.; Int'l, pg. 1850
CRITERION GLOBAL; U.S. Private, pg. 1101
CRITICAL MASS INC. - NEW YORK—See Omnicom Group Inc.; U.S. Public, pg. 1594
CRITICAL MASS INC.—See Omnicom Group Inc.; U.S. Public, pg. 1594
CRITICAL MASS INC.—See Omnicom Group Inc.; U.S. Public, pg. 1594
CRITICAL MASS - LONDON—See Omnicom Group Inc.; U.S. Public, pg. 1594
CRONIN & COMPANY, INC.; U.S. Private, pg. 1103
CROSBY MARKETING COMMUNICATIONS; U.S. Private, pg. 1103
THE CROSS AGENCY; U.S. Private, pg. 4016
CROSSBOW GROUP, LLC; U.S. Private, pg. 1105
CROSS KEYS ADVERTISING & MARKETING, INC.; U.S. Private, pg. 1105
CROSSOVER CREATIVE GROUP; U.S. Private, pg. 1107
CROWELL ADVERTISING, MARKETING AND PR; U.S. Private, pg. 1109
CROWL, MARKETING & CREATIVE, INC.; U.S. Private, pg. 1109
CROWN MARKETING GROUP, INC.; U.S. Private, pg. 1111
CRUZ/KRAVETZ:IDEAS; U.S. Private, pg. 1114
CRYSTAL CLEAR DIGITAL MARKETING, LLC; U.S. Private, pg. 1115
CS2 ADVERTISING; U.S. Private, pg. 1116
CS ADVERTISING SDN. BHD.—See Chuo Senko Advertising Co., Ltd.; Int'l, pg. 1599
THE CSI GROUP, INC.; U.S. Private, pg. 4017
CTI MEDIA; U.S. Private, pg. 1118
CUBO COMMUNICATIONS GROUP PLC; Int'l, pg. 1875
CULT360; U.S. Private, pg. 1121
CUMMINGS ADVERTISING, INC.; U.S. Private, pg. 1123
CUMMINGS GROUP; U.S. Private, pg. 1123
THE CUMMINGS GROUP; U.S. Private, pg. 4017
CUNDARI INTEGRATED ADVERTISING; Int'l, pg. 1878
CURB MEDIA LIMITED—See Wasserman Media Group, LLC; U.S. Private, pg. 4450
CURRAN & CONNORS, INC.; U.S. Private, pg. 1125
CUSTOJUSTO UNIPESSOAL, LDA; Int'l, pg. 1880
CUTWATER—See Omnicom Group Inc.; U.S. Public, pg. 1598
CVA ADVERTISING & MARKETING, INC.; U.S. Private, pg. 1132
CYBERMEDIA K.K.—See ad-comm Co., Ltd.; Int'l, pg. 123
D4 CREATIVE GROUP; U.S. Private, pg. 1143
D8; Int'l, pg. 1901
DAC GROUP/BROOME MARKETING; U.S. Private, pg. 1144

D.A. CONSORTIUM, INC.—See Hakuhodo DY Holdings Incorporated; Int'l, pg. 3220
D'ADDA, LORENZINI, VIGORELLI, BBDO—See Omnicom Group Inc.; U.S. Public, pg. 1575
DAGMAR OY; Int'l, pg. 1912
DAIFU & CO., LTD.—See Dentsu Group Inc.; Int'l, pg. 2034
DAIKO ADVERTISING, INC.—See Hakuhodo DY Holdings Incorporated; Int'l, pg. 3220
DAIKO ADVERTISING, INC.—See Hakuhodo DY Holdings Incorporated; Int'l, pg. 3220
DAIKO ADVERTISING, INC.—See Hakuhodo DY Holdings Incorporated; Int'l, pg. 3220
DAIKO ADVERTISING, INC.—See Hakuhodo DY Holdings Incorporated; Int'l, pg. 3220
DAIKO ADVERTISING, INC.—See Hakuhodo DY Holdings Incorporated; Int'l, pg. 3220
DAIKO ADVERTISING, INC.—See Hakuhodo DY Holdings Incorporated; Int'l, pg. 3220
DAIKO (BEIJING) ADVERTISING CO., LTD.—See Hakuhodo DY Holdings Incorporated; Int'l, pg. 3220
DAIKO COMMUNICATIONS ASIA CO., LTD.—See Hakuhodo DY Holdings Incorporated; Int'l, pg. 3220
DAIKO HOKURIKU INC.—See Hakuhodo DY Holdings Incorporated; Int'l, pg. 3220
DAIKO KANSAI INC.—See Hakuhodo DY Holdings Incorporated; Int'l, pg. 3220
DAIKO KOBE INC.—See Hakuhodo DY Holdings Incorporated; Int'l, pg. 3220
DAIKO KYUSYU ADVERTISING INC.—See Hakuhodo DY Holdings Incorporated; Int'l, pg. 3220
DAIKO MEDIAX INC.—See Hakuhodo DY Holdings Incorporated; Int'l, pg. 3220
DAIKO MIE INC.—See Hakuhodo DY Holdings Incorporated; Int'l, pg. 3220
DAIKO ONES OSAKA INC.—See Hakuhodo DY Holdings Incorporated; Int'l, pg. 3220
DAIKO WEST INC.—See Hakuhodo DY Holdings Incorporated; Int'l, pg. 3220
DAILEY & ASSOCIATES—See The Interpublic Group of Companies, Inc.; U.S. Public, pg. 2090
THE DALTON AGENCY, INC.; U.S. Private, pg. 4018
DAMM & BIERBAUM AGENTUR FUR MARKETING UND KOMMUNIKATION GMBH; Int'l, pg. 1957
DANIEL, BURTON, DEAN ADVERTISING & DESIGN, INC.; U.S. Private, pg. 1156
DANIELS & ROBERTS, INC.; U.S. Private, pg. 1156
DAPS ADVERTISING LTD.; Int'l, pg. 1970
D'ARCY & PARTNERS, LLC; U.S. Private, pg. 1138
DARE DIGITAL LIMITED—See You & Mr Jones Inc.; U.S. Private, pg. 4591
DARK HORSE MARKETING; U.S. Private, pg. 1159
DARWIN BBDO—See Omnicom Group Inc.; U.S. Public, pg. 1575
DARWIN-GREY COMMUNICATIONS LTD.—See Integrated Communications Corp.; U.S. Private, pg. 2099
DARWIN-GREY COMMUNICATIONS—See Integrated Communications Corp.; U.S. Private, pg. 2099
DAS HOLDINGS INC.—See Omnicom Group Inc.; U.S. Public, pg. 1579
DASSAS COMMUNICATION; Int'l, pg. 1974
DATA GENOMIX LLC—See Crawford United Corporation; U.S. Public, pg. 592
DATAMARK INC.; U.S. Private, pg. 1166
DATAMARK INC.—See Datamark Inc.; U.S. Private, pg. 1166
DATA PROCESSING SERVICES; U.S. Private, pg. 1163
DATA PRO PROXIMITY—See Omnicom Group Inc.; U.S. Public, pg. 1575
DATCHAT, INC.; U.S. Public, pg. 635
DAVID JAMES GROUP LTD.; U.S. Private, pg. 1170
DAVID K. BURNAP ADVERTISING AGENCY, INC.; U.S. Private, pg. 1170
DAVIESMOORE; U.S. Private, pg. 1172
DAVIES, PACHECO & MURPHY ADVERTISING AGENCY, INC.; U.S. Private, pg. 1172
DAVINCI SELECTWORK; U.S. Private, pg. 1172
DAVIS ADVERTISING, INC.; U.S. Private, pg. 1173
DAVIS BARONE AGENCY; U.S. Private, pg. 1173
DAVIS & CO. INC.—See Davis & Company; U.S. Private, pg. 1172
DAVIS & COMPANY; U.S. Private, pg. 1172
DAVISDENNY ADVERTISING & RELATED SERVICES, INC.; U.S. Private, pg. 1175
DAVIS-ELEN ADVERTISING, INC.; U.S. Private, pg. 1174
DAVIS-ELEN ADVERTISING, INC.—See Davis-Elen Advertising, Inc.; U.S. Private, pg. 1174
DAVIS-ELEN ADVERTISING, INC.—See Davis-Elen Advertising, Inc.; U.S. Private, pg. 1174
DAVIS HARRISON DION, INC.; U.S. Private, pg. 1173
DB ASSOCIATES ADVERTISING; U.S. Private, pg. 1178
DCA/DCPR; U.S. Private, pg. 1179
D-CREATE INC.—See Hakuhodo DY Holdings Incorporated; Int'l, pg. 3220
DDB ADVIS—See Omnicom Group Inc.; U.S. Public, pg. 1579
DDB AMSTERDAM—See Omnicom Group Inc.; U.S. Public, pg. 1579

DDB ARGENTINA—See Omnicom Group Inc.; U.S. Public, pg. 1580
DDB BARCELONA S.A.—See Omnicom Group Inc.; U.S. Public, pg. 1580
DDB BERLIN—See Omnicom Group Inc.; U.S. Public, pg. 1580
DDB BRAINSTORM—See Omnicom Group Inc.; U.S. Public, pg. 1580
DDB BRATISLAVA—See Omnicom Group Inc.; U.S. Public, pg. 1580
DDB BRAZIL—See Omnicom Group Inc.; U.S. Public, pg. 1580
DDB BUCHAREST—See Omnicom Group Inc.; U.S. Public, pg. 1580
DDB BUDAPEST—See Omnicom Group Inc.; U.S. Public, pg. 1580
DDB CANADA - EDMONTON—See Omnicom Group Inc.; U.S. Public, pg. 1580
DDB CANADA - TORONTO—See Omnicom Group Inc.; U.S. Public, pg. 1580
DDB CANADA - VANCOUVER—See Omnicom Group Inc.; U.S. Public, pg. 1580
DDB CASERS—See Omnicom Group Inc.; U.S. Public, pg. 1580
DDB CHICAGO—See Omnicom Group Inc.; U.S. Public, pg. 1580
DDB CHILE—See Omnicom Group Inc.; U.S. Public, pg. 1580
DDB CHINA - SHANGHAI—See Omnicom Group Inc.; U.S. Public, pg. 1580
DDB COMMUNICATION FRANCE—See Omnicom Group Inc.; U.S. Public, pg. 1580
DDB COSTA RICA—See Omnicom Group Inc.; U.S. Public, pg. 1580
DDB DENMARK—See Omnicom Group Inc.; U.S. Public, pg. 1580
DDB DUSSELDORF—See Omnicom Group Inc.; U.S. Public, pg. 1580
DDB EGYPT—See Omnicom Group Inc.; U.S. Public, pg. 1580
DDB ESTONIA LTD.—See Omnicom Group Inc.; U.S. Public, pg. 1580
DDB EUROPE—See Omnicom Group Inc.; U.S. Public, pg. 1580
DDB GROUP BELGIUM—See Omnicom Group Inc.; U.S. Public, pg. 1580
DDB GROUP GERMANY—See Omnicom Group Inc.; U.S. Public, pg. 1580
DDB GROUP KOREA—See Omnicom Group Inc.; U.S. Public, pg. 1579
DDB GUOAN COMMUNICATIONS BEIJING CO., LTD.—See Omnicom Group Inc.; U.S. Public, pg. 1580
DDB GUOAN - GUANGZHOU—See Omnicom Group Inc.; U.S. Public, pg. 1580
DDB HAMBURG GMBH—See Omnicom Group Inc.; U.S. Public, pg. 1580
DDB HASH THREE—See Omnicom Group Inc.; U.S. Public, pg. 1580
DDB HELSINKI—See Omnicom Group Inc.; U.S. Public, pg. 1580
DDB HONDURAS—See Omnicom Group Inc.; U.S. Public, pg. 1580
DDB INDONESIA—See Omnicom Group Inc.; U.S. Public, pg. 1580
DDB JAPAN—See Omnicom Group Inc.; U.S. Public, pg. 1580
DDB LATIN AMERICA—See Omnicom Group Inc.; U.S. Public, pg. 1580
DDB LISBOA—See Omnicom Group Inc.; U.S. Public, pg. 1580
DDB LOS ANGELES—See Omnicom Group Inc.; U.S. Public, pg. 1580
DDB MADRID, S.A.—See Omnicom Group Inc.; U.S. Public, pg. 1581
DDB MELBOURNE PTY. LTD.—See Omnicom Group Inc.; U.S. Public, pg. 1581
DDB MEXICO—See Omnicom Group Inc.; U.S. Public, pg. 1581
DDB MIAMI—See Omnicom Group Inc.; U.S. Public, pg. 1581
DDB MOZAMBIQUE—See Omnicom Group Inc.; U.S. Public, pg. 1581
DDB NEW YORK—See Omnicom Group Inc.; U.S. Public, pg. 1581
DDB NEW ZEALAND LTD.—See Omnicom Group Inc.; U.S. Public, pg. 1581
DDB OSLO A.S.—See Omnicom Group Inc.; U.S. Public, pg. 1581
DDB PARIS—See Omnicom Group Inc.; U.S. Public, pg. 1581
DDB PHILIPPINES INC.—See Omnicom Group Inc.; U.S. Public, pg. 1581
DDB PRAGUE—See Omnicom Group Inc.; U.S. Public, pg. 1581
DDB REMEDY—See Omnicom Group Inc.; U.S. Public, pg. 1579
DDB RUSSIA—See Omnicom Group Inc.; U.S. Public, pg. 1581

541810 — ADVERTISING AGENCIE...   CORPORATE AFFILIATIONS

DDB SAN FRANCISCO—See Omnicom Group Inc.; *U.S. Public*, pg. 1581
DDB SOFIA—See Omnicom Group Inc.; *U.S. Public*, pg. 1581
DDB—See Omnicom Group Inc.; *U.S. Public*, pg. 1579
DDB SOUTH AFRICA—See Omnicom Group Inc.; *U.S. Public*, pg. 1581
DDB S.R.L. ADVERTISING—See Omnicom Group Inc.; *U.S. Public*, pg. 1581
DDB SRL ADVERTISING—See Omnicom Group Inc.; *U.S. Public*, pg. 1581
DDB STOCKHOLM—See Omnicom Group Inc.; *U.S. Public*, pg. 1581
DDB SYDNEY PTY. LTD.—See Omnicom Group Inc.; *U.S. Public*, pg. 1581
DDB TRIBAL VIENNA—See Omnicom Group Inc.; *U.S. Public*, pg. 1581
DDB VIETNAM ADVERTISING—See Omnicom Group Inc.; *U.S. Public*, pg. 1581
DDB WIEN GMBH—See Omnicom Group Inc.; *U.S. Public*, pg. 1581
DDB WORLDWIDE COLOMBIA S.A.—See Omnicom Group Inc.; *U.S. Public*, pg. 1581
DDB WORLDWIDE COLOMBIA S.A.—See Omnicom Group Inc.; *U.S. Public*, pg. 1581
DDB WORLDWIDE COLOMBIA, S.A.—See Omnicom Group Inc.; *U.S. Public*, pg. 1581
DDB WORLDWIDE COMMUNICATIONS GROUP INC.—See Omnicom Group Inc.; *U.S. Public*, pg. 1579
DDB WORLDWIDE INC.—See Omnicom Group Inc.; *U.S. Public*, pg. 1581
DDB WORLDWIDE LTD.—See Omnicom Group Inc.; *U.S. Public*, pg. 1581
DDB WORLDWIDE PTY. LTD.—See Omnicom Group Inc.; *U.S. Public*, pg. 1582
DDB WORLDWIDE—See Omnicom Group Inc.; *U.S. Public*, pg. 1581
D&D INTERACTIVE; *U.S. Private*, pg. 1137
DEALER WORLD LLC; *U.S. Private*, pg. 1182
THE DEAL, LLC—See Astorg Partners S.A.S.; *Int'l*, pg. 656
THE DEAL, LLC—See Epiris Managers LLP; *Int'l*, pg. 2461
DEALON, LLC—See Gannett Co., Inc.; *U.S. Public*, pg. 899
DECAROLIS DESIGN & MARKETING, INC.; *U.S. Private*, pg. 1186
DECKER CREATIVE MARKETING; *U.S. Private*, pg. 1187
DEEPINTENT TECHNOLOGIES, INC.—See Propel Media, Inc.; *U.S. Public*, pg. 1727
DEEP—See The Marlin Network, Inc.; *U.S. Private*, pg. 4075
DE FACTO COMMUNICATIONS LTD.—See Providence Equity Partners L.L.C.; *U.S. Private*, pg. 3291
DEFI COMMUNICATION MARKETING INC.; *Int'l*, pg. 2004
DEFINITION 6, LLC—See Kelso & Company, L.P.; *U.S. Private*, pg. 2277
DEFOREST CREATIVE GROUP; *U.S. Private*, pg. 1191
DEKSIA LLC; *U.S. Private*, pg. 1192
DE LA MA/MCCANN ERICKSON—See The Interpublic Group of Companies, Inc.; *U.S. Public*, pg. 2097
DELEON GROUP, LLC; *U.S. Private*, pg. 1196
DELFINO MARKETING COMMUNICATIONS, INC.; *U.S. Private*, pg. 1196
DELIA ASSOCIATES; *U.S. Private*, pg. 1196
DELTA PUBLICIDAD - GUAYAQUIL—See Delta Publicidad; *Int'l*, pg. 2020
DELTA PUBLICIDAD; *Int'l*, pg. 2020
DELUCA FRIGOLETTO ADVERTISING, INC.; *U.S. Private*, pg. 1202
DELUCCHI +; *U.S. Private*, pg. 1202
DEMANDG, LLC; *U.S. Private*, pg. 1203
DEMNER, MERLICEK & BERGMANN WERBEGESELLSCHAFT MBH; *Int'l*, pg. 2025
DENTINO MARKETING; *U.S. Private*, pg. 1206
DENTSU AEGIS NETWORK AUSTRALIA—See Dentsu Group Inc.; *Int'l*, pg. 2036
DENTSU AEGIS NETWORK INDIA—See Dentsu Group Inc.; *Int'l*, pg. 2036
DENTSU AEGIS NETWORK ITALIA SRL—See Dentsu Group Inc.; *Int'l*, pg. 2036
DENTSU AMERICA LLC—See Dentsu Group Inc.; *Int'l*, pg. 2036
DENTSU ARGENTINA S.A.—See Dentsu Group Inc.; *Int'l*, pg. 2036
DENTSU AUSTRALIA PTY LTD—See Dentsu Group Inc.; *Int'l*, pg. 2036
DENTSUBOS—See Dentsu Group Inc.; *Int'l*, pg. 2036
DENTSU BRUSSELS GROUP—See Dentsu Group Inc.; *Int'l*, pg. 2036
DENTSU CHINA LIMITED—See Dentsu Group Inc.; *Int'l*, pg. 2036
DENTSU COMMUNICATION INSTITUTE INC.—See Dentsu Group Inc.; *Int'l*, pg. 2034
DENTSU CORPORATE ONE INC.—See Dentsu Group Inc.; *Int'l*, pg. 2034
DENTSU CREATIVE GMBH—See Dentsu Group Inc.; *Int'l*, pg. 2037
DENTSU CREATIVE IMPACT PVT. LTD.—See Dentsu Group Inc.; *Int'l*, pg. 2036
DENTSU DIGITAL CO., LTD.—See Dentsu Group Inc.; *Int'l*, pg. 2034

DENTSU DIGITAL NETWORKS INC.—See Dentsu Group Inc.; *Int'l*, pg. 2034
DENTSU EAST JAPAN INC.—See Dentsu Group Inc.; *Int'l*, pg. 2034
DENTSU EVENT OPERATIONS INC.—See Dentsu Group Inc.; *Int'l*, pg. 2034
DENTSU HOKKAIDO INC.—See Dentsu Group Inc.; *Int'l*, pg. 2034
DENTSU KOREA INC—See Dentsu Group Inc.; *Int'l*, pg. 2037
DENTSU KUOHUA—See Dentsu Group Inc.; *Int'l*, pg. 2037
DENTSU KYUSHU INC.—See Dentsu Group Inc.; *Int'l*, pg. 2038
DENTSU LATIN AMERICA PROPAGANDA LTDA.—See Dentsu Group Inc.; *Int'l*, pg. 2036
DENTSU (MALAYSIA) SDN. BHD.—See Dentsu Group Inc.; *Int'l*, pg. 2035
DENTSU MARCOM PVT. LTD.—See Dentsu Group Inc.; *Int'l*, pg. 2037
DENTSU MEDIA KOREA INC.—See Dentsu Group Inc.; *Int'l*, pg. 2037
DENTSU MEDIA (THAILAND) LTD.—See Dentsu Group Inc.; *Int'l*, pg. 2035
DENTSU MEDIA VIETNAM LTD—See Dentsu Group Inc.; *Int'l*, pg. 2037
DENTSU MEITETSU COMMUNICATIONS INC.—See Dentsu Group Inc.; *Int'l*, pg. 2038
DENTSU NEW IDEAS LLC—See Dentsu Group Inc.; *Int'l*, pg. 2037
DENTSU OPERATION PARTNERS INC.—See Dentsu Group Inc.; *Int'l*, pg. 2038
DENTSU PLUS CO., LTD—See Dentsu Group Inc.; *Int'l*, pg. 2037
DENTSU PROMOTION PLUS INC.—See Dentsu Group Inc.; *Int'l*, pg. 2038
DENTSU RESEARCH INC.—See Dentsu Group Inc.; *Int'l*, pg. 2038
DENTSU RUNWAY INC.—See Dentsu Group Inc.; *Int'l*, pg. 2038
DENTSU SINGAPORE PVT. LTD.—See Dentsu Group Inc.; *Int'l*, pg. 2037
DENTSU-SMART LLC—See Dentsu Group Inc.; *Int'l*, pg. 2037
DENTSU (TAIWAN) INC.—See Dentsu Group Inc.; *Int'l*, pg. 2035
DENTSU TEC INC.—See Dentsu Group Inc.; *Int'l*, pg. 2034
DENTSU (THAILAND) LTD.—See Dentsu Group Inc.; *Int'l*, pg. 2035
DENTSU TOP CO., LTD.—See Dentsu Group Inc.; *Int'l*, pg. 2037
DENTSU VIETNAM LTD.—See Dentsu Group Inc.; *Int'l*, pg. 2037
DENTSU WEST JAPAN INC.—See Dentsu Group Inc.; *Int'l*, pg. 2038
DENTUSBOS MONTREAL—See Dentsu Group Inc.; *Int'l*, pg. 2036
DEPARTURE; *U.S. Private*, pg. 1208
DERING ELLIOTT & ASSOCIATES; *U.S. Private*, pg. 1209
DESANTIS BREINDEL; *U.S. Private*, pg. 1211
DESAUTEL HEGE COMMUNICATIONS; *U.S. Private*, pg. 1211
DESBROW THOMPSON CHAFFE; *Int'l*, pg. 2044
DESIGN CENTER—See Omnicom Group Inc.; *U.S. Public*, pg. 1594
DESIGN CONCEPTS; *U.S. Private*, pg. 1213
DESIGN EXTENSIONS, LLC; *U.S. Private*, pg. 1213
DESIGN MARKETING GROUP, INC.; *U.S. Private*, pg. 1213
THE DESIGNORY—See Omnicom Group Inc.; *U.S. Public*, pg. 1599
DESIGN REACTOR, INC.—See XTI Aerospace, Inc.; *U.S. Public*, pg. 2393
DESIGNWORKS ADVERTISING INC.; *U.S. Private*, pg. 1215
DESTINATION MARKETING; *U.S. Private*, pg. 1215
DETROIT TRADING COMPANY; *U.S. Private*, pg. 1216
DETROW & UNDERWOOD; *U.S. Private*, pg. 1216
DEUTSCH, INC.—See The Interpublic Group of Companies, Inc.; *U.S. Public*, pg. 2090
DEUTSCH LA—See The Interpublic Group of Companies, Inc.; *U.S. Public*, pg. 2091
DEUTSCH NEW YORK—See Attivo group; *Int'l*, pg. 696
DEVELOPMENT COUNSELLORS INTERNATIONAL, LTD.; *U.S. Private*, pg. 1217
DEVINE COMMUNICATIONS CORP.; *U.S. Private*, pg. 1218
DEVITO GROUP; *U.S. Private*, pg. 1218
DEVITO/VERDI; *U.S. Private*, pg. 1218
DEWEY COMMUNICATIONS, INC.; *U.S. Private*, pg. 1219
D EXPOSITO & PARTNERS, LLC; *U.S. Private*, pg. 1136
DG COMMUNICATIONS, INC.—See Digital Garage, Inc.; *Int'l*, pg. 2121
DGWB; *U.S. Private*, pg. 1221
D. HILTON ASSOCIATES, INC.; *U.S. Private*, pg. 1140
DIABLO MEDIA LLC; *U.S. Private*, pg. 1222
DIADEIS NEW YORK, LLC—See HPS Investment Partners, LLC; *U.S. Private*, pg. 1997
DIAMOND AGENCY, INC.; *Int'l*, pg. 2105
DIAMOND MARKETING SOLUTIONS GROUP, INC.—See Aquiline Capital Partners LLC; *U.S. Private*, pg. 304

DIANOMI INC.—See Dianomi Plc; *Int'l*, pg. 2106
DIANOMI PLC; *Int'l*, pg. 2106
DIBONA, BORNSTEIN & RANDOM, INC.; *U.S. Private*, pg. 1225
DICCICCO BATTISTA COMMUNICATIONS; *U.S. Private*, pg. 1225
DICOM, INC.; *U.S. Private*, pg. 1227
DIEBOLD GLASCOCK ADVERTISING, INC.; *U.S. Private*, pg. 1228
DIESTE—See Omnicom Group Inc.; *U.S. Public*, pg. 1582
DIESTE—See Omnicom Group Inc.; *U.S. Public*, pg. 1582
DIGIKNOW, INC.—See Marcus Thomas LLC; *U.S. Private*, pg. 2573
DIGITAL ADVERTISING CONSORTIUM, INC.—See Hakuhodo DY Holdings Incorporated; *Int'l*, pg. 3220
DIGITAL CHANGE INC.—See Allied Architects, Inc.; *Int'l*, pg. 356
DIGITAL EGG INC.—See Dentsu Group Inc.; *Int'l*, pg. 2039
DIGITAL HYVE MARKETING LLC—See Butler/Till Media Services, Inc.; *U.S. Private*, pg. 697
DIGITAL MEDIA HUB GMBH—See Bertelsmann SE & Co. KGaA; *Int'l*, pg. 992
DIGITAL ONE CONSULTING SP. Z O.O.; *Int'l*, pg. 2122
DIGITAL PULP; *U.S. Private*, pg. 1231
THE DIGITAL RING, LLC; *U.S. Private*, pg. 4021
DIGITAL UNLIMITED GROUP LTD.—See Accenture plc; *Int'l*, pg. 87
DIGITAL ZEN—See Barker/DZP; *U.S. Private*, pg. 475
DIK-OCEAN ADVERTISING CO., LTD.—See Bain Capital, LP; *U.S. Private*, pg. 428
DIMENSION X CORPORATION; *U.S. Private*, pg. 1232
DIN DEL FORSALJNING AB—See Eniro Group AB; *Int'l*, pg. 2439
DIO, LLC; *U.S. Private*, pg. 1234
DIRCKS ASSOCIATES; *U.S. Private*, pg. 1234
DIRECT EFFECT MEDIA SERVICES, INC.; *U.S. Private*, pg. 1235
DIRECT IMPACT, INC.; *U.S. Private*, pg. 1235
DIRECT INNOVATIONS; *U.S. Private*, pg. 1235
DIRECT MARKETING CENTER; *U.S. Private*, pg. 1235
DIRECT PARTNERS—See Omnicom Group Inc.; *U.S. Public*, pg. 1582
DIRECT PARTNERS—See Omnicom Group Inc.; *U.S. Public*, pg. 1583
DIRECT RESPONSE ACADEMY; *U.S. Private*, pg. 1235
DIRECT RESPONSE (THAILAND) LTD.—See The Interpublic Group of Companies, Inc.; *U.S. Public*, pg. 2092
DIRECT WEB ADVERTISING, INC.; *U.S. Private*, pg. 1236
DISCIPLE DESIGN—See Thompson & Company Marketing Communications; *U.S. Private*, pg. 4158
DISPLAY BOYS; *U.S. Private*, pg. 1238
THE DIVISION—See The Interpublic Group of Companies, Inc.; *U.S. Public*, pg. 2102
DIXON SCHWABL ADVERTISING; *U.S. Private*, pg. 1246
DJD/GOLDEN ADVERTISING, INC.; *U.S. Private*, pg. 1246
DJ-LA LLC; *U.S. Private*, pg. 1246
DJS ADVERTISING; *U.S. Private*, pg. 1247
DLKW LOWE—See The Interpublic Group of Companies, Inc.; *U.S. Public*, pg. 2091
DM9 JAYME SYFU INC.—See Dentsu Group Inc.; *Int'l*, pg. 2036
DMC ADVERTISING & DIRECT MARKETING, INC.; *U.S. Private*, pg. 1248
DMN3/DALLAS—See DMN3; *U.S. Private*, pg. 1249
DMN3; *U.S. Private*, pg. 1249
DMW WORLDWIDE LLC; *U.S. Private*, pg. 1249
DNA BRAND MECHANICS; *U.S. Private*, pg. 1249
DODSON ADVERTISING; *U.S. Private*, pg. 1252
DOE-ANDERSON; *U.S. Private*, pg. 1252
DOF INC.—See Dentsu Group Inc.; *Int'l*, pg. 2040
DOG DOG BOY; *U.S. Private*, pg. 1253
DOG EAT DOG ADVERTISING; *U.S. Private*, pg. 1253
DOGUS MUSTERI SISTEMLERI A.S.—See Dogus Holding AS; *Int'l*, pg. 2154
DOGUS YAYIN GRUBU A.S.—See Dogus Holding AS; *Int'l*, pg. 2154
DO IT!—See Omnicom Group Inc.; *U.S. Public*, pg. 1594
DOM CAMERA & COMPANY, LLC; *U.S. Private*, pg. 1255
DOMINO—See Omnicom Group Inc.; *U.S. Public*, pg. 1575
DO MORE GOOD LLC; *U.S. Private*, pg. 1250
DOMUS INC.; *U.S. Private*, pg. 1257
DONALD R. HARVEY, INC.; *U.S. Private*, pg. 1260
DONATWALD+HAQUE; *U.S. Private*, pg. 1260
DONER CANADA, INC.—See Doner; *U.S. Private*, pg. 1260
DONER CANADA, INC.—See Doner; *U.S. Private*, pg. 1260
DONER CARDWELL HAWKINS—See Doner; *U.S. Private*, pg. 1260
DONER PARTNERS LLC—See Stagwell, Inc.; *U.S. Public*, pg. 1926
DONER; *U.S. Private*, pg. 1260
DONER—See Doner; *U.S. Private*, pg. 1260
DONER—See Doner; *U.S. Private*, pg. 1260
DONER—See Doner; *U.S. Private*, pg. 1260
DON JAGODA ASSOCIATES, INC.; *U.S. Private*, pg. 1258
DON JAGODA ASSOCIATES, INC.—See Don Jagoda Associates, Inc.; *U.S. Private*, pg. 1258
DONOVAN ADVERTISING & MARKETING SERVICES; *U.S. Private*, pg. 1261

DOOK MEDIA GROUP LIMITED.; *Int'l*, pg. 2172
DOOSAN ADVERTISING COMPANY—See Doosan Corporation; *Int'l*, pg. 2172
DOREMUS (HONG KONG)—See Omnicom Group Inc.; *U.S. Public*, pg. 1583
DOREMUS LONDON—See Omnicom Group Inc.; *U.S. Public*, pg. 1583
DOREMUS (SAN FRANCISCO)—See Omnicom Group Inc.; *U.S. Public*, pg. 1583
DOREMUS—See Omnicom Group Inc.; *U.S. Public*, pg. 1583
DOS: PUNTOS DDB—See Omnicom Group Inc.; *U.S. Public*, pg. 1582
DOUMOB; *Int'l*, pg. 2182
DOVETAIL PROMOTION PARTNERS; *U.S. Private*, pg. 1268
DOVETAIL; *U.S. Private*, pg. 1268
DOWLING & POPE ADVERTISING INC.; *U.S. Private*, pg. 1268
DOWNTOWN ACTION MARKETING—See Omnicom Group Inc.; *U.S. Public*, pg. 1596
DOWNTOWN PARTNERS CHICAGO—See Omnicom Group Inc.; *U.S. Public*, pg. 1583
THE DOZIER COMPANY; *U.S. Private*, pg. 4023
DPZ ARGENTINA—See Acento Advertising, Inc.; *U.S. Private*, pg. 58
DPZ-DUAILIBI, PETIT, ZARAGOZA, PROPAGANDA S.A.—See Acento Advertising, Inc.; *U.S. Private*, pg. 58
DPZ-RIO DE JANEIRO—See Acento Advertising, Inc.; *U.S. Private*, pg. 58
DRAFTFCB AD FABRIKA—See The Interpublic Group of Companies, Inc.; *U.S. Public*, pg. 2092
DRAFTFCB CANADA INC.—See The Interpublic Group of Companies, Inc.; *U.S. Public*, pg. 2092
DRAFTFCB CAPE TOWN—See The Interpublic Group of Companies, Inc.; *U.S. Public*, pg. 2092
DRAFTFCB DURBAN—See The Interpublic Group of Companies, Inc.; *U.S. Public*, pg. 2092
DRAFTFCB HEALTHCARE—See The Interpublic Group of Companies, Inc.; *U.S. Public*, pg. 2092
DRAFTFCB JOHANNESBURG—See The Interpublic Group of Companies, Inc.; *U.S. Public*, pg. 2092
DRAFTFCB MA—See The Interpublic Group of Companies, Inc.; *U.S. Public*, pg. 2092
DRAFTFCB PARTNERS WERBEAGENTUR GES.M.B.H.—See The Interpublic Group of Companies, Inc.; *U.S. Public*, pg. 2092
DRAFTFCB RUSSIA—See The Interpublic Group of Companies, Inc.; *U.S. Public*, pg. 2092
DRAFTFCB SHIMONI FINKELSTEIN—See The Interpublic Group of Companies, Inc.; *U.S. Public*, pg. 2092
DRAFTFCB—See The Interpublic Group of Companies, Inc.; *U.S. Public*, pg. 2092
DRAFTFCB—See The Interpublic Group of Companies, Inc.; *U.S. Public*, pg. 2092
DRAFTFCB—See The Interpublic Group of Companies, Inc.; *U.S. Public*, pg. 2092
DRAFTFCB (THAILAND) LTD.—See The Interpublic Group of Companies, Inc.; *U.S. Public*, pg. 2092
DRAFTFCB ULKA—See The Interpublic Group of Companies, Inc.; *U.S. Public*, pg. 2092
DRAFTFCB ULKA—See The Interpublic Group of Companies, Inc.; *U.S. Public*, pg. 2092
DRAFTFCB ULKA—See The Interpublic Group of Companies, Inc.; *U.S. Public*, pg. 2092
DRAFTFCB ULKA—See The Interpublic Group of Companies, Inc.; *U.S. Public*, pg. 2092
DRAFTFCB ULKA—See The Interpublic Group of Companies, Inc.; *U.S. Public*, pg. 2092
DRAFTFCB WEST—See The Interpublic Group of Companies, Inc.; *U.S. Public*, pg. 2093
DRAFTFCB WEST—See The Interpublic Group of Companies, Inc.; *U.S. Public*, pg. 2093
DRAKE COOPER INC.; *U.S. Private*, pg. 1272
DRILL INC.—See Dentsu Group Inc.; *Int'l*, pg. 2039
DRIVENMEDIA; *U.S. Private*, pg. 1278
DROGA5, LLC—See Accenture plc; *Int'l*, pg. 88
DROGA5—See Accenture plc; *Int'l*, pg. 88
DSC (DILEONARDO SIANO CASERTA) ADVERTISING; *U.S. Private*, pg. 1281
DS TOMBRAS—See Charles Tombras Advertising, Inc.; *U.S. Private*, pg. 854
DUDNYK ADVERTISING & PUBLIC RELATIONS, INC.—See Dudnyk Enterprises, Ltd.; *U.S. Private*, pg. 1284
DUFFY & SHANLEY, INC.; *U.S. Private*, pg. 1285
DUFOUR ADVERTISING; *U.S. Private*, pg. 1285
DUNCAN CHANNON; *U.S. Private*, pg. 1287
DUNCAN/DAY ADVERTISING; *U.S. Private*, pg. 1288
DUNN&CO.; *U.S. Private*, pg. 1290
DURHAM GROUP—See Cashman & Katz Integrated Communications; *U.S. Private*, pg. 783
DUVENJIAN; *U.S. Private*, pg. 1295
DYMUN + COMPANY, INC.—See NFM Group Inc.; *U.S. Private*, pg. 2923
DYNAMEDIA OF AMERICA, INC.; *U.S. Private*, pg. 1297
DYNAMIC LOGIC—See Bain Capital, LP; *U.S. Private*, pg. 448

DYNAMIC LOGIC—See Bain Capital, LP; *U.S. Private*, pg. 448
DYNAMIC LOGIC—See Bain Capital, LP; *U.S. Private*, pg. 448
DYNAMIC LOGIC—See Bain Capital, LP; *U.S. Private*, pg. 448
DYNAMIC MEDIA TIRANA—See Omnicom Group Inc.; *U.S. Public*, pg. 1575
DZUKA COMMUNICATIONS—See The Interpublic Group of Companies, Inc.; *U.S. Public*, pg. 2093
E21CORP; *U.S. Private*, pg. 1308
E2AMP; *U.S. Private*, pg. 1308
EARTHQUAKE MEDIA, LLC; *U.S. Private*, pg. 1314
EAST JAPAN MARKETING & COMMUNICATIONS, INC.; *Int'l*, pg. 2270
EASTWEST MARKETING GROUP, LLC; *U.S. Private*, pg. 1322
EASY CLICK WORLDWIDE NETWORK TECHNOLOGY CO., LTD.; *Int'l*, pg. 2275
EBAY SPAIN INTERNATIONAL, S.L.—See eBay Inc.; *U.S. Public*, pg. 709
E-B DISPLAY CO., INC.; *U.S. Private*, pg. 1302
THE EBELING GROUP, INC.; *U.S. Private*, pg. 4025
EBEL, SIGNORELLI & WELKE LLC; *U.S. Private*, pg. 1324
EBEN DESIGN, INC.; *U.S. Private*, pg. 1324
E.B. WALL + ASSOCIATES; *U.S. Private*, pg. 1304
ECHO MARKETING CO., LTD.; *Int'l*, pg. 2289
ECHO TORRE LAZUR—See The Interpublic Group of Companies, Inc.; *U.S. Public*, pg. 2102
EDELMANN SCOTT, INC.; *U.S. Private*, pg. 1332
EDEXPERTS; *U.S. Private*, pg. 1333
EDGECORE, LLC—See Eastport Holdings, Inc.; *U.S. Private*, pg. 1322
EDIP (EDITION-DIFFUSION-IMPRESSION-PUBLICITE); *Int'l*, pg. 2310
EDUCOM S.R.L.—See IQVIA Holdings Inc.; *U.S. Public*, pg. 1168
EDWARD J. QUIGLEY ASSOCIATES; *U.S. Private*, pg. 1341
EFFECTIVE SPEND LLC; *U.S. Private*, pg. 1343
EFPZ—See The Interpublic Group of Companies, Inc.; *U.S. Public*, pg. 2093
THE EGC GROUP; *U.S. Private*, pg. 4025
E-GRAPHICS—See Omnicom Group Inc.; *U.S. Public*, pg. 1594
EGR INTERNATIONAL, INC.; *U.S. Private*, pg. 1345
EG+ WORLDWIDE—See Omnicom Group Inc.; *U.S. Public*, pg. 1596
EHRENSTRAHLE & CO. I STOCKHOLM AB—See Omnicom Group Inc.; *U.S. Public*, pg. 1581
EICHENBAUM/ASSOCIATES, INC.; *U.S. Private*, pg. 1346
EIGEN FABRIKAAT BU—See Omnicom Group Inc.; *U.S. Public*, pg. 1580
EISENMAN ASSOCIATES INC.; *U.S. Private*, pg. 1347
EJE TBWA—See Omnicom Group Inc.; *U.S. Public*, pg. 1598
ELECTRIC GUITAR PLC; *Int'l*, pg. 2349
ELECTRONIC PRODUCTS MAGAZINE—See The Hearst Corporation; *U.S. Private*, pg. 4045
ELECTRONICS MARKETING GROUP; *U.S. Private*, pg. 1356
ELEVATION MARKETING; *U.S. Private*, pg. 1358
ELEVATION; *U.S. Private*, pg. 1358
ELEVATION—See Elevation; *U.S. Private*, pg. 1358
ELEVEN INC.—See Bluefocus Intelligent Communications Group Co., Ltd.; *Int'l*, pg. 1071
ELLISON MEDIA COMPANY; *U.S. Private*, pg. 1374
ELOCAL USA LLC—See Brookfield Corporation; *Int'l*, pg. 1189
ELRAY RESOURCES, INC.; *U.S. Public*, pg. 735
ELSER & AUCONE, INC.; *U.S. Private*, pg. 1377
THE ELTRON COMPANY; *U.S. Private*, pg. 4025
E&M ADVERTISING; *U.S. Private*, pg. 1301
EMAK WORLDWIDE, INC.; *U.S. Private*, pg. 1378
EMANATE—See Omnicom Group Inc.; *U.S. Public*, pg. 1586
EMBLEM, LLC; *U.S. Private*, pg. 1378
EMBRACE GMBH—See Bertelsmann SE & Co. KGaA; *Int'l*, pg. 992
EMERGE DIGITAL INC.; *U.S. Private*, pg. 1380
EMG - ETHNIC MARKETING GROUP, INC.; *U.S. Private*, pg. 1382
EMI/DUBLIN—See EMI Strategic Marketing, Inc.; *U.S. Private*, pg. 1382
E&M MEDIA GROUP—See E&M Advertising; *U.S. Private*, pg. 1301
EMNET INC.; *Int'l*, pg. 2385
EMNET JAPAN CO., LTD.—See eMnet Inc.; *Int'l*, pg. 2385
E. MORRIS COMMUNICATIONS, INC.; *U.S. Private*, pg. 1304
EMO; *Int'l*, pg. 2385
EMPICA LTD.; *Int'l*, pg. 2386
THE EMPIRE; *U.S. Private*, pg. 4026
EMPOWER MEDIAMARKETING—See EMI Strategic Marketing, Inc.; *U.S. Private*, pg. 1387
EMSEAS TEKNIK AB—See ad pepper media International NV; *Int'l*, pg. 122
ENERGY BBDO—See Omnicom Group Inc.; *U.S. Public*, pg. 1575
ENGAGE:BDR LIMITED; *Int'l*, pg. 2426

ENGINE COMPANY ONE; *U.S. Private*, pg. 1397
ENGINE MARKETING, LLC; *U.S. Private*, pg. 1397
THE ENGINE ROOM; *U.S. Private*, pg. 4026
ENIRO PASSAGEN AB—See Eniro Group AB; *Int'l*, pg. 2439
ENIRO SVERIGE AB—See Eniro Group AB; *Int'l*, pg. 2439
ENIRO SVERIGE FORSALJNING AB—See Eniro Group AB; *Int'l*, pg. 2439
ENIZO SP. Z O.O.—See Energoinstal S.A.; *Int'l*, pg. 2421
ENTEN & ASSOCIATES, INC.; *U.S. Private*, pg. 1403
ENYE MEDIA, LLC; *U.S. Private*, pg. 1410
EPICENTER NETWORK INC; *U.S. Private*, pg. 1413
EPICOSITY; *U.S. Private*, pg. 1413
EQUALS THREE COMMUNICATIONS; *U.S. Private*, pg. 1415
EQUATOR (SCOTLAND) LTD.—See Matthews International Corporation; *U.S. Public*, pg. 1400
EQUIFAX DIRECT MARKETING SOLUTIONS, INC.—See Bread Financial Holdings Inc.; *U.S. Public*, pg. 381
EQUI=MEDIA LIMITED; *Int'l*, pg. 2484
ERGO (ERGONOMIC COMMUNICATIONS)—See The Interpublic Group of Companies, Inc.; *U.S. Public*, pg. 2091
ERICKSEN ADVERTISING & DESIGN, INC.; *U.S. Private*, pg. 1419
ERIC MOWER AND ASSOCIATES, INC. - ALBANY—See Eric Mower and Associates, Inc.; *U.S. Private*, pg. 1419
ERIC MOWER AND ASSOCIATES, INC. - ATLANTA—See Eric Mower and Associates, Inc.; *U.S. Private*, pg. 1419
ERIC MOWER AND ASSOCIATES, INC. - BOSTON—See Eric Mower and Associates, Inc.; *U.S. Private*, pg. 1419
ERIC MOWER AND ASSOCIATES, INC. - BUFFALO—See Eric Mower and Associates, Inc.; *U.S. Private*, pg. 1419
ERIC MOWER AND ASSOCIATES, INC. - CHARLOTTE—See Eric Mower and Associates, Inc.; *U.S. Private*, pg. 1419
ERIC MOWER AND ASSOCIATES, INC. - CINCINNATI—See Eric Mower and Associates, Inc.; *U.S. Private*, pg. 1419
ERIC MOWER AND ASSOCIATES, INC. - ROCHESTER—See Eric Mower and Associates, Inc.; *U.S. Private*, pg. 1419
ERIC MOWER AND ASSOCIATES, INC.; *U.S. Private*, pg. 1419
ER MARKETING; *U.S. Private*, pg. 1417
ERVIN MARKETING CREATIVE COMMUNICATIONS; *U.S. Private*, pg. 1424
ERWIN PENLAND AND COMPANY—See Attivo group; *Int'l*, pg. 697
ES ADVERTISING; *U.S. Private*, pg. 1424
ESCALA COMUNICACAO & MARKETING LTDA.; *Int'l*, pg. 2501
ESCAPE POD; *U.S. Private*, pg. 1425
ESHAREH ADVERTISING AGENCY—See The Interpublic Group of Companies, Inc.; *U.S. Public*, pg. 2099
ESPARZA ADVERTISING; *U.S. Private*, pg. 1426
ESROCK PARTNERS; *U.S. Private*, pg. 1427
ESSENTIALLY SPORTS MARKETING LIMITED—See Wasserman Media Group, LLC; *U.S. Public*, pg. 4450
ESTEY-HOOVER INC. ADVERTISING-PUBLIC RELATIONS; *U.S. Private*, pg. 1429
ETTEPLAN B.V.—See Etteplan Oyj; *Int'l*, pg. 2524
ETTEPLAN ENGINEERING SOLUTIONS NETHERLANDS B.V.—See Etteplan Oyj; *Int'l*, pg. 2524
ETTEPLAN SWEDEN AB—See Etteplan Oyj; *Int'l*, pg. 2525
ETTEPLAN TECH POLAND S.A.—See Etteplan Oyj; *Int'l*, pg. 2525
EUROPRINT, INC.; *U.S. Private*, pg. 1434
EVANSHARDY & YOUNG, INC.; *U.S. Private*, pg. 1435
EVB-EVOLUTION BUREAU—See Omnicom Group Inc.; *U.S. Public*, pg. 1583
THE EVENT AGENCY; *U.S. Private*, pg. 4027
EVERYD MC, INC.—See McDonald's Corporation; *U.S. Public*, pg. 1406
EVINS COMMUNICATIONS, LTD.; *U.S. Private*, pg. 1441
EVOK ADVERTISING; *U.S. Private*, pg. 1442
EVOLVE TALENT AGENCY; *U.S. Private*, pg. 1444
E.W. BULLOCK ASSOCIATES, INC.; *U.S. Private*, pg. 1307
EXARING AG—See freenet AG; *Int'l*, pg. 2770
EXHICON EVENTS MEDIA SOLUTIONS LTD.; *Int'l*, pg. 2584
EXIT; *U.S. Private*, pg. 1449
EXPLORE COMMUNICATIONS; *U.S. Private*, pg. 1450
EXPONENTIAL INTERACTIVE, INC.; *U.S. Private*, pg. 1450
EXPONENT—See Stagwell, Inc.; *U.S. Public*, pg. 1926
EXUBRIO GROUP LLC; *U.S. Private*, pg. 1453
EYECON MARKETING GROUP; *U.S. Private*, pg. 1453
EZAGOO LIMITED; *Int'l*, pg. 2593
FABIANO COMMUNICATIONS, INC.; *U.S. Private*, pg. 1458
FACETIME STRATEGY; *U.S. Private*, pg. 1459
FACETIME STRATEGY—See FaceTime Strategy; *U.S. Private*, pg. 1459
FACETIME STRATEGY—See FaceTime Strategy; *U.S. Private*, pg. 1459
FACTION MEDIA; *U.S. Private*, pg. 1460
FACTORY DESIGN LABS, INC.; *U.S. Private*, pg. 1460
FAHLGREN ADVERTISING—See Peopletomysite.com, LLC; *U.S. Private*, pg. 3143

541810 — ADVERTISING AGENCIES

FAHLGREN GRIP DIGITAL—See Peopletomysite.com, LLC; *U.S. Private*, pg. 3143
FAHLGREN, INC. - CINCINNATI—See Peopletomysite.com, LLC; *U.S. Private*, pg. 3143
FAHLGREN, INC. - DAYTON—See Peopletomysite.com, LLC; *U.S. Private*, pg. 3143
FAHLGREN, INC. - FORT LAUDERDALE—See Peopletomysite.com, LLC; *U.S. Private*, pg. 3143
FAHLGREN, INC. - PARKERSBURG—See Peopletomysite.com, LLC; *U.S. Private*, pg. 3143
FAHLGREN, INC.—See Peopletomysite.com, LLC; *U.S. Private*, pg. 3143
FAHLGREN, INC. - TOLEDO—See Peopletomysite.com, LLC; *U.S. Private*, pg. 3143
FAHRENHEIT 212—See Capgemini SE; *Int'l*, pg. 1306
FAIRBROTHER & COMPANY LLC; *U.S. Private*, pg. 1462
FAIRLY PAINLESS ADVERTISING; *U.S. Private*, pg. 1464
FAIRMONT PRESS, INC.; *U.S. Private*, pg. 1464
FAIRVIEW ADVERTISING; *U.S. Private*, pg. 1464
FAIRWAY OUTDOOR ADVERTISING, LLC - ATHENS—See GTCR LLC; *U.S. Private*, pg. 1805
FAIRWAY OUTDOOR ADVERTISING, LLC - DUNCAN—See GTCR LLC; *U.S. Private*, pg. 1805
FAIRWAY OUTDOOR ADVERTISING, LLC - GREENSBORO—See GTCR LLC; *U.S. Private*, pg. 1805
FAIRWAY OUTDOOR ADVERTISING, LLC - RALEIGH—See GTCR LLC; *U.S. Private*, pg. 1805
FAKTOR 3 AG; *Int'l*, pg. 2610
FALL ADVERTISING; *U.S. Private*, pg. 1467
FALLON MEDICA LLC; *U.S. Private*, pg. 1468
THE FALLS AGENCY; *U.S. Private*, pg. 4027
FALTMAN & MALMEN AB—See The Interpublic Group of Companies, Inc.; *U.S. Public*, pg. 2093
FAMILY ADVERTISING; *Int'l*, pg. 2612
FAMOUS MARKS, INC.; *U.S. Private*, pg. 1472
FARAGO+PARTNERS; *U.S. Private*, pg. 1473
FAR EAST DDB—See Omnicom Group Inc.; *U.S. Public*, pg. 1581
FARNER TEUBER COMMUNICATION—See Omnicom Group Inc.; *U.S. Public*, pg. 1590
FARRAR & FARRAR; *U.S. Private*, pg. 1480
FASONE & PARTNERS; *U.S. Private*, pg. 1481
FASTLANE; *U.S. Private*, pg. 1482
FATHOM COMMUNICATIONS—See Omnicom Group Inc.; *U.S. Public*, pg. 1583
FATHOM COMMUNICATIONS—See Omnicom Group Inc.; *U.S. Public*, pg. 1583
FAT MEDIA LTD.; *Int'l*, pg. 2622
FAYE CLACK COMMUNICATIONS INC.; *Int'l*, pg. 2626
FCB AFRICA—See The Interpublic Group of Companies, Inc.; *U.S. Public*, pg. 2093
FCB AUSTRALIA PTY LTD—See The Interpublic Group of Companies, Inc.; *U.S. Public*, pg. 2093
FCB CHICAGO—See The Interpublic Group of Companies, Inc.; *U.S. Public*, pg. 2093
FCB CREA PUBLICIDAD—See The Interpublic Group of Companies, Inc.; *U.S. Public*, pg. 2093
FCB DOS PUNTOS CREA—See The Interpublic Group of Companies, Inc.; *U.S. Public*, pg. 2093
FCB HEALTH—See The Interpublic Group of Companies, Inc.; *U.S. Public*, pg. 2093
FCB KUALA LUMPUR—See The Interpublic Group of Companies, Inc.; *U.S. Public*, pg. 2093
FCB MANILA—See The Interpublic Group of Companies, Inc.; *U.S. Public*, pg. 2093
FCBULKA ADVERTISING—See The Interpublic Group of Companies, Inc.; *U.S. Public*, pg. 2093
FCB WORLDWIDE, INC.—See The Interpublic Group of Companies, Inc.; *U.S. Public*, pg. 2092
FD2S; *U.S. Private*, pg. 1486
FELDER COMMUNICATIONS GROUP; *U.S. Private*, pg. 1493
FERRYADS.COM—See Communication Associates; *U.S. Private*, pg. 988
FHC MARKETING; *U.S. Private*, pg. 1501
FHV BBDO—See Omnicom Group Inc.; *U.S. Public*, pg. 1575
FIELD DAY INC.; *Int'l*, pg. 2655
FIFTH RING INC.—See Fifth Ring Ltd; *Int'l*, pg. 2660
FIFTH RING LLC—See Fifth Ring Ltd; *Int'l*, pg. 2660
FIFTH RING LTD; *Int'l*, pg. 2660
FIGTREE CREATIVE SERVICES LTD.—See Prophet Brand Strategy, Inc.; *U.S. Private*, pg. 3285
FIGTREE CREATIVE SERVICES-WANCHAI—See Prophet Brand Strategy, Inc.; *U.S. Private*, pg. 3285
FILTER ADVERTISING LLC—See Splendor Design Group, Inc.; *U.S. Private*, pg. 3759
FINDLY TALENT - ATLANTA—See Symphony Technology Group, LLC; *U.S. Private*, pg. 3900
FINDLY TALENT - HOUSTON—See Symphony Technology Group, LLC; *U.S. Private*, pg. 3900
FINDLY TALENT, LLC—See Symphony Technology Group, LLC; *U.S. Private*, pg. 3900
FINDLY TALENT - NEW JERSEY—See Symphony Technology Group, LLC; *U.S. Private*, pg. 3900
FINDLY TALENT - ORLANDO—See Symphony Technology Group, LLC; *U.S. Private*, pg. 3900

FINDLY TALENT - WASHINGTON, DC—See Symphony Technology Group, LLC; *U.S. Private*, pg. 3900
FINE LIGHT, INC.; *U.S. Private*, pg. 1509
FINE LIGHT, INC.—See Fine Light, Inc.; *U.S. Private*, pg. 1509
FIORE ASSOCIATES, INC.; *U.S. Private*, pg. 1511
FIRE ADVERATINMENT—See Omnicom Group Inc.; *U.S. Public*, pg. 1581
FIREHOUSE, INC.; *U.S. Private*, pg. 1511
FIRE & RAIN, LLC—See 2e Creative; *U.S. Private*, pg. 6
FIRESPRING; *U.S. Private*, pg. 1512
FIRST CITY ADVERTISING—See Omnicom Group Inc.; *U.S. Public*, pg. 1575
FIRST MEDIA GROUP INC.; *U.S. Private*, pg. 1521
FISCHER FALA—See Hakuhodo DY Holdings Incorporated; *Int'l*, pg. 3220
FISH MARKETING; *U.S. Private*, pg. 1533
F.I.T. FAHRZEUG INGENIEURTECHNIK GMBH—See Etteplan Oyj; *Int'l*, pg. 2525
FITZGERALD+CO—See The Interpublic Group of Companies, Inc.; *U.S. Public*, pg. 2097
FITZGERALD & MASTROIANNI, INC.; *U.S. Private*, pg. 1536
FIVE BY FIVE; *Int'l*, pg. 2696
FIXATION MARKETING; *U.S. Private*, pg. 1538
FKM—See The Company of Others; *U.S. Private*, pg. 4013
FKQ ADVERTISING + MARKETING INC.; *U.S. Private*, pg. 1538
FLAMINGO—See Omnicom Group Inc.; *U.S. Public*, pg. 1583
FLASKAMP AG; *Int'l*, pg. 2698
FLEISHMAN-HILLARD CANADA INC. - TORONTO—See Omnicom Group Inc.; *U.S. Public*, pg. 1584
FLEMING & VAN METRE; *U.S. Private*, pg. 1542
FLINT COMMUNICATIONS, INC. & ADFARM; *U.S. Private*, pg. 1545
FLINT INTERACTIVE—See Flint Communications, Inc. & Adfarm; *U.S. Private*, pg. 1545
FLIPSIDE GROUP—See The Interpublic Group of Companies, Inc.; *U.S. Public*, pg. 2104
FLM HARVEST—See Land O'Lakes, Inc.; *U.S. Private*, pg. 2383
FLOURISH INC.; *U.S. Private*, pg. 1551
FLUENT, LLC—See Fluent, Inc.; *U.S. Public*, pg. 857
FLYING A; *U.S. Private*, pg. 1553
FLYING POINT MEDIA, INC.; *U.S. Private*, pg. 1553
FLYNN & FRIENDS; *U.S. Private*, pg. 1553
THE FMG GROUP; *U.S. Private*, pg. 4029
F@N COMMUNICATIONS, INC.; *Int'l*, pg. 2598
FOCUSED IMAGE; *U.S. Private*, pg. 1556
FOCUS FGW—See Freedman, Gibson & White Inc.; *U.S. Private*, pg. 1603
FOODMIX MARKETING COMMUNICATIONS; *U.S. Private*, pg. 1562
FOOTSTEPS—See Omnicom Group Inc.; *U.S. Public*, pg. 1585
FORCE MARKETING LLC; *U.S. Private*, pg. 1563
FORESIGHT RESEARCH CO., LTD.—See Hakuhodo DY Holdings Incorporated; *Int'l*, pg. 3220
FORGE MARKETING COMMUNICATIONS; *U.S. Private*, pg. 1568
FORGE WORLDWIDE; *U.S. Private*, pg. 1568
FORMIC MEDIA, INC.; *U.S. Private*, pg. 1571
FORMITAS—See Omnicom Group Inc.; *U.S. Public*, pg. 1575
FORREST & BLAKE INC.; *U.S. Private*, pg. 1572
FORSMAN & BODENFORS AB—See Stagwell, Inc.; *U.S. Public*, pg. 1926
FORSMAN & BODENFORS FACTORY AB—See Stagwell, Inc.; *U.S. Public*, pg. 1926
FORSMAN & BODENFORS INHOUSE AB—See Stagwell, Inc.; *U.S. Public*, pg. 1926
FORSMAN & BODENFORS - TORONTO—See Stagwell, Inc.; *U.S. Public*, pg. 1926
FORT FRANKLIN; *U.S. Private*, pg. 1574
FORTUNE PROMOSEVEN DUBAI—See The Interpublic Group of Companies, Inc.; *U.S. Public*, pg. 2098
FORTUNE PROMOSEVEN-HQ—See The Interpublic Group of Companies, Inc.; *U.S. Public*, pg. 2099
FORTUNE PROMOSEVEN-LEBANON—See The Interpublic Group of Companies, Inc.; *U.S. Public*, pg. 2100
FORTUNE PROMOSEVEN-QATAR—See The Interpublic Group of Companies, Inc.; *U.S. Public*, pg. 2100
FORTUNE PROMOSEVEN—See The Interpublic Group of Companies, Inc.; *U.S. Public*, pg. 2100
FORWARD MEDIA INC.; *U.S. Private*, pg. 1578
FORWARDPMX GROUP LLC—See Stagwell, Inc.; *U.S. Public*, pg. 1928
FORZA MIGLIOZZI, LLC; *U.S. Private*, pg. 1578
FOSTER MARKETING COMMUNICATIONS; *U.S. Private*, pg. 1579
FOSTER MARKETING COMMUNICATIONS—See Foster Marketing Communications; *U.S. Private*, pg. 1579
FOUR COMMUNICATIONS PLC—See Four Communications Group plc; *Int'l*, pg. 2754
FP7 ABU DHABI—See The Interpublic Group of Companies, Inc.; *U.S. Public*, pg. 2099

FP7 MCCANN ALGERIA—See The Interpublic Group of Companies, Inc.; *U.S. Public*, pg. 2099
FP7 MCCANN-TUNISIA—See The Interpublic Group of Companies, Inc.; *U.S. Public*, pg. 2099
FPO, LLC; *U.S. Private*, pg. 1586
FRANCESCHI ADVERTISING & PUBLIC RELATIONS, INC.; *U.S. Private*, pg. 1586
THE FRANK AGENCY, INC.; *U.S. Private*, pg. 4030
FRANKLIN STREET MARKETING; *U.S. Private*, pg. 1598
FRASER COMMUNICATIONS; *U.S. Private*, pg. 1599
FRCH DESIGN WORLDWIDE; *U.S. Private*, pg. 1600
FREAKOUT TAIWAN CO., LTD.—See FreakOut Holdings, Inc.; *Int'l*, pg. 2767
FREAKOUT (THAILAND) CO., LTD.—See FreakOut Holdings, Inc.; *Int'l*, pg. 2767
FREEBAIRN & CO.; *U.S. Private*, pg. 1602
FREED ADVERTISING; *U.S. Private*, pg. 1602
FREEDMAN, GIBSON & WHITE INC.; *U.S. Private*, pg. 1603
FREEDOM + PARTNERS; *U.S. Private*, pg. 1603
FRENCH/BLITZER/SCOTT LLC; *U.S. Private*, pg. 1609
FRENCH/WEST/VAUGHAN, LLC; *U.S. Private*, pg. 1609
FRENCH/WEST/VAUGHAN, LLC—See French/West/Vaughan, LLC; *U.S. Private*, pg. 1609
FRENCH/WEST/VAUGHAN, LLC—See French/West/Vaughan, LLC; *U.S. Private*, pg. 1609
FRESE & WOLFF WERBEAGENTUR GMBH; *Int'l*, pg. 2774
FRIENDABLE, INC.; *U.S. Public*, pg. 886
FRIEZE ADVERTISING INC.; *U.S. Private*, pg. 1612
FRONTAGE INC.; *Int'l*, pg. 2794
FRONTIER DIRECT INC.—See Frontier International, Inc.; *Int'l*, pg. 2795
FRONTLINE ADVERTISING, INC.; *U.S. Private*, pg. 1616
FRONT PORCH MARKETING LLC; *U.S. Private*, pg. 1613
FRP ADVISORY GROUP PLC; *Int'l*, pg. 2797
FSC MARKETING COMMUNICATIONS; *U.S. Private*, pg. 1618
FTI CONSULTING (SC) LTDA.—See FTI Consulting, Inc.; *U.S. Public*, pg. 890
FUEL AGENCY, INC.; *U.S. Private*, pg. 1619
FUEL INTERACTIVE; *U.S. Private*, pg. 1619
FUKUSHIMA HAKUHODO, INC.—See Hakuhodo DY Holdings Incorporated; *Int'l*, pg. 3221
FULLHOUSE INTERACTIVE; *U.S. Private*, pg. 1621
FULLHOUSE—See Fullhouse Interactive; *U.S. Private*, pg. 1621
FULL ON PRODUCTIONS, INC.; *U.S. Private*, pg. 1621
FUNK/LEVIS & ASSOCIATES; *U.S. Private*, pg. 1623
FURBER ADVERTISING; *U.S. Private*, pg. 1623
FURMAN, FEINER ADVERTISING—See Furman Roth Advertising; *U.S. Private*, pg. 1624
FURMAN ROTH ADVERTISING; *U.S. Private*, pg. 1623
FUSE 8 GROUP LTD; *Int'l*, pg. 2848
FUSE/IDEAS; *U.S. Private*, pg. 1625
FUSION B2B, *U.S. Private*, pg. 1625
FUSIONBOX, INC.; *U.S. Private*, pg. 1626
FUSIONFARM—See The Gazette Company; *U.S. Private*, pg. 4032
FUTURA DDB—See Omnicom Group Inc.; *U.S. Public*, pg. 1581
FUTUREBRAND GIO ROSSI—See The Interpublic Group of Companies, Inc.; *U.S. Public*, pg. 2097
FUTUREBRAND—See The Interpublic Group of Companies, Inc.; *U.S. Public*, pg. 2097
FUTUREBRAND—See The Interpublic Group of Companies, Inc.; *U.S. Public*, pg. 2097
FUTUREBRAND—See The Interpublic Group of Companies, Inc.; *U.S. Public*, pg. 2097
FUTUREBRAND—See The Interpublic Group of Companies, Inc.; *U.S. Public*, pg. 2097
FUTUREBRAND—See The Interpublic Group of Companies, Inc.; *U.S. Public*, pg. 2097
FUTUREBRAND—See The Interpublic Group of Companies, Inc.; *U.S. Public*, pg. 2097
FUTUREBRAND—See The Interpublic Group of Companies, Inc.; *U.S. Public*, pg. 2097
FUTUREBRAND—See The Interpublic Group of Companies, Inc.; *U.S. Public*, pg. 2097
FUTUREBRAND—See The Interpublic Group of Companies, Inc.; *U.S. Public*, pg. 2097
FUTUREBRAND—See The Interpublic Group of Companies, Inc.; *U.S. Public*, pg. 2097
FUTUREBRAND—See The Interpublic Group of Companies, Inc.; *U.S. Public*, pg. 2097
FUTUREBRAND—See The Interpublic Group of Companies, Inc.; *U.S. Public*, pg. 2097
FVM STRATEGIC COMMUNICATIONS; *U.S. Private*, pg. 1628
THE G3 GROUP; *U.S. Private*, pg. 4031
G5 SEARCH MARKETING, INC.—See PeakEquity Partners; *U.S. Private*, pg. 3125
GABRIEL DEGROOD BENDT LLC—See Evening Post Publishing Co.; *U.S. Private*, pg. 1436
GA COMMUNICATIONS INC.; *U.S. Private*, pg. 1632

N.A.I.C.S. INDEX
541810 — ADVERTISING AGENCIE...

GA COMMUNICATIONS—See GA Communications Inc.; *U.S. Private*, pg. 1632
GA COMMUNICATIONS—See GA Communications Inc.; *U.S. Private*, pg. 1632
GA COMMUNICATIONS—See GA Communications Inc.; *U.S. Private*, pg. 1632
GAGE; *U.S. Private*, pg. 1634
GAGE-WEST—See Gage; *U.S. Private*, pg. 1634
GALAXY ENTERPRISES INC.; *U.S. Private*, pg. 1636
GALE CREATIVE AGENCY PRIVATE LIMITED—See Stagwell, Inc.; *U.S. Private*, pg. 1926
GALE PARTNERS INC.—See Stagwell, Inc.; *U.S. Public*, pg. 1926
GALE PARTNERS LLC—See Stagwell, Inc.; *U.S. Public*, pg. 1927
GALVANEK & WAHL LLC; *U.S. Private*, pg. 1640
THE GAMS GROUP, INC.; *U.S. Private*, pg. 4032
GANNETT DIRECT MARKETING SERVICES—See TEGNA Inc.; *U.S. Public*, pg. 1990
GARBER & GOODMAN ADVERTISING, INC.; *U.S. Private*, pg. 1642
GARDEN CITY GROUP COMMUNICATIONS; *U.S. Private*, pg. 1642
GARDEN OF E; *U.S. Private*, pg. 1643
GARDNER NELSON & PARTNERS; *U.S. Private*, pg. 1644
THE GARFIELD GROUP, INC.—See Aquiline Capital Partners LLC; *U.S. Private*, pg. 305
GARRAND & COMPANY; *U.S. Private*, pg. 1645
GARWICH BBDO (QUITO)—See Omnicom Group Inc.; *U.S. Public*, pg. 1575
GARWICH BBDO—See Omnicom Group Inc.; *U.S. Public*, pg. 1575
THE GARY GROUP; *U.S. Private*, pg. 4032
GARZA CREATIVE GROUP; *U.S. Private*, pg. 1647
GAS LAMP MEDIA; *U.S. Private*, pg. 1647
GASQUE ADVERTISING, INC.; *U.S. Private*, pg. 1648
GASTON ADVERTISING; *U.S. Private*, pg. 1649
GATESMAN, INC. - CHICAGO—See Gatesman, Inc.; *U.S. Private*, pg. 1650
GATESMAN, INC.; *U.S. Private*, pg. 1650
GATESMAN, INC. - SPRINGFIELD—See Gatesman, Inc.; *U.S. Private*, pg. 1650
GAUGER + ASSOCIATES; *U.S. Private*, pg. 1652
GAUTHIER MARKETING; *U.S. Private*, pg. 1652
GBK, HEYE WERBEAGENTUR GMBH—See Omnicom Group Inc.; *U.S. Public*, pg. 1581
G&B/MILLER ADVERTISING—See Miller Advertising Agency Inc.; *U.S. Private*, pg. 2732
GCG ADVERTISING; *U.S. Private*, pg. 1653
G&D COMMUNICATIONS CORPORATION; *U.S. Private*, pg. 1628
GEARON HOFFMAN INC.; *U.S. Private*, pg. 1655
THE GEARY COMPANY; *U.S. Private*, pg. 4032
GEARY LSF GROUP, INC. - SAN DIEGO—See Geary LSF Group, Inc.; *U.S. Private*, pg. 1655
GEARY LSF GROUP, INC.; *U.S. Private*, pg. 1655
GEILE/LEON MARKETING COMMUNICATIONS; *U.S. Private*, pg. 1656
GELIA-MEDIA, INC.; *U.S. Private*, pg. 1656
GEM MINNEAPOLIS; *U.S. Private*, pg. 1657
GENDAI AGENCY INC.; *Int'l*, pg. 2917
THE GENESIS GROUP; *U.S. Private*, pg. 4032
GENIEE, INC.; *Int'l*, pg. 2923
GENOVA & PARTNERS, INC.; *U.S. Private*, pg. 1673
GENUINE INTERACTIVE, LLC—See The Interpublic Group of Companies, Inc.; *U.S. Public*, pg. 2096
GEOMEDIA N.V.—See Omnicom Group Inc.; *U.S. Public*, pg. 1585
GEORGE P. JOHNSON (AUSTRALIA) PTY., LTD.—See Project: Worldwide, Inc.; *U.S. Private*, pg. 3280
GEORGE P. JOHNSON CO. - BOSTON—See Project: Worldwide, Inc.; *U.S. Private*, pg. 3281
GEORGE P. JOHNSON CO. - EMT DIVISION—See Project: Worldwide, Inc.; *U.S. Private*, pg. 3281
GEORGE P. JOHNSON CO. - G7 ENTERTAINMENT MARKETING—See Project: Worldwide, Inc.; *U.S. Private*, pg. 3281
GEORGE P. JOHNSON COMPANY - BELGIUM—See Project: Worldwide, Inc.; *U.S. Private*, pg. 3281
GEORGE P. JOHNSON CO. - SAN CARLOS—See Project: Worldwide, Inc.; *U.S. Private*, pg. 3281
GEORGE P. JOHNSON EVENT MARKETING CO. LTD.—See Project: Worldwide, Inc.; *U.S. Private*, pg. 3281
GEORGE P. JOHNSON EVENT MARKETING CO. LTD.—See Project: Worldwide, Inc.; *U.S. Private*, pg. 3281
GEORGE P. JOHNSON EVENT MARKETING PVT. LTD.—See Project: Worldwide, Inc.; *U.S. Private*, pg. 3281
GEORGE P. JOHNSON EVENT MARKETING PVT. LTD.—See Project: Worldwide, Inc.; *U.S. Private*, pg. 3281
GEORGE P. JOHNSON (FRANCE) SARL—See Project: Worldwide, Inc.; *U.S. Private*, pg. 3281
GEORGE P. JOHNSON GMBH—See Project: Worldwide, Inc.; *U.S. Private*, pg. 3281
GEORGE P. JOHNSON HONG KONG LTD.—See Project: Worldwide, Inc.; *U.S. Private*, pg. 3281
GEORGE P. JOHNSON (JAPAN) LTD.—See Project: Worldwide, Inc.; *U.S. Private*, pg. 3281
GEORGE P. JOHNSON (KOREA) LLC—See Project: Worldwide, Inc.; *U.S. Private*, pg. 3281
GERBIG, SNELL/WEISHEIMER ADVERTISING, LLC - NEW YORK—See Elliott Management Corporation; *U.S. Private*, pg. 1366
GERBIG, SNELL/WEISHEIMER ADVERTISING, LLC - NEW YORK—See Patient Square Capital, L.P.; *U.S. Private*, pg. 3108
GERBIG, SNELL/WEISHEIMER ADVERTISING, LLC - NEW YORK—See Veritas Capital Fund Management, LLC; *U.S. Private*, pg. 4365
GERBIG, SNELL/WEISHEIMER ADVERTISING, LLC—See Elliott Management Corporation; *U.S. Private*, pg. 1366
GERBIG, SNELL/WEISHEIMER ADVERTISING, LLC—See Patient Square Capital, L.P.; *U.S. Private*, pg. 3108
GERBIG, SNELL/WEISHEIMER ADVERTISING, LLC—See Veritas Capital Fund Management, LLC; *U.S. Private*, pg. 4365
GERMAINE—See Omnicom Group Inc.; *U.S. Public*, pg. 1575
GETMYHOMESVALUE.COM; *U.S. Private*, pg. 1688
G&G ADVERTISING, INC.; *U.S. Private*, pg. 1628
G&G ADVERTISING; *U.S. Private*, pg. 1628
G&G ADVERTISING—See G&G Advertising, Inc.; *U.S. Private*, pg. 1628
GGK ZURICH WERBEAGENTUR AG; *Int'l*, pg. 2957
G&G OUTFITTERS INC.; *U.S. Private*, pg. 1629
GHA/DDB—See Omnicom Group Inc.; *U.S. Public*, pg. 1581
GHIROTTI & COMPANHIA—See Omnicom Group Inc.; *U.S. Public*, pg. 1581
GIAMBRONE + PARTNERS; *U.S. Private*, pg. 1694
GIANT CREATIVE STRATEGY LLC—See Clayton, Dubilier & Rice, LLC; *U.S. Private*, pg. 924
GIANT IDEAS; *U.S. Private*, pg. 1694
GIGANTE VAZ PARTNERS ADVERTISING, INC.; *U.S. Private*, pg. 1697
GIGIGO GROUP S.L.—See Econocom Group SA; *Int'l*, pg. 2298
GISH, SHERWOOD & FRIENDS, INC.; *U.S. Private*, pg. 1702
GIST & ERDMANN, INC.; *U.S. Private*, pg. 1702
GITAMBBDO—See Omnicom Group Inc.; *U.S. Public*, pg. 1575
G+J IMS BVBA—See Bertelsmann SE & Co. KGaA; *Int'l*, pg. 992
GKV COMMUNICATIONS; *U.S. Private*, pg. 1704
GLAM MEDIA, INC.; *U.S. Private*, pg. 1706
GLASS MCCLURE; *U.S. Private*, pg. 1706
THE GLENN GROUP; *U.S. Private*, pg. 4033
GLOBAL ADVERTISING STRATEGIES, INC.; *U.S. Private*, pg. 1711
GLOBAL FOCUS GROUP; *U.S. Private*, pg. 1714
GLOBAL STUDIO; *U.S. Private*, pg. 1718
GLOBALWORKS; *U.S. Private*, pg. 1719
GLOWAC, HARRIS, MADISON INC.; *U.S. Private*, pg. 1721
GLOW INTERACTIVE, INC.; *U.S. Private*, pg. 1721
GLYNNDEVINS ADVERTISING & MARKETING; *U.S. Private*, pg. 1721
GMC+COMPANY; *U.S. Private*, pg. 1721
GMLV-GLOBAL MARKETING WITH A LOCAL VISION; *U.S. Private*, pg. 1722
GMO DREAM WAVE INC.—See GMO Internet Group, Inc.; *Int'l*, pg. 3013
GMO NIKKO INC.—See GMO Internet Group, Inc.; *Int'l*, pg. 3014
GMR ENTERTAINMENT—See Omnicom Group Inc.; *U.S. Public*, pg. 1593
THE GMR GROUP—See Omnicom Group Inc.; *U.S. Public*, pg. 1599
GMR LONDON—See Omnicom Group Inc.; *U.S. Public*, pg. 1593
GMR MARKETING—See Omnicom Group Inc.; *U.S. Public*, pg. 1593
GMR MARKETING—See Omnicom Group Inc.; *U.S. Public*, pg. 1593
GMR MARKETING—See Omnicom Group Inc.; *U.S. Public*, pg. 1593
GMR MARKETING—See Omnicom Group Inc.; *U.S. Public*, pg. 1593
GMR MARKETING—See Omnicom Group Inc.; *U.S. Public*, pg. 1593
GMR MARKETING—See Omnicom Group Inc.; *U.S. Public*, pg. 1593
GMR MARKETING SPAIN—See Omnicom Group Inc.; *U.S. Public*, pg. 1593
GNOMI + DRAFTFCB—See The Interpublic Group of Companies, Inc.; *U.S. Public*, pg. 2093
THE GOAL INC.—See Dentsu Group Inc.; *Int'l*, pg. 2039
GOBRANDGO, LLC; *U.S. Private*, pg. 1724
GOCONVERGENCE; *U.S. Private*, pg. 1724
GODENGO, INC.; *U.S. Private*, pg. 1724
GODFREY ADVERTISING, INC.; *U.S. Private*, pg. 1724
G/O DIGITAL MARKETING, LLC—See TEGNA Inc.; *U.S. Public*, pg. 1990
GODIGITAL MEDIA GROUP, LLC; *U.S. Private*, pg. 1724
GODWIN ADVERTISING AGENCY, INC.; *U.S. Private*, pg. 1725
GODWINGROUP—See Godwin Advertising Agency, Inc.; *U.S. Private*, pg. 1725
GOLDEN GRAIL TECHNOLOGY CORP.; *U.S. Public*, pg. 950
GOLLEY SLATER CENTRAL—See Golley Slater Group Limited; *Int'l*, pg. 3036
GOLLEY SLATER GROUP LIMITED; *Int'l*, pg. 3036
GOLLEY SLATER LONDON—See Golley Slater Group Limited; *Int'l*, pg. 3036
GOLLEY SLATER RETAIL—See Golley Slater Group Limited; *Int'l*, pg. 3036
GOMAJI CORP LTD.; *Int'l*, pg. 3037
GOOD ADVERTISING, INC.; *U.S. Private*, pg. 1737
GOODBY, SILVERSTEIN & PARTNERS, INC. - NEW YORK—See Omnicom Group Inc.; *U.S. Public*, pg. 1585
GOODBY, SILVERSTEIN & PARTNERS, INC.—See Omnicom Group Inc.; *U.S. Public*, pg. 1585
GOODNESS MFG.—See Trailer Park; *U.S. Private*, pg. 4203
GORDON HANRAHAN, INC.; *U.S. Private*, pg. 1743
GORILLA NATION MEDIA, LLC; *U.S. Private*, pg. 1744
GOTHAM INCORPORATED—See The Interpublic Group of Companies, Inc.; *U.S. Public*, pg. 2094
GO WELSH!; *U.S. Private*, pg. 1723
GPJ (SINGAPORE) PTE. LTD—See Project: Worldwide, Inc.; *U.S. Private*, pg. 3280
G-PLAN, INC.—See Hakuhodo DY Holdings Incorporated; *Int'l*, pg. 3221
GRABARZ & PARTNER WERBEAGENTUR GMBH; *Int'l*, pg. 3048
GRADY BRITTON, INC.; *U.S. Private*, pg. 1750
GRAFFITI BBDO SOFIA—See Omnicom Group Inc.; *U.S. Public*, pg. 1575
GRAFFITI BBDO—See Omnicom Group Inc.; *U.S. Public*, pg. 1575
GRAFICAGROUP; *U.S. Private*, pg. 1750
GRAFICAINTER.ACTIVE, LTD.; *U.S. Private*, pg. 1750
GRAFIK MARKETING COMMUNICATIONS LTD.; *U.S. Private*, pg. 1750
GRAFIKPHARM, INC.—See Reese, Tomases & Ellick, Inc. (RT&E); *U.S. Public*, pg. 3383
GRAGG ADVERTISING; *U.S. Private*, pg. 1751
GRAHAM ADVERTISING; *U.S. Private*, pg. 1751
THE GRAHAM GROUP; *U.S. Private*, pg. 4035
THE GRAHAM GROUP—See The Graham Group; *U.S. Private*, pg. 4036
GRAMMA PUBLICIDAD—See The Interpublic Group of Companies, Inc.; *U.S. Public*, pg. 2093
GRANDESIGN ADVERTISING FIRM, INC.; *U.S. Private*, pg. 1754
GRANT MARKETING; *U.S. Private*, pg. 1756
GRAPE COMMUNICATIONS—See The Interpublic Group of Companies, Inc.; *U.S. Public*, pg. 2091
GRAPEVINE COMMUNICATIONS INTERNATIONAL INC.; *U.S. Private*, pg. 1757
GRAPHIC ANGELS DESIGN GROUP; *U.S. Private*, pg. 1757
GRA SP. Z O. O.—See Agora S.A.; *Int'l*, pg. 212
GRATTERPALM, LTD.; *Int'l*, pg. 3061
GRAVY ANALYTICS, INC.—See Unacast, Inc.; *U.S. Private*, pg. 4279
GRAYLING BARCELONA—See Clayton, Dubilier & Rice, LLC; *U.S. Private*, pg. 924
GRAYLING GLOBAL—See Clayton, Dubilier & Rice, LLC; *U.S. Private*, pg. 925
GRAYLING MADRID—See Clayton, Dubilier & Rice, LLC; *U.S. Private*, pg. 925
GRAYLING PORTUGAL—See Clayton, Dubilier & Rice, LLC; *U.S. Private*, pg. 925
GRAYLING SEVILLE—See Clayton, Dubilier & Rice, LLC; *U.S. Private*, pg. 925
GRAYLING STOCKHOLM—See Clayton, Dubilier & Rice, LLC; *U.S. Private*, pg. 925
GRAY MATTER AGENCY INC.—See Attivo group; *Int'l*, pg. 697
GREAT COMMUNICATORS, INC.; *U.S. Private*, pg. 1762
GREAT DAY ADVERTISING—See Great Day Radio; *U.S. Private*, pg. 1762
GREAT DAY RADIO; *U.S. Private*, pg. 1762
GREATER THAN ONE, INC.; *U.S. Private*, pg. 1770
GREAT WORKS AB; *Int'l*, pg. 3066
GREBSTAD HICKS COMMUNICATIONS LTD.—See Hakuhodo DY Holdings Incorporated; *Int'l*, pg. 3221
GREENBERG INC.; *U.S. Private*, pg. 1775
GREEN DOT ADVERTISING & MARKETING; *U.S. Private*, pg. 1772
GREENRUBINO; *U.S. Private*, pg. 1779
GREENSTRIPE MEDIA, INC.; *U.S. Private*, pg. 1780
GREEN TEAM ADVERTISING, INC.; *U.S. Private*, pg. 1774
GRENADIER—See Barkley; *U.S. Private*, pg. 475
GRETEMAN GROUP; *U.S. Private*, pg. 1784
GRIFFITH & COE ADVERTISING, INC.; *U.S. Private*, pg. 1788
GRIP LIMITED—See Dentsu Group Inc.; *Int'l*, pg. 2036
GROUP 5 WEST, INC.; *U.S. Private*, pg. 1793
GROUP NINE MEDIA, INC.; *U.S. Private*, pg. 1793

GROUPON FRANCE SAS—See Groupon Inc.; *U.S. Public*, pg. 972
GROUP TWO ADVERTISING, INC.; *U.S. Private*, pg. 1794
GROW INTERACTIVE; *U.S. Private*, pg. 1795
GRUPO ABC LTDA.—See Omnicom Group Inc.; *U.S. Public*, pg. 1585
GRUPO GALLEGOS; *U.S. Private*, pg. 1797
GRW ADVERTISING; *U.S. Private*, pg. 1798
GSD&M CHICAGO—See Omnicom Group Inc.; *U.S. Public*, pg. 1585
GSD&M IDEA CITY LLC—See Omnicom Group Inc.; *U.S. Public*, pg. 1585
GSP MARKETING SERVICES, INC.; *U.S. Private*, pg. 1801
GUANGDONG ADVERTISING GROUP CO., LTD.; *Int'l*, pg. 3152
GUANGDONG GUANGZHOU DAILY MEDIA CO., LTD.; *Int'l*, pg. 3155
GUANGDONG SINOFOCUS MEDIA LIMITED—See Huanxi Media Group Limited; *Int'l*, pg. 3513
GUANGZHOU FRONTOP DIGITAL CREATIVE TECHNOLOGY CO., LTD.; *Int'l*, pg. 3165
GUAVA LTD.—See Ardian SAS; *Int'l*, pg. 554
GULF MARKETING & SERVICES COMPANY LLC; *Int'l*, pg. 3181
GUMAS ADVERTISING; *U.S. Private*, pg. 1818
GUOMAI CULTURE & MEDIA CO., LTD; *Int'l*, pg. 3186
G.W. HOFFMAN MARKETING & COMMUNICATIONS; *U.S. Private*, pg. 1631
GYK ANTLER; *U.S. Private*, pg. 1821
GYRO BENELUX B.V.—See Gyro Communications Ltd; *Int'l*, pg. 3191
GYRO CHICAGO—See Gyro Communications Ltd; *Int'l*, pg. 3191
GYRO CINCINNATI—See Gyro Communications Ltd; *Int'l*, pg. 3191
GYRO COMMUNICATIONS LTD; *Int'l*, pg. 3191
GYRO DENVER—See Gyro Communications Ltd; *Int'l*, pg. 3191
GYRO DEUTSCHLAND GMBH—See Gyro Communications Ltd; *Int'l*, pg. 3191
GYRO MUNICH—See Gyro Communications Ltd; *Int'l*, pg. 3191
GYRO NEW YORK—See Gyro Communications Ltd; *Int'l*, pg. 3191
GYRO PARIS—See Gyro Communications Ltd; *Int'l*, pg. 3191
GYRO SCANDINAVIA AB—See Gyro Communications Ltd; *Int'l*, pg. 3191
HABERMAN & ASSOCIATES, INC.; *U.S. Private*, pg. 1837
H.A. BRUNO LLC—See Charterhouse Capital Partners LLP; *Int'l*, pg. 1455
HACKERAGENCY, INC.—See The Interpublic Group of Companies, Inc.; *U.S. Public*, pg. 2093
HADLEY MEDIA INC.—See Grandesign Advertising Firm, Inc.; *U.S. Private*, pg. 1754
HAFENBRACK MARKETING & PUBLIC RELATIONS, INC.—See Oxiem, LLC; *U.S. Private*, pg. 3057
HAGERTY, LOCKENVITZ ADVERTISING, INC.; *U.S. Private*, pg. 1840
H+A INTERNATIONAL, INC.; *U.S. Private*, pg. 1824
HAKUHODO AUSTRALIA PTY. LTD.—See Hakuhodo DY Holdings Incorporated; *Int'l*, pg. 3221
HAKUHODO BANGKOK CO., LTD.—See Hakuhodo DY Holdings Incorporated; *Int'l*, pg. 3221
HAKUHODO-CHEIL, INC.—See Hakuhodo DY Holdings Incorporated; *Int'l*, pg. 3221
HAKUHODO CO., LTD. TOHOKU—See Hakuhodo DY Holdings Incorporated; *Int'l*, pg. 3221
HAKUHODO COMMUNICATIONS, INC.—See Hakuhodo DY Holdings Incorporated; *Int'l*, pg. 3221
HAKUHODO CREATIVE VOX, INC.—See Hakuhodo DY Holdings Incorporated; *Int'l*, pg. 3221
HAKUHODO DEUTSCHLAND GMBH-HAMBURG OFFICE—See Hakuhodo DY Holdings Incorporated; *Int'l*, pg. 3221
HAKUHODO DEUTSCHLAND GMBH-MUNICH OFFICE—See Hakuhodo DY Holdings Incorporated; *Int'l*, pg. 3221
HAKUHODO DEUTSCHLAND GMBH—See Hakuhodo DY Holdings Incorporated; *Int'l*, pg. 3221
HAKUHODO DY CAPCO—See Hakuhodo DY Holdings Incorporated; *Int'l*, pg. 3221
HAKUHODO DY I.O INC.—See Hakuhodo DY Holdings Incorporated; *Int'l*, pg. 3221
HAKUHODO DY MEDIA PARTNERS INC.—See Hakuhodo DY Holdings Incorporated; *Int'l*, pg. 3221
HAKUHODO ERG, INC.—See Hakuhodo DY Holdings Incorporated; *Int'l*, pg. 3221
HAKUHODO FRANCE S.A.—See Hakuhodo DY Holdings Incorporated; *Int'l*, pg. 3221
HAKUHODO HONG KONG LTD.—See Hakuhodo DY Holdings Incorporated; *Int'l*, pg. 3221
HAKUHODO INC. CHUBU OFFICE—See Hakuhodo DY Holdings Incorporated; *Int'l*, pg. 3221
HAKUHODO INC. KANSAI OFFICE—See Hakuhodo DY Holdings Incorporated; *Int'l*, pg. 3221
HAKUHODO INC. KYUSHU OFFICE—See Hakuhodo DY Holdings Incorporated; *Int'l*, pg. 3221

HAKUHODO INCORPORATED—See Hakuhodo DY Holdings Incorporated; *Int'l*, pg. 3220
HAKUHODO I.O. CO., LTD.—See Hakuhodo DY Holdings Incorporated; *Int'l*, pg. 3221
HAKUHODO I-STUDIO, INC.—See Hakuhodo DY Holdings Incorporated; *Int'l*, pg. 3221
HAKUHODO MALAYSIA SDN. BHD.—See Hakuhodo DY Holdings Incorporated; *Int'l*, pg. 3221
HAKUHODO PERCEPT PVT. LTD.—See Hakuhodo DY Holdings Incorporated; *Int'l*, pg. 3221
HAKUHODO & SAIGON ADVERTISING CO., LTD.—See Hakuhodo DY Holdings Incorporated; *Int'l*, pg. 3221
HAKUHODO SINGAPORE PTE. LTD.—See Hakuhodo DY Holdings Incorporated; *Int'l*, pg. 3221
HALEY MIRANDA GROUP; *U.S. Private*, pg. 1842
HALL AND PARTNERS—See Omnicom Group Inc.; *U.S. Public*, pg. 1585
HALLOCK AGENCY; *U.S. Private*, pg. 1845
HAMILTON COMMUNICATIONS GROUP, INC.; *U.S. Private*, pg. 1847
HAMMER CREATIVE; *U.S. Private*, pg. 1849
HAMPTON ASSOCIATES LTD.; *Int'l*, pg. 3239
HAMS—See The Interpublic Group of Companies, Inc.; *U.S. Public*, pg. 2100
HANCOMM INC.—See Hanwha Group; *Int'l*, pg. 3264
HANDSTAND INNOVATIONS LLC; *U.S. Private*, pg. 1853
HANFT RABOY & PARTNERS; *U.S. Private*, pg. 1853
HANKYU ADVERTISING AGENCY INC.—See Hankyu Hanshin Holdings Inc.; *Int'l*, pg. 3255
HANKYU HANSHIN MARKETING SOLUTIONS INC.—See Hankyu Hanshin Holdings Inc.; *Int'l*, pg. 3255
HANNA & ASSOCIATES INC.; *U.S. Private*, pg. 1854
HANNA LEE COMMUNICATIONS, INC.; *U.S. Private*, pg. 1854
HANSON DODGE INC.; *U.S. Private*, pg. 1856
HANSON & HANSON ENTERPRISES LLC; *U.S. Private*, pg. 1856
HANSON WATSON ASSOCIATES; *U.S. Private*, pg. 1857
HAPPY MCGARRYBOWEN—See Dentsu Group Inc.; *Int'l*, pg. 2036
HARBURGER/SCOTT ADVERTISING; *U.S. Private*, pg. 1861
HARD BEAT COMMUNICATIONS; *U.S. Private*, pg. 1862
HARDY COMMUNICATIONS DEVELOPMENT; *U.S. Private*, pg. 1864
HARGER HOWE ADVERTISING; *U.S. Private*, pg. 1864
HARGER HOWE ADVERTISING—See Harger Howe Advertising; *U.S. Private*, pg. 1864
HARGER HOWE ADVERTISING—See Harger Howe Advertising; *U.S. Private*, pg. 1864
HARRIMAN CREATIVE, INC; *U.S. Private*, pg. 1868
HARRIS D. MCKINNEY; *U.S. Private*, pg. 1869
HARRIS MARKETING GROUP; *U.S. Private*, pg. 1869
HARRISON AND STAR—See Omnicom Group Inc.; *U.S. Public*, pg. 1585
HARRISON CREATIVE DIRECTION; *U.S. Private*, pg. 1870
HARRISON LEIFER DIMARCO, INC.; *U.S. Private*, pg. 1870
HARRISON & SHRIFTMAN LLC—See Omnicom Group Inc.; *U.S. Public*, pg. 1585
HARRISON & SHRIFTMAN—See Omnicom Group Inc.; *U.S. Public*, pg. 1585
HARRISON & SHRIFTMAN—See Omnicom Group Inc.; *U.S. Public*, pg. 1585
HARRY BARLOW LTD.; *Int'l*, pg. 3279
HARRY VIOLA ADVERTISING; *U.S. Private*, pg. 1872
HART ASSOCIATES, INC.; *U.S. Private*, pg. 1872
HARVARD IN-HOUSE AGENCY; *U.S. Private*, pg. 1875
HARVEST CREATIVE; *U.S. Private*, pg. 1875
HARVEY CAMERON GROUP LIMITED—See Attivo group; *Int'l*, pg. 697
HARVEY & DAUGHTERS, INC./ H&D BRANDING; *U.S. Private*, pg. 1877
HASAN & PARTNERS OY—See The Interpublic Group of Companies, Inc.; *U.S. Public*, pg. 2098
HASTINGS DESIGN CO; *U.S. Private*, pg. 1879
HATCH64; *Int'l*, pg. 3284
HATLING FLINT—See Flint Communications, Inc. & Adfarm; *U.S. Private*, pg. 1545
THE HAUSER GROUP—See Ames Scullin O'Haire; *U.S. Private*, pg. 262
HAWKE MEDIA, LLC; *U.S. Private*, pg. 1882
HAWKEYE, INC.; *U.S. Private*, pg. 1883
HAWKEYE—See Hawkeye, Inc.; *U.S. Private*, pg. 1883
HAYGARTH COMMUNICATIONS LIMITED—See Omnicom Group Inc.; *U.S. Public*, pg. 1592
HAYNES FURNITURE COMPANY INC.—See Haynes Furniture Company Incorporated; *U.S. Private*, pg. 1885
HAYNES MARKETING NETWORK, INC.; *U.S. Private*, pg. 1885
HB&M SPORTS, INC.—See Harris, Baio & McCullough Inc.; *U.S. Private*, pg. 1870
HC&B HEALTHCARE COMMUNICATIONS INC.; *U.S. Private*, pg. 1888
HCB HEALTH CHICAGO—See HC&B Healthcare Communications Inc.; *U.S. Private*, pg. 1888
HC INTERNATIONAL; *U.S. Private*, pg. 1888
HCK2 PARTNERS; *U.S. Private*, pg. 1889

HEADLINE PUBLISHING AGENCY—See Omnicom Group Inc.; *U.S. Public*, pg. 1596
HEADQUARTERS ADVERTISING INC.; *U.S. Private*, pg. 1891
HEALTH SCIENCE COMMUNICATIONS—See Omnicom Group Inc.; *U.S. Public*, pg. 1586
HEALTHSTAR COMMUNICATIONS, INC.; *U.S. Private*, pg. 1898
HEALTH UNLIMITED LLC—See Accenture plc; *Int'l*, pg. 87
HEARTBEAT DIGITAL; *U.S. Private*, pg. 1899
HEARTLASS INC.—See Digital Holdings, Inc.; *Int'l*, pg. 2122
HEATHCOTE COMMUNICATIONS; *U.S. Private*, pg. 1902
HEATHCOTT ASSOCIATES, INC.—See Cranford Johnson Robinson Woods, Inc.; *U.S. Private*, pg. 1085
HEAT—See Deloitte LLP; *U.S. Public*, pg. 1198
HEAT—See Deloitte Touche Tohmatsu Limited; *Int'l*, pg. 2014
HEAVYBAG MEDIA; *U.S. Private*, pg. 1902
HEAVYBAG WEST—See HeavyBag Media; *U.S. Private*, pg. 1902
HECHO STUDIOS LLC—See Stagwell, Inc.; *U.S. Public*, pg. 1927
HEILBRICE; *U.S. Private*, pg. 1904
HEINRICH HAWAII—See Heinrich Marketing; *U.S. Private*, pg. 1905
HEINRICH HISPANIDAD—See Heinrich Marketing; *U.S. Private*, pg. 1905
HEINRICH MARKETING; *U.S. Private*, pg. 1905
HEISLER GORDON & ASSOCIATES; *U.S. Private*, pg. 1905
HELLMAN ASSOCIATES, INC.; *U.S. Private*, pg. 1911
HELLMAN—See Hellman Associates, Inc.; *U.S. Private*, pg. 1911
HELVETICA CREATIVE; *U.S. Private*, pg. 1912
HENDERSON BAS PARTNERSHIP—See Stagwell, Inc.; *U.S. Public*, pg. 1928
HENRY GILL COMMUNICATIONS; *U.S. Private*, pg. 1918
HERMAN ASSOCIATES, INC.; *U.S. Private*, pg. 1925
HERMAN ASSOCIATES PUBLIC RELATIONS—See Herman Associates, Inc.; *U.S. Private*, pg. 1925
HEYE GMBH—See Omnicom Group Inc.; *U.S. Public*, pg. 1581
HEYE MEDIA OMD GMBH—See Omnicom Group Inc.; *U.S. Public*, pg. 1582
HEYE & PARTNER GMBH - HAMBURG—See Omnicom Group Inc.; *U.S. Public*, pg. 1581
HGA INC; *U.S. Private*, pg. 1928
THE HIEBING GROUP, INC.; *U.S. Private*, pg. 4052
HIGHCO DATA BENELUX NV—See HighCo S.A.; *Int'l*, pg. 3387
HIGHCO EDITING SAS—See HighCo S.A.; *Int'l*, pg. 3387
HIGHCO MINDOZA SAS—See HighCo S.A.; *Int'l*, pg. 3387
HIGHCO SHELF SERVICE NV—See HighCo S.A.; *Int'l*, pg. 3387
HIGHCO SHOPPER SL—See HighCo S.A.; *Int'l*, pg. 3387
HIGH-TOUCH COMMUNICATIONS INC.; *Int'l*, pg. 3386
HILL HOLLIDAY/NEW YORK—See Attivo group; *Int'l*, pg. 697
HILL HOLLIDAY—See Attivo group; *Int'l*, pg. 697
HI-MEDIA ITALY SRL—See AdUX SA; *Int'l*, pg. 155
HIRONS & COMPANY; *U.S. Private*, pg. 1950
HIRONS & COMPANY—See Hirons & Company; *U.S. Private*, pg. 1950
HITCHCOCK FLEMING & ASSOCIATES, INC.; *U.S. Private*, pg. 1952
H&K GRAPHICS; *U.S. Private*, pg. 1823
HLG HEALTH COMMUNICATIONS; *U.S. Private*, pg. 1954
HMC ADVERTISING LLC; *U.S. Private*, pg. 1954
HMG GROUP; *U.S. Private*, pg. 1955
HODGSON/MEYERS ADVERTISING, INC.; *U.S. Private*, pg. 1959
HOFFMAN/LEWIS; *U.S. Private*, pg. 1960
HOFFMAN/LEWIS—See Hoffman/Lewis; *U.S. Private*, pg. 1960
HOFFMAN YORK, INC.; *U.S. Private*, pg. 1960
THE HOGAN COMPANY; *U.S. Private*, pg. 4053
HOKKAIDO BALLPARK CORPORATION—See Dentsu Group Inc.; *Int'l*, pg. 2039
HOKKAIDO HAKUHODO, INC.—See Hakuhodo DY Holdings Incorporated; *Int'l*, pg. 3221
HOKURIKU HAKUHODO, INC.—See Hakuhodo DY Holdings Incorporated; *Int'l*, pg. 3221
HOLLYWOOD BRANDED INC.; *U.S. Private*, pg. 1966
HOLTON SENTIVAN + GURY; *U.S. Private*, pg. 1969
HORICH PARKS LEBOW ADVERTISING; *U.S. Private*, pg. 1980
HORIZON DRAFTFCB DUBAI—See The Interpublic Group of Companies, Inc.; *U.S. Public*, pg. 2093
HORIZON DRAFTFCB JEDDAH—See The Interpublic Group of Companies, Inc.; *U.S. Public*, pg. 2093
HORIZON.DRAFTFCB KUWAIT—See The Interpublic Group of Companies, Inc.; *U.S. Public*, pg. 2093
HORIZON.DRAFTFCB RIYADH—See The Interpublic Group of Companies, Inc.; *U.S. Public*, pg. 2093
HORIZON HOLDINGS—See The Interpublic Group of Companies, Inc.; *U.S. Public*, pg. 2093
HOST; *Int'l*, pg. 3486

N.A.I.C.S. INDEX 541810 — ADVERTISING AGENCIE...

THE HOUSE OF KAIZEN LIMITED—See House of Kaizen LLC; *U.S. Private*, pg. 1991
HOWARD, MERRELL & PARTNERS, INC.; *U.S. Private*, pg. 1995
HOWARD M. SCHWARTZ & ASSOCIATES, INC.; *U.S. Private*, pg. 1995
HRH MEDIA; *U.S. Private*, pg. 1998
HUDSONYARDS; *U.S. Private*, pg. 2002
HUGE, LLC—See The Interpublic Group of Companies, Inc.; *U.S. Public*, pg. 2094
HUGE—See The Interpublic Group of Companies, Inc.; *U.S. Public*, pg. 2091
HUGHESLEAHYKARLOVIC, INC.; *U.S. Private*, pg. 2004
HULT FRITZ MATUSZAK; *U.S. Private*, pg. 2005
HUMONGO—See Stagwell, Inc.; *U.S. Public*, pg. 1928
HUNT ADKINS; *U.S. Private*, pg. 2008
HUNTER; *U.S. Private*, pg. 2009
HUNTSWORTH HEALTH—See Clayton, Dubilier & Rice, LLC; *U.S. Private*, pg. 925
HURLEY CHANDLER & CHAFFER; *U.S. Private*, pg. 2011
HUSKY ADVERTISING, INC.; *U.S. Private*, pg. 2013
HUXLEY QUAYLE VON BISMARK, INC.; *Int'l*, pg. 3541
HW CREATIVE—See HW Publishing, LLC; *U.S. Private*, pg. 2015
HW PUBLISHING, LLC; *U.S. Private*, pg. 2015
HY CONNECT—See Myelin Health Communications, Inc.; *U.S. Private*, pg. 2824
HYDRA GROUP, INC.—See Adknowledge, Inc.; *U.S. Private*, pg. 80
HYPEBEAST LIMITED; *Int'l*, pg. 3552
HYPERDRIVE; *U.S. Private*, pg. 2019
HYPHEN DIGITAL—See Omnicom Group Inc.; *U.S. Public*, pg. 1586
IAS SMARTS LIMITED—See Stein + Partners Brand Activation; *U.S. Private*, pg. 3797
ICC HEALTH LIMITED—See The Interpublic Group of Companies, Inc.; *U.S. Public*, pg. 2093
THE ICELANDIC AD AGENCY—See Omnicom Group Inc.; *U.S. Public*, pg. 1577
ICF OLSON—See ICF International, Inc.; *U.S. Public*, pg. 1086
ICLICK INTERACTIVE (SINGAPORE) PTE. LTD.—See iClick Interactive Asia Group Limited; *Int'l*, pg. 3581
ICON INTERNATIONAL COMMUNICATIONS PTY. LTD.; *Int'l*, pg. 3583
ICON INTERNATIONAL COMMUNICATIONS SINGAPORE PTE. LTD.—See Omnicom Group Inc.; *U.S. Public*, pg. 1586
ICON INTERNATIONAL INC.; *U.S. Private*, pg. 2032
ICROSSING BRIGHTON—See The Hearst Corporation; *U.S. Private*, pg. 4049
ICROSSING CHICAGO—See The Hearst Corporation; *U.S. Private*, pg. 4049
ICROSSING DALLAS—See The Hearst Corporation; *U.S. Private*, pg. 4049
ICROSSING, INC.—See The Hearst Corporation; *U.S. Private*, pg. 4049
ICROSSING IRVINE—See The Hearst Corporation; *U.S. Private*, pg. 4049
ICROSSING LONDON—See The Hearst Corporation; *U.S. Private*, pg. 4049
ICROSSING LOS ANGELES—See The Hearst Corporation; *U.S. Private*, pg. 4049
ICROSSING SALT LAKE CITY—See The Hearst Corporation; *U.S. Private*, pg. 4049
ICROSSING SCOTTSDALE—See The Hearst Corporation; *U.S. Private*, pg. 4049
IDEA BANK MARKETING; *U.S. Private*, pg. 2035
IDEA ESTONIA—See The Interpublic Group of Companies, Inc.; *U.S. Public*, pg. 2093
IDEA FARMER LLC—See Zealot Networks, Inc.; *U.S. Private*, pg. 4599
IDEAS THAT DELIVER; *U.S. Private*, pg. 2037
IDEAWORKS, INC.; *U.S. Private*, pg. 2037
IDEAWORKS, INC.; *U.S. Private*, pg. 2037
ID KOMMUNIKATION AB; *Int'l*, pg. 3587
ID MEDIA-CHICAGO—See The Interpublic Group of Companies, Inc.; *U.S. Public*, pg. 2094
IDREAM MEDIA SERVICES GMBH—See A-TEC Industries AG; *Int'l*, pg. 21
IFTHEN, LLC; *U.S. Private*, pg. 2039
IGNITED; *U.S. Private*, pg. 2039
IGNITION BRANDING; *U.S. Private*, pg. 2039
IGNITIONONE, INC.; *U.S. Private*, pg. 2039
IKON COMMUNICATIONS; *Int'l*, pg. 3612
IMAGE ADVERTISING, INC.; *U.S. Private*, pg. 2044
THE IMAGE GROUP; *U.S. Private*, pg. 4055
IMAGEHAUS; *U.S. Private*, pg. 2045
IMAGEMARK, INC.; *U.S. Private*, pg. 2045
IMAGESTOCKHOUSE INC.; *U.S. Private*, pg. 2045
IMAGES USA; *U.S. Private*, pg. 2045
IMAGICA LAB. INC.—See Imagica Group Inc.; *Int'l*, pg. 3618
THE IMAGINATION FACTORY; *U.S. Private*, pg. 4055
IMAGINE THIS, INC.; *U.S. Private*, pg. 2045
IMAGINUITY INTERACTIVE, INC.—See Calise Partners, LLC; *U.S. Private*, pg. 721
IMARK INTEGRATED MARKETING SERVICES; *U.S. Private*, pg. 2046

IMARLIN—See The Marlin Network, Inc.; *U.S. Private*, pg. 4075
IMG BARCELONA—See Silver Lake Group, LLC; *U.S. Private*, pg. 3657
IMG BARCELONA—See William Morris Endeavor Entertainment, LLC; *U.S. Private*, pg. 4524
IMG HUNGARY—See Silver Lake Group, LLC; *U.S. Private*, pg. 3657
IMG HUNGARY—See William Morris Endeavor Entertainment, LLC; *U.S. Private*, pg. 4524
IMG MIDDLE EAST - DUBAI—See Silver Lake Group, LLC; *U.S. Private*, pg. 3657
IMG MIDDLE EAST - DUBAI—See William Morris Endeavor Entertainment, LLC; *U.S. Private*, pg. 4524
IMG MUMBAI—See Silver Lake Group, LLC; *U.S. Private*, pg. 3657
IMG MUMBAI—See William Morris Endeavor Entertainment, LLC; *U.S. Private*, pg. 4524
IMG TORONTO—See Silver Lake Group, LLC; *U.S. Private*, pg. 3657
IMG TORONTO—See William Morris Endeavor Entertainment, LLC; *U.S. Private*, pg. 4524
IMG WORLDWIDE - ASIA-PACIFIC HEADQUARTERS—See Silver Lake Group, LLC; *U.S. Private*, pg. 3657
IMG WORLDWIDE - ASIA-PACIFIC HEADQUARTERS—See William Morris Endeavor Entertainment, LLC; *U.S. Private*, pg. 4524
IMG WORLDWIDE - EMEA HEADQUARTERS—See Silver Lake Group, LLC; *U.S. Private*, pg. 3657
IMG WORLDWIDE - EMEA HEADQUARTERS—See William Morris Endeavor Entertainment, LLC; *U.S. Private*, pg. 4524
IMINDS INTERACTIVE LIMITED—See Guoen Holdings Limited; *Int'l*, pg. 3186
I-MOBILE CO., LTD.; *Int'l*, pg. 3563
IMPACT BBDO—See Omnicom Group Inc.; *U.S. Public*, pg. 1576
IMPACT BBDO—See Omnicom Group Inc.; *U.S. Public*, pg. 1576
IMPACT BBDO—See Omnicom Group Inc.; *U.S. Public*, pg. 1576
IMPACT BBDO—See Omnicom Group Inc.; *U.S. Public*, pg. 1576
IMPACT BBDO—See Omnicom Group Inc.; *U.S. Public*, pg. 1576
IMPACT BBDO—See Omnicom Group Inc.; *U.S. Public*, pg. 1576
IMPRESSIONS-A.B.A. INDUSTRIES, INC.; *U.S. Private*, pg. 2051
IMPRESSIONS MEDIA SERVICES, INC.; *U.S. Private*, pg. 2050
IMULUS, LLC; *U.S. Private*, pg. 2051
IMWOO TECHNOLOGIES, LLC; *U.S. Private*, pg. 2052
INDEX EXCHANGE, INC.; *U.S. Private*, pg. 2061
INDIGO WERBEAGENTUR GMBH—See Dentsu Group Inc.; *Int'l*, pg. 2037
INEVIDENCE LIMITED—See Providence Equity Partners L.L.C.; *U.S. Private*, pg. 3291
INFERNO LLC; *U.S. Private*, pg. 2070
INFINITY DIRECT, INC.—See Impact Mailing Of Minnesota, Inc.; *U.S. Private*, pg. 2048
INFORM, INC.; *U.S. Private*, pg. 2072
INFRONT GERMANY GMBH—See Dalian Wanda Group Corporation Ltd.; *Int'l*, pg. 1953
THE IN-HOUSE AGENCY, INC.; *U.S. Private*, pg. 4055
INITIATIVE GROUP B.V.—See The Interpublic Group of Companies, Inc.; *U.S. Public*, pg. 2095
INITIATIVE HONG KONG—See The Interpublic Group of Companies, Inc.; *U.S. Public*, pg. 2095
INITIATIVE LONDON—See The Interpublic Group of Companies, Inc.; *U.S. Public*, pg. 2095
INITIATIVE MEDIA AUSTRALIA PTY LTD—See The Interpublic Group of Companies, Inc.; *U.S. Public*, pg. 2095
INITIATIVE MOSCOW—See The Interpublic Group of Companies, Inc.; *U.S. Public*, pg. 2096
INITIATIVE UNIVERSAL MEDIA—See The Interpublic Group of Companies, Inc.; *U.S. Public*, pg. 2096
INITIO, INC.; *U.S. Private*, pg. 2077
INNERSCOPE HEARING TECHNOLOGIES, INC.; *U.S. Public*, pg. 1125
INNERWORKINGS BELGIUM SPRL/BVBA—See HH Global Group Limited; *Int'l*, pg. 3378
INNERWORKINGS BRASIL GERENCIAMENTO DE IMPRESSOES—See HH Global Group Limited; *Int'l*, pg. 3378
INNERWORKINGS CANADA—See HH Global Group Limited; *Int'l*, pg. 3378
INNIS MAGGIORE GROUP, INC.; *U.S. Private*, pg. 2080
INNOCEAN AMERICAS WORLDWIDE; *U.S. Private*, pg. 2080
INNOVATION ADS, INC.; *U.S. Private*, pg. 2081
INNOVATION ADS, INC.—See Innovation Ads, Inc.; *U.S. Private*, pg. 2081
INNOVATION DIGITAL, LLC—See COMSovereign Holding Corp.; *U.S. Public*, pg. 562
INNOVATIVE ADVERTISING, LLC; *U.S. Private*, pg. 2081
INNOVYX—See Omnicom Group Inc.; *U.S. Public*, pg. 1594

INNOVYX—See Omnicom Group Inc.; *U.S. Public*, pg. 1594
INQUEST MARKETING; *U.S. Private*, pg. 2085
INSEEV INTERACTIVE INC.; *U.S. Private*, pg. 2085
INSIDE OUT COMMUNICATIONS; *U.S. Private*, pg. 2085
INSIGHTSNOW, INC.; *U.S. Private*, pg. 2091
INSPIRA MARKETING GROUP; *U.S. Private*, pg. 2092
INSPIRE CREATIVE STUDIOS; *U.S. Private*, pg. 2092
IN SYNC BEMIS BALKIND; *U.S. Private*, pg. 2052
INTACT INFO SOLUTIONS LLC; *U.S. Private*, pg. 2097
THE INTEGER GROUP, LLC - DALLAS—See Omnicom Group Inc.; *U.S. Public*, pg. 1599
THE INTEGER GROUP, LLC - MIDWEST—See Omnicom Group Inc.; *U.S. Public*, pg. 1599
THE INTEGER GROUP, LLC—See Omnicom Group Inc.; *U.S. Public*, pg. 1599
INTEGRATED COMMUNICATIONS CORP.; *U.S. Private*, pg. 2099
INTEGRATED MARKETING WORKS; *U.S. Private*, pg. 2100
INTEGRATIVE LOGIC LLC—See Luckie & Co. Ltd.; *U.S. Private*, pg. 2511
INTELLIBRIGHT CORPORATION; *U.S. Private*, pg. 2105
INTELLIMEDIA-DBC—See Diccicco Battista Communications; *U.S. Public*, pg. 1225
INTERBRAND CORPORATION—See Omnicom Group Inc.; *U.S. Public*, pg. 1586
INTERBRAND DESIGN FORUM—See Omnicom Group Inc.; *U.S. Public*, pg. 1586
INTERBRANDHEALTH—See Omnicom Group Inc.; *U.S. Public*, pg. 1586
INTERBRAND SAN FRANCISCO—See Omnicom Group Inc.; *U.S. Public*, pg. 1586
INTERBRAND—See Omnicom Group Inc.; *U.S. Public*, pg. 1586
INTERCOMMUNICATIONS INC.; *U.S. Private*, pg. 2109
INTEREXPO COMMUNICATIONS; *U.S. Private*, pg. 2110
INTERFACE COMMUNICATIONS LTD.—See The Interpublic Group of Companies, Inc.; *U.S. Public*, pg. 2093
INTERFORM; *U.S. Private*, pg. 2110
INTERLEX COMMUNICATIONS INC; *U.S. Private*, pg. 2111
INTERLINK HEALTHCARE COMMUNICATION—See Integrated Communications Corp.; *U.S. Private*, pg. 2099
INTERMARK GROUP, INC.; *U.S. Private*, pg. 2112
INTERNATIONAL DISPLAY ADVERTISING, INC.; *U.S. Public*, pg. 1151
INTERNATIONAL MEDIA PARTNERS, INC.; *U.S. Private*, pg. 2119
INTERONE COLOGNE—See Omnicom Group Inc.; *U.S. Public*, pg. 1576
INTERONE HAMBURG—See Omnicom Group Inc.; *U.S. Public*, pg. 1576
INTERONE WORLDWIDE—See Omnicom Group Inc.; *U.S. Public*, pg. 1576
INTERSTATE LOGOS, L.L.C.—See Lamar Advertising Company; *U.S. Public*, pg. 1290
INTERTREND COMMUNICATIONS, INC.; *U.S. Private*, pg. 2127
IN TESTA HQ—See Armando Testa S.p.A.; *Int'l*, pg. 574
INVENTIV MEDICAL COMMUNICATIONS, LLC—See Elliott Management Corporation; *U.S. Private*, pg. 1366
INVENTIV MEDICAL COMMUNICATIONS, LLC—See Patient Square Capital, L.P.; *U.S. Private*, pg. 3108
INVENTIV MEDICAL COMMUNICATIONS, LLC—See Veritas Capital Fund Management, LLC; *U.S. Private*, pg. 4365
INVERSE—See Omnicom Group Inc.; *U.S. Public*, pg. 1594
INXPO INC.—See Apollo Global Management, Inc.; *U.S. Public*, pg. 152
IOMEDIA; *U.S. Private*, pg. 2133
IONIC MEDIA; *U.S. Private*, pg. 2134
IOSTUDIO; *U.S. Private*, pg. 2134
IP BELGIUM S.A.—See Bertelsmann SE & Co. KGaA; *Int'l*, pg. 992
IPG INC.—See Dentsu Group Inc.; *Int'l*, pg. 2039
IP PLURIMEDIA SA—See Bertelsmann SE & Co. KGaA; *Int'l*, pg. 994
IPROSPECT—See Dentsu Group Inc.; *Int'l*, pg. 2037
IPSH!—See Omnicom Group Inc.; *U.S. Public*, pg. 1600
IPVISTA A/S—See Arrow Electronics, Inc.; *U.S. Public*, pg. 199
IQ SOLUTIONS; *U.S. Private*, pg. 2137
IRIS GLOBAL CLINICAL TRIALS SOLUTIONS—See Omnicom Group Inc.; *U.S. Public*, pg. 1599
IRMA S. MANN, STRATEGIC MARKETING INC.; *U.S. Private*, pg. 2139
IRVINE MARKETING COMMUNICATIONS; *U.S. Private*, pg. 2141
ISA ADVERTISING; *U.S. Private*, pg. 2142
I&S BBDO INC.—See Omnicom Group Inc.; *U.S. Public*, pg. 1575
I&S/BBDO KANSAI REGIONAL HEAD OFFICE—See Omnicom Group Inc.; *U.S. Public*, pg. 1576
I&S/BBDO KYOTO REGIONAL HEAD OFFICE—See Omnicom Group Inc.; *U.S. Public*, pg. 1576
I&S/BBDO NAGOYA REGIONAL HEAD OFFICE—See Omnicom Group Inc.; *U.S. Public*, pg. 1576
I&S/BBDO SAPPORO BRANCH—See Omnicom Group Inc.; *U.S. Public*, pg. 1576

541810 — ADVERTISING AGENCIE...

I-SITE, INC.; *U.S. Private*, pg. 2026
ISOBAR AUSTRALIA—See Dentsu Group Inc.; *Int'l*, pg. 2037
ISOBAR HONG KONG—See Dentsu Group Inc.; *Int'l*, pg. 2037
ISOBAR—See Dentsu Group Inc.; *Int'l*, pg. 2037
ISOBAR—See Dentsu Group Inc.; *Int'l*, pg. 2037
IVIE & ASSOCIATES, INC.—See Quad/Graphics, Inc.; *U.S. Public*, pg. 1744
THE IVY GROUP, LTD.; *U.S. Private*, pg. 4057
THE IVY GROUP, LTD.—See The Ivy Group, Ltd.; *U.S. Private*, pg. 4058
IW GROUP, INC. - NEW YORK OFFICE—See IW Group, Inc.; *U.S. Private*, pg. 2152
IW GROUP, INC. - SAN FRANCISCO OFFICE—See IW Group, Inc.; *U.S. Private*, pg. 2152
IW GROUP, INC.; *U.S. Private*, pg. 2152
IZEA WORLDWIDE, INC.; *U.S. Public*, pg. 1179
JACK MORTON EXHIBITS—See The Interpublic Group of Companies, Inc.; *U.S. Public*, pg. 2096
JACK MORTON WORLDWIDE - SAN FRANCISCO—See The Interpublic Group of Companies, Inc.; *U.S. Public*, pg. 2097
JACK MORTON WORLDWIDE—See The Interpublic Group of Companies, Inc.; *U.S. Public*, pg. 2096
JACK MORTON WORLDWIDE—See The Interpublic Group of Companies, Inc.; *U.S. Public*, pg. 2096
JACK MORTON WORLDWIDE—See The Interpublic Group of Companies, Inc.; *U.S. Public*, pg. 2096
JACK MORTON WORLDWIDE—See The Interpublic Group of Companies, Inc.; *U.S. Public*, pg. 2096
JACK MORTON WORLDWIDE—See The Interpublic Group of Companies, Inc.; *U.S. Public*, pg. 2096
JACK MORTON WORLDWIDE—See The Interpublic Group of Companies, Inc.; *U.S. Public*, pg. 2096
JACK MORTON WORLDWIDE—See The Interpublic Group of Companies, Inc.; *U.S. Public*, pg. 2097
JACK MORTON WORLDWIDE—See The Interpublic Group of Companies, Inc.; *U.S. Public*, pg. 2097
JACK MORTON WORLDWIDE—See The Interpublic Group of Companies, Inc.; *U.S. Public*, pg. 2097
JACK MORTON WORLDWIDE—See The Interpublic Group of Companies, Inc.; *U.S. Public*, pg. 2097
JACK MORTON WORLDWIDE—See The Interpublic Group of Companies, Inc.; *U.S. Public*, pg. 2097
JACK MYERS REPORT; *U.S. Private*, pg. 2174
JACK NADEL INC. - SOUTHPORT OFFICE—See Jack Nadel Inc.; *U.S. Private*, pg. 2174
JACKSON INTEGRATED; *U.S. Private*, pg. 2177
JACKSON MARKETING GROUP, INC.; *U.S. Private*, pg. 2177
JACOBS AGENCY, INC.; *U.S. Private*, pg. 2179
JACOBS & CLEVENGER, INC.; *U.S. Private*, pg. 2179
JACOBSON ROST; *U.S. Private*, pg. 2180
JAEGER, INC.; *U.S. Private*, pg. 2181
JA INTEGRATED THINKING; *U.S. Private*, pg. 2172
JA INTEGRATED THINKING—See JA Integrated Thinking; *U.S. Private*, pg. 2172
JAJO, INC.; *U.S. Private*, pg. 2182
JAM ASSOCIATES LLC; *U.S. Private*, pg. 2182
JAMES ROSS ADVERTISING; *U.S. Private*, pg. 2185
JAMES & THOMAS, INC.; *U.S. Private*, pg. 2183
JAMISON/MCKAY LLC; *U.S. Private*, pg. 2186
JANGLE ADVERTISING; *U.S. Private*, pg. 2186
JANKOWSKICO.; *U.S. Private*, pg. 2187
JAPAN KANTAR RESEARCH—See Bain Capital, LP; *U.S. Private*, pg. 448
JAVELIN—See Omnicom Group Inc.; *U.S. Public*, pg. 1586
JAY ADVERTISING, INC.; *U.S. Private*, pg. 2191
JAYRAY ADS & PR, INC.; *U.S. Private*, pg. 2192
JBLH COMMUNICATIONS; *U.S. Private*, pg. 2194
J. BRENLIN DESIGN, INC.; *U.S. Private*, pg. 2155
JEFFREY SCOTT AGENCY, INC.; *U.S. Private*, pg. 2198
JEKYLL & HYDE BRAND BUILDERS INC—See 1CM inc.; *Int'l*, pg. 3
JESS3; *U.S. Private*, pg. 2203
JET ADVERTISING; *U.S. Private*, pg. 2203
JFD ADVERTISING & PUBLIC RELATIONS, INC.; *U.S. Private*, pg. 2206
JH&A ADVERTISING INC.; *U.S. Private*, pg. 2207
J. HUNTER ADVERTISING INC.; *U.S. Private*, pg. 2156
JIM WRIGHT ASSOCIATES; *U.S. Private*, pg. 2210
J&M ADVERTISING LLC; *U.S. Private*, pg. 2154
J&M ADVERTISING & PRODUCTIONS; *U.S. Private*, pg. 2154
JMD COMMUNICATIONS; *U.S. Private*, pg. 2215
J.M. PERRONE CO., INC.; *U.S. Private*, pg. 2169
JNS MEDIA SPECIALISTS, INC.; *U.S. Private*, pg. 2217
JOBELEPHANT.COM INC.; *U.S. Private*, pg. 2217
THE JOEY CO.; *U.S. Private*, pg. 4059
JOHN ADAMS ASSOCIATES INC.—See Kellen Communications; *U.S. Private*, pg. 2274
JOHNSON DESIGN GROUP; *U.S. Private*, pg. 2227
JOHNSON DIRECT; *U.S. Private*, pg. 2227
THE JOHNSON GROUP; *U.S. Private*, pg. 4059
JOHNSONRAUHOFF MARKETING COMMUNICATIONS—See JohnsonRauhoff; *U.S. Private*, pg. 2229
JOHNSONRAUHOFF MARKETING COMMUNICATIONS—See JohnsonRauhoff; *U.S. Private*, pg. 2229
JOHNSONRAUHOFF; *U.S. Private*, pg. 2229
JOINT VENTURE MARKETING & COMMUNICATIONS; *U.S. Private*, pg. 2230
JON BYK ADVERTISING, INC.; *U.S. Private*, pg. 2231
JONES PUBLIC AFFAIRS, INC.; *U.S. Private*, pg. 2234
JORDACHE ENTERPRISES; *U.S. Private*, pg. 2235
JOSEPH PEDOTT ADVERTISING & MARKETING, INC.; *U.S. Private*, pg. 2237
JPL INTEGRATED COMMUNICATIONS, INC.; *U.S. Private*, pg. 2239
J.R. NAVARRO & ASSOCIATES INC.; *U.S. Private*, pg. 2170
JRS ADVERTISING; *U.S. Private*, pg. 2240
J.R. THOMPSON COMPANY, LLC; *U.S. Private*, pg. 2171
JR TOKAI AGENCY CO., LTD.—See Central Japan Railway Company; *Int'l*, pg. 1408
JS2 COMMUNICATIONS—See JS2 Communications; *U.S. Private*, pg. 2241
J.S. BLADE ADVERTISING AGENCY, INC.; *U.S. Private*, pg. 2171
J. STOKES & ASSOCIATES, INC.; *U.S. Private*, pg. 2157
J.T. MEGA MARKETING COMMUNICATIONS; *U.S. Private*, pg. 2171
J-U CARTER, INC.; *U.S. Private*, pg. 2155
JUICE COMMUNICATIONS; *U.S. Private*, pg. 2243
JULIE A. LAITIN ENTERPRISES, INC.; *U.S. Private*, pg. 2243
JUMBOSHRIMP ADVERTISING INC.; *U.S. Private*, pg. 2243
JUMP2 GROUP; *U.S. Private*, pg. 2243
JUMP!; *U.S. Private*, pg. 2243
JUMP—See Omnicom Group Inc.; *U.S. Public*, pg. 1596
JUNIPER PARK LP—See Omnicom Group Inc.; *U.S. Public*, pg. 1598
JUST MEDIA, INC.; *U.S. Private*, pg. 2245
JVST, INC.—See CHR Group LLC; *U.S. Private*, pg. 889
JWALCHER COMMUNICATIONS; *U.S. Private*, pg. 2246
KAISER MARKETING, INC.; *U.S. Private*, pg. 2255
KALEIDOSCOPE—See Omnicom Group Inc.; *U.S. Public*, pg. 1586
KANAGAWA KAIHATSU KANKOU—See Dentsu Group Inc.; *Int'l*, pg. 2039
KANE COMMUNICATIONS GROUP, LLC; *U.S. Private*, pg. 2259
KANE & FINKEL HEALTHCARE COMMUNICATIONS; *U.S. Private*, pg. 2259
KAREN MORSTAD & ASSOCIATES LLC; *U.S. Private*, pg. 2262
KARLEN WILLIAMS GRAYBILL ADVERTISING; *U.S. Private*, pg. 2263
KARLIN+PIMSLER; *U.S. Private*, pg. 2263
KASTNER & PARTNERS - SAINT LOUIS—See Kastner & Partners; *U.S. Private*, pg. 2264
KASTNER & PARTNERS; *U.S. Private*, pg. 2264
KAUFMAN ADVERTISING AGENCY; *U.S. Private*, pg. 2265
KBS+P CANADA LP—See Stagwell, Inc.; *U.S. Public*, pg. 1927
K-C ADVERTISING, INC.—See Kimberly-Clark Corporation; *U.S. Public*, pg. 1229
KDNY ENTERPRISE; *U.S. Private*, pg. 2270
KDR PRODUCTIONS/DOLLARWISE PUBLICATIONS; *U.S. Private*, pg. 2270
KEA ADVERTISING; *U.S. Private*, pg. 2271
KEATING MAGEE MARKETING COMMUNICATIONS; *U.S. Private*, pg. 2271
KEENAN-NAGLE ADVERTISING; *U.S. Private*, pg. 2272
KEEN BRANDING; *U.S. Private*, pg. 2272
KEEN BRANDING—See Keen Branding; *U.S. Private*, pg. 2272
KEEN BRANDING-WEST COAST—See Keen Branding; *U.S. Private*, pg. 2272
KEILER & COMPANY; *U.S. Private*, pg. 2273
KELLEY & COMPANY; *U.S. Private*, pg. 2275
KELLEY HABIB JOHN; *U.S. Private*, pg. 2275
KELLEY SWOFFORD ROY, INC.; *U.S. Private*, pg. 2276
KELLIHER SAMETS VOLK NY—See Kelliher Samets Volk; *U.S. Private*, pg. 2276
KELLIHER SAMETS VOLK; *U.S. Private*, pg. 2276
KELLY MEDIA GROUP; *U.S. Private*, pg. 2276
KEMPERCONNECT; *U.S. Private*, pg. 2282
KENNEDY ADVERTISING—See Kennedy Automotive Group Inc.; *U.S. Private*, pg. 2284
THE KERN ORGANIZATION, INC.—See Omnicom Group Inc.; *U.S. Public*, pg. 1593
KETCHUM CHENGDU—See Omnicom Group Inc.; *U.S. Public*, pg. 1587
KETCHUM DIRECTORY ADVERTISING/KANSAS CITY—See Omnicom Group Inc.; *U.S. Public*, pg. 1587
KETCHUM DIRECTORY ADVERTISING/LOUISVILLE—See Omnicom Group Inc.; *U.S. Public*, pg. 1587
KETCHUM DIRECTORY ADVERTISING/PITTSBURGH—See Omnicom Group Inc.; *U.S. Public*, pg. 1587

CORPORATE AFFILIATIONS

KETCHUM, INC.—See Omnicom Group Inc.; *U.S. Public*, pg. 1586
KETCHUM—See Omnicom Group Inc.; *U.S. Public*, pg. 1586
KETCHUM—See Omnicom Group Inc.; *U.S. Public*, pg. 1586
KETCHUM—See Omnicom Group Inc.; *U.S. Public*, pg. 1586
KETCHUM—See Omnicom Group Inc.; *U.S. Public*, pg. 1586
KETCHUM—See Omnicom Group Inc.; *U.S. Public*, pg. 1586
KETCHUM—See Omnicom Group Inc.; *U.S. Public*, pg. 1586
KETCHUM—See Omnicom Group Inc.; *U.S. Public*, pg. 1586
KEYAD, LLC; *U.S. Private*, pg. 2294
KEYGAMES NETWORK B.V.—See Azerion Group N.V.; *Int'l*, pg. 778
KEYSEN ENGINEERING COMPANY LIMITED—See Great Eagle Holdings Limited; *Int'l*, pg. 3064
KG CREATIVE; *U.S. Private*, pg. 2301
KH ADVERTISING; *U.S. Private*, pg. 2301
KIDD GROUP; *U.S. Private*, pg. 2302
KIDVERTISERS, INC.; *U.S. Private*, pg. 2303
K I LIPTON INC.; *U.S. Private*, pg. 2249
KILLEEN FURTNEY GROUP, INC.; *U.S. Private*, pg. 2304
KILLIAN BRANDING; *U.S. Private*, pg. 2304
KINECT—See Omnicom Group Inc.; *U.S. Public*, pg. 1599
THE KING GROUP; *U.S. Private*, pg. 4065
KINGSDALE PARTNERS LP—See Stagwell, Inc.; *U.S. Public*, pg. 1927
KIROWSKI ISOBAR ZRT—See Dentsu Group Inc.; *Int'l*, pg. 2037
KIRSHENBAUM BOND SENECAL + PARTNERS - MONTREAL—See Stagwell, Inc.; *U.S. Public*, pg. 1928
KIRSHENBAUM BOND SENECAL + PARTNERS—See Stagwell, Inc.; *U.S. Public*, pg. 1928
KK BOLD; *U.S. Private*, pg. 2317
KLEIDON & ASSOCIATES; *U.S. Private*, pg. 2318
KMS ADVERTISING LTD.—See iHeartMedia, Inc.; *U.S. Public*, pg. 1095
KNIGHT MARKETING ASSOCIATES, INC.; *U.S. Private*, pg. 2322
KNSK WERBEAGENTUR GMBH—See Omnicom Group Inc.; *U.S. Public*, pg. 1576
KNUDSEN, GARDNER & HOWE, INC.; *U.S. Private*, pg. 2325
KNUPP & WATSON & WALLMAN; *U.S. Private*, pg. 2325
KOGNITIV UK LTD—See Aimia Inc.; *Int'l*, pg. 233
KOHNSTAMM COMMUNICATIONS—See Broadhead + Co.; *U.S. Private*, pg. 659
KOLLE REBBE GMBH—See Accenture plc; *Int'l*, pg. 87
KOOPMAN OSTBO; *U.S. Private*, pg. 2343
KOREY KAY & PARTNERS; *U.S. Private*, pg. 2343
KOROBERI INC.; *U.S. Private*, pg. 2344
KOSTIAL COMPANY, LLC; *U.S. Private*, pg. 2345
KOVEL/FULLER; *U.S. Private*, pg. 2345
KPA LLC; *U.S. Private*, pg. 2345
KRAUS-ANDERSON COMMUNICATIONS GROUP—See Kraus-Anderson Incorporated; *U.S. Private*, pg. 2349
KRAUSE ADVERTISING; *U.S. Private*, pg. 2350
KREATE PTY. LIMITED—See Academies Australasia Group Limited; *Int'l*, pg. 77
KRELL ADVERTISING; *U.S. Private*, pg. 2351
KRIENIK ADVERTISING, INC.; *U.S. Private*, pg. 2351
KRON & ASSOCIATES ADVERTISING INC.; *U.S. Private*, pg. 2353
KRT MARKETING, INC.—See Recruitics, LLC; *U.S. Private*, pg. 3372
KRUPP KOMMUNICATIONS; *U.S. Private*, pg. 2353
KRUSKOPF COONTZ; *U.S. Private*, pg. 2353
KSC STUDIO, LLC—See Bertram Capital Management, LLC; *U.S. Private*, pg. 540
KSL MEDIA, INC.; *U.S. Private*, pg. 2355
KUHN & WITTENBORN, INC.; *U.S. Private*, pg. 2356
KWGC, INC. ADVERTISING & DESIGN; *U.S. Private*, pg. 2359
KWITTKEN & COMPANY; *U.S. Private*, pg. 2359
KWITTKEN LP—See Stagwell, Inc.; *U.S. Public*, pg. 1927
KYK ADVERTISING MARKETING PROMOTIONS; *U.S. Private*, pg. 2360
KYODO NEWS PR WIRE—See Dentsu Group Inc.; *Int'l*, pg. 2039
KZS ADVERTISING; *U.S. Private*, pg. 2361
L2T MEDIA; *U.S. Private*, pg. 2367
LA AGENCIA DE ORCI & ASOCIADOS; *U.S. Private*, pg. 2367
LAGRAPHICO; *U.S. Private*, pg. 2373
LAIRD CHRISTIANSON ADVERTISING, INC.; *U.S. Private*, pg. 2374
LAIRD + PARTNERS NEW YORK LLC—See Stagwell, Inc.; *U.S. Public*, pg. 1927
LAMAR ADVERTISING OF COLORADO SPRINGS, INC.—See Lamar Advertising Company; *U.S. Public*, pg. 1290
LAMAR CENTRAL OUTDOOR, LLC—See Lamar Advertising Company; *U.S. Public*, pg. 1291

N.A.I.C.S. INDEX

541810 — ADVERTISING AGENCIE...

LAMAR INVESTMENTS, LLC—See Lamar Advertising Company; *U.S. Public*, pg. 1291
L&A MARKETING & ADVERTISING, INC.; *U.S. Private*, pg. 2362
LAMBESIS, INC.; *U.S. Private*, pg. 2380
LA MODE EN IMAGES—See Omnicom Group Inc.; *U.S. Public*, pg. 1596
LANDERS & PARTNERS, INC.; *U.S. Private*, pg. 2385
LANDERS & PARTNERS, INC.—See Landers & Partners, Inc.; *U.S. Private*, pg. 2385
LANDSBERRY & JAMES MARKETING PTY LTD—See Brookfield Corporation; *Int'l*, pg. 1178
LANDSBERRY & JAMES MARKETING PTY LTD—See Elliott Management Corporation; *U.S. Private*, pg. 1371
LANETERRALEVER; *U.S. Private*, pg. 2388
THE LANMARK GROUP INC.; *U.S. Private*, pg. 4067
LAPLACA COHEN; *U.S. Private*, pg. 2391
LARS & ASSOCIATES, INC.; *U.S. Private*, pg. 2393
LARSEN; *U.S. Private*, pg. 2393
LARSEN—See Larsen; *U.S. Private*, pg. 2393
THE LASTER GROUP; *U.S. Private*, pg. 4068
LATCHA+ASSOCIATES; *U.S. Private*, pg. 2396
LATIN CONNECTION—See Hanson Watson Associates; *U.S. Private*, pg. 1857
LATINWORKS MARKETING, INC.—See Omnicom Group Inc.; *U.S. Public*, pg. 1588
LATIN WORLD ENTERTAINMENT AGENCY; *U.S. Private*, pg. 2397
LATITUDE—See The Richards Group, Inc.; *U.S. Private*, pg. 4107
LATORRA, PAUL & MCCANN; *U.S. Private*, pg. 2397
THE LAUERER MARKIN GROUP, INC.; *U.S. Private*, pg. 4068
LAUGHING SAMURAI; *U.S. Private*, pg. 2397
LAUGHLIN/CONSTABLE, INC.; *U.S. Private*, pg. 2398
LAUGHLIN/CONSTABLE, INC.—See Laughlin/Constable, Inc.; *U.S. Private*, pg. 2398
LAUGHLIN/CONSTABLE NEW YORK—See Laughlin/Constable, Inc.; *U.S. Private*, pg. 2398
LAUNCH AGENCY; *U.S. Private*, pg. 2398
LAUNCHPAD ADVERTISING LLC; *U.S. Private*, pg. 2398
LAUNCHPAD; *U.S. Private*, pg. 2398
LAUNCH; *U.S. Private*, pg. 2398
LAURA DAVIDSON PUBLIC RELATIONS, INC.; *U.S. Private*, pg. 2398
LAVIDGE & ASSOCIATES INC.; *U.S. Private*, pg. 2400
THE LAVIDGE COMPANY; *U.S. Private*, pg. 4068
LAWLER BALLARD VAN DURAND; *U.S. Private*, pg. 2400
LAWLER BALLARD VAN DURAND—See Lawler Ballard Van Durand; *U.S. Private*, pg. 2401
LAWRENCE & SCHILLER, INC.; *U.S. Private*, pg. 2401
LBN PARTNERS LLC - LOS ANGELES OFFICE—See Ansira Partners, Inc.; *U.S. Private*, pg. 286
LBN PARTNERS LLC—See Ansira Partners, Inc.; *U.S. Private*, pg. 286
LDMI; *U.S. Private*, pg. 2404
LEADDOG MARKETING GROUP; *U.S. Private*, pg. 2405
THE LEADS NETWORK, LLC; *U.S. Private*, pg. 4068
LEADVISION MEDIA, LLC; *U.S. Private*, pg. 2407
LEANIN' TREE, INC.; *U.S. Private*, pg. 2407
LEAPFROG SOLUTIONS, INC.; *U.S. Private*, pg. 2407
LEC; *U.S. Private*, pg. 2409
LEE ADVERTISING; *U.S. Private*, pg. 2411
LEE REEDY INC.; *U.S. Private*, pg. 2413
LEE & WYRSCH; *U.S. Private*, pg. 2411
LEFFLER AGENCY, INC.; *U.S. Private*, pg. 2415
LEFT FIELD LABS, LLC—See Stagwell, Inc.; *U.S. Public*, pg. 1927
LEGEND CREATIVE GROUP; *U.S. Private*, pg. 2418
LEGION ADVERTISING; *U.S. Private*, pg. 2418
LEHMANMILLET EUROPE—See LehmanMillet; *U.S. Private*, pg. 2419
LEHMANMILLET; *U.S. Private*, pg. 2419
LEHMANMILLET—See LehmanMillet; *U.S. Private*, pg. 2419
LEIBLER-BRONFMAN LUBALIN; *U.S. Private*, pg. 2419
THE LEITH AGENCY—See Arsenal Capital Management LP; *U.S. Private*, pg. 338
LEO J. BRENNAN, INC.; *U.S. Private*, pg. 2422
LEOO SAS—See ADLPartner SA; *Int'l*, pg. 151
THE LESLIE CORPORATION; *U.S. Private*, pg. 4069
LESNIK, HIMMELSBACH, WILSON, & HEARL; *U.S. Private*, pg. 2432
LEVELTWO ADVERTISING; *U.S. Private*, pg. 2434
LEVELWING MEDIA; *U.S. Private*, pg. 2434
LEVENSON & HILL, INC.; *U.S. Private*, pg. 2434
LEVERAGE MARKETING GROUP; *U.S. Private*, pg. 2435
LEVINE COMMUNICATIONS OFFICE; *U.S. Private*, pg. 2435
LEVLANE ADVERTISING, PR & INTERACTIVE; *U.S. Private*, pg. 2437
LEVLANE ADVERTISING/PR/INTERACTIVE-FLORIDA—See LevLane Advertising, PR & Interactive; *U.S. Private*, pg. 2437
LEWIS ADVERTISING, INC.; *U.S. Private*, pg. 2438
LEWIS COMMUNICATIONS; *U.S. Private*, pg. 2438
LEWIS COMMUNICATIONS—See Lewis Communications; *U.S. Private*, pg. 2438

LIAISON MARKETING COMMUNICATIONS, LTD.; *U.S. Private*, pg. 2442
LIMITLESS X HOLDINGS INC.; *U.S. Public*, pg. 1316
LINDO/FCB—See The Interpublic Group of Companies, Inc.; *U.S. Public*, pg. 2093
LINEA 12/MCCANN ERICKSON—See The Interpublic Group of Companies, Inc.; *U.S. Public*, pg. 2098
LINE DIGITAL LIMITED—See Arsenal Capital Management LP; *U.S. Private*, pg. 338
LINETT & HARRISON; *U.S. Private*, pg. 2461
LINKMEDIA 360; *U.S. Private*, pg. 2462
LINX COMMUNICATIONS CORP.; *U.S. Private*, pg. 2463
LIPMAN HEARNE, INC. - WASHINGTON, DC—See Lipman Hearne, Inc.; *U.S. Private*, pg. 2465
LIPMAN SERVICES CORP.; *U.S. Private*, pg. 2465
LIPPI & CO. ADVERTISING; *U.S. Private*, pg. 2465
LISA ELIA PUBLIC RELATIONS; *U.S. Private*, pg. 2466
LITTLE BULL—See Armando Testa S.p.A.; *Int'l*, pg. 574
LITTLE & COMPANY; *U.S. Private*, pg. 2468
LITTLE DOG AGENCY INC.; *U.S. Private*, pg. 2468
LITTLEFIELD, INC.; *U.S. Private*, pg. 2469
LIVE BOARD, INC.—See Dentsu Group Inc.; *Int'l*, pg. 2039
LIVEINTENT, INC.—See Zeta Global Holdings Corp.; *U.S. Public*, pg. 2403
LIVELY GROUP, LLC; *U.S. Private*, pg. 2473
LIVERAMP UK LTD.—See LiveRamp Holdings, Inc.; *U.S. Public*, pg. 1333
LIVING BREATHING; *U.S. Private*, pg. 2473
LJF ASSOCIATES, INC.; *U.S. Private*, pg. 2474
L.K. ADVERTISING AGENCY—See The Linick Group, Inc.; *U.S. Private*, pg. 4070
LKH&S LOUISVILLE—See LKH&S; *U.S. Private*, pg. 2475
LKH&S; *U.S. Private*, pg. 2475
LLC AGORA UKRAINE—See Agora S.A.; *Int'l*, pg. 212
LLOYD & CO.; *U.S. Private*, pg. 2475
LM&O ADVERTISING; *U.S. Private*, pg. 2476
LOCAL LEADS HQ; *U.S. Private*, pg. 2477
LOCAL MARKETING GIANT, LLC; *U.S. Private*, pg. 2477
LOCAL MERCHAT SERVICES, INC.—See Telenav, Inc.; *U.S. Private*, pg. 3960
LOCAL YOKEL MEDIA LLC—See PubSquared LLC; *U.S. Private*, pg. 3301
LOCKARD & WECHSLER; *U.S. Private*, pg. 2478
LOCKNEY & ASSOCIATES, INC.; *U.S. Private*, pg. 2478
LODESTONE ADVERTISING; *U.S. Private*, pg. 2479
LOEFFLER KETCHUM MOUNTJOY (LKM); *U.S. Private*, pg. 2480
LOGISTIX—See EMAK Worldwide, Inc.; *U.S. Private*, pg. 1378
LOIS GELLER MARKETING GROUP; *U.S. Private*, pg. 2482
LOLA MADRID—See The Interpublic Group of Companies, Inc.; *U.S. Public*, pg. 2091
LOLA MULLENLOWE—See The Interpublic Group of Companies, Inc.; *U.S. Public*, pg. 2091
LONGREN & PARKS; *U.S. Private*, pg. 2493
LOOKSMART GROUP, INC.; *U.S. Private*, pg. 1342
LOOKTOURS.COM LLC—See TripAdvisor, Inc.; *U.S. Public*, pg. 2195
THE LOOMIS AGENCY; *U.S. Private*, pg. 4072
LOONEY ADVERTISING AND DESIGN; *U.S. Private*, pg. 2494
LOPEZ NEGRETE COMMUNICATIONS, INC.; *U.S. Private*, pg. 2494
LOPEZ NEGRETE COMMUNICATIONS WEST, INC.—See Lopez Negrete Communications, Inc.; *U.S. Private*, pg. 2494
LOPITO, ILEANA & HOWIE, INC.; *U.S. Private*, pg. 2494
LOREL MARKETING GROUP LLC; *U.S. Private*, pg. 2495
LOTUS ADVERTISING; *U.S. Private*, pg. 2497
LOUDMAC CREATIVE, INC.; *U.S. Private*, pg. 2498
LOVE ADVERTISING INC.; *U.S. Private*, pg. 2501
LOVGREN MARKETING GROUP; *U.S. Private*, pg. 2504
LOW + ASSOCIATES—See Crosby Marketing Communications; *U.S. Private*, pg. 1104
LOWE ADVENTA—See The Interpublic Group of Companies, Inc.; *U.S. Public*, pg. 2091
LOWE AND PARTNERS SA—See The Interpublic Group of Companies, Inc.; *U.S. Public*, pg. 2091
LOWE AVANTA—See The Interpublic Group of Companies, Inc.; *U.S. Public*, pg. 2091
LOWE BRINDFORS—See The Interpublic Group of Companies, Inc.; *U.S. Public*, pg. 2091
LOWE CHINA—See The Interpublic Group of Companies, Inc.; *U.S. Public*, pg. 2091
LOWE FMRG—See The Interpublic Group of Companies, Inc.; *U.S. Public*, pg. 2091
LOWE GGK—See The Interpublic Group of Companies, Inc.; *U.S. Public*, pg. 2091
LOWE GGK—See The Interpublic Group of Companies, Inc.; *U.S. Public*, pg. 2091
LOWE GGK—See The Interpublic Group of Companies, Inc.; *U.S. Public*, pg. 2091
LOWE GGK—See The Interpublic Group of Companies, Inc.; *U.S. Public*, pg. 2091
LOWE GGK—See The Interpublic Group of Companies, Inc.; *U.S. Public*, pg. 2091

LOWE GINKGO—See The Interpublic Group of Companies, Inc.; *U.S. Public*, pg. 2091
LOWE LDB—See The Interpublic Group of Companies, Inc.; *U.S. Public*, pg. 2091
LOWE MENA—See The Interpublic Group of Companies, Inc.; *U.S. Public*, pg. 2091
LOWE & PARTNERS—See The Interpublic Group of Companies, Inc.; *U.S. Public*, pg. 2091
LOWE & PARTNERS—See The Interpublic Group of Companies, Inc.; *U.S. Public*, pg. 2091
LOWE & PARTNERS WORLDWIDE LTD—See The Interpublic Group of Companies, Inc.; *U.S. Public*, pg. 2097
LOWE PIRELLA FRONZONI—See The Interpublic Group of Companies, Inc.; *U.S. Public*, pg. 2091
LOWE PORTA—See The Interpublic Group of Companies, Inc.; *U.S. Public*, pg. 2091
LOWE PROFERO (HK) LIMITED—See The Interpublic Group of Companies, Inc.; *U.S. Public*, pg. 2097
LOWE PROFERO IBERIA S.A.—See The Interpublic Group of Companies, Inc.; *U.S. Public*, pg. 2097
LOWE PROFERO LIMITED—See The Interpublic Group of Companies, Inc.; *U.S. Public*, pg. 2097
LOWE PROFERO PTY. LIMITED—See The Interpublic Group of Companies, Inc.; *U.S. Public*, pg. 2097
LOWE PROFERO (SHANGHAI) CO., LTD.—See The Interpublic Group of Companies, Inc.; *U.S. Public*, pg. 2097
LOWE ROCHE—See The Interpublic Group of Companies, Inc.; *U.S. Public*, pg. 2091
LOWE SCANAD—See The Interpublic Group of Companies, Inc.; *U.S. Public*, pg. 2091
LOWE SINGAPORE—See The Interpublic Group of Companies, Inc.; *U.S. Public*, pg. 2091
LOWE—See The Interpublic Group of Companies, Inc.; *U.S. Public*, pg. 2091
LOWE—See The Interpublic Group of Companies, Inc.; *U.S. Public*, pg. 2091
LOWE—See The Interpublic Group of Companies, Inc.; *U.S. Public*, pg. 2091
LOWE—See The Interpublic Group of Companies, Inc.; *U.S. Public*, pg. 2091
LOWE—See The Interpublic Group of Companies, Inc.; *U.S. Public*, pg. 2091
LOWE—See The Interpublic Group of Companies, Inc.; *U.S. Public*, pg. 2091
LOWE—See The Interpublic Group of Companies, Inc.; *U.S. Public*, pg. 2091
LOWE—See The Interpublic Group of Companies, Inc.; *U.S. Public*, pg. 2091
LOWE—See The Interpublic Group of Companies, Inc.; *U.S. Public*, pg. 2091
LOWE—See The Interpublic Group of Companies, Inc.; *U.S. Public*, pg. 2091
LOWE SSPM—See The Interpublic Group of Companies, Inc.; *U.S. Public*, pg. 2091
LOWE STRATEUS—See The Interpublic Group of Companies, Inc.; *U.S. Public*, pg. 2092
LOWE SWING COMMUNICATIONS—See The Interpublic Group of Companies, Inc.; *U.S. Public*, pg. 2092
LPK GMBH FRANKFURT—See LPK; *U.S. Private*, pg. 2507
LPK SARL GENEVA—See LPK; *U.S. Private*, pg. 2507
LPK; *U.S. Private*, pg. 2507
LST MARKETING, LLC; *U.S. Private*, pg. 2509
LUBICOM MARKETING CONSULTING; *U.S. Private*, pg. 2510
LUCID AGENCY, LLC; *U.S. Private*, pg. 2510
LUCKIE & CO. LTD.; *U.S. Private*, pg. 2511
LUKRECIJA BBDO—See Omnicom Group Inc.; *U.S. Public*, pg. 1576
LUNAR BBDO—See Omnicom Group Inc.; *U.S. Public*, pg. 1576
LUNA TBWA BELGRADE—See Omnicom Group Inc.; *U.S. Public*, pg. 1594
LUNA TBWA SARAJEVO—See Omnicom Group Inc.; *U.S. Public*, pg. 1594
LUNA TBWA—See Omnicom Group Inc.; *U.S. Public*, pg. 1594
LUNDMARK ADVERTISING + DESIGN INC.; *U.S. Private*, pg. 2515
LUQUIRE GEORGE ANDREWS, INC.; *U.S. Private*, pg. 2516
LWT COMMUNICATIONS; *U.S. Private*, pg. 2519
LYERLY AGENCY INC.; *U.S. Private*, pg. 2519
LYFE MARKETING LLC; *U.S. Private*, pg. 2519
M2L2 COMMUNICATIONS; *U.S. Private*, pg. 2530
M2 UNIVERSAL COMMUNICATIONS MANAGEMENT—See The Interpublic Group of Companies, Inc.; *U.S. Public*, pg. 2100
M5 MARKETING COMMUNICATIONS INC.—See Group m5; *Int'l*, pg. 3089
M5 MARKETING COMMUNICATIONS, INC.—See Group m5; *Int'l*, pg. 3089
MACDONALD MEDIA/LOS ANGELES—See MacDonald Media; *U.S. Private*, pg. 2535
MACDOUGALL BIOMEDICAL COMMUNICATIONS, INC.; *U.S. Private*, pg. 2535

541810 — ADVERTISING AGENCIE... CORPORATE AFFILIATIONS

MACHADO/GARCIA-SERRA PUBLICIDAD, INC.; *U.S. Private*, pg. 2535
THE MACHINE; *U.S. Private*, pg. 4073
MACQUARIUM INTELLIGENT COMMUNICATIONS; *U.S. Private*, pg. 2538
MACROMILL, INC.—See Bain Capital, LP; *U.S. Private*, pg. 442
MADDOCK DOUGLAS, INC.; *U.S. Private*, pg. 2539
MADETOORDER; *U.S. Private*, pg. 2539
MAGAPORT, INC.—See Dentsu Group Inc.; *Int'l*, pg. 2039
MAGNANI CARUSO DUTTON; *U.S. Private*, pg. 2546
MAGNER SANBORN; *U.S. Private*, pg. 2547
MAGNETIC MEDIA ONLINE, INC.; *U.S. Private*, pg. 2547
MAHER BIRD ASSOCIATES—See Omnicom Group Inc.; *U.S. Public*, pg. 1596
MAIER ADVERTISING, INC.; *U.S. Private*, pg. 2551
MAIN IDEAS; *U.S. Private*, pg. 2551
MAK MEDIA INC.; *U.S. Private*, pg. 2555
MALLOF, ABRUZINO & NASH MARKETING; *U.S. Private*, pg. 2557
MAL/TOKYO—See Omnicom Group Inc.; *U.S. Public*, pg. 1594
MAMBO-PLAK GMBH—See Bertelsmann SE & Co. KGaA; *Int'l*, pg. 993
MANAGEMENT ANALYTICS GROUP, LLC; *U.S. Private*, pg. 2560
MANASIAN INC.; *U.S. Private*, pg. 2561
MANDALA COMMUNICATIONS, INC.; *U.S. Private*, pg. 2562
MANGAN HOLCOMB PARTNERS; *U.S. Private*, pg. 2563
MANHATTAN MARKETING ENSEMBLE; *U.S. Private*, pg. 2563
MANPOWER PORTUGAL EMPRESA DE TRABALHO TEMPORARIO S.A.—See ManpowerGroup Inc.; *U.S. Public*, pg. 1359
MANSI MEDIA; *U.S. Private*, pg. 2566
MARANON & ASSOCIATES ADVERTISING; *U.S. Private*, pg. 2569
MARCA HISPANIC LLC—See MARC USA, LLC; *U.S. Private*, pg. 2571
MARCH COMMUNICATIONS, INC.—See Walker Sands, Inc.; *U.S. Private*, pg. 4429
MARCOM—See The Interpublic Group of Companies, Inc.; *U.S. Public*, pg. 2093
M/A/R/C RESEARCH—See Omnicom Group Inc.; *U.S. Public*, pg. 1588
MARC USA, LLC - CHICAGO—See MARC USA, LLC; *U.S. Private*, pg. 2571
MARC USA, LLC; *U.S. Private*, pg. 2571
MARCUS THOMAS LLC-PUBLIC RELATIONS—See Marcus Thomas LLC; *U.S. Private*, pg. 2573
MARCUS THOMAS LLC; *U.S. Private*, pg. 2573
MARDEN-KANE, INC.; *U.S. Private*, pg. 2573
MARDEN-KANE, INC.—See Marden-Kane, Inc.; *U.S. Private*, pg. 2573
THE MARINO ORGANIZATION, INC.; *U.S. Private*, pg. 4074
MARIS, WEST & BAKER, INC.; *U.S. Private*, pg. 2576
MARK BBDO—See Omnicom Group Inc.; *U.S. Public*, pg. 1576
MARK BBDO—See Omnicom Group Inc.; *U.S. Public*, pg. 1576
MARKET DEVELOPMENT GROUP, INC.; *U.S. Private*, pg. 2579
MARKETING ALTERNATIVES, INC.; *U.S. Private*, pg. 2580
THE MARKETING ARM—See Omnicom Group Inc.; *U.S. Public*, pg. 1599
THE MARKETING ARM—See Omnicom Group Inc.; *U.S. Public*, pg. 1599
MARKETING ARTS CORPORATION—See Tilt Creative + Production, LLC; *U.S. Private*, pg. 4171
THE MARKETING CENTER FOR SOCIAL SECURITY LAW PRACTICES; *U.S. Private*, pg. 4074
MARKETING CONCEPTS GROUP; *U.S. Private*, pg. 2580
MARKETING & CREATIVE SERVICES, INC.; *U.S. Private*, pg. 2579
MARKETING DOCTOR, INC.; *U.S. Private*, pg. 2580
MARKETING GROUP; *U.S. Private*, pg. 2580
MARKETING MATTERS; *U.S. Private*, pg. 2580
MARKETING & MEDIA SERVICES, LLC—See Respond2 Cmedia; *U.S. Private*, pg. 3408
MARKETING OPTIONS, LLC; *U.S. Private*, pg. 2580
MARKETING PERFORMANCE GROUP, INC.; *U.S. Private*, pg. 2580
MARKETING POWER RAPP—See Omnicom Group Inc.; *U.S. Public*, pg. 1592
THE MARKETING STORE; *U.S. Private*, pg. 4075
MARKETING SUPPORT, INC.; *U.S. Private*, pg. 2580
MARKETING VISIONS, INC.; *U.S. Private*, pg. 2580
MARKETING WORKS, INC.; *U.S. Private*, pg. 2580
MARKET MAKERS INCORPORATED LIMITED—See Centaur Media plc; *Int'l*, pg. 1402
MARKET MATCH MEDIA, INC.; *U.S. Private*, pg. 2579
MARKETOPIA, LLC; *U.S. Private*, pg. 2581
MARKET RESOURCE PARTNERS LLC—See FD Technologies PLC; *Int'l*, pg. 2628
MARKETSHARE PLUS, INC.; *U.S. Private*, pg. 2581
MARKETVISION; *U.S. Private*, pg. 2581
MARKTPLAATS B.V.—See eBay Inc.; *U.S. Public*, pg. 709
THE MARLIN NETWORK, INC.; *U.S. Private*, pg. 4075
MARLIN—See The Marlin Network, Inc.; *U.S. Private*, pg. 4075
MARQUARDT & ROCHE AND PARTNERS; *U.S. Private*, pg. 2586
MARQUEZ WORLDWIDE—See The Interpublic Group of Companies, Inc.; *U.S. Public*, pg. 2093
MARRINER MARKETING COMMUNICATIONS, INC.; *U.S. Private*, pg. 2588
MARS ADVERTISING GROUP; *U.S. Private*, pg. 2588
MARSTON WEBB INTERNATIONAL; *U.S. Private*, pg. 2593
THE MARTIN AGENCY, INC. - NEW YORK—See The Interpublic Group of Companies, Inc.; *U.S. Public*, pg. 2102
THE MARTIN AGENCY, INC.—See The Interpublic Group of Companies, Inc.; *U.S. Public*, pg. 2102
THE MARTIN GROUP LLC; *U.S. Private*, pg. 4075
MARTINI MEDIA INC.; *U.S. Private*, pg. 2596
MARTINO & BINZER, INC.—See High Road Capital Partners, LLC; *U.S. Private*, pg. 1936
MARTINO FLYNN LLC; *U.S. Private*, pg. 2596
MARTIN-SCHAFFER, INC.; *U.S. Private*, pg. 2596
MARTIN THOMAS, INC.; *U.S. Private*, pg. 2596
MARTIN THOMAS INTERNATIONAL, PUBLIC RELATIONS DIVISION—See Martin Thomas, Inc.; *U.S. Private*, pg. 2596
MARTIN/WILLIAMS ADVERTISING INC.—See Omnicom Group Inc.; *U.S. Public*, pg. 1588
MARVELOUS FINLAND—See The Interpublic Group of Companies, Inc.; *U.S. Public*, pg. 2095
MARVELOUS NORDIC—See The Interpublic Group of Companies, Inc.; *U.S. Public*, pg. 2094
MARVELOUS SVERIGE—See The Interpublic Group of Companies, Inc.; *U.S. Public*, pg. 2095
MARX MCCLELLAN THRUN; *U.S. Private*, pg. 2598
MASCOLA ADVERTISING; *U.S. Private*, pg. 2601
MASLOW LUMIA BARTORILLO ADVERTISING; *U.S. Private*, pg. 2601
MASON, INC.; *U.S. Private*, pg. 2602
MASON SELKOWITZ MARKETING, INC; *U.S. Private*, pg. 2602
MASS ADVERTISING AGENCY LTD.—See Hayel Saeed Anam Group of Companies; *Int'l*, pg. 3290
MASS CONNECTIONS, INC.; *U.S. Private*, pg. 2603
MASSEY COMMUNICATIONS, INC.—See Massey Services, Inc.; *U.S. Private*, pg. 2606
MASS HISPANIC; *U.S. Private*, pg. 2603
MASS MEDIA MARKETING; *U.S. Private*, pg. 2603
MASTERMIND MARKETING; *U.S. Private*, pg. 2608
MASTERMINDS; *U.S. Private*, pg. 2608
MATCHCRAFT, INC.—See Advance Local LLC; *U.S. Private*, pg. 83
MATLOCK ADVERTISING & PUBLIC RELATIONS; *U.S. Private*, pg. 2611
MAT SP. Z O.O.—See Grupa SMT S.A.; *Int'l*, pg. 3117
MATTER COMMUNICATIONS INC.; *U.S. Private*, pg. 2613
MATTHEWS, EVANS & ALBERTAZZI; *U.S. Private*, pg. 2614
MAUL + CO - CHR. BELSER GMBH—See Bertelsmann SE & Co. KGaA; *Int'l*, pg. 996
MAVERICK INTERACTIVE, INC.; *U.S. Private*, pg. 2616
MAX ADVERTISING; *U.S. Private*, pg. 2616
MAXIMUM DESIGN & ADVERTISING; *U.S. Private*, pg. 2618
MAXIMUM IMPACT INC.; *U.S. Private*, pg. 2618
MAXIMUM MEDIA ENTERPRISES, INC.; *U.S. Private*, pg. 2619
MAX INFORMATION—See Armando Testa S.p.A.; *Int'l*, pg. 574
MAXWELL & MILLER MARKETING COMMUNICATIONS; *U.S. Private*, pg. 2619
MAYER/MCCANN-ERICKSON S.R.O.—See The Interpublic Group of Companies, Inc.; *U.S. Public*, pg. 2099
MAYER-MCCANN—See The Interpublic Group of Companies, Inc.; *U.S. Public*, pg. 2099
MAYO ECUADOR—See The Interpublic Group of Companies, Inc.; *U.S. Public*, pg. 2093
MAYO PUBLICIDAD—See The Interpublic Group of Companies, Inc.; *U.S. Public*, pg. 2093
MAYO—See The Interpublic Group of Companies, Inc.; *U.S. Public*, pg. 2093
THE MAZEROV GROUP; *U.S. Private*, pg. 4076
MBS NURNBERG GMBH—See Bertelsmann SE & Co. KGaA; *Int'l*, pg. 997
MBT MARKETING; *U.S. Private*, pg. 2625
MC2 MARKETING INC.—See Mass Connections, Inc.; *U.S. Private*, pg. 2603
MCCANN AS—See The Interpublic Group of Companies, Inc.; *U.S. Public*, pg. 2099
MCCANN ERICKSON ADVERTISING LTD.—See The Interpublic Group of Companies, Inc.; *U.S. Public*, pg. 2100
MCCANN ERICKSON ADVERTISING PTY. LTD. - BRISBANE—See The Interpublic Group of Companies, Inc.; *U.S. Public*, pg. 2100
MCCANN ERICKSON ADVERTISING PTY. LTD. - MELBOURNE—See The Interpublic Group of Companies, Inc.; *U.S. Public*, pg. 2100
MCCANN ERICKSON ADVERTISING PTY. LTD.—See The Interpublic Group of Companies, Inc.; *U.S. Public*, pg. 2100
MCCANN ERICKSON ATHENS—See The Interpublic Group of Companies, Inc.; *U.S. Public*, pg. 2100
MCCANN ERICKSON AZERBAIJAN—See The Interpublic Group of Companies, Inc.; *U.S. Public*, pg. 2099
MCCANN ERICKSON BRAND COMMUNICATIONS AGENCY—See The Interpublic Group of Companies, Inc.; *U.S. Public*, pg. 2100
MCCANN ERICKSON BRISTOL—See The Interpublic Group of Companies, Inc.; *U.S. Public*, pg. 2100
MCCANN ERICKSON BUDAPEST—See The Interpublic Group of Companies, Inc.; *U.S. Public*, pg. 2099
MCCANN ERICKSON CAMEROON—See The Interpublic Group of Companies, Inc.; *U.S. Public*, pg. 2099
MCCANN-ERICKSON CENTRAL LIMITED—See The Interpublic Group of Companies, Inc.; *U.S. Public*, pg. 2102
MCCANN ERICKSON CENTRAL—See The Interpublic Group of Companies, Inc.; *U.S. Public*, pg. 2099
MCCANN ERICKSON CENTROAMERICANA (COSTA RICA) S.A.—See The Interpublic Group of Companies, Inc.; *U.S. Public*, pg. 2100
MCCANN ERICKSON CENTROAMERICANA (HONDURAS) S. DE R.L.—See The Interpublic Group of Companies, Inc.; *U.S. Public*, pg. 2100
MCCANN ERICKSON COMMUNICATIONS GROUP—See The Interpublic Group of Companies, Inc.; *U.S. Public*, pg. 2100
MCCANN ERICKSON COMMUNICATIONS HOUSE M.E.C.H.—See The Interpublic Group of Companies, Inc.; *U.S. Public*, pg. 2100
MCCANN ERICKSON CORP. PUBLICIDAD S.A.—See The Interpublic Group of Companies, Inc.; *U.S. Public*, pg. 2099
MCCANN ERICKSON CORP. PUBLICIDAD S.A.—See The Interpublic Group of Companies, Inc.; *U.S. Public*, pg. 2100
MCCANN ERICKSON CORP. S.A.—See The Interpublic Group of Companies, Inc.; *U.S. Public*, pg. 2100
MCCANN ERICKSON CORP. (S.A.)—See The Interpublic Group of Companies, Inc.; *U.S. Public*, pg. 2102
MCCANN-ERICKSON DEUTSCHLAND GMBH & CO MANAGEMENT PROPERTY KG—See The Interpublic Group of Companies, Inc.; *U.S. Public*, pg. 2102
MCCANN ERICKSON DEUTSCHLAND GMBH—See The Interpublic Group of Companies, Inc.; *U.S. Public*, pg. 2099
MCCANN ERICKSON DEUTSCHLAND—See The Interpublic Group of Companies, Inc.; *U.S. Public*, pg. 2100
MCCANN ERICKSON DUBLIN—See The Interpublic Group of Companies, Inc.; *U.S. Public*, pg. 2101
MCCANN ERICKSON EL SALVADOR—See The Interpublic Group of Companies, Inc.; *U.S. Public*, pg. 2101
MCCANN ERICKSON GEORGIA—See The Interpublic Group of Companies, Inc.; *U.S. Public*, pg. 2099
MCCANN ERICKSON GESELLSCHAFT M.B.H.—See The Interpublic Group of Companies, Inc.; *U.S. Public*, pg. 2101
MCCANN ERICKSON GROUP—See The Interpublic Group of Companies, Inc.; *U.S. Public*, pg. 2099
MCCANN ERICKSON GUANGMING LTD.—See The Interpublic Group of Companies, Inc.; *U.S. Public*, pg. 2099
MCCANN ERICKSON GUANGMING LTD.—See The Interpublic Group of Companies, Inc.; *U.S. Public*, pg. 2099
MCCANN ERICKSON HONG KONG LTD.—See The Interpublic Group of Companies, Inc.; *U.S. Public*, pg. 2101
MCCANN ERICKSON/HORA—See The Interpublic Group of Companies, Inc.; *U.S. Public*, pg. 2101
MCCANN ERICKSON, INC.—See The Interpublic Group of Companies, Inc.; *U.S. Public*, pg. 2101
MCCANN ERICKSON INC.—See The Interpublic Group of Companies, Inc.; *U.S. Public*, pg. 2101
MCCANN ERICKSON INDIA—See The Interpublic Group of Companies, Inc.; *U.S. Public*, pg. 2099
MCCANN ERICKSON INDIA—See The Interpublic Group of Companies, Inc.; *U.S. Public*, pg. 2099
MCCANN ERICKSON INDIA—See The Interpublic Group of Companies, Inc.; *U.S. Public*, pg. 2099
MCCANN ERICKSON ITALIANA S.P.A.—See The Interpublic Group of Companies, Inc.; *U.S. Public*, pg. 2101
MCCANN ERICKSON ITALIANA S.P.A.—See The Interpublic Group of Companies, Inc.; *U.S. Public*, pg. 2101
MCCANN ERICKSON (JAMAICA) LTD.—See The Interpublic Group of Companies, Inc.; *U.S. Public*, pg. 2099
MCCANN ERICKSON JAPAN INC.—See The Interpublic Group of Companies, Inc.; *U.S. Public*, pg. 2101
MCCANN ERICKSON KAZAKHSTAN—See The Interpublic Group of Companies, Inc.; *U.S. Public*, pg. 2099
MCCANN ERICKSON (KENYA) LTD.—See The Interpublic Group of Companies, Inc.; *U.S. Public*, pg. 2100
MCCANN ERICKSON/LOS ANGELES—See The Interpublic Group of Companies, Inc.; *U.S. Public*, pg. 2102
MCCANN ERICKSON MACEDONIA—See The Interpublic Group of Companies, Inc.; *U.S. Public*, pg. 2099
MCCANN ERICKSON (MALAYSIA) SDN. BHD.—See The

N.A.I.C.S. INDEX 541810 — ADVERTISING AGENCIE...

N.A.I.C.S. Index

Interpublic Group of Companies, Inc.; *U.S. Public*, pg. 2100
MCCANN ERICKSON MEXICO—See The Interpublic Group of Companies, Inc.; *U.S. Public*, pg. 2099
MCCANN ERICKSON (NEDERLAND) B.V.—See The Interpublic Group of Companies, Inc.; *U.S. Public*, pg. 2100
MCCANN ERICKSON/NEW YORK—See The Interpublic Group of Companies, Inc.; *U.S. Public*, pg. 2102
MCCANN ERICKSON NORTH AMERICA—See The Interpublic Group of Companies, Inc.; *U.S. Public*, pg. 2102
MCCANN ERICKSON PARIS—See The Interpublic Group of Companies, Inc.; *U.S. Public*, pg. 2101
MCCANN ERICKSON (PERU) PUBLICIDAD S.A.—See The Interpublic Group of Companies, Inc.; *U.S. Public*, pg. 2100
MCCANN ERICKSON PRAGUE—See The Interpublic Group of Companies, Inc.; *U.S. Public*, pg. 2099
MCCANN ERICKSON PUBLICIDADE LTDA.—See The Interpublic Group of Companies, Inc.; *U.S. Public*, pg. 2100
MCCANN ERICKSON PUBLICIDAD—See The Interpublic Group of Companies, Inc.; *U.S. Public*, pg. 2099
MCCANN ERICKSON RIGA—See The Interpublic Group of Companies, Inc.; *U.S. Public*, pg. 2099
MCCANN ERICKSON ROMANIA—See The Interpublic Group of Companies, Inc.; *U.S. Public*, pg. 2099
MCCANN ERICKSON S.A. DE PUBLICIDAD—See The Interpublic Group of Companies, Inc.; *U.S. Public*, pg. 2101
MCCANN ERICKSON/SALT LAKE CITY—See The Interpublic Group of Companies, Inc.; *U.S. Public*, pg. 2101
MCCANN ERICKSON SARAJEVO—See The Interpublic Group of Companies, Inc.; *U.S. Public*, pg. 2099
MCCANN ERICKSON S.A.—See The Interpublic Group of Companies, Inc.; *U.S. Public*, pg. 2101
MCCANN ERICKSON SEATTLE—See The Interpublic Group of Companies, Inc.; *U.S. Public*, pg. 2102
MCCANN ERICKSON (SINGAPORE) PRIVATE LIMITED—See The Interpublic Group of Companies, Inc.; *U.S. Public*, pg. 2099
MCCANN ERICKSON SOFIA—See The Interpublic Group of Companies, Inc.; *U.S. Public*, pg. 2099
MCCANN ERICKSON—See The Interpublic Group of Companies, Inc.; *U.S. Public*, pg. 2099
MCCANN ERICKSON—See The Interpublic Group of Companies, Inc.; *U.S. Public*, pg. 2099
MCCANN ERICKSON—See The Interpublic Group of Companies, Inc.; *U.S. Public*, pg. 2100
MCCANN ERICKSON—See The Interpublic Group of Companies, Inc.; *U.S. Public*, pg. 2102
MCCANN ERICKSON / SP—See The Interpublic Group of Companies, Inc.; *U.S. Public*, pg. 2100
MCCANN ERICKSON SWITZERLAND—See The Interpublic Group of Companies, Inc.; *U.S. Public*, pg. 2101
MCCANN ERICKSON (TRINIDAD) LTD.—See The Interpublic Group of Companies, Inc.; *U.S. Public*, pg. 2100
MCCANN ERICKSON URUGUAY—See The Interpublic Group of Companies, Inc.; *U.S. Public*, pg. 2101
MCCANN-ERICKSON USA, INC.—See The Interpublic Group of Companies, Inc.; *U.S. Public*, pg. 2102
MCCANN ERICKSON UZBEKISTAN/TASHKENT—See The Interpublic Group of Companies, Inc.; *U.S. Public*, pg. 2099
MCCANN ERICKSON VIETNAM—See The Interpublic Group of Companies, Inc.; *U.S. Public*, pg. 2099
MCCANN ERICKSON WORLDGROUP/PANAMA, S.A.—See The Interpublic Group of Companies, Inc.; *U.S. Public*, pg. 2099
MCCANN ERICKSON WORLDGROUP TURKEY—See The Interpublic Group of Companies, Inc.; *U.S. Public*, pg. 2101
MCCANN ERICKSON WORLDWIDE—See The Interpublic Group of Companies, Inc.; *U.S. Public*, pg. 2099
MCCANN HEALTHCARE MELBOURNE—See The Interpublic Group of Companies, Inc.; *U.S. Public*, pg. 2101
MCCANN HEALTHCARE—See The Interpublic Group of Companies, Inc.; *U.S. Public*, pg. 2100
MCCANN HEALTHCARE SYDNEY—See The Interpublic Group of Companies, Inc.; *U.S. Public*, pg. 2101
MCCANN HEALTH SINGAPORE—See The Interpublic Group of Companies, Inc.; *U.S. Public*, pg. 2101
MCCANN HELSINKI—See The Interpublic Group of Companies, Inc.; *U.S. Public*, pg. 2101
MCCANN JOHANNESBURG—See The Interpublic Group of Companies, Inc.; *U.S. Public*, pg. 2101
MCCANN MANCHESTER LIMITED—See The Interpublic Group of Companies, Inc.; *U.S. Public*, pg. 2101
MCCANN MANCHESTER LTD.—See The Interpublic Group of Companies, Inc.; *U.S. Public*, pg. 2100
MCCANN WORLDGROUP INDONESIA—See The Interpublic Group of Companies, Inc.; *U.S. Public*, pg. 2101
MCCANN WORLDGROUP PHILIPPINES, INC.—See The Interpublic Group of Companies, Inc.; *U.S. Public*, pg. 2101
MCCANN WORLDGROUP (SINGAPORE) PTE LTD—See The Interpublic Group of Companies, Inc.; *U.S. Public*, pg. 2101
MCCANN WORLDGROUP—See The Interpublic Group of Companies, Inc.; *U.S. Public*, pg. 2101
MCCANN WORLDGROUP—See The Interpublic Group of Companies, Inc.; *U.S. Public*, pg. 2102
MCCANN WORLDGROUP SOUTH AFRICA (PTY) LTD—See The Interpublic Group of Companies, Inc.; *U.S. Public*, pg. 2102
MCCANN WORLDGROUP THAILAND—See The Interpublic Group of Companies, Inc.; *U.S. Public*, pg. 2101
MCCANN YEREVAN—See The Interpublic Group of Companies, Inc.; *U.S. Public*, pg. 2102
MCCLENAHAN BRUER COMMUNICATIONS; *U.S. Private*, pg. 2628
M.C. COMMUNICATION, INC.; *U.S. Private*, pg. 2528
MCCORMICK COMPANY; *U.S. Private*, pg. 2630
MCCORMICK COMPANY—See McCormick Company; *U.S. Private*, pg. 2630
MCCORMICK COMPANY—See McCormick Company; *U.S. Private*, pg. 2630
MCCULLOUGH COMMUNICATIONS & MARKETING; *U.S. Private*, pg. 2631
MCEMOTION—See The Interpublic Group of Companies, Inc.; *U.S. Public*, pg. 2101
THE MCFARLAND GROUP, INC.; *U.S. Private*, pg. 4076
MCFRANK & WILLIAMS ADVERTISING AGENCY, INC.; *U.S. Private*, pg. 2634
MCGARRAH JESSEE; *U.S. Private*, pg. 2634
MCGUIRE & ASSOCIATES; *U.S. Private*, pg. 2636
MCKEE WALLWORK & COMPANY; *U.S. Private*, pg. 2638
MCKINNEY CHICAGO; *U.S. Private*, pg. 2639
MCLAUGHLIN, DELVECCHIO & CASEY, INC.; *U.S. Private*, pg. 2640
MCL MCCANN—See The Interpublic Group of Companies, Inc.; *U.S. Public*, pg. 2098
MDB COMMUNICATIONS, INC.—See Hart Associates, Inc.; *U.S. Private*, pg. 1872
MD CONNECT, INC.—See Intellibright Corporation; *U.S. Private*, pg. 2105
MDC PARTNERS INC.—See Stagwell, Inc.; *U.S. Public*, pg. 1927
MEDALLION SPORTS MEDIA, INC.—See Medallion Financial Corp.; *U.S. Public*, pg. 1411
MEDDATA GROUP, LLC—See IQVIA Holdings Inc.; *U.S. Public*, pg. 1169
MEDIA3, INC.; *U.S. Private*, pg. 2653
MEDIA ATLANTIC; *U.S. Private*, pg. 2651
MEDIABRANDS BELGIUM S.A.—See The Interpublic Group of Companies, Inc.; *U.S. Public*, pg. 2103
MEDIABRANDS EMEA LTD.—See The Interpublic Group of Companies, Inc.; *U.S. Public*, pg. 2100
MEDIA BREAKAWAY, LLC; *U.S. Private*, pg. 2651
MEDIA BUYING SERVICES, INC.; *U.S. Private*, pg. 2651
MEDIA BY DESIGN—See Hakuhodo DY Holdings Incorporated; *Int'l*, pg. 3222
MEDIA COMMUNICATIONS GROUP; *U.S. Private*, pg. 2651
THE MEDIA CREW; *U.S. Private*, pg. 4077
MEDIACROSSING, INC.; *U.S. Private*, pg. 2653
MEDIA DESIGN; *U.S. Private*, pg. 2652
MEDIA DIRECT, INC.; *U.S. Private*, pg. 2652
MEDIA DIRECTIONS ADVERTISING, INC.; *U.S. Private*, pg. 2652
MEDIA ENTERPRISES—See The Interpublic Group of Companies, Inc.; *U.S. Public*, pg. 2102
MEDIA ETC.; *U.S. Private*, pg. 2652
MEDIA FIRST PUBLIC RELATIONS; *U.S. Private*, pg. 2652
MEDIA FUSION, INC.; *U.S. Private*, pg. 2652
MEDIAHEADS 360 PROPRIETARY LIMITED—See African Media Entertainment Limited; *Int'l*, pg. 192
MEDIAHUB MINNEAPOLIS, LLC—See The Interpublic Group of Companies, Inc.; *U.S. Public*, pg. 2103
MEDIA INSIGHT; *U.S. Private*, pg. 2652
MEDIA INTELLIGENCE CO., LTD.—See Hakuhodo DY Holdings Incorporated; *Int'l*, pg. 3222
THE MEDIA INVESTMENT GROUP—See The Interpublic Group of Companies, Inc.; *U.S. Public*, pg. 2102
MEDIA LOGIC USA, LLC; *U.S. Private*, pg. 2652
MEDIA & MORE, INC.; *U.S. Private*, pg. 2651
MEDIAMORPHOSIS INC.; *U.S. Private*, pg. 2653
MEDIAMORPHOSIS—See MediaMorphosis Inc.; *U.S. Private*, pg. 2653
MEDIA PALETTE (TAIWAN) INC.—See Dentsu Group Inc.; *Int'l*, pg. 2037
MEDIA PARTNERS INC.—See Advantage Marketing, Inc.; *U.S. Private*, pg. 94
MEDIA POWER ADVERTISING; *U.S. Private*, pg. 2652
MEDIA RAIN LLC; *U.S. Private*, pg. 2652
MEDIA RESOURCES, LTD.; *U.S. Private*, pg. 2652
MEDIA RESOURCES, LTD.—See Media Resources, Ltd.; *U.S. Private*, pg. 2652
MEDIA RESPONSE, INC.; *U.S. Private*, pg. 2652
MEDIASMACK INC.—See Scorpion Design LLC; *U.S. Private*, pg. 3575
MEDIASMART MOBILE S.L.—See Affle (India) Limited; *Int'l*, pg. 188
MEDIASSOCIATES, INC.; *U.S. Private*, pg. 2654
MEDIAS & SUPPORTS—See Omnicom Group Inc.; *U.S. Public*, pg. 1596
MEDIAWHIZ; *U.S. Private*, pg. 2654
MEDIA WORKS, LTD.—See M Rogers Design, Inc.; *U.S. Private*, pg. 2523
MEDICAL MEDIA TELEVISION, INC.; *U.S. Private*, pg. 2655
MEDICCOMM CONSULTANTS, INC.; *U.S. Private*, pg. 2656
MEDINA/TURGUL DDB—See Omnicom Group Inc.; *U.S. Public*, pg. 1582
MEDMEDIA—See K I Lipton Inc.; *U.S. Private*, pg. 2249
MEDTHINK COMMUNICATIONS; *U.S. Private*, pg. 2659
MEERS ADVERTISING; *U.S. Private*, pg. 2659
MEET THE PEOPLE LLC—See Innovatus Capital Partners LLC; *U.S. Private*, pg. 2083
MEGAMEIOS - PUBLICIDADE E MEIOS, A.C.E.—See The Interpublic Group of Companies, Inc.; *U.S. Public*, pg. 2103
MEIER; *U.S. Private*, pg. 2660
MEKANISM, INC.; *U.S. Private*, pg. 2661
MELAMEDRILEY ADVERTISING, LLC; *U.S. Private*, pg. 2661
MEPLUSYOU; *U.S. Private*, pg. 2667
MEPLUSYOU—See MEplusYou; *U.S. Private*, pg. 2667
MERCURYCSC; *U.S. Private*, pg. 2671
THE MERCURY GROUP—See Ackerman McQueen, Inc.; *U.S. Private*, pg. 60
MERCURY MEDIA - BOSTON—See Mercury Media Holding Corp.; *U.S. Private*, pg. 2671
MERCURY MEDIA - PRINCETON—See Mercury Media Holding Corp.; *U.S. Private*, pg. 2671
MERCURY MEDIA -SANTA MONICA—See Mercury Media Holding Corp.; *U.S. Private*, pg. 2671
MERCURY PROMOTIONS & FULFILLMENT, INC.; *U.S. Private*, pg. 2671
MEREDITH EXELERATED MARKETING—See Meredith Corporation; *U.S. Public*, pg. 1423
MERGE DESIGN & INTERACTIVE, INC.—See Keystone Capital, Inc.; *U.S. Private*, pg. 2295
MERIDIAN CREATIVE ALLIANCE LLC; *U.S. Private*, pg. 2672
THE MERIDIAN GROUP; *U.S. Private*, pg. 4078
MERING & ASSOCIATES; *U.S. Private*, pg. 2674
MERINGCARSON—See Mering & Associates; *U.S. Private*, pg. 2674
MERKLE INC.—See Dentsu Group Inc.; *Int'l*, pg. 2036
MERKLEY + PARTNERS/HEALTHWORKS—See Omnicom Group Inc.; *U.S. Public*, pg. 1588
MERKLEY + PARTNERS—See Omnicom Group Inc.; *U.S. Public*, pg. 1588
MERRICK TOWLE COMMUNICATIONS; *U.S. Private*, pg. 2676
MERU UTAMA SDN. BHD.—See Ancom Nylex Berhad; *Int'l*, pg. 449
METAAPES GMBH—See Ardian SAS; *Int'l*, pg. 554
METAPEOPLE GMBH—See Ardian SAS; *Int'l*, pg. 554
METHOD INC.—See Hitachi, Ltd.; *Int'l*, pg. 3413
METHOD LONDON—See Hitachi, Ltd.; *Int'l*, pg. 3413
METRIX4MEDIA, LLC—See The Hearst Corporation; *U.S. Private*, pg. 4047
MEYER & WALLIS, INC.; *U.S. Private*, pg. 2692
MEYER & WALLIS, INC.—See Meyer & Wallis, Inc.; *U.S. Private*, pg. 2692
THE MEYOCKS GROUP; *U.S. Private*, pg. 4078
MGH, INC.; *U.S. Private*, pg. 2694
MGM GOLD COMMUNICATIONS; *U.S. Private*, pg. 2694
MGM MIRAGE ADVERTISING, INC.—See MGM Resorts International; *U.S. Public*, pg. 1435
MGSCOMM - MEXICO CITY—See Machado/Garcia-Serra Publicidad, Inc.; *U.S. Private*, pg. 2535
MGSCOMM - NEW YORK CITY—See Machado/Garcia-Serra Publicidad, Inc.; *U.S. Private*, pg. 2535
THE MGS GROUP; *U.S. Private*, pg. 4078
MIACO MEDIA INC.; *U.S. Private*, pg. 2696
THE MICHAEL ALAN GROUP—See BDS Marketing, LLC; *U.S. Private*, pg. 502
MICHAEL FLORA & ASSOCIATES INC.; *U.S. Private*, pg. 2697
MICHAELSWILDER; *U.S. Private*, pg. 2699
MICHAEL WALTERS ADVERTISING; *U.S. Private*, pg. 2699
MICROELECTRONICS TECHNOLOGY COMPANY; *U.S. Private*, pg. 2703
MIDDLE EAST COMMUNICATION NETWORKS - MCN—See The Interpublic Group of Companies, Inc.; *U.S. Public*, pg. 2103
MILE 9; *U.S. Private*, pg. 2727
MILESBRAND, INC.; *U.S. Private*, pg. 2728
MILESBRAND SALES—See Milesbrand, Inc.; *U.S. Private*, pg. 2728
MILES & MORE INTERNATIONAL GMBH—See Deutsche Lufthansa AG; *Int'l*, pg. 2070
MILESTONE BROADCAST; *U.S. Private*, pg. 2728
THE MILFORD AGENCY; *U.S. Private*, pg. 4079
MILK+CO—See Omnicom Group Inc.; *U.S. Public*, pg. 1582
MILKY JSC—See HighCo S.A.; *Int'l*, pg. 3387
MILLENNIUM 3 MANAGEMENT INC.; *U.S. Private*, pg. 2731
MILLENNIUM COMMUNICATIONS, INC.; *U.S. Private*, pg. 2731

541810 — ADVERTISING AGENCIE...

MILLENNIUM INTEGRATED MARKETING; *U.S. Private*, pg. 2731
MILLER ADVERTISING AGENCY INC.-CHICAGO—See Miller Advertising Agency Inc.; *U.S. Private*, pg. 2732
MILLER ADVERTISING AGENCY INC.; *U.S. Private*, pg. 2732
MILLER ADVERTISING AGENCY INC.—See Miller Advertising Agency Inc.; *U.S. Private*, pg. 2732
MILLER ADV.—See Miller Advertising Agency Inc.; *U.S. Private*, pg. 2732
THE MILLER GROUP; *U.S. Private*, pg. 4079
THE MILLER GROUP; *U.S. Private*, pg. 4079
MILLER LEGAL SERVICES—See Miller Advertising Agency Inc.; *U.S. Private*, pg. 2732
MILLER-REID, INC.; *U.S. Private*, pg. 2736
MILLER.WHITERUNKLE—See Ascentium Corporation; *U.S. Private*, pg. 348
MILLSPORT—See Omnicom Group Inc.; *U.S. Public*, pg. 1588
MILLSPORT—See Omnicom Group Inc.; *U.S. Public*, pg. 1588
MILLWARD BROWN AUSTRALIA—See Bain Capital, LP; *U.S. Private*, pg. 449
MILLWARD BROWN BRAZIL—See Bain Capital, LP; *U.S. Private*, pg. 449
MILLWARD BROWN/CENTRUM—See Bain Capital, LP; *U.S. Private*, pg. 449
MILLWARD BROWN CHINA—See Bain Capital, LP; *U.S. Private*, pg. 449
MILLWARD BROWN COLUMBIA—See Bain Capital, LP; *U.S. Private*, pg. 449
MILLWARD BROWN CZECH REPUBLIC—See Bain Capital, LP; *U.S. Private*, pg. 449
MILLWARD BROWN DELFO—See Bain Capital, LP; *U.S. Private*, pg. 449
MILLWARD BROWN DENMARK—See Bain Capital, LP; *U.S. Private*, pg. 449
MILLWARD BROWN FRANCE—See Bain Capital, LP; *U.S. Private*, pg. 449
MILLWARD BROWN GERMANY GMBH—See Bain Capital, LP; *U.S. Private*, pg. 449
MILLWARD BROWN HUNGARY—See Bain Capital, LP; *U.S. Private*, pg. 449
MILLWARD BROWN IMS—See Bain Capital, LP; *U.S. Private*, pg. 449
MILLWARD BROWN, INC.—See Bain Capital, LP; *U.S. Private*, pg. 449
MILLWARD BROWN MEDIA RESEARCH—See Bain Capital, LP; *U.S. Private*, pg. 449
MILLWARD BROWN MEXICO—See Bain Capital, LP; *U.S. Private*, pg. 449
MILLWARD BROWN PHILIPPINES—See Bain Capital, LP; *U.S. Private*, pg. 449
MILLWARD BROWN PORTUGAL—See Bain Capital, LP; *U.S. Private*, pg. 449
MILLWARD BROWN SINGAPORE—See Bain Capital, LP; *U.S. Private*, pg. 449
MILLWARD BROWN SMG/KRC—See Bain Capital, LP; *U.S. Private*, pg. 449
MILLWARD BROWN—See Bain Capital, LP; *U.S. Private*, pg. 448
MILLWARD BROWN—See Bain Capital, LP; *U.S. Private*, pg. 448
MILLWARD BROWN—See Bain Capital, LP; *U.S. Private*, pg. 449
MILLWARD BROWN SOUTH AFRICA—See Bain Capital, LP; *U.S. Private*, pg. 449
MILLWARD BROWN SPAIN—See Bain Capital, LP; *U.S. Private*, pg. 449
MILLWARD BROWN SWEDEN—See Bain Capital, LP; *U.S. Private*, pg. 449
MILLWARD BROWN TAIWAN—See Bain Capital, LP; *U.S. Private*, pg. 449
MILLWARD BROWN THAILAND—See Bain Capital, LP; *U.S. Private*, pg. 449
MILLWARD BROWN TURKEY—See Bain Capital, LP; *U.S. Private*, pg. 449
MILLWARD BROWN ULSTER—See Bain Capital, LP; *U.S. Private*, pg. 449
MINDCOMET CORPORATION; *U.S. Private*, pg. 2740
MINDCOMET—See MindComet Corporation; *U.S. Private*, pg. 2740
MINDCOMET—See MindComet Corporation; *U.S. Private*, pg. 2740
MINDPOWER INC; *U.S. Private*, pg. 2741
MINDS FCB—See The Interpublic Group of Companies, Inc.; *U.S. Public*, pg. 2093
MINDSMACK; *U.S. Private*, pg. 2741
MINDSPACE; *U.S. Private*, pg. 2741
MINDSTORM COMMUNICATIONS GROUP, INC.; *U.S. Private*, pg. 2741
MINDSTREAM MEDIA, LLC—See Eastport Holdings, Inc.; *U.S. Private*, pg. 1322
MINT ADVERTISING; *U.S. Private*, pg. 2744
MINTZ & HOKE, INC.; *U.S. Private*, pg. 2745
MIRESBALL; *U.S. Private*, pg. 2746
MISSISSIPPI PRESS SERVICES; *U.S. Private*, pg. 2748

MIST TECHNOLOGIES INC.—See Adways Inc.; *Int'l*, pg. 169
MITCHELL, LINDBERG & TAYLOR, INC.; *U.S. Private*, pg. 2751
MITCHELL & RESNIKOFF; *U.S. Private*, pg. 2750
MITHOFF BURTON PARTNERS; *U.S. Private*, pg. 2751
MITTONMEDIA—See The Company of Others; *U.S. Private*, pg. 4013
MIXPO, INC.—See Netsertive, Inc.; *U.S. Private*, pg. 2888
MJE MARKETING SERVICES; *U.S. Private*, pg. 2753
MJW HAKUHODO—See Hakuhodo DY Holdings Incorporated; *Int'l*, pg. 3222
MJW HAKUHODO—See Hakuhodo DY Holdings Incorporated; *Int'l*, pg. 3222
M/K ADVERTISING PARTNERS, LTD.; *U.S. Private*, pg. 2530
MKH—See Accord Group Limited; *Int'l*, pg. 93
MKH—See Accord Group Limited; *Int'l*, pg. 93
MKH—See Accord Group Limited; *Int'l*, pg. 93
MKTWORKS, INC.; *U.S. Private*, pg. 2753
MLT CREATIVE; *U.S. Private*, pg. 2754
MMB; *U.S. Private*, pg. 2754
MMGY GLOBAL LLC—See EagleTree Capital, LP; *U.S. Private*, pg. 1311
MMGY GLOBAL - ORLANDO—See EagleTree Capital, LP; *U.S. Private*, pg. 1311
MMI AGENCY, LLC—See Stagwell, Inc.; *U.S. Public*, pg. 1927
MNI TARGETED MEDIA INC—See Meredith Corporation; *U.S. Public*, pg. 1423
MO' BETTER MARKETING, LLC—See New West, LLC; *U.S. Private*, pg. 2908
MOBILE POSSE, INC.—See Digital Turbine, Inc.; *U.S. Public*, pg. 664
MOBIUM—See Stagwell, Inc.; *U.S. Public*, pg. 1926
MOB MEDIA; *U.S. Private*, pg. 2756
MOCHILA, INC.; *U.S. Private*, pg. 2759
MODCO CREATIVE INC.; *U.S. Private*, pg. 2759
MODEA CORP; *U.S. Private*, pg. 2759
MODERN CLIMATE; *U.S. Private*, pg. 2760
MODERNISTA!; *U.S. Private*, pg. 2763
MODERNISTA!—See Modernista!; *U.S. Private*, pg. 2763
MODERN MARKETING PARTNERS; *U.S. Private*, pg. 2761
MODOP, LLC; *U.S. Private*, pg. 2763
MOMENTUM—See The Interpublic Group of Companies, Inc.; *U.S. Public*, pg. 2102
MOMENTUM—See The Interpublic Group of Companies, Inc.; *U.S. Public*, pg. 2102
MOMENTUM—See The Interpublic Group of Companies, Inc.; *U.S. Public*, pg. 2102
MOMENTUM—See The Interpublic Group of Companies, Inc.; *U.S. Public*, pg. 2102
MOMENTUM—See The Interpublic Group of Companies, Inc.; *U.S. Public*, pg. 2102
MOMENTUM WORLDWIDE LLC—See The Interpublic Group of Companies, Inc.; *U.S. Public*, pg. 2102
THE MONKEYS PTY. LTD.—See Accenture plc; *Int'l*, pg. 88
MONO ADVERTISING LLC—See Stagwell, Inc.; *U.S. Public*, pg. 1927
MONO; *U.S. Private*, pg. 2771
MONUMETRIC, LLC; *U.S. Private*, pg. 2778
MOORE COMMUNICATIONS GROUP; *U.S. Private*, pg. 2779
MOORE, EPSTEIN, MOORE; *U.S. Private*, pg. 2780
MOORE & SCARRY ADVERTISING, INC.; *U.S. Private*, pg. 2779
MOOVE MEDIA AUSTRALIA PTY. LTD.—See ComfortDelGro Corporation Limited; *Int'l*, pg. 1713
MORBELLI, RUSSO & PARTNERS ADVERTISING, INC.; *U.S. Private*, pg. 2782
MOREY EVANS; *U.S. Private*, pg. 2782
MORGAN & COMPANY; *U.S. Private*, pg. 2783
MORGAN & MYERS, INC.—See Gibbs & Soell, Inc.; *U.S. Private*, pg. 1695
MORGAN & MYERS, INC.—See Gibbs & Soell, Inc.; *U.S. Private*, pg. 1695
MOROCH PARTNERS; *U.S. Private*, pg. 2785
MOROCH—See Moroch Partners; *U.S. Private*, pg. 2786
MOROCH—See Moroch Partners; *U.S. Private*, pg. 2786
MOROCH—See Moroch Partners; *U.S. Private*, pg. 2786
MOROCH—See Moroch Partners; *U.S. Private*, pg. 2786
MOROCH—See Moroch Partners; *U.S. Private*, pg. 2786
MOROCH—See Moroch Partners; *U.S. Private*, pg. 2786
MOROCH—See Moroch Partners; *U.S. Private*, pg. 2786
MOROCH—See Moroch Partners; *U.S. Private*, pg. 2786
MOROCH—See Moroch Partners; *U.S. Private*, pg. 2786
MOROCH—See Moroch Partners; *U.S. Private*, pg. 2786
MOROCH—See Moroch Partners; *U.S. Private*, pg. 2786
MOROCH—See Moroch Partners; *U.S. Private*, pg. 2786
MOROCH—See Moroch Partners; *U.S. Private*, pg. 2786
MOROCH—See Moroch Partners; *U.S. Private*, pg. 2786
MORONEY & GILL, INC.; *U.S. Private*, pg. 2786
MORRIS INTERNATIONAL, INC.; *U.S. Private*, pg. 2788
THE MORRISON AGENCY; *U.S. Private*, pg. 4080

MORSEKODE; *U.S. Private*, pg. 2791
MORTAR ADVERTISING; *U.S. Private*, pg. 2791
MORYA COMUNICACAO E PROPAGANDA LTDA—See Omnicom Group Inc.; *U.S. Public*, pg. 1585
MOSES ANSHELL, INC.; *U.S. Private*, pg. 2793
MOSS WARNER INC.; *U.S. Private*, pg. 2794
MOST BRAND DEVELOPMENT + ADVERTISING; *U.S. Private*, pg. 2795
MOTOR; *U.S. Private*, pg. 2796
MOVI ERECORD CINE S.A.U.—See Atresmedia Corporacion de Medios de Comunicacion, S.A.; *Int'l*, pg. 693
MOXIE SOZO; *U.S. Private*, pg. 2802
MQ&C ADVERTISING & MARKETING; *U.S. Private*, pg. 2804
MRC MEDICAL COMMUNICATIONS; *U.S. Private*, pg. 2805
M.R. DANIELSON ADVERTISING LLC; *U.S. Private*, pg. 2529
MRM CHINA—See The Interpublic Group of Companies, Inc.; *U.S. Public*, pg. 2098
MRM GILLESPIE—See The Interpublic Group of Companies, Inc.; *U.S. Public*, pg. 2098
MRM MANCHESTER—See The Interpublic Group of Companies, Inc.; *U.S. Public*, pg. 2098
MRM//MCCANN CHINA—See The Interpublic Group of Companies, Inc.; *U.S. Public*, pg. 2098
MRM//MCCANN—See The Interpublic Group of Companies, Inc.; *U.S. Public*, pg. 2098
MRM MUNICH—See The Interpublic Group of Companies, Inc.; *U.S. Public*, pg. 2098
MRM PARIS—See The Interpublic Group of Companies, Inc.; *U.S. Public*, pg. 2098
MRM PHILIPPINES—See The Interpublic Group of Companies, Inc.; *U.S. Public*, pg. 2098
MRM SPAIN—See The Interpublic Group of Companies, Inc.; *U.S. Public*, pg. 2098
MRM THAILAND—See The Interpublic Group of Companies, Inc.; *U.S. Public*, pg. 2098
MRM TURKEY—See The Interpublic Group of Companies, Inc.; *U.S. Public*, pg. 2098
MRM WORLDWIDE BRAZIL—See The Interpublic Group of Companies, Inc.; *U.S. Public*, pg. 2098
MRM WORLDWIDE - NEW YORK—See The Interpublic Group of Companies, Inc.; *U.S. Public*, pg. 2098
MRM WORLDWIDE SINGAPORE—See The Interpublic Group of Companies, Inc.; *U.S. Public*, pg. 2098
MRM WORLDWIDE—See The Interpublic Group of Companies, Inc.; *U.S. Public*, pg. 2098
MRM WORLDWIDE—See The Interpublic Group of Companies, Inc.; *U.S. Public*, pg. 2098
MRM WORLDWIDE—See The Interpublic Group of Companies, Inc.; *U.S. Public*, pg. 2098
MRM WORLDWIDE—See The Interpublic Group of Companies, Inc.; *U.S. Public*, pg. 2098
MRM WORLDWIDE—See The Interpublic Group of Companies, Inc.; *U.S. Public*, pg. 2098
MSA ADVERTISING & PUBLIC RELATIONS; *U.S. Private*, pg. 2806
MSA: THE THINK AGENCY; *U.S. Private*, pg. 2806
MSQ PARTNERS GROUP LTD.—See OEP Capital Advisors, L.P.; *U.S. Private*, pg. 2999
MUDD ADVERTISING; *U.S. Private*, pg. 2810
MUDD ADVERTISING—See Mudd Advertising; *U.S. Private*, pg. 2810
MUDRA COMMUNICATIONS PVT. LTD.—See Omnicom Group Inc.; *U.S. Public*, pg. 1582
MULLEN ADVERTISING & PUBLIC RELATIONS, INC.; *U.S. Private*, pg. 2811
MULLEN COMMUNICATIONS, INC.—See The Interpublic Group of Companies, Inc.; *U.S. Public*, pg. 2103
MULLENLOWE ACCRA—See The Interpublic Group of Companies, Inc.; *U.S. Public*, pg. 2092
MULLEN LOWE BRASIL—See The Interpublic Group of Companies, Inc.; *U.S. Public*, pg. 2092
MULLEN LOWE LINTAS GROUP—See The Interpublic Group of Companies, Inc.; *U.S. Public*, pg. 2092
MULLEN—See The Interpublic Group of Companies, Inc.; *U.S. Public*, pg. 2103
MULLEN—See The Interpublic Group of Companies, Inc.; *U.S. Public*, pg. 2103
MULLEN—See The Interpublic Group of Companies, Inc.; *U.S. Public*, pg. 2103
MULLER BRESSLER BROWN; *U.S. Private*, pg. 2811
MULLIN/ASHLEY ASSOCIATES, INC.; *U.S. Private*, pg. 2811
MULTI-MEDIA SYSTEMS—See The Interpublic Group of Companies, Inc.; *U.S. Public*, pg. 2101
MUNN RABOT LLC; *U.S. Private*, pg. 2814
MUNROE CREATIVE PARTNERS; *U.S. Private*, pg. 2814
MUNROE CREATIVE PARTNERS—See Munroe Creative Partners; *U.S. Private*, pg. 2814
MUSE COMMUNICATIONS, INC.—See Quantasy, LLC; *U.S. Public*, pg. 3322
MUSTACHE, LLC—See Daniel J. Edelman Holdings, Inc.; *U.S. Private*, pg. 1154
MVNP; *U.S. Private*, pg. 2821
MW MARKETING GROUP; *U.S. Private*, pg. 2822

N.A.I.C.S. INDEX 541810 — ADVERTISING AGENCIE...

MWW GROUP—See MWW Group LLC; *U.S. Private*, pg. 2822
MWW GROUP—See MWW Group LLC; *U.S. Private*, pg. 2822
THE MX GROUP; *U.S. Private*, pg. 4081
MYRIAD TRAVEL MARKETING—See EagleTree Capital, LP; *U.S. Private*, pg. 1311
MYRIAD TRAVEL MARKETING—See EagleTree Capital, LP; *U.S. Private*, pg. 1311
MY THEATER D.D. INC.—See Dentsu Group Inc.; *Int'l*, pg. 2039
MZD ADVERTISING; *U.S. Private*, pg. 2826
NAGA DDB SDN. BHD.—See Omnicom Group Inc.; *U.S. Public*, pg. 1582
NAGANO AD BUREAU INC.—See Dentsu Group Inc.; *Int'l*, pg. 2039
NAIL COMMUNICATIONS; *U.S. Private*, pg. 2831
NAKAHATA INC.—See Dentsu Group Inc.; *Int'l*, pg. 2039
NAKED COMMUNICATIONS LTD.—See Enero Group Limited; *Int'l*, pg. 2424
NAKED COMMUNICATIONS NORDIC—See Enero Group Limited; *Int'l*, pg. 2424
N. ARMSTRONG ADVERTISING; *U.S. Private*, pg. 2827
NATCOM MARKETING; *U.S. Private*, pg. 2838
NATIONAL CINEMEDIA, LLC—See National CineMedia, Inc.; *U.S. Public*, pg. 1494
NATIONAL MILK PRODUCERS FEDERATION; *U.S. Private*, pg. 2859
NATIONAL NEWS BUREAU AGENCY; *U.S. Private*, pg. 2859
NATIONAL OUTDOOR SPORTS ADVERTISING, INC.—See Market Development Group, Inc.; *U.S. Private*, pg. 2579
NATIONWIDE COURT SERVICES, INC.—See Nationwide Court Services, Inc.; *U.S. Private*, pg. 2865
NATIONWIDE NEWSPAPERS ADVERTISING, LLC; *U.S. Private*, pg. 2866
NATREL COMMUNICATIONS; *U.S. Private*, pg. 2866
NAVI CO., LTD.—See Crestec Inc.; *Int'l*, pg. 1841
NAYAMODE, INC.; *U.S. Private*, pg. 2874
NAYLOR, LLC—See The RLJ Companies, LLC; *U.S. Private*, pg. 4111
NEATHAWK DUBUQUE & PACKETT; *U.S. Private*, pg. 2878
NEATHAWK DUBUQUE & PACKETT—See Neathawk Dubuque & Packett; *U.S. Private*, pg. 2878
NEATHAWK DUBUQUE & PACKETT—See Neathawk Dubuque & Packett; *U.S. Private*, pg. 2878
NEBO AGENCY LLC; *U.S. Private*, pg. 2878
NEBOKO LIVE—See Omnicom Group Inc.; *U.S. Public*, pg. 1596
NEEDLEMAN DROSSMAN & PARTNERS; *U.S. Private*, pg. 2880
NEFF + ASSOCIATES, INC.; *U.S. Private*, pg. 2880
NEGOCIOS DIGITALES COLOMBIA S.A.S.—See Bancolombia S.A.; *Int'l*, pg. 828
NEHMEN-KODNER; *U.S. Private*, pg. 2880
NEHOC INC.; *U.S. Private*, pg. 2880
NEIGHBOR, INC.—See Zealot Networks, Inc.; *U.S. Private*, pg. 4599
NE KID PARIS—See Enero Group Limited; *Int'l*, pg. 2424
NELSON ADVERTISING SOLUTIONS; *U.S. Private*, pg. 2883
NELSON & GILMORE; *U.S. Private*, pg. 2882
NELSON & SCHMIDT, INC.; *U.S. Private*, pg. 2883
NEMER FIEGER; *U.S. Private*, pg. 2884
NEMO; *U.S. Private*, pg. 2884
THE NERDERY; *U.S. Private*, pg. 4082
NESTBUILDER.COM CORP.; *U.S. Public*, pg. 1506
NETBOOSTER AGENCY ITALY SRL—See Ardian SAS; *Int'l*, pg. 554
NETBOOSTER GMBH—See Ardian SAS; *Int'l*, pg. 554
NETBOOSTER MENA MIDDLE EAST & NORTH AFRICA FZ-LLC—See Ardian SAS; *Int'l*, pg. 554
NETBOOSTER SPAIN SL—See Ardian SAS; *Int'l*, pg. 555
NETBOOSTER SWEDEN AB—See Ardian SAS; *Int'l*, pg. 555
NETBOOSTER UK LIMITED—See Ardian SAS; *Int'l*, pg. 555
NETPLUS MARKETING, INC.; *U.S. Private*, pg. 2887
NETPRPRO, INC.; *U.S. Private*, pg. 2887
NETSHELTER, INC.; *U.S. Private*, pg. 2888
NET#WORK BBDO—See Omnicom Group Inc.; *U.S. Public*, pg. 1576
NEW CREATION ADVERTISING AGENCY LIMITED—See Bexcellent Group Holdings Limited; *Int'l*, pg. 1005
NEWDAY COMMUNICATIONS INC.; *U.S. Private*, pg. 2914
NEW DAY MARKETING, LTD.; *U.S. Private*, pg. 2893
NEW ENGLAND ADVERTISING CORPORATION—See Hilton Grand Vacations Inc.; *U.S. Public*, pg. 1040
NEW ENGLAND PRESS SERVICE; *U.S. Private*, pg. 2894
NEW HONOR SOCIETY, INC.—See The Interpublic Group of Companies, Inc.; *U.S. Public*, pg. 2103
NEW LONDON COMMUNICATIONS, LLC; *U.S. Private*, pg. 2898
NEWMARK ADVERTISING, INC.; *U.S. Private*, pg. 2916
NEW MEDIA STRATEGIES—See Meredith Corporation; *U.S. Public*, pg. 1423
NEW RIVER COMMUNICATIONS, INC.; *U.S. Private*, pg. 2906
NEWSQUEST (HERALD & TIMES) LIMITED—See Gannett Co., Inc.; *U.S. Public*, pg. 899
NEW TEAM LLC—See Stagwell, Inc.; *U.S. Public*, pg. 1927
NEW WEST, LLC; *U.S. Private*, pg. 2908
NEXTMEDIA GROUP, INC.—See Strategic Value Partners, LLC; *U.S. Private*, pg. 3836
NEXTMEDIA GROUP, INC.—See TPG Capital, L.P.; *U.S. Public*, pg. 2168
NEXUS DIRECT; *U.S. Private*, pg. 2922
NEXUS/H LTD.—See Hakuhodo DY Holdings Incorporated; *Int'l*, pg. 3222
NFM GROUP INC.; *U.S. Private*, pg. 2923
NFUSION GROUP, LLC; *U.S. Private*, pg. 2923
NIELSEN AUDIO, INC.—See Brookfield Corporation; *Int'l*, pg. 1179
NIELSEN AUDIO, INC.—See Elliott Management Corporation; *U.S. Private*, pg. 1371
NIIGATA HAKUHODO INC.—See Hakuhodo DY Holdings Incorporated; *Int'l*, pg. 3222
NINTHDECIMAL, INC.—See inMarket Media LLC; *U.S. Private*, pg. 2079
NITROGEN - SAN FRANCISCO—See Clayton, Dubilier & Rice, LLC; *U.S. Private*, pg. 925
NITROGEN—See Clayton, Dubilier & Rice, LLC; *U.S. Private*, pg. 925
NOBOX MARKETING GROUP, INC.; *U.S. Private*, pg. 2933
NONBOX; *U.S. Private*, pg. 2934
NONBOX—See Nonbox; *U.S. Private*, pg. 2934
NONBOX—See Nonbox; *U.S. Private*, pg. 2934
NORBELLA INC.; *U.S. Private*, pg. 2935
NORTH COAST BEHAVIORAL RESEARCH GROUP—See Wyse; *U.S. Private*, pg. 4579
NORTHEAST GROUP; *U.S. Private*, pg. 2950
NORTHLICH-COLUMBUS—See Northlich; *U.S. Private*, pg. 2956
NORTHLICH; *U.S. Private*, pg. 2956
NORTHLICH—See Northlich; *U.S. Private*, pg. 2956
NORTHLICH—See Northlich; *U.S. Private*, pg. 2956
NORTH; *U.S. Private*, pg. 2939
NORTH STAR DESTINATION STRATEGIES LLC; *U.S. Private*, pg. 2947
NORTHSTAR RESEARCH HOLDINGS CANADA INC.—See Stagwell, Inc.; *U.S. Public*, pg. 1927
NORTHSTAR RESEARCH HOLDINGS USA LP—See Stagwell, Inc.; *U.S. Public*, pg. 1927
NORTHSTAR RESEARCH PARTNERS (UK) LIMITED—See Stagwell, Inc.; *U.S. Public*, pg. 1927
THE NORTHWEST GROUP; *U.S. Private*, pg. 4084
NORTH WOODS ADVERTISING; *U.S. Private*, pg. 2948
NOUVELLE VAGUE—See Omnicom Group Inc.; *U.S. Public*, pg. 1596
NSPHERE INC.; *U.S. Private*, pg. 2970
N-TARA, INC.; *U.S. Private*, pg. 2827
NUEVO ADVERTISING GROUP, INC.; *U.S. Private*, pg. 2972
NUFFER SMITH TUCKER, INC.; *U.S. Private*, pg. 2972
THE NULMAN GROUP; *U.S. Private*, pg. 4085
NYCA; *U.S. Private*, pg. 2976
NYIAX, INC.; *U.S. Public*, pg. 1559
NYM WORLDGROUP, INC.; *U.S. Private*, pg. 2976
O2IDEAS, INC.; *U.S. Private*, pg. 2982
O2KL; *U.S. Private*, pg. 2982
O3 WORLD, LLC; *U.S. Private*, pg. 2983
OATH DENMARK APS—See Apollo Global Management, Inc.; *U.S. Public*, pg. 167
O'BERRY CAVANAUGH; *U.S. Private*, pg. 2977
OBERUBER KARGER KOMMUNIKATIONSAGENTUR GMBH—See Bertelsmann SE & Co. KGaA; *Int'l*, pg. 993
OBJEKTVISION AB—See Alma Media Corporation; *Int'l*, pg. 362
THE O'CARROLL GROUP; *U.S. Private*, pg. 4087
OCEAN BRIDGE GROUP; *U.S. Private*, pg. 2989
O'CONNOR & PARTNERS, INC.; *U.S. Private*, pg. 2977
OCTAGON ACCESS—See The Interpublic Group of Companies, Inc.; *U.S. Public*, pg. 2103
OCTAGON EMEA—See The Interpublic Group of Companies, Inc.; *U.S. Public*, pg. 2103
OCTAGON—See The Interpublic Group of Companies, Inc.; *U.S. Public*, pg. 2103
OCTAGON—See The Interpublic Group of Companies, Inc.; *U.S. Public*, pg. 2103
OCTAGON—See The Interpublic Group of Companies, Inc.; *U.S. Public*, pg. 2103
OCTAGON—See The Interpublic Group of Companies, Inc.; *U.S. Public*, pg. 2103
OCTAGON—See The Interpublic Group of Companies, Inc.; *U.S. Public*, pg. 2103
OCTAGON—See The Interpublic Group of Companies, Inc.; *U.S. Public*, pg. 2103
OCTAGON—See The Interpublic Group of Companies, Inc.; *U.S. Public*, pg. 2103
OCTAGON SYDNEY—See The Interpublic Group of Companies, Inc.; *U.S. Public*, pg. 2103
ODDFELLOWS/DENTSU HOLDINGS PTY LTD.—See Dentsu Group Inc.; *Int'l*, pg. 2036
ODEN MARKETING AND DESIGN; *U.S. Private*, pg. 2993
ODNEY ADVERTISING-FARGO—See Odney; *U.S. Private*, pg. 2993
ODNEY ADVERTISING-MINOT—See Odney; *U.S. Private*, pg. 2993
ODNEY; *U.S. Private*, pg. 2993
OFF CAMPUS PARTNERS—See CoStar Group, Inc.; *U.S. Public*, pg. 586
OFF MADISON AVE, LLC; *U.S. Private*, pg. 3000
O'HALLORAN ADVERTISING, INC.; *U.S. Private*, pg. 2978
OLDFIELD DAVIS, INC.; *U.S. Private*, pg. 3010
OLD MILL MARKETING; *U.S. Private*, pg. 3009
OLIVE INTERACTIVE DESIGN & MARKETING INC.; *U.S. Private*, pg. 3010
OLIVER RUSSELL & ASSOCIATES LLC; *U.S. Private*, pg. 3011
OLIVE; *U.S. Private*, pg. 3010
OLOGIE; *U.S. Private*, pg. 3011
OLOMANA LOOMIS ISC, INC.; *U.S. Private*, pg. 3011
OLSON CANADA, INC.—See ICF International, Inc.; *U.S. Public*, pg. 1086
OMAHA CREATIVE GROUP; *U.S. Private*, pg. 3014
O'MASTER COMMUNICATIONS (HONG KONG) LTD.—See Charm Communications Inc.; *Int'l*, pg. 1450
OMD ATLANTA—See Omnicom Group Inc.; *U.S. Public*, pg. 1589
OMD BEIJING—See Omnicom Group Inc.; *U.S. Public*, pg. 1588
OMD CANADA—See Omnicom Group Inc.; *U.S. Public*, pg. 1588
OMD FINLAND OY—See Omnicom Group Inc.; *U.S. Public*, pg. 1588
OMD GERMANY GMBH & OMD DUSSELDORF GMBH—See Omnicom Group Inc.; *U.S. Public*, pg. 1588
OMD HONG KONG—See Omnicom Group Inc.; *U.S. Public*, pg. 1589
OMD LATINO—See Omnicom Group Inc.; *U.S. Public*, pg. 1589
OMD NEDERLAND—See Omnicom Group Inc.; *U.S. Public*, pg. 1588
OMD SHANGHAI—See Omnicom Group Inc.; *U.S. Public*, pg. 1589
OMD—See Omnicom Group Inc.; *U.S. Public*, pg. 1588
OMD TURKEY—See Omnicom Group Inc.; *U.S. Public*, pg. 1589
OMD VANCOUVER—See Omnicom Group Inc.; *U.S. Public*, pg. 1589
OMD WORLDWIDE—See Omnicom Group Inc.; *U.S. Public*, pg. 1588
OMELET; *U.S. Private*, pg. 3015
OMNICOM CANADA CORP.—See Omnicom Group Inc.; *U.S. Public*, pg. 1589
OMNICOM EUROPE LIMITED—See Omnicom Group Inc.; *U.S. Public*, pg. 1589
OMNICOMM SPAIN S.L.—See ABRY Partners, LLC; *U.S. Private*, pg. 41
ONBEYOND LLC; *U.S. Private*, pg. 3019
ONE & ALL—See Omnicom Group Inc.; *U.S. Public*, pg. 1589
ONE & ALL—See Omnicom Group Inc.; *U.S. Public*, pg. 1589
ONE PLANET GROUP LLC; *U.S. Private*, pg. 3020
ONE SKY INC.—See Dentsu Group Inc.; *Int'l*, pg. 2039
ONEWORLD COMMUNICATIONS, INC.; *U.S. Private*, pg. 3026
ONE/X; *U.S. Private*, pg. 3024
ON IDEAS, INC.; *U.S. Private*, pg. 3018
ONPR—See OnPR; *U.S. Private*, pg. 3027
ONTAP—See Decker Creative Marketing; *U.S. Private*, pg. 1187
OOO EKONIVA-MEDIA—See Ekosem-Agrar GmbH; *Int'l*, pg. 2339
OPOLIS DESIGN; *U.S. Private*, pg. 3032
OPTIMA DIRECT, INC.—See Omnicom Group Inc.; *U.S. Public*, pg. 1592
OPTIMISE MEDIA GROUP LIMITED—See Clime Investment Management Limited; *Int'l*, pg. 1659
ORANGE LABEL ART & ADVERTISING; *U.S. Private*, pg. 3037
OREGON NEWSPAPER ADVERTISING CO.; *U.S. Private*, pg. 3040
ORGANIC, INC.—See Omnicom Group Inc.; *U.S. Public*, pg. 1589
ORGANIC, INC.—See Omnicom Group Inc.; *U.S. Public*, pg. 1589
ORGANIC, INC.—See Omnicom Group Inc.; *U.S. Public*, pg. 1589
ORGANIC, INC.—See Omnicom Group Inc.; *U.S. Public*, pg. 1589
ORICOM INC.—See Doosan Corporation; *Int'l*, pg. 2174
ORIENT/MCCANN—See The Interpublic Group of Companies, Inc.; *U.S. Public*, pg. 2102
ORIENT/MCCANN—See The Interpublic Group of Companies, Inc.; *U.S. Public*, pg. 2102
ORIGEN ARGENTINA—See Origen Global; *U.S. Private*, pg. 3041
ORIGEN BRAZIL—See Origen Global; *U.S. Private*, pg. 3041

541810 — ADVERTISING AGENCIE... CORPORATE AFFILIATIONS

ORIGEN COLOMBIA—See Origen Global; *U.S. Private*, pg. 3041
ORIGEN COSTA RICA—See Origen Global; *U.S. Private*, pg. 3041
ORIGEN ECUADOR—See Origen Global; *U.S. Private*, pg. 3041
ORIGEN EL SALVADOR—See Origen Global; *U.S. Private*, pg. 3041
ORIGEN ESPANA—See Origen Global; *U.S. Private*, pg. 3041
ORIGEN GLOBAL; *U.S. Private*, pg. 3041
ORIGEN GUATEMALA—See Origen Global; *U.S. Private*, pg. 3041
ORIGEN HONDURAS—See Origen Global; *U.S. Private*, pg. 3041
ORIGEN MEXICO—See Origen Global; *U.S. Private*, pg. 3042
ORIGEN NICARAGUA—See Origen Global; *U.S. Private*, pg. 3042
ORIGEN PANAMA—See Origen Global; *U.S. Private*, pg. 3042
ORION MEDIA ASSOCIATES, INC.; *U.S. Private*, pg. 3043
ORION TRADING CANADA INC.—See The Interpublic Group of Companies, Inc.; *U.S. Public*, pg. 2103
OSBORN & BARR COMMUNICATIONS; *U.S. Private*, pg. 3046
OSBORN & BARR—See Osborn & Barr Communications; *U.S. Private*, pg. 3046
O'SULLIVAN COMMUNICATIONS; *U.S. Private*, pg. 2981
OTEY WHITE & ASSOCIATES; *U.S. Private*, pg. 3049
OTTO; *U.S. Private*, pg. 3050
OTTO—See Otto; *U.S. Private*, pg. 3050
OUR MAN IN HAVANA LLC; *U.S. Private*, pg. 3050
THE OUSSET AGENCY, INC; *U.S. Private*, pg. 4089
OUTBRAIN INC.; *U.S. Public*, pg. 1624
OVATION ADVERTISING—See Omnicom Group Inc.; *U.S. Public*, pg. 1576
OVERIT MEDIA INC.; *U.S. Private*, pg. 3053
OWENS DDB—See Omnicom Group Inc.; *U.S. Public*, pg. 1582
OXFORD COMMUNICATIONS, INC.; *U.S. Private*, pg. 3056
OXIEM, LLC; *U.S. Private*, pg. 3057
OXYGEN ADVERTISING, INC.; *U.S. Private*, pg. 3057
PACE, INC.—See Integrated Communications Corp.; *U.S. Private*, pg. 2099
PACIFIC COMMUNICATIONS; *U.S. Private*, pg. 3066
PACIFIC MARKETING; *U.S. Private*, pg. 3068
PAGES BBDO—See Omnicom Group Inc.; *U.S. Public*, pg. 1576
THE PAIGE GROUP; *U.S. Private*, pg. 4090
PAIM COMUNICACAO—See The Interpublic Group of Companies, Inc.; *U.S. Public*, pg. 2100
PALIO + IGNITE, LLC—See Elliott Management Corporation; *U.S. Private*, pg. 1366
PALIO + IGNITE, LLC—See Patient Square Capital, L.P.; *U.S. Private*, pg. 3108
PALIO + IGNITE, LLC—See Veritas Capital Fund Management, LLC; *U.S. Private*, pg. 4365
PALISADES MEDIA GROUP, INC.; *U.S. Private*, pg. 3077
PANAVISTA PROMOTIONS—See Ryan Partnership, LLC; *U.S. Private*, pg. 3510
PANCOM INTERNATIONAL, INC.; *U.S. Private*, pg. 3085
PAPEL MEDIA NETWORK; *U.S. Private*, pg. 3087
THE PAPPAS GROUP, INC.—See OceanSound Partners, LP; *U.S. Private*, pg. 2991
PARACHUTE DESIGN, INC.—See Clarity Coverdale Fury Advertising, Inc.; *U.S. Private*, pg. 911
PARADIGM ASSOCIATES; *U.S. Private*, pg. 3089
PARADISE ADVERTISING & MARKETING, INC.; *U.S. Private*, pg. 3090
PARADISE ADVERTISING & MARKETING-NAPLES—See Paradise Advertising & Marketing, Inc.; *U.S. Private*, pg. 3090
PARAGON ADVERTISING; *U.S. Private*, pg. 3090
PARAGON ADVERTISING; *U.S. Private*, pg. 3090
PARAMORE THE DIGITAL AGENCY LLC—See Osborn & Barr Communications; *U.S. Private*, pg. 3046
PARKER & PARTNERS MARKETING RESOURCES, LLC; *U.S. Private*, pg. 3097
PARTNERCENTRIC, INC.—See Schaaf Consulting; *U.S. Private*, pg. 3562
PARTNERS FOR INCENTIVES INC.; *U.S. Private*, pg. 3101
PARTNERSHIP OF PACKER, OESTERLING & SMITH (PPO&S); *U.S. Private*, pg. 3103
PARTNERS + NAPIER INC. - ATLANTA OFFICE—See Project: Worldwide, Inc.; *U.S. Private*, pg. 3281
PARTNERS + NAPIER INC.—See Project: Worldwide, Inc.; *U.S. Private*, pg. 3281
PATHFINDERS ADVERTISING & MARKETING GROUP; *U.S. Private*, pg. 3105
PATIENT CONVERSATION MEDIA, INC.; *U.S. Private*, pg. 3106
THE PATIENT RECRUITING AGENCY; *U.S. Private*, pg. 4091
PATIENTS & PURPOSE, LLC—See Omnicom Group Inc.; *U.S. Public*, pg. 1579
PATRICKORTMAN, INC.; *U.S. Private*, pg. 3110
PATRIOT ADVERTISING INC.; *U.S. Private*, pg. 3110

PAUL A. DE JESSE, INC. ADVERTISING; *U.S. Private*, pg. 3112
PAULSEN MARKETING COMMUNICATIONS, INC.; *U.S. Private*, pg. 3114
PAVONE; *U.S. Private*, pg. 3115
PCGCAMPBELL; *U.S. Private*, pg. 3120
PEAKBIETY INC.; *U.S. Private*, pg. 3124
PEDONE; *U.S. Private*, pg. 3128
PENNA POWERS BRIAN HAYNES; *U.S. Private*, pg. 3135
PENN GARRITANO DIRECT RESPONSE MARKETING; *U.S. Private*, pg. 3134
PENN SCHOEN & BERLAND—See Penn Schoen Berland Associates Inc.; *U.S. Private*, pg. 3134
PENNY/OHLMANN/NEIMAN, INC.; *U.S. Private*, pg. 3138
PEOPLETOMYSITE.COM, LLC; *U.S. Private*, pg. 3143
PEPPERCORN PRODUCTIONS, INC.—See National Amusements, Inc.; *U.S. Private*, pg. 2842
THE PEPPER GROUP; *U.S. Private*, pg. 4093
PERALTASTRAWBERRYFROG—See APCO Worldwide; *U.S. Private*, pg. 291
PEREIRA & O'DELL; *U.S. Private*, pg. 3147
PERENNIAL INC.—See DATA Communications Management Corp.; *Int'l*, pg. 1976
PEREZ Y VILLA BBDO—See Omnicom Group Inc.; *U.S. Public*, pg. 1576
PERFECT FOOLS AB—See The Interpublic Group of Companies, Inc.; *U.S. Public*, pg. 2098
PERFORMANCE MARKETING OF IOWA, INC.; *U.S. Private*, pg. 3149
PERICH ADVERTISING + DESIGN; *U.S. Private*, pg. 3150
PERISCOPE, INC.—See Quad/Graphics, Inc.; *U.S. Private*, pg. 1744
PERISCOPE INTERMEDIATE CORP.—See KKR & Co. Inc.; *U.S. Public*, pg. 1267
PERRY BALLARD INCORPORATED; *U.S. Private*, pg. 3153
PERRY COMMUNICATIONS GROUP, INC.; *U.S. Private*, pg. 3153
PERRY PRODUCTIONS; *U.S. Private*, pg. 3154
PETER A. MAYER ADVERTISING, INC.; *U.S. Private*, pg. 3157
THE PETER GROUP, INC.; *U.S. Private*, pg. 4094
PETER OGNIBENE ASSOCIATES; *U.S. Private*, pg. 3159
PETERSON MILLA HOOKS; *U.S. Private*, pg. 3160
PETERSON PROBST; *U.S. Private*, pg. 3160
PHD CHICAGO—See Omnicom Group Inc.; *U.S. Public*, pg. 1589
PHD CHINA—See Omnicom Group Inc.; *U.S. Public*, pg. 1589
PHD MEDIA UK—See Omnicom Group Inc.; *U.S. Public*, pg. 1590
PHD NEW YORK—See Omnicom Group Inc.; *U.S. Public*, pg. 1590
PHD NEW ZEALAND—See Omnicom Group Inc.; *U.S. Public*, pg. 1590
PHD TORONTO—See Omnicom Group Inc.; *U.S. Public*, pg. 1590
THE PHELPS GROUP; *U.S. Private*, pg. 4094
PHENOMENON; *U.S. Private*, pg. 3167
PHIDS, INC.; *U.S. Private*, pg. 3168
PHILIP/ANDREWS DESIGN; *U.S. Private*, pg. 3170
PHILIPPEBECKER; *U.S. Private*, pg. 3170
PHILIPP UND KEUNTJE GMBH—See fischerAppelt AG; *Int'l*, pg. 2692
PHOENIX CREATIVE CO.; *U.S. Private*, pg. 3172
PHOENIX MARKETING GROUP, INC.; *U.S. Private*, pg. 3173
PHOENIX MARKETING INTERNATIONAL, INC.; *U.S. Private*, pg. 3173
PHOTOSOUND COMMUNICATIONS—See HealthSTAR Communications, Inc.; *U.S. Private*, pg. 1898
PHOTOSOUND COMMUNICATIONS—See HealthSTAR Communications, Inc.; *U.S. Private*, pg. 1898
PICKERING CREATIVE GROUP; *U.S. Private*, pg. 3176
PIER 8 GROUP—See 2Gen Net; *Int'l*, pg. 5
PIERCE COMMUNICATIONS, INC.; *U.S. Private*, pg. 3178
PIERCE-COTE ADVERTISING, INC.—See Regan Communications Group, Inc.; *U.S. Private*, pg. 3386
PIERCE PROMOTIONS & EVENT MANAGEMENT—See Omnicom Group Inc.; *U.S. Public*, pg. 1593
PI, INC.; *U.S. Private*, pg. 3175
PINCKNEY HUGO GROUP; *U.S. Private*, pg. 3181
PINGER PR AT POWERS—See Powers Agency; *U.S. Private*, pg. 3240
PINNACLE EXHIBITS, INC.; *U.S. Private*, pg. 3185
PINSTRIPE MARKETING, INC.; *U.S. Private*, pg. 3186
PIXIDIS SARL—See Ardian SAS; *Int'l*, pg. 555
PJA ADVERTISING & MARKETING, INC. - SAN FRANCISCO—See PJA Advertising & Marketing, Inc.; *U.S. Private*, pg. 3193
PJA ADVERTISING & MARKETING, INC.; *U.S. Private*, pg. 3193
PKP BBDO—See Omnicom Group Inc.; *U.S. Public*, pg. 1576
THE PLACEMAKING GROUP; *U.S. Private*, pg. 4096
PLAN B (THE AGENCY ALTERNATIVE); *U.S. Private*, pg. 3195

PLAN.NET—See The Interpublic Group of Companies, Inc.; *U.S. Public*, pg. 2097
PLATFORMQ, LLC; *U.S. Private*, pg. 3200
PLATTFORM ADVERTISING, INC.—See Arlington Capital Partners LLC; *U.S. Private*, pg. 328
PLATYPUS ADVERTISING + DESIGN; *U.S. Private*, pg. 3212
PLAYCADE INTERACTIVE GMBH—See Azerion Group N.V.; *Int'l*, pg. 778
PLAYGROUND GROUP INC; *U.S. Private*, pg. 3212
PLAYWIRE, LLC—See FreakOut Holdings, Inc.; *Int'l*, pg. 2767
PLAYWIRE MEDIA, LLC; *U.S. Private*, pg. 3212
PL&P ADVERTISING; *U.S. Private*, pg. 3194
PLUS MOBILE COMMUNICATIONS CO., LTD.—See CYBIRD Holdings Co., Ltd.; *Int'l*, pg. 1894
PLUZYNSKI/ASSOCIATES, INC.; *U.S. Private*, pg. 3215
PM ADVERTISING; *U.S. Private*, pg. 3216
PM ADVERTISING—See PM Advertising; *U.S. Private*, pg. 3216
PMK-BNC, INC.—See The Interpublic Group of Companies, Inc.; *U.S. Public*, pg. 2103
PM PUBLICIDAD; *U.S. Private*, pg. 3216
POCKET HERCULES; *U.S. Private*, pg. 3219
POINT B COMMUNICATIONS; *U.S. Private*, pg. 3221
POINT B; *U.S. Private*, pg. 3221
POINT ROLL, INC. - CHICAGO—See TEGNA Inc.; *U.S. Public*, pg. 1990
POINT ROLL, INC. - DETROIT—See TEGNA Inc.; *U.S. Public*, pg. 1990
POINT ROLL, INC.—See TEGNA Inc.; *U.S. Public*, pg. 1990
POINT TO POINT INC.; *U.S. Private*, pg. 3222
POLARIS RECRUITMENT COMMUNICATIONS; *U.S. Private*, pg. 3223
POLLER & JORDAN ADVERTISING AGENCY, INC.; *U.S. Private*, pg. 3225
PONCE BUENOS AIRES—See The Interpublic Group of Companies, Inc.; *U.S. Public*, pg. 2092
PONDELWILKINSON INC.; *U.S. Private*, pg. 3227
PONDER IDEAWORKS; *U.S. Private*, pg. 3227
POP LABS, INC; *U.S. Private*, pg. 3228
PORCARO COMMUNICATIONS; *U.S. Private*, pg. 3229
PORCARO VANCOUVER—See Porcaro Communications; *U.S. Private*, pg. 3229
PORTE ADVERTISING, INC.; *U.S. Private*, pg. 3231
PORTFOLIO MARKETING GROUP; *U.S. Private*, pg. 3232
POSNER ADVERTISING; *U.S. Private*, pg. 3234
POSNER ADVERTISING—See Posner Advertising; *U.S. Private*, pg. 3234
POWER ADS CORP.; *U.S. Private*, pg. 3237
POWER CREATIVE; *U.S. Private*, pg. 3237
POWERS AGENCY; *U.S. Private*, pg. 3239
PP+K; *U.S. Private*, pg. 3240
PRACTICE PROMOTIONS, LLC; *U.S. Private*, pg. 3241
PRAIRIE DOG/TCG—See Trozzolo Communications Group; *U.S. Private*, pg. 4244
PRAKIT & FCB VIETNAM—See The Interpublic Group of Companies, Inc.; *U.S. Public*, pg. 2093
PRECINCT—See Enero Group Limited; *Int'l*, pg. 2424
PREMISE IMMERSIVE MARKETING; *U.S. Private*, pg. 3251
PREMIUM AUDIENCE NETWORK, SL—See AdUX SA; *Int'l*, pg. 155
PRESTON KELLY, INC.; *U.S. Private*, pg. 3256
THE PRICE GROUP, INC.; *U.S. Private*, pg. 4098
PRICEWEBER MARKETING COMMUNICATIONS, INC.; *U.S. Private*, pg. 3259
PRIMA PUBLIC RELATIONS, LTD.; *U.S. Private*, pg. 3260
PRIME ACCESS, INC.—See Global Advertising Strategies, Inc.; *U.S. Private*, pg. 1712
PRINCETON PARTNERS, INC.; *U.S. Private*, pg. 3264
PRINTELECTRIC, INC.; *U.S. Private*, pg. 3265
PRIORITY MARKETING; *U.S. Private*, pg. 3266
PROBLEM SOLVERS, INC.—See Elser & Aucone, Inc.; *U.S. Private*, pg. 1377
PRODIGAL MEDIA COMPANY; *U.S. Private*, pg. 3272
PROFESSIONAL MEDIA MANAGEMENT; *U.S. Private*, pg. 3275
PROFORMA BRAND PROFORMANCE; *U.S. Private*, pg. 3277
PROFORMA STEWART & ASSOCIATES; *U.S. Private*, pg. 3277
PROGRESSIVE DIGITAL MEDIA LIMITED—See GlobalData Plc; *Int'l*, pg. 3003
PROJECT: WORLDWIDE, INC. - LOS ANGELES—See Project: Worldwide, Inc.; *U.S. Private*, pg. 3281
PROJECT: WORLDWIDE, INC.; *U.S. Private*, pg. 3280
PROMARK DIRECT INC.; *U.S. Private*, pg. 3282
PRO MEDIA GMBH—See DEAG Deutsche Entertainment AG; *Int'l*, pg. 1998
PROM KROG ALTSTIEL INC.; *U.S. Private*, pg. 3282
PROMOSEVEN-MOROCCO—See The Interpublic Group of Companies, Inc.; *U.S. Public*, pg. 2100
PROOF ADVERTISING; *U.S. Private*, pg. 3284
PROPHARMA SALES LLC; *U.S. Private*, pg. 3285
PROREKLAM-EUROPLAKAT D.O.O.—See APG/SGA SA; *Int'l*, pg. 513
PROTERRA ADVERTISING; *U.S. Private*, pg. 3290

N.A.I.C.S. INDEX

541810 — ADVERTISING AGENCIE...

PROTEUS B2B; *U.S. Private*, pg. 3290
PROVIS MEDIA GROUP; *U.S. Private*, pg. 3295
PROXIMITY BBDO—See Omnicom Group Inc.; *U.S. Public*, pg. 1575
PT. ADSTARS MEDIA PARIWARA—See Geniee, Inc.; *Int'l*, pg. 2923
PT. ADWAYS INDONESIA—See Adways Inc.; *Int'l*, pg. 169
P.T. CHUO SENKO INDONESIA—See Chuo Senko Advertising Co., Ltd.; *Int'l*, pg. 1599
PT. DENTSU STRAT—See Dentsu Group Inc.; *Int'l*, pg. 2037
PT FLEISHMAN-HILLIARD—See Omnicom Group Inc.; *U.S. Public*, pg. 1585
PT. FREAKOUT DEWINA INDONESIA—See FreakOut Holdings, Inc.; *Int'l*, pg. 2767
PT GEMA TEKNOLOGI CAHAYA GEMILANG—See FreakOut Holdings, Inc.; *Int'l*, pg. 2767
PT ICON INTERNATIONAL COMMUNICATIONS INDONESIA—See ICON International Communications Pty. Ltd.; *Int'l*, pg. 3583
PUBLICENTRO—See The Interpublic Group of Companies, Inc.; *U.S. Public*, pg. 2093
PUBLICIDAD COMERCIAL—See The Interpublic Group of Companies, Inc.; *U.S. Public*, pg. 2092
PUBLICIDAD INTERAMERICA—See The Interpublic Group of Companies, Inc.; *U.S. Public*, pg. 2092
PUBLICIDAD MCCANN ERICKSON CENTROAMERICANA (GUATEMALA) S.A.—See The Interpublic Group of Companies, Inc.; *U.S. Public*, pg. 2101
PUBLICIDAD VIRTUAL, S.A. DE C.V.—See Grupo Televisa, S.A.B.; *Int'l*, pg. 3136
PUBLICO MCCANN—See The Interpublic Group of Companies, Inc.; *U.S. Public*, pg. 2102
PUBLIFUTURA AFFICHAGE ITALIA SRL—See APG/SGA SA; *Int'l*, pg. 513
PUBLISHERS ADVERTISING ASSOCIATES; *U.S. Private*, pg. 3301
PUBSQUARED LLC; *U.S. Private*, pg. 3301
PULSAR ADVERTISING, INC.; *U.S. Private*, pg. 3303
PULSAR ADVERTISING, INC.—See Pulsar Advertising, Inc.; *U.S. Private*, pg. 3303
PULSAR ADVERTISING, INC.—See Pulsar Advertising, Inc.; *U.S. Private*, pg. 3303
THE PULSE NETWORK, INC.; *U.S. Private*, pg. 4101
PURDIE ROGERS, INC.; *U.S. Private*, pg. 3305
PURDIE ROGERS, INC.—See Purdie Rogers, Inc.; *U.S. Private*, pg. 3305
PURE AUTO LLC—See Diversis Capital, LLC; *U.S. Private*, pg. 1244
PURE AUTO LLC—See Stage 1 Ventures, LLC; *U.S. Private*, pg. 3775
PURE BRAND COMMUNICATIONS, LLC; *U.S. Private*, pg. 3305
PURE BRAND COMMUNICATIONS—See Pure Brand Communications, LLC; *U.S. Private*, pg. 3305
PUROHIT NAVIGATION, INC.; *U.S. Private*, pg. 3306
PUSH CREATIVE; *U.S. Private*, pg. 3307
PUSH SEVEN, INC.—See Pipitone Group; *U.S. Private*, pg. 3190
PUSH; *U.S. Private*, pg. 3307
P&V BBDO—See Omnicom Group Inc.; *U.S. Public*, pg. 1576
Q1MEDIA; *U.S. Private*, pg. 3312
Q, INC.—See DZ BANK AG Deutsche Zentral-Genossenschaftsbank; *Int'l*, pg. 2244
QUADRANT COMMUNICATIONS LTD.—See The Interpublic Group of Companies, Inc.; *U.S. Public*, pg. 2092
QUADRANT CREATIVE PTY LTD—See Adcorp Australia Limited; *Int'l*, pg. 127
QUAKER CITY MERCANTILE; *U.S. Private*, pg. 3316
QUALIA, INC.; *U.S. Private*, pg. 3317
QUALICONTACT—See Omnicom Group Inc.; *U.S. Public*, pg. 1596
QUALLY & COMPANY, INC.; *U.S. Private*, pg. 3322
QUANTA ADVERTISING; *U.S. Private*, pg. 3322
QUANTASY, LLC; *U.S. Private*, pg. 3322
QUANTUM COMMUNICATIONS; *U.S. Private*, pg. 3322
QUANTUMWORK ADVISORY—See Allegis Group, Inc.; *U.S. Private*, pg. 177
QUATTRO DIRECT LLC; *U.S. Private*, pg. 3324
THE QUEST BUSINESS AGENCY, INC.; *U.S. Private*, pg. 4101
QUEST CORPORATION OF AMERICA, INC.; *U.S. Private*, pg. 3325
QUEUE CREATIVE; *U.S. Private*, pg. 3326
QUIET LIGHT COMMUNICATIONS INC.; *U.S. Private*, pg. 3327
QUILL/AWA ENTERPRISES; *U.S. Private*, pg. 3327
QUINLAN MARKETING COMMUNICATIONS; *U.S. Private*, pg. 3328
QUINN FABLE ADVERTISING; *U.S. Private*, pg. 3328
QUORUM INTEGRATED; *U.S. Private*, pg. 3331
QVC DEUTSCHLAND INC. & CO. KG—See Qurate Retail, Inc.; *U.S. Public*, pg. 1758
R2C GROUP, INC.; *U.S. Private*, pg. 3340
R2INTEGRATED—See Robert Half Inc.; *U.S. Public*, pg. 1803
RABUCK STRANGER; *U.S. Private*, pg. 3341
RADARWORKS, INC.; *U.S. Private*, pg. 3342

RADARWORKS, INC.—See Radarworks, Inc.; *U.S. Private*, pg. 3342
RADIATE GROUP—See Omnicom Group Inc.; *U.S. Public*, pg. 1593
RADIATE GROUP—See Omnicom Group Inc.; *U.S. Public*, pg. 1593
@RADICAL MEDIA; *U.S. Private*, pg. 17
R.A. DINKEL & ASSOCIATES, INC.; *U.S. Private*, pg. 3334
RADIO DIRECT RESPONSE; *U.S. Private*, pg. 3343
RADIX COMMUNICATIONS, INC.; *U.S. Private*, pg. 3345
RAGUS MEDIA, LLC; *U.S. Private*, pg. 3346
RAINS BIRCHARD INC.; *U.S. Private*, pg. 3348
RAIN; *U.S. Private*, pg. 3346
RAIN; *U.S. Private*, pg. 3346
THE RAMEY AGENCY LLC; *U.S. Private*, pg. 4102
THE RAMEY AGENCY—See The Ramey Agency LLC; *U.S. Private*, pg. 4102
THE RAMEY AGENCY—See The Ramey Agency LLC; *U.S. Private*, pg. 4102
THE RAMEY AGENCY—See The Ramey Agency LLC; *U.S. Private*, pg. 4102
RAMONA—See Stagwell, Inc.; *U.S. Public*, pg. 1928
RAMSEY ADVERTISING; *U.S. Private*, pg. 3352
RANKINGS.IO, LLC; *U.S. Private*, pg. 3355
RAPID RESPONSE MARKETING LLC; *U.S. Private*, pg. 3356
RAPIER COMMUNICATIONS LIMITED—See CHI & Partners Limited; *Int'l*, pg. 1474
RAPP ARGENTINA—See Omnicom Group Inc.; *U.S. Public*, pg. 1592
RAPP BARCELONA—See Omnicom Group Inc.; *U.S. Public*, pg. 1592
RAPP BRAZIL—See Omnicom Group Inc.; *U.S. Public*, pg. 1592
RAPP BUDAPEST—See Omnicom Group Inc.; *U.S. Public*, pg. 1592
RAPP CENTRO AMERICA—See Omnicom Group Inc.; *U.S. Public*, pg. 1592
RAPP DALLAS—See Omnicom Group Inc.; *U.S. Public*, pg. 1592
RAPPDATA COMPANY—See Omnicom Group Inc.; *U.S. Public*, pg. 1592
RAPPDIGITAL BRAZIL—See Omnicom Group Inc.; *U.S. Public*, pg. 1592
RAPP HEALTHCARE—See Omnicom Group Inc.; *U.S. Public*, pg. 1592
RAPP HONG KONG—See Omnicom Group Inc.; *U.S. Public*, pg. 1592
RAPP LONDON—See Omnicom Group Inc.; *U.S. Public*, pg. 1592
RAPP MALAYSIA—See Omnicom Group Inc.; *U.S. Public*, pg. 1592
RAPPMEDIA—See Omnicom Group Inc.; *U.S. Public*, pg. 1592
RAPP MEXICO—See Omnicom Group Inc.; *U.S. Public*, pg. 1592
RAPP NEW YORK—See Omnicom Group Inc.; *U.S. Public*, pg. 1592
RAPP PARIS—See Omnicom Group Inc.; *U.S. Public*, pg. 1592
RAPP—See Omnicom Group Inc.; *U.S. Public*, pg. 1592
RAPP TOKYO—See Omnicom Group Inc.; *U.S. Public*, pg. 1592
RAPP/TRIBAL—See Omnicom Group Inc.; *U.S. Public*, pg. 1582
RAPP UK—See Omnicom Group Inc.; *U.S. Public*, pg. 1592
RAPP UK—See Omnicom Group Inc.; *U.S. Public*, pg. 1592
RAPP WORLDWIDE—See Omnicom Group Inc.; *U.S. Public*, pg. 1592
RARITAN ADVERTISING AGENCY; *U.S. Private*, pg. 3356
RATTLE ADVERTISING; *U.S. Private*, pg. 3357
RAVENNA DESIGN; *U.S. Private*, pg. 3357
RBMM—See The Richards Group, Inc.; *U.S. Private*, pg. 4107
RCG PRODUCTIONS; *U.S. Private*, pg. 3362
RDA INTERNATIONAL; *U.S. Private*, pg. 3364
REACHLOCAL EUROPE BV—See Gannett Co., Inc.; *U.S. Public*, pg. 899
REACHLOCAL GMBH—See Gannett Co., Inc.; *U.S. Public*, pg. 899
REACHLOCAL JAPAN SERVICES G.K.—See Gannett Co., Inc.; *U.S. Public*, pg. 899
REACH SPORTS MARKETING GROUP; *U.S. Private*, pg. 3365
READE COMMUNICATIONS GROUP; *U.S. Private*, pg. 3366
READE COMMUNICATIONS GROUP—See Reade Communications Group; *U.S. Private*, pg. 3366
READING ROOM, LTD.—See Fat Media Ltd.; *Int'l*, pg. 2622
REALLY GOOD COPY CO.; *U.S. Private*, pg. 3368
REALMAD MEDIA, LLC; *U.S. Private*, pg. 3368
REBOLUCION, LLC; *U.S. Private*, pg. 3370
RECIPROCAL RESULTS; *U.S. Private*, pg. 3370
RED212; *U.S. Private*, pg. 3376
RED7E; *U.S. Private*, pg. 3377
RED BALL TIGER; *U.S. Private*, pg. 3373
REDBERRY OUTDOORS SDN. BHD.—See Ancom Nylex Berhad; *Int'l*, pg. 449

RED BROWN KLE; *U.S. Private*, pg. 3373
RED DELUXE BRAND DEVELOPMENT; *U.S. Private*, pg. 3374
RED DOOR INTERACTIVE, INC.; *U.S. Private*, pg. 3374
RED FROG MARKETING—See Highland Productions, LLC; *U.S. Private*, pg. 1939
REDGROUP SP. Z O.O.—See Cyber_Folks S.A.; *Int'l*, pg. 1892
REDHEAD COMPANIES; *U.S. Private*, pg. 3378
RED HOUSE NORTH AMERICA, INC.; *U.S. Private*, pg. 3375
REDLEVER, INC.—See Adconion Media Group Ltd.; *Int'l*, pg. 127
REDMAS ARGENTINA, S.A.—See Entravision Communications Corporation; *U.S. Public*, pg. 779
REDMAS COLUMBIA, S.A.S.—See Entravision Communications Corporation; *U.S. Public*, pg. 779
REDMAS PERU, S.A.C.—See Entravision Communications Corporation; *U.S. Public*, pg. 779
RED MOON MARKETING LLC; *U.S. Private*, pg. 3375
THE RED PEAK GROUP LLC—See Hakuhodo DY Holdings Incorporated; *Int'l*, pg. 3222
REDPEG MARKETING, INC.; *U.S. Private*, pg. 3379
RED PEPPER INC.; *U.S. Private*, pg. 3375
RED PEPPER, INC—See Red Pepper Inc.; *U.S. Private*, pg. 3375
REDSCOUT LLC - SAN FRANCISCO—See Stagwell, Inc.; *U.S. Public*, pg. 1927
REDSCOUT LLC—See Stagwell, Inc.; *U.S. Public*, pg. 1927
RED SIX MEDIA, LLC; *U.S. Private*, pg. 3376
RED SQUARE; *U.S. Private*, pg. 3376
REDSTONE COMMUNICATIONS INC.; *U.S. Private*, pg. 3380
RED URBAN—See Omnicom Group Inc.; *U.S. Public*, pg. 1593
RED WAGON ADVERTISING & DESIGN; *U.S. Private*, pg. 3376
REED SENDECKE KREBSBACH; *U.S. Private*, pg. 3382
REESE, TOMASES & ELLICK, INC. (RT&E); *U.S. Private*, pg. 3383
REGAN CAMPBELL WARD MCCANN—See The Interpublic Group of Companies, Inc.; *U.S. Public*, pg. 2101
REGAN CAMPBELL WARD WEST—See The Interpublic Group of Companies, Inc.; *U.S. Public*, pg. 2101
REGBERG & ASSOCIATES, INC.; *U.S. Private*, pg. 3386
RE:GROUP; *U.S. Private*, pg. 3365
REID/O'DONAHUE & ASSOCIATES INC.; *U.S. Private*, pg. 3391
RE:INTERACTION; *U.S. Private*, pg. 3365
RELATIONSHIP TRAVEL & EVENT SOLUTIONS—See Aimia Inc.; *Int'l*, pg. 233
RELATIVITY, INC.; *U.S. Private*, pg. 3393
RELEVANT ADS, INC.; *U.S. Private*, pg. 3393
REMER INC. CREATIVE MARKETING; *U.S. Private*, pg. 3396
RENEGADE; *U.S. Private*, pg. 3397
RENNA COMMUNICATIONS; *U.S. Private*, pg. 3398
REN SCOTT CREATIVE MARKETING; *U.S. Private*, pg. 3396
REPEQUITY INC.—See Trinity Hunt Management, L.P.; *U.S. Private*, pg. 4235
REPEQUITY; *U.S. Private*, pg. 3400
REPRISE MEDIA ASIA—See The Interpublic Group of Companies, Inc.; *U.S. Public*, pg. 2104
REPRISE MEDIA AUSTRALIA—See The Interpublic Group of Companies, Inc.; *U.S. Public*, pg. 2104
REPRISE MEDIA, INC.—See The Interpublic Group of Companies, Inc.; *U.S. Public*, pg. 2104
REPUTATION PARTNERS, LLC; *U.S. Private*, pg. 3403
RESEARCH DEVELOPMENT & PROMOTIONS; *U.S. Private*, pg. 3404
RESEARCH INTERNATIONAL LIMITED—See Bain Capital, LP; *U.S. Public*, pg. 448
RESH MARKETING CONSULTANTS, INC.; *U.S. Private*, pg. 3405
RESOLUTION MEDIA—See Omnicom Group Inc.; *U.S. Public*, pg. 1593
RESOURCE/AMMIRATI—See International Business Machines Corporation; *U.S. Public*, pg. 1150
RESPOND2 CMEDIA; *U.S. Private*, pg. 3407
RESPONSE MARKETING GROUP LLC; *U.S. Private*, pg. 3408
RESPONSE MEDIA, INC.; *U.S. Private*, pg. 3408
THE RESPONSE SHOP, INC.; *U.S. Private*, pg. 4105
RESTAURANT RECRUIT, INC.; *U.S. Private*, pg. 3408
RESTORATION MEDIA; *U.S. Private*, pg. 3410
RESULTS DIRECT MARKETING; *U.S. Private*, pg. 3410
RETAILNEXT RP UK LTD.—See RetailNext, Inc.; *U.S. Private*, pg. 3411
RETELE COMPANY; *U.S. Private*, pg. 3411
RE:THINK GROUP; *U.S. Private*, pg. 3365
REVERB-DBC—See Diccicco Battista Communications; *U.S. Private*, pg. 1225
REVISION; *U.S. Private*, pg. 3416
REWARDS ARVATO SERVICES GMBH—See Bertelsmann SE & Co. KGaA; *Int'l*, pg. 996
REWIND INC.—See Dentsu Group Inc.; *Int'l*, pg. 2039
REX DIRECT NET, INC.; *U.S. Private*, pg. 3417

541810 — ADVERTISING AGENCIE...

REZN8 PRODUCTIONS, INC.; *U.S. Private*, pg. 3419
R/GA LONDON—See The Interpublic Group of Companies, Inc.; *U.S. Public*, pg. 2104
R/GA LOS ANGELES—See The Interpublic Group of Companies, Inc.; *U.S. Public*, pg. 2104
R/GA MEDIA GROUP, INC.—See The Interpublic Group of Companies, Inc.; *U.S. Public*, pg. 2103
R/GA SAN FRANCISCO—See The Interpublic Group of Companies, Inc.; *U.S. Public*, pg. 2104
R/GA SAO PAULO—See The Interpublic Group of Companies, Inc.; *U.S. Public*, pg. 2104
RGT ADVERTISING AGENCY; *U.S. Private*, pg. 3420
RHYMES AND COMPANY ADVERTISING; *U.S. Private*, pg. 3424
RIBECK & CO.; *U.S. Private*, pg. 3425
RICHARDS/CARLBERG; *U.S. Private*, pg. 3429
THE RICHARDS GROUP, INC.; *U.S. Private*, pg. 4106
THE RICHARDS GROUP, INC.—See The Richards Group, Inc.; *U.S. Private*, pg. 4107
RICHARDS/LERMA—See The Richards Group, Inc.; *U.S. Private*, pg. 4107
THE RICHARDS ORGANIZATION; *U.S. Private*, pg. 4107
RICHARDS PARTNERS—See The Richards Group, Inc.; *U.S. Private*, pg. 4107
RICHTER7; *U.S. Private*, pg. 3430
RICK JOHNSON & COMPANY, INC.; *U.S. Private*, pg. 3431
RICOCHET PARTNERS, INC.; *U.S. Private*, pg. 3431
RIECHESBAIRD, INC.; *U.S. Private*, pg. 3434
RIESTER-ROBB—See Riester; *U.S. Private*, pg. 3434
RIESTER; *U.S. Private*, pg. 3434
RIGER ADVERTISING AGENCY, INC.; *U.S. Private*, pg. 3435
RILEY HAYES ADVERTISING; *U.S. Private*, pg. 3437
RING2 MEDIA—See Osceola Capital Management, LLC; *U.S. Private*, pg. 3047
RISDALL MARKETING GROUP, LLC; *U.S. Private*, pg. 3440
RISE INTERACTIVE, INC.; *U.S. Private*, pg. 3440
RISE INTERACTIVE SRL—See Quad/Graphics, Inc.; *U.S. Public*, pg. 1745
RITTENHOUSE MARKETING ASSOCIATES; *U.S. Private*, pg. 3442
RIVER COMMUNICATIONS, INC.; *U.S. Private*, pg. 3443
RIVET MARKCOM MIDWEST, INC. - CHICAGO OFFICE—See The Interpublic Group of Companies, Inc.; *U.S. Public*, pg. 2103
RIZZUTI/AUSTIN MARKETING GROUP; *U.S. Private*, pg. 3449
R&J ADVERTISING INC.—See Ron Jon Surf Shop; *U.S. Private*, pg. 3477
R.K. SWAMY BBDO—See Omnicom Group Inc.; *U.S. Public*, pg. 1576
R.K. SWAMY/BBDO—See Omnicom Group Inc.; *U.S. Public*, pg. 1576
R.K. SWAMY/BBDO—See Omnicom Group Inc.; *U.S. Public*, pg. 1576
R.K. SWAMY/BBDO—See Omnicom Group Inc.; *U.S. Public*, pg. 1576
R.K. SWAMY/BBDO—See Omnicom Group Inc.; *U.S. Public*, pg. 1577
R.K. SWAMY/BBDO—See Omnicom Group Inc.; *U.S. Public*, pg. 1577
RL PUBLIC RELATIONS + MARKETING—See RL Public Relations + Marketing; *U.S. Private*, pg. 3450
RLR ADVERTISING INC.; *U.S. Private*, pg. 3450
RLR ADVERTISING; *U.S. Private*, pg. 3450
R.M. BARROWS, INC. ADVERTISING & PUBLIC RELATIONS; *U.S. Private*, pg. 3338
RMG MEDIA, LLC; *U.S. Private*, pg. 3451
RMI MARKETING & ADVERTISING; *U.S. Private*, pg. 3452
RMR & ASSOCIATES, INC.; *U.S. Private*, pg. 3452
ROBERT A. SHERMAN & ASSOCIATES, INC.; *U.S. Private*, pg. 3457
ROBERT FLEEGE & PARTNERS; *U.S. Private*, pg. 3458
ROBERT J. BERNS ADVERTISING LTD.; *U.S. Private*, pg. 3458
ROBERTS COMMUNICATIONS INC.; *U.S. Private*, pg. 3459
ROBERTS + LANGER DDB—See Omnicom Group Inc.; *U.S. Public*, pg. 1582
ROBERTSON WOOD ADVERTISING; *U.S. Private*, pg. 3460
ROBFRANKEL.COM; *U.S. Private*, pg. 3460
ROBIN SHEPHERD STUDIOS, INC.; *U.S. Private*, pg. 3460
ROBIN SHEPHERD STUDIOS, INC.—See Robin Shepherd Studios, Inc.; *U.S. Private*, pg. 3460
ROBINSON CREATIVE INC.; *U.S. Private*, pg. 3461
ROBINSON & MAITES, INC.; *U.S. Private*, pg. 3461
ROBINSON RADIO, INC.; *U.S. Private*, pg. 3462
ROCKERHEADS—See Omnicom Group Inc.; *U.S. Public*, pg. 1585
ROCKETCREATIVE; *U.S. Private*, pg. 3466
ROCKEY & ROCKWELL ADVERTISING, INC.; *U.S. Private*, pg. 3466
THE ROCKFORD GROUP; *U.S. Private*, pg. 4111
RODGERS TOWNSEND, LLC—See Omnicom Group Inc.; *U.S. Public*, pg. 1593
ROKKAN; *U.S. Private*, pg. 3473

ROME & COMPANY; *U.S. Private*, pg. 3476
RONALD R. WREN ADVERTISING, INC.; *U.S. Private*, pg. 3477
RONIN ADVERTISING GROUP; *U.S. Private*, pg. 3478
ROOFTOP COMMUNICATIONS; *U.S. Private*, pg. 3479
ROOM 214 INC.; *U.S. Private*, pg. 3479
ROSBERG FOZMAN ROLANDELLI ADVERTISING; *U.S. Private*, pg. 3481
ROSE & KINDEL—See Clayton, Dubilier & Rice, LLC; *U.S. Private*, pg. 925
ROSE & KINDEL—See Clayton, Dubilier & Rice, LLC; *U.S. Private*, pg. 925
ROSEN & BRICHTA; *U.S. Private*, pg. 3483
ROSKA DIRECT; *U.S. Private*, pg. 3484
THE ROSS AGENCY; *U.S. Private*, pg. 4112
ROTTER GROUP INC.; *U.S. Private*, pg. 3487
ROTTER GROUP INC.—See Rotter Group Inc.; *U.S. Private*, pg. 3487
ROUNDHOUSE MARKETING & PROMOTION, INC.; *U.S. Private*, pg. 3488
ROUNDPEG; *U.S. Private*, pg. 3488
RPM ADVERTISING; *U.S. Private*, pg. 3495
RPMC EUROPE LTD.—See RPMC, Inc.; *U.S. Private*, pg. 3496
RPMC - NEW YORK—See RPMC, Inc.; *U.S. Private*, pg. 3496
RPM CONNECT—See Ryan Partnership, LLC; *U.S. Private*, pg. 3510
RPM/DETROIT—See RPM Advertising; *U.S. Private*, pg. 3495
RPM/LAS VEGAS—See RPM Advertising; *U.S. Private*, pg. 3495
RPM RADAR REKLAM PAZARLAMA MUSAVIRLIK A.S.—See Dentsu Group Inc.; *Int'l*, pg. 2037
R&R PARTNERS; *U.S. Private*, pg. 3333
R&R PARTNERS—See R&R Partners; *U.S. Private*, pg. 3333
R&R PARTNERS—See R&R Partners; *U.S. Private*, pg. 3333
R&R PARTNERS—See R&R Partners; *U.S. Private*, pg. 3333
R&R PARTNERS—See R&R Partners; *U.S. Private*, pg. 3333
RS ENTERPRISES; *U.S. Private*, pg. 3496
RTK.IO, INC.—See Magnite, Inc.; *U.S. Public*, pg. 1354
THE RUBICON PROJECT LTD.—See Magnite, Inc.; *U.S. Public*, pg. 1354
RUBICON PROJECT SERVICOS DE INTERNET LTDA.—See Magnite, Inc.; *U.S. Public*, pg. 1354
RUBIN POSTAER & ASSOCIATES - ATLANTA OFFICE—See Rubin Postaer & Associates; *U.S. Private*, pg. 3500
RUBIN POSTAER & ASSOCIATES - CHICAGO OFFICE—See Rubin Postaer & Associates; *U.S. Private*, pg. 3500
RUBIN POSTAER & ASSOCIATES - DALLAS OFFICE—See Rubin Postaer & Associates; *U.S. Private*, pg. 3500
RUBIN POSTAER & ASSOCIATES - DENVER OFFICE—See Rubin Postaer & Associates; *U.S. Private*, pg. 3500
RUBIN POSTAER & ASSOCIATES - MOORESTOWN OFFICE—See Rubin Postaer & Associates; *U.S. Private*, pg. 3500
RUBIN POSTAER & ASSOCIATES - PORTLAND OFFICE—See Rubin Postaer & Associates; *U.S. Private*, pg. 3500
RUBIN POSTAER & ASSOCIATES; *U.S. Private*, pg. 3500
RUECKERT ADVERTISING; *U.S. Private*, pg. 3502
RUMBLE, INC.; *U.S. Public*, pg. 1825
RUMBLETREE, INC.; *U.S. Private*, pg. 3503
RUNYON SALTZMAN & EINHORN; *U.S. Private*, pg. 3504
RUSSELL HERDER; *U.S. Private*, pg. 3506
RUSSELL HERDER—See Russell Herder; *U.S. Private*, pg. 3506
RW ADVERTISING, INC.; *U.S. Private*, pg. 3508
RYAN PARTNERSHIP, LLC; *U.S. Private*, pg. 3510
RYAN PARTNERSHIP—See Ryan Partnership, LLC; *U.S. Private*, pg. 3510
RYAN PARTNERSHIP—See Ryan Partnership, LLC; *U.S. Private*, pg. 3510
S360S; *U.S. Private*, pg. 3519
S3 MEDIA INC.; *U.S. Private*, pg. 3519
SABRE MARKETING; *U.S. Private*, pg. 3521
SACHS MEDIA GROUP; *U.S. Private*, pg. 3522
SACUNAS, INC.; *U.S. Private*, pg. 3522
SAGARMATHA SAS—See Hopscotch Groupe S.A.; *Int'l*, pg. 3474
SAGE ADVERTISING; *U.S. Private*, pg. 3526
SAGE COLLECTIVE INC.—See Omnicom Group Inc.; *U.S. Public*, pg. 1593
SAGE COMMUNICATIONS, LLC; *U.S. Private*, pg. 3526
THE SAGE GROUP; *U.S. Private*, pg. 4113
SAGON-PHIOR—See Sagon-Phior; *U.S. Private*, pg. 3528
SALES DEVELOPMENT ASSOCIATES, INC.; *U.S. Private*, pg. 3532
SALESFACTORY + WOODBINE, INC.; *U.S. Private*, pg. 3532
SALTWATER COLLECTIVE LLC—See Innovatus Capital Partners LLC; *U.S. Private*, pg. 2083
SALVA O'RENICK; *U.S. Private*, pg. 3535

SALVETRIBAL WORLDWIDE—See Omnicom Group Inc.; *U.S. Public*, pg. 1585
SAMURAI ADWAYS INC.—See Adways Inc.; *Int'l*, pg. 169
SANCHO BBDO—See Omnicom Group Inc.; *U.S. Public*, pg. 1577
THE SANDBOX GROUP LLC—See Keystone Capital, Inc.; *U.S. Private*, pg. 2295
SANG AM & ASSOCIATES. INC.—See Daesang Corporation; *Int'l*, pg. 1909
SANGAM & ASSOCIATES; *U.S. Private*, pg. 3546
THE SAN JOSE GROUP LTD.; *U.S. Private*, pg. 4113
SANNA MATTSON MACLEOD, INC.; *U.S. Private*, pg. 3546
SAPUTO DESIGN, INC.; *U.S. Private*, pg. 3548
SAVAGLIO TBWA—See Omnicom Group Inc.; *U.S. Public*, pg. 1594
THE SAWTOOTH GROUP; *U.S. Private*, pg. 4114
SAXO-PHON GMBH—See Bertelsmann SE & Co. KGaA; *Int'l*, pg. 996
SAXTON HORNE ADVERTISING; *U.S. Private*, pg. 3558
SBC ADVERTISING; *U.S. Private*, pg. 3559
SCALES ADVERTISING; *U.S. Private*, pg. 3560
SCA PROMOTIONS, INC.; *U.S. Private*, pg. 3560
THE SCHAECHTER ADVERTISING AGENCY; *U.S. Private*, pg. 4114
SCHAWK USA, INC. - ATLANTA—See Matthews International Corporation; *U.S. Public*, pg. 1401
SCHAWK USA, INC. - KALAMAZOO—See Matthews International Corporation; *U.S. Public*, pg. 1401
SCHAWK USA, INC. - MINNEAPOLIS—See Matthews International Corporation; *U.S. Public*, pg. 1401
SCHAWK USA, INC. - REDMOND—See Matthews International Corporation; *U.S. Public*, pg. 1401
SCHAWK USA, INC.—See Matthews International Corporation; *U.S. Public*, pg. 1401
SCHEIBEL HALASKA, INC.; *U.S. Private*, pg. 3564
SCHERMER, INC.; *U.S. Private*, pg. 3564
SCHIFINO/LEE, INC.; *U.S. Private*, pg. 3564
SCHNEIDER ELECTRIC'S AGENCY; *U.S. Private*, pg. 3566
SCHREIBER & ROMAN, INC.; *U.S. Private*, pg. 3569
SCHUBERT COMMUNICATIONS, INC.; *U.S. Private*, pg. 3570
SCHUPP COMPANY, INC.; *U.S. Private*, pg. 3571
SCI DIRECT, INC.—See Service Corporation International; *U.S. Public*, pg. 1870
SCOPPECHIO; *U.S. Private*, pg. 3575
SCOTT BROWN MEDIA GROUP; *U.S. Private*, pg. 3576
SCOTT-MCRAE ADVERTISING INC.—See Scott-McRae Automotive Group Inc.; *U.S. Private*, pg. 3578
SCREENSHOT DIGITAL, INC.—See TEGNA Inc.; *U.S. Public*, pg. 1990
SCRIBBLE TECHNOLOGIES INC.—See e.Bricks Ventures; *Int'l*, pg. 2251
SEA GULL ADVERTISING SDN. BHD.—See Hai-O Enterprise Berhad; *Int'l*, pg. 3209
THE SEARCH AGENCY—See Stagwell, Inc.; *U.S. Public*, pg. 1928
SEARCH LIFE, INC.—See Hakuhodo DY Holdings Incorporated; *Int'l*, pg. 3222
SEARCH MOJO; *U.S. Private*, pg. 3586
SECOND STREET MEDIA, INC.—See Upland Software, Inc.; *U.S. Public*, pg. 2264
SECURITYCLEARANCEEXPO.COM; *U.S. Private*, pg. 3597
SEGAL LICENSING—See The Interpublic Group of Companies, Inc.; *U.S. Public*, pg. 2093
SEG MEDIA GROUP INC.; *U.S. Private*, pg. 3598
THE SEIDEN GROUP; *U.S. Private*, pg. 4116
SEITER & MILLER ADVERTISING, INC.; *U.S. Private*, pg. 3600
SELECTNY.BERLIN GMBH—See SelectNY L.P.; *U.S. Private*, pg. 3601
SELECTNY GMBH—See SelectNY L.P.; *U.S. Private*, pg. 3601
SELECTNY.KOBLENZ GMBH—See SelectNY L.P.; *U.S. Private*, pg. 3601
SELECTNY.LONDON LTD.—See SelectNY L.P.; *U.S. Private*, pg. 3601
SELECTNY L.P.; *U.S. Private*, pg. 3601
SELECTNY.PARIS—See SelectNY L.P.; *U.S. Private*, pg. 3601
SELF OPPORTUNITY, INC.; *U.S. Private*, pg. 3602
SELLING SOLUTIONS, INC.; *U.S. Private*, pg. 3603
SELMARQ; *U.S. Private*, pg. 3603
SEMBERA VANAK/FCB—See The Interpublic Group of Companies, Inc.; *U.S. Public*, pg. 2093
SENA REIDER, INC.; *U.S. Private*, pg. 3605
SENA REIDER, INC.—See Sena Reider, Inc.; *U.S. Private*, pg. 3605
SENDTRAFFIC.COM, INC.—See Protagenic Therapeutics, Inc.; *U.S. Public*, pg. 1729
SENSIS INC.; *U.S. Private*, pg. 3608
SEO.COM LLC; *U.S. Private*, pg. 3611
SEOFABRYKA SP. Z O.O.—See Cyber_Folks S.A.; *Int'l*, pg. 1892
SEO ONE INC.; *U.S. Private*, pg. 3611
SEOP; *U.S. Private*, pg. 3611
SERINO COYNE LLC—See Omnicom Group Inc.; *U.S. Public*, pg. 1593

N.A.I.C.S. INDEX 541810 — ADVERTISING AGENCIE...

N.A.I.C.S. Index

SERLE DESIGN; *U.S. Private*, pg. 3614
SEROKA; *U.S. Private*, pg. 3614
SERWER SMS POLSKA SP. Z O.O.—See Cyber_Folks S.A.; *Int'l*, pg. 1892
SET CREATIVE; *U.S. Private*, pg. 3617
SEVENTH POINT; *U.S. Private*, pg. 3619
SGW INTEGRATED MARKETING COMMUNICATIONS, INC.; *U.S. Private*, pg. 3622
SHAKER RECRUITMENT ADVERTISING & COMMUNICATIONS, INC.; *U.S. Private*, pg. 3623
SHAKER RECRUITMENT ADVERTISING & COMMUNICATIONS, INC.—See Shaker Recruitment Advertising & Communications, Inc.; *U.S. Private*, pg. 3623
THE SHAND GROUP; *U.S. Private*, pg. 4117
SHANGHAI ASATSU ADVERTISING CO., LTD.—See Bain Capital, LP; *U.S. Private*, pg. 428
SHANGHAI ASIARAY ADVERTISING—See Asiaray Media Group Limited; *Int'l*, pg. 620
SHANGHAI DAIKO MAOCU ADVERTISING CO., LTD.—See Hakuhodo DY Holdings Incorporated; *Int'l*, pg. 3220
SHANGHAI DAIKO MAOCU ADVERTISING CO., LTD.—See Hakuhodo DY Holdings Incorporated; *Int'l*, pg. 3220
SHARAVSKY COMMUNICATIONS; *U.S. Private*, pg. 3625
SHARKREACH, INC.; *U.S. Private*, pg. 3626
SHARP & CO.—See Sensis Inc.; *U.S. Private*, pg. 3608
SHEEHY & ASSOCIATES; *U.S. Private*, pg. 3629
SHEILA DONNELLY & ASSOCIATES; *U.S. Private*, pg. 3630
SHELTON INTERACTIVE—See Advantage Media Group, Inc.; *U.S. Private*, pg. 94
SHERRY MATTHEWS ADVOCACY MARKETING; *U.S. Private*, pg. 3634
SHIFT GLOBAL; *U.S. Private*, pg. 3636
SHINGATA INC.—See Dentsu Group Inc.; *Int'l*, pg. 2039
SHINKEN-AD CO., LTD.—See EQT AB; *Int'l*, pg. 2467
SHIODOME URBAN ENERGY CORP.—See Dentsu Group Inc.; *Int'l*, pg. 2039
SHIZUOKA HAKUHODO INC.—See Hakuhodo DY Holdings Incorporated; *Int'l*, pg. 3222
SHOULTZ & ASSOCIATES ADVERTISING, INC.; *U.S. Private*, pg. 3643
SIA CITY24—See Alma Media Corporation; *Int'l*, pg. 362
SIDDALL, INC.; *U.S. Private*, pg. 3645
SIDES & ASSOCIATES, INC.; *U.S. Private*, pg. 3645
SID LEE INTERNATIONAL LLC—See Hakuhodo DY Holdings Incorporated; *Int'l*, pg. 3222
SID LEE—See Hakuhodo DY Holdings Incorporated; *Int'l*, pg. 3222
SID LEE—See Hakuhodo DY Holdings Incorporated; *Int'l*, pg. 3222
SID LEE—See Hakuhodo DY Holdings Incorporated; *Int'l*, pg. 3222
SID LEE—See Omnicom Group Inc.; *U.S. Public*, pg. 1593
SID LEE USA—See Hakuhodo DY Holdings Incorporated; *Int'l*, pg. 3222
SID PATERSON ADVERTISING, INC.; *U.S. Private*, pg. 3645
SID SPORTMARKETING & COMMUNICATION SERVICES GMBH—See Agence France-Presse; *Int'l*, pg. 205
SIEGEL+GALE - LOS ANGELES—See Omnicom Group Inc.; *U.S. Public*, pg. 1593
SIEGEL+GALE—See Omnicom Group Inc.; *U.S. Public*, pg. 1593
SIGMA MARKETING GROUP LLC—See DeltaPoint Capital Management, LLC; *U.S. Private*, pg. 1202
SIGMAWORKS GROUP—See Omnicom Group Inc.; *U.S. Public*, pg. 1594
SIGNAL POINT MARKETING+DESIGN; *U.S. Private*, pg. 3649
SIGNALTREE MARKETING & ADVERTISING; *U.S. Private*, pg. 3649
SIGNATURE COMMUNICATIONS; *U.S. Private*, pg. 3650
SIGNATURE GRAPHICS—See Omnicom Group Inc.; *U.S. Public*, pg. 1593
SIITE INTERACTIVE LLC; *U.S. Private*, pg. 3651
SILLERY AND PARTNERS; *U.S. Private*, pg. 3653
SILLERY AND PARTNERS—See Sillery and Partners; *U.S. Private*, pg. 3653
SILLERY AND PARTNERS—See Sillery and Partners; *U.S. Private*, pg. 3653
SILTANEN & PARTNERS; *U.S. Private*, pg. 3653
SILVERSCAPE TECHNOLOGIES, INC.; *U.S. Private*, pg. 3663
SIMMONS FLINT—See Flint Communications, Inc. & Adfarm; *U.S. Private*, pg. 1545
SIMONS MICHELSON ZIEVE, INC.; *U.S. Private*, pg. 3666
SIMON WORLDWIDE, INC.; *U.S. Private*, pg. 3666
SIMPLIFI HOLDINGS INC.—See GTCR LLC; *U.S. Private*, pg. 1806
SIMPLY ZESTY LIMITED—See News Corporation; *U.S. Public*, pg. 1520
SINGLETON & PARTNERS, LTD.; *U.S. Private*, pg. 3670
SINUATE MEDIA, LLC.; *U.S. Private*, pg. 3670
SIQUIS, LTD.; *U.S. Private*, pg. 3671
SITEK MARKETING & COMMUNICATIONS; *U.S. Private*, pg. 3676
SITEWIRE; *U.S. Private*, pg. 3676
SIZMEK TECHNOLOGIES, INC.—See Vector Capital Management, L.P.; *U.S. Private*, pg. 4352
SJ COMMUNICATIONS; *U.S. Private*, pg. 3678
SJI FULFILLMENT—See SJI, Inc.; *U.S. Private*, pg. 3678
SJI, INC.; *U.S. Private*, pg. 3678
SK+G ADVERTISING; *U.S. Private*, pg. 3680
SKILLUP VIDEO TECHNOLOGIES CORPORATION—See Digital Holdings, Inc.; *Int'l*, pg. 2122
SKM GROUP; *U.S. Private*, pg. 3683
SKSW ADVERTISING; *U.S. Private*, pg. 3683
SKY ADVERTISING-CHICAGO—See Sky Advertising, Inc.; *U.S. Private*, pg. 3683
SKY ADVERTISING, INC.; *U.S. Private*, pg. 3683
SKYTYPERS, INC.; *U.S. Private*, pg. 3686
SKYWORKS TECHNOLOGIES, INC.; *U.S. Private*, pg. 3686
SLAUGHTER GROUP; *U.S. Private*, pg. 3687
SLEDGE—See Enero Group Limited; *Int'l*, pg. 2424
SLINGSHOT, LLC; *U.S. Private*, pg. 3689
SMALL ARMY, INC.—See Ruder Finn Group, Inc.; *U.S. Private*, pg. 3501
SMARTCLIP EUROPE GMBH—See Bertelsmann SE & Co. KGaA; *Int'l*, pg. 996
SMARTLITE; *U.S. Private*, pg. 3692
SMBOLOGY, INC.; *U.S. Private*, pg. 3693
SMITHGIFFORD; *U.S. Private*, pg. 3697
SMITH & JONES; *U.S. Private*, pg. 3694
SMITH/JUNGER/WELLMAN; *U.S. Private*, pg. 3696
SMITH, KAPLAN, ALLEN & REYNOLDS, INC.; *U.S. Private*, pg. 3696
SMITH, PHILLIPS & DI PIETRO; *U.S. Private*, pg. 3696
SMITH; *U.S. Private*, pg. 3693
SMITH—See SMITH; *U.S. Private*, pg. 3693
SMITH WALKER DESIGN; *U.S. Private*, pg. 3696
SMIZER PERRY; *U.S. Private*, pg. 3698
SNAP AGENCY, INC.; *U.S. Private*, pg. 3699
SNS MARKETING; *U.S. Private*, pg. 3701
SNYDER GROUP INCORPORATED; *U.S. Private*, pg. 3701
THE SNYDER GROUP; *U.S. Private*, pg. 4119
SOAP LINKED BY ISOBAR—See Dentsu Group Inc.; *Int'l*, pg. 2037
SOAR COMMUNICATIONS; *U.S. Private*, pg. 3702
SOBE SPORT S.R.L.—See Iervolino & Lady Bacardi Entertainment S.p.A.; *Int'l*, pg. 3597
SOCIALCOM INC.; *U.S. Private*, pg. 3703
SO DO IT, LLC; *U.S. Private*, pg. 3702
SOGEI INC.-SAPPORO BRANCH—See Digital Garage, Inc.; *Int'l*, pg. 2121
SOGEI INC.-SENDAI BRANCH—See Digital Garage, Inc.; *Int'l*, pg. 2122
SOLAR VELOCITY; *U.S. Private*, pg. 3707
SOLEM & ASSOCIATES; *U.S. Private*, pg. 3708
SOLOMON FRIEDMAN ADVERTISING LLC; *U.S. Private*, pg. 3709
SOLTYS SCHNITZLER SCHIRMER LLC; *U.S. Private*, pg. 3710
SOLUTIONS BY DESIGN, INC.; *U.S. Private*, pg. 3711
SOMERSET SPORTART; *U.S. Private*, pg. 3712
SONIC PROMOS; *U.S. Private*, pg. 3713
SONNHALTER; *U.S. Private*, pg. 3714
SOPEXA ITALIA S.A.—See Hopscotch Groupe S.A.; *Int'l*, pg. 3474
SOPEXA JAPON CO., LTD.—See Hopscotch Groupe S.A.; *Int'l*, pg. 3474
SOPEXA USA—See Hopscotch Groupe S.A.; *Int'l*, pg. 3474
SOUND COMMUNICATIONS, INC.; *U.S. Private*, pg. 3717
SOURCE COMMUNICATIONS; *U.S. Private*, pg. 3718
SOURCE COMMUNICATIONS—See Source Communications; *U.S. Private*, pg. 3718
SOURCE MARKETING LLC—See Stagwell, Inc.; *U.S. Public*, pg. 1928
SOUTHWEST MEDIA GROUP, LLC; *U.S. Private*, pg. 3740
SPACETIME, INC.; *U.S. Private*, pg. 3744
SPA-HAKUHODO CO., LTD.—See Hakuhodo DY Holdings Incorporated; *Int'l*, pg. 3222
SPARK451 INC.—See Jenzabar, Inc.; *U.S. Private*, pg. 2201
THE SPARK AGENCY, INC.; *U.S. Private*, pg. 4120
SPARK; *U.S. Private*, pg. 3745
SPARK; *U.S. Private*, pg. 3745
SPARXOO, LLC—See Big Sea, Inc.; *U.S. Private*, pg. 554
SPAWN IDEAS, INC.; *U.S. Private*, pg. 3747
SPEARHALL ADVERTISING & PUBLIC RELATIONS; *U.S. Private*, pg. 3747
SPEAR MARKETING GROUP LLC; *U.S. Private*, pg. 3747
SPECIALIST UK LTD.—See Omnicom Group Inc.; *U.S. Public*, pg. 1593
SPECIFIC MEDIA INC.; *U.S. Private*, pg. 3751
SPECTRUM MARKETING, INC.; *U.S. Private*, pg. 3753
SPECTRUM REACH, LLC—See Charter Communications, Inc.; *U.S. Public*, pg. 483
SPIKE ADVERTISING INC.; *U.S. Private*, pg. 3757
SPIKE/DDB—See Omnicom Group Inc.; *U.S. Public*, pg. 1582
SPIKER COMMUNICATIONS, INC.; *U.S. Private*, pg. 3757
SPIN RECRUITMENT ADVERTISING; *U.S. Private*, pg. 3757
SPIRO & ASSOCIATES MARKETING, ADVERTISING & PUBLIC RELATIONS; *U.S. Private*, pg. 3758
SPM MARKETING & COMMUNICATIONS, LLC—See Amulet Capital Partners, L.P.; *U.S. Private*, pg. 268
SPORT1 MEDIA GMBH—See Highlight Communications AG; *Int'l*, pg. 3388
SPORTS & BYTES GMBH—See Borussia Dortmund GmbH & Co. KGaA; *Int'l*, pg. 1115
SPOT BEHAVIOR MEDIA, LLC; *U.S. Private*, pg. 3761
SPOTLIGHT ADVERTISING; *U.S. Private*, pg. 3761
SPRINGBOX, LTD.; *U.S. Private*, pg. 3763
SPRING, O'BRIEN & CO. INC.; *U.S. Private*, pg. 3763
SPRIZA, INC.; *U.S. Public*, pg. 1920
SQUARE ONE, INC.; *U.S. Private*, pg. 3766
SQUARE ONE MARKETING; *U.S. Private*, pg. 3766
STALELIFE STUDIOS; *U.S. Private*, pg. 3776
STAMATS; *U.S. Private*, pg. 3776
STANDARD ADVERTISING, INC.—See The Interpublic Group of Companies, Inc.; *U.S. Public*, pg. 2092
STANDARD BUSINESS SERVICES; *U.S. Private*, pg. 3778
STAN & LOU ADVERTISING; *U.S. Private*, pg. 3777
STAN STONER, INC.; *U.S. Private*, pg. 3777
STAR MARKETING SERVICES—See Omnicom Group Inc.; *U.S. Public*, pg. 1594
STARMARK GLOBAL, INC.—See MARC USA, LLC; *U.S. Private*, pg. 2571
STARMARK INTERNATIONAL, INC.; *U.S. Private*, pg. 3787
STAR MEDIA NETWORK; *U.S. Private*, pg. 3785
STARR TINCUP; *U.S. Private*, pg. 3787
START.IO, INC; *U.S. Private*, pg. 3788
STASZAK COMMUNICATIONS; *U.S. Private*, pg. 3790
STAUCH VETROMILE & MITCHELL ADVERTISING, INC.; *U.S. Private*, pg. 3794
ST. CLAIRE GROUP; *U.S. Private*, pg. 3771
STEEL BRANDING; *U.S. Private*, pg. 3795
STEELE+; *U.S. Private*, pg. 3796
STEINER SPORTS MARKETING—See Omnicom Group Inc.; *U.S. Public*, pg. 1594
STEIN + PARTNERS BRAND ACTIVATION; *U.S. Private*, pg. 3797
STEINREICH COMMUNICATIONS, LLC; *U.S. Private*, pg. 3798
STEIN ROGAN + PARTNERS; *U.S. Private*, pg. 3798
STEPHAN & BRADY, INC.; *U.S. Private*, pg. 3801
STEPHENS & ASSOCIATES ADVERTISING, INC.; *U.S. Private*, pg. 3803
THE STEPHENZ GROUP, INC.; *U.S. Private*, pg. 4121
STERLING ADVERTISING CO.; *U.S. Private*, pg. 3804
STERLING BRANDS—See Omnicom Group Inc.; *U.S. Public*, pg. 1594
STERLING RICE GROUP; *U.S. Private*, pg. 3807
STEVENS ADVERTISING; *U.S. Private*, pg. 3809
STEVENS STRATEGIC COMMUNICATIONS, INC.; *U.S. Private*, pg. 3810
THE STEVEN STYLE GROUP; *U.S. Private*, pg. 4123
STEWARD MARKETING, LLC; *U.S. Private*, pg. 3811
STIEGLER, WELLS, BRUNSWICK & ROTH, INC.; *U.S. Private*, pg. 3812
STIR ADVERTISING & INTEGRATED MARKETING; *U.S. Private*, pg. 3813
STIRISTA, LLC; *U.S. Private*, pg. 3813
ST. JOHN & PARTNERS; *U.S. Private*, pg. 3771
STOLTZ MARKETING GROUP; *U.S. Private*, pg. 3816
STONER BUNTING ADVERTISING; *U.S. Private*, pg. 3830
STONE & SIMONS ADVERTISING; *U.S. Private*, pg. 3816
STONE WARD; *U.S. Private*, pg. 3826
STORAKERS MCCANN—See The Interpublic Group of Companies, Inc.; *U.S. Public*, pg. 2102
STOREBOARD MEDIA LLC—See Leonard Green & Partners, L.P.; *U.S. Private*, pg. 2423
STOWE AREA ASSOCIATION AGENCY; *U.S. Private*, pg. 3832
STRAIGHT NORTH LLC; *U.S. Private*, pg. 3833
STRATEGIC AMERICA; *U.S. Private*, pg. 3834
STRATEGIC MEDIA, INC.; *U.S. Private*, pg. 3835
STRATEGIES, A MARKETING COMMUNICATIONS CORPORATION; *U.S. Private*, pg. 3836
STRATEGIS; *U.S. Private*, pg. 3836
STRATMAR RETAIL SERVICES; *U.S. Private*, pg. 3837
STRAWBERRYFROG—See APCO Worldwide; *U.S. Private*, pg. 291
STREAM COMPANIES; *U.S. Private*, pg. 3838
STREAMLINE MARKETING, LLC—See Mountaingate Capital Management, L.P.; *U.S. Private*, pg. 2801
STREET CANCE MARKETING COMMUNICATIONS; *U.S. Private*, pg. 3838
STRONGMAIL SYSTEMS, INC.; *U.S. Private*, pg. 3841
STRONGMAIL SYSTEMS UK LTD.—See StrongMail Systems, Inc.; *U.S. Private*, pg. 3841
STROUD DESIGN, INC.; *U.S. Private*, pg. 3841
STUDIO98, LLC; *U.S. Private*, pg. 3844
STUN CREATIVE, LLC—See Known Global LLC; *U.S. Private*, pg. 2324
THE STURGESS COMPANY; *U.S. Private*, pg. 4123
SUCCESS ADVERTISING; *U.S. Private*, pg. 3848
SUCCESS ADVERTISING—See Success Advertising; *U.S. Private*, pg. 3848
SUCCESS ADVERTISING—See Success Advertising; *U.S. Private*, pg. 3848

541810 — ADVERTISING AGENCIE...   CORPORATE AFFILIATIONS

SUCCESS ADVERTISING—See Success Advertising; *U.S. Private*, pg. 3848
SUCCESS ADVERTISING—See Success Advertising; *U.S. Private*, pg. 3848
SUCCESS ADVERTISING—See Success Advertising; *U.S. Private*, pg. 3848
SUCCESS COMMUNICATIONS GROUP—See Success Advertising; *U.S. Private*, pg. 3848
SUKLE ADVERTISING, INC.; *U.S. Private*, pg. 3850
SULLIVAN & COMPANY; *U.S. Private*, pg. 3850
SULLIVAN CREATIVE SERVICES, LTD.; *U.S. Private*, pg. 3851
SULLIVAN CREATIVE—See Sullivan Creative Services, Ltd.; *U.S. Private*, pg. 3851
SULLIVAN HIGDON & SINK INCORPORATED; *U.S. Private*, pg. 3851
SULLIVAN HIGDON & SINK INCORPORATED—See Sullivan Higdon & Sink Incorporated; *U.S. Private*, pg. 3851
SULLIVAN HIGDON & SINK INCORPORATED—See Sullivan Higdon & Sink Incorporated; *U.S. Private*, pg. 3851
SULLIVAN PERKINS; *U.S. Private*, pg. 3851
SUMMIT MARKETING GROUP—See Summit Marketing; *U.S. Private*, pg. 3855
SUMMIT MARKETING; *U.S. Private*, pg. 3855
SUMMIT MARKETING—See Summit Marketing; *U.S. Private*, pg. 3855
SUMMIT MARKETING—See Summit Marketing; *U.S. Private*, pg. 3855
SUMMIT MARKETING—See Summit Marketing; *U.S. Private*, pg. 3855
SUMMIT MARKETING—See Summit Marketing; *U.S. Private*, pg. 3855
SUMMIT MARKETING—See Summit Marketing; *U.S. Private*, pg. 3855
SUNDIN ASSOCIATES, INC.; *U.S. Private*, pg. 3866
SUNDOG; *U.S. Private*, pg. 3866
THE SUNFLOWER GROUP; *U.S. Private*, pg. 4125
THE SUNFLOWER GROUP—See The Sunflower Group; *U.S. Private*, pg. 4125
THE SUNFLOWER GROUP—See The Sunflower Group; *U.S. Private*, pg. 4125
THE SUNFLOWER GROUP—See The Sunflower Group; *U.S. Private*, pg. 4125
SUNKEN STONE INC.; *U.S. Private*, pg. 3867
SUNRISE ADVERTISING; *U.S. Private*, pg. 3869
SUNSET COMUNICACAO—See Omnicom Group Inc.; *U.S. Public*, pg. 1585
SUOMEN BUSINESS VIESTINTA SBV OY—See Alma Media Corporation; *Int'l*, pg. 362
SUPEROXYGEN, INC.; *U.S. Private*, pg. 3881
SUPERSHIP HOLDINGS CO., LTD.—See Dentsu Group Inc.; *Int'l*, pg. 2039
SUPERSIGNS POLSKA SP ZO.O.—See iHeartMedia, Inc.; *U.S. Public*, pg. 1096
SUSAN DAVIS INTERNATIONAL; *U.S. Private*, pg. 3885
SWAG PROMO, INC.; *U.S. Private*, pg. 3889
SWANSON RUSSELL ASSOCIATES; *U.S. Private*, pg. 3891
SWANSON RUSSELL ASSOCIATES—See Swanson Russell Associates; *U.S. Private*, pg. 3891
SWEENEY; *U.S. Private*, pg. 3891
SWEENEY—See SWEENEY; *U.S. Private*, pg. 3891
SWING MEDIA; *U.S. Private*, pg. 3894
SYDYS CORPORATION; *U.S. Private*, pg. 3898
SYNAPTIC DIGITAL, INC.—See DMA Media Ltd.; *Int'l*, pg. 2142
TAG CREATIVE LIMITED—See Dentsu Group Inc.; *Int'l*, pg. 2039
TAG MENA FZE—See Dentsu Group Inc.; *Int'l*, pg. 2039
TAG WORLDWIDE AUSTRALIA PTY LTD.—See Dentsu Group Inc.; *Int'l*, pg. 2039
TAG WORLDWIDE (SHANGHAI) CO LTD.—See Dentsu Group Inc.; *Int'l*, pg. 2039
TAIGMARKS INC.; *U.S. Private*, pg. 3923
TAIWAN HAKUHODO MEDIA INC.—See Hakuhodo DY Holdings Incorporated; *Int'l*, pg. 3222
TALK, INC.; *U.S. Private*, pg. 3926
TAM-TAM/TBWA—See Omnicom Group Inc.; *U.S. Public*, pg. 1598
TANNAHILL ADVERTISING; *U.S. Private*, pg. 3931
TARGETABLE MARKETING SERVICES LLC; *U.S. Private*, pg. 3933
TARGETBASE CLAYDON HEELEY—See Omnicom Group Inc.; *U.S. Public*, pg. 1599
TARGETBASE - GREENSBORO—See Omnicom Group Inc.; *U.S. Public*, pg. 1599
TARGET DATA, INC.—See ARS Advertising, LLC.; *U.S. Private*, pg. 337
TARGET MARKETING MAINE; *U.S. Private*, pg. 3933
TARGET + RESPONSE INC.; *U.S. Private*, pg. 3933
TARTAN MARKETING; *U.S. Private*, pg. 3934
TATANGO, INC.; *U.S. Private*, pg. 3935
TBA GLOBAL, LLC - CHICAGO—See TBA Global, LLC; *U.S. Private*, pg. 3941
TBA GLOBAL, LLC - NASHVILLE—See TBA Global, LLC; *U.S. Private*, pg. 3941
TBA GLOBAL, LLC; *U.S. Private*, pg. 3941
TBC DIRECT, INC.—See TBC Inc.; *U.S. Private*, pg. 3941

TBC INC.; *U.S. Private*, pg. 3941
TBC SALES PROMOTION—See Ted Barkus Company, Inc.; *U.S. Private*, pg. 3957
TBWA ADRIATIC REGION—See Omnicom Group Inc.; *U.S. Public*, pg. 1594
TBWA/ALIF—See Omnicom Group Inc.; *U.S. Public*, pg. 1597
TBWA AME MED—See Omnicom Group Inc.; *U.S. Public*, pg. 1597
TBWA ATHENS—See Omnicom Group Inc.; *U.S. Public*, pg. 1594
TBWA/AUSTRALIA—See Omnicom Group Inc.; *U.S. Public*, pg. 1595
TBWA & BBDO A/S—See Omnicom Group Inc.; *U.S. Public*, pg. 1577
TBWA BELARUS—See Omnicom Group Inc.; *U.S. Public*, pg. 1594
TBWA BRUSSELS—See Omnicom Group Inc.; *U.S. Public*, pg. 1596
TBWA BUDAPEST—See Omnicom Group Inc.; *U.S. Public*, pg. 1594
TBWA CALIFORNIA—See Omnicom Group Inc.; *U.S. Public*, pg. 1598
TBWA CENTRAL ASIA—See Omnicom Group Inc.; *U.S. Public*, pg. 1596
TBWA/CHIAT/DAY LOS ANGELES INC.—See Omnicom Group Inc.; *U.S. Public*, pg. 1598
TBWA CHIAT DAY LOS ANGELES—See Omnicom Group Inc.; *U.S. Public*, pg. 1598
TBWA CHIAT DAY NEW YORK—See Omnicom Group Inc.; *U.S. Public*, pg. 1598
TBWA/COLOMBIA SUIZA DE PUBLICIDAD LTDA—See Omnicom Group Inc.; *U.S. Public*, pg. 1599
TBWA/COMPACT—See Omnicom Group Inc.; *U.S. Public*, pg. 1596
TBWA COMPANY GROUP—See Omnicom Group Inc.; *U.S. Public*, pg. 1596
TBWA CONCEPT UNIT—See Omnicom Group Inc.; *U.S. Public*, pg. 1596
TBWA COPENHAGEN—See Omnicom Group Inc.; *U.S. Public*, pg. 1595
TBWA CORPORATE—See Omnicom Group Inc.; *U.S. Public*, pg. 1596
TBWA COSTA RICA—See Omnicom Group Inc.; *U.S. Public*, pg. 1596
TBWA (DEUTSCHLAND) HOLDING GMBH—See Omnicom Group Inc.; *U.S. Public*, pg. 1594
TBWA/DUBLIN—See Omnicom Group Inc.; *U.S. Public*, pg. 1597
TBWA DURBAN—See Omnicom Group Inc.; *U.S. Public*, pg. 1597
TBWA/EL SALVADOR—See Omnicom Group Inc.; *U.S. Public*, pg. 1599
TBWA EMCG—See Omnicom Group Inc.; *U.S. Public*, pg. 1595
TBWA ESTONIA—See Omnicom Group Inc.; *U.S. Public*, pg. 1595
TBWA EUROPE—See Omnicom Group Inc.; *U.S. Public*, pg. 1596
TBWA FKGB—See Omnicom Group Inc.; *U.S. Public*, pg. 1596
TBWA FRANCE—See Omnicom Group Inc.; *U.S. Public*, pg. 1596
TBWA FREDERICK—See Omnicom Group Inc.; *U.S. Public*, pg. 1597
TBWA/G1—See Omnicom Group Inc.; *U.S. Public*, pg. 1596
TBWA GREATER CHINA—See Omnicom Group Inc.; *U.S. Public*, pg. 1595
TBWA/GROUP GERMANY—See Omnicom Group Inc.; *U.S. Public*, pg. 1595
TBWA GROUP POLAND—See Omnicom Group Inc.; *U.S. Public*, pg. 1595
TBWA GROUP—See Omnicom Group Inc.; *U.S. Public*, pg. 1596
TBWA/ GROUP VIETNAM—See Omnicom Group Inc.; *U.S. Public*, pg. 1595
TBWA/GUATEMALA—See Omnicom Group Inc.; *U.S. Public*, pg. 1599
TBWA HEALTH A.G.—See Omnicom Group Inc.; *U.S. Public*, pg. 1595
TBWA HONG KONG LIMITED—See Omnicom Group Inc.; *U.S. Public*, pg. 1595
TBWA HUNT LASCARIS (CAPE TOWN) PROPRIETARY LIMITED—See Omnicom Group Inc.; *U.S. Public*, pg. 1597
TBWA HUNT LASCARIS (DURBAN) PTY. LTD.—See Omnicom Group Inc.; *U.S. Public*, pg. 1597
TBWA HUNT LASCARIS (JOHANNESBURG) PTY. LTD.—See Omnicom Group Inc.; *U.S. Public*, pg. 1597
TBWA INDIA CORPORATE—See Omnicom Group Inc.; *U.S. Public*, pg. 1597
TBWA INDIA—See Omnicom Group Inc.; *U.S. Public*, pg. 1595
TBWA INDIA—See Omnicom Group Inc.; *U.S. Public*, pg. 1597
TBWA INDIA—See Omnicom Group Inc.; *U.S. Public*, pg. 1597

TBWA INDIA—See Omnicom Group Inc.; *U.S. Public*, pg. 1597
TBWA INDIA—See Omnicom Group Inc.; *U.S. Public*, pg. 1597
TBWA INTERACTIVE—See Omnicom Group Inc.; *U.S. Public*, pg. 1595
TBWA ISC MALAYSIA—See Omnicom Group Inc.; *U.S. Public*, pg. 1595
TBWA ISTANBUL—See Omnicom Group Inc.; *U.S. Public*, pg. 1595
TBWA ITALIA—See Omnicom Group Inc.; *U.S. Public*, pg. 1595
TBWA/JAIMEURIBE—See Omnicom Group Inc.; *U.S. Public*, pg. 1599
TBWA KOREA—See Omnicom Group Inc.; *U.S. Public*, pg. 1595
TBWA LATVIJA—See Omnicom Group Inc.; *U.S. Public*, pg. 1595
TBWA LISBON—See Omnicom Group Inc.; *U.S. Public*, pg. 1597
TBWA/LONDON LIMITED—See Omnicom Group Inc.; *U.S. Public*, pg. 1597
TBWA/MANCHESTER—See Omnicom Group Inc.; *U.S. Public*, pg. 1597
TBWA/MEDIA ARTS LAB—See Omnicom Group Inc.; *U.S. Public*, pg. 1598
TBWA MERLIN—See Omnicom Group Inc.; *U.S. Public*, pg. 1595
TBWA MOSCOW—See Omnicom Group Inc.; *U.S. Public*, pg. 1595
TBWA NEBOKO—See Omnicom Group Inc.; *U.S. Public*, pg. 1597
TBWA OSLO—See Omnicom Group Inc.; *U.S. Public*, pg. 1597
TBWA PALING WALTERS—See Omnicom Group Inc.; *U.S. Public*, pg. 1597
TBWA/PARAGON—See Omnicom Group Inc.; *U.S. Public*, pg. 1595
TBWA PARIS—See Omnicom Group Inc.; *U.S. Public*, pg. 1596
TBWA PERU—See Omnicom Group Inc.; *U.S. Public*, pg. 1597
TBWA PHS—See Omnicom Group Inc.; *U.S. Public*, pg. 1595
TBWA PRAHA—See Omnicom Group Inc.; *U.S. Public*, pg. 1595
TBWA PR—See Omnicom Group Inc.; *U.S. Public*, pg. 1595
TBWA RAAD—See Omnicom Group Inc.; *U.S. Public*, pg. 1597
TBWA ROMA—See Omnicom Group Inc.; *U.S. Public*, pg. 1595
TBWA SANTIAGO MANGADA PUNO—See Omnicom Group Inc.; *U.S. Public*, pg. 1595
TBWA SHANGHAI—See Omnicom Group Inc.; *U.S. Public*, pg. 1595
TBWA SINGAPORE—See Omnicom Group Inc.; *U.S. Public*, pg. 1595
TBWA SOFIA—See Omnicom Group Inc.; *U.S. Public*, pg. 1595
TBWA SOUTH AFRICA GROUP—See Omnicom Group Inc.; *U.S. Public*, pg. 1597
TBWA STOCKHOLM—See Omnicom Group Inc.; *U.S. Public*, pg. 1597
TBWA SWITZERLAND A.G.—See Omnicom Group Inc.; *U.S. Public*, pg. 1595
TBWA TANGO/ HELSINKI—See Omnicom Group Inc.; *U.S. Public*, pg. 1597
TBWA THAILAND—See Omnicom Group Inc.; *U.S. Public*, pg. 1595
TBWA TORONTO—See Omnicom Group Inc.; *U.S. Public*, pg. 1595
TBWA UKRAINE—See Omnicom Group Inc.; *U.S. Public*, pg. 1595
TBWA UNITED—See Omnicom Group Inc.; *U.S. Public*, pg. 1597
TBWA VANCOUVER—See Omnicom Group Inc.; *U.S. Public*, pg. 1598
TBWA VENEZUELA—See Omnicom Group Inc.; *U.S. Public*, pg. 1597
TBWA VILNIUS—See Omnicom Group Inc.; *U.S. Public*, pg. 1595
TBWA WARSZAWA—See Omnicom Group Inc.; *U.S. Public*, pg. 1595
TBWA WHYBIN LIMITED—See Omnicom Group Inc.; *U.S. Public*, pg. 1597
TBWA WIEN—See Omnicom Group Inc.; *U.S. Public*, pg. 1595
TBWA WORLDHEALTH CHICAGO INC.—See Omnicom Group Inc.; *U.S. Public*, pg. 1599
TBWA/WORLDHEALTH NEW YORK—See Omnicom Group Inc.; *U.S. Public*, pg. 1599
TBWA/WORLDHEALTH—See Omnicom Group Inc.; *U.S. Public*, pg. 1598
TBWA WORLDWIDE INC.—See Omnicom Group Inc.; *U.S. Public*, pg. 1594
TBWA ZAGREB—See Omnicom Group Inc.; *U.S. Public*, pg. 1595
TCAA; *U.S. Private*, pg. 3942

N.A.I.C.S. INDEX

541810 — ADVERTISING AGENCIE...

TCP-TBWA INDONESIA—See Omnicom Group Inc.; *U.S. Public*, pg. 1595
TCS MEDIA, INC.; *U.S. Private*, pg. 3943
TDA ADVERTISING & DESIGN; *U.S. Private*, pg. 3944
TEAM/ATHENS—See Omnicom Group Inc.; *U.S. Public*, pg. 1573
TEAM EPIPHANY—See Stagwell, Inc.; *U.S. Public*, pg. 1928
TEAMSPIRIT LIMITED—See Providence Equity Partners L.L.C.; *U.S. Private*, pg. 3292
TEAM VELOCITY MARKETING LLC; *U.S. Private*, pg. 3950
TED BARKUS COMPANY, INC.; *U.S. Private*, pg. 3957
TEKNICKS LLC; *U.S. Private*, pg. 3958
TELESCOPE UK LTD.—See Bally's Corporation; *U.S. Public*, pg. 268
TELIA & PAVLA BBDO—See Omnicom Group Inc.; *U.S. Public*, pg. 1577
TELMAR (ASIA) LTD.—See Splashlight LLC; *U.S. Private*, pg. 3759
TELMAR INTERNATIONAL INC.—See Splashlight LLC; *U.S. Private*, pg. 3759
TELMAR PEAKTIME B.V.—See Splashlight LLC; *U.S. Private*, pg. 3759
TELMAR SOFTWARE (SHANGHAI) LTD.—See Splashlight LLC; *U.S. Private*, pg. 3759
TEMKIN & TEMKIN; *U.S. Private*, pg. 3963
TENNESSEE PRESS SERVICE, INC; *U.S. Private*, pg. 3968
TEQUILA AUSTRIA—See Omnicom Group Inc.; *U.S. Public*, pg. 1598
TEQUILA BELGIUM—See Omnicom Group Inc.; *U.S. Public*, pg. 1598
TEQUILA BR—See Omnicom Group Inc.; *U.S. Public*, pg. 1598
TEQUILA CHINA—See Omnicom Group Inc.; *U.S. Public*, pg. 1598
TEQUILA DIGITAL—See Omnicom Group Inc.; *U.S. Public*, pg. 1598
TEQUILA DURBAN MARKETING SERVICES—See Omnicom Group Inc.; *U.S. Public*, pg. 1598
TEQUILA ESECE—See Omnicom Group Inc.; *U.S. Public*, pg. 1598
TEQUILA FRANCE—See Omnicom Group Inc.; *U.S. Public*, pg. 1598
TEQUILA GUATEMALA—See Omnicom Group Inc.; *U.S. Public*, pg. 1598
TEQUILA HONG KONG—See Omnicom Group Inc.; *U.S. Public*, pg. 1598
TEQUILA INDIA—See Omnicom Group Inc.; *U.S. Public*, pg. 1598
TEQUILA IRELAND—See Omnicom Group Inc.; *U.S. Public*, pg. 1598
TEQUILA ITALIA—See Omnicom Group Inc.; *U.S. Public*, pg. 1598
TEQUILA ITALIA—See Omnicom Group Inc.; *U.S. Public*, pg. 1598
TEQUILA JOHANNESBURG—See Omnicom Group Inc.; *U.S. Public*, pg. 1598
TEQUILA LONDON—See Omnicom Group Inc.; *U.S. Public*, pg. 1598
TEQUILA MANILA—See Omnicom Group Inc.; *U.S. Public*, pg. 1598
TEQUILA MYALO—See Omnicom Group Inc.; *U.S. Public*, pg. 1598
TEQUILA POLSKA SP ZOO—See Omnicom Group Inc.; *U.S. Public*, pg. 1598
TEQUILA PORTUGAL—See Omnicom Group Inc.; *U.S. Public*, pg. 1598
TEQUILA RAAD—See Omnicom Group Inc.; *U.S. Public*, pg. 1598
TEQUILA SINGAPORE—See Omnicom Group Inc.; *U.S. Public*, pg. 1598
TEQUILA SWITZERLAND AG—See Omnicom Group Inc.; *U.S. Public*, pg. 1598
TERAN TBWA—See Omnicom Group Inc.; *U.S. Public*, pg. 1599
TEXAS PRESS ASSOCIATION; *U.S. Private*, pg. 3977
TEXTUEL LA MINE—See Omnicom Group Inc.; *U.S. Public*, pg. 1597
TEXTUEL—See Omnicom Group Inc.; *U.S. Public*, pg. 1597
TG MADISON; *U.S. Private*, pg. 3979
THABASCO—See Omnicom Group Inc.; *U.S. Public*, pg. 1597
THAYER MEDIA, INC.; *U.S. Private*, pg. 3980
THELMA LAGER & ASSOCIATES; *U.S. Private*, pg. 4141
THERAPYSITES.COM LLC; *U.S. Private*, pg. 4142
THIELEN IDEACORP; *U.S. Private*, pg. 4144
THE THINK TANK; *U.S. Private*, pg. 4126
THE THINK TANK—See The Think Tank; *U.S. Private*, pg. 4126
THE THINK TANK—See The Think Tank; *U.S. Private*, pg. 4126
THOMASARTS HOLDING, INC.—See Integrity Marketing Group LLC; *U.S. Private*, pg. 2104
THOMAS KAUBISCH GMBH—See Avnet, Inc.; *U.S. Public*, pg. 254
THOMAS MEDIA GROUP, LLC; *U.S. Private*, pg. 4157
THOMPSON & COMPANY MARKETING COMMUNICATIONS; *U.S. Private*, pg. 4158
THOMPSON MARKETING; *U.S. Private*, pg. 4160

THRESHOLD INTERACTIVE—See Zealot Networks, Inc.; *U.S. Private*, pg. 4599
THUNDER TECH INC.; *U.S. Private*, pg. 4166
TIBUS—See Anderson Spratt Group; *Int'l*, pg. 450
TIC TOC; *U.S. Private*, pg. 4167
TIEMPO BBDO—See Omnicom Group Inc.; *U.S. Public*, pg. 1577
TIEMPO BBDO—See Omnicom Group Inc.; *U.S. Public*, pg. 1577
TIERNEY COMMUNICATIONS—See The Interpublic Group of Companies, Inc.; *U.S. Public*, pg. 2104
TILLMAN, ALLEN, GREER; *U.S. Private*, pg. 4171
TILT CREATIVE + PRODUCTION, LLC; *U.S. Private*, pg. 4171
TIMBES & YEAGER, LLC; *U.S. Private*, pg. 4172
TIMELY ADVERTISING, INC.; *U.S. Private*, pg. 4172
TIME & SPACE—See Williams Whittle Associates, Inc.; *U.S. Private*, pg. 4527
TIMMONS & COMPANY, INC.; *U.S. Private*, pg. 4173
TINSLEY ADVERTISING; *U.S. Private*, pg. 4175
TIPTON & MAGLIONE INC.; *U.S. Private*, pg. 4176
TITAN OUTDOOR—See Titan; *U.S. Private*, pg. 4176
TITAN SEO INC.; *U.S. Private*, pg. 4177
TITAN; *U.S. Private*, pg. 4176
TITAN WORLDWIDE—See Titan; *U.S. Private*, pg. 4177
TITAN WORLDWIDE—See Titan; *U.S. Private*, pg. 4177
TITAN WORLDWIDE—See Titan; *U.S. Private*, pg. 4177
TIVOLI PARTNERS; *U.S. Private*, pg. 4177
TIZIANI & WHITMYRE, INC.; *U.S. Private*, pg. 4177
TLG MULTICULTURAL COMMUNICATIONS; *U.S. Private*, pg. 4178
TM ADVERTISING, LLC; *U.S. Private*, pg. 4179
TMP (UK) LIMITED—See TrueBlue, Inc.; *U.S. Public*, pg. 2198
TMP WORLDWIDE ADVERTISING & COMMUNICATIONS LLC—See Gemspring Capital Management, LLC; *U.S. Private*, pg. 1659
TMP WORLDWIDE/ADVERTISING & COMMUNICATIONS—See Gemspring Capital Management, LLC; *U.S. Private*, pg. 1659
TMP WORLDWIDE/ADVERTISING & COMMUNICATIONS—See Gemspring Capital Management, LLC; *U.S. Private*, pg. 1659
TMP WORLDWIDE/ADVERTISING & COMMUNICATIONS—See Gemspring Capital Management, LLC; *U.S. Private*, pg. 1659
TMP WORLDWIDE/ADVERTISING & COMMUNICATIONS—See Gemspring Capital Management, LLC; *U.S. Private*, pg. 1659
TMP WORLDWIDE/ADVERTISING & COMMUNICATIONS—See Gemspring Capital Management, LLC; *U.S. Private*, pg. 1659
TMP WORLDWIDE/ADVERTISING & COMMUNICATIONS—See Gemspring Capital Management, LLC; *U.S. Private*, pg. 1659
TMP WORLDWIDE/ADVERTISING & COMMUNICATIONS—See Gemspring Capital Management, LLC; *U.S. Private*, pg. 1659
TMP WORLDWIDE/DIRECTIONAL MARKETING—See Gemspring Capital Management, LLC; *U.S. Private*, pg. 1659
TMRG, INC.—See comScore, Inc.; *U.S. Public*, pg. 561
TOBE DIRECT; *U.S. Private*, pg. 4180
TOCQUIGNY DESIGN, INC.; *U.S. Private*, pg. 4180
TOHOKU HAKUHODO INC.—See Hakuhodo DY Holdings Incorporated; *Int'l*, pg. 3222
TOM, DICK & HARRY ADVERTISING; *U.S. Private*, pg. 4183
TOMSHEEHAN WORLDWIDE; *U.S. Private*, pg. 4184
TOPAK MARKETING INC.—See The Peter Group, Inc.; *U.S. Private*, pg. 4094
TOPETE/STONEFIELD, INCORPORATED; *U.S. Private*, pg. 4187
TOP OF MIND NETWORKS, LLC—See Intercontinental Exchange, Inc.; *U.S. Public*, pg. 1142
TORRE LAZUR HEALTHCARE GROUP, LLC—See The Interpublic Group of Companies, Inc.; *U.S. Public*, pg. 2102
TOTAL MEDIA; *U.S. Private*, pg. 4191
TOTAL PROMOTIONS; *U.S. Private*, pg. 4191
TOTH, INC.; *U.S. Private*, pg. 4192
TOUCHE PHD—See Omnicom Group Inc.; *U.S. Public*, pg. 1590
TOV DELFI—See AS Ekspress Grupp; *Int'l*, pg. 590
TPG DIRECT—See Omnicom Group Inc.; *U.S. Public*, pg. 1599
TPN INC.—See Omnicom Group Inc.; *U.S. Public*, pg. 1599
TRACK—See Omnicom Group Inc.; *U.S. Public*, pg. 1592
TRACO ADVERTISING, INC.; *U.S. Private*, pg. 4201

TRACTION CORPORATION; *U.S. Private*, pg. 4201
TRACTORBEAM; *U.S. Private*, pg. 4201
TRACYLOCKE—See Omnicom Group Inc.; *U.S. Public*, pg. 1599
TRACYLOCKE—See Omnicom Group Inc.; *U.S. Public*, pg. 1599
TRACYLOCKE - WILTON OFFICE—See Omnicom Group Inc.; *U.S. Public*, pg. 1599
THE TRADE DESK AUSTRALIA PTY LTD—See The Trade Desk, Inc.; *U.S. Public*, pg. 2135
THE TRADE DESK GMBH—See The Trade Desk, Inc.; *U.S. Public*, pg. 2135
THE TRADE DESK JAPAN K.K.—See The Trade Desk, Inc.; *U.S. Public*, pg. 2135
THE TRADE DESK KOREA YUHAN HOESA—See The Trade Desk, Inc.; *U.S. Public*, pg. 2135
THE TRADE DESK (SINGAPORE) PTE. LTD.—See The Trade Desk, Inc.; *U.S. Public*, pg. 2135
THE TRADE DESK SPAIN SRL—See The Trade Desk, Inc.; *U.S. Public*, pg. 2135
TRAILER PARK; *U.S. Private*, pg. 4203
TRANS.AD SOLUTIONS COMPANY LIMITED—See BTS Group Holdings Public Company Limited; *Int'l*, pg. 1206
TRANSCEND MEDIA LLC; *U.S. Private*, pg. 4207
TRANSCOM WORLDWIDE SPAIN SL—See Altor Equity Partners AB; *Int'l*, pg. 396
TRANSLATION LLC—See The Interpublic Group of Companies, Inc.; *U.S. Public*, pg. 2104
TRANSWORLD ADVERTISING, INC.; *U.S. Private*, pg. 4212
TRAVELERS MARKETING LLC; *U.S. Private*, pg. 4214
TRAVEL SPIKE, LLC; *U.S. Private*, pg. 4213
TRENMEDIA, S.A.—See ACS, Actividades de Construccion y Servicios, S.A.; *Int'l*, pg. 116
TREPOINT BARC; *U.S. Private*, pg. 4218
TREPOINTBARC—See Trepoint Barc; *U.S. Private*, pg. 4218
TREW MARKETING; *U.S. Private*, pg. 4219
TRI-AUTO ENTERPRISES, LLC; *U.S. Private*, pg. 4221
TRIBAL DDB ATHENS—See Omnicom Group Inc.; *U.S. Public*, pg. 1582
TRIBAL DDB BARCELONA—See Omnicom Group Inc.; *U.S. Public*, pg. 1582
TRIBAL DDB BUDAPEST—See Omnicom Group Inc.; *U.S. Public*, pg. 1582
TRIBAL DDB CHICAGO—See Omnicom Group Inc.; *U.S. Public*, pg. 1582
TRIBAL DDB COLOMBIA—See Omnicom Group Inc.; *U.S. Public*, pg. 1582
TRIBAL DDB COPENHAGEN—See Omnicom Group Inc.; *U.S. Public*, pg. 1582
TRIBAL DDB HONG KONG—See Omnicom Group Inc.; *U.S. Public*, pg. 1582
TRIBAL DDB INDIA—See Omnicom Group Inc.; *U.S. Public*, pg. 1582
TRIBAL DDB MADRID—See Omnicom Group Inc.; *U.S. Public*, pg. 1582
TRIBAL DDB MALAYSIA—See Omnicom Group Inc.; *U.S. Public*, pg. 1582
TRIBAL DDB MELBOURNE—See Omnicom Group Inc.; *U.S. Public*, pg. 1582
TRIBAL DDB MILAN—See Omnicom Group Inc.; *U.S. Public*, pg. 1582
TRIBAL DDB NORTH AMERICA/NEW YORK—See Omnicom Group Inc.; *U.S. Public*, pg. 1582
TRIBAL DDB OSLO—See Omnicom Group Inc.; *U.S. Public*, pg. 1582
TRIBAL DDB PARIS—See Omnicom Group Inc.; *U.S. Public*, pg. 1582
TRIBAL DDB SAN FRANCISCO—See Omnicom Group Inc.; *U.S. Public*, pg. 1582
TRIBAL DDB SAO PAULO—See Omnicom Group Inc.; *U.S. Public*, pg. 1582
TRIBAL DDB SINGAPORE—See Omnicom Group Inc.; *U.S. Public*, pg. 1582
TRIBAL DDB—See Omnicom Group Inc.; *U.S. Public*, pg. 1582
TRIBAL DDB SYDNEY—See Omnicom Group Inc.; *U.S. Public*, pg. 1582
TRIBAL DDB TEL AVIV—See Omnicom Group Inc.; *U.S. Public*, pg. 1582
TRIBAL DDB TOKYO—See Omnicom Group Inc.; *U.S. Public*, pg. 1582
TRIBAL DDB TORONTO—See Omnicom Group Inc.; *U.S. Public*, pg. 1582
TRIBAL DDB VANCOUVER—See Omnicom Group Inc.; *U.S. Public*, pg. 1582
TRIBAL DDB WORLDWIDE—See Omnicom Group Inc.; *U.S. Public*, pg. 1582
TRIBAL FUSION, INC.; *U.S. Private*, pg. 4227
TRIBAL WORLDWIDE LONDON—See Omnicom Group Inc.; *U.S. Public*, pg. 1582
TRIBE; *U.S. Private*, pg. 4227
TRICKEY JENNUS INC.; *U.S. Private*, pg. 4229
TRILOGIC OUTDOOR; *U.S. Private*, pg. 4231
TRIMEDIA K.K.—See ad-comm Co., Ltd.; *Int'l*, pg. 123
TRINET INTERNET SOLUTIONS, INC.; *U.S. Private*, pg. 4232

541810 — ADVERTISING AGENCIE...   CORPORATE AFFILIATIONS

TRINET INTERNET SOLUTIONS, INC.—See Trinet Internet Solutions, Inc.; *U.S. Private*, pg. 4232
TRIO ADVERTISING. DESIGN. SOLUTIONS; *U.S. Private*, pg. 4236
TRIPLEINK—See Omnicom Group Inc.; *U.S. Public*, pg. 1588
TRI-STATE ADVERTISING CO., INC.; *U.S. Private*, pg. 4223
TRITON COMMERCE, LLC; *U.S. Private*, pg. 4239
TROIKA, INC.—See Troika Media Group, Inc.; *U.S. Public*, pg. 2197
TRONE BRAND ENERGY, INC.; *U.S. Private*, pg. 4241
TROZZOLO COMMUNICATIONS GROUP; *U.S. Private*, pg. 4244
TRUEFFECT, INC.; *U.S. Private*, pg. 4248
TRUE NORTH INC.; *U.S. Private*, pg. 4248
TRUE NORTH INTERACTIVE—See True North Inc.; *U.S. Private*, pg. 4248
TRUMPET LLC; *U.S. Private*, pg. 4250
TSUNAMI MARKETING; *U.S. Private*, pg. 4254
TUDO EVENTOS E PROMOCOES LTDA—See Omnicom Group Inc.; *U.S. Public*, pg. 1585
TUFFY ADVERTISING; *U.S. Private*, pg. 4257
TUKAIZ LLC; *U.S. Private*, pg. 4257
TULLO MARSHALL WARREN LTD.—See Accenture plc; *Int'l*, pg. 87
TURBINE; *U.S. Private*, pg. 4258
TURCHETTE ADVERTISING AGENCY LLC; *U.S. Private*, pg. 4259
TURCOTTE O'KEEFFE, INC.; *U.S. Private*, pg. 4259
TUREC ADVERTISING ASSOCIATES, INC.; *U.S. Private*, pg. 4259
TURKEL; *U.S. Private*, pg. 4259
TURTLEDOVE CLEMENS, INC.; *U.S. Private*, pg. 4262
TVER INC—See Dentsu Group Inc.; *Int'l*, pg. 2039
TV, INC.; *U.S. Private*, pg. 4263
TV, INC.—See TV, Inc.; *U.S. Private*, pg. 4263
TVNORTE, S. DE R.L. DE C.V.—See Entravision Communications Corporation; *U.S. Public*, pg. 779
TWENTY FOUR SEVEN, INC.; *U.S. Private*, pg. 4264
TWENTY FOUR SEVEN—See Twenty Four Seven, Inc.; *U.S. Private*, pg. 4264
TWIN CITIES AD; *U.S. Private*, pg. 4264
TWO WEST, INC.; *U.S. Private*, pg. 4267
UENO, LLC; *U.S. Private*, pg. 4274
THE UK TRADE DESK LTD—See The Trade Desk, Inc.; *U.S. Public*, pg. 2135
THE UNGAR GROUP; *U.S. Private*, pg. 4129
UNI COMMUNICATIONS INC—See Ildong Pharmaceutical Co., Ltd.; *Int'l*, pg. 3613
UNION ADVERTISING CANADA LP—See Stagwell, Inc.; *U.S. Public*, pg. 1928
UNITED ASATSU INTERNATIONAL LTD.—See Bain Capital, LP; *U.S. Private*, pg. 428
UNITED COMMUNICATION GROUP—See Hakuhodo DY Holdings Incorporated; *Int'l*, pg. 3221
UNITED LANDMARK ASSOCIATES, INC.; *U.S. Private*, pg. 4293
UNITREND LTD.—See The Interpublic Group of Companies, Inc.; *U.S. Public*, pg. 2102
UNIVERSAL COMMUNICATION—See The Interpublic Group of Companies, Inc.; *U.S. Public*, pg. 2103
UNIVERSAL MCCANN GMBH—See The Interpublic Group of Companies, Inc.; *U.S. Public*, pg. 2101
UNIVERSAL MCCANN—See The Interpublic Group of Companies, Inc.; *U.S. Public*, pg. 2101
UNIVERSAL MCCANN—See The Interpublic Group of Companies, Inc.; *U.S. Public*, pg. 2101
UNIVERSAL MCCANN—See The Interpublic Group of Companies, Inc.; *U.S. Public*, pg. 2103
UNIVERSAL MCCANN—See The Interpublic Group of Companies, Inc.; *U.S. Public*, pg. 2103
UNIVERSAL MCCANN—See The Interpublic Group of Companies, Inc.; *U.S. Public*, pg. 2103
UNIVERSAL MCCANN WORLDWIDE, INC.—See The Interpublic Group of Companies, Inc.; *U.S. Public*, pg. 2102
UNIVERSAL MEDIA SEVEN FZ-LLC—See The Interpublic Group of Companies, Inc.; *U.S. Public*, pg. 2104
UNIVERSAL MEDIA—See The Interpublic Group of Companies, Inc.; *U.S. Public*, pg. 2103
UNIWORLD GROUP-DETROIT—See Uniworld Group, Inc.; *U.S. Private*, pg. 4310
UNIWORLD GROUP, INC.; *U.S. Private*, pg. 4310
UNLEADED COMMUNICATIONS, INC.; *U.S. Private*, pg. 4310
THE UNREAL AGENCY; *U.S. Private*, pg. 4129
UPCURVE, INC.—See Gannett Co., Inc.; *U.S. Public*, pg. 906
UPSHOT INC.—See Leonard Green & Partners, L.P.; *U.S. Private*, pg. 2423
UPTON FULTON MCCANN PVT. LTD.—See The Interpublic Group of Companies, Inc.; *U.S. Public*, pg. 2103
URI, INC.; *U.S. Private*, pg. 4315
US MEDIA CONSULTING; *U.S. Private*, pg. 4319
USMP—See Omnicom Group Inc.; *U.S. Public*, pg. 1599
THE VANDERBILT ADVERTISING AGENCY, INC.—See Arnold Bernhard & Co.; *U.S. Private*, pg. 333
VANGUARDCOMM - CORAL GABLES—See Vanguard-Comm; *U.S. Private*, pg. 4344
VANGUARDCOMM; *U.S. Private*, pg. 4344
VANGUARD COMMUNICATIONS; *U.S. Private*, pg. 4343
VANKSEN GROUP—See Datawords Datasia SARL; *Int'l*, pg. 1981
VAN SCHOUWEN ASSOCIATES, LLC; *U.S. Private*, pg. 4341
VANTAGEPOINT, INC.; *U.S. Private*, pg. 4345
VAN WAGNER COMMUNICATIONS, LLC; *U.S. Private*, pg. 4341
VAN WAGNER SPORTS GROUP LLC—See Van Wagner Communications, LLC; *U.S. Private*, pg. 4341
VARSITY—See Pavone; *U.S. Private*, pg. 3115
VAUGHN WEDEEN KUHN; *U.S. Private*, pg. 4348
VAVINEL SAS—See HPS Investment Partners, LLC; *U.S. Private*, pg. 1997
VAYAN MARKETING GROUP, LLC; *U.S. Private*, pg. 4348
VCCP BLUE LIMITED—See Providence Equity Partners L.L.C.; *U.S. Private*, pg. 3292
VCCP HEALTH LIMITED—See Providence Equity Partners L.L.C.; *U.S. Private*, pg. 3292
VCCP LIMITED—See Providence Equity Partners L.L.C.; *U.S. Private*, pg. 3292
VCCP PTY. LTD.—See Providence Equity Partners L.L.C.; *U.S. Private*, pg. 3292
VCCP SEARCH LIMITED—See Providence Equity Partners L.L.C.; *U.S. Private*, pg. 3292
VCCP S.R.O.—See Providence Equity Partners L.L.C.; *U.S. Private*, pg. 3292
VELOCITY LOCAL, INC.—See Live Ventures Incorporated; *U.S. Public*, pg. 1332
VENABLES, BELL & PARTNERS; *U.S. Private*, pg. 4355
VENE INTERNATIONAL GMBH—See freenet AG; *Int'l*, pg. 2770
VENEZIA DESIGN INC.; *U.S. Private*, pg. 4356
VENTURA ASSOCIATES INTERNATIONAL LLC; *U.S. Private*, pg. 4357
VERBA S.R.L. ADVERTISING—See Omnicom Group Inc.; *U.S. Public*, pg. 1582
VERGE180, LLC; *U.S. Private*, pg. 4360
VERIFONE MEDIA, LLC—See British Columbia Investment Management Corp.; *Int'l*, pg. 1170
VERIFONE MEDIA, LLC—See Francisco Partners Management, LP; *U.S. Private*, pg. 1592
VERSANT, INC. - NEW YORK OFFICE—See Versant, Inc.; *U.S. Private*, pg. 4369
VERSANT, INC.; *U.S. Private*, pg. 4369
VERSO ADVERTISING, INC.; *U.S. Private*, pg. 4369
VERTICAL MARKETING NETWORK LLC; *U.S. Private*, pg. 4370
VERY, INC.; *U.S. Private*, pg. 4371
VEST ADVERTISING; *U.S. Private*, pg. 4371
VESTA—See Hypemarks, Inc.; *U.S. Private*, pg. 2019
VEVA COMMUNICATIONS; *U.S. Private*, pg. 4374
THE VIA GROUP LLC; *U.S. Private*, pg. 4130
VIA MARKETING, INC.; *U.S. Private*, pg. 4375
VIBE INC.—See BANDAI NAMCO Holdings Inc.; *Int'l*, pg. 829
VIBRANT MEDIA FRANCE—See Vibrant Media; *U.S. Private*, pg. 4376
VIBRANT MEDIA GMBH—See Vibrant Media; *U.S. Private*, pg. 4376
VIBRANT MEDIA LTD.—See Vibrant Media; *U.S. Private*, pg. 4376
VIBRANT MEDIA; *U.S. Private*, pg. 4376
VIBRANT MEDIA—See Vibrant Media; *U.S. Private*, pg. 4376
VICE SQUAD; *U.S. Private*, pg. 4376
VIDEOAMP, INC.; *U.S. Private*, pg. 4380
VIDEO RESEARCH INTERACTIVE INC.—See Dentsu Group Inc.; *Int'l*, pg. 2039
VIDEO RESEARCH LTD.—See Dentsu Group Inc.; *Int'l*, pg. 2040
VILLADCO INC.—See Banfi Product Corp.; *U.S. Private*, pg. 465
VILLAGE GREEN COMMUNICATIONS, INC.; *U.S. Private*, pg. 4383
VILLING & COMPANY, INC.; *U.S. Private*, pg. 4384
VIRTUAL FARM CREATIVE INC.; *U.S. Private*, pg. 4389
VIRTUAL MARKETING SERVICES (UK) LIMITED—See evoke plc; *Int'l*, pg. 2572
VISION CREATIVE GROUP, INC.; *U.S. Private*, pg. 4390
VISION MEDIA & MARKETING LLC; *U.S. Private*, pg. 4391
VISIORAMA AG—See APG/SGA SA; *Int'l*, pg. 513
VISUAL IMAGE ADVERTISING; *U.S. Private*, pg. 4404
VISUALMAX; *U.S. Private*, pg. 4404
VITAL MARKETING GROUP LLC; *U.S. Private*, pg. 4405
VITERI/TBWA—See Omnicom Group Inc.; *U.S. Public*, pg. 1599
VITRO PARTNERS LLC—See Stagwell, Inc.; *U.S. Public*, pg. 1928
VITROROBERTSON LLC—See Stagwell, Inc.; *U.S. Public*, pg. 1928
VITTLES; *U.S. Private*, pg. 4405
VIVA MEDIA—See Viva Partnership, Inc.; *U.S. Private*, pg. 4406
VIVA PARTNERSHIP, INC.; *U.S. Private*, pg. 4406
VIVIAL, INC.; *U.S. Private*, pg. 4406
VIVIDFRONT, LLC; *U.S. Private*, pg. 4406
VIZERGY; *U.S. Private*, pg. 4406
VIZEUM CANADA INC.—See Dentsu Group Inc.; *Int'l*, pg. 2038
VIZEUM CANADA INC. - VANCOUVER—See Dentsu Group Inc.; *Int'l*, pg. 2038
VIZEUM USA—See Dentsu Group Inc.; *Int'l*, pg. 2038
VLADIMIR JONES; *U.S. Private*, pg. 4407
VLADIMIR JONES—See Vladimir Jones; *U.S. Private*, pg. 4407
VLG ADVERTISING; *U.S. Private*, pg. 4408
VLYBY DIGITAL GMBH—See Azerion Group N.V.; *Int'l*, pg. 778
VOIDU B.V.—See Azerion Group N.V.; *Int'l*, pg. 778
VSA PARTNERS, INC.—See Innovatus Capital Partners LLC; *U.S. Private*, pg. 2083
VSA PARTNERS, INC.—See Innovatus Capital Partners LLC; *U.S. Private*, pg. 2083
VSBLTY GROUPE TECHNOLOGIES CORP.; *U.S. Public*, pg. 2312
VVL BBDO—See Omnicom Group Inc.; *U.S. Public*, pg. 1577
WAGGENER EDSTROM GMBH—See Waggener Edstrom; *U.S. Private*, pg. 4425
WAGGENER EDSTROM—See Waggener Edstrom; *U.S. Private*, pg. 4425
WAGGENER EDSTROM—See Waggener Edstrom; *U.S. Private*, pg. 4425
WAGGENER EDSTROM—See Waggener Edstrom; *U.S. Private*, pg. 4425
WAHLSTROM GROUP—See The Interpublic Group of Companies, Inc.; *U.S. Public*, pg. 2096
WAKEFLY; *U.S. Private*, pg. 4427
WALKER ADVERTISING, INC.; *U.S. Private*, pg. 4428
WALKER & ASSOCIATES, INC.; *U.S. Private*, pg. 4428
WALLWORK CURRY MCKENNA; *U.S. Private*, pg. 4431
WALRUS; *U.S. Private*, pg. 4432
WALSH SHEPPARD; *U.S. Private*, pg. 4433
WALTER F. CAMERON ADVERTISING INC.; *U.S. Private*, pg. 4433
WALTER LYONS & ASSOCIATES; *U.S. Private*, pg. 4434
WALTER LYONS & ASSOCIATES—See Walter Lyons & Associates; *U.S. Private*, pg. 4434
WALZ TETRICK ADVERTISING; *U.S. Private*, pg. 4435
WANDERLUST; *U.S. Private*, pg. 4435
THE WARD GROUP; *U.S. Private*, pg. 4133
WARHAFTIG & LITTMAN ADV/SALES PROMOTION/PR; *U.S. Private*, pg. 4442
WARREN MARKETING, INC.; *U.S. Private*, pg. 4444
WATAUGA GROUP LLC; *U.S. Private*, pg. 4451
WATERSWIDGREN/TBWA AB—See Omnicom Group Inc.; *U.S. Public*, pg. 1599
WEAPON 7—See Omnicom Group Inc.; *U.S. Public*, pg. 1599
WEBB PR; *U.S. Private*, pg. 4464
WEBGAINS GMBH—See ad pepper media International NV; *Int'l*, pg. 122
WEBGAINS LTD.—See ad pepper media International NV; *Int'l*, pg. 122
WEBGAINS S.L.—See ad pepper media International NV; *Int'l*, pg. 122
WEBMARKETING123; *U.S. Private*, pg. 4466
WEBPAGEFX INC.; *U.S. Private*, pg. 4466
WEBSCOPE; *U.S. Private*, pg. 4466
WEBSITEBIZ, INC.; *U.S. Private*, pg. 4466
WEBTEGRITY, LLC—See AiAdvertising, Inc.; *U.S. Public*, pg. 63
WEBWORKS ALLIANCE; *U.S. Private*, pg. 4467
WEINRICH ADVERTISING & COMMUNICATIONS, INC.; *U.S. Private*, pg. 4472
THE WEINSTEIN ORGANIZATION, INC.; *U.S. Private*, pg. 4134
WEINSTEIN OTTERMAN & ASSOCIATES; *U.S. Private*, pg. 4472
WEINTRAUB ADVERTISING; *U.S. Private*, pg. 4472
WELCOMM, INC.; *U.S. Private*, pg. 4473
WELLS COMMUNICATIONS, INC.; *U.S. Private*, pg. 4476
WEMMERS CONSULTING GROUP INC.; *U.S. Private*, pg. 4480
WENDT, INC.; *U.S. Private*, pg. 4481
WENSTROM COMMUNICATIONS, INC.; *U.S. Private*, pg. 4481
WESLEY DAY & COMPANY, INC.; *U.S. Private*, pg. 4482
WEST ADVERTISING/PUBLIC RELATIONS, INC.—See KOA Holdings Inc.; *U.S. Private*, pg. 2325
WEST ADVERTISING; *U.S. Private*, pg. 4483
WESTBOUND COMMUNICATIONS, INC.; *U.S. Private*, pg. 4485
WEST END ADVERTISING; *U.S. Private*, pg. 4485
WESTERN CREATIVE, INC.; *U.S. Private*, pg. 4492
WEST MEDIA GROUP, INC.; *U.S. Private*, pg. 4486
WESTMORELANDFLINT—See Flint Communications, Inc. & Adfarm; *U.S. Private*, pg. 1545
WESTREC PROPERTIES, INC.—See Centerbridge Partners, L.P.; *U.S. Private*, pg. 816
WHAM! ADVERTISING; *U.S. Private*, pg. 4503
WHEATLEY & TIMMONS; *U.S. Private*, pg. 4504
WHITE GOOD & CO. ADVERTISING; *U.S. Private*, pg. 4509

N.A.I.C.S. INDEX

WHITEHALL ADVERTISING INC.—See Chatam International Incorporated; *U.S. Private*, pg. 860
WHITEMYER ADVERTISING, INC.; *U.S. Private*, pg. 4511
WHITE & PARTNERS; *U.S. Private*, pg. 4508
WHITESPACE CREATIVE; *U.S. Private*, pg. 4512
WHITESPACE DESIGN GROUP, INC.; *U.S. Private*, pg. 4512
WHITESPACE (SCOTLAND) LIMITED—See Dentsu Group Inc.; *Int'l*, pg. 2038
WHITESPEED; *U.S. Private*, pg. 4512
WHITE/THOMPSON, LLC; *U.S. Private*, pg. 4510
WHOLE WHEAT CREATIVE; *U.S. Private*, pg. 4514
WHYBIN TBWA—See Omnicom Group Inc.; *U.S. Public*, pg. 1596
WIDMEYER COMMUNICATIONS—See Ruder Finn Group, Inc.; *U.S. Private*, pg. 3502
WIEDEN + KENNEDY - AMSTERDAM—See Wieden + Kennedy, Inc.; *U.S. Private*, pg. 4516
WIEDEN + KENNEDY, INC.; *U.S. Private*, pg. 4516
WIEDEN + KENNEDY INDIA—See Wieden + Kennedy, Inc.; *U.S. Private*, pg. 4516
WIEDEN + KENNEDY JAPAN—See Wieden + Kennedy, Inc.; *U.S. Private*, pg. 4516
WIEDEN + KENNEDY-NEW YORK—See Wieden + Kennedy, Inc.; *U.S. Private*, pg. 4516
WIEDEN + KENNEDY—See Wieden + Kennedy, Inc.; *U.S. Private*, pg. 4516
WIEDEN + KENNEDY UK LIMITED—See Wieden + Kennedy, Inc.; *U.S. Private*, pg. 4516
WIKREATE; *U.S. Private*, pg. 4517
WILDFIRE LLC; *U.S. Private*, pg. 4519
WILEN PRESS—See Wilen New York; *U.S. Private*, pg. 4519
WILKINS MEDIA COMPANY—See Wilkins Media Company; *U.S. Private*, pg. 4520
WILKINS MEDIA COMPANY—See Wilkins Media Company; *U.S. Private*, pg. 4520
WILLIAMS/CRAWFORD & ASSOCIATES; *U.S. Private*, pg. 4527
WILLIAMS WHITTLE ASSOCIATES, INC.; *U.S. Private*, pg. 4527
WILLIS CASE HARWOOD MARKETING COMMUNICATIONS INC.; *U.S. Private*, pg. 4527
THE WIMBLEY GROUP, INC.; *U.S. Private*, pg. 4137
W INC.; *U.S. Private*, pg. 4417
WINGMAN MEDIA; *U.S. Private*, pg. 4541
WINK, INCORPORATED; *U.S. Private*, pg. 4542
WINNER COMMUNICATIONS, INC.; *U.S. Private*, pg. 4542
WINSPER INC.; *U.S. Private*, pg. 4543
WINSTANLEY PARTNERS; *U.S. Private*, pg. 4543
WINSTON ADVERTISING; *U.S. Private*, pg. 4544
WIRE STONE, LLC; *U.S. Private*, pg. 4546
WIRESTONE, LLC—See Wire Stone, LLC; *U.S. Private*, pg. 4546
WIRESTONE—See Wire Stone, LLC; *U.S. Private*, pg. 4546
WIRESTONE—See Wire Stone, LLC; *U.S. Private*, pg. 4546
WIRESTONE—See Wire Stone, LLC; *U.S. Private*, pg. 4546
WIRESTONE—See Wire Stone, LLC; *U.S. Private*, pg. 4546
WIRESTONE—See Wire Stone, LLC; *U.S. Private*, pg. 4546
WIRZ COMMUNICATIONS AG—See Anton Borer Immobilien AG; *Int'l*, pg. 484
WIRZ & HAFNER WERBEBERATUNG GMBH—See Anton Borer Immobilien AG; *Int'l*, pg. 484
WIRZ WERBEAGENTUR GMBH—See Anton Borer Immobilien AG; *Int'l*, pg. 484
WOL DIRECT; *U.S. Private*, pg. 4553
WOLFBONE MARKETING; *U.S. Private*, pg. 4554
WOLFE/DOYLE ADVERTISING; *U.S. Private*, pg. 4554
WOLFF OLINS-NEW YORK—See Omnicom Group Inc.; *U.S. Public*, pg. 1599
WOLFF OLINS—See Omnicom Group Inc.; *U.S. Public*, pg. 1599
THE WOOD AGENCY; *U.S. Private*, pg. 4139
WOODRUFF SWEITZER CANADA INC.—See Woodruff Sweitzer; *U.S. Private*, pg. 4560
WOODS WITT DEALY & SONS, INC.; *U.S. Private*, pg. 4560
WORDSMITH DESIGN & ADVERTISING—See 2Gen Net; *Int'l*, pg. 5
WORKBOOK SOFTWARE A/S—See Roper Technologies, Inc.; *U.S. Public*, pg. 1814
WORKER BEES, INC.; *U.S. Private*, pg. 4563
WORKHOUSE PUBLICITY; *U.S. Private*, pg. 4563
WORKING CLASS, INC.; *U.S. Private*, pg. 4564
WORKING MEDIA GROUP; *U.S. Private*, pg. 4564
WORKPLACE IMPACT; *U.S. Private*, pg. 4564
WORLDWAYS, INC.; *U.S. Private*, pg. 4569
WORLD WRITERS LIMITED—See Dentsu Group Inc.; *Int'l*, pg. 2039
WRAY WARD MARKETING COMMUNICATIONS; *U.S. Private*, pg. 4572
WRIGHTIMC, LLC.; *U.S. Private*, pg. 4573
WRIGHTWAY CREATIVE GROUP; *U.S. Private*, pg. 4573
WRL ADVERTISING, INC.; *U.S. Private*, pg. 4574
WWAV RAPP COLLINS WEST—See Omnicom Group Inc.; *U.S. Public*, pg. 1592
WWAV—See Omnicom Group Inc.; *U.S. Public*, pg. 1593
WWWINS ISOBAR—See Dentsu Group Inc.; *Int'l*, pg. 2037

WYBLE ADVERTISING; *U.S. Private*, pg. 4575
WYSE ADVERTISING, INC.—See Falls Communications, Inc; *U.S. Private*, pg. 1468
WYSE; *U.S. Private*, pg. 4579
X-LINE HYPERMEDIA LTD.—See Dentsu Group Inc.; *Int'l*, pg. 2038
XPR LLC; *U.S. Private*, pg. 4582
X! PROMOS; *U.S. Private*, pg. 4579
XSTATIC PUBLIC RELATIONS; *U.S. Private*, pg. 4582
X STUDIOS INC.; *U.S. Private*, pg. 4579
YAAKOV SERLE ADVERTISING; *U.S. Private*, pg. 4584
YAFFE/DEUTSER—See Yaffe Group; *U.S. Private*, pg. 4584
YAFFE DIRECT—See Yaffe Group; *U.S. Private*, pg. 4584
YAFFE GROUP; *U.S. Private*, pg. 4584
YAHOO! GLOBAL PARTNER SOLUTIONS—See Apollo Global Management, Inc.; *U.S. Public*, pg. 167
YAMAGATA AD BUREAU CORP.—See Dentsu Group Inc.; *Int'l*, pg. 2040
YAMAMOTO MOSS AND MACKENZIE MARKETING; *U.S. Private*, pg. 4585
YAPPN CORP.; *U.S. Public*, pg. 2398
YARRUM MARKETING, INC.; *U.S. Private*, pg. 4586
YASHI, INC.—See Nexstar Media Group, Inc.; *U.S. Public*, pg. 1525
YEHOSHUA TBWA—See Omnicom Group Inc.; *U.S. Public*, pg. 1599
YELLOWHAMMER, LLC.; *U.S. Private*, pg. 4587
YELLOW PAGES COMMERCE COMPANY LIMITED—See Advanced Info Service Plc; *Int'l*, pg. 160
YES& HOLDINGS, LLC; *U.S. Private*, pg. 4588
YMARKETING, LLC—See Keystone Capital, Inc.; *U.S. Private*, pg. 2295
YODLE WEB.COM, INC.—See Siris Capital Group, LLC; *U.S. Private*, pg. 3675
YOMIKO ADVERTISING INC.—See Hakuhodo DY Holdings Incorporated; *Int'l*, pg. 3222
YOMIKO ADVERTISING—See Hakuhodo DY Holdings Incorporated; *Int'l*, pg. 3222
YOMIKO ADVERTISING—See Hakuhodo DY Holdings Incorporated; *Int'l*, pg. 3222
YOMIKO ADVERTISING—See Hakuhodo DY Holdings Incorporated; *Int'l*, pg. 3222
YOMIKO ADVERTISING—See Hakuhodo DY Holdings Incorporated; *Int'l*, pg. 3222
YOMIKO ADVERTISING—See Hakuhodo DY Holdings Incorporated; *Int'l*, pg. 3222
YOMIKO ADVERTISING—See Hakuhodo DY Holdings Incorporated; *Int'l*, pg. 3222
YOUNG COMPANY CREATIVE MARKETING COMMUNICATIONS, INC.; *U.S. Private*, pg. 4592
YOUNG & LARAMORE; *U.S. Private*, pg. 4592
YOUTECH & ASSOCIATES, INC.; *U.S. Private*, pg. 4594
ZAMBEZI; *U.S. Private*, pg. 4597
ZANZICO; *U.S. Private*, pg. 4598
ZAVOD BBDO—See Omnicom Group Inc.; *U.S. Public*, pg. 1577
ZEA BBDO—See Omnicom Group Inc.; *U.S. Public*, pg. 1577
ZEBRA RAPP MADRID—See Omnicom Group Inc.; *U.S. Public*, pg. 1593
ZEHNDER COMMUNICATIONS, INC.; *U.S. Private*, pg. 4599
ZEHNDER COMMUNICATIONS—See Zehnder Communications, Inc.; *U.S. Private*, pg. 4599
ZHONGYING DENTSU TEC ADVERTISING CO., LTD.—See Dentsu Group Inc.; *Int'l*, pg. 2038
ZIG.MARKETING; *U.S. Private*, pg. 4604
ZIMMERMAN ADVERTISING LLC - CHICAGO—See Omnicom Group Inc.; *U.S. Public*, pg. 1600
ZIMMERMAN ADVERTISING LLC - LOS ANGELES—See Omnicom Group Inc.; *U.S. Public*, pg. 1600
ZIMMERMAN ADVERTISING LLC - NEW YORK—See Omnicom Group Inc.; *U.S. Public*, pg. 1600
ZIMMERMAN ADVERTISING LLC—See Omnicom Group Inc.; *U.S. Public*, pg. 1600
THE ZIMMERMAN AGENCY LLC; *U.S. Private*, pg. 4140
THE ZIMMERMAN GROUP; *U.S. Private*, pg. 4140
ZION & ZION; *U.S. Private*, pg. 4605
ZIPLINE COMMUNICATIONS, INC.; *U.S. Private*, pg. 4606
THE ZISES GROUP; *U.S. Private*, pg. 4140
ZIZZO GROUP, INC.; *U.S. Private*, pg. 4606
ZK ADVERTISING—See The Interpublic Group of Companies, Inc.; *U.S. Public*, pg. 2103
ZLOKOWER COMPANY LLC—See CHR Group LLC; *U.S. Private*, pg. 889
THE ZLOTNICK GROUP; *U.S. Private*, pg. 4140
ZLR IGNITION—See Whitemyer Advertising, Inc.; *U.S. Private*, pg. 4511
ZOAR INTERACTIVE—See Whitemyer Advertising, Inc.; *U.S. Private*, pg. 4511
ZOCALO GROUP—See Omnicom Group Inc.; *U.S. Public*, pg. 1587
ZONE 5; *U.S. Private*, pg. 4608
ZOOM ADVERTISING; *U.S. Private*, pg. 4608
ZOOMEDIA, INC.—See Harris D. McKinney, Inc.; *U.S. Private*, pg. 1869
ZUCHELLI & JOHNSON HEALTHCARE COMMUNICATIONS; *U.S. Private*, pg. 4609

541820 — PUBLIC RELATIONS AGENCIES

360 PUBLIC RELATIONS LLC; *U.S. Private*, pg. 8
42WEST LLC—See Dolphin Entertainment, Inc.; *U.S. Public*, pg. 673
5W PUBLIC RELATIONS; *U.S. Private*, pg. 16
5W PUBLIC RELATIONS—See 5W Public Relations; *U.S. Private*, pg. 16
ABI ASIA—See Ruder Finn Group, Inc.; *U.S. Private*, pg. 3501
ABI EUROPE—See Ruder Finn Group, Inc.; *U.S. Private*, pg. 3501
ABI MARKETING PUBLIC RELATIONS—See Ruder Finn Group, Inc.; *U.S. Private*, pg. 3501
A. BRIGHT IDEA; *U.S. Private*, pg. 22
A. BRIGHT IDEA—See A. Bright Idea; *U.S. Private*, pg. 22
ACCENT MEDIA PRODUCTIONS, INC.; *U.S. Private*, pg. 50
ACCESS EMANATE COMMUNICATIONS—See Omnicom Group Inc.; *U.S. Public*, pg. 1586
ACKERMANN PR; *U.S. Private*, pg. 60
AC-SANAFOR—See The Interpublic Group of Companies, Inc.; *U.S. Public*, pg. 2104
ACTION GLOBAL COMMUNICATIONS LTD.—See The Interpublic Group of Companies, Inc.; *U.S. Public*, pg. 2094
ACTION HELLAS—See The Interpublic Group of Companies, Inc.; *U.S. Public*, pg. 2094
A.D. ADAMS ADVERTISING, INC.; *U.S. Private*, pg. 25
ADAM FRIEDMAN ASSOCIATES; *U.S. Private*, pg. 73
ADAMS UNLIMITED; *U.S. Private*, pg. 75
ADPR LTD.; *Int'l*, pg. 152
AGENCE SCHILLING COMMUNICATION; *Int'l*, pg. 205
AGENCY 33; *U.S. Private*, pg. 126
AGENDA; *U.S. Private*, pg. 126
AGENDA—See Agenda; *U.S. Private*, pg. 127
AIGNER PRENSKY MARKETING GROUP; *U.S. Private*, pg. 132
AIRFOIL PUBLIC RELATIONS; *U.S. Private*, pg. 141
ALAN WEINKRANTZ & COMPANY; *U.S. Private*, pg. 150
ALLEN & CARON INC.—See Dresner Corporate Services Inc.; *U.S. Private*, pg. 1276
ALLISON & PARTNERS LLC; *U.S. Private*, pg. 192
ALLISON & PARTNERS—See Allison & Partners LLC; *U.S. Private*, pg. 192
ALLISON & PARTNERS—See Allison & Partners LLC; *U.S. Private*, pg. 192
ALLISON & PARTNERS—See Allison & Partners LLC; *U.S. Private*, pg. 192
ALLISON & PARTNERS—See Allison & Partners LLC; *U.S. Private*, pg. 192
AMADA LASER AMERICA INC.—See Amada Holdings Co., Ltd.; *Int'l*, pg. 404
AMI COMMUNICATIONS SLOVAKIA—See Daniel J. Edelman, Inc.; *U.S. Private*, pg. 1154
AMI COMMUNICATIONS—See Daniel J. Edelman, Inc.; *U.S. Private*, pg. 1154
ANDOVER COMMUNICATIONS, INC.; *U.S. Private*, pg. 279
ANNE KLEIN COMMUNICATIONS GROUP, LLC; *U.S. Private*, pg. 284
ANREDER & COMPANY—See Anreder & Co.; *U.S. Private*, pg. 285
ANREDER & CO.; *U.S. Private*, pg. 285
ANTENNA GROUP, INC.—See Beckerman Group; *U.S. Private*, pg. 511
APCO WORLDWIDE - PARIS—See APCO Worldwide; *U.S. Private*, pg. 291
APCO WORLDWIDE—See APCO Worldwide; *U.S. Private*, pg. 290
APCO WORLDWIDE—See APCO Worldwide; *U.S. Private*, pg. 291
APCO WORLDWIDE—See APCO Worldwide; *U.S. Private*, pg. 291
APCO WORLDWIDE—See APCO Worldwide; *U.S. Private*, pg. 291
APCO WORLDWIDE—See APCO Worldwide; *U.S. Private*, pg. 291
APCO WORLDWIDE—See APCO Worldwide; *U.S. Private*, pg. 291
APCO WORLDWIDE—See APCO Worldwide; *U.S. Private*, pg. 291
APCO WORLDWIDE—See APCO Worldwide; *U.S. Private*, pg. 291
APCO WORLDWIDE—See APCO Worldwide; *U.S. Private*, pg. 291
APCO WORLDWIDE—See APCO Worldwide; *U.S. Private*, pg. 291
APCO WORLDWIDE—See APCO Worldwide; *U.S. Private*, pg. 291
APCO WORLDWIDE—See APCO Worldwide; *U.S. Private*, pg. 291
APCO WORLDWIDE—See APCO Worldwide; *U.S. Private*, pg. 291
APCO WORLDWIDE—See APCO Worldwide; *U.S. Private*, pg. 291

541820 — PUBLIC RELATIONS AG...

APRA PORTER NOVELLI—See Omnicom Group Inc.; *U.S. Public*, pg. 1590
APT RESOURCES & SERVICES SRL; *Int'l*, pg. 523
THE ARDELL GROUP; *U.S. Private*, pg. 3987
ARGENTINA PORTER NOVELLI—See Omnicom Group Inc.; *U.S. Public*, pg. 1590
ARTICULATE COMMUNICATIONS INC.; *U.S. Private*, pg. 342
ARTICULATE COMMUNICATIONS INC.—See Articulate Communications Inc.; *U.S. Private*, pg. 342
ARTS & COMMUNICATIONS COUNSELORS—See Ruder Finn Group, Inc.; *U.S. Private*, pg. 3501
ATD PORTER NOVELLI—See Omnicom Group Inc.; *U.S. Public*, pg. 1590
AT THE TABLE PUBLIC RELATIONS; *U.S. Private*, pg. 363
AUTOCOM ASSOCIATES; *U.S. Private*, pg. 398
AVIAREPS MARKETING GARDEN LTD.; *Int'l*, pg. 741
AVIAREPS MARKETING GARDEN LTD.—See AVIAREPS Marketing Garden Ltd.; *Int'l*, pg. 741
AVIAREPS MARKETING GARDEN—See AVIAREPS Marketing Garden Ltd.; *Int'l*, pg. 741
AXIA PUBLIC RELATIONS; *U.S. Private*, pg. 412
THE BAILIWICK COMPANY; *U.S. Private*, pg. 3990
BALTZ & COMPANY - DENVER—See Baltz & Company; *U.S. Private*, pg. 463
BALTZ & COMPANY; *U.S. Private*, pg. 463
BALTZ & COMPANY—See Baltz & Company; *U.S. Private*, pg. 463
BAMBOO MARKETING; *U.S. Private*, pg. 463
BANGKOK PR PORTER NOVELLI—See Omnicom Group Inc.; *U.S. Public*, pg. 1590
THE BATEMAN GROUP; *U.S. Private*, pg. 3992
THE BATEMAN GROUP—See The Bateman Group; *U.S. Private*, pg. 3992
THE BAWMANN GROUP; *U.S. Private*, pg. 3992
BEATTIE COMMUNICATIONS GROUP—See Beattie Communications Group; *Int'l*, pg. 933
BEATTIE COMMUNICATIONS GROUP—See Beattie Communications Group; *Int'l*, pg. 933
BEATTIE COMMUNICATIONS GROUP—See Beattie Communications Group; *Int'l*, pg. 933
BEAUPRE & CO. PUBLIC RELATIONS INC.—See Omnicom Group Inc.; *U.S. Public*, pg. 1577
BECKERMAN GROUP; *U.S. Private*, pg. 511
BEHAN COMMUNICATIONS, INC.; *U.S. Private*, pg. 514
BENCHMARK DISPLAYS; *U.S. Private*, pg. 523
BENDER/HELPER IMPACT, INC.—See Dolphin Entertainment, Inc.; *U.S. Public*, pg. 673
BENTLEY PORTER NOVELLI-SHANGHAI—See Omnicom Group Inc.; *U.S. Public*, pg. 1590
BERRY ECKE ASSOCIATES; *U.S. Private*, pg. 538
B/HI COMMUNICATIONS, INC.—See Dolphin Entertainment, Inc.; *U.S. Public*, pg. 673
BIANCHI PUBLIC RELATIONS INC.; *U.S. Private*, pg. 550
BIG INK PR & MARKETING; *U.S. Private*, pg. 553
BIOSPACE, INC.—See Ziff Davis, Inc.; *U.S. Public*, pg. 2404
BIRNBACH COMMUNICATIONS, INC.; *U.S. Private*, pg. 565
BITNER GOODMAN; *U.S. Private*, pg. 567
BITNER HENNESSY—See Bitner Goodman; *U.S. Private*, pg. 567
THE BLAINE GROUP; *U.S. Private*, pg. 3995
BLINNPR; *U.S. Private*, pg. 581
BLISSPR—See Bliss Integrated Communication; *U.S. Private*, pg. 582
BLITZ MEDIA-DIRECT—See The Linick Group, Inc.; *U.S. Private*, pg. 4070
BLUECHIP AGENTUR FOR PUBLIC RELATIONS & STRATEGY GMBH—See Dentsu Group Inc.; *Int'l*, pg. 2035
BLUE LOTUS COMMUNICATIONS CONSULTANCY; *Int'l*, pg. 1068
BLUE WORLDWIDE—See Daniel J. Edelman, Inc.; *U.S. Private*, pg. 1154
THE BOHLE COMPANY; *U.S. Private*, pg. 3995
BOOKE & COMPANY, INC.; *U.S. Private*, pg. 615
BOXER CREATIVE—See The Marketing Store; *U.S. Private*, pg. 4075
BRACY TUCKER BROWN & VALANZANO; *U.S. Private*, pg. 630
BRADFORD EQUITIES MANAGEMENT, LLC; *U.S. Private*, pg. 631
BREAKAWAY COMMUNICATIONS LLC; *U.S. Private*, pg. 642
BREAKAWAY COMMUNICATIONS LLC—See Breakaway Communications LLC; *U.S. Private*, pg. 642
BRODEUR BRAZIL—See Omnicom Group Inc.; *U.S. Public*, pg. 1577
BRODEUR MARTEC—See Omnicom Group Inc.; *U.S. Public*, pg. 1577
BRODEUR PARTNERS—See Omnicom Group Inc.; *U.S. Public*, pg. 1577
BRODEUR PARTNERS—See Omnicom Group Inc.; *U.S. Public*, pg. 1578
BRODEUR PARTNERS—See Omnicom Group Inc.; *U.S. Public*, pg. 1578
BRODEUR PARTNERS—See Omnicom Group Inc.; *U.S. Public*, pg. 1578
BROOKLINE PUBLIC RELATIONS INC.; *Int'l*, pg. 1194
BROTMAN WINTER FRIED COMMUNICATIONS; *U.S. Private*, pg. 665
BUCKLEY & KALDENBACH; *U.S. Private*, pg. 678
BURNS360; *U.S. Private*, pg. 691
BUSINESS STRATEGIES & BEYOND LLC; *U.S. Private*, pg. 695
CANALE COMMUNICATIONS INC.—See Clayton, Dubilier & Rice, LLC; *U.S. Private*, pg. 927
CAPITAL-IMAGE—See Environics Communications; *U.S. Private*, pg. 1407
CAPONIGRO PUBLIC RELATIONS, INC.; *U.S. Private*, pg. 745
CAPSTRAT; *U.S. Private*, pg. 746
CARMICHAEL LYNCH RELATE—See The Interpublic Group of Companies, Inc.; *U.S. Public*, pg. 2090
CARMICHAEL LYNCH SPONG—See The Interpublic Group of Companies, Inc.; *U.S. Public*, pg. 2090
CAROLINA PUBLIC RELATIONS/MARKETING ASSOCIATES, INC.—See Chernoff Newman, LLC; *U.S. Private*, pg. 873
CAROLYN GRISKO & ASSOCIATES INC.; *U.S. Private*, pg. 769
CASEY & SAYRE; *U.S. Private*, pg. 782
CATAPULT PR-IR, L.L.C.; *U.S. Private*, pg. 787
CAUGHERTY HAHN COMMUNICATIONS, INC.; *U.S. Private*, pg. 794
CECE FEINBERG PUBLIC RELATIONS; *U.S. Private*, pg. 804
CENERGIST LIMITED—See Eneraqua Technologies Plc; *Int'l*, pg. 2418
CENTROAMERICA PORTER NOVELLI-COSTA RICA—See Omnicom Group Inc.; *U.S. Public*, pg. 1590
CENTROAMERICA PORTER NOVELLI-EL SALVADOR—See Omnicom Group Inc.; *U.S. Public*, pg. 1590
CENTROAMERICA PORTER NOVELLI-GUATEMALA—See Omnicom Group Inc.; *U.S. Public*, pg. 1590
CENTROAMERICA PORTER NOVELLI-NICARAGUA—See Omnicom Group Inc.; *U.S. Public*, pg. 1590
CENTURION STRATEGIES LLC; *U.S. Private*, pg. 831
CERRELL ASSOCIATES, INC.; *U.S. Private*, pg. 841
CFM STRATEGIC COMMUNICATIONS, INC.; *U.S. Private*, pg. 843
CFM STRATEGIC COMMUNICATIONS, INC.—See CFM Strategic Communications, Inc.; *U.S. Private*, pg. 844
CGPR LLC—See Off Madison Ave, LLC; *U.S. Private*, pg. 3000
CHAMBERLAIN HEALTHCARE PUBLIC RELATIONS—See Elliott Management Corporation; *U.S. Private*, pg. 1366
CHAMBERLAIN HEALTHCARE PUBLIC RELATIONS—See Patient Square Capital, L.P.; *U.S. Private*, pg. 3108
CHAMBERLAIN HEALTHCARE PUBLIC RELATIONS—See Veritas Capital Fund Management, LLC; *U.S. Private*, pg. 4365
CHARISMA! COMMUNICATIONS; *U.S. Private*, pg. 851
CHARTWELL AGENCY; *U.S. Private*, pg. 859
CHARTWELL AGENCY—See Chartwell Agency; *U.S. Private*, pg. 859
CHARTWELL AGENCY—See Chartwell Agency; *U.S. Private*, pg. 859
CHENGDU INFORMATION TECHNOLOGY OF CHINESE ACADEMY OF SCIENCES CO., LTD.; *Int'l*, pg. 1468
CHEN PR; *U.S. Private*, pg. 872
CHLOPAK, LEONARD, SCHECHTER & ASSOCIATES—See Omnicom Group Inc.; *U.S. Public*, pg. 1587
CISION SVERIGE AB—See Platinum Equity, LLC; *U.S. Private*, pg. 3201
CITIGATE CUNNINGHAM—See Clayton, Dubilier & Rice, LLC; *U.S. Private*, pg. 924
CITIGATE CUNNINGHAM—See Clayton, Dubilier & Rice, LLC; *U.S. Private*, pg. 924
CITIGATE DEWE ROGERSON—See Clayton, Dubilier & Rice, LLC; *U.S. Private*, pg. 924
CITIZEN BRANDO LIMITED—See Bluefocus Intelligent Communications Group Co., Ltd.; *Int'l*, pg. 1071
CITIZEN RELATIONS INC. - TORONTO—See Bluefocus Intelligent Communications Group Co., Ltd.; *Int'l*, pg. 1071
CITIZEN RELATIONS INC. - VANCOUVER—See Bluefocus Intelligent Communications Group Co., Ltd.; *Int'l*, pg. 1071
CITIZEN RELATIONS LLC - IRVINE—See Bluefocus Intelligent Communications Group Co., Ltd.; *Int'l*, pg. 1071
CITIZEN RELATIONS LLC - NEW YORK—See Bluefocus Intelligent Communications Group Co., Ltd.; *Int'l*, pg. 1071
CITIZEN RELATIONS LLC—See Bluefocus Intelligent Communications Group Co., Ltd.; *Int'l*, pg. 1071
CITOYEN RELATIONS INC. - QUEBEC CITY—See Bluefocus Intelligent Communications Group Co., Ltd.; *Int'l*, pg. 1071
CITOYEN RELATIONS INC.—See Bluefocus Intelligent Communications Group Co., Ltd.; *Int'l*, pg. 1071
CITY PUBLIC RELATIONS PTY LIMITED—See Enero Group Limited; *Int'l*, pg. 2423
C.I. VISIONS INC.; *U.S. Private*, pg. 707
CJ AMERICA, INC.—See CJ Corporation; *Int'l*, pg. 1631
CLARK COMMUNICATIONS LIMITED; *Int'l*, pg. 1650
CLIFFORD/BRATSKEIR PUBLIC RELATIONS LLC—See Stagwell, Inc.; *U.S. Public*, pg. 1926
CLIFF ROSS; *U.S. Private*, pg. 943
CLOCKWORK MARKETING SERVICES, INC.; *U.S. Private*, pg. 945
C-MATRIX COMMUNICATIONS AG—See Omnicom Group Inc.; *U.S. Public*, pg. 1586
CM PORTER NOVELLI-SCOTLAND—See Omnicom Group Inc.; *U.S. Public*, pg. 1590
CO-COMMUNICATIONS, INC.; *U.S. Private*, pg. 953
COLES MARKETING COMMUNICATIONS, INC.; *U.S. Private*, pg. 967
COMMUNICATION BY DESIGN—See Omnicom Group Inc.; *U.S. Public*, pg. 1578
COMMUNIQUE—See Daniel J. Edelman, Inc.; *U.S. Private*, pg. 1154
COMPASS PORTER NOVELLI—See Omnicom Group Inc.; *U.S. Public*, pg. 1590
COMPUTER WORLD; *U.S. Private*, pg. 1005
COMUNICADORA NEXUS—See The Interpublic Group of Companies, Inc.; *U.S. Public*, pg. 2094
COMUNICA—See The Interpublic Group of Companies, Inc.; *U.S. Public*, pg. 2094
CONCENTRIC COMMUNICATIONS—See Omnicom Group Inc.; *U.S. Public*, pg. 1586
CONNECTING POINT COMMUNICATIONS—See Clayton, Dubilier & Rice, LLC; *U.S. Private*, pg. 924
CONNECT PUBLIC RELATIONS; *U.S. Private*, pg. 1015
CONNECT PUBLIC RELATIONS—See Connect Public Relations; *U.S. Private*, pg. 1015
COOKSEY COMMUNICATIONS, INC.; *U.S. Private*, pg. 1039
COORDINAMOS PORTER NOVELLI—See Omnicom Group Inc.; *U.S. Public*, pg. 1590
CORBIN-HILLMAN COMMUNICATIONS; *U.S. Private*, pg. 1047
CORKERY GROUP UNLIMITED—See Accenture plc; *Int'l*, pg. 87
CORNERSTONE PROMOTION, INC.; *U.S. Private*, pg. 1052
CORPORATE INK PUBLIC RELATIONS, LTD.; *U.S. Private*, pg. 1055
CORPORATE VOICE-WEBER SHANDWICK—See The Interpublic Group of Companies, Inc.; *U.S. Public*, pg. 2104
CORPORATE VOICE-WEBER SHANDWICK—See The Interpublic Group of Companies, Inc.; *U.S. Public*, pg. 2104
COTTON INCORPORATED; *U.S. Private*, pg. 1064
COYNE PUBLIC RELATIONS; *U.S. Private*, pg. 1079
CRC PUBLIC RELATIONS; *U.S. Private*, pg. 1087
CREATIVE COMMUNICATIONS CONSULTANTS, INC.; *U.S. Private*, pg. 1088
CREATIVE MEDIA MARKETING INC.; *U.S. Private*, pg. 1089
CRENSHAW COMMUNICATIONS, LLC—See ModOp, LLC; *U.S. Private*, pg. 2763
CRISTOFOLI KEELING, INC.; *U.S. Private*, pg. 1101
CRITICAL PR; *U.S. Private*, pg. 1102
CROSSROADS—See Barkley; *U.S. Private*, pg. 475
CSM SPORT & ENTERTAINMENT LLP—See Wasserman Media Group, LLC; *U.S. Private*, pg. 4450
CUSTOMERVILLE, INC.—See EQT AB; *Int'l*, pg. 2477
CYPRESS MEDIA GROUP; *U.S. Private*, pg. 1135
DANIEL J. EDELMAN, INC.; *U.S. Private*, pg. 1154
DAVID CHAPMAN ASSOCIATES LTD.—See The Interpublic Group of Companies, Inc.; *U.S. Public*, pg. 2104
DAVID PEARSON ASSOCIATES; *U.S. Private*, pg. 1171
DAVID X. MANNERS CO., INC.; *U.S. Private*, pg. 1171
DAVIES; *U.S. Private*, pg. 1172
DCA/DCPR CHICAGO—See DCA/DCPR; *U.S. Private*, pg. 1179
DCA/DCPR—See DCA/DCPR; *U.S. Private*, pg. 1179
DCI GROUP; *U.S. Private*, pg. 1180
DCI-WEST—See Development Counsellors International, Ltd.; *U.S. Private*, pg. 1217
DEALER IGNITION, LLC; *U.S. Private*, pg. 1182
DE LA GARZA PUBLIC RELATIONS, INC.; *U.S. Private*, pg. 1181
DENNIS PR GROUP; *U.S. Private*, pg. 1205
DERA, ROSLAN & CAMPION PUBLIC RELATIONS; *U.S. Private*, pg. 1209
DEVRIES PUBLIC RELATIONS—See The Interpublic Group of Companies, Inc.; *U.S. Public*, pg. 2090
DIAMOND PUBLIC RELATIONS; *U.S. Private*, pg. 1223
DICKEY-JOHN INTERNATIONAL LTD.—See Churchill Equity, Inc.; *U.S. Public*, pg. 895
DIGENNARO COMMUNICATIONS; *U.S. Private*, pg. 1229
DITTOE PUBLIC RELATIONS, INC.; *U.S. Private*, pg. 1240
DIX & EATON INCORPORATED; *U.S. Private*, pg. 1244
DIXON SCHWABL INC.; *U.S. Private*, pg. 1246
DODGE COMMUNICATIONS, INC.—See Myelin Health Communications, Inc.; *U.S. Private*, pg. 2824
DOERR ASSOCIATES; *U.S. Private*, pg. 1253
DOMINICANA PORTER NOVELLI—See Omnicom Group Inc.; *U.S. Public*, pg. 1590
DOTTED LINE COMMUNICATIONS; *U.S. Private*, pg. 1265
DOTTED LINE COMMUNICATIONS—See Dotted Line

N.A.I.C.S. INDEX

541820 — PUBLIC RELATIONS AG...

Communications; *U.S. Private*, pg. 1265
DOVETAIL PUBLIC RELATIONS; *U.S. Private*, pg. 1268
DOVETAIL SOLUTIONS INC.; *U.S. Private*, pg. 1268
DPR GROUP, INC.; *U.S. Private*, pg. 1270
DPR GROUP, INC.—See DPR Group, Inc.; *U.S. Private*, pg. 1271
DRESNER ALLEN CARON—See Dresner Corporate Services Inc.; *U.S. Private*, pg. 1276
DRESNER CORPORATE SERVICES INC.; *U.S. Private*, pg. 1276
DRURY COMMUNICATIONS LIMITED; *Int'l*, pg. 2206
D-TRIX NV—See DPG Media Group NV; *Int'l*, pg. 2189
DUBLIN & ASSOCIATES, INC.; *U.S. Private*, pg. 1283
DUFFEY COMMUNICATIONS, INC.; *U.S. Private*, pg. 1285
DUO PR; *U.S. Private*, pg. 1291
DVL SEIGENTHALER, INC.—See Ruder Finn Group, Inc.; *U.S. Private*, pg. 3501
EASTWEST PUBLIC RELATIONS—See Omnicom Group Inc.; *U.S. Public*, pg. 1578
EBA COMMUNICATIONS - BEIJING—See Omnicom Group Inc.; *U.S. Public*, pg. 1578
EBA COMMUNICATIONS LTD—See Omnicom Group Inc.; *U.S. Public*, pg. 1578
EBA COMMUNICATIONS - SHANGHAI—See Omnicom Group Inc.; *U.S. Public*, pg. 1578
E. BOINEAU & COMPANY; *U.S. Private*, pg. 1303
EDELMAN BEIJING—See Daniel J. Edelman, Inc.; *U.S. Private*, pg. 1155
EDELMAN HONG KONG—See Daniel J. Edelman, Inc.; *U.S. Private*, pg. 1155
EDELMAN RUSSIA—See Daniel J. Edelman, Inc.; *U.S. Private*, pg. 1155
EDELMAN—See Daniel J. Edelman, Inc.; *U.S. Private*, pg. 1154
EDELMAN—See Daniel J. Edelman, Inc.; *U.S. Private*, pg. 1154
EDELMAN—See Daniel J. Edelman, Inc.; *U.S. Private*, pg. 1154
EDELMAN—See Daniel J. Edelman, Inc.; *U.S. Private*, pg. 1154
EDELMAN—See Daniel J. Edelman, Inc.; *U.S. Private*, pg. 1154
EDELMAN—See Daniel J. Edelman, Inc.; *U.S. Private*, pg. 1154
EDELMAN—See Daniel J. Edelman, Inc.; *U.S. Private*, pg. 1154
EDELMAN—See Daniel J. Edelman, Inc.; *U.S. Private*, pg. 1155
EDELMAN—See Daniel J. Edelman, Inc.; *U.S. Private*, pg. 1155
EDELMAN—See Daniel J. Edelman, Inc.; *U.S. Private*, pg. 1155
EDELMAN—See Daniel J. Edelman, Inc.; *U.S. Private*, pg. 1155
EDELMAN—See Daniel J. Edelman, Inc.; *U.S. Private*, pg. 1155
EDELMAN—See Daniel J. Edelman, Inc.; *U.S. Private*, pg. 1155
EDELMAN—See Daniel J. Edelman, Inc.; *U.S. Private*, pg. 1155
EDELMAN—See Daniel J. Edelman, Inc.; *U.S. Private*, pg. 1155
EDELMAN—See Daniel J. Edelman, Inc.; *U.S. Private*, pg. 1155
EDELMAN—See Daniel J. Edelman, Inc.; *U.S. Private*, pg. 1155
EDELMAN—See Daniel J. Edelman, Inc.; *U.S. Private*, pg. 1155
EDELMAN—See Daniel J. Edelman, Inc.; *U.S. Private*, pg. 1155
EDELMAN—See Daniel J. Edelman, Inc.; *U.S. Private*, pg. 1155
EDELMAN—See Daniel J. Edelman, Inc.; *U.S. Private*, pg. 1155
EDELMAN SOUTH AFRICA—See Daniel J. Edelman, Inc.; *U.S. Private*, pg. 1155
EDELMAN SOUTHWEST - DALLAS—See Daniel J. Edelman, Inc.; *U.S. Private*, pg. 1155
EDELMAN SOUTHWEST—See Daniel J. Edelman, Inc.; *U.S. Private*, pg. 1155
EDELMAN S.R.L.—See Daniel J. Edelman, Inc.; *U.S. Private*, pg. 1155
EDGE COMMUNICATIONS, INC.; *U.S. Private*, pg. 1334
ELIZABETH CHRISTIAN PUBLIC RELATIONS LLC; *U.S. Private*, pg. 1362
EMA PUBLIC RELATIONS SERVICES—See Eric Mower and Associates, Inc.; *U.S. Private*, pg. 1419
ENGAGE PR; *U.S. Private*, pg. 1397
ENGLANDER KNABE & ALLEN; *U.S. Private*, pg. 1399
ENVIRONICS COMMUNICATIONS INC.—See Environics Communications; *U.S. Private*, pg. 1407
ENVIRONICS COMMUNICATIONS; *U.S. Private*, pg. 1407
ENVIRONICS COMMUNICATIONS—See Environics Communications; *U.S. Private*, pg. 1407
ENVIRONICS COMUNICATIONS INC.—See Environics Communications; *U.S. Private*, pg. 1407
EPROMOS PROMOTIONAL PRODUCTS, INC.; *U.S. Private*, pg. 1414
EVENT MANAGEMENT SERVICES, INC.; *U.S. Private*, pg. 1436
EWING PUBLIC RELATIONS, S.R.O.; *Int'l*, pg. 2576
EXTEND COMUNICACIONES-WEBER SHANDWICK—See The Interpublic Group of Companies, Inc.; *U.S. Public*, pg. 2104
EXXONMOBIL CORPORATION—See Exxon Mobil Corporation; *U.S. Public*, pg. 815
FAHLGREN MORTINE PUBLIC RELATIONS—See Peopletomysite.com, LLC; *U.S. Private*, pg. 3143
FAISS FOLEY WARREN; *U.S. Private*, pg. 1465
FALLS COMMUNICATIONS, INC; *U.S. Private*, pg. 1468
FAMA PR, INC.; *U.S. Private*, pg. 1468
FARNER CONSULTING AG—See Omnicom Group Inc.; *U.S. Public*, pg. 1590
FARNER PORTER NOVELLI—See Omnicom Group Inc.; *U.S. Public*, pg. 1590
FEDERATION OF RESPONSIBLE CITIZENS, INC.; *U.S. Private*, pg. 1492
FEINTUCH COMMUNICATIONS, INC.—See Roher Public Relations; *U.S. Private*, pg. 3473
FETCHING COMMUNICATIONS—See French/West/Vaughan, LLC; *U.S. Private*, pg. 1609
F&H PORTER NOVELLI—See Omnicom Group Inc.; *U.S. Public*, pg. 1590
FINANCIAL DYNAMICS IRELAND LTD.—See FTI Consulting, Inc.; *U.S. Public*, pg. 890
FINEMAN PR—See Off Madison Ave, LLC; *U.S. Private*, pg. 3000
FINN PARTNERS, INC.—See Ruder Finn Group, Inc.; *U.S. Private*, pg. 3501
FISHBURN HEDGES; *Int'l*, pg. 2692
FISH CONSULTING, LLC—See Greens Farms Capital LLC; *U.S. Private*, pg. 1779
FISH CONSULTING, LLC—See Landon Capital Partners, LLC; *U.S. Private*, pg. 2386
FISHMAN PUBLIC RELATIONS; *U.S. Private*, pg. 1535
FLEISHMAN-HILLARD AUSTRALIA PTY. LTD.—See Omnicom Group Inc.; *U.S. Public*, pg. 1583
FLEISHMAN-HILLARD BEIJING—See Omnicom Group Inc.; *U.S. Public*, pg. 1583
FLEISHMAN-HILLARD B.V.—See Omnicom Group Inc.; *U.S. Public*, pg. 1583
FLEISHMAN-HILLARD CANADA INC. - CALGARY—See Omnicom Group Inc.; *U.S. Public*, pg. 1584
FLEISHMAN-HILLARD CANADA INC. - OTTAWA—See Omnicom Group Inc.; *U.S. Public*, pg. 1584
FLEISHMAN-HILLARD CANADA INC. - VANCOUVER—See Omnicom Group Inc.; *U.S. Public*, pg. 1584
FLEISHMAN-HILLARD CZECH REPUBLIC—See Omnicom Group Inc.; *U.S. Public*, pg. 1583
FLEISHMAN-HILLARD FRANCE—See Omnicom Group Inc.; *U.S. Public*, pg. 1583
FLEISHMAN-HILLARD GERMANY GMBH - BERLIN—See Omnicom Group Inc.; *U.S. Public*, pg. 1583
FLEISHMAN-HILLARD GERMANY GMBH - MUNICH—See Omnicom Group Inc.; *U.S. Public*, pg. 1583
FLEISHMAN-HILLARD GERMANY GMBH—See Omnicom Group Inc.; *U.S. Public*, pg. 1583
FLEISHMAN-HILLARD GROUP LTD. - EDINBURGH—See Omnicom Group Inc.; *U.S. Public*, pg. 1583
FLEISHMAN-HILLARD GROUP LTD.—See Omnicom Group Inc.; *U.S. Public*, pg. 1583
FLEISHMAN-HILLARD GUANGZHOU—See Omnicom Group Inc.; *U.S. Public*, pg. 1583
FLEISHMANHILLARD HIGHROAD—See Omnicom Group Inc.; *U.S. Public*, pg. 1584
FLEISHMAN-HILLARD HONG KONG LTD.—See Omnicom Group Inc.; *U.S. Public*, pg. 1583
FLEISHMAN-HILLARD INC. - BOSTON—See Omnicom Group Inc.; *U.S. Public*, pg. 1584
FLEISHMAN-HILLARD INC. - IRVINE—See Omnicom Group Inc.; *U.S. Public*, pg. 1584
FLEISHMAN-HILLARD INC. - PUERTO RICO—See Omnicom Group Inc.; *U.S. Public*, pg. 1584
FLEISHMAN-HILLARD INC.—See Omnicom Group Inc.; *U.S. Public*, pg. 1583
FLEISHMAN-HILLARD INC.—See Omnicom Group Inc.; *U.S. Public*, pg. 1583
FLEISHMAN-HILLARD INC.—See Omnicom Group Inc.; *U.S. Public*, pg. 1583
FLEISHMAN-HILLARD INC.—See Omnicom Group Inc.; *U.S. Public*, pg. 1583
FLEISHMAN-HILLARD INC.—See Omnicom Group Inc.; *U.S. Public*, pg. 1583
FLEISHMAN-HILLARD INC.—See Omnicom Group Inc.; *U.S. Public*, pg. 1584
FLEISHMAN-HILLARD INC.—See Omnicom Group Inc.; *U.S. Public*, pg. 1584
FLEISHMAN-HILLARD INC.—See Omnicom Group Inc.; *U.S. Public*, pg. 1584
FLEISHMAN-HILLARD INC.—See Omnicom Group Inc.; *U.S. Public*, pg. 1584
FLEISHMAN-HILLARD INC.—See Omnicom Group Inc.; *U.S. Public*, pg. 1584
FLEISHMAN-HILLARD INC.—See Omnicom Group Inc.; *U.S. Public*, pg. 1584
FLEISHMAN-HILLARD INC.—See Omnicom Group Inc.; *U.S. Public*, pg. 1584
FLEISHMAN-HILLARD INC.—See Omnicom Group Inc.; *U.S. Public*, pg. 1584
FLEISHMAN-HILLARD INC.—See Omnicom Group Inc.; *U.S. Public*, pg. 1584
FLEISHMAN-HILLARD INC.—See Omnicom Group Inc.; *U.S. Public*, pg. 1584
FLEISHMAN-HILLARD INC.—See Omnicom Group Inc.; *U.S. Public*, pg. 1584
FLEISHMAN-HILLARD ITALIA S.R.L.—See Omnicom Group Inc.; *U.S. Public*, pg. 1584
FLEISHMAN-HILLARD JAPAN KK—See Omnicom Group Inc.; *U.S. Public*, pg. 1584
FLEISHMAN-HILLARD KOREA—See Omnicom Group Inc.; *U.S. Public*, pg. 1584
FLEISHMAN-HILLARD LIMITED—See Omnicom Group Inc.; *U.S. Public*, pg. 1584
FLEISHMAN-HILLARD MANILA—See Omnicom Group Inc.; *U.S. Public*, pg. 1584
FLEISHMAN-HILLARD MEXICO, S.A. DE C.V.—See Omnicom Group Inc.; *U.S. Public*, pg. 1584
FLEISHMAN-HILLARD POLSKA SP. Z O.O.—See Omnicom Group Inc.; *U.S. Public*, pg. 1584
FLEISHMAN-HILLARD PTE. LTD.—See Omnicom Group Inc.; *U.S. Public*, pg. 1584
FLEISHMAN-HILLARD SA/NV—See Omnicom Group Inc.; *U.S. Public*, pg. 1584
FLEISHMANHILLARD—See Omnicom Group Inc.; *U.S. Public*, pg. 1583
FLEISHMAN-HILLARD SOUTH AFRICA (PTY) LTD.—See Omnicom Group Inc.; *U.S. Public*, pg. 1584
FLEISHMAN-HILLARD SPAIN, S.A.—See Omnicom Group Inc.; *U.S. Public*, pg. 1584
FLORIDIAN PARTNERS, LLC; *U.S. Private*, pg. 1551
FOCUSED COMMUNICATIONS CO., LTD.—See Allison & Partners LLC; *U.S. Public*, pg. 192
FORGE3, LIMITED—See FMG Suite, LLC; *U.S. Private*, pg. 1554
FORGE SPONSORSHIP CONSULTING, LLC; *U.S. Private*, pg. 1568
FORMULA; *U.S. Private*, pg. 1572
FRANCO PUBLIC RELATIONS GROUP; *U.S. Private*, pg. 1593
FRANK PR AUSTRALIA PTY LIMITED—See Enero Group Limited; *Int'l*, pg. 2424
FRANK PR LIMITED—See Enero Group Limited; *Int'l*, pg. 2424
FREEBAIRN & COMPANY PUBLIC RELATIONS—See Freebairn & Co.; *U.S. Private*, pg. 1602
FREEMAN PUBLIC RELATIONS; *U.S. Private*, pg. 1605
FRENCH-AMERICAN FOUNDATION; *U.S. Private*, pg. 1609
FRERE-BOURGEOIS; *Int'l*, pg. 2773
FRESHBAKED PR LTD; *Int'l*, pg. 2781
FRESHWATER CONSUMER LIMITED—See Freshwater UK PLC; *Int'l*, pg. 2782
FRESHWATER HEALTHCARE LIMITED—See Freshwater UK PLC; *Int'l*, pg. 2782
FRESHWATER SCOTLAND LIMITED—See Freshwater UK PLC; *Int'l*, pg. 2782
FRESHWATER SOUTHERN LIMITED—See Freshwater UK PLC; *Int'l*, pg. 2782
FRESHWATER TECHNOLOGY LIMITED—See Freshwater UK PLC; *Int'l*, pg. 2782
FRESHWATER TECHNOLOGY; *Int'l*, pg. 2781
FRESHWATER UK PLC; *Int'l*, pg. 2782
FTC—See Omnicom Group Inc.; *U.S. Public*, pg. 1590
FTI CONSULTING SC GMBH—See FTI Consulting, Inc.; *U.S. Public*, pg. 890
FTI CONSULTING (SC) INC.—See FTI Consulting, Inc.; *U.S. Public*, pg. 890
FUESSLER GROUP INC.; *U.S. Private*, pg. 1619
FUSE LLC; *U.S. Private*, pg. 1625

4763

541820 — PUBLIC RELATIONS AG...

FUSION PUBLIC RELATIONS, INC.—See Fusion Public Relations; *U.S. Private*, pg. 1625
FUSION PUBLIC RELATIONS; *U.S. Private*, pg. 1625
FUTURA SERVICES; *U.S. Private*, pg. 1626
GABRIELLE SHAW COMMUNICATIONS; *Int'l*, pg. 2867
GARNIER BBDO—See Omnicom Group Inc.; *U.S. Public*, pg. 1575
GASPAR & ASOCIADOS—See The Interpublic Group of Companies, Inc.; *U.S. Public*, pg. 2104
GATEHOUSE CONSULTING LIMITED—See Arthur J. Gallagher & Co.; *U.S. Public*, pg. 205
GBRITT P.R. & MARKETING; *U.S. Private*, pg. 1653
GEELMUYDEN-KIESE—See The Interpublic Group of Companies, Inc.; *U.S. Public*, pg. 2104
GEELMUYDEN-KIESE—See The Interpublic Group of Companies, Inc.; *U.S. Public*, pg. 2104
GEORGE KLEITZ + ASSOCIATES, INC., PUBLIC RELATIONS DIVISION; *U.S. Private*, pg. 1682
GETO & DEMILLY INC.; *U.S. Private*, pg. 1688
GIBBS & SOELL - CHICAGO—See Gibbs & Soell, Inc.; *U.S. Private*, pg. 1695
GIBBS & SOELL GMBH—See Gibbs & Soell, Inc.; *U.S. Private*, pg. 1695
GIBBS & SOELL, INC.; *U.S. Private*, pg. 1695
GIBBS & SOELL - RALEIGH—See Gibbs & Soell, Inc.; *U.S. Private*, pg. 1695
GILLIAN GAMSY INTERNATIONAL—See The Interpublic Group of Companies, Inc.; *U.S. Public*, pg. 2105
GIRAUDY VIACOM OUTDOOR S.A.—See National Amusements, Inc.; *U.S. Private*, pg. 2841
GITAM PORTER NOVELLI—See Omnicom Group Inc.; *U.S. Public*, pg. 1590
GLOBAL-5, INC.; *U.S. Private*, pg. 1719
GLOBAL COMMUNICATION EXPERTS GMBH; *Int'l*, pg. 2994
GLOBALFLUENCY; *U.S. Private*, pg. 1719
GLOBALFLUENCY—See GlobalFluency; *U.S. Private*, pg. 1719
GMMB INC. - SEATTLE—See Omnicom Group Inc.; *U.S. Public*, pg. 1585
GMMB INC.—See Omnicom Group Inc.; *U.S. Public*, pg. 1584
GMR MARKETING LLC—See Omnicom Group Inc.; *U.S. Public*, pg. 1593
GOGERTY STARK MARRIOTT; *U.S. Private*, pg. 1726
GOLDMAN & ASSOCIATES; *U.S. Private*, pg. 1735
GOLIN/HARRIS INTERNATIONAL, INC.—See The Interpublic Group of Companies, Inc.; *U.S. Public*, pg. 2093
GOLINHARRIS/PANACHE—See The Interpublic Group of Companies, Inc.; *U.S. Public*, pg. 2094
GOLINHARRIS—See The Interpublic Group of Companies, Inc.; *U.S. Public*, pg. 2094
GOLINHARRIS—See The Interpublic Group of Companies, Inc.; *U.S. Public*, pg. 2094
GOLINHARRIS—See The Interpublic Group of Companies, Inc.; *U.S. Public*, pg. 2094
GOLINHARRIS—See The Interpublic Group of Companies, Inc.; *U.S. Public*, pg. 2094
GOLINHARRIS—See The Interpublic Group of Companies, Inc.; *U.S. Public*, pg. 2094
GOLINHARRIS—See The Interpublic Group of Companies, Inc.; *U.S. Public*, pg. 2094
GOLINHARRIS—See The Interpublic Group of Companies, Inc.; *U.S. Public*, pg. 2094
GOLINHARRIS—See The Interpublic Group of Companies, Inc.; *U.S. Public*, pg. 2094
GOLINHARRIS—See The Interpublic Group of Companies, Inc.; *U.S. Public*, pg. 2094
GOLINHARRIS—See The Interpublic Group of Companies, Inc.; *U.S. Public*, pg. 2094
GOLINHARRIS—See The Interpublic Group of Companies, Inc.; *U.S. Public*, pg. 2094
GOLINHARRIS—See The Interpublic Group of Companies, Inc.; *U.S. Public*, pg. 2094
GOLINHARRIS—See The Interpublic Group of Companies, Inc.; *U.S. Public*, pg. 2094
GOLINHARRIS—See The Interpublic Group of Companies, Inc.; *U.S. Public*, pg. 2094
GOLINHARRIS—See The Interpublic Group of Companies, Inc.; *U.S. Public*, pg. 2094
GOLINHARRIS—See The Interpublic Group of Companies, Inc.; *U.S. Public*, pg. 2094
GOOD RELATIONS LIMITED—See Providence Equity Partners L.L.C.; *U.S. Private*, pg. 3291
GRAND SOLUTIONS LLC—See LST Marketing, LLC; *U.S. Private*, pg. 2509

GRAYLING AUSTRIA—See Clayton, Dubilier & Rice, LLC; *U.S. Private*, pg. 924
GRAYLING BELGIUM—See Clayton, Dubilier & Rice, LLC; *U.S. Private*, pg. 924
GRAYLING BULGARIA—See Clayton, Dubilier & Rice, LLC; *U.S. Private*, pg. 924
GRAYLING CHINA—See Clayton, Dubilier & Rice, LLC; *U.S. Private*, pg. 924
GRAYLING CROATIA—See Clayton, Dubilier & Rice, LLC; *U.S. Private*, pg. 924
GRAYLING CZECH REPUBLIC—See Clayton, Dubilier & Rice, LLC; *U.S. Private*, pg. 924
GRAYLING DEUTSCHLAND GMBH—See Clayton, Dubilier & Rice, LLC; *U.S. Private*, pg. 924
GRAYLING DEUTSCHLAND GMBH—See Clayton, Dubilier & Rice, LLC; *U.S. Private*, pg. 925
GRAYLING DEUTSCHLAND GMBH—See Clayton, Dubilier & Rice, LLC; *U.S. Private*, pg. 925
GRAYLING FRANCE—See Clayton, Dubilier & Rice, LLC; *U.S. Private*, pg. 925
GRAYLING GLOBAL—See Clayton, Dubilier & Rice, LLC; *U.S. Private*, pg. 924
GRAYLING GLOBAL—See Clayton, Dubilier & Rice, LLC; *U.S. Private*, pg. 925
GRAYLING GLOBAL—See Clayton, Dubilier & Rice, LLC; *U.S. Private*, pg. 925
GRAYLING GLOBAL—See Clayton, Dubilier & Rice, LLC; *U.S. Private*, pg. 925
GRAYLING HUNGARY—See Clayton, Dubilier & Rice, LLC; *U.S. Private*, pg. 925
GRAYLING NETHERLANDS—See Clayton, Dubilier & Rice, LLC; *U.S. Private*, pg. 925
GRAYLING POLAND—See Clayton, Dubilier & Rice, LLC; *U.S. Private*, pg. 925
GRAYLING ROMANIA—See Clayton, Dubilier & Rice, LLC; *U.S. Private*, pg. 925
GRAYLING RUSSIA—See Clayton, Dubilier & Rice, LLC; *U.S. Private*, pg. 925
GRAYLING SCHWEIZ AG—See Clayton, Dubilier & Rice, LLC; *U.S. Private*, pg. 925
GRAYLING SLOVAKIA—See Clayton, Dubilier & Rice, LLC; *U.S. Private*, pg. 925
GRAYLING SLOVENIA—See Clayton, Dubilier & Rice, LLC; *U.S. Private*, pg. 925
GRAYLING SUISSE SA—See Clayton, Dubilier & Rice, LLC; *U.S. Private*, pg. 925
GRAYLING UKRAINE—See Clayton, Dubilier & Rice, LLC; *U.S. Private*, pg. 925
GRAY MEDIA GROUP, INC.—See Gray Television, Inc.; *U.S. Public*, pg. 960
GREENOUGH COMMUNICATIONS; *U.S. Private*, pg. 1779
GREGORY FCA; *U.S. Private*, pg. 1783
GRIFFIN & ASSOCIATES; *U.S. Private*, pg. 1786
GRIFFIN & ASSOCIATES—See Griffin & Associates; *U.S. Private*, pg. 1787
GRIFFIN INTEGRATED COMMUNICATIONS; *U.S. Private*, pg. 1788
GROUP 5 WEST, INC.—See Group 5 West, Inc.; *U.S. Private*, pg. 1793
GRP. PUBLIC RELATIONS LIMITED—See Providence Equity Partners L.L.C.; *U.S. Private*, pg. 3291
GRUPO ALBION; *Int'l*, pg. 3119
G.S. SCHWARTZ & CO. INC.; *U.S. Private*, pg. 1631
GULLERS GROUP PORTER NOVELLI—See Omnicom Group Inc.; *U.S. Public*, pg. 1590
GUTENBERG COMMUNICATIONS; *U.S. Private*, pg. 1820
GUTENBERG COMMUNICATIONS—See Gutenberg Communications; *U.S. Private*, pg. 1820
GUTHRIE/MAYES; *U.S. Private*, pg. 1820
H2O CREATIVE; *Int'l*, pg. 3200
HAGER SHARP INC.; *U.S. Private*, pg. 1839
HALPERN LTD.—See CHI & Partners Limited; *Int'l*, pg. 1474
HAMILTON PUBLIC RELATIONS—See Bodden Partners; *U.S. Private*, pg. 607
HANSER & ASSOCIATES PUBLIC RELATIONS; *U.S. Private*, pg. 1856
HANSER & ASSOCIATES PUBLIC RELATIONS—See Hanser & Associates Public Relations; *U.S. Private*, pg. 1856
HARRIS, BAIO & MCCULLOUGH INC.; *U.S. Private*, pg. 1870
HARRISON LEIFER DIMARCO PUBLIC RELATIONS—See Harrison Leifer DiMarco, Inc.; *U.S. Private*, pg. 1870
HASLIMANN TAYLOR PUBLIC RELATIONS—See Clayton, Dubilier & Rice, LLC; *U.S. Private*, pg. 925
THE HATCHER GROUP; *U.S. Private*, pg. 4043
THE HERALD NEWS—See Chicago Public Media, Inc.; *U.S. Private*, pg. 879
HETRICK COMMUNICATIONS, INC.; *U.S. Private*, pg. 1928
HIGHFIELD COMMUNICATIONS LLC—See Kearney O'Doherty Public Affairs, LLC; *U.S. Private*, pg. 2271
HIGH ROAD COMMUNICATIONS—See Omnicom Group Inc.; *U.S. Public*, pg. 1585
HIGH ROAD COMMUNICATIONS—See Omnicom Group Inc.; *U.S. Public*, pg. 1585
HIGH ROAD COMMUNICATIONS—See Omnicom Group Inc.; *U.S. Public*, pg. 1585
HILLMER INC.; *U.S. Private*, pg. 1946

HILSINGER MENDELSON PUBLIC RELATIONS; *U.S. Private*, pg. 1948
HILSINGER MENDELSON PUBLIC RELATIONS—See Hilsinger Mendelson Public Relations; *U.S. Private*, pg. 1948
HODGE SCHINDLER INTEGRATED COMMUNICATIONS; *U.S. Private*, pg. 1959
THE HOFFMAN AGENCY; *U.S. Private*, pg. 4053
THE HOFFMAN AGENCY—See The Hoffman Agency; *U.S. Private*, pg. 4053
THE HOFFMAN AGENCY—See The Hoffman Agency; *U.S. Private*, pg. 4053
THE HOFFMAN AGENCY—See The Hoffman Agency; *U.S. Private*, pg. 4053
THE HOFFMAN AGENCY—See The Hoffman Agency; *U.S. Private*, pg. 4053
THE HOFFMAN AGENCY—See The Hoffman Agency; *U.S. Private*, pg. 4053
THE HOFFMAN AGENCY—See The Hoffman Agency; *U.S. Private*, pg. 4053
THE HOFFMAN AGENCY—See The Hoffman Agency; *U.S. Private*, pg. 4053
THE HOFFMAN AGENCY—See The Hoffman Agency; *U.S. Private*, pg. 4053
THE HOFFMAN AGENCY—See The Hoffman Agency; *U.S. Private*, pg. 4053
HOPSCOTCH AFRICA S.A.—See Hopscotch Groupe S.A.; *Int'l*, pg. 3474
HOPSCOTCH EUROPE LTD.—See Hopscotch Groupe S.A.; *Int'l*, pg. 3474
HORN GROUP INC.—See Ruder Finn Group, Inc.; *U.S. Private*, pg. 3501
HORN GROUP - NEW YORK—See Ruder Finn Group, Inc.; *U.S. Private*, pg. 3501
HOTWIRE PUBLIC RELATION ITALY S.R.L.—See Enero Group Limited; *Int'l*, pg. 2424
HOTWIRE PUBLIC RELATIONS GMBH—See Enero Group Limited; *Int'l*, pg. 2424
HOTWIRE PUBLIC RELATIONS LIMITED—See Enero Group Limited; *Int'l*, pg. 2424
HOTWIRE PUBLIC RELATIONS SARL—See Enero Group Limited; *Int'l*, pg. 2424
HOTWIRE PUBLIC RELATIONS SL—See Enero Group Limited; *Int'l*, pg. 2424
HPR, INC.; *U.S. Private*, pg. 1997
HPR, INC.—See HPR, Inc.; *U.S. Private*, pg. 1997
HUNTER PUBLIC RELATIONS, LLC—See Stagwell, Inc.; *U.S. Public*, pg. 1927
HVR GROUP—See Omnicom Group Inc.; *U.S. Public*, pg. 1596
HWH PUBLIC RELATIONS; *U.S. Private*, pg. 2015
HWH PUBLIC RELATIONS—See HWH Public Relations; *U.S. Private*, pg. 2015
HYDE PARK COMMUNICATIONS; *U.S. Private*, pg. 2017
ICR, LLC; *U.S. Private*, pg. 2033
IDENTITY; *U.S. Private*, pg. 2037
I & E CONSULTANTS; *Int'l*, pg. 3561
IGM CREATIVE GROUP; *U.S. Private*, pg. 2039
IKON PORTER NOVELLI—See Omnicom Group Inc.; *U.S. Public*, pg. 1590
ILCC CO., LTD; *Int'l*, pg. 3613
IMPACT BBDO—See Omnicom Group Inc.; *U.S. Public*, pg. 1576
IMPACT PORTER NOVELLI DUBAI—See Omnicom Group Inc.; *U.S. Public*, pg. 1590
IMPACT PORTER NOVELLI—See Omnicom Group Inc.; *U.S. Public*, pg. 1590
IMPACT PORTER NOVELLI—See Omnicom Group Inc.; *U.S. Public*, pg. 1590
IMPRESS PUBLIC RELATIONS, INC.; *U.S. Private*, pg. 2050
IMPRESS PUBLIC RELATIONS, INC.—See Impress Public Relations, Inc.; *U.S. Private*, pg. 2050
IMPRESS PUBLIC RELATIONS, INC.—See Impress Public Relations, Inc.; *U.S. Private*, pg. 2050
IMRE, LLC; *U.S. Private*, pg. 2051
INCOMM BRODEUR—See Omnicom Group Inc.; *U.S. Public*, pg. 1578
INDOPACIFIC EDELMAN—See Daniel J. Edelman, Inc.; *U.S. Private*, pg. 1155
INKHOUSE—See O2 Investment Partners, LLC; *U.S. Private*, pg. 2982
INK, INC. PR; *U.S. Private*, pg. 2077
INK; *U.S. Private*, pg. 2077
INPRESS PORTER NOVELLI-SAO PAULO—See Omnicom Group Inc.; *U.S. Public*, pg. 1590
IN PRESS PORTER NOVELLI—See Omnicom Group Inc.; *U.S. Public*, pg. 1590
INTEGRATED MARKETING SERVICES; *U.S. Private*, pg. 2100
INTERPROSE INC.; *U.S. Private*, pg. 2123
INTERSTAR MARKETING & PUBLIC RELATIONS; *U.S. Private*, pg. 2123
INVESTORCOM INC.; *U.S. Private*, pg. 2132
ITAGROUP, INC. - INDIANAPOLIS—See ITAGroup, Inc.; *U.S. Private*, pg. 2148
IT GIRL PUBLIC RELATIONS; *U.S. Private*, pg. 2148
JACK HORNER COMMUNICATIONS; *U.S. Private*, pg. 2174
JACKIE COOPER PUBLIC RELATIONS—See Daniel J.

N.A.I.C.S. INDEX 541820 — PUBLIC RELATIONS AG...

Edelman, Inc.; *U.S. Private*, pg. 1155
JACK MORTON WORLDWIDE—See The Interpublic Group of Companies, Inc; *U.S. Public*, pg. 2096
JACMAR FOOD SERVICE—See Jacmar Companies, Inc.; *U.S. Private*, pg. 2179
JASCULCA/TERMAN AND ASSOCIATES; *U.S. Private*, pg. 2189
JB CUMBERLAND PR—See Didit.com, Inc.; *U.S. Private*, pg. 1227
JC MARKETING ASSOCIATES INC.; *U.S. Private*, pg. 2194
JCM EVENTS—See JC Marketing Associates Inc.; *U.S. Private*, pg. 2194
JC PUBLIC RELATIONS, INC.; *U.S. Private*, pg. 2194
THE JEWISH FEDERATIONS OF NORTH AMERICA, INC.; *U.S. Private*, pg. 4059
J.F. MILLS/WORLDWIDE; *U.S. Private*, pg. 2164
JMPR, INC.—See IMRE, LLC; *U.S. Private*, pg. 2051
JOAN B. MARCUS COMMUNICATIONS LLC; *U.S. Private*, pg. 2217
JOHNSTONWELLS PUBLIC RELATIONS; *U.S. Private*, pg. 2230
JOP, OVE & MYRTHU—See Omnicom Group Inc.; *U.S. Public*, pg. 1591
JOP, OVE & MYRTHU—See Omnicom Group Inc.; *U.S. Public*, pg. 1591
JOTO PR AGENCY; *U.S. Private*, pg. 2238
J PUBLIC RELATIONS, INC.; *U.S. Private*, pg. 2153
JS2 COMMUNICATIONS; *U.S. Private*, pg. 2241
KANAN, CORBIN, SCHUPAK & ARONOW, INC.; *U.S. Private*, pg. 2259
KARWOSKI & COURAGE—See Omnicom Group Inc.; *U.S. Public*, pg. 1588
KCD, INC.; *U.S. Private*, pg. 2269
KEATING & CO.; *U.S. Private*, pg. 2271
KEENE PROMOTIONS, INC.; *U.S. Private*, pg. 2272
KEENE PROMOTIONS, INC.—See Keene Promotions, Inc.; *U.S. Private*, pg. 2272
KEENE PROMOTIONS, INC.—See Keene Promotions, Inc.; *U.S. Private*, pg. 2272
KELLEN COMMUNICATIONS; *U.S. Private*, pg. 2274
KELLEN COMMUNICATIONS—See Kellen Communications; *U.S. Private*, pg. 2274
KELLEN COMMUNICATIONS—See Kellen Communications; *U.S. Private*, pg. 2274
KELLEN COMMUNICATIONS—See Kellen Communications; *U.S. Private*, pg. 2274
KELLEN EUROPE—See Kellen Communications; *U.S. Private*, pg. 2274
KELLIHER SAMETS VOLK—See Kelliher Samets Volk; *U.S. Private*, pg. 2276
KEMPERLESNIK; *U.S. Private*, pg. 2282
KEO MARKETING INC.; *U.S. Private*, pg. 2290
KETCHUM CANADA—See Omnicom Group Inc.; *U.S. Public*, pg. 1586
KETCHUM PLEON GMBH—See Omnicom Group Inc.; *U.S. Public*, pg. 1587
KETCHUM PLEON MILANO—See Omnicom Group Inc.; *U.S. Public*, pg. 1587
KETCHUM PLEON ROMA—See Omnicom Group Inc.; *U.S. Public*, pg. 1587
KETCHUM PLEON—See Omnicom Group Inc.; *U.S. Public*, pg. 1587
KETCHUM PLEON—See Omnicom Group Inc.; *U.S. Public*, pg. 1587
KETCHUM PLEON—See Omnicom Group Inc.; *U.S. Public*, pg. 1587
KETCHUM PLEON STUTTGART—See Omnicom Group Inc.; *U.S. Public*, pg. 1587
KETCHUM PUBLICO—See Omnicom Group Inc.; *U.S. Public*, pg. 1587
KETCHUM-PUBLIC RELATIONS LTD.—See Omnicom Group Inc.; *U.S. Public*, pg. 1587
KETCHUM-PUBLIC RELATIONS—See Omnicom Group Inc.; *U.S. Public*, pg. 1587
KETCHUM-PUBLIC RELATIONS—See Omnicom Group Inc.; *U.S. Public*, pg. 1587
KETCHUM-PUBLIC RELATIONS—See Omnicom Group Inc.; *U.S. Public*, pg. 1587
KETCHUM SAMPARK PVT. LTD—See Omnicom Group Inc.; *U.S. Public*, pg. 1587
KETCHUM—See Omnicom Group Inc.; *U.S. Public*, pg. 1586
KETCHUM—See Omnicom Group Inc.; *U.S. Public*, pg. 1586
KETCHUM—See Omnicom Group Inc.; *U.S. Public*, pg. 1586
KETCHUM—See Omnicom Group Inc.; *U.S. Public*, pg. 1586
KETCHUM SPAIN—See Omnicom Group Inc.; *U.S. Public*, pg. 1587
KETCHUM TAIPEI—See Omnicom Group Inc.; *U.S. Public*, pg. 1587
KING + COMPANY; *U.S. Private*, pg. 2308
KINGDON-NICHOLS LLC; *U.S. Private*, pg. 2310
KORCOM PORTER NOVELLI—See Omnicom Group Inc.; *U.S. Public*, pg. 1591
THE KOTERET GROUP—See Omnicom Group Inc.; *U.S. Public*, pg. 1578
KRC RESEARCH—See The Interpublic Group of Companies, Inc.; *U.S. Public*, pg. 2105
KRC RESEARCH—See The Interpublic Group of Companies, Inc.; *U.S. Public*, pg. 2105
KREAB AB—See Omnicom Group Inc.; *U.S. Public*, pg. 1587
KREAB BRUSSELS—See Omnicom Group Inc.; *U.S. Public*, pg. 1587
KREAB ESPANA S.L. - BARCELONA—See Omnicom Group Inc.; *U.S. Public*, pg. 1587
KREAB ESPANA S.L.—See Omnicom Group Inc.; *U.S. Public*, pg. 1587
KREAB (HONG KONG) LIMITED—See Omnicom Group Inc.; *U.S. Public*, pg. 1587
KREAB K.K.—See Omnicom Group Inc.; *U.S. Public*, pg. 1587
KREAB LIMITED—See Omnicom Group Inc.; *U.S. Public*, pg. 1587
KREAB LISBON—See Omnicom Group Inc.; *U.S. Public*, pg. 1588
KREAB OY—See Omnicom Group Inc.; *U.S. Public*, pg. 1588
KREAB PTE. LTD.—See Omnicom Group Inc.; *U.S. Public*, pg. 1588
KUBIN-NICHOLSON CORP., NEW YORK—See Kubin-Nicholson Corporation; *U.S. Private*, pg. 2356
KULESA FAUL INC.; *U.S. Private*, pg. 2356
KUNDELL COMMUNICATIONS, INC.; *U.S. Private*, pg. 2357
KURMAN COMMUNICATIONS, INC.; *U.S. Private*, pg. 2357
KWE PARTNERS, INC.; *U.S. Private*, pg. 2359
KWITTKEN & COMPANY LIMITED—See Stagwell, Inc.; *U.S. Public*, pg. 1927
KWT GLOBAL, LLC—See Stagwell, Inc.; *U.S. Public*, pg. 1927
KWT GLOBAL LP—See Stagwell, Inc.; *U.S. Public*, pg. 1927
KWT GLOBAL LTD.—See Stagwell, Inc.; *U.S. Public*, pg. 1927
LABRECHE; *U.S. Private*, pg. 2371
LAMBERT & CO.; *U.S. Private*, pg. 2379
LANA DUKE CONSULTING; *U.S. Private*, pg. 2381
LANDIS COMMUNICATIONS INC.; *U.S. Private*, pg. 2385
LANE MARKETING—See Lane PR; *U.S. Private*, pg. 2388
LANE PR; *U.S. Private*, pg. 2388
LAUREY PEAT & ASSOCIATES INC.; *U.S. Private*, pg. 2399
LAVOIE STRATEGIC COMMUNICATIONS GROUP, INC.; *U.S. Private*, pg. 2400
LAWRENCE RAGAN COMMUNICATIONS, INC.; *U.S. Private*, pg. 2402
LAZAR PARTNERS LTD.—See Finn Partners, Inc.; *U.S. Private*, pg. 1510
L.C. WILLIAMS & ASSOCIATES, LLC; *U.S. Private*, pg. 2365
THE LEDLIE GROUP; *U.S. Private*, pg. 4068
LEE & ASSOCIATES, INC.; *U.S. Private*, pg. 2411
LEONARD & FINCO PUBLIC RELATIONS INC.—See Kane Communications Group, LLC; *U.S. Private*, pg. 2259
LEOPOLD KETEL & PARTNERS; *U.S. Private*, pg. 2431
LERNER ENTERPRISES, INC.; *U.S. Private*, pg. 2431
LESIC & CAMPER COMMUNICATIONS; *U.S. Private*, pg. 2432
LESIC & CAMPER COMMUNICATIONS—See Lesic & Camper Communications; *U.S. Private*, pg. 2432
LESTELLE COMMUNICATIONS, LLC; *U.S. Private*, pg. 2432
LEVICK STRATEGIC COMMUNICATIONS, LP; *U.S. Private*, pg. 2435
LEXICON COMMUNICATIONS CORP.; *U.S. Private*, pg. 2440
LHC PORTER NOVELLI—See Omnicom Group Inc.; *U.S. Public*, pg. 1591
THE LILIAN RAJI AGENCY; *U.S. Private*, pg. 4070
LINHART PUBLIC RELATIONS, LLP; *U.S. Private*, pg. 2461
LIPMAN HEARNE, INC.; *U.S. Private*, pg. 2465
LIPPINCOTT—See Marsh & McLennan Companies, Inc.; *U.S. Public*, pg. 1387
THE LIPPIN GROUP, INC. - NEW YORK—See The Lippin Group; *U.S. Private*, pg. 4070
THE LIPPIN GROUP; *U.S. Private*, pg. 4070
THE LIPPIN GROUP—See The Lippin Group; *U.S. Private*, pg. 4070
LITLAMP COMMUNICATIONS GROUP; *U.S. Private*, pg. 2468
LOIS PAUL & PARTNERS—See Omnicom Group Inc.; *U.S. Public*, pg. 1585
LOIS PAUL & PARTNERS—See Omnicom Group Inc.; *U.S. Public*, pg. 1585
LOOK MEDIA USA, LLC; *U.S. Private*, pg. 2493
LORRIE WALKER COMMUNICATIONS INC.; *U.S. Private*, pg. 2496
LOU HAMMOND & ASSOCIATES, INC.; *U.S. Private*, pg. 2498
LOVELL PUBLIC RELATIONS, INC.; *U.S. Private*, pg. 2503
LOVIO GEORGE INC.; *U.S. Private*, pg. 2504
LVM GROUP, INC.—See Didit.com, Inc.; *U.S. Private*, pg. 1228
LYNX PORTER NOVELLI AS—See Omnicom Group Inc.; *U.S. Public*, pg. 1591
LYNX PR—See Freshwater UK PLC; *Int'l*, pg. 2782
M45 MARKETING SERVICES; *U.S. Private*, pg. 2530
MAGNA CARTA—See Omnicom Group Inc.; *U.S. Public*, pg. 1597
THE MAHONEY COMPANY; *U.S. Private*, pg. 4074
MAKOVSKY & COMPANY, INC.; *U.S. Private*, pg. 2556
MALONEY & FOX—See Waggener Edstrom; *U.S. Private*, pg. 4425
MANTRA PUBLIC RELATIONS, INC.; *U.S. Private*, pg. 2567
MANUFACTURING AFFINITY PROGRAM—See TR Cutler, Inc.; *U.S. Private*, pg. 4200
MAPR.AGENCY, INC.; *U.S. Private*, pg. 2569
MARGIE KORSHAK INC.; *U.S. Private*, pg. 2573
MARKETCOM PUBLIC RELATIONS, LLC; *U.S. Private*, pg. 2579
THE MARKET CONNECTION; *U.S. Private*, pg. 4074
MARKETING GARDEN LTD.—See AVIAREPS Marketing Garden Ltd.; *Int'l*, pg. 741
MARKETING MANIACS, INC.; *U.S. Private*, pg. 2580
THE MARKETING STORE—See The Marketing Store; *U.S. Private*, pg. 4075
THE MARKETING STORE—See The Marketing Store; *U.S. Private*, pg. 4075
THE MARKETING STORE—See The Marketing Store; *U.S. Private*, pg. 4075
THE MARKETING STORE—See The Marketing Store; *U.S. Private*, pg. 4075
THE MARKETING STORE WORLDWIDE (EUROPE) LIMITED—See The Marketing Store; *U.S. Private*, pg. 4075
MARLO MARKETING COMMUNICATIONS; *U.S. Private*, pg. 2585
MARTEC PORTER NOVELLI—See Omnicom Group Inc.; *U.S. Public*, pg. 1591
MASSMEDIA CORPORATE COMMUNICATIONS; *U.S. Private*, pg. 2606
MATLOCK ADVERTISING & PUBLIC RELATIONS-NY—See Matlock Advertising & Public Relations; *U.S. Private*, pg. 2611
MAX BORGES AGENCY; *U.S. Private*, pg. 2617
MCCULLOUGH PUBLIC RELATIONS, INC.; *U.S. Private*, pg. 2631
MCNEELY, PIGOTT & FOX; *U.S. Private*, pg. 2643
MCNEIL, GRAY & RICE; *U.S. Private*, pg. 2643
MCNEILL COMMUNICATIONS GROUP INC.—See Steinreich Communications, LLC; *U.S. Private*, pg. 3798
THE MCRAE AGENCY; *U.S. Private*, pg. 4077
MCS HEALTHCARE PUBLIC RELATIONS; *U.S. Private*, pg. 2644
THE MEDIA FOUNDRY INTERNATIONAL LIMITED—See Cubo Communications Group Plc; *Int'l*, pg. 1875
MEDIA RELATIONS, INC.; *U.S. Private*, pg. 2652
MELISSA DEVOLENTINE PUBLIC RELATIONS; *U.S. Private*, pg. 2662
MERCK & CO. INC.—See Merck & Co., Inc.; *U.S. Public*, pg. 1418
MERRITT GROUP; *U.S. Private*, pg. 2676
METZGER ASSOCIATES; *U.S. Private*, pg. 2691
MICHAEL J. LONDON & ASSOCIATES; *U.S. Private*, pg. 2698
MIKE WILSON PUBLIC RELATIONS, INC.; *U.S. Private*, pg. 2726
THE MILLERSCHIN GROUP, INC.—See French/West/Vaughan, LLC; *U.S. Private*, pg. 1609
MIRAMAR EVENTS; *U.S. Private*, pg. 2746
MISSY FARREN & ASSOCIATES LTD.—See Finn Partners, Inc.; *U.S. Private*, pg. 1510
MITCHELL MANNING ASSOCIATES, LTD.; *U.S. Private*, pg. 2750
MKG CHICAGO—See Acceleration Community of Companies; *U.S. Private*, pg. 49
MKG PRODUCTIONS, LLC—See Acceleration Community of Companies; *U.S. Private*, pg. 49
MKG WEST—See Acceleration Community of Companies; *U.S. Private*, pg. 49
MMGY GLOBAL - NEW YORK—See EagleTree Capital, LP; *U.S. Private*, pg. 1311
MMI PUBLIC RELATIONS; *U.S. Private*, pg. 2755
MMI PUBLIC RELATIONS—See MMI Public Relations; *U.S. Private*, pg. 2755
MOMENTUM—See The Interpublic Group of Companies, Inc.; *U.S. Public*, pg. 2102
MORGAN MARKETING & PUBLIC RELATIONS LLC; *U.S. Private*, pg. 2784
MORRISSEY & COMPANY; *U.S. Private*, pg. 2790
M&R SALES & SERVICE INC.—See M&R Holdings Inc.; *U.S. Private*, pg. 2525
M STRATEGIES, INC.; *U.S. Private*, pg. 2523
MURPHY O'BRIEN, INC.; *U.S. Private*, pg. 2815
MUTO COMMUNICATIONS, LLC; *U.S. Private*, pg. 2819
MWW GROUP LLC; *U.S. Private*, pg. 2822
THE MWW GROUP—See MWW Group LLC; *U.S. Private*, pg. 2822
THE MWW GROUP—See MWW Group LLC; *U.S. Private*, pg. 2822

541820 — PUBLIC RELATIONS AG...

THE MWW GROUP—See MWW Group LLC; *U.S. Private,* pg. 2822
THE MWW GROUP—See MWW Group LLC; *U.S. Private,* pg. 2822
THE MWW GROUP—See MWW Group LLC; *U.S. Private,* pg. 2822
MYNEWSDESK AB—See Fred. Olsen & Co.; *Int'l,* pg. 2768
MYNEWSDESK APS—See Fred. Olsen & Co.; *Int'l,* pg. 2768
MYNEWSDESK AS—See Fred. Olsen & Co.; *Int'l,* pg. 2768
MYNEWSDESK GMBH—See Fred. Olsen & Co.; *Int'l,* pg. 2768
MYNEWSDESK- GOTHENBURG—See Fred. Olsen & Co.; *Int'l,* pg. 2768
MYNEWSDESK LTD.—See Fred. Olsen & Co.; *Int'l,* pg. 2768
MYNEWSDESK- MALMO—See Fred. Olsen & Co.; *Int'l,* pg. 2768
MYNEWSDESK OY—See Fred. Olsen & Co.; *Int'l,* pg. 2768
MYNEWSDESK- UMEA—See Fred. Olsen & Co.; *Int'l,* pg. 2768
NADEL PHELAN, INC.; *U.S. Private,* pg. 2830
NANCY MARSHALL COMMUNICATIONS; *U.S. Private,* pg. 2833
NATIONAL STRATEGIES PUBLIC RELATIONS, LLC; *U.S. Private,* pg. 2863
NELSON BOSTOCK GROUP LIMITED—See Accenture plc; *Int'l,* pg. 87
NEOTROPE; *U.S. Private,* pg. 2885
NETPR, INC.; *U.S. Private,* pg. 2887
NICOLAZZO & ASSOCIATES INC.; *U.S. Private,* pg. 2926
NIKE COMMUNICATIONS, INC.; *U.S. Private,* pg. 2927
NM MARKETING COMMUNICATIONS, INC.; *U.S. Private,* pg. 2931
NOESIS COMMUNICAZIONE—See Clayton, Dubilier & Rice, LLC; *U.S. Private,* pg. 925
NORDS PORTER NOVELLI—See Omnicom Group Inc.; *U.S. Public,* pg. 1591
NOREEN HERON & ASSOCIATES; *U.S. Private,* pg. 2937
NORTHLICH PUBLIC RELATIONS—See Northlich; *U.S. Private,* pg. 2956
NORTHSTAR COUNSELORS INC.; *U.S. Private,* pg. 2957
NORTHWEST STRATEGIES; *U.S. Private,* pg. 2961
NORTHWINDS MARKETING GROUP LLC—See American Express Company; *U.S. Public,* pg. 102
NPC CREATIVE SERVICES, LLC; *U.S. Private,* pg. 2969
NUEVA COMUNICACION-WEBER SHANDWICK—See The Interpublic Group of Companies, Inc.; *U.S. Public,* pg. 2105
NUEVA COMUNICACION-WEBER SHANDWICK—See The Interpublic Group of Companies, Inc.; *U.S. Public,* pg. 2105
NYHUS COMMUNICATIONS LLC; *U.S. Private,* pg. 2976
O'CONNELL & GOLDBERG; *U.S. Private,* pg. 2977
OFF THE GRID PUBLIC RELATIONS; *U.S. Private,* pg. 3001
OGAN/DALLAL ASSOCIATES, INC.; *U.S. Private,* pg. 3003
O'KEEFFE & CO.; *U.S. Private,* pg. 2978
O'KEEFFE & CO.—See O'Keeffe & Co.; *U.S. Private,* pg. 2978
O'KEEFFE & CO.—See O'Keeffe & Co.; *U.S. Private,* pg. 2978
O'KEEFFE & CO.—See O'Keeffe & Co.; *U.S. Private,* pg. 2978
O'KEEFFE & CO.—See O'Keeffe & Co.; *U.S. Private,* pg. 2978
OLSON ENGAGE—See ICF International, Inc.; *U.S. Public,* pg. 1086
O'MALLEY HANSEN COMMUNICATIONS; *U.S. Private,* pg. 2978
OMNICOM PUBLIC RELATIONS GROUP, INC.—See Omnicom Group Inc.; *U.S. Public,* pg. 1589
ONPR GMBH—See OnPR; *U.S. Private,* pg. 3027
ONPR; *U.S. Private,* pg. 3027
OPUS SOLUTIONS, LLC; *U.S. Private,* pg. 3036
PADILLACRT - LOS ANGELES—See Padilla Speer Beardsley Inc.; *U.S. Private,* pg. 3074
PADILLACRT - NEW YORK—See Padilla Speer Beardsley Inc.; *U.S. Private,* pg. 3074
PADILLACRT - NORFOLK—See Padilla Speer Beardsley Inc.; *U.S. Private,* pg. 3074
PADILLACRT - RICHMOND—See Padilla Speer Beardsley Inc.; *U.S. Private,* pg. 3074
PADILLA SPEER BEARDSLEY INC.; *U.S. Private,* pg. 3073
PAGE ONE PR, LLC; *U.S. Private,* pg. 3074
PAIGE HENDRICKS PUBLIC RELATIONS INC; *U.S. Private,* pg. 3075
PAN COMMUNICATIONS; *U.S. Private,* pg. 3084
PARQUET PUBLIC AFFAIRS, LLC—See The Parquet Group; *U.S. Private,* pg. 4091
PEGASUS COMMUNICATIONS—See Daniel J. Edelman, Inc.; *U.S. Private,* pg. 1155
PEPPERCOM, INC.; *U.S. Private,* pg. 3144
PEPPERCOM—See Peppercom, Inc.; *U.S. Private,* pg. 3144
PEPPERCOM UK LTD.—See Peppercom, Inc.; *U.S. Private,* pg. 3145
PERFECT RELATIONS PVT. LTD.—See Dentsu Group Inc.; *Int'l,* pg. 2036

PICTURE MARKETING, INC.; *U.S. Private,* pg. 3176
PIERCE MATTIE COMMUNICATIONS; *U.S. Private,* pg. 3178
PIERPONT COMMUNICATIONS, INC.; *U.S. Private,* pg. 3179
PIERPONT COMMUNICATIONS, INC.—See Pierpont Communications, Inc.; *U.S. Private,* pg. 3179
PILOT GROUP—See Hakuhodo DY Holdings Incorporated; *Int'l,* pg. 3221
PIPELINE PUBLIC RELATIONS & MARKETING; *U.S. Private,* pg. 3189
PLANNED TELEVISION ARTS—See Ruder Finn Group, Inc.; *U.S. Private,* pg. 3501
PLEON IMPACT—See Omnicom Group Inc.; *U.S. Public,* pg. 1576
PLESSER HOLLAND ASSOCIATES; *U.S. Private,* pg. 3213
PMK*BNC—See The Interpublic Group of Companies, Inc.; *U.S. Public,* pg. 2102
PMK*BNC—See The Interpublic Group of Companies, Inc.; *U.S. Public,* pg. 2102
POINTER PR LLC; *U.S. Private,* pg. 3222
POLLOCK COMMUNICATIONS; *U.S. Private,* pg. 3225
PORTER, LEVAY & ROSE, INC.; *U.S. Private,* pg. 3232
PORTER NOVELLI-AUSTIN—See Omnicom Group Inc.; *U.S. Public,* pg. 1591
PORTER NOVELLI AUSTRALIA-MELBOURNE—See Omnicom Group Inc.; *U.S. Public,* pg. 1591
PORTER NOVELLI-BAY AREA-SAN FRANCISCO—See Omnicom Group Inc.; *U.S. Public,* pg. 1591
PORTER NOVELLI-BEIJING—See Omnicom Group Inc.; *U.S. Public,* pg. 1591
PORTER NOVELLI-BOSTON—See Omnicom Group Inc.; *U.S. Public,* pg. 1591
PORTER NOVELLI CANADA-MONTREAL—See Omnicom Group Inc.; *U.S. Public,* pg. 1591
PORTER NOVELLI-CHICAGO—See Omnicom Group Inc.; *U.S. Public,* pg. 1591
PORTER NOVELLI-FT. LAUDERDALE—See Omnicom Group Inc.; *U.S. Public,* pg. 1591
PORTER NOVELLI-IRVINE—See Omnicom Group Inc.; *U.S. Public,* pg. 1591
PORTER NOVELLI-LONDON—See Omnicom Group Inc.; *U.S. Public,* pg. 1591
PORTER NOVELLI-LOS ANGELES—See Omnicom Group Inc.; *U.S. Public,* pg. 1591
PORTER NOVELLI NEW ZEALAND-AUCKLAND—See Omnicom Group Inc.; *U.S. Public,* pg. 1591
PORTER NOVELLI-PARIS—See Omnicom Group Inc.; *U.S. Public,* pg. 1591
PORTER NOVELLI PTE. LTD. - SINGAPORE—See Omnicom Group Inc.; *U.S. Public,* pg. 1591
PORTER NOVELLI-SAN DIEGO—See Omnicom Group Inc.; *U.S. Public,* pg. 1591
PORTER NOVELLI-SEATTLE—See Omnicom Group Inc.; *U.S. Public,* pg. 1591
PORTER NOVELLI—See Omnicom Group Inc.; *U.S. Public,* pg. 1590
PORTER NOVELLI—See Omnicom Group Inc.; *U.S. Public,* pg. 1591
PORTER NOVELLI—See Omnicom Group Inc.; *U.S. Public,* pg. 1591
PORTER NOVELLI—See Omnicom Group Inc.; *U.S. Public,* pg. 1591
PORTER NOVELLI—See Omnicom Group Inc.; *U.S. Public,* pg. 1591
PORTER NOVELLI—See Omnicom Group Inc.; *U.S. Public,* pg. 1591
PORTER NOVELLI—See Omnicom Group Inc.; *U.S. Public,* pg. 1591
PORTER NOVELLI—See Omnicom Group Inc.; *U.S. Public,* pg. 1591
PORTER NOVELLI SYDNEY—See Omnicom Group Inc.; *U.S. Public,* pg. 1591
PORTER NOVELLI TASMANIA—See Omnicom Group Inc.; *U.S. Public,* pg. 1591
PORTER NOVELLI-TORONTO—See Omnicom Group Inc.; *U.S. Public,* pg. 1591
PORTER NOVELLI-WASHINGTON—See Omnicom Group Inc.; *U.S. Public,* pg. 1591
POST+BEAM; *U.S. Private,* pg. 3234
POWELL TATE-WEBER SHANDWICK—See The Interpublic Group of Companies, Inc.; *U.S. Public,* pg. 2105
POWERS BRAND COMMUNICATIONS LLC—See 360 Public Relations LLC; *U.S. Private,* pg. 8
POWERSCOURT LIMITED—See TPG Capital, L.P.; *U.S. Public,* pg. 2177
THE PRACTICE PORTER NOVELLI—See Omnicom Group Inc.; *U.S. Public,* pg. 1592
PR CONSULTING DENTSU INC.—See Dentsu Group Inc.; *Int'l,* pg. 2039
THE PR CONSULTING GROUP, INC.-LOS ANGELES—See The PR Consulting Group, Inc.; *U.S. Private,* pg. 4097
THE PR CONSULTING GROUP, INC.; *U.S. Private,* pg. 4097
THE PR CONSULTING GROUP, INC.-WASHINGTON—See The PR Consulting Group, Inc.; *U.S. Private,* pg. 4097

PRG PASKAL LIGHTING—See The Jordan Company, L.P.; *U.S. Private,* pg. 4061
THE PR GROUP, INC.; *U.S. Private,* pg. 4097
PRIME TIME—See The Interpublic Group of Companies, Inc.; *U.S. Public,* pg. 2105
PRINCETON PUBLIC AFFAIRS GROUP, INC.—See Winning Strategies Public Relations; *U.S. Private,* pg. 4543
PRIORITY PUBLIC RELATIONS; *U.S. Private,* pg. 3267
PRIORITY PUBLIC RELATIONS—See Priority Public Relations; *U.S. Private,* pg. 3267
PRISMA PUBLIC RELATIONS—See Omnicom Group Inc.; *U.S. Public,* pg. 1578
PR NEWSCHANNEL—See Selig Multimedia Inc.; *U.S. Private,* pg. 3602
PR NEWSWIRE ASIA LTD—See Platinum Equity, LLC; *U.S. Private,* pg. 3202
PROAMERICAS; *U.S. Private,* pg. 3271
PROFILE PLUS (UK) LTD.—See Freshwater UK PLC; *Int'l,* pg. 2782
PROSEK PARTNERS; *U.S. Private,* pg. 3286
PROSEK PARTNERS—See Prosek Partners; *U.S. Private,* pg. 3286
PROSEK PARTNERS—See Prosek Partners; *U.S. Private,* pg. 3286
PRP-PUBLIC RELATIONS & PROMOTION GROUP—See The Interpublic Group of Companies, Inc.; *U.S. Public,* pg. 2105
PR PUNDIT PORTER NOVELLI—See Omnicom Group Inc.; *U.S. Public,* pg. 1591
PRXDIGITAL; *U.S. Private,* pg. 3296
PUBLIC AND INVESTOR RELATIONS PIR SVERIGE AB—See Platinum Equity, LLC; *U.S. Private,* pg. 3202
THE PUBLICITY AGENCY—See Selig Multimedia Inc.; *U.S. Private,* pg. 3602
QUASAR COMUNICACIONES PORTER NOVELLI—See Omnicom Group Inc.; *U.S. Public,* pg. 1591
QUINN/BREIN PUBLIC RELATIONS; *U.S. Private,* pg. 3328
QUIXOTE RESEARCH, MARKETING & PUBLIC RELATIONS; *U.S. Private,* pg. 3329
RAKER GOLDSTEIN & CO., INC.—See CHR Group LLC; *U.S. Private,* pg. 889
RANDALL PR, LLC; *U.S. Private,* pg. 3353
RAS ASSOCIATES LLC—See EQT AB; *Int'l,* pg. 2483
RAWLE MURDY ASSOCIATES, INC.—See Troon Golf L.L.C.; *U.S. Private,* pg. 4242
RBB PUBLIC RELATIONS, LLC; *U.S. Private,* pg. 3360
R.C. AULETTA & CO. LLC; *U.S. Private,* pg. 3334
RECOGNITION PUBLIC RELATIONS—See Omnicom Group Inc.; *U.S. Public,* pg. 1578
THE RED CONSULTANCY—See Clayton, Dubilier & Rice, LLC; *U.S. Private,* pg. 925
THE RED CONSULTANCY—See Clayton, Dubilier & Rice, LLC; *U.S. Private,* pg. 925
THE RED CONSULTANCY—See Clayton, Dubilier & Rice, LLC; *U.S. Private,* pg. 925
REDLINE—See The Interpublic Group of Companies, Inc.; *U.S. Public,* pg. 2093
REELTIME RENTALS, INC.; *U.S. Public,* pg. 1771
REEVES LAVERDURE PUBLIC RELATIONS; *U.S. Private,* pg. 3384
REGAN COMMUNICATIONS GROUP, INC. - FLORIDA—See Regan Communications Group, Inc.; *U.S. Private,* pg. 3386
REGAN COMMUNICATIONS GROUP, INC. - PROVIDENCE—See Regan Communications Group, Inc.; *U.S. Private,* pg. 3386
REGAN COMMUNICATIONS GROUP, INC.; *U.S. Private,* pg. 3386
REPORT PORTER NOVELLI-ROME—See Omnicom Group Inc.; *U.S. Public,* pg. 1592
REPORT PORTER NOVELLI—See Omnicom Group Inc.; *U.S. Public,* pg. 1592
REVELL COMMUNICATIONS; *U.S. Private,* pg. 3413
REVOLUTION PUBLIC RELATIONS; *U.S. Private,* pg. 3416
RF BINDER PARTNERS—See Ruder Finn Group, Inc.; *U.S. Private,* pg. 3501
RF BINDER PARTNERS—See Ruder Finn Group, Inc.; *U.S. Private,* pg. 3501
THE RHOADS GROUP—See The Interpublic Group of Companies, Inc.; *U.S. Public,* pg. 2105
RIEGNER & ASSOCIATES, INC.; *U.S. Private,* pg. 3434
RIGGS PARTNERS; *U.S. Private,* pg. 3435
RIMON COHEN-WEBER SHANDWICK—See The Interpublic Group of Companies, Inc.; *U.S. Public,* pg. 2105
R.I.M. PORTER NOVELLI—See Omnicom Group Inc.; *U.S. Public,* pg. 1591
RISDALL PUBLIC RELATIONS—See Risdall Marketing Group, LLC; *U.S. Private,* pg. 3440
R.J. DALE ADVERTISING & PUBLIC RELATIONS; *U.S. Private,* pg. 3337
RLM PUBLIC RELATIONS, INC.; *U.S. Private,* pg. 3450
RL PUBLIC RELATIONS + MARKETING; *U.S. Private,* pg. 3450
ROAR MEDIA LLC; *U.S. Private,* pg. 3454
ROBIN LEEDY & ASSOCIATES; *U.S. Private,* pg. 3460
ROCKET SCIENCE; *U.S. Private,* pg. 3466
ROGERS & COWAN—See The Interpublic Group of Companies, Inc.; *U.S. Public,* pg. 2105

N.A.I.C.S. INDEX

541820 — PUBLIC RELATIONS AG...

ROGERS & COWAN—See The Interpublic Group of Companies, Inc.; *U.S. Public*, pg. 2105
THE ROGERS GROUP—See Ruder Finn Group, Inc.; *U.S. Private*, pg. 3501
ROHER PUBLIC RELATIONS; *U.S. Private*, pg. 3473
ROHER PUBLIC RELATIONS—See Roher Public Relations; *U.S. Private*, pg. 3473
RON SONNTAG PUBLIC RELATIONS; *U.S. Private*, pg. 3477
ROOP & CO.; *U.S. Private*, pg. 3479
ROSECOMM, INC.; *U.S. Private*, pg. 3482
THE ROSEN GROUP; *U.S. Private*, pg. 4112
ROSICA STRATEGIC PUBLIC RELATIONS; *U.S. Private*, pg. 3484
ROUSSO/FISHER PUBLIC RELATIONS, INC.; *U.S. Private*, pg. 3489
RR PUBLIC RELATIONS, INC.; *U.S. Private*, pg. 3496
RT&E INTEGRATED COMMUNICATIONS—See Reese, Tomases & Ellick, Inc. (RT&E); *U.S. Private*, pg. 3383
RU&A PORTER NOVELLI—See Omnicom Group Inc.; *U.S. Public*, pg. 1591
RUBENSTEIN ASSOCIATES, INC.; *U.S. Private*, pg. 3499
RUBENSTEIN PUBLIC RELATIONS, INC.—See Rubenstein Associates, Inc.; *U.S. Private*, pg. 3499
RUDER FINN FRANCE, SARL—See Ruder Finn Group, Inc.; *U.S. Private*, pg. 3501
RUDER FINN HEALTHCARE—See Ruder Finn Group, Inc.; *U.S. Private*, pg. 3501
RUDER FINN, INC.—See Ruder Finn Group, Inc.; *U.S. Private*, pg. 3501
RUDER FINN, INC.—See Ruder Finn Group, Inc.; *U.S. Private*, pg. 3501
RUDER FINN—See Ruder Finn Group, Inc.; *U.S. Private*, pg. 3501
RUDER FINN UK, LTD.—See Ruder Finn Group, Inc.; *U.S. Private*, pg. 3501
RUDER FINN WEST—See Ruder Finn Group, Inc.; *U.S. Private*, pg. 3501
S2PUBLICOM WEBER SHANDWICK—See The Interpublic Group of Companies, Inc.; *U.S. Public*, pg. 2094
SAGON-PHIOR; *U.S. Private*, pg. 3528
SAGON-PHIOR—See Sagon-Phior; *U.S. Private*, pg. 3528
SAGON-PHIOR—See Sagon-Phior; *U.S. Private*, pg. 3528
SALTERMITCHELL, INC.; *U.S. Private*, pg. 3534
SANDRA EVANS & ASSOCIATES; *U.S. Private*, pg. 3544
SAUNDERS UNSWORTH LIMITED—See Daniel J. Edelman, Inc.; *U.S. Private*, pg. 1155
SAVVY INC.; *U.S. Private*, pg. 3557
SAWYER MILLER ADVERTISING—See The Interpublic Group of Companies, Inc.; *U.S. Public*, pg. 2105
SAWYER MILLER ADVERTISING—See The Interpublic Group of Companies, Inc.; *U.S. Public*, pg. 2105
SAXUM PUBLIC RELATIONS; *U.S. Private*, pg. 3558
SBPR CORP.; *U.S. Private*, pg. 3560
SCHNEIDER ASSOCIATES; *U.S. Private*, pg. 3566
SCHWARTZ PUBLIC RELATIONS ASSOCIATES, INC.; *U.S. Private*, pg. 3572
SCORR MARKETING; *U.S. Private*, pg. 3575
SCOTT PEYRON & ASSOCIATES, INC.; *U.S. Private*, pg. 3577
SCOTT PUBLIC RELATIONS; *U.S. Private*, pg. 3577
SEFIN MARKETING—See Omnicom Group Inc.; *U.S. Public*, pg. 1578
SELIG MULTIMEDIA INC.; *U.S. Private*, pg. 3602
SEVENTY SEVEN PR—See Fishburn Hedges; *Int'l*, pg. 2692
SEYFERTH & ASSOCIATES INC.; *U.S. Private*, pg. 3620
SHERMAN COMMUNICATIONS & MARKETING; *U.S. Private*, pg. 3634
SHOREY PUBLIC RELATIONS LLC; *U.S. Private*, pg. 3642
SIGMA INTERNATIONAL (POLAND) LTD.—See The Interpublic Group of Companies, Inc.; *U.S. Public*, pg. 2105
SILVERMAN MEDIA & MARKETING GROUP, INC.; *U.S. Private*, pg. 3663
SITRICK & CO.; *U.S. Private*, pg. 3676
SLOANE & COMPANY LLC—See Stagwell, Inc.; *U.S. Public*, pg. 1927
SOCIALRADIUS; *U.S. Private*, pg. 3703
SOLOMON MCCOWN & COMPANY, INC.; *U.S. Private*, pg. 3710
SOPEXA (CANADA) LTD.—See Hopscotch Groupe S.A.; *Int'l*, pg. 3474
SOUTHARD COMMUNICATIONS; *U.S. Private*, pg. 3724
SPARK COMMUNICATIONS—See Omnicom Group Inc.; *U.S. Public*, pg. 1578
SPARKPR; *U.S. Private*, pg. 3746
SPEAKERBOX COMMUNICATIONS, LLC—See Trinity Hunt Management, L.P.; *U.S. Private*, pg. 4235
SPECTOR & ASSOCIATES, INC.; *U.S. Private*, pg. 3751
SPEM COMMUNICATION GROUP—See Omnicom Group Inc.; *U.S. Public*, pg. 1592
SPEM PORTER NOVELLI-CROATIA—See Omnicom Group Inc.; *U.S. Public*, pg. 1592
SPI GROUP LLC—See Ruder Finn Group, Inc.; *U.S. Private*, pg. 3501
SPOT ON PUBLIC RELATIONS—See Omnicom Group Inc.; *U.S. Public*, pg. 1578

SPRINGBOARD COMMUNICATIONS; *U.S. Private*, pg. 3763
S&S PUBLIC RELATIONS, INC.; *U.S. Private*, pg. 3514
S&S PUBLIC RELATIONS, INC.—See S&S Public Relations, Inc.; *U.S. Private*, pg. 3514
STANDING PARTNERSHIP; *U.S. Private*, pg. 3782
STANDING PARTNERSHIP—See Standing Partnership; *U.S. Private*, pg. 3782
STANIFORTH/—See Omnicom Group Inc.; *U.S. Public*, pg. 1596
STANTON COMMUNICATIONS, INC.; *U.S. Private*, pg. 3783
STANTON COMMUNICATIONS INC.—See Stanton Communications, Inc.; *U.S. Private*, pg. 3783
STANTON COMMUNICATIONS INC.—See Stanton Communications, Inc.; *U.S. Private*, pg. 3783
STARRTECH INTERACTIVE; *U.S. Private*, pg. 3788
STC ASSOCIATES; *U.S. Private*, pg. 3794
STEPHANIE CHURCHILL PR—See Clayton, Dubilier & Rice, LLC; *U.S. Private*, pg. 925
STEPHENSON GROUP; *U.S. Private*, pg. 3803
STEPHENSON GROUP—See Stephenson Group; *U.S. Private*, pg. 3803
STERLING COMMUNICATIONS; *U.S. Private*, pg. 3804
THE STERLING CORPORATION—See Lambert & Co.; *U.S. Private*, pg. 2380
STERN + ASSOCIATES—See Stern Strategy Group; *U.S. Private*, pg. 3807
STERN INVESTOR RELATIONS, INC.—See Precision Medicine Group, Inc.; *U.S. Private*, pg. 3245
STERN STRATEGY GROUP; *U.S. Private*, pg. 3807
STEVENS FKM PUBLIC RELATIONS—See The Company of Others; *U.S. Private*, pg. 4013
STORYLINE STRATEGIES LLC—See Stagwell, Inc.; *U.S. Public*, pg. 1928
STRATACOMM LLC - DETROIT OFFICE—See Omnicom Group Inc.; *U.S. Public*, pg. 1585
STRATACOMM LLC—See Omnicom Group Inc.; *U.S. Public*, pg. 1585
STRATEGY COMMUNICATIONS; *U.S. Private*, pg. 3836
STRAUSS MEDIA STRATEGIES, INC.; *U.S. Private*, pg. 3837
STRAUSS MEDIA STRATEGIES, INC.—See Strauss Media Strategies, Inc.; *U.S. Private*, pg. 3837
SUGAR HELSINKI OY—See Adelis Equity Partners AB; *Int'l*, pg. 142
SWORDFISH COMMUNICATIONS; *U.S. Private*, pg. 3895
SYLVIA MARKETING & PUBLIC RELATIONS, LLC; *U.S. Private*, pg. 3898
SYMPOINT COMMUNICATIONS; *U.S. Private*, pg. 3902
TATEAUSTINHAHN; *U.S. Private*, pg. 3936
TAYLOR GLOBAL INC.; *U.S. Private*, pg. 3940
TAYLOR GLOBAL INC.—See Taylor Global Inc.; *U.S. Private*, pg. 3940
TBC INC.—See TBC Inc.; *U.S. Private*, pg. 3941
TBC PUBLIC RELATIONS—See TBC Inc.; *U.S. Private*, pg. 3941
TBC PUBLIC RELATIONS—See Ted Barkus Company, Inc.; *U.S. Private*, pg. 3957
TECH IMAGE—See SmithBucklin Corporation; *U.S. Private*, pg. 3697
TERPIN COMMUNICATIONS GROUP; *U.S. Private*, pg. 3970
THOMAS J. PAYNE MARKET DEVELOPMENT; *U.S. Private*, pg. 4156
THOMAS J. PAYNE MARKET DEVELOPMENT—See Thomas J. Payne Market Development; *U.S. Private*, pg. 4156
THOMPSON & BENDER LLC; *U.S. Private*, pg. 4158
THOMPSON & BERRY—See Thompson & Company Marketing Communications; *U.S. Private*, pg. 4158
THOMPSON & CO. NEW YORK—See Thompson & Co. Public Relations; *U.S. Private*, pg. 4158
THOMPSON & CO. PUBLIC RELATIONS; *U.S. Private*, pg. 4158
THORP & COMPANY; *U.S. Private*, pg. 4163
TIER ONE PARTNERS; *U.S. Private*, pg. 4169
TOGORUN; *U.S. Private*, pg. 4181
TOMSHEEHAN WORLDWIDE—See tomsheehan worldwide; *U.S. Private*, pg. 4184
TONIC LIFE COMMUNICATIONS LTD.—See Clayton, Dubilier & Rice, LLC; *U.S. Private*, pg. 925
TORME LAURICELLA; *U.S. Private*, pg. 4189
TOTAL MEDIA GGI—See The Interpublic Group of Companies, Inc.; *U.S. Public*, pg. 2105
TRAINER COMMUNICATIONS; *U.S. Private*, pg. 4204
TRANSMEDIA GROUP; *U.S. Private*, pg. 4209
TR CUTLER, INC.; *U.S. Private*, pg. 4200
TRYLON SMR; *U.S. Private*, pg. 4252
TTC GROUP, INC.; *U.S. Private*, pg. 4254
TUCKER/HALL, INC.; *U.S. Private*, pg. 4256
TUERFF-DAVIS ENVIROMEDIA; *U.S. Private*, pg. 4257
TUNHEIM PARTNERS; *U.S. Private*, pg. 4258
TURBOLIN PR—See Omnicom Group Inc.; *U.S. Public*, pg. 1578
TURNER PUBLIC RELATIONS, INC. - NEW YORK—See Peopletomysite.com, LLC; *U.S. Private*, pg. 3143
TURNER PUBLIC RELATIONS, INC.—See Peopletomysite.com, LLC; *U.S. Private*, pg. 3143

THE ULUM GROUP; *U.S. Private*, pg. 4129
VANCOREJONES COMMUNICATIONS INC.; *U.S. Private*, pg. 4342
THE VANDIVER GROUP, INC.—See Lambert & Co.; *U.S. Private*, pg. 2380
VERGE PROMOTIONAL MARKETING; *U.S. Private*, pg. 4359
VERSE COMMUNICATIONS; *U.S. Private*, pg. 4369
VISITECH, INC.; *U.S. Private*, pg. 4392
VISTA GROUP INC.; *U.S. Private*, pg. 4403
VOCE COMMUNICATIONS—See Omnicom Group Inc.; *U.S. Public*, pg. 1592
VOLUME PUBLIC RELATIONS; *U.S. Private*, pg. 4411
W2O GROUP—See New Mountain Capital, LLC; *U.S. Private*, pg. 2903
WAGGENER EDSTROM; *U.S. Private*, pg. 4425
WAGGENER EDSTROM—See Waggener Edstrom; *U.S. Private*, pg. 4425
WAGGENER EDSTROM—See Waggener Edstrom; *U.S. Private*, pg. 4425
WAGGENER EDSTROM—See Waggener Edstrom; *U.S. Private*, pg. 4425
WAGGENER EDSTROM—See Waggener Edstrom; *U.S. Private*, pg. 4425
WAGGENER EDSTROM—See Waggener Edstrom; *U.S. Private*, pg. 4425
WAGGENER EDSTROM—See Waggener Edstrom; *U.S. Private*, pg. 4425
WALEK & ASSOCIATES—See Peppercom, Inc.; *U.S. Private*, pg. 3145
WALL STREET COMMUNICATIONS; *U.S. Private*, pg. 4430
WALT & COMPANY COMMUNICATIONS INC.; *U.S. Private*, pg. 4433
WARNER COMMUNICATIONS—See Millwright Holdings LLC; *U.S. Private*, pg. 2738
WARSCHAWSKI; *U.S. Private*, pg. 4445
WARSCHAWSKI—See Warschawski; *U.S. Private*, pg. 4445
WCG—See New Mountain Capital, LLC; *U.S. Private*, pg. 2904
WEBBERMCJ—See McGarrah Jessee; *U.S. Private*, pg. 2634
WEBER SHANDWICK-ATLANTA—See The Interpublic Group of Companies, Inc.; *U.S. Public*, pg. 2106
WEBER SHANDWICK-AUSTIN—See The Interpublic Group of Companies, Inc.; *U.S. Public*, pg. 2106
WEBER SHANDWICK-BALTIMORE—See The Interpublic Group of Companies, Inc.; *U.S. Public*, pg. 2106
WEBER SHANDWICK-BOSTON—See The Interpublic Group of Companies, Inc.; *U.S. Public*, pg. 2106
WEBER SHANDWICK-CHICAGO—See The Interpublic Group of Companies, Inc.; *U.S. Public*, pg. 2106
WEBER SHANDWICK-DALLAS—See The Interpublic Group of Companies, Inc.; *U.S. Public*, pg. 2106
WEBER SHANDWICK-DENVER—See The Interpublic Group of Companies, Inc.; *U.S. Public*, pg. 2106
WEBER SHANDWICK-DETROIT—See The Interpublic Group of Companies, Inc.; *U.S. Public*, pg. 2106
WEBER SHANDWICK-LOS ANGELES—See The Interpublic Group of Companies, Inc.; *U.S. Public*, pg. 2106
WEBER SHANDWICK-MINNEAPOLIS—See The Interpublic Group of Companies, Inc.; *U.S. Public*, pg. 2106
WEBER SHANDWICK - MUMBAI—See The Interpublic Group of Companies, Inc.; *U.S. Public*, pg. 2106
WEBER SHANDWICK-SAINT LOUIS—See The Interpublic Group of Companies, Inc.; *U.S. Public*, pg. 2106
WEBER SHANDWICK-SAN FRANCISCO—See The Interpublic Group of Companies, Inc.; *U.S. Public*, pg. 2106
WEBER SHANDWICK-SEATTLE—See The Interpublic Group of Companies, Inc.; *U.S. Public*, pg. 2106
WEBER SHANDWICK—See The Interpublic Group of Companies, Inc.; *U.S. Public*, pg. 2104
WEBER SHANDWICK—See The Interpublic Group of Companies, Inc.; *U.S. Public*, pg. 2105
WEBER SHANDWICK—See The Interpublic Group of Companies, Inc.; *U.S. Public*, pg. 2105
WEBER SHANDWICK—See The Interpublic Group of Companies, Inc.; *U.S. Public*, pg. 2105
WEBER SHANDWICK—See The Interpublic Group of Companies, Inc.; *U.S. Public*, pg. 2105
WEBER SHANDWICK—See The Interpublic Group of Companies, Inc.; *U.S. Public*, pg. 2105
WEBER SHANDWICK—See The Interpublic Group of Companies, Inc.; *U.S. Public*, pg. 2105
WEBER SHANDWICK—See The Interpublic Group of Companies, Inc.; *U.S. Public*, pg. 2105
WEBER SHANDWICK—See The Interpublic Group of Companies, Inc.; *U.S. Public*, pg. 2105
WEBER SHANDWICK—See The Interpublic Group of Companies, Inc.; *U.S. Public*, pg. 2105
WEBER SHANDWICK—See The Interpublic Group of Companies, Inc.; *U.S. Public*, pg. 2105
WEBER SHANDWICK—See The Interpublic Group of Companies, Inc.; *U.S. Public*, pg. 2105
WEBER SHANDWICK—See The Interpublic Group of Companies, Inc.; *U.S. Public*, pg. 2105

541820 — PUBLIC RELATIONS AG...

WEBER SHANDWICK—See The Interpublic Group of Companies, Inc.; *U.S. Public*, pg. 2105
WEBER SHANDWICK—See The Interpublic Group of Companies, Inc.; *U.S. Public*, pg. 2105
WEBER SHANDWICK—See The Interpublic Group of Companies, Inc.; *U.S. Public*, pg. 2105
WEBER SHANDWICK—See The Interpublic Group of Companies, Inc.; *U.S. Public*, pg. 2105
WEBER SHANDWICK—See The Interpublic Group of Companies, Inc.; *U.S. Public*, pg. 2106
WEBER SHANDWICK—See The Interpublic Group of Companies, Inc.; *U.S. Public*, pg. 2106
WEBER SHANDWICK—See The Interpublic Group of Companies, Inc.; *U.S. Public*, pg. 2106
WEBER SHANDWICK—See The Interpublic Group of Companies, Inc.; *U.S. Public*, pg. 2106
WEBER SHANDWICK—See The Interpublic Group of Companies, Inc.; *U.S. Public*, pg. 2106
WEBER SHANDWICK—See The Interpublic Group of Companies, Inc.; *U.S. Public*, pg. 2106
WEBER SHANDWICK—See The Interpublic Group of Companies, Inc.; *U.S. Public*, pg. 2106
WEBER SHANDWICK—See The Interpublic Group of Companies, Inc.; *U.S. Public*, pg. 2106
WEBER SHANDWICK—See The Interpublic Group of Companies, Inc.; *U.S. Public*, pg. 2106
WEBER SHANDWICK—See The Interpublic Group of Companies, Inc.; *U.S. Public*, pg. 2106
WEBER SHANDWICK—See The Interpublic Group of Companies, Inc.; *U.S. Public*, pg. 2106
WEBER SHANDWICK-SUNNYVALE—See The Interpublic Group of Companies, Inc.; *U.S. Public*, pg. 2106
WEBER SHANDWICK UK—See The Interpublic Group of Companies, Inc.; *U.S. Public*, pg. 2106
WEBER SHANDWICK WORLDWIDE—See The Interpublic Group of Companies, Inc.; *U.S. Public*, pg. 2106
WIDMEYER COMMUNICATIONS, INC.—See Ruder Finn Group, Inc.; *U.S. Private*, pg. 3501
WILDFIRE SALES INC.—See CI Capital Partners LLC; *U.S. Private*, pg. 895
WILEN MEDIA; *U.S. Private*, pg. 4519
WILSON STRATEGIC COMMUNICATIONS, INC.—See Health Management Associates, Inc.; *U.S. Private*, pg. 1894
WINNING STRATEGIES PUBLIC RELATIONS; *U.S. Private*, pg. 4543
WINNING STRATEGIES WASHINGTON—See Winning Strategies Public Relations; *U.S. Private*, pg. 4543
WOLF PRESS & PUBLIC RELATIONS—See Daniel J. Edelman, Inc.; *U.S. Private*, pg. 1155
WOMANWISE LLC; *U.S. Private*, pg. 4555
WRAGG & CASAS PUBLIC RELATIONS, INC.; *U.S. Private*, pg. 4571
WRAGG & CASAS PUBLIC RELATIONS, INC.—See Wragg & Casas Public Relations, Inc.; *U.S. Private*, pg. 4572
WRAGG & CASAS PUBLIC RELATIONS, INC.—See Wragg & Casas Public Relations, Inc.; *U.S. Private*, pg. 4572
W.S. ADAMSON & ASSOCIATES, INC.; *U.S. Private*, pg. 4422
XENOPHON STRATEGIES; *U.S. Private*, pg. 4581
XFACT, INC.; *U.S. Private*, pg. 4581
YAMAMOTO MOSS MACKENZIE—See Stagwell, Inc.; *U.S. Public*, pg. 1928
ZAPWATER COMMUNICATIONS, INC.; *U.S. Private*, pg. 4598
ZENO GROUP; *U.S. Private*, pg. 4601
ZENO GROUP—See ZENO Group; *U.S. Private*, pg. 4601
ZENO GROUP—See ZENO Group; *U.S. Private*, pg. 4601
ZENO GROUP—See ZENO Group; *U.S. Private*, pg. 4601
ZENZI COMMUNICATIONS; *U.S. Private*, pg. 4602
ZEPPOS & ASSOCIATES, INC.; *U.S. Private*, pg. 4602
ZIGMAN JOSEPH PR; *U.S. Private*, pg. 4604
ZIMAT CONSULTORES—See The Interpublic Group of Companies, Inc.; *U.S. Public*, pg. 2094
ZIMAT-WEBER SHANDWICK—See The Interpublic Group of Companies, Inc.; *U.S. Public*, pg. 2106
ZORCH INTERNATIONAL, INC.—See Satori Capital, LLC; *U.S. Private*, pg. 3553

541830 — MEDIA BUYING AGENCIES

3Q DIGITAL, INC.; *U.S. Private*, pg. 14
AC ADVERTISING; *U.S. Private*, pg. 45
ACTION MEDIA, INC.; *U.S. Private*, pg. 67
ACTIVE INTERNATIONAL CORPORATE TRADING SPAIN S.L.—See Active Media Services, Inc.; *U.S. Private*, pg. 69
ACTIVE INTERNATIONAL POLAND SP. Z O.O.—See Active Media Services, Inc.; *U.S. Private*, pg. 69
ADCOMM, INC; *U.S. Private*, pg. 76
ADCONION GMBH—See Adconion Media Group Ltd.; *Int'l*, pg. 127
ADCONION GMBH—See Adconion Media Group Ltd.; *Int'l*, pg. 127
ADCONION GMBH—See Adconion Media Group Ltd.; *Int'l*, pg. 127
ADCONION MEDIA, INC.—See Adconion Media Group Ltd.; *Int'l*, pg. 127
ADCONION MEDIA INC.—See Adconion Media Group Ltd.; *Int'l*, pg. 127
ADCONION S.L.—See Adconion Media Group Ltd.; *Int'l*, pg. 127
ADVANCE LOCAL LLC; *U.S. Private*, pg. 83
ADVANTAGE MARKETING, INC.; *U.S. Private*, pg. 94
AERIAL ADVERTISING SERVICES; *U.S. Private*, pg. 117
ALLIANCE MEDIA GROUP; *U.S. Private*, pg. 183
AMERICAN COMMUNICATIONS GROUP, INC.; *U.S. Private*, pg. 227
AMERICAN NEWSPAPER REPRESENTATIVES, INC.; *U.S. Private*, pg. 242
ANVIL MEDIA, INC.—See Deksia LLC; *U.S. Private*, pg. 1192
APPLEGATE MEDIA GROUP; *U.S. Private*, pg. 297
ATWELL MEDIA SERVICES, INC.; *U.S. Private*, pg. 384
AWIN AG—See Axel Springer SE; *Int'l*, pg. 765
AWIN INC.—See Axel Springer SE; *Int'l*, pg. 765
AXIS MEDIA; *U.S. Private*, pg. 413
BAGS-ENERGOTEHNIKA D.D.; *Int'l*, pg. 799
BERGFREUNDE GMBH—See Decathlon SA; *Int'l*, pg. 1999
BILLBOARD CONNECTION; *U.S. Private*, pg. 559
BILLUPS, INC.; *U.S. Private*, pg. 559
BLACK DIAMOND MEDIA; *U.S. Private*, pg. 571
BOSS CREATIVE; *U.S. Private*, pg. 620
BRAXTON STRATEGIC GROUP; *U.S. Private*, pg. 641
BRIGGS & CALDWELL; *U.S. Private*, pg. 650
BRILLIANT MEDIA; *Int'l*, pg. 1163
BRILLIANT MEDIA—See Brilliant Media; *Int'l*, pg. 1163
BRILLIANT MEDIA—See Brilliant Media; *Int'l*, pg. 1163
BUTLER/TILL MEDIA SERVICES, INC.; *U.S. Private*, pg. 697
BUY ADS DIRECT; *U.S. Private*, pg. 698
CARAT ARGENTINA S.A.—See Dentsu Group Inc.; *Int'l*, pg. 2036
CARAT ASIA PACIFIC—See Dentsu Group Inc.; *Int'l*, pg. 2035
CARAT - EDINBURGH—See Dentsu Group Inc.; *Int'l*, pg. 2035
CARAT GUANGZHOU—See Dentsu Group Inc.; *Int'l*, pg. 2035
CARAT KOREA—See Dentsu Group Inc.; *Int'l*, pg. 2035
CARAT MEXICANA—See Dentsu Group Inc.; *Int'l*, pg. 2036
CARAT MUMBAI—See Dentsu Group Inc.; *Int'l*, pg. 2035
CARAT NEW DELHI—See Dentsu Group Inc.; *Int'l*, pg. 2035
CARAT NORGE AS—See Dentsu Group Inc.; *Int'l*, pg. 2035
CARAT SWEDEN AB—See Dentsu Group Inc.; *Int'l*, pg. 2035
CENTRO MEDIA, INC.; *U.S. Private*, pg. 830
CIVIC ENTERTAINMENT GROUP, LLC—See Ryan Seacrest Enterprises, Inc.; *U.S. Private*, pg. 3510
CLEVELAND COMMUNICATIONS; *U.S. Private*, pg. 940
CLICKBOOTH.COM LLC—See Centre Lane Partners, LLC; *U.S. Private*, pg. 827
CNHI-CAN—See The Retirement Systems of Alabama; *U.S. Private*, pg. 4106
COMPAS, INC.; *U.S. Private*, pg. 998
COMPASS POINT MEDIA; *U.S. Private*, pg. 999
CORINTHIAN MEDIA, INC.; *U.S. Private*, pg. 1050
CRN INTERNATIONAL, INC.; *U.S. Private*, pg. 1102
DCD PUBLISHING LIMITED—See DCD Media plc; *Int'l*, pg. 1991
DELIVERY AGENT, INC.; *U.S. Private*, pg. 1197
DENTSU AEGIS NETWORK ASIA PACIFIC—See Dentsu Group Inc.; *Int'l*, pg. 2036
DENTSU AEGIS NETWORK—See Dentsu Group Inc.; *Int'l*, pg. 2036
DEUTSCHMEDIA—See The Interpublic Group of Companies, Inc.; *U.S. Public*, pg. 2092
DLP INTERACTIVE MEDIA—See Don Wenner Home Selling, Inc.; *U.S. Private*, pg. 1259
DRM PARTNERS, INC.; *U.S. Private*, pg. 1279
DWA MEDIA; *U.S. Private*, pg. 1295
ECIT MARKETING AS—See TowerBrook Capital Partners, L.P.; *U.S. Private*, pg. 4194
EFX MEDIA—See Yes& Holdings, LLC; *U.S. Private*, pg. 4588
ELITE MEDIA, INC.; *U.S. Private*, pg. 1361
EMC OUTDOOR; *U.S. Private*, pg. 1379
ENVERSA COMPANIES; *U.S. Private*, pg. 1406
FACTOR 3 MEDIA—See Masterminds; *U.S. Private*, pg. 2608
FAZE HOLDINGS INC.—See GameSquare Holdings, Inc.; *Int'l*, pg. 2877
FIRST CLASS, INC.; *U.S. Private*, pg. 1516
GADNIUM GROUP LLC; *U.S. Private*, pg. 1633
GALAXIA SM INC.; *Int'l*, pg. 2871
GENERAL MOTORS R*WORKS—See The Interpublic Group of Companies, Inc.; *U.S. Public*, pg. 2093
GOLDEN MEDIA; *U.S. Private*, pg. 1732
GRP MEDIA, INC.; *U.S. Private*, pg. 1796
HARMELIN MEDIA; *U.S. Private*, pg. 1866
HAWORTH MARKETING & MEDIA COMPANY; *U.S. Private*, pg. 1883
HAWORTH MARKETING & MEDIA COMPANY—See Haworth Marketing & Media Company; *U.S. Private*, pg. 1883
HELEN THOMPSON MEDIA; *U.S. Private*, pg. 1905
HORIZON MEDIA, INC. - LOS ANGELES—See Horizon Media, Inc.; *U.S. Private*, pg. 1982
HORIZON MEDIA, INC.; *U.S. Private*, pg. 1981
HORIZON OUT-OF-HOME—See Horizon Media, Inc.; *U.S. Private*, pg. 1982
HORIZON PRINT SERVICES GROUP—See Horizon Media, Inc.; *U.S. Private*, pg. 1982
HUDSON MEDIA SERVICES LLC; *U.S. Private*, pg. 2002
ICON INTERNATIONAL INC.—See Omnicom Group Inc.; *U.S. Public*, pg. 1586
ID MEDIA-LOS ANGELES—See The Interpublic Group of Companies, Inc.; *U.S. Public*, pg. 2094
ID MEDIA—See The Interpublic Group of Companies, Inc.; *U.S. Public*, pg. 2094
IMG COLLEGE—See Silver Lake Group, LLC; *U.S. Private*, pg. 3657
IMG COLLEGE—See William Morris Endeavor Entertainment, LLC; *U.S. Private*, pg. 4524
IMG WORLDWIDE, INC.—See Silver Lake Group, LLC; *U.S. Private*, pg. 3657
IMG WORLDWIDE, INC.—See William Morris Endeavor Entertainment, LLC; *U.S. Private*, pg. 4523
INGENUITY MEDIA GROUP AT THE MARTIN AGENCY—See The Interpublic Group of Companies, Inc.; *U.S. Public*, pg. 2102
INITIATIVE ATHENS—See The Interpublic Group of Companies, Inc.; *U.S. Public*, pg. 2095
INITIATIVE ATLANTA—See The Interpublic Group of Companies, Inc.; *U.S. Public*, pg. 2095
INITIATIVE BANGKOK—See The Interpublic Group of Companies, Inc.; *U.S. Public*, pg. 2095
INITIATIVE BARCELONA—See The Interpublic Group of Companies, Inc.; *U.S. Public*, pg. 2095
INITIATIVE BEIRUT—See The Interpublic Group of Companies, Inc.; *U.S. Public*, pg. 2095
INITIATIVE BOGOTA—See The Interpublic Group of Companies, Inc.; *U.S. Public*, pg. 2095
INITIATIVE BRUSSELS—See The Interpublic Group of Companies, Inc.; *U.S. Public*, pg. 2095
INITIATIVE BUDAPEST—See The Interpublic Group of Companies, Inc.; *U.S. Public*, pg. 2095
INITIATIVE BUENOS AIRES—See The Interpublic Group of Companies, Inc.; *U.S. Public*, pg. 2095
INITIATIVE CARACAS—See The Interpublic Group of Companies, Inc.; *U.S. Public*, pg. 2095
INITIATIVE DUBAI—See The Interpublic Group of Companies, Inc.; *U.S. Public*, pg. 2095
INITIATIVE DUBLIN—See The Interpublic Group of Companies, Inc.; *U.S. Public*, pg. 2095
INITIATIVE HAMBURG—See The Interpublic Group of Companies, Inc.; *U.S. Public*, pg. 2095
INITIATIVE JAKARTA—See The Interpublic Group of Companies, Inc.; *U.S. Public*, pg. 2095
INITIATIVE LIMA—See The Interpublic Group of Companies, Inc.; *U.S. Public*, pg. 2095
INITIATIVE LISBON—See The Interpublic Group of Companies, Inc.; *U.S. Public*, pg. 2095
INITIATIVE LOS ANGELES—See The Interpublic Group of Companies, Inc.; *U.S. Public*, pg. 2095
INITIATIVE MADRID—See The Interpublic Group of Companies, Inc.; *U.S. Public*, pg. 2095
INITIATIVE MELBOURNE—See The Interpublic Group of Companies, Inc.; *U.S. Public*, pg. 2095
INITIATIVE MEXICO CITY—See The Interpublic Group of Companies, Inc.; *U.S. Public*, pg. 2095
INITIATIVE MIAMI—See The Interpublic Group of Companies, Inc.; *U.S. Public*, pg. 2095
INITIATIVE MILAN—See The Interpublic Group of Companies, Inc.; *U.S. Public*, pg. 2095
INITIATIVE MUMBAI—See The Interpublic Group of Companies, Inc.; *U.S. Public*, pg. 2096
INITIATIVE PARIS—See The Interpublic Group of Companies, Inc.; *U.S. Public*, pg. 2096
INITIATIVE PERTH—See The Interpublic Group of Companies, Inc.; *U.S. Public*, pg. 2096
INITIATIVE PRAGUE—See The Interpublic Group of Companies, Inc.; *U.S. Public*, pg. 2096
INITIATIVE SAN DIEGO—See The Interpublic Group of Companies, Inc.; *U.S. Public*, pg. 2096
INITIATIVE SANTIAGO—See The Interpublic Group of Companies, Inc.; *U.S. Public*, pg. 2096
INITIATIVE SINGAPORE—See The Interpublic Group of Companies, Inc.; *U.S. Public*, pg. 2096
INITIATIVE—See The Interpublic Group of Companies, Inc.; *U.S. Public*, pg. 2095
INITIATIVE—See The Interpublic Group of Companies, Inc.; *U.S. Public*, pg. 2095
INITIATIVE—See The Interpublic Group of Companies, Inc.; *U.S. Public*, pg. 2095
INITIATIVE SYDNEY—See The Interpublic Group of Companies, Inc.; *U.S. Public*, pg. 2096
INITIATIVE TAIPEI—See The Interpublic Group of Companies, Inc.; *U.S. Public*, pg. 2096
INITIATIVE TOKYO—See The Interpublic Group of Compa-

N.A.I.C.S. INDEX
541840 — MEDIA REPRESENTATIV...
N.A.I.C.S. Index

nies, Inc.; *U.S. Public*, pg. 2096
INITIATIVE TORONTO—See The Interpublic Group of Companies, Inc.; *U.S. Public*, pg. 2096
INITIATIVE UNIVERSAL COPENHAGEN—See The Interpublic Group of Companies, Inc.; *U.S. Public*, pg. 2096
INITIATIVE UNIVERSAL OSLO—See The Interpublic Group of Companies, Inc.; *U.S. Public*, pg. 2096
INITIATIVE UNIVERSAL WARSAW—See The Interpublic Group of Companies, Inc.; *U.S. Public*, pg. 2096
INITIATIVE VIENNA—See The Interpublic Group of Companies, Inc.; *U.S. Public*, pg. 2096
INITIATIVE WORLDWIDE—See The Interpublic Group of Companies, Inc.; *U.S. Public*, pg. 2095
INITIATIVE ZURICH—See The Interpublic Group of Companies, Inc.; *U.S. Public*, pg. 2096
INNOVISION MEDIA GROUP; *U.S. Private*, pg. 2084
INTEGRAL MEDIA COMPANY; *U.S. Private*, pg. 2098
THE INTERCONNECT GROUP; *U.S. Private*, pg. 4057
INTERSECT MEDIA SOLUTIONS—See Florida Press Association Inc.; *U.S. Private*, pg. 1550
IPG MEDIABRANDS—See The Interpublic Group of Companies, Inc.; *U.S. Public*, pg. 2094
ISOSBAR—See Dentsu Group Inc.; *Int'l*, pg. 2037
JL MEDIA, INC.; *U.S. Private*, pg. 2212
JSML MEDIA, LLC; *U.S. Private*, pg. 2241
JSML MEDIA, LLC—See JSML Media, LLC; *U.S. Private*, pg. 2241
JUST KID, INC.; *U.S. Private*, pg. 2245
JUST MEDIA LTD.—See Just Media, Inc.; *U.S. Private*, pg. 2245
KELLY, SCOTT & MADISON; *U.S. Private*, pg. 2277
KELLY, SCOTT & MADISON—See Kelly, Scott & Madison; *U.S. Private*, pg. 2277
KLUNK & MILLAN ADVERTISING INC.; *U.S. Private*, pg. 2321
KMBH ADVERTISING; *U.S. Private*, pg. 2321
KSL MEDIA, INC.—See KSL Media, Inc.; *U.S. Private*, pg. 2355
LEADGENESYS; *U.S. Private*, pg. 2406
LEAPFROG RESEARCH & PLANNING LIMITED—See Arsenal Capital Management LP; *U.S. Private*, pg. 338
LINCOLN MEDIA SERVICES, INC.; *U.S. Private*, pg. 2458
LOS ANGELES BROADCASTING PARTNERS, LLC—See iHeartMedia, Inc.; *U.S. Public*, pg. 1095
MACDONALD MEDIA; *U.S. Private*, pg. 2535
THE MARKETING AGENCY LLC; *U.S. Private*, pg. 4074
MARSHALL ADVERTISING, INC.; *U.S. Private*, pg. 2592
MATRIX MEDIA SERVICES, INC.; *U.S. Private*, pg. 2612
MAYOSEITZ MEDIA; *U.S. Private*, pg. 2622
MBS WEST—See Media Buying Services, Inc.; *U.S. Private*, pg. 2651
MD-DE-DC AD PLACEMENT SERVICE; *U.S. Private*, pg. 2646
MEDIA BROKERS INTERNATIONAL, INC.; *U.S. Private*, pg. 2651
MEDIA BUYING DECISIONS; *U.S. Private*, pg. 2651
MEDIA CANDO LLC; *U.S. Private*, pg. 2651
MEDIACOMP, INC.; *U.S. Private*, pg. 2653
MEDIA DEPARTMENT II, INC.; *U.S. Private*, pg. 2652
MEDIA DIRECTION—See Omnicom Group Inc.; *U.S. Public*, pg. 1575
MEDIA EDGE, INC.; *U.S. Private*, pg. 2652
MEDIA EXPERTS—See The Interpublic Group of Companies, Inc.; *U.S. Public*, pg. 2095
MEDIA EXPERTS—See The Interpublic Group of Companies, Inc.; *U.S. Public*, pg. 2095
MEDIA PARTNERSHIP CORPORATION—See The Interpublic Group of Companies, Inc.; *U.S. Public*, pg. 2096
MEDIASMITH INC.; *U.S. Private*, pg. 2653
MEDIA SOLUTIONS, INC.; *U.S. Private*, pg. 2652
MEDIASPACE SOLUTIONS; *U.S. Private*, pg. 2653
MEDIA SPADE, INC.; *U.S. Private*, pg. 2652
MEDIASPOT, INC.; *U.S. Private*, pg. 2654
MEDIA STORM LLC; *U.S. Private*, pg. 2653
MEDIA STRATEGIES & RESEARCH; *U.S. Private*, pg. 2653
MEDIA WHIZ HOLDINGS, LLC; *U.S. Private*, pg. 2653
MEDIA WORKS CHARLOTTE—See M Rogers Design, Inc.; *U.S. Private*, pg. 2523
MERCURY MEDIA HOLDING CORP.; *U.S. Private*, pg. 2671
MIDWEST COMMUNICATIONS & MEDIA; *U.S. Private*, pg. 2720
MJS COMMUNICATIONS; *U.S. Private*, pg. 2753
MOSAIC INTERACTIVE; *U.S. Private*, pg. 2792
MULTI MEDIA SERVICES CORP.; *U.S. Private*, pg. 2812
MULTI-NET MARKETING, INC.; *U.S. Private*, pg. 2812
MUSICTODAY II, LLC; *U.S. Private*, pg. 2818
NAIL MEDIA GROUP; *U.S. Private*, pg. 2831
THE NARRATIVE GROUP LLC—See Bluefocus Intelligent Communications Group Co., Ltd.; *Int'l*, pg. 1071
NEW & IMPROVED MEDIA; *U.S. Private*, pg. 2892
NEWSPAPER SERVICES OF AMERICA, INC.—See The Interpublic Group of Companies, Inc.; *U.S. Public*, pg. 2096
NEWTON MEDIA ASSOCIATES, INC.; *U.S. Private*, pg. 2918
NEXGEN MEDIA WORLDWIDE, INC.; *U.S. Private*, pg. 2919
NOVUS MEDIA INC—See Omnicom Group Inc.; *U.S. Public*, pg. 1588
NSA MEDIA—See The Interpublic Group of Companies, Inc.; *U.S. Public*, pg. 2103
OCEAN MEDIA INC.; *U.S. Private*, pg. 2989
OCEANOS, INC.; *U.S. Private*, pg. 2990
OLANDER MEDIA GROUP; *U.S. Private*, pg. 3008
OMD CHICAGO—See Omnicom Group Inc.; *U.S. Public*, pg. 1589
OMD DALLAS—See Omnicom Group Inc.; *U.S. Public*, pg. 1589
OMD LOS ANGELES—See Omnicom Group Inc.; *U.S. Public*, pg. 1589
OMD NEW ZEALAND/AUCKLAND—See Omnicom Group Inc.; *U.S. Public*, pg. 1589
OMD PHILIPPINES—See Omnicom Group Inc.; *U.S. Public*, pg. 1589
OMD SAN FRANCISCO—See Omnicom Group Inc.; *U.S. Public*, pg. 1589
OMD SEATTLE—See Omnicom Group Inc.; *U.S. Public*, pg. 1589
OMD SINGAPORE—See Omnicom Group Inc.; *U.S. Public*, pg. 1589
OMD UK—See Omnicom Group Inc.; *U.S. Public*, pg. 1589
OMNICOM MEDIA GROUP—See Omnicom Group Inc.; *U.S. Public*, pg. 1589
OPTICOMM MEDIA LIMITED—See Arsenal Capital Management LP; *U.S. Private*, pg. 338
ORION TRADING—See The Interpublic Group of Companies, Inc.; *U.S. Public*, pg. 2103
OUTDOOR ADVERTISING GROUP - DETROIT OFFICE—See The Interpublic Group of Companies, Inc.; *U.S. Public*, pg. 2096
OUTDOOR ADVERTISING GROUP - LOS ANGELES OFFICE—See The Interpublic Group of Companies, Inc.; *U.S. Public*, pg. 2096
OUTDOOR ADVERTISING GROUP—See The Interpublic Group of Companies, Inc.; *U.S. Public*, pg. 2096
OUTDOOR FIRST, INC.—See Wilkins Media Company; *U.S. Private*, pg. 4520
PARR MEDIA GROUP; *U.S. Private*, pg. 3099
PERKINS NICHOLS MEDIA—See Young & Laramore; *U.S. Private*, pg. 4592
PHD DETROIT—See Omnicom Group Inc.; *U.S. Public*, pg. 1589
PHD LOS ANGELES—See Omnicom Group Inc.; *U.S. Public*, pg. 1589
PHD SAN FRANCISCO—See Omnicom Group Inc.; *U.S. Public*, pg. 1590
PHD—See Omnicom Group Inc.; *U.S. Public*, pg. 1589
PLANETE INTERACTIVE—See Dentsu Group Inc.; *Int'l*, pg. 2037
PRIMEDIA, INC.; *U.S. Private*, pg. 3263
PROMETHEUS—See Omnicom Group Inc.; *U.S. Public*, pg. 1589
PROVING GROUND MEDIA, INC.; *U.S. Private*, pg. 3295
PURE MEDIA LIMITED—See Providence Equity Partners L.L.C.; *U.S. Private*, pg. 3292
RED COMMA MEDIA, INC.; *U.S. Private*, pg. 3374
RIVENDELL MEDIA INC.; *U.S. Private*, pg. 3443
RJW MEDIA; *U.S. Private*, pg. 3449
ROUND2 COMMUNICATIONS, LLC; *U.S. Private*, pg. 3488
ROUND2/SF—See Round2 Communications, LLC; *U.S. Private*, pg. 3488
RPMC, INC.; *U.S. Private*, pg. 3495
RPM-RIGHT PLACE MEDIA; *U.S. Private*, pg. 3495
SINGER DIRECT LLC—See Omnicom Group Inc.; *U.S. Public*, pg. 1593
SMARTCEO PUBLISHING; *U.S. Private*, pg. 3691
SMY MEDIA, INC.; *U.S. Private*, pg. 3699
SPECIALIZED MEDIA SERVICES, INC.; *U.S. Private*, pg. 3749
STUDIO ONE NETWORKS INC.—See CHR Group LLC; *U.S. Private*, pg. 889
TANGIBLE MEDIA, INC.; *U.S. Private*, pg. 3930
TARGET ENTERPRISES LTD.; *U.S. Private*, pg. 3933
TARGETING GROUP—See The Company of Others; *U.S. Private*, pg. 4013
TEC DIRECT MEDIA, INC.; *U.S. Private*, pg. 3951
TOTAL COMMUNICATIONS GROUP; *U.S. Private*, pg. 4190
TRANSIT MEDIA GROUP; *U.S. Private*, pg. 4208
TRUE MEDIA; *U.S. Private*, pg. 4247
UNDERSCORE MARKETING LLC; *U.S. Private*, pg. 4279
UNIVERSAL COMMUNICATION—See The Interpublic Group of Companies, Inc.; *U.S. Public*, pg. 2103
UNIVERSAL MCCANN, S.A.—See The Interpublic Group of Companies, Inc.; *U.S. Public*, pg. 2103
UNIVERSAL MCCANN—See The Interpublic Group of Companies, Inc.; *U.S. Public*, pg. 2101
UNIVERSAL MCCANN—See The Interpublic Group of Companies, Inc.; *U.S. Public*, pg. 2103
UNIVERSAL MCCANN—See The Interpublic Group of Companies, Inc.; *U.S. Public*, pg. 2103
UNIVERSAL MCCANN—See The Interpublic Group of Companies, Inc.; *U.S. Public*, pg. 2103
UNIVERSAL MEDIA HELLAS SA—See The Interpublic Group of Companies, Inc.; *U.S. Public*, pg. 2103
UNIVERSAL MEDIA INC.; *U.S. Private*, pg. 4305
URBAN COMMUNICATIONS; *U.S. Private*, pg. 4313
U.S. INTERNATIONAL MEDIA; *U.S. Private*, pg. 4271
US NEWSPAPERS; *U.S. Private*, pg. 4319
VALPO MEDIOS, INC.; *U.S. Private*, pg. 4337
VIZEUM UK LTD.—See Dentsu Group Inc.; *Int'l*, pg. 2038
VOLICON INC.—See Apollo Global Management, Inc.; *U.S. Public*, pg. 167
WAHLSTROM GROUP—See The Interpublic Group of Companies, Inc.; *U.S. Public*, pg. 2096
WAHLSTROM GROUP—See The Interpublic Group of Companies, Inc.; *U.S. Public*, pg. 2096
WALSH ADVERTISING INC.; *U.S. Private*, pg. 4432
WILKINS MEDIA COMPANY; *U.S. Private*, pg. 4520
YELLIN/MCCARRON, INC.; *U.S. Private*, pg. 4587
ZEPHYR MEDIA GROUP—See Zephyr Media Group; *U.S. Private*, pg. 4602
ZEPHYR MEDIA GROUP—See Zephyr Media Group; *U.S. Private*, pg. 4602

541840 — MEDIA REPRESENTATIVES

1091 MEDIA—See JDS Capital Management, Inc.; *U.S. Private*, pg. 2196
AARKI, LLC—See Skillz Inc.; *U.S. Public*, pg. 1892
ACCEL MEDIA VENTURES LTD.—See Accel Limited; *Int'l*, pg. 79
ALINK INTERNET, INC.; *Int'l*, pg. 329
ALLIED TECH CAMP CO., LTD.—See Allied Architects, Inc.; *Int'l*, pg. 356
AMARU, INC.; *Int'l*, pg. 412
AMSIVE DIGITAL INC.—See H.I.G. Capital, LLC; *U.S. Private*, pg. 1829
ANCHOR WORLDWIDE, LLC; *U.S. Private*, pg. 273
THE AROUNDCAMPUS GROUP; *U.S. Private*, pg. 3988
ASC COMMUNICATIONS, LLC; *U.S. Private*, pg. 345
ASMIQ AG—See Die Schweizerische Post AG; *Int'l*, pg. 2112
ATI NETWORKS INC; *U.S. Public*, pg. 222
AUTOMOTIVE INTERNET MEDIA, INC.; *U.S. Private*, pg. 400
BAUER MEDIA AS—See Heinrich Bauer Verlag KG; *Int'l*, pg. 3323
BAUER MEDIA GROUP AB—See Heinrich Bauer Verlag KG; *Int'l*, pg. 3323
BAUER MEDIA OY—See Heinrich Bauer Verlag KG; *Int'l*, pg. 3323
THE BEACON NEWS—See Chicago Public Media, Inc.; *U.S. Private*, pg. 879
BERTELSMANN CORPORATE SERVICES INDIA PRIVATE LIMITED—See Bertelsmann SE & Co. KGaA; *Int'l*, pg. 990
BILLY GENE IS MARKETING, INC.; *U.S. Private*, pg. 559
BLEACH INC.; *Int'l*, pg. 1063
BLUELINK INTERNATIONAL AUSTRALIA PTY. LTD.—See Air France-KLM S.A.; *Int'l*, pg. 237
BLUELINK INTERNATIONAL CHILE SPA.—See Air France-KLM S.A.; *Int'l*, pg. 237
BLUELINK INTERNATIONAL STRASBOURG SA—See Air France-KLM S.A.; *Int'l*, pg. 237
BRANDBUCKET MEDIA & TECHNOLOGY LIMITED; *Int'l*, pg. 1139
BRAND MEDIA SOLUTIONS GMBH—See Hubert Burda Media Holding Kommanditgesellschaft; *Int'l*, pg. 3519
BRAVE BISON ASIA PACIFIC PTE. LTD.—See Brave Bison Group plc; *Int'l*, pg. 1141
BRAVE BISON LIMITED—See Brave Bison Group plc; *Int'l*, pg. 1141
BURDA SERVICES GMBH—See Hubert Burda Media Holding Kommanditgesellschaft; *Int'l*, pg. 3519
CANADIAN BROADCAST SALES—See Corus Entertainment Inc.; *Int'l*, pg. 1808
CATENA MEDIA PLC; *Int'l*, pg. 1359
CBS INTERNATIONAL HOLDINGS B.V.—See National Amusements, Inc.; *U.S. Private*, pg. 2840
C CHANNEL CORPORATION; *Int'l*, pg. 1237
CEGEDIM MEDIA SARL—See Cegedim S.A.; *Int'l*, pg. 1390
CJ E&M AMERICA INC.—See CJ Corporation; *Int'l*, pg. 1631
CLEAR CHANNEL (GUANGZHOU) LTD.—See Clear Channel Outdoor Holdings, Inc.; *U.S. Public*, pg. 511
CLEAR CHANNEL RADIO SALES—See iHeartMedia, Inc.; *U.S. Public*, pg. 1096
CONTINENTAL TELEVISION SALES—See iHeartMedia, Inc.; *U.S. Public*, pg. 1096
COSMO SPACE CO., LTD.—See Imagica Group Inc.; *Int'l*, pg. 3618
COX CROSS MEDIA—See Apollo Global Management, Inc.; *U.S. Public*, pg. 163
COX REPS—See Apollo Global Management, Inc.; *U.S. Public*, pg. 163
CRAID INC.—See FreeBit Co., Ltd.; *Int'l*, pg. 2769
CROSS MEDIAWORKS, INC.; *U.S. Private*, pg. 1105
CYBER BUZZ, INC.; *Int'l*, pg. 1891
DAAR COMMUNICATIONS PLC; *Int'l*, pg. 1902
DEKRA MEDIA GMBH—See DEKRA e.V.; *Int'l*, pg. 2009
DIE MEHRWERTMACHER GMBH—See Bertelsmann SE & Co. KGaA; *Int'l*, pg. 992
DIGICONTENT LIMITED; *Int'l*, pg. 2119

541840 — MEDIA REPRESENTATIV...

DIGITAL360 S.P.A.; *Int'l*, pg. 2123
DIGITAL MEDIA SOLUTIONS, LLC—See Digital Media Solutions, Inc.; *U.S. Public*, pg. 663
DISCOVERY, INC. - DETROIT OFFICE—See Warner Bros. Discovery, Inc.; *U.S. Public*, pg. 2326
DOOSAN MAGAZINE—See Doosan Corporation; *Int'l*, pg. 2173
DURRANTS LTD.—See Exponent Private Equity LLP; *Int'l*, pg. 2589
EAGLE DIRECT, INC —See National Amusements, Inc.; *U.S. Private*, pg. 2841
EAGLE TELEVISION SALES—See iHeartMedia, Inc.; *U.S. Public*, pg. 1096
EASTMAN RADIO SALES—See iHeartMedia, Inc.; *U.S. Public*, pg. 1096
EBIQUITY ITALY MEDIA ADVISOR S.R.L.—See Ebiquity plc; *Int'l*, pg. 2285
EBIZAUTOS; *U.S. Private*, pg. 1324
EDGEWARE AB; *Int'l*, pg. 2309
EKSPRESS MEEDIA AS—See AS Ekspress Grupp; *Int'l*, pg. 590
ELECTRECORD SA; *Int'l*, pg. 2348
ENCOMPASS ASIA—See Encompass Digital Media; *U.S. Private*, pg. 1390
ENCOMPASS DIGITAL MEDIA; *U.S. Private*, pg. 1390
EQUAL ENTERTAINMENT LLC; *U.S. Private*, pg. 1415
ETS GROUP LIMITED; *Int'l*, pg. 2524
EVEO INC.—See ALPHAEON Corporation; *U.S. Private*, pg. 200
FAME PRODUCTIONS, INC.; *U.S. Public*, pg. 821
FELIX MEDIA SOLUTIONS, INC.; *U.S. Private*, pg. 1493
FILMOLUX BENELUX B.V.—See Blue Cap AG; *Int'l*, pg. 1067
FNL TECHNOLOGIES, INC.; *U.S. Public*, pg. 1555
FOR IT INC.—See FreeBit Co., Ltd.; *Int'l*, pg. 2769
FOX ASSOCIATES INC.; *U.S. Private*, pg. 1584
FOX STATIONS SALES, INC.—See Fox Corporation; *U.S. Public*, pg. 876
FROSTPROOF NEWS—See Independent Newspapers, Inc.; *U.S. Private*, pg. 2060
FUJIKURA SHANGHAI TRADING CO., LTD.—See Fujikura Ltd.; *Int'l*, pg. 2829
FUNSHINE CULTURE GROUP CO., LTD.; *Int'l*, pg. 2846
FUTURE MEDIA (INDIA) LIMITED—See Future Corporate Resources Limited; *Int'l*, pg. 2853
GAMELANCER MEDIA CORP.; *Int'l*, pg. 2877
GAZPROM-MEDIA HOLDING JSC—See Gazprombank JSC; *Int'l*, pg. 2892
GJ INTERNATIONAL MEDIA SALES LTD.—See Bertelsmann SE & Co. KGaA; *Int'l*, pg. 992
G+J INTERNATIONAL SALES ITALY S.R.L.—See Bertelsmann SE & Co. KGaA; *Int'l*, pg. 992
GMO MEDIA, INC.—See GMO Internet Group, Inc.; *Int'l*, pg. 3014
GOODCONCERT CO., LTD.—See CJ Corporation; *Int'l*, pg. 1634
GORKANA—See Platinum Equity, LLC; *U.S. Private*, pg. 3201
GRAND PRIX INTERNATIONAL PUBLIC COMPANY LIMITED; *Int'l*, pg. 3056
GRAND VISION MEDIA HOLDINGS PLC; *Int'l*, pg. 3057
GUANGDONG INSIGHT BRAND MARKETING GROUP CO., LTD.; *Int'l*, pg. 3156
GUANGDONG SOUTH NEW MEDIA CO., LTD.; *Int'l*, pg. 3160
HARRINGTON, RIGHTER & PARSONS, LLC—See Apollo Global Management, Inc.; *U.S. Public*, pg. 163
HAYMARKET MEDIA ASIA PTE LTD—See Haymarket Group Limited; *Int'l*, pg. 3292
HAYMARKET MEDIA GMBH & CO. KG—See Haymarket Group Limited; *Int'l*, pg. 3292
HAYMARKET MEDIA (INDIA) PVT LTD—See Haymarket Group Limited; *Int'l*, pg. 3292
HAYMARKET MEDIA LIMITED—See Haymarket Group Limited; *Int'l*, pg. 3292
HESPERIA STAR—See Gannett Co., Inc.; *U.S. Public*, pg. 904
HJEMMET MORTENSEN AS; *Int'l*, pg. 3428
HOLOGRAPHIC STORAGE LTD.; *U.S. Public*, pg. 1045
THE HOMER GROUP; *U.S. Private*, pg. 4054
IDNNT SA; *Int'l*, pg. 3595
IGNITE SOCIAL MEDIA LLC; *U.S. Private*, pg. 2039
IMAGICA DIGITAL SCAPE CO., LTD.—See Imagica Group Inc.; *Int'l*, pg. 3618
IMAGICA LIVE CORP.—See Imagica Group Inc.; *Int'l*, pg. 3618
INTEGRATED MEDIA SOLUTIONS, LCC—See Stagwell, Inc.; *U.S. Public*, pg. 1927
KATZ 360 DIGITAL SALES—See iHeartMedia, Inc.; *U.S. Public*, pg. 1096
KATZ ADVANTAGE—See iHeartMedia, Inc.; *U.S. Public*, pg. 1096
KATZ NET RADIO SALES, INC.—See iHeartMedia, Inc.; *U.S. Public*, pg. 1096
KATZ RADIO GROUP—See iHeartMedia, Inc.; *U.S. Public*, pg. 1096
KATZ TELEVISION GROUP—See iHeartMedia, Inc.; *U.S. Public*, pg. 1096
KINETIC WORLDWIDE LTD—See Beelk Holding AG; *Int'l*, pg. 939
KUBOO, INC.; *U.S. Public*, pg. 1277
LEMONLIGHT MEDIA, INC.; *U.S. Private*, pg. 2421
LINK MEDIA GEORGIA, LLC—See Boston Omaha Corporation; *U.S. Public*, pg. 372
LIVESYSTEMS AG—See Die Schweizerische Post AG; *Int'l*, pg. 2113
LOWP CO., LTD.—See AJIS Co., Ltd.; *Int'l*, pg. 258
MACREPORT.NET, INC.; *U.S. Public*, pg. 1353
MEDIA BUSINESS INSIGHT LIMITED—See GlobalData Plc; *Int'l*, pg. 3003
MEDIA & COMMUNICATION SYSTEMS (MCS) GMBH—See Bavaria Film GmbH; *Int'l*, pg. 899
MEDIA IMPACT INC.—See Axel Springer SE; *Int'l*, pg. 766
MEDIANET—See Australian Associated Press Pty Ltd; *Int'l*, pg. 721
MEGAN DRISCOLL, LLC; *U.S. Private*, pg. 2660
MENERGIA INC.—See Aucnet Inc.; *Int'l*, pg. 700
MERGENCE CORP.; *U.S. Public*, pg. 1424
METRO-PUCK COMICS NETWORK—See Gemini Communications; *U.S. Private*, pg. 1657
METRO SUNDAY NEWSPAPERS—See Gemini Communications; *U.S. Private*, pg. 1657
MEZZOMEDIA INC.—See CJ Corporation; *Int'l*, pg. 1634
MIDCONTINENT COMMUNICATIONS INVESTOR LLC—See Midcontinent Media Inc.; *U.S. Private*, pg. 2711
MIDSTATES GROUP COMPANY; *U.S. Private*, pg. 2718
MIRACLE SOUND OULU OY—See Warner Bros. Discovery, Inc.; *U.S. Public*, pg. 2327
MIRACLE SOUND OY—See Warner Bros. Discovery, Inc.; *U.S. Public*, pg. 2327
MMT SALES, LLC—See Apollo Global Management, Inc.; *U.S. Public*, pg. 164
MNI TARGETED MEDIA INC.—See Warner Bros. Discovery, Inc.; *U.S. Public*, pg. 2327
MONSTER MEDIA, LLC; *U.S. Private*, pg. 2774
NEWS WORLD COMMUNICATIONS, INC.—See Family Federation for World Peace & Unification; *U.S. Private*, pg. 1469
NOW GMBH—See Bertelsmann SE & Co. KGaA; *Int'l*, pg. 993
OLIVER MARKETING LIMITED—See You & Mr Jones Inc.; *U.S. Private*, pg. 4592
OMD-USA—See Omnicom Group Inc.; *U.S. Public*, pg. 1589
OPTIMUM SOURCE INTERNATIONAL, LTD.; *U.S. Public*, pg. 1609
ORLANDO BUSINESS JOURNAL—See Advance Publications, Inc.; *U.S. Private*, pg. 84
OUTBRAIN AUSTRALIA PTY LTD—See Outbrain Inc.; *U.S. Public*, pg. 1624
OUTBRAIN BELGIUM BVBA—See Outbrain Inc.; *U.S. Public*, pg. 1624
OUTBRAIN FRANCE SAS—See Outbrain Inc.; *U.S. Public*, pg. 1624
OUTBRAIN GERMANY GMBH—See Outbrain Inc.; *U.S. Public*, pg. 1624
OUTBRAIN INDIA PRIVATE LIMITED—See Outbrain Inc.; *U.S. Public*, pg. 1624
OUTBRAIN ISRAEL LTD.—See Outbrain Inc.; *U.S. Public*, pg. 1624
OUTBRAIN ITALY SRL—See Outbrain Inc.; *U.S. Public*, pg. 1624
OUTBRAIN JAPAN KK—See Outbrain Inc.; *U.S. Public*, pg. 1624
OUTBRAIN NETHERLANDS B.V.—See Outbrain Inc.; *U.S. Public*, pg. 1624
OUTBRAIN SERVICES MONETIZACAO DE CONTEUDO LTDA—See Outbrain Inc.; *U.S. Public*, pg. 1624
OUTBRAIN SINGAPORE PTE. LTD.—See Outbrain Inc.; *U.S. Public*, pg. 1624
OUTBRAIN SPAIN S.L.—See Outbrain Inc.; *U.S. Public*, pg. 1624
OUTBRAIN UK LIMITED—See Outbrain Inc.; *U.S. Public*, pg. 1624
PARAMOUNT ADVERTISER SERVICES INC.—See National Amusements, Inc.; *U.S. Private*, pg. 2843
PETRY MEDIA CORPORATION—See Patriarch Partners, LLC; *U.S. Private*, pg. 3109
PETRY TELEVISION INC.—See Patriarch Partners, LLC; *U.S. Private*, pg. 3109
PIEMME SPA—See Caltagirone Editore S.p.A.; *Int'l*, pg. 1266
PLACEIQ, INC.—See Clearlake Capital Group, L.P.; *U.S. Private*, pg. 936
PLACEIQ, INC.—See TA Associates, Inc.; *U.S. Private*, pg. 3917
POKERVISION MEDIA INC.—See ePlay Digital Inc.; *Int'l*, pg. 2463
PORTFOLIO METRICA LTD.—See Exponent Private Equity LLP; *Int'l*, pg. 2589
PRETTYWORK CREATIVE LLC—See CCL Industries Inc.; *Int'l*, pg. 1368
PRIDE MEDIA INC.—See Equal Entertainment LLC; *U.S. Private*, pg. 1415
PROFESSIONAL EDUCATION INSTITUTE; *U.S. Private*, pg. 3275
PT DENTSU MEDIA INDONESIA—See Dentsu Group Inc.; *Int'l*, pg. 2037
RAW ARTISTS, INC.; *U.S. Private*, pg. 3358
REDBERRY AMBIENT SDN. BHD.—See Ancom Nylex Berhad; *Int'l*, pg. 449
REDBERRY SDN. BHD.—See Ancom Nylex Berhad; *Int'l*, pg. 449
RESERVOIR MEDIA, INC.; *U.S. Public*, pg. 1789
SADDLE RANCH MEDIA, INC.; *U.S. Public*, pg. 1834
SCAN FRANCE SARL—See Badger Meter, Inc.; *U.S. Public*, pg. 263
SHANGHAI HAKUHODO ADVERTISING CO., LTD.—See Hakuhodo DY Holdings Incorporated; *Int'l*, pg. 3222
SHAREROCKET, INC.—See Nexstar Media Group, Inc.; *U.S. Public*, pg. 1524
SMARTBUG OPERATING LLC; *U.S. Private*, pg. 3691
SOCIALFLY LLC; *U.S. Private*, pg. 3703
SOCIAL FULCRUM LLC—See ARS Advertising, LLC.; *U.S. Private*, pg. 337
TELEREP, LLC—See Apollo Global Management, Inc.; *U.S. Public*, pg. 164
TNS MEDIA INTELLIGENCE/CMR—See Bain Capital, LP; *U.S. Private*, pg. 448
TRUEPOINT COMMUNICATIONS, LLC; *U.S. Private*, pg. 4249
TURNER SPORTS, INC.—See Warner Bros. Discovery, Inc.; *U.S. Public*, pg. 2328
UNIVISION RADIO NATIONAL SALES—See iHeartMedia, Inc.; *U.S. Public*, pg. 1096
VANGUARD MEDIA GROUP; *U.S. Public*, pg. 4343
VIEWPOINT COMPUTER ANIMATION, INCORPORATED—See Dolphin Entertainment, Inc.; *U.S. Public*, pg. 673
VOGEL DRUCK UND MEDIENSERVICE GMBH—See Bertelsmann SE & Co. KGaA; *Int'l*, pg. 996
VUNGLE, INC.—See Blackstone Inc.; *U.S. Public*, pg. 361
WILLIAM MORRIS ENDEAVOR ENTERTAINMENT (U.K.) LIMITED—See Silver Lake Group, LLC; *U.S. Private*, pg. 3654

541850 — INDOOR AND OUTDOOR DISPLAY ADVERTISING

2020 EXHIBITS, INC.; *U.S. Private*, pg. 5
ACE-HI INC.—See The Schafer Company Inc.; *U.S. Private*, pg. 4114
ADNOSTIC—See Future plc; *Int'l*, pg. 2857
ADTHEORENT, INC.—See AdTheorent Holding Company, Inc.; *U.S. Public*, pg. 43
ALLGEMEINE PLAKATGESELLSCHAFT APG—See APG/SGA SA; *Int'l*, pg. 513
ALLOVER MEDIA, INC.—See Audax Group, Limited Partnership; *U.S. Private*, pg. 386
ANDO HOLDINGS LTD.; *Int'l*, pg. 451
APPTNESS MEDIA GROUP, LLC—See Zeta Global Holdings Corp.; *U.S. Public*, pg. 2403
ASHBY STREET OUTDOOR LLC—See Lamar Advertising Company; *U.S. Public*, pg. 1290
ASIARAY MEDIA GROUP LIMITED; *Int'l*, pg. 620
ASTRAL OUT-OF-HOME—See BCE Inc.; *Int'l*, pg. 927
AVALON EXHIBITS, INC.; *U.S. Private*, pg. 403
BAUER DIGITAL KG—See Heinrich Bauer Verlag KG; *Int'l*, pg. 3324
B & P OUTDOOR BV—See Clear Channel Outdoor Holdings, Inc.; *U.S. Public*, pg. 511
BRANDED ONLINE INC.—See Nogin, Inc.; *U.S. Public*, pg. 1532
CABCHARGE PAYMENTS PTY. LTD.—See ComfortDelGro Corporation Limited; *Int'l*, pg. 1712
CANADIAN TODS LIMITED—See Lamar Advertising Company; *U.S. Public*, pg. 1290
CENTERFIELD MEDIA HOLDINGS, LLC—See Platinum Equity, LLC; *U.S. Private*, pg. 3201
CHINA 33 MEDIA GROUP LIMITED; *Int'l*, pg. 1481
CINEPLEX DIGITAL MEDIA INC.—See Cineplex Inc.; *Int'l*, pg. 1610
CINEPLEX DIGITAL NETWORKS INC.—See Cineplex Inc.; *Int'l*, pg. 1610
CLEAR CHANNEL AIRPORTS—See Clear Channel Outdoor Holdings, Inc.; *U.S. Public*, pg. 511
CLEAR CHANNEL CHILE PUBLICIDAD LTDA—See iHeartMedia, Inc.; *U.S. Public*, pg. 1095
CLEAR CHANNEL INTERNATIONAL LTD.—See iHeartMedia, Inc.; *U.S. Public*, pg. 1096
CLEAR CHANNEL MALLS—See Clear Channel Outdoor Holdings, Inc.; *U.S. Public*, pg. 511
CLEAR CHANNEL OUTDOOR - AKRON/CANTON—See Clear Channel Outdoor Holdings, Inc.; *U.S. Public*, pg. 511
CLEAR CHANNEL OUTDOOR - ATLANTA—See Clear Channel Outdoor Holdings, Inc.; *U.S. Public*, pg. 511
CLEAR CHANNEL OUTDOOR - BOSTON—See Clear Channel Outdoor Holdings, Inc.; *U.S. Public*, pg. 511
CLEAR CHANNEL OUTDOOR - CHICAGO—See Clear Channel Outdoor Holdings, Inc.; *U.S. Public*, pg. 512
CLEAR CHANNEL OUTDOOR COMPANY CANADA—See

N.A.I.C.S. INDEX

541860 — DIRECT MAIL ADVERTI...

Clear Channel Outdoor Holdings, Inc.; *U.S. Public*, pg. 512
CLEAR CHANNEL OUTDOOR - DAYTONA BEACH/MELBOURNE—See Clear Channel Outdoor Holdings, Inc.; *U.S. Public*, pg. 511
CLEAR CHANNEL OUTDOOR - EASTERN REGIONAL OFFICE—See Clear Channel Outdoor Holdings, Inc.; *U.S. Public*, pg. 511
CLEAR CHANNEL OUTDOOR - HOUSTON—See Clear Channel Outdoor Holdings, Inc.; *U.S. Public*, pg. 512
CLEAR CHANNEL OUTDOOR, INC.—See Clear Channel Outdoor Holdings, Inc.; *U.S. Public*, pg. 511
CLEAR CHANNEL OUTDOOR - INDIANAPOLIS—See Clear Channel Outdoor Holdings, Inc.; *U.S. Public*, pg. 511
CLEAR CHANNEL OUTDOOR - JACKSONVILLE—See Clear Channel Outdoor Holdings, Inc.; *U.S. Public*, pg. 511
CLEAR CHANNEL OUTDOOR - LAS VEGAS—See Clear Channel Outdoor Holdings, Inc.; *U.S. Public*, pg. 512
CLEAR CHANNEL OUTDOOR - LOS ANGELES—See Clear Channel Outdoor Holdings, Inc.; *U.S. Public*, pg. 512
CLEAR CHANNEL OUTDOOR - MIAMI—See Clear Channel Outdoor Holdings, Inc.; *U.S. Public*, pg. 511
CLEAR CHANNEL OUTDOOR - MILWAUKEE—See Clear Channel Outdoor Holdings, Inc.; *U.S. Public*, pg. 512
CLEAR CHANNEL OUTDOOR - ORLANDO—See Clear Channel Outdoor Holdings, Inc.; *U.S. Public*, pg. 511
CLEAR CHANNEL OUTDOOR - PHILADELPHIA—See Clear Channel Outdoor Holdings, Inc.; *U.S. Public*, pg. 511
CLEAR CHANNEL OUTDOOR - SACRAMENTO—See Clear Channel Outdoor Holdings, Inc.; *U.S. Public*, pg. 512
CLEAR CHANNEL OUTDOOR - SAN ANTONIO—See Clear Channel Outdoor Holdings, Inc.; *U.S. Public*, pg. 512
CLEAR CHANNEL OUTDOOR - SAN DIEGO—See Clear Channel Outdoor Holdings, Inc.; *U.S. Public*, pg. 512
CLEAR CHANNEL OUTDOOR - SAN FRANCISCO—See Clear Channel Outdoor Holdings, Inc.; *U.S. Public*, pg. 512
CLEAR CHANNEL OUTDOOR - WASHINGTON, D.C./BALTIMORE—See Clear Channel Outdoor Holdings, Inc.; *U.S. Public*, pg. 511
CLEAR CHANNEL OUTDOOR - WESTERN REGIONAL OFFICE—See Clear Channel Outdoor Holdings, Inc.; *U.S. Public*, pg. 511
CLEAR CHANNEL OUTDOOR - WICHITA—See Clear Channel Outdoor Holdings, Inc.; *U.S. Public*, pg. 512
CLEAR CHANNEL OUTDOOR - WILMINGTON—See Clear Channel Outdoor Holdings, Inc.; *U.S. Public*, pg. 511
CLEAR CHANNEL POLAND SP ZO.O.—See iHeartMedia, Inc.; *U.S. Public*, pg. 1096
CLEAR CHANNEL UK LIMITED—See Clear Channel Outdoor Holdings, Inc.; *U.S. Public*, pg. 511
COLORADO LOGOS, INC.—See Lamar Advertising Company; *U.S. Public*, pg. 1290
CREO RETAIL MARKETING LTD—See DS Smith Plc; *Int'l*, pg. 2208
D2C MEDIA INC.—See Cars.com Inc.; *U.S. Public*, pg. 444
DEFI DEUTSCHLAND GMBH—See DEFI Group SAS; *Int'l*, pg. 2004
DEFI FRANCE SAS—See DEFI Group SAS; *Int'l*, pg. 2004
DEFI GROUP ASIA LTD.—See DEFI Group SAS; *Int'l*, pg. 2004
DEFI GROUP SAS; *Int'l*, pg. 2004
DEFI HUNGARY KFT—See DEFI Group SAS; *Int'l*, pg. 2004
DEFI ITALIA S.P.A.—See DEFI Group SAS; *Int'l*, pg. 2004
DEFI NEOLUX—See DEFI Group SAS; *Int'l*, pg. 2004
DEFI POLAND SP. Z O.O.—See DEFI Group SAS; *Int'l*, pg. 2004
DELAWARE LOGOS, L.L.C.—See Lamar Advertising Company; *U.S. Public*, pg. 1290
DIGITAL BLUE DOG, INC.; *U.S. Private*, pg. 1230
DIMENSION DESIGN; *U.S. Private*, pg. 1232
DIVA LABORATORIES LTD.; *Int'l*, pg. 2137
DNP SP TECH CO., LTD.—See Dai Nippon Printing Co., Ltd.; *Int'l*, pg. 1915
D SCREENS SIA—See AS Ekspress Grupp; *Int'l*, pg. 589
DS SMITH AD—See DS Smith Plc; *Int'l*, pg. 2209
E FOR L AIM PUBLIC COMPANY LIMITED; *Int'l*, pg. 2246
EUROPLAKAT BULGARIA OOD—See APG/SGA SA; *Int'l*, pg. 513
EUROPLAKAT D.O.O.—See APG/SGA SA; *Int'l*, pg. 513
EUROPLAKAT KFT—See APG/SGA SA; *Int'l*, pg. 513
EXCALIBUR EXHIBITS; *U.S. Private*, pg. 1445
EXTERION MEDIA (IRELAND) LIMITED—See Platinum Equity, LLC; *U.S. Private*, pg. 3203
EXTERION MEDIA (NETHERLANDS) B.V.—See Platinum Equity, LLC; *U.S. Private*, pg. 3203
EXTERION MEDIA SPAIN, S.A.—See Platinum Equity, LLC; *U.S. Private*, pg. 3203
FAIRWAY OUTDOOR ADVERTISING, LLC - CHATTANOOGA—See GTCR LLC; *U.S. Private*, pg. 1805
FAIRWAY OUTDOOR ADVERTISING, LLC - PRESTONSBURG—See GTCR LLC; *U.S. Private*, pg. 1805

FAIRWAY OUTDOOR ADVERTISING, LLC - ROCHESTER—See GTCR LLC; *U.S. Private*, pg. 1805
FAIRWAY OUTDOOR ADVERTISING, LLC—See GTCR LLC; *U.S. Private*, pg. 1805
FAIRWAY OUTDOOR ADVERTISING, LLC - VALDOSTA—See GTCR LLC; *U.S. Private*, pg. 1805
FRAMTIDSUTVECKLING I SVERIGE AB—See AcadeMedia AB; *Int'l*, pg. 76
GEORGIA LOGOS, L.L.C.—See Lamar Advertising Company; *U.S. Public*, pg. 1290
GREENLIGHT COMMERCE LIMITED—See Brave Bison Group plc; *Int'l*, pg. 1141
IBERDEFI—See DEFI Group SAS; *Int'l*, pg. 2004
ICON CULTURE GLOBAL COMPANY LIMITED; *Int'l*, pg. 3583
INNOVATEMAP LLC; *U.S. Private*, pg. 2081
IN-SYSTCOM, INC.; *U.S. Private*, pg. 1114
INTERNATIONAL METROPOLIS MEDIA D.O.O.—See APG/SGA SA; *Int'l*, pg. 513
IN-TER-SPACE SERVICES, INC.—See iHeartMedia, Inc.; *U.S. Public*, pg. 1095
KANSAS LOGOS, INC.—See Lamar Advertising Company; *U.S. Public*, pg. 1290
KENTUCKY LOGOS, LLC—See Lamar Advertising Company; *U.S. Public*, pg. 1290
KEY OUTDOOR INC.—See Boston Omaha Corporation; *U.S. Public*, pg. 372
LAMAR ADVERTISING COMPANY - SEATTLE—See Clear Channel Outdoor Holdings, Inc.; *U.S. Public*, pg. 512
LAMAR ADVERTISING OF MICHIGAN, INC.—See Lamar Advertising Company; *U.S. Public*, pg. 1290
LAMAR ADVERTISING OF OKLAHOMA, INC.—See Lamar Advertising Company; *U.S. Public*, pg. 1290
LAMAR ADVERTISING OF PENN, LLC—See Lamar Advertising Company; *U.S. Public*, pg. 1290
LAMAR ADVERTISING OF SOUTH DAKOTA, INC.—See Lamar Advertising Company; *U.S. Public*, pg. 1290
LAMAR ADVERTISING OF YOUNGSTOWN, INC.—See Lamar Advertising Company; *U.S. Public*, pg. 1290
LAMAR CORPORATION—See Lamar Advertising Company; *U.S. Public*, pg. 1290
LAMAR MEDIA CORP.—See Lamar Advertising Company; *U.S. Public*, pg. 1291
LAMAR OBIE CORPORATION—See Lamar Advertising Company; *U.S. Public*, pg. 1291
LAMAR PENSACOLA TRANSIT, INC.—See Lamar Advertising Company; *U.S. Public*, pg. 1291
LAMAR TENNESSEE, L.L.C.—See Lamar Advertising Company; *U.S. Public*, pg. 1291
LAMAR TEXAS LIMITED PARTNERSHIP—See Lamar Advertising Company; *U.S. Public*, pg. 1291
LAMAR TRANSIT ADVERTISING CANADA LTD.—See Lamar Advertising Company; *U.S. Public*, pg. 1291
LEADID LLC; *U.S. Private*, pg. 2406
LONGNECK & THUNDERFOOT LLC; *U.S. Private*, pg. 2492
LOUISIANA INTERSTATE LOGOS, L.L.C.—See Lamar Advertising Company; *U.S. Public*, pg. 1291
LUMENAD INC.; *U.S. Private*, pg. 2514
MALKA MEDIA GROUP LLC—See MoneyLion Inc.; *U.S. Public*, pg. 1464
MICHIGAN LOGOS, INC.—See Lamar Advertising Company; *U.S. Public*, pg. 1291
MILLENIUM BILLBOARDS L.L.C.—See OUTFRONT Media Inc.; *U.S. Public*, pg. 1625
MINNESOTA LOGOS, INC.—See Lamar Advertising Company; *U.S. Public*, pg. 1291
MISSISSIPPI LOGOS, L.L.C.—See Lamar Advertising Company; *U.S. Public*, pg. 1291
MISSOURI LOGOS, LLC—See Lamar Advertising Company; *U.S. Public*, pg. 1291
MONTANA LOGOS, L.L.C.—See Lamar Advertising Company; *U.S. Public*, pg. 1291
NEBRASKA LOGOS, INC.—See Lamar Advertising Company; *U.S. Public*, pg. 1291
NEONLIGHT KFT—See APG/SGA SA; *Int'l*, pg. 513
NEVADA LOGOS, INC.—See Lamar Advertising Company; *U.S. Public*, pg. 1291
NEW MEXICO LOGOS, INC.—See Lamar Advertising Company; *U.S. Public*, pg. 1291
OHIO LOGOS, INC.—See Lamar Advertising Company; *U.S. Public*, pg. 1291
OKLAHOMA LOGOS, L.L.C.—See Lamar Advertising Company; *U.S. Public*, pg. 1291
ONDISPLAY ADVERTISING LLC—See Federated Media Inc.; *U.S. Private*, pg. 1492
OOH MEDIA SOLUTION, INC.—See Dentsu Group Inc.; *Int'l*, pg. 2039
OUTFRONT MEDIA CANADA LP—See OUTFRONT Media Inc.; *U.S. Public*, pg. 1625
OUTFRONT MEDIA CHICAGO LLC—See OUTFRONT Media Inc.; *U.S. Public*, pg. 1625
OUTFRONT MEDIA LLC—See OUTFRONT Media Inc.; *U.S. Public*, pg. 1625
OUTFRONT MEDIA - PHOENIX—See OUTFRONT Media Inc.; *U.S. Public*, pg. 1625
OUTSIDE INTERACTIVE, INC.; *U.S. Private*, pg. 3051
PEARL MEDIA LLC; *U.S. Private*, pg. 3125

PRIMESIGHT LTD.—See GMT Communications Partners LLP; *Int'l*, pg. 3015
QUANTUM STRUCTURES & DESIGN—See Clear Channel Outdoor Holdings, Inc.; *U.S. Public*, pg. 512
RBN ROMANIAN BILLBOARD NETWORK SRL—See APG/SGA SA; *Int'l*, pg. 513
RED STAR OUTDOOR LLC—See Shamrock Capital Advisors, LLC; *U.S. Private*, pg. 3624
REYNOLDS OUTDOOR MEDIA—See OUTFRONT Media Inc.; *U.S. Public*, pg. 1625
RSA MEDIA, INC.—See American Tower Corporation; *U.S. Public*, pg. 111
SAXON CAPITAL GROUP, INC.; *U.S. Public*, pg. 1842
SD3IT, LLC; *U.S. Private*, pg. 3581
SIA CLEAR CHANNEL LATVIA—See iHeartMedia, Inc.; *U.S. Public*, pg. 1096
SIGNAL OUTDOOR ADVERTISING LLC—See MSouth Equity Partners, LLC; *U.S. Private*, pg. 2808
SIGNAL OUTDOOR ADVERTISING—See MSouth Equity Partners, LLC; *U.S. Private*, pg. 2808
SIGNAL OUTDOOR ADVERTISING—See MSouth Equity Partners, LLC; *U.S. Private*, pg. 2808
SIGNAL OUTDOOR ADVERTISING—See MSouth Equity Partners, LLC; *U.S. Private*, pg. 2808
SIGNAL OUTDOOR ADVERTISING—See MSouth Equity Partners, LLC; *U.S. Private*, pg. 2808
SIGNAL OUTDOOR ADVERTISING—See MSouth Equity Partners, LLC; *U.S. Private*, pg. 2808
SIGNAL OUTDOOR ADVERTISING—See MSouth Equity Partners, LLC; *U.S. Private*, pg. 2808
SIGNAL OUTDOOR ADVERTISING—See MSouth Equity Partners, LLC; *U.S. Private*, pg. 2808
SOUTH CAROLINA LOGOS, INC.—See Lamar Advertising Company; *U.S. Public*, pg. 1291
SPARKS CUSTOM RETAIL, LLC—See Freeman Decorating Co.; *U.S. Private*, pg. 1605
STANDARD OUTDOOR LLC—See Turning Point Brands, Inc.; *U.S. Public*, pg. 2205
STRATEGIC DIGITAL SERVICES INC.; *U.S. Private*, pg. 3834
STREET SMART OUTDOOR CORP.—See Sun Pacific Holding Corp; *U.S. Public*, pg. 1963
SUPERIOR DIGITAL DISPLAYS, LLC—See PennantPark Investment Corporation; *U.S. Public*, pg. 1663
TACO TRUCK CREATIVE, LLC; *U.S. Private*, pg. 3920
TAMMY LYNN OUTDOOR, LLC—See Boston Omaha Corporation; *U.S. Public*, pg. 372
TARHEEL BILLBOARD, INC.; *U.S. Private*, pg. 3934
TRANDS AD VIETNAM JOINT STOCK COMPANY—See BTS Group Holdings Public Company Limited; *Int'l*, pg. 1206
UAB CLEAR CHANNEL LIETUVA—See iHeartMedia, Inc.; *U.S. Public*, pg. 1096
UTAH LOGOS, INC.—See Lamar Advertising Company; *U.S. Public*, pg. 1291
VENDOR PUBLICIDAD EXTERIOR S DE RL DE CV—See National Amusements, Inc.; *U.S. Private*, pg. 2844
VIRGINIA LOGOS, LLC—See Lamar Advertising Company; *U.S. Public*, pg. 1291
VIRTUMUNDO, INC.; *U.S. Private*, pg. 4389
WHITECO INDUSTRIES INC.; *U.S. Private*, pg. 4511
YOUNG ELECTRIC SIGN CO. - PHOENIX—See Young Electric Sign Company; *U.S. Private*, pg. 4593
ZAO DEFI RUSSIE—See DEFI Group SAS; *Int'l*, pg. 2004

541860 — DIRECT MAIL ADVERTISING

A.B. DATA, LTD.; *U.S. Private*, pg. 24
ACCESS WORLDWIDE, INC.—See Passport Global Inc.; *U.S. Private*, pg. 3104
ACUMBAMAIL SL—See Growens S.p.A.; *Int'l*, pg. 3112
ADVERTISING DISTRIBUTORS OF AMERICA INC.; *U.S. Private*, pg. 110
ALCHEMY WORX LIMITED—See SellUp Inc.; *U.S. Private*, pg. 3603
ALLISON & PARTNERS-WASHINGTON D.C.—See Allison & Partners LLC; *U.S. Private*, pg. 192
ALLMEDIA, INC.; *U.S. Private*, pg. 192
AMERICAN LIST COUNSEL, INC.; *U.S. Private*, pg. 240
AMERICAN MARKETING & MAILING SERVICES, INC.; *U.S. Private*, pg. 240
AMERIMARK DIRECT, LLC—See JH Partners LLC; *U.S. Private*, pg. 2207
AMERIMARK DIRECT, LLC—See Prudential Financial, Inc.; *U.S. Public*, pg. 1732
APPLIED RESEARCH ASSOCIATES EMERALD COAST DIVISION—See Applied Research Associates, Inc.; *U.S. Private*, pg. 299
ARENA COMMUNICATIONS; *U.S. Private*, pg. 318
ARIIX, LLC—See NewAge, Inc.; *U.S. Public*, pg. 1513
ARROWHEAD PROMOTION & FULFILLMENT COMPANY, INC.; *U.S. Private*, pg. 336
ASHTON-DRAKE GALLERIES, LTD.—See The Bradford Group; *U.S. Private*, pg. 3999
BAKKER CONTINENTAL B.V.—See Chepri Holding B.V.; *Int'l*, pg. 1471
BETTERWARE DE MEXICO S.A.P.I. DE C.V.; *Int'l*, pg. 1004
BORNS GROUP, INC.; *U.S. Private*, pg. 619
BROADRIDGE FINANCIAL SOLUTIONS, INC.—See Auto-

N.A.I.C.S. Index

541860 — DIRECT MAIL ADVERTI... CORPORATE AFFILIATIONS

matic Data Processing, Inc.; *U.S. Public*, pg. 230
BROADRIDGE INVESTOR COMMUNICATIONS CORPORATION—See Broadridge Financial Solutions, Inc.; *U.S. Public*, pg. 391
CDR FUNDRAISING GROUP—See Moore DM Group, LLC; *U.S. Private*, pg. 2780
CENTURY DIRECT LLC; *U.S. Private*, pg. 832
CIL GROUP SL; *Int'l*, pg. 1607
CITYTWIST; *U.S. Private*, pg. 907
CLIPPER MAGAZINE, LLC; *U.S. Private*, pg. 945
CLUB INTERNACIONAL DEL LIBRO, MARKETING DIRECTO, S.L.—See CIL Group SL; *Int'l*, pg. 1607
THE CORPORATE COMMUNICATIONS GROUP; *U.S. Private*, pg. 4015
CSG SYSTEMS, INC.—See CSG Systems International, Inc.; *U.S. Public*, pg. 601
DDM-DIGITAL IMAGING, DATA PROCESSING AND MAILING SERVICES, L.C.—See Chatham Asset Management, LLC; *U.S. Private*, pg. 863
DEPENDABLE MAIL SERVICES INC.; *U.S. Private*, pg. 1209
DIRECTGROUP BERTELSMANN—See Bertelsmann SE & Co. KGaA; *Int'l*, pg. 992
DIRECT MAIL EXPRESS, INC.; *U.S. Private*, pg. 1235
DIRECT MARKETING SOLUTIONS, INC.; *U.S. Private*, pg. 1235
DIRECT MEDIA MILLARD, INC.—See CCMP Capital Advisors, LP; *U.S. Private*, pg. 800
DIRECT RESPONSE MEDIA GROUP INC.; *Int'l*, pg. 2130
DITTBORN & UNZUETA MRM—See The Interpublic Group of Companies, Inc.; *U.S. Public*, pg. 2098
DM SOLUTIONS CO., LTD; *Int'l*, pg. 2142
DUNHILL INTERNATIONAL LIST CO., INC.; *U.S. Private*, pg. 1289
DUNNDATA COMPANY; *U.S. Private*, pg. 1290
DYNAMICARD, INC.; *U.S. Private*, pg. 1299
ENGAGE; *U.S. Private*, pg. 1397
EVALUE VENTURES AG; *Int'l*, pg. 2560
FOLEY-BELSAW INSTITUTE—See Foley-Belsaw Company; *U.S. Private*, pg. 1558
FRESHADDRESS, LLC—See TowerData, Inc.; *U.S. Private*, pg. 4196
GETTY IMAGES, INC.—See CC Capital Partners, LLC; *U.S. Private*, pg. 797
GLOBEDIRECT, LLC—See NE Media Group, Inc.; *U.S. Private*, pg. 2877
GLOBE SPECIALTY PRODUCTS, INC.—See NE Media Group, Inc.; *U.S. Private*, pg. 2877
GROUP O DIRECT INC.—See Group O Inc.; *U.S. Private*, pg. 1794
GS MARKETING, INC.; *U.S. Private*, pg. 1800
GUIDESTAR DIRECT CORP.; *U.S. Private*, pg. 1813
HANDSOME REWARDS—See Starcrest Products of California; *U.S. Private*, pg. 3786
HARTE-HANKS DIRECT MARKETING/DALLAS, INC.—See Harte Hanks, Inc.; *U.S. Public*, pg. 986
HARTE-HANKS DIRECT MARKETING/DALLAS, L.P.—See Harte Hanks, Inc.; *U.S. Public*, pg. 986
HARTE-HANKS FLYER, INC.—See Harte Hanks, Inc.; *U.S. Public*, pg. 986
HARTE HANKS, INC.; *U.S. Public*, pg. 986
HARTE-HANKS, INC.—See Harte Hanks, Inc.; *U.S. Public*, pg. 986
HARTE-HANKS, INC.—See Harte Hanks, Inc.; *U.S. Public*, pg. 986
HARTE-HANKS MARKET INTELLIGENCE EUROPE B.V.—See Harte Hanks, Inc.; *U.S. Public*, pg. 986
HAWKEYE FFWD—See Hawkeye, Inc.; *U.S. Private*, pg. 1883
THE HIBBERT GROUP; *U.S. Private*, pg. 4052
HUGO DUNHILL MAILING LISTS, INC.; *U.S. Private*, pg. 2004
IMPACT MAILING OF MINNESOTA, INC.; *U.S. Private*, pg. 2048
INFOGROUP DIRECT MARKETING SOLUTIONS—See CCMP Capital Advisors, LP; *U.S. Private*, pg. 800
INFOGROUP/EDITH ROMAN ASSOCIATES—See CCMP Capital Advisors, LP; *U.S. Private*, pg. 800
INNOVYX—See Omnicom Group Inc.; *U.S. Public*, pg. 1594
INNOVYX—See Omnicom Group Inc.; *U.S. Public*, pg. 1594
INTERNATIONAL BUSINESS SYSTEMS, INC.—See Maestro Print Management LLC; *U.S. Private*, pg. 2545
IRON MOUNTAIN ASSURANCE CORPORATION—See Iron Mountain Incorporated; *U.S. Public*, pg. 1172
IWCO DIRECT INC.—See Cerberus Capital Management, L.P.; *U.S. Private*, pg. 838
JOHNSON & QUIN, INC.; *U.S. Private*, pg. 2226
KROLL DIRECT MARKETING INC.; *U.S. Private*, pg. 2353
LAKE GROUP MEDIA, INC.; *U.S. Private*, pg. 2375
LEAD RESEARCH GROUP, LLC; *U.S. Private*, pg. 2405
LEON HENRY, INC.; *U.S. Private*, pg. 2422
LEWIS DIRECT, INC.; *U.S. Private*, pg. 2438
THE LINICK GROUP, INC.; *U.S. Private*, pg. 4070
L.I.S.T. INC.; *U.S. Private*, pg. 2366
LIST SERVICES CORPORATION; *U.S. Private*, pg. 2466
MAIL CUSTOMER CENTER CO., LTD.—See Bain Capital, LP; *U.S. Private*, pg. 449
MAILER'S CHOICE, INC.—See DNI Corp.; *U.S. Private*, pg. 1249
MAILING SERVICES OF PITTSBURGH, INC.—See Direct Marketing Solutions, Inc.; *U.S. Private*, pg. 1235
MAILINGS UNLIMITED; *U.S. Private*, pg. 2551
MAILING SYSTEMS, INC.; *U.S. Private*, pg. 2551
MAIL SHARK; *U.S. Private*, pg. 2551
MAILSOUTH, INC.; *U.S. Private*, pg. 2551
MARKET FIRST, INC.; *U.S. Private*, pg. 2579
MARKETING INFORMATICS, INC.; *U.S. Private*, pg. 2580
MARKETING SOLUTIONS UNLIMITED, LLC; *U.S. Private*, pg. 2580
MARKETSHARE PUBLICATIONS, INC.; *U.S. Private*, pg. 2581
MCH, INC.; *U.S. Private*, pg. 2636
MERITDIRECT, LLC; *U.S. Private*, pg. 2674
MERITDIRECT UK—See MeritDirect, LLC; *U.S. Private*, pg. 2674
METARESPONSE GROUP, INC.; *U.S. Private*, pg. 2682
MILLER'S PRESORT, INC.—See Pitney Bowes Inc.; *U.S. Public*, pg. 1694
MONEY MAILER, LLC—See Local Marketing Solutions Group, Inc.; *U.S. Private*, pg. 2477
MONEY SAVER COUPON BOOK INC.; *U.S. Private*, pg. 2770
MRM BRAZIL—See The Interpublic Group of Companies, Inc.; *U.S. Public*, pg. 2098
MRM LONDON—See The Interpublic Group of Companies, Inc.; *U.S. Public*, pg. 2098
MRM MEXICO—See The Interpublic Group of Companies, Inc.; *U.S. Public*, pg. 2098
MRM PARTNERS DIALOGO—See The Interpublic Group of Companies, Inc.; *U.S. Public*, pg. 2098
MRM WORLDWIDE HONG KONG—See The Interpublic Group of Companies, Inc.; *U.S. Public*, pg. 2098
MRM WORLDWIDE INDIA—See The Interpublic Group of Companies, Inc.; *U.S. Public*, pg. 2098
MRM WORLDWIDE PARAGUAY—See The Interpublic Group of Companies, Inc.; *U.S. Public*, pg. 2098
MRM WORLDWIDE—See The Interpublic Group of Companies, Inc.; *U.S. Public*, pg. 2098
MRM WORLDWIDE—See The Interpublic Group of Companies, Inc.; *U.S. Public*, pg. 2098
MRM WORLDWIDE SPAIN—See The Interpublic Group of Companies, Inc.; *U.S. Public*, pg. 2098
NEXT DAY FLYERS; *U.S. Private*, pg. 2919
NOBLE VENTURES CORP.; *U.S. Private*, pg. 2933
ON-DEMAND MAIL SERVICES, LLC; *U.S. Private*, pg. 3018
ONETONE RESEARCH SRL—See Fullsix S.p.A.; *Int'l*, pg. 2843
OUR TOWN AMERICA, INC.; *U.S. Private*, pg. 3050
PARADYSZ MATERA COMPANY, INC.; *U.S. Private*, pg. 3090
POINT IT INC.—See Add3, LLC; *U.S. Private*, pg. 77
POSTCARDMANIA; *U.S. Private*, pg. 3235
PRECISION DIALOGUE DIRECT, INC.—See Chatham Asset Management, LLC; *U.S. Private*, pg. 864
PREFERRED GROUP INC.; *U.S. Private*, pg. 3248
PRIMENET DIRECT MARKETING SOLUTIONS, LLC; *U.S. Private*, pg. 3263
PRODUCTION SOLUTIONS, INC.—See LA Associates, Inc.; *U.S. Private*, pg. 2367
QUANTUMDIGITAL, INC.; *U.S. Private*, pg. 3323
RAPP LOS ANGELES—See Omnicom Group Inc.; *U.S. Public*, pg. 1592
RESOURCE SOLUTIONS INC.; *U.S. Private*, pg. 3407
RESPONSE MAIL EXPRESS INC.; *U.S. Private*, pg. 3408
RESULTS GENERATION; *U.S. Private*, pg. 3410
R & R DIRECT MAIL, INC.; *U.S. Private*, pg. 3331
S.A. DE PROMOCIONES Y EDICIONES—See CIL Group SL; *Int'l*, pg. 1607
SELEKTVRACHT B.V.—See Deutsche Post AG; *Int'l*, pg. 2082
SELLUP INC.; *U.S. Private*, pg. 3603
SOUTHWEST PUBLISHING & MAILING CORP.—See Moore DM Group, LLC; *U.S. Private*, pg. 2780
SPECIALISTS MARKETING SERVICES, INC.; *U.S. Private*, pg. 3748
TAUBENPOST MAILING, INC.—See Taubenpost, Inc.; *U.S. Private*, pg. 3936
THINKDIRECT MARKETING GROUP, INC.—See Blackstreet Capital Management, LLC; *U.S. Private*, pg. 577
THINK INK MARKETING & DIRECT MAIL SERVICES, INC.; *U.S. Private*, pg. 4144
TRIBUNE DIRECT MARKETING, INC.—See Tribune Publishing Company; *U.S. Private*, pg. 4228
TRIBUNE DIRECT MARKETING—See Tribune Publishing Company; *U.S. Private*, pg. 4228
TRI-WIN; *U.S. Private*, pg. 4225
UNITED MAILING SERVICES, INC.; *U.S. Private*, pg. 4293
VALASSIS CANADA INC.—See Direct Response Media Group Inc.; *Int'l*, pg. 2130
VALASSIS DIRECT MAIL, INC.—See MacAndrews & Forbes Incorporated; *U.S. Private*, pg. 2532
VALPAK DIRECT MARKETING SYSTEMS, INC.; *U.S. Private*, pg. 4337
WELCOME WAGON INTERNATIONAL, INC.—See South Florida Media Group, LLC; *U.S. Private*, pg. 3722
WINMO, LLC—See Northlane Capital Partners, LLC; *U.S. Private*, pg. 2956
WORLDATA INFOCENTER, INC.; *U.S. Private*, pg. 4568

541870 — ADVERTISING MATERIAL DISTRIBUTION SERVICES

ADREXO SAS; *Int'l*, pg. 152
ADVANTEX MARKETING INTERNATIONAL INC.; *Int'l*, pg. 166
ALL CAMPUS LLC; *U.S. Private*, pg. 170
A.MANZONI AND C. SPA—See Giovanni Agnelli B.V.; *Int'l*, pg. 2978
AMTD DIGITAL INC.—See AMTD Group Company Limited; *Int'l*, pg. 441
ASPIRE GLOBAL INC.; *Int'l*, pg. 631
ATLAS—See Meta Platforms, Inc.; *U.S. Public*, pg. 1426
ATLAS—See Meta Platforms, Inc.; *U.S. Public*, pg. 1427
AT&T—See AT&T Inc.; *U.S. Public*, pg. 218
AUDIOBOOM GROUP PLC; *Int'l*, pg. 701
B2B MEDIA—See Vomela Specialty Company; *U.S. Private*, pg. 4412
BECKETT & BECKETT, INC.—See Beckett & Beckett, Inc.; *U.S. Private*, pg. 511
BEIJING YUANLONG YATO CULTURE DISSEMINATION CO., LTD.; *Int'l*, pg. 961
BEIJING ZHONGKEHAIXUN DIGITAL S & T CO., LTD.; *Int'l*, pg. 961
BIRDMAN, INC.; *Int'l*, pg. 1047
B-LINE APPAREL, INC.; *U.S. Private*, pg. 419
BLITZ MEDIA, INC.; *U.S. Private*, pg. 582
BLUESTAR MARKETING, INC.; *U.S. Private*, pg. 598
BVK DIRECT, INC.—See BVK, Inc.; *U.S. Private*, pg. 700
CARAT BEIJING—See Dentsu Group Inc.; *Int'l*, pg. 2035
CARAT HONG KONG—See Dentsu Group Inc.; *Int'l*, pg. 2035
CARAT SHANGHAI—See Dentsu Group Inc.; *Int'l*, pg. 2035
CLINICALMIND LLC; *U.S. Private*, pg. 944
COCONALA, INC.; *Int'l*, pg. 1687
COPUS KOREA CO., LTD.; *Int'l*, pg. 1794
COUPONS.COM LIMITED—See Charlesbank Capital Partners, LLC; *U.S. Private*, pg. 855
COUPONS, INC.—See Charlesbank Capital Partners, LLC; *U.S. Private*, pg. 855
COX DIGITAL SOLUTIONS, LLC—See Apollo Global Management, Inc.; *U.S. Public*, pg. 163
CPM USA—See Omnicom Group Inc.; *U.S. Public*, pg. 1578
CRITICAL MASS INC. - CHICAGO—See Omnicom Group Inc.; *U.S. Public*, pg. 1594
CTM MEDIA GROUP - CANADIAN DIVISION—See CTM Media Group, Inc.; *U.S. Private*, pg. 1119
CTM MEDIA GROUP, INC.; *U.S. Private*, pg. 1119
DEFY MEDIA, LLC—See ZelnickMedia Corp.; *U.S. Private*, pg. 4600
DISTRIBUTECH INC.—See Redfin Corporation; *U.S. Public*, pg. 1770
DISTRIBUTECH—See Redfin Corporation; *U.S. Public*, pg. 1770
DISTRIBUTECH - SOUTHWEST REGION—See Redfin Corporation; *U.S. Public*, pg. 1770
DLOCAL LTD.; *Int'l*, pg. 2141
EEC ACQUISITION LLC—See Wind Point Advisors LLC; *U.S. Private*, pg. 4536
ELEVENTH DAY ENTERTAINMENT INC.; *U.S. Private*, pg. 1358
ENCOUNTER TECHNOLOGIES, INC.; *U.S. Public*, pg. 760
EURIZON MEDIA—See Horizon Media, Inc.; *U.S. Private*, pg. 1982
FEEDFORCE GROUP, INC.; *Int'l*, pg. 2632
FLIVA APS; *Int'l*, pg. 2706
FRANK PRODUCTIONS, INC.—See Live Nation Entertainment, Inc.; *U.S. Public*, pg. 1328
FRONTIER INTERNATIONAL, INC.; *Int'l*, pg. 2795
GEOCODE CO., LTD.; *Int'l*, pg. 2932
GIIR COMMUNICATIONS PVT. LTD.—See HS Ad Inc.; *Int'l*, pg. 3502
GLOBAL SUPPLY LLC; *U.S. Private*, pg. 1718
GMO UNITEX INC.—See GMO Internet Group, Inc.; *Int'l*, pg. 3014
GUANGDONG BRANDMAX MARKETING CO., LTD.; *Int'l*, pg. 3153
HARTE-HANKS DIRECT, INC.—See Harte Hanks, Inc.; *U.S. Public*, pg. 986
HARTE-HANKS DIRECT MARKETING/BALTIMORE, INC.—See Harte Hanks, Inc.; *U.S. Public*, pg. 986
HARTE HANKS DIRECT MARKETING/CINCINNATI, INC.—See Harte Hanks, Inc.; *U.S. Public*, pg. 986
HARTE-HANKS DIRECT MARKETING/FULLERTON, INC.—See Harte Hanks, Inc.; *U.S. Public*, pg. 986
HARTE-HANKS DIRECT MARKETING/JACKSONVILLE, LLC—See Harte Hanks, Inc.; *U.S. Public*, pg. 986
HARTE-HANKS DIRECT MARKETING/KANSAS CITY, LLC—See Harte Hanks, Inc.; *U.S. Public*, pg. 986
HARTE-HANKS FLORIDA, INC.—See Harte Hanks, Inc.; *U.S. Public*, pg. 986
HARTE-HANKS RESPONSE MANAGEMENT/BOSTON,

N.A.I.C.S. INDEX

541890 — OTHER SERVICES RELA...

INC.—See Harte Hanks, Inc.; *U.S. Public*, pg. 986
HYLINK DIGITAL SOLUTION CO., LTD.; *Int'l*, pg. 3549
INTEGRATED MERCHANDISING SYSTEMS—See Omnicom Group Inc.; *U.S. Public*, pg. 1586
INTIMATE MERGER, INC.—See FreakOut Holdings, Inc.; *Int'l*, pg. 2767
JOHN MENZIES DISTRIBUTION—See Endless LLP; *Int'l*, pg. 2403
KC DISTRIBUTING, LLC—See Glazer's Family of Companies; *U.S. Private*, pg. 1707
KURIER DIREKTSERVICE DRESDEN GMBH—See Bertelsmann SE & Co. KGaA; *Int'l*, pg. 993
LENDWAY, INC.; *U.S. Public*, pg. 1305
LIGHTNING GOLF AND PROMOTIONS, INC.—See HH Global Group Limited; *Int'l*, pg. 3379
LOCALEDGE—See The Hearst Corporation; *U.S. Private*, pg. 4047
MBX SYSTEMS—See Berkshire Partners LLC; *U.S. Private*, pg. 534
MC GROUP; *U.S. Private*, pg. 2625
MEDIA ITALIA HQ—See Armando Testa S.p.A.; *Int'l*, pg. 574
MERCHANDISING WORKSHOP, INC.; *U.S. Private*, pg. 2669
MNET MOBILE PTY. LTD.—See The Interpublic Group of Companies, Inc.; *U.S. Public*, pg. 2103
MONEY CLIP MAGAZINE; *U.S. Private*, pg. 2770
NEWSCON INC.—See Envipro Holdings Inc.; *Int'l*, pg. 2454
NEXGEN RXMARKETING LLC—See Insignia Capital Group, L.P.; *U.S. Private*, pg. 2091
OMD AUSTRALIA—See Omnicom Group Inc.; *U.S. Public*, pg. 1588
OMD GUANGZHOU—See Omnicom Group Inc.; *U.S. Public*, pg. 1588
PAYBACK AUSTRIA GMBH—See American Express Company; *U.S. Public*, pg. 102
PEOPLES RURAL TELEPHONE COOPERATIVE; *U.S. Private*, pg. 3142
PHD CANADA—See Omnicom Group Inc.; *U.S. Public*, pg. 1590
PINCHME.COM, INC.; *U.S. Private*, pg. 3181
PLANET EVENTS S.A.—See Live Nation Entertainment, Inc.; *U.S. Public*, pg. 1330
PRO MOTION, INC.; *U.S. Private*, pg. 3270
RABBIT REWARDS CO., LTD.—See BTS Group Holdings Public Company Limited; *Int'l*, pg. 1206
RXSAVER, INC.—See MacAndrews & Forbes Incorporated; *U.S. Private*, pg. 2532
RYAN RETAIL ZONE—See Ryan Partnership, LLC; *U.S. Private*, pg. 3510
SANHO CORPORATION—See Targus Group International, Inc.; *U.S. Private*, pg. 3934
SIZMEK SPAIN, S.L.—See Vector Capital Management, L.P.; *U.S. Private*, pg. 4352
SIZMEK TECHNOLOGIES GMBH—See Vector Capital Management, L.P.; *U.S. Private*, pg. 4352
SIZMEK TECHNOLOGIES LTD.—See Vector Capital Management, L.P.; *U.S. Private*, pg. 4353
SIZMEK TECHNOLOGIES LTD.—See Vector Capital Management, L.P.; *U.S. Private*, pg. 4353
SIZMEK TECHNOLOGIES PTY. LTD.—See Vector Capital Management, L.P.; *U.S. Private*, pg. 4353
SOUTHERN EQUIPMENT DISTRIBUTORS, INC.—See Cal-Maine Foods, Inc.; *U.S. Public*, pg. 421
SPECIFICITY INC.; *U.S. Public*, pg. 1915
STACI SAS—See Ardian SAS; *Int'l*, pg. 556
STREAMWORKS LLC; *U.S. Private*, pg. 3838
SUNFLOWER MARKETING—See M-C Industries Inc.; *U.S. Private*, pg. 2525
THE SWARM AGENCY, INC.; *U.S. Private*, pg. 4125
TURNER BROADCASTING SALES TAIWAN INC.—See Warner Bros. Discovery, Inc.; *U.S. Public*, pg. 2328
WEBBMASON, INC.; *U.S. Private*, pg. 4464
WOVEN DIGITAL, INC.; *U.S. Private*, pg. 4571
ZEPHYR MEDIA GROUP; *U.S. Private*, pg. 4602
ZIP INC.—See EQT AB; *Int'l*, pg. 2467

541890 — OTHER SERVICES RELATED TO ADVERTISING

1000MERCIS S.A.; *Int'l*, pg. 1
1220 EXHIBITS, INC.; *U.S. Private*, pg. 2
1BG LLC; *U.S. Private*, pg. 3
3 BIRDS MARKETING LLC—See Digital Air Strike Inc.; *U.S. Private*, pg. 1229
3BL MEDIA LLC; *U.S. Private*, pg. 8
3D EXHIBITS, INC.—See Freeman Decorating Co.; *U.S. Private*, pg. 1605
4IMPRINT INC.—See 4imprint Group plc; *Int'l*, pg. 12
6DEGREES INTEGRATED COMMUNICATIONS CORP.—See Stagwell, Inc.; *U.S. Public*, pg. 1925
888 MEDIA CO., LTD.—See BTS Group Holdings Public Company Limited; *Int'l*, pg. 1205
8VI HOLDINGS LIMITED; *Int'l*, pg. 16
966850 ONTARIO INC; *Int'l*, pg. 16
A9.COM, INC.—See Amazon.com, Inc.; *U.S. Public*, pg. 91
ACCENTHEALTH LLC—See Catterton Management Company, LLC; *U.S. Private*, pg. 794

ACQUIRE MEDIA 1 UK LIMITED—See Moody's Corporation; *U.S. Public*, pg. 1466
ACRONYM ASIA PTE. LTD.—See Acronym Media Inc.; *U.S. Private*, pg. 66
ACRONYM EUROPE—See Acronym Media Inc.; *U.S. Private*, pg. 66
ACRONYM MEDIA INC.; *U.S. Private*, pg. 66
ACRONYM MEDIA—See Acronym Media Inc.; *U.S. Private*, pg. 66
ACXION FOODSERVICE—See Prospect Hill Growth Partners, L.P.; *U.S. Private*, pg. 3288
ADAPTIVE AD SYSTEMS, INC.; *U.S. Public*, pg. 39
ADARE GROUP LIMITED—See Endless LLP; *Int'l*, pg. 2403
ADCHECK PROPRIETARY LIMITED—See Caxton and CTP Publishers and Printers Ltd.; *Int'l*, pg. 1363
ADCLOUD OPERATIONS SPAIN S.L.—See Deutsche Post AG; *Int'l*, pg. 2071
ADCOLONY, INC.—See Digital Turbine, Inc.; *U.S. Public*, pg. 664
ADFONIC GMBH—See Adfonic Ltd.; *Int'l*, pg. 145
ADFONIC INC.—See Adfonic Ltd.; *Int'l*, pg. 145
ADFONIC LTD.; *Int'l*, pg. 145
ADKNOWLEDGE, INC.; *U.S. Private*, pg. 80
ADMARKETPLACE, INC.; *U.S. Private*, pg. 80
ADROLL, INC.; *U.S. Private*, pg. 82
ADS DIRECT MEDIA INC.; *U.S. Private*, pg. 82
ADSHEL (BRAZIL) LTDA—See Clear Channel Outdoor Holdings, Inc.; *U.S. Public*, pg. 511
ADSHEL IRELAND LIMITED—See Clear Channel Outdoor Holdings, Inc.; *U.S. Public*, pg. 511
ADSLOT LTD.; *Int'l*, pg. 154
ADSPACE NETWORKS, INC.; *U.S. Private*, pg. 83
ADUX SA; *Int'l*, pg. 154
AD-VANTAGENET, INC.; *U.S. Private*, pg. 72
ADVENT, LLC; *U.S. Private*, pg. 108
ADVOC8, LLC; *U.S. Private*, pg. 110
A&E TELEVISION NETWORKS, LLC - DETROIT OFFICE—See The Hearst Corporation; *U.S. Private*, pg. 4045
A&E TELEVISION NETWORKS, LLC - DETROIT OFFICE—See The Walt Disney Company; *U.S. Public*, pg. 2137
AFFILIATEFUTURE INC.—See GlobalData Plc; *Int'l*, pg. 3003
AFFILIATEFUTURE UK—See GlobalData Plc; *Int'l*, pg. 3003
AFFINITAS MARKETING, INC.—See Affinitas Corporation; *U.S. Private*, pg. 122
AFFINITY EXPRESS, INC.—See Ayala Corporation; *Int'l*, pg. 774
AGILE MEDIA NETWORK, INC.; *Int'l*, pg. 209
AIA CORPORATION; *U.S. Private*, pg. 131
AIRSHIP & BALLOON COMPANY LTD.; *Int'l*, pg. 248
ALCHEMIST MEDIA, INC.; *U.S. Private*, pg. 153
ALEXANDER GLOBAL PROMOTIONS, INC.; *U.S. Private*, pg. 163
ALGORITHM MEDIA LIMITED—See Fidelity Bank Plc.; *Int'l*, pg. 2654
ALI SPECIALTIES; *U.S. Private*, pg. 166
ALIVE COMPANIES, INC.—See Skybridge Americas, Inc.; *U.S. Private*, pg. 3684
ALLIANCE FOR AUDITED MEDIA; *U.S. Private*, pg. 182
ALLIANCE INTERACTIVE INC.; *U.S. Private*, pg. 183
ALLIED FARMERS LIMITED; *Int'l*, pg. 357
ALMA QUATTRO D.O.O.—See APG/SGA SA; *Int'l*, pg. 513
ALTITUDE GROUP PLC; *Int'l*, pg. 393
ANTEVENIO SA; *Int'l*, pg. 482
APOSITION—See Dentsu Group Inc.; *Int'l*, pg. 2035
AQABA TECHNOLOGIES; *U.S. Private*, pg. 302
ARKNETMEDIA INC.; *U.S. Private*, pg. 326
ASATSU-DK VIETNAM INC.—See Bain Capital, LP; *U.S. Private*, pg. 428
ASIA MEDIA GROUP BERHAD; *Int'l*, pg. 613
ASM MESSEPROFIS AG; *Int'l*, pg. 626
ASTERI HOLDINGS; *U.S. Private*, pg. 360
ASTRO PRODUCTIONS SDN. BHD.—See Astro Malaysia Holdings Bhd; *Int'l*, pg. 662
ATTACK MARKETING, LLC; *U.S. Private*, pg. 383
AUDIENCE LABS SA; *Int'l*, pg. 701
AUDIENCESCIENCE INC.; *U.S. Private*, pg. 391
AVANT MARKETING GROUP; *U.S. Private*, pg. 404
AXELERO SPA; *Int'l*, pg. 767
AXEL MARK INC.; *Int'l*, pg. 765
BACKBONE MEDIA, INC.; *U.S. Private*, pg. 423
BADGE-A-MINIT LTD—See Malcolm Group Inc.; *U.S. Private*, pg. 2557
BAIDU (HONG KONG) LIMITED—See Baidu, Inc.; *Int'l*, pg. 801
BATANGA, INC.; *U.S. Private*, pg. 486
BAYSHORE SOLUTIONS INC.; *U.S. Private*, pg. 497
BBN NETWORKS, INC.; *U.S. Private*, pg. 498
BEAN CREATIVE, INC.; *U.S. Private*, pg. 506
BEL USA LLC; *U.S. Private*, pg. 516
BERLIN ROSEN LTD.—See O2 Investment Partners, LLC; *U.S. Private*, pg. 2982
BEST EDGE SEO, INC.; *U.S. Private*, pg. 542
BEYOND COMMERCE, INC.; *U.S. Public*, pg. 327
BLUE ACORN, LLC—See Beringer Capital; *Int'l*, pg. 981
BLUE CALYPSO, INC.; *U.S. Public*, pg. 364

BLUEGLASS INTERACTIVE, INC.; *U.S. Private*, pg. 596
BLUEGLASS INTERACTIVE UK INC.—See BlueGlass Interactive, Inc.; *U.S. Private*, pg. 596
BLUE GLOBAL MEDIA; *U.S. Private*, pg. 588
BLUE INTERACTIVE AGENCY; *U.S. Private*, pg. 589
BLUE PHOENIX MEDIA, INC.; *U.S. Private*, pg. 590
BLUESPIRE, INC. - MONTVALE—See High Road Capital Partners, LLC; *U.S. Private*, pg. 1936
BLUEWATER MEDIA LLC; *U.S. Private*, pg. 598
BOOM MARKETING INC.—See Stagwell, Inc.; *U.S. Public*, pg. 1926
BOUNTY UK LTD.; *Int'l*, pg. 1120
BRANDED CITIES NETWORK, LLC—See Shamrock Capital Advisors, LLC; *U.S. Private*, pg. 3624
BRANDVIA ALLIANCE, INC.; *U.S. Private*, pg. 639
BRAVE; *Int'l*, pg. 1141
BRIGHTCOM GROUP LTD.; *Int'l*, pg. 1162
BROADSTREET PRODUCTIONS, LLC; *U.S. Private*, pg. 659
BROWN & BIGELOW, INC.; *U.S. Private*, pg. 666
BRUCE CLAY AUSTRALIA PTY LTD—See Bruce Clay, Inc.; *U.S. Private*, pg. 670
BRUCE CLAY EUROPE—See Bruce Clay, Inc.; *U.S. Private*, pg. 670
BRUCE CLAY, INC.; *U.S. Private*, pg. 670
BRUCE CLAY INDIA PVT LTD—See Bruce Clay, Inc.; *U.S. Private*, pg. 670
BRUCE CLAY JAPAN, INC.—See Bruce Clay, Inc.; *U.S. Private*, pg. 671
BUCK LA; *U.S. Private*, pg. 676
BUCK NY—See Buck LA; *U.S. Private*, pg. 676
BURDA COMMUNITY NETWORK GMBH—See Hubert Burda Media Holding Kommanditgesellschaft; *Int'l*, pg. 3519
BUSINESSONLINE INC.; *U.S. Private*, pg. 695
CABOT INVESTMENT TECHNOLOGY, INC.—See FactSet Research Systems Inc.; *U.S. Public*, pg. 819
CALIENDO SAVIO ENTERPRISES, INC.—See TPG Capital, L.P.; *U.S. Private*, pg. 2176
CAM GROUP, INC.; *Int'l*, pg. 1266
CANOE VENTURES LLC—See Altice USA, Inc.; *U.S. Public*, pg. 87
CANOE VENTURES LLC—See Charter Communications, Inc.; *U.S. Public*, pg. 483
CANOE VENTURES LLC—See Comcast Corporation; *U.S. Public*, pg. 537
CANOE VENTURES LLC—See Cox Enterprises, Inc.; *U.S. Private*, pg. 1078
CARSALES.COM LIMITED; *Int'l*, pg. 1346
CASTA DIVA GROUP; *Int'l*, pg. 1355
CATALINA MARKETING CORPORATION—See Berkshire Partners LLC; *U.S. Private*, pg. 534
CDK GLOBAL, INC.—See Brookfield Corporation; *Int'l*, pg. 1175
CDK GLOBAL (NETHERLAND) BV—See Brookfield Corporation; *Int'l*, pg. 1175
CENERGY COMMUNICATIONS, LLC; *U.S. Private*, pg. 808
CGS INTERNATIONAL, INC.; *Int'l*, pg. 1435
CHAMBERLAIN AND ASSOCIATES; *U.S. Private*, pg. 845
CHINA CENTURY DRAGON MEDIA, INC.; *Int'l*, pg. 1488
CHINA MASS MEDIA CORP.; *Int'l*, pg. 1517
CHINA TIME SHARE MEDIA CO. LTD.; *Int'l*, pg. 1559
CIVITAS PUBLIC AFFAIRS GROUP LLC—See O2 Investment Partners, LLC; *U.S. Private*, pg. 2982
CJS PLV; *Int'l*, pg. 1634
CLEAR CHANNEL FRANCE SA—See Clear Channel Outdoor Holdings, Inc.; *U.S. Public*, pg. 1096
CLEAR CHANNEL HILLENAAR BV—See iHeartMedia, Inc.; *U.S. Public*, pg. 1096
CLEAR CHANNEL LATVIA—See iHeartMedia, Inc.; *U.S. Public*, pg. 1096
CLEAR CHANNEL NORWAY AS—See iHeartMedia, Inc.; *U.S. Public*, pg. 1096
CLEAR CHANNEL OUTDOOR MEXICO, OPERACIONES SA DE CV—See iHeartMedia, Inc.; *U.S. Public*, pg. 1096
CLEAR CHANNEL SVERIGE AB—See iHeartMedia, Inc.; *U.S. Public*, pg. 1096
CLEAR MEDIA LIMITED; *Int'l*, pg. 1656
COALMARCH PRODUCTIONS LLC; *U.S. Private*, pg. 954
COMCAST SPOTLIGHT—See Comcast Corporation; *U.S. Public*, pg. 537
COME AND STAY S.A.; *Int'l*, pg. 1709
CONCENTRIC PARTNERS LLC—See Accenture plc; *Int'l*, pg. 87
CONTINENTAL PREMIUM CORPORATION; *U.S. Private*, pg. 1030
COVARIO CHINA—See Covario, Inc.; *U.S. Private*, pg. 1071
COVARIO EUROPE—See Covario, Inc.; *U.S. Private*, pg. 1071
COVARIO, INC.; *U.S. Private*, pg. 1071
COVARIO JAPAN—See Covario, Inc.; *U.S. Private*, pg. 1071
COVARIO SINGAPORE—See Covario, Inc.; *U.S. Private*, pg. 1071
CRAFTSMEN INDUSTRIES, INC.; *U.S. Private*, pg. 1082
CREATIVE GENIUS, INC.—See Vera Bradley, Inc.; *U.S. Public*, pg. 2279
CREATIVE PRODUCTIONS; *U.S. Private*, pg. 1090

541890 — OTHER SERVICES RELA...

CREATIVE SOLUTIONS GROUP, INC.; *U.S. Private*, pg. 1090
CREATIVE VISION ALLIANCE CORP.; *U.S. Private*, pg. 1090
CRITEO S.A.; *Int'l*, pg. 1850
CROWN EQUITY HOLDINGS INC.; *U.S. Public*, pg. 597
CYBERAGENT, INC.; *Int'l*, pg. 1892
DAI NIPPON PRINTING CO. (AUSTRALIA) PTY. LTD.—See Dai Nippon Printing Co., Ltd.; *Int'l*, pg. 1915
DAI NIPPON PRINTING (EUROPA) GMBH—See Dai Nippon Printing Co., Ltd.; *Int'l*, pg. 1915
DARK BLUE SEA LIMITED—See Enero Group Limited; *Int'l*, pg. 2423
DCODR DIGITAL AGENCY; *Int'l*, pg. 1992
DEALER FUSION, INC.—See Flick Fusion LLC; *U.S. Private*, pg. 1544
DENA CO., LTD.; *Int'l*, pg. 2026
DENTSU 24/7 SEARCH HOLDINGS B.V.—See Dentsu Group Inc.; *Int'l*, pg. 2036
DENTSU AD-GEAR INC.—See Dentsu Group Inc.; *Int'l*, pg. 2034
DENTSUBOS - ANTIBODY HEALTHCARE COMMUNICATIONS DIVISION—See Dentsu Group Inc.; *Int'l*, pg. 2036
DENTSU CASTING AND ENTERTAINMENT INC.—See Dentsu Group Inc.; *Int'l*, pg. 2034
DENTSU CREATIVE FORCE INC.—See Dentsu Group Inc.; *Int'l*, pg. 2034
DENTSU ISOBAR, INC.—See Dentsu Group Inc.; *Int'l*, pg. 2034
DENTSU MEDIA HONG KONG LTD.—See Dentsu Group Inc.; *Int'l*, pg. 2037
DENTSU TABLE MEDIA COMMUNICATIONS INC—See Dentsu Group Inc.; *Int'l*, pg. 2038
DESIGN HOTELS AG—See Marriott International, Inc.; *U.S. Public*, pg. 1371
DIDIT.COM, INC.; *U.S. Private*, pg. 1227
DIGITAL PLUS INC.; *Int'l*, pg. 2123
DIGITOUCH S.P.A.; *Int'l*, pg. 2124
DIRECT ONLINE MARKETING, LLC; *U.S. Private*, pg. 1235
DIRECT PARTNER SOLUTIONS, INC.; *U.S. Private*, pg. 1235
DISCOUNTMUGS.COM—See BEL USA LLC; *U.S. Private*, pg. 516
DK ADVERTISING (HK) LTD.—See Bain Capital, LP; *U.S. Private*, pg. 428
DMC SRL—See Fullsix S.p.A.; *Int'l*, pg. 2843
DNP (SINGAPORE) PTE. LTD.—See Dai Nippon Printing Co., Ltd.; *Int'l*, pg. 1914
DNP (UK) CO. LTD.—See Dai Nippon Printing Co., Ltd.; *Int'l*, pg. 1914
DOGTIME MEDIA, INC.—See Evolve Media, LLC; *U.S. Private*, pg. 1443
DOLPHIN ENTERTAINMENT, INC.; *U.S. Public*, pg. 672
DOMINION ENERGY HOLDINGS, INC.—See Dominion Energy, Inc.; *U.S. Public*, pg. 673
DOTDIGITAL GROUP PLC; *Int'l*, pg. 2180
DSNR MEDIA GROUP; *Int'l*, pg. 2210
DYOMO CORPORATION—See Brightcom Group Ltd.; *Int'l*, pg. 1162
ECAMPUSCASH INC.; *U.S. Private*, pg. 1326
ECHOMAIL, INC.; *U.S. Private*, pg. 1327
ECOM PRODUCTS GROUP CORPORATION; *U.S. Public*, pg. 717
ECOMSYSTEMS, INC.; *U.S. Private*, pg. 1329
EDENRED PTE LIMITED—See Edenred S.A.; *Int'l*, pg. 2308
EEI GLOBAL, INC.; *U.S. Private*, pg. 1343
ELSINORE SERVICES, INC.; *U.S. Private*, pg. 1377
E-MACHITOWN CO., LTD.—See Hikari Tsushin, Inc.; *Int'l*, pg. 3390
EMAILERI OY—See Enento Group Plc; *Int'l*, pg. 2415
ENEIGHBORHOODS INC.—See Irish Times; *U.S. Private*, pg. 2138
EPHRICON WEB MARKETING LLC; *U.S. Private*, pg. 1412
EPIC SEATS, INC.; *U.S. Private*, pg. 1412
ESCALATE MEDIA, L.P.—See H.I.G. Capital, LLC; *U.S. Private*, pg. 1829
EUROPLAKAT YUGOSLAVIA D.O.O.—See APG/SGA SA; *Int'l*, pg. 513
EVOLVE MEDIA, LLC; *U.S. Private*, pg. 1443
EXHIBIT WORKS INC.; *U.S. Private*, pg. 1448
EXTRACTABLE, INC.; *U.S. Private*, pg. 1452
EXTREME REACH, INC.; *U.S. Private*, pg. 1452
EZANGA.COM, INC.; *U.S. Private*, pg. 1454
FERN EXPOSITION SERVICES LLC—See MSouth Equity Partners, LLC; *U.S. Private*, pg. 2808
FFW—See ICTA AB; *Int'l*, pg. 3587
FFW—See ICTA AB; *Int'l*, pg. 3587
FIGARO CLASSIFIEDS S.A.—See Groupe Industriel Marcel Dassault S.A.; *Int'l*, pg. 3105
FIKSU, INC.—See Clickdealer Asia Pte Ltd.; *Int'l*, pg. 1658
FINDOLOGY INTERACTIVE MEDIA—See Enero Group Limited; *Int'l*, pg. 2424
FINE PROMOTIONS, INC.; *U.S. Private*, pg. 1509
FITZMARTIN INC.; *U.S. Private*, pg. 1536
FLICK FUSION LLC; *U.S. Private*, pg. 1544
FLYTXT; *Int'l*, pg. 2716
FOCUS UNIVERSAL INC.; *U.S. Private*, pg. 862

FREEMANXP—See Freeman Decorating Co.; *U.S. Private*, pg. 1605
FREESTYLE MARKETING, LLC—See Touchstone Merchandise Group, LLC; *U.S. Private*, pg. 4193
FRINGE81 CO., LTD.; *Int'l*, pg. 2793
FYBER GMBH—See Digital Turbine, Inc.; *U.S. Public*, pg. 664
GALAXY MARKETING SOLUTIONS LLC; *U.S. Private*, pg. 1636
GENIS PRODUCTIONS, INC.; *U.S. Private*, pg. 1671
GENOME, INC.—See Apollo Global Management, Inc.; *U.S. Public*, pg. 167
GETTY IMAGES FRANCE—See CC Capital Partners, LLC; *U.S. Private*, pg. 797
GETTY IMAGES PTY. LTD.—See CC Capital Partners, LLC; *U.S. Private*, pg. 797
GETTY IMAGES (UK) LIMITED—See CC Capital Partners, LLC; *U.S. Private*, pg. 797
GIFA, INC.; *U.S. Public*, pg. 936
G+J ELECTRONIC MEDIA SALES GMBH—See Bertelsmann SE & Co. KGaA; *Int'l*, pg. 992
GLADIFI; *U.S. Private*, pg. 1704
GLADSON INTERACTIVE, LLC; *U.S. Private*, pg. 1705
GLIMMER, INC.; *U.S. Private*, pg. 1711
GLOBAL EXPERIENCE SPECIALISTS, INC.—See Viad Corp.; *U.S. Public*, pg. 2291
GMO AD PARTNERS INC.—See GMO Internet Group, Inc.; *Int'l*, pg. 3013
GMO TECH, INC.—See GMO Internet Group, Inc.; *Int'l*, pg. 3014
GOLF COURSE MEDIA NETWORK; *U.S. Private*, pg. 1735
GOMEEKI PTY LTD.; *Int'l*, pg. 3037
GREENLIGHT; *Int'l*, pg. 3075
GROUP DELPHI, INC.; *U.S. Private*, pg. 1793
GROUPON INC.; *U.S. Public*, pg. 972
GSG DESIGN; *U.S. Private*, pg. 1800
GUPPY MEDIA INC; *U.S. Private*, pg. 1819
HALO BRANDED SOLUTIONS, INC.—See TPG Capital, L.P.; *U.S. Public*, pg. 2176
HEARST INTEGRATED MEDIA—See The Hearst Corporation; *U.S. Private*, pg. 4046
HI-MEDIA DEUTSCHLAND AG—See AdUX SA; *Int'l*, pg. 155
HI-MEDIA NEDERLAND BV—See AdUX SA; *Int'l*, pg. 155
HIT PROMOTIONAL PRODUCTS INC.; *U.S. Private*, pg. 1952
HOKKAIDO AJINOMOTO CO., INC.—See Ajinomoto Company, Inc.; *Int'l*, pg. 257
HOOPLAH INC.; *Int'l*, pg. 3472
HOTLINE PRODUCTS—See Brown & Bigelow, Inc.; *U.S. Private*, pg. 666
HUNAN EDUCATION TELEVISION MEDIA CO., LTD.—See China South Publishing & Media Group Co., Ltd.; *Int'l*, pg. 1553
ICAR ASIA LIMITED—See Carsome Sdn. Bhd.; *Int'l*, pg. 1347
ICROSSING RESTON—See The Hearst Corporation; *U.S. Private*, pg. 4049
ICTA AB; *Int'l*, pg. 3587
IEEE GLOBALSPEC, INC.—See Institute of Electrical and Electronics Engineers, Inc.; *U.S. Private*, pg. 2093
IMPACT RADIUS, INC.—See Silversmith Management, L.P.; *U.S. Private*, pg. 3664
IMPACT SALES & MARKETING SAS—See 21 Investimenti Societa' di Gestione del Risparmio S.p.A.; *Int'l*, pg. 4
IMPACT UNLIMITED GMBH—See asm Messeprofis AG; *Int'l*, pg. 626
IMPACT UNLIMITED INC.; *U.S. Private*, pg. 2048
IMPACT UNLIMITED LTDA.—See Impact Unlimited Inc.; *U.S. Private*, pg. 2048
INKHEAD PROMOTIONAL PRODUCTS—See Deluxe Corporation; *U.S. Public*, pg. 653
INKWELL GLOBAL MARKETING; *U.S. Private*, pg. 2078
INMARKET MEDIA LLC; *U.S. Private*, pg. 2079
INNERWORKINGS RUS LLC—See HH Global Group Limited; *Int'l*, pg. 3378
INTEGRACLICK, LLC; *U.S. Private*, pg. 2098
INTERPUBLIC GROUP DEUTSCHLAND GMBH—See The Interpublic Group of Companies, Inc.; *U.S. Public*, pg. 2096
INTERUPS INC.; *U.S. Public*, pg. 1158
INVENDA CORPORATION; *U.S. Private*, pg. 2131
INVIDI TECHNOLOGIES CORPORATION—See AT&T Inc.; *U.S. Public*, pg. 220
INVNT, LLC; *U.S. Private*, pg. 2133
IQVIA SOLUTIONS UK LIMITED—See IQVIA Holdings Inc.; *U.S. Public*, pg. 1169
JACK NADEL INC.; *U.S. Private*, pg. 2174
JOHN BROWN MEDIA GROUP LTD.—See Dentsu Group Inc.; *Int'l*, pg. 2037
KAESER & BLAIR INCORPORATED; *U.S. Private*, pg. 2254
KOBIE MARKETING, INC.; *U.S. Private*, pg. 2326
KOCHAVA, INC.; *U.S. Private*, pg. 2335
KOTIS DESIGN LLC; *U.S. Private*, pg. 2345
LAMAR ALLIANCE AIRPORT ADVERTISING CO.—See Lamar Advertising Company; *U.S. Public*, pg. 1290
LEBHAR-FRIEDMAN INC.; *U.S. Private*, pg. 2409

CORPORATE AFFILIATIONS

LESPAC NETWORK INC.—See Thoma Bravo, L.P.; *U.S. Private*, pg. 4154
LEVERAGE MARKETING, LLC—See Hawke Media, LLC; *U.S. Private*, pg. 1882
LEWIS ENTERPRISES; *U.S. Private*, pg. 2438
LINKAD INC.—See FreeBit Co., Ltd.; *Int'l*, pg. 2769
LIVE MARKETING, INC.; *U.S. Private*, pg. 2472
LODGING INTERACTIVE; *U.S. Private*, pg. 2479
LOGO PLUS LIMITED—See Global Strategic Group Limited; *Int'l*, pg. 3001
LOST PLANET; *U.S. Private*, pg. 2497
LOST PLANET—See Lost Planet; *U.S. Private*, pg. 2497
MAGNITE, INC.; *U.S. Public*, pg. 1354
MALCOLM GROUP INC.; *U.S. Private*, pg. 2557
MARCHEX SALES, LLC—See Marchex, Inc.; *U.S. Public*, pg. 1365
MARKET TRACK, LLC—See Vista Equity Partners, LLC; *U.S. Public*, pg. 4398
MASCUS A/S—See Alma Media Corporation; *Int'l*, pg. 362
MEDIASHIFT, INC.; *U.S. Private*, pg. 2653
MEDIUM BLUE MULTIMEDIA GROUP LLC; *U.S. Private*, pg. 2657
MILLENNIAL MEDIA LLC—See Apollo Global Management, Inc.; *U.S. Public*, pg. 167
MMG—See Omnicom Group Inc.; *U.S. Public*, pg. 1588
MOBIQUITY NETWORKS, INC.—See Mobiquity Technologies, Inc.; *U.S. Public*, pg. 1454
MOBIQUITY TECHNOLOGIES, INC.; *U.S. Public*, pg. 1454
MOJIVA INC.; *U.S. Private*, pg. 2766
MOJIVA UK LTD.—See Mojiva Inc.; *U.S. Private*, pg. 2766
MOTIVATORS INC.; *U.S. Private*, pg. 2796
MOTIVE INTERACTIVE INC.; *U.S. Private*, pg. 2796
MP DISPLAYS, LLC; *U.S. Private*, pg. 2803
MSP MEDIEN-SERVICE UND PROMOTION GMBH—See Bertelsmann SE & Co. KGaA; *Int'l*, pg. 993
MTV PUBBLICITA S.R.L.—See National Amusements, Inc.; *U.S. Private*, pg. 2842
NATIONAL CINEMEDIA, INC.; *U.S. Public*, pg. 1494
NATIONAL PREMIUM, INC.; *U.S. Private*, pg. 2861
NCM FATHOM—See National CineMedia, Inc.; *U.S. Public*, pg. 1494
NDS SWEDEN—See Cisco Systems, Inc.; *U.S. Public*, pg. 499
NETT SOLUTIONS INC.; *U.S. Private*, pg. 2888
NEWS AMERICA MARKETING IN-STORE SERVICES L.L.C.—See Charlesbank Capital Partners, LLC; *U.S. Private*, pg. 854
NEWS AMERICA MARKETING INTERACTIVE L.L.C.—See Charlesbank Capital Partners, LLC; *U.S. Private*, pg. 854
NZME ONLINE LIMITED—See ARN Media Limited; *Int'l*, pg. 576
OATH (AMERICAS) INC.—See Apollo Global Management, Inc.; *U.S. Public*, pg. 167
ONE TECHNOLOGIES, LTD.; *U.S. Private*, pg. 3024
OPPSOURCE INC.; *U.S. Private*, pg. 3033
OXAMEDIA CORPORATION; *U.S. Private*, pg. 3056
PAEDAE, INC.; *U.S. Private*, pg. 3074
PAID, INC.; *U.S. Public*, pg. 1634
PANELES NAPSA, S.A.—See Clear Channel Outdoor Holdings, Inc.; *U.S. Public*, pg. 512
PEP PRINTING, INC.; *U.S. Private*, pg. 3143
PERFORMANCE AWARDS INC.—See ITAGroup, Inc.; *U.S. Private*, pg. 2148
PETER E. KLEINE CO.—See American Solutions for Business; *U.S. Private*, pg. 254
PHYSICIANS INTERACTIVE INC.—See KKR & Co. Inc.; *U.S. Public*, pg. 1253
PIPELINE PACKAGING CORPORATION—See Cleveland Steel Container Corporation; *U.S. Private*, pg. 941
POINTCLEAR, LLC; *U.S. Private*, pg. 3222
PORTENT, INC.—See Creadev SAS; *Int'l*, pg. 1831
POSITION RESEARCH—See Etica Entertainment Inc.; *U.S. Private*, pg. 1432
POWER DIRECT; *U.S. Private*, pg. 3237
PRECISION DIALOGUE MARKETING, LLC—See Chatham Asset Management, LLC; *U.S. Private*, pg. 864
PRECISION FOR VALUE - NEW JERSEY—See Precision Medicine Group, Inc.; *U.S. Private*, pg. 3245
PRIZELOGIC, LLC—See Marlin Equity Partners, LLC; *U.S. Private*, pg. 2584
PRODEGE, LLC—See Great Hill Partners, L.P.; *U.S. Private*, pg. 1763
PROFF AB—See Enento Group Plc; *Int'l*, pg. 2415
PROFF APS—See Enento Group Plc; *Int'l*, pg. 2415
PROFROMGO INTERNET MARKETING, LLC; *U.S. Private*, pg. 3277
PROGRESSIVE PROMOTIONS, INC.—See Consolidated Marketing Services, Inc. of MA; *U.S. Private*, pg. 1021
PROSPECTSPLUS!, INC.; *U.S. Private*, pg. 3288
PT INOVATIF SINERGI INTERNATIONAL—See I Synergy Group Limited; *Int'l*, pg. 3562
PURCH GROUP, INC.; *U.S. Private*, pg. 3305
PURE RED CREATIVE—See GA Communications Inc.; *U.S. Private*, pg. 1632
PURO.EARTH OY—See Nasdaq, Inc.; *U.S. Public*, pg. 1492
QUOTIENT TECHNOLOGY INC.—See Charlesbank Capital Partners, LLC; *U.S. Private*, pg. 855

N.A.I.C.S. INDEX

541910 — MARKETING RESEARCH ...

RABBIT DIGITAL GROUP CO., LTD.—See AOI TYO Holdings Inc.; *Int'l*, pg. 488
RANDALL-REILLY, LLC—See Aurora Capital Group, LLC; *U.S. Private*, pg. 394
RAUEN INCORPORATED; *U.S. Private*, pg. 3357
RD&F ADVERTISING, INC.—See Quad/Graphics, Inc.; *U.S. Public*, pg. 1744
REACHLOCAL AUSTRALIA PTY LTD—See Gannett Co., Inc.; *U.S. Public*, pg. 899
REACHLOCAL, INC.—See Gannett Co., Inc.; *U.S. Public*, pg. 899
REACH MARKETING LLC; *U.S. Private*, pg. 3365
READER'S DIGEST SALES & SERVICES, INC.—See RDA Holding Co.; *U.S. Private*, pg. 3363
READER'S DIGEST SALES & SERVICES, INC.—See RDA Holding Co.; *U.S. Private*, pg. 3363
RE-AD MARKETING INC.; *U.S. Private*, pg. 3364
RECOMMERCE HOLDINGS, LLC; *U.S. Private*, pg. 3371
RELEVATE HEALTH, LLC—See Mountaingate Capital Management, L.P.; *U.S. Private*, pg. 2801
RETAILMENOT, FRANCE, SAS—See MacAndrews & Forbes Incorporated; *U.S. Private*, pg. 2532
RETAILMENOT, INC.—See MacAndrews & Forbes Incorporated; *U.S. Private*, pg. 2532
RETAILMENOT UK LTD.—See MacAndrews & Forbes Incorporated; *U.S. Private*, pg. 2532
RETAIL RADIO; *U.S. Private*, pg. 3411
REVENUEADS—See LeadVision Media, LLC; *U.S. Private*, pg. 2407
RMG NETWORKS, INC.—See RMG Networks Holding Corporation; *U.S. Private*, pg. 3451
ROCTEC GLOBAL PUBLIC COMPANY LIMITED—See BTS Group Holdings Public Company Limited; *Int'l*, pg. 1206
SALEM WEB NETWORK, LLC—See Salem Media Group, Inc.; *U.S. Public*, pg. 1836
SAVEAROUND; *U.S. Private*, pg. 3556
SAY MEDIA, INC.—See The Arena Group Holdings, Inc; *U.S. Public*, pg. 2035
SCREENTONIC S.A.—See Microsoft Corporation; *U.S. Public*, pg. 1441
SCREENVISION CINEMA NETWORK LLC—See ABRY Partners, LLC; *U.S. Private*, pg. 43
SENSIS PTY. LTD.—See Thryv Holdings, Inc.; *U.S. Public*, pg. 2157
SEO INC.; *U.S. Private*, pg. 3611
THE SHADOWLIGHT GROUP, LTD—See TC Studios, LLC; *U.S. Private*, pg. 3942
SHAREASALE.COM, INC.—See Axel Springer SE; *Int'l*, pg. 765
SHECKY'S MARKETING; *U.S. Private*, pg. 3629
SHOP EAT LIVE, INC.; *U.S. Private*, pg. 3640
SHOPLOCAL, LLC—See Liquidus Marketing, Inc.; *U.S. Private*, pg. 2466
SINNERSCHRADER CONTENT GMBH—See Accenture plc; *Int'l*, pg. 88
SITOUR ITALIA S.R.L.—See Feratel Media Technologies AG; *Int'l*, pg. 2635
SITOUR MARKETING GMBH—See Feratel Media Technologies AG; *Int'l*, pg. 2635
SITOUR SPOL. S R.O.—See Feratel Media Technologies AG; *Int'l*, pg. 2635
SITOUR USA—See Feratel Media Technologies AG; *Int'l*, pg. 2635
SIZMEK DSP, INC.—See Zeta Interactive Corporation; *U.S. Private*, pg. 4603
SIZMEK TECHNOLOGIES K.K.—See Vector Capital Management, L.P.; *U.S. Private*, pg. 4353
SKY MEDIA GMBH—See Comcast Corporation; *U.S. Public*, pg. 541
SMAATO INC.—See FS Development Investment Holdings; *Int'l*, pg. 2797
SNC TRAVAUX PUBLICS DE PROVENCE—See Eiffage S.A.; *Int'l*, pg. 2331
SOCIAL MEDIA VENTURES, INC.; *U.S. Private*, pg. 3703
SOCI, INC.; *U.S. Private*, pg. 3702
SOCIUS MARKETING INC.; *U.S. Private*, pg. 3704
SOLOVIS, INC.—See Nasdaq, Inc.; *U.S. Public*, pg. 1492
SOMETHING UNIQUE, INC.—See Rauen Incorporated; *U.S. Private*, pg. 3357
SOUND MARKETING CONCEPTS OF CT LLC—See The Jordan Company, L.P.; *U.S. Private*, pg. 4062
SPAFINDER WELLNESS UK, LTD.—See SpaFinder, Inc.; *U.S. Private*, pg. 3744
SPECIAL T'S, INC.; *U.S. Private*, pg. 3748
SPECTRIO, LLC—See The Jordan Company, L.P.; *U.S. Private*, pg. 4062
SPLASH MEDIA LP; *U.S. Private*, pg. 3759
SPLENDOR DESIGN GROUP, INC.; *U.S. Private*, pg. 3759
STAPLES PROMOTIONAL PRODUCTS CANADA LTD.—See Sycamore Partners Management, LP; *U.S. Private*, pg. 3898
STAPLES PROMOTIONAL PRODUCTS—See Sycamore Partners Management, LP; *U.S. Private*, pg. 3898
STAPLES PROMOTIONAL PRODUCTS—See Sycamore Partners Management, LP; *U.S. Private*, pg. 3898
STARCO BRANDS, INC.; *U.S. Public*, pg. 1939
STAR EXHIBITS & ENVIRONMENTS, INC.; *U.S. Private*, pg. 3784

STEEL MEDIA INC.—See SRAX, Inc.; *U.S. Public*, pg. 1922
SUBSCRIBERMAIL, LLC—See MacAndrews & Forbes Incorporated; *U.S. Private*, pg. 2532
SVG MEDIA PVT. LTD.—See Dentsu Group Inc.; *Int'l*, pg. 2037
SYMPLESOFT SDN. BHD.—See Citra Nusa Holdings Berhad; *Int'l*, pg. 1626
TABOOLA.COM LTD.—See Nexstar Media Group, Inc.; *U.S. Public*, pg. 1524
TABOR COMMUNICATIONS, INC.; *U.S. Private*, pg. 3920
TAPJOY, INC.; *U.S. Private*, pg. 3932
TARGET MARKETING GROUP—See Banyan Technologies Group, LLC; *U.S. Private*, pg. 470
TELARIA, INC.—See Magnite, Inc.; *U.S. Public*, pg. 1354
TELENAV KOREA, LIMITED—See Telenav, Inc.; *U.S. Private*, pg. 3961
TERRESTRIAL RF LICENSING, INC.—See iHeartMedia, Inc.; *U.S. Public*, pg. 1096
THINKINGMAN.COM NEW MEDIA; *U.S. Private*, pg. 4144
TIANWEN DIGITAL MEDIA TECHNOLOGY (BEIJING) CO., LTD.—See China South Publishing & Media Group Co., Ltd.; *Int'l*, pg. 1553
TOM GROUP LIMITED—See CK Hutchison Holdings Limited; *Int'l*, pg. 1638
TOP BRANDS, INC.; *U.S. Private*, pg. 4186
TOUCHSTONE MERCHANDISE GROUP, LLC; *U.S. Private*, pg. 4193
THE TOWNSEND GROUP, INC.—See SmithBucklin Corporation; *U.S. Private*, pg. 3697
TRADA; *U.S. Private*, pg. 4201
TRAFFIX, INC.—See Protagenic Therapeutics, Inc.; *U.S. Public*, pg. 1729
TRIALPAY, INC.—See Visa, Inc.; *U.S. Public*, pg. 2301
TRIBUNE 365, LLC—See Tribune Publishing Company; *U.S. Private*, pg. 4228
TRI-STAGE, INC.—See Bain Capital, LP; *U.S. Private*, pg. 449
TYO INC.—See AOI TYO Holdings Inc.; *Int'l*, pg. 488
TYROO MEDIA PVT. LTD.—See Dentsu Group Inc.; *Int'l*, pg. 2038
UHSOME, LLC; *U.S. Private*, pg. 4274
UMLAUT; *U.S. Private*, pg. 4278
UNITED COMMUNICATION PARTNERS INC.; *U.S. Public*, pg. 2229
UNIVERSAL MEDIA GROUP INC.; *U.S. Public*, pg. 2262
U & U INC.—See GENDAI AGENCY INC.; *Int'l*, pg. 2917
VANTAGE MEDIA, LLC; *U.S. Private*, pg. 4345
VERIZON YELLOW PAGES—See Verizon Communications Inc.; *U.S. Public*, pg. 2286
THE VERNON COMPANY; *U.S. Private*, pg. 4130
VGI PUBLIC COMPANY LIMITED—See BTS Group Holdings Public Company Limited; *Int'l*, pg. 1205
VIACOM BRAND SOLUTIONS LIMITED—See National Amusements, Inc.; *U.S. Private*, pg. 2844
VIRURL, INC.—See Revenue.com Corporation; *U.S. Private*, pg. 3414
VISIONS PRODUCTIONS, INC.—See National Amusements, Inc.; *U.S. Private*, pg. 2844
WALKER SANDS, INC.; *U.S. Private*, pg. 4429
WATSON-CRICK INC.—See Dentsu Group Inc.; *Int'l*, pg. 2040
WEB SHOP MANAGER; *U.S. Private*, pg. 4464
WELCOME S.R.L.—See General Motors Company; *U.S. Public*, pg. 928
WENDT PRODUCTIONS, INC.; *U.S. Private*, pg. 4481
WHEREOWARE LLC; *U.S. Private*, pg. 4506
WILD CRAZE INC.; *U.S. Private*, pg. 4518
WILDFIRE INTERACTIVE, INC.—See Alphabet Inc.; *U.S. Public*, pg. 84
WOOL AND TUSK LTD.; *U.S. Private*, pg. 4561
WORLDMEDIA INTERACTIVE; *U.S. Private*, pg. 4568
WOWIO, INC.; *U.S. Public*, pg. 2383
WPROMOTE, LLC—See ZelnickMedia Corp.; *U.S. Private*, pg. 4600
XA, THE EXPERIENTIAL AGENCY, INC.; *U.S. Private*, pg. 4579
XAVIER CREATIVE HOUSE LLC; *U.S. Private*, pg. 4580
ZEALNET INC.—See GENDAI AGENCY INC.; *Int'l*, pg. 2917
ZUCKS INC—See CyberAgent, Inc.; *Int'l*, pg. 1892

541910 — MARKETING RESEARCH AND PUBLIC OPINION POLLING

20/20 RESEARCH INC.—See Schlesinger Group; *U.S. Private*, pg. 3565
2CV INC—See Arsenal Capital Management LP; *U.S. Private*, pg. 337
2CV LIMITED—See Arsenal Capital Management LP; *U.S. Private*, pg. 337
500 GROUP INC.—See Boxabl Inc.; *U.S. Private*, pg. 626
84.51 LLC—See The Kroger Co.; *U.S. Public*, pg. 2107
ABI RESEARCH SINGAPORE—See Allied Business Intelligence, Inc.; *U.S. Private*, pg. 185
ABI RESEARCH SWITZERLAND—See Allied Business Intelligence, Inc.; *U.S. Private*, pg. 185
ABI RESEARCH UK—See Allied Business Intelligence, Inc.; *U.S. Private*, pg. 185

ABT ASSOCIATES INC.—See Abt Associates Inc.; *U.S. Private*, pg. 45
ABT SRBI, INC.—See Abt Associates Inc.; *U.S. Private*, pg. 45
ACCESS TCA INC.; *U.S. Private*, pg. 52
ACNIELSEN AB—See Brookfield Corporation; *Int'l*, pg. 1177
ACNIELSEN AB—See Elliott Management Corporation; *U.S. Private*, pg. 1369
ACNIELSEN ARGENTINA S.A.—See Brookfield Corporation; *Int'l*, pg. 1177
ACNIELSEN ARGENTINA S.A.—See Elliott Management Corporation; *U.S. Private*, pg. 1369
ACNIELSEN CAMEROON SARL—See Brookfield Corporation; *Int'l*, pg. 1177
ACNIELSEN CAMEROON SARL—See Elliott Management Corporation; *U.S. Private*, pg. 1369
ACNIELSEN COMPANY (BELGIUM) S.A.—See Brookfield Corporation; *Int'l*, pg. 1177
ACNIELSEN COMPANY (BELGIUM) S.A.—See Elliott Management Corporation; *U.S. Private*, pg. 1370
A.C. NIELSEN COMPANY, LLC—See Brookfield Corporation; *Int'l*, pg. 1176
A.C. NIELSEN COMPANY, LLC—See Elliott Management Corporation; *U.S. Private*, pg. 1369
ACNIELSEN COMPANY LTD.—See Brookfield Corporation; *Int'l*, pg. 1177
ACNIELSEN COMPANY LTD.—See Elliott Management Corporation; *U.S. Private*, pg. 1370
ACNIELSEN COMPANY OF CANADA—See Brookfield Corporation; *Int'l*, pg. 1177
ACNIELSEN COMPANY OF CANADA—See Elliott Management Corporation; *U.S. Private*, pg. 1369
A.C. NIELSEN COMPANY, S.L.—See Brookfield Corporation; *Int'l*, pg. 1177
A.C. NIELSEN COMPANY, S.L.—See Elliott Management Corporation; *U.S. Private*, pg. 1369
ACNIELSEN CORPORATION JAPAN—See Brookfield Corporation; *Int'l*, pg. 1178
ACNIELSEN CORPORATION JAPAN—See Brookfield Corporation; *Int'l*, pg. 1178
ACNIELSEN CORPORATION JAPAN—See Elliott Management Corporation; *U.S. Private*, pg. 1370
ACNIELSEN CORPORATION JAPAN—See Elliott Management Corporation; *U.S. Private*, pg. 1370
ACNIELSEN CORPORATION—See Brookfield Corporation; *Int'l*, pg. 1176
ACNIELSEN CORPORATION—See Elliott Management Corporation; *U.S. Private*, pg. 1369
ACNIELSEN CYPRUS LIMITED—See Brookfield Corporation; *Int'l*, pg. 1177
ACNIELSEN CYPRUS LIMITED—See Elliott Management Corporation; *U.S. Private*, pg. 1369
A.C. NIELSEN DE VENEZUELA, S.A.—See Brookfield Corporation; *Int'l*, pg. 1177
A.C. NIELSEN DE VENEZUELA, S.A.—See Elliott Management Corporation; *U.S. Private*, pg. 1369
A.C. NIELSEN DO BRASIL LTDA.—See Brookfield Corporation; *Int'l*, pg. 1177
A.C. NIELSEN DO BRASIL LTDA.—See Elliott Management Corporation; *U.S. Private*, pg. 1369
ACNIELSEN ECUADOR S.A.—See Brookfield Corporation; *Int'l*, pg. 1177
ACNIELSEN ECUADOR S.A.—See Elliott Management Corporation; *U.S. Private*, pg. 1369
ACNIELSEN EUROPE—See Brookfield Corporation; *Int'l*, pg. 1177
ACNIELSEN EUROPE—See Elliott Management Corporation; *U.S. Private*, pg. 1369
A.C. NIELSEN GESELLSCHAFT M.B.H.—See Brookfield Corporation; *Int'l*, pg. 1177
A.C. NIELSEN GESELLSCHAFT M.B.H.—See Elliott Management Corporation; *U.S. Private*, pg. 1369
ACNIELSEN GHANA LIMITED—See Brookfield Corporation; *Int'l*, pg. 1177
ACNIELSEN GHANA LIMITED—See Elliott Management Corporation; *U.S. Private*, pg. 1369
A.C. NIELSEN GMBH—See Brookfield Corporation; *Int'l*, pg. 1177
A.C. NIELSEN GMBH—See Elliott Management Corporation; *U.S. Private*, pg. 1369
ACNIELSEN GROUP LIMITED—See Brookfield Corporation; *Int'l*, pg. 1178
ACNIELSEN GROUP LIMITED—See Elliott Management Corporation; *U.S. Private*, pg. 1370
ACNIELSEN KAZAKHSTAN LTD.—See Brookfield Corporation; *Int'l*, pg. 1177
ACNIELSEN KAZAKHSTAN LTD.—See Elliott Management Corporation; *U.S. Private*, pg. 1369
ACNIELSEN (KOREA) LTD.—See Brookfield Corporation; *Int'l*, pg. 1178
ACNIELSEN (KOREA) LTD.—See Elliott Management Corporation; *U.S. Private*, pg. 1370
ACNIELSEN LIMITED LIABILITY COMPANY—See Brookfield Corporation; *Int'l*, pg. 1177
ACNIELSEN LIMITED LIABILITY COMPANY—See Elliott Management Corporation; *U.S. Private*, pg. 1369
ACNIELSEN (NEDERLAND) B.V.—See Brookfield Corporation; *Int'l*, pg. 1177

541910 — MARKETING RESEARCH ...

ACNIELSEN (NEDERLAND) B.V.—See Elliott Management Corporation; *U.S. Private*, pg. 1370
ACNIELSEN NIGERIA LIMITED—See Brookfield Corporation; *Int'l*, pg. 1177
ACNIELSEN NIGERIA LIMITED—See Elliott Management Corporation; *U.S. Private*, pg. 1369
ACNIELSEN NORGE AS—See Brookfield Corporation; *Int'l*, pg. 1177
ACNIELSEN NORGE AS—See Elliott Management Corporation; *U.S. Private*, pg. 1370
ACNIELSEN (N.Z.) LTD.—See Brookfield Corporation; *Int'l*, pg. 1178
ACNIELSEN (N.Z.) LTD.—See Elliott Management Corporation; *U.S. Private*, pg. 1370
A.C. NIELSEN OF IRELAND LIMITED—See Brookfield Corporation; *Int'l*, pg. 1177
A.C. NIELSEN OF IRELAND LIMITED—See Elliott Management Corporation; *U.S. Private*, pg. 1369
A.C. NIELSEN PORTUGAL—See Brookfield Corporation; *Int'l*, pg. 1177
A.C. NIELSEN PORTUGAL—See Elliott Management Corporation; *U.S. Private*, pg. 1369
ACNIELSEN PUERTO RICO INC.—See Brookfield Corporation; *Int'l*, pg. 1177
ACNIELSEN PUERTO RICO INC.—See Elliott Management Corporation; *U.S. Private*, pg. 1369
ACNIELSEN SARL—See Brookfield Corporation; *Int'l*, pg. 1177
ACNIELSEN SARL—See Elliott Management Corporation; *U.S. Private*, pg. 1369
ACNIELSEN S.A.—See Brookfield Corporation; *Int'l*, pg. 1177
ACNIELSEN S.A.—See Brookfield Corporation; *Int'l*, pg. 1177
ACNIELSEN SA—See Brookfield Corporation; *Int'l*, pg. 1178
ACNIELSEN S.A.—See Elliott Management Corporation; *U.S. Private*, pg. 1369
ACNIELSEN S.A.—See Elliott Management Corporation; *U.S. Private*, pg. 1370
ACNIELSEN SA—See Elliott Management Corporation; *U.S. Private*, pg. 1370
A.C. NIELSEN, S. DE RL DE C.V.—See Brookfield Corporation; *Int'l*, pg. 1177
A.C. NIELSEN, S. DE RL DE C.V.—See Elliott Management Corporation; *U.S. Private*, pg. 1369
ACNIELSEN—See Brookfield Corporation; *Int'l*, pg. 1177
ACNIELSEN—See Brookfield Corporation; *Int'l*, pg. 1177
ACNIELSEN—See Elliott Management Corporation; *U.S. Private*, pg. 1369
ACNIELSEN—See Elliott Management Corporation; *U.S. Private*, pg. 1369
ACNIELSEN (TANZANIA) LTD.—See Brookfield Corporation; *Int'l*, pg. 1177
ACNIELSEN (TANZANIA) LTD.—See Elliott Management Corporation; *U.S. Private*, pg. 1369
ACNIELSEN (US), INC.—See Brookfield Corporation; *Int'l*, pg. 1176
ACNIELSEN (US), INC.—See Elliott Management Corporation; *U.S. Private*, pg. 1369
ADMOSPHERE, S.R.O.—See Brookfield Corporation; *Int'l*, pg. 1178
ADMOSPHERE, S.R.O.—See Elliott Management Corporation; *U.S. Private*, pg. 1370
AFFINNOVA FRANCE SARL—See Brookfield Corporation; *Int'l*, pg. 1178
AFFINNOVA FRANCE SARL—See Elliott Management Corporation; *U.S. Private*, pg. 1370
AGB NIELSEN, MEDIJSKE RAZISKAVE, D.O.O—See Brookfield Corporation; *Int'l*, pg. 1178
AGB NIELSEN, MEDIJSKE RAZISKAVE, D.O.O—See Elliott Management Corporation; *U.S. Private*, pg. 1370
AGB STAT IPSOS SAL—See Brookfield Corporation; *Int'l*, pg. 1178
AGB STAT IPSOS SAL—See Elliott Management Corporation; *U.S. Private*, pg. 1370
A. J. EDMOND COMPANY—See OceanSound Partners, LP; *U.S. Private*, pg. 2991
AKQURACY; *U.S. Private*, pg. 146
ALDPRO CORPORATE SERVICES SDN. BHD.—See Aldrich Resources Bhd; *Int'l*, pg. 305
ALEXA INTERNET, INC.—See Amazon.com, Inc.; *U.S. Public*, pg. 90
ALLEGIANCE, INC.; *U.S. Private*, pg. 176
ALLIED BUSINESS INTELLIGENCE, INC.; *U.S. Private*, pg. 185
ALPHASENSE USA, INC.—See AMETEK, Inc.; *U.S. Public*, pg. 120
AMSTAT CORP.—See The Hearst Corporation; *U.S. Private*, pg. 4044
AMTEC CORPORATION; *U.S. Private*, pg. 268
ANIMAL DERMATOLOGY REFERRAL CLINIC—See Percheron Investment Management LP; *U.S. Private*, pg. 3146
APACS; *Int'l*, pg. 500
A SQUARED PRODUCTIONS GROUP, INC.—See Duncan Channon; *U.S. Private*, pg. 1287
ATENEA COMUNICACION Y MECENAZGO, S.A.—See Lone Star Funds; *U.S. Private*, pg. 2485

AXIOMETRICS LLC—See Thoma Bravo, L.P.; *U.S. Private*, pg. 4152
B4UTRADE.COM, CORP.; *U.S. Private*, pg. 421
BARE INTERNATIONAL, INC.; *U.S. Private*, pg. 474
BASELINE LLC—See Brookfield Corporation; *Int'l*, pg. 1178
BASELINE LLC—See Elliott Management Corporation; *U.S. Private*, pg. 1370
BASES—See Brookfield Corporation; *Int'l*, pg. 1180
BASES—See Elliott Management Corporation; *U.S. Private*, pg. 1373
BCB COMMUNICATIONS—See Barbados Shipping & Trading Co. Ltd.; *Int'l*, pg. 858
BCD MEETINGS & EVENTS GERMANY GMBH—See BCD Holdings N.V.; *Int'l*, pg. 926
BCD MEETINGS & EVENTS SWITZERLAND AG—See BCD Holdings N.V.; *Int'l*, pg. 926
BESTMARK, INC.—See Generation Growth Capital, Inc.; *U.S. Private*, pg. 1668
BILENDI AB—See Bilendi SA; *Int'l*, pg. 1023
BILENDI A/S—See Bilendi SA; *Int'l*, pg. 1023
BILENDI GMBH—See Bilendi SA; *Int'l*, pg. 1023
BILENDI OY—See Bilendi SA; *Int'l*, pg. 1023
BIZRATE.COM; *U.S. Private*, pg. 567
BIZRATE INSIGHTS INC.—See Meredith Corporation; *U.S. Public*, pg. 1422
BRANDBANK (HUNGARY) KFT.—See Brookfield Corporation; *Int'l*, pg. 1178
BRANDBANK (HUNGARY) KFT.—See Elliott Management Corporation; *U.S. Private*, pg. 1370
BRANDBANK (IRELAND) LIMITED.—See Brookfield Corporation; *Int'l*, pg. 1178
BRANDBANK (IRELAND) LIMITED.—See Elliott Management Corporation; *U.S. Private*, pg. 1370
BRANDBANK (NETHERLANDS) B.V.—See Brookfield Corporation; *Int'l*, pg. 1178
BRANDBANK (NETHERLANDS) B.V.—See Elliott Management Corporation; *U.S. Private*, pg. 1370
BRANDBANK (POLAND) SP. Z .O.O.—See Brookfield Corporation; *Int'l*, pg. 1178
BRANDBANK (POLAND) SP. Z .O.O.—See Elliott Management Corporation; *U.S. Private*, pg. 1370
BRANDBANK (SLOVAKIA) S.R.O.—See Brookfield Corporation; *Int'l*, pg. 1178
BRANDBANK (SLOVAKIA) S.R.O.—See Elliott Management Corporation; *U.S. Private*, pg. 1370
BRAND DATA BANK INC.—See Bain Capital, LP; *U.S. Private*, pg. 442
BRIDGETOWER MEDIA, LLC—See Transom Capital Group, LLC; *U.S. Private*, pg. 4209
B/R/S GROUP INC.; *U.S. Private*, pg. 421
BURKE INC.; *U.S. Private*, pg. 688
BWG STRATEGY LLC—See Infinedi Partners LP; *U.S. Private*, pg. 2070
BZZAGENT, INC.—See Battery Ventures, L.P.; *U.S. Private*, pg. 488
CABLE TELEVISION LABORATORIES, INC.; *U.S. Private*, pg. 711
THE CENTER FOR STUDYING HEALTH SYSTEM CHANGE INC.—See Mathematica Inc.; *U.S. Private*, pg. 2610
CENTRAL FOCUS, INC.—See Aloysius, Butler & Clark Associates, Inc.; *U.S. Private*, pg. 196
CHEETAH DIGITAL—See Vector Capital Management, L.P.; *U.S. Private*, pg. 4350
CINT AUSTRALIA PTY. LTD.—See Cint Group AB; *Int'l*, pg. 1611
CINT UK LTD.—See Cint Group AB; *Int'l*, pg. 1611
CIVICSCIENCE, INC.; *U.S. Private*, pg. 908
CLARITAS, INC.—See Brookfield Corporation; *Int'l*, pg. 1180
CLARITAS, INC.—See Brookfield Corporation; *Int'l*, pg. 1180
CLARITAS, INC.—See Elliott Management Corporation; *U.S. Private*, pg. 1373
CLARITAS, INC.—See Elliott Management Corporation; *U.S. Private*, pg. 1373
CLARITAS LLC—See The Carlyle Group Inc.; *U.S. Public*, pg. 2045
COGENCY GLOBAL INC.—See Bertram Capital Management, LLC; *U.S. Private*, pg. 540
COLEMAN INSIGHTS; *U.S. Private*, pg. 967
COMMERCIAL KITCHEN PARTS & SERVICE; *U.S. Private*, pg. 984
COMMUNICORP, INC.—See Aflac Incorporated; *U.S. Public*, pg. 57
COMSCORE MEDIA METRIX, INC.—See comScore, Inc.; *U.S. Public*, pg. 562
CONFERO, INC.; *U.S. Private*, pg. 1013
CONFIRMIT ASA—See EQT AB; *Int'l*, pg. 2475
CONSTRUCTION MONITOR LLC—See Byggfakta Group Nordic HoldCo AB; *Int'l*, pg. 1234
CORNERSTONE BUSINESS SERVICES, INC.—See Pacific Avenue Capital Partners, LLC; *U.S. Private*, pg. 3065
CORPORATE DOCUMENT SOLUTIONS, INC.; *U.S. Private*, pg. 1054
CORPORATE RESEARCH INTERNATIONAL; *U.S. Private*, pg. 1055
COTTERWEB ENTERPRISES, INC.—See Great Hill Partners, L.P.; *U.S. Private*, pg. 1763

CREDITSIGHTS, INC.—See The Hearst Corporation; *U.S. Private*, pg. 4044
CRISIL IREVNA INFORMATION TECHNOLOGY (HANGZHOU) COMPANY LTD.—See S&P Global Inc.; *U.S. Public*, pg. 1830
CRITICAL MASS MEDIA, INC.—See iHeartMedia, Inc.; *U.S. Public*, pg. 1096
CRM METRIX, INC.; *U.S. Private*, pg. 1102
CROSSIX SOLUTIONS INC.—See Veeva Systems, Inc.; *U.S. Public*, pg. 2277
CROSS MARKETING ASIA PTE. LTD.—See Cross Marketing Group Inc.; *Int'l*, pg. 1856
CROSS MARKETING INC.—See Cross Marketing Group Inc.; *Int'l*, pg. 1856
CROSS PROPWORKS INC.—See Cross Marketing Group Inc.; *Int'l*, pg. 1856
C&R RESEARCH, INC.; *U.S. Private*, pg. 703
CUNNINGHAM FIELD & RESEARCH SERVICE; *U.S. Private*, pg. 1123
DAIWA HOUSE EUROPE B.V.—See Daiwa House Industry Co., Ltd.; *Int'l*, pg. 1945
DATA LOCATOR GROUP LIMITED—See DM plc; *Int'l*, pg. 2142
DBS BANK-LONDON BRANCH—See DBS Group Holdings Ltd.; *Int'l*, pg. 1988
DECISION RESOURCES, LLC—See Clarivate PLC; *Int'l*, pg. 1649
DENTSU MARKETING EAST ASIA INC.—See Dentsu Group Inc.; *Int'l*, pg. 2038
DEUTSCHE POST DHL RESEARCH AND INNOVATION GMBH—See Deutsche Post AG; *Int'l*, pg. 2079
DEYTA LLC; *U.S. Private*, pg. 1220
DI ASIA INC.—See Dream Incubator Inc.; *Int'l*, pg. 2202
DIGITAL ONLINE MEDIA GMBH; *Int'l*, pg. 2123
D. K. SHIFFLET & ASSOCIATES, LTD.—See EagleTree Capital, LP; *U.S. Private*, pg. 1311
D&M, INC.—See Cross Marketing Group Inc.; *Int'l*, pg. 1856
DPRA INCORPORATED; *U.S. Private*, pg. 1271
DYNATA, LLC - LEHI—See Court Square Capital Partners, L.P.; *U.S. Private*, pg. 1069
DYNATA, LLC—See Court Square Capital Partners, L.P.; *U.S. Private*, pg. 1069
EASTERN RESEARCH SERVICES INC.; *U.S. Private*, pg. 1321
EASTLAN RESOURCES LLC; *U.S. Private*, pg. 1322
EBIQUITY ASSOCIATES LIMITED—See Brookfield Corporation; *Int'l*, pg. 1179
EBIQUITY ASSOCIATES LIMITED—See Elliott Management Corporation; *U.S. Private*, pg. 1372
EBIQUITY PLC; *Int'l*, pg. 2285
EC RESEARCH CORP.—See Cross Marketing Group Inc.; *Int'l*, pg. 1856
EDISON MEDIA RESEARCH; *U.S. Private*, pg. 1336
EDLP MARKETING, LDA.—See Edel SE & Co. KGaA; *Int'l*, pg. 2305
ELDER RESEARCH INC.; *U.S. Private*, pg. 1351
ELECPRO USA INC.—See DEA General Aviation Holding Co., Ltd.; *Int'l*, pg. 1997
EMARKETER INC.—See Axel Springer SE; *Int'l*, pg. 766
EMEDIA COMMUNICATIONS, LLC—See Ziff Davis, Inc.; *U.S. Public*, pg. 2404
ENCIMA GLOBAL LLC—See Strategas Research Partners, LLC; *U.S. Private*, pg. 3834
ENVIROSELL INC.—See Cross Marketing Group Inc.; *Int'l*, pg. 1856
E-POLL MARKET RESEARCH; *U.S. Private*, pg. 1302
E-REWARDS, INC.; *U.S. Private*, pg. 1302
ESCALENT, INC.—See Symphony Technology Group, LLC; *U.S. Private*, pg. 3900
ESHA MEDIA RESEARCH LIMITED; *Int'l*, pg. 2503
EUROFINS MARKETING RESEARCH SAS—See Eurofins Scientific S.E.; *Int'l*, pg. 2543
EU YAN SANG MARKETING PTE LTD—See Eu Yan Sang International Ltd.; *Int'l*, pg. 2525
EVIDERA MARKET ACCESS LIMITED—See Thermo Fisher Scientific Inc.; *U.S. Public*, pg. 2150
EXEVO INDIA PRIVATE LTD.—See Moody's Corporation; *U.S. Public*, pg. 1467
EXHIBIT SURVEYS, INC.—See Freeman Decorating Co.; *U.S. Private*, pg. 1605
EXPERIAN SIMMONS—See Symphony Technology Group, LLC; *U.S. Private*, pg. 3900
FACTSET RESEARCH SYSTEMS INC. - CONTENT COLLECTION—See FactSet Research Systems Inc.; *U.S. Public*, pg. 820
FACTUM INVENIO—See Bain Capital, LP; *U.S. Private*, pg. 447
FIRST MARKET RESEARCH CORP.; *U.S. Private*, pg. 1521
FIZZIOLOGY LLC—See Kohlberg & Company, LLC; *U.S. Private*, pg. 2338
FLASPOHLER RESEARCH GROUP, INC; *U.S. Private*, pg. 1540
FORESEE RESULTS, INC.—See Verint Systems Inc.; *U.S. Public*, pg. 2281
FORRESTER MARKET ADVISORY (BEIJING) CO., LTD.—See Forrester Research, Inc; *U.S. Public*, pg. 868
FORRESTER RESEARCH, INC.; *U.S. Public*, pg. 868

N.A.I.C.S. INDEX

541910 — MARKETING RESEARCH ...

FORRESTER RESEARCH SAS—See Forrester Research, Inc.; *U.S. Public*, pg. 868
FORS MARSH GROUP LLC.; *U.S. Private*, pg. 1572
FOSTER ASSOCIATES, INC.; *U.S. Private*, pg. 1578
FRANK N. MAGID ASSOCIATES, INC.; *U.S. Private*, pg. 1595
THE FREEDONIA GROUP, INC.—See MarketResearch.com; *U.S. Private*, pg. 2581
FULCRUM ANALYTICS, INC.; *U.S. Private*, pg. 1620
FULCRUM RESEARCH GROUP, LLC; *U.S. Private*, pg. 1620
FULD & COMPANY, INC.; *U.S. Private*, pg. 1620
THE FUTURES COMPANY—See Bain Capital, LP; *U.S. Private*, pg. 448
THE GALLUP ORGANIZATION-PRINCETON—See The Gallup Organization; *U.S. Private*, pg. 4031
THE GALLUP ORGANIZATION; *U.S. Private*, pg. 4031
GAP FISH GMBH—See Cint Group AB; *Int'l*, pg. 1611
GARTNER BEIJING—See Gartner, Inc.; *U.S. Public*, pg. 907
GARTNER FINLAND OY—See Gartner, Inc.; *U.S. Public*, pg. 907
GARTNER HONG KONG, LIMITED—See Gartner, Inc.; *U.S. Public*, pg. 907
GARTNER JAPAN LTD.—See Gartner, Inc.; *U.S. Public*, pg. 907
GARTNER POLAND SP Z.O.O—See Gartner, Inc.; *U.S. Public*, pg. 907
GARTNER RUS LLC—See Gartner, Inc.; *U.S. Public*, pg. 907
GARTNER SAUDI ARABIA LTD—See Gartner, Inc.; *U.S. Public*, pg. 907
GARTNER TURKEY TEKNOLOJI ARASTIRMA VE DANISMANLIK HIZMETLERI LIMITED SIRKETI—See Gartner, Inc.; *U.S. Public*, pg. 907
GARTNER U.K. LIMITED—See Gartner, Inc.; *U.S. Public*, pg. 907
GENERALPLUS TECHNOLOGY (SHENZHEN) INC.—See Generalplus Technology Inc.; *Int'l*, pg. 2920
GFK CUSTOM RESEARCH, LLC - MINNEAPOLIS—See Advent International Corporation; *U.S. Private*, pg. 105
GFK CUSTOM RESEARCH, LLC - PRINCETON—See Advent International Corporation; *U.S. Private*, pg. 105
GFK CUSTOM RESEARCH, LLC—See Advent International Corporation; *U.S. Private*, pg. 105
GFK NOP LTD.—See Advent International Corporation; *U.S. Private*, pg. 105
GFK SE—See Advent International Corporation; *U.S. Private*, pg. 105
GMO JAPAN MARKET INTELLIGENCE K.K.—See GMO Internet Group, Inc.; *Int'l*, pg. 3014
GMO RESEARCH & AI, INC.—See GMO Internet Group, Inc.; *Int'l*, pg. 3014
GONGOS RESEARCH; *U.S. Private*, pg. 1737
GRAPHISADS LIMITED; *Int'l*, pg. 3060
GRASS ROOTS SL—See P2 Capital Partners, LLC; *U.S. Private*, pg. 3061
GRASS ROOTS SL—See Silver Lake Group, LLC; *U.S. Private*, pg. 3656
GREENWICH ASSOCIATES LLC—See S&P Global Inc.; *U.S. Public*, pg. 1831
GROUP SALES DIVISON—See Family Inns of America, Inc.; *U.S. Private*, pg. 1470
HEALTHSTREAM RESEARCH—See HealthStream, Inc.; *U.S. Public*, pg. 1017
HEALTHSTREAM RESEARCH—See HealthStream, Inc.; *U.S. Public*, pg. 1017
HEDGEYE POTOMAC RESEARCH—See Hedgeye Risk Management LLC; *U.S. Private*, pg. 1903
HITACHI ZOSEN U.S.A. LTD.—See Hitachi Zosen Corporation; *Int'l*, pg. 3411
HITACHI ZOSEN U.S.A. LTD.—See Hitachi Zosen Corporation; *Int'l*, pg. 3411
HONDA R&D AMERICAS, INC.—See Honda Motor Co., Ltd.; *Int'l*, pg. 3462
HUMANCENTRIC; *U.S. Private*, pg. 2006
IBISWORLD INC.—See IBISWorld Pty Ltd; *Int'l*, pg. 3576
IBISWORLD LTD—See IBISWorld Pty Ltd; *Int'l*, pg. 3576
IBISWORLD PTY LTD; *Int'l*, pg. 3576
IBOPE ERATINGS.COM DO BRASIL LTDA.—See Brookfield Corporation; *Int'l*, pg. 1178
IBOPE ERATINGS.COM DO BRASIL LTDA.—See Elliott Management Corporation; *U.S. Private*, pg. 1371
ICC/DECISION SERVICES—See Thoma Bravo, L.P.; *U.S. Private*, pg. 4149
ICOM INFORMATION & COMMUNICATIONS L.P.—See Bread Financial Holdings Inc.; *U.S. Public*, pg. 381
ICONOCULTURE, INC.—See Gartner, Inc.; *U.S. Public*, pg. 906
ID FACTOR LIMITED—See GlobalData Plc; *Int'l*, pg. 3003
IDG COMMUNICATIONS MEDIA AG—See China Oceanwide Holdings Group Co., Ltd.; *Int'l*, pg. 1537
IDG COMMUNICATIONS MEDIA AG—See IDG Capital; *Int'l*, pg. 3594
IGNITE MEDIA SOLUTIONS LLC; *U.S. Private*, pg. 2039
IID INC.; *Int'l*, pg. 3607
IMAGITAS, INC.—See Red Ventures, LLC; *U.S. Private*, pg. 3376

IMODERATE LLC; *U.S. Private*, pg. 2047
IMPACT RECHERCHE—See Bluefocus Intelligent Communications Group Co., Ltd.; *Int'l*, pg. 1071
IMPACTRX, INC.—See IQVIA Holdings Inc.; *U.S. Public*, pg. 1169
IMRA AMERICA, INC.—See AISIN Corporation; *Int'l*, pg. 252
IMS HEALTH MARKET RESEARCH CONSULTING (SHANGHAI) CO. LTD.—See IQVIA Holdings Inc.; *U.S. Public*, pg. 1168
INDICUS ANALYTICS PRIVATE LIMITED—See Brookfield Corporation; *Int'l*, pg. 1179
INDICUS ANALYTICS PRIVATE LIMITED—See Elliott Management Corporation; *U.S. Private*, pg. 1371
INFORMATION RESOURCES, INC.—See Hellman & Friedman LLC; *U.S. Private*, pg. 1910
INFORMZ, LLC—See Higher Logic, LLC; *U.S. Private*, pg. 1937
INFOSURV, INC.; *U.S. Private*, pg. 2074
INFOTRIEVE INC.; *U.S. Private*, pg. 2074
INKTEL CHICAGO—See Inktel Direct Inc.; *U.S. Private*, pg. 2078
INNERSCOPE RESEARCH, INC.—See Brookfield Corporation; *Int'l*, pg. 1179
INNERSCOPE RESEARCH, INC.—See Elliott Management Corporation; *U.S. Private*, pg. 1371
INSIGHT TECH INC.—See en-japan Inc.; *Int'l*, pg. 2395
INTEGRATED MARKETING SYSTEMS, INC.—See Symphony Technology Group, LLC; *U.S. Private*, pg. 3900
INTELLIGENT OPTICAL SYSTEMS—See Mercury Systems, Inc.; *U.S. Public*, pg. 1422
INTELLIGENT RESULTS, INC.—See Fiserv, Inc.; *U.S. Public*, pg. 851
INTERACTIONS CONSUMER EXPERIENCE MARKETING INC.—See Bain Capital, LP; *U.S. Private*, pg. 439
INTERFACE IN DESIGN, INC.—See IID Inc.; *Int'l*, pg. 3607
INTERNATIONAL DATA CORPORATION (CANADA) LTD—See China Oceanwide Holdings Group Co., Ltd.; *Int'l*, pg. 1538
INTERNATIONAL DATA CORPORATION (CANADA) LTD—See IDG Capital; *Int'l*, pg. 3594
INTERNET SPORTS MARKETING LIMITED—See AsianLogic Limited; *Int'l*, pg. 620
INTER-PACIFIC RESEARCH SDN BHD—See Berjaya Corporation Berhad; *Int'l*, pg. 982
INTERVIEWING SERVICE OF AMERICA; *U.S. Private*, pg. 2128
INVOKE SOLUTIONS, INC.—See Kohlberg & Company, LLC; *U.S. Private*, pg. 2338
IRONTRAFFIC.COM; *U.S. Private*, pg. 2140
ISSUES & ANSWERS NETWORK, INC.—See Beyond Commerce, Inc.; *U.S. Public*, pg. 327
ITT INDUSTRIES INC.—See ITT Inc.; *U.S. Public*, pg. 1178
JACKSON ADEPT RESEARCH—See Jackson Associates, Inc.; *U.S. Private*, pg. 2175
THE JAMES MADISON INSTITUTE; *U.S. Private*, pg. 4058
J.D. POWER—See Thoma Bravo, L.P.; *U.S. Private*, pg. 4148
JG BLACK BOOK OF TRAVEL; *U.S. Private*, pg. 2206
JOAN PEARCE RESEARCH ASSOCIATES; *U.S. Private*, pg. 2217
JOHN BURNS REAL ESTATE CONSULTING, INC.; *U.S. Private*, pg. 2220
J. RECKNER ASSOCIATES INC.; *U.S. Private*, pg. 2157
JUPITER MR SOLUTIONS CO., LTD.—See Cross Marketing Group Inc.; *Int'l*, pg. 1856
KADENCE INTERNATIONAL BUSINESS RESEARCH PTE. LTD.—See Cross Marketing Group Inc.; *Int'l*, pg. 1856
KADENCE INTERNATIONAL INC.—See Cross Marketing Group Inc.; *Int'l*, pg. 1856
KADENCE INTERNATIONAL LIMITED—See Cross Marketing Group Inc.; *Int'l*, pg. 1856
KADENCE INTERNATIONAL LTD.—See Cross Marketing Group Inc.; *Int'l*, pg. 1856
KADENCE INTERNATIONAL PVT., LTD.—See Cross Marketing Group Inc.; *Int'l*, pg. 1856
KADENCE INTERNATIONAL (THAILAND) CO., LTD.—See Cross Marketing Group Inc.; *Int'l*, pg. 1856
KANTAR DEUTSCHLAND GMBH—See Bain Capital, LP; *U.S. Private*, pg. 447
THE KANTAR GROUP LIMITED—See Bain Capital, LP; *U.S. Private*, pg. 447
KANTAR IBOPE MEDIA—See Bain Capital, LP; *U.S. Private*, pg. 448
KANTAR MEDIA—See Bain Capital, LP; *U.S. Private*, pg. 448
KANTAR WORLDPANEL—See Bain Capital, LP; *U.S. Private*, pg. 447
KNOWLEDGE NETWORKS, INC.—See Advent International Corporation; *U.S. Private*, pg. 105
THE LEADING EDGE MARKET RESEARCH CONSULTANTS PTY LIMITED—See Enero Group Limited; *Int'l*, pg. 2424
LEO J. SHAPIRO & ASSOCIATES, LLC; *U.S. Private*, pg. 2422
LOUIS HARRIS FRANCE SA—See Bain Capital, LP; *U.S. Private*, pg. 448
LUTH RESEARCH, LLC; *U.S. Private*, pg. 2516

MACRO INTERNATIONAL INC.—See ICF International, Inc.; *U.S. Public*, pg. 1086
MAGA DESIGN GROUP; *U.S. Private*, pg. 2545
MAGUIRE ASSOCIATES, INC.—See Carnegie Dartlet LLC; *U.S. Public*, pg. 766
MARITZ MARKETING RESEARCH, INC.—See Maritz Holdings Inc.; *U.S. Private*, pg. 2577
MARITZ RESEARCH GMBH—See Maritz Holdings Inc.; *U.S. Private*, pg. 2577
MARKELYTICS SOLUTIONS INDIA PRIVATE LIMITED—See Cross Marketing Group Inc.; *Int'l*, pg. 1856
MARKETCAST INC.—See Kohlberg & Company, LLC; *U.S. Private*, pg. 2338
MARKET DATA RETRIEVAL—See Cannae Holdings, Inc.; *U.S. Public*, pg. 430
MARKET DATA RETRIEVAL—See CC Capital Partners, LLC; *U.S. Private*, pg. 798
MARKET DATA RETRIEVAL—See Intercontinental Exchange, Inc.; *U.S. Public*, pg. 1142
MARKET ENHANCEMENT GROUP, INC.; *U.S. Private*, pg. 2579
MARKETING ANALYTICS, INC—See Brookfield Corporation; *Int'l*, pg. 1178
MARKETING ANALYTICS, INC—See Elliott Management Corporation; *U.S. Private*, pg. 1371
MARKETING WORKSHOP INC.; *U.S. Private*, pg. 2581
MARKETLAB RESEARCH, INC.—See Schlesinger Group; *U.S. Private*, pg. 3565
MARKET METRIX LLC—See Canada Pension Plan Investment Board; *Int'l*, pg. 1281
MARKET METRIX LLC—See Silver Lake Group, LLC; *U.S. Private*, pg. 3655
MARKET PROBE INC.; *U.S. Private*, pg. 2579
MASLANSKY, LUNTZ & PARTNERS—See Omnicom Group Inc.; *U.S. Public*, pg. 1588
MATERIAL HOLDINGS, LLC—See Tailwind Capital Group, LLC; *U.S. Private*, pg. 3924
MATERIAL US, INC.—See Tailwind Capital Group, LLC; *U.S. Private*, pg. 3924
MATHEMATICA INC.; *U.S. Private*, pg. 2610
MEDIA FOCUS SCHWEIZ GMBH—See Brookfield Corporation; *Int'l*, pg. 1178
MEDIA FOCUS SCHWEIZ GMBH—See Elliott Management Corporation; *U.S. Private*, pg. 1371
MEDIAKIX, LLC—See Stadiumred Group; *U.S. Private*, pg. 3774
MEDIASCORE GESELLSCHAFT FUR MEDIEN- UND KOMMUNIKATIONSFORSCHUNG MBH—See Bertelsmann SE & Co. KGaA; *Int'l*, pg. 995
MEDILEAD INC.—See Cross Marketing Group Inc.; *Int'l*, pg. 1856
MEREDITH LIST MARKETING—See Meredith Corporation; *U.S. Public*, pg. 1423
METROSTUDY, INC.—See MidOcean Partners, LLP; *U.S. Private*, pg. 2717
MILENIUM ESPACIO SOFT, S.A.—See Brookfield Corporation; *Int'l*, pg. 1178
MILENIUM ESPACIO SOFT, S.A.—See Elliott Management Corporation; *U.S. Private*, pg. 1371
MILLWARD BROWN CANADA—See Bain Capital, LP; *U.S. Private*, pg. 449
MILLWARD BROWN INC.—See Bain Capital, LP; *U.S. Private*, pg. 448
MILLWARD BROWN MARKET RESEACH SERVICES—See Bain Capital, LP; *U.S. Private*, pg. 449
MILLWARD BROWN—See Bain Capital, LP; *U.S. Private*, pg. 448
MKTG INC.; *U.S. Private*, pg. 2753
MR2 GROUP, INC.; *U.S. Private*, pg. 2805
MSD POLSKA DYSTRYBUCJA SP. Z.O.O.—See Merck & Co., Inc.; *U.S. Public*, pg. 1418
THE MSR GROUP; *U.S. Private*, pg. 4081
MUELLER DENMARK APS—See Mueller Water Products, Inc.; *U.S. Public*, pg. 1486
NATIONAL OPINION RESEARCH CENTER COLORADO; *U.S. Private*, pg. 2860
NED DAVIS RESEARCH INC.—See Astorg Partners S.A.S.; *Int'l*, pg. 656
NED DAVIS RESEARCH INC.—See Epiris Managers LLP; *Int'l*, pg. 2461
NETRATINGS FRANCE SAS—See Brookfield Corporation; *Int'l*, pg. 1179
NETRATINGS FRANCE SAS—See Elliott Management Corporation; *U.S. Private*, pg. 1371
NETRATINGS, LLC—See Brookfield Corporation; *Int'l*, pg. 1179
NETRATINGS, LLC—See Elliott Management Corporation; *U.S. Private*, pg. 1371
NEUROFOCUS, INC.—See Brookfield Corporation; *Int'l*, pg. 1179
NEUROFOCUS, INC.—See Elliott Management Corporation; *U.S. Private*, pg. 1371
THE NEW WAVE RESEARCH LTD.—See Brookfield Corporation; *Int'l*, pg. 1180
THE NEW WAVE RESEARCH LTD.—See Elliott Management Corporation; *U.S. Private*, pg. 1372
NEXIUM PORTUGAL - CONSULTARIO E SOFTWARE

N.A.I.C.S. Index

541910 — MARKETING RESEARCH ... CORPORATE AFFILIATIONS

LDA.—See Brookfield Corporation; *Int'l*, pg. 1178
NEXIUM PORTUGAL - CONSULTARIO E SOFTWARE LDA.—See Elliott Management Corporation; *U.S. Private*, pg. 1371
NEXIUM SOFTWARE FACTORY, S.L.—See Brookfield Corporation; *Int'l*, pg. 1179
NEXIUM SOFTWARE FACTORY, S.L.—See Elliott Management Corporation; *U.S. Private*, pg. 1371
NIELSEN ADMOSPHERE, A.S—See Brookfield Corporation; *Int'l*, pg. 1177
NIELSEN ADMOSPHERE, A.S—See Elliott Management Corporation; *U.S. Private*, pg. 1370
NIELSEN AUDIENCE MEASUREMENT (CYPRUS) LTD.—See Brookfield Corporation; *Int'l*, pg. 1179
NIELSEN AUDIENCE MEASUREMENT (CYPRUS) LTD.—See Elliott Management Corporation; *U.S. Private*, pg. 1371
NIELSEN AUDIENCE MEASUREMENT DOO BEOGRAD—See Brookfield Corporation; *Int'l*, pg. 1179
NIELSEN AUDIENCE MEASUREMENT DOO BEOGRAD—See Elliott Management Corporation; *U.S. Private*, pg. 1371
THE NIELSEN COMPANY - ADVISORY SERVICES—See Brookfield Corporation; *Int'l*, pg. 1180
THE NIELSEN COMPANY - ADVISORY SERVICES—See Elliott Management Corporation; *U.S. Private*, pg. 1373
THE NIELSEN COMPANY (AUSTRALIA) PTY. LTD.—See Brookfield Corporation; *Int'l*, pg. 1178
THE NIELSEN COMPANY (AUSTRALIA) PTY. LTD.—See Elliott Management Corporation; *U.S. Private*, pg. 1370
THE NIELSEN COMPANY (BANGLADESH) LTD.—See Brookfield Corporation; *Int'l*, pg. 1180
THE NIELSEN COMPANY (BANGLADESH) LTD.—See Elliott Management Corporation; *U.S. Private*, pg. 1372
THE NIELSEN COMPANY B.V.—See Brookfield Corporation; *Int'l*, pg. 1176
THE NIELSEN COMPANY B.V.—See Elliott Management Corporation; *U.S. Private*, pg. 1369
THE NIELSEN COMPANY (GREECE) S.A.—See Brookfield Corporation; *Int'l*, pg. 1180
THE NIELSEN COMPANY (GREECE) S.A.—See Elliott Management Corporation; *U.S. Private*, pg. 1372
THE NIELSEN COMPANY (ITALY) S.R.L.—See Brookfield Corporation; *Int'l*, pg. 1178
THE NIELSEN COMPANY (ITALY) S.R.L.—See Elliott Management Corporation; *U.S. Private*, pg. 1370
THE NIELSEN COMPANY JAPAN—See Brookfield Corporation; *Int'l*, pg. 1180
THE NIELSEN COMPANY JAPAN—See Elliott Management Corporation; *U.S. Private*, pg. 1373
THE NIELSEN COMPANY (MALAYSIA) SDN. BHD.—See Brookfield Corporation; *Int'l*, pg. 1180
THE NIELSEN COMPANY (MALAYSIA) SDN. BHD.—See Elliott Management Corporation; *U.S. Private*, pg. 1372
THE NIELSEN COMPANY NEPAL PVT LTD.—See Brookfield Corporation; *Int'l*, pg. 1179
THE NIELSEN COMPANY NEPAL PVT LTD.—See Elliott Management Corporation; *U.S. Private*, pg. 1371
THE NIELSEN COMPANY (PHILIPPINES), INC.—See Brookfield Corporation; *Int'l*, pg. 1180
THE NIELSEN COMPANY (PHILIPPINES), INC.—See Elliott Management Corporation; *U.S. Private*, pg. 1372
THE NIELSEN COMPANY TAIWAN LTD.—See Brookfield Corporation; *Int'l*, pg. 1178
THE NIELSEN COMPANY TAIWAN LTD.—See Elliott Management Corporation; *U.S. Private*, pg. 1370
THE NIELSEN COMPANY (US), LLC—See Brookfield Corporation; *Int'l*, pg. 1176
THE NIELSEN COMPANY (US), LLC—See Elliott Management Corporation; *U.S. Private*, pg. 1369
NIELSEN CONSULTANCY LLC—See Brookfield Corporation; *Int'l*, pg. 1179
NIELSEN CONSULTANCY LLC—See Elliott Management Corporation; *U.S. Private*, pg. 1371
NIELSEN CONSUMER INSIGHTS, INC—See Brookfield Corporation; *Int'l*, pg. 1179
NIELSEN CONSUMER INSIGHTS, INC—See Elliott Management Corporation; *U.S. Private*, pg. 1371
NIELSEN CONSUMER LLC—See Advent International Corporation; *U.S. Private*, pg. 105
NIELSEN ENTERTAINMENT, LLC—See Brookfield Corporation; *Int'l*, pg. 1179
NIELSEN ENTERTAINMENT, LLC—See Elliott Management Corporation; *U.S. Private*, pg. 1371
NIELSEN FOR CONSULTANCIES LIMITED LIABILITY COMPANY—See Brookfield Corporation; *Int'l*, pg. 1180
NIELSEN FOR CONSULTANCIES LIMITED LIABILITY COMPANY—See Elliott Management Corporation; *U.S. Private*, pg. 1372
NIELSEN IBOPE DOMINICANA, S.R.L.—See Brookfield Corporation; *Int'l*, pg. 1179
NIELSEN IBOPE DOMINICANA, S.R.L.—See Elliott Management Corporation; *U.S. Private*, pg. 1371
NIELSEN (INDIA) PRIVATE LIMITED—See Brookfield Corporation; *Int'l*, pg. 1179
NIELSEN (INDIA) PRIVATE LIMITED—See Elliott Management Corporation; *U.S. Private*, pg. 1371
NIELSEN INNOVATE LTD.—See Brookfield Corporation; *Int'l*, pg. 1179
NIELSEN INNOVATE LTD.—See Elliott Management Corporation; *U.S. Private*, pg. 1371
NIELSEN KOREA LTD.—See Brookfield Corporation; *Int'l*, pg. 1179
NIELSEN KOREA LTD.—See Elliott Management Corporation; *U.S. Private*, pg. 1371
NIELSEN KOZONSEGMERES KFT.—See Brookfield Corporation; *Int'l*, pg. 1179
NIELSEN KOZONSEGMERES KFT.—See Elliott Management Corporation; *U.S. Private*, pg. 1371
NIELSEN MEDIA RESEARCH, INC.—See Brookfield Corporation; *Int'l*, pg. 1179
NIELSEN MEDIA RESEARCH, INC.—See Elliott Management Corporation; *U.S. Private*, pg. 1371
NIELSEN MMRD (MYANMAR) CO., LTD—See Brookfield Corporation; *Int'l*, pg. 1179
NIELSEN MMRD (MYANMAR) CO., LTD—See Elliott Management Corporation; *U.S. Private*, pg. 1371
NIELSEN NATIONAL RESEARCH GROUP, INC.—See Stagwell, Inc.; *U.S. Public*, pg. 1928
THE NIELSEN NEPAL PVT. LTD.—See Brookfield Corporation; *Int'l*, pg. 1178
THE NIELSEN NEPAL PVT. LTD.—See Elliott Management Corporation; *U.S. Private*, pg. 1370
NIELSEN SCARBOROUGH—See Brookfield Corporation; *Int'l*, pg. 1179
NIELSEN SCARBOROUGH—See Elliott Management Corporation; *U.S. Private*, pg. 1372
NIELSEN SERVICES ITALY S.R.L.—See Brookfield Corporation; *Int'l*, pg. 1178
NIELSEN SERVICES ITALY S.R.L.—See Elliott Management Corporation; *U.S. Private*, pg. 1370
NIELSEN SERVICES POLAND SP. Z.O.O.—See Brookfield Corporation; *Int'l*, pg. 1179
NIELSEN SERVICES POLAND SP. Z.O.O.—See Elliott Management Corporation; *U.S. Private*, pg. 1372
NIELSEN SERVICES SPAIN, S.L.—See Brookfield Corporation; *Int'l*, pg. 1179
NIELSEN SERVICES SPAIN, S.L.—See Elliott Management Corporation; *U.S. Private*, pg. 1372
NIELSEN SERVICES SWEDEN AB—See Brookfield Corporation; *Int'l*, pg. 1177
NIELSEN SERVICES SWEDEN AB—See Elliott Management Corporation; *U.S. Private*, pg. 1370
NIELSEN SOUNDSCAN—See Brookfield Corporation; *Int'l*, pg. 1179
NIELSEN SOUNDSCAN—See Elliott Management Corporation; *U.S. Private*, pg. 1371
NIELSEN TUNISIA SARL—See Brookfield Corporation; *Int'l*, pg. 1180
NIELSEN TUNISIA SARL—See Elliott Management Corporation; *U.S. Private*, pg. 1372
NIELSEN TV AUDIENCE MEASUREMENT S.R.L.—See Brookfield Corporation; *Int'l*, pg. 1180
NIELSEN TV AUDIENCE MEASUREMENT S.R.L.—See Elliott Management Corporation; *U.S. Private*, pg. 1372
NIPO BV—See Bain Capital, LP; *U.S. Private*, pg. 447
NM INCITE, LLC—See Brookfield Corporation; *Int'l*, pg. 1178
NM INCITE, LLC—See Elliott Management Corporation; *U.S. Private*, pg. 1371
NORTHSTAR RESEARCH PARTNERS (USA) LLC—See Stagwell, Inc.; *U.S. Public*, pg. 1927
THE NPD GROUP, INC.; *U.S. Private*, pg. 4085
OBSERVANT LLC; *U.S. Private*, pg. 2987
OPINION LEADER RESEARCH LIMITED—See Providence Equity Partners L.L.C.; *U.S. Private*, pg. 3292
OPINION RESEARCH CORPORATION—See Lake Capital Management LLC; *U.S. Private*, pg. 2374
OPINION SEARCH INC.—See Brookfield Corporation; *Int'l*, pg. 1179
OPINION SEARCH INC.—See Elliott Management Corporation; *U.S. Private*, pg. 1371
OPPENHEIMER & CO. INC.—See Oppenheimer Holdings Inc.; *U.S. Public*, pg. 1608
ORC AUS PTY LTD—See Lake Capital Management LLC; *U.S. Private*, pg. 2374
O.R.C. INTERNATIONAL LTD.—See Lake Capital Management LLC; *U.S. Private*, pg. 2374
OUTSELL, INC.; *U.S. Private*, pg. 3051
OWENSMORRIS COMMUNICATIONS, INC.; *U.S. Private*, pg. 3055
PENN SCHOEN BERLAND ASSOCIATES INC.; *U.S. Private*, pg. 3134
PERSONAL MARKETING RESEARCH; *U.S. Private*, pg. 3155
THE PERT GROUP; *U.S. Private*, pg. 4093
PERYAM & KROLL RESEARCH CORP.; *U.S. Private*, pg. 3156
PEW RESEARCH CENTER—See The Pew Charitable Trusts; *U.S. Private*, pg. 4094
PGM INCORPORATED; *U.S. Private*, pg. 3165
PHOTON GROUP SINGAPORE PTE LIMITED—See Enero Group Limited; *Int'l*, pg. 2424
PIXLEE, INC.; *U.S. Private*, pg. 3193
POINTLOGIC USA INC.—See Brookfield Corporation; *Int'l*, pg. 1180
POINTLOGIC USA INC.—See Elliott Management Corporation; *U.S. Private*, pg. 1372
POLYPHENOLICS LLC—See Constellation Brands, Inc.; *U.S. Public*, pg. 571
POWERFORCE FIELD MARKETING & RETAIL SERVICES LTD—See Enero Group Limited; *Int'l*, pg. 2424
THE PRETESTING COMPANY, INC.; *U.S. Private*, pg. 4098
PROGRESSIVE IMPRESSIONS INTERNATIONAL—See Taylor Corporation; *U.S. Private*, pg. 3939
PT. NIELSEN AUDIENCE MEASUREMENT—See Brookfield Corporation; *Int'l*, pg. 1180
PT. NIELSEN AUDIENCE MEASUREMENT—See Elliott Management Corporation; *U.S. Private*, pg. 1372
PT. THE NIELSEN COMPANY INDONESIA—See Brookfield Corporation; *Int'l*, pg. 1180
PT. THE NIELSEN COMPANY INDONESIA—See Elliott Management Corporation; *U.S. Private*, pg. 1372
PUBLIC OPINION STRATEGIES LLC; *U.S. Private*, pg. 3299
QUANTUM RESEARCH SERVICES, INC.; *U.S. Private*, pg. 3323
QUICK TEST/HEAKIN—See MVL Group, Inc.; *U.S. Private*, pg. 2821
RACHEL KAY PUBLIC RELATIONS LLC—See Finn Partners, Inc.; *U.S. Private*, pg. 1510
RADIANT RESEARCH INC.—See Kinderhook Industries, LLC; *U.S. Private*, pg. 2307
RADIUS EMEA—See Radius Global Market Research; *U.S. Private*, pg. 3344
RADIUS GLOBAL MARKET RESEARCH; *U.S. Private*, pg. 3344
RADIUS GLOBAL MARKET RESEARCH—See Radius Global Market Research; *U.S. Private*, pg. 3344
RADIUS GLOBAL MARKET RESEARCH—See Radius Global Market Research; *U.S. Private*, pg. 3344
RADIUS GLOBAL MARKET RESEARCH—See Radius Global Market Research; *U.S. Private*, pg. 3344
RADIUS GLOBAL MARKET RESEARCH—See Radius Global Market Research; *U.S. Private*, pg. 3344
RADIUS GLOBAL MARKET RESEARCH—See Radius Global Market Research; *U.S. Private*, pg. 3344
RADIUS GLOBAL MARKET RESEARCH—See Radius Global Market Research; *U.S. Private*, pg. 3344
RAPIDTRON, INC.; *U.S. Private*, pg. 3356
REGIONAL INDUSTRIAL DEVELOPMENT CORPORATION OF SOUTHWESTERN PENNSYLVANIA INC.; *U.S. Private*, pg. 3388
RENTECH SERVICES CORPORATION—See Rentech, Inc.; *U.S. Private*, pg. 3400
RESEARCH AMERICA, INC.; *U.S. Private*, pg. 3403
RESEARCH BY DESIGN LLC; *U.S. Private*, pg. 3403
RESEARCH & DEVELOPMENT, INC.—See Cross Marketing Group Inc.; *Int'l*, pg. 1856
RESEARCH NOW PLC—See e-Rewards, Inc.; *U.S. Private*, pg. 1302
RESEARCH SOLUTIONS, INC.; *U.S. Public*, pg. 1789
ROCKY RESEARCH—See Honeywell International Inc.; *U.S. Public*, pg. 1051
SAEXPLORATION (CANADA) LTD.—See SAExploration Holdings, Inc.; *U.S. Private*, pg. 3523
SAVITZ RESEARCH CENTER INC.; *U.S. Private*, pg. 3557
SCHIRESON ASSOCIATES, INC.—See Known Global LLC; *U.S. Private*, pg. 2324
SCIENTIFIC RESEARCH CORP.; *U.S. Private*, pg. 3574
SEARCH TECHNOLOGIES LIMITED—See Accenture plc; *Int'l*, pg. 88
SECOND TO NONE, INC.; *U.S. Private*, pg. 3593
SENTIENT SERVICES—See Interviewing Service of America; *U.S. Private*, pg. 2128
SEQUEL RESPONSE, LLC—See Guggenheim Partners, LLC; *U.S. Private*, pg. 1811
SI2 TECHNOLOGIES, INC.—See Antenna Research Associates, Incorporated; *U.S. Private*, pg. 287
SIDOTI & COMPANY, LLC; *U.S. Private*, pg. 3646
THE SIGMA GROUP, LLC—See Research America, Inc.; *U.S. Private*, pg. 3403
SILLOH MARKET RESEARCH LLC—See Silloh Industries Inc.; *U.S. Private*, pg. 3653
SLI.DO S.R.O.—See Cisco Systems, Inc.; *U.S. Public*, pg. 501
SMARTPROS LTD.—See Graham Holdings Company; *U.S. Public*, pg. 956
SMARTREVENUE, INC.; *U.S. Private*, pg. 3692
SPECTRA MARKETING SYSTEMS, INC.—See Brookfield Corporation; *Int'l*, pg. 1180
SPECTRA MARKETING SYSTEMS, INC.—See Elliott Management Corporation; *U.S. Private*, pg. 1373
SPEND MATTERS—See Azul Partners, Inc.; *U.S. Private*, pg. 416
S&P GLOBAL COMMODITIES UK LIMITED—See S&P Global Inc.; *U.S. Public*, pg. 1831
S&P GLOBAL GERMANY GMBH—See S&P Global Inc.; *U.S. Public*, pg. 1831
S&P GLOBAL ITALY S.R.L—See S&P Global Inc.; *U.S. Public*, pg. 1831
SPORTCAL GLOBAL COMMUNICATIONS LIMITED—See GlobalData Plc; *Int'l*, pg. 3003
STRATEGIC MANAGEMENT DECISIONS LLC—See Ares

N.A.I.C.S. INDEX

Management Corporation; *U.S. Public*, pg. 190
STRATEGIC MANAGEMENT DECISIONS LLC—See Leonard Green & Partners, L.P.; *U.S. Private*, pg. 2427
STRATEGY ANALYTICS GMBH—See CVC Capital Partners SICAV-FIS S.A.; *Int'l*, pg. 1888
STRATEGY ANALYTICS, INC.—See CVC Capital Partners SICAV-FIS S.A.; *Int'l*, pg. 1888
STRATEGY ANALYTICS INC.—See CVC Capital Partners SICAV-FIS S.A.; *Int'l*, pg. 1888
STRATEGY ANALYTICS INC.—See CVC Capital Partners SICAV-FIS S.A.; *Int'l*, pg. 1888
STRATEGY ANALYTICS INC.—See CVC Capital Partners SICAV-FIS S.A.; *Int'l*, pg. 1888
STRATEGY ANALYTICS LTD.—See CVC Capital Partners SICAV-FIS S.A.; *Int'l*, pg. 1888
STRATEGY ANALYTICS—See CVC Capital Partners SICAV-FIS S.A.; *Int'l*, pg. 1888
STR, INC.—See CoStar Group, Inc.; *U.S. Public*, pg. 586
SUDDEN IMPACT MARKETING INC.; *U.S. Private*, pg. 3849
SURVEYVITALS, INC.; *U.S. Private*, pg. 3885
SWISS POSTER RESEARCH PLUS AG—See APG/SGA SA; *Int'l*, pg. 513
SYNTACTX, LLC—See ArchiMed SAS; *Int'l*, pg. 549
TANGIBLE GROUP LIMITED—See Arsenal Capital Management LP; *U.S. Private*, pg. 338
TARP WORLDWIDE EUROPE—See TARP Worldwide; *U.S. Private*, pg. 3934
TARP WORLDWIDE; *U.S. Private*, pg. 3934
TAYLOR NELSON SOFRES AUSTRALIA PTY. LTD.—See Bain Capital, LP; *U.S. Private*, pg. 448
TAYLOR NELSON SOFRES S.A.—See Bain Capital, LP; *U.S. Private*, pg. 448
TAYLOR NELSON SOFRES—See Bain Capital, LP; *U.S. Private*, pg. 448
THE TELEPHONE CENTRE, INC.; *U.S. Private*, pg. 4126
TEXAS MARKET RESEARCH GROUP LLC; *U.S. Private*, pg. 3976
TEXAS TRIBUNE INC.; *U.S. Private*, pg. 3978
THIRD WAVE RESEARCH GROUP, LTD.—See Vestar Capital Partners, LLC; *U.S. Private*, pg. 4372
THOMAS REGISTER OF AMERICAN MANUFACTURERS—See Thomas Publishing Company LLC; *U.S. Private*, pg. 4157
THOROUGHBRED RESEARCH GROUP, INC.; *U.S. Private*, pg. 4163
TIDEWATCH SELECT, LLC—See B. Riley Financial, Inc.; *U.S. Public*, pg. 261
TMR INC.—See 1-800 We Answer, Inc.; *U.S. Private*, pg. 1
TMW MARKETING COMPANY, INC.—See Tailored Brands, Inc.; *U.S. Public*, pg. 1979
TNS CANADIAN FACTS—See Bain Capital, LP; *U.S. Private*, pg. 447
TNS EMNID—See Bain Capital, LP; *U.S. Private*, pg. 447
TNS GALLUP AS—See Bain Capital, LP; *U.S. Private*, pg. 447
TNS GALLUP SA—See Bain Capital, LP; *U.S. Private*, pg. 447
TNS INDIA PVT. LTD.—See Bain Capital, LP; *U.S. Private*, pg. 447
TNS INTERSEARCH—See Bain Capital, LP; *U.S. Private*, pg. 448
TNS MALAYSIA SDN. BHD.—See Bain Capital, LP; *U.S. Private*, pg. 447
TNS NEW ZEALAND—See Bain Capital, LP; *U.S. Private*, pg. 448
TNS PHILIPPINES—See Bain Capital, LP; *U.S. Private*, pg. 448
TNS PROGNOSTICS LTD—See Bain Capital, LP; *U.S. Private*, pg. 448
TNS PROGNOSTICS—See Bain Capital, LP; *U.S. Private*, pg. 448
TNS SECODIP—See Bain Capital, LP; *U.S. Private*, pg. 448
TNS SINGAPORE—See Bain Capital, LP; *U.S. Private*, pg. 448
TNS UK LIMITED—See Bain Capital, LP; *U.S. Private*, pg. 448
TNS US, LLC—See Bain Capital, LP; *U.S. Private*, pg. 448
TNS US, LLC - TOLEDO OFFICE—See Bain Capital, LP; *U.S. Private*, pg. 448
TOLUNA GROUP LIMITED.—See Brookfield Corporation; *Int'l*, pg. 1180
TOLUNA GROUP LIMITED.—See Elliott Management Corporation; *U.S. Private*, pg. 1373
TROYRESEARCH; *U.S. Private*, pg. 4243
UAB ACNIELSEN BALTICS—See Brookfield Corporation; *Int'l*, pg. 1177
UAB ACNIELSEN BALTICS—See Elliott Management Corporation; *U.S. Private*, pg. 1369
VLSI RESEARCH, INC.—See CVC Capital Partners SICAV-FIS S.A.; *Int'l*, pg. 1888
VOTER CONSUMER RESEARCH, INC.—See Texas Market Research Group LLC; *U.S. Private*, pg. 3976
WALKER INFORMATION INC.; *U.S. Private*, pg. 4429
WEAVER & HOLIHAN, INC.; *U.S. Private*, pg. 4463
W&E SOURCE CORP.; *U.S. Public*, pg. 2315
WILLOW MARKETING; *U.S. Private*, pg. 4528
WILSON PERKINS ALLEN OPINION RESEARCH (WPA); *U.S. Private*, pg. 4531
WORTHPOINT CORPORATION; *U.S. Private*, pg. 4570
YGI, INC.—See 451 Group, LLC; *U.S. Private*, pg. 15

541921 — PHOTOGRAPHY STUDIOS, PORTRAIT

THE ASPEN BRANDS; *U.S. Private*, pg. 3989
BN PRODUCTIONS INC.—See National Amusements, Inc.; *U.S. Private*, pg. 2842
CANDID COLOR PHOTOGRAPHY, INC.—See Candid Color Systems, Inc.; *U.S. Private*, pg. 733
CHERRY HILL PROGRAMS, INC.—See Keystone Capital, Inc.; *U.S. Private*, pg. 2295
DA LUE INTERNATIONAL HOLDING CO., LTD.; *Int'l*, pg. 1901
DEUTSCHE BORSE PHOTOGRAPHY FOUNDATION GGMBH—See Deutsche Borse AG; *Int'l*, pg. 2063
DOM DEUTSCHE ONLINE MEDIEN GMBH—See Carl Bennet AB; *Int'l*, pg. 1332
GEORGE STREET PHOTO & VIDEO, LLC; *U.S. Private*, pg. 1683
HAGADONE PHOTOGRAPHY INC.—See The Hagadone Corporation; *U.S. Private*, pg. 4041
HENRY SCHEIN, INC.-PENNSYLVANIA—See Henry Schein, Inc.; *U.S. Public*, pg. 1027
LIFE365 PORTRAITS; *U.S. Private*, pg. 2449
LIFETOUCH CHURCH DIRECTORIES AND PORTRAITS INC.—See Apollo Global Management, Inc.; *U.S. Public*, pg. 159
LIFETOUCH, INC.—See Apollo Global Management, Inc.; *U.S. Public*, pg. 159
MYPHOTOALBUM, INC.; *U.S. Public*, pg. 1488
NATIONWIDE STUDIOS, INC.; *U.S. Private*, pg. 2866
NOON FILMTECHNIK SPOL.S R.O.—See Bavaria Film GmbH; *Int'l*, pg. 899
PHILIPPINE ANIMATION STUDIO INC—See Astro All Asia Networks plc; *Int'l*, pg. 662
PICTURE PEOPLE INC.—See Hallmark Cards, Inc.; *U.S. Private*, pg. 1845
PLAYBOY STUDIO WEST—See PLBY Group, Inc.; *U.S. Public*, pg. 1698
PORTRAIT INNOVATIONS HOLDING COMPANY; *U.S. Private*, pg. 3233
SHUTTERFLY LIFETOUCH, LLC—See Apollo Global Management, Inc.; *U.S. Public*, pg. 159
SIMPLY COLOR LAB INC.; *U.S. Private*, pg. 3668
THOMAS D. MANGELSEN, INC.; *U.S. Private*, pg. 4155
YOKOHAMA SUPER FACTORY CO., LTD.—See Dentsu Group Inc.; *Int'l*, pg. 2040

541922 — COMMERCIAL PHOTOGRAPHY

THE ALDERMAN COMPANY; *U.S. Private*, pg. 3983
AP IMAGES—See The Associated Press; *U.S. Private*, pg. 3989
ASTRAL IMAGES CORPORATION—See Astrotech Corporation; *U.S. Public*, pg. 218
BG PICTURES LLC; *U.S. Private*, pg. 548
BLEND IMAGES, LLC; *U.S. Private*, pg. 580
BLUEWATER EDITIONS—See Southeastern Printing Company Inc.; *U.S. Private*, pg. 3728
CLAROCITY CORPORATION; *U.S. Public*, pg. 507
COLORVISION INTERNATIONAL, INC.; *U.S. Private*, pg. 975
COMSTOCK IMAGES—See Mecklermedia Corporation; *U.S. Private*, pg. 2649
DCC RETOUCHING & PHOTOGRAPHY SERVICES; *U.S. Private*, pg. 1179
DNP MEDIA CREATE CO., LTD.—See Dai Nippon Printing Co., Ltd.; *Int'l*, pg. 1915
ERIK KELLAR PHOTOGRAPHY—See Osprey Capital LLC; *U.S. Private*, pg. 3048
FORTUNE STAR ENTERTAINMENT (HK) LIMITED—See The Walt Disney Company; *U.S. Public*, pg. 2140
FOTOLIA—See Adobe Inc.; *U.S. Public*, pg. 42
HIFSA—See Airtificial Intelligence Structures SA; *Int'l*, pg. 249
IINO MEDIA PRO CO., LTD.—See Iino Kaiun Kaisha Ltd.; *Int'l*, pg. 3608
JOSTENS, INC.—See Platinum Equity, LLC; *U.S. Private*, pg. 3205
KREBER GRAPHICS INC.; *U.S. Private*, pg. 2350
MOM365, INC.; *U.S. Private*, pg. 2767
OMEGA STUDIOS-SOUTHWEST INC.—See Chatham Asset Management, LLC; *U.S. Private*, pg. 864
PHOTOCREATE CO., LTD.—See Culture Convenience Club Co., Ltd.; *Int'l*, pg. 1877
PHOTOGENIC, INC.—See Keystone Capital, Inc.; *U.S. Private*, pg. 2295
PRIMARY COLOR SYSTEMS CORP; *U.S. Private*, pg. 3260
PROGRAM PRODUCTIONS, INC.; *U.S. Private*, pg. 3278
PROPERTYPHOTOS.COM LLC—See Thoma Bravo, L.P.; *U.S. Private*, pg. 4153
QUADRAS, INC.; *U.S. Private*, pg. 3316

R & R IMAGES, INC.—See Apollo Global Management, Inc.; *U.S. Public*, pg. 159
SHOWTIME PICTURES; *U.S. Private*, pg. 3643
SHUTTERSTOCK, INC.; *U.S. Public*, pg. 1876
SHUTTERSTOCK (UK) LTD.—See Shutterstock, Inc.; *U.S. Public*, pg. 1876
TC STUDIOS, LLC; *U.S. Private*, pg. 3942
ZUMA PRESS, INC.; *U.S. Private*, pg. 4610

541930 — TRANSLATION AND INTERPRETATION SERVICES

1-STOP TRANSLATION USA, LLC; *U.S. Private*, pg. 1
ABEXTRA, INC.—See Huseby, LLC; *U.S. Private*, pg. 2013
ALBORS & ASSOCIATES, INC.—See Interpreters Unlimited, Inc.; *U.S. Private*, pg. 2123
APPLIED LANGUAGE SOLUTIONS—See Capita plc; *Int'l*, pg. 1308
BABYLON SOFTWARE LTD.—See Babylon Ltd.; *Int'l*, pg. 793
BEIJING YAXINCHENG MEDICAL INFOTECH CO. LTD.—See Hangzhou Tigermed Consulting Co., Ltd.; *Int'l*, pg. 3251
BITS PRIVATE LIMITED; *Int'l*, pg. 1050
CANON TECHNICAL INFORMATION SERVICES INC.—See Canon Inc.; *Int'l*, pg. 1296
CERTIFIED LANGUAGES INTERNATIONAL, INC.; *U.S. Private*, pg. 841
CETRA, INC.; *U.S. Private*, pg. 843
COMMAND LANGUAGES, INC.; *U.S. Private*, pg. 982
COMMUNICATIONS INTERNATIONAL (NY); *U.S. Private*, pg. 988
CORE MISSION SOLUTIONS, LLC—See Citadel Federal Solutions LLC; *U.S. Private*, pg. 901
CRESTEC EUROPE B.V.—See Crestec Inc.; *Int'l*, pg. 1841
CYRACOM INTERNATIONAL, INC.; *U.S. Private*, pg. 1135
DYNAMIC LANGUAGE CENTER, LTD.; *U.S. Private*, pg. 1298
ERIKSEN TRANSLATIONS, INC.; *U.S. Private*, pg. 1421
ERIKSEN TRANSLATIONS S.R.L.—See Eriksen Translations, Inc.; *U.S. Private*, pg. 1421
FIPAS, INC.—See Honyaku Center Inc.; *Int'l*, pg. 3472
FLASR, INC.; *Int'l*, pg. 2698
FLITTO INC.; *Int'l*, pg. 2706
GENEVA WORLDWIDE, INC.; *U.S. Private*, pg. 1670
GETBLEND INC.; *U.S. Private*, pg. 1688
GLOBAL LANGUAGE SOLUTIONS, LLC—See Welocalize, Inc.; *U.S. Private*, pg. 4479
HC LANGUAGE SOLUTIONS, INC.—See Honyaku Center Inc.; *Int'l*, pg. 3472
HONYAKU CENTER INC.; *Int'l*, pg. 3472
INTELLIGERE; *U.S. Private*, pg. 2106
INTERPRETERS UNLIMITED, INC.; *U.S. Private*, pg. 2123
JUNCTION INTERNATIONAL, LLC; *U.S. Private*, pg. 2244
KJ INTERNATIONAL RESOURCES LTD.—See Leonard Green & Partners, L.P.; *U.S. Private*, pg. 2428
KJ INTERNATIONAL RESOURCES LTD.—See TTCP Management Services, LLC.; *U.S. Private*, pg. 4254
LANGUAGELINE SOLUTIONS, INC.—See ABRY Partners, LLC; *U.S. Private*, pg. 42
LANGUAGE SCIENTIFIC, INC.; *U.S. Private*, pg. 2390
LANGUAGE SERVICES ASSOCIATES, INC.; *U.S. Private*, pg. 2390
LANGUAGE TRANSLATION INC.—See Lingualinx Inc.; *U.S. Private*, pg. 2461
THE LANGUAGE WORKS, INC.—See Euromezzanine Conseil SAS; *Int'l*, pg. 2554
LEXICON CONSULTING, INC.; *U.S. Private*, pg. 2440
LINGUALINX, INC.; *U.S. Private*, pg. 2461
LIONBRIDGE TESTING SERVICES OY—See H.I.G. Capital, LLC; *U.S. Private*, pg. 1830
MANPOWERGROUP PUBLIC SECTOR INC.—See ManpowerGroup Inc.; *U.S. Public*, pg. 1360
MEDIA RESEARCH, INC.—See Honyaku Center Inc.; *Int'l*, pg. 3472
METAFORM LANGUES SARL—See CDS Co., Ltd.; *Int'l*, pg. 1371
MGS LANGUAGE SERVICES—See ManpowerGroup Inc.; *U.S. Public*, pg. 1358
MISSION ESSENTIAL PERSONNEL, LLC; *U.S. Private*, pg. 2747
MOTIONPOINT CORP.; *U.S. Private*, pg. 2796
NETWORKOMNI; *U.S. Private*, pg. 2889
OPTIMAL PHONE INTERPRETERS, INC.—See Kinderhook Industries, LLC; *U.S. Private*, pg. 2306
PARA-PLUS TRANSLATIONS, INC.; *U.S. Private*, pg. 3089
PERVOICE S.P.A.—See Almawave S.p.A.; *Int'l*, pg. 363
PROPIO LANGUAGE SERVICES, LLC.—See Leonard Green & Partners, L.P.; *U.S. Private*, pg. 2428
PROPIO LANGUAGE SERVICES, LLC.—See TTCP Management Services, LLC.; *U.S. Private*, pg. 4254
PROTRANSLATING, INC.—See MSouth Equity Partners, LLC; *U.S. Private*, pg. 2808
SAS SB TRADUCTION—See CDS Co., Ltd.; *Int'l*, pg. 1371
SB TRADUCTION SARL—See CDS Co., Ltd.; *Int'l*, pg. 1371
SIGNTALK, LLC; *U.S. Private*, pg. 3651
STAR-USA LLC; *U.S. Private*, pg. 3786

541930 — TRANSLATION AND INT...

STRATUS VIDEO, LLC—See Kinderhook Industries, LLC; *U.S. Private,* pg. 2306
SYSTEMATECH TECHNICAL MANAGEMENT SERVICES, INC.—See Kinderhook Industries, LLC; *U.S. Private,* pg. 2306
TECHNICIS SAS—See Groupe BPCE; *Int'l,* pg. 3095
TELELANGUAGE INC.—See Leonard Green & Partners, L.P.; *U.S. Private,* pg. 2428
TELELANGUAGE INC.—See TTCP Management Services, LLC; *U.S. Private,* pg. 4254
TORINDO CO., LTD—See CDS Co., Ltd.; *Int'l,* pg. 1371
TRANSLATIONS.COM; *U.S. Private,* pg. 4208
TRANSPERFECT TRANSLATIONS INTERNATIONAL INC.—See TransPerfect Global, Inc.; *U.S. Private,* pg. 4210
UBIQUS SAS—See Euromezzanine Conseil SAS; *Int'l,* pg. 2554
UBIQUS UK LIMITED—See Euromezzanine Conseil SAS; *Int'l,* pg. 2554
UNIVERSAL LANGUAGE SERVICE, INC.; *U.S. Private,* pg. 4305
U.S. TRANSLATION COMPANY; *U.S. Private,* pg. 4272
WELOCALIZE GMBH—See Welocalize, Inc.; *U.S. Private,* pg. 4479
WELOCALIZE, INC.; *U.S. Private,* pg. 4479
WELOCALIZE IRELAND—See Welocalize, Inc.; *U.S. Private,* pg. 4479

541940 — VETERINARY SERVICES

AGNES BANKS EQUINE CLINIC PTY. LIMITED—See Apiam Animal Health Limited; *Int'l,* pg. 515
ALBAVET LIMITED—See CVS Group Plc; *Int'l,* pg. 1890
AMLAN INTERNATIONAL—See Oil-Dri Corporation of America; *U.S. Public,* pg. 1565
ANICOM PAFE, INC.—See Anicom Holdings, Inc.; *Int'l,* pg. 471
ANICOM SPECIALTY MEDICAL INSTITUTE. INC.—See Anicom Holdings, Inc.; *Int'l,* pg. 471
ANIMAID PET HOSPITAL; *U.S. Private,* pg. 283
ANIMAL DERMATOLOGY & ALLERGY—See Percheron Investment Management LP; *U.S. Private,* pg. 3146
ANIMAL DERMATOLOGY CLINIC—See Percheron Investment Management LP; *U.S. Private,* pg. 3146
ANIMAL DERMATOLOGY GROUP, INC.—See Percheron Investment Management LP; *U.S. Private,* pg. 3146
ANIMAL EMERGENCY CENTRE CENTRAL COAST PTY LTD.—See TPG Capital, L.P.; *U.S. Public,* pg. 2176
ANIMAL EMERGENCY CENTRE (FRANKSTON) PTY LTD.—See TPG Capital, L.P.; *U.S. Public,* pg. 2176
ANIMAL EMERGENCY CENTRE HALLAM PTY LTD.—See TPG Capital, L.P.; *U.S. Public,* pg. 2176
ANIMAL EMERGENCY CENTRE PTY LTD.—See TPG Capital, L.P.; *U.S. Public,* pg. 2176
ANIMAL EMERGENCY CENTRE WOOLLOONGABBA PTY LTD.—See TPG Capital, L.P.; *U.S. Public,* pg. 2176
ANIMAL HEALTH CENTRE LIMITED—See CVS Group Plc; *Int'l,* pg. 1890
ANTECH DIAGNOSTICS CANADA LTD.—See Mars, Incorporated; *U.S. Private,* pg. 2590
AVACTA ANIMAL HEALTH LIMITED—See Avacta Group plc; *Int'l,* pg. 733
BIO-VET, INC.—See Anpario plc; *Int'l,* pg. 475
BLUEPEARL VETERINARY PARTNERS LLC; *U.S. Private,* pg. 597
CAMPSIE VETERINARY CENTRE LIMITED—See CVS Group Plc; *Int'l,* pg. 1890
C.A.P.L. LIMITED—See Patterson Companies, Inc.; *U.S. Public,* pg. 1653
CARTHAGE VETERINARY SERVICE, LTD.; *U.S. Private,* pg. 776
CHERMSIDE VETERINARY HOSPITAL PTY LTD.—See TPG Capital, L.P.; *U.S. Public,* pg. 2176
COEN DIERENARTS B.V.—See CVS Group Plc; *Int'l,* pg. 1890
COVETRUS, INC.—See Clayton, Dubilier & Rice, LLC; *U.S. Private,* pg. 921
COVETRUS, INC.—See TPG Capital, L.P.; *U.S. Public,* pg. 2170
CRITICAL CARE & VETERINARY SPECIALISTS OF SARASOTA LLC; *U.S. Private,* pg. 1101
C.V. SANCHINARRO, S.L.—See Helvetia Holding AG; *Int'l,* pg. 3339
CVS GROUP PLC; *Int'l,* pg. 1889
CVS (UK) LIMITED—See CVS Group Plc; *Int'l,* pg. 1890
DEMETER-RIDGEFIELD DIVISION—See Demeter LP; *U.S. Private,* pg. 1203
DIERENARTSENPRAKTIJK NOP B.V—See CVS Group Plc; *Int'l,* pg. 1890
DIERENARTSENPRAKTIJK ZUID-WEST FRIESLAND B.V—See CVS Group Plc; *Int'l,* pg. 1890
DIERENZIEKENHUIS DRACHTEN B.V.—See CVS Group Plc; *Int'l,* pg. 1890
ECUPHAR BV—See Animalcare Group plc; *Int'l,* pg. 471
ELANCO HUNGARY KFT.—See Elanco Animal Health Incorporated; *U.S. Public,* pg. 722

EMANCIPET CENTRAL AUSTIN—See Emancipet, Inc.; *U.S. Private,* pg. 1378
EMANCIPET, INC.; *U.S. Private,* pg. 1378
ENDELL VETERINARY GROUP LIMITED—See CVS Group Plc; *Int'l,* pg. 1890
EPARK PET LIFE INC.—See extreme Co., Ltd,; *Int'l,* pg. 2592
FISH VET GROUP LIMITED—See Zoetis, Inc.; *U.S. Public,* pg. 2409
GATOR VET INC.; *U.S. Private,* pg. 1651
GOLD COAST ANIMAL REFERRAL & EMERGENCY PTY LTD.—See TPG Capital, L.P.; *U.S. Public,* pg. 2176
GREENCROSS LIMITED—See TPG Capital, L.P.; *U.S. Public,* pg. 2176
GREENCROSS NSW PTY LTD.—See TPG Capital, L.P.; *U.S. Public,* pg. 2176
GREENCROSS VETS SOUTHCOAST PTY. LTD.—See TPG Capital, L.P.; *U.S. Public,* pg. 2176
GREENDALE VETERINARY DIAGNOSTICS LIMITED—See CVS Group Plc; *Int'l,* pg. 1890
GRIBBLES VETERINARY PATHOLOGY LIMITED; *Int'l,* pg. 3082
GYMPIE & DISTRICT VETERINARY SERVICES PTY. LTD.—See Apiam Animal Health Limited; *Int'l,* pg. 515
HEARTLAND VETERINARY PHARMACY LLC—See Pet Assistant Holdings, LLC; *U.S. Private,* pg. 3156
HELIOS KLINIK HERZBERG/OSTERODE GMBH—See Fresenius SE & Co. KGaA; *Int'l,* pg. 2779
HELIOS VOGTLAND-KLINIKUM PLAUEN GMBH—See Fresenius SE & Co. KGaA; *Int'l,* pg. 2780
IDEXX DIAVET AG—See IDEXX Laboratories, Inc.; *U.S. Public,* pg. 1092
IDEXX LABORATORIES SP. Z O.O.—See IDEXX Laboratories, Inc.; *U.S. Public,* pg. 1093
IDEXX REFERENCE LABORATORIES LTD.—See IDEXX Laboratories, Inc.; *U.S. Public,* pg. 1093
IDEXX TELEMEDICINE CONSULTANTS—See IDEXX Laboratories, Inc.; *U.S. Public,* pg. 1093
INNOVETIVE PETCARE HOLDINGS LLC; *U.S. Private,* pg. 2083
INSPIRE VETERINARY PARTNERS, INC.; *U.S. Public,* pg. 1131
INTERVET EGYPT FOR ANIMAL HEALTH SAE—See Merck & Co., Inc.; *U.S. Public,* pg. 1416
INTERVET K.K.—See Merck & Co., Inc.; *U.S. Public,* pg. 1416
INTERVET MIDDLE EAST LTD—See Merck & Co., Inc.; *U.S. Public,* pg. 1417
INTERVET NORBIO A.S.—See Merck & Co., Inc.; *U.S. Public,* pg. 1417
INTERVET NORBIO SINGAPORE PTE LTD—See Merck & Co., Inc.; *U.S. Public,* pg. 1417
INTERVET NORGE AS—See Merck & Co., Inc.; *U.S. Public,* pg. 1417
INTERVET OY—See Merck & Co., Inc.; *U.S. Public,* pg. 1417
J & J CALIBRATION SERVICES, INC—See Aldinger Company; *U.S. Private,* pg. 160
KENNEL VACCINE VET SUPPLY CO.; *U.S. Private,* pg. 2285
LAP OF LOVE, INC.; *U.S. Private,* pg. 2391
THE MASON COMPANY, LLC—See Midmark Corporation; *U.S. Private,* pg. 2716
MEDICAL MANAGEMENT INTERNATIONAL INC.—See Mars, Incorporated; *U.S. Private,* pg. 2590
MEDICAL MODELING INC.—See 3D Systems Corporation; *U.S. Public,* pg. 4
MOVET OY—See IDEXX Laboratories, Inc.; *U.S. Public,* pg. 1093
MSD ANIMAL HEALTH K.K.—See Merck & Co., Inc.; *U.S. Public,* pg. 1417
NEWPORT LABORATORIES, INC.—See C.H. Boehringer Sohn AG & Co. KG; *Int'l,* pg. 1243
PATTERSON VETERINARY SUPPLY, INC.—See Patterson Companies, Inc.; *U.S. Public,* pg. 1654
PAWS/LA; *U.S. Private,* pg. 3115
PET ACCIDENT & EMERGENCY PTY. LTD.—See TPG Capital, L.P.; *U.S. Public,* pg. 2176
PETMED EXPRESS, INC.; *U.S. Public,* pg. 1678
PETRAYS; *U.S. Private,* pg. 3161
PETWELL PARTNERS LLC; *U.S. Private,* pg. 3163
PHOENIX CENTRAL LABORATORY FOR VETERINARIANS, INC.—See Zoetis, Inc.; *U.S. Public,* pg. 2409
PORTEC VETERINARY SERVICES PTY. LTD.—See Apiam Animal Health Limited; *Int'l,* pg. 515
PT. LOHMANN ANIMAL HEALTH INDONESIA—See Eli Lilly & Company; *U.S. Public,* pg. 734
RITMA PRESTASI SDN BHD—See Emerging Glory Sdn Bhd; *Int'l,* pg. 2379
SANTAMIX IBERICA SL—See Element Solutions Inc.; *U.S. Public,* pg. 728
SCIL ANIMAL CARE COMPANY FRANCE SARL—See Mars, Incorporated; *U.S. Private,* pg. 2588
SCIL ANIMAL CARE COMPANY SL—See Mars, Incorporated; *U.S. Private,* pg. 2588
SCIL ANIMAL CARE COMPANY SRL—See Mars, Incorporated; *U.S. Private,* pg. 2588

CORPORATE AFFILIATIONS

SCIL DIAGNOSTICS SDN. BHD.—See Mars, Incorporated; *U.S. Private,* pg. 2589
SCOTTSDALE VETERINARY SERVICES PTY. LTD.—See Apiam Animal Health Limited; *Int'l,* pg. 515
SENTRX ANIMAL CARE, INC.—See Domes Pharma SA; *Int'l,* pg. 2159
SIMCRO LIMITED—See Datamars SA; *Int'l,* pg. 1978
SIMCRO (UK) LIMITED—See Datamars SA; *Int'l,* pg. 1978
SMITHTON VETERINARY SERVICE PTY. LTD.—See Apiam Animal Health Limited; *Int'l,* pg. 515
SOUND TECHNOLOGIES, INC.—See Mars, Incorporated; *U.S. Private,* pg. 2590
ST ELMO VETERINARY CLINIC LIMITED—See CVS Group Plc; *Int'l,* pg. 1890
SUMMIT PET PRODUCTS DISTRIBUTORS, INC.; *U.S. Private,* pg. 3856
SYNBIOTICS EUROPE S.A.S.—See Zoetis, Inc.; *U.S. Public,* pg. 2409
UNITED SCIENCES TESTING INC.—See TRC Companies, Inc.; *U.S. Private,* pg. 4215
VCA ANIMAL HOSPITALS, INC.—See Mars, Incorporated; *U.S. Private,* pg. 2590
VCA INC.—See Mars, Incorporated; *U.S. Private,* pg. 2590
VETLAB OY—See IDEXX Laboratories, Inc.; *U.S. Public,* pg. 1093
VICAR OPERATING, INC.—See Mars, Incorporated; *U.S. Private,* pg. 2590
VIRTUAL RECALL LIMITED—See Zoetis, Inc.; *U.S. Public,* pg. 2410
WARRNAMBOOL VETERINARY CLINIC PTY. LTD.—See Apiam Animal Health Limited; *Int'l,* pg. 515
WILLIAMSTOWN VETERINARY HOSPITAL PTY LTD.—See TPG Capital, L.P.; *U.S. Public,* pg. 2176
ZNLABS, LLC—See Zoetis, Inc.; *U.S. Public,* pg. 2410

541990 — ALL OTHER PROFESSIONAL, SCIENTIFIC, AND TECHNICAL SERVICES

99DESIGNS INC.—See Cimpress plc; *Int'l,* pg. 1609
ACCEL ENTERTAINMENT, LLC—See Accel Entertainment, Inc.; *U.S. Public,* pg. 31
ACCESS MEDIA 3, INC.; *U.S. Private,* pg. 52
ACO SMARTCARE CO., LTD.—See Compal Electronics, Inc.; *Int'l,* pg. 1746
ACUMEN DETECTION, LLC—See SRC, Inc.; *U.S. Private,* pg. 3767
ACUREN INSPECTION, INC. - NORTH REGION—See Acuren Corporation; *Int'l,* pg. 121
ACUREN INSPECTION, INC.—See Acuren Corporation; *Int'l,* pg. 121
ACUREN INSPECTION, INC. - SOUTH REGION—See Acuren Corporation; *Int'l,* pg. 121
ADR GROUP; *U.S. Private,* pg. 82
ADVANCED CONCEPTS & TECHNOLOGIES INTERNATIONAL, LLC - ARLINGTON—See Advanced Concepts & Technologies International, LLC; *U.S. Private,* pg. 88
ADVANTICOM, INC.; *U.S. Private,* pg. 95
AEEC LLC; *U.S. Private,* pg. 116
AESKU.DIAGNOSTICS GMBH & CO. KG; *Int'l,* pg. 182
AGRIA GROUP HOLDING JSC; *Int'l,* pg. 216
AINSWORTH, INC.—See GDI Integrated Facility Services Inc.; *Int'l,* pg. 2896
AIRLINES REPORTING CORPORATION; *U.S. Private,* pg. 141
ALADDIN; *U.S. Private,* pg. 148
ALIGN TECHNOLOGY—See HitecVision AS; *Int'l,* pg. 3425
ALLEGRA NETWORK LLC—See Alliance Franchise Brands LLC; *U.S. Private,* pg. 182
ALL OCEANS CLOSINGS LLC—See OneWater Marine Inc.; *U.S. Public,* pg. 1604
AL PRIME ENERGY CONSULTANT INC.; *U.S. Private,* pg. 147
AMAG TECHNOLOGY LTD.—See Allied Universal Manager LLC; *U.S. Private,* pg. 188
AMA XPERTEYE INC.—See AMA Corporation Plc; *Int'l,* pg. 403
AMERGENT, INC.—See Moore DM Group, LLC; *U.S. Private,* pg. 2780
AMERGINT TECHNOLOGIES, INC.; *U.S. Private,* pg. 219
AMERICAN CONSUMER CREDIT COUNSELING, INC.; *U.S. Private,* pg. 228
AMERICAN TECHNOLOGY SERVICES INC; *U.S. Private,* pg. 256
AMERICAN TRANSMISSION COMPANY LLC—See ATC Management Inc.; *U.S. Private,* pg. 365
AMERICAN WASTE MANAGEMENT SERVICES, INC.—See Avalon Holdings Corporation; *U.S. Public,* pg. 239
AMI INVESTMENTS, LLC—See McWane, Inc.; *U.S. Private,* pg. 2645
AON GLOBAL LIMITED—See Aon plc; *Int'l,* pg. 495
APAVE SA; *Int'l,* pg. 501
APIXIO INC.—See New Mountain Capital, LLC; *U.S. Private,* pg. 2900
APPLICATION CONSULTING TRAINING SOLUTIONS INC.; *U.S. Private,* pg. 298
APPLUS NORCONTROL REPUBLICA DOMINICANA,

N.A.I.C.S. INDEX

541990 — ALL OTHER PROFESSIO...

S.R.L.—See I Squared Capital Advisors (US) LLC; *U.S. Private*, pg. 2022
APPLUS SERVICES, S.A.—See I Squared Capital Advisors (US) LLC; *U.S. Private*, pg. 2021
APPLUS+ TECHNOLOGIES, INC.—See Searchlight Capital Partners, L.P.; *U.S. Private*, pg. 3590
ARGUS VICKERS AMERICAN EQUITY RESEARCH LTD.—See The Argus Research Group, Inc.; *U.S. Private*, pg. 3988
ARMENI CONSULTING SERVICES, LLC—See KCI Holdings Inc.; *U.S. Private*, pg. 2269
ASCOM NETWORK TESTING AG—See Ascom Holding AG; *Int'l*, pg. 602
ASPEED TECHNOLOGY (U.S.A.) INC.—See ASPEED Technology Inc.; *Int'l*, pg. 628
ATLAS MATERIAL TESTING TECHNOLOGY LLC—See AMETEK, Inc.; *U.S. Public*, pg. 117
AUBAY ITALIA S.P.A.—See Aubay SA; *Int'l*, pg. 698
AUBAY LUXEMBOURG S.A.—See Aubay SA; *Int'l*, pg. 698
AUBAY PORTUGAL—See Aubay SA; *Int'l*, pg. 698
AUBAY SA; *Int'l*, pg. 698
AUBAY SPAIN S.L.—See Aubay SA; *Int'l*, pg. 698
AUC FINANCIAL PARTNERS INC—See Aucnet Inc.; *Int'l*, pg. 700
AUDIO VISUAL SERVICES GROUP, LLC—See Blackstone Inc.; *U.S. Public*, pg. 348
AUTHENTIC AUTOGRAPHS UNLIMITED, INC.; *U.S. Private*, pg. 396
AZOLVER DANMARK APS—See Francotyp-Postalia Holding AG; *Int'l*, pg. 2760
AZOLVER NORGE AS—See Francotyp-Postalia Holding AG; *Int'l*, pg. 2760
AZOLVER SUOMI OY—See Francotyp-Postalia Holding AG; *Int'l*, pg. 2760
AZOLVER SWITZERLAND AG—See Francotyp-Postalia Holding AG; *Int'l*, pg. 2761
BABEL MEDIA LIMITED—See Canada Pension Plan Investment Board; *Int'l*, pg. 1280
BABEL MEDIA LIMITED—See EQT AB; *Int'l*, pg. 2482
THE BAKER-MEEKINS COMPANY INC.—See Evergreen Advisors, LLC; *U.S. Private*, pg. 1438
BANDIT LITES, INC.; *U.S. Private*, pg. 465
BANDIT LITES—See Bandit Lites, Inc.; *U.S. Private*, pg. 465
BARR AIR PATROL, LLC; *U.S. Private*, pg. 479
BEACON APPLICATION SERVICES CORPORATION; *U.S. Private*, pg. 503
BID4ASSETS, INC.; *U.S. Private*, pg. 551
BIDCLERK, INC.—See Roper Technologies, Inc.; *U.S. Public*, pg. 1810
BILFINGER INDUSTRIAL SERVICES GERMANY GMBH—See Bilfinger SE; *Int'l*, pg. 1027
BILFINGER INDUSTRIAL SERVICES SWITZERLAND AG—See Bilfinger SE; *Int'l*, pg. 1027
BINARI SONORI AMERICA INC.—See Canada Pension Plan Investment Board; *Int'l*, pg. 1280
BINARI SONORI AMERICA INC.—See EQT AB; *Int'l*, pg. 2482
BJ SERVICES CO. (SINGAPORE) PTE LTD—See Baker Hughes Company; *U.S. Public*, pg. 264
BJ TUBULAR SERVICES LIMITED—See Baker Hughes Company; *U.S. Public*, pg. 264
B&L TELEPHONE LLC—See Fortran Corporation; *U.S. Public*, pg. 872
BLUENRGY, LLC—See BlueNRGY Group Limited; *Int'l*, pg. 1072
BLUE STAR JETS, INC.; *U.S. Private*, pg. 593
BLUE ZONES, LLC—See Adventist Health System; *U.S. Private*, pg. 108
BMT ARGOSS B.V.—See BMT Group Limited; *Int'l*, pg. 1077
BMT ARGOSS LIMITED—See BMT Group Limited; *Int'l*, pg. 1077
BMT NIGEL GEE LTD—See BMT Group Limited; *Int'l*, pg. 1078
BOLT UNDERWATER SERVICES, INC.—See Volkert, Inc.; *U.S. Private*, pg. 4410
BOZEMAN TREE SERVICE, INC.—See Apax Partners LLP; *Int'l*, pg. 506
BRAGG CRANE & RIGGING—See Bragg Investment Company, Inc.; *U.S. Private*, pg. 634
BRAND ENERGY & INFRASTRUCTURE SERVICES—See Brand Industrial Services, Inc.; *U.S. Private*, pg. 636
BREEDON BOW HIGHWAYS LIMITED—See Breedon Group plc; *Int'l*, pg. 1144
BRIGHTLANE.COM, INC.—See DLH Holdings Corp.; *U.S. Public*, pg. 670
BROADBEAN INC.—See Veritone, Inc.; *U.S. Public*, pg. 2283
BRUNEL TECHNICAL SERVICES (THAILAND) LIMITED—See Brunel International N.V.; *Int'l*, pg. 1200
B-SOFT CO., LTD.; *Int'l*, pg. 785
THE BUFFALO GROUP, LLC—See Jacobs Engineering Group, Inc.; *U.S. Public*, pg. 1186
BUILDING CONTROLS & SOLUTIONS; *U.S. Private*, pg. 682
BYTE POWER GROUP LIMITED; *Int'l*, pg. 1236
CABRINI TECHNOLOGY SERVICES—See Cabrini Health Limited; *Int'l*, pg. 1246
CALIAN LTD.—See Calian Group Ltd.; *Int'l*, pg. 1263

CAMBRIDGE SOUND MANAGEMENT INC.—See AMETEK, Inc.; *U.S. Public*, pg. 118
CAPMAN PROCUREMENT SERVICES (CAPS) OY—See CapMan PLC; *Int'l*, pg. 1315
CASA CIENTIFICA—See Standard Industries Holdings Inc.; *U.S. Private*, pg. 3779
CAS, INC.—See KBR, Inc.; *U.S. Public*, pg. 1216
CAVOK—See Marsh & McLennan Companies, Inc.; *U.S. Public*, pg. 1386
CCI-TELECOM, INC.—See Fortran Corporation; *U.S. Public*, pg. 872
CECO PIPELINE SERVICES COMPANY, INC.—See Compressor Engineering Corporation; *U.S. Private*, pg. 1003
CEGEDIM CUSTOMER INFORMATION SRL—See Cegedim S.A.; *Int'l*, pg. 1390
CEGEDIM MAROC SARL—See Cegedim S.A.; *Int'l*, pg. 1390
CEGEDIM SRH LTD.—See Cegedim S.A.; *Int'l*, pg. 1390
CEGEDIM SRH SA—See Cegedim S.A.; *Int'l*, pg. 1390
CERTARA UK LIMITED—See Certara, Inc.; *U.S. Public*, pg. 476
CERTIFIED ENVIRONMENTAL PARTICULATE AIR, INC.—See Levine Leichtman Capital Partners, LLC; *U.S. Private*, pg. 2436
CERTIPATH, INC.; *U.S. Private*, pg. 842
CHAMPION GLOBAL SERVICES LIMITED—See Great Eagle Holdings Limited; *Int'l*, pg. 3064
CHINA TECHFAITH WIRELESS COMMUNICATION TECHNOLOGY LIMITED; *Int'l*, pg. 1557
CHRISTIAN BERNER TECH TRADE AB; *Int'l*, pg. 1586
CHRISTIE GROUP CENTRAL SERVICES LIMITED—See Christie Group plc; *Int'l*, pg. 1587
CHURCHILL DOWNS RACETRACK, LLC—See Churchill Downs, Inc.; *U.S. Public*, pg. 493
CIPEC CONSTRUCTION INC.—See CTCI Corporation; *Int'l*, pg. 1870
CITOC INC.; *U.S. Private*, pg. 904
CLARIVATE PLC; *Int'l*, pg. 1649
CLARKSON VALUATIONS LIMITED—See Clarkson PLC; *Int'l*, pg. 1651
CLEAN AIR ENGINEERING INC.; *U.S. Private*, pg. 931
CLEAN HARBORS, INC.; *U.S. Public*, pg. 508
CLS AMERICA, INC.—See Collecte Localisation Satellites; *Int'l*, pg. 1699
COAST CRANE CO.-BAKERSFIELD—See Apollo Global Management, Inc.; *U.S. Public*, pg. 153
COAST CRANE CO.-CITY OF INDUSTRY—See Apollo Global Management, Inc.; *U.S. Public*, pg. 153
COAST CRANE CO.-PORTLAND—See Apollo Global Management, Inc.; *U.S. Public*, pg. 153
COAST CRANE CO.-SAN LEANDRO—See Apollo Global Management, Inc.; *U.S. Public*, pg. 153
COAST CRANE CO.—See Apollo Global Management, Inc.; *U.S. Public*, pg. 153
COAST CRANE CO.-TACOMA—See Apollo Global Management, Inc.; *U.S. Public*, pg. 153
COAST CRANE LTD.—See Apollo Global Management, Inc.; *U.S. Public*, pg. 153
COLLECTE LOCALISATION SATELLITES; *Int'l*, pg. 1699
COMTEC SOLUTIONS; *U.S. Private*, pg. 1006
CONCAT AG IT SOLUTIONS—See Meridian Group International, Inc.; *U.S. Private*, pg. 2673
CONCERN WORLDWIDE; *Int'l*, pg. 1764
CONNECTED SERVICES GROUP PTY. LTD.—See FUJIFILM Holdings Corporation; *Int'l*, pg. 2825
CONSUMER CREDIT COUNSELING SERVICE OF SAN FRANCISCO; *U.S. Private*, pg. 1025
CONVERCENT, INC.—See OneTrust LLC; *U.S. Private*, pg. 3026
COPT DC-6, LLC—See COPT Defense Properties; *U.S. Public*, pg. 575
THE CORETEC GROUP INC.; *U.S. Public*, pg. 2066
COURAGE SERVICES, INC.—See Amentum Services, Inc.; *U.S. Private*, pg. 219
CRANE INSPECTION & CERTIFICATION BUREAU L.L.C.; *U.S. Private*, pg. 1085
CREDENCE RESOURCE MANAGEMENT, LLC—See Kriya Capital, LLC; *U.S. Private*, pg. 2352
CREDITO AFIANZADOR, S.A.—See Grupo BAL; *Int'l*, pg. 3121
CREW TECHNICAL SERVICES; *U.S. Private*, pg. 1099
CRITICAL PROCESS SYSTEMS GROUP, INC.—See Wynnchurch Capital, L.P.; *U.S. Private*, pg. 4577
CSA FRANCHISING, LLC—See CSA Service Solutions, LLC; *U.S. Private*, pg. 1116
CSG COMMUNICATIONS PTY. LTD.—See FUJIFILM Holdings Corporation; *Int'l*, pg. 2825
CSG PRINT SERVICES PTY. LTD.—See FUJIFILM Holdings Corporation; *Int'l*, pg. 2825
CTCI ARABIA LTD.—See CTCI Corporation; *Int'l*, pg. 1870
CTCI SHANGHAI CO., LTD.—See CTCI Corporation; *Int'l*, pg. 1870
CTCI VIETNAM COMPANY LIMITED—See CTCI Corporation; *Int'l*, pg. 1870
CTR INVESTMENTS & CONSULTING, INC.; *U.S. Public*, pg. 602
CURRIE & BROWN (CI) LIMITED—See Currie & Brown Holdings Limited; *Int'l*, pg. 1879

CURRIE & BROWN, INC.—See Currie & Brown Holdings Limited; *Int'l*, pg. 1879
CURRIE & BROWN UK LIMITED—See Currie & Brown Holdings Limited; *Int'l*, pg. 1879
CYBERSETTLE, INC.; *U.S. Private*, pg. 1133
CYMAT TECHNOLOGIES LTD.; *Int'l*, pg. 1896
D3T LTD.—See Canada Pension Plan Investment Board; *Int'l*, pg. 1281
D3T LTD.—See EQT AB; *Int'l*, pg. 2483
DADE MOELLER AND ASSOCIATES, INC.—See NV5 Global, Inc.; *U.S. Public*, pg. 1557
DAISY CORPORATE SERVICES LIMITED—See Daisy Group Limited; *Int'l*, pg. 1942
DAMOVO BELGIUM N.V/S.A—See Eli Global, LLC; *U.S. Private*, pg. 1359
DAMOVO DEUTSCHLAND GMBH & CO. KG—See Eli Global, LLC; *U.S. Private*, pg. 1359
DAMOVO POLSKA SP. Z O.O.—See Eli Global, LLC; *U.S. Private*, pg. 1359
DAMOVO SCHWEIZ AG—See Eli Global, LLC; *U.S. Private*, pg. 1359
DAMOVO USA, INC.—See Eli Global, LLC; *U.S. Private*, pg. 1359
DATA CAPTURE SOLUTIONS INC.; *U.S. Private*, pg. 1162
DBI, INC.—See ERI Solutions, LLC; *U.S. Private*, pg. 1419
DEFINITIVE MEDIA CORP.—See JLL Partners, LLC; *U.S. Private*, pg. 2212
DEFINITIVE MEDIA CORP.—See Water Street Healthcare Partners, LLC; *U.S. Private*, pg. 4452
DEKRA AMBIO S.A.U.—See DEKRA e.V.; *Int'l*, pg. 2007
DELTA SOLUTIONS & STRATEGIES, LLC—See Hammond, Kennedy, Whitney & Company, Inc.; *U.S. Private*, pg. 1850
DESPATCH INDUSTRIES GMBH EMEA OPERATION—See Illinois Tool Works Inc.; *U.S. Public*, pg. 1102
DET NORSKE VERITAS CERTIFICATION INC.—See DNV GL Group AS; *Int'l*, pg. 2151
DET NORSKE VERITAS CERTIFICATION—See DNV GL Group AS; *Int'l*, pg. 2151
DETRON ICT SOLUTIONS BV; *Int'l*, pg. 2048
THE DEWBERRY COMPANIES INC.; *U.S. Private*, pg. 4020
DICTOR CAPITAL CORPORATION; *U.S. Private*, pg. 1227
DINE DEVELOPMENT CORPORATION; *U.S. Private*, pg. 1233
DIRECT HOLDINGS AMERICAS INC.—See Mosaic Media Investment Partners LLC; *U.S. Private*, pg. 2792
DIRECT HOLDINGS LIBRARIES INC.—See Mosaic Media Investment Partners LLC; *U.S. Private*, pg. 2792
DISNEYLAND RESORTS—See The Walt Disney Company; *U.S. Public*, pg. 2138
DOMINICA SERVICES, INC.—See Adtalem Global Education Inc.; *U.S. Public*, pg. 43
DOWD ASSOCIATES INC.—See RFE Investment Partners; *U.S. Private*, pg. 3420
DPA GROUP N.V.—See Gilde Equity Management (GEM) Benelux Partners B.V.; *Int'l*, pg. 2975
DRIVER TRETT (CANADA) LTD.—See Diales; *Int'l*, pg. 2104
DRIVER TRETT (HONG KONG) LTD.—See Diales; *Int'l*, pg. 2104
DRIVER TRETT (SINGAPORE) PTE. LTD.—See Diales; *Int'l*, pg. 2104
DRYPATROL, LLC—See FirstService Corporation; *Int'l*, pg. 2691
DSYS INC; *U.S. Private*, pg. 1282
THE DUBIN GROUP, INC.—See HireQuest, Inc.; *U.S. Public*, pg. 1042
DUPONT SPECIALTY PRODUCTS GMBH & CO. KG—See DuPont de Nemours, Inc.; *U.S. Public*, pg. 693
DYMEDEX CONSULTING, LLC—See Bain Capital, LP; *U.S. Private*, pg. 432
DYNCORP INTERNATIONAL LLC—See Cerberus Capital Management, L.P.; *U.S. Private*, pg. 838
EAGLECLAW MIDSTREAM VENTURES, LLC—See Kayne Anderson Capital Advisors, L.P.; *U.S. Private*, pg. 2267
E.A. HUGHES & CO., INC.—See Solomon-Page Group LLC; *U.S. Private*, pg. 3710
EARLY WARNING NETWORK PTY. LTD.—See Aeeris Limited; *Int'l*, pg. 173
EATON TECHNOLOGIES LIMITED—See Eaton Corporation plc; *Int'l*, pg. 2281
ECOASSET SOLUTIONS, LLC—See Lykes Brothers Inc.; *U.S. Private*, pg. 2519
ECONOMICS PARTNERS, LLC—See Ryan, LLC; *U.S. Private*, pg. 3511
EDDYFI NDT, INC.; *Int'l*, pg. 2304
EDGE SERVICES, INC.; *U.S. Private*, pg. 1334
EEII AG; *Int'l*, pg. 2317
EMERALD TECHNOLOGY VALUATIONS, LLC—See Gordon Brothers Group, LLC; *U.S. Private*, pg. 1742
ENCAVIS TECHNICAL SERVICES GMBH—See Encavis AG; *Int'l*, pg. 2401
ENDRESS+HAUSER CONDUCTA GMBH+CO. KG—See Endress+Hauser (International) Holding AG; *Int'l*, pg. 2407
ENERGIE STEIERMARK SERVICE GMBH—See Energie Steiermark AG; *Int'l*, pg. 2420
ENGINEERING AND INFORMATION TECHNOLOGIES,

541990 — ALL OTHER PROFESSIO...

INC.; *U.S. Private*, pg. 1398
ENQUERO, INC.—See Genpact Limited; *Int'l*, pg. 2926
ENVISION PHARMA INC.—See Ardian SAS; *Int'l*, pg. 555
ENVISION PHARMA INC.—See GHO Capital Partners LLP; *Int'l*, pg. 2959
ENVISION PHARMA LIMITED—See Ardian SAS; *Int'l*, pg. 555
ENVISION PHARMA LIMITED—See GHO Capital Partners LLP; *Int'l*, pg. 2959
ENVISTA FORENSICS, LLC—See Engle Martin & Associates, LLC; *U.S. Private*, pg. 1399
EPROCESS INTERNATIONAL S.A.—See Ecobank Transnational Incorporated; *Int'l*, pg. 2294
EPROTEX, LLC—See Ascension Health Alliance; *U.S. Private*, pg. 346
EUROFINS E&E CML LIMITED—See Eurofins Scientific S.E.; *Int'l*, pg. 2540
EUROFINS GFA GMBH—See Eurofins Scientific S.E.; *Int'l*, pg. 2543
EUROFINS HONG KONG LTD.—See Eurofins Scientific S.E.; *Int'l*, pg. 2543
EUROFINS TECHNOLOGY SERVICE (SUZHOU) LTD.—See Eurofins Scientific S.E.; *Int'l*, pg. 2549
EVERGY SERVICES, INC.—See Evergy, Inc.; *U.S. Public*, pg. 801
EXAMWORKS GROUP, INC.—See GIC Pte. Ltd.; *Int'l*, pg. 2964
EXAMWORKS GROUP, INC.—See Leonard Green & Partners, L.P.; *U.S. Private*, pg. 2425
EXASERV, INC.; *U.S. Private*, pg. 1445
EXPAND, LLC—See DYN365, Inc.; *U.S. Private*, pg. 1297
EXXONMOBIL GLOBAL SERVICES COMPANY—See Exxon Mobil Corporation; *U.S. Public*, pg. 815
FACTSET HONG KONG LIMITED—See FactSet Research Systems Inc.; *U.S. Public*, pg. 819
FACTSET RESEARCH LIMITED—See FactSet Research Systems Inc.; *U.S. Public*, pg. 820
FALCON TECHNOLOGIES AND SERVICES, INC.—See CARBO Ceramics Inc.; *U.S. Public*, pg. 748
FAST ENERGY SDN. BHD.—See Fast Energy Holdings Berhad; *Int'l*, pg. 2621
FAST TECHNOLOGY SDN. BHD.—See Fast Energy Holdings Berhad; *Int'l*, pg. 2621
FATA GULF CO WLL—See Danieli & C. Officine Meccaniche S.p.A.; *Int'l*, pg. 1963
F. CHRISTIANA & CO.—See US Foods Holding Corp.; *U.S. Public*, pg. 2266
FEDERATED INTERACTIVE LLC—See Federated Media Inc.; *U.S. Private*, pg. 1491
FIELD SERVICE DEUTSCHLAND FSD GMBH—See freenet AG; *Int'l*, pg. 2770
FINITE CARBON CORPORATION—See BP plc; *Int'l*, pg. 1131
FIREFLY IT SERVICES INC.—See CloudScale365, Inc.; *U.S. Private*, pg. 947
FIRSTCARBON SOLUTIONS CORPORATION—See The ADEC Group; *U.S. Private*, pg. 3981
FIVES MACHINING SYSTEMS, INC. - GLOBAL SERVICES, CHATSWORTH—See FIVES, Societe Anonyme; *Int'l*, pg. 2696
FLETCHER MCNEILL & PARTNERS LIMITED—See Baqus Group Limited; *Int'l*, pg. 857
FLIGHT LANDATA, INC.—See Jacobs Engineering Group, Inc.; *U.S. Public*, pg. 1186
FM FACILITY MAINTENANCE, LLC; *U.S. Private*, pg. 1553
FONTEVA INC.—See GI Manager L.P.; *U.S. Private*, pg. 1694
FOODBUY PTY LTD—See Compass Group PLC; *Int'l*, pg. 1752
FOODCHAIN ID TECHNICAL SERVICES, INC—See Berkshire Partners LLC; *U.S. Private*, pg. 534
FORCE COMMUNICATIONS, LLC—See Keystone Group, L.P.; *U.S. Private*, pg. 2299
FORTRAN COMMUNICATIONS, INC.—See Fortran Corporation; *U.S. Public*, pg. 872
FRESENIUS KABI MEDTECH SERVICES GMBH—See Fresenius SE & Co. KGaA; *Int'l*, pg. 2778
GAS ATACAMA CHILE SA—See Enel S.p.A.; *Int'l*, pg. 2414
GENERATIONE CONSULTING, LLC—See Lotus Innovations LLC; *U.S. Private*, pg. 2497
GENPACT CANADA SERVICES COMPANY—See Genpact Limited; *Int'l*, pg. 2926
GENPACT ISRAEL LTD.—See Genpact Limited; *Int'l*, pg. 2926
GENPACT OUTSOURCING SERVICES COSTA RICA, S.R.L.—See Genpact Limited; *Int'l*, pg. 2927
GEODIGITAL INTERNATIONAL CORP.—See GeoDigital International Inc.; *Int'l*, pg. 2933
GLOBAL-ENTECH CO., LTD—See Chung-Hsin Electric & Machinery Manufacturing Corp.; *Int'l*, pg. 1597
GLOBAL NEURO-DIAGNOSTICS, LP—See ArchiMed SAS; *Int'l*, pg. 1131
GLOBAL OLED TECHNOLOGY LLC—See Idemitsu Kosan Co., Ltd.; *Int'l*, pg. 3590
GLOBAL TEST SUPPLY, LLC; *U.S. Private*, pg. 1718
GMZ ENERGY, INC.—See Evident Thermoelectrics; *U.S. Private*, pg. 1441

GOLDBELT FALCON, LLC—See Gold Belt Incorporated; *U.S. Private*, pg. 1727
GOODRICH CONTROL SYSTEMS GMBH—See RTX Corporation; *U.S. Public*, pg. 1823
GRAPHIC SYSTEMS INC.; *U.S. Private*, pg. 1758
GREEK RESOURCE SERVICES, INC.—See GI Manager L.P.; *U.S. Private*, pg. 1694
GROUPE OPEN NEDERLAND B.V.—See Groupe OPEN S.A.; *Int'l*, pg. 3109
GROUPE OPEN S.A.; *Int'l*, pg. 3109
GULF SCIENTIFIC CORPORATION—See Waters Corporation; *U.S. Public*, pg. 2334
HANNET CO., LTD.; *Int'l*, pg. 3257
HAPPIEST MINDS TECHNOLOGIES PVT. LTD.; *Int'l*, pg. 3268
HAZTEK, INC.; *U.S. Private*, pg. 1886
HCT CO., LTD.; *Int'l*, pg. 3299
HEIDELBERGCEMENT TECHNOLOGY CENTER GMBH—See Heidelberg Materials AG; *Int'l*, pg. 3315
HERITAGE AVIATION LTD.—See Patriarch Partners, LLC; *U.S. Private*, pg. 3109
HH ASSOCIATES US, INC.—See HH Global Group Limited; *Int'l*, pg. 3378
HIGH VOLTAGE MAINTENANCE - NORTHEAST ELECTRICAL TESTING—See Emerson Electric Co.; *U.S. Public*, pg. 748
HILDI INCORPORATED—See Caisse de Depot et Placement du Quebec; *Int'l*, pg. 1256
HILDI INCORPORATED—See KKR & Co. Inc.; *U.S. Public*, pg. 1265
HIRERIGHT ESTONIA AS—See Corporate Risk Holdings LLC; *U.S. Private*, pg. 1056
HMY YACHT SALES, INC.; *U.S. Private*, pg. 1955
HOOVER'S, INC.—See Cannae Holdings, Inc.; *U.S. Public*, pg. 430
HOOVER'S, INC.—See CC Capital Partners, LLC; *U.S. Private*, pg. 798
HOOVER'S, INC.—See Intercontinental Exchange, Inc.; *U.S. Public*, pg. 1142
HORIZON PROPERTIES OF PENSACOLA; *U.S. Private*, pg. 1982
HP INSPECTIONS, INC.; *U.S. Private*, pg. 1996
HUNTER MARITIME ACQUISITION CORP.; *Int'l*, pg. 3536
HYDROMAX USA, LLC—See Gallant Capital Partners, LLC; *U.S. Private*, pg. 1639
HYPERVIEW INC.; *Int'l*, pg. 3553
HYTERA COMMUNICATIONS (AUSTRALIA) PTY LTD—See Hytera Communications Corporation Limited; *Int'l*, pg. 3554
IBERDROLA QSTP, LLC—See Iberdrola, S.A.; *Int'l*, pg. 3572
IBIB GROUP CONSULTANTS (ISRAEL) LTD.—See ARCADIS N.V.; *Int'l*, pg. 542
IBI GROUP ARCHITECTS (USA) INC.—See ARCADIS N.V.; *Int'l*, pg. 542
IBI GROUP CONSULTANTS (IRELAND) LIMITED—See ARCADIS N.V.; *Int'l*, pg. 542
IBI GROUP GEOMATICS (CANADA) INC.—See ARCADIS N.V.; *Int'l*, pg. 542
IBI GROUP GREECE BUSINESS CONSULTANTS SINGLE MEMBER SOCIETE ANONYME IBI HELLAS S.A.—See ARCADIS N.V.; *Int'l*, pg. 542
IBI GROUP INDIA PRIVATE LIMITED—See ARCADIS N.V.; *Int'l*, pg. 542
IBI GROUP PROFESSIONAL SERVICES (USA) INC.—See ARCADIS N.V.; *Int'l*, pg. 542
IBI GROUP SAUDI LIMITED COMPANY—See ARCADIS N.V.; *Int'l*, pg. 542
IBI-MAAK CARIBBEAN LIMITED—See ARCADIS N.V.; *Int'l*, pg. 542
ICTS INTERNATIONAL, N.V.; *Int'l*, pg. 3587
IDEO, LLC; *U.S. Private*, pg. 2037
I-FREEK MOBILE INC.; *Int'l*, pg. 3563
INCOTEC GROUP B.V.—See Croda International plc; *Int'l*, pg. 1852
INCOTEC INTEGRATED COATING & SEED TECHNOLOGY, INC.—See Croda International plc; *Int'l*, pg. 1852
INEOQUEST TECHNOLOGIES LTD.—See Genstar Capital, LLC; *U.S. Private*, pg. 1679
INFO RETAIL COMPANY; *U.S. Private*, pg. 2072
INNOVATIVE TECHNICAL SOLUTIONS, INC.—See Corning Incorporated; *U.S. Public*, pg. 579
INSTITUTE OF NUCLEAR POWER OPERATIONS; *U.S. Private*, pg. 2093
INTALYTICS, INC.—See Hanover Investors Management LLP; *Int'l*, pg. 3258
INTEGRA TECHNOLOGIES LLC; *U.S. Private*, pg. 2098
INTEGREVIEW, LLC—See Genstar Capital, LLC; *U.S. Private*, pg. 1673
INTERICA LIMITED—See ALS Limited; *Int'l*, pg. 378
INTERNATIONAL CERTIFICATION SERVICES, INC.—See Where Food Comes From, Inc.; *U.S. Public*, pg. 2366
INTERNATIONAL PAPER COMPANY—See International Paper Company; *U.S. Public*, pg. 1156
ISOVERA, LLC; *U.S. Private*, pg. 2146
IST RESEARCH CORP.—See The Carlyle Group Inc.; *U.S. Public*, pg. 2056
IT AMERICA INC.; *U.S. Private*, pg. 2147

ITERIS, INC. - GRAND FORKS—See Almaviva S.p.A.; *Int'l*, pg. 363
JANICKI ENVIRONMENTAL, INC.—See Environmental Science Associates; *U.S. Private*, pg. 1408
JAN X-RAY SERVICES INCORPORATED; *U.S. Private*, pg. 2186
JBR MEDIA VENTURES LLC; *U.S. Private*, pg. 2194
THE JELLYVISION LAB, INC.; *U.S. Private*, pg. 4058
JHM FINANCIAL GROUP, LLC; *U.S. Private*, pg. 2207
J.M. RODGERS CO., INC.; *U.S. Private*, pg. 2169
JNS-SMITHCHEM, LLC; *U.S. Private*, pg. 2217
JOHN L. HINKLE HOLDINGS CO., INC.—See Riverside Partners, LLC; *U.S. Private*, pg. 3446
JOHNSTON INTEGRATION TECHNOLOGY LLC—See Johnston Industrial Supply Inc.; *U.S. Private*, pg. 2230
JOHOR SHIPYARD & ENGINEERING SDN BHD—See E.A Technique (M) Bhd; *Int'l*, pg. 2250
KEJR, INC.; *U.S. Private*, pg. 2274
KEYSTONE GROUP HOLDINGS INC.; *U.S. Private*, pg. 2296
KEYWORDS INTERNATIONAL CO. LIMITED—See Canada Pension Plan Investment Board; *Int'l*, pg. 1280
KEYWORDS INTERNATIONAL CO. LIMITED—See EQT AB; *Int'l*, pg. 2482
KEYWORDS INTERNATIONAL CORPORATION INC.—See Canada Pension Plan Investment Board; *Int'l*, pg. 1280
KEYWORDS INTERNATIONAL CORPORATION INC.—See EQT AB; *Int'l*, pg. 2482
KEYWORDS INTERNATIONAL INC.—See Canada Pension Plan Investment Board; *Int'l*, pg. 1280
KEYWORDS INTERNATIONAL INC.—See EQT AB; *Int'l*, pg. 2482
KEYWORDS INTERNATIONAL PTE. LIMITED—See Canada Pension Plan Investment Board; *Int'l*, pg. 1280
KEYWORDS INTERNATIONAL PTE. LIMITED—See EQT AB; *Int'l*, pg. 2482
KEYWORDS ITALIA SRL—See Canada Pension Plan Investment Board; *Int'l*, pg. 1280
KEYWORDS ITALIA SRL—See EQT AB; *Int'l*, pg. 2482
KEYWORDS STUDIOS PLC—See Canada Pension Plan Investment Board; *Int'l*, pg. 1280
KEYWORDS STUDIOS PLC—See EQT AB; *Int'l*, pg. 2482
K.J.P. LTD.—See Cinven Limited; *Int'l*, pg. 1612
KOCH REFINING INTERNATIONAL PTE, LTD.—See Koch Industries, Inc.; *U.S. Private*, pg. 2332
KOMARKETING ASSOCIATES LLC—See Walker Sands, Inc.; *U.S. Private*, pg. 4429
KRUEGER-GILBERT HEALTH PHYSICS, INC.—See Blue Sea Capital Management LLC; *U.S. Private*, pg. 592
K & T HEATING SERVICES LIMITED—See Cap10 Partners LLP; *Int'l*, pg. 1301
LAB PRODUCTS, INC.—See Bio Medic Corporation; *U.S. Private*, pg. 561
LARAGEN INCORPORATED—See Thompson Street Capital Manager LLC; *U.S. Private*, pg. 4161
LEADING EDGE AVIATION SOLUTIONS, LLC; *U.S. Private*, pg. 2406
LEAD INTELLIGENCE, INC.—See Verisk Analytics, Inc.; *U.S. Public*, pg. 2283
LIANDON B.V.—See Alliander N.V.; *Int'l*, pg. 341
LIANDON MEETBEDRIJF N.V.—See Alliander N.V.; *Int'l*, pg. 341
LIFE SAFETY SERVICES; *U.S. Private*, pg. 2449
LIQUIDITY SERVICES UK LTD—See Liquidity Services, Inc.; *U.S. Public*, pg. 1321
LOEB EQUIPMENT & APPRAISAL CO.; *U.S. Private*, pg. 2479
LOXA BEAUTY LLC—See Sally Beauty Holdings, Inc.; *U.S. Public*, pg. 1839
MACROSTIE HISTORIC ADVISORS, LLC—See Ryan, LLC; *U.S. Private*, pg. 3511
MAERSK SUPPLY SERVICE APOIO MARITIMO LTDA.—See A.P. Moller-Maersk A/S; *Int'l*, pg. 27
THE MANOFF GROUP, INC.—See John Snow, Inc.; *U.S. Private*, pg. 2224
MARCUS INVESTMENTS, LLC; *U.S. Private*, pg. 2572
MAR (MD), LLC—See GF Capital Management & Advisors, LLC; *U.S. Private*, pg. 1689
MASCO PRODUCT DESIGN, INC.—See Masco Corporation; *U.S. Public*, pg. 1391
MATCO SERVICES, INC.—See Valmont Industries, Inc.; *U.S. Public*, pg. 2274
MATRIX CAPITAL ADVISORS LLC—See CI Financial Corporation; *Int'l*, pg. 1601
MATRIX HEALTH MANAGEMENT CORP.—See GIC Pte. Ltd.; *Int'l*, pg. 2964
MATRIX HEALTH MANAGEMENT CORP.—See Leonard Green & Partners, L.P.; *U.S. Private*, pg. 2425
MAUI ESTATES INTERNATIONAL, LLC—See Hawaii Life; *U.S. Private*, pg. 1881
MAXIM CRANE WORKS, L.P. - SEATTLE—See Apollo Global Management, Inc.; *U.S. Public*, pg. 153
MAXVANTAGE LLC—See Dart Appraisal.com, Inc.; *U.S. Private*, pg. 1159
MCBEE STRATEGIC CONSULTING, LLC—See Wiley Rein LLP; *U.S. Private*, pg. 4520
MCGINLEY & ASSOCIATES, INC.—See Universal Engineering Sciences, LLC; *U.S. Private*, pg. 4304

N.A.I.C.S. INDEX
541990 — ALL OTHER PROFESSIO...

MEDICIM NV—See Danaher Corporation; *U.S. Public*, pg. 628
MEDNET SOLUTIONS, INC.; *U.S. Private*, pg. 2658
MELVILLE SURGERY CENTER, LLC—See North Shore Lij Health Systems; *U.S. Private*, pg. 2946
METZ & ASSOCIATES, LTD.—See Metz Enterprises Inc.; *U.S. Private*, pg. 2691
MICRON TECHNOLOGIES, INC.—See Arlington Capital Partners LLC; *U.S. Private*, pg. 328
MILLER/ZELL, INC.; *U.S. Private*, pg. 2736
MONTROSE ENVIRONMENTAL CORP.; *U.S. Private*, pg. 2777
THE MORAN COMPANY, LLC—See Health Management Associates, Inc.; *U.S. Private*, pg. 1894
MRO CORPORATION—See PCP Enterprise, L.P.; *U.S. Private*, pg. 3121
MSP CORPORATION—See TSI Incorporated; *U.S. Private*, pg. 4253
MULTIBASE S.A.—See DuPont de Nemours, Inc.; *U.S. Public*, pg. 694
NABROS INC; *U.S. Private*, pg. 2829
NATHAN ASSOCIATES INC.; *U.S. Private*, pg. 2838
NATIONAL TRANSFER SERVICES, LLC—See Stewart Information Services Corporation; *U.S. Public*, pg. 1947
NAUTRONIX BRASIL LTDA.—See Riverstone Holdings LLC; *U.S. Private*, pg. 3447
NAUTRONIX LTD—See Riverstone Holdings LLC; *U.S. Private*, pg. 3447
NETFUSION, INC.—See Tonka Bay Equity Partners LLC; *U.S. Private*, pg. 4185
NETWORK DYNAMICS INC.—See Global Convergence, Inc.; *U.S. Private*, pg. 1713
NEUDESIC, LLC—See International Business Machines Corporation; *U.S. Public*, pg. 1149
NEUGER COMMUNICATIONS GROUP, INC.; *U.S. Private*, pg. 2890
NEW LEAF PAPER, LLC; *U.S. Private*, pg. 2898
NEW WAVE YACHTS, DEALERSHIP—See New Wave Yachts; *U.S. Private*, pg. 2908
NEW YORK CRUISE LINES INC.; *U.S. Private*, pg. 2909
NEXANT, INC.—See BV Investment Partners, LLC; *U.S. Private*, pg. 699
NIJECT SERVICES COMPANY—See Ingersoll Rand Inc.; *U.S. Public*, pg. 1122
NORTHROP GRUMMAN - CORPORATE GOVERNMENT RELATIONS—See Northrop Grumman Corporation; *U.S. Public*, pg. 1539
NORTHROP GRUMMAN TECHNICAL SERVICES, INC.—See Northrop Grumman Corporation; *U.S. Public*, pg. 1541
NOV TUBOSCOPE NL B.V.—See NOV, Inc.; *U.S. Public*, pg. 1545
NRG CURTAILMENT SOLUTIONS, INC.—See NRG Energy, Inc.; *U.S. Public*, pg. 1550
NYPRO DENMARK APS—See Jabil Inc.; *U.S. Public*, pg. 1181
OBJECT CTALK INC.; *U.S. Private*, pg. 2987
OBSIDIAN TECHNOLOGIES, INC.—See Converge Technology Solutions Corp.; *Int'l*, pg. 1787
OFFIS SA/NV—See Aubay SA; *Int'l*, pg. 698
OKEANUS SCIENCE & TECHNOLOGY, LLC; *U.S. Private*, pg. 3006
OKI AUTO AUCTION, INC.—See Dealer's Auto Auction Group; *U.S. Private*, pg. 1182
OMEGA PARTNERS III LLC; *U.S. Private*, pg. 3015
ONCOLOGY THERAPEUTIC NETWORK CORPORATION—See McKesson Corporation; *U.S. Public*, pg. 1408
ONSITE INNOVATIONS, INC.—See Athletico Ltd.; *U.S. Private*, pg. 368
OPERATIONAL TECHNOLOGIES CORPORATION-MIDWEST REGIONAL OFFICE—See Operational Technologies Corporation; *U.S. Private*, pg. 3032
OPERATIONAL TECHNOLOGIES CORPORATION; *U.S. Private*, pg. 3032
OVATION CREDIT SERVICES, INC.—See LendingTree, Inc.; *U.S. Public*, pg. 1305
PACCESS LLC; *U.S. Private*, pg. 3063
PARASTAR, INC.—See Beaumont Health; *U.S. Private*, pg. 508
PCS RETIREMENT, LLC; *U.S. Private*, pg. 3121
PEARLFISHER; *U.S. Private*, pg. 3125
PENTA ELECTROMEC PVT. LTD.—See Daeyang Electric Co., Ltd.; *Int'l*, pg. 1911
PEREGRINE TECHNICAL SERVICES, LLC—See Gold Belt Incorporated; *U.S. Private*, pg. 1727
PERFORMANCE SPECIALTY PRODUCTS (INDIA) PRIVATE LIMITED—See DuPont de Nemours, Inc.; *U.S. Public*, pg. 694
PERFORMANCE SPECIALTY PRODUCTS (SINGAPORE) PTE. LTD.—See DuPont de Nemours, Inc.; *U.S. Public*, pg. 694
PLAINS LPG SERVICES GP LLC—See Plains All American Pipeline, L.P.; *U.S. Public*, pg. 1696
PLUNKETT & LYNCH ASSOCIATES; *U.S. Private*, pg. 3215
PORT INC.—See Targus Group International, Inc.; *U.S. Private*, pg. 3934

POS DIGICERT SDN. BHD.—See DRB-HICOM Berhad; *Int'l*, pg. 2202
POYRY ENERGY GMBH—See AFRY AB; *Int'l*, pg. 195
PREMIER EQUIPMENT CO. INC.—See Premier Machinery Inc.; *U.S. Private*, pg. 3250
PREMIER SERVICES, LLC—See Premier, Inc.; *U.S. Public*, pg. 1715
PRI ASPHALT TECHNOLOGIES, INC.—See OceanSound Partners, LP; *U.S. Private*, pg. 2991
PRIMESCAPE SOLUTIONS, INC.—See HighPoint Global, LLC; *U.S. Private*, pg. 1941
PRINT RESOURCES, INC.; *U.S. Private*, pg. 3265
PRISMONE GROUP, INC.; *U.S. Public*, pg. 1722
PROLINE GROUP AB—See Carl Bennet AB; *Int'l*, pg. 1332
PROMONITORING BV—See Eurofins Scientific S.E.; *Int'l*, pg. 2551
PROMOTIC BELGIUM SA/NV—See Aubay SA; *Int'l*, pg. 698
PROVIDOR LIMITED—See Cap10 Partners LLP; *Int'l*, pg. 1301
PT CTCI INTERNATIONAL INDONESIA—See CTCI Corporation; *Int'l*, pg. 1870
PTS, INC.; *U.S. Public*, pg. 1735
PULLMAN STT, INC.—See Structural Group, Inc.; *U.S. Private*, pg. 3841
QED SYSTEMS, INC. - HONOLULU OFFICE—See QED Systems, Inc.; *U.S. Private*, pg. 3312
QED SYSTEMS, INC. - PORT ORCHARD OFFICE—See QED Systems, Inc.; *U.S. Private*, pg. 3313
QED SYSTEMS, INC. - SAN DIEGO OFFICE—See QED Systems, Inc.; *U.S. Private*, pg. 3313
QED SYSTEMS, INC.; *U.S. Private*, pg. 3312
QUEST INTEGRITY USA, LLC—See Baker Hughes Company; *U.S. Public*, pg. 265
QUIKTRAK INC.—See Bureau Veritas S.A.; *Int'l*, pg. 1222
RAYTHEON AUSTRALIA AIR WARFARE DESTROYER—See RTX Corporation; *U.S. Public*, pg. 1824
RAYTHEON AUSTRALIA MISSION SUPPORT—See RTX Corporation; *U.S. Public*, pg. 1824
RAYTHEON AUSTRALIA SECURITY SOLUTIONS—See RTX Corporation; *U.S. Public*, pg. 1824
RAYTHEON CANADA LIMITED SUPPORT SERVICES DIVISION—See RTX Corporation; *U.S. Public*, pg. 1824
RAYTHEON INTELLIGENCE, INFORMATION & SERVICES—See RTX Corporation; *U.S. Public*, pg. 1824
RAYTHEON TECHNICAL SERVICES COMPANY LLC—See RTX Corporation; *U.S. Public*, pg. 1825
RBJ & ASSOCIATES LLC—See Berkshire Hathaway Inc.; *U.S. Public*, pg. 313
READING SCIENTIFIC SERVICES LTD.—See Mondelez International, Inc.; *U.S. Public*, pg. 1461
RE.ALTO-ENERGY B.V./S.R.L.—See Elia Group SA; *Int'l*, pg. 2360
RECORDTRAK INC.; *U.S. Private*, pg. 3371
REGISTER.COM, INC.—See Siris Capital Group, LLC; *U.S. Private*, pg. 3675
REMOTE ACCESS TECHNOLOGY INTERNATIONAL—See Rockwood Holdings Limited Partnership; *U.S. Private*, pg. 3468
RGC VENTURES OF VIRGINIA, INC.—See RGC Resources, Inc.; *U.S. Public*, pg. 1796
ROHM & HAAS ELECTRONIC MATERIALS K.K.—See DuPont de Nemours, Inc.; *U.S. Public*, pg. 694
RONTGEN TECHNISCHE DIENST B.V.—See I Squared Capital Advisors (US) LLC; *U.S. Private*, pg. 2023
SAFETY NETACCESS, INC.; *U.S. Private*, pg. 3524
SALESFORCE.COM ITALY S.R.L.—See Salesforce, Inc.; *U.S. Public*, pg. 1837
SALLY BEAUTY MILITARY SUPPLY LLC—See Sally Beauty Holdings, Inc.; *U.S. Public*, pg. 1839
SCIFLUENT COMMUNICATIONS INC—See Arsenal Capital Management LP; *U.S. Private*, pg. 338
SEMI DICE, LLC—See Behrman Brothers Management Corp.; *U.S. Private*, pg. 515
SENTRY DATA SYSTEMS, INC.—See Craneware plc; *Int'l*, pg. 1828
SERVASSURE LIMITED—See Daisy Group Limited; *Int'l*, pg. 1943
SGS TUNISIE S.A.R.L.—See Concentrix Corporation; *U.S. Public*, pg. 565
SHYFT GLOBAL SERVICES, INC.—See TD Synnex Corp; *U.S. Public*, pg. 1984
SIGMA AB—See Danir Resources AB; *Int'l*, pg. 1963
SIGMA ACQUISITION LLC—See Repay Holdings Corporation; *Int'l*, pg. 1784
SIGNALFIRE TELEMETRY INC.—See The TASI Group; *U.S. Private*, pg. 4126
SIMPLION TECHNOLOGIES INC.; *U.S. Private*, pg. 3668
SINGLE PATH; *U.S. Private*, pg. 3670
SMARTECH ELECTRONICS (SHENZHEN) CO., LTD—See Fuji Corporation; *Int'l*, pg. 2810
SMARTECH ENTERPRISE CO., LTD.—See Fuji Corporation; *Int'l*, pg. 2810
SMARTECH EQUIPMENT (SHENZHEN) CO., LTD.—See Fuji Corporation; *Int'l*, pg. 2810
SNIP BIOTECH GMBH & CO. KG—See Eurofins Scientific S.E.; *Int'l*, pg. 2551

SOLUTIONSIQ, LLC—See Accenture plc; *Int'l*, pg. 86
SOLVE ADVISORS INC.; *U.S. Private*, pg. 3711
SOMA MEDICAL ASSESSMENTS CORP.—See GIC Pte. Ltd.; *Int'l*, pg. 2964
SOMA MEDICAL ASSESSMENTS CORP.—See Leonard Green & Partners, L.P.; *U.S. Private*, pg. 2425
SOUTHERN CROSS AVIATION INC.; *U.S. Private*, pg. 3730
SPARKFACTOR DESIGN; *U.S. Private*, pg. 3745
SPECIALTY PRODUCTS TURKEY ENDUSTRI URUNLERI LIMITED SIRKETI—See DuPont de Nemours, Inc.; *U.S. Public*, pg. 694
SPERRY RAIL, INC.—See Rockwood Holdings Limited Partnership; *U.S. Private*, pg. 3468
SPIRA-LOC—See EMCOR Group, Inc.; *U.S. Public*, pg. 737
STACKS CONSULTING E INGENIERA EN SOFTWARE SL—See Cegedim S.A.; *Int'l*, pg. 1390
STEM, INC.—See Stem, Inc.; *U.S. Public*, pg. 1945
STERIGENICS U.S., LLC—See Warburg Pincus LLC; *U.S. Private*, pg. 4439
STG, INC.—See STG Group, Inc.; *U.S. Public*, pg. 1949
STORMGEO BRASIL AS—See Alfa Laval AB; *Int'l*, pg. 312
STORMGEO JAPAN KK—See Alfa Laval AB; *Int'l*, pg. 312
STORMGEO PH INC.—See Alfa Laval AB; *Int'l*, pg. 312
STORMGEO PTE. LTD.—See Alfa Laval AB; *Int'l*, pg. 312
SUNBELT BUSINESS ADVISORS NETWORK, LLC—See Merrymeeting, Inc.; *U.S. Private*, pg. 2677
SUPPLIER MANAGEMENT SOLUTIONS, INC.—See Ardian SAS; *Int'l*, pg. 556
SURE MAINTENANCE LIMITED—See Cap10 Partners LLP; *Int'l*, pg. 1301
SVAM, INDIA-NORTH SHORE TECHNOLOGIES—See SVAM International, Inc.; *U.S. Private*, pg. 3888
SVITZER AUSTRALIA PTY LTD.—See A.P. Moller-Maersk A/S; *Int'l*, pg. 28
SYMBOTIC LLC—See Symbotic, Inc.; *U.S. Public*, pg. 1969
TAYLOR ENERGY, LLC; *U.S. Private*, pg. 3939
TAYLOR INTERNATIONAL CO. INC.; *U.S. Private*, pg. 3940
TAYLOR & MARTIN ENTERPRISES INC.; *U.S. Private*, pg. 3937
TAYLOR STUDIOS, INC.; *U.S. Private*, pg. 3940
TCI SERVICES, INC.—See Team, Inc.; *U.S. Public*, pg. 1988
TEAM, INC.; *U.S. Public*, pg. 1987
TEAM INDUSTRIAL SERVICES MALAYSIA SDN BHD—See Team, Inc.; *U.S. Public*, pg. 1988
TEAM NATIONAL; *U.S. Private*, pg. 3949
TECHNICAL SALES INTERNATIONAL, LLC (TSI); *U.S. Private*, pg. 3954
TELECOMMUNICATION SUPPORT SERVICES, INC.—See Acorn Growth Companies, LC; *U.S. Private*, pg. 63
TEMPUS APPLIED SOLUTIONS, LLC—See Tempus Applied Solutions Holdings, Inc.; *U.S. Public*, pg. 2000
TENEO BLUE RUBICON LIMITED—See CVC Capital Partners SICAV-FIS S.A.; *Int'l*, pg. 1889
TENEO BLUE RUBICON - SINGAPORE—See CVC Capital Partners SICAV-FIS S.A.; *Int'l*, pg. 1889
TENEO HOLDINGS LLC—See CVC Capital Partners SICAV-FIS S.A.; *Int'l*, pg. 1888
TENTH AVENUE HOLDINGS LLC; *U.S. Private*, pg. 3968
THERMO SCIENTIFIC SERVICES, INC.—See Thermo Fisher Scientific Inc.; *U.S. Public*, pg. 2154
THERMOSET TECHNOLOGIES (MIDDLE EAST) LLC—See Dubai Investments PJSC; *Int'l*, pg. 2219
THX LTD.—See Razer Inc.; *U.S. Private*, pg. 3359
TLC CORPORATE SERVICES LLC—See The Kroger Co.; *U.S. Public*, pg. 2109
TOHOKU PIONEER EG CORPORATION—See Denso Corporation; *Int'l*, pg. 2033
TOUCHTUNES MUSIC CORPORATION—See Searchlight Capital Partners, L.P.; *U.S. Private*, pg. 3590
TOX PATH SPECIALISTS, LLC—See Ampersand Management LLC; *U.S. Private*, pg. 265
TPI EUROPE LTD.—See Information Services Group, Inc.; *U.S. Public*, pg. 1118
TQT S.R.L.—See FLY Srl; *Int'l*, pg. 2716
TRANSCEND UNITED TECHNOLOGIES LLC—See Black Box Limited; *Int'l*, pg. 1058
TRANSNATIONAL FOODS; *U.S. Private*, pg. 4209
TRETT LTD.—See Diales; *Int'l*, pg. 2104
TRIMEDX, LLC—See Ascension Health Alliance; *U.S. Private*, pg. 346
TRITON DIVING SERVICES, LLC; *U.S. Private*, pg. 4239
TRIUMPH ENTERPRISES INC; *U.S. Private*, pg. 4239
TRYNEX, INC.—See Douglas Dynamics, Inc.; *U.S. Public*, pg. 677
T&T SOLUTIONS, INC.; *U.S. Private*, pg. 3910
TWC PRODUCT AND TECHNOLOGY, LLC—See International Business Machines Corporation; *U.S. Public*, pg. 1151
UAB STORMGEO—See Alfa Laval AB; *Int'l*, pg. 312
UBICARE; *U.S. Private*, pg. 4273
UK INDEPENDENT MEDICAL SERVICES LIMITED—See GIC Pte. Ltd.; *Int'l*, pg. 2964
UK INDEPENDENT MEDICAL SERVICES LIMITED—See Leonard Green & Partners, L.P.; *U.S. Private*, pg. 2425
UMIAQ, LLC—See Ukpeagvik Inupiat Corporation; *U.S. Private*, pg. 4275
UNITED DEALER SERVICES L.L.C.—See Arthur J. Gallagher & Co.; *U.S. Public*, pg. 207

541990 — ALL OTHER PROFESSIO...

UNITED FOREST PRODUCTS INC.; *U.S. Private*, pg. 4292
UPLAND SOFTWARE I, INC.—See Upland Software, Inc.; *U.S. Public*, pg. 2264
U.S. PT THERAPY SERVICES, INC.—See U.S. Physical Therapy, Inc.; *U.S. Public*, pg. 2216
UTC AEROSPACE SYSTEMS - ENGINE CONTROL SERVICES—See RTX Corporation; *U.S. Public*, pg. 1823
VALUATION RESEARCH CORP.; *U.S. Private*, pg. 4337
VALUE MANAGEMENT GROUP LLC—See Northlane Capital Partners, LLC; *U.S. Private*, pg. 2956
VANASSE HANGEN BRUSTLIN, INC.; *U.S. Private*, pg. 4341
VCE EUROPE GMBH—See HPI AG; *Int'l*, pg. 3500
VELOSI (VIETNAM) CO LTD.—See I Squared Capital Advisors (US) LLC; *U.S. Private*, pg. 2023
VELTEC AS—See ELKA Beteiligungs GmbH; *Int'l*, pg. 2364
VELTEC GMBH—See ELKA Beteiligungs GmbH; *Int'l*, pg. 2364
VELTEC INDUSTRIAL SERVICES A/S—See ELKA Beteiligungs GmbH; *Int'l*, pg. 2364
VELTEC N.V.—See ELKA Beteiligungs GmbH; *Int'l*, pg. 2364
VERTEX AEROSPACE LLC—See V2X, Inc.; *U.S. Public*, pg. 2270
VISONEX, LLC—See Renesan Software; *U.S. Private*, pg. 3398
VT SERVICES, INC. - JACKSONVILLE DIVISION—See Alvarez & Marsal, Inc.; *U.S. Private*, pg. 213
VT SERVICES, INC. - MADISON DIVISION—See Alvarez & Marsal, Inc.; *U.S. Private*, pg. 213
WASSENBURG MEDICAL B.V.—See Hoya Corporation; *Int'l*, pg. 3498
WEATHERFORD U.S., INC.—See Weatherford International plc; *U.S. Public*, pg. 2341
WEATHER MAP CO., LTD.—See Imagica Group Inc.; *Int'l*, pg. 3619
WESDYNE INTERNATIONAL, INC.—See Brookfield Corporation; *Int'l*, pg. 1186
WEST COAST PIPE INSPECTION & MAINTENANCE INC.—See J.D. Rush Company Inc.; *U.S. Private*, pg. 2161
WHEATLAND SEED INC.; *U.S. Private*, pg. 4504
WIENER FINANCIAL MANAGEMENT—See Keystone Group, L.P.; *U.S. Private*, pg. 2298
WILLIAMS GAS PIPELINE—See The Williams Companies, Inc.; *U.S. Public*, pg. 2143
WISPRY, INC.—See AAC Technologies Holdings Inc.; *Int'l*, pg. 31
WLI (UK) LIMITED—See Castik Capital S.a.r.l.; *Int'l*, pg. 1356
WORLD INSPECTION NETWORK INTERNATIONAL, INC.—See Agamya Capital LLC; *U.S. Private*, pg. 126
WORLD WIDE TECHNOLOGY ASYNCHRONY LABS, LLC—See World Wide Technology Holding Co., LLC; *U.S. Private*, pg. 4568
WSI CORPORATION—See International Business Machines Corporation; *U.S. Public*, pg. 1151
WYG MANAGEMENT SERVICES LIMITED—See Tetra Tech, Inc.; *U.S. Public*, pg. 2024
WYLE LABORATORIES, INC.—See KBR, Inc.; *U.S. Public*, pg. 1216
XINDI ENERGY ENGINEERING TECHNOLOGY CO., LTD.—See ENN Natural Gas Co., Ltd.; *Int'l*, pg. 2443
ZERODAY TECHNOLOGY SOLUTIONS, INC.—See Warren Equity Partners, LLC; *U.S. Private*, pg. 4443
ZUBERANCE, INC.—See IZEA Worldwide, Inc.; *U.S. Public*, pg. 1179

551111 — OFFICES OF BANK HOLDING COMPANIES

1864 BANCORP, INC; *U.S. Private*, pg. 3
1867 WESTERN FINANCIAL CORPORATION; *U.S. Public*, pg. 2
1895 BANCORP OF WISCONSIN, INC.; *U.S. Public*, pg. 2
1ST CONSTITUTION BANCORP—See Provident Financial Services, Inc.; *U.S. Public*, pg. 1730
1ST SOURCE CORPORATION; *U.S. Public*, pg. 2
1ST SUMMIT BANCORP JOHNSTOWN, INC.; *U.S. Public*, pg. 3
215 HOLDING CO.; *U.S. Private*, pg. 5
3MV BANCORP, INC.; *U.S. Private*, pg. 13
ABC HOLDINGS LIMITED—See Atlas Mara Limited; *Int'l*, pg. 686
ABDO INVESTMENTS, INC.; *U.S. Private*, pg. 37
ABH FINANCIAL LIMITED—See ABH Holdings S.A.; *Int'l*, pg. 60
ABN AMRO GROUP N.V.; *Int'l*, pg. 63
ABSA GROUP LIMITED; *Int'l*, pg. 69
ABSECON BANCORP; *U.S. Public*, pg. 27
ACNB CORPORATION; *U.S. Public*, pg. 35
ADAM BANK GROUP, INC.—See The Adam Corporation/Group; *U.S. Private*, pg. 3981
ADIRONDACK BANKCORP, INC.; *U.S. Private*, pg. 79
AFFINITY BANCSHARES, INC.; *U.S. Public*, pg. 56
AIB GROUP PLC; *Int'l*, pg. 227
AICHI FINANCIAL GROUP CO., LTD.; *Int'l*, pg. 229
AINAVO HOLDINGS CORPORATION; *Int'l*, pg. 234
AJJ BANCORP, INC.; *U.S. Private*, pg. 144
ALBANY BANCORP, INC.; *U.S. Private*, pg. 151
ALERUS FINANCIAL CORPORATION; *U.S. Public*, pg. 74
ALLEGIANCE BANCSHARES, INC.—See Stellar Bancorp, Inc.; *U.S. Public*, pg. 1944
ALLIANCE BANCORP; *U.S. Private*, pg. 181
ALLIED FIRST BANCORP, INC.; *U.S. Private*, pg. 186
ALPINE BANKS OF COLORADO; *U.S. Public*, pg. 85
ALTABANCORP—See Glacier Bancorp, Inc.; *U.S. Public*, pg. 938
ALTAPACIFIC BANCORP—See Banner Corporation; *U.S. Public*, pg. 275
ALTRUST FINANCIAL SERVICES, INC.; *U.S. Public*, pg. 89
AMALGAMATED FINANCIAL CORP.; *U.S. Public*, pg. 89
AMALGAMATED INVESTMENTS CO.; *U.S. Private*, pg. 215
AMARILLO NATIONAL BANCORP, INC.; *U.S. Private*, pg. 216
AMB FINANCIAL CORP.; *U.S. Public*, pg. 91
AMBOY BANCORPORATION; *U.S. Private*, pg. 218
AMERANT BANCORP INC.; *U.S. Public*, pg. 94
AMERIBANCSHARES, INC.; *U.S. Private*, pg. 220
AMERICAN BANCOR, LTD.; *U.S. Private*, pg. 223
AMERICAN BANCORP, INC.; *U.S. Public*, pg. 97
AMERICAN BANCORPORATION OF MINNESOTA, INC.; *U.S. Private*, pg. 223
AMERICAN BANK HOLDING INC.; *U.S. Private*, pg. 223
AMERICAN BANK INCORPORATED; *U.S. Public*, pg. 97
AMERICAN CONTINENTAL BANCORP; *U.S. Private*, pg. 228
AMERICAN NATIONAL BANKSHARES INC.—See Atlantic Union Bankshares Corporation; *U.S. Public*, pg. 223
AMERICAN NATIONAL CORPORATION; *U.S. Private*, pg. 241
AMERICAN RIVER BANKSHARES—See Bank of Marin Bancorp; *U.S. Public*, pg. 273
AMERICAN STATE BANCSHARES, INC.; *U.S. Private*, pg. 255
AMERICAN STATE BANK HOLDING COMPANY, INC.; *U.S. Private*, pg. 255
AMERI FINANCIAL GROUP, INC.; *U.S. Private*, pg. 220
AMERIS BANCORP; *U.S. Public*, pg. 114
AMERISERV FINANCIAL, INC.; *U.S. Public*, pg. 115
AMES NATIONAL CORPORATION; *U.S. Public*, pg. 115
AMFIN FINANCIAL CORP.; *U.S. Public*, pg. 122
AMI (HOLDINGS), LLC—See Apollo Global Management, Inc.; *U.S. Private*, pg. 146
ANDOVER BANCORP, INC.; *U.S. Public*, pg. 136
ANZ (DELAWARE) INC.—See Australia & New Zealand Banking Group Limited; *Int'l*, pg. 719
ANZ INTERNATIONAL (HONG KONG) LTD.—See Australia & New Zealand Banking Group Limited; *Int'l*, pg. 719
ANZ INTERNATIONAL PTE. LTD.—See Australia & New Zealand Banking Group Limited; *Int'l*, pg. 719
ANZ NATIONAL BANK LTD.—See Australia & New Zealand Banking Group Limited; *Int'l*, pg. 720
APAMAN CO., LTD.; *Int'l*, pg. 500
APOLLO BANCORP, INC.; *U.S. Public*, pg. 145
APOLLO BANCSHARES, INC.—See Seacoast Banking Corporation of Florida; *U.S. Public*, pg. 1851
APPLE CREEK BANC CORP.; *U.S. Private*, pg. 296
AQUESTA FINANCIAL HOLDINGS, INC.—See United Community Banks, Inc.; *U.S. Public*, pg. 2230
ARBOR BANCORP, INC.; *U.S. Private*, pg. 308
ARIF HABIB CORPORATION LIMITED; *Int'l*, pg. 564
ARROW FINANCIAL CORPORATION; *U.S. Public*, pg. 200
ARVEST BANK GROUP, INC.; *U.S. Private*, pg. 344
ASB HAWAII, INC.—See Hawaiian Electric Industries, Inc.; *U.S. Public*, pg. 989
ASCENT BANCORP; *U.S. Private*, pg. 348
ASHTON BANCSHARES, INC.; *U.S. Private*, pg. 350
ASSABET VALLEY BANCORP; *U.S. Private*, pg. 353
ASSOCIATED BANC-CORP; *U.S. Public*, pg. 214
ASSOCIATED COMMUNITY BANCORP, INC.; *U.S. Private*, pg. 355
ASTAREAL HOLDINGS CO., LTD.—See Fuji Chemical Industries Co., Ltd; *Int'l*, pg. 2808
ATLANTIC CAPITAL BANCSHARES, INC.—See SouthState Corporation; *U.S. Public*, pg. 1912
ATLANTIC UNION BANKSHARES CORPORATION; *U.S. Public*, pg. 222
AUBURN BANCORP, INC.; *U.S. Private*, pg. 225
AUBURN NATIONAL BANCORPORATION, INC.; *U.S. Public*, pg. 225
AUSTRALIA & NEW ZEALAND BANKING GROUP LIMITED; *Int'l*, pg. 719
AVIDBANK HOLDINGS, INC.; *U.S. Private*, pg. 246
AXOS FINANCIAL, INC.; *U.S. Public*, pg. 256
BAC HOLDING INTERNATIONAL CORP.; *Int'l*, pg. 793
BAINBRIDGE BANCSHARES, INC.; *U.S. Private*, pg. 453
BAIYU HOLDINGS, INC.; *Int'l*, pg. 803
BAKER BOYER BANCORP; *U.S. Private*, pg. 264
BANCA FINNAT EURAMERICA S.P.A.; *Int'l*, pg. 814
BANCA ITALEASE S.P.A.—See Banco BPM S.p.A.; *Int'l*, pg. 818
BANCA SELLA HOLDINGS S.P.A.; *Int'l*, pg. 816
BANCFIRST CORPORATION; *U.S. Public*, pg. 269
BANCINDEPENDENT INC.; *U.S. Private*, pg. 464
BANCINSURANCE CORPORATION; *U.S. Private*, pg. 464
BANCO BPM S.P.A.; *Int'l*, pg. 818
BANC OF CALIFORNIA, INC.; *U.S. Public*, pg. 268
BANCORP 34, INC.; *U.S. Public*, pg. 269
THE BANCORP, INC.; *U.S. Public*, pg. 2036
BANCORP OF SOUTHERN INDIANA; *U.S. Private*, pg. 269
BANCO SANTANDER, S.A.; *Int'l*, pg. 825
BANK7 CORP.; *U.S. Public*, pg. 274
BANKERS BANCORP OF OKLAHOMA, INC.; *U.S. Private*, pg. 467
BANKERS' BANCORPORATION, INC.; *U.S. Private*, pg. 468
BANKFINANCIAL CORPORATION; *U.S. Public*, pg. 274
BANKFIRST CAPITAL CORPORATION; *U.S. Private*, pg. 274
BANK FIRST CORPORATION; *U.S. Public*, pg. 269
BANK IOWA CORPORATION; *U.S. Private*, pg. 466
BANKMANAGERS CORP.—See Old National Bancorp; *U.S. Public*, pg. 1566
BANK OF AMERICA CORPORATION; *U.S. Public*, pg. 270
BANK OF COMMERCE HOLDINGS; *U.S. Public*, pg. 272
BANK OF GEORGIA GROUP PLC; *Int'l*, pg. 843
BANK OF HAWAII CORPORATION; *U.S. Public*, pg. 272
BANK OF IDAHO HOLDING COMPANY; *U.S. Public*, pg. 273
BANK OF IRELAND GROUP PLC; *Int'l*, pg. 843
BANK OF MARIN BANCORP; *U.S. Public*, pg. 273
THE BANK OF NEW YORK MELLON CORPORATION; *U.S. Public*, pg. 2036
BANK OF SOUTH CAROLINA CORPORATION; *U.S. Public*, pg. 273
BANK OF THE JAMES FINANCIAL GROUP, INC.; *U.S. Public*, pg. 273
BANK OF THE PHILIPPINE ISLANDS; *Int'l*, pg. 848
BANK OZK; *U.S. Public*, pg. 273
BANKPLUS CORPORATION; *U.S. Private*, pg. 468
BANKPROV; *U.S. Public*, pg. 274
BANKWELL FINANCIAL GROUP, INC.; *U.S. Public*, pg. 274
BANNER CORPORATION; *U.S. Public*, pg. 275
BANNER COUNTY BAN CORPORATION; *U.S. Private*, pg. 469
BANQUE DEGROOF S.A.; *Int'l*, pg. 853
BANQUE DE NEUFLIZE OBC S.A.—See ABN AMRO Group N.V.; *Int'l*, pg. 65
BANTERRA CORP.; *U.S. Private*, pg. 469
BARABOO BANCORPORATION, INC.; *U.S. Private*, pg. 275
BARCLAYS PLC; *Int'l*, pg. 859
BAR HARBOR BANKSHARES; *U.S. Public*, pg. 275
BAWAG GROUP AG; *Int'l*, pg. 900
BAWAG P.S.K. BANK FUR ARBEIT UND WIRTSCHAFT UND OSTERREICHISCHE POSTSPARKASSE AKTIENGESELLSCHAFT; *Int'l*, pg. 900
BAY BANKS OF VIRGINIA, INC.—See Blue Ridge Bankshares, Inc.; *U.S. Public*, pg. 364
BAYCOM CORP; *U.S. Public*, pg. 284
BAYFIRST FINANCIAL CORP.; *U.S. Public*, pg. 284
BBVA USA BANCSHARES, INC.—See The PNC Financial Services Group, Inc.; *U.S. Public*, pg. 2119
BBVA USA BANCSHARES, INC.—See The PNC Financial Services Group, Inc.; *U.S. Public*, pg. 2119
BCB BANCORP, INC.; *U.S. Public*, pg. 285
BDO STRATEGIC HOLDINGS, INC.—See BDO Unibank, Inc.; *Int'l*, pg. 930
BEACH COMMUNITY BANCSHARES, INC.; *U.S. Public*, pg. 285
BENCHMARK BANKSHARES INC.; *U.S. Public*, pg. 295
BENEFICIAL STATE BANCORP, INC.—See Beneficial State Foundation; *U.S. Private*, pg. 525
BENTON FINANCIAL CORP.; *U.S. Public*, pg. 297
BEO BANCORP; *U.S. Public*, pg. 297
BERKSHIRE BANCORP INC.; *U.S. Private*, pg. 533
BERKSHIRE FINANCIAL SERVICES, INC.; *U.S. Private*, pg. 533
BERKSHIRE HILLS BANCORP, INC.; *U.S. Public*, pg. 319
BERMUDA INTERNATIONAL FINANCE LTD.—See HSBC Holdings plc; *Int'l*, pg. 3504
THE BESSEMER GROUP, INCORPORATED; *U.S. Private*, pg. 3994
BFA TENEDORA DE ACCIONES, S.A.U.; *Int'l*, pg. 1006
BLACKHAWK BANCORP INC.—See First Mid Bancshares, Inc.; *U.S. Public*, pg. 846
BLUE FOUNDRY BANCORP; *U.S. Public*, pg. 364
BLUE RIDGE BANCSHARES INC.; *U.S. Private*, pg. 591
BLUE RIDGE BANKSHARES, INC.; *U.S. Public*, pg. 364
BLUE VALLEY BAN CORP.—See Heartland Financial USA, Inc.; *U.S. Public*, pg. 1018
BMO FINANCIAL CORP.—See Bank of Montreal; *Int'l*, pg. 846
BNCCORP, INC.; *U.S. Public*, pg. 366
BNH FINANCIAL; *U.S. Private*, pg. 601
BNK FINANCIAL GROUP INC.; *Int'l*, pg. 1079
BNP PARIBAS FORTIS YATIRIMLAR HOLDING A.S.—See BNP Paribas SA; *Int'l*, pg. 1084
BNP PARIBAS SA; *Int'l*, pg. 1079

551111 — OFFICES OF BANK HOL...

N.A.I.C.S. INDEX

BNPP YATIRIMLAR HOLDING AS—See BNP Paribas SA; *Int'l*, pg. 1088
BOA GROUP S.A.; *Int'l*, pg. 1094
BOC HONG KONG (HOLDINGS) LIMITED—See Bank of China, Ltd.; *Int'l*, pg. 841
BOGOTA FINANCIAL CORP.; *U.S. Public*, pg. 367
BOK FINANCIAL CORPORATION; *U.S. Public*, pg. 367
BOL BANCSHARES, INC.; *U.S. Public*, pg. 367
BOSP BANCSHARES, INC.; *U.S. Private*, pg. 620
BOSTON PRIVATE FINANCIAL HOLDINGS, INC.; *U.S. Public*, pg. 372
BOU BANCORP, INC.; *U.S. Private*, pg. 623
BOYLE BANCORP INC.; *U.S. Public*, pg. 378
BPCE S.A.—See Groupe BPCE; *Int'l*, pg. 3094
BPER BANCA S.P.A; *Int'l*, pg. 1131
BRADLEY BANCORP, INC.; *U.S. Private*, pg. 632
BRADLEY BANCSHARES, INC.; *U.S. Private*, pg. 632
BREMER FINANCIAL CORPORATION; *U.S. Private*, pg. 645
BRENHAM BANCSHARES, INC.; *U.S. Private*, pg. 645
BRIDGEVIEW BANCORP, INC.—See Old National Bancorp; *U.S. Public*, pg. 1567
BRIDGEWATER BANCSHARES, INC.; *U.S. Public*, pg. 382
BROADWAY BANCSHARES, INC.; *U.S. Private*, pg. 660
BROOKLINE BANCORP, INC.; *U.S. Public*, pg. 395
BROTHERHOOD BANCSHARES, INC.; *U.S. Public*, pg. 396
BRUNSWICK BANCORP—See Mid Penn Bancorp, Inc.; *U.S. Public*, pg. 1444
BRYN MAWR BANK CORPORATION; *U.S. Public*, pg. 408
BSJ BANCSHARES, INC.; *U.S. Private*, pg. 675
BTC FINANCIAL CORPORATION; *U.S. Private*, pg. 675
BTG PACTUAL HOLDING S.A.; *Int'l*, pg. 1204
BUCKEYE STATE BANCSHARES, INC.; *U.S. Private*, pg. 677
BUNKYODO GROUP HOLDINGS CO., LTD.; *Int'l*, pg. 1216
BUREAU VERITAS S.A.; *Int'l*, pg. 1221
BURKE & HERBERT FINANCIAL SERVICES CORP.—See Burke & Herbert Bank & Trust Company; *U.S. Private*, pg. 687
BURTON BANCSHARES, INC.; *U.S. Private*, pg. 693
BUSINESS FIRST BANCSHARES, INC.; *U.S. Public*, pg. 413
BV FINANCIAL, INC.—See Bay-Vanguard, M.H.C.; *U.S. Private*, pg. 495
BYLINE BANCORP, INC.; *U.S. Public*, pg. 413
C3 BANCORP; *U.S. Private*, pg. 710
CAB FINANCIAL CORPORATION—See Park National Corporation; *U.S. Public*, pg. 1638
CACHE VALLEY BANKING COMPANY; *U.S. Private*, pg. 712
CALDWELL COUNTY BANCSHARES, INC.; *U.S. Private*, pg. 716
CALIFORNIA BANCORP; *U.S. Public*, pg. 423
CALIFORNIA FIRST NATIONAL BANCORP; *U.S. Private*, pg. 719
CALUMET BANCORPORATION, INC.; *U.S. Private*, pg. 724
CAMBRIDGE BANCORP; *U.S. Public*, pg. 425
CAMBRIDGE FINANCIAL GROUP, INC.; *U.S. Private*, pg. 726
CAMDEN NATIONAL CORPORATION; *U.S. Public*, pg. 426
CAMPELLO BANCORP, INC.; *U.S. Private*, pg. 731
CANADA LANDS COMPANY LIMITED; *Int'l*, pg. 1278
CANADIAN IMPERIAL HOLDINGS INC.—See Canadian Imperial Bank of Commerce; *Int'l*, pg. 1283
CANANDAIGUA NATIONAL CORPORATION; *U.S. Public*, pg. 428
CAPITAL BANCORP, INC.; *U.S. Public*, pg. 431
CAPITAL CITY BANK GROUP, INC.; *U.S. Public*, pg. 431
CAPITAL FUNDING BANCORP, INC.—See Capital Funding Group, Inc.; *U.S. Private*, pg. 740
CAPITAL ONE FINANCIAL CORPORATION; *U.S. Public*, pg. 431
CAPITAL ONE HOLDINGS LIMITED—See Capital One Financial Corporation; *U.S. Public*, pg. 431
CAPITEC BANK HOLDINGS LIMITED; *Int'l*, pg. 1314
CAPITOL FEDERAL FINANCIAL, INC.; *U.S. Public*, pg. 432
CAPSTAR FINANCIAL HOLDINGS, INC.—See Old National Bancorp; *U.S. Public*, pg. 1566
CAPTEX BANCSHARES, INC.; *U.S. Public*, pg. 746
CARDINAL BANCORP INC.; *U.S. Private*, pg. 749
CARDTRONICS HOLDINGS, LLC—See NCR Voyix Corporation.; *U.S. Public*, pg. 1501
CARIBBEAN INVESTMENT HOLDINGS LIMITED; *Int'l*, pg. 1330
CARPENTER BANK PARTNERS, INC.—See CCFW, Inc.; *U.S. Private*, pg. 799
CARSON FINANCIAL HOLDING COMPANY, INC.; *U.S. Private*, pg. 774
CARTER BANKSHARES, INC.; *U.S. Public*, pg. 445
CARTU GROUP JSC; *Int'l*, pg. 1348
CASSA CENTRALE BANCA-CREDITO COOPERATIVO DEL NORD EST SPA; *Int'l*, pg. 1354
CATALYST BANCORP, INC.; *U.S. Public*, pg. 449
CATHAY GENERAL BANCORP; *U.S. Public*, pg. 454
CATSKILL HUDSON BANCORP, INC.; *U.S. Public*, pg. 454
CBB BANCORP, INC.; *U.S. Public*, pg. 455
CBC BANCORP; *U.S. Private*, pg. 796

CBC HOLDING COMPANY; *U.S. Public*, pg. 455
CB FINANCIAL SERVICES, INC.; *U.S. Public*, pg. 455
CBM BANCORP, INC.; *U.S. Public*, pg. 459
CB&S BANK, INC.; *U.S. Private*, pg. 796
CB&T HOLDING CORPORATION; *U.S. Private*, pg. 796
CCB GROUP EAD—See Chimimport AD; *Int'l*, pg. 1479
CCSB FINANCIAL CORP.; *U.S. Public*, pg. 461
CECIL BANCORP, INC.; *U.S. Public*, pg. 463
CENTRABANC CORPORATION; *U.S. Private*, pg. 818
CENTRAL BANCOMPANY, INC.; *U.S. Public*, pg. 472
CENTRAL FINANCE COMPANY PLC; *Int'l*, pg. 1406
CENTRAL FINANCIAL HOLDINGS, INC.; *U.S. Private*, pg. 820
CENTRAL PACIFIC FINANCIAL CORPORATION; *U.S. Public*, pg. 473
CENTRAL PLAINS BANCSHARES, INC.; *U.S. Public*, pg. 473
CENTRAL SERVICE CORP.; *U.S. Public*, pg. 474
CENTRE 1 BANCORP, INC.; *U.S. Private*, pg. 827
CENTRIC FINANCIAL CORP.—See First Commonwealth Financial Corporation; *U.S. Public*, pg. 842
CENTURY BANCORP, INC.—See Eastern Bankshares, Inc.; *U.S. Public*, pg. 703
CENTURY BANCSHARES, INC.; *U.S. Private*, pg. 831
CENTURY BANCSHARES, INC.; *U.S. Private*, pg. 832
CENTURY BANCSHARES OF FLORIDA, INC.; *U.S. Private*, pg. 831
CENTURY NEXT FINANCIAL CORPORATION; *U.S. Public*, pg. 475
CERTUSHOLDINGS, INC.; *U.S. Private*, pg. 842
CF BANKSHARES INC.; *U.S. Public*, pg. 476
C&F FINANCIAL CORPORATION; *U.S. Public*, pg. 414
CFSB BANCORP, INC.; *U.S. Public*, pg. 477
CHAMBERS BANCSHARES INC.; *U.S. Private*, pg. 846
CHAMPLAIN BANK CORPORATION; *U.S. Private*, pg. 847
CHARTER BANKSHARES, INC.—See Nicolet Bankshares, Inc.; *U.S. Public*, pg. 1528
CHASE VENTURES HOLDINGS INC.—See JPMorgan Chase & Co.; *U.S. Public*, pg. 1209
CHEAHA FINANCIAL GROUP, INC.—See Investar Holding Corporation; *U.S. Public*, pg. 1164
CHEBELLE CORPORATION; *U.S. Private*, pg. 868
CHESAPEAKE BANCORP; *U.S. Public*, pg. 485
CHESAPEAKE FINANCIAL SHARES, INC.; *U.S. Public*, pg. 485
CHESTER BANCORP, INC.; *U.S. Public*, pg. 486
CHINA DEVELOPMENT BANK CORPORATION; *Int'l*, pg. 1497
CHINO COMMERCIAL BANCORP; *U.S. Public*, pg. 489
CHOICE FINANCIAL HOLDINGS, INC.—See Northlane Capital Partners, LLC; *U.S. Private*, pg. 2956
CHOICEONE FINANCIAL SERVICES, INC.; *U.S. Public*, pg. 490
CHUGIN FINANCIAL GROUP, INC.; *Int'l*, pg. 1594
CIB MARINE BANCSHARES, INC.; *U.S. Public*, pg. 494
CIMB GROUP HOLDINGS BERHAD; *Int'l*, pg. 1607
CIMB GROUP SDN. BHD.—See CIMB Group Holdings Berhad; *Int'l*, pg. 1607
CITBA FINANCIAL CORP.; *U.S. Public*, pg. 501
CITCO COMMUNITY BANCSHARES, INC.; *U.S. Private*, pg. 901
CIT GROUP INC.—See First Citizens BancShares, Inc.; *U.S. Public*, pg. 841
CITIC INTERNATIONAL FINANCIAL HOLDINGS LIMITED—See CITIC Group Corporation; *Int'l*, pg. 1620
CITIGROUP INC.; *U.S. Public*, pg. 501
CITIZENS BANCORP INVESTMENT, INC.; *U.S. Public*, pg. 504
CITIZENS BANCORPORATION OF NEW ULM, INC.; *U.S. Private*, pg. 902
CITIZENS BANCSHARES CORPORATION; *U.S. Private*, pg. 902
CITIZENS BANCSHARES CORPORATION; *U.S. Private*, pg. 504
CITIZENS BANCSHARES CO.—See Southern Missouri Bancorp, Inc.; *U.S. Public*, pg. 1911
CITIZENS BANCSHARES, INC.; *U.S. Private*, pg. 902
CITIZENS BANCSHARES, INC.; *U.S. Private*, pg. 903
CITIZENS BANCSHARES OF BATESVILLE, INC.; *U.S. Private*, pg. 902
CITIZENS BANCSHARES OF HUTCHINSON, INC.; *U.S. Private*, pg. 902
CITIZENS BANKSHARES INC.; *U.S. Private*, pg. 903
CITIZENS B & T HOLDINGS, INC.; *U.S. Private*, pg. 902
CITIZENS COMMERCE BANCSHARES, INC.—See City Holding Company; *U.S. Public*, pg. 506
CITIZENS COMMUNITY BANCORP, INC.; *U.S. Public*, pg. 504
CITIZENS CORPORATION; *U.S. Private*, pg. 903
CITIZENS FINANCIAL CORP.; *U.S. Public*, pg. 505
CITIZENS FINANCIAL GROUP, INC.; *U.S. Public*, pg. 505
CITIZENS FINANCIAL SERVICES, INC.; *U.S. Public*, pg. 506
CITIZENS HOLDING COMPANY; *U.S. Public*, pg. 506
CITIZENS INDEPENDENT BANCORP, INC.—See The Merchants National Bank; *U.S. Private*, pg. 4078
CITIZENS NATIONAL CORPORATION; *U.S. Public*, pg. 506

CITIZENS & NORTHERN CORPORATION; *U.S. Public*, pg. 504
CITIZENS UNION BANCORP OF SHELBYVILLE, INC.—See German American Bancorp, Inc.; *U.S. Public*, pg. 934
CITY HOLDING COMPANY; *U.S. Public*, pg. 506
CIVISTA BANCSHARES, INC.; *U.S. Public*, pg. 507
CLAYTON HC, INC.; *U.S. Private*, pg. 918
CLEVER LEAVES HOLDINGS INC.; *U.S. Public*, pg. 514
CLINTON BANCSHARES, INC.; *U.S. Private*, pg. 944
CMS ENERGY CORPORATION; *U.S. Public*, pg. 518
CNB BANK SHARES, INC.; *U.S. Public*, pg. 519
CNB COMMUNITY BANCORP, INC.; *U.S. Public*, pg. 519
CNB CORPORATION; *U.S. Public*, pg. 519
CNB CORPORATION; *U.S. Public*, pg. 519
CNB FINANCIAL CORPORATION; *U.S. Public*, pg. 519
CNL FINANCIAL GROUP, INC.; *U.S. Private*, pg. 952
COASTAL CAROLINA BANCSHARES, INC.; *U.S. Public*, pg. 520
COASTAL FINANCIAL CORPORATION; *U.S. Public*, pg. 520
COASTAL SOUTH BANCSHARES, INC.; *U.S. Public*, pg. 520
CODORUS VALLEY BANCORP, INC.—See Orrstown Financial Services, Inc.; *U.S. Public*, pg. 1618
COEUR D'ALENE BANCORP, INC.; *U.S. Public*, pg. 521
COLONY BANKCORP, INC.; *U.S. Public*, pg. 533
COLUMBIA BANKING SYSTEM, INC.; *U.S. Public*, pg. 534
COLUMBIA FINANCIAL, INC.; *U.S. Public*, pg. 534
COMERICA INCORPORATED; *U.S. Public*, pg. 542
COMERICA LEASING CORPORATION—See Comerica Incorporated; *U.S. Public*, pg. 542
COMET HOLDING AG; *Int'l*, pg. 1710
COMMERCE BANCSHARES, INC.; *U.S. Private*, pg. 982
COMMERCE BANCSHARES, INC.; *U.S. Public*, pg. 544
COMMERCIAL BANCGROUP, INC.; *U.S. Private*, pg. 983
COMMERCIAL FINANCIAL CORP.; *U.S. Private*, pg. 983
COMMERCIAL NATIONAL FINANCIAL CORPORATION; *U.S. Public*, pg. 547
COMMERZBANK AG; *Int'l*, pg. 1715
COMMONWEALTH BANCSHARES, INC.—See Stock Yards Bancorp, Inc.; *U.S. Public*, pg. 1950
COMMUNITIES FIRST FINANCIAL CORPORATION; *U.S. Public*, pg. 549
COMMUNITY BANCORP, INC.; *U.S. Public*, pg. 549
COMMUNITY BANCORP OF LOUISIANA, INC.; *U.S. Private*, pg. 989
COMMUNITY BANCSHARES, INC.; *U.S. Public*, pg. 549
COMMUNITY BANCSHARES OF MISSISSIPPI, INC.; *U.S. Private*, pg. 989
COMMUNITY BANKERS; *U.S. Public*, pg. 550
COMMUNITY BANKERS TRUST CORPORATION—See United Bankshares, Inc.; *U.S. Public*, pg. 2229
COMMUNITY BANK HOLDINGS OF TEXAS, INC.; *U.S. Private*, pg. 990
COMMUNITY BANK OF MISSISSIPPI—See Community Bancshares of Mississippi, Inc.; *U.S. Private*, pg. 990
COMMUNITY BANKSHARES, INC.; *U.S. Private*, pg. 990
COMMUNITY BANK SYSTEM, INC.; *U.S. Public*, pg. 549
COMMUNITY CAPITAL BANCSHARES, INC.; *U.S. Public*, pg. 550
THE COMMUNITY FINANCIAL CORPORATION—See Shore Bancshares, Inc.; *U.S. Public*, pg. 1875
COMMUNITY FINANCIAL CORP; *U.S. Private*, pg. 991
COMMUNITY FIRST BANCORPORATION; *U.S. Public*, pg. 550
COMMUNITY FIRST BANCSHARES, INC.; *U.S. Private*, pg. 991
COMMUNITY FIRST BANCSHARES, INC.—See Affinity Bancshares, Inc.; *U.S. Public*, pg. 56
COMMUNITY HERITAGE FINANCIAL, INC.; *U.S. Public*, pg. 558
COMMUNITY INVESTMENT GROUP, LTD.; *U.S. Private*, pg. 995
COMMUNITY INVESTORS BANCORP, INC.; *U.S. Public*, pg. 558
COMMUNITY NATIONAL BANK & TRUST; *U.S. Private*, pg. 996
COMMUNITY SAVINGS BANCORP, INC.; *U.S. Public*, pg. 558
COMMUNITY TRUST BANCORP INC; *U.S. Public*, pg. 558
COMMUNITY WEST BANCSHARES; *U.S. Public*, pg. 558
COMMUNITY WEST BANCSHARES—See Community West Bancshares; *U.S. Public*, pg. 558
COMPAGNIE DE L'OCCIDENT POUR LA FINANCE ET L'INDUSTRIE S.A.; *Int'l*, pg. 1722
COMUNIBANC CORP.—See Civista Bancshares, Inc.; *U.S. Public*, pg. 507
CONCORDIA FINANCIAL GROUP, LTD.; *Int'l*, pg. 1765
CONGRESSIONAL BANCSHARES, INC.; *U.S. Private*, pg. 1013
CONNECTONE BANCORP, INC.; *U.S. Public*, pg. 567
CONSTELLATION INSURANCE HOLDINGS INC.—See Caisse de Depot et Placement du Quebec; *Int'l*, pg. 1254
CONSUMERS BANCORP, INC.; *U.S. Public*, pg. 573
COOPERATIEVE CENTRALE RAIFFEISEN-BOERENLEENBANK B.A.; *Int'l*, pg. 1791

551111 — OFFICES OF BANK HOL...

CORNERSTONE COMMUNITY BANCORP; *U.S. Public*, pg. 577
CORNERSTONE FINANCIAL CORPORATION—See Princeton Bancorp, Inc.; *U.S. Public*, pg. 1719
CORNHUSKER GROWTH CORPORATION; *U.S. Private*, pg. 1053
CORTLAND BANCORP, INC.—See Farmers National Banc Corp.; *U.S. Public*, pg. 822
COSTAR LIMITED—See CoStar Group, Inc.; *U.S. Public*, pg. 585
COUNTRY BANK HOLDING COMPANY, INC.—See OceanFirst Financial Corp.; *U.S. Public*, pg. 1563
COUNTRY BANK SHARES, INC.; *U.S. Private*, pg. 1066
COUNTY BANCORP, INC.—See Nicolet Bankshares, Inc.; *U.S. Public*, pg. 1528
CRANE CREDIT UNION; *U.S. Public*, pg. 1085
CRAZY WOMAN CREEK BANCORP, INC.; *U.S. Public*, pg. 592
CREDICORP LTD.; *Int'l*, pg. 1834
CREDIT MUTUEL ARKEA S.A.—See Confederation Nationale du Credit Mutuel; *Int'l*, pg. 1767
CREDITO EMILIANO S.P.A.; *Int'l*, pg. 1836
CREDITOS Y AHORRO CREDIFINANCIERA S.A., COMPANIA DE FINANCIAMIENTO; *Int'l*, pg. 1837
CREDITO VALTELLINESE SOCIETA COOPERATIVA; *Int'l*, pg. 1837
CRELANCO CVBA; *Int'l*, pg. 1838
CREWS BANKING CORPORATION; *U.S. Private*, pg. 1099
CROSS COUNTY BANCSHARES INC.; *U.S. Private*, pg. 1104
CROSSFIRST BANKSHARES, INC.; *U.S. Public*, pg. 596
CSB BANCORP, INC.; *U.S. Public*, pg. 600
C.S.B. BANCSHARES, INC.; *U.S. Private*, pg. 709
CSS HOLDINGS, LTD.; *Int'l*, pg. 1867
CTBC BANK CO., LTD.—See CTBC Financial Holding Co., Ltd.; *Int'l*, pg. 1869
CULLEN/FROST BANKERS, INC.; *U.S. Public*, pg. 604
CULLMAN BANCORP, INC.; *U.S. Public*, pg. 604
CUMBERLAND VALLEY FINANCIAL CORPORATION; *U.S. Private*, pg. 1123
CUSTOMERS BANCORP, INC.; *U.S. Public*, pg. 612
CVB FINANCIAL CORP.; *U.S. Public*, pg. 613
DACOTAH BANKS, INC.; *U.S. Public*, pg. 620
DAH SING FINANCIAL HOLDINGS LIMITED; *Int'l*, pg. 1912
DAINGERFIELD HOLDING COMPANY; *U.S. Private*, pg. 1145
DAKOTA COMMUNITY BANSHARES, INC.; *U.S. Private*, pg. 1147
DBS GROUP HOLDINGS LTD.; *Int'l*, pg. 1988
DEERWOOD BANCSHARES, INC.; *U.S. Private*, pg. 1190
DELMARVA BANCSHARES, INC.; *U.S. Private*, pg. 1197
DELTA BANCSHARES COMPANY—See First Mid Bancshares, Inc.; *U.S. Public*, pg. 846
DENALI BANCORP INC.; *U.S. Public*, pg. 653
DENMARK BANCSHARES, INC.—See Bank First Corporation; *U.S. Public*, pg. 270
DENTEL BANCORPORATION; *U.S. Private*, pg. 1206
DENVER BANKSHARES, INC.; *U.S. Public*, pg. 656
DEUTSCHE ASIA PACIFIC HOLDINGS PTE LTD.—See Deutsche Bank Aktiengesellschaft; *Int'l*, pg. 2057
DEWAVRIN GROUPE; *Int'l*, pg. 2091
DEXIA SA; *Int'l*, pg. 2092
DGB FINANCIAL GROUP CO., LTD.; *Int'l*, pg. 2096
DH DENMARK HOLDING APS—See Danaher Corporation; *U.S. Public*, pg. 625
DICKINSON FINANCIAL CORPORATION; *U.S. Private*, pg. 1227
DIMECO INC.; *U.S. Public*, pg. 666
DIME COMMUNITY BANCSHARES, INC.; *U.S. Public*, pg. 666
D.L. EVANS BANCORP; *U.S. Private*, pg. 1142
DMG BANCSHARES, INC.; *U.S. Private*, pg. 1248
DNB FINANCIAL CORPORATION—See S&T Bancorp, Inc.; *U.S. Public*, pg. 1832
DOCKING BANCSHARES, INC.; *U.S. Private*, pg. 1251
DOLLAR MUTUAL BANCORP; *U.S. Private*, pg. 1254
DRUMMOND BANKING COMPANY; *U.S. Private*, pg. 1279
DSA FINANCIAL CORP.; *U.S. Public*, pg. 688
DUCLARKEE, INC.; *U.S. Private*, pg. 1284
DURANT BANCORP, INC.; *U.S. Private*, pg. 1292
DZ BANK AG DEUTSCHE ZENTRAL-GENOSSENSCHAFTSBANK; *Int'l*, pg. 2243
EAGLE BANCORP, INC.; *U.S. Public*, pg. 701
EAGLE BANCORP MONTANA, INC.; *U.S. Public*, pg. 701
EAGLE FINANCIAL BANCORP, INC.—See LCNB Corp.; *U.S. Public*, pg. 1296
EAGLE FINANCIAL SERVICES, INC.; *U.S. Public*, pg. 702
EASTER ENTERPRISES, INC.; *U.S. Private*, pg. 1319
EASTERN BANKSHARES, INC.; *U.S. Public*, pg. 703
EAST TEXAS BANCSHARES, INC.; *U.S. Private*, pg. 1318
EAST TEXAS FINANCIAL CORPORATION; *U.S. Private*, pg. 1318
EAST WEST BANCORP, INC.; *U.S. Public*, pg. 708
ECB BANCORP, INC.; *U.S. Public*, pg. 710
ECOBANK TRANSNATIONAL INCORPORATED; *Int'l*, pg. 2293
EDGEWATER BANCORP, INC.—See United Federal Credit Union; *U.S. Private*, pg. 4292

EDISON BANCSHARES, INC.; *U.S. Private*, pg. 1336
EDMOND DE ROTHSCHILD HOLDING S.A.; *Int'l*, pg. 2312
EFG BANK EUROPEAN FINANCIAL GROUP SA; *Int'l*, pg. 2319
ELMER BANCORP, INC.; *U.S. Public*, pg. 735
EMCLAIRE FINANCIAL CORP—See Farmers National Banc Corp.; *U.S. Public*, pg. 822
EMMETSBURG BANK SHARES, INC.; *U.S. Private*, pg. 1383
EMORY BANCSHARES, INC.; *U.S. Private*, pg. 1383
EMPIRE BANCORP, INC.—See Flushing Financial Corporation; *U.S. Public*, pg. 860
EMPRESAS JUAN YARUR S.A.C.; *Int'l*, pg. 2391
ENB FINANCIAL CORP.; *U.S. Public*, pg. 754
ENTEGRA FINANCIAL CORP.—See First Citizens BancShares, Inc.; *U.S. Public*, pg. 842
ENTERPRISE BANCORP, INC.; *U.S. Public*, pg. 777
ENTERPRISE FINANCIAL SERVICES GROUP, INC.; *U.S. Public*, pg. 778
EQUITABLE FINANCIAL CORP.; *U.S. Public*, pg. 788
EQUITY BANCSHARES, INC.; *U.S. Public*, pg. 790
ERSTE GROUP BANK AG; *Int'l*, pg. 2497
ES BANCSHARES, INC.; *U.S. Public*, pg. 793
ESQUIRE FINANCIAL HOLDINGS, INC.; *U.S. Public*, pg. 794
ESSA BANCORP, INC.; *U.S. Public*, pg. 794
E.SUN VENTURE CAPITAL CORP.—See E. Sun Financial Holding Co., Ltd.; *Int'l*, pg. 2250
EUREKA HOMESTEAD BANCORP, INC.; *U.S. Public*, pg. 797
EVANS BANCORP, INC.; *U.S. Public*, pg. 799
EVERLY BANCORPORATION; *U.S. Private*, pg. 1440
EXECUTIVE CATERERS INC.; *U.S. Private*, pg. 1447
EXTRACO CORPORATION; *U.S. Private*, pg. 1452
FAIRFIELD BANCSHARES INC.; *U.S. Public*, pg. 1463
FAIRFIELD COUNTY BANK CORP.—See Fairfield County Bank, MHC; *U.S. Private*, pg. 1463
FAIRFIELD NATIONAL BANK—See Fairfield Bancshares Inc.; *U.S. Private*, pg. 1463
FARMERS AND MERCHANTS BANCSHARES, INC.; *U.S. Public*, pg. 822
FARMERS BANCORP INC.; *U.S. Public*, pg. 822
FARMERS BANCORPORATION, INC.; *U.S. Private*, pg. 1476
FARMERS BANCSHARES INC.; *U.S. Private*, pg. 1476
FARMERS BANKSHARES, INC.—See Towne Bank; *U.S. Public*, pg. 2165
FARMERS & MERCHANTS BANCORP, INC.; *U.S. Public*, pg. 821
FARMERS & MERCHANTS BANCORP; *U.S. Public*, pg. 821
THE FARMERS & MERCHANTS BANKSHARES, INC.; *U.S. Private*, pg. 4027
FARMERS & MERCHANTS FINANCIAL SERVICES—See F&M Bank Corp.; *U.S. Public*, pg. 818
FARMERS & MERCHANTS INVESTMENT INC.; *U.S. Private*, pg. 1475
FARMERS NATIONAL BANC CORP.; *U.S. Public*, pg. 822
FARMERS STATE BANK—See Farmers Bancshares Inc.; *U.S. Private*, pg. 1476
FARMINGTON BANCORP, INC.; *U.S. Private*, pg. 1480
FAUQUIER BANKSHARES, INC.—See Virginia National Bankshares Corporation; *U.S. Public*, pg. 2299
FB FINANCIAL CORPORATION; *U.S. Public*, pg. 824
FBN HOLDINGS PLC; *Int'l*, pg. 2627
FCB FINANCIAL CORP.; *U.S. Private*, pg. 1485
FENTURA FINANCIAL, INC.; *U.S. Public*, pg. 829
FFD FINANCIAL CORPORATION; *U.S. Public*, pg. 830
FFW CORPORATION; *U.S. Public*, pg. 830
FIDEA HOLDINGS CO. LTD.; *Int'l*, pg. 2653
FIDELITY D & D BANCORP, INC.; *U.S. Public*, pg. 830
FIDELITY FEDERAL BANCORP; *U.S. Public*, pg. 830
FIDELITY FINANCIAL CORPORATION; *U.S. Private*, pg. 1502
FIDELITY MUTUAL HOLDING COMPANY—See Mutual Bancorp; *U.S. Private*, pg. 2819
FIFTH THIRD BANCORP; *U.S. Public*, pg. 833
FINANCIAL CORPORATION OF LOUISIANA; *U.S. Private*, pg. 1506
FINANCIAL FEDCORP, INC.; *U.S. Private*, pg. 1507
FINANCIAL INSTITUTIONS, INC.; *U.S. Public*, pg. 834
FINANCIERE SYZ & CO SA; *Int'l*, pg. 2669
FINEMARK HOLDINGS, INC.; *U.S. Public*, pg. 834
FINLAYSON BANCSHARES, INC.; *U.S. Private*, pg. 1510
FINWARD BANCORP; *U.S. Public*, pg. 835
FINWISE BANCORP; *U.S. Public*, pg. 835
FIRST ADVANTAGE BANCORP—See United Community Banks, Inc.; *U.S. Public*, pg. 2230
FIRST AMERICAN BANCSHARES, INC.; *U.S. Private*, pg. 1512
FIRST AMERICAN BANK CORPORATION; *U.S. Private*, pg. 1512
FIRST ANTLERS BANCORPORATION, INC.; *U.S. Private*, pg. 1513
FIRST ARKANSAS BANCSHARES, INC.; *U.S. Private*, pg. 1513
FIRST ARTESIA BANCSHARES, INC.; *U.S. Private*, pg. 1513

FIRSTBANC OF ALABAMA, INC.; *U.S. Private*, pg. 1531
THE FIRST BANCORP, INC.; *U.S. Public*, pg. 2073
FIRST BANCORP OF INDIANA, INC.; *U.S. Public*, pg. 839
FIRST BANCORPORATION INC.; *U.S. Private*, pg. 1513
FIRST BANCORP; *U.S. Public*, pg. 838
FIRST BANCORP; *U.S. Public*, pg. 839
FIRST BANCSHARES CORPORATION; *U.S. Private*, pg. 1513
FIRST BANCSHARES INC.; *U.S. Private*, pg. 1513
THE FIRST BANCSHARES, INC.; *U.S. Public*, pg. 2073
FIRST BANCSHARES, INC.; *U.S. Public*, pg. 839
FIRST BANCSHARES, INC.; *U.S. Public*, pg. 839
FIRST BANKERS TRUSTSHARES INC.; *U.S. Public*, pg. 840
FIRST BANKS, INC.; *U.S. Private*, pg. 1514
FIRST BELLS BANKSHARES, INC.; *U.S. Private*, pg. 1514
FIRST BERNE FINANCIAL CORPORATION; *U.S. Private*, pg. 1514
FIRST BROKEN ARROW CORPORATION; *U.S. Private*, pg. 1514
FIRST BUSEY CORPORATION; *U.S. Public*, pg. 840
FIRST BUSINESS BANCORP CO.; *U.S. Private*, pg. 1515
FIRST CAPITAL BANCSHARES INC; *U.S. Public*, pg. 841
FIRST CAPITAL, INC.; *U.S. Public*, pg. 841
FIRST CAROLINA FINANCIAL SERVICES, INC.; *U.S. Private*, pg. 1515
FIRST CECILIAN BANCORP, INC.; *U.S. Private*, pg. 1515
FIRST CENTURY BANCORP; *U.S. Private*, pg. 1515
FIRST CHOICE BANCORP—See Enterprise Financial Services Corp; *U.S. Public*, pg. 778
FIRST CITIZENS BANCSHARES, INC.; *U.S. Public*, pg. 841
FIRST CITIZENS BANCSHARES, INC.; *U.S. Public*, pg. 841
FIRST CITIZENS FINANCIAL CORP.; *U.S. Private*, pg. 1515
FIRST CITRUS BANCORPORATION, INC.; *U.S. Private*, pg. 1515
FIRST COMMONWEALTH FINANCIAL CORPORATION; *U.S. Public*, pg. 842
FIRST COMMUNITY BANCSHARES, INC.; *U.S. Private*, pg. 1516
FIRST COMMUNITY BANCSHARES, INC.; *U.S. Private*, pg. 1516
FIRST COMMUNITY BANKSHARES, INC.; *U.S. Public*, pg. 842
FIRST COMMUNITY CORPORATION; *U.S. Public*, pg. 842
FIRST COMMUNITY FINANCIAL CORPORATION; *U.S. Public*, pg. 843
FIRST FARMERS AND MERCHANTS CORPORATION; *U.S. Public*, pg. 843
FIRST FARMERS FINANCIAL CORPORATION; *U.S. Private*, pg. 1517
FIRSTFED BANCORP, INC.; *U.S. Private*, pg. 1532
FIRST FEDERAL BANCORP, INC.; *U.S. Private*, pg. 1517
FIRST FEDERAL MHC; *U.S. Private*, pg. 1518
FIRST FIDELITY BANCORP, INC.; *U.S. Private*, pg. 1518
FIRST FINANCIAL BANCORP.; *U.S. Public*, pg. 843
FIRST FINANCIAL BANKSHARES, INC.; *U.S. Public*, pg. 843
FIRST FINANCIAL CORPORATION; *U.S. Public*, pg. 843
FIRST FINANCIAL NORTHWEST, INC.; *U.S. Public*, pg. 843
FIRST FOUNDATION INC.; *U.S. Public*, pg. 844
FIRST GILMER BANKSHARES, INC.; *U.S. Private*, pg. 1519
FIRST GROESBECK HOLDING COMPANY; *U.S. Private*, pg. 1519
FIRST GUARANTY BANCSHARES, INC.; *U.S. Public*, pg. 844
FIRST HORIZON CORPORATION; *U.S. Public*, pg. 844
FIRST ILLINOIS BANCORP, INC.; *U.S. Private*, pg. 1520
FIRST INDEPENDENCE CORPORATION; *U.S. Private*, pg. 1520
FIRST INTERNET BANCORP; *U.S. Public*, pg. 845
FIRST INTERSTATE BANCSYSTEM, INC.; *U.S. Public*, pg. 845
FIRST KANSAS BANCSHARES, INC.; *U.S. Private*, pg. 1520
FIRST KEYES BANCSHARES, INC.; *U.S. Private*, pg. 1520
FIRST KEYSTONE CORPORATION; *U.S. Public*, pg. 845
FIRST LIBERTY CAPITAL CORPORATION; *U.S. Private*, pg. 1520
FIRST LIGHT BANCORP—See Indiana Members Credit Union; *U.S. Private*, pg. 2062
FIRST LINDEN BANCSHARES, INC.; *U.S. Private*, pg. 1520
FIRST MERCHANTS CORPORATION; *U.S. Public*, pg. 845
FIRST MIAMI BANCORP, INC.—See United Community Banks, Inc.; *U.S. Public*, pg. 2230
FIRST MIAMI BANCSHARES, INC.; *U.S. Private*, pg. 1521
FIRST MID BANCSHARES, INC.; *U.S. Public*, pg. 845
FIRST MIDWEST ACQUISITION CORP.; *U.S. Private*, pg. 1521
FIRST MIDWEST BANCORP, INC.—See Old National Bancorp; *U.S. Public*, pg. 1566
FIRST MUTUAL OF RICHMOND, INC.; *U.S. Private*, pg. 1521
FIRST NATIONAL BANCORP, INC.; *U.S. Private*, pg. 1521
FIRST NATIONAL BANKERS BANKSHARES, INC.; *U.S. Private*, pg. 1523

551111 — OFFICES OF BANK HOL...

FIRST NATIONAL BANK OF BEMIDJI; *U.S. Private*, pg. 1522
THE FIRST NATIONAL BANK & TRUST COMPANY OF BROKEN ARROW—See First Broken Arrow Corporation; *U.S. Private*, pg. 1514
FIRST NATIONAL CORPORATION OF ARDMORE, INC.; *U.S. Private*, pg. 1523
FIRST NATIONAL CORPORATION OF WYNNE; *U.S. Private*, pg. 1523
FIRST NATIONAL CORPORATION; *U.S. Public*, pg. 846
FIRST NATIONAL FINANCIAL SERVICES, INC.; *U.S. Private*, pg. 1523
FIRST NATIONAL OF NEBRASKA, INC.; *U.S. Private*, pg. 1523
FIRST NILES FINANCIAL, INC.; *U.S. Public*, pg. 846
FIRST NORTHERN COMMUNITY BANCORP; *U.S. Public*, pg. 846
FIRST NORTHWEST BANCORP; *U.S. Public*, pg. 846
THE FIRST OF LONG ISLAND CORPORATION; *U.S. Public*, pg. 2074
FIRST OKMULGEE CORPORATION; *U.S. Public*, pg. 1524
FIRST PALMETTO FINANCIAL CORP.; *U.S. Private*, pg. 1524
FIRST PARAGOULD BANKSHARES, INC.; *U.S. Private*, pg. 1524
FIRST PEOPLES BANKSHARES, INC.; *U.S. Private*, pg. 1524
FIRSTPERRYTON BANCORP, INC.; *U.S. Private*, pg. 1532
FIRST PIONEER BANK CORP.; *U.S. Private*, pg. 1524
FIRST PULASKI NATIONAL CORPORATION; *U.S. Private*, pg. 1524
FIRSTRAND BANK HOLDINGS LIMITED—See FirstRand Limited; *Int'l*, pg. 2690
FIRSTRAND BANK LIMITED—See FirstRand Limited; *Int'l*, pg. 2690
FIRST RELIANCE BANCSHARES, INC.; *U.S. Public*, pg. 847
FIRST ROBINSON FINANCIAL CORPORATION; *U.S. Public*, pg. 847
FIRST RUSHMORE BANCORPORATION, INC.; *U.S. Private*, pg. 1527
FIRST SAVINGS FINANCIAL GROUP, INC.; *U.S. Public*, pg. 847
FIRST SEACOAST BANCORP, INC.; *U.S. Public*, pg. 847
FIRST SECURITY BANCORP, INC.—See Wirtz Corporation; *U.S. Private*, pg. 4547
FIRST SECURITY BANCORP; *U.S. Private*, pg. 1527
FIRST SECURITY BANKSHARES INC.; *U.S. Private*, pg. 1527
FIRST SLEEPY EYE BANCORPORATION, INC.; *U.S. Private*, pg. 1527
FIRST SONORA BANCSHARES, INC.; *U.S. Private*, pg. 1527
FIRST SOUTHERN BANCORP, INC.; *U.S. Private*, pg. 1528
FIRST SOUTHWEST CORPORATION; *U.S. Private*, pg. 1528
FIRST STATE BANCORP, INC.; *U.S. Private*, pg. 1528
FIRST STATE BANCORPORATION, INC.; *U.S. Private*, pg. 1528
FIRST STATE BANCSHARES INC.; *U.S. Private*, pg. 1528
FIRST STATE BANCSHARES INC.; *U.S. Private*, pg. 1528
FIRST STATE BANCSHARES, INC.; *U.S. Private*, pg. 1528
FIRST STATE HOLDING CO.; *U.S. Private*, pg. 1529
FIRSTSUN CAPITAL BANCORP; *U.S. Public*, pg. 849
FIRST TEXAS BANCORP, INC.; *U.S. Private*, pg. 1529
FIRST UNITED CORPORATION; *U.S. Public*, pg. 848
FIRST US BANCSHARES, INC.; *U.S. Public*, pg. 848
FIRST VANDALIA CORP.; *U.S. Private*, pg. 1530
FIRST VOLUNTEER CORPORATION; *U.S. Private*, pg. 1530
FIRST WATERLOO BANCSHARES, INC.; *U.S. Private*, pg. 1530
FIRST WESTERN FINANCIAL, INC.; *U.S. Public*, pg. 848
FIRST YORK BAN CORP.; *U.S. Private*, pg. 1531
FISHBACK FINANCIAL CORPORATION; *U.S. Private*, pg. 1533
FIVE STAR BANCORP; *U.S. Public*, pg. 852
FLAGLER BANCSHARES CORPORATION; *U.S. Private*, pg. 1539
FLAGSHIP FINANCIAL GROUP, INC.; *U.S. Private*, pg. 1539
FLAGSTAR BANCORP, INC.—See New York Community Bancorp, Inc.; *U.S. Public*, pg. 1512
FLORIDA BANCSHARES, INC.; *U.S. Private*, pg. 1547
FLUSHING FINANCIAL CORPORATION; *U.S. Public*, pg. 860
F&M BANCORP; *U.S. Public*, pg. 818
F&M BANK CORP.; *U.S. Public*, pg. 818
FMBCAPITAL HOLDINGS PLC; *Int'l*, pg. 2717
FMB OF S.C. BANCSHARES, INCORPORATED; *U.S. Private*, pg. 1553
F&M FINANCIAL CORPORATION; *U.S. Private*, pg. 1455
FNB BANCSHARES INC.; *U.S. Private*, pg. 1555
FNB BANCSHARES OF CENTRAL ALABAMA, INC.—See BankFirst Capital Corporation; *U.S. Public*, pg. 274
F.N.B.C. OF LA GRANGE, INC.; *U.S. Private*, pg. 1456
F.N.B. CORPORATION; *U.S. Public*, pg. 818

FNBH BANCORP, INC.; *U.S. Private*, pg. 1555
FNB, INC.; *U.S. Public*, pg. 862
FNBK HOLDINGS, INC.; *U.S. Private*, pg. 1555
FNBT BANCSHARES, PERRY, OK, INC.; *U.S. Private*, pg. 1555
FORCHT BANCORP, INC.—See Forcht Group of Kentucky, Inc.; *U.S. Private*, pg. 1563
FORESIGHT FINANCIAL GROUP INC.; *U.S. Public*, pg. 867
FORTITUDE GROUP HOLDINGS, LLC—See The Carlyle Group Inc.; *U.S. Public*, pg. 2047
FRANDSEN FINANCIAL CORPORATION—See Frandsen Corporation; *U.S. Private*, pg. 1593
FRANKFORT FIRST BANCORP, INC.—See First Federal MHC; *U.S. Private*, pg. 1518
FRANKLIN BANCORP INC.; *U.S. Private*, pg. 1596
FRANKLIN FINANCIAL NETWORK, INC.—See FB Financial Corporation; *U.S. Public*, pg. 824
FRANKLIN FINANCIAL SERVICES CORPORATION; *U.S. Public*, pg. 879
FREDERICK COUNTY BANCORP, INC.—See ACNB Corporation; *U.S. Public*, pg. 36
FREMONT BANCORPORATION; *U.S. Private*, pg. 1608
FS BANCORP, INC.; *U.S. Public*, pg. 888
F.S. BANCORP; *U.S. Private*, pg. 1457
FSC BANCSHARES, INC.; *U.S. Private*, pg. 1618
FTS FINANCIAL, INC.; *U.S. Private*, pg. 1619
FUKUOKA FINANCIAL GROUP, INC.; *Int'l*, pg. 2840
FULL SERVICE INSURANCE AGENCY, INC.; *U.S. Private*, pg. 1621
FULTON FINANCIAL CORPORATION; *U.S. Public*, pg. 892
FVCBANKCORP, INC.; *U.S. Public*, pg. 893
GENERALI HOLDING VIENNA AG—See Assicurazioni Generali S.p.A.; *Int'l*, pg. 645
GENERATIONS BANCORP NY, INC.; *U.S. Public*, pg. 929
GENTERA, S.A.B. DE C.V.; *Int'l*, pg. 2928
GERMAN AMERICAN BANCORP, INC.; *U.S. Public*, pg. 934
GIACOM (CLOUD) HOLDINGS LIMITED; *Int'l*, pg. 2961
GILLETTE HOLDING GMBH—See The Procter & Gamble Company; *U.S. Public*, pg. 2124
GLACIER BANCORP, INC.; *U.S. Public*, pg. 938
GLEN BURNIE BANCORP; *U.S. Public*, pg. 940
GOLDEN PACIFIC BANCORP, INC.; *U.S. Public*, pg. 950
GOLDEN STATE BANCORP; *U.S. Public*, pg. 951
THE GOLDMAN SACHS GROUP, INC.; *U.S. Public*, pg. 2076
GOPPERT FINANCIAL CORP.; *U.S. Private*, pg. 1741
GORHAM BANCORP, MHC; *U.S. Private*, pg. 1743
GOUVERNEUR BANCORP, INC.—See Cambray Mutual Holding Company; *U.S. Private*, pg. 726
GRACE INVESTMENT COMPANY, INC.; *U.S. Private*, pg. 1749
GRAND BANCORP, INC.; *U.S. Private*, pg. 1752
GRAND BANK CORPORATION; *U.S. Public*, pg. 956
GRAND RIVER COMMERCE, INC.; *U.S. Public*, pg. 957
GRANDSOUTH BANCORPORATION—See First Bancorp; *U.S. Public*, pg. 839
GRANITE BANK; *U.S. Private*, pg. 1755
GRANT BANCSHARES, INC.; *U.S. Private*, pg. 1756
GREAT AMERICAN BANCORP, INC.; *U.S. Public*, pg. 961
GREAT RIVER HOLDING COMPANY; *U.S. Private*, pg. 1767
GREAT SOUTHERN BANCORP, INC.; *U.S. Public*, pg. 962
GREAT SOUTHERN CAPITAL CORP.; *U.S. Private*, pg. 1768
GREAT WESTERN BANCORP, INC.; *U.S. Public*, pg. 962
GREEN BANCORP, INC.—See Veritex Holdings, Inc.; *U.S. Public*, pg. 2283
GREENE COUNTY BANCORP, INC.; *U.S. Public*, pg. 964
GREENFIELD BANCORPORATION LTD.; *U.S. Private*, pg. 1777
GREENFIELD BANCSHARES INC.; *U.S. Private*, pg. 1777
GREENVILLE FEDERAL FINANCIAL CORPORATION; *U.S. Public*, pg. 965
GREENWAY BANK; *U.S. Public*, pg. 965
GREENWOODS FINANCIAL GROUP, INC.; *U.S. Private*, pg. 1782
GRINNELL BANCSHARES, INC.; *U.S. Private*, pg. 1790
GROESBECK BANCSHARES, INC.; *U.S. Private*, pg. 1791
GRUPO ALIADO S.A.; *Int'l*, pg. 3119
GRUPO AVAL ACCIONES Y VALORES S.A.; *Int'l*, pg. 3121
GRUPO FINANCIERO BANAMEX, S.A. DE C.V.—See Citigroup Inc.; *U.S. Public*, pg. 504
GRUPO FINANCIERO GALICIA S.A.; *Int'l*, pg. 3129
GRUPO FINANCIERO HSBC, S.A. DE C.V.—See HSBC Holdings plc; *Int'l*, pg. 3503
GRUPO FINANCIERO INBURSA, S.A. DE C.V.; *Int'l*, pg. 3129
GRUPO MUNDIAL TENEDORA, S.A.; *Int'l*, pg. 3133
GSD HOLDING A.S.; *Int'l*, pg. 3144
GUARANTY BANCORP—See Independent Bank Group, Inc.; *U.S. Public*, pg. 1116
GUARANTY BANCSHARES, INC.; *U.S. Public*, pg. 973
GUARANTY CAPITAL CORP; *U.S. Private*, pg. 1809
GUARANTY DEVELOPMENT COMPANY; *U.S. Private*, pg. 1809
GUARANTY FEDERAL BANCSHARES, INC.—See QCR Holdings, Inc.; *U.S. Public*, pg. 1742

GUARANTY FINANCIAL CORP.; *U.S. Public*, pg. 973
HABERER REGISTERED INVESTMENT ADVISOR, INC.—See Huntington Bancshares Incorporated; *U.S. Public*, pg. 1071
HABIB ALLIED INTERNATIONAL BANK PLC.—See Habib Bank Limited; *Int'l*, pg. 3203
HANA FINANCIAL GROUP, INC.; *Int'l*, pg. 3240
HANCOCK WHITNEY CORPORATION; *U.S. Public*, pg. 982
HANMI FINANCIAL CORPORATION; *U.S. Public*, pg. 983
HANOVER BANCORP INC.; *U.S. Public*, pg. 983
HAPPY BANCSHARES, INC.—See Home BancShares, Inc.; *U.S. Public*, pg. 1045
HARBOR BANKSHARES CORPORATION; *U.S. Public*, pg. 984
HARBORONE BANCORP, INC.; *U.S. Public*, pg. 984
HARDIN COUNTY BANCORPORATION; *U.S. Private*, pg. 1863
HARLEYSVILLE FINANCIAL CORPORATION; *U.S. Public*, pg. 985
THE HARTFORD FINANCIAL SERVICES GROUP, INC.; *U.S. Public*, pg. 2087
HARVARD ILLINOIS BANCORP, INC.; *U.S. Public*, pg. 1875
HAUCK & AUFHAUSER PRIVATBANKIERS AG—See Fosun International Limited; *Int'l*, pg. 2751
HAVEN BANCORP, INC.—See Haven Bancorp, MHC; *U.S. Private*, pg. 1880
HAWAII NATIONAL BANCSHARES, INC.; *U.S. Public*, pg. 1881
HAWTHORN BANCSHARES, INC.; *U.S. Public*, pg. 989
HAZLEHURST INVESTORS, INC.; *U.S. Private*, pg. 1886
HBANCORPORATION INC.; *U.S. Public*, pg. 990
HBT FINANCIAL, INC.; *U.S. Public*, pg. 990
H.C.B. FINANCIAL CORP.; *U.S. Public*, pg. 978
HEARTLAND BANCCORP; *U.S. Public*, pg. 1017
HEARTLAND FINANCIAL USA, INC.; *U.S. Public*, pg. 1017
HENDERSON BANCSHARES, INC.; *U.S. Private*, pg. 1913
HERITAGE BANCSHARES GROUP, INC.; *U.S. Private*, pg. 1922
HERITAGE COMMERCE CORP; *U.S. Public*, pg. 1028
HERITAGE FEDERAL CREDIT UNION; *U.S. Private*, pg. 1922
HERITAGE FINANCIAL CORPORATION; *U.S. Public*, pg. 1028
HERITAGE NOLA BANCORP, INC.; *U.S. Public*, pg. 1028
HERITAGE SOUTHEAST BANCORPORATION, INC.—See The First Bancshares, Inc.; *U.S. Public*, pg. 2073
HERKY HAWK FINANCIAL CORP.; *U.S. Private*, pg. 1925
HERRING BANCORP, INC.; *U.S. Private*, pg. 1926
HFB FINANCIAL CORPORATION; *U.S. Public*, pg. 1034
HIGH COUNTRY BANCORP, INC.; *U.S. Public*, pg. 1034
HIGHLAND BANKSHARES INC.; *U.S. Public*, pg. 1938
HIGHLANDS BANCORP, INC.—See Provident Financial Services, Inc.; *U.S. Public*, pg. 1730
HIGHLANDS BANKSHARES, INC.—See First Community Bankshares, Inc.; *U.S. Public*, pg. 842
HILLS BANCORPORATION; *U.S. Public*, pg. 1038
HILLTOP HOLDINGS INC.; *U.S. Public*, pg. 1038
HILLTOP SECURITIES HOLDINGS LLC—See Hilltop Holdings Inc.; *U.S. Public*, pg. 1038
HMN FINANCIAL, INC.—See Alerus Financial Corporation; *U.S. Public*, pg. 75
HOCKING VALLEY BANCSHARES, INC.; *U.S. Public*, pg. 1044
HOKKOKU FINANCIAL HOLDINGS, INC.; *Int'l*, pg. 3443
HOKUHOKU FINANCIAL GROUP, INC.; *Int'l*, pg. 3444
HOLLAND BANCORP, INC.; *U.S. Private*, pg. 1964
HOME BANCGROUP, INC.; *U.S. Private*, pg. 1970
HOME BANCORP, INC.; *U.S. Public*, pg. 1045
HOME BANCORP WISCONSIN, INC.; *U.S. Public*, pg. 1045
HOME BANCSHARES, INC.; *U.S. Public*, pg. 1045
HOME FEDERAL BANCORP, INC. OF LOUISIANA; *U.S. Public*, pg. 1046
HOME FEDERAL BANCORP; *U.S. Public*, pg. 1046
HOME LOAN FINANCIAL CORPORATION; *U.S. Public*, pg. 1046
HOME STATE BANCORP, INC.; *U.S. Private*, pg. 1972
HOMESTREET, INC.; *U.S. Public*, pg. 1046
HOMETOWN BANKSHARES CORPORATION—See Atlantic Union Bankshares Corporation; *U.S. Public*, pg. 223
HOMETOWN COMMUNITY BANCORP, INC.; *U.S. Private*, pg. 1975
HOMETOWN FINANCIAL GROUP, INC.; *U.S. Private*, pg. 1975
HOMETRUST BANCSHARES, INC.; *U.S. Public*, pg. 1046
HONAT BANCORP INC.; *U.S. Public*, pg. 1046
THE HONG KONG AND SHANGHAI BANKING CORPORATION LIMITED—See HSBC Holdings plc; *Int'l*, pg. 3506
HOOKER NATIONAL BANCSHARES, INC.; *U.S. Private*, pg. 1978
HOPE BANCORP, INC.; *U.S. Public*, pg. 1052
HOPKINS FINANCIAL CORPORATION; *U.S. Private*, pg. 1979
HORIZON BANCORP, INC.; *U.S. Public*, pg. 1053
HOUSEHOLD CREDIT SERVICES INC.—See HSBC Holdings plc; *Int'l*, pg. 3505

551111 — OFFICES OF BANK HOL...   CORPORATE AFFILIATIONS

HOWARD BANCORP, INC.—See F.N.B. Corporation; *U.S. Public*, pg. 818
HOYNE FINANCIAL CORPORATION; *U.S. Private*, pg. 1996
HSBC GLOBAL ASSET MANAGEMENT LIMITED—See HSBC Holdings plc; *Int'l*, pg. 3504
HSBC HOLDINGS PLC; *Int'l*, pg. 3503
HS HOLDINGS CO., LTD.; *Int'l*, pg. 3503
HUNTINGTON BANCSHARES INCORPORATED; *U.S. Public*, pg. 1071
HUNTINGTON BANCSHARES INC.; *U.S. Private*, pg. 2010
HURON VALLEY BANCORP, INC.; *U.S. Public*, pg. 1076
IBERIABANK CORPORATION—See First Horizon Corporation; *U.S. Public*, pg. 844
IBW FINANCIAL CORPORATION; *U.S. Public*, pg. 1083
ICCREA HOLDING S.P.A.; *Int'l*, pg. 3578
ICHISHIN HOLDINGS CO., LTD.; *Int'l*, pg. 3581
IDA GROVE BANCSHARES, INC.; *U.S. Private*, pg. 2034
IDAHO TRUST BANCORP; *U.S. Private*, pg. 2035
IF BANCORP, INC.; *U.S. Public*, pg. 1095
IFB HOLDINGS, INC.; *U.S. Public*, pg. 1095
ILLINOIS COMMUNITY BANCORP, INC.; *U.S. Public*, pg. 1101
INBANKSHARES CORP.; *U.S. Public*, pg. 1114
INDEPENDENCE BANCSHARES, INC.; *U.S. Private*, pg. 2055
INDEPENDENT BANCORP., LIMITED; *U.S. Private*, pg. 2058
INDEPENDENT BANCSHARES, INC.; *U.S. Private*, pg. 2058
INDEPENDENT BANK CORPORATION; *U.S. Public*, pg. 1116
INDEPENDENT BANK CORP.; *U.S. Public*, pg. 1116
INDEPENDENT BANKERS FINANCIAL CORPORATION; *U.S. Private*, pg. 2058
INDEPENDENT BANK GROUP, INC.; *U.S. Public*, pg. 1116
INDEPENDENT SOUTHERN BANCSHARES, INC.; *U.S. Private*, pg. 2061
INLAND BANCORP, INC.—See Byline Bancorp, Inc.; *U.S. Public*, pg. 414
INSCORP, INC.; *U.S. Public*, pg. 1128
INTEGRATED FINANCIAL HOLDINGS, INC.—See Capital Bancorp, Inc.; *U.S. Public*, pg. 431
INTERNATIONAL BANCSHARES CORPORATION; *U.S. Public*, pg. 1145
INTERNATIONAL BANCSHARES OF OKLAHOMA, INC.; *U.S. Private*, pg. 2114
INTERNATIONAL BANK OF COMMERCE, OKLAHOMA—See International Bancshares Corporation; *U.S. Public*, pg. 1145
INTRUST FINANCIAL CORPORATION; *U.S. Private*, pg. 2130
INVESCO VERWALTUNGSGESELLSCHAFT MBH—See Invesco Ltd.; *U.S. Public*, pg. 1163
INVESTAR HOLDING CORPORATION; *U.S. Public*, pg. 1164
INVESTORS BANCORP, INC.—See Citizens Financial Group, Inc.; *U.S. Public*, pg. 505
INVESTORS TITLE COMPANY—See FB Financial Corporation; *U.S. Public*, pg. 824
INWOOD BANCSHARES INC.; *U.S. Private*, pg. 2133
ION FINANCIAL, MHC; *U.S. Private*, pg. 2133
IOWA FIRST BANCSHARES CORP.—See MidWestOne Financial Group, Inc.; *U.S. Public*, pg. 1446
IOWA RIVER BANCORP, INC.; *U.S. Private*, pg. 2135
ISABELLA BANK CORPORATION; *U.S. Public*, pg. 1174
ITASCA BANCORP INC.; *U.S. Private*, pg. 2149
ITHMAAR HOLDING B.S.C.—See Dar Al-Maal Al-Islami Trust; *Int'l*, pg. 1971
JACKASS CREEK LAND & LIVESTOCK COMPANY; *U.S. Private*, pg. 2175
JACKSON FINANCIAL INC.; *U.S. Public*, pg. 1183
JAMESMARK BANCSHARES, INC.; *U.S. Private*, pg. 2185
JBNV HOLDING CORP.; *U.S. Private*, pg. 2194
J. CARL H. BANCORPORATION; *U.S. Private*, pg. 2155
JEFF DAVIS BANCSHARES, INC.; *U.S. Private*, pg. 2196
JEFFERSONVILLE BANCORP; *U.S. Public*, pg. 1189
JOHN MARSHALL BANCORP, INC.; *U.S. Public*, pg. 1192
JOHN R. TURNER HOLDING COMPANY; *U.S. Private*, pg. 2224
JOHNSON FINANCIAL GROUP, INC.—See S.C. Johnson & Son, Inc.; *U.S. Private*, pg. 3516
J.P. MORGAN BANK—See JPMorgan Chase & Co.; *U.S. Public*, pg. 1209
JPMORGAN CHASE BANK, N.A.—See JPMorgan Chase & Co.; *U.S. Public*, pg. 1209
JPMORGAN CHASE & CO.; *U.S. Public*, pg. 1206
J.P. MORGAN CHASE (UK) HOLDINGS LTD.—See JPMorgan Chase & Co.; *U.S. Public*, pg. 1209
J.P. MORGAN GRUPO FINANCIERO S.A. DE C.V.—See JPMorgan Chase & Co.; *U.S. Public*, pg. 1208
J.P. MORGAN INTERNATIONAL INC.—See JPMorgan Chase & Co.; *U.S. Public*, pg. 1209
J. SAFRA SARASIN HOLDING AG—See Banco Safra S.A.; *Int'l*, pg. 824
JTNB BANCORP, INC.; *U.S. Public*, pg. 1210
JUNIATA VALLEY FINANCIAL CORP.; *U.S. Public*, pg. 1210

KATAHDIN BANKSHARES CORP.; *U.S. Public*, pg. 1214
K CAPITAL CORPORATION; *U.S. Private*, pg. 2249
KEARNY FINANCIAL CORP.; *U.S. Public*, pg. 1217
KEB HANA BANK—See Hana Financial Group, Inc.; *Int'l*, pg. 3240
KENNEBEC SAVINGS BANK, MHC; *U.S. Private*, pg. 2284
KENTUCKY BANCSHARES, INC.—See Stock Yards Bancorp, Inc.; *U.S. Public*, pg. 1951
KENTUCKY FIRST FEDERAL BANCORP—See First Federal MHC; *U.S. Public*, pg. 1518
KEYCORP; *U.S. Public*, pg. 1225
KEYSTONE BANCSHARES, INC.; *U.S. Private*, pg. 2295
KILLBUCK BANCSHARES, INC.; *U.S. Public*, pg. 1228
KIRKWOOD BANCORPORATION CO.; *U.S. Private*, pg. 2315
KISH BANCORP, INC.; *U.S. Public*, pg. 1236
KLEBERG & COMPANY BANKERS, INC.; *U.S. Private*, pg. 2318
KOSS-WINN BANCSHARES, INC.; *U.S. Private*, pg. 2344
KS BANCORP INC.; *U.S. Public*, pg. 1277
LA COMPAGNIE FINANCIERE EDMOND DE ROTHSCHILD—See Edmond de Rothschild Holding S.A.; *Int'l*, pg. 2313
LAKELAND BANCORP, INC.—See Provident Financial Services, Inc.; *U.S. Public*, pg. 1730
LAKELAND FINANCIAL CORPORATION; *U.S. Public*, pg. 1288
LAKE SHORE BANCORP, INC.; *U.S. Public*, pg. 1288
LAKESIDE BANCSHARES, INC.; *U.S. Public*, pg. 1289
LANDESBANK BERLIN HOLDING AG—See Deutscher Sparkassen- und Giroverband e.V.; *Int'l*, pg. 2085
LANDMARK BANCORP, INC.; *U.S. Public*, pg. 1292
LANDRUM COMPANY; *U.S. Private*, pg. 2386
LASALLE BANCORP, INC.; *U.S. Private*, pg. 2394
LATIN AMERICAN INVESTMENT BANK BAHAMAS LIMITED—See Citigroup Inc.; *U.S. Public*, pg. 504
LAWRENCE FINANCIAL CORPORATION; *U.S. Private*, pg. 2401
LCNB CORP.; *U.S. Public*, pg. 1296
LEACKCO BANK HOLDING COMPANY, INC.; *U.S. Private*, pg. 2405
THE LEADERS GROUP, INC.; *U.S. Private*, pg. 4068
LEAR CANADA INVESTMENTS LTD.—See Lear Corporation; *U.S. Public*, pg. 1297
LEDYARD FINANCIAL GROUP, INC.; *U.S. Public*, pg. 1298
LEGACYTEXAS FINANCIAL GROUP, INC.—See Prosperity Bancshares, Inc.; *U.S. Public*, pg. 1728
LIBERTY BANCSHARES INC.—See Middlefield Banc Corp.; *U.S. Public*, pg. 1445
LIBERTY FINANCIAL SERVICES, INC.; *U.S. Private*, pg. 2444
LIFESTORE FINANCIAL GROUP; *U.S. Public*, pg. 1313
LIMESTONE BANCORP, INC.—See Peoples Bancorp Inc.; *U.S. Public*, pg. 1667
LINCOLN COUNTY BANCORP., INC.; *U.S. Private*, pg. 2457
LINKBANCORP, INC.; *U.S. Public*, pg. 1320
LIVE OAK BANCSHARES CORPORATION; *U.S. Private*, pg. 2473
LIVE OAK BANCSHARES, INC.; *U.S. Public*, pg. 1331
LIZTON FINANCIAL CORPORATION; *U.S. Private*, pg. 2474
LOGAN INVESTMENT CORPORATION; *U.S. Private*, pg. 2480
LOGANSPORT FINANCIAL CORP.; *U.S. Public*, pg. 1340
LOLYN FINANCIAL CORPORATION; *U.S. Private*, pg. 2483
LONE STAR NATIONAL BANCSHARES-TEXAS, INC.; *U.S. Private*, pg. 2489
LONE STAR STATE BANCSHARES, INC.—See Prosperity Bancshares, Inc.; *U.S. Public*, pg. 1728
LWCBANCORP, INC.; *U.S. Private*, pg. 2518
M3-BRIGADE ACQUISITION V CORP.; *U.S. Public*, pg. 1351
MABREY BANCORPORATION INC.; *U.S. Private*, pg. 2531
MACATAWA BANK CORPORATION—See Wintrust Financial Corporation; *U.S. Public*, pg. 2375
MACKEY BANCO, INC.; *U.S. Private*, pg. 2537
MACKINAC FINANCIAL CORPORATION; *U.S. Public*, pg. 1352
MADISON COUNTY FINANCIAL, INC.; *U.S. Public*, pg. 1353
MAGNOLIA BANKING CORPORATION; *U.S. Private*, pg. 2548
MAGYAR BANCORP, INC.—See Magyar Bancorp, MHC; *U.S. Private*, pg. 2550
MAGYAR BANCORP, MHC; *U.S. Private*, pg. 2550
MAINE COMMUNITY BANCORP, MHC; *U.S. Private*, pg. 2552
MAINSTREET BANCSHARES, INC.; *U.S. Public*, pg. 1355
MAIN STREET FINANCIAL SERVICES CORP.; *U.S. Public*, pg. 1355
MALAGA FINANCIAL CORP.; *U.S. Public*, pg. 1355
MALVERN BANCORP, INC.—See First Bank; *U.S. Public*, pg. 840
MAPLE CITY SAVINGS, MHC; *U.S. Private*, pg. 2568
MARATHON BANCORP, INC.; *U.S. Public*, pg. 1363
MARINE BANCORP, INC.; *U.S. Private*, pg. 2574

MARINE BANCORP OF FLORIDA, INC.; *U.S. Public*, pg. 1366
MARQUETTE NATIONAL CORPORATION; *U.S. Public*, pg. 1370
MARQUIS BANCORP, INC.; *U.S. Private*, pg. 2587
MARS BANCORP, INC.—See NexTier, Inc.; *U.S. Private*, pg. 2921
MASCOMA MUTUAL FINANCIAL SERVICES CORPORATION; *U.S. Private*, pg. 2601
MASON BANCSHARES, INC.; *U.S. Private*, pg. 2601
MATHIAS BANCSHARES, INC.; *U.S. Private*, pg. 2611
MB BANCORP, INC.—See Bay-Vanguard, M.H.C.; *U.S. Private*, pg. 495
MB FINANCIAL, INC.—See Fifth Third Bancorp; *U.S. Public*, pg. 833
M C BANCSHARES, INC.; *U.S. Private*, pg. 2523
MCHENRY BANCORP, INC.; *U.S. Public*, pg. 1407
MCLEOD BANCSHARES, INC.; *U.S. Private*, pg. 2641
MCNB BANKS, INC.; *U.S. Public*, pg. 1409
MECHANICS BANC HOLDING COMPANY; *U.S. Private*, pg. 2649
MELROSE BANCORP, INC.; *U.S. Public*, pg. 2663
MERCANTILE BANK CORPORATION; *U.S. Public*, pg. 1414
MERCER BANCORP, INC.; *U.S. Public*, pg. 1415
MERCER COUNTY STATE BANCORP; *U.S. Private*, pg. 2669
MERCER COUNTY STATE BANK—See Mercer County State Bancorp; *U.S. Private*, pg. 2669
MERCHANTS BANCORP; *U.S. Public*, pg. 1415
MERCHANTS & MARINE BANCORP, INC.; *U.S. Public*, pg. 1415
MERIDIAN BANCORP, INC.; *U.S. Public*, pg. 1424
MERIDIAN CORPORATION; *U.S. Public*, pg. 1424
MERRILL LYNCH & CO., INC.—See Bank of America Corporation; *U.S. Public*, pg. 272
METROCITY BANKSHARES, INC.; *U.S. Public*, pg. 1431
M&F BANCORP, INC.; *U.S. Private*, pg. 2524
M&F BANCORP, INC.; *U.S. Public*, pg. 1350
MGB BANCSHARES, INC.; *U.S. Private*, pg. 2694
MIDAMERICA NATIONAL BANCSHARES, INC.; *U.S. Private*, pg. 2710
MIDCOUNTRY ACQUISITION CORP.; *U.S. Private*, pg. 2711
MIDCOUNTRY FINANCIAL CORP.; *U.S. Private*, pg. 2711
MIDDLEBURY NATIONAL CORP.; *U.S. Public*, pg. 1445
MIDDLEFIELD BANC CORP.; *U.S. Public*, pg. 1445
MIDDLESEX BANCORP, MHC; *U.S. Private*, pg. 2714
MIDLAND CAPITAL HOLDINGS CORP.; *U.S. Private*, pg. 2714
MIDLAND FINANCIAL CO.; *U.S. Private*, pg. 2715
MIDLAND STATES BANCORP, INC.; *U.S. Public*, pg. 1445
MID-MISSOURI HOLDING COMPANY, INC.; *U.S. Private*, pg. 2708
MID PENN BANCORP, INC.; *U.S. Public*, pg. 1444
MID-SOUTHERN BANCORP, INC.; *U.S. Public*, pg. 1445
MIDSTATE BANCORP, INC.; *U.S. Public*, pg. 2717
MIDWEST BANCO CORPORATION; *U.S. Private*, pg. 2720
MIDWEST BANCORPORATION, INC.; *U.S. Private*, pg. 2720
MIDWEST BANKCENTRE, INC.—See Stupp Bros., Inc.; *U.S. Private*, pg. 3844
MIDWEST COMMUNITY BANCSHARES, INC.; *U.S. Private*, pg. 2720
MIDWEST MINNESOTA COMMUNITY DEVELOPMENT CORPORATION; *U.S. Private*, pg. 2722
MIDWESTONE FINANCIAL GROUP, INC.; *U.S. Public*, pg. 1445
MIFFLINBURG BANCORP, INC.; *U.S. Private*, pg. 2724
MILLE LACS BANCORPORATION, INC.; *U.S. Private*, pg. 2731
MINERS AND MERCHANTS BANCORP, INC.; *U.S. Private*, pg. 2742
MINNWEST CORPORATION; *U.S. Private*, pg. 2744
MISSION BANCORP; *U.S. Public*, pg. 1450
MNB BANCSHARES, INC.; *U.S. Public*, pg. 2755
MNB HOLDINGS CORPORATION; *U.S. Private*, pg. 1453
MONONA BANKSHARES, INC.; *U.S. Private*, pg. 2772
MOODY BANCSHARES, INC.; *U.S. Private*, pg. 2778
MORGAN STANLEY; *U.S. Public*, pg. 1471
MORGAN STANLEY SWISS HOLDINGS GMBH—See Morgan Stanley; *U.S. Public*, pg. 1473
MORLEY BANCSHARES CORPORATION; *U.S. Private*, pg. 2785
MORRIS STATE BANCSHARES, INC.; *U.S. Public*, pg. 1477
MOSCOW BANCSHARES, INC.; *U.S. Private*, pg. 2792
MOUNTAIN COMMERCE BANCORP, INC.; *U.S. Public*, pg. 1479
MOUNTAIN PACIFIC BANCORP, INC.; *U.S. Public*, pg. 1479
MOUNTAIN-VALLEY BANCSHARES, INC.; *U.S. Private*, pg. 2800
MSB FINANCIAL CORP.—See Kearny Financial Corp.; *U.S. Public*, pg. 1217
MSB MUTUAL HOLDING COMPANY; *U.S. Private*, pg. 2806
M&T BANK CORPORATION; *U.S. Public*, pg. 1350

N.A.I.C.S. INDEX
551111 — OFFICES OF BANK HOL...

MUNCY BANK FINANCIAL, INC.—See Muncy Columbia Financial Corporation; *U.S. Public*, pg. 1487
MUNCY COLUMBIA FINANCIAL CORPORATION; *U.S. Public*, pg. 1486
MUTUAL BANCORP; *U.S. Private*, pg. 2819
MUTUALFIRST FINANCIAL, INC.—See Northwest Bancshares, Inc.; *U.S. Public*, pg. 1541
MVB FINANCIAL CORP.; *U.S. Public*, pg. 1487
NARRAGANSETT FINANCIAL CORP.; *U.S. Private*, pg. 2835
NASB FINANCIAL, INC.; *U.S. Public*, pg. 1491
NATCOM BANCSHARES, INC.; *U.S. Private*, pg. 2838
NATIONAL BANK HOLDINGS CORPORATION; *U.S. Public*, pg. 1493
THE NATIONAL BANK OF INDIANAPOLIS CORPORATION; *U.S. Private*, pg. 4082
NATIONAL BANKSHARES, INC.; *U.S. Public*, pg. 1493
NATIXIS LUXEMBOURG S.A.—See Groupe BPCE; *Int'l*, pg. 3097
NATIXIS, S.A.—See Groupe BPCE; *Int'l*, pg. 3094
NBC CORP. OF OKLAHOMA; *U.S. Private*, pg. 2874
NBE BANCSHARES, INC.; *U.S. Private*, pg. 2874
N.B.M. CORPORATION; *U.S. Private*, pg. 2827
NBT BANCORP INC.; *U.S. Public*, pg. 1500
NEB CORPORATION; *U.S. Private*, pg. 2878
NEBRASKA BANKSHARES, INC.; *U.S. Private*, pg. 2878
NEFFS BANCORP, INC.; *U.S. Public*, pg. 1504
NEISEN BANCSHARES, INC.; *U.S. Private*, pg. 2882
NEWFIELD BANCORP INC.; *U.S. Private*, pg. 2914
NEW PEOPLES BANKSHARES, INC.; *U.S. Public*, pg. 1512
NEW SOUTH BANCSHARES INC.; *U.S. Private*, pg. 2906
NEW TRIPOLI BANCORP, INC.; *U.S. Public*, pg. 1512
NEW YORK PRIVATE BANK & TRUST CORPORATION; *U.S. Private*, pg. 2911
NEW ZEALAND HOLDINGS (UK) LTD—See Alliance Group Limited; *Int'l*, pg. 339
NEXBANK CAPITAL, INC.; *U.S. Private*, pg. 2918
NEXTIER, INC.; *U.S. Private*, pg. 2921
NIBC HOLDING N.V.—See Blackstone Inc.; *U.S. Public*, pg. 356
NICOLET BANKSHARES, INC.; *U.S. Public*, pg. 1528
NORTHBRIDGE FINANCIAL CORPORATION—See Fairfax Financial Holdings Limited; *Int'l*, pg. 2607
NORTHEAST COMMUNITY BANCORP, INC.; *U.S. Public*, pg. 1537
NORTHEAST INDIANA BANCORP, INC.; *U.S. Public*, pg. 1537
NORTHERN CALIFORNIA BANCORP, INC.—See PCB Financial, Inc; *U.S. Public*, pg. 3119
NORTHERN MISSOURI BANCSHARES, INC.; *U.S. Private*, pg. 2953
NORTHERN TRUST CORPORATION; *U.S. Public*, pg. 1538
NORTHFIELD BANCORP, INC.; *U.S. Public*, pg. 1539
NORTHRIM BANCORP, INC.; *U.S. Public*, pg. 1539
NORTH SHORE BANCORP; *U.S. Public*, pg. 2946
NORTH SHORE FINANCIAL CORPORATION; *U.S. Private*, pg. 2946
NORTH STATE BANCORP; *U.S. Private*, pg. 2948
NORTHUMBERLAND BANCORP; *U.S. Public*, pg. 1541
NORTHWAY FINANCIAL, INC.; *U.S. Public*, pg. 1541
NORTHWEST BANCSHARES, INC.; *U.S. Public*, pg. 1541
NORTHWESTERN BANCSHARES, INC.; *U.S. Private*, pg. 2962
NORTHWEST FINANCIAL CORP.; *U.S. Private*, pg. 2960
NORTHWEST INDIANA BANCORP, INC.; *U.S. Public*, pg. 1542
NORWAY BANCORP, INC.; *U.S. Private*, pg. 2964
NORWOOD FINANCIAL CORP.; *U.S. Public*, pg. 1543
NSTS BANCORP, INC.; *U.S. Public*, pg. 1551
NW SERVICES CORPORATION; *U.S. Private*, pg. 2975
OAK RIDGE FINANCIAL SERVICES, INC.; *U.S. Public*, pg. 1560
OAKSTAR BANCSHARES, INC.; *U.S. Private*, pg. 2985
OAK VALLEY BANCORP; *U.S. Public*, pg. 1560
OCEAN BANKSHARES, INC.; *U.S. Private*, pg. 2988
OCEANFIRST FINANCIAL CORP.; *U.S. Public*, pg. 1563
OCONEE FEDERAL FINANCIAL CORP.; *U.S. Public*, pg. 1563
OCONOMOWOC BANCSHARES, INC.; *U.S. Public*, pg. 1563
OFG BANCORP; *U.S. Public*, pg. 1564
OHIO VALLEY BANC CORP.; *U.S. Public*, pg. 1565
OHIO VALLEY BANCORP, INC.; *U.S. Private*, pg. 3005
OLD MISSION BANCORP, INC.; *U.S. Private*, pg. 3009
OLD NATIONAL BANCORP; *U.S. Public*, pg. 1566
OLD O'BRIEN BANC SHARES, INC.; *U.S. Private*, pg. 3009
OLD POINT FINANCIAL CORPORATION; *U.S. Public*, pg. 1567
OLNEY BANCSHARES OF TEXAS, INC.; *U.S. Private*, pg. 3011
OLYMPIC BANCORP; *U.S. Private*, pg. 3012
OP BANCORP; *U.S. Public*, pg. 1605
OPORTUN, INC.; *U.S. Private*, pg. 3032
OPTIMUMBANK HOLDINGS INC.; *U.S. Public*, pg. 1609
ORANGE COUNTY BANCORP, INC.; *U.S. Public*, pg. 1614
OREGON BANCORP, INC.; *U.S. Private*, pg. 1615
OREGON PACIFIC BANCORP; *U.S. Public*, pg. 1615
ORIENT BANCORPORATION INC.; *U.S. Private*, pg. 3041

ORIGIN BANCORP, INC.; *U.S. Public*, pg. 1617
ORITANI FINANCIAL CORP.—See Valley National Bancorp; *U.S. Public*, pg. 2273
ORRSTOWN FINANCIAL SERVICES, INC.; *U.S. Public*, pg. 1618
OSAGE BANCSHARES, INC.—See American Heritage Bank; *U.S. Private*, pg. 236
OSSIAN FINANCIAL SERVICES, INC.—See Farmers & Merchants Bancorp, Inc.; *U.S. Public*, pg. 822
OTKRITIE HOLDING JSC—See Central Bank of the Russian Federation; *Int'l*, pg. 1405
OTTAWA BANCORP, INC.; *U.S. Public*, pg. 1623
OVATION HOLDINGS, INC.; *U.S. Private*, pg. 3052
OVERTON FINANCIAL CORPORATION; *U.S. Private*, pg. 3054
OWEN FINANCIAL CORPORATION; *U.S. Private*, pg. 3054
OXFORD BANK CORPORATION; *U.S. Public*, pg. 1628
PACIFIC CREST BANCORP, INC.; *U.S. Private*, pg. 3067
PACIFIC ENTERPRISE BANCORP; *U.S. Public*, pg. 1631
PACIFIC FINANCIAL CORPORATION; *U.S. Public*, pg. 1631
PACIFIC MERCANTILE BANCORP—See Banc of California, Inc.; *U.S. Public*, pg. 269
PACIFIC PREMIER BANCORP, INC.; *U.S. Public*, pg. 1632
PACWEST BANCORP—See Banc of California, Inc.; *U.S. Public*, pg. 268
PADUCAH BANK SHARES, INC.; *U.S. Private*, pg. 3074
PALMER BANCSHARES, INC.; *U.S. Private*, pg. 3080
PALMETTO STATE BANKSHARES, INC.; *U.S. Private*, pg. 3081
PARAGON FINANCIAL SOLUTIONS, INC.; *U.S. Public*, pg. 1637
PARKE BANCORP, INC.; *U.S. Public*, pg. 1640
PARKER CANADA HOLDING CO.—See Parker Hannifin Corporation; *U.S. Public*, pg. 1644
PARK FINANCIAL GROUP, INC.; *U.S. Private*, pg. 3096
PARK NATIONAL CORPORATION; *U.S. Public*, pg. 1638
PARKWAY BANCORP, INC.; *U.S. Private*, pg. 3098
PASSUMPSIC BANCORP INC.; *U.S. Private*, pg. 3104
PATHFINDER BANCORP, INC.; *U.S. Public*, pg. 1651
PATHWARD FINANCIAL, INC.; *U.S. Public*, pg. 1652
PATRIOT NATIONAL BANCORP, INC.; *U.S. Public*, pg. 1653
PAYFLEX HOLDINGS, INC.—See ABRY Partners, LLC; *U.S. Private*, pg. 42
PB BANCORP, INC.—See Centreville Bank; *U.S. Private*, pg. 829
PB BANKSHARES, INC.; *U.S. Public*, pg. 1657
PB FINANCIAL CORPORATION; *U.S. Public*, pg. 1657
PCB BANCORP; *U.S. Public*, pg. 1658
PCSB FINANCIAL CORPORATION—See Brookline Bancorp, Inc.; *U.S. Public*, pg. 396
PDL COMMUNITY BANCORP; *U.S. Public*, pg. 1658
PEAPACK-GLADSTONE FINANCIAL CORPORATION; *U.S. Public*, pg. 1659
PEDESTAL BANCSHARES, INC.—See Business First Bancshares, Inc.; *U.S. Public*, pg. 413
PELLA FINANCIAL GROUP, INC.; *U.S. Public*, pg. 3131
PENN COMMUNITY FINANCIAL CORPORATION; *U.S. Private*, pg. 3134
PENNS WOODS BANCORP, INC.; *U.S. Public*, pg. 1663
PEOPLE FIRST BANCSHARES, INC.; *U.S. Private*, pg. 3140
PEOPLES BANCORP INC.; *U.S. Public*, pg. 1667
PEOPLES BANCORP OF MT. PLEASANT, INC.—See Consumers Bancorp, Inc.; *U.S. Public*, pg. 573
PEOPLES BANCORP; *U.S. Private*, pg. 3141
PEOPLES BANCSHARES-POINTE COUPEE, INC.—See Synergy Bancshares Inc.; *U.S. Private*, pg. 3904
PEOPLES BANKSHARES, INC.; *U.S. Private*, pg. 3141
PEOPLES EXCHANGE BANCSHARES, INC.; *U.S. Private*, pg. 3142
PEOPLES FEDERAL SAVINGS & LOAN ASSOCIATION OF SIDNEY—See Farmers & Merchants Bancorp, Inc.; *U.S. Public*, pg. 822
PEOPLES FINANCIAL CORPORATION; *U.S. Public*, pg. 1667
PEOPLES FINANCIAL SERVICES CORP.; *U.S. Public*, pg. 1667
PEOPLES INDEPENDENT BANCSHARES, INC.; *U.S. Private*, pg. 3142
PEOPLES LTD.; *U.S. Public*, pg. 1667
PEOPLES-SIDNEY FINANCIAL CORPORATION—See Farmers & Merchants Bancorp, Inc.; *U.S. Public*, pg. 822
PEOPLESSOUTH BANCSHARES, INC.; *U.S. Private*, pg. 3142
PEOPLE'S UNITED FINANCIAL, INC.—See M&T Bank Corporation; *U.S. Public*, pg. 1351
PFBS HOLDINGS, INC.; *U.S. Private*, pg. 3164
PIEDMONT BANCORP, INC.; *U.S. Private*, pg. 3176
PIEDMONT COMMUNITY BANK GROUP, INC.; *U.S. Public*, pg. 1690
PIEDMONT FINANCIAL HOLDING COMPANY; *U.S. Private*, pg. 3177
PILOT BANCSHARES, INC.—See Lake Michigan Credit Union; *U.S. Private*, pg. 2375
PINNACLE BANCORP, INC.; *U.S. Private*, pg. 3184
PINNACLE BANCSHARES, INC.; *U.S. Public*, pg. 1691

PINNACLE BANKSHARES CORP.; *U.S. Public*, pg. 1691
PINNACLE FINANCIAL CORPORATION; *U.S. Private*, pg. 3185
PINNACLE FINANCIAL PARTNERS, INC.; *U.S. Public*, pg. 1691
PIONEER BANCORP, INC.; *U.S. Public*, pg. 1692
PIONEER BANCSHARES, INC.—See FirstSun Capital Bancorp; *U.S. Public*, pg. 850
PIONEER BANKCORP, INC.; *U.S. Public*, pg. 1692
PIONEER BANKSHARES, INC.; *U.S. Public*, pg. 1692
PLAINSCAPITAL CORPORATION—See Hilltop Holdings Inc.; *U.S. Public*, pg. 1039
PLANTERS FINANCIAL GROUP, INC.; *U.S. Private*, pg. 3197
PLANTERS HOLDING COMPANY INC.; *U.S. Private*, pg. 3197
PLATTE VALLEY FINANCIAL SERVICE COMPANIES INC.; *U.S. Private*, pg. 3211
PLUMAS BANCORP; *U.S. Public*, pg. 1699
PNC BANCORP, INC.—See The PNC Financial Services Group, Inc.; *U.S. Public*, pg. 2119
THE PNC FINANCIAL SERVICES GROUP, INC.; *U.S. Public*, pg. 2118
PONTIAC BANCORP, INC.; *U.S. Public*, pg. 1701
PONY EXPRESS BANCORP, INC.; *U.S. Private*, pg. 3227
POPULAR, INC.; *U.S. Public*, pg. 1702
PPS DATA, LLC—See Zions Bancorporation, National Association; *U.S. Public*, pg. 2408
PRAIRIE BANCSHARES CORPORATION; *U.S. Private*, pg. 3242
PREFERRED BANCSHARES, INC.; *U.S. Private*, pg. 3247
PREMIER FINANCIAL BANCORP, INC.; *U.S. Public*, pg. 1715
PREMIER FINANCIAL CORP.; *U.S. Public*, pg. 1715
PRIME MERIDIAN HOLDING COMPANY; *U.S. Public*, pg. 1717
PRIMERICA, INC.; *U.S. Public*, pg. 1717
PRIMESOUTH BANCSHARES, INC.; *U.S. Private*, pg. 3263
PRIMIS FINANCIAL CORP.; *U.S. Public*, pg. 1717
PRIORITYONE CAPITAL CORPORATION; *U.S. Private*, pg. 3267
PRIVATE BANCORP OF AMERICA, INC.; *U.S. Public*, pg. 1722
PROFESSIONAL HOLDING CORP.; *U.S. Public*, pg. 1724
PROSPECT CAPITAL CORPORATION; *U.S. Public*, pg. 1728
PROSPERITY BANCSHARES, INC.; *U.S. Public*, pg. 1728
PROTECTIVE CAPITAL STRUCTURES CORP.; *U.S. Public*, pg. 1729
PROVIDENCE FINANCIAL CORPORATION; *U.S. Private*, pg. 3294
PROVIDENT FINANCIAL HOLDINGS, INC.; *U.S. Public*, pg. 1730
PROVIDENT FINANCIAL SERVICES, INC.; *U.S. Public*, pg. 1730
PRUDENTIAL BANCORP, INC.—See Fulton Financial Corporation; *U.S. Public*, pg. 892
PSB HOLDING CORP.—See Summit Financial Group, Inc.; *U.S. Public*, pg. 1959
PSB HOLDINGS, INC.; *U.S. Public*, pg. 1734
PT KROM BANK INDONESIA TBK—See FinAccel Pte Ltd.; *Int'l*, pg. 2664
PUEBLO BANCORPORATION; *U.S. Private*, pg. 3301
PUTNAM-GREENE FINANCIAL CORPORATION; *U.S. Private*, pg. 3307
QCR HOLDINGS, INC.; *U.S. Public*, pg. 1742
QNB CORP.; *U.S. Public*, pg. 1743
QUAINT OAK BANCORP, INC.; *U.S. Public*, pg. 1745
RADIUS BANCORP INC.—See LendingClub Corporation; *U.S. Public*, pg. 1305
RAMSEY FINANCIAL CORPORATION; *U.S. Private*, pg. 3352
RANDOLPH BANCORP, INC.—See Hometown Financial Group, Inc.; *U.S. Private*, pg. 1975
RBAZ BANCORP, INC.; *U.S. Public*, pg. 1765
RBB BANCORP; *U.S. Public*, pg. 1766
RBC, INC.; *U.S. Private*, pg. 3360
RCB HOLDING COMPANY, INC.; *U.S. Private*, pg. 3361
R CORP FINANCIAL; *U.S. Private*, pg. 3331
RED RIVER BANCSHARES, INC.; *U.S. Public*, pg. 1769
REGENT CAPITAL CORPORATION; *U.S. Private*, pg. 3387
REGIONS FINANCIAL CORPORATION; *U.S. Public*, pg. 1776
RELIANCE BANCORP, INC.; *U.S. Private*, pg. 3394
RELIANCE BANCSHARES, INC.—See Simmons First National Corporation; *U.S. Public*, pg. 1881
RELIANT BANCORP, INC.—See United Community Banks, Inc.; *U.S. Public*, pg. 2230
RELTCO, INC.—See Live Oak Bancshares, Inc.; *U.S. Public*, pg. 1331
RENASANT CORPORATION; *U.S. Public*, pg. 1782
REPUBLIC BANCORP CO.; *U.S. Private*, pg. 3401
REPUBLIC BANCORP, INC.; *U.S. Public*, pg. 1785
REPUBLIC BANCSHARES, INC.; *U.S. Private*, pg. 3401
RESOURCE BANK; *U.S. Private*, pg. 3406
RHINEBECK BANCORP, INC.; *U.S. Public*, pg. 1796
RICHWOOD BANCSHARES, INC.; *U.S. Private*, pg. 3431
RIVER FINANCIAL CORPORATION; *U.S. Public*, pg. 1801

551111 — OFFICES OF BANK HOL... CORPORATE AFFILIATIONS

RIVER VALLEY BANCORPORATION, INC.; *U.S. Private*, pg. 3444
RIVERVIEW BANCORP, INC.; *U.S. Public*, pg. 1801
RIVERVIEW FINANCIAL CORPORATION—See Mid Penn Bancorp, Inc.; *U.S. Public*, pg. 1444
RMB BANCSHARES, INC.; *U.S. Private*, pg. 3451
ROSCOE FINANCIAL CORPORATION; *U.S. Private*, pg. 3481
ROYAL BANCSHARES, INC.; *U.S. Private*, pg. 3491
ROYAL BANCSHARES, INC.; *U.S. Private*, pg. 3491
ROYAL FINANCIAL, INC.; *U.S. Public*, pg. 1815
RSNB BANCORP; *U.S. Private*, pg. 3497
SABINE BANCSHARES INC.; *U.S. Private*, pg. 3521
SAGICOR GROUP JAMAICA LIMITED—See Alignvest Management Corporation; *Int'l*, pg. 327
SALEM FIVE BANCORP; *U.S. Private*, pg. 3531
SALISBURY BANCORP, INC.—See NBT Bancorp Inc.; *U.S. Public*, pg. 1501
SAMMONS ENTERPRISES, INC.; *U.S. Private*, pg. 3537
SANDY SPRING BANCORP, INC.; *U.S. Public*, pg. 1840
SANTANDER BANCORP—See First BanCorp; *U.S. Public*, pg. 839
SANTANDER BANESPA GRUPO—See Banco Santander, S.A.; *Int'l*, pg. 826
SANTANDER BANK POLSKA S.A.—See Banco Santander, S.A.; *Int'l*, pg. 826
SANTANDER CONSUMER USA HOLDINGS INC.—See Banco Santander, S.A.; *Int'l*, pg. 827
SANTANDER HOLDINGS USA, INC.—See Banco Santander, S.A.; *Int'l*, pg. 827
SANTANDER UK GROUP HOLDINGS PLC—See Banco Santander, S.A.; *Int'l*, pg. 827
SANTANDER UK PLC—See Banco Santander, S.A.; *Int'l*, pg. 827
S.B.C.P. BANCORP, INC.; *U.S. Public*, pg. 1832
SB FINANCIAL GROUP, INC.; *U.S. Public*, pg. 1842
SBT BANCSHARES, INC.; *U.S. Private*, pg. 3560
SEACOAST BANKING CORPORATION OF FLORIDA; *U.S. Public*, pg. 1851
SECURITY AGENCY, INC.; *U.S. Private*, pg. 3594
SECURITY BANCORP, INC.; *U.S. Public*, pg. 1855
SECURITY BANCORP OF TENNESSEE, INC.; *U.S. Private*, pg. 3594
SECURITY CHICAGO CORPORATION; *U.S. Private*, pg. 3595
SECURITY FEDERAL CORPORATION; *U.S. Public*, pg. 1855
SECURITY FINANCIAL SERVICES CORPORATION; *U.S. Private*, pg. 3595
SECURITY STATE CORPORATION; *U.S. Private*, pg. 3596
SELECT BANCORP, INC.—See First Bancorp; *U.S. Public*, pg. 839
SENECA FINANCIAL CORP.; *U.S. Public*, pg. 1864
SERVISFIRST BANCSHARES, INC.; *U.S. Public*, pg. 1872
SEVIER COUNTY BANCSHARES, INC.; *U.S. Public*, pg. 1873
SFB BANCORP INC.; *U.S. Public*, pg. 1873
SFSB, INC.; *U.S. Public*, pg. 1873
S G BANCSHARES INC.—See First Keyes Bancshares, Inc.; *U.S. Private*, pg. 1520
SHAMROCK BANCSHARES, INC.; *U.S. Private*, pg. 3624
SHF HOLDINGS, INC.; *U.S. Public*, pg. 1874
SHORE BANCSHARES, INC.; *U.S. Public*, pg. 1875
SIERRA BANCORP; *U.S. Public*, pg. 1877
SI FINANCIAL GROUP, INC.—See Berkshire Hills Bancorp, Inc.; *U.S. Public*, pg. 320
SILVERGATE CAPITAL CORPORATION; *U.S. Public*, pg. 1880
SIMMONS FIRST NATIONAL CORPORATION; *U.S. Public*, pg. 1881
SKYLINE BANKSHARES, INC.; *U.S. Public*, pg. 1892
SMARTFINANCIAL, INC.; *U.S. Public*, pg. 1895
SNB HOLDINGS, INC.; *U.S. Private*, pg. 3700
SOFI TECHNOLOGIES, INC.; *U.S. Public*, pg. 1899
SOLERA NATIONAL BANCORP, INC.; *U.S. Public*, pg. 1900
SOLVAY BANK CORP.; *U.S. Public*, pg. 1901
SOMERVILLE BANCORP.; *U.S. Private*, pg. 3712
SOONER SOUTHWEST BANKSHARES, INC.; *U.S. Private*, pg. 3715
SOUND FINANCIAL BANCORP, INC.; *U.S. Public*, pg. 1910
SOUTH ATLANTIC BANCSHARES, INC.; *U.S. Public*, pg. 1910
SOUTHCREST FINANCIAL GROUP, INC.—See Colony Bankcorp, Inc.; *U.S. Public*, pg. 533
SOUTH DAKOTA BANCSHARES, INC.; *U.S. Private*, pg. 3722
SOUTHEAST BANCSHARES, INC.; *U.S. Private*, pg. 3725
SOUTHEASTERN BANCORP, INC.; *U.S. Private*, pg. 3727
SOUTHEASTERN BANCORP, INC.; *U.S. Private*, pg. 3727
SOUTHEASTERN FINANCIAL, INC.; *U.S. Private*, pg. 3727
THE SOUTHERN BANC COMPANY, INC.; *U.S. Public*, pg. 2130
SOUTHERN BANCORP, INC.; *U.S. Private*, pg. 3729
SOUTHERN BANCSHARES (N.C.), INC.; *U.S. Public*, pg. 1911
SOUTHERN COMMUNITY BANCSHARES, INC.; *U.S. Public*, pg. 1911

SOUTHERN FIRST BANCSHARES, INC.; *U.S. Public*, pg. 1911
SOUTHERN MICHIGAN BANCORP INC.; *U.S. Public*, pg. 1911
SOUTHERN MISSOURI BANCORP, INC.; *U.S. Public*, pg. 1911
SOUTHERN NATIONAL BANKS, INC.; *U.S. Private*, pg. 3734
SOUTHERN STATES BANCSHARES, INC.; *U.S. Public*, pg. 1912
SOUTHFIRST BANCSHARES, INC.; *U.S. Private*, pg. 3736
SOUTH PLAINS FINANCIAL, INC.; *U.S. Public*, pg. 1911
SOUTHPOINT BANCSHARES, INC.; *U.S. Private*, pg. 3738
SOUTHSIDE BANCSHARES, INC.; *U.S. Public*, pg. 1912
SOUTHSTATE CORPORATION; *U.S. Public*, pg. 1912
SOUTHWEST BANCSHARES, INC.; *U.S. Private*, pg. 3738
SOUTHWESTERN BANCORP, INC.; *U.S. Private*, pg. 3741
SPEARMAN BANCSHARES, INC.; *U.S. Private*, pg. 3748
SPECTAIRE HOLDINGS INC.; *U.S. Public*, pg. 1915
SPIRIT OF TEXAS BANCSHARES, INC.—See Sentinel Capital Partners, L.L.C.; *U.S. Private*, pg. 3609
SPRING BANCORP, INC.; *U.S. Private*, pg. 3763
SPRINT INDUSTRIAL HOLDINGS LLC; *U.S. Private*, pg. 3764
SR BANCORP, INC.; *U.S. Public*, pg. 1922
SSB BANCORP, INC.; *U.S. Public*, pg. 1924
SSB COMMUNITY BANCORP INC.—See SSB Community Bancorp MHC; *U.S. Private*, pg. 3768
SSB COMMUNITY BANCORP MHC; *U.S. Private*, pg. 3768
STAR FINANCIAL GROUP INC.; *U.S. Public*, pg. 1937
STARK BANK GROUP LTD.; *U.S. Private*, pg. 3786
STATE BANKSHARES, INC.; *U.S. Private*, pg. 3791
STATE CENTER FINANCIAL, INC.; *U.S. Private*, pg. 3791
STATE STREET BANK EUROPE LIMITED—See State Street Corporation; *U.S. Public*, pg. 1940
STATE STREET CORPORATION; *U.S. Public*, pg. 1940
STATE STREET FINANCIAL SERVICES—See State Street Corporation; *U.S. Public*, pg. 1941
STATION CASINOS LLC—See Red Rock Resorts, Inc.; *U.S. Public*, pg. 1769
S&T BANCORP, INC.; *U.S. Public*, pg. 1832
STEARNS FINANCIAL SERVICES, INC.; *U.S. Private*, pg. 3795
STEELE HOLDINGS, INC.; *U.S. Private*, pg. 3796
STELLAR BANCORP, INC.; *U.S. Public*, pg. 1944
STERLING BANCORP; *U.S. Public*, pg. 1946
STERLING BANCSHARES, INC.; *U.S. Private*, pg. 3804
STEWARDSHIP FINANCIAL CORPORATION—See Columbia Financial, Inc.; *U.S. Public*, pg. 534
STOCKMENS FINANCIAL CORPORATION; *U.S. Private*, pg. 3815
STOCK YARDS BANCORP, INC.; *U.S. Public*, pg. 1950
STRATFORD BANCSHARES, INC.; *U.S. Private*, pg. 3837
STURGIS BANCORP, INC.; *U.S. Public*, pg. 1958
SUGAR CREEK FINANCIAL CORP.; *U.S. Public*, pg. 3849
SUMMIT FINANCIAL GROUP, INC.; *U.S. Public*, pg. 1959
SUMNER FINANCIAL CORPORATION; *U.S. Private*, pg. 3857
SUNRISE BANCSHARES, INC.; *U.S. Private*, pg. 3869
SUNSOUTH BANCSHARES, INC.; *U.S. Private*, pg. 3872
SUNTRUST BANK HOLDING COMPANY—See Truist Financial Corporation; *U.S. Public*, pg. 2199
SUNTRUST BANKS, INC.—See Truist Financial Corporation; *U.S. Public*, pg. 2199
SUNWEST BANCORP, INC.; *U.S. Private*, pg. 3874
SURREY BANCORP—See First Community Bankshares, Inc.; *U.S. Public*, pg. 842
SURU GROUP LTD.—See Haldane McCall PLC; *Int'l*, pg. 3227
SVB FINANCIAL GROUP; *U.S. Public*, pg. 1968
SVB&T CORPORATION; *U.S. Private*, pg. 3888
SYNERGY BANCSHARES INC.; *U.S. Private*, pg. 3904
SYNOVUS FINANCIAL CORP.; *U.S. Public*, pg. 1971
TAHOKA FIRST BANCORP INC.; *U.S. Private*, pg. 3923
TAMPA BANKING CO.; *U.S. Private*, pg. 3928
T BANCSHARES, INC.—See Tectonic Financial, Inc.; *U.S. Public*, pg. 1989
TBI BANK EAD—See 4finance Holding S.A.; *Int'l*, pg. 11
TC BANCSHARES, INC.; *U.S. Public*, pg. 1983
TCM COMPANY; *U.S. Private*, pg. 3942
TEB BANCORP, INC.; *U.S. Public*, pg. 1988
TEB HOLDING ANONIM SIRKETI—See BNP Paribas SA; *Int'l*, pg. 1093
TENNESSEE VALLEY FINANCIAL HOLDINGS, INC.; *U.S. Public*, pg. 2016
TERME BANCORP, INC.; *U.S. Public*, pg. 2020
TERRITORIAL BANCORP INC.; *U.S. Public*, pg. 2021
TEXAS CAPITAL BANCSHARES, INC.; *U.S. Public*, pg. 2025
TEXAS CITIZENS BANCORP, INC.—See Business First Bancshares, Inc.; *U.S. Public*, pg. 413
TEXAS COMMUNITY BANCSHARES, INC.; *U.S. Public*, pg. 2025
TEXAS INDEPENDENT BANCSHARES, INC.—See Preferred Bancshares, Inc.; *U.S. Private*, pg. 3247
TEXAS PEOPLES NATIONAL BANCSHARES, INC.; *U.S. Private*, pg. 3976
TEXAS STATE BANKSHARES, INC.; *U.S. Private*, pg. 3977

TGR FINANCIAL INC.; *U.S. Private*, pg. 3979
THIRD COAST BANCSHARES, INC.; *U.S. Public*, pg. 2155
THOMASVILLE BANCSHARES, INC.; *U.S. Public*, pg. 2156
THREE SHORES BANCORPORATION, INC.—See United Community Banks, Inc.; *U.S. Public*, pg. 2230
THUMB BANCORP, INC.; *U.S. Private*, pg. 4165
TIAA FSB HOLDINGS, INC.—See Teachers Insurance Association - College Retirement Fund; *U.S. Private*, pg. 3948
TIMBERLAND BANCORP, INC.; *U.S. Public*, pg. 2159
TOMPKINS FINANCIAL CORPORATION; *U.S. Public*, pg. 2162
TOUCHMARK BANCSHARES, INC.; *U.S. Public*, pg. 2165
TRANS PACIFIC BANCORP; *U.S. Private*, pg. 4205
TREYNOR BANCSHARES, INC.; *U.S. Private*, pg. 4219
TRICO BANCSHARES; *U.S. Public*, pg. 2189
TRI-COUNTY FINANCIAL GROUP, INC.; *U.S. Public*, pg. 2188
TRIDENT MICROSYSTEMS, INC.; *U.S. Private*, pg. 4230
TRINITY CAPITAL CORPORATION—See Enterprise Financial Services Corp; *U.S. Public*, pg. 778
TRISTATE CAPITAL HOLDINGS, INC.—See Raymond James Financial, Inc.; *U.S. Public*, pg. 1765
TRIUMPH FINANCIAL, INC.; *U.S. Public*, pg. 2196
TRUIST FINANCIAL CORPORATION; *U.S. Public*, pg. 2199
TRUSTCO BANK CORP NY; *U.S. Public*, pg. 2201
TRUSTMARK CORPORATION; *U.S. Public*, pg. 2202
TRUXTON CORP.; *U.S. Public*, pg. 2202
TRV HOLDINGS LLC—See Citigroup Inc.; *U.S. Public*, pg. 504
TSB BANKING GROUP PLC—See Banco de Sabadell, S.A.; *Int'l*, pg. 821
TSB BANKSHARES, INC.; *U.S. Public*, pg. 4252
TSB SERVICES INC.; *U.S. Private*, pg. 4252
TWO RIVER BANCORP—See OceanFirst Financial Corp.; *U.S. Public*, pg. 1563
TWO RIVERS FINANCIAL GROUP, INC.; *U.S. Public*, pg. 2207
TXRB HOLDINGS, INC.; *U.S. Private*, pg. 4267
TZ FINANCIAL COMPANY; *U.S. Private*, pg. 4269
UBC INVESTMENTS, INC.—See United Bancshares, Inc.; *U.S. Public*, pg. 2229
UCBH HOLDINGS, INC.; *U.S. Private*, pg. 4273
UFS BANCORP; *U.S. Private*, pg. 4274
U & I FINANCIAL CORP.; *U.S. Public*, pg. 2211
UMB FINANCIAL CORPORATION; *U.S. Public*, pg. 2224
UNION BANKSHARES, INC.; *U.S. Public*, pg. 2226
UNION FINANCIAL CORP.; *U.S. Public*, pg. 2226
UNION STATE BANCSHARES, INC.; *U.S. Private*, pg. 4285
UNITED BANCORP, INC.; *U.S. Public*, pg. 2229
UNITED BANCORPORATION OF ALABAMA, INC.; *U.S. Public*, pg. 2229
UNITED BANCSHARES, INC.; *U.S. Public*, pg. 4288
UNITED BANCSHARES, INC.; *U.S. Public*, pg. 2229
UNITED BANK CORPORATION; *U.S. Public*, pg. 4288
UNITED BANCSHARES, INC.; *U.S. Public*, pg. 2229
UNITED COMMUNITY BANCORP, INC.; *U.S. Private*, pg. 4289
UNITED COMMUNITY BANKS, INC.; *U.S. Public*, pg. 2229
UNITED NATIONAL CORPORATION; *U.S. Private*, pg. 4295
UNITED SECURITY BANCSHARES; *U.S. Public*, pg. 2235
UNITED TENNESSEE BANKSHARES, INC.; *U.S. Public*, pg. 2237
UNITY BANCORP, INC.; *U.S. Public*, pg. 2253
UNIVERSITY BANCORP, INC.; *U.S. Public*, pg. 2262
UNIVEST FINANCIAL CORPORATION; *U.S. Public*, pg. 2262
U.S. BANCORP; *U.S. Public*, pg. 2212
UWHARRIE CAPITAL CORP.; *U.S. Public*, pg. 2268
VALLEY NATIONAL BANCORP; *U.S. Public*, pg. 2273
VALLEY VIEW BANCSHARES, INC.; *U.S. Private*, pg. 4336
VAN DIEST INVESTMENT COMPANY—See Van Diest Family, LLC; *U.S. Private*, pg. 4339
VBS MORTGAGE, LLC—See F&M Bank Corp.; *U.S. Public*, pg. 818
VBT FINANCIAL CORPORATION; *U.S. Public*, pg. 4348
VECTA INC.; *U.S. Private*, pg. 4349
VERABANK, INC.; *U.S. Private*, pg. 4359
VERITEX HOLDINGS, INC.; *U.S. Public*, pg. 2283
VERMILION BANCSHARES CORPORATION; *U.S. Private*, pg. 4367
VERSAILLES FINANCIAL CORPORATION; *U.S. Public*, pg. 2287
THE VICTORY BANCORP, INC.; *U.S. Public*, pg. 2136
VIKING FINANCIAL CORPORATION; *U.S. Private*, pg. 4382
VILLAGE BANCSHARES, INC.; *U.S. Private*, pg. 4383
VILLAGE BANK & TRUST FINANCIAL CORP.; *U.S. Public*, pg. 2297
VIRGINIA BANK BANKSHARES, INC.; *U.S. Public*, pg. 4387
VIRGINIA COMMUNITY BANKSHARES, INC.—See Blue Ridge Bankshares, Inc.; *U.S. Public*, pg. 365
VIRGINIA NATIONAL BANKSHARES CORPORATION; *U.S. Public*, pg. 2299
VISION BANCSHARES, INC.; *U.S. Private*, pg. 4390

WAFD, INC.; *U.S. Public*, pg. 2321
WAITAKI INTERNATIONAL LTD—See Alliance Group Limited; *Int'l*, pg. 339
WAKE FOREST BANCSHARES, INC.; *U.S. Public*, pg. 2321
WALLKILL VALLEY BANCORP INC.; *U.S. Private*, pg. 4431
WAMEGO BANCSHARES, INC.; *U.S. Private*, pg. 4435
WASHCO BANCSHARES, INC.; *U.S. Private*, pg. 4445
WASHINGTON TRUST BANCORP, INC.; *U.S. Public*, pg. 2329
WATERSTONE FINANCIAL, INC.; *U.S. Public*, pg. 2336
WAYNE SAVINGS BANCSHARES, INC.—See Main Street Financial Services Corp.; *U.S. Public*, pg. 1355
WCF BANCORP, INC.; *U.S. Public*, pg. 2338
WEBSTER FINANCIAL CORPORATION; *U.S. Public*, pg. 2341
WEED INVESTMENT GROUP, INC.; *U.S. Private*, pg. 4468
WELLS FARGO BANK, N.A.—See Wells Fargo & Company; *U.S. Public*, pg. 2346
WELLS FARGO & COMPANY; *U.S. Public*, pg. 2343
WESBANCO, INC.; *U.S. Public*, pg. 2349
WESTAMERICA BANCORPORATION; *U.S. Public*, pg. 2354
WEST BANCORPORATION INC.; *U.S. Public*, pg. 2352
WESTBURY BANCORP, INC.; *U.S. Public*, pg. 2354
WEST COAST COMMUNITY BANCORP; *U.S. Public*, pg. 2352
WESTERN ALLIANCE BANCORPORATION; *U.S. Public*, pg. 2354
WESTERN BANCORPORATION, INC.; *U.S. Private*, pg. 4490
WESTERN BANCSHARES OF CLOVIS, INC.; *U.S. Private*, pg. 4491
WESTERN CAPITAL CORPORATION; *U.S. Private*, pg. 4491
WESTERN ILLINOIS BANCSHARES, INC.; *U.S. Private*, pg. 4493
WESTERN NEW ENGLAND BANCORP, INC.; *U.S. Public*, pg. 2356
WESTERN STATE AGENCY, INC.; *U.S. Private*, pg. 4496
WESTERN STATES BANCORPORATION; *U.S. Private*, pg. 4497
WESTFIELD BANCORP, INC.—See Ohio Farmers Insurance Company; *U.S. Private*, pg. 3004
WEST FLORIDA BANK CORPORATION; *U.S. Private*, pg. 4485
WEST SHORE BANK CORPORATION; *U.S. Public*, pg. 2353
WESTSTAR BANK HOLDING COMPANY, INC.; *U.S. Private*, pg. 4501
WEST SUBURBAN BANCORP, INC.—See Old Second Bancorp, Inc.; *U.S. Public*, pg. 1569
WHITAKER BANK CORPORATION OF KENTUCKY; *U.S. Private*, pg. 4507
WHITCORP FINANCIAL COMPANY; *U.S. Private*, pg. 4507
WILCOX BANCSHARES, INC.; *U.S. Private*, pg. 4518
WILLIAM PENN BANCORPORATION; *U.S. Public*, pg. 2371
WILMINGTON TRUST CORPORATION—See M&T Bank Corporation; *U.S. Public*, pg. 1351
WILSON BANK HOLDING COMPANY; *U.S. Public*, pg. 2372
WINTRUST FINANCIAL CORPORATION; *U.S. Public*, pg. 2374
WOLCOTT BANCORP; *U.S. Private*, pg. 4553
WOLF RIVER BANCORP, INC.; *U.S. Private*, pg. 4553
WOLSELEY HOLDINGS CANADA INC.—See Ferguson plc; *Int'l*, pg. 2638
WONDER BANCORP, INC.; *U.S. Private*, pg. 4556
WOODLANDS FINANCIAL SERVICES COMPANY; *U.S. Public*, pg. 2377
WRZ BANKSHARES, INC.; *U.S. Private*, pg. 4574
WSFS FINANCIAL CORP.; *U.S. Public*, pg. 2383
W.T.B. FINANCIAL CORPORATION; *U.S. Public*, pg. 2318
WVS FINANCIAL CORP.; *U.S. Public*, pg. 2384
XALLES HOLDINGS INC.; *U.S. Public*, pg. 2385
YORK HOLDINGS, INC.; *U.S. Private*, pg. 4590
YORKTOWN FINANCIAL HOLDINGS, INC.; *U.S. Private*, pg. 4591

551112 — OFFICES OF OTHER HOLDING COMPANIES

10X CAPITAL VENTURE ACQUISITION CORP. III; *U.S. Public*, pg. 1
1100 HOLDINGS LLC; *U.S. Public*, pg. 2
1520 GROUP OF COMPANIES; *Int'l*, pg. 2
17 EDUCATION & TECHNOLOGY GROUP INC.; *Int'l*, pg. 2
1834 INVESTMENTS LIMITED; *Int'l*, pg. 3
1847 HOLDINGS LLC; *U.S. Public*, pg. 2
18TH PLACE HEALTH HOLDINGS LLC—See CareTrust REIT, Inc.; *U.S. Public*, pg. 435
1SPATIAL HOLDINGS LIMITED—See 1Spatial Plc; *Int'l*, pg. 3
21 INVESTIMENTI SOCIETA' DI GESTIONE DEL RISPARMIO S.P.A.; *Int'l*, pg. 4
21ST CENTURY ONCOLOGY HOLDINGS, INC.—See Vestar Capital Partners, LLC; *U.S. Private*, pg. 4371
2929 ENTERTAINMENT LP; *U.S. Private*, pg. 6
2INVEST AG; *Int'l*, pg. 5
360 CAPITAL GROUP LIMITED—See Centuria Capital Limited; *Int'l*, pg. 1416
360 LUDASHI HOLDINGS LIMITED; *Int'l*, pg. 6
365 HF; *Int'l*, pg. 7
36KR HOLDINGS INC.; *Int'l*, pg. 7
3E (CYPRUS) LIMITED—See Coca-Cola HBC AG; *Int'l*, pg. 1685
3I GROUP PLC; *Int'l*, pg. 7
3M JAPAN HOLDINGS COMPANY—See 3M Company; *U.S. Public*, pg. 6
3M REAL ESTATE GMBH & CO. KG—See 3M Company; *U.S. Public*, pg. 5
3SBIO INC.; *Int'l*, pg. 9
3 STEP IT GROUP OY; *Int'l*, pg. 5
3U HOLDING AG; *Int'l*, pg. 10
3W POWER S.A.; *Int'l*, pg. 10
451 GROUP, LLC; *U.S. Private*, pg. 15
4CS HOLDINGS CO., LTD.; *Int'l*, pg. 11
4FINANCE HOLDING S.A.; *Int'l*, pg. 11
4SIGHT HOLDINGS LTD.; *Int'l*, pg. 12
4TH STREET HOLDINGS LLC—See CareTrust REIT, Inc.; *U.S. Public*, pg. 435
555 1290 HOLDINGS LLC—See Vornado Realty Trust; *U.S. Public*, pg. 2310
5G NETWORKS LIMITED; *Int'l*, pg. 13
5I5J HOLDING GROUP CO., LTD.; *Int'l*, pg. 13
600SA HOLDINGS (PTY) LTD.—See enX Group Limited; *Int'l*, pg. 2456
6D GLOBAL TECHNOLOGIES, INC.; *U.S. Public*, pg. 9
7DAYS GROUP GMBH & CO. KG; *Int'l*, pg. 15
7ROAD HOLDINGS LIMITED; *Int'l*, pg. 15
8I HOLDINGS LIMITED; *Int'l*, pg. 16
9938982 CANADA INC.—See Fairfax Financial Holdings Limited; *Int'l*, pg. 2605
9F INC.; *Int'l*, pg. 16
9R CANARY SDN. BHD.—See 9R Limited; *Int'l*, pg. 17
9R LEISURE SDN. BHD.—See 9R Limited; *Int'l*, pg. 17
AAA AUTO INTERNATIONAL A.S.—See Abris Capital Partners Sp. z o.o.; *Int'l*, pg. 69
AAB HOLDINGS PTY LIMITED; *Int'l*, pg. 30
AAC CAPITAL PARTNERS HOLDING B.V.; *Int'l*, pg. 30
AAC GROUP HOLDING CORP.—See Fenway Partners, LLC; *U.S. Private*, pg. 1495
AAC HOLDINGS, INC.; *U.S. Private*, pg. 30
AAC TECHNOLOGIES HOLDINGS INC.; *Int'l*, pg. 31
AALBERTS N.V.; *Int'l*, pg. 32
AAM INTERNATIONAL HOLDINGS, INC.—See American Axle & Manufacturing Holdings, Inc.; *U.S. Public*, pg. 96
AAR AIRCRAFT SERVICES, INC.—See AAR Corp.; *U.S. Public*, pg. 13
AARTI INDUSTRIES LTD.; *Int'l*, pg. 38
AARTSENFRUIT HOLDING B.V.; *Int'l*, pg. 38
AASTRA TELECOM EUROPE A/S—See Searchlight Capital Partners, L.P.; *U.S. Private*, pg. 3588
ABACO ENERGY TECHNOLOGIES LLC—See Riverstone Holdings LLC; *U.S. Private*, pg. 3447
ABAKAN INC.; *U.S. Public*, pg. 34
ABANS HOLDINGS LIMITED; *Int'l*, pg. 48
ABBEY GROUP LIMITED—See Gallagher Holdings Ltd.; *Int'l*, pg. 2873
ABBEY PROTECTION PLC—See Markel Group Inc.; *U.S. Public*, pg. 1367
ABBEY ROAD GROUP LLC; *U.S. Private*, pg. 34
ABBOTT EQUITY HOLDINGS LTD.—See Abbott Laboratories; *U.S. Public*, pg. 16
ABBOTT HOLDING GMBH—See Abbott Laboratories; *U.S. Public*, pg. 15
ABBOTT HOLDINGS B.V.—See Abbott Laboratories; *U.S. Public*, pg. 15
ABBOTT LABORATORIES TRUSTEE COMPANY LIMITED—See Abbott Laboratories; *U.S. Public*, pg. 16
ABBOTT (UK) HOLDINGS LIMITED—See Abbott Laboratories; *U.S. Public*, pg. 16
ABB SCHWEIZ HOLDING AG—See ABB Ltd.; *Int'l*, pg. 54
ABC NEWS HOLDING COMPANY, INC.—See The Walt Disney Company; *U.S. Public*, pg. 2137
ABDULLA AHMED NASS GROUP WLL; *Int'l*, pg. 58
ABDULLAH & SAID M.O. BINZAGR COMPANY—See Binzagr Company; *Int'l*, pg. 1035
ABDUL LATIF JAMEEL GROUP OF COMPANIES; *Int'l*, pg. 58
THE ABERDEEN GROUP, LLC—See Ziff Davis, Inc.; *U.S. Public*, pg. 2404
ABH HOLDINGS S.A.; *Int'l*, pg. 60
ABH HOLDINGS S.A.—See Alfa Group; *Int'l*, pg. 308
ABICO GROUP; *Int'l*, pg. 61
ABICO HOLDINGS PUBLIC COMPANY LIMITED; *Int'l*, pg. 61
AB INDUSTRIVARDEN; *Int'l*, pg. 41
ABI SAB GROUP HOLDING LIMITED—See Anheuser-Busch InBev SA/NV; *Int'l*, pg. 464
ABLAK HOLDINGS, LLC; *U.S. Private*, pg. 39
ABO-GROUP NV/SA; *U.S. Private*, pg. 66
ABOUT YOU HOLDING SE; *Int'l*, pg. 67
ABP INDUCTION LLC; *U.S. Private*, pg. 39
ABPRO HOLDINGS, INC.; *U.S. Public*, pg. 26
ABRAAJ CAPITAL LIMITED; *Int'l*, pg. 67
ABRA AUTO BODY & GLASS LP—See Hellman & Friedman LLC; *U.S. Private*, pg. 1907
ABRDN PLC; *Int'l*, pg. 68
ABS GROUP OF COMPANIES, INC.—See American Bureau of Shipping; *U.S. Private*, pg. 225
ABT HOLDING COMPANY—See Healios K.K.; *Int'l*, pg. 3302
ABU DHABI DEVELOPMENTAL HOLDING COMPANY PJSC; *Int'l*, pg. 71
ABU DHABI GROUP; *Int'l*, pg. 71
ABU DHABI INVESTMENT AUTHORITY; *Int'l*, pg. 71
AB VOLVO; *Int'l*, pg. 42
ACACIA DIVERSIFIED HOLDINGS, INC.; *U.S. Public*, pg. 27
ACADEMEDIA AB; *Int'l*, pg. 75
ACADEMY SPORTS AND OUTDOORS, INC.; *U.S. Public*, pg. 27
ACADIA HEALTHCARE COMPANY, INC.; *U.S. Public*, pg. 27
ACADIA - YFCS HOLDINGS, INC.—See Acadia Healthcare Company, Inc.; *U.S. Public*, pg. 27
ACAL EUROPE HOLDING BV—See discoverIE Group plc; *Int'l*, pg. 2132
ACCEL ENTERTAINMENT, INC.; *U.S. Public*, pg. 31
ACCEL GROUP HOLDINGS LIMITED; *Int'l*, pg. 79
ACCELMED PARTNERS II MANAGEMENT, LLC; *U.S. Private*, pg. 50
ACCENTURE CANADA HOLDINGS INC.—See Accenture plc; *Int'l*, pg. 83
ACCENTURE HOLDINGS FRANCE SAS—See Accenture plc; *Int'l*, pg. 84
ACCENTURE HOLDINGS PLC—See Accenture plc; *Int'l*, pg. 82
ACCENTURE PLC; *Int'l*, pg. 82
ACCESS GROUP HOLDINGS CO., LTD.; *Int'l*, pg. 89
ACCESS INDUSTRIES, INC.; *U.S. Private*, pg. 51
ACC HOLDING, INC.; *U.S. Private*, pg. 47
ACCIONA LOGISTICA, S.A.—See Acciona, S.A.; *Int'l*, pg. 90
ACCIONA, S.A.; *Int'l*, pg. 90
ACCO EUROPE LIMITED—See ACCO Brands Corporation; *U.S. Public*, pg. 32
ACCOLADE WINES HOLDINGS AUSTRALIA PTY LIMITED—See The Carlyle Group Inc.; *U.S. Public*, pg. 2043
ACCOLADE WINES HOLDINGS EUROPE LIMITED—See The Carlyle Group Inc.; *U.S. Public*, pg. 2044
ACCORD GROUP LIMITED; *Int'l*, pg. 93
ACCOR S.A.; *Int'l*, pg. 91
ACCOR (U.K.) LIMITED—See Accor S.A.; *Int'l*, pg. 91
ACCOUNT CONTROL TECHNOLOGY HOLDINGS, INC.—See Platinum Equity, LLC; *U.S. Private*, pg. 3209
ACCRELIST LTD.; *Int'l*, pg. 93
ACCUDYNE INDUSTRIES, LLC—See BC Partners LLP; *Int'l*, pg. 922
ACCUDYNE INDUSTRIES, LLC—See The Carlyle Group Inc.; *U.S. Public*, pg. 2044
ACC-U-TUNE—See Icahn Enterprises L.P.; *U.S. Public*, pg. 1083
ACE ACHIEVE INFOCOM LIMITED; *Int'l*, pg. 94
ACE EUROPEAN HOLDINGS LIMITED—See Chubb Limited; *Int'l*, pg. 1590
ACEK DESARROLLO Y GESTION INDUSTRIAL SL; *Int'l*, pg. 96
ACELITY HOLDINGS, INC.—See 3M Company; *U.S. Public*, pg. 7
AC ENERGY HOLDINGS, INC.—See Ayala Corporation; *Int'l*, pg. 773
ACESA-DRIVES S.A. DE C.V.; *Int'l*, pg. 102
ACESO LIFE SCIENCE GROUP LIMITED; *Int'l*, pg. 102
ACHARI VENTURES HOLDINGS CORP. I; *U.S. Public*, pg. 34
ACH, D.D.; *Int'l*, pg. 102
ACHEM TECHNOLOGY CORPORATION; *Int'l*, pg. 103
ACHMEA B.V.; *Int'l*, pg. 103
ACHP PLC—See Financiere Pinault SCA; *Int'l*, pg. 2668
ACINO HOLDING AG—See Avista Capital Partners, L.P.; *U.S. Private*, pg. 408
A.C. ISRAEL ENTERPRISES, INC.; *U.S. Private*, pg. 24
ACI WORLDWIDE, INC.; *U.S. Public*, pg. 34
ACMAT CORPORATION; *U.S. Public*, pg. 35
ACME HOLDINGS, INC.; *U.S. Private*, pg. 61
ACME INTERNATIONAL HOLDINGS LIMITED; *Int'l*, pg. 107
ACORN ENERGY, INC.; *U.S. Public*, pg. 36
ACORN GROWTH COMPANIES, LC; *U.S. Private*, pg. 63
ACOTEC SCIENTIFIC HOLDINGS LIMITED; *Int'l*, pg. 108
ACOT GROUP OF COMPANIES; *Int'l*, pg. 108
ACREAGE HOLDINGS, INC.; *U.S. Public*, pg. 36
ACRE, LLC; *U.S. Private*, pg. 65
ACROMAS HOLDINGS LTD.—See Charterhouse Capital Partners LLP; *Int'l*, pg. 1454
ACROMAS HOLDINGS LTD.—See CVC Capital Partners SICAV-FIS S.A.; *Int'l*, pg. 1881
ACSTAR HOLDINGS, INC.—See ACMAT Corporation; *U.S. Public*, pg. 35

ACTION ASIA LIMITED; *Int'l*, pg. 119
ACTION GROUP HOLDINGS COMPANY K.S.C.C.; *Int'l*, pg. 119
ACTIVAR CONSTRUCTION PRODUCTS GROUP, INC.—See Activar, Inc.; *U.S. Private*, pg. 68
ACTIVA RESOURCES AG; *Int'l*, pg. 119
ACTIVAR, INC.; *U.S. Private*, pg. 68
ACTIVAR INDUSTRIAL PRODUCTS GROUP, INC.—See Activar, Inc.; *U.S. Private*, pg. 68
ACTIVAR PLASTIC PRODUCTS GROUP, INC.—See Activar, Inc.; *U.S. Private*, pg. 68
ACTIVAR TECHNICAL PRODUCTS GROUP, INC.—See Activar, Inc.; *U.S. Private*, pg. 68
ACTIVATED HOLDINGS LLC; *U.S. Private*, pg. 68
ACTIVATION GROUP HOLDINGS LIMITED; *Int'l*, pg. 119
ACTUA CORPORATION; *U.S. Private*, pg. 71
ACUREN GROUP INC.—See Acuren Corporation; *Int'l*, pg. 121
AD1 HOLDINGS LIMITED; *Int'l*, pg. 123
ADAMAS INCORPORATION PUBLIC COMPANY LIMITED; *Int'l*, pg. 124
ADAMA TECHNOLOGIES CORP.; *U.S. Private*, pg. 73
THE ADAM CORPORATION/GROUP; *U.S. Private*, pg. 3981
ADAMS INVESTMENT COMPANY; *U.S. Private*, pg. 74
ADAMS RESOURCES & ENERGY, INC.; *U.S. Public*, pg. 38
ADASTRIA CO., LTD.; *Int'l*, pg. 126
A&D AUSTRALASIA PTY. LTD.—See A&D Co., Ltd.; *Int'l*, pg. 18
AD-BASE GROUP, INC.; *U.S. Private*, pg. 72
AD BEL LTD.; *U.S. Private*, pg. 71
ADCONION MEDIA GROUP LTD.; *Int'l*, pg. 127
ADCS CLINICS, LLC—See Harvest Partners L.P.; *U.S. Private*, pg. 1876
ADCURAM GROUP AG; *Int'l*, pg. 128
ADD NEW ENERGY INVESTMENT HOLDINGS GROUP LIMITED; *Int'l*, pg. 128
ADECCO GROUP AG; *Int'l*, pg. 136
THE ADEC GROUP; *U.S. Private*, pg. 3981
ADEIA INC.; *U.S. Public*, pg. 40
ADEPTUS HEALTH INC.; *U.S. Private*, pg. 78
ADHESIVE APPLICATIONS, INC.; *U.S. Private*, pg. 79
ADIDAS AMERICA, INC.—See adidas AG; *Int'l*, pg. 146
ADIL BEY HOLDING A.S.; *Int'l*, pg. 148
ADIRONDACK BEVERAGES—See Polar Beverages; *U.S. Private*, pg. 3223
ADK HOLDINGS INC.—See Bain Capital, LP; *U.S. Private*, pg. 428
ADLAI NORTYE LTD.; *U.S. Public*, pg. 41
ADMORE INVESTMENTS LIMITED—See Hysan Development Company Limited; *Int'l*, pg. 3554
ADOBE VENTURES—See Adobe Inc.; *U.S. Public*, pg. 42
A&D PHARMA HOLDINGS S.R.L.; *Int'l*, pg. 19
AD PK SOMBOR HOLDING CO.; *Int'l*, pg. 122
ADRITEC GROUP INTERNATIONAL, E.C.; *Int'l*, pg. 153
ADS-TEC ENERGY PUBLIC LIMITED COMPANY; *Int'l*, pg. 154
ADT INC.—See Apollo Global Management, Inc.; *U.S. Public*, pg. 146
ADTRAN HOLDINGS, INC.; *U.S. Public*, pg. 43
THE ADT SECURITY CORPORATION—See Apollo Global Management, Inc.; *U.S. Public*, pg. 146
ADVANCE COMMUNICATION CORP.—See Advance Publications, Inc.; *U.S. Private*, pg. 84
ADVANCED BATTERY TECHNOLOGIES, INC.; *U.S. Private*, pg. 88
ADVANCED EMISSIONS SOLUTIONS, INC.; *U.S. Public*, pg. 46
ADVANCED ENGINEERING HOLDINGS PTE. LTD.—See Advanced Holdings Ltd.; *Int'l*, pg. 159
ADVANCED ENVIRONMENTAL TECHNOLOGIES PTE. LTD.—See Advanced Holdings Ltd.; *Int'l*, pg. 159
THE ADVANCED GROUP OF COMPANIES; *U.S. Private*, pg. 3982
ADVANCED HOLDINGS LTD.; *Int'l*, pg. 159
ADVANCED HOMECARE HOLDINGS, INC.—See Encompass Health Corporation; *U.S. Public*, pg. 754
ADVANCED LIGHTING TECHNOLOGIES, INC.—See Saratoga Partners L.P.; *U.S. Private*, pg. 3549
ADVANCED MEDICAL SOLUTIONS (UK) LTD.—See Advanced Medical Solutions Group plc; *Int'l*, pg. 161
ADVANCED METALS GROUP, LLC; *U.S. Private*, pg. 91
ADVANCED SPORTS, INC.; *U.S. Private*, pg. 92
ADVANCEPIERRE FOODS HOLDINGS, INC.—See Tyson Foods, Inc.; *U.S. Public*, pg. 2209
ADVANCER GLOBAL LIMITED; *Int'l*, pg. 163
ADVANCING EYECARE HOLDINGS, INC.—See Atlantic Street Capital Management LLC; *U.S. Private*, pg. 374
ADVANTECH B&B SMARTWORX S.R.O.—See Advantech Co., Ltd.; *Int'l*, pg. 165
ADVANTECH CO., LTD.; *Int'l*, pg. 164
ADVANTECH CORPORATION (THAILAND) CO., LTD.—See Advantech Co., Ltd.; *Int'l*, pg. 164
ADVANTECH ELECTRONICS, S.DE R.L.DE C.—See Advantech Co., Ltd.; *Int'l*, pg. 164
ADVANTECH EUROPE HOLDING B.V—See Advantech Co., Ltd.; *Int'l*, pg. 164

ADVANTECH POLAND SP Z O.O.—See Advantech Co., Ltd.; *Int'l*, pg. 164
ADVANTECH VIETNAM TECHNOLOGY COMPANY LIMITED—See Advantech Co., Ltd.; *Int'l*, pg. 165
ADVANTEST-ENGINEERING (MALAYSIA) SDN. BHD.—See Advantest Corporation; *Int'l*, pg. 165
ADVANZ PHARMA CORP.; *Int'l*, pg. 166
ADVAZONE INTERNATIONAL LTD.—See Elitegroup Computer Systems Co., Ltd.; *Int'l*, pg. 2363
ADVENTZ GROUP; *Int'l*, pg. 167
ADVISOR GROUP, INC.—See Reverence Capital Partners LLC; *U.S. Private*, pg. 3414
AEA INTERNATIONAL HOLDINGS PTE. LTD.; *Int'l*, pg. 170
AEBI SCHMIDT HOLDING AG; *Int'l*, pg. 170
AEGON N.V.; *Int'l*, pg. 173
AEI SERVICES LLC—See Ashmore Group plc; *Int'l*, pg. 608
AEMULUS HOLDINGS BERHAD; *Int'l*, pg. 175
AEON BIOPHARMA, INC.; *U.S. Public*, pg. 52
AEON CO., LTD.; *Int'l*, pg. 176
AEON GLOBAL HEALTH CORP.; *U.S. Private*, pg. 117
AEROFLEX HOLDING CORP.—See Advent International Corporation; *U.S. Private*, pg. 98
AEROJET INTERNATIONAL, INC.—See L3Harris Technologies, Inc.; *U.S. Public*, pg. 1279
AERO LLOYD FLUGREISEN GMBH & CO. LUFTVERKEHRS-KG—See BayernLB Holding AG; *Int'l*, pg. 913
AEROSPACE COMMMUNICATIONS HOLDINGS GROUP CO., LTD.; *Int'l*, pg. 181
AEROSPACE HI-TECH HOLDING GROUP CO., LTD.; *Int'l*, pg. 181
AEROSTAR AIRPORT HOLDINGS, LLC—See Grupo Aeroportuario del Sureste, S.A.B. de C.V.; *Int'l*, pg. 3119
AEROWORKS EUROPE B.V.—See HEICO Corporation; *U.S. Public*, pg. 1019
AERSALE HOLDINGS, INC.—See Leonard Green & Partners, L.P.; *U.S. Private*, pg. 2423
AES DPL HOLDINGS, LLC—See The AES Corporation; *U.S. Public*, pg. 2030
AES DRAX POWER FINANCE HOLDINGS LIMITED—See The AES Corporation; *U.S. Public*, pg. 2030
AESTHETIC MEDICAL INTERNATIONAL HOLDINGS GROUP LIMITED; *Int'l*, pg. 183
A&E TELEVISION NETWORKS, LLC—See The Hearst Corporation; *U.S. Private*, pg. 4045
A&E TELEVISION NETWORKS, LLC—See The Walt Disney Company; *U.S. Public*, pg. 2137
AET HOLDINGS, LLC; *U.S. Public*, pg. 120
AETNA HEALTH HOLDINGS, LLC—See CVS Health Corporation; *U.S. Public*, pg. 614
AEV CRH HOLDINGS, INC.—See Aboitiz Equity Ventures, Inc.; *Int'l*, pg. 66
AEV CRH HOLDINGS, INC.—See CRH plc; *Int'l*, pg. 1842
AFCV HOLDINGS, LLC—See Summit Partners, L.P.; *U.S. Private*, pg. 3855
AFCV HOLDINGS, LLC—See TA Associates, Inc.; *U.S. Private*, pg. 3914
THE AFE GROUP LTD.—See Ali Holding S.r.l; *Int'l*, pg. 322
AFFIDEA GROUP B.V.—See B-FLEXION Group Holdings SA; *Int'l*, pg. 785
AFFILIATED FOOD STORES, INC.; *U.S. Private*, pg. 121
AFFIRMA CAPITAL LIMITED; *Int'l*, pg. 187
AFFIRMATIVE INSURANCE HOLDINGS, INC.—See J.C. Flowers & Co. LLC; *U.S. Private*, pg. 2159
AFFIRM HOLDINGS, INC.; *U.S. Public*, pg. 57
AFFLUENT PARTNERS HOLDINGS LIMITED; *Int'l*, pg. 188
AFG HOLDINGS, INC.; *U.S. Private*, pg. 123
AFGLOBAL CORPORATION—See First Reserve Management, L.P.; *U.S. Private*, pg. 1525
AF GLOBAL LIMITED—See Aspial Corporation Limited; *Int'l*, pg. 630
AF GLOBAL LIMITED—See Fragrance Group Limited; *Int'l*, pg. 2758
AFH FINANCIAL GROUP PLC—See Edwards Capital, LLC; *U.S. Private*, pg. 1341
AFI DEVELOPMENT PLC; *Int'l*, pg. 189
AF LEGAL GROUP LTD.; *Int'l*, pg. 184
AFM HOLDING CORPORATION—See Compass Diversified Holdings; *U.S. Public*, pg. 559
AF MUTUAL HOLDING CO., INC.; *U.S. Private*, pg. 121
AFRICA ISRAEL PROPERTIES LTD.—See Africa Israel Investments Ltd.; *Int'l*, pg. 190
AFRICA ISRAEL TRADE & AGENCIES LTD.—See Africa Israel Investments Ltd.; *Int'l*, pg. 190
AFRICAN AGRICULTURE HOLDINGS INC.; *U.S. Public*, pg. 57
AFRY AB; *Int'l*, pg. 193
AFTERMARKET CONTROLS HOLDINGS CORP.—See Superior Capital Partners LLC; *U.S. Private*, pg. 3876
AFTERPAY LIMITED—See Block, Inc.; *U.S. Public*, pg. 361
AGALAWATTE PLANTATIONS PLC; *Int'l*, pg. 199
AG ANADOLU GRUBU HOLDING A.S.; *Int'l*, pg. 196
AGAPE ATP CORPORATION; *Int'l*, pg. 199
AGA RANGEMASTER GROUP PLC—See The Middleby Corporation; *U.S. Public*, pg. 2114
AGATOS S.P.A.; *Int'l*, pg. 200
A.G. BARR PLC; *Int'l*, pg. 23

AGC AMERICA, INC.—See AGC Inc.; *Int'l*, pg. 200
AGCO HOLDING BV—See AGCO Corporation; *U.S. Public*, pg. 58
AGCO HOLDINGS (SINGAPORE) PTE. LTD—See AGCO Corporation; *U.S. Public*, pg. 58
AGEAGLE AERIAL SYSTEMS INC.; *U.S. Public*, pg. 60
AGEAS N.V.—See Ageas SA/NV; *Int'l*, pg. 205
AGEAS SA/NV; *Int'l*, pg. 204
AGEL ENTERPRISES INTERNATIONAL SDN. BHD.—See JRjr33, Inc.; *U.S. Public*, pg. 2240
AGEL INTERNATIONAL SRL—See JRjr33, Inc.; *U.S. Private*, pg. 2240
AGENNIX AG; *Int'l*, pg. 205
AGESCA NEDERLAND NV—See BNP Paribas SA; *Int'l*, pg. 1090
AGESCA NEDERLAND NV—See Frere-Bourgeois; *Int'l*, pg. 2773
AGGREGATE INDUSTRIES HOLDINGS LIMITED—See Holcim Ltd.; *Int'l*, pg. 3446
AGGREGATO GLOBAL PTY. LTD.; *Int'l*, pg. 209
AGGREKO HOLDINGS, INC.—See I Squared Capital Advisors (US) LLC; *U.S. Private*, pg. 2021
AGGREKO HOLDINGS LTD.—See I Squared Capital Advisors (US) LLC; *U.S. Private*, pg. 2021
AGILE GROUP HOLDINGS LIMITED; *Int'l*, pg. 209
AGILE MALTA HOLDINGS LIMITED—See Aurobindo Pharma Ltd.; *Int'l*, pg. 712
AGILITI, INC.—See Thomas H. Lee Partners, L.P.; *U.S. Private*, pg. 4155
AGILITY FUEL SOLUTIONS HOLDINGS INC.—See Hexagon Composites ASA; *Int'l*, pg. 3370
AGILITY HEALTH, INC.; *Int'l*, pg. 210
AGMO HOLDINGS BERHAD; *Int'l*, pg. 211
AGN AGROINDUSTRIAL, PROJETOS E PARTICIPACOES LTDA.; *Int'l*, pg. 211
AGNUS HOLDINGS PVT. LTD.; *Int'l*, pg. 212
AGORA DIGITAL HOLDINGS, INC.; *U.S. Private*, pg. 128
AGORA HOLDINGS INC.; *Int'l*, pg. 212
AGORA, INC.; *U.S. Public*, pg. 62
AGORA S.A.; *Int'l*, pg. 212
AGRI-FINTECH HOLDINGS, INC.; *U.S. Public*, pg. 63
AGRIMARINE HOLDINGS INC.—See Dundee Corporation; *Int'l*, pg. 2225
AGRIOS GLOBAL HOLDINGS LTD.; *Int'l*, pg. 217
AGRIPURE HOLDINGS COMPANY LIMITED; *Int'l*, pg. 217
AGRITEK HOLDINGS, INC.; *U.S. Private*, pg. 129
AGROFERT HOLDING, A.S.; *Int'l*, pg. 218
AGROFRESH ITALIA SRL—See Paine Schwartz Partners, LLC; *U.S. Private*, pg. 3075
AGROFRESH SOLUTIONS, INC.—See Paine Schwartz Partners, LLC; *U.S. Private*, pg. 3075
AGRO-IRON, INC.; *U.S. Private*, pg. 130
AGROLI GROUP; *Int'l*, pg. 220
AGV GROUP LIMITED; *Int'l*, pg. 222
AH HOLDINGS, LLC—See Ascension Health Alliance; *U.S. Private*, pg. 346
AHLSELL AB; *Int'l*, pg. 223
AHLSTROM-MUNKSJO GERMANY GMBH—See Ahlstrom Capital Oy; *Int'l*, pg. 224
AHLSTROM-MUNKSJO GERMANY GMBH—See Bain Capital, LP; *U.S. Private*, pg. 429
AHLSTROM-MUNKSJO GERMANY HOLDING GMBH—See Ahlstrom Capital Oy; *Int'l*, pg. 224
AHLSTROM-MUNKSJO GERMANY HOLDING GMBH—See Bain Capital, LP; *U.S. Private*, pg. 429
AHP HOLDINGS PTY. LIMITED—See Pfizer Inc.; *U.S. Public*, pg. 1679
AHS OKLAHOMA HOLDINGS, INC.—See Ventas, Inc.; *U.S. Public*, pg. 2277
AIA GROUP LIMITED; *Int'l*, pg. 227
AICHI USA INC.—See Aichi Steel Corporation; *Int'l*, pg. 230
AI CLAIMS SOLUTIONS PLC; *Int'l*, pg. 226
AI CONVERSATION SYSTEMS LTD.; *Int'l*, pg. 226
AIDIGONG MATERNAL & CHILD HEALTH LIMITED; *Int'l*, pg. 231
AID PARTNERS TECHNOLOGY HOLDINGS LIMITED; *Int'l*, pg. 230
AIG APAC HOLDINGS PTE. LTD.—See American International Group, Inc.; *U.S. Public*, pg. 105
AIG HOLDINGS, LLC—See Tenet Healthcare Corporation; *U.S. Public*, pg. 2009
AIG JAPAN HOLDINGS KABUSHIKI KAISHA—See American International Group, Inc.; *U.S. Public*, pg. 104
AIG LIFE & RETIREMENT—See American International Group, Inc.; *U.S. Public*, pg. 104
AIG MEA HOLDINGS LIMITED—See American International Group, Inc.; *U.S. Public*, pg. 105
AIM MEDIA TEXAS, LLC; *U.S. Private*, pg. 132
AIP/AEROSPACE HOLDINGS, LLC—See AIP, LLC; *U.S. Private*, pg. 133
AIRA CAPITAL PUBLIC COMPANY LIMITED; *Int'l*, pg. 241
AIRBUS GROUP, INC.—See Airbus SE; *Int'l*, pg. 243
AIRBUS HELICOPTERS HOLDING SAS—See Airbus SE; *Int'l*, pg. 243
AIRCRAFT SERVICE INTERNATIONAL GROUP, INC.—See Agility; *Int'l*, pg. 210
AIRESIS S.A.; *Int'l*, pg. 247
AIR INDUSTRIES GROUP; *U.S. Public*, pg. 64

N.A.I.C.S. INDEX

551112 — OFFICES OF OTHER HO...

AIRINMAR HOLDINGS LIMITED—See AAR Corp.; *U.S. Public*, pg. 13
AIR METHODS CORPORATION—See American Securities LLC; *U.S. Private*, pg. 247
AIR T, INC.; *U.S. Public*, pg. 67
AIR WIS SERVICES, INC.—See United Airlines Holdings, Inc.; *U.S. Public*, pg. 2228
AIRXCEL, INC.—See Thor Industries, Inc.; *U.S. Public*, pg. 2156
AISIN HOLDINGS OF AMERICA, INC.—See AISIN Corporation; *Int'l*, pg. 252
AJIA INNOGROUP HOLDINGS, LTD.; *U.S. Public*, pg. 68
AJISEN CHINA HOLDINGS LTD.; *Int'l*, pg. 258
A.K.A. BRANDS HOLDING CORP.; *U.S. Public*, pg. 12
A.K. AL-MUHAIDIB & SONS GROUP OF COMPANIES; *Int'l*, pg. 24
AKASTOR ASA; *Int'l*, pg. 260
AKATSUKI CORP.; *Int'l*, pg. 260
AKBAR GROUP; *Int'l*, pg. 261
AKDENIZ FAKTORING A.S.; *Int'l*, pg. 261
AKELA PHARMA, INC.; *U.S. Private*, pg. 144
AKER CAPITAL AS—See Aker ASA; *Int'l*, pg. 262
AKER SOLUTIONS ASA; *Int'l*, pg. 262
AK FAKTORING AS; *Int'l*, pg. 259
AKFEN HOLDING A.S.; *Int'l*, pg. 263
AK HOLDINGS, INC.; *Int'l*, pg. 259
AK RETAIL HOLDINGS LIMITED; *Int'l*, pg. 259
AKROTEX, INC.; *U.S. Private*, pg. 146
AKTIESELSKABET SCHOUW & CO.; *Int'l*, pg. 265
AKTIO HOLDINGS CORPORATION; *Int'l*, pg. 267
AKZO NOBEL N.V.; *Int'l*, pg. 268
AL-ABRAJ HOLDING COMPANY KSCC; *Int'l*, pg. 284
ALAM GROUP OF COMPANIES; *Int'l*, pg. 289
ALAMOGORDO FINANCIAL CORP.—See AF Mutual Holding Co., Inc.; *U.S. Private*, pg. 121
ALAMO GROUP INC.; *U.S. Public*, pg. 70
AL ANWAR HOLDINGS S.A.O.G—See Al Yousef Group; *Int'l*, pg. 283
ALARM.COM HOLDINGS, INC.—See ABS Capital Partners, L.P.; *U.S. Private*, pg. 43
ALASKA AIR GROUP, INC.; *U.S. Public*, pg. 71
ALASKA BASIC INDUSTRIES, INC.—See MDU Resources Group, Inc.; *U.S. Public*, pg. 1409
ALASKA NATIONAL CORPORATION; *U.S. Private*, pg. 151
ALASKA POWER & TELEPHONE COMPANY; *U.S. Public*, pg. 72
ALBERCO HOLDING B.V.; *Int'l*, pg. 293
ALBERTA NEWSPAPER GROUP INC.—See Glacier Media Inc.; *Int'l*, pg. 2987
ALBERT BALLIN KG; *Int'l*, pg. 294
ALBIREO ENERGY, LLC—See Huron Capital Partners LLC; *U.S. Private*, pg. 2011
ALBORZ INVESTMENT COMPANY; *Int'l*, pg. 299
ALCANTARA GROUP; *Int'l*, pg. 300
ALCHEMIST LTD; *Int'l*, pg. 300
ALCOA AUSTRALIAN HOLDINGS PTY. LTD.—See Alcoa Corporation; *U.S. Public*, pg. 74
ALCOA CORPORATION; *U.S. Public*, pg. 74
ALCOA HOLDING FRANCE SAS—See Howmet Aerospace Inc.; *U.S. Public*, pg. 1061
ALCUMUS HOLDINGS LTD; *Int'l*, pg. 303
ALEADRI-SCHINNI PARTICIPACOES E REPRESENTACOES S.A.; *Int'l*, pg. 305
ALE GROUP HOLDING LIMITED; *Int'l*, pg. 305
ALEPH GROUP, INC.; *Int'l*, pg. 306
ALERA GROUP, INC.—See Genstar Capital, LLC; *U.S. Private*, pg. 1673
ALERISLIFE INC.; *U.S. Private*, pg. 160
ALESSANDRO ROSSO GROUP S.P.A.; *Int'l*, pg. 306
ALEXANDER & BALDWIN, INC.; *U.S. Public*, pg. 75
ALEX LEE, INC.; *U.S. Private*, pg. 162
ALFA CORPORATION; *U.S. Private*, pg. 164
ALFAGOMMA S.P.A.; *Int'l*, pg. 315
AL FAHIM GROUP; *Int'l*, pg. 277
AL FIRDOUS HOLDINGS (P.J.S.C.); *Int'l*, pg. 277
ALFRESA HOLDINGS CORPORATION; *Int'l*, pg. 317
AL GHURAIR GROUP; *Int'l*, pg. 277
AL GHURAIR INVESTMENT LLC; *Int'l*, pg. 278
ALGOMA STEEL GROUP INC.; *Int'l*, pg. 318
AL-HAJ GROUP OF COMPANIES; *Int'l*, pg. 285
ALHAMRANI GROUP; *Int'l*, pg. 319
AL-HEJAILAN GROUP; *Int'l*, pg. 286
ALH HOLDINGS, LLC—See Ventas, Inc.; *U.S. Public*, pg. 2277
ALI ABDULLAH AL TAMIMI COMPANY; *Int'l*, pg. 319
ALIANCYS (CHINA) HOLDING B.V.—See CVC Capital Partners SICAV-FIS S.A.; *Int'l*, pg. 1886
ALIANCYS HOLDING INTERNATIONAL B.V.—See CVC Capital Partners SICAV-FIS S.A.; *Int'l*, pg. 1886
ALIAXIS HOLDING ITALIA SPA—See Aliaxis S.A./N.V.; *Int'l*, pg. 323
ALIAXIS HOLDINGS UK LTD—See Aliaxis S.A./N.V.; *Int'l*, pg. 323
ALIBABA GROUP HOLDING LIMITED; *Int'l*, pg. 325
ALIBABA PICTURES GROUP LTD; *Int'l*, pg. 326
A. LIBENTAL HOLDINGS LTD.; *Int'l*, pg. 21
ALI BIN ALI ESTABLISHMENT; *Int'l*, pg. 320
ALICROS S.P.A.; *Int'l*, pg. 327

ALIGNA AG; *Int'l*, pg. 327
ALIGN AEROSPACE HOLDINGS, INC.—See AVIC International Holdings Limited; *Int'l*, pg. 742
ALIGN FINANCIAL GROUP, LLC; *U.S. Private*, pg. 168
ALI HOLDING S.R.L.; *Int'l*, pg. 320
ALIJARAH HOLDING QSC; *Int'l*, pg. 328
ALISTHE INVESTMENTS PTY LTD; *Int'l*, pg. 329
AL JABER GROUP; *Int'l*, pg. 279
AL-JAZEERA SATELLITE NETWORK; *Int'l*, pg. 286
ALJ REGIONAL HOLDINGS, INC.; *U.S. Public*, pg. 77
ALL AMERICAN AUTO SALES GROUP; *U.S. Private*, pg. 169
ALLEANZA HOLDINGS CO., LTD.; *Int'l*, pg. 334
ALLEGHANY CORPORATION—See Berkshire Hathaway Inc.; *U.S. Public*, pg. 298
ALLEGION PUBLIC LIMITED COMPANY; *Int'l*, pg. 334
ALLEGION US HOLDING COMPANY INC.—See Allegion Public Limited Company; *Int'l*, pg. 335
ALLEGIS GROUP, INC.; *U.S. Private*, pg. 177
ALLEGIS GROUP LTD.—See Allegis Group, Inc.; *U.S. Private*, pg. 177
ALLEGRO MICROSYSTEMS, INC.; *U.S. Public*, pg. 78
ALLEN HOLDING INC.; *U.S. Private*, pg. 179
ALLERGAN, INC.—See AbbVie Inc.; *U.S. Public*, pg. 22
ALLERGAN PLC—See AbbVie Inc.; *U.S. Public*, pg. 22
ALLER HOLDING A/S; *Int'l*, pg. 336
ALLER MEDIA AS—See Aller Holding A/S; *Int'l*, pg. 336
ALLETE, INC.; *U.S. Public*, pg. 79
ALLGEIER SE; *Int'l*, pg. 336
ALLIANCE AUTOMOTIVE HOLDING LIMITED—See Blackstone Inc.; *U.S. Public*, pg. 359
ALLIANCE BENEFIT GROUP, LLC; *U.S. Private*, pg. 181
ALLIANCE BOOTS HOLDINGS LIMITED—See Walgreens Boots Alliance, Inc.; *U.S. Public*, pg. 2321
ALLIANCE FINANCE COMPANY PLC; *Int'l*, pg. 338
ALLIANCE GLOBAL GROUP, INC.; *Int'l*, pg. 339
ALLIANCE HOLDINGS GP, L.P.; *U.S. Public*, pg. 183
ALLIANCE HOLDINGS, INC.; *U.S. Private*, pg. 183
ALLIANCE INTERNATIONAL EDUCATION LEASING HOLDINGS LIMITED; *Int'l*, pg. 340
ALLIANCE LAUNDRY HOLDINGS LLC—See BDT Capital Partners, LLC; *U.S. Private*, pg. 502
ALLIANT ENERGY CORPORATION; *U.S. Public*, pg. 79
ALLIANZ DEUTSCHLAND AG—See Allianz SE; *Int'l*, pg. 344
ALLIANZ EUROPE B.V.—See Allianz SE; *Int'l*, pg. 345
ALLIANZ OF AMERICA, INC.—See Allianz SE; *Int'l*, pg. 351
ALLIANZ PLC—See Allianz SE; *Int'l*, pg. 351
ALLIANZ SE; *Int'l*, pg. 341
ALLIANZ SUBALPINA HOLDING S.P.A.—See Allianz SE; *Int'l*, pg. 350
ALLIED GROUP LIMITED; *Int'l*, pg. 357
ALLIED HEALTHCARE GROUP HOLDINGS LIMITED—See Charterhouse Capital Partners LLP; *Int'l*, pg. 1454
ALLIED HEALTHCARE GROUP HOLDINGS LIMITED—See CVC Capital Partners SICAV-FIS S.A.; *Int'l*, pg. 1882
ALLIED HEALTHCARE HOLDINGS LIMITED—See Charterhouse Capital Partners LLP; *Int'l*, pg. 1454
ALLIED HEALTHCARE HOLDINGS LIMITED—See CVC Capital Partners SICAV-FIS S.A.; *Int'l*, pg. 1882
ALLIED HEALTHCARE INTERNATIONAL INC.—See Charterhouse Capital Partners LLP; *Int'l*, pg. 1454
ALLIED HEALTHCARE INTERNATIONAL INC.—See CVC Capital Partners SICAV-FIS S.A.; *Int'l*, pg. 1882
ALLIED HEALTHCARE—See Charterhouse Capital Partners LLP; *Int'l*, pg. 1454
ALLIED HEALTHCARE—See CVC Capital Partners SICAV-FIS S.A.; *Int'l*, pg. 1882
ALLIED HOLDINGS LTD.; *Int'l*, pg. 357
ALLIED MINDS PLC; *U.S. Public*, pg. 80
ALLIED UNIVERSAL HOLDING CORPORATION; *U.S. Private*, pg. 188
ALLIED UNIVERSAL MANAGER LLC; *U.S. Private*, pg. 188
ALLIED VAUGHN INC.; *U.S. Private*, pg. 191
ALLISON REED GROUP, INC.; *U.S. Private*, pg. 192
ALLISON TRANSMISSION HOLDINGS, INC.; *U.S. Public*, pg. 81
ALL MEDIA BALTICS—See Providence Equity Partners L.L.C.; *U.S. Private*, pg. 3291
ALLNEX HOLDING II GERMANY GMBH—See Advent International Corporation; *U.S. Private*, pg. 98
ALLNEX HOLDING S.A.R.L.—See Advent International Corporation; *U.S. Private*, pg. 98
ALLOY MEDIA HOLDINGS, L.L.C.—See Warner Bros. Discovery, Inc.; *U.S. Public*, pg. 2327
ALLSTATE NON-INSURANCE HOLDINGS, INC.—See The Allstate Corporation; *U.S. Public*, pg. 2032
ALL-TEX ERECTION SYSTEMS INC.; *U.S. Public*, pg. 174
ALLURION TECHNOLOGIES, INC.; *U.S. Public*, pg. 81
ALLVUE SYSTEMS HOLDINGS, INC.; *U.S. Private*, pg. 194
ALLY FINANCIAL INC.; *U.S. Public*, pg. 81
ALMA MEDIA CORPORATION; *Int'l*, pg. 361
ALMAVIVA S.P.A.; *Int'l*, pg. 363
AL-MAZAYA HOLDING COMPANY K.S.C.P.; *Int'l*, pg. 287
ALMENDRAL S.A.; *Int'l*, pg. 364
ALMOGIM HOLDINGS LTD.; *Int'l*, pg. 364
ALMOST FAMILY, INC.—See UnitedHealth Group Incorporated; *U.S. Public*, pg. 2243

AL MOWASAT HEALTHCARE COMPANY K.S.C.C.; *Int'l*, pg. 281
AL-NAWADI HOLDING COMPANY - KPSC; *Int'l*, pg. 287
ALON ISRAEL OIL COMPANY LTD.; *Int'l*, pg. 365
AL-OSAISI INTERNATIONAL HOLDING COMPANY; *Int'l*, pg. 287
AL-OTHAIM HOLDING COMPANY; *Int'l*, pg. 288
AL PACKER, INC.; *U.S. Public*, pg. 147
ALPHA AND OMEGA SEMICONDUCTOR LIMITED; *Int'l*, pg. 366
ALPHABET INC.; *U.S. Public*, pg. 82
ALPHACARE HOLDINGS, INC.—See Centene Corporation; *U.S. Public*, pg. 469
ALPHA DHABI HOLDING PJSC; *Int'l*, pg. 367
ALPHA DX GROUP LIMITED; *Int'l*, pg. 368
ALPHA GRISSIN S.A.; *Int'l*, pg. 368
THE ALPHA GROUP—See EnerSys; *U.S. Public*, pg. 767
ALPHA HOLDING TWO B.V.—See HP Inc.; *U.S. Public*, pg. 1062
ALPHA MEDIA LLC; *U.S. Private*, pg. 198
ALPHATEC HOLDINGS, INC.; *U.S. Public*, pg. 84
ALPICO HOLDINGS CO., LTD.; *Int'l*, pg. 371
ALPINE 4 HOLDINGS, INC.; *U.S. Public*, pg. 85
THE ALPINE GROUP, INC.; *U.S. Private*, pg. 3984
ALPINE HOLDING GMBH; *Int'l*, pg. 371
ALPIQ HOLDING AG; *Int'l*, pg. 371
A.L. PROCHOICE GROUP PUBLIC LTD.; *Int'l*, pg. 25
ALPRO HOLDINGS, BVBA—See Danone; *Int'l*, pg. 1967
AL-SAFWA GROUP HOLDING CO. K.P.S.C.; *Int'l*, pg. 288
ALSCO INC.; *U.S. Private*, pg. 202
AL SHAFAR DEVELOPMENT—See Al Shafar Group; *Int'l*, pg. 282
AL SHAFAR GROUP; *Int'l*, pg. 282
ALSHAMEL INTERNATIONAL HOLDING COMPANY K.S.C.P.; *Int'l*, pg. 379
ALS INDUSTRIAL HOLDINGS PTY. LTD.—See ALS Limited; *Int'l*, pg. 378
ALSO HOLDING AG—See Droege Group AG; *Int'l*, pg. 2204
ALST CASINO HOLDCO, LLC—See Boyd Gaming Corporation; *U.S. Public*, pg. 377
ALSTOM BELGIUM SA—See Alstom S.A.; *Int'l*, pg. 380
ALSTOM (CHINA) INVESTMENT CO. LTD—See Alstom S.A.; *Int'l*, pg. 380
ALSTOM ESPANA IB—See Alstom S.A.; *Int'l*, pg. 380
ALSTOM HOLDINGS—See Alstom S.A.; *Int'l*, pg. 380
ALSTOM MEXICO SA DE CV—See Alstom S.A.; *Int'l*, pg. 381
ALSTOM NEW ZEALAND LTD—See Alstom S.A.; *Int'l*, pg. 381
ALSTOM N.V.—See Alstom S.A.; *Int'l*, pg. 381
ALSTOM S.P.A.—See Alstom S.A.; *Int'l*, pg. 381
ALSUWAIKET TRADING & CONTRACTING CO.; *Int'l*, pg. 383
ALTA COMMUNICATIONS, INC.; *U.S. Private*, pg. 203
ALTA EAST, INC.; *U.S. Private*, pg. 203
ALTAIR CORPORATION; *U.S. Public*, pg. 86
ALTAIR US HOLDINGS, INC.—See Altair Nanotechnologies Inc.; *U.S. Public*, pg. 204
ALTA MESA RESOURCES, INC.; *U.S. Private*, pg. 203
AL TAYER GROUP LLC; *Int'l*, pg. 283
ALTEC HOLDINGS S.A.; *Int'l*, pg. 388
ALTERNERGY HOLDINGS CORPORATION; *Int'l*, pg. 392
ALTERRA MOUNTAIN COMPANY—See KSL Capital Partners, LLC; *U.S. Private*, pg. 2354
ALTEX INDUSTRIES, INC.; *U.S. Public*, pg. 87
ALTHEA GROUP HOLDINGS LIMITED; *Int'l*, pg. 392
AL-THEMAR INTERNATIONAL HOLDING CO. (K.S.C.); *Int'l*, pg. 289
ALTICE EUROPE N.V.; *Int'l*, pg. 392
ALTICE USA, INC.; *U.S. Public*, pg. 87
ALTICOR INC.; *U.S. Private*, pg. 208
ALTI GLOBAL, INC.; *U.S. Public*, pg. 87
ALTIMMUNE, INC; *U.S. Public*, pg. 88
ALTRAD HOLDING S.A.—See Altrad Investment Authority SAS; *Int'l*, pg. 397
ALTRAD INVESTMENT AUTHORITY SAS; *Int'l*, pg. 397
ALTRA INDUSTRIAL MOTION CORP.—See Regal Rexnord Corporation; *U.S. Public*, pg. 1772
ALTRIA GROUP, INC.; *U.S. Public*, pg. 88
ALTRUIST TECHNOLOGIES PVT. LTD.; *Int'l*, pg. 399
AL-TUWAIRQI GROUP; *Int'l*, pg. 289
ALUF HOLDINGS, INC.; *U.S. Public*, pg. 89
ALUMIFUEL POWER CORPORATION; *U.S. Public*, pg. 89
ALVAREZ & MARSAL, INC.; *U.S. Private*, pg. 212
AL-WAZZAN HOLDING GROUP; *Int'l*, pg. 289
AL YOUSEF GROUP; *Int'l*, pg. 283
AMADA NORTH AMERICA, INC.—See Amada Holdings Co., Ltd.; *Int'l*, pg. 404
AMADEUS IT GROUP, S.A.; *Int'l*, pg. 405
AMADEUS NORTH AMERICA, INC.—See Amadeus IT Group, S.A.; *Int'l*, pg. 406
AMALGAMATED METAL (AUSTRALIA) LTD—See Amalgamated Metal Corporation PLC; *Int'l*, pg. 408
AMALGAMATED METAL CORPORATION PLC; *Int'l*, pg. 408
AMALGAMATED REGIONAL TRADING (ART) HOLDINGS LTD.; *Int'l*, pg. 409
AMANET MANAGEMENT & SYSTEMS LTD.; *Int'l*, pg. 410

551112 — OFFICES OF OTHER HO...

AMATA B.GRIMM POWER HOLDING LTD.—See B. Grimm Group; *Int'l*, pg. 788
AMATHEON AGRI HOLDING N.V.; *Int'l*, pg. 413
AMAYA GLOBAL HOLDINGS CORP.; *U.S. Public*, pg. 90
AMAZON EU SARL—See Amazon.com, Inc.; *U.S. Public*, pg. 90
AMBAC FINANCIAL GROUP, INC.; *U.S. Public*, pg. 91
AMBA HOLDINGS INC.—See Moody's Corporation; *U.S. Public*, pg. 1466
AMBASSADOR ENTERPRISES, LLC; *U.S. Private*, pg. 217
AMBEON HOLDINGS PLC; *Int'l*, pg. 414
AMBIT ENERGY HOLDINGS, LLC—See Vistra Corp.; *U.S. Public*, pg. 2306
AMBROISIE CAPITAL HOLDING S.A.S.; *Int'l*, pg. 415
AMC ENTERTAINMENT HOLDINGS, INC.—See Dalian Wanda Group Corporation Ltd.; *Int'l*, pg. 1953
AMCO GROUP INC.; *U.S. Private*, pg. 218
AMCORP GROUP BERHAD; *Int'l*, pg. 418
AMCOR PLC; *Int'l*, pg. 416
AMDOCS LIMITED; *Int'l*, pg. 418
AMECO HOLDINGS, INC.—See OEP Capital Advisors, L.P.; *U.S. Private*, pg. 2998
AMEN PROPERTIES, INC.; *U.S. Public*, pg. 94
AMERICAN AIRLINES GROUP INC.; *U.S. Public*, pg. 95
AMERICAN-AMICABLE HOLDINGS, INC.—See iA Financial Corporation Inc.; *Int'l*, pg. 3567
AMERICAN AUTO AUCTION GROUP, LLC—See Huron Capital Partners LLC; *U.S. Private*, pg. 2011
AMERICAN AXLE & MANUFACTURING DE MEXICO HOLDINGS S. DE R.L. DE C.V.—See American Axle & Manufacturing Holdings, Inc.; *U.S. Public*, pg. 96
AMERICAN AXLE & MANUFACTURING HOLDINGS, INC.; *U.S. Public*, pg. 96
AMERICAN BANKNOTE CORPORATION; *U.S. Private*, pg. 224
AMERICAN BLUE RIBBON HOLDINGS, LLC—See Fidelity National Financial, Inc.; *U.S. Public*, pg. 830
AMERICAN BRIDGE HOLDING COMPANY—See Continental Holdings Corp.; *Int'l*, pg. 1784
AMERICAN CANNABIS INNOVATIONS CONGLOMERATED; *U.S. Private*, pg. 226
AMERICAN CASINO & ENTERTAINMENT PROPERTIES LLC—See Golden Entertainment, Inc.; *U.S. Public*, pg. 950
AMERICAN COASTAL INSURANCE CORPORATION; *U.S. Public*, pg. 98
AMERICAN COMMERCE SOLUTIONS, INC.; *U.S. Private*, pg. 227
AMERICAN CONSOLIDATED MEDIA LP; *U.S. Private*, pg. 228
AMERICAN CONSOLIDATED NATURAL RESOURCES, INC.; *U.S. Private*, pg. 228
AMERICAN DIVERSIFIED HOLDINGS CORPORATION; *U.S. Public*, pg. 98
AMERICAN ENTERPRISE GROUP, INC.—See American Enterprise Mutual Holding Company; *U.S. Private*, pg. 232
AMERICAN ENTERPRISE MUTUAL HOLDING COMPANY; *U.S. Private*, pg. 232
AMERICAN EQUITY INVESTMENT LIFE HOLDING COMPANY—See Brookfield Reinsurance Ltd.; *Int'l*, pg. 1193
AMERICAN EXPRESS HOLDINGS (FRANCE) SAS—See American Express Company; *U.S. Public*, pg. 100
AMERICAN EXPRESS INTERNATIONAL, INC.—See American Express Company; *U.S. Public*, pg. 101
AMERICAN FINANCIAL GROUP, INC.; *U.S. Public*, pg. 102
AMERICAN GIRL BRANDS, LLC—See Mattel, Inc.; *U.S. Public*, pg. 1398
AMERICAN HOLDCO INC.; *U.S. Private*, pg. 236
AMERICAN HOMETOWN PUBLISHING, INC.—See West End Holdings LLC; *U.S. Public*, pg. 4485
AMERICAN INDEPENDENCE CORP.—See Geneve Holdings Corp.; *U.S. Private*, pg. 1670
AMERICAN INDUSTRIAL ACQUISITION CORPORATION; *U.S. Private*, pg. 237
AMERICAN INTERNATIONAL GROUP, INC.; *U.S. Public*, pg. 104
AMERICAN INTERNATIONAL HOLDINGS CORP.; *U.S. Public*, pg. 107
AMERICAN INTERNATIONAL INDUSTRIES, INC.; *U.S. Public*, pg. 107
AMERICAN MARINE HOLDINGS, LLC; *U.S. Private*, pg. 240
AMERICAN MARITIME HOLDINGS, INC.; *U.S. Private*, pg. 240
AMERICAN MEDIA, INC.—See Chatham Asset Management, LLC; *U.S. Private*, pg. 860
AMERICAN NATIONAL GROUP, INC.—See Brookfield Corporation; *Int'l*, pg. 1174
AMERICAN ONCOLOGY NETWORK, INC.; *U.S. Public*, pg. 108
AMERICAN OVERSEAS GROUP LIMITED; *Int'l*, pg. 422
AMERICAN PLASTICS, LLC—See Highview Capital, LLC; *U.S. Private*, pg. 1942
AMERICAN PLASTICS, LLC—See Victory Park Capital Advisors, LLC; *U.S. Private*, pg. 4379

AMERICAN RESOURCES CORPORATION; *U.S. Public*, pg. 109
AMERICAN RESTAURANT HOLDINGS, INC.; *U.S. Private*, pg. 246
AMERICAN SOCCER CORPORATION; *U.S. Private*, pg. 253
AMERICAN SURGICAL HOLDINGS, INC.—See Great Point Partners, LLC; *U.S. Private*, pg. 1767
AMERICAN TEXTILE HOLDINGS, LLC—See Monomoy Capital Partners LLC; *U.S. Private*, pg. 2772
AMERICAN TIRE DISTRIBUTORS HOLDINGS, INC.—See TPG Capital, L.P.; *U.S. Public*, pg. 2166
AMERICAN TOOL COMPANIES HOLDING B.V.—See Newell Brands Inc.; *U.S. Public*, pg. 1513
AMERICAN TOWER INVESTMENTS LLC—See American Tower Corporation; *U.S. Public*, pg. 110
AMERICAN UNITED MUTUAL INSURANCE HOLDING COMPANY; *U.S. Private*, pg. 257
AMERICAN VANGUARD CORPORATION; *U.S. Public*, pg. 111
AMERICAN ZINC RECYCLING CORP.—See Befesa S.A.; *Int'l*, pg. 939
AMERICA'S CAR-MART, INC.; *U.S. Public*, pg. 95
AMERICATOWNE HOLDINGS, INC.; *U.S. Private*, pg. 259
AMERI-FORCE, INC.; *U.S. Private*, pg. 220
AMERIGAS, INC.—See UGI Corporation; *U.S. Public*, pg. 2221
AMERIGAS PARTNERS, L.P.—See UGI Corporation; *U.S. Public*, pg. 2221
AMERI METRO, INC.; *U.S. Private*, pg. 220
AMERINAC HOLDING CORP.; *U.S. Private*, pg. 260
AMERINST INSURANCE GROUP, LTD.; *Int'l*, pg. 423
AMERISAFE, INC.; *U.S. Public*, pg. 115
AMERITAS MUTUAL HOLDING COMPANY; *U.S. Private*, pg. 260
AMERON HOLDINGS II PTE LTD—See NOV, Inc.; *U.S. Public*, pg. 1543
A METAVERSE COMPANY; *Int'l*, pg. 18
AMETEK MATERIAL ANALYSIS HOLDINGS GMBH—See AMETEK, Inc.; *U.S. Public*, pg. 119
AMEXDRUG CORPORATION; *U.S. Public*, pg. 122
AMGEN ROCKVILLE, INC.—See Amgen Inc.; *U.S. Public*, pg. 123
AMG LITHIUM GMBH—See AMG Critical Materials N.V.; *Int'l*, pg. 425
AM GROUP HOLDINGS LIMITED; *Int'l*, pg. 402
AMICORP GROUP AG; *Int'l*, pg. 427
AMIGO HOLDINGS PLC; *Int'l*, pg. 427
AMINVESTMENT BANK GROUP—See AMMB Holdings Berhad; *Int'l*, pg. 429
AMNEAL PHARMACEUTICALS, INC.; *U.S. Public*, pg. 125
AMOREPACIFIC GROUP; *Int'l*, pg. 430
AMOS GROUP LIMITED; *Int'l*, pg. 430
AMOS MIDDLE EAST HOLDINGS FZE—See AMOS Group Limited; *Int'l*, pg. 430
AMOTIV LIMITED; *Int'l*, pg. 431
AMPAC HOLDINGS, LLC—See The Pritzker Group - Chicago, LLC; *U.S. Public*, pg. 4099
AMP AUSTRALIAN FINANCIAL SERVICES HOLDINGS LIMITED—See AMP Limited; *Int'l*, pg. 431
AMP CAPITAL HOLDINGS LIMITED—See AMP Limited; *Int'l*, pg. 431
AMP CAPITAL INVESTORS INTERNATIONAL HOLDINGS LIMITED—See AMP Limited; *Int'l*, pg. 431
AMP HOLDINGS LIMITED—See AMP Limited; *Int'l*, pg. 432
AMPLEX AB; *Int'l*, pg. 433
AMPLIFON GROUPE FRANCE SA—See Amplifon S.p.A.; *Int'l*, pg. 435
AMPLIFY ENERGY HOLDINGS LLC—See Amplify Energy Corp.; *U.S. Public*, pg. 133
AMRIT CORP. LIMITED; *Int'l*, pg. 438
AMSONS GROUP; *Int'l*, pg. 441
AMTD GROUP COMPANY LIMITED; *Int'l*, pg. 441
AMTECK, LLC—See Comfort Systems USA, Inc.; *U.S. Public*, pg. 543
AMTRADA HOLDING B.V.; *Int'l*, pg. 442
AMTROL HOLDINGS INC.—See Worthington Industries, Inc.; *U.S. Public*, pg. 2382
AMVIS HOLDINGS, INC.; *Int'l*, pg. 443
ANADOLU ENDUSTRI HOLDING A.S.—See AG Anadolu Grubu Holding A.S.; *Int'l*, pg. 197
ANAREN, INC.—See TTM Technologies, Inc.; *U.S. Public*, pg. 2203
ANCALA PARTNERS LLP; *Int'l*, pg. 448
ANCAP MANAGEMENT LP; *U.S. Private*, pg. 272
ANCHOR RETAIL INVESTMENTS N.V.—See Fiba Holding A.S.; *Int'l*, pg. 2651
ANCHUN INTERNATIONAL HOLDINGS LTD.; *Int'l*, pg. 449
ANDEAVOR LLC—See Marathon Petroleum Corporation; *U.S. Public*, pg. 1363
ANDERSEN CORPORATION; *U.S. Private*, pg. 275
ANDERSON COMPANIES, INC.; *U.S. Private*, pg. 276
ANDIAMO CORPORATION; *U.S. Private*, pg. 136
ANDINA BOTTLING INVESTMENTS SA—See Embotelladora Andina S.A.; *U.S. Public*, pg. 2375
ANDLAUER HEALTHCARE GROUP, INC.; *Int'l*, pg. 451
THE ANDOVER COMPANIES; *U.S. Private*, pg. 3986
ANDRITZ AG; *Int'l*, pg. 452

ANEKA JARINGAN HOLDINGS BERHAD; *Int'l*, pg. 457
ANEMOI INTERNATIONAL LTD; *Int'l*, pg. 458
ANGELCARE HOLDING INC.; *Int'l*, pg. 459
ANGEL ISLAND CAPITAL, L.P.—See Golden Gate Capital Management II, LLC; *U.S. Private*, pg. 1730
ANGELO MORATTI S.A.P.A.; *Int'l*, pg. 460
ANGI INC.—See IAC Inc.; *U.S. Public*, pg. 1081
ANGLIAN WATER GROUP LIMITED—See Canada Pension Plan Investment Board; *Int'l*, pg. 1278
ANGLIAN WATER GROUP LIMITED—See Commonwealth Bank of Australia; *Int'l*, pg. 1720
ANGLO AMERICAN PLC; *Int'l*, pg. 461
ANGLO AMERICAN SUR SA—See Anglo American PLC; *Int'l*, pg. 461
ANGLO BASE METALS (IRELAND) LTD.—See Anglo American PLC; *Int'l*, pg. 461
ANGLOGOLD ASHANTI NORTH AMERICA INC.—See AngloGold Ashanti plc; *Int'l*, pg. 463
ANGUS MONTGOMERY LTD.; *Int'l*, pg. 463
ANHEUSER-BUSCH COMPANIES, LLC—See Anheuser-Busch InBev SA/NV; *Int'l*, pg. 465
ANHEUSER-BUSCH INBEV GERMANY HOLDING GMBH—See Anheuser-Busch InBev SA/NV; *Int'l*, pg. 465
ANHEUSER-BUSCH INBEV SA/NV; *Int'l*, pg. 464
ANHUI GUJING GROUP CO., LTD.; *Int'l*, pg. 467
ANHUI ZHONGDING HOLDING (GROUP) CO., LTD.; *Int'l*, pg. 470
ANHYDRO A/S—See Lone Star Funds; *U.S. Private*, pg. 2486
ANIMA HOLDING S.P.A.; *Int'l*, pg. 471
ANITTEL GROUP LIMITED—See 5G Networks Limited; *Int'l*, pg. 13
ANIXTER INTERNATIONAL INC.—See WESCO International, Inc.; *U.S. Public*, pg. 2350
ANKARSRUM INDUSTRIES AB—See Duroc AB; *Int'l*, pg. 2229
ANLEV (UK) HOLDINGS LIMITED—See Analogue Holdings Limited; *Int'l*, pg. 446
ANNICA HOLDINGS LIMITED; *Int'l*, pg. 474
ANN INC.—See Sycamore Partners Management, LP; *U.S. Private*, pg. 3895
ANRIKA GROUP SCANDINAVIA AB; *Int'l*, pg. 475
ANSA MCAL (BARBADOS) LIMITED—See ANSA McAL Limited; *Int'l*, pg. 476
ANSA MCAL LIMITED; *Int'l*, pg. 476
THE ANSCHUTZ CORPORATION; *U.S. Private*, pg. 3986
ANSCHUTZ FILM GROUP, LLC—See The Anschutz Corporation; *U.S. Private*, pg. 3987
AN-SHIN FOOD SERVICES CO., LTD.; *Int'l*, pg. 443
ANTARES RESTAURANT GROUP LIMITED—See Blackstone Inc.; *U.S. Public*, pg. 360
ANTELOPE ENTERPRISE HOLDINGS LTD.; *Int'l*, pg. 482
ANTHEM HOLDING CORP.—See Elevance Health, Inc.; *U.S. Public*, pg. 729
ANTICIMEX INTERNATIONAL AB—See EQT AB; *Int'l*, pg. 2467
ANTILLES GOLD LIMITED; *Int'l*, pg. 483
ANTIN INFRASTRUCTURE PARTNERS SAS; *Int'l*, pg. 483
ANUVU—See PAR Capital Management, Inc.; *U.S. Private*, pg. 3089
ANXIAN YUAN CHINA HOLDINGS LIMITED; *Int'l*, pg. 486
ANXIAN YUAN (HK) LIMITED—See Anxian Yuan China Holdings Limited; *Int'l*, pg. 486
ANYWHERE REAL ESTATE INC.; *U.S. Public*, pg. 140
AOI TYO HOLDINGS INC.; *Int'l*, pg. 488
AON CASH MANAGEMENT B.V.—See Aon plc; *Int'l*, pg. 490
AON GROUP HOLDINGS INTERNATIONAL 1 B.V.—See Aon plc; *Int'l*, pg. 491
AON HEWITT WEALTH MANAGEMENT PTE. LTD.—See Alight, Inc.; *U.S. Public*, pg. 76
AON PLC; *Int'l*, pg. 488
AON REINSURANCE SOLUTIONS ASIA PTE. LTD.—See Aon plc; *Int'l*, pg. 490
THE AOT GROUP PTY. LTD.—See Helloworld Travel Limited; *Int'l*, pg. 3337
A. O. WATER PRODUCTS COMPANY—See A. O. Smith Corporation; *U.S. Public*, pg. 11
APA CORPORATION; *U.S. Public*, pg. 143
APA HOLDINGS CO., LTD.; *Int'l*, pg. 500
APC BRANDS, INC.—See Court Square Capital Partners, L.P.; *U.S. Private*, pg. 1069
APEX EQUITY HOLDINGS BERHAD; *Int'l*, pg. 509
APEX FUND SERVICES HOLDINGS LTD.; *Int'l*, pg. 509
APEX HOLDING LIMITED; *Int'l*, pg. 511
APEX OIL COMPANY, INC.; *U.S. Private*, pg. 293
APEX PARTNERS PROPRIETARY LIMITED; *Int'l*, pg. 512
APEX TOOL GROUP, LLC—See Bain Capital, LP; *U.S. Private*, pg. 430
APG/SGA SA; *Int'l*, pg. 513
API GROUP CORPORATION; *Int'l*, pg. 513
API GROUP PLC—See Steel Partners Holdings L.P.; *U.S. Public*, pg. 1942
APLEONA GMBH—See EQT AB; *Int'l*, pg. 2468
A.P. MOLLER HOLDING A/S; *Int'l*, pg. 25
A.P. MOLLER-MAERSK A/S; *Int'l*, pg. 25
APN NEW ZEALAND LIMITED—See ARN Media Limited; *Int'l*, pg. 576

N.A.I.C.S. INDEX 551112 — OFFICES OF OTHER HO...

N.A.I.C.S. Index

APOLLO EDUCATION GROUP, INC.—See Apollo Global Management, Inc.; *U.S. Public*, pg. 146
APOLLO EDUCATION GROUP, INC.—See The Vistria Group, LP; *U.S. Private*, pg. 4131
APOLLO ENDOSURGERY, INC.—See Boston Scientific Corporation; *U.S. Public*, pg. 373
APOLLO ENTERPRISE SOLUTIONS, LTD.; *U.S. Private*, pg. 294
APOLLO GLOBAL CAPITAL, INC.; *Int'l*, pg. 517
APOLLO GLOBAL MANAGEMENT, INC.; *U.S. Public*, pg. 145
APOLLO PIPES LIMITED; *Int'l*, pg. 518
APOTEX PHARMACEUTICAL HOLDINGS INC.—See SK Capital Partners, LP; *U.S. Private*, pg. 3678
APPAREL GROUP PTY. LTD.; *Int'l*, pg. 519
APPGATE, INC.; *U.S. Public*, pg. 168
APPLE AMERICAN GROUP LLC; *U.S. Private*, pg. 296
APPLE LEISURE GROUP; *U.S. Private*, pg. 296
APPLIED MEXICO HOLDINGS, S.A. DE C.V.—See Applied Industrial Technologies, Inc.; *U.S. Public*, pg. 170
APPLIED UV, INC.; *U.S. Public*, pg. 173
THE APPOINTMENT GROUP LIMITED—See ECI Partners LLP; *Int'l*, pg. 2289
APPRECIATE HOLDINGS, INC.; *U.S. Public*, pg. 173
APR ENERGY PLC—See ACON Investments, LLC; *U.S. Private*, pg. 62
APR ENERGY PLC—See Fairfax Financial Holdings Limited; *Int'l*, pg. 2605
AP RENTALS HOLDINGS LTD.; *Int'l*, pg. 499
APRIL CORNELL HOLDINGS; *U.S. Private*, pg. 301
APRIL GROUP SA—See CVC Capital Partners SICAV-FIS S.A.; *Int'l*, pg. 1882
APS ENTERPRISES HOLDING COMPANY, INC.—See Cencora, Inc.; *U.S. Public*, pg. 466
APTEC HOLDING EGYPT LLC—See Hainan Traffic Administration Holding Co., Ltd.; *Int'l*, pg. 3213
APTEC HOLDINGS LIMITED—See Hainan Traffic Administration Holding Co., Ltd.; *Int'l*, pg. 3213
APTITUDE SOFTWARE GROUP PLC; *Int'l*, pg. 523
APTIV PLC; *Int'l*, pg. 524
APT SATELLITE INTERNATIONAL COMPANY LIMITED; *Int'l*, pg. 523
AP WIP INVESTMENTS HOLDINGS, LP—See EQT AB; *Int'l*, pg. 2479
AQUAFIN HOLDING S.P.A.; *Int'l*, pg. 527
AQUAMARINE SUBSEA AS—See HitecVision AS; *Int'l*, pg. 3426
AQUA PHARMACEUTICAL HOLDINGS INC.—See Almirall, S.A.; *Int'l*, pg. 364
ARABIAN INTERNATIONAL HEALTHCARE HOLDING COMPANY; *Int'l*, pg. 533
ARABI HOLDING GROUP COMPANY K.S.C.C.; *Int'l*, pg. 532
ARAB PALESTINIAN INVESTMENT COMPANY; *Int'l*, pg. 531
ARAB SUPPLY & TRADING CO.; *Int'l*, pg. 532
ARABTEC HOLDING PJSC; *Int'l*, pg. 534
ARAD INVESTMENT & INDUSTRIAL DEVELOPMENT LTD.; *Int'l*, pg. 534
ARAFA HOLDING; *Int'l*, pg. 534
ARAMARK CHINA HOLDINGS LIMITED—See Aramark; *U.S. Public*, pg. 177
ARAMARK CORPORATION—See Aramark; *U.S. Public*, pg. 175
ARAMARK FOOD AND SUPPORT SERVICES GROUP, INC.—See Aramark; *U.S. Public*, pg. 176
ARAMARK HOLDINGS GMBH & CO. KG—See Aramark; *U.S. Public*, pg. 176
ARAMARK INTERMEDIATE HOLDCO CORPORATION—See Aramark; *U.S. Public*, pg. 175
ARAMARK IRELAND HOLDINGS LIMITED—See Aramark; *U.S. Public*, pg. 177
ARAMARK; *U.S. Public*, pg. 175
ARA REAL ESTATE INVESTORS XVIII PTE. LTD—See ESR Group Limited; *Int'l*, pg. 2508
A RAYMOND TINNERMAN MANUFACTURING, INC.—See A. Raymond & Cie SCS; *Int'l*, pg. 22
ARBONIA AG; *Int'l*, pg. 537
ARBY'S RESTAURANT GROUP, INC.—See Roark Capital Group Inc.; *U.S. Private*, pg. 3455
ARCADIS N.V.; *Int'l*, pg. 540
ARC DOCUMENT SOLUTIONS, INC.; *U.S. Public*, pg. 178
ARCELORMITTAL S.A.; *Int'l*, pg. 543
ARC GROUP, INC.; *U.S. Public*, pg. 179
ARC GROUP WORLDWIDE, INC.; *U.S. Public*, pg. 179
ARCHITECTURAL SURFACES GROUP, LLC; *U.S. Private*, pg. 311
ARCHROCK, INC.; *U.S. Public*, pg. 185
ARCHROCK PARTNERS, L.P.—See Archrock, Inc.; *U.S. Public*, pg. 186
ARCLIGHT CAPITAL HOLDINGS, LLC; *U.S. Private*, pg. 312
ARCONIC INTERNATIONAL HOLDING COMPANY LLC—See Howmet Aerospace Inc.; *U.S. Public*, pg. 1062
ARCONIC INVERSIONES ESPANA S.L.—See Howmet Aerospace Inc.; *U.S. Public*, pg. 1062
ARCTECH SOLAR HOLDING CO., LTD.; *Int'l*, pg. 551
ARC TERMINALS JOLIET HOLDINGS LLC—See Warburg Pincus LLC; *U.S. Private*, pg. 4440
ARCTIC FISH HOLDING AS; *Int'l*, pg. 551
ARCTIC GLACIER HOLDINGS INC.—See H.I.G. Capital, LLC; *U.S. Private*, pg. 1829
ARCTIC SLOPE REGIONAL CORPORATION; *U.S. Private*, pg. 315
ARCTURUS THERAPEUTICS HOLDINGS INC.; *U.S. Public*, pg. 186
ARCUS ASA; *Int'l*, pg. 552
ARDAGH GROUP S.A.; *Int'l*, pg. 553
ARDEN GROUP, INC.—See TPG Capital, L.P.; *U.S. Public*, pg. 2168
ARD FINANCE S.A.; *Int'l*, pg. 553
ARDURRA GROUP, LLC—See Littlejohn & Co., LLC; *U.S. Private*, pg. 2469
ARENA FAKTORING A.S.; *Int'l*, pg. 558
ARENA HOLDING S.P.A.; *Int'l*, pg. 558
ARETEC GROUP, INC.—See RCAP Holdings, LLC; *U.S. Private*, pg. 3361
ARETE INDUSTRIES, INC.; *U.S. Public*, pg. 191
ARGAN, INC.; *U.S. Public*, pg. 191
ARGENT FINANCIAL GROUP, INC.; *U.S. Private*, pg. 319
AR GLOBAL INVESTMENTS, LLC; *U.S. Private*, pg. 306
ARGO FINANZIARIA S.P.A.; *Int'l*, pg. 561
ARGO GROUP INTERNATIONAL HOLDINGS, LTD.—See Brookfield Reinsurance Ltd.; *Int'l*, pg. 1193
THE ARGUS RESEARCH GROUP, INC.; *U.S. Private*, pg. 3988
ARIAN RESOURCES CORP.; *Int'l*, pg. 564
ARI-INDUSTRIAL PRODUCTS GROUP—See ITE Management L.P.; *U.S. Private*, pg. 2149
ARISON HOLDINGS (1998) LTD.; *Int'l*, pg. 566
ARISON INVESTMENTS LTD.—See Arison Holdings (1998) Ltd.; *Int'l*, pg. 566
ARISTA FINANCIAL CORP.; *U.S. Private*, pg. 323
ARISTOCRAT LEISURE LIMITED; *Int'l*, pg. 566
ARISTON HOLDING N.V.; *Int'l*, pg. 567
ARIS WATER SOLUTIONS, INC.; *U.S. Public*, pg. 192
ARIZANT HOLDINGS INC.—See 3M Company; *U.S. Public*, pg. 8
ARKADIA CAPITAL CORP.; *Int'l*, pg. 568
ARKANSAS CASUALTY INVESTMENT—See Arkansas Farm Bureau Federation; *U.S. Private*, pg. 325
ARKO HOLDINGS LTD.—See Haymaker Acquisition Corp.; *U.S. Private*, pg. 1885
ARKRAY GLOBAL BUSINESS, INC.—See ARKRAY, Inc.; *Int'l*, pg. 571
ARK RESTAURANTS CORP.; *U.S. Public*, pg. 192
ARLA DP HOLDING A/S—See Arla Foods amba; *Int'l*, pg. 572
ARLA FOODS AMBA; *Int'l*, pg. 572
ARLA FOODS INGREDIENTS GMBH—See Arla Foods amba; *Int'l*, pg. 572
ARLA FOODS SA—See Arla Foods amba; *Int'l*, pg. 573
ARLA FOODS UK PLC—See Arla Foods amba; *Int'l*, pg. 573
ARMADA GROUP, LTD.; *U.S. Private*, pg. 329
ARMADA PARENT, INC.—See Stellex Capital Management LP; *U.S. Private*, pg. 3800
ARMAN HOLDINGS LIMITED; *Int'l*, pg. 574
ARMEYSKI HOLDING AD; *Int'l*, pg. 574
ARMON INC.; *U.S. Private*, pg. 330
ARMOUR AUTOMOTIVE GROUP LIMITED—See AAMP of Florida, Inc.; *U.S. Private*, pg. 32
ARMSTRONG CHINA HOLDINGS, LIMITED—See Armstrong World Industries, Inc.; *U.S. Public*, pg. 194
ARMSTRONG ENERGY GLOBAL LIMITED; *Int'l*, pg. 575
ARMSTRONG HOLDINGS, INC.; *U.S. Private*, pg. 331
ARMSTRONG MCCALL HOLDINGS, INC.—See Sally Beauty Holdings, Inc.; *U.S. Public*, pg. 1838
ARMSTRONG METALLDECKEN HOLDINGS AG—See Armstrong World Industries, Inc.; *U.S. Public*, pg. 194
ARNOLD HOLDINGS LIMITED; *Int'l*, pg. 576
ARO LIQUIDATION, INC.; *U.S. Private*, pg. 333
ARPICO FINANCE COMPANY PLC—See Associated Motor Finance Company PLC; *Int'l*, pg. 649
ARRAY TECHNOLOGIES, INC.; *U.S. Public*, pg. 194
ARRIBATEC SOLUTIONS ASA; *Int'l*, pg. 579
ARRIS - BOCA RATON—See CommScope Holding Company, Inc.; *U.S. Public*, pg. 548
ARRIS ENTERPRISES LLC—See CommScope Holding Company, Inc.; *U.S. Public*, pg. 547
ARRIS GROUP EUROPE HOLDING B.V.—See CommScope Holding Company, Inc.; *U.S. Public*, pg. 548
ARRIS INTERNATIONAL PLC—See CommScope Holding Company, Inc.; *U.S. Public*, pg. 547
ARROW ALTECH HOLDINGS (PTY) LTD.—See Arrow Electronics, Inc.; *U.S. Public*, pg. 195
ARROW CAPITAL CORP.; *Int'l*, pg. 579
ARROW CENTRAL EUROPE HOLDING MUNICH GMBH—See Arrow Electronics, Inc.; *U.S. Public*, pg. 195
ARROWCREST GROUP PTY. LTD.; *Int'l*, pg. 579
ARROW ELECTRONICS ANZ HOLDINGS PTY LTD.—See Arrow Electronics, Inc.; *U.S. Public*, pg. 196
ARROW ELECTRONICS NORWEGIAN HOLDINGS AS—See Arrow Electronics, Inc.; *U.S. Public*, pg. 197
ARROW GLOBAL GROUP PLC; *Int'l*, pg. 579
ARROW-INTECHRA LLC—See Arrow Electronics, Inc.; *U.S. Public*, pg. 198
ARROW MIDSTREAM HOLDINGS, LLC—See Crestwood Equity Partners LP; *U.S. Public*, pg. 594
ARTAL GROUP S.A.; *Int'l*, pg. 581
ARTCURIAL HOLDING SA—See Groupe Industriel Marcel Dassault S.A.; *Int'l*, pg. 3104
ARTEMIS CAPITAL PARTNERS MANAGEMENT CO., LLC; *U.S. Private*, pg. 340
ARTEMIS HOLDING AG; *Int'l*, pg. 582
ARTEMIS S.A.—See Financiere Pinault SCA; *Int'l*, pg. 2668
ARTERA SERVICES, LLC—See Clayton, Dubilier & Rice, LLC; *U.S. Private*, pg. 919
ARTE SALON HOLDINGS, INC.; *Int'l*, pg. 581
ARTESYN HOLDING GMBH—See Advanced Energy Industries, Inc.; *U.S. Public*, pg. 47
ART GROUP HOLDINGS LIMITED; *Int'l*, pg. 580
ARTHUR J. GALLAGHER & CO.; *U.S. Public*, pg. 202
ARTHUR'S ENTERPRISES, INC.; *U.S. Private*, pg. 342
ARTINI HOLDINGS LIMITED; *Int'l*, pg. 584
ARTIO GLOBAL INVESTORS INC.—See abrdn PLC; *Int'l*, pg. 68
ARTISAN DESIGN GROUP, LLC—See The Sterling Group, L.P.; *U.S. Private*, pg. 4121
ARTISAN PARTNERS HOLDINGS LP—See Artisan Partners Asset Management Inc.; *U.S. Public*, pg. 208
ARTISAN (UK) PLC; *Int'l*, pg. 584
ARTISSIMO HOLDINGS, INC.; *U.S. Private*, pg. 343
ARTRONIQ BERHAD; *Int'l*, pg. 585
ARVATO FINANCE AS—See Bertelsmann SE & Co. KGaA; *Int'l*, pg. 996
ARVIG ENTERPRISES, INC.; *U.S. Private*, pg. 344
ARVIND MAFATLAL GROUP; *Int'l*, pg. 587
ARX HOLDING CORP.—See The Progressive Corporation; *U.S. Public*, pg. 2124
ARYT INDUSTRIES LTD.; *Int'l*, pg. 588
ASAHI GROUP HOLDINGS LTD.; *Int'l*, pg. 593
ASAHI KASEI CORPORATION; *Int'l*, pg. 594
ASA HOLDING D.O.O.; *Int'l*, pg. 591
ASCEND LEARNING, LLC—See Blackstone Inc.; *U.S. Public*, pg. 348
ASCEND LEARNING, LLC—See Canada Pension Plan Investment Board; *Int'l*, pg. 1278
ASCENDO INTERNATIONAL HOLDINGS PTE. LTD.; *Int'l*, pg. 602
ASCEND WELLNESS HOLDINGS, INC.; *U.S. Public*, pg. 210
ASCENT CAPITAL GROUP, INC.; *U.S. Private*, pg. 348
ASC GLOBAL INC.; *U.S. Private*, pg. 345
ASCOM HOLDING AG; *Int'l*, pg. 602
ASCO RENEWABLES S.P.A.—See Ascopiave S.p.A.; *Int'l*, pg. 603
ASDION BERHAD.; *Int'l*, pg. 604
ASEED HOLDINGS CO., LTD.; *Int'l*, pg. 605
ASEP MEDICAL HOLDINGS INC.; *Int'l*, pg. 606
ASE TECHNOLOGY HOLDING CO., LTD.; *Int'l*, pg. 604
ASHLAND INC.; *U.S. Public*, pg. 211
ASHLAND INTERNATIONAL HOLDINGS, INC.—See Ashland Inc.; *U.S. Public*, pg. 211
ASHLAND RHINE HOLDINGS B.V.—See Ashland Inc.; *U.S. Public*, pg. 212
ASHLAND SWITZERLAND HOLDINGS GMBH—See Ashland Inc.; *U.S. Public*, pg. 212
ASHOK PIRAMAL GROUP; *Int'l*, pg. 608
ASIA ALLIED INFRASTRUCTURE HOLDINGS LIMITED; *Int'l*, pg. 609
ASIA AMALGAMATED HOLDINGS CORPORATION; *Int'l*, pg. 610
ASIA CARBON INDUSTRIES, INC.; *Int'l*, pg. 610
ASIA CEMENT (CHINA) HOLDINGS CORPORATION—See Asia Cement Corporation; *Int'l*, pg. 611
ASIA-EXPRESS LOGISTICS HOLDINGS LIMITED; *Int'l*, pg. 616
ASIA FASHION HOLDINGS LIMITED; *Int'l*, pg. 612
ASIAFIN HOLDINGS CORP.; *Int'l*, pg. 616
ASIA HOLDINGS CO., LTD.; *Int'l*, pg. 612
ASIAINFO, INC.—See CITIC Group Corporation; *Int'l*, pg. 1619
ASIAN MICRO HOLDINGS LTD.; *Int'l*, pg. 618
ASIA PARAGON INTERNATIONAL LIMITED—See Delong Holdings Limited; *Int'l*, pg. 2015
ASIAPHARMA HOLDINGS LTD.; *Int'l*, pg. 620
ASIA POLY HOLDINGS BERHAD; *Int'l*, pg. 614
ASIA TELE-NET & TECHNOLOGY CORPORATION LIMITED; *Int'l*, pg. 615
ASIATRAVEL.COM HOLDINGS LIMITED; *Int'l*, pg. 620
AS INFORTAR; *Int'l*, pg. 590
ASM GROUP S.A.; *Int'l*, pg. 625
ASML HOLDING N.V.; *Int'l*, pg. 627
A-SONIC AEROSPACE LIMITED; *Int'l*, pg. 20
ASOS PLC; *Int'l*, pg. 628
ASPEN GROVE LANDSCAPE COMPANIES, LLC; *U.S. Private*, pg. 352
ASPEN PHARMACARE HOLDINGS LIMITED; *Int'l*, pg. 629
ASPEN TECHNOLOGY, INC.—See Emerson Electric Co.; *U.S. Public*, pg. 741
ASPIRITY HOLDINGS, LLC; *U.S. Private*, pg. 353
ASPIRO AB—See Block, Inc.; *U.S. Public*, pg. 362
ASPOCOMP GROUP OYJ; *Int'l*, pg. 632
ASPO OYJ; *Int'l*, pg. 631

551112 — OFFICES OF OTHER HO...   CORPORATE AFFILIATIONS

ASR NEDERLAND N.V.; *Int'l*, pg. 632
ASSA ABLOY DOOR SECURITY SOLUTIONS—See ASSA ABLOY AB; *Int'l*, pg. 636
ASSA ABLOY, INC.—See ASSA ABLOY AB; *Int'l*, pg. 636
ASSA ABLOY LIMITED—See ASSA ABLOY AB; *Int'l*, pg. 636
ASSECO POLAND S.A.; *Int'l*, pg. 641
ASSETWISE PUBLIC COMPANY LIMITED; *Int'l*, pg. 643
ASSICURAZIONI GENERALI S.P.A.; *Int'l*, pg. 643
ASSOCIATED BRITISH PORTS HOLDINGS LTD.—See GIC Pte. Ltd.; *Int'l*, pg. 2964
ASSOCIATED BRITISH PORTS HOLDINGS LTD.—See The Goldman Sachs Group, Inc.; *U.S. Public*, pg. 2076
ASSOCIATED FOOD STORES, INC.; *U.S. Private*, pg. 355
ASSOCIATED INTERNATIONAL HOTELS LTD.; *Int'l*, pg. 649
ASSOCIATED MATERIALS GROUP, INC.—See Hellman & Friedman LLC; *U.S. Private*, pg. 1907
ASSOCIATED SERVICE SPECIALIST; *U.S. Private*, pg. 357
ASSOCIATED STEEL GROUP, LLC—See Promus Holdings, LLC; *U.S. Private*, pg. 3283
ASSURAMED, INC.—See Cardinal Health, Inc.; *U.S. Public*, pg. 433
ASSURED GUARANTY LTD.; *Int'l*, pg. 649
ASSURED GUARANTY RE OVERSEAS LTD—See Assured Guaranty Ltd.; *Int'l*, pg. 649
ASSURED NEACE LUKENS INSURANCE AGENCY, INC.—See GTCR LLC; *U.S. Private*, pg. 1802
ASSUREDPARTNERS, INC.—See GTCR LLC; *U.S. Private*, pg. 1802
ASSURE HOLDINGS CORP.; *U.S. Public*, pg. 216
ASSURIA N.V.; *Int'l*, pg. 650
ASSURITY SECURITY GROUP INC.; *U.S. Private*, pg. 359
ASTA HOLDINGS GMBH—See Global Equity Partners Beteiligungs-Management AG; *Int'l*, pg. 2996
ASTEC INDUSTRIES, INC.; *U.S. Public*, pg. 216
ASTELLAS US LLC—See Astellas Pharma Inc.; *Int'l*, pg. 653
ASTIKA HOLDINGS, INC.; *Int'l*, pg. 655
ASTON MARTIN LAGONDA GLOBAL HOLDINGS PLC; *Int'l*, pg. 655
ASTRAZENECA PLC; *Int'l*, pg. 659
ASTRIUM HOLDING S.A.S.—See Airbus SE; *Int'l*, pg. 245
ASTRO AEROSPACE LTD.; *U.S. Public*, pg. 217
ASTRO MALAYSIA HOLDINGS BHD; *Int'l*, pg. 662
ASX LIMITED; *Int'l*, pg. 664
ASYAD HOLDING GROUP; *Int'l*, pg. 664
ATAI LIFE SCIENCES N.V.; *Int'l*, pg. 665
ATA IMS BERHAD; *Int'l*, pg. 665
ATARI, SA; *Int'l*, pg. 666
ATC GERMANY HOLDINGS GMBH—See American Tower Corporation; *U.S. Public*, pg. 110
ATCO AUSTRALIA PTY. LTD.—See ATCO Ltd.; *Int'l*, pg. 666
ATCO GAS & PIPELINES LTD.—See ATCO Ltd.; *Int'l*, pg. 667
ATD CORPORATION—See TPG Capital, L.P.; *U.S. Public*, pg. 2166
A-TEC INDUSTRIES AG; *Int'l*, pg. 21
ATEK COMPANIES, INC.; *U.S. Private*, pg. 365
ATELIER SERVICES—See BNP Paribas SA; *Int'l*, pg. 1080
ATENTO S.A.—See Bain Capital, LP; *U.S. Private*, pg. 430
ATERIAN, INC.; *U.S. Public*, pg. 220
ATHEEB GROUP; *Int'l*, pg. 669
ATHENA BITCOIN GLOBAL; *U.S. Public*, pg. 221
ATHENE HOLDING LTD.—See Apollo Global Management, Inc.; *U.S. Public*, pg. 147
ATHENEX, INC.; *U.S. Public*, pg. 221
ATHLETICS INVESTMENT GROUP, LLC; *U.S. Private*, pg. 368
ATHLON HOLDINGS, INC.; *U.S. Private*, pg. 368
ATIF HOLDINGS LIMITED; *Int'l*, pg. 670
ATILIM FAKTORING A.S.; *Int'l*, pg. 670
AT INDUSTRIES, INC.; *U.S. Private*, pg. 363
ATKINSREALIS GROUP INC.; *Int'l*, pg. 670
ATKORE INC.—See Clayton, Dubilier & Rice, LLC; *U.S. Private*, pg. 919
ATKORE INTERNATIONAL HOLDINGS INC.—See Clayton, Dubilier & Rice, LLC; *U.S. Private*, pg. 919
ATLANTA BRAVES HOLDINGS, INC.; *U.S. Public*, pg. 222
ATLANTIC COASTAL ACQUISITION CORP.; *U.S. Private*, pg. 372
ATLANTIC GROUP; *Int'l*, pg. 674
ATLANTIC METHANOL ASSOCIATES LLC—See Chevron Corporation; *U.S. Public*, pg. 487
ATLANTIC METHANOL ASSOCIATES LLC—See Conoco-Phillips; *U.S. Public*, pg. 569
ATLANTIC NAVIGATION HOLDINGS (SINGAPORE) LIMITED; *Int'l*, pg. 675
ATLANTIC POWER CORPORATION—See I Squared Capital Advisors (US) LLC; *U.S. Private*, pg. 2025
ATLANTIC POWER LIMITED PARTNERSHIP—See I Squared Capital Advisors (US) LLC; *U.S. Private*, pg. 2025
ATLANTIC SOCIETE FRANCAISE DEVELOP THERMIQUE S.A.; *Int'l*, pg. 675
ATLANTICUS HOLDINGS CORPORATION; *U.S. Public*, pg. 223
ATLANTIS SUBMARINES INTERNATIONAL INC.; *Int'l*, pg. 676
ATLANTIS YATIRIM HOLDING A.S.; *Int'l*, pg. 676

ATLAS AIR WORLDWIDE HOLDINGS, INC.—See Apollo Global Management, Inc.; *U.S. Public*, pg. 148
ATLAS AIR WORLDWIDE HOLDINGS, INC.—See J.F. Lehman & Company, Inc.; *U.S. Private*, pg. 2162
ATLAS COPCO BELGIUM N.V.—See Atlas Copco AB; *Int'l*, pg. 678
ATLAS COPCO DYNAPAC AB—See FAYAT SAS; *Int'l*, pg. 2624
ATLAS COPCO FRANCE HOLDING S.A.—See Atlas Copco AB; *Int'l*, pg. 678
ATLAS COPCO NORTH AMERICA LLC—See Atlas Copco AB; *Int'l*, pg. 680
ATLAS ENERGY GROUP, LLC; *U.S. Public*, pg. 223
ATLAS FINANCIAL HOLDINGS, INC.; *U.S. Public*, pg. 224
ATLAS GROUP OF COMPANIES; *Int'l*, pg. 685
ATLAS HOLDINGS, LLC; *U.S. Public*, pg. 376
ATLAS HOTELS, INC.; *U.S. Public*, pg. 378
ATLAS MARA LIMITED; *Int'l*, pg. 686
ATLAS WORLD GROUP, INC.; *U.S. Private*, pg. 380
ATN HOLDINGS, INC.; *U.S. Public*, pg. 687
ATON GMBH; *Int'l*, pg. 688
ATOS IT SOLUTIONS AND SERVICES GMBH—See Atos SE; *Int'l*, pg. 690
ATOUR LIFESTYLE HOLDINGS LIMITED; *Int'l*, pg. 693
ATRIA WEALTH SOLUTIONS, LLC—See Lee Equity Partners LLC; *U.S. Private*, pg. 2412
ATRIUM CORPORATION—See Kenner & Company, Inc.; *U.S. Private*, pg. 2285
ATRIUM CORPORATION—See North Cove Partners; *U.S. Private*, pg. 2944
ATTAIN FINANCE CANADA, INC.—See CURO Group Holdings Corp.; *U.S. Public*, pg. 611
ATTENSITY GROUP, INC.; *U.S. Private*, pg. 383
ATT HOLDING COMPANY—See Griffon Corporation; *U.S. Public*, pg. 969
AT&T INC.; *U.S. Public*, pg. 218
ATTIS INDUSTRIES INC.; *U.S. Public*, pg. 383
ATTITUDE DRINKS INCORPORATED; *U.S. Private*, pg. 383
ATW COMPANIES INC.; *U.S. Private*, pg. 384
A.T. WILLIAMS OIL COMPANY; *U.S. Private*, pg. 28
AUCHAN HOLDING S.A.; *Int'l*, pg. 699
AUCTUS INVESTMENT GROUP LIMITED; *Int'l*, pg. 700
AUDACY, INC.; *U.S. Public*, pg. 226
AUDAX GROUP, LIMITED PARTNERSHIP; *U.S. Private*, pg. 385
AUDIA INTERNATIONAL, INC.; *U.S. Private*, pg. 390
AUDIO GROUP GREECE B.V.; *Int'l*, pg. 701
AUDIO VISUAL SERVICES CORPORATION—See Blackstone Inc.; *U.S. Public*, pg. 348
AUGA GROUP, AB; *Int'l*, pg. 702
AUGEAN PLC—See Ancala Partners LLP; *Int'l*, pg. 448
AUGEAN PLC—See Fiera Capital Corporation; *Int'l*, pg. 2659
AUGUST FRANCE HOLDING COMPANY S.A.S.—See Sensata Technologies Holding plc; *U.S. Public*, pg. 1865
AULT ALLIANCE, INC.; *U.S. Public*, pg. 227
AUNA S.A.A.; *Int'l*, pg. 705
AUREA, S.A.; *Int'l*, pg. 707
AURIC POOL, S.A.—See Fluidra SA; *Int'l*, pg. 2714
AURIGA INDUSTRIES A/S; *Int'l*, pg. 710
AURI, INC.; *U.S. Public*, pg. 227
AURIZON HOLDINGS LIMITED; *Int'l*, pg. 711
AURORA DIAGNOSTICS HOLDINGS, LLC; *U.S. Private*, pg. 394
AURUBIS AG; *Int'l*, pg. 714
AURUBIS NV/SA—See Aurubis AG; *Int'l*, pg. 715
AUSTRALIAN BOND EXCHANGE HOLDINGS LIMITED; *Int'l*, pg. 721
AUSTRALIAN CLINICAL LABS LIMITED—See Crescent Capital Partners Ltd.; *Int'l*, pg. 1839
AUSTRALIAN OILSEEDS HOLDINGS LIMITED; *Int'l*, pg. 722
AUSTRIACARD HOLDINGS AG; *Int'l*, pg. 723
AUTANIA AG—See Dr. Helmut Rothenberger Holding GmbH; *Int'l*, pg. 2191
AUTHENTIC RESTAURANT BRANDS—See Garnett Station Partners, LLC; *U.S. Private*, pg. 1645
AUTHORITY BRANDS US HOME SERVICES, INC.—See Apax Partners LLP; *U.S. Private*, pg. 502
AUTOBACS SEVEN CO., LTD.; *Int'l*, pg. 725
AUTOCANADA INC.; *Int'l*, pg. 726
AUTOCORP HOLDING PUBLIC COMPANY LIMITED; *Int'l*, pg. 726
AUTO CREDIT INVESTMENTS OF GEORGIA INC.—See Scott-McRae Automotive Group Inc.; *U.S. Private*, pg. 3578
AUTODESK ASIA PTE. LTD.—See Autodesk, Inc.; *U.S. Public*, pg. 228
AUTODESK (EMEA) SARL—See Autodesk, Inc.; *U.S. Public*, pg. 228
AUTOGARD HOLDINGS LIMITED—See Zurn Elkay Water Solutions Corporation; *U.S. Public*, pg. 2412
AUTOGRILL S.P.A.—See Avolta AG; *Int'l*, pg. 749
AUTOINFO, INC.—See Comvest Group Holdings LLC; *U.S. Private*, pg. 1007
AUTO ITALIA HOLDINGS LIMITED; *Int'l*, pg. 724
AUTOKINITON GLOBAL GROUP, LP—See KPS Capital Partners, LP; *U.S. Private*, pg. 2346
AUTOLIV HOLDING AB—See Autoliv, Inc.; *Int'l*, pg. 729
AUTOLOGIC HOLDINGS LIMITED—See DBAY Advisors Limited; *Int'l*, pg. 1986
AUTOMATIC DATA PROCESSING, INC.; *U.S. Public*, pg. 229
AUTOMOTIVE MANAGEMENT SERVICES, INC.; *U.S. Private*, pg. 400
AUTONAVI HOLDINGS LIMITED—See Alibaba Group Holding Limited; *Int'l*, pg. 326
AUTO-OWNERS INSURANCE GROUP; *U.S. Private*, pg. 397
AUTOPLEX AUTOMOTIVE LP; *U.S. Private*, pg. 401
AUTOSTORE HOLDINGS LTD.; *Int'l*, pg. 732
AVALAND BERHAD; *Int'l*, pg. 734
AVANTHA GROUP; *Int'l*, pg. 735
AVANTI COMMUNICATIONS GROUP PLC; *Int'l*, pg. 736
AVANTOR, INC.; *U.S. Public*, pg. 241
AVARGA LIMITED; *Int'l*, pg. 736
AVAST SOFTWARE B.V.—See Gen Digital Inc.; *U.S. Public*, pg. 910
AVAYA GMBH & CO. KG—See Silver Lake Group, LLC; *U.S. Private*, pg. 3656
AVAYA GMBH & CO. KG—See TPG Capital, L.P.; *U.S. Public*, pg. 2169
AVAYA HOLDINGS CORP.—See Silver Lake Group, LLC; *U.S. Private*, pg. 3655
AVAYA HOLDINGS CORP.—See TPG Capital, L.P.; *U.S. Public*, pg. 2168
AVEANNA HEALTHCARE HOLDINGS INC.; *U.S. Public*, pg. 242
AVENTAS MANUFACTURING GROUP LIMITED; *Int'l*, pg. 738
AVENZA HOLDINGS INC.; *Int'l*, pg. 739
AVERON PARK LIMITED; *Int'l*, pg. 739
AVERY DENNISON HONG KONG HOLDING I B.V.—See Avery Dennison Corporation; *U.S. Public*, pg. 243
AVERY WEIGH-TRONIX HOLDINGS LIMITED—See Illinois Tool Works Inc.; *U.S. Public*, pg. 1101
AVESI PARTNERS, LLC; *U.S. Private*, pg. 405
AVESORO HOLDINGS LIMITED; *Int'l*, pg. 739
AVEX INC.; *Int'l*, pg. 740
AV HOMES, INC.—See Brookfield Corporation; *Int'l*, pg. 1183
AVIAT NETWORKS, INC.; *U.S. Public*, pg. 245
AVIC INTERNATIONAL HOLDINGS LIMITED; *Int'l*, pg. 742
AVIC JOY HOLDINGS (HK) LIMITED; *Int'l*, pg. 742
AVID LIFE MEDIA INC.; *Int'l*, pg. 743
AVID TECHNOLOGY HOLDING GMBH—See Symphony Technology Group, LLC; *U.S. Private*, pg. 3901
AVIDXCHANGE HOLDINGS, INC.; *U.S. Public*, pg. 246
AVINEON, INC.; *U.S. Private*, pg. 407
AVINTIV INC.—See Berry Global Group, Inc; *U.S. Public*, pg. 320
AVIO GLOBAL, INC.; *U.S. Private*, pg. 407
AVI-SPL, INC.—See Marlin Equity Partners, LLC; *U.S. Private*, pg. 2583
AVISTA CAPITAL HOLDINGS, L.P.—See Avista Capital Partners, L.P.; *U.S. Private*, pg. 408
AVISTO CAPITAL PARTNERS, LLC; *U.S. Private*, pg. 409
AVIVA GROUP IRELAND PLC—See Aviva plc; *Int'l*, pg. 745
AVL MICHIGAN HOLDING CORPORATION—See AVL List GmbH; *Int'l*, pg. 748
AVNET (HOLDINGS) LTD—See Avnet, Inc.; *U.S. Public*, pg. 250
AVNET HOLDINGS UK LIMITED—See Avnet, Inc.; *U.S. Public*, pg. 251
AVNET, INC.; *U.S. Public*, pg. 249
AVRIL SCA; *Int'l*, pg. 750
AVRUPA YATIRIM HOLDING AS; *Int'l*, pg. 750
AVTOTEHNA, D.D.; *Int'l*, pg. 751
AWAYSIS CAPITAL, INC.; *U.S. Public*, pg. 254
AWETA HOLDING B.V.—See FPS Food Processing Systems B.V.; *Int'l*, pg. 2757
AWMS HOLDINGS, LLC—See Avalon Holdings Corporation; *U.S. Public*, pg. 239
AXA ASIA PACIFIC HOLDINGS LIMITED—See AMP Limited; *Int'l*, pg. 432
AXA ASSISTANCE S.A.—See AXA S.A.; *Int'l*, pg. 754
AXA HOLDINGS BELGIUM—See AXA S.A.; *Int'l*, pg. 756
AXA INVESTMENT MANAGERS GS LIMITED—See AXA S.A.; *Int'l*, pg. 756
AXA INVESTMENT MANAGERS S.A.—See AXA S.A.; *Int'l*, pg. 756
AXALTA COATING SYSTEMS LTD.; *U.S. Public*, pg. 254
AXAR ACQUISITION CORP.—See Axar Capital Management L.P.; *U.S. Private*, pg. 411
AXA S.A.; *Int'l*, pg. 754
AXAS HOLDINGS CO., LTD.; *Int'l*, pg. 761
AXEL JOHNSON AB—See Axel Johnson Gruppen AB; *Int'l*, pg. 762
AXEL JOHNSON GRUPPEN AB; *Int'l*, pg. 762
AXFLOW HOLDING AB—See Axel Johnson Gruppen AB; *Int'l*, pg. 762
AXFOOD AB—See Axel Johnson Gruppen AB; *Int'l*, pg. 764
AXIALL CORPORATION—See Westlake Corporation; *U.S. Public*, pg. 2360

N.A.I.C.S. INDEX

551112 — OFFICES OF OTHER HO...

AXINDUSTRIES AB—See Axel Johnson Gruppen AB; *Int'l*, pg. 763
AXIS AB—See Canon Inc.; *Int'l*, pg. 1293
AXIS CAPITAL HOLDINGS LIMITED; *Int'l*, pg. 769
AXIS-SHIELD LIMITED—See Abbott Laboratories; *U.S. Public*, pg. 19
AXIUM PHARMACY HOLDINGS, INC.—See The Kroger Co.; *U.S. Public*, pg. 2107
AXLE GROUP HOLDINGS LIMITED—See Halfords Group plc; *Int'l*, pg. 3229
AXLETECH INTERNATIONAL HOLDINGS, INC.—See Cummins Inc.; *U.S. Public*, pg. 608
AXOGEN, INC.; *U.S. Public*, pg. 255
AXOLOT SOLUTIONS HOLDING AB; *Int'l*, pg. 770
AXON ACTIVE AG; *Int'l*, pg. 770
AXON GROUP LIMITED—See HCL Technologies Ltd.; *Int'l*, pg. 3298
AXON HOLDINGS S.A.; *Int'l*, pg. 770
AXPO HOLDING AG; *Int'l*, pg. 771
AXPO SOLUTIONS AG—See Axpo Holding AG; *Int'l*, pg. 771
AXTERIA GROUP BERHAD; *Int'l*, pg. 772
AXYZ AUTOMATION GROUP INC.; *Int'l*, pg. 773
AYALA AUTOMOTIVE HOLDINGS CORPORATION—See Ayala Corporation; *Int'l*, pg. 773
AYALA CORPORATION; *Int'l*, pg. 773
AYALA INTERNATIONAL PTE. LTD.—See Ayala Corporation; *Int'l*, pg. 774
AYALALAND LOGISTICS HOLDINGS CORP.; *Int'l*, pg. 774
AYALON INSURANCE COMPANY LTD.; *Int'l*, pg. 774
AYRES-DELTA IMPLEMENT, INC.; *U.S. Private*, pg. 414
THE AYRES GROUP, LLC; *U.S. Private*, pg. 3990
AYS VENTURES BERHAD; *Int'l*, pg. 775
AZBIL CORPORATION; *Int'l*, pg. 776
THE AZEK COMPANY INC.; *U.S. Public*, pg. 2035
AZ MEDIEN AG—See BT Holding AG; *Int'l*, pg. 1204
AZRIELI GROUP LTD.; *Int'l*, pg. 781
AZZ WSI HOLDING B.V.—See AZZ, Inc.; *U.S. Public*, pg. 259
B12 CAPITAL PARTNERS LLC; *U.S. Private*, pg. 421
BABCOCK WANSON HOLDING SA—See CNIM Constructions Industrielles de la Mediterranee SA; *Int'l*, pg. 1676
BABCOCK & WILCOX ENTERPRISES, INC.; *U.S. Public*, pg. 262
BABYLON HOLDINGS LIMITED; *U.S. Public*, pg. 263
BACARDI LIMITED; *Int'l*, pg. 793
BACHEM HOLDING AG; *Int'l*, pg. 794
BADR INVESTMENT GROUP LLC; *Int'l*, pg. 796
BAE SYSTEMS PLATFORMS & SERVICES—See BAE Systems plc; *Int'l*, pg. 797
BAE SYSTEMS PLC; *Int'l*, pg. 796
BA GLASS B.V.; *Int'l*, pg. 791
BAGO GROUP; *Int'l*, pg. 799
BAHEMA EDUCACAO SA; *Int'l*, pg. 799
BAHNSON HOLDINGS, INC.; *U.S. Private*, pg. 425
BAHRAIN MUMTALAKAT HOLDING COMPANY B.S.C.; *Int'l*, pg. 800
BAIDU HOLDINGS LIMITED—See Baidu, Inc.; *Int'l*, pg. 801
BAIDU, INC.; *Int'l*, pg. 801
BAIERL AUTOMOTIVE CORPORATION—See Lithia Motors, Inc.; *U.S. Public*, pg. 1321
BAIJIAYUN GROUP LTD; *Int'l*, pg. 801
BAIKANG BIOLOGICAL GROUP HOLDINGS LIMITED; *Int'l*, pg. 802
BAILIAN GROUP CO., LTD.; *Int'l*, pg. 802
BAIRD FINANCIAL GROUP, INC.; *U.S. Private*, pg. 453
BAIYIN NONFERROUS METAL (GROUP) CO., LTD.; *Int'l*, pg. 803
BAJAJ HOLDINGS & INVESTMENT LIMITED—See Bajaj Auto Ltd.; *Int'l*, pg. 804
BAKER HUGHES COMPANY; *U.S. Public*, pg. 264
BAKER TILLY UK HOLDINGS LIMITED; *Int'l*, pg. 805
BAKKAVOR GROUP PLC; *Int'l*, pg. 805
BAKKAVOR HOLDINGS LIMITED—See Bakkavor Group plc; *Int'l*, pg. 805
BAKKT HOLDINGS, LLC—See Intercontinental Exchange, Inc.; *U.S. Public*, pg. 1141
THE BALDWIN INSURANCE GROUP, INC.; *U.S. Public*, pg. 2035
BALDWIN SWEDEN HOLDING AB—See Forsyth Capital Investors LLC; *U.S. Private*, pg. 1573
BALDWIN U.K. HOLDING LIMITED—See Forsyth Capital Investors LLC; *U.S. Private*, pg. 1573
BALHOUSIE HOLDINGS LIMITED; *Int'l*, pg. 808
BALL ASIA PACIFIC LIMITED—See Ball Corporation; *U.S. Public*, pg. 266
BALL CORPORATION; *U.S. Public*, pg. 266
BALL PACKAGING EUROPE HOLDING GMBH & CO. KG—See Ball Corporation; *U.S. Public*, pg. 267
BALL TECHNOLOGIES HOLDINGS CORP.—See Ball Corporation; *U.S. Public*, pg. 267
BALLY'S CORPORATION; *U.S. Public*, pg. 268
BALLY TECHNOLOGIES AUSTRALIA HOLDINGS I PTY LTD—See Light & Wonder, Inc.; *U.S. Public*, pg. 1314
BALMORAL INTERNATIONAL LAND HOLDINGS PLC; *Int'l*, pg. 810
BALMORAL INTERNATIONAL LAND PROPERTY HOLDINGS BV—See Balmoral International Land Holdings plc; *Int'l*, pg. 810

BALOISE HOLDING AG; *Int'l*, pg. 810
BALTIC BRIDGE S.A.; *Int'l*, pg. 812
BALT INTERNATIONAL SAS—See Bridgepoint Group Plc; *Int'l*, pg. 1154
BAMBORA GROUP AB—See Apollo Global Management, Inc.; *U.S. Public*, pg. 151
BAM ENTERPRISES, INC.; *U.S. Private*, pg. 463
B&A MINERACAO S.A.—See AGN Agroindustrial, Projetos e Participacoes Ltda.; *Int'l*, pg. 211
B&A MINERACAO S.A.—See BTG Pactual Holding S.A.; *Int'l*, pg. 1204
BANC OF AMERICA FSC HOLDINGS, INC.—See Bank of America Corporation; *U.S. Public*, pg. 270
BANC ONE CAPITAL HOLDINGS LLC—See JPMorgan Chase & Co.; *U.S. Public*, pg. 1206
BANDAI NAMCO GAMES INC.—See BANDAI NAMCO Holdings Inc.; *Int'l*, pg. 829
BANDAI NAMCO HOLDINGS INC.; *Int'l*, pg. 828
BANDAI NAMCO HOLDINGS UK LTD.—See BANDAI NAMCO Holdings Inc.; *Int'l*, pg. 829
BANDAI NAMCO HOLDINGS (USA) INC.—See BANDAI NAMCO Holdings Inc.; *Int'l*, pg. 829
BANDHAN FINANCIAL HOLDINGS LIMITED—See Bandhan Financial Services Ltd.; *Int'l*, pg. 830
BANG HOLDINGS CORP.; *U.S. Public*, pg. 269
BANGKOK DUSIT MEDICAL SERVICES PUBLIC COMPANY LIMITED; *Int'l*, pg. 833
BANGOR NATURAL GAS COMPANY—See First Reserve Management, L.P.; *U.S. Private*, pg. 1525
BANKERS LIFE HOLDING CORP.—See CNO Financial Group, Inc.; *U.S. Public*, pg. 519
BANKS HOLDINGS LIMITED—See Anheuser-Busch InBev SA/NV; *Int'l*, pg. 464
BANTAM CAPITAL CORP.; *Int'l*, pg. 855
BANYAN ACQUISITION CORPORATION; *U.S. Public*, pg. 275
BANYAN TREE HOLDINGS LTD.; *Int'l*, pg. 855
BAOSHENG MEDIA GROUP HOLDINGS LIMITED; *Int'l*, pg. 856
BAOSHIDA INTERNATIONAL HOLDING GROUP CO., LTD.; *Int'l*, pg. 856
BAOSHIDA SWISSMETAL LTD.—See Baoshida International Holding Group Co., Ltd.; *Int'l*, pg. 856
BAPCOR NEW ZEALAND LIMITED—See Bapcor Limited; *Int'l*, pg. 857
BARANCORP, LTD.; *U.S. Private*, pg. 471
BARBADOS SHIPPING & TRADING CO. LTD.; *Int'l*, pg. 858
BARBICAN GROUP HOLDINGS LTD.—See Arch Capital Group Ltd.; *Int'l*, pg. 547
BARCELO SWITZERLAND, S.A—See Barcelo Corporacion Empresarial S.A.; *Int'l*, pg. 859
BARDEN COMPANIES, INC.; *U.S. Private*, pg. 474
BARD HOLDINGS NETHERLANDS BV—See Becton, Dickinson & Company; *U.S. Public*, pg. 290
BAREFOOT LUXURY, INC.; *U.S. Private*, pg. 474
BARKAWI HOLDING GMBH; *Int'l*, pg. 865
BARLOWORLD HOLDINGS PLC—See Barloworld Ltd.; *Int'l*, pg. 866
BARLOWORLD LTD.; *Int'l*, pg. 866
BARNES GROUP INC.; *U.S. Public*, pg. 276
BARNES & NOBLE, INC.—See Elliott Management Corporation; *U.S. Private*, pg. 1364
BARRICK GOLD OF NORTH AMERICA, INC.—See Barrick Gold Corporation; *Int'l*, pg. 869
BARRON COLLIER COMPANY, LTD.; *U.S. Private*, pg. 480
BARROWGATE LIMITED—See Hysan Development Company Limited; *Int'l*, pg. 3554
BARTEC TOP HOLDING GMBH—See Charterhouse Capital Partners LLP; *Int'l*, pg. 1455
BARTON GOLD HOLDINGS LIMITED; *Int'l*, pg. 870
BASE D'INFORMATIONS LEGALES HOLDING S.A.S.; *Int'l*, pg. 871
BASER FAKTORING A.S.; *Int'l*, pg. 871
BASF COATINGS AG—See BASF SE; *Int'l*, pg. 872
BASF COATINGS HOLDING B.V.—See BASF SE; *Int'l*, pg. 872
BASF CONSTRUCTION CHEMICALS GMBH—See BASF SE; *Int'l*, pg. 874
BASF CORPORATION—See BASF SE; *Int'l*, pg. 875
BASF CROP PROTECTION DIVISION—See BASF SE; *Int'l*, pg. 877
BASF EAST ASIA REGIONAL HEADQUARTERS LTD.—See BASF SE; *Int'l*, pg. 877
BASF FRANCE S.A.S.—See BASF SE; *Int'l*, pg. 878
BASF PERFORMANCE PRODUCTS PLC—See BASF SE; *Int'l*, pg. 882
BASF PLANT SCIENCE COMPANY GMBH—See BASF SE; *Int'l*, pg. 877
BASF SE; *Int'l*, pg. 871
BASF SOUTH EAST ASIA PTE. LTD.—See BASF SE; *Int'l*, pg. 878
BASIN HOLDINGS US LLC—See J Fitzgibbons LLC; *U.S. Private*, pg. 2153
BASIN TOOLS, LP—See J Fitzgibbons LLC; *U.S. Private*, pg. 2153
BASS ENTERPRISES PRODUCTION CO.—See Keystone Group, L.P.; *U.S. Private*, pg. 2296

BASS PRO GROUP, LLC—See The Great American Outdoors Group LLC; *U.S. Private*, pg. 4037
BASTOGI S.P.A.; *Int'l*, pg. 888
BATESVILLE HOLDING UK, LIMITED—See Hillenbrand, Inc.; *U.S. Public*, pg. 1035
BATS GLOBAL MARKETS, INC.—See Cboe Global Markets, Inc.; *U.S. Public*, pg. 459
BAUER COMP HOLDING AG; *Int'l*, pg. 894
BAULAND GMBH—See BayernLB Holding AG; *Int'l*, pg. 913
BAUMER HOLDING AG; *Int'l*, pg. 895
BAUSCH HEALTH COMPANIES INC.; *Int'l*, pg. 895
BAUSCH + LOMB CORPORATION—See Bausch Health Companies Inc.; *Int'l*, pg. 895
BAUUNTERNEHMAN ECHTERHOFF GMBH & CO. KG; *Int'l*, pg. 898
BAVARIA IMMOBILIEN-BETEILIGUNGS-GESELLSCHAFT MBH & CO. OBJEKT FURTH KG—See BayernLB Holding AG; *Int'l*, pg. 913
BAWANG INTERNATIONAL GROUP HOLDING (HK) LIMITED—See BaWang International (Group) Holding Limited; *Int'l*, pg. 900
BAXTER HEALTHCARE HOLDING GMBH—See Baxter International Inc.; *U.S. Public*, pg. 281
BAXTER HEALTHCARE (HOLDINGS) LIMITED—See Baxter International Inc.; *U.S. Public*, pg. 280
BAY AREA NEWS GROUP—See Alden Global Capital LLC; *U.S. Private*, pg. 155
BAYCORP HOLDINGS, LTD.—See Tavistock Group, Inc.; *U.S. Private*, pg. 3937
BAYER AKTIENGESELLSCHAFT; *Int'l*, pg. 901
BAYERN BANKETT GASTRONOMIE GMBH—See BayernLB Holding AG; *Int'l*, pg. 913
BAYERNINVEST KAPITALANLAGEGESELLSCHAFT MBH—See BayernLB Holding AG; *Int'l*, pg. 913
BAYERNLB CAPITAL PARTNER GMBH—See BayernLB Holding AG; *Int'l*, pg. 913
BAYLOR SCOTT & WHITE HOLDINGS; *U.S. Private*, pg. 496
BAYSIDE CORP.; *U.S. Public*, pg. 284
BAYTEX ENERGY USA, INC.—See Baytex Energy Corp.; *Int'l*, pg. 915
BAY-VANGUARD, M.H.C.; *U.S. Private*, pg. 495
B&B CORPORATE HOLDINGS, INC.; *U.S. Private*, pg. 417
B. BRAUN MELSUNGEN AG; *Int'l*, pg. 785
BBR HOLDINGS (S) LTD.; *Int'l*, pg. 921
BB SEGURIDADE PARTICIPACOES S/A—See Banco do Brasil S.A.; *Int'l*, pg. 822
B&B SMARTWORX LIMITED—See Advantech Co., Ltd.; *Int'l*, pg. 165
B+B VAKMEDIANET GROEP B.V.; *Int'l*, pg. 784
BBX SWEET HOLDINGS, LLC—See Hilton Grand Vacations Inc.; *U.S. Public*, pg. 1039
BCD HOLDINGS N.V.; *Int'l*, pg. 926
BCE INC.; *Int'l*, pg. 926
BCII ENTERPRISES, INC.; *U.S. Public*, pg. 285
BCL LIMITED; *Int'l*, pg. 928
BCLO BRISA PUNTA CANA, BV—See Barcelo Corporacion Empresarial S.A.; *Int'l*, pg. 859
BCM ALLIANCE BERHAD; *Int'l*, pg. 928
BCP INC.; *U.S. Private*, pg. 499
B&D INDUSTRIAL, INC.; *U.S. Private*, pg. 418
BDO INTERNATIONAL LIMITED; *Int'l*, pg. 930
B & D STRATEGIC HOLDINGS LIMITED; *Int'l*, pg. 783
B.DUCK SEMK HOLDINGS INTERNATIONAL LIMITED; *Int'l*, pg. 789
BD WHITE BIRCH PAPER INVESTMENT LLC—See Black Diamond Capital Holdings, LLC; *U.S. Private*, pg. 570
BEACHSIDE CAPITAL PARTNERS; *U.S. Private*, pg. 503
BEACON HEALTH HOLDINGS LLC; *U.S. Private*, pg. 504
BEACON POINTE HOLDINGS, LLC; *U.S. Private*, pg. 505
BEACON RISE HOLDINGS PLC; *Int'l*, pg. 932
B/E AEROSPACE HOLDINGS GMBH—See RTX Corporation; *U.S. Public*, pg. 1822
BEAL GROUP; *U.S. Public*, pg. 505
BEAMTREE HOLDINGS LIMITED; *Int'l*, pg. 932
BEARINGPOINT HOLDINGS EUROPE B.V.; *Int'l*, pg. 933
BEASLEY BROADCAST GROUP, INC.; *U.S. Public*, pg. 287
BEASLEY MEZZANINE HOLDINGS, LLC—See Beasley Broadcast Group, Inc.; *U.S. Public*, pg. 287
BEAULIEU INTERNATIONAL GROUP NV; *Int'l*, pg. 934
BEAUTYGE PARTICIPATIONS, S.L.—See MacAndrews & Forbes Incorporated; *U.S. Private*, pg. 2533
THE BEAUTY HEALTH COMPANY; *U.S. Public*, pg. 2038
BEAVER ENTECH LIMITED; *Int'l*, pg. 935
BEC ASSET CO., LTD.—See BEC World Public Company Limited; *Int'l*, pg. 936
BEC INC.; *U.S. Private*, pg. 509
BECK ARNLEY HOLDINGS LLC—See Icahn Enterprises L.P.; *U.S. Public*, pg. 1084
BECTON DICKINSON AUSTRIA HOLDINGS GMBH—See Becton, Dickinson & Company; *U.S. Public*, pg. 289
BECTON DICKINSON SWITZERLAND GLOBAL HOLDINGS SARL—See Becton, Dickinson & Company; *U.S. Public*, pg. 290
BEDROCK INDUSTRIES GP, LLC; *U.S. Private*, pg. 512
BEE STREET HOLDINGS LLC; *U.S. Private*, pg. 513
BEGBIES TRAYNOR GROUP PLC; *Int'l*, pg. 940

551112 — OFFICES OF OTHER HO...

BEHN MEYER (D) HOLDING AG & CO.; *Int'l*, pg. 941
BEHR HOLDINGS CORPORATION—See Masco Corporation; *U.S. Public*, pg. 1389
BEHRINGER HARVARD HOLDINGS, LLC; *U.S. Private*, pg. 515
BEIJING CAPITAL AGRIBUSINESS GROUP CO., LTD.; *Int'l*, pg. 946
BEIJING CAPITAL DEVELOPMENT HOLDING GROUP CO., LTD; *Int'l*, pg. 947
BEIJING CAPITAL GRAND LIMITED; *Int'l*, pg. 947
BEIJING CAPITAL GROUP CO., LTD.; *Int'l*, pg. 947
BEIJING CENTERGATE TECHNOLOGIES (HOLDING) CO., LTD.; *Int'l*, pg. 947
BEIJING ENTERPRISES HOLDINGS LIMITED; *Int'l*, pg. 949
BEIJING GEHUA CULTURAL DEVELOPMENT GROUP CO., LTD; *Int'l*, pg. 950
BEIJING INFRASTRUCTURE INVESTMENT CO., LTD.; *Int'l*, pg. 952
BEIJING JINGCHENG MACHINERY ELECTRIC HOLDING CO., LTD.; *Int'l*, pg. 952
BEIJING KAWIN TECHNOLOGY SHARE-HOLDING CO., LTD.; *Int'l*, pg. 953
BEIJING SWT COMMUNICATIONS CO., LTD.; *Int'l*, pg. 958
BEIJING UNITED FAMILY HOSPITAL MANAGEMENT CO., LTD.—See TPG Capital, L.P.; *U.S. Public*, pg. 2169
BEING HOLDING CO., LTD.; *Int'l*, pg. 962
BEIREN GROUP CORPORATION—See Beijing Jingcheng Machinery Electric Holding Co., Ltd.; *Int'l*, pg. 953
BEISEN HOLDING LTD.; *Int'l*, pg. 962
BELARTO GROUP—See HAL Trust N.V.; *Int'l*, pg. 3224
BELDEN HOLDINGS, INC.—See Belden, Inc.; *U.S. Public*, pg. 293
BELDEN VENLO HOLDING B.V.—See Belden, Inc.; *U.S. Public*, pg. 294
THE BELET GROUP, INC.; *U.S. Private*, pg. 3993
BELGICA INSURANCE HOLDING S.A.—See Assicurazioni Generali S.p.A.; *Int'l*, pg. 647
BELHASA GROUP OF COMPANIES; *Int'l*, pg. 963
BELL DEUTSCHLAND HOLDING GMBH—See Coop-Gruppe Genossenschaft; *Int'l*, pg. 1789
BELLE CORPORATION; *Int'l*, pg. 966
BELLE INTERNATIONAL HOLDINGS LIMITED—See Hillhouse Investment Management Limited; *Int'l*, pg. 3392
BELLEVUE LIFE SCIENCES ACQUISITION CORP.; *U.S. Public*, pg. 295
BELL FOOD GROUP AG—See Coop-Gruppe Genossenschaft; *Int'l*, pg. 1789
BELL INDUSTRIES, INC.; *U.S. Public*, pg. 295
BELL MEDIA INC.—See BCE Inc.; *Int'l*, pg. 926
BELO CORP.—See TEGNA Inc.; *U.S. Public*, pg. 1989
BELPHAR LTD.; *Int'l*, pg. 968
BELTON FINANCIAL HOLDING—See Chimera Investments LLC; *Int'l*, pg. 1479
BENCHMARK TELECAST INTEGRATION PTE LTD; *Int'l*, pg. 970
BENEFITFOCUS, INC.—See Voya Financial, Inc.; *U.S. Public*, pg. 2311
BENESSE HOLDINGS, INC.—See EQT AB; *Int'l*, pg. 2467
BENGAL GROUP; *Int'l*, pg. 973
BENG SOON MACHINERY HOLDINGS LIMITED; *Int'l*, pg. 973
BENIHANA INC.—See TPG Capital, L.P.; *U.S. Public*, pg. 2167
BENNER HOLDING GMBH; *Int'l*, pg. 974
BENNETT, COLEMAN & CO. LTD.; *Int'l*, pg. 974
BENTALL KENNEDY LP; *Int'l*, pg. 975
BENTELER NETHERLANDS HOLDING B.V.—See Benteler International AG; *Int'l*, pg. 977
BEN THANH SERVICE JSC; *Int'l*, pg. 969
BENTLEY REID (HOLDINGS) LIMITED; *Int'l*, pg. 977
BENZER PHARMACY HOLDING LLC; *U.S. Private*, pg. 529
BERA HOLDING A.S.; *Int'l*, pg. 978
BERBERIAN BROS INC.; *U.S. Private*, pg. 529
BERETTA HOLDING S.P.A.—See Fabbrica d'Armi Pietro Beretta S.p.A.; *Int'l*, pg. 2598
BERG & BERG ENTERPRISES, INC.; *U.S. Private*, pg. 530
BERGER HOLDING GMBH; *Int'l*, pg. 979
BERGE Y CIA SA; *Int'l*, pg. 979
BERGIO INTERNATIONAL, INC.; *U.S. Public*, pg. 297
BERGMAN & BEVING SAFETY AB—See Bergman & Beving AB; *Int'l*, pg. 980
BERJAYA CAPITAL BERHAD—See Berjaya Corporation Berhad; *Int'l*, pg. 982
BERJAYA FOOD BERHAD—See Berjaya Corporation Berhad; *Int'l*, pg. 982
BERJAYA GROUP BERHAD—See Berjaya Corporation Berhad; *Int'l*, pg. 982
BERKS GROUP—See News-Press & Gazette Company; *U.S. Public*, pg. 2917
BERKSHIRE HATHAWAY AUTOMOTIVE INC.—See Berkshire Hathaway Inc.; *U.S. Public*, pg. 300
BERKSHIRE HATHAWAY ENERGY COMPANY—See Berkshire Hathaway Inc.; *U.S. Public*, pg. 300
BERKSHIRE HATHAWAY INC.; *U.S. Public*, pg. 297
BERLIN CITY AUTO GROUP—See Booth Creek Management Corporation; *U.S. Private*, pg. 617

BERLITZ CORPORATION—See Quad Partners, LLC; *U.S. Private*, pg. 3314
BERNER SE; *Int'l*, pg. 988
BERRY GLOBAL GROUP, INC; *U.S. Public*, pg. 320
BERRY INVESTMENTS INC.; *U.S. Private*, pg. 538
BERTEL O. STEEN AS; *Int'l*, pg. 989
BERTELSMANN INC.—See Bertelsmann SE & Co. KGaA; *Int'l*, pg. 990
BERTELSMANN SE & CO. KGAA; *Int'l*, pg. 989
BEST FOOD HOLDING COMPANY LIMITED; *Int'l*, pg. 999
BESTLIFE 3 INTERNATIONAL GMBH & CO. KG—See BayernLB Holding AG; *Int'l*, pg. 913
BEST LINKING GROUP HOLDINGS LIMITED; *Int'l*, pg. 999
BEST MART 360 HOLDINGS LIMITED; *Int'l*, pg. 999
BEST PACIFIC INTERNATIONAL HOLDINGS LIMITED; *Int'l*, pg. 999
BESTWAY (HOLDINGS) LIMITED; *Int'l*, pg. 1000
BESTWAY PANACEA HOLDINGS LTD—See Bestway (Holdings) Limited; *Int'l*, pg. 1001
BETBULL HOLDING SE; *Int'l*, pg. 1002
BETER BED HOLDING N.V.; *Int'l*, pg. 1002
THE BETESH GROUP, INC.; *U.S. Private*, pg. 3994
BETFAIR GROUP LIMITED—See Flutter Entertainment plc; *Int'l*, pg. 2715
BETFAIR HOLDING (MALTA) LIMITED—See Flutter Entertainment plc; *Int'l*, pg. 2715
BET HOLDINGS LLC—See National Amusements, Inc.; *U.S. Private*, pg. 2839
BET SHEMESH ENGINES HOLDINGS (1997) LTD.; *Int'l*, pg. 1001
BETTERLIFE HOLDING LIMITED; *Int'l*, pg. 1003
BETTER THERAPEUTICS, INC.; *U.S. Public*, pg. 327
BEXIL CORPORATION; *U.S. Public*, pg. 327
BEZEQ - THE ISRAEL TELECOMMUNICATION CORP. LIMITED; *Int'l*, pg. 1006
BF1 MOTORSPORT HOLDINGS LTD.; *Int'l*, pg. 1006
BF BOLTHOUSE HOLDCO LLC—See Campbell Soup Company; *U.S. Public*, pg. 426
B-FLEXION GROUP HOLDINGS SA; *Int'l*, pg. 785
B GAON HOLDINGS LTD.; *Int'l*, pg. 783
BGC INTERNATIONAL, L.P.—See BGC Group, Inc.; *U.S. Public*, pg. 328
B&G FOODS, INC.; *U.S. Public*, pg. 260
BGL GROUP LIMITED; *Int'l*, pg. 1008
B. GRIMM HOLDING CO., LTD.—See B. Grimm Group; *Int'l*, pg. 788
B.GRIMM JOINT VENTURE HOLDING LTD.—See B. Grimm Group; *Int'l*, pg. 788
BHARTI ENTERPRISES LIMITED; *Int'l*, pg. 1011
BHATIA BROTHERS GROUP; *Int'l*, pg. 1013
B+H MANAGEMENT LTD.—See B+H Ocean Carriers Ltd.; *Int'l*, pg. 784
BH MEDIA GROUP INC.—See Lee Enterprises, Incorporated; *U.S. Public*, pg. 1298
BHP GROUP LIMITED; *Int'l*, pg. 1015
BH SHOE HOLDINGS, INC.—See Berkshire Hathaway Inc.; *U.S. Public*, pg. 299
BIANCAMANO S.P.A.; *Int'l*, pg. 1017
BIBBY HOLDINGS LIMITED—See Bibby Line Group Limited; *Int'l*, pg. 1018
BIBBY LINE GROUP LIMITED; *Int'l*, pg. 1017
BIBOJEE SERVICES PRIVATE LIMITED; *Int'l*, pg. 1018
BICAPITAL CORPORATION; *Int'l*, pg. 1018
BICKFORD SENIOR LIVING GROUP, LLC; *U.S. Private*, pg. 550
BICOASTAL MEDIA, LLC; *U.S. Private*, pg. 550
BIFFA GROUP LIMITED; *Int'l*, pg. 1020
BIGCOMMERCE HOLDINGS, INC.; *U.S. Public*, pg. 331
BIG THREE RESTAURANTS, INC.; *U.S. Private*, pg. 554
BIG TIME HOLDINGS, INC.; *U.S. Public*, pg. 331
BIGTINCAN HOLDINGS LIMITED; *U.S. Public*, pg. 331
BIG TREE CLOUD HOLDINGS LIMITED; *Int'l*, pg. 1022
BII RAILWAY TRANSPORTATION TECHNOLOGY HOLDINGS COMPANY LIMITED—See Beijing Infrastructure Investment Co., Ltd.; *Int'l*, pg. 952
BIJOUX TERNER, INC.; *U.S. Private*, pg. 556
BIKE24 HOLDING AG; *Int'l*, pg. 1022
BILCARE LIMITED; *Int'l*, pg. 1023
BILFINGER BERGER POLSKA S.A.—See Bilfinger SE; *Int'l*, pg. 1026
BILFINGER BERGER UMWELTTECHNIK GMBH—See Bilfinger SE; *Int'l*, pg. 1027
BILFINGER POWER SYSTEMS GMBH—See Bilfinger SE; *Int'l*, pg. 1027
BILGIN ENERJI YATIRIM HOLDING A.S.; *Int'l*, pg. 1029
BILLERUD AMERICAS CORPORATION—See Billerud AB; *Int'l*, pg. 1030
BILL HOLDINGS, INC.; *U.S. Public*, pg. 331
BILLION HOLDING INC.; *Int'l*, pg. 1031
BILLION MOTORS, INC.; *U.S. Public*, pg. 559
BILTMORE HOLDING ARIZONA L.L.C.; *U.S. Private*, pg. 560
BINSWANGER INTERNATIONAL LTD.—See Binswanger Management Corp.; *U.S. Private*, pg. 561
BINTULU PORT SDN. BHD.—See Bintulu Port Holdings Berhad; *Int'l*, pg. 1034
BIO-AMD, INC.; *Int'l*, pg. 1035
BIOAUTHORIZE HOLDINGS, INC.; *U.S. Private*, pg. 561

BIOCARDIA, INC.; *U.S. Public*, pg. 335
BIOFISH HOLDING AS; *Int'l*, pg. 1037
BIOFOCUS DPI (HOLDINGS) LIMITED—See Charles River Laboratories International, Inc.; *U.S. Public*, pg. 480
BIOKARPET S.A.; *Int'l*, pg. 1038
BIOMET EUROPE B.V.—See Zimmer Biomet Holdings, Inc.; *U.S. Public*, pg. 2405
BIONOR HOLDING AS; *Int'l*, pg. 1040
BIOPLUS LIFE CORP.; *Int'l*, pg. 1041
BIOSTIME HONG KONG LIMITED—See Health and Happiness (H&H) International Holdings Limited; *Int'l*, pg. 3303
BIO-TECHNE CORPORATION; *U.S. Public*, pg. 334
BIOTHERA HOLDING CORP.; *U.S. Private*, pg. 563
BIOVENTUS INC.; *U.S. Public*, pg. 339
BIPADOSA SA; *Int'l*, pg. 1045
BIR HOLDINGS, LLC; *U.S. Private*, pg. 563
BIRKENSTOCK HOLDING PLC.; *Int'l*, pg. 1047
BIRMINGHAM HOLDINGS, LLC—See Community Health Systems, Inc.; *U.S. Public*, pg. 551
BIRMINGHAM SPORTS HOLDINGS LIMITED; *Int'l*, pg. 1048
BIS INDUSTRIAL SERVICES SWEDEN AB—See Bilfinger SE; *Int'l*, pg. 1025
BIT BROTHER LIMITED; *Int'l*, pg. 1049
BITECH TECHNOLOGIES CORPORATION; *U.S. Public*, pg. 339
BIT MINING LTD.; *Int'l*, pg. 1049
BITTIUM OYJ; *Int'l*, pg. 1050
BITZER SE; *Int'l*, pg. 1051
BIZLAB, INC.; *U.S. Private*, pg. 567
BJ'S WHOLESALE CLUB HOLDINGS, INC.; *U.S. Public*, pg. 340
BKN BIOSTROM AG; *Int'l*, pg. 1054
BLACKBURN RADIO INC; *Int'l*, pg. 1060
BLACK CREEK GROUP, LLC; *U.S. Private*, pg. 570
BLACK & DECKER INTERNATIONAL—See Stanley Black & Decker, Inc.; *U.S. Public*, pg. 1936
BLACK DIAMOND CAPITAL HOLDINGS, LLC; *U.S. Private*, pg. 570
BLACK DIAMOND ENERGY HOLDINGS LLC—See Legend Oil and Gas, Ltd.; *U.S. Public*, pg. 1301
BLACK DIAMOND GROUP LIMITED; *Int'l*, pg. 1059
BLACKFRIARS CORP.; *U.S. Private*, pg. 574
BLACKHAWK INDUSTRIAL DISTRIBUTION, INC.—See TruArc Partners, L.P.; *U.S. Private*, pg. 4244
BLACK KNIGHT, INC.—See Intercontinental Exchange, Inc.; *U.S. Public*, pg. 1141
BLACK KNIGHT INFOSERV, LLC—See Intercontinental Exchange, Inc.; *U.S. Public*, pg. 1141
BLACK KNIGHT SPORTS & ENTERTAINMENT LLC; *U.S. Private*, pg. 572
BLACKOUT MEDIA CORP.; *Int'l*, pg. 1061
BLACKSTREET CAPITAL HOLDINGS LLC; *U.S. Private*, pg. 576
BLACK & VEATCH HOLDING COMPANY; *U.S. Private*, pg. 569
BLACKWELL LTD.—See Elliott Management Corporation; *U.S. Private*, pg. 1365
BLAKE HOLDINGS LIMITED; *Int'l*, pg. 1062
BLANCCO TECHNOLOGY GROUP PLC—See Francisco Partners Management, LP; *U.S. Private*, pg. 1588
BLEP HOLDING GMBH—See Bausch Health Companies Inc.; *Int'l*, pg. 896
BLISS COMMUNICATIONS, INC.—See Adams Publishing Group, LLC; *U.S. Private*, pg. 74
BLME HOLDINGS PLC; *Int'l*, pg. 1064
BLOCKCHAIN GROUP COMPANY LIMITED; *Int'l*, pg. 1064
BLOOMBERG L.P.; *U.S. Private*, pg. 583
BLOOMBERRY RESORTS CORPORATION; *Int'l*, pg. 1065
BLOOM HOLDCO LLC; *U.S. Private*, pg. 583
BLOOMIN' BRANDS, INC.; *U.S. Public*, pg. 362
BLUBUZZARD, INC.; *U.S. Public*, pg. 363
BLUEBET HOLDINGS LTD.; *Int'l*, pg. 1070
BLUE BIRD CORPORATION—See American Securities LLC; *U.S. Private*, pg. 247
BLUE CANYON HOLDINGS AB—See GTCR LLC; *U.S. Private*, pg. 1804
BLUEFOCUS INTELLIGENT COMMUNICATIONS GROUP CO., LTD.; *Int'l*, pg. 1071
BLUEFOCUS INTERNATIONAL LIMITED—See Bluefocus Intelligent Communications Group Co., Ltd.; *Int'l*, pg. 1071
BLUEGREEN VACATIONS HOLDING CORPORATION—See Hilton Grand Vacations Inc.; *U.S. Public*, pg. 1039
BLUE HOLDING S.P.A.—See Green Holding S.p.A.; *Int'l*, pg. 3071
BLUELINX HOLDINGS, INC.—See Cerberus Capital Management, L.P.; *U.S. Private*, pg. 837
BLUE MOON GROUP HOLDINGS LIMITED; *Int'l*, pg. 1069
BLUENRGY GROUP LIMITED; *Int'l*, pg. 1072
BLUEONE CARD, INC.; *U.S. Public*, pg. 365
BLUE OVAL HOLDINGS LIMITED—See Ford Motor Company; *U.S. Public*, pg. 865
BLUEPRINT TECHNOLOGIES, INC.; *U.S. Public*, pg. 366
BLUE RIDGE INDUSTRIES, INC.; *U.S. Private*, pg. 592
BLUE RIDGE MOUNTAIN RESOURCES, INC.—See Expand Energy Corporation; *U.S. Public*, pg. 808

551112 — OFFICES OF OTHER HO...

BLUESKY HOTELS & RESORTS INC.; *Int'l*, pg. 1074
BLUESTAR ALLIANCE LLC; *U.S. Private*, pg. 597
BLUESTEM GROUP INC.; *U.S. Public*, pg. 366
BLUE WATER GLOBAL GROUP, INC.; *Int'l*, pg. 1070
BLVD COMPANIES; *U.S. Private*, pg. 600
BMC STOCK HOLDINGS, INC.—See Builders FirstSource, Inc.; *U.S. Public*, pg. 409
BMH LTD.; *Int'l*, pg. 1076
BMI SYSTEMS CORPORATION; *U.S. Private*, pg. 600
BM MOBILITY LTD.; *Int'l*, pg. 1075
BMT GROUP LIMITED; *Int'l*, pg. 1077
BMWC GROUP INC.; *U.S. Private*, pg. 601
BMW HOLDING B.V.—See Bayerische Motoren Werke Aktiengesellschaft; *Int'l*, pg. 911
BN MEDIA LLC; *U.S. Private*, pg. 601
BNP PARIBAS CARDIF SA—See BNP Paribas SA; *Int'l*, pg. 1083
BNP PARIBAS USA, INC.—See BNP Paribas SA; *Int'l*, pg. 1087
BNT HOLDING D.D.; *Int'l*, pg. 1093
BOA HOLDINGS INC.—See Compass Diversified Holdings; *U.S. Public*, pg. 560
BOARDROOM LIMITED—See G. K. Goh Holdings Limited; *Int'l*, pg. 2864
BOATZON HOLDINGS, LLC—See MarineMax, Inc.; *U.S. Public*, pg. 1366
BOBST GROUP S.A.; *Int'l*, pg. 1095
BODY CENTRAL CORP.—See WestView Capital Partners, L.P.; *U.S. Private*, pg. 4501
BOEHRINGER INGELHEIM CORP.—See C.H. Boehringer Sohn AG & Co. KG; *Int'l*, pg. 1241
BOEHRINGER INGELHEIM EUROPE GMBH—See C.H. Boehringer Sohn AG & Co. KG; *Int'l*, pg. 1241
BOEHRINGER INGELHEIM GMBH—See C.H. Boehringer Sohn AG & Co. KG; *Int'l*, pg. 1242
BOEHRINGER INGELHEIM (PTY.) LTD.—See C.H. Boehringer Sohn AG & Co. KG; *Int'l*, pg. 1241
BOEING AUSTRALIA HOLDINGS PROPRIETARY LIMITED—See The Boeing Company; *U.S. Public*, pg. 2040
BOEING INTERNATIONAL CORPORATION—See The Boeing Company; *U.S. Public*, pg. 2040
BOELS TOPHOLDING B.V.; *Int'l*, pg. 1099
BOE VARITRONIX LIMITED—See BOE Technology Group Co., Ltd.; *Int'l*, pg. 1099
BOILL HEALTHCARE HOLDINGS LIMITED; *Int'l*, pg. 1101
BOING US HOLDCO, INC.—See Roark Capital Group Inc.; *U.S. Private*, pg. 3454
BOISSET, LA FAMILLE DES GRANDS VINS; *Int'l*, pg. 1101
THE BOLDT GROUP INC.; *U.S. Private*, pg. 3995
BOLD VENTURES INC.; *Int'l*, pg. 1102
THE BOLER COMPANY; *U.S. Private*, pg. 3996
BOLIGA GRUPPEN A/S; *Int'l*, pg. 1102
BOLINA HOLDING CO., LTD.; *Int'l*, pg. 1102
BOLLORE S.A.—See Financiere de L'Odet; *Int'l*, pg. 2666
BOLTEK HOLDINGS LIMITED; *Int'l*, pg. 1103
BOMAR EXO LLC; *U.S. Private*, pg. 612
BONHEUR ASA—See Fred. Olsen & Co.; *Int'l*, pg. 2768
BON NATURAL LIFE LIMITED; *Int'l*, pg. 1105
BONNIER AB; *Int'l*, pg. 1108
BONNIER BOOKS AB—See Bonnier AB; *Int'l*, pg. 1108
BONNIER BUSINESS PRESS AB—See Bonnier AB; *Int'l*, pg. 1108
BONNIER MAGAZINE GROUP AB—See Bonnier AB; *Int'l*, pg. 1108
BONNY INTERNATIONAL HOLDING LTD.; *Int'l*, pg. 1109
BONVESTS HOLDINGS LIMITED; *Int'l*, pg. 1109
BOOSEY & HAWKES LIMITED—See HgCapital Trust plc; *Int'l*, pg. 3376
BOOST TECHNOLOGIES, LLC; *U.S. Private*, pg. 616
BOOT BARN HOLDINGS, INC.; *U.S. Public*, pg. 368
BOOTH CREEK MANAGEMENT CORPORATION; *U.S. Private*, pg. 616
BOOTH CREEK SKI HOLDINGS, INC.—See Booth Creek Management Corporation; *U.S. Private*, pg. 616
BOOTH SECURITIES LTD.; *Int'l*, pg. 1111
THE BOOTS COMPANY PLC—See Walgreens Boots Alliance, Inc.; *U.S. Public*, pg. 2323
BOOZ ALLEN HAMILTON HOLDING CORPORATION; *U.S. Public*, pg. 368
BOPARAN HOLDINGS LIMITED; *Int'l*, pg. 1111
BOQII HOLDING LIMITED; *Int'l*, pg. 1112
BORA CORPORATION; *Int'l*, pg. 1112
BORDEN DAIRY COMPANY—See Capitol Peak Partners, LLC; *U.S. Private*, pg. 744
BORDEN DAIRY COMPANY—See KKR & Co. Inc.; *U.S. Public*, pg. 1241
BORDURE LIMITED—See Camellia Plc; *Int'l*, pg. 1271
BOREALIS EXPLORATION LIMITED; *Int'l*, pg. 1113
BORGESS HEALTH ALLIANCE, INC.—See Ascension Health Alliance; *U.S. Private*, pg. 346
BORGWARNER EUROPE GMBH—See BorgWarner Inc.; *U.S. Public*, pg. 369
BORGWARNER HOLDINGS LIMITED—See BorgWarner Inc.; *U.S. Public*, pg. 371
BORGWARNER INC.; *U.S. Public*, pg. 369
BORNEO OIL BERHAD; *Int'l*, pg. 1114

BOROUGE PLC—See Abu Dhabi National Oil Company; *Int'l*, pg. 73
BORR DRILLING LIMITED; *Int'l*, pg. 1114
BOSSARD HOLDING AG; *Int'l*, pg. 1117
BOSS HOLDINGS, INC.; *U.S. Public*, pg. 371
BOSS SYSTEMS LIMITED—See China Trends Holdings Limited; *Int'l*, pg. 1561
BOSTON BASKETBALL PARTNERS LLC; *U.S. Private*, pg. 621
BOSTON INTERNATIONAL HOLDINGS PLC; *Int'l*, pg. 1118
BOSTON OMAHA CORPORATION; *U.S. Public*, pg. 371
BOT GORNICTWO I ENERGETYKA SA—See Elektrownia Belchatow S.A.; *Int'l*, pg. 2357
THE BOUCHER GROUP, INC.; *U.S. Private*, pg. 3998
BOUSSARD & GAVAUDAN GESTION S.A.S.—See Boussard & Gavaudan Holding Limited; *Int'l*, pg. 1120
BOUSTEAD SINGAPORE LIMITED; *Int'l*, pg. 1120
BOUYGUES E&S UK LTD.—See Bouygues S.A.; *Int'l*, pg. 1122
BOUYGUES S.A.; *Int'l*, pg. 1121
BOWLEN SPORTS, INC.; *U.S. Private*, pg. 625
BOYALIFE GROUP; *Int'l*, pg. 1124
BOYAUDERIE ORLEANAISE SA—See Danish Crown AmbA; *Int'l*, pg. 1964
BOYAUX BRESSANS SA—See Danish Crown AmbA; *Int'l*, pg. 1964
BOYD GAMING CORPORATION; *U.S. Public*, pg. 377
BOZLU HOLDING; *Int'l*, pg. 1125
BPB PLC—See Compagnie de Saint-Gobain SA; *Int'l*, pg. 1725
BP CORPORATION NORTH AMERICA INC.—See BP plc; *Int'l*, pg. 1126
BP CORPORATION NORTH AMERICA INC.—See BP plc; *Int'l*, pg. 1126
BP EXPLORATION OPERATING COMPANY LIMITED—See BP plc; *Int'l*, pg. 1128
BP NEDERLAND HOLDINGS B.V.—See BP plc; *Int'l*, pg. 1129
BP PLC; *Int'l*, pg. 1125
BPPL HOLDINGS PLC; *Int'l*, pg. 1133
BPREX BRAZIL HOLDING INC.—See Berry Global Group, Inc; *U.S. Public*, pg. 320
THE BRADY COMPANIES; *U.S. Private*, pg. 3999
BRADY PLC; *Int'l*, pg. 1135
BRAEMAR PLC; *Int'l*, pg. 1135
BRAES CAPITAL LLC; *U.S. Private*, pg. 633
BRAGG GROUP OF COMPANIES; *Int'l*, pg. 1136
BRAHIM'S HOLDINGS BERHAD; *Int'l*, pg. 1136
BRAKE BROS LIMITED—See Sysco Corporation; *U.S. Public*, pg. 1973
BRAMBLES USA INC.—See Brambles Limited; *Int'l*, pg. 1138
BRANDIMAGE BELGIQUE HOLDINGS SA—See Matthews International Corporation; *U.S. Public*, pg. 1400
BRANDMARK INTERNATIONAL HOLDING B.V.—See Matthews International Corporation; *U.S. Public*, pg. 1400
BRANDT HOLDINGS COMPANY; *U.S. Private*, pg. 638
BRANDT INDUSTRIES LTD.; *Int'l*, pg. 1140
THE BRANDYWINE COMPANIES, LLC; *U.S. Private*, pg. 4000
BRANFORD CASTLE, INC.; *U.S. Private*, pg. 639
BRASWELL MILLING COMPANY; *U.S. Private*, pg. 640
BRAVERN VENTURES LLC; *Int'l*, pg. 1141
BRAVIDA AB—See Bravida Holding AB; *Int'l*, pg. 1142
BRAVIDA HOLDING AB; *Int'l*, pg. 1141
BRAVO MULTINATIONAL INCORPORATED; *U.S. Public*, pg. 380
BRAZOS PRIVATE EQUITY PARTNERS, LLC; *U.S. Private*, pg. 642
BRC INC.; *U.S. Public*, pg. 380
BREADTALK GROUP PTE LTD.; *Int'l*, pg. 1143
BREAKTHRU BEVERAGE GROUP, LLC; *U.S. Private*, pg. 643
BRECKENRIDGE HOLDING COMPANY; *U.S. Private*, pg. 644
BRECO HOLDINGS, INC; *U.S. Private*, pg. 644
BREGAL MILESTONE LLP; *Int'l*, pg. 1144
THE BRENLIN GROUP; *U.S. Private*, pg. 4000
BRERA HOLDINGS PLC; *Int'l*, pg. 1150
BRF B.V.—See BRF S.A.; *Int'l*, pg. 1150
BRF S.A.; *Int'l*, pg. 1150
BRG GROUP JOINT STOCK CO.; *Int'l*, pg. 1151
BRG SPORTS, INC.—See Fenway Partners, LLC; *U.S. Private*, pg. 1495
BR. HOLDINGS CORPORATION; *Int'l*, pg. 1133
BR HOMEBUILDING GROUP, L.P.; *U.S. Private*, pg. 630
BRIAN BEMIS AUTOMOTIVE GROUP, LTD.; *U.S. Private*, pg. 647
BRICK INVESTMENT PARTNERS LLC; *U.S. Private*, pg. 648
BRIDAS CORPORATION; *Int'l*, pg. 1152
BRIDGE INVESTMENT GROUP HOLDINGS INC.; *U.S. Public*, pg. 381
BRIDGEMERE UK PLC; *Int'l*, pg. 1153
BRIDGEPOINT ADVISERS GROUP LIMITED—See Bridgepoint Group Plc; *Int'l*, pg. 1153
BRIDGEPOINT GROUP PLC; *Int'l*, pg. 1153

BRIDGER AEROSPACE GROUP HOLDINGS, INC.; *U.S. Public*, pg. 382
BRIDGER AEROSPACE GROUP HOLDINGS, LLC—See Bridger Aerospace Group Holdings, Inc.; *U.S. Public*, pg. 382
BRIDGETOWN 3 HOLDINGS LIMITED; *Int'l*, pg. 1160
BRIDGEWATER RESOURCES CORPORATION; *U.S. Private*, pg. 650
BRIDGEWAY NATIONAL CORP.; *U.S. Public*, pg. 382
BRIGGS INTERNATIONAL, INC.—See Sammons Enterprises, Inc.; *U.S. Private*, pg. 3537
BRIGGS & STRATTON INTERNATIONAL HOLDING BV—See Briggs & Stratton Corporation; *U.S. Private*, pg. 651
BRIGHT FOOD (GROUP) CO., LTD.; *Int'l*, pg. 1161
BRIGHT FUTURE TECHNOLOGY HOLDINGS LTD.; *Int'l*, pg. 1161
BRIGHTLANE ACQUISITION CORP.; *U.S. Private*, pg. 652
BRIGHT MOUNTAIN MEDIA, INC.; *U.S. Public*, pg. 383
BRIGHTVIEW HOLDINGS, INC.; *U.S. Public*, pg. 383
B. RILEY FINANCIAL, INC.; *U.S. Public*, pg. 260
B. RILEY WEALTH MANAGEMENT, INC.—See B. Riley Financial, Inc.; *U.S. Public*, pg. 260
BRILLIANCE CHINA AUTOMOTIVE HOLDINGS LIMITED; *Int'l*, pg. 1163
BRILLIANT EARTH GROUP, INC.; *U.S. Public*, pg. 384
BRIMSTONE INVESTMENT CORPORATION LTD.; *Int'l*, pg. 1164
BR INDUSTRIER AS; *Int'l*, pg. 1133
THE BRINK'S COMPANY; *U.S. Public*, pg. 2041
BRINK'S INTERNATIONAL HOLDINGS AG—See The Brink's Company; *U.S. Public*, pg. 2042
BRINK'S SECURITY INTERNATIONAL, INC.—See The Brink's Company; *U.S. Public*, pg. 2042
BRISA INTERNACIONAL, SGPS, S.A.—See APG Asset Management NV; *Int'l*, pg. 512
BRISA - SERVICOS VIARIOS, SGPS, S.A.—See APG Asset Management NV; *Int'l*, pg. 512
BRISBANE BRONCOS LIMITED—See News Corporation; *U.S. Public*, pg. 1520
BRISTOL BAY NATIVE CORPORATION; *U.S. Private*, pg. 655
BRISTOW GROUP, INC.; *U.S. Public*, pg. 387
BRITISH AAMERICAN TOBACCO HOLDINGS (THE NETHERLANDS) B.V.—See British American Tobacco plc; *Int'l*, pg. 1165
BRITISH AMERICAN INVESTMENT CO. (MTIUS) LTD.; *Int'l*, pg. 1165
BRITISH AMERICAN TOBACCO PLC; *Int'l*, pg. 1165
BRITISH VITA GROUP SOCIETE A RESPONSABILITE LIMITEE—See TPG Capital, L.P.; *U.S. Public*, pg. 2175
BRITVIC PLC; *Int'l*, pg. 1171
BRIX HOLDINGS, LLC; *U.S. Private*, pg. 657
BRIXMOR OPERATING PARTNERSHIP LP—See Blackstone Inc.; *U.S. Public*, pg. 352
BROADCOM INC.; *U.S. Public*, pg. 388
BROADRIDGE FINANCIAL SOLUTIONS, INC.; *U.S. Public*, pg. 391
BROADSPECTRUM PTY. LTD.—See Apollo Global Management, Inc.; *U.S. Public*, pg. 166
BROADWAY ENTERPRISES, INC.; *U.S. Private*, pg. 660
BROADWAY INDUSTRIAL GROUP LIMITED; *Int'l*, pg. 1172
BROADWAY SYSTEMS & TECHNOLOGY CO., LTD.—See Platinum Equity, LLC; *U.S. Private*, pg. 3201
BROASTER COMPANY; *U.S. Private*, pg. 660
BROCK ENTERPRISES, LLC—See AIP, LLC; *U.S. Private*, pg. 134
BROCKHAUS TECHNOLOGIES AG—See Brockhaus Private Equity GmbH; *Int'l*, pg. 1172
BROCK HOLDINGS III, INC.—See Goldberg Lindsay & Co., LLC; *U.S. Private*, pg. 1729
BROCKMAN MINING LIMITED; *Int'l*, pg. 1173
BRONSSTADET AB; *Int'l*, pg. 1174
BROOKFIELD BRASIL, S.A.—See Brookfield Corporation; *Int'l*, pg. 1175
BROOKFIELD BUSINESS PARTNERS L.P.—See Brookfield Corporation; *Int'l*, pg. 1175
BROOKFIELD CORPORATION; *Int'l*, pg. 1174
BROOKFIELD INFRASTRUCTURE PARTNERS L.P.; *Int'l*, pg. 1189
BROOKFIELD MULTIPLEX GROUP LIMITED—See Brookfield Corporation; *Int'l*, pg. 1185
BROOKFIELD OAKTREE HOLDINGS, LLC—See Brookfield Corporation; *Int'l*, pg. 1181
BROOKHOLLOW CORPORATION—See Martin Marietta Materials, Inc.; *U.S. Public*, pg. 1389
BROOKS AUTO SUPPLY INC.; *U.S. Private*, pg. 664
BROOKSTONE HOLDINGS, INC.; *U.S. Private*, pg. 665
BROTHER CORPORATION (ASIA) LTD.—See Brother Industries, Ltd.; *Int'l*, pg. 1196
BROWN & BROWN, INC.; *U.S. Public*, pg. 396
BROWN & BROWN OF BARTLESVILLE, INC.—See Brown & Brown, Inc.; *U.S. Public*, pg. 398
BROWN-DAUB INC.; *U.S. Private*, pg. 669
BROWN-FORMAN CORPORATION; *U.S. Public*, pg. 403
BROWNS CAPITAL PLC; *Int'l*, pg. 1199
BRS VENTURES INVESTMENT LTD; *Int'l*, pg. 1199
BRUCKNER GROUP GMBH; *Int'l*, pg. 1199

551112 — OFFICES OF OTHER HO...   CORPORATE AFFILIATIONS

BRUDERMAN & CO., LLC; *U.S. Private*, pg. 671
BRUNSWICK INTERNATIONAL LIMITED—See Brunswick Corporation; *U.S. Public*, pg. 407
BRYTON MARINE GROUP; *Int'l*, pg. 1201
BSA INDUSTRIES, INC.—See EssilorLuxottica SA; *Int'l*, pg. 2513
B&S GROUP S.A.; *Int'l*, pg. 784
BSM GROUP LIMITED; *Int'l*, pg. 1202
BTC DIGITAL LTD.; *Int'l*, pg. 1204
BT GROUP PLC; *Int'l*, pg. 1202
BT HOLDING AG; *Int'l*, pg. 1204
BTS GROUP HOLDINGS PUBLIC COMPANY LIMITED; *Int'l*, pg. 1205
BTU INTERNATIONAL, INC.—See Amtech Systems, Inc.; *U.S. Public*, pg. 133
THE BUCCINI/POLLIN GROUP, INC.; *U.S. Private*, pg. 4002
BUCHER INDUSTRIES AG; *Int'l*, pg. 1206
BUCKINGHAM & COMPANY; *U.S. Private*, pg. 677
BUCKINGHAM FOUNTAIN LP; *U.S. Private*, pg. 678
BUCKMAN LABORATORIES INTERNATIONAL, INC.—See Bulab Holdings, Inc.; *U.S. Private*, pg. 683
BUCYRUS INTERNATIONAL, INC.—See Caterpillar, Inc.; *U.S. Public*, pg. 450
BUFA GMBH & CO. KG; *Int'l*, pg. 1211
BUFFALO WILD WINGS, INC.—See Roark Capital Group Inc.; *U.S. Private*, pg. 3455
BUFFET CRAMPON HOLDINGS SAS—See Fondations Capital SA; *Int'l*, pg. 2725
BUFFET PARTNERS HOLDING COMPANY, LLC—See Food Management Partners, Inc.; *U.S. Private*, pg. 1561
BUILD-A-BEAR WORKSHOP UK HOLDINGS LTD.—See Build-A-Bear Workshop, Inc.; *U.S. Public*, pg. 409
BUILDERS FIRSTSOURCE, INC.; *U.S. Public*, pg. 409
BUILDERS FIRSTSOURCE - SOUTHEAST GROUP, LLC—See Builders FirstSource, Inc.; *U.S. Public*, pg. 410
BUILDING DREAMSTAR TECHNOLOGY INC.; *Int'l*, pg. 1212
BUKIT SEMBAWANG ESTATES LTD; *Int'l*, pg. 1213
BULAB HOLDINGS, INC.; *U.S. Private*, pg. 683
BULGAR CZECH INVEST HOLDING AD; *Int'l*, pg. 1213
BULGARIA HOLDING CO AD-SOFIA; *Int'l*, pg. 1213
BULGARIAN INVESTMENT HOLDING; *Int'l*, pg. 1213
BULGARSKI TRANSPORTEN HOLDING AD; *Int'l*, pg. 1213
BULL BROS., INC.; *U.S. Private*, pg. 684
BULLFROG AI HOLDINGS, INC.; *U.S. Public*, pg. 410
BULOVA TECHNOLOGIES GROUP, INC.; *U.S. Private*, pg. 685
BULTEN AB; *Int'l*, pg. 1214
BUMRUNGRAD HEALTH NETWORK CO., LTD.—See Bumrungrad Hospital Public Company Limited; *Int'l*, pg. 1215
BUNDABERG SUGAR GROUP LTD.—See Finasucre S.A.; *Int'l*, pg. 2669
BUNGE ARGENTINA S.A.—See Bunge Limited; *U.S. Public*, pg. 411
BUNGE LODERS CROKLAAN GROUP B.V.—See Bunge Limited; *U.S. Public*, pg. 411
BUNGE MEXICO HOLDINGS, INC.—See Bunge Limited; *U.S. Public*, pg. 411
BUNZL PLC; *Int'l*, pg. 1216
BURDA PUBLICATIONS, INC.—See Hubert Burda Media Holding Kommanditgesellschaft; *Int'l*, pg. 3519
BURE EQUITY AB; *Int'l*, pg. 1221
BURELLE S.A.; *Int'l*, pg. 1222
BURGENLAND HOLDING AG—See EVN AG; *Int'l*, pg. 2570
BURGMANN INDUSTRIES HOLDING GMBH—See Freudenberg SE; *Int'l*, pg. 2783
BURLINGTON NORTHERN SANTA FE, LLC—See Berkshire Hathaway Inc.; *U.S. Public*, pg. 303
BURLINGTON STORES, INC.—See Bain Capital, LP; *U.S. Private*, pg. 437
BURNHAM HOLDINGS, INC.; *U.S. Public*, pg. 412
BURNING ROCK BIOTECH LIMITED; *Int'l*, pg. 1226
BUSH O'DONNELL & CO., INC.; *U.S. Private*, pg. 694
BUSHVELD MINERALS LIMITED; *Int'l*, pg. 1228
BUSINESS CONNEXION GROUP LIMITED; *Int'l*, pg. 1228
BUYANG INTERNATIONAL HOLDING INC.; *Int'l*, pg. 1230
B.V. ALGEMENE HOLDING EN FINANCIERINGS MAATSCHAPPIJ—See Assicurazioni Generali S.p.A.; *Int'l*, pg. 645
BVE HOLDING SE; *Int'l*, pg. 1231
BVZ HOLDING AG; *Int'l*, pg. 1231
BWAB, INC.; *U.S. Private*, pg. 700
BWAY CORPORATION—See Stone Canyon Industries, LLC; *U.S. Private*, pg. 3817
BW GROUP LTD.; *Int'l*, pg. 1231
BW MARITIME PTE LTD.—See BW Group Ltd.; *Int'l*, pg. 1231
BWX TECHNOLOGIES, INC.; *U.S. Public*, pg. 413
BYSTRONIC AG; *Int'l*, pg. 1235
C3G, L.P.; *U.S. Private*, pg. 710
C4X DISCOVERY HOLDINGS PLC; *Int'l*, pg. 1245
CABANA HOLDINGS LLC; *U.S. Private*, pg. 710
CABKA GROUP GMBH; *Int'l*, pg. 1245
CABLE MANAGEMENT PRODUCTS LTD.—See ABB Ltd.; *Int'l*, pg. 52

CABLEVISION HOLDING S.A.; *Int'l*, pg. 1246
CABLEVISION SYSTEMS CORPORATION—See Altice USA, Inc.; *U.S. Public*, pg. 87
CABNET HOLDING BERHAD; *Int'l*, pg. 1246
CABOT CREDIT MANAGEMENT GROUP LIMITED—See Encore Capital Group, Inc.; *U.S. Public*, pg. 759
CABOT CREDIT MANAGEMENT LIMITED—See Encore Capital Group, Inc.; *U.S. Public*, pg. 759
CAC HOLDINGS CORPORATION; *Int'l*, pg. 1247
CA CULTURAL TECHNOLOGY GROUP LIMITED; *Int'l*, pg. 1245
CADAC GROUP HOLDING B.V.; *Int'l*, pg. 1247
CADBURY LIMITED—See Mondelez International, Inc.; *U.S. Public*, pg. 1460
CADRE HOLDINGS, INC.; *U.S. Public*, pg. 419
CAESARS ENTERTAINMENT, INC.; *U.S. Public*, pg. 419
CAESARS ENTERTAINMENT WINDSOR HOLDING INC.—See Caesars Entertainment, Inc.; *U.S. Public*, pg. 420
CAESARS GROUP; *Int'l*, pg. 1249
CAESARS GROWTH PARTNERS, LLC—See Caesars Entertainment, Inc.; *U.S. Public*, pg. 420
CAESARS HOLDINGS, INC.—See Caesars Entertainment, Inc.; *U.S. Public*, pg. 419
CAFE DE CORAL HOLDINGS LIMITED; *Int'l*, pg. 1249
CAG HOLDING GMBH; *Int'l*, pg. 1250
CAIANO AS; *Int'l*, pg. 1252
CAIRN UK HOLDINGS LIMITED—See Capricorn Energy PLC; *Int'l*, pg. 1316
CAIRO MEZZ PLC; *Int'l*, pg. 1253
CAISSE DES DEPOTS ET CONSIGNATIONS; *Int'l*, pg. 1257
CAJAVEC A.D.; *Int'l*, pg. 1260
CALATLANTIC GROUP, INC.—See Lennar Corporation; *U.S. Public*, pg. 1305
CALDER DEVELOPMENT ASSOCIATES, INC.; *U.S. Private*, pg. 716
CALEY LTD.—See HSBC Holdings plc; *Int'l*, pg. 3503
CALIBURN INTERNATIONAL CORPORATION; *U.S. Private*, pg. 717
CALIDA HOLDING AG; *Int'l*, pg. 1264
CALIDI BIOTHERAPEUTICS, INC.; *U.S. Public*, pg. 423
CALIDUS HOLDINGS, LLC—See Benjamin Macfarland Company, LLC; *U.S. Private*, pg. 526
CALIFORNIA NEWSPAPERS PARTNERSHIP—See Alden Global Capital LLC; *U.S. Private*, pg. 155
CALIFORNIA TECHNOLOGY VENTURES, LLC; *U.S. Private*, pg. 721
CALIFORNIA WATER SERVICE GROUP; *U.S. Public*, pg. 423
CALLITAS HEALTH INC.; *U.S. Private*, pg. 722
CALSPAN TECHNOLOGY HOLDING CORPORATION; *U.S. Private*, pg. 723
CALTEX AUSTRALIA MANAGEMENT PTY LTD—See Ampol Limited; *Int'l*, pg. 436
CALTRON CASE COMPANY; *U.S. Private*, pg. 724
CALUMET, INC.; *U.S. Public*, pg. 425
CALVALLEY ENERGY LTD.; *Int'l*, pg. 1266
CALVERT HOLDINGS, INC.; *U.S. Private*, pg. 724
CALVERT INVESTMENTS, INC.—See Ameritas Mutual Holding Company; *U.S. Private*, pg. 261
CALVIAS GMBH—See DPE Deutsche Private Equity GmbH; *Int'l*, pg. 2187
CALYX VENTURES INC.; *Int'l*, pg. 1266
CAMARGO CORREA S.A.; *Int'l*, pg. 1267
CAMBIA HEALTH SOLUTIONS, INC.; *U.S. Private*, pg. 725
CAMBIUM NETWORKS CORPORATION; *U.S. Public*, pg. 425
CAMBRAY MUTUAL HOLDING COMPANY; *U.S. Private*, pg. 726
CAMBRIDGE INFORMATION GROUP, INC.; *U.S. Private*, pg. 727
CAMELLIA PLC; *Int'l*, pg. 1270
CAMERON NORGE HOLDING AS—See Schlumberger Limited; *U.S. Public*, pg. 1843
CAMERON THOMSON GROUP LTD.; *Int'l*, pg. 1272
CAMFIN S.P.A.; *Int'l*, pg. 1272
CAMPANIA HOLDING COMPANY, INC.—See The Hanover Insurance Group, Inc.; *U.S. Public*, pg. 2087
CAMPING WORLD HOLDINGS, INC.; *U.S. Public*, pg. 427
CAMPLIFY HOLDINGS LIMITED; *Int'l*, pg. 1275
CAMPOSOL HOLDING PLC; *Int'l*, pg. 1275
CAMSING HEALTHCARE LIMITED; *Int'l*, pg. 1275
CAMUTO LLC—See Schottenstein Stores Corporation; *U.S. Private*, pg. 3569
CANADA GOOSE HOLDINGS INC.—See Bain Capital, LP; *U.S. Private*, pg. 437
CANADA HOUSE WELLNESS GROUP INC.; *Int'l*, pg. 1278
CANADIAN UTILITIES LIMITED—See ATCO Ltd.; *Int'l*, pg. 666
CANAL CORPORATION; *U.S. Private*, pg. 733
CANARGO ENERGY CORPORATION; *Int'l*, pg. 1288
CANARY WHARF GROUP PLC—See Brookfield Corporation; *Int'l*, pg. 1187
CANBURG LIMITED; *Int'l*, pg. 1288
CANCOM SE; *Int'l*, pg. 1288
CANDLE ACQUISITION CORPORATION; *U.S. Private*, pg. 733

CANDYKING HOLDING AB—See Cloetta AB; *Int'l*, pg. 1660
CANFOR CORPORATION; *Int'l*, pg. 1290
CANGEN HOLDINGS, INC.—See Hillenbrand, Inc.; *U.S. Public*, pg. 1037
CANICA AS; *Int'l*, pg. 1291
CANNABIST CO HOLDINGS INC.; *U.S. Public*, pg. 429
CANNAE HOLDINGS, INC.; *U.S. Public*, pg. 429
CANN AMERICAN CORP; *U.S. Public*, pg. 428
CANNERY CASINO RESORTS, LLC; *U.S. Private*, pg. 734
CANNONDALE INVESTMENTS, INC.—See GTCR LLC; *U.S. Private*, pg. 1804
CANOPIUS GROUP LIMTED—See Centerbridge Partners, L.P.; *U.S. Private*, pg. 813
CANTERBURY PARK HOLDING CORPORATION; *U.S. Public*, pg. 430
CANTINE RIUNITE & CIV S.C.AGR.; *Int'l*, pg. 1299
CANUCKS SPORTS & ENTERTAINMENT—See Aquilini Investment Group; *Int'l*, pg. 528
CANUM CAPITAL MANAGEMENT, L.P.; *U.S. Private*, pg. 736
CAPALLIANZ HOLDINGS LIMITED; *Int'l*, pg. 1301
CAPARO GROUP LTD.; *Int'l*, pg. 1301
CAPARO INDUSTRIES PLC—See Caparo Group Ltd.; *Int'l*, pg. 1301
CAPARO PLC—See Caparo Group Ltd.; *Int'l*, pg. 1301
CAPCELLENCE HOLDING GMBH & CO. KG—See Cerberus Capital Management, L.P.; *U.S. Private*, pg. 838
CAPCELLENCE HOLDING GMBH & CO. KG—See Golden-Tree Asset Management LP; *U.S. Private*, pg. 1734
CAPCELLENCE HOLDING GMBH & CO. KG—See J.C. Flowers & Co. LLC; *U.S. Private*, pg. 2159
CAP-CON AUTOMOTIVE TECHNOLOGIES, INC.—See The Jordan Company, L.P.; *U.S. Private*, pg. 4060
CAPE GROUP PTE. LTD.—See Buckthorn Partners LLP; *Int'l*, pg. 1210
CAPE GROUP PTE. LTD.—See OEP Capital Advisors, L.P.; *U.S. Private*, pg. 2997
CAPE PLC—See Altrad Investment Authority SAS; *Int'l*, pg. 398
THE CAPFINANCIAL GROUP, LLC; *U.S. Private*, pg. 4004
CAPGEMINI ASIA PACIFIC—See Capgemini SE; *Int'l*, pg. 1303
CAPGEMINI DEUTSCHLAND HOLDING GMBH—See Capgemini SE; *Int'l*, pg. 1304
CAPGEMINI FRANCE S.A.S.—See Capgemini SE; *Int'l*, pg. 1305
CAPGEMINI NEDERLAND B.V.—See Capgemini SE; *Int'l*, pg. 1306
CAPGEMINI SE; *Int'l*, pg. 1303
CAPITAL A BHD; *Int'l*, pg. 1309
CAPITAL AIRPORTS HOLDING COMPANY (CAH); *Int'l*, pg. 1309
CAPITALAND CHINA HOLDINGS PTE LTD—See CapitaLand Investment Limited; *Int'l*, pg. 1313
CAPITALAND COMMERCIAL TRUST MANAGEMENT LIMITED—See CapitaLand Investment Limited; *Int'l*, pg. 1313
CAPITALAND (VIETNAM) HOLDINGS PTE LTD—See CapitaLand Investment Limited; *Int'l*, pg. 1313
CAPITAL BEVERAGE CORPORATION; *U.S. Private*, pg. 738
CAPITAL CITY HOME LOANS INC.; *U.S. Private*, pg. 739
CAPITAL CLEAN ENERGY CARRIERS CORP.; *Int'l*, pg. 1310
CAPITAL ENVIRONMENT HOLDINGS LIMITED; *Int'l*, pg. 1310
CAPITAL EYE INVESTMENTS LIMITED; *Int'l*, pg. 1310
CAPITAL FINANCE HOLDINGS LIMITED; *Int'l*, pg. 1311
CAPITAL FINANCIAL HOLDINGS, INC.; *U.S. Public*, pg. 431
CAPITAL FUNDING GROUP, INC.; *U.S. Private*, pg. 740
CAPITAL GRAND EST SAS; *Int'l*, pg. 1311
CAPITAL INDUSTRIAL FINANCIAL SERVICES GROUP LIMITED; *Int'l*, pg. 1311
CAPITAL INTERNATIONAL GROUP LIMITED; *Int'l*, pg. 1311
CAPITAL SPORTS GROUP OF COMPANIES; *Int'l*, pg. 1312
CAPITAL WORLD LIMITED; *Int'l*, pg. 1313
CAPITOL AUTO GROUP, INC.; *U.S. Private*, pg. 743
CAPITOL PEAK PARTNERS, LLC; *U.S. Private*, pg. 744
CAPITOL RADIO NETWORK, INC.—See Capitol Broadcasting Company, Inc.; *U.S. Private*, pg. 743
CAPMAN PLC; *Int'l*, pg. 1315
CAPRICORN ENERGY LIMITED—See Capricorn Energy PLC; *Int'l*, pg. 1316
CAPRI HOLDINGS LIMITED; *Int'l*, pg. 1316
CAPSTONE INFRASTRUCTURE CORPORATION—See iCON Infrastructure LLP; *Int'l*, pg. 3583
CAPTII LIMITED; *Int'l*, pg. 1317
CARASENT ASA; *Int'l*, pg. 1319
CARAVELLE SA; *Int'l*, pg. 1320
CARBOLINE CORP.—See RPM International Inc.; *U.S. Public*, pg. 1818
CARDAX, INC.—See Cardax Pharmaceuticals, Inc.; *U.S. Private*, pg. 749
CARDAX PHARMACEUTICALS, INC.; *U.S. Private*, pg. 749

N.A.I.C.S. INDEX

551112 — OFFICES OF OTHER HO...

CARDIFF LEXINGTON CORPORATION; *U.S. Public,* pg. 433
CARDINAL HEALTH, INC.; *U.S. Public,* pg. 433
CARDNO LIMITED; *Int'l,* pg. 1321
CARDTRONICS, INC.—See NCR Voyix Corporation.; *U.S. Public,* pg. 1501
CARDTRONICS PLC—See NCR Voyix Corporation.; *U.S. Public,* pg. 1501
CARECLIX HOLDINGS, INC.; *U.S. Private,* pg. 752
CAREMORE HEALTH GROUP, INC.—See Elevance Health, Inc.; *U.S. Public,* pg. 729
CAREMORE HOLDINGS, INC.—See Elevance Health, Inc.; *U.S. Public,* pg. 729
CARFINCO FINANCIAL GROUP INC.—See Banco Santander, S.A.; *Int'l,* pg. 825
CARGILL INVESTMENTS (CHINA) LTD.—See Cargill, Inc.; *U.S. Private,* pg. 757
CARIBE MEDIA, INC.; *U.S. Private,* pg. 761
CARIBOU CORPORATION; *U.S. Private,* pg. 761
CARL BENNET AB; *Int'l,* pg. 1331
CARLEX GLASS AMERICA, LLC—See Central Glass Co., Ltd.; *Int'l,* pg. 1406
CARLISLE COMPANIES INCORPORATED; *U.S. Public,* pg. 435
CARLIT CO., LTD.; *Int'l,* pg. 1338
CARLO GAVAZZI HOLDING AG; *Int'l,* pg. 1338
CARLO MANAGEMENT CORPORATION; *U.S. Private,* pg. 764
CARLSON COMPANIES INC.; *U.S. Private,* pg. 764
CARLSON RESTAURANTS WORLDWIDE INC.—See Carlson Companies Inc.; *U.S. Private,* pg. 765
CARLUCCIO'S LTD.; *Int'l,* pg. 1341
THE CARLYLE GROUP INC; *U.S. Public,* pg. 2043
CARMEN ANTHONY RESTAURANT GROUP, LLC; *U.S. Private,* pg. 766
CARMIKE CINEMAS, LLC—See Dalian Wanda Group Corporation Ltd.; *Int'l,* pg. 1953
CARNIVAL CORPORATION; *U.S. Public,* pg. 437
CARNIVAL PLC—See Carnival Corporation; *U.S. Public,* pg. 437
CAROLINE HOLDINGS LLC—See Tiptree Inc.; *U.S. Public,* pg. 2159
CARREFOUR CHINA HOLDINGS BV—See Carrefour SA; *Int'l,* pg. 1344
CARREFOUR LATIN AMERICA—See Carrefour SA; *Int'l,* pg. 1344
CARREFOUR SA; *Int'l,* pg. 1343
CARRIER CORPORATION—See Carrier Global Corporation; *U.S. Public,* pg. 440
CARRIER GLOBAL CORPORATION; *U.S. Public,* pg. 440
CARRIS FINANCIAL CORP.; *U.S. Private,* pg. 772
CARRIX, INC.; *U.S. Private,* pg. 772
CARR'S GROUP PLC; *Int'l,* pg. 1343
CARS.COM INC.; *U.S. Public,* pg. 444
CARSGEN THERAPEUTICS HOLDINGS LIMITED; *Int'l,* pg. 1347
CARSON CUMBERBATCH PLC; *Int'l,* pg. 1347
CARTER'S, INC.; *U.S. Public,* pg. 445
CARUSO AFFILIATED; *U.S. Private,* pg. 776
CARVAJAL S.A.; *Int'l,* pg. 1348
CASA HOLDINGS LTD.; *Int'l,* pg. 1349
CASCADE KELLY HOLDINGS LLC—See Global Partners LP; *U.S. Public,* pg. 942
CASCO BAY VENDING ENTERPRISES, LLC; *U.S. Private,* pg. 781
CASCO HOLDINGS GMBH—See Amphenol Corporation; *U.S. Public,* pg. 129
CASE FOODS, INC.; *U.S. Private,* pg. 781
CASIL TELECOMMUNICATIONS HOLDINGS LIMITED; *Int'l,* pg. 1352
CASINOS AUSTRIA INTERNATIONAL HOLDINGS GMBH—See Casinos Austria AG; *Int'l,* pg. 1353
CASI PHARMACEUTICALS, INC.; *Int'l,* pg. 1352
CASTLETON COMMODITIES INTERNATIONAL LLC; *U.S. Private,* pg. 785
CATALENT ITALY HOLDING SRL—See Catalent, Inc.; *U.S. Public,* pg. 448
CATALENT PHARMA SOLUTIONS LIMITED—See Catalent, Inc.; *U.S. Public,* pg. 448
CATALINA HOLDINGS (BERMUDA) LTD.—See Apollo Global Management, Inc.; *U.S. Public,* pg. 148
CATALINA HOLDINGS UK LIMITED—See Apollo Global Management, Inc.; *U.S. Public,* pg. 148
CATALINA RESTAURANT GROUP INC.—See Food Management Partners, Inc.; *U.S. Private,* pg. 1561
CATALOG HOLDINGS, INC.—See Golden Gate Capital Management II, LLC; *U.S. Private,* pg. 1731
CATALYSIS HOLDING CORPORATION; *U.S. Private,* pg. 786
CAT RESOURCE & ASSET HOLDINGS, INC.; *Int'l,* pg. 1358
CAUSAM ENERGY, INC.; *U.S. Private,* pg. 794
CAVALIER BREMWORTH (AUSTRALIA) LIMITED—See Bremworth Limited; *Int'l,* pg. 1145
CAVATINA HOLDING SA; *Int'l,* pg. 1361
CAVMONT CAPITAL HOLDINGS ZAMBIA PLC.; *Int'l,* pg. 1362
CAYMUS EQUITY PARTNERS LLC; *U.S. Private,* pg. 795

CB GROUP MANAGEMENT CO., LTD.; *Int'l,* pg. 1364
CBOCS WEST, INC.—See Cracker Barrel Old Country Store, Inc.; *U.S. Public,* pg. 589
CBOE GLOBAL MARKETS, INC.; *U.S. Public,* pg. 459
CBRE GLOBAL INVESTORS (ASIA PACIFIC) LIMITED—See CBRE Group, Inc.; *U.S. Public,* pg. 460
CBRE GLOBAL INVESTORS EUROPE B.V.—See CBRE Group, Inc.; *U.S. Public,* pg. 460
C.C. CLARK, INC.; *U.S. Private,* pg. 706
CC DUTCH PROPERTY HOLDING B.V.—See Cintas Corporation; *U.S. Public,* pg. 495
CCF HOLDINGS LLC; *U.S. Public,* pg. 461
CCFW, INC.; *U.S. Private,* pg. 799
CCHN GROUP HOLDINGS, INC.—See Frazier & Company, Inc.; *U.S. Private,* pg. 1599
CCHN GROUP HOLDINGS, INC.—See ModivCare, Inc.; *U.S. Public,* pg. 1455
CCMC AFFILIATES, INC.—See Connecticut Children's Medical Center Corporation, Inc.; *U.S. Private,* pg. 1015
CC NEUBERGER PRINCIPAL HOLDINGS I—See CC Capital Partners, LLC; *U.S. Private,* pg. 797
CCO HOLDINGS CAPITAL CORP.—See Charter Communications, Inc.; *U.S. Public,* pg. 483
CCO HOLDINGS, LLC—See Charter Communications, Inc.; *U.S. Public,* pg. 483
C&C ORGANIZATION INC.; *U.S. Private,* pg. 702
CCS MEDICAL HOLDINGS, INC.; *U.S. Private,* pg. 801
CCT FORTIS HOLDINGS LIMITED; *Int'l,* pg. 1369
CCT RAIL SYSTEM CORPORATION; *U.S. Private,* pg. 801
CDC DATA, LLC; *U.S. Private,* pg. 802
CDF INTERNATIONAL COOPERATIEF U.A.; *Int'l,* pg. 1370
CDM HOLDINGS LLC—See Energy Transfer LP; *U.S. Public,* pg. 762
CDM INVESTMENT GROUP, INC.; *U.S. Private,* pg. 802
CDP CAPITAL FINANCING INC.—See Caisse de Depot et Placement du Quebec; *Int'l,* pg. 1253
CDP EQUITY SPA—See Cassa Depositi e Prestiti S.p.A.; *Int'l,* pg. 1354
CDP HOLDINGS, LTD.; *Int'l,* pg. 1371
CDT ENVIRONMENTAL TECHNOLOGY INVESTMENT HOLDINGS LIMITED; *Int'l,* pg. 1371
CDW HOLDING LTD.; *Int'l,* pg. 1372
CEC ENTERTAINMENT, INC.—See Apollo Global Management, Inc.; *U.S. Public,* pg. 148
CECEP COSTIN NEW MATERIALS GROUP LIMITED; *Int'l,* pg. 1372
CECG INTERNATIONAL HOLDINGS, INC.—See Constellation Energy Corporation; *U.S. Public,* pg. 571
CEC INTERNATIONAL HOLDINGS LIMITED; *Int'l,* pg. 1372
CECO GROUP GLOBAL HOLDINGS LLC—See CECO Environmental Corp.; *U.S. Public,* pg. 463
CEDAR AMERICAN RAIL HOLDINGS, INC.—See Canadian Pacific Kansas City Limited; *Int'l,* pg. 1285
CEDAR ENTERPRISES INC.; *U.S. Private,* pg. 804
CEFC ANHUI INTERNATIONAL HOLDING CO., LTD.; *Int'l,* pg. 1389
CEFC CHINA ENERGY COMPANY LIMITED; *Int'l,* pg. 1389
CEFLA S.C.; *Int'l,* pg. 1389
CEF (SOC) LIMITED; *Int'l,* pg. 1389
CEGEDEL PARTICIPATIONS S.A.—See Enovos International S.A.; *Int'l,* pg. 2444
CEGEKA GROEP NV; *Int'l,* pg. 1390
CEGEKA NEDERLAND HOLDING B.V.—See Cegeka Groep NV; *Int'l,* pg. 1391
CE HOLDINGS CO., LTD.; *Int'l,* pg. 1372
CELADON E-COMMERCE, INC.—See Celadon Group, Inc.; *U.S. Public,* pg. 464
CELADON GROUP, INC.; *U.S. Public,* pg. 464
CELANESE GMBH—See Celanese Corporation; *U.S. Public,* pg. 465
CELEBI HOLDING A.S.; *Int'l,* pg. 1391
CELEXUS, INC.; *U.S. Private,* pg. 806
CELLCO PARTNERSHIP—See Verizon Communications Inc.; *U.S. Public,* pg. 2284
THE CELLER ORGANIZATION; *U.S. Private,* pg. 4006
CELL MEDX CORP.; *U.S. Public,* pg. 465
CELLNEX TELECOM, S.A.; *Int'l,* pg. 1394
CELSYS, INC.; *Int'l,* pg. 1396
CELULOSA ARAUCO Y CONSTITUCION S.A.—See AntarChile S.A.; *Int'l,* pg. 481
CEMAT A/S; *Int'l,* pg. 1396
CEMENTIR HOLDING N.V.; *Int'l,* pg. 1397
CEMEX ASIA HOLDINGS LTD.—See CEMEX, S.A.B. de C.V.; *Int'l,* pg. 1398
CEMEX DEUTSCHLAND AG—See CEMEX, S.A.B. de C.V.; *Int'l,* pg. 1398
CEMEX, S.A.B. DE C.V.; *Int'l,* pg. 1398
CEMEX UK MATERIALS LIMITED—See CEMEX, S.A.B. de C.V.; *Int'l,* pg. 1399
CENGAGE LEARNING HOLDINGS II, INC.—See Apax Partners LLP; *Int'l,* pg. 502
CENGAGE LEARNING HOLDINGS II, INC.—See Apollo Global Management, Inc.; *U.S. Public,* pg. 168
CENGAGE LEARNING HOLDINGS II, INC.—See KKR & Co. Inc.; *U.S. Public,* pg. 1256
CENGAGE LEARNING HOLDINGS II, INC.—See Searchlight Capital Partners, L.P.; *U.S. Public,* pg. 3587
CENNTRO ELECTRIC GROUP LIMITED; *Int'l,* pg. 1401

CENOTEC CO., LTD.; *Int'l,* pg. 1401
CENTAMIN EGYPT LIMITED—See Centamin plc; *Int'l,* pg. 1402
CENTAMIN PLC; *Int'l,* pg. 1402
CENTAUR MEDIA PLC; *Int'l,* pg. 1402
CENTEN AG LLC—See Corteva, Inc.; *U.S. Public,* pg. 581
CENTENARY UNITED HOLDINGS LIMITED; *Int'l,* pg. 1402
CENTENNIAL ENERGY HOLDINGS, INC.—See MDU Resources Group, Inc.; *U.S. Public,* pg. 1409
CENTENNIAL HOLDING COMPANY, LLC—See Century Communities, Inc.; *U.S. Public,* pg. 475
CENTESSA PHARMACEUTICALS PLC; *Int'l,* pg. 1403
CENTOGENE N.V.; *Int'l,* pg. 1403
CENTRAIS ELETRICAS BRASILEIRAS S.A.; *Int'l,* pg. 1403
CENTRAIS ELETRICAS DE SANTA CATARINA S.A. - CELESC; *Int'l,* pg. 1403
CENTRAL DEVELOPMENT HOLDINGS LTD.; *Int'l,* pg. 1405
CENTRAL EUROPEAN DISTRIBUTION CORPORATION—See CJSC Russian Standard Corporation; *Int'l,* pg. 1634
CENTRAL GROUP COMPANY LIMITED; *Int'l,* pg. 1407
CENTRAL IOWA ENERGY COOPERATIVE—See Central Iowa Power Cooperative; *U.S. Public,* pg. 822
CENTRAL NETWORK RETAIL GROUP, LLC—See Tyndale Advisors, LLC; *U.S. Private,* pg. 4268
CENTRAL PLAZA HOTEL PUBLIC COMPANY LIMITED; *Int'l,* pg. 1409
CENTRAL STATES INC.; *U.S. Private,* pg. 825
CENTRAL VALLEY MEAT HOLDING COMPANY; *U.S. Private,* pg. 826
CENTRAL WEALTH GROUP HOLDINGS LIMITED; *Int'l,* pg. 1410
CENTRICA PLC; *Int'l,* pg. 1413
CENTRIC HOLDING B.V.; *Int'l,* pg. 1412
CENTRIC NETHERLANDS HOLDING B.V.—See Centric Holding B.V.; *Int'l,* pg. 1412
CENTRICUS PARTNERS LP; *Int'l,* pg. 1413
CENTRUS ENERGY CORP.; *U.S. Public,* pg. 474
CENTURI GROUP, INC.—See Southwest Gas Holdings, Inc.; *U.S. Public,* pg. 1913
CENTURION CORPORATION LIMITED; *Int'l,* pg. 1416
CENTURY ENERGY INTERNATIONAL HOLDINGS LIMITED; *Int'l,* pg. 1418
CENTURY GINWA RETAIL HOLDINGS LIMITED; *Int'l,* pg. 1418
CENTURY II—See Paychex, Inc.; *U.S. Public,* pg. 1655
CENTURY INTERNATIONAL ARMS CORPORATION; *U.S. Private,* pg. 833
CENVEO CORP. - CUSTOM RESALE GROUP—See Cenveo, Inc.; *U.S. Private,* pg. 834
CENVEO, INC.; *U.S. Private,* pg. 834
CEPS PLC; *Int'l,* pg. 1420
CEQUEL COMMUNICATIONS HOLDINGS I, LLC—See Altice USA, Inc.; *U.S. Public,* pg. 88
CEQUEL DATA CENTERS, LLC—See Cequel III, LLC; *U.S. Private,* pg. 835
CEQUEL DATA CENTERS, LLC—See Charterhouse Group, Inc.; *U.S. Private,* pg. 859
CEQUEL DATA CENTERS, LLC—See Thompson Street Capital Manager LLC; *U.S. Private,* pg. 4160
CERA SCRL; *Int'l,* pg. 1421
CEREVEL THERAPEUTICS HOLDINGS, INC.—See AbbVie Inc.; *U.S. Public,* pg. 24
CEREVEL THERAPEUTICS, INC.—See AbbVie Inc.; *U.S. Public,* pg. 24
CERION, LLC—See MW Universal Inc.; *U.S. Private,* pg. 2822
CERIUM HOLDINGS, INC.; *U.S. Private,* pg. 841
CEROS HOLDING AG; *Int'l,* pg. 1422
CERTINA HOLDING AG; *Int'l,* pg. 1423
CERVED GROUP S.P.A—See GIC Pte. Ltd.; *Int'l,* pg. 2964
CES EDUCATION PTE. LTD.—See Chip Eng Seng Corporation Ltd.; *Int'l,* pg. 1572
CES SYNERGIES, INC.; *U.S. Public,* pg. 476
CE STAR HOLDINGS, LLC; *U.S. Private,* pg. 803
CETERA FINANCIAL HOLDINGS, INC.—See Genstar Capital, LLC; *U.S. Private,* pg. 1676
CEVA GROUP PLC—See CMA CGM S.A.; *Int'l,* pg. 1666
CFC GROUP PTY. LTD.; *Int'l,* pg. 1429
CF HOLDING COMPANY, INC.; *U.S. Private,* pg. 843
CFI HOLDING S.A.; *Int'l,* pg. 1429
CFI HOLDINGS LIMITED; *Int'l,* pg. 1429
C.F. JORDAN CONSTRUCTION LLC—See C.F. Jordan L.P.; *U.S. Public,* pg. 707
CFS BRANDS LLC—See The Jordan Company, L.P.; *U.S. Private,* pg. 4060
CGE ENERGY INC.; *U.S. Public,* pg. 477
C&G ENVIRONMENTAL PROTECTION HOLDINGS LIMITED; *Int'l,* pg. 1238
CGG AMERICAS INC.—See CGG; *Int'l,* pg. 1431
CGG DATA SERVICES AG—See CGG; *Int'l,* pg. 1431
CGG SERVICES HOLDING B.V.—See CGG; *Int'l,* pg. 1432
CGG SERVICES HOLDING (LATIN AMERICA) B.V.—See CGG; *Int'l,* pg. 1432
CGG; *Int'l,* pg. 1431
CGI LIMITED—See CGI Inc.; *Int'l,* pg. 1433
CGN MINING CO. LTD.; *Int'l,* pg. 1434

CGNPC URANIUM RESOURCES CO., LTD.—See China Guangdong Nuclear Power Holding Co., Ltd.; *Int'l*, pg. 1506
CGRH, LLC—See Graham Holdings Company; *U.S. Public*, pg. 954
CHAILEASE HOLDING COMPANY LIMITED; *Int'l*, pg. 1436
CHALLENGER LIFE HOLDINGS PTY LIMITED—See Challenger Limited; *Int'l*, pg. 1438
CHALMERS GROUP OF COMPANIES; *Int'l*, pg. 1438
CHAMAK HOLDINGS LTD.; *Int'l*, pg. 1439
CHAMBERLIN PLC; *Int'l*, pg. 1439
CHAM GROUP AG; *Int'l*, pg. 1439
CHAMPION ENTERPRISES HOLDINGS, LLC—See Champion Homes, Inc.; *U.S. Public*, pg. 477
CHAMPION HOMES, INC.; *U.S. Public*, pg. 477
CHANDLER CORPORATION; *Int'l*, pg. 1441
CHANGCHUN GROUP; *Int'l*, pg. 1442
CHANGDA INTERNATIONAL HOLDINGS, INC.; *Int'l*, pg. 1443
CHANGFENG (GROUP) CO., LTD.; *Int'l*, pg. 1443
CHANGSHA TONGCHENG HOLDINGS CO., LTD.; *Int'l*, pg. 1444
CHANGSHENG INTERNATIONAL GROUP LIMITED; *U.S. Private*, pg. 848
CHANNEL MICRON HOLDINGS COMPANY LIMITED; *Int'l*, pg. 1446
CHANSON INTERNATIONAL HOLDING; *Int'l*, pg. 1446
CHAOJU EYE CARE HOLDINGS LIMITED; *Int'l*, pg. 1447
CHAPMAN AUTOMOTIVE GROUP LLC; *U.S. Private*, pg. 849
CHAPS HOLDING SAS; *Int'l*, pg. 1448
CHARISMA ENERGY SERVICES LIMITED; *Int'l*, pg. 1450
THE CHARLES SCHWAB CORPORATION; *U.S. Public*, pg. 2058
CHARLWOOD PACIFIC GROUP; *Int'l*, pg. 1450
CHARMACY PHARMACEUTICAL CO., LTD.; *Int'l*, pg. 1451
CHARMWELL HOLDINGS LTD.; *Int'l*, pg. 1451
CHAROEN POKPHAND FOODS PUBLIC COMPANY LIMITED; *Int'l*, pg. 1451
CHAROEN POKPHAND GROUP CO., LTD.; *Int'l*, pg. 1453
CHARTER LTD.—See Enovis Corporation; *U.S. Public*, pg. 770
CHASWOOD RESOURCES HOLDINGS LTD.; *Int'l*, pg. 1457
C.H. BOEHRINGER SOHN AG & CO. KG; *Int'l*, pg. 1240
CHELCO GROUP OF COMPANIES INC.; *U.S. Private*, pg. 869
CHELSEA FC PLC—See Clearlake Capital Group, L.P.; *U.S. Private*, pg. 933
CHELSEY DIRECT, LLC; *U.S. Private*, pg. 870
CHELTON INC.—See Advent International Corporation; *U.S. Private*, pg. 99
CHEMICAINVEST HOLDING B.V.—See CVC Capital Partners SICAV-FIS S.A.; *Int'l*, pg. 1886
CHEMICAL EXCHANGE INDUSTRIES, INC.; *U.S. Private*, pg. 871
CHEMICAL INDUSTRIES (FAR EAST) LTD.; *Int'l*, pg. 1461
CHEMITHON ENTERPRISES, INC.; *U.S. Private*, pg. 872
CHEMTRADE LOGISTICS INCOME FUND; *Int'l*, pg. 1464
CHEM-TREND HOLDING LP—See Freudenberg SE; *Int'l*, pg. 2782
CH ENERGY GROUP, INC.—See Fortis Inc.; *Int'l*, pg. 2739
CHENGDU TIANQI INDUSTRY (GROUP) CO., LTD.; *Int'l*, pg. 1469
CHEN HSONG HOLDINGS LTD.; *Int'l*, pg. 1464
CHENIERE CORPUS CHRISTI HOLDINGS, LLC; *U.S. Private*, pg. 872
CHENIERE ENERGY PARTNERS LP HOLDINGS, LLC—See Cheniere Energy, Inc.; *U.S. Public*, pg. 485
CHEN LIN EDUCATION GROUP HOLDINGS LIMITED; *Int'l*, pg. 1465
CHEROKEE NATION BUSINESSES; *U.S. Private*, pg. 873
CHERVON HOLDINGS LIMITED; *Int'l*, pg. 1472
CHESAPEAKE INVESTMENT COMPANY—See Chesapeake Utilities Corporation; *U.S. Public*, pg. 485
CHESAPEAKE LOUISANA, L.P—See Expand Energy Corporation; *U.S. Public*, pg. 808
CHESNARA PLC; *Int'l*, pg. 1472
CHETTINAD GROUP OF COMPANIES; *Int'l*, pg. 1473
CHEVALIER INTERNATIONAL HOLDINGS LIMITED; *Int'l*, pg. 1473
CHEVROLET EUROPE GMBH—See General Motors Company; *U.S. Public*, pg. 926
CHEYNET S.A.S; *Int'l*, pg. 1474
CHICAGO BRIDGE & IRON COMPANY N.V.—See McDermott International, Inc.; *U.S. Public*, pg. 1404
CHICAGO BRIDGE & IRON COMPANY—See McDermott International, Inc.; *U.S. Public*, pg. 1405
CHICAGO PIZZA HOSPITALITY HOLDING, INC.—See BJ'S RESTAURANTS, INC.; *U.S. Public*, pg. 340
CHICAGO PUBLIC MEDIA, INC.; *U.S. Private*, pg. 879
CHICAGO TRIBUNE COMPANY, LLC—See Tribune Publishing Company; *U.S. Private*, pg. 4227
CHICKASAW HOLDING COMPANY; *U.S. Private*, pg. 880
CHICKASAW NATION INDUSTRIES, INC.—See The Chickasaw Nation; *U.S. Private*, pg. 4008
CHICO'S FAS, INC.—See Sycamore Partners Management, LP; *U.S. Private*, pg. 3895

CHI KAN HOLDINGS LIMITED; *Int'l*, pg. 1475
CHILLED & FROZEN LOGISTICS HOLDING CO., LTD.; *Int'l*, pg. 1478
CHIME COMMUNICATIONS LIMITED—See Providence Equity Partners L.L.C.; *U.S. Private*, pg. 3291
CHI MEI GROUP; *Int'l*, pg. 1475
CHIMIMPORT AD; *Int'l*, pg. 1479
CHINA AGRI-INDUSTRIES HOLDINGS LIMITED—See COFCO Limited; *Int'l*, pg. 1692
CHINA ASIA VALLEY GROUP LIMITED; *Int'l*, pg. 1483
CHINA ASSURANCE FINANCE GROUP LIMITED; *Int'l*, pg. 1483
CHINA AUTOMOBILE NEW RETAIL (HOLDINGS) LIMITED; *Int'l*, pg. 1484
CHINA AUTOMOBILE PARTS HOLDINGS LIMITED; *Int'l*, pg. 1484
CHINA BAOLI TECHNOLOGIES HOLDINGS LTD.; *Int'l*, pg. 1485
CHINA BAOWU STEEL GROUP CORP., LTD.; *Int'l*, pg. 1485
CHINA BIOTECH SERVICES HOLDINGS LIMITED; *Int'l*, pg. 1487
CHINA BOZZA DEVELOPMENT HOLDINGS LIMITED; *Int'l*, pg. 1487
CHINA BPIC SURVEYING INSTRUMENTS AG; *Int'l*, pg. 1487
CHINA BRILLIANT GLOBAL LIMITED; *Int'l*, pg. 1487
CHINACACHE INTERNATIONAL HOLDINGS LTD.; *Int'l*, pg. 1568
CHINA CARBON NEUTRAL DEVELOPMENT GROUP LIMITED; *Int'l*, pg. 1487
CHINA CBM GROUP COMPANY LIMITED; *Int'l*, pg. 1488
CHINA CITY INFRASTRUCTURE GROUP LIMITED; *Int'l*, pg. 1489
CHINA CONCENTRIC CAPITAL GROUP, INC.; *U.S. Private*, pg. 885
CHINA CONCH ENVIRONMENT PROTECTION HOLDINGS LIMITED; *Int'l*, pg. 1491
CHINA CONCH VENTURE HOLDINGS LIMITED; *Int'l*, pg. 1491
CHINA COSCO SHIPPING CORPORATION LIMITED; *Int'l*, pg. 1491
CHINA CRYSTAL NEW MATERIAL HOLDINGS CO., LTD; *Int'l*, pg. 1496
CHINA CYTS TOURS HOLDING CO., LTD.; *Int'l*, pg. 1496
CHINA DILI GROUP; *Int'l*, pg. 1498
CHINA EAST EDUCATION HOLDINGS LIMITED; *Int'l*, pg. 1498
CHINA ECO-MATERIALS GROUP CO., LIMITED; *Int'l*, pg. 1498
CHINAEDU HOLDINGS LTD.; *Int'l*, pg. 1568
CHINA ELECTRONICS CORPORATION; *Int'l*, pg. 1499
CHINA ENERGY RESERVE & CHEMICALS GROUP CO., LTD.; *Int'l*, pg. 1500
CHINA ENTERPRISES LIMITED; *Int'l*, pg. 1500
CHINA ENVIRONMENTAL ENERGY INVESTMENT LIMITED; *Int'l*, pg. 1500
CHINA EVERBRIGHT GROUP LIMITED; *Int'l*, pg. 1501
CHINA EVERBRIGHT LIMITED—See China Everbright Group Limited; *Int'l*, pg. 1501
CHINA EVERGRANDE GROUP; *Int'l*, pg. 1501
CHINA FINANCE INVESTMENT HOLDINGS LIMITED; *Int'l*, pg. 1502
CHINA FINANCIAL INTERNATIONAL INVESTMENTS LIMITED; *Int'l*, pg. 1502
CHINA FINANCIAL LEASING GROUP LIMITED; *Int'l*, pg. 1502
CHINA FINANCIAL SERVICES HOLDINGS LIMITED; *Int'l*, pg. 1502
CHINA FOODS HOLDINGS LTD.; *Int'l*, pg. 1503
CHINA FOODS LIMITED—See COFCO Limited; *Int'l*, pg. 1692
CHINA FORTUNE INVESTMENTS (HOLDING) LIMITED; *Int'l*, pg. 1503
CHINA GAS HOLDINGS LIMITED; *Int'l*, pg. 1503
CHINA GAS INDUSTRY INVESTMENT HOLDINGS CO., LTD.; *Int'l*, pg. 1504
CHINA GENERAL TECHNOLOGY (GROUP) HOLDING CO., LTD.; *Int'l*, pg. 1504
CHINA GREAT LAND HOLDINGS LTD.; *Int'l*, pg. 1505
CHINA GREAT STAR INTERNATIONAL LIMITED; *Int'l*, pg. 1505
CHINA GUANGDONG NUCLEAR POWER HOLDING CO., LTD.; *Int'l*, pg. 1506
CHINA GUODIAN CORPORATION; *Int'l*, pg. 1506
CHINA HAOHUA CHEMICAL GROUP CO., LTD.—See China National Chemical Corporation; *Int'l*, pg. 1526
CHINA HAO RAN RECYCLING CO., LTD.; *Int'l*, pg. 1506
CHINA HEALTHWISE HOLDINGS LIMITED; *Int'l*, pg. 1507
CHINA HI-TECH GROUP CORPORATION; *Int'l*, pg. 1507
CHINA HONGGUANG HOLDINGS LIMITED; *Int'l*, pg. 1508
CHINA-HONG KONG PHOTO PRODUCTS HOLDINGS LIMITED; *Int'l*, pg. 1568
CHINA HUANENG GROUP CO., LTD.; *Int'l*, pg. 1509
CHINA HUIRONG FINANCIAL HOLDINGS LIMITED; *Int'l*, pg. 1509
CHINA INDEX HOLDINGS LIMITED; *Int'l*, pg. 1509
CHINA INDUSTRIAL STEEL INC.; *U.S. Public*, pg. 489

CHINA INTERNATIONAL HOLDINGS LIMITED; *Int'l*, pg. 1510
CHINA INVESTMENTS HOLDINGS LIMITED; *Int'l*, pg. 1513
CHINA JICHENG HOLDINGS LIMITED; *Int'l*, pg. 1513
CHINA KELI ELECTRIC COMPANY LTD.; *Int'l*, pg. 1514
CHINA KINGHO ENERGY GROUP CO., LTD.; *Int'l*, pg. 1514
CHINA KUNDA TECHNOLOGY HOLDINGS LIMITED; *Int'l*, pg. 1514
CHINA LIBERAL EDUCATION HOLDINGS LIMITED; *Int'l*, pg. 1514
CHINA LONGYI GROUP INTERNATIONAL HOLDINGS LIMITED; *Int'l*, pg. 1515
CHINA MEDIA INC.; *Int'l*, pg. 1518
CHINA MEIDONG AUTO HOLDINGS LIMITED; *Int'l*, pg. 1519
CHINA MERCHANTS GROUP LIMITED; *Int'l*, pg. 1520
CHINA MERCHANTS HOLDINGS (PACIFIC) LIMITED—See China Merchants Group Limited; *Int'l*, pg. 1520
CHINA MERCHANTS PORT GROUP CO., LTD.—See China Merchants Group Limited; *Int'l*, pg. 1521
CHINA MERCHANTS SHEKOU INDUSTRIAL ZONE HOLDINGS CO., LTD.; *Int'l*, pg. 1523
CHINA MERCHANTS TECHNOLOGY HOLDINGS CO., LTD.—See China Merchants Group Limited; *Int'l*, pg. 1521
CHINA METALLURGICAL GROUP CORPORATION—See China Rare Earth Resources And Technology Co., Ltd.; *Int'l*, pg. 1545
CHINA METRO-RURAL HOLDINGS LIMITED; *Int'l*, pg. 1524
CHINA MINING INTERNATIONAL LIMITED; *Int'l*, pg. 1524
CHINA MINSHENG INVESTMENT GROUP CORP., LTD.; *Int'l*, pg. 1524
CHINA MOBILE COMMUNICATIONS CORPORATION; *Int'l*, pg. 1524
CHINA MOBILE GAMES & ENTERTAINMENT GROUP LIMITED—See Changjiang Securities Company Limited; *Int'l*, pg. 1443
CHINA MOTION HOLDINGS LIMITED—See Hua Yin International Holdings Ltd.; *Int'l*, pg. 3510
CHINA MOTION UNITED TELECOM LIMITED—See Hua Yin International Holdings Ltd.; *Int'l*, pg. 3510
CHINA NATIONAL AVIATION HOLDING COMPANY; *Int'l*, pg. 1525
CHINA NATIONAL BUILDING MATERIAL GROUP CO., LTD.; *Int'l*, pg. 1525
CHINA NATIONAL CHEMICAL CORPORATION; *Int'l*, pg. 1526
CHINA NATIONAL NUCLEAR CORPORATION; *Int'l*, pg. 1532
CHINA NATIONAL PETROLEUM CORPORATION; *Int'l*, pg. 1533
CHINA NATURAL RESOURCES, INC.; *Int'l*, pg. 1534
CHINA NETCOM TECHNOLOGY HOLDINGS LIMITED; *Int'l*, pg. 1534
CHINA NEW TOWN DEVELOPMENT COMPANY LIMITED; *Int'l*, pg. 1535
CHINA NORTH INDUSTRIES GROUP CORPORATION; *Int'l*, pg. 1535
CHINA NUTRIFRUIT GROUP LIMITED; *Int'l*, pg. 1536
CHINA OCEAN GROUP DEVELOPMENT LIMITED; *Int'l*, pg. 1536
CHINA OCEANWIDE HOLDINGS GROUP CO., LTD.; *Int'l*, pg. 1536
CHINA OCEANWIDE HOLDINGS LTD.—See China Oceanwide Holdings Group Co., Ltd.; *Int'l*, pg. 1538
CHINA OILFIELD SERVICES LIMITED—See China National Offshore Oil Corp.; *Int'l*, pg. 1532
CHINA ORIENTED INTERNATIONAL HOLDINGS LIMITED; *Int'l*, pg. 1538
CHINA OUTFITTERS HOLDINGS LTD.; *Int'l*, pg. 1538
CHINA OVERSEAS PROPERTY HOLDINGS LTD.; *Int'l*, pg. 1539
CHINA PETROCHEMICAL CORPORATION; *Int'l*, pg. 1539
CHINA PETROLEUM & CHEMICAL CORPORATION—See China Petrochemical Corporation; *Int'l*, pg. 1539
CHINA PHARMA HOLDINGS, INC.; *Int'l*, pg. 1540
CHINA PRIMARY ENERGY HOLDINGS LIMITED; *Int'l*, pg. 1542
CHINA RAILWAY GROUP LIMITED; *Int'l*, pg. 1543
CHINA RAILWAY SIGNAL & COMMUNICATION CORPORATION LTD.; *Int'l*, pg. 1544
CHINA RARE EARTH HOLDINGS LIMITED; *Int'l*, pg. 1544
CHINA REGENERATIVE MEDICINE INTERNATIONAL CO., LTD.; *Int'l*, pg. 1547
CHINA RESOURCES BEER (HOLDINGS) COMPANY LIMITED—See China Resources (Holdings) Co., Ltd.; *Int'l*, pg. 1547
CHINA RESOURCES GAS GROUP LIMITED—See China Resources (Holdings) Co., Ltd.; *Int'l*, pg. 1548
CHINA RESOURCES (HOLDINGS) CO., LTD.; *Int'l*, pg. 1547
CHINA RESOURCES MICROELECTRONICS LTD.—See China Resources (Holdings) Co., Ltd.; *Int'l*, pg. 1548
CHINA RESOURCES POWER HOLDINGS CO., LTD.—See China Resources (Holdings) Co., Ltd.; *Int'l*, pg. 1548

CHINA RESOURCES RETAIL (GROUP) CO., LTD.—See China Resources (Holdings) Co., Ltd.; *Int'l*, pg. 1548
CHINA RESOURCES SNOW BREWERIES LTD.—See China Resources (Holdings) Co., Ltd.; *Int'l*, pg. 1547
CHINA RESOURCES TEXTILES (HOLDINGS) CO., LTD.—See China Resources (Holdings) Co., Ltd.; *Int'l*, pg. 1548
CHINA RONGZHONG FINANCIAL HOLDINGS CO. LTD.; *Int'l*, pg. 1549
CHINA SAFTOWER INTERNATIONAL HOLDING GROUP LIMITED; *Int'l*, pg. 1549
CHINA SCE GROUP HOLDINGS LIMITED; *Int'l*, pg. 1549
CHINA SHUIFA SINGYES ENERGY HOLDINGS LIMITED; *Int'l*, pg. 1551
CHINA SHUN KE LONG HOLDINGS LTD.—See CCOOP Group Co., Ltd.; *Int'l*, pg. 1369
CHINA SINOSTAR GROUP COMPANY LIMITED; *Int'l*, pg. 1552
CHINA SMARTPAY GROUP HOLDINGS LIMITED; *Int'l*, pg. 1552
CHINA STARCH HOLDINGS LTD.; *Int'l*, pg. 1553
CHINA TAIPING INSURANCE HOLDINGS COMPANY LIMITED; *Int'l*, pg. 1557
CHINA TANGSHANG HOLDINGS LIMITED; *Int'l*, pg. 1557
CHINA TECHNOLOGY INDUSTRY GROUP LIMITED; *Int'l*, pg. 1557
CHINA TELECOM CORPORATION LIMITED—See China Telecommunications Corporation; *Int'l*, pg. 1557
CHINA TELECOMMUNICATIONS CORPORATION; *Int'l*, pg. 1557
CHINA TELETECH HOLDING, INC.; *Int'l*, pg. 1558
CHINA THREE GORGES BRASIL ENERGIA LTDA.—See China Three Gorges Corporation; *Int'l*, pg. 1558
CHINA TING GROUP HOLDINGS LIMITED; *Int'l*, pg. 1559
CHINA TRENDS HOLDINGS LIMITED; *Int'l*, pg. 1561
CHINA TRUSTFUL GROUP LIMITED; *Int'l*, pg. 1561
CHINA UNION HOLDINGS LTD.; *Int'l*, pg. 1561
CHINA UNITED NETWORK COMMUNICATIONS GROUP COMPANY LIMITED; *Int'l*, pg. 1561
CHINA UNITED VENTURE INVESTMENT LIMITED; *Int'l*, pg. 1561
CHINA UPTOWN GROUP COMPANY LIMITED; *Int'l*, pg. 1561
CHINA VITUP HEALTH CARE HOLDINGS, INC.; *Int'l*, pg. 1562
CHINA WAFER LEVEL CSP CO., LTD.; *Int'l*, pg. 1562
CHINA YIDA HOLDING, CO.; *Int'l*, pg. 1564
CHINA YOUNGMAN AUTOMOBILE GROUP CO., LTD.; *Int'l*, pg. 1565
CHINA YUCHAI INTERNATIONAL LIMITED—See Hong Leong Investment Holdings Pte. Ltd.; *Int'l*, pg. 3468
CHINA ZHONGDI DAIRY HOLDINGS COMPANY LIMITED; *Int'l*, pg. 1567
CHINDATA GROUP HOLDINGS LIMITED—See Bain Capital, LP; *U.S. Private*, pg. 431
CHINESE ENERGY HOLDINGS LIMITED; *Int'l*, pg. 1569
CHINESE FOOD & BEVERAGE GROUP LIMITED; *Int'l*, pg. 1569
CHINESE STRATEGIC HOLDINGS LIMITED; *Int'l*, pg. 1569
CHINLINK INTERNATIONAL HOLDINGS LIMITED; *Int'l*, pg. 1570
CHINNEY INVESTMENTS, LIMITED; *Int'l*, pg. 1570
CHINNEY KIN WING HOLDINGS LTD.—See Chinney Alliance Group Limited; *Int'l*, pg. 1570
CHINT GROUP CORPORATION; *Int'l*, pg. 1571
CHINYANG HOLDINGS CORPORATION; *Int'l*, pg. 1571
CHIP GANASSI RACING TEAMS, INC.; *U.S. Private*, pg. 886
CHIQUITA BRANDS INTERNATIONAL SARL—See Banco Safra S.A.; *Int'l*, pg. 824
CHIRAL QUEST CORP.; *U.S. Private*, pg. 886
CHISHOLM ENERGY HOLDINGS, LLC—See Warburg Pincus LLC; *U.S. Private*, pg. 4437
C.H. JAMES RESTAURANT HOLDINGS, LLC; *U.S. Private*, pg. 707
CHLORIDE GROUP PLC—See Vertiv Holdings Co; *U.S. Public*, pg. 2288
CH MEDIA HOLDING AG; *Int'l*, pg. 1435
CHOBANI INC.; *U.S. Private*, pg. 887
CHOCOLADEFABRIKEN LINDT & SPRUNGLI AG; *Int'l*, pg. 1576
CHOICE FOOD GROUP, INC.; *U.S. Private*, pg. 888
CHOLAMANDALAM FINANCIAL HOLDINGS LIMITED; *Int'l*, pg. 1578
CHONG FAI JEWELLERY GROUP HOLDINGS COMPANY LIMITED; *Int'l*, pg. 1578
CHONGQING CASIN GROUP CO., LTD.; *Int'l*, pg. 1579
CHONGQING HELICOPTER INVESTMENT CO. LTD.; *Int'l*, pg. 1579
CHONGQING MACHINERY & ELECTRONICS HOLDING (GROUP) CO., LTD.; *Int'l*, pg. 1580
CHOO CHOO PARTNERS L.P.; *U.S. Private*, pg. 888
CHORUS AVIATION INC.; *Int'l*, pg. 1584
CHOW ENERGY PUBLIC COMPANY LIMITED; *Int'l*, pg. 1584
CHOWGULE & COMPANY PVT. LTD.; *Int'l*, pg. 1585
CHOW TAI FOOK ENTERPRISES LIMITED; *Int'l*, pg. 1584
CHOW TAI FOOK JEWELLERY GROUP LIMITED—See Chow Tai Fook Enterprises Limited; *Int'l*, pg. 1584
CHR GROUP LLC; *U.S. Private*, pg. 889
CHRISTCHURCH CITY HOLDINGS LTD.; *Int'l*, pg. 1585
CHRISTIE'S INTERNATIONAL PLC—See Financiere Pinault SCA; *Int'l*, pg. 2668
CHRISTOF HOLDING AG; *Int'l*, pg. 1587
C.H. ROBINSON EUROPE B.V.—See C.H. Robinson Worldwide, Inc.; *U.S. Public*, pg. 414
C.H. ROBINSON WORLDWIDE, INC.; *U.S. Public*, pg. 414
CHROMADEX CORPORATION; *U.S. Public*, pg. 490
CHRYSAOR HOLDING LIMITED—See Harbour Energy plc; *Int'l*, pg. 3271
CHS CAPITAL LLC; *U.S. Private*, pg. 893
CHS INC.; *U.S. Public*, pg. 490
CHUBB GROUP MANAGEMENT & HOLDINGS LTD.—See Chubb Limited; *Int'l*, pg. 1590
CHUBB HOLDINGS AUSTRALIA PTY LIMITED—See Chubb Limited; *Int'l*, pg. 1592
CHUBB INA HOLDINGS INC.—See Chubb Limited; *Int'l*, pg. 1590
CHUBB INSURANCE S.A.-N.V.—See Chubb Limited; *Int'l*, pg. 1592
CHUBB LIMITED; *Int'l*, pg. 1590
CHUBB SECURITY HOLDINGS AUSTRALIA PTY LTD—See Carrier Global Corporation; *U.S. Public*, pg. 441
CHUBU-NIPPON BROADCASTING CO., LTD.; *Int'l*, pg. 1594
CHU KONG SHIPPING ENTERPRISES (HOLDING) CO. LTD.; *Int'l*, pg. 1589
CHURCHILL INDUSTRIES, INC.—See Churchill Equity, Inc.; *U.S. Private*, pg. 895
CHUY'S HOLDINGS, INC.—See Darden Restaurants, Inc.; *U.S. Public*, pg. 633
CHYY DEVELOPMENT GROUP LIMITED; *Int'l*, pg. 1600
CIA DE INVERSIONES LA ESPANOLA SA; *Int'l*, pg. 1601
CIBA HOLDING AG—See BASF SE; *Int'l*, pg. 882
CIBA SPECIALTY CHEMICALS HOLDING INC.—See BASF SE; *Int'l*, pg. 883
CIBC (U.K.) HOLDINGS LIMITED—See Canadian Imperial Bank of Commerce; *Int'l*, pg. 1602
CIBER HOLDING GMBH—See HTC Global Services Inc.; *U.S. Private*, pg. 1999
CIC HOLDINGS LIMITED; *Int'l*, pg. 1602
CIDB INVENTURES SDN BHD—See IJM Corporation Berhad; *Int'l*, pg. 3608
CIDEON HOLDING GMBH & CO. KG—See Friedhelm Loh Stiftung & Co. KG; *Int'l*, pg. 2791
CIE FINANCIERE DE L'OUEST AFRICAIN SA; *Int'l*, pg. 1605
CIFC CORP.—See Centricus Partners LP; *Int'l*, pg. 1413
CIFC LLC—See Centricus Partners LP; *Int'l*, pg. 1413
CIFI HOLDINGS (GROUP) CO. LTD.; *Int'l*, pg. 1605
CI FINANCIAL CORPORATION; *Int'l*, pg. 1600
CIFIN S.R.L.; *Int'l*, pg. 1605
THE CIGARETTE STORE CORP.; *U.S. Public*, pg. 4010
CIGNA GLOBAL HOLDINGS, INC.—See The Cigna Group; *U.S. Public*, pg. 2060
THE CIGNA GROUP; *U.S. Public*, pg. 2059
CIGNA HOLDING COMPANY—See The Cigna Group; *U.S. Public*, pg. 2060
CIGNA HOLDINGS, INC.—See The Cigna Group; *U.S. Public*, pg. 2060
C&I HOLDINGS INC.; *U.S. Public*, pg. 703
CILAG HOLDING AG—See Johnson & Johnson; *U.S. Public*, pg. 1196
CIL HOLDINGS LIMITED; *Int'l*, pg. 1607
CIMC ENRIC TANK & PROCESS B.V.—See China International Marine Containers (Group) Co., Ltd.; *Int'l*, pg. 1511
CIMCOOL EUROPE B.V.—See Altas Partners LP; *Int'l*, pg. 386
CIMIC GROUP LIMITED—See ACS, Actividades de Construccion y Servicios, S.A.; *Int'l*, pg. 112
CIMPOR BETAO - SOCIEDADE GESTORA DE PARTICIPACOES SOCIAIS S.A.—See Camargo Correa S.A.; *Int'l*, pg. 1267
CIMPOR BRASIL PARTICIPACOES LTDA—See Camargo Correa S.A.; *Int'l*, pg. 1267
CIMPOR INTERNACIONAL SGPS S.A.—See Camargo Correa S.A.; *Int'l*, pg. 1268
CIMPOR INVESTIMENTOS SGPS S.A.—See Camargo Correa S.A.; *Int'l*, pg. 1268
CIMPRESS PLC; *Int'l*, pg. 1609
CINCINNATI BANCORP, INC.—See LCNB Corp.; *U.S. Public*, pg. 1296
CINCINNATI FINANCIAL CORPORATION; *U.S. Public*, pg. 494
CINDERELLA TARGET VALUE ZONES INC.; *U.S. Public*, pg. 495
CINEDIGM ENTERTAINMENT HOLDINGS, LLC—See Cineverse Corp.; *U.S. Public*, pg. 495
CINEMARK HOLDINGS, INC.; *U.S. Public*, pg. 495
CINEPLEX INC.; *Int'l*, pg. 1610
CINER GROUP; *Int'l*, pg. 1610
CINGULATE INC.; *U.S. Public*, pg. 495
CINIUM FINANCIAL SERVICES CORPORATION; *U.S. Private*, pg. 898
CIRCLE HEALTH HOLDINGS LIMITED—See Centene Corporation; *U.S. Public*, pg. 468
CIRCLE INTERNATIONAL HOLDINGS LIMITED; *Int'l*, pg. 1617
CIR S.P.A.—See Compagnia Finanziaria de Benedetti S.p.A.; *Int'l*, pg. 1721
CIRTEK HOLDINGS LIMITED; *Int'l*, pg. 1618
CIRTEK HOLDINGS PHILIPPINES CORP.; *Int'l*, pg. 1618
CISCO ISH B.V.—See Cisco Systems, Inc.; *U.S. Public*, pg. 497
CISCOM CORP.; *Int'l*, pg. 1618
CISCO NORWAY HOLDINGS AS—See Cisco Systems, Inc.; *U.S. Public*, pg. 497
CITADEL COMMUNICATIONS LLC; *U.S. Private*, pg. 901
CITAGLOBAL BERHAD; *Int'l*, pg. 1619
CITIBASE HOLDINGS PLC; *Int'l*, pg. 1619
CITIC ENVIROTECH LTD—See CITIC Group Corporation; *Int'l*, pg. 1620
CITIC GROUP CORPORATION; *Int'l*, pg. 1619
CITIC HONG KONG (HOLDINGS) LTD.—See CITIC Group Corporation; *Int'l*, pg. 1620
CITIC INDUSTRIAL INVESTMENT GROUP CORP., LTD.—See CITIC Group Corporation; *Int'l*, pg. 1620
CITIC INVESTMENT HOLDINGS LTD.—See CITIC Group Corporation; *Int'l*, pg. 1620
CITIC LTD.—See CITIC Group Corporation; *Int'l*, pg. 1620
CITIC SECURITIES CO., LTD.; *Int'l*, pg. 1622
CITIC TIANJIN INVESTMENT HOLDING CO., LTD.—See CITIC Group Corporation; *Int'l*, pg. 1621
CITIGROUP GLOBAL MARKETS ASIA LIMITED—See Citigroup Inc.; *U.S. Public*, pg. 503
CITIGROUP GLOBAL MARKETS EUROPE FINANCE LIMITED—See Citigroup Inc.; *U.S. Public*, pg. 503
CITIGROUP GLOBAL MARKETS FINANCE CORPORATION & CO. BESCHRANKT HAFTENDE KG—See Citigroup Inc.; *U.S. Public*, pg. 502
CITIGROUP GLOBAL MARKETS HOLDINGS, INC.—See Citigroup Inc.; *U.S. Public*, pg. 503
CITIGROUP GLOBAL MARKETS SWITZERLAND HOLDING GMBH—See Citigroup Inc.; *U.S. Public*, pg. 503
CITI OVERSEAS INVESTMENTS BAHAMAS INC.—See Citigroup Inc.; *U.S. Public*, pg. 502
CITI VENTURES, INC.—See Citigroup Inc.; *U.S. Public*, pg. 502
CITIZEN MACHINERY EUROPE GMBH—See Citizen Watch Co., Ltd.; *Int'l*, pg. 1624
CITIZENS FINANCIAL CORPORATION; *U.S. Public*, pg. 505
CITIZENS, INC.; *U.S. Public*, pg. 506
CITIZEN WATCH CO., LTD.; *Int'l*, pg. 1623
CITOXLAB GROUP SAS—See Charles River Laboratories International, Inc.; *U.S. Public*, pg. 480
CIT RAIL HOLDINGS (EUROPE) SAS—See Morgan Stanley; *U.S. Public*, pg. 1476
CITRIX SYSTEMS INTERNATIONAL GMBH—See Elliott Management Corporation; *U.S. Private*, pg. 1367
CITRIX SYSTEMS INTERNATIONAL GMBH—See Vista Equity Partners, LLC; *U.S. Private*, pg. 4396
CITY & COUNTY HEALTHCARE GROUP LIMITED—See Graphite Capital Management LLP; *Int'l*, pg. 3060
CITY HOLDINGS (AUS) PTY LTD—See City Refrigeration Holdings (UK) Limited; *Int'l*, pg. 1627
CITY INDEX (HOLDINGS) LTD.—See StoneX Group Inc.; *U.S. Public*, pg. 1952
CITYWIRE HOLDINGS LTD.; *Int'l*, pg. 1630
CJ CORPORATION; *Int'l*, pg. 1631
CJP HOLDINGS INC.—See Citigroup Inc.; *U.S. Public*, pg. 502
CJSC RUSSIAN STANDARD CORPORATION; *Int'l*, pg. 1634
CJSC S7 GROUP; *Int'l*, pg. 1634
CK ASSET HOLDINGS LIMITED; *Int'l*, pg. 1634
CK BIRLA GROUP; *Int'l*, pg. 1636
CKE, INC.—See Roark Capital Group Inc.; *U.S. Private*, pg. 3454
CK HUTCHISON HOLDINGS LIMITED; *Int'l*, pg. 1636
CK LIFE SCIENCES INTERNATIONAL, (HOLDINGS) INC.—See CK Hutchison Holdings Limited; *Int'l*, pg. 1637
C&K OIL CO. INC.—See Lank Oil Co. Inc.; *U.S. Private*, pg. 2390
CLAAS FRANCE HOLDING S.A.S.—See Claas KGaA mbH; *Int'l*, pg. 1640
CLAAS HOLDINGS LTD.—See Claas KGaA mbH; *Int'l*, pg. 1641
CLAAS KGAA MBH; *Int'l*, pg. 1640
CLAAS NORTH AMERICA HOLDINGS INC.—See Claas KGaA mbH; *Int'l*, pg. 1640
CLAIRE'S INC.—See Apollo Global Management, Inc.; *U.S. Public*, pg. 148
CLAL INDUSTRIES LTD.—See Access Industries, Inc.; *U.S. Private*, pg. 51
CLAL INSURANCE ENTERPRISES HOLDINGS LTD.—See IDB Development Corporation Ltd.; *Int'l*, pg. 3588
CLANCY'S INC.; *U.S. Private*, pg. 910
CLARIANT AG; *Int'l*, pg. 1645
CLARIANT HOLDINGS UK LTD.—See Clariant AG; *Int'l*, pg. 1648
CLARIOS GLOBAL GP LLC—See Brookfield Corporation; *Int'l*, pg. 1175

CLARIOS GLOBAL GP LLC—See Caisse de Depot et Placement du Quebec; *Int'l*, pg. 1254
CLARIS LIFESCIENCES LTD.; *Int'l*, pg. 1649
CLARITY MEDIA GROUP, INC.—See The Anschutz Corporation; *U.S. Private*, pg. 3987
CLARITY MEDICAL GROUP HOLDING LIMITED; *Int'l*, pg. 1649
CLARITY TELECOM, LLC—See Keystone Group, L.P.; *U.S. Private*, pg. 2297
CLARITY TELECOM, LLC—See Pamlico Capital Management, L.P.; *U.S. Private*, pg. 3083
CLARK ASSOCIATES, INC.; *U.S. Private*, pg. 912
CLARKE INC.; *Int'l*, pg. 1650
CLARK HOLDINGS, INC.—See Atlas Holdings, LLC; *U.S. Private*, pg. 376
CLASSITA HOLDINGS BERHAD; *Int'l*, pg. 1653
CLAYTON HOLDINGS UK, LTD.—See Radian Group, Inc.; *U.S. Public*, pg. 1759
CLC GROUP LIMITED—See H.I.G. Capital, LLC; *U.S. Private*, pg. 1827
CLEAN EARTH HOLDINGS, INC.—See Compass Diversified Holdings; *U.S. Public*, pg. 559
CLEANHILL PARTNERS; *U.S. Private*, pg. 931
CLEANSPACE HOLDINGS LIMITED; *Int'l*, pg. 1655
CLEAR2PAY SCOTLAND HOLDINGS LIMITED—See Fidelity National Infor; *U.S. Public*, pg. 832
CLEAR BLUE FINANCIAL HOLDINGS LLC; *U.S. Private*, pg. 932
CLEAR CHANNEL HOLDINGS LIMITED—See Clear Channel Outdoor Holdings, Inc.; *U.S. Public*, pg. 511
CLEAR CHANNEL OUTDOOR HOLDINGS, INC.; *U.S. Public*, pg. 511
CLEARCIRCLE ENVIRONMENTAL LIMITED—See Madison Dearborn Partners, LLC; *U.S. Public*, pg. 2541
CLEAR CREEK HOLDINGS, LLC—See Tetra Tech, Inc.; *U.S. Public*, pg. 2022
CLEARDEBT GROUP PLC; *Int'l*, pg. 1656
THE CLEARING CORPORATION—See Intercontinental Exchange, Inc.; *U.S. Public*, pg. 1143
CLEARWATER ANALYTICS HOLDINGS, INC.; *U.S. Public*, pg. 513
CLEARWATER FINE FOODS INCORPORATED; *Int'l*, pg. 1657
CLEARY GULL HOLDINGS INC.—See Canadian Imperial Bank of Commerce; *Int'l*, pg. 1283
CLEOPATRA HOLDING B.V.—See Masco Corporation; *U.S. Public*, pg. 1390
CLERE AG; *Int'l*, pg. 1658
CLEVELAND GROUP, INC.; *U.S. Private*, pg. 941
CL FINANCIAL LIMITED; *Int'l*, pg. 1640
CLIENTELE LIMITED; *Int'l*, pg. 1658
CLIFFSIDE CAPITAL LTD.—See Cliffside Ltd.; *Int'l*, pg. 1659
CLIME INVESTMENT MANAGEMENT LIMITED; *Int'l*, pg. 1659
CLINISYS GROUP LIMITED—See Roper Technologies, Inc.; *U.S. Public*, pg. 1810
CLIO HOLDINGS LLC—See O2 Investment Partners, LLC; *U.S. Private*, pg. 2982
CLIO HOLDINGS LLC—See Oakland Standard Co., LLC; *U.S. Private*, pg. 2984
CLIVE CHRISTIAN LIMITED; *Int'l*, pg. 1660
CLK HOLDING A.S.; *Int'l*, pg. 1660
CLONDALKIN GROUP HOLDINGS BV—See Egeria Capital Management B.V.; *Int'l*, pg. 2323
CLONDALKIN GROUP HOLDINGS LTD.—See Egeria Capital Management B.V.; *Int'l*, pg. 2323
CLOOPEN GROUP HOLDING LIMITED; *Int'l*, pg. 1661
THE CLOROX INTERNATIONAL COMPANY—See The Clorox Company; *U.S. Public*, pg. 2063
CLOSE BROTHERS GROUP PLC; *Int'l*, pg. 1661
CLOUD INVESTMENT HOLDINGS LIMITED; *Int'l*, pg. 1662
CLOUDMINDS INC.; *Int'l*, pg. 1662
CLOUD PEAK ENERGY INC.; *U.S. Private*, pg. 946
CLP HOLDINGS LIMITED; *Int'l*, pg. 1663
CLS HOLDINGS PLC; *Int'l*, pg. 1663
CLS HOLDINGS USA, INC.; *U.S. Public*, pg. 515
C.L. THOMAS, INC.; *U.S. Private*, pg. 708
CLUBCORP HOLDINGS, INC.—See Apollo Global Management, Inc.; *U.S. Public*, pg. 149
CLYDE BERGEMANN POWER GROUP—See Clyde Blowers Capital IM LLP; *Int'l*, pg. 1664
CLYDE BLOWERS CAPITAL IM LLP; *Int'l*, pg. 1664
CLYDE UNION (FRANCE) S.A.S.—See Lone Star Funds; *U.S. Private*, pg. 2485
CMC GROUP INC.; *U.S. Private*, pg. 950
CME GROUP AUSTRALIA PTY. LTD.—See CME Group, Inc.; *U.S. Public*, pg. 516
CME GROUP, INC.; *U.S. Public*, pg. 515
CMFG LIFE INSURANCE COMPANY; *U.S. Private*, pg. 950
CMG FINANCIAL SERVICES INC.; *U.S. Private*, pg. 950
C.M. HOLDING CO., INC.—See Mid Oaks Investments LLC; *U.S. Private*, pg. 2706
CMIC HOLDINGS CO., LTD.; *Int'l*, pg. 1670
CML MICROSYSTEMS PLC; *Int'l*, pg. 1671
THE C. M. PAULA COMPANY; *U.S. Private*, pg. 4003
CNA FINANCIAL CORPORATION—See Loews Corporation; *U.S. Public*, pg. 1339
CNB SECURITIES CORPORATION—See CNB Financial Corporation; *U.S. Public*, pg. 519
CNE GAS HOLDINGS, LLC—See Constellation Energy Corporation; *U.S. Public*, pg. 571
CN ENERGY GROUP, INC.; *Int'l*, pg. 1672
CNFINANCE HOLDINGS LIMITED; *Int'l*, pg. 1673
CNH CO., LTD.; *Int'l*, pg. 1674
CNH INDUSTRIAL N.V.; *Int'l*, pg. 1674
CN LOGISTICS INTERNATIONAL HOLDINGS LIMITED; *Int'l*, pg. 1673
CNNC INTERNATIONAL LIMITED—See China National Nuclear Corporation; *Int'l*, pg. 1532
CNO FINANCIAL GROUP, INC.; *U.S. Public*, pg. 519
CNOVA N.V.—See Finatis SA; *Int'l*, pg. 2670
CNQC INTERNATIONAL HOLDINGS LTD.; *Int'l*, pg. 1678
CNS CORPORATION; *U.S. Private*, pg. 953
CNT GROUP LIMITED; *Int'l*, pg. 1678
CNX MIDSTREAM PARTNERS LP—See CNX Resources Corporation; *U.S. Public*, pg. 520
CNX RESOURCES CORPORATION; *U.S. Public*, pg. 520
COASIA HOLDINGS CO., LTD.; *Int'l*, pg. 1680
COAST 2 COAST FINANCIAL GROUP, LLC; *U.S. Private*, pg. 954
COASTAL CAPITAL ACQUISITION CORP.; *U.S. Private*, pg. 955
COAST ENTERTAINMENT HOLDINGS LIMITED; *Int'l*, pg. 1681
COATS GROUP PLC; *Int'l*, pg. 1681
COATS PLC—See Coats Group plc; *Int'l*, pg. 1682
COBHAM PLC—See Advent International Corporation; *U.S. Private*, pg. 98
COBURG GROUP PLC; *Int'l*, pg. 1683
COCA-COLA AMATIL LIMITED—See COCA-COLA EUROPACIFIC PARTNERS PLC; *Int'l*, pg. 1684
COCA-COLA ENTERPRISES GREAT BRITAIN LIMITED—See COCA-COLA EUROPACIFIC PARTNERS PLC; *Int'l*, pg. 1685
COCA-COLA EUROPACIFIC PARTNERS PLC; *Int'l*, pg. 1684
COCA-COLA EUROPEAN PARTNERS US, LLC—See COCA-COLA EUROPACIFIC PARTNERS PLC; *Int'l*, pg. 1685
COCA-COLA FEMSA, S.A.B. DE C.V.—See Fomento Economico Mexicano, S.A.B. de C.V.; *Int'l*, pg. 2723
COCA-COLA HBC AG; *Int'l*, pg. 1685
COCA-COLA REFRESHMENTS USA, INC.—See The Coca-Cola Company; *U.S. Public*, pg. 2064
COCRYSTAL PHARMA, INC.; *U.S. Public*, pg. 521
CODI GROUP BV—See Active Capital Company Holding BV; *Int'l*, pg. 120
COFACE AUSTRIA HOLDING AG—See Coface S.A.; *Int'l*, pg. 1690
COFACE HOLDING AG—See Coface S.A.; *Int'l*, pg. 1690
COFACE ITALIA S.P.A.—See Coface S.A.; *Int'l*, pg. 1691
COFACE NORTH AMERICA HOLDING COMPANY—See Coface S.A.; *Int'l*, pg. 1691
COFACE UK HOLDING LTD.—See Coface S.A.; *Int'l*, pg. 1691
COFFEE DAY ENTERPRISES LIMITED—See Affirma Capital Limited; *Int'l*, pg. 187
COFFEE REPUBLIC TRADING LTD.; *Int'l*, pg. 1692
COFFEY INTERNATIONAL DEVELOPMENT HOLDINGS LIMITED—See Tetra Tech, Inc.; *U.S. Public*, pg. 2022
COFFEY INTERNATIONAL LIMITED—See Tetra Tech, Inc.; *U.S. Public*, pg. 2022
COFRA HOLDING AG; *Int'l*, pg. 1693
COGECO INC.—See Gestion Audem, Inc.; *Int'l*, pg. 2946
COGENT COMMUNICATIONS HOLDINGS, INC.; *U.S. Public*, pg. 522
COGENT HOLDINGS LIMITED—See China COSCO Shipping Corporation Limited; *Int'l*, pg. 1492
COGNIS GMBH—See BASF SE; *Int'l*, pg. 883
COIL STEELS GROUP PTY LIMITED—See Commercial Metals Company; *U.S. Public*, pg. 546
COLBOND HOLDING BV—See Freudenberg SE; *Int'l*, pg. 2789
COLBOND INVESTMENTS BV—See Freudenberg SE; *Int'l*, pg. 2789
COLDSTREAM HOLDINGS, INC.; *U.S. Private*, pg. 966
COLEFAX GROUP PLC; *Int'l*, pg. 1697
COLES GROUP LIMITED; *Int'l*, pg. 1698
COLES GROUP PROPERTIES HOLDINGS LTD—See Coles Group Limited; *Int'l*, pg. 1698
COLIAN HOLDING S.A.; *Int'l*, pg. 1698
COLINA HOLDINGS BAHAMAS LIMITED; *Int'l*, pg. 1698
COLLABORATIVE CARE HOLDINGS, LLC—See UnitedHealth Group Incorporated; *U.S. Public*, pg. 2240
COLLEGIUM HOLDINGS, INC.; *U.S. Private*, pg. 968
COLLIER ENTERPRISES, INC.; *U.S. Private*, pg. 969
COLLIERS INTERNATIONAL GROUP INC.; *Int'l*, pg. 1700
COLLIERS INTERNATIONAL HOLDINGS (AUSTRALIA) LIMITED—See Colliers International Group Inc.; *Int'l*, pg. 1701
COLLIERS INTERNATIONAL HOLDINGS (USA), INC.—See Colliers International Group Inc.; *Int'l*, pg. 1700
COLLINS AEROSPACE—See RTX Corporation; *U.S. Public*, pg. 1821
COLLPLANT BIOTECHNOLOGIES LTD.; *Int'l*, pg. 1702
COLONIAL AUTOMOTIVE GROUP, INC.; *U.S. Private*, pg. 970
COLONIAL FIRST STATE GROUP LIMITED—See Commonwealth Bank of Australia; *Int'l*, pg. 1719
COLONY GLOBAL ACQUISITION CORP.—See DigitalBridge Group, Inc.; *U.S. Public*, pg. 664
COLORMATRIX EUROPE LIMITED—See Avient Corporation; *U.S. Public*, pg. 247
COLOR ME MINE ENTERPRISES, INC.; *U.S. Private*, pg. 973
COLRICH (SAC) LTD—See Guardian Holdings Limited; *Int'l*, pg. 3171
COLTALA HOLDINGS, LLC; *U.S. Private*, pg. 976
COLT CZ GROUP SE; *Int'l*, pg. 1705
COLTENE HOLDING AG; *Int'l*, pg. 1705
COLT GROUP S.A.—See FMR LLC; *U.S. Private*, pg. 1554
COMBA TELECOM SYSTEMS HOLDINGS LIMITED; *Int'l*, pg. 1708
COMBEST HOLDINGS LIMITED; *Int'l*, pg. 1708
COMBINED MOTOR HOLDINGS LIMITED; *Int'l*, pg. 1709
COMBINE WILL INTERNATIONAL HOLDINGS LIMITED; *Int'l*, pg. 1708
COMCAST SPECTACOR, L.P.—See Comcast Corporation; *U.S. Public*, pg. 537
COMERA LIFE SCIENCES HOLDINGS, INC.; *U.S. Public*, pg. 542
COMFORT GLOVES BERHAD; *Int'l*, pg. 1711
COMMERCE GROUP CORP.; *U.S. Public*, pg. 545
COMMERCEHUB, INC.—See Insight Venture Management, LLC; *U.S. Private*, pg. 2087
COMMERCE ONE HOLDINGS, INC.; *Int'l*, pg. 1714
COMMERCIAL CREDIT, INC.—See BDT Capital Partners, LLC; *U.S. Private*, pg. 502
COMMERCIAL WARRANTY SOLUTIONS, LLC; *U.S. Private*, pg. 985
COMMONWEALTH VENTURE FUNDING GROUP; *U.S. Private*, pg. 987
COMMSCOPE HOLDING COMPANY, INC.; *U.S. Public*, pg. 547
COMMUNE HOTELS & RESORTS, LLC; *U.S. Private*, pg. 987
COMMUNICATIONS INFRASTRUCTURE INVESTMENTS, LLC; *U.S. Private*, pg. 988
COMMUNITY BRANDS HOLDCO, LLC—See Insight Venture Management, LLC; *U.S. Private*, pg. 2088
COMMUNITY HEALTH SYSTEMS, INC.; *U.S. Public*, pg. 550
COMMUNITY INVESTMENT HOLDINGS (PTY) LIMITED; *Int'l*, pg. 1721
COMPAGNIA FINANZIARIA DE BENEDETTI S.P.A.; *Int'l*, pg. 1721
COMPAGNIE DE SAINT-GOBAIN SA; *Int'l*, pg. 1722
COMPAGNIE DES TRAMWAYS DE ROUEN SA; *Int'l*, pg. 1739
COMPAGNIE DU BOIS SAUVAGE SA; *Int'l*, pg. 1740
COMPAGNIE FINANCIERE RICHEMONT S.A.; *Int'l*, pg. 1740
COMPAGNIE GENERALE DES ETABLISSEMENTS MICHELIN SCA; *Int'l*, pg. 1741
COMPAGNIE LEBON SA; *Int'l*, pg. 1745
COMPAGNIE MERCOSUR GRECEMAR SA; *Int'l*, pg. 1746
COMPAGNIE NATIONALE A PORTEFEUILLE S.A.—See BNP Paribas SA; *Int'l*, pg. 1090
COMPAGNIE NATIONALE A PORTEFEUILLE S.A.—See Frere-Bourgeois; *Int'l*, pg. 2773
COMPASS ADVISERS GROUP LLC; *U.S. Private*, pg. 998
COMPASS DIVERSIFIED HOLDINGS; *U.S. Public*, pg. 559
COMPASS ELECTRONICS GROUP—See Compass Group, LLC; *U.S. Private*, pg. 999
COMPASS GROUP DIVERSIFIED HOLDINGS LLC—See Compass Diversified Holdings; *U.S. Public*, pg. 560
COMPASS GROUP HOLDINGS PLC—See Compass Group PLC; *Int'l*, pg. 1750
COMPASS GROUP INTERNATIONAL BV—See Compass Group PLC; *Int'l*, pg. 1750
COMPASS GROUP NEDERLAND HOLDING BV—See Compass Group PLC; *Int'l*, pg. 1750
COMPASS GROUP PLC; *Int'l*, pg. 1750
COMPASS GROUP USA, INC.—See Compass Group PLC; *Int'l*, pg. 1750
COMPASS HEALTH BRANDS CORP.—See Tenex Capital Management, L.P.; *U.S. Private*, pg. 3966
COMPASS MINERALS UK HOLDINGS LIMITED—See Compass Minerals International, Inc.; *U.S. Public*, pg. 560
COMPASS PATHWAYS PLC; *Int'l*, pg. 1752
COMPLETE FINANCIAL SOLUTIONS, INC.; *U.S. Public*, pg. 561
COMPUGATES HOLDINGS BERHAD; *Int'l*, pg. 1755
COMPUGROUP MEDICAL SE & CO. KGAA; *Int'l*, pg. 1755
COMPUTACENTER PLC; *Int'l*, pg. 1757
COMPUTER PROCESS CONTROLS, INC.—See Emerson Electric Co.; *U.S. Public*, pg. 743
COMPUTER TASK GROUP (HOLDINGS) LTD.—See Cegeka Groep NV; *Int'l*, pg. 1391
COMSYS HOLDINGS CORPORATION; *Int'l*, pg. 1761
COMTRADE GROUP B.V.; *Int'l*, pg. 1762

N.A.I.C.S. INDEX

551112 — OFFICES OF OTHER HO...

CONCENTRA INC.—See Select Medical Holdings Corporation; *U.S. Public*, pg. 1857
CONCENTRA INC.—See Welsh, Carson, Anderson & Stowe; *U.S. Private*, pg. 4479
CONCENTRA NV; *Int'l*, pg. 1763
CONCORDANCE HEALTHCARE SOLUTIONS, LLC; *U.S. Private*, pg. 1010
THE CONCORDE GROUP, INC.; *U.S. Private*, pg. 4013
CONCORDE HOTEL NEW YORK INC.—See Hotel Properties Limited; *Int'l*, pg. 3488
CONCORDIA INTERNATIONAL RX UK LTD—See Advanz Pharma Corp.; *Int'l*, pg. 166
CONDUENT INCORPORATED; *U.S. Public*, pg. 566
CONDUIT HOLDINGS LIMITED; *Int'l*, pg. 1766
CONERGY GLOBAL SOLUTIONS GMBH—See Kawa Capital Management, Inc.; *U.S. Private*, pg. 2266
CONFIDENCE INTELLIGENCE HOLDINGS LIMITED; *Int'l*, pg. 1768
CONFIE SEGUROS INSURANCE SERVICES, INC.—See Stone Point Capital LLC; *U.S. Private*, pg. 3818
CONIFER HOLDINGS, INC.; *U.S. Public*, pg. 567
CONNECTICUT WATER SERVICE, INC.—See SJW Group; *U.S. Public*, pg. 1891
CONOCOPHILLIPS NORGE—See ConocoPhillips; *U.S. Public*, pg. 568
CONRAIL INC.—See CSX Corporation; *U.S. Public*, pg. 602
CONRAIL INC.—See Norfolk Southern Corporation; *U.S. Public*, pg. 1535
CONRAN HOLDINGS LIMITED; *Int'l*, pg. 1769
CONSOL ENERGY INC.; *U.S. Public*, pg. 569
CONSOLIDATED CATFISH COMPANIES, LLC; *U.S. Private*, pg. 1020
CONSOLIDATED COMMUNICATIONS HOLDINGS, INC.; *U.S. Public*, pg. 569
CONSOLIDATED EDISON, INC.; *U.S. Public*, pg. 570
CONSOLIDATED FINVEST & HOLDINGS LIMITED; *Int'l*, pg. 1770
CONSOLIDATED GLASS HOLDING—See Grey Mountain Partners, LLC; *U.S. Private*, pg. 1784
CONSOLIDATED MACHINE & TOOL HOLDINGS, LLC—See White Wolf Capital LLC; *U.S. Private*, pg. 4510
CONSOLIDATED MEDIA HOLDINGS PTY LIMITED—See News Corporation; *U.S. Public*, pg. 1518
CONSOLIDATED PRESS HOLDINGS LIMITED; *Int'l*, pg. 1771
CONSOLIDATED STORAGE COMPANIES, INC.; *U.S. Private*, pg. 1022
CONSORCIO COMEX, S.A. DE C.V.—See PPG Industries, Inc.; *U.S. Public*, pg. 1709
CONSTELLATION BRANDS BEACH HOLDINGS, INC.—See Constellation Brands, Inc.; *U.S. Public*, pg. 570
CONSTELLATION ENERGY NUCLEAR GROUP, LLC—See Constellation Energy Corporation; *U.S. Public*, pg. 571
CONSTELLATION ENERGY PARTNERS HOLDINGS, LLC—See Constellation Energy Corporation; *U.S. Public*, pg. 572
CONSTELLATION, INC.—See Curi Holdings, Inc.; *U.S. Private*, pg. 1124
CONSTELLIS HOLDINGS, INC.—See Apollo Global Management, Inc.; *U.S. Public*, pg. 150
CONSTELLIUM SE; *Int'l*, pg. 1776
CONTANDA, LLC—See EQT AB; *U.S. Private*, pg. 2473
CONTANGO GROUP PTY. LTD.; *Int'l*, pg. 1779
CONTENT VENTURES LIMITED; *Int'l*, pg. 1779
CONTIKI TOURS INTERNATIONAL LIMITED; *Int'l*, pg. 1780
CONTINENTAL AEROSPACE TECHNOLOGIES HOLDING LIMITED—See Aviation Industry Corporation of China; *Int'l*, pg. 741
CONTINENTALE HOLDING AG; *Int'l*, pg. 1784
CONTINENTAL GRAIN COMPANY; *U.S. Private*, pg. 1029
CONTINENTAL HOLDING COMPANY; *U.S. Private*, pg. 1029
CONTINENTAL HOLDINGS CORP.; *Int'l*, pg. 1783
CONTOURGLOBAL LIMITED; *Int'l*, pg. 1785
CONTOUR GLOBAL LLC—See ContourGlobal Limited; *Int'l*, pg. 1785
CONTRAN CORPORATION; *U.S. Private*, pg. 1033
CONTROL RISKS GROUP HOLDINGS LTD.; *Int'l*, pg. 1785
CONVERGEONE HOLDINGS, INC.—See CVC Capital Partners SICAV-FIS S.A.; *Int'l*, pg. 1883
CONVERGYS CORPORATION—See Concentrix Corporation; *U.S. Public*, pg. 564
CONVERGYS HOLDINGS (UK) LTD.—See Concentrix Corporation; *U.S. Public*, pg. 565
CONVERSIONPOINT HOLDINGS, INC.; *U.S. Public*, pg. 573
CONVEY HEALTH SOLUTIONS HOLDINGS, INC.—See TPG Capital, L.P.; *U.S. Public*, pg. 2169
THE COOK & BOARDMAN GROUP, LLC—See Platinum Equity, LLC; *U.S. Private*, pg. 3208
COOKE, INC.; *Int'l*, pg. 1788
COOK GROUP INCORPORATED; *U.S. Private*, pg. 1037
COOK INLET REGION, INC.; *U.S. Private*, pg. 1038
COOLPAD GROUP LIMITED; *Int'l*, pg. 1789
CO-OPERATIVE BANKING GROUP LIMITED—See Co-operative Group Limited; *Int'l*, pg. 1679
COOPER COATED COIL MANAGEMENT LIMITED; *Int'l*, pg. 1790
THE COOPER COMPANIES, INC.; *U.S. Public*, pg. 2065
COOPER GAY SWETT & CRAWFORD LIMITED—See Lightyear Capital LLC; *U.S. Private*, pg. 2454
COOPER INDUSTRIES, LLC—See Eaton Corporation plc; *Int'l*, pg. 2277
COOPER-STANDARD HOLDINGS INC.; *U.S. Public*, pg. 573
COOPER TIRE & RUBBER HOLDING NETHERLANDS 1 B.V.—See The Goodyear Tire & Rubber Company; *U.S. Public*, pg. 2083
COOPER TIRE & RUBBER HOLDING NETHERLANDS 2 B.V.—See The Goodyear Tire & Rubber Company; *U.S. Public*, pg. 2083
COOP-GRUPPE GENOSSENSCHAFT; *Int'l*, pg. 1789
COPEL COMPANHIA ENERGIA S/A—See Companhia Paranaense de Energia; *Int'l*, pg. 1748
COPPERPOINT MUTUAL INSURANCE HOLDING COMPANY; *U.S. Private*, pg. 1045
COPRO HOLDINGS CO., LTD.; *Int'l*, pg. 1794
CORBUS PHARMACEUTICALS HOLDINGS, INC.; *U.S. Public*, pg. 575
CORDILLERA CORPORATION; *U.S. Private*, pg. 1047
CORECARD CORPORATION; *U.S. Public*, pg. 576
CORELLE BRANDS HOLDINGS INC.—See Cornell Capital Management LLC; *U.S. Private*, pg. 1051
CORESTAFF SERVICES, LP—See HFBG Holding B.V.; *Int'l*, pg. 3374
CORNELIUS EUROPE SA—See Berkshire Hathaway Inc.; *U.S. Public*, pg. 309
CORNELIUS (PACIFIC) LTD.—See Berkshire Hathaway Inc.; *U.S. Public*, pg. 309
CORNERSTONE BUILDING BRANDS, INC.—See Clayton, Dubilier & Rice, LLC; *U.S. Private*, pg. 920
CORNERSTONECAPITAL VERWALTUNGS AG; *Int'l*, pg. 1801
CORNERSTONE FINANCIAL HOLDINGS LIMITED; *Int'l*, pg. 1801
CORNING HOLDING GMBH—See Corning Incorporated; *U.S. Public*, pg. 578
CORNING HOLDING JAPAN GK—See Corning Incorporated; *U.S. Public*, pg. 578
CORNING INTERNATIONAL CORPORATION—See Corning Incorporated; *U.S. Public*, pg. 578
CORNING NATURAL GAS HOLDING CORPORATION—See Argo Infrastructure Partners LLC; *U.S. Private*, pg. 320
CORPACQ HOLDINGS LIMITED; *Int'l*, pg. 1802
CORPORACION AMERICA ITALIA S.P.A.—See Corporacion America Airports S.A.; *Int'l*, pg. 1803
CORPORACION AMERICA S.A.; *Int'l*, pg. 1803
CORPORACION FINANCIERA ALBA S.A.—See Alba Grupo March; *Int'l*, pg. 292
CORPORACION GESTAMP SL; *Int'l*, pg. 1803
CORPORATION TSESNA JSC; *Int'l*, pg. 1806
CORPRO GROUP LIMITED—See ALS Limited; *Int'l*, pg. 378
CORTELCO SYSTEMS HOLDING CORP.; *U.S. Private*, pg. 1060
CORTEVA, INC.; *U.S. Public*, pg. 580
COSALT PLC; *Int'l*, pg. 1809
COSAN LIMITED—See Cosan S.A.; *Int'l*, pg. 1809
COSCO CONTAINER INDUSTRIES LIMITED—See COSCO Shipping Holdings Co., Ltd.; *Int'l*, pg. 1810
COSCO (HK) FREIGHT SERVICE HOLDINGS LTD.—See China COSCO Shipping Corporation Limited; *Int'l*, pg. 1492
COSCO SHIPPING FINANCIAL HOLDINGS CO., LIMITED—See China COSCO Shipping Corporation Limited; *Int'l*, pg. 1493
COSCO SHIPPING HOLDINGS CO., LTD.; *Int'l*, pg. 1809
COSCO SHIPPING (HONG KONG) CO., LIMITED—See China COSCO Shipping Corporation Limited; *Int'l*, pg. 1492
COSCO SHIPPING INTERNATIONAL (HONG KONG) CO., LTD.—See China COSCO Shipping Corporation Limited; *Int'l*, pg. 1492
COSCO SHIPPING LINES (NORTH AMERICA) INC.—See China COSCO Shipping Corporation Limited; *Int'l*, pg. 1493
COSCO SHIPPING PORTS LIMITED—See COSCO Shipping Holdings Co., Ltd.; *Int'l*, pg. 1810
COSCO SHIPPING (SOUTH EAST ASIA) PTE. LTD.—See China COSCO Shipping Corporation Limited; *Int'l*, pg. 1492
COSERV UTILITY HOLDINGS, L.P.; *U.S. Private*, pg. 1062
COSL HOLDING AS—See China National Offshore Oil Corp.; *Int'l*, pg. 1532
COSL NORWEGIAN AS—See China National Offshore Oil Corp.; *Int'l*, pg. 1533
COSMO ENERGY HOLDINGS CO., LTD.; *Int'l*, pg. 1811
COSMO LADY (CHINA) HOLDINGS COMPANY LIMITED; *Int'l*, pg. 1812
COSMOPOLITAN INTERNATIONAL HOLDINGS LIMITED—See Century City International Holdings Ltd; *Int'l*, pg. 1417
COSMOS GROUP HOLDINGS INC.; *Int'l*, pg. 1813
COSMOS YATIRIM HOLDING A.S.; *Int'l*, pg. 1814
COSTA GROUP HOLDINGS LIMITED—See British Columbia Investment Management Corp.; *Int'l*, pg. 1169
COSTA GROUP HOLDINGS LIMITED—See Driscoll's, Inc; *U.S. Private*, pg. 1278
COSTA GROUP HOLDINGS LIMITED—See Paine Schwartz Partners, LLC; *U.S. Private*, pg. 3075
COSTA GROUP OF COMPANIES; *Int'l*, pg. 1814
COSTA INC.—See EssilorLuxottica SA; *Int'l*, pg. 2513
COSTAIN GROUP PLC; *Int'l*, pg. 1814
COSTAMP GROUP S.P.A.—See Co.Stamp - Srl; *Int'l*, pg. 1680
CO.STAMP - SRL; *Int'l*, pg. 1680
COST PLUS, INC.—See Kingswood Capital Management LLC; *U.S. Private*, pg. 2312
COTIVITI CORPORATION—See Veritas Capital Fund Management, LLC; *U.S. Private*, pg. 4366
COTIVITI HOLDINGS, INC.—See Veritas Capital Fund Management, LLC; *U.S. Private*, pg. 4365
COTTBUSER ENERGIEVERWALTUNGSGESELLSCHAFT MBH—See BayernLB Holding AG; *Int'l*, pg. 913
COTTCO HOLDINGS LIMITED; *Int'l*, pg. 1817
COTTCO INTERNATIONAL (PROPRIETARY) LIMITED—See Cottco Holdings Limited; *Int'l*, pg. 1817
COTT LIMITED—See Primo Water Corporation; *U.S. Public*, pg. 1718
COTTON HOLDINGS, INC.; *U.S. Private*, pg. 1064
COUGHLAN COMPANIES, INC.; *U.S. Private*, pg. 1064
COULSON GROUP OF COMPANIES; *Int'l*, pg. 1817
COUNT LIMITED; *Int'l*, pg. 1817
COUNTRY GARDEN HOLDINGS COMPANY LIMITED; *Int'l*, pg. 1818
COUNTRY GARDEN SERVICES HOLDINGS COMPANY LIMITED; *Int'l*, pg. 1818
COUNTRY GROUP HOLDINGS PUBLIC COMPANY LIMITED; *Int'l*, pg. 1818
COUNTY WELDING PRODUCTS, INC.—See CI Capital Partners LLC; *U.S. Private*, pg. 895
COURT CAVENDISH LIMITED; *Int'l*, pg. 1819
COURTESY GARAGE LTD.—See Goddard Enterprises Limited; *Int'l*, pg. 3018
COURTOIS SA; *Int'l*, pg. 1819
COVANT MANAGEMENT, INC.—See Madison Dearborn Partners, LLC; *U.S. Private*, pg. 2540
COVEA GROUPE S.A.S.; *Int'l*, pg. 1820
COVERIS ADVANCED COATINGS HOLDINGS (UK) LTD.—See Sun Capital Partners, Inc.; *U.S. Private*, pg. 3858
COVERIS HOLDING CORP.—See Sun Capital Partners, Inc.; *U.S. Private*, pg. 3858
COVERIS HOLDINGS S.A.—See Sun Capital Partners, Inc.; *U.S. Private*, pg. 3858
COVIUS HOLDINGS, INC.; *U.S. Private*, pg. 1073
COWELL E HOLDINGS INC.; *Int'l*, pg. 1821
COWLES COMPANY; *U.S. Private*, pg. 1073
CP2 GROUP LIMITED; *Int'l*, pg. 1823
CPA GLOBAL LIMITED—See Clarivate PLC; *Int'l*, pg. 1649
CPA GLOBAL NORTH AMERICA LLC—See Clarivate PLC; *Int'l*, pg. 1649
CPH CHEMIE + PAPIER HOLDING AG; *Int'l*, pg. 1824
CP HOLDINGS LTD.; *Int'l*, pg. 1823
CPM GROUP LIMITED—See CNT Group Limited; *Int'l*, pg. 1678
CPOWER HOLDINGS, LLC—See Exelon Corporation; *U.S. Public*, pg. 806
CPPGROUP PLC; *Int'l*, pg. 1826
C.P. POKPHAND CO. LTD.—See Charoen Pokphand Foods Public Company Limited; *Int'l*, pg. 1452
CRACKEN, HARKEY & CO., LLC; *U.S. Private*, pg. 1081
CRACOW HOLDINGS PTY LTD—See Newmont Corporation; *U.S. Public*, pg. 1517
CRANE AEROSPACE & ELECTRONICS—See Crane NXT, Co.; *U.S. Public*, pg. 589
CRANE GROUP CO.; *U.S. Private*, pg. 1085
CRANE GROUP LIMITED; *Int'l*, pg. 1827
CRANE INTERNATIONAL HOLDINGS, INC.—See Crane NXT, Co.; *U.S. Public*, pg. 590
CRAYON GROUP HOLDING ASA; *Int'l*, pg. 1829
CRAZY SPORTS GROUP LIMITED; *Int'l*, pg. 1830
CRC-EVANS INTERNATIONAL, INC.; *U.S. Private*, pg. 1087
CRC HEALTH GROUP, INC.—See Acadia Healthcare Company, Inc.; *U.S. Public*, pg. 28
CREAM HOLDINGS LIMITED—See Live Nation Entertainment, Inc.; *U.S. Public*, pg. 1328
CREATIONS, INC.; *U.S. Private*, pg. 1087
CREATIVE EDGE NUTRITION, INC.; *U.S. Public*, pg. 593
CREATIVE MASTER BERMUDA LTD.; *Int'l*, pg. 1832
CREATIVE MEDICAL TECHNOLOGY HOLDINGS, INC.; *U.S. Public*, pg. 593
CRED HOLDING CO., LTD.; *Int'l*, pg. 1834
CREDIT EUROPE GROUP N.V.—See Fiba Holding A.S.; *Int'l*, pg. 2651
CREDO TECHNOLOGY GROUP HOLDING LTD.; *U.S. Public*, pg. 593
CREEK INDIAN ENTERPRISES; *U.S. Private*, pg. 1092
CREO RETAIL MARKETING HOLDINGS LIMITED—See DS Smith Plc; *Int'l*, pg. 2208

CRESCENDAS PTE. LTD.; *Int'l*, pg. 1839
CRESCENDO INDUSTRIES; *Int'l*, pg. 1839
CREST GROUP INC.; *U.S. Private*, pg. 1095
CREST INDUSTRIES, LLC; *U.S. Private*, pg. 1096
CREST NICHOLSON HOLDINGS PLC; *Int'l*, pg. 1840
CRESTWOOD EQUITY PARTNERS LP; *U.S. Public*, pg. 594
CRG HOLDING COMPANY, INC.; *U.S. Private*, pg. 1100
CRG HOLDINGS CO., LTD.; *Int'l*, pg. 1842
CRH FRANCE SAS—See CRH plc; *Int'l*, pg. 1843
CRH PLC; *Int'l*, pg. 1842
CRICKET ENERGY HOLDINGS, INC.; *Int'l*, pg. 1849
CRICKET MEDIA GROUP LTD.; *U.S. Private*, pg. 1100
CRIMSON SOLUTIONS, LLC; *U.S. Private*, pg. 1101
CRIMSON WINE GROUP, LTD.; *U.S. Public*, pg. 594
CRITERIA CAIXA, S.A.—See Fundacion Bancaria Caixa d'Estalvis i Pensions de Barcelona, la Caixa; *Int'l*, pg. 2845
CROSSCO INVESTMENT AB—See Enerpac Tool Group Corp.; *U.S. Public*, pg. 765
THE CROSS COUNTRY GROUP, LLC; *U.S. Private*, pg. 4016
CROSS FINANCIAL CORPORATION; *U.S. Private*, pg. 1104
CROSS MARKETING GROUP INC.; *Int'l*, pg. 1855
CROSS RAPIDS CAPITAL LP; *U.S. Private*, pg. 1105
CROSSROADS AUTOMOTIVE GROUP; *U.S. Private*, pg. 1108
CROSSWIND INDUSTRIES, INC.—See Archer-Daniels-Midland Company; *U.S. Public*, pg. 184
CROTON HOLDING COMPANY; *U.S. Private*, pg. 1108
CROWDSTRIKE HOLDINGS, INC.; *U.S. Public*, pg. 596
CROWE GROUP LLP; *U.S. Private*, pg. 1109
CROW FAMILY HOLDINGS REALTY PARTNERS, L.P.; *U.S. Private*, pg. 1109
CROWN AMERICAS LLC—See Crown Holdings, Inc.; *U.S. Public*, pg. 597
CROWN CANADIAN HOLDINGS ULC—See Crown Holdings, Inc.; *U.S. Public*, pg. 598
CROWN EQUITY HOLDINGS INC.; *U.S. Public*, pg. 597
CROWN FOODCAN GERMANY GMBH—See Crown Holdings, Inc.; *U.S. Public*, pg. 597
CROWN HOLDINGS, INC.; *U.S. Public*, pg. 597
CROWN INVESTMENTS CORPORATION OF SASKATCHEWAN; *Int'l*, pg. 1857
CROWN MEDIA HOLDINGS, INC.—See Hallmark Cards, Inc.; *U.S. Private*, pg. 1844
CROWN PACKAGING UK PLC—See Crown Holdings, Inc.; *U.S. Public*, pg. 598
CROWN WORLDWIDE HOLDINGS LTD.; *Int'l*, pg. 1858
CRS HOLDING AG; *Int'l*, pg. 1859
CRUMBS BAKE SHOP, INC.—See Fisher Enterprises, LLC; *U.S. Private*, pg. 1534
CRUM & FORSTER HOLDINGS CORP.—See Fairfax Financial Holdings Limited; *Int'l*, pg. 2606
CRUMP GROUP, INC.—See J.C. Flowers & Co. LLC; *U.S. Private*, pg. 2159
CRUNCH, LLC—See TPG Capital, L.P.; *U.S. Public*, pg. 2176
CRW, INC.; *U.S. Private*, pg. 1114
CRYOCORD SDN. BHD.; *Int'l*, pg. 1859
CRYOVAC INTERNATIONAL HOLDINGS, INC.—See Sealed Air Corporation; *U.S. Public*, pg. 1852
CRYSTAL GLOBE LIMITED; *Int'l*, pg. 1860
CSA AMERICA, INC.—See CSA Group; *Int'l*, pg. 1861
CSBH LLC; *U.S. Private*, pg. 1116
CSC GENERATION HOLDINGS, INC.; *U.S. Private*, pg. 1116
CSC HOLDINGS LIMITED; *Int'l*, pg. 1862
CSC HOLDINGS, LLC—See Altice USA, Inc.; *U.S. Public*, pg. 87
C.S. GENERAL INC.; *U.S. Private*, pg. 709
CSG HOLDINGS LIMITED; *Int'l*, pg. 1864
CSG LIMITED—See FUJIFILM Holdings Corporation; *Int'l*, pg. 2825
CSG SYSTEMS INTERNATIONAL, INC.; *U.S. Public*, pg. 601
CSI HOLDINGS INC.; *U.S. Private*, pg. 1117
CSM BAKERY SOLUTIONS EUROPE HOLDING B.V.—See Rhone Group, LLC; *U.S. Private*, pg. 3423
C. STEIN, INC.; *U.S. Private*, pg. 705
CST GROUP LIMITED; *Int'l*, pg. 1868
CSW INDUSTRIALS, INC.; *U.S. Public*, pg. 601
CSX CORPORATION; *U.S. Public*, pg. 602
CTBC FINANCIAL HOLDING CO., LTD.; *Int'l*, pg. 1869
CTI GROUP (HOLDINGS) INC.—See Enghouse Systems Limited; *Int'l*, pg. 2427
CTR HOLDINGS LIMITED; *Int'l*, pg. 1872
CTV INC.—See BCE Inc.; *Int'l*, pg. 927
CTX HOLDINGS JOINT STOCK COMPANY; *Int'l*, pg. 1874
CUATTRO, LLC; *U.S. Private*, pg. 1119
CUBIC (UK) LIMITED—See Elliott Management Corporation; *U.S. Private*, pg. 1367
CUBIC (UK) LIMITED—See Veritas Capital Fund Management, LLC; *U.S. Private*, pg. 4361
CU INC.—See ATCO Ltd.; *Int'l*, pg. 667
CUKIERMAN & CO. INVESTMENT HOUSE LTD.; *Int'l*, pg. 1876

CUKUROVA HOLDING A.S.; *Int'l*, pg. 1876
CUMBERLAND TECHNOLOGIES, INC.; *U.S. Private*, pg. 1122
CUMMINS-ALLISON CORPORATION—See Crane NXT, Co.; *U.S. Public*, pg. 591
CUMULUS MEDIA HOLDINGS, INC.—See Cumulus Media Inc.; *U.S. Public*, pg. 609
CUMULUS MEDIA INC.; *U.S. Public*, pg. 609
CUPRIC CANYON CAPITAL LLC; *U.S. Private*, pg. 1124
CURAEGIS TECHNOLOGIES, INC.; *U.S. Private*, pg. 1124
CURBELL, INC.; *U.S. Private*, pg. 1124
CUREVAC N.V.; *Int'l*, pg. 1878
CURI HOLDINGS, INC.; *U.S. Private*, pg. 1124
CURIUM NETHERLANDS HOLDINGS B.V.—See Curium SAS; *Int'l*, pg. 1878
CURO GROUP HOLDINGS CORP.; *U.S. Public*, pg. 610
CURRAX HOLDINGS LLC—See JPMorgan Chase & Co.; *U.S. Public*, pg. 1207
CURRAX HOLDINGS USA LLC—See JPMorgan Chase & Co.; *U.S. Public*, pg. 1207
CURRIE & BROWN HOLDINGS LIMITED; *Int'l*, pg. 1879
CURRO HOLDINGS LTD.; *Int'l*, pg. 1879
CURTIS SCREW CO., INC.; *U.S. Private*, pg. 1127
CURVES HOLDINGS CO., LTD.; *Int'l*, pg. 1880
CUSHMAN & WAKEFIELD PLC—See TPG Capital, L.P.; *U.S. Public*, pg. 2170
CUSTOM SPA; *Int'l*, pg. 1880
CUSTOM TRUCK ONE SOURCE, INC.; *U.S. Public*, pg. 612
CUTTER HOLDING CO.; *U.S. Private*, pg. 1131
CUTTER OF MAUI, INC.; *U.S. Private*, pg. 1131
CVA S.P.A. A S.U.; *Int'l*, pg. 1881
CVC CAPITAL PARTNERS SICAV-FIS S.A.; *Int'l*, pg. 1881
CV INDUSTRIES INC.; *U.S. Private*, pg. 1132
CVR ENERGY, INC.—See Icahn Enterprises L.P.; *U.S. Public*, pg. 1084
CVR PARTNERS, LP—See Icahn Enterprises L.P.; *U.S. Public*, pg. 1084
CVS HEALTH CORPORATION; *U.S. Public*, pg. 613
C.V. STARR & CO., INC.; *U.S. Public*, pg. 709
CWG HOLDINGS BERHAD; *Int'l*, pg. 1890
CW GROUP HOLDINGS LIMITED; *Int'l*, pg. 1890
CXI HEALTHCARE TECHNOLOGY GROUP LIMITED; *Int'l*, pg. 1891
CXLOYALTY GROUP, INC.—See JPMorgan Chase & Co.; *U.S. Public*, pg. 1210
CYALUME TECHNOLOGIES HOLDINGS, INC.—See Arsenal Capital Management LP; *U.S. Private*, pg. 337
CYANCO HOLDING CORP.—See Cerberus Capital Management, L.P.; *U.S. Private*, pg. 837
CYBERCATCH HOLDINGS, INC.; *Int'l*, pg. 1892
CYBERGY HOLDINGS, INC.; *U.S. Private*, pg. 1133
CYBIRD HOLDINGS CO., LTD.; *Int'l*, pg. 1894
CYCLE HOLDINGS, LLC—See Penske Automotive Group, Inc.; *U.S. Public*, pg. 1664
CYCLO THERAPEUTICS, INC.; *U.S. Public*, pg. 617
CYNERGISTEK, INC.—See Altaris Capital Partners, LLC; *U.S. Private*, pg. 206
CYNERGY CAPITAL LTD.; *Int'l*, pg. 1896
CYPRESS PARTNERS, LLC; *U.S. Private*, pg. 1135
CYWEB HOLDINGS INC.; *U.S. Private*, pg. 1136
CZECH MEDIA INVEST AS; *Int'l*, pg. 1898
D3 INC.—See BANDAI NAMCO Holdings Inc.; *Int'l*, pg. 829
DABBAGH GROUP HOLDING COMPANY LTD.; *Int'l*, pg. 1902
DACO CORPORATION; *U.S. Private*, pg. 1144
DADA NEXUS LIMITED; *Int'l*, pg. 1904
D.A. DAVIDSON COMPANIES; *U.S. Private*, pg. 1140
DAE CAPITAL HOLDINGS COOPERATIEF U.A.—See Dubai Aerospace Enterprise Ltd; *Int'l*, pg. 2218
DAEDUCK CO., LTD.; *Int'l*, pg. 1906
DAEJAN HOLDINGS PLC—See Centremanor Ltd.; *Int'l*, pg. 1411
DAESANG HOLDINGS CO., LTD.; *Int'l*, pg. 1909
DAESUNG HOLDINGS CO., LTD.; *Int'l*, pg. 1909
DAETWYLER GLOBAL TEC HOLDING AG; *Int'l*, pg. 1909
DAE WOONG CO., LTD.; *Int'l*, pg. 1905
DAGGETT VENTURES, LLC; *U.S. Private*, pg. 1144
DAGI YATIRIM HOLDING A.S.; *Int'l*, pg. 1912
DAH CHONG HONG HOLDINGS LTD.—See CITIC Group Corporation; *Int'l*, pg. 1620
DAH SING COMPANY LIMITED—See Dah Sing Financial Holdings Limited; *Int'l*, pg. 1913
DAIFUKU WEBB HOLDING COMPANY—See Daifuku Co., Ltd.; *Int'l*, pg. 1925
DAIICHI KOUTSU SANGYO CO., LTD.; *Int'l*, pg. 1928
DAI-ICHI LIFE HOLDINGS, INC.; *Int'l*, pg. 1917
DAIICHI SANKYO CO., LTD.; *Int'l*, pg. 1929
DAIICHI SANKYO EUROPE GMBH—See Daiichi Sankyo Co., Ltd.; *Int'l*, pg. 1929
DAIMLER TRUCK HOLDING AG; *Int'l*, pg. 1938
DAIRIBORD HOLDINGS LIMITED; *Int'l*, pg. 1940
DAISHI HOKUETSU FINANCIAL GROUP, INC.; *Int'l*, pg. 1941
DAISHO MICROLINE HOLDINGS LIMITED; *Int'l*, pg. 1942
DAISY GROUP LIMITED; *Int'l*, pg. 1942
DAIWA CAPITAL MARKETS AMERICA HOLDINGS INC.—See Daiwa Securities Group Inc.; *Int'l*, pg. 1948
DAIWA HOUSE INDUSTRY CO., LTD.; *Int'l*, pg. 1944

DAIWA SECURITIES GROUP INC.; *Int'l*, pg. 1947
DALET HOLDING SAS—See Long Path Partners, LP; *U.S. Private*, pg. 2491
DALGASGROUP A/S—See Det Danske Hedeselskab; *Int'l*, pg. 2047
DALIAN DAFU HOLDINGS CO., LTD.; *Int'l*, pg. 1951
DALIAN SHIDE GROUP CO., LTD.; *Int'l*, pg. 1952
DALIAN SUNAISA TOURISM HOLDINGS CO., LTD.; *Int'l*, pg. 1952
DALIAN TOP-EASTERN GROUP CO., LTD.; *Int'l*, pg. 1952
DALIAN WANDA GROUP CORPORATION LTD.; *Int'l*, pg. 1953
DALIPAL HOLDINGS LIMITED; *Int'l*, pg. 1953
DALLAH AL BARAKA HOLDING COMPANY E.C.; *Int'l*, pg. 1953
DALLASNEWS CORPORATION; *U.S. Public*, pg. 621
DALRADIAN RESOURCES INC.—See Orion Resource Partners (USA) LP; *U.S. Private*, pg. 3043
DAL-TILE INTERNATIONAL INC.—See Mohawk Industries, Inc.; *U.S. Public*, pg. 1457
DALTON INVESTMENTS LLC; *U.S. Private*, pg. 1150
DAMAC GROUP; *Int'l*, pg. 1955
DAMSTRA HOLDINGS LTD.; *Int'l*, pg. 1957
DANA AUSTRALIA (HOLDINGS) PTY. LTD.—See Dana Incorporated; *U.S. Public*, pg. 622
DANAHER HOLDING B.V.—See Danaher Corporation; *U.S. Public*, pg. 626
DANA INCORPORATED; *U.S. Public*, pg. 621
DANBURY AEROSPACE, INC.; *U.S. Private*, pg. 1152
DANFOSS A/S; *Int'l*, pg. 1959
DANIEL J. EDELMAN HOLDINGS, INC.; *U.S. Private*, pg. 1154
DANIELS ENTERPRISES INC.; *U.S. Private*, pg. 1156
DANIEL THWAITES PLC; *Int'l*, pg. 1962
DANIR RESOURCES AB; *Int'l*, pg. 1963
DANLAW, INC.; *U.S. Private*, pg. 1157
DANNY'S FAMILY CAROUSEL, INC.—See Danny's Family Companies, LLC; *U.S. Private*, pg. 1157
DANNY'S FAMILY COMPANIES, LLC; *U.S. Private*, pg. 1157
DANONE ASIA-PACIFIC HOLDINGS PTE. LTD.—See Danone; *Int'l*, pg. 1965
DANONE BABY & MEDICAL NUTRITION B.V.—See Danone; *Int'l*, pg. 1965
DANONE BEHEER B.V.—See Danone; *Int'l*, pg. 1966
DANONE NEDERLAND B.V.—See Danone; *Int'l*, pg. 1968
DANONE; *Int'l*, pg. 1965
DANONE US, INC.—See Danone; *Int'l*, pg. 1967
DAN PERKINS AUTO GROUP; *U.S. Private*, pg. 1151
DANRAD HOLDING APS—See Danaher Corporation; *U.S. Public*, pg. 625
DANSK INDUSTRI INVEST A/S; *Int'l*, pg. 1968
DANTO HOLDINGS CORPORATION; *Int'l*, pg. 1969
DAN WOLF INCORPORATED; *U.S. Private*, pg. 1152
DANYA DUTCH BV—See Africa Israel Investments Ltd.; *Int'l*, pg. 190
DANZER AG; *Int'l*, pg. 1969
DANZER EUROPE VENEER AG—See Danzer AG; *Int'l*, pg. 1969
DAPD MEDIA HOLDING AG; *Int'l*, pg. 1970
DART HOLDING COMPANY LTD.—See Bristow Group, Inc.; *U.S. Public*, pg. 387
DART HOLDING COMPANY LTD.—See Eagle Copters Ltd.; *Int'l*, pg. 2264
DASEKE COMPANIES, INC.—See Daseke, Inc.; *U.S. Private*, pg. 1161
DASEKE, INC.; *U.S. Private*, pg. 1161
DASSAULT SYSTEMES AMERICAS CORP.—See Dassault Systemes S.A.; *Int'l*, pg. 1974
DATAGROUP SE; *Int'l*, pg. 1977
DATALEX PLC; *Int'l*, pg. 1978
DATALOGIC HOLDINGS, INC.—See Datalogic S.p.A.; *Int'l*, pg. 1978
DATRONIX HOLDINGS LIMITED; *Int'l*, pg. 1982
DAT-SCHAUB A/S—See Danish Crown AmbA; *Int'l*, pg. 1964
DATTO HOLDING CORP.—See Insight Venture Management, LLC; *U.S. Private*, pg. 2090
DAUN & CIE. AG; *Int'l*, pg. 1982
DAUPHIN HUMANDESIGN GROUP GMBH & CO. KG; *Int'l*, pg. 1982
DAUPHIN REALTY CORPORATION—See Berkshire Hathaway Inc.; *U.S. Public*, pg. 306
DAVCO ACQUISITION HOLDING INC.; *U.S. Private*, pg. 1168
DAVE CANTIN GROUP, LLC; *U.S. Private*, pg. 1168
DAVIDSON HOTEL COMPANY LLC—See Nautic Partners, LLC; *U.S. Private*, pg. 2868
DAVIDSON PIPE COMPANY INC.—See Ferguson plc; *Int'l*, pg. 2637
DAVIDSON PIPE SUPPLY CO. INC.—See Ferguson plc; *Int'l*, pg. 2637
DAWN PROPERTIES LIMITED; *Int'l*, pg. 1984
DAWOOD CORPORATION (PVT.) LTD.; *Int'l*, pg. 1984
DAWSON GEOPHYSICAL COMPANY—See Wilks Brothers LLC; *U.S. Private*, pg. 4521
DAWSON INTERNATIONAL PLC; *Int'l*, pg. 1984
DAYANG ENTERPRISE HOLDINGS BERHAD; *Int'l*, pg. 1985

N.A.I.C.S. INDEX 551112 — OFFICES OF OTHER HO...

N.A.I.C.S. Index

DAY STAR RESTAURANT HOLDINGS, LLC; *U.S. Private*, pg. 1176
DA YU FINANCIAL HOLDINGS LTD.; *Int'l*, pg. 1902
THE DAY & ZIMMERMANN GROUP, INC.; *U.S. Private*, pg. 4019
DAZN GROUP LIMITED—See Vista Equity Partners, LLC; *U.S. Private*, pg. 4401
DBA GROUP SRL; *Int'l*, pg. 1986
DBAPPAREL S.A.S.—See Hanesbrands Inc.; *U.S. Public*, pg. 982
DB ARKANSAS HOLDINGS, INC.—See Gannett Co., Inc.; *U.S. Public*, pg. 896
D&B GROUP HOLDINGS (UK)—See Cannae Holdings, Inc.; *U.S. Public*, pg. 429
D&B GROUP HOLDINGS (UK)—See CC Capital Partners, LLC; *U.S. Private*, pg. 798
D&B GROUP HOLDINGS (UK)—See Intercontinental Exchange, Inc.; *U.S. Public*, pg. 1141
D&B HOLDINGS AUSTRALIA LIMITED—See Cannae Holdings, Inc.; *U.S. Public*, pg. 429
D&B HOLDINGS AUSTRALIA LIMITED—See CC Capital Partners, LLC; *U.S. Private*, pg. 798
D&B HOLDINGS AUSTRALIA LIMITED—See Intercontinental Exchange, Inc.; *U.S. Public*, pg. 1141
D&B MANAGEMENT SERVICES CO.—See Cannae Holdings, Inc.; *U.S. Public*, pg. 429
D&B MANAGEMENT SERVICES CO.—See CC Capital Partners, LLC; *U.S. Private*, pg. 798
D&B MANAGEMENT SERVICES CO.—See Intercontinental Exchange, Inc.; *U.S. Public*, pg. 1141
DBM GLOBAL INC.—See INNOVATE Corp.; *U.S. Public*, pg. 1125
DB SCHENKER RAIL (UK) LIMITED—See Deutsche Bahn AG; *Int'l*, pg. 2050
DBSI HOUSING INC.—See DBSI, Inc.; *U.S. Private*, pg. 1179
DBSI, INC.; *U.S. Private*, pg. 1179
DB TEXAS HOLDINGS, INC.—See Gannett Co., Inc.; *U.S. Public*, pg. 896
DCA OUTDOOR, INC.; *U.S. Private*, pg. 1179
DCC ENERGY—See DCC plc; *Int'l*, pg. 1989
DCC ENVIRONMENTAL—See DCC plc; *Int'l*, pg. 1989
DCC FOOD & BEVERAGE—See DCC plc; *Int'l*, pg. 1989
DCC PLC; *Int'l*, pg. 1989
DCD-DORBYL (PTY) LTD.; *Int'l*, pg. 1991
DC ENERGY, LLC.; *U.S. Private*, pg. 1179
DCH AUTO GROUP (USA) INC.—See Lithia Motors, Inc.; *U.S. Public*, pg. 1322
DCH HOLDINGS LLC—See Lithia Motors, Inc.; *U.S. Public*, pg. 1322
DCP MIDSTREAM, LLC—See Phillips 66 Company; *U.S. Public*, pg. 1688
DC RADIO ASSETS, LLC—See Cumulus Media Inc.; *U.S. Public*, pg. 610
THE DDC GROUP; *U.S. Private*, pg. 4019
DD HOLDINGS CO., LTD.; *Int'l*, pg. 1993
DDI HOLDING AS—See Aban Offshore Limited; *Int'l*, pg. 48
DDM HOLDING AG; *Int'l*, pg. 1993
DDS WIRELESS INTERNATIONAL INC.; *Int'l*, pg. 1993
DEACONESS HOLDINGS, LLC—See Community Health Systems, Inc.; *U.S. Public*, pg. 552
DEA GENERAL AVIATION HOLDING CO., LTD.; *Int'l*, pg. 1997
DE AGOSTINI S.P.A.; *Int'l*, pg. 1994
DEAN DAIRY HOLDINGS, LLC—See Dean Foods Company; *U.S. Private*, pg. 1183
DEAN OPERATIONS, INC.; *U.S. Private*, pg. 1184
DEARBORN RESOURCES, INC.; *U.S. Private*, pg. 1185
DEBARTOLO CORPORATION; *U.S. Private*, pg. 1186
DEBARTOLO HOLDINGS, LLC; *U.S. Private*, pg. 1186
DE BEERS GROUP OF COMPANIES—See Anglo American PLC; *Int'l*, pg. 462
DE BOERTIEN GROEP B.V.; *Int'l*, pg. 1995
DECHRA PHARMACEUTICALS PLC—See EQT AB; *Int'l*, pg. 2474
DECISION INSIGHT INFORMATION GROUP (EUROPE) LIMITED—See Daily Mail & General Trust plc; *Int'l*, pg. 1937
DECISION INSIGHT INFORMATION GROUP, INC.—See TPG Capital, L.P.; *U.S. Public*, pg. 2173
DECORATIVE CASTINGS INC.; *U.S. Private*, pg. 1187
DECOR HOLDINGS, INC.; *U.S. Private*, pg. 1187
DECURION CORP.; *U.S. Private*, pg. 1188
DEDALO GRUPO GRAFICO, S.L.; *Int'l*, pg. 2001
DEFENCE TECH HOLDING S.P.A. SB; *Int'l*, pg. 2004
DEFINITIVE HEALTHCARE CORP.; *U.S. Public*, pg. 648
DEFRAQ VENTURES AG; *Int'l*, pg. 2004
DEGG'S IMMOBILIENPROJEKTENTWICKLUNG GMBH & CO. EINKAUFSPASSAGE KG—See BayernLB Holding AG; *Int'l*, pg. 913
DEILMANN-HANIEL INTERNATIONAL MINING & TUNNELING GMBH—See ATON GmbH; *Int'l*, pg. 688
DEKA BETEILIGUNGS GMBH—See DekaBank; *Int'l*, pg. 2005
DEKRA INTERNATIONAL GMBH—See DEKRA e.V.; *Int'l*, pg. 2008
DE LAGE LANDEN INTERNATIONAL BV—See Cooperatieve Centrale Raiffeisen-Boerenleenbank B.A.; *Int'l*, pg. 1791
DELANCE LIMITED; *Int'l*, pg. 2010
DELANY CAPITAL MANAGEMENT CORP.; *U.S. Private*, pg. 1193
DELEK GROUP LTD.; *Int'l*, pg. 2011
DELEK US HOLDINGS, INC.—See Delek Group Ltd.; *Int'l*, pg. 2011
DELFORTGROUP AG; *Int'l*, pg. 2013
DELIMOBIL HOLDING S.A.; *Int'l*, pg. 2013
DELINIAN LIMITED—See Astorg Partners S.A.S.; *Int'l*, pg. 656
DELINIAN LIMITED—See Epiris Managers LLP; *Int'l*, pg. 2460
DELIVRA HEALTH BRANDS INC.—See Hygrovest Limited; *Int'l*, pg. 3549
DELL TECHNOLOGIES INC.; *U.S. Public*, pg. 649
DELO GROUP; *Int'l*, pg. 2014
DELOITTE BULGARIA EOOD; *Int'l*, pg. 2014
DELOITTE HOLDING B.V.; *Int'l*, pg. 2014
DELOITTE LLP; *U.S. Private*, pg. 1197
DE'LONGHI S.P.A.; *Int'l*, pg. 1997
DELPHI HOLDINGS LUXEMBOURG S.A R.L.—See Aptiv PLC; *Int'l*, pg. 525
DEL TACO RESTAURANTS, INC.—See Jack in the Box Inc.; *U.S. Public*, pg. 1183
DELTA GROUP PTY LTD; *Int'l*, pg. 2018
DELTA HOLDINGS, INC.; *U.S. Private*, pg. 1200
DELTA HOLDING; *Int'l*, pg. 2018
DELTATHREE, INC.; *U.S. Private*, pg. 1202
DELTA TUCKER HOLDINGS, INC.—See Cerberus Capital Management, L.P.; *U.S. Private*, pg. 837
DELTON AG; *Int'l*, pg. 2021
DEMAAGD ENTERPRISES, LLC; *U.S. Private*, pg. 1203
DEMANT A/S; *Int'l*, pg. 2022
DEMATIC GMBH—See KKR & Co. Inc.; *U.S. Public*, pg. 1254
DEMATIC GMBH—See The Goldman Sachs Group, Inc.; *U.S. Public*, pg. 2078
DEMATIC HOLDINGS PTY. LTD.—See KKR & Co. Inc.; *U.S. Public*, pg. 1254
DEMATIC HOLDINGS PTY. LTD.—See The Goldman Sachs Group, Inc.; *U.S. Public*, pg. 2079
DEMCO EUROPE LIMITED—See Wall Family Enterprise, Inc.; *U.S. Private*, pg. 4430
DEMOS LLC; *Int'l*, pg. 2025
DEMPSEY GROUP, INC.—See CI Capital Partners LLC; *U.S. Private*, pg. 895
DEM. TH. BERTZELETOS & BROS. SA; *Int'l*, pg. 2022
DENALI MEDIA HOLDINGS, CORP.—See Liberty Broadband Corporation; *U.S. Public*, pg. 1310
DENBURY INC.—See Exxon Mobil Corporation; *U.S. Public*, pg. 813
DENEL SOC LTD.; *Int'l*, pg. 2026
DEN HARTOGH HOLDING BV; *Int'l*, pg. 2026
DENSO INTERNATIONAL ASIA PTE. LTD.—See Denso Corporation; *Int'l*, pg. 2031
DENSO INTERNATIONAL AUSTRALIA PTY. LTD.—See Denso Corporation; *Int'l*, pg. 2031
DENTSPLY SIRONA INC.; *U.S. Public*, pg. 654
DENTSU AEGIS JAPAN INC.—See Dentsu Group Inc.; *Int'l*, pg. 2034
DENTSU AEGIS NETWORK NETHERLANDS B.V.—See Dentsu Group Inc.; *Int'l*, pg. 2036
DENTSU GROUP INC.; *Int'l*, pg. 2034
DENTSU HOLDINGS PHILIPPINES INC.—See Dentsu Group Inc.; *Int'l*, pg. 2036
DENTSU INTERNATIONAL LIMITED—See Dentsu Group Inc.; *Int'l*, pg. 2035
DENTSU SOLARI INC.—See Dentsu Group Inc.; *Int'l*, pg. 2038
DENWAY MOTORS LTD—See Guangzhou Automobile Industry Group Co., Ltd.; *Int'l*, pg. 3164
DENYO AMERICA CORPORATION—See Denyo Co., Ltd.; *Int'l*, pg. 2040
DEPO HOLDINGS, LLC—See Trinity Hunt Management, L.P.; *U.S. Private*, pg. 4234
DEPUY INTERNATIONAL (HOLDINGS) LTD.—See Johnson & Johnson; *U.S. Public*, pg. 1195
DEPUY SYNTHES, INC.—See Johnson & Johnson; *U.S. Public*, pg. 1195
DEREK POBJOY INVESTMENTS LTD.; *Int'l*, pg. 2041
DERICHEBOURG MULTISERVICES SAS—See Derichebourg S.A.; *Int'l*, pg. 2042
DERMTECH, INC.—See DermTech, LLC; *U.S. Private*, pg. 1210
DESCOURS & CABAUD SA; *Int'l*, pg. 2044
DESERET MANAGEMENT CORPORATION; *U.S. Private*, pg. 1212
DESERT FIRE HOLDINGS, INC.—See MDU Resources Group, Inc.; *U.S. Public*, pg. 1410
DESRI INC.; *U.S. Private*, pg. 1215
DETAI NEW ENERGY GROUP LIMITED; *Int'l*, pg. 2047
DEUTSCHE ASSET MANAGEMENT ITALY S.P.A.—See Deutsche Bank Aktiengesellschaft; *Int'l*, pg. 2059
DEUTSCHE BAHN AG; *Int'l*, pg. 2049
DEUTSCHE BORSE IT-HOLDING GMBH—See Deutsche Borse AG; *Int'l*, pg. 2063
DEUTSCHE GAMMA GMBH—See Gilde Buy Out Partners B.V.; *Int'l*, pg. 2974
DEUTSCHE LUFTHANSA AG; *Int'l*, pg. 2066
DEUTSCHE WOHNEN SE; *Int'l*, pg. 2085
DEVA HOLDING A.S.—See Eastpharma Ltd.; *Int'l*, pg. 2274
DE VERE GROUP LIMITED; *Int'l*, pg. 1997
DEVILS HOLDINGS, LLC; *U.S. Private*, pg. 1218
DEVKI GROUP OF COMPANIES; *Int'l*, pg. 2089
DEVONSHIRE SWITZERLAND HOLDINGS GMBH—See RTX Corporation; *U.S. Public*, pg. 1823
DEVOTION ENERGY GROUP LIMITED; *Int'l*, pg. 2090
DEVVSTREAM HOLDINGS INC.—See DevvStream Corp.; *U.S. Public*, pg. 657
DEXELANCE S.P.A.; *Int'l*, pg. 2091
DEYUN HOLDING LTD.; *Int'l*, pg. 2093
DFC GLOBAL CORP.—See Lone Star Global Acquisitions, LLC; *U.S. Private*, pg. 2487
DFDS SEAWAYS HOLDING AB—See DFDS A/S; *Int'l*, pg. 2095
DFG CANADA, INC.—See Lone Star Global Acquisitions, LLC; *U.S. Private*, pg. 2487
DF KING WORLDWIDE—See The Riverside Company; *U.S. Private*, pg. 4108
DFL HOLDINGS PTY LTD; *Int'l*, pg. 2095
DFP HOLDINGS LIMITED; *Int'l*, pg. 2096
DFZ CAPITAL BERHAD—See Atlan Holdings Berhad; *Int'l*, pg. 673
DGB GROUP N.V.; *Int'l*, pg. 2096
DH HOLDINGS CO., LTD.; *Int'l*, pg. 2097
DH HOLDINGS CORP.—See Danaher Corporation; *U.S. Public*, pg. 625
DHI GROUP, INC.; *U.S. Public*, pg. 657
DHISCO, INC.—See H.I.G. Capital, LLC; *U.S. Private*, pg. 1829
DHL VERWALTUNGS GMBH—See Deutsche Post AG; *Int'l*, pg. 2078
DIAGEO CAPITAL PLC—See Diageo plc; *Int'l*, pg. 2102
DIAGEO PLC; *Int'l*, pg. 2101
DIAMOND ELECTRIC HOLDINGS CO., LTD.; *Int'l*, pg. 2105
DIAMOND RESORTS HOLDINGS, LLC—See Apollo Global Management, Inc.; *U.S. Public*, pg. 150
DIAMOND RESORTS HOLDINGS, LLC—See Reverence Capital Partners LLC; *U.S. Private*, pg. 3415
DIAMOND RESORTS INTERNATIONAL, INC.—See Apollo Global Management, Inc.; *U.S. Public*, pg. 150
DIAMOND RESORTS INTERNATIONAL, INC.—See Reverence Capital Partners LLC; *U.S. Private*, pg. 3415
DICK BLICK HOLDINGS INC.; *U.S. Private*, pg. 1225
DICK BROWNING, INC.; *U.S. Private*, pg. 1225
THE DICKERSON GROUP, INC.; *U.S. Private*, pg. 4021
DICK SMITH ELECTRONICS LIMITED—See Anchorage Capital Partners Pty. Limited; *Int'l*, pg. 448
DICK SMITH HOLDINGS LIMITED—See Anchorage Capital Partners Pty. Limited; *Int'l*, pg. 448
DIEBOLD INTERNATIONAL LIMITED—See Diebold Nixdorf, Inc.; *U.S. Public*, pg. 660
DIEBOLD LATIN AMERICA HOLDING COMPANY, LLC—See Diebold Nixdorf, Inc.; *U.S. Public*, pg. 660
DIEBOLD MEXICO HOLDING COMPANY, INC.—See Diebold Nixdorf, Inc.; *U.S. Public*, pg. 660
DIEBOLD NIXDORF, INC.; *U.S. Public*, pg. 659
DIEFENTHAL HOLDINGS, LLC; *U.S. Private*, pg. 1228
DIEHL STIFTUNG & CO. KG; *Int'l*, pg. 2114
DIETHELM KELLER HOLDING LIMITED; *Int'l*, pg. 2116
DIFFER GROUP HOLDING CO., LTD.; *Int'l*, pg. 2118
DIF MANAGEMENT HOLDING B.V.; *Int'l*, pg. 2117
DIGERATI TECHNOLOGIES, INC.; *U.S. Public*, pg. 661
DIGIA PLC; *Int'l*, pg. 2118
DIGITALBOX PLC; *Int'l*, pg. 2123
DIGITAL CHINA GROUP CO., LTD.; *Int'l*, pg. 2120
DIGITAL CHINA HOLDINGS LIMITED; *Int'l*, pg. 2121
DIGITAL COLONY MANAGEMENT, LLC—See DigitalBridge Group, Inc.; *U.S. Public*, pg. 664
DIGITAL DOMAIN HOLDINGS LIMITED; *Int'l*, pg. 2121
DIGITAL HEARTS HOLDINGS CO., LTD.; *Int'l*, pg. 2122
DIGITAL HOLDINGS, INC.; *Int'l*, pg. 2122
DIGITALOCEAN HOLDINGS, INC.; *U.S. Public*, pg. 665
DIGITAL VIRGO GROUP SAS; *Int'l*, pg. 2123
DIMENSIONAL MUSIC PUBLISHING, LLC—See JDS Capital Management, Inc.; *U.S. Private*, pg. 2196
DINAIR GROUP AB—See Daikin Industries, Ltd.; *Int'l*, pg. 1936
DINE BRANDS GLOBAL, INC.; *U.S. Public*, pg. 666
DIN GLOBAL CORP.; *U.S. Private*, pg. 1233
DINGYI GROUP INVESTMENT LIMITED; *Int'l*, pg. 2127
DIOS RIOS PARTNERS, LP; *U.S. Private*, pg. 1234
DIPLOMAT HOLDINGS LTD.; *Int'l*, pg. 2129
DIRECT DIGITAL HOLDINGS, INC.; *U.S. Public*, pg. 667
DIRECT ENERGY, LP—See NRG Energy, Inc.; *U.S. Public*, pg. 1549
DIRECT ENERGY MARKETING LIMITED—See NRG Energy, Inc.; *U.S. Public*, pg. 1549
DIRECT ENERGY SERVICES, LLC—See NRG Energy, Inc.; *U.S. Public*, pg. 1549
DIRECT LINE GROUP LIMITED—See Direct Line Insurance Group plc; *Int'l*, pg. 2129
DIRECT LINE INSURANCE GROUP PLC; *Int'l*, pg. 2129

551112 — OFFICES OF OTHER HO...   CORPORATE AFFILIATIONS

DIRECT TRAVEL, INC.—See ABRY Partners, LLC; *U.S. Private*, pg. 41
DISCOUNT INVESTMENT CORP. LTD.—See IDB Development Corporation Ltd.; *Int'l*, pg. 3588
DISCOVERY LIMITED; *Int'l*, pg. 2134
DISH NETWORK CORPORATION—See EchoStar Corporation; *U.S. Public*, pg. 711
DISOSWAY, INC.; *U.S. Private*, pg. 1238
DISPATCH BROADCAST GROUP—See The Dispatch Printing Company; *U.S. Public*, pg. 4021
THE DISPATCH PRINTING COMPANY; *U.S. Private*, pg. 4021
DISTRIBUTION FINANCE CAPITAL HOLDINGS PLC; *Int'l*, pg. 2136
DITECH NETWORKS, INC.—See Microsoft Corporation; *U.S. Public*, pg. 1442
DIVERSCO INC.—See ABM Industries, Inc.; *U.S. Public*, pg. 26
DIVERSEY EUROPE B.V.—See Platinum Equity, LLC; *U.S. Private*, pg. 3204
DIVERSEY HOLDINGS, LTD.—See Platinum Equity, LLC; *U.S. Private*, pg. 3204
DIVERSIFIED COMMUNICATIONS; *U.S. Private*, pg. 1241
DIVERSIFIED ENERGY COMPANY PLC; *U.S. Public*, pg. 670
DIVERSIFIED FOODSERVICE SUPPLY, INC.—See New Mountain Capital, LLC; *U.S. Private*, pg. 2901
DIWANG INDUSTRIAL HOLDINGS LIMITED; *Int'l*, pg. 2138
DIX 1898, INC; *U.S. Private*, pg. 1244
DKB FINANCE GMBH—See BayernLB Holding AG; *Int'l*, pg. 913
DKB GRUNDBESITZVERMITTLUNG GMBH—See BayernLB Holding AG; *Int'l*, pg. 913
DKB IMMOBILIEN BETEILIGUNGS GMBH—See BayernLB Holding AG; *Int'l*, pg. 913
DKB IT-SERVICES GMBH—See BayernLB Holding AG; *Int'l*, pg. 913
DK CROWN HOLDINGS INC.—See DraftKings Inc.; *U.S. Public*, pg. 687
DKSH HOLDING LIMITED—See Diethelm Keller Holding Limited; *Int'l*, pg. 2116
DKSH HOLDINGS (MALAYSIA) BERHAD—See Diethelm Keller Holding Limited; *Int'l*, pg. 2116
DLA PIPER INTERNATIONAL LLP—See DLA Piper Global; *Int'l*, pg. 2140
D&L INDUSTRIES, INC.; *Int'l*, pg. 1899
D'LONG INTERNATIONAL STRATEGIC INVESTMENT CO., LTD.—See China CITIC Financial Asset Management Co., Ltd.; *Int'l*, pg. 1489
DLP HEALTHCARE, LLC—See Apollo Global Management, Inc.; *U.S. Public*, pg. 155
DLR HOLDING, LLC; *U.S. Private*, pg. 1247
D MARINE INVESTMENT HOLDING B.V.—See Dogus Holding AS; *Int'l*, pg. 2154
DMB DR. DIETER MURMANN BETEILIGUNGSGESELLSCHAFT MBH; *Int'l*, pg. 2142
DMCI HOLDINGS, INC.; *Int'l*, pg. 2142
DMCI MINING CORPORATION—See DMCI Holdings, Inc.; *Int'l*, pg. 2142
DMEP CORPORATION; *U.S. Private*, pg. 1248
DMG AMERICA INC.—See DMG MORI Co., Ltd.; *Int'l*, pg. 2145
D&M HOLDINGS U.S. INC.—See Bain Capital, LP; *U.S. Private*, pg. 438
DMI TECHNOLOGY CORP.—See Delany Capital Management Corp.; *U.S. Private*, pg. 1194
DM PLC; *Int'l*, pg. 2142
DN HOLDINGS CO.,LTD; *Int'l*, pg. 2147
DNO NORTH SEA PLC; *Int'l*, pg. 2148
DNOW INC.; *U.S. Public*, pg. 671
DNV GL GROUP AS; *Int'l*, pg. 2148
DOBRUDZHA HOLDING AD; *Int'l*, pg. 2153
DOCTOR'S ASSOCIATES INC.; *U.S. Private*, pg. 1251
DOEDIJNS GROUP INTERNATIONAL B.V.—See IK Investment Partners Limited; *Int'l*, pg. 3609
DOERS EDUCATION ASEAN LIMITED; *U.S. Private*, pg. 1253
DOGGETT EQUIPMENT SERVICES, LTD.; *U.S. Private*, pg. 1253
DOGUS HOLDING AS; *Int'l*, pg. 2154
DOHLE HANDELSGRUPPE HOLDING GMBH & CO. KG; *Int'l*, pg. 2155
THE DOLAN COMPANY; *U.S. Private*, pg. 4022
DOLE HOLDING COMPANY, LLC—See Dole plc; *Int'l*, pg. 2157
DOLE PLC; *Int'l*, pg. 2157
DOLFIN GROUP LTD.; *Int'l*, pg. 2158
DOLLAR TREE, INC.; *U.S. Public*, pg. 672
DOLPHINS ENTERPRISES, LLC; *U.S. Private*, pg. 1255
DOMAINE POWER HOLDINGS LIMITED—See Hainan Traffic Administration Holding Co., Ltd.; *Int'l*, pg. 3213
DOMESTIC INDUSTRIES INC.; *U.S. Private*, pg. 1255
DOMETIC GROUP AB; *Int'l*, pg. 2160
DOMETIC INTERNATIONAL AB—See Dometic Group AB; *Int'l*, pg. 2160
DOMINION ENERGY, INC.; *U.S. Public*, pg. 673
DOMINION ENERGY QUESTAR CORPORATION—See Dominion Energy, Inc.; *U.S. Public*, pg. 674

DOMINION ENERGY SOLUTIONS, INC.—See Dominion Energy, Inc.; *U.S. Public*, pg. 674
DOMINION HOLDING CORPORATION; *Int'l*, pg. 2161
DOMINO'S PIZZA GROUP PLC; *Int'l*, pg. 2162
DOMINO'S PIZZA (ISLE OF MAN) LIMITED—See Domino's Pizza Group plc; *Int'l*, pg. 2162
DOMO NV; *Int'l*, pg. 2162
DOMUS FIN S.A.; *Int'l*, pg. 2162
DONALDSON EUROPE, B.V.B.A.—See Donaldson Company, Inc.; *U.S. Public*, pg. 675
DONALDSON FILTRATION DEUTSCHLAND GMBH—See Donaldson Company, Inc.; *U.S. Public*, pg. 675
DONCASTERS GROUP LTD.—See Dubai Holding LLC; *Int'l*, pg. 2218
DON DAVIS AUTO GROUP, INC.; *U.S. Private*, pg. 1257
DONEGAL INVESTMENT GROUP PLC; *Int'l*, pg. 2163
DONGBU GROUP; *Int'l*, pg. 2165
DONGGUAN DEVELOPMENT (HOLDINGS) CO., LTD.; *Int'l*, pg. 2167
DONGPENG HOLDINGS COMPANY LIMITED; *Int'l*, pg. 2169
DONGSUNG HOLDINGS CO., LTD.—See Dongsung Chemical Co., Ltd.; *Int'l*, pg. 2170
DONGWHA AUSTRALIA HOLDINGS PTY LTD.—See DONGWHA HOLDINGS CO., LTD.; *Int'l*, pg. 2170
DONGWON ENTERPRISE CO., LTD.; *Int'l*, pg. 2170
DONKEYREPUBLIC HOLDING A/S; *Int'l*, pg. 2172
DONNELLEY FINANCIAL SOLUTIONS CANADA CORPORATION—See Donnelley Financial Solutions, Inc.; *U.S. Public*, pg. 677
DONNELLEY FINANCIAL SOLUTIONS, INC.; *U.S. Public*, pg. 676
DONNELLEY FINANCIAL SOLUTIONS UK LIMITED—See Donnelley Financial Solutions, Inc.; *U.S. Public*, pg. 677
DOOSAN CORPORATION; *Int'l*, pg. 2172
DOPPELMAYR ANDORRA S.A.—See Doppelmayr Group; *Int'l*, pg. 2174
DOPPELMAYR GROUP; *Int'l*, pg. 2174
DOPPELMAYR HOLDING AG—See Doppelmayr Group; *Int'l*, pg. 2174
DOPPELMAYR LANOVE DRAHY, SPOL. S R. O.—See Doppelmayr Group; *Int'l*, pg. 2175
DORCHESTER GROUP OF COMPANIES; *Int'l*, pg. 2175
DORMAKABA HOLDING AG; *Int'l*, pg. 2177
DORMAN INDUSTRIES, LLC; *U.S. Private*, pg. 1263
DOSAL CAPITAL, LLC; *U.S. Private*, pg. 1264
DOT FAMILY HOLDINGS LLC; *U.S. Private*, pg. 1264
DOUBLEVERIFY HOLDINGS, INC.; *U.S. Public*, pg. 677
DOUTOR-NICHIRES HOLDINGS CO., LTD.; *Int'l*, pg. 2182
DOUYU INTERNATIONAL HOLDINGS LIMITED; *Int'l*, pg. 2182
DOVER COMMUNICATION TECHNOLOGIES, INC.—See Dover Corporation; *U.S. Public*, pg. 679
DOVER CORPORATION; *U.S. Public*, pg. 678
DOVER MOTORSPORTS, INC.—See Sonic Financial Corporation; *U.S. Private*, pg. 3713
DOVER PCS HOLDING LLC—See Dover Corporation; *U.S. Public*, pg. 680
DOWA HOLDINGS CO., LTD.; *Int'l*, pg. 2182
DOW CHEMICAL (CHINA) INVESTMENT COMPANY LIMITED—See Dow Inc.; *U.S. Public*, pg. 683
THE DOW CHEMICAL COMPANY—See Dow Inc.; *U.S. Public*, pg. 683
DOW EUROPE HOLDINGS B.V.—See Dow Inc.; *U.S. Public*, pg. 685
DOW FINANCIAL HOLDINGS INC.—See Dow Inc.; *U.S. Public*, pg. 684
DOW HOLDINGS LLC—See Dow Inc.; *U.S. Public*, pg. 684
DOW INC.; *U.S. Public*, pg. 683
DOW INTERBRANCH B.V.—See Dow Inc.; *U.S. Public*, pg. 685
DOW INTERNATIONAL HOLDINGS COMPANY—See Dow Inc.; *U.S. Public*, pg. 684
DOW INTERNATIONAL HOLDINGS S.A.—See Dow Inc.; *U.S. Public*, pg. 684
DOWNER EDI MINING HOLDING PTY LTD.—See Downer EDI Limited; *Int'l*, pg. 2185
DOWNER GROUP FINANCE PTY LIMITED—See Downer EDI Limited; *Int'l*, pg. 2186
DP FOX VENTURES, LLC; *U.S. Private*, pg. 1270
DPG MEDIA BV—See DPG Media Group NV; *Int'l*, pg. 2188
DPG MEDIA GROUP NV; *Int'l*, pg. 2188
DPI HOLDINGS BERHAD; *Int'l*, pg. 2189
DPS BRISTOL (HOLDINGS) LTD.; *Int'l*, pg. 2189
DPS RESOURCES BERHAD; *Int'l*, pg. 2189
DRAFTKINGS HOLDINGS INC.—See DraftKings Inc.; *U.S. Public*, pg. 687
DRAFTKINGS INC.; *U.S. Public*, pg. 687
DR. AICHHORN GMBH; *Int'l*, pg. 2190
DR. AUGUST OETKER KG; *Int'l*, pg. 2190
DRAX BIOMASS INTERNATIONAL INC.—See Drax Group plc; *Int'l*, pg. 2200
DRB HOLDING CO., LTD.; *Int'l*, pg. 2201
DREAMEAST GROUP LIMITED; *Int'l*, pg. 2203
DREAM FINDERS HOMES, INC.; *U.S. Public*, pg. 687
DREFA MEDIA HOLDING GMBH; *Int'l*, pg. 2204
DREISON INTERNATIONAL, INC.; *U.S. Private*, pg. 1276

DR. HELMUT ROTHENBERGER HOLDING GMBH; *Int'l*, pg. 2191
DRIVEN BRANDS HOLDINGS INC.; *U.S. Public*, pg. 688
DRIVEN BRANDS, INC.—See Roark Capital Group Inc.; *U.S. Private*, pg. 3455
DRIVER-HARRIS COMPANY; *U.S. Private*, pg. 1278
DR. PENG TELECOM & MEDIA GROUP CO., LTD.; *Int'l*, pg. 2194
DRYSHIPS INC.; *Int'l*, pg. 2207
DRYVIT HOLDINGS, INC.—See RPM International Inc.; *U.S. Public*, pg. 1819
DSCS HOLDINGS LLC; *U.S. Private*, pg. 1281
DS-FRANCE S.A.S.—See Danish Crown AmbA; *Int'l*, pg. 1964
DTE ENERGY COMPANY; *U.S. Public*, pg. 689
DTLR HOLDING, INC.—See Bruckmann, Rosser, Sherrill & Co., LLC; *U.S. Private*, pg. 671
DTV SERVICES LIMITED—See British Broadcasting Corporation; *Int'l*, pg. 1169
DTV SERVICES LIMITED—See Comcast Corporation; *U.S. Public*, pg. 541
DUBAI GROUP—See Dubai Holding LLC; *Int'l*, pg. 2218
DUBAI HOLDING LLC; *Int'l*, pg. 2218
DUBAI INSURANCE GROUP—See Dubai Holding LLC; *Int'l*, pg. 2218
DUBAI WORLD CORPORATION; *Int'l*, pg. 2220
THE DUCHOSSOIS GROUP, INC.; *U.S. Private*, pg. 4023
DUCKER FSG HOLDINGS LLC; *U.S. Private*, pg. 1284
DUDNYK ENTERPRISES, LTD.; *U.S. Private*, pg. 1284
DUFFY'S HOLDINGS INC.; *U.S. Private*, pg. 1285
DUFU TECHNOLOGY CORP. BERHAD; *Int'l*, pg. 2223
DULCICH, INC.; *U.S. Private*, pg. 1286
DUMMEN ORANGE HOLDING B.V.; *Int'l*, pg. 2225
DUNA HOUSE HOLDING PUBLIC COMPANY LIMITED; *Int'l*, pg. 2225
DUN & BRADSTREET HOLDINGS, INC.; *U.S. Public*, pg. 691
DUNDEE CORPORATION; *Int'l*, pg. 2225
DUNELM GROUP PLC; *Int'l*, pg. 2226
DUNKIN' BRANDS GROUP, INC.—See Roark Capital Group Inc.; *U.S. Private*, pg. 3455
DUNSTAN THOMAS GROUP LIMITED; *Int'l*, pg. 2227
DUOYUAN INVESTMENTS LIMITED; *Int'l*, pg. 2227
DUPONT DE NEMOURS, INC.; *U.S. Public*, pg. 692
THE DURACELL COMPANY—See Berkshire Hathaway Inc.; *U.S. Public*, pg. 316
DURAVANT LLC—See Warburg Pincus LLC; *U.S. Private*, pg. 4437
DURO DAKOVIC HOLDING D.D.; *Int'l*, pg. 2228
DURR AG; *Int'l*, pg. 2230
DUSSMANN STIFTUNG & CO. KGAA; *Int'l*, pg. 2234
DUTCH BROS INC.; *U.S. Public*, pg. 694
DUTECH HOLDINGS LIMITED; *Int'l*, pg. 2235
DUTY FREE CARIBBEAN HOLDINGS LTD.—See Avolta AG; *Int'l*, pg. 749
DUTY FREE CARIBBEAN HOLDINGS LTD.—See Cave Shepherd & Co., Ltd.; *Int'l*, pg. 1362
DW BETON GMBH—See Bain Capital, LP; *U.S. Private*, pg. 438
D.W. CAMPBELL, INC.; *U.S. Private*, pg. 1143
DW MANAGEMENT SERVICES, LLC; *Int'l*, pg. 2236
DXC TECHNOLOGY COMPANY; *U.S. Public*, pg. 694
DYCOM INDUSTRIES, INC.; *U.S. Public*, pg. 698
DYDO GROUP HOLDINGS, INC.; *Int'l*, pg. 2238
DYEHARD FAN SUPPLY, LLC—See Teall Capital Partners, LLC; *U.S. Private*, pg. 3948
DYER HOLDING PTY. LTD.; *Int'l*, pg. 2238
DYNACARE INC.—See Laboratory Corporation of America Holdings; *U.S. Public*, pg. 1286
DYNACTION SA; *Int'l*, pg. 2239
DYNA GROUP INTERNATIONAL INC.; *U.S. Public*, pg. 699
DYNAMIC BRANDS; *U.S. Private*, pg. 1297
DYNAMIC GROUP HOLDINGS LIMITED; *Int'l*, pg. 2240
DYNAMIC HOLDINGS LIMITED; *Int'l*, pg. 2240
DYNAMIC TECHNOLOGIES GROUP INC.; *Int'l*, pg. 2241
DYNAMIX BALWAS GROUP OF COMPANIES; *Int'l*, pg. 2241
DYNNIQ GROUP B.V.—See Egeria Capital Management B.V.; *Int'l*, pg. 2323
DYSON, DYSON & DUNN INC.; *U.S. Private*, pg. 1300
THE DYSON-KISSNER-MORAN CORPORATION; *U.S. Private*, pg. 4024
EAC INVEST AS; *Int'l*, pg. 2261
EACO CORPORATION; *U.S. Public*, pg. 701
EAF HOLDING GMBH; *Int'l*, pg. 2262
EAG-BETEILIGUNGS AG; *Int'l*, pg. 2263
EAGLE EYE SOLUTIONS GROUP PLC; *Int'l*, pg. 2264
EAGLE INDUSTRY CO., LTD.; *Int'l*, pg. 2264
EAGLE MATERIALS INC.; *U.S. Public*, pg. 702
EAGLE POINT INCOME COMPANY INC.; *U.S. Public*, pg. 703
EAGLESTONE, LLC—See Aterian Investment Management, L.P.; *U.S. Private*, pg. 366
EA HOLDINGS BERHAD; *Int'l*, pg. 2261
E.A. JUFFALI & BROTHERS COMPANY; *Int'l*, pg. 2250
E&A LIMITED; *Int'l*, pg. 2246
EARTHLINK HOLDINGS, LLC—See Windstream Holdings, Inc.; *U.S. Public*, pg. 2373

EARTHPORT PLC; *Int'l*, pg. 2268
EASE2PAY N.V.; *Int'l*, pg. 2269
EAST ASIA HOLDINGS INVESTMENT LIMITED; *Int'l*, pg. 2269
EAST BALT. INC.—See Grupo Bimbo, S.A.B. de C.V.; *Int'l*, pg. 3122
EAST BAY NEWSPAPERS—See Alden Global Capital LLC; *U.S. Private*, pg. 155
EASTBRIDGE GROUP; *Int'l*, pg. 2271
EAST COAST DIVERSIFIED CORPORATION; *U.S. Private*, pg. 1316
EASTERN ENERGY GAS HOLDINGS, LLC—See Dominion Energy, Inc.; *U.S. Public*, pg. 674
EASTERN HOLDINGS LTD.; *Int'l*, pg. 2272
EASTERN INSURANCE HOLDINGS, INC.—See ProAssurance Corporation; *U.S. Public*, pg. 1723
EASTHAM ENTERPRISES INC.; *U.S. Private*, pg. 1321
EAST JAPAN RAILWAY COMPANY; *Int'l*, pg. 2270
EASTPORT HOLDINGS, INC.; *U.S. Private*, pg. 1322
EASYJET PLC; *Int'l*, pg. 2276
EASY SMART GROUP HOLDINGS LIMITED; *Int'l*, pg. 2275
EASYVISTA HOLDING SAS—See Eurazeo SE; *Int'l*, pg. 2528
EAT & BEYOND GLOBAL HOLDINGS INC.; *Int'l*, pg. 2277
EATON CORPORATION PLC; *Int'l*, pg. 2277
EATON CORPORATION—See Eaton Corporation plc; *Int'l*, pg. 2277
EATON ELECTRIC HOLDINGS LLC—See Eaton Corporation plc; *Int'l*, pg. 2280
EATON INDUSTRIES MANUFACTURING GMBH—See Eaton Corporation plc; *Int'l*, pg. 2281
EBANG INTERNATIONAL HOLDINGS INC.; *Int'l*, pg. 2282
EB HOLDINGS CORP.—See WEX, Inc.; *U.S. Public*, pg. 2364
EBI ASIA PACIFIC PTE LTD—See Eagle Industry Co., Ltd.; *Int'l*, pg. 2265
EBI, LLC—See Zimmer Biomet Holdings, Inc.; *U.S. Public*, pg. 2406
EBUSCO HOLDING N.V.; *Int'l*, pg. 2287
EBX GROUP LTD.; *Int'l*, pg. 2287
ECARGO HOLDINGS LIMITED; *Int'l*, pg. 2287
ECARX HOLDINGS, INC.; *Int'l*, pg. 2287
E.CF SAS—See Groupe BPCE; *Int'l*, pg. 3095
ECHO, LLC; *U.S. Private*, pg. 1327
ECKERT & ZIEGLER STRAHLEN- UND MEDIZINTECHNIK AG; *Int'l*, pg. 2290
ECKES AG; *Int'l*, pg. 2290
ECKES-GRANINI GROUP GMBH—See Eckes AG; *Int'l*, pg. 2290
ECL WESTERN HOLDINGS LIMITED—See Empire Company Limited; *Int'l*, pg. 2387
ECOGREEN MANUFACTURING—See EcoGreen International Group Limited; *Int'l*, pg. 2295
ECO INNOVATION GROUP, INC.; *U.S. Public*, pg. 712
ECONACH HOLDINGS CO., LTD.; *Int'l*, pg. 2296
ECONOCOM SA—See Econocom Group SA; *Int'l*, pg. 2298
ECONOMEDIA; *Int'l*, pg. 2298
ECO - PHU HOLDING—See Derichebourg S.A.; *Int'l*, pg. 2041
ECO SCIENCE SOLUTIONS, INC.; *U.S. Private*, pg. 1328
ECOTEL COMMUNICATION AG; *Int'l*, pg. 2300
ECOWISE HOLDINGS LIMITED; *Int'l*, pg. 2300
ECS IT BERHAD; *Int'l*, pg. 2301
ECUHOLD N.V.—See Allcargo Logistics Limited; *Int'l*, pg. 333
ECZACIBASI HOLDING A.S.; *Int'l*, pg. 2301
ECZACIBASI YATIRIM HOLDING ORTAKLIGI A.S.; *Int'l*, pg. 2302
EDAG ENGINEERING GROUP AG—See ATON GmbH; *Int'l*, pg. 688
EDC COMMUNICATIONS LIMITED—See Mill Road Capital Management LLC; *U.S. Private*, pg. 2730
EDCON HOLDINGS LIMITED; *Int'l*, pg. 2304
EDDIE STOBART LOGISTICS PLC—See DBAY Advisors Limited; *Int'l*, pg. 1986
EDEN INC. BERHAD; *Int'l*, pg. 2306
EDENSOFT HOLDINGS LIMITED; *Int'l*, pg. 2308
EDF INTERNATIONAL SA—See Electricite de France S.A.; *Int'l*, pg. 2350
EDGE GROUP LIMITED; *Int'l*, pg. 2309
EDGEWELL PERSONAL CARE COMPANY; *U.S. Public*, pg. 717
EDGEWOOD COMPANIES; *U.S. Private*, pg. 1335
EDG/SW HOLDINGS LLC; *U.S. Private*, pg. 1333
EDIZIONE S.R.L.; *Int'l*, pg. 2311
EDP - ENERGIAS DO BRASIL S.A.—See EDP - Energias de Portugal, S.A.; *Int'l*, pg. 2314
EDSCHA HOLDING GMBH—See Acek Desarrollo y Gestion Industrial SL; *Int'l*, pg. 96
EDTECHX HOLDINGS ACQUISITION CORP.; *Int'l*, pg. 2315
EDUCATE, INC.—See Sterling Partners; *U.S. Private*, pg. 3807
EDUCATION AFFILIATES INC.—See JLL Partners, LLC; *U.S. Private*, pg. 2212
EDUCATION CORPORATION OF AMERICA; *U.S. Private*, pg. 1338

EDUCATION MEDIA & PUBLISHING GROUP (CHINA) LIMITED; *Int'l*, pg. 2315
EDVANTAGE GROUP HOLDINGS LIMITED; *Int'l*, pg. 2316
EDWARD B. BEHARRY & CO. LTD.; *Int'l*, pg. 2316
EDWARD ROSE COMPANY; *U.S. Private*, pg. 1341
EEKA FASHION HOLDINGS LIMITED; *Int'l*, pg. 2317
EEW ENERGY FROM WASTE GMBH—See Beijing Enterprises Holdings Limited; *Int'l*, pg. 950
EFACEC CAPITAL, SGPS, S.A.; *Int'l*, pg. 2318
EFAD REAL ESTATE COMPANY; *Int'l*, pg. 2318
EFFICIENT E-SOLUTIONS BERHAD; *Int'l*, pg. 2319
EFUTURE HOLDING INC.—See Beijing Shiji Information Technology Co., Ltd.; *Int'l*, pg. 956
EGCO PEARL CO., LTD.—See Electricity Generating Public Co., Ltd.; *Int'l*, pg. 2352
EGELI & CO. YATIRIM HOLDING A.S.; *Int'l*, pg. 2322
EGGPLANT GROUP LIMITED—See Keysight Technologies, Inc.; *U.S. Public*, pg. 1227
EGIDE USA, LLC—See Egide SA; *Int'l*, pg. 2324
EGL HOLDINGS COMPANY LIMITED; *Int'l*, pg. 2324
EGMONT HOLDING AB—See Egmont Fonden; *Int'l*, pg. 2325
EGMONT HOLDING OY—See Egmont Fonden; *Int'l*, pg. 2325
EGMONT INTERNATIONAL HOLDING A/S—See Egmont Fonden; *Int'l*, pg. 2325
EGYPTAIR HOLDING COMPANY; *Int'l*, pg. 2327
EGYPT KUWAIT HOLDING CO. S.A.E; *Int'l*, pg. 2327
EHANG HOLDINGS LIMITED; *Int'l*, pg. 2327
EHEALTH, INC.; *U.S. Public*, pg. 721
E-HOME HOUSEHOLD SERVICE HOLDINGS LIMITED; *Int'l*, pg. 2248
E-HOUSE (CHINA) HOLDINGS LIMITED; *Int'l*, pg. 2248
EIDESVIK HOLDING A/S; *Int'l*, pg. 2328
EIGER BIOPHARMACEUTICALS, INC.; *U.S. Public*, pg. 721
EIGHTCO HOLDINGS INC.; *U.S. Public*, pg. 721
EIKENBERRY CORPORATION; *U.S. Private*, pg. 1347
EIRCOM HOLDINGS (IRELAND) LIMITED; *Int'l*, pg. 2334
EISAI CORPORATION OF NORTH AMERICA—See Eisai Co., Ltd.; *Int'l*, pg. 2335
EISAI EUROPE LTD.—See Eisai Co., Ltd.; *Int'l*, pg. 2335
EI TOWERS S.P.A.; *Int'l*, pg. 2328
EJ HOLDINGS INC.; *Int'l*, pg. 2337
EK CHOR CHINA MOTORCYCLE CO., LTD.—See Charoen Pokphand Group Co., Ltd.; *Int'l*, pg. 1453
EKIP-98 HOLDING AD; *Int'l*, pg. 2338
EKO HOLDING SA—See Eurocash S.A.; *Int'l*, pg. 2533
EKO INTERNATIONAL CORP.; *U.S. Public*, pg. 721
EKOSEM-AGRAR GMBH; *Int'l*, pg. 2339
EKWIENOX LIMITED; *Int'l*, pg. 2340
EL-AD GROUP, LTD.; *U.S. Private*, pg. 1349
ELAGHMORE GP LLP; *Int'l*, pg. 2342
ELAH HOLDINGS, INC.; *U.S. Public*, pg. 722
E-LAND WORLD LTD.; *Int'l*, pg. 2248
ELAUT INTERNATIONAL N.V.; *Int'l*, pg. 2343
ELAVON EUROPEAN HOLDINGS B.V.—See U.S. Bancorp; *U.S. Public*, pg. 2212
ELAVON EUROPEAN HOLDINGS C.V.—See U.S. Bancorp; *U.S. Public*, pg. 2212
ELB EQUIPMENT HOLDINGS LIMITED—See ELB Group Limited; *Int'l*, pg. 2343
ELDER AUTOMOTIVE GROUP OF TAMPA BAY, INC.—See Elder Automotive Group; *U.S. Private*, pg. 1350
ELDER AUTOMOTIVE GROUP; *U.S. Private*, pg. 1350
ELDERS LIMITED; *Int'l*, pg. 2346
ELECTROLUX NORTH AMERICA, INC.—See AB Electrolux; *Int'l*, pg. 40
ELECTROLUX ZANUSSI ITALIA SPA—See AB Electrolux; *Int'l*, pg. 41
ELECTRON HOUSE (OVERSEAS) LIMITED—See Avnet, Inc.; *U.S. Public*, pg. 253
ELECTRONIC TRANSACTION GROUP NORDIC HOLDING AB—See British Columbia Investment Management Corp.; *Int'l*, pg. 1170
ELECTRONIC TRANSACTION GROUP NORDIC HOLDING AB—See Francisco Partners Management, LP; *U.S. Private*, pg. 1592
ELEGANCE OPTICAL INVESTMENTS LIMITED—See Elegance Optical International Holdings Ltd.; *Int'l*, pg. 2355
ELEKTRIM S.A.; *Int'l*, pg. 2356
ELEMENT GLOBAL, INC.; *U.S. Public*, pg. 725
ELEMENT SOLUTIONS INC.; *U.S. Public*, pg. 725
ELEVANCE HEALTH, INC.; *U.S. Public*, pg. 728
ELEVATE HOLDINGS, INC.; *U.S. Public*, pg. 1358
E-L FINANCIAL CORPORATION LIMITED; *Int'l*, pg. 2248
ELIA GRID INTERNATIONAL GMBH—See Elia Group SA; *Int'l*, pg. 2360
ELIA GRID INTERNATIONAL LLC—See Elia Group SA; *Int'l*, pg. 2360
ELIA GRID INTERNATIONAL NV/SA—See Elia Group SA; *Int'l*, pg. 2360
ELI GLOBAL, LLC; *U.S. Private*, pg. 1359
ELI LILLY GROUP LIMITED—See Eli Lilly & Company; *U.S. Public*, pg. 732
ELI LILLY INTERNATIONAL CORPORATION—See Eli Lilly & Company; *U.S. Public*, pg. 732
ELION CLEAN ENERGY CO., LTD.; *Int'l*, pg. 2361

ELITE HEALTH SYSTEMS HOLDINGS INC.—See Elite Health Systems Inc.; *U.S. Public*, pg. 734
ELITE HEALTH SYSTEMS INC.; *U.S. Public*, pg. 734
ELITE PERFORMANCE HOLDING CORP.; *U.S. Private*, pg. 1361
ELITE STOR CAPITAL PARTNERS, LLC—See Benjamin Macfarland Company, LLC; *U.S. Private*, pg. 526
ELKA BETEILIGUNGS GMBH; *Int'l*, pg. 2364
ELK GROUP INTERNATIONAL, INC.; *U.S. Private*, pg. 1362
ELLAKTOR S.A.; *Int'l*, pg. 2364
ELLA'S KITCHEN GROUP LIMITED—See The Hain Celestial Group, Inc.; *U.S. Public*, pg. 2086
ELL ENVIRONMENTAL HOLDINGS LIMITED; *Int'l*, pg. 2364
ELLERINE HOLDINGS LTD.; *Int'l*, pg. 2365
ELLERMAN INVESTMENTS LTD.; *Int'l*, pg. 2365
ELLEVATE FINANCIAL, INC.; *U.S. Public*, pg. 1363
ELLIS, MCQUARY, STANLEY & ASSOCIATES LLC; *U.S. Private*, pg. 1374
ELLOMAY CAPITAL LTD.; *Int'l*, pg. 2367
ELMC HOLDINGS, LLC; *U.S. Private*, pg. 1376
ELMORE GROUP LTD.; *U.S. Private*, pg. 1376
ELONG POWER HOLDING LIMITED; *Int'l*, pg. 2369
EL ORO LTD.; *Int'l*, pg. 2341
ELOY ESD SOLAR HOLDINGS, LLC—See The AES Corporation; *U.S. Public*, pg. 2031
EL PASO LLC—See Kinder Morgan, Inc.; *U.S. Public*, pg. 1232
EL POLLO LOCO HOLDINGS, INC.—See Trimaran Capital Partners, LLC; *U.S. Private*, pg. 4232
ELSTER GROUP GMBH—See Honeywell International Inc.; *U.S. Public*, pg. 1047
ELTEL AB; *Int'l*, pg. 2370
ELTEL GROUP CORPORATION—See Eltel AB; *Int'l*, pg. 2370
ELVISRIDGE CAPITAL, LLC; *U.S. Private*, pg. 1377
ELXSI CORPORATION—See SPX Technologies, Inc.; *U.S. Public*, pg. 1921
EMAMI GROUP; *Int'l*, pg. 2373
EMBRACE GROUP LIMITED—See D. E. Shaw & Co., L.P.; *U.S. Private*, pg. 1139
EMBRACE GROUP LIMITED—See Varde Partners, Inc.; *U.S. Private*, pg. 4346
EMC CORPORATION—See Dell Technologies Inc.; *U.S. Public*, pg. 650
EMC INSURANCE GROUP INC.—See Employers Mutual Casualty Company; *U.S. Private*, pg. 1386
EMCOR CONSTRUCTION SERVICES, INC.—See EMCOR Group, Inc.; *U.S. Public*, pg. 736
EMCOR FACILITIES SERVICES, INC.—See EMCOR Group, Inc.; *U.S. Public*, pg. 737
EMCOR GROUP, INC.; *U.S. Public*, pg. 736
E MEDIA HOLDINGS LIMITED; *Int'l*, pg. 2246
EMERA, INC.; *Int'l*, pg. 2377
EMERALD PLANTATION HOLDINGS LIMITED; *Int'l*, pg. 2377
EMERGENT CAPITAL, INC.; *U.S. Private*, pg. 1381
EMERGING GLORY SDN BHD; *Int'l*, pg. 2379
EMERGING TOWNS & CITIES SINGAPORE LTD.; *Int'l*, pg. 2379
EMERSON ELECTRIC (ASIA) LIMITED—See Emerson Electric Co.; *U.S. Public*, pg. 744
EMERSON ELECTRIC DO BRASIL LTDA—See Emerson Electric Co.; *U.S. Public*, pg. 744
EMERSON ELECTRIC (U.S.) HOLDING CORPORATION—See Emerson Electric Co.; *U.S. Public*, pg. 742
EMERSON SWEDEN AB—See Emerson Electric Co.; *U.S. Public*, pg. 747
EMI GROUP LIMITED—See Citigroup Inc.; *U.S. Public*, pg. 504
EMINENCE ENTERPRISE LIMITED—See Easyknit International Holdings Ltd.; *Int'l*, pg. 2276
EMIS GROUP PLC; *Int'l*, pg. 2382
EMMIS PUBLISHING CORPORATION—See Emmis Communications Corporation; *U.S. Public*, pg. 753
EMPERADOR INC.—See Alliance Global Group, Inc.; *Int'l*, pg. 339
EMPEROR ENTERTAINMENT HOTEL LIMITED; *Int'l*, pg. 2386
EMPIRE COMPANY LIMITED; *Int'l*, pg. 2386
EMPLOYEE OWNED HOLDINGS, INC.; *U.S. Private*, pg. 1386
EMPLOYERS HOLDINGS, INC.; *U.S. Public*, pg. 754
EMPRESA GENERAL DE INVERSIONES, S.A.; *Int'l*, pg. 2388
EMPRESAS BECHARA, INC.; *U.S. Private*, pg. 1388
EMPRESAS PENTA S.A.; *Int'l*, pg. 2391
EMPRESAS POLAR; *Int'l*, pg. 2391
EMPRESAS TAGAROPULOS, S.A.; *Int'l*, pg. 2392
EMR EMERSON HOLDINGS (SWITZERLAND) GMBH—See Emerson Electric Co.; *U.S. Public*, pg. 743
EMR US HOLDINGS LLC—See Emerson Electric Co.; *U.S. Public*, pg. 743
EMTEC INTERNATIONAL HOLDING GMBH—See Dexxon Groupe SA; *Int'l*, pg. 2093
ENABLE HOLDINGS, INC.; *U.S. Public*, pg. 754

ENACT HOLDINGS, INC.—See Genworth Financial, Inc.; *U.S. Public*, pg. 933
ENBRIDGE INC.; *Int'l*, pg. 2396
ENBW ENERGIE BADEN-WURTTEMBERG AG; *Int'l*, pg. 2397
ENCANA GLOBAL HOLDINGS S.A R.L.—See Ovintiv Inc.; *U.S. Public*, pg. 1625
ENCANTO RESTAURANTS, INC; *U.S. Private*, pg. 1389
ENCI HOLDING N.V.—See Heidelberg Materials AG; *Int'l*, pg. 3309
ENDEAVOR GROUP HOLDINGS, INC.—See Silver Lake Group, LLC; *U.S. Private*, pg. 3653
ENDEAVOUR AIR, INC.—See Delta Air Lines, Inc.; *U.S. Public*, pg. 652
ENDOCHOICE HOLDINGS, INC.—See Boston Scientific Corporation; *U.S. Public*, pg. 375
ENDO INTERNATIONAL PLC; *Int'l*, pg. 2403
ENDURANCE ENERGY LTD.—See Warburg Pincus LLC; *U.S. Private*, pg. 4438
ENDURANCE INTERNATIONAL GROUP HOLDINGS, INC.—See Clearlake Capital Group, L.P.; *U.S. Private*, pg. 934
ENDURANCE INTERNATIONAL GROUP HOLDINGS, INC.—See Siris Capital Group, LLC; *U.S. Private*, pg. 3673
ENDURANCE OVERSEAS S.R.L.—See Affirma Capital Limited; *Int'l*, pg. 187
ENDUR ASA; *Int'l*, pg. 2409
END USER SERVICES, INC.—See Ad-Base Group, Inc.; *U.S. Private*, pg. 72
ENECO HOLDING N.V.; *Int'l*, pg. 2411
ENEFCO INTERNATIONAL, INC.—See Argosy Capital Group, LLC; *U.S. Private*, pg. 321
ENEL BRASIL S.A.—See Enel S.p.A.; *Int'l*, pg. 2412
ENEL IBEROAMERICA SL—See Enel S.p.A.; *Int'l*, pg. 2413
ENEL LATINOAMERICA SA—See Enel S.p.A.; *Int'l*, pg. 2413
ENEL S.P.A.; *Int'l*, pg. 2411
ENEOS HOLDINGS, INC.; *Int'l*, pg. 2415
ENER1 GROUP, INC.; *U.S. Private*, pg. 1392
ENERCO GROUP INCORPORATED; *U.S. Private*, pg. 1392
ENERFAB, INC.; *U.S. Private*, pg. 1392
ENERGETICKY A PRUMYSLOVY HOLDING, A.S.; *Int'l*, pg. 2419
ENERGIEDIENST HOLDING AG—See EnBW Energie Baden-Wurttemberg AG; *Int'l*, pg. 2398
ENERGIE STEIERMARK AG; *Int'l*, pg. 2420
ENERGIZER HOLDINGS, INC.; *U.S. Public*, pg. 760
ENERGIZER MANAGEMENT HOLDING VERWALTUNGS GMBH—See Energizer Holdings, Inc.; *U.S. Public*, pg. 761
ENERGY & EXPLORATION PARTNERS, INC.; *U.S. Private*, pg. 1393
ENERGY HARDWARE HOLDINGS, INC.—See Barings BDC, Inc.; *U.S. Public*, pg. 276
ENERGY PLUS HOLDINGS LLC—See NRG Energy, Inc.; *U.S. Public*, pg. 1550
ENERGY SERVICES HOLDINGS, LLC—See Cadent Energy Partners, LLC; *U.S. Private*, pg. 713
ENERJISA ENERJI A.S.—See E.ON SE; *Int'l*, pg. 2257
ENERJISA ENERJI A.S.—See Haci Omer Sabanci Holding A.S.; *Int'l*, pg. 3204
ENERKON SOLAR INTERNATIONAL, INC.; *U.S. Public*, pg. 765
ENERO GROUP LIMITED; *Int'l*, pg. 2423
ENERPHASE INDUSTRIAL SOLUTIONS, INC.; *U.S. Private*, pg. 1396
ENFUSION, INC.; *U.S. Public*, pg. 768
ENGAGE TECHNOLOGIES CORP.; *U.S. Private*, pg. 1397
ENGENE HOLDINGS INC.; *Int'l*, pg. 2427
ENGIE NORTH AMERICA INC.—See ENGIE SA; *Int'l*, pg. 2428
ENGIE SA; *Int'l*, pg. 2428
ENGIE SERVICES AUSTRALIA & NEW ZEALAND HOLDINGS PTY. LTD.—See ENGIE SA; *Int'l*, pg. 2431
ENGILITY HOLDINGS, INC.—See Science Applications International Corporation; *U.S. Public*, pg. 1848
ENGLOBAL CORPORATION; *U.S. Public*, pg. 768
EN+ GROUP LTD.; *Int'l*, pg. 2395
ENI INTERNATIONAL B.V.—See Eni S.p.A.; *Int'l*, pg. 2437
ENIRO INTERNATIONAL AB—See Eniro Group AB; *Int'l*, pg. 2439
ENI UK LTD—See Eni S.p.A.; *Int'l*, pg. 2437
ENKA HOLDING B.V.—See Enka Insaat ve Sanayi A.S.; *Int'l*, pg. 2440
ENL COMMERCIAL LIMITED—See ENL Limited; *Int'l*, pg. 2441
ENLINK MIDSTREAM, LLC; *U.S. Public*, pg. 768
ENL LIMITED; *Int'l*, pg. 2440
ENMAX CORPORATION; *Int'l*, pg. 2442
ENMAX POWER CORPORATION—See ENMAX Corporation; *Int'l*, pg. 2442
ENM HOLDINGS LIMITED; *Int'l*, pg. 2442
ENNIA CARIBE HOLDING NV—See Banco di Caribe N.V.; *Int'l*, pg. 822
ENN NATURAL GAS CO., LTD.; *Int'l*, pg. 2442
ENOVOS INTERNATIONAL S.A; *Int'l*, pg. 2444
ENPOWER CORP.; *U.S. Private*, pg. 1401

ENSEMBLE HEALTH PARTNERS, INC.; *U.S. Private*, pg. 1402
ENSO GROUP; *Int'l*, pg. 2448
ENTAIN PLC; *Int'l*, pg. 2449
ENTEGRIS JAPAN HOLDING K.K.—See Entegris, Inc.; *U.S. Public*, pg. 776
ENTERCOM MEDIA CORP.—See AUDACY, INC.; *U.S. Public*, pg. 226
ENTERPRISE DEVELOPMENT HOLDINGS LIMITED; *Int'l*, pg. 2451
ENTERPRISE HOLDING CORPORATION—See Securian Financial Group, Inc.; *U.S. Private*, pg. 3594
ENTERPRISE HOLDINGS, INC.; *U.S. Private*, pg. 1403
ENTERTAINMENT HOLDINGS, INC.; *U.S. Private*, pg. 1404
ENTERTAINMENT TECHNOLOGY PARTNERS LLC; *U.S. Private*, pg. 1405
ENTHUSIAST GAMING HOLDINGS, INC.; *Int'l*, pg. 2452
ENTRETENIMIENTO GM DE MEXICO SA DE CV; *Int'l*, pg. 2453
ENTREX CARBON MARKET, LLC; *U.S. Public*, pg. 779
ENVERIC BIOSCIENCES, INC.; *U.S. Public*, pg. 780
ENVESTNET, INC.—See Bain Capital, LP; *U.S. Private*, pg. 439
ENVIPRO HOLDINGS INC.; *Int'l*, pg. 2453
ENVIRON GROUP (INVESTMENTS) PLC; *Int'l*, pg. 2454
ENVIRONMENTAL ENGINUITY GROUP LLC; *U.S. Private*, pg. 1407
ENVIRONMENTAL INFRASTRUCTURE HOLDINGS CORP.; *U.S. Private*, pg. 1408
ENVIRONMENTAL SOLUTIONS GROUP—See Terex Corporation; *U.S. Public*, pg. 2019
ENVISION HEALTHCARE HOLDINGS, INC.—See KKR & Co. Inc.; *U.S. Public*, pg. 1249
ENVISTA HOLDINGS CORPORATION; *U.S. Public*, pg. 781
ENVOY AVIATION GROUP, INC.—See American Airlines Group Inc.; *U.S. Public*, pg. 96
ENX LEASING INVESTMENTS PROPRIETARY LIMITED—See enX Group Limited; *Int'l*, pg. 2456
EOM PHARMACEUTICAL HOLDINGS, INC.; *U.S. Public*, pg. 782
E.ON SE; *Int'l*, pg. 2251
EOS INTERNATIONAL, INC.; *U.S. Private*, pg. 1411
E.P. BARRUS LTD.; *Int'l*, pg. 2260
EP ENERGY CORPORATION—See Access Industries, Inc.; *U.S. Private*, pg. 51
EP ENERGY CORPORATION—See Apollo Global Management, Inc.; *U.S. Public*, pg. 150
EP ENERGY CORPORATION—See Riverstone Holdings LLC; *U.S. Private*, pg. 3447
EPICQUEST EDUCATION GROUP INTERNATIONAL LIMITED; *U.S. Public*, pg. 783
EPISERVER PTY. LTD.—See Insight Venture Management, LLC; *U.S. Private*, pg. 2090
EQGP HOLDINGS, LP—See EQT Corporation; *U.S. Public*, pg. 785
EQ HOLDINGS, INC.—See Republic Services, Inc.; *U.S. Public*, pg. 1787
EQM TECHNOLOGIES & ENERGY, INC.; *U.S. Public*, pg. 784
EQS ASIA LIMITED—See Thoma Bravo, L.P.; *U.S. Private*, pg. 4147
EQT AB; *Int'l*, pg. 2467
EQT RE, LLC—See EQT Corporation; *U.S. Public*, pg. 784
EQUIFAX AUSTRALIA PTY. LTD.—See Equifax Inc.; *U.S. Public*, pg. 786
EQUIFAX CANADIAN HOLDINGS CO.—See Equifax Inc.; *U.S. Public*, pg. 786
EQUIFAX DO BRASIL HOLDINGS LTDA.—See Equifax Inc.; *U.S. Public*, pg. 786
EQUINITI GROUP PLC—See Siris Capital Group, LLC; *U.S. Private*, pg. 3673
EQUINIX (NETHERLANDS) HOLDINGS BV—See Equinix, Inc.; *U.S. Public*, pg. 787
EQUINOR ASA; *Int'l*, pg. 2484
EQUINOR US HOLDINGS INC.—See Equinor ASA; *Int'l*, pg. 2485
EQUIPMAKE HOLDINGS PLC; *Int'l*, pg. 2485
EQUITABLE HOLDINGS, INC.; *U.S. Public*, pg. 788
EQUITAL LTD.; *Int'l*, pg. 2487
EQUITAS HOLDINGS LIMITED; *Int'l*, pg. 2487
EQUITY GROUP INVESTMENTS, LLC—See TowerBrook Capital Partners, L.P.; *U.S. Private*, pg. 4195
EQUUS HOLDINGS, INC.; *U.S. Private*, pg. 1417
EQUUS TOTAL RETURN, INC.; *U.S. Public*, pg. 792
EQVA ASA; *Int'l*, pg. 2488
ERA HELICOPTERS, LLC—See Bristow Group, Inc.; *U.S. Public*, pg. 387
ERA LEASING LLC—See Bristow Group, Inc.; *U.S. Public*, pg. 387
ERA MED LLC—See Bristow Group, Inc.; *U.S. Public*, pg. 387
ERAYAK POWER SOLUTION GROUP INC.; *Int'l*, pg. 2489
ERBE SA—See BNP Paribas SA; *Int'l*, pg. 1090
ERBE SA—See Frere-Bourgeois; *Int'l*, pg. 2773
E.R. CAPITAL HOLDING GMBH & CIE. KG; *Int'l*, pg. 2260
EREDIVISIE BEHEER B.V.—See The Walt Disney Company; *U.S. Public*, pg. 2140
EREN GROUPE SA; *Int'l*, pg. 2490

ERG S.P.A.; *Int'l*, pg. 2491
ERIE INDEMNITY COMPANY; *U.S. Public*, pg. 792
ERI HOLDINGS CO., LTD.; *Int'l*, pg. 2491
E. RITTER AGRIBUSINESS HOLDINGS, INC.—See E. Ritter & Company; *U.S. Private*, pg. 1304
E. RITTER AGRIBUSINESS HOLDINGS, INC.—See Grain Management, LLC; *U.S. Private*, pg. 1751
E. RITTER COMMUNICATIONS HOLDINGS, INC.—See E. Ritter & Company; *U.S. Private*, pg. 1304
E. RITTER COMMUNICATIONS HOLDINGS, INC.—See Grain Management, LLC; *U.S. Private*, pg. 1751
E. RITTER & COMPANY; *U.S. Private*, pg. 1304
ERNEST BOREL HOLDINGS LIMITED—See Citychamp Watch & Jewellery Group Limited; *Int'l*, pg. 1629
ERNEST HEALTH, INC.; *U.S. Private*, pg. 1421
ERNST GOHNER STIFTUNG; *Int'l*, pg. 2495
EROGLU HOLDING AS; *Int'l*, pg. 2496
EROS INTERNATIONAL PLC; *Int'l*, pg. 2496
EROS INTERNATIONAL USA INC.—See Eros International Plc; *Int'l*, pg. 2496
ESAS HOLDING A.S.; *Int'l*, pg. 2501
ESCALATE MEDIA HOLDINGS, LLC—See H.I.G. Capital, LLC; *U.S. Private*, pg. 1829
ESCHENBACH HOLDING GMBH—See Equistone Partners Europe Limited; *Int'l*, pg. 2486
ESCO TECHNOLOGIES HOLDING INC.—See ESCO Technologies, Inc.; *U.S. Public*, pg. 793
ESCOY HOLDINGS BHD.—See Amalgamated Metal Corporation PLC; *Int'l*, pg. 408
ESENCIA GROUP; *Int'l*, pg. 2502
ESENCIA GROUP—See Esencia Group; *Int'l*, pg. 2502
ESENCIA GROUP—See Esencia Group; *Int'l*, pg. 2502
ESGL HOLDINGS LIMITED; *Int'l*, pg. 2503
E.S.I. HOLDOING CORP.; *U.S. Private*, pg. 1307
ESKEN LIMITED; *Int'l*, pg. 2503
ESMARK INCORPORATED; *U.S. Private*, pg. 1426
ESMARK STEEL GROUP, LLC—See Esmark Incorporated; *U.S. Private*, pg. 1426
ESPN, INC.—See The Walt Disney Company; *U.S. Public*, pg. 2138
ESPRIT INTERNATIONAL GP, INC.—See Esprit Holdings Limited; *Int'l*, pg. 2507
ESRT MH HOLDINGS, L.L.C.—See Empire State Realty Trust, Inc.; *U.S. Public*, pg. 753
ESSAR ENERGY PLC—See Essar Global Limited; *Int'l*, pg. 2508
ESSAR GLOBAL LIMITED; *Int'l*, pg. 2508
ESSEL CORPORATE RESOURCES PVT. LTD.; *Int'l*, pg. 2509
ESSELTE AB—See ACCO Brands Corporation; *U.S. Public*, pg. 32
ESSENT GROUP LTD.; *Int'l*, pg. 2510
ESTABLISHMENT LABS HOLDINGS, INC.; *Int'l*, pg. 2517
ESTATIA AG; *Int'l*, pg. 2517
ESTORIL SOL, SGPS, S.A.; *Int'l*, pg. 2518
E. SUN FINANCIAL HOLDING CO., LTD.; *Int'l*, pg. 2250
ESURE GROUP PLC—See Bain Capital, LP; *U.S. Private*, pg. 452
ETALON-LENSPETSSMU CONSTRUCTION HOLDING COMPANY; *Int'l*, pg. 2520
ETE COMMON HOLDINGS, LLC—See Energy Transfer LP; *U.S. Public*, pg. 763
ETERNAL BEST INDUSTRIAL LIMITED; *Int'l*, pg. 2520
ETERNITY INVESTMENT LIMITED; *Int'l*, pg. 2521
ETHIAS FINANCE SA/NV; *Int'l*, pg. 2523
ETICA ENTERTAINMENT INC.; *U.S. Private*, pg. 1432
E*TRADE FINANCIAL CORPORATION; *U.S. Private*, pg. 1302
ETX HOLDINGS, INC.—See Blue Point Capital Partners, LLC; *U.S. Private*, pg. 590
EUMUNDI GROUP LIMITED; *Int'l*, pg. 2526
EURASIAN NATURAL RESOURCES CORPORATION LIMITED; *Int'l*, pg. 2527
EUREMIS HOLDING SA; *Int'l*, pg. 2530
EUROBANK ERGASIAS SERVICES AND HOLDINGS S.A.; *Int'l*, pg. 2532
EUROCHEM MINERAL CHEMICAL COMPANY, OJSC; *Int'l*, pg. 2533
EURO DISNEY COMMANDITE SAS—See The Walt Disney Company; *U.S. Public*, pg. 2139
EURO DISNEY S.C.A.—See The Walt Disney Company; *U.S. Public*, pg. 2139
EURODRY LTD.; *Int'l*, pg. 2534
EUROFINS FRANCE HOLDING SAS—See Eurofins Scientific S.E.; *Int'l*, pg. 2542
EUROFINS SCIENTIFIC S.E.; *Int'l*, pg. 2535
EUROGRID INTERNATIONAL CVBA/SCRL—See Elia Group SA; *Int'l*, pg. 2360
EUROHOLD BULGARIA AD; *Int'l*, pg. 2552
EUROKAI GMBH & CO. KGAA; *Int'l*, pg. 2553
EUROLIFE ERB INSURANCE GROUP HOLDINGS S.A.—See Fairfax Financial Holdings Limited; *Int'l*, pg. 2606
EUROMAINT GRUPPEN AB—See Construcciones y Auxiliar de Ferrocarriles S.A.; *Int'l*, pg. 1777
EUROMOBILIARE FIDUCIARIA SPA—See Credito Emiliano S.p.A.; *Int'l*, pg. 1836
EURONEXT N.V.; *Int'l*, pg. 2554

N.A.I.C.S. INDEX

551112 — OFFICES OF OTHER HO...

EUROPEAN CANNABIS CORPORATION LIMITED; *Int'l*, pg. 2555
EUROPEAN GOLD REFINERIES HOLDING SA—See Newmont Corporation; *U.S. Public*, pg. 1516
EUROPEAN METAL RECYCLING LIMITED; *Int'l*, pg. 2556
EURO TECH (FAR EAST) LTD.—See Euro Tech Holdings Company Limited; *Int'l*, pg. 2531
EUROVITA HOLDING S.P.A.—See Cinven Limited; *Int'l*, pg. 1612
EURO YATIRIM HOLDING AS; *Int'l*, pg. 2531
EUSU HOLDINGS CO., LTD.; *Int'l*, pg. 2559
EU YAN SANG INTERNATIONAL LTD.; *Int'l*, pg. 2525
EVANS NATIONAL FINANCIAL SERVICES, LLC—See Evans Bancorp, Inc.; *Int'l*, pg. 799
EVCI CAREER COLLEGES HOLDING CORP.; *U.S. Private*, pg. 1435
EV DYNAMICS (HOLDINGS) LIMITED; *Int'l*, pg. 2560
EVENING POST PUBLISHING CO.; *U.S. Private*, pg. 1436
EVENT HOSPITALITY & ENTERTAINMENT LIMITED; *Int'l*, pg. 2562
EVENT SUPPORT CORPORATION—See National Association for Stock Car Auto Racing, Inc.; *U.S. Private*, pg. 2845
EVERCHINA INT'L HOLDINGS COMPANY LIMITED; *Int'l*, pg. 2563
EVERCORE GROUP LLC—See Evercore, Inc.; *U.S. Public*, pg. 800
EVEREST REINSURANCE HOLDINGS, INC.—See Everest Group, Ltd.; *Int'l*, pg. 2564
EVER-GOTESCO RESOURCES & HOLDINGS, INC.; *Int'l*, pg. 2563
EVERGREEN CORPORATION; *Int'l*, pg. 2565
THE EVERGREEN GROUP VENTURES, LLC; *U.S. Private*, pg. 4027
EVERGREEN SERVICES GROUP LLC—See Alpine Investors; *U.S. Private*, pg. 201
EVERGY, INC.; *U.S. Public*, pg. 800
EVERI HOLDINGS INC.; *U.S. Public*, pg. 801
EVERJOY HEALTH GROUP CO., LTD.; *Int'l*, pg. 2567
EVERSAFE RUBBER BERHAD; *Int'l*, pg. 2568
EVERSHINE GROUP HOLDINGS LIMITED; *Int'l*, pg. 2568
EVERTEC, INC.; *U.S. Public*, pg. 802
EVN FINANZSERVICE GMBH—See EVN AG; *Int'l*, pg. 2571
EVOAIR HOLDINGS INC.; *Int'l*, pg. 2572
EVOKE PLC; *Int'l*, pg. 2572
EVOLUTION HEALTHCARE PTY. LTD.; *Int'l*, pg. 2572
EVOLUTION JAPAN CO., LTD.—See Evolution Capital Management LLC; *U.S. Private*, pg. 1443
EVOLVE TRANSITION INFRASTRUCTURE LP; *U.S. Public*, pg. 804
EV PRIVATE EQUITY; *Int'l*, pg. 2560
EVRAZ GROUP S.A.—See Evraz plc; *Int'l*, pg. 2573
EVRAZ LLC—See Evraz plc; *Int'l*, pg. 2573
EVRAZ PLC; *Int'l*, pg. 2573
EWC-HH&B HOLDINGS, LLC—See EverWatch Capital; *U.S. Private*, pg. 1441
EWEIN BERHAD; *Int'l*, pg. 2576
EXACT EMEA B.V.—See KKR & Co. Inc.; *U.S. Public*, pg. 1250
EXACT HOLDING N.V.—See KKR & Co. Inc.; *U.S. Public*, pg. 1250
EXACT NEDERLAND B.V.—See KKR & Co. Inc.; *U.S. Public*, pg. 1250
EXACT SOFTWARE ASIA SDN. BHD.—See KKR & Co. Inc.; *U.S. Public*, pg. 1250
EXAMWORKS GROUP, INC.—See GIC Pte. Ltd.; *Int'l*, pg. 2964
EXAMWORKS GROUP, INC.—See Leonard Green & Partners, L.P.; *U.S. Private*, pg. 2425
EXCEL GROUP, INC.; *U.S. Private*, pg. 1445
EXCEL HOMES GROUP, LLC—See Innovative Building Systems LLC; *U.S. Private*, pg. 2082
EXCELLENT RETAIL BRANDS B.V.; *Int'l*, pg. 2578
EXCELLERATE HOLDINGS LTD.; *Int'l*, pg. 2578
EXCEPTIONAL INNOVATION BV; *Int'l*, pg. 2579
EXCITE HOLDINGS CO., LTD.; *Int'l*, pg. 2579
EXCITE TECHNOLOGY SERVICES LIMITED; *Int'l*, pg. 2579
EXEDY HOLDINGS OF AMERICA CORPORATION—See Exedy Corporation; *Int'l*, pg. 2581
EXELON CORPORATION; *U.S. Public*, pg. 806
EXOR N.V.—See Giovanni Agnelli B.V.; *Int'l*, pg. 2978
EXPAND FAST HOLDINGS (SINGAPORE) PTE. LIMITED—See Essel Corporate Resources Pvt. Ltd.; *Int'l*, pg. 2510
EXPEDIA GROUP, INC.; *U.S. Public*, pg. 809
EXPLORNATION ENERGY, INC.; *U.S. Private*, pg. 1450
EXPRESS SCRIPTS HOLDING COMPANY—See The Cigna Group; *U.S. Public*, pg. 2061
EXPRO GROUP HOLDINGS N.V.; *Int'l*, pg. 2591
EXSITEC HOLDING AB; *Int'l*, pg. 2591
EXTERION MEDIA—See Platinum Equity, LLC; *U.S. Private*, pg. 3203
EXTERRAN GP LLC—See Archrock, Inc.; *U.S. Public*, pg. 186
EXTRACT GROUP LIMITED; *Int'l*, pg. 2592
EXTRAWELL PHARMACEUTICAL HOLDINGS LTD.; *Int'l*, pg. 2592

EXTREME HOLDINGS, INC.; *U.S. Private*, pg. 1452
EXXONMOBIL CENTRAL EUROPE HOLDING GMBH—See Exxon Mobil Corporation; *U.S. Public*, pg. 814
EXXON MOBIL CORPORATION; *U.S. Public*, pg. 813
EXXONMOBIL INTERNATIONAL HOLDINGS INC.—See Exxon Mobil Corporation; *U.S. Public*, pg. 815
EYE HEALTH AMERICA—See Independence Capital Partners, LLC; *U.S. Private*, pg. 2056
EYP, INC.; *U.S. Private*, pg. 1454
EZFILL HOLDINGS INC.; *U.S. Public*, pg. 818
EZGO TECHNOLOGIES INC.; *Int'l*, pg. 2594
EZRAIDER CO.; *U.S. Public*, pg. 818
EZZ LIFE SCIENCE HOLDINGS LIMITED; *Int'l*, pg. 2594
F45 TRAINING HOLDINGS INC.; *U.S. Public*, pg. 1457
FABREL AG; *Int'l*, pg. 2599
FACIL CORPORATE BVBA; *Int'l*, pg. 2600
FACT CORPORATION; *Int'l*, pg. 2601
FAGERDALA WORLD FOAMS AB; *Int'l*, pg. 2601
FAGERHULT GROUP AB; *Int'l*, pg. 2601
FAGRON NV; *Int'l*, pg. 2602
FAH MAI HOLDINGS, INC.; *Int'l*, pg. 2604
FAIRFAX FINANCIAL HOLDINGS LIMITED; *Int'l*, pg. 2605
FAIRFAX INDIA HOLDINGS CORPORATION—See Fairfax Financial Holdings Limited; *Int'l*, pg. 2606
FAIRFIELD COUNTY BANK, MHC; *U.S. Private*, pg. 1463
FAIRMONT RAFFLES HOTELS INTERNATIONAL INC.—See Accor S.A.; *Int'l*, pg. 91
FAIRPOINT GROUP PLC; *Int'l*, pg. 2609
FAIRWAY GROUP HOLDINGS CORP.—See Sterling Investment Partners, L.P.; *U.S. Private*, pg. 3805
FALANX CYBER SECURITY LTD; *Int'l*, pg. 2610
FAM AB; *Int'l*, pg. 2611
FAMILY DOLLAR STORES, INC.—See Dollar Tree, Inc.; *U.S. Public*, pg. 672
FANDANGO HOLDINGS PLC; *Int'l*, pg. 2613
FANGDD NETWORK GROUP LTD.; *Int'l*, pg. 2613
FANNIE MAY CONFECTIONS BRANDS, INC.—See Ferrero International S.A.; *Int'l*, pg. 2640
FANSTEEL, INC.; *U.S. Private*, pg. 1472
FANTASISTA CO., LTD.; *Int'l*, pg. 2613
FARADAY FUTURE INTELLIGENT ELECTRIC INC.; *U.S. Public*, pg. 821
FARADAY HOLDINGS LIMITED—See Berkshire Hathaway Inc.; *U.S. Public*, pg. 301
FAR BANK ENTERPRISES, INC.—See Joshua Green Corporation; *U.S. Private*, pg. 2237
FAR EAST ORGANIZATION PTE. LTD.; *Int'l*, pg. 2616
FARMER BUSINESS DEVELOPMENTS PLC; *Int'l*, pg. 2619
FARMINVESTE SGPS S.A.; *Int'l*, pg. 2620
FARM PRIDE FOODS LTD.; *Int'l*, pg. 2619
FARNBOROUGH LIMITED—See Global Business Travel Group, Inc.; *U.S. Public*, pg. 941
FASTBUCKS HOLDING CORPORATION; *U.S. Private*, pg. 1482
FAST FINANCE 24 HOLDING AG; *Int'l*, pg. 2621
FASTIGHETS AB BRIGGEN—See Castellum AB; *Int'l*, pg. 1356
FASTIGHETS AB CORALLEN—See Castellum AB; *Int'l*, pg. 1356
FAST LINE HLDG, INC.; *U.S. Public*, pg. 2621
FAST RETAILING CO., LTD.; *Int'l*, pg. 2621
FATHOM HOLDINGS INC.; *U.S. Public*, pg. 824
FATIMA FERTILIZER COMPANY LIMITED; *Int'l*, pg. 2623
FAYAT SAS; *Int'l*, pg. 2624
FBA II, INC.; *U.S. Private*, pg. 1485
FBD HOLDINGS PLC; *Int'l*, pg. 2627
F&B GROUP; *Int'l*, pg. 2595
F&C (CI) LIMITED—See Bank of Montreal; *Int'l*, pg. 847
FCCI MUTUAL INSURANCE HOLDING COMPANY; *U.S. Private*, pg. 1485
F&C GROUP (HOLDINGS) LIMITED—See Bank of Montreal; *Int'l*, pg. 847
F&C GROUP MANAGEMENT LIMITED—See Bank of Montreal; *Int'l*, pg. 847
FCSTONE GROUP, INC.—See StoneX Group Inc.; *U.S. Public*, pg. 1951
FDG ELECTRIC VEHICLES LIMITED; *Int'l*, pg. 2629
FDS GROUP SA—See Bridgepoint Group Plc; *Int'l*, pg. 1154
FECTO GROUP OF COMPANIES; *Int'l*, pg. 2629
FEDERAL EXPRESS INTERNATIONAL, INC.—See FedEx Corporation; *U.S. Public*, pg. 828
FEDERAL-MOGUL ACQUISITION COMPANY LIMITED—See Apollo Global Management, Inc.; *U.S. Public*, pg. 162
FEDERAL-MOGUL ASIA INVESTMENTS LIMITED—See Apollo Global Management, Inc.; *U.S. Public*, pg. 160
FEDERAL-MOGUL CHASSIS LLC—See Apollo Global Management, Inc.; *U.S. Public*, pg. 160
FEDERAL-MOGUL FRICTION PRODUCTS INTERNATIONAL GMBH—See Apollo Global Management, Inc.; *U.S. Public*, pg. 161
FEDERAL-MOGUL HOLDINGS DEUTSCHLAND GMBH—See Apollo Global Management, Inc.; *U.S. Public*, pg. 161
FEDERAL-MOGUL HOLDINGS LLC—See Apollo Global Management, Inc.; *U.S. Public*, pg. 160
FEDERAL-MOGUL MOTORPARTS MINORITY HOLDING B.V.—See Apollo Global Management, Inc.; *U.S. Public*, pg. 161
FEDERAL-MOGUL POWERTRAIN ITALY S.R.L—See Apollo Global Management, Inc.; *U.S. Public*, pg. 161
FEDERAL-MOGUL SAS—See Apollo Global Management, Inc.; *U.S. Public*, pg. 161
FEDERAL-MOGUL SOROCABA-HOLDING LTDA—See Apollo Global Management, Inc.; *U.S. Public*, pg. 162
FEDERAL-MOGUL UK HOLDING LTD.—See Apollo Global Management, Inc.; *U.S. Public*, pg. 162
FEDERAL-MOGUL VALVETRAIN LA SOURCE SAS—See Apollo Global Management, Inc.; *U.S. Public*, pg. 162
FEDERAL-MOGUL VALVETRAIN SCHIRMECK SAS—See Apollo Global Management, Inc.; *U.S. Public*, pg. 162
FEDERAL-MOGUL WORLD WIDE, INC.—See Apollo Global Management, Inc.; *U.S. Public*, pg. 162
FEDERATED HEALTHCARE SUPPLY HOLDINGS, INC.; *U.S. Private*, pg. 1491
FEDERATED MEDIA INC.; *U.S. Private*, pg. 1491
FEDERATED PUBLICATIONS, INC.—See Gannett Co., Inc.; *U.S. Public*, pg. 897
FEDERATION ASSET MANAGEMENT PTY. LTD.; *Int'l*, pg. 2631
FEDERMANN ENTERPRISES, LTD.; *Int'l*, pg. 2631
FEDEX CORPORATION; *U.S. Public*, pg. 827
FEDNAT HOLDING COMPANY; *U.S. Public*, pg. 828
FEED ONE CO., LTD.; *Int'l*, pg. 2631
FEINTOOL INTERNATIONAL HOLDING AG—See Artemis Holding AG; *Int'l*, pg. 582
FE INVESTMENTS LIMITED; *Int'l*, pg. 2629
FEISHANG MINING HOLDING LIMITED—See China Natural Resources, Inc.; *Int'l*, pg. 1534
FEIYANG INTERNATIONAL HOLDINGS GROUP LIMITED; *Int'l*, pg. 2632
FELDA GLOBAL VENTURES PERLIS SDN BHD—See FGV Holdings Bhd; *Int'l*, pg. 2649
FELDA HOLDINGS BHD.—See FGV Holdings Bhd; *Int'l*, pg. 2649
FELIX GROUP HOLDINGS LIMITED; *Int'l*, pg. 2633
FELIX SCHOELLER HOLDING GMBH & CO. KG; *Int'l*, pg. 2633
FENBO HOLDINGS LIMITED; *Int'l*, pg. 2633
FENIX PARENT LLC—See Stellex Capital Management LP; *U.S. Private*, pg. 3800
FENNER DUNLOP AMERICAS, LLC—See Compagnie Generale des Etablissements Michelin SCA; *Int'l*, pg. 1744
FENNER GROUP HOLDINGS LIMITED—See Compagnie Generale des Etablissements Michelin SCA; *Int'l*, pg. 1744
FENWAY SPORTS GROUP HOLDINGS, LLC; *U.S. Private*, pg. 1496
FERALLOY INDIANA CORP.—See Reliance Steel & Aluminum Co.; *U.S. Public*, pg. 1780
FERALLOY OHIO CORP.—See Reliance Steel & Aluminum Co.; *U.S. Public*, pg. 1780
FERALLOY OREGON CORP.—See Reliance Steel & Aluminum Co.; *U.S. Public*, pg. 1780
FERD AS; *Int'l*, pg. 2635
FERFINA S.P.A.; *Int'l*, pg. 2637
FERGUSON ELECTRIC HOLDINGS CORP.; *U.S. Private*, pg. 1496
FERGUSON ENTERPRISES MIDWEST, INC.—See Ferguson plc; *Int'l*, pg. 2637
FERGUSON PLC; *Int'l*, pg. 2637
FERRARI N.V.; *Int'l*, pg. 2639
FERRELLGAS, L.P.—See Ferrellgas Partners, L.P.; *U.S. Public*, pg. 829
FERRERO INTERNATIONAL S.A.; *Int'l*, pg. 2640
FERRING HOLDING SA; *Int'l*, pg. 2641
FERRO B.V.—See American Securities LLC; *U.S. Private*, pg. 251
FERROGLOBE PLC—See Grupo Villar Mir, S.A.U.; *Int'l*, pg. 3138
FERROVIE DELLO STATO ITALIANE S.P.A.; *Int'l*, pg. 2645
FERTITTA ENTERTAINMENT, INC.; *U.S. Private*, pg. 1499
FESTA HOLDING PLC; *Int'l*, pg. 2646
FET HOLDINGS LLC—See Forum Energy Technologies, Inc.; *U.S. Public*, pg. 873
FEVERTREE DRINKS PLC; *Int'l*, pg. 2648
FFG EUROPE S.P.A.—See Fair Friend Group; *Int'l*, pg. 2604
FFI HOLDINGS, INC.—See Simple Management Group, Inc.; *U.S. Private*, pg. 3666
FFT GMBH & CO. KGAA—See Fosun International Limited; *Int'l*, pg. 2750
F&G ANNUITIES & LIFE, INC.—See Fidelity National Financial, Inc.; *U.S. Public*, pg. 831
FGL HOLDINGS—See Fidelity National Financial, Inc.; *U.S. Public*, pg. 831
FGV HOLDINGS BHD; *Int'l*, pg. 2649
FGX INTERNATIONAL, INC.—See EssilorLuxottica SA; *Int'l*, pg. 2514
FHC HOLDING COMPANY; *U.S. Private*, pg. 1501
FHP HOLDING GMBH—See Freudenberg SE; *Int'l*, pg. 2785
FIAMMA HOLDINGS BERHAD; *Int'l*, pg. 2650
FIAT INDUSTRIAL S.P.A.—See CNH Industrial N.V.; *Int'l*, pg. 1675
FIBA HOLDING A.S.; *Int'l*, pg. 2651

551112 — OFFICES OF OTHER HO...

FIBA PORTFOY YONETIMI A.S.—See Fiba Holding A.S.; *Int'l*, pg. 2651
FIBER GLASS SYSTEMS HOLDINGS, LLC—See NOV, Inc.; *U.S. Public*, pg. 1544
FIBI HOLDINGS LTD.; *Int'l*, pg. 2652
FIBRANT HOLDING B.V.—See Highsun Holding Group Co., Ltd.; *Int'l*, pg. 3388
FIDELIS INSURANCE HOLDINGS LIMITED; *Int'l*, pg. 2654
THE FIDELITY INVESTMENT COMPANY—See Fidelity Financial Corporation; *U.S. Private*, pg. 1503
FIDELITY SECURITY GROUP (PTY) LTD.; *Int'l*, pg. 2654
FIDUCIAN GROUP LIMITED; *Int'l*, pg. 2655
FIELD SOLUTIONS HOLDINGS LIMITED; *Int'l*, pg. 2655
FIESTA RESTAURANT GROUP, INC.—See Garnett Station Partners, LLC; *U.S. Private*, pg. 1645
FIFTH STREET ASSET MANAGEMENT INC.; *U.S. Private*, pg. 1505
FIH GROUP PLC; *Int'l*, pg. 2661
FIJIAN HOLDINGS LIMITED; *Int'l*, pg. 2661
FILINVEST DEVELOPMENT CORPORATION; *Int'l*, pg. 2662
FILLAUER COMPANIES, INC.—See Patient Square Capital, L.P.; *U.S. Private*, pg. 3107
FILTA GROUP HOLDINGS PLC—See Franchise Brands plc; *Int'l*, pg. 2760
FIMOPART GROUP; *Int'l*, pg. 2664
FINANCIAL & ENERGY EXCHANGE LIMITED; *Int'l*, pg. 2665
FINANCIAL GUARANTY INSURANCE COMPANY; *U.S. Private*, pg. 1507
FINANCIAL HOLDING CORP.; *U.S. Private*, pg. 1507
FINANCIAL STREET HOLDING CO., LTD.; *Int'l*, pg. 2665
FINANCIERE DE L'ODET; *Int'l*, pg. 2665
FINANCIERE DESSANGE SASU—See Eurazeo SE; *Int'l*, pg. 2528
FINANCIERE EIFFARIE—See Eiffage S.A.; *Int'l*, pg. 2331
FINANCIERE MONCEY SA; *Int'l*, pg. 2668
FINANCIERE OFIC—See Astorg Partners S.A.S.; *Int'l*, pg. 656
FINANCIERE PINAULT SCA; *Int'l*, pg. 2668
FINANCIERE QUICK S.A.S.; *Int'l*, pg. 2669
FINASTRA GROUP HOLDINGS LIMITED—See Vista Equity Partners, LLC; *U.S. Private*, pg. 4397
FINASUCRE HOLDINGS (AUSTRALIA) PTY LTD—See Finasucre S.A.; *Int'l*, pg. 2670
FINASUCRE INVESTMENTS (AUSTRALIA) PTY LTD—See Finasucre S.A.; *Int'l*, pg. 2670
FINATIS SA; *Int'l*, pg. 2670
FINCANTIERI MARINE GROUP HOLDINGS INC.—See Fincantieri S.p.A.; *Int'l*, pg. 2671
FINCOR HOLDINGS, INC.—See Coverys; *U.S. Private*, pg. 1072
FINCRAFT RESOURCES JSC; *Int'l*, pg. 2672
FINDER ENERGY HOLDINGS LIMITED; *Int'l*, pg. 2672
FINE SOUNDS S.P.A.; *Int'l*, pg. 2673
FININVEST S.P.A.; *Int'l*, pg. 2675
FINISHING BRANDS HOLDINGS INC.—See Carlisle Companies Incorporated; *U.S. Public*, pg. 436
FINNAIR PLC; *Int'l*, pg. 2675
FINNING INTERNATIONAL INC.; *Int'l*, pg. 2676
FINOLEX GROUP; *Int'l*, pg. 2676
FINTEC GLOBAL BERHAD; *Int'l*, pg. 2677
FINTECH SCION LIMITED; *Int'l*, pg. 2677
FIRMA HOLDINGS CORP.; *U.S. Public*, pg. 835
FIRMENICH INTERNATIONAL SA; *Int'l*, pg. 2679
FIRST ABACUS FINANCIAL HOLDINGS CORPORATION; *Int'l*, pg. 2681
FIRST ADVANTAGE CORPORATION—See Silver Lake Group, LLC; *U.S. Private*, pg. 3654
FIRST COAST LOGISTICS SERVICES; *U.S. Private*, pg. 1516
FIRST CREDIT FINANCE GROUP LIMITED; *Int'l*, pg. 2683
FIRST EAGLE HOLDINGS, INC.—See Blackstone Inc.; *U.S. Public*, pg. 353
FIRST EAGLE HOLDINGS, INC.—See Corsair Capital, LLC; *U.S. Private*, pg. 1059
FIRSTENERGY CORP.; *U.S. Public*, pg. 849
FIRST EQUITY GROUP, INC.; *U.S. Private*, pg. 1517
FIRST FINANCIAL HOLDING CO., LTD.; *Int'l*, pg. 2683
FIRST GUARANTY INSURANCE, CO.—See Security National Financial Corporation; *U.S. Public*, pg. 1856
FIRST HIGH-SCHOOL EDUCATION GROUP CO., LTD.; *Int'l*, pg. 2684
FIRSTLINK INVESTMENTS CORPORATION LIMITED; *Int'l*, pg. 2689
FIRST LOOK HOLDINGS, LLC—See Nu Image, Inc.; *U.S. Private*, pg. 2971
FIRSTMAC HOLDINGS LTD.; *Int'l*, pg. 2689
FIRST MINING GOLD CORP.; *Int'l*, pg. 2685
FIRST PACIFIC COMPANY LIMITED; *Int'l*, pg. 2686
FIRST PERSON LTD.; *Int'l*, pg. 2686
FIRST QUALITY ENTERPRISES, INC.; *U.S. Private*, pg. 1524
FIRSTRAND LIMITED; *Int'l*, pg. 2689
FIRSTRAND NAMIBIA LTD.—See FirstRand Limited; *Int'l*, pg. 2690
FIRSTSERVICE CORPORATION; *Int'l*, pg. 2690
FIRST SURGICAL PARTNERS INC.; *U.S. Private*, pg. 1529

FIRST TRINITY FINANCIAL CORPORATION; *U.S. Private*, pg. 1530
FIRST WATCH RESTAURANT GROUP, INC.; *U.S. Public*, pg. 848
FISCHERWERKE GMBH & CO. KG; *Int'l*, pg. 2692
FISHER SCIENTIFIC HOLDING U.K., LIMITED—See Thermo Fisher Scientific Inc.; *U.S. Public*, pg. 2148
FISKEBY INTERNATIONAL HOLDING AB; *Int'l*, pg. 2695
FIT BOXX HOLDINGS LIMITED; *Int'l*, pg. 2695
FITZROY RIVER CORPORATION LTD; *Int'l*, pg. 2695
FIVE CORE EXIM LIMITED; *Int'l*, pg. 2696
FJ MANAGEMENT, INC.; *U.S. Private*, pg. 1538
FLABEG HOLDING GMBH—See CORDET Capital Partners, LLP; *Int'l*, pg. 1796
FLACKS HOMES LLC; *U.S. Private*, pg. 1538
FLAG INTERMEDIATE HOLDINGS CORPORATION—See Reliance Steel & Aluminum Co.; *U.S. Public*, pg. 1780
FLAGSHIP CREDIT CORPORATION; *U.S. Private*, pg. 1539
FLAKK HOLDING AS; *Int'l*, pg. 2697
FLAVUS BETEILIGUNGEN AG; *Int'l*, pg. 2698
FLEETGISTICS HOLDINGS, INC.—See Harbour Group Industries, Inc.; *U.S. Private*, pg. 1860
FLEETPARTNERS GROUP LIMITED; *Int'l*, pg. 2698
FLETCHER BUILDING HOLDINGS LIMITED—See Fletcher Building Limited; *Int'l*, pg. 2700
FLEXCON CORPORATION; *U.S. Private*, pg. 1543
FLEXIBLE PACKAGING HOLDING B.V.; *Int'l*, pg. 2704
FLEXICARE (GROUP) LIMITED; *Int'l*, pg. 2704
FLIGHT CENTRE TRAVEL GROUP LIMITED; *Int'l*, pg. 2705
FLIGHT CENTRE USA HOLDING CORP.—See Flight Centre Travel Group Limited; *Int'l*, pg. 2706
FLIGHT SOLUTIONS CO., LTD.; *Int'l*, pg. 2706
FLINT CORP.; *Int'l*, pg. 2706
FLINT EQUIPMENT HOLDINGS, INC.; *U.S. Private*, pg. 1545
FLINT GROUP SA—See Koch Industries, Inc.; *U.S. Private*, pg. 2327
FLINT GROUP SA—See The Goldman Sachs Group, Inc.; *U.S. Public*, pg. 2076
FLJ GROUP LIMITED; *Int'l*, pg. 2706
FLOATEL INTERNATIONAL LTD.; *Int'l*, pg. 2707
FLORENS ASSET MANAGEMENT COMPANY LIMITED—See China COSCO Shipping Corporation Limited; *Int'l*, pg. 1492
FLORIDA ICE AND FARM CO. S.A.; *Int'l*, pg. 2707
FLORIDIENNE SA; *Int'l*, pg. 2708
FLOWERS FOODS, INC.; *U.S. Public*, pg. 853
FLSMIDTH—See FLSmidth & Co. A/S; *Int'l*, pg. 2710
FLUENCE ENERGY, INC.; *U.S. Public*, pg. 857
FLUENT, INC.; *U.S. Public*, pg. 857
FLUOR ARABIA LIMITED—See Fluor Corporation; *U.S. Public*, pg. 858
FLUOR CORPORATION; *U.S. Public*, pg. 857
FLUOR EUROPE BV—See Fluor Corporation; *U.S. Public*, pg. 858
FLUTTER ENTERTAINMENT PLC; *Int'l*, pg. 2715
FMC ASIA-PACIFIC, INC.—See FMC Corporation; *U.S. Public*, pg. 861
FMC CORPORATION; *U.S. Public*, pg. 861
FMC GLOBALSAT HOLDINGS, INC.; *U.S. Private*, pg. 1554
FMS WERTMANAGEMENT AOR; *Int'l*, pg. 2717
F-M TRADEMARKS LTD.—See Apollo Global Management, Inc.; *U.S. Public*, pg. 162
FNM S.P.A.; *Int'l*, pg. 2718
FOCALTECH SYSTEMS CO., LTD.; *Int'l*, pg. 2718
FOCUS BRANDS, INC.—See Roark Capital Group Inc.; *U.S. Private*, pg. 3454
FOCUS FINANCIAL PARTNERS INC.—See Clayton, Dubilier & Rice, LLC; *U.S. Private*, pg. 923
FOCUS FINANCIAL PARTNERS INC.—See Stone Point Capital LLC; *U.S. Private*, pg. 3824
FOCUS MEDIA HOLDING LIMITED; *Int'l*, pg. 2719
FOCUS MEDIA INFORMATION TECHNOLOGY CO., LTD.—See Focus Media Holding Limited; *Int'l*, pg. 2719
FOCUS VENTURE PARTNERS, INC.; *U.S. Private*, pg. 1556
FOG CUTTER CAPITAL GROUP INC.; *U.S. Private*, pg. 1556
FOGO DE CHAO, INC.—See Rhone Group, LLC; *U.S. Private*, pg. 3423
FOGO HOSPITALITY, INC.; *U.S. Private*, pg. 1557
FOKKER TECHNOLOGIES HOLDING B.V.—See GKN plc; *Int'l*, pg. 2983
FOLEY FAMILY WINES HOLDINGS INC; *U.S. Private*, pg. 1558
FOLLETT CORPORATION; *U.S. Private*, pg. 1559
FOLLI FOLLIE S.A.; *Int'l*, pg. 2721
FOODCHAIN ID GROUP, INC.—See Berkshire Partners LLC; *U.S. Private*, pg. 534
FOODFIRST GLOBAL RESTAURANTS, INC.—See GP Investments, Ltd.; *Int'l*, pg. 3045
FOOD MANAGEMENT PARTNERS, INC.; *U.S. Private*, pg. 1561
FOOD PLANET, INC.; *Int'l*, pg. 2727
FORBES MEDIA LLC; *U.S. Private*, pg. 1563

FORBION CAPITAL PARTNERS MANAGEMENT HOLDING BV; *Int'l*, pg. 2729
FORBO AMERICA INC.—See Forbo Holding Ltd.; *Int'l*, pg. 2729
FORBO INTERNATIONAL SA—See Forbo Holding Ltd.; *Int'l*, pg. 2729
FORBO S.R.O.—See Forbo Holding Ltd.; *Int'l*, pg. 2730
FORBO UK LTD.—See Forbo Holding Ltd.; *Int'l*, pg. 2730
FORCEPOINT INTERNATIONAL LIMITED—See Francisco Partners Management, L.P.; *U.S. Private*, pg. 1590
FORCHT GROUP OF KENTUCKY, INC.; *U.S. Private*, pg. 1563
FORD COMMUNICATIONS, INC.—See Ford Motor Company; *U.S. Public*, pg. 864
FORD CREDIT INTERNATIONAL, INC.—See Ford Motor Company; *U.S. Public*, pg. 866
FORD HOLDING COMPANY INC.; *U.S. Private*, pg. 1564
FORD PLASTIC & TRIM PRODUCTS INTERNATIONAL, INC.—See Ford Motor Company; *U.S. Public*, pg. 866
FORD RETAIL GROUP LIMITED—See Ford Motor Company; *U.S. Public*, pg. 866
FORENINGEN AP PENSION F.M.B.A.; *Int'l*, pg. 2731
FORESIGHT GROUP LLP; *Int'l*, pg. 2732
FORESTAR GROUP INC.; *U.S. Public*, pg. 867
FORESTERS FINANCIAL HOLDING COMPANY, INC.—See Golden Gate Capital Management II, LLC; *U.S. Private*, pg. 1731
FORGE COMPANY INC.; *U.S. Private*, pg. 1567
FORMAN GROUP LIMITED—See Fletcher Building Limited; *Int'l*, pg. 2700
FORMATION MINERALS, INC.; *U.S. Public*, pg. 868
FORMULA SYSTEMS (1985) LTD.—See Asseco Poland S.A.; *Int'l*, pg. 642
FORNACA INC.; *U.S. Private*, pg. 1572
FORTEGRA FINANCIAL CORPORATION—See Tiptree Inc.; *U.S. Public*, pg. 2159
THE FORTEGRA GROUP, INC.—See Tiptree Inc.; *U.S. Public*, pg. 2159
FORTERRA, INC.—See The Quikrete Companies, LLC; *U.S. Public*, pg. 4101
FORTERRA PLC—See Lone Star Global Acquisitions, LLC; *U.S. Private*, pg. 2487
FORTIANA HOLDINGS LTD; *Int'l*, pg. 2738
FORTISBC HOLDINGS INC.—See Fortis Inc.; *Int'l*, pg. 2739
FORTIS INC.; *Int'l*, pg. 2739
FORTIS PROPERTIES CORPORATION—See Fortis Inc.; *Int'l*, pg. 2739
FORTIVE CORPORATION; *U.S. Public*, pg. 870
FORTRAN CORPORATION; *U.S. Public*, pg. 872
FORTREA HOLDINGS INC.; *U.S. Public*, pg. 872
FORTUNE BRANDS INNOVATIONS, INC.; *U.S. Public*, pg. 872
FORTUNE CAPITAL PARTNERS, INC.; *U.S. Private*, pg. 1577
FORTUNE FOUNTAIN (BEIJING) HOLDING GROUP CO., LTD.; *Int'l*, pg. 2743
FORUM BIOSCIENCE HOLDINGS LTD.—See Bain Capital, LP; *U.S. Private*, pg. 443
FORUM BIOSCIENCE HOLDINGS LTD.—See Cinven Limited; *Int'l*, pg. 1613
FORWARD FASHION INTERNATIONAL HOLDINGS COMPANY LIMITED; *Int'l*, pg. 2747
FOSSIL GROUP, INC.; *U.S. Public*, pg. 874
FOSTER HOLDING GROUP INC.; *U.S. Private*, pg. 1578
FOSUN INTERNATIONAL LIMITED; *Int'l*, pg. 2750
FOTO ELECTRIC SUPPLY CO., INC.; *U.S. Private*, pg. 1579
FOUAD ALGHANIM & SONS GROUP OF COMPANIES; *Int'l*, pg. 2753
FOUNDATION BUILDING MATERIALS, INC.—See American Securities LLC; *U.S. Private*, pg. 248
FOUNDATION HEALTHCARE, INC.; *U.S. Public*, pg. 1580
FOUNDPAC GROUP BERHAD; *Int'l*, pg. 2753
FOURACE INDUSTRIES GROUP HOLDINGS LIMITED; *Int'l*, pg. 2755
FOUR COMMUNICATIONS GROUP PLC; *Int'l*, pg. 2754
FOUR M HOLDINGS LLC; *U.S. Private*, pg. 1582
FOURSHORE CAPITAL LLC; *U.S. Private*, pg. 1583
FOURTH DIMENSION DISPLAY LTD.—See Kopin Corporation; *U.S. Public*, pg. 1271
FOXCONN INTERCONNECT TECHNOLOGY LIMITED—See Hon Hai Precision Industry Co., Ltd.; *Int'l*, pg. 3456
FOX CORPORATION; *U.S. Public*, pg. 875
FOX ENTERTAINMENT GROUP, INC.—See The Walt Disney Company; *U.S. Public*, pg. 2140
FOX TELEVISION STATIONS, LLC—See Fox Corporation; *U.S. Public*, pg. 876
FOXTRONICS EMS; *U.S. Private*, pg. 1585
FP ASSET MANAGEMENT HOLDINGS LIMITED—See Bank of Montreal; *Int'l*, pg. 847
FPIC INSURANCE GROUP, INC.—See The Doctors Company; *U.S. Public*, pg. 4021
FPS FOOD PROCESSING SYSTEMS B.V.; *Int'l*, pg. 2757
FRAGRANCE GROUP LIMITED; *Int'l*, pg. 2758
F. RAMADA INVESTIMENTOS, SGPS, S.A.; *Int'l*, pg. 2596
FRANCAISE DE GASTRONOMIE—See Floridienne SA; *Int'l*, pg. 2708

N.A.I.C.S. INDEX

551112 — OFFICES OF OTHER HO...

FRANCESCA'S HOLDINGS CORPORATION—See Terra-Mar Capital LLC; *U.S. Private*, pg. 3971
FRANCHISE BANCORP INC.; *Int'l*, pg. 2760
FRANCHISE BRANDS PLC; *Int'l*, pg. 2760
FRANCHISE GROUP, INC.—See B. Riley Financial, Inc.; *U.S. Public*, pg. 261
FRANCHISE GROUP, INC.—See Irradiant Partners, LP; *U.S. Private*, pg. 2140
FRANCOIS-CHARLES OBERTHUR FIDUCIAIRE S.A.; *Int'l*, pg. 2760
FRANCOUDI & STEPHANOU LTD.; *Int'l*, pg. 2761
FRANDSEN CORPORATION; *U.S. Private*, pg. 1593
THE FRANGOS GROUP, LLC; *U.S. Private*, pg. 4030
FRANK CONSOLIDATED ENTERPRISES; *U.S. Private*, pg. 1594
FRANKE HOLDING AG—See Artemis Holding AG; *Int'l*, pg. 582
FRANK FLETCHER COMPANIES, LTD.; *U.S. Private*, pg. 1594
FRANKLIN HILL ACQUISITION CORPORATION; *U.S. Private*, pg. 1597
FRANKLIN RESOURCES, INC.; *U.S. Public*, pg. 879
FRANKLY INC.—See GameSquare Holdings, Inc.; *Int'l*, pg. 2878
FRANK RUSSELL COMPANY—See The Northwestern Mutual Life Insurance Company; *U.S. Private*, pg. 4085
FRANZ HANIEL & CIE. GMBH; *Int'l*, pg. 2762
FRAUENTHAL AUTOMOTIVE ADMINISTRATION GMBH—See Frauenthal Holding AG; *Int'l*, pg. 2767
FRAUENTHAL AUTOMOTIVE SAXONY GMBH—See Frauenthal Holding AG; *Int'l*, pg. 2767
FRED. OLSEN & CO.; *Int'l*, pg. 2767
FREEDOM HOLDING CORP.; *Int'l*, pg. 2769
FREEDOM RESOURCES HOLDINGS CORP.; *Int'l*, pg. 2769
FREEDOMROADS, LLC—See Camping World Holdings, Inc.; *U.S. Public*, pg. 428
FREENET AG; *Int'l*, pg. 2770
FREIGHTLINER GROUP LIMITED—See Brookfield Infrastructure Partners L.P.; *Int'l*, pg. 1191
FREIGHTLINER GROUP LIMITED—See GIC Pte. Ltd.; *Int'l*, pg. 2965
FRENCH CONNECTION GROUP PLC; *Int'l*, pg. 2772
FRENCH CONNECTION HOLDINGS, INC.—See French Connection Group plc; *Int'l*, pg. 2772
FRENKEL TOPPING GROUP PLC; *Int'l*, pg. 2773
FRESENIUS MEDICAL CARE AG; *Int'l*, pg. 2774
FRESENIUS SE & CO. KGAA; *Int'l*, pg. 2777
FRESH ALTERNATIVES, LLC—See Boyne Capital Management, LLC; *U.S. Private*, pg. 628
FRESH EXPRESS DELIVERY HOLDINGS GROUP CO., LTD.; *Int'l*, pg. 2781
THE FRESH MARKET HOLDINGS, INC.; *U.S. Public*, pg. 2074
FRESHPOINT CALIFORNIA, INC.—See Sysco Corporation; *U.S. Public*, pg. 1974
FREUDENBERG CHEMICAL SPECIALITIES SE & CO. KG—See Freudenberg SE; *Int'l*, pg. 2785
FREUDENBERG SE; *Int'l*, pg. 2782
FRIENDS LIFE GROUP LIMITED—See Aviva plc; *Int'l*, pg. 746
FRISCH'S RESTAURANTS, INC.—See NRD Capital Management, LLC; *U.S. Private*, pg. 2969
FRIT INCORPORATED; *U.S. Private*, pg. 1612
FRONTAGE HOLDINGS CORPORATION—See Hangzhou Tigermed Consulting Co., Ltd.; *Int'l*, pg. 3251
FRONT GATE HOLDINGS, LLC—See Live Nation Entertainment, Inc.; *U.S. Public*, pg. 1328
FRONTIER COMMUNICATIONS PARENT, INC.; *U.S. Public*, pg. 887
FRONTIER MEDEX GROUP LIMITED—See UnitedHealth Group Incorporated; *U.S. Public*, pg. 2241
FRONTIER NATURAL GAS COMPANY—See First Reserve Management, L.P.; *U.S. Private*, pg. 1525
FRONTIER WEALTH ENTERPRISES, LLC; *U.S. Private*, pg. 1616
FRONTMATEC GROUP APS—See KKR & Co. Inc.; *U.S. Public*, pg. 1241
FRONTSTREAM HOLDINGS LLC; *U.S. Private*, pg. 1616
FSA INDUSTRIES, LLC—See Fort Sill Apache Tribe of Oklahoma; *U.S. Private*, pg. 1575
FS BRANDS, INC.—See FirstService Corporation; *Int'l*, pg. 2691
FSC HOLDINGS, LLC—See AVADEL PHARMACEUTICALS PLC; *Int'l*, pg. 734
FSE SERVICES GROUP LIMITED; *Int'l*, pg. 2798
FS HOLDING AD; *Int'l*, pg. 2797
FSII SWEDEN HOLDINGS AB—See Thermo Fisher Scientific Inc.; *U.S. Public*, pg. 2147
FSM HOLDINGS LIMITED; *Int'l*, pg. 2798
FTD COMPANIES, INC.; *U.S. Private*, pg. 1618
FTD GROUP, INC.—See Nexus Capital Management LP; *U.S. Private*, pg. 2922
FTGROUP CO LTD.; *Int'l*, pg. 2800
FTI CONSULTING — FD AUSTRALIA HOLDINGS PTY LTD—See FTI Consulting, Inc.; *U.S. Public*, pg. 890
FTS INTERNATIONAL, INC.; *U.S. Private*, pg. 1619
FUBON FINANCIAL HOLDING CO. LTD.; *Int'l*, pg. 2801

FUCHS AUSTRALIA PTY. LTD.—See FUCHS SE; *Int'l*, pg. 2803
FUCHS LUBRICANTS (UK) PLC—See FUCHS SE; *Int'l*, pg. 2802
FUEGO ENTERPRISES, INC.; *U.S. Public*, pg. 891
FUELSTREAM, INC.; *U.S. Public*, pg. 891
FUER INTERNATIONAL, INC.; *Int'l*, pg. 2804
FUJIFILM EUROPE B.V.—See FUJIFILM Holdings Corporation; *Int'l*, pg. 2821
FUJIFILM HOLDINGS CORPORATION; *Int'l*, pg. 2820
FUJI MEDIA HOLDINGS, INC.; *Int'l*, pg. 2813
FUJI OIL HOLDINGS INC.; *Int'l*, pg. 2815
FUKUI COMPUTER HOLDINGS INC.; *Int'l*, pg. 2840
FULCRUM IT PARTNERS; *Int'l*, pg. 2841
FULHAM & CO., INC.; *U.S. Private*, pg. 1620
FULLERTON TOWERS HOLDINGS, LLC—See Wells Fargo & Company; *U.S. Public*, pg. 2343
FULL MOON HOLDINGS LIMITED; *Int'l*, pg. 2842
FULU HOLDINGS LIMITED; *Int'l*, pg. 2844
FULUM GROUP HOLDINGS LIMITED; *Int'l*, pg. 2844
FUNAI SOKEN HOLDINGS INCORPORATED; *Int'l*, pg. 2845
FUN-BRANDS OF TEMPE, LLC—See Tregaron Management, LLC; *U.S. Private*, pg. 4217
FUNDAMENTAL GLOBAL INC.—See Kingsway Financial Services Inc.; *U.S. Public*, pg. 1234
FURUKAWA CO., LTD.; *Int'l*, pg. 2846
FU SHEK FINANCIAL HOLDINGS LIMITED; *Int'l*, pg. 2801
FUTU HOLDINGS LIMITED; *Int'l*, pg. 2852
FUTURE CORPORATE RESOURCES LIMITED; *Int'l*, pg. 2853
FUTURE INTERNATIONAL GROUP CORP.; *Int'l*, pg. 2856
FUTURE PLC; *Int'l*, pg. 2857
FUTURE RETAIL LIMITED—See Future Corporate Resources Limited; *Int'l*, pg. 2853
FUTURE WORLD HOLDINGS LIMITED; *Int'l*, pg. 2857
FUTURIS PTY. LTD.—See Clearlake Capital Group, L.P.; *U.S. Private*, pg. 934
FUTURUM, LLC; *U.S. Private*, pg. 1627
FUYAO GLASS INDUSTRY GROUP CO., LTD.; *Int'l*, pg. 2858
FWA EQUIPMENT & MUD COMPANY, INC.—See ConocoPhillips; *U.S. Public*, pg. 569
FXCM HOLDINGS, LLC—See Global Brokerage, Inc.; *U.S. Public*, pg. 940
G3 EXPLORATION LIMITED; *Int'l*, pg. 2866
G6 HOSPITALITY LLC—See Blackstone Inc.; *U.S. Public*, pg. 353
G7 ENTREPRISES; *Int'l*, pg. 2867
G7 INTERNATIONAL PTE. LTD.—See G-7 HOLDINGS Inc.; *Int'l*, pg. 2862
GABETTI PROPERTY SOLUTIONS SPA; *Int'l*, pg. 2867
GABRIEL'S HOLDINGS LTD.; *U.S. Private*, pg. 1632
GADANG HOLDINGS BERHAD; *Int'l*, pg. 2868
GAF MATERIALS CORPORATION; *U.S. Private*, pg. 1633
G.A. HOLDINGS LIMITED; *Int'l*, pg. 2865
GAIA, INC.; *U.S. Public*, pg. 894
GA INDUSTRIES HOLDINGS, LLC—See Zurn Elkay Water Solutions Corporation; *U.S. Public*, pg. 2412
GALA TECHNOLOGY HOLDING LIMITED; *Int'l*, pg. 2870
GALAXY NEXT GENERATION, INC.; *U.S. Public*, pg. 894
GALDERMA HOLDING S.A.—See Abu Dhabi Investment Authority; *Int'l*, pg. 71
GALDERMA HOLDING S.A.—See EQT Corporation; *U.S. Public*, pg. 785
GALDERMA PHARMA S.A.—See Abu Dhabi Investment Authority; *Int'l*, pg. 71
GALDERMA PHARMA S.A.—See EQT Corporation; *U.S. Public*, pg. 785
GALE FORCE HOLDINGS, LP; *U.S. Private*, pg. 1636
GALLAGHER HOLDINGS LTD.; *Int'l*, pg. 2873
GALLANT CAPITAL PARTNERS, LLC; *U.S. Private*, pg. 1639
GALP ENERGIA SGPS, S.A.; *Int'l*, pg. 2875
GAL-TEX HOTEL CORPORATION; *U.S. Private*, pg. 1635
GAMBLING.COM GROUP LIMITED; *Int'l*, pg. 2877
GAMBRO HOLDING AB—See Baxter International Inc.; *U.S. Public*, pg. 282
GAMCO INVESTORS, INC.; *U.S. Public*, pg. 895
GAME PLAN HOLDINGS, INC.; *U.S. Private*, pg. 1640
GAMESQUARE ESPORTS INC.—See GameSquare Holdings, Inc.; *Int'l*, pg. 2878
GAMESQUARE HOLDINGS, INC.; *Int'l*, pg. 2877
GAM HOLDING AG; *Int'l*, pg. 2876
GAMIDA FOR LIFE B.V.; *Int'l*, pg. 2878
GAMING REALMS PLC; *Int'l*, pg. 2878
GAMMA HOLDING N.V.—See Gilde Buy Out Partners B.V.; *Int'l*, pg. 2974
GANGDONG INDUSTRY CO., LTD.; *Int'l*, pg. 2880
GANGER ROLF ASA—See Fred. Olsen & Co.; *Int'l*, pg. 2768
GAN LIMITED; *U.S. Public*, pg. 896
GANNETT CO., INC.; *U.S. Public*, pg. 896
GANNETT MEDIA CORP.—See Gannett Co., Inc.; *U.S. Public*, pg. 896
GANSU GANGTAI HOLDING GROUP CO., LTD.; *Int'l*, pg. 2881
GAOTU TECHEDU INC.; *Int'l*, pg. 2882
GARANT INVEST HOLDING AD; *Int'l*, pg. 2883

GARDENA AG—See Husqvarna AB; *Int'l*, pg. 3538
THE GARDEN CITY COMPANY; *U.S. Public*, pg. 2074
GARDNER DENVER INDUSTRIES SA—See Ingersoll Rand Inc.; *U.S. Public*, pg. 1119
GARDRUM HOLDINGS LIMITED; *Int'l*, pg. 2884
THE GART COMPANIES, INC.; *U.S. Private*, pg. 4032
G.A.S. CAPITAL, INC.; *U.S. Private*, pg. 1630
GASLOG LTD.; *Int'l*, pg. 2888
GASLOG PARTNERS LP—See GasLog Ltd.; *Int'l*, pg. 2888
GASPARI NUTRA LLC; *U.S. Private*, pg. 1648
GATE PETROLEUM COMPANY; *U.S. Private*, pg. 1649
GATX CORPORATION; *U.S. Public*, pg. 907
GAYLORD INTEREST, LLC; *U.S. Private*, pg. 1652
THE GAZETTE COMPANY; *U.S. Private*, pg. 4032
GAZ METRO INC.—See Caisse de Depot et Placement du Quebec; *Int'l*, pg. 1255
G.B. GROUP CORPORATION; *Int'l*, pg. 2865
GB GROUP S.A.; *Int'l*, pg. 2892
GBI HOLDINGS PTY., LTD.; *Int'l*, pg. 2893
GCA CORPORATION—See Houlihan Lokey, Inc.; *U.S. Public*, pg. 1055
GC AESTHETICS PLC; *Int'l*, pg. 2893
GC CONSTRUCTION HOLDINGS LTD.; *Int'l*, pg. 2894
GCL NEW ENERGY HOLDINGS LIMITED—See Golden Concord Holdings Limited; *Int'l*, pg. 3028
G-CLUSTER GLOBAL CORPORATION; *Int'l*, pg. 2862
GCM GROSVENOR INC.; *U.S. Public*, pg. 908
GCP CAPITAL PARTNERS HOLDINGS LLC; *U.S. Private*, pg. 1654
GC RIEBER AS; *Int'l*, pg. 2894
GD CULTURE GROUP LIMITED; *Int'l*, pg. 2895
GD EUROPEAN LAND SYSTEMS HOLDING GMBH—See General Dynamics Corporation; *U.S. Public*, pg. 913
GDF SUEZ ENERGY INTERNATIONAL—See ENGIE SA; *Int'l*, pg. 2431
GDH GUANGNAN (HOLDINGS) LIMITED—See GDH Limited; *Int'l*, pg. 2896
GDH LIMITED; *Int'l*, pg. 2896
GDP COMPANIES, INC.—See One Rock Capital Partners, LLC; *U.S. Private*, pg. 3022
GD POWER DEVELOPMENT CO., LTD.—See China Guodian Corporation; *Int'l*, pg. 1506
GDP VENDOME; *Int'l*, pg. 2896
GDS HOLDINGS LIMITED; *Int'l*, pg. 2896
GE ALBANY US HOLDINGS LLC—See General Electric Company; *U.S. Public*, pg. 916
GEAR4MUSIC (HOLDINGS) PLC; *Int'l*, pg. 2904
GEA WESTFALIA SEPARATOR GROUP GMBH—See GEA Group Aktiengesellschaft; *Int'l*, pg. 2900
GEBERIT BETEILIGUNGSVERWALTUNG GMBH—See Geberit AG; *Int'l*, pg. 2904
GEBERIT HOLDING AG—See Geberit AG; *Int'l*, pg. 2904
GEBERIT INTERNATIONAL B.V.—See Geberit AG; *Int'l*, pg. 2904
GECOS S.P.A.; *Int'l*, pg. 2909
GEDIK YATIRIM HOLDING AS; *Int'l*, pg. 2910
GEE GROUP INC.; *U.S. Public*, pg. 909
GEESINK GROUP B.V.; *Int'l*, pg. 2911
GEFINOR S.A.; *Int'l*, pg. 2911
GEFRAN ASIA PTE. LTD.—See Gefran S.p.A.; *Int'l*, pg. 2912
THE GEHR GROUP; *U.S. Private*, pg. 4032
GEICO CORPORATION—See Berkshire Hathaway Inc.; *U.S. Public*, pg. 305
GE INVESTMENTS, INC.—See General Electric Company; *U.S. Public*, pg. 917
GEK TERNA SOCIETE ANONYME HOLDINGS REAL ESTATE CONSTRUCTIONS; *Int'l*, pg. 2912
GELLERT GLOBAL GROUP; *U.S. Private*, pg. 1656
GEMDALE PROPERTIES AND INVESTMENT CORPORATION LIMITED—See Gemdale Corporation; *Int'l*, pg. 2915
GEMINI COMMUNICATIONS; *U.S. Private*, pg. 1657
GENDIS INC.; *Int'l*, pg. 2917
GENERAC HOLDINGS INC.; *U.S. Public*, pg. 912
GENERA D.D.—See EQT AB; *Int'l*, pg. 2474
GENERAL ATOMICS; *U.S. Private*, pg. 1663
GENERAL ELECTRIC CAPITAL SERVICES, INC.—See General Electric Company; *U.S. Public*, pg. 918
GENERAL ELECTRIC COMPANY; *U.S. Public*, pg. 916
GENERALI BRASIL SEGUROS S.A.—See Assicurazioni Generali S.p.A.; *Int'l*, pg. 644
GENERALI BULGARIA HOLDING AD—See Assicurazioni Generali S.p.A.; *Int'l*, pg. 644
GENERALI DO BRASIL PARTIPACOES S.A.—See Assicurazioni Generali S.p.A.; *Int'l*, pg. 647
GENERALI ESPANA, HOLDING DE ENTIDADES DE SEGUROS, S.A.—See Assicurazioni Generali S.p.A.; *Int'l*, pg. 644
GENERALI FRANCE HOLDING S.A.—See Assicurazioni Generali S.p.A.; *Int'l*, pg. 644
GENERALI KENT B.V.—See Assicurazioni Generali S.p.A.; *Int'l*, pg. 647
GENERALI PPF HOLDING BV—See Assicurazioni Generali S.p.A.; *Int'l*, pg. 646
GENERAL MILLS—See General Mills, Inc.; *U.S. Public*, pg. 921
GENERAL MOTORS ASIA PACIFIC HOLDINGS, LLC—See

551112 — OFFICES OF OTHER HO...

General Motors Company; *U.S. Public*, pg. 924
GENERAL NICE DEVELOPMENT LIMITED; *Int'l*, pg. 2919
GENERATIONAL EQUITY GROUP, INC.; *U.S. Private*, pg. 1668
GENESIS BIOTECHNOLOGY GROUP, LLC; *U.S. Private*, pg. 1669
GENESIS FINANCIAL HOLDINGS LIMITED; *Int'l*, pg. 2921
GENESIS HEALTHCARE, INC.—See Formation Capital, LLC; *U.S. Private*, pg. 1569
GENESIS HEALTH, INC.; *U.S. Private*, pg. 1669
GENESIS UNICORN CAPITAL CORP.; *U.S. Public*, pg. 930
GENETRON HOLDINGS LIMITED; *Int'l*, pg. 2922
GENEVE CORPORATION—See Geneve Holdings Corp.; *U.S. Private*, pg. 1670
GENEVE HOLDINGS CORP.; *U.S. Private*, pg. 1670
GENISYS CONTROLS, LLC; *U.S. Private*, pg. 1671
GENPACT LIMITED; *Int'l*, pg. 2926
GENTHERM GMBH—See Gentherm Incorporated; *U.S. Public*, pg. 931
GENTING BERHAD; *Int'l*, pg. 2928
GENTING HONG KONG LIMITED; *Int'l*, pg. 2929
GENTING OIL & GAS SDN BHD—See Genting Berhad; *Int'l*, pg. 2928
GENTLEMENS EQUITY S.A.; *Int'l*, pg. 2929
GENUIT GROUP PLC; *Int'l*, pg. 2930
GEOMETRIC LIMITED—See HCL Technologies Ltd.; *Int'l*, pg. 3298
GEOPROMINING LTD.; *Int'l*, pg. 2934
GEORGE FORREST INTERNATIONAL S.A.; *Int'l*, pg. 2938
GEORGE K. BAUM HOLDINGS, INC.; *U.S. Private*, pg. 1682
GEORGE P. REINTJES CO., INC.; *U.S. Private*, pg. 1682
GEORG FISCHER HOLDING (N.V.)—See Georg Fischer AG; *Int'l*, pg. 2936
GEORGIAN PARTNERS GROWTH LP; *Int'l*, pg. 2939
GEORGSMARIENHUTTE HOLDING GMBH; *Int'l*, pg. 2940
GEOVERA HOLDINGS, INC.—See Edwards Capital, LLC; *U.S. Private*, pg. 1341
GEPE HOLDING AG; *Int'l*, pg. 2942
GE POWER—See General Electric Company; *U.S. Public*, pg. 917
THE GERBER GROUP, INC.—See Boyd Group Services Inc.; *Int'l*, pg. 1124
GERMAIN AUTOMOTIVE PARTNERSHIP, INC.—See Germain Motor Company; *U.S. Private*, pg. 1687
GESTION AUDEM, INC.; *Int'l*, pg. 2946
GESTION CLAUDE ROBERT INC.; *Int'l*, pg. 2946
GESTION MARTIN POITRAS INC; *Int'l*, pg. 2946
GETEC ENERGIE HOLDING GMBH; *Int'l*, pg. 2947
GET HOLDINGS LIMITED; *Int'l*, pg. 2946
GETINGE AB; *Int'l*, pg. 2947
GETTY IMAGES HOLDINGS, INC.; *U.S. Public*, pg. 935
GETTY REALTY CORP.; *U.S. Public*, pg. 935
GFE GESELLSCHAFT FUR ELEKTROMETALLURGIE MBH—See AMG Critical Materials N.V.; *Int'l*, pg. 426
GFE-MIR HOLDINGS AG; *Int'l*, pg. 2956
GFG ALLIANCE LIMITED; *Int'l*, pg. 2956
GF MANAGEMENT, INC.; *U.S. Private*, pg. 1689
GFM SERVICES BERHAD; *Int'l*, pg. 2957
GHADIR INVESTMENT COMPANY; *Int'l*, pg. 2958
GHD GROUP PTY LTD.; *Int'l*, pg. 2959
GHM CORP.; *U.S. Private*, pg. 1690
GHN AGRISPAN HOLDING COMPANY; *Int'l*, pg. 2959
GHR ACQUISITION, LLC—See Platform Partners LLC; *U.S. Private*, pg. 3200
GHX HOLDINGS, LLC—See Clayton, Dubilier & Rice, LLC; *U.S. Private*, pg. 926
GHY CULTURE & MEDIA HOLDING CO., LIMITED; *Int'l*, pg. 2960
GIA ENTERPRISES; *U.S. Private*, pg. 1694
GIANT BIOGENE HOLDING CO., LTD.; *Int'l*, pg. 2961
GIANT CEMENT HOLDING, INC.—See Grupo Empresarial Kaluz S.A. de C.V.; *Int'l*, pg. 3127
GIAT INDUSTRIES S.A.; *Int'l*, pg. 2962
GIBCA LIMITED; *Int'l*, pg. 2962
GIBRALTAR INDUSTRIES, INC.; *U.S. Public*, pg. 935
GIBSON ENERGY ULC—See Gibson Energy Inc.; *Int'l*, pg. 2963
GIBUI HOLDING LTD.; *Int'l*, pg. 2963
GICHNER HOLDINGS, INC.—See Kratos Defense & Security Solutions, Inc.; *U.S. Public*, pg. 1276
GIC PTE. LTD.; *Int'l*, pg. 2963
GIFT SAS; *Int'l*, pg. 2970
GILEAD SCIENCES EUROPE LTD.—See Gilead Sciences, Inc.; *U.S. Public*, pg. 937
GILMAN BUILDING PRODUCTS COMPANY; *U.S. Private*, pg. 1700
GIMMAL GROUP, INC.; *U.S. Private*, pg. 1701
GIOVANNI AGNELLI B.V.; *Int'l*, pg. 2978
GITI TIRE (CHINA) INVESTMENT CO., LTD.—See Giti Tire Pte. Ltd.; *Int'l*, pg. 2979
GITI TIRE PTE. LTD.; *Int'l*, pg. 2979
GK ENTERPRISES, INC.; *U.S. Private*, pg. 1703
GKN DO BRASIL LTDA.—See GKN plc; *Int'l*, pg. 2986
GKN DRIVELINE LOHMAR—See GKN plc; *Int'l*, pg. 2984
GKN THOMPSON CHASSIS LTD—See GKN plc; *Int'l*, pg. 2985

GLANBIA CO-OPERATIVE SOCIETY LIMITED; *Int'l*, pg. 2987
GLANBIA FOODS B.V.—See Glanbia Co-Operative Society Limited; *Int'l*, pg. 2988
GLANBIA INVESTMENTS (IRELAND) LIMITED—See Glanbia Co-Operative Society Limited; *Int'l*, pg. 2988
GLANTUS HOLDINGS PLC—See Accel Partners L.P.; *U.S. Private*, pg. 48
GLANTUS HOLDINGS PLC—See KKR & Co. Inc.; *U.S. Public*, pg. 1238
GLANTUS HOLDINGS PLC—See Long Path Partners, LP; *U.S. Private*, pg. 2491
GLASSBRIDGE ENTERPRISES, INC.; *U.S. Public*, pg. 939
GLASS LLC—See Dubai Investments PJSC; *Int'l*, pg. 2219
GLASS MOUNTAIN HOLDING, LLC—See Energy Transfer LP; *U.S. Public*, pg. 764
GLATFELTER CANADA, INC.—See Glatfelter Corporation; *U.S. Public*, pg. 939
GLATFELTER FALKENHAGEN HOLDINGS GMBH—See Glatfelter Corporation; *U.S. Public*, pg. 939
GLAXOSMITHKLINE HOLDINGS (AMERICAS) INC.—See GSK plc; *Int'l*, pg. 3147
GLAXOSMITHKLINE HOLDINGS (ONE) LIMITED—See GSK plc; *Int'l*, pg. 3147
GLAXOSMITHKLINE INTERNATIONAL (LUXEMBOURG) S.A.R.L—See GSK plc; *Int'l*, pg. 3148
GLAXOSMITHKLINE PHARMACEUTICALS EUROPE B.V.—See GSK plc; *Int'l*, pg. 3148
GLAXO WELLCOME INTERNATIONAL B.V.—See GSK plc; *Int'l*, pg. 3145
GLAZER'S FAMILY OF COMPANIES; *U.S. Private*, pg. 1707
G & L BEIJER A/S—See Beijer Ref AB; *Int'l*, pg. 944
GLENCORE INTERNATIONAL AG—See Glencore plc; *Int'l*, pg. 2990
GLENCORE PLC; *Int'l*, pg. 2990
GLENCORE QUEENSLAND LIMITED—See Glencore plc; *Int'l*, pg. 2991
GLENCORE (SCHWEIZ) AG—See Glencore plc; *Int'l*, pg. 2990
GLENHILL ADVISORS, LLC; *U.S. Private*, pg. 1710
GLENMARK HOLDING S.A.—See Glenmark Pharmaceuticals Limited; *Int'l*, pg. 2992
GL GROUP, INC.; *U.S. Private*, pg. 1704
GL LIMITED—See Hong Leong Investment Holdings Pte. Ltd.; *Int'l*, pg. 3468
GLOBAL ARENA HOLDING, INC.; *U.S. Public*, pg. 940
GLOBAL ATLANTIC FINANCIAL GROUP LIMITED—See KKR & Co. Inc.; *U.S. Public*, pg. 1251
GLOBAL AVIATION HOLDINGS, INC.—See MatlinPatterson Global Advisers LLC; *U.S. Private*, pg. 2611
GLOBAL AXCESS CORP.; *U.S. Public*, pg. 1712
GLOBAL BANKERS INSURANCE GROUP, LLC—See Eli Global, LLC; *U.S. Private*, pg. 1359
GLOBAL BLUE GROUP HOLDING AG; *Int'l*, pg. 2993
GLOBAL BROKERAGE, INC.; *U.S. Public*, pg. 940
GLOBAL CITY HOLDINGS N.V.; *Int'l*, pg. 2994
GLOBAL CONVERGENCE, INC.; *U.S. Private*, pg. 1713
GLOBAL CROSSING AIRLINES GROUP INC.; *U.S. Public*, pg. 941
GLOBALDATA PLC; *Int'l*, pg. 3003
GLOBAL DIGITAL CREATIONS HOLDINGS LIMITED; *Int'l*, pg. 2994
GLOBAL DRAGON LIMITED; *Int'l*, pg. 2995
GLOBAL FINANCIAL INVESTMENTS HOLDING SAOG; *Int'l*, pg. 2996
GLOBAL HEMP GROUP INC.; *Int'l*, pg. 2997
GLOBAL INDEMNITY GROUP, INC.—See Paine Schwartz Partners, LLC; *U.S. Private*, pg. 3075
GLOBAL INDEMNITY GROUP, LLC—See Paine Schwartz Partners, LLC; *U.S. Private*, pg. 3075
GLOBAL LINK COMMUNICATIONS HOLDINGS LIMITED—See Goldstream Investment Limited; *Int'l*, pg. 3034
GLOBAL LOGISTIC PROPERTIES LIMITED; *Int'l*, pg. 2999
GLOBAL MASTERMIND HOLDINGS LTD.; *Int'l*, pg. 2999
GLOBAL NEW MATERIAL INTERNATIONAL HOLDINGS LIMITED; *Int'l*, pg. 2999
GLOBAL PHILATELIC NETWORK; *Int'l*, pg. 3000
GLOBAL SAE-A CO., LTD; *Int'l*, pg. 3000
GLOBALTEC FORMATION BERHAD; *Int'l*, pg. 3004
GLOBAL-TECH ADVANCED INNOVATIONS INC.; *Int'l*, pg. 3003
GLOBALTECH HOLDINGS, INC.; *U.S. Public*, pg. 946
GLOBAL UIN INTELLIGENCE HOLDINGS LIMITED; *Int'l*, pg. 3002
GLOBAL UNICORN HOLDINGS, INC.; *U.S. Private*, pg. 1718
GLOBAL WATER RESOURCES, INC.; *U.S. Public*, pg. 945
GLOBAVEND HOLDINGS LIMITED; *Int'l*, pg. 3005
GLOBE LIFE INC.; *U.S. Public*, pg. 946
GLOBELTR ENERGY, INC.—See Clearlake Capital Group, L.P.; *U.S. Private*, pg. 934
GLOBE SPECIALTY METALS, INC.—See Grupo Villar Mir, S.A.U.; *Int'l*, pg. 3138
GLOME HOLDING, INC.; *U.S. Public*, pg. 3008
GLORY HEALTH INDUSTRY LIMITED; *Int'l*, pg. 3009
GLORY SUN FINANCIAL GROUP LIMITED; *Int'l*, pg. 3010

GLYNWED PACIFIC HOLDINGS PTY LTD—See Aliaxis S.A./N.V.; *Int'l*, pg. 324
GMAC INTERNATIONAL HOLDINGS B.V.—See General Motors Company; *U.S. Public*, pg. 925
GMA HOLDING B.V.—See Mistras Group, Inc.; *U.S. Public*, pg. 1451
G MEDICAL INNOVATIONS HOLDINGS LTD.; *Int'l*, pg. 2861
GMG GLOBAL LIMITED—See China Hainan Rubber Industry Group Co., Ltd.; *Int'l*, pg. 1506
GMI HOLDING, INC.; *U.S. Public*, pg. 1722
GM LAAM HOLDINGS, LLC—See General Motors Company; *U.S. Public*, pg. 924
GMO FINANCIAL HOLDINGS, INC.—See GMO Internet Group, Inc.; *Int'l*, pg. 3013
GMS INC.; *U.S. Public*, pg. 947
GMSS HOLDINGS, LLC; *U.S. Private*, pg. 1723
GNCC CAPITAL, INC.; *U.S. Public*, pg. 949
GNC CORPORATION—See Ares Management Corporation; *U.S. Public*, pg. 189
GNC HOLDINGS INC.—See Ares Management Corporation; *U.S. Public*, pg. 189
GNCO, INC.; *U.S. Private*, pg. 1723
GNC PARENT LLC—See Ares Management Corporation; *U.S. Public*, pg. 189
THE GO-AHEAD GROUP PLC—See GLOBALVIA Inversiones, S.A.U.; *Int'l*, pg. 3005
GO-AHEAD LONDON—See GLOBALVIA Inversiones, S.A.U.; *Int'l*, pg. 3005
GOALS SOCCER CENTRES PLC; *Int'l*, pg. 3018
GO COMPANIES, LLC; *U.S. Private*, pg. 1723
GODADDY, INC.—See KKR & Co. Inc.; *U.S. Public*, pg. 1252
GODADDY, INC.—See Silver Lake Group, LLC; *U.S. Private*, pg. 3657
GODADDY, INC.—See TCMI, Inc.; *U.S. Private*, pg. 3943
GODDARD CATERING GROUP INC.—See Goddard Enterprises Limited; *Int'l*, pg. 3019
GODDARD ENTERPRISES LIMITED; *Int'l*, pg. 3018
GODREJ & BOYCE MFG. CO. LTD.; *Int'l*, pg. 3020
GOFF CAPITAL, INC.; *U.S. Private*, pg. 1726
GOGOX HOLDINGS LIMITED; *Int'l*, pg. 3022
GOHEALTH, INC.; *U.S. Public*, pg. 949
GOINDUSTRY-DOVEBID LIMITED—See Liquidity Services, Inc.; *U.S. Public*, pg. 1320
GOKURAKUYU HOLDINGS CO., LTD.; *Int'l*, pg. 3023
GOLAR LNG LIMITED; *Int'l*, pg. 3023
GOLD BOND GROUP LTD.; *Int'l*, pg. 3023
GOLDBOND GROUP; *Int'l*, pg. 3027
GOLD COIN HOLDINGS SDN BHD; *Int'l*, pg. 3024
GOLDEN AGRI-RESOURCES LTD.; *Int'l*, pg. 3027
GOLDENBRIDGE NO.4 SPECIAL PURPOSE ACQUISITION CO., LTD.; *Int'l*, pg. 3032
GOLDEN CAPITAL INVESTMENT LIMITED—See Hysan Development Company Limited; *Int'l*, pg. 3554
GOLDEN CONCORD HOLDINGS LIMITED; *Int'l*, pg. 3028
GOLDEN ENTERTAINMENT, INC.; *U.S. Public*, pg. 950
GOLDEN HEAVEN GROUP HOLDINGS LTD.; *Int'l*, pg. 3029
GOLDEN LEAF HOLDINGS LTD.; *Int'l*, pg. 3030
GOLDEN MEDITECH (BVI) COMPANY LIMITED—See Golden Meditech Holdings Limited; *Int'l*, pg. 3030
GOLDEN MEDITECH HERBAL TREATMENT (BVI) COMPANY LIMITED—See Golden Meditech Holdings Limited; *Int'l*, pg. 3030
GOLDEN OCEAN GROUP LTD.; *Int'l*, pg. 3030
GOLDEN THROAT HOLDINGS GROUP CO. LTD.; *Int'l*, pg. 3032
GOLDEN TOUCH IMPORTS, INC.; *U.S. Private*, pg. 1733
GOLDENTREE ASSET MANAGEMENT LP; *U.S. Private*, pg. 1734
GOLDEN TRIANGLE VENTURES, INC.; *U.S. Public*, pg. 951
GOLDEN WEST PACKAGING GROUP LLC—See Goldberg Lindsay & Co., LLC; *U.S. Private*, pg. 1729
GOLDEN WHEEL TIANDI HOLDINGS COMPANY LIMITED; *Int'l*, pg. 3032
GOLD FLORA CORP.; *U.S. Public*, pg. 949
GOLDMAN SACHS AUSTRALIA GROUP HOLDINGS PTY LTD—See The Goldman Sachs Group, Inc.; *U.S. Public*, pg. 2081
GOLDMAN SACHS GROUP HOLDINGS (U.K.)—See The Goldman Sachs Group, Inc.; *U.S. Public*, pg. 2081
GOLD PEAK TECHNOLOGY GROUP LIMITED; *Int'l*, pg. 3025
GOLD ROCK HOLDINGS INC.; *U.S. Public*, pg. 950
GOLD'S GYM INTERNATIONAL, INC.—See TRT Holdings, Inc.; *U.S. Public*, pg. 4244
GOLFLAND ENTERTAINMENT CENTERS; *U.S. Private*, pg. 1736
GOLIATH INTERNATIONAL HOLDING BV; *Int'l*, pg. 3036
GOME FINANCE TECHNOLOGY CO., LTD.; *Int'l*, pg. 3037
GOOD EATS HOLDING COMPANY INC.—See Cracken, Harkey & Co., LLC; *U.S. Private*, pg. 1081
GOOD FELLOW HEALTHCARE HOLDINGS LIMITED; *Int'l*, pg. 3038
GOOD FOOD HOLDINGS LLC; *U.S. Private*, pg. 1738
GOODMAN LIMITED; *Int'l*, pg. 3040

551112 — OFFICES OF OTHER HO...

GOOD RESOURCES HOLDINGS LIMITED; *Int'l*, pg. 3038
GOODRICH PETROLEUM CORPORATION—See EnCap Investments L.P.; *U.S. Private*, pg. 1390
GOODRX HOLDINGS, INC.; *U.S. Public*, pg. 951
GOOD SAM ENTERPRISES, LLC—See Camping World Holdings, Inc.; *U.S. Public*, pg. 428
GOODWIN PLC; *Int'l*, pg. 3041
GOODYEAR DUNLOP TIRES EUROPE B.V.—See The Goodyear Tire & Rubber Company; *U.S. Public*, pg. 2083
GOODYEAR TYRE & RUBBER HOLDINGS (PTY) LTD—See The Goodyear Tire & Rubber Company; *U.S. Public*, pg. 2084
GOOGLE INTERNATIONAL LLC—See Alphabet Inc.; *U.S. Public*, pg. 83
GOOGLE IRELAND HOLDINGS—See Alphabet Inc.; *U.S. Public*, pg. 83
GOOI GLOBAL; *U.S. Public*, pg. 952
GORAZDZE KRUSZYWA—See Heidelberg Materials AG; *Int'l*, pg. 3310
GORDON BROTHERS GROUP, LLC; *U.S. Private*, pg. 1741
THE GORES GROUP, LLC; *U.S. Private*, pg. 4035
GO SOUTH COAST LIMITED—See GLOBALVIA Inversiones, S.A.U.; *Int'l*, pg. 3005
GOSTA TORSSELL HOLDING AB; *Int'l*, pg. 3043
GOSUN HOLDING CO., LTD.; *Int'l*, pg. 3043
GOTHIA FINANCIAL GROUP AB—See Bertelsmann SE & Co. KGaA; *Int'l*, pg. 996
GOVERNMENT REVENUE SOLUTIONS, LLC—See Guggenheim Partners, LLC; *U.S. Private*, pg. 1812
GOVIA LIMITED—See GLOBALVIA Inversiones, S.A.U.; *Int'l*, pg. 3005
GOWANDA COMPONENTS GROUP—See The Jordan Company, L.P.; *U.S. Private*, pg. 4063
GOXUS INC.; *Int'l*, pg. 3045
GPC ASIA PACIFIC HOLDINGS PTY LTD—See Genuine Parts Company; *U.S. Public*, pg. 932
GPC PARTICIPACOES SA; *Int'l*, pg. 3046
GPI S.P.A.; *Int'l*, pg. 3046
GPS ALLIANCE HOLDINGS LIMITED; *Int'l*, pg. 3046
GPS ALLIANCE HOLDINGS PTE. LTD.—See GPS Alliance Holdings Limited; *Int'l*, pg. 3047
GPS HOLDING GERMANY GMBH—See Aliaxis S.A./N.V.; *Int'l*, pg. 324
GPSI HOLDINGS, LLC—See Ingersoll Rand Inc.; *U.S. Public*, pg. 1120
GQG PARTNERS (AUSTRALIA) PTY LTD—See GQG Partners Inc.; *U.S. Public*, pg. 952
GRAB HOLDINGS LIMITED; *Int'l*, pg. 3048
GRACE CONTAINER, S. A. DE C. V.—See Standard Industries Holdings Inc.; *U.S. Private*, pg. 3779
GRACE HOLDINGS, S.A. DE C.V.—See Standard Industries Holdings Inc.; *U.S. Private*, pg. 3780
GRACE MANAGEMENT GROUP, LLC; *U.S. Private*, pg. 1749
GRADIANT CORPORATION; *Int'l*, pg. 3049
GRAEBEL COMPANIES, INC.; *U.S. Private*, pg. 1750
GRAHAM CORPORATION; *U.S. Public*, pg. 954
THE GRAHAM GROUP, INC.; *U.S. Private*, pg. 4036
GRAHAM HOLDINGS COMPANY; *U.S. Public*, pg. 954
GRAHAM NEWSPAPERS, INC.—See Alden Global Capital LLC; *U.S. Private*, pg. 156
GRAHAM PACKAGING HOLDINGS COMPANY—See Pactiv Evergreen Inc.; *U.S. Public*, pg. 1633
GRAINCORP MALT—See GrainCorp Limited; *Int'l*, pg. 3052
GRAINGER INTERNATIONAL, INC.—See W.W. Grainger, Inc.; *U.S. Public*, pg. 2320
GRAINGER LUXEMBOURG GERMANY HOLDINGS SARL—See Grainger plc; *Int'l*, pg. 3052
GRANARIA HOLDINGS B.V.; *Int'l*, pg. 3054
GRAND FIELD GROUP HOLDINGS LIMITED; *Int'l*, pg. 3054
GRAND GENEVA RESORT & SPA—See The Marcus Corporation; *U.S. Public*, pg. 2112
GRAND INVESTMENT INTERNATIONAL LIMITED; *Int'l*, pg. 3055
GRAND PEACE GROUP HOLDINGS LIMITED; *Int'l*, pg. 3056
GRAND PHARMACEUTICAL GROUP LIMITED; *Int'l*, pg. 3056
GRAND TALENTS GROUP HOLDINGS LIMITED; *Int'l*, pg. 3057
GRAND T G GOLD HOLDINGS LIMITED; *Int'l*, pg. 3057
GRANGE MUTUAL CASUALTY COMPANY; *U.S. Private*, pg. 1754
GRANINVESTIMENTOS SA; *Int'l*, pg. 3058
GRANITE BROADCASTING CORPORATION—See Silver Point Capital, L.P.; *U.S. Private*, pg. 3661
GRANITE CONSTRUCTION INCORPORATED; *U.S. Public*, pg. 957
GRANITE HACARMEL INVESTMENTS LTD.—See Azrieli Group Ltd.; *Int'l*, pg. 781
GRANT PRIDECO NETHERLANDS B.V.—See NOV, Inc.; *U.S. Public*, pg. 1544
GRAPHEX GROUP LIMITED; *Int'l*, pg. 3060
GRAPHIC COMMUNICATIONS HOLDINGS, INC.—See Clayton, Dubilier & Rice, LLC; *U.S. Public*, pg. 929
GRAPHIC CONVERTING INC.; *U.S. Private*, pg. 1757

GRAPHIC PACKAGING HOLDING COMPANY; *U.S. Public*, pg. 958
GRAPHIC PACKAGING INTERNATIONAL BOX HOLDINGS LIMITED—See Graphic Packaging Holding Company; *U.S. Public*, pg. 958
GRAPHIC PACKAGING INTERNATIONAL HOLDING SWEDEN AB—See Graphic Packaging Holding Company; *U.S. Public*, pg. 959
GRAPHIC PACKAGING INTERNATIONAL PARTNERS, LLC—See Graphic Packaging Holding Company; *U.S. Public*, pg. 958
GRAYCOR INC.; *U.S. Private*, pg. 1761
GRAY ENERGY SERVICES, LLC—See Centre Partners Management LLC; *U.S. Private*, pg. 828
GRAY INC.; *U.S. Private*, pg. 1759
GRAY TELEVISION, INC.; *U.S. Public*, pg. 959
GREAT AMERICAN FINANCIAL RESOURCES, INC.—See American Financial Group, Inc.; *U.S. Public*, pg. 102
THE GREAT AMERICAN OUTDOORS GROUP LLC; *U.S. Private*, pg. 4037
GREAT EAGLE HOLDINGS LIMITED; *Int'l*, pg. 3064
GREATER CHINA FINANCIAL HOLDINGS LTD.; *Int'l*, pg. 3067
GREATER NEW YORK MUTUAL INSURANCE COMPANY; *U.S. Private*, pg. 1770
GREAT PLAINS COMPANIES, INC.; *U.S. Private*, pg. 1766
GREAT PLAINS MEDIA, INC.; *U.S. Private*, pg. 1767
GREAT PLAINS VENTURES, INC.; *U.S. Private*, pg. 1767
GREATSTAR GROUP CO., LTD.; *Int'l*, pg. 3067
GREATTOWN HOLDINGS LTD.; *Int'l*, pg. 3068
GREATWALLE INC.; *Int'l*, pg. 3068
GREAT WALL PAN ASIA HOLDINGS LIMITED—See China Great Wall Asset Management Corporation; *Int'l*, pg. 1505
GREAT WESTERN CORPORATION PTY. LTD.; *Int'l*, pg. 3066
GREAT WHITE SHARK ENTERPRISES, INC.; *U.S. Private*, pg. 1768
GREAT WOLF RESORTS, INC.—See Centerbridge Partners, L.P.; *U.S. Private*, pg. 814
GREAT WORLD COMPANY HOLDINGS LIMITED; *Int'l*, pg. 3066
GREDE HOLDINGS LLC—See Gamut Capital Management, L.P.; *U.S. Private*, pg. 1641
GREE GROUP CO., LTD.; *Int'l*, pg. 3069
GREEN AQUA COMPANY SGPS, S.A.; *Int'l*, pg. 3069
GREENAUER HOLDING INC.; *U.S. Private*, pg. 1774
GREENBERG SPORTS GROUP INC.; *U.S. Private*, pg. 1775
GREENBRIER RAIL SERVICES WHEEL DIVISION—See The Greenbrier Companies, Inc.; *U.S. Public*, pg. 2086
GREEN COAST ENTERPRISES LLC; *Int'l*, pg. 3070
GREEN CROSS HK HOLDINGS LIMITED—See China Resources Boya Bio-pharmaceutical Group Co., Ltd.; *Int'l*, pg. 1548
GREEN CROSS HOLDINGS CORP.; *Int'l*, pg. 3070
GREENE KING PLC—See CK Asset Holdings Limited; *Int'l*, pg. 1635
GREEN ENERGY GROUP LIMITED; *Int'l*, pg. 3071
GREENERGY HOLDINGS INC.; *Int'l*, pg. 3074
GREENFIELDS HOLDING BV—See ABN AMRO Group N.V.; *Int'l*, pg. 64
GREENFIELDS HOLDING BV—See Gilde Buy Out Partners B.V.; *Int'l*, pg. 2974
GREEN GIANT INC.; *Int'l*, pg. 3071
GREEN GRASS ECOLOGICAL TECHNOLOGY DEVELOPMENT CO., LTD.; *Int'l*, pg. 3071
GREEN HOLDING S.P.A.; *Int'l*, pg. 3071
GREENHOUSE HOLDINGS, INC.—See root9B Holdings, Inc.; *U.S. Public*, pg. 1810
GREEN HYGIENICS HOLDINGS INC.; *U.S. Public*, pg. 963
GREENIDGE GENERATION HOLDINGS INC.; *U.S. Public*, pg. 964
GREEN INTERNATIONAL HOLDINGS LIMITED; *Int'l*, pg. 3071
GREENKO DUTCH B.V.; *Int'l*, pg. 3075
GREENLAND HOLDING A/S; *Int'l*, pg. 3075
GREENLAND HOLDING GROUP CO., LTD.—See Greenland Holdings Corporation Limited; *Int'l*, pg. 3075
GREENLAND HONG KONG HOLDINGS LIMITED—See Greenland Holdings Corporation Limited; *Int'l*, pg. 3075
GREENLANE HOLDINGS, INC.; *U.S. Public*, pg. 964
GREENLIT VENTURES, INC.; *U.S. Private*, pg. 3075
GREENLOOP IT, INC.; *U.S. Private*, pg. 1779
GREEN OCEAN CORPORATION BERHAD; *Int'l*, pg. 3072
GREEN PLANET BIOENGINEERING CO., LTD.; *U.S. Public*, pg. 964
GREENSONS BASEBALL II INC.—See Greenberg Sports Group Inc.; *U.S. Private*, pg. 1775
THE GREENSPUN CORPORATION; *U.S. Private*, pg. 4039
GREEN STREAM HOLDINGS INC.; *U.S. Public*, pg. 964
GREENTECH TECHNOLOGY INTERNATIONAL LIMITED; *Int'l*, pg. 3076
GREENTOWN MANAGEMENT HOLDINGS COMPANY LIMITED—See Greentown China Holdings Limited; *Int'l*, pg. 3076
GREENWAY TECHNOLOGIES, INC.; *U.S. Public*, pg. 965
GREENWICH AEROGROUP, INC.; *U.S. Private*, pg. 1781

GREENWOOD RACING INC.—See International Turf Investment Co., Inc.; *U.S. Private*, pg. 2121
GREGORY DISTRIBUTION (HOLDINGS) LIMITED; *Int'l*, pg. 3078
GREIF FLEXIBLES TRADING HOLDING B.V.—See Greif Inc.; *U.S. Public*, pg. 968
GREIF FRANCE HOLDINGS SAS—See Greif Inc.; *U.S. Public*, pg. 968
GREIF INTERNATIONAL HOLDING SUPRA II C.V.—See Greif Inc.; *U.S. Public*, pg. 968
GREINER HOLDING AG; *Int'l*, pg. 3078
GREKA DRILLING LIMITED; *Int'l*, pg. 3080
GRENSON LIMITED; *Int'l*, pg. 3081
GRE VENTURES, INC.; *U.S. Private*, pg. 1761
GREYSTAR REAL ESTATE PARTNERS, LLC; *U.S. Private*, pg. 1785
GREYSTONE INCORPORATED; *U.S. Private*, pg. 1786
GRIESHABER HOLDING GMBH; *Int'l*, pg. 3083
GRIFFIN COMMUNICATIONS, LLC; *U.S. Private*, pg. 1787
GRIFFIN HOLDINGS INC.; *U.S. Private*, pg. 1788
GRIFFITH HOLDINGS INC.; *U.S. Private*, pg. 1789
GRIFFITHS CORPORATION; *U.S. Private*, pg. 1789
GRIFOLS, INC.—See Grifols, S.A.; *Int'l*, pg. 3084
GRIFOLS INTERNATIONAL, S.A.—See Grifols, S.A.; *Int'l*, pg. 3084
GRIMALDI INDUSTRI AB; *Int'l*, pg. 3085
GRINDROD SHIPPING HOLDINGS LTD.; *Int'l*, pg. 3086
GRIZZLY ENERGY, LLC; *U.S. Public*, pg. 970
GRN HOLDING CORPORATION—See GRN Funds, LLC; *U.S. Private*, pg. 1791
THE GROCERS SUPPLY CO., INC.; *U.S. Private*, pg. 4039
GROCERY OUTLET HOLDING CORP.; *U.S. Public*, pg. 970
GROGANS TOWNE CHRYSLER DODGE INC.; *U.S. Private*, pg. 1791
GROLSCH INTERNATIONAL B.V.—See Asahi Group Holdings Ltd.; *Int'l*, pg. 593
GROUPE AB S.A.; *Int'l*, pg. 3091
GROUPE BAUMGARTNER HOLDING SA—See Banque Cantonale Vaudoise; *Int'l*, pg. 853
GROUPE BPCE; *Int'l*, pg. 3092
GROUPE BRUXELLES LAMBERT SA; *Int'l*, pg. 3099
GROUPE CENTENNIAL HOLDING SAH; *Int'l*, pg. 3101
GROUPE DUBREUIL SA; *Int'l*, pg. 3102
GROUPE EGIS S.A.; *Int'l*, pg. 3102
GROUPE GRIMAUD LA CORBIERE SA; *Int'l*, pg. 3103
GROUPE INDUSTRIEL MARCEL DASSAULT S.A.; *Int'l*, pg. 3104
GROUPE LAGASSE INC.; *Int'l*, pg. 3106
GROUPE LEGRIS INDUSTRIES; *Int'l*, pg. 3106
GROUPE LIMAGRAIN HOLDING—See Groupe Limagrain Holding SA; *Int'l*, pg. 3107
GROUPEMENT FLO; *Int'l*, pg. 3112
GROUPE MONITEUR HOLDING—See Bridgepoint Group Plc; *Int'l*, pg. 1155
GROUPE OMERIN; *Int'l*, pg. 3109
GROUPE SECHE SAS; *Int'l*, pg. 3110
GROUPE SFPI SA; *Int'l*, pg. 3111
GROUPE SIPAREX; *Int'l*, pg. 3111
GROUPE UNIPEX SAS; *Int'l*, pg. 3112
GROUP M5; *Int'l*, pg. 3089
GROUP ONE THOUSAND ONE, LLC; *U.S. Private*, pg. 1794
GROW CAPITAL, INC.; *U.S. Public*, pg. 972
GROWN UP GROUP INVESTMENT HOLDINGS LIMITED; *Int'l*, pg. 3113
GROWTH CATALYST PARTNERS, LLC; *U.S. Private*, pg. 1796
GROWTHCURVE CAPITAL LP; *U.S. Private*, pg. 1796
GROWWW MEDIA CO., LTD.—See Hakuhodo DY Holdings Incorporated; *Int'l*, pg. 3221
GR PROPERTIES LIMITED; *Int'l*, pg. 3047
GRUBB & ELLIS COMPANY—See BGC Group, Inc.; *U.S. Public*, pg. 329
GRUPA FORTIS D.O.O. BANJA LUKA; *Int'l*, pg. 3116
GRUPA GRASS SP. Z O.O.; *Int'l*, pg. 3116
GRUPA SMT S.A.; *Int'l*, pg. 3117
GRUPE, S.A.B. DE C.V.; *Int'l*, pg. 3118
GRUPO AEROMEXICO, S.A.B. DE C.V.; *Int'l*, pg. 3118
GRUPO ANTOLIN-AMSTERDAM, B.V.—See Grupo Antolin-Irausa, S.A.; *Int'l*, pg. 3119
GRUPO ARGOS S.A.; *Int'l*, pg. 3120
GRUPO BAL; *Int'l*, pg. 3121
GRUPO BOLIVAR S.A.; *Int'l*, pg. 3123
GRUPO BRASIL PARTICIPACOES; *Int'l*, pg. 3123
GRUPO BRITT N.V.; *Int'l*, pg. 3123
GRUPO CARSO, S.A.B. DE C.V.; *Int'l*, pg. 3123
GRUPO CLARIN S.A.; *Int'l*, pg. 3124
GRUPO EMPRESARIAL ANGELES, S.A. DE C.V.; *Int'l*, pg. 3126
GRUPO EMPRESARIAL KALUZ S.A. DE C.V.; *Int'l*, pg. 3126
GRUPO EMPRESARIAL SAN JOSE, S.A.; *Int'l*, pg. 3128
GRUPO FERRER INTERNACIONAL, S.A.; *Int'l*, pg. 3129
GRUPO FERROATLANTICA, S.A.U.—See Sixth Street Partners LLC; *U.S. Private*, pg. 3677
GRUPO FERROMINERO, S.A. DE C.V.; *Int'l*, pg. 3129
GRUPO FINACCESS S.A.P.I. DE C.V.; *Int'l*, pg. 3129
GRUPO FINANCIERO SANTANDER MEXICO, S.A.B. DE

C.V.—See Banco Santander, S.A.; *Int'l*, pg. 825
GRUPO INMOBILIARIO DE CAPITAL PRIVADO I (GICAP I) LTD.; *Int'l*, pg. 3130
GRUPO KONECTANET S.L.; *Int'l*, pg. 3130
GRUPO KUO, S.A.B. DE C.V.; *Int'l*, pg. 3130
GRUPO MRF CARTUJA SL; *Int'l*, pg. 3133
GRUPO MZ; *Int'l*, pg. 3133
GRUPONUEVA S.A.; *Int'l*, pg. 3139
GRUPO PROEZA, S.A.P.I. DE C.V.; *Int'l*, pg. 3134
GRUPO PROTEXA S.A. DE C.V.; *Int'l*, pg. 3134
GRUPO ROMERO; *Int'l*, pg. 3134
GRUPO SALVADOR CAETANO (SGPS) S.A.; *Int'l*, pg. 3135
GRUPO TECNOLOGICO E INDUSTRIAL GMV, S.A.; *Int'l*, pg. 3135
GRUPO TERRA S.A. DE C.V.; *Int'l*, pg. 3137
GRUPO VILLAR MIR, S.A.U.; *Int'l*, pg. 3138
GRUPO VIPS—See Alsea, S.A.B. de C.V.; *Int'l*, pg. 379
GRUPO XTRA S.A. DE C.V.; *Int'l*, pg. 3139
GRUPPO ITALIANO VINI S.P.A.—See Cantine Riunite & CIV S.C.Agr.; *Int'l*, pg. 1299
GRUPPO LACTALIS ITALIA S.P.A.—See Groupe Lactalis SA; *Int'l*, pg. 3106
GRUPPO MINERALI MAFFEI S.P.A.; *Int'l*, pg. 3140
GRUPPO PAM S.P.A.—See GECOS S.p.A.; *Int'l*, pg. 2909
GRUPPO RIELLO SISTEMI S.P.A.; *Int'l*, pg. 3141
GRUPPO WASTE ITALIA S.P.A.; *Int'l*, pg. 3141
GRYPHON DIGITAL MINING, INC.; *U.S. Public*, pg. 973
GSC ENTERPRISES, INC.; *U.S. Private*, pg. 1800
GSE HOLDING, INC.—See Littlejohn & Co., LLC; *U.S. Private*, pg. 2470
GSE HOLDING, INC.—See Strategic Value Partners, LLC; *U.S. Private*, pg. 3836
G.S. GALATARIOTIS & SONS LTD.; *Int'l*, pg. 2866
GS HOLDINGS CORP.; *Int'l*, pg. 3141
GS YUASA CORPORATION; *Int'l*, pg. 3143
GT CAPITAL HOLDINGS, INC.; *Int'l*, pg. 3150
G THREE HOLDINGS CORP.; *Int'l*, pg. 2861
GTI HOLDINGS LIMITED; *Int'l*, pg. 3151
GTM HOLDINGS CORPORATION; *Int'l*, pg. 3151
GTN LIMITED—See GTCR LLC; *U.S. Private*, pg. 1805
GTS HOLDINGS, INC.; *U.S. Private*, pg. 1807
GUANGDONG AVCIT TECHNOLOGY HOLDING CO., LTD.; *Int'l*, pg. 3152
GUANGDONG GUANGHONG HOLDINGS CO., LTD.; *Int'l*, pg. 3155
GUANGDONG HONGTU TECHNOLOGY (HOLDINGS) CO., LTD.; *Int'l*, pg. 3155
GUANGDONG KITECH NEW MATERIAL HOLDING CO., LTD.; *Int'l*, pg. 3158
GUANGDONG LAND HOLDINGS LIMITED—See GDH Limited; *Int'l*, pg. 2896
GUANGDONG RISING ASSETS MANAGEMENT CO., LTD.; *Int'l*, pg. 3159
GUANGDONG YUDEAN GROUP CO., LTD.; *Int'l*, pg. 3162
GUANGHUI LOGISTICS CO., LTD.; *Int'l*, pg. 3162
GUANGZHOU BAIYUNSHAN PHARMACEUTICAL HOLDINGS COMPANY LIMITED; *Int'l*, pg. 3164
GUANGZHOU HENGYUN ENTERPRISES HOLDING LTD.; *Int'l*, pg. 3165
GUANGZHOU RADIO GROUP CO., LTD.; *Int'l*, pg. 3167
GUANGZHOU RISONG INTELLIGENT TECHNOLOGY HOLDING CO., LTD.; *Int'l*, pg. 3167
GUANGZHOU SECURITIES CO., LTD.—See CITIC Securities Co., Ltd.; *Int'l*, pg. 1622
GUANGZHOU YUEXIU CAPITAL HOLDINGS GROUP CO., LTD.; *Int'l*, pg. 3168
GUANHUA CORP.; *U.S. Private*, pg. 1808
GUANZE MEDICAL INFORMATION INDUSTRY (HOLDING) CO., LTD.; *Int'l*, pg. 3169
GUARANTEE INSURANCE GROUP, INC.; *U.S. Private*, pg. 1809
GUARANTY CORPORATION; *U.S. Public*, pg. 973
GUARANTY TRUST HOLDING COMPANY PLC; *Int'l*, pg. 3169
GUARDFORCE AI CO., LIMITED; *Int'l*, pg. 3169
GUARDIAN ASSET MANAGEMENT LTD—See Guardian Holdings Limited; *Int'l*, pg. 3171
GUARDIAN HOLDINGS INC.; *U.S. Private*, pg. 1810
GUARDIAN HOLDINGS LIMITED; *Int'l*, pg. 3170
GUARD INSURANCE GROUP, INC.—See Berkshire Hathaway Inc.; *U.S. Public*, pg. 302
GUCKENHEIMER ENTERPRISE, INC.—See EQT AB; *Int'l*, pg. 2476
GUCKENHEIMER ENTERPRISE, INC.—See The Goldman Sachs Group, Inc.; *U.S. Public*, pg. 2077
GUESS? INC.; *U.S. Public*, pg. 974
GUESS MOTORS, INC.; *U.S. Private*, pg. 1810
GUGGENHEIM BASEBALL MANAGEMENT, L.P.; *U.S. Private*, pg. 1811
GUGGENHEIM PARTNERS, LLC; *U.S. Private*, pg. 1811
GUIDEHOUSE LLP—See Bain Capital, LP; *U.S. Private*, pg. 432
GUIDEWELL MUTUAL HOLDING CORPORATION; *U.S. Private*, pg. 1813
GUILD HOLDINGS COMPANY—See McCarthy Group, LLC; *U.S. Private*, pg. 2626

GUITAR CENTER HOLDINGS, INC.—See Bain Capital, LP; *U.S. Private*, pg. 440
GUIZHOU CHANGZHENG TIANCHENG HOLDING CO., LTD.; *Int'l*, pg. 3174
GUJARAT LEASE FINANCING LIMITED; *Int'l*, pg. 3176
GUJARAT STATE PETROLEUM CORPORATION LIMITED; *Int'l*, pg. 3177
GULER YATIRIM HOLDING A.S.; *Int'l*, pg. 3178
GULF DISTRIBUTING HOLDINGS LLC; *U.S. Private*, pg. 1816
GULF INTERNATIONAL CORPORATION; *U.S. Private*, pg. 1816
GULL HOLDINGS, LTD.; *U.S. Private*, pg. 1817
GULTECH INTERNATIONAL PTE LTD—See Gul Technologies Singapore Ltd.; *Int'l*, pg. 3178
GUMA GROUP; *Int'l*, pg. 3183
GUNDERSON LLC—See The Greenbrier Companies, Inc.; *U.S. Public*, pg. 2086
GUNVOR GROUP LTD.; *Int'l*, pg. 3185
GUNVOR INTERNATIONAL B.V.—See Gunvor Group Ltd.; *Int'l*, pg. 3185
GUOCO GROUP LTD.—See Hong Leong Investment Holdings Pte. Ltd.; *Int'l*, pg. 3467
GUOTAI JUNAN FINANCIAL HOLDINGS CO., LTD—See Guotai Junan Securities Co., Ltd.; *Int'l*, pg. 3187
GUSHENGTANG HOLDINGS LIMITED; *Int'l*, pg. 3188
GUS MACHADO ENTERPRISES, INC.; *U.S. Private*, pg. 1819
GUTHY-RENKER CORPORATION; *U.S. Private*, pg. 1820
GUTTMAN HOLDINGS, INC.; *U.S. Private*, pg. 1820
GVW GROUP, LLC; *U.S. Private*, pg. 1821
GYRE THERAPEUTICS, INC.—See GNI Group Ltd.; *Int'l*, pg. 3017
GYROSCOPE THERAPEUTICS HOLDINGS PLC; *Int'l*, pg. 3191
H2G GREEN LIMITED; *Int'l*, pg. 3200
HAAS & HAAS, LLC; *U.S. Private*, pg. 1837
HAAS HOLDINGS, LLC—See Platinum Equity, LLC; *U.S. Private*, pg. 3210
HABERKORN HOLDING AG; *Int'l*, pg. 3202
HABIA CABLE AB—See Beijer Alma AB; *Int'l*, pg. 942
HABIB GROUP OF COMPANIES; *Int'l*, pg. 3203
HACI OMER SABANCI HOLDING A.S.; *Int'l*, pg. 3203
HADDAD RESTAURANT GROUP, INC.; *U.S. Private*, pg. 1839
HAEGER INDUSTRIES, INC.; *U.S. Private*, pg. 1839
THE HAGADONE CORPORATION; *U.S. Private*, pg. 4041
THE HAGERTY GROUP, LLC—See Hagerty, Inc.; *U.S. Public*, pg. 979
HAGERTY, INC.; *U.S. Public*, pg. 979
HAGLEITNER HYGIENE INTERNATIONAL GMBH; *Int'l*, pg. 3207
HAICHANG OCEAN PARK HOLDINGS LTD.; *Int'l*, pg. 3209
HAIDILAO INTERNATIONAL HOLDING LTD.; *Int'l*, pg. 3209
HAILIANG GROUP CO. LTD.; *Int'l*, pg. 3211
HAILIANG INTERNATIONAL HOLDINGS LIMITED—See Hailiang Group Co. Ltd.; *Int'l*, pg. 3211
HAINA INTELLIGENT EQUIPMENT INTERNATIONAL HOLDINGS LIMITED; *Int'l*, pg. 3211
HAINAN JINGLIANG HOLDINGS CO., LTD.; *Int'l*, pg. 3212
HAINAN TRAFFIC ADMINISTRATION HOLDING CO., LTD.; *Int'l*, pg. 3212
HAISAN RESOURCES BERHAD; *Int'l*, pg. 3217
HAITONG INTERNATIONAL HOLDINGS LIMITED—See Haitong Securities Co., Ltd.; *Int'l*, pg. 3218
HAITONG INTERNATIONAL HOLDINGS (UK) LIMITED—See Haitong Securities Co., Ltd.; *Int'l*, pg. 3218
HAKI SAFETY AB; *Int'l*, pg. 3219
HAKKANI GROUP; *Int'l*, pg. 3219
HAKUHODO DY HOLDINGS INCORPORATED; *Int'l*, pg. 3220
HALBERG A/S; *Int'l*, pg. 3227
HALCROW HOLDINGS LIMITED—See Jacobs Engineering Group, Inc.; *U.S. Public*, pg. 1184
HALCYON COAST INVESTMENT (CANADA) LTD.; *Int'l*, pg. 3227
HALDANE MCCALL PLC; *Int'l*, pg. 3227
HAL HOLDING N.V.—See HAL Trust N.V.; *Int'l*, pg. 3223
HALIFAX MEDIA HOLDINGS, LLC—See Gannett Co., Inc.; *U.S. Public*, pg. 905
HALLA GROUP; *Int'l*, pg. 3229
HALL CAPITAL, LLC; *U.S. Private*, pg. 1843
HALLENSTEIN GLASSON HOLDINGS LIMITED; *Int'l*, pg. 3230
HALLIBURTON COMPANY; *U.S. Public*, pg. 980
HALLIBURTON ENERGY SERVICES LIMITED—See Halliburton Company; *U.S. Public*, pg. 980
HALLIBURTON GLOBAL AFFILIATES HOLDINGS B.V.—See Halliburton Company; *U.S. Public*, pg. 980
HALLWOOD GROUP, LLC; *U.S. Private*, pg. 1845
HALMA HOLDINGS INC.—See Halma plc; *Int'l*, pg. 3231
HALMA PLC; *Int'l*, pg. 3230
HALMEK HOLDINGS CO., LTD.; *Int'l*, pg. 3233
HALO TECHNOLOGIES HOLDINGS LTD.; *Int'l*, pg. 3233
HALO TECHNOLOGY HOLDINGS, INC.; *U.S. Private*, pg. 1845

HAMBLEDON MINING COMPANY LIMITED—See Altyn-Gold plc; *Int'l*, pg. 400
HAMELN GROUP GMBH; *Int'l*, pg. 3237
HAMILTON BEACH BRANDS HOLDING COMPANY; *U.S. Public*, pg. 981
HAMILTON INSURANCE GROUP, LTD.; *Int'l*, pg. 3238
HAMILTON SUNDSTRAND CORPORATION—See RTX Corporation; *U.S. Public*, pg. 1821
HAMMER TECHNOLOGY HOLDINGS; *U.S. Public*, pg. 982
HAMPDEN CAPITAL PLC—See Hampden Holdings Limited; *Int'l*, pg. 3239
HAMPDEN HOLDINGS LIMITED; *Int'l*, pg. 3239
HAMPDEN PLC—See Hampden Holdings Limited; *Int'l*, pg. 3239
HANCAP AB; *Int'l*, pg. 3241
HANDAL ENERGY BERHAD; *Int'l*, pg. 3243
HANDS FORM HOLDINGS LIMITED; *Int'l*, pg. 3243
HANEDA ZENITH HOLDINGS CO., LTD.; *Int'l*, pg. 3244
HANERGY HOLDING GROUP LIMITED; *Int'l*, pg. 3244
HANG FAR COMPANY LIMITED—See Hang Lung Group Limited; *Int'l*, pg. 3245
HANG PIN LIVING TECHNOLOGY COMPANY LIMITED; *Int'l*, pg. 3245
HANG TAI YUE GROUP HOLDINGS LIMITED; *Int'l*, pg. 3245
HANGZHOU HOTA M & E HOLDINGS CO., LTD.; *Int'l*, pg. 3248
HANHUA FINANCIAL HOLDING CO., LTD.; *Int'l*, pg. 3252
HANIL CEMENT CO., LTD.—See Hanil Holdings Co., Ltd; *Int'l*, pg. 3252
HANIL HOLDINGS CO., LTD; *Int'l*, pg. 3252
HANJIN KAL CORP.; *Int'l*, pg. 3252
HANKEY GROUP; *U.S. Private*, pg. 1853
HANKYU HANSHIN HOLDINGS INC.; *Int'l*, pg. 3254
HANMI SCIENCE CO., LTD.; *Int'l*, pg. 3256
HANNA HOLDINGS, INC.; *U.S. Private*, pg. 1854
HANNSPREE EUROPE HOLDINGS B.V.—See HannStar Display Corporation; *Int'l*, pg. 3258
HANNSTAR BOARD INTERNATIONAL HOLDINGS LIMITED; *Int'l*, pg. 3257
THE HANOVER INSURANCE GROUP, INC.; *U.S. Public*, pg. 2087
HANOVER R.S. LIMITED PARTNERSHIP; *U.S. Private*, pg. 1855
HANRYU HOLDINGS, INC.; *Int'l*, pg. 3258
HANSA CHEMIE INTERNATIONAL AG; *Int'l*, pg. 3259
HANSAE YES24 HOLDINGS CO., LTD.; *Int'l*, pg. 3259
HANSEN TECHNOLOGIES LIMITED; *Int'l*, pg. 3260
HANSER HOLDINGS INTERNATIONAL; *U.S. Private*, pg. 1856
HANSOL GROUP; *Int'l*, pg. 3260
HANSON AUSTRALIA (HOLDINGS) PTY. LIMITED—See Heidelberg Materials AG; *Int'l*, pg. 3311
HANSON LIMITED—See Heidelberg Materials AG; *Int'l*, pg. 3311
HANTZ GROUP, INC.; *U.S. Private*, pg. 1857
HANWHA GROUP; *Int'l*, pg. 3264
HAO TIAN INTERNATIONAL CONSTRUCTION INVESTMENT GROUP LIMITED; *Int'l*, pg. 3267
HAPPY HARRY'S DISCOUNT DRUG STORES, INC.—See Walgreens Boots Alliance, Inc.; *U.S. Public*, pg. 2323
HAP SENG CONSOLIDATED BERHAD; *Int'l*, pg. 3268
HAP SENG PLANTATIONS HOLDINGS BERHAD—See Hap Seng Consolidated Berhad; *Int'l*, pg. 3268
HARALD QUANDT HOLDING GMBH; *Int'l*, pg. 3269
HARBERT MANAGEMENT CORPORATION; *U.S. Private*, pg. 1857
HARBISONWALKER INTERNATIONAL, INC.—See Platinum Equity, LLC; *U.S. Private*, pg. 3203
HARBOR FOODS GROUP INC.; *U.S. Private*, pg. 1859
HARBOUR ENERGY LTD.—See EIG Global Energy Partners, LLC; *U.S. Private*, pg. 1347
HARBOUR ENERGY PLC; *Int'l*, pg. 3271
HARBOUR EQUINE HOLDINGS LIMITED; *Int'l*, pg. 3271
HARBOUR GROUP INDUSTRIES, INC.; *U.S. Private*, pg. 1860
HARDY UNDERWRITING BERMUDA LIMITED—See Loews Corporation; *U.S. Public*, pg. 1340
HAREL MALLAC & CO. LTD.; *Int'l*, pg. 3274
HARIM HOLDINGS CO., LTD.; *Int'l*, pg. 3275
HARKINS AMUSEMENT ENTERPRISES, INC.; *U.S. Private*, pg. 1864
HARLEY-DAVIDSON EUROPE LIMITED—See Harley-Davidson, Inc.; *U.S. Public*, pg. 984
HARMON GROUP; *U.S. Private*, pg. 1866
HARMONICARE MEDICAL HOLDINGS LTD.; *Int'l*, pg. 3278
HARMONY BIOSCIENCES HOLDINGS, INC.; *U.S. Public*, pg. 986
HARMONY GOLD (AUSTRALIA) PTY. LTD.—See Harmony Gold Mining Company Limited; *Int'l*, pg. 3278
HARPERCOLLINS (UK)—See News Corporation; *U.S. Public*, pg. 1519
HARPER HOLDING SARL—See Enstar Group Limited; *Int'l*, pg. 2449
HARPO, INC.; *U.S. Private*, pg. 1868
HARRIS ASIA PACIFIC (M) SDN. BHD.—See L3Harris Technologies, Inc.; *U.S. Public*, pg. 1279
HARRIS BUSINESS GROUP INC.; *U.S. Private*, pg. 1869

HARRIS CANADA, INC.—See L3Harris Technologies, Inc.; *U.S. Public*, pg. 1279
HARRIS FARMS, INC.; *U.S. Private*, pg. 1869
HARRIS RANCH BEEF HOLDING COMPANY—See Central Valley Meat Holding Company; *U.S. Private*, pg. 826
HARRIS TEETER SUPERMARKETS, INC.—See The Kroger Co.; *U.S. Public*, pg. 2108
HARRY & DAVID HOLDINGS, INC.—See 1-800-FLOWERS.COM, Inc.; *U.S. Public*, pg. 1
HARTALEGA HOLDINGS BERHAD; *Int'l*, pg. 3279
HARTAMAS GROUP BHD.; *Int'l*, pg. 3279
HARTFORD LIFE & ACCIDENT INSURANCE COMPANY—See Sixth Street Specialty Lending, Inc.; *U.S. Public*, pg. 1891
HARTZELL INDUSTRIES, INC.; *U.S. Private*, pg. 1874
THE HARTZ GROUP, INC.; *U.S. Private*, pg. 4043
HARU HOLDING CORP.—See TPG Capital, L.P.; *U.S. Public*, pg. 2167
HARUYAMA HOLDINGS INC.; *Int'l*, pg. 3280
HARVEST HILL BEVERAGE COMPANY—See Brynwood Partners Management LLC; *U.S. Private*, pg. 674
HARVEST OIL & GAS CORP.—See EnerVest, Ltd.; *U.S. Private*, pg. 1397
HARVEY NASH GROUP LTD—See DBAY Advisors Limited; *Int'l*, pg. 1987
HARWICH HOLDING GMBH—See Aptiv PLC; *Int'l*, pg. 525
HASBRO NETHERLANDS HOLDINGS, B.V.—See Hasbro, Inc.; *U.S. Public*, pg. 988
HASEEB WAQAS GROUP OF COMPANIES; *Int'l*, pg. 3282
HASGO GROUP LTD.; *Int'l*, pg. 3283
HASGROVE PLC; *Int'l*, pg. 3283
HASHWANI GROUP; *Int'l*, pg. 3283
HATTERAS FUNDS LLC—See RCAP Holdings, LLC; *U.S. Private*, pg. 3361
HAVELL'S HOLDINGS INTERNATIONAL, LLC—See Havell's India Ltd.; *Int'l*, pg. 3286
HAVEN BANCORP, MHC; *U.S. Private*, pg. 1880
HAVILA HOLDING AS; *Int'l*, pg. 3287
HAWAIIAN ELECTRIC INDUSTRIES, INC.; *U.S. Public*, pg. 988
HAWAIIAN HOLDINGS, INC.—See Alaska Air Group, Inc.; *U.S. Public*, pg. 71
HAWESKO HOLDING AG; *Int'l*, pg. 3288
HAWKEYE ENERGY HOLDINGS LLC—See Thomas H. Lee Partners, L.P.; *U.S. Private*, pg. 4156
HAWK HOLDING COMPANY, LLC—See KSL Capital Partners, LLC; *U.S. Private*, pg. 2354
HAWTAI MOTOR GROUP LIMITED; *Int'l*, pg. 3289
HAXC HOLDINGS (BEIJING) CO., LTD.; *Int'l*, pg. 3289
HAYAKAWA DENSEN KOGYO CO., LTD.; *Int'l*, pg. 3289
HAYDALE GRAPHENE INDUSTRIES PLC; *Int'l*, pg. 3290
HAYDALE TECHNOLOGIES, INC.—See Haydale Graphene Industries plc; *Int'l*, pg. 3290
HAYEL SAEED ANAM GROUP OF COMPANIES; *Int'l*, pg. 3290
HAY ISLAND HOLDING CORPORATION; *U.S. Private*, pg. 1884
HAYLEYS PLC; *Int'l*, pg. 3291
HAYMARKET GROUP LIMITED; *Int'l*, pg. 3292
HAYS HOLDINGS LIMITED—See Hays PLC; *Int'l*, pg. 3293
HAYS PLC; *Int'l*, pg. 3293
HAYWARD HOLDINGS, INC.; *U.S. Public*, pg. 990
HAYWARD INDUSTRIES, INC.—See CCMP Capital Advisors, LP; *U.S. Private*, pg. 800
HAYWARD INDUSTRIES, INC.—See MSD Capital, L.P.; *U.S. Private*, pg. 2807
HAZELETT STRIP-CASTING CORP.—See Stave Island Ltd. Partnership; *U.S. Private*, pg. 3794
H.B. FULLER DEUTSCHLAND HOLDING GMBH—See H.B. Fuller Company; *U.S. Public*, pg. 977
HB GLOBAL LIMITED; *Int'l*, pg. 3295
HBM HOLDINGS COMPANY; *U.S. Private*, pg. 1887
HBO EUROPE HOLDINGS, INC.—See Warner Bros. Discovery, Inc.; *U.S. Public*, pg. 2327
HBV HOLDING UND BETEILIGUNGSVERWALTUNG GMBH—See BAWAG Group AG; *Int'l*, pg. 900
HCA HEALTHCARE, INC.; *U.S. Public*, pg. 990
HCAP PARTNERS, LLC; *U.S. Private*, pg. 1888
HCGI HARTFORD—See Avnet, Inc.; *U.S. Public*, pg. 253
HCG TECHNOLOGIES INC.; *U.S. Private*, pg. 1888
HCK CAPITAL GROUP BERHAD; *Int'l*, pg. 3297
HCK COMMUNICATIONS SDN. BHD.—See HCK Capital Group Berhad; *Int'l*, pg. 3297
HCL INFOSYSTEMS LIMITED; *Int'l*, pg. 3297
H-D ADVANCED MANUFACTURING COMPANY—See Hicks Holdings, LLC; *U.S. Private*, pg. 1934
H-D ADVANCED MANUFACTURING COMPANY—See The Riverside Company; *U.S. Private*, pg. 4108
H-D ADVANCED MANUFACTURING COMPANY—See Weinberg Capital Group, Inc.; *U.S. Private*, pg. 4471
HD DUNAV AD; *Int'l*, pg. 3299
HD HYUNDAI CO., LTD; *Int'l*, pg. 3299
HD SUPPLY HOLDINGS, INC.—See The Home Depot, Inc.; *U.S. Public*, pg. 2089
HDV HOLDINGS, INC.—See Genstar Capital, LLC; *U.S. Private*, pg. 1676
HEAD HOLDING UNTERNEHMENSBETEILIGUNG GMBH—See Head B.V.; *Int'l*, pg. 3300
HEAD INVEST OY; *Int'l*, pg. 3300
HEALTHCARE LOCUMS PLC—See Ares Management Corporation; *U.S. Public*, pg. 188
HEALTHCARE OF TODAY, INC; *U.S. Private*, pg. 1895
HEALTHCARE REALTY HOLDINGS, L.P.—See Healthcare Realty Trust Incorporated; *U.S. Public*, pg. 1015
HEALTH CARE SERVICE CORPORATION; *U.S. Private*, pg. 1892
HEALTHFUSION HOLDINGS, INC.—See Thoma Bravo, L.P.; *U.S. Private*, pg. 4150
HEALTH HORIZONS ENTERPRISES PTE. LTD.—See Bumrungrad Hospital Public Company Limited; *Int'l*, pg. 1215
HEALTHIER CHOICES MANAGEMENT CORP.; *U.S. Public*, pg. 1016
THE HEALTH MANAGEMENT GROUP, INC.; *U.S. Private*, pg. 4043
HEALTHMARKETS, INC.—See Blackstone Inc.; *U.S. Public*, pg. 354
HEALTH NET, LLC—See Centene Corporation; *U.S. Public*, pg. 469
HEALTHPLAN HOLDINGS, INC.—See Water Street Healthcare Partners, LLC; *U.S. Private*, pg. 4452
HEALTHSCOPE NEW ZEALAND LIMITED—See Brookfield Corporation; *Int'l*, pg. 1176
HEALTHSCOPE PTY. LTD.—See Brookfield Corporation; *Int'l*, pg. 1176
HEALTHSMART HOLDINGS, INC.; *U.S. Private*, pg. 1897
HEALTHSPRING, INC.—See The Cigna Group; *U.S. Public*, pg. 2061
HEALTHTECH SOLUTIONS, INC.; *U.S. Public*, pg. 1017
HEALTHYDAYS GROUP PLC; *Int'l*, pg. 3304
HEAR.COM N.V.; *Int'l*, pg. 3304
THE HEARST CORPORATION; *U.S. Private*, pg. 4044
HEARST TELEVISION, INC.—See The Hearst Corporation; *U.S. Private*, pg. 4048
HEARTHSTONE UTILITIES, INC.—See First Reserve Management, L.P.; *U.S. Private*, pg. 1525
HEARTLAND GROUP HOLDINGS LIMITED; *Int'l*, pg. 3304
HEARTLAND MEDIA, LLC; *U.S. Private*, pg. 1900
HEATHPATCH LTD.; *Int'l*, pg. 3305
HEBEI LIHUA HAT MANUFACTURING GROUP CO., LTD.; *Int'l*, pg. 3306
HEBSON HOLDINGS PLC; *Int'l*, pg. 3306
HECTOR COMMUNICATIONS CORPORATION—See Arvig Enterprises, Inc.; *U.S. Private*, pg. 344
HECTOR COMMUNICATIONS CORPORATION—See Blue Earth Valley Communications; *U.S. Private*, pg. 588
HECTOR COMMUNICATIONS CORPORATION—See Nuvera Communications, Inc.; *U.S. Public*, pg. 1556
HEDEF INTERNATIONAL HOLDINGS BV—See Walgreens Boots Alliance, Inc.; *U.S. Public*, pg. 2322
HEELING HOLDING CORPORATION—See Sequential Brands Group, Inc.; *U.S. Public*, pg. 1868
HEELYS, INC.—See Sequential Brands Group, Inc.; *U.S. Public*, pg. 1868
HEICO AEROSPACE HOLDINGS CORP.—See HEICO Corporation; *U.S. Public*, pg. 1019
THE HEICO COMPANIES, L.L.C.; *U.S. Private*, pg. 4050
HEICO CORPORATION; *U.S. Public*, pg. 1019
HEICO ELECTRONIC TECHNOLOGIES CORP.—See HEICO Corporation; *U.S. Public*, pg. 1020
HEICO FLIGHT SUPPORT CORP.—See HEICO Corporation; *U.S. Public*, pg. 1021
HEIDE & COOK MECHANICAL CONTRACTORS; *U.S. Private*, pg. 1904
HEIDELBERG CEMENT, INC.—See Heidelberg Materials AG; *Int'l*, pg. 3314
HEIDRICK & STRUGGLES INTERNATIONAL, INC.; *U.S. Public*, pg. 1022
HEIN DE WINDT B.V.—See FUCHS SE; *Int'l*, pg. 2804
HEINRICH BAUER VERLAG KG; *Int'l*, pg. 3323
HEINZE GRUPPE GMBH; *Int'l*, pg. 3325
HEINZ EUROPEAN HOLDING B.V.—See 3G Capital Inc.; *U.S. Private*, pg. 9
HEINZ EUROPEAN HOLDING B.V.—See Berkshire Hathaway Inc.; *U.S. Public*, pg. 317
HEITKAMP & THUMANN KG; *Int'l*, pg. 3326
HEIWA CORPORATION; *Int'l*, pg. 3327
HELENS INTERNATIONAL HOLDINGS COMPANY LIMITED; *Int'l*, pg. 3329
HELIOGEN, INC.; *U.S. Public*, pg. 1023
HELIOS FAIRFAX PARTNERS CORPORATION—See Helios Investment Partners LLP; *Int'l*, pg. 3330
HELIOS TECHNO HOLDING CO., LTD.; *Int'l*, pg. 3330
HELIOS UNDERWRITING PLC; *Int'l*, pg. 3330
HELIX INDUSTRIES LTD.—See Cinven Limited; *Int'l*, pg. 1612
HELIX OFFSHORE INTERNATIONAL HOLDINGS S.A R.L.—See Helix Energy Solutions Group, Inc.; *U.S. Public*, pg. 1024
HELLENIC EXCHANGES-ATHENS STOCK EXCHANGE S.A.; *Int'l*, pg. 3333
HELLENIQ ENERGY HOLDINGS S.A; *Int'l*, pg. 3334
HELLERMANNTYTON GROUP PLC—See Aptiv PLC; *Int'l*, pg. 525
HELLY HANSEN GROUP AS—See Canadian Tire Corporation Limited; *Int'l*, pg. 1286
THE HELM GROUP; *U.S. Private*, pg. 4051
HELVAR MERCA OY AB; *Int'l*, pg. 3339
HELVETIA HOLDING AG; *Int'l*, pg. 3339
HELVITIA VITA COMPAGNIA SA—See Helvetia Holding AG; *Int'l*, pg. 3340
HEMAS HOLDINGS PLC; *Int'l*, pg. 3340
HEM HOLDINGS & TRADING LTD.; *Int'l*, pg. 3340
HEMISPHERE MEDIA GROUP, INC.; *U.S. Private*, pg. 1913
HENAN ENERGY & CHEMICAL INDUSTRY GROUP CO., LTD.; *Int'l*, pg. 3342
HENAN YUNENG HOLDINGS CO., LTD.; *Int'l*, pg. 3344
HENDALE CAPITAL; *Int'l*, pg. 3344
HENDERSON LAND DEVELOPMENT CO. LTD.; *Int'l*, pg. 3344
HENDERSON PRODUCTS, INC.—See Douglas Dynamics, Inc.; *U.S. Public*, pg. 677
THE HENDRICK COMPANIES, LLC; *U.S. Private*, pg. 4051
HENDRICKS HOLDING COMPANY, INC.; *U.S. Private*, pg. 1914
HENGGUANG HOLDING CO., LIMITED; *Int'l*, pg. 3346
HENG SHENG HOLDING GROUP LTD.; *Int'l*, pg. 3345
HENKEL AG & CO. KGAA; *Int'l*, pg. 3348
HENKEL ASIA-PACIFIC LTD.—See Henkel AG & Co. KGaA; *Int'l*, pg. 3348
HENLEY MANAGEMENT COMPANY; *U.S. Private*, pg. 1916
HENRY BOOT PLC; *Int'l*, pg. 3354
HENRY CROWN & COMPANY; *U.S. Private*, pg. 1917
HENRY LAMOTTE GMBH; *Int'l*, pg. 3355
HENRY SCHEIN ANIMAL HEALTH HOLDINGS LIMITED—See Clayton, Dubilier & Rice, LLC; *U.S. Private*, pg. 921
HENRY SCHEIN ANIMAL HEALTH HOLDINGS LIMITED—See TPG Capital, L.P.; *U.S. Public*, pg. 2170
HENRY SCHEIN UK HOLDINGS LIMITED—See Henry Schein, Inc.; *U.S. Public*, pg. 1026
HENRY S. MILLER MANAGEMENT CORP.; *U.S. Private*, pg. 1919
HENSOLDT HOLDING GERMANY GMBH—See HENSOLDT AG; *Int'l*, pg. 3355
HEPHAESTUS HOLDINGS LIMITED; *Int'l*, pg. 3356
HERAEUS HOLDING GMBH; *Int'l*, pg. 3357
HERAEUS MEDICAL GMBH—See Heraeus Holding GmbH; *Int'l*, pg. 3358
HERC HOLDINGS INC.; *U.S. Public*, pg. 1027
HERE TO SERVE HOLDING CORP.; *U.S. Public*, pg. 1028
HERITAGE DISTILLING HOLDING COMPANY, INC.; *U.S. Private*, pg. 1922
HERITAGE DISTRIBUTION HOLDINGS—See Beijer Ref AB; *Int'l*, pg. 944
HERITAGE HOME GROUP, LLC; *U.S. Private*, pg. 1923
HERITAGE INSURANCE HOLDINGS, INC.; *U.S. Public*, pg. 1028
HERITAGE LANDSCAPE SUPPLY GROUP, INC.—See Leonard Green & Partners, L.P.; *U.S. Private*, pg. 2429
HERMALUX SARL—See CLS Holdings plc; *Int'l*, pg. 1664
HERMILL INVESTMENTS PTE LTD—See Hotel Properties Limited; *Int'l*, pg. 3488
HERO AG; *Int'l*, pg. 3363
HERO CORP.; *Int'l*, pg. 3363
HERSHA ENTERPRISES, LTD.; *U.S. Private*, pg. 1926
HERTZ CLAIM MANAGEMENT B.V.—See Hertz Global Holdings, Inc.; *U.S. Public*, pg. 1029
HERTZ CLAIM MANAGEMENT GMBH—See Hertz Global Holdings, Inc.; *U.S. Public*, pg. 1029
HERTZ GLOBAL HOLDINGS, INC.; *U.S. Public*, pg. 1029
HESCO GROUP LIMITED—See CVC Capital Partners SICAV-FIS S.A.; *Int'l*, pg. 1885
HESKA CORPORATION—See Mars, Incorporated; *U.S. Private*, pg. 2588
HESS GROUP AG; *Int'l*, pg. 3365
HESTA AG; *Int'l*, pg. 3365
HETTICH HOLDING GMBH & CO. OHG; *Int'l*, pg. 3365
HEW-KABEL HOLDING GMBH; *Int'l*, pg. 3367
HEWLETT-PACKARD ASIA PACIFIC PTE. LTD.—See Hewlett Packard Enterprise Company; *U.S. Public*, pg. 1031
HEWLETT-PACKARD EUROPA HOLDING B.V.—See HP Inc.; *U.S. Public*, pg. 1063
HEWLETT-PACKARD INTERNATIONAL PTE. LTD.—See HP Inc.; *U.S. Public*, pg. 1064
HEWLETT-PACKARD INTERNATIONAL SARL—See Hewlett Packard Enterprise Company; *U.S. Public*, pg. 1031
HEXAGON COMPOSITES ASA; *Int'l*, pg. 3369
HEXCEL-CHINA HOLDINGS CORP.—See Hexcel Corporation; *U.S. Public*, pg. 1033
HEXION HOLDINGS CORPORATION—See American Securities LLC; *U.S. Private*, pg. 249
HEXION TOPCO, LLC—See Apollo Global Management, Inc.; *U.S. Public*, pg. 151
HEXTAR GLOBAL BERHAD; *Int'l*, pg. 3373
HEXTAR HOLDINGS SDN. BHD.; *Int'l*, pg. 3373
HEZHONG INTERNATIONAL (HOLDING) LIMITED; *Int'l*, pg. 3374
HFBG HOLDING B.V.; *Int'l*, pg. 3374
HF SINCLAIR CORPORATION; *U.S. Public*, pg. 1033
HFT INTL. (GUERNSEY) LTD—See Banque Heritage (Suisse) S.A.; *Int'l*, pg. 854
H.G. HASTINGS CO.; *U.S. Private*, pg. 1826

551112 — OFFICES OF OTHER HO...   CORPORATE AFFILIATIONS

HG HOLDINGS, INC.; *U.S. Public*, pg. 1034
HGS HOLDINGS, INC.—See Kratos Defense & Security Solutions, Inc.; *U.S. Public*, pg. 1276
HGV HAMBURGER GESELLSCHAFT FUR VERMOGENS- UND BETEILIGUNGSMANAGEMENT MBH; *Int'l*, pg. 3378
HH GLOBAL GROUP LIMITED; *Int'l*, pg. 3378
H&H GROUP PLC; *Int'l*, pg. 3191
HHI GROUP HOLDINGS, LLC—See American Axle & Manufacturing Holdings, Inc.; *U.S. Public*, pg. 96
HHJ HOLDINGS LIMITED; *U.S. Private*, pg. 1931
HH&L ACQUISITION CO.; *Int'l*, pg. 3379
HIADVANCE INC.; *U.S. Private*, pg. 1932
HIBU GROUP 2013 LIMITED; *Int'l*, pg. 3383
HICKS HOLDINGS, LLC; *U.S. Private*, pg. 1934
HICKS SPORTS GROUP, LLC—See Hicks Holdings, LLC; *U.S. Private*, pg. 1934
HICOM HOLDINGS BHD—See DRB-HICOM Berhad; *Int'l*, pg. 2201
HIDRIA D.O.O.; *Int'l*, pg. 3384
HIGGINBOTHAM INSURANCE GROUP, INC.—See Galiot Insurance Services, Inc.; *U.S. Private*, pg. 1638
HIGHEST PERFORMANCES HOLDINGS INC.; *Int'l*, pg. 3387
HIGHGATE HOTELS, L.P.; *U.S. Private*, pg. 1937
HIGHLAND ACQUISITION CORPORATION—See Highland Capital Management, L.P.; *U.S. Private*, pg. 1938
HIGHLAND PRODUCTIONS, LLC; *U.S. Private*, pg. 1938
HIGHLAND VENTURES, LTD.; *U.S. Private*, pg. 1939
HIGHLIGHT COMMUNICATIONS AG; *Int'l*, pg. 3388
HIGHLIGHT EVENT & ENTERTAINMENT AG; *Int'l*, pg. 3388
HIGH PEAK ROYALTIES LIMITED; *Int'l*, pg. 3385
HIGH REAL ESTATE GROUP LLC; *U.S. Private*, pg. 1936
HIGHSUN HOLDING GROUP CO., LTD.; *Int'l*, pg. 3388
HIGH TECH COMPUTER ASIA PACIFIC PTE. LTD.—See HTC Corporation; *Int'l*, pg. 3508
HIGHTOWER HOLDING LLC; *U.S. Private*, pg. 1941
HIGHWAY INSURANCE HOLDINGS PLC; *Int'l*, pg. 3389
HIGH WIRE NETWORKS INC.; *U.S. Public*, pg. 1035
HII INDUSTRIES, INC.; *U.S. Private*, pg. 1943
HIKARI HOLDINGS CO., LTD.; *Int'l*, pg. 3389
HILCO TRADING, LLC; *U.S. Private*, pg. 1943
HILI VENTURES LTD; *Int'l*, pg. 3391
HILLCREST CAPITAL PARTNERS LP; *U.S. Private*, pg. 1946
HILLENBRAND GERMANY HOLDING GMBH—See Hillenbrand, Inc.; *U.S. Public*, pg. 1036
THE HILLMAN COMPANIES, INC.—See Hillman Solutions Corp.; *U.S. Public*, pg. 1038
THE HILLMAN COMPANY; *U.S. Private*, pg. 4052
THE HILLMAN FLUID POWER GROUP—See The Hillman Company; *U.S. Private*, pg. 4053
HILLMAN SOLUTIONS CORP.; *U.S. Public*, pg. 1038
HILL-ROM HOLDINGS, INC.—See Baxter International Inc.; *U.S. Public*, pg. 282
THE HILLSHIRE BRANDS COMPANY—See Tyson Foods, Inc.; *U.S. Public*, pg. 2210
HILLS LIMITED; *Int'l*, pg. 3393
HILL & SMITH PLC; *Int'l*, pg. 3391
HILONG ENERGY LIMITED—See Hilong Holding Limited; *Int'l*, pg. 3393
HILTON GRAND VACATIONS INC.; *U.S. Public*, pg. 1039
HILTON WORLDWIDE HOLDINGS INC.; *U.S. Public*, pg. 1040
HILZINGER HOLDING GMBH; *Int'l*, pg. 3395
HINES CORPORATION; *U.S. Private*, pg. 1948
HING LEE (HK) HOLDINGS LIMITED; *Int'l*, pg. 3400
HIN SANG GROUP (INTERNATIONAL) HOLDING CO. LTD.; *Int'l*, pg. 3397
HIPAGES GROUP HOLDINGS LIMITED; *Int'l*, pg. 3402
HIPPO HOLDINGS INC.; *U.S. Public*, pg. 1042
HI-REL GROUP, LLC—See Windjammer Capital Investors, LLC; *U.S. Private*, pg. 4537
HIRERIGHT HOLDINGS CORPORATION—See General Atlantic Service Company, L.P.; *U.S. Public*, pg. 1662
HIRERIGHT HOLDINGS CORPORATION—See Stone Point Capital LLC; *U.S. Private*, pg. 3825
HIROCA HOLDINGS LTD.; *Int'l*, pg. 3404
HIROGIN HOLDINGS, INC.; *Int'l*, pg. 3404
HIROSE HOLDINGS & CO.,LTD.; *Int'l*, pg. 3405
HISENSE CO., LTD.; *Int'l*, pg. 3407
HITACHI AMERICA, LTD.—See Hitachi, Ltd.; *Int'l*, pg. 3413
HITACHI ASIA LTD.—See Hitachi, Ltd.; *Int'l*, pg. 3414
HITACHI ASTEMO, LTD.; *Int'l*, pg. 3408
HITACHI EUROPE LTD.—See Hitachi, Ltd.; *Int'l*, pg. 3417
HITACHI, LTD.; *Int'l*, pg. 3412
HITACHI MEDICAL SYSTEMS EUROPE HOLDING AG—See Hitachi, Ltd.; *Int'l*, pg. 3420
HITAY INVESTMENT HOLDINGS A.S.; *Int'l*, pg. 3425
HITEJINRO HOLDINGS CO., LTD.; *Int'l*, pg. 3426
HITIM GROUP; *Int'l*, pg. 3426
HITIT HOLDING A.S.; *Int'l*, pg. 3426
HITO COMMUNICATIONS HOLDINGS, INC.; *Int'l*, pg. 3427
HK ELECTRIC INVESTMENTS LIMITED; *Int'l*, pg. 3428
HKS METALS B.V.—See Alfa Acciai SpA; *Int'l*, pg. 307
HKS METALS B.V.—See CRONIMET Holding GmbH; *Int'l*, pg. 1855

HL GLOBAL ENTERPRISES LIMITED; *Int'l*, pg. 3429
HL HOLDINGS CORPORATION—See Halla Group; *Int'l*, pg. 3229
HLK BIOTECH HOLDING GROUP, INC.; *U.S. Public*, pg. 1042
HL MULTI-FAMILY HOLDINGS, LLC—See Howard Hughes Holdings Inc.; *U.S. Public*, pg. 1060
HLP (CHINA) LIMITED—See Hang Lung Group Limited; *Int'l*, pg. 3245
HLP TREASURY SERVICES LIMITED—See Hang Lung Group Limited; *Int'l*, pg. 3245
HLT GLOBAL BERHAD; *Int'l*, pg. 3431
H&M HENNES & MAURITZ HOLDING BV—See H&M Hennes & Mauritz AB; *Int'l*, pg. 3192
HM INSURANCE GROUP, INC.—See Highmark Health; *U.S. Private*, pg. 1940
HMK ENTERPRISES, INC.; *U.S. Private*, pg. 1955
HML HOLDINGS PLC; *Int'l*, pg. 3432
HMS HOLDINGS CORP.—See Veritas Capital Fund Management, LLC; *U.S. Private*, pg. 4362
HNA CAPITAL HOLDING CO., LTD.—See Hainan Traffic Administration Holding Co., Ltd.; *Int'l*, pg. 3213
HNA GROUP CO., LTD.—See Hainan Traffic Administration Holding Co., Ltd.; *Int'l*, pg. 3212
HNA TECHNOLOGY CO., LTD.—See Hainan Traffic Administration Holding Co., Ltd.; *Int'l*, pg. 3213
HNH INTERNATIONAL LTD.; *Int'l*, pg. 3434
HNO INTERNATIONAL, INC.; *U.S. Public*, pg. 1043
HOANG ANH GIA LAI JOINT STOCK COMPANY; *Int'l*, pg. 3436
HOBART ENTERPRISES LTD; *Int'l*, pg. 3436
HOB ENTERTAINMENT, INC.—See Live Nation Entertainment, Inc.; *U.S. Public*, pg. 1329
HOB-LOB LIMITED PARTNERSHIP; *U.S. Private*, pg. 1958
HOCHDORF HOLDING AG; *Int'l*, pg. 3437
HOCHSCHILD MINING PLC; *Int'l*, pg. 3437
HOCHTIEF AMERICAS GMBH—See ACS, Actividades de Construccion y Servicios, S.A.; *Int'l*, pg. 113
HOCHTIEF ASIA PACIFIC GMBH—See ACS, Actividades de Construccion y Servicios, S.A.; *Int'l*, pg. 113
HOEGH LNG HOLDING LTD.; *Int'l*, pg. 3439
HOERBIGER ANTRIEBSTECHNIK HOLDING GMBH—See Hoerbiger Holding AG; *Int'l*, pg. 3440
HOERBIGER HOLDING AG; *Int'l*, pg. 3439
HOGG ROBINSON GROUP LIMITED—See Global Business Travel Group, Inc.; *U.S. Public*, pg. 941
HOGG ROBINSON LIMITED—See Global Business Travel Group, Inc.; *U.S. Public*, pg. 941
HOI SANG LIMITED—See Hang Lung Group Limited; *Int'l*, pg. 3245
HOJGAARD HOLDING A/S; *Int'l*, pg. 3442
HOKKAN HOLDINGS LIMITED; *Int'l*, pg. 3443
HOKUYAKU TAKEYAMA HOLDINGS, INC.; *Int'l*, pg. 3445
HOLDEN INDUSTRIES, INC.; *U.S. Private*, pg. 1962
HOLDERFIN B.V.—See Holcim Ltd.; *Int'l*, pg. 3448
HOLDER HOSPITALITY GROUP INC.; *U.S. Private*, pg. 1962
HOLDERS TECHNOLOGY PLC; *Int'l*, pg. 3449
HOLDING BERCY INVESTISSEMENT SCA—See Charterhouse Capital Partners LLP; *Int'l*, pg. 1455
HOLDING COOP-YUG AD; *Int'l*, pg. 3450
HOLDING D'INFRASTRUCTURES DE TRANSPORT SAS—See ACS, Actividades de Construccion y Servicios, S.A.; *Int'l*, pg. 112
HOLDING FINANCIERE DIMOTRANS SA; *Int'l*, pg. 3450
HOLDING LE DUFF SA; *Int'l*, pg. 3450
HOLDING SOCOTEC S.A.S.—See Cobepa S.A.; *Int'l*, pg. 1683
HOLDING SOLINA SA—See Ardian SAS; *Int'l*, pg. 555
HOLDUX BETEILIGUNGSGESELLSCHAFT—See Assicurazioni Generali S.p.A.; *Int'l*, pg. 646
HOLIDAYCHECK GROUP AG—See Hubert Burda Media Holding Kommanditgesellschaft; *Int'l*, pg. 3520
HOLLEY GROUP CO., LTD.—See Holley Holding, Ltd.; *Int'l*, pg. 3451
HOLLEY HOLDING, LTD.; *Int'l*, pg. 3451
HOLLEY INC.; *U.S. Public*, pg. 1044
HOLLYFRONTIER CORPORATION—See HF Sinclair Corporation; *U.S. Public*, pg. 1033
HOLLYLAND GROUP HOLDINGS LIMITED; *Int'l*, pg. 3452
HOLLYSYS AUTOMATION TECHNOLOGIES LTD.; *Int'l*, pg. 3452
HOLLYWOOD ENTERTAINMENT EDU HOLDING, INC.; *U.S. Private*, pg. 1966
HOLMAN AUTOMOTIVE GROUP, INC.; *U.S. Private*, pg. 1967
HOLOGIC INTERNATIONAL HOLDINGS B.V.—See Hologic, Inc.; *U.S. Public*, pg. 1045
HOLOGRAPHIX LLC—See Headwall Photonics, Inc.; *U.S. Private*, pg. 1891
HOLOPHANE EUROPE LTD.—See Acuity Brands, Inc.; *U.S. Public*, pg. 37
THE HOME DEPOT, INC.; *U.S. Public*, pg. 2089
HOME MERIDIAN INTERNATIONAL, INC.—See Hooker Furnishings Corporation; *U.S. Public*, pg. 1052
HOMEOWNERS OF AMERICA HOLDING CORPORATION—See Porch Group, Inc.; *U.S. Public*, pg. 1702

HOMESMART HOLDINGS, INC.; *U.S. Private*, pg. 1974
HOMESQUARE HOLDINGS LLC; *U.S. Private*, pg. 1974
HOME SWEET HOME HOLDINGS INC.; *U.S. Private*, pg. 1972
HOME TEAM SERVICES,LLC; *U.S. Private*, pg. 1972
HOMEWOOD HOLDINGS, LLC—See Bain Capital, LP; *U.S. Private*, pg. 450
HONG FOK CORPORATION LIMITED; *Int'l*, pg. 3465
HONG KONG AEROSPACE TECHNOLOGY GROUP LIMITED—See Hong Kong Aerospace Technology Holdings Limited; *Int'l*, pg. 3465
HONG KONG AEROSPACE TECHNOLOGY HOLDINGS LIMITED; *Int'l*, pg. 3465
HONG KONG FOOD INVESTMENT HOLDINGS LIMITED; *Int'l*, pg. 3466
HONG KONG JOHNSON HOLDINGS COMPANY LIMITED; *Int'l*, pg. 3466
HONG KONG LIFE SCIENCES & TECHNOLOGIES GROUP LIMITED; *Int'l*, pg. 3467
HONG LEONG ASIA LTD.—See Hong Leong Investment Holdings Pte. Ltd.; *Int'l*, pg. 3468
HONG LEONG COMPANY (MALAYSIA) BERHAD—See Hong Leong Investment Holdings Pte. Ltd.; *Int'l*, pg. 3467
HONG LEONG CORPORATION HOLDINGS PTE. LTD.—See Hong Leong Investment Holdings Pte. Ltd.; *Int'l*, pg. 3468
HONG LEONG FINANCIAL GROUP BERHAD—See Hong Leong Investment Holdings Pte. Ltd.; *Int'l*, pg. 3468
HONG LEONG HOLDINGS LTD.—See Hong Leong Investment Holdings Pte. Ltd.; *Int'l*, pg. 3469
HONG LEONG INVESTMENT HOLDINGS PTE. LTD.; *Int'l*, pg. 3467
HONGLI GROUP INC.; *Int'l*, pg. 3471
HONG SENG CONSOLIDATED BERHAD; *Int'l*, pg. 3469
HON HAI PRECISION INDUSTRY CO., LTD.; *Int'l*, pg. 3456
HON KWOK LAND INVESTMENT CO., LTD.; *Int'l*, pg. 3459
HOOSIER INVESTMENT LLC; *U.S. Private*, pg. 1978
HOOSIERS HOLDINGS; *Int'l*, pg. 3472
HOOVER FERGUSON GROUP, INC.—See First Reserve Management, L.P.; *U.S. Private*, pg. 1525
HOPE LIFE INTERNATIONAL HOLDINGS LIMITED; *Int'l*, pg. 3473
HOREN NEDERLAND BEHEER BV—See Amplifon S.p.A.; *Int'l*, pg. 435
HORIZON HOLDINGS, INC.; *U.S. Private*, pg. 1981
HORIZON THERAPEUTICS PLC—See Amgen Inc.; *U.S. Public*, pg. 123
HORMANN HOLDING GMBH & CO. KG; *Int'l*, pg. 3479
HORNETS SPORTS & ENTERTAINMENT—See MJ Basketball Holdings, LLC; *U.S. Private*, pg. 2752
HORNG SHIUE HOLDING CO., LTD.; *Int'l*, pg. 3482
HORST WELLNESS GMBH & CO. KG; *Int'l*, pg. 3482
HOSHIZAKI EUROPE HOLDINGS B.V.—See Hoshizaki Corporation; *Int'l*, pg. 3483
HOSHIZAKI USA HOLDINGS, INC.—See Hoshizaki Corporation; *Int'l*, pg. 3484
HOSPEDIA HOLDINGS LIMITED—See Marlin Equity Partners, LLC; *U.S. Public*, pg. 2584
HOSPIRA, INC.—See Pfizer Inc.; *U.S. Public*, pg. 1680
HOSPIRA PTY LIMITED—See Pfizer Inc.; *U.S. Public*, pg. 1680
HOTELBEDS GROUP, S.L.U.—See Canada Pension Plan Investment Board; *Int'l*, pg. 1279
HOTELBEDS GROUP, S.L.U.—See Cinven Limited; *Int'l*, pg. 1612
HOTEL OKURA CO., LTD.; *Int'l*, pg. 3488
HOTEL PROPERTIES LIMITED; *Int'l*, pg. 3488
HOTEL SHILLA CO., LTD.; *Int'l*, pg. 3489
HOUGHTON MIFFLIN HARCOURT COMPANY—See Veritas Capital Fund Management, LLC; *U.S. Private*, pg. 4362
HOUR MEDIA GROUP, LLC; *U.S. Private*, pg. 1990
HOUSE FOODS GROUP INC.; *Int'l*, pg. 3490
HOUSE OF HABIB; *Int'l*, pg. 3491
HOUSTON BASEBALL PARTNERS LLC; *U.S. Private*, pg. 1993
HOVNANIAN ENTERPRISES, INC.; *U.S. Public*, pg. 1056
HOV SERVICES LIMITED; *Int'l*, pg. 3492
HOWARD MILLER COMPANY; *U.S. Private*, pg. 1995
HOWDEN BROKING GROUP LIMITED—See Howden Group Holdings Limited; *Int'l*, pg. 3493
HOWDEN GROUP SOUTH AFRICA LIMITED—See Chart Industries, Inc.; *U.S. Public*, pg. 482
HOWDEN UK GROUP LIMITED—See Howden Group Holdings Limited; *Int'l*, pg. 3494
HOWKINGTECH INTERNATIONAL HOLDING LIMITED; *Int'l*, pg. 3494
HOWMET AEROSPACE INC.; *U.S. Public*, pg. 1061
HOWMET HOLDINGS CORPORATION—See Howmet Aerospace Inc.; *U.S. Public*, pg. 1061
HOWMET INTERNATIONAL, INC.—See Howmet Aerospace Inc.; *U.S. Public*, pg. 1061
HOYA HOLDINGS ASIA PACIFIC PTE. LTD.—See Hoya Corporation; *Int'l*, pg. 3495
HOYA HOLDINGS N.V.—See Hoya Corporation; *Int'l*, pg. 3496
HPC INDUSTRIES LLC; *U.S. Private*, pg. 1996
HPMT HOLDING BERHAD; *Int'l*, pg. 3501

551112 — OFFICES OF OTHER HO...

HPP HOLDINGS BERHAD; *Int'l*, pg. 3501
HPQ HOLDINGS, LLC—See HP Inc.; *U.S. Public*, pg. 1063
HQ CAPITAL GMBH & CO. KG—See Harald Quandt Holding GmbH; *Int'l*, pg. 3269
H&R BLOCK, INC.; *U.S. Public*, pg. 976
HSBC HOLDINGS PLC; *Int'l*, pg. 3507
HSBC NORTH AMERICA HOLDINGS INC.—See HSBC Holdings plc; *Int'l*, pg. 3505
HSBC (SINGAPORE) NOMINEES PTE. LTD.—See HSBC Holdings plc; *Int'l*, pg. 3506
HSBC TRUSTEE (CI) LIMITED—See HSBC Holdings plc; *Int'l*, pg. 3505
HSH FACILITY MANAGEMENT GMBH—See Cerberus Capital Management, L.P.; *U.S. Private*, pg. 838
HSH FACILITY MANAGEMENT GMBH—See GoldenTree Asset Management LP; *U.S. Private*, pg. 1734
HSH FACILITY MANAGEMENT GMBH—See J.C. Flowers & Co. LLC; *U.S. Private*, pg. 2159
HSH N FINANCIAL SECURITIES LLC—See Cerberus Capital Management, L.P.; *U.S. Private*, pg. 838
HSH N FINANCIAL SECURITIES LLC—See GoldenTree Asset Management LP; *U.S. Private*, pg. 1734
HSH N FINANCIAL SECURITIES LLC—See J.C. Flowers & Co. LLC; *U.S. Private*, pg. 2159
HS HOLDINGS, LLC; *U.S. Private*, pg. 1998
HSIN CHONG GROUP HOLDINGS LIMITED; *Int'l*, pg. 3507
HSINJING HOLDING CO., LTD.; *Int'l*, pg. 3507
H.S. MORGAN LIMITED PARTNERSHIP; *U.S. Private*, pg. 1835
HS OPTIMUS HOLDINGS LIMITED; *Int'l*, pg. 3503
H-SOURCE HOLDINGS LTD.; *Int'l*, pg. 3194
HSS ENGINEERS BERHAD; *Int'l*, pg. 3507
HTC HOLDING A.S.; *Int'l*, pg. 3508
H&T GROUP PLC; *Int'l*, pg. 3193
HTI HIGH TECH INDUSTRIES AG; *Int'l*, pg. 3508
HTM INTERNATIONAL HOLDING LTD.; *Int'l*, pg. 3508
HUABANG TECHNOLOGY HOLDINGS LIMITED; *Int'l*, pg. 3510
HUADI INTERNATIONAL GROUP CO., LTD.; *Int'l*, pg. 3511
HUAKE HOLDING BIOLOGY CO., LTD.; *Int'l*, pg. 3512
HUA LIEN INTERNATIONAL (HOLDING) COMPANY LIMITED—See China National Complete Plant Import & Export Corporation; *Int'l*, pg. 1531
HUA NAN FINANCIAL HOLDINGS CO., LTD.; *Int'l*, pg. 3509
HUAN HSIN HOLDINGS LTD.; *Int'l*, pg. 3513
HUANXI MEDIA GROUP LIMITED; *Int'l*, pg. 3513
HUARONG (HK) INTERNATIONAL HOLDINGS LIMITED—See China CITIC Financial Asset Management Co., Ltd.; *Int'l*, pg. 1489
HUARONG INTERNATIONAL FINANCIAL HOLDINGS LIMITED—See China CITIC Financial Asset Management Co., Ltd.; *Int'l*, pg. 1489
HUARUI INTERNATIONAL NEW MATERIAL LIMITED; *Int'l*, pg. 3514
HUASU HOLDINGS CO., LTD.; *Int'l*, pg. 3514
HUAT LAI RESOURCES BERHAD; *Int'l*, pg. 3514
HUAWEI INVESTMENT & HOLDING CO., LTD.; *Int'l*, pg. 3514
HUAXI HOLDINGS COMPANY LIMITED; *Int'l*, pg. 3515
HUAZHONG IN-VEHICLE HOLDINGS COMPANY LIMITED; *Int'l*, pg. 3516
HUBBARD BROADCASTING, INC.; *U.S. Private*, pg. 2000
HUBEI HUARONG HOLDINGS CO., LTD.; *Int'l*, pg. 3517
HUBERGROUP DEUTSCHLAND GMBH; *Int'l*, pg. 3519
HUBERT BURDA MEDIA HOLDING KOMMANDITGESELLSCHAFT; *Int'l*, pg. 3519
HUB INTERNATIONAL NORTHEAST LIMITED—See Hellman & Friedman LLC; *U.S. Private*, pg. 1909
HUDSON BLVD. GROUP LLC; *U.S. Private*, pg. 2001
HUDSON EUROPE BV—See Hudson Global, Inc; *U.S. Public*, pg. 1068
HUDSON GLOBAL, INC; *U.S. Public*, pg. 1068
HUDSON HIGHLAND (APAC) PTY. LIMITED; *Int'l*, pg. 3522
HUFFINES AUTO GROUP; *U.S. Private*, pg. 2002
HUGHES GROUP, INC.; *U.S. Private*, pg. 2003
H.U. GROUP HOLDINGS, INC.; *Int'l*, pg. 3196
HUHTAMAKI, INC.—See Huhtamaki Oyj; *Int'l*, pg. 3526
HUIJING HOLDINGS COMPANY LIMITED; *Int'l*, pg. 3526
HUI YING FINANCIAL HOLDINGS CORPORATION; *Int'l*, pg. 3526
HUIYIN SMART COMMUNITY CO., LTD.; *Int'l*, pg. 3527
HUIZE HOLDING LIMITED; *Int'l*, pg. 3527
HUIZENGA HOLDINGS, INC.; *U.S. Private*, pg. 2004
HUIZENGA MANUFACTURING GROUP, INC.; *U.S. Private*, pg. 2004
HULMAN & COMPANY; *U.S. Private*, pg. 2005
HUMAN CREATION HOLDINGS, INC.; *Int'l*, pg. 3528
HUMAX HOLDINGS CO., LTD.; *Int'l*, pg. 3530
HUME CEMENT INDUSTRIES BERHAD; *Int'l*, pg. 3530
HUMMER WINBLAD OPERATING CO., LLC; *U.S. Private*, pg. 2007
HUMM GROUP LIMITED; *Int'l*, pg. 3531
HUNAN TIANRUN DIGITAL ENTERTAINMENT & CULTURAL MEDIA CO., LTD.; *Int'l*, pg. 3534
HUNAN YONKER INVESTMENT GROUP CO., LTD.; *Int'l*, pg. 3534

HUNNIWELL LAKE VENTURES LLC; *U.S. Private*, pg. 2008
HUNT COMPANIES, INC.; *U.S. Private*, pg. 2008
HUNT CONSOLIDATED, INC.; *U.S. Private*, pg. 2008
THE HUNT CORPORATION; *U.S. Private*, pg. 2008
HUNTER DOUGLAS HOLDINGS LTD.—See 3G Capital Partners L.P.; *U.S. Private*, pg. 12
HUNTING DOG CAPITAL CORP.; *U.S. Private*, pg. 2010
HUNTSMAN CORPORATION CANADA INC.—See Huntsman Corporation; *U.S. Public*, pg. 1074
HUNTSMAN CORPORATION; *U.S. Public*, pg. 1072
HUNTSMAN FAMILY HOLDINGS COMPANY LLC—See Huntsman Family Investments, LLC; *U.S. Private*, pg. 2011
HUNTSMAN (HOLDINGS) NETHERLANDS B.V.—See Huntsman Corporation; *U.S. Public*, pg. 1073
HUNTSMAN PIGMENTS HOLDING GMBH—See Huntsman Corporation; *U.S. Public*, pg. 1073
HURON CONSULTING GROUP INC.; *U.S. Public*, pg. 1076
HURRICANES HOLDINGS, LLC; *U.S. Private*, pg. 2013
HUSSMANN INTERNATIONAL, INC.—See Clayton, Dubilier & Rice, LLC; *U.S. Private*, pg. 924
HUT 8 CORP.; *U.S. Public*, pg. 1076
HUT 8 MINING CORP.—See Hut 8 Corp.; *U.S. Public*, pg. 1076
HUTCHMED (CHINA) LIMITED—See CK Hutchison Holdings Limited; *Int'l*, pg. 1637
HUTTER & SCHRANTZ PMS GES.M.B.H; *Int'l*, pg. 3540
HWA HONG CORPORATION LIMITED; *Int'l*, pg. 3541
HWH INVESTMENTS LIMITED; *Int'l*, pg. 3543
HYDRAULEX INTERNATIONAL HOLDINGS LTD.—See Clearlake Capital Group, L.P.; *U.S. Private*, pg. 933
HYDRODEC GROUP PLC; *Int'l*, pg. 3547
HYDROFARM HOLDINGS GROUP, INC.; *U.S. Public*, pg. 1079
HYDRO ONE LIMITED; *Int'l*, pg. 3546
HYDRO OTTAWA HOLDING INC.; *Int'l*, pg. 3546
HYGIEIA GROUP LIMITED; *Int'l*, pg. 3549
HYGROVEST LIMITED; *Int'l*, pg. 3549
HYOSUNG HOLDINGS USA, INC.—See Hyosung Corporation; *Int'l*, pg. 3551
HYPERFINE, INC.; *U.S. Public*, pg. 1079
HYPERION PARTNERS LP; *U.S. Private*, pg. 2019
HYPO REAL ESTATE HOLDING AG; *Int'l*, pg. 3553
HYSTER-YALE GROUP, INC.—See Hyster-Yale Materials Handling, Inc.; *U.S. Public*, pg. 1080
HYSTER-YALE MATERIALS HANDLING, INC.; *U.S. Public*, pg. 1079
HYUNDAI GROUP; *Int'l*, pg. 3557
HYWIN HOLDINGS LTD.; *Int'l*, pg. 3561
HZ HRVATSKE ZELJEZNICE HOLDING D.O.O.; *Int'l*, pg. 3561
I3 VERTICALS, INC.; *U.S. Public*, pg. 1081
IA FINANCIAL CORPORATION INC.; *Int'l*, pg. 3567
IANTHUS CAPITAL HOLDINGS, INC.; *U.S. Public*, pg. 1083
IAT REINSURANCE COMPANY, LTD.; *U.S. Private*, pg. 2028
IBERDROLA DIVERSIFICACION, S.A.U.—See Iberdrola, S.A.; *Int'l*, pg. 3572
IBERDROLA ENERGIA, S.A.U.—See Iberdrola, S.A.; *Int'l*, pg. 3572
IBERIA INDUSTRY CAPITAL GROUP SARL; *Int'l*, pg. 3574
IBG ADRIATICA HOLDINGS, INC.—See Independent Bank Group, Inc.; *U.S. Public*, pg. 1116
IBG REAL ESTATE HOLDINGS, INC.—See Independent Bank Group, Inc.; *U.S. Public*, pg. 1116
IBIDEN EUROPEAN HOLDINGS B.V.—See Ibiden Co., Ltd.; *Int'l*, pg. 3575
IBIDEN INTERNATIONAL, INC.—See Ibiden Co., Ltd.; *Int'l*, pg. 3575
I-BIMSA ULUSLARARASI IS BILGI VEYONETIM SISTEMLERI A.S.—See Haci Omer Sabanci Holding A.S.; *Int'l*, pg. 3204
I-BIMSA ULUSLARARASI IS BILGI VEYONETIM SISTEMLERI A.S.—See International Business Machines Corporation; *U.S. Public*, pg. 1145
IBM UNITED KINGDOM HOLDINGS LIMITED—See International Business Machines Corporation; *U.S. Public*, pg. 1148
IBRACO BERHAD; *Int'l*, pg. 3576
IBS GROUP HOLDING LTD.; *Int'l*, pg. 3576
IBSTOCK GROUP LIMITED—See Ibstock plc; *Int'l*, pg. 3577
IBSTOCK PLC; *Int'l*, pg. 3577
ICA GRUPPEN AB; *Int'l*, pg. 3577
ICAHN ENTERPRISES HOLDINGS L.P.—See Icahn Enterprises L.P.; *U.S. Public*, pg. 1084
ICAHN ENTERPRISES L.P.; *U.S. Public*, pg. 1083
ICARE S.A.—See BNP Paribas SA; *Int'l*, pg. 1083
ICC HOLDINGS, INC.; *U.S. Public*, pg. 1085
ICELANDIC GROUP HF—See Enterprise Investment Fund slhf.; *Int'l*, pg. 2451
ICF GROUP; *U.S. Private*, pg. 2031
ICHINEN HOLDINGS CO., LTD.; *Int'l*, pg. 3580
ICIMS HOLDING CORP.; *U.S. Private*, pg. 2031
ICM HOLDINGS INC.; *U.S. Private*, pg. 2031
ICM LIMITED; *Int'l*, pg. 3581
ICON NY HOLDINGS LLC—See Iconix Acquisition LLC; *U.S. Private*, pg. 2033

ICORECONNECT INC.; *U.S. Public*, pg. 1086
ICS CARGO CLEAN—See Stone Canyon Industries, LLC; *U.S. Private*, pg. 3817
ICZOOM GROUP INC.; *Int'l*, pg. 3587
IDACORP, INC.; *U.S. Public*, pg. 1087
IDAHO COPPER CORPORATION; *U.S. Public*, pg. 1088
IDB DEVELOPMENT CORPORATION LTD.; *Int'l*, pg. 3588
IDB TOURISM (2009) LTD.—See IDB Development Corporation Ltd.; *Int'l*, pg. 3588
IDEALAB HOLDINGS, LLC; *U.S. Private*, pg. 2036
THE IDEAL GROUP, INC.; *U.S. Private*, pg. 4055
IDEAL SETECH HOLDCO, INC.—See The Ideal Group, Inc.; *U.S. Private*, pg. 4055
IDEAL UNITED BINTANG BERHAD; *Int'l*, pg. 3589
IDEANOMICS, INC.; *U.S. Public*, pg. 1088
IDEATEK SYSTEMS, INC.—See DigitalBridge Group, Inc.; *U.S. Public*, pg. 665
IDEATEK SYSTEMS, INC.—See EQT AB; *Int'l*, pg. 2482
IDEX HOLDINGS GMBH—See IDEX Corp; *U.S. Public*, pg. 1090
IDEXX HOLDING B.V.—See IDEXX Laboratories, Inc.; *U.S. Public*, pg. 1092
IDEXX REFERENCE LABORATORIES, INC.—See IDEXX Laboratories, Inc.; *U.S. Public*, pg. 1093
IDFC SECURITIES LIMITED; *Int'l*, pg. 3593
IDI HOLDINGS, LLC—See Red Violet, Inc.; *U.S. Public*, pg. 1770
IDI SCA; *Int'l*, pg. 3594
IDIS HOLDINGS CO., LTD.; *Int'l*, pg. 3595
IDORSIA LTD.; *Int'l*, pg. 3595
IDQ HOLDINGS, INC.—See Spectrum Brands Holdings, Inc.; *U.S. Public*, pg. 1915
IEP INVEST SA; *Int'l*, pg. 3597
IES HOLDINGS, INC.; *U.S. Public*, pg. 1094
IES HOLDINGS LTD.; *Int'l*, pg. 3597
IES SUBSIDIARY HOLDINGS, INC.—See IES Holdings, Inc.; *U.S. Public*, pg. 1094
IEX GROUP, INC.; *U.S. Private*, pg. 2038
IFG COMPANIES; *U.S. Private*, pg. 2038
IFIT HEALTH & FITNESS INC.; *U.S. Private*, pg. 2039
IF&P FOODS LLC—See Wind Point Advisors LLC; *U.S. Private*, pg. 4534
IFS CAPITAL HOLDINGS (THAILAND) LIMITED—See IFS Capital Limited; *Int'l*, pg. 3600
IFS CAPITAL LIMITED; *Int'l*, pg. 3599
IFS HOLDINGS, LLC; *U.S. Private*, pg. 2039
IG GROUP HOLDINGS PLC; *Int'l*, pg. 3601
IGI HOLDINGS LIMITED; *Int'l*, pg. 3602
IGNITE TECHNOLOGIES, INC.—See ESW Capital, LLC; *U.S. Private*, pg. 1430
IGUATEMI S.A.; *Int'l*, pg. 3603
IHAG HOLDING AG; *Int'l*, pg. 3603
IHEARTMEDIA, INC.; *U.S. Public*, pg. 1095
IHLAS HOLDING A.S.; *Int'l*, pg. 3606
IHLAS YAYIN HOLDING A.S.; *Int'l*, pg. 3606
IHS HOLDING LIMITED; *Int'l*, pg. 3607
IHUMAN INC.; *Int'l*, pg. 3607
IIDA GROUP HOLDINGS CO., LTD.; *Int'l*, pg. 3607
III EXPLORATION COMPANY—See Intermountain Industries, Inc.; *U.S. Private*, pg. 2113
IKF S.P.A.; *Int'l*, pg. 3610
IKM GRUPPEN AS; *Int'l*, pg. 3611
IKO ENTERPRISES LTD.; *Int'l*, pg. 3612
IKONIX GROUP, INC.; *U.S. Private*, pg. 2041
ILDONG HOLDINGS CO., LTD.; *Int'l*, pg. 3613
ILFC HOLDINGS, INC.—See American International Group, Inc.; *U.S. Public*, pg. 107
ILITCH HOLDINGS, INC.; *U.S. Private*, pg. 2041
ILJIN HOLDINGS CO., LTD.; *Int'l*, pg. 3614
ILLINOIS CORN PROCESSING HOLDINGS INC.—See Alto Ingredients, Inc.; *U.S. Public*, pg. 88
ILLINOIS HEALTH & SCIENCE; *U.S. Private*, pg. 2042
ILLINOVA CORPORATION—See Vistra Corp.; *U.S. Public*, pg. 2306
I-MAB; *Int'l*, pg. 3563
IMAC HOLDINGS, INC.; *U.S. Public*, pg. 1112
IMAGE HOLDINGS CORPORATION; *U.S. Private*, pg. 2044
IMAGELINX PLC; *Int'l*, pg. 3618
IMAX CHINA HOLDING, INC.—See Imax Corporation; *Int'l*, pg. 3620
IMB PARTNERS; *U.S. Private*, pg. 2046
IMCD GROUP B.V.—See IMCD N.V.; *Int'l*, pg. 3621
IMCD N.V.; *Int'l*, pg. 3621
IMC (GERMANY) HOLDINGS GMBH—See Berkshire Hathaway Inc.; *U.S. Public*, pg. 307
IMC GROUP USA HOLDINGS, INC.—See Berkshire Hathaway Inc.; *U.S. Public*, pg. 307
IMC HOLDINGS, INC.; *U.S. Private*, pg. 2046
IMC INDUSTRIAL PTE. LTD.—See IMC Pan Asia Alliance Pte. Ltd.; *Int'l*, pg. 3621
IMC INTERNATIONAL MARKETMAKERS COMBINATION B.V.; *Int'l*, pg. 3620
IMC INTERNATIONAL METALWORKING COMPANIES B.V.—See Berkshire Hathaway Inc.; *U.S. Public*, pg. 307
IMC PAN ASIA ALLIANCE PTE. LTD.; *Int'l*, pg. 3621
IMEG CORP.; *U.S. Private*, pg. 2046
IMERYS SA—See Groupe Bruxelles Lambert SA; *Int'l*, pg. 3099

551112 — OFFICES OF OTHER HO...   CORPORATE AFFILIATIONS

I&M GROUP PLC; *Int'l*, pg. 3562
IMG WORLDWIDE, INC. - CLEVELAND—See Silver Lake Group, LLC; *U.S. Private*, pg. 3657
IMG WORLDWIDE, INC. - CLEVELAND—See William Morris Endeavor Entertainment, LLC; *U.S. Private*, pg. 4524
IMIMOBILE PLC—See Cisco Systems, Inc.; *U.S. Public*, pg. 499
IMPAXX, INC.; *U.S. Private*, pg. 2049
IMPELLAM GROUP PLC—See HFBG Holding B.V.; *Int'l*, pg. 3374
IMPERATIVE LOGISTICS GROUP—See Littlejohn & Co., LLC; *U.S. Private*, pg. 2470
IMPERIAL LOGISTICS LIMITED—See Dubai World Corporation; *Int'l*, pg. 2221
IMPERO ELECTRONICS, INC.; *U.S. Private*, pg. 2050
I.M.P. GROUP INTERNATIONAL INC.; *Int'l*, pg. 3566
IMPREGLON GMBH—See Aalberts N.V.; *Int'l*, pg. 34
IMPRESO, INC.; *U.S. Public*, pg. 1114
IMS HEALTH HOLDINGS, INC.—See IQVIA Holdings Inc.; *U.S. Public*, pg. 1168
IMTT HOLDINGS LLC—See Riverstone Holdings LLC; *U.S. Private*, pg. 3447
IMX HOLDINGS, LLC—See HCA Healthcare, Inc.; *U.S. Public*, pg. 999
IMX SOFTWARE GROUP LIMITED—See Holley Holland Limited; *Int'l*, pg. 3451
INCIPIO, LLC; *U.S. Private*, pg. 2053
INDEL, INC.; *U.S. Private*, pg. 2055
INDEPENDENCE CAPITAL PARTNERS, LLC; *U.S. Private*, pg. 2055
INDEPENDENCE HOLDING COMPANY—See Geneve Holdings Corp.; *U.S. Private*, pg. 1670
INDEPENDENT BREWERS UNITED, INC.—See Florida Ice and Farm Co. S.A.; *Int'l*, pg. 2707
INDIANAPOLIS MOTOR SPEEDWAY CORPORATION—See Penske Corporation; *U.S. Private*, pg. 3138
INDUSTRIA AUTOMOTRIZ CIFUNSA, S.A. DE C.V.—See Grupo Industrial Saltillo S.A. de C.V.; *Int'l*, pg. 3130
INDUSTRIAL DIELECTRICS HOLDINGS, INC.; *U.S. Private*, pg. 2065
INDUSTRIAL GALVANIZERS AMERICA HOLDINGS, INC.—See Valmont Industries, Inc.; *U.S. Public*, pg. 2273
INDVR BRANDS, INC.; *U.S. Public*, pg. 1117
INFINEX FINANCIAL HOLDINGS, INC.; *U.S. Private*, pg. 2070
INFINITAS LEARNING HOLDING B.V.—See Bridgepoint Group Plc; *Int'l*, pg. 1154
INFINITY GROUP, L.L.C.—See Kemper Corporation; *U.S. Public*, pg. 1220
INFOGROUP INC.—See CCMP Capital Advisors, LP; *U.S. Private*, pg. 800
INFOGROUP INTERACTIVE—See CCMP Capital Advisors, LP; *U.S. Private*, pg. 800
INFOSPACE HOLDINGS LLC—See OpenMail LLC; *U.S. Private*, pg. 3031
INFRASOURCE, LLC—See Quanta Services, Inc.; *U.S. Public*, pg. 1751
INGENICO VENTURES SAS—See Apollo Global Management, Inc.; *U.S. Public*, pg. 152
INGERSOLL-DRESSER PUMPS S.R.L.—See Flowserve Corporation; *U.S. Public*, pg. 856
INGERSOLL-RAND COMPANY LIMITED—See Ingersoll Rand Inc.; *U.S. Public*, pg. 1120
INGERSOLL RAND INC.; *U.S. Public*, pg. 1118
INGERSOLL-RAND US TRANE HOLDINGS CORPORATION—See Ingersoll Rand Inc; *U.S. Public*, pg. 1121
INGEVITY CORPORATION; *U.S. Public*, pg. 1122
INGEVITY HOLDINGS SPRL—See Ingevity Corporation; *U.S. Public*, pg. 1122
INGRAM INDUSTRIES, INC.; *U.S. Private*, pg. 2076
INGRAM MICRO CFS INTERNATIONAL B.V.—See Hainan Traffic Administration Holding Co., Ltd.; *Int'l*, pg. 3214
INGRAM MICRO HOLDINGS (AUSTRALIA) PTY LTD—See Hainan Traffic Administration Holding Co., Ltd.; *Int'l*, pg. 3214
INGRAM MICRO HOLDINGS LIMITED—See Hainan Traffic Administration Holding Co., Ltd.; *Int'l*, pg. 3214
INIZIO GROUP LIMITED—See Clayton, Dubilier & Rice, LLC; *U.S. Private*, pg. 924
INLAND INDUSTRIES, INC.; *U.S. Private*, pg. 2078
THE INLAND REAL ESTATE GROUP OF COMPANIES, INC.; *U.S. Private*, pg. 4055
INMAN HOLDING CO. INC.; *U.S. Private*, pg. 2079
INMARSAT GROUP LIMITED—See ViaSat, Inc.; *U.S. Public*, pg. 2291
INMUSIC, LLC; *U.S. Private*, pg. 2080
INNO HOLDINGS, INC.; *U.S. Public*, pg. 1125
INNOPHOS HOLDINGS, INC.—See One Rock Capital Partners, LLC; *U.S. Private*, pg. 3022
INNOVANCE, INC.; *U.S. Private*, pg. 2081
INNOVATE CORP.; *U.S. Public*, pg. 1125
INNOVATION TECHNOLOGY GROUP; *U.S. Private*, pg. 2081
INNOVATIVE BUILDING SYSTEMS LLC; *U.S. Private*, pg. 2081
INNOVATIVE CHEMICAL PRODUCTS GROUP, LLC—See Audax Group, Limited Partnership; *U.S. Private*, pg. 388
INNOVATIVE DIVERSIFIED TECHNOLOGIES INC.; *U.S. Private*, pg. 2082
INNOVEST GLOBAL, INC.; *U.S. Public*, pg. 1127
INNOVIA MEDICAL, INC.—See The Graham Group, Inc.; *U.S. Private*, pg. 4037
INOVALON HOLDINGS, INC.; *U.S. Public*, pg. 1128
INSENSYS HOLDINGS LTD.—See Moog Inc.; *U.S. Public*, pg. 1469
INSIDE IDEAS GROUP LTD.—See You & Mr Jones Inc.; *U.S. Private*, pg. 4591
INSIGHT HEALTH SERVICES HOLDINGS CORP.—See Black Diamond Capital Holdings, LLC; *U.S. Private*, pg. 570
INSOMNIAC HOLDINGS, LLC—See Live Nation Entertainment, Inc.; *U.S. Public*, pg. 1329
INSPIRE BRANDS, INC.—See Roark Capital Group Inc.; *U.S. Private*, pg. 3455
INSTRUCTURE HOLDINGS, INC.—See KKR & Co. Inc.; *U.S. Public*, pg. 1253
THE INSURANCE PARTNERSHIP HOLDINGS LIMITED—See Marsh & McLennan Companies, Inc.; *U.S. Public*, pg. 1388
INTEA HOLDINGS INC.—See Hikari Tsushin, Inc.; *Int'l*, pg. 3390
INTEGER HOLDINGS CORPORATION; *U.S. Public*, pg. 1134
INTEGRACORE, INC.; *U.S. Private*, pg. 2098
INTEGRAL AD SCIENCE HOLDING CORP.; *U.S. Public*, pg. 1136
INTEGRA LIFESCIENCES HOLDINGS CORPORATION; *U.S. Public*, pg. 1135
INTEGRATED COMMUNICATIONS GROUP PTE LTD.—See Hakuhodo DY Holdings Incorporated; *Int'l*, pg. 3221
INTEGRATED POLYMER SOLUTIONS, INC.—See Arcline Investment Management LP; *U.S. Private*, pg. 314
INTEGRA TELECOM OF OREGON INC.—See Warburg Pincus LLC; *U.S. Private*, pg. 4438
INTEGREON GLOBAL; *U.S. Public*, pg. 2102
INTEGRIS—See Frontenac Company LLC; *U.S. Private*, pg. 1613
INTEGRITY MUTUAL INSURANCE COMPANY—See Grange Mutual Casualty Company; *U.S. Private*, pg. 1754
INTEGRYS HOLDING, INC.—See WEC Energy Group, Inc.; *U.S. Public*, pg. 2342
INTELECOM GROUP AS—See Herkules Capital AS; *Int'l*, pg. 3362
INTELEK LIMITED—See Teledyne Technologies Incorporated; *U.S. Public*, pg. 1994
INTEL HOLDINGS B.V.—See Intel Corporation; *U.S. Public*, pg. 1138
INTELLICENTRICS GLOBAL HOLDINGS LTD.; *U.S. Public*, pg. 1139
INTELLIGENT BIO SOLUTIONS INC.; *U.S. Public*, pg. 1139
INTERBULK GROUP LIMITED—See Den Hartogh Holding BV; *Int'l*, pg. 2026
INTERCALL ASIA PACIFIC HOLDINGS PTE. LTD.—See Apollo Global Management, Inc.; *U.S. Public*, pg. 152
INTERCONTINENTAL EXCHANGE HOLDINGS, INC.—See Intercontinental Exchange, Inc.; *U.S. Public*, pg. 1143
INTERCONTINENTAL EXCHANGE, INC.; *U.S. Public*, pg. 1141
INTERFACE AUST. HOLDINGS PTY LIMITED—See Interface, Inc.; *U.S. Public*, pg. 1144
INTERFACE EUROPE B.V.—See Interface, Inc.; *U.S. Public*, pg. 1144
INTERFACE, INC.; *U.S. Public*, pg. 1144
INTERFACE OVERSEAS HOLDINGS, INC.—See Interface, Inc.; *U.S. Public*, pg. 1144
INTERFOODS OF AMERICA, INC.; *U.S. Public*, pg. 2110
INTERIOR LOGIC GROUP HOLDINGS, LLC—See Littlejohn & Co., LLC; *U.S. Private*, pg. 2470
INTERIOR LOGIC GROUP HOLDINGS, LLC—See Platinum Equity, LLC; *U.S. Private*, pg. 3205
INTERMEX WIRE TRANSFERS DE GUATEMALA S.A.—See International Money Express Inc.; *U.S. Public*, pg. 1155
INTERMOUNTAIN INDUSTRIES, INC.; *U.S. Private*, pg. 2113
INTERMOUNTAIN WEST COMMUNICATIONS COMPANY; *U.S. Private*, pg. 2113
INTERNAP HOLDING LLC; *U.S. Public*, pg. 2113
INTERNATIONAL DAIRY QUEEN, INC.—See Berkshire Hathaway Inc.; *U.S. Public*, pg. 308
INTERNATIONAL DATA GROUP, INC.—See China Oceanwide Holdings Group Co., Ltd.; *Int'l*, pg. 1536
INTERNATIONAL DATA GROUP, INC.—See IDG Capital; *Int'l*, pg. 3593
INTERNATIONAL EQUIPMENT SOLUTIONS, LLC—See KPS Capital Partners, LP; *U.S. Private*, pg. 2347
INTERNATIONAL FIBRES GROUP (HOLDINGS) LIMITED—See Duroc AB; *Int'l*, pg. 2230
INTERNATIONAL FLAVORS & FRAGRANCES (NEDERLAND) HOLDING B.V.—See International Flavors & Fragrances Inc.; *U.S. Public*, pg. 1153
INTERNATIONAL MANUFACTURING COMPANY LLC—See Summa Holdings, Inc.; *U.S. Private*, pg. 3852
INTERNATIONAL MONETARY SYSTEMS, LTD.; *U.S. Public*, pg. 1154
INTERNATIONAL MONEY EXPRESS INC.; *U.S. Public*, pg. 1154
INTERNATIONAL PORT HOLDINGS LTD.—See BlackRock, Inc.; *U.S. Public*, pg. 346
INTERNATIONAL POWER PLC—See ENGIE SA; *Int'l*, pg. 2432
INTERNATIONAL SAINT-GOBAIN—See Compagnie de Saint-Gobain SA; *Int'l*, pg. 1723
INTERNATIONAL SPECIALTY PRODUCTS, INC.—See Ashland Inc.; *U.S. Public*, pg. 212
INTERNATIONAL SPEEDWAY CORPORATION—See National Association for Stock Car Auto Racing, Inc.; *U.S. Private*, pg. 2845
INTERNATIONAL TURF INVESTMENT CO., INC.; *U.S. Private*, pg. 2121
INTERNATIONAL VOYAGER HOLDINGS, INC.; *U.S. Private*, pg. 2121
INTERNATIONAL WINE & SPIRITS LTD.—See Altria Group, Inc.; *U.S. Public*, pg. 89
INTERNET BRANDS, INC.—See KKR & Co. Inc.; *U.S. Public*, pg. 1253
INTERPACE BIOSCIENCES, INC.; *U.S. Public*, pg. 1158
INTER PARFUMS HOLDINGS, S.A.—See Inter Parfums, Inc.; *U.S. Public*, pg. 1140
INTERPLEX HOLDINGS PTE. LTD.—See Blackstone Inc.; *U.S. Public*, pg. 354
THE INTERPUBLIC GROUP OF COMPANIES, INC.; *U.S. Public*, pg. 2089
INTERPUBLIC LIMITED—See The Interpublic Group of Companies, Inc.; *U.S. Public*, pg. 2096
INTERSTATE GROUP HOLDINGS, INC.; *U.S. Private*, pg. 2124
INTERSTATE INTERNATIONAL, INC.; *U.S. Private*, pg. 2125
THE INTERTECH GROUP, INC.; *U.S. Private*, pg. 4057
INTERTRUST B.V.—See Corporation Service Company; *U.S. Private*, pg. 1057
INTERTRUST GROUP B.V.—See Corporation Service Company; *U.S. Private*, pg. 1057
INTERTRUST GROUP HOLDING S.A.—See Corporation Service Company; *U.S. Private*, pg. 1057
INTERWEST CORPORATION; *U.S. Private*, pg. 2128
INTERXION HOLDING N.V.—See Digital Realty Trust, Inc.; *U.S. Public*, pg. 663
INTIVA INC.; *U.S. Private*, pg. 2128
INTRALINKS EMEA HOLDINGS B.V.—See SS&C Technologies Holdings, Inc.; *U.S. Public*, pg. 1923
INTRALINKS HOLDINGS, INC.—See SS&C Technologies Holdings, Inc.; *U.S. Public*, pg. 1923
INVACARE CANADIAN HOLDINGS, INC.—See Invacare Corporation; *U.S. Private*, pg. 2130
INVACARE GERMANY HOLDING GMBH—See Invacare Corporation; *U.S. Private*, pg. 2130
INVACARE HOLDINGS AS—See Invacare Corporation; *U.S. Private*, pg. 2131
INVACARE HOLDINGS C.V.—See Invacare Corporation; *U.S. Private*, pg. 2131
INVESCO ADMINISTRATION SERVICES LIMITED—See Invesco Ltd.; *U.S. Public*, pg. 1161
INVESCO ASSET MANAGEMENT LTD.—See Invesco Ltd.; *U.S. Public*, pg. 1163
INVESCO HONG KONG LIMITED—See Invesco Ltd.; *U.S. Public*, pg. 1162
INVESCO (HYDERABAD) PRIVATE LIMITED—See Invesco Ltd.; *U.S. Public*, pg. 1161
INVESCO LTD.; *U.S. Public*, pg. 1161
INVESCO NORTH AMERICAN HOLDINGS, INC.—See Invesco Ltd.; *U.S. Public*, pg. 1163
INVESCO TRUSTEE PVT. LTD.—See Invesco Ltd.; *U.S. Public*, pg. 1162
INVESCO UK LTD.—See Invesco Ltd.; *U.S. Public*, pg. 1163
INVESTMENT PARTNERS GROUP, INC.; *U.S. Private*, pg. 2132
INVESTORS CORPORATION OF VERMONT; *U.S. Private*, pg. 2132
INVESTORS MANAGEMENT CORPORATION; *U.S. Private*, pg. 2132
INVESTORS TITLE COMPANY; *U.S. Public*, pg. 1165
INVISIONS HOLDING B.V.—See National Amusements, Inc.; *U.S. Public*, pg. 2841
INVOCO HOLDING GMBH—See Conduent Incorporated; *U.S. Public*, pg. 566
ION MEDIA NETWORKS, INC.—See The E.W. Scripps Company; *U.S. Public*, pg. 2067
IOS HOLDINGS, INC.—See L.B. Foster Company; *U.S. Public*, pg. 1278
IOWA TELECOMMUNICATIONS SERVICES, INC.—See Windstream Holdings, Inc.; *U.S. Public*, pg. 2373
IOWA TURKEY GROWERS COOPERATIVE; *U.S. Private*, pg. 2136
IPALCO ENTERPRISES, INC.—See The AES Corporation; *U.S. Public*, pg. 2031
IPC HEALTHCARE, INC.—See Blackstone Inc.; *U.S. Public*, pg. 359

N.A.I.C.S. INDEX
551112 — OFFICES OF OTHER HO...

IPL PLASTICS INC—See Madison Dearborn Partners, LLC; *U.S. Private*, pg. 2541
IQVIA HOLDINGS INC.; *U.S. Public*, pg. 1168
IR BIOSCIENCES HOLDINGS, INC.; *U.S. Public*, pg. 1171
I'ROM GROUP CO., LTD.; *Int'l*, pg. 3562
IRON HORSE HOLDINGS INC—See LendingTree, Inc.; *U.S. Public*, pg. 1305
IRON MINING GROUP, INC.; *U.S. Private*, pg. 2139
IRON MOUNTAIN EUROPE LIMITED—See Iron Mountain Incorporated; *U.S. Public*, pg. 1172
IRON MOUNTAIN HOLDINGS GROUP, INC.—See Iron Mountain Incorporated; *U.S. Public*, pg. 1173
IRON MOUNTAIN INTERNATIONAL HOLDINGS B.V.—See Iron Mountain Incorporated; *U.S. Public*, pg. 1173
IRONSHORE AUSTRALIA HOLDINGS PTY LIMITED—See Liberty Mutual Holding Company Inc.; *U.S. Private*, pg. 2445
IRONSHORE HOLDINGS (U.S.) INC.—See Liberty Mutual Holding Company Inc.; *U.S. Private*, pg. 2445
IRONWAVE TECHNOLOGIES LLC; *U.S. Private*, pg. 2140
IRWIN INTERNATIONAL, INC.; *U.S. Private*, pg. 2142
ISHIN HOTELS GROUP CO., LTD.—See Alpine Grove Partners LLP; *U.S. Private*, pg. 201
ISHIN HOTELS GROUP CO., LTD.—See Hoshino Resorts Inc.; *Int'l*, pg. 3483
ISLAND CAPITAL GROUP LLC; *U.S. Private*, pg. 2144
ISLAND HOLDINGS, INC.; *U.S. Private*, pg. 2145
ISLET SCIENCES, INC.; *U.S. Private*, pg. 2146
ISMECA SEMICONDUCTOR HOLDING SA—See Cohu, Inc.; *U.S. Public*, pg. 529
ISQFT PARENT CORPORATION—See Roper Technologies, Inc.; *U.S. Public*, pg. 1814
ISS A/S—See EQT AB; *Int'l*, pg. 2476
ISS A/S—See The Goldman Sachs Group, Inc.; *U.S. Public*, pg. 2077
ISS GLOBAL A/S—See EQT AB; *Int'l*, pg. 2476
ISS GLOBAL A/S—See The Goldman Sachs Group, Inc.; *U.S. Public*, pg. 2077
ISS HOLDING A/S—See EQT AB; *Int'l*, pg. 2476
ISS HOLDING A/S—See The Goldman Sachs Group, Inc.; *U.S. Public*, pg. 2077
ISS SCHWEIZ AG—See EQT AB; *Int'l*, pg. 2477
ISS SCHWEIZ AG—See The Goldman Sachs Group, Inc.; *U.S. Public*, pg. 2078
ISS UK LIMITED—See EQT AB; *Int'l*, pg. 2477
ISS UK LIMITED—See The Goldman Sachs Group, Inc.; *U.S. Public*, pg. 2078
ISTAR APARTMENT HOLDINGS LLC—See Safehold Inc.; *U.S. Public*, pg. 1834
ISTONISH HOLDING COMPANY, INC.; *U.S. Private*, pg. 2147
ITALCEMENTI S.P.A.—See Heidelberg Materials AG; *Int'l*, pg. 3316
ITALEASE GESTIONE BENI S.P.A.—See Banco BPM S.p.A.; *Int'l*, pg. 818
ITC HOLDING COMPANY, LLC; *U.S. Private*, pg. 2149
ITC HOLDINGS CORP.—See Fortis Inc.; *Int'l*, pg. 2739
ITEFIN PARTICIPATIONS SAS—See Apax Partners LLP; *Int'l*, pg. 504
ITG HOLDINGS LLC; *U.S. Private*, pg. 2149
ITR INDUSTRIES INC.; *U.S. Private*, pg. 2150
ITRON HOLDING GERMANY GMBH—See Itron, Inc.; *U.S. Public*, pg. 1176
ITT KOREA HOLDING B.V.—See ITT Inc.; *U.S. Public*, pg. 1178
ITW BUILDING COMPONENTS GROUP INC.—See Illinois Tool Works Inc.; *U.S. Public*, pg. 1104
ITW INTERNATIONAL HOLDINGS LLC—See Illinois Tool Works Inc.; *U.S. Public*, pg. 1106
ITW SPAIN HOLDINGS, S.L.—See Illinois Tool Works Inc.; *U.S. Public*, pg. 1107
IVARI CANADA ULC—See Vestar Capital Partners, LLC; *U.S. Private*, pg. 4373
IVC-USA INC.; *U.S. Private*, pg. 2150
IZICO HOLDING B.V.—See Egeria Capital Management B.V.; *Int'l*, pg. 2323
JAC HOLDINGS, LLC—See Argonaut Private Equity, LLC; *U.S. Private*, pg. 321
JAC HOLDINGS, LLC—See Hall Capital, LLC; *U.S. Private*, pg. 1843
JACK CREEK INVESTMENT CORP.—See Bridger Aerospace Group Holdings, Inc.; *U.S. Public*, pg. 382
JACK GRAHAM INC.; *U.S. Private*, pg. 2174
JACKSON FAMILY WINES, INC.; *U.S. Private*, pg. 2176
JACOBS BRASIL HOLDINGS S.A.—See Jacobs Engineering Group, Inc.; *U.S. Public*, pg. 1184
JACOBS ENTERTAINMENT, INC.; *U.S. Private*, pg. 2179
JACOBS EUROPEAN HOLDINGS LIMITED—See Jacobs Engineering Group, Inc.; *U.S. Public*, pg. 1185
JAMBA, INC.—See Roark Capital Group Inc.; *U.S. Private*, pg. 3454
JAMES RIVER GROUP HOLDINGS, LTD.—See D. E. Shaw & Co., L.P.; *U.S. Private*, pg. 1139
JAMF HOLDING CORP.; *U.S. Public*, pg. 1187
JAMS MEDIA LLC; *U.S. Private*, pg. 2186
JANSSEN INTERNATIONAAL CVBA—See Johnson & Johnson; *U.S. Public*, pg. 1197

J. ARON HOLDINGS L.P.—See The Goldman Sachs Group, Inc.; *U.S. Public*, pg. 2081
JASON HOLDING GMBH—See Jason Industries, Inc.; *U.S. Private*, pg. 2189
JASON HOLDINGS UK LIMITED—See Jason Industries, Inc.; *U.S. Private*, pg. 2189
JASON INDUSTRIES, INC.; *U.S. Private*, pg. 2189
JBC HOLDING CO.; *U.S. Private*, pg. 2193
J&B GROUP, INC.; *U.S. Private*, pg. 2153
J.C. PENNEY COMPANY, INC.; *U.S. Private*, pg. 2160
JDA SOFTWARE GROUP, INC.—See New Mountain Capital, LLC; *U.S. Private*, pg. 2902
JDH CAPITAL HOLDINGS, L.P.; *U.S. Private*, pg. 2195
J.D.S. FINANCE LIMITED—See Landon Capital Partners, LLC; *U.S. Private*, pg. 2386
JEAN-CLAUDE BOISSET WINES U.S.A., INC.—See Boisset, La Famille des Grands Vins; *Int'l*, pg. 1101
JEFFERIES FINANCIAL GROUP INC.; *U.S. Public*, pg. 1188
JEFFERIES GROUP LLC—See Jefferies Financial Group Inc.; *U.S. Public*, pg. 1188
JEFFERIES INTERNATIONAL (HOLDINGS) LIMITED—See Jefferies Financial Group Inc.; *U.S. Public*, pg. 1188
JEFF WYLER AUTOMOTIVE FAMILY, INC.; *U.S. Private*, pg. 2197
JENCAP HOLDINGS LLC—See The Carlyle Group Inc.; *U.S. Public*, pg. 2047
JERASH HOLDINGS (US), INC.; *U.S. Public*, pg. 1189
JET AVIATION HOLDING GMBH—See General Dynamics Corporation; *U.S. Public*, pg. 916
JETCENTERS, INC.—See Cordillera Corporation; *U.S. Private*, pg. 1047
J FITZGIBBONS LLC; *U.S. Private*, pg. 2153
THE J.G. WENTWORTH COMPANY—See JLL Partners, LLC; *U.S. Private*, pg. 2213
J.H. BERRA HOLDING CO., INC.; *U.S. Private*, pg. 2165
JIMMY JOHN'S LLC—See Roark Capital Group Inc.; *U.S. Private*, pg. 3455
J.L. DAVIS COMPANIES; *U.S. Private*, pg. 2167
JMD PROPERTIES INC.; *U.S. Private*, pg. 1190
JMI SERVICES, INC.; *U.S. Private*, pg. 2215
JMK OPERATIONS INC.—See JMK International, Inc.; *U.S. Private*, pg. 2216
JMP COAL HOLDINGS, LLC; *U.S. Private*, pg. 2216
JMP GROUP INC.—See Citizens Financial Group, Inc.; *U.S. Public*, pg. 505
JMP GROUP LLC—See Citizens Financial Group, Inc.; *U.S. Public*, pg. 505
JOANN INC.; *U.S. Public*, pg. 1190
JOHN BEAN TECHNOLOGIES INTERNATIONAL AB—See John Bean Technologies Corporation; *U.S. Public*, pg. 1191
JOHN DEERE GMBH & CO. KG—See Deere & Company; *U.S. Public*, pg. 646
JOHN EAGLE A MANAGEMENT, LLC; *U.S. Private*, pg. 2221
JOHN RICH & SONS—See Woolrich, Inc.; *U.S. Private*, pg. 4562
JOHN S. FREY ENTERPRISES; *U.S. Private*, pg. 2224
JOHN SHEARER (HOLDINGS) LIMITED—See Arrowcrest Group Pty. Ltd.; *Int'l*, pg. 580
JOHNS MANVILLE CORPORATION—See Berkshire Hathaway Inc.; *U.S. Public*, pg. 308
JOHNSON HOLDING CO.; *U.S. Private*, pg. 2228
JOHNSON & JOHNSON GROUP HOLDINGS GMBH—See Johnson & Johnson; *U.S. Public*, pg. 1198
JOHNSON & JOHNSON HOLDCO (NA) INC.—See Johnson & Johnson; *U.S. Public*, pg. 1197
JOHNSON & JOHNSON HOLDING AB—See Johnson & Johnson; *U.S. Public*, pg. 1198
JOHNSON & JOHNSON HOLDING GMBH—See Johnson & Johnson; *U.S. Public*, pg. 1198
JOHNSON & JOHNSON INTERNATIONAL—See Johnson & Johnson; *U.S. Public*, pg. 1198
JOHNSON & JOHNSON MEDICAL PTY. LIMITED—See Johnson & Johnson; *U.S. Public*, pg. 1199
JOHNSTON ENTERPRISES INC.; *U.S. Private*, pg. 2230
JOIN ENTERTAINMENT HOLDINGS, INC.; *U.S. Private*, pg. 2230
JOINT HOLDINGS/BASIC METAL INDUSTRIES, INC.; *U.S. Private*, pg. 2230
JONES LANG LASALLE HOLDINGS BV—See Jones Lang LaSalle Incorporated; *U.S. Public*, pg. 1203
JONES LANG LASALLE INCORPORATED; *U.S. Public*, pg. 1201
JONES MOTOR GROUP, INC.—See Transport Investments, Inc.; *U.S. Private*, pg. 4210
JORDAN INDUSTRIES, INC.; *U.S. Private*, pg. 2235
JOSHUA GREEN CORPORATION; *U.S. Private*, pg. 2237
JOURNAL MEDIA GROUP, INC.—See Gannett Co., Inc.; *U.S. Public*, pg. 898
JOY CITY PROPERTY LTD.—See COFCO Limited; *Int'l*, pg. 1692
J.P.B. ENTERPRISES, INC.; *U.S. Private*, pg. 2170
JPN HOLDINGS COMPANY, LIMITED—See Credit Saison Co., Ltd.; *Int'l*, pg. 1836
J. RAY MCDERMOTT (AUST.) HOLDING PTY LIMITED—See McDermott International, Inc.; *U.S. Public*, pg. 1405
JRJR33, INC.; *U.S. Private*, pg. 2240
JRS HOLDING, INC.; *U.S. Private*, pg. 2240
JSA HEALTHCARE NEVADA, LLC.—See DaVita Inc.; *U.S. Public*, pg. 640
JSC LIBERTY CONSUMER—See Bank of Georgia Group PLC; *Int'l*, pg. 843
JUBILEE HOLDINGS LIMITED—See Aga Khan Development Network; *Int'l*, pg. 199
JUNIPER INDUSTRIAL HOLDINGS, INC.—See Clearlake Capital Group, L.P.; *U.S. Private*, pg. 935
JUNIPER NETWORKS HOLDINGS INTERNATIONAL, INC.—See Juniper Networks, Inc.; *U.S. Public*, pg. 1211
JUNIPER NETWORKS, INC.; *U.S. Public*, pg. 1210
JUSHI HOLDINGS INC.; *U.S. Public*, pg. 1211
JUUT HOLDINGS INC.; *U.S. Private*, pg. 2246
JVC HOLDINGS, INC.—See LTC Properties, Inc.; *U.S. Public*, pg. 1344
JX NIPPON OIL & GAS EXPLORATION CORPORATION—See ENEOS Holdings, Inc.; *Int'l*, pg. 2416
JXTG NIPPON OIL & ENERGY CORPORATION—See ENEOS Holdings, Inc.; *Int'l*, pg. 2417
K2-MDV HOLDINGS, LP—See Kohlberg & Company, LLC; *U.S. Private*, pg. 2338
K2M GROUP HOLDINGS, INC.—See Stryker Corporation; *U.S. Public*, pg. 1955
KAHALA CORP.; *U.S. Private*, pg. 2254
KALAHARI MINERALS PLC—See China Development Bank Corporation; *Int'l*, pg. 1497
KALAHARI MINERALS PLC—See China Guangdong Nuclear Power Holding Co., Ltd.; *Int'l*, pg. 1506
KALIN ENTERPRISES, INC.; *U.S. Private*, pg. 2257
KAMAN AEROSPACE GROUP, INC.—See Arcline Investment Management LP; *U.S. Private*, pg. 314
KANDERS & COMPANY, INC.; *U.S. Private*, pg. 2259
KANDMAD - SOCIEDADE GESTORA DE PARTICIPACOES SOCIAIS LDA—See Camargo Correa S.A.; *Int'l*, pg. 1268
KANSAS CABLE HOLDINGS, INC.—See Gladstone Management Corporation; *U.S. Public*, pg. 1705
KANSAS CITY SOUTHERN—See Canadian Pacific Kansas City Limited; *Int'l*, pg. 1285
KAPSTONE PAPER & PACKAGING CORPORATION—See WestRock Company; *U.S. Public*, pg. 2361
KASHIMA AROMATICS CO., LTD.—See ENEOS Holdings, Inc.; *Int'l*, pg. 2417
KASHIMA OIL CO., LTD.—See ENEOS Holdings, Inc.; *Int'l*, pg. 2417
THE KASPAR COMPANIES; *U.S. Private*, pg. 4064
KAYSER AUTOMOTIVE GROUP, LLC; *U.S. Private*, pg. 2267
KBR HOLDINGS PTY LTD.—See KBR, Inc.; *U.S. Public*, pg. 1216
KBR, INC.; *U.S. Public*, pg. 1215
KCP HOLDCO, INC.; *U.S. Private*, pg. 2270
K.C.S.A. HOLDINGS (PTY.) LTD.—See Kimberly-Clark Corporation; *U.S. Public*, pg. 1229
KCS LIMITED—See CVC Capital Partners SICAV-FIS S.A.; *Int'l*, pg. 1886
KD HOLDING CORPORATION—See CTCI Corporation; *Int'l*, pg. 1870
KEANE GROUP HOLDINGS, LLC; *U.S. Private*, pg. 2271
KEB ENTERPRISES LP; *U.S. Private*, pg. 2271
KEDI HOLDINGS S.A.R.L.—See KKR & Co. Inc.; *U.S. Public*, pg. 1254
THE KEELEY COMPANIES; *U.S. Private*, pg. 4064
KELDA GROUP LIMITED—See Citigroup Inc.; *U.S. Public*, pg. 503
KELDA GROUP LIMITED—See GIC Pte. Ltd.; *Int'l*, pg. 2965
KELDA GROUP LIMITED—See HSBC Holdings plc; *Int'l*, pg. 3504
KELLOGG AUSTRALIA HOLDINGS PTY LTD—See Kellanova; *U.S. Public*, pg. 1217
KELLOGG BROWN & ROOT INTERNATIONAL, INC.—See KBR, Inc.; *U.S. Public*, pg. 1216
KELLOGG USA INC.—See WK Kellogg Co; *U.S. Public*, pg. 2376
KEMA INC.—See DNV GL Group AS; *Int'l*, pg. 2151
KEMA N.V.—See DNV GL Group AS; *Int'l*, pg. 2151
KEMMONS WILSON, INC.; *U.S. Private*, pg. 2281
KENDALL AUTOMOTIVE GROUP INC.; *U.S. Private*, pg. 2283
KENEX HOLDINGS LLC; *U.S. Private*, pg. 2284
KENMAR GROUP INC.—See Ambroisie Capital Holding S.A.S.; *Int'l*, pg. 415
KENNAMETAL GMBH—See Kennametal Inc.; *U.S. Public*, pg. 1222
KENNAMETAL HOLDINGS EUROPE INC.—See Kennametal Inc.; *U.S. Public*, pg. 1222
KENNAMETAL HOLDINGS, LLC LUXEMBOURG S.C.S.—See Kennametal Inc.; *U.S. Public*, pg. 1222
KENNEDY WILSON EUROPE LIMITED—See Kennedy-Wilson Holdings, Inc.; *U.S. Public*, pg. 1223
KENNEDY-WILSON HOLDINGS, INC.; *U.S. Public*, pg. 1223
KENT CORPORATION; *U.S. Private*, pg. 2287

551112 — OFFICES OF OTHER HO...

KENTUCKY NATIONAL INSURANCE GROUP, LLC—See Forcht Group of Kentucky, Inc.; *U.S. Private,* pg. 1564
KENVUE INC.; *U.S. Public,* pg. 1223
KESTRA FINANCIAL, INC.—See Warburg Pincus LLC; *U.S. Private,* pg. 4439
KEWILL HOLDING B.V—See Francisco Partners Management, LP; *U.S. Private,* pg. 1589
KEY AUTO GROUP; *U.S. Private,* pg. 2292
KEYEDIN SOLUTIONS HOLDINGS LIMITED—See KeyedIn Solutions, Inc.; *U.S. Private,* pg. 2294
KEY EQUIPMENT FINANCE INC.—See KeyCorp; *U.S. Public,* pg. 1225
KEYSTONE AUTOMOTIVE OPERATIONS, INC.—See LKQ Corporation; *U.S. Public,* pg. 1334
KEYSTONE GROUP, L.P.; *U.S. Private,* pg. 2296
KEYSTONE INSURERS GROUP, INC; *U.S. Private,* pg. 2300
KFC HOLDINGS JAPAN LTD.—See The Carlyle Group Inc.; *U.S. Public,* pg. 2048
K&F INDUSTRIES HOLDINGS, INC.—See Parker Hannifin Corporation; *U.S. Public,* pg. 1642
KFM ENTERPRISES, LLC; *U.S. Private,* pg. 2300
KICK ICT GROUP LTD.—See BGF Group PLC; *Int'l,* pg. 1007
KIDDE INTERNATIONAL LIMITED—See Carrier Global Corporation; *U.S. Public,* pg. 441
KIMBERLY-CLARK AUSTRALIA HOLDINGS PTY. LIMITED—See Kimberly-Clark Corporation; *U.S. Public,* pg. 1229
KIMBERLY-CLARK COLOMBIA HOLDING LIMITADA—See Kimberly-Clark Corporation; *U.S. Public,* pg. 1229
KIMBERLY-CLARK HOLDING LTD—See Kimberly-Clark Corporation; *U.S. Public,* pg. 1230
KIMBERLY-CLARK HOLDING SRL—See Kimberly-Clark Corporation; *U.S. Public,* pg. 1230
KIMBLE CHASE LIFE SCIENCE & RESEARCH PRODUCTS LLC—See OEP Capital Advisors, L.P.; *U.S. Private,* pg. 2999
KIMBLE COMPANIES INC.; *U.S. Private,* pg. 2305
KIMBRELL INVESTMENTS INC.—See Furniture Distributors Inc.; *U.S. Private,* pg. 1624
KINDERCARE LEARNING COMPANIES, INC.; *U.S. Public,* pg. 1234
KINDER MORGAN G.P., INC.—See Kinder Morgan, Inc.; *U.S. Public,* pg. 1233
KING INTERNATIONAL FINANCIAL HOLDINGS LIMITED—See Aceso Life Science Group Limited; *Int'l,* pg. 102
KINGSBRIDGE HOLDINGS LLC; *U.S. Private,* pg. 2311
KING'S SAFETYWEAR LIMITED—See Honeywell International Inc.; *U.S. Public,* pg. 1049
KINGSWAY FINANCIAL SERVICES INC.; *U.S. Public,* pg. 1234
KINPLEX CORP.; *U.S. Private,* pg. 2313
KION GROUP AG—See KKR & Co. Inc.; *U.S. Public,* pg. 1254
KION GROUP AG—See The Goldman Sachs Group, Inc.; *U.S. Public,* pg. 2078
KIRBY CORPORATION; *U.S. Public,* pg. 1235
KIRINDO HOLDINGS CO., LTD.—See Bain Capital, LP; *U.S. Private,* pg. 441
KIRK BEAUTY ONE GMBH—See CVC Capital Partners SICAV-FIS S.A.; *Int'l,* pg. 1883
KKR FINANCIAL HOLDINGS LLC—See KKR & Co. Inc.; *U.S. Public,* pg. 1256
KLC HOLDINGS, LTD.; *U.S. Private,* pg. 2318
KLEIN BROS. HOLDINGS, LTD.; *U.S. Private,* pg. 2318
KLEINFELDER INTERNATIONAL, INC.—See Goldberg Lindsay & Co., LLC; *U.S. Private,* pg. 1729
KLEOPATRA HOLDINGS 2 S.C.A.—See Strategic Value Partners, LLC; *U.S. Private,* pg. 3836
KLX ENERGY SERVICES HOLDINGS, INC.; *U.S. Public,* pg. 1269
K-MAC ENTERPRISES, INC.—See Brentwood Associates; *U.S. Private,* pg. 646
KNAUF GIPS KG—See Gebr. Knauf KG; *Int'l,* pg. 2906
KNAUF INSULATION HOLDING AG—See Gebr. Knauf KG; *Int'l,* pg. 2907
KNAUF INSULATION HOLDING GMBH—See Gebr. Knauf KG; *Int'l,* pg. 2907
KNIGHT-SWIFT TRANSPORTATION HOLDINGS INC.; *U.S. Public,* pg. 1269
KNL HOLDINGS INC.; *U.S. Private,* pg. 2322
KNOLOGY, INC.—See WideOpenWest, Inc.; *U.S. Public,* pg. 2370
KNOWLES ELECTRONICS HOLDINGS, INC.—See Knowles Corporation; *U.S. Public,* pg. 1270
KN RUBBER, LLC—See Kinderhook Industries, LLC; *U.S. Private,* pg. 2307
KOCH FERTILIZER, LLC—See Koch Industries, Inc.; *U.S. Private,* pg. 2333
KOCH INDUSTRIES, INC.; *U.S. Private,* pg. 2326
KODA ENTERPRISES GROUP, LLC; *U.S. Private,* pg. 2335
KODAK HOLDING GMBH—See Eastman Kodak Company; *U.S. Public,* pg. 707
KODIAK BUILDING PARTNERS LLC; *U.S. Private,* pg. 2336

KODIAK GAS SERVICES, INC.—See EQT AB; *Int'l,* pg. 2478
KOFAX HOLDING AG—See Clearlake Capital Group, L.P.; *U.S. Private,* pg. 936
KOFAX HOLDING AG—See TA Associates, Inc.; *U.S. Private,* pg. 3916
KO HUTS, INC.; *U.S. Private,* pg. 2325
KOKUSAI ELECTRIC CORPORATION—See KKR & Co. Inc.; *U.S. Public,* pg. 1257
KOLLMAN LABEL GROUP, LLC; *U.S. Private,* pg. 2341
KOMAR COMPANY; *U.S. Private,* pg. 2341
KOMATSU CUMMINS CHILE LTDA.—See Cummins Inc.; *U.S. Public,* pg. 608
KONATEL, INC.; *U.S. Public,* pg. 1271
KONINKLIJKE TEN CATE, B.V.—See ABN AMRO Group N.V.; *Int'l,* pg. 64
KONINKLIJKE TEN CATE, B.V.—See Gilde Buy Out Partners B.V.; *Int'l,* pg. 2974
KONINKLIJKE WEGENER B.V.—See DPG Media Group NV; *Int'l,* pg. 2189
KONTOOR BRANDS, INC.; *U.S. Public,* pg. 1271
KONTORA FAMILY OFFICE GMBH—See Cerberus Capital Management, L.P.; *U.S. Private,* pg. 838
KONTORA FAMILY OFFICE GMBH—See GoldenTree Asset Management LP; *U.S. Private,* pg. 1734
KONTORA FAMILY OFFICE GMBH—See J.C. Flowers & Co. LLC; *U.S. Private,* pg. 2159
KOOR INDUSTRIES LTD.—See IDB Development Corporation Ltd.; *Int'l,* pg. 3588
KOOSHAREM, LLC—See Affiliated Managers Group, Inc.; *U.S. Public,* pg. 54
KOOSHAREM, LLC—See Anchorage Capital Group, L.L.C.; *U.S. Private,* pg. 274
KORE WIRELESS GROUP, INC.; *U.S. Private,* pg. 2343
KORIAN DEUTSCHLAND AG—See Clariane SE; *Int'l,* pg. 1643
KORN FERRY; *U.S. Public,* pg. 1272
KOU YOU KAI, LTD.; *U.S. Private,* pg. 2345
KPC HEALTHCARE HOLDINGS, INC.; *U.S. Private,* pg. 2346
KPC PROMISE HEALTHCARE, LLC—See KPC Healthcare Holdings, Inc.; *U.S. Private,* pg. 2346
KPS AG—See Bridgepoint Group Plc; *Int'l,* pg. 1154
KRACIE HOLDINGS, LTD.—See Hoyu Co., Ltd.; *Int'l,* pg. 3499
KRAFT FOODS ENTITY HOLDINGS B.V.—See Mondelez International, Inc.; *U.S. Public,* pg. 1462
THE KRAFT GROUP LLC; *U.S. Public,* pg. 4065
THE KRAFT HEINZ COMPANY—See 3G Capital Inc.; *U.S. Private,* pg. 9
THE KRAFT HEINZ COMPANY—See Berkshire Hathaway Inc.; *U.S. Public,* pg. 317
KRATON CORPORATION—See Daelim Industrial Co., Ltd.; *Int'l,* pg. 1908
KRATOS DEFENSE & SECURITY SOLUTIONS, INC.; *U.S. Public,* pg. 1275
KRAUSSMAFFEI TECHNOLOGIES GMBH—See China National Chemical Corporation; *Int'l,* pg. 1528
KREAB WORLDWIDE AB—See Omnicom Group Inc.; *U.S. Public,* pg. 1587
THE KRETSINGER GROUP, INC.; *U.S. Private,* pg. 4066
KRISPY KREME DOUGHNUTS, INC.—See Krispy Kreme, Inc.; *U.S. Public,* pg. 1277
KRISPY KREME, INC.; *U.S. Public,* pg. 1277
KROENKE SPORTS & ENTERTAINMENT, LLC; *U.S. Private,* pg. 2352
KRONOS TITAN A/S—See Contran Corporation; *U.S. Private,* pg. 1033
KROPP HOLDINGS, INC.—See World Kinect Corporation; *U.S. Public,* pg. 2380
KRUGER BROWN HOLDINGS, LLC; *U.S. Private,* pg. 2353
KS INTERNATIONAL HOLDINGS CORP.; *U.S. Public,* pg. 1277
KS INTERNATIONAL INVESTMENT CORP.; *U.S. Private,* pg. 2354
KTVU, INC.—See Apollo Global Management, Inc.; *U.S. Public,* pg. 164
KUNI ENTERPRISES, INC.—See Holman Automotive Group, Inc.; *U.S. Private,* pg. 1967
KUONI REISEN HOLDING AG—See EQT AB; *Int'l,* pg. 2478
KUVARE US HOLDINGS, INC.; *U.S. Private,* pg. 2358
KV HOLDING CO., INC.—See Hubbell Incorporated; *U.S. Public,* pg. 1067
KYNDRYL HOLDINGS INC.; *U.S. Public,* pg. 1278
L3HARRIS TECHNOLOGIES, INC.; *U.S. Public,* pg. 1279
LA ASSOCIATES, INC.; *U.S. Private,* pg. 2367
LAB M HOLDINGS—See Neogen Corporation; *U.S. Public,* pg. 1505
LABORATORY CORPORATION OF AMERICA HOLDINGS; *U.S. Public,* pg. 1285
LABWIRE, INC.; *U.S. Public,* pg. 1287
THE LACKEY GROUP; *U.S. Private,* pg. 4067
LADBROKES CORAL GROUP LIMITED—See Entain PLC; *Int'l,* pg. 2450
LADDER CAPITAL FINANCE HOLDINGS LLLP—See Ladder Capital Corp.; *U.S. Public,* pg. 1288
LADENBURG THALMANN ANNUITY INSURANCE SER-

CORPORATE AFFILIATIONS

VICES, LLC—See Reverence Capital Partners LLC; *U.S. Private,* pg. 3414
LADENBURG THALMANN FINANCIAL SERVICES INC.—See Reverence Capital Partners LLC; *U.S. Private,* pg. 3414
LAFARGE AFRICA PLC.—See Holcim Ltd.; *Int'l,* pg. 3448
LAFARGEHOLCIM BANGLADESH LIMITED—See Cementos Molins S.A.; *Int'l,* pg. 1398
LAFARGEHOLCIM BANGLADESH LIMITED—See Holcim Ltd.; *Int'l,* pg. 3449
LAFARGE MAROC HOLDING—See Holcim Ltd.; *Int'l,* pg. 3448
LAFARGE NORTH AMERICA INC.—See Holcim Ltd.; *Int'l,* pg. 3449
LAFARGE SOUTH AFRICA HOLDINGS (PTY) LTD.—See Holcim Ltd.; *Int'l,* pg. 3448
LAIRD LIMITED—See DuPont de Nemours, Inc.; *U.S. Public,* pg. 693
LAKE REGION MEDICAL HOLDINGS, INC—See Integer Holdings Corporation; *U.S. Public,* pg. 1135
LAMB WESTON HOLDINGS, INC.; *U.S. Public,* pg. 1291
LAM RESEARCH INTERNATIONAL HOLDING COMPANY—See Lam Research Corporation; *U.S. Public,* pg. 1290
LANCASTER COLONY CORPORATION; *U.S. Public,* pg. 1291
LANCASTER PLC—See Lithia Motors, Inc.; *U.S. Public,* pg. 1323
LANDRY'S, INC.—See Fertitta Entertainment, Inc.; *U.S. Private,* pg. 1499
LANDS' END, INC.; *U.S. Public,* pg. 1292
LANDS END MARINA HOLDING COMPANY, INC.; *U.S. Private,* pg. 2387
LANDSTAR SYSTEM HOLDINGS, INC.—See Landstar System, Inc.; *U.S. Public,* pg. 1292
LANDSTAR SYSTEM, INC.; *U.S. Public,* pg. 1292
LANNETT HOLDINGS, INC.—See Lannett Company, Inc.; *U.S. Public,* pg. 1293
LANS HOLDINGS, INC.; *U.S. Public,* pg. 1293
LANTHEUS HOLDINGS, INC.—See Avista Capital Partners, L.P.; *U.S. Private,* pg. 408
LANVIN GROUP HOLDINGS LIMITED—See Fosun International Limited; *Int'l,* pg. 2751
LANYON, INC.—See Blackstone Inc.; *U.S. Public,* pg. 353
LA ROSA HOLDINGS CORP.; *U.S. Private,* pg. 2369
LARRY H. MILLER GROUP OF COMPANIES; *U.S. Private,* pg. 2392
LARRY H. MILLER SPORTS & ENTERTAINMENT GROUP OF COMPANIES—See Larry H. Miller Group of Companies; *U.S. Private,* pg. 2393
LARSON FINANCIAL HOLDINGS, LLC; *U.S. Private,* pg. 2394
LASERCARD CORPORATION—See ASSA ABLOY AB; *Int'l,* pg. 637
LATHAM GROUP, INC.; *U.S. Public,* pg. 1294
LATIN UNUM AMERICA HOLDINGS—See Unum Group; *U.S. Public,* pg. 2263
LAURA ASHLEY CER COUNTRIES BV—See Gordon Brothers Group, LLC; *U.S. Private,* pg. 1742
LAURA ASHLEY HOLDINGS PLC—See Gordon Brothers Group, LLC; *U.S. Private,* pg. 1742
LAYNE CHRISTENSEN COMPANY—See Granite Construction Incorporated; *U.S. Public,* pg. 957
L B INDUSTRIES, INC.; *U.S. Private,* pg. 2361
L.B.O. HOLDING, INC.—See Vail Resorts, Inc.; *U.S. Public,* pg. 2271
LCI INDUSTRIES; *U.S. Public,* pg. 1295
LD&D AUSTRALIA PTY. LTD.—See Bega Cheese Ltd.; *Int'l,* pg. 940
LDI LTD., LLC; *U.S. Private,* pg. 2404
LEACHGARNER—See Berkshire Hathaway Inc.; *U.S. Public,* pg. 316
LEAR CORPORATION BETEILIGUNGS GMBH—See Lear Corporation; *U.S. Public,* pg. 1297
LEARNING ANNEX HOLDINGS, LLC; *U.S. Private,* pg. 2408
LECHASE CONSTRUCTION SERVICES, LLC; *U.S. Private,* pg. 2409
LEEDS WELD & CO.; *U.S. Private,* pg. 2415
LEE ENTERPRISES, INCORPORATED; *U.S. Public,* pg. 1298
LEE METAL GROUP LTD.—See BRC Asia Limited; *Int'l,* pg. 1143
LEGACY VIVINT SMART HOME, INC.—See NRG Energy, Inc.; *U.S. Public,* pg. 1551
LEHMAN BROTHERS HOLDINGS INC. PLAN TRUST; *U.S. Private,* pg. 2419
LEHMAN BROTHERS HOLDINGS PLC—See Lehman Brothers Holdings Inc. Plan Trust; *U.S. Private,* pg. 2419
LEISURE HOTEL CORPORATION; *U.S. Private,* pg. 2420
LEISURE HOTEL LLC—See Leisure Hotel Corporation; *U.S. Private,* pg. 2420
LEISURE RE ADVISORS LLC—See Leisure Hotel Corporation; *U.S. Private,* pg. 2420
LEMIEUX GROUP L.P.; *U.S. Private,* pg. 2421
LEMONADE, INC.; *U.S. Public,* pg. 1305
LEONG HUP HOLDINGS BERHAD—See Emerging Glory Sdn Bhd; *Int'l,* pg. 2379

LEPERCQ, DE NEUFLIZE & CO. INC; *U.S. Private*, pg. 2431
LESAFFRE INTERNATIONAL CORP.—See Compagnie des Levures Lesaffre SA; *Int'l*, pg. 1739
LESJOFORS AB—See Beijer Alma AB; *Int'l*, pg. 943
LES SCHWAB HOLDING COMPANY—See Les Schwab Tire Centers of Oregon, Inc.; *U.S. Private*, pg. 2432
LETTS INDUSTRIES, INC.; *U.S. Private*, pg. 2433
LEUCADIA LLC—See Jefferies Financial Group Inc.; *U.S. Public*, pg. 1189
LEVEL 3 PARENT, LLC—See Lumen Technologies, Inc.; *U.S. Public*, pg. 1347
LEVEL EQUITY MANAGEMENT, LLC; *U.S. Private*, pg. 2434
L.E.W. HOLDING CO. INC; *U.S. Private*, pg. 2365
LEWIS ONE PLAZA CENTER CORPORATION; *U.S. Private*, pg. 2439
LEWIS TRANSPORTATION SYSTEMS; *U.S. Private*, pg. 2439
LEXA INTERNATIONAL CORPORATION; *U.S. Private*, pg. 2440
LEXICON, INC.; *U.S. Private*, pg. 2440
LF GEORGE HOLDINGS, INC.; *U.S. Private*, pg. 2441
LGA HOLDINGS, INC.; *U.S. Public*, pg. 1309
THE LGL GROUP, INC.; *U.S. Public*, pg. 2109
LH TRADING (HOLDING) AG—See Holcim Ltd.; *Int'l*, pg. 3448
LIBERATOR MEDICAL HOLDINGS, INC.—See Becton, Dickinson & Company; *U.S. Public*, pg. 291
LIBERTY ENERGY INC.; *U.S. Public*, pg. 1311
LIBERTY EXPEDIA HOLDINGS, INC.—See Expedia Group, Inc.; *U.S. Public*, pg. 809
LIBERTY GROUP LIMITED—See Abengoa S.A.; *Int'l*, pg. 59
LIBERTY GROUP LIMITED—See Algonquin Power & Utilities Corp.; *Int'l*, pg. 319
LIBERTY INTERACTIVE LLC—See Qurate Retail, Inc.; *U.S. Public*, pg. 1758
LIBERTY MEDIA CORPORATION; *U.S. Public*, pg. 1311
LIBERTY MUTUAL GROUP INC.—See Liberty Mutual Holding Company Inc.; *U.S. Private*, pg. 2445
LIBERTY MUTUAL HOLDING COMPANY INC.; *U.S. Private*, pg. 2445
LIBERTY PARTNERS, L.P.; *U.S. Private*, pg. 2446
LIBERTY SYSTEMS, INC.; *U.S. Private*, pg. 2447
LIBERTY TELECOMS HOLDINGS, INC.—See Globe Telecom, Inc.; *Int'l*, pg. 3006
LIFEPOINT HEALTH, INC.—See Apollo Global Management, Inc.; *U.S. Public*, pg. 154
LIFE SCIENCES HOLDINGS FRANCE SAS—See Danaher Corporation; *U.S. Public*, pg. 628
LIFE SCIENCES INTERNATIONAL HOLDINGS BV—See Thermo Fisher Scientific Inc.; *U.S. Public*, pg. 2148
LIFE & SPECIALTY VENTURES, LLC—See USAble Corporation; *U.S. Private*, pg. 4322
LIFESTANCE HEALTH GROUP, INC.; *U.S. Public*, pg. 1313
LIFE TIME FITNESS, INC.—See Leonard Green & Partners, L.P.; *U.S. Private*, pg. 2426
LIFE TIME FITNESS, INC.—See TPG Capital, L.P.; *U.S. Public*, pg. 2174
LIFE TIME GROUP HOLDINGS, INC.; *U.S. Public*, pg. 1312
THE LIFETIME HEALTHCARE COMPANIES; *U.S. Private*, pg. 4069
LIFFE (HOLDINGS) LTD.—See Intercontinental Exchange, Inc.; *U.S. Public*, pg. 1143
LIGHTBAY MANAGEMENT, LLC; *U.S. Private*, pg. 2452
LIGHTHOUSE HOLDINGS, INC.—See Pharos Capital Group, LLC; *U.S. Private*, pg. 3166
LIGHTHOUSE HOLDINGS, INC.—See TPG Capital, L.P.; *U.S. Public*, pg. 2174
THE LIGHTSTONE GROUP, LLC; *U.S. Private*, pg. 4070
LILLY HOLDINGS, LLC—See Eli Lilly & Company; *U.S. Public*, pg. 733
LILLY PHARMA HOLDING GMBH—See Eli Lilly & Company; *U.S. Public*, pg. 733
LIME ROCK MANAGEMENT, L.P.—See Lime Rock Partners, LLC; *U.S. Private*, pg. 2456
LIMNES BOTTLING ACQUISITION CO.; *U.S. Private*, pg. 2456
LINCOLN HOLDINGS LLC; *U.S. Private*, pg. 2457
LINDBLAD EXPEDITIONS HOLDINGS, INC.; *U.S. Public*, pg. 1319
LINEAGE LOGISTICS HOLDINGS LLC—See Bay Grove Capital LLC; *U.S. Private*, pg. 492
LINESTAR INTEGRITY SERVICES LLC—See First Reserve Management, L.P.; *U.S. Private*, pg. 1526
THE LINN CONTRACTING COMPANIES INC.; *U.S. Private*, pg. 4070
LINN ENERGY HOLDINGS, LLC—See Citizen Energy Operating LLC; *U.S. Private*, pg. 902
LINN ENERGY, INC.—See Citizen Energy Operating LLC; *U.S. Private*, pg. 902
LINPAC GROUP LIMITED—See Strategic Value Partners, LLC; *U.S. Private*, pg. 3836
LINTHICUM CORPORATION; *U.S. Private*, pg. 2463
LINTON PARK PLC—See Camellia Plc; *Int'l*, pg. 1271
LION COPOLYMER HOLDINGS, LLC; *U.S. Private*, pg. 2463
LIPMAN & LIPMAN, INC.; *U.S. Private*, pg. 2464

LIQUIDITY SERVICES, INC.; *U.S. Public*, pg. 1320
LISTA HOLDING AG—See GreatStar Group Co., Ltd.; *Int'l*, pg. 3068
LITHIA MOTORS, INC.; *U.S. Public*, pg. 1321
LITTELFUSE MEXICO HOLDING LLC—See Littelfuse, Inc.; *U.S. Public*, pg. 1327
LITTLE ROCK HMA, INC.—See Community Health Systems, Inc.; *U.S. Public*, pg. 554
LITTLE SHEEP GROUP LIMITED—See Yum China Holdings, Inc.; *U.S. Public*, pg. 2399
LIVEIT INVESTMENTS, INC.—See Ayala Corporation; *Int'l*, pg. 774
LIVE NATION ENTERTAINMENT, INC.; *U.S. Public*, pg. 1327
LIVEONE, INC.; *U.S. Public*, pg. 1332
LIVEOPS, INC.; *U.S. Private*, pg. 2473
LIVETILES LIMITED; *U.S. Public*, pg. 2473
LJUNGBERG GRUPPEN HOLDING AB—See Atrium Ljungberg AB; *Int'l*, pg. 694
LMC EAST VILLAGE I HOLDINGS, LLC—See Lennar Corporation; *U.S. Public*, pg. 1306
LMHC MASSACHUSETTS HOLDINGS INC.—See Liberty Mutual Holding Company Inc.; *U.S. Private*, pg. 2445
LM LAND HOLDINGS, LP—See Forestar Group Inc.; *U.S. Public*, pg. 867
LMNEXT UK LTD.—See Bravofly Rumbo Group N.V.; *Int'l*, pg. 1142
LMP AUTOMOTIVE HOLDINGS, INC.; *U.S. Public*, pg. 1337
LNI VERKKO HOLDING OY—See 3i Group plc; *Int'l*, pg. 9
LNI VERKKO HOLDING OY—See The Goldman Sachs Group, Inc.; *U.S. Public*, pg. 2080
LOANDEPOT, INC.; *U.S. Public*, pg. 1337
LOCKER GROUP HOLDINGS PTY. LTD.—See Valmont Industries, Inc.; *U.S. Public*, pg. 2273
LOCKHEED MARTIN GLOBAL, INC.—See Lockheed Martin Corporation; *U.S. Public*, pg. 1338
LOCKTON COMPANIES LLP—See The Lockton Companies, LLC; *U.S. Private*, pg. 4071
LOCKTON OVERSEAS LTD.—See The Lockton Companies, LLC; *U.S. Private*, pg. 4071
LOEHMANN'S HOLDINGS INC.—See Dubai World Corporation; *Int'l*, pg. 2222
LOEWS CORPORATION; *U.S. Public*, pg. 1339
LOGISTAR INTERNATIONAL HOLDING COMPANY LIMITED—See Cal-Comp Electronics (Thailand) pcl; *Int'l*, pg. 1261
LOGITECH ASIA PACIFIC LIMITED—See Logitech International S.A.; *U.S. Public*, pg. 1341
LOGITECH EUROPE SA—See Logitech International S.A.; *U.S. Public*, pg. 1341
LOGOPLASTE INVESTIMENTO, S.G.P.S., S.A.—See The Carlyle Group Inc.; *U.S. Public*, pg. 2048
LOJAS AMERICANAS S.A.—See Americanas S.A.; *Int'l*, pg. 423
LOKEY MOTOR COMPANY; *U.S. Private*, pg. 2482
LONDON BROADCASTING COMPANY, INC.—See SunTx Capital Partners, L.P.; *U.S. Private*, pg. 3874
LONDON CLUBS MANAGEMENT LIMITED—See Caesars Entertainment, Inc.; *U.S. Public*, pg. 420
LONDON CLUBS (OVERSEAS) LIMITED—See Caesars Entertainment, Inc.; *U.S. Public*, pg. 420
THE LONG & FOSTER COMPANIES, INC.; *U.S. Private*, pg. 4072
LONGHOUSE HOSPITALITY—See J.E. Robert Company; *U.S. Private*, pg. 2162
LONGKLOOF LTD.—See E Media Holdings Limited; *Int'l*, pg. 2246
LONGWOOD INDUSTRIES HOLDINGS, LLC; *U.S. Private*, pg. 2499
THE LOS ANGELES RAMS, LLC; *U.S. Private*, pg. 4072
LOSINGER HOLDING AG—See Bouygues S.A.; *Int'l*, pg. 1122
LOTS INTERMEDIATE CO.—See Tiptree Inc.; *U.S. Public*, pg. 2159
LOUISIANA MEDIA COMPANY, LLC; *U.S. Private*, pg. 2499
LOUNORA INDUSTRIES INC.; *U.S. Private*, pg. 2500
LOVE REAL ESTATE COMPANY; *U.S. Private*, pg. 2501
LOWE ENTERPRISES, INC.; *U.S. Private*, pg. 2504
LOWE'S COMPANIES, INC.; *U.S. Public*, pg. 1343
LOZINAK PROFESSIONAL BASEBALL LLC; *U.S. Private*, pg. 2506
LPL FINANCIAL HOLDINGS INC.; *U.S. Public*, pg. 1343
L&P SWISS HOLDING GMBH—See Leggett & Platt, Incorporated; *U.S. Public*, pg. 1302
LPX, INC.; *U.S. Public*, pg. 2507
LRI HOLDINGS, INC.—See Kelso & Company, L.P.; *U.S. Private*, pg. 2278
LSB INDUSTRIES, INC.; *U.S. Public*, pg. 1344
LSC COMMUNICATIONS LLC—See Atlas Holdings, LLC; *U.S. Private*, pg. 376
LSG LUFTHANSA SERVICE EUROPA/AFRIKA GMBH—See Deutsche Lufthansa AG; *Int'l*, pg. 2067
LSG LUFTHANSA SERVICE HOLDING AG—See Deutsche Lufthansa AG; *Int'l*, pg. 2066
LSG/SKY CHEFS EUROPE HOLDINGS LTD.—See Deutsche Lufthansa AG; *Int'l*, pg. 2068
LSG SKY CHEFS NORTH AMERICA SOLUTIONS, INC.—See Deutsche Lufthansa AG; *Int'l*, pg. 2067
LSG SKY CHEFS (THAILAND) LTD.—See Deutsche Lufthansa AG; *Int'l*, pg. 2067
LS POWER DEVELOPMENT, LLC; *U.S. Private*, pg. 2508
LTP MANAGEMENT GROUP, INC.; *U.S. Private*, pg. 2510
LT TRUST COMPANY; *U.S. Private*, pg. 2509
LUBY'S HOLDINGS, INC.—See Luby's, Inc.; *U.S. Public*, pg. 1345
LUCID GROUP, INC.; *U.S. Public*, pg. 1345
LUCKY BUCKS LLC—See Trive Capital Inc.; *U.S. Private*, pg. 4240
LUFTHANSA COMMERCIAL HOLDING GMBH—See Deutsche Lufthansa AG; *Int'l*, pg. 2069
LULU'S FASHION LOUNGE HOLDINGS, INC.; *U.S. Public*, pg. 1345
LUMASENSE TECHNOLOGIES EUROPE GMBH—See Advanced Energy Industries, Inc.; *U.S. Public*, pg. 47
LUMATA HOLDINGS LIMITED—See Francisco Partners Management, LP; *U.S. Private*, pg. 1590
LUMINOR FINANCIAL HOLDINGS LIMITED—See GRP Limited; *Int'l*, pg. 3113
LUSE HOLDINGS, INC.; *U.S. Private*, pg. 2516
LUZ SAUDE, S.A.—See Fosun International Limited; *Int'l*, pg. 2751
LYON & DITTRICH HOLDING COMPANY; *U.S. Private*, pg. 2522
MAB DEVELOPMENT GROUP B.V.—See Cooperatieve Centrale Raiffeisen-Boerenleenbank B.A.; *Int'l*, pg. 1791
MACANDREWS & FORBES INCORPORATED; *U.S. Private*, pg. 2531
MACARI-HEALEY PUBLISHING COMPANY, LLC; *U.S. Private*, pg. 2534
MACDERMID GROUP, INC.—See Element Solutions Inc.; *U.S. Public*, pg. 726
MACDERMID UK LTD—See Element Solutions Inc.; *U.S. Public*, pg. 727
MACH7 TECHNOLOGIES LIMITED; *U.S. Public*, pg. 1352
MACHTEN, INC.; *U.S. Public*, pg. 1352
MACKLOWE MANAGEMENT CO., INC.—See Macklowe Properties, L.L.C.; *U.S. Private*, pg. 2537
MACLEAN-FOGG COMPANY; *U.S. Private*, pg. 2537
MACLEAN-FOGG COMPONENT SOLUTIONS, LLC—See MacLean-Fogg Company; *U.S. Private*, pg. 2537
MACLEAN INVESTMENT PARTNERS, LLC—See MacLean-Fogg Company; *U.S. Private*, pg. 2537
MACOM TECHNOLOGY SOLUTIONS HOLDINGS, INC.; *U.S. Public*, pg. 1352
MADEWELL GROUP, INC.; *U.S. Private*, pg. 2539
MADISON AVENUE HOLDINGS, INC.; *U.S. Private*, pg. 2539
MADISON MARQUETTE DEVELOPMENT CORPORATION; *U.S. Private*, pg. 2544
MADISON ONE HOLDINGS; *U.S. Private*, pg. 2544
MADISON RIVER HOLDINGS LLC—See Lumen Technologies, Inc.; *U.S. Public*, pg. 1347
MADISON SQUARE GARDEN ENTERTAINMENT CORP.; *U.S. Public*, pg. 1353
MADISON SQUARE GARDEN SPORTS CORP.; *U.S. Public*, pg. 1353
MADISON TECHNOLOGIES INC.; *U.S. Public*, pg. 1354
MAERSK BENELUX B.V.—See A.P. Moller-Maersk A/S; *Int'l*, pg. 26
MAERSK LINE AGENCY HOLDING A/S—See A.P. Moller-Maersk A/S; *Int'l*, pg. 27
MAGANG (GROUP) HOLDING COMPANY LIMITED—See China Baowu Steel Group Corp., Ltd.; *Int'l*, pg. 1486
MAG IAS HOLDINGS, INC.; *U.S. Private*, pg. 2545
MAGNITUDE SOFTWARE, INC.—See TA Associates, Inc.; *U.S. Private*, pg. 3915
MAGYARCOM HOLDING GMBH—See Deutsche Telekom AG; *Int'l*, pg. 2083
MAHWAH BERGEN RETAIL GROUP, INC.; *U.S. Private*, pg. 2550
MAIDEN REINSURANCE NORTH AMERICA, INC.—See Enstar Group Limited; *Int'l*, pg. 2449
MAINSTREAM ENERGY CORPORATION; *U.S. Private*, pg. 2553
MAINSTREAM GROUP HOLDINGS LIMITED—See Apex Fund Services Holdings Ltd.; *Int'l*, pg. 510
THE MAIN STREET AMERICA GROUP—See American Family Mutual Insurance Company; *U.S. Private*, pg. 233
MAINSTREET INVESTMENT COMPANY, LLC; *U.S. Private*, pg. 2554
MAIN STREET REAL ESTATE HOLDINGS, LLC—See Waterstone Financial, Inc.; *U.S. Private*, pg. 2336
MAJESTIC STAR CASINO & HOTEL; *U.S. Private*, pg. 2554
MAJOR LEAGUE BASEBALL PROPERTIES, INC.—See Major League Baseball; *U.S. Private*, pg. 2555
MAKKE LLC; *U.S. Private*, pg. 2556
MAMMOTH RESORTS LLC—See KSL Capital Partners, LLC; *U.S. Private*, pg. 2354
MANAGEMENT PARTNERS, INC.; *U.S. Private*, pg. 2560
MANCHESTER MARKETING, INC.; *U.S. Private*, pg. 2562
MANDALAY BASEBALL PROPERTIES, LLC—See Mandalay Entertainment Group; *U.S. Private*, pg. 2562
MANDALAY BASEBALL PROPERTIES, LLC—See Seaport Capital, LLC; *U.S. Private*, pg. 3586

551112 — OFFICES OF OTHER HO...

MANDALAY ENTERTAINMENT GROUP; *U.S. Private*, pg. 2562
MANDALAY SPORTS ENTERTAINMENT LLC—See Mandalay Entertainment Group; *U.S. Private*, pg. 2562
MANGINO HOLDING CORP.; *U.S. Private*, pg. 2563
THE MANHATTAN INSURANCE GROUP; *U.S. Private*, pg. 4074
MANIFOLD CAPITAL CORP.; *U.S. Private*, pg. 2564
THE MANITOWOC COMPANY, INC.; *U.S. Public*, pg. 2111
MANITOWOC CRANE COMPANIES, INC.—See The Manitowoc Company, Inc.; *U.S. Public*, pg. 2111
MANITOWOC FOODSERVICE COMPANIES, LLC—See Ali Holding S.r.l; *Int'l*, pg. 322
MANNHEIM HOLDINGS, LLC—See Mannheim, LLC; *U.S. Private*, pg. 2565
MANN+HUMMEL VOKES AIR TREATMENT HOLDINGS LIMITED—See SPX Technologies, Inc.; *U.S. Public*, pg. 1921
MANPOWERGROUP HOLDING GMBH—See ManpowerGroup Inc.; *U.S. Public*, pg. 1360
MANPOWER HOLDING CORP.; *U.S. Private*, pg. 2566
MANSFIELD ENERGY CORP.; *U.S. Private*, pg. 2566
MANTIS INNOVATION GROUP, LLC—See O2 Investment Partners, LLC; *U.S. Private*, pg. 2982
MANTRA GROUP LIMITED—See Accor S.A.; *Int'l*, pg. 91
MAPLE LEAF SPORTS & ENTERTAINMENT LTD.—See BCE Inc.; *Int'l*, pg. 927
MAPLETON COMMUNICATIONS, LLC; *U.S. Private*, pg. 2568
MAQUIA CAPITAL ACQUISITION CORPORATION; *U.S. Public*, pg. 1363
MARATHON AUTOMOTIVE GROUP LLC—See Marathon Asset Management LP; *U.S. Private*, pg. 2570
MARATHON OIL CORPORATION—See ConocoPhillips; *U.S. Public*, pg. 568
MARATHON OIL HOLDINGS U.K. LIMITED—See ConocoPhillips; *U.S. Public*, pg. 569
MARAVAI LIFESCIENCES HOLDINGS, INC.; *U.S. Public*, pg. 1364
MARBULK CANADA INC.—See Algoma Central Corporation; *Int'l*, pg. 318
MARCOU TRANSPORTATION GROUP LLC; *U.S. Private*, pg. 2572
MARCUS & MILLICHAP, INC.; *U.S. Public*, pg. 1365
MARDECK LIMITED; *U.S. Private*, pg. 2573
MARELLI HOLDINGS CO., LTD.—See KKR & Co. Inc.; *U.S. Public*, pg. 1260
MARIE CALLENDER'S, INC.; *U.S. Private*, pg. 2574
MARIMED INC.; *U.S. Public*, pg. 1365
MARINA DISTRICT DEVELOPMENT HOLDING CO., LLC—See MGM Resorts International; *U.S. Public*, pg. 1435
MARINA INVESTMENT MANAGEMENT INC.; *U.S. Private*, pg. 2574
MARINER WEALTH ADVISORS, LLC; *U.S. Private*, pg. 2575
MAR-JAC HOLDINGS INC.; *U.S. Private*, pg. 2569
MARKEL GROUP INC.; *U.S. Public*, pg. 1367
MARKEL INTERNATIONAL LIMITED—See Markel Group Inc.; *U.S. Public*, pg. 1368
MARKEM-IMAJE HOLDING—See Dover Corporation; *U.S. Public*, pg. 682
MARKETAXESS HOLDINGS INC.; *U.S. Public*, pg. 1369
MARKET LEADER, INC.—See Constellation Software Inc.; *Int'l*, pg. 1772
MARKTKAUF HOLDING GMBH—See EDEKA Zentrale AG & Co. KG; *Int'l*, pg. 2305
THE MARMON GROUP LLC—See Berkshire Hathaway Inc.; *U.S. Public*, pg. 308
MARMON HOLDINGS, INC.—See Berkshire Hathaway Inc.; *U.S. Public*, pg. 308
MARNELL SHER GAMING LLC—See Marnell Corrao Associates, Inc.; *U.S. Private*, pg. 2586
MARRIOTT VACATIONS WORLDWIDE CORPORATION; *U.S. Public*, pg. 1373
MARSDEN HOLDING, L.L.C.; *U.S. Private*, pg. 2591
MARSHALL & STERLING ENTERPRISES, INC.; *U.S. Private*, pg. 2592
MARSH HOLDING AB—See Marsh & McLennan Companies, Inc.; *U.S. Public*, pg. 1378
MARSH & MCLENNAN COMPANIES, INC.; *U.S. Public*, pg. 1374
MARSH MERCER HOLDINGS (AUSTRALIA) PTY LTD—See Marsh & McLennan Companies, Inc.; *U.S. Public*, pg. 1383
MARTIN FLETCHER ASSOCIATES HOLDINGS, INC.—See HCA Healthcare, Inc.; *U.S. Public*, pg. 1001
MARUZEN CHI HOLDINGS CO., LTD.—See Dai Nippon Printing Co., Ltd.; *Int'l*, pg. 1915
MARVEL ENTERTAINMENT INTERNATIONAL LIMITED—See The Walt Disney Company; *U.S. Public*, pg. 2139
MARY KAY HOLDING CORPORATION; *U.S. Private*, pg. 2598
MASCHHOFF FAMILY FOODS, LLC; *U.S. Private*, pg. 2600
THE MASCHHOFFS, LLC—See Maschhoff Family Foods, LLC; *U.S. Private*, pg. 2601
MASCO CORPORATION OF INDIANA—See Masco Corporation; *U.S. Public*, pg. 1391
MASCO EUROPE S.A.R.L.—See Masco Corporation; *U.S. Public*, pg. 1391
MASCO GERMANY HOLDING GMBH—See Masco Corporation; *U.S. Public*, pg. 1391
MASONITE CHILE HOLDINGS—See Owens Corning; *U.S. Public*, pg. 1627
MASONITE INTERNATIONAL CORPORATION—See Owens Corning; *U.S. Public*, pg. 1626
MASTERBRAND, INC.; *U.S. Public*, pg. 1394
MASTERCARD INCORPORATED; *U.S. Public*, pg. 1394
MASTERCRAFT BOAT HOLDINGS, INC.; *U.S. Public*, pg. 1394
THE MATCO GROUP, INC.; *U.S. Private*, pg. 4075
MATEC INSTRUMENT COMPANIES, INC.; *U.S. Private*, pg. 2609
MATERION CORPORATION; *U.S. Public*, pg. 1395
MATERION HOLDINGS LIMITED—See Materion Corporation; *U.S. Public*, pg. 1395
MATSON ALASKA, INC.—See Matson, Inc.; *U.S. Public*, pg. 1398
MATSON, INC.; *U.S. Public*, pg. 1397
MATTEL EUROPE HOLDINGS B.V.—See Mattel, Inc.; *U.S. Public*, pg. 1398
MATTEL FOREIGN HOLDINGS, LTD.—See Mattel, Inc.; *U.S. Public*, pg. 1398
MATTEL OVERSEAS, INC.—See Mattel, Inc.; *U.S. Public*, pg. 1399
MATTHEWSDANIEL LIMITED—See Bureau Veritas S.A.; *Int'l*, pg. 1222
MATTHEWS EUROPE GMBH—See Matthews International Corporation; *U.S. Public*, pg. 1399
MATTHEWS INTERNATIONAL GMBH—See Matthews International Corporation; *U.S. Public*, pg. 1400
MAUSER GROUP N.V.—See Stone Canyon Industries, LLC; *U.S. Private*, pg. 3817
MAXEDA B.V.—See KKR & Co. Inc.; *U.S. Public*, pg. 1261
MAXS OF SAN FRANCISCO INC.; *U.S. Private*, pg. 2619
MAXWELL TECHNOLOGIES, INC.—See Tesla, Inc.; *U.S. Public*, pg. 2021
MAXXAM, INC.; *U.S. Private*, pg. 2620
MAYOR'S JEWELERS, INC.—See Apollo Global Management, Inc.; *U.S. Public*, pg. 167
MBAC BRAZIL HOLDINGS B.V.—See Itafos Inc.; *U.S. Public*, pg. 1175
MB AEROSPACE HOLDINGS INC.—See Barnes Group Inc.; *U.S. Public*, pg. 277
M&B CORPORATION; *U.S. Private*, pg. 2524
MBDA HOLDINGS S.A.S.—See Airbus SE; *Int'l*, pg. 247
MBDA HOLDINGS S.A.S—See BAE Systems plc; *Int'l*, pg. 798
MB HOLDING GMBH—See BayernLB Holding AG; *Int'l*, pg. 914
MB INVESTMENTS, INC.; *U.S. Private*, pg. 2623
MB TECHNOLOGY HOLDINGS, LLC; *U.S. Private*, pg. 2624
M-B-W INC.; *U.S. Private*, pg. 2525
MCA COMMUNICATIONS, LLC; *U.S. Private*, pg. 2625
MCCANN WORLDGROUP, LLC—See The Interpublic Group of Companies, Inc.; *U.S. Public*, pg. 2097
MCCARTHY HOLDINGS, INC.; *U.S. Private*, pg. 2627
MCC MAGAZINES, LLC—See Shivers Trading & Operating Company; *U.S. Private*, pg. 3638
MCCOLLISTER'S TRANSPORTATION GROUP INC.; *U.S. Private*, pg. 2629
MCCOMBIE GROUP, LLC; *U.S. Private*, pg. 2629
MCCORMICK EUROPE LTD.—See McCormick & Company, Incorporated; *U.S. Public*, pg. 1404
MCCORMICK INTERNATIONAL HOLDINGS LTD.—See McCormick & Company, Incorporated; *U.S. Public*, pg. 1404
MCDONALD'S HOLDINGS CO. (JAPAN), LTD.—See McDonald's Corporation; *U.S. Public*, pg. 1406
MC EKONIVA-APK HOLDING—See Ekosem-Agrar GmbH; *Int'l*, pg. 2339
MCI, LC; *U.S. Private*, pg. 2636
THE MCKENZIE RIVER CORPORATION; *U.S. Private*, pg. 4077
MCKINLEY GROUP, INC.; *U.S. Private*, pg. 2639
MCLAREN HEALTH CARE CORPORATION; *U.S. Private*, pg. 2640
MCLARTY CAPITAL PARTNERS UK LLP; *U.S. Private*, pg. 2640
MCNEEL INTERNATIONAL CORPORATION; *U.S. Private*, pg. 2643
MCVEIGH GLOBAL MEETINGS & EVENTS, LLC—See InteleTravel.com; *U.S. Private*, pg. 2104
MDB CAPITAL HOLDINGS, LLC; *U.S. Public*, pg. 1409
MDU CONSTRUCTION SERVICES GROUP, INC.—See MDU Resources Group, Inc.; *U.S. Public*, pg. 1410
MDU RESOURCES GROUP, INC.; *U.S. Public*, pg. 1409
MEADOWBROOK INSURANCE GROUP, INC.—See Fosun International Limited; *Int'l*, pg. 2751
MECALUX, S.A.—See Acerolux SL; *Int'l*, pg. 101
MECHANICAL REPS INC.; *U.S. Private*, pg. 2649
MECHEL BLUESTONE INC.; *U.S. Private*, pg. 2649
MEDCO HEALTH SOLUTIONS, INC.—See The Cigna Group; *U.S. Public*, pg. 2061

CORPORATE AFFILIATIONS

MEDIAALPHA, INC.; *U.S. Public*, pg. 1411
MEDIACO HOLDING INC.; *U.S. Public*, pg. 1411
THE MEDIA GLOBO CORPORATION; *U.S. Public*, pg. 2113
MEDIA PAL HOLDINGS, CORP.; *U.S. Public*, pg. 1411
MEDIAWORKS HOLDINGS LIMITED—See Brookfield Corporation; *Int'l*, pg. 1181
MEDICA HEALTH PLANS OF FLORIDA, INC.—See UnitedHealth Group Incorporated; *U.S. Public*, pg. 2251
MEDICAL CARD SYSTEM, INC.—See JLL Partners, LLC; *U.S. Private*, pg. 2212
MEDICAN ENTERPRISES, INC.; *U.S. Public*, pg. 1412
MEDICIS PHARMACEUTICAL CORPORATION—See Bausch Health Companies Inc.; *Int'l*, pg. 898
MEDICONSTANT HOLDING SDN. BHD.—See Bioalpha Holdings Berhad; *Int'l*, pg. 1036
MEDIFAST, INC.; *U.S. Public*, pg. 1412
MEDIQ B.V.—See Advent International Corporation; *U.S. Private*, pg. 104
MEDITE EUROPE LTD.—See Coillte Ltd.; *Int'l*, pg. 1696
MEDLEY MANAGEMENT INC.; *U.S. Public*, pg. 1413
MEDOS INTERNATIONAL SARL—See Johnson & Johnson; *U.S. Public*, pg. 1199
MEDTEK DEVICES, INC.—See Madison Industries Holdings LLC; *U.S. Private*, pg. 2543
MED-X, INC.; *U.S. Private*, pg. 2650
MEGA BROADBAND INVESTMENTS, LLC—See GTCR LLC; *U.S. Private*, pg. 1805
MEIRAGTX HOLDINGS PLC; *U.S. Public*, pg. 1414
MELINTA THERAPEUTICS, INC.—See Deerfield Management Company L.P.; *U.S. Private*, pg. 1190
MELITA CAPITAL PLC—See EQT AB; *Int'l*, pg. 2478
MERCHANTS METALS RECYCLING II CD, LLC; *U.S. Private*, pg. 2670
MERCK SHARP & DOHME BV—See Merck & Co., Inc.; *U.S. Public*, pg. 1419
MERCK SHARP & DOHME (HOLDINGS) PTY LTD—See Merck & Co., Inc.; *U.S. Public*, pg. 1419
MERCURI INTERNATIONAL GROUP AB—See Bure Equity AB; *Int'l*, pg. 1221
MERCURIUS GROEP B.V.—See HAL Trust N.V.; *Int'l*, pg. 3224
MEREDITH INTEGRATED MARKETING—See Meredith Corporation; *U.S. Public*, pg. 1423
MEREX HOLDING CORPORATION; *U.S. Private*, pg. 2672
MERIDIAN BIOSCIENCE S.A.—See Meridian Bioscience Inc.; *U.S. Public*, pg. 1424
MERIDIAN GENERAL, LLC; *U.S. Private*, pg. 2672
MERISEL, INC.—See Saints Capital, LLC; *U.S. Public*, pg. 3530
MERITUM ENERGY HOLDINGS, LP; *U.S. Private*, pg. 2675
MERRIMAN HOLDINGS, INC.; *U.S. Private*, pg. 2676
MERRITT MANAGEMENT CORPORATION; *U.S. Private*, pg. 2676
MERSCORP HOLDINGS, INC.—See Intercontinental Exchange, Inc.; *U.S. Public*, pg. 1143
MERUELO CONSTRUCTION—See Meruelo Group LLC; *U.S. Private*, pg. 2677
MERUELO ENTERPRISES, INC.—See Meruelo Group LLC; *U.S. Private*, pg. 2677
MERUELO FOODS, INC.—See Meruelo Group LLC; *U.S. Private*, pg. 2677
MERUELO GROUP LLC; *U.S. Private*, pg. 2677
MERUELO PROPERTIES, INC.—See Meruelo Group LLC; *U.S. Private*, pg. 2677
MESA AIR GROUP, INC.; *U.S. Public*, pg. 1425
MESIROW FINANCIAL HOLDINGS, INC.; *U.S. Private*, pg. 2678
MESQUITE GAMING, LLC; *U.S. Private*, pg. 2679
MESSER INDUSTRIES USA, INC.—See CVC Capital Partners SICAV-FIS S.A.; *Int'l*, pg. 1885
MESTEK, INC.; *U.S. Public*, pg. 1426
METALIS HOLDING SAS—See Aalberts N.V.; *Int'l*, pg. 35
METALLURGICAL CORPORATION OF CHINA LIMITED—See China Rare Earth Resources And Technology Co., Ltd.; *Int'l*, pg. 1545
METAL MANAGEMENT, INC.—See Sims Limited; *U.S. Public*, pg. 1883
METALS USA HOLDINGS CORP.—See Reliance Steel & Aluminum Co.; *U.S. Public*, pg. 1780
META PLATFORMS, INC.; *U.S. Public*, pg. 1426
METHODE ELECTRONICS MALTA HOLDINGS LTD.—See Methode Electronics, Inc.; *U.S. Public*, pg. 1428
METLIFE, INC.; *U.S. Public*, pg. 1429
METLIFE INTERNATIONAL HOLDINGS, LLC—See MetLife, Inc.; *U.S. Public*, pg. 1431
METRO-GOLDWYN-MAYER INC.; *U.S. Private*, pg. 2687
METROMEDIA COMPANY; *U.S. Private*, pg. 2687
METRONET HOLDINGS, LLC—See Keystone Group, L.P.; *U.S. Private*, pg. 2299
METROPOLITAN CORPORATION; *U.S. Private*, pg. 2688
METTLER-TOLEDO HOLDING AG—See Mettler-Toledo International, Inc.; *U.S. Public*, pg. 1432
METTLER-TOLEDO MANAGEMENT HOLDING DEUTSCHLAND GMBH—See Mettler-Toledo International, Inc.; *U.S. Public*, pg. 1433
METTLER-TOLEDO UK HOLDINGS LIMITED—See Mettler-Toledo International, Inc.; *U.S. Public*, pg. 1433
MFG PARTNERS LLC; *U.S. Private*, pg. 2693

N.A.I.C.S. INDEX

MFI HOLDING CORPORATION—See Post Holdings, Inc.; *U.S. Public*, pg. 1703
M FINANCIAL HOLDINGS INCORPORATED; *U.S. Private*, pg. 2523
M & F WORLDWIDE CORP.—See MacAndrews & Forbes Incorporated; *U.S. Private*, pg. 2532
MGM RESORTS INTERNATIONAL; *U.S. Public*, pg. 1435
MGT CAPITAL INVESTMENTS, INC.; *U.S. Public*, pg. 1436
MHG MEDIA HOLDINGS AG—See The Jordan Company, L.P.; *U.S. Private*, pg. 4061
MHHC ENTERPRISES INC; *U.S. Public*, pg. 1436
MICHAEL KORS RETAIL, INC.—See Capri Holdings Limited; *Int'l*, pg. 1316
MICHAEL KORS (USA), INC.—See Capri Holdings Limited; *Int'l*, pg. 1316
MICHAEL O'BRIEN ENTERPRISES, INC.; *U.S. Private*, pg. 2698
THE MICHAELS COMPANIES, INC.—See Apollo Global Management, Inc.; *U.S. Private*, pg. 164
MICHELIN SIAM GROUP CO., LTD.—See Compagnie Generale des Etablissements Michelin SCA; *Int'l*, pg. 1743
MICHIGAN CRYSTAL FLASH PETRO; *U.S. Private*, pg. 2700
MICROSEMI CORPORATION—See Microchip Technology Incorporated; *U.S. Public*, pg. 1436
MICROSOFT EMEA—See Microsoft Corporation; *U.S. Public*, pg. 1439
MICROS RETAIL SERVICES UK LIMITED—See Oracle Corporation; *U.S. Public*, pg. 1612
MIDAMERICAN FUNDING, LLC—See Berkshire Hathaway Inc.; *U.S. Public*, pg. 300
MIDAS OPCO HOLDINGS LLC—See Stagwell, Inc.; *U.S. Public*, pg. 1925
MID ATLANTIC CAPITAL GROUP, INC.; *U.S. Private*, pg. 2705
MID-MISSOURI LIMESTONE, LLC—See Summit Materials, Inc.; *U.S. Public*, pg. 1959
MIDOCEAN PARTNERS, LLP; *U.S. Private*, pg. 2716
MIDWEST COMMUNICATIONS, INC.; *U.S. Private*, pg. 2720
MIDWEST DEVELOPMENT CO. INC.—See Skogman Construction Company of Iowa Inc.; *U.S. Private*, pg. 3683
MIDWEST HOLDING INC.—See Antarctica Capital, LLC; *U.S. Private*, pg. 286
MI EUROPEAN HOLDINGS CV—See Koch Industries, Inc.; *U.S. Private*, pg. 2333
MIGC, LLC—See Western Midstream Partners, LP; *U.S. Public*, pg. 2356
M-I HOLDINGS BV—See Schlumberger Limited; *U.S. Public*, pg. 1844
MIKE CASTRUCCI, LLC; *U.S. Private*, pg. 2725
MILACRON B.V.—See Hillenbrand, Inc.; *U.S. Public*, pg. 1037
MILACRON HOLDINGS CORP.—See Hillenbrand, Inc.; *U.S. Public*, pg. 1037
MILAN LASER INC.; *U.S. Public*, pg. 1446
MILLER ENTERPRISES OF MANATEE, INC.; *U.S. Private*, pg. 2734
THE MILLER GROUP INC.—See Bouygues S.A.; *Int'l*, pg. 1122
MILLER MCASPHALT CORPORATION—See Bouygues S.A.; *Int'l*, pg. 1122
MILLHOUSE GROUP, INC.; *U.S. Private*, pg. 2736
MILLS AUTO GROUP, INC.—See Mills Fleet Farm, Inc.; *U.S. Private*, pg. 2737
MILLS FLEET FARM, INC.; *U.S. Private*, pg. 2737
MILLWRIGHT HOLDINGS LLC; *U.S. Private*, pg. 2738
MINARA RESOURCES HOLDINGS PTY LTD—See Glencore plc; *Int'l*, pg. 2991
MINERALS TECHNOLOGIES HOLDINGS LTD.—See Minerals Technologies, Inc.; *U.S. Public*, pg. 1449
MINILUXE HOLDING CORP.; *U.S. Public*, pg. 1449
MINNESOTA HOCKEY VENTURES GROUP, LP; *U.S. Private*, pg. 2743
MINSAL LIMITED—See Hysan Development Company Limited; *Int'l*, pg. 3554
MINTRA HOLDING AS—See Ferd AS; *Int'l*, pg. 2636
MINVIELLE & CHASTANET INSURANCE BROKERS LIMITED—See Arthur J. Gallagher & Co.; *U.S. Public*, pg. 206
MIRACLE INDUSTRIES, INC—See Icahn Enterprises L.P.; *U.S. Public*, pg. 1084
MIRION TECHNOLOGIES, INC.; *U.S. Public*, pg. 1450
MIRION TECHNOLOGIES (US), INC.—See Mirion Technologies, Inc.; *U.S. Public*, pg. 1450
MISSION BROADCASTING, INC.; *U.S. Private*, pg. 2747
MITCHELL COMPANIES; *U.S. Private*, pg. 2750
MITEK INDUSTRIES, INC.—See Berkshire Hathaway Inc.; *U.S. Public*, pg. 312
MITTERA GROUP, INC.; *U.S. Private*, pg. 2751
MJ BASKETBALL HOLDINGS, LLC; *U.S. Private*, pg. 2752
MJV HOLDINGS, LLC; *U.S. Private*, pg. 2753
MKS GERMAN HOLDING GMBH—See MKS Instruments, Inc.; *U.S. Public*, pg. 1452
MKS GERMANY HOLDING GMBH—See MKS Instruments, Inc.; *U.S. Public*, pg. 1452
M. LEVIN & COMPANY HOLDINGS, INC.; *U.S. Private*, pg. 2527

MMG LIMITED—See China Rare Earth Resources And Technology Co., Ltd.; *Int'l*, pg. 1545
MMI HOLDINGS LIMITED—See KKR & Co. Inc.; *U.S. Public*, pg. 1259
MNO-BMADSEN—See Pokagon Band of Potawatomi Indians; *U.S. Private*, pg. 3223
MODERN GROUP LTD.; *U.S. Private*, pg. 2760
MODERN HOLDINGS INCORPORATED; *U.S. Private*, pg. 2761
MODINE HOLDING GMBH—See Modine Manufacturing Company; *U.S. Public*, pg. 1455
MOELIS ASSET MANAGEMENT LP; *U.S. Private*, pg. 2764
MOELIS & COMPANY; *U.S. Public*, pg. 1456
MOJO BRANDS MEDIA, LLC; *U.S. Private*, pg. 2766
MOLDMAKERS MANAGEMENT INC.—See MGS Manufacturing Group, Inc.; *U.S. Private*, pg. 2695
MOLEX EUROPEAN HOLDINGS BV—See Koch Industries, Inc.; *U.S. Private*, pg. 2334
MOLEX HOLDING GMBH—See Koch Industries, Inc.; *U.S. Private*, pg. 2334
MOLINA HEALTHCARE, INC.; *U.S. Public*, pg. 1458
MOLSON COORS BEVERAGE COMPANY; *U.S. Public*, pg. 1459
MOLSON COORS CENTRAL EUROPE S.R.O.—See Molson Coors Beverage Company; *U.S. Public*, pg. 1459
MOLSON COORS NETHERLANDS BV—See Molson Coors Beverage Company; *U.S. Public*, pg. 1459
MOLSON COORS (UK) HOLDINGS LLP—See Molson Coors Beverage Company; *U.S. Public*, pg. 1459
MONARCH CASINO & RESORT, INC.; *U.S. Public*, pg. 1460
MONARCH SERVICES, INC.; *U.S. Public*, pg. 1460
MONDAIS HOLDINGS B.V.—See Crane NXT, Co.; *U.S. Public*, pg. 591
MONDELEZ AUSTRALIA HOLDINGS PTY. LTD.—See Mondelez International, Inc.; *U.S. Public*, pg. 1462
MONDELEZ INTERNATIONAL, INC.; *U.S. Public*, pg. 1460
MONEYGRAM INTERNATIONAL HOLDINGS LTD.—See Madison Dearborn Partners, LLC; *U.S. Private*, pg. 2541
MONEYGRAM INTERNATIONAL, INC.—See Madison Dearborn Partners, LLC; *U.S. Private*, pg. 2541
MONROE GUARANTY COMPANIES INC.—See FCCI Mutual Insurance Holding Company; *U.S. Private*, pg. 1485
MONSTER BEVERAGE CORPORATION; *U.S. Public*, pg. 1465
MONSTER, INC.—See Monster Products, Inc.; *U.S. Private*, pg. 2774
MONSTER PRODUCTS, INC.; *U.S. Private*, pg. 2774
MONUMENT & CATHEDRAL HOLDINGS, LLC; *U.S. Private*, pg. 2777
MONUMENT CHEMICALS, INC.—See Heritage Group; *U.S. Private*, pg. 1923
MOODY'S ASIA PACIFIC LTD.—See Moody's Corporation; *U.S. Public*, pg. 1468
MOODY'S CORPORATION; *U.S. Public*, pg. 1466
MOONEY AEROSPACE GROUP, LTD.; *U.S. Private*, pg. 2779
MOORE DM GROUP, LLC; *U.S. Private*, pg. 2780
MOORE HOLDINGS INC.; *U.S. Private*, pg. 2780
MORGAN AUTO GROUP, LLC; *U.S. Private*, pg. 2783
MORGAN BUILDINGS & SPAS, INC.—See GHM Corp.; *U.S. Private*, pg. 1690
MORGAN GROUP HOLDING CO.; *U.S. Public*, pg. 1471
MORGAN JOSEPH TRIARTISAN GROUP INC.; *U.S. Private*, pg. 2784
MORGAN STANLEY CAPITAL MANAGEMENT, LLC—See Morgan Stanley; *U.S. Public*, pg. 1472
MORGAN STANLEY DOMESTIC CAPITAL, INC.—See Morgan Stanley; *U.S. Public*, pg. 1472
MORGAN STANLEY LATIN AMERICA INCORPORATED—See Morgan Stanley; *U.S. Public*, pg. 1473
MORGAN STANLEY PROPERTIES, INC.—See Morgan Stanley; *U.S. Public*, pg. 1475
MORGANTI GROUP/SKH HOLDINGS INC.; *U.S. Private*, pg. 2785
MORINDA HOLDINGS INC.—See NewAge, Inc.; *U.S. Public*, pg. 1513
MORPHIC HOLDING, INC.—See Eli Lilly & Company; *U.S. Public*, pg. 734
MORRIE'S IMPORTS, INC.; *U.S. Private*, pg. 2786
MORRIS PUBLISHING GROUP, LLC—See Shivers Trading & Operating Company; *U.S. Private*, pg. 3638
MORTON'S RESTAURANT GROUP, INC.; *U.S. Private*, pg. 2792
MOSSIMO HOLDINGS LLC—See Iconix Acquisition LLC; *U.S. Private*, pg. 2033
MOTION INDUSTRIES (CANADA) INC.—See Genuine Parts Company; *U.S. Public*, pg. 933
MOTOMOVA, INC.; *U.S. Public*, pg. 1477
MOTOR FUEL GROUP LTD.—See Clayton, Dubilier & Rice, LLC; *U.S. Private*, pg. 926
MOTORSPORT GAMES INC.—See GMF Capital LLC; *U.S. Private*, pg. 1721
MOTT'S HOLDINGS, INC.; *U.S. Private*, pg. 2797
MOTTS SUPERMARKETS—See Mott's Holdings, Inc.; *U.S. Private*, pg. 2797

MOUNTAIN ACQUISITION COMPANY, LLC; *U.S. Private*, pg. 2798
MOUNTAIN GAS RESOURCES, LLC—See Western Midstream Partners, LP; *U.S. Public*, pg. 2356
MOUNTAIN VIEW ELECTRIC ASSOCIATION; *U.S. Private*, pg. 2800
MOVADO GROUP, INC.; *U.S. Public*, pg. 1479
MOVADO RETAIL GROUP, INC.—See Movado Group, Inc.; *U.S. Public*, pg. 1480
MOVE, INC.—See News Corporation; *U.S. Public*, pg. 1519
MOXIAN (HONG KONG) LIMITED—See Abits Group Inc.; *Int'l*, pg. 62
MRC GLOBAL INC.; *U.S. Public*, pg. 1480
MRC HOLDINGS, INC.—See Citigroup Inc.; *U.S. Public*, pg. 504
MR. COOPER GROUP INC.; *U.S. Public*, pg. 1480
MRC TRANSMARK HOLDINGS UK LTD.—See MRC Global Inc.; *U.S. Public*, pg. 1481
MRO HOLDINGS LP; *U.S. Private*, pg. 2805
MSA EUROPE HOLDINGS GMBH—See MSA Safety Incorporated; *U.S. Public*, pg. 1481
MSD HUMAN HEALTH HOLDING B.V.—See Merck & Co., Inc.; *U.S. Public*, pg. 1418
MSD INTERNATIONAL HOLDINGS GMBH—See Merck & Co., Inc.; *U.S. Public*, pg. 1418
MSGN HOLDINGS, L.P.—See Sphere Entertainment Co.; *U.S. Public*, pg. 1918
MSL SOLUTIONS LIMITED—See FirstRand Limited; *Int'l*, pg. 2690
MSM MALAYSIA HOLDINGS BERHAD—See FGV Holdings Bhd; *Int'l*, pg. 2649
MTECH ACQUISITION CORP.—See Gryphon Digital Mining, Inc.; *U.S. Public*, pg. 973
MTGLQ INVESTORS, L.P.—See The Goldman Sachs Group, Inc.; *U.S. Public*, pg. 2082
THE MTL INSTRUMENTS GROUP LTD.—See Eaton Corporation plc; *Int'l*, pg. 2278
MTPCS, LLC; *U.S. Private*, pg. 2809
MTS HOLDINGS FRANCE, SARL—See Amphenol Corporation; *U.S. Public*, pg. 131
MTV OY—See Bonnier AB; *Int'l*, pg. 1109
MUELLER INDUSTRIES, INC.; *U.S. Public*, pg. 1484
MUELLER PROPERTY HOLDINGS, LLC—See Mueller Water Products, Inc.; *U.S. Public*, pg. 1486
MULLEN AUTOMOTIVE, INC.; *U.S. Public*, pg. 1486
MULTIMEDIA GAMES HOLDING COMPANY, INC.—See Everi Holdings Inc.; *U.S. Public*, pg. 801
MULTINER S.A.—See Bolognesi Empreendimentos Ltda.; *Int'l*, pg. 1103
MULTI PACKAGING SOLUTIONS INTERNATIONAL LIMITED—See WestRock Company; *U.S. Public*, pg. 2362
MULTI-PACK SOLUTIONS LLC—See Cameron Holdings Corporation; *U.S. Private*, pg. 728
MURDOCK HOLDINGS, LLC; *U.S. Private*, pg. 2814
MURRAY ENERGY CORPORATION—See American Consolidated Natural Resources, Inc.; *U.S. Private*, pg. 228
MUSCATO GROUP, INC.—See Digital Payments PLC; *Int'l*, pg. 2123
MUTUAL CAPITAL GROUP, INC.; *U.S. Private*, pg. 2819
MUTUAL OF OMAHA INSURANCE COMPANY; *U.S. Private*, pg. 2820
MVC HOLDINGS LLC; *U.S. Private*, pg. 2821
MVL GROUP, INC.; *U.S. Private*, pg. 2821
MWI VETERINARY SUPPLY, CO.—See Cencora, Inc.; *U.S. Public*, pg. 467
MYDIGITALOFFICE HOLDINGS INC.; *U.S. Private*, pg. 2824
NABRO ABLE LLC; *U.S. Private*, pg. 2829
NADACE AGROFERT HOLDING—See Agrofert Holding, a.s.; *Int'l*, pg. 219
NAERODYNAMICS, INC.; *U.S. Public*, pg. 1490
NALCO DUTCH HOLDINGS B.V.—See Ecolab Inc.; *U.S. Public*, pg. 715
NALCO HOLDING COMPANY—See Ecolab Inc.; *U.S. Public*, pg. 715
NALCO HOLDINGS G.M.B.H.—See Ecolab Inc.; *U.S. Public*, pg. 715
NALCO INTERNATIONAL HOLDINGS B.V.—See Ecolab Inc.; *U.S. Public*, pg. 716
NALLEY AUTOMOTIVE GROUP—See Asbury Automotive Group, Inc.; *U.S. Public*, pg. 209
NANO MAGIC INC.; *U.S. Public*, pg. 1490
NANTWORKS, LLC; *U.S. Private*, pg. 2833
NASDAQ, INC.; *U.S. Public*, pg. 1491
NASDAQ OMX NORDIC OY—See Nasdaq, Inc.; *U.S. Public*, pg. 1492
NASH HOLDINGS LLC; *U.S. Private*, pg. 2835
NASHVILLE PREDATORS, LLC; *U.S. Private*, pg. 2836
NASSAU REINSURANCE GROUP HOLDINGS L.P.—See Golden Gate Capital Management II, LLC; *U.S. Private*, pg. 1731
NATIONAL AMERICAN UNIVERSITY HOLDINGS, INC.; *U.S. Public*, pg. 1493
NATIONAL AMUSEMENTS, INC.; *U.S. Private*, pg. 2839
NATIONAL BEDDING CO.—See Ares Management Corporation; *U.S. Public*, pg. 190

NATIONAL ENERGY SERVICES, INC.; *U.S. Private*, pg. 2853
NATIONAL FIRE HOLDINGS PTY. LIMITED—See Evergreen Capital L.P.; *U.S. Private*, pg. 1438
NATIONAL GENERAL HOLDINGS CORP.—See The Allstate Corporation; *U.S. Public*, pg. 2033
NATIONAL HEALTHCARE DISTRIBUTION, INC.; *U.S. Private*, pg. 2856
NATIONAL HOLDINGS CORPORATION—See B. Riley Financial, Inc.; *U.S. Public*, pg. 261
NATIONAL INTERSTATE CORPORATION—See American Financial Group, Inc.; *U.S. Public*, pg. 103
NATIONAL LLOYDS CORPORATION—See Align Financial Group, LLC; *U.S. Private*, pg. 168
NATIONAL MENTOR HOLDINGS, LLC—See Centerbridge Partners, L.P.; *U.S. Private*, pg. 814
NATIONAL RESTAURANT DEVELOPMENT, INC.; *U.S. Private*, pg. 2862
NATIONAL RETAIL SYSTEMS, INC.; *U.S. Private*, pg. 2862
NATIONAL SEMICONDUCTOR (PTE) LIMITED—See Texas Instruments Incorporated; *U.S. Public*, pg. 2025
NATIONAL STARCH & CHEMICAL (HOLDINGS) LTD.—See Ingredion Incorporated; *U.S. Public*, pg. 1124
NATIONAL SURGERY CENTER HOLDINGS, INC.—See Tenet Healthcare Corporation; *U.S. Public*, pg. 2005
NATIONAL TECHNICAL SYSTEMS, INC.—See Aurora Capital Group, LLC; *U.S. Private*, pg. 393
NATIONAL URGENT CARE HOLDINGS, INC.—See Tenet Healthcare Corporation; *U.S. Public*, pg. 2005
NATIONAL WESTERN LIFE GROUP, INC.—See Prosperity Group Holdings, LP; *U.S. Public*, pg. 3289
NATION'S BEST HOLDINGS, LLC; *U.S. Private*, pg. 2839
NATIONWIDE ARGOSY SOLUTIONS, LLC; *U.S. Private*, pg. 2865
NATIXIS ASSURANCES S.A.—See Groupe BPCE; *Int'l*, pg. 3096
NATIXIS GLOBAL ASSET MANAGEMENT CANADA CORP.—See Groupe BPCE; *Int'l*, pg. 3096
NATIXIS GLOBAL ASSET MANAGEMENT (FRANCE)—See Groupe BPCE; *Int'l*, pg. 3096
NATIXIS GLOBAL ASSET MANAGEMENT, L.P.—See Groupe BPCE; *Int'l*, pg. 3096
NATIXIS GLOBAL ASSET MANAGEMENT S.A.—See Groupe BPCE; *Int'l*, pg. 3096
NATIXIS GLOBAL ASSOCIATES, LLC—See Groupe BPCE; *Int'l*, pg. 3096
NATIXIS NORTH AMERICA INC.—See Groupe BPCE; *Int'l*, pg. 3094
NATURAL FOOD HOLDINGS, INC.—See Perdue Farms Incorporated; *U.S. Private*, pg. 3147
NATURAL RESOURCE PARTNERS L.P.; *U.S. Public*, pg. 1499
NATURAL WELLNESS USA, INC.—See Essel Corporate Resources Pvt. Ltd.; *Int'l*, pg. 2509
NATURE'S MIRACLE HOLDING INC.; *U.S. Public*, pg. 1499
NATURE'S WAY HOLDING CO.—See Dr. Willmar Schwabe GmbH & Co. KG; *Int'l*, pg. 2195
NAUTIC PARTNERS, LLC; *U.S. Private*, pg. 2868
NAVICO HOLDING AS—See Brunswick Corporation; *U.S. Public*, pg. 408
NAVIGANT ECONOMICS, LLC—See Bain Capital, LP; *U.S. Private*, pg. 432
THE NAVIGATORS GROUP, INC.—See The Hartford Financial Services Group, Inc.; *U.S. Public*, pg. 2088
NAVIGATORS HOLDINGS UK LTD.—See The Hartford Financial Services Group, Inc.; *U.S. Public*, pg. 2088
NBC NEWS WORLDWIDE LLC—See Comcast Corporation; *U.S. Public*, pg. 539
NBC SPORTS VENTURES LLC—See Comcast Corporation; *U.S. Public*, pg. 539
NBC UNIVERSAL DIGITAL SOLUTIONS LLC—See Comcast Corporation; *U.S. Public*, pg. 540
NBCUNIVERSAL INTERNATIONAL LIMITED—See Comcast Corporation; *U.S. Public*, pg. 540
NBCUNIVERSAL MEDIA, LLC—See Comcast Corporation; *U.S. Public*, pg. 539
NBL TEXAS, LLC—See Chevron Corporation; *U.S. Public*, pg. 487
NCI, INC.—See H.I.G. Capital, LLC; *U.S. Private*, pg. 1831
NCL CORPORATION LTD.—See Norwegian Cruise Line Holdings Ltd.; *U.S. Public*, pg. 1543
NCMIC GROUP INC.; *U.S. Private*, pg. 2876
NDS HOLDINGS B.V.—See Cisco Systems, Inc.; *U.S. Public*, pg. 499
NEACE VENTURES; *U.S. Private*, pg. 2877
NEAPCO HOLDINGS, LLC; *U.S. Private*, pg. 2877
NEBRASKA BOOK HOLDINGS, INC.—See Concise Capital Management LP; *U.S. Private*, pg. 1009
NEENAH ENTERPRISES, INC.—See Charlotte Pipe & Foundry Company; *U.S. Private*, pg. 857
NEIMAN MARCUS GROUP, INC.—See Ares Management Corporation; *U.S. Public*, pg. 190
NEIMAN MARCUS GROUP, INC.—See Canada Pension Plan Investment Board; *Int'l*, pg. 1281
NEIMAN MARCUS GROUP LTD LLC—See Ares Management Corporation; *U.S. Public*, pg. 190
NEIMAN MARCUS GROUP LTD LLC—See Canada Pension Plan Investment Board; *Int'l*, pg. 1281

NEL GROUP, INC.; *U.S. Private*, pg. 2882
NEMA PROPERTIES, LLC—See AMEN Properties, Inc.; *U.S. Public*, pg. 94
NE MEDIA GROUP, INC.; *U.S. Private*, pg. 2876
NEOVASC INC.—See Johnson & Johnson; *U.S. Public*, pg. 1200
NEPTUNE ENERGY GROUP LIMITED—See Eni S.p.A.; *Int'l*, pg. 2438
NER HOLDINGS INC.; *U.S. Private*, pg. 2885
NESBITT INVESTMENT COMPANY; *U.S. Private*, pg. 2885
NESCHEN AG—See Blue Cap AG; *Int'l*, pg. 1067
NESCO, INC.; *U.S. Private*, pg. 2886
NETAPP ASIA PACIFIC HOLDINGS B.V.—See NetApp, Inc.; *U.S. Public*, pg. 1507
NETBOOSTER HOLDING A/S—See Ardian SAS; *Int'l*, pg. 554
NETNAMES HOLDINGS LIMITED—See HgCapital Trust plc; *Int'l*, pg. 3377
NETS A/S—See Advent International Corporation; *U.S. Private*, pg. 105
NETS A/S—See Bain Capital, LP; *U.S. Private*, pg. 442
NETS A/S—See GIC Pte. Ltd.; *Int'l*, pg. 2965
NETS A/S—See Hellman & Friedman LLC; *U.S. Private*, pg. 1910
NETSPEND HOLDINGS, INC.—See Global Payments Inc.; *U.S. Public*, pg. 944
NETWORKERS INTERNATIONAL LIMITED—See Gattaca plc; *Int'l*, pg. 2890
NETZSCH USA HOLDINGS, INC.—See Erich Netzsch GmbH & Co. Holding KG; *Int'l*, pg. 2492
NEUBERGER BERMAN GROUP LLC; *U.S. Private*, pg. 2890
NEUTRAHEALTH PLC—See Elder Pharmaceuticals Ltd.; *Int'l*, pg. 2346
NEVA ONE LLC; *U.S. Private*, pg. 2891
NEW ALBERTSON'S, INC.—See Cerberus Capital Management, L.P.; *U.S. Private*, pg. 836
NEWAVE ENERGY HOLDING SA—See ABB Ltd.; *Int'l*, pg. 54
NEW AXIA HOLDINGS INC.—See Aurora Capital Group, LLC; *U.S. Private*, pg. 394
NEW CALIFORNIA LIFE HOLDINGS, INC.—See Financiere Pinault SCA; *Int'l*, pg. 2668
NEW CENTAUR, LLC—See Caesars Entertainment, Inc.; *U.S. Public*, pg. 420
NEW CHINA HOMES LTD.—See Far East Consortium International Limited; *Int'l*, pg. 2615
NEWCOR, INC.—See Cie Automotive S.A.; *Int'l*, pg. 1604
NEWELL BRANDS INC.; *U.S. Public*, pg. 1513
NEW FRONTIER MEDIA, INC.—See L.F.P., Inc.; *U.S. Private*, pg. 2365
NEW GROWTH PLUS B.V.—See Electricity Generating Public Co., Ltd.; *Int'l*, pg. 2352
NEWHOLD ENTERPRISES LLC; *U.S. Private*, pg. 2915
NEW HORIZONS WORLDWIDE, INC.—See Camden Partners Holdings, LLC; *U.S. Private*, pg. 728
NEW JERSEY RESOURCES CORPORATION; *U.S. Public*, pg. 1511
NEW KLEINFONTEIN MINING COMPANY LIMITED—See Baiyin Nonferrous Metal (Group) Co., Ltd.; *Int'l*, pg. 803
NEWLINE UNDERWRITING MANAGEMENT LTD.—See Fairfax Financial Holdings Limited; *Int'l*, pg. 2607
NEW LOOK RETAIL GROUP LIMITED—See Brait S.E.; *Int'l*, pg. 1137
NEW PENDULUM CORPORATION; *U.S. Private*, pg. 2905
NEWPORT CORPORATION—See MKS Instruments, Inc.; *U.S. Public*, pg. 1453
NEWREGEN, INC.; *U.S. Public*, pg. 1518
NEW RESOURCES COMPANIES; *U.S. Private*, pg. 2905
NEW RITE AID, LLC; *U.S. Private*, pg. 2905
NEWS CORPORATION; *U.S. Public*, pg. 1518
NEWSDAY LLC—See Altice USA, Inc.; *U.S. Public*, pg. 87
NEWS-PRESS & GAZETTE COMPANY; *U.S. Private*, pg. 2917
NEW TALENT MEDIA COMPANY LIMITED—See Creative China Holdings Limited; *Int'l*, pg. 1832
NEWTON-WELLESLEY HEALTHCARE SYSTEM—See Partners HealthCare System, Inc.; *U.S. Private*, pg. 3101
NEW VENTURE PARTNERS LLC; *U.S. Private*, pg. 2907
NEW WINCUP HOLDINGS, INC.—See ATAR Capital, LLC; *U.S. Private*, pg. 364
NEW WORLD HOTELS (HOLDINGS) LIMITED—See Chow Tai Fook Enterprises Limited; *Int'l*, pg. 1585
NEW YORK COMMUNITY BANCORP, INC.; *U.S. Public*, pg. 1512
NEW YORK LIFE INTERNATIONAL INVESTMENT—See New York Life Insurance Company; *U.S. Private*, pg. 2910
NEW YORK LIFE INVESTMENT MANAGEMENT GUARANTEED PRODUCTS—See New York Life Insurance Company; *U.S. Private*, pg. 2911
NEW YORK YANKEES PARTNERSHIP; *U.S. Private*, pg. 2912
NEXEO SOLUTIONS HOLDINGS, LLC—See Apollo Global Management, Inc.; *U.S. Public*, pg. 165
NEXEO SOLUTIONS, INC.—See Apollo Global Management, Inc.; *U.S. Public*, pg. 165
NEXEYA SAS—See HENSOLDT AG; *Int'l*, pg. 3355

NEXSAN CORPORATION; *U.S. Private*, pg. 2919
NEXSTAR FINANCE HOLDINGS, INC.—See Nexstar Media Group, Inc.; *U.S. Public*, pg. 1524
NEXSTAR MEDIA GROUP, INC.; *U.S. Public*, pg. 1522
NEXTCARE HOLDINGS, INC.; *U.S. Private*, pg. 2920
NEXT CENTURY TECHNOLOGIES, INC.; *U.S. Private*, pg. 2919
NEXTERA ENERGY, INC.; *U.S. Public*, pg. 1526
NEXTGEN HEALTHCARE, INC.—See Thoma Bravo, L.P.; *U.S. Private*, pg. 4150
NEXTTRIP HOLDINGS, INC.; *U.S. Private*, pg. 2921
NFCO INC.; *U.S. Private*, pg. 2922
NFP CORP.—See Aon plc; *Int'l*, pg. 495
NGEN TECHNOLOGIES HOLDINGS CORP.; *U.S. Public*, pg. 1527
NICKLAUS COMPANIES, LLC; *U.S. Private*, pg. 2926
NICOR GAS COMPANY—See The Southern Company; *U.S. Public*, pg. 2131
NIELSEN HOLDINGS PLC—See Brookfield Corporation; *Int'l*, pg. 1176
NIELSEN HOLDINGS PLC—See Elliott Management Corporation; *U.S. Public*, pg. 1369
NI HOLDINGS, INC.; *U.S. Public*, pg. 1527
NILORNGRUPPEN AB—See Duroc AB; *Int'l*, pg. 2229
NIPPON BOEHRINGER INGELHEIM CO. LTD.—See C.H. Boehringer Sohn AG & Co. KG; *Int'l*, pg. 1243
NIPPON HOTEL CO. LTD.—See East Japan Railway Company; *Int'l*, pg. 2270
NISCAYAH HOLDING SPAIN, S.L.—See Stanley Black & Decker, Inc.; *U.S. Public*, pg. 1933
NIVEL HOLDINGS, LLC—See Morgan Stanley; *U.S. Public*, pg. 1474
NL INDUSTRIES, INC.—See Contran Corporation; *U.S. Private*, pg. 1033
NM GROUP GLOBAL LLC—See Alpha Capital Partners, Ltd.; *U.S. Private*, pg. 197
NMHG AUSTRALIA HOLDING PTY LTD.—See Hyster-Yale Materials Handling, Inc.; *U.S. Public*, pg. 1080
NMI HOLDINGS, INC.; *U.S. Public*, pg. 1530
NN INVESTMENT PARTNERS HOLDINGS N.V.—See The Goldman Sachs Group, Inc.; *U.S. Public*, pg. 2082
NOBEL BIOCARE ASIA-AFRICA HOLDING AG—See Danaher Corporation; *U.S. Public*, pg. 628
NOEL GROUP, LLC; *U.S. Private*, pg. 2933
NOLAN CAPITAL, INC.; *U.S. Private*, pg. 2934
NORCRAFT HOLDINGS, L.P.—See MasterBrand, Inc.; *U.S. Public*, pg. 1394
NORD ANGLIA EDUCATION, INC.—See Canada Pension Plan Investment Board; *Int'l*, pg. 1281
NORD ANGLIA EDUCATION, INC.—See EQT AB; *Int'l*, pg. 2470
NORD ANGLIA EDUCATION LIMITED—See Canada Pension Plan Investment Board; *Int'l*, pg. 1281
NORD ANGLIA EDUCATION LIMITED—See EQT AB; *Int'l*, pg. 2470
NORDCAPITAL GMBH—See E.R. CAPITAL HOLDING GmbH & Cie. KG; *Int'l*, pg. 2260
NORFOLK SOUTHERN CORPORATION; *U.S. Public*, pg. 1535
NORFOLK SOUTHERN PROPERTIES, INC.—See Norfolk Southern Corporation; *U.S. Public*, pg. 1535
NORICAN GROUP APS—See Altor Equity Partners AB; *Int'l*, pg. 395
NORIT (UK) HOLDING LIMITED—See Cabot Corporation; *U.S. Public*, pg. 417
NOR-MAR INC.; *U.S. Private*, pg. 2935
NORSEA GROUP AS—See Eidesvik Holding A/S; *Int'l*, pg. 2329
NORTEL INVERSORA S.A.—See Gregorio, Numo y Noel Werthein S.A.; *Int'l*, pg. 3078
NORTH AMERICAN BREWERIES, INC.—See Florida Ice and Farm Co. S.A.; *Int'l*, pg. 2707
NORTH AMERICAN ESSENTIAL HOME SERVICES—See Gryphon Investors, LLC; *U.S. Private*, pg. 1799
NORTH AMERICAN INTERNATIONAL HOLDING CORPORATION—See Madison Dearborn Partners, LLC; *U.S. Private*, pg. 2542
NORTH AMERICAN TRANSMISSION & DISTRIBUTION GROUP—See Falfurrias Capital Partners, LP; *U.S. Private*, pg. 1467
NORTH ATLANTIC TRADING COMPANY, INC.; *U.S. Private*, pg. 2942
NORTHEAST INDUSTRIES GROUP CO., LTD.—See China North Industries Group Corporation; *Int'l*, pg. 1536
NORTHERN CONTOURS HOLDING CORP.; *U.S. Private*, pg. 2952
NORTHERN FOODS LIMITED—See Boparan Holdings Limited; *Int'l*, pg. 1111
NORTHERN STEEL GROUP, INC.—See Aurora Capital Group, LLC; *U.S. Private*, pg. 394
NORTHERN TIER ENERGY LLC—See Marathon Petroleum Corporation; *U.S. Public*, pg. 1363
NORTHGATE INFORMATION SOLUTIONS HOLDINGS LIMITED—See Alight, Inc.; *U.S. Public*, pg. 76
NORTHGATE INFORMATION SOLUTIONS LIMITED—See Alight, Inc.; *U.S. Public*, pg. 76
NORTHMARQ COMPANIES LLC—See Pohlad Companies; *U.S. Private*, pg. 3220

N.A.I.C.S. INDEX

551112 — OFFICES OF OTHER HO...

NORTH POLE INVESTMENT COMPANY LIMITED—See Electricity Generating Public Co., Ltd.; *Int'l*, pg. 2352
NORTHROP GRUMMAN CORPORATION; *U.S. Public*, pg. 1539
NORTHROP GRUMMAN INNOVATION SYSTEMS, INC.—See Northrop Grumman Corporation; *U.S. Public*, pg. 1540
NORTHROP GRUMMAN UK LIMITED—See Northrop Grumman Corporation; *U.S. Public*, pg. 1541
NORTHSTAR GROUP HOLDINGS, LLC—See J.F. Lehman & Company, Inc.; *U.S. Private*, pg. 2163
NORTHSTAR GROUP SERVICES, INC.—See J.F. Lehman & Company, Inc.; *U.S. Private*, pg. 2164
THE NORTHVIEW GROUP LIMITED—See Barclays PLC; *Int'l*, pg. 860
NORTHWEST BROADCASTING, INC.; *U.S. Private*, pg. 2959
NORTHWESTERN ENGINEERING COMPANY; *U.S. Private*, pg. 2962
NORTHWEST NATURAL HOLDING COMPANY; *U.S. Public*, pg. 1542
NORTH WIND, INC.—See Cook Inlet Region, Inc.; *U.S. Private*, pg. 1038
NORTON ABRASIVE EXPORTS—See Compagnie de Saint-Gobain SA; *Int'l*, pg. 1730
NORTON COMPANY—See Compagnie de Saint-Gobain SA; *Int'l*, pg. 1730
NORWEGIAN CRUISE LINE HOLDINGS LTD.; *U.S. Public*, pg. 1543
NORWIX INC.; *U.S. Public*, pg. 1543
NOURYON CHEMICALS HOLDING B.V.—See GIC Pte. Ltd.; *Int'l*, pg. 2967
NOURYON CHEMICALS HOLDING B.V.—See The Carlyle Group Inc.; *U.S. Public*, pg. 2050
NOURYON CHEMICALS INTERNATIONAL B.V.—See GIC Pte. Ltd.; *Int'l*, pg. 2967
NOURYON CHEMICALS INTERNATIONAL B.V.—See The Carlyle Group Inc.; *U.S. Public*, pg. 2050
NOVANTA INC.; *U.S. Public*, pg. 1547
NOVARIA HOLDINGS LLC—See KKR & Co. Inc.; *U.S. Public*, pg. 1262
NOVATION COMPANIES, INC.; *U.S. Public*, pg. 1548
NOVA VENTURES GROUP CORP.; *U.S. Private*, pg. 2966
NOVERCO INC.—See Caisse de Depot et Placement du Quebec; *Int'l*, pg. 1255
NOVETTA SOLUTIONS, LLC—See The Carlyle Group Inc.; *U.S. Public*, pg. 2051
NOVM HOLDING LLC—See NOV, Inc.; *U.S. Public*, pg. 1545
NOVVIA GROUP—See Kelso & Company, L.P.; *U.S. Private*, pg. 2278
NRC GROUP HOLDINGS, LLC—See Republic Services, Inc.; *U.S. Public*, pg. 1788
NSI-MI TECHNOLOGIES, LLC—See AMETEK, Inc.; *U.S. Public*, pg. 121
NSM HOLDINGS, INC.—See American International Group, Inc.; *U.S. Public*, pg. 106
NSM INSURANCE GROUP, LLC—See The Carlyle Group Inc.; *U.S. Public*, pg. 2050
NSTAR LLC—See Eversource Energy; *U.S. Public*, pg. 801
NTS CORPORATION; *U.S. Private*, pg. 2971
NTS, INC.—See Keystone Group, L.P.; *U.S. Private*, pg. 2297
NTS, INC.—See Pamlico Capital Management, L.P.; *U.S. Private*, pg. 3083
NUMET HOLDINGS PTY. LTD.—See Tupperware Brands Corporation; *U.S. Public*, pg. 2204
NU SKIN MALAYSIA HOLDINGS SDN. BHD.—See Nu Skin Enterprises, Inc.; *U.S. Public*, pg. 1552
NUSTAR GP HOLDINGS, LLC—See Sunoco LP; *U.S. Public*, pg. 1964
NUTEX HEALTH INC.; *U.S. Public*, pg. 1555
NUTRICIA HOLDINGS LTD.—See Danone; *Int'l*, pg. 1966
NUTRICIA NETHERLANDS B.V.—See Danone; *Int'l*, pg. 1967
NUTRICIA (RUSSIA) LLC—See Danone; *Int'l*, pg. 1966
NUTRICIA S.A.—See Danone; *Int'l*, pg. 1967
THE NUTTING COMPANY, INC.; *U.S. Private*, pg. 4086
N.V. DELI MAATSCHAPPIJ—See Blackstone Inc.; *U.S. Public*, pg. 356
NV ENERGY, INC.—See Berkshire Hathaway Inc.; *U.S. Public*, pg. 300
NVEST, INC.; *U.S. Private*, pg. 2975
NWS HOLDINGS LIMITED—See Chow Tai Fook Enterprises Limited; *Int'l*, pg. 1584
NYPRO GLOBAL HOLDINGS CV—See Jabil Inc.; *U.S. Public*, pg. 1181
NYSE CHICAGO HOLDINGS, INC.—See Intercontinental Exchange, Inc.; *U.S. Public*, pg. 1143
NYSE GROUP, INC.—See Intercontinental Exchange, Inc.; *U.S. Public*, pg. 1143
NYT MANAGEMENT SERVICES, INC.—See The New York Times Company; *U.S. Public*, pg. 2116
NZJ HOLDINGS, INC.; *U.S. Public*, pg. 1559
OAKLAND INDUSTRIES BLOCKER CORP.—See Oakland Standard Co., LLC; *U.S. Private*, pg. 2985
OAKTREE SPECIALTY LENDING CORPORATION—See Fifth Street Capital LLC; *U.S. Private*, pg. 1505

OB COMPANIES—See Brookfield Corporation; *Int'l*, pg. 1189
OBERTHUR CARD SYSTEMS—See Advent International Corporation; *U.S. Private*, pg. 102
OBN HOLDINGS, INC.; *U.S. Public*, pg. 2987
OBSIDIAN ENTERPRISES, INC.; *U.S. Private*, pg. 2988
OCCIDENTAL CHEMICAL HOLDING CORPORATION—See Occidental Petroleum Corporation; *U.S. Public*, pg. 1561
OCEAN BIOMEDICAL HOLDINGS, INC.—See Ocean Biomedical, Inc.; *U.S. Public*, pg. 1562
OCEANFREIGHT INC.—See DryShips Inc.; *Int'l*, pg. 2207
OCEANWIDE HOLDINGS CO., LTD.—See China Oceanwide Holdings Group Co., Ltd.; *Int'l*, pg. 1538
OCLARO, INC.—See Lumentum Holdings Inc.; *U.S. Public*, pg. 1348
OC LATIN AMERICAN HOLDINGS GMBH—See Owens Corning; *U.S. Public*, pg. 1627
OCM HOLDCO, LLC—See Brookfield Corporation; *Int'l*, pg. 1182
THE O'CONNELL COMPANIES, INCORPORATED; *U.S. Private*, pg. 4087
OFFICE DEPOT ASIA HOLDING LIMITED—See The ODP Corporation; *U.S. Public*, pg. 2117
OFFICE DEPOT EUROPE B.V.—See Aurelius Equity Opportunities SE & Co. KGaA; *Int'l*, pg. 709
OFFICEMAX INCORPORATED—See The ODP Corporation; *U.S. Public*, pg. 2117
OFFSHORE HELICOPTER SUPPORT SERVICES, INC.—See Bristow Group, Inc.; *U.S. Public*, pg. 388
OFFSITE ARCHIVE STORAGE & INTEGRATED SERVICES LIMITED—See Housatonic Partners Management Co., Inc.; *U.S. Private*, pg. 1991
OFFSITE ARCHIVE STORAGE & INTEGRATED SERVICES LIMITED—See Sverica Capital Management LP; *U.S. Private*, pg. 3888
THE OGDEN NEWSPAPERS, INC.—See The Nutting Company, Inc.; *U.S. Private*, pg. 4086
OGE ENERGY CORP.; *U.S. Public*, pg. 1564
OHIO CASUALTY CORPORATION—See Liberty Mutual Holding Company Inc.; *U.S. Private*, pg. 2446
OHIO FARMERS INSURANCE COMPANY; *U.S. Private*, pg. 3004
OHIO NATIONAL FINANCIAL SERVICES, INC.—See Caisse de Depot et Placement du Quebec; *Int'l*, pg. 1254
OHIO NATIONAL HOLDINGS, INC.—See Caisse de Depot et Placement du Quebec; *Int'l*, pg. 1254
OHIO/OKLAHOMA HEARST-ARGYLE TELEVISION, INC.—See The Hearst Corporation; *U.S. Private*, pg. 4048
OHTORI CORPORATION—See Ichinen Holdings Co., Ltd.; *Int'l*, pg. 3580
OIL AIR HOLDINGS INC.—See Parker Hannifin Corporation; *U.S. Public*, pg. 1643
OLAPLEX HOLDINGS, INC.; *U.S. Public*, pg. 1566
OLDCASTLE MATERIALS, INC.—See CRH plc; *Int'l*, pg. 1846
OLDENBURG GROUP, INC.; *U.S. Private*, pg. 3009
OLD REPUBLIC GENERAL INSURANCE GROUP, INC.—See Old Republic International Corporation; *U.S. Public*, pg. 1567
OLD REPUBLIC INTERNATIONAL CORPORATION; *U.S. Public*, pg. 1567
OLD REPUBLIC LIFE INSURANCE GROUP, INC.—See Old Republic International Corporation; *U.S. Public*, pg. 1568
OLD REPUBLIC MORTGAGE GUARANTY GROUP, INC.—See Old Republic International Corporation; *U.S. Public*, pg. 1568
OLD REPUBLIC NATIONAL TITLE HOLDING COMPANY—See Old Republic International Corporation; *U.S. Public*, pg. 1568
OLD REPUBLIC TITLE HOLDING COMPANY, INC.—See Old Republic International Corporation; *U.S. Public*, pg. 1569
OLD REPUBLIC TITLE INSURANCE GROUP, INC.—See Old Republic International Corporation; *U.S. Public*, pg. 1568
OLGOONIK CORPORATION; *U.S. Private*, pg. 3010
OLGOONIK DEVELOPMENT, LLC—See Olgoonik Corporation; *U.S. Private*, pg. 3010
OLINK HOLDING AB—See Thermo Fisher Scientific Inc.; *U.S. Public*, pg. 2149
OLLIE'S BARGAIN OUTLET HOLDINGS, INC.—See CCMP Capital Advisors, LP; *U.S. Private*, pg. 800
OLYMPUS HOLDINGS, LLC; *U.S. Private*, pg. 3012
OLYMPUS POWER, LLC—See Olympus Holdings, LLC; *U.S. Private*, pg. 3013
OLYMPUS PRODUCTIONS, LLC—See Olympus Holdings, LLC; *U.S. Private*, pg. 3013
OMAM INC.—See BrightSphere Investment Group Inc.; *U.S. Public*, pg. 383
OMEGA ENTERPRISES INC.; *U.S. Private*, pg. 3015
OMG MIDWEST, INC.—See CRH plc; *Int'l*, pg. 1847
OMID HOLDINGS, INC.; *U.S. Private*, pg. 1572
OMINTO, INC.; *U.S. Public*, pg. 1572
OMNICOM GROUP INC.; *U.S. Public*, pg. 1573
OMNICOM MEDIA GROUP HOLDINGS INC—See Omnicom Group Inc.; *U.S. Public*, pg. 1589

OMNI HOTELS MANAGEMENT CORPORATION—See TRT Holdings, Inc.; *U.S. Private*, pg. 4244
OMNIMAX HOLDINGS, INC.; *U.S. Private*, pg. 3017
OMNISOURCE SOUTHEAST, LLC—See Steel Dynamics, Inc.; *U.S. Public*, pg. 1942
ONE51 PLASTICS HOLDINGS LIMITED—See Madison Dearborn Partners, LLC; *U.S. Private*, pg. 2541
O'NEAL INDUSTRIES, INC.; *U.S. Private*, pg. 2979
ONEAMERICA FINANCIAL PARTNERS, INC.—See American United Mutual Insurance Holding Company; *U.S. Private*, pg. 257
ONEOK PARTNERS, L.P.—See ONEOK, Inc.; *U.S. Public*, pg. 1603
ONEONTA TRADING CORPORATION; *U.S. Private*, pg. 3025
ONESOFT SOLUTIONS INC.—See Blackstone Inc.; *U.S. Public*, pg. 355
ONESPAWORLD HOLDINGS LIMITED; *U.S. Public*, pg. 1604
ONETOUCHPOINT CORP.—See ICV Partners, LLC; *U.S. Private*, pg. 2034
ONEWATER MARINE HOLDINGS LLC; *U.S. Private*, pg. 3026
ONFOLIO HOLDINGS INC.; *U.S. Public*, pg. 1604
ONITY GROUP INC.; *U.S. Public*, pg. 1604
ONSITE HOLDING LLC—See Walgreens Boots Alliance, Inc.; *U.S. Public*, pg. 2322
ON-TIME STEEL MANAGEMENT HOLDING, INC.—See INNOVATE Corp.; *U.S. Public*, pg. 1126
ONTO INNOVATION INC.; *U.S. Public*, pg. 1605
OOCL (EUROPE) LTD—See China COSCO Shipping Corporation Limited; *Int'l*, pg. 1495
OONA HOLDINGS PTE. LTD.—See Warburg Pincus LLC; *U.S. Private*, pg. 4439
OOO NET ELEMENT RUSSIA—See Mullen Automotive, Inc.; *U.S. Public*, pg. 1486
OPDENERGY HOLDING SA—See Antin Infrastructure Partners SAS; *Int'l*, pg. 483
OPEL GROUP GMBH—See General Motors Company; *U.S. Public*, pg. 926
OPENAI, INC.; *U.S. Public*, pg. 3030
OPENDOOR TECHNOLOGIES INC.; *U.S. Public*, pg. 1606
OPEN GRID EUROPE GMBH—See British Columbia Investment Management Corp.; *Int'l*, pg. 1169
OPENLANE, INC.; *U.S. Public*, pg. 1606
OPENLANE US, INC.—See OPENLANE, Inc.; *U.S. Public*, pg. 1607
OPEN ROAD AUTO GROUP; *U.S. Private*, pg. 3029
OPORTUN FINANCIAL CORPORATION; *U.S. Public*, pg. 1608
OPPENHEIMERFUNDS, INC.—See Invesco Ltd.; *U.S. Public*, pg. 1163
OPTIGROUP AB—See Altor Equity Partners AB; *Int'l*, pg. 395
OPTIMA SPECIALTY STEEL, INC.; *U.S. Private*, pg. 3034
OPTIMUS STEEL, LLC; *U.S. Private*, pg. 3035
OPTION CARE HEALTH, INC.; *U.S. Public*, pg. 1609
OPTUM GOVERNMENT SOLUTIONS, INC.—See UnitedHealth Group Incorporated; *U.S. Public*, pg. 2243
OPUS GLOBAL HOLDINGS LLC—See GTCR LLC; *U.S. Private*, pg. 1806
OPUS HOLDING, LLC; *U.S. Private*, pg. 3036
ORACLE AMERICA, INC.—See Oracle Corporation; *U.S. Public*, pg. 1611
ORACLE DEUTSCHLAND B.V. & CO. KG—See Oracle Corporation; *U.S. Public*, pg. 1612
ORAZUL ENERGY CORPORATION—See I Squared Capital Advisors (US) LLC; *U.S. Private*, pg. 2025
ORBITEL HOLDINGS, LLC—See Schurz Communications, Inc.; *U.S. Private*, pg. 3571
ORBITZ WORLDWIDE, LLC—See Expedia Group, Inc.; *U.S. Public*, pg. 809
ORCHARD PARADE HOLDINGS LTD.—See Far East Organization Pte. Ltd.; *Int'l*, pg. 2617
ORCHESTRA BIOMED HOLDINGS, INC.; *U.S. Public*, pg. 1615
O'REILLY AUTOMOTIVE, INC.; *U.S. Public*, pg. 1559
ORGANICELL REGENERATIVE MEDICINE, INC.; *U.S. Public*, pg. 1615
ORGANOGENESIS HOLDINGS INC.; *U.S. Public*, pg. 1615
O'RIELLY MOTOR COMPANY; *U.S. Private*, pg. 2980
ORIENTAL SINO LIMITED—See Danish Crown AmbA; *Int'l*, pg. 1964
ORIENT CAPITAL VENTURES LIMITED—See AsianLogic Limited; *Int'l*, pg. 620
ORI GREAT WEST HOLDING, INC.—See Old Republic International Corporation; *U.S. Public*, pg. 1567
ORION ENGINEERED CARBONS HOLDINGS GMBH—See Rhone Group, LLC; *U.S. Private*, pg. 3424
ORION S.A.—See Rhone Group, LLC; *U.S. Private*, pg. 3424
ORKIM SDN. BHD.—See Ekuiti Nasional Berhad; *Int'l*, pg. 2340
ORLEANS HOMEBUILDERS, INC.; *U.S. Private*, pg. 3044
O'ROURKE MEDIA GROUP, LLC; *U.S. Private*, pg. 2980
ORSCHELN GROUP; *U.S. Private*, pg. 3045
ORTHO CLINICAL DIAGNOSTICS HOLDINGS PLC—See QuidelOrtho Corporation; *U.S. Public*, pg. 1756

551112 — OFFICES OF OTHER HO...   CORPORATE AFFILIATIONS

ORWAK GROUP AB—See Accent Equity Partners AB; *Int'l*, pg. 81
THE OSAWATOMIE AGENCY INC.; *U.S. Private*, pg. 4089
OSCAR HEALTH, INC.; *U.S. Public*, pg. 1619
OSCEOLA CAPITAL MANAGEMENT, LLC; *U.S. Private*, pg. 3046
OSL HOLDINGS INC.; *U.S. Private*, pg. 3048
OSLO BORS VPS HOLDING ASA—See Euronext N.V.; *Int'l*, pg. 2554
OSMOSE UTILITIES SERVICES, INC.—See EQT AB; *Int'l*, pg. 2479
OTIS INTERNATIONAL HOLDINGS GMBH—See Otis Worldwide Corporation; *U.S. Public*, pg. 1623
OTIS WORLDWIDE CORPORATION; *U.S. Public*, pg. 1622
OUTDOOR CHANNEL HOLDINGS, INC.—See Kroenke Sports & Entertainment, LLC; *U.S. Private*, pg. 2352
OUTDOOR & SPORTS COMPANY (HOLDINGS) LIMITED—See Bollin Group Ltd.; *Int'l*, pg. 1103
OUTFRONT MEDIA INC.; *U.S. Public*, pg. 1624
OVAL PARTNERS; *U.S. Private*, pg. 3052
OVATION ENTERPRISES, INC.; *U.S. Private*, pg. 3052
OVINTIV INC.; *U.S. Public*, pg. 1625
OWENS CORNING HOLDINGS HOLLAND B.V.—See Owens Corning; *U.S. Public*, pg. 1628
OWENS-CORNING ONTARIO HOLDINGS INC.—See Owens Corning; *U.S. Public*, pg. 1628
OWENS-ILLINOIS INTERNATIONAL B.V.—See O-I Glass, Inc.; *U.S. Public*, pg. 1559
OWENS & MINOR, INC.; *U.S. Public*, pg. 1625
OWNERSEDGE INC.; *U.S. Private*, pg. 3055
P10 HOLDINGS, INC.—See P10, Inc.; *U.S. Public*, pg. 1630
PAAMCO PRISMA HOLDINGS, LLC; *U.S. Private*, pg. 3062
PACIFIC AMERICAN GROUP, LLC; *U.S. Private*, pg. 3065
PACIFIC HOUSING GROUP, LLC; *U.S. Private*, pg. 3067
PACIFIC INTERNATIONAL MARKETING, INC.; *U.S. Private*, pg. 3068
PACIFIC LIFECORP—See Pacific Mutual Holding Company; *U.S. Private*, pg. 3068
PACIFIC MUTUAL HOLDING COMPANY; *U.S. Private*, pg. 3068
PACIFIC VENTURES GROUP, INC.; *U.S. Public*, pg. 1632
PACKABLE HOLDINGS, LLC; *U.S. Private*, pg. 3072
PACTIV EVERGREEN INC.; *U.S. Public*, pg. 1633
PAE INCORPORATED—See Amentum Services, Inc.; *U.S. Private*, pg. 219
PAGNOTTI ENTERPRISES INC.; *U.S. Private*, pg. 3075
PALACE SPORTS & ENTERTAINMENT, INC.—See Platinum Equity, LLC; *U.S. Private*, pg. 3206
PALESTINE INDUSTRIAL INVESTMENT CO. LTD.—See Arab Supply & Trading Co.; *Int'l*, pg. 532
PALM CREEK HOLDINGS LLC—See Sun Communities, Inc.; *U.S. Public*, pg. 1961
PALM ENTERTAINMENT PROPERTIES LLC; *U.S. Private*, pg. 3079
PALOMA PARTNERS VI HOLDINGS, LLC—See EnCap Investments L.P.; *U.S. Private*, pg. 1390
PALOMAR TECHNOLOGIES COMPANIES, LLC; *U.S. Private*, pg. 3082
PAMALICAN ISLAND HOLDINGS, INC.—See A. Soriano Corporation; *Int'l*, pg. 22
PAMARCO GLOBAL GRAPHICS—See J.P. Kotts & Co.; *U.S. Private*, pg. 2170
PAMC, LTD.; *U.S. Private*, pg. 3083
PANACEA LIFE SCIENCES HOLDINGS, INC.; *U.S. Public*, pg. 1635
PANAMERA HOLDINGS CORPORATION; *U.S. Public*, pg. 1635
PANCON CORPORATION—See Milestone Partners Ltd.; *U.S. Private*, pg. 2728
PANDA RESTAURANT GROUP, INC.; *U.S. Private*, pg. 3085
PANGAEA LOGISTICS SOLUTIONS LTD.; *U.S. Public*, pg. 1635
PANMURE GORDON & CO. LIMITED—See Atlas Merchant Capital LLC; *U.S. Private*, pg. 379
PANTHER SUMMIT INDUSTRIES INC.; *U.S. Private*, pg. 3087
PAPA GINOS-DEANGELO HOLDING CORPORATION, INC.; *U.S. Private*, pg. 3087
PAPERWEIGHT DEVELOPMENT CORP.; *U.S. Private*, pg. 3088
PAPPAS TELECASTING COMPANIES; *U.S. Private*, pg. 3088
PARADIGM PRECISION HOLDINGS, LLC—See AeroEquity Partners, LLC; *U.S. Private*, pg. 118
PARADIGM PRECISION HOLDINGS, LLC—See The Carlyle Group Inc.; *U.S. Public*, pg. 2046
PARAGON GLOBAL RESOURCES, INC.; *U.S. Private*, pg. 3091
PARAGON TECHNOLOGIES, INC.; *U.S. Public*, pg. 1637
PARASOLE RESTAURANT HOLDINGS, INC.; *U.S. Private*, pg. 3093
PARATEK PHARMACEUTICALS, INC.—See Gurnet Point Capital LLC; *U.S. Private*, pg. 1819
PARGESA HOLDING S.A.—See BNP Paribas SA; *Int'l*, pg. 1090
PARGESA HOLDING S.A.—See Frere-Bourgeois; *Int'l*, pg. 2773

PARJOINTCO N.V.—See BNP Paribas SA; *Int'l*, pg. 1090
PARJOINTCO N.V.—See Frere-Bourgeois; *Int'l*, pg. 2773
PARKER DRILLING MANAGEMENT SERVICES, INC.—See Parker Wellbore Company; *U.S. Public*, pg. 1650
PARKER HANNIFIN HOLDING, S. DE R.L. DE C.V.—See Parker Hannifin Corporation; *U.S. Public*, pg. 1647
PARKER HANNIFIN HONG KONG LTD.—See Parker Hannifin Corporation; *U.S. Public*, pg. 1647
PARKER HANNIFIN JAPAN HOLDINGS GK—See Parker Hannifin Corporation; *U.S. Public*, pg. 1648
PARKER HANNIFIN NETHERLANDS HOLDINGS B.V.—See Parker Hannifin Corporation; *U.S. Public*, pg. 1648
PARKER HOLDING COMPANY, INC.; *U.S. Private*, pg. 3097
PARKER ONTARIO HOLDING INC.—See Parker Hannifin Corporation; *U.S. Public*, pg. 1649
PARK-OHIO HOLDINGS CORP.; *U.S. Public*, pg. 1638
PARMAN HOLDING CORPORATION; *U.S. Private*, pg. 3099
PAR PACIFIC HOLDINGS, INC.; *U.S. Public*, pg. 1636
PAR PHARMACEUTICAL COMPANIES, INC.—See Endo International plc; *Int'l*, pg. 2404
PARTICIPATIE MAATSCHAPPIJ GRAAFSCHAP HOLLAND N.V.—See Assicurazioni Generali S.p.A.; *Int'l*, pg. 647
PARTY CITY HOLDCO, INC.—See Thomas H. Lee Partners, L.P.; *U.S. Private*, pg. 4156
PARTY CITY HOLDINGS, INC.—See Thomas H. Lee Partners, L.P.; *U.S. Private*, pg. 4156
PASS CREEK RESOURCES LLC; *U.S. Private*, pg. 3104
PATAGONIA WORKS, INC.; *U.S. Private*, pg. 3105
PATHEON N.V.—See Thermo Fisher Scientific Inc.; *U.S. Public*, pg. 2151
PATHFINDER COMMUNICATIONS CORPORATION—See Federated Media Inc.; *U.S. Private*, pg. 1492
PATRIOT TRANSPORTATION HOLDING, INC.—See Gregmar, Inc.; *U.S. Private*, pg. 1783
PATTEN ENERGY SOLUTIONS GROUP, INC.; *U.S. Public*, pg. 1653
PAVONIA HOLDINGS (US), INC.—See Eli Global, LLC; *U.S. Private*, pg. 1360
PAYCOR HCM, INC.; *U.S. Public*, pg. 1656
PAYLESS HOLDINGS LLC; *U.S. Private*, pg. 3117
PAYLESS SHOESOURCE WORLDWIDE, LLC—See Payless Holdings LLC; *U.S. Private*, pg. 3117
PAYLOCITY HOLDING CORPORATION; *U.S. Public*, pg. 1656
PAYMENTUS HOLDINGS, INC.; *U.S. Public*, pg. 1656
THE PAYNE INVESTMENT COMPANY—See Brittany Stamping, LLC; *U.S. Private*, pg. 657
PAYPAL HOLDINGS, INC.; *U.S. Public*, pg. 1656
PBF HOLDING COMPANY LLC—See PBF Energy Inc.; *U.S. Public*, pg. 1657
PBS ENTERPRISES, INC.—See Public Broadcasting Service; *U.S. Private*, pg. 3298
PCI MEDIA, INC.; *U.S. Private*, pg. 3120
PDI GROUP INC.; *U.S. Private*, pg. 3122
PD PORTS GROUP LIMITED—See Brookfield Infrastructure Partners L.P.; *Int'l*, pg. 1190
PD PORTS LTD.—See Brookfield Infrastructure Partners L.P.; *Int'l*, pg. 1190
PEABODY HOLDING COMPANY INC.—See Peabody Energy Corporation; *U.S. Public*, pg. 1659
PEAK GLOBAL HOLDINGS, LLC; *U.S. Private*, pg. 3123
PEAK RESORTS, INC.—See Vail Resorts, Inc.; *U.S. Public*, pg. 2271
PEARL COMPANIES; *U.S. Private*, pg. 3125
PEDRO'S LIST, INC.; *U.S. Public*, pg. 1660
PEI, INC.; *U.S. Private*, pg. 3130
PENDAFORM CORPORATION—See Kruger Brown Holdings, LLC; *U.S. Private*, pg. 2353
PENGUIN RANDOM HOUSE LTD.—See Bertelsmann SE & Co. KGaA; *Int'l*, pg. 991
THE PENNANT GROUP, INC.; *U.S. Public*, pg. 2118
PENN NATIONAL HOLDING CORP.—See Pennsylvania National Mutual Casualty Insurance Company; *U.S. Private*, pg. 3137
PENNSYLVANIA REAL ESTATE INVESTMENT TRUST; *U.S. Public*, pg. 1663
PENN TREATY AMERICAN CORPORATION; *U.S. Private*, pg. 3135
PENSKE AUTOMOTIVE GROUP, INC.; *U.S. Public*, pg. 1664
PENTAX OF AMERICA, INC.—See Hoya Corporation; *Int'l*, pg. 3495
PENTAX SINTAI HOLDING CO., LTD.—See Hoya Corporation; *Int'l*, pg. 3495
PEOPLE'S JEWELRY COMPANY, INC.; *U.S. Private*, pg. 3141
PEPCO HOLDINGS LLC—See Exelon Corporation; *U.S. Public*, pg. 807
PEP INDUSTRIES LLC—See Nautic Partners, LLC; *U.S. Private*, pg. 2871
PEP INDUSTRIES LLC—See The Jordan Company, L.P.; *U.S. Private*, pg. 4061
PEPPER CONSTRUCTION GROUP, LLC; *U.S. Private*, pg. 3144

PEPSICO AMERICAS BEVERAGES—See PepsiCo, Inc.; *U.S. Public*, pg. 1669
PEPSICO CANADA ULC—See PepsiCo, Inc.; *U.S. Public*, pg. 1671
PEPSICO DO BRASIL HOLDING LTDA.—See PepsiCo, Inc.; *U.S. Public*, pg. 1671
PEPSICO INDIA HOLDINGS PRIVATE LIMITED—See PepsiCo, Inc.; *U.S. Public*, pg. 1671
PEPSI-COLA & NATIONAL BRAND BEVERAGES, LTD.; *U.S. Private*, pg. 3145
PERCEPTION CAPITAL CORP. III; *U.S. Public*, pg. 1673
PERFORMANCE FOOD GROUP COMPANY; *U.S. Public*, pg. 1674
PERFORMANCE HEALTH HOLDINGS, INC.—See Madison Dearborn Partners, LLC; *U.S. Private*, pg. 2542
PERKINELMER HOLDING GMBH—See Revvity, Inc.; *U.S. Public*, pg. 1795
PERMASTEELISA PACIFIC HOLDINGS LTD.—See Atlas Holdings, LLC; *U.S. Private*, pg. 377
PERMASWAGE HOLDINGS, INC.—See Berkshire Hathaway Inc.; *U.S. Public*, pg. 314
PERMIAN RESOURCES CORP; *U.S. Public*, pg. 1677
PERNIX THERAPEUTICS HOLDINGS, INC.; *U.S. Private*, pg. 3152
PERPETUAL CORPORATION—See Sinclair, Inc.; *U.S. Public*, pg. 1885
PERSEUS BOOKS, LLC; *U.S. Private*, pg. 3155
PERSHING SQUARE SPARC HOLDINGS, LTD.; *U.S. Private*, pg. 3155
PERSPECTA INC.—See Veritas Capital Fund Management, LLC; *U.S. Private*, pg. 4363
PERSPECTIVE THERAPEUTICS, INC.; *U.S. Public*, pg. 1678
PESTCO HOLDINGS, LLC—See Thompson Street Capital Manager LLC; *U.S. Private*, pg. 4161
PETCO HEALTH AND WELLNESS COMPANY, INC.; *U.S. Public*, pg. 1678
PETCO HOLDINGS, INC.—See Canada Pension Plan Investment Board; *Int'l*, pg. 1281
PETCO HOLDINGS, INC.—See CVC Capital Partners SICAV-FIS S.A.; *Int'l*, pg. 1885
PETE HARKNESS AUTO GROUP, INC.; *U.S. Private*, pg. 3157
PETER KIEWIT SONS', INC.; *U.S. Private*, pg. 3158
PETRA NOVA PARISH HOLDINGS LLC—See ENEOS Holdings, Inc.; *Int'l*, pg. 2417
PETRO USA, INC.; *U.S. Public*, pg. 1678
PETRUS BRANDS, INC.; *U.S. Private*, pg. 3163
PETTY HOLDINGS LLC—See BV Investment Partners, LLC; *U.S. Private*, pg. 699
PFB CORP.—See The Riverside Company; *U.S. Private*, pg. 4109
P.F. CHANG'S CHINA BISTRO, INC.—See Centerbridge Partners, L.P.; *U.S. Private*, pg. 815
PF CONCEPT INTERNATIONAL B.V.—See Charlesbank Capital Partners, LLC; *U.S. Private*, pg. 855
PFIZER ASIA INTERNATIONAL B.V.—See Pfizer Inc.; *U.S. Public*, pg. 1680
PFIZER HOLDINGS INTERNATIONAL LUXEMBOURG (PHIL) SARL—See Pfizer Inc.; *U.S. Public*, pg. 1681
PFIZER MEDICAMENTOS GENERICOS E PARTICIPACOES LTDA.—See Pfizer Inc.; *U.S. Public*, pg. 1682
PFIZER PFE NEW ZEALAND HOLDING B.V.—See Pfizer Inc.; *U.S. Public*, pg. 1682
PGL GROUP LIMITED—See Cox & Kings Limited; *Int'l*, pg. 1823
PGM HOLDINGS K.K.—See Heiwa Corporation; *Int'l*, pg. 3327
PGT INNOVATIONS, INC.—See Koch Industries, Inc.; *U.S. Private*, pg. 2332
PHARAOH GOLD MINES NL—See Centamin plc; *Int'l*, pg. 1402
PHAZAR CORP.; *U.S. Public*, pg. 3166
THE PHILADELPHIA CONTRIBUTIONSHIP; *U.S. Private*, pg. 4094
PHILADELPHIA ENERGY SOLUTIONS INC.—See Energy Transfer LP; *U.S. Public*, pg. 764
PHILADELPHIA FINANCIAL GROUP, INC.—See Blackstone Inc.; *U.S. Public*, pg. 356
PHILADELPHIA FLYERS, LLC—See Comcast Corporation; *U.S. Public*, pg. 538
PHILADELPHIA MEDIA HOLDINGS, LLC; *U.S. Private*, pg. 3169
PHILIP MORRIS INTERNATIONAL INC.; *U.S. Public*, pg. 1685
PHILLIPS 66 COMPANY; *U.S. Public*, pg. 1688
PHILLIPS SERVICE INDUSTRIES, INC. (PSI); *U.S. Private*, pg. 3171
PHIPPS VENTURES INC.; *U.S. Private*, pg. 3172
PHMC, INC.; *U.S. Private*, pg. 3172
THE PHOENIX COMPANIES, INC.—See Golden Gate Capital Management II, LLC; *U.S. Private*, pg. 1731
PHOENIX GROUP HOLDINGS LLC; *U.S. Private*, pg. 3173
THE PHOENIX HOLDINGS LTD.—See Delek Group Ltd.; *Int'l*, pg. 2011
PHOENIX MOTOR INC.; *U.S. Public*, pg. 1689
PHYSICAL REHABILITATION NETWORK, LLC—See Gryphon Investors, LLC; *U.S. Private*, pg. 1799

551112 — OFFICES OF OTHER HO...

PHYSICIANS FORMULA HOLDINGS, INC.—See Markwins International Corporation; *U.S. Private*, pg. 2582
PIEDMONT ENERGY PARTNERS, INC.—See Duke Energy Corporation; *U.S. Public*, pg. 691
PIEDMONT MINERALS—See Thiele Kaolin Company; *U.S. Private*, pg. 4144
PIERCE MANAGEMENT GROUP; *U.S. Private*, pg. 3178
PIERPOINT CAPITAL LLC; *U.S. Private*, pg. 3179
PINE GROVE HOLDINGS, LLC; *U.S. Private*, pg. 3182
PINE TREE EQUITY MANAGEMENT, LP.; *U.S. Private*, pg. 3183
PING IDENTITY HOLDING CORP.—See Thoma Bravo, L.P.; *U.S. Private*, pg. 4150
PINNACLE ENTERTAINMENT, INC.—See PENN Entertainment, Inc.; *U.S. Public*, pg. 1662
PINNACLE FOODS FINANCE LLC—See Conagra Brands, Inc.; *U.S. Public*, pg. 564
PINNACLE FOODS GROUP LLC—See Conagra Brands, Inc.; *U.S. Public*, pg. 564
PINNACLE FOODS INC.—See Conagra Brands, Inc.; *U.S. Public*, pg. 564
PINNACLE SUMMER INVESTMENTS, INC.—See Lee Equity Partners LLC; *U.S. Private*, pg. 2412
PINNACLE WEST CAPITAL CORPORATION; *U.S. Public*, pg. 1692
PIONEER MERGER CORP.; *U.S. Public*, pg. 1693
PIONEER PUMP HOLDINGS, INC.—See Franklin Electric Co., Inc.; *U.S. Public*, pg. 878
PIPER SANDLER COMPANIES; *U.S. Public*, pg. 1693
PIRELLI NORTH AMERICA INC.—See China National Chemical Corporation; *Int'l*, pg. 1528
PIRELLI UK LIMITED—See China National Chemical Corporation; *Int'l*, pg. 1529
PIRIFORM LTD.—See Gen Digital Inc.; *U.S. Public*, pg. 910
PISTON GROUP, LLC; *U.S. Private*, pg. 3190
PITTSBURGH BASEBALL HOLDINGS, INC.—See The Nutting Company, Inc.; *U.S. Private*, pg. 4086
PIVOT TECHNOLOGY SOLUTIONS, INC.; *U.S. Public*, pg. 1695
PIVOT TECHNOLOGY SOLUTIONS, LTD.—See Pivot Technology Solutions, Inc.; *U.S. Public*, pg. 1695
PKDM HOLDINGS, INC.; *U.S. Private*, pg. 3193
PLACEMAKERS LIMITED—See Fletcher Building Limited; *Int'l*, pg. 2701
PLACID HOLDING COMPANY; *U.S. Private*, pg. 3194
PLA-FIT HOLDINGS, LLC—See Planet Fitness, Inc.; *U.S. Public*, pg. 1697
PLAINS GP HOLDINGS, L.P.; *U.S. Public*, pg. 1696
PLANET 13 HOLDINGS, INC.; *U.S. Public*, pg. 1697
PLANET FITNESS HOLDINGS, LLC—See Planet Fitness, Inc.; *U.S. Public*, pg. 1697
PLANET GREEN HOLDINGS CORP.; *U.S. Public*, pg. 1697
PLANTATION PETROLEUM HOLDINGS IV, LLC (PPH); *U.S. Private*, pg. 3197
PLANT SYSTEMS & SERVICES PSS GMBH—See ELKA Beteiligungs GmbH; *Int'l*, pg. 2364
PLASTIPAK EUROPE—See Plastipak Holdings, Inc.; *U.S. Private*, pg. 3199
PLASTIPAK HOLDINGS, INC.; *U.S. Private*, pg. 3199
PLASTIQUE HOLDINGS LIMITED—See Sonoco Products Company; *U.S. Public*, pg. 1904
PLATEAU GROUP INC.; *U.S. Private*, pg. 3200
PLAYBOY ENTERPRISES, INC.—See PLBY Group, Inc.; *U.S. Public*, pg. 1698
PLAY COMMUNICATIONS S.A.—See Iliad S.A.; *Int'l*, pg. 3614
PLAYCORE HOLDINGS, INC.—See Court Square Capital Partners, L.P.; *U.S. Private*, pg. 1069
PLAYTEX MARKETING CORP.—See Edgewell Personal Care Company; *U.S. Public*, pg. 718
PLEXUS ASIA, LTD.—See Plexus Corp.; *U.S. Public*, pg. 1698
PLURALSIGHT, INC.; *U.S. Public*, pg. 1699
PLX PHARMA INC.; *U.S. Public*, pg. 1699
PLY GEM HOLDINGS, INC.—See Clayton, Dubilier & Rice, LLC; *U.S. Public*, pg. 921
PLYMOUTH INDUSTRIES INC.—See Hines Corporation; *U.S. Private*, pg. 1949
PMA COMPANIES, INC.—See Old Republic International Corporation; *U.S. Public*, pg. 1568
PMC CAPITAL PARTNERS, LLC; *U.S. Private*, pg. 3217
PMC GROUP, INC.; *U.S. Private*, pg. 3218
PMC, INC.—See PMC Capital Partners, LLC; *U.S. Private*, pg. 3217
POHLAD COMPANIES; *U.S. Private*, pg. 3220
POINT BLANK ENTERPRISES, INC.—See JLL Partners, LLC; *U.S. Private*, pg. 2213
POINT BROADCASTING COMPANY; *U.S. Private*, pg. 3221
THE POINT GROUP; *U.S. Private*, pg. 4097
POLE POSITION RACEWAY, INC.—See K1 Speed, LLC; *U.S. Private*, pg. 2253
POLYCEL HOLDINGS INC.; *U.S. Private*, pg. 3225
POLYNT GROUP HOLDING INC.—See Reichhold, Inc.; *U.S. Private*, pg. 3390
POLYPORE INTERNATIONAL, LP—See Asahi Kasei Corporation; *Int'l*, pg. 597
POP DISPLAYS USA, LLC—See CounterPoint Capital Partners, LLC; *U.S. Private*, pg. 1066
PORTAGE PHARMA LTD.; *U.S. Private*, pg. 3231
PORT AMHERST, LTD.; *U.S. Private*, pg. 3229
PORTILLO'S, INC.; *U.S. Public*, pg. 1702
POSILLICO, INC.; *U.S. Private*, pg. 3233
POSITIVE PHYSICIANS HOLDINGS, INC.; *U.S. Public*, pg. 1703
POSNAVITAS RETAIL SERVICES, INC.; *U.S. Private*, pg. 3234
POST HOLDINGS, INC.; *U.S. Public*, pg. 1703
POSTMEDIA NETWORK CANADA CORP.—See Chatham Asset Management, LLC; *U.S. Public*, pg. 860
POTBELLY CORPORATION; *U.S. Public*, pg. 1704
POTNETWORK HOLDINGS, INC.; *U.S. Public*, pg. 3235
POTOMAC RIVER HOLDINGS, LLC—See Veritex Holdings, Inc.; *U.S. Public*, pg. 2283
POWDR CORP.; *U.S. Private*, pg. 3236
POWER INTEGRATIONS SWITZERLAND HOLDING GMBH—See Power Integrations, Inc.; *U.S. Public*, pg. 1705
POWER PRODUCTS, LLC—See Brunswick Corporation; *U.S. Public*, pg. 408
POWERSCHOOL HOLDINGS, INC.—See Bain Capital, LP; *U.S. Private*, pg. 442
POWERS HOLDINGS, INC.; *U.S. Private*, pg. 3240
POYRY PLC—See AFRY AB; *Int'l*, pg. 194
PPD, INC.—See Thermo Fisher Scientific Inc.; *U.S. Public*, pg. 2150
PPG INDUSTRIES SECURITIES, INC.—See PPG Industries, Inc.; *U.S. Public*, pg. 1709
PPLA PARTICIPATIONS LTD.—See BTG Pactual Holding S.A.; *Int'l*, pg. 1204
PPL CORPORATION; *U.S. Public*, pg. 1711
PPL GLOBAL, LLC—See PPL Corporation; *U.S. Public*, pg. 1712
PPS HOLDINGS AUSTRALIA PTY. LTD.—See Penske Automotive Group, Inc.; *U.S. Public*, pg. 1665
PPS, INC.; *U.S. Private*, pg. 3240
PQ HOLDINGS INC.—See The Carlyle Group Inc.; *U.S. Public*, pg. 2052
PRAESIDIAN CAPITAL CORP.; *U.S. Private*, pg. 3241
PRAIRIE BAND, LLC—See Prairie Band Potawatomi Nation; *U.S. Private*, pg. 3242
PRAISE INTERNATIONAL NORTH AMERICA, INC.; *U.S. Private*, pg. 3243
PRECISION GEAR HOLDINGS LLC—See Zurn Elkay Water Solutions Corporation; *U.S. Public*, pg. 2413
PRECISION INVESTMENT GROUP LLC—See Precision Environmental Co.; *U.S. Private*, pg. 3244
PRECISION MEDICINE GROUP, INC.; *U.S. Private*, pg. 3245
PRECISION PARTNERS HOLDING COMPANY—See Cleveland-Cliffs, Inc.; *U.S. Public*, pg. 514
THE PREDICTIVE INDEX LLC; *U.S. Private*, pg. 4097
PREFERRED CARE PARTNERS HOLDING, CORP.—See UnitedHealth Group Incorporated; *U.S. Public*, pg. 2249
PREFERRED FINANCIAL CORPORATION—See Health Care Service Corporation; *U.S. Private*, pg. 1892
PREMDOR U.K. HOLDINGS LIMITED—See Owens Corning; *U.S. Public*, pg. 1627
PREMETALCO INC.—See Amalgamated Metal Corporation PLC; *Int'l*, pg. 409
PREMIER BRANDS GROUP HOLDINGS LLC; *U.S. Private*, pg. 3249
PREMIERE GLOBAL SERVICES, INC.—See Siris Capital Group, LLC; *U.S. Private*, pg. 3673
PREMIER FARNELL CORP.—See Avnet, Inc.; *U.S. Public*, pg. 254
PREMIER FARNELL LIMITED—See Avnet, Inc.; *U.S. Public*, pg. 253
PREMIER HOLDING CORP.; *U.S. Public*, pg. 1715
PREMIER MORTGAGE SERVICE LIMITED—See Aviva plc; *Int'l*, pg. 746
PREMIER NEEDLE ARTS, INC.—See Blue Point Capital Partners, LLC; *U.S. Public*, pg. 590
PREMIER PRODUCT GROUP, INC.; *U.S. Public*, pg. 1715
PREMIER VENTURES, INC.; *U.S. Private*, pg. 3251
PREMIUM LEISURE CORP.—See Belle Corporation; *Int'l*, pg. 966
PREMIUM WATER HOLDINGS, INC.—See Hikari Tsushin, Inc.; *Int'l*, pg. 3390
PRESIDIO, INC.—See BC Partners LLP; *Int'l*, pg. 925
PRESS GANEY HOLDINGS, INC.—See Ares Management Corporation; *U.S. Public*, pg. 190
PRESS GANEY HOLDINGS, INC.—See Leonard Green & Partners, L.P.; *U.S. Private*, pg. 2427
PRESSURE THERMAL DYNAMICS B.V.—See BENCIS Capital Partners B.V.; *Int'l*, pg. 970
PRESTIGE CRUISE HOLDINGS, INC—See Norwegian Cruise Line Holdings Ltd.; *U.S. Public*, pg. 1543
PREZZO LIMITED—See TPG Capital, L.P.; *U.S. Private*, pg. 2175
PRGX UK HOLDINGS LTD—See PRGX Global, Inc.; *U.S. Private*, pg. 3257
PRIDE TREE HOLDINGS, INC.; *U.S. Private*, pg. 3260
PRIME ABA, LP—See Godspeed Capital Management LP; *U.S. Private*, pg. 1725
PRIME HEALTHCARE SERVICES, INC.; *U.S. Private*, pg. 3261
PRIME RISK PARTNERS INC.—See Keystone Group, L.P.; *U.S. Private*, pg. 2299
PRIMORIS SERVICES CORPORATION; *U.S. Public*, pg. 1718
PRIMO WATER CORPORATION; *U.S. Public*, pg. 1717
PRIMUS TELECOM PTY. LTD.—See Aware Super Pty Ltd; *Int'l*, pg. 752
PRINCIPAL FINANCIAL GROUP, INC.; *U.S. Public*, pg. 1719
PRINCIPAL INTERNATIONAL (ASIA) LIMITED—See Principal Financial Group, Inc.; *U.S. Public*, pg. 1721
PRINCIPAL INTERNATIONAL, INC.—See Principal Financial Group, Inc.; *U.S. Public*, pg. 1721
PRIORITY AVIATION, INC.; *U.S. Private*, pg. 3266
THE PRITZKER ORGANIZATION, LLC; *U.S. Private*, pg. 4100
PRIVETERRA ACQUISITION CORP. II; *U.S. Public*, pg. 1722
PROALLIANCE CORPORATION; *U.S. Private*, pg. 3271
PROAMPAC LLC—See The Pritzker Group - Chicago, LLC; *U.S. Private*, pg. 4099
PROASSURANCE CORPORATION; *U.S. Public*, pg. 1722
PROCACCI HOLDINGS LLC; *U.S. Private*, pg. 3271
PROCESS INSIGHTS HOLDINGS LLC—See IGP Industries, LLC; *U.S. Private*, pg. 2040
PROCESS SOLUTIONS—See One Rock Capital Partners, LLC; *U.S. Private*, pg. 3023
PROCTER & GAMBLE JAPAN K.K.—See The Procter & Gamble Company; *U.S. Public*, pg. 2122
PRODIGY HEALTH GROUP, INC.—See CVS Health Corporation; *U.S. Public*, pg. 615
PRODWAYS GROUP SA—See Groupe Gorge S.A.; *Int'l*, pg. 3103
THE PROFESSIONAL BASKETBALL CLUB, LLC; *U.S. Private*, pg. 4100
PROFESSIONAL PLUMBING GROUP, INC.—See Dunes Point Capital, LLC; *U.S. Private*, pg. 1289
PROFRAC HOLDING CORP.; *U.S. Public*, pg. 1724
PROG HOLDINGS, INC.; *U.S. Public*, pg. 1724
THE PROGRESSIVE CORPORATION; *U.S. Public*, pg. 2124
PROGRESSIVE FINANCE HOLDINGS, LLC—See Aaron's Company, Inc.; *U.S. Public*, pg. 13
PROGRESS RAIL SIGNALING S.P.A.—See Caterpillar, Inc.; *U.S. Public*, pg. 453
PROGRESS SOFTWARE EUROPE B.V.—See Progress Software Corporation; *U.S. Public*, pg. 1725
PROJECT RENDEZVOUS HOLDING CORPORATION—See Star Equity Holdings, Inc.; *U.S. Public*, pg. 1937
PROLIANCE HOLDINGS, LLC—See CenterPoint Energy, Inc.; *U.S. Public*, pg. 472
PROLOGIS, L.P.—See Prologis, Inc.; *U.S. Public*, pg. 1727
PRO MACH GROUP, INC.—See Leonard Green & Partners, L.P.; *U.S. Private*, pg. 2427
PROMETHEUS GLOBAL MEDIA LLC—See Valence Media Group; *U.S. Private*, pg. 4330
PROMISE HOLDINGS, LLC; *U.S. Private*, pg. 3283
PROMONTORIA MMB SAS—See Cerberus Capital Management, L.P.; *U.S. Private*, pg. 839
PROMUS HOLDINGS, LLC; *U.S. Private*, pg. 3283
PROPEL MEDIA, INC.; *U.S. Public*, pg. 1727
PROSERV HOLDINGS LIMITED—See Riverstone Holdings LLC; *U.S. Private*, pg. 3447
PROTECTIVE LIFE CORPORATION—See Dai-ichi Life Holdings, Inc.; *U.S. Public*, pg. 1917
PROTECT PHARMACEUTICAL CORPORATION; *U.S. Public*, pg. 1729
PROTON HOLDINGS BERHAD—See DRB-HICOM Berhad; *Int'l*, pg. 2202
PROVENTIA GROUP OY—See Head Invest Oy; *Int'l*, pg. 3301
PROVIMI HOLDING B.V.—See Cargill, Inc.; *U.S. Private*, pg. 759
PROVIMI S.A.—See Cargill, Inc.; *U.S. Private*, pg. 759
PROVISION HOLDING, INC.; *U.S. Public*, pg. 1730
PROXES GMBH—See Capvis AG; *Int'l*, pg. 1318
PRP HOLDINGS, LLC—See Bloomin' Brands, Inc.; *U.S. Public*, pg. 363
PRUDENTIAL DO BRASIL SEGUROS DE VIDA S.A.—See Prudential Financial, Inc.; *U.S. Public*, pg. 1733
PRUDENTIAL HEALTH HOLDINGS LIMITED—See Discovery Limited; *Int'l*, pg. 2134
PRUDENTIAL INTERNATIONAL INSURANCE HOLDINGS, LTD.—See Prudential Financial, Inc.; *U.S. Public*, pg. 1732
PRUDENTIAL INTERNATIONAL INVESTMENTS CORPORATION—See Prudential Financial, Inc.; *U.S. Public*, pg. 1732
PSA HOLDINGS, INC.; *U.S. Private*, pg. 3296
PSC, LLC—See Littlejohn & Co., LLC; *U.S. Private*, pg. 2471
PSYC CORPORATION; *U.S. Public*, pg. 1734
PT ADVANTECH INTERNATIONAL—See Advantech Co., Ltd.; *Int'l*, pg. 165
PT HOLDING COMPANY, LLC—See Duke Energy Corporation; *U.S. Public*, pg. 691

N.A.I.C.S. Index

551112 — OFFICES OF OTHER HO... CORPORATE AFFILIATIONS

PT HOLDING INVESTMENT B.V.—See Energeticky a Prumyslovy Holding, a.s.; *Int'l*, pg. 2420
PT HOLDINGS, LLC—See Berkshire Partners LLC; *U.S. Private*, pg. 535
PT PORTUGAL, SGPS, S.A.—See Altice Europe N.V.; *Int'l*, pg. 392
PUBCO CORPORATION; *U.S. Private*, pg. 3298
PUBLIC POLICY HOLDING COMPANY; *U.S. Public*, pg. 1735
PUBLICSQ. INC.; *U.S. Public*, pg. 1736
PUBLIX SUPER MARKETS, INC.; *U.S. Private*, pg. 3301
PUERTO RICO SUPPLY GROUP; *U.S. Private*, pg. 3302
PUGET ENERGY, INC.—See Alberta Investment Management Corporation; *Int'l*, pg. 298
PUGET ENERGY, INC.—See British Columbia Investment Management Corp.; *Int'l*, pg. 1169
PUGET ENERGY, INC.—See Canada Pension Plan Investment Board; *Int'l*, pg. 1281
PULTEGROUP, INC.; *U.S. Public*, pg. 1737
PURECYCLE TECHNOLOGIES, INC.; *U.S. Public*, pg. 1738
PURPLE INNOVATION, INC.; *U.S. Public*, pg. 1738
PVI HOLDINGS INC.—See MiddleGround Management, LP; *U.S. Private*, pg. 2712
PWS INVESTMENTS, INC.; *U.S. Private*, pg. 3308
PYBAR HOLDINGS PTY. LTD.—See ACS, Actividades de Construccion y Servicios, S.A.; *Int'l*, pg. 113
PYBAR HOLDINGS PTY. LTD.—See Elliott Management Corporation; *U.S. Private*, pg. 1365
PYRRHA INVESTMENTS B.V.—See Caterpillar, Inc.; *U.S. Public*, pg. 453
PYXUS INTERNATIONAL, INC.; *U.S. Public*, pg. 1740
Q2 HOLDINGS, INC.; *U.S. Public*, pg. 1741
QCE FINANCE LLC; *U.S. Private*, pg. 3312
QONTIGO GMBH—See Deutsche Borse AG; *Int'l*, pg. 2064
QORVO, INC.; *U.S. Public*, pg. 1743
QORVO US, INC.—See Qorvo, Inc.; *U.S. Public*, pg. 1743
QUADRANT METALS TECHNOLOGIES, LLC—See ARC Group Worldwide, Inc.; *U.S. Public*, pg. 179
QUADRIGA WORLDWIDE LIMITED—See Exceptional Innovation BV; *Int'l*, pg. 2579
QUAKER HOLDINGS (UK) LTD.—See PepsiCo, Inc.; *U.S. Public*, pg. 1670
QUALITY DISTRIBUTION, INC.—See Apax Partners LLP; *Int'l*, pg. 505
QUALITY PRODUCTS INC.; *U.S. Private*, pg. 3320
QUALUS POWER SERVICES CORP.—See New Mountain Capital, LLC; *U.S. Private*, pg. 2903
QUANTA SERVICES, INC.; *U.S. Public*, pg. 1750
QUANTUM COMPUTING INC.; *U.S. Public*, pg. 1753
QUANTUM UTILITY GENERATION, LLC—See Quantum Energy Partners, LLC; *U.S. Private*, pg. 3323
QUESTE CAPITAL; *U.S. Private*, pg. 3326
QUEXCO INCORPORATED; *U.S. Private*, pg. 3326
QUIDELORTHO CORPORATION; *U.S. Public*, pg. 1756
QUIKRETE HOLDINGS, INC.—See The Quikrete Companies, LLC; *U.S. Private*, pg. 4101
QUORUM HEALTH CORPORATION; *U.S. Private*, pg. 3329
QURATE RETAIL GROUP, INC.—See Qurate Retail, Inc.; *U.S. Public*, pg. 1758
QURATE RETAIL, INC.; *U.S. Public*, pg. 1757
QWEST COMMUNICATIONS INTERNATIONAL INC.—See Lumen Technologies, Inc.; *U.S. Public*, pg. 1347
QXO, INC.; *U.S. Public*, pg. 1758
R1 RCM HOLDCO INC.—See R1 RCM Inc.; *U.S. Public*, pg. 1758
R.A.B. HOLDINGS, INC.; *U.S. Private*, pg. 3334
RABO VASTGOEDGROEP HOLDING N.V.—See Cooperatieve Centrale Raiffeisen-Boerenleenbank B.A.; *Int'l*, pg. 1791
RACO HOLDINGS, LLC—See The Graham Group, Inc.; *U.S. Private*, pg. 4037
RADIANT GLOBAL LOGISTICS LTD.—See Radiant Logistics, Inc.; *U.S. Public*, pg. 1759
RADIANT LOGISTICS, INC.; *U.S. Public*, pg. 1759
RADIOMETER GMBH—See Danaher Corporation; *U.S. Public*, pg. 630
RADIOMETER (UK) LTD.—See Danaher Corporation; *U.S. Public*, pg. 630
RADISSON HOSPITALITY AB—See Carlson Companies Inc.; *U.S. Private*, pg. 764
RADIUS GLOBAL INFRASTRUCTURE, INC.—See EQT AB; *Int'l*, pg. 2479
RADIX DEVELOPMENT COMPANY LIMITED—See Fullsun International Holdings Group Co., Limited; *Int'l*, pg. 2843
RAFAEL HOLDINGS, INC.; *U.S. Public*, pg. 1761
RAFFERTY HOLDINGS, LLC; *U.S. Private*, pg. 3345
RAG-BETEILIGUNGS-AKTIEN—See EVN AG; *Int'l*, pg. 2571
RA GLOBAL SERVICES, INC.; *U.S. Public*, pg. 1758
RAINEY ROAD HOLDINGS, INC.; *U.S. Private*, pg. 3347
RAINIER PARTNERS LP; *U.S. Private*, pg. 3348
RALLY AUTO GROUP, INC.; *U.S. Private*, pg. 3350
RALLYE S.A.—See Finatis SA; *Int'l*, pg. 2670
RANADIVE GROUP; *U.S. Private*, pg. 3352
RANDA CORP.; *U.S. Private*, pg. 3353
RANDOLPH GROUP, INC.; *U.S. Private*, pg. 3354
RANDY MARION INCORPORATED; *U.S. Private*, pg. 3354
RANGER AEROSPACE LLC; *U.S. Private*, pg. 3354
RANGE RESOURCES-LOUISIANA, INC.—See Range Resources Corporation; *U.S. Public*, pg. 1762
RANI THERAPEUTICS HOLDINGS, INC.; *U.S. Public*, pg. 1762
RA SUSHI HOLDING CORP.—See TPG Capital, L.P.; *U.S. Public*, pg. 2167
RATIONAL GROUP LIMITED—See Flutter Entertainment plc; *Int'l*, pg. 2715
RAY LAETHEM, INC.; *U.S. Private*, pg. 3358
RAYMOND JAMES FINANCIAL, INC.; *U.S. Public*, pg. 1763
RAYMOND JAMES SOUTH AMERICAN HOLDINGS, INC.—See Raymond James Financial, Inc.; *U.S. Public*, pg. 1765
R.B. PAMPLIN CORPORATION; *U.S. Private*, pg. 3334
RCAP HOLDINGS, LLC; *U.S. Private*, pg. 3361
RCI HOSPITALITY HOLDINGS, INC.; *U.S. Public*, pg. 1767
RCM TECHNOLOGIES, INC.; *U.S. Public*, pg. 1767
RDA HOLDING CO.; *U.S. Private*, pg. 3363
R.D. OFFUTT COMPANY; *U.S. Private*, pg. 3335
RDV CORPORATION; *U.S. Private*, pg. 3364
RDV SPORTS, INC.—See RDV Corporation; *U.S. Private*, pg. 3364
THE READING GROUP, LLC—See J.B. Poindexter & Co., Inc.; *U.S. Private*, pg. 2159
READING INTERNATIONAL, INC.; *U.S. Public*, pg. 1768
READY MIX USA, INC.; *U.S. Private*, pg. 3367
REAL ALLOY HOLDING, INC.—See Elah Holdings, Inc.; *U.S. Public*, pg. 722
REALTY USA LLC; *U.S. Private*, pg. 3369
RECRUITER.COM GROUP, INC.—See Chicken Soup for the Soul Entertainment, Inc.; *U.S. Public*, pg. 488
REC SOLAR HOLDINGS AS—See China National Chemical Corporation; *Int'l*, pg. 1527
RED APPLE GROUP, INC.; *U.S. Private*, pg. 3372
RED CAT HOLDINGS, INC.; *U.S. Public*, pg. 1769
RED DOG HOLDINGS, LLC—See EZCORP, Inc.; *U.S. Public*, pg. 818
REDDY ICE HOLDINGS, INC.—See Centerbridge Partners, L.P.; *U.S. Private*, pg. 815
REDHAWK HOLDINGS CORP.; *U.S. Public*, pg. 1770
RED HOLDINGS GROUP INC.; *U.S. Private*, pg. 3374
REDOZE HOLDING N.V.—See Assicurazioni Generali S.p.A.; *Int'l*, pg. 647
THE REDPATH GROUP—See ATON GmbH; *Int'l*, pg. 688
RED ROCK RESORTS, INC.; *U.S. Public*, pg. 1769
THE REDSTONE COMPANIES, L.P.; *U.S. Private*, pg. 4103
REDSTONE GROUP HOLDINGS LTD—See GI Manager L.P.; *U.S. Private*, pg. 1693
RED VIOLET, INC.; *U.S. Public*, pg. 1770
REES-JONES FAMILY HOLDINGS LP; *U.S. Private*, pg. 3383
REFRESCO GROUP N.V.—See KKR & Co. Inc.; *U.S. Public*, pg. 1263
REGAL CINEMAS CORPORATION—See Cineworld Group plc; *Int'l*, pg. 1611
REGAL CINEMAS, INC.—See Cineworld Group plc; *Int'l*, pg. 1611
REGAL PLASTIC SUPPLY CO.; *U.S. Private*, pg. 3385
REGAN HOLDING CORPORATION; *U.S. Private*, pg. 3386
REGENERSIS (NEDERLAND) BV—See Francisco Partners Management, LP; *U.S. Private*, pg. 1588
REGENERSIS (SPAIN) COMANDITARIA SIMPLE—See Francisco Partners Management, LP; *U.S. Private*, pg. 1588
REGENT ENTERTAINMENT PARTNERSHIP, L.P.; *U.S. Private*, pg. 3387
REGIONAL BRANDS INC.; *U.S. Public*, pg. 1775
REGIONALCARE HOSPITAL PARTNERS, INC.—See Apollo Global Management, Inc.; *U.S. Public*, pg. 154
REGIONAL ENERGY HOLDINGS, INC.; *U.S. Private*, pg. 3388
REICH & TANG, INC.; *U.S. Private*, pg. 3390
REKOR SYSTEMS, INC.; *U.S. Public*, pg. 1778
REKTGLOBAL, INC.—See Infinite Realty; *U.S. Private*, pg. 2071
THE RELATED COMPANIES, L.P.; *U.S. Private*, pg. 4103
RELATIVITY ACQUISITION CORP.; *U.S. Private*, pg. 3392
RELIANCE FINANCIAL CORPORATION—See Fidelity National Infor; *U.S. Public*, pg. 832
RELIANCE GLOBAL GROUP, INC.; *U.S. Public*, pg. 1778
RELIANT ENERGY RETAIL HOLDINGS, LLC—See NRG Energy, Inc.; *U.S. Public*, pg. 1550
RELIANT HOLDINGS, INC.; *U.S. Public*, pg. 1782
REMARK HOLDINGS, INC.; *U.S. Public*, pg. 1782
RE/MAX HOLDINGS, INC.; *U.S. Public*, pg. 1768
REMEDI SENIORCARE HOLDING CORPORATION; *U.S. Private*, pg. 3396
REMITLY GLOBAL, INC.; *U.S. Public*, pg. 1782
REMORA ROYALTIES, INC.; *U.S. Private*, pg. 3396
RENAISSANCE PHARMA INC.—See RoundTable Healthcare Management, Inc.; *U.S. Private*, pg. 3489
RENAISSANCE POWER SYSTEMS, LLC—See Mill City Capital, L.P.; *U.S. Private*, pg. 2730
RENAISSANCE SPORTS & ENTERTAINMENT, LLC; *U.S. Private*, pg. 3397
THE RENCO GROUP INC.; *U.S. Private*, pg. 4104
RENEGY HOLDINGS, INC.; *U.S. Private*, pg. 3397
RENEWABLE FUNDING GROUP, INC.; *U.S. Private*, pg. 3398
RENEWABLE RESOURCES GROUP INC.; *U.S. Private*, pg. 3398
RENNOVA HEALTH, INC.; *U.S. Public*, pg. 1783
RENOVUS CAPITAL PARTNERS; *U.S. Private*, pg. 3399
REPARCO NEDERLAND B.V.—See H2 Equity Partners B.V.; *Int'l*, pg. 3199
REPUBLIC AIRWAYS HOLDINGS INC.; *U.S. Private*, pg. 3401
RESERVOIR GROUP LIMITED—See ALS Limited; *Int'l*, pg. 378
RESOURCE GROUP INTERNATIONAL; *U.S. Private*, pg. 3407
RESTAURANTS OF AMERICA, INC.; *U.S. Private*, pg. 3408
RETAIL NETWORK BV—See CVC Capital Partners SICAV-FIS S.A.; *Int'l*, pg. 1886
REVAL HOLDINGS, INC.; *U.S. Private*, pg. 3413
REVENUE.COM CORPORATION; *U.S. Private*, pg. 3414
REVERE INDUSTRIES, LLC; *U.S. Private*, pg. 3414
REVIMA GROUP SAS—See Ardian SAS; *Int'l*, pg. 556
REVITALIZE CAPITAL; *U.S. Private*, pg. 3416
REVLON, INC.—See MacAndrews & Forbes Incorporated; *U.S. Private*, pg. 2532
REVLON INTERNATIONAL CORPORATION—See MacAndrews & Forbes Incorporated; *U.S. Private*, pg. 2533
REV RENEWABLES, INC.; *U.S. Private*, pg. 3412
REXALL PHARMACY GROUP LTD.—See McKesson Corporation; *U.S. Public*, pg. 1408
REXAM LIMITED—See Ball Corporation; *U.S. Public*, pg. 267
REX FEATURES LTD.—See Shutterstock, Inc.; *U.S. Public*, pg. 1876
REXNORD-ZURN HOLDINGS, INC.—See Zurn Elkay Water Solutions Corporation; *U.S. Public*, pg. 2413
REYDEL AUTOMOTIVE HOLDINGS B.V.—See Cerberus Capital Management, L.P.; *U.S. Private*, pg. 839
REYES HOLDINGS, LLC; *U.S. Private*, pg. 3417
REYNOLDS AMERICAN INC.—See British American Tobacco plc; *Int'l*, pg. 1168
RF2M LTD.—See AEA Investors LP; *U.S. Private*, pg. 113
RGC RESOURCES, INC.; *U.S. Public*, pg. 1796
RGP HOLDING, INC.; *U.S. Private*, pg. 3420
RHI HOLDING LLC—See NOV, Inc.; *U.S. Public*, pg. 1546
RHO ACCELERATION, L.P.—See Rho Capital Partners, Inc.; *U.S. Private*, pg. 3421
RHODIUS GMBH—See Equistone Partners Europe Limited; *Int'l*, pg. 2487
RHONE GROUP, LLC; *U.S. Private*, pg. 3422
RHON-KLINIKUM AKTIENGESELLSCHAFT—See Asklepios Kliniken GmbH & Co. KGaA; *Int'l*, pg. 624
RH; *U.S. Public*, pg. 1796
RIALTO HOLDINGS, LLC—See Lennar Corporation; *U.S. Public*, pg. 1307
RIBBON COMMUNICATIONS INC.; *U.S. Public*, pg. 1796
RIBBON COMMUNICATIONS OPERATING COMPANY, INC.—See Ribbon Communications Inc.; *U.S. Public*, pg. 1797
RICE AUTOMOTIVE GROUP; *U.S. Private*, pg. 3425
RICHARD O'BRIEN COMPANIES, INC.; *U.S. Private*, pg. 3428
RICH ENTERTAINMENT GROUP, LLC—See Rich Holdings, Inc.; *U.S. Private*, pg. 3426
RICH HOLDINGS, INC.; *U.S. Private*, pg. 3426
RICK CASE ENTERPRISES, INC.; *U.S. Private*, pg. 3431
RIDGETOP HOLDING CO., INC.; *U.S. Private*, pg. 3433
RIDLEY USA INC.—See Alltech, Inc.; *U.S. Private*, pg. 194
RIETER AUTOMOTIVE (INTERNATIONAL) AG—See Autoneum Holding Ltd.; *Int'l*, pg. 731
RIGHT LANE INDUSTRIES, LLC; *U.S. Private*, pg. 3435
RIGHT SIDE CAPITAL MANAGEMENT, LLC; *U.S. Private*, pg. 3436
RILEY EXPLORATION GROUP, LLC; *U.S. Private*, pg. 3436
RIMROCK HOLDINGS CORPORATION—See Lincoln Electric Holdings, Inc.; *U.S. Public*, pg. 1318
RIO MINAS ENERGIA PARTICIPACOES S.A.—See Companhia Energetica de Minas Gerais - CEMIG; *Int'l*, pg. 1747
RIO PARANAPANEMA PARTICIPACOES S.A.—See China Three Gorges Corporation; *Int'l*, pg. 1558
RIO PROPERTIES, INC.—See Caesars Entertainment, Inc.; *U.S. Public*, pg. 420
RIPPE & KINGSTON, LLC; *U.S. Private*, pg. 3439
RISANAMENTO S.P.A.—See Domus Fin S.A.; *Int'l*, pg. 2162
RISING INDIA, INC.; *U.S. Private*, pg. 3440
RISING PHOENIX HOLDINGS CORPORATION; *U.S. Private*, pg. 3440
RISKON INTERNATIONAL, INC.; *U.S. Public*, pg. 1799
R.I.S.N. OPERATIONS INC.; *U.S. Private*, pg. 3336
RITA RESTAURANT CORP.—See Food Management Partners, Inc.; *U.S. Private*, pg. 1561
RITTENHOUSE SENIOR LIVING; *U.S. Private*, pg. 3442
RIVA FINANCIAL INC.; *U.S. Private*, pg. 3442
RIVERBED TECHNOLOGY, INC.—See Vector Capital Management, L.P.; *U.S. Private*, pg. 4351
RIVERLAKE PARTNERS, LLC; *U.S. Private*, pg. 3444
RIVER & MERCANTILE GROUP PLC—See AssetCo plc; *Int'l*, pg. 643

551112 — OFFICES OF OTHER HO...

RIVERSTONE GROUP, INC.; *U.S. Private*, pg. 3446
THE RIVERSTONE GROUP, LLC; *U.S. Private*, pg. 4110
R.J. O'BRIEN (EUROPE) LIMITED—See R.J. O'Brien & Associates, LLC; *U.S. Private*, pg. 3337
R.J. REYNOLDS TOBACCO COMPANY—See British American Tobacco plc; *Int'l*, pg. 1168
R.J. REYNOLDS TOBACCO HOLDINGS, INC.—See British American Tobacco plc; *Int'l*, pg. 1168
R.J. REYNOLDS TOBACCO INTERNATIONAL, INC.—See British American Tobacco plc; *Int'l*, pg. 1168
RJW, INC.; *U.S. Private*, pg. 3449
THE RLJ COMPANIES, LLC; *U.S. Private*, pg. 4110
RLJ ENTERTAINMENT, INC.—See AMC Networks Inc.; *U.S. Public*, pg. 92
RLJ-MCLARTY-LANDERS AUTOMOTIVE HOLDINGS, LLC—See The RLJ Companies, LLC; *U.S. Private*, pg. 4111
RLR, INC.; *U.S. Private*, pg. 3450
RM CROWE MANAGEMENT COMPANY; *U.S. Private*, pg. 3451
RMG NETWORKS HOLDING CORPORATION; *U.S. Private*, pg. 3451
THE RMR GROUP INC.; *U.S. Public*, pg. 2125
ROADMASTER DRIVERS SCHOOL OF TAMPA, INC.—See Career Path Training Corp.; *U.S. Private*, pg. 752
ROADRUNNER TRANSPORTATION SYSTEMS, INC.; *U.S. Public*, pg. 1802
ROBERT FINVARB COMPANIES, LLC; *U.S. Private*, pg. 3458
ROBERT HALF INC.; *U.S. Public*, pg. 1802
ROBERTSON BOIS DICKSON ANDERSON LIMITED—See Camellia Plc; *Int'l*, pg. 1271
ROBERTS PROPERTIES, INC.; *U.S. Private*, pg. 3460
ROBUR INDUSTRY SERVICE GROUP GMBH—See Clayton, Dubilier & Rice, LLC; *U.S. Private*, pg. 926
ROCKHILL HOLDING COMPANY—See State Automobile Mutual Insurance Company; *U.S. Private*, pg. 3461
ROCKPOINT GAS STORAGE LP—See Brookfield Infrastructure Partners L.P.; *Int'l*, pg. 1190
ROCKRESORTS INTERNATIONAL, LLC—See Vail Resorts, Inc.; *U.S. Public*, pg. 2271
ROCK VENTURES LLC; *U.S. Private*, pg. 3465
ROCKVILLE PIKE HOLDINGS, LLC—See Saul Centers, Inc.; *U.S. Public*, pg. 1842
ROCKWOOD HOLDINGS LIMITED PARTNERSHIP; *U.S. Private*, pg. 3468
ROCKWOOD SERVICE CORPORATION—See Rockwood Holdings Limited Partnership; *U.S. Private*, pg. 3468
ROCKY MOUNTAIN CHOCOLATE FACTORY, INC.; *U.S. Public*, pg. 1807
ROFAN SERVICES LLC—See Dow Inc.; *U.S. Public*, pg. 685
ROLAND RECHTSSCHUTZ BETEILIGUNGS GMBH—See Baloise Holding AG; *Int'l*, pg. 811
ROOFING SUPPLY GROUP, LLC—See Beacon Roofing Supply, Inc.; *U.S. Public*, pg. 286
ROONEY HOLDINGS, INC.; *U.S. Private*, pg. 3479
ROSEBUD MEDIA, LLC; *U.S. Private*, pg. 3482
ROSE DESIGN BUILD, INC.; *U.S. Private*, pg. 3481
ROSEMORE HOLDINGS INC.—See Rosemore Inc.; *U.S. Private*, pg. 3483
ROSEN HOTELS & RESORTS, INC.; *U.S. Private*, pg. 3483
ROSENS DIVERSIFIED, INC.; *U.S. Private*, pg. 3483
THE ROSEWOOD CORPORATION; *U.S. Private*, pg. 4112
ROSNER MANAGEMENT GROUP, LLC; *U.S. Private*, pg. 3485
THE ROSSI GROUP, LLC—See H.I.G. Capital, LLC; *U.S. Private*, pg. 1832
ROTECH HEALTHCARE HOLDINGS INC.; *U.S. Public*, pg. 1815
ROTHENBERGER AG—See Dr. Helmut Rothenberger Holding GmbH; *Int'l*, pg. 2191
ROTHENBERGER WERKZEUGE GMBH—See Dr. Helmut Rothenberger Holding GmbH; *Int'l*, pg. 2191
ROUND2 TECHNOLOGIES, INC.—See Avnet, Inc.; *U.S. Public*, pg. 254
ROUND ROOM LLC; *U.S. Private*, pg. 3488
ROUNDTREE AUTOMOTIVE GROUP, LLC; *U.S. Private*, pg. 3489
ROUSH ENTERPRISES, INC.; *U.S. Private*, pg. 3489
ROV HOLDING, INC.—See Energizer Holdings, Inc.; *U.S. Public*, pg. 761
ROV INTERNATIONAL HOLDINGS LLC—See Energizer Holdings, Inc.; *U.S. Public*, pg. 761
THE ROWMAN & LITTLEFIELD PUBLISHING GROUP, INC.; *U.S. Private*, pg. 4112
ROYAL HOSPITALITY CORP.; *U.S. Private*, pg. 3492
ROYAL OAK VENTURES INC.—See Brookfield Corporation; *Int'l*, pg. 1189
ROYAL ORCHID HOTEL (THAILAND) PUBLIC COMPANY LIMITED—See Grande Asset Hotels & Property Public Company Limited; *Int'l*, pg. 3057
ROYAL SCANDINAVIA A/S—See Axcel Management A/S; *Int'l*, pg. 762
ROYALTY PHARMA PLC; *U.S. Public*, pg. 1816
ROYAL UNITED MINT BV—See Groep Heylen Business & Building BV; *Int'l*, pg. 3087

THE ROZIER MERCANTILE COMPANY; *U.S. Private*, pg. 4113
RP MANAGEMENT, LLC; *U.S. Private*, pg. 3495
RPM CONSUMER HOLDING COMPANY—See RPM International Inc.; *U.S. Public*, pg. 1817
RPM INDUSTRIAL HOLDING CO.—See RPM International Inc.; *U.S. Public*, pg. 1817
RPM INTERNATIONAL INC.; *U.S. Public*, pg. 1816
RPM WOOD FINISHES GROUP, INC.—See RPM International Inc.; *U.S. Public*, pg. 1819
RR DONNELLEY (CHINA) HOLDING CO., LTD.—See Chatham Asset Management, LLC; *U.S. Private*, pg. 865
RTL GROUP S.A.—See Bertelsmann SE & Co. KGaA; *Int'l*, pg. 993
RTS HOLDINGS, LLC—See Ridgemont Partners Management LLC; *U.S. Private*, pg. 3433
R.T. VANDERBILT HOLDING COMPANY, INC.; *U.S. Private*, pg. 3339
RTX CORPORATION; *U.S. Public*, pg. 1820
RUBICON FINANCIAL INCORPORATED; *U.S. Private*, pg. 3499
RUBIN INDUSTRIAL CO. INC.—See GenNx360 Capital Partners, L.P.; *U.S. Private*, pg. 1672
RUDER FINN GROUP, INC.; *U.S. Private*, pg. 3501
RUGBY HOLDINGS LLC—See Hardwoods Distribution Inc.; *Int'l*, pg. 3273
RULMECA HOLDING SPA—See Rulmeca Corporation; *U.S. Private*, pg. 3503
RUMPKE CONSOLIDATED COMPANIES, INC.; *U.S. Private*, pg. 3503
RUSH ENTERPRISES, INC.; *U.S. Public*, pg. 1826
RUSSELL HOBBS, INC.—See Spectrum Brands Holdings, Inc.; *U.S. Public*, pg. 1916
RUSS SMALE, INC.; *U.S. Private*, pg. 3506
RUST-OLEUM INTERNATIONAL, LLC—See RPM International Inc.; *U.S. Public*, pg. 1817
RUTAN REALTY, LLC—See Johnson & Johnson; *U.S. Public*, pg. 1200
RUTH'S HOSPITALITY GROUP, INC.—See Darden Restaurants, Inc.; *U.S. Public*, pg. 633
RYAN SANDERS BASEBALL, L.P.; *U.S. Private*, pg. 3510
RYAN SEACREST ENTERPRISES, INC.; *U.S. Private*, pg. 3510
RYAN SPECIALTY GROUP, LLC—See Ryan Specialty Holdings, Inc.; *U.S. Public*, pg. 1827
RYAN SPECIALTY HOLDINGS, INC.; *U.S. Public*, pg. 1827
RYDER SYSTEM, INC.; *U.S. Public*, pg. 1828
RYERSON HOLDING CORPORATION; *U.S. Public*, pg. 1828
SAAD'S HEALTHCARE SERVICES, INC.; *U.S. Private*, pg. 3519
SABA INFRAESTRUCTURAS, S.A.—See Fundacion Bancaria Caixa d'Estalvis i Pensions de Barcelona, la Caixa; *Int'l*, pg. 2845
SABAL HOLDINGS INC.; *U.S. Private*, pg. 3520
SABINE OIL & GAS HOLDINGS, INC.; *U.S. Private*, pg. 3521
SA BPI-GROUPE—See Caisse des Depots et Consignations; *Int'l*, pg. 1258
SA BPI-GROUPE—See EPIC Bpifrance; *Int'l*, pg. 2460
SABRE HOLDINGS CORPORATION—See Sabre Corporation; *U.S. Public*, pg. 1833
SABSA HOLDINGS (PTY) LTD.—See Anheuser-Busch InBev SA/NV; *Int'l*, pg. 464
SACHS HOLDING COMPANY; *U.S. Private*, pg. 3521
SACKETT NATIONAL HOLDINGS, INC.; *U.S. Private*, pg. 3522
SADDLEBROOK HOLDINGS, INC.; *U.S. Private*, pg. 3522
SAFE AUTO INSURANCE GROUP, INC.; *U.S. Private*, pg. 3523
SAFE & GREEN HOLDINGS CORP.; *U.S. Public*, pg. 1834
SAFEGUARD SCIENTIFICS, INC.; *U.S. Public*, pg. 1834
SAFEMARK INC.—See MSouth Equity Partners, LLC; *U.S. Private*, pg. 2808
SAFETY-KLEEN, INC.—See Clean Harbors, Inc.; *U.S. Public*, pg. 510
SAFETY TECHNOLOGY HOLDINGS, INC.—See Bridgepoint Group Plc; *Int'l*, pg. 1155
SAFEWAY INC.—See Cerberus Capital Management, L.P.; *U.S. Private*, pg. 836
SAFIRE REHABILITATION OF AMHERST, LLC; *U.S. Private*, pg. 3525
SAGA GROUP LIMITED—See Charterhouse Capital Partners LLP; *Int'l*, pg. 1454
SAGA GROUP LIMITED—See CVC Capital Partners SICAV-FIS S.A.; *Int'l*, pg. 1881
SAGE HOLDING COMPANY; *U.S. Private*, pg. 3526
SAGE INVESTMENT HOLDINGS; *U.S. Private*, pg. 3526
SAGICOR FINANCIAL CORPORATION LIMITED—See Alignvest Management Corporation; *Int'l*, pg. 327
SAGICOR USA, INC.—See Alignvest Management Corporation; *Int'l*, pg. 328
SAGITTARIUS BRANDS, INC.—See Charlesbank Capital Partners, LLC; *U.S. Private*, pg. 856
SAGITTARIUS BRANDS, INC.—See Grotech Ventures; *U.S. Private*, pg. 1793
SAGITTARIUS BRANDS, INC.—See Leonard Green & Partners, L.P.; *U.S. Private*, pg. 2429

SAIA-BURGESS ELECTRONICS HOLDING AG—See Honeywell International Inc.; *U.S. Public*, pg. 1051
SAILBRI COOPER INC.—See Hebei Sailhero Environmental Protection High-Tech Co., Ltd.; *Int'l*, pg. 3306
SAINT-GOBAIN CORPORATION—See Compagnie de Saint-Gobain SA; *Int'l*, pg. 1729
SAINT-GOBAIN DEUTSCHE GLAS GMBH—See Compagnie de Saint-Gobain SA; *Int'l*, pg. 1732
SAINT-GOBAIN—See Compagnie de Saint-Gobain SA; *Int'l*, pg. 1730
SAINT-GOBAIN WEBER—See Compagnie de Saint-Gobain SA; *Int'l*, pg. 1726
SAKS INCORPORATED—See Abrams Capital, LLC; *U.S. Private*, pg. 40
SAKS INCORPORATED—See Rhone Group, LLC; *U.S. Private*, pg. 3423
SAKS INCORPORATED—See WeWork Inc.; *U.S. Public*, pg. 2364
SALESFORCE, INC.; *U.S. Public*, pg. 1836
SALESFUSION INC.—See Accel Partners L.P.; *U.S. Private*, pg. 49
SALESFUSION INC.—See KKR & Co. Inc.; *U.S. Public*, pg. 1238
SALVO TECHNOLOGIES, INC.; *U.S. Private*, pg. 3535
SAMALAJU INDUSTRIES SDN. BHD.—See Cahya Mata Sarawak Berhad; *Int'l*, pg. 1251
SAMBA HOLDINGS, INC.—See ABRY Partners, LLC; *U.S. Private*, pg. 43
SAMMONS FINANCIAL GROUP, INC.—See Sammons Enterprises, Inc.; *U.S. Private*, pg. 3537
SANDATA HOLDINGS, INC.; *U.S. Private*, pg. 3542
SAND OAK CAPITAL LLC; *U.S. Private*, pg. 3542
SANDPIPER CI LIMITED—See Duke Street Capital Limited; *Int'l*, pg. 2224
SANDPIPER CI RETAIL LIMITED—See Duke Street Capital Limited; *Int'l*, pg. 2224
SANDRIDGE HOLDINGS, INC.—See SandRidge Energy, Inc.; *U.S. Public*, pg. 1839
SANDS CHINA LTD.—See Las Vegas Sands Corp.; *U.S. Public*, pg. 1293
SANDSTON CORPORATION; *U.S. Public*, pg. 1840
SANDSTONE GROUP, INC.; *U.S. Private*, pg. 3545
SAN FRANCISCO BASEBALL ASSOCIATES, L.P.; *U.S. Private*, pg. 3540
SARA LEE TRADEMARK HOLDINGS AUSTRALASIA LLC—See Tyson Foods, Inc.; *U.S. Public*, pg. 2210
SA RECYCLING LLC—See Sims Limited; *U.S. Public*, pg. 1883
THE SARPES GROUP, INC.; *U.S. Private*, pg. 4114
SASSER FAMILY HOLDINGS, INC.; *U.S. Private*, pg. 3552
SAT & CO. HOLDING A.S.—See Fincraft Resources JSC; *Int'l*, pg. 2672
SATELLITE HOLDINGS, INC.; *U.S. Private*, pg. 3553
SAUER-DANFOSS CHINA HOLDING COMPANY APS—See Danfoss A/S; *Int'l*, pg. 1961
SAVCOR—See Trimble, Inc.; *U.S. Public*, pg. 2191
SAVEDAILY, INC.; *U.S. Private*, pg. 3556
THE SAVE MART COMPANIES, LLC—See Kingswood Capital Management LLC; *U.S. Private*, pg. 2312
SAVERS VALUE VILLAGE, INC.; *U.S. Public*, pg. 1842
SAVEUR FOOD GROUP, LLC; *U.S. Private*, pg. 3556
SAVILLE & HOLDSWORTH LIMITED—See Exponent Private Equity LLP; *Int'l*, pg. 2589
SBEEG HOLDINGS, LLC; *U.S. Private*, pg. 3559
SBI INCORPORATED; *U.S. Private*, pg. 3559
SBP HOLDINGS INC.—See AEA Investors LP; *U.S. Private*, pg. 115
SBR EVENTS GROUP; *U.S. Private*, pg. 3560
SB/RH HOLDINGS, LLC; *U.S. Private*, pg. 3559
SCALEWORKS, INC.; *U.S. Private*, pg. 3561
SCEPTER HOLDINGS, INC.; *U.S. Private*, pg. 3562
SCEPTER HOLDINGS, INC.; *U.S. Private*, pg. 1843
SCF PARTNERS LTD.; *U.S. Private*, pg. 3562
THE SCHAFER COMPANY INC.; *U.S. Private*, pg. 4114
SCHALTBAU HOLDING AG—See The Carlyle Group Inc.; *U.S. Public*, pg. 2052
SCHAUBACH HOLDINGS INC.; *U.S. Private*, pg. 3563
SCHAWK HOLDINGS AUSTRALIA PTY. LTD.—See Matthews International Corporation; *U.S. Public*, pg. 1400
SCHLEGEL UK (2006) LIMITED—See Quanex Building Products Corp.; *U.S. Public*, pg. 1750
SCHLOSSMANN INVESTMENT CORP.; *U.S. Private*, pg. 3565
SCHLUMBERGER LIMITED; *U.S. Public*, pg. 1843
SCHNEIDER NATIONAL, INC.; *U.S. Public*, pg. 1846
SCHOCH HOLDING AG—See PPG Industries, Inc.; *U.S. Public*, pg. 1710
SCHOLASTIC CORPORATION; *U.S. Public*, pg. 1847
SCHOLLE CORPORATION; *U.S. Private*, pg. 3567
SCHONFELD GROUP HOLDINGS, LLC; *U.S. Private*, pg. 3568
SCHOTTENSTEIN STORES CORPORATION; *U.S. Private*, pg. 3568
THE SCHUMACHER GROUP OF LOUISIANA, INC.—See Subsidium Healthcare, LLC; *U.S. Private*, pg. 3847
SCHURZ COMMUNICATIONS, INC.; *U.S. Private*, pg. 3571
THE SCHWARTZBERG COMPANIES; *U.S. Private*, pg. 4115

551112 — OFFICES OF OTHER HO...

SCHWARZ PARTNERS, LP; *U.S. Private*, pg. 3572
SCIENCE 37 HOLDINGS, INC.—See eMed, LLC; *U.S. Private*, pg. 1379
SCIENTURE HOLDINGS, INC.; *U.S. Public*, pg. 1849
SCILEX HOLDING COMPANY; *U.S. Public*, pg. 1849
SCM SINGAPORE HOLDINGS PTE. LTD.—See Caterpillar, Inc.; *U.S. Public*, pg. 453
SCORES HOLDING COMPANY, INC.; *U.S. Public*, pg. 1849
SCOTSMAN INDUSTRIES, INC.—See Ali Holding S.r.l; *Int'l*, pg. 321
SCOTTISHPOWER FINANCIAL SERVICES, INC.—See Iberdrola, S.A.; *Int'l*, pg. 3574
SCOTTISHPOWER GROUP HOLDINGS COMPANY—See Iberdrola, S.A.; *Int'l*, pg. 3573
SCOTTS HOLDINGS LIMITED—See Exponent Private Equity LLP; *Int'l*, pg. 2590
THE SCOTTS MIRACLE-GRO COMPANY; *U.S. Public*, pg. 2126
SD GROUP SERVICE COMPANY LTD.—See Dow Inc.; *U.S. Public*, pg. 686
SEABOARD SOLAR HOLDINGS, LLC; *U.S. Private*, pg. 3583
SEABRIGHT HOLDINGS, INC.—See Enstar Group Limited; *Int'l*, pg. 2449
SEACOR MARINE HOLDINGS INC.; *U.S. Public*, pg. 1851
SEALED AIR (ASIA) HOLDINGS B.V.—See Sealed Air Corporation; *U.S. Public*, pg. 1854
SEALED AIR CORPORATION (US)—See Sealed Air Corporation; *U.S. Public*, pg. 1854
SEALED AIR NETHERLANDS HOLDINGS IV COOPERATIEF U.A.—See Sealed Air Corporation; *U.S. Public*, pg. 1854
SEALS ENTERTAINMENT CORPORATION; *U.S. Private*, pg. 3585
SEARS HOMETOWN AND OUTLET STORES, INC.; *U.S. Public*, pg. 1855
SEAWRIGHT HOLDINGS, INC.; *U.S. Private*, pg. 3592
SECURIAN FINANCIAL GROUP, INC.; *U.S. Private*, pg. 3594
SEDONA CORP.—See Dominion Energy, Inc.; *U.S. Public*, pg. 674
THE SEGAL GROUP, INC.; *U.S. Private*, pg. 4115
SELECTIVE INSURANCE GROUP, INC.; *U.S. Public*, pg. 1862
SELECT MANAGEMENT HOLDINGS, INC.; *U.S. Private*, pg. 3600
SELECT MEDICAL HOLDINGS CORPORATION; *U.S. Public*, pg. 1857
SELECTQUOTE, INC.; *U.S. Public*, pg. 1863
SEMANAL MEDIA, LLC; *U.S. Private*, pg. 3603
SEMGROUP HOLDINGS, L.P.—See Energy Transfer LP; *U.S. Public*, pg. 764
SEMINOLE HOLDINGS GROUP, LLC; *U.S. Private*, pg. 3604
SEMPRA ENERGY HOLDINGS XI B.V.—See Sempra; *U.S. Public*, pg. 1863
SEMPRA MIDSTREAM, INC.—See Sempra; *U.S. Public*, pg. 1863
SEMPRA; *U.S. Public*, pg. 1863
SEMPRA TEXAS HOLDINGS CORP.—See Sempra; *U.S. Public*, pg. 1863
SEMRUSH HOLDINGS, INC.; *U.S. Public*, pg. 1864
SENSATA TECHNOLOGIES B.V.—See Sensata Technologies Holding plc; *U.S. Public*, pg. 1865
SENSATA TECHNOLOGIES HOLDING PLC; *U.S. Public*, pg. 1865
SENSORYEFFECTS, INC.—See Balchem Corporation; *U.S. Public*, pg. 266
SENTRYCARE, INC.; *U.S. Private*, pg. 3611
SEQENS SAS—See Eurazeo SE; *Int'l*, pg. 2529
SEQUENTIAL BRANDS GROUP, INC.; *U.S. Public*, pg. 1868
SERCEL HOLDING SA—See CGG; *Int'l*, pg. 1432
SERRA AUTOMOTIVE, INC.; *U.S. Private*, pg. 3614
SERVICE CORPORATION INTERNATIONAL; *U.S. Public*, pg. 1869
SERVICES GROUP, INC.; *U.S. Private*, pg. 3616
SERVICES GROUP OF AMERICA, INC.; *U.S. Private*, pg. 3616
SESAME BANKHALL GROUP LIMITED—See Aviva plc; *Int'l*, pg. 746
SF HOLDING CORP.; *U.S. Private*, pg. 3621
SFW HOLDING CORP.—See United Natural Foods, Inc.; *U.S. Public*, pg. 2232
SGK LLC—See Matthews International Corporation; *U.S. Public*, pg. 1400
S GROUP INC.; *U.S. Private*, pg. 3512
THE SHANE GROUP, LLC—See Worth Investment Group, LLC; *U.S. Private*, pg. 4570
SHANGHAI ANSHIJIE REAL ESTATE CONSULTANT CO., LTD—See IFM Investments Limited; *Int'l*, pg. 3599
SHANGPHARMA CORPORATION—See TPG Capital, L.P.; *U.S. Private*, pg. 2175
SHAPES/ARCH HOLDINGS, LLC—See H.I.G. Capital, LLC; *U.S. Private*, pg. 1831
SHARING SERVICES GLOBAL CORPORATION; *U.S. Public*, pg. 1873
SHARKNINJA, INC.; *U.S. Public*, pg. 1873

SHARP HOLDING CO.; *U.S. Private*, pg. 3626
SHARP (TAIWAN) ELECTRONICS CORPORATION—See Hon Hai Precision Industry Co., Ltd.; *Int'l*, pg. 3457
SHENYANG HEJIN HOLDING INVESTMENT CO., LTD.—See China CITIC Financial Asset Management Co., Ltd.; *Int'l*, pg. 1489
SHENZHEN CITY NEW CHINA WATER ELECTRIC POWER LIMITED—See China Water Industry Group Limited; *Int'l*, pg. 1563
SHG HOLDINGS CORP.; *U.S. Private*, pg. 3635
SHIFT4 PAYMENTS, INC.; *U.S. Public*, pg. 1874
SHIVERS TRADING & OPERATING COMPANY; *U.S. Private*, pg. 3638
SHL FRANCE SAS—See Exponent Private Equity LLP; *Int'l*, pg. 2589
SHO-DEEN INC.; *U.S. Private*, pg. 3639
SHOP 'N SAVE WAREHOUSE FOODS, INC.—See United Natural Foods, Inc.; *U.S. Public*, pg. 2232
SHULTS MANAGEMENT GROUP, INC.; *U.S. Private*, pg. 3644
SHURE EUROPE GMBH—See Shure Incorporated; *U.S. Private*, pg. 3644
SHUTTLE PHARMACEUTICALS HOLDINGS, INC.; *U.S. Public*, pg. 1876
THE SHYFT GROUP, INC.; *U.S. Public*, pg. 2130
SIDEREAL CAPITAL GROUP, LLC; *U.S. Private*, pg. 3645
SIGLER COMPANIES, INC.; *U.S. Private*, pg. 3648
SIGNATURE AVIATION LIMITED—See BlackRock, Inc.; *U.S. Public*, pg. 346
SIGNATURE AVIATION LIMITED—See Blackstone Inc.; *U.S. Public*, pg. 358
SIGNATURE AVIATION LIMITED—See Cascade Investment LLC; *U.S. Public*, pg. 780
SIGNATURE STYLES, LLC—See Patriarch Partners, LLC; *U.S. Private*, pg. 3109
SIGNET HEALTHCARE PARTNERS, LLC; *U.S. Private*, pg. 3650
SIGNIFY HEALTH, INC.—See CVS Health Corporation; *U.S. Public*, pg. 616
SIGNODE INDUSTRIAL GROUP LLC—See Crown Holdings, Inc.; *U.S. Public*, pg. 599
SILEX HOLDINGS, INC.; *U.S. Private*, pg. 3652
SILGAN WHITE CAP HOLDINGS SPAIN, S.L.—See Silgan Holdings, Inc.; *U.S. Public*, pg. 1879
SILICON MOUNTAIN HOLDINGS, INC.; *U.S. Private*, pg. 3652
SILLOH INDUSTRIES INC.; *U.S. Private*, pg. 3653
SILVER POINT CAPITAL FUND INVESTMENTS LLC—See Silver Point Capital, L.P.; *U.S. Public*, pg. 3662
SILVER POINT CAPITAL, L.P.; *U.S. Private*, pg. 3661
SIMON HOLDINGS LLC; *U.S. Private*, pg. 3666
SIMPLICITY GROUP HOLDINGS—See Simplicity Financial Marketing Holdings Inc.; *U.S. Private*, pg. 3667
SIMPSON INVESTMENT COMPANY; *U.S. Private*, pg. 3668
SIMS GROUP AUSTRALIA HOLDINGS LIMITED—See Sims Limited; *U.S. Public*, pg. 1884
SIMS GROUP CANADA HOLDINGS LIMITED—See Sims Limited; *U.S. Public*, pg. 1883
SIMS GROUP UK HOLDINGS LIMITED—See Sims Limited; *U.S. Public*, pg. 1884
SIMS LIMITED; *U.S. Public*, pg. 1883
SIMS RECYCLING SOLUTIONS HOLDINGS INC.—See Sims Limited; *U.S. Public*, pg. 1884
SIMS RECYCLING SOLUTIONS UK HOLDINGS LTD.—See Sims Limited; *U.S. Public*, pg. 1884
SINCLAIR, INC.; *U.S. Public*, pg. 1885
SINCLAIR KNIGHT MERZ (NZ) HOLDINGS LTD—See Jacobs Engineering Group, Inc.; *U.S. Public*, pg. 1186
SINCLAIR TELEVISION GROUP, INC.—See Sinclair, Inc.; *U.S. Public*, pg. 1885
SINCLAIR TELEVISION OF CHARLESTON, INC.—See Sinclair, Inc.; *U.S. Public*, pg. 1886
SINCLAIR TELEVISION OF DAYTON, INC.—See Sinclair, Inc.; *U.S. Public*, pg. 1886
SINCLAIR TELEVISION OF NEVADA, INC.—See Sinclair, Inc.; *U.S. Public*, pg. 1886
SINCLAIR TELEVISION OF SEATTLE, INC.—See Sinclair, Inc.; *U.S. Public*, pg. 1886
SINCLAIR TELEVISION OF TENNESSEE, INC.—See Sinclair, Inc.; *U.S. Public*, pg. 1886
SINCLAIR TELEVISION STATIONS, LLC—See Sinclair, Inc.; *U.S. Public*, pg. 1885
SINGLETON MARINE GROUP; *U.S. Private*, pg. 3670
SINIAT INTERNATIONAL SA—See Etex SA/NV; *Int'l*, pg. 2522
SINO GAS & ENERGY HOLDINGS LIMITED—See Lone Star Global Acquisitions; *U.S. Private*, pg. 2489
SINOMEM TECHNOLOGY LIMITED—See CDH China Management Company Limited; *Int'l*, pg. 1370
SINOPEC INTERNATIONAL PETROLEUM EXPLORATION & PRODUCTION CORPORATION—See China Petrochemical Corporation; *Int'l*, pg. 1540
SINOTRANS (HONG KONG) HOLDINGS LTD.—See China Merchants Group Limited; *Int'l*, pg. 1522
SINTONIA S.P.A—See Edizione S.r.l.; *Int'l*, pg. 2312
SIRIUS XM HOLDINGS INC.—See Liberty Media Corporation; *U.S. Public*, pg. 1311

CORPORATE AFFILIATIONS

SITECORE CORPORATION A/S—See EQT AB; *Int'l*, pg. 2480
SITEONE LANDSCAPE SUPPLY, INC.; *U.S. Public*, pg. 1888
SITNASUAK NATIVE CORP.; *U.S. Private*, pg. 3676
SITUS HOLDINGS, LLC—See Stone Point Capital LLC; *U.S. Private*, pg. 3825
SIZMEK INC.—See Vector Capital Management, L.P.; *U.S. Private*, pg. 4352
SJL BROADCAST MANAGEMENT CORP.; *U.S. Private*, pg. 3678
SJW GROUP; *U.S. Public*, pg. 1891
SKANDIA RETAIL EUROPE HOLDING GMBH—See Cinven Limited; *Int'l*, pg. 1616
SKILLSOFT CORPORATION—See Charterhouse Capital Partners LLP; *Int'l*, pg. 1456
SKILLSOFT CORPORATION—See Clarivate PLC; *Int'l*, pg. 1650
SKM INVESTMENTS AUSTRALIA PTY LTD—See Jacobs Engineering Group, Inc.; *U.S. Public*, pg. 1186
SKULLCANDY, INC.—See Mill Road Capital Management LLC; *U.S. Private*, pg. 2730
SKY FOX INVESTMENT LIMITED—See Fullsun International Holdings Group Co., Limited; *Int'l*, pg. 2843
SKY LIMITED—See Comcast Corporation; *U.S. Public*, pg. 541
SKY PETROLEUM, INC.; *U.S. Public*, pg. 1892
SKYWARD SPECIALTY INSURANCE GROUP, INC.; *U.S. Public*, pg. 1893
SLEEP COUNTRY CANADA HOLDINGS, INC.—See Fairfax Financial Holdings Limited; *Int'l*, pg. 2608
SLEEP COUNTRY CANADA INCOME FUND—See Birch Hill Equity Partners Management Inc.; *Int'l*, pg. 1046
SLIMWARE UTILITIES HOLDINGS, INC.—See IAC Inc.; *U.S. Public*, pg. 1082
SLR INVESTMENT CORP.; *U.S. Public*, pg. 1894
SMALL BUSINESS DEVELOPMENT GROUP, INC.; *U.S. Public*, pg. 1895
SMARTLINE HOME LOANS PTY. LTD.—See News Corporation; *U.S. Public*, pg. 1520
SMARTOPTICS HOLDINGS AS—See Coherent Corp.; *U.S. Public*, pg. 528
SMARTRAC N.V.—See Avery Dennison Corporation; *U.S. Public*, pg. 245
SMART WORLDWIDE HOLDINGS, INC.—See Penguin Solutions, Inc.; *U.S. Public*, pg. 1661
SMC COMPANIES; *U.S. Private*, pg. 3693
SMILEDIRECTCLUB, INC.; *U.S. Public*, pg. 1896
SMILE VUN GROUP PVT LTD.—See Dentsu Group Inc.; *Int'l*, pg. 2037
THE SMITHERS GROUP; *U.S. Private*, pg. 4118
SMITHGROUP COMPANIES, INC.; *U.S. Private*, pg. 3697
SMITH INDUSTRIES, INC.—See European Metal Recycling Limited; *Int'l*, pg. 2556
SMITH INVESTMENT COMPANY—See A. O. Smith Corporation; *U.S. Public*, pg. 12
SMITH & WESSON BRANDS, INC.; *U.S. Public*, pg. 1896
SMOKY SYSTEMS, LLC; *U.S. Private*, pg. 3698
SMOOTHIE KING CO., INC.—See Affirma Capital Limited; *Int'l*, pg. 187
SMS HOLDINGS CORPORATION; *U.S. Private*, pg. 3699
SMSJ TUCSON HOLDINGS, LLC—See Tenet Healthcare Corporation; *U.S. Public*, pg. 2006
SM SPEAKER CORP.—See Gibson Brands, Inc.; *U.S. Private*, pg. 1696
SM SUMMIT HOLDINGS PTE LTD.—See Centurion Corporation Limited; *Int'l*, pg. 1417
SNAIL, INC.; *U.S. Public*, pg. 1897
SNAKE RIVER SUGAR CO.; *U.S. Private*, pg. 3699
SNAM INTERNATIONAL HOLDING A.G.—See Eni S.p.A.; *Int'l*, pg. 2437
SNAM S.P.A.—See Eni S.p.A.; *Int'l*, pg. 2438
SNAP ONE HOLDINGS CORP—See Resideo Technologies, Inc.; *U.S. Public*, pg. 1790
SNAP-ON TOOLS INTERNATIONAL, LTD.—See Snap-on Incorporated; *U.S. Public*, pg. 1898
SNC-LAVALIN INTERNATIONAL INC.—See AtkinsRealis Group Inc.; *Int'l*, pg. 671
SNC-LAVALIN INTERNATIONAL—See AtkinsRealis Group Inc.; *Int'l*, pg. 672
SNM GLOBAL HOLDINGS; *U.S. Public*, pg. 1899
SNORKEL INTERNATIONAL HOLDINGS, LLC—See Xtreme Manufacturing, LLC; *U.S. Private*, pg. 4583
SNOW PEAK CAPITAL, LLC; *U.S. Private*, pg. 3701
SNTC HOLDING, INC.—See KKR & Co. Inc.; *U.S. Public*, pg. 1254
SNYDER ASSOCIATED COMPANIES, INC.—See The Snyder Group, Inc.; *U.S. Private*, pg. 4119
THE SNYDER GROUP, INC.; *U.S. Private*, pg. 4119
SOAVE ENTERPRISES, LLC; *U.S. Private*, pg. 3702
SOBEYS GROUP INC.—See Empire Company Limited; *Int'l*, pg. 2387
SOCIAL CAPITAL HEDOSOPHIA HOLDINGS CORP. IV; *U.S. Private*, pg. 3702
SOCIAL CAPITAL HEDOSOPHIA HOLDINGS CORP. VI; *U.S. Private*, pg. 3702
SOCIAL CUBE INC.; *U.S. Private*, pg. 3703

N.A.I.C.S. INDEX

551112 — OFFICES OF OTHER HO...

SOFIBEL S.A.S.—See Church & Dwight Co., Inc.; *U.S. Public*, pg. 493
SOFIPROTEOL S.A.—See Avril SCA; *Int'l*, pg. 750
SOFTINTEREST HOLDING AG—See Silver Lake Group, LLC; *U.S. Private*, pg. 3659
SOFTPRINT HOLDINGS, INC.; *U.S. Private*, pg. 3705
SOLANBRIDGE GROUP INC.; *U.S. Public*, pg. 1899
SOLAR INTEGRATED ROOFING CORPORATION; *U.S. Public*, pg. 1899
SOLAR SPECTRUM HOLDINGS LLC—See Hercules Capital, Inc.; *U.S. Public*, pg. 1028
SOLAR SPECTRUM HOLDINGS LLC—See Northern Pacific Group; *U.S. Private*, pg. 2954
SOLARWINDS CORPORATION; *U.S. Public*, pg. 1900
SOLERA HOLDINGS, INC.—See Vista Equity Partners, LLC; *U.S. Private*, pg. 4399
SOMERS LIMITED—See ICM Limited; *Int'l*, pg. 3582
SONAR ENTERTAINMENT, INC.—See Chicken Soup for the Soul Entertainment, Inc.; *U.S. Public*, pg. 488
SONDER HOLDINGS, INC.; *U.S. Private*, pg. 1902
SONESTA INTERNATIONAL HOTELS CORPORATION—See The RMR Group Inc.; *U.S. Public*, pg. 2126
SONNET BIOTHERAPEUTICS HOLDINGS, INC.; *U.S. Public*, pg. 1903
SONOCO DEUTSCHLAND HOLDINGS GMBH—See Sonoco Products Company; *U.S. Public*, pg. 1906
SONOCO HOLDINGS (UK) LTD.—See Sonoco Products Company; *U.S. Public*, pg. 1906
SONOCO LUXEMBOURG S.A.R.L.—See Sonoco Products Company; *U.S. Public*, pg. 1906
SONOCO NETHERLANDS B.V.—See Sonoco Products Company; *U.S. Public*, pg. 1907
SONSRAY, INC.; *U.S. Private*, pg. 3714
SOPHOS GROUP PLC—See Apax Partners LLP; *Int'l*, pg. 506
SOREX HOLDINGS LTD.—See BASF SE; *Int'l*, pg. 882
SOTERA HEALTH LLC—See Warburg Pincus LLC; *U.S. Private*, pg. 4439
SOTHEBY'S; *U.S. Public*, pg. 1909
SOURCE TECHNOLOGIES HOLDINGS, LLC—See StoneCalibre, LLC; *U.S. Private*, pg. 3828
SOUTH BEACH SPIRITS, INC.; *U.S. Public*, pg. 1911
SOUTHBRIDGE INSURANCE COMPANY—See Fairfax Financial Holdings Limited; *Int'l*, pg. 2608
SOUTH CHESTER TUBE COMPANY; *U.S. Private*, pg. 3721
SOUTHCOMM, INC.; *U.S. Private*, pg. 3724
SOUTHCROSS HOLDINGS LP—See Charlesbank Capital Partners, LLC; *U.S. Private*, pg. 856
SOUTHCROSS HOLDINGS LP—See EIG Global Energy Partners, LLC; *U.S. Private*, pg. 1347
SOUTHCROSS HOLDINGS LP—See Tailwater Capital LLC; *U.S. Private*, pg. 3923
SOUTHEAST DIESEL CORP.; *U.S. Private*, pg. 3725
SOUTHEASTERN GROCERS, INC.—See Aldi Einkauf SE & Co. oHG; *Int'l*, pg. 304
THE SOUTHERN COMPANY; *U.S. Public*, pg. 2130
SOUTHERN HOSPITALITY AUTO GROUP OF VIRGINIA; *U.S. Private*, pg. 3732
SOUTHERN TRUST SECURITIES HOLDING CORP.; *U.S. Private*, pg. 3735
SOUTH JERSEY ENERGY SOLUTIONS, LLC—See JPMorgan Chase & Co.; *U.S. Public*, pg. 1210
SOUTH JERSEY INDUSTRIES, INC.—See JPMorgan Chase & Co.; *U.S. Public*, pg. 1210
SOUTHLAND HOLDINGS, INC.; *U.S. Public*, pg. 1912
SOUTH PACIFIC POWER PTY. LIMITED—See Electricity Generating Public Co., Ltd.; *Int'l*, pg. 2352
SOUTH STAFFORDSHIRE PLC—See Arjun Infrastructure Partners Limited; *Int'l*, pg. 568
SOUTHWEST GAS HOLDINGS, INC.; *U.S. Public*, pg. 1913
SOUZA CRUZ, S.A.—See British American Tobacco plc; *Int'l*, pg. 1168
SOVEREIGN REIT HOLDINGS, INC.—See Banco Santander, S.A.; *Int'l*, pg. 827
SOVRANO LLC; *U.S. Private*, pg. 3743
SPAFI—See Compagnie de Saint-Gobain SA; *Int'l*, pg. 1737
THE SPANCRETE GROUP, INC.—See Wells Concrete Products Company Inc.; *U.S. Private*, pg. 4476
SPANGLER COMPANIES, INC.; *U.S. Private*, pg. 3745
SPARC HOLDING COMPANY; *U.S. Private*, pg. 3745
SPARTANBURG REGIONAL HEALTH SERVICES DISTRICT, INC.; *U.S. Private*, pg. 3746
SPARX HOLDINGS GROUP, INC.; *U.S. Public*, pg. 1914
SPAY, INC.—See Genstar Capital, LLC; *U.S. Private*, pg. 1678
SPECIALIZED MEDICAL DEVICES, LLC—See Teleflex Incorporated; *U.S. Public*, pg. 1996
SPECIAL PHAGE HOLDINGS PTY LTD—See Armata Pharmaceuticals, Inc.; *U.S. Public*, pg. 193
SPECIALTY BUILDING PRODUCTS, INC.; *U.S. Private*, pg. 3749
SPECIALTY BUILDING PRODUCTS, LLC; *U.S. Private*, pg. 3749
SPECIALTY RETAIL VENTURES LLC; *U.S. Private*, pg. 3750
SPECIALTY THERAPEUTIC CARE HOLDINGS, LLC—See Centene Corporation; *U.S. Public*, pg. 470
SPECTRUM BRANDS HOLDINGS, INC.; *U.S. Public*, pg. 1915
SPECTRUM BRANDS, INC. - HARDWARE & HOME IMPROVEMENT—See Spectrum Brands Holdings, Inc.; *U.S. Public*, pg. 1916
SPECTRUM BRANDS, INC.—See Spectrum Brands Holdings, Inc.; *U.S. Public*, pg. 1916
SPECTRUM BRANDS LEGACY, INC.—See Spectrum Brands Holdings, Inc.; *U.S. Public*, pg. 1915
SPECTRUM CAPITAL ENTERPRISES, INC.; *U.S. Private*, pg. 3752
SPECTRUM GROUP INTERNATIONAL, INC.; *U.S. Public*, pg. 1917
SPECTRUM MANAGEMENT HOLDING COMPANY, LLC—See Charter Communications, Inc.; *U.S. Public*, pg. 483
SPEEDWAY MOTORSPORTS, LLC—See Sonic Financial Corporation; *U.S. Private*, pg. 3713
SPENCER MAC CORPORATION; *U.S. Private*, pg. 3755
S&P GLOBAL INC.; *U.S. Public*, pg. 1830
SPHERE ENTERTAINMENT CO.; *U.S. Public*, pg. 1918
SPIE SA—See Clayton, Dubilier & Rice, LLC; *U.S. Private*, pg. 926
SPIKES BASEBALL LP—See Greenberg Sports Group Inc.; *U.S. Private*, pg. 1775
SPINAL ELEMENTS HOLDINGS, INC.; *U.S. Private*, pg. 3757
SPIRE, INC; *U.S. Public*, pg. 1918
SPITZER MANAGEMENT, INC.; *U.S. Private*, pg. 3758
SPL ASSOCIATES INC; *U.S. Private*, pg. 3759
SPORTINGBET AUSTRALIA PTY LIMITED—See Entain PLC; *Int'l*, pg. 2450
SPORTSMAN'S WAREHOUSE HOLDINGS, INC.; *U.S. Public*, pg. 1919
SP PLUS CORPORATION—See Eldridge Industries LLC; *U.S. Private*, pg. 1351
SPRAGUE RESOURCES LP—See Brookfield Corporation; *Int'l*, pg. 1182
SPRINGER SCIENCE+BUSINESS MEDIA S.A.—See BC Partners LLP; *Int'l*, pg. 925
SPRINT CORPORATION—See Deutsche Telekom AG; *Int'l*, pg. 2084
SPURS SPORTS & ENTERTAINMENT; *U.S. Private*, pg. 3765
SPX FLOW, INC.—See Lone Star Funds; *U.S. Private*, pg. 2485
SPX GERMANY HOLDING GMBH—See SPX Technologies, Inc.; *U.S. Public*, pg. 1921
SQUAW VALLEY SKI HOLDINGS, LLC—See KSL Capital Partners, LLC; *U.S. Private*, pg. 2354
SRAM INTERNATIONAL CORPORATION; *U.S. Private*, pg. 3767
SRC COMMERCIAL HOLDINGS, INC.—See SRC, Inc.; *U.S. Private*, pg. 3767
SRC INTERNATIONAL, INC.—See SRC, Inc.; *U.S. Private*, pg. 3767
SRC VENTURES, INC.—See SRC, Inc.; *U.S. Private*, pg. 3767
SRG GLOBAL, INC.—See Koch Industries, Inc.; *U.S. Private*, pg. 2329
SR TECHNICS HOLDCO I GMBH—See Hainan Traffic Administration Holding Co., Ltd.; *Int'l*, pg. 3215
SS&C TECHNOLOGIES HOLDINGS, INC.; *U.S. Public*, pg. 1922
SSMB PACIFIC HOLDING COMPANY, INC.; *U.S. Private*, pg. 3769
SSW HOLDING COMPANY, INC.—See Trive Capital Inc.; *U.S. Private*, pg. 4240
STACK INFRASTRUCTURE, INC.—See ICONIQ Capital, LLC; *U.S. Private*, pg. 2032
STACK INFRASTRUCTURE, INC.—See Iron Point Partners, LLC; *U.S. Private*, pg. 2139
STADIUMRED GROUP; *U.S. Private*, pg. 3774
STAGE STORES, INC.; *U.S. Public*, pg. 1925
STAGWELL, INC.; *U.S. Public*, pg. 1925
STALLERGENES GREER HOLDINGS INC.—See B-FLEXION Group Holdings SA; *Int'l*, pg. 785
STALLERGENES GREER PLC—See B-FLEXION Group Holdings SA; *Int'l*, pg. 785
STANDARD COMPANIES INC.—See Bain Capital, LP; *U.S. Private*, pg. 451
STANDARD INDUSTRIES HOLDINGS INC.; *U.S. Private*, pg. 3779
STANDARD PREMIUM FINANCE HOLDINGS, INC.; *U.S. Public*, pg. 1929
STANDARD-TAYLOR INDUSTRIES, INC.; *U.S. Private*, pg. 3782
STANDBY HOLDINGS PTY LTD—See Expedia Group, Inc.; *U.S. Public*, pg. 810
STANLEY CONSULTANTS CO.; *U.S. Private*, pg. 3782
STAPLES FRANCE HOLDING SAS—See Sycamore Partners Management, LP; *U.S. Private*, pg. 3898
STAPLES, INC.—See Sycamore Partners Management, LP; *U.S. Private*, pg. 3896
STAPLES INTERNATIONAL B.V.—See Sycamore Partners Management, LP; *U.S. Private*, pg. 3897
STAPLES NEDERLAND HOLDING B.V.—See Sycamore Partners Management, LP; *U.S. Private*, pg. 3898
STAPLES SOLUTIONS B.V.—See Cerberus Capital Management, L.P.; *U.S. Private*, pg. 839
STARBUCKS COFFEE HOLDINGS (UK) LIMITED—See Starbucks Corporation; *U.S. Public*, pg. 1939
STARBUCKS EMEA HOLDINGS LTD—See Starbucks Corporation; *U.S. Public*, pg. 1939
STAR ENERGY INTERNATIONAL CORPORATION; *U.S. Private*, pg. 3784
STARGAMES AUSTRALIA PTY LIMITED—See Light & Wonder, Inc.; *U.S. Public*, pg. 1315
STAR GROUP NEWSPAPERS—See Alden Global Capital LLC; *U.S. Private*, pg. 156
STAR HOLDINGS, INC.; *U.S. Public*, pg. 1938
STARMARK MANAGEMENT HOLDINGS LLC; *U.S. Private*, pg. 3787
STARR INVESTMENT HOLDINGS LLC—See C.V. Starr & Co., Inc.; *U.S. Private*, pg. 709
STARRY GROUP HOLDINGS, INC.; *U.S. Public*, pg. 1939
THE STARS GROUP INC.—See Flutter Entertainment plc; *Int'l*, pg. 2715
STAR TRIBUNE MEDIA COMPANY LLC; *U.S. Private*, pg. 3785
STARWOOD HOTELS & RESORTS WORLDWIDE, LLC—See Marriott International, Inc.; *U.S. Public*, pg. 1371
STATER BROTHERS HOLDINGS—See La Cadena Investments; *U.S. Private*, pg. 2368
STATIA TERMINALS, INC.—See Sunoco LP; *U.S. Public*, pg. 1965
STATIONSERV HOLDINGS, LLC—See The Rosewood Corporation; *U.S. Private*, pg. 4112
STA TRAVEL (HOLDINGS) PTE LTD—See Diethelm Keller Holding Limited; *Int'l*, pg. 2117
STAVE ISLAND LTD. PARTNERSHIP; *U.S. Private*, pg. 3794
STEADFAST COMPANIES; *U.S. Private*, pg. 3794
STEELE OCEANIC CORP; *U.S. Public*, pg. 1941
STEEL PARTNERS HOLDINGS GP INC.—See Steel Partners Holdings L.P.; *U.S. Public*, pg. 1943
STEEL PARTNERS HOLDINGS L.P.; *U.S. Public*, pg. 1942
STEIN INDUSTRIES, INC.; *U.S. Private*, pg. 3797
STEINWAY MUSICAL INSTRUMENTS HOLDINGS, INC.; *U.S. Private*, pg. 3798
STELCO HOLDINGS, INC.—See Cleveland-Cliffs, Inc.; *U.S. Public*, pg. 514
STELLA POINT CAPITAL, LP; *U.S. Private*, pg. 3799
STEPHENS MEDIA GROUP MANAGEMENT, LLC; *U.S. Private*, pg. 3803
STEPHENSON GOBIN LTD—See British Engines Ltd.; *Int'l*, pg. 1171
STEPSTONE GMBH—See Axel Springer SE; *Int'l*, pg. 766
STERLING CONSOLIDATED CORP.; *U.S. Public*, pg. 1946
STERLING ENTERTAINMENT ENTERPRISES, LLC—See Sterling Equities, Inc.; *U.S. Private*, pg. 3805
STERLING INDUSTRIES LTD.—See Caledonia Investments plc; *Int'l*, pg. 1262
THE STEVENS & LEE COMPANIES, LLC; *U.S. Private*, pg. 4123
STEVENS & WILKINSON, INC.—See SSOE Group; *U.S. Private*, pg. 3769
STEWART ENTERPRISES, INC.—See Service Corporation International; *U.S. Public*, pg. 1871
STEWART INFORMATION SERVICES CORPORATION; *U.S. Public*, pg. 1947
STEWART'S CLASSICS, INC.—See Lithia Motors, Inc.; *U.S. Public*, pg. 1326
STIFEL FINANCIAL CORP.; *U.S. Public*, pg. 1949
S&T INSURANCE GROUP, LLC—See S&T Bancorp, Inc.; *U.S. Public*, pg. 1832
STIX HOLDINGS, LLC—See West Coast Capital LLC; *U.S. Private*, pg. 4484
ST MEDIA HOLDINGS, LLC—See Chicago Public Media, Inc.; *U.S. Private*, pg. 879
STM INDUSTRIES, INC.; *U.S. Private*, pg. 3813
STO BUILDING GROUP INC.; *U.S. Private*, pg. 3813
STONEBRIDGE REALTY ADVISORS, INC.; *U.S. Private*, pg. 3827
STONE CANYON INDUSTRIES, LLC; *U.S. Private*, pg. 3817
STONEX GROUP INC.; *U.S. Public*, pg. 1951
STORK B.V.—See Fluor Corporation; *U.S. Public*, pg. 859
STORK HOLDING B.V.—See Fluor Corporation; *U.S. Public*, pg. 859
STORK TECHNICAL SERVICES HOLDCO B.V.—See Fluor Corporation; *U.S. Public*, pg. 860
STRATA-TAC, INC.—See OpenGate Capital Management, LLC; *U.S. Private*, pg. 3030
STRATEGIC CAPITAL HOLDINGS, LLC; *U.S. Private*, pg. 3834
STRATEGIC DISTRIBUTION, INC.—See Independence Capital Partners, LLC; *U.S. Private*, pg. 2056
STRATEGIC DISTRIBUTION, INC.—See Pouschine Cook Capital Management LLC; *U.S. Private*, pg. 3236
STRATUS TECHNOLOGIES BERMUDA LTD.—See Siris Capital Group, LLC; *U.S. Private*, pg. 3674
STRATUS TECHNOLOGIES GROUP, S.A.—See Siris Capital Group, LLC; *U.S. Private*, pg. 3674

STRATUS TECHNOLOGIES INTERNATIONAL S.A.R.L.—See Siris Capital Group, LLC; *U.S. Private*, pg. 3674
STR HOLDINGS, INC.; *U.S. Public*, pg. 1953
STRONG GLOBAL ENTERTAINMENT, INC.—See Kingsway Financial Services Inc.; *U.S. Public*, pg. 1234
STRONGHOLD, LTD.—See Quanta Services, Inc.; *U.S. Public*, pg. 1753
STRONGWOOD INSURANCE HOLDINGS CORP.; *U.S. Private*, pg. 3841
STS AVIATION GROUP; *U.S. Private*, pg. 3842
STUDER HOLDINGS, INC.—See Huron Consulting Group Inc.; *U.S. Public*, pg. 1076
STUPP BROS., INC.; *U.S. Private*, pg. 3844
SUBURBAN MOTORS COMPANY, LLC; *U.S. Private*, pg. 3848
SUCCESS TRADE, INC.; *U.S. Private*, pg. 3849
SUCCESS TRADE SECURITIES, INC.—See Success Trade, Inc.; *U.S. Private*, pg. 3849
SUEZ-TRACTEBEL SA—See ENGIE SA; *Int'l*, pg. 2431
SUIC WORLDWIDE HOLDINGS LTD.; *U.S. Public*, pg. 1959
SUMMA HOLDINGS, INC.; *U.S. Private*, pg. 3852
SUMMER INFANT, INC.—See Kids2, Inc.; *U.S. Private*, pg. 2303
SUMMIT AUTOMOTIVE PARTNERS, LLC—See Booth Creek Management Corporation; *U.S. Private*, pg. 616
SUMMIT FINANCIAL SERVICES GROUP, INC.—See RCAP Holdings, LLC; *U.S. Private*, pg. 3361
SUMMIT HOLDING SOUTHEAST, INC.—See American Financial Group, Inc.; *U.S. Public*, pg. 103
SUMMIT MATERIALS, INC.; *U.S. Public*, pg. 1959
SUMMIT MEDICAL GROUP LIMITED—See Apposite Capital LLP; *Int'l*, pg. 522
SUMMIT UTILITIES INC.; *U.S. Private*, pg. 3857
SUNCHASE HOLDINGS, INC.; *U.S. Private*, pg. 3865
SUN COUNTRY AIRLINES HOLDINGS, INC.; *U.S. Public*, pg. 1963
THE SUNDT COMPANIES, INC.; *U.S. Private*, pg. 4125
SUNEDISON HOLDINGS CORPORATION—See SunEdison, Inc.; *U.S. Private*, pg. 3867
SUNEDISON, INC.; *U.S. Private*, pg. 3866
SUNGARD AVAILABILITY SERVICES CAPITAL, INC.; *U.S. Private*, pg. 3867
SUN HUNG KAI & CO. LIMITED—See Allied Group Limited; *Int'l*, pg. 357
SUNNOVA ENERGY INTERNATIONAL INC.; *U.S. Public*, pg. 1964
SUNRISE ACQUISITION CORP.; *U.S. Private*, pg. 3869
SUNRISE SPORTS & ENTERTAINMENT LLLP; *U.S. Private*, pg. 3870
SUNROAD HOLDING CORPORATION; *U.S. Private*, pg. 3870
SUNS LEGACY PARTNERS, LLC; *U.S. Private*, pg. 3870
SUNSOUTH LLC; *U.S. Private*, pg. 3872
SUNSTAR INSURANCE GROUP, LLC—See Reverence Capital Partners LLC; *U.S. Private*, pg. 3415
SUPERIOR EQUIPMENT SOLUTIONS; *U.S. Private*, pg. 3877
SUPERIOR INVESTMENT HOLDINGS PTE. LTD.—See Crown Holdings, Inc.; *U.S. Public*, pg. 599
SUPERIOR WASTE INDUSTRIES LLC; *U.S. Private*, pg. 3881
SUPER SERVICE HOLDINGS, LLC—See Wayzata Investment Partners LLC; *U.S. Private*, pg. 4461
SUPERVALU INC.—See United Natural Foods, Inc.; *U.S. Public*, pg. 2231
SUPPLYONE HOLDINGS COMPANY, INC.—See Meridian Venture Partners; *U.S. Private*, pg. 2673
SUREWEST COMMUNICATIONS—See Consolidated Communications Holdings, Inc.; *U.S. Public*, pg. 570
SURF AIR MOBILITY INC.; *U.S. Public*, pg. 1967
SURGALIGN HOLDINGS, INC.; *U.S. Public*, pg. 1967
SURMA HOLDINGS B.V.—See Cementos Molins S.A.; *Int'l*, pg. 1398
SURMA HOLDINGS B.V.—See Holcim Ltd.; *Int'l*, pg. 3449
SUSPECT DETECTION SYSTEMS INC.; *U.S. Private*, pg. 3885
SUSSER HOLDINGS CORPORATION—See Sunoco LP; *U.S. Public*, pg. 1965
SUTERA HARBOUR RESORT SDN BHD—See GSH Corporation Limited; *Int'l*, pg. 3144
SUTLIFF AUTO GROUP; *U.S. Private*, pg. 3887
SVILUPPO ITALIA ABRUZZO S.P.A.—See Agenzia Nazionale per l'Attrazione degli Investimenti e lo Sviluppo d'Impresa SpA; *Int'l*, pg. 206
SVP WORLDWIDE, LLC—See Platinum Equity, LLC; *U.S. Private*, pg. 3207
SWANK CAPITAL, LLC; *U.S. Private*, pg. 3890
SWEPI LP—See ConocoPhillips; *U.S. Public*, pg. 569
SWH MIMI'S CAFE, LLC—See Holding Le Duff SA; *Int'l*, pg. 3450
SWISHER HYGIENE INC.; *U.S. Private*, pg. 3894
SYAN HOLDINGS LIMITED—See Xerox Holdings Corporation; *U.S. Public*, pg. 2388
SYLVANIA EUROPE HOLDING CO. LTD. (GERMAN BRANCH)—See Havell's India Ltd.; *Int'l*, pg. 3286
SYMMETRY SURGICAL INC.—See Audax Group, Limited Partnership; *U.S. Private*, pg. 386

SYNEOS HEALTH CLINICAL, LLC—See Elliott Management Corporation; *U.S. Private*, pg. 1365
SYNEOS HEALTH CLINICAL, LLC—See Patient Square Capital, L.P.; *U.S. Private*, pg. 3108
SYNEOS HEALTH CLINICAL, LLC—See Veritas Capital Fund Management, LLC; *U.S. Private*, pg. 4365
SYNEOS HEALTH COMMUNICATIONS, INC.—See Elliott Management Corporation; *U.S. Private*, pg. 1366
SYNEOS HEALTH COMMUNICATIONS, INC.—See Patient Square Capital, L.P.; *U.S. Private*, pg. 3108
SYNEOS HEALTH COMMUNICATIONS, INC.—See Veritas Capital Fund Management, LLC; *U.S. Private*, pg. 4365
SYNEOS HEALTH, INC.—See Elliott Management Corporation; *U.S. Private*, pg. 1365
SYNEOS HEALTH, INC.—See Patient Square Capital, L.P.; *U.S. Private*, pg. 3108
SYNEOS HEALTH, INC.—See Veritas Capital Fund Management, LLC; *U.S. Private*, pg. 4364
SYNEOS HEALTH, LLC—See Elliott Management Corporation; *U.S. Private*, pg. 1365
SYNEOS HEALTH, LLC—See Patient Square Capital, L.P.; *U.S. Private*, pg. 3108
SYNEOS HEALTH, LLC—See Veritas Capital Fund Management, LLC; *U.S. Private*, pg. 4365
SYNERGY COMMUNICATIONS MANAGEMENT; *U.S. Private*, pg. 3904
SYNGENTA CORPORATION—See China National Chemical Corporation; *Int'l*, pg. 1529
SYNIVERSE HOLDINGS, INC.—See The Carlyle Group Inc.; *U.S. Public*, pg. 2054
SYNLAB INTERNATIONAL GMBH—See Cinven Limited; *Int'l*, pg. 1614
SYNTEC OPTICS HOLDING, INC.; *U.S. Public*, pg. 1972
SYSCO CORPORATION; *U.S. Public*, pg. 1972
T1T LAB—See Enerfund, LLC; *U.S. Public*, pg. 1393
T2 PARTNERS GROUP, LLC; *U.S. Private*, pg. 3913
TAC HOLDINGS LLC—See Tredegar Corporation; *U.S. Public*, pg. 2187
TAG HOLDINGS, LLC; *U.S. Private*, pg. 3922
TAILWIND TECHNOLOGIES INC.; *U.S. Private*, pg. 3924
TAIPING FINANCIAL HOLDINGS COMPANY LIMITED—See China Taiping Insurance Holdings Company Limited; *Int'l*, pg. 1557
TALBOT HOLDINGS INC.; *U.S. Private*, pg. 3925
TALCOTT RESOLUTION LIFE INSURANCE COMPANY—See Sixth Street Specialty Lending, Inc.; *U.S. Public*, pg. 1891
TALEN ENERGY CORPORATION—See Riverstone Holdings LLC; *U.S. Private*, pg. 3447
TAL HOLDINGS LLC; *U.S. Private*, pg. 3925
TALLGRASS ENERGY PARTNERS, LP—See Blackstone Inc.; *U.S. Public*, pg. 359
TALL TREE FOODS, INC.—See Altamont Capital Partners; *U.S. Private*, pg. 205
TALLY ENERGY SERVICES—See RedBird Capital Partners L.P.; *U.S. Private*, pg. 3377
TALON GROUP LLC; *U.S. Private*, pg. 3927
TALOS ENERGY INC.; *U.S. Public*, pg. 1980
TAM CERAMICS GROUP OF NY, LLC; *U.S. Private*, pg. 3927
TAMCO HOLDINGS, LLC; *U.S. Private*, pg. 3928
TAMER MEDIA, LLC; *U.S. Private*, pg. 3928
TAMPA BAY SPORTS & ENTERTAINMENT LLC; *U.S. Private*, pg. 3929
TANG CITY PROPERTIES PTE LIMITED.—See Far East Consortium International Limited; *Int'l*, pg. 2615
TANK HOLDING CORP.—See Olympus Partners; *U.S. Private*, pg. 3013
TARGA PIPELINE PARTNERS LP—See Targa Resources Corp.; *U.S. Public*, pg. 1982
TARGA RESOURCES CORP.; *U.S. Public*, pg. 1981
TARGA RESOURCES LLC—See Targa Resources Corp.; *U.S. Public*, pg. 1981
TARGET CORPORATION; *U.S. Public*, pg. 1982
TARMAC HOLDINGS LIMITED—See CRH plc; *Int'l*, pg. 1848
TAT HONG HOLDINGS LTD.—See Affirma Capital Limited; *Int'l*, pg. 187
TATUM DEVELOPMENT CORP.; *U.S. Private*, pg. 3936
TAUBENPOST, INC.; *U.S. Private*, pg. 3936
TAURUS MINERAL LIMITED—See China Development Bank Corporation; *Int'l*, pg. 1497
TAURUS MINERAL LIMITED—See China Guangdong Nuclear Power Holding Co., Ltd.; *Int'l*, pg. 1506
TAVISTOCK RESTAURANTS, LLC—See Tavistock Group, Inc.; *U.S. Private*, pg. 3937
TAWA ASSOCIATES LTD.—See Financiere Pinault SCA; *Int'l*, pg. 2669
TAYLOR COMMUNICATIONS, INC.—See Taylor Corporation; *U.S. Private*, pg. 3939
TAYLOR MORRISON HOME CORPORATION—See Brookfield Corporation; *Int'l*, pg. 1183
TAYLOR UNITED INC.; *U.S. Private*, pg. 3940
TBG HOLDINGS CORP.; *U.S. Private*, pg. 3941
TBWA UK GROUP LIMITED—See Omnicom Group Inc.; *U.S. Public*, pg. 1597
TD AMERITRADE HOLDING CORPORATION—See The Charles Schwab Corporation; *U.S. Public*, pg. 2058

TDC HOLDING A/S—See Arbejdsmarkedets Tillaegspension; *Int'l*, pg. 537
TD FOOD GROUP, INC.—See Grupo Finaccess S.A.P.I. de C.V.; *Int'l*, pg. 3129
TEACHERS INSURANCE ASSOCIATION - COLLEGE RETIREMENT FUND; *U.S. Private*, pg. 3945
TEAM HEALTH HOLDINGS, INC.—See Blackstone Inc.; *U.S. Public*, pg. 359
TEAM INDUSTRIES, INC.; *U.S. Private*, pg. 3949
TEAM TANKERS INTERNATIONAL LTD.; *U.S. Private*, pg. 3950
TECHLAW HOLDINGS, INC.; *U.S. Private*, pg. 3952
TECHNIKS INDUSTRIES—See Audax Group, Limited Partnership; *U.S. Private*, pg. 389
TECHNOSYSTEMS CONSOLIDATED CORPORATION; *U.S. Private*, pg. 3956
TECTA AMERICA CORP.—See Altas Partners LP; *Int'l*, pg. 386
TECTONIC FINANCIAL, INC.; *U.S. Public*, pg. 1989
TEGNA INC.; *U.S. Public*, pg. 1989
TELE GROUP CORP.; *U.S. Public*, pg. 1992
TELLABS, INC.—See Marlin Equity Partners, LLC; *U.S. Private*, pg. 2585
TELMEX INTERNACIONAL, S.A.B. DE C.V.—See America Movil, S.A.B. de C.V.; *Int'l*, pg. 422
TELRITE HOLDINGS, INC.; *U.S. Private*, pg. 3962
TEMPRESS SYSTEMS B.V.—See Amtech Systems, Inc.; *U.S. Public*, pg. 134
TEMP-RITE INTERNATIONAL HOLDING B.V.—See Ali Holding S.r.l; *Int'l*, pg. 322
TEMPUS APPLIED SOLUTIONS HOLDINGS, INC.; *U.S. Public*, pg. 2000
TENABLE HOLDINGS, INC.; *U.S. Public*, pg. 2000
TEN CATE ADVANCED TEXTILES BV—See ABN AMRO Group N.V.; *Int'l*, pg. 64
TEN CATE ADVANCED TEXTILES BV—See Gilde Buy Out Partners B.V.; *Int'l*, pg. 2974
TENCATE GRASS HOLDING BV—See Crestview Partners, L.P.; *U.S. Private*, pg. 1099
TENDYNE HOLDINGS, INC.—See Abbott Laboratories; *U.S. Public*, pg. 21
TENERITY, INC.; *U.S. Private*, pg. 3966
TENGJUN BIOTECHNOLOGY CORP.; *U.S. Public*, pg. 2015
TENIR INVESTMENTS INC.; *U.S. Private*, pg. 3967
TEN NETWORK HOLDINGS LIMITED—See National Amusements, Inc.; *U.S. Private*, pg. 2844
TEN: THE ENTHUSIAST NETWORK, INC.; *U.S. Private*, pg. 3964
TEO SENG CAPITAL BERHAD—See Emerging Glory Sdn Bhd; *Int'l*, pg. 2379
TERADATA CORPORATION; *U.S. Public*, pg. 2016
TERM HOLDINGS, LLC—See Blackstone Inc.; *U.S. Public*, pg. 349
TERM HOLDINGS, LLC—See Five Point Energy LLC; *U.S. Private*, pg. 1537
TERRAFORM POWER, INC.—See Brookfield Corporation; *Int'l*, pg. 1189
TERRA-GEN POWER, LLC—See ArcLight Capital Holdings, LLC; *U.S. Private*, pg. 312
TERRA MILLENIUM CORPORATION; *U.S. Private*, pg. 3970
TERRIER MEDIA BUYER, INC.—See Apollo Global Management, Inc.; *U.S. Public*, pg. 163
TESEQ HOLDING AG—See AMETEK, Inc.; *U.S. Public*, pg. 119
TETCO, INC.; *U.S. Private*, pg. 3973
TETRA APPLIED HOLDING COMPANY—See TETRA Technologies, Inc.; *U.S. Public*, pg. 2024
TEUPEN MASCHINENBAU GMBH—See Altec Industries Inc.; *U.S. Private*, pg. 206
TEXANS CUSO SERVICES—See Texans Credit Union; *U.S. Private*, pg. 3974
TEXAS AMERICAN RESOURCES I, LLC—See Venado Oil & Gas, LLC; *U.S. Private*, pg. 4355
TEXAS REPUBLIC CAPITAL CORPORATION; *U.S. Private*, pg. 3977
TEXTRON ATLANTIC HOLDING GMBH—See Textron Inc.; *U.S. Public*, pg. 2028
TEXTRON INC.; *U.S. Public*, pg. 2027
TEXTRON SYSTEMS ELECTRONIC SYSTEMS UK (HOLDINGS) LIMITED—See Textron Inc.; *U.S. Public*, pg. 2029
TFI INC.; *U.S. Private*, pg. 3978
TFS-ICAP HOLDINGS LLC—See CME Group, Inc.; *U.S. Public*, pg. 518
T.G.I. FRIDAY'S INC.—See Carlson Companies Inc.; *U.S. Private*, pg. 765
TG VALENTINE, LLC; *U.S. Private*, pg. 3979
THARCO PACKAGING, INC.—See Packaging Corporation of America; *U.S. Public*, pg. 1633
THB GROUP LIMITED—See AmWINS Group, Inc.; *U.S. Private*, pg. 269
THC FARMACEUTICALS, INC.; *U.S. Public*, pg. 2030
THERMADYNE BRAZIL HOLDINGS LTD—See Enovis Corporation; *U.S. Public*, pg. 773
THERMAL ENGINEERING INTERNATIONAL (USA), INC.—See Babcock Power, Inc.; *U.S. Private*, pg. 422

N.A.I.C.S. INDEX 551112 — OFFICES OF OTHER HO...

N.A.I.C.S. Index

THERMO FISHER SCIENTIFIC (BREDA) HOLDING BV—See Thermo Fisher Scientific Inc.; *U.S. Public*, pg. 2154
THERMO FISHER SCIENTIFIC LIFE SENIOR HOLDINGS II C.V.—See Thermo Fisher Scientific Inc.; *U.S. Public*, pg. 2154
THERMO LUXEMBOURG HOLDING S.A.R.L.—See Thermo Fisher Scientific Inc.; *U.S. Public*, pg. 2154
THERMON GROUP HOLDINGS, INC.; *U.S. Public*, pg. 2155
THERMO TELECOM PARTNERS, LLC; *U.S. Private*, pg. 4143
T&H GLOBAL HOLDINGS, LLC—See The Carlyle Group Inc.; *U.S. Public*, pg. 2054
THINGAP HOLDINGS, LLC—See Sensata Technologies Holding plc; *U.S. Public*, pg. 1866
THOMAS INVESTMENTS INC.; *U.S. Private*, pg. 4156
THOMAS JAMES HOMES, INC.; *U.S. Private*, pg. 4156
THOMAS WEISEL PARTNERS GROUP, INC.—See Stifel Financial Corp.; *U.S. Public*, pg. 1950
THOMPSON DISTRIBUTION, LLC; *U.S. Private*, pg. 4159
THORPE SPECIALTY SERVICES CORPORATION—See The CapStreet Group LLC; *U.S. Private*, pg. 4005
THOUGHTWORKS HOLDING, INC.—See Apax Partners LLP; *Int'l*, pg. 507
THREESIXTY GROUP LIMITED—See AEA Investors LP; *U.S. Private*, pg. 116
THRYV HOLDINGS, INC.; *U.S. Public*, pg. 2157
THUNDERBIRD LLC; *U.S. Private*, pg. 4166
THYSSENKRUPP ACCESSIBILITY HOLDING GMBH—See Advent International Corporation; *U.S. Private*, pg. 106
THYSSENKRUPP ACCESSIBILITY HOLDING GMBH—See Cinven Limited; *Int'l*, pg. 1614
TI AUTOMOTIVE EURO HOLDINGS LIMITED—See Bain Capital, LP; *U.S. Private*, pg. 447
TICKETMASTER ENTERTAINMENT LLC—See Live Nation Entertainment, Inc.; *U.S. Public*, pg. 1331
THE TIFFEN COMPANY LLC—See Topspin Partners, L.P.; *U.S. Private*, pg. 4188
TILE SHOP HOLDINGS, INC.; *U.S. Public*, pg. 2158
TIMBERLAND (GIBRALTAR) HOLDING LIMITED—See V. F. Corporation; *U.S. Public*, pg. 2268
TIMBERLAND SWITZERLAND HOLDING GMBH—See V. F. Corporation; *U.S. Public*, pg. 2269
TIMES HOLDING CO.; *U.S. Private*, pg. 4172
TIMICO TECHNOLOGY GROUP LIMITED—See Horizon Capital LLP; *Int'l*, pg. 3479
TIMIOS HOLDINGS CORP.—See Ideanomics, Inc.; *U.S. Public*, pg. 1088
TIML RADIO LTD.—See Bennett, Coleman & Co. Ltd.; *Int'l*, pg. 975
TINICUM ENTERPRISES, INC.; *U.S. Private*, pg. 4173
TIPTREE INC.; *U.S. Public*, pg. 2159
TITAN ENERGY, LLC—See Atlas Energy Group, LLC; *U.S. Public*, pg. 223
TITAN ENERGY PARTNERS, L.P.—See UGI Corporation; *U.S. Public*, pg. 2222
TITAN INTERNATIONAL, INC.; *U.S. Public*, pg. 2159
TIVO CORPORATION—See Adeia Inc.; *U.S. Public*, pg. 41
T.J. HAGGERTY, INC.; *U.S. Private*, pg. 3912
TK ELEVATOR GMBH—See Advent International Corporation; *U.S. Private*, pg. 106
TK ELEVATOR GMBH—See Cinven Limited; *Int'l*, pg. 1614
TKO GROUP HOLDINGS, INC.—See Silver Lake Group, LLC; *U.S. Private*, pg. 3654
T-MOBILE US, INC.—See Deutsche Telekom AG; *Int'l*, pg. 2084
TNS GROUP HOLDINGS PLC—See Bain Capital, LP; *U.S. Private*, pg. 447
TOC HOLDINGS CO.; *U.S. Private*, pg. 4180
TOKEN COMMUNITIES LTD.—See ASC Global Inc.; *U.S. Private*, pg. 345
TOLL BROTHERS, INC.; *U.S. Public*, pg. 2161
TOP RIGHT GROUP LIMITED—See Apax Partners LLP; *Int'l*, pg. 507
TOPS HOLDING II CORPORATION; *U.S. Private*, pg. 4188
TOPS HOLDING LLC—See Tops Holding II Corporation; *U.S. Private*, pg. 4188
TORGO, LTD.; *U.S. Private*, pg. 4189
TORRE HOLDINGS (PTY) LTD.—See Apex Partners Proprietary Limited; *Int'l*, pg. 512
TORRE HOLDINGS (PTY) LTD.—See TRG Management LP; *U.S. Private*, pg. 4220
TORRE INDUSTRIES LIMITED—See Apex Partners Proprietary Limited; *Int'l*, pg. 512
TORRE INDUSTRIES LIMITED—See TRG Management LP; *U.S. Private*, pg. 4219
TORRE PARTS AND COMPONENTS—See Apex Partners Proprietary Limited; *Int'l*, pg. 512
TORRE PARTS AND COMPONENTS—See TRG Management LP; *U.S. Private*, pg. 4220
TORRID HOLDINGS INC.; *U.S. Public*, pg. 2164
TORTOISE INVESTMENTS, LLC—See Lovell Minnick Partners LLC; *U.S. Private*, pg. 2503
TOTAL INSIGHT, LLC; *U.S. Private*, pg. 4191
TOTAL PRODUCE PLC—See Dole plc; *Int'l*, pg. 2158
TOT GROUP, INC.—See Mullen Automotive, Inc.; *U.S. Public*, pg. 1486
TOUCH HOLDINGS PTY. LIMITED—See Block, Inc.; *U.S. Public*, pg. 361
TOUYUN BIOTECH GROUP LTD—See CC Land Holdings Limited; *Int'l*, pg. 1366
TOWER AUTOMOTIVE HOLDINGS EUROPE B.V.—See Financiere SNOP Dunois SA; *Int'l*, pg. 2669
TOWER HOLDINGS, INC.—See Amneal Pharmaceuticals, Inc.; *U.S. Public*, pg. 125
TOWNE BANCORP, INC.; *U.S. Private*, pg. 4198
TOWN SPORTS INTERNATIONAL HOLDINGS, INC.; *U.S. Private*, pg. 4197
TOWNSQUARE MEDIA, INC.—See Brookfield Corporation; *Int'l*, pg. 1183
TOWNSQUARE MEDIA - SQUARE DIVISION—See Brookfield Corporation; *Int'l*, pg. 1183
TOWNSQUARE MEDIA - TOWN DIVISION—See Brookfield Corporation; *Int'l*, pg. 1184
TOYS "R" US, INC.—See WHP Global; *U.S. Private*, pg. 4515
TOYS "R" US INTERNATIONAL, LLC—See WHP Global; *U.S. Private*, pg. 4515
TPC HOLDINGS, INC.; *U.S. Private*, pg. 4199
TPG HOLDINGS LIMITED—See CK Hutchison Holdings Limited; *Int'l*, pg. 1638
T.P. INDUSTRIAL HOLDING S.P.A.—See China National Chemical Corporation; *Int'l*, pg. 1529
TPS PARKING MANAGEMENT, LLC—See Green Courte Partners, LLC; *U.S. Private*, pg. 1772
TRACINDA CORPORATION; *U.S. Private*, pg. 4200
TRAC INTERMODAL LLC—See Stonepeak Partners L.P.; *U.S. Private*, pg. 3829
TRADEMARK GLOBAL, LLC—See Bertram Capital Management, LLC; *U.S. Private*, pg. 540
TRADEWEB MARKETS INC.; *U.S. Public*, pg. 2178
TRADEWEB MARKETS LLC—See Tradeweb Markets Inc.; *U.S. Public*, pg. 2178
TRADITIONAL SERVICE CORPORATION; *U.S. Private*, pg. 4203
TRADITIONS HEALTH, LLC—See Dorilton Capital Advisors LLC; *U.S. Private*, pg. 1263
TRANSCOM WORLDWIDE AB—See Altor Equity Partners AB; *Int'l*, pg. 396
TRANSDIGM GROUP INCORPORATED; *U.S. Public*, pg. 2180
TRANSFORM HOLDCO LLC; *U.S. Private*, pg. 4208
TRANSGLOBAL ASSETS, INC.; *U.S. Public*, pg. 2183
TRANSMEDICS GROUP, INC.; *U.S. Public*, pg. 2183
TRANSMONTAIGNE GP L.L.C.—See ArcLight Capital Holdings, LLC; *U.S. Private*, pg. 312
TRANSPERFECT GLOBAL, INC.; *U.S. Private*, pg. 4210
TRANSPORT INVESTMENTS, INC.; *U.S. Private*, pg. 4210
TRANS-RESOURCES, INC.; *U.S. Private*, pg. 4206
TRANSTAR HOLDING COMPANY—See Blue Point Capital Partners, LLC; *U.S. Private*, pg. 590
TRANSUNION; *U.S. Public*, pg. 2184
TRAUSON HOLDINGS COMPANY LIMITED—See Stryker Corporation; *U.S. Public*, pg. 1957
TRAVELCENTERS OF AMERICA INC.—See BP plc; *Int'l*, pg. 1127
THE TRAVELERS COMPANIES, INC.; *U.S. Public*, pg. 2135
TRAVELJIGSAW HOLDINGS LIMITED—See Booking Holdings, Inc.; *U.S. Public*, pg. 368
TRAVEL LEADERS FRANCHISE GROUP, LLC—See Travel Leaders Group, LLC; *U.S. Private*, pg. 4213
TRAVEL LEADERS GROUP, LLC; *U.S. Private*, pg. 4213
TRAVEL & LEISURE CO.; *U.S. Public*, pg. 2185
TRAVELLERS INTERNATIONAL HOTEL GROUP, INC.—See Alliance Global Group, Inc.; *Int'l*, pg. 339
TRAVELLERS INTERNATIONAL HOTEL GROUP, INC.—See Genting Hong Kong Limited; *Int'l*, pg. 2929
TREAN INSURANCE GROUP, INC.—See Altaris Capital Partners, LLC; *U.S. Private*, pg. 206
TREECON RESOURCES, INC.; *U.S. Public*, pg. 2187
TREEN BOX & PALLET CORP.; *U.S. Private*, pg. 4217
TREES CORPORATION; *U.S. Public*, pg. 2188
TRENCAP L.P.—See Caisse de Depot et Placement du Quebec; *Int'l*, pg. 1255
TRG HOLDINGS, LLC; *U.S. Private*, pg. 4219
TRIAD FOODS GROUP; *U.S. Private*, pg. 4225
TRIBUNE BROADCASTING COMPANY—See Nexstar Media Group, Inc.; *U.S. Public*, pg. 1524
TRIBUNE MEDIA COMPANY—See Nexstar Media Group, Inc.; *U.S. Public*, pg. 1524
TRIBUNE PUBLISHING COMPANY; *U.S. Private*, pg. 4227
TRILOGY ENTERPRISES, INC.—See ESW Capital, LLC; *U.S. Private*, pg. 1430
TRILOGY INTERNATIONAL PARTNERS INC.—See SG Enterprises II, LLC; *U.S. Private*, pg. 3622
TRIMBLE HOLDINGS GMBH—See Trimble, Inc.; *U.S. Public*, pg. 2192
TRINIDAD/BENHAM HOLDING CO; *U.S. Private*, pg. 4233
TRINIDAD MATCH LIMITED—See ANSA McAL Limited; *Int'l*, pg. 477
TRINITY CO2 INVESTMENTS LLC—See Morgan Stanley; *U.S. Public*, pg. 1474
TRINITY INDUSTRIES DE MEXICO, S. DE R.L. DE C.V.—See Trinity Industries, Inc.; *U.S. Public*, pg. 2194
TRINITY PARTS & COMPONENTS, LLC—See Trinity Industries, Inc.; *U.S. Public*, pg. 2194
TRINTECH GROUP LIMITED—See Summit Partners, L.P.; *U.S. Private*, pg. 3856
TRIPADVISOR, INC.; *U.S. Public*, pg. 2195
TRIPLE J ENTERPRISES, INC.; *U.S. Private*, pg. 4237
TRIPLE PEAKS, LLC—See Vail Resorts, Inc.; *U.S. Public*, pg. 2271
TRIPLE-S STEEL HOLDINGS INC.; *U.S. Private*, pg. 4237
TRI POINTE HOLDINGS, INC.—See Tri Pointe Homes, Inc.; *U.S. Public*, pg. 2188
TRI-POINT OIL & GAS PRODUCTION SYSTEMS, LLC—See First Reserve Management, L.P.; *U.S. Private*, pg. 1526
TRISTYLE MODE GMBH—See Equistone Partners Europe Limited; *Int'l*, pg. 2487
TRITON CONSOLIDATED, INC.; *U.S. Private*, pg. 4239
TRITON MEDIA, LLC—See Brookfield Corporation; *Int'l*, pg. 1184
TRIUMPH GROUP, INC.; *U.S. Public*, pg. 2196
TRIVASCULAR TECHNOLOGIES, INC.—See Endologix, Inc.; *U.S. Private*, pg. 1392
TRONOX GLOBAL HOLDINGS PTY LIMITED—See Tronox Holdings plc; *U.S. Public*, pg. 2197
TRONOX US HOLDINGS INC.—See Tronox Holdings plc; *U.S. Public*, pg. 2197
TROPICANA LAS VEGAS HOTEL & CASINO, INC.—See PENN Entertainment, Inc.; *U.S. Public*, pg. 1663
TROPRIA HOLDING B.V.—See Edgewell Personal Care Company; *U.S. Public*, pg. 718
TRT HOLDINGS, INC.; *U.S. Private*, pg. 4244
TRUCEPT INC.; *U.S. Public*, pg. 2198
TRUCK BODIES & EQUIPMENT INTERNATIONAL, INC.—See Federal Signal Corporation; *U.S. Public*, pg. 826
TRUIST INSURANCE HOLDINGS, INC.—See Clayton, Dubilier & Rice, LLC; *U.S. Private*, pg. 927
TRUIST INSURANCE HOLDINGS, INC.—See Stone Point Capital LLC; *U.S. Private*, pg. 3825
TRULIEVE CANNABIS CORP.; *U.S. Public*, pg. 2201
THE TRUMP ORGANIZATION, INC.; *U.S. Private*, pg. 4128
TRUSTHOUSE SERVICES GROUP, INC.—See Charterhouse Capital Partners LLP; *Int'l*, pg. 1455
TRUSTMARK MUTUAL HOLDING COMPANY; *U.S. Private*, pg. 4251
TRUSTWAVE HOLDINGS, INC.—See The Chertoff Group, LLC; *U.S. Private*, pg. 4008
TSAY CORPORATION; *U.S. Private*, pg. 4252
TSL ENGINEERED PRODUCTS, LLC—See Tinicum Enterprises, Inc.; *U.S. Private*, pg. 4174
TSOGO INVESTMENT HOLDING COMPANY (PTY) LIMITED—See Hosken Consolidated Investments Limited; *Int'l*, pg. 3485
TSOGO SUN LIMITED—See Hosken Consolidated Investments Limited; *Int'l*, pg. 3485
TTEC HOLDINGS, INC.; *U.S. Public*, pg. 2202
TUBEX HOLDING GMBH—See CAG Holding GmbH; *Int'l*, pg. 1251
TURBONETICS HOLDINGS, INC.—See Westinghouse Air Brake Technologies Corporation; *U.S. Public*, pg. 2359
TURKEY HILL, L.P.—See Peak Rock Capital LLC; *U.S. Private*, pg. 3124
TURNER VALLEY OIL & GAS, INC.; *U.S. Public*, pg. 2205
TURNONGREEN, INC.—See Ault Alliance, Inc.; *U.S. Public*, pg. 227
TUSIMPLE HOLDINGS INC.; *U.S. Public*, pg. 2205
TUXIS CORP.; *U.S. Public*, pg. 2206
TV GUIDE ONLINE HOLDINGS LLC—See National Amusements, Inc.; *U.S. Private*, pg. 2844
TWDC ENTERPRISES 18 CORP.—See The Walt Disney Company; *U.S. Public*, pg. 2137
TWENTY-FIRST CENTURY FOX, INC.—See The Walt Disney Company; *U.S. Public*, pg. 2140
TWINLAB CONSOLIDATED HOLDINGS, INC.; *U.S. Public*, pg. 2207
TWINLAB HOLDINGS, INC.—See Twinlab Consolidated Holdings, Inc.; *U.S. Public*, pg. 2207
TWIN RIVERS TECHNOLOGIES HOLDINGS, INC.—See FGV Holdings Bhd; *Int'l*, pg. 2649
TWINS SPORTS, INC.—See Pohlad Companies; *U.S. Private*, pg. 3220
TWO RIVER GROUP HOLDINGS, LLC; *U.S. Private*, pg. 4266
TXNM ENERGY, INC.; *U.S. Public*, pg. 2208
TYONEK CONSTRUCTION GROUP, INC.—See The Tyonek Native Corporation; *U.S. Private*, pg. 4128
TYONEK MANUFACTURING GROUP, INC.—See The Tyonek Native Corporation; *U.S. Private*, pg. 4128
THE TYONEK NATIVE CORPORATION; *U.S. Private*, pg. 4128
TYONEK SERVICES GROUP, INC.—See The Tyonek Native Corporation; *U.S. Private*, pg. 4128
UBUYHOLDINGS, INC.; *U.S. Public*, pg. 2217
UCOMMUNE GROUP HOLDINGS LIMITED—See Ucommune International Ltd.; *U.S. Public*, pg. 2217
UCOMMUNE INTERNATIONAL LTD.; *U.S. Public*, pg. 2217
UELS HOLDING, LLC—See Wells Fargo & Company; *U.S. Public*, pg. 2345
UFG GROUP, INC.; *U.S. Private*, pg. 4274

551112 — OFFICES OF OTHER HO...   CORPORATE AFFILIATIONS

UFP INDUSTRIES, INC.; *U.S. Public*, pg. 2218
UGI CORPORATION; *U.S. Public*, pg. 2221
UGI ENTERPRISES, LLC—See UGI Corporation; *U.S. Public*, pg. 2222
U-HAUL HOLDING COMPANY; *U.S. Public*, pg. 2211
UIC COMMERCIAL SERVICES, LLC—See Ukpeagvik Inupiat Corporation; *U.S. Private*, pg. 4275
UIC TECHNICAL SERVICES, LLC—See Ukpeagvik Inupiat Corporation; *U.S. Private*, pg. 4275
UKG INC.—See Hellman & Friedman LLC; *U.S. Private*, pg. 1910
UK MAIL GROUP LIMITED—See Deutsche Post AG; *Int'l*, pg. 2083
U.K. MEDICAL LIMITED—See Becton, Dickinson & Company; *U.S. Public*, pg. 292
UKPEAGVIK INUPIAT CORPORATION; *U.S. Private*, pg. 4275
ULLICO INC.; *U.S. Private*, pg. 4276
ULLINK GLOBAL SAS—See Broadridge Financial Solutions, Inc.; *U.S. Public*, pg. 392
ULTIMATE EVERCARE HOLDINGS, LLC; *U.S. Private*, pg. 4277
UMBRA APPLIED TECHNOLOGIES GROUP, INC.; *U.S. Public*, pg. 2224
UM HOLDINGS LIMITED; *U.S. Private*, pg. 4278
UNICO AMERICAN CORPORATION; *U.S. Public*, pg. 2225
UNICOM GLOBAL, INC.; *U.S. Private*, pg. 4281
UNIFIED COMMERCE GROUP; *U.S. Private*, pg. 4282
UNIFIED FINANCIAL SERVICES, INC.; *U.S. Private*, pg. 4282
UNIFIED LOGISTICS HOLDINGS LLC—See ACI Capital Co. LLC; *U.S. Private*, pg. 59
UNION PACIFIC CORPORATION; *U.S. Public*, pg. 2226
UNIPROP, INC.; *U.S. Private*, pg. 4285
UNIQUE LOGISTICS HOLDINGS LTD.—See Unique Logistics International Inc.; *U.S. Public*, pg. 2227
UNISA HOLDINGS INCORPORATED; *U.S. Private*, pg. 4286
UNITEAM HOLDING AS—See IKM Gruppen AS; *Int'l*, pg. 3612
UNITED ACQUISITION CORP.—See Red Apple Group, Inc.; *U.S. Private*, pg. 3373
UNITED AIRLINES HOLDINGS, INC.; *U.S. Public*, pg. 2228
THE UNITED DISTRIBUTION GROUP, INC.—See Clayton, Dubilier & Rice, LLC; *U.S. Private*, pg. 926
UNITEDHEALTH GROUP INCORPORATED; *U.S. Public*, pg. 2238
UNITED PANAM FINANCIAL CORP.—See Pine Brook Partners, LLC; *U.S. Private*, pg. 3182
UNITED REFINING INC.—See Red Apple Group, Inc.; *U.S. Private*, pg. 3373
UNITED RENTALS, INC.; *U.S. Public*, pg. 2234
UNITED SUPER MARKETS HOLDINGS, INC.—See AEON Co., Ltd.; *Int'l*, pg. 178
UNITED TECHNOLOGIES AUSTRALIA HOLDINGS LIMITED—See RTX Corporation; *U.S. Public*, pg. 1825
UNITIL CORPORATION; *U.S. Public*, pg. 2253
UNIVAR EUROPE HOLDINGS B.V.—See Apollo Global Management, Inc.; *U.S. Public*, pg. 165
UNIVAR SOLUTIONS INC.—See Apollo Global Management, Inc.; *U.S. Public*, pg. 165
UNIVEG GROUP—See CVC Capital Partners SICAV-FIS S.A.; *Int'l*, pg. 1886
UNIVERSAL AMERICAN CORP.—See Centene Corporation; *U.S. Public*, pg. 471
UNIVERSAL CORPORATION; *U.S. Public*, pg. 2254
UNIVERSAL INSURANCE HOLDING CO.—See Universal Insurance Holdings, Inc.; *U.S. Public*, pg. 2261
UNIVERSAL INSURANCE HOLDINGS, INC.; *U.S. Public*, pg. 2261
UNIVERSAL LOGISTICS HOLDINGS, INC.; *U.S. Public*, pg. 2261
UNIVERSAL PICTURES INTERNATIONAL ENTERTAINMENT LIMITED—See Comcast Corporation; *U.S. Public*, pg. 541
UNIVERSAL SOLAR TECHNOLOGY, INC.; *U.S. Public*, pg. 2262
UNIVERSAL STUDIOS LLC—See Comcast Corporation; *U.S. Public*, pg. 540
UNIVISION COMMUNICATIONS INC.—See ForgeLight, LLC; *U.S. Private*, pg. 1568
UNIVISION COMMUNICATIONS INC.—See Searchlight Capital Partners, L.P.; *U.S. Private*, pg. 3590
UNIVISION HOLDINGS, INC.—See ForgeLight, LLC; *U.S. Private*, pg. 1568
UNIVISION HOLDINGS, INC.—See Searchlight Capital Partners, L.P.; *U.S. Private*, pg. 3590
UNOCHROME INDUSTRIES LIMITED—See Camellia Plc; *Int'l*, pg. 1271
UNS ENERGY CORPORATION—See Fortis Inc.; *Int'l*, pg. 2740
UNUM EUROPEAN HOLDING COMPANY LIMITED—See Unum Group; *U.S. Public*, pg. 2263
UNUM GROUP; *U.S. Public*, pg. 2263
UPG ENTERPRISES LLC; *U.S. Private*, pg. 4311
UPLAND SOFTWARE, INC.; *U.S. Public*, pg. 2264
UPS SCS HOLDING LIMITED—See United Parcel Service, Inc.; *U.S. Public*, pg. 2233

UPSTART HOLDINGS, INC.; *U.S. Public*, pg. 2264
UPWORK GLOBAL INC.; *U.S. Private*, pg. 4313
URBAN-GRO, INC.; *U.S. Public*, pg. 2265
URBAN ONE, INC.; *U.S. Public*, pg. 2265
URBN FNB HOLDINGS LLC—See Urban Outfitters, Inc.; *U.S. Public*, pg. 2265
URS HOLDINGS, INC. - PANAMANIAN BRANCH—See AECOM; *U.S. Public*, pg. 51
URS WORLDWIDE HOLDINGS UK LIMITED—See AECOM; *U.S. Public*, pg. 52
USABLE CORPORATION; *U.S. Private*, pg. 4322
USA COMPRESSION GP, LLC—See Energy Transfer LP; *U.S. Public*, pg. 765
USA COMPRESSION PARTNERS, LP—See Riverstone Holdings LLC; *U.S. Private*, pg. 3447
US BIOSERVICES; *U.S. Private*, pg. 4317
USCB FINANCIAL HOLDINGS, INC.; *U.S. Public*, pg. 2267
US COMMERCIAL CORP. S.A. DE C.V.—See Grupo Carso, S.A.B. de C.V.; *Int'l*, pg. 3124
U.S. EAGLE CORPORATION; *U.S. Private*, pg. 4270
US ECOLOGY, INC.—See Republic Services, Inc.; *U.S. Public*, pg. 1787
US ECOLOGY VERNON, INC.—See Republic Services, Inc.; *U.S. Public*, pg. 1788
U.S. ENERGY TECHNOLOGIES, INC.; *U.S. Private*, pg. 4270
U.S. EXCHANGE HOLDINGS, INC.—See Deutsche Borse AG; *Int'l*, pg. 2064
U.S. FARATHANE HOLDINGS CORP.—See The Gores Group, LLC; *U.S. Private*, pg. 4035
U.S. FIDUCIARY SERVICES, INC.; *U.S. Private*, pg. 4270
US FOODS HOLDING CORP.; *U.S. Public*, pg. 2266
USG NETHERLANDS GLOBAL HOLDINGS B.V.—See Gebr. Knauf KG; *Int'l*, pg. 2908
U.S HEALTHCARE HOLDINGS, LLC—See CVS Health Corporation; *U.S. Public*, pg. 615
US HOLDINGS CORPORATION; *U.S. Private*, pg. 4319
USI HOLDINGS CORPORATION—See Caisse de Depot et Placement du Quebec; *Int'l*, pg. 1256
USI HOLDINGS CORPORATION—See KKR & Co. Inc.; *U.S. Public*, pg. 1264
U.S. LBM HOLDINGS, LLC—See Bain Capital, LP; *U.S. Private*, pg. 450
USLEGAL, INC.; *U.S. Private*, pg. 4323
US LIGHTING GROUP, INC.; *U.S. Public*, pg. 2266
U.S. LOGISTICS, INC.; *U.S. Private*, pg. 4271
U.S. MERCHANTS FINANCIAL GROUP, INC.; *U.S. Private*, pg. 4271
USPI HOLDING COMPANY, INC.—See Tenet Healthcare Corporation; *U.S. Public*, pg. 2009
USPI HOLDINGS, INC.—See Tenet Healthcare Corporation; *U.S. Public*, pg. 2013
U.S. RISK INSURANCE GROUP, INC.—See Caisse de Depot et Placement du Quebec; *Int'l*, pg. 1256
U.S. RISK INSURANCE GROUP, INC.—See KKR & Co. Inc.; *U.S. Public*, pg. 1265
USS HOLDINGS, INC.—See Apollo Global Management, Inc.; *U.S. Public*, pg. 165
U.S. TRUST, BANK OF AMERICA PRIVATE WEALTH MANAGEMENT—See Bank of America Corporation; *U.S. Public*, pg. 271
U-SWIRL, INC.—See Rocky Mountain Chocolate Factory, Inc.; *U.S. Public*, pg. 1807
U.S. XPRESS ENTERPRISES, INC.—See Knight-Swift Transportation Holdings Inc.; *U.S. Public*, pg. 1269
UTG, INC.; *U.S. Public*, pg. 2267
UTICA ENTERPRISES, INC.; *U.S. Private*, pg. 4325
UTICA NATIONAL INSURANCE GROUP; *U.S. Private*, pg. 4325
UTILITY ONE SOURCE L.P.; *U.S. Private*, pg. 4326
UWM CORPORATION—See The Gores Group, LLC; *U.S. Private*, pg. 4035
VAIL HOLDINGS, INC.—See Vail Resorts, Inc.; *U.S. Public*, pg. 2271
VALENCE MEDIA GROUP; *U.S. Private*, pg. 4330
VALERO RENEWABLE FUELS COMPANY, LLC—See Valero Energy Corporation; *U.S. Public*, pg. 2272
VALHI, INC.—See Contran Corporation; *U.S. Private*, pg. 1033
VALIDOR CAPITAL LLC; *U.S. Private*, pg. 4332
VALIDUS HOLDINGS, LTD.—See American International Group, Inc.; *U.S. Public*, pg. 107
THE VALLEY GROUP, INC.; *U.S. Private*, pg. 4130
VALLEY-HI AUTOMOTIVE GROUP—See Dick Browning, Inc.; *U.S. Private*, pg. 1225
VALLEY RIDGE INVESTMENT PARTNERS; *U.S. Private*, pg. 4335
VALORA HOLDING AG—See Fomento Economico Mexicano, S.A.B. de C.V.; *Int'l*, pg. 2724
VALORA HOLDING GERMANY GMBH—See Fomento Economico Mexicano, S.A.B. de C.V.; *Int'l*, pg. 2724
VALVOLINE INC.; *U.S. Public*, pg. 2274
VANDE HEY BRANTMEIER ENTERPRISES, INC.; *U.S. Private*, pg. 4342
VAN DE POL ENTERPRISES, INC.; *U.S. Private*, pg. 4339
VAN DIEST FAMILY, LLC; *U.S. Private*, pg. 4339
VANGEO TECHNOLOGY GROUP, LLC; *U.S. Private*, pg. 4343

VANKE OVERSEAS INVESTMENT HOLDING COMPANY LIMITED—See China Vanke Co., Ltd.; *Int'l*, pg. 1562
VANKE REAL ESTATE (HONG KONG) CO., LTD.—See China Vanke Co., Ltd.; *Int'l*, pg. 1562
VANTAGE DELAWARE HOLDINGS LLC—See Vantage Drilling Company; *U.S. Public*, pg. 2275
VANTAGE DRILLING COMPANY; *U.S. Public*, pg. 2275
VANTAGE ENERGY INC.—See Lime Rock Partners, LLC; *U.S. Private*, pg. 2456
VANTAGE ENERGY INC.—See Quantum Energy Partners, LLC; *U.S. Private*, pg. 3323
VANTAGE ENERGY INC.—See Riverstone Holdings LLC; *U.S. Private*, pg. 3448
VANTAGE SPECIALTIES, INC.—See H.I.G. Capital, LLC; *U.S. Private*, pg. 1832
VANTEC CORPORATION—See KKR & Co. Inc.; *U.S. Public*, pg. 1259
VAN TUYL GROUP, LLC—See Berkshire Hathaway Inc.; *U.S. Public*, pg. 300
VARD GROUP AS—See Fincantieri S.p.A.; *Int'l*, pg. 2671
VAREX IMAGING CORPORATION; *U.S. Public*, pg. 2275
VAREX IMAGING HOLDINGS, INC.—See Varex Imaging Corporation; *U.S. Public*, pg. 2275
VARISTAR CORPORATION—See Otter Tail Corporation; *U.S. Public*, pg. 1624
VARO ENERGY HOLDING S.A.—See AtlasInvest; *Int'l*, pg. 686
VARSITY BRANDS HOLDING CO., INC.—See Bain Capital, LP; *U.S. Private*, pg. 451
VARTA AG—See Global Equity Partners Beteiligungs-Management AG; *Int'l*, pg. 2996
VAXART, INC.; *U.S. Public*, pg. 2276
VBI VACCINES INC.; *U.S. Public*, pg. 2276
VCST N.V.—See Gimv NV; *Int'l*, pg. 2976
VECTIVBIO HOLDING AG—See Ironwood Pharmaceuticals, Inc.; *U.S. Public*, pg. 1174
VECTOR 21 HOLDINGS, INC.; *U.S. Public*, pg. 2276
VECTRA CO.—See Apollo Global Management, Inc.; *U.S. Public*, pg. 166
VECTREN CORPORATION—See CenterPoint Energy, Inc.; *U.S. Public*, pg. 472
VECTREN UTILITY HOLDINGS, INC.—See CenterPoint Energy, Inc.; *U.S. Public*, pg. 472
VEEVA U.K. HOLDINGS LIMITED—See Veeva Systems, Inc.; *U.S. Public*, pg. 2277
VELATEL GLOBAL COMMUNICATIONS, INC.; *U.S. Private*, pg. 4354
VENATOR GROUP—See Huntsman Corporation; *U.S. Public*, pg. 1075
VENCAP INDUSTRIER AB—See Grimaldi Industri AB; *Int'l*, pg. 3086
VENCAP TECHNOLOGIES, LLC; *U.S. Private*, pg. 4356
VENTUREDYNE, LTD.; *U.S. Private*, pg. 4358
VERADIGM INC.; *U.S. Public*, pg. 2279
VERANO HOLDINGS CORP.; *U.S. Public*, pg. 2280
VERA VARLIK YONETIM A.S.—See Bogazici Varlik Yonetim A.S.; *Int'l*, pg. 1100
VERDE BIO HOLDINGS, INC.—See Formation Minerals, Inc.; *U.S. Public*, pg. 868
VERDE MEDIA GROUP, INC.; *U.S. Public*, pg. 2280
VERETECH HOLDINGS, INC.—See The Hearst Corporation; *U.S. Private*, pg. 4045
VERICITY, INC.—See iA Financial Corporation Inc.; *Int'l*, pg. 3568
VERIFONE SYSTEMS, INC.—See British Columbia Investment Management Corp.; *Int'l*, pg. 1170
VERIFONE SYSTEMS, INC.—See Francisco Partners Management, LP; *U.S. Private*, pg. 1592
VERISK ANALYTICS, INC.; *U.S. Public*, pg. 2282
VERITAS FARMS, INC.; *U.S. Public*, pg. 2283
VERITIV CORPORATION—See Clayton, Dubilier & Rice, LLC; *U.S. Private*, pg. 928
VERMOGENSVERWALTUNG EMAILLIERWERK GMBH—See Helaba Landesbank Hessen-Thuringen; *Int'l*, pg. 3328
VERSA COMPANIES; *U.S. Private*, pg. 4368
VERSATA, INC.—See ESW Capital, LLC; *U.S. Private*, pg. 1430
VERSO PAPER HOLDINGS LLC—See Billerud AB; *Int'l*, pg. 1030
VERTEC—See Compagnie de Saint-Gobain SA; *Int'l*, pg. 1737
VERTIKOM GMBH—See ASM Group S.A.; *Int'l*, pg. 625
VERTIV HOLDINGS, LLC—See Vertiv Holdings Co; *U.S. Public*, pg. 2288
VERTIV (HONG KONG) LTD.—See Vertiv Holdings Co; *U.S. Public*, pg. 2289
VESTAR/GRAY INVESTORS LLC; *U.S. Private*, pg. 4373
VESTIN GROUP, INC.; *U.S. Private*, pg. 4373
VESTIS CORP; *U.S. Public*, pg. 2290
VESTIS RETAIL GROUP, LLC—See Independence Capital Partners, LLC; *U.S. Private*, pg. 2057
VETRI HOLDINGS LLC; *U.S. Private*, pg. 4374
VEXCEL HOLDINGS, INC.; *U.S. Private*, pg. 4374
V. F. CORPORATION; *U.S. Public*, pg. 2268
VF WORLDWIDE HOLDINGS LTD.—See EQT AB; *Int'l*, pg. 2478
VGTEL, INC.; *U.S. Public*, pg. 2290

N.A.I.C.S. INDEX

551112 — OFFICES OF OTHER HO...

VHS ACQUISITION CORPORATION—See Tenet Healthcare Corporation; *U.S. Public*, pg. 2014
VIAD CORP.; *U.S. Public*, pg. 2290
VIANT MEDICAL, INC.-SOUTH PLAINFIELD—See Viant Medical, LLC; *U.S. Private*, pg. 4375
VIATEL HOLDING (EUROPE) LIMITED—See Digiweb Ltd.; *Int'l*, pg. 2124
VICTORY AUTOMOTIVE GROUP, INC.; *U.S. Private*, pg. 4378
VICTORY COMMERCIAL MANAGEMENT, INC.; *U.S. Private*, pg. 4378
VICTORY OF WEST VIRGINIA, INC.; *U.S. Private*, pg. 4379
VICTURA CONSTRUCTION GROUP, INC.—See Saint James Holding & Investment Company Trust; *U.S. Private*, pg. 3529
VIDLER WATER RESOURCES, INC.—See D.R. Horton, Inc.; *U.S. Public*, pg. 620
VIGILANT DIVERSIFIED HOLDINGS, INC.; *U.S. Private*, pg. 4382
VIGOR INDUSTRIAL LLC—See Stellex Capital Management LP; *U.S. Private*, pg. 3800
VIGOR INDUSTRIAL LLC—See The Carlyle Group Inc.; *U.S. Public*, pg. 2056
VIKING ENERGY GROUP, INC.—See Camber Energy, Inc.; *U.S. Public*, pg. 425
VILLAGE CHEVROLET CO.—See North American Automotive Services, Inc.; *U.S. Private*, pg. 2940
VILLAGE VOICE MEDIA HOLDINGS, LLC; *U.S. Private*, pg. 4384
VIMEO, INC.; *U.S. Public*, pg. 2297
VINCE HOLDING CORP.—See Sun Capital Partners, Inc.; *U.S. Private*, pg. 3859
VINDA HOUSEHOLD PAPER (HONG KONG) LIMITED—See Essity Aktiebolag; *Int'l*, pg. 2517
VINDA INTERNATIONAL HOLDINGS LIMITED—See Essity Aktiebolag; *Int'l*, pg. 2517
VINE ENERGY INC.—See Expand Energy Corporation; *U.S. Public*, pg. 809
VINYTHAI HOLDING PTE. LTD.—See AGC Inc.; *Int'l*, pg. 204
VIRGIN GALACTIC HOLDINGS, INC.; *U.S. Public*, pg. 2299
VIRIDIUM HOLDING AG—See Cinven Limited; *Int'l*, pg. 1616
VIRNETX HOLDING CORP.; *U.S. Public*, pg. 2299
VIRTU GETCO HOLDING COMPANY, LLC—See Virtu Financial, Inc.; *U.S. Public*, pg. 2300
VIRTU KCG HOLDINGS LLC—See Virtu Financial, Inc.; *U.S. Public*, pg. 2300
VISION 7 INTERNATIONAL ULC—See Bluefocus Intelligent Communications Group Co., Ltd.; *Int'l*, pg. 1071
VISIUM TECHNOLOGIES, INC.; *U.S. Public*, pg. 2304
VISTAGEN THERAPEUTICS, INC.; *U.S. Public*, pg. 2305
VISTA GOLD HOLDINGS INC.—See Hycroft Mining Holding Corporation; *U.S. Public*, pg. 1079
VISTA OUTDOOR INC.; *U.S. Public*, pg. 2304
VISTEON EUROPEAN HOLDINGS, INC.—See Visteon Corporation; *U.S. Public*, pg. 2306
VISTEON HOLDINGS FRANCE SAS—See Visteon Corporation; *U.S. Public*, pg. 2306
VISTEON HOLDINGS GMBH—See Visteon Corporation; *U.S. Public*, pg. 2306
VISTRA GROUP HOLDINGS S.A.—See EQT AB; *Int'l*, pg. 2472
VITAMIN SHOPPE, INC.—See B. Riley Financial, Inc.; *U.S. Public*, pg. 261
VITAMIN SHOPPE, INC.—See Irradiant Partners, LP; *U.S. Private*, pg. 2140
VITERRA INC.—See Glencore plc; *Int'l*, pg. 2990
VIVAKOR, INC.; *U.S. Public*, pg. 2307
VIVAT N.V.—See Apollo Global Management, Inc.; *U.S. Public*, pg. 147
VIVINT SOLAR, INC.—See Sunrun Inc.; *U.S. Public*, pg. 1965
VIZIO HOLDING CORP.; *U.S. Public*, pg. 2307
VOLARIS GROUP INC.—See Constellation Software Inc.; *Int'l*, pg. 1775
VOLTARI CORPORATION; *U.S. Private*, pg. 4411
VOLT DELTA RESOURCES, INC.—See ESW Capital, LLC; *U.S. Private*, pg. 1431
VOLT EUROPE HOLDINGS LIMITED—See American CyberSystems, Inc.; *U.S. Private*, pg. 230
VOLVO FINANCIAL SERVICES AB—See AB Volvo; *Int'l*, pg. 44
VOLVO FINANCIAL SERVICES LLC—See AB Volvo; *Int'l*, pg. 44
VON HOUSEN'S MOTORS; *U.S. Private*, pg. 4412
VOUVRAY ACQUISITION LIMITED—See Ackermans & van Haaren NV; *Int'l*, pg. 106
VOX COMMUNICATIONS GROUP LLC; *U.S. Private*, pg. 4414
VOXX GERMAN HOLDINGS GMBH—See VOXX International Corporation; *U.S. Public*, pg. 2311
VOYA FINANCIAL, INC.; *U.S. Public*, pg. 2311
VOYAGER SPACE HOLDINGS, INC.; *U.S. Private*, pg. 4414
VOYA INVESTMENT MANAGEMENT—See Voya Financial, Inc.; *U.S. Public*, pg. 2311
VOYA SERVICES COMPANY—See Voya Financial, Inc.; *U.S. Public*, pg. 2312

VPI ACQUISITION CORP.—See Spell Capital Partners, LLC; *U.S. Private*, pg. 3754
VSM GROUP AB—See Platinum Equity, LLC; *U.S. Private*, pg. 3208
VSR GROUP, INC.—See RCAP Holdings, LLC; *U.S. Private*, pg. 3361
VTG AKTIENGESELLSCHAFT—See Morgan Stanley; *U.S. Public*, pg. 1476
VTG CORP.; *U.S. Private*, pg. 4415
VTL HOLDING, INC.—See Littlejohn & Co., LLC; *U.S. Private*, pg. 2472
VTV THERAPEUTICS INC.—See MacAndrews & Forbes Incorporated; *U.S. Private*, pg. 2534
VULCAN INC.; *U.S. Private*, pg. 4416
VULCAN SPORTS & ENTERTAINMENT LLC—See Vulcan Inc.; *U.S. Private*, pg. 4416
VWR CORPORATION—See Avantor, Inc.; *U.S. Public*, pg. 241
VWR FUNDING, INC.—See Avantor, Inc.; *U.S. Public*, pg. 241
WABASH TECHNOLOGIES, INC. - TROY PLANT—See Sensata Technologies Holding plc; *U.S. Public*, pg. 1866
WAB HOLDINGS, LLC—See Walgreens Boots Alliance, Inc.; *U.S. Public*, pg. 2323
WADDINGTON GROUP, INC.—See Apollo Global Management, Inc.; *U.S. Public*, pg. 154
WAGMAN COMPANIES, INC.; *U.S. Private*, pg. 4426
W.A. HOLDING COMPANY—See KSL Capital Partners, LLC; *U.S. Private*, pg. 2355
WAITTCORP LLC; *U.S. Private*, pg. 4427
WALGREEN ARIZONA DRUG CO.—See Walgreens Boots Alliance, Inc.; *U.S. Public*, pg. 2323
WALGREEN HASTINGS CO.—See Walgreens Boots Alliance, Inc.; *U.S. Public*, pg. 2323
WALGREENS BOOTS ALLIANCE, INC.; *U.S. Public*, pg. 2321
WALGREENS HEALTH SERVICES—See Walgreens Boots Alliance, Inc.; *U.S. Public*, pg. 2324
WALGREENS HEALTH & WELLNESS—See Walgreens Boots Alliance, Inc.; *U.S. Public*, pg. 2324
WALKER & DUNLOP, INC.; *U.S. Public*, pg. 2324
WALLACE AUTOMOTIVE MANAGEMENT CORPORATION, INC.; *U.S. Private*, pg. 4430
WALL FAMILY ENTERPRISE, INC.; *U.S. Private*, pg. 4430
WAL-MART DE MEXICO, S.A. DE C.V.—See Walmart Inc.; *U.S. Public*, pg. 2325
WALSER AUTOMOTIVE GROUP, LLC; *U.S. Private*, pg. 4432
THE WALSH GROUP; *U.S. Private*, pg. 4133
THE WALT DISNEY COMPANY; *U.S. Public*, pg. 2137
WALTON INTERNATIONAL GROUP INC.—See Giordano International Limited; *Int'l*, pg. 2978
WANDA SPORTS GROUP COMPANY LIMITED—See Dalian Wanda Group Corporation Ltd.; *Int'l*, pg. 1953
WANG-ZHENG BERHAD—See Hengan International Group Co. Ltd.; *Int'l*, pg. 3346
WANTAGE AVENUE HOLDING COMPANY, INC.—See Selective Insurance Group, Inc.; *U.S. Public*, pg. 1863
WARBIRD CORPORATION—See Coteminas Companhia de Tecidos Norte de Minas; *Int'l*, pg. 1817
WARBIRD CORPORATION—See Springs Global, Inc.; *U.S. Private*, pg. 3764
WARNER BROS. DISCOVERY, INC.; *U.S. Public*, pg. 2326
WARNER MEDIA, LLC—See Warner Bros. Discovery, Inc.; *U.S. Public*, pg. 2327
WARREN EQUITY PARTNERS, LLC; *U.S. Private*, pg. 4443
WARRIOR GIRL CORP.; *U.S. Public*, pg. 2329
WARWICK HOLDING GMBH—See Morgan Stanley; *U.S. Public*, pg. 1475
WASHINGTON CORPORATIONS; *U.S. Private*, pg. 4446
WASTE ASSOCIATES, LLC—See BlackEagle Partners, LLC; *U.S. Private*, pg. 573
WASTEBUILT ENVIRONMENTAL SOLUTIONS, LLC—See H.I.G. Capital, LLC; *U.S. Private*, pg. 1833
WASTE PRO USA, INC.; *U.S. Private*, pg. 4450
WATCHES OF SWITZERLAND OPERATIONS LIMITED—See Apollo Global Management, Inc.; *U.S. Public*, pg. 167
WATCO COMPANIES, LLC—See Kinder Morgan, Inc.; *U.S. Public*, pg. 1233
WATCO RAILROAD COMPANY HOLDINGS, INC.—See Kinder Morgan, Inc.; *U.S. Public*, pg. 1233
WATERFORD GAMING, LLC—See Waterford Group, LLC; *U.S. Private*, pg. 4453
WATERJET HOLDINGS, INC.—See AIP, LLC; *U.S. Private*, pg. 137
WATERLOGIC PLC—See Castik Capital S.a.r.l.; *Int'l*, pg. 1356
WATERMAN INTERNATIONAL HOLDINGS LIMITED—See CTI Engineering Co., Ltd.; *Int'l*, pg. 1871
WATERMARK GROUP, INC.; *U.S. Private*, pg. 4454
WATERWAY HOTEL HOLDINGS, LLC—See Howard Hughes Holdings Inc.; *U.S. Public*, pg. 1061
WATFORD HOLDINGS LTD.—See Arch Capital Group Ltd.; *Int'l*, pg. 547
WATKINS ASSOCIATED INDUSTRIES INC.; *U.S. Private*, pg. 4454

WATTENBERG HOLDING, LLC—See Energy Transfer LP; *U.S. Public*, pg. 764
WAVEDIVISION HOLDINGS, LLC—See Stonepeak Partners L.P.; *U.S. Private*, pg. 3829
WAXMAN INDUSTRIES, INC.; *U.S. Private*, pg. 4459
WAYBILL USA INC.; *U.S. Private*, pg. 4459
WAYFAIR INC.; *U.S. Public*, pg. 2338
WAYPOINT CAPITAL PARTNERS; *U.S. Private*, pg. 4460
WBI HOLDINGS, INC.—See MDU Resources Group, Inc.; *U.S. Public*, pg. 1410
W.C. BRADLEY FARMS INC.—See W.C. Bradley Co.; *U.S. Private*, pg. 4419
WC HOLDING, INC.; *U.S. Private*, pg. 4461
WCS, INC.; *U.S. Private*, pg. 4462
WDF/NAGELBUSH HOLDING CORP—See Tutor Perini Corporation; *U.S. Public*, pg. 2206
W-DIAMOND GROUP CORPORATION; *U.S. Private*, pg. 4417
WEATHERFORD INTERNATIONAL PLC; *U.S. Public*, pg. 2339
WEBER INC.—See BDT Capital Partners, LLC; *U.S. Private*, pg. 503
WEBMD HEALTH CORP.—See KKR & Co. Inc.; *U.S. Public*, pg. 1253
WEC ENERGY GROUP, INC.; *U.S. Public*, pg. 2342
WECHCO, INC.; *U.S. Private*, pg. 4468
WEDOTALK INC.; *U.S. Public*, pg. 2342
WEED, INC.; *U.S. Public*, pg. 2342
WEGENER KONINKLIJKE B.V.—See DPG Media Group NV; *Int'l*, pg. 2189
WEIN WOLF HOLDING GMBH & CO. KG—See Hawesko Holding AG; *Int'l*, pg. 3288
WEISS GROUP, LLC; *U.S. Private*, pg. 4473
WELBILT, INC.—See Ali Holding S.r.l; *Int'l*, pg. 322
WELCIA HOLDINGS CO., LTD.—See AEON Co., Ltd.; *Int'l*, pg. 178
WELD NORTH LLC—See Silver Lake Group, LLC; *U.S. Private*, pg. 3661
WELLINGTON EQUESTRIAN PARTNERS, LLC; *U.S. Private*, pg. 4475
WELLINGTON INSURANCE GROUP, INC.—See Clayton, Dubilier & Rice, LLC; *U.S. Private*, pg. 927
WELLINGTON INSURANCE GROUP, INC.—See Stone Point Capital LLC; *U.S. Private*, pg. 3826
WELLMONT HEALTH SYSTEM—See Mountain States Health Alliance; *U.S. Private*, pg. 2800
WELLS FARGO CAPITAL FINANCE, INC.—See Wells Fargo & Company; *U.S. Public*, pg. 2346
WELLS FARGO INSURANCE, INC.—See Wells Fargo & Company; *U.S. Public*, pg. 2346
WELLS HOLDINGS, INC.—See Corporate Partners LLC; *U.S. Private*, pg. 1055
WENCOR GROUP, LLC—See HEICO Corporation; *U.S. Public*, pg. 1021
THE WENDY'S COMPANY; *U.S. Public*, pg. 2141
WENTWORTH MANAGEMENT SERVICES LLC; *U.S. Private*, pg. 4481
WESCO AIRCRAFT HOLDINGS, INC.—See Platinum Equity, LLC; *U.S. Private*, pg. 3209
WESTERN ELITE INCORPORATED SERVICES; *U.S. Private*, pg. 4492
WESTERN GAS HOLDINGS, LLC—See Western Midstream Partners, LP; *U.S. Public*, pg. 2356
WESTERN MIDSTREAM OPERATING, LP—See Western Midstream Partners, LP; *U.S. Public*, pg. 2356
WESTERN MIDSTREAM PARTNERS, LP; *U.S. Public*, pg. 2356
WESTERN PETROLEUM LLC—See Berkshire Hathaway Inc.; *U.S. Public*, pg. 313
WESTERN & SOUTHERN FINANCIAL GROUP, INC.; *U.S. Private*, pg. 4490
WESTERN WORLD INSURANCE GROUP, INC.—See American International Group, Inc.; *U.S. Public*, pg. 107
WESTFALL TECHNIK, INC.—See BlackBern Partners LLC; *U.S. Private*, pg. 573
WESTFALL TECHNIK, INC.—See Lee Equity Partners LLC; *U.S. Private*, pg. 2412
WESTHOUSE HOLDINGS PLC—See ICM Limited; *Int'l*, pg. 3582
WESTMED PRACTICE PARTNERS LLC—See UnitedHealth Group Incorporated; *U.S. Public*, pg. 2252
WESTMINSTER FOODS, LLC—See LSCG Management, Inc.; *U.S. Private*, pg. 2509
WESTMORELAND COAL COMPANY; *U.S. Private*, pg. 4499
WESTMORELAND ENERGY LLC—See Westmoreland Coal Company; *U.S. Private*, pg. 4500
WESTMORELAND RESOURCES GP, LLC—See Westmoreland Coal Company; *U.S. Private*, pg. 4500
WEST PARTNERS LLC; *U.S. Public*, pg. 4486
WEST PHARMACEUTICAL SERVICES HOLDING DANMARK APS—See West Pharmaceutical Services, Inc.; *U.S. Public*, pg. 2353
WEST PHARMACEUTICAL SERVICES HOLDING FRANCE SAS—See West Pharmaceutical Services, Inc.; *U.S. Public*, pg. 2353
WEST PHARMACEUTICAL SERVICES HOLDING

GMBH—See West Pharmaceutical Services, Inc.; U.S. Public, pg. 2353
WEST PHARMACEUTICAL SERVICES SINGAPORE (HOLDING) PTE. LIMITED—See West Pharmaceutical Services, Inc.; U.S. Public, pg. 2353
WESTPOINT INTERNATIONAL, INC.—See Icahn Enterprises L.P.; U.S. Public, pg. 1085
WESTROCK COMPANY; U.S. Public, pg. 2361
WEST SIDE UNLIMITED CORPORATION; U.S. Private, pg. 4487
WETZEL HOLDING AG—See Matthews International Corporation; U.S. Public, pg. 1401
WEWORK INC.; U.S. Public, pg. 2364
WEX, INC.; U.S. Public, pg. 2364
WFS GLOBAL SAS—See Cerberus Capital Management, L.P.; U.S. Private, pg. 840
WGL HOLDINGS, INC.—See AltaGas Ltd.; Int'l, pg. 384
WHANAU INTERESTS LLC; U.S. Private, pg. 4503
WHEELS GROUP INC.—See Radiant Logistics, Inc.; U.S. Public, pg. 1759
WHIRLPOOL OVERSEAS HOLDINGS, LLC—See Whirlpool Corporation; U.S. Public, pg. 2368
WHISTLER BLACKCOMB HOLDINGS INC.—See Vail Resorts, Inc.; U.S. Public, pg. 2272
WHITCOM PARTNERS, INC.; U.S. Private, pg. 4507
WHITEBIRCH ENTERPRISES, INC.; U.S. Private, pg. 4511
WHITE KNIGHT BROADCASTING, INC.; U.S. Private, pg. 4509
WHITE LODGE EDUCATION GROUP SERVICES PTE. LTD.—See Chip Eng Seng Corporation Ltd.; Int'l, pg. 1572
WHITE MOUNTAINS INSURANCE GROUP, LTD.; U.S. Public, pg. 2368
WHITE MOUNTAINS RE BERMUDA LTD.—See White Mountains Insurance Group, Ltd.; U.S. Public, pg. 2369
WHITE RIVER CAPITAL, INC.—See PCP Enterprise, L.P.; U.S. Public, pg. 3121
WHITESELL INTERNATIONAL CORPORATION—See Whitesell Corporation; U.S. Private, pg. 4512
WHITING CANADIAN HOLDING COMPANY ULC—See Chord Energy Corporation; U.S. Public, pg. 490
WHITING HOLDINGS LLC—See Chord Energy Corporation; U.S. Public, pg. 490
WHITING PETROLEUM CORPORATION—See Chord Energy Corporation; U.S. Public, pg. 490
WHYTE & MACKAY GROUP LIMITED—See Alliance Global Group, Inc.; Int'l, pg. 339
WICKLAND PROPERTIES—See Wickland Oil Corporation; U.S. Private, pg. 4516
WIDEOPENWEST FINANCE, LLC—See WideOpenWest, Inc.; U.S. Public, pg. 2369
WILBERT INC.—See Berkshire Hathaway Inc.; U.S. Public, pg. 298
WILHELMINA INTERNATIONAL, INC.; U.S. Public, pg. 2370
WILILOY LIMITED—See Hang Lung Group Limited; Int'l, pg. 3245
WILLDAN GROUP, INC.; U.S. Public, pg. 2370
WILLIAM LYON HOMES, INC.—See Brookfield Corporation; Int'l, pg. 1183
WILLIAM MORRIS ENDEAVOR ENTERTAINMENT, LLC; U.S. Private, pg. 4523
WILLIAMS GROUP LLC; U.S. Private, pg. 4526
WILLIAMS INDUSTRIES, INC.; U.S. Private, pg. 4526
WILLIAMS INTERNATIONAL COMPANY—See The Williams Companies, Inc.; U.S. Public, pg. 2142
WILLISTON HOLDING CO., INC.; U.S. Public, pg. 2372
WILLSCOT MOBILE MINI HOLDINGS CORP.; U.S. Public, pg. 2372
WILMINGTON INVESTMENTS INC.—See The Hillman Company; U.S. Private, pg. 4053
WILMOT-BREEDEN HOLDINGS LIMITED—See Cummins Inc.; U.S. Public, pg. 609
WILSONART INTERNATIONAL HOLDINGS LLC—See Clayton, Dubilier & Rice, LLC; U.S. Private, pg. 930
WILSON HOLDINGS, INC.—See Service Corporation International; U.S. Public, pg. 1871
WILTON RE HOLDINGS LTD.—See Vestar Capital Partners, LLC; U.S. Private, pg. 4372
WINCANTON HOLDINGS LIMITED—See GXO Logistics, Inc.; U.S. Public, pg. 976
WINCANTON INTERNATIONAL LIMITED—See GXO Logistics, Inc.; U.S. Public, pg. 976
WINCANTON PLC—See GXO Logistics, Inc.; U.S. Public, pg. 976
WINCO GENERATORS; U.S. Private, pg. 4533
WINCOVE PRIVATE HOLDINGS, LP; U.S. Private, pg. 4533
WINDSOR PROPERTY MANAGEMENT COMPANY—See GID Investment Advisor LLC; U.S. Private, pg. 1697
THE WINEBOW GROUP, LLC; U.S. Private, pg. 4137
THE WINE GROUP, INC.; U.S. Private, pg. 4137
WINGARC1ST INC.—See The Carlyle Group Inc.; U.S. Public, pg. 2057
WINGSTOP INC.—See Roark Capital Group Inc.; U.S. Private, pg. 3456
WINN-DIXIE STORES, INC.—See Aldi Einkauf SE & Co. oHG; Int'l, pg. 304

WINS FINANCE GROUP LTD.—See Arta TechFin Corporation Limited; Int'l, pg. 581
WINS FINANCE HOLDINGS INC.—See Arta TechFin Corporation Limited; Int'l, pg. 581
WINSTON HARTON HOLDINGS, LLC; U.S. Private, pg. 4544
WINSUPPLY INC.; U.S. Private, pg. 4544
WINTERSHALL DEA AG—See BASF SE; Int'l, pg. 885
WINVEST GROUP LTD.; U.S. Public, pg. 2376
WIRELESS GROUP LIMITED—See News Corporation; U.S. Public, pg. 1520
WIRTGEN GROUP HOLDING GMBH—See Deere & Company; U.S. Public, pg. 647
WIRTZ CORPORATION; U.S. Private, pg. 4547
WISE SIGMA INTERNATIONAL HOLDING COMPANY LIMITED—See Cal-Comp Electronics (Thailand) pcl; Int'l, pg. 1261
WITHERS BROADCASTING COMPANY OF WEST VIRGINIA; U.S. Private, pg. 4550
WITTUR HOLDING GMBH—See Bain Capital, LP; U.S. Private, pg. 452
WK KELLOGG CO; U.S. Public, pg. 2376
WKO INVESTMENTS INC.; U.S. Private, pg. 4551
WMCR CO. LLC; U.S. Private, pg. 4552
WMI LIQUIDATING TRUST; U.S. Private, pg. 4552
WNDRCO HOLDINGS, LLC; U.S. Private, pg. 4552
WOLSELEY OVERSEAS LTD.—See Ferguson plc; Int'l, pg. 2638
WOMENSFORUM MEDIA GROUP—See H.I.G. Capital, LLC; U.S. Private, pg. 1829
THE WONDERFUL COMPANY LLC; U.S. Private, pg. 4138
WONDER INTERNATIONAL EDUCATION & INVESTMENT GROUP CORPORATION; U.S. Private, pg. 4556
WOODBOLT DISTRIBUTION, LLC; U.S. Private, pg. 4557
WOODSAGE HOLDINGS, LLC; U.S. Private, pg. 4560
WOODVINE GROUP, LLC; U.S. Private, pg. 4561
WORD ENTERTAINMENT LLC—See Curb Records, Inc.; U.S. Private, pg. 1124
WORKSHOP HOLDING AS—See ManpowerGroup Inc.; U.S. Public, pg. 1362
WORLD DUTY FREE GROUP S.A.U.—See Avolta AG; Int'l, pg. 749
WORLD DUTY FREE S.P.A.—See Avolta AG; Int'l, pg. 749
WORLDONE, INC.; U.S. Private, pg. 4569
WORLD POINT TERMINALS, INC.; U.S. Private, pg. 4566
WORLDSOURCE HOLDING CORP.—See Guardian Capital Group Limited; Int'l, pg. 3170
WORLD TRAVEL HOLDINGS, INC.; U.S. Private, pg. 4567
WORLD WIDE TECHNOLOGY HOLDING CO., LLC; U.S. Private, pg. 4567
WORLD WRESTLING ENTERTAINMENT, LLC—See Silver Lake Group, LLC; U.S. Private, pg. 3654
WORTHINGTON INDUSTRIES, INC.; U.S. Public, pg. 2382
WORTH INVESTMENT GROUP, LLC; U.S. Private, pg. 4570
WOTIF.COM HOLDINGS PTY. LTD.—See Expedia Group, Inc.; U.S. Public, pg. 810
W.R. BERKLEY CORPORATION; U.S. Public, pg. 2316
WRCC HOLDINGS, LLC—See Howard Hughes Holdings Inc.; U.S. Public, pg. 1060
WREN CORPORATION; U.S. Private, pg. 4572
W.R. HESS COMPANY; U.S. Private, pg. 4422
WRKCO INC.—See WestRock Company; U.S. Public, pg. 2362
WSG PARTNERS, LLC; U.S. Private, pg. 4574
WUEST'S INC.; U.S. Private, pg. 4574
WW INTERNATIONAL, INC.; U.S. Public, pg. 2384
WWRD UNITED KINGDOM LIMITED—See Fiskars Oyj Abp; Int'l, pg. 2694
WWRD US, LLC—See Fiskars Oyj Abp; Int'l, pg. 2694
WW VENTURE CORP.—See World-Wide Holdings Corp.; U.S. Private, pg. 4568
WYANDOTTE TRIBAL CORPORATION; U.S. Private, pg. 4575
WYNIT, INC.; U.S. Private, pg. 4576
WYNYARD PROPERTIES HOLDINGS LIMITED—See Brookfield Corporation; Int'l, pg. 1189
XANTERRA LEISURE HOLDING, LLC—See The Anschutz Corporation; U.S. Private, pg. 3987
X CORP.; U.S. Private, pg. 4579
XERIS BIOPHARMA HOLDINGS, INC.; U.S. Public, pg. 2386
XERIUM GERMANY HOLDING GMBH—See ANDRITZ AG; Int'l, pg. 457
XEROX HOLDING DEUTSCHLAND GMBH—See Xerox Holdings Corporation; U.S. Public, pg. 2390
XEROX HOLDINGS CORPORATION; U.S. Public, pg. 2386
XFL PROPERTIES LLC—See RedBird Capital Partners L.P.; U.S. Private, pg. 3377
XL INSURANCE (UK) HOLDINGS LIMITED—See AXA S.A.; Int'l, pg. 760
XO HOLDINGS, INC.; U.S. Private, pg. 4581
XPERI CORPORATION—See Adeia Inc.; U.S. Public, pg. 40
XPERI INC.; U.S. Public, pg. 2391
XPO HOLDINGS UK & IRELAND LIMITED—See XPO, Inc.; U.S. Public, pg. 2392
XPO, INC.; U.S. Public, pg. 2392

XPO LOGISTICS EUROPE S.A.—See XPO, Inc.; U.S. Public, pg. 2392
XPONENTIAL, INC.; U.S. Private, pg. 4582
XSTELOS HOLDINGS, INC.; U.S. Private, pg. 4582
XTRAC GROUP LIMITED—See MiddleGround Management, LP; U.S. Private, pg. 2713
XYLEM AUSTRALIA HOLDINGS PTY LTD—See Xylem Inc.; U.S. Public, pg. 2395
XYLEM INC.; U.S. Public, pg. 2393
YAHOO HOLDINGS, INC.—See Apollo Global Management, Inc.; U.S. Public, pg. 167
YALE SECURITY PRODUCTS (HONG KONG) LIMITED—See ASSA ABLOY AB; Int'l, pg. 636
YARD HOUSE USA, INC.—See Darden Restaurants, Inc.; U.S. Public, pg. 633
YASHENG GROUP; U.S. Public, pg. 2398
YASHILI INTERNATIONAL HOLDINGS LTD.—See China Mengniu Dairy Company Limited; Int'l, pg. 1520
YELLOW CORPORATION; U.S. Public, pg. 2398
YELLOWSTONE COMMUNICATIONS; U.S. Private, pg. 4587
YEO HIAP SENG LIMITED—See Far East Organization Pte. Ltd.; Int'l, pg. 2617
YERBAE BRANDS CORP.; U.S. Public, pg. 2398
YETI HOLDINGS, INC.; U.S. Public, pg. 2398
YGOMI LLC; U.S. Private, pg. 4589
YIDA CHINA HOLDINGS LIMITED—See China Minsheng Investment Group Corp., Ltd.; Int'l, pg. 1524
YMF MEDIA LLC; U.S. Private, pg. 4589
THE YORK GROUP, INC.—See Matthews International Corporation; U.S. Public, pg. 1401
YORK RISK SERVICES GROUP, INC.—See The Carlyle Group Inc.; U.S. Public, pg. 2054
YOUNEEQAI TECHNICAL SERVICES, INC.; U.S. Public, pg. 2399
YOUNGEVITY INTERNATIONAL CORP.; U.S. Public, pg. 2399
YOUNG INNOVATIONS, INC.—See The Jordan Company, L.P.; U.S. Private, pg. 4063
YOUNG'S HOLDINGS, INC.; U.S. Private, pg. 4593
YRC NORTH AMERICAN TRANSPORTATION, INC.—See Yellow Corporation; U.S. Public, pg. 2398
THE YUCAIPA COMPANIES LLC; U.S. Private, pg. 4139
YUM! BRANDS, INC.; U.S. Public, pg. 2400
YUM CHINA HOLDINGS, INC.; U.S. Public, pg. 2399
YUM! RESTAURANTS INTERNATIONAL—See Yum! Brands, Inc.; U.S. Public, pg. 2400
ZACHRY CORPORATION—See Zachry Holdings, Inc.; U.S. Private, pg. 4596
ZACHRY HOLDINGS, INC.; U.S. Private, pg. 4596
ZAIS GROUP HOLDINGS, INC.; U.S. Private, pg. 4597
ZAYO GROUP HOLDINGS, INC.—See DigitalBridge Group, Inc.; U.S. Public, pg. 665
ZAYO GROUP HOLDINGS, INC.—See EQT AB; Int'l, pg. 2481
ZEALOT NETWORKS, INC.; U.S. Private, pg. 4598
ZEE MULTIMEDIA WORLDWIDE (MAURITIUS) LIMITED—See Essel Corporate Resources. Pvt. Ltd.; Int'l, pg. 2510
ZELIS HEALTHCARE CORPORATION—See PCP Enterprise, L.P.; U.S. Public, pg. 3121
ZENDEX HOLDINGS, INC.; U.S. Private, pg. 4601
ZENITH NATIONAL INSURANCE CORP.—See Fairfax Financial Holdings Limited; Int'l, pg. 2609
ZENOVIA DIGITAL EXCHANGE CORPORATION; U.S. Public, pg. 2402
ZENTIVA N.V.—See Advent International Corporation; U.S. Private, pg. 108
ZEP EUROPE B.V.—See New Mountain Capital, LLC; U.S. Private, pg. 2904
ZEP INC.—See New Mountain Capital, LLC; U.S. Private, pg. 2904
ZEROFOX HOLDINGS, INC.—See Whanau Interests LLC.; U.S. Private, pg. 4503
ZETA GLOBAL HOLDINGS CORP.; U.S. Public, pg. 2403
ZETTLER COMPONENTS, INC.; U.S. Private, pg. 4603
ZHENGZHOU CHINA RESOURCES GAS CO., LTD.—See China Resources (Holdings) Co., Ltd.; Int'l, pg. 1548
ZHONGDING SEALING PARTS (USA), INC.—See Anhui Zhongding Holding (Group) Co., Ltd.; Int'l, pg. 470
ZHONGDING U.S.A., INC.—See Anhui Zhongding Holding (Group) Co., Ltd.; Int'l, pg. 470
ZHRH CORPORATION; U.S. Public, pg. 2403
ZILBER LTD.; U.S. Private, pg. 4604
ZILLOW GROUP, INC.; U.S. Public, pg. 2404
ZIMMER AUSTRALIA HOLDING PTY. LTD.—See Zimmer Biomet Holdings, Inc.; U.S. Public, pg. 2406
ZIMMER BIOMET HOLDINGS, INC.; U.S. Public, pg. 2405
ZIMMER GERMANY HOLDINGS GMBH—See Zimmer Biomet Holdings, Inc.; U.S. Public, pg. 2407
ZIMMERMAN HOLDING COMPANY; U.S. Private, pg. 4605
ZINSSER HOLDINGS, LLC—See RPM International Inc.; U.S. Public, pg. 1817
ZL STAR INC.; U.S. Private, pg. 4606
ZODIAC EUROPEAN POOLS—See The Carlyle Group Inc.; U.S. Public, pg. 2057
ZODIAC INTERNATIONAL—See The Carlyle Group Inc.; U.S. Public, pg. 2057

N.A.I.C.S. INDEX

ZODIAC MARINE & POOL—See The Carlyle Group Inc.; *U.S. Private*, pg. 2057
ZOM HOLDING, INC.; *U.S. Private*, pg. 4607
ZOOMINFO TECHNOLOGIES INC.; *U.S. Public*, pg. 2411
ZOTTI GROUP AVIATION, INC.; *U.S. Private*, pg. 4609
ZYLA LIFE SCIENCES—See Assertio Holdings, Inc.; *U.S. Public*, pg. 214

551114 — CORPORATE, SUBSIDIARY, AND REGIONAL MANAGING OFFICES

ABS EUROPE LTD.—See American Bureau of Shipping; *U.S. Private*, pg. 225
ABS PACIFIC—See American Bureau of Shipping; *U.S. Private*, pg. 226
AEGION HOLDING COMPANY, LLC—See New Mountain Capital, LLC; *U.S. Private*, pg. 2899
AEP OHIO—See American Electric Power Company, Inc.; *U.S. Public*, pg. 100
AEROVIAS DE MEXICO, S.A. DE C.V. - USA SALES OFFICE—See Grupo Aeromexico, S.A.B. de C.V.; *Int'l*, pg. 3118
AFFIDEA B.V. - OPERATIONS HEADQUARTERS—See B-FLEXION Group Holdings SA; *Int'l*, pg. 785
AGRAVIS RAIFFEISEN AG - HANNOVER HEAD OFFICE—See AGRAVIS Raiffeisen AG; *Int'l*, pg. 215
ALL3MEDIA HOLDINGS LTD—See Warner Bros. Discovery, Inc.; *U.S. Public*, pg. 2326
ALLEGION PLC - EUROPE, MIDDLE EAST, INDIA & AFRICA MAIN OFFICE—See Allegion Public Limited Company; *Int'l*, pg. 335
ALPS HOLDINGS INC—See SS&C Technologies Holdings, Inc.; *U.S. Public*, pg. 1923
ALVAREZ & MARSAL NORTH AMERICA, LLC—See Alvarez & Marsal, Inc.; *U.S. Private*, pg. 212
AMERICAN INTEGRATION TECHNOLOGIES LLC—See Ultra Clean Holdings, Inc.; *U.S. Public*, pg. 2223
AMG ADVANCED METALLURGICAL GROUP N.V.—See AMG Critical Materials N.V.; *Int'l*, pg. 425
AMPHENOL GLOBAL INTERCONNECT SYSTEMS—See Amphenol Corporation; *U.S. Public*, pg. 127
ANTHONY EQUITY HOLDINGS, INC.—See Dover Corporation; *U.S. Public*, pg. 678
ANTHONY MEXICO HOLDINGS S. DE R.L. DE C.V.—See Dover Corporation; *U.S. Public*, pg. 678
ANZ ASIA PACIFIC DIVISION—See Australia & New Zealand Banking Group Limited; *Int'l*, pg. 719
ANZ NATIONAL BANK LTD.—See Australia & New Zealand Banking Group Limited; *Int'l*, pg. 720
APPLE AB—See Apple Inc.; *U.S. Public*, pg. 169
APPLE CANADA INC.—See Apple Inc.; *U.S. Public*, pg. 169
ARC TERMINALS HOLDINGS LLC—See Warburg Pincus LLC; *U.S. Private*, pg. 4440
AVERY DENNISON BELGIUM MANAGEMENT SERVICES SPRL—See Avery Dennison Corporation; *U.S. Public*, pg. 243
AXIS BANK LIMITED - CORPORATE OFFICE—See Axis Bank Limited; *Int'l*, pg. 769
AXPO TRADING AG - HEAD OFFICE & TRADING CENTER—See Axpo Holding AG; *Int'l*, pg. 771
BANCO POPULAR PUERTO RICO - VIRGIN ISLANDS REGIONAL OFFICE—See Popular, Inc.; *U.S. Public*, pg. 1702
BANK 34 - ARIZONA DIVISION—See Bancorp 34, Inc.; *U.S. Public*, pg. 269
BANKIA INVERSIONES FINANCIERAS, S.A.U.—See Lone Star Funds; *U.S. Private*, pg. 2485
BBA AVIATION ENGINE REPAIR & OVERHAUL GROUP—See BlackRock, Inc.; *U.S. Public*, pg. 346
BBA AVIATION ENGINE REPAIR & OVERHAUL GROUP—See Blackstone Inc.; *U.S. Public*, pg. 358
BBA AVIATION ENGINE REPAIR & OVERHAUL GROUP—See Cascade Investment LLC; *U.S. Private*, pg. 780
BBA AVIATION LEGACY SUPPORT GROUP—See BlackRock, Inc.; *U.S. Public*, pg. 346
BBA AVIATION LEGACY SUPPORT GROUP—See Blackstone Inc.; *U.S. Public*, pg. 358
BBA AVIATION LEGACY SUPPORT GROUP—See Cascade Investment LLC; *U.S. Private*, pg. 780
THE BESSEMER GROUP, INCORPORATED - NEW YORK OFFICE—See The Bessemer Group, Incorporated; *U.S. Private*, pg. 3994
BINTULU PORT HOLDINGS BERHAD; *Int'l*, pg. 1034
BORGWARNER TURBO SYSTEMS WORLDWIDE HEADQUARTERS GMBH—See BorgWarner Inc.; *U.S. Public*, pg. 371
BOXX MODULAR INC. - DENVER OFFICE—See Black Diamond Group Limited; *Int'l*, pg. 1059
BRAVIDA SVERIGE AB - NORTH DIVISION—See Bravida Holding AB; *Int'l*, pg. 1142
BRAVIDA SVERIGE AB - SOUTH DIVISION—See Bravida Holding AB; *Int'l*, pg. 1142
BUND CENTER INVESTMENT LTD.; *Int'l*, pg. 1215
CAESARS ENTERTAINMENT OPERATING COMPANY, INC.—See Caesars Entertainment, Inc.; *U.S. Public*, pg. 419

CAMPBELL NORTH AMERICA—See Campbell Soup Company; *U.S. Public*, pg. 426
CASTLETON COMMODITIES INTERNATIONAL LLC - HOUSTON OFFICE—See Castleton Commodities International LLC; *U.S. Private*, pg. 785
CENTRAL FINANCE COMPANY PLC - CITY OFFICE—See Central Finance Company PLC; *Int'l*, pg. 1406
CHAMPION IRON LIMITED - TORONTO HEAD OFFICE—See Champion Iron Limited; *Int'l*, pg. 1440
CHEP ASIA-PACIFIC—See Brambles Limited; *Int'l*, pg. 1138
CHEP EMEA—See Brambles Limited; *Int'l*, pg. 1138
CHEP EUROPE—See Brambles Limited; *Int'l*, pg. 1138
CHINA NEW TOWN DEVELOPMENT COMPANY LIMITED - CORPORATE OFFICE—See China New Town Development Company Limited; *Int'l*, pg. 1535
THE CLOROX INTERNATIONAL COMPANY - MIAMI OFFICE—See The Clorox Company; *U.S. Public*, pg. 2063
COMERICA BANK - MICHIGAN MARKET—See Comerica Incorporated; *U.S. Public*, pg. 542
COMERICA BANK - WESTERN MARKET—See Comerica Incorporated; *U.S. Public*, pg. 542
COMMUNISIS EUROPE LIMITED—See Aquiline Capital Partners LLC; *U.S. Private*, pg. 304
COMPASS GROUP NORTH AMERICA—See Compass Group PLC; *Int'l*, pg. 1750
CONSOLIS OY AB—See Bain Capital, LP; *U.S. Private*, pg. 438
CONSOLIS SAS—See Bain Capital, LP; *U.S. Private*, pg. 438
COTT CORPORATION - US CORPORATE HEADQUARTERS—See Primo Water Corporation; *U.S. Public*, pg. 1718
CS HOLDINGS CO., LTD.; *Int'l*, pg. 1861
DENTSU AEGIS NETWORK AMERICAS—See Dentsu Group Inc.; *Int'l*, pg. 2036
DEX MEDIA HOLDINGS, INC.—See Thryv Holdings, Inc.; *U.S. Public*, pg. 2157
DOVER SPAIN HOLDINGS, S.L.—See Dover Corporation; *U.S. Public*, pg. 681
EAGLE BIDCO 2018 LIMITED—See KKR & Co. Inc.; *U.S. Public*, pg. 1256
EASIOPTION LTD.—See J.C. Flowers & Co. LLC; *U.S. Private*, pg. 2160
EAST JAPAN RAILWAY COMPANY - NEW YORK OFFICE—See East Japan Railway Company; *Int'l*, pg. 2270
EMERSON ELECTRIC (U.S.) HOLDING CORPORATION (CHILE) LIMITADA—See Emerson Electric Co.; *U.S. Public*, pg. 744
ENTERPRISE SERVICES - EUROPE, MIDDLE EAST & AFRICA—See Veritas Capital Fund Management, LLC; *U.S. Private*, pg. 4363
E SERVICES SINGAPORE PTE. LTD.—See Veritas Capital Fund Management, LLC; *U.S. Private*, pg. 4363
EXCO HOLDING MLP, INC.—See EXCO Resources, Inc.; *U.S. Public*, pg. 805
FABORY CZ HOLDING S.R.O.—See W.W. Grainger, Inc.; *U.S. Public*, pg. 2319
FAST ENERGY HOLDINGS BERHAD; *Int'l*, pg. 2621
FLINT GROUP GMBH—See Koch Industries, Inc.; *U.S. Private*, pg. 2327
FLINT GROUP GMBH—See The Goldman Sachs Group, Inc.; *U.S. Public*, pg. 2076
FMC FORET S.A.—See FMC Corporation; *U.S. Public*, pg. 862
FORTUNE REAL ESTATE INVESTMENT TRUST; *Int'l*, pg. 2744
FRANKLINS HOLDINGS, LLC—See TEGNA Inc.; *U.S. Public*, pg. 1990
FUCHS LUBRICANTS - ASIA PACIFIC REGIONAL HEADQUARTERS—See FUCHS SE; *Int'l*, pg. 2803
GARTNER, INC.; *U.S. Public*, pg. 906
GENERAL DYNAMICS ARMAMENT & TECHNICAL PRODUCTS—See General Dynamics Corporation; *U.S. Public*, pg. 913
GRAINGER SERVICE HOLDING COMPANY, INC.—See W.W. Grainger, Inc.; *U.S. Public*, pg. 2320
GRUPO EMPRESARIAL SAN JOSE, S.A. - CENTRAL OFFICE—See Grupo Empresarial San Jose, S.A.; *Int'l*, pg. 3128
HABIT HOLDINGS, INC.—See Acadia Healthcare Company, Inc.; *U.S. Public*, pg. 29
HENRY SCHEIN HOLDING GMBH—See Henry Schein, Inc.; *U.S. Public*, pg. 1025
HEWLETT-PACKARD LATIN AMERICA—See Hewlett Packard Enterprise Company; *U.S. Public*, pg. 1032
HILTON WORLDWIDE - MEMPHIS OPERATIONS CENTER—See Hilton Worldwide Holdings Inc.; *U.S. Public*, pg. 1041
HRNETGROUP LIMITED; *Int'l*, pg. 3501
IBP HOLDINGS, LLC—See Installed Building Products, Inc.; *U.S. Public*, pg. 1132
IDEX HOLDINGS, INC.—See IDEX Corp; *U.S. Public*, pg. 1091
IHEARTMEDIA + ENTERTAINMENT, INC. - TULSA CORPORATE OFFICE—See iHeartMedia, Inc.; *U.S. Public*, pg. 1100

INDEPENDENT NEWSPAPERS, INC. - ARIZONA—See Independent Newspapers, Inc.; *U.S. Public*, pg. 2060
INSTRUMENTARIUM DENTAL S.A.R.L.—See Danaher Corporation; *U.S. Public*, pg. 630
IRISH STUDIO, LLC - IRELAND CORPORATE OFFICE—See Irish Studio, LLC; *U.S. Private*, pg. 2138
ITW AUSTRALIA PROPERTY HOLDINGS PTY LTD.—See Illinois Tool Works Inc.; *U.S. Public*, pg. 1104
KELLWOOD COMPANY - NEW YORK OFFICE—See Sun Capital Partners, Inc.; *U.S. Private*, pg. 3859
LANDIS HOLDINGS LLC—See The Manitowoc Company, Inc.; *U.S. Public*, pg. 2111
MAXIM INTEGRATED PRODUCTS (IRELAND) HOLDINGS LIMITED—See Analog Devices, Inc.; *U.S. Public*, pg. 135
MMG LIMITED - CORPORATE OFFICE—See China Rare Earth Resources And Technology Co., Ltd.; *Int'l*, pg. 1545
MOUNT SAINT JOSEPH; *U.S. Private*, pg. 2798
MULTI PACKAGING SOLUTIONS, INC.—See WestRock Company; *U.S. Public*, pg. 2362
NASDAQ AUSTRALIA HOLDINGS PTY. LTD.—See Nasdaq, Inc.; *U.S. Public*, pg. 1491
NASDAQ OMX EUROPE LIMITED—See Nasdaq, Inc.; *U.S. Public*, pg. 1492
OIL STATES ENERGY SERVICES HOLDING, INC.—See Oil States International, Inc.; *U.S. Public*, pg. 1565
ORACLE CANADA ULC—See Oracle Corporation; *U.S. Public*, pg. 1611
PARKWAY BANK & TRUST COMPANY - ARIZONA DIVISION—See Parkway Bancorp, Inc.; *U.S. Private*, pg. 3098
PEPSICO BEVERAGES AMERICAS—See PepsiCo, Inc.; *U.S. Public*, pg. 1670
PHOENIX VENEZUELA—See Genstar Capital, LLC; *U.S. Private*, pg. 1679
PMC SPECIALTY LEADERS IN CHEMICALS, INC.—See PMC Capital Partners, LLC; *U.S. Private*, pg. 3217
PROSPERITY BANK - CENTRAL OKLAHOMA REGIONAL OFFICE—See Prosperity Bancshares, Inc.; *U.S. Public*, pg. 1728
PROSPERITY BANK - EAST TEXAS/TYLER REGIONAL OFFICE—See Prosperity Bancshares, Inc.; *U.S. Public*, pg. 1728
PROSPERITY BANK - SOUTH TEXAS/VICTORIA REGIONAL OFFICE—See Prosperity Bancshares, Inc.; *U.S. Public*, pg. 1729
PROSPERITY BANK - WEST TEXAS REGIONAL OFFICE—See Prosperity Bancshares, Inc.; *U.S. Public*, pg. 1729
PUBLIX SUPER MARKETS, INC. - GA, SC, TN & AL—See Publix Super Markets, Inc.; *U.S. Private*, pg. 3301
PUBLIX SUPER MARKETS, INC. - NORTH FLORIDA/SOUTHEAST GEORGIA—See Publix Super Markets, Inc.; *U.S. Private*, pg. 3301
PUBLIX SUPER MARKETS, INC. - SOUTH EAST FLORIDA—See Publix Super Markets, Inc.; *U.S. Private*, pg. 3301
RABOBANK AUSTRALIA & NEW ZEALAND GROUP—See Cooperatieve Centrale Raiffeisen-Boerenleenbank B.A.; *Int'l*, pg. 1792
RENASANT BANK - ALABAMA REGION HEADQUARTERS—See Renasant Corporation; *U.S. Public*, pg. 1783
RENASANT BANK - GEORGIA REGION HEADQUARTERS—See Renasant Corporation; *U.S. Public*, pg. 1783
RENASANT BANK - TENNESSEE REGION HEADQUARTERS—See Renasant Corporation; *U.S. Public*, pg. 1783
RIMPORTS, LLC—See Compass Diversified Holdings; *U.S. Public*, pg. 560
ROONEY HOLDINGS, INC.—See Rooney Holdings, Inc.; *U.S. Private*, pg. 3479
RSF REIT V SP, L.L.C.—See Welltower Inc.; *U.S. Public*, pg. 2349
SFXE NETHERLANDS HOLDINGS B.V.—See LiveStyle, Inc.; *U.S. Private*, pg. 2473
SIMS METAL MANAGEMENT LIMITED - AUSTRALIA HEAD OFFICE—See Sims Limited; *U.S. Public*, pg. 1883
SK HOLDING COMPANY, INC.—See Clean Harbors, Inc.; *U.S. Public*, pg. 510
STEWART TITLE INSURANCE CORP. - UPSTATE CORPORATE OFFICE—See Stewart Information Services Corporation; *U.S. Public*, pg. 1948
SUNTRUST BANK, CENTRAL FLORIDA DIVISION HEADQUARTERS—See Truist Financial Corporation; *U.S. Public*, pg. 2199
SUNTRUST BANK, EAST TENNESSEE REGION HEADQUARTERS—See Truist Financial Corporation; *U.S. Public*, pg. 2199
SUNTRUST BANK, GEORGIA REGION HEADQUARTERS—See Truist Financial Corporation; *U.S. Public*, pg. 2199
SUNTRUST BANK, MID-ATLANTIC DIVISION HEADQUARTERS—See Truist Financial Corporation; *U.S. Public*, pg. 2199
SUNTRUST BANK, NASHVILLE REGION

551114 — CORPORATE, SUBSIDIA...

N.A.I.C.S. Index

HEADQUARTERS—See Truist Financial Corporation; *U.S. Public*, pg. 2199
SUNTRUST BANK, SOUTH FLORIDA DIVISION HEADQUARTERS—See Truist Financial Corporation; *U.S. Public*, pg. 2199
SUNTRUST BANK, SOUTHWEST FLORIDA REGION HEADQUARTERS—See Truist Financial Corporation; *U.S. Public*, pg. 2200
SUNTRUST BANK, TAMPA REGION HEADQUARTERS—See Truist Financial Corporation; *U.S. Public*, pg. 2200
TARMAC TRADING LIMITED—See CRH plc; *Int'l*, pg. 1848
TBWA ASIA PACIFIC—See Omnicom Group Inc.; *U.S. Public*, pg. 1595
TBWA/CHIAT/DAY—See Omnicom Group Inc.; *U.S. Public*, pg. 1597
TI AUTOMOTIVE, LLC—See Bain Capital, LP; *U.S. Private*, pg. 447
TJX AUSTRIA HOLDING GMBH—See The TJX Companies, Inc.; *U.S. Public*, pg. 2134
TJX NEDERLAND B.V.—See The TJX Companies, Inc.; *U.S. Public*, pg. 2134
TRADE SERVICE HOLDINGS INC.—See Trimble, Inc.; *U.S. Public*, pg. 2191
TRIUMPH AEROSTRUCTURES GROUP—See Triumph Group, Inc.; *U.S. Public*, pg. 2196
TUNDRA HOLDINGS, INC.—See Cadence Design Systems, Inc.; *U.S. Public*, pg. 419
UNIVERSAL TABLETOP, INC.—See EveryWare Global, Inc.; *U.S. Private*, pg. 1441
VELOCITY OUTDOOR INC.—See Compass Diversified Holdings; *U.S. Public*, pg. 560
VERITIV—See Clayton, Dubilier & Rice, LLC; *U.S. Private*, pg. 929
VISTEON ENGINEERING SERVICES LIMITED—See Visteon Corporation; *U.S. Public*, pg. 2306
VULCAN MATERIALS CO. - CENTRAL REGION—See Vulcan Materials Company; *U.S. Public*, pg. 2314
VULCAN MATERIALS CO. - EAST REGION—See Vulcan Materials Company; *U.S. Public*, pg. 2314
VULCAN MATERIALS CO. - SOUTH REGION—See Vulcan Materials Company; *U.S. Public*, pg. 2314
VULCAN MATERIALS CO. - WEST REGION—See Vulcan Materials Company; *U.S. Public*, pg. 2314

561110 — OFFICE ADMINISTRATIVE SERVICES

139 ENTERPRISES LIMITED—See Central Wealth Group Holdings Limited; *Int'l*, pg. 1410
ABBOTT MANAGEMENT GMBH—See Abbott Laboratories; *U.S. Public*, pg. 15
ABC FRONTIER HOLDINGS, INC.—See Asahi Broadcasting Group Holdings Corporation; *Int'l*, pg. 592
ACCENTIA TECHNOLOGIES - COCHIN UNIT—See Accentia Technologies Limited; *Int'l*, pg. 81
ACCENTIA TECHNOLOGIES LTD. - TRIVANDRUM UNIT—See Accentia Technologies Limited; *Int'l*, pg. 82
ACCENTURE MANAGEMENT GMBH—See Accenture plc; *Int'l*, pg. 83
ACCOR HOTELES ESPANA S.A.—See Accor S.A.; *Int'l*, pg. 91
ADKORE STAFFING GROUP; *U.S. Private*, pg. 80
ADVENTIST HEALTH CENTRAL VALLEY NETWORK—See Adventist Health System; *U.S. Private*, pg. 108
ADVOCATE CHARITABLE FOUNDATION—See Advocate Health Care Network; *U.S. Private*, pg. 111
AERO INVENTORY (HONG KONG) LIMITED—See Aero Inventory plc; *Int'l*, pg. 180
AERO INVENTORY (UK) LIMITED—See Aero Inventory plc; *Int'l*, pg. 180
AES SERVICIOS AMERICA S.R. L.—See The AES Corporation; *U.S. Public*, pg. 2031
AFFINITY HEALTH SYSTEM; *U.S. Private*, pg. 123
AGENZIA ITALIA S.P.A.—See Gruppo MutuiOnline S.p.A; *Int'l*, pg. 3140
AGRO HARAPAN LESTAR (PRIVATE) LIMITED—See Carson Cumberbatch PLC; *Int'l*, pg. 1347
AGS CAPITAL, LLC—See PlayAGS, Inc.; *U.S. Public*, pg. 1697
AIMBRIDGE HOSPITALITY, LLC—See Advent International Corporation; *U.S. Private*, pg. 97
AKEBONO COOPERATION (THAILAND) CO., LTD.—See Akebono Brake Industry Co., Ltd.; *Int'l*, pg. 261
AKIMA INTRA-DATA, LLC—See Nana Regional Corporation, Inc.; *U.S. Private*, pg. 2832
ALAN JAY AUTOMOTIVE MANAGEMENT, INC.; *U.S. Private*, pg. 149
ALL ABOUT STAFFING, INC.—See HCA Healthcare, Inc.; *U.S. Public*, pg. 990
ALLABOUTXPERT (PTY) LIMITED—See Adcorp Holdings Limited; *Int'l*, pg. 127
ALLERGAN USA, INC.—See AbbVie Inc.; *U.S. Public*, pg. 23
ALLIANCE HEALTHCARE MANAGEMENT SERVICES LIMITED—See Walgreens Boots Alliance, Inc.; *U.S. Public*, pg. 2322

ALLIANCE HOSPITALITY MANAGEMENT, LLC; *U.S. Private*, pg. 183
ALLIANZ CAPITAL PARTNERS OF AMERICA LLC—See Allianz SE; *Int'l*, pg. 344
ALLIANZ CAPITAL PARTNERS VERWALTUNGS GMBH—See Allianz SE; *Int'l*, pg. 344
ALLIED DIGITAL SERVICES LLC—See Allied Digital Services Limited; *Int'l*, pg. 357
ALPINE ACCESS CANADA, INC—See Creadev SAS; *Int'l*, pg. 1831
ALSTOM LTD.—See Alstom S.A.; *Int'l*, pg. 380
ALTAMONT CAPITAL MANAGEMENT, LLC; *U.S. Private*, pg. 204
ALTRIA CLIENT SERVICES INC.—See Altria Group, Inc.; *U.S. Public*, pg. 89
AMEREN SERVICES INC.—See Ameren Corporation; *U.S. Public*, pg. 94
AMERIGAS PROPANE, INC.—See UGI Corporation; *U.S. Public*, pg. 2221
AMOS AZERBAIJAN LLC—See AMOS Group Limited; *Int'l*, pg. 430
AMOS INTERNATIONAL (HK) LIMITED—See AMOS Group Limited; *Int'l*, pg. 430
AMOS INTERNATIONAL (SHANGHAI) CO., LTD—See AMOS Group Limited; *Int'l*, pg. 430
AMOS INTERNATIONAL (S) PTE LTD—See AMOS Group Limited; *Int'l*, pg. 430
AMOS KAZAKHSTAN LLP—See AMOS Group Limited; *Int'l*, pg. 430
AMOS KOREA CO LTD—See AMOS Group Limited; *Int'l*, pg. 430
AMOS MALAYSIA SDN BHD—See AMOS Group Limited; *Int'l*, pg. 430
AMOS MIDDLE EAST FZE—See AMOS Group Limited; *Int'l*, pg. 430
AMOS SUPPLY KOREA CO., LTD.—See AMOS Group Limited; *Int'l*, pg. 430
AMOS SUPPLY PTE LTD—See AMOS Group Limited; *Int'l*, pg. 430
AMOS VIETNAM PTE LTD—See AMOS Group Limited; *Int'l*, pg. 430
AN CENTRAL REGION MANAGEMENT, LLC—See AutoNation, Inc.; *U.S. Public*, pg. 231
ANCHOR INNOVATION, INC.; *U.S. Private*, pg. 273
AQUA HOSPITALITY LLC—See Marriott Vacations Worldwide Corporation; *U.S. Public*, pg. 1373
ARAMARK SERVICES OF PUERTO RICO, INC.—See Aramark; *U.S. Public*, pg. 176
ARCELORMITTAL ESCAZU SA—See ArcelorMittal S.A.; *Int'l*, pg. 544
ARCHON GROUP, L.P.—See The Goldman Sachs Group, Inc.; *U.S. Public*, pg. 2076
ARDENT LEISURE MANAGEMENT LIMITED—See Coast Entertainment Holdings Limited; *Int'l*, pg. 1681
ARMED FORCES INSURANCE EXCHANGE; *U.S. Private*, pg. 330
ARVEST BANK OPERATIONS, INC.—See Arvest Bank Group, Inc.; *U.S. Private*, pg. 344
ASMO CATERING MALAYSIA SDN. BHD.—See Asmo Corporation; *Int'l*, pg. 628
ASSOCIATED COST ENGINEERS INC.; *U.S. Private*, pg. 355
ASTERION DM FINLAND A.B.—See Exela Technologies, Inc.; *U.S. Public*, pg. 806
ATHENA HEALTH CARE SYSTEMS; *U.S. Private*, pg. 367
AT&T MOBILITY LLC—See AT&T Inc.; *U.S. Public*, pg. 219
AT&T—See AT&T Inc.; *U.S. Public*, pg. 218
AVENU INSIGHTS & ANALYTICS LLC—See Arlington Capital Partners LLC; *U.S. Private*, pg. 327
THE AXIOM GROUP, INC.—See Apax Partners LLP; *Int'l*, pg. 503
BACK OFFICE SERVICES ESTONIA OU—See Finnair Plc; *Int'l*, pg. 2675
BANKIA, S.A. MADRID OPERATIONAL HEADQUARTERS—See Lone Star Funds; *U.S. Private*, pg. 2485
BARARI NATURAL RESOURCES LLC—See Alpha Dhabi Holding PJSC; *Int'l*, pg. 367
BATTLERS CORP.; *Int'l*, pg. 890
BAXTER RENAL DIVISION—See Baxter International Inc.; *U.S. Public*, pg. 280
BAYSTATE HEALTH SYSTEM, INC.; *U.S. Private*, pg. 497
BBS I, LLC—See Barrett Business Services, Inc.; *U.S. Public*, pg. 278
BEIJING DIGITAL CHINA LIMITED—See Digital China Holdings Limited; *Int'l*, pg. 2121
BENESSE CORPORATION - TOKYO HEAD OFFICE—See EQT AB; *Int'l*, pg. 2467
BERNHARD SCHULTE SHIPMANAGEMENT (SINGAPORE) PTE. LTD.,—See Bernhard Schulte Shipmanagement (Cyprus) Ltd.; *Int'l*, pg. 989
BGP CORP.; *U.S. Private*, pg. 549
BGR OPERATIONS, LLC—See Sonnet BioTherapeutics Holdings, Inc.; *U.S. Public*, pg. 1904
BIOARTIGAS—See Ente Vasco de la Energia; *Int'l*, pg. 2450
BJC HEALTH SYSTEM; *U.S. Private*, pg. 568
BLUE LYNX MEDIA, LLC—See Tribune Publishing Company; *U.S. Private*, pg. 4227

CORPORATE AFFILIATIONS

BMK TURIZM VE OTELCILIK HIZMETLERI A.S.—See Dogus Holding AS; *Int'l*, pg. 2154
BMO GROUP RETIREMENT SERVICES INC.—See Bank of Montreal; *Int'l*, pg. 846
BOEING NORTH AMERICAN SERVICES INC.—See The Boeing Company; *U.S. Public*, pg. 2041
BPO HOLDCO COOPERATIEF U.A.—See TD Synnex Corp; *U.S. Public*, pg. 1983
BRENCAL CONTRACTORS INC.—See BEC Inc.; *U.S. Private*, pg. 509
BRISBANE BRONCOS MANAGEMENT CORPORATION PTY. LTD.—See News Corporation; *U.S. Public*, pg. 1520
BRISBANE WATERS ADMINISTRATION PTY. LTD.—See Brookfield Corporation; *Int'l*, pg. 1176
BROWN & BROWN, INC. - TAMPA CORPORATE OFFICE—See Brown & Brown, Inc.; *U.S. Public*, pg. 400
BRRH CORPORATION; *U.S. Public*, pg. 670
BSI DIVERSIFIED LLC; *U.S. Private*, pg. 675
BUFFALO & PITTSBURGH RAILROAD, INC.—See Brookfield Infrastructure Partners L.P.; *Int'l*, pg. 1190
BUFFALO & PITTSBURGH RAILROAD, INC.—See GIC Pte. Ltd.; *Int'l*, pg. 2965
BURCH MANAGEMENT CO., INC.; *U.S. Private*, pg. 686
BUYCASTINGS.COM; *U.S. Private*, pg. 699
C2 TECHNOLOGIES, INC.; *U.S. Private*, pg. 709
CAL POLY CORPORATION; *U.S. Private*, pg. 715
CAMPBELL GLOBAL, LLC—See BrightSphere Investment Group Inc.; *U.S. Public*, pg. 383
CARDLINK SYSTEMS LIMITED—See Corpay, Inc.; *U.S. Public*, pg. 579
CAREMORE MEDICAL MANAGEMENT COMPANY—See Elevance Health, Inc.; *U.S. Public*, pg. 729
CARGILL ANIMAL NUTRITION—See Cargill, Inc.; *U.S. Private*, pg. 755
CARONDELET MANAGEMENT COMPANY, INC.—See Ascension Health Alliance; *U.S. Private*, pg. 347
CARROLL & CARROLL INCORPORATED; *U.S. Private*, pg. 773
CASH E-TRADE LIMITED—See CASH Financial Services Group Limited; *Int'l*, pg. 1352
CASSIDY & ASSOCIATES/WEBER SHANDWICK GOVERNMENT RELATIONS—See The Interpublic Group of Companies, Inc.; *U.S. Public*, pg. 2104
CATERPILLAR COMMERCIAL HOLDING S.A.R.L.—See Caterpillar, Inc.; *U.S. Public*, pg. 449
CDM SERVICE GROUP, INC.—See CDM Investment Group, Inc.; *U.S. Private*, pg. 802
CENTRASTATE HEALTHCARE SYSTEM INC.; *U.S. Private*, pg. 826
CENTURION PIPELINE—See Occidental Petroleum Corporation; *U.S. Public*, pg. 1561
CEP SERVICES COMPANY, INC.—See Evolve Transition Infrastructure LP; *U.S. Public*, pg. 804
CHEROKEE LANDING CORPORATION—See Equity LifeStyle Properties, Inc.; *U.S. Public*, pg. 790
CHINA RAILWAY DEVELOPMENT & INVESTMENT CO., LTD.—See China Railway Group Limited; *Int'l*, pg. 1543
CHINA RAILWAY INVESTMENT GROUP CO., LTD.—See China Railway Group Limited; *Int'l*, pg. 1543
CHRISTIE + CO OY—See Christie Group plc; *Int'l*, pg. 1586
CHRISTIE + CO SARL—See Christie Group plc; *Int'l*, pg. 1587
CHUGIN ASSET MANAGEMENT COMPANY, LIMITED—See Chugin Financial Group, Inc.; *Int'l*, pg. 1594
CICOR MANAGEMENT AG—See Cicor Technologies Ltd.; *Int'l*, pg. 1603
CITRA NUSA HOLDINGS BERHAD; *Int'l*, pg. 1626
CITY LODGE BRYANSTON (PTY) LIMITED—See City Lodge Hotels Limited; *Int'l*, pg. 1627
CITY LODGE HOLDINGS (SHARE BLOCK) (PTY) LTD—See City Lodge Hotels Limited; *Int'l*, pg. 1627
CLAYTON GROUP HOLDINGS INC.—See Radian Group, Inc.; *U.S. Public*, pg. 1759
CLICKIT VENTURES, LLC; *U.S. Private*, pg. 942
CLOCK RESTAURANT INC.; *U.S. Private*, pg. 945
COMPASS AMERICA INC.—See Information Services Group, Inc.; *U.S. Public*, pg. 1117
COMPLETE HEALTHCARE RESOURCES INC; *U.S. Private*, pg. 1000
COMPUTERIZED MANAGEMENT SERVICES, INC.—See GTCR LLC; *U.S. Private*, pg. 1807
CONNOR FOREST INDUSTRIES, INC.—See Bridgewater Resources Corporation; *U.S. Private*, pg. 650
COPPER ROCK CAPITAL PARTNERS LLC—See BrightSphere Investment Group Inc.; *U.S. Public*, pg. 383
CORPOREX DEVELOPMENT—See Corporex Companies, Inc.; *U.S. Private*, pg. 1058
COS BUSINESS PRODUCTS & INTERIORS, INC.—See The ODP Corporation; *U.S. Public*, pg. 2117
COSIMO'S MANAGEMENT, INC.; *U.S. Private*, pg. 1062
COST PLUS MANAGEMENT SERVICES, INC.—See Kingswood Capital Management LLC; *U.S. Private*, pg. 2312
COX AND KINGS GLOBAL SERVICES PRIVATE LIMITED—See Cox & Kings Limited; *Int'l*, pg. 1822
CPF DENTAL, LLC; *U.S. Private*, pg. 1080

N.A.I.C.S. INDEX

561110 — OFFICE ADMINISTRATI...

CREATIVE TECHNOLOGY LTD.—See The Carlyle Group Inc.; *U.S. Public*, pg. 2049
CREMONINI S.P.A. - ADMINISTRATIVE HEADQUARTERS—See Cremonini S.p.A.; *Int'l*, pg. 1838
CROWN CENTER REDEVELOPMENT CORP—See Hallmark Cards, Inc.; *U.S. Private*, pg. 1844
CSS HOTELS SERVICES INC.; *U.S. Private*, pg. 1118
CUTTER MANAGEMENT CO.—See Cutter of Maui, Inc.; *U.S. Private*, pg. 1131
DAICEL SAKAI JITSUGYO CO. LTD.—See Daicel Corporation; *Int'l*, pg. 1919
DAIOHS CORPORATION; *Int'l*, pg. 1940
DALRADA FINANCIAL CORPORATION; *U.S. Public*, pg. 621
DANUBIUS HOTEL AND SPA NYRT.—See CP Holdings Ltd.; *Int'l*, pg. 1823
DAUGHTERS OF CHARITY HEALTH SYSTEM; *U.S. Private*, pg. 1167
DBX, INC.—See Mahwah Bergen Retail Group, Inc.; *U.S. Private*, pg. 2550
DEUTSCHE ASSET & WEALTH MANAGEMENT—See Deutsche Bank Aktiengesellschaft; *Int'l*, pg. 2057
DIAGEO NORTH AMERICA—See Diageo plc; *Int'l*, pg. 2102
DOCTORS BILLING SERVICE, INC.—See KKR & Co. Inc.; *U.S. Public*, pg. 1249
DOF MANAGEMENT ARGENTINA S.A.—See DOF Group ASA; *Int'l*, pg. 2154
DOTBOX LLC—See Stagwell, Inc.; *U.S. Public*, pg. 1926
D OTEL MARMARIS TURIZM ISLETMECILIGI TICARET VE SANAYI A.S.—See Dogus Holding AS; *Int'l*, pg. 2154
DOUBLETREE LLC—See Hilton Worldwide Holdings Inc.; *U.S. Public*, pg. 1040
DOUGLAS TELECOMMUNICATIONS; *U.S. Private*, pg. 1267
DOVER (SHANGHAI) TRADING COMPANY—See Dover Corporation; *U.S. Public*, pg. 679
DOVRE GROUP INC.—See Dovre Group Plc; *Int'l*, pg. 2182
DOWNER NEW ZEALAND LIMITED—See Downer EDI Limited; *Int'l*, pg. 2186
DRAEGER'S SUPER MARKETS INC.; *U.S. Private*, pg. 1271
DUO SOFTWARE (PVT.) LIMITED—See Duo World, Inc.; *U.S. Public*, pg. 691
DUVAL MOTORS AT THE AVENUES INC—See Scott-McRae Automotive Group Inc.; *U.S. Private*, pg. 3578
E&A INDUSTRIES, INC.; *U.S. Private*, pg. 1301
EAKIN-YOUNGENTOB ASSOCIATES INC.; *U.S. Private*, pg. 1312
EBARA EARNEST CO., LTD.—See Ebara Corporation; *Int'l*, pg. 2282
ECHO HEALTH, INC; *U.S. Private*, pg. 1327
ECPH MANAGEMENT INC.; *U.S. Private*, pg. 1330
EDWARDO'S RESTAURANT, INC.—See Bravo Restaurants Inc.; *U.S. Private*, pg. 641
EDX AUSTRALIA PTY LIMITED—See Equifax Inc.; *U.S. Public*, pg. 785
EGMONT ADMINISTRATION A/S—See Egmont Fonden; *Int'l*, pg. 2325
ELC MANAGEMENT LLC—See The Estee Lauder Companies Inc.; *U.S. Public*, pg. 2073
ELDERWOOD ADMINISTRATIVE SERVICES, LLC—See Post Acute Partners, LLC; *U.S. Private*, pg. 3234
ELEMENT VEHICLE MANAGEMENT SERVICES, LLC—See Element Fleet Management Corporation; *Int'l*, pg. 2358
ELLIOTT GROUP HOLDINGS, INC.—See Ebara Corporation; *Int'l*, pg. 2284
EMAGINE GMBH; *Int'l*, pg. 2373
EMBASSY SUITES MANAGEMENT LLC—See Hilton Worldwide Holdings Inc.; *U.S. Public*, pg. 1040
ENGAGE HOSPITALITY LLC; *U.S. Private*, pg. 1397
ENPOWER MANAGEMENT CORP.—See Enpower Corp.; *U.S. Private*, pg. 1401
ENPOWER OPERATIONS CORP.—See Enpower Corp.; *U.S. Private*, pg. 1401
EPYX FRANCE SAS—See Corpay, Inc.; *U.S. Public*, pg. 579
EPYX LIMITED—See Corpay, Inc.; *U.S. Public*, pg. 579
EQUIFAX ANALYTICS PRIVATE LIMITED—See Equifax Inc.; *U.S. Public*, pg. 785
EQUIFAX AUSTRALASIA GROUP SERVICES PTY LIMITED—See Equifax Inc.; *U.S. Public*, pg. 786
EQUIFAX AUSTRALIA COMMERCIAL SERVICES AND SOLUTIONS PTY LIMITED—See Equifax Inc.; *U.S. Public*, pg. 786
EQUIFAX NEW ZEALAND INFORMATION SERVICES AND SOLUTIONS LIMITED—See Equifax Inc.; *U.S. Public*, pg. 786
EQUIOM (GUERNSEY) LIMITED—See Equiom (Isle of Man) Limited; *Int'l*, pg. 2485
EQUIOM (JERSEY) LIMITED—See Equiom (Isle of Man) Limited; *Int'l*, pg. 2485
EQUIOM (MALTA) LIMITED—See Equiom (Isle of Man) Limited; *Int'l*, pg. 2485
ESQUIRE DEPOSITION SOLUTIONS, LLC - PHILADELPHIA—See H.I.G. Capital, LLC; *U.S. Private*, pg. 1827

EVERTEC COSTA RICA, S.A.—See EVERTEC, Inc.; *U.S. Public*, pg. 802
EVERTEC DOMINICANA, SAS—See EVERTEC, Inc.; *U.S. Public*, pg. 802
EVERTEC GUATEMALA, S.A.—See EVERTEC, Inc.; *U.S. Public*, pg. 802
EVERTEC MEXICO SERVICIOS DE PROCESAMIENTO, S.A. DE C.V.—See EVERTEC, Inc.; *U.S. Public*, pg. 802
EVERTEC PANAMA, S.A.—See EVERTEC, Inc.; *U.S. Public*, pg. 802
EVOLUTION HEALTHCARE MANAGEMENT PTY. LTD.—See Evolution Healthcare Pty. Ltd.; *Int'l*, pg. 2572
FAIR FRIEND ENTERPRISE GROUP—See Fair Friend Group; *Int'l*, pg. 2604
FCER MANAGEMENT LLC—See Adeptus Health Inc.; *U.S. Private*, pg. 78
FERTITTA ENTERTAINMENT, LLC—See Red Rock Resorts, Inc.; *U.S. Public*, pg. 1769
FGL GROUP MANAGEMENT SERVICE CO., LTD.—See Fuyo General Lease Co., Ltd.; *Int'l*, pg. 2859
FIDUCIAL, INC.—See Fiducial; *Int'l*, pg. 2655
FI-MED MANAGEMENT, INC.; *U.S. Private*, pg. 1501
FINANCIALOGIC, INC.; *U.S. Private*, pg. 1508
FINANCO, LLC—See Raymond James Financial, Inc.; *U.S. Public*, pg. 1764
FIRST SHANGHAI NOMINEES LIMITED—See First Shanghai Investments Limited; *Int'l*, pg. 2687
FLEETCOR DEUTSCHLAND GMBH—See Corpay, Inc.; *U.S. Public*, pg. 579
FMP RESTAURANT MANAGEMENT, LLC—See Food Management Partners, Inc.; *U.S. Private*, pg. 1561
FM SERVICES COMPANY—See Freeport-McMoRan Inc.; *U.S. Public*, pg. 884
FORMOSA INTERNATIONAL HOTELS CORP.; *Int'l*, pg. 2734
FOUNDER'S CONSULTANTS HOLDINGS, INC.; *Int'l*, pg. 2753
FRANCE QUICK S.A.S.—See Groupe Bertrand SARL; *Int'l*, pg. 3092
FREEDOM 1, LLC—See US 1 Industries, Inc.; *U.S. Private*, pg. 4317
FRUITION PARTNERS CANADA LTD.—See DXC Technology Company; *U.S. Public*, pg. 696
FUJIAN HOLDINGS LIMITED; *Int'l*, pg. 2818
FUJIYA SYSTEM CENTER CO., LTD.—See Fujiya Co., Ltd.; *Int'l*, pg. 2838
FULCRUM LOGIC, INC.; *U.S. Private*, pg. 1620
FUTABA (TIANJIN) CO., LTD.—See Futaba Industrial Co., Ltd.; *Int'l*, pg. 2851
G4S BEHEER BV—See Allied Universal Manager LLC; *U.S. Private*, pg. 188
GABELLI & COMPANY, INC.—See GAMCO Investors, Inc.; *U.S. Public*, pg. 895
GECASA—See Ente Vasco de la Energia; *Int'l*, pg. 2450
GENERAL HEALTH SYSTEM FOUNDATION, INC.—See General Health System Inc.; *U.S. Private*, pg. 1665
GENERAL HEALTH SYSTEM INC.; *U.S. Private*, pg. 1665
GENEVA MANAGEMENT INC.; *U.S. Private*, pg. 1670
GEX MANAGEMENT, INC.; *U.S. Private*, pg. 935
G-FACTORY CO., LTD.; *Int'l*, pg. 2862
GF MANAGEMENT, LLC—See GF Management, Inc.; *U.S. Private*, pg. 1689
GLANBIA CHEESE—See Glanbia Co-Operative Society Limited; *Int'l*, pg. 2988
GLOBAL CLIENT SOLUTIONS LLC—See Anywhere Real Estate Inc.; *U.S. Public*, pg. 141
GLOBEOSS PTE LTD—See Captii Limited; *Int'l*, pg. 1317
GLOBEOSS SDN BHD—See Captii Limited; *Int'l*, pg. 1317
GOLDEN EAGLES LESSEE LLC—See Pebblebrook Hotel Trust; *U.S. Public*, pg. 1660
GOODMAN MANAGEMENT HOLDINGS (LUX) SARL—See Goodman Limited; *Int'l*, pg. 3040
GOODMAN PROPERTY SERVICES (NZ) LIMITED—See Goodman Limited; *Int'l*, pg. 3040
GPI INTERNATIONAL LIMITED—See Gold Peak Technology Group Limited; *Int'l*, pg. 3025
GPI MANAGEMENT SERVICES (PROPRIETARY) LIMITED—See Grand Parade Investments Limited; *Int'l*, pg. 3056
GRAINGER MANAGEMENT LLC—See W.W. Grainger, Inc.; *U.S. Public*, pg. 2320
GRAND CENTRAL ENTERPRISES BHD.; *Int'l*, pg. 3054
GRAND HOTEL UNION BUSINESS D.D.—See Grand Hotel Union d.d.; *Int'l*, pg. 3055
GREAT EAGLE HOTELS (UK) LIMITED—See Great Eagle Holdings Limited; *Int'l*, pg. 3064
THE GREATER CANNABIS COMPANY, INC.; *U.S. Public*, pg. 2085
GREENE KING RETAIL SERVICES LIMITED—See CK Asset Holdings Limited; *Int'l*, pg. 1635
GREENE KING SERVICES LIMITED—See CK Asset Holdings Limited; *Int'l*, pg. 1635
GREENKO ENERGIES PVT. LTD.—See Greenko Dutch B.V.; *Int'l*, pg. 3075
GREEN VIEW DEVELOPMENT SERVICES LIMITED—See Dangote Group Limited; *Int'l*, pg. 1962
GRINDROD MANAGEMENT SERVICES (PTY) LIMITED—See Grindrod Limited; *Int'l*, pg. 3086

GRUPO INFFINIX, S.A. DE C.V.—See Equifax Inc.; *U.S. Public*, pg. 786
GUANGDONG GUANGSHENG HOTEL GROUP CO., LTD.—See Guangdong Rising Assets Management Co., Ltd.; *Int'l*, pg. 3159
GY COMMERCE CO LTD; *Int'l*, pg. 3190
HALLMARK SYSTEMS INC.; *U.S. Private*, pg. 1845
HAMPTON INNS LLC—See Hilton Worldwide Holdings Inc.; *U.S. Public*, pg. 1040
HAND ENTERPRISE USA, INC.—See Hand Enterprise Solutions Co., Ltd.; *Int'l*, pg. 3243
HANGOUT HOTELS INTERNATIONAL PTE LTD—See Cathay Organisation Holdings Ltd; *Int'l*, pg. 1360
HCFS HEALTH CARE FINANCIAL SERVICES, LLC—See Blackstone Inc.; *U.S. Public*, pg. 359
HEADCOUNT MANAGEMENT, INC.; *U.S. Private*, pg. 1891
HEALTH CARE MANAGEMENT, INC.—See Key Family of Companies; *U.S. Private*, pg. 2293
HELABA INTERNATIONAL FINANCE PLC—See Helaba Landesbank Hessen-Thuringen; *Int'l*, pg. 3328
HILTON GARDEN INNS MANAGEMENT LLC—See Hilton Worldwide Holdings Inc.; *U.S. Public*, pg. 1040
HILTON MANAGEMENT LLC—See Hilton Worldwide Holdings Inc.; *U.S. Public*, pg. 1041
HI-P MANAGEMENT SERVICES PTE. LTD.—See Hi-P International Limited; *Int'l*, pg. 3381
HM INTERNATIONAL HOLDINGS LIMITED; *Int'l*, pg. 3431
HOME NURSING AGENCY; *U.S. Private*, pg. 1971
HOMEWOOD SUITES MANAGEMENT LLC—See Hilton Worldwide Holdings Inc.; *U.S. Public*, pg. 1041
HOPEWELL HOTELS MANAGEMENT LIMITED—See Hopewell Holdings Limited; *Int'l*, pg. 3473
HOSPITAL SISTERS HEALTH SYSTEM; *U.S. Private*, pg. 1987
HOSPITAL SOLUTIONS, INC.; *U.S. Private*, pg. 1987
HOTEL CONSULTING SERVICES INC.; *U.S. Private*, pg. 1989
HOTELIM SA; *Int'l*, pg. 3489
HOTEL MAJESTIC CANNES SA; *Int'l*, pg. 3488
HOTEL MONTELEONE INC.; *U.S. Private*, pg. 1989
HOTEL ROYAL LIMITED; *Int'l*, pg. 3489
HOTELS.COM GP, LLC—See Expedia Group, Inc.; *U.S. Public*, pg. 809
HOTEL SIGIRIYA PLC; *Int'l*, pg. 3489
HOYAS LESSEE LLC—See Pebblebrook Hotel Trust; *U.S. Public*, pg. 1660
HUANGSHAN INTERNATIONAL HOTEL CO., LTD.—See Huangshan Tourism Development Co., Ltd.; *Int'l*, pg. 3513
HUBBARD RADIO, LLC—See Hubbard Broadcasting, Inc.; *U.S. Private*, pg. 2000
HULIC HOTEL MANAGEMENT CO., LTD.—See Hulic Co., Ltd.; *Int'l*, pg. 3528
HUMPERDINK'S TEXAS LLC; *U.S. Private*, pg. 2007
HUNTSMAN VERWALTUNGS GMBH—See Huntsman Corporation; *U.S. Public*, pg. 1073
HUNTSWOOD CTC LIMITED—See ResultsCX; *U.S. Private*, pg. 3410
HV FOOD PRODUCTS COMPANY—See The Clorox Company; *U.S. Public*, pg. 2062
HYATT CHAIN SERVICES LIMITED—See Hyatt Hotels Corporation; *U.S. Public*, pg. 1077
HYDE PARK HOLDINGS LLC; *U.S. Private*, pg. 2017
IBIL—See Ente Vasco de la Energia; *Int'l*, pg. 2450
INDUSTRIAL MARKETING INC.—See Slay Industries Inc.; *U.S. Private*, pg. 3687
INDUSTRIAL PROMOTION SERVICES S.A.—See Aga Khan Development Network; *Int'l*, pg. 199
INDUSTRIAL PROMOTION SERVICES (WEST AFRICA) S.A.—See Aga Khan Development Network; *Int'l*, pg. 199
INNOVIM LLC; *U.S. Private*, pg. 2084
INTOWARE LTD.—See Kopin Corporation; *U.S. Public*, pg. 1271
I.Q. DATA INTERNATIONAL, INC.—See Assurant, Inc.; *U.S. Public*, pg. 215
ISLAND HOSPITALITY MANAGEMENT, LLC; *U.S. Private*, pg. 2145
ISLAND OPERATING COMPANY INC.; *U.S. Private*, pg. 2145
JACOBY & MEYERS, LLC—See Jacoby & Meyers, P.C.; *U.S. Private*, pg. 2180
JANUS HOTELS & RESORTS, INC.; *U.S. Private*, pg. 2188
JBS PROJECT MANAGEMENT LLC—See H.I.G. Capital, LLC; *U.S. Private*, pg. 1827
JIM KOONS MANAGEMENT COMPANY—See Asbury Automotive Group, Inc.; *U.S. Public*, pg. 209
J.M. HUBER CORP.-NATURAL RESOURCES—See J.M. Huber Corporation; *U.S. Private*, pg. 2168
JX NIPPON MINING ECOMANAGEMENT, INC.—See ENEOS Holdings, Inc.; *Int'l*, pg. 2416
KAPOOR ENTERPRISES; *U.S. Private*, pg. 2261
THE KEN BLANCHARD COMPANIES; *U.S. Private*, pg. 4064
KERN & ASSOCIATES; *U.S. Private*, pg. 2290
KINGSWAY FINANCIAL ASSESSMENTS PTY LTD—See Equifax Inc.; *U.S. Public*, pg. 786
KINGWOOD MEMORIAL PARK ASSOCIATION—See Axar Capital Management L.P.; *U.S. Private*, pg. 411

K-MASTER SRL—See Edizione S.r.l.; *Int'l*, pg. 2312
KONECTA ARGENTINA—See Grupo Konectanet S.L.; *Int'l*, pg. 3130
KONECTA CHILE SA—See Grupo Konectanet S.L.; *Int'l*, pg. 3130
KONECTA PORTUGAL, LDA—See Grupo Konectanet S.L.; *Int'l*, pg. 3130
KONECTA UK LTD—See Grupo Konectanet S.L.; *Int'l*, pg. 3130
KOWLOON PANDA HOTEL LIMITED—See Hopewell Holdings Limited; *Int'l*, pg. 3473
KPC HEALTHCARE, INC.—See KPC Healthcare Holdings, Inc.; *U.S. Private*, pg. 2346
KROGER DELTA MARKETING AREA—See The Kroger Co.; *U.S. Private*, pg. 2108
LAND O'LAKES FINANCE CO.—See Land O'Lakes, Inc.; *U.S. Private*, pg. 2383
LAUREL HEALTH SYSTEMS; *U.S. Private*, pg. 2398
L.C. HOTELS PTE LTD—See A-Smart Holdings Ltd.; *Int'l*, pg. 20
L.C. (LONDON) LTD—See Aspial Corporation Limited; *Int'l*, pg. 630
L.C. (LONDON) LTD—See Fragrance Group Limited; *Int'l*, pg. 2758
LEANCOR LLC—See TPG Capital, L.P.; *U.S. Public*, pg. 2177
LIBERTY MANAGEMENT GROUP, INC.; *U.S. Private*, pg. 2444
LIFESPAN CORP.; *U.S. Private*, pg. 2451
LINROC COMMUNITY SERVICE CORPORATION; *U.S. Private*, pg. 2462
LMG INSIGHT & COMMUNICATION—See Aimia Inc.; *Int'l*, pg. 233
LOCKHEED MARTIN SERVICES, INC.—See Lockheed Martin Corporation; *U.S. Public*, pg. 1338
LODGING UNLIMITED, INC.; *U.S. Private*, pg. 2479
LONESTAR FREIGHTLINER GROUP, LTD.; *U.S. Private*, pg. 2489
LONESTAR TRANSPORTATION, LLC—See Daseke, Inc.; *U.S. Private*, pg. 1161
LOVELACE HEALTH SYSTEM—See Ventas, Inc.; *U.S. Public*, pg. 2279
LUFTHANSA PROCESS MANAGEMENT GMBH—See Deutsche Lufthansa AG; *Int'l*, pg. 2069
LV YANG OFFSHORE EQUIPMENT CO., LTD.—See AMOS Group Limited; *Int'l*, pg. 430
MACERICH LAKEWOOD LP—See The Macerich Company; *U.S. Public*, pg. 2110
MADER CONSTRUCTION CORP; *U.S. Private*, pg. 2539
MAJORS MANAGEMENT, LLC; *U.S. Private*, pg. 2555
MARRIOTT HOTELMANAGEMENT COLOGNE GMBH—See Marriott International, Inc.; *U.S. Public*, pg. 1371
MARSH LANDING MANAGEMENT COMPANY, INC.; *U.S. Private*, pg. 2591
MARTIN GOTTLIEB & ASSOCIATES, LLC—See Varsity Management Company, LP; *U.S. Private*, pg. 4347
M-B COMPANIES, INC.; *U.S. Private*, pg. 2525
MEDXCEL, LLC—See Ascension Health Alliance; *U.S. Private*, pg. 346
MERRY MAIDS LIMITED PARTNERSHIP—See Roark Capital Group Inc.; *U.S. Private*, pg. 3456
METROPOLITAN-SAINT LOUIS SEWER DISTRICT INC.; *U.S. Private*, pg. 2690
MIHLFELD & ASSOCIATES INC.; *U.S. Private*, pg. 2724
MISSISSIPPI VALLEY COMPANY—See U.S. Bancorp; *U.S. Public*, pg. 2212
MONMOUTH MEDICAL CENTER—See Barnabas Health, Inc.; *U.S. Private*, pg. 476
MONSANTO NL BV—See Bayer Aktiengesellschaft; *Int'l*, pg. 909
MONTGOMERY PROFESSIONAL SERVICES CORP.—See Global Upside, Inc.; *U.S. Private*, pg. 1718
MOODY PUBLISHERS—See Moody Bible Institute; *U.S. Private*, pg. 2778
MORGAN MANAGEMENT CORPORATION—See GHM Corp.; *U.S. Private*, pg. 1691
MOSAIC—See Caregiver, Inc.; *U.S. Private*, pg. 753
MRC MANAGEMENT COMPANY—See MRC Global Inc.; *U.S. Public*, pg. 1481
MSI/CANTERBURY CORP.—See Canterbury Consulting Group, Inc.; *U.S. Private*, pg. 735
MTHOMBO IT SERVICES (PTY) LIMITED—See EOH HOLDINGS LIMITED; *Int'l*, pg. 2457
NATIONAL SURGICAL HOSPITALS, INC.—See Bain Capital, LP; *U.S. Private*, pg. 445
NATIONAL UTILITY SERVICE, S.A.—See National Utility Service, Inc.; *U.S. Private*, pg. 2864
NATIONAL UTILITY SERVICE, S.A.—See National Utility Service, Inc.; *U.S. Private*, pg. 2864
NATIONWIDE PAYMENT SOLUTIONS, LLC; *U.S. Private*, pg. 2866
NCH HEALTHCARE SYSTEM, INC.; *U.S. Private*, pg. 2876
NEMO (AKS) LIMITED—See Xerox Holdings Corporation; *U.S. Public*, pg. 2388
NEWARK BETH ISRAEL MEDICAL CENTER—See Barnabas Health, Inc.; *U.S. Private*, pg. 476

NEW COUNTRY MOTOR CAR GROUP INC.; *U.S. Private*, pg. 2893
NJ TRANSIT MERCER, INC.—See NJ Transit Corporation; *U.S. Private*, pg. 2930
NORIAN ACCOUNTING OY—See TowerBrook Capital Partners, L.P.; *U.S. Private*, pg. 4195
NORTHROP GRUMMAN OHIO CORPORATION—See Northrop Grumman Corporation; *U.S. Public*, pg. 1541
NOVANT HEALTH, INC.; *U.S. Private*, pg. 2966
NUS DEUTSCHLAND GMBH—See National Utility Service, Inc.; *U.S. Private*, pg. 2864
NUS INTERNATIONAL PTY. LTD.—See National Utility Service, Inc.; *U.S. Private*, pg. 2864
NUS ITALIA, S.R.L.—See National Utility Service, Inc.; *U.S. Private*, pg. 2864
OCEANEERING SERVICES AUSTRALIA PTY LTD.—See Oceaneering International, Inc.; *U.S. Public*, pg. 1563
ON THE SCENE; *U.S. Private*, pg. 3018
OPPENHEIM PRIVATE EQUITY VERWALTUNGSGESELLSCHAFT MBH—See Deutsche Bank Aktiengesellschaft; *Int'l*, pg. 2062
ORION ADMINISTRATIVE SERVICES, INC.—See Orion Group Holdings, Inc.; *U.S. Public*, pg. 1618
ORPAK SYSTEMS LTD—See Vontier Corporation; *U.S. Public*, pg. 2309
OS (THAILAND) CO., LTD.—See Bain Capital, LP; *U.S. Private*, pg. 434
OUTRIGGER HOTELS HAWAII—See KSL Capital Partners, LLC; *U.S. Private*, pg. 2355
OUTRIGGER LODGING SERVICES LIMITED PARTNERSHIP; *U.S. Private*, pg. 3051
PACKARD ELECTRIC EUROPA GES.M.B.H.—See General Motors Company; *U.S. Public*, pg. 928
PADUS GRUNDSTUCKSVERMIETUNGSGESELLSCHAFT MBH—See Deutsche Bank Aktiengesellschaft; *Int'l*, pg. 2061
PA KOMPETENS LON AB—See TowerBrook Capital Partners, L.P.; *U.S. Private*, pg. 4195
PALM RESTAURANT GROUP; *U.S. Private*, pg. 3079
PARKSON CORPORATION—See Axel Johnson Gruppen AB; *Int'l*, pg. 765
PEQUOT PHARMACEUTICAL NETWORK MANAGEMENT SERVICES—See Mashantucket Pequot Gaming Enterprise Inc.; *U.S. Private*, pg. 2601
PIER 4 LLC—See UDR, Inc.; *U.S. Public*, pg. 2218
PITNEY BOWES CREDIT AUSTRALIA LIMITED—See Pitney Bowes Inc.; *U.S. Public*, pg. 1694
PM HOSPITALITY STRATEGIES, INC.—See The Buccini/Pollin Group, Inc.; *U.S. Private*, pg. 4002
POST FOODS, LLC - PARSIPPANY ADMINISTRATIVE OFFICE—See Post Holdings, Inc.; *U.S. Public*, pg. 1704
POWERFLEET SYSTEMS LTD—See PowerFleet, Inc.; *U.S. Public*, pg. 1706
PRECISION ENTERPRISES INC—See Precision Resources Inc.; *U.S. Private*, pg. 3246
PREMIER INSURANCE MANAGEMENT SERVICES, INC.—See Premier, Inc.; *U.S. Public*, pg. 1715
PRESBYTERIAN MANORS OF MID-AMERICA INC.; *U.S. Private*, pg. 3253
THE PRIVATE TRUST COMPANY, N.A.—See LPL Financial Holdings, Inc.; *U.S. Public*, pg. 1343
PROCTER & GAMBLE INTERNATIONAL OPERATIONS SA-ROHQ—See The Procter & Gamble Company; *U.S. Public*, pg. 2122
PROVIDENT FINANCIAL MANAGEMENT, INC.; *U.S. Private*, pg. 3295
PRUDENTIAL FUNDING LLC—See Prudential Financial, Inc.; *U.S. Public*, pg. 1732
PSEG SERVICES CORP.—See Public Service Enterprise Group Incorporated; *U.S. Public*, pg. 1736
PT AMOS UTAMA INDONESIA—See AMOS Group Limited; *Int'l*, pg. 430
PT HUNTSMAN INDONESIA—See Huntsman Corporation; *U.S. Public*, pg. 1075
QATAR PROJECT MANAGEMENT COMPANY Q.P.S.C.—See Barwa Real Estate Company Q.P.S.C.; *Int'l*, pg. 870
Q-CHECK SYSTEMS—See Synergis Technologies Group; *U.S. Private*, pg. 3903
QUALITY VISION INTERNATIONAL INC.; *U.S. Private*, pg. 3321
RAILWAY APPROVALS LTD—See Deutsche Bahn AG; *Int'l*, pg. 2052
RAKYAT HARTANAH SDN BHD—See Bank Kerjasama Rakyat Malaysia Berhad; *Int'l*, pg. 838
RAKYAT MANAGEMENT SERVICES SDN BHD—See Bank Kerjasama Rakyat Malaysia Berhad; *Int'l*, pg. 838
RAKYAT NIAGA SDN BHD—See Bank Kerjasama Rakyat Malaysia Berhad; *Int'l*, pg. 838
RAPHAEL HOTEL GROUP; *U.S. Private*, pg. 3355
REACHTEL PTY LTD—See Equifax Inc.; *U.S. Public*, pg. 787
REGAL HOTELS INVESTMENT & MANAGEMENT (SHANGHAI) LTD—See Century City International Holdings Ltd; *Int'l*, pg. 1418
REGENCY FRANCHISE GROUP, LLC—See The ODP Corporation; *U.S. Public*, pg. 2118

REGENT BERLIN GMBH—See Formosa International Hotels Corp.; *Int'l*, pg. 2734
REGIONAL MANAGEMENT RECEIVABLES, LLC—See Regional Management Corp.; *U.S. Public*, pg. 1776
RENAISSANCE DUSSELDORF HOTEMMANAGMENT GMBH—See Marriott International, Inc.; *U.S. Public*, pg. 1371
RESOURCES GLOBAL PROFESSIONALS, INC.—See Resources Connection, Inc.; *U.S. Public*, pg. 1792
RESTAURANTS OF AMERICA MANAGEMENT, INC.—See Restaurants of America, Inc.; *U.S. Private*, pg. 3408
RESULTSCX; *U.S. Private*, pg. 3410
RHA HEALTH SERVICES INC.—See Blue Wolf Capital Partners LLC; *U.S. Private*, pg. 595
RSR MANAGEMENT CORP.—See RSR Group Inc.; *U.S. Private*, pg. 3497
RTKL ASSOCIATES INC.—See ARCADIS N.V.; *Int'l*, pg. 541
RUBY RECEPTIONISTS—See Updata Partners; *U.S. Private*, pg. 4311
RUSH HEALTH SYSTEMS INC.; *U.S. Private*, pg. 3505
RYUGIN OFFICE SERVICE CO., LTD.—See Bank of The Ryukyus, Ltd.; *Int'l*, pg. 849
SAFECORE, INC; *U.S. Private*, pg. 3524
SAINT BARNABAS MEDICAL CENTER—See Barnabas Health, Inc.; *U.S. Private*, pg. 477
SAMOS VERMOGENSVERWALTUNGS GMBH—See Deutsche Bank Aktiengesellschaft; *Int'l*, pg. 2061
SCOTTISH FOOD SYSTEMS INC.—See ZV Pate Inc.; *U.S. Private*, pg. 4610
SECURE SENTINEL AUSTRALIA PTY LIMITED—See Equifax Inc.; *U.S. Public*, pg. 787
SECURE SENTINEL NEW ZEALAND LIMITED—See Equifax Inc.; *U.S. Public*, pg. 787
SEMINOLE GAMING—See Seminole Tribe of Florida, Inc.; *U.S. Private*, pg. 3604
SERVICE BIRMINGHAM LIMITED—See Capita plc; *Int'l*, pg. 1309
SERVICIOS ADMINISTRATIVOS LAMOSA, S.A. DE C.V.—See Grupo Lamosa S.A. de C.V.; *Int'l*, pg. 3132
SERVIZI AZIENDALI PIRELLI S.C.P.A.—See China National Chemical Corporation; *Int'l*, pg. 1529
SHERATON TUCSON HOTEL & SUITES—See Marriott International, Inc.; *U.S. Public*, pg. 1372
SOFICA GROUP AD—See TTEC Holdings, Inc.; *U.S. Public*, pg. 2203
SOLUTION MINDS (UK) LIMITED—See 1Spatial Plc; *Int'l*, pg. 3
SPRINGER DEVELOPMENT LLC—See Banner Corporation; *U.S. Public*, pg. 275
SPRINGHILL HEALTH SERVICES INC.—See Southern Medical Health Systems Inc.; *U.S. Private*, pg. 3733
STAMFORD HEALTH SYSTEM INC.; *U.S. Private*, pg. 3776
STERIGENICS INTERNATIONAL LLC - SHARED SERVICES CENTER—See Warburg Pincus LLC; *U.S. Private*, pg. 4439
STERLING SOLUTIONS, LLC—See Where Food Comes From, Inc.; *U.S. Public*, pg. 2366
STEYRERMUHL SAGEWERKSGESELLSCHAFT M.B.H. NFG KG—See Heinzel Holding GmbH; *Int'l*, pg. 3325
STORED VALUE SOLUTIONS INTERNATIONAL B.V.—See Corpay, Inc.; *U.S. Public*, pg. 580
STRAUBE CENTER LLC; *U.S. Private*, pg. 3837
STREAM NEW YORK INC.—See Concentrix Corporation; *U.S. Public*, pg. 565
SUMMIT MATERIALS, LLC—See Summit Materials, Inc.; *U.S. Public*, pg. 1959
SUNRX, INC.; *U.S. Private*, pg. 3870
SURGICAL CARE AFFILIATES, LLC—See UnitedHealth Group Incorporated; *U.S. Public*, pg. 2250
SUVARNABHUMI AIRPORT HOTEL COMPANY LIMITED—See Airports of Thailand Public Company Limited; *Int'l*, pg. 248
SYKES ENTERPRISES MANAGEMENT GMBH—See Creadev SAS; *Int'l*, pg. 1831
SYSTRAN FINANCIAL SERVICES CORP.—See Textron Inc.; *U.S. Public*, pg. 2029
TAIWAN KYUSYUYA CO., LTD.—See Air Water Inc.; *Int'l*, pg. 241
TARGA RESOURCES GP LLC—See Targa Resources Corp.; *U.S. Public*, pg. 1981
TATE & LYLE NORTH AMERICAN SUGARS INC.—See Florida Crystals Corporation; *U.S. Public*, pg. 1548
T-C OIL COMPANY INC.; *U.S. Private*, pg. 3910
TOAD HOLLOW VINEYARDS, INC.; *U.S. Private*, pg. 4180
TORESCO ENTERPRISES; *U.S. Private*, pg. 4188
TRADEBE BRASIL—See Grupo Tradebe Medioambiente S.L.; *Int'l*, pg. 3138
TRADEBE S.A.R.L.—See Grupo Tradebe Medioambiente S.L.; *Int'l*, pg. 3138
TRUCKERS B2B, LLC—See WEX, Inc.; *U.S. Public*, pg. 2364
TRUE CAPITAL MANAGEMENT, LLC—See Cresset Asset Management, LLC; *U.S. Private*, pg. 1095
TRUMP INTERNATIONAL HOTELS MANAGEMENT LLC—See The Trump Organization, Inc.; *U.S. Private*, pg. 4128
TUPPERWARE SERVICES GMBH—See Tupperware Brands Corporation; *U.S. Public*, pg. 2204

N.A.I.C.S. INDEX

UCS SOLUTIONS (PROPRIETARY) LIMITED—See Business Connexion Group Limited; *Int'l*, pg. 1228
UNISON PACIFIC CORPORATION; *U.S. Private*, pg. 4286
UNITIL SERVICE CORP.—See Unitil Corporation; *U.S. Public*, pg. 2253
UNIVERSAL MANAGEMENT CORP.—See The Rados Companies; *U.S. Private*, pg. 4102
UNIVERSITY HEALTH CARE, INC.; *U.S. Private*, pg. 4308
UPCURVE CLOUD LLC—See Gannett Co., Inc.; *U.S. Public*, pg. 906
UP IMAGING MANAGEMENT SERVICES, LLC—See Apollo Global Management, Inc.; *U.S. Private*, pg. 159
U.S. COLLECTIONS, INC.—See HCA Healthcare, Inc.; *U.S. Public*, pg. 1013
USS PORTFOLIO DELAWARE, INC.—See United States Steel Corporation; *U.S. Public*, pg. 2237
VAN BEUREN MANAGEMENT, INC.; *U.S. Private*, pg. 4338
VASONA MANAGEMENT; *U.S. Private*, pg. 4347
VB SERVICIOS, COMERCIO E ADMINISTRACAO LTDA.—See Corpay, Inc.; *U.S. Public*, pg. 580
VELOCITEL MANAGEMENT SERVICES—See Willis Stein & Partners, LLC; *U.S. Private*, pg. 4528
VELOSI CERTIFICATION W.L.L—See I Squared Capital Advisors (US) LLC; *U.S. Private*, pg. 2024
VENTURE FOR AMERICA; *U.S. Private*, pg. 4358
VETRI MANAGEMENT CORPORATION—See Vetri Holdings LLC; *U.S. Private*, pg. 4374
VIRTUALEX HOLDINGS, INC.—See The Carlyle Group Inc.; *U.S. Public*, pg. 2055
VOXEO CORPORATION—See Vector Capital Management, L.P.; *U.S. Private*, pg. 4350
WACHTER MANAGEMENT COMPANY INC.; *U.S. Private*, pg. 4424
WADCORPP INDIAN PRIVATE LIMITED—See Franklin Electric Co., Inc.; *U.S. Public*, pg. 879
WALDORF ASTORIA MANAGEMENT LLC—See Hilton Worldwide Holdings Inc.; *U.S. Public*, pg. 1041
THE WARRANTY GROUP AUSTRALIA PTY. LTD.—See Assurant, Inc.; *U.S. Public*, pg. 215
THE WARRANTY GROUP COLOMBIA S.A.—See Assurant, Inc.; *U.S. Public*, pg. 215
WATERSTREET COMPANY; *U.S. Private*, pg. 4454
WAVERLY REGENCY, LLC—See Regency Centers Corporation; *U.S. Public*, pg. 1774
WEEZ SRL—See DBA Group SRL; *Int'l*, pg. 1986
WESTIN CROWN CENTER HOTEL—See Hallmark Cards, Inc.; *U.S. Private*, pg. 1845
WESTREC PROPERTIES, INC.—See Centerbridge Partners, L.P.; *U.S. Private*, pg. 816
?WHAT IF! HOLDINGS LIMITED—See Accenture plc; *Int'l*, pg. 82
WILKINSON REAL ESTATE ADVISORS INC; *U.S. Private*, pg. 4521
WILLIAMS MERCHANT SERVICES CO.—See The Williams Companies, Inc.; *U.S. Public*, pg. 2143
WINDERMERE REAL ESTATE SERVICES COMPANY; *U.S. Private*, pg. 4537
WISCONSIN CHEESE INC.; *U.S. Private*, pg. 4548
WOODMERE MANAGEMENT INC.—See Delta Holdings, Inc.; *U.S. Private*, pg. 1200
WRIGHT MANAGEMENT COMPANY, LLC; *U.S. Private*, pg. 4573
XCHANGING, INC.—See DXC Technology Company; *U.S. Public*, pg. 697
XCHANGING ITALY S.P.A.—See DXC Technology Company; *U.S. Public*, pg. 697
YARD HOUSE RESTAURANTS, LLC—See Darden Restaurants, Inc.; *U.S. Public*, pg. 633
YUKI SANGYO CO., LTD.—See ES-CON JAPAN Ltd.; *Int'l*, pg. 2500
ZABALGARBI, S.A.—See Ente Vasco de la Energia; *Int'l*, pg. 2450
ZMC HOTELS; *U.S. Private*, pg. 4606
ZV PATE INC.; *U.S. Private*, pg. 4610

561210 — FACILITIES SUPPORT SERVICES

11TH HOUR BUSINESS CENTERS, LLC; *U.S. Private*, pg. 2
14FORTY LIMITED—See Compass Group PLC; *Int'l*, pg. 1750
A2A CALORE & SERVIZI S.R.L.—See A2A S.p.A.; *Int'l*, pg. 29
ABM FACILITY SOLUTIONS GROUP, LLC—See ABM Industries, Inc.; *U.S. Public*, pg. 25
ABM HEALTHCARE SUPPORT SERVICES, INC.—See ABM Industries, Inc.; *U.S. Public*, pg. 25
ACCIONA FACILITY SERVICES, S.A.—See Acciona, S.A.; *Int'l*, pg. 90
ADVANCED FEDERAL SERVICES; *U.S. Private*, pg. 89
ADVANFACILITIES CO., LTD.—See Advantest Corporation; *Int'l*, pg. 165
AECOM GOVERNMENT SERVICES, INC.—See AECOM; *U.S. Public*, pg. 51
AEK ENERGIE AG—See BKW AG; *Int'l*, pg. 1054
AHTNA TECHNICAL SERVICES INC.—See Ahtna Incorporated; *U.S. Private*, pg. 131
AKIMA FACILITIES MANAGEMENT, LLC—See Nana Regional Corporation, Inc.; *U.S. Private*, pg. 2832
ALAMO 1; *U.S. Private*, pg. 149
ALTUS FIRE & LIFE SAFETY—See Apax Partners LLP; *Int'l*, pg. 501
APCOA BELGIUM N.V.—See Centerbridge Partners, L.P.; *U.S. Private*, pg. 811
APCOA PARKING AG—See Centerbridge Partners, L.P.; *U.S. Private*, pg. 811
APCOA PARKING AUSTRIA GMBH—See Centerbridge Partners, L.P.; *U.S. Private*, pg. 811
APCOA PARKING IRELAND LTD.—See Centerbridge Partners, L.P.; *U.S. Private*, pg. 812
APCOA PARKING NEDERLAND B.V.—See Centerbridge Partners, L.P.; *U.S. Private*, pg. 812
APCOA PARKING POLSKA SP.Z O.O.—See Centerbridge Partners, L.P.; *U.S. Private*, pg. 812
APCOA PARKING SWITZERLAND AG—See Centerbridge Partners, L.P.; *U.S. Private*, pg. 812
APCOA PARKING TURKEY—See Centerbridge Partners, L.P.; *U.S. Private*, pg. 812
APCOA PARKING (UK) LTD—See Centerbridge Partners, L.P.; *U.S. Private*, pg. 811
APLEONA AHR HEALTHCARE & SERVICES GMBH—See EQT AB; *Int'l*, pg. 2468
APLEONA HSG AG—See EQT AB; *Int'l*, pg. 2468
APLEONA HSG A/S—See EQT AB; *Int'l*, pg. 2468
APLEONA HSG EOOD—See EQT AB; *Int'l*, pg. 2468
APLEONA HSG GMBH—See EQT AB; *Int'l*, pg. 2468
APLEONA HSG GMBH—See EQT AB; *Int'l*, pg. 2468
APLEONA HSG KFT.—See EQT AB; *Int'l*, pg. 2468
APLEONA HSG LIMITED—See EQT AB; *Int'l*, pg. 2468
APLEONA HSG LIMITED—See EQT AB; *Int'l*, pg. 2468
APLEONA HSG NORD GMBH—See EQT AB; *Int'l*, pg. 2468
APLEONA HSG NORDOST GMBH—See EQT AB; *Int'l*, pg. 2468
APLEONA HSG O.O.O.—See EQT AB; *Int'l*, pg. 2468
APLEONA HSG OST GMBH—See EQT AB; *Int'l*, pg. 2468
APLEONA HSG RHEIN-MAIN GMBH—See EQT AB; *Int'l*, pg. 2468
APLEONA HSG S.A.R.L.—See EQT AB; *Int'l*, pg. 2469
APLEONA HSG S.A.—See EQT AB; *Int'l*, pg. 2468
APLEONA HSG S.P.A.—See EQT AB; *Int'l*, pg. 2468
APLEONA HSG SP. Z O.O.—See EQT AB; *Int'l*, pg. 2468
APLEONA HSG SRL—See EQT AB; *Int'l*, pg. 2468
APLEONA HSG S.R.O.—See EQT AB; *Int'l*, pg. 2469
APLEONA HSG S.R.O.—See EQT AB; *Int'l*, pg. 2469
APLEONA HSG SUDOST GMBH—See EQT AB; *Int'l*, pg. 2468
APLEONA HSG TOV—See EQT AB; *Int'l*, pg. 2468
APLEONA HSG WURTTEMBERG GMBH—See EQT AB; *Int'l*, pg. 2469
APLEONA PPP LIMITED—See EQT AB; *Int'l*, pg. 2468
APS SINERGIA S.P.A.—See ACEGAS-APS SpA; *Int'l*, pg. 95
ARA GROUP LIMITED; *Int'l*, pg. 528
ARAMARK CANADA LTD.—See Aramark; *U.S. Public*, pg. 176
ATALIAN GLOBAL SERVICES; *Int'l*, pg. 665
ATI, INC.—See CNH Industrial N.V.; *Int'l*, pg. 1674
ATLANTIC ENERGY CONCEPTS, INC.—See Schaedler/Yesco Distribution, Inc.; *U.S. Private*, pg. 3563
BABCOCK BORSIG SERVICE GMBH—See Bilfinger SE; *Int'l*, pg. 1027
BAE SYSTEMS-INTEGRATED O & M SOLUTIONS—See BAE Systems plc; *Int'l*, pg. 797
BAYER INDUSTRY SERVICES GMBH & CO. OHG—See Bayer Aktiengesellschaft; *Int'l*, pg. 905
BEM SYSTEMS, INC.—See Bernhard Capital Partners Management, LP; *U.S. Private*, pg. 536
BEM SYSTEMS - NEWPORT NEWS—See Bernhard Capital Partners Management, LP; *U.S. Private*, pg. 536
BEM SYSTEMS - ORLANDO—See Bernhard Capital Partners Management, LP; *U.S. Private*, pg. 536
BILLY MOORE CORRECTIONAL CENTER—See Management & Training Corporation; *U.S. Private*, pg. 2560
THE BIONETICS CORPORATION; *U.S. Private*, pg. 3995
BOUYGUES E&S FM UK LIMITED—See Bouygues S.A.; *Int'l*, pg. 1122
BOUYGUES E&S INTEC SCHWEIZ AG—See Bouygues S.A.; *Int'l*, pg. 1123
BROOKS & BROOKS SERVICES INC.; *U.S. Private*, pg. 664
THE BUDD GROUP INC. - CHARLOTTE OFFICE—See The Budd Group Inc.; *U.S. Private*, pg. 4002
THE BUDD GROUP INC. - DURHAM OFFICE—See The Budd Group Inc.; *U.S. Private*, pg. 4002
THE BUDD GROUP INC. - GREENSBORO OFFICE—See The Budd Group Inc.; *U.S. Private*, pg. 4002
THE BUDD GROUP INC. - GREENVILLE/SPARTANBURG, SC OFFICE—See The Budd Group Inc.; *U.S. Private*, pg. 4002
THE BUDD GROUP INC. - ORLANDO OFFICE—See The Budd Group Inc.; *U.S. Private*, pg. 4002
THE BUDD GROUP INC.; *U.S. Private*, pg. 4002
THE BUDD GROUP INC. - TAMPA OFFICE—See The Budd Group Inc.; *U.S. Private*, pg. 4002
BUILDINGSTARS; *U.S. Private*, pg. 683
BURGOS GROUP LLC—See Prairie Band Potawatomi Nation; *U.S. Private*, pg. 3242
BWXT Y-12, LLC—See BWX Technologies, Inc.; *U.S. Public*, pg. 413
CALL HENRY, INC.; *U.S. Private*, pg. 721
CAR.E FACILITY MANAGEMENT GMBH—See Clayton, Dubilier & Rice, LLC; *U.S. Private*, pg. 926
CARILLION (AMBS) LTD—See Carillion plc; *Int'l*, pg. 1330
CARILLION FACILITIES MANAGEMENT—See Carillion plc; *Int'l*, pg. 1330
CARILLION PLANNED MAINTENANCE—See Carillion plc; *Int'l*, pg. 1330
CARILLION PLC; *Int'l*, pg. 1330
CCA TRS, LLC—See Corecivic, Inc.; *U.S. Public*, pg. 577
CENTOSTAZIONI S.P.A.—See Altarea SCA; *Int'l*, pg. 385
THE CENTURION GROUP, INC.—See Marsh & McLennan Companies, Inc.; *U.S. Public*, pg. 1382
CHATEAUD'EAU SA—See Eden International SA; *Int'l*, pg. 2306
CHINA SUPPLY CHAIN HOLDINGS LIMITED; *Int'l*, pg. 1556
CHUGACH ALASKA CORPORATION; *U.S. Private*, pg. 893
CIVEO CORPORATION; *U.S. Public*, pg. 506
CIVEO PTY LTD—See Civeo Corporation; *U.S. Public*, pg. 506
CIVEO PTY LTD—See Civeo Corporation; *U.S. Public*, pg. 506
CIVEO PTY LTD—See Civeo Corporation; *U.S. Public*, pg. 506
CIVEO PTY LTD—See Civeo Corporation; *U.S. Public*, pg. 506
CMIC HEALTHCARE INSTITUTE CO., LTD.—See CMIC Holdings Co., Ltd.; *Int'l*, pg. 1670
CNCS FACILITY SOLUTIONS PRIVATE LIMITED.—See A2Z Infra Engineering Limited; *Int'l*, pg. 30
COBALT SERVICE PARTNERS, LLC—See Alpine Investors; *U.S. Private*, pg. 201
COFELY FMO—See ENGIE SA; *Int'l*, pg. 2430
COFELY GEBAUDETECHNIK GMBH—See ENGIE SA; *Int'l*, pg. 2431
COFELY WORKPLACE LIMITED—See ENGIE SA; *Int'l*, pg. 2430
COMMUNITY CORRECTIONAL CENTER OF LINCOLN—See Nebraska Department of Correctional Services; *U.S. Private*, pg. 2878
CONTAMINANT CONTROL INC.; *U.S. Private*, pg. 1027
COOR SERVICE MANAGEMENT AS—See Cinven Limited; *Int'l*, pg. 1612
COOR SERVICE MANAGEMENT A/S—See Cinven Limited; *Int'l*, pg. 1612
COOR SERVICE MANAGEMENT HOLDING AB—See Cinven Limited; *Int'l*, pg. 1611
COOR SERVICE MANAGEMENT NV—See Cinven Limited; *Int'l*, pg. 1612
COOR SERVICE MANAGEMENT OY—See Cinven Limited; *Int'l*, pg. 1612
CORDANT GROUP PLC; pg. 1795
CORPORACION DE INVERSION Y DESARROLLO BES, S.A.—See BES Engineering Corporation; *Int'l*, pg. 998
CORRECTIONAL ALTERNATIVES, LLC—See Corecivic, Inc.; *U.S. Public*, pg. 577
CSG GMBH—See Deutsche Post AG; *Int'l*, pg. 2072
CSG GMBH—See EQT AB; *Int'l*, pg. 2469
CSK SP. Z O.O.—See Commerzbank AG; *Int'l*, pg. 1715
DAIKIN FACILITIES CO., LTD.—See Daikin Industries, Ltd.; *Int'l*, pg. 1934
DAY & ZIMMERMANN NPS, INC.—See The Day & Zimmermann Group, Inc.; *U.S. Private*, pg. 4019
DENTSU FACILITY MANAGEMENT INC.—See Dentsu Group Inc.; *Int'l*, pg. 2034
DERICHEBOURG PROPRETE SAS—See Derichebourg S.A.; *Int'l*, pg. 2042
D'HUY ENGINEERING, INC. (DEI)—See H.I.G. Capital, LLC; *U.S. Private*, pg. 1827
DIVISIONS, INC.—See Roark Capital Group Inc.; *U.S. Private*, pg. 3454
DNP FACILITY SERVICES CO., LTD.—See Dai Nippon Printing Co., Ltd.; *Int'l*, pg. 1914
DUSSMANN GULF LLC—See Dussmann Stiftung & Co. KGaA; *Int'l*, pg. 2234
DUSSMANN MIDDLE EAST GMBH—See Dussmann Stiftung & Co. KGaA; *Int'l*, pg. 2234
DUSSMANN SERVICE DEUTSCHLAND GMBH—See Dussmann Stiftung & Co. KGaA; *Int'l*, pg. 2234
DUSSMANN SERVICE S.R.L.—See Dussmann Stiftung & Co. KGaA; *Int'l*, pg. 2234
THE DWYER GROUP, INC.—See Harvest Partners L.P.; *U.S. Private*, pg. 1877
DYNAMAC INTERNATIONAL INC.; *U.S. Private*, pg. 1297
DZSP 21 LLC—See Parsons Corporation; *U.S. Public*, pg. 1650
EATON S.A.—See Eaton Corporation plc; *Int'l*, pg. 2281
EATON TECHNOLOGIES G.M.B.H.—See Eaton Corporation plc; *Int'l*, pg. 2281
EDEN INTERNATIONAL SA; *Int'l*, pg. 2306
EDEN SPRINGS (DENMARK) A/S—See Eden International SA; *Int'l*, pg. 2306

561210 — FACILITIES SUPPORT ...

EDEN SPRINGS ESPANA S.A.—See Eden International SA; *Int'l*, pg. 2307
EDEN SPRINGS (ESTONIA) OU—See Eden International SA; *Int'l*, pg. 2306
EDEN SPRINGS LATVIA SIA—See Eden International SA; *Int'l*, pg. 2307
EDEN SPRINGS (NEDERLAND) BV—See Eden International SA; *Int'l*, pg. 2306
EDEN SPRINGS (NORWAY) A/S—See Eden International SA; *Int'l*, pg. 2306
EDEN SPRINGS OY FINLAND—See Eden International SA; *Int'l*, pg. 2307
EDEN SPRINGS (POLAND) SP. Z O.O.—See Eden International SA; *Int'l*, pg. 2306
EDEN SPRINGS PORTUGAL SA—See Eden International SA; *Int'l*, pg. 2307
EDEN SPRINGS (SWEDEN) AB—See Eden International SA; *Int'l*, pg. 2306
EDEN SPRINGS (SWITZERLAND) SA—See Eden International SA; *Int'l*, pg. 2306
EDEN SPRINGS (UK) LIMITED—See Eden International SA; *Int'l*, pg. 2307
EDEN WATER & COFFEE DEUTSCHLAND GMBH—See Eden International SA; *Int'l*, pg. 2307
EMCON ASSOCIATES, INC.—See TPG Capital, L.P.; *U.S. Public*, pg. 2173
EMCOR FACILITIES SERVICES - SITE BASED SERVICES—See EMCOR Group, Inc.; *U.S. Public*, pg. 737
EMCOR GOVERNMENT SERVICES, INC.—See EMCOR Group, Inc.; *U.S. Public*, pg. 737
EMERALD COMPANIES, INC.; *U.S. Private*, pg. 1379
ENTECH ENGINEERING INC.—See Entech Engineering Inc.; *U.S. Private*, pg. 1402
ENVIRONMENTAL CONTRACTORS OF ILLINOIS INC.—See William Charles, Ltd.; *U.S. Private*, pg. 4522
ENVIRONMENTAL SERVICES OF NORTH AMERICA, INC.; *U.S. Private*, pg. 1408
ESG HOLDINGS, LTD.—See Advantage Partners LLP; *Int'l*, pg. 164
ETIHAD INTERNATIONAL HOSPITALITY LLC - SOLE PROPRIETORSHIP LLC—See Alpha Dhabi Holding PJSC; *Int'l*, pg. 367
EUREST SERVICES B.V.—See Compass Group PLC; *Int'l*, pg. 1752
EUREST SERVICES, INC.—See Compass Group PLC; *Int'l*, pg. 1751
EUROFOAM G.E.I.E.—See Greiner Holding AG; *Int'l*, pg. 3078
THE FACILITIES GROUP NATIONAL LLC—See Greenbriar Equity Group, L.P.; *U.S. Private*, pg. 1776
THE FACILITIES GROUP NATIONAL LLC—See Revolent Capital Solutions; *U.S. Private*, pg. 3416
FACILITYSOURCE, LLC—See CBRE Group, Inc.; *U.S. Public*, pg. 460
FEDERAL SOLUTIONS GROUP LLC—See Vornado Realty Trust; *U.S. Public*, pg. 2309
FERROSER—See Ferrovial S.A.; *Int'l*, pg. 2644
FERROVIAL SERVICOS, S.A.—See Ferrovial S.A.; *Int'l*, pg. 2644
FINNAIR FACILITIES MANAGEMENT OY—See Finnair Plc; *Int'l*, pg. 2676
FIRSTPORT LIMITED—See Equistone Partners Europe Limited; *Int'l*, pg. 2486
FIRST SERVICE NETWORKS, INC.; *U.S. Private*, pg. 1527
FLAGSHIP FACILITY SERVICES, INC.; *U.S. Private*, pg. 1539
FORWARD SOLUTIONS; *U.S. Private*, pg. 1578
FRONTSTREET FACILITY SOLUTIONS, INC.—See Charterhouse Group, Inc.; *U.S. Private*, pg. 859
FRONTSTREET MANAGEMENT GROUP LLC—See Charterhouse Group, Inc.; *U.S. Private*, pg. 859
FUJITA BUILDING MAINTENANCE INC.—See Daiwa House Industry Co., Ltd.; *Int'l*, pg. 1946
GATEWAY MOTORSPORTS PARK; *U.S. Private*, pg. 1650
GCA SERVICES GROUP, INC.—See ABM Industries, Inc.; *U.S. Public*, pg. 26
GDI INTEGRATED FACILITY SERVICES INC.; *Int'l*, pg. 2896
GEBZE IZMIR OTOYOLU ISLETME A.S.—See Groupe Egis S.A.; *Int'l*, pg. 3102
GEK SERVICES S.A.—See Gek Terna Societe Anonyme Holdings Real Estate Constructions; *Int'l*, pg. 2913
GEPSA—See ENGIE SA; *Int'l*, pg. 2431
GE.S.IN. GESTIONE SERVIZI INTEGRATI - SOCIETA COOPERATIVA—See CAMST-Cooperativa Albergo Mensa Spettacolo e Turismo, Soc. Coop. a.r.l.; *Int'l*, pg. 1275
GOVERNMENT CONTRACTING RESOURCES, INC.; *U.S. Private*, pg. 1746
GRAINGER S.A. DE C.V.—See W.W. Grainger, Inc.; *U.S. Public*, pg. 2320
GRANDI STAZIONI S.P.A.—See Ferrovie dello Stato Italiane S.p.A.; *Int'l*, pg. 2645
GREEN TOTAL SOLUTIONS, INC.—See Huron Capital Partners LLC; *U.S. Private*, pg. 2011
HART, CROWSER, INC.—See Haley & Aldrich Inc.; *U.S. Private*, pg. 1842

HITACHI BUILDING SYSTEMS BUSINESS SUPPORT CO., LTD.—See Hitachi, Ltd.; *Int'l*, pg. 3415
HSG ZANDER FS GMBH—See EQT AB; *Int'l*, pg. 2469
INDUSTRIOUS NATIONAL MANAGEMENT COMPANY LLC; *U.S. Private*, pg. 2069
IN DYNE INC.; *U.S. Private*, pg. 2052
INFRAPOST AG—See Die Schweizerische Post AG; *Int'l*, pg. 2113
INTEGRAL UK LTD—See Jones Lang LaSalle Incorporated; *U.S. Public*, pg. 1202
ISS EASTPOINT FACILITY SERVICES LIMITED—See EQT AB; *Int'l*, pg. 2476
ISS EASTPOINT FACILITY SERVICES LIMITED—See The Goldman Sachs Group, Inc.; *U.S. Public*, pg. 2077
ISS FACILITY SERVICES AB—See EQT AB; *Int'l*, pg. 2476
ISS FACILITY SERVICES AB—See The Goldman Sachs Group, Inc.; *U.S. Public*, pg. 2077
ISS FACILITY SERVICES A.E.—See EQT AB; *Int'l*, pg. 2476
ISS FACILITY SERVICES A.E.—See The Goldman Sachs Group, Inc.; *U.S. Public*, pg. 2077
ISS FACILITY SERVICES AG—See EQT AB; *Int'l*, pg. 2477
ISS FACILITY SERVICES AG—See The Goldman Sachs Group, Inc.; *U.S. Public*, pg. 2078
ISS FACILITY SERVICES A/S—See EQT AB; *Int'l*, pg. 2476
ISS FACILITY SERVICES A/S—See EQT AB; *Int'l*, pg. 2476
ISS FACILITY SERVICES A/S—See The Goldman Sachs Group, Inc.; *U.S. Public*, pg. 2077
ISS FACILITY SERVICES A/S—See The Goldman Sachs Group, Inc.; *U.S. Public*, pg. 2077
ISS FACILITY SERVICES AUSTRALIA LIMITED—See EQT AB; *Int'l*, pg. 2476
ISS FACILITY SERVICES AUSTRALIA LIMITED—See The Goldman Sachs Group, Inc.; *U.S. Public*, pg. 2077
ISS FACILITY SERVICES GMBH—See EQT AB; *Int'l*, pg. 2476
ISS FACILITY SERVICES GMBH—See EQT AB; *Int'l*, pg. 2476
ISS FACILITY SERVICES GMBH—See The Goldman Sachs Group, Inc.; *U.S. Public*, pg. 2077
ISS FACILITY SERVICES GMBH—See The Goldman Sachs Group, Inc.; *U.S. Public*, pg. 2077
ISS FACILITY SERVICES, INC. - AUSTIN REGIONAL OFFICE—See EQT AB; *Int'l*, pg. 2476
ISS FACILITY SERVICES, INC. - AUSTIN REGIONAL OFFICE—See The Goldman Sachs Group, Inc.; *U.S. Public*, pg. 2077
ISS FACILITY SERVICES, INC. - DALLAS REGIONAL OFFICE—See EQT AB; *Int'l*, pg. 2476
ISS FACILITY SERVICES, INC. - DALLAS REGIONAL OFFICE—See The Goldman Sachs Group, Inc.; *U.S. Public*, pg. 2077
ISS FACILITY SERVICES, INC. - GREENSBORO REGIONAL OFFICE—See EQT AB; *Int'l*, pg. 2476
ISS FACILITY SERVICES, INC. - GREENSBORO REGIONAL OFFICE—See The Goldman Sachs Group, Inc.; *U.S. Public*, pg. 2077
ISS FACILITY SERVICES, INC. - HOUSTON REGIONAL OFFICE—See EQT AB; *Int'l*, pg. 2476
ISS FACILITY SERVICES, INC. - HOUSTON REGIONAL OFFICE—See The Goldman Sachs Group, Inc.; *U.S. Public*, pg. 2077
ISS FACILITY SERVICES, INC. - KANSAS CITY REGIONAL OFFICE—See EQT AB; *Int'l*, pg. 2476
ISS FACILITY SERVICES, INC. - KANSAS CITY REGIONAL OFFICE—See The Goldman Sachs Group, Inc.; *U.S. Public*, pg. 2078
ISS FACILITY SERVICES, INC. - LAS VEGAS REGIONAL OFFICE—See EQT AB; *Int'l*, pg. 2476
ISS FACILITY SERVICES, INC. - LAS VEGAS REGIONAL OFFICE—See The Goldman Sachs Group, Inc.; *U.S. Public*, pg. 2078
ISS FACILITY SERVICES, INC. - MEMPHIS REGIONAL OFFICE—See EQT AB; *Int'l*, pg. 2476
ISS FACILITY SERVICES, INC. - MEMPHIS REGIONAL OFFICE—See The Goldman Sachs Group, Inc.; *U.S. Public*, pg. 2078
ISS FACILITY SERVICES, INC. - PHOENIX REGIONAL OFFICE—See EQT AB; *Int'l*, pg. 2476
ISS FACILITY SERVICES, INC. - PHOENIX REGIONAL OFFICE—See The Goldman Sachs Group, Inc.; *U.S. Public*, pg. 2078
ISS FACILITY SERVICES, INC. - SAN ANTONIO REGIONAL OFFICE—See EQT AB; *Int'l*, pg. 2476
ISS FACILITY SERVICES, INC. - SAN ANTONIO REGIONAL OFFICE—See The Goldman Sachs Group, Inc.; *U.S. Public*, pg. 2078
ISS FACILITY SERVICES, INC.—See EQT AB; *Int'l*, pg. 2476
ISS FACILITY SERVICES, INC.—See The Goldman Sachs Group, Inc.; *U.S. Public*, pg. 2077
ISS FACILITY SERVICES LDA—See EQT AB; *Int'l*, pg. 2476
ISS FACILITY SERVICES LDA—See The Goldman Sachs Group, Inc.; *U.S. Public*, pg. 2077
ISS FACILITY SERVICES LIMITED—See EQT AB; *Int'l*, pg. 2476
ISS FACILITY SERVICES LIMITED—See EQT AB; *Int'l*, pg. 2477

CORPORATE AFFILIATIONS

ISS FACILITY SERVICES LIMITED—See The Goldman Sachs Group, Inc.; *U.S. Public*, pg. 2077
ISS FACILITY SERVICES LIMITED—See The Goldman Sachs Group, Inc.; *U.S. Public*, pg. 2078
ISS FACILITY SERVICES LTD. - LONDON—See EQT AB; *Int'l*, pg. 2477
ISS FACILITY SERVICES LTD. - LONDON—See The Goldman Sachs Group, Inc.; *U.S. Public*, pg. 2078
ISS FACILITY SERVICES S.A.—See EQT AB; *Int'l*, pg. 2476
ISS FACILITY SERVICES S.A.—See The Goldman Sachs Group, Inc.; *U.S. Public*, pg. 2077
ISS FACILITY SERVICES—See EQT AB; *Int'l*, pg. 2476
ISS FACILITY SERVICES—See The Goldman Sachs Group, Inc.; *U.S. Public*, pg. 2078
ISS FACILITY SERVICES SPOL. S R.O.—See EQT AB; *Int'l*, pg. 2476
ISS FACILITY SERVICES SPOL. S R.O.—See The Goldman Sachs Group, Inc.; *U.S. Public*, pg. 2077
ISS FACILITY SERVICES S.R.O.—See EQT AB; *Int'l*, pg. 2476
ISS FACILITY SERVICES S.R.O.—See The Goldman Sachs Group, Inc.; *U.S. Public*, pg. 2077
ISS IRELAND LTD.—See EQT AB; *Int'l*, pg. 2476
ISS IRELAND LTD.—See The Goldman Sachs Group, Inc.; *U.S. Public*, pg. 2078
ISS ISLAND EHF.—See EQT AB; *Int'l*, pg. 2476
ISS ISLAND EHF.—See The Goldman Sachs Group, Inc.; *U.S. Public*, pg. 2078
ISS NEDERLAND B.V.—See EQT AB; *Int'l*, pg. 2476
ISS NEDERLAND B.V.—See The Goldman Sachs Group, Inc.; *U.S. Public*, pg. 2078
ISS N.V.—See EQT AB; *Int'l*, pg. 2476
ISS N.V.—See The Goldman Sachs Group, Inc.; *U.S. Public*, pg. 2078
ISS PALVELUT OY—See EQT AB; *Int'l*, pg. 2477
ISS PALVELUT OY—See The Goldman Sachs Group, Inc.; *U.S. Public*, pg. 2078
ISS SERVISYSTEM DO BRASIL LTDA.—See EQT AB; *Int'l*, pg. 2477
ISS SERVISYSTEM DO BRASIL LTDA.—See The Goldman Sachs Group, Inc.; *U.S. Public*, pg. 2078
ISS SERVISYSTEM D.O.O.—See EQT AB; *Int'l*, pg. 2477
ISS SERVISYSTEM D.O.O.—See The Goldman Sachs Group, Inc.; *U.S. Public*, pg. 2078
ISS SERVISYSTEM KFT.—See EQT AB; *Int'l*, pg. 2477
ISS SERVISYSTEM KFT.—See The Goldman Sachs Group, Inc.; *U.S. Public*, pg. 2078
ISS TMC SERVICES, INC.—See EQT AB; *Int'l*, pg. 2476
ISS TMC SERVICES, INC.—See The Goldman Sachs Group, Inc.; *U.S. Public*, pg. 2078
IST MANAGEMENT SERVICES, INC.; *U.S. Private*, pg. 2147
ITEMFIELD LIMITED—See Canada Pension Plan Investment Board; *Int'l*, pg. 1280
K2 INDUSTRIAL INC.—See The Halifax Group LLC; *U.S. Private*, pg. 4042
KELLERMEYER BERGENSONS SERVICES, LLC—See Cerberus Capital Management, L.P.; *U.S. Private*, pg. 839
KIRA, INC.—See Tlingit Haida Tribal Business Corporation; *U.S. Private*, pg. 4179
MAJOR AFFILIATES INC.; *U.S. Private*, pg. 2555
MARTIN PLANT SERVICES—See MSCO Inc.; *U.S. Private*, pg. 2806
MCKINSTRY ESSENTION, INC.—See McKinstry Co., LLC; *U.S. Private*, pg. 2639
MEY EDEN IL—See Eden International SA; *Int'l*, pg. 2307
MINER CENTRAL TEXAS—See On-Point Group, LLC; *U.S. Private*, pg. 3019
THE MINER CORPORATION—See On-Point Group, LLC; *U.S. Private*, pg. 3018
MINER DALLAS—See On-Point Group, LLC; *U.S. Private*, pg. 3019
MINER EL PASO—See On-Point Group, LLC; *U.S. Private*, pg. 3019
MINER HOUSTON—See On-Point Group, LLC; *U.S. Private*, pg. 3019
MINER SOUTHWEST, LLC—See On-Point Group, LLC; *U.S. Private*, pg. 3019
MODIGENT LLC; *U.S. Private*, pg. 2763
NAMCO OPERATIONS EUROPE LTD.—See BANDAI NAMCO Holdings Inc.; *Int'l*, pg. 829
NATIONAL DEFENSE CORP.—See National Presto Industries, Inc; *U.S. Public*, pg. 1497
NAVARRO RESEARCH & ENGINEERING, INC.; *U.S. Private*, pg. 2872
NMS—See Nana Regional Corporation, Inc.; *U.S. Private*, pg. 2832
OM OBJEKTMANAGEMENT GMBH—See Erste Group Bank AG; *Int'l*, pg. 2499
O,R&L FACILITY SERVICES—See O,R&L Construction Corp.; *U.S. Private*, pg. 2981
PAE (NEW ZEALAND) LIMITED—See Amentum Services, Inc.; *U.S. Public*, pg. 219
PAPERPLUS—See Clayton, Dubilier & Rice, LLC; *U.S. Private*, pg. 929
PARAMOUNT BUILDING SOLUTIONS, LLC—See GDI Integrated Facility Services Inc.; *Int'l*, pg. 2896

N.A.I.C.S. INDEX

561311 — EMPLOYMENT PLACEMEN...

PEARL ENERGY PHILIPPINES OPERATING, INC.—See Electricity Generating Public Co., Ltd.; *Int'l*, pg. 2352
PM SERVICES COMPANY; *U.S. Private*, pg. 3217
POWERHOUSE RETAIL SERVICES, LLC—See Lincolnshire Management, Inc.; *U.S. Private*, pg. 2459
PROLIPHIX, INC.—See Yardi Systems, Inc.; *U.S. Private*, pg. 4586
PROTERTIA FM—See Electricite de France S.A.; *Int'l*, pg. 2352
PYRAMID BUILDING MAINTENANCE CORPORATION—See TPG Capital, L.P.; *U.S. Public*, pg. 2171
PYRAMID SERVICES, INC.; *U.S. Private*, pg. 3310
R. BAKER & SON ALL INDUSTRIAL SERVICES; *U.S. Private*, pg. 3333
REGIONAL UTILITY SERVICES, INC.; *U.S. Private*, pg. 3389
REGIONS FACILITY SERVICES INC.; *U.S. Private*, pg. 3389
RESOURCE ENVIRONMENTAL SOLUTIONS, LLC—See KKR & Co. Inc.; *U.S. Public*, pg. 1263
RKB HANDYMAN SERVICES, INC.; *U.S. Private*, pg. 3450
RT FACILITY MANAGEMENT GMBH & CO. KG—See ADLER Group SA; *Int'l*, pg. 150
SAFIRA FACILITY SERVICES SA—See Derichebourg S.A.; *Int'l*, pg. 2042
SAVA, LLC—See Nana Regional Corporation, Inc.; *U.S. Private*, pg. 2832
SCHWABISCH HALL FACILITY MANAGEMENT GMBH—See DZ BANK AG Deutsche Zentral-Genossenschaftsbank; *Int'l*, pg. 2244
SEACREST SERVICES, INC.; *U.S. Private*, pg. 3584
SIEMENS GEBAUDEMANAGEMENT & -SERVICES G.M.B.H.—See EQT AB; *Int'l*, pg. 2469
SKYLARK D&M CO., LTD.—See Bain Capital, LP; *U.S. Private*, pg. 444
SNC-LAVALIN OPERATIONS & MAINTENANCE INC.—See AtkinsRealis Group Inc.; *Int'l*, pg. 673
SPECTRA VENUE MANAGEMENT—See Atairos Group, Inc.; *U.S. Private*, pg. 364
SPECTRA VENUE MANAGEMENT—See Comcast Corporation; *U.S. Public*, pg. 538
SPOTLESS FACILITY SERVICES PTY LTD—See Downer EDI Limited; *Int'l*, pg. 2185
SPOTLESS GROUP HOLDINGS LIMITED—See Downer EDI Limited; *Int'l*, pg. 2185
SSG A/S—See BWB Partners P/S; *Int'l*, pg. 1232
STV INC.—See STV Group, Inc.; *U.S. Private*, pg. 3845
SWEEPING SOUTH, INC.—See Warburg Pincus LLC; *U.S. Private*, pg. 4440
SYMAG SASU—See BNP Paribas SA; *Int'l*, pg. 1093
TEAM SOLUTIONS PROJECT GROUP, INC.; *U.S. Private*, pg. 3950
THE TENDIT GROUP, LLC—See Osceola Capital Management, LLC; *U.S. Private*, pg. 3047
TFS, LTD.—See Southfield Capital Advisors, LLC; *U.S. Private*, pg. 3736
THOMPSON INDUSTRIAL SERVICES, LLC; *U.S. Private*, pg. 4159
T&H SERVICES, LLC—See Tlingit Haida Tribal Business Corporation; *U.S. Private*, pg. 4179
TIBA PARKING LLC; *U.S. Private*, pg. 4166
TRASH BUTLER, LLC—See Republic Services, Inc.; *U.S. Public*, pg. 1787
TWASOL BUSINESS MEN SERVICE LLC—See Alpha Dhabi Holding PJSC; *Int'l*, pg. 368
UAB EDEN SPRINGS LIETUVA—See Eden International SA; *Int'l*, pg. 2307
ULTEAM SARL—See Derichebourg S.A.; *Int'l*, pg. 2042
UND SPORTS FACILITIES INC.; *U.S. Private*, pg. 4279
UNITED STATES SERVICES GROUP, LLC.; *U.S. Private*, pg. 4300
U.S. FACILITIES, INC.—See PRWT Services, Inc.; *U.S. Private*, pg. 3296
VAMED MANAGEMENT UND SERVICE GMBH & CO KG—See Fresenius SE & Co. KGaA; *Int'l*, pg. 2781
VIOX SERVICES, INC.—See EMCOR Group, Inc.; *U.S. Public*, pg. 737
VT GRIFFIN SERVICES, INC.—See Babcock International Group PLC; *Int'l*, pg. 793
WILLIAMS FOOD WORKS AND DISTRIBUTION, LLC—See Tyson Foods, Inc.; *U.S. Public*, pg. 2210
YULISTA MANAGEMENT SERVICES, INC.—See Chiulista Services, Inc.; *U.S. Private*, pg. 887

561311 — EMPLOYMENT PLACEMENT AGENCIES

20/20 FORESIGHT EXECUTIVE SEARCH LLC; *U.S. Private*, pg. 4
24 SEVEN, LLC; *U.S. Private*, pg. 6
2ND CITY RESOURCING LIMITED—See Empresaria Group Plc; *Int'l*, pg. 2388
9008 GROUP INC.; *U.S. Private*, pg. 17
ABACUS GROUP LLC; *U.S. Private*, pg. 33
ABBOTT STAFFING GROUP—See The Eastridge Group, Inc.; *U.S. Private*, pg. 4024
ABC CONTRACT SERVICES LTD.—See HFBG Holding B.V.; *Int'l*, pg. 3374
A.B. CLOSING CORPORATION; *U.S. Private*, pg. 24
ACCLAIM TECHNICAL SERVICES—See Blue Delta Capital Partners LLC; *U.S. Private*, pg. 588
ACCOLO, INC.; *U.S. Private*, pg. 53
ACCOUNTING PRINCIPALS INC.—See Adecco Group AG; *Int'l*, pg. 136
THE ACCURO GROUP, INC.; *U.S. Private*, pg. 3981
ACT 1 PERSONNEL SERVICES; *U.S. Private*, pg. 66
ACTION LABOR MANAGEMENT, LLC; *U.S. Private*, pg. 67
ADECCO EMPLOYMENT SERVICES LIMITED—See Adecco Group AG; *Int'l*, pg. 138
ADECCO FRANCE SASU—See Adecco Group AG; *Int'l*, pg. 137
ADECCO MOROCCO—See Adecco Group AG; *Int'l*, pg. 137
ADECCO PERSONALDIENSTLEISTUNGEN GMBH—See Adecco Group AG; *Int'l*, pg. 137
ADECCO PERSONEELSDIENSTEN BV—See Adecco Group AG; *Int'l*, pg. 137
ADECCO PUERTO RICO—See Adecco Group AG; *Int'l*, pg. 138
ADECCO RESURSE UMANE SRL—See Adecco Group AG; *Int'l*, pg. 138
ADECCO SWEDEN AB—See Adecco Group AG; *Int'l*, pg. 138
ADECCO SZEMELYZETI KOZVETITO KFT.—See Adecco Group AG; *Int'l*, pg. 138
ADELANTE LIVE INC.; *U.S. Private*, pg. 77
ADRIAN UPFITTING COMPANY INC.—See Adrian Steel Company Inc.; *U.S. Private*, pg. 82
ADVANCED MEDICAL PERSONNEL SERVICES, INC.—See AMN Healthcare Services, Inc.; *U.S. Public*, pg. 125
ADVANCED PERSONNEL, INC.—See Elwood Staffing Services, Inc.; *U.S. Private*, pg. 1377
ADVANCED TECHNICAL RESOURCES INC.; *U.S. Private*, pg. 93
ADVANCED TRAVEL NURSING—See AMN Healthcare Services, Inc.; *U.S. Public*, pg. 125
AD-VANCE TALENT SOLUTIONS, INC.; *U.S. Private*, pg. 72
ADVANTAGE NURSING SERVICES, INC.; *U.S. Private*, pg. 94
ADVANTAGE ON CALL, LLC—See Cross Country Healthcare, Inc.; *U.S. Public*, pg. 595
ADVANTAGE RN, LLC—See Cross Country Healthcare, Inc.; *U.S. Public*, pg. 595
ADVANTEX PROFESSIONAL SERVICES—See Kimco Staffing Services Inc.; *U.S. Private*, pg. 2305
ADVANTIS GLOBAL, INC.; *U.S. Private*, pg. 95
ADVTECH RESOURCING (PTY) LTD - COMMUNICATE PERSONNEL DIVISION—See ADvTECH Limited; *Int'l*, pg. 168
ADVTECH RESOURCING (PTY) LTD - INSOURCE.ICT DIVISION—See ADvTECH Limited; *Int'l*, pg. 168
ADVTECH RESOURCING (PTY) LTD - IT EDGE DIVISION—See ADvTECH Limited; *Int'l*, pg. 168
ADVTECH RESOURCING (PTY) LTD - NETWORK RECRUITMENT DIVISION—See ADvTECH Limited; *Int'l*, pg. 168
ADVTECH RESOURCING (PTY) LTD - PRO REC RECRUITMENT DIVISION—See ADvTECH Limited; *Int'l*, pg. 168
AJILON PROFESSIONAL STAFFING LLC—See Adecco Group AG; *Int'l*, pg. 138
AJILON TECHNOLOGY PROFESSIONALS B.V.—See Adecco Group AG; *Int'l*, pg. 140
A.J. O'NEAL & ASSOCIATES, INC.; *U.S. Private*, pg. 26
AKIMA MANAGEMENT SERVICES LLC; *U.S. Private*, pg. 145
AKRAYA, INC.; *U.S. Private*, pg. 146
ALBACORE CONSULTING GROUP PTY LTD.—See Bain Capital, LP; *U.S. Private*, pg. 433
ALIGN TECHNICAL RESOURCES, LLC; *U.S. Private*, pg. 168
ALLGEIER EXPERTS GMBH—See Allgeier SE; *Int'l*, pg. 336
ALLGEIER SECION GMBH—See Allgeier SE; *Int'l*, pg. 337
ALLIANCE SOLUTIONS GROUP; *U.S. Private*, pg. 184
ALLIANCE WORKFORCE SOLUTIONS LLC; *U.S. Private*, pg. 184
ALLIED EMPLOYER GROUP; *U.S. Private*, pg. 186
ALLIED HEALTH PROFESSIONALS LIMITED—See Ares Management Corporation; *U.S. Public*, pg. 188
ALLIED WORK FORCE CHRISTCHURCH LIMITED—See AWF Madison Group Limited; *Int'l*, pg. 753
ALLIED WORK FORCE DUNEDIN LIMITED—See AWF Madison Group Limited; *Int'l*, pg. 753
ALLIED WORK FORCE HAMILTON LIMITED—See AWF Madison Group Limited; *Int'l*, pg. 753
ALLIED WORK FORCE NELSON LIMITED—See AWF Madison Group Limited; *Int'l*, pg. 753
ALLIED WORK FORCE PALMERSTON NORTH LIMITED—See AWF Madison Group Limited; *Int'l*, pg. 753
ALLIED WORK FORCE TAURANGA LIMITED—See AWF Madison Group Limited; *Int'l*, pg. 753
ALLIED WORK FORCE WELLINGTON LIMITED—See AWF Madison Group Limited; *Int'l*, pg. 753
ALLIED WORK FORCE WHANGAREI LIMITED—See AWF Madison Group Limited; *Int'l*, pg. 753
ALL LEGAL STAFF INC.; *U.S. Private*, pg. 171
ALL TEMPS PERSONNEL SERVICE; *U.S. Private*, pg. 173
ALLUVION STAFFING, INC.—See Olympus Partners; *U.S. Private*, pg. 3013
AL-OSAIS HIRING CO.—See Al-Osais International Holding Company; *Int'l*, pg. 287
ALPS CAREER DESIGNING CORPORATION—See Altech Corporation; *Int'l*, pg. 389
ALTECH SHINE CO., LTD.—See Altech Corporation; *Int'l*, pg. 389
ALTERNATIVE SOLUTIONS, INC.; *U.S. Private*, pg. 207
AMBITION GROUP LIMITED - AMBITION TECHNOLOGY DIVISION—See Ambition Group Limited; *Int'l*, pg. 415
AMBITION GROUP LIMITED - FINANCE DIVISION—See Ambition Group Limited; *Int'l*, pg. 415
THE AMBITION GROUP LIMITED (HK)—See Ambition Group Limited; *Int'l*, pg. 415
THE AMBITION GROUP LIMITED (UK)—See Ambition Group Limited; *Int'l*, pg. 415
AMBITION GROUP SINGAPORE PTE LIMITED—See Ambition Group Limited; *Int'l*, pg. 415
AMBITION RECRUIT PTY LIMITED—See Ambition Group Limited; *Int'l*, pg. 415
AMERICAN CHECKED, LLC—See Insight Venture Management, LLC; *U.S. Private*, pg. 2088
AMERICAN CRYSTAL HOLDINGS, INC.; *U.S. Private*, pg. 229
AMERICANS FOR JOB SECURITY; *U.S. Private*, pg. 259
AMERICA WORKS OF NEW YORK INC.; *U.S. Private*, pg. 220
AMERI-FORCE CRAFT SERVICES, INC.—See Ameri-Force, Inc.; *U.S. Private*, pg. 220
AMERI-FORCE INDUSTRIAL SERVICES, INC.—See Ameri-Force, Inc.; *U.S. Private*, pg. 220
AMERI-FORCE LABOR SERVICES, INC.—See Ameri-Force, Inc.; *U.S. Private*, pg. 220
AMERI-FORCE PROFESSIONAL SERVICES, INC.—See Ameri-Force, Inc.; *U.S. Private*, pg. 220
AMICUS SEARCH GROUP LLC; *U.S. Private*, pg. 263
AMS STAFF LEASING; *U.S. Private*, pg. 267
ANDREW MACALLISTER SA; *Int'l*, pg. 451
ANGEL HUMAN RESOUCES LTD; *Int'l*, pg. 459
ANGEL STAFFING, INC.; *U.S. Private*, pg. 281
ANJANEYAP GLOBAL INC.; *U.S. Private*, pg. 284
ANU RESOURCES, INC.; *U.S. Private*, pg. 289
API HEALTHCARE CORPORATION - SAN DIEGO—See Clearlake Capital Group, L.P.; *U.S. Private*, pg. 937
API HEALTHCARE CORPORATION - SAN DIEGO—See SkyKnight Capital LLC; *U.S. Private*, pg. 3685
APPLE ONE SERVICE ARIZONA INC.; *U.S. Private*, pg. 297
APPLEONE SERVICES LTD; *Int'l*, pg. 521
AP PROFESSIONALS OF WNY LLC; *U.S. Private*, pg. 290
APR CONSULTING INC.; *U.S. Private*, pg. 300
AQUENT INC.; *U.S. Private*, pg. 303
ARAMARK INDIA PRIVATE LIMITED—See Aramark; *U.S. Public*, pg. 177
ARGYLL SCOTT HONG KONG LTD.—See Hydrogen Group Plc; *Int'l*, pg. 3547
ARGYLL SCOTT INTERNATIONAL (SINGAPORE) LTD.—See Hydrogen Group Plc; *Int'l*, pg. 3547
ARGYLL SCOTT MALAYSIA SDN BHD—See Hydrogen Group Plc; *Int'l*, pg. 3547
ARGYLL SCOTT RECRUITMENT (THAILAND) LTD.—See Hydrogen Group Plc; *Int'l*, pg. 3547
ARLINGTON RESOURCES, INC.; *U.S. Private*, pg. 329
ARTNER CO., LTD.; *Int'l*, pg. 585
ASAHI JINZAI SERVICE CO., LTD.—See Asahi Printing Co., Ltd.; *Int'l*, pg. 598
ASCENDO RESOURCES, LLC; *U.S. Private*, pg. 346
ASHLEY SERVICES GROUP LIMITED; *Int'l*, pg. 607
ASIRO INC.; *Int'l*, pg. 621
ASK STAFFING, INC.; *U.S. Private*, pg. 351
ASMARQ CO., LTD.; *Int'l*, pg. 627
ASPEN OF DC; *U.S. Private*, pg. 352
ASSET STAFFING INCORPORATED; *U.S. Private*, pg. 354
ASTYRA CORPORATION; *U.S. Private*, pg. 362
ATC HEALTHCARE, INC.; *U.S. Private*, pg. 365
ATC HEALTHCARE SERVICES, INC.—See ATC Healthcare, Inc.; *U.S. Private*, pg. 365
ATLANTIC PARTNERS CORP.; *U.S. Private*, pg. 373
ATLAST FULFILLMENT; *U.S. Private*, pg. 381
ATR INTERNATIONAL, INC.; *U.S. Private*, pg. 381
ATRIUM STAFFING SERVICES LTD.; *U.S. Private*, pg. 382
AUBAY UK LIMITED—See Aubay SA; *Int'l*, pg. 698
AUSTIN BENN LTD.—See HFBG Holding B.V.; *Int'l*, pg. 3374
AUSTIN FRASER GMBH—See Austin Fraser Limited; *Int'l*, pg. 718
AUSTIN FRASER INC—See Austin Fraser Limited; *Int'l*, pg. 718
AUSTIN FRASER LIMITED; *Int'l*, pg. 718
AUSTIN-MCGREGOR INTERNATIONAL; *U.S. Private*, pg. 396

561311 — EMPLOYMENT PLACEMEN...   CORPORATE AFFILIATIONS

AVITEA GMBH—See Hella GmbH & Co. KGaA; *Int'l*, pg. 3333
AXIOS INC.; *U.S. Private*, pg. 413
AYERS GROUP INC.—See Silver Oak Services Partners, LLC; *U.S. Private*, pg. 3661
AZTECH PROFESSIONAL SERVICES, INC.—See EGS, Inc.; *U.S. Private*, pg. 1346
B2B CFO PARTNERS, LLC; *U.S. Private*, pg. 421
B2B STAFFING SERVICES, INC.; *U.S. Private*, pg. 421
BAMBOOS HEALTH CARE HOLDINGS LIMITED; *Int'l*, pg. 813
BANNER PERSONNEL SERVICE INC.; *U.S. Private*, pg. 469
BARBARA PERSONNEL INC.; *Int'l*, pg. 858
BARCLAY MEADE LTD.—See Gattaca plc; *Int'l*, pg. 2890
BASF JOBMARKT GMBH—See BASF SE; *Int'l*, pg. 879
BAYSIDE SOLUTIONS, INC.; *U.S. Private*, pg. 497
BE ACTIVE CORP.; *U.S. Private*, pg. 503
BECOME RECRUITMENT LIMITED—See Empresaria Group Plc; *Int'l*, pg. 2388
BELFLEX STAFFING NETWORK, LLC—See Elwood Staffing Services, Inc.; *U.S. Private*, pg. 1377
BERESFORD WILSON & PARTNERS FZ-LLC—See Empresaria Group Plc; *Int'l*, pg. 2388
BEYOND.COM, INC.; *U.S. Private*, pg. 548
BG AMIA SP. Z O.O.—See Endur ASA; *Int'l*, pg. 2409
BGSF, INC.; *U.S. Public*, pg. 330
BIZMATES, INC.; *Int'l*, pg. 1053
BLUESTONE GLOBAL LIMITED; *Int'l*, pg. 1074
BMEC PTE. LTD.—See Boustead Singapore Limited; *Int'l*, pg. 1120
BOOM TALENT LIMITED—See Boomerang Plus plc; *Int'l*, pg. 1110
BOSS GROUP LTD.—See Drake New Zealand Ltd.; *Int'l*, pg. 2200
BOS STAFFING; *U.S. Private*, pg. 619
BOSTONAIR LTD; *Int'l*, pg. 1118
BRADDOCKMATTHEWSBARRETT, LLC; *U.S. Private*, pg. 631
BRADSBY GROUP; *U.S. Private*, pg. 633
BRIAN CORK HUMAN CAPITAL; *U.S. Private*, pg. 647
BRIDGE TECHNICAL SOLUTIONS; *U.S. Private*, pg. 649
BROOK STREET (UK) LIMITED—See ManpowerGroup Inc.; *U.S. Public*, pg. 1359
BRUNEL CANADA LTD—See Brunel International N.V.; *Int'l*, pg. 1199
BRUNEL ENERGY CANADA INC—See Brunel International N.V.; *Int'l*, pg. 1199
BRUNEL ENERGY INC.—See Brunel International N.V.; *Int'l*, pg. 1199
BRUNEL INTERNATIONAL N.V.; *Int'l*, pg. 1199
BRUNEL INTERNATIONAL UK LTD—See Brunel International N.V.; *Int'l*, pg. 1200
BRUNEL NEDERLAND BV—See Brunel International N.V.; *Int'l*, pg. 1200
BTI CONSULTANTS PTE. LTD.—See Kelly Services, Inc.; *U.S. Public*, pg. 1218
BTI EXECUTIVE PLACEMENT (THAILAND) CO.—See Kelly Services, Inc.; *U.S. Public*, pg. 1219
BUFFALO AND ERIE COUNTY WORKFORCE DEVELOPMENT CONSORTIUM, INC.; *U.S. Private*, pg. 680
THE BURNETT COMPANIES CONSOLIDATED INC.; *U.S. Private*, pg. 4003
BUTLER AMERICA, INC.; *U.S. Private*, pg. 696
C&A INDUSTRIES INC.—See TPG Capital, L.P.; *U.S. Public*, pg. 2176
CALVIN GROUP; *U.S. Private*, pg. 724
CAMERON SEARCH & STAFFING LLC; *U.S. Private*, pg. 729
CANCOM NSG GIS GMBH—See CANCOM SE; *Int'l*, pg. 1288
CANDLE IT & T RECRUITMENT LIMITED—See Ignite Limited; *Int'l*, pg. 3602
CANDLE IT & T RECRUITMENT PTY LIMITED—See Ignite Limited; *Int'l*, pg. 3602
CANON RECRUITING GROUP LLC; *U.S. Private*, pg. 735
CAPITAL TECHSEARCH, INC.; *U.S. Private*, pg. 742
THE CAPSTONE GROUP RECRUITMENT AND CONSULTING (THAILAND) LTD.—See en-japan Inc.; *Int'l*, pg. 2395
CARBON60 LIMITED—See HFBG Holding B.V.; *Int'l*, pg. 3374
CARDINAL SERVICES INC.—See Owner Resource Group, LLC; *U.S. Private*, pg. 3055
CAREER AGENT CO., LTD.—See Bain Capital, LP; *U.S. Private*, pg. 433
CAREER CONCEPTS STAFFING SERVICES, INC.; *U.S. Private*, pg. 752
CAREERINDEX, INC.; *Int'l*, pg. 1323
CAREERLINK CO., LTD.; *Int'l*, pg. 1324
CAREERLINK, INC.; *U.S. Private*, pg. 752
CAREERMAG.COM—See Jameson Publishing Inc.; *U.S. Private*, pg. 2185
CAREER RESOURCES, INC.—See Adecco Group AG; *Int'l*, pg. 138
CAREERSOURCE BREVARD; *U.S. Private*, pg. 752
CAREERSUSA, INC.; *U.S. Private*, pg. 752
CAREER TIMES ONLINE LIMITED—See Hong Kong Economic Times Holdings Ltd; *Int'l*, pg. 3465
CAREERXCHANGE, INC.; *U.S. Private*, pg. 753
CAREERXCHANGE, INC.—See Careerxchange, Inc.; *U.S. Private*, pg. 753
CARLISLE CLEANING SERVICES LTD.—See HFBG Holding B.V.; *Int'l*, pg. 3374
CARLISLE STAFFING PLC—See HFBG Holding B.V.; *Int'l*, pg. 3374
THE CARNEY GROUP; *U.S. Private*, pg. 4005
CARNIVAL SUPPORT SERVICES INDIA PRIVATE LIMITED—See Carnival Corporation; *U.S. Public*, pg. 438
CASCADE HEALTH SERVICES; *U.S. Private*, pg. 779
CASSEL & COMPANY—See ADvTECH Limited; *Int'l*, pg. 168
CATALINA CONSULTANTS PTY. LTD.—See Azimut Holding SpA; *Int'l*, pg. 779
CBASE CORPORATION—See en-japan Inc.; *Int'l*, pg. 2395
CBS BUTLER LIMITED—See Staffing 360 Solutions, Inc.; *U.S. Public*, pg. 1925
CEJKA SEARCH, INC.—See Cross Country Healthcare, Inc.; *U.S. Public*, pg. 595
CENTER FOR EMPLOYMENT OPPORTUNITIES INC; *U.S. Private*, pg. 810
CENTER FOR TALENT REPORTING, INC—See ROI Institute, Inc.; *U.S. Private*, pg. 3473
CENTERLINE DRIVERS, LLC—See TrueBlue, Inc.; *U.S. Public*, pg. 2198
CFO SELECTIONS, LLC; *U.S. Private*, pg. 844
CHADWICK NOTT—See HFBG Holding B.V.; *Int'l*, pg. 3374
CHALLENGER, GRAY & CHRISTMAS, INC.; *U.S. Private*, pg. 845
CHAMELEON TECHNOLOGIES, INC.; *U.S. Private*, pg. 846
CHESAPEAKE MEDICAL STAFFING, LLC—See Great Point Partners, LLC; *U.S. Private*, pg. 1767
CHG HEALTHCARE SERVICES, INC.—See Ares Management Corporation; *U.S. Public*, pg. 188
CHG HEALTHCARE SERVICES, INC.—See Leonard Green & Partners, L.P.; *U.S. Private*, pg. 2425
CHG MANAGEMENT, INC.—See Ares Management Corporation; *U.S. Public*, pg. 188
CHG MANAGEMENT, INC.—See Leonard Green & Partners, L.P.; *U.S. Private*, pg. 2425
CHG MEDICAL STAFFING, INC.—See Ares Management Corporation; *U.S. Public*, pg. 188
CHG MEDICAL STAFFING, INC.—See Leonard Green & Partners, L.P.; *U.S. Private*, pg. 2425
CHRC LLC—See Pebblebrook Hotel Trust; *U.S. Public*, pg. 1660
CINE MAGNETICS VIDEO & DIGITAL LABORATORIES—See Cine Magnetics, Inc.; *U.S. Private*, pg. 898
CIRRUS CONCEPT CONSULTING, INC.—See Littlejohn & Co., LLC; *U.S. Private*, pg. 2470
CIRRUS MEDICAL STAFFING, INC.—See Webster Equity Partners, LLC; *U.S. Private*, pg. 4467
CITADEL FEDERAL SOLUTIONS LLC; *U.S. Private*, pg. 901
CITITEC ASSOCIATES LIMITED; *Int'l*, pg. 1623
CLARITY RESOURCE GROUP; *U.S. Private*, pg. 912
CLEARBRIDGE TECHNOLOGY GROUP; *U.S. Private*, pg. 932
CLEMENT MAY LIMITED—See Staffing 360 Solutions, Inc.; *U.S. Public*, pg. 1925
CLIMBER.COM—See Mingle, LLC; *U.S. Private*, pg. 2742
CLUB STAFFING—See AMN Healthcare Services, Inc.; *U.S. Public*, pg. 125
CONE FINANCIAL GROUP INC.; *U.S. Private*, pg. 1012
CONNEXION SYSTEMS & ENGINEERING, INC.; *U.S. Private*, pg. 1018
CONSOL PARTNERS LLC—See Empresaria Group Plc; *Int'l*, pg. 2388
CONSULTING FOR ARCHITECTS INC.; *U.S. Private*, pg. 1025
CONTRACTED LABOR SERVICES INC.; *U.S. Private*, pg. 1032
CORE MEDICAL GROUP; *U.S. Private*, pg. 1049
CORESTAFF SUPPORT SERVICES, INC.—See HFBG Holding B.V.; *Int'l*, pg. 3374
CORNERSTONE RPO, LLC; *U.S. Private*, pg. 1052
CORPORATE SERVICES INC.; *U.S. Private*, pg. 1056
COUPON EXPRESS, INC.; *U.S. Private*, pg. 1068
COWORX STAFFING SERVICES LLC; *U.S. Private*, pg. 1074
THE CPI GROUP, INC.; *U.S. Private*, pg. 4015
CPL JOBS TUNISIE SARL—See Bain Capital, LP; *U.S. Private*, pg. 433
CPL RESOURCES LIMITED—See Bain Capital, LP; *U.S. Private*, pg. 433
CPL RESOURCES PLC—See Bain Capital, LP; *U.S. Private*, pg. 433
CPL SOLUTIONS LIMITED—See Bain Capital, LP; *U.S. Private*, pg. 433
CRESCENT SOLUTIONS; *U.S. Private*, pg. 1094
CRIT MAROC—See Groupe Crit, S.A.; *Int'l*, pg. 3101
CRIT TUNISIE—See Groupe Crit, S.A.; *Int'l*, pg. 3101
CROSS COUNTRY STAFFING, INC.—See Cross Country Healthcare, Inc.; *U.S. Public*, pg. 595
CSG RESOURCINGS PROPRIETARY LIMITED—See CSG Holdings Limited; *Int'l*, pg. 1864
CSRA PROBATION SERVICES, INC.; *U.S. Private*, pg. 1117
CURAMED STAFFING, LLC; *U.S. Private*, pg. 1124
CYBERSECURITY SERVICE LLC—See System1, Inc.; *U.S. Public*, pg. 1977
DAISHI HOKUETSU CAREER BRIDGE, CO., LTD.—See Daishi Hokuetsu Financial Group, Inc.; *Int'l*, pg. 1941
DAL GLOBAL SERVICES—See Delta Air Lines, Inc.; *U.S. Public*, pg. 651
DAL ZEITARBEIT GMBH—See Derichebourg S.A.; *Int'l*, pg. 2041
DANA'S HOUSEKEEPING PERSONNEL SERVICES; *U.S. Private*, pg. 1152
DANIEL & YEAGER, LLC—See Blackstone Inc.; *U.S. Public*, pg. 359
DATROSE; *U.S. Private*, pg. 1167
DAVIS COMPANIES—See The Davis Companies Inc.; *U.S. Private*, pg. 4018
DAVIS COMPANIES—See The Davis Companies Inc.; *U.S. Private*, pg. 4018
DAV PROFESSIONAL PLACEMENT GROUP (PTY) LIMITED—See Adcorp Holdings Limited; *Int'l*, pg. 127
DAWSON RESOURCES, INC.; *U.S. Private*, pg. 1176
DEANNA ENTERPRISES INC.; *U.S. Private*, pg. 1185
DEAN'S PROFESSIONAL SERVICES, INC.; *U.S. Private*, pg. 1184
DE CAPUA ENTERPRISES INC.; *U.S. Private*, pg. 1181
DEDICARE AB; *Int'l*, pg. 2002
DEDICARE AS—See Dedicare AB; *Int'l*, pg. 2002
DEKRA ARBEIT AG—See DEKRA e.V.; *Int'l*, pg. 2006
DEKRA ARBEIT GMBH—See DEKRA e.V.; *Int'l*, pg. 2008
DEKRA ARBEIT (SCHWEIZ) HOLDING AG—See DEKRA e.V.; *Int'l*, pg. 2006
DEKRA ARBEIT (SCHWEIZ) VERWALTUNGS AG—See DEKRA e.V.; *Int'l*, pg. 2006
DEKRA JOB APS—See DEKRA e.V.; *Int'l*, pg. 2006
DELFONT MACKINTOSH THEATRES LIMITED; *Int'l*, pg. 2013
THE DELTA COMPANIES; *U.S. Private*, pg. 4019
DELTAFORCE PERSONNEL SERVICES, INC.—See The Supporting Cast, Inc.; *U.S. Private*, pg. 4125
DES COMPANIES; *U.S. Private*, pg. 1210
DESERT PERSONNEL SERVICES—See AtWorkGroup LLC; *U.S. Private*, pg. 384
DICE CAREERS GMBH—See DHI Group, Inc.; *U.S. Public*, pg. 657
DICE CAREERS LIMITED—See DHI Group, Inc.; *U.S. Public*, pg. 658
DICE CAREER SOLUTIONS, INC.—See DHI Group, Inc.; *U.S. Public*, pg. 658
DIRECTEMPLOYERS ASSOCIATION, INC.; *U.S. Private*, pg. 1236
DIVERSIFIED MEDICAL STAFFING, LLC; *U.S. Private*, pg. 1243
DLH HOLDINGS CORP.; *U.S. Public*, pg. 670
DLSI SA; *Int'l*, pg. 2142
DOMARI & ASSOCIATES, INC.; *U.S. Private*, pg. 1255
DRAKE AUSTRALIA PTY LTD—See Drake New Zealand Ltd.; *Int'l*, pg. 2200
DRAKE NEW ZEALAND LTD.; *Int'l*, pg. 2200
DRAKKAR & ASSOCIES INC.; *Int'l*, pg. 2200
DRAKKAR MAK INC.—See Drakkar & Associes Inc.; *Int'l*, pg. 2200
E2 RECRUITING, INC.; *U.S. Private*, pg. 1308
E4E BUSINESS SOLUTIONS INDIA PRIVATE LIMITED—See e4e Inc.; *U.S. Private*, pg. 1308
EAGLE PROFESSIONAL RESOURCES INC.—See Cornell Capital LLC; *U.S. Private*, pg. 1051
EARLYPAY LTD.; *Int'l*, pg. 2267
EASTERN KENTUCKY CONCENTRATED EMPLOYMENT PROGRAM, INC.; *U.S. Private*, pg. 1320
THE EASTRIDGE GROUP, INC.; *U.S. Private*, pg. 4024
EASTRIDGE PERSONNEL OF LAS VEGAS—See The Eastridge Group, Inc.; *U.S. Private*, pg. 4024
EC SOLUTIONS INC.—See Alan Allman Associates SA; *Int'l*, pg. 290
EFINANCIALCAREERS GMBH—See DHI Group, Inc.; *U.S. Public*, pg. 658
EGS, INC.; *U.S. Private*, pg. 1346
EHD TECHNOLOGIES, LLC—See Groupe Crit, S.A.; *Int'l*, pg. 3101
EIT PROFESSIONALS CORP.; *U.S. Private*, pg. 1348
ELIASSEN GROUP, LLC—See Stone Point Capital LLC; *U.S. Private*, pg. 3823
ELIGO S.P.A.; *Int'l*, pg. 2361
ELWOOD STAFFING SERVICES, INC.; *U.S. Private*, pg. 1377
EMAGINE GMBH—See emagine GmbH; *Int'l*, pg. 2373
EMERALD HEALTH SERVICES; *U.S. Private*, pg. 1379
EMERGENCY COVERAGE CORPORATION—See Blackstone Inc.; *U.S. Public*, pg. 359
EMERGENETICS INTERNATIONAL-ASIA (EGI-A)—See Emergenetics, LLC; *U.S. Private*, pg. 1381
EMERGENETICS INTERNATIONAL—See Emergenetics, LLC; *U.S. Private*, pg. 1381

N.A.I.C.S. INDEX

561311 — EMPLOYMENT PLACEMEN...

EMERGENETICS, LLC; *U.S. Private*, pg. 1380
EMPLOYEE SOLUTIONS; *U.S. Private*, pg. 1386
EMPLOYEES ONLY; *U.S. Private*, pg. 1386
EMPLOYER FLEXIBLE—See Employer Flexible Management, LLC; *U.S. Private*, pg. 1386
EMPLOYER FLEXIBLE—See Employer Flexible Management, LLC; *U.S. Private*, pg. 1386
EMPLOYMENT GROUP INC.—See Employment Group Holding Corp.; *U.S. Private*, pg. 1387
EMPLOYMENT SOLUTIONS; *U.S. Private*, pg. 1387
EMPLOYUS, LLC—See The Staffing Group Ltd.; *U.S. Private*, pg. 4120
EMPRESARIA LIMITED—See Empresaria Group Plc; *Int'l*, pg. 2388
ENCADRIA STAFFING SOLUTIONS, INC.—See Koch Industries, Inc.; *U.S. Private*, pg. 2327
ENGLISH LANGUAGE INSTITUTE/CHINA; *U.S. Private*, pg. 1400
ENSCICON CORPORATION; *U.S. Private*, pg. 1401
ENSURE RECRUITMENT PTY LIMITED; *Int'l*, pg. 2449
ENTEGEE INC.—See Adecco Group AG; *Int'l*, pg. 141
ENTERTAINMENT PARTNERS GROUP INC; *U.S. Private*, pg. 1404
EN WORLD HONG-KONG LIMITED.—See en-japan Inc.; *Int'l*, pg. 2395
EN WORLD JAPAN K.K.—See en-japan Inc.; *Int'l*, pg. 2395
EN WORLD KOREA CO., LTD—See en-japan Inc.; *Int'l*, pg. 2395
EP-FORCE CO., LTD.—See EPS Holdings, Inc.; *Int'l*, pg. 2465
EPIC HEALTH SERVICES, INC.—See Bain Capital, LP; *U.S. Private*, pg. 439
ESSENTIAL PERSONNEL, INC.; *U.S. Private*, pg. 1427
ETTAIN GROUP INC.—See ManpowerGroup Inc.; *U.S. Public*, pg. 1362
EUROTUNNEL SERVICES LIMITED—See Getlink SE; *Int'l*, pg. 2953
EVERSTAFF; *U.S. Private*, pg. 1440
EVINS PERSONNEL CONSULTANTS, INC.; *U.S. Private*, pg. 1442
EWORK HEALTHCARE—See Workway, Inc.; *U.S. Private*, pg. 4564
EXACT STAFF, INC.; *U.S. Private*, pg. 1445
EXCEL SEARCH GROUP, LLC—See Profectus, LLC; *U.S. Private*, pg. 3274
EXPERIS MANPOWERGROUP, S.L.—See ManpowerGroup Inc.; *U.S. Public*, pg. 1358
EXPRESS EMPLOYMENT PROFESSIONALS; *U.S. Private*, pg. 1451
FACILITY ASSOCIATES RECRUITMENT LIMITED—See Jones Lang LaSalle Incorporated; *U.S. Public*, pg. 1201
FASTAFF—See Clarion Capital Partners, LLC; *U.S. Private*, pg. 911
FEDCAP REHABILITATION SERVICES, INC.; *U.S. Private*, pg. 1486
FEDERAL PRISON INDUSTRIES INC.; *U.S. Private*, pg. 1489
FEDERAL STAFFING RESOURCES, LLC; *U.S. Private*, pg. 1491
FERRERI SEARCH LLC; *U.S. Private*, pg. 1498
FGP INTERNATIONAL; *U.S. Private*, pg. 1501
FILTER LLC—See 24 Seven, LLC; *U.S. Private*, pg. 6
FIRCROFT AUSTRALIA PTY LTD—See AEA Investors LP; *U.S. Private*, pg. 115
FIRCROFT CANADA INC—See AEA Investors LP; *U.S. Private*, pg. 115
FIRCROFT ENGINEERING SERVICES LTD.—See AEA Investors LP; *U.S. Private*, pg. 114
FIRCROFT INC—See AEA Investors LP; *U.S. Private*, pg. 115
FIRCROFT NORGE AS—See AEA Investors LP; *U.S. Private*, pg. 115
FIRCROFT PTE LTD—See AEA Investors LP; *U.S. Private*, pg. 115
FIRCROFT QATAR LLC—See AEA Investors LP; *U.S. Private*, pg. 115
FIRCROFT RUSSIA, LLC.—See AEA Investors LP; *U.S. Private*, pg. 115
FIRCROFT THAILAND LIMITED—See AEA Investors LP; *U.S. Private*, pg. 115
FIRCROFT (VIETNAM) COMPANY LTD—See AEA Investors LP; *U.S. Private*, pg. 115
FIRST ASSIST INC; *U.S. Private*, pg. 1513
FIRST COAST WORKFORCE DEVELOPMENT, INC.; *U.S. Private*, pg. 1516
FIRST RATE STAFFING CORPORATION; *U.S. Private*, pg. 1524
FITTIO INC.—See Cross Marketing Group Inc.; *Int'l*, pg. 1856
FOCUS FORWARD LLC; *U.S. Private*, pg. 1556
FOCUS SEARCH PARTNERS LLC—See Olympus Partners; *U.S. Private*, pg. 3014
FORTE GROUP INC—See The Point Group; *U.S. Private*, pg. 4097
FORTUS GROUP INC.; *U.S. Private*, pg. 1577
FORUM ENGINEERING, INC.; *Int'l*, pg. 2744
FORUM PERSONNEL INC.; *U.S. Private*, pg. 1577
THE FOUNTAIN GROUP, LLC; *U.S. Private*, pg. 4030

FREELANCER LTD.; *Int'l*, pg. 2770
FREEMARKET (SWITZERLAND) GMBH—See Freelancer Ltd.; *Int'l*, pg. 2770
FRONTLINE RECRUITMENT (PTY), LTD.—See Adcorp Holdings Limited; *Int'l*, pg. 127
FSO OUTSOURCING—See FSO Onsite Outsourcing; *U.S. Private*, pg. 1618
FSO OUTSOURCING—See FSO Onsite Outsourcing; *U.S. Private*, pg. 1618
FSS STAFFING SOLUTIONS—See FSO Onsite Outsourcing; *U.S. Private*, pg. 1618
FST CANADA INC.—See Federal Signal Corporation; *U.S. Public*, pg. 826
FUEL TALENT, LLC; *U.S. Private*, pg. 1619
FUN TO FUN INC.—See Hirayama Holdings Co., Ltd.; *Int'l*, pg. 3404
FUTURE FORCE PERSONNEL SERVICES; *U.S. Private*, pg. 1627
GALAXY SOFTWARE SOLUTIONS INC.; *U.S. Private*, pg. 1636
GARICH INC.; *U.S. Private*, pg. 1644
GARY D. NELSON ASSOCIATES, INC.; *U.S. Private*, pg. 1646
GATTACA PLC; *Int'l*, pg. 2890
GATTACA PROJECTS LIMITED—See Gattaca plc; *Int'l*, pg. 2890
GATTACA SOLUTIONS LIMITED—See Gattaca plc; *Int'l*, pg. 2890
GENERAL LABOR STAFFING SERVICES INC; *U.S. Private*, pg. 1665
GEOMETRIC RESULTS, INC.—See Bain Capital, LP; *U.S. Private*, pg. 441
GLOBAL EMPLOYMENT SOLUTIONS, INC.—See ManpowerGroup Inc.; *U.S. Public*, pg. 1362
GLOBAL IT, INC.—See Brightcom Group Ltd.; *Int'l*, pg. 1162
GMO CARD SYSTEM, INC.—See GMO Internet Group, Inc.; *Int'l*, pg. 3013
GOODWILL INDUSTRIES OF THE VALLEYS, INC.—See Goodwill Industries International, Inc.; *U.S. Private*, pg. 1740
GOODWILL KEYSTONE AREA, INC.—See Goodwill Industries International, Inc.; *U.S. Private*, pg. 1740
GRATWICK ENTERPRISES INC.; *U.S. Private*, pg. 1758
GREENE RESOURCES, INC.; *U.S. Private*, pg. 1777
GREYCOAT LUMLEYS LTD.—See Empresaria Group Plc; *Int'l*, pg. 2389
GREYTHORN, INC.—See Olympus Partners; *U.S. Private*, pg. 3014
GRUPA PRACUJ S.A.; *Int'l*, pg. 3117
GT HIRING SOLUTIONS (2005) INC.—See MAXIMUS, Inc.; *U.S. Public*, pg. 1402
GTN TECHNICAL STAFFING; *U.S. Private*, pg. 1807
GULF ASIA INTERNATIONAL CORPORATION—See EEI Corporation; *Int'l*, pg. 2317
GUNTHER DOUGLAS, INC.; *U.S. Private*, pg. 1818
HAITI ENTREPRENEURIAL INITIATIVE; *U.S. Private*, pg. 1841
HAMILTON-RYKER COMPANY; *U.S. Private*, pg. 1848
HARBINGER PARTNERS, INC.; *U.S. Private*, pg. 1858
HARRIS VENTURES, INC.; *U.S. Private*, pg. 1870
HARVARD STUDENT AGENCIES, INC.; *U.S. Private*, pg. 1875
HARVEY NASH AG—See DBAY Advisors Limited; *Int'l*, pg. 1987
HARVEY NASH BV—See DBAY Advisors Limited; *Int'l*, pg. 1987
HARVEY NASH INC—See DBAY Advisors Limited; *Int'l*, pg. 1987
HARVEY NASH IT CONSULTING NV—See DBAY Advisors Limited; *Int'l*, pg. 1987
HARVEY NASH LIMITED—See DBAY Advisors Limited; *Int'l*, pg. 1987
HARVEY NASH (VIETNAM) LTD—See DBAY Advisors Limited; *Int'l*, pg. 1987
HAYS AG—See Hays PLC; *Int'l*, pg. 3293
HAYS BUSINESS SOLUTIONS PRIVATE LIMITED—See Hays PLC; *Int'l*, pg. 3293
HAYS COLOMBIA SAS—See Hays PLC; *Int'l*, pg. 3293
HAYS CZECH REPUBLIC, S.R.O.—See Hays PLC; *Int'l*, pg. 3293
HAYS HOLDING GMBH—See Hays PLC; *Int'l*, pg. 3293
HAYS OSTERREICH GMBH—See Hays PLC; *Int'l*, pg. 3293
HAYS PROFESSIONAL SOLUTIONS OSTERREICH GMBH—See Hays PLC; *Int'l*, pg. 3293
HAYS SASU—See Hays PLC; *Int'l*, pg. 3293
HAYS (SCHWEIZ) AG—See Hays PLC; *Int'l*, pg. 3293
HAYS SLOVAKIA S.R.O.—See Hays PLC; *Int'l*, pg. 3293
HAYS SOLUTIONS S.R.L—See Hays PLC; *Int'l*, pg. 3293
HAYS SPECIALIST RECRUITMENT (AUSTRALIA) PTY LIMITED—See Hays PLC; *Int'l*, pg. 3293
HAYS SPECIALIST RECRUITMENT BELGIUM—See Hays PLC; *Int'l*, pg. 3294
HAYS SPECIALIST RECRUITMENT BRAZIL—See Hays PLC; *Int'l*, pg. 3294
HAYS SPECIALIST RECRUITMENT CANADA—See Hays PLC; *Int'l*, pg. 3294
HAYS SPECIALIST RECRUITMENT DENMARK—See Hays PLC; *Int'l*, pg. 3294

HAYS SPECIALIST RECRUITMENT DUBAI UAE—See Hays PLC; *Int'l*, pg. 3294
HAYS SPECIALIST RECRUITMENT FRANCE—See Hays PLC; *Int'l*, pg. 3294
HAYS SPECIALIST RECRUITMENT HONG KONG—See Hays PLC; *Int'l*, pg. 3294
HAYS SPECIALIST RECRUITMENT HUNGARY—See Hays PLC; *Int'l*, pg. 3294
HAYS SPECIALIST RECRUITMENT IRELAND—See Hays PLC; *Int'l*, pg. 3294
HAYS SPECIALIST RECRUITMENT ITALY—See Hays PLC; *Int'l*, pg. 3294
HAYS SPECIALIST RECRUITMENT JAPAN KK—See Hays PLC; *Int'l*, pg. 3294
HAYS SPECIALIST RECRUITMENT LUXEMBOURG—See Hays PLC; *Int'l*, pg. 3294
HAYS SPECIALIST RECRUITMENT NETHERLANDS—See Hays PLC; *Int'l*, pg. 3294
HAYS SPECIALIST RECRUITMENT NEW ZEALAND—See Hays PLC; *Int'l*, pg. 3294
HAYS SPECIALIST RECRUITMENT PORTUGAL—See Hays PLC; *Int'l*, pg. 3294
HAYS SPECIALIST RECRUITMENT PTE LIMITED—See Hays PLC; *Int'l*, pg. 3294
HAYS SPECIALIST RECRUITMENT SPAIN—See Hays PLC; *Int'l*, pg. 3294
HAYS SPECIALIST RECRUITMENT SWEDEN—See Hays PLC; *Int'l*, pg. 3294
HAYS SPECIALIST RECRUITMENT WARSAW—See Hays PLC; *Int'l*, pg. 3294
HAYS (SWITZERLAND) LTD.—See Hays PLC; *Int'l*, pg. 3293
HAYS TALENT SOLUTIONS ESPANA S.L.—See Hays PLC; *Int'l*, pg. 3294
HAYS TECHNOLOGY SOLUTIONS GMBH—See Hays PLC; *Int'l*, pg. 3294
HAYS TECHNOLOGY SOLUTIONS ROMANIA S.R.L.—See Hays PLC; *Int'l*, pg. 3294
HAYS TRAVAIL TEMPORAIRE LUXEMBOURG S.A.R.L.—See Hays PLC; *Int'l*, pg. 3294
HCL BBL MEDICAL LIMITED—See Ares Management Corporation; *U.S. Public*, pg. 188
HCL GPS LIMITED—See Ares Management Corporation; *U.S. Public*, pg. 188
HCL HEALTHCARE LIMITED—See Ares Management Corporation; *U.S. Public*, pg. 188
HCL THAMES MEDICS LIMITED—See Ares Management Corporation; *U.S. Public*, pg. 188
HEADHUNTER GROUP PLC; *Int'l*, pg. 3301
THE HEADHUNTERS RECRUITMENT, INC.—See Hire Technologies, Inc.; *Int'l*, pg. 3404
HEADWAY CORPORATE STAFFING SERVICES OF NORTH CAROLINA INC.—See Headway Corporate Resources Inc.; *U.S. Private*, pg. 1891
HEADWAY HOLDING GMBH—See Empresaria Group Plc; *Int'l*, pg. 2389
HEALTH ADVOCATES NETWORK, INC.; *U.S. Private*, pg. 1892
HEALTHCARE SUPPORT STAFFING, INC.; *U.S. Private*, pg. 1895
HEALTH CAROUSEL, LLC; *U.S. Private*, pg. 1892
HEALTHTRUST WORKFORCE SOLUTIONS, LLC—See HCA Healthcare, Inc.; *U.S. Public*, pg. 998
HEIDRICK & STRUGGLES, INC.—See Heidrick & Struggles International, Inc.; *U.S. Public*, pg. 1023
HEIWA IRONWORKS CO., LTD.—See Hirayama Holdings Co., Ltd.; *Int'l*, pg. 3404
HIGH FINANCE LTD.; *Int'l*, pg. 3385
HIM CONNECTIONS, LLC; *U.S. Private*, pg. 1948
HIRAYAMA GLOBAL SUPPORTER CO., LTD.—See Hirayama Holdings Co., Ltd.; *Int'l*, pg. 3404
HIRAYAMA HOLDINGS CO., LTD.; *Int'l*, pg. 3404
HIRAYAMA VIETNAM COMPANY LIMITED—See Hirayama Holdings Co., Ltd.; *Int'l*, pg. 3404
HIRED HANDS, INC.; *U.S. Private*, pg. 1950
HIREGY, INC.; *U.S. Private*, pg. 1950
HIREMII LIMITED; *Int'l*, pg. 3404
HIRE POWER, INC.; *U.S. Private*, pg. 1950
HIRESYNERGY, INC.—See Odyssey Investment Partners, LLC; *U.S. Private*, pg. 2994
HIREVERGENCE LLC—See My Job Matcher, Inc.; *U.S. Private*, pg. 2823
HOWROYD-WRIGHT EMPLOYMENT AGENCY INC.; *U.S. Private*, pg. 1996
HP RESOURCES INC.; *U.S. Private*, pg. 1996
HR FORCE, INC.—See Funai Soken Holdings Incorporated; *Int'l*, pg. 2845
HR MAX—See Legacy Partners Inc.; *U.S. Private*, pg. 2416
HUDSON BELGIUM SA/NV; *Int'l*, pg. 3522
HUDSON GLOBAL RESOURCES (AUSTRALIA) PTY LIMITED—See Hudson Highland (APAC) Pty. Limited; *Int'l*, pg. 3522
HUDSON GLOBAL RESOURCES HONG KONG LTD.—See Hudson Highland (APAC) Pty. Limited; *Int'l*, pg. 3522
HUDSON GLOBAL RESOURCES MANAGEMENT, INC.—See Hudson Global, Inc; *U.S. Public*, pg. 1068
HUDSON GLOBAL RESOURCES (NZ) LTD.—See Hudson Highland (APAC) Pty. Limited; *Int'l*, pg. 3522

561311 — EMPLOYMENT PLACEMEN...

HUDSON LUXEMBOURG S.A.—See Hudson Belgium SA/NV; *Int'l*, pg. 3522
HUDSON RECRUITMENT SHANGHAI LIMITED—See Hudson Highland (APAC) Pty. Limited; *Int'l*, pg. 3522
HUMAN GLOBAL TALENT CO., LTD.—See Human Holdings Co., Ltd.; *Int'l*, pg. 3529
HUMAN INTERNATIONAL CO., LTD.—See Human Holdings Co., Ltd.; *Int'l*, pg. 3529
HUMAN (SHANGHAI) COMMERCE CONSULTANTS CO., LTD.—See Human Holdings Co., Ltd.; *Int'l*, pg. 3529
HUMCAP LP; *U.S. Private*, pg. 2007
HUNTER WEST LEGAL RECRUITMENT LTD.; *Int'l*, pg. 3536
HYDROGEN GROUP PTY. LIMITED—See Hydrogen Group Plc; *Int'l*, pg. 3547
HYDROGEN GROUP SDN. BHD.—See Hydrogen Group Plc; *Int'l*, pg. 3547
HYDROGEN INTERNATIONAL LIMITED—See Hydrogen Group Plc; *Int'l*, pg. 3547
HYDROGEN UK LIMITED—See Hydrogen Group Plc; *Int'l*, pg. 3547
HY-PHEN.COM LIMITED—See Adecco Group AG; *Int'l*, pg. 138
ICON MEDICAL NETWORK LLC; *U.S. Private*, pg. 2032
IDC TECHNOLOGIES, INC.; *U.S. Private*, pg. 2035
IGNITE LIMITED; *Int'l*, pg. 3602
IINO MARINE SERVICE CO., LTD.—See Iino Kaiun Kaisha Ltd.; *Int'l*, pg. 3608
IMPACT BUSINESS GROUP INC.; *U.S. Private*, pg. 2048
IMPACT EXECUTIVES LTD—See DBAY Advisors Limited; *Int'l*, pg. 1987
IMPACT STAFFING SOLUTIONS—See Impact Logistics, Inc.; *U.S. Private*, pg. 2048
INCENDIA PARTNERS, INC.; *U.S. Private*, pg. 2053
INCEPTURE INC.—See GuideWell Mutual Holding Corporation; *U.S. Private*, pg. 1814
INDEPENDENCE ANESTHESIA SERVICES—See ICON Medical Network LLC; *U.S. Private*, pg. 2032
INDEX ROOT CO., LTD.—See MAXIMUS, Inc.; *U.S. Public*, pg. 1402
INFINITY CONSULTING SOLUTIONS, INC.—See Korn Ferry; *U.S. Public*, pg. 1272
INFO CUBIC LLC—See Boathouse Capital Management, LLC; *U.S. Private*, pg. 603
INFOCUS PARTNERS, INC.; *U.S. Private*, pg. 2072
INFORMATION TECHNOLOGY ENGINEERING CORP.—See Global Employment Holdings, Inc.; *U.S. Private*, pg. 1713
INNSTAFF (PTY) LTD—See Adcorp Holdings Limited; *Int'l*, pg. 127
INSIGHT GLOBAL, INC.—See Harvest Partners L.P.; *U.S. Private*, pg. 1876
INSPERITY EMPLOYMENT SCREENING, L.L.C—See Insperity, Inc.; *U.S. Public*, pg. 1131
INSTANT TECHNOLOGY, LLC; *U.S. Private*, pg. 2092
INSTITUTE FOR CORPORATE PRODUCTIVITY, INC.; *U.S. Private*, pg. 2093
INSURANCE OVERLOAD SERVICES, INC.; *U.S. Private*, pg. 2095
INTEGRATED RESOURCES, INC.; *U.S. Private*, pg. 2101
INTELLECT RESOURCES, INC.; *U.S. Private*, pg. 2105
INTERIM PHYSICIANS, LLC; *U.S. Private*, pg. 2110
INVO HEALTHCARE ASSOCIATES, INC.—See Golden Gate Capital Management II, LLC; *U.S. Private*, pg. 1731
IPLACEMENT, INC.; *U.S. Private*, pg. 2136
IRISH RECRUITMENT CONSULTANTS LIMITED—See HFBG Holding B.V.; *Int'l*, pg. 3375
IRONWORKER MANAGEMENT PROGRESSIVE ACTION COOPERATIVE TRUST; *U.S. Private*, pg. 2140
ISS INC.—See Business Brain Showa-Ota Inc.; *Int'l*, pg. 1228
IT ASCENT, INC.; *U.S. Private*, pg. 2147
IT ASCENT, INC.-WALNUT CREEK—See IT Ascent, Inc.; *U.S. Private*, pg. 2148
ITN MARK (UK)—See Core Education and Technologies Ltd.; *Int'l*, pg. 1797
IT RESOURCES CORP.; *U.S. Private*, pg. 2148
JAMES DRURY PARTNERS, LTD.; *U.S. Private*, pg. 2183
JEWISH VOCATIONAL SERVICE AND EMPLOYMENT CENTER; *U.S. Private*, pg. 2206
JJ&H LTD.; *U.S. Private*, pg. 2211
THE JM GROUP (IT RECRUITMENT) LIMITED—See Staffing 360 Solutions, Inc.; *U.S. Public*, pg. 1925
JOBBOT, INC.; *U.S. Private*, pg. 2217
JOBREQ.COM, INC.; *U.S. Private*, pg. 2217
JOBTARGET LLC; *U.S. Private*, pg. 2217
JOULE INC.—See System One Holdings, LLC; *U.S. Private*, pg. 3906
JSMN INTERNATIONAL INC.; *U.S. Private*, pg. 2241
KAPELE APPOINTMENTS (PTY) LIMITED - THE WORKING EARTH DIVISION—See ADvTECH Limited; *Int'l*, pg. 168
KATE COWHIG INTERNATIONAL RECRUITMENT LIMITED—See Bain Capital, LP; *U.S. Private*, pg. 433
KAZTRONIX, LLC; *U.S. Private*, pg. 2268
KELLY LAW REGISTRY—See TrustPoint International, LLC; *U.S. Private*, pg. 4251

KELLY SERVICES GMBH NCO OHG—See Kelly Services, Inc.; *U.S. Public*, pg. 1219
KELLY SERVICES GMBH—See Kelly Services, Inc.; *U.S. Public*, pg. 1218
KELLY SERVICES (INDIA) PVT. LTD.—See Kelly Services, Inc.; *U.S. Public*, pg. 1219
KELLY SERVICES INTERIM (BELGIUM)—See Kelly Services, Inc.; *U.S. Public*, pg. 1219
KELLY SERVICES (MALAYSIA) SDN. BHD.—See Kelly Services, Inc.; *U.S. Public*, pg. 1219
KELLY SERVICES (NEW ZEALAND), LTD.—See Kelly Services, Inc.; *U.S. Public*, pg. 1219
KELLY SERVICES S.A.R.L.—See Kelly Services, Inc.; *U.S. Public*, pg. 1219
KELLY SERVICES SOCIETA DI FORNITURA DI LAVORO TEMPORANEO S.P.A.—See Kelly Services, Inc.; *U.S. Public*, pg. 1219
KELLY SERVICES—See Kelly Services, Inc.; *U.S. Public*, pg. 1219
KELLY SERVICES (S) PTE LTD—See Kelly Services, Inc.; *U.S. Public*, pg. 1218
KENEXA LIMITED—See International Business Machines Corporation; *U.S. Public*, pg. 1148
KEY RESOURCES, INC.—See Staffing 360 Solutions, Inc.; *U.S. Public*, pg. 1925
KFORCE GOVERNMENT HOLDINGS, INC.—See Kforce Inc.; *U.S. Public*, pg. 1227
KFORCE—See Kforce Inc.; *U.S. Public*, pg. 1227
KINGWOOD PERSONNEL—See Murray Resources, Ltd.; *U.S. Private*, pg. 2816
KORN FERRY RPO (SWEDEN) AB—See Korn Ferry; *U.S. Public*, pg. 1272
KROLL, BECKER & WING, LLC; *U.S. Private*, pg. 2353
KWIK JOBS, INC.—See Labor Smart Inc.; *U.S. Public*, pg. 1285
LABORATORY STAFFING INC.—See Xenspire, Inc.; *U.S. Private*, pg. 4581
LABOR READY SOUTHEAST, INC.—See TrueBlue, Inc.; *U.S. Public*, pg. 2198
LABOUR SOLUTIONS AUSTRALIA PROPRIETARY LIMITED—See Adcorp Holdings Limited; *Int'l*, pg. 127
LARKIN ENTERPRISES, INC.; *U.S. Private*, pg. 2392
LAUNCH TECHNICAL WORKFORCE SOLUTIONS, LLC—See The Argentum Group; *U.S. Private*, pg. 3988
LAWCROSSING, INC.; *U.S. Private*, pg. 2400
LES COMPAGNONS—See Groupe Crit, S.A.; *Int'l*, pg. 3101
LES SOLUTIONS VICTRIX INC.—See Alan Allman Associates SA; *Int'l*, pg. 290
LFI FORT PIERCE INC.; *U.S. Private*, pg. 2441
LGC ASSOCIATES, LLC; *U.S. Private*, pg. 2441
LIBERTY PERSONNEL SERVICES; *U.S. Private*, pg. 2447
LIGHTHOUSE PLACEMENT SERVICES, INC.—See Staffing 360 Solutions, Inc.; *U.S. Public*, pg. 1925
LINGO STAFFING, INC.; *U.S. Private*, pg. 2461
LINK STAFFING SERVICES, INC.; *U.S. Private*, pg. 2461
LLOYD MORGAN CHINA LIMITED—See Ignite Limited; *Int'l*, pg. 3603
LLOYD MORGAN HONG KONG LIMITED—See Ignite Limited; *Int'l*, pg. 3603
LLOYD MORGAN INTERNATIONAL PTY LIMITED—See Ignite Limited; *Int'l*, pg. 3603
LMA RECRUITMENT SINGAPORE PTE. LIMITED—See Empresaria Group Plc; *Int'l*, pg. 2389
LOGIX HEALTHCARE SEARCH PARTNERS, LLC—See Maxim Healthcare Services, Inc.; *U.S. Private*, pg. 2618
LOYAL SOURCE GOVERNMENT SERVICES, LLC; *U.S. Private*, pg. 2506
LUCAS ASSOCIATES INC.—See H.I.G. Capital, LLC; *U.S. Private*, pg. 1830
LUCAS GROUP—See H.I.G. Capital, LLC; *U.S. Private*, pg. 1830
LYNEER STAFFING SOLUTIONS, LLC; *U.S. Private*, pg. 2521
MADISON APPROACH STAFFING, INC.; *U.S. Private*, pg. 2539
MALONE WORKFORCE SOLUTIONS; *U.S. Private*, pg. 2558
MANAGEMENT ANALYSIS & UTILIZATION, INC.; *U.S. Private*, pg. 2560
MANAGEMENT RECRUITERS INTERNATIONAL, INC.; *U.S. Private*, pg. 2560
MANAGEMENT TRAINING & CONSULTING INC.; *U.S. Private*, pg. 2561
MANPOWER BUSINESS CONSULTING (SHANGHAI) CO. LTD.—See ManpowerGroup Inc.; *U.S. Public*, pg. 1358
MANPOWER DEUTSCHLAND GMBH—See ManpowerGroup Inc.; *U.S. Public*, pg. 1358
MANPOWER FRANCE SAS—See ManpowerGroup Inc.; *U.S. Public*, pg. 1360
MANPOWERGROUP CO., LTD.—See ManpowerGroup Inc.; *U.S. Public*, pg. 1360
MANPOWERGROUP INC.; *U.S. Public*, pg. 1357
MANPOWERGROUP KOREA, INC.—See ManpowerGroup Inc.; *U.S. Public*, pg. 1360
MANPOWERGROUP SP. Z O.O.—See ManpowerGroup Inc.; *U.S. Public*, pg. 1361
MANPOWER HR SRL—See ManpowerGroup Inc.; *U.S. Public*, pg. 1358

CORPORATE AFFILIATIONS

MANPOWER (IRELAND) LIMITED—See ManpowerGroup Inc.; *U.S. Public*, pg. 1358
MANPOWER (ISRAEL) LTD.—See ManpowerGroup Inc.; *U.S. Public*, pg. 1358
MANPOWER KOREA, INC.—See ManpowerGroup Inc.; *U.S. Public*, pg. 1359
MANPOWER OY—See ManpowerGroup Inc.; *U.S. Public*, pg. 1359
MANPOWER S.A. DE C.V.—See ManpowerGroup Inc.; *U.S. Public*, pg. 1359
MANPOWER S.A.—See ManpowerGroup Inc.; *U.S. Public*, pg. 1359
MANPOWER SERVICES (AUSTRALIA) PTY. LTD.—See ManpowerGroup Inc.; *U.S. Public*, pg. 1359
MANPOWER SERVICES (HONG KONG) LIMITED—See ManpowerGroup Inc.; *U.S. Public*, pg. 1359
MANPOWER STAFFING (AUSTRALIA) PTY LIMITED—See ManpowerGroup Inc.; *U.S. Public*, pg. 1359
MANPOWER STAFFING SERVICES (SINGAPORE) PTE. LTD.—See ManpowerGroup Inc.; *U.S. Public*, pg. 1359
MANPOWER STUDENT AB—See ManpowerGroup Inc.; *U.S. Public*, pg. 1359
MARKS SATTIN (AUSTRALIA) PTY LIMITED—See ManpowerGroup Inc.; *U.S. Public*, pg. 1361
MARY KRAFT AND ASSOCIATES INC.—See Imagine Staffing Technology, Inc.; *U.S. Private*, pg. 2045
MASER ENGINEERING SA—See Groupe Crit, S.A.; *Int'l*, pg. 3101
MASTERYWORKS, INC.—See Adecco Group AG; *Int'l*, pg. 139
MATCHTECH GROUP UK LTD—See Gattaca plc; *Int'l*, pg. 2890
MAXIM PHYSICIAN RESOURCES, LLC—See Maxim Healthcare Services, Inc.; *U.S. Private*, pg. 2618
MAXIM STAFFING SOLUTIONS - TRAVELMAX DIVISION—See Maxim Healthcare Services, Inc.; *U.S. Private*, pg. 2618
MAXIMUM TALENT AGENCY—See The Block Agency, Inc.; *U.S. Private*, pg. 3995
MAXIMUS EMPLOYMENT & TRAINING LIMITED—See MAXIMUS, Inc.; *U.S. Public*, pg. 1402
MCKINLEY FINANCE, INC.—See McKinley Group, Inc.; *U.S. Private*, pg. 2639
MECHANICAL CONTRACTING SERVICES INC.; *U.S. Private*, pg. 2648
MEDACS HEALTHCARE PLC—See HFBG Holding B.V.; *Int'l*, pg. 3375
MEDICAL DOCTOR ASSOCIATES INC.; *U.S. Private*, pg. 2655
MEDICAL RECRUITMENT SPECIALISTS—See Bain Capital, LP; *U.S. Private*, pg. 433
MEDICAL RECRUITMENT STRATEGIES, LLC—See Empresaria Group Plc; *Int'l*, pg. 2389
MEDICAL SOLUTIONS LLC—See TPG Capital, L.P.; *U.S. Public*, pg. 2176
MEDIX STAFFING SOLUTIONS INC.; *U.S. Private*, pg. 2657
MEDSTAFF, INC.; *U.S. Private*, pg. 2658
MERCER HUMAN RESOURCE CONSULTING LTD.—See Marsh & McLennan Companies, Inc.; *U.S. Public*, pg. 1385
MERCER HUMAN RESOURCE CONSULTING, S.L.—See Marsh & McLennan Companies, Inc.; *U.S. Public*, pg. 1386
MERCER HUMAN RESOURCE CONSULTING SRL—See Marsh & McLennan Companies, Inc.; *U.S. Public*, pg. 1385
METASYS TECHNOLOGIES, INC.; *U.S. Private*, pg. 2682
MICROGEN MANAGEMENT SERVICES LIMITED—See Aptitude Software Group Plc; *Int'l*, pg. 523
MILLER RESOURCES INTERNATIONAL, INC.; *U.S. Private*, pg. 2735
MILWAUKEE AREA WORKFORCE INVESTMENT BOARD INC.; *U.S. Public*, pg. 2739
MINDSEEKER, INC.; *U.S. Private*, pg. 2741
MINGLE, LLC; *U.S. Private*, pg. 2742
MISOURCE INC.; *U.S. Private*, pg. 2746
MITCHELL MARTIN, INC.; *U.S. Private*, pg. 2750
MODIS AMSTERDAM—See Adecco Group AG; *Int'l*, pg. 140
MODIS CANADA INC.—See Adecco Group AG; *Int'l*, pg. 140
MODIS, INC.—See Adecco Group AG; *Int'l*, pg. 140
MODIS INTERNATIONAL-BRUSSELS—See Adecco Group AG; *Int'l*, pg. 140
MODIS LONDON—See Adecco Group AG; *Int'l*, pg. 140
MODIS POLSKA SP.Z.O.O—See Adecco Group AG; *Int'l*, pg. 140
THE MOM CORPS, INC.; *U.S. Private*, pg. 4080
MOMENTUM SPECIALIZED STAFFING—See AtWorkGroup, LLC; *U.S. Private*, pg. 384
MONDO—See Odyssey Investment Partners, LLC; *U.S. Private*, pg. 2994
MONROE CONSULTING GROUP VIETNAM LIMITED LIABILITY COMPANY—See Empresaria Group Plc; *Int'l*, pg. 2389
MONROE GROUP INC.; *U.S. Private*, pg. 2773
MONROE RECRUITMENT CONSULTING GROUP COM-

N.A.I.C.S. INDEX 561311 — EMPLOYMENT PLACEMEN...

PANY LIMITED—See Empresaria Group Plc; *Int'l*, pg. 2389
MONTAPLAN GMBH—See ManpowerGroup Inc.; *U.S. Public*, pg. 1361
MORALES GROUP INC.; *U.S. Private*, pg. 2781
MOTEN TATE, INC. (MTI); *U.S. Private*, pg. 2795
MOTION RECRUITMENT PARTNERS, LLC—See Littlejohn & Co., LLC; *U.S. Private*, pg. 2471
MPS MEDIZINISCHE PERSONAL- UND SERVICEGE- SELLSCHAFT MBH KETTWIG—See Asklepios Kliniken GmbH & Co. KGaA; *Int'l*, pg. 623
MTCI-NORTHEAST—See Management Training & Consulting Inc.; *U.S. Private*, pg. 2561
MTCI-SOUTH CENTRAL—See Management Training & Consulting Inc.; *U.S. Private*, pg. 2561
MURRAY RESOURCES, LTD.; *U.S. Private*, pg. 2816
NAGLER GROUP; *U.S. Private*, pg. 2830
NA ORION INTERNATIONAL CONSULTING GROUP, INC.; *U.S. Private*, pg. 2829
NAPOLI MANAGEMENT GROUP—See Blue Equity, LLC; *U.S. Private*, pg. 588
NATIONAL OLDER WORKER CAREER CENTER; *U.S. Private*, pg. 2860
NAVIGA BUSINESS SERVICES, LLC; *U.S. Private*, pg. 2872
NAVIGOS GROUP JOINT STOCK COMPANY—See en-japan Inc.; *Int'l*, pg. 2395
NAVIGOS SEARCH—See en-japan Inc.; *Int'l*, pg. 2395
NETWORKERS INTERNATIONAL (CHINA) CO. LTD—See Gattaca plc; *Int'l*, pg. 2890
NETWORKERS INTERNATIONAL LLC—See Gattaca plc; *Int'l*, pg. 2890
NETWORKERS INTERNATIONAL (MALAYSIA) SDN BHD—See Gattaca plc; *Int'l*, pg. 2890
NETWORKERS TELECOMMUNICATIONS PTY LTD—See Gattaca plc; *Int'l*, pg. 2890
NEW ERA INDIA CONSULTANCY PVT. LTD.—See en-japan Inc.; *Int'l*, pg. 2395
NEXTAFF, LLC—See Malone Workforce Solutions; *U.S. Private*, pg. 2558
NEXTECH SOLUTIONS, INC.; *U.S. Public*, pg. 1526
NINETY NINE PTY. LTD.—See Hipages Group Holdings Limited; *Int'l*, pg. 3402
NOLL HUMAN RESOURCE SERVICE; *U.S. Private*, pg. 2934
NOOR, INC.; *U.S. Private*, pg. 2935
NORTH BAY REHABILITATION SERVICES; *U.S. Private*, pg. 2942
NORTH GATE EXECUTIVE SEARCH LIMITED—See Diales; *Int'l*, pg. 2104
NORTHPOINTE PERSONNEL—See Asset Staffing Incorporated; *U.S. Private*, pg. 354
NORTHSIDE RECRUITMENT SERVICES LIMITED—See Bain Capital, LP; *U.S. Private*, pg. 434
NOVAPRO—See Cross Country Healthcare, Inc.; *U.S. Public*, pg. 595
NOVOTUS, LLC—See L2 Capital Partners; *U.S. Private*, pg. 2367
NOVOTUS, LLC—See Lakewood Capital, LLC; *U.S. Private*, pg. 2379
NSC TECHNOLOGIES, INC.; *U.S. Private*, pg. 2970
NTELICOR, LP; *U.S. Private*, pg. 2970
NURSEFINDERSUK LIMITED—See Bain Capital, LP; *U.S. Private*, pg. 434
NUVEI TECHNOLOGIES; *U.S. Private*, pg. 2975
ODESUS INC.; *U.S. Private*, pg. 2993
OHIO MUTUAL INSURANCE GROUP; *U.S. Private*, pg. 3005
OMNIPOINT, INC.; *U.S. Private*, pg. 3017
THE ONE UMBRELLA PTY LIMITED—See Ignite Limited; *Int'l*, pg. 3603
ONFORCE, INC.—See Adecco Group AG; *Int'l*, pg. 141
OPTIMUM HEALTHCARE IT, LLC—See Achieve Partners Management, LLC; *U.S. Private*, pg. 59
ORION INTERNATIONAL CONSULTING GROUP, LLC—See L2 Capital Partners; *U.S. Private*, pg. 2367
ORION INTERNATIONAL CONSULTING GROUP, LLC—See Lakewood Capital, LLC; *U.S. Private*, pg. 2379
ORIZON GMBH—See Bain Capital, LP; *U.S. Private*, pg. 435
ORIZON HOLDING GMBH—See Bain Capital, LP; *U.S. Private*, pg. 435
OS POWER VIETNAM CO., LTD.—See Bain Capital, LP; *U.S. Private*, pg. 435
OUTSOURCE TECHNICAL; *U.S. Private*, pg. 3052
OUTSOURCING OCEANIA PTY LTD.—See Bain Capital, LP; *U.S. Private*, pg. 435
OVERSEAS EMPLOYMENT SERVICES—See Fauji Foundation; *Int'l*, pg. 2623
OXFORD GLOBAL RESOURCES, INC.—See H.I.G. Capital, LLC; *U.S. Private*, pg. 1831
P2P STAFFING CORP.; *U.S. Private*, pg. 3062
PACIFIC ASIAN CONSORTIUM IN EMPLOYMENT; *U.S. Private*, pg. 3065
PALADIN COMPANIES INC.—See Adecco Group AG; *Int'l*, pg. 141
PARC AVIATION, LTD.—See CAE Inc.; *Int'l*, pg. 1249

PARKER & LYNCH—See Adecco Group AG; *Int'l*, pg. 136
PARTNERSHIP EMPLOYMENT; *U.S. Private*, pg. 3103
PARTNERS TWO INC.; *U.S. Private*, pg. 3103
PATHFINDERS; *U.S. Private*, pg. 3105
PATINA SOLUTIONS GROUP INC.—See Korn Ferry; *U.S. Public*, pg. 1275
PATINA SOLUTIONS GROUP INC.—See Korn Ferry; *U.S. Public*, pg. 1275
PATINA SOLUTIONS GROUP INC.—See Korn Ferry; *U.S. Public*, pg. 1275
PATINA SOLUTIONS GROUP INC.—See Korn Ferry; *U.S. Public*, pg. 1275
PATINA SOLUTIONS GROUP INC.—See Korn Ferry; *U.S. Public*, pg. 1275
PATINA SOLUTIONS GROUP INC.—See Korn Ferry; *U.S. Public*, pg. 1275
PATINA SOLUTIONS GROUP INC.—See Korn Ferry; *U.S. Public*, pg. 1275
PATINA SOLUTIONS GROUP INC.—See Korn Ferry; *U.S. Public*, pg. 1275
PDS SERVICES, LLC; *U.S. Private*, pg. 3122
PEAK RESOURCE GROUP, INC.; *U.S. Private*, pg. 3123
PENCOM SYSTEMS INCORPORATED; *U.S. Private*, pg. 3132
PEOPLESCOUT PTY, LTD—See TrueBlue, Inc.; *U.S. Public*, pg. 2198
PEOPLE SOURCE CONSULTING LIMITED—See ManpowerGroup Inc.; *U.S. Public*, pg. 1361
PEOPULSE—See Groupe Crit, S.A.; *Int'l*, pg. 3101
PERCISION GMBH—See adesso SE; *Int'l*, pg. 145
PERFORMANCE PERSONNEL PARTNERS, LLC; *U.S. Private*, pg. 3149
PERITUS INC.; *U.S. Private*, pg. 3151
PERSONALITY IT PEOPLE POWER GMBH—See Adecco Group AG; *Int'l*, pg. 140
PERSONNEL PLUS, INC.; *U.S. Private*, pg. 3156
PERSONNEL SOURCE INC.; *U.S. Private*, pg. 3156
PHARMALOGICS RECRUITING LLC—See Webster Equity Partners, LLC; *U.S. Private*, pg. 4467
PHARMASCENT—See IT Ascent, Inc.; *U.S. Private*, pg. 2148
PI SOUTHEAST LLC—See The Predictive Index LLC; *U.S. Private*, pg. 4097
PLANETECHS, LLC—See The Argentum Group; *U.S. Private*, pg. 3988
THE PLANET GROUP LLC—See Odyssey Investment Partners, LLC; *U.S. Private*, pg. 2996
PORTER GROUP, INC.; *U.S. Private*, pg. 3231
PORTFOLIO CREATIVE; *U.S. Private*, pg. 3232
PRACTICELINK, LTD; *U.S. Private*, pg. 3241
PRAGMATIC WORKS INC.—See Gryphon Investors, LLC; *U.S. Private*, pg. 1798
THE PREMIER GROUP, INC.; *U.S. Private*, pg. 4097
PRESTIGE STAFFING; *U.S. Private*, pg. 3256
PRIMESTAFF, LLC—See Health Advocates Network, Inc.; *U.S. Private*, pg. 1892
PRIME TIME HEALTHCARE LLC—See OEP Capital Advisors, L.P.; *U.S. Private*, pg. 2999
PRIMUS GLOBAL SERVICES INC.; *U.S. Private*, pg. 3263
PRIORITY PERSONNEL, INC.—See Hamilton-Ryker Company; *U.S. Private*, pg. 1848
PRIORITY STAFFING SOLUTIONS, INC.; *U.S. Private*, pg. 3267
PRN HEALTH SERVICES, INC.—See McLarty Capital Partners UK LLP; *U.S. Private*, pg. 2640
PRN RECRUITMENT LTD.—See HFBG Holding B.V.; *Int'l*, pg. 3375
PROCARE ONE NURSES LLC—See ShiftMed, LLC; *U.S. Private*, pg. 3636
PRODIGY RESOURCES LLC; *U.S. Private*, pg. 3272
PROFESSIONAL EMPLOYMENT SOLUTIONS, INC.; *U.S. Private*, pg. 3275
PROFESSIONAL PLACEMENT RESOURCES, LLC—See TPG Capital, L.P.; *U.S. Public*, pg. 2176
THE PROFESSIONAL SEARCH GROUP—See The Reserves Network Inc.; *U.S. Private*, pg. 4105
PROFESSIONAL SOLUTIONS; *U.S. Private*, pg. 3276
PROGRESSIVE DRIVER SERVICES, INC.; *U.S. Private*, pg. 3279
PROGRESSUS THERAPY, INC.—See Golden Gate Capital Management II, LLC; *U.S. Private*, pg. 1731
PROPARTNER ZEITARBEIT + HANDELSAGENTUR GMBH—See Groupe Crit, S.A.; *Int'l*, pg. 3101
PROTIVITI HONG KONG CO. LTD.—See Robert Half Inc.; *U.S. Public*, pg. 1803
PROVIDUS GROUP; *U.S. Private*, pg. 3295
PROXY PERSONNEL LLC; *U.S. Private*, pg. 3295
P-SERV PTE. LTD.—See Kelly Services, Inc.; *U.S. Public*, pg. 2198
PSINAPSE TECHNOLOGY LTD.; *U.S. Private*, pg. 3297
PSI SERVICES LLC—See Educational Testing Service Inc.; *U.S. Private*, pg. 1339
PT. FIRCROFT INDONESIA—See AEA Investors LP; *U.S. Private*, pg. 115
P.T. MANPOWER BUSINESS SOLUTIONS INDONESIA—See ManpowerGroup Inc.; *U.S. Public*, pg. 1361
PTS STAFFING SOLUTIONS; *U.S. Private*, pg. 3298

QPS COMPANIES INC.; *U.S. Private*, pg. 3313
QUEST FLEXIBLE STAFFING SOLUTIONS (PTY) LIMITED—See Adcorp Holdings Limited; *Int'l*, pg. 127
THE QUEST GROUP, INC.; *U.S. Private*, pg. 4101
QUIN WORKFORCE LIMITED—See AWF Madison Group Limited; *Int'l*, pg. 753
RAZOR TECHNICAL STAFFING; *U.S. Private*, pg. 3360
REARDON ASSOCIATES INC.; *U.S. Private*, pg. 3370
RECRUITING FORCE LLC; *U.S. Private*, pg. 3372
RED APPOINTMENTS PTY LTD.—See Bain Capital, LP; *U.S. Private*, pg. 435
REDF; *U.S. Private*, pg. 3378
RED RIVER SOLUTIONS; *U.S. Private*, pg. 3375
REDWAVE BV—See Cooperatieve Centrale Raiffeisen-Boerenleenbank B.A.; *Int'l*, pg. 1792
REFLECTX SERVICES—See Maxim Healthcare Services, Inc.; *U.S. Private*, pg. 2618
REGIONALHELPWANTED.COM, INC.—See Ziff Davis, Inc.; *U.S. Public*, pg. 2404
REHABABILITIES, INC.; *U.S. Private*, pg. 3389
REICHARD STAFFING, INC.; *U.S. Private*, pg. 3390
REMEDY INTELLIGENT STAFFING, INC.—See Affiliated Managers Group, Inc.; *U.S. Public*, pg. 54
REMEDY INTELLIGENT STAFFING, INC.—See Anchorage Capital Group, L.L.C.; *U.S. Private*, pg. 274
REMPLOY LIMITED—See MAXIMUS, Inc.; *U.S. Public*, pg. 1402
RESOLVE INTERIM SOLUTIONS LIMITED—See Empresaria Group Plc; *Int'l*, pg. 2389
RESOURCES CONNECTION, INC.; *U.S. Public*, pg. 1791
RESOURCES CONNECTION LLC—See Resources Connection, Inc.; *U.S. Public*, pg. 1791
RIA ROHR- UND INDUSTRIEANLAGENBAU GMBH—See Christof Holding AG; *Int'l*, pg. 1587
RIGHT MANAGEMENT ARGENTINA S.A.—See ManpowerGroup Inc.; *U.S. Public*, pg. 1361
RIGHT MANAGEMENT CONSULTANTS, INC.—See ManpowerGroup Inc.; *U.S. Public*, pg. 1361
RIGHT MANAGEMENT CONSULTING (SHANGHAI) CO., LTD—See ManpowerGroup Inc.; *U.S. Public*, pg. 1361
RIGHT MANAGEMENT TAIWAN CO., LTD.—See ManpowerGroup Inc.; *U.S. Public*, pg. 1361
RITASUE SIEGEL RESOURCES—See Aquent Inc.; *U.S. Private*, pg. 303
RM PERSONNEL INC.; *U.S. Private*, pg. 3451
ROBERT HALF BVBA—See Robert Half Inc.; *U.S. Public*, pg. 1803
ROBERT HALF CONSULTING SERVICES BVBA—See Robert Half Inc.; *U.S. Public*, pg. 1803
ROBERT HALF CORPORATION - FINANCE & ACCOUNTING DIVISION—See Robert Half Inc.; *U.S. Public*, pg. 1803
ROBERT HALF INTERNATIONAL IRELAND LIMITED—See Robert Half Inc.; *U.S. Public*, pg. 1804
ROBERT HALF INTERNATIONAL S.A./N.V.—See Robert Half Inc.; *U.S. Public*, pg. 1804
ROBERT HALF LIMITED—See Robert Half Inc.; *U.S. Public*, pg. 1804
ROEVIN TECHNICAL PEOPLE LIMITED—See Adecco Group AG; *Int'l*, pg. 138
RONIN STAFFING LLC; *U.S. Private*, pg. 3478
ROYS & ASSOCIATES; *U.S. Private*, pg. 3494
RSI HOLDINGS INC.; *U.S. Private*, pg. 3496
RUBICON PROGRAMS; *U.S. Private*, pg. 3499
RUMPF CORPORATION; *U.S. Private*, pg. 3503
RURAL CAPITAL AREA WORKFORCE DEVELOPMENT BOARD, INC.; *U.S. Private*, pg. 3504
RUSSELL REYNOLDS ASSOCIATES, FRANCE—See Russell Reynolds Associates Inc.; *U.S. Private*, pg. 3506
RUSSELL REYNOLDS ASSOCIATES, HAMBURG—See Russell Reynolds Associates Inc.; *U.S. Private*, pg. 3507
RUSSELL REYNOLDS ASSOCIATES LTD.—See Russell Reynolds Associates Inc.; *U.S. Private*, pg. 3506
SAISON PERSONALPLUS CO., LTD.—See Credit Saison Co., Ltd.; *Int'l*, pg. 1836
SALES PARTNERSHIPS, INC.; *U.S. Private*, pg. 3532
S.A. MANPOWER (BELGIUM) N.V.—See ManpowerGroup Inc.; *U.S. Public*, pg. 1362
SAN DIEGO WORKFORCE PARTNERSHIP; *U.S. Private*, pg. 3540
SAONGROUP LIMITED—See Axel Springer SE; *Int'l*, pg. 766
SASR WORKFORCE SOLUTIONS, LLC; *U.S. Private*, pg. 3552
SAVI TECHNOLOGIES , INC; *U.S. Private*, pg. 3557
SCHERER STAFFING LLC; *U.S. Private*, pg. 3564
S & C PERMANENT PLACEMENT INC.—See Sullivan & Cogliano Designers Inc.; *U.S. Private*, pg. 3850
SEARCH INC.; *U.S. Private*, pg. 3586
SEARCHPROS SOLUTIONS; *U.S. Private*, pg. 3591
SEARCH WIZARDS INC.; *U.S. Private*, pg. 3586
SECURE NURSING SERVICE, INC.—See Kingsway Financial Services Inc.; *U.S. Public*, pg. 1235
SECURITEC SCREENING SOLUTIONS, INC.—See Appriss Holdings, Inc.; *U.S. Private*, pg. 300
SELECT GROUP; *U.S. Private*, pg. 3600
SELPRO S.A.—See Activa Capital S.A.S.; *Int'l*, pg. 119
SHANGHAI HUMAN RESOURCE CO., LTD.—See Human

561311 — EMPLOYMENT PLACEMEN...

Holdings Co., Ltd.; *Int'l*, pg. 3529
SHL BELGIUM SA—See Exponent Private Equity LLP; *Int'l*, pg. 2589
SHL SVERIGE AB—See Exponent Private Equity LLP; *Int'l*, pg. 2589
SIEBENLIST, GREY & PARTNER GMBH—See Manpower-Group Inc.; *U.S. Public*, pg. 1362
SILVERMAN MCGOVERN STAFFING AND RECRUITING; *U.S. Private*, pg. 3663
SIMOS INSOURCING SOLUTIONS, LLC—See TrueBlue, Inc.; *U.S. Public*, pg. 2198
S.I. SYSTEMS ULC—See Cornell Capital LLC; *U.S. Private*, pg. 1051
SKILLHOUSE STAFFING SOLUTIONS K.K.—See Empresaria Group Plc; *Int'l*, pg. 2389
SKILLSET GROUP, LLC; *U.S. Private*, pg. 3682
SKYBRIDGE RESOURCES, LLC; *U.S. Private*, pg. 3684
SMARTIT STAFFING INC.; *U.S. Private*, pg. 3692
SMITH TEMPORARIES, INC.; *U.S. Private*, pg. 3696
SNELLING PERSONNEL SERVICES—See Patriarch Partners, LLC; *U.S. Private*, pg. 3109
SNI COMPANIES—See GEE Group Inc.; *U.S. Public*, pg. 910
SOCIAL WORK ASSOCIATES LIMITED—See Empresaria Group Plc; *Int'l*, pg. 2389
SOFTNICE; *U.S. Private*, pg. 3705
SOFTWORLD, INC.—See Kelly Services, Inc.; *U.S. Public*, pg. 1220
SOLOMON-PAGE GROUP LLC; *U.S. Private*, pg. 3710
SOLU TECHNOLOGY PARTNERS - PHOENIX OFFICE—See Solu Technology Partners; *U.S. Private*, pg. 3710
SOLU TECHNOLOGY PARTNERS; *U.S. Private*, pg. 3710
SOPHLOGIC GLOBAL, LLC; *U.S. Private*, pg. 3715
SOURCE SELECT GROUP, LLC; *U.S. Private*, pg. 3718
SOUTH BAY WORKFORCE INVESTMENT BOARD; *U.S. Private*, pg. 3719
SOUTHEAST TEXAS WORKFORCE DEVELOPMENT BOARD; *U.S. Private*, pg. 3726
SOUTHERN PROMOTIONS, INC.—See Live Nation Entertainment, Inc.; *U.S. Public*, pg. 1330
SOUTHERN STAFFING INC.; *U.S. Private*, pg. 3735
SPECIAL COUNSEL INC.—See Adecco Group AG; *Int'l*, pg. 141
SPECTRUM HEALTHCARE SERVICES, INC.—See Blackstone Inc.; *U.S. Public*, pg. 359
SPECTRUM PRIMARY CARE, INC.—See Blackstone Inc.; *U.S. Public*, pg. 359
SPENCER REED GROUP, LLC; *U.S. Private*, pg. 3755
SPINKS—See DBAY Advisors Limited; *Int'l*, pg. 1987
SPRINGBOARD; *U.S. Private*, pg. 3763
SPRING GROUP LIMITED—See Adecco Group AG; *Int'l*, pg. 138
SPRING LAKE CONSULTING—See Mitchell Martin, Inc.; *U.S. Private*, pg. 2751
SPRING PERSONNEL LIMITED—See Adecco Group AG; *Int'l*, pg. 138
SPRING PROFESSIONAL SINGAPORE PTE LTD—See Adecco Group AG; *Int'l*, pg. 138
SPRING TECHNOLOGY STAFFING SERVICES LIMITED—See Adecco Group AG; *Int'l*, pg. 138
SRG CLINICAL—See HFBG Holding B.V.; *Int'l*, pg. 3375
SRG ENGINEERING—See HFBG Holding B.V.; *Int'l*, pg. 3375
SRG—See HFBG Holding B.V.; *Int'l*, pg. 3375
SRG WOOLF GROUP, INC.—See HFBG Holding B.V.; *Int'l*, pg. 3375
STAFFING 360 SOLUTIONS, INC.; *U.S. Public*, pg. 1924
STAFFING NOW, INC.—See GEE Group Inc.; *U.S. Public*, pg. 910
THE STAFFING RESOURCE GROUP, INC.; *U.S. Private*, pg. 4120
STAFFING SERVICES LLC; *U.S. Private*, pg. 3775
STAFF MATTERS INC.—See NSC Technologies, Inc.; *U.S. Private*, pg. 2970
STAFFWORKS GROUP; *U.S. Private*, pg. 3775
STAR COLLABORATIVE; *U.S. Private*, pg. 3784
STAR MULTI CARE SERVICES INC.; *U.S. Private*, pg. 3785
STAT NURSING SERVICES INC.; *U.S. Private*, pg. 3790
STERLING ENGINEERING, INC.; *U.S. Private*, pg. 3805
STEVERSON & COMPANY, INC.—See Hamilton-Ryker Company; *U.S. Private*, pg. 1848
ST. JOSEPH, INC.; *U.S. Private*, pg. 3772
STOWE GROUP HEALTHCARE, LLC—See Manpower-Group Inc.; *U.S. Public*, pg. 1362
STRATACUITY STAFFING PARTNERS, INC.—See ASGN Incorporated; *U.S. Public*, pg. 211
STRATEGIC GOVERNMENT RESOURCES INC.; *U.S. Private*, pg. 3835
STRATEGIC NURSE STAFFING, INC.; *U.S. Private*, pg. 3835
STRIDE & ASSOCIATES INC.; *U.S. Private*, pg. 3840
STS TECHNICAL SERVICES LLC—See STS Aviation Group; *U.S. Private*, pg. 3842
SULLIVAN & COGLIANO TRAINING CENTER INC.—See Sullivan & Cogliano Designers Inc.; *U.S. Private*, pg. 3850

SUPERIOR DESIGN INTERNATIONAL, INC.; *U.S. Private*, pg. 3876
SUPOTANT CO., LTD.—See Cross Marketing Group Inc.; *Int'l*, pg. 1856
SURESTAFF, LLC—See Owner Resource Group, LLC; *U.S. Private*, pg. 3055
SVS GROUP INC.; *U.S. Private*, pg. 3889
SYNERFAC TECHNICAL STAFFING; *U.S. Private*, pg. 3903
SYNOVA, INC.; *U.S. Private*, pg. 3904
SZANCA SOLUTIONS, INC.; *U.S. Private*, pg. 3908
TACOMA GOODWILL INDUSTRIES, INC.—See Goodwill Industries International, Inc.; *U.S. Private*, pg. 1740
TALASCEND, LLC; *U.S. Private*, pg. 3925
TALENT BRIDGE, LLC; *U.S. Private*, pg. 3926
TALENTBURST—See TalentBurst, Inc.; *U.S. Private*, pg. 3926
TALLIENCE LLC—See Steven Douglas Associates, Inc.; *U.S. Private*, pg. 3808
TAMPA BAY WORKFORCE ALLIANCE; *U.S. Private*, pg. 3929
TANDEMSEVEN, INC.—See Genpact Limited; *Int'l*, pg. 2927
TARGETED JOB FAIRS, INC.—See DHI Group, Inc.; *U.S. Public*, pg. 658
TASKUS; *U.S. Private*, pg. 3935
TAYLOR ASSOCIATES; *U.S. Private*, pg. 3937
TAYLOR & HILL, INC.; *U.S. Private*, pg. 3937
TAYLOR WHITE SPECIALIZED STAFFING SERVICES, INC.; *U.S. Private*, pg. 3940
TEACH FOR AMERICA; *U.S. Private*, pg. 3944
TEAM-ONE STAFFING SERVICES; *U.S. Private*, pg. 3950
TEAMSALES LIMITED—See Empresaria Group Plc; *Int'l*, pg. 2389
TEAMSOURCE INC.; *U.S. Private*, pg. 3951
TECHLINK SYSTEMS, INC.; *U.S. Private*, pg. 3952
TECHNICAL ASSOCIATES OF GEORGIA INC.; *U.S. Private*, pg. 3953
TECHNOLOGY SERVICE PARTNERS, INC.—See DXC Technology Company; *U.S. Public*, pg. 696
TECHNOLOGY STAFFING ON CALL; *U.S. Private*, pg. 3955
TECHNOPRO HOLDINGS, INC.—See CVC Capital Partners SICAV-FIS S.A.; *Int'l*, pg. 1885
TEKFOR SERVICES GMBH—See Amtek Auto Limited; *Int'l*, pg. 441
TEKFOR SERVICES INC.—See Amtek Auto Limited; *Int'l*, pg. 441
TEKPARTNERS—See P2P Staffing Corp.; *U.S. Private*, pg. 3062
TELESEARCH INC.; *U.S. Private*, pg. 3961
TEMPLAR INTERNATIONAL CONSULTANTS LIMITED-GUANGZHOU—See Adecco Group AG; *Int'l*, pg. 139
TEMPSTAFF (HONG KONG) LIMITED—See Kelly Services, Inc.; *U.S. Public*, pg. 1219
TEMPUS IT STAFFING; *U.S. Private*, pg. 3964
TERRA SEARCH PARTNERS, LLC—See RFE Investment Partners; *U.S. Private*, pg. 3420
THAT'S GOOD HR; *U.S. Private*, pg. 3980
THELADDERS.COM, INC.; *U.S. Private*, pg. 4141
THERAPY STAFF, LLC - DETROIT REGIONAL DIVISION—See L2 Capital Partners; *U.S. Private*, pg. 2367
THERAPY STAFF, LLC - DETROIT REGIONAL DIVISION—See Lakewood Capital, LLC; *U.S. Private*, pg. 2379
THERAPY STAFF, LLC - NATIONAL TRAVEL DIVISION—See L2 Capital Partners; *U.S. Private*, pg. 2367
THERAPY STAFF, LLC - NATIONAL TRAVEL DIVISION—See Lakewood Capital, LLC; *U.S. Private*, pg. 2379
THERAPY STAFF, LLC—See L2 Capital Partners; *U.S. Private*, pg. 2367
THERAPY STAFF, LLC—See Lakewood Capital, LLC; *U.S. Private*, pg. 2379
TIMELINE RECRUITING, LLC—See Maxim Healthcare Services, Inc.; *U.S. Private*, pg. 2618
TOP ENGINEERING INC.—See Hirayama Holdings Co., Ltd.; *Int'l*, pg. 3404
TOPSOURCE INC.; *U.S. Private*, pg. 4188
TRADESMEN INTERNATIONAL, LLC—See Blackstone Inc.; *U.S. Public*, pg. 361
TRADESOURCE INC.; *U.S. Private*, pg. 4202
TRADES UNLIMITED; *U.S. Private*, pg. 4202
TRAINICO TRAINING UND AUSBILDUNG COOPERATION IN BERLIN BRANDENBURG GMBH—See Deutsche Lufthansa AG; *Int'l*, pg. 2070
TRANSFORCE, INC.—See Palladium Equity Partners, LLC; *U.S. Private*, pg. 3078
TRENDHR SERVICES; *U.S. Private*, pg. 4218
TRIAD PERSONNEL SERVICES, INC.—See GEE Group Inc.; *U.S. Public*, pg. 910
TRIAGE PARTNERS, LLC—See Broadtree Partners, LLC; *U.S. Private*, pg. 659
TRIAGE STAFFING INC.; *U.S. Private*, pg. 4225
TRINITE; *U.S. Private*, pg. 4233
TRS CONSULTANTS JLT—See Fluor Corporation; *U.S. Public*, pg. 858

TRS STAFFING SOLUTIONS (AUSTRALIA) PTY LTD—See Fluor Corporation; *U.S. Public*, pg. 860
TRS STAFFING SOLUTIONS INDIA PRIVATE LIMITED—See Fluor Corporation; *U.S. Public*, pg. 860
TRS STAFFING SOLUTIONS (PTY) LTD—See Fluor Corporation; *U.S. Public*, pg. 860
TRUEBLUE OUTSOURCING SOLUTIONS—See TrueBlue, Inc.; *U.S. Public*, pg. 2198
TYLER STAFFING SERVICES INC.; *U.S. Private*, pg. 4268
UNITED STAFFING ASSOCIATES; *U.S. Private*, pg. 4298
UNITED SURGICAL ASSISTANTS, INC.; *U.S. Private*, pg. 4300
UNIVERSAL BACKGROUND SCREENING, INC.—See Sackett National Holdings, Inc.; *U.S. Private*, pg. 3522
UPDATE LEGAL, INC.—See Driven, Inc.; *U.S. Private*, pg. 1278
UROOJ LLC; *U.S. Private*, pg. 4316
US NURSING CORPORATION—See Clarion Capital Partners, LLC; *U.S. Private*, pg. 911
VACO, LLC—See Olympus Partners; *U.S. Private*, pg. 3013
VALLEY HEALTHCARE SYSTEMS, INC.; *U.S. Private*, pg. 4334
VANDERHOUWEN & ASSOCIATES, INC.; *U.S. Private*, pg. 4343
VEREDUS CORP.—See Hays PLC; *Int'l*, pg. 3294
VERIGENT, LLC.; *U.S. Private*, pg. 4360
VERTEK SOLUTIONS INC; *U.S. Private*, pg. 4369
VICTORY PERSONNEL SERVICES, INC.; *U.S. Private*, pg. 4379
VIRPIE INC.; *U.S. Private*, pg. 4388
VIRPIE TECH—See Virpie Inc.; *U.S. Private*, pg. 4388
VISION Y COMPROMISO; *U.S. Private*, pg. 4392
VISTA STAFFING SOLUTIONS, INC.—See KKR & Co. Inc.; *U.S. Public*, pg. 1249
VOLARIS EXEC RECRUITMENT LIMITED—See Manpower-Group Inc.; *U.S. Public*, pg. 1362
WATERMARK SEARCH INTERNATIONAL PTY LIMITED—See Ambition Group Limited; *Int'l*, pg. 415
WCG INTERNATIONAL CONSULTANTS LTD.—See Modiv-Care, Inc.; *U.S. Public*, pg. 1456
WEATHERBY HEALTHCARE—See Ares Management Corporation; *U.S. Public*, pg. 188
WEATHERBY HEALTHCARE—See Leonard Green & Partners, L.P.; *U.S. Private*, pg. 2425
THE WELLSPRING GROUP; *U.S. Private*, pg. 4134
WESTWAYS STAFFING SERVICES INC.; *U.S. Private*, pg. 4501
WHITAKER TECHNICAL—See The Whitaker Companies, Inc.; *U.S. Private*, pg. 4134
WHITE GLOVE PLACEMENT INC.; *U.S. Private*, pg. 4509
WINTER, WYMAN & COMPANY, INC.—See Odyssey Investment Partners, LLC; *U.S. Private*, pg. 2996
WORKFORCE INVESTMENT BOARD OF THE SOUTHWEST REGION, INC.; *U.S. Private*, pg. 4563
WORKFORCE OUTSOURCE SERVICES, INC.; *U.S. Private*, pg. 4563
WORKFORCE SOLUTIONS CAMERON; *U.S. Private*, pg. 4563
WORKFORCE SOLUTIONS CAPITAL AREA WORKFORCE BOARD; *U.S. Private*, pg. 4563
WORKFORCE SOLUTIONS FOR SOUTH TEXAS; *U.S. Private*, pg. 4563
WORKNET PINELLAS INC.; *U.S. Private*, pg. 4564
THE WORKPLACE, INC.; *U.S. Private*, pg. 4139
WORKWAY, INC.; *U.S. Private*, pg. 4564
WORLDWIDE TRAVEL STAFFING, LIMITED; *U.S. Private*, pg. 4570
WRITING ASSISTANCE, INC.—See Orbis Technologies, Inc.; *U.S. Private*, pg. 3038
XSELL RESOURCES, INC.; *U.S. Private*, pg. 4582
YOURCAREERGROUP GMBH—See Axel Springer SE; *Int'l*, pg. 767
ZEKU CORPORATION—See en-japan Inc.; *Int'l*, pg. 2395
ZEMPLEO, INC.; *U.S. Private*, pg. 4601
ZIPRECRUITER, INC.; *U.S. Public*, pg. 2409

561312 — EXECUTIVE SEARCH SERVICES

ALGOE EXECUTIVE—See Algoe; *Int'l*, pg. 318
ARMSTRONG CRAVEN LIMITED; *Int'l*, pg. 575
AXELERATE; *U.S. Private*, pg. 412
BARKERGILMORE; *U.S. Private*, pg. 475
BARTECH TECHNICAL SERVICES OF CANADA LIMITED—See HFBG Holding B.V.; *Int'l*, pg. 3374
B.E. SMITH, INC.—See AMN Healthcare Services, Inc.; *U.S. Public*, pg. 125
BIE EXECUTIVE LIMITED—See Barclays PLC; *Int'l*, pg. 859
BIOQUEST, INC.—See Diversified Search, LLC; *U.S. Private*, pg. 1243
BLU-ALLIANCE LIFESCIENCE; *U.S. Private*, pg. 585
BOTTOM LINE MARKETING & PUBLIC RELATIONS, INC.—See Michael, Best & Friedrich LLP; *U.S. Private*, pg. 2699
THE BOWDOIN GROUP, INC.; *U.S. Private*, pg. 3998
BROOKE CHASE ASSOCIATES, INC.; *U.S. Private*, pg. 663

N.A.I.C.S. INDEX

561320 — TEMPORARY HELP SERV...

CA GLOBAL FINANCE (PTY) LTD.—See ADvTECH Limited; *Int'l*, pg. 169
CA GLOBAL HEADHUNTERS (PTY) LTD.—See ADvTECH Limited; *Int'l*, pg. 169
CA MINING (PTY) LTD.—See ADvTECH Limited; *Int'l*, pg. 169
CA OIL & GAS (PTY) LTD.—See ADvTECH Limited; *Int'l*, pg. 169
CAREER TEACHERS LIMITED—See HFBG Holding B.V.; *Int'l*, pg. 3374
CATENON S.A.; *Int'l*, pg. 1359
COMENSURA PTY LIMITED—See HFBG Holding B.V.; *Int'l*, pg. 3374
CREATIVE ALIGNMENTS, LLC; *U.S. Private*, pg. 1087
CRITERION EXECUTIVE SEARCH, INC.; *U.S. Private*, pg. 1101
DELIGHTFUL.COM, LLC—See IAC Inc.; *U.S. Public*, pg. 1082
DELTA CONSTRUCTION PARTNERS, INC.; *U.S. Private*, pg. 1199
DEVON ROYCE, INC.—See International Business Machines Corporation; *U.S. Public*, pg. 1148
DHR INTERNATIONAL, INC. - MILWAUKEE—See DHR International, Inc.; *U.S. Private*, pg. 1221
DHR INTERNATIONAL, INC. - NEW YORK—See DHR International, Inc.; *U.S. Private*, pg. 1221
DHR INTERNATIONAL, INC.; *U.S. Private*, pg. 1221
DIVERSIFIED SEARCH, LLC; *U.S. Private*, pg. 1243
THE ELLIOT GROUP LLC; *U.S. Private*, pg. 4025
EPIC PERSONNEL PARTNERS LLC; *U.S. Private*, pg. 1412
EXPERIS EXECUTIVE CO. LTD.—See ManpowerGroup Inc.; *U.S. Public*, pg. 1357
FELIX GLOBAL CORP.; *Int'l*, pg. 2632
GLOBAL MEDICS NZ LIMITED—See HFBG Holding B.V.; *Int'l*, pg. 3374
GLOBAL MEDICS PTY LIMITED—See HFBG Holding B.V.; *Int'l*, pg. 3374
HILL INTERNATIONAL (GERMANY) GMBH—See Global Infrastructure Solutions, Inc.; *U.S. Private*, pg. 1715
HRX PTY, LTD.—See TrueBlue, Inc.; *U.S. Public*, pg. 2198
HUGHES CASTELL (HONG KONG) LTD.; *Int'l*, pg. 3524
HUNTER TECHNICAL RESOURCES LLC—See Cognizant Technology Solutions Corporation; *U.S. Public*, pg. 524
KORN/FERRY INTERNATIONAL S.A.—See Korn Ferry; *U.S. Public*, pg. 1274
KORN FERRY LEADERSHIP CONSULTING CORPORATION—See Korn Ferry; *U.S. Public*, pg. 1273
KORN FERRY LLC—See Korn Ferry; *U.S. Public*, pg. 1274
KORN FERRY RECRUITMENT (THAILAND) LTD.—See Korn Ferry; *U.S. Public*, pg. 1274
KORN FERRY (SWEDEN) AB—See Korn Ferry; *U.S. Public*, pg. 1273
L.J. KUSHNER & ASSOCIATES, L.L.C.—See BGSF, Inc.; *U.S. Public*, pg. 330
MAJOR, LINDSEY & AFRICA, LLC—See Allegis Group, Inc.; *U.S. Private*, pg. 177
MANPOWERGROUP (IRELAND) LIMITED—See ManpowerGroup Inc.; *U.S. Public*, pg. 1360
PARADIGM TECHNOLOGY CONSULTING, LLC—See Geisinger Health System; *U.S. Private*, pg. 1656
PERSONNEL DECISIONS INTERNATIONAL SCANDINAVIA A.B.—See Korn Ferry; *U.S. Public*, pg. 1274
SAENGER ASSOCIATES—See 20/20 Foresight Executive Search LLC; *U.S. Private*, pg. 5
SJB CORPORATE LIMITED—See ManpowerGroup Inc.; *U.S. Public*, pg. 1360
SOURCING INTERESTS GROUP (SIG); *U.S. Private*, pg. 3719
STEGPLUS PERSONAL GMBH—See ManpowerGroup Inc.; *U.S. Public*, pg. 1362
T2 TOKYO K.K.—See Allegis Group, Inc.; *U.S. Private*, pg. 177
TALENT2 UK EXECUTIVE LIMITED—See Allegis Group, Inc.; *U.S. Private*, pg. 177
TEEMA SOLUTIONS GROUP INC.; *U.S. Private*, pg. 3958
TRI-WORTH SOLUTIONS, LLC—See The Advanced Group of Companies; *U.S. Private*, pg. 3982
TYLER & CO.—See Jackson Healthcare, LLC; *U.S. Private*, pg. 2177
WILSON HUMAN CAPITAL GROUP, LLC; *U.S. Private*, pg. 4530
YOUNIFI LIMITED—See HFBG Holding B.V.; *Int'l*, pg. 3375
YOURCAREERGROUP AUSTRIA GMBH—See Axel Springer SE; *Int'l*, pg. 767

561320 — TEMPORARY HELP SERVICES

104 CORPORATION; *Int'l*, pg. 1
A-1 TEMPS; *U.S. Private*, pg. 21
AARVI ENCON FZE—See Aarvi Encon Ltd.; *Int'l*, pg. 38
AARVI ENCON LTD.; *Int'l*, pg. 38
ACCRUEPARTNERS, INC.; *U.S. Private*, pg. 54
ACLOCHE; *U.S. Private*, pg. 60
ACRO SERVICE CORP.; *U.S. Private*, pg. 65
ADECCO BULGARIA EOOD—See Adecco Group AG; *Int'l*, pg. 136
ADECCO-COLOMBIA—See Adecco Group AG; *Int'l*, pg. 139
ADECCO H.R. D.O.O.—See Adecco Group AG; *Int'l*, pg. 137
ADECCO IRVINE—See Adecco Group AG; *Int'l*, pg. 138
ADECCO MEDICAL SASU—See Adecco Group AG; *Int'l*, pg. 137
ADECCO OUTSOURCING D.O.O.—See Adecco Group AG; *Int'l*, pg. 137
ADECCO ROMANIA SRL—See Adecco Group AG; *Int'l*, pg. 138
ADECCO SLOVAKIA, S.R.O—See Adecco Group AG; *Int'l*, pg. 138
ADECCO USA, INC.—See Adecco Group AG; *Int'l*, pg. 138
ADECCO VIETNAM JOINT STOCK COMPANY—See Adecco Group AG; *Int'l*, pg. 139
ADVANCED RESOURCES INC.—See The Advanced Group of Companies; *U.S. Private*, pg. 3982
ADVANCED RESOURCES LLC—See The Advanced Group of Companies; *U.S. Private*, pg. 3982
ADVANCED TEMPORARIES INC.; *U.S. Private*, pg. 93
ADVANCED TEMPORARIES, INC.; *U.S. Private*, pg. 93
ADVANTAGE STAFFING; *U.S. Private*, pg. 95
AGENSI PEKERJAAN KERJAYA SUKSES SDN. BHD—See Kelly Services, Inc.; *U.S. Public*, pg. 1219
ALCEA TECHNOLOGIES INC.; *Int'l*, pg. 300
ALKU, LLC—See FFL Partners, LLC; *U.S. Private*, pg. 1500
ALLIED HEALTH GROUP, LLC—See Cross Country Healthcare, Inc.; *U.S. Public*, pg. 595
ALPS AGRI CAREER CORPORATION—See Altech Corporation; *Int'l*, pg. 389
ALTERNATE STAFFING INC.; *U.S. Private*, pg. 207
ALTERNATIVE STAFFING INC.; *U.S. Private*, pg. 207
AMADEUS FIRE AG; *Int'l*, pg. 405
AMERICAN CRITICAL CARE SERVICES; *U.S. Private*, pg. 229
AMERITEMPS INC.; *U.S. Private*, pg. 261
AMN ALLIED SERVICES, LLC—See AMN Healthcare Services, Inc.; *U.S. Public*, pg. 125
AMN HEALTHCARE ALLIED, INC.—See AMN Healthcare Services, Inc.; *U.S. Public*, pg. 125
AMN HEALTHCARE, INC.—See AMN Healthcare Services, Inc.; *U.S. Public*, pg. 125
AMN HEALTHCARE SERVICES, INC.; *U.S. Public*, pg. 124
AMN SERVICES, LLC—See AMN Healthcare Services, Inc.; *U.S. Public*, pg. 125
AMN STAFFING SERVICES, LLC—See AMN Healthcare Services, Inc.; *U.S. Public*, pg. 125
ANCHOR STAFFING, INC.—See Lyneer Staffing Solutions, LLC; *U.S. Private*, pg. 2521
ANDERSELITE LTD.; *Int'l*, pg. 450
ANYHELP INTERNATIONAL, S.L.U.—See ManpowerGroup Inc.; *U.S. Public*, pg. 1357
APEX SYSTEMS, INC.—See ASGN Incorporated; *U.S. Public*, pg. 210
ARG FINANCIAL STAFFING; *U.S. Private*, pg. 319
ARGUS TECHNICAL SERVICES INC.; *U.S. Private*, pg. 322
ARIZONA LABOR FORCE INC.; *U.S. Private*, pg. 324
ASGN INCORPORATED; *U.S. Public*, pg. 210
ASHLEY ELLIS LLC—See GEE Group Inc.; *U.S. Public*, pg. 909
THE ASPEN GROUP, INC.; *U.S. Private*, pg. 3989
ASSENT CONSULTING—See Cross Country Healthcare, Inc.; *U.S. Public*, pg. 595
ASSIGNED COUNSEL INCORPORATED.; *U.S. Private*, pg. 354
ASSIGNMENT AMERICA, LLC—See Cross Country Healthcare, Inc.; *U.S. Public*, pg. 595
ASTREYA PARTNERS, INC.; *U.S. Private*, pg. 361
AUGMENTITY SYSTEMS; *U.S. Private*, pg. 392
AUTOMATION PERSONNEL SERVICES, INC.; *U.S. Private*, pg. 399
AVAN AS—See ManpowerGroup Inc.; *U.S. Public*, pg. 1357
AVANT HEALTHCARE PROFESSIONALS, LLC—See Jackson Healthcare, LLC; *U.S. Private*, pg. 2177
AVIATIONSTAFFMANAGEMENT GMBH—See ManpowerGroup Inc.; *U.S. Public*, pg. 1357
AVIATIONSTAFF MANAGEMENT—See ManpowerGroup Inc.; *U.S. Public*, pg. 1357
AWF MADISON GROUP LIMITED; *Int'l*, pg. 753
BABERS INC.; *U.S. Private*, pg. 422
BALANCE STAFFING, INC.; *U.S. Private*, pg. 457
BAR 2 LIMITED; *Int'l*, pg. 857
BARRETT BUSINESS SERVICES, INC.; *U.S. Public*, pg. 278
BARRETT BUSINESS SERVICES—See Barrett Business Services, Inc.; *U.S. Public*, pg. 278
THE BARTECH GROUP, INC.—See HFBG Holding B.V.; *Int'l*, pg. 3375
BARTLETT, INC.—See BHI Energy; *U.S. Private*, pg. 549
BEACON HILL STAFFING GROUP LLC; *U.S. Private*, pg. 504
BENEFITS S.A.—See ManpowerGroup Inc.; *U.S. Public*, pg. 1357
BIG TRADING CO., LTD.—See Gun Ei Chemical Industry Co., Ltd.; *Int'l*, pg. 3183
BILFINGER PERSONALSERVICE OSTERREICH GMBH—See Bilfinger SE; *Int'l*, pg. 1027
BJM AND ASSOCIATES INC.; *U.S. Private*, pg. 568
BOUNTYJOBS INC.; *U.S. Private*, pg. 624
BTI CONSULTANTS HONG KONG LIMITED—See Kelly Services, Inc.; *U.S. Public*, pg. 1219
BURLINGTON HEALTHCARE PROVIDERS, INC.; *U.S. Private*, pg. 689
BUSINESS INTEGRA TECHNOLOGY SOLUTIONS, INC.; *U.S. Private*, pg. 695
BUTLER DESIGN SERVICES, INC.—See Butler America, Inc.; *U.S. Private*, pg. 696
BUTLER FLEET SERVICES, INC.—See Butler America, Inc.; *U.S. Private*, pg. 696
BUTLER SERVICE GROUP, INC.—See Butler America, Inc.; *U.S. Private*, pg. 696
BUTLER TECHNOLOGY SOLUTIONS, INC.—See Butler America, Inc.; *U.S. Private*, pg. 696
BUTLER UTILITY SERVICE, INC.—See Butler America, Inc.; *U.S. Private*, pg. 696
CAMERON & COMPANY, INC.; *U.S. Private*, pg. 728
CAPITAL OUTSOURCING GROUP (PTY) LIMITED—See Adcorp Holdings Limited; *Int'l*, pg. 127
CARDINAL HEALTH 102, INC.—See Cardinal Health, Inc.; *U.S. Public*, pg. 433
CARDINAL HEALTH, INC. - HOUSTON—See Cardinal Health, Inc.; *U.S. Public*, pg. 434
CAREER TRAINING CONCEPTS, INC.; *U.S. Private*, pg. 752
CARIBBEAN TEMPORARY SERVICES INC.; *U.S. Private*, pg. 761
CARING MATTERS HOME CARE; *U.S. Private*, pg. 761
CAROLINA LEGAL STAFFING LLC; *U.S. Private*, pg. 768
CAROLINAS CONSTRUCTIONS SOLUTIONS, INC.; *U.S. Private*, pg. 769
CARPENTRY CONTRACTORS CORP.—See Bain Capital, LP; *U.S. Private*, pg. 450
CC STAFFING, INC.—See Cross Country Healthcare, Inc.; *U.S. Public*, pg. 595
CEC MANAGEMENT, INC.—See Perdoceo Education Corporation; *U.S. Public*, pg. 1673
CENERGY INTERNATIONAL SERVICES, LLC—See First Tek, Inc.; *U.S. Private*, pg. 1529
CENERGY PARTNERS LLC; *U.S. Private*, pg. 808
CERTIFIED COMPANIES, INC.; *U.S. Private*, pg. 841
CHAMPION TEMPORARIES INC—See Teamsource Inc.; *U.S. Private*, pg. 3951
CHASE TECHNOLOGY CONSULTANTS, LLC; *U.S. Private*, pg. 860
CK HOBBIE INC.; *U.S. Private*, pg. 909
CLINICAL RESOURCES LLC; *U.S. Private*, pg. 944
CLP HOLDINGS CORP—See TrueBlue, Inc.; *U.S. Public*, pg. 2198
CMIC-CP CO. LTD.—See CMIC Holdings Co., Ltd.; *Int'l*, pg. 1670
CMIC SOLUTIONS CO., LTD.—See CMIC Holdings Co., Ltd.; *Int'l*, pg. 1670
CN TEC, INC.—See Sharp Decisions Inc.; *U.S. Private*, pg. 3626
COMFORCE CORPORATION—See American CyberSystems, Inc.; *U.S. Private*, pg. 229
COMFORCE INFORMATION TECHNOLOGIES, INC.—See American CyberSystems, Inc.; *U.S. Private*, pg. 229
COMFORCE TECHNICAL SERVICES, INC.—See American CyberSystems, Inc.; *U.S. Private*, pg. 229
COMFORCE TELECOM, INC.—See American CyberSystems, Inc.; *U.S. Private*, pg. 229
COMPANION PROFESSIONAL SERVICES LLC; *U.S. Private*, pg. 998
COMPUTER PROFESSIONALS, INC.; *U.S. Private*, pg. 1005
CONTEMPORARY STAFFING SOLUTIONS INC.; *U.S. Private*, pg. 1027
CONTINENTAL DESIGN & ENGINEERING, INC.; *U.S. Private*, pg. 1028
CONTINENTAL LABOR RESOURCES INC.; *U.S. Private*, pg. 1030
CONTRACT PROFESSIONALS INC.; *U.S. Private*, pg. 1032
COUNSEL ON CALL; *U.S. Private*, pg. 1065
CPC LOGISTICS INC.; *U.S. Private*, pg. 1080
CRASSOCIATES, INC.; *U.S. Private*, pg. 1086
CREATIVE CIRCLE, LLC—See ASGN Incorporated; *U.S. Public*, pg. 210
CREATIVE FINANCIAL STAFFING LLC; *U.S. Private*, pg. 1088
CREEKSIDE INDUSTRIES; *U.S. Private*, pg. 1092
CRIE ANABUKI INC.; *Int'l*, pg. 1849
CROSS COUNTRY HEALTHCARE, INC.; *U.S. Public*, pg. 595
CROSS COUNTRY TRAVCORPS, INC.—See Cross Country Healthcare, Inc.; *U.S. Public*, pg. 595
CROWN SERVICES INC.; *U.S. Private*, pg. 1112
CWU, INC.; *U.S. Private*, pg. 1133
CYNERGIES CONSULTING, INC.; *U.S. Private*, pg. 1134
THE DAISHI STAFF SERVICE CO., LTD.—See Daishi Hokuetsu Financial Group, Inc.; *Int'l*, pg. 1941
THE DAVIS COMPANIES INC.; *U.S. Private*, pg. 4018
THE DAVIS COMPANIES INC—See The Davis Companies Inc.; *U.S. Private*, pg. 4018
DBTS INC.; *U.S. Private*, pg. 1179
DD & SF INVESTMENTS, INC.; *U.S. Private*, pg. 1180

561320 — TEMPORARY HELP SERV...

DEBBIE'S STAFFING SERVICES; *U.S. Private*, pg. 1186
DEKRA ARBEIT AUSTRIA GMBH—See DEKRA e.V.; *Int'l*, pg. 2006
DEPENDABLE HEALTH SERVICES, INC.; *U.S. Private*, pg. 1209
DERICHEBOURG ATIS GMBH—See Derichebourg S.A.; *Int'l*, pg. 2042
DERICHEBOURG INTERIM AERONAUTIQUE SAS—See Derichebourg S.A.; *Int'l*, pg. 2042
DERICHEBOURG INTERIM SAS—See Derichebourg S.A.; *Int'l*, pg. 2042
DIAL TEMPORARY HELP SERVICE; *U.S. Private*, pg. 1222
DIVERSANT, LLC; *U.S. Private*, pg. 1240
DLH SOLUTIONS, INC.—See DLH Holdings Corp.; *U.S. Public*, pg. 670
DOBBS TEMPORARY SERVICES, INC.; *U.S. Private*, pg. 1250
DOCS INTERNATIONAL BV—See ICON plc; *Int'l*, pg. 3584
DOHERTY EMPLOYMENT GROUP, INC.; *U.S. Private*, pg. 1253
DOHERTY STAFFING SOLUTIONS—See Doherty Employment Group, Inc.; *U.S. Private*, pg. 1253
DUBAI AIRPORT FREE ZONE—See ManpowerGroup Inc.; *U.S. Public*, pg. 1357
DYNAMIC SERVICES & SECURITY LIMITED; *Int'l*, pg. 2240
EBARA MEISTER CO., LTD.—See Ebara Corporation; *Int'l*, pg. 2283
EGW TEMPORARIES INC.; *U.S. Private*, pg. 1346
EKS GROUP LLC; *U.S. Private*, pg. 1348
ELAN GROUP LTD.—See ManpowerGroup Inc.; *U.S. Public*, pg. 1357
ELAN PARTNERS; *U.S. Private*, pg. 1350
ELITE STAFFING INC; *U.S. Private*, pg. 1361
ELWOOD STAFFING SERVICES, INC. - GRAND RAPIDS—See Elwood Staffing Services, Inc.; *U.S. Private*, pg. 1377
EMPLOYBRIDGE, LLC—See Apollo Global Management, Inc.; *U.S. Public*, pg. 151
EMPLOYER FLEXIBLE MANAGEMENT, LLC; *U.S. Private*, pg. 1386
EMPLOYERS RESOURCE MANAGEMENT INC.; *U.S. Private*, pg. 1387
EMPLOYERS TEMPORARY SERVICE; *U.S. Private*, pg. 1387
EMPLOYMENT CONTROL INC.; *U.S. Private*, pg. 1387
EMPLOYMENT ENTERPRISES INC.; *U.S. Private*, pg. 1387
EMPLOYMENT GROUP HOLDING CORP.; *U.S. Private*, pg. 1387
ENEOS CAREER SUPPORT CORPORATION—See ENEOS Holdings, Inc.; *Int'l*, pg. 2415
ENERGY SERVICES GROUP INTERNATIONAL INC. (ESG); *U.S. Private*, pg. 1396
EPMATE CO., LTD.—See EPS Holdings, Inc.; *Int'l*, pg. 2465
EQUIS STAFFING; *U.S. Private*, pg. 1415
ETCON INC.; *U.S. Private*, pg. 1431
EVENTPRO STRATEGIES, INC.; *U.S. Private*, pg. 1437
EXPERIS BELGIUM SA—See ManpowerGroup Inc.; *U.S. Public*, pg. 1357
EXPERIS EXECUTIVE FRANCE—See ManpowerGroup Inc.; *U.S. Public*, pg. 1358
EXPERIS EXECUTIVE LYON SAS—See ManpowerGroup Inc.; *U.S. Public*, pg. 1358
EXPERIS GMBH—See ManpowerGroup Inc.; *U.S. Public*, pg. 1358
EXPERIS (M) SDN BHD—See ManpowerGroup Inc.; *U.S. Public*, pg. 1357
EXPERIS S.R.L.—See ManpowerGroup Inc.; *U.S. Public*, pg. 1358
EXPERIS TECHNOLOGY FUTURES CO. LTD.—See ManpowerGroup Inc.; *U.S. Public*, pg. 1358
EXPRESS EMPLOYMENT PROFESSIONALS, INC.; *U.S. Private*, pg. 1451
FARO RECRUITMENT (HONG KONG) CO., LIMITED—See Bain Capital, LP; *U.S. Private*, pg. 434
FARO RECRUITMENT (SINGAPORE) PTE. LTD.—See Bain Capital, LP; *U.S. Private*, pg. 434
FAVORITE HEALTHCARE STAFFING, INC.; *U.S. Private*, pg. 1484
FIRST CALL TEMPORARY SERVICES; *U.S. Private*, pg. 1515
FISCHER & FUNKE GESELLSCHAFT FUR PERSONAL-DIENSTLEISTUNGEN MBH—See BayernLB Holding AG; *Int'l*, pg. 914
FLEX-TEAM INC.—See Lingo Staffing, Inc.; *U.S. Private*, pg. 2461
FOODTEAM INC.; *U.S. Private*, pg. 1562
FORGE STAFFING INC.; *U.S. Private*, pg. 1568
FRANKEL STAFFING PARTNERS; *U.S. Private*, pg. 1596
FREIGHT HANDLERS INC.; *U.S. Private*, pg. 1607
FSO ONSITE OUTSOURCING; *U.S. Private*, pg. 1618
FULLCAST TECHNOLOGY CO., LTD.—See Fullcast Holdings Co., Ltd.; *Int'l*, pg. 2842
FULL-O-PEP APPLIANCES INCORPORATED; *U.S. Private*, pg. 1621
FURSTSTAFFING, INC.; *U.S. Private*, pg. 1624
FUSCO PERSONNEL, INC.; *U.S. Private*, pg. 1625

FUTURE FOCUS INFOTECH PVT. LTD.—See en-japan Inc.; *Int'l*, pg. 2395
FYI SYSTEMS, INC.; *U.S. Private*, pg. 1628
G&A OUTSOURCING, INC.; *U.S. Private*, pg. 1628
G.D. BARRI & ASSOCIATES INC.; *U.S. Private*, pg. 1630
GDH CONSULTING, INC.; *U.S. Private*, pg. 1654
GECKO HOSPITALITY INC—See Triumph Higher Education Group, LLC; *U.S. Private*, pg. 4239
GEOMETRIC RESULTS HOLDINGS LIMITED—See Bain Capital, LP; *U.S. Private*, pg. 441
GEORGIA HOME MEDICAL, INC.—See AdaptHealth Corp.; *U.S. Public*, pg. 38
GEOTEMPS INC.; *U.S. Private*, pg. 1685
GLOBAL EMPLOYMENT HOLDINGS, INC.; *U.S. Private*, pg. 1713
GLOBAL MEDICAL STAFFING LIMITED, INC.—See Ares Management Corporation; *U.S. Public*, pg. 188
GLOBAL MEDICAL STAFFING LIMITED, INC.—See Leonard Green & Partners, L.P.; *U.S. Private*, pg. 2425
GLOTEL INC.—See The Gores Group, LLC; *U.S. Private*, pg. 4034
GONZALES LABOR SYSTEMS INC.; *U.S. Private*, pg. 1737
GROUPE CRIT, S.A.; *Int'l*, pg. 3101
G-TECH SERVICES, INC.; *U.S. Private*, pg. 1630
GURU.COM; *U.S. Private*, pg. 1819
HALLMARK AVIATION SERVICES LP; *U.S. Private*, pg. 1844
HAWKINS ASSOCIATES INC.; *U.S. Private*, pg. 1883
HEADWAY CORPORATE RESOURCES INC.; *U.S. Private*, pg. 1891
HINNI AG—See BKW AG; *Int'l*, pg. 1055
HIRENETWORKS; *U.S. Private*, pg. 1950
HIREQUEST, INC.; *U.S. Private*, pg. 1042
HIRESTRATEGY, INC.—See Odyssey Investment Partners, LLC; *U.S. Private*, pg. 2994
HKA ENTERPRISES, LLC—See Cenergy Partners LLC; *U.S. Private*, pg. 808
HORIZON STAFFING INC.; *U.S. Private*, pg. 1982
HTSS, INC.; *U.S. Private*, pg. 1999
HUMAN CAPITAL STAFFING, L.L.C.; *U.S. Private*, pg. 2005
HUMANIX CORP.; *U.S. Private*, pg. 2006
HUTCO INC.; *U.S. Private*, pg. 2014
ICONMA, LLC; *U.S. Private*, pg. 2033
IJOBS B.V.—See ManpowerGroup Inc.; *U.S. Public*, pg. 1362
IMPRIMIS GROUP; *U.S. Private*, pg. 2051
INCONEN CORPORATION; *U.S. Private*, pg. 2054
INDUSTRIAL STAFFING SERVICES, INC.; *U.S. Private*, pg. 2068
INFOMEDIA GROUP INC; *U.S. Private*, pg. 2072
INTEGRAL SEARCH & SELECTION LIMITED—See ManpowerGroup Inc.; *U.S. Public*, pg. 1358
INTEGRA STAFFING & SEARCH; *U.S. Private*, pg. 2098
INTEGRITY STAFFING SOLUTIONS; *U.S. Private*, pg. 2104
INTEPROS CONSULTING INC; *U.S. Private*, pg. 2106
INTERIM HEALTHCARE INC.—See The Halifax Group LLC; *U.S. Private*, pg. 4042
INTERIM HEALTHCARE OF HARTFORD, INC.; *U.S. Private*, pg. 2110
INTERPRETA, INC.—See Centene Corporation; *U.S. Public*, pg. 469
IQ PIPELINE; *U.S. Private*, pg. 2137
JAPAN PRO STAFF CO., LTD—See Bell-Park Co., Ltd.; *Int'l*, pg. 966
J.C. MALONE ASSOCIATES—See Malone Workforce Solutions; *U.S. Private*, pg. 2558
JEAN SIMPSON PERSONNEL SERVICES, INC.; *U.S. Private*, pg. 2196
J&J STAFFING RESOURCES INC.; *U.S. Private*, pg. 2154
JOB STORE INC.; *U.S. Private*, pg. 2217
JOHNSON SERVICE GROUP INC.; *U.S. Private*, pg. 2229
JOULE STAFFING SERVICES, INC.—See System One Holdings, LLC; *U.S. Private*, pg. 3907
K2 PARTNERING SOLUTIONS, INC.; *U.S. Private*, pg. 2253
KABLE STAFFING RESOURCES LLC; *U.S. Private*, pg. 2253
KANE STAFFING SERVICES, LLC—See The Kane Company; *U.S. Private*, pg. 4064
KB STAFFING; *U.S. Private*, pg. 2268
KELLY AUTOMOTIVE SERVICES GROUP—See Kelly Services, Inc.; *U.S. Public*, pg. 1220
KELLY ENGINEERING RESOURCES—See Kelly Services, Inc.; *U.S. Public*, pg. 1220
KELLY INFORMATION TECHNOLOGY RESOURCES—See Kelly Services, Inc.; *U.S. Public*, pg. 1220
KELLY SCIENTIFIC RESOURCES—See Kelly Services, Inc.; *U.S. Public*, pg. 1220
KELLY SERVICES AB—See Kelly Services, Inc.; *U.S. Public*, pg. 1219
KELLY SERVICES AUSTRALIA—See Kelly Services, Inc.; *U.S. Public*, pg. 1219
KELLY SERVICES - EMPRESSA DE TRABALHO TEMPORARIO, UNIPESSOAL, LDA.—See Kelly Services, Inc.; *U.S. Public*, pg. 1219

CORPORATE AFFILIATIONS

KELLY SERVICES FRANCE S.A.—See Kelly Services, Inc.; *U.S. Public*, pg. 1219
KELLY SERVICES, INC. - INTERNATIONAL DIVISION—See Kelly Services, Inc.; *U.S. Public*, pg. 1218
KELLY SERVICES, INC. - PROFESSIONAL TECHNICAL & STAFFING ALTERNATIVES DIVISION—See Kelly Services, Inc.; *U.S. Public*, pg. 1219
KELLY SERVICES, INC.; *U.S. Public*, pg. 1218
KELLY SERVICES (IRELAND), LTD.—See Kelly Services, Inc.; *U.S. Public*, pg. 1219
KELLY SERVICES LUXEMBOURG, S.A.R.L.—See Kelly Services, Inc.; *U.S. Public*, pg. 1219
KELLY SERVICES MANAGEMENT S.A.R.L.—See Kelly Services, Inc.; *U.S. Public*, pg. 1219
KELLY SERVICES MEXICO S.A. DE C.V.—See Kelly Services, Inc.; *U.S. Public*, pg. 1219
KELLY SERVICES NORGE A/S—See Kelly Services, Inc.; *U.S. Public*, pg. 1219
KELLY SERVICES OF DENMARK, INC.—See Kelly Services, Inc.; *U.S. Public*, pg. 1219
KELLY SERVICES STAFFING & RECRUITMENT (THAILAND) CO., LTD.—See Kelly Services, Inc.; *U.S. Public*, pg. 1219
KELLY SERVICES (SUISSE) S.A.—See Kelly Services, Inc.; *U.S. Public*, pg. 1219
KFORCE INC.; *U.S. Public*, pg. 1227
KIMCO STAFFING SERVICES INC.; *U.S. Private*, pg. 2305
KINETICOM, INC.; *U.S. Private*, pg. 2308
KINETICOM LTD.—See Kineticom, Inc.; *U.S. Private*, pg. 2308
LABOR READY MID-ATLANTIC, INC.—See TrueBlue, Inc.; *U.S. Public*, pg. 2198
LABOR READY MIDWEST, INC.—See TrueBlue, Inc.; *U.S. Public*, pg. 2198
LABOR READY SOUTHWEST, INC.—See TrueBlue, Inc.; *U.S. Public*, pg. 2198
LABOR SMART INC.; *U.S. Public*, pg. 1285
LABOR STAFFING, INC.; *U.S. Private*, pg. 2370
LAKESHORE STAFFING INC.—See Jordan Industries, Inc.; *U.S. Private*, pg. 2235
LANDRUM STAFFING SERVICES, INC.—See Landrum Human Resource Companies, Inc.; *U.S. Private*, pg. 2386
LEE HECHT HARRISON POLSKA SP. Z O.O.—See Adecco Group AG; *Int'l*, pg. 141
LHH RECRUITMENT SOLUTIONS—See Adecco Group AG; *Int'l*, pg. 136
LIFEGIFT ORGAN DONATION CENTER; *U.S. Private*, pg. 2450
LLOYD STAFFING INC.; *U.S. Private*, pg. 2476
LOCKHEED MARTIN SPACE SYSTEMS CO. - EL PASO—See Lockheed Martin Corporation; *U.S. Public*, pg. 1338
LOCUM LEADERS; *U.S. Private*, pg. 2479
LOVING HANDS LTD.; *U.S. Private*, pg. 2504
MAGNUM STAFFING SERVICES INC.; *U.S. Private*, pg. 2549
MAINSTAY BUSINESS SOLUTIONS; *U.S. Private*, pg. 2553
MANCAN INC.; *U.S. Private*, pg. 2562
MANPOWER B.V.—See ManpowerGroup Inc.; *U.S. Public*, pg. 1358
MANPOWER CARE LTD.—See ManpowerGroup Inc.; *U.S. Public*, pg. 1358
MANPOWER EL & TELE AB—See ManpowerGroup Inc.; *U.S. Public*, pg. 1360
MANPOWERGROUP BUSINESS SOLUTIONS LTD.—See ManpowerGroup Inc.; *U.S. Public*, pg. 1360
MANPOWERGROUP CO. LIMITED—See ManpowerGroup Inc.; *U.S. Public*, pg. 1360
MANPOWERGROUP GMBH—See ManpowerGroup Inc.; *U.S. Public*, pg. 1360
MANPOWERGROUP S.A.—See ManpowerGroup Inc.; *U.S. Public*, pg. 1360
MANPOWERGROUP SERVICES INDIA PVT. LTD.—See ManpowerGroup Inc.; *U.S. Public*, pg. 1361
MANPOWERGROUP S R.O.—See ManpowerGroup Inc.; *U.S. Public*, pg. 1361
MANPOWER GUATEMALA S.A.—See ManpowerGroup Inc.; *U.S. Public*, pg. 1358
MANPOWER HONDURAS, S.A.—See ManpowerGroup Inc.; *U.S. Public*, pg. 1359
MANPOWER, INC. / CALIFORNIA PENINSULA—See ManpowerGroup Inc.; *U.S. Public*, pg. 1360
MANPOWER, INCORPORATED OF SOUTHERN NEVADA—See Manpower Holding Corp.; *U.S. Private*, pg. 2566
MANPOWER INC. - SAN DIEGO—See ManpowerGroup Inc.; *U.S. Public*, pg. 1359
MANPOWER (IRELAND) GROUP LIMITED—See ManpowerGroup Inc.; *U.S. Public*, pg. 1358
MANPOWER KAZ LLC—See ManpowerGroup Inc.; *U.S. Public*, pg. 1359
MANPOWER LUXEMBOURG S.A.—See ManpowerGroup Inc.; *U.S. Public*, pg. 1359
MANPOWER MONACO SAM—See ManpowerGroup Inc.; *U.S. Public*, pg. 1359
MANPOWER NICARAGUA S.A.—See ManpowerGroup Inc.; *U.S. Public*, pg. 1359

N.A.I.C.S. INDEX

561320 — TEMPORARY HELP SERV...

MANPOWER PANAMA S.A.—See ManpowerGroup Inc.; *U.S. Public*, pg. 1359
MANPOWER PARAGUAY S.R.L.—See ManpowerGroup Inc.; *U.S. Public*, pg. 1359
MANPOWER ROMANIA SRL—See ManpowerGroup Inc.; *U.S. Public*, pg. 1359
MANPOWER, S.A. DE C.V.—See ManpowerGroup Inc.; *U.S. Public*, pg. 1360
MANPOWER SAVJETOVANJE DOO—See ManpowerGroup Inc.; *U.S. Public*, pg. 1359
MANPOWER S.R.L—See ManpowerGroup Inc.; *U.S. Public*, pg. 1359
MARISTAFF INC.; *U.S. Private*, pg. 2576
MARKETING Y PROMOCIONES S.A.—See Empresaria Group Plc; *Int'l*, pg. 2389
MAS MEDICAL STAFFING; *U.S. Private*, pg. 2600
MAU WORKFORCE SOLUTIONS; *U.S. Private*, pg. 2614
MAXIM HEALTHCARE SERVICES, INC.; *U.S. Private*, pg. 2618
MAXIM HEALTHCARE SERVICES INC.—See Maxim Healthcare Services, Inc.; *U.S. Private*, pg. 2618
MCCALLION STAFFING; *U.S. Private*, pg. 2626
MCDERMOTT & WIEDEMANN, LLC—See Health Carousel, LLC; *U.S. Private*, pg. 1892
MEADOR STAFFING SERVICES INC.; *U.S. Private*, pg. 2647
MEDACS HEALTHCARE AUSTRALIA (PTY) LIMITED—See HFBG Holding B.V.; *Int'l*, pg. 3375
MEDACS HEALTHCARE LIMITED—See HFBG Holding B.V.; *Int'l*, pg. 3375
MEDICAL SEARCH SOLUTIONS, INC.—See Subsidium Healthcare, LLC; *U.S. Private*, pg. 3847
MEDIRADIX OY—See Empresaria Group Plc; *Int'l*, pg. 2389
MED-STAFF, INC.—See Cross Country Healthcare, Inc.; *U.S. Public*, pg. 595
MEDVANTX, INC.; *U.S. Private*, pg. 2659
MEIRXRS; *U.S. Private*, pg. 2660
MERCURY STAFFING CO., LTD.—See FUJISOFT INCORPORATED; *Int'l*, pg. 2830
MERRITT, HAWKINS & ASSOCIATES—See AMN Healthcare Services, Inc.; *U.S. Public*, pg. 125
METRO SYSTEMS INC.—See Great Mill Rock LLC; *U.S. Private*, pg. 1766
M FORCE STAFFING; *U.S. Private*, pg. 2523
MGA EMPLOYEE SERVICES INC.; *U.S. Private*, pg. 2694
THE MHA GROUP, INC.—See AMN Healthcare Services, Inc.; *U.S. Public*, pg. 125
MICROTECH STAFFING GROUP INC.; *U.S. Private*, pg. 2704
MIDCOM WORKFORCE SOLUTIONS—See Cenergy Partners LLC; *U.S. Private*, pg. 808
MINT MEDICAL PHYSICIAN STAFFING, LP—See Cross Country Healthcare, Inc.; *U.S. Public*, pg. 595
MISS PAIGE LTD.; *U.S. Private*, pg. 2746
MONROE STAFFING SERVICES, LLC—See Staffing 360 Solutions, Inc.; *U.S. Public*, pg. 1925
MRA SEARCH, INC.—See Cross Country Healthcare, Inc.; *U.S. Public*, pg. 595
MYSIGN AG—See Allgeier SE; *Int'l*, pg. 337
NES HOLDINGS, INC.; *U.S. Private*, pg. 2885
NETWORK ADVANTAGE—See DD & SF Investments, Inc.; *U.S. Private*, pg. 1180
NEXT MEDICAL STAFFING LLC—See Health Carousel, LLC; *U.S. Private*, pg. 1893
NORDIC TALENT PROFESSIONALS—See ManpowerGroup Inc.; *U.S. Public*, pg. 1360
NORTHWEST STAFFING RESOURCES INC.; *U.S. Private*, pg. 2961
NRI INC.; *U.S. Private*, pg. 2969
NUMBERWORKS, LLC; *U.S. Private*, pg. 2973
NURSEFINDERS, LLC—See AMN Healthcare Services, Inc.; *U.S. Public*, pg. 125
OFFICE ANGELS LIMITED—See Adecco Group AG; *Int'l*, pg. 138
OFFICE FURNITURE RENTAL ALLIANCE LLC; *U.S. Private*, pg. 3001
O'GRADY-PEYTON INTERNATIONAL (USA), INC.—See AMN Healthcare Services, Inc.; *U.S. Public*, pg. 125
OLYMPIC STAFFING SERVICES; *U.S. Private*, pg. 3012
ONIN STAFFING; *U.S. Private*, pg. 3026
ORANGE TREE EMPLOYMENT SCREENING LLC—See Boathouse Capital Management, LLC; *U.S. Private*, pg. 603
OUTSOURCE INC.; *U.S. Private*, pg. 3052
OUT-SOURCING SYSTEM CONSULTING INC.—See Bain Capital, LP; *U.S. Private*, pg. 435
PALADIN CONSULTING, INC.—See GEE Group Inc.; *U.S. Public*, pg. 910
PALKAR INC.; *U.S. Private*, pg. 3077
PATEL CONSULTANTS CORPORATION; *U.S. Private*, pg. 3105
PAYROLL MANAGEMENT, INC.; *U.S. Private*, pg. 3117
PDQ TEMPORARIES INCORPORATED; *U.S. Private*, pg. 3122
PDS TECH, INC.—See Adecco Group AG; *Int'l*, pg. 140
PDS TECHNICAL SERVICES—See Adecco Group AG; *Int'l*, pg. 140

PDS TECHNICAL SERVICES—See Adecco Group AG; *Int'l*, pg. 140
PDS TECHNICAL SERVICES, WICHITA BRANCH—See Adecco Group AG; *Int'l*, pg. 140
PDZ PERSONALDIENSTE & ZEITARBEIT GMBH—See DZ BANK AG Deutsche Zentral-Genossenschaftsbank; *Int'l*, pg. 2244
PEAK TECHNICAL SERVICES, INC.; *U.S. Private*, pg. 3124
PEAK TECHNICAL SERVICES, IRVINE—See Peak Technical Services, Inc.; *U.S. Private*, pg. 3124
PEAK TECHNICAL SERVICES, NATIONAL DIVISON—See Peak Technical Services, Inc.; *U.S. Private*, pg. 3124
PEOPLE 2.0 GLOBAL, LLC—See TPG Capital, L.P.; *U.S. Public*, pg. 2177
PEOPLELINK STAFFING SOLUTIONS INC.—See Groupe Crit S.A.; *Int'l*, pg. 3101
PEOPLEMARK, INC.—See Allied Universal Manager LLC; *U.S. Private*, pg. 190
PERFORMANCE GROUP, INC.; *U.S. Private*, pg. 3149
PERSONALLY YOURS STAFFING; *U.S. Private*, pg. 3156
PERSONNEL PARTNERS INC.; *U.S. Private*, pg. 3156
PERSONNEL PLACEMENTS LLC; *U.S. Private*, pg. 3156
PHIPPS REPORTING, INC.—See Trinity Hunt Management, L.P.; *U.S. Private*, pg. 4234
PHOENIX PERSONNEL; *U.S. Private*, pg. 3173
PHYSICAL DISTRIBUTION SERVICES; *U.S. Private*, pg. 3174
PINNACLE STAFFING INC.; *U.S. Private*, pg. 3185
PLANT MAINTENANCE, INC.; *U.S. Private*, pg. 3197
PLUS GROUP INC.; *U.S. Private*, pg. 3215
POCH PERSONNEL, INC.; *U.S. Private*, pg. 3219
POWER ADVOCATE, INC.—See Veritas Capital Fund Management, LLC; *U.S. Private*, pg. 4366
PRECISION STAFFING INCORPORATED; *U.S. Private*, pg. 3246
PREMIER STAFFING, INC.—See Elwood Staffing Services, Inc.; *U.S. Private*, pg. 1377
PRIMARY SERVICES LP; *U.S. Private*, pg. 3261
PRIME MANPOWER RESOURCES DEVELOPMENT INC.—See ManpowerGroup Inc.; *U.S. Public*, pg. 1361
PRIME STAFFING INC.; *U.S. Private*, pg. 3262
PRINCIPLE SOLUTIONS GROUP, LLC—See Stone Point Capital LLC; *U.S. Private*, pg. 3823
PRODUCTION DESIGN SERVICES; *U.S. Private*, pg. 3273
PRODUCTION SUPPORT SERVICES INCORPORATED (PSS)—See Energy Services Group International Inc. (ESG); *U.S. Private*, pg. 1396
PROFESSIONAL EMERGENCY CARE PC; *U.S. Private*, pg. 3275
PROFESSIONAL RESOURCES IN INFORMATION SYSTEMS MANAGEMENT, INC.; *U.S. Private*, pg. 3276
PROFESSIONAL STAFFING A BTS INC.; *U.S. Private*, pg. 3276
PROFESSIONAL STAFFING CORPORATION; *U.S. Private*, pg. 3276
PROGRESSIVE NURSING STAFFERS INC.—See Flexibility & Co., LLC; *U.S. Private*, pg. 1544
PRO RESOURCES INC.; *U.S. Private*, pg. 3270
PRO SOURCE INC.; *U.S. Private*, pg. 3270
PROTIVITI SHANGHAI CO., LTD.—See Robert Half Inc.; *U.S. Public*, pg. 1803
PROTOCALL NJ INC.; *U.S. Private*, pg. 3290
QUALITEMPS INC.; *U.S. Private*, pg. 3317
QUALITY TEMPORARY SERVICES; *U.S. Private*, pg. 3321
QUANTIX, INC.; *U.S. Private*, pg. 3322
REEDY CREEK ENERGY SERVICES—See The Walt Disney Company; *U.S. Public*, pg. 2139
REGAL TEMPORARY SERVICES INC.; *U.S. Private*, pg. 3386
REGISTRY NETWORK, INC.; *U.S. Private*, pg. 3389
RENHILL GROUP INC.; *U.S. Private*, pg. 3398
RENOVO EMPLOYMENT GROUP LIMITED—See Bain Capital, LP; *U.S. Private*, pg. 435
THE RESERVES NETWORK INC.; *U.S. Private*, pg. 4104
RIGHT MANAGEMENT KOREA CO. LTD.—See ManpowerGroup Inc.; *U.S. Public*, pg. 1361
RIGHT MANAGEMENT LIMITED—See ManpowerGroup Inc.; *U.S. Public*, pg. 1361
RIGHT MANAGEMENT LUXEMBOURG SA—See ManpowerGroup Inc.; *U.S. Public*, pg. 1361
RIGHT MANAGEMENT MEXICO, S.A. DE C.V.—See ManpowerGroup Inc.; *U.S. Public*, pg. 1361
RIGHT MANAGEMENT NEDERLAND B.V.—See ManpowerGroup Inc.; *U.S. Public*, pg. 1361
RIGHT MANAGEMENT S.A.—See ManpowerGroup Inc.; *U.S. Public*, pg. 1361
RIGHT MANAGEMENT SPAIN, S.L.U.—See ManpowerGroup Inc.; *U.S. Public*, pg. 1361
RIGHT MANAGEMENT SWEDEN AB—See ManpowerGroup Inc.; *U.S. Public*, pg. 1361
RIOJAS ENTERPRISES INC.; *U.S. Private*, pg. 3438
RITA STAFFING INC.; *U.S. Private*, pg. 3441
ROBERT HALF ASSESSORIA EM RECURSOS HUMANOS LTDA.—See Robert Half Inc.; *U.S. Public*, pg. 1803
ROBERT HALF AUSTRALIA PTY. LTD.—See Robert Half Inc.; *U.S. Public*, pg. 1803
ROBERT HALF AUSTRIA GMBH—See Robert Half Inc.; *U.S. Public*, pg. 1803

ROBERT HALF CANADA INC.—See Robert Half Inc.; *U.S. Public*, pg. 1803
ROBERT HALF CORPORATION - ACCOUNTEMPS DIVISION—See Robert Half Inc.; *U.S. Public*, pg. 1803
ROBERT HALF CORPORATION - LEGAL DIVISION—See Robert Half Inc.; *U.S. Public*, pg. 1803
ROBERT HALF CORPORATION - MANAGEMENT RESOURCES DIVISION—See Robert Half Inc.; *U.S. Public*, pg. 1803
ROBERT HALF CORPORATION - OFFICETEAM DIVISION—See Robert Half Inc.; *U.S. Public*, pg. 1803
ROBERT HALF CORPORATION—See Robert Half Inc.; *U.S. Public*, pg. 1803
ROBERT HALF CORPORATION - TECHNOLOGY DIVISION—See Robert Half Inc.; *U.S. Public*, pg. 1803
ROBERT HALF CORPORATION - THE CREATIVE GROUP DIVISION—See Robert Half Inc.; *U.S. Public*, pg. 1803
ROBERT HALF DEUTSCHLAND BETEILIGUNGSGESELLSCHAFT GMBH—See Robert Half Inc.; *U.S. Public*, pg. 1803
ROBERT HALF HONG KONG LIMITED—See Robert Half Inc.; *U.S. Public*, pg. 1803
ROBERT HALF HUMAN RESOURCES SHANGHAI COMPANY LIMITED—See Robert Half Inc.; *U.S. Public*, pg. 1804
ROBERT HALF INTERNATIONAL B.V.—See Robert Half Inc.; *U.S. Public*, pg. 1804
ROBERT HALF INTERNATIONAL (DUBAI) LTD.—See Robert Half Inc.; *U.S. Public*, pg. 1804
ROBERT HALF INTERNATIONAL PTE. LTD.—See Robert Half Inc.; *U.S. Public*, pg. 1804
ROBERT HALF JAPAN LTD.—See Robert Half Inc.; *U.S. Public*, pg. 1804
ROBERT HALF NEDERLAND B.V.—See Robert Half Inc.; *U.S. Public*, pg. 1804
ROBERT HALF SARL—See Robert Half Inc.; *U.S. Public*, pg. 1804
ROBINSON AVIATION (RVA) INC.; *U.S. Private*, pg. 3461
ROPER PERSONNEL SERVICES INC.; *U.S. Private*, pg. 3480
RTG MEDICAL; *U.S. Private*, pg. 3498
SAFESEARCH PTY LIMITED—See ManpowerGroup Inc.; *U.S. Public*, pg. 1362
SAGE STAFFING, INC.; *U.S. Private*, pg. 3527
SALARISPROFS B.V.—See ManpowerGroup Inc.; *U.S. Public*, pg. 1362
THE SALEM GROUP; *U.S. Private*, pg. 4113
SAMPO IP, LLC—See Marathon Digital Holdings, Inc.; *U.S. Public*, pg. 1363
SEEK CAREERS/STAFFING, INC.; *U.S. Private*, pg. 3598
SELECTEMP CORPORATION; *U.S. Private*, pg. 3601
SELECTREMEDY—See Affiliated Managers Group, Inc.; *U.S. Public*, pg. 54
SELECTREMEDY—See Anchorage Capital Group, L.L.C.; *U.S. Private*, pg. 274
SELECT STAFFING—See Affiliated Managers Group, Inc.; *U.S. Public*, pg. 54
SELECT STAFFING—See Anchorage Capital Group, L.L.C.; *U.S. Private*, pg. 274
SELECT STAFFING—See Comarco, Inc.; *U.S. Private*, pg. 980
SELECT TEMPORARIES INC.; *U.S. Private*, pg. 3601
SENTECH SERVICES, INC.; *U.S. Private*, pg. 3608
SHORE CONSTRUCTION LLC; *U.S. Private*, pg. 3641
SIGNATURE CONSULTANTS LLC—See Digital Intelligence Systems, LLC; *U.S. Private*, pg. 1230
SITE PERSONNEL SERVICES INC.; *U.S. Private*, pg. 3676
SKI HI MECHANICAL SERVICES INC.—See Ski Hi Enterprises Ltd.; *U.S. Private*, pg. 3681
SKILLED SERVICES CORPORATION—See TrueBlue, Inc.; *U.S. Public*, pg. 2198
SMART SOURCE, LLC—See Guggenheim Partners, LLC; *U.S. Private*, pg. 1812
SNELLING STAFFING SERVICES—See Patriarch Partners, LLC; *U.S. Private*, pg. 3109
SOLIANT HEALTH INC.—See Olympus Partners; *U.S. Private*, pg. 3013
SOURCE ONE MEDICAL MANAGEMENT; *U.S. Private*, pg. 3718
SOURCE ONE STAFFING LLC; *U.S. Private*, pg. 3718
SPHERION OF LIMA INC.; *U.S. Private*, pg. 3756
SPRING PROFESSIONAL LUXEMBOURG SA.—See Adecco Group AG; *Int'l*, pg. 141
STAFFBUILDERSHR, LLC; *U.S. Private*, pg. 3775
STAFF CARE, INC.—See AMN Healthcare Services, Inc.; *U.S. Public*, pg. 125
STAFF FORCE INC.; *U.S. Private*, pg. 3774
STAFFING ASSOCIATES INC.; *U.S. Private*, pg. 3775
STAFF MANAGEMENT SOLUTIONS, LLC—See TrueBlue, Inc.; *U.S. Public*, pg. 2199
STAFF ON SITE, INC.; *U.S. Private*, pg. 3775
STARK TALENT; *U.S. Private*, pg. 3787
STEGMANN PERSONALDIENSTLEISTUNG GMBH—See ManpowerGroup Inc.; *U.S. Public*, pg. 1362
STIVERS TEMPORARY PERSONNEL INC.; *U.S. Private*, pg. 3813
THE STOLLER GROUP; *U.S. Private*, pg. 4123

561320 — TEMPORARY HELP SERV...

STRIDE ONLINE TUTORING, INC.—See Stride, Inc.; *U.S. Public*, pg. 1955
STS SERVICES, INC.—See STS Holdings, Inc.; *U.S. Private*, pg. 3842
SULLIVAN & COGLIANO—See Sullivan & Cogliano Designers Inc.; *U.S. Private*, pg. 3850
SUMMIT TECHNICAL SERVICES, INC.; *U.S. Private*, pg. 3857
SUN TECHNICAL SERVICES, INC.—See Bernhard Capital Partners Management, LP; *U.S. Private*, pg. 537
THE SUPPORTING CAST, INC.; *U.S. Private*, pg. 4125
SURGICAL STAFF, INC.; *U.S. Private*, pg. 3885
SYGNETICS INCORPORATED; *U.S. Private*, pg. 3898
TAC WORLDWIDE COMPANIES—See American Crystal Holdings, Inc.; *U.S. Private*, pg. 229
TAILORED MANAGEMENT, INC.; *U.S. Private*, pg. 3923
TALLO LLC—See Stride, Inc.; *U.S. Public*, pg. 1955
TALON PROFESSIONAL SERVICES, LLC; *U.S. Private*, pg. 3927
TAOS MOUNTAIN LLC—See International Business Machines Corporation; *U.S. Public*, pg. 1151
TCC SERVICE COMPANY LIMITED—See KKR & Co. Inc.; *U.S. Public*, pg. 1259
TECHNICAL STAFFING DIVISION—See Resilience Capital Partners, LLC; *U.S. Private*, pg. 3405
TECHNOLOGY PLUS INC.; *U.S. Private*, pg. 3955
TECH USA INC.; *U.S. Private*, pg. 3952
TEMPORARY SOLUTIONS INC.—See Employment Enterprises Inc.; *U.S. Private*, pg. 1387
TEMPORARY SYSTEMS INC.—See Meador Staffing Services Inc.; *U.S. Private*, pg. 2647
TEMPWISE, INC.—See The Reserves Network Inc.; *U.S. Private*, pg. 4105
THREEWIRE, INC.—See Leonard Green & Partners, L.P.; *U.S. Private*, pg. 2430
TOPS STAFFING, LLC; *U.S. Private*, pg. 4188
TOTAL STAFFING SOLUTIONS INC.; *U.S. Private*, pg. 4191
TOWNE PARK LTD—See Greenbriar Equity Group, L.P.; *U.S. Private*, pg. 1776
TRANSPORT DRIVERS INC.; *U.S. Private*, pg. 4210
TRANSPORT LEASING/CONTRACT; *U.S. Private*, pg. 4210
TRAVEL NURSE ACROSS AMERICA, LLC; *U.S. Private*, pg. 4213
TRC STAFFING SERVICES, INC.; *U.S. Private*, pg. 4215
TRUEBLUE, INC.; *U.S. Public*, pg. 2198
TRUE NORTH RECRUITING, LLC; *U.S. Private*, pg. 4248
TRUSTAFF, INC.; *U.S. Private*, pg. 4251
TSL LTD.; *U.S. Private*, pg. 4254
T-STAFF, INC.; *U.S. Private*, pg. 3911
TTEC DIGITAL LLC—See TTEC Holdings, Inc.; *U.S. Public*, pg. 2203
TUNTEX EXECUTIVE PARK INC.—See Universal Paragon Corporation; *U.S. Private*, pg. 4306
UNITED STAFFING SOLUTIONS INC.; *U.S. Private*, pg. 4298
UNIVERSAL CONSOLIDATED SERVICES; *U.S. Private*, pg. 4304
VANGUARD TEMPORARIES INC.; *U.S. Private*, pg. 4344
VANPIKE INC.; *U.S. Private*, pg. 4344
VELOSI ANGOLA LDA—See I Squared Capital Advisors (US) LLC; *U.S. Private*, pg. 2024
VELOSI THAI CO., LTD.—See I Squared Capital Advisors (US) LLC; *U.S. Private*, pg. 2024
VIP STAFFING, INC.; *U.S. Private*, pg. 4387
VISIONAIRE PARTNERS; *U.S. Private*, pg. 4392
VOLT EUROPE (FRANCE) SARL—See American CyberSystems, Inc.; *U.S. Private*, pg. 230
VOLT INFORMATION SCIENCES, INC.—See American CyberSystems, Inc.; *U.S. Private*, pg. 229
VOLT TECHNICAL RESOURCES, LLC—See American CyberSystems, Inc.; *U.S. Private*, pg. 230
WESTAFF (AUSTRALIA) PTY. LTD.—See Bluestone Global Limited; *Int'l*, pg. 1075
WESTAFF NZ LIMITED—See Bluestone Global Limited; *Int'l*, pg. 1075
THE WHITAKER COMPANIES, INC.; *U.S. Private*, pg. 4134
WINGFOOT ENTERPRISES INC.; *U.S. Private*, pg. 4541
WINSTON RESOURCES, LLC; *U.S. Private*, pg. 4544
XCEL MANAGEMENT, INC.; *U.S. Private*, pg. 4580
YORKSON LEGAL INC.—See Apax Partners LLP; *Int'l*, pg. 503
ZEROCHAOS, LLC—See TruArc Partners, L.P.; *U.S. Private*, pg. 4246

561330 — PROFESSIONAL EMPLOYER ORGANIZATIONS

A-1 CONTRACT STAFFING, LLC; *U.S. Private*, pg. 21
ABACUS CORPORATION; *U.S. Private*, pg. 33
AB STAFFING SOLUTIONS, LLC; *U.S. Private*, pg. 33
ACCESS POINT LLC—See Management Recruiters International, Inc.; *U.S. Private*, pg. 2560
ACCORD HUMAN RESOURCES, INC.—See Virgo Capital; *U.S. Private*, pg. 4388

ADECCO AUSTRALIA PTY LTD.—See Adecco Group AG; *Int'l*, pg. 136
ADECCO CALEDONIE SARL—See Adecco Group AG; *Int'l*, pg. 136
ADECCO DENMARK A/S—See Adecco Group AG; *Int'l*, pg. 136
ADECCO DO BRASIL LTDA.—See Adecco Group AG; *Int'l*, pg. 139
ADECCO FINLAND OY—See Adecco Group AG; *Int'l*, pg. 136
ADECCO GMBH—See Adecco Group AG; *Int'l*, pg. 137
ADECCO GROUPE FRANCE—See Adecco Group AG; *Int'l*, pg. 137
ADECCO HIZMET VE DANISNANLIK A/S—See Adecco Group AG; *Int'l*, pg. 137
ADECCO IBERIA SA—See Adecco Group AG; *Int'l*, pg. 137
ADECCO IRELAND LTD.—See Adecco Group AG; *Int'l*, pg. 138
ADECCO ISRAEL STAFFING SERVICES LTD.—See Adecco Group AG; *Int'l*, pg. 137
ADECCO ITALY SPA—See Adecco Group AG; *Int'l*, pg. 137
ADECCO KFT—See Adecco Group AG; *Int'l*, pg. 137
ADECCO-KUALA LUMPUR—See Adecco Group AG; *Int'l*, pg. 139
ADECCO LTD.—See Adecco Group AG; *Int'l*, pg. 137
ADECCO LUXEMBOURG S.A.—See Adecco Group AG; *Int'l*, pg. 137
ADECCO MONACO SAM—See Adecco Group AG; *Int'l*, pg. 137
ADECCO NETHERLANDS BEHEER B.V.—See Adecco Group AG; *Int'l*, pg. 137
ADECCO NORGE AS—See Adecco Group AG; *Int'l*, pg. 137
ADECCO PERSONNEL CONSULTANTS CO., LTD. TAIWAN—See Adecco Group AG; *Int'l*, pg. 137
ADECCO PERSONNEL LIMITED—See Adecco Group AG; *Int'l*, pg. 136
ADECCO PERSONNEL PTE. LTD.—See Adecco Group AG; *Int'l*, pg. 137
ADECCO PERSONNEL SERVICES S.A.—See Adecco Group AG; *Int'l*, pg. 137
ADECCO PERU S.A.—See Adecco Group AG; *Int'l*, pg. 137
ADECCO PHAHOLYOTHIN—See Adecco Group AG; *Int'l*, pg. 137
ADECCO POLAND SP. Z O.O.—See Adecco Group AG; *Int'l*, pg. 137
ADECCO RECRUITMENT SERVICES—See Adecco Group AG; *Int'l*, pg. 137
ADECCO RECURSOS HUMANOS S.A.—See Adecco Group AG; *Int'l*, pg. 138
ADECCO RECURSOS HUMANOS—See Adecco Group AG; *Int'l*, pg. 138
ADECCO RESSOURCES HUMAINES S.A.—See Adecco Group AG; *Int'l*, pg. 138
ADECCO-SHANGHAI—See Adecco Group AG; *Int'l*, pg. 139
ADECCO SPOL. S R.O.—See Adecco Group AG; *Int'l*, pg. 139
ADECCO-STOCKHOLM—See Adecco Group AG; *Int'l*, pg. 139
ADECCO UK LTD.—See Adecco Group AG; *Int'l*, pg. 138
ADECCO URUGUAY S.A.—See Adecco Group AG; *Int'l*, pg. 139
ADECCO-VENEZUELA—See Adecco Group AG; *Int'l*, pg. 139
ADECCO-WANCHAI—See Adecco Group AG; *Int'l*, pg. 139
ADIA FRANCE—See Adecco Group AG; *Int'l*, pg. 137
ADMINISTRATIVE CONCEPT CORP.; *U.S. Private*, pg. 80
AEROTEK, INC.—See Allegis Group, Inc.; *U.S. Private*, pg. 177
AGILE RESOURCES, INC.—See GEE Group Inc.; *U.S. Public*, pg. 909
ALTECH CORPORATION; *Int'l*, pg. 388
AMBROSE EMPLOYER GROUP, LLC—See General Atlantic Service Company, L.P.; *U.S. Private*, pg. 1663
ANDERSELITE LTD. - LONDON—See AndersElite Ltd.; *Int'l*, pg. 450
AP VERITAS—See Management Recruiters International, Inc.; *U.S. Private*, pg. 2560
ARROW STRATEGIES, LLC; *U.S. Private*, pg. 336
ATLAS STAFFING INC.; *U.S. Private*, pg. 380
THE BERYL COMPANIES; *U.S. Private*, pg. 3994
BICI-BAIL DE COTE D'IVOIRE—See BNP Paribas SA; *Int'l*, pg. 1080
THE BLOCK AGENCY, INC.; *U.S. Private*, pg. 3995
BNP PARIBAS LEASE GROUP SP. Z O.O.—See BNP Paribas SA; *Int'l*, pg. 1085
BUTLER SERVICE GROUP - U.K. LTD.—See Butler America, Inc.; *U.S. Private*, pg. 696
CAREER PERSONNEL LIMITED—See HRnetGroup Limited; *Int'l*, pg. 3501
CARLISLE SECURITY SERVICES LTD.—See HFBG Holding B.V.; *Int'l*, pg. 3374
CATAPULT EMPLOYERS ASSOCIATION, INC.; *U.S. Private*, pg. 787
CERTIGY INC.; *U.S. Private*, pg. 842
CO-ADVANTAGE RESOURCES INC.; *U.S. Private*, pg. 953
CYBER 360 SOLUTIONS—See Staffing 360 Solutions, Inc.; *U.S. Public*, pg. 1925

CYPRESS HUMAN CAPITAL MANAGEMENT, LLC.; *U.S. Private*, pg. 1135
DEWINTER HOLDINGS, LLC.—See New Heritage Capital LLC; *U.S. Private*, pg. 2896
DIS AG—See Adecco Group AG; *Int'l*, pg. 141
ELWOOD PROFESSIONAL—See Elwood Staffing Services, Inc.; *U.S. Private*, pg. 1377
EMERGENCY MEDICINE CONSULTANTS, LTD.—See Blackstone Inc.; *U.S. Public*, pg. 359
EMPLOYER'S DEPOT INC.; *U.S. Private*, pg. 1386
EMPLOYER SERVICES CORPORATION—See Stone Point Capital LLC; *U.S. Private*, pg. 3822
EMPO CORPORATION; *U.S. Private*, pg. 1386
EUROTUNNEL SERVICES GIE—See Getlink SE; *Int'l*, pg. 2953
FAHRENHEIT IT, INC.—See Global Employment Holdings, Inc.; *U.S. Private*, pg. 1713
FIRSTSOURCEHR, INC.; *U.S. Private*, pg. 1532
FORREST SOLUTIONS GROUP; *U.S. Private*, pg. 1572
FORTUNE INDUSTRIES INC.—See Paychex, Inc.; *U.S. Public*, pg. 1655
FRANKCRUM; *U.S. Private*, pg. 1596
GLOBAL TECHNICAL SERVICES, INC.; *U.S. Private*, pg. 1718
HARBOR AMERICA; *U.S. Private*, pg. 1858
HITECH GROUP AUSTRALIA LIMITED; *Int'l*, pg. 3425
HOWARD LEASING INC.; *U.S. Private*, pg. 1995
HR AMERICA INC.; *U.S. Private*, pg. 1997
HR, INC.; *U.S. Private*, pg. 1998
HR STRATEGIES COMPANY; *U.S. Private*, pg. 1998
HSP, INC.—See Brookfield Corporation; *Int'l*, pg. 1183
HUMAN RESOURCES INCORPORATED; *U.S. Private*, pg. 2006
ICON RECRUITMENT LIMITED—See Adecco Group AG; *Int'l*, pg. 136
ICON RECRUITMENT LTD.—See Adecco Group AG; *Int'l*, pg. 136
INTEGRITY EMPLOYEE LEASING, INC.; *U.S. Private*, pg. 2102
INTERNATIONAL MANAGEMENT SERVICES COMPANY; *U.S. Private*, pg. 2118
IVY EXEC, INC.; *U.S. Private*, pg. 2152
KELLY FINANCIAL RESOURCES—See Kelly Services, Inc.; *U.S. Public*, pg. 1220
KELLY MANAGED SERVICES—See Kelly Services, Inc.; *U.S. Public*, pg. 1220
KELLY SERVICES (NEDERLAND) B.V.—See Kelly Services, Inc.; *U.S. Public*, pg. 1219
KELLY SERVICES (UK) LTD.—See Kelly Services, Inc.; *U.S. Public*, pg. 1219
KENBAR SERVICES INC.; *U.S. Private*, pg. 2283
LANDRUM PROFESSIONAL EMPLOYER SERVICES, INC.—See Landrum Human Resource Companies, Inc.; *U.S. Private*, pg. 2386
LEE HECHT HARRISON AG—See Adecco Group AG; *Int'l*, pg. 139
MARKETSOURCE, INC.—See Allegis Group, Inc.; *U.S. Private*, pg. 177
MARKET STAFF INC.; *U.S. Private*, pg. 2579
MODERN BUSINESS ASSOCIATES, INC.; *U.S. Private*, pg. 2759
MODIS—See Adecco Group AG; *Int'l*, pg. 136
MOMENTUM RESOURCES, INC.—See Aquiline Capital Partners LLC; *U.S. Private*, pg. 304
MOVADIS SA—See Adecco Group AG; *Int'l*, pg. 137
OASIS OUTSOURCING, INC.—See Paychex, Inc.; *U.S. Public*, pg. 1655
OASIS OUTSOURCING—See Paychex, Inc.; *U.S. Public*, pg. 1655
OPPORTUNITIES, INC.; *U.S. Private*, pg. 3033
PEAK TECHNICAL SERVICES, TROY—See Peak Technical Services, Inc.; *U.S. Private*, pg. 3124
PEOPLE INC.; *U.S. Private*, pg. 3140
PEOPLE PREMIER, INC.; *U.S. Private*, pg. 3140
PEOPLESERVE, INC.—See Staffing 360 Solutions, Inc.; *U.S. Public*, pg. 1925
PREMIUM ENTERPRISES INC.—See Premium Transportation Staffing, Inc.; *U.S. Private*, pg. 3252
PREMIUM OF NORTH CAROLINA INC.—See Premium Transportation Staffing, Inc.; *U.S. Private*, pg. 3252
PREMIUM OF TENNESSEE INC.—See Premium Transportation Staffing, Inc.; *U.S. Private*, pg. 3252
PREMIUM TRANSPORTATION STAFFING, INC.; *U.S. Private*, pg. 3252
THE PROVEN METHOD INC.—See Marathon TS, Inc.; *U.S. Private*, pg. 2570
QED NATIONAL; *U.S. Private*, pg. 3312
RECRUIT EXPRESS PTE. LTD.—See HRnetGroup Limited; *Int'l*, pg. 3502
RECRUITFIRST LIMITED—See HRnetGroup Limited; *Int'l*, pg. 3502
RECRUITFIRST PTE. LTD.—See HRnetGroup Limited; *Int'l*, pg. 3502
REMEDY EMPLOYER SERVICES, LLC—See Aquiline Capital Partners LLC; *U.S. Private*, pg. 304
RESOURCE MANAGEMENT INC.—See Vensure Employer Services, Inc.; *U.S. Private*, pg. 4357
RICHFIELD INDUSTRIES, CORP.; *U.S. Private*, pg. 3430

N.A.I.C.S. INDEX

ROEVIN LIMITED—See Adecco Group AG; *Int'l*, pg. 138
ROEVIN MANAGEMENT SERVICES LTD.—See Adecco Group AG; *Int'l*, pg. 138
SCI COMPANIES—See People Inc.; *U.S. Private*, pg. 3140
SEARCHASIA CONSULTING PTE. LTD.—See HRnetGroup Limited; *Int'l*, pg. 3502
SIMPLIFIED BUSINESS SOLUTIONS, INC.—See iSolved HCM LLC; *U.S. Private*, pg. 2146
SKILSTAF INC.; *U.S. Private*, pg. 3682
SOUTHEAST PERSONNEL LEASING, INC.; *U.S. Private*, pg. 3726
SPECIAL COUNSEL INC.—See Adecco Group AG; *Int'l*, pg. 141
SPRING GROUP AUSTRALIA PTY LIMITED—See Adecco Group AG; *Int'l*, pg. 138
STEGDOC GMBH—See ManpowerGroup Inc.; *U.S. Public*, pg. 1362
STEPHEN JAMES ASSOCIATES, INC.—See Allegis Group, Inc.; *U.S. Private*, pg. 177
SUBSIDIUM HEALTHCARE, LLC; *U.S. Private*, pg. 3847
SULLIVAN & COGLIANO DESIGNERS INC.; *U.S. Private*, pg. 3850
TALENTSCALE, LLC—See SCST, Inc.; *U.S. Private*, pg. 3581
TECHNICAL STAFFING RESOURCES, LLC—See KBR, Inc.; *U.S. Public*, pg. 1216
TECHNOPRO SMILE, INC.—See CVC Capital Partners SICAV-FIS S.A.; *Int'l*, pg. 1885
TEKSYSTEMS, INC.—See Allegis Group, Inc.; *U.S. Private*, pg. 177
TEMPLAR HUMAN SEARCH INC—See Adecco Group AG; *Int'l*, pg. 139
TEMPLAR INTERNATIONAL CONSULTANTS LIMITED—See Adecco Group AG; *Int'l*, pg. 139
TFE GROUP INC.—See International Management Services Company; *U.S. Private*, pg. 2118
TOWER LEGAL STAFFING, INC.—See Surge Private Equity LLC; *U.S. Private*, pg. 3884
TRANSPORT LABOR CONTRACT/LEASING—See Berggruen Holdings, Inc.; *U.S. Private*, pg. 531
TRANSPORT LABOR CONTRACT/LEASING—See High Street Capital Management, Inc.; *U.S. Private*, pg. 1937
TRANSPORT LABOR CONTRACT/LEASING—See SE Capital, LLC; *U.S. Private*, pg. 3582
TRS STAFFING SOLUTIONS, S. DE R.L. DE C.V.—See Fluor Corporation; *U.S. Public*, pg. 860
UNIVERSAL SELECT INC.; *U.S. Private*, pg. 4306
VISIONIT; *U.S. Private*, pg. 4392
VISION TECHNOLOGY SERVICES, LLC—See BGSF, Inc.; *U.S. Public*, pg. 330

561410 — DOCUMENT PREPARATION SERVICES

ACCENTUS INC.—See Microsoft Corporation; *U.S. Public*, pg. 1442
ALLSCRIPTS HEALTHCARE, LLC—See Veradigm Inc.; *U.S. Public*, pg. 2279
ALLSCRIPTS SOFTWARE, LLC—See Veradigm Inc.; *U.S. Public*, pg. 2280
AMADA DOCUMECH CO., LTD.—See Amada Holdings Co., Ltd.; *Int'l*, pg. 403
AMPHION MEDICAL SOLUTIONS, LLC—See iMedX, Inc.; *U.S. Private*, pg. 2046
ANACOMP, INC.; *U.S. Public*, pg. 134
ANTENNA HOUSE, INC.; *Int'l*, pg. 482
APN EDUCATIONAL MEDIA—See ARN Media Limited; *Int'l*, pg. 576
ARCHERHALL, LLC; *U.S. Private*, pg. 311
BARRISTER REPORTING SERVICE, INC.—See Apax Partners LLP; *Int'l*, pg. 503
BUSINESS BROKERS OF SAN ANTONIO; *U.S. Private*, pg. 694
CERENCE SWITZERLAND AG—See Microsoft Corporation; *U.S. Public*, pg. 1442
CF COMUNICACION, S.L.; *Int'l*, pg. 1429
CHARLES TAYLOR ADMINISTRATION SERVICES LIMITED—See Lovell Minnick Partners LLC; *U.S. Private*, pg. 2502
CINTAS DOCUMENT MANAGEMENT INC.—See Cintas Corporation; *U.S. Public*, pg. 495
CINTAS DOCUMENT MANAGEMENT, LLC—See Cintas Corporation; *U.S. Public*, pg. 495
CMC ASIA PACIFIC CO., LTD.—See CMC Corporation; *Int'l*, pg. 1669
CREDENTIALS INC.—See SCRIP-SAFE Security Products, Inc.; *U.S. Private*, pg. 3579
CRESTEC ELECTRONICS TECHNOLOGY (ZHUHAI) CO., LTD.—See Crestec Inc.; *Int'l*, pg. 1841
CRESTEC INC.; *Int'l*, pg. 1841
CRESTEC (SHANGHAI) CO., LTD.—See Crestec Inc.; *Int'l*, pg. 1841
CRITICAL TECHNOLOGIES, INC.—See General Electric Company; *U.S. Public*, pg. 918
DIGITAL TRANSCRIPTION SYSTEM, INC.—See Travis Business Systems Inc.; *U.S. Private*, pg. 4214

DRS IMAGING SERVICES, LLC—See The HiGro Group LLC; *U.S. Private*, pg. 4052
DTSV INC.; *U.S. Private*, pg. 1282
EBYLINE, INC.—See IZEA Worldwide, Inc.; *U.S. Public*, pg. 1179
EDGARIZING SOLUTIONS, INC.; *U.S. Private*, pg. 1333
EDICO FINANCIAL PRESS SERVICES LIMITED—See EDICO Holdings Limited; *Int'l*, pg. 2309
EIGHT CROSSINGS; *U.S. Private*, pg. 1347
ESKER DOCUMENTS AUTOMATION ASIA PTE LTD—See Esker S.A.; *Int'l*, pg. 2503
EXBO SERVICES INTERNATIONAL SA/NV—See bpost NV/SA; *Int'l*, pg. 1133
FIRST SHANGHAI MANAGEMENT SERVICES LIMITED—See First Shanghai Investments Limited; *Int'l*, pg. 2687
FRASER ADVANCED INFORMATION SYSTEMS; *U.S. Private*, pg. 1599
FUJI XEROX DOCUMENT MANAGEMENT SOLUTIONS ASIA LIMITED—See FUJIFILM Holdings Corporation; *Int'l*, pg. 2825
FUJI XEROX DOCUMENT MANAGEMENT SOLUTIONS PTY LTD—See FUJIFILM Holdings Corporation; *Int'l*, pg. 2825
GCMC INFORMATION TECHNOLOGY CO., LTD.—See CMC Corporation; *Int'l*, pg. 1669
GENERAL FINANCIAL SUPPLY, INC. - VIRGINIA—See Ennis, Inc.; *U.S. Public*, pg. 769
GRACE TECHNOLOGY, INC.; *Int'l*, pg. 3048
GRANDFLOW, INC.—See Smart Source of Georgia, LLC; *U.S. Private*, pg. 3691
HUMAN GLOBAL COMMUNICATIONS CO., LTD.—See Human Holdings Co., Ltd.; *Int'l*, pg. 3529
IFIS JAPAN LTD.—See Daiwa Securities Group Inc.; *Int'l*, pg. 1949
IMAGICA KADOKAWA EDITORIAL CO., LTD.—See Imagica Group Inc.; *Int'l*, pg. 3618
LAW CENTRAL CO. PTY. LTD.—See Count Limited; *Int'l*, pg. 1818
LIKEABLE MEDIA; *U.S. Private*, pg. 2455
MAIN CO., LTD.—See CMC Corporation; *Int'l*, pg. 1669
MARUBOSHI EUROPE B.V.—See CMC Corporation; *Int'l*, pg. 1669
MARUBOSHI THAILAND CO., LTD.—See CMC Corporation; *Int'l*, pg. 1669
MARUZEN CO., LTD. - LONDON OFFICE—See Dai Nippon Printing Co., Ltd.; *Int'l*, pg. 1915
MARUZEN MEGA PASARAYA—See Dai Nippon Printing Co., Ltd.; *Int'l*, pg. 1915
MARUZEN PASARAYA MANGGARAI—See Dai Nippon Printing Co., Ltd.; *Int'l*, pg. 1916
MAXIM HEALTH INFORMATION SERVICES—See Maxim Healthcare Services, Inc.; *U.S. Private*, pg. 2618
MEDHEALTH PTY LIMITED—See GIC Pte. Ltd.; *Int'l*, pg. 2964
MEDHEALTH PTY LIMITED—See Leonard Green & Partners, L.P.; *U.S. Private*, pg. 2425
MENDIP MEDIA GROUP LIMITED—See Appen Limited; *Int'l*, pg. 519
MERRILL CORPORATION—See aPriori Capital Partners L.P.; *U.S. Private*, pg. 301
MERRILL FRANCE S.A.R.L.—See aPriori Capital Partners L.P.; *U.S. Private*, pg. 302
MERRILL GERMANY GMBH—See aPriori Capital Partners L.P.; *U.S. Private*, pg. 302
MILNER DOCUMENT PRODUCTS, INC.; *U.S. Private*, pg. 2738
MIMEO.COM, INC.; *U.S. Private*, pg. 2740
NEUROSTAR SOLUTIONS, INC.—See Microsoft Corporation; *U.S. Public*, pg. 1442
NOVITEX GOVERNMENT SOLUTIONS, LLC—See Exela Technologies, Inc.; *U.S. Public*, pg. 806
NOVUS LAW, LLC—See Rock Gate Partners LLC; *U.S. Private*, pg. 3464
NUANCE DOCUMENT IMAGING ULC—See Microsoft Corporation; *U.S. Public*, pg. 1442
NUANCE TRANSCRIPTION SERVICES, INC.—See Microsoft Corporation; *U.S. Public*, pg. 1443
PMC CO., LTD.—See CDS Co., Ltd.; *Int'l*, pg. 1371
PT. HITACHI HIGH-TECH INDONESIA—See Hitachi, Ltd.; *Int'l*, pg. 3424
REVSPRING, INC.—See GTCR LLC; *U.S. Private*, pg. 1806
SCRIP-SAFE SECURITY PRODUCTS, INC.; *U.S. Private*, pg. 3579
SECOND IMAGE NATIONAL, INC.—See Aquiline Capital Partners LLC; *U.S. Private*, pg. 304
SERVICELINK NATIONAL FLOOD, LLC—See Fidelity National Financial, Inc.; *U.S. Public*, pg. 831
SIGNIUS COMMUNICATIONS—See AnswerNet, Inc.; *U.S. Private*, pg. 286
SPEOS BELGIUM SA/NV—See bpost NV/SA; *Int'l*, pg. 1133
SUTHERLAND GLOBAL SERVICES EGYPT, LLC—See Sutherland Global Services, Inc.; *U.S. Private*, pg. 3886
SUTHERLAND GLOBAL SERVICES JLT—See Sutherland Global Services, Inc.; *U.S. Private*, pg. 3886
SUTHERLAND (SUZHOU) INFORMATION CONSULTING CO., LTD.—See Sutherland Global Services, Inc.; *U.S. Private*, pg. 3886

TRANSPERFECT DOCUMENT MANAGEMENT, INC.—See TransPerfect Global, Inc.; *U.S. Private*, pg. 4210
UPSTREAM PRINT SOLUTIONS AUSTRALIA PTY LTD—See FUJIFILM Holdings Corporation; *Int'l*, pg. 2826
VERIZON DIRECTORY SUPPORT CENTER—See Verizon Communications Inc.; *U.S. Public*, pg. 2286
VOICE SIGNAL IRELAND LIMITED—See Microsoft Corporation; *U.S. Public*, pg. 1443
WONDERWARE, INC.; *U.S. Private*, pg. 4556
WRITERACCESS—See Blackstone Inc.; *U.S. Public*, pg. 353
WRITERACCESS—See Vista Equity Partners, LLC; *U.S. Private*, pg. 4396
ZENO OFFICE SOLUTIONS, INC.; *U.S. Private*, pg. 4601
ZERT AB—See AFRY AB; *Int'l*, pg. 196

561421 — TELEPHONE ANSWERING SERVICES

1-800 WE ANSWER, INC.; *U.S. Private*, pg. 1
ADVANCED SERVICES, INC.—See Haier Smart Home Co., Ltd.; *Int'l*, pg. 3210
ALBATROS SERVICE CENTER GMBH—See Deutsche Lufthansa AG; *Int'l*, pg. 2066
A MESSAGE CENTER INC.; *U.S. Private*, pg. 18
ANSAFONE CONTACT CENTERS; *U.S. Private*, pg. 285
ANSWER-1 COMMUNICATIONS; *U.S. Private*, pg. 286
ANSWERFIRST COMMUNICATIONS, INC.; *U.S. Private*, pg. 286
ANSWERNET, INC.; *U.S. Private*, pg. 286
ANSWERPHONE; *U.S. Private*, pg. 286
APPLETREE ANSWERING SERVICES, INC.; *U.S. Private*, pg. 297
ATENTO INVERSIONES Y TELESERVICIOS, S.A.U.—See Bain Capital, LP; *U.S. Private*, pg. 430
ATENTO TELESERVICIOS ESPANA, S.A.U.—See Bain Capital, LP; *U.S. Private*, pg. 430
ATLANTA DATACOM INC.; *U.S. Private*, pg. 370
BASIN TELECOMMUNICATION, INC.—See Basin Electric Power Cooperative; *U.S. Private*, pg. 485
BEEPER COMMUNICATIONS ISRAEL LTD.—See Motorola Solutions, Inc.; *U.S. Public*, pg. 1478
BUNKERFUELS CORPORATION—See World Kinect Corporation; *U.S. Public*, pg. 2380
CALL EXPERTS; *U.S. Private*, pg. 721
CALLITECH LIMITED—See ECI Partners LLP; *Int'l*, pg. 2289
CALLOGIX, INC.; *U.S. Private*, pg. 722
CALVERT SHAREHOLDER SERVICES, INC.—See Ameritas Mutual Holding Company; *U.S. Private*, pg. 261
CARECALL INC.; *U.S. Private*, pg. 752
CARGO FUTURE COMMUNICATIONS (CFC) GMBH—See Deutsche Lufthansa AG; *Int'l*, pg. 2069
CUSTOMER CONTACT SERVICES CCS; *U.S. Private*, pg. 1130
ELUON LBS CORP.—See ELUON Corporation; *Int'l*, pg. 2371
ENABLX, INC.; *U.S. Private*, pg. 1389
EXAMINATION MANAGEMENT SERVICES, INC. - NATIONAL SERVICE CENTER—See Beecken Petty O'Keefe & Company, LLC; *U.S. Private*, pg. 514
FINGER LAKES BUSINESS SERVICES; *U.S. Private*, pg. 1509
FLEXTRONICS ITALY S.P.A—See Flex Ltd.; *Int'l*, pg. 2703
FUJIKURA TECHNOLOGY EUROPE GMBH—See Fujikura Ltd.; *Int'l*, pg. 2829
GLOBAL RESPONSE CORPORATION; *U.S. Private*, pg. 1717
GLOBAL TELE SALES PTY LIMITED—See Deutsche Lufthansa AG; *Int'l*, pg. 2069
GLOBAL TELE SALES (PTY) LTD.—See Deutsche Lufthansa AG; *Int'l*, pg. 2069
GP COMMUNICATIONS, LLC—See Oblong, Inc.; *U.S. Public*, pg. 1560
HELLO, INC.; *U.S. Private*, pg. 1911
HYPER CORPORATION; *Int'l*, pg. 3552
ILD CORP.—See ILD Corp.; *U.S. Public*, pg. 2041
IMAGE OFFICE SERVICES—See Arvig Enterprises, Inc.; *U.S. Private*, pg. 345
IMPET SP. Z O.O.—See Grupa Kety S.A.; *Int'l*, pg. 3117
INTELLIVERSE—See The Gores Group, LLC; *U.S. Private*, pg. 4035
INTERACTIVE COMMUNICATIONS INC; *U.S. Private*, pg. 2108
INTERNATIONAL SOS ASSISTANCE, INC.—See AEA International Holdings Pte. Ltd.; *Int'l*, pg. 170
INTERNATIONAL SOS (FRANCE) S.A.—See AEA International Holdings Pte. Ltd.; *Int'l*, pg. 170
INTERNATIONAL SOS PTE. LTD.—See AEA International Holdings Pte. Ltd.; *Int'l*, pg. 170
INVENTERGY GLOBAL, INC.; *U.S. Public*, pg. 1161
J.LODGE, LLC; *U.S. Private*, pg. 2168
KUSTOMER, INC.—See Meta Platforms, Inc.; *U.S. Public*, pg. 1427
MAP COMMUNICATIONS INC.; *U.S. Private*, pg. 2568

561421 — TELEPHONE ANSWERING...

NEXICORE SERVICES, LLC - CALL CENTER—See Avnet, Inc.; *U.S. Public*, pg. 253
NORSTAN, INC.—See Black Box Limited; *Int'l*, pg. 1058
THE OFFICE GURUS, LTD.—See Superior Group Of Companies, Inc.; *U.S. Private*, pg. 1966
PAGEONE COMMUNICATIONS LIMITED—See Erisbeg Holdings Limited; *Int'l*, pg. 2493
REALVOICE LLC; *U.S. Private*, pg. 3369
THE RESULTS COMPANIES LLC—See OEP Capital Advisors, L.P.; *U.S. Private*, pg. 3000
SERPRO INC.; *U.S. Private*, pg. 3614
SIGNIUS CORP.—See AnswerNet, Inc.; *U.S. Private*, pg. 286
SIGNIUS INVESTMENT CORPORATION—See AnswerNet, Inc.; *U.S. Private*, pg. 286
SKY DEUTSCHLAND SERVICE CENTER GMBH—See Comcast Corporation; *U.S. Public*, pg. 541
SOUND TELECOM; *U.S. Private*, pg. 3717
TELELINK SERVICES INC.—See FirstService Corporation; *Int'l*, pg. 2691
TELEMESSAGING SERVICES INC.; *U.S. Private*, pg. 3960
TELEREACH, INC.—See Aquiline Capital Partners LLC; *U.S. Private*, pg. 305
VAIL SYSTEMS INC.; *U.S. Private*, pg. 4329
VERIZON COMMUNICATIONS INC. - ROANOKE, VA—See Verizon Communications Inc.; *U.S. Public*, pg. 2285
XENTEL INC.—See iMarketing Solutions Group Inc.; *Int'l*, pg. 3620

561422 — TELEMARKETING BUREAUS AND OTHER CONTACT CENTERS

ALBEDO SDN. BHD.—See China Medical (International) Group Limited; *Int'l*, pg. 1518
ALMA INTERMEDIA OY—See Alma Media Corporation; *Int'l*, pg. 361
ALTA RESOURCES CORPORATION; *U.S. Private*, pg. 203
ALTA RESOURCES - PHILIPPINES—See Alta Resources Corporation; *U.S. Private*, pg. 203
ALTEC PRODUCTS INC.—See Beyond Limits, Inc.; *U.S. Private*, pg. 548
AMERIDIAL, INC.; *U.S. Private*, pg. 259
ANA TELEMART CO., LTD.—See ANA Holdings Inc.; *Int'l*, pg. 444
ARMATIS SA—See Activa Capital S.A.S.; *Int'l*, pg. 119
ARTERIA S.A.; *Int'l*, pg. 583
CA MOBILE LTD.—See CyberAgent, Inc.; *Int'l*, pg. 1892
CAREER HORIZONS, INC.; *U.S. Private*, pg. 752
CERIDA—See AnswerNet, Inc.; *U.S. Private*, pg. 286
CHINA CUSTOMER RELATIONS CENTERS, INC.; *Int'l*, pg. 1496
COMDATA SPA—See The Carlyle Group Inc.; *U.S. Public*, pg. 2045
COMPUTACENTER SERVICES (IBERIA) SLU—See Computacenter plc; *Int'l*, pg. 1758
CONNECT ASSIST LIMITED—See MAXIMUS, Inc.; *U.S. Public*, pg. 1402
CONSORZIO STABILE CENTO ORIZZONTI SCARL—See GPI S.p.A.; *Int'l*, pg. 3046
CONVERGYS GLOBAL SERVICES GMBH—See Concentrix Corporation; *U.S. Public*, pg. 565
CONVERGYS GROUP SERVICIOS DE APOYO INFORMATICO, S.L.—See Concentrix Corporation; *U.S. Public*, pg. 565
CONVERGYS INTERNATIONAL BULGARIA EOOD—See Concentrix Corporation; *U.S. Public*, pg. 565
CONVERGYS INTERNATIONAL NORDIC AB—See Concentrix Corporation; *U.S. Public*, pg. 565
CONVERGYS IRELAND LIMITED—See Concentrix Corporation; *U.S. Public*, pg. 565
CONVERGYS MALAYSIA SDN BHD—See Concentrix Corporation; *U.S. Public*, pg. 565
CONVERGYS PHILIPPINES INC.—See Concentrix Corporation; *U.S. Public*, pg. 565
CONVERGYS SERVICES PHILIPPINES, INC.—See Concentrix Corporation; *U.S. Public*, pg. 565
CONVERGYS SERVICES SINGAPORE PTE. LTD.—See Concentrix Corporation; *U.S. Public*, pg. 565
CONVERGYS STREAM PVT. LTD.—See Concentrix Corporation; *U.S. Public*, pg. 565
CORFACTS, INC.; *U.S. Private*, pg. 1050
CR DYNAMICS & ASSOCIATES; *U.S. Private*, pg. 1081
CSP CREATIVE SERVICE CO., LTD—See Central Security Patrols Co., Ltd.; *Int'l*, pg. 1410
CSSC CUSTOMER SALES SERVICE CENTER GMBH—See Erste Group Bank AG; *Int'l*, pg. 2498
DATACONTACT SP. Z O.O.—See Gimv NV; *Int'l*, pg. 2976
DATALINKS CORPORATION; *Int'l*, pg. 1978
DESIGN MILK CO. LIMITED; *Int'l*, pg. 2045
DESIGN YOUR HOME HOLDING AB; *Int'l*, pg. 2045
DIXIE HOMECRAFTERS INC.; *U.S. Private*, pg. 1245
DOUBLEDAY CANADA LIMITED—See Pride Tree Holdings, Inc.; *U.S. Private*, pg. 3260
DSP LABS LIMITED—See Mitek Systems, Inc.; *U.S. Public*, pg. 1452
DYNAMICS MARKETING INC.; *U.S. Private*, pg. 1299

EBSCO TELESERVICES—See EBSCO Industries, Inc.; *U.S. Private*, pg. 1325
EGAIN FRANCE S.A.R.L.—See eGain Corporation; *U.S. Public*, pg. 721
ENERGIE STEIERMARK KUNDEN GMBH—See Energie Steiermark AG; *Int'l*, pg. 2420
EPRO TELECOM HOLDINGS LIMITED—See ETS Group Limited; *Int'l*, pg. 2524
ESD ENERGIE SERVICE DEUTSCHLAND GMBH—See EnBW Energie Baden-Wurttemberg AG; *Int'l*, pg. 2398
ETELECARE PHILIPPINES, INC.—See Concentrix Corporation; *U.S. Public*, pg. 565
EXCEL REALTY N INFRA LTD.; *Int'l*, pg. 2577
FCR, LLC—See Republic Services, Inc.; *U.S. Public*, pg. 1786
FIRST LEADS, LLC—See RE/MAX Holdings, Inc.; *U.S. Public*, pg. 1768
FREECHARGE PAYMENT TECHNOLOGIES PVT. LTD.—See Axis Bank Limited; *Int'l*, pg. 769
GA-COM TELEKOMMUNIKATION UND TELEMATIK GMBH—See Alpiq Holding AG; *Int'l*, pg. 372
GASLIGHT PROMOTIONAL CONSULTING, INC.—See CE Competitive Edge LLC; *U.S. Private*, pg. 803
GLOBAL TELESOURCING, LLC; *U.S. Private*, pg. 1718
GRUPO TELVISTA, S.A. DE C.V.—See America Movil, S.A.B. de C.V.; *Int'l*, pg. 421
GS TELESERVICE INC—See GS Holdings Corp.; *Int'l*, pg. 3142
HAINES & COMPANY, INC. - HAINES DIRECT DIVISION—See Haines & Company, Inc.; *U.S. Private*, pg. 1840
IBEX GLOBAL SOLUTIONS LIMITED—See The Resource Group International Ltd.; *U.S. Private*, pg. 4105
ICTV BRANDS INC.; *U.S. Public*, pg. 1086
INCALL SYSTEMS PTE. LTD.—See Challenger Technologies Ltd.; *Int'l*, pg. 1438
INFOCISION MANAGEMENT CORP.; *U.S. Private*, pg. 2072
INKTEL DIRECT INC.; *U.S. Private*, pg. 2078
INSERVICE AMERICA INCORPORATED; *U.S. Private*, pg. 2085
INTERACTIVE RESPONSE TECHNOLOGIES; *U.S. Private*, pg. 2108
IRT OF TEXAS—See Interactive Response Technologies; *U.S. Private*, pg. 2108
LEAD GENERATION SOLUTIONS; *U.S. Private*, pg. 2405
LIFEBOAT DISTRIBUTION, EMEA B.V.—See Climb Global Solutions, Inc.; *U.S. Public*, pg. 515
LIFEBOAT DISTRIBUTION, INC.—See Climb Global Solutions, Inc.; *U.S. Public*, pg. 515
MARK FACEY & COMPANY; *U.S. Private*, pg. 2577
MBNA MARKETING SYSTEMS, INC.—See Bank of America Corporation; *U.S. Public*, pg. 271
MEDCOMM SOLUTIONS, LLC—See Dohmen Co.; *U.S. Private*, pg. 2761
MEDICAL DATA MANAGEMENT, INC.—See IQVIA Holdings Inc.; *U.S. Public*, pg. 1169
MIDCO OF SOUTH DAKOTA, INC.—See Midcontinent Media Inc.; *U.S. Private*, pg. 2711
NOBLE VOICE LLC—See Professional Diversity Network, Inc.; *U.S. Public*, pg. 1724
NOVO 1, INC.; *U.S. Private*, pg. 2968
ONECOMMAND, INC.—See Affinitiv, Inc.; *U.S. Private*, pg. 122
PCMG INC.—See Insight Enterprises, Inc.; *U.S. Public*, pg. 1130
PEKAO DIRECT SP. Z O.O—See Bank Polska Kasa Opieki Spolka Akcyjna; *Int'l*, pg. 850
PORTWAY INTERNATIONAL INC.—See Vista Equity Partners, LLC; *U.S. Private*, pg. 4395
PREZAKAZNICKA A.S.—See EnBW Energie Baden-Wurttemberg AG; *Int'l*, pg. 2399
SENTURE, LLC—See Kingswood Capital Management LLC; *U.S. Private*, pg. 2312
SMART COMMUNICATIONS INC.—See Hakuhodo DY Holdings Incorporated; *Int'l*, pg. 3220
STREAM GLOBAL SERVICES - AZ, INC.—See Concentrix Corporation; *U.S. Public*, pg. 565
STREAM GLOBAL SERVICES EL SALVADOR, S.A. DE C.V.—See Concentrix Corporation; *U.S. Public*, pg. 565
STREAM GLOBAL SERVICES HONDURAS, S.A.—See Concentrix Corporation; *U.S. Public*, pg. 565
STREAM GLOBAL SERVICES NICARAGUA, S.A.—See Concentrix Corporation; *U.S. Public*, pg. 565
STREAM INTERNATIONAL CANADA ULC—See Concentrix Corporation; *U.S. Public*, pg. 565
STREAM INTERNATIONAL COSTA RICA S.A.—See Concentrix Corporation; *U.S. Public*, pg. 565
STREAM INTERNATIONAL SP. Z O.O.—See Concentrix Corporation; *U.S. Public*, pg. 565
STREAM TUNISIE, S.A.R.L.—See Concentrix Corporation; *U.S. Public*, pg. 565
SUORAMARKKINOINTI MEGA OY—See Alma Media Corporation; *Int'l*, pg. 361
SYKES ASSISTANCE SERVICES CORPORATION—See Creadev SAS; *Int'l*, pg. 1831
SYKES DATASVAR SUPPORT AB—See Creadev SAS; *Int'l*, pg. 1831

SYKES EL SALVADOR, LTDA—See Creadev SAS; *Int'l*, pg. 1831
SYKES ENTERPRISES BERLIN GMBH & CO. KG—See Creadev SAS; *Int'l*, pg. 1831
SYKES ENTERPRISES BOCHUM GMBH & CO. KG—See Creadev SAS; *Int'l*, pg. 1831
SYKES ENTERPRISES DENMARK APS—See Creadev SAS; *Int'l*, pg. 1831
SYKES ENTERPRISES EASTERN EUROPE S.R.L.—See Creadev SAS; *Int'l*, pg. 1831
SYKES ENTERPRISES (INDIA) PVT LTD—See Creadev SAS; *Int'l*, pg. 1831
SYKES ENTERPRISES NORWAY AS—See Creadev SAS; *Int'l*, pg. 1831
SYKES GLOBAL SERVICES LTD.—See Creadev SAS; *Int'l*, pg. 1831
SYKES REALTY, INC.—See Creadev SAS; *Int'l*, pg. 1831
SYKES (SHANGHAI) CO. LTD—See Creadev SAS; *Int'l*, pg. 1831
SYKES SLOVAKIA SRO—See Creadev SAS; *Int'l*, pg. 1831
SYKES SWEDEN AB—See Creadev SAS; *Int'l*, pg. 1831
TALK2REP, INC.; *U.S. Private*, pg. 3926
TCIM SERVICES INC.; *U.S. Private*, pg. 3942
TELECONCEPTS, INC.—See AbleNet, Inc.; *U.S. Private*, pg. 39
TELEMARKETING CO., INC.—See TTC Marketing Solutions; *U.S. Private*, pg. 4254
TELEMARKET SIA—See Alma Media Corporation; *Int'l*, pg. 361
TELE RESOURCES, INC.; *U.S. Private*, pg. 3959
TELESERVICES DIRECT—See Career Horizons, Inc.; *U.S. Private*, pg. 752
TELETECH NORTH AMERICA—See TTEC Holdings, Inc.; *U.S. Public*, pg. 2203
TELISIMO INTERNATIONAL CORPORATION; *U.S. Private*, pg. 3962
THANE INTERNATIONAL, INC.—See H.I.G. Capital, LLC; *U.S. Private*, pg. 1832
THOMAS L. CARDELLA & ASSOCIATES INC; *U.S. Private*, pg. 4157
TSD GLOBAL INC.—See Career Horizons, Inc.; *U.S. Private*, pg. 752
TTC MARKETING SOLUTIONS; *U.S. Private*, pg. 4254
TTEC EASTERN EUROPE EAD—See TTEC Holdings, Inc.; *U.S. Public*, pg. 2203
USAN, INC.; *U.S. Private*, pg. 4322
VELOCITI (PROPRIETARY) LIMITED—See Blue Label Telecoms Limited; *Int'l*, pg. 1068
VENDORNET, INC.—See eBay Inc.; *U.S. Public*, pg. 709
VPAY INC.—See UnitedHealth Group Incorporated; *U.S. Public*, pg. 2248

561431 — PRIVATE MAIL CENTERS

ACCESS MAIL PROCESSING SERVICES, INC.; *U.S. Private*, pg. 52
AERO FULFILLMENT SERVICES CORPORATION; *U.S. Private*, pg. 118
AIRMAIL CENTER FRANKFURT GMBH—See Fraport AG; *Int'l*, pg. 2764
APTAR CALI SAS—See AptarGroup, Inc.; *U.S. Public*, pg. 174
DENSO BLOSSOM CO., LTD.—See Denso Corporation; *Int'l*, pg. 2031
EARTH CLASS MAIL, INC.—See LegalZoom.com, Inc.; *U.S. Public*, pg. 1301
EASTBIZ CORP.; *U.S. Private*, pg. 1319
EXPRESS POSTAL OPTIONS INTERNATIONAL LLC—See Chatham Asset Management, LLC; *U.S. Private*, pg. 863
FEDERAL EXPRESS CANADA LTD.—See FedEx Corporation; *U.S. Public*, pg. 828
FEDERAL EXPRESS CORPORATION—See FedEx Corporation; *U.S. Public*, pg. 828
FEDERAL EXPRESS EUROPE, MIDDLE EAST & AFRICA—See FedEx Corporation; *U.S. Public*, pg. 828
FEDERAL EXPRESS LATIN AMERICA-CARIBBEAN—See FedEx Corporation; *U.S. Public*, pg. 828
FREESORT GMBH—See Francotyp-Postalia Holding AG; *Int'l*, pg. 2764
LETTERSTREAM, INC.; *U.S. Private*, pg. 2433
NORTH AMERICAN COMMUNICATIONS, INC. (NAC)—See North American Communications Inc.; *U.S. Private*, pg. 2940
NORTH AMERICAN COMMUNICATIONS INC.; *U.S. Private*, pg. 2940
PITNEY BOWES BUSINESS SYSTEMS-INTERNATIONAL—See Pitney Bowes Inc.; *U.S. Public*, pg. 1695
PRESORT SOLUTIONS; *U.S. Private*, pg. 3255
R.R. DONNELLEY—See Chatham Asset Management, LLC; *U.S. Private*, pg. 864
R.R. DONNELLEY—See Chatham Asset Management, LLC; *U.S. Private*, pg. 864
SUNLINE DIRECT MAIL LTD.—See CEPS PLC; *Int'l*, pg. 1420
THREE DOG LOGISTICS; *U.S. Private*, pg. 4164

561439 — OTHER BUSINESS SERVICE CENTERS (INCLUDING COPY SHOPS)

A10 CENTER WILDAU GMBH—See Deutsche EuroShop AG; *Int'l*, pg. 2065
ACQUIRENT, LLC; *U.S. Private*, pg. 64
ADVANCED CONTACT CENTER CO., LTD.—See Advanced Info Service Plc; *Int'l*, pg. 159
AGS TRANSACT TECHNOLOGIES LTD.; *Int'l*, pg. 221
AL FARAZDAQ COMPANY W.L.L.—See Aamal Company Q.S.C.; *Int'l*, pg. 36
ALTMARKT-GALERIE DRESDEN GMBH & CO. KG—See Deutsche EuroShop AG; *Int'l*, pg. 2065
ASSOCIATED PRODUCE DEALERS & BROKERS OF L.A - INSURANCE TRUST; *U.S. Private*, pg. 357
BREMBO DO BRASIL LTDA.—See Brembo S.p.A.; *Int'l*, pg. 1145
BUNZL OUTSOURCING SERVICES BV—See Bunzl plc; *Int'l*, pg. 1217
CALTEX AUSTRALIA FINANCE PTY LTD—See Ampol Limited; *Int'l*, pg. 436
CLIENT SOLUTION ARCHITECTS; *U.S. Private*, pg. 943
CORNERSTONE TECHNOLOGIES HOLDINGS LIMITED; *Int'l*, pg. 1801
CREATIVE DOCUMENT IMAGING, INC.—See Hackworth Reprographics, Inc.; *U.S. Private*, pg. 1838
C&R LEGAL AGENCY, CO., LTD.—See CREEK & RIVER Co., Ltd.; *Int'l*, pg. 1837
CTI RECORDS MANAGEMENT PTY LTD—See CTI Logistics Limited; *Int'l*, pg. 1871
DATABANK TECHNOLOGIES PTY LIMITED—See Freightways Group Limited; *Int'l*, pg. 2771
DMS INK—See Revitalize Capital; *U.S. Private*, pg. 3416
DOCUSOURCE PRINT MANAGEMENT; *U.S. Private*, pg. 1252
DX MAIL—See Freightways Group Limited; *Int'l*, pg. 2771
EBANNER SOLUTION SDN. BHD.—See eprint Group Limited; *Int'l*, pg. 2465
EDL GROUP OPERATIONS PTY LTD—See CK Hutchison Holdings Limited; *Int'l*, pg. 1636
EGURIDAD PRIVADA ACTIVE SECURITY COMPANY A.S.C. CIA. LTDA.—See Bain Capital, LP; *U.S. Private*, pg. 434
EQUUS GROUP, LLC; *U.S. Private*, pg. 1416
ERRAND SOLUTIONS, LLC; *U.S. Private*, pg. 1423
EURO-DRUCKSERVICE GMBH—See DPE Deutsche Private Equity GmbH; *Int'l*, pg. 2188
FUKUGIN BUSINESS OPERATION SERVICE CO., LTD.—See Fukuoka Financial Group, Inc.; *Int'l*, pg. 2840
GEFRAN BRASIL ELETROELETRONICA LTDA.—See Gefran S.p.A.; *Int'l*, pg. 2912
GORDON DOCUMENT PRODUCTS INC.; *U.S. Private*, pg. 1743
GUNZE OFFICE SERVICES CO., LTD.—See Gunze Limited; *Int'l*, pg. 3185
GURIT SERVICES AG—See Gurit Holding AG; *Int'l*, pg. 3188
HACKWORTH REPROGRAPHICS, INC.; *U.S. Private*, pg. 1838
HANKYU SHOPPING CENTER DEVELOPMENT CO LTD—See H2O Retailing Corp.; *Int'l*, pg. 3200
HYOSUNG ITX CO., LTD.; *Int'l*, pg. 3552
INFOMAT N.V.—See KKR & Co. Inc.; *U.S. Public*, pg. 1257
ISID BUSINESS CONSULTING, LTD.—See Dentsu Group Inc.; *Int'l*, pg. 2039
IVOX SOLUTIONS, LLC; *U.S. Private*, pg. 2151
KANSAI BEVERAGE SERVICE COMPANY LIMITED—See Coca-Cola Bottlers Japan Holdings Inc.; *Int'l*, pg. 1684
KNOWLEDGE ADVANTAGE INC.; *U.S. Private*, pg. 2323
LDISCOVERY, LLC - PHILADELPHIA—See Pivotal Acquisition Corp.; *U.S. Private*, pg. 3192
MACHINETOOLS.COM; *U.S. Private*, pg. 2536
MAIN-TAUNUS-ZENTRUM KG—See Deutsche EuroShop AG; *Int'l*, pg. 2065
MULTIFAMILY TECHNOLOGY SOLUTIONS, INC.—See Thoma Bravo, L.P.; *U.S. Private*, pg. 4153
NORTHEAST BLUEPRINT & SUPPLY CO., INC.; *U.S. Private*, pg. 2949
OBJEKT CITY-POINT KASSEL GMBH & CO. KG—See Deutsche EuroShop AG; *Int'l*, pg. 2065
OCEAN TERMINAL LIMITED—See Arcus Infrastructure Partners LLP; *Int'l*, pg. 552
OLYMPIA BRNO S.R.O.—See Deutsche EuroShop AG; *Int'l*, pg. 2065
ONLINE SECURITY SERVICES LIMITED—See Freightways Group Limited; *Int'l*, pg. 2772
PACIFIC GLOBAL INC.; *U.S. Private*, pg. 3067
PALLADIUM PRAHA S.R.O.—See Helaba Landesbank Hessen-Thuringen; *Int'l*, pg. 3328
PERDIGAO HOLLAND B.V.—See BRF S.A.; *Int'l*, pg. 1151
PERDIGAO INTERNATIONAL LTD.—See BRF S.A.; *Int'l*, pg. 1151
PERDIGAO UK LTD.—See BRF S.A.; *Int'l*, pg. 1151
PERFORMANCE INDICATOR, LLC; *U.S. Private*, pg. 3149
PLAZA ANTOFAGASTA S.A.—See Falabella S.A.; *Int'l*, pg. 2610
PLAZA DEL TREBOL SPA—See Falabella S.A.; *Int'l*, pg. 2610
PLAZA OESTE SPA—See Falabella S.A.; *Int'l*, pg. 2610
PLAZA TOBALABA SPA—See Falabella S.A.; *Int'l*, pg. 2610
PLAZA VESPUCIO SPA—See Falabella S.A.; *Int'l*, pg. 2610
PREFERRED IMAGING, INC.—See JLL Partners, LLC; *U.S. Private*, pg. 2213
THE PURSUANT GROUP, INC.—See Allegiance Fundraising LLC; *U.S. Private*, pg. 176
QDISCOVERY, LLC—See JLL Partners, LLC; *U.S. Private*, pg. 2213
SANDYMAC S.R.L.—See Biesse S.p.A.; *Int'l*, pg. 1020
SERVICIOS NUTRESA S.A.S.—See Grupo Nutresa S.A.; *Int'l*, pg. 3133
SIMCENTER ENTERPRISES, INC.; *U.S. Private*, pg. 3665
SNOWDEN TECHNOLOGIES PTY LTD.—See Downer EDI Limited; *Int'l*, pg. 2186
SOURCE ONE MANAGEMENT, INC.; *U.S. Private*, pg. 3718
SPIE BELGIUM SA-ICS DIVISION—See Clayton, Dubilier & Rice, LLC; *U.S. Private*, pg. 926
STEAMBOAT VENTURES ASIA, L.P.—See The Walt Disney Company; *U.S. Public*, pg. 2139
TREELINE, INCORPORATED; *U.S. Private*, pg. 4217
TRM COPY CENTERS, LLC—See Marlin Equity Partners, LLC; *U.S. Private*, pg. 2584
VERTEK CORP; *U.S. Private*, pg. 4369
XEROX CORPORATION—See Xerox Holdings Corporation; *U.S. Public*, pg. 2387
XEROX (NEDERLAND) BV—See Xerox Holdings Corporation; *U.S. Public*, pg. 2389

561440 — COLLECTION AGENCIES

ABACUS (FINANCIAL CONSULTANTS) LIMITED—See ClearDebt Group Plc; *Int'l*, pg. 1656
ABC/AMEGA INC.—See Trivest Partners, LP; *U.S. Private*, pg. 4240
ACB AMERICAN INC.; *U.S. Private*, pg. 47
ACCOUNT CONTROL TECHNOLOGY, INC.—See Platinum Equity, LLC; *U.S. Private*, pg. 3209
ACCOUNT RECOVERY SPECIALISTS, INC. (ARSI); *U.S. Private*, pg. 53
ADAMS, COOPER & MARKS—See I.C. System, Inc.; *U.S. Private*, pg. 2026
AD ASTRA RECOVERY SERVICES INC.—See CURO Group Holdings Corp.; *U.S. Public*, pg. 611
AEROMEDICAL COLLECTION SERVICES, INC.; *U.S. Private*, pg. 119
AG GUARANTEE CO., LTD.—See AIFUL Corporation; *Int'l*, pg. 231
AG LOAN SERVICES CORPORATION—See AIFUL Corporation; *Int'l*, pg. 231
AK SVERIGE AB—See PRA Group, Inc.; *U.S. Public*, pg. 1712
AKTIV KAPITAL INVESTMENT AS—See PRA Group, Inc.; *U.S. Public*, pg. 1712
ALLIANCEONE INC.; *U.S. Private*, pg. 184
AMADA FRANCHISE CENTER CO., LTD.—See Amada Holdings Co., Ltd.; *Int'l*, pg. 404
AMERICAN ACCOUNTS & ADVISERS; *U.S. Private*, pg. 221
AMERICAN RECOVERY SERVICE INC.; *U.S. Private*, pg. 245
AMERICOLLECT, INC.; *U.S. Private*, pg. 259
AMERIWORKS FINANCIAL SERVICES, INC.; *U.S. Public*, pg. 115
A.R.M. SOLUTIONS, INC.; *U.S. Private*, pg. 28
ARROW FINANCIAL SERVICES LLC—See SLM Corporation; *U.S. Public*, pg. 1894
ARROW GLOBAL LIMITED—See Arrow Global Group PLC; *Int'l*, pg. 579
ASSOCIATED CREDITORS EXCHANGE, INC.; *U.S. Private*, pg. 355
ASSOCIATED RECOVERY SYSTEMS; *U.S. Private*, pg. 357
ATLANTIC CREDIT & FINANCE, INC.—See Encore Capital Group, Inc.; *U.S. Public*, pg. 759
ATRADIUS COLLECTIONS B.V.—See Grupo Catalana Occidente, S.A.; *Int'l*, pg. 3124
ATRADIUS COLLECTIONS, INC.—See Grupo Catalana Occidente, S.A.; *Int'l*, pg. 3124
A.TREDS LTD.—See Axis Bank Limited; *Int'l*, pg. 769
AUSECO, S.A.—See Lone Star Funds; *U.S. Private*, pg. 2485
AUTOMATED COLLECTION SERVICES, INC. (ACSI); *U.S. Private*, pg. 399
AXACTOR FINLAND OY—See Axactor SE; *Int'l*, pg. 761
AXACTOR NORWAY AS—See Axactor SE; *Int'l*, pg. 761
BARR CREDIT SERVICES, INC.; *U.S. Private*, pg. 479
BAYCORP HOLDINGS (NZ) LIMITED—See Encore Capital Group, Inc.; *U.S. Public*, pg. 759
BAYCORP (NZ) LIMITED—See Encore Capital Group, Inc.; *U.S. Public*, pg. 759
BAYCORP (WA) PTY LIMITED—See Encore Capital Group, Inc.; *U.S. Public*, pg. 759
BENJAMIN MICHAEL & ASSOCIATES, INC.; *U.S. Private*, pg. 526
BEST S.A.; *Int'l*, pg. 999
BILL BARTMANN ENTERPRISES; *U.S. Private*, pg. 556
BONNEVILLE BILLING & COLLECTIONS; *U.S. Private*, pg. 615
BROWN & JOSEPH LTD.; *U.S. Private*, pg. 666
BURGEL INTERNATIONALE INKASSOGESELLSCHAFT GMBH—See Allianz SE; *Int'l*, pg. 351
BURGEL WIRTSCHAFTSINFORMATIONEN GMBH & CO. KG—See Allianz SE; *Int'l*, pg. 351
CABOT FINANCIAL FRANCE—See Encore Capital Group, Inc.; *U.S. Public*, pg. 759
CARDWORKS, INC.; *U.S. Private*, pg. 751
CARDWORKS SERVICING, LLC—See CardWorks, Inc.; *U.S. Private*, pg. 751
CBE GROUP; *U.S. Public*, pg. 797
CENTRAL CREDIT AUDIT, INC.—See Creditech, Inc.; *U.S. Private*, pg. 1092
CENTRIX FINANCIAL LLC; *U.S. Private*, pg. 830
CHOICE RECOVERY, INC.—See Wakefield & Associates, LLC; *U.S. Private*, pg. 4427
C L FINANCE LIMITED—See Cattles Limited; *Int'l*, pg. 1361
CLIENT SERVICES INC.; *U.S. Private*, pg. 943
CLINICAL REVENUE MANAGEMENT SERVICES, LLC—See AAC Holdings, Inc.; *U.S. Private*, pg. 31
COAST PROFESSIONAL, INC.; *U.S. Private*, pg. 954
COFACE COLLECTIONS NORTH AMERICA, INC.—See Coface S.A.; *Int'l*, pg. 1691
COFACE SOUTH AFRICA PTY LTD—See Groupe BPCE; *Int'l*, pg. 3093
COLLECTION HOUSE LIMITED; *Int'l*, pg. 1699
COMMERCIAL SERVICES GROUP INCORPORATED; *U.S. Private*, pg. 984
COMPLETE RECOVERY CORPORATION; *U.S. Private*, pg. 1001
COMPUTER CHEQUE—See Paradigm Recovery Solutions, LLC; *U.S. Private*, pg. 3089
CONDUENT PAYMENT INTEGRITY SOLUTIONS, INC.—See Conduent Incorporated; *U.S. Public*, pg. 566
CONSERVE; *U.S. Private*, pg. 1019
CONSUMER RECOVERY ASSOCIATES, LLC; *U.S. Private*, pg. 1025
CONVERGENT COMMERCIAL, INC.—See Platinum Equity, LLC; *U.S. Private*, pg. 3209
CONVERGENT HEALTHCARE RECOVERIES, INC.—See Platinum Equity, LLC; *U.S. Private*, pg. 3209
CONVERGENT OUTSOURCING, INC.—See Platinum Equity, LLC; *U.S. Private*, pg. 3209
CONVERGENT RESOURCES, INC.—See Platinum Equity, LLC; *U.S. Private*, pg. 3209
CORROHEALTH, INC.; *U.S. Private*, pg. 1059
CREDCO RECEIVABLES CORP.—See American Express Company; *U.S. Public*, pg. 101
CREDIT ANSWERS, LLC; *U.S. Private*, pg. 1091
CREDIT COLLECTIONS BUREAU COLLECTION AGENCY; *U.S. Private*, pg. 1091
CREDIT CONTROL, LLC; *U.S. Private*, pg. 1091
CREDIT CONTROL SERVICES INC.; *U.S. Private*, pg. 1091
CREDIT CORP AUSTRALIA PTY LIMITED—See Credit Corp Group Limited; *Int'l*, pg. 1835
CREDIT CORP COLLECTIONS PTY LIMITED—See Credit Corp Group Limited; *Int'l*, pg. 1835
CREDIT CORP FACILITIES PTY LIMITED—See Credit Corp Group Limited; *Int'l*, pg. 1835
CREDIT CORP SERVICES PTY LIMITED—See Credit Corp Group Limited; *Int'l*, pg. 1835
CREDITECH, INC.; *U.S. Private*, pg. 1092
CREDITORS INTERCHANGE RECEIVABLES MANAGEMENT LLC; *U.S. Private*, pg. 1092
CREDIT RECOVERY ASSOCIATES, INC.—See Regional Management Corp.; *U.S. Public*, pg. 1776
CREDITREFORM LATVIJA SIA—See B2Holding AS; *Int'l*, pg. 790
CRIBIS TELESERVICE S.R.L.—See CRIF S.p.A.; *Int'l*, pg. 1849
CRIF ALACAK YONETIM VE DANISMANLIK HIZMETLERI ANONIM SIRKETI—See CRIF S.p.A.; *Int'l*, pg. 1849
DAL, INC.—See Trivest Partners, LP; *U.S. Private*, pg. 4240
DEBITOR-INKASSO GMBH—See IK Investment Partners Limited; *Int'l*, pg. 3609
THE DEBT ADVICE PORTAL LIMITED—See ClearDebt Group Plc; *Int'l*, pg. 1657
DGB CREDIT INFORMATION CO., LTD.—See DGB Financial Group Co., Ltd.; *Int'l*, pg. 2096
DOUGLAS, KNIGHT & ASSOCIATES, INC.; *U.S. Private*, pg. 1267
DXC INSURANCE SOLUTIONS AUSTRALIA PTY LTD—See DXC Technology Company; *U.S. Public*, pg. 696
DXC TECHNOLOGY AUSTRALIA PTY. LIMITED—See DXC Technology Company; *U.S. Public*, pg. 696
ECSI; *U.S. Private*, pg. 1331
EDGEIQ, INC.—See DXC Technology Company; *U.S. Public*, pg. 696
E-KANCELARIA GRUPA PRAWNO-FINANSOWA S.A.; *Int'l*, pg. 2248
EL ISTIFA SA—See Groupe BPCE; *Int'l*, pg. 3094

561440 — COLLECTION AGENCIES

EMERALD AR SYSTEMS; *U.S. Private*, pg. 1379
ENTERPRISE RECOVERY SYSTEMS, INC.—See Audax Group, Limited Partnership; *U.S. Private*, pg. 390
EQUIANT FINANCIAL SERVICES, INC.—See Concord Servicing Corp.; *U.S. Private*, pg. 1010
ES FIELD DELIVERY FRANCE SAS—See DXC Technology Company; *U.S. Public*, pg. 696
ES FIELD DELIVERY NEDERLAND B.V.—See DXC Technology Company; *U.S. Public*, pg. 696
ES FIELD DELIVERY SPAIN, S.L.U.—See DXC Technology Company; *U.S. Public*, pg. 696
ES IMMOBILIEN GMBH—See DXC Technology Company; *U.S. Public*, pg. 696
ETAN INDUSTRIES INC.; *U.S. Private*, pg. 1431
ETRANSMEDIA TECHNOLOGY INC.—See Northwell Health, Inc.; *U.S. Private*, pg. 2958
EULER HERMES COLLECTIONS GMBH—See Allianz SE; *Int'l*, pg. 352
EULER HERMES COLLECTIONS UK LIMITED—See Allianz SE; *Int'l*, pg. 352
EULER HERMES FORDERUNGSMANAGEMENT GMBH—See Allianz SE; *Int'l*, pg. 352
EULER HERMES SFAC RECOUVREMENT S.A.S.—See Allianz SE; *Int'l*, pg. 353
EULER HERMES UMA INC.—See Allianz SE; *Int'l*, pg. 353
FIDELITY NATIONAL CREDIT SERVICES LTD.—See American CyberSystems, Inc.; *U.S. Private*, pg. 230
FINANCIAL RECOVERY SERVICES, INC.; *U.S. Private*, pg. 1508
FINANCIAL TELEMARKETING SERVICES LTD.—See BNP Paribas SA; *Int'l*, pg. 1091
FIRST RECOVERY GROUP, LLC—See New Mountain Capital, LLC; *U.S. Private*, pg. 2902
FMA ALLIANCE LTD.; *U.S. Private*, pg. 1553
FOCUS RECEIVABLES MANAGEMENT, LLC; *U.S. Private*, pg. 1556
FRANKLIN COLLECTION SERVICE, INC.; *U.S. Private*, pg. 1596
FRONTEX INTERNATIONAL EAD—See AG Capital; *Int'l*, pg. 197
FUKUOKA SERVICING CO., LTD.—See Fukuoka Financial Group, Inc.; *Int'l*, pg. 2840
GB COLLECTS, LLC; *U.S. Private*, pg. 1653
GEBBS HEALTHCARE SOLUTIONS INC.—See ChrysCapital Management Co.; *Int'l*, pg. 1588
GENERAL MOTORS FINANCIAL OF CANADA LIMITED—See General Motors Company; *U.S. Public*, pg. 925
GENESIS FINANCIAL SOLUTIONS, INC.—See Castlelake, L.P.; *U.S. Private*, pg. 785
GETBACK SPOLKA AKCYJNA; *Int'l*, pg. 2947
GFS CANADA—See Castlelake, L.P.; *U.S. Private*, pg. 785
GILA, LLC—See Navient Corporation; *U.S. Public*, pg. 1500
GLASS MOUNTAIN CAPITAL, LLC; *U.S. Private*, pg. 1706
GRIMLEY FINANCIAL CORPORATION; *U.S. Private*, pg. 1790
GULF COAST COLLECTION BUREAU, INC.; *U.S. Private*, pg. 1815
HOIST FINANCE CRAIOVA S.R.L.—See Hoist Finance AB; *Int'l*, pg. 3442
HOIST POLSKA SP. Z O.O.—See Hoist Finance AB; *Int'l*, pg. 3442
HUDSON & KEYSE, LLC; *U.S. Private*, pg. 2001
HUNTER WARFIELD; *U.S. Private*, pg. 2010
I.C. SYSTEM, INC.; *U.S. Private*, pg. 2026
IKASSA FINLAND OY—See Lone Star Global Acquisitions, LLC; *U.S. Private*, pg. 2487
INNOVA TAXFREE BELGIUM SPRL—See Euronet Worldwide, Inc.; *U.S. Public*, pg. 798
INNOVA TAX FREE FRANCE SAS—See Euronet Worldwide, Inc.; *U.S. Public*, pg. 798
INNOVA TAXFREE IRELAND LIMITED—See Euronet Worldwide, Inc.; *U.S. Public*, pg. 798
INNOVA TAXFREE ITALY S.R.L.—See Euronet Worldwide, Inc.; *U.S. Public*, pg. 798
INNOVA TAXFREE NETHERLANDS B.V.—See Euronet Worldwide, Inc.; *U.S. Public*, pg. 798
INNOVA TAXFREE PORTUGAL UNIPESSOAL LDA.—See Euronet Worldwide, Inc.; *U.S. Public*, pg. 798
INNOVA TAXFREE SPAIN S.L.—See Euronet Worldwide, Inc.; *U.S. Public*, pg. 798
INNOVA TAX FREE (UK) LIMITED—See Euronet Worldwide, Inc.; *U.S. Public*, pg. 798
INNOVATIVE BANKING SOLUTIONS AG—See DXC Technology Company; *U.S. Public*, pg. 695
INTEGRATEC—See Bread Financial Holdings Inc.; *U.S. Public*, pg. 381
INTERKREDITT AS—See B2Holding AS; *Int'l*, pg. 790
IQOR, INC.—See HGGC, LLC; *U.S. Private*, pg. 1930
ISOFT INC.—See DXC Technology Company; *U.S. Public*, pg. 696
JEFFERSON CAPITAL SYSTEMS, LLC—See J.C. Flowers & Co. LLC; *U.S. Private*, pg. 2159
J J MARSHALL & ASSOCIATES, INC.—See Arena Investors, LP; *U.S. Private*, pg. 318
LAMONT HANLEY & ASSOCIATES; *U.S. Private*, pg. 2380
LEADING EDGE RECOVERY SOLUTIONS, LLC; *U.S. Private*, pg. 2406
LEIB SOLUTIONS, INC.; *U.S. Private*, pg. 2419
LUCANIA GESTION, S.L.—See Encore Capital Group, Inc.; *U.S. Public*, pg. 759
LUCAS ET DEGAND S.A R.L.—See Encore Capital Group, Inc.; *U.S. Public*, pg. 759
LUXOFT BULGARIA E.O.O.D.—See DXC Technology Company; *U.S. Public*, pg. 696
LUXOFT UK LIMITED—See DXC Technology Company; *U.S. Public*, pg. 696
LUXOFT UKRAINE LLC—See DXC Technology Company; *U.S. Public*, pg. 696
LVNV FUNDING, LLC—See Sherman Financial Group LLC; *U.S. Private*, pg. 3634
MERCHANTS' CREDIT GUIDE CO.; *U.S. Private*, pg. 2670
MICROBILT COLLECTION AGENCY, INC.—See Bristol Investments, Ltd.; *U.S. Private*, pg. 657
MIDSTATE CREDITCOLLECT PTY LTD—See Collection House Limited; *Int'l*, pg. 1699
MONARCH RECOVERY MANAGEMENT INC.; *U.S. Private*, pg. 2769
MULTIGESTION IBERIA 2014, S.L.—See D. E. Shaw & Co., L.P.; *U.S. Private*, pg. 1140
NATIONAL CREDIT MANAGEMENT LIMITED—See Credit Corp Group Limited; *Int'l*, pg. 1835
NATIONAL RECOVERY AGENCY; *U.S. Private*, pg. 2861
NATIONWIDE CREDIT, INC.; *U.S. Private*, pg. 2865
NCC BUSINESS SERVICES INC.—See Platinum Equity, LLC; *U.S. Private*, pg. 3209
NETWORK COMMERCIAL SERVICE, INC.; *U.S. Private*, pg. 2889
NORTHLAND GROUP—See Radius Global Solutions LLC; *U.S. Private*, pg. 3345
OK INCURE OU—See B2Holding AS; *Int'l*, pg. 790
OK PERINTA OY—See B2Holding AS; *Int'l*, pg. 790
OPERATING TAX SYSTEMS, LLC—See The Riverside Company; *U.S. Private*, pg. 4109
PARADIGM RECOVERY SOLUTIONS, LLC; *U.S. Private*, pg. 3089
PAYMENTONE CORPORATION; *U.S. Private*, pg. 3117
PERFORMANT RECOVERY, INC.—See Performant Financial Corporation; *U.S. Public*, pg. 1676
PHILLIPS & COHEN ASSOCIATES LTD.; *U.S. Private*, pg. 3170
PHOENIX COMMERCIAL COLLECTIONS LIMITED—See Bain Capital, LP; *U.S. Private*, pg. 435
PHOENIX FINANCIAL SERVICES, LLC; *U.S. Private*, pg. 3172
PIONEER CREDIT RECOVERY, INC.—See SLM Corporation; *U.S. Public*, pg. 1894
PLAZA RECOVERY, INC.—See Audax Group, Limited Partnership; *U.S. Private*, pg. 390
POSTPOINT SERVICES LIMITED—See An Post LLC; *Int'l*, pg. 443
PRA GROUP EUROPE PORTFOLIO AS—See PRA Group, Inc.; *U.S. Public*, pg. 1712
PRA GROUP, INC.; *U.S. Public*, pg. 1712
PRA GROUP NORGE AS—See PRA Group, Inc.; *U.S. Public*, pg. 1712
PRA GROUP NORGE AS—See PRA Group, Inc.; *U.S. Public*, pg. 1712
PRA GROUP NORGE AS—See PRA Group, Inc.; *U.S. Public*, pg. 1712
PRA GROUP NORGE AS—See PRA Group, Inc.; *U.S. Public*, pg. 1712
PRA GROUP OSTERREICH PORTFOLIO GMBH—See PRA Group, Inc.; *U.S. Public*, pg. 1712
PRA GROUP SVERIGE AB—See PRA Group, Inc.; *U.S. Public*, pg. 1712
PRA GROUP (UK) LIMITED—See PRA Group, Inc.; *U.S. Public*, pg. 1712
PRA IBERIA SLU—See PRA Group, Inc.; *U.S. Public*, pg. 1712
PRA SUOMI OY—See PRA Group, Inc.; *U.S. Public*, pg. 1712
PRA SUOMI OY—See PRA Group, Inc.; *U.S. Public*, pg. 1712
PRA SUOMI OY—See PRA Group, Inc.; *U.S. Public*, pg. 1712
PRA SUOMI OY—See PRA Group, Inc.; *U.S. Public*, pg. 1712
PRINCE-PARKER & ASSOCIATES INC—See Complete Recovery Corporation; *U.S. Private*, pg. 1001
PROFESSIONAL RECOVERY CONSULTANTS, INC.—See Longshore Capital Partners; *U.S. Private*, pg. 2493
RADIUS GLOBAL SOLUTIONS LLC; *U.S. Private*, pg. 3344
RCB PLANEJAMENTO FINANCEIRO LTDA.—See PRA Group, Inc.; *U.S. Public*, pg. 1712
RCB PORTFOLIOS LTDA.—See PRA Group, Inc.; *U.S. Public*, pg. 1712
RECEIVABLES MANAGEMENT (NZ) LIMITED—See Collection House Limited; *Int'l*, pg. 1699
RECEIVABLES MANAGEMENT PARTNERS, LLC—See Thompson Street Capital Manager LLC; *U.S. Private*, pg. 4161
RECEIVABLE SOLUTIONS SPECIALIST, INC.—See Kriya Capital, LLC; *U.S. Private*, pg. 2352
RECEIVABLES OUTSOURCING, LLC—See Cognizant Technology Solutions Corporation; *U.S. Public*, pg. 523
RESURGENCE FINANCIAL, LLC; *U.S. Private*, pg. 3410
REVENUE ENTERPRISES LLC; *U.S. Private*, pg. 3413
RIVERWALK HOLDINGS, LTD.—See Sunoco LP; *U.S. Public*, pg. 1964
ROYAL MERCANTILE TRUST CORP. OF AMERICA; *U.S. Private*, pg. 3492
SAISON BUSINESS SUPPORT, INC.—See Credit Saison Co., Ltd.; *Int'l*, pg. 1836
SALTBUSH CONSULTING PTY LTD—See DXC Technology Company; *U.S. Public*, pg. 697
SEATTLE SERVICE BUREAU INC.; *U.S. Private*, pg. 3592
SILEO KAPITAL AB—See B2Holding AS; *Int'l*, pg. 791
SPT INKASSO OU—See Axactor SE; *Int'l*, pg. 761
STA INTERNATIONAL INC.; *U.S. Private*, pg. 3774
STELLAR RECOVERY, INC.; *U.S. Private*, pg. 3799
STIRLING PARK LLP—See Capita plc; *Int'l*, pg. 1309
STONELEIGH RECOVERY ASSOCIATES LLC; *U.S. Private*, pg. 3828
STRATEGIC AR; *U.S. Private*, pg. 3834
TDX INDIGO IBERIA S.L.U—See Equifax Inc.; *U.S. Public*, pg. 786
TFC ASSOCIATES, LLC; *U.S. Private*, pg. 3978
TRANSCOM WORLDWIDE CZECH REPUBLIC S.R.O.—See Altor Equity Partners AB; *Int'l*, pg. 396
TRANSWORLD SYSTEMS, INC.—See Platinum Equity, LLC; *U.S. Private*, pg. 3209
TREZ COMMERCIAL FINANCES LP—See Groupe BPCE; *Int'l*, pg. 3099
TUCKER ALBIN & ASSOCIATES, INC.; *U.S. Private*, pg. 4256
ULTIMO SP. Z O.O.—See B2Holding AS; *Int'l*, pg. 791
UNITED RECOVERY SYSTEMS, LP—See Audax Group, Limited Partnership; *U.S. Private*, pg. 390
VAN RU CREDIT CORPORATION; *U.S. Private*, pg. 4341
VENGROFF WILLIAMS, INC.; *U.S. Private*, pg. 4356
WAKEFIELD & ASSOCIATES, LLC; *U.S. Private*, pg. 4427
WESCOT CREDIT SERVICES LIMITED—See Encore Capital Group, Inc.; *U.S. Public*, pg. 760
WEST ASSET MANAGEMENT; *U.S. Private*, pg. 4483
XTEND HEALTHCARE LLC—See CorroHealth, Inc.; *U.S. Private*, pg. 1059
YOURCASH LIMITED—See Euronet Worldwide, Inc.; *U.S. Public*, pg. 798

561450 — CREDIT BUREAUS

ACUITY KNOWLEDGE PARTNERS COSTA RICA SOCIEDAD ANONIMA—See Equistone Partners Europe Limited; *Int'l*, pg. 2486
ACUITY KNOWLEDGE PARTNERS (UK) LIMITED—See Equistone Partners Europe Limited; *Int'l*, pg. 2486
AMERICAN REPORTING COMPANY, LLC; *U.S. Private*, pg. 246
AMRENT INC.—See CBC Companies Inc.; *U.S. Private*, pg. 796
ARGUS RESEARCH COMPANY—See The Argus Research Group, Inc.; *U.S. Private*, pg. 3988
AUSTIN CONSOLIDATED HOLDINGS, INC.—See Equifax Inc.; *U.S. Public*, pg. 785
AXACTOR ESPANA PLATFORM SA—See Axactor SE; *Int'l*, pg. 761
AXACTOR ITALY SPA—See Axactor SE; *Int'l*, pg. 761
AXACTOR SWEDEN AB—See Axactor SE; *Int'l*, pg. 761
BRC INVESTOR SERVICES S.A.—See S&P Global Inc.; *U.S. Public*, pg. 1830
BUREAU VAN DIJK ELECTRONIC PUBLISHING INC.—See Moody's Corporation; *U.S. Public*, pg. 1467
BUREAU VAN DIJK E.P. DMCC—See Moody's Corporation; *U.S. Public*, pg. 1466
BUREAU VAN DIJK PUBLICACAO ELECTRONICA LTDA—See Moody's Corporation; *U.S. Public*, pg. 1467
BUREAU VAN DIJK PUBLICACIONES ELECTRONICAS SA—See Moody's Corporation; *U.S. Public*, pg. 1467
CARE RATINGS NEPAL LTD.—See CARE Ratings Limited; *Int'l*, pg. 1323
CBC COMPANIES INC.; *U.S. Private*, pg. 796
CBC COMPANIES INC.—See CBC Companies Inc.; *U.S. Private*, pg. 796
CBCS—See CBC Companies Inc.; *U.S. Private*, pg. 796
CERVED CREDIT MANAGEMENT GROUP SRL—See GIC Pte. Ltd.; *Int'l*, pg. 2964
CERVED CREDIT MANAGEMENT SPA—See GIC Pte. Ltd.; *Int'l*, pg. 2964
CERVED GROUP SPA—See GIC Pte. Ltd.; *Int'l*, pg. 2964
CERVED RATING AGENCY S.P.A.—See GIC Pte. Ltd.; *Int'l*, pg. 2964
THE CHUGIN CREDIT GUARANTEE CO., LIMITED—See Chugin Financial Group, Inc.; *Int'l*, pg. 1595
COALITION SINGAPORE PTE. LTD.—See S&P Global Inc.; *U.S. Public*, pg. 1830
CONSUMERINFO.COM, INC.—See Experian plc; *Int'l*, pg. 2587
CORELOGIC CREDCO LLC—See Insight Venture Management, LLC; *U.S. Public*, pg. 2088
CORELOGIC CREDCO LLC—See Stone Point Capital LLC; *U.S. Private*, pg. 3822

N.A.I.C.S. INDEX

561492 — COURT REPORTING AND...

THE CREDIT BUREAU INC.—See CBC Companies Inc.; *U.S. Private*, pg. 796
THE CREDIT BUREAU OF BATON ROUGE, INC.; *U.S. Private*, pg. 4016
CREDIT BUREAU OF GREATER LANSING INC.—See CBC Companies Inc.; *U.S. Private*, pg. 796
CREDIT BUREAU (SINGAPORE) PTE. LTD.—See Credit Bureau Asia Limited; *Int'l*, pg. 1835
CREDITINFORM AS—See Experian plc; *Int'l*, pg. 2587
CREDIT KARMA, INC.—See Intuit Inc.; *U.S. Public*, pg. 1160
CREDIT LENDERS SERVICE AGENCY; *U.S. Private*, pg. 1091
CREDIT PLUS INC.—See Lovell Minnick Partners LLC; *U.S. Private*, pg. 2503
CREDIT RATING & COLLECTION COMPANY KSCC; *Int'l*, pg. 1835
CREDITWORKS AUSTRALIA PTY LTD—See Equifax Inc.; *U.S. Public*, pg. 785
CRIF BEIJING LTD.—See CRIF S.p.A.; *Int'l*, pg. 1849
CRIF CORPORATION—See CRIF S.p.A.; *Int'l*, pg. 1849
CRIF GMBH—See CRIF S.p.A.; *Int'l*, pg. 1849
CRIF HIGH MARK CREDIT INFORMATION SERVICES PVT. LTD.—See CRIF S.p.A.; *Int'l*, pg. 1849
CRIF HONG KONG LIMITED—See CRIF S.p.A.; *Int'l*, pg. 1849
CRIF - SLOVAK CREDIT BUREAU, S.R.O.—See CRIF S.p.A.; *Int'l*, pg. 1849
CRIF SOLUTIONS PRIVATE LIMITED—See CRIF S.p.A.; *Int'l*, pg. 1849
DATALINK BANKCARD SERVICES, CO.; *U.S. Private*, pg. 1165
DATAX LTD.—See Equifax Inc.; *U.S. Public*, pg. 785
D&B AUSTRALASIA PTY. LTD.—See Archer Capital Pty. Ltd.; *Int'l*, pg. 547
D&B (THAILAND) CO., LTD.—See Business Online Public Company Limited; *Int'l*, pg. 1229
DUN & BRADSTREET CIS—See Cannae Holdings, Inc.; *U.S. Public*, pg. 429
DUN & BRADSTREET CIS—See CC Capital Partners, LLC; *U.S. Private*, pg. 798
DUN & BRADSTREET CIS—See Intercontinental Exchange, Inc.; *U.S. Public*, pg. 1142
DUN & BRADSTREET (D&B) MALAYSIA SDN. BHD.—See Credit Bureau Asia Limited; *Int'l*, pg. 1835
DUN & BRADSTREET (HK) LTD.—See Cannae Holdings, Inc.; *U.S. Public*, pg. 429
DUN & BRADSTREET (HK) LTD.—See CC Capital Partners, LLC; *U.S. Private*, pg. 798
DUN & BRADSTREET (HK) LTD.—See Intercontinental Exchange, Inc.; *U.S. Public*, pg. 1141
DUN & BRADSTREET INTERNATIONAL CONSULTANT (SHANGHAI) LTD.—See Cannae Holdings, Inc.; *U.S. Public*, pg. 429
DUN & BRADSTREET INTERNATIONAL CONSULTANT (SHANGHAI) LTD.—See CC Capital Partners, LLC; *U.S. Private*, pg. 798
DUN & BRADSTREET INTERNATIONAL CONSULTANT (SHANGHAI) LTD.—See Intercontinental Exchange, Inc.; *U.S. Public*, pg. 1142
DUN & BRADSTREET (ISRAEL) LTD.—See Cannae Holdings, Inc.; *U.S. Public*, pg. 429
DUN & BRADSTREET (ISRAEL) LTD.—See CC Capital Partners, LLC; *U.S. Private*, pg. 798
DUN & BRADSTREET (ISRAEL) LTD.—See Intercontinental Exchange, Inc.; *U.S. Public*, pg. 1141
DUN & BRADSTREET SPA—See Cannae Holdings, Inc.; *U.S. Public*, pg. 429
DUN & BRADSTREET SPA—See CC Capital Partners, LLC; *U.S. Private*, pg. 798
DUN & BRADSTREET SPA—See Intercontinental Exchange, Inc.; *U.S. Public*, pg. 1142
DVBS, INC.—See Moody's Corporation; *U.S. Public*, pg. 1467
EFX DE COSTA RICA, S.A.—See Equifax Inc.; *U.S. Public*, pg. 786
EQUIFAX AMERICAS B.V.—See Equifax Inc.; *U.S. Public*, pg. 786
EQUIFAX CANADA CO.—See Equifax Inc.; *U.S. Public*, pg. 786
EQUIFAX COMMERCIAL SERVICES LTD.—See Equifax Inc.; *U.S. Public*, pg. 786
EQUIFAX DO BRASIL LTDA.—See Equifax Inc.; *U.S. Public*, pg. 786
EQUIFAX INC.; *U.S. Public*, pg. 785
EQUIFAX INFORMATION SERVICES LLC—See Equifax Inc.; *U.S. Public*, pg. 786
EQUIFAX INFORMATION SERVICES OF PUERTO RICO, INC.—See Equifax Inc.; *U.S. Public*, pg. 786
EQUIFAX LTD.—See Equifax Inc.; *U.S. Public*, pg. 786
EQUIFAX SECURE UK LTD.—See Equifax Inc.; *U.S. Public*, pg. 786
EQUIFAX SPAIN HOLDINGS S.L.—See Equifax Inc.; *U.S. Public*, pg. 786
EQUIFAX SPECIAL SERVICES LLC—See Equifax Inc.; *U.S. Public*, pg. 786
EQUIFAX URUGUAY S.A.—See Equifax Inc.; *U.S. Public*, pg. 786
EQUILIBRIUM CALIFICADORA DE RIESGO S.A.—See Moody's Corporation; *U.S. Public*, pg. 1467
EQUILIBRIUM CLASIFICADORA DE RIESGO S.A.—See Moody's Corporation; *U.S. Public*, pg. 1467
EXPERIAN INFORMATION SOLUTIONS, INC. - CHICAGO—See Experian plc; *Int'l*, pg. 2587
EXPERIAN INFORMATION SOLUTIONS, INC.—See Experian plc; *Int'l*, pg. 2587
EXPERIAN LTD.—See Experian plc; *Int'l*, pg. 2587
EXPERIAN PLC; *Int'l*, pg. 2586
EXPERIAN SINGAPORE PTE. LTD.—See Experian plc; *Int'l*, pg. 2587
EXPERIAN SOUTH AFRICA—See Experian plc; *Int'l*, pg. 2587
FARM CREDIT SERVICES OF NORTH DAKOTA; *U.S. Private*, pg. 1475
FITCH RATINGS, INC. - CHICAGO—See The Hearst Corporation; *U.S. Private*, pg. 4044
FITCH RATINGS, INC. - SAN FRANCISCO—See The Hearst Corporation; *U.S. Private*, pg. 4044
FITCH RATINGS, INC.—See The Hearst Corporation; *U.S. Private*, pg. 4044
HAMILTON INVESTMENTS, INC.—See Kingsway Financial Services Inc.; *U.S. Public*, pg. 1234
ICRA LANKA LIMITED—See Moody's Corporation; *U.S. Public*, pg. 1467
ICRA LIMITED—See Moody's Corporation; *U.S. Public*, pg. 1467
ICRA NEPAL LIMITED—See Moody's Corporation; *U.S. Public*, pg. 1467
INCHARGE INSTITUTE OF AMERICA, INC.; *U.S. Private*, pg. 2053
INFORMATIVE RESEARCH INC.; *U.S. Private*, pg. 2073
IXI CORPORATION—See Equifax Inc.; *U.S. Public*, pg. 786
JIM SMOLICH MOTORS, INC.—See Lithia Motors, Inc.; *U.S. Public*, pg. 1323
KOREA INVESTORS SERVICE, INC.—See Moody's Corporation; *U.S. Public*, pg. 1467
LUMBERMEN'S CREDIT ASSOCIATION OF BROWARD COUNTY INC.; *U.S. Private*, pg. 2513
MA KNOWLEDGE SERVICES RESEARCH (INDIA) PRIVATE LIMITED—See Moody's Corporation; *U.S. Public*, pg. 1468
MIDROOG LTD.—See Moody's Corporation; *U.S. Public*, pg. 1468
MOODY'S ANALYTICS AUSTRALIA PTY. LTD.—See Moody's Corporation; *U.S. Public*, pg. 1468
MOODY'S ANALYTICS CZECH REPUBLIC S.R.O.—See Moody's Corporation; *U.S. Public*, pg. 1468
MOODY'S ANALYTICS DEUTSCHLAND GMBH—See Moody's Corporation; *U.S. Public*, pg. 1468
MOODY'S ANALYTICS JAPAN KK—See Moody's Corporation; *U.S. Public*, pg. 1468
MOODYS ANALYTICS KNOWLEDGE SERVICES (INDIA) PVT. LTD.—See Equistone Partners Europe Limited; *Int'l*, pg. 2486
MOODYS ANALYTICS KNOWLEDGE SERVICES LANKA (PRIVATE) LIMITED—See Equistone Partners Europe Limited; *Int'l*, pg. 2486
MOODY'S ANALYTICS SAS—See Moody's Corporation; *U.S. Public*, pg. 1468
MOODY'S EASTERN EUROPE LLC—See Moody's Corporation; *U.S. Public*, pg. 1468
MOODYS FRANCE SAS—See Moody's Corporation; *U.S. Public*, pg. 1469
MOODY'S INTERFAX RATING AGENCY LTD—See Moody's Corporation; *U.S. Public*, pg. 1468
MOODY'S INVESTORS SERVICE CYPRUS LTD.—See Moody's Corporation; *U.S. Public*, pg. 1468
MOODY'S INVESTORS SERVICE ESPANA, S.A.—See Moody's Corporation; *U.S. Public*, pg. 1468
MOODY'S INVESTORS SERVICE, INC.—See Moody's Corporation; *U.S. Public*, pg. 1468
MOODY'S INVESTORS SERVICE (KOREA) INC.—See Moody's Corporation; *U.S. Public*, pg. 1468
MOODY'S INVESTORS SERVICE LTD.—See Moody's Corporation; *U.S. Public*, pg. 1468
MOODY'S INVESTORS SERVICE PTY. LTD.—See Moody's Corporation; *U.S. Public*, pg. 1468
MOODY'S INVESTORS SERVICE (SOUTH AFRICA) PTY. LTD.—See Moody's Corporation; *U.S. Public*, pg. 1468
NAVIGANT CONSULTING (EUROPE) LIMITED—See Bain Capital, LP; *U.S. Private*, pg. 432
NAVIGANT CONSULTING (PI) LLC—See Bain Capital, LP; *U.S. Private*, pg. 432
NEUSTAR TECHNOLOGIES LIMITED—See TransUnion; *U.S. Public*, pg. 2184
NORTHEAST MERCHANT SYSTEMS INC—See Ryvyl Inc.; *U.S. Public*, pg. 1830
PRA GROUP EUROPE FINANCIAL SERVICES AS—See PRA Group, Inc.; *U.S. Public*, pg. 1712
PROGREXION HOLDINGS INC.; *U.S. Private*, pg. 3279
PT CRIF—See CRIF S.p.A.; *Int'l*, pg. 1849
PT ICRA INDONESIA—See Moody's Corporation; *U.S. Public*, pg. 1469
RMCN CREDIT SERVICES, INC.; *U.S. Private*, pg. 3451
RUSSIAN STANDARD CREDIT BUREAU LLC—See CJSC Russian Standard Corporation; *Int'l*, pg. 1634
SEAFAX, INC.—See Stone Point Capital LLC; *U.S. Private*, pg. 3819
SERASA S.A.—See Experian plc; *Int'l*, pg. 2588
SP GLOBAL FINANCIAL IBERIA, S.L.U.—See S&P Global Inc.; *U.S. Public*, pg. 1831
S&P GLOBAL RATINGS FRANCE SAS—See S&P Global Inc.; *U.S. Public*, pg. 1831
S&P GLOBAL RATINGS SINGAPORE PTE. LTD.—See S&P Global Inc.; *U.S. Public*, pg. 1831
S&P GLOBAL SWEDEN AB—See S&P Global Inc.; *U.S. Public*, pg. 1831
SPRINGBOARD NONPROFIT CONSUMER CREDIT MANAGEMENT, INC.; *U.S. Private*, pg. 3763
STANDARD & POORS HONG KONG LIMITED—See S&P Global Inc.; *U.S. Public*, pg. 1832
STANDARD & POORS SINGAPORE PTE. LTD.—See S&P Global Inc.; *U.S. Public*, pg. 1832
STELLAR COLLECTIONS LIMITED—See Geneva Finance Limited; *Int'l*, pg. 2922
TALX CORPORATION—See Equifax Inc.; *U.S. Public*, pg. 786
TELETRACK, LLC—See Equifax Inc.; *U.S. Public*, pg. 787
TRANSUNION CORP.—See TransUnion; *U.S. Public*, pg. 2184
TRANS UNION COSTA RICA, S.A.—See TransUnion; *U.S. Public*, pg. 2184
TRANSUNION CREDIT BUREAU NAMIBIA (PTY) LTD.—See TransUnion; *U.S. Public*, pg. 2184
TRANSUNION CREDIT BUREAU (PTY) LTD.—See TransUnion; *U.S. Public*, pg. 2184
TRANS UNION GUATEMALA, S.A.—See TransUnion; *U.S. Public*, pg. 2184
TRANSUNION LLC—See TransUnion; *U.S. Public*, pg. 2184
TRANSUNION RWANDA LIMITED—See TransUnion; *U.S. Public*, pg. 2184
TRUSTEDID, INC.—See Equifax Inc.; *U.S. Public*, pg. 787
VANTAGESCORE SOLUTIONS, LLC—See Equifax Inc.; *U.S. Public*, pg. 787
VANTAGESCORE SOLUTIONS, LLC—See Experian plc; *Int'l*, pg. 2587
VANTAGESCORE SOLUTIONS, LLC—See TransUnion; *U.S. Public*, pg. 2184
YELLOW MAPLE II B.V.—See Moody's Corporation; *U.S. Public*, pg. 1469

561491 — REPOSSESSION SERVICES

HOSPITAL BILLING & COLLECTION SERVICE, LTD.; *U.S. Private*, pg. 1987
INTERFLASH D.O.O.—See APG/SGA SA; *Int'l*, pg. 513
NETSTAR PROPRIETARY LIMITED—See Altron Limited.; *Int'l*, pg. 399
PARON AG—See APG/SGA SA; *Int'l*, pg. 513
RASTRAC; *U.S. Private*, pg. 3357
SAN ANTONIO RECOVERY SERVICES—See Webster Equity Partners, LLC; *U.S. Private*, pg. 4466

561492 — COURT REPORTING AND STENOTYPE SERVICES

ALDERSON REPORTING CO., INC.—See TrustPoint International, LLC; *U.S. Private*, pg. 4251
APTUS COURT REPORTING, LLC; *U.S. Private*, pg. 302
ATKINSON-BAKER, INC; *U.S. Private*, pg. 369
ATM ROZRYWKA SP. Z.O.O.—See ATM Grupa S.A.; *Int'l*, pg. 687
AVERY WOODS REPORTING SERVICE—See Stevens Koenig Reporting; *U.S. Private*, pg. 3809
BARRISTERS' REPORTING SERVICE, INC.—See Aptus Court Reporting, LLC; *U.S. Private*, pg. 302
BENCHMARK REPORTING AGENCY, INC.—See Apax Partners LLP; *Int'l*, pg. 503
CAPTION IT, LLC—See Ai-Media Technologies Limited; *Int'l*, pg. 227
DEPOSITION SOLUTIONS, LLC—See Apax Partners LLP; *Int'l*, pg. 503
DOWNTOWN REPORTING LLC; *U.S. Private*, pg. 1269
EDWARDS REPORTING INC.—See Huseby, LLC; *U.S. Private*, pg. 2013
ESQUIRE DEPOSITION SOLUTIONS, LLC - CHICAGO—See H.I.G. Capital, LLC; *U.S. Private*, pg. 1827
ESQUIRE DEPOSITION SOLUTIONS, LLC - LONG ISLAND—See H.I.G. Capital, LLC; *U.S. Private*, pg. 1827
ESQUIRE DEPOSITION SOLUTIONS, LLC - SAN DIEGO—See H.I.G. Capital, LLC; *U.S. Private*, pg. 1827
ESQUIRE DEPOSITION SOLUTIONS, LLC—See H.I.G. Capital, LLC; *U.S. Private*, pg. 1827
ESQUIRE DEPOSITION SOLUTIONS, LLC - WOODBRIDGE—See H.I.G. Capital, LLC; *U.S. Private*, pg. 1827
EXECUTIVE REPORTING SERVICE; *U.S. Private*, pg. 1448
HUSEBY, LLC; *U.S. Private*, pg. 2013
IMBER COURT REPORTERS INC.—See Apax Partners LLP; *Int'l*, pg. 503

561492 — COURT REPORTING AND...

KIM THAYER & ASSOCIATES—See Litigation Services, LLC; *U.S. Private*, pg. 2468
LEGAL GRAPHICWORKS, INC.; *U.S. Private*, pg. 2417
LITIGATION SERVICES, LLC; *U.S. Private*, pg. 2468
M.A.R. REPORTING GROUP, LLC.—See Planet Depos, LLC; *U.S. Private*, pg. 3196
MEDSCRIBE INFORMATION SYSTEMS, INC.; *U.S. Private*, pg. 2658
NATIONAL CENTER FOR STATE COURTS; *U.S. Private*, pg. 2850
NEXTGEN REPORTING LLC; *U.S. Private*, pg. 2921
OASIS REPORTING SERVICES LLC—See Apax Partners LLP; *Int'l*, pg. 503
PLANET DEPOS, LLC; *U.S. Private*, pg. 3196
PRECISION REPORTING, INC.; *U.S. Private*, pg. 3246
REGENCY-BRENTANO, INC.—See Odyssey Investment Partners, LLC; *U.S. Private*, pg. 2995
SCLAFANI WILLIAMS COURT REPORTERS, INC.—See U.S. Legal Support, Inc.; *U.S. Private*, pg. 4271
STEVENS KOENIG REPORTING; *U.S. Private*, pg. 3809
UBIQUS REPORTING, INC.—See Euromezzanine Conseil SAS; *Int'l*, pg. 2554
VERBATIM REPORTING SERVICES—See Litigation Services, LLC; *U.S. Private*, pg. 2468
WEBMEDX INC.—See Microsoft Corporation; *U.S. Public*, pg. 1443
WILCOX & FETZER LTD.—See NextGen Reporting LLC; *U.S. Private*, pg. 2921
XEROX GLOBAL SERVICES LTD.—See Xerox Holdings Corporation; *U.S. Public*, pg. 2389

561499 — ALL OTHER BUSINESS SUPPORT SERVICES

1ST AMERICAN CARD SERVICE; *U.S. Private*, pg. 3
3I PLC—See 3i Group plc; *Int'l*, pg. 8
70 CC, LLC—See Howard Hughes Holdings Inc.; *U.S. Public*, pg. 1060
A2Z INFRASERVICES LANKA PRIVATE LIMITED—See A2Z Infra Engineering Limited; *Int'l*, pg. 30
AAR ALLEN ASSET MANAGEMENT—See AAR Corp.; *U.S. Public*, pg. 13
ABBEY HOLDINGS LIMITED—See Gallagher Holdings Ltd.; *Int'l*, pg. 2873
ABB INC.—See ABB Ltd.; *Int'l*, pg. 51
ABB SERVICE CO. LTD.—See ABB Ltd.; *Int'l*, pg. 54
ABERDEEN ADVISORS INC.; *U.S. Private*, pg. 38
ACCELERATE COMMERCE GMBH—See Ceconomy AG; *Int'l*, pg. 1373
ACCELERATED TECHNOLOGIES HOLDING CORP.; *U.S. Public*, pg. 32
ACCELOGIX LLC—See Black Lake Capital, LLC; *U.S. Private*, pg. 572
ACCEL, S.A.B. DE C.V.; *Int'l*, pg. 79
ACCENTURE 2, INC.—See Accenture plc; *Int'l*, pg. 85
ACCENTURE A.B.—See Accenture plc; *Int'l*, pg. 82
ACCENTURE AG—See Accenture plc; *Int'l*, pg. 82
ACCENTURE ARGENTINA—See Accenture plc; *Int'l*, pg. 82
ACCENTURE A.S.—See Accenture plc; *Int'l*, pg. 82
ACCENTURE AUSTRALIA—See Accenture plc; *Int'l*, pg. 82
ACCENTURE AUSTRIA—See Accenture plc; *Int'l*, pg. 82
ACCENTURE BELGIUM—See Accenture plc; *Int'l*, pg. 82
ACCENTURE (BOTSWANA) (PTY) LTD.—See Accenture plc; *Int'l*, pg. 82
ACCENTURE BPM IS YONETIMI LIMITED SIRKETI—See Accenture plc; *Int'l*, pg. 82
ACCENTURE BPM S.A.—See Accenture plc; *Int'l*, pg. 82
ACCENTURE BRAZIL—See Accenture plc; *Int'l*, pg. 82
ACCENTURE BUSINESS SERVICES FOR UTILITIES INC.—See Accenture plc; *Int'l*, pg. 82
ACCENTURE BUSINESS SERVICES OF BRITISH COLUMBIA LIMITED PARTNERSHIP—See Accenture plc; *Int'l*, pg. 82
ACCENTURE CANADA—See Accenture plc; *Int'l*, pg. 83
ACCENTURE CENTRAL EUROPE B. V.—See Accenture plc; *Int'l*, pg. 83
ACCENTURE CHILE ASESORIAS Y SERVICIOS LTDA.—See Accenture plc; *Int'l*, pg. 83
ACCENTURE COLOMBIA—See Accenture plc; *Int'l*, pg. 83
ACCENTURE CO LTD.—See Accenture plc; *Int'l*, pg. 83
ACCENTURE CO. LTD. (TAIWAN)—See Accenture plc; *Int'l*, pg. 83
ACCENTURE COMPANY LTD.—See Accenture plc; *Int'l*, pg. 83
ACCENTURE DENMARK—See Accenture plc; *Int'l*, pg. 83
ACCENTURE DIENSTLEISTUNGEN GMBH—See Accenture plc; *Int'l*, pg. 83
ACCENTURE DO BRASIL LTDA—See Accenture plc; *Int'l*, pg. 85
ACCENTURE EUROPEAN SERVICE CENTRE LTD.—See Accenture plc; *Int'l*, pg. 82
ACCENTURE FINANCE AND ACCOUNTING BPO SERVICES SPA—See Accenture plc; *Int'l*, pg. 83
ACCENTURE GLOBAL SERVICES LTD.—See Accenture plc; *Int'l*, pg. 82
ACCENTURE GMBH—See Accenture plc; *Int'l*, pg. 83

ACCENTURE HEALTHCARE PROCESSING INC.—See Accenture plc; *Int'l*, pg. 83
ACCENTURE INDIA PRIVATE LTD.—See Accenture plc; *Int'l*, pg. 83
ACCENTURE (IRELAND)—See Accenture plc; *Int'l*, pg. 82
ACCENTURE JAPAN LTD.—See Accenture plc; *Int'l*, pg. 83
ACCENTURE (KOREA) LTD.—See Accenture plc; *Int'l*, pg. 82
ACCENTURE LLC—See Accenture plc; *Int'l*, pg. 85
ACCENTURE LTDA—See Accenture plc; *Int'l*, pg. 83
ACCENTURE LTD. NIGERIA—See Accenture plc; *Int'l*, pg. 83
ACCENTURE MAURITIUS LTD.—See Accenture plc; *Int'l*, pg. 83
ACCENTURE (MAURITIUS) ONSHORE LTD.—See Accenture plc; *Int'l*, pg. 83
ACCENTURE MIDDLE EAST B.V.—See Accenture plc; *Int'l*, pg. 83
ACCENTURE NV SA—See Accenture plc; *Int'l*, pg. 83
ACCENTURE OOO—See Accenture plc; *Int'l*, pg. 83
ACCENTURE OUTSOURCING SERVICES S.A.—See Accenture plc; *Int'l*, pg. 83
ACCENTURE OY—See Accenture plc; *Int'l*, pg. 83
ACCENTURE PARTICIPATIONS BV—See Accenture plc; *Int'l*, pg. 83
ACCENTURE SARL—See Accenture plc; *Int'l*, pg. 84
ACCENTURE S.A.—See Accenture plc; *Int'l*, pg. 84
ACCENTURE SAS—See Accenture plc; *Int'l*, pg. 84
ACCENTURE SDN. BHD.—See Accenture plc; *Int'l*, pg. 84
ACCENTURE SERVICE CENTRE MOROCCO SA—See Accenture plc; *Int'l*, pg. 84
ACCENTURE SERVICES AG—See Accenture plc; *Int'l*, pg. 84
ACCENTURE SERVICES GMBH—See Accenture plc; *Int'l*, pg. 84
ACCENTURE SERVICES OY—See Accenture plc; *Int'l*, pg. 84
ACCENTURE SERVICES PRIVATE LTD.—See Accenture plc; *Int'l*, pg. 84
ACCENTURE SERVICES SP. Z.O.O.—See Accenture plc; *Int'l*, pg. 84
ACCENTURE SERVICES S.R.O—See Accenture plc; *Int'l*, pg. 84
ACCENTURE SERVICES S.R.O.—See Accenture plc; *Int'l*, pg. 84
ACCENTURE, S.L.—See Accenture plc; *Int'l*, pg. 86
ACCENTURE SOLUTIONS CO. LTD.—See Accenture plc; *Int'l*, pg. 84
ACCENTURE (SOUTH AFRICA) PTY. LTD.—See Accenture plc; *Int'l*, pg. 82
ACCENTURE SPA—See Accenture plc; *Int'l*, pg. 84
ACCENTURE SP. Z.O.O.—See Accenture plc; *Int'l*, pg. 84
ACCENTURE S.R.O.—See Accenture plc; *Int'l*, pg. 85
ACCENTURE TECHNOLOGY SERVICES LTDA.—See Accenture plc; *Int'l*, pg. 84
ACCENTURE TECHNOLOGY SOLUTIONS A/S—See Accenture plc; *Int'l*, pg. 84
ACCENTURE TECHNOLOGY SOLUTIONS-CANADA, INC.—See Accenture plc; *Int'l*, pg. 85
ACCENTURE TECHNOLOGY SOLUTIONS (DALIAN) CO LTD.—See Accenture plc; *Int'l*, pg. 84
ACCENTURE TECHNOLOGY SOLUTIONS GMBH—See Accenture plc; *Int'l*, pg. 84
ACCENTURE TECHNOLOGY SOLUTIONS GMBH—See Accenture plc; *Int'l*, pg. 84
ACCENTURE TECHNOLOGY SOLUTIONS (HK) CO. LTD.—See Accenture plc; *Int'l*, pg. 84
ACCENTURE TECHNOLOGY SOLUTIONS OY—See Accenture plc; *Int'l*, pg. 84
ACCENTURE TECHNOLOGY SOLUTIONS-SOLUCOES INFORMATICAS INTEGRADOS, S.A.—See Accenture plc; *Int'l*, pg. 85
ACCENTURE TURKEY—See Accenture plc; *Int'l*, pg. 85
ACCESS BUSINESS GROUP LLC—See Alticor Inc.; *U.S. Private*, pg. 208
ACCESS WORLDWIDE COMMUNICATIONS, INC.; *U.S. Public*, pg. 32
ACCOUNTABILITY OUTSOURCING, INC.; *U.S. Private*, pg. 54
ACEWIN AGRITECK LIMITED; *Int'l*, pg. 102
ACKROO INC.; *Int'l*, pg. 106
ACTEOS S.A.; *Int'l*, pg. 117
ACTIVE INTERNATIONAL LLC.—See Active Media Services, Inc.; *U.S. Private*, pg. 69
ACUATIVE - SERVICE CONTRACT ADMINISTRATION—See Acuative Corp.; *U.S. Private*, pg. 71
ADARE INTERNATIONAL LIMITED—See HH Global Group Limited; *Int'l*, pg. 3378
ADARE SEC LIMITED—See Endless LLP; *Int'l*, pg. 2403
ADEC SOLUTIONS USA, INC.—See The ADEC Group; *U.S. Private*, pg. 3981
ADFITECH, INC.—See Mortgage Connect, LP; *U.S. Private*, pg. 2791
ADIDAS SERVICES LIMITED—See adidas AG; *Int'l*, pg. 147
ADM ITALIA S.R.L.—See Archer-Daniels-Midland Company; *U.S. Public*, pg. 182

CORPORATE AFFILIATIONS

ADP ATLANTIC, LLC—See Automatic Data Processing, Inc.; *U.S. Public*, pg. 230
ADP BUSINESS SERVICES (SHANGHAI) CO., LTD.—See Automatic Data Processing, Inc.; *U.S. Public*, pg. 229
ADP GLOBALVIEW B.V.—See Automatic Data Processing, Inc.; *U.S. Public*, pg. 230
ADP TAX CREDIT SERVICES—See Automatic Data Processing, Inc.; *U.S. Public*, pg. 230
ADUT S.R.O—See Africa Israel Investments Ltd.; *Int'l*, pg. 189
ADVANCED RESOURCES INC.—See The Advanced Group of Companies; *U.S. Private*, pg. 3982
ADVANCED SYNERGIC PTE. LTD.—See ASM Technologies Limited; *Int'l*, pg. 627
ADVANTAGE SOLUTIONS INC.; *U.S. Public*, pg. 49
ADVANTEX; *U.S. Private*, pg. 95
ADVARRA, INC.—See Genstar Capital, LLC; *U.S. Private*, pg. 1673
AEM SERVICE S.R.L.—See A2A S.p.A.; *Int'l*, pg. 29
AEON COMPASS CO., LTD.—See AEON Co., Ltd.; *Int'l*, pg. 177
AEOREMA COMMUNICATIONS PLC; *Int'l*, pg. 179
AE OUTFITTERS RETAIL CO.—See American Eagle Outfitters, Inc.; *U.S. Public*, pg. 99
AFCO CREDIT CORPORATION—See Truist Financial Corporation; *U.S. Public*, pg. 2201
AFG MANAGEMENT AG—See Arbonia AG; *Int'l*, pg. 537
AFOGNAK NATIVE CORPORATION; *U.S. Private*, pg. 123
AGCO FUNDING CORPORATION—See AGCO Corporation; *U.S. Public*, pg. 58
AGC SHANGHAI CO., LTD.—See AGC Inc.; *Int'l*, pg. 202
AG FINANCIAL PRODUCTS INC.—See Assured Guaranty Ltd.; *Int'l*, pg. 650
AGNIV, INC.—See Clayton, Dubilier & Rice, LLC; *U.S. Private*, pg. 920
AGNIV, INC.—See KKR & Co. Inc.; *U.S. Public*, pg. 1243
AGS PRO SERVICE CO., LTD.—See AGS Corporation; *Int'l*, pg. 221
AHTNA SUPPORT AND TRAINING SERVICES, LLC—See Ahtna Incorporated; *U.S. Private*, pg. 131
AIGIN BUSINESS SERVICE CO., LTD.—See Aichi Financial Group Co., Ltd.; *Int'l*, pg. 229
AIG SHARED SERVICES CORPORATION—See American International Group, Inc.; *U.S. Public*, pg. 106
AIMIA INC.; *Int'l*, pg. 233
AIR COMPRESSOR SOLUTIONS; *U.S. Private*, pg. 138
AJG CAPITAL, INC.—See Arthur J. Gallagher & Co.; *U.S. Public*, pg. 202
AJG FINANCIAL SERVICES, LLC—See Arthur J. Gallagher & Co.; *U.S. Public*, pg. 202
AJG TWO PIERCE, INC.—See Arthur J. Gallagher & Co.; *U.S. Public*, pg. 202
ALACRA, INC.—See GTCR LLC; *U.S. Private*, pg. 1806
ALBA GRUPO MARCH; *Int'l*, pg. 292
ALBERT'S ORGANICS INC.—See United Natural Foods, Inc.; *U.S. Public*, pg. 2231
ALCIDION GROUP LIMITED; *Int'l*, pg. 301
ALCOA REMEDIATION MANAGEMENT, INC.—See Alcoa Corporation; *U.S. Public*, pg. 74
ALEXIUM INTERNATIONAL GROUP LIMITED; *Int'l*, pg. 307
AL-FUTTAIM PRIVATE COMPANY LLC; *Int'l*, pg. 285
ALIBABA TECHNOLOGY (SHANGHAI) CO., LTD.—See Alibaba Group Holding Limited; *Int'l*, pg. 326
AL-JAZEIRA SERVICES CO. SAOG—See DAMAC Group; *Int'l*, pg. 1955
ALLEGIANT PROFESSIONAL BUSINESS SERVICES, INC.; *U.S. Private*, pg. 176
ALLIANDER FINANCE B.V.—See Alliander N.V.; *Int'l*, pg. 341
ALLIN DIGITAL IMAGING—See Allin Corporation; *U.S. Public*, pg. 81
ALL IPO PLC—See ADVFN PLC; *Int'l*, pg. 167
ALLSCRIPTS—See Veradigm Inc.; *U.S. Public*, pg. 2279
ALORICA INC.; *U.S. Private*, pg. 195
ALPHA CARD SERVICES INC.; *U.S. Private*, pg. 197
ALPHAPURCHASE CO., LTD—See ASKUL Corporation; *Int'l*, pg. 625
ALPHASTAFF GROUP, INC.; *U.S. Private*, pg. 200
ALPS BUSINESS SERVICE CORPORATION—See Altech Corporation; *Int'l*, pg. 389
THE ALTA GROUP, LLC - ASSET MANAGEMENT PRACTICE—See The Alta Group, LLC; *U.S. Private*, pg. 3985
ALTEN ITALIA SPA—See Alten S.A.; *Int'l*, pg. 389
ALUTIIQ, LLC—See Afognak Native Corporation; *U.S. Private*, pg. 123
AMARAS AG—See Bechtle AG; *Int'l*, pg. 937
AMBIT GROUP LLC—See OceanSound Partners, LP; *U.S. Private*, pg. 2991
AMERICAN BANCARD, LLC; *U.S. Private*, pg. 223
AMERICAN EAGLE EXPRESS INC.; *U.S. Public*, pg. 231
AMERICAN FINANCIAL SOLUTIONS—See North Seattle Community College Foundation; *U.S. Private*, pg. 2946
AMERICAN INCORPORATORS LTD.; *U.S. Private*, pg. 237
AMERICANN INC.; *U.S. Public*, pg. 113
AMERICAN PUBLISHERS LLC—See M2 Media Group, LLC; *U.S. Private*, pg. 2530

N.A.I.C.S. INDEX

561499 — ALL OTHER BUSINESS ...

AMERICAN REPROGRAPHICS COMPANY, LLC—See ARC DOCUMENT SOLUTIONS, INC.; *U.S. Public*, pg. 179

AMERICAN VIDEO TELECONFERENCING CORP.; *U.S. Public*, pg. 112

AMERICROWN SERVICE CORPORATION—See National Association for Stock Car Auto Racing, Inc.; *U.S. Private*, pg. 2845

AMPER KLINIKEN AG—See Fresenius SE & Co. KGaA; *Int'l*, pg. 2778

AMP FINANCE SERVICES LIMITED—See AMP Limited; *Int'l*, pg. 432

AMP GBS LIMITED—See AMP Limited; *Int'l*, pg. 432

AMP GROUP HOLDINGS LIMITED—See AMP Limited; *Int'l*, pg. 432

AMP INVESTMENT SERVICES PTY LIMITED—See AMP Limited; *Int'l*, pg. 432

A.M. PRODUCTIONS—See Financiere de L'Odet; *Int'l*, pg. 2666

AMRISC, LP—See Clayton, Dubilier & Rice, LLC; *U.S. Private*, pg. 927

AMRISC, LP—See Stone Point Capital LLC; *U.S. Private*, pg. 3826

ANDALE INC.; *U.S. Private*, pg. 275

ANDERSON TAIWAN (CENTRAL)—See Anderson Industrial Corporation; *Int'l*, pg. 450

ANNABIDIOL CORP.; *U.S. Public*, pg. 137

ANSONIA CREDIT DATA, INC.—See Equifax Inc.; *U.S. Public*, pg. 786

APEIRON SYSTEMS, INC.—See KonaTel, Inc.; *U.S. Public*, pg. 1271

APOLLO HEALTH STREET, INC.—See Sutherland Global Services, Inc.; *U.S. Private*, pg. 3886

APOLLO HEALTH STREET LTD—See Sutherland Global Services, Inc.; *U.S. Private*, pg. 3886

APOLLO INTERNATIONAL MANAGEMENT, L.P.—See Apollo Global Management, Inc.; *U.S. Public*, pg. 146

APP ANNIE LTD.; *Int'l*, pg. 519

APPIER PTE LTD.—See Appier Group, Inc.; *Int'l*, pg. 520

APPLIED MATERIALS, INC.—See Applied Materials, Inc.; *U.S. Public*, pg. 172

ARAKOR CO. LTD.—See Aramark; *U.S. Public*, pg. 177

ARAMARK CHINA—See Aramark; *U.S. Public*, pg. 176

ARAMARK ENTERTAINMENT SERVICES (CANADA), INC.—See Aramark; *U.S. Public*, pg. 176

ARAMARK MANNING SERVICES LIMITED—See Aramark; *U.S. Public*, pg. 176

ARAMARK MEXICO S.A. DE C.V.—See Aramark; *U.S. Public*, pg. 176

ARBITRATION FORUMS, INC.; *U.S. Private*, pg. 308

ARCH REINSURANCE LTD.—See Arch Capital Group Ltd.; *Int'l*, pg. 546

ARC MIDCO L.L.C.—See ARC DOCUMENT SOLUTIONS, INC.; *U.S. Public*, pg. 179

ARGANO, LLC—See Trinity Hunt Management, L.P.; *U.S. Private*, pg. 4234

ARGO MANAGEMENT HOLDINGS, LTD.—See Brookfield Reinsurance Ltd.; *Int'l*, pg. 1193

ARISE VIRTUAL SOLUTIONS, INC.—See Warburg Pincus LLC; *U.S. Private*, pg. 4440

ARMADA DATA CORPORATION; *Int'l*, pg. 573

ARMILAR BUSINESS SERVICES S.L.—See Byggfakta Group Nordic HoldCo AB; *Int'l*, pg. 1234

AROMATIC FUSION; *U.S. Private*, pg. 334

ARVATO AG—See Bertelsmann SE & Co. KGaA; *Int'l*, pg. 996

ASAHI PRINTING BUSINESS SUPPORT CO., LTD.—See Asahi Printing Co., Ltd.; *Int'l*, pg. 598

ASAP, INC.—See Grossman Marketing Group; *U.S. Private*, pg. 1792

ASE TECHNOLOGY INC.; *U.S. Private*, pg. 348

ASHOKA; *U.S. Private*, pg. 350

ASIA-PACIFIC INFORMATION SERVICES SDN. BHD.—See Deutsche Post AG; *Int'l*, pg. 2071

ASITE SOLUTIONS LTD.; *Int'l*, pg. 621

ASM EUROPE B.V.—See ASM INTERNATIONAL N.V.; *Int'l*, pg. 626

ASM TECHNOLOGIES LIMITED; *Int'l*, pg. 626

ASPERMONT MEDIA—See Aspermont Limited; *Int'l*, pg. 629

ASPYRA TECHNOLOGIES LTD.—See ASPYRA, INC.; *U.S. Public*, pg. 213

ASRY MARKETING SERVICES LTD.—See Arab Shipbuilding & Repair Yard Co.; *Int'l*, pg. 532

ASSET STRATEGY RETIREMENT CONSULTANTS, LLC; *U.S. Private*, pg. 354

ASSYRIAN NATIONAL COUNCIL OF ILLINOIS; *U.S. Private*, pg. 359

ASTADIA CONSULTING - INDIA—See The Gores Group, LLC; *U.S. Private*, pg. 4034

ASTADIA CONSULTING UK LIMITED—See The Gores Group, LLC; *U.S. Private*, pg. 4034

ASTADIA INC.—See The Gores Group, LLC; *U.S. Private*, pg. 4034

ASTERION BELGIUM, NV—See Exela Technologies, Inc.; *U.S. Public*, pg. 806

ASTERION DENMARK A/S—See Exela Technologies, Inc.; *U.S. Public*, pg. 806

ASTERION FRANCE S.A.S.—See Exela Technologies, Inc.; *U.S. Public*, pg. 806

ASTERION INTERNATIONAL GMBH—See Exela Technologies, Inc.; *U.S. Public*, pg. 806

ASURION LLC; *U.S. Private*, pg. 362

ASX OPERATIONS PTY. LIMITED—See ASX Limited; *Int'l*, pg. 664

ATEC SYSTEMS, INC.—See Cadiz Inc.; *U.S. Public*, pg. 419

ATHENAHEALTH, INC.—See Bain Capital, LP; *U.S. Private*, pg. 452

ATHENAHEALTH, INC.—See Hellman & Friedman LLC; *U.S. Private*, pg. 1911

ATMA PARTICIPACOES S.A.; *Int'l*, pg. 687

ATTACHE; *U.S. Private*, pg. 382

AUDACIOUS INQUIRY, LLC; *U.S. Private*, pg. 385

AUDIENCE PARTNERS, LLC—See Altice USA, Inc.; *U.S. Public*, pg. 87

AURES GMBH—See Aures Technologies; *Int'l*, pg. 710

AUTHENTIDATE, INC.—See Aeon Global Health Corp.; *U.S. Private*, pg. 117

AUTHORITY BRANDS, LLC—See Apax Partners LLP; *Int'l*, pg. 502

AUTOCRIB, INC.—See Snap-on Incorporated; *U.S. Public*, pg. 1897

AUTOLIV - AIRBAG INFLATOR FACILITY—See Autoliv, Inc.; *Int'l*, pg. 729

AUTOMATED TECHNOLOGY MACHINES INCORPORATED; *U.S. Private*, pg. 399

AUTOMATED TOUCHSTONE MACHINES LIMITED; *Int'l*, pg. 730

AUTOVIA MEDINACELI-CALATAYUD SOC.CONCES.ESTADO, S.A.—See ACS, Actividades de Construccion y Servicios, S.A.; *Int'l*, pg. 110

AUTOVIN, INC.—See OPENLANE, Inc.; *U.S. Public*, pg. 1607

AVANT SERVICES CORPORATION; *U.S. Private*, pg. 404

AVENDRA, LLC—See Aramark; *U.S. Public*, pg. 177

AVI SYSTEMS, INC.; *U.S. Private*, pg. 406

AXA BUSINESS SERVICES PRIVATE LIMITED—See AXA S.A.; *Int'l*, pg. 755

AXA CUSTOMER SERVICES LTD—See AXA S.A.; *Int'l*, pg. 755

AXEL SPRINGER HY GMBH—See Axel Springer SE; *Int'l*, pg. 766

AXINGTON INC.; *Int'l*, pg. 768

AXWAY NORDIC AB—See Axway Software SA; *Int'l*, pg. 772

AZURE HEALTHCARE LIMITED; *Int'l*, pg. 782

BABCOCK INTERNATIONAL SUPPORT SERVICES LIMITED—See Babcock International Group PLC; *Int'l*, pg. 792

BACKS GROUP INC.—See Hakuhodo DY Holdings Incorporated; *Int'l*, pg. 3220

BAHRAIN DUTY FREE SHOP COMPLEX BSC; *Int'l*, pg. 800

BALL EUROPE GMBH—See Ball Corporation; *U.S. Public*, pg. 266

BANCVUE, LTD.; *U.S. Private*, pg. 464

BANDAI NAMCO BUSINESS ARC INC.—See BANDAI NAMCO Holdings Inc.; *Int'l*, pg. 829

BANKERS BUSINESS MANAGEMENT SERVICES, INC.; *U.S. Private*, pg. 467

BANKERS WARRANTY GROUP—See Bankers International Financial Corporation; *U.S. Private*, pg. 468

BANTA GLOBAL TURNKEY (SINGAPORE) PTE LTD—See Chatham Asset Management, LLC; *U.S. Private*, pg. 862

THE BARBOUR GROUP, LLC; *U.S. Private*, pg. 3991

BARCHART.COM, INC.; *U.S. Private*, pg. 473

BARCLAYS SHARED SERVICES PRIVATE LIMITED—See Barclays PLC; *Int'l*, pg. 860

BARLOWORLD INFORMATION SYSTEMS (PTY) LIMITED—See Barloworld Ltd.; *Int'l*, pg. 866

BARON LRMS LIMITED—See Heritage Group Ltd.; *Int'l*, pg. 3361

BARRETT CORPORATION; *Int'l*, pg. 869

BARTON COTTON—See Moore DM Group, LLC; *U.S. Private*, pg. 2780

BASEPOINT BUSINESS CENTRES; *Int'l*, pg. 871

BAXENDALE ADVISORY LIMITED; *Int'l*, pg. 900

BAYER DIRECT SERVICES GMBH—See Bayer Aktiengesellschaft; *Int'l*, pg. 902

BAYER (SCHWEIZ) AG—See Bayer Aktiengesellschaft; *Int'l*, pg. 901

BAYER-UNTERSTUTZUNGSKASSE GMBH—See Bayer Aktiengesellschaft; *Int'l*, pg. 906

BAYER U.S. LLC—See Bayer Aktiengesellschaft; *Int'l*, pg. 902

BBX CHINA CO., LTD—See BBX Minerals Limited; *Int'l*, pg. 921

BCD MEETINGS & EVENTS LLC—See BCD Holdings N.V.; *Int'l*, pg. 926

BCF SOLUTIONS, INC.; *U.S. Private*, pg. 499

BEBIT INFORMATIONSTECHNIK GMBH—See Bilfinger SE; *Int'l*, pg. 1029

BEENVERIFIED.COM; *U.S. Private*, pg. 514

BENEFIT IP SPOLKA Z OGRANICZONA ODPOWIEDZIALNOSCIA SP.K.—See Benefit Systems SA; *Int'l*, pg. 972

BENEFIT SYSTEMS INTERNATIONAL SP. Z O.O.—See Benefit Systems SA; *Int'l*, pg. 972

BENESSE BUSINESS-MATE, INC.—See EQT AB; *Int'l*, pg. 2467

BERGBAHNEN ENGELBERG-TRUBSEE-TITLIS AG; *Int'l*, pg. 979

BERG EAST IMPORTS INC.; *U.S. Private*, pg. 530

BERGMAN & BEVING DEVELOPMENT AB—See Bergman & Beving AB; *Int'l*, pg. 980

BEVSOURCE, INC.; *U.S. Private*, pg. 548

BIDPAL, INC.; *U.S. Private*, pg. 551

BIG M. AGENCY—See Grinnell Mutual Reinsurance Company Inc.; *U.S. Private*, pg. 1790

BILLING SERVICES GROUP, LLC; *U.S. Private*, pg. 559

BILL ME LATER, INC.—See PayPal Holdings, Inc.; *U.S. Public*, pg. 1656

BINARY NETWORKS PTY. LTD.—See Comms Group Ltd; *Int'l*, pg. 1720

BIRSE GROUP SERVICES—See Balfour Beatty plc; *Int'l*, pg. 807

BI-STATE PROFESSIONAL SERVICES, INC.—See Beecken Petty O'Keefe & Company, LLC; *U.S. Private*, pg. 514

BITTNET SYSTEMS SA BUCURESTI; *Int'l*, pg. 1050

BIZCENTRAL USA, INC.; *U.S. Private*, pg. 567

BIZCONF TELECOM CO., LTD.; *Int'l*, pg. 1052

BLACKBOARD STUDENT SERVICES—See Class Technologies Inc.; *U.S. Private*, pg. 915

BLACKSTONE VALLEY OFFICE SYSTEMS—See Xerox Holdings Corporation; *U.S. Public*, pg. 2389

BLDY CO., LTD.—See Bain Capital, LP; *U.S. Private*, pg. 444

BLUE JEANS NETWORK, INC.—See Verizon Communications Inc.; *U.S. Public*, pg. 2284

BLUE STAR PARTNERS LLC; *U.S. Private*, pg. 593

BMS MANAGEMENT SERVICES LTD.—See BMS Group Ltd.; *Int'l*, pg. 1077

BMT SMART LTD—See BMT Group Limited; *Int'l*, pg. 1078

BOLDER OUTREACH SOLUTIONS, LLC—See Cognizant Technology Solutions Corporation; *U.S. Public*, pg. 523

BORGWARNER GERMANY GMBH—See BorgWarner Inc.; *U.S. Public*, pg. 369

BOS AGENCY INC—See Uwharrie Capital Corp.; *U.S. Public*, pg. 2268

BOUVET SYD AB—See Bouvet ASA; *Int'l*, pg. 1121

BPA SERVEIS, SA—See Banca Privada D'Andorra, SA; *Int'l*, pg. 816

BPI FOREX CORPORATION—See Bank of the Philippine Islands; *Int'l*, pg. 848

BPO HOUSE—See Alna AB; *Int'l*, pg. 364

BRIGHTON CORPORATION—See Enerfab, Inc.; *U.S. Private*, pg. 1393

BRINDERSON CONSTRUCTORS, INC.—See New Mountain Capital, LLC; *U.S. Private*, pg. 2899

BRINK'S DIAMOND & JEWELLERY SERVICES (INTERNATIONAL) LTD.—See The Brink's Company; *U.S. Public*, pg. 2042

THE BRITISH SCHOOL SP. Z O.O.—See Canada Pension Plan Investment Board; *Int'l*, pg. 1281

THE BRITISH SCHOOL SP. Z O.O.—See EQT AB; *Int'l*, pg. 2470

BROADBAND ENTERPRISES, INC.—See Specific Media Inc.; *U.S. Private*, pg. 3751

BROADRIDGE FINANCIAL SOLUTIONS, INC. - JERSEY CITY—See Broadridge Financial Solutions, Inc.; *U.S. Public*, pg. 391

BROADRIDGE FINANCIAL SOLUTIONS LIMITED—See Broadridge Financial Solutions, Inc.; *U.S. Public*, pg. 391

BROOKESIDE VENTURES INC.; *U.S. Private*, pg. 663

BRUNEL ENERGY EUROPE BV—See Brunel International N.V.; *Int'l*, pg. 1199

BRUNEL ENERGY HOLDING BV—See Brunel International N.V.; *Int'l*, pg. 1199

BRUNSWICK GROUP (BEIJING) CO., LTD.—See Brunswick Group Limited; *Int'l*, pg. 1200

BRUNSWICK GROUP GMBH—See Brunswick Group Limited; *Int'l*, pg. 1200

BRUNSWICK GROUP (HK) CO., LTD.—See Brunswick Group Limited; *Int'l*, pg. 1200

BRUNSWICK GROUP LIMITED; *Int'l*, pg. 1200

BRUNSWICK GROUP LLC—See Brunswick Group Limited; *Int'l*, pg. 1201

BRUNSWICK GROUP NV/SA—See Brunswick Group Limited; *Int'l*, pg. 1201

BRUNSWICK GROUP (PTY) LTD.—See Brunswick Group Limited; *Int'l*, pg. 1200

BRUNSWICK GULF LTD.—See Brunswick Group Limited; *Int'l*, pg. 1201

BRUNSWICK HAW PAR HOLDINGS PTE LTD.—See Haw Par Corporation Limited; *Int'l*, pg. 3287

BT CONFERENCING, INC.—See BT Group plc; *Int'l*, pg. 1203

BT CONFERENCING—See BT Group plc; *Int'l*, pg. 1203

BT FLEET LIMITED—See Aurelius Equity Opportunities SE & Co. KGaA; *Int'l*, pg. 707

BTS BUSINESS CONSULTING (THAILAND) CO., LTD.—See BTS Group AB; *Int'l*, pg. 1205

BTS PHILADELPHIA—See BTS Group AB; *Int'l*, pg. 1205

BTS TAIPEI—See BTS Group AB; *Int'l*, pg. 1205

BUILDING INFORMATION SYSTEMS LLC—See CBRE

561499 — ALL OTHER BUSINESS ...

Group, Inc.; *U.S. Public*, pg. 459
THE BUSEY GROUP; *U.S. Private*, pg. 4003
BUSINESS ANCHOR CORPORATION—See Chori Co., Ltd.; *Int'l*, pg. 1583
BUSINESS ELECTRONICS CORP.—See R.J. Young Co., Inc.; *U.S. Private*, pg. 3337
BUSINESS ONLINE PUBLIC COMPANY LIMITED; *Int'l*, pg. 1229
C3 CUSTOMER CONTACT CHANNELS & HOLDINGS L.P.; *U.S. Private*, pg. 710
CAETECH INTERNATIONAL, INC.; *U.S. Private*, pg. 714
CAFO, INC.—See Truist Financial Corporation; *U.S. Public*, pg. 2201
CALERIS, INC.—See Iowa Network Services Inc.; *U.S. Private*, pg. 2135
CALL CENTRE TECHNOLOGY LIMITED—See Capita plc; *Int'l*, pg. 1308
CALLCOPY, INC.; *U.S. Private*, pg. 722
CALL US ASSISTANCE INTERNATIONAL GMBH—See AXA S.A.; *Int'l*, pg. 754
CALMARE THERAPEUTICS INCORPORATED; *U.S. Public*, pg. 425
CAMBRIDGE ADVISORY GROUP, INC.—See Kelso & Company, L.P.; *U.S. Private*, pg. 2279
CAMEN INTERNATIONAL TRADING, INC.—See ALFA, S.A.B. de C.V.; *Int'l*, pg. 313
CANADIAN COMMERCIAL CORPORATION; *Int'l*, pg. 1283
CANADIAN STANDARDS ASSOCIATION (FAR EAST OPERATIONS) LTD.—See CSA Group; *Int'l*, pg. 1861
CANCER FUND OF AMERICA, INC.; *U.S. Private*, pg. 733
CANON BUSINESS PROCESS SERVICES, INC.—See Canon Inc.; *Int'l*, pg. 1297
CANON BUSINESS SUPPORT INC.—See Canon Inc.; *Int'l*, pg. 1295
CANON CUSTOMER SUPPORT INC.—See Canon Inc.; *Int'l*, pg. 1296
CANON MAILCOM MALAYSIA SDN. BHD.—See Canon Inc.; *Int'l*, pg. 1296
CAPCO PRIVATE LTD.—See Central Automotive Products Ltd.; *Int'l*, pg. 1404
CAPGEMINI BUSINESS SERVICES BV—See Capgemini SE; *Int'l*, pg. 1306
CAPGEMINI BUSINESS SERVICES GUATEMALA S.A.—See Capgemini SE; *Int'l*, pg. 1304
CAPGEMINI BUSINESS SERVICES (INDIA) LTD.—See Capgemini SE; *Int'l*, pg. 1304
CAPGEMINI BUSINESS SERVICES USA LLC—See Capgemini SE; *Int'l*, pg. 1304
CAPGEMINI OUTSOURCING SERVICES GMBH—See Capgemini SE; *Int'l*, pg. 1304
CAPGEMINI OUTSOURCING SERVICES S.A.S.—See Capgemini SE; *Int'l*, pg. 1306
CAPGEMINI SHARED SERVICES BV—See Capgemini SE; *Int'l*, pg. 1306
CAPILLION INTERNATIONAL PTE. LTD.; *Int'l*, pg. 1308
CAPITA COMMERCIAL SERVICES LIMITED—See Capita plc; *Int'l*, pg. 1308
CAPITAL INSTITUTIONAL SERVICES, INC.; *U.S. Private*, pg. 740
CAPITAL MANAGEMENT ASSOCIATES INC.—See Central Iowa Power Cooperative; *U.S. Private*, pg. 822
CAPSULE TECHNOLOGIES, INC.—See Francisco Partners Management, LP; *U.S. Private*, pg. 1589
CARDCONNECT CORPORATION—See Fiserv, Inc.; *U.S. Public*, pg. 850
CARE ENTREE—See Aon plc; *Int'l*, pg. 489
CARE KALYPTO RISK TECHNOLOGIES AND ADVISORY SERVICES PVT. LTD.—See CARE Ratings Limited; *Int'l*, pg. 1323
CARE RATINGS LIMITED; *Int'l*, pg. 1323
CARLO CAPPELLARI ITALIA S.R.L.—See Fritz Egger GmbH & Co.; *Int'l*, pg. 2793
CARLSBERG FINANS A/S—See Carlsberg A/S; *Int'l*, pg. 1340
CAROLINE LLC—See Primo Water Corporation; *U.S. Public*, pg. 2718
CARY STREET PARTNERS FINANCIAL LLC; *U.S. Private*, pg. 777
CASA DE CAMBIO DELGADO INC.—See Delgado Travel Agency Corporation; *U.S. Private*, pg. 1196
CASCADES TECHNOLOGIES, INC.; *U.S. Private*, pg. 781
CASCADIA MOTIVATION INC; *Int'l*, pg. 1351
CASS INFORMATION SYSTEMS, INC.; *U.S. Public*, pg. 447
CATAMARAN SOLUTIONS, LLC; *U.S. Private*, pg. 787
CB SCIENTIFIC, INC.; *U.S. Public*, pg. 455
C&B SERVICES, INC.—See Crochet & Borel, Inc.; *U.S. Private*, pg. 1102
CCA GLOBAL PARTNERS, INC.; *U.S. Private*, pg. 799
CCB FINANCE, S.R.O.—See Banco Santander, S.A.; *Int'l*, pg. 825
CDG GROUP, LLC—See FTI Consulting, Inc.; *U.S. Public*, pg. 890
CEMAC (HONG KONG) LIMITED—See Fletcher Building Limited; *Int'l*, pg. 2699
CEM INTERNATIONAL LTD.; *Int'l*, pg. 1396
CENTER CAPITAL GENERAL AVIATION DIVISION—See Webster Financial Corporation; *U.S. Public*, pg. 2341

CENTURY II SERVICES, INC.—See Paychex, Inc.; *U.S. Public*, pg. 1655
CENTURY II STAFFING, INC.—See Paychex, Inc.; *U.S. Public*, pg. 1655
CERTEGY CHECK SERVICES, INC.—See Variant Equity Advisors, LLC; *U.S. Private*, pg. 4346
CERTIFICATION INTERNATIONAL (UK) LIMITED—See Cobepa S.A.; *Int'l*, pg. 1683
CEVA LOGISTICS ARGENTINA—See CMA CGM S.A.; *Int'l*, pg. 1666
CEVA LOGISTICS AUSTRIA GMBH—See CMA CGM S.A.; *Int'l*, pg. 1666
CEVA LOGISTICS BELGIUM—See CMA CGM S.A.; *Int'l*, pg. 1666
CEVA LOGISTICS B.V.—See CMA CGM S.A.; *Int'l*, pg. 1666
CEVA LOGISTICS CZECH REPUBLIC—See CMA CGM S.A.; *Int'l*, pg. 1666
CEVA LOGISTICS NORTH AMERICA INC.—See CMA CGM S.A.; *Int'l*, pg. 1667
CEVA LOGISTICS POLAND—See CMA CGM S.A.; *Int'l*, pg. 1667
CGF MARKETING SERVICES LTD.—See The DDC Group; *U.S. Private*, pg. 4019
CGI BUSINESS PROCESS OUTSOURCING BV—See CGI Inc.; *Int'l*, pg. 1433
CGM MEDISTAR SYSTEMHAUS GMBH—See CompuGroup Medical SE & Co. KGaA; *Int'l*, pg. 1756
CHALLENGER LIMITED—See Challenger Limited; *Int'l*, pg. 1438
CHAMBERLIN EDMONDS & ASSOCIATES, INC.—See McKesson Corporation; *U.S. Public*, pg. 1407
CHANGYOU ALLIANCE GROUP LIMITED; *Int'l*, pg. 1444
CHAROEN POKPHAND INTERTRADE SINGAPORE (PTE) LTD.—See Charoen Pokphand Group Co., Ltd.; *Int'l*, pg. 1453
CHARTER SCHOOL BUSINESS MANAGEMENT; *U.S. Private*, pg. 858
CHIA TAI COMPANY LIMITED—See Charoen Pokphand Group Co., Ltd.; *Int'l*, pg. 1453
CHIME INSIGHT & ENGAGEMENT LIMITED—See Providence Equity Partners L.L.C.; *U.S. Private*, pg. 3291
CHINA CONSTRUCTION IMPORT & EXPORT CO.—See China State Construction Engineering Corporation Limited; *Int'l*, pg. 1554
CHINA ECOTOURISM GROUP LIMITED; *Int'l*, pg. 1498
CHINA EVERGRANDE NEW ENERGY VEHICLE GROUP LIMITED—See China Evergrande Group; *Int'l*, pg. 1501
CHINA VERED FINANCIAL HOLDING CORPORATION LIMITED; *Int'l*, pg. 1562
CHIPOTLE MEXICAN GRILL U.S. FINANCE CO., LLC—See Chipotle Mexican Grill, Inc.; *U.S. Public*, pg. 489
CH JONES LIMITED—See Corpay, Inc.; *U.S. Public*, pg. 579
CHN SOLUTIONS—See Consolidated Services Group; *U.S. Private*, pg. 1022
CHOICE LOGISTICS INC.; *U.S. Private*, pg. 888
CHRISTIE + CO GMBH—See Christie Group plc; *Int'l*, pg. 1586
CHRISTIE, OWEN & DAVIES SL—See Christie Group plc; *Int'l*, pg. 1587
CHRISTIE'S AUSTRALIA PTY. LTD.—See Financiere Pinault SCA; *Int'l*, pg. 2668
CHRISTIE'S HONG KONG LTD.—See Financiere Pinault SCA; *Int'l*, pg. 2668
CHRISTIE'S (INTERNATIONAL) S.A. - FILIALE ITALIANA, ROME—See Financiere Pinault SCA; *Int'l*, pg. 2668
CHRISTIE'S INTERNATIONAL SINGAPORE PTE. LTD.—See Financiere Pinault SCA; *Int'l*, pg. 2668
CHRISTIE'S MONACO S.A.M.—See Financiere Pinault SCA; *Int'l*, pg. 2668
CHRISTIE'S SCOTLAND LIMITED—See Financiere Pinault SCA; *Int'l*, pg. 2668
CHRISTIE'S ZURICH S.A.—See Financiere Pinault SCA; *Int'l*, pg. 2668
CHRISTOVICH & ASSOCIATES, LLC; *U.S. Private*, pg. 892
C&H TESTING SERVICE, LLC—See The Aleut Corporation; *U.S. Private*, pg. 3984
CHUBB ASSET MANAGERS, INC.—See Chubb Limited; *Int'l*, pg. 1591
CIGNA INTERNATIONAL SERVICES AUSTRALIA PTY. LTD.—See The Cigna Group; *U.S. Public*, pg. 2061
CIJ NEXT CO., LTD.—See Computer Institute of Japan Ltd.; *Int'l*, pg. 1759
CIMPOR - SERVICOS DE APOIO A GESTAO DE EMPRESAS S.A.—See Camargo Correa S.A.; *Int'l*, pg. 1267
CIRCA INC.; *U.S. Private*, pg. 899
CISCO-EAGLE, INC. - LITTLE ROCK—See Cisco-Eagle Inc.; *U.S. Private*, pg. 900
CISCO SYSTEMS CAPITAL (AUSTRALIA) PTY. LTD.—See Cisco Systems, Inc.; *U.S. Public*, pg. 498
CISION FINLAND OY—See Platinum Equity, LLC; *U.S. Private*, pg. 3201
CISION GERMANY GMBH—See Platinum Equity, LLC; *U.S. Private*, pg. 3201
CISION PORTUGAL S.A.—See Platinum Equity, LLC; *U.S. Private*, pg. 3201
CISION SCANDINAVIA AS—See Platinum Equity, LLC; *U.S. Private*, pg. 3201

CISION UK LTD.—See Platinum Equity, LLC; *U.S. Private*, pg. 3201
CISION US INC.—See Platinum Equity, LLC; *U.S. Private*, pg. 3201
CITATION LTD.—See ECI Partners LLP; *Int'l*, pg. 2289
CITIGATE FIRST FINANCIAL B.V.—See Clayton, Dubilier & Rice, LLC; *U.S. Private*, pg. 924
CITIGATE MARCHCOM—See Clayton, Dubilier & Rice, LLC; *U.S. Private*, pg. 924
CITIGATE PUBLIC AFFAIRS—See Clayton, Dubilier & Rice, LLC; *U.S. Private*, pg. 924
CITIGATE SANCHIS—See Clayton, Dubilier & Rice, LLC; *U.S. Private*, pg. 924
CITIGATE SA—See Clayton, Dubilier & Rice, LLC; *U.S. Private*, pg. 924
CITY ADVERTISING LLC; *U.S. Private*, pg. 905
CLASS LIMITED—See HUB24 Limited; *Int'l*, pg. 3516
CLAYTON HOLDINGS, INC.—See Radian Group, Inc.; *U.S. Public*, pg. 1759
CLEAN VISION CORPORATION; *U.S. Public*, pg. 510
CLEAR HARBOR, LLC; *U.S. Private*, pg. 932
C-LEVELED LLC—See Direct Online Marketing, LLC; *U.S. Private*, pg. 1235
CMEC INTERNATIONAL EXHIBITION CO., LTD.—See China Machinery Engineering Corporation; *Int'l*, pg. 1516
CMIC-BS CO.LTD.—See CMIC Holdings Co., Ltd.; *Int'l*, pg. 1670
CMIC-CRC CO. LTD.—See CMIC Holdings Co., Ltd.; *Int'l*, pg. 1670
CMO PUBLIC COMPANY LIMITED; *Int'l*, pg. 1671
COAST TO COAST TICKETS LLC; *U.S. Private*, pg. 955
COFFEE FOR LESS; *U.S. Private*, pg. 961
COFFEY PROJECTS (NEW ZEALAND) LIMITED—See Tetra Tech, Inc.; *U.S. Public*, pg. 2022
COGITO MEDIA GROUP INC.; *Int'l*, pg. 1695
COGNIZANT TECHNOLOGY SOLUTIONS AUSTRALIA PTY. LTD.—See Cognizant Technology Solutions Corporation; *U.S. Public*, pg. 524
COHERIS INFOCAT LTD.—See Coheris SA; *Int'l*, pg. 1695
COILLTE PANEL PRODUCTS (UK) LIMITED—See Coillte Ltd.; *Int'l*, pg. 1696
COLLINS CO., LTD.; *Int'l*, pg. 1702
COLORADO RETAIL VENTURES SERVICES, LLC—See CHS INC.; *U.S. Public*, pg. 492
COLOUR LIMITED—See FedEx Corporation; *U.S. Public*, pg. 827
COLUMBIA INSURANCE GROUP INC.—See Columbia Insurance Group, Inc.; *U.S. Private*, pg. 977
COMDATA HOLDING SA—See The Carlyle Group Inc.; *U.S. Public*, pg. 2046
COMFORTDELGRO DRIVING CENTRE PTE. LTD.—See ComfortDelGro Corporation Limited; *Int'l*, pg. 1713
COMMONWEALTH TECHNOLOGY, INC.—See Veritas Capital Fund Management, LLC; *U.S. Private*, pg. 4360
COMMUNICATIONS DATA GROUP, INC.; *U.S. Private*, pg. 988
COMMUNITY ASSOCIATION MANAGEMENT SPECIALIST, INC.; *U.S. Private*, pg. 989
THE COMPANY CORPORATION—See Corporation Service Company; *U.S. Private*, pg. 1058
COMPLETE PURCHASING SERVICES INC.—See Aramark; *U.S. Public*, pg. 177
COMPREHENSIVE FINANCE, INC.; *U.S. Private*, pg. 1003
COMPUGROUP MEDICAL MANAGEMENTGESELLSCHAFT MBH—See CompuGroup Medical SE & Co. KGaA; *Int'l*, pg. 1756
COMPUPOWER CORPORATION—See Arnold Bernhard & Co.; *U.S. Private*, pg. 333
COMPUTER PLACEMENT LIMITED—See Bain Capital, LP; *U.S. Private*, pg. 433
COMPUTERSHARE LIMITED; *Int'l*, pg. 1760
COMPUTERSHARE SCHWEIZ AG—See Computershare Limited; *Int'l*, pg. 1760
CONCORD SERVICING CORP.; *U.S. Private*, pg. 1010
CONDECO LTD.; *Int'l*, pg. 1766
CONDUENT FEDERAL SOLUTIONS, LLC—See Conduent Incorporated; *U.S. Public*, pg. 566
CONDUENT MORTGAGE SERVICES, INC.—See Conduent Incorporated; *U.S. Public*, pg. 566
CONECTUM S.A. DE C.V.—See Grupo Posadas S.A.B. de C.V.; *Int'l*, pg. 3134
CONFIANCE GROUP—See Confiance Group; *U.S. Private*, pg. 1013
CONNECT2ONE—See National Association of College Stores, Inc.; *U.S. Private*, pg. 2846
THE CONNECTION; *U.S. Private*, pg. 4014
CONNXUS, INC.—See Thoma Bravo, L.P.; *U.S. Private*, pg. 4147
CONSERVICE; *U.S. Private*, pg. 1019
CONSTANT CONTACT, INC.—See Clearlake Capital Group, L.P.; *U.S. Private*, pg. 933
CONSTANT CONTACT, INC.—See Siris Capital Group, LLC; *U.S. Private*, pg. 3672
CONTINUUM GLOBAL SOLUTIONS, LLC—See Skyview Capital, LLC; *U.S. Private*, pg. 3686
CONVERGYS CUSTOMER MANAGEMENT GROUP INC.—See Concentrix Corporation; *U.S. Public*, pg. 565

N.A.I.C.S. INDEX 561499 — ALL OTHER BUSINESS ...

N.A.I.C.S. Index

CONWAY, DIERKING & HILLMAN, INC.; *U.S. Private*, pg. 1036
CONZZETA MANAGEMENT AG—See Bystronic AG; *Int'l*, pg. 1236
COOPER CONSOLIDATED—See Cooper/T. Smith Corporation; *U.S. Private*, pg. 1041
COOPER MARINE & TIMBERLANDS—See Cooper/T. Smith Corporation; *U.S. Private*, pg. 1041
COOPER/T. SMITH MOORING—See Cooper/T. Smith Corporation; *U.S. Private*, pg. 1041
COOPER/T. SMITH STEVEDORING - CALIFORNIA—See Cooper/T. Smith Corporation; *U.S. Private*, pg. 1042
COOPER/T. SMITH STEVEDORING—See Cooper/T. Smith Corporation; *U.S. Private*, pg. 1041
COOPER/T. SMITH STEVEDORING—See Cooper/T. Smith Corporation; *U.S. Private*, pg. 1041
COOPER/T. SMITH STEVEDORING—See Cooper/T. Smith Corporation; *U.S. Private*, pg. 1041
COOPER/T. SMITH STEVEDORING—See Cooper/T. Smith Corporation; *U.S. Private*, pg. 1041
COOPER/T. SMITH STEVEDORING—See Cooper/T. Smith Corporation; *U.S. Private*, pg. 1042
COOPER/T. SMITH STEVEDORING - TEXAS—See Cooper/T. Smith Corporation; *U.S. Private*, pg. 1042
COOPER-WILKINS WELDING & MACHINE CO., INC.—See Cooper/T. Smith Corporation; *U.S. Private*, pg. 1041
COPART OF KANSAS, INC.—See Copart, Inc.; *U.S. Public*, pg. 575
CORP2000, INC.—See Apax Partners LLP; *Int'l*, pg. 503
CORPORATE BANK TRANSIT; *U.S. Private*, pg. 1054
CORPORATION SERVICE COMPANY (UK) LIMITED—See Corporation Service Company; *U.S. Private*, pg. 1057
THE CORRIDOR GROUP, INC.—See HealthEdge Investment Partners, LLC; *U.S. Private*, pg. 1896
COSTAR GROUP, INC.; *U.S. Public*, pg. 585
COTIVITI, LLC - HEALTHCARE DIVISION—See Veritas Capital Fund Management, LLC; *U.S. Private*, pg. 4366
COTIVITI, LLC—See Veritas Capital Fund Management, LLC; *U.S. Private*, pg. 4366
COVENTRY FINANCIAL MANAGEMENT SERVICES, INC.—See CVS Health Corporation; *U.S. Public*, pg. 614
COVERDELL—See Vertrue Inc.; *U.S. Private*, pg. 4370
CP INTERTRADE COMPANY LIMITED—See Charoen Pokphand Group Co., Ltd.; *Int'l*, pg. 1453
CPM BRAXIS OUTSOURCING S.A.—See Capgemini SE; *Int'l*, pg. 1303
C P & O, LLC—See Cooper/T. Smith Corporation; *U.S. Private*, pg. 1041
CREATIVE TECHNOLOGY CHICAGO—See The Carlyle Group Inc.; *U.S. Public*, pg. 2049
CREATIVE TECHNOLOGY SAN FRANCISCO—See The Carlyle Group Inc.; *U.S. Public*, pg. 2049
CREDIT SOLUTIONS, INC.; *U.S. Private*, pg. 1091
CREST INVESTMENTS CO., LTD.; *Int'l*, pg. 1840
CRIF AG—See CRIF S.p.A.; *Int'l*, pg. 1849
CRIF (SHANGHAI) BUSINESS INFORMATION SERVICE CO. LTD—See CRIF S.p.A.; *Int'l*, pg. 1849
CRIF S.P.A.; *Int'l*, pg. 1849
CRISIL LTD.—See S&P Global Inc.; *U.S. Public*, pg. 1831
CRITICAL CONTROL ENERGY SERVICES CORP.; *Int'l*, pg. 1851
CROCHET & BOREL, INC.; *U.S. Private*, pg. 1102
CROWN CONSULTING, INC.; *U.S. Private*, pg. 1110
CSA EQUIPMENT COMPANY LLC—See Cooper/T. Smith Corporation; *U.S. Private*, pg. 1041
CSA GROUP EUROPE GMBH—See CSA Group; *Int'l*, pg. 1861
CSA GROUP ITALY S.R.L.—See CSA Group; *Int'l*, pg. 1861
CSA GROUP; *Int'l*, pg. 1861
CSA GROUP SWITZERLAND GMBH—See CSA Group; *Int'l*, pg. 1861
CSA SERVICE SOLUTIONS, LLC; *U.S. Private*, pg. 1116
CSA SERVICES—See Cooper/T. Smith Corporation; *U.S. Private*, pg. 1041
CSE-GLOBAL (UK) LIMITED—See CSE Global Ltd.; *Int'l*, pg. 1863
CSG SYSTEMS—See CSG Systems International, Inc.; *U.S. Public*, pg. 601
CTI RESOURCE MANAGEMENT SERVICES, INC.; *U.S. Private*, pg. 1118
CTQ MEDIA—See Cyger Media; *U.S. Private*, pg. 1134
CUBIC DEFENSE APPLICATIONS, INC.—See Elliott Management Corporation; *U.S. Private*, pg. 1368
CUBIC DEFENSE APPLICATIONS, INC.—See Veritas Capital Fund Management, LLC; *U.S. Private*, pg. 4361
CUBIC DE MEXICO—See Elliott Management Corporation; *U.S. Private*, pg. 1368
CUBIC DE MEXICO—See Veritas Capital Fund Management, LLC; *U.S. Private*, pg. 4362
CU COOPERATIVE SYSTEMS, INC.; *U.S. Private*, pg. 1119
CURRENT ANALYSIS, INC.—See GlobalData Plc; *Int'l*, pg. 3003
CUSTOMER VALUE PARTNERS; *U.S. Private*, pg. 1130
CU VENTURES INC.—See CU Cooperative Systems, Inc.; *U.S. Private*, pg. 1119
DAHER SUPPORT MANAGEMENT—See DAHER Group; *Int'l*, pg. 1913
DAIICHI SANKYO BUSINESS ASSOCIE CO., LTD.—See Daiichi Sankyo Co., Ltd.; *Int'l*, pg. 1929
DAIICHI SANKYO HAPPINESS CO., LTD.—See Daiichi Sankyo Co., Ltd.; *Int'l*, pg. 1930
DAIWA SECURITIES BUSINESS CENTER CO., LTD.—See Daiwa Securities Group Inc.; *Int'l*, pg. 1948
DALIAN ANCHOR BUSINESS SERVICE CO., LTD.—See Chori Co., Ltd.; *Int'l*, pg. 1583
DALIAN XINHUA INFOTECH CO., LTD—See Chinasoft International Ltd.; *Int'l*, pg. 1569
DANIELS CORPORATE ADVISORY COMPANY, INC.; *U.S. Public*, pg. 632
DATA MANAGEMENT, INCORPORATED—See CCL Industries Inc.; *Int'l*, pg. 1369
DATAMATICS TECHNOLOGIES GMBH—See Datamatics Global Services Ltd.; *Int'l*, pg. 1979
DATAMATICS TECHNOLOGIES U.K. LIMITED—See Datamatics Global Services Ltd.; *Int'l*, pg. 1979
DATASCAN FIELD SERVICES, LLC—See JM Family Enterprises Inc.; *U.S. Private*, pg. 2214
DATASEA INC.; *Int'l*, pg. 1979
DATASOURCE CONSULTING, LLC—See ExlService Holdings, Inc.; *U.S. Public*, pg. 807
DAV PRODUCTIONS, INC.; *U.S. Private*, pg. 1168
DAY & ZIMMERMANN VALIDATION SERVICES—See The Day & Zimmermann Group, Inc.; *U.S. Private*, pg. 4019
DEALERS UNITED LLC; *U.S. Private*, pg. 1182
DECISIONHEALTH LLC—See United Communications Group; *U.S. Private*, pg. 4289
DELGADO COMMUNICATIONS INC.—See Delgado Travel Agency Corporation; *U.S. Private*, pg. 1196
DELICARD AB—See Edenred S.A.; *Int'l*, pg. 2307
DELICARD GROUP AB—See Edenred S.A.; *Int'l*, pg. 2307
DELL CAPITAL PARTNERS, L.P.; *U.S. Private*, pg. 1197
DELUXE CORPORATION; *U.S. Public*, pg. 652
DEMAND SCIENCE GROUP, LLC; *U.S. Private*, pg. 1203
DENSO TEN (CHINA) LIMITED—See Denso Corporation; *Int'l*, pg. 2030
DENTSU OPERATIONS DEVELOPMENT INC.—See Dentsu Group Inc.; *Int'l*, pg. 2038
DEUTSCHE POST COM GMBH—See Deutsche Post AG; *Int'l*, pg. 2079
DEUTSCHE POST CUSTOMER SERVICE CENTER GMBH—See Deutsche Post AG; *Int'l*, pg. 2079
DEUTSCHE POST DIREKT GMBH—See Deutsche Post AG; *Int'l*, pg. 2079
DHOOT INDUSTRIAL FINANCE LIMITED; *Int'l*, pg. 2100
DIALOGUE MARKETING, INC.; *U.S. Private*, pg. 1222
DIGISCRIBE INTERNATIONAL, LLC—See Longshore Capital Partners; *U.S. Private*, pg. 2493
DIGITAL ROADS, INC.—See Advanced Network Management, Inc.; *U.S. Private*, pg. 91
DIMACO UK LIMITED—See Colruyt Group N.V.; *Int'l*, pg. 1705
DISCOVERY ALLIANCE, LLC—See Capital Southwest Corporation; *U.S. Public*, pg. 432
DIV DEUTSCHE IMMOBILIENFONDS GMBH—See Helaba Landesbank Hessen-Thuringen; *Int'l*, pg. 3327
DIVERSE COMPUTER MARKETERS, INC.—See SB Financial Group, Inc.; *U.S. Public*, pg. 1842
DNV BUSINESS ASSURANCE INDIA PRIVATE LTD—See DNV GL Group AS; *Int'l*, pg. 2148
THE DOCTORS' MANAGEMENT COMPANY—See The Doctors Company; *U.S. Private*, pg. 4022
DOMINION ENTERPRISES—See Irish Times; *U.S. Private*, pg. 2138
DOMINO'S IP HOLDER LLC—See Domino's Pizza, Inc.; *U.S. Public*, pg. 674
DONGBU CORP - CONSTRUCTION—See Dongbu Group; *Int'l*, pg. 2166
DONGBU TECHNOLOGY INSTITUTE—See Dongbu Group; *Int'l*, pg. 2166
DONNELLEY FINANCIAL, LLC—See Donnelley Financial Solutions, Inc.; *U.S. Public*, pg. 677
DOUBLE STANDARD INC.; *Int'l*, pg. 2181
DOUGLAS EINKAUFS- UND SERVICEGESELLSCHAFT MBH & CO. KG—See CVC Capital Partners SICAV-FIS S.A.; *Int'l*, pg. 1883
DOUGLAS-GUARDIAN SERVICES CORPORATION; *U.S. Private*, pg. 1267
DOVETAIL SERVICES (UK) LIMITED—See British Broadcasting Corporation; *Int'l*, pg. 1169
DOWA KOHSAN CO., LTD.—See Dowa Holdings Co., Ltd.; *Int'l*, pg. 2183
DOWA MANAGEMENT SERVICES CO., LTD.—See Dowa Holdings Co., Ltd.; *Int'l*, pg. 2183
DOWA TECHNOLOGY CO., LTD.—See Dowa Holdings Co., Ltd.; *Int'l*, pg. 2184
DOWNER PTE LTD—See Downer EDI Limited; *Int'l*, pg. 2186
DRAKES BAY FUNDRAISING, INC.—See Next Generation Fundraising, Inc.; *U.S. Private*, pg. 2920
DRB-HICOM AUTO SOLUTIONS SDN BHD—See DRB-HICOM Berhad; *Int'l*, pg. 2201
DRS PRODUCT RETURNS LLC—See Leading Ridge Management, LLC; *U.S. Private*, pg. 2406
DUCON INFRATECHNOLOGIES LIMITED—See Telidyne Inc.; *U.S. Public*, pg. 1998
DUFRY MANAGEMENT LTD.—See Avolta AG; *Int'l*, pg. 749
DUN & BRADSTREET NETPROSPEX—See Cannae Holdings, Inc.; *U.S. Public*, pg. 429
DUN & BRADSTREET NETPROSPEX—See CC Capital Partners, LLC; *U.S. Private*, pg. 798
DUN & BRADSTREET NETPROSPEX—See Intercontinental Exchange, Inc.; *U.S. Public*, pg. 1142
DUNCAN LAWRIE—See Camellia Plc; *Int'l*, pg. 1271
DUNCAN-PARNELL, INC.; *U.S. Private*, pg. 1288
DUNGARVIN, INC.; *U.S. Private*, pg. 1289
DUPONT (CHINA) RESEARCH & DEVELOPMENT AND MANAGEMENT CO., LTD.—See DuPont de Nemours, Inc.; *U.S. Public*, pg. 693
DYNAM BUSINESS SUPPORT CO., LTD.—See Dynam Japan Holdings, Co., Ltd.; *Int'l*, pg. 2239
E4E INC.; *U.S. Private*, pg. 1308
EADS SUPPLY & SERVICES, INC.—See Airbus SE; *Int'l*, pg. 243
EAGLE SYSTEMS & SERVICES, INC.; *U.S. Private*, pg. 1310
EARTHPORT MIDDLE EAST LTD.—See Earthport Plc; *Int'l*, pg. 2268
EASIOPTION BPO SERVICES PRIVATE LTD.—See J.C. Flowers & Co. LLC; *U.S. Private*, pg. 2160
EASTMAN CHEMICAL COMPANY FOUNDATION, INC.—See Eastman Chemical Company; *U.S. Public*, pg. 704
EAST WEST CONNECTION, INC.; *U.S. Private*, pg. 1318
EASY MONEY GROUP (EMG); *U.S. Private*, pg. 1323
EASY VISIBLE SUPPLY CHAIN MANAGEMENT CO., LTD.; *Int'l*, pg. 2276
EBC HR & PAYROLL SOLUTIONS, INC.; *U.S. Private*, pg. 1323
EBSO, INC.; *U.S. Private*, pg. 1325
EBSO, INC.—See EBSO, Inc.; *U.S. Private*, pg. 1325
ECKOH PLC; *Int'l*, pg. 2291
ECLERX LIMITED—See eClerx Services Ltd; *Int'l*, pg. 2291
ECLIPSE ADVANTAGE, LLC—See LSCG Management, Inc.; *U.S. Private*, pg. 2508
ECOAST SALES SOLUTIONS, LTD.; *U.S. Private*, pg. 1329
ECONTACTLIVE, INC.; *U.S. Private*, pg. 1330
ECTEON, INC.—See TA Associates, Inc.; *U.S. Private*, pg. 3917
EDDIE STOBART PROMOTIONS LIMITED—See DBAY Advisors Limited; *Int'l*, pg. 1986
EDENRED ARGENTINA—See Edenred S.A.; *Int'l*, pg. 2307
EDENRED BELGIUM SA—See Edenred S.A.; *Int'l*, pg. 2307
EDENRED DEUTSCHLAND GMBH—See Edenred S.A.; *Int'l*, pg. 2307
EDENRED ESPANA S.A.—See Edenred S.A.; *Int'l*, pg. 2307
EDENRED INCENTIVES & REWARDS DEUTSCHLAND—See Edenred S.A.; *Int'l*, pg. 2307
EDENRED MEXICO—See Edenred S.A.; *Int'l*, pg. 2308
EDENRED S.A.; *Int'l*, pg. 2307
EDENRED SWEDEN AB—See Edenred S.A.; *Int'l*, pg. 2308
EDENRED UK—See Edenred S.A.; *Int'l*, pg. 2308
EDENRED VOUCHERS DEUTSCHLAND—See Edenred S.A.; *Int'l*, pg. 2308
EDGE GLOBAL LIMITED; *Int'l*, pg. 2309
EDGIL ASSOCIATES, INC.—See Gladifi; *U.S. Private*, pg. 1704
EIGHT TO GO LLC.; *U.S. Private*, pg. 1347
EINHELL ARGENTINA S. A—See Einhell Germany AG; *Int'l*, pg. 2332
ELDERS RURAL SERVICES AUSTRALIA LIMITED—See Elders Limited; *Int'l*, pg. 2346
ELDERS RURAL SERVICES LIMITED—See Elders Limited; *Int'l*, pg. 2346
ELECTRICAL RELIABILITY SERVICES, INC.—See Emerson Electric Co.; *U.S. Public*, pg. 746
ELI LILLY ASIA, INC.—See Eli Lilly & Company; *U.S. Public*, pg. 732
ELI RESEARCH INDIA PVT. LTD.—See Eli Global, LLC; *U.S. Private*, pg. 1359
ELMAR FAR EAST PTY LTD—See NOV, Inc.; *U.S. Public*, pg. 1544
EMAGIC.COM LLC—See MGIC Investment Corporation; *U.S. Public*, pg. 1435
EMCOM HOLDINGS CO., LTD.; *Int'l*, pg. 2376
EMERA ENERGY—See Emera, Inc.; *Int'l*, pg. 2377
EMERSON NETWORK POWER—See Vertiv Holdings Co; *U.S. Public*, pg. 2288
EMIDA CORPORATION; *U.S. Private*, pg. 1382
EMIDA CORPORATION—See Emida Corporation; *U.S. Private*, pg. 1382
EMPLOYEESCREENIQ, INC.—See Caisse de Depot et Placement du Quebec; *Int'l*, pg. 1255
EMPLOYEESCREENIQ, INC.—See The Goldman Sachs Group, Inc.; *U.S. Public*, pg. 2081
EMS CO., LTD—See EPS Holdings, Inc.; *Int'l*, pg. 2465
EMS-INTERNATIONAL FINANCE (GUERNSEY) LTD.—See EMS-Chemie Holding AG; *Int'l*, pg. 2393
ENBRIDGE G & P (NORTH TEXAS) L P—See Enbridge Inc.; *Int'l*, pg. 2397
ENBW TRADING GMBH—See EnBW Energie Baden-Wurttemberg AG; *Int'l*, pg. 2398
ENDEAVOR IP, INC.; *U.S. Private*, pg. 1391
ENDESCO SERVICES CORPORATION—See Gas Technology Institute; *U.S. Private*, pg. 1647

561499 — ALL OTHER BUSINESS ...

ENDEXX CORPORATION; *U.S. Public*, pg. 760
ENEX (MAURITIUS) LIMITED—See ENL Limited; *Int'l*, pg. 2442
ENL FINANCE LIMITED—See ENL Limited; *Int'l*, pg. 2441
ENL FOUNDATION—See ENL Limited; *Int'l*, pg. 2441
ENL HOUSE LIMITED—See ENL Limited; *Int'l*, pg. 2441
ENMAX ENCOMPASS INC.—See ENMAX Corporation; *Int'l*, pg. 2442
ENRC MANAGEMENT (UK) LIMITED—See Eurasian Natural Resources Corporation Limited; *Int'l*, pg. 2527
ENSERVE GROUP LIMITED—See Grovepoint Capital LLP; *Int'l*, pg. 3112
ENVIRO SHRED INC—See Greymart Metal Company Inc.; *U.S. Private*, pg. 1785
ENVISTA, LLC; *U.S. Private*, pg. 1410
E.ON SZOLGALTATO KFT.—See E.ON SE; *Int'l*, pg. 2253
EPEAT, INC.; *U.S. Private*, pg. 1411
EPS HOLDINGS, INC.; *Int'l*, pg. 2465
EQUIMARK-NFC DEVELOPMENT CORPORATION—See BDO Unibank, Inc.; *Int'l*, pg. 930
EQUINITI LIMITED—See Siris Capital Group, LLC; *U.S. Private*, pg. 3673
EQUIOM (ISLE OF MAN) LIMITED; *Int'l*, pg. 2485
EQUIOM MARINE & AVIATION SERVICES (JERSEY) LIMITED—See Equiom (Isle of Man) Limited; *Int'l*, pg. 2485
EQUIOM TRUST COMPANY (CYPRUS) LIMITED—See Equiom (Isle of Man) Limited; *Int'l*, pg. 2485
EQUISOFT INC.; *U.S. Private*, pg. 1415
ESPREON LIMITED—See EQT AB; *Int'l*, pg. 2471
ESTACIONAMIENTOS Y SERVICIOS, S.A.—See H.I.G. Capital, LLC; *U.S. Private*, pg. 1827
E-STET; *U.S. Private*, pg. 1303
ETECH, INC.; *U.S. Private*, pg. 1431
EURODEV BV; *Int'l*, pg. 2534
EURODEV SARL—See EuroDev BV; *Int'l*, pg. 2534
EUROFINS LABORATORIES LTD.—See Eurofins Scientific S.E.; *Int'l*, pg. 2545
EUROSERVICES BAYER S.L.—See Bayer Aktiengesellschaft; *Int'l*, pg. 908
EVA- THE BASEL LIFE SCIENCES START-UP AGENCY—See Basellandschaftliche Kantonalbank; *Int'l*, pg. 871
EVCO WHOLESALE FOODS; *U.S. Private*, pg. 1436
EVERYDAY HERO LTD.—See Blackbaud, Inc.; *U.S. Public*, pg. 341
EVERYDAY HERO PTY. LTD.—See Blackbaud, Inc.; *U.S. Public*, pg. 341
EXAMINATION MANAGEMENT SERVICES, INC.—See Beecken Petty O'Keefe & Company, LLC; *U.S. Private*, pg. 514
EXAMWORKS CLINICAL SOLUTIONS, LLC—See GIC Pte. Ltd.; *Int'l*, pg. 2964
EXAMWORKS CLINICAL SOLUTIONS, LLC—See Leonard Green & Partners, L.P.; *U.S. Private*, pg. 2425
EXCEED CORPORATION; *U.S. Private*, pg. 1445
EXCEET SECURE SOLUTIONS GMBH—See EQT AB; *Int'l*, pg. 2481
EXCEL CORPORATION; *U.S. Public*, pg. 805
EXCELL AGENT SERVICES LLC; *U.S. Private*, pg. 1445
EXECUTIVE COURIER, INC.—See Storage & Transportation Co., Inc.; *U.S. Private*, pg. 3831
EXELIS SERVICES A/S—See V2X, Inc.; *U.S. Public*, pg. 2270
EXEO DIGITAL SOLUTIONS, INC.—See EXEO Group Inc.; *Int'l*, pg. 2583
EXLSERVICE COLOMBIA, S.A.S.—See ExlService Holdings, Inc.; *U.S. Public*, pg. 807
EXLSERVICE.COM, INC.—See ExlService Holdings, Inc.; *U.S. Public*, pg. 807
EXLSERVICE.COM (INDIA) PRIVATE LIMITED—See ExlService Holdings, Inc.; *U.S. Public*, pg. 807
EXLSERVICE CZECH REPUBLIC S.R.O.—See ExlService Holdings, Inc.; *U.S. Public*, pg. 807
EXLSERVICE HOLDINGS, INC.; *U.S. Public*, pg. 807
EXLSERVICE PHILIPPINES, INC.—See ExlService Holdings, Inc.; *U.S. Public*, pg. 807
EXLSERVICE ROMANIA PRIVATE LIMITED S.R.L.—See ExlService Holdings, Inc.; *U.S. Public*, pg. 807
EXLSERVICE TECHNOLOGY SOLUTIONS, LLC—See ExlService Holdings, Inc.; *U.S. Public*, pg. 807
EXPERIAN FRANCE—See Experian plc; *Int'l*, pg. 2587
EXPERIAN SCOREX US, LLC—See Experian plc; *Int'l*, pg. 2587
EXPLOTACION COMERCIAL DE INTERCAMBIADORES, S.A.—See ACS, Actividades de Construccion y Servicios, S.A.; *Int'l*, pg. 112
EXPRESS KCS INC.; *U.S. Private*, pg. 1451
EXTREME NETWORKS AUSTRALIA PTE, LTD.—See Extreme Networks, Inc.; *U.S. Public*, pg. 813
EXTREME NETWORKS HONG KONG LTD.—See Extreme Networks, Inc.; *U.S. Public*, pg. 813
EXTREME NETWORKS JAPAN, K.K.—See Extreme Networks, Inc.; *U.S. Public*, pg. 813
EXXONMOBIL OIL CORPORATION—See Exxon Mobil Corporation; *U.S. Public*, pg. 815
FANEUIL, INC.—See Skyview Capital, LLC; *U.S. Private*, pg. 3686

FARM CREDIT MID-AMERICA; *U.S. Private*, pg. 1474
FASTMARKETS LIMITED—See Astorg Partners S.A.S.; *Int'l*, pg. 656
FCSTONE DO BRASIL LTDA.—See StoneX Group Inc.; *U.S. Public*, pg. 1952
FEDERATED PAYMENT SYSTEMS LLC—See Global Payments Inc.; *U.S. Public*, pg. 943
FEDEX CORPORATE SERVICES, INC.—See FedEx Corporation; *U.S. Public*, pg. 827
FERRELLGAS FINANCE CORP.—See Ferrellgas Partners, L.P.; *U.S. Public*, pg. 829
FERROVIAL SERVICIOS S.A.—See Ferrovial S.A.; *Int'l*, pg. 2644
FERSERVIZI S.P.A.—See Ferrovie dello Stato Italiane S.p.A.; *Int'l*, pg. 2645
FIELD NATION, LLC; *U.S. Private*, pg. 1504
FIFTH GEAR, INC.—See Speed Commerce, Inc.; *U.S. Public*, pg. 1917
FILING SERVICES CANADA INC.—See Issuer Direct Corporation; *U.S. Public*, pg. 1175
FIMALAC S.A.; *Int'l*, pg. 2664
FINANCIAL SUPERMARKETS, INC.—See Market Contractors Ltd.; *U.S. Private*, pg. 2579
FINCERA INC.; *Int'l*, pg. 2672
FINDLY, LLC—See Symphony Technology Group, LLC; *U.S. Private*, pg. 3900
FINNAIR BUSINESS SERVICES OU—See Finnair Plc; *Int'l*, pg. 2675
FINSINA S.P.A.—See Argo Finanziaria S.p.A.; *Int'l*, pg. 561
FINVIS BUSINESS SERVICES GMBH—See AGRAVIS Raiffeisen AG; *Int'l*, pg. 215
FIRST ADVANTAGE CANADA INC.—See Silver Lake Group, LLC; *U.S. Private*, pg. 3654
FIRST ADVANTAGE ENTERPRISE SCREENING CORPORATION—See Silver Lake Group, LLC; *U.S. Private*, pg. 3654
FIRST ADVANTAGE JAPAN K.K.—See Silver Lake Group, LLC; *U.S. Private*, pg. 3654
FIRST ADVANTAGE OCCUPATIONAL HEALTH SERVICES CORP.—See Silver Lake Group, LLC; *U.S. Private*, pg. 3654
FIRST CHOICE HEALTHCARE SOLUTIONS, INC.; *U.S. Public*, pg. 841
FIRST DATA MERCHANT SERVICES CORPORATION—See Fiserv, Inc.; *U.S. Public*, pg. 850
FIRST EFFORT INVESTMENTS LTD.; *Int'l*, pg. 2683
FIRST FINANCIAL EMPLOYEE LEASING, INC.; *U.S. Private*, pg. 1519
FIRST INSURANCE FUNDING CORP.—See Wintrust Financial Corporation; *U.S. Public*, pg. 2375
FIRST PUNJAB MODARABA; *Int'l*, pg. 2686
FIRSTSOURCE SOLUTIONS LIMITED; *Int'l*, pg. 2691
FIRST TEK, INC.; *U.S. Private*, pg. 1529
FLEET MAINTANCE—See VSE Corporation; *U.S. Public*, pg. 2313
FLEXXRAY LLC—See Tilia Holdings LLC; *U.S. Private*, pg. 4170
FLEXXRAY LLC—See Warburg Pincus LLC; *U.S. Private*, pg. 4438
FLYWHEEL ADVANCED TECHNOLOGY, INC.; *U.S. Public*, pg. 861
F&M CO., LTD.; *Int'l*, pg. 2595
FMS PURCHASING & SERVICES, INC.; *U.S. Private*, pg. 1555
FONDSDEPOT BANK GMBH—See Caisse de Depot et Placement du Quebec; *Int'l*, pg. 1254
FONDSDEPOT BANK GMBH—See Generation Investment Management LLP; *Int'l*, pg. 2920
FOOTPRINT RETAIL SERVICES; *U.S. Private*, pg. 1562
FORD CREDIT AUTO RECEIVABLES CORPORATION—See Ford Motor Company; *U.S. Public*, pg. 865
FORD MOTOR COMPANY SWITZERLAND S.A.—See Ford Motor Company; *U.S. Public*, pg. 865
FORESIDE FINANCIAL GROUP LLC—See Genstar Capital, LLC; *U.S. Private*, pg. 1689
FORSYTHE MCARTHUR ASSOCIATES, INC.—See CDW Corporation; *U.S. Public*, pg. 463
FORTIS ADVISORS, LLC; *U.S. Private*, pg. 1576
FORTUNE SOFTWARE (BEIJING) CO., LTD—See China Finance Online Co. Limited; *Int'l*, pg. 1502
FOURTH DIMENSION SOLUTIONS LIMITED; *Int'l*, pg. 2755
FRANCHISE CONCEPTS LIMITED; *Int'l*, pg. 2760
FRANCOTYP-POSTALIA HOLDING AG; *Int'l*, pg. 2760
FRANKLIN COVEY BRASIL LTDA.—See Franklin Covey Company; *U.S. Public*, pg. 877
FRANKLIN COVEY CANADA, LTD.—See Franklin Covey Company; *U.S. Public*, pg. 877
FRANKLIN COVEY DE MEXICO, S. DE R.L. DE C.V.—See Franklin Covey Company; *U.S. Public*, pg. 878
FRANKLIN COVEY EUROPE, LTD.—See Franklin Covey Company; *U.S. Public*, pg. 877
FRANKLIN COVEY FRANCE SARL—See Franklin Covey Company; *U.S. Public*, pg. 877
FRANKLIN COVEY GERMANY—See Franklin Covey Company; *U.S. Public*, pg. 877
FRANKLIN COVEY JAPAN CO. LTD.—See Franklin Covey Company; *U.S. Public*, pg. 877
FRANKLIN COVEY NETHERLANDS BV—See Franklin Covey Company; *U.S. Public*, pg. 877
FRANKLIN COVEY PROPRIETARY LIMITED—See Franklin Covey Company; *U.S. Public*, pg. 878
FRASERS PROPERTY (THAILAND) PUBLIC COMPANY LIMITED—See Frasers Property Limited; *Int'l*, pg. 2766
FRED'S CAPITAL MANAGEMENT COMPANY, INC.—See Fred's Inc.; *U.S. Public*, pg. 883
FRINGE BENEFIT GROUP LP; *U.S. Private*, pg. 1612
FROESE FORENSIC PARTNERS LTD.—See Delta Consulting Group, Inc.; *U.S. Private*, pg. 1199
FROG DESIGN, INC.—See Capgemini SE; *Int'l*, pg. 1305
FRONTIER MANAGEMENT LLC; *U.S. Private*, pg. 1615
FUJAIRAH TRADE CENTRE COMPANY; *Int'l*, pg. 2808
FUJIFILM BUSINESS SUPPLY CO., LTD.—See FUJIFILM Holdings Corporation; *Int'l*, pg. 2821
FUJITSU A/S—See Fujitsu Limited; *Int'l*, pg. 2833
FUJITSU FSAS INC.—See Fujitsu Limited; *Int'l*, pg. 2834
FUNAI SOKEN CORPORATE RELATIONS, INC.—See Funai Soken Holdings Incorporated; *Int'l*, pg. 2845
GAFISA VENDAS INTERMEDIACAO IMOBILIARIA LTDA.—See Gafisa S.A.; *Int'l*, pg. 2868
GANNETT SUPPLY CORPORATION—See Gannett Co., Inc.; *U.S. Public*, pg. 897
GAP SOLUTIONS, INC.—See System One Holdings, LLC; *U.S. Private*, pg. 3906
GARLOCK HYGIENIC TECHNOLOGIES, LLC—See Enpro Inc.; *U.S. Public*, pg. 775
GAS STRATEGIES GROUP LTD—See S&P Global Inc.; *U.S. Public*, pg. 1831
THE GATORADE COMPANY OF AUSTRALIA PTY LIMITED—See PepsiCo, Inc.; *U.S. Public*, pg. 1672
GCA (MACAU) S.A.—See Everi Holdings Inc.; *U.S. Public*, pg. 801
GDF, INC.—See New Rite Aid, LLC; *U.S. Private*, pg. 2905
GECI GMBH—See GECI International SA; *Int'l*, pg. 2909
GECI PORTUGAL—See GECI International SA; *Int'l*, pg. 2909
GEFINOR FINANCE S.A.—See Gefinor S.A.; *Int'l*, pg. 2911
GENERAL ATOMICS ELECTRONIC SYSTEMS, INC.—See General Atomics; *U.S. Private*, pg. 1663
GENERAL DE PRODUCCIONES Y DISENO, S.A.—See Acciona, S.A.; *Int'l*, pg. 90
GENERAL DYNAMICS INFORMATION TECHNOLOGY—See General Dynamics Corporation; *U.S. Public*, pg. 914
GENERAL MARKETING SRL—See CEMBRE S.p.A.; *Int'l*, pg. 1396
GENERAL PAYMENT SYSTEMS, INC.; *U.S. Public*, pg. 929
GENPACT (DALIAN) CO. LTD.—See Genpact Limited; *Int'l*, pg. 2926
GENPACT INDIA—See Genpact Limited; *Int'l*, pg. 2926
GENPACT LLC—See Genpact Limited; *Int'l*, pg. 2926
GENPACT NETHERLANDS B.V.—See Genpact Limited; *Int'l*, pg. 2927
GENPACT RESOURCING SERVICES B.V.—See Genpact Limited; *Int'l*, pg. 2927
GENPACT SERVICES LLC—See Genpact Limited; *Int'l*, pg. 2926
GENPACT SOUTH AFRICA (PROPRIETARY) LIMITED—See Genpact Limited; *Int'l*, pg. 2927
GEN SERV, INC.; *U.S. Private*, pg. 1660
GEORGE E. FERN COMPANY—See Budco Group, Inc.; *U.S. Private*, pg. 679
GEORGE GROUP INC; *U.S. Private*, pg. 1682
GEORG FISCHER RISK MANAGEMENT AG—See Georg Fischer AG; *Int'l*, pg. 2936
GEORGIA DUPLICATING PRODUCTS, INC.—See Xerox Holdings Corporation; *U.S. Public*, pg. 2387
GESTION COMPARTIDA S.A.—See Grupo Clarin S.A.; *Int'l*, pg. 3125
GETRONICS BELGIUM NV/SA; *Int'l*, pg. 2953
GETRONICS (UK) LIMITED—See Aurelius Equity Opportunities SE & Co. KGaA; *Int'l*, pg. 708
GEVELOT S.A.; *Int'l*, pg. 2954
GIESECKE & DEVRIENT AMERICA-PRINT INSPECTION DIVISION—See Giesecke & Devrient GmbH; *Int'l*, pg. 2969
GILLETTE BETEILIGUNGS GMBH—See The Procter & Gamble Company; *U.S. Public*, pg. 2124
GLENCORE SERVICES UK LIMITED—See Glencore plc; *Int'l*, pg. 2991
GLENDENNING PTY LIMITED—See AMP Limited; *Int'l*, pg. 432
GLOBAL BUSINESS CENTERS CORP.; *U.S. Private*, pg. 1712
GLOBAL DATA SERVICES OF INDIA LIMITED—See S&P Global Inc.; *U.S. Public*, pg. 1831
GLOBAL FILE REGISTRY, INC.—See Brilliant Digital Entertainment, Inc.; *U.S. Private*, pg. 654
GLOBAL INVENTURES, INC.—See SmithBucklin Corporation; *U.S. Private*, pg. 3697
GLOBAL LOGISTICS INC.; *U.S. Private*, pg. 1716
GLOBAL PROFESSIONAL MEDIA LIMITED—See Apax Partners LLP; *Int'l*, pg. 504
GLOBAL RESALE LLC; *U.S. Private*, pg. 1717
GLOBAL UPSIDE, INC.; *U.S. Private*, pg. 1718

N.A.I.C.S. INDEX

561499 — ALL OTHER BUSINESS ...

GLOBELEQ ADVISORS LIMITED—See General Atlantic Service Company, L.P.; *U.S. Private*, pg. 1661
GLOBEOP FINANCIAL SERVICES LLC—See SS&C Technologies Holdings, Inc.; *U.S. Public*, pg. 1923
GLOBETRONICS MEDICAL TECHNOLOGY SDN BHD—See Globetronics Technology Bhd.; *Int'l*, pg. 3007
GMM GRAMMY PUBLIC COMPANY LIMITED; *Int'l*, pg. 3012
GOBI LIBRARY SOLTUIONS—See EBSCO Industries, Inc.; *U.S. Private*, pg. 1325
GOLDEN TIME NETWORK MARKETING LTD.; *U.S. Public*, pg. 951
GOLDSTREAM INVESTMENT LIMITED; *Int'l*, pg. 3034
GPV ASIA (HONG KONG), LTD.—See Aktieselskabet Schouw & Co.; *Int'l*, pg. 266
GRAND PEQUOT TOWER—See Mashantucket Pequot Gaming Enterprise Inc.; *U.S. Private*, pg. 2601
GREAT AMERICAN GROUP, LLC—See B. Riley Financial, Inc.; *U.S. Public*, pg. 261
GREATER GIVING—See Global Payments Inc.; *U.S. Public*, pg. 944
GREATER NY FINANCIAL CONSULTANTS—See Principal Financial Group, Inc.; *U.S. Public*, pg. 1721
GREATER TALENT NETWORK, INC.—See United Talent Agency, Inc.; *U.S. Private*, pg. 4301
GREELEY CONTAINMENT AND REWORK INC.; *Int'l*, pg. 3069
GREENBRIER INTERNATIONAL, INC.—See Dollar Tree, Inc.; *U.S. Public*, pg. 672
GREENHY2 LIMITED; *Int'l*, pg. 3075
GREENSILL CAPITAL (UK) LIMITED; *Int'l*, pg. 3076
GREEN TEC CORPORATION; *Int'l*, pg. 3073
GREGGS (LEASING) LIMITED—See Greggs plc; *Int'l*, pg. 3078
GROSSMAN Y ASOCIADOS, S.A. DE C.V.—See Arca Continental, S.A.B. de C.V.; *Int'l*, pg. 540
GROUP125 LLC; *U.S. Private*, pg. 1794
GROUPE ACTICALL SAS—See Creadev SAS; *Int'l*, pg. 1830
GS HOLDINGS LIMITED; *Int'l*, pg. 3142
GUEST PACKAGING, LLC—See Sysco Corporation; *U.S. Public*, pg. 1974
GUIDELINE, INC.—See Lake Capital Management LLC; *U.S. Private*, pg. 2374
GULF FRANCHISING HOLDING COMPANY K.S.C.C.; *Int'l*, pg. 3180
GUN.IO INCORPORATED; *U.S. Private*, pg. 1818
GURIT SCANDINAVIA APS—See Gurit Holding AG; *Int'l*, pg. 3188
GUSHEN, INC.; *U.S. Public*, pg. 975
HAFSLUND FAKTURASERVICE AS—See Hafslund ASA; *Int'l*, pg. 3206
HAFSLUND KUNDESENTER AS—See Hafslund ASA; *Int'l*, pg. 3206
HAGU CO., LTD.—See AB&Company Co., Ltd.; *Int'l*, pg. 47
HAIGOOD & CAMPBELL LLC; *U.S. Private*, pg. 1840
HAKKANI CORPORATION—See Hakkani Group; *Int'l*, pg. 3219
HALLVARSSON & HALVARSSON AB; *Int'l*, pg. 3230
HAMPDEN AGENCIES LIMITED—See Hampden Holdings Limited; *Int'l*, pg. 3239
HANCOM FINTECH, INC.—See Hancom, Inc.; *Int'l*, pg. 3242
HANKYU HANSHIN CLEAN SERVICE CO., LTD.—See Hankyu Hanshin Holdings Inc.; *Int'l*, pg. 3255
HANKYU HANSHIN TECHNO SERVICE CO., LTD.—See Hankyu Hanshin Holdings Inc.; *Int'l*, pg. 3255
HANNOVER LEASING GMBH & CO. KG—See Helaba Landesbank Hessen-Thuringen; *Int'l*, pg. 3328
HANWHA DEFENSE SYSTEMS CO., LTD.—See Hanwha Group; *Int'l*, pg. 3265
HAPPYDOO SA; *Int'l*, pg. 3269
HARGREAVES SERVICES PLC; *Int'l*, pg. 3275
HARLAND CLARKE CORP.—See MacAndrews & Forbes Incorporated; *U.S. Private*, pg. 2532
HARRIS WILLIAMS & CO.—See The PNC Financial Services Group, Inc.; *U.S. Public*, pg. 2119
HAUPT PHARMA SALES GMBH—See BC Partners LLP; *Int'l*, pg. 922
HAW PAR SECURITIES (PRIVATE) LIMITED—See Haw Par Corporation Limited; *Int'l*, pg. 3287
HAYLEYS BUSINESS SOLUTIONS INTERNATIONAL (PVT) LTD.—See Hayleys PLC; *Int'l*, pg. 3292
HCL BPO SERVICES (NI) LIMITED—See HCL Technologies Ltd.; *Int'l*, pg. 3298
HCL EXPENSE MANAGEMENT SERVICES INC.—See HCL Technologies Ltd.; *Int'l*, pg. 3298
HCL INSURANCE BPO SERVICES LTD.—See HCL Technologies Ltd.; *Int'l*, pg. 3298
HCL TECHNOLOGIES BPO SERVICES LTD—See HCL Technologies Ltd.; *Int'l*, pg. 3299
THE H.D. LEE COMPANY, INC.—See V. F. Corporation; *U.S. Public*, pg. 2268
HEALTHLINK, INC.—See Elevance Health, Inc.; *U.S. Public*, pg. 730
HEALTH REVENUE ASSURANCE HOLDINGS, INC.; *U.S. Public*, pg. 1015
THE HEARST SERVICE CENTER, IN CHARLOTTE,
N.C.—See The Hearst Corporation; *U.S. Private*, pg. 4049
HEARTLAND EXPRESS, INC., OF IOWA—See Heartland Express, Inc.; *U.S. Public*, pg. 1017
HELABA BETEILIGUNGS-MANAGEMENT GESELLSCHAFT MBH—See Helaba Landesbank Hessen-Thuringen; *Int'l*, pg. 3328
HIDIS GMBH; *Int'l*, pg. 3384
HIFX AUSTRALIA PTY LTD—See Euronet Worldwide, Inc.; *U.S. Public*, pg. 798
HIFX LIMITED—See Euronet Worldwide, Inc.; *U.S. Public*, pg. 798
HIFX SPAIN S.L.—See Euronet Worldwide, Inc.; *U.S. Public*, pg. 798
HILCO APPRAISAL LIMITED—See Hilco Trading, LLC; *U.S. Private*, pg. 1943
HILCO APPRAISAL SERVICES, LLC—See Hilco Trading, LLC; *U.S. Private*, pg. 1943
HINDUJA GLOBAL SOLUTIONS LTD.; *Int'l*, pg. 3397
HINDUJA GLOBAL SOLUTIONS (UK) LIMITED—See Hinduja Global Solutions Ltd.; *Int'l*, pg. 3398
HIQ CORPORATE SERVICES, INC.—See Apax Partners LLP; *Int'l*, pg. 503
HITACHI EUROPE GMBH - EUROPEAN PROCUREMENT & SOURCING GROUP—See Hitachi, Ltd.; *Int'l*, pg. 3417
HITACHI ZOSEN CORPORATION - TOKYO OFFICE—See Hitachi Zosen Corporation; *Int'l*, pg. 3410
HOKKAIDO RECORDS MANAGEMENT CO., INC.—See Hokkaido Electric Power Co., Inc.; *Int'l*, pg. 3443
HONDA BANK GMBH—See Honda Motor Co., Ltd.; *Int'l*, pg. 3460
HONG KONG AIRPORT SERVICES LTD.—See Cathay Pacific Airways Limited; *Int'l*, pg. 1360
HONGLI CLEAN ENERGY TECHNOLOGIES CORP.; *Int'l*, pg. 3471
HOOYU LTD.—See Mitek Systems, Inc.; *U.S. Public*, pg. 1452
HORD COPLAN MACHT, INC.; *U.S. Private*, pg. 1980
HORMEL FOODS INTERNATIONAL CORPORATION—See Hormel Foods Corporation; *U.S. Public*, pg. 1054
HOSPECO BRANDS GROUP; *U.S. Private*, pg. 1985
HOSPITAL CORPORATION OF AMERICA; *U.S. Private*, pg. 1987
HOSPITALITY INT. THAILANDE—See Accor S.A.; *Int'l*, pg. 91
HOSPITALITY MARKETING CONCEPTS, (ASIA PACIFIC) INC—See Hospitality Marketing Concepts, Inc.; *U.S. Private*, pg. 1987
HOSPITALITY PURVEYOR INC.; *U.S. Private*, pg. 1988
HOT SHOT EXPRESS INC.; *U.S. Private*, pg. 1988
HOULIHAN LOKEY (CORPORATE FINANCE) LIMITED—See Houlihan Lokey, Inc.; *U.S. Public*, pg. 1055
HOUSTON COPART SALVAGE AUTO AUCTIONS LP—See Copart, Inc.; *U.S. Public*, pg. 575
HPC WIRELESS SERVICES; *U.S. Private*, pg. 1996
HPI SOURCING GMBH & CO. KG—See HPI AG; *Int'l*, pg. 3500
HR ACCESS SOLUTIONS SAS—See FMR LLC; *U.S. Private*, pg. 1555
HR ACCESS SOLUTIONS S.L.—See FMR LLC; *U.S. Private*, pg. 1555
HRMALL INC.—See Ayala Corporation; *Int'l*, pg. 774
HRQ, INC.; *U.S. Private*, pg. 1998
HUBEI CENTURY NETWORK TECHNOLOGY INC; *Int'l*, pg. 3517
HUNYADY AUCTION COMPANY; *U.S. Private*, pg. 2011
HWGG ENTERTAINMENT LIMITED; *Int'l*, pg. 3543
HYPERSPRING, LLC—See GSE Systems, Inc.; *U.S. Public*, pg. 973
I3 VERTICALS, LLC—See i3 Verticals, Inc.; *U.S. Public*, pg. 1081
IBIDEN CAREER TECHNO CORP.—See Ibiden Co., Ltd.; *Int'l*, pg. 3575
IBIDEN ELECTRONICS (SHANGHAI) CO., LTD.—See Ibiden Co., Ltd.; *Int'l*, pg. 3575
ICB GLOBAL MANAGEMENT SDN. BHD.—See ICB Financial Group Holdings AG; *Int'l*, pg. 3578
ICON PROFESSIONAL SERVICES LLC—See Serent Capital Management Company, LLC; *U.S. Private*, pg. 3613
ICONTACT MARKETING CORP.—See Ziff Davis, Inc.; *U.S. Public*, pg. 2404
I-CONTROL HOLDINGS LIMITED; *Int'l*, pg. 3563
ICX GROUP INC.; *U.S. Private*, pg. 2034
IDC ASEAN—See China Oceanwide Holdings Group Co., Ltd.; *Int'l*, pg. 1536
IDC ASEAN—See IDG Capital; *Int'l*, pg. 3593
IDC CHINA—See China Oceanwide Holdings Group Co., Ltd.; *Int'l*, pg. 1537
IDC CHINA—See IDG Capital; *Int'l*, pg. 3593
IDC INDIA LTD.—See China Oceanwide Holdings Group Co., Ltd.; *Int'l*, pg. 1537
IDC INDIA LTD.—See IDG Capital; *Int'l*, pg. 3593
IDC KOREA LTD.—See China Oceanwide Holdings Group Co., Ltd.; *Int'l*, pg. 1537
IDC KOREA LTD.—See IDG Capital; *Int'l*, pg. 3593
IDC NORDIC (DENMARK) A/S—See China Oceanwide Holdings Group Co., Ltd.; *Int'l*, pg. 1537
IDC NORDIC (DENMARK) A/S—See IDG Capital; *Int'l*, pg. 3593
IDC NORDIC (SWEDEN)—See China Oceanwide Holdings Group Co., Ltd.; *Int'l*, pg. 1537
IDC NORDIC (SWEDEN)—See IDG Capital; *Int'l*, pg. 3593
IDC PHILIPPINES—See China Oceanwide Holdings Group Co., Ltd.; *Int'l*, pg. 1537
IDC PHILIPPINES—See IDG Capital; *Int'l*, pg. 3593
IDC POLSKA—See China Oceanwide Holdings Group Co., Ltd.; *Int'l*, pg. 1537
IDC POLSKA—See IDG Capital; *Int'l*, pg. 3594
IDC RESEARCH, INC.—See China Oceanwide Holdings Group Co., Ltd.; *Int'l*, pg. 1537
IDC RESEARCH, INC.—See IDG Capital; *Int'l*, pg. 3594
IDC TAIWAN—See China Oceanwide Holdings Group Co., Ltd.; *Int'l*, pg. 1537
IDC TAIWAN—See IDG Capital; *Int'l*, pg. 3594
IDEAL SETECH, L.L.C.—See The Ideal Group, Inc.; *U.S. Private*, pg. 4055
IDEAS INTERNATIONAL LIMITED—See Gartner, Inc.; *U.S. Public*, pg. 907
IDT (JAPAN) LIMITED—See IDT International Limited; *Int'l*, pg. 3596
IENERGIZER LIMITED; *Int'l*, pg. 3597
IHS INC.—See S&P Global Inc.; *U.S. Public*, pg. 1830
IKB CAPITAL CORPORATION—See Lone Star Global Acquisitions, LLC; *U.S. Private*, pg. 2488
IKF TECHNOLOGIES LIMITED; *Int'l*, pg. 3610
ILLINOIS ENERGY SOLUTIONS, USA, LLC—See The Southern Company; *U.S. Public*, pg. 2131
IMARKETING SOLUTIONS GROUP INC; *Int'l*, pg. 3619
IMPACT HD INC.—See Bain Capital, LP; *U.S. Private*, pg. 433
IMPACT RESOURCES, LLC—See National Product Services; *U.S. Private*, pg. 2861
INCOGNITO SOFTWARE SYSTEMS INC.—See Constellation Software Inc.; *Int'l*, pg. 1775
INCORPORATING SERVICES, LTD; *U.S. Private*, pg. 2054
INDIA INDEX SERVICES AND PRODUCTS LIMITED—See S&P Global Inc.; *U.S. Public*, pg. 1831
INFINITY DISTRIBUTION, INC.; *U.S. Private*, pg. 2071
INFOVISION TECHNOLOGIES—See Infovision Technologies Inc.; *U.S. Private*, pg. 2074
INFOVISION TECHNOLOGIES—See Infovision Technologies Inc.; *U.S. Private*, pg. 2074
INNOVAPOST, INC.—See Canada Post Corporation; *Int'l*, pg. 1282
INNOVAPOST, INC.—See CGI Inc.; *Int'l*, pg. 1433
INNOVATIONONE, LLC—See The Chickasaw Nation; *U.S. Private*, pg. 4008
INNOVATIONSFONDS HESSEN GMBH & CO. KG—See Helaba Landesbank Hessen-Thuringen; *Int'l*, pg. 3328
INOVINE BH D.O.O.—See British American Tobacco plc; *Int'l*, pg. 1168
INSIGHT RESOURCE GROUP; *U.S. Private*, pg. 2086
INSIGHT SOURCING GROUP, INC.; *U.S. Private*, pg. 2087
INSURMARK, INC.; *U.S. Private*, pg. 2096
INTEC BILLING IRELAND—See CSG Systems International, Inc.; *U.S. Public*, pg. 601
INTEC TELECOM SYSTEMS LIMITED—See CSG Systems International, Inc.; *U.S. Public*, pg. 601
INTEGRATED BUSINESS TECHNOLOGIES, LLC—See The 20 Msp Group LLC; *U.S. Private*, pg. 3980
INTELCOM EXPRESS INC.—See Canada Post Corporation; *Int'l*, pg. 1282
INTELLICORP RECORDS, INC.—See Verisk Analytics, Inc.; *U.S. Public*, pg. 2283
THE INTELLIGENT OFFICE, INC.—See MidOcean Partners, LLP; *U.S. Private*, pg. 2717
INTERACTIVE SYSTEMS, INC.—See Triple-S Management Corp.; *U.S. Public*, pg. 2195
INTER-CITY MPC (M) SDN. BHD.—See HeiTech Padu Berhad; *Int'l*, pg. 3326
INTERNATIONAL BUSINESS EXCHANGE CORPORATION; *U.S. Private*, pg. 2115
INTERNATIONAL LOGISTICS COMPANY, INC.—See Cooper/T. Smith Corporation; *U.S. Private*, pg. 1042
INTERNATIONAL TOOLING SOLUTIONS LLC; *U.S. Private*, pg. 2121
INTERNATIONAL VIDEO-CONFERENCING, INC.; *U.S. Private*, pg. 2121
INTERTRUST (SUISSE) S.A.—See Corporation Service Company; *U.S. Private*, pg. 1057
INVENTUS, LLC—See HGGC, LLC; *U.S. Private*, pg. 1930
IVESHARE INC.; *U.S. Private*, pg. 2131
INVESTMENTS AFRICA ISRAEL S.R.O.—See Africa Israel Investments Ltd.; *Int'l*, pg. 190
INVITA B.S.C.—See BBK B.S.C.; *Int'l*, pg. 920
IQ BACKOFFICE, INC.—See Ayala Corporation; *Int'l*, pg. 774
IQ OFFICE PRODUCTS LLC; *U.S. Private*, pg. 2137
IQVIA GOVERNMENT SOLUTIONS, INC.—See IQVIA Holdings Inc.; *U.S. Public*, pg. 1168
IRB COMPANY INC.—See Genstar Capital, LLC; *U.S. Private*, pg. 1673
ISHIR, INC.; *U.S. Private*, pg. 2143
ISID ASSIST, LTD.—See Dentsu Group Inc.; *Int'l*, pg. 2038
ISSUER DIRECT CORPORATION; *U.S. Public*, pg. 1175

561499 — ALL OTHER BUSINESS ...

ITALEASE GESTIONE BENI - OPERATIONAL HEADQUARTERS—See Banco BPM S.p.A.; *Int'l*, pg. 819
ITEMION GMBH & CO. KG—See Edenred S.A.; *Int'l*, pg. 2308
ITEX CORPORATION; *U.S. Public*, pg. 1175
IT'S JUST LUNCH INTERNATIONAL LLC—See The Riverside Company; *U.S. Private*, pg. 4109
ITS MAGHIELSE LLC—See International Tooling Solutions LLC; *U.S. Private*, pg. 2121
I.T. SOURCE; *U.S. Private*, pg. 2027
ITT COMMUNITY DEVELOPMENT CORP.—See ITT Inc.; *U.S. Public*, pg. 1178
ITT DELAWARE INVESTMENTS INC.—See ITT Inc.; *U.S. Public*, pg. 1178
IVCI, LLC; *U.S. Private*, pg. 2151
JAWOOD BUSINESS PROCESS SOLUTIONS, LLC—See Genpact Limited; *Int'l*, pg. 2927
JEFFERSON WELLS INTERNATIONAL, INC.—See ManpowerGroup Inc.; *U.S. Public*, pg. 1358
JMR FINANCIAL GROUP, INC.; *U.S. Private*, pg. 2216
JOHNS MANVILLE—See Berkshire Hathaway Inc.; *U.S. Public*, pg. 308
JOMO-NET CO., LTD.—See ENEOS Holdings, Inc.; *Int'l*, pg. 2417
JOSEPH A. BARANSKI LITERARY AGENCY—See Barancorp, Ltd.; *U.S. Private*, pg. 471
JOSEPH C. SANSONE COMPANY; *U.S. Private*, pg. 2236
JP BUSINESS SERVICE CORPORATION—See Electric Power Development Co., Ltd.; *Int'l*, pg. 2349
JUMPSTART AUTOMOTIVE MEDIA—See The Hearst Corporation; *U.S. Private*, pg. 4049
K3 ENTERPRISES INC.; *U.S. Private*, pg. 2253
KAMEX LTD.—See Triumph Group, Inc.; *U.S. Public*, pg. 2196
KAPLAN EDUCATION PTY. LIMITED—See Graham Holdings Company; *U.S. Public*, pg. 955
KARIMS INTERNATIONAL USA; *U.S. Private*, pg. 2262
KATAHDIN INDUSTRIES, INC.; *U.S. Private*, pg. 2264
KATALYST PARTNERS, LLC; *U.S. Private*, pg. 2264
KAYA HOLDINGS, INC.; *U.S. Public*, pg. 1215
KCS HONG KONG LTD.—See CVC Capital Partners SICAV-FIS S.A.; *Int'l*, pg. 1886
KEEPONPROSPECTING.COM—See Response Mail Express Inc.; *U.S. Private*, pg. 3408
KELLYMITCHELL GROUP, INC.; *U.S. Private*, pg. 2277
KELTIC FINANCIAL SERVICES, LLC—See Ares Management Corporation; *U.S. Public*, pg. 189
KEMA USA INC.—See DNV GL Group AS; *Int'l*, pg. 2151
KERR BROTHERS (EXPORTS) PTY LIMITED—See Grove International Pty Limited; *Int'l*, pg. 3112
KEYMARK, INC. - NORTHEAST—See Keymark, Inc.; *U.S. Private*, pg. 2294
KIERSTED SYSTEMS, L.P.—See Driven, Inc.; *U.S. Private*, pg. 1278
KIESWERK MAAS-ROELOFFS VERWALTUNGSGESELLSCHAFT MBH—See Heidelberg Materials AG; *Int'l*, pg. 3317
KITCHENMAN TERMINAL CO.—See George S. Coyne Chemical Co. Inc.; *U.S. Private*, pg. 1683
KITCHNER & PIERRO COMPANY, INC.; *U.S. Private*, pg. 2316
KNOWLEDGEBANK, INC.; *U.S. Private*, pg. 2323
KNOWLEDGEPOINT360 GROUP LLC—See Clayton, Dubilier & Rice, LLC; *U.S. Private*, pg. 928
KONECTA BTO, S.L.—See Grupo Konectanet S.L.; *Int'l*, pg. 3130
KOWLOONBAY INTERNATIONAL TRADE & EXHIBITION CENTRE—See Hopewell Holdings Limited; *Int'l*, pg. 3473
KOYA LEADERSHIP PARTNERS LLC; *U.S. Private*, pg. 2345
KPF, LLC—See The Kroger Co.; *U.S. Public*, pg. 2108
KS INTERNATIONAL LLC—See D.C. Capital Partners, LLC; *U.S. Private*, pg. 1141
KYRUUS, INC.; *U.S. Private*, pg. 2360
LANDMARK SERVICE CO. LLC—See Worth & Co., Inc.; *U.S. Private*, pg. 4570
LANDMARKS SA—See Hasgrove plc; *Int'l*, pg. 3283
LANE BRYANT CHARITIES, INC.—See Sycamore Partners Management, LP; *U.S. Private*, pg. 3896
LAZER SPOT, INC.—See Harvest Partners L.P.; *U.S. Private*, pg. 1876
LEASE A SALES REP; *U.S. Private*, pg. 2408
LEDIC MANAGEMENT GROUP; *U.S. Private*, pg. 2410
THE LEGACY COMPANIES; *U.S. Private*, pg. 4069
LESTER INC.; *U.S. Private*, pg. 2433
LESTER INDIA—See Lester Inc.; *U.S. Private*, pg. 2433
LEVEL 11; *U.S. Private*, pg. 2434
LEVIATHAN CORP.; *U.S. Private*, pg. 2435
LEWELLYN TECHNOLOGY, LLC—See Align Capital Partners, LLC; *U.S. Private*, pg. 167
LH TRADING LTD—See Holcim Ltd.; *Int'l*, pg. 3448
LIBERATA UK LTD.—See Bain Capital, LP; *U.S. Private*, pg. 434
LIFEWOOD DATA TECHNOLOGY LIMITED—See China Electronics Corporation; *Int'l*, pg. 1499
LIMITED BRAND & CREATIVE SERVICES—See Bath & Body Works, Inc.; *U.S. Public*, pg. 279
LINEWISE SERVICES AB—See Addnode Group AB; *Int'l*, pg. 130
LINKIA, LLC—See Patient Square Capital, L.P.; *U.S. Private*, pg. 3107
LINQ SERVICES; *U.S. Private*, pg. 2462
LIONEL HENDERSON & CO., INC.; *U.S. Private*, pg. 2464
LISTEN UP ESPANOL INC. (LUE); *U.S. Private*, pg. 2466
LIVE AUCTIONEERS, LLC—See Auction Technology Group PLC; *Int'l*, pg. 700
LLC WILLIAMS LEA—See Deutsche Post AG; *Int'l*, pg. 2081
L&M TECHNOLOGIES, INC.; *U.S. Private*, pg. 2363
LOGTEK LIMITED—See OEP Capital Advisors, L.P.; *U.S. Private*, pg. 3000
LOGWIN AG—See Delton AG; *Int'l*, pg. 2021
LONGROOT (THAILAND) LTD.—See Axion Ventures Inc.; *Int'l*, pg. 769
LOREN COMMUNICATIONS INTERNATIONAL LTD., INC.; *U.S. Private*, pg. 2495
LORIEN RESOURCING LIMITED - LEEDS—See HFBG Holding B.V.; *Int'l*, pg. 3375
LORIEN RESOURCING LIMITED - LONDON—See HFBG Holding B.V.; *Int'l*, pg. 3375
LORIEN RESOURCING LIMITED - MANCHESTER—See HFBG Holding B.V.; *Int'l*, pg. 3375
LOTUS AGRAR GMBH—See AGRAVIS Raiffeisen AG; *Int'l*, pg. 215
LOYALTYONE US, INC.—See Bread Financial Holdings Inc.; *U.S. Public*, pg. 381
LOZANO ENTERPRISES, LP; *U.S. Private*, pg. 2506
L&P TEHNOLOGIJE D.O.O.—See Leggett & Platt, Incorporated; *U.S. Public*, pg. 1302
M2 COMMANDER PTY. LTD.—See Aware Super Pty Ltd; *Int'l*, pg. 752
M2 MEDIA GROUP, LLC; *U.S. Private*, pg. 2530
MAAG PUMP SYSTEMS (SWITZERLAND) AG—See Dover Corporation; *U.S. Public*, pg. 682
MAALI ENTERPRISES INC.; *U.S. Private*, pg. 2530
MACY'S MERCHANDISING GROUP, INC.—See Macy's, Inc.; *U.S. Public*, pg. 1353
MADATA IT, S.A. DE C.V.—See GCC, S.A.B. de C.V.; *Int'l*, pg. 2895
MAIN STREET HUB INC.—See KKR & Co. Inc.; *U.S. Public*, pg. 1252
MAIN STREET HUB INC.—See Silver Lake Group, LLC; *U.S. Private*, pg. 3657
MAIN STREET HUB INC.—See TCMI, Inc.; *U.S. Private*, pg. 3943
MANAGEMENT SERVICES NORTHWEST; *U.S. Private*, pg. 2561
MANHEIM OF PHOENIX—See Cox Enterprises, Inc.; *U.S. Private*, pg. 1077
MAN-MACHINES SYSTEMS ASSESSMENT, INC.; *U.S. Private*, pg. 2559
MANNING & NAPIER BENEFITS, LLC—See Callodine Acquisition Corporation; *U.S. Public*, pg. 424
MARATHON DIGITAL HOLDINGS, INC.; *U.S. Public*, pg. 1363
MARINA ENERGY LLC—See JPMorgan Chase & Co.; *U.S. Public*, pg. 1210
MARKEM-IMAJE INDUSTRIES LIMITED—See Dover Corporation; *U.S. Public*, pg. 682
MARKETING PRODUCTION SYSTEMS, LLC—See Ambassador Programs, Inc.; *U.S. Private*, pg. 217
MARKETRX INC.—See Cognizant Technology Solutions Corporation; *U.S. Public*, pg. 525
MARKETRX INDIA PRIVATE LIMITED—See Cognizant Technology Solutions Corporation; *U.S. Public*, pg. 525
MARMAXX OPERATING CORP.—See The TJX Companies, Inc.; *U.S. Public*, pg. 2134
MARQUINARIAS INGERSOLL-RAND DE COLOMBIA S.A.—See Ingersoll Rand Inc.; *U.S. Public*, pg. 1122
MARSH WORTHAM—See Marsh & McLennan Companies, Inc.; *U.S. Public*, pg. 1382
MAST TECHNOLOGY SERVICES, INC.—See Bath & Body Works, Inc.; *U.S. Public*, pg. 279
MATRIX MANAGEMENT SOLUTIONS, LLC—See Thoma Bravo, L.P.; *U.S. Private*, pg. 4150
MATRIXONESOURCE, LLC—See GPB Capital Holdings, LLC; *U.S. Private*, pg. 1748
MAXIFY SOLUTIONS INC.; *U.S. Private*, pg. 2618
M. CALL, S.A.—See APG Asset Management NV; *Int'l*, pg. 512
MCDASH ANALYTICS, LLC—See Fidelity National Financial, Inc.; *U.S. Public*, pg. 831
MDVIP, LLC—See Charlesbank Capital Partners, LLC; *U.S. Private*, pg. 855
MDVIP, LLC—See The Goldman Sachs Group, Inc.; *U.S. Public*, pg. 2081
MEDIAFLAG OKINAWA INC.—See Bain Capital, LP; *U.S. Private*, pg. 433
MEDICAL AIRPORT SERVICE GMBH—See Fraport AG; *Int'l*, pg. 2764
MEDICAL EXPRESS—See AMN Healthcare Services, Inc.; *U.S. Public*, pg. 125
MEDISKED LLC—See Symphony Technology Group, LLC; *U.S. Private*, pg. 3901
MEDISOUTH, INC.; *U.S. Private*, pg. 2657

CORPORATE AFFILIATIONS

MEDKINETICS, LLC—See Clearlake Capital Group, L.P.; *U.S. Private*, pg. 937
MEDKINETICS, LLC—See SkyKnight Capital LLC; *U.S. Private*, pg. 3685
MEGAS, INC.; *U.S. Private*, pg. 2660
MEMBERWORKS CANADA CORPORATION—See Vertrue Inc.; *U.S. Private*, pg. 4370
MERIDIAN GROUP INTERNATIONAL, INC.; *U.S. Private*, pg. 2673
MERITS & BENEFITS NV—See Edenred S.A.; *Int'l*, pg. 2308
MERKLE RESPONSE MANAGEMENT GROUP—See Moore DM Group, LLC; *U.S. Private*, pg. 2780
MESIROW FINANCIAL, INC. - PITTSBURGH—See Mesirow Financial Holdings, Inc.; *U.S. Private*, pg. 2679
METASOURCE, LLC—See Longshore Capital Partners; *U.S. Private*, pg. 2493
METER-U LIMITED—See Grovepoint Capital LLP; *Int'l*, pg. 3112
METRO APPRAISAL, INC.—See The Carlyle Group Inc.; *U.S. Public*, pg. 2053
METRON SUSTAINABLE SERVICES INC.—See Caisse de Depot et Placement du Quebec; *Int'l*, pg. 1255
METRO ONE TELECOMMUNICATIONS, INC.; *U.S. Public*, pg. 1431
METRO PARKING (S) PTE. LTD.—See Damansara Realty Berhad; *Int'l*, pg. 1955
MICROGEN UK LIMITED—See Aptitude Software Group Plc; *Int'l*, pg. 524
MICROLAB LLC—See Artemis Capital Partners Management Co., LLC; *U.S. Private*, pg. 341
MICROS SYSTEMS UK LIMITED—See Oracle Corporation; *U.S. Public*, pg. 1612
MIDWEST INDUSTRIAL METALS CORPORATION; *U.S. Private*, pg. 2721
MIDWEST TELEMARK INTERNATIONAL INC; *U.S. Private*, pg. 2723
MIRIFEX SYSTEMS, LLC; *U.S. Private*, pg. 2746
MIRO CONSULTING, INC.; *U.S. Private*, pg. 2746
MNP STEEL & WIRE/UTICA WASHER DIVISION—See MNP Corporation; *U.S. Private*, pg. 2756
MOBIL OIL CORPORATION—See Exxon Mobil Corporation; *U.S. Public*, pg. 817
MOC PORTFOLIO DELAWARE, INC.—See ConocoPhillips; *U.S. Public*, pg. 569
MODUS EDISCOVERY, INC.—See JLL Partners, LLC; *U.S. Private*, pg. 2193
MODUSLINK AUSTRALIA PTY LIMITED—See Steel Connect, Inc.; *U.S. Public*, pg. 1941
MONDELEZ CANADA, INC.—See Mondelez International, Inc.; *U.S. Public*, pg. 1462
MONEYONMOBILE, INC.; *U.S. Public*, pg. 1464
MONTAGE SERVICES, INC.—See EQT AB; *Int'l*, pg. 2472
MOORESTOWN FINANCE, INC.—See Sbar's, Inc.; *U.S. Private*, pg. 3559
MOOSE CHARITIES, INC.; *U.S. Private*, pg. 2781
MORTGAGE CONTRACTING SERVICES LLC—See American Securities LLC; *U.S. Private*, pg. 250
MOTOROLA RECEIVABLES CORPORATION—See Motorola Solutions, Inc.; *U.S. Public*, pg. 1478
MOULTON LOGISTICS MANAGEMENT—See Rotunda Capital Partners LLC; *U.S. Private*, pg. 3488
MOVERO, INC.; *U.S. Private*, pg. 2802
MSDSONLINE, INC.—See CVC Capital Partners SICAV-FIS S.A.; *Int'l*, pg. 1885
MSPACE; *U.S. Private*, pg. 2808
MTS ASIA LTD.—See SharpLink Gaming, Inc.; *U.S. Public*, pg. 1873
MURIEL SIEBERT & CO., INC.—See Siebert Financial Corp.; *U.S. Public*, pg. 1876
MURPHY BUSINESS & FINANCIAL CORPORATION; *U.S. Private*, pg. 2815
MXSECURE, INC.; *U.S. Private*, pg. 2823
MYBENEFIT SP. Z O.O.—See Benefit Systems SA; *Int'l*, pg. 972
NAKOMA GROUP ENTERPRISE SOLUTIONS—See Nakoma Group; *U.S. Private*, pg. 2831
NATIONAL ASSOCIATION FOR THE SELF-EMPLOYED, INC.; *U.S. Private*, pg. 2846
NATIONAL EXPERT WITNESS NETWORK; *U.S. Private*, pg. 2853
NATIONAL PRODUCT SERVICES; *U.S. Private*, pg. 2861
NATIONAL PURCHASING CORP; *U.S. Private*, pg. 2864
NATIONAL VETERINARY SERVICES LIMITED—See Patterson Companies, Inc.; *U.S. Public*, pg. 1654
NATIONWIDE NTERTAINMENT SERVICES, INC.—See GLOBAL AXCESS CORP.; *U.S. Private*, pg. 1712
NAVITAIRE INTERNATIONAL INC.—See Amadeus IT Group, S.A.; *Int'l*, pg. 406
NEBS PAYROLL SERVICE LIMITED—See Deluxe Corporation; *U.S. Public*, pg. 652
NEOVIA LOGISTICS SERVICES SPAIN S.A.—See Rhone Group, LLC; *U.S. Private*, pg. 3424
NEOVIA LOGISTICS SERVICES SPAIN S.A.—See The Goldman Sachs Group, Inc.; *U.S. Public*, pg. 2080
NETSCALIBUR LTD.—See Claranet Limited; *Int'l*, pg. 1642
NETWORK FOR GOOD, INC.; *U.S. Private*, pg. 2889
NEVADA STATE CORPORATE NETWORK, INC.; *U.S. Private*, pg. 2891

N.A.I.C.S. INDEX

561499 — ALL OTHER BUSINESS ...

NEWBUCKS OPERATIONS PTY., LTD.—See FirstRand Limited; *Int'l*, pg. 2690
NEWCOAST FINANCIAL SERVICES, INC.—See MarineMax, Inc.; *U.S. Public*, pg. 1367
N.E.W. CUSTOMER SERVICES COMPANIES, INC.; *U.S. Private*, pg. 2827
NEWRY CORP; *U.S. Private*, pg. 2916
NEWTEKONE, INC.; *U.S. Public*, pg. 1521
NEXION—See Travel Leaders Group, LLC; *U.S. Private*, pg. 4213
NEXMART GMBH & CO. KG—See Dr. Helmut Rothenberger Holding GmbH; *Int'l*, pg. 2192
NEXT GENERATION FUNDRAISING, INC.; *U.S. Private*, pg. 2919
NIIT SMART SERVE LTD—See Coforge Ltd.; *Int'l*, pg. 1693
NIKKO METALS TRADING & SERVICES (SHANGHAI) CO., LTD.—See ENEOS Holdings, Inc.; *Int'l*, pg. 2416
NOBEL BIOCARE MANAGEMENT AG—See Danaher Corporation; *U.S. Public*, pg. 629
NOMINA PLC—See Hampden Holdings Limited; *Int'l*, pg. 3239
NOORDKOEL B.V.—See China International Marine Containers (Group) Co., Ltd.; *Int'l*, pg. 1512
NORAM INTERNATIONAL PARTNERS LLC; *U.S. Private*, pg. 2935
NORTH CUTTING SYSTEMS, LLC—See Windway Capital Corp.; *U.S. Private*, pg. 4539
NORTH STATE ACCEPTANCE, LLC—See Fourshore Capital LLC; *U.S. Private*, pg. 1583
NOVINIUM, INC.—See Southwire Company, LLC; *U.S. Private*, pg. 3742
NOVITEX ENTERPRISE SOLUTIONS, INC.—See Exela Technologies, Inc.; *U.S. Public*, pg. 806
NOW COURIER INC.; *U.S. Private*, pg. 2968
NRI USA LLC; *U.S. Private*, pg. 2969
NV KEMA—See DNV GL Group AS; *Int'l*, pg. 2151
NYMBUS, INC.; *U.S. Private*, pg. 2976
OAL INC.—See Canon Inc.; *Int'l*, pg. 1296
OBERTHUR TECHNOLOGIES ITALIA SRL—See Advent International Corporation; *U.S. Private*, pg. 103
OBVERSE CORPORATION; *U.S. Private*, pg. 2988
OCEANEERING TECHNOLOGIES—See Oceaneering International, Inc.; *U.S. Public*, pg. 1563
THE OHANA COMPANIES, LLC—See 360insights.com Canada, Inc.; *Int'l*, pg. 6
OLDWEBSITES.COM, INC.; *U.S. Private*, pg. 3010
OMNIA WELLNESS, INC.; *U.S. Public*, pg. 1572
OMNI WORKSPACE COMPANY—See HNI Corporation; *U.S. Public*, pg. 1043
ONPOINT WARRANTY SOLUTIONS, LLC; *U.S. Private*, pg. 3027
ON SERVICES—See Viad Corp.; *U.S. Public*, pg. 2291
OOO KAUKO RUS—See Aspo Oyj; *Int'l*, pg. 631
OPEN AMERICA INC.; *U.S. Private*, pg. 3028
OPEN CHANNEL SOLUTIONS B.V.—See Steel Connect, Inc.; *U.S. Public*, pg. 1942
OPEN CHANNEL SOLUTIONS—See Steel Connect, Inc.; *U.S. Public*, pg. 1942
OPENSPACE GMBH—See Commerzbank AG; *Int'l*, pg. 1719
OPERACIONES ACCENTURE S.A. DE C.V.—See Accenture plc; *Int'l*, pg. 86
OPERON SYSTEMS, L.L.C.—See Dunsirn Partners LLC; *U.S. Private*, pg. 1291
OPPENHEIMER & CO. INC. - NEW YORK, PARK AVE—See Oppenheimer Holdings Inc.; *U.S. Public*, pg. 1608
OPTION 1 NUTRITION HOLDINGS, LLC—See Bain Capital, LP; *U.S. Private*, pg. 439
OPTUM FRONTIER THERAPIES, LLC—See UnitedHealth Group Incorporated; *U.S. Public*, pg. 2247
ORION FINANCIAL GROUP, INC.—See Longshore Capital Partners; *U.S. Private*, pg. 2493
OSRP, LLC—See Insight Enterprises, Inc.; *U.S. Public*, pg. 1130
THE OUTSOURCE GROUP, INC.—See HCA Healthcare, Inc.; *U.S. Public*, pg. 1006
OUTSOURCE PARTNERS INTERNATIONAL SDN BHD—See ExlService Holdings, Inc.; *U.S. Public*, pg. 808
OUTSOURCING INC.—See Bain Capital, LP; *U.S. Private*, pg. 433
OY FORD AB—See Ford Motor Company; *U.S. Public*, pg. 867
PACIFIC COAST COMPANIES, INC.—See Pacific Coast Building Products, Inc.; *U.S. Private*, pg. 3066
PACIFIC EMERGING TECHNOLOGIES LIMITED—See Fiji National Provident Fund; *Int'l*, pg. 2661
PACIFIC HORIZON LIMITED—See Hinduja Global Solutions Ltd.; *Int'l*, pg. 3398
PAMELA LOREN LIMITED, INC.—See Loren Communications International Ltd., Inc.; *U.S. Private*, pg. 2495
PANHANDLE-PLAINS HIGHER EDUCATION AUTHORITY INC; *U.S. Private*, pg. 3086
PAPERSAVE; *U.S. Private*, pg. 3088
PARAGON CUSTOMER COMMUNICATIONS LIMITED—See SS&C Technologies Holdings, Inc.; *U.S. Public*, pg. 1923
PARAGON DATA ANALYTICS LIMITED—See SS&C Technologies Holdings, Inc.; *U.S. Public*, pg. 1923
PARKLAND PROJECTS LTD.—See Tetra Tech, Inc.; *U.S. Public*, pg. 2023
PARTS ID, INC.; *U.S. Public*, pg. 1651
PATTONAIR DERBY LIMITED—See Platinum Equity, LLC; *U.S. Private*, pg. 3207
PATTONAIR LIMITED—See Platinum Equity, LLC; *U.S. Private*, pg. 3206
PATTONAIR SAS—See Platinum Equity, LLC; *U.S. Private*, pg. 3207
PCQUOTE.COM, INC.—See Money.net, Inc.; *U.S. Private*, pg. 2770
PEPPERS & ROGERS GROUP - BELGIUM—See TTEC Holdings, Inc.; *U.S. Public*, pg. 2202
PEPSI-COLA NORTH AMERICA—See PepsiCo, Inc.; *U.S. Public*, pg. 1670
PERCEPTA UK LIMITED—See TTEC Holdings, Inc.; *U.S. Public*, pg. 2203
PERFORMANCE BROKERAGE SERVICES, INC.; *U.S. Private*, pg. 3148
PERFORMANCE REVIEW INSTITUTE, INC.; *U.S. Private*, pg. 3149
PERIODICAL PUBLISHERS' SERVICE BUREAU, LLC—See Subco Inc.; *U.S. Private*, pg. 3847
PHARMALINK CONSULTING OPERATIONS LTD.—See Genpact Limited; *Int'l*, pg. 2927
PHARMALINK CONSULTING OPERATIONS PVT. LTD.—See Genpact Limited; *Int'l*, pg. 2927
PHARMALINK CONSULTING PTE. LTD.—See Genpact Limited; *Int'l*, pg. 2927
PHARMAMED, INC.; *U.S. Private*, pg. 3165
PHOENIX AMERICAN FINANCIAL SERVICES, INC.—See Phoenix American Incorporated; *U.S. Private*, pg. 3172
PHOENIX MARKETING SOLUTIONS LLC—See Phoenix Group Holdings LLC; *U.S. Private*, pg. 3173
PHONEX HOLDINGS, INC; *U.S. Public*, pg. 1689
PHYSICIANS WORLD, LLC—See Veeva Systems, Inc.; *U.S. Public*, pg. 2277
PINNACLE TALENT INC.—See ASM Technologies Limited; *Int'l*, pg. 627
PIPELINE BRICKELL; *U.S. Private*, pg. 3189
P&I PERSONAL & INFORMATIK AG—See HgCapital Trust plc; *Int'l*, pg. 3377
PITNEY BOWES DANMARK A/S—See Pitney Bowes Inc.; *U.S. Public*, pg. 1694
PITNEY BOWES FRANCE—See Pitney Bowes Inc.; *U.S. Public*, pg. 1694
PITNEY BOWES ITALIA S.R.L.—See Pitney Bowes Inc.; *U.S. Public*, pg. 1695
PITNEY BOWES PRESORT SERVICES, INC.—See Pitney Bowes Inc.; *U.S. Public*, pg. 1695
PIVOTAL RESOURCES, INC.; *U.S. Private*, pg. 3192
PLATINUM DATA SOLUTIONS, INC.—See Insight Venture Management, LLC; *U.S. Private*, pg. 2089
PLATINUM DATA SOLUTIONS, INC.—See Stone Point Capital LLC; *U.S. Private*, pg. 3822
PLUM BENEFITS, LLC—See Entertainment Benefits Group, LLC; *U.S. Private*, pg. 1404
PLURIDIS—See AXA S.A.; *Int'l*, pg. 754
POLAR COVE, INC.; *U.S. Private*, pg. 3223
POLARIS CONTRACT MANUFACTURING, INC.—See Lockheed Martin Corporation; *U.S. Public*, pg. 1338
POLATIS INCORPORATED—See Huber + Suhner AG; *Int'l*, pg. 3519
POLYPATHS, LLC—See Genstar Capital, LLC; *U.S. Private*, pg. 1678
POWERSECURE SERVICE, INC.—See The Southern Company; *U.S. Public*, pg. 2131
PPG ITALIA BUSINESS SUPPORT S.R.L—See PPG Industries, Inc.; *U.S. Public*, pg. 1709
PPL DEVELOPMENT CORPORATION—See PPL Corporation; *U.S. Public*, pg. 1711
PRAIRIE OPERATING CO.; *U.S. Public*, pg. 1712
PRATT & LAMBERT PAINTS—See The Sherwin-Williams Company; *U.S. Public*, pg. 2128
PREDICTIVE SAFETY LLC; *U.S. Private*, pg. 3247
PREMIERE CONFERENCING E.U.R.L.—See Siris Capital Group, LLC; *U.S. Private*, pg. 3674
PREMIERE CONFERENCING GMBH—See Siris Capital Group, LLC; *U.S. Private*, pg. 3674
PREMIERE CONFERENCING (JAPAN), INC.—See Siris Capital Group, LLC; *U.S. Private*, pg. 3674
PREMIERE CONFERENCING PTE. LTD.—See Siris Capital Group, LLC; *U.S. Private*, pg. 3674
PREMIERE CONFERENCING (UK) LIMITED—See Siris Capital Group, LLC; *U.S. Private*, pg. 3674
PREMIERE GLOBAL SERVICES DENMARK APS—See Siris Capital Group, LLC; *U.S. Private*, pg. 3674
PREMIERE GLOBAL SERVICES, INC. - COLORADO SPRINGS—See Siris Capital Group, LLC; *U.S. Private*, pg. 3674
PREMIERE GLOBAL SERVICES ITALY SRL—See Siris Capital Group, LLC; *U.S. Private*, pg. 3674
PREMIERE GLOBAL SERVICES KOREA LTD.—See Siris Capital Group, LLC; *U.S. Private*, pg. 3674
PREMIERE GLOBAL SERVICES SWEDEN AB—See Siris Capital Group, LLC; *U.S. Private*, pg. 3674
PREMIERE GLOBAL SERVICES SWITZERLAND GMBH—See Siris Capital Group, LLC; *U.S. Private*, pg. 3674
PRGX GLOBAL, INC.; *U.S. Private*, pg. 3257
PRIME PERFORMANCE, INC.—See Lincoln Property Company; *U.S. Private*, pg. 2458
PRIMERITUS FINANCIAL SERVICES, INC—See Kinderhook Industries, LLC; *U.S. Private*, pg. 2307
PRINTGLOBE, INC.; *U.S. Public*, pg. 3266
PRINT, INC.—See Pitney Bowes Inc.; *U.S. Public*, pg. 1695
PRINTPOST LIMITED—See An Post LLC; *Int'l*, pg. 443
PRISM TECHNOLOGIES GROUP, INC.; *U.S. Public*, pg. 1722
PROCTER & GAMBLE DISTRIBUTING COMPANY—See The Procter & Gamble Company; *U.S. Public*, pg. 2121
PRODUCT DEVELOPMENT CORPORATION; *U.S. Private*, pg. 3273
PROFESSIONAL STAFF MANAGEMENT, INC.—See Paychex, Inc.; *U.S. Public*, pg. 1655
PROFORMA PROMOTIONALLY YOURS; *U.S. Private*, pg. 3277
PROGENY BIOVENTURES LIMITED—See ANGLE plc; *Int'l*, pg. 461
PROGISTIX-SOLUTIONS INC.—See Canada Post Corporation; *Int'l*, pg. 1282
PROKARMA INC.—See Concentrix Corporation; *U.S. Public*, pg. 565
PROKARMA INC. - WASHINGTON—See Concentrix Corporation; *U.S. Public*, pg. 565
PROPERTY DAMAGE APPRAISERS, INC.—See Alacrity Solutions Group, Inc.; *U.S. Private*, pg. 148
PROSYS—See Bridgepoint Group Plc; *Int'l*, pg. 1155
PROTOCOL GLOBAL SOLUTIONS—See Protocol Inc.; *U.S. Private*, pg. 3290
PROTOCOL INC.; *U.S. Private*, pg. 3290
PRO UNLIMITED GLOBAL JAPAN (YK) LTD.—See Harvest Partners L.P.; *U.S. Private*, pg. 1876
PRO UNLIMITED, INC.—See Harvest Partners L.P.; *U.S. Private*, pg. 1876
PROVISTA, LLC—See Vizient, Inc.; *U.S. Private*, pg. 4407
PROWEBCE SA—See Edenred S.A.; *Int'l*, pg. 2308
PRWT SERVICES, INC.; *U.S. Private*, pg. 3296
PSM FINANCIAL SERVICES, LLC—See Paychex, Inc.; *U.S. Public*, pg. 1655
P.T. ACCENTURE—See Accenture plc; *Int'l*, pg. 86
PUBLISHERS CIRCULATION FULFILLMENT INC.; *U.S. Private*, pg. 3301
PUBLISHER'S CREATIVE SYSTEMS; *U.S. Private*, pg. 3301
PURCHASING POWER, LLC—See Edwards Capital, LLC; *U.S. Private*, pg. 1342
PURE SOLUTIONS NA, LLC—See Ashford Inc.; *U.S. Public*, pg. 211
PURE WATER TECH OF SAN DIEGO—See BDT Capital Partners, LLC; *U.S. Private*, pg. 503
PUTNAM ASSOCIATES, LLC—See Clayton, Dubilier & Rice, LLC; *U.S. Private*, pg. 928
PUYALLUP TRIBE OF INDIANS; *U.S. Private*, pg. 3308
QC DATA LLC—See General Atlantic Service Company, L.P.; *U.S. Private*, pg. 1662
QMI - SAI CANADA LIMITED—See EQT AB; *Int'l*, pg. 2471
QUANTA GOVERNMENT SOLUTIONS, INC.—See Quanta Services, Inc.; *U.S. Public*, pg. 1752
QUARAS INC.—See Fuji Media Holdings, Inc.; *Int'l*, pg. 2814
QUESTLINE, INC.—See Constellation Software Inc.; *Int'l*, pg. 1774
RADIAL, INC.—See bpost NV/SA; *Int'l*, pg. 1133
RADIANT CUSTOMS SERVICES, INC.—See Radiant Logistics, Inc.; *U.S. Public*, pg. 1759
RAET B.V.—See HgCapital Trust plc; *Int'l*, pg. 3377
RASA FLOORS & CARPET CLEANING, LLC; *U.S. Private*, pg. 3356
RATEGAIN TECHNOLOGIES INC.; *U.S. Private*, pg. 3357
RAZORBACK FOUNDATION; *U.S. Private*, pg. 3360
RCM TECHNOLOGIES (USA), INC.—See RCM Technologies, Inc.; *U.S. Public*, pg. 1767
RECEM S.A.—See Heidelberg Materials AG; *Int'l*, pg. 3319
THE RECOVRE GROUP PTY LIMITED—See Marsh & McLennan Companies, Inc.; *U.S. Public*, pg. 1377
RED CARPET TICKETS INC.; *U.S. Private*, pg. 3373
REED BRENNAN MEDIA ASSOCIATES, INC.—See The Hearst Corporation; *U.S. Private*, pg. 4046
REGULATORY DATACORP, INC.—See Moody's Corporation; *U.S. Public*, pg. 1469
RELIANT INVENTORY SERVICES, INC.—See Reliant Inventory Services; *U.S. Private*, pg. 3395
RELIANT INVENTORY SERVICES; *U.S. Private*, pg. 3395
RENAULT TRUCKS UK LTD.—See AB Volvo; *Int'l*, pg. 45
RESIN PARTNERS INC.; *U.S. Private*, pg. 3405
RESOLUTION CONSULTING, INC.—See Grant Avenue Capital, LLC; *U.S. Private*, pg. 1756
THE RESOURCE GROUP INTERNATIONAL LTD.; *U.S. Private*, pg. 4105
RESOURCE PLUS OF NORTH FLORIDA, INC.—See SPAR Group, Inc.; *U.S. Public*, pg. 1914
RESOURCE PRO, LLC; *U.S. Private*, pg. 3407
RESOURCE PROVIDERS, INC.; *U.S. Private*, pg. 3407
RETAIL VENTURES SERVICES, INC.—See Schottenstein Stores Corporation; *U.S. Private*, pg. 3569

561499 — ALL OTHER BUSINESS ... CORPORATE AFFILIATIONS

N.A.I.C.S. Index

REVERE DATA, LLC—See FactSet Research Systems Inc.; *U.S. Public*, pg. 820
REVOLUTION ENVIRONMENTAL SOLUTIONS ACQUISITION GP INC.—See Birch Hill Equity Partners Management Inc.; *Int'l*, pg. 1046
REWARDS NETWORK INC.—See TowerBrook Capital Partners, L.P.; *U.S. Private*, pg. 4195
RGIS—See Blackstone Inc.; *U.S. Public*, pg. 357
RIGHTSCORP, INC.; *U.S. Public*, pg. 1798
RIMHUB, INC.; *U.S. Private*, pg. 3437
RIMHUB INDIA PVT. LTD.—See Rimhub, Inc.; *U.S. Private*, pg. 3437
RISE GROUP, INC.—See Thielsch Engineering, Inc.; *U.S. Private*, pg. 4144
RMH ACQUISITION, LLC.; *U.S. Private*, pg. 3452
RMK HOLDINGS CORP.; *U.S. Private*, pg. 3452
ROCKALL TECHNOLOGIES LIMITED—See Broadridge Financial Solutions, Inc.; *U.S. Public*, pg. 392
ROCK RIDGE RESOURCES, INC.; *U.S. Public*, pg. 1804
ROGERS GRAIN INC.; *U.S. Private*, pg. 3472
ROMEO ENTERTAINMENT GROUP, INC.; *U.S. Private*, pg. 3476
ROOT WIRELESS, INC.—See Ziff Davis, Inc.; *U.S. Public*, pg. 2403
ROQUEMORE & ROQUEMORE INC.—See Kinderhook Industries, LLC; *U.S. Private*, pg. 2307
ROTORCRAFT LEASING COMPANY, L.L.C.—See H.I.G. Capital, LLC; *U.S. Private*, pg. 1831
ROUND SKY INC; *U.S. Private*, pg. 3488
R&R ASSOCIATES LLC - QUALITY ASSURANCE DIVISION—See R&R Associates LLC; *U.S. Private*, pg. 3332
R.R. DONNELLEY—See Chatham Asset Management, LLC; *U.S. Private*, pg. 864
R.R. DONNELLEY—See Chatham Asset Management, LLC; *U.S. Private*, pg. 864
RSB RIGGING SOLUTIONS S.L.—See Windway Capital Corp.; *U.S. Private*, pg. 4540
RUFFALO NOEL LEVITZ, LLC; *U.S. Private*, pg. 3502
R & U WEBER GMBH & CO. KG—See GERRY WEBER International AG; *Int'l*, pg. 2945
RYUGIN BUSINESS SERVICE CO., LTD.—See Bank of The Ryukyus, Ltd.; *Int'l*, pg. 849
SAFESOFT SOLUTIONS INC.; *U.S. Private*, pg. 3524
SAGE TREE LLC—See Leonard Green & Partners, L.P.; *U.S. Private*, pg. 2423
SAGEWORKS, INC.; *U.S. Private*, pg. 3528
SAI GLOBAL LIMITED—See EQT AB; *Int'l*, pg. 2471
SAI-MED PARTNERS LLC—See Northlane Capital Partners, LLC; *U.S. Private*, pg. 2956
SALES BENCHMARK INDEX LLC; *U.S. Private*, pg. 3531
SALIENT BUSINESS SOLUTIONS, LTD.—See Walgreens Boots Alliance, Inc.; *U.S. Public*, pg. 2323
SAMMONS CORPORATION—See Sammons Enterprises, Inc.; *U.S. Private*, pg. 3537
SAMPCO INC.; *U.S. Private*, pg. 3537
SANTANDER FINANCIAL PRODUCTS, LTD.—See Banco Santander, S.A.; *Int'l*, pg. 827
SAVI SHOP LTD.—See ENL Limited; *Int'l*, pg. 2441
SAYBROOK CORPORATE OPPORTUNITY FUND LP; *U.S. Private*, pg. 3558
SB CAPITAL CORPORATION—See Bayer Aktiengesellschaft; *Int'l*, pg. 902
SCHAAF CONSULTING; *U.S. Private*, pg. 3562
SCHENCK TECHNOLOGIE UND INDUSTRIEPARK GMBH—See Durr AG; *Int'l*, pg. 2233
SDG CORPORATION; *U.S. Private*, pg. 3581
SDI INTERNATIONAL CORP.; *U.S. Private*, pg. 3581
SE2 INC.—See Guggenheim Partners, LLC; *U.S. Private*, pg. 1812
SEALED AIR S.R.O—See Sealed Air Corporation; *U.S. Public*, pg. 1855
SECURIS; *U.S. Private*, pg. 3594
SECURITY CHECK LLC; *U.S. Private*, pg. 3595
SEEDINVEST, LLC—See Startengine Crowdfunding, Inc.; *U.S. Private*, pg. 3788
SEI LLC—See Solugenix Corp.; *U.S. Private*, pg. 3710
SENA SYSTEMS (INDIA) PVT. LTD.—See Aurionpro Solutions Limited; *Int'l*, pg. 711
SERVICE CONCIERGE SAS—See Accor S.A.; *Int'l*, pg. 92
SERVICE MANAGEMENT GROUP, INC.; *U.S. Private*, pg. 3615
SERVICE ROUNDTABLE; *U.S. Private*, pg. 3616
SERVICIOS CORPORATIVOS TWC, S.A. DE C.V.—See ACS, Actividades de Construccion y Servicios, S.A.; *Int'l*, pg. 116
SFP HOLDING, INC.—See BlackRock, Inc.; *U.S. Public*, pg. 346
SGG BELGIUM S.A.—See Astorg Partners S.A.S.; *Int'l*, pg. 657
SGG NETHERLANDS N.V.—See Astorg Partners S.A.S.; *Int'l*, pg. 657
SGRP MERIDIAN (PTY), LTD.—See SPAR Group, Inc.; *U.S. Public*, pg. 1914
SHANGHAI EURO TECH LTD.—See Euro Tech Holdings Company Limited; *Int'l*, pg. 2531
SHERLOQ SOLUTIONS; *U.S. Private*, pg. 3633
SHL US LLC—See Exponent Private Equity LLP; *Int'l*, pg. 2589
SIGNIA FINANCIAL GROUP INC—See GraceKennedy Limited; *Int'l*, pg. 3049
SIIBER LLC; *U.S. Private*, pg. 3651
SILVERBIRCH HOTELS & RESORTS—See British Columbia Investment Management Corp.; *Int'l*, pg. 1169
SIMCO SALES SERVICE OF PA INC.; *U.S. Private*, pg. 3665
SIMPLE PRODUCTS CORPORATION; *U.S. Private*, pg. 3667
SIRA CONSULTING LIMITED—See CSA Group; *Int'l*, pg. 1861
SIRIUS SOLUTIONS LLC; *U.S. Private*, pg. 3675
SITEL WORLDWIDE CORPORATION—See Creadev SAS; *Int'l*, pg. 1830
SKYCOM (PTY) LTD—See Allied Universal Manager LLC; *U.S. Private*, pg. 190
SKYLINE FUNDING INC.—See Skyline Credit Ride Inc.; *U.S. Private*, pg. 3685
SKYWORD INC.—See Progress Partners, Inc.; *U.S. Private*, pg. 3278
SKYWORD INC.—See Rho Capital Partners, Inc.; *U.S. Private*, pg. 3421
SLACK & COMPANY, LLC; *U.S. Private*, pg. 3686
SLIDESTORM LLC—See Columbia Ventures Corporation; *U.S. Private*, pg. 978
SMARTPRICE SALES & MARKETING INC.; *U.S. Private*, pg. 3692
SMITHBUCKLIN CORPORATION; *U.S. Private*, pg. 3696
SNC-LAVALIN DEFENCE PROGRAMS INC.—See AtkinsRealis Group Inc.; *Int'l*, pg. 671
SNC-LAVALIN INTERNATIONAL INC. - TUNISIA—See AtkinsRealis Group Inc.; *Int'l*, pg. 672
SNC-LAVALIN PROJETOS LTDA.—See AtkinsRealis Group Inc.; *Int'l*, pg. 673
SNS INVESTMENT COMPANY—See Biglari Holdings Inc.; *U.S. Public*, pg. 331
SNTIAL TECHNOLOGIES, INC.; *U.S. Private*, pg. 3701
SOBC DARAG HOLDINGS LTD.—See DARAG Group Limited; *Int'l*, pg. 1972
SOBC DARAG HOLDINGS LTD.—See SOBC Corp.; *U.S. Private*, pg. 3702
SOCIETE REUNION—See ENL Limited; *Int'l*, pg. 2442
SOFTWARE & INFORMATION INDUSTRY ASSOCIATION, INC.; *U.S. Private*, pg. 3705
SOLOMONEDWARDSGROUP, LLC; *U.S. Private*, pg. 3710
SOLUTIONSTAR REALTY SERVICES LLC—See Mr. Cooper Group Inc.; *U.S. Public*, pg. 1480
SOURCEHOV L.L.C.—See Gainline Capital Partners LP; *U.S. Private*, pg. 1635
THE SOURCING GROUP LLC; *U.S. Private*, pg. 4119
SOUTHERN CALIFORNIA SECTION OF THE PGA OF AMERICA; *U.S. Private*, pg. 3730
SOUTH JERSEY RESOURCES GROUP, LLC—See JPMorgan Chase & Co.; *U.S. Public*, pg. 1210
SOUTHWEST DEALERS SERVICES, INC.—See Spencer Capital Holdings, Ltd.; *U.S. Private*, pg. 3754
SOUTH WESTERN COMMUNICATIONS, INC.—See Koch Enterprises, Inc.; *U.S. Private*, pg. 2326
SPAR GROUP, INC.; *U.S. Public*, pg. 1914
SPAR, INC.—See SPAR Group, Inc.; *U.S. Public*, pg. 1914
SPARK SERVICES LTD—See Gresham House Strategic plc; *Int'l*, pg. 3082
SPEED COMMERCE, INC.; *U.S. Public*, pg. 1917
SPENDSMART NETWORKS, INC.; *U.S. Private*, pg. 3755
SPOTLESS SERVICES AUSTRALIA LIMITED—See Downer EDI Limited; *Int'l*, pg. 2185
SQA SERVICES, INC.; *U.S. Private*, pg. 3765
THE SR GROUP (UK) LTD.—See Baird Financial Group, Inc.; *U.S. Private*, pg. 453
SS&C TECHNOLOGIES, INC.—See SS&C Technologies Holdings, Inc.; *U.S. Public*, pg. 1924
STARIZON, INC.; *U.S. Private*, pg. 3786
STARTEK CANADA SERVICES, LTD.—See StarTek, Inc.; *U.S. Private*, pg. 3788
STARTEK, INC.; *U.S. Private*, pg. 3788
STERILIZATION SERVICES OF VIRGINIA—See Altair Corporation; *U.S. Public*, pg. 86
STERLING INFOSYSTEMS, INC.—See Caisse de Depot et Placement du Quebec; *Int'l*, pg. 1255
STERLING INFOSYSTEMS, INC.—See The Goldman Sachs Group, Inc.; *U.S. Public*, pg. 2080
STGI INC.; *U.S. Private*, pg. 3812
STITCH LABS, INC.—See Block, Inc.; *U.S. Public*, pg. 362
ST. MODWEN VENTURES LIMITED—See Blackstone Inc.; *U.S. Public*, pg. 358
STP INVESTMENT SERVICES; *U.S. Private*, pg. 3832
STRATEGIC DISTRIBUTION MARKETING DE MEXICO, S.A. DE C.V.—See Independence Capital Partners, LLC; *U.S. Private*, pg. 2056
STRATEGIC DISTRIBUTION MARKETING DE MEXICO, S.A. DE C.V.—See Pouschine Cook Capital Management LLC; *U.S. Private*, pg. 3236
STRATEGIC ENVIRONMENTAL & ENERGY RESOURCES, INC.; *U.S. Public*, pg. 1954
STRATEGIC FULFILLMENT GROUP LLC—See Dynamic Resource Group, Inc.; *U.S. Private*, pg. 1299
STRATEGIC OUTSOURCING, INC.—See General Atlantic Service Company, L.P.; *U.S. Private*, pg. 1663
STV INC.—See STV Group, Inc.; *U.S. Private*, pg. 3845
STV INC.—See STV Group, Inc.; *U.S. Private*, pg. 3845
SUMMIT TECH CONSULTING; *U.S. Private*, pg. 3857
SUN ENERGY SOLUTIONS; *U.S. Private*, pg. 3863
SUNGARD AVAILABILITY SERVICES LP—See SunGard Availability Services Capital, Inc.; *U.S. Private*, pg. 3867
SYKES LATIN AMERICA, S.A.—See Creadev SAS; *Int'l*, pg. 1831
SYNERGETIC, INC.; *U.S. Private*, pg. 3903
SYSTEMS FINANCE GROUP INC.; *U.S. Private*, pg. 3907
SYSTEMS PLANNING AND ANALYSIS, INC.—See Arlington Capital Partners LLC; *U.S. Private*, pg. 328
T2 OPTIMISE PTY. LTD.—See Allegis Group, Inc.; *U.S. Private*, pg. 177
TAK CO., LTD.—See Ibiden Co., Ltd.; *Int'l*, pg. 3576
TARSUS GROUP PLC—See Charterhouse Capital Partners LLP; *Int'l*, pg. 1456
TASKUS—See TaskUS; *U.S. Private*, pg. 3935
TEAMBONDING; *U.S. Private*, pg. 3951
TEAM JO-ANN STORES, INC.—See Leonard Green & Partners, L.P.; *U.S. Private*, pg. 2426
TECHEAD; *U.S. Private*, pg. 3952
TECHEM DANMARK A/S—See Caisse de Depot et Placement du Quebec; *Int'l*, pg. 1255
TECHEM DO BRASIL SERVICOS DE MEDICAO DE AGUA LTDA.—See Caisse de Depot et Placement du Quebec; *Int'l*, pg. 1255
TECHEM ENERGY SERVICES B.V.—See Caisse de Depot et Placement du Quebec; *Int'l*, pg. 1255
TECHEM ENERGY SERVICES MIDDLE EAST FZCO—See Caisse de Depot et Placement du Quebec; *Int'l*, pg. 1255
TECHEM ENERGY SERVICES S.R.L.—See Caisse de Depot et Placement du Quebec; *Int'l*, pg. 1255
TECHEM ENERJI HIZMETLERI SANAYI VE TICARET LIMITED SIRKETI—See Caisse de Depot et Placement du Quebec; *Int'l*, pg. 1255
TECHEM GMBH—See Caisse de Depot et Placement du Quebec; *Int'l*, pg. 1255
TECHEM NORGE A/S—See Caisse de Depot et Placement du Quebec; *Int'l*, pg. 1255
TECHEM SAS—See Caisse de Depot et Placement du Quebec; *Int'l*, pg. 1255
TECHEM (SCHWEIZ) AG—See Caisse de Depot et Placement du Quebec; *Int'l*, pg. 1255
TECHEM SERVICES E.O.O.D.—See Caisse de Depot et Placement du Quebec; *Int'l*, pg. 1255
TECHEM SPOL. S R. O.—See Caisse de Depot et Placement du Quebec; *Int'l*, pg. 1255
TECHEM SPOL. S R. O.—See Caisse de Depot et Placement du Quebec; *Int'l*, pg. 1255
TECHEM S.R.L.—See Caisse de Depot et Placement du Quebec; *Int'l*, pg. 1255
TECHEM SVERIGE AB—See Caisse de Depot et Placement du Quebec; *Int'l*, pg. 1255
TECHEM TECHNIKI POMIAROWE SP. Z O.O.—See Caisse de Depot et Placement du Quebec; *Int'l*, pg. 1255
TEKLINK INTERNATIONAL INC.—See Hinduja Global Solutions Ltd.; *Int'l*, pg. 3398
TELETECH CUSTOMER CARE MANAGEMENT COSTA RICA, S.A.—See TTEC Holdings, Inc.; *U.S. Public*, pg. 2203
TELETECH GOVERNMENT SOLUTIONS, LLC—See TTEC Holdings, Inc.; *U.S. Public*, pg. 2203
TELETECH INTERNATIONAL PTY LTD—See TTEC Holdings, Inc.; *U.S. Public*, pg. 2203
TEMPO PARTICIPACOES S.A.—See The Carlyle Group Inc.; *U.S. Public*, pg. 2055
TERRYBERRY COMPANY LLC; *U.S. Private*, pg. 3972
THEATRE DEVELOPMENT FUND; *U.S. Private*, pg. 4141
THEBLAZE INC.; *U.S. Private*, pg. 4141
TICKET EXPRESS HUNGARY KFT.—See CTS Eventim AG & Co. KGAA; *Int'l*, pg. 1874
TICKET SERVICE, S.R.O.—See Edenred S.A.; *Int'l*, pg. 2308
TICKET SERVICOS S.A.—See Edenred S.A.; *Int'l*, pg. 2308
TIME WARNER GLOBAL MEDIA GROUP—See Warner Bros. Discovery, Inc.; *U.S. Public*, pg. 2328
TIPPING POINT COMMUNITY; *U.S. Private*, pg. 4176
TITAN HEALTH MANAGEMENT SOLUTIONS, INC.—See Certive Solutions Inc.; *U.S. Public*, pg. 476
TITAN TECHNOLOGY PARTNERS, LTD.—See Accenture plc; *Int'l*, pg. 87
TLINGIT HAIDA TRIBAL BUSINESS CORPORATION; *U.S. Private*, pg. 4179
TMC GROUP INC.; *U.S. Private*, pg. 4179
TMG HEALTH, INC.—See Cognizant Technology Solutions Corporation; *U.S. Public*, pg. 525
TMS INTERNATIONAL SERVICES UK LIMITED—See The Pritzker Organization, LLC; *U.S. Private*, pg. 4100
TMW MERCHANTS LLC—See Tailored Brands, Inc.; *U.S. Public*, pg. 1979
TMW PURCHASING LLC—See Tailored Brands, Inc.; *U.S. Public*, pg. 1979
TOM JONES INC.; *U.S. Private*, pg. 4182
TONSA AUTOMOTIVE INC.; *U.S. Private*, pg. 4185
TOTALPAAS, INC.; *U.S. Private*, pg. 4192

TPI BILLING SOLUTIONS; *U.S. Private*, pg. 4200
TRACTMANAGER, INC.—See Clearlake Capital Group, L.P.; *U.S. Private*, pg. 937
TRACTMANAGER, INC.—See SkyKnight Capital LLC; *U.S. Private*, pg. 3685
THE TRADEMARK COMPANY; *U.S. Private*, pg. 4127
TRADEPORT HONG KONG LTD.—See Fraport AG; *Int'l*, pg. 2764
TRAFERA, LLC—See Rotunda Capital Partners LLC; *U.S. Private*, pg. 3488
TRANSCEND SERVICES, INC.—See Microsoft Corporation; *U.S. Public*, pg. 1443
TRANSCEPTA LLC; *U.S. Private*, pg. 4207
TRANSCOM AB—See Altor Equity Partners AB; *Int'l*, pg. 396
TRANSCOM A/S—See Altor Equity Partners AB; *Int'l*, pg. 396
TRANSCOM WORLDWIDE BELGIUM SA—See Altor Equity Partners AB; *Int'l*, pg. 396
TRANSCOM WORLDWIDE D.O.O.—See Altor Equity Partners AB; *Int'l*, pg. 396
TRANSCOM WORLDWIDE FRANCE SAS—See Altor Equity Partners AB; *Int'l*, pg. 396
TRANSCOM WORLDWIDE ROSTOCK GMBH—See Altor Equity Partners AB; *Int'l*, pg. 396
TRANSCOM WORLDWIDE VILNIUS UAB—See Altor Equity Partners AB; *Int'l*, pg. 396
TRANSFER ENTERPRISES, INC.; *U.S. Private*, pg. 4207
TRANSPORTATION CONSULTANTS OF AMERICA, INC.; *U.S. Private*, pg. 4211
TRANSTECH SOLUTIONS, INC.; *U.S. Private*, pg. 4211
TRANSVOICE AB—See Altor Equity Partners AB; *Int'l*, pg. 396
TRANSWORLD PRODUCTS, INC.—See Peterson Manufacturing Company Inc.; *U.S. Private*, pg. 3160
TRICOM, INC.—See Wintrust Financial Corporation; *U.S. Public*, pg. 2375
TRIGO SAS—See Ardian SAS; *Int'l*, pg. 556
TRILEGIANT CORPORATION—See JPMorgan Chase & Co.; *U.S. Public*, pg. 1210
TRINET GROUP, INC.—See General Atlantic Service Company, L.P.; *U.S. Private*, pg. 1663
TRIOPTIMA UK LIMITED—See CME Group, Inc.; *U.S. Public*, pg. 518
TRONOX FINANCE B.V.—See Tronox Holdings plc; *U.S. Public*, pg. 2197
TRUECONTEXT INC.—See Battery Ventures, L.P.; *U.S. Private*, pg. 489
T&T INSPECTIONS & ENGINEERING LTD.—See Hyduke Energy Services Inc.; *Int'l*, pg. 3548
TUBE CITY IMS BELGIUM BVBA—See The Pritzker Organization, LLC; *U.S. Private*, pg. 4100
TUBE CITY IMS TAIWAN LIMITED—See The Pritzker Organization, LLC; *U.S. Private*, pg. 4100
TUNGSTEN NETWORK INC—See Clearlake Capital Group, L.P.; *U.S. Private*, pg. 936
TUNGSTEN NETWORK INC—See TA Associates, Inc.; *U.S. Private*, pg. 3916
TURNER INTERNATIONAL, INC.—See Warner Bros. Discovery, Inc.; *U.S. Public*, pg. 2328
TYLER TECHNOLOGIES, INC. - CLT—See Tyler Technologies, Inc.; *U.S. Public*, pg. 2209
UCDP FINANCE, INC.—See Comcast Corporation; *U.S. Public*, pg. 541
UDG HEALTHCARE PLC—See Clayton, Dubilier & Rice, LLC; *U.S. Public*, pg. 927
ULTRAEX, INC.; *U.S. Private*, pg. 4278
ULTRAPURE & INDUSTRIAL SERVICES, LLC—See Driessen Water I Inc.; *U.S. Private*, pg. 1277
UNDERWATER WORLD SINGAPORE PTE. LTD.—See Haw Par Corporation Limited; *Int'l*, pg. 3288
UNIMAC GRAPHICS; *U.S. Private*, pg. 4283
UNISHIPPERS ASSOCIATION INC.; *U.S. Private*, pg. 4286
UNITED CANNABIS CORPORATION; *U.S. Private*, pg. 4288
UNITED FOAM—See UFP Technologies, Inc.; *U.S. Public*, pg. 2221
UNITEDLEX CORPORATION; *U.S. Private*, pg. 4302
UPDATEPOWER CORPORATION; *U.S. Private*, pg. 4311
UPLAND SOFTWARE VI, LLC—See Upland Software, Inc.; *U.S. Public*, pg. 2264
UPONOR BUSINESS SOLUTIONS OY—See Georg Fischer AG; *Int'l*, pg. 2937
USA FINANCIAL MARKETING CORPORATION; *U.S. Private*, pg. 4321
U.S. MEDGROUP, P.A.—See Select Medical Holdings Corporation; *U.S. Public*, pg. 1862
UTEK EUROPE LTD.—See INNOVARO, INC.; *U.S. Private*, pg. 2081
VALIANT INTEGRATED SERVICES LLC; *U.S. Private*, pg. 4331
VALLI INFORMATION SYSTEMS, INCORPORATED; *U.S. Private*, pg. 4336
VARD BREVIK HOLDING AS—See Fincantieri S.p.A.; *Int'l*, pg. 2671
VARD OFFSHORE BREVIK AS—See Fincantieri S.p.A.; *Int'l*, pg. 2672
VARD SINGAPORE PTE. LTD.—See Fincantieri S.p.A.; *Int'l*, pg. 2672

VCOM SOLUTIONS INC.; *U.S. Private*, pg. 4349
VCUSTOMER; *U.S. Private*, pg. 4349
VELOSI LIMITED—See I Squared Capital Advisors (US) LLC; *U.S. Private*, pg. 2023
VENDOR CREDENTIALING SERVICE LLC—See Clearlake Capital Group, L.P.; *U.S. Private*, pg. 937
VENDOR CREDENTIALING SERVICE LLC—See SkyKnight Capital LLC; *U.S. Private*, pg. 3685
VERITEST, INC.—See H.I.G. Capital, LLC; *U.S. Private*, pg. 1830
VERLAG AUTOMOBIL WIRTSCHAFT (PTY) LTD.—See Bertelsmann SE & Co. KGaA; *Int'l*, pg. 996
VERTEX BUSINESS SERVICES LLC—See Keystone Group, L.P.; *U.S. Private*, pg. 2300
VERTEX CUSTOMER SERVICES INDIA PRIVATE LIMITED—See Keystone Group, L.P.; *U.S. Private*, pg. 2300
VERTEX DATA SCIENCE LIMITED—See Keystone Group, L.P.; *U.S. Private*, pg. 2300
VERTRUE INC.; *U.S. Private*, pg. 4370
VESTA CORP.; *U.S. Private*, pg. 4371
VFS GLOBAL SERVICES PVT. LTD.—See EQT AB; *Int'l*, pg. 2478
VIANT, INC.—See MultiPlan Corp.; *U.S. Public*, pg. 1486
VIBCO VIBRATION PRODUCTS—See Vibco Inc.; *U.S. Private*, pg. 4376
VIDEOJET TECHNOLOGIES (I) PVT. LTD—See Danaher Corporation; *U.S. Public*, pg. 631
VIDERA OY—See Elisa Corporation; *Int'l*, pg. 2362
VIEWPOINTE ARCHIVE SERVICES, LLC—See Truist Financial Corporation; *U.S. Public*, pg. 2200
VILSMEIER AUCTION CO.—See Hunyady Auction Company; *U.S. Private*, pg. 2011
VINCENT & VINCENT COMPANIES, INC.; *U.S. Private*, pg. 4385
VIREXIT TECHNOLOGIES, INC.; *U.S. Public*, pg. 2299
VIRTEVA LLC—See The RLJ Companies, LLC; *U.S. Private*, pg. 4111
VIS CO., LTD.—See Freudenberg SE; *Int'l*, pg. 2790
VISION CAPITAL LP; *U.S. Private*, pg. 4390
VISTRA HOLDINGS (USA) LLC—See EQT AB; *Int'l*, pg. 2472
VISTRA IE UK LTD.—See EQT AB; *Int'l*, pg. 2472
VIZUAL HUMAN RESOURCES PLC—See Automatic Data Processing, Inc.; *U.S. Public*, pg. 230
VORSIGHT LLC—See Acquirent, LLC; *U.S. Private*, pg. 65
VOYA INVESTMENTS DISTRIBUTOR, LLC—See Voya Financial, Inc.; *U.S. Public*, pg. 2311
VOYA SERVICES CO.—See Voya Financial, Inc.; *U.S. Public*, pg. 2312
VT SERVICES, INC. - PENSACOLA DIVISION—See Alvarez & Marsal, Inc.; *U.S. Private*, pg. 213
VXI GLOBAL SOLUTIONS, INC.—See Bain Capital, LP; *U.S. Private*, pg. 451
WAGEWORKS, INC.—See HealthEquity, Inc.; *U.S. Public*, pg. 1016
WALTER SERVICES GMBH—See H.I.G. Capital, LLC; *U.S. Private*, pg. 1828
WALTER SERVICES POLAND SP. Z. O. O.—See H.I.G. Capital, LLC; *U.S. Private*, pg. 1828
WALTER SERVICES SWISS AG—See H.I.G. Capital, LLC; *U.S. Private*, pg. 1828
WAND PARTNERS INC.; *U.S. Private*, pg. 4435
WATERLOGIC USA (WEST)—See Castik Capital S.a.r.l.; *Int'l*, pg. 1356
WAVETABLE LABS LLC; *U.S. Private*, pg. 4458
WBT SYSTEMS LTD.—See TD Synnex Corp; *U.S. Public*, pg. 1985
WEBSTER CAPITAL FINANCE, INC.—See Webster Financial Corporation; *U.S. Public*, pg. 2341
WELLFLEET FLEA MARKET; *U.S. Private*, pg. 4475
WELLS FARGO ENERGY CAPITAL, INC.—See Wells Fargo & Company; *U.S. Public*, pg. 2324
WELL VENTURES, LLC—See Walgreens Boots Alliance, Inc.; *U.S. Public*, pg. 2324
WEST COAST SALES & ASSOCIATES LLC; *U.S. Private*, pg. 4484
WESTERN UNION—See The Western Union Company; *U.S. Public*, pg. 2141
WESTROCK FINANCIAL, INC.—See WestRock Company; *U.S. Public*, pg. 2363
WILLIAMS LEA (BEIJING) LIMITED—See Advent International Corporation; *U.S. Private*, pg. 107
WILLIAMS LEA (BRAZIL) ASSESSORIA EM SOLUCOES EMPRESARIAIS LTDA.—See Advent International Corporation; *U.S. Private*, pg. 107
WILLIAMS LEA FRANCE SAS—See Advent International Corporation; *U.S. Private*, pg. 107
WILLIAMS LEA GMBH—See Advent International Corporation; *U.S. Private*, pg. 107
WILLIAMS LEA HOLDINGS PLC—See Advent International Corporation; *U.S. Private*, pg. 107
WILLIAMS LEA INDIA PRIVATE LIMITED—See Advent International Corporation; *U.S. Private*, pg. 107
WILLIAMS LEA IRELAND LIMITED—See Advent International Corporation; *U.S. Private*, pg. 107
WILLIAMS LEA JAPAN LIMITED—See Advent International Corporation; *U.S. Private*, pg. 108

WILLIAMS LEA LIMITED—See Advent International Corporation; *U.S. Private*, pg. 108
WILLIAMS LEA PRIVATE LIMITED—See Advent International Corporation; *U.S. Private*, pg. 108
WILLIAMS LEA PTY LIMITED—See Advent International Corporation; *U.S. Private*, pg. 108
WILLIAMS LEA (US ACQUISITIONS) LIMITED—See Advent International Corporation; *U.S. Private*, pg. 107
WILLIS GROUP LLC; *U.S. Private*, pg. 4527
WILSHIRE ASSOCIATES EUROPE B.V.—See Wilshire Associates, Inc.; *U.S. Private*, pg. 4529
WILSHIRE ASSOCIATES, INC.; *U.S. Private*, pg. 4529
WILSHIRE AUSTRALIA PTY LIMITED—See Wilshire Associates, Inc.; *U.S. Private*, pg. 4529
WINEDIRECT, INC.; *U.S. Private*, pg. 4540
WINKLER+DUNNEBIER GMBH—See Barry-Wehmiller Companies, Inc.; *U.S. Private*, pg. 482
WIS INTERNATIONAL—See Ares Management Corporation; *U.S. Public*, pg. 191
WORLD RESOURCE PARTNERS—See G&T Industries Inc.; *U.S. Private*, pg. 1629
WORLDSPAN SERVICES LTD.—See Elliott Management Corporation; *U.S. Public*, pg. 1373
WORLDSPAN SERVICES LTD.—See Siris Capital Group, LLC; *U.S. Private*, pg. 3674
WORLDWIDE RECRUITING AND STAFFING SERVICES LLC—See Cerberus Capital Management, L.P.; *U.S. Private*, pg. 838
WORLDWIDE STRATEGIES, INC.; *U.S. Public*, pg. 2382
WRIDGWAYS AUSTRALIA LIMITED - WRIDGWAYS MOVE SOLUTIONS—See EAC Invest AS; *Int'l*, pg. 2262
W SQUARED DYNAMICS, INC.—See Comprehensive Health Services, Inc.; *U.S. Private*, pg. 1003
W.T. COX SUBSCRIPTIONS, INC.; *U.S. Private*, pg. 4423
XCHANGING LIMITED—See DXC Technology Company; *U.S. Public*, pg. 695
XEROX CORP.—See Xerox Holdings Corporation; *U.S. Public*, pg. 2390
XPRESS SOURCE—See Echo, LLC; *U.S. Private*, pg. 1327
XTI AEROSPACE, INC.; *U.S. Public*, pg. 2393
YAHOO! CANADA CO.—See Apollo Global Management, Inc.; *U.S. Public*, pg. 167
YAHOO! DE MEXICO, S.A. DE C.V.—See Apollo Global Management, Inc.; *U.S. Public*, pg. 168
YAHOO! DO BRASIL INTERNET LTDA.—See Apollo Global Management, Inc.; *U.S. Public*, pg. 168
YAP AH SHAK HOUSE SDN. BHD.—See Advance Synergy Berhad; *Int'l*, pg. 157
YET2.COM, INC.; *U.S. Private*, pg. 4588
ZELIS NETWORK SOLUTIONS, LLC—See PCP Enterprise, L.P.; *U.S. Private*, pg. 3121
ZIRMED, INC.—See Canada Pension Plan Investment Board; *Int'l*, pg. 1282
ZIRMED, INC.—See EQT AB; *Int'l*, pg. 2481

561510 — TRAVEL AGENCIES

AAMAL TRAVEL & TOURISM W.L.L.—See Aamal Company Q.S.C.; *Int'l*, pg. 36
ABERCROMBIE & KENT USA, LLC; *U.S. Private*, pg. 37
ACROMAS HOLIDAYS LIMITED—See Charterhouse Capital Partners LLP; *Int'l*, pg. 1454
ACROMAS HOLIDAYS LIMITED—See CVC Capital Partners SICAV-FIS S.A.; *Int'l*, pg. 1882
ACROMAS SHIPPING LIMITED—See Charterhouse Capital Partners LLP; *Int'l*, pg. 1454
ACROMAS SHIPPING LIMITED—See CVC Capital Partners SICAV-FIS S.A.; *Int'l*, pg. 1882
ACTION TRAVEL CENTER, INC.—See ABRY Partners, LLC; *U.S. Private*, pg. 41
ADELMAN TRAVEL SYSTEMS, INC.—See BCD Holdings N.V.; *Int'l*, pg. 926
ADVENTURE LIFE; *U.S. Private*, pg. 109
AEOLOS LIMITED—See Francoudi & Stephanou Ltd.; *Int'l*, pg. 2761
AGE D'OR EXPANSION SA—See CNP Assurances SA; *Int'l*, pg. 1677
AGENCIA DE VIAGENS E TURISMO GRAND, LIMITADA—See China Travel International Investment Hong Kong Ltd; *Int'l*, pg. 1560
AGIITO LIMITED—See Capita plc; *Int'l*, pg. 1308
AIKO SERVICE CO., LTD.—See Aichi Steel Corporation; *Int'l*, pg. 230
AIR NEW ZEALAND LTD. (U.S.A.)—See Air New Zealand Limited; *Int'l*, pg. 239
AIR PARTNER INC—See Wheels Up Experience Inc.; *U.S. Public*, pg. 2366
AIR PARTNER INTERNATIONAL GMBH—See Wheels Up Experience Inc.; *U.S. Public*, pg. 2366
AIR PARTNER INTERNATIONAL SAS—See Wheels Up Experience Inc.; *U.S. Public*, pg. 2366
AIR PARTNER SWITZERLAND AG—See Wheels Up Experience Inc.; *U.S. Public*, pg. 2366
AIR PARTNER TRAVEL CONSULTANTS LTD—See Wheels Up Experience Inc.; *U.S. Public*, pg. 2366
AIRPLUS INTERNATIONAL S.R.L.—See Deutsche Lufthansa AG; *Int'l*, pg. 2068

561510 — TRAVEL AGENCIES

AIRTREKS; *U.S. Private*, pg. 142
AIRTRIP CORP.; *Int'l*, pg. 250
A & I TRAVEL SERVICE; *U.S. Private*, pg. 18
THE ALAMO TRAVEL GROUP, INC.; *U.S. Private*, pg. 3983
ALASKA DENALI TRAVEL—See Viad Corp.; *U.S. Public*, pg. 2291
ALBANY TRAVEL UNLIMITED INC.; *U.S. Private*, pg. 152
AL-FUTTAIM TRAVEL—See Al-Futtaim Private Company LLC; *Int'l*, pg. 285
ALICE EVENEMENTS; *Int'l*, pg. 327
ALLEGIANT NONSTOP MICHIGAN, LLC—See Allegiant Travel Company; *U.S. Public*, pg. 78
ALLER-RETOUR; *Int'l*, pg. 336
ALL HORIZONS TRAVEL INC.—See Frosch International Travel Inc.; *U.S. Private*, pg. 1616
ALLIED T-PRO INC.—See Fairfax Financial Holdings Limited; *Int'l*, pg. 2608
ALL SEASONS TRAVEL AGENCY INC.; *U.S. Private*, pg. 172
ALL WORLD TRAVEL INC.; *U.S. Private*, pg. 173
ALSUWAIKET TRAVEL & TOURISM DIVISION—See AlSuwaiket Trading & Contracting Co.; *Int'l*, pg. 383
ALTOUR INTERNATIONAL, INC.; *U.S. Private*, pg. 210
AMADEUS FRANCE SNC—See Amadeus IT Group, S.A.; *Int'l*, pg. 405
AMADEUS HELLAS ELECTRONIC TRAVEL INFORMATION SERVICES SINGLE MEMBER SOCIETE ANONYME—See Amadeus IT Group, S.A.; *Int'l*, pg. 405
AMADEUS MAROC S.A.S.—See Amadeus IT Group, S.A.; *Int'l*, pg. 406
AMADEUS NORTH AMERICA, INC. - E-TRAVEL BUSINESS—See Amadeus IT Group, S.A.; *Int'l*, pg. 406
AMATHUS TRAVEL LTD.—See Amathus Public Limited; *Int'l*, pg. 413
AMATHUS (UK) LTD.—See Amathus Public Limited; *Int'l*, pg. 413
AMBASSADOR TRAVEL LTD.; *U.S. Private*, pg. 217
AMBER TRAVEL, INC.—See Grueninger Tours & Cruises Inc.; *U.S. Private*, pg. 1797
AMERICAN EXPRESS BARCELO VIAJES SL—See American Express Company; *U.S. Public*, pg. 101
AMERICAN EXPRESS BUSINESS TRAVEL AB—See Global Business Travel Group, Inc.; *U.S. Public*, pg. 941
AMERICAN EXPRESS BUSINESS TRAVEL AS—See Global Business Travel Group, Inc.; *U.S. Public*, pg. 941
AMERICAN EXPRESS DENMARK A/S—See American Express Company; *U.S. Public*, pg. 101
AMERICAN EXPRESS EUROPE LIMITED—See American Express Company; *U.S. Public*, pg. 100
AMERICAN EXPRESS INTERNATIONAL SA—See American Express Company; *U.S. Public*, pg. 101
AMERICAN INTERNATIONAL TRAVEL LIMITED—See Flight Centre Travel Group Limited; *Int'l*, pg. 2705
AMEX AGENZIA ASSICURATIVA S.R.L.—See American Express Company; *U.S. Public*, pg. 101
AMEX ASESORES DE SEGUROS, S.A.—See American Express Company; *U.S. Public*, pg. 101
AMNET NEW YORK, INC.; *U.S. Private*, pg. 264
ANC WORLDCHOICE HOLIDAYS LTD.—See Amathus Public Limited; *Int'l*, pg. 413
ANDAVO TRAVEL; *U.S. Private*, pg. 275
ANDREW HARPER, LLC—See Travel Leaders Group, LLC; *U.S. Private*, pg. 4213
ANDREW JONES TRAVEL PTY LTD.—See Corporate Travel Management Limited; *Int'l*, pg. 1805
ANTIPODES VOYAGES SA; *Int'l*, pg. 483
APPLE VACATIONS, LLC—See Apple Leisure Group; *U.S. Private*, pg. 296
ARRIVA TOURING BV—See I Squared Capital Advisors (US) LLC; *U.S. Private*, pg. 2075
ARS DREAM PNG LTD.—See IBJ Inc.; *Int'l*, pg. 3576
ARS DREAM TRAVEL & TOURS CORP.—See IBJ Inc.; *Int'l*, pg. 3576
ARTIST & BUSINESS TRANSPORT GROUP B.V.—See Live Nation Entertainment, Inc.; *U.S. Public*, pg. 1328
ASIA MIDDLE EAST TOURS (L.L.C.)—See Asiatravel.com Holdings Limited; *Int'l*, pg. 620
ASIA MILES LIMITED—See Cathay Pacific Airways Limited; *Int'l*, pg. 1360
ASIAN TRAILS LTD.—See Fairfax Financial Holdings Limited; *Int'l*, pg. 2608
ASIA TRAVEL NETWORK LTD.—See Asiatravel.com Holdings Limited; *Int'l*, pg. 620
ASTAKA HOLDINGS LIMITED; *Int'l*, pg. 651
ATLANTIS TRAVEL & TOURS—See ECI Partners LLP; *Int'l*, pg. 2289
ATLAS TRAVEL INTERNATIONAL; *U.S. Private*, pg. 380
ATLAS WORLD-CLASS TRAVEL—See Atlas World Group, Inc.; *U.S. Private*, pg. 380
AT PHIL., INC.—See Asiatravel.com Holdings Limited; *Int'l*, pg. 620
AUDLEY TRAVEL US, INC.; *U.S. Private*, pg. 391
AUSTRALIAN TOURS MANAGEMENT PTY LTD.—See Fairfax Financial Holdings Limited; *Int'l*, pg. 2608
AUTOPREVOZTURIST A.D.; *Int'l*, pg. 732
AVALON TRAVEL, INC.—See Avalon Holdings Corporation; *U.S. Public*, pg. 239
AVIAREPS AG; *Int'l*, pg. 741

AVOLTA AG; *Int'l*, pg. 749
BALBOA TRAVEL MANAGEMENT; *U.S. Private*, pg. 458
BARBADOS TOURISM AUTHORITY; *U.S. Private*, pg. 472
BARRHEAD TRAVEL SERVICE LIMITED—See Travel Leaders Group, LLC; *U.S. Private*, pg. 4213
BAVARIA LLOYD REISEBUERO GMBH—See Bayerische Motoren Werke Aktiengesellschaft; *Int'l*, pg. 912
BCD TRAVEL—See BCD Holdings N.V.; *Int'l*, pg. 926
BCD TRAVEL—See BCD Holdings N.V.; *Int'l*, pg. 926
BEES.TRAVEL LIMITED—See Corporate Travel Management Limited; *Int'l*, pg. 1805
BEIJING WESTMINSTER AIR SERVICE LIMITED—See Corporate Travel Management Limited; *Int'l*, pg. 1805
BESTONE.COM CO., LTD.; *Int'l*, pg. 1000
BESTTRAVEL DORTMUND GMBH—See Borussia Dortmund GmbH & Co. KGaA; *Int'l*, pg. 1115
BLACK COACH NETWORK, INC.; *U.S. Private*, pg. 570
BLACK TIE TRANSPORTATION LLC; *U.S. Private*, pg. 573
BLACK & WHITE SPORTSWEAR CO., LTD.—See Goldwin, Inc.; *Int'l*, pg. 3035
BLUE SKY REUNION SAS—See ENL Limited; *Int'l*, pg. 2441
BOCA RATON TRAVEL & CRUISES, INC.; *U.S. Private*, pg. 607
BOODAI AVIATION AGENCIES CO WLL—See City Group Company KSCP; *Int'l*, pg. 1626
BOODAI AVIATION CO. WLL—See City Group Company KSCP; *Int'l*, pg. 1626
BOOKCYPRUS.COM—See Francoudi & Stephanou Ltd.; *Int'l*, pg. 2761
BOWEN TRAVEL SERVICES INC.; *U.S. Private*, pg. 625
BREWSTER TRAVEL CANADA INC.—See Viad Corp.; *U.S. Public*, pg. 2291
BRINDLEY BEACH VACATIONS & SALES; *U.S. Private*, pg. 654
BURSCH TRAVEL - SHERIDAN—See Bursch Travel Agency, Inc.; *U.S. Private*, pg. 692
CANADIAN UNIVERSITIES TRAVEL SERVICE LIMITED; *Int'l*, pg. 1286
CAPPY DEVLIN INTERNATIONAL; *U.S. Private*, pg. 745
CARLSON TRAVEL/LET'S TALK TRAVEL INC.—See Carlson Companies Inc.; *U.S. Private*, pg. 765
CASINO TRAVEL & TOURS, LLC—See Remark Holdings, Inc.; *U.S. Private*, pg. 1782
CASINO VACANCES SNC—See Finatis SA; *Int'l*, pg. 2670
CB TRAVEL CORP.; *U.S. Private*, pg. 796
CENTURY TRAVEL SERVICE INC.; *U.S. Private*, pg. 834
CHANGBAI MOUNTAIN TOURISM CO., LTD.; *Int'l*, pg. 1442
CHINA TRAVEL HI-TECH COMPUTER HONG KONG LTD.—See China Travel International Investment Hong Kong Ltd; *Int'l*, pg. 1560
CHINA TRAVEL SERVICE (AUSTRALIA) PTY. LTD.—See China Travel International Investment Hong Kong Ltd; *Int'l*, pg. 1560
CHINA TRAVEL SERVICE (HONG KONG) LTD.—See China Travel International Investment Hong Kong Ltd; *Int'l*, pg. 1560
CHINA TRAVEL SERVICE (KOREA) CO., LTD.—See China Travel International Investment Hong Kong Ltd; *Int'l*, pg. 1560
CHINA TRAVEL SERVICE (N.Z.) LTD.—See China Travel International Investment Hong Kong Ltd; *Int'l*, pg. 1560
CHINA TRAVEL SERVICE (U.K.) LTD.—See China Travel International Investment Hong Kong Ltd; *Int'l*, pg. 1560
CHINA TRAVEL SERVICE (U.S.A.), INC.—See China Travel International Investment Hong Kong Ltd; *Int'l*, pg. 1560
CHINA TRAVEL & TRADING (DEUTSCHLAND) GMBH—See China Travel International Investment Hong Kong Ltd; *Int'l*, pg. 1560
CINESE INTERNATIONAL GROUP HOLDINGS LIMITED; *Int'l*, pg. 1610
CITIC TRAVEL CO., LTD.—See CITIC Group Corporation; *Int'l*, pg. 1621
CITY-NAV SP. Z O.O.—See Axel Springer SE; *Int'l*, pg. 766
CLASSIC COACHES (CONTINENTAL) LIMITED—See Deutsche Bahn AG; *Int'l*, pg. 2049
CLIO; *Int'l*, pg. 1660
CLUB MEDITERRANEE K.K.—See Fosun International Limited; *Int'l*, pg. 2750
CLUB MEDITERRANEE S.A. BELGE—See Fosun International Limited; *Int'l*, pg. 2750
CLUB MED SALES, INC.—See Fosun International Limited; *Int'l*, pg. 2750
CONTIKI HOLIDAYS (AUSTRALIA) PTY. LTD—See Contiki Tours International Limited; *Int'l*, pg. 1780
COOK TRAVEL STATION—See Travel Station; *U.S. Private*, pg. 4213
COOP-ITS-TRAVEL AG—See Coop-Gruppe Genossenschaft; *Int'l*, pg. 1790
CORPORATE TRAVEL MANAGEMENT GROUP PTY LTD—See Corporate Travel Management Limited; *Int'l*, pg. 1805
CORPORATE TRAVEL MANAGEMENT GROUP; *U.S. Private*, pg. 1056
CORPORATE TRAVEL MANAGEMENT LIMITED—See Corporate Travel Management Limited; *Int'l*, pg. 1805
CORPORATE TRAVEL MANAGEMENT NORTH AMERICA INC.—See Corporate Travel Management Limited; *Int'l*, pg. 1805
CORPORATE TRAVEL MANAGEMENT (S) PTE. LIMITED—See Corporate Travel Management Limited; *Int'l*, pg. 1806
CORPORATE TRAVEL MANAGEMENT (UK) LIMITED—See Corporate Travel Management Limited; *Int'l*, pg. 1805
CORPORATE TRAVEL PLANNERS, INC.—See Corporate Travel Management Limited; *Int'l*, pg. 1805
COSCO INTERNATIONAL TRAVEL (HK) CO., LTD.—See China COSCO Shipping Corporation Limited; *Int'l*, pg. 1492
COSTAMAR TRAVEL, CRUISE & TOURS INC.; *U.S. Private*, pg. 1063
CROSSROADS TRAVEL, INC.—See ABRY Partners, LLC; *U.S. Private*, pg. 41
CRUISESONLY INC.—See World Travel Holdings, Inc.; *U.S. Private*, pg. 4567
CWT CANADA—See Carlson Companies Inc.; *U.S. Private*, pg. 765
DANDONG CHINA INTERNATIONAL TRAVEL SERVICE CO., LTD.—See China Tourism Group Duty Free Corporation Limited; *Int'l*, pg. 1560
DB BAHN ITALIA S.R.L.—See Deutsche Bahn AG; *Int'l*, pg. 2049
DB BUSVERKEHR HESSEN GMBH—See Deutsche Bahn AG; *Int'l*, pg. 2049
DB DIALOG GMBH—See Deutsche Bahn AG; *Int'l*, pg. 2050
DELGADO TRAVEL AGENCY CORPORATION; *U.S. Private*, pg. 1196
DESERT ADVENTURES TOURISM LLC—See Fairfax Financial Holdings Limited; *Int'l*, pg. 2608
DESTINATION ITALIA SPA; *Int'l*, pg. 2046
DESTINATIONS UNLIMITED, INC.; *U.S. Private*, pg. 1215
DEUTSCHE BAHN FRANCE VOYAGES&TOURISME SAS—See Deutsche Bahn AG; *Int'l*, pg. 2051
DFB-REISEBUERO GMBH—See Global Business Travel Group, Inc.; *U.S. Public*, pg. 940
DISCOVERY WORLD TRAVEL, INC.; *U.S. Private*, pg. 1238
DJOSER-DIVANTOURA BVBA—See Cox & Kings Limited; *Int'l*, pg. 1822
DOWN UNDER ANSWERS, LLC; *U.S. Private*, pg. 1269
DYNASTY HOLIDAYS, INC.—See China Airlines Ltd.; *Int'l*, pg. 1482
EASEMYTRIP TOURS LLC—See Easy Trip Planners Limited; *Int'l*, pg. 2276
EAST YORKSHIRE MOTOR SERVICES LIMITED—See GLOBALVIA Inversiones, S.A.U.; *Int'l*, pg. 3005
EASY TRIP PLANNERS LIMITED; *Int'l*, pg. 2276
EDENRED TRAVEL LIMITED—See Edenred S.A.; *Int'l*, pg. 2308
EGENCIA GMBH—See Expedia Group, Inc.; *U.S. Public*, pg. 809
EGENCIA UK LTD.—See Expedia Group, Inc.; *U.S. Public*, pg. 809
ELITE TRAVEL MANAGEMENT GROUP; *U.S. Private*, pg. 1361
ELJOSA TRAVEL & TOURS PROPRIETARY LIMITED—See Frontier Transport Holdings Limited; *Int'l*, pg. 2796
ELLISON TRAVEL & TOURS LTD.; *Int'l*, pg. 2367
ENTAS NAKLIYAT VE TURIZM ANONIM SIRKETI—See Enka Insaat ve Sanayi A.S.; *Int'l*, pg. 2440
ESCAPOLOGY LLC; *U.S. Private*, pg. 1425
ESG INC.—See Goldwin, Inc.; *Int'l*, pg. 3035
EURASIA TRAVEL CO., LTD.; *Int'l*, pg. 2527
EUROP ASSISTANCE MALAYSIA SDN. BHD.—See Assicurazioni Generali S.p.A.; *Int'l*, pg. 644
EUROP ASSISTANCE (THAILAND) COMPANY LIMITED—See Assicurazioni Generali S.p.A.; *Int'l*, pg. 644
EVENT SOLUTIONS LLC; *U.S. Private*, pg. 1437
EXECUTIVE TRAVEL, INC.—See BCD Holdings N.V.; *Int'l*, pg. 926
EXPEDIA FRANCE S.A.S.—See Expedia Group, Inc.; *U.S. Public*, pg. 809
EXPEDIA.NL B.V.—See Expedia Group, Inc.; *U.S. Public*, pg. 809
EXPEDIA ONLINE TRAVEL SERVICES INDIA PRIVATE LIMITED—See Expedia Group, Inc.; *U.S. Public*, pg. 809
EXPEDIA SPAIN, S.L.—See Expedia Group, Inc.; *U.S. Public*, pg. 809
EXPEDIA SWEDEN AB—See Expedia Group, Inc.; *U.S. Public*, pg. 809
EXPLORICA CANADA INC.—See Eurazeo SE; *Int'l*, pg. 2530
EZFLY INTERNATIONAL TRAVEL AGENT CO., LTD.; *Int'l*, pg. 2594
FCM BANNOCKBURN; *U.S. Private*, pg. 1486
FC USA INC.—See Flight Centre Travel Group Limited; *Int'l*, pg. 2706
FELDA TRAVEL SDN. BHD.—See FGV Holdings Bhd; *Int'l*, pg. 2649
FIDITOUR JOINT STOCK COMPANY; *Int'l*, pg. 2655
FINLAND TRAVEL BUREAU LTD.—See Finnair Plc; *Int'l*, pg. 2675
FIRST TRAVEL SOLUTIONS LIMITED—See FirstGroup plc; *Int'l*, pg. 2689

N.A.I.C.S. INDEX

561510 — TRAVEL AGENCIES

FISH & GAME FRONTIERS, INC.; *U.S. Private*, pg. 1533
FLIGHT CENTRE (UK) LIMITED—See Flight Centre Travel Group Limited; *Int'l*, pg. 2706
FLIPKEY, INC.—See TripAdvisor, Inc.; *U.S. Public*, pg. 2195
FOX WORLD TRAVEL; *U.S. Private*, pg. 1585
FULL SERVICE TRAVEL INC.; *U.S. Private*, pg. 1621
F.W. VAN ZILE POPULAR TOURS INC.; *U.S. Private*, pg. 1457
GALILEO DEUTSCHLAND GMBH—See Elliott Management Corporation; *U.S. Private*, pg. 1373
GALILEO DEUTSCHLAND GMBH—See Siris Capital Group, LLC; *U.S. Private*, pg. 3674
GARBER'S TRAVEL SERVICE, INC.—See Flight Centre Travel Group Limited; *Int'l*, pg. 2706
GBT III B.V.—See Global Business Travel Group, Inc.; *U.S. Public*, pg. 940
GEORGIA INTERNATIONAL TRAVEL, INC.—See ABRY Partners, LLC; *U.S. Private*, pg. 41
GLOBAL MARINE TRAVEL LLC—See Ackermans & van Haaren NV; *Int'l*, pg. 106
GLOBALSTAR EMEA LTD.; *Int'l*, pg. 3004
GLOBALSTAR SLOVAKIA, S.R.O.—See Globalstar, Inc.; *U.S. Public*, pg. 946
GLOBAL TRAVEL INTERNATIONAL, INC.; *U.S. Private*, pg. 1718
GO-AHEAD TRANSPORT SERVICES (DUBLIN) LIMITED—See GLOBALVIA Inversiones, S.A.U.; *Int'l*, pg. 3005
GOLDWIN AMERICA, INC.—See Goldwin, Inc.; *Int'l*, pg. 3035
GOLDWIN DEVELOPMENT INC.—See Goldwin, Inc.; *Int'l*, pg. 3035
GOLDWIN ENTERPRISE INC.—See Goldwin, Inc.; *Int'l*, pg. 3035
GOLDWIN EUROPE AG—See Goldwin, Inc.; *Int'l*, pg. 3035
GOLDWIN LOGITEM INC.—See Goldwin, Inc.; *Int'l*, pg. 3035
GOLDWIN TECHNICAL CENTER INC.—See Goldwin, Inc.; *Int'l*, pg. 3035
GOLDWIN TRADING INC.—See Goldwin, Inc.; *Int'l*, pg. 3035
GO VOYAGES—See Accor S.A.; *Int'l*, pg. 91
GRAND CENTRAL RAILWAY COMPANY LIMITED—See Deutsche Bahn AG; *Int'l*, pg. 2051
GRAND CIRCLE CORPORATION; *U.S. Private*, pg. 1752
GREAT DESTINATIONS, INC.—See Marriott Vacations Worldwide Corporation; *U.S. Public*, pg. 1373
GREAT DESTINATIONS, INC.—See Marriott Vacations Worldwide Corporation; *U.S. Public*, pg. 1373
GREENLANDS REJSEBUREAU A/S—See Air Greenland A/S; *Int'l*, pg. 238
GROTTES DE HAN-SUR-LESSE; *Int'l*, pg. 3088
GROWINGTON VENTURES INDIA LIMITED; *Int'l*, pg. 3112
GRUENINGER MUSIC TOURS—See Grueninger Tours & Cruises Inc.; *U.S. Private*, pg. 1797
GRUENINGER TOURS & CRUISES INC.; *U.S. Private*, pg. 1797
GUANGZHOU WESTMINSTER TRAVEL SERVICES LTD.—See Corporate Travel Management Limited; *Int'l*, pg. 1806
GUILIN TOURISM CORPORATION LIMITED; *Int'l*, pg. 3174
GUINNESS STOREHOUSE LIMITED—See Diageo plc; *Int'l*, pg. 2102
GULF STATES FINANCIAL SERVICES, INC.; *U.S. Private*, pg. 1817
GYEONGJU WORLD RESORT CO., LTD.—See Asia Holdings Co., Ltd.; *Int'l*, pg. 613
HANATOUR SERVICE, INC.; *Int'l*, pg. 3241
HANKYU TRAVEL SUPPORT CO., LTD.—See Hankyu Hanshin Holdings Inc.; *Int'l*, pg. 3255
HANSEAT REISEBURO GMBH—See Global Business Travel Group, Inc.; *U.S. Public*, pg. 941
HAREL MALLAC TRAVEL AND LEISURE LTD—See Harel Mallac & Co. Ltd.; *Int'l*, pg. 3274
HARVEY WORLD TRAVEL GROUP PTY. LTD.—See Helloworld Travel Limited; *Int'l*, pg. 3337
HARVEY WORLD TRAVEL SOUTHERN AFRICA (PTY) LIMITED—See Helloworld Travel Limited; *Int'l*, pg. 3337
HEINEMANN ASIA PACIFIC PTE. LTD.—See Gebr. Heinemann SE & Co. KG; *Int'l*, pg. 2905
HELLENIC TOURS S.A.—See EQT AB; *Int'l*, pg. 2478
HELLO METRO; *U.S. Private*, pg. 1911
HELLOWORLD TRAVEL LIMITED; *Int'l*, pg. 3337
HEMAS TRAVELS (PTE) LTD—See Hemas Holdings PLC; *Int'l*, pg. 3340
H.I.S. AUSTRALIA PTY. LTD.—See H.I.S. Co., Ltd.; *Int'l*, pg. 3195
H.I.S. CANADA INC.—See H.I.S. Co., Ltd.; *Int'l*, pg. 3195
H.I.S.-MERIT TRAVEL INC.—See H.I.S. Co., Ltd.; *Int'l*, pg. 3195
HMJ INC.; *U.S. Private*, pg. 1955
HOGG ROBINSON AUSTRALIA PTY LIMITED—See Global Business Travel Group, Inc.; *U.S. Public*, pg. 941
HOGG ROBINSON GERMANY GMBH & CO. KG—See Global Business Travel Group, Inc.; *U.S. Public*, pg. 941
HOGG ROBINSON MAGYARORSZAG KFT.—See Global Business Travel Group, Inc.; *U.S. Public*, pg. 941
HOGG ROBINSON SINGAPORE PTE LIMITED—See Global Business Travel Group, Inc.; *U.S. Public*, pg. 941
HOLY LANDS SUN TOURS—See Isram Wholesale Tours & Travel Ltd.; *U.S. Private*, pg. 2147
HOTWIRE, INC.—See Expedia Group, Inc.; *U.S. Public*, pg. 809
HUDSON LTD.—See Avolta AG; *Int'l*, pg. 749
IGNITE TRAVEL GROUP—See Flight Centre Travel Group Limited; *Int'l*, pg. 2706
INSPIRE TRAVEL MANAGEMENT PTY. LTD.—See Corporate Travel Management Limited; *Int'l*, pg. 1805
INTELETRAVEL.COM; *U.S. Private*, pg. 2104
INTERNATIONAL MANAGEMENT SERVICES GROUP, INC.; *U.S. Private*, pg. 2118
INTERNATIONAL TRAVEL ASSOCIATES CORP.—See ITA-Group, Inc.; *U.S. Private*, pg. 2148
IN THE KNOW EXPERIENCES; *U.S. Private*, pg. 2052
JECKING TOURS & TRAVEL LIMITED—See Corporate Travel Management Limited; *Int'l*, pg. 1805
JOURNEY MEXICO; *U.S. Private*, pg. 2238
JR TOKAI TOURS, INC.—See Central Japan Railway Company; *Int'l*, pg. 1408
KAMOME CO., LTD.—See IBJ Inc.; *Int'l*, pg. 3576
KATMAILAND, INC.—See Bristol Bay Native Corporation; *U.S. Private*, pg. 656
KEY TOURS INTERNATIONAL INC.—See United Rail, Inc.; *U.S. Public*, pg. 2234
KOBAYASHI TRAVEL SERVICE LTD. INC.; *U.S. Private*, pg. 2326
LA FOURCHETTE NETHERLANDS B.V.—See TripAdvisor, Inc.; *U.S. Public*, pg. 2195
LAKELAND TOURS, LLC—See Eurazeo SE; *Int'l*, pg. 2529
LEGACY HEALTHCARE ADVISORS LLC; *U.S. Private*, pg. 2416
LEISURE CORP PRIVATE LIMITED—See Ebix Inc.; *U.S. Public*, pg. 710
LIJIANG CHINA INTERNATIONAL TRAVEL SERVICE CO., LTD.—See China Tourism Group Duty Free Corporation Limited; *Int'l*, pg. 1560
LINK WITH HOME TRAVEL INC.—See Home Hardware Stores Limited; *Int'l*, pg. 3454
LIVETRAVEL, INC.—See American International Group, Inc.; *U.S. Public*, pg. 106
LOCOMOTE IP PTY. LTD.—See Elliott Management Corporation; *U.S. Private*, pg. 1373
LOCOMOTE IP PTY. LTD.—See Siris Capital Group, LLC; *U.S. Private*, pg. 3674
LOTUS TOURS LIMITED—See Corporate Travel Management Limited; *Int'l*, pg. 1805
LUFTHANSA CITY CENTER INTERNATIONAL GMBH—See Deutsche Lufthansa AG; *Int'l*, pg. 2068
LUFTHANSA INDUSTRY SOLUTIONS GMBH & CO. KG—See Deutsche Lufthansa AG; *Int'l*, pg. 2069
LUXE RV, INC.; *U.S. Private*, pg. 2518
LUXE TRAVEL MANAGEMENT, INC.—See Frosch International Travel Inc.; *U.S. Private*, pg. 1616
MARITZ TRAVEL CO.—See Maritz Holdings Inc.; *U.S. Private*, pg. 2577
MARKET SQUARE TRAVEL LLC—See Travel Leaders Group, LLC; *U.S. Private*, pg. 4213
MENNO TRAVEL SERVICE, INC.; *U.S. Private*, pg. 2666
MERCURY HIMALAYAN EXPLORATIONS LTD.—See Ebix Inc.; *U.S. Public*, pg. 710
MERIBEL ALPINA SAS—See Compagnie des Alpes S.A.; *Int'l*, pg. 1738
MILLENNIUM TOURS; *U.S. Private*, pg. 2732
MILL-RUN TOURS INC.; *U.S. Private*, pg. 2730
MLT VACATIONS, INC.—See Delta Air Lines, Inc.; *U.S. Public*, pg. 652
MORRIS MURDOCK, LLC; *U.S. Private*, pg. 2788
MTS TRAVEL - COLORADO SPRINGS—See Menno Travel Service, Inc.; *U.S. Private*, pg. 2666
MVP HOLDINGS, INC.; *U.S. Public*, pg. 1487
OFF THE BEATEN PATH, LLC—See Lindblad Expeditions Holdings, Inc.; *U.S. Public*, pg. 1319
OMEGA WORLD TRAVEL, INC.; *U.S. Private*, pg. 3015
ONLINE VACATION CENTER HOLDINGS CORP.; *U.S. Public*, pg. 1605
ONLINE VACATION CENTER, INC.—See Online Vacation Center Holdings Corp.; *U.S. Public*, pg. 1605
ORIENT ESCAPE TRAVEL (SABAH) SDN. BHD.—See Advance Synergy Berhad; *Int'l*, pg. 156
ORIENT FLEXI-PAX TOURS—See Isram Wholesale Tours & Travel Ltd.; *U.S. Private*, pg. 2147
OU TALLINK TRAVEL CLUB—See AS Infortar; *Int'l*, pg. 590
OUTDOOR TRAVELER DESTINATIONS, LLC—See Hilton Grand Vacations Inc.; *U.S. Public*, pg. 1040
OVATION TRAVEL GROUP, INC—See Global Business Travel Group, Inc.; *U.S. Public*, pg. 941
OVATION TRAVEL GROUP UK LIMITED—See Global Business Travel Group, Inc.; *U.S. Public*, pg. 941
OVATION TRAVEL, LLC—See Global Business Travel Group, Inc.; *U.S. Public*, pg. 941
OV INTERNATIONAL PTE LTD—See Asiatravel.com Holdings Limited; *Int'l*, pg. 620
PAR AVION TRAVEL, INC.; *U.S. Private*, pg. 3089
PEAK TRAVEL GROUP, INC.—See ABRY Partners, LLC; *U.S. Private*, pg. 41
PELLA TRAVEL INC.; *U.S. Private*, pg. 3131
PENTRAVEL (PTY) LTD—See Cullinan Holdings Limited; *Int'l*, pg. 1877
PIROVANO STELVIO SPA—See Banca Popolare di Sondrio S.p.A.; *Int'l*, pg. 816
PLAZA TRAVEL, INC.—See BCD Holdings N.V.; *Int'l*, pg. 926
PORT SOLENT MARINA LIMITED—See BAE Systems plc; *Int'l*, pg. 798
POTHOS, INC.; *U.S. Private*, pg. 3235
PREFERRED TRAVEL OF NAPLES INC.; *U.S. Private*, pg. 3248
PREMIER TRAVELS, INC.—See Diplomat Hotel Corporation; *U.S. Private*, pg. 1234
PRESTIGE TRAVEL, INC.; *U.S. Private*, pg. 3256
PRESTIGE TRAVEL, INC.; *U.S. Private*, pg. 3256
PRESTIGE TRAVEL SYSTEMS, INC.; *U.S. Private*, pg. 3256
PRIVATE SAFARIS (EAST AFRICA) LTD.—See Fairfax Financial Holdings Limited; *Int'l*, pg. 2608
PRIVATE SAFARIS (PTY) LTD.—See Fairfax Financial Holdings Limited; *Int'l*, pg. 2608
PROFESSIONAL TRAVEL INC.—See ABRY Partners, LLC; *U.S. Private*, pg. 41
PROTRAVEL/AUSTIN—See Travel Leaders Group, LLC; *U.S. Private*, pg. 4213
PROTRAVEL INTERNATIONAL INC.—See Travel Leaders Group, LLC; *U.S. Private*, pg. 4213
PROTRAVEL—See Travel Leaders Group, LLC; *U.S. Private*, pg. 4213
PT. ADYA TOURS - INDONESIA—See Ebix Inc.; *U.S. Public*, pg. 710
QST TRAVEL GROUP INC.; *U.S. Private*, pg. 3314
RADO TRAVEL SERVICE CO., LTD.—See Adventure Inc.; *Int'l*, pg. 167
RA TRAVEL, INC.—See Corporate Travel Management Limited; *Int'l*, pg. 1805
RCI TRAVEL—See Travel & Leisure Co.; *U.S. Public*, pg. 2185
REGALE INTERNATIONAL TRAVEL COMPANY LTD.—See EQT AB; *Int'l*, pg. 2478
REGAL TRAVEL, INC.—See International Management Services Group, Inc.; *U.S. Private*, pg. 2118
REGENCY TRAVEL INC.; *U.S. Private*, pg. 3386
REISEBURO KUONI GES.M.B.H.—See EQT AB; *Int'l*, pg. 2478
RENNERT TRAVEL—See Corporate Travel Management Limited; *Int'l*, pg. 1805
RESTPLATZBORSE GES.M.B.H.—See EQT AB; *Int'l*, pg. 2478
RIO GRANDE TRAVEL CENTERS, INC.; *U.S. Private*, pg. 3438
ROBERT'S HAWAII TOURS INC.—See Robert's Hawaii Inc.; *U.S. Private*, pg. 3459
SABRE ASIA PACIFIC PTE. LTD.—See Sabre Corporation; *U.S. Public*, pg. 1833
SABRE AUSTRIA GMBH—See Sabre Corporation; *U.S. Public*, pg. 1833
SABRE BELGIUM SA—See Sabre Corporation; *U.S. Public*, pg. 1833
SABRE DEUTSCHLAND MARKETING GMBH—See Sabre Corporation; *U.S. Public*, pg. 1833
SABRE MARKETING NEDERLAND B.V.—See Sabre Corporation; *U.S. Public*, pg. 1833
SABRE POLSKA SP. Z O.O.—See Sabre Corporation; *U.S. Public*, pg. 1833
SABRE SEYAHAT DAGITIM SISTERNLERI A.S.—See Sabre Corporation; *U.S. Public*, pg. 1833
SABRE SVERIGE AB—See Sabre Corporation; *U.S. Public*, pg. 1833
SABRE TRAVEL NETWORK (CENTRAL ASIA) LLP—See Sabre Corporation; *U.S. Public*, pg. 1833
SABRE TRAVEL NETWORK (HONG KONG) LIMITED—See Sabre Corporation; *U.S. Public*, pg. 1833
SABRE TRAVEL NETWORK JORDAN LLC—See Sabre Corporation; *U.S. Public*, pg. 1834
SABRE TRAVEL NETWORK (MALAYSIA) SDN. BHD.—See Sabre Corporation; *U.S. Public*, pg. 1833
SABRE TRAVEL NETWORK MIDDLE EAST W.L.L.—See Sabre Corporation; *U.S. Public*, pg. 1834
SABRE TRAVEL NETWORK ROMANIA S.R.L.—See Sabre Corporation; *U.S. Public*, pg. 1834
SABRE TRAVEL NETWORK (THAILAND) LTD.—See Sabre Corporation; *U.S. Public*, pg. 1834
SAFAR TRAVEL SERVICES—See Al Fahim Group; *Int'l*, pg. 277
SAINTEN PTY LTD—See Corporate Travel Management Limited; *Int'l*, pg. 1806
SAVEONRESORTS.COM, LLC; *U.S. Private*, pg. 3556
SCHEDULED AIRLINES TRAFFIC OFFICES, INC.—See Carlson Companies Inc.; *U.S. Private*, pg. 765
SCOTT DUNN LIMITED—See Flight Centre Travel Group Limited; *Int'l*, pg. 2706
SCOTT DUNN USA—See Flight Centre Travel Group Limited; *Int'l*, pg. 2706
SCV DOMAINE SKIABLE SA—See Compagnie des Alpes S.A.; *Int'l*, pg. 1738
SEVABEL SAS—See Compagnie des Alpes S.A.; *Int'l*, pg. 1738

561510 — TRAVEL AGENCIES

SHADOW CONCEPTS LLC; *U.S. Private*, pg. 3622
SHELTER CO.; *U.S. Private*, pg. 3631
SHORT'S TRAVEL MANAGEMENT, INC.; *U.S. Private*, pg. 3643
SH TOURS PTE LTD—See Asiatravel.com Holdings Limited; *Int'l*, pg. 620
SIGNATURE TRANSPORTATION GROUP, LLC; *U.S. Private*, pg. 3650
SILVERSEA CRUISES AUSTRALIA PTY. LTD.—See Royal Caribbean Cruises Ltd.; *U.S. Public*, pg. 1815
SINGER TRAVEL; *U.S. Private*, pg. 3670
SKYAUCTION.COM, INC.; *U.S. Private*, pg. 3684
SKY BIRD TRAVEL & TOUR INC.; *U.S. Private*, pg. 3683
SKYPASS TRAVEL, INC—See Mondee Holdings, Inc.; *U.S. Public*, pg. 1460
SOCIETE D'EXPLOITATION D'AGENCES DE VOYAGES ET DE TOURISME SA—See Accor S.A.; *Int'l*, pg. 92
SOTC TRAVEL SERVICES PRIVATE LIMITED—See Fairfax Financial Holdings Limited; *Int'l*, pg. 2608
SOUTHEAST TRAVEL SERVICES USA CO. LTD.; *U.S. Private*, pg. 3726
STARLITE FERRIES, INC.—See Chelsea Logistics and Infrastructure Holdings Corp.; *Int'l*, pg. 1460
STA TRAVEL, INC—See Diethelm Keller Holding Limited; *Int'l*, pg. 2117
STA TRAVEL LTD.—See Diethelm Keller Holding Limited; *Int'l*, pg. 2117
STA TRAVEL PTY LTD—See Diethelm Keller Holding Limited; *Int'l*, pg. 2117
STELLA GROUP PTY LTD.—See CVC Capital Partners SICAV-FIS S.A.; *Int'l*, pg. 1885
STELLA TRAVEL SERVICES (AUSTRALIA) PTY LTD—See Helloworld Travel Limited; *Int'l*, pg. 3337
STUDENTCITY.COM INC.; *U.S. Private*, pg. 3843
STVI SAS—See Compagnie des Alpes S.A.; *Int'l*, pg. 1738
SUBMARINO VIAGENS LTDA—See CVC Brasil Operadora e Agencia de Viagens S.A.; *Int'l*, pg. 1881
SUPERSTAR HOLIDAYS LTD—See El Al Airlines Ltd.; *Int'l*, pg. 2340
SYNERGY TOURS SDN. BHD.2002—See Advance Synergy Berhad; *Int'l*, pg. 157
SYS INC.—See H.I.S. Co., Ltd.; *Int'l*, pg. 3196
TAIPEI WESTMINSTER TRAVEL LIMITED (TAIWAN)—See Corporate Travel Management Limited; *Int'l*, pg. 1806
TAMPA PALMS TRAVELWORLD; *U.S. Private*, pg. 3929
TIGER ENTERPRISES LTD—See Giordano International Limited; *Int'l*, pg. 2978
TRADING PLACES INTERNATIONAL, LLC—See Marriott Vacations Worldwide Corporation; *U.S. Public*, pg. 1374
TRAIN TRAVEL, INC.—See United Rail, Inc.; *U.S. Public*, pg. 2234
TRANSPORTATION COMMUNICATIONS UNIONIAM; *U.S. Private*, pg. 4211
TRAVEL ALL RUSSIA LLC; *U.S. Private*, pg. 4212
TRAVEL AUDIENCE, GMBH—See Amadeus IT Group, S.A.; *Int'l*, pg. 407
TRAVELCORP HOLDINGS PTY LTD.—See Corporate Travel Management Limited; *Int'l*, pg. 1806
TRAVEL DESTINATIONS MANAGEMENT GROUP, INC.—See ABRY Partners, LLC; *U.S. Private*, pg. 41
TRAVELDOO SAS—See Expedia Group, Inc.; *U.S. Public*, pg. 810
TRAVEL EXCHANGE; *U.S. Private*, pg. 4213
TRAVEL INCORPORATED; *U.S. Private*, pg. 4213
TRAVEL-IT GMBH & CO. KG—See Elliott Management Corporation; *U.S. Private*, pg. 1373
TRAVEL-IT GMBH & CO. KG—See Siris Capital Group, LLC; *U.S. Private*, pg. 3674
TRAVEL LEADERS OF CHARLESTON—See Travel Leaders Group, LLC; *U.S. Private*, pg. 4213
TRAVEL MANAGEMENT PARTNERS INC.; *U.S. Private*, pg. 4213
TRAVELMATE.COM.AU PTY. LTD.—See Helloworld Travel Limited; *Int'l*, pg. 3337
TRAVELNET SOLUTIONS, INC.; *U.S. Private*, pg. 4214
TRAVEL-ON LTD., INC.; *U.S. Private*, pg. 4213
TRAVEL PLUS N.V.—See Exmar N.V.; *Int'l*, pg. 2585
TRAVELPORT DIGITAL LIMITED—See Elliott Management Corporation; *U.S. Private*, pg. 1373
TRAVELPORT DIGITAL LIMITED—See Siris Capital Group, LLC; *U.S. Private*, pg. 3674
TRAVELPORT, LP—See Elliott Management Corporation; *U.S. Private*, pg. 1373
TRAVELPORT, LP—See Siris Capital Group, LLC; *U.S. Private*, pg. 3674
TRAVEL RESOURCES LIMITED—See Corporate Travel Management Limited; *Int'l*, pg. 1806
TRAVELSCAPE, LLC—See Expedia Group, Inc.; *U.S. Public*, pg. 810
TRAVEL STATION; *U.S. Private*, pg. 4213
THE TRAVEL TEAM, INC.—See Rich Holdings, Inc.; *U.S. Private*, pg. 3426
TRAVEL & TRANSPORT INC.; *U.S. Private*, pg. 4212
TRAVELZOO; *U.S. Public*, pg. 2186
TRAVIAUSTRIA DATENSERVICE FUR REISE UND TOURISTIK GESELLSCHAFT M.B.H. & CO NFG. KG—See Deutsche Lufthansa AG; *Int'l*, pg. 2070
TRIPBORN, INC.; *U.S. Public*, pg. 2195
TRIPOS TRAVEL PROPRIETARY LIMITED—See AYO Technology Solutions Ltd.; *Int'l*, pg. 775
TRIPRESERVATIONS.COM—See Prestige Travel, Inc.; *U.S. Private*, pg. 3256
TTA, INC.—See Altour International, Inc.; *U.S. Private*, pg. 210
UNITED VACATIONS, INC.—See United Airlines Holdings, Inc.; *U.S. Public*, pg. 2229
VACATION CENTRAL—See Travel Network Vacation Central; *U.S. Private*, pg. 4213
VACATION.COM, INC.—See Travel Leaders Group, LLC; *U.S. Private*, pg. 4213
VALERIE WILSON TRAVEL, INC.—See Frosch International Travel Inc.; *U.S. Private*, pg. 1616
VANTAGE DELUXE WORLD TRAVEL; *U.S. Private*, pg. 4345
VGF VERKEHRS-GEMEINSCHAFT LANDKREIS FREUDENSTADT GMBH—See Deutsche Bahn AG; *Int'l*, pg. 2055
VIAJES CARREFOUR, S.L.U.—See Carrefour SA; *Int'l*, pg. 1345
VIAJES EL CORTE INGLES, S.A.—See El Corte Ingles, S.A.; *Int'l*, pg. 2340
VIAJES EROSKI SA—See Grupo Eroski; *Int'l*, pg. 3128
VIAJES KUONI, S.A.—See EQT AB; *Int'l*, pg. 2478
VIAJES PARIS S.A.—See Cencosud S.A.; *Int'l*, pg. 1400
VIA PHILIPPINES TRAVEL CORPORATION—See Ebix Inc.; *U.S. Public*, pg. 710
VIP TRAVEL OF WOOSTER, INC.—See ABRY Partners, LLC; *U.S. Private*, pg. 41
VIRTUOSO LTD.; *U.S. Private*, pg. 4389
VISIT NAPA VALLEY; *U.S. Private*, pg. 4392
VISUAL TURISMO LTDA—See CVC Brasil Operadora e Agencia de Viagens S.A.; *Int'l*, pg. 1881
VONLANE, LLC; *U.S. Private*, pg. 4412
WESTMINSTER TRAVEL CONSULTANCY (GUANGZHOU) LIMITED—See Corporate Travel Management Limited; *Int'l*, pg. 1806
WESTMINSTER TRAVEL LIMITED—See Corporate Travel Management Limited; *Int'l*, pg. 1806
WESTMINSTER TRAVEL LIMITED—See Corporate Travel Management Limited; *Int'l*, pg. 1806
W.L. TOURISME—See Accor S.A.; *Int'l*, pg. 92
WMPH VACATIONS, LLC—See 3i Group plc; *Int'l*, pg. 8
WORLDSTRIDES PTY. LTD.—See Eurazeo SE; *Int'l*, pg. 2530
WORLD TOURIST REJSEBUREAU A/S—See Accor S.A.; *Int'l*, pg. 92
WORLD TRAVEL HOLDINGS—See World Travel Holdings, Inc.; *U.S. Private*, pg. 4567
WORLD TRAVEL PARTNERS ORLANDO; *U.S. Private*, pg. 4567
WRIGHT TRAVEL AGENCY INC.; *U.S. Private*, pg. 4573
WRIGHT TRAVEL CORPORATION—See EchoStar Corporation; *U.S. Public*, pg. 711
WUYISHAN CHINA INTERNATIONAL TRAVEL SERVICE CO., LTD.—See China Tourism Group Duty Free Corporation Limited; *Int'l*, pg. 1560
WYNDHAM JADE LLC; *U.S. Private*, pg. 4576
YEMEN TRAVEL AGENCIES—See Hayel Saeed Anam Group of Companies; *Int'l*, pg. 3291
YILU TRAVEL SERVICES GMBH—See Deutsche Lufthansa AG; *Int'l*, pg. 2071
YMT VACATIONS; *U.S. Private*, pg. 4589
YOUNGONE OUTDOOR CORPORATION—See Goldwin, Inc.; *Int'l*, pg. 3035
YOUR TRAVEL CENTER, INC.; *U.S. Private*, pg. 4594
ZEROG GMBH—See Deutsche Lufthansa AG; *Int'l*, pg. 2071
ZHANGJIAJIE CHINA INTERNATIONAL TRAVEL SERVICE CO., LTD.—See China Tourism Group Duty Free Corporation Limited; *Int'l*, pg. 1560
ZHEJIANG CHINA INTERNATIONAL TRAVEL SERVICE CO., LTD.—See China Tourism Group Duty Free Corporation Limited; *Int'l*, pg. 1560

561520 — TOUR OPERATORS

734758 ONTARIO LIMITED; *Int'l*, pg. 14
ACADEMIC TRAVEL ABROAD, INC.; *U.S. Private*, pg. 46
ACADEMY BUS LLC; *U.S. Private*, pg. 46
ADVENTURE BOUND ALASKA; *U.S. Private*, pg. 109
ADVENTURES BY DISNEY—See The Walt Disney Company; *U.S. Public*, pg. 2138
AGGRESSOR ADVENTURES, LLC; *U.S. Private*, pg. 127
AIRPLUS AIR TRAVEL CARD VERTRIEBSGESELLSCHAFT MBH—See Deutsche Lufthansa AG; *Int'l*, pg. 2068
AITKEN SPENCE PLC; *Int'l*, pg. 254
ALPITOUR S.P.A.; *Int'l*, pg. 373
AL SHARQ INVESTMENTS PROJECTS(HOLDING) P.L.C.; *Int'l*, pg. 283
AMERICAN COUNCIL FOR INTERNATIONAL STUDIES, INC. - ENCORE TOURS DIVISION—See American Institute for Foreign Study, Inc.; *U.S. Private*, pg. 237
AMERICAN EXPRESS BUSINESS TRAVEL APS—See Global Business Travel Group, Inc.; *U.S. Public*, pg. 941

ANHUI JIUHUA MOUNTAIN TOURISM DEVELOPMENT CO., LTD; *Int'l*, pg. 468
ANTUR TURIZM A.S.—See Dogus Holding AS; *Int'l*, pg. 2154
AOT BUSINESS CONSULTING (SHANGHAI) INC.—See Helloworld Travel Limited; *Int'l*, pg. 3337
AOVO TOURISTIK AG; *Int'l*, pg. 498
ASIAN TRAILS TOUR LTD.—See Fairfax Financial Holdings Limited; *Int'l*, pg. 2608
ATLANTIS ADVENTURES, LLC.—See Atlantis Submarines International Inc.; *Int'l*, pg. 676
ATLANTIS SUBMARINES HAWAII, INC.—See Atlantis Submarines International Inc.; *Int'l*, pg. 676
AT LAOS CO., LTD.—See Fairfax Financial Holdings Limited; *Int'l*, pg. 2608
ATPI LIMITED; *Int'l*, pg. 693
ATS PACIFIC FIJI LIMITED—See Helloworld Travel Limited; *Int'l*, pg. 3337
ATS PACIFIC (NZ) LTD—See Helloworld Travel Limited; *Int'l*, pg. 3337
ATTAS ALARKO TURISTIK TESISLER A.S.—See Alarko Holding A.S.; *Int'l*, pg. 291
AURINKO OU—See Finnair Plc; *Int'l*, pg. 2675
AVIATION LINKS LTD.; *Int'l*, pg. 742
AVILLION BERHAD; *Int'l*, pg. 743
AYLA OASIS DEVELOPMENT COMPANY—See Arab Supply & Trading Co.; *Int'l*, pg. 532
BACKROADS INC.; *U.S. Private*, pg. 423
BCD TRAVEL SERVICES B.V.—See BCD Holdings N.V.; *Int'l*, pg. 926
BEIJING JINGXI CULTURE & TOURISM CO., LTD.; *Int'l*, pg. 953
BELHASA, TOURISM, TRAVEL & CARGO CO., L.L.C.—See Belhasa Group of Companies; *Int'l*, pg. 964
BERGE & MEER TOURISTIK GMBH—See Genui GmbH; *Int'l*, pg. 2930
BEST TOURS ITALIA S.P.A.—See Alessandro Rosso Group S.p.A.; *Int'l*, pg. 306
BEST TOURS S.P.A.—See Alessandro Rosso Group S.p.A.; *Int'l*, pg. 306
BLUE MOUNTAIN ECO TOURS INC.; *Int'l*, pg. 1069
BOC TRAVELS (PRIVATE) LIMITED—See Bank of Ceylon; *Int'l*, pg. 840
BOSTON HARBOR CRUISES; *U.S. Private*, pg. 621
BREWSTER CHARTER SERVICES—See Viad Corp.; *U.S. Public*, pg. 2291
BRF HOLIDAYS PTE LTD—See Gallant Venture Ltd.; *Int'l*, pg. 2873
BTG HOTELS GROUP CO., LTD.; *Int'l*, pg. 1204
CARAVAN TOURS, INC.; *U.S. Private*, pg. 748
CARNIVAL CORPORATION HONG KING LIMITED—See Carnival Corporation; *U.S. Public*, pg. 438
CARNIVAL CORPORATION KOREA LTD.—See Carnival Corporation; *U.S. Public*, pg. 438
CATC ALASKA TOURISM CORPORATION—See Viad Corp.; *U.S. Public*, pg. 2291
CELLNEX IRELAND LIMITED—See Cellnex Telecom, S.A.; *Int'l*, pg. 1394
CELLNEX UK LIMITED—See Cellnex Telecom, S.A.; *Int'l*, pg. 1394
CH. CHARILAOU GROUP PLC; *Int'l*, pg. 1435
CHINA DUTY FREE GROUP CORPORATION—See China Tourism Group Duty Free Corporation Limited; *Int'l*, pg. 1560
CHINA INTERNATIONAL TRAVEL SERVICE DALIAN CO., LTD.—See China Tourism Group Duty Free Corporation Limited; *Int'l*, pg. 1560
CHINA INTERNATIONAL TRAVEL SERVICE (QINGDAO) CO., LTD.—See China Tourism Group Duty Free Corporation Limited; *Int'l*, pg. 1560
CHINA TRAVEL INTERNATIONAL INVESTMENT HONG KONG LTD; *Int'l*, pg. 1560
CHINA TRAVEL SERVICE (CANADA) INC.—See China Travel International Investment Hong Kong Ltd; *Int'l*, pg. 1560
CHONGQING CHINA INTERNATIONAL TRAVEL SERVICE CO., LTD.—See China Tourism Group Duty Free Corporation Limited; *Int'l*, pg. 1560
CITS GROUP SHANGHAI CO., LTD.—See China Tourism Group Duty Free Corporation Limited; *Int'l*, pg. 1560
CITY TOURS INC.; *U.S. Private*, pg. 907
CLASSIC JOURNEYS, LLC—See Lindblad Expeditions Holdings, Inc.; *U.S. Public*, pg. 1319
CLASSIC VACATIONS, LLC—See Expedia Group, Inc.; *U.S. Public*, pg. 809
CLUB 7 HOLIDAYS LIMITED—See Centrum Capital Ltd.; *Int'l*, pg. 1415
CLUB MEDITERRANEE HELLAS S.A.—See Fosun International Limited; *Int'l*, pg. 2750
CM.COM DENMARK AS—See CM.com N.V.; *Int'l*, pg. 1666
CM.COM JAPAN KK—See CM.com N.V.; *Int'l*, pg. 1666
COACH USA, INC.—See Variant Equity Advisors, LLC; *U.S. Private*, pg. 4346
COLLETTE TRAVEL SERVICES; *U.S. Private*, pg. 968
CONCEPTS FOR TRAVEL LIMITED—See CPPGroup Plc; *Int'l*, pg. 1826
CONSOLIDATED TOURS INC.; *U.S. Private*, pg. 1022
CONTEXT TRAVEL; *U.S. Private*, pg. 1028

561591 — CONVENTION AND VISI...

COSTA CRUCEROS S.A.—See Carnival Corporation; *U.S. Public*, pg. 438
COX & KINGS GLOBAL SERVICES SWEDEN AB—See Cox & Kings Limited; *Int'l*, pg. 1822
COX & KINGS JAPAN LIMITED—See Cox & Kings Limited; *Int'l*, pg. 1822
COX & KINGS TOURS LLC—See Cox & Kings Limited; *Int'l*, pg. 1822
COX & KINGS (UK) LIMITED—See Cox & Kings Limited; *Int'l*, pg. 1822
COZUMEL CRUISE TERMINAL S.A. DE C.V.—See Carnival Corporation; *U.S. Public*, pg. 438
CP FRANCHISING, LLC.; *U.S. Private*, pg. 1079
CROWN TOURS LIMITED; *Int'l*, pg. 1858
CRUISE PLANET CO., LTD.—See H.I.S. Co., Ltd.; *Int'l*, pg. 3195
CULLINAN HOLDINGS LIMITED; *Int'l*, pg. 1877
CULLINAN NAMIBIA (PTY) LTD—See Cullinan Holdings Limited; *Int'l*, pg. 1877
CVC BRASIL OPERADORA E AGENCIA DE VIAGENS S.A.; *Int'l*, pg. 1881
DADABHAI TRAVEL LLC—See Dadabhai Group; *Int'l*, pg. 1904
DEPOT STARVILLAS SARL—See Cox & Kings Limited; *Int'l*, pg. 1822
DHOFAR TOURISM COMPANY SAOG; *Int'l*, pg. 2100
DIETHELM TRAVEL SRI LANKA—See Hemas Holdings PLC; *Int'l*, pg. 3340
DJOSER B.V.—See Cox & Kings Limited; *Int'l*, pg. 1822
DXN COMFORT TOURS SDN. BHD.—See DXN Holdings Bhd.; *Int'l*, pg. 2237
EASTGATE SAFARIS & TRANSFERS—See Cullinan Holdings Limited; *Int'l*, pg. 1877
EAST INDIA TRAVEL COMPANY, INC.—See Cox & Kings Limited; *Int'l*, pg. 1822
EFES TURIZM ISLETMELERI A.S.—See AG Anadolu Grubu Holding A.S.; *Int'l*, pg. 197
EF INSTITUTE FOR CULTURAL EXCHANGE INC.; *U.S. Private*, pg. 1343
EGENCIA AUSTRALIA PTY. LTD.—See Expedia Group, Inc.; *U.S. Public*, pg. 809
EMEI SHAN TOURISM COMPANY LIMITED; *Int'l*, pg. 2376
ENC DIGITAL TECHNOLOGY CO., LTD.; *Int'l*, pg. 2401
ESCALATUR VIAGENS, LDA.—See Barcelo Corporacion Empresarial S.A.; *Int'l*, pg. 859
EUROPEAN STUDY TOURS LIMITED—See Cox & Kings Limited; *Int'l*, pg. 1822
EUROSITES AS—See Cox & Kings Limited; *Int'l*, pg. 1822
EUROSITES BV—See Cox & Kings Limited; *Int'l*, pg. 1822
EXPLORE WORLDWIDE LIMITED—See Cox & Kings Limited; *Int'l*, pg. 1822
EXPLORICA, INC.—See Eurazeo SE; *Int'l*, pg. 2529
FLAP KONGRE TOPLANTI HIZMETLERI OTOMOTIV VE TURIZM A.S.; *Int'l*, pg. 2698
FRED. OLSEN TRAVEL AS—See Fred. Olsen & Co.; *Int'l*, pg. 2768
FUSION MARKETING—See Silver Lake Group, LLC; *U.S. Private*, pg. 3657
FUSION MARKETING—See William Morris Endeavor Entertainment, LLC; *U.S. Private*, pg. 4523
GABBIT CORP.; *Int'l*, pg. 2867
G ADVENTURES, INC.; *Int'l*, pg. 2861
GENERAL TOURS WORLD TRAVELER, INC.; *U.S. Private*, pg. 1667
GLOBALSTAR ARGENTINA S.R.L.—See Globalstar, Inc.; *U.S. Public*, pg. 946
GRINDROD TRAVEL (PTY) LIMITED—See Grindrod Limited; *Int'l*, pg. 3086
GROUP VOYAGERS, INC.; *U.S. Private*, pg. 1794
GUIZHOU CHINA INTERNATIONAL TRAVEL SERVICE CO., LTD.—See China Tourism Group Duty Free Corporation Limited; *Int'l*, pg. 1560
GULF DUNES LLC—See Fairfax Financial Holdings Limited; *Int'l*, pg. 2608
HAINAN BESTCHAIN INFORMATION SYSTEM CO., LTD.—See Hainan Traffic Administration Holding Co., Ltd.; *Int'l*, pg. 3215
HANATOUR JAPAN CO., LTD.—See Hanatour Service, Inc.; *Int'l*, pg. 3241
HEILONGJIANG CHINA INTERNATIONAL TRAVEL SERVICE LIMITED—See China Tourism Group Duty Free Corporation Limited; *Int'l*, pg. 1560
H.I.S. DEUTSCHLAND TOURISTIK GMBH—See H.I.S. Co., Ltd.; *Int'l*, pg. 3195
H.I.S. EUROPE ITALY S.R.L.—See H.I.S. Co., Ltd.; *Int'l*, pg. 3195
H.I.S. EUROPE LIMITED—See H.I.S. Co., Ltd.; *Int'l*, pg. 3195
HIS (HONG KONG) COMPANY LIMITED—See H.I.S. Co., Ltd.; *Int'l*, pg. 3195
HIS INTERNATIONAL TOURS FRANCE SAS—See H.I.S. Co., Ltd.; *Int'l*, pg. 3195
H.I.S. INTERNATIONAL TRAVEL PTE. LTD.—See H.I.S. Co., Ltd.; *Int'l*, pg. 3195
H.I.S.-RED LABEL VACATIONS INC.—See H.I.S. Co., Ltd.; *Int'l*, pg. 3195
H.I.S. TOURS CO., LTD.—See H.I.S. Co., Ltd.; *Int'l*, pg. 3195
HIS ULUSLARARASI TURIZM SEYAHAT ACENTASI LIMITED SIRKETI—See H.I.S. Co., Ltd.; *Int'l*, pg. 3195
HNA INNOVATION HAINAN CO., LTD.; *Int'l*, pg. 3433
HNA SOUTHERN TOURISM HOLDING GROUP CO., LTD.—See Hainan Traffic Administration Holding Co., Ltd.; *Int'l*, pg. 3213
HOLIDAYBREAK LTD.—See Cox & Kings Limited; *Int'l*, pg. 1822
HOLIDAYBREAK REISEVERMITTLUNG GMBH—See Cox & Kings Limited; *Int'l*, pg. 1822
HOLLAND AMERICA LINE INC.—See Carnival Corporation; *U.S. Public*, pg. 438
HOTELBEDS HONG KONG LIMITED—See Canada Pension Plan Investment Board; *Int'l*, pg. 1279
HOTELBEDS HONG KONG LIMITED—See Cinven Limited; *Int'l*, pg. 1612
HOTELBEDS PTE. LTD.—See Canada Pension Plan Investment Board; *Int'l*, pg. 1279
HOTELBEDS PTE. LTD.—See Cinven Limited; *Int'l*, pg. 1612
HUANGSHAN CHINA INTERNATIONAL TRAVEL SERVICE CO., LTD.—See China Tourism Group Duty Free Corporation Limited; *Int'l*, pg. 1560
HUANGSHAN TOURISM DEVELOPMENT CO., LTD.; *Int'l*, pg. 3513
HUIS TEN BOSCH CO., LTD.—See H.I.S. Co., Ltd.; *Int'l*, pg. 3195
HYLTON ROSS TOURS (PTY) LTD—See Cullinan Holdings Limited; *Int'l*, pg. 1877
HYUNDAI DREAM TOUR CO., LTD.—See Hyundai GF Holdings Co., Ltd.; *Int'l*, pg. 3556
ICONIC WORLDWIDE BHD; *Int'l*, pg. 3586
IDAHO DIVISION OF TOURISM DEVELOPMENT—See Idaho Department of Commerce; *U.S. Private*, pg. 2034
IFA HOTEL & TOURISTIK AG; *Int'l*, pg. 3598
IKAPA COACH CHARTERS—See Cullinan Holdings Limited; *Int'l*, pg. 1877
IKAPA TOURS & TRAVEL (PTY) LTD—See Cullinan Holdings Limited; *Int'l*, pg. 1877
INTERCRUISES SHORESIDE & PORT SERVICES PTY LTD—See Canada Pension Plan Investment Board; *Int'l*, pg. 1279
INTERCRUISES SHORESIDE & PORT SERVICES PTY LTD—See Cinven Limited; *Int'l*, pg. 1612
ISRAM WHOLESALE TOURS & TRAVEL LTD.; *U.S. Private*, pg. 2147
ITAGROUP, INC.-CHICAGO—See ITAGroup, Inc.; *U.S. Private*, pg. 2148
JAPAN HOLIDAY TRAVEL CO., LTD.—See H.I.S. Co., Ltd.; *Int'l*, pg. 3195
JONVIEW CANADA INC.—See H.I.S. Co., Ltd.; *Int'l*, pg. 3195
J-YADO INC.—See Cybozu Inc.; *Int'l*, pg. 1894
KEYCAMP HOLIDAYS NETHERLANDS B.V.—See Cox & Kings Limited; *Int'l*, pg. 1822
KEY HOLIDAYS—See United Rail, Inc.; *U.S. Public*, pg. 2234
KUNMING CHINA INTERNATIONAL TRAVEL SERVICE CO., LTD.—See China Tourism Group Duty Free Corporation Limited; *Int'l*, pg. 1560
KUONI TRAVEL (CHINA) LTD.—See Fairfax Financial Holdings Limited; *Int'l*, pg. 2608
LEITNER TOURISTIK GMBH—See ECM Equity Capital Management GmbH; *Int'l*, pg. 2291
MARINER INTERNATIONAL TRAVEL INC.; *U.S. Private*, pg. 2575
MAUPINTOUR INC.; *U.S. Private*, pg. 2615
MC&A INC.; *U.S. Private*, pg. 2625
MOUNT ROBERTS TRAMWAY, LTD.—See Gold Belt Incorporated; *U.S. Private*, pg. 1727
MUSEUM HACK, LLC; *U.S. Private*, pg. 2817
NST LIMITED—See Cox & Kings Limited; *Int'l*, pg. 1822
NST TRAVEL GROUP LIMITED—See Cox & Kings Limited; *Int'l*, pg. 1822
OBZOR PUTOVANJA D.O.O—See Croatia Airlines d.d.; *Int'l*, pg. 1851
OHSHU EXPRESS LTD.—See H.I.S. Co., Ltd.; *Int'l*, pg. 3195
OLD TOWN TROLLEY TOURS OF SAN DIEGO INC—See Historic Tours of America Inc.; *U.S. Private*, pg. 1952
OLD TOWN TROLLEY TOURS OF SAVANNAH INC.—See Historic Tours of America Inc.; *U.S. Private*, pg. 1952
OMTEL ESTRUCTURAS DE COMUNICACOES S.A.—See Cellnex Telecom, S.A.; *Int'l*, pg. 1394
ORION TOUR CO., LTD.—See H.I.S. Co., Ltd.; *Int'l*, pg. 3196
PANTURIST DIONICKO DRUSTVO ZA PRIJEVOZ PUTNIKA I TURIZAM D.D.—See Deutsche Bahn AG; *Int'l*, pg. 2052
PBP ORBIS SP. Z O.O.—See Accor S.A.; *Int'l*, pg. 92
PGL TRAVEL LIMITED—See Cox & Kings Limited; *Int'l*, pg. 1823
PINK JEEP TOURS, INC.—See Herschend Family Entertainment Corp.; *U.S. Private*, pg. 1926
PLAN ASIA, INC.; *U.S. Private*, pg. 3195
PLEASANT HOLIDAYS LLC; *U.S. Private*, pg. 3213
PRIVATE SAFARIS NAMIBIA (PTY) LTD—See Fairfax Financial Holdings Limited; *Int'l*, pg. 2608
PUERTO RICO TOURISM COMPANY; *U.S. Private*, pg. 3302
RENDEZVOUS TOURS, INC.—See International Management Services Group, Inc.; *U.S. Private*, pg. 2118
THE RETAIL BUS TOUR, INC.; *U.S. Private*, pg. 4105
ROCKY MOUNTAIN TOURS—See Summit Sports, Inc.; *U.S. Private*, pg. 3857
ROYAL CELEBRITY TOURS INC.—See Royal Caribbean Cruises Ltd.; *U.S. Public*, pg. 1815
R&R PARTNERS—See R&R Partners; *U.S. Private*, pg. 3333
SAEFERDIR EHF.—See Eimskipafelag Islands Hf.; *Int'l*, pg. 2332
SILVER STATE COACH, INC.—See Silverado Stages, Inc.; *U.S. Private*, pg. 3662
SILVERTON TRAVEL (PTY) LTD—See Cullinan Holdings Limited; *Int'l*, pg. 1877
SIXTHMAN, LLC; *U.S. Private*, pg. 3678
SMALL WORLD VACATIONS, INC.; *U.S. Private*, pg. 3690
SPRINGBOK ATLAS TOURS & SAFARIS PTY LTD—See Cullinan Holdings Limited; *Int'l*, pg. 1877
SUNLOVER HOLIDAYS PTY LTD—See Helloworld Travel Limited; *Int'l*, pg. 3337
SUNSHINE HELICOPTERS, INC.; *U.S. Private*, pg. 3871
SUNSHINE TOURS—See Abu Dhabi National Hotels PJSC; *Int'l*, pg. 72
SUPERBREAK MINI HOLIDAYS GROUP LTD.—See Cox & Kings Limited; *Int'l*, pg. 1823
SYNERGY TOURS SDN. BHD.—See Advance Synergy Berhad; *Int'l*, pg. 157
SZ-REISEN GMBH—See Bertelsmann SE & Co. KGaA; *Int'l*, pg. 996
TAMARIND TOURS PRIVATE LIMITED—See Crest Ventures Limited; *Int'l*, pg. 1841
TENON TOURS; *U.S. Private*, pg. 3968
THEBE TOURISM GROUP PTY LIMITED—See Futuregrowth Asset Management Pty. Ltd.; *Int'l*, pg. 2858
THOMPSONS GATEWAY (PTE) LTD—See Cullinan Holdings Limited; *Int'l*, pg. 1877
TOURAM LIMITED PARTNERSHIP—See Air Canada; *Int'l*, pg. 236
TOURICO HOLIDAYS, INC.—See Canada Pension Plan Investment Board; *Int'l*, pg. 1279
TOURICO HOLIDAYS, INC.—See Cinven Limited; *Int'l*, pg. 1612
TOURS ON LOCATION INC; *U.S. Private*, pg. 4193
TOUR WAVE CO., LTD.—See H.I.S. Co., Ltd.; *Int'l*, pg. 3196
TRALLIANCE CORPORATION—See theglobe.com, inc.; *U.S. Public*, pg. 2144
TRANS NATIONAL GROUP SERVICES, LLC—See Apple Leisure Group; *U.S. Private*, pg. 297
TRANSPORTATION AND LOGISTICS SYSTEMS, INC.; *U.S. Public*, pg. 2184
TRAVEL IMPRESSIONS, LTD.—See Apple Leisure Group; *U.S. Private*, pg. 297
TRAVELPLUS GROUP GMBH—See Cox & Kings Limited; *Int'l*, pg. 1823
TRAVELTAINMENT POLSKA SP. Z O.O.—See Amadeus IT Group, S.A.; *Int'l*, pg. 407
TUI CRUISES GMBH—See Royal Caribbean Cruises Ltd.; *U.S. Public*, pg. 1815
UAB KRANTAS TRAVEL—See DFDS A/S; *Int'l*, pg. 2095
UVET AMERICAN EXPRESS CORPORATE TRAVEL S.P.A.—See American Express Company; *U.S. Public*, pg. 102
VACASA, INC.; *U.S. Public*, pg. 2270
VEGAS BRAZIL LLC; *U.S. Private*, pg. 4354
VIAJES INTEROPA, S.A—See Barcelo Corporacion Empresarial S.A.; *Int'l*, pg. 859
VILLAGE CHARTERS, INC.; *U.S. Private*, pg. 4383
VILLAGE TOURS, LLC—See Village Charters, Inc.; *U.S. Private*, pg. 4383
VIVIC CORP.; *U.S. Public*, pg. 2307
VOUCHER TRAVEL CLUB LIMITED—See Co-operative Group Limited; *Int'l*, pg. 1679
WELCOME TRAVEL GROUP S.P.A.—See Carnival Corporation; *U.S. Public*, pg. 438
WILLIMENT TRAVEL GROUP LIMITED—See Helloworld Travel Limited; *Int'l*, pg. 3337
WORLD CHOICE LIMITED—See Co-operative Group Limited; *Int'l*, pg. 1679
WORLD CLASS DRIVING; *U.S. Private*, pg. 4565
XIAN CHINA INTERNATIONAL TRAVEL SERVICE CO., LTD.—See China Tourism Group Duty Free Corporation Limited; *Int'l*, pg. 1560
ZAZITKOVA AKADEMIE S.R.O.—See Erlebnis Akademie AG; *Int'l*, pg. 2494
ZHUHAI CHINA INTERNATIONAL TRAVEL SERVICE CO., LTD.—See China Tourism Group Duty Free Corporation Limited; *Int'l*, pg. 1560

561591 — CONVENTION AND VISITORS BUREAUS

ABADGARAN IRAN TOURISM AND WELFARE COMPLEXES (PUBLIC LIMITED COMPANY); *Int'l*, pg. 47

561591 — CONVENTION AND VISI...

ADRIA RESORTS D.O.O.—See Adris Grupa d.d.; *Int'l*, pg. 153
ALABAMA BUREAU OF TOURISM & TRAVEL; *U.S. Private*, pg. 148
ALASKA TRAVEL INDUSTRY ASSOCIATION; *U.S. Private*, pg. 151
CMC PUTEX SP.Z O.O.—See Commercial Metals Company; *U.S. Public*, pg. 545
CRUISE LINES INTERNATIONAL ASSOCIATION; *U.S. Private*, pg. 1114
DALLAS TOURISM PUBLIC IMPROVEMENT DISTRICT; *U.S. Private*, pg. 1150
FERATEL DEVELOPMENT CENTER EOOD—See Feratel Media Technologies AG; *Int'l*, pg. 2635
FLORIDA TOURISM INDUSTRY MARKETING CORPORATION; *U.S. Private*, pg. 1550
GREATER HOUSTON CONVENTION & VISITORS BUREAU—See Houston First Corporation; *U.S. Private*, pg. 1993
GREATER MIAMI CONVENTION & VISITORS BUREAU; *U.S. Private*, pg. 1769
GREATER MINNEAPOLIS CONVENTION & VISITORS ASSOCIATION; *U.S. Private*, pg. 1770
GREATER PITTSBURGH CONVENTION & VISITORS BUREAU; *U.S. Private*, pg. 1770
GREEK NATIONAL TOURIST ORGANIZATION—See Greek National Tourist Organization; *Int'l*, pg. 3069
HOT SPRINGS CONVENTION & VISITORS BUREAU; *U.S. Private*, pg. 1988
HOUSTON FIRST CORPORATION; *U.S. Private*, pg. 1993
HUANGSHAN HUASHAN MYSTERY CAVE TOURISM DEVELOPMENT CO., LTD.—See Huangshan Tourism Development Co., Ltd.; *Int'l*, pg. 3513
LA TOURISM & CONVENTION BOARD; *U.S. Private*, pg. 2370
LEISURE PASS GROUP LIMITED—See Exponent Private Equity LLP; *Int'l*, pg. 2589
MEXICAN GOVERNMENT TOURISM OFFICES; *U.S. Private*, pg. 2692
MEXICO TOURISM BOARD-LOS ANGELES—See Mexican Government Tourism Offices; *U.S. Private*, pg. 2692
NASSAU PARADISE ISLAND PROMOTION BOARD; *U.S. Private*, pg. 2837
NEW ORLEANS METROPOLITAN CONVENTION & VISITORS BUREAU; *U.S. Private*, pg. 2904
SCOTTSDALE CONVENTION & VISITORS BUREAU; *U.S. Private*, pg. 3578
SEATTLE KING COUNTY CONVENTION AND VISITORS BUREAU; *U.S. Private*, pg. 3592
SHANGHAI EVERBRIGHT CONVENTION AND EXHIBITION CENTRE LIMITED—See China Everbright Group Limited; *Int'l*, pg. 1501
SITOUR CESKA REPUBLIKA S.R.O.—See Feratel Media Technologies AG; *Int'l*, pg. 2635
SITOUR JAPAN KK—See Feratel Media Technologies AG; *Int'l*, pg. 2635
TAMPA BAY & CO.; *U.S. Private*, pg. 3928
UTAH OFFICE OF TOURISM; *U.S. Private*, pg. 4324
VISIT INDY, INC.; *U.S. Private*, pg. 4392
VISIT ORLANDO; *U.S. Private*, pg. 4392

561599 — ALL OTHER TRAVEL ARRANGEMENT AND RESERVATION SERVICES

30 SECONDSTOFLY (THAILAND) CO., LTD.—See Global Business Travel Group, Inc.; *U.S. Public*, pg. 940
AAA AUTO CLUB SOUTH—See The American Automobile Association, Inc.; *U.S. Private*, pg. 3985
AAA MID-ATLANTIC INC.—See The American Automobile Association, Inc.; *U.S. Private*, pg. 3985
AAA NORTHERN CALIFORNIA, NEVADA & UTAH—See The American Automobile Association, Inc.; *U.S. Private*, pg. 3985
AAA NORTHWEST OHIO—See The American Automobile Association, Inc.; *U.S. Private*, pg. 3985
ABEC EXHIBITIONS & CONFERENCES PVT. LTD.—See Providence Equity Partners L.L.C.; *U.S. Private*, pg. 3292
ABEC EXHIBITIONS & CONFERENCES PVT. LTD.—See Searchlight Capital Partners, L.P.; *U.S. Private*, pg. 3587
ACCESS DESTINATION SERVICES - CHICAGO—See ACCESS Destination Services; *U.S. Private*, pg. 50
ACCESS DESTINATION SERVICES - LAFAYETTE—See ACCESS Destination Services; *U.S. Private*, pg. 50
ACCESS DESTINATION SERVICES; *U.S. Private*, pg. 50
ACCESS DESTINATION SERVICES—See ACCESS Destination Services; *U.S. Private*, pg. 50
ACCESS DESTINATION SERVICES—See ACCESS Destination Services; *U.S. Private*, pg. 50
ACCESS DESTINATION SERVICES—See ACCESS Destination Services; *U.S. Private*, pg. 50
ACCESS DESTINATION SERVICES—See ACCESS Destination Services; *U.S. Private*, pg. 50
ACCESS DESTINATION SERVICES—See ACCESS Destination Services; *U.S. Private*, pg. 50
ACCESS DESTINATION SERVICES—See ACCESS Destination Services; *U.S. Private*, pg. 50
ACCESS DESTINATION SERVICES—See ACCESS Destination Services; *U.S. Private*, pg. 50
A.C.N. 079 010 772 PTY LTD—See Expedia Group, Inc.; *U.S. Public*, pg. 809
ACP MARKETING US INC.—See ACP Marketing, Inc.; *Int'l*, pg. 108
ADMIRAL TRAVEL INTERNATIONAL, INC.; *U.S. Private*, pg. 81
AENA SME, S.A.—See ENAIRE; *Int'l*, pg. 2396
AERODROMI REPUBLIKE SRPSKE A.D.; *Int'l*, pg. 181
AEROLINK UGANDA LIMITED—See AirKenya Aviation Ltd.; *Int'l*, pg. 247
AIRBNB, INC.; *U.S. Public*, pg. 68
AIR INDIA—See Air India Limited; *Int'l*, pg. 238
AIRNET TECHNOLOGY INC.; *Int'l*, pg. 248
ALDEASA CHILE, LTD.—See Avolta AG; *Int'l*, pg. 749
ALESSANDRO ROSSO INCENTIVE S.R.L.—See Alessandro Rosso Group S.p.A.; *Int'l*, pg. 306
ALLIED FRANCE—See Allied International Ltd.; *Int'l*, pg. 358
ALLIED INTERNATIONAL LTD.; *Int'l*, pg. 357
ALLIEDPRA, INC.—See EagleTree Capital, LP; *U.S. Private*, pg. 1311
ALLIEDPRA MONACO—See Allied International Ltd.; *Int'l*, pg. 358
ALLIED SPAIN—See Allied International Ltd.; *Int'l*, pg. 358
ALLIED UK—See Allied International Ltd.; *Int'l*, pg. 358
AMERICAN AIRLINES CARGO—See American Airlines Group Inc.; *U.S. Public*, pg. 95
AMERICAN EXPRESS COMPANY (MEXICO) S.A. DE C.V.—See American Express Company; *U.S. Public*, pg. 101
AMERICAN EXPRESS CORPORATE TRAVEL BVBA—See Global Business Travel Group, Inc.; *U.S. Public*, pg. 941
AMERICAN EXPRESS HOLDING AB—See American Express Company; *U.S. Public*, pg. 101
AMERICAN EXPRESS HUNGARY KFT—See American Express Company; *U.S. Public*, pg. 101
AMERICAN EXPRESS LOCAZIONI FINANZIARIE S.R.L.—See American Express Company; *U.S. Public*, pg. 101
AMERICAN EXPRESS NIPPON TRAVEL AGENCY, INC.—See American Express Company; *U.S. Public*, pg. 100
AMERICAN EXPRESS POLAND SP Z O O—See American Express Company; *U.S. Public*, pg. 101
AMERICAN EXPRESS REISEBURO GMBH—See American Express Company; *U.S. Public*, pg. 101
AMERICAN EXPRESS SERVICES EUROPE LIMITED—See American Express Company; *U.S. Public*, pg. 101
AMERICAN EXPRESS TRAVEL RELATED SERVICES COMPANY, INC.—See American Express Company; *U.S. Public*, pg. 101
AMERICAN EXPRESS VOYAGES SAS—See American Express Company; *U.S. Public*, pg. 101
ANA SALES CO., LTD.—See ANA Holdings Inc.; *Int'l*, pg. 444
APPMIRA B.V.BA.—See CM.com N.V.; *Int'l*, pg. 1666
THE APPOINTMENT GROUP (UK) LIMITED—See ECI Partners LLP; *Int'l*, pg. 2289
AQUA LUANA OPERATOR LLC—See Marriott Vacations Worldwide Corporation; *U.S. Public*, pg. 1373
ARENA MANAGEMENT GMBH—See CTS Eventim AG & Co. KGAA; *Int'l*, pg. 1872
ARGO KONZERTE GMBH—See CTS Eventim AG & Co. KGAA; *Int'l*, pg. 1872
ARMA SERVICES, INC.; *U.S. Public*, pg. 193
ASIA TRAVEL NETWORK LTD—See Asiatravel.com Holdings Limited; *Int'l*, pg. 620
ASIATRAVEL ONLINE SDN BHD—See Asiatravel.com Holdings Limited; *Int'l*, pg. 620
ASIA WEB DIRECT CO., LTD.—See Expedia Group, Inc.; *U.S. Public*, pg. 809
ASIA WEB DIRECT (HK) LIMITED—See Expedia Group, Inc.; *U.S. Public*, pg. 809
AT EXPRESS PTE. LTD.—See Asiatravel.com Holdings Limited; *Int'l*, pg. 620
AT RESERVATION PTE LTD—See Asiatravel.com Holdings Limited; *Int'l*, pg. 620
AUSTRALIAN ONLINE TRAVEL PTY. LTD.—See Helloworld Travel Limited; *Int'l*, pg. 3337
AUSTRALIAN OPCO PTY. LTD.—See Flight Centre Travel Group Limited; *Int'l*, pg. 2706
AUTO ESCAPE GROUP—See Expedia Group, Inc.; *U.S. Public*, pg. 809
AUTO EUROPE, LLC; *U.S. Private*, pg. 397
THE AUTOMOBILE ASSOCIATION LIMITED—See Charterhouse Capital Partners LLP; *Int'l*, pg. 1455
THE AUTOMOBILE ASSOCIATION LIMITED—See CVC Capital Partners SICAV-FIS S.A.; *Int'l*, pg. 1882
BERJAYA AIR SDN BHD—See Berjaya Corporation Berhad; *Int'l*, pg. 982
BEST OF 52 LLC—See INSPIRATO INCORPORATED; *U.S. Public*, pg. 1131
BEST WESTERN INTERNATIONAL, INC.; *U.S. Private*, pg. 544
BILESU PARADIZE SIA—See AS Ekspress Grupp; *Int'l*, pg. 589
BOOKING.COM BRASIL SERVICOS DE RESERVA DE HOTEIS LTDA—See Booking Holdings, Inc.; *U.S. Public*, pg. 368
BOOKING HOLDINGS, INC.; *U.S. Public*, pg. 368
BOOKIT B.V.—See Cox & Kings Limited; *Int'l*, pg. 1822
BRAVOFLY RUMBO GROUP N.V.; *Int'l*, pg. 1142
BRINKER LOUISIANA, INC.—See Brinker International, Inc.; *U.S. Public*, pg. 384
BRIT AIR—See Air France-KLM S.A.; *Int'l*, pg. 237
BRITT SHOP—See Grupo Britt N.V.; *Int'l*, pg. 3123
BROWN PAPER TICKETS LLC—See Events.com, Inc.; *U.S. Private*, pg. 1437
BUSINESS RESERVATIONS CENTRE HOLLAND B.V.—See Cox & Kings Limited; *Int'l*, pg. 1822
B.V. WEEKENDJEWEG.NL—See Cox & Kings Limited; *Int'l*, pg. 1822
CAESARS HOLIDAYS—See Caesars Group; *Int'l*, pg. 1249
CAESARS TRAVEL COMPANY—See Caesars Group; *Int'l*, pg. 1249
CAR DEL MAR FERIENAUTOVERMIETUNG GMBH—See Expedia Group, Inc.; *U.S. Public*, pg. 809
CARLSON WAGONLIT TRAVEL, INC.—See Carlson Companies Inc.; *U.S. Private*, pg. 765
CARREFOUR VOYAGES SAS—See Carrefour SA; *Int'l*, pg. 1345
CASTO TRAVEL US, LLC—See Flight Centre Travel Group Limited; *Int'l*, pg. 2706
CATHAY PACIFIC AIRWAYS LIMITED; *Int'l*, pg. 1360
CEO TOURISM JOINT STOCK COMPANY—See C.E.O Group Joint Stock Company; *Int'l*, pg. 1240
CEYBANK HOLIDAY HOMES (PVT) LTD—See Bank of Ceylon; *Int'l*, pg. 840
CHARTWELL TRAVEL LTD.—See Global Business Travel Group, Inc.; *U.S. Public*, pg. 940
CHEAPCARIBBEAN.COM, INC.—See Apple Leisure Group; *U.S. Private*, pg. 296
CHILI'S OF MARYLAND, INC.—See Brinker International, Inc.; *U.S. Public*, pg. 384
CHINA PALACE INTERNATIONAL TRAVEL SERVICE—See China Rare Earth Resources And Technology Co., Ltd.; *Int'l*, pg. 1545
CHOICE HOTELS ASIA-PAC PTY. LTD.—See Choice Hotels International, Inc.; *U.S. Public*, pg. 489
CHRISTIE & CO S.A.S.—See Christie Group plc; *Int'l*, pg. 1586
CITY JET LTD—See Air France-KLM S.A.; *Int'l*, pg. 237
CLC GROUP, INC.—See Corpay, Inc.; *U.S. Public*, pg. 579
CLUB MED BRASIL SA—See Fosun International Limited; *Int'l*, pg. 2750
CLUB MED FERIAS—See Fosun International Limited; *Int'l*, pg. 2750
CLUB MEDITERRANEE HOLLAND BV—See Fosun International Limited; *Int'l*, pg. 2750
CLUB MEDITERRANEE HONG KONG LTD—See Fosun International Limited; *Int'l*, pg. 2750
CLUB MEDITERRANEE SERVICES INDIA PRIVATE LTD—See Fosun International Limited; *Int'l*, pg. 2750
CLUB MEDITERRANEE SUISSE—See Fosun International Limited; *Int'l*, pg. 2750
CLUB MED MANAGEMENT SERVICES INC—See Fosun International Limited; *Int'l*, pg. 2750
CLUB MED SALES CANADA INC—See Fosun International Limited; *Int'l*, pg. 2750
CLUB MED VACANCES (TAIWAN) LTD—See Fosun International Limited; *Int'l*, pg. 2750
CLUB MED VIAGENS UNIPESSOAL, LDA—See Fosun International Limited; *Int'l*, pg. 2750
CLUB MED VILLAS ET CHALETS HOLDING—See Fosun International Limited; *Int'l*, pg. 2750
CLUB MED VILLAS ET CHALETS—See Fosun International Limited; *Int'l*, pg. 2750
CNG TRAVEL GROUP PLC; *Int'l*, pg. 1673
COGNIUS, INC.; *U.S. Private*, pg. 962
CONSUMER CLUB INC.—See Booking Holdings, Inc.; *U.S. Public*, pg. 368
CORPORATE TRAVEL MANAGEMENT LIMITED; *Int'l*, pg. 1805
COX & KINGS LIMITED; *Int'l*, pg. 1822
CREA INFORMATICA S.R.L.—See CTS Eventim AG & Co. KGAA; *Int'l*, pg. 1874
CREATIVE LODGING SOLUTIONS, LLC—See Corpay, Inc.; *U.S. Public*, pg. 579
CRUISE NOW INC.—See 3i Group plc; *Int'l*, pg. 8
CRUISEONE AND CRUISES INC.—See World Travel Holdings, Inc.; *U.S. Private*, pg. 4567
CSC TRAVEL GROUP INC.—See Expedia Group, Inc.; *U.S. Public*, pg. 809
CTS EVENTIM AUSTRIA GMBH—See CTS Eventim AG & Co. KGAA; *Int'l*, pg. 1872
CTS EVENTIM NEDERLAND B.V.—See CTS Eventim AG & Co. KGAA; *Int'l*, pg. 1872
CWT FRANCE—See Carlson Companies Inc.; *U.S. Private*, pg. 765
CYGNIFIC B.V.—See Air France-KLM S.A.; *Int'l*, pg. 237
DENSO COMMUNICATIONS CORPORATION—See Denso Corporation; *Int'l*, pg. 2029
DENSO YUSEN TRAVEL CORPORATION—See Denso Corporation; *Int'l*, pg. 2031
DESPEGAR.COM, CORP.; *Int'l*, pg. 2046

N.A.I.C.S. INDEX
561599 — ALL OTHER TRAVEL AR...

DI & GI S.R.L.—See CTS Eventim AG & Co. KGAA; *Int'l*, pg. 1872
DUFRY FRANCE SA—See Avolta AG; *Int'l*, pg. 749
EASEMYTRIP THAI CO., LTD.—See Easy Trip Planners Limited; *Int'l*, pg. 2276
EHOTEL AG; *Int'l*, pg. 2328
ENCORE TICKETS LTD.—See Great Hill Partners, L.P.; *U.S. Private*, pg. 1763
ENERGETYKA POZNANSKA ZAKLAD OBSLUGI SOCJALNEJ ENERGO-TOUR SP. Z O.O.—See ENEA S.A.; *Int'l*, pg. 2410
ENTERTAINMENT BENEFITS GROUP, LLC; *U.S. Private*, pg. 1404
ENTRADAS EVENTIM S.A.—See CTS Eventim AG & Co. KGAA; *Int'l*, pg. 1872
E-TABLE ONLINE RESTAURANT RESERVATION SERVICES SINGLE MEMBER P.C.—See Delivery Hero SE; *Int'l*, pg. 2013
EUROWINGS GMBH—See Deutsche Lufthansa AG; *Int'l*, pg. 2066
EVENTIM BG O.O.D.—See CTS Eventim AG & Co. KGAA; *Int'l*, pg. 1872
EVENTIM D.O.O.—See CTS Eventim AG & Co. KGAA; *Int'l*, pg. 1873
EVENTIM NORGE AS—See CTS Eventim AG & Co. KGAA; *Int'l*, pg. 1872
EVENTIM RU S.R.L.—See CTS Eventim AG & Co. KGAA; *Int'l*, pg. 1873
EVENTIM SI D.O.O.—See CTS Eventim AG & Co. KGAA; *Int'l*, pg. 1872
EVENTIM SK, S.R.O.—See CTS Eventim AG & Co. KGAA; *Int'l*, pg. 1872
EVENTIM SVERIGE AB—See CTS Eventim AG & Co. KGAA; *Int'l*, pg. 1872
EVENTIM UK LIMITED—See CTS Eventim AG & Co. KGAA; *Int'l*, pg. 1872
EXECUTIVE BUSINESS CENTERS; *U.S. Private*, pg. 1447
EXECUTIVE TRAVEL ASSOCIATES LLC—See Global Business Travel Group, Inc.; *U.S. Public*, pg. 941
EXPEDIA LODGING PARTNER SERVICES SARL—See Expedia Group, Inc.; *U.S. Public*, pg. 809
EXPEDIA US, INC.—See Expedia Group, Inc.; *U.S. Public*, pg. 809
FASTTRACK S.A.—See AUTOHELLAS S.A.; *Int'l*, pg. 727
FC BAYERN TOURS GMBH—See Global Business Travel Group, Inc.; *U.S. Public*, pg. 940
FCM TRAVEL SOLUTIONS (INDIA) PRIVATE LIMITED—See Flight Centre Travel Group Limited; *Int'l*, pg. 2706
FCM TRAVEL SOLUTIONS (L.L.C)—See Flight Centre Travel Group Limited; *Int'l*, pg. 2706
FCM TRAVEL SOLUTIONS SINGAPORE PTE. LTD.—See Flight Centre Travel Group Limited; *Int'l*, pg. 2706
FCM TRAVEL SOLUTIONS USA—See Flight Centre Travel Group Limited; *Int'l*, pg. 2706
FIFA TICKETING AG—See Federation Internationale de Football Association; *Int'l*, pg. 2631
FIRST CLASS & MORE FZE—See Asmallworld AG; *Int'l*, pg. 627
FIRST CLASS & MORE INTERNATIONAL AG—See Asmallworld AG; *Int'l*, pg. 627
FIRST GREATER WESTERN LIMITED—See FirstGroup plc; *Int'l*, pg. 2689
FLIGHT CENTRE TECHNOLOGY PTY. LTD.—See Flight Centre Travel Group Limited; *Int'l*, pg. 2706
FLIGHT DELAY SERVICES LIMITED—See Deutsche Bahn AG; *Int'l*, pg. 2051
FORBES TRAVEL INTERNATIONAL LTD.; *Int'l*, pg. 2729
FORTUNE VACATION TRAVEL LTD.; *Int'l*, pg. 2744
FRIEDRICHSBAU VARIETE BETRIEBS- UND VERWALTUNGS GMBH—See DEAG Deutsche Entertainment AG; *Int'l*, pg. 1998
FROSCH INTERNATIONAL TRAVEL INC.; *U.S. Private*, pg. 1616
FUNJET VACATIONS INC.—See Apple Leisure Group; *U.S. Private*, pg. 296
G7 TAXI SERVICE—See G7 Entreprises; *Int'l*, pg. 2867
GBT CR, S.R.O.—See Global Business Travel Group, Inc.; *U.S. Public*, pg. 941
GBT INDIA PRIVATE LIMITED—See Global Business Travel Group, Inc.; *U.S. Public*, pg. 941
GBT TRAVEL SERVICES UK LTD.—See Global Business Travel Group, Inc.; *U.S. Public*, pg. 941
GD ASSIST LTD.—See Green Delta Insurance Company Limited; *Int'l*, pg. 3070
GERMAN VALUES PROPERTY GROUP AG; *Int'l*, pg. 2943
GET-A-TICKET B.V.—See CM.com N.V.; *Int'l*, pg. 1666
GLOBAL ADRENALINE INC.—See The Walt Disney Company; *U.S. Public*, pg. 2140
GLOBAL BUSINESS TRAVEL GROUP, INC.; *U.S. Public*, pg. 940
GLOBALINK, LTD.; *Int'l*, pg. 3004
GLOBAL TELE SALES BRNO S.R.O.—See Deutsche Lufthansa AG; *Int'l*, pg. 2069
GLOBAL TELESALES OF CANADA, INC.—See Deutsche Lufthansa AG; *Int'l*, pg. 2069
GOWAII VACATION HOLDING S.L.; *Int'l*, pg. 3044
GRAND INCENTIVES, INC.; *U.S. Private*, pg. 1753

GREENBANK HOLIDAYS LIMITED—See The Carlyle Group Inc.; *U.S. Public*, pg. 2047
GUARDIAN TRAVEL, INC.—See Assurant, Inc.; *U.S. Public*, pg. 215
HANSHIN ELECTRIC RAILWAY CO., LTD.—See Hankyu Hanshin Holdings Inc.; *Int'l*, pg. 3255
HAWAIIAN BEACH RENTALS—See RealVoice LLC; *U.S. Private*, pg. 3369
HAYLEYS TRAVELS (PVT) LTD.—See Hayleys PLC; *Int'l*, pg. 3292
HEMAS AIR SERVICES (PTE) LTD—See Hemas Holdings PLC; *Int'l*, pg. 3340
HEMAS AIR SERVICES (PVT.) LTD.—See Hemas Holdings PLC; *Int'l*, pg. 3340
HILTON GRAND VACATIONS COMPANY, LLC—See Hilton Grand Vacations Inc.; *U.S. Public*, pg. 1040
HILTON RESERVATIONS & CUSTOMER CARE—See Hilton Worldwide Holdings Inc.; *U.S. Public*, pg. 1041
HILTON RESERVATIONS WORLDWIDE LLC—See Hilton Worldwide Holdings Inc.; *U.S. Public*, pg. 1041
H.I.S. CO., LTD.; *Int'l*, pg. 3195
HOFFMAN VACATION RENTALS LLC; *U.S. Private*, pg. 1960
HOGG ROBINSON GROUP POLAND—See Global Business Travel Group, Inc.; *U.S. Public*, pg. 941
HOGG ROBINSON NORDIC AB—See Global Business Travel Group, Inc.; *U.S. Public*, pg. 941
HOGG ROBINSON NORDIC OY—See Global Business Travel Group, Inc.; *U.S. Public*, pg. 941
HOGG ROBINSON (TRAVEL) LIMITED—See Global Business Travel Group, Inc.; *U.S. Public*, pg. 941
HOLIDAY LETTINGS LIMITED—See TripAdvisor, Inc.; *U.S. Public*, pg. 2195
HOLIDAY VILLAGE OF SANDPIPER INC.—See Fosun International Limited; *Int'l*, pg. 2750
HOMEAWAY, INC.—See Expedia Group, Inc.; *U.S. Public*, pg. 809
HOME & TRAVEL LIMITED—See Arthur J. Gallagher & Co.; *U.S. Public*, pg. 206
HOTELBEDS SPAIN, S.L.U.—See Canada Pension Plan Investment Board; *Int'l*, pg. 1279
HOTELBEDS SPAIN, S.L.U.—See Cinven Limited; *Int'l*, pg. 1612
HOTELES CANCUN K20, S. DE R.L. DE C.V.—See Marriott Vacations Worldwide Corporation; *U.S. Public*, pg. 1373
HOTELS.COM, L.P.—See Expedia Group, Inc.; *U.S. Public*, pg. 809
HRG BELGIUM NV—See Global Business Travel Group, Inc.; *U.S. Public*, pg. 941
I GRANDI VIAGGI S.P.A.; *Int'l*, pg. 3561
ILG, LLC—See Marriott Vacations Worldwide Corporation; *U.S. Public*, pg. 1373
INTERNATIONAL RESERVATIONS LIMITED—See Hyatt Hotels Corporation; *U.S. Public*, pg. 1078
ISLANDIAN SARL—See ENL Limited; *Int'l*, pg. 2442
JETTICKET SOFTWARE GMBH—See CTS Eventim AG & Co. KGAA; *Int'l*, pg. 1873
JUST ARRIVE, LLC—See Weldon, Williams & Lick, Inc.; *U.S. Private*, pg. 4474
KAI MANAGEMENT SERVICES, LLC—See Marriott Vacations Worldwide Corporation; *U.S. Public*, pg. 1373
KARTENHAUS TICKETSERVICE GMBH—See Live Nation Entertainment, Inc.; *U.S. Public*, pg. 1331
KAYAK SOFTWARE CORPORATION—See Booking Holdings, Inc.; *U.S. Public*, pg. 368
KEITH PROWSE LIMITED—See Compass Group PLC; *Int'l*, pg. 1752
KINOHELD GMBH—See CTS Eventim AG & Co. KGAA; *Int'l*, pg. 1873
KNOWLAND GROUP INC.; *U.S. Private*, pg. 2323
LA FOURCHETTE SAS—See TripAdvisor, Inc.; *U.S. Public*, pg. 2195
LAFOURCHETTE SWEDEN AB—See TripAdvisor, Inc.; *U.S. Public*, pg. 2195
LASTMINUTE.COM.AU PTY. LIMITED—See Expedia Group, Inc.; *U.S. Public*, pg. 810
LEISURELINK INC.—See VacationRoost Group Inc.; *U.S. Private*, pg. 4329
LEXYL TRAVEL TECHNOLOGIES LLC; *U.S. Private*, pg. 2441
LIPPUPISTE OY—See CTS Eventim AG & Co. KGAA; *Int'l*, pg. 1873
LODGE OF FOUR SEASONS; *U.S. Private*, pg. 2479
LODGING PARTNER SERVICES DENMARK APS—See Expedia Group, Inc.; *U.S. Public*, pg. 809
LOLA TRAVEL CO., INC.; *U.S. Private*, pg. 2483
LUFTHANSA SYSTEMS PASSENGER SERVICES GMBH—See Deutsche Lufthansa AG; *Int'l*, pg. 2069
MAGGIANO'S BEVERAGE COMPANY—See Brinker International, Inc.; *U.S. Public*, pg. 384
MANITOBA MOTOR LEAGUE—See CAA Club Group; *Int'l*, pg. 1245
MAUI ELDORADO KAANAPALI BY OUTRIGGER—See KSL Capital Partners, LLC; *U.S. Private*, pg. 2355
MAUI LEONES LLC; *U.S. Private*, pg. 2614
MAUI RESORT RENTALS INC.; *U.S. Private*, pg. 2614
MEETINGS & INCENTIVES; *U.S. Private*, pg. 2660

MILEAGE PLUS, INC.—See United Airlines Holdings, Inc.; *U.S. Public*, pg. 2229
MOVIETICKETS.CO.UK, LTD.—See Comcast Corporation; *U.S. Public*, pg. 540
MYTABLE SRL—See TripAdvisor, Inc.; *U.S. Public*, pg. 2195
NATIONAL AUTOMOBILE CLUB, INC.; *U.S. Private*, pg. 2847
NAUTALIA VIAJES, S.L.—See Gowaii Vacation Holding S.L.; *Int'l*, pg. 3044
NURSESRX—See AMN Healthcare Services, Inc.; *U.S. Public*, pg. 125
OMNI AIR INTERNATIONAL, LLC—See Air Transport Services Group, Inc.; *U.S. Public*, pg. 68
ONE SMOOTH STONE, INC.—See EagleTree Capital, LP; *U.S. Private*, pg. 1311
OPODO LIMITED—See Ardian SAS; *Int'l*, pg. 556
OTS GESELLSCHAFT ZUM VERTRIEB ELEKTRONISCHER EINTRITTSKARTEN MBH—See CTS Eventim AG & Co. KGAA; *Int'l*, pg. 1873
OY EBOOKERS FINLAND LTD—See Expedia Group, Inc.; *U.S. Public*, pg. 809
PARADISE VACATION ADVENTURES, LLC—See Marriott Vacations Worldwide Corporation; *U.S. Public*, pg. 1374
PETER RIEGER KONZERTAGENTUR GMBH & CO. KG—See CTS Eventim AG & Co. KGAA; *Int'l*, pg. 1873
PETER RIEGER KONZERTAGENTUR HOLDING GMBH—See CTS Eventim AG & Co. KGAA; *Int'l*, pg. 1873
PETER RIEGER VERWALTUNGS GMBH—See CTS Eventim AG & Co. KGAA; *Int'l*, pg. 1873
PHOCUSWRIGHT INC.—See EagleTree Capital, LP; *U.S. Private*, pg. 1312
PLASTER CASTER, INC.; *U.S. Private*, pg. 3198
P&O CRUISES LIMITED—See Carnival Corporation; *U.S. Public*, pg. 438
POINTS OF COLORADO, INC.—See Marriott Vacations Worldwide Corporation; *U.S. Public*, pg. 1374
POLAR CRUISES; *U.S. Private*, pg. 3223
PREMIUM DESTINATIONS, INC.; *U.S. Private*, pg. 3251
PUCKRUP HALL HOTEL LIMITED—See Hilton Worldwide Holdings Inc.; *U.S. Public*, pg. 1041
QUNAR CAYMAN ISLANDS LIMITED—See Baidu, Inc.; *Int'l*, pg. 801
RADIXX SOLUTIONS INTERNATIONAL, INC.—See Sabre Corporation; *U.S. Public*, pg. 1833
RAILREST S.A.—See Cremonini S.p.A.; *Int'l*, pg. 1838
RAKYAT TRAVEL SDN BHD—See Bank Kerjasama Rakyat Malaysia Berhad; *Int'l*, pg. 838
RAZORGATOR, INC.; *U.S. Private*, pg. 3360
RCL (UK) LTD.—See Royal Caribbean Cruises Ltd.; *U.S. Public*, pg. 1815
REEDEREI HIDDENSEE GMBH—See FRS GmbH & Co. KG; *Int'l*, pg. 2797
REGAL WINGS, INC.; *U.S. Private*, pg. 3386
REGIONAL AIR SERVICES—See AirKenya Aviation Ltd.; *Int'l*, pg. 248
REGIONAL COMPAGNIE AERIENNE EUROPEENNE—See Air France-KLM S.A.; *Int'l*, pg. 238
RESERVEAMERICA INC.—See IAC Inc.; *U.S. Public*, pg. 1082
RESY NETWORK, INC.—See American Express Company; *U.S. Private*, pg. 101
ROBERT'S TOURS & TRANSPORTATION INC.—See Robert's Hawaii Inc.; *U.S. Private*, pg. 3459
ROMO-SYLT LINIE GMBH & CO. KG—See FRS GmbH & Co. KG; *Int'l*, pg. 2797
ROYAL SEA CLIFF KONA BY OUTRIGGER—See KSL Capital Partners, LLC; *U.S. Private*, pg. 2355
SABRE TRAVEL NETWORK—See Sabre Corporation; *U.S. Public*, pg. 1833
SARA ENTERPRISES—See Corporate Travel Management Limited; *Int'l*, pg. 1806
SCEPTRE HOSPITALITY RESOURCES; *U.S. Private*, pg. 3562
SCHOLASTIC BOOK FAIRS, LTD.—See Scholastic Corporation; *U.S. Public*, pg. 1847
SCOREBIG.COM—See TicketNetwork, Inc.; *U.S. Private*, pg. 4167
SDI TRAVEL & INCENTIVES—See SmithBucklin Corporation; *U.S. Private*, pg. 3697
SEATWAVE NEDERLAND B.V.—See Live Nation Entertainment, Inc.; *U.S. Public*, pg. 1330
SEI MEETINGS AND INCENTIVES; *U.S. Private*, pg. 3599
SEMMEL CONCERTS ENTERTAINMENT GMBH—See CTS Eventim AG & Co. KGAA; *Int'l*, pg. 1873
SITEMINDER LIMITED—See Bailador Technology Investments Limited; *Int'l*, pg. 802
SKYLINK TRAVEL; *U.S. Private*, pg. 3686
SKYRUN BRECKENRIDGE, LLC; *U.S. Private*, pg. 3686
SKYWEST INC.; *U.S. Public*, pg. 1893
SMART DESTINATIONS, INC.; *U.S. Private*, pg. 3691
SMARTER TRAVEL MEDIA LLC—See Cognius, Inc.; *U.S. Private*, pg. 962
SPECIAL OPERATIONS GROUP INC.; *U.S. Private*, pg. 3748
STARGARAGE AG—See CTS Eventim AG & Co. KGAA; *Int'l*, pg. 1873
STAR TRAVEL SERVICES, INC.—See Cook Group Incor-

561599 — ALL OTHER TRAVEL AR...

porated; *U.S. Private*, pg. 1038
STERLING HOLIDAY RESORTS (INDIA) LIMITED—See Fairfax Financial Holdings Limited; *Int'l*, pg. 2608
STERLING VALLEY SYSTEMS, INC.—See EagleTree Capital, LP; *U.S. Private*, pg. 1312
STRATEJIC SOLUTIONS S.A. DE C.V.—See Maritz Holdings Inc.; *U.S. Private*, pg. 2577
SUNDANCE VACATIONS; *U.S. Private*, pg. 3866
SUPERBREAK MINI-HOLIDAYS LIMITED—See Cox & Kings Limited; *Int'l*, pg. 1823
SURF AIR INC.—See Surf Air Mobility Inc.; *U.S. Public*, pg. 1967
SYNDICATED RESORTS ASSOCIATION, INC.; *U.S. Private*, pg. 3903
SYSTEM TECHNIK GMBH—See Cabka N.V.; *Int'l*, pg. 1246
TABLET, INC.—See Compagnie Generale des Etablissements Michelin SCA; *Int'l*, pg. 1745
TEMPORARY ACCOMMODATIONS, INC.—See The Carlyle Group Inc.; *U.S. Private*, pg. 2054
TEX HUNGARY KFT.—See CTS Eventim AG & Co. KGAA; *Int'l*, pg. 1873
THAI TICKET MAJOR CO., LTD.—See BEC World Public Company Limited; *Int'l*, pg. 936
THOMAS COOK (INDIA) LIMITED—See Fairfax Financial Holdings Limited; *Int'l*, pg. 2608
THE TICKET EXPERIENCE, LLC; *U.S. Private*, pg. 4127
TICKETFORCE, LLC—See Intelli-Mark Technologies, Inc.; *U.S. Private*, pg. 2105
TICKETLEAP INC.; *U.S. Private*, pg. 4167
TICKETMASTER CANADA LTD.—See Live Nation Entertainment, Inc.; *U.S. Public*, pg. 1331
TICKETMASTER ISRAEL LTD—See Live Nation Entertainment, Inc.; *U.S. Public*, pg. 1331
TICKETMASTER LLC—See Live Nation Entertainment, Inc.; *U.S. Public*, pg. 1331
TICKETMASTER SCHWEIZ AG—See Live Nation Entertainment, Inc.; *U.S. Public*, pg. 1331
TICKETMASTER-SINGAPORE PTE. LTD.—See Live Nation Entertainment, Inc.; *U.S. Public*, pg. 1331
TICKETNETWORK, INC.; *U.S. Private*, pg. 4167
TICKETPRO POLSKA SP ZOO—See Live Nation Entertainment, Inc.; *U.S. Public*, pg. 1331
TICKETS.COM, INC.—See Major League Baseball; *U.S. Private*, pg. 2555
TICKETSNOW.COM, INC.—See Live Nation Entertainment, Inc.; *U.S. Public*, pg. 1331
TICKETS & TOURS—See Entertainment Benefits Group, LLC; *U.S. Private*, pg. 1404
TICKETWEB LLC—See Live Nation Entertainment, Inc.; *U.S. Public*, pg. 1331
TIMESHARE RELIEF, INC.; *U.S. Private*, pg. 4173
TIMESHARES BY OWNER; *U.S. Private*, pg. 4173
T.O.S.C. - TICKETONE SISTEMI CULTURALI S.R.L.—See CTS Eventim AG & Co. KGAA; *Int'l*, pg. 1874
TOUR-HOUSE VERANSTALTUNGS-, KONZERT-, TV- UND MEDIA-CONSULTING GMBH—See CTS Eventim AG & Co. KGAA; *Int'l*, pg. 1874
TOURIST BUREAU MARKETING, INC.—See Travel & Leisure Co.; *U.S. Public*, pg. 2185
THE TRAFFIC MARSHAL PTY LTD.—See AVADA Group Limited; *Int'l*, pg. 734
TRAINLINE PLC—See Exponent Private Equity LLP; *Int'l*, pg. 2590
TRAVCO HOTELS LIMITED—See Co-operative Group Limited; *Int'l*, pg. 1679
TRAVELBOARD GMBH—See Bayer Aktiengesellschaft; *Int'l*, pg. 910
TRAVEL-BY-NET, INC.—See Cappy Devlin International; *U.S. Private*, pg. 745
TRAVEL HOLDINGS, INC.; *U.S. Private*, pg. 4213
THE TRAVEL NETWORK—See Travel Network Vacation Central; *U.S. Private*, pg. 4213
TRAVEL NETWORK VACATION CENTRAL; *U.S. Private*, pg. 4213
TRAVELPORT GDS—See Elliott Management Corporation; *U.S. Private*, pg. 1373
TRAVELPORT GDS—See Siris Capital Group, LLC; *U.S. Private*, pg. 3674
TRAVELPORT INC.—See Elliott Management Corporation; *U.S. Private*, pg. 1373
TRAVELPORT INC.—See Siris Capital Group, LLC; *U.S. Private*, pg. 3674
TRAVELPORT WORLDWIDE LIMITED—See Elliott Management Corporation; *U.S. Private*, pg. 1373
TRAVELPORT WORLDWIDE LIMITED—See Siris Capital Group, LLC; *U.S. Private*, pg. 3674
TRAVEL & RECREATION GROUP—See Viad Corp.; *U.S. Public*, pg. 2291
TRAVELTAINMENT UK LTD.—See Amadeus IT Group, S.A.; *Int'l*, pg. 407
TRAVELZOO (EUROPE) LIMITED—See Travelzoo; *U.S. Public*, pg. 2186
TRIP NETWORK, INC.—See Expedia Group, Inc.; *U.S. Public*, pg. 809
TRIVAGO SPAIN, S.L.—See Expedia Group, Inc.; *U.S. Public*, pg. 810
TZELL TRAVEL GROUP—See Travel Leaders Group, LLC; *U.S. Private*, pg. 4213

VACANCES (PTY) LTD—See Fosun International Limited; *Int'l*, pg. 2750
VADDI CONCERTS GMBH—See CTS Eventim AG & Co. KGAA; *Int'l*, pg. 1874
VEGAS.COM, LLC—See Vivid Seats, Inc.; *U.S. Public*, pg. 2307
VIA EGENCIA AS—See Expedia Group, Inc.; *U.S. Public*, pg. 810
VIA EGENCIA DENMARK A/S—See Expedia Group, Inc.; *U.S. Public*, pg. 810
VIVID SEATS, INC.; *U.S. Public*, pg. 2307
VRX STUDIOS INC.—See Symphony Technology Group, LLC; *U.S. Private*, pg. 3902
WEBJET MARKETING NORTH AMERICA LLC; *U.S. Private*, pg. 4466
WEST END THEATRE BOOKINGS LIMITED—See Great Hill Partners, L.P.; *U.S. Private*, pg. 1763
WESTMINSTER TRAVEL LIMITED—See Corporate Travel Management Limited; *Int'l*, pg. 1806
WORLD DUTY FREE GROUP GERMANY GMBH—See Avolta AG; *Int'l*, pg. 749
WOTIF.COM (NZ) LTD.—See Expedia Group, Inc.; *U.S. Public*, pg. 810
WOTIF.COM PTY. LTD.—See Expedia Group, Inc.; *U.S. Public*, pg. 810
XPLORE TRAVEL GROUP—See Symphony Technology Group, LLC; *U.S. Private*, pg. 3902
YOUR TICKET PROVIDER B.V.—See CM.com N.V.; *Int'l*, pg. 1666
YTB INTERNATIONAL, INC.; *U.S. Private*, pg. 4595
ZAO BTI RUSSIA—See Global Business Travel Group, Inc.; *U.S. Public*, pg. 941
ZENON NATIONAL DISTRIBUTION CENTRE LTD.—See Cyprus Airways Public Limited; *Int'l*, pg. 1897
ZOOMAWAY TRAVEL, INC.; *U.S. Public*, pg. 2411

561611 — INVESTIGATION SERVICES

ALLIANCE 2020, INC.; *U.S. Private*, pg. 181
ALTEGRITY RISK INTERNATIONAL, INC.—See Corporate Risk Holdings LLC; *U.S. Private*, pg. 1056
AMERICAN BACKGROUND SERVICES, INC.—See General Catalyst Partners; *U.S. Private*, pg. 1664
AMERICAN BACKGROUND SERVICES, INC.—See iSubscribed Inc.; *U.S. Private*, pg. 2147
AMERICAN BACKGROUND SERVICES, INC.—See WndrCo Holdings, LLC; *U.S. Private*, pg. 4552
AMERIGUARD SECURITY SERVICES, INC.; *U.S. Public*, pg. 113
ANDREWS INTERNATIONAL GOVERNMENT SERVICES, INC.—See Audax Group, Limited Partnership; *U.S. Private*, pg. 386
ASSET SOURCE INTERNATIONAL, INC.—See STA International; *U.S. Private*, pg. 3774
BATES GROUP LLC; *U.S. Private*, pg. 486
BIRN SERBIA; *Int'l*, pg. 1048
CAPCON ARGEN LIMITED—See Capcon Limited; *Int'l*, pg. 1303
CAPCON LIMITED; *Int'l*, pg. 1303
CAREERBUILDER EMPLOYMENT SCREENING, LLC—See Boathouse Capital Management, LLC; *U.S. Private*, pg. 603
CENTRAL GLASS EUROPE LIMITED—See Central Glass Co., Ltd.; *Int'l*, pg. 1406
CLEAR INVESTIGATIVE ADVANTAGE, LLC.; *U.S. Private*, pg. 932
COMBINED INVESTIGATORS, INC—See Ethos Risk Services LLC; *U.S. Private*, pg. 1432
COMMERCIAL INVESTIGATION & SECURITY—See Security Solutions of America; *U.S. Private*, pg. 3596
CORELOGIC SAFERENT, LLC—See Insight Venture Management, LLC; *U.S. Private*, pg. 2089
CORELOGIC SAFERENT, LLC—See Stone Point Capital LLC; *U.S. Private*, pg. 3822
CORPDIRECT AGENTS, INC.; *U.S. Private*, pg. 1053
CORPORATE RISK HOLDINGS LLC; *U.S. Private*, pg. 1056
DIAMOND DETECTIVE AGENCY INC.; *U.S. Private*, pg. 1223
THE DIAMOND GROUP INC.; *U.S. Private*, pg. 4021
EASYBACKGROUNDS, INC.—See Audax Group, Limited Partnership; *U.S. Private*, pg. 387
EFI GLOBAL CANADA—See The Carlyle Group Inc.; *U.S. Public*, pg. 2053
EFI GLOBAL, INC.—See The Carlyle Group Inc.; *U.S. Public*, pg. 2053
EMPLOYMENT SCREENING SERVICES (ESS)—See Audax Group, Limited Partnership; *U.S. Private*, pg. 387
EQUISEARCH SERVICES INC.—See Palladian Capital Partners LLC; *U.S. Private*, pg. 3077
EVIDENT, LLC—See TruBridge, Inc.; *U.S. Public*, pg. 2198
EXERA MYANMAR LIMITED—See Asia Strategic Holdings Limited; *Int'l*, pg. 615
FINGERPRINT SOLUTIONS, LLC—See General Atlantic Service Company, L.P.; *U.S. Private*, pg. 1663
FINGERPRINT SOLUTIONS, LLC—See Stone Point Capital LLC; *U.S. Private*, pg. 3825

FIRST ADVANTAGE EUROPE LTD.—See Silver Lake Group, LLC; *U.S. Private*, pg. 3654
FIRST ADVANTAGE INVESTIGATIVE SERVICES—See Silver Lake Group, LLC; *U.S. Private*, pg. 3654
FRASCO, INC.; *U.S. Private*, pg. 1599
G4S COMPLIANCE & NVESTIGATIONS (IRELAND) LIMITED—See Allied Universal Manager LLC; *U.S. Private*, pg. 188
GLOBAL INVESTIGATIVE SERVICES, LLC—See Kinderhook Industries, LLC; *U.S. Private*, pg. 2307
GLORIA GMBH—See Carrier Global Corporation; *U.S. Public*, pg. 443
GUTS INVESTIGATION CO., LTD.—See Guts Group Inc.; *Int'l*, pg. 3189
HERMES TRANSPORTES BLINDADOS SA; *Int'l*, pg. 3363
HIRERIGHT AU PTY LTD—See General Atlantic Service Company, L.P.; *U.S. Private*, pg. 1663
HIRERIGHT AU PTY LTD—See Stone Point Capital LLC; *U.S. Private*, pg. 3825
HIRERIGHT CANADA CORPORATION—See Corporate Risk Holdings LLC; *U.S. Private*, pg. 1056
HORSEMEN, INC.; *U.S. Private*, pg. 1984
IDENTIGEN LIMITED—See Merck & Co., Inc.; *U.S. Public*, pg. 1416
IDENTIGEN NORTH AMERICA INC.—See Merck & Co., Inc.; *U.S. Public*, pg. 1416
IDENTIGEN SWITZERLAND AG—See Merck & Co., Inc.; *U.S. Public*, pg. 1416
IDENTITY THEFT GUARD SOLUTIONS, INC.—See Whanau Interests LLC; *U.S. Private*, pg. 4504
IDEX AMERICA INC.—See IDEX Biometrics ASA; *Int'l*, pg. 3592
IDEX BIOMETRICS AMERICA INC.—See IDEX Biometrics ASA; *Int'l*, pg. 3592
INFORTAL ASSOCIATES; *U.S. Private*, pg. 2074
IUNLIMITED INC.; *U.S. Private*, pg. 2150
JSSF, INC.—See Frasco, Inc.; *U.S. Private*, pg. 1599
JUDICIAL CORRECTION SERVICES, INC.; *U.S. Private*, pg. 2242
MATTHEWS-DANIEL COMPANY—See Bureau Veritas S.A.; *Int'l*, pg. 1222
MATTHEWS-DANIEL INTERNATIONAL (LONDON) LIMITED—See Bureau Veritas S.A.; *Int'l*, pg. 1222
NARDELLO & CO. LLC; *U.S. Private*, pg. 2835
NATIONAWIDE SCREENING SERVICES, INC.; *U.S. Private*, pg. 2865
NAUTILUS INVESTIGATIONS, INC.—See The Carlyle Group Inc.; *U.S. Public*, pg. 2053
PRIVATE EYES, INC.; *U.S. Private*, pg. 3268
PROBE INFORMATION SERVICES, LLC—See Trinity Hunt Management, L.P.; *U.S. Private*, pg. 4235
SAPIENT INVESTIGATIONS INC.; *U.S. Private*, pg. 3548
SEDGWICK FACTUAL PHOTO, INC.—See The Carlyle Group Inc.; *U.S. Public*, pg. 2053
SOUTHWESTERN SECURITY SERVICES; *U.S. Private*, pg. 3742
STAYSAFE RESEARCH SYSTEMS LTD.; *U.S. Private*, pg. 3794
STERLING CHECK CORP.; *U.S. Public*, pg. 1946
THE SWARTHMORE GROUP, INC.; *U.S. Private*, pg. 4125
TEAM LEGAL—See Apax Partners LLP; *Int'l*, pg. 503
UNIFIED INVESTIGATIONS & SCIENCES, INC.—See The Carlyle Group Inc.; *U.S. Public*, pg. 2054
UNITECH POWER SYSTEMS AS—See Aker Solutions ASA; *Int'l*, pg. 263
US INVESTIGATIONS SERVICES, LLC—See Corporate Risk Holdings LLC; *U.S. Private*, pg. 1056
USIS COMMERCIAL SERVICES—See Corporate Risk Holdings LLC; *U.S. Private*, pg. 1056
VERACITY RESEARCH CO.—See Trinity Hunt Management, L.P.; *U.S. Private*, pg. 4235
WELLTHERM DRILLING LTD.—See Eneraqua Technologies Plc; *Int'l*, pg. 2418

561612 — SECURITY GUARDS AND PATROL SERVICES

3 SIXTY RISK SOLUTIONS LTD.; *Int'l*, pg. 5
ABC SECURITY SERVICE, INC.; *U.S. Private*, pg. 36
ABDUL MOHSIN BADER AL KHORAFI EST. CO. FOR GEN. TRADING & CONTRACTING WLL—See Aiphone Co., Ltd.; *Int'l*, pg. 235
ACADEMI LLC—See Apollo Global Management, Inc.; *U.S. Public*, pg. 150
A CONE ZONE, INC.—See Trilantic Capital Management L.P.; *U.S. Private*, pg. 4231
ADC LTD. NM; *U.S. Private*, pg. 76
ADMIRAL SECURITY SERVICES—See Red Coats Inc.; *U.S. Private*, pg. 3373
ADMIRAL SECURITY SERVICES—See Red Coats Inc.; *U.S. Private*, pg. 3373
AEON DELIGHT SECURITY CO., LTD.—See AEON Co., Ltd.; *Int'l*, pg. 176
AEPS CORPORATION; *U.S. Private*, pg. 117
AGENCIAS PAN AMERICANAS, S DE R.L. DE C.V.—See Aiphone Co., Ltd.; *Int'l*, pg. 235
AKAL SECURITY, INC.; *U.S. Private*, pg. 144

N.A.I.C.S. INDEX 561612 — SECURITY GUARDS AND...

AKDENIZ YATIRIM HOLDING AS; *Int'l*, pg. 261
ALL PHASE SECURITY, INC.—See Allied Universal Manager LLC; *U.S. Private*, pg. 191
ALLSTAR FINANCIAL GROUP INC.; *U.S. Private*, pg. 193
ALROD ENTERPRISES INC.; *U.S. Private*, pg. 202
AMERICAN SECURITY, L.L.C.; *U.S. Private*, pg. 253
AMERICAN SECURITY PROGRAMS INC.—See Allied Universal Manager LLC; *U.S. Private*, pg. 191
AMERICAN SERVICES, INC.—See Allied Universal Manager LLC; *U.S. Private*, pg. 188
ARROW SECURITY, INC.; *U.S. Private*, pg. 336
ASKARI GUARDS (PVT) LIMITED—See Army Welfare Trust LLC; *Int'l*, pg. 575
ASSET PROTECTION ASSOCIATES, INC.—See Allied Universal Manager LLC; *U.S. Private*, pg. 190
ASSET PROTECTION & SECURITY SERVICES, L. P.; *U.S. Private*, pg. 354
AVARN SECURITY OY—See Avarn Security Group Holding AS; *Int'l*, pg. 737
AWAKE SECURITY LLC—See Arista Networks, Inc.; *U.S. Public*, pg. 192
BECHTLE NETWORK & SECURITY SOLUTIONS GMBH—See Bechtle AG; *Int'l*, pg. 937
BETHLEHEM ADVANCED TECHNOLOGIES CO., LTD.—See Aiphone Co., Ltd.; *Int'l*, pg. 235
BLUE ARMOR SECURITY SERVICES, INC.; *U.S. Private*, pg. 585
BLUE LINE PROTECTION GROUP, INC.; *U.S. Public*, pg. 364
BOWLES CORPORATE SERVICES INC.; *U.S. Private*, pg. 626
BRAAVOS, INC.; *U.S. Private*, pg. 630
BRINK'S ARGENTINA S.A.—See The Brink's Company; *U.S. Public*, pg. 2042
BRINK'S AUSTRALIA PTY. LTD—See The Brink's Company; *U.S. Public*, pg. 2042
BRINK'S BOLIVIA S.A.—See The Brink's Company; *U.S. Public*, pg. 2042
BRINK'S CANADA LIMITED—See The Brink's Company; *U.S. Public*, pg. 2042
BRINK'S CASH SERVICES (IRELAND) LIMITED—See The Brink's Company; *U.S. Public*, pg. 2042
BRINK'S CASH & VALUABLE SERVICES S.A.—See The Brink's Company; *U.S. Public*, pg. 2041
BRINK'S C.L. HUNGARIA LIMITED—See The Brink's Company; *U.S. Public*, pg. 2042
BRINK'S CYPRUS (PRIVATE SECURITY SERVICES) LIMITED—See The Brink's Company; *U.S. Public*, pg. 2042
BRINK'S EMEA SAS—See The Brink's Company; *U.S. Public*, pg. 2042
BRINK'S FAR EAST LIMITED—See The Brink's Company; *U.S. Public*, pg. 2042
BRINK'S GLOBAL SERVICES ANTWERP BVBA—See The Brink's Company; *U.S. Public*, pg. 2042
BRINK'S GLOBAL SERVICES FZE—See The Brink's Company; *U.S. Public*, pg. 2042
BRINK'S GLOBAL SERVICES POLAND SP.ZO.O.—See The Brink's Company; *U.S. Public*, pg. 2042
BRINK'S GLOBAL SERVICES S.R.L.—See The Brink's Company; *U.S. Public*, pg. 2042
BRINK'S GUVENLIK HIZMETLERI ANONIM SIRKETI—See The Brink's Company; *U.S. Public*, pg. 2042
BRINK'S HONG KONG LIMITED—See The Brink's Company; *U.S. Public*, pg. 2042
BRINK'S, INCORPORATED—See The Brink's Company; *U.S. Public*, pg. 2042
BRINK'S INDIA PRIVATE LIMITED—See The Brink's Company; *U.S. Public*, pg. 2042
BRINK'S IRELAND LIMITED—See The Brink's Company; *U.S. Public*, pg. 2042
BRINK'S (ISRAEL) LIMITED—See The Brink's Company; *U.S. Public*, pg. 2042
BRINK'S JAPAN LIMITED—See The Brink's Company; *U.S. Public*, pg. 2042
BRINK'S LIMITED (BAHRAIN) EC—See The Brink's Company; *U.S. Public*, pg. 2042
BRINK'S LUXEMBOURG S.A.—See The Brink's Company; *U.S. Public*, pg. 2042
BRINKS MONGOLIA LLC—See The Brink's Company; *U.S. Public*, pg. 2043
BRINK'S NEDERLAND B.V.—See The Brink's Company; *U.S. Public*, pg. 2042
BRINK'S PUERTO RICO, INC.—See The Brink's Company; *U.S. Public*, pg. 2042
BRINK'S SECURITY SERVICES, B.V.—See The Brink's Company; *U.S. Public*, pg. 2042
BRINK'S SECURITY TRANSPORTATION (SHANGHAI) COMPANY LIMITED—See The Brink's Company; *U.S. Public*, pg. 2043
BRINK'S SINGAPORE PTE LTD.—See The Brink's Company; *U.S. Public*, pg. 2042
BRINK'S (UK) LIMITED—See The Brink's Company; *U.S. Public*, pg. 2042
BRINK'S U.S.—See The Brink's Company; *U.S. Public*, pg. 2043
BRINK'S WORLDBRIDGE SECURE LOGISTICS CO., LTD.—See The Brink's Company; *U.S. Public*, pg. 2042

CANTOR FITZGERALD INTERNATIONAL—See Cantor Fitzgerald, L.P.; *U.S. Public*, pg. 736
CDA INCORPORATED; *U.S. Private*, pg. 802
CENTERRA GROUP, LLC—See Apollo Global Management, Inc.; *U.S. Public*, pg. 150
CENTRAL SECURITY PATROLS CO., LTD.; *Int'l*, pg. 1409
CHENEGA INTEGRATED SYSTEMS, LLC—See Chenega Corporation; *U.S. Private*, pg. 872
CHUANG'S PROPERTIES (CENTRAL PLAZA) SDN. BHD.—See Chuang's China Investments Limited; *Int'l*, pg. 1590
CLF-SATREM—See Groupe Gorge S.A.; *Int'l*, pg. 3103
COASTAL INTERNATIONAL SECURITY, INC.—See Akal Security, Inc.; *U.S. Private*, pg. 144
COMMAND DECISIONS SYSTEMS & SOLUTIONS, INCORPORATED; *U.S. Private*, pg. 982
CONCORD SECURITY CORP.; *Int'l*, pg. 1765
CONRAD SECURITY LIMITED—See Allied Group Limited; *Int'l*, pg. 357
CONSTELLIS, LLC—See Apollo Global Management, Inc.; *U.S. Public*, pg. 150
CONTEMPORARY SERVICES CORP.; *U.S. Private*, pg. 1027
CONTINENTAL SECRET SERVICE BUREAU; *U.S. Private*, pg. 1031
COSTA SECURITY SERVICES, LLC; *U.S. Private*, pg. 1063
CREATIVE HARDWARE FOR INTEGRATED PRODUCTS SAL—See Aiphone Co., Ltd.; *Int'l*, pg. 235
DAVIS SECURITY SERVICES INC.—See Owen Security Solutions Inc.; *U.S. Private*, pg. 3054
DAY & ZIMMERMANN SECURITY SERVICES—See The Day & Zimmermann Group, Inc.; *U.S. Private*, pg. 4019
DB STATION&SERVICE AKTIENGESELLSCHAFT—See Deutsche Bahn AG; *Int'l*, pg. 2051
DC INFOTECH & COMMUNICATION LTD.; *Int'l*, pg. 1989
D C SECURITY INC; *Int'l*, pg. 1899
DEFENSE ACADEMICS—See Excelsior Defense, Inc.; *U.S. Private*, pg. 1446
DENSO UNITY SERVICE CORPORATION—See Denso Corporation; *Int'l*, pg. 2031
DIQU TECH PRIVATE LIMITED—See Aiphone Co., Ltd.; *Int'l*, pg. 235
DOTHAN SECURITY INC.; *U.S. Private*, pg. 1265
DYNAMIC SECURITY INC.; *U.S. Private*, pg. 1299
EASTERN SECURITY, INC.—See Allied Universal Manager LLC; *U.S. Private*, pg. 190
EGYPT & MIDDLE EAST IMPORT-EXPORT LTD. CO.—See Aiphone Co., Ltd.; *Int'l*, pg. 235
ELECTROCOM S.A.—See Aiphone Co., Ltd.; *Int'l*, pg. 235
ELTEK DISTRIBUTION SRL—See Aiphone Co., Ltd.; *Int'l*, pg. 235
ENIGMA-BULWARK, LIMITED; *U.S. Private*, pg. 1400
ESSENTIAL SECURITY, INC.; *U.S. Private*, pg. 1427
ESSENTRA PACKAGING - NOTTINGHAM—See Essentra plc; *Int'l*, pg. 2511
ETS PIERRE KESS ET FILS S.A.—See The Brink's Company; *U.S. Public*, pg. 2043
EUROSERVE GUVENLIK A.S.—See Compass Group PLC; *Int'l*, pg. 1752
EVERGREEN INTERNATIONAL NZ, LLC—See Evergreen Capital L.P.; *U.S. Private*, pg. 1438
EXCELSIOR DEFENSE, INC.; *U.S. Private*, pg. 1446
FAURE QEI S.A.—See Groupe Gorge S.A.; *Int'l*, pg. 3103
FGV SECURITY SERVICES SDN. BHD.—See FGV Holdings Bhd; *Int'l*, pg. 2649
FIDELITY SECURITY SERVICES (PTY) LTD.—See Fidelity Security Group (Pty) Ltd.; *Int'l*, pg. 2654
FIRSTLINE TRANSPORTATION SECURITY, INC.—See SMS Holdings Corporation; *U.S. Private*, pg. 3699
FIRST SECURITY SERVICES—See First Alarm Security & Patrol, Inc.; *U.S. Private*, pg. 1512
FJC SECURITY SERVICES, INC.—See Allied Universal Manager LLC; *U.S. Private*, pg. 190
FRAPORT SECURITY SERVICES GMBH—See Fraport AG; *Int'l*, pg. 2764
THE FUJI FACILITY SERVICE, INC.—See First Brothers Co., Ltd.; *Int'l*, pg. 2682
FULLCAST ADVANCE CO., LTD.—See Fullcast Holdings Co., Ltd.; *Int'l*, pg. 2842
FULL IMAGE SDN. BHD.—See Digistar Corporation Berhad; *Int'l*, pg. 2120
G4S KENYA LIMITED—See Allied Universal Manager LLC; *U.S. Private*, pg. 189
G4S KESZPENZLOGISZTIKAI KFT—See Allied Universal Manager LLC; *U.S. Private*, pg. 189
G4S PLC—See Allied Universal Manager LLC; *U.S. Private*, pg. 188
G4S SECURE SOLUTIONS (USA) INC.—See Allied Universal Manager LLC; *U.S. Private*, pg. 189
G4S SECURITY SERVICES AG—See Allied Universal Manager LLC; *U.S. Private*, pg. 190
G4S SECURITY SERVICES A/S—See Allied Universal Manager LLC; *U.S. Private*, pg. 190
G4S SECURITY SERVICES (INDIA) PVT. LIMITED—See Allied Universal Manager LLC; *U.S. Private*, pg. 189
G4S SECURITY SERVICES SA/NV—See Allied Universal Manager LLC; *U.S. Private*, pg. 190
G4S SECURITY SOLUTIONS AB—See Allied Universal Manager LLC; *U.S. Private*, pg. 190
G4S SECURITY SOLUTIONS SARL—See Allied Universal Manager LLC; *U.S. Private*, pg. 190
G4S SOLUCIONES DE SEGURIDAD S.A.—See Allied Universal Manager LLC; *U.S. Private*, pg. 190
GATEWAY GROUP ONE; *U.S. Private*, pg. 1650
GATEWAY GROUP ONE—See Gateway Group One; *U.S. Private*, pg. 1650
GENERAL SECURITY SERVICES CORPORATION; *U.S. Private*, pg. 1667
GEOTRON CIA. LTDA.—See Aiphone Co., Ltd.; *Int'l*, pg. 235
GITTINGS PROTECTIVE SECURITY, INC.; *U.S. Private*, pg. 1703
GLOBAL ASSET ADVISORS, LLC—See StoneX Group Inc.; *U.S. Public*, pg. 1952
GLOBAL GUARDIAN, LLC; *U.S. Private*, pg. 1714
GOLDBELT SECURITY SERVICES, LLC—See Gold Belt Incorporated; *U.S. Private*, pg. 1727
GUARDFORCE LIMITED—See China Security Co., Ltd.; *Int'l*, pg. 1550
GUARDFORCE (MACAU) LIMITED—See China Security Co., Ltd.; *Int'l*, pg. 1550
GUARD ONE SECURITY, INC.—See Security Solutions of America; *U.S. Private*, pg. 3596
GUARD-SYSTEMS, INC.; *U.S. Private*, pg. 1809
GUOYUAN SECURITIES CO., LTD.; *Int'l*, pg. 3187
GUTS OPERATION CO., LTD.—See Guts Group Inc.; *Int'l*, pg. 3189
HAYNES SECURITY INC.; *U.S. Private*, pg. 1885
HEAVENLY VALLEY, LIMITED PARTNERSHIP—See Vail Resorts, Inc.; *U.S. Public*, pg. 2271
HI-TECH ASSET PROTECTION PROPRIETARY LIMITED—See CSG Holdings Limited; *Int'l*, pg. 1864
HI-TECH NELSPRUIT PROPRIETARY LIMITED—See CSG Holdings Limited; *Int'l*, pg. 1864
ICD AMERICAS, INC.—See The Brink's Company; *U.S. Public*, pg. 2043
ICD ENGINEERING (BEIJING) CO., LTD.—See The Brink's Company; *U.S. Public*, pg. 2043
ICD SECURITY SOLUTIONS (HK) LIMITED—See The Brink's Company; *U.S. Public*, pg. 2043
ICD SECURITY SOLUTIONS (INDIA) PRIVATE LTD.—See The Brink's Company; *U.S. Public*, pg. 2043
ICD SECURITY SOLUTIONS PTE. LTD.—See The Brink's Company; *U.S. Public*, pg. 2043
ICTS TECHNOLOGIES USA, INC.—See ICTS International, N.V.; *Int'l*, pg. 3587
INOVONICS CORPORATION—See Roper Technologies, Inc.; *U.S. Public*, pg. 1812
INTEL, S.A.—See Aiphone Co., Ltd.; *Int'l*, pg. 235
INTER-CON SECURITY SYSTEMS, INC.; *U.S. Private*, pg. 2107
I-SEC INTERNATIONAL SECURITY B.V.—See ICTS International, N.V.; *Int'l*, pg. 3587
I-SEC INTERNATIONAL SECURITY B.V.—See ICTS International, N.V.; *Int'l*, pg. 3587
JIHSUN SECURITIES CO., LTD.—See Fubon Financial Holding Co. Ltd.; *Int'l*, pg. 2802
KANSAI CSP K.K.—See Central Security Patrols Co., Ltd.; *Int'l*, pg. 1410
KHAI QUOC TRADING & TECHNOLOGY DEVELOPMENT CO., LTD.—See Aiphone Co., Ltd.; *Int'l*, pg. 235
KIMBERLITE CORP.; *U.S. Private*, pg. 2305
KING FORCE SECURITY LIMITED—See Greatwalle Inc.; *Int'l*, pg. 3068
KLINIKUM ERFURT BEWACHUNGS GMBH—See Fresenius SE & Co. KGaA; *Int'l*, pg. 2780
KNIGHTHAWK PROTECTION, LLC—See Veteran Infrastructure Products LLC; *U.S. Private*, pg. 4373
KNIGHT PROTECTIVE SERVICE, INC.; *U.S. Private*, pg. 2322
KRATOS MID-ATLANTIC, INC.—See Kratos Defense & Security Solutions, Inc.; *U.S. Public*, pg. 1276
LABOR MANAGEMENT CONCEPTS, INC.; *U.S. Private*, pg. 2370
LANCE INVESTIGATION SERVICE; *U.S. Private*, pg. 2382
LANDMARK EVENT STAFFING SERVICES, INC.—See Allied Universal Manager LLC; *U.S. Private*, pg. 190
LEVY SECURITY CORPORATION; *U.S. Private*, pg. 2437
LIFE ALERT EMERGENCY RESPONSE INC.; *U.S. Private*, pg. 2448
MACO LITORAL S.A.—See The Brink's Company; *U.S. Public*, pg. 2043
MASSY SECURITY (GUYANA) INC.—See Amalgamated Security Services Limited; *Int'l*, pg. 409
MAXIMUS CONSULTING (HONG KONG) LTD.—See Future Data Group Limited; *Int'l*, pg. 2854
MAXSENT INC.—See CDA Incorporated; *U.S. Private*, pg. 802
MC2 SECURITY INC.; *U.S. Private*, pg. 2625
MCROBERTS PROTECTIVE AGENCY, INC.—See Allied Universal Manager LLC; *U.S. Private*, pg. 191
MEGA HERTZ TECHNOLOGIES SDN. BHD.—See Aiphone Co., Ltd.; *Int'l*, pg. 235
MEGASTRENGTH SECURITY SERVICES COMPANY LIMITED—See Henderson Land Development Co. Ltd.; *Int'l*, pg. 3345

561612 — SECURITY GUARDS AND...

MERCHANTS BUILDING MAINTENANCE CO.; *U.S. Private*, pg. 2670
MIKE GARCIA MERCHANT SECURITY, INC.; *U.S. Private*, pg. 2725
MURRAY GUARD, INC.; *U.S. Private*, pg. 2816
MYDATT SERVICES, INC.—See SMS Holdings Corporation; *U.S. Private*, pg. 3699
NAGANOKEN PATROL CO.—See Central Security Patrols Co., Ltd.; *Int'l*, pg. 1410
THE NATIONAL INSTITUTE FOR HOMETOWN SECURITY; *U.S. Private*, pg. 4082
NEW HORIZON SECURITY SERVICES, INC.—See Allied Universal Manager LLC; *U.S. Private*, pg. 190
NIK. M. KOURAKOS & CO., LTD.—See Aiphone Co., Ltd.; *Int'l*, pg. 235
NISCAYAH, INC.—See Stanley Black & Decker, Inc.; *U.S. Public*, pg. 1935
NOVEL LIMITED—See Aiphone Co., Ltd.; *Int'l*, pg. 235
NUCLEACTION—See Groupe Gorge S.A.; *Int'l*, pg. 3103
OBSIDIAN SOLUTIONS GROUP LLC; *U.S. Private*, pg. 2988
OHIO SECURITY SYSTEMS INC.; *U.S. Private*, pg. 3005
OLYMPIC SECURITY SERVICES, INC.; *U.S. Private*, pg. 3012
OY HEDENGREN SECURITY AB—See Aiphone Co., Ltd.; *Int'l*, pg. 235
PERIMETER SECURITY PARTNERS, LLC; *U.S. Private*, pg. 3150
PROTECS A & A CMS SDN. BHD.—See Digistar Corporation Berhad; *Int'l*, pg. 2120
PT BRINKS SOLUTIONS INDONESIA—See The Brink's Company; *U.S. Public*, pg. 2043
PUF SECURITY CORPORATION—See eMemory Technology, Inc.; *Int'l*, pg. 2377
PULTE HOMES OF TEXAS, L.P. - HOUSTON—See Pulte-Group, Inc.; *U.S. Public*, pg. 1737
RAV INVESTIGATIVE & SECURITIES SERVICES LTD; *U.S. Private*, pg. 3357
RAXA SECURITY SERVICES LIMITED—See GMR Airports Infrastructure Limited; *Int'l*, pg. 3015
REDWIRE LLC; *U.S. Private*, pg. 3380
REEFCO, LLC—See Carrier Global Corporation; *U.S. Public*, pg. 444
REES CONTRACT SERVICE INC.; *U.S. Private*, pg. 3383
RETAIL SECURITY SERVICES, INC.; *U.S. Private*, pg. 3411
RUIZ PROTECTIVE SERVICES, INC.; *U.S. Private*, pg. 3503
RURAL/METRO CORPORATION—See KKR & Co. Inc.; *U.S. Public*, pg. 1249
SAFEGUARD SECURITY SERVICES INC.; *U.S. Private*, pg. 3524
SAFEGUARDS SECURICOR SDN BHD—See Allied Universal Manager LLC; *U.S. Private*, pg. 190
SAFETY CONSULTING ENGINEERS INC.—See DEKRA e.V.; *Int'l*, pg. 2009
SECURAMERICA, LLC—See Allied Universal Manager LLC; *U.S. Private*, pg. 191
SECURIGUARD, INC.; *U.S. Private*, pg. 3594
SECURITY ALLIANCE GROUP, LLC; *U.S. Private*, pg. 3594
SECURITY COMPANY SECURITY B.V.—See Live Nation Entertainment, Inc.; *U.S. Public*, pg. 1330
SECURITY GRADE PROTECTIVE SERVICES, LTD.—See Forian Inc.; *U.S. Public*, pg. 868
SECURITY GUARD INC.—See St. John Holdings Inc.; *U.S. Private*, pg. 3772
SECURITY INDUSTRY SPECIALISTS, INC.; *U.S. Private*, pg. 3596
SECURITY SERVICES HOLDINGS, LLC—See Southfield Capital Advisors, LLC; *U.S. Private*, pg. 3736
SECURITY SOLUTIONS OF AMERICA; *U.S. Private*, pg. 3596
SERVICIO PANAMERICANO DE VIGILANCIA CURACAO, N.V.—See The Brink's Company; *U.S. Public*, pg. 2043
SIN CHEW ALARM COMPANY LIMITED—See Aiphone Co., Ltd.; *Int'l*, pg. 235
SMITH PROTECTIVE SERVICES INC.; *U.S. Private*, pg. 3695
SONITROL DISTRIBUTION CANADA, INC.—See Stanley Black & Decker, Inc.; *U.S. Public*, pg. 1934
SONITROL SECURITY SYSTEMS OF BUFFALO, INC.—See Stanley Black & Decker, Inc.; *U.S. Public*, pg. 1934
SOS SECURITY LLC—See Allied Universal Manager LLC; *U.S. Private*, pg. 190
SPARTAN SECURITY SERVICES, INC.—See ATALIAN Global Services; *Int'l*, pg. 665
SP PLUS SECURITY SERVICES, INC.—See Eldridge Industries LLC; *U.S. Private*, pg. 1351
ST. MORITZ SECURITY SERVICES, INC.; *U.S. Private*, pg. 3773
SUMMIT SECURITY SERVICES INC.; *U.S. Private*, pg. 3857
TECH & HOUSE S.A.—See Aiphone Co., Ltd.; *Int'l*, pg. 235
TECHNOLOGY OF ENERGY & CONTROLS CO., LTD.—See Aiphone Co., Ltd.; *Int'l*, pg. 235
TOP GUN SECURITY SERVICES—See BC Partners LLP; *Int'l*, pg. 924
TRINITY TECHNOLOGY GROUP, INC.; *U.S. Private*, pg. 4235
TSLELAY GITIT LTD.—See Aiphone Co., Ltd.; *Int'l*, pg. 235
TWIN CITY SECURITY, INC.; *U.S. Private*, pg. 4265
UNITED AMERICAN SECURITY, LLC—See BC Partners LLP; *Int'l*, pg. 924
UNIVERSAL PROTECTION SERVICE, LP—See Allied Universal Manager LLC; *U.S. Private*, pg. 191
UNIVERSAL SERVICES OF AMERICA, LP—See Allied Universal Manager LLC; *U.S. Private*, pg. 190
U.S. SECURITY ASSOCIATES, INC.—See Allied Universal Manager LLC; *U.S. Private*, pg. 191
U.S. SECURITY ASSOCIATES, INC.—See Allied Universal Manager LLC; *U.S. Private*, pg. 191
VANCE INTERNATIONAL DE MEXICO, S.A. DE C.V.—See Audax Group, Limited Partnership; *U.S. Private*, pg. 386
VIGILANT ASIA (M) SDN BHD—See Efficient E-Solutions Berhad; *Int'l*, pg. 2319
VINSON GUARD SERVICE INC.—See Allied Universal Manager LLC; *U.S. Private*, pg. 191
WEISER SECURITY SERVICES INC.; *U.S. Private*, pg. 4472
WFD SECURITIES, INC.—See Western New England Bancorp, Inc.; *U.S. Public*, pg. 2356
WHELAN SECURITY CO., INC.; *U.S. Private*, pg. 4506
WORLD SECURITY FZE—See Dubai World Corporation; *Int'l*, pg. 2222
WRAP TECHNOLOGIES, INC.; *U.S. Public*, pg. 2383
YALE ENFORCEMENT SERVICES, INC.—See Allied Universal Manager LLC; *U.S. Private*, pg. 191
ZAHRA SECURITY SYSTEMS & ELECTRICALS LLC—See Aiphone Co., Ltd.; *Int'l*, pg. 235

561613 — ARMORED CAR SERVICES

APPLETON SECURITY CORP.—See The O'Connell Companies, Incorporated; *U.S. Private*, pg. 4087
BAE SYSTEMS SURVIVABILITY SYSTEMS LLC—See BAE Systems plc; *Int'l*, pg. 796
BRINK'S DIAMOND & JEWELRY SERVICES BVBA—See The Brink's Company; *U.S. Public*, pg. 2042
DUNBAR ARMORED INC.—See The Brink's Company; *U.S. Public*, pg. 2043
G4S CASH SOLUTIONS BV—See Allied Universal Manager LLC; *U.S. Private*, pg. 188
GARDA CL NORTHWEST, INC.—See BC Partners LLP; *Int'l*, pg. 924
LITIGATION INSIGHTS, INC.—See IMS Consulting & Expert Services; *U.S. Private*, pg. 2051
MULLIGAN SECURITY CORP.—See Southfield Capital Advisors, LLC; *U.S. Private*, pg. 3736
MVM, INC.; *U.S. Private*, pg. 2821
RAPID ARMORED CORPORATION—See Founders Equity, Inc.; *U.S. Private*, pg. 1581
RENT-A-WRECK SYSTEMS INC—See Franchise Services of North America Inc.; *U.S. Private*, pg. 1587
SECTEK INC.; *U.S. Private*, pg. 3593
SECTRAN SECURITY, INC.; *U.S. Private*, pg. 3593
SECURITAS HOLDINGS INC.; *U.S. Private*, pg. 3594
STAFF PRO SERVICES INC.—See Staff Pro Inc.; *U.S. Private*, pg. 3775
USIS INTELLIGENCE AND INVESTIGATIONS SERVICES—See Corporate Risk Holdings LLC; *U.S. Private*, pg. 1056
WALDEN SECURITY COMPANY; *U.S. Private*, pg. 4428

561621 — SECURITY SYSTEMS SERVICES (EXCEPT LOCKSMITHS)

3D-ID, LLC—See LogicMark, Inc.; *U.S. Public*, pg. 1340
3S INCORPORATED—See APi Group Corporation; *Int'l*, pg. 513
3XLOGIC FLORIDA, LLC—See Stanley Black & Decker, Inc.; *U.S. Public*, pg. 1931
3XLOGIC, INC.—See Stanley Black & Decker, Inc.; *U.S. Public*, pg. 1931
3XLOGIC INDIANA, LLC—See Stanley Black & Decker, Inc.; *U.S. Public*, pg. 1931
A10 NETWORKS, INC.; *U.S. Public*, pg. 12
AAA FIRE SAFETY & ALARM INC.—See Pye-Barker Fire & Safety, LLC; *U.S. Private*, pg. 3309
ABSOLUTE SOFTWARE, INC.—See Crosspoint Capital Partners LP; *U.S. Private*, pg. 1107
ACCEL PROTECTION & TECHNOLOGIES, LLC.—See American Integration Contractors, LLC; *U.S. Private*, pg. 238
AC TECHNICAL SYSTEMS LTD.—See Creative Vistas Inc.; *Int'l*, pg. 1833
ACTS-AVIATION SECURITY, INC.; *U.S. Private*, pg. 70
ADARE SEC LIMITED - REDDITCH—See Endless LLP; *Int'l*, pg. 2403
ADI GLOBAL DISTRIBUTION—See Honeywell International Inc.; *U.S. Public*, pg. 1049
ADT COMMERCIAL LLC—See GTCR LLC; *U.S. Private*, pg. 1801
ADT LLC - CARROLLTON OFFICE—See Apollo Global Management, Inc.; *U.S. Public*, pg. 146
ADT LLC - LOUISVILLE OFFICE—See Apollo Global Management, Inc.; *U.S. Public*, pg. 146
ADT LLC - MELVILLE OFFICE—See Apollo Global Management, Inc.; *U.S. Public*, pg. 146
ADT LLC - NEW YORK OFFICE—See Apollo Global Management, Inc.; *U.S. Public*, pg. 146
ADT LLC - SAN ANTONIO OFFICE—See Apollo Global Management, Inc.; *U.S. Public*, pg. 146
ADT LLC—See Apollo Global Management, Inc.; *U.S. Public*, pg. 146
ADT LLC - TOTOWA OFFICE—See Apollo Global Management, Inc.; *U.S. Public*, pg. 146
ADT SECURITY SERVICES, LLC - AURORA OFFICE—See Apollo Global Management, Inc.; *U.S. Public*, pg. 146
ADVANCED FIRE & SECURITY, INC.—See FirstService Corporation; *Int'l*, pg. 2691
ADVENICA AB; *Int'l*, pg. 166
AEWIN TECH INC.—See AEWIN Technologies Co., Ltd.; *Int'l*, pg. 183
AFA MASSACHUSETTS, INC.—See Wind Point Advisors LLC; *U.S. Private*, pg. 4535
AFA PROTECTIVE SYSTEMS, INC. - ALTAMONTE SPRINGS, FLORIDA—See Wind Point Advisors LLC; *U.S. Private*, pg. 4535
AFA PROTECTIVE SYSTEMS, INC. - NATIONAL ACCOUNTS DIVISION—See Wind Point Advisors LLC; *U.S. Private*, pg. 4535
AFA PROTECTIVE SYSTEMS, INC. - NORTHERN NEW JERSEY—See Wind Point Advisors LLC; *U.S. Private*, pg. 4535
AFA PROTECTIVE SYSTEMS, INC.—See Wind Point Advisors LLC; *U.S. Private*, pg. 4535
AFA SOUTHEAST, INC.—See Wind Point Advisors LLC; *U.S. Private*, pg. 4535
AFFINITECH, INC.; *U.S. Private*, pg. 122
AFFORDABLE ALARM & MONITORING, INC. (AAMI); *U.S. Private*, pg. 123
A.G.S. GROEP B.V.—See The Brink's Company; *U.S. Public*, pg. 2041
AGS INTEGRATION PTE. LTD.—See Advancer Global Limited; *Int'l*, pg. 163
AIZAWA SECURITIES GROUP CO., LTD.; *Int'l*, pg. 255
ALARM.COM INC.—See ABS Capital Partners, L.P.; *U.S. Private*, pg. 43
ALARM DETECTION SYSTEMS, INC.; *U.S. Private*, pg. 150
ALARMGUARD SECURITY INC.—See Pye-Barker Fire & Safety, LLC; *U.S. Private*, pg. 3309
ALARM LOCK SYSTEMS, INC.—See Napco Security Technologies, Inc.; *U.S. Public*, pg. 1491
ALARM NEW ENGLAND LLC; *U.S. Private*, pg. 150
ALARM SPECIALISTS, INC.—See Pye-Barker Fire & Safety, LLC; *U.S. Private*, pg. 3309
ALARM TECH SOLUTIONS LLC—See GTCR LLC; *U.S. Private*, pg. 1801
ALERT HOLDINGS GROUP, INC.; *U.S. Private*, pg. 162
ALLEN-VANGUARD CORPORATION—See Independence Capital Partners, LLC; *U.S. Private*, pg. 2057
ALLEN-VANGUARD LIMITED—See Independence Capital Partners, LLC; *U.S. Private*, pg. 2057
ALLIANCE SECURITY INC.; *U.S. Private*, pg. 184
ALLIED PROTECTIVE SYSTEMS, INC.—See Summit Partners, L.P.; *U.S. Private*, pg. 3855
ALPHA SECURITY PRODUCTS—See CCL Industries Inc.; *Int'l*, pg. 1367
ALTRAD ITALIA SRL—See Altrad Investment Authority SAS; *Int'l*, pg. 397
AMALGAMATED SECURITY SERVICES LIMITED; *Int'l*, pg. 409
AMERICAN ALARM & COMMUNICATIONS, INC.; *U.S. Private*, pg. 222
AMHERST ALARM, INC.—See Pye-Barker Fire & Safety, LLC; *U.S. Private*, pg. 3309
AMP SECURITY; *U.S. Private*, pg. 264
ANAVEO SAS—See Bridgepoint Group Plc; *Int'l*, pg. 1154
ANDREWS INTERNATIONAL—See Audax Group, Limited Partnership; *U.S. Private*, pg. 386
ANV SECURITY GROUP, INC.; *Int'l*, pg. 486
ANXIN-CHINA HOLDINGS LIMITED; *Int'l*, pg. 486
ANY SECURITY PRINTING COMPANY PLC; *Int'l*, pg. 486
APEXCCTV; *U.S. Private*, pg. 293
APLEONA HSG SECURITY & SERVICES GMBH—See EQT AB; *Int'l*, pg. 2468
APPLIED DNA SCIENCES, INC.; *U.S. Public*, pg. 170
AQUILA SA; *Int'l*, pg. 528
ARECONT VISION LLC—See IDIS Co., Ltd.; *Int'l*, pg. 3595
ARGOTEK, INC.—See Parsons Corporation; *U.S. Public*, pg. 1650
AS G4S EESTI—See Allied Universal Manager LLC; *U.S. Private*, pg. 188
ASGENT, INC.; *Int'l*, pg. 606
A/S GUNNEBO NORDIC—See Gunnebo AB; *Int'l*, pg. 3184
ASSA ABLOY AB; *Int'l*, pg. 632
ASSA ABLOY COLOMBIA S.A.S.—See ASSA ABLOY AB; *Int'l*, pg. 633
ASSA ABLOY ENTRANCE SYSTEMS AB—See ASSA ABLOY AB; *Int'l*, pg. 633
ASSA ABLOY GECIS SISTEMLERI A.S.—See ASSA ABLOY AB; *Int'l*, pg. 635

N.A.I.C.S. INDEX

561621 — SECURITY SYSTEMS SE...

ASSA ABLOY IP AB—See ASSA ABLOY AB; *Int'l*, pg. 635
ASSA ABLOY MOBILE SERVICES AB—See ASSA ABLOY AB; *Int'l*, pg. 636
ATWEC TECHNOLOGIES, INC.; *U.S. Public*, pg. 225
AU10TIX B.V.—See ICTS International, N.V.; *Int'l*, pg. 3587
AUSTRALIAN SECURITY GROUP PTY LTD.—See China Security Co., Ltd.; *Int'l*, pg. 1550
AUTOSCOPE TECHNOLOGIES CORPORATION; *U.S. Public*, pg. 238
AVANTE CORP; *Int'l*, pg. 735
AVANTE SECURITY INC.—See Avante Corp; *Int'l*, pg. 735
AVA RISK GROUP LIMITED; *Int'l*, pg. 733
AVARN SECURITY GROUP HOLDING AS; *Int'l*, pg. 737
AVERTIUM, LLC—See Sunstone Partners Management LLC; *U.S. Private*, pg. 3873
AVI INTEGRATORS INC.—See Gemspring Capital Management, LLC; *U.S. Private*, pg. 1658
AXIS COMMUNICATIONS AB—See Canon Inc.; *Int'l*, pg. 1293
B3SYSTEM S.A.; *Int'l*, pg. 791
BARRACUDA NETWORKS, INC.—See KKR & Co. Inc.; *U.S. Public*, pg. 1241
BARRACUDA NETWORKS JAPAN, K.K.—See KKR & Co. Inc.; *U.S. Public*, pg. 1241
BARRACUDA NETWORKS TECHNOLOGY CO. LTD.—See KKR & Co. Inc.; *U.S. Public*, pg. 1241
BASS SECURITY SERVICES INC.—See Platinum Equity, LLC; *U.S. Private*, pg. 3208
BATTIKHA SECURITY INC.; *Int'l*, pg. 890
BAY ALARM COMPANY INC.; *U.S. Private*, pg. 491
B&B ARMR CORPORATION; *U.S. Private*, pg. 417
BCE FRANCE SAS—See Bertelsmann SE & Co. KGaA; *Int'l*, pg. 990
BEGHELLI S.P.A.; *Int'l*, pg. 941
BELLRINGER SECURITY, INC.—See Pye-Barker Fire & Safety, LLC; *U.S. Private*, pg. 3309
BENTLY NEVADA FRANCE S.A.R.L.—See General Electric Company; *U.S. Public*, pg. 919
BEOZASTITA A.D.; *Int'l*, pg. 978
BEST FENCING GROUP B.V.; *Int'l*, pg. 999
BEYOND SECURITY, INC.—See HGGC, LLC; *U.S. Private*, pg. 1929
BFPE INTERNATIONAL INC.; *U.S. Private*, pg. 548
BI INCORPORATED—See The GEO Group, Inc.; *U.S. Public*, pg. 2075
BLACKWATCH INTERNATIONAL CORP.; *U.S. Private*, pg. 577
BLUE RIDGE SECURITY SYSTEMS—See Blue Ridge Electric Cooperative Inc.; *U.S. Private*, pg. 591
BONIAL INTERNATIONAL GMBH—See Axel Springer SE; *Int'l*, pg. 766
BQT SOLUTIONS (AUSTRALIA) PTY. LTD.—See Ava Risk Group Limited; *Int'l*, pg. 733
BQT SOLUTIONS (NZ) LTD.—See Ava Risk Group Limited; *Int'l*, pg. 733
BQT SOLUTIONS (UK) LTD.—See Ava Risk Group Limited; *Int'l*, pg. 733
BRANDPROTECT INC.; *Int'l*, pg. 1140
BREKOM GMBH—See EWE Aktiengesellschaft; *Int'l*, pg. 2575
BRICKHOUSE SECURITY; *U.S. Private*, pg. 648
BRINK'S GLOBAL HOLDINGS B.V.—See The Brink's Company; *U.S. Public*, pg. 2042
BRISCOE PROTECTIVE SYSTEMS, INC.—See Pye-Barker Fire & Safety, LLC; *U.S. Private*, pg. 3309
BRYANT-DURHAM ALARM CO. INC.—See Bryant-Durham Electric Co., Inc.; *U.S. Private*, pg. 674
B SAFE INC.—See Pye-Barker Fire & Safety, LLC; *U.S. Private*, pg. 3309
BUDDI LIMITED—See Big Technologies Plc; *Int'l*, pg. 1021
BUDDI US LLC—See Big Technologies Plc; *Int'l*, pg. 1021
BURGARELLO ALARM INC.—See Fire Protection Services Corp.; *U.S. Private*, pg. 1511
BWM OUTCOMES, LLC—See Hammond, Kennedy, Whitney & Company, Inc.; *U.S. Private*, pg. 1850
CALIFORNIA SUPPRESSION SYSTEMS INC.; *U.S. Private*, pg. 721
CAM CONNECTIONS, INC.—See Apollo Global Management, Inc.; *U.S. Public*, pg. 146
CANADIAN LOCKER COMPANY OF CANADA, LTD.—See American Locker Group Incorporated; *U.S. Private*, pg. 240
CANTRONIC SYSTEMS INC.; *Int'l*, pg. 1299
CAPITOL DOOR SERVICES—See ASSA ABLOY AB; *Int'l*, pg. 639
CARAT DUCHATELET S.A.—See Capital People S.A.; *Int'l*, pg. 1312
CAR MART COMUNICACIONES, S.A. DE C.V.—See CalAmp Corp.; *U.S. Public*, pg. 422
CARRIER FIRE & SECURITY AMERICAS CORPORATION—See Carrier Global Corporation; *U.S. Public*, pg. 440
CARTER BROTHERS, LLC; *U.S. Private*, pg. 775
CARVE SYSTEMS LLC—See iVision Scale, LLC; *U.S. Private*, pg. 2151
CENTIGON FRANCE—See Capital People S.A.; *Int'l*, pg. 1312
CENTRAL STATION MONITORING; *U.S. Private*, pg. 825

CEREBRA MIDDLE EAST FZCO—See Cerebra Integrated Technologies Ltd.; *Int'l*, pg. 1422
CERTEGO OY—See ASSA ABLOY AB; *Int'l*, pg. 639
CETC CYBERSPACE SECURITY TECHNOLOGY CO., LTD.; *Int'l*, pg. 1424
CHECKPOINT DO BRASIL LTDA.—See CCL Industries Inc.; *Int'l*, pg. 1368
CHECKPOINT PORTUGAL LDA—See CCL Industries Inc.; *Int'l*, pg. 1367
CHECK POINT SOFTWARE TECHNOLOGIES (SWITZERLAND) A.G.—See Check Point Software Technologies Ltd.; *Int'l*, pg. 1458
CHECKPOINT SOLUTIONS GMBH—See CCL Industries Inc.; *Int'l*, pg. 1367
CHECKPOINT SYSTEMS (AUST/NZ) PTY LTD.—See CCL Industries Inc.; *Int'l*, pg. 1367
CHECKPOINT SYSTEMS BENELUX B.V.—See CCL Industries Inc.; *Int'l*, pg. 1368
CHECKPOINT SYSTEMS CEE SP. Z.O.O.—See CCL Industries Inc.; *Int'l*, pg. 1368
CHECKPOINT SYSTEMS ESPANA S.L.U.—See CCL Industries Inc.; *Int'l*, pg. 1368
CHECKPOINT SYSTEMS FRANCE SASU—See CCL Industries Inc.; *Int'l*, pg. 1368
CHECKPOINT SYSTEMS GMBH—See CCL Industries Inc.; *Int'l*, pg. 1368
CHECKPOINT SYSTEMS ITALIA S.P.A.—See CCL Industries Inc.; *Int'l*, pg. 1368
CHECKPOINT SYSTEMS MEXICO—See CCL Industries Inc.; *Int'l*, pg. 1368
CHECKPOINT SYSTEMS (M) SDN. BHD.—See CCL Industries Inc.; *Int'l*, pg. 1368
CHECKPOINT SYSTEMS S.A.—See CCL Industries Inc.; *Int'l*, pg. 1368
CHECKPOINT SYSTEMS SVERIGE AB—See CCL Industries Inc.; *Int'l*, pg. 1368
CHECKPOINT SYSTEMS (UK) LTD.—See CCL Industries Inc.; *Int'l*, pg. 1368
CHECKVIDEO, LLC—See Kastle Systems International LLC; *U.S. Private*, pg. 2264
CHINA FIRE & SECURITY GROUP, INC.—See Bain Capital, LP; *U.S. Private*, pg. 437
CHINA SECURITY CO., LTD.; *Int'l*, pg. 1550
CHINA SECURITY & SURVEILLANCE TECHNOLOGY, INC.; *Int'l*, pg. 1550
CHINA STEEL SECURITY CORPORATION—See China Steel Corporation; *Int'l*, pg. 1555
CHT SECURITY CO., LTD.—See Chunghwa Telecom Co., Ltd.; *Int'l*, pg. 1598
CHUBB DELTA TELESURVEILLANCE—See Carrier Global Corporation; *U.S. Public*, pg. 443
CHUBB FIRE & SECURITY B.V.—See Carrier Global Corporation; *U.S. Public*, pg. 443
CHUBB FIRE & SECURITY LIMITED—See Carrier Global Corporation; *U.S. Public*, pg. 440
CHUBB HONG KONG LTD.—See Carrier Global Corporation; *U.S. Public*, pg. 441
CHUBB IRELAND LIMITED—See Carrier Global Corporation; *U.S. Public*, pg. 443
CHUBB NEW ZEALAND—See Carrier Global Corporation; *U.S. Public*, pg. 443
CHUBB OSTERREICH GMBH—See Carrier Global Corporation; *U.S. Public*, pg. 443
CHUBB SECURITY SYSTEMS B.V.B.A.—See Carrier Global Corporation; *U.S. Public*, pg. 443
CHUBB SYSTEMS LIMITED—See Carrier Global Corporation; *U.S. Public*, pg. 441
CKP (CZ) S.R.O.—See CCL Industries Inc.; *Int'l*, pg. 1367
CLARKE SECURITY SERVICES INCORPORATED—See Stanley Black & Decker, Inc.; *U.S. Public*, pg. 1932
COMMERCIAL FIRE & COMMUNICATIONS, INC.; *U.S. Private*, pg. 983
COMMUNICATION ELECTRONICS INC.—See Pye-Barker Fire & Safety, LLC; *U.S. Private*, pg. 3309
COMP S.A.; *Int'l*, pg. 1721
COMTEC SYSTEMS, INC.; *U.S. Private*, pg. 1006
CONNEX GROUP SA—See Stanley Black & Decker, Inc.; *U.S. Public*, pg. 1932
CONTRACT FIRE SYSTEMS LTD.—See Stanley Black & Decker, Inc.; *U.S. Public*, pg. 1932
CONVERGED SECURITY SOLUTIONS LLC; *U.S. Private*, pg. 1035
CONVERGINT TECHNOLOGIES, LLC—See Ares Management Corporation; *U.S. Public*, pg. 188
CORERO NETWORK SECURITY, INC.—See Corero Network Security plc; *Int'l*, pg. 1799
CORPORACION CERRAJERA ALBA, S.A. DE C.V.—See dormakaba Holding AG; *Int'l*, pg. 2177
CORPORATE ARMOR, INC.—See Tiversa, Inc.; *U.S. Private*, pg. 4177
CORRIGAN CANADA, LTD.—See OSI Systems, Inc.; *U.S. Public*, pg. 1621
COSTAR TECHNOLOGIES INC.—See IDIS Co., Ltd.; *Int'l*, pg. 3595
CREATIVE VISTAS INC.; *Int'l*, pg. 1833
CRESCO ID SYSTEMS INC.—See Cresco, Ltd.; *Int'l*, pg. 1840

CRIME INTERVENTION ALARM CO INC—See Apax Partners LLP; *Int'l*, pg. 501
CRIME PREVENTION INC.; *U.S. Private*, pg. 1100
CRITICAL ALERT SYSTEMS, LLC—See TigerConnect, Inc.; *U.S. Private*, pg. 4170
CROMA SECURITY SOLUTIONS GROUP PLC; *Int'l*, pg. 1853
CROSS FIRE & SECURITY CO., INC.—See AE Industrial Partners, LP; *U.S. Private*, pg. 112
CROSSWORD CYBERSECURITY PLC; *Int'l*, pg. 1856
CRU DATA SECURITY GROUP, LLC; *U.S. Private*, pg. 1113
CSA HOLDINGS INC.; *U.S. Private*, pg. 1116
CSMI; *U.S. Private*, pg. 1117
CTEK SECURITY, INC.—See Altaris Capital Partners, LLC; *U.S. Private*, pg. 206
CTI SECURITY SERVICES PTY LTD—See CTI Logistics Limited; *Int'l*, pg. 1871
CTI SECURITY SYSTEMS PTY LTD—See CTI Logistics Limited; *Int'l*, pg. 1871
CUBIC GLOBAL TRACKING SOLUTIONS, INC.—See Elliott Management Corporation; *U.S. Private*, pg. 1368
CUBIC GLOBAL TRACKING SOLUTIONS, INC.—See Veritas Capital Fund Management, LLC; *U.S. Private*, pg. 4361
CULPEPPER & ASSOCIATES SECURITY SERVICES, INC.; *U.S. Private*, pg. 1121
CURBSOFT, LLC—See Sensata Technologies Holding plc; *U.S. Public*, pg. 1865
CYBERMAXX, LLC—See Periscope Equity LLC; *U.S. Private*, pg. 3151
CYBERTRUST BELGIUM N.V.—See Verizon Communications Inc.; *U.S. Public*, pg. 2285
DAIFUKU BUSINESS SERVICE CORPORATION—See Daifuku Co., Ltd.; *Int'l*, pg. 1925
DATADOT TECHNOLOGY - TAIWAN—See DataDot Technology Ltd; *Int'l*, pg. 1977
DATADOT TECHNOLOGY (UK) LTD.—See DataDot Technology Ltd; *Int'l*, pg. 1977
DATAGUISE, INC.—See Thompson Street Capital Manager LLC; *U.S. Private*, pg. 4161
DATA TRACEID (EUROPE) LIMITED—See DataDot Technology Ltd; *Int'l*, pg. 1977
DD PERFORMANCE RESEARCH LLC—See HKS CO., LTD.; *U.S. Private*, pg. 3429
DEFENDER SECURITY COMPANY; *U.S. Private*, pg. 1190
DEFENSE TECHNOLOGIES INTERNATIONAL CORP.; *U.S. Public*, pg. 648
DEFENX PLC; *Int'l*, pg. 2004
DE LA RUE SECURITY PAPERS—See De La Rue plc; *Int'l*, pg. 1996
DELEGO SOFTWARE ULC—See Global Payments Inc.; *U.S. Public*, pg. 943
DETECTOR ELECTRONICS CORPORATION—See Carrier Global Corporation; *U.S. Public*, pg. 440
DETERMINA INC.; *U.S. Private*, pg. 1216
DETERRENT TECHNOLOGIES INC.; *U.S. Private*, pg. 1216
DIGITAL BARRIERS PLC; *Int'l*, pg. 2120
DIGITAL DEFENSE, INC.—See HGGC, LLC; *U.S. Private*, pg. 1929
DISASTER PREPAREDNESS SYSTEMS, INC.; *Int'l*, pg. 2131
DIT CO., LTD.—See Future Corporation; *Int'l*, pg. 2853
DORMAKABA AUSTRIA GMBH—See dormakaba Holding AG; *Int'l*, pg. 2178
DORMAKABA BELGIUM N.V.—See dormakaba Holding AG; *Int'l*, pg. 2178
DORMAKABA DEUTSCHLAND GMBH—See dormakaba Holding AG; *Int'l*, pg. 2178
DORMAKABA FRANCE S.A.S—See dormakaba Holding AG; *Int'l*, pg. 2178
DORMAKABA HOLDING AUSTRALIA PTY. LTD.—See dormakaba Holding AG; *Int'l*, pg. 2178
DORMAKABA JAPAN CO., LTD.—See dormakaba Holding AG; *Int'l*, pg. 2179
DORMAKABA NEDERLAND B.V.—See dormakaba Holding AG; *Int'l*, pg. 2179
DORMAKABA SVERIGE AB—See dormakaba Holding AG; *Int'l*, pg. 2179
DORMAKABA UK HOLDING LIMITED—See dormakaba Holding AG; *Int'l*, pg. 2179
DORMAKABA UK LIMITED - TIVERTON OFFICE—See dormakaba Holding AG; *Int'l*, pg. 2179
DORMAKABA ZRT.—See dormakaba Holding AG; *Int'l*, pg. 2179
DOYLE GROUP INC.; *U.S. Private*, pg. 1270
DOYLE SECURITY SYSTEMS INC.—See Doyle Group Inc.; *U.S. Private*, pg. 1270
DRAEGER SAFETY S.A. DE C.V.—See Draegerwerk AG & Co. KGaA; *Int'l*, pg. 2197
DRONE GUARDER, INC.—See Video River Networks, Inc.; *U.S. Public*, pg. 2297
DTI GROUP LTD; *Int'l*, pg. 2217
DTIQ TECHNOLOGIES, INC.; *U.S. Private*, pg. 1282
E2M TECHNOLOGIES B.V.—See Amphenol Corporation; *U.S. Public*, pg. 130
E2M TECHNOLOGIES INC.—See Amphenol Corporation; *U.S. Public*, pg. 131

561621 — SECURITY SYSTEMS SE...

EASAT ANTENNAS LTD.—See Goodwin PLC; *Int'l*, pg. 3041
THE EASTERN COMPANY; *U.S. Public*, pg. 2069
EASTERN SECURITY & PROTECTION SERVICES, INC.; *Int'l*, pg. 2274
ECI TECHNOLOGY HOLDINGS LIMITED; *Int'l*, pg. 2289
ECONOCOM DIGITAL SECURITY SAS—See Atos SE; *Int'l*, pg. 692
EDISON O&M SERVICES—See Edison International; *U.S. Public*, pg. 719
EID PASSPORT, INC.; *U.S. Private*, pg. 1346
EJ2 COMMUNICATIONS, INC.; *U.S. Private*, pg. 1348
ELECTRIC GUARD DOG, LLC—See TruArc Partners, L.P.; *U.S. Private*, pg. 4245
ELECTRONIC CONTRACTING COMPANY; *U.S. Private*, pg. 1355
ELECTRONIC CONTROL SECURITY INC.; *U.S. Public*, pg. 724
ELSIM ELEKTROTEKNIK SISTEMLER SANAYI VE TICARET A.S.—See Regal Rexnord Corporation; *U.S. Public*, pg. 1772
ELVEY GROUP LTD—See Hudaco Industries Limited; *Int'l*, pg. 3521
EMERGE MONITORING, INC.—See Track Group, Inc.; *U.S. Public*, pg. 2178
EMERGENCY24, INC.; *U.S. Private*, pg. 1380
EMERGENCY RESPONSE TECHNOLOGIES, INC.—See Ilustrato Pictures International Inc.; *Int'l*, pg. 3616
EMIRATES GATEWAY SECURITIES SERVICES LLC—See Alpha Dhabi Holding PJSC; *Int'l*, pg. 367
EMKA-BESCHLAGTEILE GMBH & CO. KG; *Int'l*, pg. 2383
ENGINEERED PROTECTION SYSTEMS, INC.; *U.S. Private*, pg. 1398
ENGIWEB SECURITY S.R.L.—See Apax Partners LLP; *Int'l*, pg. 504
ENNTE AS—See CCL Industries Inc.; *Int'l*, pg. 1368
ENTERPRISE SECURITY, INC.; *U.S. Private*, pg. 1404
ENTRANCE CONTROLS INTEGRATED SECURITY—See Christenson Electric, Inc.; *U.S. Private*, pg. 890
ENVERA SYSTEMS LLC—See Wind Point Advisors LLC; *U.S. Private*, pg. 4534
ESENTIRE, INC.; *Int'l*, pg. 2502
ESSENTRA PACKAGING & SECURITY LIMITED—See Essentra plc; *Int'l*, pg. 2511
ETHOS RISK SERVICES LLC; *U.S. Private*, pg. 1432
EVERGREEN FIRE ALARMS, LLC; *U.S. Private*, pg. 1439
EVERGREEN SECURITY, INC.—See Bay Alarm Company Inc.; *U.S. Private*, pg. 491
THE EVERMEDIA GROUP, INC.; *U.S. Public*, pg. 2073
EVERSPRING INDUSTRY CO.; *Int'l*, pg. 2569
EVIGILANT SECURITY; *U.S. Private*, pg. 1441
EYES ON THE GO, INC.; *U.S. Private*, pg. 1453
F24 CZECH REPUBLIC S.R.O.—See HgCapital Trust plc; *Int'l*, pg. 3376
F24 FRANCE SARL—See HgCapital Trust plc; *Int'l*, pg. 3376
F24 SERVICIOS DE COMUNICACION, S.L.U.—See HgCapital Trust plc; *Int'l*, pg. 3376
FACEKEY CORPORATION; *U.S. Public*, pg. 819
FICHET SECURITY SOLUTIONS BELGIUM SA/NV—See OpenGate Capital Management, LLC; *U.S. Private*, pg. 3030
FICHET SECURITY SOLUTIONS FRANCE SAS—See OpenGate Capital Management, LLC; *U.S. Private*, pg. 3030
FICHET SECURITY SOLUTIONS—See OpenGate Capital Management, LLC; *U.S. Private*, pg. 3030
FINGERPRINT CARDS AB; *Int'l*, pg. 2675
FIRE ALARM SERVICES, INC.—See Pye-Barker Fire & Safety, LLC; *U.S. Private*, pg. 3309
FIRE PROTECTION SERVICES CORP.; *U.S. Private*, pg. 1511
FIRST ALARM SECURITY & PATROL, INC.; *U.S. Private*, pg. 1512
FIRST ALARM—See First Alarm Security & Patrol, Inc.; *U.S. Private*, pg. 1512
FIRSTLINE SECURITY SYSTEMS, INC.—See Ares Management Corporation; *U.S. Public*, pg. 189
FIRST NATIONAL ALARMCAP LP/PREMIERE SOCIETE EN COMMANDITE NATIONALE ALARMCAP—See Stanley Black & Decker, Inc.; *U.S. Public*, pg. 1932
FJERBY AS—See AF Gruppen ASA; *Int'l*, pg. 184
FLEENOR SECURITY SYSTEMS, INC.; *U.S. Private*, pg. 1541
FLORIDA STATE SECURITY, INC.; *U.S. Private*, pg. 1550
FORD AUDIO-VIDEO SYSTEMS INC.; *U.S. Private*, pg. 1564
FORTHINK CO., LTD.—See Abalance Corporation Ltd.; *Int'l*, pg. 48
FORTINET BV—See Fortinet, Inc.; *U.S. Public*, pg. 869
FOUNDSTONE; *U.S. Private*, pg. 1581
FRASEC FRAPORT SECURITY SERVICES GMBH—See Fraport AG; *Int'l*, pg. 2764
FREEUS, LLC; *U.S. Private*, pg. 1607
FREJA EID GROUP AB; *Int'l*, pg. 2772
FS DEPOT, INC.—See Federal Signal Corporation; *U.S. Public*, pg. 826
FUVA BRAIN LIMITED; *Int'l*, pg. 2858
G4S (BOTSWANA) LTD.—See Allied Universal Manager LLC; *U.S. Private*, pg. 188
G4S CASH SOLUTIONS (BELGIUM) SA/NV—See Allied Universal Manager LLC; *U.S. Private*, pg. 188
G4S CASH SOLUTIONS (IRELAND) LIMITED—See Allied Universal Manager LLC; *U.S. Private*, pg. 188
G4S CASH SOLUTIONS SRL—See Allied Universal Manager LLC; *U.S. Private*, pg. 188
G4S (DRC) S.A.R.L.—See Allied Universal Manager LLC; *U.S. Private*, pg. 188
G4S FIRE & SAFETY BV—See Allied Universal Manager LLC; *U.S. Private*, pg. 189
G4S (HELLAS), S.A.—See Allied Universal Manager LLC; *U.S. Private*, pg. 188
G4S HOLDINGS (HONG KONG) LTD.—See Allied Universal Manager LLC; *U.S. Private*, pg. 189
G4S (HONG KONG - HOLDING) LTD.—See Allied Universal Manager LLC; *U.S. Private*, pg. 188
G4S INTERNATIONAL LOGISITICS (HONG KONG) LTD.—See Allied Universal Manager LLC; *U.S. Private*, pg. 189
G4S INTERNATIONAL LOGISTICS (GERMANY) GMBH—See Allied Universal Manager LLC; *U.S. Private*, pg. 189
G4S INTERNATIONAL LOGISTICS (USA), INC.—See Allied Universal Manager LLC; *U.S. Private*, pg. 189
G4S (MALI) SARL—See Allied Universal Manager LLC; *U.S. Private*, pg. 188
G4S RISK CONSULTING LTD.—See Allied Universal Manager LLC; *U.S. Private*, pg. 189
G4S SECURE SOLUTIONS AG—See Allied Universal Manager LLC; *U.S. Private*, pg. 189
G4S SECURE SOLUTIONS (CANADA) LIMITED—See Allied Universal Manager LLC; *U.S. Private*, pg. 189
G4S SECURE SOLUTIONS (CI) SA—See Allied Universal Manager LLC; *U.S. Private*, pg. 189
G4S SECURE SOLUTIONS (CYPRUS) LIMITED—See Allied Universal Manager LLC; *U.S. Private*, pg. 189
G4S SECURE SOLUTIONS D.O.O.—See Allied Universal Manager LLC; *U.S. Private*, pg. 189
G4S SECURE SOLUTIONS (EGYPT) LLC—See Allied Universal Manager LLC; *U.S. Private*, pg. 189
G4S SECURE SOLUTIONS FRANCE SAS—See Allied Universal Manager LLC; *U.S. Private*, pg. 189
G4S SECURE SOLUTIONS (GAMBIA) LTD.—See Allied Universal Manager LLC; *U.S. Private*, pg. 189
G4S SECURE SOLUTIONS JAPAN K.K.—See Allied Universal Manager LLC; *U.S. Private*, pg. 189
G4S SECURE SOLUTIONS (MACAU) LTD.—See Allied Universal Manager LLC; *U.S. Private*, pg. 189
G4S SECURE SOLUTIONS MOCAMBIQUE LIMITADA—See Allied Universal Manager LLC; *U.S. Private*, pg. 189
G4S SECURE SOLUTIONS NIGERIA LTD.—See Allied Universal Manager LLC; *U.S. Private*, pg. 189
G4S SECURE SOLUTIONS (SA) (PTY) LIMITED—See Allied Universal Manager LLC; *U.S. Private*, pg. 189
G4S SECURE SOLUTIONS (SINGAPORE) PTE. LTD.—See Allied Universal Manager LLC; *U.S. Private*, pg. 189
G4S SECURE SOLUTIONS (SL) LTD.—See Allied Universal Manager LLC; *U.S. Private*, pg. 189
G4S SECURE SOLUTIONS (TRINIDAD) LTD.—See Allied Universal Manager LLC; *U.S. Private*, pg. 189
G4S SECURE SOLUTIONS (UK) LIMITED—See Allied Universal Manager LLC; *U.S. Private*, pg. 189
G4S SECURE SOLUTIONS (URUGUAY) S.A.—See Allied Universal Manager LLC; *U.S. Private*, pg. 189
G4S SECURE SOLUTIONS ZAMBIA LTD.—See Allied Universal Manager LLC; *U.S. Private*, pg. 189
G4S SECURITY SERVICES CANADA LTD.—See Allied Universal Manager LLC; *U.S. Private*, pg. 190
G4S SECURITY SERVICES (MAURITANIA) SA—See Allied Universal Manager LLC; *U.S. Private*, pg. 190
G4S SECURITY SERVICES NEPAL (P) LTD.—See Allied Universal Manager LLC; *U.S. Private*, pg. 190
G4S SECURITY SERVICES (THAILAND) LIMITED—See Allied Universal Manager LLC; *U.S. Private*, pg. 190
G4S SECURITY SYSTEMS GMBH—See Allied Universal Manager LLC; *U.S. Private*, pg. 190
G4S SECURITY SYSTEMS LEBANON SAL—See Allied Universal Manager LLC; *U.S. Private*, pg. 190
G4S WACKENHUT (UK) LTD.—See Allied Universal Manager LLC; *U.S. Private*, pg. 189
GABBA LLC; *U.S. Private*, pg. 1632
GARDA SECURITY SCREENING INC.—See BC Partners LLP; *Int'l*, pg. 924
GARDA WORLD SECURITY CORPORATION—See BC Partners LLP; *Int'l*, pg. 924
GATEKEEPER SERVICES LIMITED—See Mastercard Incorporated; *U.S. Public*, pg. 1394
GATEKEEPER USA, INC.; *U.S. Public*, pg. 907
GHS INTERACTIVE SECURITY, LLC—See Arena Investors, LP; *U.S. Private*, pg. 318
GIGA PRIZE CO., LTD.; *Int'l*, pg. 2971
THE GILBERTSON GROUP, INC.—See Argosy Capital Group, LLC; *U.S. Private*, pg. 321
GLOBAL LOCK SAFETY (INTERNATIONAL) GROUP CO., LTD.; *Int'l*, pg. 2999
GLOBAL SECURITY AGENCY INC.; *U.S. Private*, pg. 1717
GLOBLEX SECURITES CO., LTD.—See Globlex Holding Management Public Company Limited; *Int'l*, pg. 3007
GMO GLOBALSIGN CHINA CO., LTD.—See GMO Internet Group, Inc.; *Int'l*, pg. 3013
GOTHAM SECURITY, INC.—See Abacus Group LLC; *U.S. Private*, pg. 34
GOVANGUARD, LLC—See Abacus Group LLC; *U.S. Private*, pg. 33
GREEN RADAR (SG) PTE LIMITED—See Edvance International Holdings Limited; *Int'l*, pg. 2316
GREEN THREADS, LLC; *U.S. Private*, pg. 1774
GRUPO WACKENHUT S.A. DE C.V.—See Allied Universal Manager LLC; *U.S. Private*, pg. 189
GS4 PERU, S.A.—See Allied Universal Manager LLC; *U.S. Private*, pg. 189
GUARDIAN 8 HOLDINGS; *U.S. Private*, pg. 1809
GUARDIAN ALARM COMPANY; *U.S. Private*, pg. 1809
GUARDIAN ALARM OF TOLEDO—See Guardian Alarm Company; *U.S. Private*, pg. 1809
GUARDIAN FIRE PROTECTION SERVICE, LLC.—See Knox Lane LP; *U.S. Private*, pg. 2324
GUARDIANLINK; *U.S. Private*, pg. 1810
GUARDIAN PROTECTION SERVICES, INC.—See Armstrong Holdings, Inc.; *U.S. Private*, pg. 331
GUARDIAN SECURITY SYSTEMS, INC.; *U.S. Private*, pg. 1810
GULF WEST SECUTIRY NETWORK, INC.; *U.S. Public*, pg. 975
GUNNEBO AB; *Int'l*, pg. 3184
GUNNEBO AUSTRALIA PTY LTD—See Gunnebo AB; *Int'l*, pg. 3184
GUNNEBO CANADA INC.—See Gunnebo AB; *Int'l*, pg. 3184
GUNNEBO CZ S.R.O.—See Gunnebo AB; *Int'l*, pg. 3184
GUNNEBO DEUTSCHLAND GMBH—See Gunnebo AB; *Int'l*, pg. 3184
GUNNEBO ENTRANCE CONTROL, INC.—See Gunnebo AB; *Int'l*, pg. 3184
GUNNEBO ESPANA SA—See Gunnebo AB; *Int'l*, pg. 3184
GUNNEBO HOLDING GMBH—See Gunnebo AB; *Int'l*, pg. 3184
GUNNEBO INDIA LTD—See Gunnebo AB; *Int'l*, pg. 3184
GUNNEBO INDONESIA—See Gunnebo AB; *Int'l*, pg. 3184
GUNNEBO ITALIA S.P.A—See Gunnebo AB; *Int'l*, pg. 3184
GUNNEBO MAGYARORSZAG KFT.—See Gunnebo AB; *Int'l*, pg. 3184
GUNNEBO MIDDLE EAST FZE—See Gunnebo AB; *Int'l*, pg. 3184
GUNNEBO NEDERLAND BV—See Gunnebo AB; *Int'l*, pg. 3184
GUNNEBO NORDIC AB—See Gunnebo AB; *Int'l*, pg. 3184
GUNNEBO NORDIC OY—See Gunnebo AB; *Int'l*, pg. 3184
GUNNEBO OSTERREICH GMBH—See Gunnebo AB; *Int'l*, pg. 3184
GUNNEBO PERIMETER PROTECTION AB—See Gunnebo AB; *Int'l*, pg. 3184
GUNNEBO POLSKA SP. Z O.O.—See Gunnebo AB; *Int'l*, pg. 3184
GUNNEBO PORTUGAL S.A.—See Gunnebo AB; *Int'l*, pg. 3184
GUNNEBO SAFEPAY AB—See Gunnebo AB; *Int'l*, pg. 3184
GUNNEBO SECURITY (CHINA) CO., LTD—See Gunnebo AB; *Int'l*, pg. 3184
GUNNEBO SINGAPORE PTE LTD—See Gunnebo AB; *Int'l*, pg. 3184
GUNNEBO SOUTH AFRICA (PTY) LTD—See Gunnebo AB; *Int'l*, pg. 3184
GUNNEBO (SUISSE) SA—See Gunnebo AB; *Int'l*, pg. 3184
GUNNEBO TREASURY SA—See Gunnebo AB; *Int'l*, pg. 3184
GUNNEBO UK LTD—See Gunnebo AB; *Int'l*, pg. 3184
GUTS GROUP INC.; *Int'l*, pg. 3189
GUTS SECURITECH CO., LTD.—See Guts Group Inc.; *Int'l*, pg. 3189
HABITEC SECURITY INC.; *U.S. Private*, pg. 1837
HAIG'S SERVICE CORPORATION; *U.S. Private*, pg. 1840
HANKYU HANSHIN SECURITY SERVICE CO., LTD.—See Hankyu Hanshin Holdings Inc.; *Int'l*, pg. 3255
HARRIS COMPANIES - WASATCH CONTROLS DIVISION—See Harris Companies; *U.S. Private*, pg. 1869
THE HARTLINE ALARM CO, LLC—See Pye-Barker Fire & Safety, LLC; *U.S. Private*, pg. 3309
HAWKEYE ELECTRONIC SECURITY LTD.; *Int'l*, pg. 3289
HEMABH TECHNOLOGY PRIVATE LIMITED—See CMS Info Systems Limited; *Int'l*, pg. 1672
HENSOLDT AG; *Int'l*, pg. 3355
HERAS CLOTURE S.A.R.L.—See CRH plc; *Int'l*, pg. 1843
HERAS MOBILZAUN GMBH—See CRH plc; *Int'l*, pg. 1844
HID GLOBAL SAS—See ASSA ABLOY AB; *Int'l*, pg. 639
HIGHMARK TRAFFIC SERVICES, INC.—See Federal Signal Corporation; *U.S. Public*, pg. 826
HIGH SECURITY SYSTEM CO., LTD.—See Hankyu Hanshin Holdings Inc.; *Int'l*, pg. 3256
HIGH TECH CRIME INSTITUTE INC.; *U.S. Private*, pg. 1937
HILLARD HEINTZE, LLC—See Gryphon Investors, LLC; *U.S. Private*, pg. 1798
HILL & ASSOCIATES (INDIA) PVT. LTD.—See Allied Universal Manager LLC; *U.S. Private*, pg. 190

N.A.I.C.S. INDEX

561621 — SECURITY SYSTEMS SE...

HILL & ASSOCIATES (PRC) LTD.—See Allied Universal Manager LLC; *U.S. Private*, pg. 190
THE HILLER COMPANIES, INC.—See Littlejohn & Co., LLC; *U.S. Private*, pg. 2471
HOCHIKI THAILAND CO., LTD.—See Hochiki Corporation; *Int'l*, pg. 3437
HOLOGRAM. INDUSTRIES RESEARCH GMBH—See Hologram. Industries SA; *Int'l*, pg. 3453
HOLOGRAM. INDUSTRIES SA; *Int'l*, pg. 3453
HOME AUTOMATION (FE) PTE. LTD.—See Hi Sharp Electronics Co., Ltd.; *Int'l*, pg. 3379
HOMELAND SECURITY CORPORATION; *U.S. Public*, pg. 1046
HONEYWELL ADEMCO SECURITY—See Honeywell International Inc.; *U.S. Public*, pg. 1049
HONEYWELL SECURITY—See Honeywell International Inc.; *U.S. Public*, pg. 1049
HONEYWELL SECURITY UK LIMITED—See Honeywell International Inc.; *U.S. Public*, pg. 1050
HONEYWELL VIDEO SYSTEMS—See Honeywell International Inc.; *U.S. Public*, pg. 1050
HUB CYBER SECURITY LTD.; *Int'l*, pg. 3516
HUNTLEIGH CORPORATION—See ICTS International, N.V.; *Int'l*, pg. 3587
HURONIA ALARM & FIRE SECURITY INC.; *Int'l*, pg. 3538
ICOP DIGITAL, INC.—See Safety Vision, LLC; *U.S. Private*, pg. 3525
IDEAL INNOVATIONS, INC.; *U.S. Private*, pg. 2036
IDEMIA FRANCE SAS—See Advent International Corporation; *U.S. Private*, pg. 102
IDEMIA IDENTITY & SECURITY FRANCE SAS—See Advent International Corporation; *U.S. Private*, pg. 102
IDEMIA IDENTITY & SECURITY USA, LLC—See Advent International Corporation; *U.S. Private*, pg. 102
IDENTICARD SYSTEMS CANADA LTD.—See Brady Corporation; *U.S. Public*, pg. 379
IDENTITY REHAB CORPORATION—See Equifax Inc.; *U.S. Public*, pg. 786
IDEX BIOMETRICS ASA; *Int'l*, pg. 3592
IDO SECURITY INC.; *U.S. Private*, pg. 2038
ILLUMINATE OPERATIONS LLC; *U.S. Private*, pg. 2042
IMAGE SENSING SYSTEMS UK LIMITED—See Autoscope Technologies Corporation; *U.S. Public*, pg. 239
IMATRA BV—See DPG Media Group NV; *Int'l*, pg. 2189
INDIGOVISION GROUP PLC—See Motorola Solutions, Inc.; *U.S. Public*, pg. 1477
INEO DEFENSE—See ENGIE SA; *Int'l*, pg. 2430
INFASTECH THAI COMPANY LIMITED—See Stanley Black & Decker, Inc.; *U.S. Public*, pg. 1933
INFOBLOX INC.—See Vista Equity Partners, LLC; *U.S. Private*, pg. 4398
INFRASAFE, INC.; *U.S. Private*, pg. 2074
INGERSOLL-RAND SECURITY TECHNOLOGIES CONSULTANTS—See Allegion Public Limited Company; *Int'l*, pg. 335
INILEX, INC.—See Greenbriar Equity Group, L.P.; *U.S. Private*, pg. 1776
INKAS FINANCIAL CORP. LTD.—See 3 Sixty Secure Corp.; *Int'l*, pg. 5
INTEC COMPANY, INC.; *U.S. Private*, pg. 2097
INTEGRATED FIRE SYSTEMS, INC.—See Performance Systems Integration, LLC; *U.S. Private*, pg. 3150
INTEGRATED, LLC; *U.S. Private*, pg. 2101
INTEGRATED OPENINGS SOLUTIONS, LLC—See Frontenac Company LLC; *U.S. Private*, pg. 1613
INTEGRATED SECURITY SYSTEMS—See Ares Management Corporation; *U.S. Public*, pg. 189
INTEGRATED VIDEO SUPPLY—See Integrated, LLC; *U.S. Private*, pg. 2101
INTELLI CENTRICS INC.; *U.S. Private*, pg. 2105
INTELLIGENT ACCESS SYSTEMS OF NORTH CAROLINA LLC—See Allied Universal Manager LLC; *U.S. Private*, pg. 191
INTELLIMAR, INC.; *U.S. Private*, pg. 2106
INTERFACE SECURITY SYSTEMS, LLC; *U.S. Private*, pg. 2110
INTRALOGIC SOLUTIONS INC.; *U.S. Private*, pg. 2129
I-SYS CORPORATION—See System Development.Integration LLC; *U.S. Private*, pg. 3906
IVEDA SOLUTIONS, INC.; *U.S. Public*, pg. 1179
IVERIFY US, INC.; *U.S. Private*, pg. 2151
JENKINS SECURITY CONSULTANTS, INC.; *U.S. Private*, pg. 2199
JOHNS BROTHERS SECURITY INC.—See Schaubach Holdings Inc.; *U.S. Private*, pg. 3563
KABA DO BRASIL LTDA.—See dormakaba Holding AG; *Int'l*, pg. 2177
KABA GALLENSCHUTZ GMBH—See dormakaba Holding AG; *Int'l*, pg. 2177
KABA GMBH—See dormakaba Holding AG; *Int'l*, pg. 2177
KABA ILCO INC.—See dormakaba Holding AG; *Int'l*, pg. 2177
KABA IMMOBILIEN GMBH—See dormakaba Holding AG; *Int'l*, pg. 2177
KABA NEW ZEALAND LIMITED—See dormakaba Holding AG; *Int'l*, pg. 2177
KABA S.A.S.—See dormakaba Holding AG; *Int'l*, pg. 2177
KABA SRL—See dormakaba Holding AG; *Int'l*, pg. 2177

KASTLE SYSTEMS INTERNATIONAL LLC; *U.S. Private*, pg. 2264
KASTLE SYSTEMS LLC—See Kastle Systems International LLC; *U.S. Private*, pg. 2264
KENNA SECURITY, INC.—See Cisco Systems, Inc.; *U.S. Public*, pg. 499
KH SECURITY PTE. LTD.—See Advancer Global Limited; *Int'l*, pg. 163
KNOWBE4, LLC; *U.S. Private*, pg. 2323
KNOW LABS, INC.; *U.S. Public*, pg. 1270
KURSANA AG—See Dussmann Stiftung & Co. KGaA; *Int'l*, pg. 2234
L-3 ADVANCED LASER SYSTEMS TECHNOLOGY—See L3Harris Technologies, Inc.; *U.S. Public*, pg. 1281
L-3 APPLIED SIGNAL & IMAGE TECHNOLOGY—See L3Harris Technologies, Inc.; *U.S. Public*, pg. 1281
L-3 AVISYS—See L3Harris Technologies, Inc.; *U.S. Public*, pg. 1281
L-3 CINCINNATI ELECTRONICS—See L3Harris Technologies, Inc.; *U.S. Public*, pg. 1281
L-3 COMMUNICATIONS COMMUNICATION SYSTEMS-EAST—See L3Harris Technologies, Inc.; *U.S. Public*, pg. 1282
L-3 COMMUNICATIONS COMMUNICATION SYSTEMS-WEST—See L3Harris Technologies, Inc.; *U.S. Public*, pg. 1282
L-3 COMMUNICATIONS INFRARED PRODUCTS—See L3Harris Technologies, Inc.; *U.S. Public*, pg. 1282
L-3 COMMUNICATIONS MAPPS INC.—See L3Harris Technologies, Inc.; *U.S. Public*, pg. 1282
L-3 COMMUNICATIONS OCEAN SYSTEMS—See L3Harris Technologies, Inc.; *U.S. Public*, pg. 1282
L-3 COMMUNICATIONS SPACE & NAVIGATION—See EMCORE Corporation; *U.S. Public*, pg. 739
L-3 ELECTRON TECHNOLOGIES, INC.—See L3Harris Technologies, Inc.; *U.S. Public*, pg. 1283
L-3 FUZING & ORDNANCE SYSTEMS—See L3Harris Technologies, Inc.; *U.S. Public*, pg. 1283
L-3 PHOTONICS—See L3Harris Technologies, Inc.; *U.S. Public*, pg. 1282
L3 SECURITY & DETECTION SYSTEMS, INC.—See L3Harris Technologies, Inc.; *U.S. Public*, pg. 1284
LAN CONTROL SYSTEMS LIMITED—See Halma plc; *Int'l*, pg. 3232
LAW ENFORCEMENT ASSOCIATES CORPORATION; *U.S. Private*, pg. 2400
LIFE SAFETY COMMERCIAL FIRE & SECURITY SERVICES, INC.; *U.S. Private*, pg. 2449
LIVEWATCH SECURITY, LLC; *U.S. Private*, pg. 2473
LP INNOVATIONS, INC.—See DTIQ Technologies, Inc.; *U.S. Private*, pg. 1282
MAGNA MAKINE SAN. VE TIC. LTD.STI.—See Arcure; *Int'l*, pg. 552
MAXIMUM ALARM & SECURITY INC.—See Co-op Atlantic; *Int'l*, pg. 1679
MEGANET CORPORATION; *U.S. Public*, pg. 1414
METO FENIX HANDELS GMBH—See CCL Industries Inc.; *Int'l*, pg. 1368
MICROTEC ENTERPRISES, INC.—See Stanley Black & Decker, Inc.; *U.S. Public*, pg. 1935
MIDSTATE SECURITY COMPANY LLC—See Allied Universal Manager LLC; *U.S. Private*, pg. 190
MIDWEST MONITORING & SURVEILLANCE INC.; *U.S. Private*, pg. 2722
MINDA SILCA ENGINEERING PVT. LTD.—See dormakaba Holding AG; *Int'l*, pg. 2177
MONITRONICS INTERNATIONAL, INC.—See Ascent Capital Group, Inc.; *U.S. Private*, pg. 348
MORGAN STANLEY ASIA (TAIWAN) LTD.—See Morgan Stanley; *U.S. Public*, pg. 1472
MORGAN STANLEY DURANGO LLC—See Morgan Stanley; *U.S. Public*, pg. 1472
MSA CANADA—See MSA Safety Incorporated; *U.S. Public*, pg. 1481
MUL-T-LOCK LTD.—See ASSA ABLOY AB; *Int'l*, pg. 640
MUTUAL CENTRAL ALARM SERVICE INC.—See Kastle Systems International LLC; *U.S. Private*, pg. 2264
MY ALARM CENTER LLC; *U.S. Private*, pg. 2823
MYRTLE BEACH COMMUNICATIONS, INC.—See Sentinel Capital Partners, L.L.C.; *U.S. Private*, pg. 3609
NABCO, INC.; *U.S. Private*, pg. 2829
NAPCO SECURITY TECHNOLOGIES, INC.; *U.S. Public*, pg. 1491
NATIONAL ALARM & PROTECTION; *U.S. Private*, pg. 2839
NATIONWIDE SECURITY SOLUTIONS INC.; *U.S. Private*, pg. 2866
NCC SYSTEMS INC.—See Frontier Communications Parent, Inc.; *U.S. Public*, pg. 887
NDI RECOGNITION SYSTEMS; *U.S. Private*, pg. 2876
NETCITADEL, INC.—See Thoma Bravo, L.P.; *U.S. Private*, pg. 4151
NEXTGEN SECURITY, LLC—See Dunes Point Capital, LLC; *U.S. Private*, pg. 1288
NISCAYAH AB—See Stanley Black & Decker, Inc.; *U.S. Public*, pg. 1935
NIXU CORPORATION—See DNV GL Group AS; *Int'l*, pg. 2151

NOKAS AS—See Avarn Security Group Holding AS; *Int'l*, pg. 737
NORDIC RETAIL A/S—See CCL Industries Inc.; *Int'l*, pg. 1368
NORTH AMERICAN VIDEO, INC.—See The Halifax Group LLC; *U.S. Private*, pg. 4042
NORTH AMERICAN VIDEO - NORTH EAST REGIONAL HEADQUARTERS—See The Halifax Group LLC; *U.S. Private*, pg. 4042
NOTIFIER INERTIA FIRE SYSTEM—See Honeywell International Inc.; *U.S. Public*, pg. 1050
OBERTHUR CASH PROTECTION S.A.—See Francois-Charles Oberthur Fiduciaire S.A.; *Int'l*, pg. 2760
OCEASOFT SAS—See May River Capital, LLC; *U.S. Private*, pg. 2620
OCTIO AS—See Equinor ASA; *Int'l*, pg. 2485
THE O'GARA GROUP, INC.; *U.S. Private*, pg. 4087
OJO TECHNOLOGY, INC.—See Ares Management Corporation; *U.S. Public*, pg. 189
OMNIPLEX WORLD SERVICES CORPORATION—See Altamont Capital Partners; *U.S. Private*, pg. 205
OPAQ NETWORKS, INC—See Fortinet, Inc.; *U.S. Public*, pg. 869
OPTIVIA BANKING EQUIPMENT & SERVICES—See Loth MBI, Inc.; *U.S. Private*, pg. 2497
ORLACO PRODUCTS B.V.—See Stoneridge, Inc.; *U.S. Public*, pg. 1951
OWEN SECURITY SOLUTIONS INC.; *U.S. Private*, pg. 3054
OWL CYBER DEFENSE SOLUTIONS, LLC—See D.C. Capital Partners, LLC; *U.S. Private*, pg. 1141
PACIFIC AUXILIARY FIRE ALARM COMPANY—See Financial Investments Corporation; *U.S. Private*, pg. 1507
PACKAGE CONCIERGE, INC.—See Gibraltar Industries, Inc.; *U.S. Public*, pg. 936
PACOM GROUP AB—See Stanley Black & Decker, Inc.; *U.S. Public*, pg. 1933
PACOM SYSTEMS ESPANA SL—See Stanley Black & Decker, Inc.; *U.S. Public*, pg. 1933
PACOM SYSTEMS PTY LIMITED—See Stanley Black & Decker, Inc.; *U.S. Public*, pg. 1933
PALADION NETWORKS PRIVATE LIMITED—See Atos SE; *Int'l*, pg. 692
PASEK CORPORATION; *U.S. Private*, pg. 3104
PCO INCORPORATED; *U.S. Private*, pg. 3121
P. DUSSMANN EESTI OU—See Dussmann Stiftung & Co. KGaA; *Int'l*, pg. 2234
P. DUSSMANN GES.M.B.H.—See Dussmann Stiftung & Co. KGaA; *Int'l*, pg. 2234
P. DUSSMANN GUVENLIK, TEMIZLIK, BAKIM, ONARIM, HIZMET LIMITED SIRKETI—See Dussmann Stiftung & Co. KGaA; *Int'l*, pg. 2234
P. DUSSMANN HONG KONG LTD.—See Dussmann Stiftung & Co. KGaA; *Int'l*, pg. 2234
P. DUSSMANN SPOL. S.R.O.—See Dussmann Stiftung & Co. KGaA; *Int'l*, pg. 2234
P. DUSSMANN SP.ZO.O.—See Dussmann Stiftung & Co. KGaA; *Int'l*, pg. 2234
P. DUSSMANN TNHH—See Dussmann Stiftung & Co. KGaA; *Int'l*, pg. 2234
P. DUSSMANN UAB—See Dussmann Stiftung & Co. KGaA; *Int'l*, pg. 2234
PEDUS SERVICE S.A.R.L.—See Dussmann Stiftung & Co. KGaA; *Int'l*, pg. 2235
PELCO INC.—See Motorola Solutions, Inc.; *U.S. Public*, pg. 1479
PER MAR SECURITY SERVICES; *U.S. Private*, pg. 3146
PETER DUSSMANN - VOSTOK—See Dussmann Stiftung & Co. KGaA; *Int'l*, pg. 2235
PIEPER GMBH—See Moog Inc.; *U.S. Public*, pg. 1471
PINNACLE ELECTRONIC SYSTEMS—See Construction Management Service; *U.S. Private*, pg. 1024
POINTER RECUPERACION DE MEXICO S.A. DE C.V.—See PowerFleet, Inc.; *U.S. Public*, pg. 1706
POINTER TELOCATION LTD.—See PowerFleet, Inc.; *U.S. Public*, pg. 1706
POWER HOME TECHNOLOGIES INC.; *U.S. Private*, pg. 3238
PRECINTIA INTERNATIONAL, S.A.—See Bertram Capital Management, LLC; *U.S. Private*, pg. 540
PRECINTIA INTERNATIONAL, S.A.—See Crimson Investment; *U.S. Private*, pg. 1100
PRECISION MARKETING INFORMATION LIMITED—See An Post LLC; *Int'l*, pg. 443
PREMIER SECURITY SOLUTIONS CORP—See Wind Point Advisors LLC; *U.S. Private*, pg. 4535
PREMIER STEEL DOORS & FRAMES—See ASSA ABLOY AB; *Int'l*, pg. 640
THE PRIDE GROUP (QLD) PTY. LTD.—See VISION ENERGY CORPORATION; *U.S. Public*, pg. 2304
PRIMION TECHNOLOGY AG—See AZKOYEN S.A; *Int'l*, pg. 780
PROFESSIONAL SECURITY TECHNOLOGIES LLC; *U.S. Private*, pg. 3276
PROJECT DEVELOPERS, INC.; *U.S. Private*, pg. 3280
PROOF AUTHENTICATION CORPORATION; *U.S. Private*, pg. 3284

561621 — SECURITY SYSTEMS SE...

PROOFPOINT NETHERLANDS B.V.—See Thoma Bravo, L.P.; *U.S. Private*, pg. 4151
PROTEC, INC.—See Apollo Global Management, Inc.; *U.S. Public*, pg. 146
PROTECT AMERICA, INC.—See RockBridge Growth Equity, LLC; *U.S. Private*, pg. 3465
PROTECTION 24 SACA—See BNP Paribas SA; *Int'l*, pg. 1092
PUBLICENGINES INC.; *U.S. Private*, pg. 3300
PUGET SOUND ALARM INC.—See Guardian Security Systems, Inc.; *U.S. Private*, pg. 1810
PULENG TECHNOLOGIES PROPRIETARY LIMITED—See AYO Technology Solutions Ltd.; *Int'l*, pg. 775
QUALYS AUSTRALIA PTY LTD.—See Qualys, Inc.; *U.S. Public*, pg. 1748
QUALYS GMBH—See Qualys, Inc.; *U.S. Public*, pg. 1748
QUALYS HONG KONG LIMITED—See Qualys, Inc.; *U.S. Public*, pg. 1748
QUALYS INTERNATIONAL, INC.—See Qualys, Inc.; *U.S. Public*, pg. 1748
QUALYS JAPAN K.K.—See Qualys, Inc.; *U.S. Public*, pg. 1748
QUALYS LTD.—See Qualys, Inc.; *U.S. Public*, pg. 1748
QUALYS MIDDLE EAST FZE—See Qualys, Inc.; *U.S. Public*, pg. 1748
QUALYS SECURITY TECHSERVICES PRIVATE LTD.—See Qualys, Inc.; *U.S. Public*, pg. 1748
QUALYS TECHNOLOGIES, S.A.—See Qualys, Inc.; *U.S. Public*, pg. 1748
QUANTA SYSTEMS, LLC—See Black Box Limited; *Int'l*, pg. 1058
RAPID SECURITY SOLUTIONS, LLC; *U.S. Private*, pg. 3356
RAPISCAN SYSTEMS, INC.—See OSI Systems, Inc.; *U.S. Public*, pg. 1622
RAPISCAN SYSTEMS PTE. LTD.—See OSI Systems, Inc.; *U.S. Public*, pg. 1622
RDC RAFAEL DEVELOPMENT CORPORATION LTD.—See Elron Ventures Ltd; *Int'l*, pg. 2370
REAL AUTO DYNAMICS INC.—See HKS CO., LTD.; *Int'l*, pg. 3429
REVERT RISK MANAGEMENT SOLUTIONS (PTY) LTD.—See CSG Holdings Limited; *Int'l*, pg. 3678
RFI ELECTRONICS, INC.—See Wind Point Advisors LLC; *U.S. Private*, pg. 4535
RISK ASSISTANCE NETWORK + EXCHANGE NETWORK, INC.; *U.S. Private*, pg. 3440
ROLLKALL TECHNOLOGIES LLC; *U.S. Private*, pg. 3475
RSA SECURITY LLC—See Symphony Technology Group, LLC; *U.S. Private*, pg. 3901
RSA SECURITY LLC—See The Carlyle Group Inc.; *U.S. Public*, pg. 2044
SABAH INTERNATIONAL, INC.; *U.S. Private*, pg. 3520
SABA INC.—See Mainco Investments Inc.; *U.S. Private*, pg. 2552
SAFE ALARM SYSTEMS INC.; *U.S. Private*, pg. 3523
SAFE ELECTRONICS, INC.—See Apollo Global Management, Inc.; *U.S. Public*, pg. 146
SAFE FLEET HOLDINGS LLC—See Genstar Capital, LLC; *U.S. Private*, pg. 1676
SAFE-T USA INC.—See Alarum Technologies Ltd.; *Int'l*, pg. 291
SAFETY VISION, LLC; *U.S. Private*, pg. 3525
SAN FERNANDO VALLEY ALARM, INC.—See Armet Alarm & Electronics Inc.; *U.S. Private*, pg. 330
SANYO VIDEO VERTRIEB AG—See Burg-Wachter KG; *Int'l*, pg. 1223
SARGENT & GREENLEAF S.A.—See OpenGate Capital Management, LLC; *U.S. Private*, pg. 3031
SCHLAGE ELECTRONIC SECURITY—See Allegion Public Limited Company; *Int'l*, pg. 335
SEALING TECHNOLOGIES, INC.—See Parsons Corporation; *U.S. Public*, pg. 1651
SEARCH ORGANIZACION DE SEGURIDAD, S.A.—See Allied Universal Manager LLC; *U.S. Private*, pg. 190
SECION GMBH—See Allgeier SE; *Int'l*, pg. 337
SECTIGO LIMITED—See Francisco Partners Management, LP; *U.S. Private*, pg. 1591
SECURADYNE SYSTEMS LLC—See Allied Universal Manager LLC; *U.S. Private*, pg. 191
SECURE EXCHANGE SOLUTIONS, INC.; *U.S. Private*, pg. 3593
SECURE IDEAS, LLC; *U.S. Private*, pg. 3593
SECUREINFO CORPORATION—See Kratos Defense & Security Solutions, Inc.; *U.S. Public*, pg. 1277
SECUREUSA INC.—See CVC Capital Partners SICAV-FIS S.A.; *Int'l*, pg. 1886
SECURITAS DIRECT AB—See Bain Capital, LP; *U.S. Private*, pg. 444
SECURITAS DIRECT AB—See Hellman & Friedman LLC; *U.S. Private*, pg. 1910
SECURITY ALARM FINANCING ENTERPRISES, INC.—See ICV Partners, LLC; *U.S. Private*, pg. 2034
SECURITY ALLIANCE OF FLORIDA, LLC—See Sealaska Corporation; *U.S. Private*, pg. 3585
SECURITY BY DESIGN INC.; *U.S. Private*, pg. 3595
SECURITY CORPORATION; *U.S. Private*, pg. 3595
SECURITYCOVERAGE INC.—See National Rural Telecommunications Cooperative; *U.S. Private*, pg. 2862
SECURITYHUNTER, INC.; *U.S. Private*, pg. 3597
SECURITY IDENTIFICATION SYSTEMS CORPORATION—See ACRE, LLC; *U.S. Private*, pg. 65
SECURITY INNOVATIONS INC—See TTIK Inc.; *U.S. Private*, pg. 4255
SECURITY MONITORING CENTRE B.V.B.A./S.P.R.L—See Carrier Global Corporation; *U.S. Public*, pg. 444
SECURITY MONITORING CENTRE B.V.—See Carrier Global Corporation; *U.S. Public*, pg. 444
SECURITY NETWORKS LLC—See Ascent Capital Group, Inc.; *U.S. Public*, pg. 348
SECURITY SOLUTIONS & MANAGEMENT LLC—See Ares Management Corporation; *U.S. Public*, pg. 189
SEGURIDAD INTEGRAL METROPOLITANA, S.A.—See ACS, Actividades de Construccion y Servicios, S.A.; *Int'l*, pg. 116
SENTINEL OFFENDER SERVICES, LLC—See CSRA Probation Services, Inc.; *U.S. Private*, pg. 1117
SENTINEL SECURITY SOLUTIONS, INC.; *U.S. Private*, pg. 3610
SENTINEL SILENT ALARM CO., INC.—See Alert Holdings Group, Inc.; *U.S. Private*, pg. 162
SENTRILLION CORPORATION; *U.S. Private*, pg. 3610
SENTRY COMMUNICATIONS & SECURITY; *U.S. Private*, pg. 3610
SENTRY DETECTION INC.; *U.S. Private*, pg. 3610
SENTRY TECHNOLOGY CANADA INC.—See Sentry Technology Corporation; *U.S. Public*, pg. 1868
SERVICE WORKS, INC.—See Allied Universal Manager LLC; *U.S. Private*, pg. 191
SHAGRIR MOTOR VEHICLE SYSTEMS LTD.—See PowerFleet, Inc.; *U.S. Public*, pg. 1706
SHEKOU CONTAINER TERMINALS (PHASE III) CO., LTD—See China Merchants Group Limited; *Int'l*, pg. 1521
SHENZHEN COSON TECHNOLQGY CO., LTD.—See China Security Co., Ltd.; *Int'l*, pg. 1550
SHENZHEN CYBER-HARBOUR NETWORK CO. LIMITED—See China Merchants Group Limited; *Int'l*, pg. 1521
SHENZHEN HAOEN SAFETY TECHNOLOGY CO., LTD.—See China Security Co., Ltd.; *Int'l*, pg. 1550
SHENZHEN JINHANG INDUSTRY CO., LTD.—See Aiphone Co., Ltd.; *Int'l*, pg. 235
SHENZHEN WEIDA MEDICAL SYSTEM ENGINEERING CO., LTD.—See China Security Co., Ltd.; *Int'l*, pg. 1550
SHIVER SECURITY SYSTEMS, INC.—See Pye-Barker Fire & Safety, LLC; *U.S. Private*, pg. 3309
SIA P. DUSSMANN—See Dussmann Stiftung & Co. KGaA; *Int'l*, pg. 2235
SIGNAL ONE FIRE AND COMMUNICATION, LLC—See APi Group Corporation; *Int'l*, pg. 514
SILCA GMBH—See dormakaba Holding AG; *Int'l*, pg. 2177
SILCA KEY SYSTEMS S.A.—See dormakaba Holding AG; *Int'l*, pg. 2177
SILCA LTD.—See dormakaba Holding AG; *Int'l*, pg. 2178
SILCA S.A.S.—See dormakaba Holding AG; *Int'l*, pg. 2178
SILCA S.P.A.—See dormakaba Holding AG; *Int'l*, pg. 2177
SIZEMORE GROUP; *U.S. Private*, pg. 3678
SIZEMORE PERSONNEL INC.—See Sizemore Group; *U.S. Private*, pg. 3678
SMARTER SECURITY, INC.; *U.S. Private*, pg. 3692
SMARTWATCH SECURITY & SOUND, LLC—See The Carlyle Group Inc.; *U.S. Public*, pg. 2053
SOLIS SECURITY INC.—See Frontenac Company LLC; *U.S. Private*, pg. 1614
SOLUS SECURITY SYSTEMS PRIVATE LIMITED—See dormakaba Holding AG; *Int'l*, pg. 2178
SONITROL FRANCHISE COMPANY, L.L.C.—See Stanley Black & Decker, Inc.; *U.S. Public*, pg. 1934
SOS INTERNATIONAL LLC; *U.S. Private*, pg. 3716
STAFF PRO INC.; *U.S. Private*, pg. 3775
STANLEY BLACK & DECKER SWEDEN AB—See Stanley Black & Decker, Inc.; *U.S. Public*, pg. 1934
STANLEY MECHANICAL SOLUTIONS—See Stanley Black & Decker, Inc.; *U.S. Public*, pg. 1935
STANLEY SECURITY ALARMCENTRALE B.V.—See Stanley Black & Decker, Inc.; *U.S. Public*, pg. 1935
STANLEY SECURITY AS—See Stanley Black & Decker, Inc.; *U.S. Public*, pg. 1935
STANLEY SECURITY B.V.—See Stanley Black & Decker, Inc.; *U.S. Public*, pg. 1935
STANLEY SECURITY DENMARK APS—See Stanley Black & Decker, Inc.; *U.S. Public*, pg. 1935
STANLEY SECURITY DEUTSCHLAND ADMINISTRATION GMBH—See Stanley Black & Decker, Inc.; *U.S. Public*, pg. 1935
STANLEY SECURITY DEUTSCHLAND GMBH—See Stanley Black & Decker, Inc.; *U.S. Public*, pg. 1935
STANLEY SECURITY ESPANA, S. L.—See Stanley Black & Decker, Inc.; *U.S. Public*, pg. 1935
STANLEY SECURITY EUROPE BVBA—See Stanley Black & Decker, Inc.; *U.S. Public*, pg. 1935
STANLEY SECURITY NEDERLAND B.V.—See Stanley Black & Decker, Inc.; *U.S. Public*, pg. 1935
STANLEY SECURITY PORTUGAL, UNIPESSOAL, LDA—See Stanley Black & Decker, Inc.; *U.S. Public*, pg. 1935
STANLEY SECURITY SINGAPORE PTE LTD—See Stanley Black & Decker, Inc.; *U.S. Public*, pg. 1935
STANLEY SECURITY SOLUTIONS AUSTRALIA PTY. LTD.—See Stanley Black & Decker, Inc.; *U.S. Public*, pg. 1935
STANLEY SECURITY SOLUTIONS (NI) LIMITED—See Stanley Black & Decker, Inc.; *U.S. Public*, pg. 1935
STANLEY SECURITY SOLUTIONS TAIWAN LTD.—See Stanley Black & Decker, Inc.; *U.S. Public*, pg. 1935
STANLEY SECURITY SVERIGE AB—See Stanley Black & Decker, Inc.; *U.S. Public*, pg. 1935
STANLEY SECURITY SWITZERLAND SARL—See Stanley Black & Decker, Inc.; *U.S. Public*, pg. 1935
STANLEY WORKS (EUROPE) GMBH—See Stanley Black & Decker, Inc.; *U.S. Public*, pg. 1936
STARTRAK PRODUCTS, INC.; *U.S. Private*, pg. 3788
STING ALARM INC.; *U.S. Private*, pg. 3813
STRONG SYSTEMS INTERNATIONAL, INC.—See RAF Industries, Inc.; *U.S. Private*, pg. 3345
STRYKER COMMUNICATIONS LIMITED—See Digital Barriers plc; *Int'l*, pg. 2120
SUSPECT DETECTION SYSTEMS LTD.—See Suspect Detection Systems Inc.; *U.S. Public*, pg. 3885
SWEETWATER SECURITY SYSTEMS LLC; *U.S. Private*, pg. 3892
SYNERGISTICS, INC.; *U.S. Private*, pg. 3903
SYSTEMHOUSE SOLUTIONS AB—See Bravida Holding AB; *Int'l*, pg. 1142
TAPESTRY TECHNOLOGIES, INC.—See The Carlyle Group Inc.; *U.S. Public*, pg. 2049
TASCOR SERVICES LIMITED—See Capita plc; *Int'l*, pg. 1309
TEAM SERVICES, INC.; *U.S. Private*, pg. 3950
TEKNON CORPORATION—See LINX LLLP; *U.S. Private*, pg. 2463
TEO HONG PHAISAN CO., LTD.—See Aiphone Co., Ltd.; *Int'l*, pg. 235
TERACO DATA ENVIRONMENTS PROPRIETARY LIMITED—See Digital Realty Trust, Inc.; *U.S. Public*, pg. 663
THAYERMAHAN, INC.; *U.S. Private*, pg. 3980
TILLEY FIRE EQUIPMENT COMPANY INC—See Tustin Mechanical Services (Lehigh Valley), LLC; *U.S. Private*, pg. 4262
TIMELOX AB—See ASSA ABLOY AB; *Int'l*, pg. 640
TOEPFER SECURITY CORP.—See Alpine Investors; *U.S. Private*, pg. 201
TOLL BROTHERS SMART HOME TECHNOLOGIES, INC.—See Toll Brothers, Inc.; *U.S. Public*, pg. 2162
TRACK GROUP, INC.; *U.S. Public*, pg. 2178
TRANS-ALARM, INC.—See iVerify US, Inc.; *U.S. Private*, pg. 2151
TRANSQUEST TAG & TRACING SOLUTIONS B.V.—See dormakaba Holding AG; *Int'l*, pg. 2178
TRAQUEUR S.A.—See Coyote System SAS; *Int'l*, pg. 1823
TR CONSULTING KFT.—See 4iG Nyrt.; *Int'l*, pg. 12
TRIPLE CANOPY, INC.—See Apollo Global Management, Inc.; *U.S. Public*, pg. 150
TRI-SIGNAL INTEGRATION, INC.; *U.S. Private*, pg. 4223
TSI PRISM—See Black Creek Integrated Systems Corporation; *U.S. Private*, pg. 570
TUNEHOUSE PTY. LTD.—See HKS CO., LTD.; *Int'l*, pg. 3429
TUNSTALL AMERICAS—See ConnectAmerica.com, LLC; *U.S. Private*, pg. 1015
TUVAN-STANGSEL AB—See CRH plc; *Int'l*, pg. 1848
UAB MANO SAUGA LT—See City Service SE; *Int'l*, pg. 1628
UNIVERSAL PROTECTION SECURITY SYSTEMS, LP—See Allied Universal Manager LLC; *U.S. Private*, pg. 191
US SECURITY INC.; *U.S. Private*, pg. 4320
UTC FIRE & SECURITY CORPORATION—See Carrier Global Corporation; *U.S. Public*, pg. 440
VANGUARD PRODUCTS GROUP, INC.; *U.S. Private*, pg. 4344
VARONIS SYSTEMS (NETHERLANDS) B.V.—See Varonis Systems Inc.; *U.S. Public*, pg. 2276
VBRICK SYSTEMS INC.; *U.S. Private*, pg. 4348
VERISURE—See Bain Capital, LP; *U.S. Private*, pg. 444
VERISURE—See Hellman & Friedman LLC; *U.S. Private*, pg. 1910
VERODIN, LLC—See Alphabet Inc.; *U.S. Public*, pg. 84
VIDEO NETWORKS, INC.; *U.S. Private*, pg. 4380
VIDEOTRONIX INC.; *U.S. Private*, pg. 4381
VIGILANT SECURITY (SCOTLAND) LIMITED—See Croma Security Solutions Group Plc; *Int'l*, pg. 1853
VINDICATOR SECURITY SOLUTIONS—See Honeywell International Inc.; *U.S. Public*, pg. 1049
VINDICIA, INC.—See Amdocs Limited; *Int'l*, pg. 420
VINTAGE SECURITY LLC—See Armstrong Holdings, Inc.; *U.S. Private*, pg. 331
VIRTUALARMOUR, LLC—See VirtualArmour International, Inc.; *U.S. Public*, pg. 2300
VISCOUNT SYSTEMS, INC.—See Identiv, Inc.; *U.S. Public*, pg. 1089
VISIOCOM INTERNATIONAL PTE LTD—See Stanley Black

N.A.I.C.S. INDEX

561710 — EXTERMINATING AND P...

& Decker, Inc.; *U.S. Public*, pg. 1936
VISION SECURITY LLC; *U.S. Private*, pg. 4391
VIZER GROUP, INC.; *U.S. Private*, pg. 4406
VSC FIRE & SECURITY, INC.; *U.S. Private*, pg. 4415
VSK ELECTRONICS N.V.—See Blum Capital Partners, L.P.; *U.S. Private*, pg. 599
WACKENHUT CAMEROON S.A.—See Allied Universal Manager LLC; *U.S. Private*, pg. 189
WACKENHUT DE BOLIVIA S.A.—See Allied Universal Manager LLC; *U.S. Private*, pg. 189
WACKENHUT DEL ECUADOR S.A.—See Allied Universal Manager LLC; *U.S. Private*, pg. 189
WACKENHUT DOMINICANA, S.A.—See Allied Universal Manager LLC; *U.S. Private*, pg. 189
WACKENHUT EL SALVADOR S.A.—See Allied Universal Manager LLC; *U.S. Private*, pg. 189
WACKENHUT PARAGUAY S.A.—See Allied Universal Manager LLC; *U.S. Private*, pg. 189
WACKENHUT S.A.—See Allied Universal Manager LLC; *U.S. Private*, pg. 189
WACKENHUT VENEZOLANA C.A.—See Allied Universal Manager LLC; *U.S. Private*, pg. 189
WAVE SINE TECHNOLOGY LTD.—See Hi Sharp Electronics Co., Ltd.; *Int'l*, pg. 3379
WESTAR INDUSTRIES, INC.—See Evergy, Inc.; *U.S. Public*, pg. 801
W.H.B. IDENTIFICATION SOLUTIONS, INC.—See Brady Corporation; *U.S. Public*, pg. 379
WHITEHAT LTD.—See EPAM Systems, Inc.; *U.S. Public*, pg. 783
THE WHITESTONE GROUP, INC.; *U.S. Private*, pg. 4135
WILLDAN HOMELAND SOLUTIONS—See Willdan Group, Inc.; *U.S. Public*, pg. 2371
WOODSTREAM EUROPE LTD.—See Vestar Capital Partners, LLC; *U.S. Private*, pg. 4372
WORLD WIDE SECURITY GROUP; *U.S. Private*, pg. 4567
WORMALD AUSTRALIA PTY. LTD.—See Evergreen Capital L.P.; *U.S. Private*, pg. 1438
XTRALIS, INC.—See Blum Capital Partners, L.P.; *U.S. Private*, pg. 599
XTRALIS PTY. LTD.—See Blum Capital Partners, L.P.; *U.S. Private*, pg. 599
XTRALIS UK LTD.—See Blum Capital Partners, L.P.; *U.S. Private*, pg. 599
ZAFE CARE SYSTEMS AB—See AddLife AB; *Int'l*, pg. 130

561622 — LOCKSMITHS

BATES SECURITY, LLC—See Pye-Barker Fire & Safety, LLC; *U.S. Private*, pg. 3309
CITYWIDE LOCKSMITHS LTD.—See Avante Corp; *Int'l*, pg. 735
FAR EAST VAULT LIMITED—See Far East Consortium International Limited; *Int'l*, pg. 2615
MEDECO SECURITY LOCKS INC—See ASSA ABLOY AB; *Int'l*, pg. 640
NATIONWIDE SECURITY & BUILDING SERVICES; *U.S. Private*, pg. 2866
SCHLAGE LOCK CO.—See Allegion Public Limited Company; *Int'l*, pg. 335
YALELOCK SPAIN—See ASSA ABLOY AB; *Int'l*, pg. 641

561710 — EXTERMINATING AND PEST CONTROL SERVICES

5 STAR TERMITE & PEST CONTROL, INC.—See Arrow Exterminators Inc.; *U.S. Private*, pg. 335
A-ACTIVE TERMITE & PEST CONTROL COMPANY; *U.S. Private*, pg. 22
ABC HOME & COMMERCIAL SERVICES; *U.S. Private*, pg. 35
ADAMS PEST CONTROL PTY LTD—See Rollins, Inc.; *U.S. Public*, pg. 1809
AK KRAUS UND HILLER SCHADLINGSBEKAMPFUNG GMBH—See Ecolab Inc.; *U.S. Public*, pg. 712
ALBANY ENVIRONMENTAL SERVICES LTD.—See Rollins, Inc.; *U.S. Public*, pg. 1809
ALLIANCE COMMERCIAL PEST CONTROL, INC.—See Thompson Street Capital Manager LLC; *U.S. Private*, pg. 4161
ALPINE MATERIALS LLC—See SiteOne Landscape Supply, Inc.; *U.S. Public*, pg. 1888
ALTA ASSOCIATES, INC.—See Diversified Search, LLC; *U.S. Private*, pg. 1243
AMERICAN PEST CONTROL-MNTGMRY—See EQT AB; *Int'l*, pg. 2467
AMERICAN PEST MANAGEMENT, INC.—See EQT AB; *Int'l*, pg. 2467
AMES GROUP LIMITED—See Rollins, Inc.; *U.S. Public*, pg. 1808
ANTICIMEX AB—See EQT AB; *Int'l*, pg. 2467
ANTICIMEX A/S—See EQT AB; *Int'l*, pg. 2467
ANTICIMEX AS—See EQT AB; *Int'l*, pg. 2468
ANTICIMEX BENELUX B.V.—See EQT AB; *Int'l*, pg. 2468
ANTICIMEX GMBH & CO. KG—See EQT AB; *Int'l*, pg. 2468

ANTIMITE ASSOCIATES INC.—See Terminix Service, Inc.; *U.S. Private*, pg. 3969
ARROW EXTERMINATORS INC.; *U.S. Private*, pg. 335
BARNES QUALITY PEST CONTROL, INC.—See Senske Lawn & Tree Care, Inc.; *U.S. Private*, pg. 3608
BAROQUE (S.W.) LIMITED—See Rollins, Inc.; *U.S. Public*, pg. 1809
BASF AGRICULTURAL SPECIALITIES LIMITED—See BASF SE; *Int'l*, pg. 872
BATZNER PEST MANAGEMENT, INC.; *U.S. Private*, pg. 490
BIOBEST S.A.—See Floridienne SA; *Int'l*, pg. 2708
BIO-SERV CORPORATION; *U.S. Private*, pg. 561
BUG BUSTERS, INC.; *U.S. Private*, pg. 681
BUG BUSTERS USA, INC.; *U.S. Private*, pg. 681
BUGMASTER TERMITE & PEST CONTROL—See Arrow Exterminators Inc.; *U.S. Private*, pg. 335
BUSY BEE CLEANING SERVICES LTD.; *Int'l*, pg. 1229
CANNON PEST CONTROL—See Arrow Exterminators Inc.; *U.S. Private*, pg. 335
CATSEYE PEST CONTROL, INC.; *U.S. Private*, pg. 792
CENTURY STRONG LIMITED—See Asia Resources Holdings Limited; *Int'l*, pg. 615
CERTUS PEST, INC.; *U.S. Private*, pg. 842
CHEMTEC PEST CONTROL CORP.—See EQT AB; *Int'l*, pg. 2468
CLARK PEST CONTROL, INC.—See Rollins, Inc.; *U.S. Public*, pg. 1809
CLARK PEST CONTROL OF STOCKTON INC.—See Rollins, Inc.; *U.S. Public*, pg. 1809
CLARK PEST CONTROT OF NEVADA, LLC—See Rollins, Inc.; *U.S. Public*, pg. 1809
CLEGG'S TERMITE AND PEST CONTROL, INC.; *U.S. Private*, pg. 939
CONTROL SOLUTIONS INC.—See China National Chemical Corporation; *Int'l*, pg. 1526
COOK'S PEST CONTROL, INC.—See Flash Exterminating, Inc.; *U.S. Private*, pg. 1540
COOPER PEST SOLUTION, INC.; *U.S. Private*, pg. 1041
COPESAN SERVICES INC.—See Roark Capital Group Inc.; *U.S. Private*, pg. 3456
CRANE PEST CONTROL, INC.—See Rollins, Inc.; *U.S. Public*, pg. 1809
DC SCIENTIFIC PEST CONTROL, INC.—See Arrow Exterminators Inc.; *U.S. Private*, pg. 335
DENTON COUNTY TERMITE & HOUSE LEVELING, INC.; *U.S. Private*, pg. 1206
DEWEY SERVICES INCORPORATED; *U.S. Private*, pg. 1219
DODSON BROTHERS EXTERMINATING COMPANY, INC.; *U.S. Private*, pg. 1252
ECOLAB PEST ELIMINATION—See Ecolab Inc.; *U.S. Public*, pg. 713
ECOLAB PEST FRANCE SAS—See Ecolab Inc.; *U.S. Public*, pg. 714
ECOTEAM, LLC—See Thompson Street Capital Manager LLC; *U.S. Private*, pg. 4161
EG SYSTEMS, LLC—See TruGreen Limited Partnership; *U.S. Private*, pg. 4249
ENTOPEST ENVIRONMENTAL SERVICES SDN. BHD.—See Ancom Nylex Berhad; *Int'l*, pg. 449
ENVIROPEST CONTROL SERVICES LTD.—See Rollins, Inc.; *U.S. Public*, pg. 1809
ENVIRO-SERV, INC.; *U.S. Public*, pg. 781
ENVIROTROL PEST MANAGEMENT SYSTEMS INC.; *U.S. Private*, pg. 1409
ENVIROTROL PEST SOLUTIONS LLC—See Thompson Street Capital Manager LLC; *U.S. Private*, pg. 4161
EUROPEST ENVIRONMENTAL SERVICES LIMITED—See Rollins, Inc.; *U.S. Public*, pg. 1809
EXPERT PEST CONTROL—See Rollins, Inc.; *U.S. Public*, pg. 1810
FLASH EXTERMINATING, INC.; *U.S. Private*, pg. 1540
FLOWER CITY PEST ELIMINATION—See Rollins, Inc.; *U.S. Public*, pg. 1810
FLOWTRON OUTDOOR PRODUCTS—See Armatron International, Inc.; *U.S. Private*, pg. 330
FOX PEST CONTROL - ALBANY LLC—See Rollins, Inc.; *U.S. Public*, pg. 1809
FOX PEST CONTROL - LONG ISLAND, LLC—See Rollins, Inc.; *U.S. Public*, pg. 1809
FOX PEST CONTROL - LOUISIANA LLC—See Rollins, Inc.; *U.S. Public*, pg. 1809
FOX PEST CONTROL - MCALLEN TX, LLC—See Rollins, Inc.; *U.S. Public*, pg. 1809
FOX PEST CONTROL - ORLANDO WEST, LLC—See Rollins, Inc.; *U.S. Public*, pg. 1809
FOX PEST CONTROL - PITTSBURGH, LLC—See Rollins, Inc.; *U.S. Public*, pg. 1809
FOX PEST CONTROL - RHODE ISLAND, LLC—See Rollins, Inc.; *U.S. Public*, pg. 1809
FOX PEST CONTROL - VIRGINIA BEACH, LLC—See Rollins, Inc.; *U.S. Public*, pg. 1809
FOX PEST SERVICES, LLC—See Rollins, Inc.; *U.S. Public*, pg. 1809
FRYE EXTERMINATING CO—See Arrow Exterminators Inc.; *U.S. Private*, pg. 335
GIDDY-UP GO TERMITE & PEST CONTROL, INC.—See

TORCO Termite & Pest Control Company, LLC; *U.S. Private*, pg. 4188
GOOD NEWS PEST SOLUTIONS; *U.S. Private*, pg. 1738
GREEN LAWN FERTILIZING, INC.; *U.S. Private*, pg. 1773
GUANGZHOU GREEN HARBOUR ENVIRONMENTAL OPERATION LTD.—See Ecolab Inc.; *U.S. Public*, pg. 714
GUARDIAN HYGIENE SERVICES LIMITED—See Rollins, Inc.; *U.S. Public*, pg. 1809
HEDLEY TECHNOLOGIES LTD.—See BioSyent Inc.; *Int'l*, pg. 1042
HOME PARAMONT PEST CONTROL COMPANIES; *U.S. Private*, pg. 1972
HOMETEAM PEST DEFENSE, LLC—See Rollins, Inc.; *U.S. Public*, pg. 1809
HOSKINS PEST CONTROL INC.—See Certus Pest, Inc.; *U.S. Private*, pg. 842
HUGHES EXTERMINATORS, INC.—See Arrow Exterminators Inc.; *U.S. Private*, pg. 335
INDUSTRIAL FUMIGANT COMPANY—See Rollins, Inc.; *U.S. Public*, pg. 1809
INNOVATIVE PEST MANAGEMENT, LLC—See EQT AB; *Int'l*, pg. 2467
INSIGHT PEST SOLUTIONS, LLC—See Massey Services, Inc.; *U.S. Private*, pg. 2606
INTERNATIONAL FOOD CONSULTANTS, LLC—See Rollins, Inc.; *U.S. Public*, pg. 1809
ISLAND PEST CONTROL INC.—See Massey Services, Inc.; *U.S. Private*, pg. 2606
ISOTECH PEST MANAGEMENT, INC.; *U.S. Private*, pg. 2146
JEFF'S PEST CONTROL SERVICE, INC.—See Rollins, Inc.; *U.S. Public*, pg. 1809
J & J EXTERMINATING CO. INC.; *U.S. Private*, pg. 2152
JODY MILLARD PEST CONTROL, LLC—See Rollins, Inc.; *U.S. Public*, pg. 1809
JP MCHALE PEST MANAGEMENT, LLC—See EQT AB; *Int'l*, pg. 2468
KESTREL PEST CONTROL LIMITED—See Rollins, Inc.; *U.S. Public*, pg. 1809
KINRO INVESTMENTS, INC.—See Rollins, Inc.; *U.S. Public*, pg. 1809
LEADSONLINE LLC; *U.S. Private*, pg. 2407
LIVE OAK PEST CONTROL INC.—See Thompson Street Capital Manager LLC; *U.S. Private*, pg. 4161
LLOYD PEST CONTROL COMPANY INCORPORATED; *U.S. Private*, pg. 2476
MASSEY SERVICES, INC. - PORT CHARLOTTE—See Massey Services, Inc.; *U.S. Private*, pg. 2606
MASSEY SERVICES, INC.; *U.S. Private*, pg. 2606
MASSEY SERVICES INC.—See Massey Services, Inc.; *U.S. Private*, pg. 2606
MATHIS EXTERMINATING; *U.S. Private*, pg. 2611
MICKS EXTERMINATING; *U.S. Private*, pg. 2702
MILLER TECHNICAL SERVICE—See Honeywell International Inc.; *U.S. Public*, pg. 1049
MOSQUITONIX FRANCHISE SYSTEMS, LTD.; *U.S. Private*, pg. 2793
MOSQUITO SQUAD FRANCHISING CORPORATION; *U.S. Private*, pg. 2793
MOTOMCO; *U.S. Private*, pg. 2796
NADER'S PEST RAIDERS, INC.—See Arrow Exterminators Inc.; *U.S. Private*, pg. 335
NATRAN LLC; *U.S. Private*, pg. 2866
NBC ENVIRONMENT LIMITED—See Rollins, Inc.; *U.S. Public*, pg. 1809
NOON TURF CARE; *U.S. Private*, pg. 2935
NORTHWEST EXTERMINATING CO., INC.—See EQT AB; *Int'l*, pg. 2468
NORTHWEST EXTERMINATING, LLC—See Rollins, Inc.; *U.S. Public*, pg. 1809
O'DONNELL'S TERMITE & PEST CONTROL, INC.; *U.S. Private*, pg. 2978
OLIVER EXTERMINATING CORP.; *U.S. Private*, pg. 3010
OPC PEST CONTROL, INC.—See Rollins, Inc.; *U.S. Public*, pg. 1809
ORKIN CANADA—See Rollins, Inc.; *U.S. Public*, pg. 1809
ORKIN CANADA—See Rollins, Inc.; *U.S. Public*, pg. 1809
ORKIN CANADA—See Rollins, Inc.; *U.S. Public*, pg. 1809
ORKIN, INC.—See Rollins, Inc.; *U.S. Public*, pg. 1809
PATRICK EXTERMINATING, INC.—See Certus Pest, Inc.; *U.S. Private*, pg. 842
PCO ACQUISITIONS, INC.—See Rollins, Inc.; *U.S. Public*, pg. 1809
PERMATREAT PEST CONTROL COMPANY INC.—See Rollins, Inc.; *U.S. Public*, pg. 1809
PESTCO, LLC—See Thompson Street Capital Manager LLC; *U.S. Private*, pg. 4161
PESTPROOF LIMITED—See Rollins, Inc.; *U.S. Public*, pg. 1809
PEST SOLUTIONS, LLC—See Roark Capital Group Inc.; *U.S. Private*, pg. 3456
PLUNKETT'S PEST CONTROL, INC.; *U.S. Private*, pg. 3215
P&M SOLUTIONS, LLC; *U.S. Private*, pg. 3059
POINTE PEST CONTROL-ID LLC—See Thompson Street Capital Manager LLC; *U.S. Private*, pg. 4161
POINTE PEST CONTROL-IL, LLC—See Thompson Street Capital Manager LLC; *U.S. Private*, pg. 4161

561710 — EXTERMINATING AND P...

R.J. ROBERTS, INC.—See PTS Advance; *U.S. Private,* pg. 3298
RK ENVIRONMENTAL SERVICES LLC; *U.S. Private,* pg. 3450
ROLLINS, INC.; *U.S. Public,* pg. 1808
ROSE EXTERMINATOR CO.; *U.S. Private,* pg. 3481
ROYAL PEST SOLUTIONS INC.—See Ecolab Inc.; *U.S. Public,* pg. 716
SAFEGUARD PEST CONTROL AND ENVIRONMENTAL SERVICES LIMITED—See Rollins, Inc.; *U.S. Public,* pg. 1809
SANDWICH ISLE PEST SOLUTIONS—See Roark Capital Group Inc.; *U.S. Private,* pg. 3456
SAWYER EXTERMINATING, INC.—See Rollins, Inc.; *U.S. Public,* pg. 1809
SCIENTIFIC SPRAY SERVICE, INC.—See Senske Lawn & Tree Care, Inc.; *U.S. Private,* pg. 3608
SCOTT EXTERMINATING CO—See Bug Busters USA, Inc.; *U.S. Private,* pg. 681
SENSKE LAWN & TREE CARE, INC.; *U.S. Private,* pg. 3608
SERVICEMASTER CONSUMER SERVICES LIMITED PARTNERSHIP—See Roark Capital Group Inc.; *U.S. Private,* pg. 3456
SEXTON PEST CONTROL, INC.; *U.S. Private,* pg. 3620
SPRAGUE PEST SOLUTIONS, INC.; *U.S. Private,* pg. 3762
STATEWIDE ROLLINS PTY LTD—See Rollins, Inc.; *U.S. Public,* pg. 1809
STERLING INTERNATIONAL INC.; *U.S. Private,* pg. 3805
SUTERRA LLC—See The Wonderful Company LLC; *U.S. Private,* pg. 4138
TARGET PEST CONTROL, INC.—See Rollins, Inc.; *U.S. Public,* pg. 1809
THE TERMINIX INTERNATIONAL COMPANY LIMITED PARTNERSHIP—See Roark Capital Group Inc.; *U.S. Private,* pg. 3456
TERMINIX SERVICE, INC.; *U.S. Private,* pg. 3969
TMC PEST MANAGEMENT, INC.—See Sprague Pest Solutions, Inc.; *U.S. Private,* pg. 3762
TORCO TERMITE & PEST CONTROL COMPANY, LLC; *U.S. Private,* pg. 4188
TOXIDO PEST CONTROL LLC—See Al Jaber Group; *Int'l,* pg. 280
TRULY NOLEN OF AMERICA INC.; *U.S. Private,* pg. 4250
VAN VYNCK ENVIRONMENTAL SERVICES LTD.—See Rollins, Inc.; *U.S. Public,* pg. 1809
VIKING TERMITE & PEST CONTROL, LLC—See EQT AB; *Int'l,* pg. 2468
WALTHAM SERVICES LLC—See Rollins, Inc.; *U.S. Public,* pg. 1810
W.B. MCCLOUD & COMPANY, INC.; *U.S. Private,* pg. 4419
WELLMARK INTERNATIONAL—See Central Garden & Pet Company; *U.S. Public,* pg. 473
WESTERN PEST SERVICES—See Rollins, Inc.; *U.S. Public,* pg. 1810
YOUNGER BROTHERS EXTERMINATING—See Younger Brothers Group Inc.; *U.S. Private,* pg. 4594

561720 — JANITORIAL SERVICES

4M BUILDING SOLUTIONS, INC.—See O2 Investment Partners, LLC; *U.S. Private,* pg. 2982
4M; *U.S. Private,* pg. 15
AAMAL SERVICES W.L.L.—See Aamal Company Q.S.C.; *Int'l,* pg. 36
ABM ELECTRICAL & LIGHTING SOLUTIONS, INC.—See ABM Industries, Inc.; *U.S. Public,* pg. 25
ABM FACILITY SERVICES, INC.—See ABM Industries, Inc.; *U.S. Public,* pg. 25
ABM FACILITY SERVICES—See ABM Industries, Inc.; *U.S. Public,* pg. 25
ABM INDUSTRIES, INC.; *U.S. Public,* pg. 25
ABM JANITORIAL SERVICES COMPANY, LTD.—See ABM Industries, Inc.; *U.S. Public,* pg. 26
ABM JANITORIAL SERVICES - HAWAIIAN REGION—See ABM Industries, Inc.; *U.S. Public,* pg. 25
ABM JANITORIAL SERVICES, INC.—See ABM Industries, Inc.; *U.S. Public,* pg. 25
ABM JANITORIAL SERVICES - MID-ATLANTIC REGION—See ABM Industries, Inc.; *U.S. Public,* pg. 25
ABM JANITORIAL SERVICES - MIDWEST REGION—See ABM Industries, Inc.; *U.S. Public,* pg. 25
ABM JANITORIAL SERVICES - NATIONAL ACCOUNTS—See ABM Industries, Inc.; *U.S. Public,* pg. 25
ABM JANITORIAL SERVICES - NORTH CENTRAL REGION—See ABM Industries, Inc.; *U.S. Public,* pg. 25
ABM JANITORIAL SERVICES - NORTHERN CALIFORNIA REGION—See ABM Industries, Inc.; *U.S. Public,* pg. 25
ABM JANITORIAL SERVICES - NORTHWEST MOUNTAIN REGION—See ABM Industries, Inc.; *U.S. Public,* pg. 26
ABM JANITORIAL SERVICES - NORTHWEST PACIFIC REGION—See ABM Industries, Inc.; *U.S. Public,* pg. 26
ABM JANITORIAL SERVICES - SOUTH CENTRAL REGION—See ABM Industries, Inc.; *U.S. Public,* pg. 26
ABM JANITORIAL SERVICES - SOUTHEAST REGION—See ABM Industries, Inc.; *U.S. Public,* pg. 26
ABM JANITORIAL SERVICES - WEST CENTRAL & WEST PACIFIC REGION—See ABM Industries, Inc.; *U.S. Public,* pg. 26
ABM ONSITE SERVICES, INC.—See ABM Industries, Inc.; *U.S. Public,* pg. 25
ACME BUILDING MAINTENANCE COMPANY; *U.S. Private,* pg. 60
ADMIRAL SECURITY SERVICES—See Red Coats Inc.; *U.S. Private,* pg. 3373
ADMIRAL SECURITY SERVICES—See Red Coats Inc.; *U.S. Private,* pg. 3373
AERO SNOW REMOVAL, LLC—See Guggenheim Partners, LLC; *U.S. Private,* pg. 1811
AETNA BUILDING MAINTENANCE, INC.; *U.S. Private,* pg. 120
AFRIBOOM PROPRIETARY LIMITED—See CSG Holdings Limited; *Int'l,* pg. 1864
AFS HEALTHCARE SUPPORT SERVICES—See AFS Janitorial LLC; *U.S. Private,* pg. 124
AFS JANITORIAL LLC; *U.S. Private,* pg. 124
AIRPORT TERMINAL SERVICES INC.; *U.S. Private,* pg. 142
ALLAN INDUSTRIES INC.; *U.S. Private,* pg. 174
AL TAJAMOUAT FOR CATERING & HOUSING COMPANY, PLC.; *Int'l,* pg. 283
AMERICAN EAGLE READY MIX UTAH, LLC—See Quanta Services, Inc.; *U.S. Public,* pg. 1750
AMERICAN FACILITY SERVICES; *U.S. Private,* pg. 232
AMERICAN NATIONAL SKYLINE, INC.—See Valcourt Building Services LLC; *U.S. Private,* pg. 4330
AMERICAN PRODUCT DISTRIBUTORS, INC.; *U.S. Private,* pg. 244
AMERI-KLEEN; *U.S. Private,* pg. 220
A.M.E. SERVICES, INC.; *U.S. Private,* pg. 27
AMPCO SYSTEM PARKING—See ABM Industries, Inc.; *U.S. Public,* pg. 26
ANDREWS & CO, LLC; *U.S. Private,* pg. 280
ANTILLES CLEANING SERVICE INC.; *U.S. Private,* pg. 288
APLEONA AHR CARECLEAN GMBH—See EQT AB; *Int'l,* pg. 2468
APOLLO 8 MAINTENANCE SERVICES LTD.; *Int'l,* pg. 517
AQUATECH ENVIRONMENTAL, INC.—See MPW Industrial Services Group, Inc.; *U.S. Private,* pg. 2804
AQUTIA CO., LTD.—See AEON Co., Ltd.; *Int'l,* pg. 177
ARAMARK FACILITIES MANAGEMENT, LLC—See Aramark; *U.S. Public,* pg. 176
ARAMARK FACILITY SERVICES—See Aramark; *U.S. Public,* pg. 176
ASTRO PAK CORPORATION; *U.S. Private,* pg. 362
AVIATION GROUND SERVICE COMPANY LTD.—See Cam Ranh International Airport Services JSC; *Int'l,* pg. 1266
AVNET FINANCE B.V.—See Avnet, Inc.; *U.S. Public,* pg. 251
AWNCLEAN U. S. A., INC.—See Valcourt Building Services LLC; *U.S. Private,* pg. 4330
AZTEC FACILITY SERVICES INCORPORATED; *U.S. Private,* pg. 416
BALDER GERMANY GMBH—See Fastighets AB Balder; *Int'l,* pg. 2622
BEE LINE, INC.; *U.S. Private,* pg. 512
BERKELEYS FRANCHISE SERVICES PTY. LTD.—See Downer EDI Limited; *Int'l,* pg. 2185
BEST FACILITY SERVICES; *U.S. Private,* pg. 542
BOB POPP BUILDING SERVICES, INC.—See Osceola Capital Management, LLC; *U.S. Private,* pg. 3047
BPCL-KIAL FUEL FARM PRIVATE LIMITED—See Bharat Petroleum Corporation Limited; *Int'l,* pg. 1011
BRETTING DEVELOPMENT CORP., INC.—See C. G. Bretting Manufacturing Co., Inc.; *U.S. Private,* pg. 705
BROADWAY SERVICES, INC.; *U.S. Private,* pg. 660
BUILDING MAINTENANCE SERVICE LLC—See Vornado Realty Trust; *U.S. Public,* pg. 2310
BUNZL UK LTD—See Bunzl plc; *Int'l,* pg. 1217
CAPE EAST PHILIPPINES INC—See Altrad Investment Authority SAS; *Int'l,* pg. 398
CAPE EAST (THAILAND) LIMITED—See Altrad Investment Authority SAS; *Int'l,* pg. 398
CAPITAL SERVICES, INC.—See O2 Investment Partners, LLC; *U.S. Private,* pg. 2982
CAPITOL CLEANING CONTRACTORS, INC.; *U.S. Private,* pg. 743
CARE FOR BUILDINGS AND CITIES CLEANING CONTRACTING COMPANY - WLL—See Gulf Cable & Electrical Industries Co. K.S.C.; *Int'l,* pg. 3179
CAVALIER SERVICES, INC.; *U.S. Private,* pg. 795
CENTAUR BUILDING SERVICES, INC.; *U.S. Private,* pg. 809
CITRON HYGIENE LTD—See Birch Hill Equity Partners Management Inc.; *Int'l,* pg. 1046
CITY WIDE MAINTENANCE OF COLORADO; *U.S. Private,* pg. 907
CLEAN AIR, INC.—See Ingersoll Rand Inc.; *U.S. Public,* pg. 1120
CLEAN HARBORS ENERGY AND INDUSTRIAL SERVICES LP—See Clean Harbors, Inc.; *U.S. Public,* pg. 509
CLEANING BUTLERS INTERNATIONAL, INC.; *U.S. Private,* pg. 931
CLEANPOWER LLC—See Marsden Holding, L.L.C.; *U.S. Private,* pg. 2591
CLECE, S.A.—See ACS, Actividades de Construccion y Servicios, S.A.; *Int'l,* pg. 110
CODDING MAINTENANCE INC—See Codding Enterprises; *U.S. Private,* pg. 960
COMMERCIAL CLEANING SYSTEMS, INC.—See Silver Oak Services Partners, LLC; *U.S. Private,* pg. 3661
CONTROL BUILDING SERVICES INC.; *U.S. Private,* pg. 1034
COTAC CORPORATION—See Ansell Limited; *Int'l,* pg. 478
CROSS GATE SERVICES, INC.—See The Budd Group Inc.; *U.S. Private,* pg. 4002
CROTHALL SERVICES GROUP, INC.—See Compass Group PLC; *Int'l,* pg. 1751
CROWN BUILDING MAINTENANCE CO.—See ABM Industries, Inc.; *U.S. Public,* pg. 26
CWS-BOCO BELUX N.V.—See Franz Haniel & Cie. GmbH; *Int'l,* pg. 2762
CWS-BOCO BULGARIA, EOOD—See Franz Haniel & Cie. GmbH; *Int'l,* pg. 2762
CWS-BOCO CESKA REPUBLIKA S.R.O.—See Franz Haniel & Cie. GmbH; *Int'l,* pg. 2762
CWS-BOCO DEUTSCHLAND GMBH—See Franz Haniel & Cie. GmbH; *Int'l,* pg. 2762
CWS-BOCO D.O.O.—See Franz Haniel & Cie. GmbH; *Int'l,* pg. 2762
CWS-BOCO HIGIENSKI SISTEMI IN VZDRZEVANJE D.O.O.—See Franz Haniel & Cie. GmbH; *Int'l,* pg. 2762
CWS-BOCO HUNGARY KFT.—See Franz Haniel & Cie. GmbH; *Int'l,* pg. 2762
CWS-BOCO ITALIA S.P.A—See Franz Haniel & Cie. GmbH; *Int'l,* pg. 2762
CWS-BOCO OSTERREICH GESELLSCHAFT M.B.H.—See Franz Haniel & Cie. GmbH; *Int'l,* pg. 2762
CWS-BOCO POLSKA SP. Z O.O.—See Franz Haniel & Cie. GmbH; *Int'l,* pg. 2762
CWS-BOCO ROMANIA S.R.L.—See Franz Haniel & Cie. GmbH; *Int'l,* pg. 2762
CWS-BOCO SLOVENSKO, S. R. O.—See Franz Haniel & Cie. GmbH; *Int'l,* pg. 2762
CWS-BOCO SUISSE SA—See Franz Haniel & Cie. GmbH; *Int'l,* pg. 2762
CWS-BOCO SWEDEN AB—See Franz Haniel & Cie. GmbH; *Int'l,* pg. 2762
CWS NEDERLAND B.V.—See Franz Haniel & Cie. GmbH; *Int'l,* pg. 2762
DAYCARE CLEANING SERVICES, INC.; *U.S. Private,* pg. 1177
DBI INDUSTRIAL SERVICES LIMITED—See Altrad Investment Authority SAS; *Int'l,* pg. 398
DCS SANITATION MANAGEMENT; *U.S. Private,* pg. 1180
DEFENDER SERVICES, INC.; *U.S. Private,* pg. 1190
DE LOGE SCHOONMAAKDIENSTEN B.V.—See EQT AB; *Int'l,* pg. 2476
DE LOGE SCHOONMAAKDIENSTEN B.V.—See The Goldman Sachs Group, Inc.; *U.S. Public,* pg. 2078
DIVERSEY EGYPT LIMITED—See Sealed Air Corporation; *U.S. Public,* pg. 1852
DIVERSEY LLC—See Sealed Air Corporation; *U.S. Public,* pg. 1853
DIVERSEY ROMANIA S.R.L.—See Sealed Air Corporation; *U.S. Public,* pg. 1853
DIVERSIFIED MAINTENANCE SYSTEMS, LLC; *U.S. Private,* pg. 1243
DMS FACILITY SERVICES INC.; *U.S. Private,* pg. 1249
DO SERVICE CO., LTD.—See AEON Co., Ltd.; *Int'l,* pg. 177
ECOLAB MANUFACTURING INC.—See Ecolab Inc.; *U.S. Public,* pg. 713
THE ELITE GROUP LLC—See ABRY Partners, LLC; *U.S. Private,* pg. 42
EMPIRE BUILDING & ENVIRONMENTAL SERVICES; *U.S. Private,* pg. 1384
EMPIRE MAINTENANCE INDUSTRIES INC.; *Int'l,* pg. 2387
ENG LENG THAILAND CO., LTD.—See Hygieia Group Limited; *Int'l,* pg. 3549
ENVIRONMENT AND GENERAL SERVICES, INC.—See APC Group, Inc.; *Int'l,* pg. 507
ERMC II, L.P.—See Allied Universal Manager LLC; *U.S. Private,* pg. 191
EUROFINS INPAC MEDIZINTECHNIK GMBH—See Eurofins Scientific S.E.; *Int'l,* pg. 2544
EXCLUSIVE CONTRACT SERVICES LIMITED; *Int'l,* pg. 2580
EXECUTIVE MANAGEMENT SERVICES INC.; *U.S. Private,* pg. 1447
EXTERIOR DIAGNOSTIC SERVICES, INC.—See Valcourt Building Services LLC; *U.S. Private,* pg. 4330
FBG SERVICE CORPORATION; *U.S. Private,* pg. 1485
FEDERAL BUILDING SERVICES, INC.; *U.S. Private,* pg. 1487
FIRST PENSION CUSTODIAN LTD.—See FBN Holdings PLC; *Int'l,* pg. 2627
FISH WINDOW CLEANING SERVICES INC.; *U.S. Private,* pg. 1533
FOUR-STATE HYGIENE, INC.—See Ecolab Inc.; *U.S. Public,* pg. 714
GCS GESELLSCHAFT FUR CLEANING SERVICE MBH &

N.A.I.C.S. INDEX

561730 — LANDSCAPING SERVICE...

CO. AIRPORT FRANKFURT/ MAIN KG—See Fraport AG; *Int'l*, pg. 2764
GDI INTEGRATED FACILITY SERVICES USA INC.—See GDI Integrated Facility Services Inc.; *Int'l*, pg. 2896
GDI TECHNICAL SERVICES—See GDI Integrated Facility Services Inc.; *Int'l*, pg. 2896
GEMINI GROUP SERVICE CORPORATION; *U.S. Private*, pg. 1657
GENERAL BUILDING MAINTENANCE, INC.; *U.S. Private*, pg. 1664
GPI CHILE SPA—See GPI S.p.A.; *Int'l*, pg. 3046
GREAT LAKES CLEANING INC.; *U.S. Private*, pg. 1764
GREAT LAKES SERVICES, LLC—See Centerbridge Partners, L.P.; *U.S. Private*, pg. 815
GREENHOMES AMERICA, LLC—See ABM Industries, Inc.; *U.S. Public*, pg. 25
HANIEL TEXTILE SERVICE GMBH—See Franz Haniel & Cie. GmbH; *Int'l*, pg. 2762
HARTCO, INC.—See Osceola Capital Management, LLC; *U.S. Private*, pg. 3047
HARVARD MAINTENANCE, INC.; *U.S. Private*, pg. 1875
HEITS BUILDING SERVICES, INC.; *U.S. Private*, pg. 1905
HOEN CO., LTD.—See Howa Machinery, Ltd.; *Int'l*, pg. 3493
HOME PERFECT RESTORATION, INC.; *U.S. Private*, pg. 1972
HORIZON SERVICES CORPORATION—See O2 Investment Partners, LLC; *U.S. Private*, pg. 2982
HORWATH HTL LIMITED—See Beijing Shiji Information Technology Co., Ltd.; *Int'l*, pg. 956
HOSPITALITY STAFFING SOLUTIONS, LLC—See Cerberus Capital Management, L.P.; *U.S. Private*, pg. 839
IH SERVICES, INC.—See GDI Integrated Facility Services Inc.; *Int'l*, pg. 2896
INDOOR ENVIRONMENTAL TECHNOLOGY INC.—See Team Solutions Project Group, Inc.; *U.S. Private*, pg. 3950
INNOCLEAN S.A.—See Compass Group PLC; *Int'l*, pg. 1752
INTEGRATED PROPERTY MANAGEMENT PTE LTD—See Bonvests Holdings Limited; *Int'l*, pg. 1110
INTEGRITY JANITORIAL SERVICES, INC.; *U.S. Private*, pg. 2103
JANI-KING INTERNATIONAL, INC.; *U.S. Private*, pg. 2186
JANI KING OF CALIFORNIA, INC.—See Jani-King International, Inc.; *U.S. Private*, pg. 2187
JANI KING OF DALLAS—See Jani-King International, Inc.; *U.S. Private*, pg. 2187
JANI KING OF ILLINOIS, INC.—See Jani-King International, Inc.; *U.S. Private*, pg. 2187
JANI KING OF MINNESOTA, INC.—See Jani-King International, Inc.; *U.S. Private*, pg. 2187
JANI KING OF NASHVILLE, INC.—See Jani-King International, Inc.; *U.S. Private*, pg. 2187
JANI KING OF NEW YORK, INC.—See Jani-King International, Inc.; *U.S. Private*, pg. 2187
JANI-KING OF PHOENIX—See Jani-King International, Inc.; *U.S. Private*, pg. 2187
JANITRONICS INC.; *U.S. Private*, pg. 2187
JDK REAL ESTATE, LLC—See Kenco Group Inc.; *U.S. Private*, pg. 2283
J. M. MURRAY CENTER INC—See J.M. Murray Center Inc.; *U.S. Private*, pg. 2169
JOHNSON CLEANING SERVICES COMPANY LIMITED—See Hong Kong Johnson Holdings Company Limited; *Int'l*, pg. 3466
KANKYOUSEIBI CO., LTD.—See AEON Co., Ltd.; *Int'l*, pg. 177
KB BUILDING SERVICES, INC.; *U.S. Private*, pg. 2268
KLEENMARK SERVICES CORP.; *U.S. Private*, pg. 2318
KLEEN-TECH BUILDING SERVICES; *U.S. Private*, pg. 2318
KLEEN-TECH SERVICES, LLC—See Concierge Building Services, LLC; *U.S. Private*, pg. 1009
KRYSTAL KLEAN INC.—See ACON Investments, LLC; *U.S. Private*, pg. 62
KTSC JANITORIAL INC.—See Concierge Building Services, LLC; *U.S. Private*, pg. 1009
LEGACY BUILDING SERVICES, INC.—See Dempsey Construction, Inc.; *U.S. Private*, pg. 1204
MACLELLAN INTEGRATED SERVICES; *U.S. Private*, pg. 2538
MAJOR COMMERCIAL CLEANING INC.—See O2 Investment Partners, LLC; *U.S. Private*, pg. 2982
MARSDEN BUILDING MAINTENANCE COMPANY, L.L.C.—See Marsden Holding, L.L.C.; *U.S. Private*, pg. 2591
MASTERCORP INC.; *U.S. Private*, pg. 2608
MCLEMORE BUILDING MAINTENANCE INC.; *U.S. Private*, pg. 2641
MCP, INC.—See Hillenbrand, Inc.; *U.S. Public*, pg. 1035
MC SERVICE GMBH—See Asklepios Kliniken GmbH & Co. KGaA; *Int'l*, pg. 623
METROCLEAN EXPRESS CORP.—See GTJ REIT, Inc.; *U.S. Private*, pg. 1807
METRO COMPUTER FACILITIES CLEANING CORP.—See Paris Maintenance Co. Inc.; *U.S. Private*, pg. 3095
METRO MAINTENANCE SERVICE SYSTEMS, INC.—See Paris Maintenance Co. Inc.; *U.S. Private*, pg. 3095

MICRONCLEAN IRELAND LTD.—See Franz Haniel & Cie. GmbH; *Int'l*, pg. 2763
MID-AMERICAN CLEANING CONTRACTORS; *U.S. Private*, pg. 2707
THE MILLARD GROUP; *U.S. Private*, pg. 4079
MILLARD MAINTENANCE SERVICE COMPANY INC.—See The Millard Group; *U.S. Private*, pg. 4079
MOLLY MAID, INC.; *U.S. Private*, pg. 2767
MPW INDUSTRIAL CLEANING CORP.—See MPW Industrial Services Group, Inc.; *U.S. Private*, pg. 2804
MPW INDUSTRIAL SERVICES GROUP—See MPW Industrial Services Group, Inc.; *U.S. Private*, pg. 2804
MPW INDUSTRIAL SERVICES GROUP—See MPW Industrial Services Group, Inc.; *U.S. Private*, pg. 2804
MUNDY CONTRACT MAINTENANCE—See The Mundy Companies; *U.S. Private*, pg. 4081
NALCO COMPANY LLC—See Ecolab Inc.; *U.S. Public*, pg. 715
NATIONAL BUILDING MAINTENANCE, INC.; *U.S. Private*, pg. 2849
NCH BELGIUM INC—See NCH Corporation; *U.S. Private*, pg. 2875
NCH CHILE S.A.—See NCH Corporation; *U.S. Private*, pg. 2875
NCH CROATIA D.O.O.—See NCH Corporation; *U.S. Private*, pg. 2875
NCH KOREA LTD—See NCH Corporation; *U.S. Private*, pg. 2876
NEU INTERNATIONAL RAILWAYS S.A.S.—See Groupe SFPI SA; *Int'l*, pg. 3111
NORTHWEST PIONEER INC—See Pioneer Packing Inc.; *U.S. Private*, pg. 3187
OKSA KIMYA SANAYI A.S.—See Ecolab Inc.; *U.S. Public*, pg. 716
OMNI FACILITY SERVICES, INC.; *U.S. Private*, pg. 3016
OPENWORKS; *U.S. Private*, pg. 3031
PACKERS HOLDINGS, LLC—See Harvest Partners L.P.; *U.S. Private*, pg. 1877
PACKERS SANITATION SERVICES, INC.—See Blue Point Capital Partners, LLC; *U.S. Private*, pg. 590
PARIS MAINTENANCE CO. INC.; *U.S. Private*, pg. 3095
PARIS MAINTENANCE CO. INC.—See Paris Maintenance Co. Inc.; *U.S. Private*, pg. 3095
PCM SERVICES INC.; *U.S. Private*, pg. 3120
PEGASUS COMMERCIAL & RESIDENTIAL CLEANING LLC; *U.S. Private*, pg. 3129
PENINSULA CLEANING SERVICE INC.; *U.S. Private*, pg. 3133
THE PERFORMANCE COMPANIES INC.; *U.S. Private*, pg. 4093
PERFORMANCE PLUS—See The Performance Companies Inc.; *U.S. Private*, pg. 4093
PLURAL SERVICEPOOL GMBH—See Compass Group PLC; *Int'l*, pg. 1752
POLYKING SERVICES LIMITED—See Allied Group Limited; *Int'l*, pg. 357
P&R ENTERPRISES INC.; *U.S. Private*, pg. 3059
PREVENTIVE MAINTENANCE MEDICAL INC.—See Atlantic Street Capital Management LLC; *U.S. Private*, pg. 374
PRIDE INDUSTRIES INC.; *U.S. Private*, pg. 3259
PRINCIPAL BUILDING SERVICES, INC.; *U.S. Private*, pg. 3264
PRITCHARD INDUSTRIES, INC.—See Littlejohn & Co., LLC; *U.S. Private*, pg. 2471
PRITCHARD INDUSTRIES SOUTHWEST INC.—See Littlejohn & Co., LLC; *U.S. Private*, pg. 2471
PROSPERITY LAND CLEANING SERVICE LIMITED—See Asia Orient Holdings Limited; *Int'l*, pg. 613
P.T. ECOLAB INDONESIA—See Ecolab Inc.; *U.S. Public*, pg. 716
R B HILTON SAUDI ARABIA LIMITED—See Altrad Investment Authority SAS; *Int'l*, pg. 398
RED COATS INC. - NORTH CAROLINA DIVISION—See Red Coats Inc.; *U.S. Private*, pg. 3374
RED COATS INC. - NORTH FLORIDA DIVISION—See Red Coats Inc.; *U.S. Private*, pg. 3374
RED COATS INC.; *U.S. Private*, pg. 3373
RED COATS INC.—See Red Coats Inc.; *U.S. Private*, pg. 3374
RED COATS INC. - SOUTH FLORIDA DIVISION—See Red Coats Inc.; *U.S. Private*, pg. 3374
RED COATS INC. - VIRGINIA SOUTHERN DIVISION—See Red Coats Inc.; *U.S. Private*, pg. 3374
RESEARCH ANALYSIS & MAINTENANCE, INC.; *U.S. Private*, pg. 3403
REVIEWPRO ASIA PACIFIC PTE LTD—See Beijing Shiji Information Technology Co., Ltd.; *Int'l*, pg. 956
REVIEWPRO, INC—See Beijing Shiji Information Technology Co., Ltd.; *Int'l*, pg. 956
REVIEW RANK S.A.—See Beijing Shiji Information Technology Co., Ltd.; *Int'l*, pg. 956
RITE WAY SERVICE INC—See Diversified Maintenance Systems, LLC; *U.S. Private*, pg. 1243
ROMARCO NV—See Eiffage S.A.; *Int'l*, pg. 2331
RONELL INDUSTRIES INC.; *U.S. Private*, pg. 3478
ROZALADO & CO.; *U.S. Private*, pg. 3494
SDQ, LTD.; *U.S. Private*, pg. 3581
SERVICE BY MEDALLION; *U.S. Private*, pg. 3614

SERVICE MANAGEMENT SYSTEMS, INC.—See SMS Holding Corporation; *U.S. Private*, pg. 3699
SERVICEMASTER LTD.—See Roark Capital Group Inc.; *U.S. Private*, pg. 3456
SERVICEMASTER OF CANADA LTD.—See Roark Capital Group Inc.; *U.S. Private*, pg. 3456
SERVICON SYSTEMS INC.; *U.S. Private*, pg. 3617
SERVI-TEK LLC; *U.S. Private*, pg. 3614
SERVPRO OF THE QUAD CITIES, LLC—See Blackstone Inc.; *U.S. Public*, pg. 358
SEVENSON INDUSTRIAL SERVICES, INC.—See Sevenson Environmental Services, Inc.; *U.S. Private*, pg. 3619
SHAMROCK BUILDING SERVICES CORP.; *U.S. Private*, pg. 3624
SHELTERCLEAN, INC.—See GTJ REIT, Inc.; *U.S. Private*, pg. 1807
SMS ASSIST LLC; *U.S. Private*, pg. 3698
SOUTH SHORE BUILDING SERVICES, INC.—See Valcourt Building Services LLC; *U.S. Private*, pg. 4330
SPARKLE MAINTENANCE, INC.; *U.S. Private*, pg. 3746
SPARKLE MAINTENANCE, INC.—See Silver Oak Services Partners LLC; *U.S. Private*, pg. 3661
SPARTAN SECURITY SERVICES, INC. - NEW JERSEY—See ATALIAN Global Services; *Int'l*, pg. 666
SPECIALIZED MAINTENANCE AND SERVICES, INC.—See Carylon Corporation; *U.S. Private*, pg. 777
SSC SERVICE SOLUTIONS—See Compass Group PLC; *Int'l*, pg. 1751
STEVENS AVIATION INC.; *U.S. Private*, pg. 3809
SWISHER HYGIENE FRANCHISE CORP.—See Ecolab Inc.; *U.S. Public*, pg. 716
SWISH WHITE RIVER LTD.—See Kelso & Company, L.P.; *U.S. Private*, pg. 2279
SWISH WHITE RIVER LTD.—See Warburg Pincus LLC; *U.S. Private*, pg. 4437
SWS RE-DISTRIBUTION COMPANY, INC.; *U.S. Private*, pg. 3895
TEMCO SERVICE INDUSTRIES, INC.—See ATALIAN Global Services; *Int'l*, pg. 665
TITAN FACILITIES MANAGEMENT PTE. LTD.—See Hygieia Group Limited; *Int'l*, pg. 3549
TOP GUN PRESSURE WASHING, INC.—See Osceola Capital Management, LLC; *U.S. Private*, pg. 3047
TOTALFACILITY, INC.—See Lincolnshire Management, Inc.; *U.S. Private*, pg. 2459
TOWER CLEANING SYSTEMS INC.; *U.S. Private*, pg. 4193
TRIANGLE SERVICES, INC.; *U.S. Private*, pg. 4226
UAB MANO APLINKA—See City Service SE; *Int'l*, pg. 1628
UNIBAR MAINTENANCE SERVICES; *U.S. Private*, pg. 4281
UNITED SERVICE COMPANIES INC.; *U.S. Private*, pg. 4297
UNITED STATES SERVICE INDUSTRIES INC.; *U.S. Private*, pg. 4300
USI SERVICES GROUP; *U.S. Private*, pg. 4323
VANGUARD CLEANING SYSTEMS INC; *U.S. Private*, pg. 4343
VARSITY CONTRACTORS, INC.; *U.S. Private*, pg. 4347
VENTROLLA LIMITED—See Quanex Building Products Corp.; *U.S. Public*, pg. 1750
WASTE CONSOLIDATORS, INC.—See Ally Waste Services, LLC; *U.S. Private*, pg. 194
WBM ENTERPRISES INC.; *U.S. Private*, pg. 4461
WESTERN BUILDING MAINTENANCE—See WBM Enterprises Inc.; *U.S. Private*, pg. 4461
WINGFOOT CORPORATION—See The Goodyear Tire & Rubber Company; *U.S. Public*, pg. 2085
WORLD CLEAN FACILITY SERVICES PTE. LTD.—See Advancer Global Limited; *Int'l*, pg. 163
WYNDHAM RESORT AT FAIRFIELD PLANTATION—See Travel & Leisure Co.; *U.S. Public*, pg. 2186
XANITOS, INC.—See Angeles Equity Partners, LLC; *U.S. Private*, pg. 282

561730 — LANDSCAPING SERVICES

1611 SUMMIT, INC.—See Apax Partners LLP; *Int'l*, pg. 505
ABSOLUTELY OUTDOORS; *U.S. Private*, pg. 44
ABUNDANT TREE CARE SERVICES LLC—See Apax Partners LLP; *Int'l*, pg. 505
ACE OF BLADES LLC—See Senske Lawn & Tree Care, Inc.; *U.S. Private*, pg. 3608
AGROLUX NEDERLAND B.V.—See The Scotts Miracle-Gro Company; *U.S. Public*, pg. 2126
AKKM CO., LTD.—See AISIN Corporation; *Int'l*, pg. 252
ALL-GREEN TURF MANAGEMENT CORP.—See Rahn Contracting, Inc.; *U.S. Private*, pg. 3346
AMADA PLANTECH CO., LTD.—See Amada Holdings Co., Ltd.; *Int'l*, pg. 404
ARBOR ART TREE CARE INC.—See Apax Partners LLP; *Int'l*, pg. 506
ARBORCHEM PRODUCTS—See Asplundh Tree Expert Co.; *U.S. Private*, pg. 353
ARBORGUARD, INC.—See The Davey Tree Expert Company; *U.S. Private*, pg. 4018
ARBORMETRICS SOLUTIONS, INC.—See Asplundh Tree Expert Co.; *U.S. Private*, pg. 353

561730 — LANDSCAPING SERVICES

ARBOR-NOMICS TURF, INC.—See Senske Lawn & Tree Care, Inc.; *U.S. Private*, pg. 3608
ARBOR TREE SERVICE INC.—See The Davey Tree Expert Company; *U.S. Private*, pg. 4018
ARBORWELL, INC.—See Apax Partners LLP; *Int'l*, pg. 506
ARTISTREE LANDSCAPE MAINTENANCE & DESIGN; *U.S. Private*, pg. 343
ASCENT PREP INTERNATIONAL EDUCATION LIMITED—See Bexcellent Group Holdings Limited; *Int'l*, pg. 1005
ASPLUNDH CANADA ULC—See Asplundh Tree Expert Co.; *U.S. Private*, pg. 353
ASPLUNDH TREE EXPERT (AUSTRALIA) PTY LTD—See Asplundh Tree Expert Co.; *U.S. Private*, pg. 353
ASPLUNDH TREE EXPERT CO.; *U.S. Private*, pg. 353
ASPLUNDH TREE EXPERT (NZ) LTD.—See Asplundh Tree Expert Co.; *U.S. Private*, pg. 353
ASPLUNDH TREE SERVICE ULC—See Asplundh Tree Expert Co.; *U.S. Private*, pg. 353
BAILEY NURSERIES INC. — SAUVIE IS DIVISION—See Bailey Nurseries Inc.; *U.S. Private*, pg. 426
BAILEY NURSERIES INC. - SUNNYSIDE DIVISION—See Bailey Nurseries Inc.; *U.S. Private*, pg. 426
BARTLETT TREE SERVICE—See The F.A. Bartlett Tree Expert Company; *U.S. Private*, pg. 4027
BLADES OF GREEN, INC.—See Senske Lawn & Tree Care, Inc.; *U.S. Private*, pg. 3608
BLUME TREE SERVICES, INC.—See Asplundh Tree Expert Co.; *U.S. Private*, pg. 353
BOLKE HANDEL GMBH—See BayWa AG; *Int'l*, pg. 917
BRIGHTREE SERVICES LLC—See ResMed Inc.; *U.S. Public*, pg. 1790
BRITISH INTERNATIONAL SCHOOL OF TBILISI LLC—See Georgia Capital PLC; *Int'l*, pg. 2939
BROTHER LIVING CO., LTD.—See Brother Industries, Ltd.; *Int'l*, pg. 1197
BRUCE COMPANY OF WISCONSIN, INC.; *U.S. Private*, pg. 671
BUCCANEER LANDSCAPE MANAGEMENT CORPORATION; *U.S. Private*, pg. 676
BUCKEYE SWEEPING, INC.—See Warburg Pincus LLC; *U.S. Private*, pg. 4440
BUCKSWOOD INTERNATIONAL SCHOOL - TBILISI, LLC—See Georgia Capital PLC; *Int'l*, pg. 2939
CAGWIN & DORWARD; *U.S. Private*, pg. 714
CAROLINA TREE CARE; *U.S. Private*, pg. 769
CHAPEL VALLEY LANDSCAPE COMPANY; *U.S. Private*, pg. 849
CHAPIN INTERNATIONAL, INC.; *U.S. Private*, pg. 849
CHINA WAN TONG YUAN (HOLDINGS) LTD.; *Int'l*, pg. 1562
CITYGREEN GARTENGESTALTUNGS GMBH—See BayWa AG; *Int'l*, pg. 917
CLARENCE DAVIDS & COMPANY; *U.S. Private*, pg. 910
CLEAN CUT LAWNS, LLC—See BrightView Holdings, Inc.; *U.S. Public*, pg. 383
CLS SCOTLAND LIMITED—See CLS Holdings plc; *Int'l*, pg. 1664
COMMERCIAL LAWN CARE SERVICES INC.; *U.S. Private*, pg. 984
COMMERCIAL TREE CARE, INC.—See BrightView Holdings, Inc.; *U.S. Public*, pg. 383
CONTRACT SWEEPERS & EQUIPMENT COMPANY—See Warburg Pincus LLC; *U.S. Private*, pg. 4440
CORNERSTONE SOLUTIONS GROUP; *U.S. Private*, pg. 1052
DAITO KENTAKU PARTNERS CO., LTD.—See Daito Trust Construction Co., Ltd.; *Int'l*, pg. 1943
DANIEL STONE & LANDSCAPING SUPPLIES, INC.—See SiteOne Landscape Supply, Inc.; *U.S. Public*, pg. 1888
DAQIAN ECOLOGY & ENVIRONMENT GROUP CO., LTD.; *Int'l*, pg. 1971
DAVEY TREE EXPERT COMPANY OF CANADA, LTD.—See The Davey Tree Expert Company; *U.S. Private*, pg. 4018
DAVEY TREE SURGERY COMPANY—See The Davey Tree Expert Company; *U.S. Private*, pg. 4018
DAVID J. FRANK LANDSCAPE CONTRACTING, INC.; *U.S. Private*, pg. 1170
DE ENK GROEN & GOLF B.V.; *Int'l*, pg. 1995
DELTA ELECTRONICS (UK) LTD.—See Delta Electronics, Inc.; *Int'l*, pg. 2018
DELUXE FAMILY CO., LTD.; *Int'l*, pg. 2022
DENT ENTERPRISES INC.; *U.S. Private*, pg. 1206
DERICHEBOURG ESPACES VERTS SAS—See Derichebourg S.A.; *Int'l*, pg. 2042
DIETER'S SOD SERVICE, INC.—See Agro-Iron, Inc.; *U.S. Private*, pg. 130
DIXIE LANDSCAPE CO. INC.; *U.S. Private*, pg. 1245
D'ONOFRIO & SON LANDSCAPING, INC.; *U.S. Private*, pg. 1139
DUNN & CO. INC.; *U.S. Private*, pg. 1290
ELITE GROUNDS, L.C.—See Stratton & Bratt Landscapes, LLC; *U.S. Private*, pg. 3837
ELK CREEK LAWN & TREE CARE, LLC—See Senske Lawn & Tree Care, Inc.; *U.S. Private*, pg. 3608
ELTEK POWER CO., LTD.—See Delta Electronics, Inc.; *Int'l*, pg. 2018

EMERALD ISLE LANDSCAPING, INC.—See Osceola Capital Management, LLC; *U.S. Private*, pg. 3047
EMERALD LANDSCAPE COMPANY, INC.—See BrightView Holdings, Inc.; *U.S. Public*, pg. 384
EMERALD LANDSCAPE SERVICES, INC.—See Stay-Green, Inc.; *U.S. Private*, pg. 3794
EMERALD TREE FARM; *U.S. Private*, pg. 1380
ENHANCED LANDSCAPE MANAGEMENT, LLC—See Landscape Developmental Inc.; *U.S. Private*, pg. 2387
ENVIRONMENTAL AND LANDSCAPE SERVICES SDN. BHD.—See AWC Berhad; *Int'l*, pg. 752
ENVIRONMENTAL DESIGN, INC.—See Audax Group, Limited Partnership; *U.S. Private*, pg. 389
ENVIRONMENTAL EARTHSCAPES INCORPORATED; *U.S. Private*, pg. 1407
ENVIRONMENTAL TURF SERVICES, INC.—See XFit Brands, Inc.; *U.S. Public*, pg. 2391
ESP LANDSCAPERS LTD.—See ENL Limited; *Int'l*, pg. 2441
EUROGREEN AUSTRIA GMBH—See BayWa AG; *Int'l*, pg. 917
EVERGREEN GARDEN CARE AUSTRALIA PTY LTD.—See Exponent Private Equity LLP; *Int'l*, pg. 2590
EVERGREEN GARDEN CARE BELGIUM BVBA—See Exponent Private Equity LLP; *Int'l*, pg. 2590
EVERGREEN GARDEN CARE POLAND SP. Z O.O.—See Exponent Private Equity LLP; *Int'l*, pg. 2590
THE F.A. BARTLETT TREE EXPERT COMPANY; *U.S. Private*, pg. 4027
FAIRWAY GREEN INC.—See CenterOak Partners LLC; *U.S. Private*, pg. 816
FAIRWAY LAWNS, LLC; *U.S. Private*, pg. 1465
FIELDSTONE LANDSCAPE SERVICES LLC; *U.S. Private*, pg. 1504
FIRST KONTACT LLC—See Advantage Communications, Inc.; *Int'l*, pg. 164
FIT TURF, INC.—See Senske Lawn & Tree Care, Inc.; *U.S. Private*, pg. 3608
FLORIDA LANDSCAPE CONSULTANTS INC.; *U.S. Private*, pg. 1549
FLORIDA LANDSCAPE DOCTOR, INC.; *U.S. Private*, pg. 1549
FLOWER KING ECO-ENGINEERING INC.; *Int'l*, pg. 2709
GARDENVISION, LLC—See Markel Group Inc.; *U.S. Public*, pg. 1368
G & G LAWN CARE, INC.—See Senske Lawn & Tree Care, Inc.; *U.S. Private*, pg. 3608
GIFU LANDSCAPE ARCHITECT CO., LTD.; *Int'l*, pg. 2970
G.K. SMART FARMING CO., LTD.—See Gunkul Engineering Co., Ltd.; *Int'l*, pg. 3183
GLM LANDSCAPE SUPPLY, LLC; *U.S. Private*, pg. 1711
GOLD LANDSCAPE, LLC—See Guggenheim Partners, LLC; *U.S. Private*, pg. 1811
GOTHIC LANDSCAPE, INC.; *U.S. Private*, pg. 1745
GOTHIC LANDSCAPING INC.; *U.S. Private*, pg. 1745
GRASSCOR LAWN & LANDSCAPES, LLC—See Schill Landscaping & Lawn Services, Inc.; *U.S. Private*, pg. 3565
GRASS & MORE OUTDOOR SERVICES, INC.; *U.S. Private*, pg. 1758
GREENBRIER FARMS, INC.; *U.S. Private*, pg. 1776
GREENERY OF CHARLESTON, LLC—See Ruppert Landscape, LLC; *U.S. Private*, pg. 3504
GREENHAVEN, INC.—See Apax Partners LLP; *Int'l*, pg. 506
GREEN LANDSCAPING AB—See FSN Capital Partners AS; *Int'l*, pg. 2799
GREEN MOUNTAIN LAWN & TREE CARE—See Senske Lawn & Tree Care, Inc.; *U.S. Private*, pg. 3608
GREENSCAPE, INC.; *U.S. Private*, pg. 1780
GREENSCAPES OF SOUTHWEST FLORIDA, INC.; *U.S. Private*, pg. 1780
GREENVIEW LANDSCAPING, INC.; *U.S. Private*, pg. 1780
GRITIT; *Int'l*, pg. 3087
GTI NEVADA, LLC—See Green Thumb Industries, Inc.; *U.S. Public*, pg. 964
GUANGDONG WENKE GREEN TECHNOLOGY CORP., LTD.; *Int'l*, pg. 3161
GUNZE GREEN CO., LTD.—See Gunze Limited; *Int'l*, pg. 3185
HANGZHOU LANDSCAPING CO., LTD.; *Int'l*, pg. 3249
HARDEMAN LANDSCAPE NURSERY, INC.; *U.S. Private*, pg. 1862
HASTINGS LANDSCAPE & DESIGN GROUP—See H.G. Hastings Co.; *U.S. Private*, pg. 1826
HEAVILAND ENTERPRISES, INC.—See BrightView Holdings, Inc.; *U.S. Public*, pg. 384
HIGHRIDGE—See Plantscapes, Inc.; *U.S. Private*, pg. 3198
HOLMES LANDSCAPE COMPANY—See Landscape Developmental Inc.; *U.S. Private*, pg. 2387
HONG KONG ISLAND LANDSCAPE COMPANY LIMITED—See FSE Services Group Limited; *Int'l*, pg. 2798
HOUSE LEAVE CO., LTD.—See Daito Trust Construction Co., Ltd.; *Int'l*, pg. 1943
HVAC CONSOLIDATED PTY. LTD.—See Beijer Ref AB; *Int'l*, pg. 944

IRELAND GANNON ASSOCIATES INC.; *U.S. Private*, pg. 2137
ISLAND PLANT COMPANY, LLC—See BrightView Holdings, Inc.; *U.S. Public*, pg. 384
JACOBSEN PROFESSIONAL LAWN CARE INC.—See Textron Inc.; *U.S. Public*, pg. 2028
KEEPSAKE PLANTS LTD—See Aris Horticulture, Inc.; *U.S. Private*, pg. 323
KENS TREE CARE INC.—See Apax Partners LLP; *Int'l*, pg. 506
KNIGHT SOLUTIONS; *U.S. Private*, pg. 2322
KOCH & ASSOCIATES INC.—See Dover Corporation; *U.S. Public*, pg. 679
LANDCARE LANDSCAPING, INC.; *U.S. Private*, pg. 2384
LANDSCAPE CARE CO.—See Bruce Company of Wisconsin, Inc.; *U.S. Private*, pg. 671
LANDSCAPE DEVELOPMENTAL INC.; *U.S. Private*, pg. 2387
LANDSCAPE WORKSHOP, INC.—See Carousel Capital Partners; *U.S. Private*, pg. 769
LAWNAMERICA, INC.—See TruGreen Limited Partnership; *U.S. Private*, pg. 4249
LAWN BUTLER INC.; *U.S. Private*, pg. 2401
LAWN PRIDE INC.—See Harvest Partners L.P.; *U.S. Private*, pg. 1876
LEN-TRAN, INC.; *U.S. Private*, pg. 2421
LEWIS TREE SERVICE INC.; *U.S. Private*, pg. 2440
LIMAGRAIN GMBH—See Groupe Limagrain Holding SA; *Int'l*, pg. 3107
LIMAGRAIN NEDERLAND BV—See Groupe Limagrain Holding SA; *Int'l*, pg. 3107
LK ESTATE SERVICES, INC.—See Fairway Lawns, LLC; *U.S. Private*, pg. 1465
LOU GIROUD TREE SERVICE, INC.—See Apax Partners LLP; *Int'l*, pg. 506
LOUISIANA LANDSCAPE SPECIALTY, INC.—See Carousel Capital Partners; *U.S. Private*, pg. 769
LUKE BROTHERS, INC.; *U.S. Private*, pg. 2513
MERIT SERVICE SOLUTIONS—See Eureka Equity Partners, L.P.; *U.S. Private*, pg. 1433
MONARCH LANDSCAPE HOLDINGS LLC—See Audax Group, Limited Partnership; *U.S. Private*, pg. 389
MOUNTAIN HIGH TREE SERVICE, INC.—See Apax Partners LLP; *Int'l*, pg. 506
MR. AMOTO LAWN & TREE SERVICE, LLC—See Apax Partners LLP; *Int'l*, pg. 506
MTD SCHWEIZ AG—See Stanley Black & Decker, Inc.; *U.S. Public*, pg. 1933
MUNIE GREENCARE—See Munie Outdoor Services, Inc.; *U.S. Private*, pg. 2814
MUNIE OUTDOOR SERVICES, INC.; *U.S. Private*, pg. 2814
MY ENT SPECIALIST PTE. LTD.—See Alliance Healthcare Group Limited; *Int'l*, pg. 340
NATIONAL TURF SERVICE-CLINTON M. QUINN, INC.—See Senske Lawn & Tree Care, Inc.; *U.S. Private*, pg. 3608
NATURAL DESIGNS LANDSCAPING INC.; *U.S. Private*, pg. 2867
NATURAL WAY, INC.; *U.S. Private*, pg. 2867
NELSON TREE SERVICE INC.; *U.S. Private*, pg. 2883
NEW GARDEN LANDSCAPING & NURSERY INC.; *U.S. Private*, pg. 2896
NEWMAN LAWN CARE INC.—See Crux Capital Ltd; *U.S. Private*, pg. 1114
NEW URBAN FORESTRY, LLC—See Warren Equity Partners, LLC; *U.S. Private*, pg. 4443
NIGERIAN EAGLE FLOUR MILLS LIMITED—See Flour Mills of Nigeria Plc.; *Int'l*, pg. 2709
O'CONNELL LANDSCAPE MAINTENANCE; *U.S. Private*, pg. 2977
O'DONNELL LANDSCAPES, INC.; *U.S. Private*, pg. 2978
ORTO PARQUES Y JARDINES, S.L.—See ACS, Actividades de Construccion y Servicios, S.A.; *Int'l*, pg. 115
OUTDOOR SERVICES, LLC—See Cerberus Capital Management, L.P.; *U.S. Private*, pg. 838
PACIFIC OUTDOOR LIVING; *U.S. Private*, pg. 3069
PACIFIC PAVINGSTONE—See Pacific Outdoor Living; *U.S. Private*, pg. 3069
PAFF LANDSCAPE, INC.; *U.S. Private*, pg. 3074
PARADIGM ENTERPRISES, INC.—See Babcock Power, Inc.; *U.S. Private*, pg. 422
PARK WEST LANDSCAPE INC.—See Tracy Industries Inc.; *U.S. Private*, pg. 4201
PARK WEST LANDSCAPE INC.—See Tracy Industries Inc.; *U.S. Private*, pg. 4201
PAVING MAINTENANCE SUPPLY, INC.—See Ergon, Inc.; *U.S. Private*, pg. 1418
PICKSEED WEST INC.—See DLF AmbA; *Int'l*, pg. 2140
PISCATAQUA LANDSCAPIING & TREE SERVICE; *U.S. Private*, pg. 3190
PROFESSIONAL GROUNDS MANAGEMENT; *U.S. Private*, pg. 3275
PROPERTY CARE SPECILISTS INC.; *U.S. Private*, pg. 3285
PRO-QUAL INDUSTRIES, LLC—See Sperber Landscape Cos, LLC; *U.S. Private*, pg. 3756
PROSCAPE LANDSCAPE MANAGEMENT CORPORATION; *U.S. Private*, pg. 3286

N.A.I.C.S. INDEX

QGS DEVELOPMENT INC.; *U.S. Private*, pg. 3313
RED CEDAR ARBORISTS & LANDSCAPERS, INC.—See Apax Partners LLP.—*Int'l*, pg. 506
RIPS PROFESSIONAL LAWN CARE, INC.—See Juniper Landscaping, Inc.; *U.S. Private*, pg. 2244
ROCKLAND TREE EXPERT CO, INC.—See The Davey Tree Expert Company; *U.S. Private*, pg. 4018
ROCK & WATERSCAPE SYSTEMS INC.; *U.S. Private*, pg. 3464
ROTOLO CONSULTANTS, INC.; *U.S. Private*, pg. 3487
RUPPERT LANDSCAPE, LLC; *U.S. Private*, pg. 3504
SAVATREE, LLC—See Apax Partners LLP; *Int'l*, pg. 505
THE SCOTTS COMPANY—See The Scotts Miracle-Gro Company; *U.S. Public*, pg. 2127
SCOTT'S LANDSCAPING INC.—See Ruppert Landscape, LLC; *U.S. Private*, pg. 3504
THE SIEBENTHALER CO.; *U.S. Private*, pg. 4118
SOUTHERN LANDSCAPE SUPPLY LLC—See SiteOne Landscape Supply, Inc.; *U.S. Public*, pg. 1889
SPECIALTY TREE SERVICES, LLC—See Tree Medic, LLC; *U.S. Private*, pg. 4216
SPRING-GREEN LAWN CARE CORPORATION; *U.S. Private*, pg. 3763
STAY-GREEN, INC.; *U.S. Private*, pg. 3794
ST. CROIX TREE SERVICE, INC.; *U.S. Private*, pg. 3771
STERLING GROUP SERVICES PTY LTD—See CityWide Service Solutions Pty Ltd; *Int'l*, pg. 1630
STOCKNER'S NURSERY, INC.; *U.S. Private*, pg. 3815
STRATTON & BRATT LANDSCAPES, LLC; *U.S. Private*, pg. 3837
SUNGROW LANDSCAPE SERVICES; *U.S. Private*, pg. 3867
SUNRISE LANDSCAPE, INC.; *U.S. Private*, pg. 3870
SUNSET PROPERTY SERVICES, INC.—See Warburg Pincus LLC; *U.S. Private*, pg. 4440
SUPERSCAPES, INC.—See Crux Capital Ltd; *U.S. Private*, pg. 1114
SUSTAINABLE GREEN TEAM LTD.; *U.S. Public*, pg. 1968
SWEEPING CORPORATION OF AMERICA, INC.—See Warburg Pincus LLC; *U.S. Private*, pg. 4439
SWINGLE, INC.—See Apax Partners LLP; *Int'l*, pg. 506
TADDIKEN TREE COMPANY—See Apax Partners LLP; *Int'l*, pg. 506
TAK TAI ENVIROSCAPE LIMITED—See Baguio Green Group Limited; *Int'l*, pg. 799
TEUFEL LANDSCAPE, INC.; *U.S. Private*, pg. 3974
TEUFEL NURSERY INC.—See Teufel Landscape, Inc.; *U.S. Private*, pg. 3974
THAI STICK HERB CO., LTD.—See Gunkul Engineering Co., Ltd.; *Int'l*, pg. 3184
THRIVE, INC.—See Apax Partners LLP; *Int'l*, pg. 506
TIMBERLAND SERVICES—See Landvest Inc.; *U.S. Private*, pg. 2387
THE TODD GROUP, INC.; *U.S. Private*, pg. 4127
TORO EUROPE N.V.—See The Toro Company; *U.S. Public*, pg. 2135
TORRE & BRUGLIO INC.; *U.S. Private*, pg. 4189
TOVAR SNOW PROFESSIONALS, INC.—See Guggenheim Partners, LLC; *U.S. Private*, pg. 1811
TRACY INDUSTRIES INC.; *U.S. Private*, pg. 4201
TRACY & RYDER LANDSCAPE INC.—See Tracy Industries Inc.; *U.S. Private*, pg. 4201
TREE MEDICS, INC.—See The F.A. Bartlett Tree Expert Company; *U.S. Private*, pg. 4027
TREE MEN INC.—See A Plus Tree, LLC; *U.S. Private*, pg. 19
TREE-TECH, INC.—See Apax Partners LLP; *Int'l*, pg. 506
TROPEX PLANT SALES LEASING & MAINTENANCE, INC.; *U.S. Private*, pg. 4242
TRUGREEN COMPANIES LLC—See TruGreen Limited Partnership; *U.S. Private*, pg. 4249
TRUGREEN LIMITED PARTNERSHIP; *U.S. Private*, pg. 4249
TURF MASTERS BRANDS, INC.—See CenterOak Partners LLC; *U.S. Private*, pg. 816
TURF MASTERS LAWN CARE, INC.—See CenterOak Partners LLC; *U.S. Private*, pg. 816
TURFTENDERS LANDSCAPE SERVICES INC—See Greenscape, Inc.; *U.S. Private*, pg. 1780
UNDERWOOD BROS INCORPORATED; *U.S. Private*, pg. 4280
UNITED LAND SERVICES, INC.—See Centre Partners Management LLC; *U.S. Private*, pg. 829
UNITED LAND SERVICES, INC.—See LP First Capital; *U.S. Private*, pg. 2507
URBACET, S.L.—See ACS, Actividades de Construccion y Servicios, S.A.; *Int'l*, pg. 116
USA SERVICES OF FLORIDA, INC.—See Warburg Pincus LLC; *U.S. Private*, pg. 4440
U.S. LAWNS INC.—See The Riverside Company; *U.S. Private*, pg. 4110
VILA & SON LANDSCAPING CORP.; *U.S. Private*, pg. 4383
VINE & BRANCH, INC.—See Apax Partners LLP; *Int'l*, pg. 506
WEBER ENVIRONMENTAL SERVICE, INC.; *U.S. Private*, pg. 4465
WEST BAY LANDSCAPE, INC.—See BrightView Holdings, Inc.; *U.S. Public*, pg. 384
WESTCOAST LANDSCAPE & LAWNS, INC.; *U.S. Private*, pg. 4489
WOLF TREE, INC.—See The Davey Tree Expert Company; *U.S. Private*, pg. 4018
WOODWARD LANDSCAPE SUPPLY, INC.; *U.S. Private*, pg. 4561
WRIGHT TREE SERVICE INC.; *U.S. Private*, pg. 4573
YELLOWSTONE TREE SURGEONS, INC.—See Apax Partners LLP; *Int'l*, pg. 506
YOUNG'S NURSERIES INC.; *U.S. Private*, pg. 4593
ZHONG YA INTERNATIONAL LTD; *U.S. Public*, pg. 2403
ZUKE'S LANDSCAPE, INC.—See Landscape Developmental Inc.; *U.S. Private*, pg. 2387

561740 — CARPET AND UPHOLSTERY CLEANING SERVICES

ALFRED KARCHER GES.M.B.H.—See Alfred Karcher GmbH & Co. KG; *Int'l*, pg. 316
ALFRED KARCHER GMBH & CO. KG; *Int'l*, pg. 316
ALFRED KARCHER VERTRIEBS-GMBH—See Alfred Karcher GmbH & Co. KG; *Int'l*, pg. 316
AL QURAISHI MARKETING CO. LTD.—See Ali Zaid Al-Quraishi & Brothers Co.; *Int'l*, pg. 323
ASIATIC CARPETS LTD; *Int'l*, pg. 620
BAGUIO GREEN GROUP LIMITED; *Int'l*, pg. 799
BIOCLEANSE LTD.—See Getinge AB; *Int'l*, pg. 2949
BIOKARPET BULGARIA E.O.O.D.—See Biokarpet S.A.; *Int'l*, pg. 1038
BMS ENTERPRISES INC.; *U.S. Private*, pg. 601
BUCHER MUNICIPAL A/S—See Bucher Industries AG; *Int'l*, pg. 1207
CHEM-TECH FINISHERS INC.; *U.S. Private*, pg. 871
COIT SERVICES, INC.; *U.S. Private*, pg. 965
COIT SERVICES PENNSYLVANIA INC—See Coit Services, Inc.; *U.S. Private*, pg. 965
COIT SERVICES—See Coit Services, Inc.; *U.S. Private*, pg. 965
COLORADO CLEANUP SERVICES, INC.; *U.S. Private*, pg. 973
C-TECH INDUSTRIES DE MEXICO, S. DE R.L. DE C.F.—See Alfred Karcher GmbH & Co. KG; *Int'l*, pg. 316
DIXIE CARPET INSTALLATIONS INC.—See The Sterling Group, L.P.; *U.S. Private*, pg. 4122
ECOPPIA SCIENTIFIC LTD.; *Int'l*, pg. 2299
GETINGE LANCER SAS—See Getinge AB; *Int'l*, pg. 2950
GEYEN GROUP, INC.; *U.S. Private*, pg. 1689
HARRIS RESEARCH, INC.—See Baird Financial Group, Inc.; *U.S. Private*, pg. 453
HPC INDUSTRIAL SERVICES, LLC—See Clean Harbors, Inc.; *U.S. Public*, pg. 510
KARCHER ANLAGENVERMIETUNGS GMBH—See Alfred Karcher GmbH & Co. KG; *Int'l*, pg. 316
KARCHER B.V.—See Alfred Karcher GmbH & Co. KG; *Int'l*, pg. 316
KARCHER CANADA, INC.—See Alfred Karcher GmbH & Co. KG; *Int'l*, pg. 316
KARCHER CLEANING SYSTEMS A.E.—See Alfred Karcher GmbH & Co. KG; *Int'l*, pg. 316
KARCHER CO., LTD. (SOUTH KOREA)—See Alfred Karcher GmbH & Co. KG; *Int'l*, pg. 316
KARCHER HUNGARIA KFT.—See Alfred Karcher GmbH & Co. KG; *Int'l*, pg. 316
KARCHER INDUSTRIA E COMERCIO LTDA.—See Alfred Karcher GmbH & Co. KG; *Int'l*, pg. 316
KARCHER (JAPAN) CO., LTD.—See Alfred Karcher GmbH & Co. KG; *Int'l*, pg. 316
KARCHER LEASING GMBH—See Alfred Karcher GmbH & Co. KG; *Int'l*, pg. 316
KARCHER LTD—See Alfred Karcher GmbH & Co. KG; *Int'l*, pg. 316
KARCHER N.V.—See Alfred Karcher GmbH & Co. KG; *Int'l*, pg. 316
KARCHER OY—See Alfred Karcher GmbH & Co. KG; *Int'l*, pg. 316
KARCHER POLAND LTD. SP. Z O.O.—See Alfred Karcher GmbH & Co. KG; *Int'l*, pg. 316
KARCHER PTY. LTD.—See Alfred Karcher GmbH & Co. KG; *Int'l*, pg. 317
KARCHER RENGORINGSSYSTEMER A/S—See Alfred Karcher GmbH & Co. KG; *Int'l*, pg. 317
KARCHER RESIDENTIAL SOLUTIONS, INC.—See Alfred Karcher GmbH & Co. KG; *Int'l*, pg. 317
KARCHER, S.A.—See Alfred Karcher GmbH & Co. KG; *Int'l*, pg. 317
KARCHER S.A.S.—See Alfred Karcher GmbH & Co. KG; *Int'l*, pg. 317
KARCHER SERVIS TICARET A.S.—See Alfred Karcher GmbH & Co. KG; *Int'l*, pg. 317
KARCHER (SHANGHAI) CLEANING SYSTEMS CO., LTD.—See Alfred Karcher GmbH & Co. KG; *Int'l*, pg. 316
KARCHER SOUTH EAST ASIA PTE LTD—See Alfred Karcher GmbH & Co. KG; *Int'l*, pg. 317
KARCHER S.P.A.—See Alfred Karcher GmbH & Co. KG; *Int'l*, pg. 317
KARCHER SPOL. S R.O.—See Alfred Karcher GmbH & Co. KG; *Int'l*, pg. 317

RAINBOW INTERNATIONAL LLC—See Harvest Partners L.P.; *U.S. Private*, pg. 1877
RICKY'S OIL & ENVIRONMENTAL SERVICES, LLC—See Clean Harbors, Inc.; *U.S. Public*, pg. 510
SERVIS LIMITED—See Angostura Holdings Limited; *Int'l*, pg. 463
SOLID RESTORATION INC.—See Grays Peak Capital LP; *U.S. Private*, pg. 1761
SOLID RESTORATION INC.—See Timoneer Strategic Partners, LLC; *U.S. Private*, pg. 4173
SPAULDING DECON, LLC; *U.S. Private*, pg. 3747
STANLEY STEEMER ATLANTA—See Stanley Steemer International, Inc.; *U.S. Private*, pg. 3783
STANLEY STEEMER INTERNATIONAL, INC.; *U.S. Private*, pg. 3783
STANLEY STEEMER OF CHARLESTON—See Stanley Steemer International, Inc.; *U.S. Private*, pg. 3783
UCS; *U.S. Private*, pg. 4274
ZEROREZ MINNESOTA; *U.S. Private*, pg. 4602

561790 — OTHER SERVICES TO BUILDINGS AND DWELLINGS

ABM ELECTRICAL & LIGHTING SERVICES, LLC—See ABM Industries, Inc.; *U.S. Public*, pg. 25
ABM GROUP UK LIMITED—See ABM Industries, Inc.; *U.S. Public*, pg. 26
ACEA ENERGIA S.P.A.—See ACEA S.p.A.; *Int'l*, pg. 95
AEON DELIGHT (CHINA) CO., LTD.—See AEON Co., Ltd.; *Int'l*, pg. 176
AEON DELIGHT CO., LTD.—See AEON Co., Ltd.; *Int'l*, pg. 176
AEP PLANUNG UND BERATUNG GESELLSCHAFT MBH—See BKW AG; *Int'l*, pg. 1054
AFRICA ISRAEL RESIDENCES LTD.—See Africa Israel Investments Ltd.; *Int'l*, pg. 190
AILSEN LIMITED.; *Int'l*, pg. 232
AMERICAN BUILDING SERVICES LLC—See Platinum Equity, LLC; *U.S. Private*, pg. 3208
AMERICAN POOL MANAGEMENT CORP.; *U.S. Private*, pg. 244
ASTRY LOAN SERVICES CORPORATION—See AIFUL Corporation; *Int'l*, pg. 232
A TO Z SERVICE CO., LTD.—See AEON Co., Ltd.; *Int'l*, pg. 178
AUSTIN DATA, INC.—See D.R. Horton, Inc.; *U.S. Public*, pg. 619
BALFOUR BEATTY BUILDING MANAGEMENT & SERVICES—See Balfour Beatty plc; *Int'l*, pg. 807
BEIJING WOODWORKING FACTORY CO., LTD—See BBMG Corporation; *Int'l*, pg. 921
BIKEN TECHNO CORPORATION LTD.; *Int'l*, pg. 1023
BUCHER MUNICIPAL LTD.—See Bucher Industries AG; *Int'l*, pg. 1207
BUCHER MUNICIPAL NORTH AMERICA—See Bucher Industries AG; *Int'l*, pg. 1207
BUCHER MUNICIPAL SIA—See Bucher Industries AG; *Int'l*, pg. 1207
CDC CORPORATION—See Owens Corning; *U.S. Public*, pg. 1626
CHEVALIER (CONSTRUCTION) COMPANY LIMITED—See Chevalier International Holdings Limited; *Int'l*, pg. 1473
CHINESE GLOBAL INVESTORS GROUP LTD.; *Int'l*, pg. 1569
CLC CONTRACTORS LTD.—See H.I.G. Capital, LLC; *U.S. Private*, pg. 1827
THE CLEANING AUTHORITY LLC—See Apax Partners LLP; *Int'l*, pg. 502
CNA-HTE VIETNAM CO., LTD.—See CNA Group Ltd.; *Int'l*, pg. 1673
CONSTI OYJ; *Int'l*, pg. 1776
CORAL TECHNOLOGIES—See Coral Chemical Company; *U.S. Private*, pg. 1046
CPG FACILITIES MANAGEMENT PTE LTD.—See China Architecture Design & Research Group; *Int'l*, pg. 1483
CRYSTAL CLEAR CONTRACTOR PTE. LTD.—See Daiki Axis Co., Ltd.; *Int'l*, pg. 1932
DANINGER + PARTNER ENGINEERING GMBH—See BKW AG; *Int'l*, pg. 1055
DAOJIA LIMITED; *Int'l*, pg. 1970
DEDINJE A.D.; *Int'l*, pg. 2002
DEYAAR FACILITIES MANAGEMENT LLC—See Deyaar Development PJSC; *Int'l*, pg. 2093
DIMNICAR A.D.; *Int'l*, pg. 2126
DOMINION HOME PROTECTION SERVICES, INC.—See Dominion Energy, Inc.; *U.S. Public*, pg. 674
DONOHOE CONSTRUCTION COMPANY—See The Donohoe Companies, Inc.; *U.S. Private*, pg. 4022
DONOHOE DEVELOPMENT COMPANY—See The Donohoe Companies, Inc.; *U.S. Private*, pg. 4022
DONOHOE HOSPITALITY SERVICES, LLC—See The Donohoe Companies, Inc.; *U.S. Private*, pg. 4022
DONOHOE REAL ESTATE SERVICES—See The Donohoe Companies, Inc.; *U.S. Private*, pg. 4023
D-SS INC.—See Datasection Inc.; *Int'l*, pg. 1979
DVS LIMITED—See Fletcher Building Limited; *Int'l*, pg. 2699

561790 — OTHER SERVICES TO B...

ECO WINDOW SYSTEMS LLC—See Koch Industries, Inc.; *U.S. Private*, pg. 2332
EQ TERMINAL SERVICES LLC—See Republic Services, Inc.; *U.S. Public*, pg. 1787
FELIX HOLTKEN GMBH—See Asterion Industrial Partners SGEIC SA; *Int'l*, pg. 654
GENERAL SERVICES, INC.—See AEON Co., Ltd.; *Int'l*, pg. 177
GREATSOLUTIONS PTE. LTD.—See GS Holdings Limited; *Int'l*, pg. 3143
GUILBERT PROPRETE; *Int'l*, pg. 3173
HANKYU MAINTENANCE SERVICE CO LTD—See H2O Retailing Corp.; *Int'l*, pg. 3200
HASEKO COMMUNITY OKINAWA INC.—See Haseko Corporation; *Int'l*, pg. 3283
HAWKINS BUILDING SERVICES OF SAINT LOUIS, LLC—See Hercules Window Cleaning Co.; *U.S. Private*, pg. 1921
HERCULES WINDOW CLEANING CO.; *U.S. Private*, pg. 1921
HIGIJENA A.D.; *Int'l*, pg. 3389
HOME & DRY LIMITED—See Fletcher Building Limited; *Int'l*, pg. 2700
HOMEMAID AB; *Int'l*, pg. 3455
HOSS INDUSTRIAL LLC; *U.S. Private*, pg. 1988
INAYA FACILITIES MANAGEMENT SERVICES—See Belhasa Group of Companies; *Int'l*, pg. 964
INFINITE POOL FINISHES, LLC; *U.S. Private*, pg. 2071
INSTITUTO DE GESTION SANITARIA, S.A.U.—See Grupo Villar Mir, S.A.U.; *Int'l*, pg. 3138
JAGER & CO. GESELLSCHAFT MIT BESCHRANKTER HAFTUNG—See CEZ, a.s.; *Int'l*, pg. 1428
JOBS BUILDING SERVICES LLC—See Valcourt Building Services LLC; *U.S. Private*, pg. 4330
KAJITAKU INC.—See AEON Co., Ltd.; *Int'l*, pg. 177
KARL WAECHTER AG—See BKW AG; *Int'l*, pg. 1055
KURASHINO SAISON CO., LTD.—See Credit Saison Co., Ltd.; *Int'l*, pg. 1836
LINIO COLOMBIA S.A.S.—See Falabella S.A.; *Int'l*, pg. 2610
LUTZ BODENMULLER AG—See BKW AG; *Int'l*, pg. 1055
MANSELL PLC—See Balfour Beatty plc; *Int'l*, pg. 807
MARZOLO & PARTNER AG—See BKW AG; *Int'l*, pg. 1055
METRO ROD LIMITED—See Franchise Brands plc; *Int'l*, pg. 2760
MPW INDUSTRIAL SERVICES GROUP, INC.; *U.S. Private*, pg. 2804
NEUKOM INSTALLATIONEN AG—See BKW AG; *Int'l*, pg. 1055
OMNI SERV LIMITED—See ABM Industries, Inc.; *U.S. Public*, pg. 26
PICOI CO., LTD.—See Freesia Macross Corporation; *Int'l*, pg. 2771
POOL AND PATIO WORKS INC.—See Anchor Industries, Inc.; *U.S. Private*, pg. 273
POOL & ELECTRICAL PRODUCTS INC.; *U.S. Private*, pg. 3227
RABOUD ENERGIE SA—See BKW AG; *Int'l*, pg. 1056
R. MONNET & CIE SA—See BKW AG; *Int'l*, pg. 1056
ROBERT L. HANSON INC.; *U.S. Private*, pg. 3458
ROBERTS ONSITE INC.—See Black & McDonald Limited; *Int'l*, pg. 1056
RUEFER INGENIEURE AG—See BKW AG; *Int'l*, pg. 1056
THE SANKEI BUILDING MANAGEMENT CO., LTD.—See Fuji Media Holdings, Inc.; *Int'l*, pg. 2814
S.C.BOG'ART BUILDING MANAGEMENT S.R.L.—See Bog'Art S.R.L.; *Int'l*, pg. 1100
SCOTTIE'S BUILDING SERVICES, LLC—See Valcourt Building Services LLC; *U.S. Private*, pg. 4330
THE SERVICEMASTER COMPANY, LLC—See Roark Capital Group Inc.; *U.S. Private*, pg. 3456
THE SHAMROCK COMPANY—See The Shamrock Companies Inc.; *U.S. Private*, pg. 4117
SOCIETE DES FORCES ELECTRIQUES DE LA GOULE SA—See BKW AG; *Int'l*, pg. 1056
SOIL-AWAY CLEANING & RESTORATION SERVICES—See Insurcomm Construction, Inc.; *U.S. Private*, pg. 2095
STELTECH STRUCTURAL LTD.—See BlueScope Steel Limited; *Int'l*, pg. 1074
SUMMIT DISPOSAL INC.—See Waste Management, Inc.; *U.S. Public*, pg. 2332
SWISHER HYGIENE USA OPERATIONS, INC.—See Ecolab Inc.; *U.S. Public*, pg. 716
TECNOCONTROL SERVICIOS, S.A.U.—See Grupo Empresarial San Jose, S.A.; *Int'l*, pg. 3128
TID TECHNISCHE INFORMATIONEN & DIENSTLEISTUNGEN P. TSCHANNEN GMBH—See BKW AG; *Int'l*, pg. 1056
TODD HARRIS CO. INC.; *U.S. Private*, pg. 4181
TOTAL CORROSION CONTROL PTY. LTD.—See Altrad Investment Authority SAS; *Int'l*, pg. 398
TSI ASSET HOLDINGS, LLC—See Lezzer Lumber, Inc.; *U.S. Private*, pg. 2441
UAB CITY SERVICE ENGINEERING—See City Service SE; *Int'l*, pg. 1628
UEG ARAUCARIA S.A.—See Companhia Paranaense de Energia; *Int'l*, pg. 1748
UNITED BUILDING MAINTENANCE, INC.; *U.S. Private*, pg. 4288
VALCOURT BUILDING SERVICES LLC; *U.S. Private*, pg. 4330
VAMED-KMB—See Fresenius SE & Co. KGaA; *Int'l*, pg. 2781
WEBER AG—See BKW AG; *Int'l*, pg. 1056
WERNER ELECTRO AG—See BKW AG; *Int'l*, pg. 1056
WINKELMANN ELEKTRO AG—See BKW AG; *Int'l*, pg. 1056
WORRY FREE TEA HOUSE HOLDINGS CO; *U.S. Public*, pg. 2382

561910 — PACKAGING AND LABELING SERVICES

AARON THOMAS CO. INC.; *U.S. Private*, pg. 32
ABC FULFILLMENT LLC—See Hub Group, Inc.; *U.S. Public*, pg. 1066
ACCUPAC, INC.—See Palladium Equity Partners, LLC; *U.S. Private*, pg. 3077
ACCU-TEC INC.; *U.S. Private*, pg. 54
ACME PAPER & SUPPLY CO., INC.—See Acme Paper & Supply Co. Inc.; *U.S. Private*, pg. 61
ADHESIVE MATERIALS GROUP—See Distribution Solutions Group, Inc.; *U.S. Public*, pg. 668
A.D. SCHINNER CO.—See Bunzl plc; *Int'l*, pg. 1218
ADVANCED LABELS N. W.—See Ares Management Corporation; *U.S. Public*, pg. 190
ADVANTAGE LABEL & PACKAGING, INC.—See UFP Industries, Inc.; *U.S. Public*, pg. 2218
ALCO HIGH-TECH PLASTICS, INC.; *U.S. Private*, pg. 153
ALDUS PTY. LTD.; *Int'l*, pg. 305
ALL AMERICAN FOODS, INC.; *U.S. Private*, pg. 169
ALL AMERICAN LABEL & PACKAGING—See Heartwood Partners, LLC; *U.S. Private*, pg. 1901
AMCOR FLEXIBLES (AUSTRALIA) PTY LTD—See Amcor plc; *Int'l*, pg. 416
AMCOR FLEXIBLES BANGKOK PUBLIC COMPANY LIMITED—See Amcor plc; *Int'l*, pg. 417
AMCOR FLEXIBLES EUROPA SUR S.L.—See Amcor plc; *Int'l*, pg. 417
AMCOR FLEXIBLES INC.—See Amcor plc; *Int'l*, pg. 417
AMCOR FLEXIBLES PHETCHABURI CO., LTD.—See Amcor plc; *Int'l*, pg. 417
AMCOR FLEXIBLES RORSCHACH AG—See Amcor plc; *Int'l*, pg. 417
AMCOR PACKAGING UK LIMITED—See Amcor plc; *Int'l*, pg. 417
AMCOR RIGID PLASTICS DE MEXICO S.A. DE C.V.—See Amcor plc; *Int'l*, pg. 417
AMD INDUSTRIES LIMITED; *Int'l*, pg. 418
AMERICAN PASTEURIZATION COMPANY; *U.S. Private*, pg. 243
AMPLE INDUSTRIES, INC.—See Ares Management Corporation; *U.S. Public*, pg. 190
ANDPAK, INC.—See ADDEV Material SAS; *Int'l*, pg. 128
ANHEUSER-BUSCH PACKAGING GROUP, INC.—See Anheuser-Busch InBev SA/NV; *Int'l*, pg. 465
APEX PRODUCTS COMPANY—See Keystone Laboratories, Inc.; *U.S. Private*, pg. 2300
APTAR MEZZOVICO S.A.—See AptarGroup, Inc.; *U.S. Public*, pg. 175
AQL DECORATING CO., INC.—See O. Berk Company L.L.C.; *U.S. Private*, pg. 2981
ARDAGH METAL PACKAGING USA, INC.—See Ardagh Group S.A.; *Int'l*, pg. 553
ASE ASSEMBLY & TEST (SHANGHAI) LIMITED—See ASE Technology Holding Co., Ltd.; *Int'l*, pg. 604
A+ SECURE PACKAGING, LLC—See Cardinal Health, Inc.; *U.S. Public*, pg. 433
ASEPTIC SYSTEMS CO., LTD.—See Dai Nippon Printing Co., Ltd.; *Int'l*, pg. 1914
ASIA SIYAKA COMMODITIES PLC; *Int'l*, pg. 615
ASSOCIATED PRODUCTION SERVICE; *U.S. Private*, pg. 357
ASTRAFLEX (PTY) LTD—See Berry Global Group, Inc; *U.S. Public*, pg. 323
ATLANTIC CORPORATION - CHARLESTON FACILITY—See Atlantic Corporation; *U.S. Private*, pg. 372
ATLANTIC CORPORATION - CHARLOTTE FACILITY—See Atlantic Corporation; *U.S. Private*, pg. 372
ATLANTIC CORPORATION - GREENSBORO FACILITY—See Atlantic Corporation; *U.S. Private*, pg. 372
ATLANTIC PACKAGING AS—See Atlantic Group; *Int'l*, pg. 674
ATLANTIC PACKAGING PRODUCTS LTD.; *Int'l*, pg. 675
ATLANTIC ZEISER GMBH & CO.; *Int'l*, pg. 676
ATOBATC SHIPPING CYPRUS LTD.—See Aspo Oyj; *Int'l*, pg. 631
AVERY DENNISON CENTRAL EUROPE GMBH—See Avery Dennison Corporation; *U.S. Public*, pg. 243
AVERY DENNISON CORPORATION; *U.S. Public*, pg. 243
AVERY DENNISON CORP. - RETAIL BRANDING & INFORMATION SOLUTIONS—See Avery Dennison Corporation; *U.S. Public*, pg. 243

CORPORATE AFFILIATIONS

AXIOM CORP.; *Int'l*, pg. 769
AXIOM LABEL, LLC—See Ares Management Corporation; *U.S. Public*, pg. 190
BALL AEROSOL PACKAGING INDIA PRIVATE LIMITED—See Ball Corporation; *U.S. Public*, pg. 266
BALL BEVERAGE PACKAGING EGYPT SAE—See Ball Corporation; *U.S. Public*, pg. 266
BANTAS BANDIRMA AMBALAJ SANAYI VE TICARET AS; *Int'l*, pg. 855
BAOSTEEL METAL CO., LTD.—See China Baowu Steel Group Corp., Ltd.; *Int'l*, pg. 1485
BAY CONVERTING INC.—See Bay Industries Inc.; *U.S. Private*, pg. 493
BEKUPLAST BENELUX B.V.—See bekuplast GmbH; *Int'l*, pg. 962
BEKUPLAST POLSKA SP. Z O.O—See bekuplast GmbH; *Int'l*, pg. 962
BELUGA LIMITED—See Hung Hing Printing Group Limited; *Int'l*, pg. 3535
BERKELEY CONTRACT PACKAGING LLC—See Summit Container Corporation; *U.S. Private*, pg. 3854
BERRY PACK INC.—See Goldberg Lindsay & Co., LLC; *U.S. Public*, pg. 1729
BOSCH PACKAGING TECHNOLOGY LTD.—See CVC Capital Partners SICAV-FIS S.A.; *Int'l*, pg. 1884
BOVEDA INC.; *U.S. Private*, pg. 624
BROOK & WHITTLE LIMITED—See Genstar Capital, LLC; *U.S. Private*, pg. 1676
BUDUCNOST JAGODINA A.D.; *Int'l*, pg. 1211
BUNZL CANADA, INC.—See Bunzl plc; *Int'l*, pg. 1217
CADILLAC PRODUCTS PACKAGING COMPANY - DALLAS PLANT—See Cadillac Products, Inc.; *U.S. Private*, pg. 713
CADILLAC PRODUCTS PACKAGING COMPANY - PARIS PLANT—See Cadillac Products, Inc.; *U.S. Private*, pg. 713
CARGILL MEAT SOLUTIONS—See Cargill, Inc.; *U.S. Private*, pg. 758
CARRIS REELS, INC.-NORTH CAROLINA WOOD DIV—See Carris Financial Corp.; *U.S. Private*, pg. 772
CARVAJAL EMPAQUES SA; *Int'l*, pg. 1348
CASTLE COLOURS LTD.—See American Securities LLC; *U.S. Private*, pg. 253
CATALENT SHIGA K.K.—See Catalent, Inc.; *U.S. Public*, pg. 448
CATALENT U.K. PACKAGING LIMITED—See Catalent, Inc.; *U.S. Public*, pg. 448
CATALENT USA WOODSTOCK, INC.—See Catalent, Inc.; *U.S. Public*, pg. 448
CCL INDUSTRIES CORP.—See CCL Industries Inc.; *Int'l*, pg. 1367
CCL INDUSTRIES INC.; *Int'l*, pg. 1367
CCL INSERTCO, LLC—See CCL Industries Inc.; *Int'l*, pg. 1367
CCL LABEL/AUTO-SLEEVE—See CCL Industries Inc.; *Int'l*, pg. 1367
CCL LABEL DO BRASIL S/A—See CCL Industries Inc.; *Int'l*, pg. 1368
CCL LABEL GMBH—See CCL Industries Inc.; *Int'l*, pg. 1368
CCL LABEL (GUANGZHOU) CO., LTD.—See CCL Industries, Inc.; *Int'l*, pg. 1368
CCL LABEL (HEFEI) CO., LTD—See CCL Industries Inc.; *Int'l*, pg. 1368
CCL LABEL MEERANE GMBH—See CCL Industries Inc.; *Int'l*, pg. 1368
CCL LABEL PORTLAND, INC—See CCL Industries Inc.; *Int'l*, pg. 1367
CCL LABEL S.A.S—See CCL Industries Inc.; *Int'l*, pg. 1368
CCL LABEL SIOUX FALLS, INC—See CCL Industries Inc.; *Int'l*, pg. 1367
CCL LABEL—See CCL Industries Inc.; *Int'l*, pg. 1367
CCL LABEL—See CCL Industries Inc.; *Int'l*, pg. 1367
CCL LABEL—See CCL Industries Inc.; *Int'l*, pg. 1368
CCL LABEL—See CCL Industries Inc.; *Int'l*, pg. 1368
CCL LABEL SP Z O.O—See CCL Industries Inc.; *Int'l*, pg. 1368
CCL LABEL (THAI) LTD.—See CCL Industries Inc.; *Int'l*, pg. 1368
CCL LABEL TUBEDEC—See CCL Industries Inc.; *Int'l*, pg. 1367
CCL LABEL VIETNAM COMPANY LIMITED—See CCL Industries Inc.; *Int'l*, pg. 1368
CCL PACKAGE LABEL S.N.C—See CCL Industries Inc.; *Int'l*, pg. 1368
CCL TUBE (WILKES-BARRE), INC—See CCL Industries Inc.; *Int'l*, pg. 1367
CENVEO PUBLISHER SERVICES INDIA LIMITED—See Cenveo, Inc.; *U.S. Private*, pg. 835
CHASE PACKAGING CORPORATION; *U.S. Public*, pg. 483
CHINA ACE SHIPPING PTE. LTD.—See Chinese Maritime Transport Ltd.; *Int'l*, pg. 1569
GIMPLAST EMBALAGENS IMPORTACAO, EXPORTACAO E. COMERCIO S.A.—See Greif Inc.; *U.S. Public*, pg. 967
CLINICAL SYSTEMS, INC.—See CCL Industries Inc.; *Int'l*, pg. 1369
CLOUD PACKAGING SOLUTIONS LLC—See Warburg Pincus LLC; *U.S. Private*, pg. 4437
C.M. JACKSON ASSOCIATES, INC.—See HPS Investment

561910 — PACKAGING AND LABEL...

Partners, LLC; *U.S. Private*, pg. 1997
COIN WRAP INC.; *U.S. Private*, pg. 964
COLLICO VERPACKUNGSLOGISTIK UND SERVICE GMBH—See DSV A/S; *Int'l*, pg. 2211
COLLOTYPE LABELS CHILE SA—See Platinum Equity, LLC; *U.S. Private*, pg. 3206
COMPLETE PACKAGING, INC.—See Altamont Capital Partners; *U.S. Private*, pg. 205
CONSTANTIA PACKAGING AG—See OEP Capital Advisors, L.P.; *U.S. Private*, pg. 2998
CONSUPAQ (PTY) LTD—See Berry Global Group, Inc; *U.S. Public*, pg. 324
COSMETIC SPECIALTIES INTERNATIONAL LLC—See Airlite Plastics Company; *U.S. Private*, pg. 141
COVERIS FLEXIBLES US LLC - CONSUMER FOOD DIVISION—See Sun Capital Partners, Inc.; *U.S. Private*, pg. 3859
CROWN COMMERCIAL GERMANY GMBH & CO. KG—See Crown Holdings, Inc.; *U.S. Public*, pg. 597
CTS GLOBAL LOGISTICS(CANADA) INC.—See CTS International Logistics Corporation Limited; *Int'l*, pg. 1874
CTS GLOBAL LOGISTICS(THAILAND)CO., LTD.—See CTS International Logistics Corporation Limited; *Int'l*, pg. 1874
CTS INTERNATIONAL FREIGHT (SPAIN) S.L.—See CTS International Logistics Corporation Limited; *Int'l*, pg. 1874
CTS INTERNATIONAL LOGISTICS (JAPAN) CO., LTD.—See CTS International Logistics Corporation Limited; *Int'l*, pg. 1874
CTS INTERNATIONAL LOGISTICS TANZANIA LIMITED—See CTS International Logistics Corporation Limited; *Int'l*, pg. 1874
CTS INTERNATIONAL LOGISTICS (VIET NAM) CO., LTD.—See CTS International Logistics Corporation Limited; *Int'l*, pg. 1874
CUBBISON COMPANY; *U.S. Private*, pg. 1119
DAH MEI SILK WEAVING FTY CO., LTD.—See Avery Dennison Corporation; *U.S. Public*, pg. 244
DATA2 CORPORATION; *U.S. Private*, pg. 1164
DEUFOL BERLIN GMBH—See Deufol SE; *Int'l*, pg. 2048
DEUFOL BOCHUM GMBH—See Deufol SE; *Int'l*, pg. 2048
DEUFOL FRANKFURT GMBH—See Deufol SE; *Int'l*, pg. 2048
DEUFOL HAMBURG GMBH—See Deufol SE; *Int'l*, pg. 2048
DEUFOL MUNCHEN GMBH—See Deufol SE; *Int'l*, pg. 2048
DEUFOL NORD GMBH—See Deufol SE; *Int'l*, pg. 2048
DEUFOL NURNBERG GMBH—See Deufol SE; *Int'l*, pg. 2048
DEUFOL SE; *Int'l*, pg. 2048
DEUFOL SUD GMBH—See Deufol SE; *Int'l*, pg. 2048
DEUFOL SUNMAN INC.—See Deufol SE; *Int'l*, pg. 2048
DEUFOL TAILLEUR GMBH—See Deufol SE; *Int'l*, pg. 2048
DEUFOL WEST GMBH—See Deufol SE; *Int'l*, pg. 2048
DFDS LOGISTICS POLSKA SP. Z O.O.—See DFDS A/S; *Int'l*, pg. 2094
DFDS SIA—See DFDS A/S; *Int'l*, pg. 2095
DIMENSIONAL MERCHANDISING, INC.; *U.S. Private*, pg. 1233
DISC GRAPHICS LABEL GROUP INC.—See Dunsirn Partners LLC; *U.S. Private*, pg. 1291
DISC GRAPHICS LABEL GROUP INC.—See Pfingsten Partners, LLC; *U.S. Private*, pg. 3164
DIVERSAPACK, LLC—See Universal Packaging Systems, Inc.; *U.S. Private*, pg. 4306
DIVERSE LABELLING CONSULTANTS (PTY) LTD—See Berry Global Group, Inc; *U.S. Public*, pg. 324
DIXIE TOGA SA—See Amcor plc; *Int'l*, pg. 418
DM LABEL GROUP—See Avery Dennison Corporation; *U.S. Public*, pg. 244
DONBY SHIPPERS SUPPLY, CO.—See Benchmark Industrial, Inc.; *U.S. Private*, pg. 524
DPS CHILE COMERCIAL LIMITADA—See Bunzl plc; *Int'l*, pg. 1218
DYNIC SINGAPORE PTE. LTD.—See Dynic Corporation; *Int'l*, pg. 2243
EDELMANN GMBH; *Int'l*, pg. 2305
ELIF GLOBAL PACKAGING S.A.E.—See Huhtamaki India Limited; *Int'l*, pg. 3524
ELIF GLOBAL S.A.—See Huhtamaki India Limited; *Int'l*, pg. 3524
ELIF HOLDING ANONIM SIRKETI—See Huhtamaki Oyj; *Int'l*, pg. 3524
ELIF HOLDING ANONIM SIRKET—See Huhtamaki India Limited; *Int'l*, pg. 3524
ELOCOAT B.V.—See Ferd AS; *Int'l*, pg. 2635
ELOPAK AB—See Ferd AS; *Int'l*, pg. 2635
ELOPAK B.V.—See Ferd AS; *Int'l*, pg. 2635
ELOPAK B.V.—See Ferd AS; *Int'l*, pg. 2636
ELOPAK B.V.—See Ferd AS; *Int'l*, pg. 2636
ELOPAK FRANCE B.V.—See Ferd AS; *Int'l*, pg. 2635
ELOPAK GES.M.B.H—See Ferd AS; *Int'l*, pg. 2635
ELOPAK GMBH—See Ferd AS; *Int'l*, pg. 2635
ELOPAK HUNGARY—See Ferd AS; *Int'l*, pg. 2635
ELOPAK LTD.—See Ferd AS; *Int'l*, pg. 2635
ELOPAK MALAYSIA SDN BHD—See Ferd AS; *Int'l*, pg. 2635
ELOPAK OBEIKAN LTD.—See Ferd AS; *Int'l*, pg. 2635
ELOPAK OY—See Ferd AS; *Int'l*, pg. 2635
ELOPAK S.A.—See Ferd AS; *Int'l*, pg. 2635
ELOPAK—See Ferd AS; *Int'l*, pg. 2635
ELOPAK S.P.A.—See Ferd AS; *Int'l*, pg. 2636
ELOPAK SYSTEMS AG—See Ferd AS; *Int'l*, pg. 2636
ELOPAK UK LTD.—See Ferd AS; *Int'l*, pg. 2636
ELOPAK UKRAINE—See Ferd AS; *Int'l*, pg. 2636
ENVASES ELOPAK S.A. DE C.V.—See Ferd AS; *Int'l*, pg. 2636
ENWRAP LOGISTIC & PACKAGING S.R.L.—See UFP Industries, Inc.; *U.S. Public*, pg. 2219
ERNEST PAPER PRODUCTS, INC. - FRESNO FACILITY—See Ernest Paper Products, Inc.; *U.S. Private*, pg. 1421
ERNEST PAPER PRODUCTS, INC. - HOUSTON FACILITY—See Ernest Paper Products, Inc.; *U.S. Private*, pg. 1422
ERNEST PAPER PRODUCTS, INC. - LAS VEGAS FACILITY—See Ernest Paper Products, Inc.; *U.S. Private*, pg. 1422
ERNEST PAPER PRODUCTS, INC. - PORTLAND FACILITY—See Ernest Paper Products, Inc.; *U.S. Private*, pg. 1422
ERNEST PAPER PRODUCTS, INC. - RALEIGH-DURHAM FACILITY—See Ernest Paper Products, Inc.; *U.S. Private*, pg. 1422
ERNEST PAPER PRODUCTS, INC. - RENO FACILITY—See Ernest Paper Products, Inc.; *U.S. Private*, pg. 1422
ERNEST PAPER PRODUCTS, INC. - SACRAMENTO FACILITY—See Ernest Paper Products, Inc.; *U.S. Private*, pg. 1422
ERNEST PAPER PRODUCTS, INC. - SAN DIEGO FACILITY—See Ernest Paper Products, Inc.; *U.S. Private*, pg. 1422
ESSENTRA PACKAGING - CARDIFF—See Essentra plc; *Int'l*, pg. 2511
ETIMEX PRIMARY PACKAGING GMBH—See Etimex GmbH; *Int'l*, pg. 2523
ETIQUETAS CCL S.A. DE C.V.—See CCL Industries Inc.; *Int'l*, pg. 1368
EVERGREEN LOGISTICS MALAYSIA SDN. BHD.—See Evergreen International Storage & Transport Corp.; *Int'l*, pg. 2566
FABBIT PHILIPPINES INC.—See Apaman Co., Ltd.; *Int'l*, pg. 500
FIBRO CORPORATION—See Genstar Capital, LLC; *U.S. Private*, pg. 1678
FIRST CHOICE PACKAGING INC.; *U.S. Private*, pg. 1515
FLEXITUFF VENTURES INTERNATIONAL LIMITED; *Int'l*, pg. 2705
FORT DEARBORN COMPANY—See Advent International Corporation; *U.S. Private*, pg. 101
FORT DEARBORN - FORT WORTH—See Advent International Corporation; *U.S. Private*, pg. 101
FORTIS SOLUTIONS GROUP LLC—See Harvest Partners L.P.; *U.S. Private*, pg. 1876
FOSTER INTERNATIONAL PACKAGING (PTY.) LTD.—See Close the Loop Limited; *Int'l*, pg. 1661
FRIDENSON AIR & OCEAN LTD.—See Fridenson Logistic Services Ltd.; *Int'l*, pg. 2791
FTX LOGISTICS LIMITED—See KBR, Inc.; *U.S. Public*, pg. 1215
FULFILLMENT SPECIALISTS OF AMERICA—See The Van Hoof Companies; *U.S. Private*, pg. 4130
FUSION PACKAGING I, LLC—See AptarGroup, Inc.; *U.S. Public*, pg. 174
FUSTIPLAST DO BRASIL LTDA—See Greif Inc.; *U.S. Public*, pg. 967
GARVEY PRODUCTS INC.—See Taylor Corporation; *U.S. Private*, pg. 3938
GENESEE PACKAGING INC.; *U.S. Private*, pg. 1669
GERRESHEIMER RESPIMETRIX GMBH—See Gerresheimer AG; *Int'l*, pg. 2944
GRAFFO PARANAENSE DE EMBALAGENS S.A—See Sonoco Products Company; *U.S. Public*, pg. 1904
GREENCORE USA - CPG PARTNERS, LLC—See Charlesbank Capital Partners, LLC; *U.S. Private*, pg. 855
GREIF FLEXIBLES CHANGZHOU CO. LTD—See Greif Inc.; *U.S. Public*, pg. 967
GREIF FLEXIBLES GERMANY GMBH & CO. KG—See Greif Inc.; *U.S. Public*, pg. 967
GREIF PACKAGING MOROCCO S.A.—See Greif Inc.; *U.S. Public*, pg. 968
GREIF THOLU B.V.—See Greif Inc.; *U.S. Public*, pg. 968
GRINDING & SIZING COMPANY LLC—See American Securities LLC; *U.S. Private*, pg. 253
GSC PACKAGING, INC.; *U.S. Private*, pg. 1800
GUALA CLOSURES TURKEY AMBALAJ VE KAPAK SISTEMLERI SANAYI VE TICARET ANONIM SIRKETI—See Guala Closures S.p.A.; *Int'l*, pg. 3152
GUY CHEMICAL COMPANY, INC.; *U.S. Private*, pg. 1820
HANG SANG (SIU PO) INTERNATIONAL HOLDING COMPANY LIMITED; *Int'l*, pg. 3245
HAUPT PHARMA BERLIN GMBH - BRACKENHEIM—See BC Partners LLP; *Int'l*, pg. 922
HCP PACKAGING FRANCE SAS—See TPG Capital, L.P.; *U.S. Public*, pg. 2173
HCP PACKAGING GROUP—See TPG Capital, L.P.; *U.S. Public*, pg. 2173
HCP PACKAGING HONG KONG LTD.—See TPG Capital, L.P.; *U.S. Public*, pg. 2173
HCP PACKAGING (HUAI AN) CO., LTD.—See TPG Capital, L.P.; *U.S. Public*, pg. 2173
HCP PACKAGING (SHANGHAI) CO. LTD.—See TPG Capital, L.P.; *U.S. Public*, pg. 2173
HCP PACKAGING UK LTD.—See TPG Capital, L.P.; *U.S. Public*, pg. 2173
HCP PACKAGING USA, INC. - HINSDALE PLANT—See TPG Capital, L.P.; *U.S. Public*, pg. 2174
HCP PACKAGING USA, INC.—See TPG Capital, L.P.; *U.S. Public*, pg. 2174
HEARTHSIDE FOOD SOLUTIONS, LLC - GIBSON CITY—See Charlesbank Capital Partners, LLC; *U.S. Private*, pg. 855
HELM43, LLC—See Banyan Technologies Group, LLC; *U.S. Private*, pg. 470
HELM HOLDING COMPANY; *U.S. Private*, pg. 1911
HERMETIC SOLUTIONS GROUP, LLC—See Windjammer Capital Investors, LLC; *U.S. Private*, pg. 4537
HOMEMOVEBOX LTD.—See Citipost Group; *Int'l*, pg. 1623
HORST LANGE GMBH—See Deufol SE; *Int'l*, pg. 2048
HOUSTON CRATING, INC.—See Olympus Partners; *U.S. Private*, pg. 3013
HUANGSHAN CHINA OVERSEAS TRAVEL SERVICE MANAGEMENT CO., LTD.—See Huangshan Tourism Development Co., Ltd.; *Int'l*, pg. 3513
HUANGSHAN TAIPING LAKE CULTURAL TOURISM CO., LTD.—See Huangshan Tourism Development Co., Ltd.; *Int'l*, pg. 3513
HUANGSHAN TUMAMART TOURISM E-COMMERCE CO., LTD.—See Huangshan Tourism Development Co., Ltd.; *Int'l*, pg. 3513
HUHTAMAKI FLEXIBLES ITALY S.R.L.—See Huhtamaki Oyj; *Int'l*, pg. 3525
HUHTAMAKI FOODSERVICE FRANCE S.A.S.—See Huhtamaki Oyj; *Int'l*, pg. 3525
HUISHANGGULI HOTEL OF HUANGSHAN TOURISM DEVELOPMENT CO., LTD.—See Huangshan Tourism Development Co., Ltd.; *Int'l*, pg. 3513
HUNTSMAN PIGMENTS & ADDITIVES—See Huntsman Corporation; *U.S. Public*, pg. 1074
HY-TEST PACKAGING CORP.; *U.S. Private*, pg. 2015
ICT LOGISTICS UAB—See DFDS A/S; *Int'l*, pg. 2095
INLAND LABEL & MARKETING SERVICES, LLC; *U.S. Private*, pg. 2078
INNOVATIVE PLASTICS WEST CORP.—See Global Supply LLC; *U.S. Private*, pg. 1718
INTERNATIONAL CONVERTER LLC—See Apollo Global Management, Inc.; *U.S. Public*, pg. 154
INTERNATIONAL DISPENSING CORPORATION; *U.S. Public*, pg. 1151
INTRAPAC GROUP—See CI Capital Partners LLC; *U.S. Private*, pg. 895
JAMES ALEXANDER CORPORATION; *U.S. Private*, pg. 2183
JENCO PRODUCTIONS INC.; *U.S. Private*, pg. 2199
JOHNS-BYRNE CO.; *U.S. Private*, pg. 2226
J-PAC, LLC—See Public Pension Capital, LLC; *U.S. Private*, pg. 3300
KEENPAC ITALIA S.R.L.—See Bunzl plc; *Int'l*, pg. 1218
KEENPAC (SWITZERLAND) SA—See Bunzl plc; *Int'l*, pg. 1218
KENDALL PACKAGING CORPORATION - PITTSBURG FACILITY—See Kendall Packaging Corporation; *U.S. Private*, pg. 2283
KLISCHEEWERKSTATT SCHOLLER GMBH—See Matthews International Corporation; *U.S. Public*, pg. 1399
KUSHCO HOLDINGS, INC.—See Greenlane Holdings, Inc.; *U.S. Public*, pg. 964
LABEL-AIRE A/S—See Impaxx, Inc.; *U.S. Private*, pg. 2049
LABEL ART—See Platinum Equity, LLC; *U.S. Private*, pg. 3206
LABEL CRAFTS JAMAICA LTD.—See Goddard Enterprises Limited; *Int'l*, pg. 3019
LABELWORX INC.—See Resilience Capital Partners, LLC; *U.S. Private*, pg. 3405
LA CROMOGRAFICA SRL—See Platinum Equity, LLC; *U.S. Private*, pg. 3206
LOS ANDES SERVICIOS CORPORATIVOS S.A.C.—See China Three Gorges Corporation; *Int'l*, pg. 1558
MAPLE MOUNTAIN CO-PACKERS LLC—See Ryder System, Inc.; *U.S. Public*, pg. 1828
MARATHON CHEESE CORP.; *U.S. Private*, pg. 2570
MARK-LYNN FOODS, INC.—See Hormel Foods Corporation; *U.S. Public*, pg. 1054
MATERIALS PROCESSING INC.; *U.S. Private*, pg. 2610
MAUSER PACKAGING SOLUTIONS—See Stone Canyon Industries, LLC; *U.S. Private*, pg. 3817
MAX SOLUTIONS INC.; *U.S. Private*, pg. 2617
MCC-NORWAY, LLC—See Platinum Equity, LLC; *U.S. Private*, pg. 3206
MECHELEN RIGID PAPER—See Sonoco Products Company; *U.S. Public*, pg. 1904
MEDALLION LABORATORIES—See General Mills, Inc.; *U.S. Public*, pg. 922
MEICHALEY ZAHAV PACKAGES LTD.—See Bunzl plc; *Int'l*, pg. 1219

561910 — PACKAGING AND LABEL...

MEIER VERPACKUNGEN GMBH—See Bunzl plc; *Int'l*, pg. 1219
MERUS REFRESHMENT SERVICES INC.—See Castik Capital S.a.r.l.; *Int'l*, pg. 1356
MILAGRO PACKAGING, LLC; *U.S. Private*, pg. 2726
MILL ROCK PACKAGING PARTNERS LLC—See Great Mill Rock LLC; *U.S. Private*, pg. 1766
MINNESOTA DIVERSIFIED INDUSTRIES; *U.S. Private*, pg. 2743
MIVEPA GMBH—See DS Smith Plc; *Int'l*, pg. 2209
MKF-SCHIMANSKI-ERGIS GMBH—See Ergis S.A.; *Int'l*, pg. 2491
MOD-PAC CORP.; *U.S. Private*, pg. 2759
MSI EXPRESS, INC.—See HCI Equity Management, L.P.; *U.S. Private*, pg. 1889
MULTI-COLOR (BAROSSA) PTY. LTD.—See Platinum Equity, LLC; *U.S. Private*, pg. 3206
MULTI-COLOR LABEL CANADA CORPORATION—See Platinum Equity, LLC; *U.S. Private*, pg. 3206
MULTI-COLOR (QLD) PTY LTD—See Platinum Equity, LLC; *U.S. Private*, pg. 3206
MULTI-PACK - ATLANTA—See Cameron Holdings Corporation; *U.S. Private*, pg. 729
MULTI-PACK - CHICAGO—See Wind Point Advisors LLC; *U.S. Private*, pg. 4536
MULTI-PACK - MILWAUKEE—See Cameron Holdings Corporation; *U.S. Private*, pg. 729
NELSON PACKAGING SUPPLIES LIMITED—See Bunzl plc; *Int'l*, pg. 1219
NEUTECH PACKAGING SYSTEMS, LLC; *U.S. Private*, pg. 2890
NEWAY PACKAGING CORP.; *U.S. Private*, pg. 2913
NEW TRANSPORT APPLICATIONS, S.A. DE C.V.—See Deutsche Post AG; *Int'l*, pg. 2082
NILORN AB—See Duroc AB; *Int'l*, pg. 2229
NILORN BELGIUM NV—See Duroc AB; *Int'l*, pg. 2229
NILORN DENMARK A/S—See Duroc AB; *Int'l*, pg. 2229
NILORN EAST ASIA LTD.—See Duroc AB; *Int'l*, pg. 2229
NILORN ETIKET SA. VE TIC. LTD. STI.—See Duroc AB; *Int'l*, pg. 2229
NILORN GERMANY GMBH—See Duroc AB; *Int'l*, pg. 2229
NILORN PORTUGAL LDA.—See Duroc AB; *Int'l*, pg. 2229
NILORN UK LTD.—See Duroc AB; *Int'l*, pg. 2229
NORTH AMERICAN PACKAGING LLC; *U.S. Private*, pg. 2941
NOSCO, INC.—See Holden Industries, Inc.; *U.S. Private*, pg. 1962
NOVOLEX HOLDINGS, LLC—See Apollo Global Management, Inc.; *U.S. Public*, pg. 153
NUTRA MED PACKAGING, INC.—See GenNx360 Capital Partners, L.P.; *U.S. Private*, pg. 1672
OMNIBLEND PTY. LTD.—See Halo Food Co. Limited; *Int'l*, pg. 3233
OMNI SYSTEMS INC.; *U.S. Private*, pg. 3016
ONEPAK, INC.; *U.S. Private*, pg. 3025
OSM WORLDWIDE; *U.S. Private*, pg. 3048
OUTLOOK GROUP CORP.—See Aterian Investment Management, L.P.; *U.S. Private*, pg. 366
PACKAGE ALL CORP.—See Ares Management Corporation; *U.S. Public*, pg. 191
PACKAGING COORDINATORS, INC.—See Kohlberg & Company, LLC; *U.S. Private*, pg. 2338
PACKAGING INNOVATORS, LLC—See Goldberg Lindsay & Co., LLC; *U.S. Private*, pg. 1729
PACKAGING PERSONIFIED, INC.—See Packaging Personified, Inc.; *U.S. Private*, pg. 3072
PACKAGING SYSTEMS, LLC; *U.S. Private*, pg. 3072
PAKETPLUS MARKETING GMBH—See Hubert Burda Media Holding Kommanditgesellschaft; *Int'l*, pg. 3520
PAK-RITE, LTD.—See UFP Industries, Inc.; *U.S. Public*, pg. 2219
PAPERPLUS—See Clayton, Dubilier & Rice, LLC; *U.S. Private*, pg. 929
PAPERPLUS—See Clayton, Dubilier & Rice, LLC; *U.S. Private*, pg. 929
PAPERPLUS—See Clayton, Dubilier & Rice, LLC; *U.S. Private*, pg. 929
PCI PHARMA SERVICES - ROCKFORD—See Kohlberg & Company, LLC; *U.S. Private*, pg. 2339
PCI PHARMA SERVICES—See Kohlberg & Company, LLC; *U.S. Private*, pg. 2339
PEARSON PACKAGING SYSTEMS; *U.S. Private*, pg. 3126
PEEK PACKAGING SOLUTIONS; *U.S. Private*, pg. 3128
PERFORMANCE PACKAGING; *U.S. Private*, pg. 3149
PERLEN PACKAGING AG—See CPH Chemie + Papier Holding AG; *Int'l*, pg. 1824
PERLEN PACKAGING ANAPOLIS, INDUSTRIA E COMERCIO LTDA.—See CPH Chemie + Papier Holding AG; *Int'l*, pg. 1824
PERLEN PACKAGING GMBH—See CPH Chemie + Papier Holding AG; *Int'l*, pg. 1824
PERLEN PACKAGING L.L.C.—See CPH Chemie + Papier Holding AG; *Int'l*, pg. 1824
PERLEN PACKAGING (SUZHOU) CO., LTD.—See CPH Chemie + Papier Holding AG; *Int'l*, pg. 1824
PITNEY BOWES BUSINESS SUPPLIES & SERVICES—See Pitney Bowes Inc.; *U.S. Public*, pg. 1694

PLASTIPAK PACKAGING DO BRASIL LTDA.—See Plastipak Holdings, Inc.; *U.S. Private*, pg. 3200
PREMIERE PACKAGING INDUSTRIES, INC.—See Central National Gottesman Inc.; *U.S. Private*, pg. 823
PREMIER PACKAGING CORPORATION—See DSS, Inc.; *U.S. Public*, pg. 689
PREMIER PLASTICS, INC.; *U.S. Private*, pg. 3250
PRESENTATION PACKAGING—See Liberty Diversified International Inc.; *U.S. Private*, pg. 2443
PRIDE PRODUCTS, INC.; *U.S. Private*, pg. 3260
PRINT CRAFT, INC.—See Taylor Corporation; *U.S. Private*, pg. 3939
PROSTAR PACKAGING INC.—See South Atlantic Packaging Corp.; *U.S. Private*, pg. 3719
PROSYS INNOVATIVE PACKAGING EQUIPMENT INC.—See Wynnchurch Capital, L.P.; *U.S. Private*, pg. 4578
P.T. PACIFIC LABEL INCORPORATED—See Avery Dennison Corporation; *U.S. Public*, pg. 244
QPSI / IPC—See Quality Packaging Specialists, Inc.; *U.S. Private*, pg. 3320
QUALITY PACKAGING SPECIALISTS, INC.; *U.S. Private*, pg. 3320
RADIOSHACK PACKAGING—See RS Legacy Corporation; *U.S. Private*, pg. 3496
RANPAK BV—See Ranpak Holdings Corp.; *U.S. Public*, pg. 1763
RAPID ACTION PACKAGING LTD.—See The Pritzker Group - Chicago, LLC; *U.S. Private*, pg. 4099
REMAR, INC.—See Fideltone, Inc.; *U.S. Private*, pg. 1502
REPRO BUSEK DRUCKVORSTUFENTECHNICK GMBH & CO. KG—See Matthews International Corporation; *U.S. Public*, pg. 1400
RIDEAU PACKAGING, INC.; *U.S. Private*, pg. 3432
RISDON INTERNATIONAL, INC.; *U.S. Private*, pg. 3440
RPC ASTRAPAK—See Berry Global Group, Inc; *U.S. Public*, pg. 323
R.R. DONNELLEY—See Chatham Asset Management, LLC; *U.S. Private*, pg. 864
SAFECOR HEALTH, LLC—See Vesey Street Capital Partners, L.L.C; *U.S. Private*, pg. 4371
SANCAP LINER TECHNOLOGY, INC.—See Genstar Capital, LLC; *U.S. Private*, pg. 1679
SCHOLLE CANADA, LTD.—See Scholle Corporation; *U.S. Private*, pg. 3567
SCHOLLE EUROPE, B.V.—See Scholle Corporation; *U.S. Private*, pg. 3567
SCHOLLE EUROPE FRANCE SAS—See Scholle Corporation; *U.S. Private*, pg. 3567
SCHOLLE EUROPE GMBH—See Scholle Corporation; *U.S. Private*, pg. 3567
SCHOLLE EUROPE, LTD.—See Scholle Corporation; *U.S. Private*, pg. 3567
SCHOLLE INDUSTRIES, PTY, LTD.—See Scholle Corporation; *U.S. Private*, pg. 3567
SCHOLLE PACKAGING, LTDA.—See Scholle Corporation; *U.S. Private*, pg. 3567
SCHOTT NORTH AMERICA, INC. - PHARMACEUTICAL PACKAGING DIVISION—See Carl-Zeiss-Stiftung; *Int'l*, pg. 1337
SCHOTT XINKANG PHARMACEUTICAL PACKAGING CO., LTD.—See Carl-Zeiss-Stiftung; *Int'l*, pg. 1337
SCHUTZ GROUP GMBH & CO. KG—See BayernLB Holding AG; *Int'l*, pg. 914
SEALED AIR GMBH—See Sealed Air Corporation; *U.S. Public*, pg. 1854
SEALED AIR HONG KONG LIMITED—See Sealed Air Corporation; *U.S. Public*, pg. 1854
SEALED AIR HUNGARY KFT.—See Sealed Air Corporation; *U.S. Public*, pg. 1854
SEALED AIR (ISRAEL) LTD.—See Sealed Air Corporation; *U.S. Public*, pg. 1854
SEALED AIR (SINGAPORE) PTE. LTD.—See Sealed Air Corporation; *U.S. Public*, pg. 1854
SEALED AIR (TAIWAN) LIMITED—See Sealed Air Corporation; *U.S. Public*, pg. 1854
SEALED AIR (THAILAND) LTD.—See Sealed Air Corporation; *U.S. Public*, pg. 1854
SEALED AIR URUGUAY S.A.—See Sealed Air Corporation; *U.S. Public*, pg. 1855
SEAPAC INC.; *U.S. Private*, pg. 3585
SETON NAME PLATE COMPANY; *U.S. Private*, pg. 3617
SHARP CLINICAL SERVICES (UK) LIMITED—See Clayton, Dubilier & Rice, LLC; *U.S. Private*, pg. 928
SHIELD PACKAGING OF CALIFORNIA; *U.S. Private*, pg. 3635
SIGNODE BRASILEIRA LTDA.—See Crown Holdings, Inc.; *U.S. Public*, pg. 599
SIGNODE INDUSTRIAL GROUP AB—See Crown Holdings, Inc.; *U.S. Public*, pg. 599
SIGNODE INDUSTRIAL GROUP GMBH—See Crown Holdings, Inc.; *U.S. Public*, pg. 599
SISTEMA PLASTICS LIMITED—See Newell Brands Inc.; *U.S. Public*, pg. 1514
SISTEMA PLASTICS UK LIMITED—See Newell Brands Inc.; *U.S. Public*, pg. 1515
SIXARP LLC—See Huizenga Manufacturing Group, Inc.; *U.S. Private*, pg. 2005

SOBEYS CAPITAL INCORPORATED.—See Empire Company Limited; *Int'l*, pg. 2387
SONOCO DEUTSCHLAND GMBH—See Sonoco Products Company; *U.S. Public*, pg. 1906
SONOCO PRODUCTS COMPANY - BAKER DIVISION—See Sonoco Products Company; *U.S. Public*, pg. 1908
SOURCENTRA, INC.; *U.S. Private*, pg. 3718
SOUTH ATLANTIC PACKAGING CORP.; *U.S. Private*, pg. 3719
SPAN PACKAGING SERVICES LLC—See Cameron Holdings Corporation; *U.S. Private*, pg. 729
SPARFLEX SA—See Cobepa S.A.; *Int'l*, pg. 1683
SPEARSYSTEM PACKAGING AFRICA (PTY) LTD—See Spear USA LLC; *U.S. Private*, pg. 3747
SPEARSYSTEM PACKAGING ASIA PTE LTD.—See Spear USA LLC; *U.S. Private*, pg. 3747
SQUARE PEG PACKAGING & PRINTING, LLC—See Atlas Holdings, LLC; *U.S. Private*, pg. 378
STEPHEN GOULD CORPORATION; *U.S. Private*, pg. 3802
STEPHEN GOULD OF PUERTO RICO, INC.—See Stephen Gould Corporation; *U.S. Private*, pg. 3802
SUN PACKING, INC.; *U.S. Private*, pg. 3863
SYNPRODO BV—See BEWi ASA; *Int'l*, pg. 1004
SYSTEMS FORMULATIONS AND INTEGRATIONS INCORPORATED—See FUJISOFT INCORPORATED; *Int'l*, pg. 2830
TACT GROUP LIMITED—See Matthews International Corporation; *U.S. Public*, pg. 1401
TAILORED LABEL PRODUCTS, INC.; *U.S. Private*, pg. 3923
TARANTO CRUISE PORT S.R.L.—See Global Yatirim Holding A.S.; *Int'l*, pg. 3003
TECH-PAK—See President Container Group, Inc.; *U.S. Private*, pg. 3254
TEMPERPACK TECHNOLOGIES, INC.; *U.S. Private*, pg. 3963
THERMOPAC (PTY) LTD—See Berry Global Group, Inc; *U.S. Public*, pg. 324
TOTAL INNOVATIVE PACKAGING, INC.—See AptarGroup, Inc.; *U.S. Public*, pg. 175
TRIPLE P PACKAGING & PAPER PRODUCTS, INC.; *U.S. Private*, pg. 4237
TWELVE NYC; *U.S. Private*, pg. 4264
UNIMAC PACKAGING GROUP—See Unimac Graphics; *U.S. Private*, pg. 4284
UNIVERSAL PACKAGING SYSTEMS, INC.; *U.S. Private*, pg. 4306
VALLEY PACKAGING INDUSTRIES, INC.; *U.S. Private*, pg. 4334
VERITIV CANADA, INC.—See Bain Capital, LP; *U.S. Private*, pg. 441
VERITIV EXPRESS—See Clayton, Dubilier & Rice, LLC; *U.S. Private*, pg. 929
VERITIV, S.A. DE C.V.—See Clayton, Dubilier & Rice, LLC; *U.S. Private*, pg. 930
VERSATILE PACKAGERS, INC.; *U.S. Private*, pg. 4369
VICTORY PACKAGING MAQUILLA DORA LLC—See WestRock Company; *U.S. Public*, pg. 2361
VIDYA BRANDS GROUP LLC; *U.S. Private*, pg. 4381
VIRTUAL IMAGES—See Taylor Corporation; *U.S. Private*, pg. 3939
VISTA INTERNATIONAL PACKAGING, LLC.—See Keystone Capital, Inc.; *U.S. Private*, pg. 2295
VISUAL PAK COMPANY; *U.S. Private*, pg. 4404
VPI PACKAGING INC.—See O. Berk Company L.L.C.; *U.S. Private*, pg. 2981
VULSAY INDUSTRIES, LTD.—See Greif Inc.; *U.S. Public*, pg. 969
WALLE CORPORATION - FLEXOGRAPHIC DIVISION—See Walle Corporation; *U.S. Private*, pg. 4431
WALLE CORPORATION - LITHOGRAPHIC DIVISION—See Walle Corporation; *U.S. Private*, pg. 4431
WALPA GESELLSCHAFT FUR UBERSEE- UND SPEZIALVERPACKUNG MBH—See Deufol SE; *Int'l*, pg. 2049
WARREN INDUSTRIES INC.; *U.S. Private*, pg. 4444
WEBER MARKING SYSTEMS (THAILAND) LTD.—See Weber Packaging Solutions, Inc.; *U.S. Private*, pg. 4465
WHITE LABEL LIQUID, INC.; *U.S. Public*, pg. 2368
XGILITY, LLC.—See Applied Information Sciences, Inc.; *U.S. Private*, pg. 299
ZAO ELOPAK—See Ferd AS; *Int'l*, pg. 2636
ZEBRA TECHNOLOGIES LATIN AMERICA, LLC—See Zebra Technologies Corporation; *U.S. Public*, pg. 2402
THE ZIPPERTUBING COMPANY - ZIPTAPE LABEL ID SYSTEMS DIVISION—See The Zippertubing Company; *U.S. Private*, pg. 4140

561920 — CONVENTION AND TRADE SHOW ORGANIZERS

ACE EXHIBITS, INC.; *U.S. Private*, pg. 56
AGIDENS INTERNATIONAL NV—See Ackermans & van Haaren NV; *Int'l*, pg. 104
ALLIED CONVENTION SERVICE, INC.—See New State

N.A.I.C.S. INDEX

561920 — CONVENTION AND TRAD...

Capital Partners LLC; *U.S. Private*, pg. 2907
AL OULA MIDDLE EAST LLC—See Al-Oula Company; *Int'l*, pg. 288
ALTER ECO; *U.S. Private*, pg. 206
APLEONA HSG EVENT SERVICES GMBH—See EQT AB; *Int'l*, pg. 2468
AQUARIAN, LLC—See Shepard Exposition Services Inc.; *U.S. Private*, pg. 3632
THE ARMORY SHOW INC.—See Vornado Realty Trust; *U.S. Public*, pg. 2310
AUDIO VISUAL MANAGEMENT SOLUTIONS, INC.; *U.S. Private*, pg. 391
AXICA KONGRESS- UND TAGUNGSZENTRUM PARISER PLATZ 3 GMBH—See DZ BANK AG Deutsche Zentral-Genossenschaftsbank; *Int'l*, pg. 2243
BEC-TERO EXHIBITIONS CO., LTD.—See BEC World Public Company Limited; *Int'l*, pg. 936
BEIJING DOWWAY CULTURAL DEVELOPMENT COMPANY LIMITED—See Dowway Holdings Ltd.; *Int'l*, pg. 2187
BEIJING GEHUA MEDIA CENTER CO., LTD.—See Beijing Gehua Cultural Development Group Co., Ltd.; *Int'l*, pg. 950
BEIJING GEHUA SCIENCE & TECHNOLOGY CENTER CO., LTD.—See Beijing Gehua Cultural Development Group Co., Ltd.; *Int'l*, pg. 950
BIG TOURS S.L.—See CTS Eventim AG & Co. KGAA; *Int'l*, pg. 1872
BILETIX BILET DAGITIM BASIM VE TICARET AS—See Live Nation Entertainment, Inc.; *U.S. Public*, pg. 1328
BILLETNET AS—See Live Nation Entertainment, Inc.; *U.S. Public*, pg. 1329
BILLETTSERVICE AS—See Live Nation Entertainment, Inc.; *U.S. Public*, pg. 1330
BLUEPOOL GMBH; *Int'l*, pg. 1072
BRAND NEW LIVE BV—See Live Nation Entertainment, Inc.; *U.S. Public*, pg. 1328
B.V. EXPLOITATIEMAATSCHAPPIJ GELREDOME—See Live Nation Entertainment, Inc.; *U.S. Public*, pg. 1328
C 2 CONCERTS GMBH—See DEAG Deutsche Entertainment AG; *Int'l*, pg. 1997
C3 EVENT MANAGEMENT, INC.; *U.S. Private*, pg. 710
CANADA'S OUTDOOR SHOWS LIMITED PARTNERSHIP—See GVIC Communications Corp.; *Int'l*, pg. 3189
CARLISLE PRODUCTIONS, INC.; *U.S. Private*, pg. 764
CHICAGO EXHIBIT PRODUCTIONS, INC.; *U.S. Private*, pg. 877
CHICAGO EXHIBIT PRODUCTIONS INC.—See Chicago Exhibit Productions, Inc.; *U.S. Private*, pg. 877
CHRISTMAS GARDEN DEUTSCHLAND GMBH—See DEAG Deutsche Entertainment AG; *Int'l*, pg. 1997
C I (EVENTS) LIMITED—See Live Nation Entertainment, Inc.; *U.S. Public*, pg. 1328
CIPA FIERA MILANO PUBLICACOES E EVENTOS LTDA.—See Fiera Milano SpA; *Int'l*, pg. 2660
CLARION EVENTS LTD.—See Blackstone Inc.; *U.S. Public*, pg. 360
THE CM GROUP, LLC; *U.S. Private*, pg. 4011
COASTAL INTERNATIONAL INC.; *U.S. Private*, pg. 956
CONCERT SUPPLIES SP. Z O.O.—See Live Nation Entertainment, Inc.; *U.S. Public*, pg. 1328
CORCORAN GROUP LLC—See Anywhere Real Estate Inc.; *U.S. Public*, pg. 142
COURTESY ASSOCIATES—See SmithBucklin Corporation; *U.S. Private*, pg. 3697
CRAIGMICHAELS, INC.; *U.S. Private*, pg. 1083
CSI WORLDWIDE INC.; *U.S. Private*, pg. 1117
DEUTSCHE MESSE AG; *Int'l*, pg. 2071
DEUTSCHE MESSE INTERACTIVE GMBH—See Deutsche Messe AG; *Int'l*, pg. 2071
D.F. CONCERTS LIMITED—See Live Nation Entertainment, Inc.; *U.S. Public*, pg. 1328
DIRK BECKER ENTERTAINMENT GMBH—See CTS Eventim AG & Co. KGAA; *Int'l*, pg. 1872
DIVERSIFIED BUSINESS COMMUNICATIONS CANADA—See Diversified Communications; *U.S. Private*, pg. 1241
DIVERSIFIED BUSINESS COMMUNICATIONS—See Diversified Communications; *U.S. Private*, pg. 1241
DIVERSIFIED PRODUCTION SERVICES, LLC—See Live Nation Entertainment, Inc.; *U.S. Public*, pg. 1328
DMG EVENTS ASIA PACIFIC PTE LTD—See Daily Mail & General Trust plc; *Int'l*, pg. 1937
DMG EVENTS (CANADA) INC.—See Daily Mail & General Trust plc; *Int'l*, pg. 1937
DMG EVENTS (DUBAI) LIMITED—See Daily Mail & General Trust plc; *Int'l*, pg. 1937
DMG EVENTS EGYPT LTD.—See Daily Mail & General Trust plc; *Int'l*, pg. 1937
DMG EVENTS LIMITED—See Daily Mail & General Trust plc; *Int'l*, pg. 1937
DMG EVENTS, LLC—See Daily Mail & General Trust plc; *Int'l*, pg. 1937
DMG EVENTS (USA) INC. - DIGITAL MARKETING—See Daily Mail & General Trust plc; *Int'l*, pg. 1937
DMG EVENTS (USA) INC.—See Daily Mail & General Trust plc; *Int'l*, pg. 1937

E FACTOR EXPERIENCES LIMITED; *Int'l*, pg. 2246
ELIFE HOLDINGS LIMITED; *Int'l*, pg. 2361
ENCORE PRODUCTIONS, INC.—See Freeman Decorating Co.; *U.S. Private*, pg. 1605
ENMOTIVE COMPANY LLC—See Gannett Co., Inc.; *U.S. Public*, pg. 896
E-PLUS LIMITED; *Int'l*, pg. 2249
ESP AFRIKA PROPRIETARY LIMITED—See AYO Technology Solutions Ltd.; *Int'l*, pg. 775
ETM TRAVEL PTY LTD.—See Corporate Travel Management Limited; *Int'l*, pg. 1805
EVENTFUL LIMITED—See Aeorema Communications Plc; *Int'l*, pg. 179
EVENTIMPRESENTS GMBH & CO. KG—See CTS Eventim AG & Co. KGAA; *Int'l*, pg. 1874
EVENTIM SP. Z O.O.—See CTS Eventim AG & Co. KGAA; *Int'l*, pg. 1872
EVENT IT AG—See Deutsche Messe AG; *Int'l*, pg. 2071
EVENTS CLUB OY—See Live Nation Entertainment, Inc.; *U.S. Public*, pg. 1330
THE EVENTS COMPANY—See Fertitta Entertainment, Inc.; *U.S. Private*, pg. 1499
THE EVENT SUPPORT COMPANY BV—See Live Nation Entertainment, Inc.; *U.S. Public*, pg. 1331
EXHIBITS USA, INC.; *U.S. Private*, pg. 1448
THE EXPO GROUP, INC.—See New State Capital Partners LLC; *U.S. Private*, pg. 2907
EXPOS2 INC.; *U.S. Private*, pg. 1451
EXPO SERVICES, A ROGERS COMPANY LLC—See The Rogers Company; *U.S. Private*, pg. 4112
FESTIVALS LIMBURG B.V.—See Live Nation Entertainment, Inc.; *U.S. Public*, pg. 1328
FIERA MILANO CONGRESSI SPA—See Fiera Milano SpA; *Int'l*, pg. 2660
FIERA MILANO EXHIBITIONS AFRICA PTY. LTD.—See Fiera Milano SpA; *Int'l*, pg. 2660
FIFTY FIFTY ANTWERPEN B.V.—See Live Nation Entertainment, Inc.; *U.S. Public*, pg. 1328
FILM EXPO GROUP LLC—See Shamrock Capital Advisors, LLC; *U.S. Private*, pg. 3624
FKP SCORPIO NORGE AS—See CTS Eventim AG & Co. KGAA; *Int'l*, pg. 1873
FKP SCORPIO SVERIGE AB—See CTS Eventim AG & Co. KGAA; *Int'l*, pg. 1873
FOURCAR BELGIUM SA—See Carrefour SA; *Int'l*, pg. 1344
FOURTH WALL EVENTS, INC.—See InteleTravel.com; *U.S. Private*, pg. 2104
FOX NET, INC.—See Fox Corporation; *U.S. Public*, pg. 876
FREEMAN DECORATING CO.; *U.S. Private*, pg. 1605
GENERALI AKADEMIE GMBH I.L.—See Assicurazioni Generali S.p.A.; *Int'l*, pg. 644
GES CANADA LIMITED—See Viad Corp.; *U.S. Public*, pg. 2291
GES EXPOSITION SERVICES, INC.—See Viad Corp.; *U.S. Public*, pg. 2291
GETELMAN CORP.; *U.S. Private*, pg. 1688
GIGTECH B.V.—See Live Nation Entertainment, Inc.; *U.S. Public*, pg. 1328
GLOBAL EXPERIENCE SPECIALISTS (GES) EXHIBITION SERVICES LLC—See Viad Corp.; *U.S. Public*, pg. 2291
GLOW EVENTS, LLC—See Live Nation Entertainment, Inc.; *U.S. Public*, pg. 1329
GUYO ENTERTAINMENT, INC.—See Live Nation Entertainment, Inc.; *U.S. Public*, pg. 1329
HAKUTEN CORPORATION; *Int'l*, pg. 3222
HANNOVER CONSULTANCY B.V.—See Deutsche Messe AG; *Int'l*, pg. 2071
HANNOVER FAIRS AUSTRALIA PTY. LTD.—See Deutsche Messe AG; *Int'l*, pg. 2071
HANNOVER FAIRS DO BRASIL S/C LTDA—See Deutsche Messe AG; *Int'l*, pg. 2071
HANNOVER FAIRS TURKEY FUARCILIK A.S.—See Deutsche Messe AG; *Int'l*, pg. 2071
HANNOVER FAIRS USA INC.—See Deutsche Messe AG; *Int'l*, pg. 2071
HANNOVERMASSANS SVERIGEKONTOR AB—See Deutsche Messe AG; *Int'l*, pg. 2071
HANNOVER MILANO FAIRS CHINA LTD.—See Deutsche Messe AG; *Int'l*, pg. 2071
HANNOVER MILANO FAIRS INDIA PVT. LTD.—See Deutsche Messe AG; *Int'l*, pg. 2071
HANNOVER MILANO FAIRS SHANGHAI LTD.—See Deutsche Messe AG; *Int'l*, pg. 2071
HARD EVENTS LLC—See Live Nation Entertainment, Inc.; *U.S. Public*, pg. 1329
HAYMARKET EXHIBITIONS LTD.—See Haymarket Group Limited; *Int'l*, pg. 3292
HELLO! CALIFORNIA—See Hello! Florida Destination Management, Inc.; *U.S. Private*, pg. 1911
HELLO! FLORIDA DESTINATION MANAGEMENT, INC.; *U.S. Private*, pg. 1911
HOUSE OF BLUES DALLAS RESTAURANT CORP.—See Live Nation Entertainment, Inc.; *U.S. Public*, pg. 1329
HOUSE OF BLUES HOUSTON RESTAURANT CORP.—See Live Nation Entertainment, Inc.; *U.S. Public*, pg. 1329
HOUSE OF BLUES LAS VEGAS RESTAURANT CORP.—See Live Nation Entertainment, Inc.; *U.S. Public*, pg. 1329
HYVE GROUP PLC—See Providence Equity Partners L.L.C.; *U.S. Private*, pg. 3292
HYVE GROUP PLC—See Searchlight Capital Partners, L.P.; *U.S. Private*, pg. 3587
HYVE INDIA PRIVATE LTD.—See Providence Equity Partners L.L.C.; *U.S. Private*, pg. 3292
HYVE INDIA PRIVATE LTD.—See Searchlight Capital Partners, L.P.; *U.S. Private*, pg. 3587
IDG WORLD EXPO CORPORATION—See China Oceanwide Holdings Group Co., Ltd.; *Int'l*, pg. 1538
IDG WORLD EXPO CORPORATION—See IDG Capital; *Int'l*, pg. 3594
I-MOTION GMBH EVENTS & COMMUNICATION—See DEAG Deutsche Entertainment AG; *Int'l*, pg. 1998
INTERPLAN GROUP—See Hakuhodo DY Holdings Incorporated; *Int'l*, pg. 3221
INVESTMENT SEMINARS, INC.; *U.S. Private*, pg. 2132
ITE EURASIAN EXHIBITIONS FZ LLC—See Providence Equity Partners L.L.C.; *U.S. Private*, pg. 3292
ITE EURASIAN EXHIBITIONS FZ LLC—See Searchlight Capital Partners, L.P.; *U.S. Private*, pg. 3588
JOSE SILVA CARVALHO CATERING, S.A.—See Ibersol S.G.P.S., S.A.; *Int'l*, pg. 3574
K.B. HALLEN MANAGEMENT A/S—See CTS Eventim AG & Co. KGAA; *Int'l*, pg. 1873
KESSEL FESTIVAL GMBH—See DEAG Deutsche Entertainment AG; *Int'l*, pg. 1997
KULTUR IM PARK GMBH—See DEAG Deutsche Entertainment AG; *Int'l*, pg. 1998
LAFFITTE MANAGEMENT GROUP LLC—See Live Nation Entertainment, Inc.; *U.S. Public*, pg. 1329
LDJ PRODUCTIONS; *U.S. Private*, pg. 2404
LIMINAL COLLECTIVE, INC.—See Logitech International S.A.; *U.S. Public*, pg. 1341
LIVE NATION AUSTRALIA PTY LTD—See Live Nation Entertainment, Inc.; *U.S. Public*, pg. 1329
LIVE NATION BALTICS OU—See Live Nation Entertainment, Inc.; *U.S. Public*, pg. 1329
LIVE NATION DENMARK APS—See Live Nation Entertainment, Inc.; *U.S. Public*, pg. 1329
LIVE NATION DENMARK MANAGEMENT APS—See Live Nation Entertainment, Inc.; *U.S. Public*, pg. 1329
LIVE NATION ESPANA SAU—See Live Nation Entertainment, Inc.; *U.S. Public*, pg. 1329
LIVE NATION (HK) LIMITED—See Live Nation Entertainment, Inc.; *U.S. Public*, pg. 1329
LIVE NATION ITALIA S.R.L.—See Live Nation Entertainment, Inc.; *U.S. Public*, pg. 1329
LIVE NATION LGTOURS (USA), LLC—See Live Nation Entertainment, Inc.; *U.S. Public*, pg. 1329
LIVE NATION LUSHINGTON (HONG KONG) LIMITED—See Live Nation Entertainment, Inc.; *U.S. Public*, pg. 1329
LIVE NATION MIDDLE EAST FZ-LLC—See Live Nation Entertainment, Inc.; *U.S. Public*, pg. 1329
LIVE NATION NORDIC AB—See Live Nation Entertainment, Inc.; *U.S. Public*, pg. 1329
LIVE NATION NORWAY AS—See Live Nation Entertainment, Inc.; *U.S. Public*, pg. 1330
LIVE NATION SP. Z.O.O.—See Live Nation Entertainment, Inc.; *U.S. Public*, pg. 1330
LIVE NATION SWEDEN AB—See Live Nation Entertainment, Inc.; *U.S. Public*, pg. 1330
LIVE NATION VENUES (NETHERLANDS) BV—See Live Nation Entertainment, Inc.; *U.S. Public*, pg. 1330
LOLLAPALOOZA, LLC—See Live Nation Entertainment, Inc.; *U.S. Public*, pg. 1330
LUGERINC AB—See Live Nation Entertainment, Inc.; *U.S. Public*, pg. 1330
MADRID DEPORTES Y ESPECTACULOS SA—See Live Nation Entertainment, Inc.; *U.S. Public*, pg. 1329
MAP MARKETING & INCENTIVES, LLC—See Frosch International Travel Inc.; *U.S. Private*, pg. 1616
MARKETPLACE EVENTS LLC—See Sentinel Capital Partners, L.L.C.; *U.S. Private*, pg. 3609
MEETING ALLIANCE, LLC; *U.S. Private*, pg. 2660
THE MEETINGHOUSE COMPANIES, INC.—See SBR Events Group; *U.S. Private*, pg. 3560
METROPOLITAN PIER & EXPOSITION AUTHORITY; *U.S. Private*, pg. 2689
MEWES ENTERTAINMENT GROUP GMBH—See DEAG Deutsche Entertainment AG; *Int'l*, pg. 1998
MINNEAPOLIS SOCIETY OF FINE ARTS; *U.S. Private*, pg. 2743
MOJO CONCERTS B.V.—See Live Nation Entertainment, Inc.; *U.S. Public*, pg. 1330
MONEYSHOW.COM, LLC; *U.S. Private*, pg. 2770
MONTGOMERY EXHIBITIONS LTD.—See Angus Montgomery Ltd.; *Int'l*, pg. 463
MOONDOG ENTERTAINMENT AB—See Live Nation Entertainment, Inc.; *U.S. Public*, pg. 1330
M ROGERS DESIGN, INC.; *U.S. Private*, pg. 2523
MUSIC MARKETING SP. Z.O.O.—See Live Nation Entertainment, Inc.; *U.S. Public*, pg. 1330
MYTIC MYTICKET AG—See DEAG Deutsche Entertainment AG; *Int'l*, pg. 1998

561920 — CONVENTION AND TRAD...

N200 HOLDING B.V.—See Viad Corp.; *U.S. Public*, pg. 2291
N200 LIMITED—See Viad Corp.; *U.S. Public*, pg. 2291
NTH DEGREE EMEA—See MSouth Equity Partners, LLC; *U.S. Private*, pg. 2808
NTH DEGREE GERMANY—See MSouth Equity Partners, LLC; *U.S. Private*, pg. 2808
NTH DEGREE INC.—See MSouth Equity Partners, LLC; *U.S. Private*, pg. 2808
OOO DEUTSCHE MESSE RUS—See Deutsche Messe AG; *Int'l*, pg. 2071
OPENAIR ST.GALLEN AG—See CTS Eventim AG & Co. KGAA; *Int'l*, pg. 1873
PACIFIC EVENT PRODUCTIONS; *U.S. Private*, pg. 3067
POTEL ET CHABOT SAS—See 21 Investimenti Societa' di Gestione del Risparmio S.p.A.; *Int'l*, pg. 4
PRODUCTION SERVICE SWITZERLAND AG—See CTS Eventim AG & Co. KGAA; *Int'l*, pg. 1873
PUERTO RICO TOURISM COMPANY - NEW YORK—See Puerto Rico Tourism Company; *U.S. Private*, pg. 3302
QUIETUS MANAGEMENT LIMITED—See Live Nation Entertainment, Inc.; *U.S. Public*, pg. 1330
REACTION AUDIO VISUAL LLC; *U.S. Private*, pg. 3366
REED SINOPHARM EXHIBITIONS CO., LTD.—See China National Pharmaceutical Group Corporation; *Int'l*, pg. 1534
RIDER PRODUCTIONS LLC—See Comcast Corporation; *U.S. Public*, pg. 541
ROCK IN RIO MADRID SA—See Live Nation Entertainment, Inc.; *U.S. Public*, pg. 1329
THE ROGERS COMPANY; *U.S. Private*, pg. 4111
ROSECLAIM LIMITED—See Live Nation Entertainment, Inc.; *U.S. Public*, pg. 1330
THE SECURITY COMPANY UTRECHT HOLLAND HOLDING BV—See Live Nation Entertainment, Inc.; *U.S. Public*, pg. 1331
SENSIBLE EVENTS LIMITED—See Live Nation Entertainment, Inc.; *U.S. Public*, pg. 1330
SHANGHAI AIR WATER INTERNATIONAL TRADING CO., LTD.—See Air Water Inc.; *Int'l*, pg. 240
SHEPARD EXPOSITION SERVICES INC.; *U.S. Private*, pg. 3632
SHERPA.BE SA—See Live Nation Entertainment, Inc.; *U.S. Public*, pg. 1330
SHORELINE AMPHITHEATRE, LTD.—See Live Nation Entertainment, Inc.; *U.S. Public*, pg. 1330
SHOWSEC INTERNATIONAL LIMITED—See Live Nation Entertainment, Inc.; *U.S. Public*, pg. 1330
SH WORLDWIDE, LLC; *U.S. Private*, pg. 3622
SKYLINE EXHIBITS OF LOS ANGELES INC—See Skyline Displays Inc.; *U.S. Private*, pg. 3685
SKYLINE EXHIBITS—See Skyline Displays Inc.; *U.S. Private*, pg. 3685
SOCIO LABS LLC—See Cisco Systems, Inc.; *U.S. Public*, pg. 500
SPARKS EXHIBITS & ENVIRONMENTS CORP.—See Freeman Decorating Co.; *U.S. Private*, pg. 1605
SPARKS MARKETING GROUP LLC—See Freeman Decorating Co.; *U.S. Private*, pg. 1605
SPECIALISED EXHIBITIONS (PTY.) LIMITED—See Angus Montgomery Ltd.; *Int'l*, pg. 463
SPRING MESSE MANAGEMENT GMBH—See Deutsche Messe AG; *Int'l*, pg. 2071
STAGING CONNECTIONS GROUP LIMITED—See Freeman Decorating Co.; *U.S. Private*, pg. 1605
STRAIGHT INTERNATIONAL SECURITY BV—See Live Nation Entertainment, Inc.; *U.S. Public*, pg. 1330
STREAMLINEVENTS INC.; *U.S. Private*, pg. 3838
SUMMERDAYS FESTIVAL AG—See CTS Eventim AG & Co. KGAA; *Int'l*, pg. 1873
TARSUS EXPOSITIONS INC—See Charterhouse Capital Partners LLP; *Int'l*, pg. 1456
TARSUS FRANCE—See Charterhouse Capital Partners LLP; *Int'l*, pg. 1456
TATRO & WHEELER CORP.; *U.S. Private*, pg. 3936
TEN CUE PRODUCTIONS—See Opus Solutions, LLC; *U.S. Private*, pg. 3036
T.F. COLLETTE COMPANIES, INC.; *U.S. Private*, pg. 3912
THEBE REED EXHIBITIONS PTY LIMITED—See Futuregrowth Asset Management Pty. Ltd.; *Int'l*, pg. 2858
THREE SIX ZERO GRP LIMITED—See Live Nation Entertainment, Inc.; *U.S. Public*, pg. 1331
TICKETMASTER GMBH—See Live Nation Entertainment, Inc.; *U.S. Public*, pg. 1331
TICKETMASTER NZ LIMITED—See Live Nation Entertainment, Inc.; *U.S. Public*, pg. 1331
TICKETMASTER POLAND SP. Z.O.O.—See Live Nation Entertainment, Inc.; *U.S. Public*, pg. 1331
TICKETMASTER SUOMI OY—See Live Nation Entertainment, Inc.; *U.S. Public*, pg. 1330
TICKETMASTER SYSTEMS LIMITED—See Live Nation Entertainment, Inc.; *U.S. Public*, pg. 1331
TICKETMASTER UK LIMITED—See Live Nation Entertainment, Inc.; *U.S. Public*, pg. 1331
TIMEOUT AGENCY & CONCERTS AS—See Live Nation Entertainment, Inc.; *U.S. Public*, pg. 1331
URBAN EXPOSITIONS; *U.S. Private*, pg. 4314
VIVA ENTERTAINMENT, LLC; *U.S. Private*, pg. 4406

VIVO CONCERTI S.R.L.—See CTS Eventim AG & Co. KGAA; *Int'l*, pg. 1873
VOLI FUAR HIZMETLERI A.S.—See Ihlas Holding A.S.; *Int'l*, pg. 3606
WE FEST HOLDINGS, LLC—See Live Nation Entertainment, Inc.; *U.S. Public*, pg. 1331
WELLDONE LR OY—See Live Nation Entertainment, Inc.; *U.S. Public*, pg. 1330
WIZARD PROMOTIONS KONZERTAGENTUR GMBH—See DEAG Deutsche Entertainment AG; *Int'l*, pg. 1998
WORD ON THE STREET (UK EVENTS) LIMITED—See Aramark; *U.S. Public*, pg. 178
YOURTROVE, INC.—See Live Nation Entertainment, Inc.; *U.S. Public*, pg. 1331

561990 — ALL OTHER SUPPORT SERVICES

15 EDISON ROAD, LLC—See Welltower Inc.; *U.S. Public*, pg. 2347
3M SECURITY PRINTING AND SYSTEMS LTD.—See 3M Company; *U.S. Public*, pg. 7
3P CORP.—See Dentsu Group Inc.; *Int'l*, pg. 2034
3-RD CO., LTD.—See GMM Grammy Public Company Limited; *Int'l*, pg. 3012
4IMPRINT GROUP PLC; *Int'l*, pg. 12
THE 501 ALLIANCE; *U.S. Private*, pg. 3980
AAC GLOBAL AB—See Groupe BPCE; *Int'l*, pg. 3095
AAC GLOBAL DENMARK—See Groupe BPCE; *Int'l*, pg. 3095
AAC GLOBAL OY—See Groupe BPCE; *Int'l*, pg. 3095
AA PLC—See TowerBrook Capital Partners, L.P.; *U.S. Private*, pg. 4194
AA PLC—See Warburg Pincus LLC; *U.S. Private*, pg. 4436
ADS ENVIRONMENTAL SERVICES—See IDEX Corp; *U.S. Public*, pg. 1089
ADS STRUCTURES, INC.—See Advanced Drainage Systems, Inc.; *U.S. Public*, pg. 46
AETNA SERVICE CENTER—See CVS Health Corporation; *U.S. Public*, pg. 615
AF-AUTOMATIKKA OU—See AFRY AB; *Int'l*, pg. 193
AGILITY LOGISTICS GMBH—See Agility; *Int'l*, pg. 210
AIRIQ, INC.; *Int'l*, pg. 247
AJIS CO., LTD.; *Int'l*, pg. 258
AJIS (HONG KONG) CO., LIMITED—See AJIS Co., Ltd.; *Int'l*, pg. 258
AJIS (THAILAND) CO., LTD.—See AJIS Co., Ltd.; *Int'l*, pg. 258
ALLSTATE TRAFFIC CONTROL, LLC—See Kohlberg & Company, LLC; *U.S. Private*, pg. 2337
ALTAIR GLOBAL RELOCATION; *U.S. Private*, pg. 204
AMANO SECURE JAPAN CORPORATION—See Amano Corporation; *Int'l*, pg. 411
AMBOILE SERVICES SAS—See Ecolab Inc.; *U.S. Public*, pg. 712
AMERICAN ASSOCIATION FOR LABORATORY ACCREDITATION; *U.S. Private*, pg. 223
AMERICAN HEARING AID ASSOCIATES, INC.—See Demant A/S; *Int'l*, pg. 2023
AMERICAN REGISTRY FOR DIAGNOSTIC MEDICAL SONOGRAPHY, INC.; *U.S. Private*, pg. 245
AMERICAN SOCIETY OF MECHANICAL ENGINEERS; *U.S. Private*, pg. 254
AN PHU IRRADIATION J.S.C.; *Int'l*, pg. 443
APATOR RECTOR SP. Z O.O.—See Apator S.A.; *Int'l*, pg. 501
AQUASHIELD, INC.—See Komline-Sanderson Corporation; *U.S. Private*, pg. 2342
ARAMARK REFRESHMENT SERVICES, INC.—See Aramark; *U.S. Public*, pg. 176
ARAMBHAN HOSPITALITY SERVICES LIMITED—See Arambhan Group; *Int'l*, pg. 535
ATLANTIQUE DRAGAGE SARL—See HAL Trust N.V.; *Int'l*, pg. 3224
ATOM INSTRUMENT LLC—See Advanced Holdings Ltd.; *Int'l*, pg. 159
AUCNET CONSUMER PRODUCTS USA, LLC—See Aucnet Inc.; *Int'l*, pg. 700
AUTO DRIVEAWAY FRANCHISE SYSTEMS, LLC—See Evanston Partners, LLC; *U.S. Private*, pg. 1435
AVIBANK SERVICES, LLC—See Berkshire Hathaway Inc.; *U.S. Public*, pg. 313
BANFF HOSPITALITY RESIDENCE LTD.—See Viad Corp.; *U.S. Public*, pg. 2291
BANGKOK AIRWAYS GROUND SERVICES CO. LTD.—See Bangkok Airways Public Company Limited; *Int'l*, pg. 832
BANK OF AMERICA CAPITAL MANAGEMENT COMPANY—See Bank of America Corporation; *U.S. Public*, pg. 270
BANSEI ROYAL RESORTS HIKKADUWA PLC; *Int'l*, pg. 854
BAS KUNDENSERVICE GMBH & CO. KG—See ENGIE SA; *Int'l*, pg. 2429
BAS KUNDENSERVICE GMBH & CO. KG—See E.ON SE; *Int'l*, pg. 2257
BAY VALUATION ADVISORS, LLC—See Kelso & Company, L.P.; *U.S. Private*, pg. 2281

BBS OUTSOURCING KUMAMOTO INC.—See Business Brain Showa-Ota Inc.; *Int'l*, pg. 1228
BBX CENTROAMERICA LA URUCA—See BBX Minerals Limited; *Int'l*, pg. 921
BBX MANAGEMENT LTD—See BBX Minerals Limited; *Int'l*, pg. 921
BBX MANAGEMENT PTY. LTD—See BBX Minerals Limited; *Int'l*, pg. 921
BEACH MOLD & TOOL INC.—See NYX Inc.; *U.S. Private*, pg. 2977
BGLOBAL METERING LIMITED—See Astatine Investment Partners LLC; *U.S. Private*, pg. 360
BIG C CORPORATION; *U.S. Private*, pg. 552
BILFINGER HEIGHT SPECIALISTS B.V.—See Bilfinger SE; *Int'l*, pg. 1027
BLAINE CONVENTION SERVICES; *U.S. Private*, pg. 577
BLUE SKY EXHIBITS; *U.S. Private*, pg. 593
BODY WAVES INC.; *U.S. Private*, pg. 608
BONUSKAD LOYALTY SDN BHD—See AMMB Holdings Berhad; *Int'l*, pg. 429
BOSKALIS B.V.—See HAL Trust N.V.; *Int'l*, pg. 3225
BRAGG INVESTMENT COMPANY, INC.; *U.S. Private*, pg. 634
BRANDED ENTERTAINMENT NETWORK, INC. - NEW YORK OFFICE—See Branded Entertainment Network, Inc.; *U.S. Private*, pg. 637
BRIAN TAYLOR INTERNATIONAL LLC; *U.S. Private*, pg. 647
BRISTOW HELICOPTER GROUP, LIMITED—See Bristow Group, Inc.; *U.S. Public*, pg. 387
BUREAU VERITAS AUSTRALIA PTY. LTD.—See Bureau Veritas S.A.; *Int'l*, pg. 1221
BUREAU VERITAS UK LIMITED—See Bureau Veritas S.A.; *Int'l*, pg. 1222
BURKHALTER AUTOMATION AG—See Burkhalter Holding AG; *Int'l*, pg. 1224
BURRELLE'S INFORMATION SERVICES LLC; *U.S. Private*, pg. 691
BUSINESS WATCH INTERNATIONAL INC.—See Leadsonline LLC; *U.S. Private*, pg. 2407
CALIFORNIA SUITES INC.; *U.S. Private*, pg. 720
CAPITAL AUTO & TRUCK AUCTION; *U.S. Private*, pg. 738
CARD CENTRE NIGERIA LIMITED—See Chams Holding Company; *Int'l*, pg. 1440
CAROLINA CANNERS MEDIA—See Carolina Canners Inc.; *U.S. Private*, pg. 767
CARTUS CORPORATION PTE. LTD.—See Anywhere Real Estate Inc.; *U.S. Public*, pg. 140
CARTUS CORPORATION—See Anywhere Real Estate Inc.; *U.S. Public*, pg. 140
CARTUS UK PLC—See Anywhere Real Estate Inc.; *U.S. Public*, pg. 140
CBIZ ACCOUNTING, TAX & ADVISORY OF FLORIDA, LLC—See CBIZ, Inc.; *U.S. Public*, pg. 456
CBIZ RISK & ADVISORY SERVICES, LLC—See CBIZ, Inc.; *U.S. Public*, pg. 457
CELEBRATION WORLD RESORT LTD.; *U.S. Private*, pg. 806
CENTRAL ASIA DEVELOPMENT GROUP, INC.; *Int'l*, pg. 1404
CHAMPION INTERNATIONAL MOVING, LTD.—See Atlas World Group, Inc.; *U.S. Private*, pg. 381
CHICAGO STEEL LIMITED PARTNERSHIP; *U.S. Private*, pg. 879
CHIRONET LLC; *U.S. Private*, pg. 886
CHOPPER TRADING LLC—See DRW Holdings, LLC; *U.S. Private*, pg. 1280
CHRISTIE MANSON & WOODS LIMITED—See Financiere Pinault SCA; *Int'l*, pg. 2668
CHRISTIE'S AMSTERDAM B.V.—See Financiere Pinault SCA; *Int'l*, pg. 2668
CHRISTIE'S (INTERNATIONAL) S.A.—See Financiere Pinault SCA; *Int'l*, pg. 2668
CHRISTIE'S (ISRAEL) LTD.—See Financiere Pinault SCA; *Int'l*, pg. 2668
CHRISTIE'S SOUTH KENSINGTON LTD.—See Financiere Pinault SCA; *Int'l*, pg. 2668
CHUBB FIRE & SECURITY LIMITED—See Carrier Global Corporation; *U.S. Public*, pg. 441
CHUBB FIRE & SECURITY PTY LTD—See Carrier Global Corporation; *U.S. Public*, pg. 441
CIPPERMAN COMPLIANCE SERVICES LLC—See Genstar Capital, LLC; *U.S. Private*, pg. 1677
CITIZENHAWK, INC.—See Astorg Partners S.A.S.; *Int'l*, pg. 655
CITY RESPONSE LIMITED—See Guinness Northern Counties Ltd; *Int'l*, pg. 3174
CLARK PEST CONTROL OF NEVADA, LLC—See Rollins, Inc.; *U.S. Public*, pg. 1809
CLUB DEMONSTRATION SERVICES, INC.; *U.S. Private*, pg. 948
CMIT SOLUTIONS LLC—See Hammond, Kennedy, Whitney & Company, Inc.; *U.S. Private*, pg. 1850
COFELY AG—See ENGIE SA; *Int'l*, pg. 2429
COFELY AG - WINTERTHUR—See ENGIE SA; *Int'l*, pg. 2429
COFELY A.S.—See ENGIE SA; *Int'l*, pg. 2430

N.A.I.C.S. INDEX

561990 — ALL OTHER SUPPORT S...

COFELY DEUTSCHLAND GMBH—See ENGIE SA; *Int'l*, pg. 2429

COFELY ESPANA, S.A.U. - BARCELONA—See ENGIE SA; *Int'l*, pg. 2430

COFELY ESPANA, S.A.U.—See ENGIE SA; *Int'l*, pg. 2430

COFELY HELLAS A.E.—See ENGIE SA; *Int'l*, pg. 2430

COFELY NEDERLAND N.V.—See ENGIE SA; *Int'l*, pg. 2430

COFELY SERVICES INC.—See ENGIE SA; *Int'l*, pg. 2430

COFELY SERVICES SA/NV - LIEGE—See ENGIE SA; *Int'l*, pg. 2430

COFELY SERVICES SA/NV - MECHELEN—See ENGIE SA; *Int'l*, pg. 2430

COFELY SERVICES SA/NV—See ENGIE SA; *Int'l*, pg. 2429

COFELY SERVICES S.A.—See ENGIE SA; *Int'l*, pg. 2430

COFELY SERVICES SP. Z O.O.—See ENGIE SA; *Int'l*, pg. 2430

COFELY SOUTH EAST ASIA PTE. LTD.—See ENGIE SA; *Int'l*, pg. 2430

COFELY (THAILAND) PTE. LTD.—See ENGIE SA; *Int'l*, pg. 2430

COFRA B.V.—See HAL Trust N.V.; *Int'l*, pg. 3225

COLLECTION HOUSE INTERNATIONAL BPO, INC.—See Collection House Limited; *Int'l*, pg. 1699

COLLECTORS UNIVERSE INC.—See Cohen Private Ventures, LLC; *U.S. Private*, pg. 963

COLLECTORS UNIVERSE INC.—See D1 Capital Partners L.P.; *U.S. Private*, pg. 1143

COMMAND MANAGEMENT SERVICES, INC.; *U.S. Private*, pg. 982

COMMISSION ON ACCREDITATION OF REHABILITATION FACILITIES; *U.S. Private*, pg. 985

COMMUNITY HEALTH ACCREDITATION PARTNER, INC.; *U.S. Private*, pg. 993

COMMUNITY HEALTH NETWORK FOUNDATION; *U.S. Private*, pg. 993

COMPUTING SYSTEM INNOVATIONS; *U.S. Private*, pg. 1006

CONESTOGA AUCTION COMPANY, INC.—See John M. Hess Auction Service, Inc.; *U.S. Private*, pg. 2223

CORINPHILA AUKTIONEN AG—See Global Philatelic Network; *Int'l*, pg. 3000

CORINPHILA VEILINGEN BV—See Global Philatelic Network; *Int'l*, pg. 3000

CORPORATE ESSENTIALS, LLC.; *U.S. Private*, pg. 1054

CORPORATE SUITES, LLC; *U.S. Private*, pg. 1056

CORTEX BUSINESS SOLUTIONS INC.—See Hellman & Friedman LLC; *U.S. Private*, pg. 1908

CREATIVE RESOURCE GROUP, LLC; *U.S. Private*, pg. 1090

CREATIVE TECHNOLOGY GMBH CO. KG—See The Carlyle Group Inc.; *U.S. Public*, pg. 2049

CULLIGAN SOFT WATER SERVICE CO.; *U.S. Private*, pg. 1121

CULLIGAN WATER—See BDT Capital Partners, LLC; *U.S. Private*, pg. 502

CZARNOWSKI EXHIBIT SERVICE INC.; *U.S. Private*, pg. 1136

DACSIS LLC—See Pye-Barker Fire & Safety, LLC; *U.S. Private*, pg. 3309

DAIDO ENVIRONMENT ENGINEERING CO.,LTD.,—See Daido Steel Co., Ltd.; *Int'l*, pg. 1922

DARAMIC HOLDING S.A.S.—See Asahi Kasei Corporation; *Int'l*, pg. 597

DARKTRACE COLOMBIA S.A.S.—See Thoma Bravo, L.P.; *U.S. Private*, pg. 4147

DARKTRACE JAPAN KK—See Thoma Bravo, L.P.; *U.S. Private*, pg. 4147

DARKTRACE MEXICO, S.A. DE C.V.—See Thoma Bravo, L.P.; *U.S. Private*, pg. 4147

DARKTRACE SINGAPORE PTE. LTD.—See Thoma Bravo, L.P.; *U.S. Private*, pg. 4147

DDINNOVATION CO., LTD.—See Daiwa House Industry Co., Ltd.; *Int'l*, pg. 1945

D&D SERVICES (AUSTRALIA) PTY LTD.—See AVADA Group Limited; *Int'l*, pg. 734

DECKSIDE POOL SERVICE; *U.S. Private*, pg. 1187

DEKRA CZ A.S.—See DEKRA e.V.; *Int'l*, pg. 2006

THE DESIGN AGENCY INC.; *U.S. Private*, pg. 4020

DEUTZ DITER S.A.—See DEUTZ AG; *Int'l*, pg. 2086

DEWBERRY TECHNOLOGIES, INC.—See Dewberry LLC; *U.S. Private*, pg. 1219

D-FLIGHT S.P.A.—See ENAV S.p.A.; *Int'l*, pg. 2396

DH (DALIAN) ADMINISTRATIVE MANAGEMENT CONSULTING CENTER CO., LTD.—See Daiwa House Industry Co., Ltd.; *Int'l*, pg. 1945

DIGICO INC.—See National Amusements, Inc.; *U.S. Private*, pg. 2842

DLIGHT BVBA—See BASF SE; *Int'l*, pg. 883

DMS INC.; *Int'l*, pg. 2146

DNT SERVICE CO., LTD.—See Dai Nippon Toryo Co., Ltd.; *Int'l*, pg. 1916

DNV GL—See DNV GL Group AS; *Int'l*, pg. 2151

EAGLE PACKAGING INC.—See Anheuser-Busch InBev SA/NV; *Int'l*, pg. 465

EARLY WARNING SYSTEM GMBH—See Federation Internationale de Football Association; *Int'l*, pg. 2631

EASTERN JASON FABRICATION SERVICES PTE LTD—See Federal International (2000) Ltd; *Int'l*, pg. 2630

ECMS, INC.—See L.N. Curtis & Sons; *U.S. Private*, pg. 2366

EDENRED PERU SA—See Edenred S.A.; *Int'l*, pg. 2308

E&E EXHIBITS; *U.S. Private*, pg. 1301

EFFILIO AG—See Bossard Holding AG; *Int'l*, pg. 1117

ELAN INFORMATION TECHNOLOGY GROUP—See ELAN Microelectronic Corp.; *Int'l*, pg. 2342

EL CAMINO RESOURCES LLC; *U.S. Private*, pg. 1348

ELECTION SERVICES CORPORATION; *U.S. Private*, pg. 1351

ELNET TECHNOLOGIES LIMITED; *Int'l*, pg. 2368

E-MID SIM S.P.A.—See CME Group, Inc.; *U.S. Public*, pg. 518

EMPOWER OY—See AAC Capital Partners Holding B.V.; *Int'l*, pg. 31

EMT DISTRIBUTION PTY. LTD.—See Crayon Group Holding ASA; *Int'l*, pg. 1829

ENCORE HOMES LIMITED—See Guinness Northern Counties Ltd; *Int'l*, pg. 3174

ENCORE UNLIMITED LLC—See Summit Partners, L.P.; *U.S. Private*, pg. 3856

ENFINITEC B.V.—See Acer Incorporated; *Int'l*, pg. 99

ENTERPRISE DIVERSIFIED, INC.—See ENDI Corp.; *U.S. Public*, pg. 760

E.ON BAYERN AG—See E.ON SE; *Int'l*, pg. 2252

EQUATION RECYCLING PTE. LTD.—See DISA LIMITED; *Int'l*, pg. 2131

EQUIMAR SHIPHOLDINGS, LTD.—See B+H Ocean Carriers Ltd.; *Int'l*, pg. 784

ERMAN RETIREMENT ADVISORY, INC.—See Hellman & Friedman LLC; *U.S. Private*, pg. 1908

ERSTE GROUP PROCUREMENT—See Erste Group Bank AG; *Int'l*, pg. 2498

ESCAPES!—See Cooper Communities, Inc.; *U.S. Private*, pg. 1041

ES-LINK CO., LTD.—See EPS Holdings, Inc.; *Int'l*, pg. 2465

EUROPTRONIC GREEN ENERGY PTE. LTD.—See Europtronic Group Ltd.; *Int'l*, pg. 2557

EUROTOLL SAS—See ACS, Actividades de Construccion y Servicios, S.A.; *Int'l*, pg. 112

EVENT SALES INC.; *U.S. Private*, pg. 1437

EVERGREEN AVIATION TECHNOLOGIES CORP.—See Evergreen Marine Corporation (Taiwan) Ltd.; *Int'l*, pg. 2566

EVERPIA JOINT STOCK COMPANY - DONG NAI FACTORY—See Everpia Joint Stock Company; *Int'l*, pg. 2568

EVERPIA JOINT STOCK COMPANY - HANOI FACTORY—See Everpia Joint Stock Company; *Int'l*, pg. 2568

EVERPIA JOINT STOCK COMPANY; *Int'l*, pg. 2568

EXCHANGE ENTERPRISES LIMITED—See Gannett Co., Inc.; *U.S. Public*, pg. 897

EXHIBIT EDGE INC.—See Star Exhibits & Environments, Inc.; *U.S. Private*, pg. 3784

EXPO EXPERTS, LLC—See Professional Diversity Network, Inc.; *U.S. Public*, pg. 1724

FECTO ORIENT (PVT.) LTD.—See Fecto Group of Companies; *Int'l*, pg. 2629

FIELD AVIATION COMPANY INC.—See Hunting Plc; *Int'l*, pg. 3536

FIERA MILANO SPA; *Int'l*, pg. 2660

FLAGGER FORCE; *U.S. Private*, pg. 1539

FLUKE PROCESS INSTRUMENTS—See Fortive Corporation; *U.S. Public*, pg. 870

FOCAL THERAPEUTICS INC.—See Hologic, Inc.; *U.S. Public*, pg. 1044

FORUM INDUSTRIES, INC.—See Blue Point Capital Partners, LLC; *U.S. Private*, pg. 590

FP DIGITAL BUSINESS SOLUTIONS GMBH—See Francotyp-Postalia Holding AG; *Int'l*, pg. 2761

FRAMOS GMBH; *Int'l*, pg. 2759

FUJIFILM BUSINESS EXPERT CORPORATION—See FUJIFILM Holdings Corporation; *Int'l*, pg. 2821

FUTURE NRG SDN BHD—See FITTERS Diversified Berhad; *Int'l*, pg. 2695

GASAG SOLUTION PLUS GMBH—See ENGIE SA; *Int'l*, pg. 2429

GASAG SOLUTION PLUS GMBH—See E.ON SE; *Int'l*, pg. 2257

GASTON & SHEEHAN AUCTIONEERS, INC.; *U.S. Private*, pg. 1648

GBN,LLC—See MetLife, Inc.; *U.S. Public*, pg. 1430

GENERAL DYNAMICS INFORMATION SYSTEMS & TECHNOLOGY GROUP—See General Dynamics Corporation; *U.S. Public*, pg. 914

GENNIUS, INC.—See Thoma Bravo, L.P.; *U.S. Private*, pg. 4150

GES GMBH & CO. KG—See Viad Corp.; *U.S. Public*, pg. 2291

GET PREPPED LLC—See Manhattan Review Inc.; *U.S. Private*, pg. 2563

G&G TECHNICAL INC.; *U.S. Private*, pg. 1629

GLOBAL MARINE SEARCH, LTD—See INNOVATE Corp.; *U.S. Public*, pg. 1126

GLOBAL TECHNICAL SYSTEMS - GTS INFORMATION AND SENSOR SYSTEMS FACILITY—See Global Technical Systems; *U.S. Private*, pg. 1718

GLOBETRONICS (KL) SDN. BHD.—See Globetronics Technology Bhd.; *Int'l*, pg. 3007

GLOBETRONICS SDN. BHD.—See Globetronics Technology Bhd.; *Int'l*, pg. 3007

GO GREEN (OH) LLC—See W.P. Carey Inc.; *U.S. Public*, pg. 2315

GOLDARD WATER TECHNOLOGY CO., LTD.—See Goldcard Smart Group Co., Ltd.; *Int'l*, pg. 3027

GOODWILL INDUSTRIES OF CENTRAL INDIANA, INC.—See Goodwill Industries International, Inc.; *U.S. Private*, pg. 1740

GOVERNMENTAUCTIONS.ORG—See Cyweb Holdings Inc.; *U.S. Private*, pg. 1136

GPO PLUS, INC.; *U.S. Public*, pg. 952

GPS BULGARIA AD—See America Movil, S.A.B. de C.V.; *Int'l*, pg. 421

GREAT LAKES SCRIP CENTER, LLC—See Bold Orange Company, LLC; *U.S. Private*, pg. 610

GREAT TEAM BACKEND FOUNDRY, INC.—See Hong Tai Electric Industrial Co., Ltd.; *Int'l*, pg. 3469

GREENBAX ENTERPRISES INC.; *U.S. Private*, pg. 1774

GULF INTERSTATE FIELD SERVICES, INC.—See Gulf International Corporation; *U.S. Private*, pg. 1816

HANKYU JOB YELL CO LTD—See H2O Retailing Corp.; *Int'l*, pg. 3200

HAWK INCENTIVES HOLDINGS LIMITED—See P2 Capital Partners, LLC; *U.S. Private*, pg. 3061

HAWK INCENTIVES HOLDINGS LIMITED—See Silver Lake Group, LLC; *U.S. Private*, pg. 3656

HEINRICH KOHLER AUCTIONSHAUS GMBH & CO. KG—See Global Philatelic Network; *Int'l*, pg. 3000

HENROB CORPORATION—See Atlas Copco AB; *Int'l*, pg. 681

HENROB CORPORATION—See Atlas Copco AB; *Int'l*, pg. 681

HERA COMM MEDITERRANEA S.R.L.—See Hera S.p.A.; *Int'l*, pg. 3356

HERCULES EQUIPAMENTOS DE PROTECAO LTDA.—See Ansell Limited; *Int'l*, pg. 478

HIGHTIMES HOLDING CORP.; *U.S. Private*, pg. 1941

HIRAGA CO., LTD.; *Int'l*, pg. 3402

HMC CONSULTING (SHANGHAI) CO. LTD—See Hospitality Marketing Concepts, Inc.; *U.S. Private*, pg. 1987

HOMESERVE USA CORP.—See Brookfield Corporation; *Int'l*, pg. 1188

H.R. HARMER, GLOBAL PHILATELIC NETWORK, INC.—See Global Philatelic Network; *Int'l*, pg. 3000

HUNTER DOUGLAS FABRICATION CO.—See 3G Capital Partners L.P.; *U.S. Private*, pg. 13

HUNTER LANE, LLC—See New Rite Aid, LLC; *U.S. Private*, pg. 2905

HYOSUNG TRADING PERFORMANCE GROUP—See Hyosung Corporation; *Int'l*, pg. 3551

IBH ENGINEERING GMBH—See Enka Insaat ve Sanayi A.S.; *Int'l*, pg. 2440

IDS AIRNAV S.R.L.—See ENAV S.p.A.; *Int'l*, pg. 2396

IGAS, INC.; *U.S. Private*, pg. 2039

I-K-I MANUFACTURING CO. INC.; *U.S. Private*, pg. 2026

INSPECTMYRIDE LLC—See JM Family Enterprises Inc.; *U.S. Private*, pg. 2214

INTELLIGENT TECHNOLOGIES & SERVICES, INC.—See Fike Corporation; *U.S. Private*, pg. 1505

INTERNATIONAL MISSING PERSONS FOUNDATION; *U.S. Private*, pg. 2119

INTERNATIONAL SOCIETY OF AUTOMATION; *U.S. Private*, pg. 2120

INTER PARTNER ASISTENCIA SERVICIOS ESPANA SA—See AXA S.A.; *Int'l*, pg. 754

INTER PARTNER ASSISTANCE ALGERIE SPA—See AXA S.A.; *Int'l*, pg. 754

INTER PARTNER ASSISTANCE HONG-KONG LTD—See AXA S.A.; *Int'l*, pg. 755

INTER PARTNER ASSISTANCE POLSKA S.A.—See AXA S.A.; *Int'l*, pg. 755

INTER PARTNER ASSISTANCE S/C LTDA—See AXA S.A.; *Int'l*, pg. 755

INTER PARTNER ASSISTANCE TURKEY—See AXA S.A.; *Int'l*, pg. 755

INVENTION SUBMISSION CORPORATION—See Technosystems Consolidated Corporation; *U.S. Private*, pg. 3956

ISID-AO, LTD.—See Dentsu Group Inc.; *Int'l*, pg. 2038

ISO TECHNOLOGY SDN. BHD.—See Globetronics Technology Bhd.; *Int'l*, pg. 3007

IZAMAX VENTURES, INC.—See Legal Graphicworks, Inc.; *U.S. Private*, pg. 2417

JAMES G. MURPHY CO. INC.; *U.S. Private*, pg. 2184

JOHN BULL STAMP AUCTIONS, LTD.—See Global Philatelic Network; *Int'l*, pg. 3000

JOHN CONTI COFFEE CO.; *U.S. Private*, pg. 2221

JOHN M. HESS AUCTION SERVICE, INC.; *U.S. Private*, pg. 2223

JOHNSONS WAX (EAST AFRICA) LTD.—See S.C. Johnson & Son, Inc.; *U.S. Private*, pg. 3516

JSL SOLUTIONS LLC—See Zebulon Solutions LLC; *U.S. Private*, pg. 4599

561990 — ALL OTHER SUPPORT S...

JUDITH HEFT ASSOCIATES, LLC—See Aon plc; *Int'l*, pg. 498
KART, SPOL. S R.O.—See CEZ, a.s.; *Int'l*, pg. 1428
KATHRYN BEICH FUNDRAISING—See Lincolnshire Management, Inc.; *U.S. Private*, pg. 2459
KEMA SERVICES INC. - ANAHEIM—See DNV GL Group AS; *Int'l*, pg. 2151
KEMA SERVICES INC. - MADISON—See DNV GL Group AS; *Int'l*, pg. 2151
KEMA SERVICES INC. - OAKLAND—See DNV GL Group AS; *Int'l*, pg. 2151
KEMA SERVICES INC.—See DNV GL Group AS; *Int'l*, pg. 2151
KIRTAS TECHNOLOGIES, INC.—See i2S SA; *Int'l*, pg. 3566
KLEENEZE UK LIMITED—See JRjr33, Inc.; *U.S. Private*, pg. 2240
L-3 MICRODYNE OUTSOURCING, INC.—See L3Harris Technologies, Inc.; *U.S. Public*, pg. 1283
LEGS (SHANGHAI) CULTURAL & CREATIVE COMPANY, LTD.—See CL Holdings Inc.; *Int'l*, pg. 1640
LENATI LLC—See Concentrix Corporation; *U.S. Public*, pg. 565
LIBERTY LEASING CO.—See BNP Paribas SA; *Int'l*, pg. 1091
LOVABLE ITALIANA INTERNATIONAL LIMITED—See Hanesbrands Inc.; *U.S. Public*, pg. 983
LOVELL COMMUNICATIONS INC.—See Health Management Associates, Inc.; *U.S. Private*, pg. 1893
MAE.CH GMBH—See Gesco AG; *Int'l*, pg. 2945
MASTER PROTECTION CORPORATION; *U.S. Private*, pg. 2607
MEDCEN COMMUNITY HEALTH FOUNDATION INC.—See Central Georgia Health System Inc.; *U.S. Private*, pg. 821
MEDIALIVE INTERNATIONAL INC.; *U.S. Private*, pg. 2653
MERCATOR INTERNATIONAL AB—See Axel Johnson Gruppen AB; *Int'l*, pg. 765
MEXICOHOSOKAWA MICRON DE MEXICO S.A. DE C.V.—See Hosokawa Micron Corporation; *Int'l*, pg. 3486
MIRTH, LLC—See Thoma Bravo, L.P.; *U.S. Private*, pg. 4150
MOBILE.INTERNATIONAL GMBH—See eBay Inc.; *U.S. Public*, pg. 709
MOBILITY SERVICES INTERNATIONAL LLC; *U.S. Private*, pg. 2758
MORGAN STANLEY CORPORATE TRADER—See Morgan Stanley; *U.S. Public*, pg. 1472
M.T. DONAHOE & ASSOCIATES, LLC—See AmWINS Group, Inc.; *U.S. Private*, pg. 269
MYRON BOWLING AUCTIONEERS INC.; *U.S. Private*, pg. 2826
NAPC DEFENSE, INC.; *U.S. Public*, pg. 1491
NATIONAL HERITAGE FOUNDATION, INC.; *U.S. Private*, pg. 2856
NAVY SEAL FOUNDATION, INC.; *U.S. Private*, pg. 2873
NEJ, INC.; *U.S. Private*, pg. 2882
NEWPORT DIVERSIFIED INC.; *U.S. Private*, pg. 2916
NEWSTREAM ENTERPRISES, LLC.—See SRC Holdings Corporation; *U.S. Private*, pg. 3767
NEX ABIDE TRADE REPOSITORY AB—See CME Group, Inc.; *U.S. Public*, pg. 516
NEX SERVICES LIMITED—See CME Group, Inc.; *U.S. Public*, pg. 518
NEX TREASURY—See CME Group, Inc.; *U.S. Public*, pg. 517
NONPROFIT VOTE; *U.S. Private*, pg. 2934
NORTHEAST DATA DESTRUCTION & RECYCLING, LLC—See National Waste Management Holdings, Inc.; *U.S. Public*, pg. 1498
NORTHWEST CRANE SERVICE, LLC.; *U.S. Private*, pg. 2959
OBSCURA DIGITAL, INC.—See Sphere Entertainment Co.; *U.S. Public*, pg. 1918
OFFSITE ARCHIVE STORAGE & INTEGRATED SERVICES (IRELAND) LIMITED—See Housatonic Partners Management Co., Inc.; *U.S. Private*, pg. 1991
OFFSITE ARCHIVE STORAGE & INTEGRATED SERVICES (IRELAND) LIMITED—See Sverica Capital Management LP; *U.S. Private*, pg. 3888
THE OLIVER GROUP LLC—See JLL Partners, LLC; *U.S. Private*, pg. 2213
OMNI OPHTHALMIC MANAGEMENT CONSULTANTS LLC—See NMS Capital Services, LLC; *U.S. Private*, pg. 2931
ON-SITE MANAGER, INC.—See Thoma Bravo, L.P.; *U.S. Private*, pg. 4153
OPENGATE CONSULTING, INC.—See SolomonEdwardsGroup, LLC; *U.S. Private*, pg. 3710
ORGANIZATIONAL DEVELOPMENT INC.; *U.S. Private*, pg. 3041
ORLIN, INC.—See Avis Budget Group, Inc.; *U.S. Public*, pg. 249
ORRIDGE & CO LTD.—See Blackstone Inc.; *U.S. Public*, pg. 357
ORTEC MESSE UND KONGRESS GMBH—See Bertelsmann SE & Co. KGaA; *Int'l*, pg. 993
OSES INTERNATIONAL, LLC—See Oil States International, Inc.; *U.S. Public*, pg. 1565
PACIFIC TOLL PROCESSING, INC.; *U.S. Private*, pg. 3071

PALLMANN MASCHINENFABRIK GMBH & CO. KG—See G. Siempelkamp GmbH & Co. KG; *Int'l*, pg. 2864
PARKER OIL COMPANY, INC. - ENVIRONMENTAL MANAGEMENT SERVICES DIVISION—See Parker Holding Company, Inc.; *U.S. Private*, pg. 3097
PHARMACY TECHNICIAN CERTIFICATION BOARD; *U.S. Private*, pg. 3165
PHILLIPS DE PURY & COMPANY; *U.S. Private*, pg. 3170
PLANTSCAPES, INC.; *U.S. Private*, pg. 3198
PLLYPORE K.K.—See Asahi Kasei Corporation; *Int'l*, pg. 597
P&R DENTAL STRATEGIES, LLC—See The Beekman Group, LLC; *U.S. Private*, pg. 3993
PRECISION ROLL GRINDERS, INC.; *U.S. Private*, pg. 3246
PREMIER BROKERAGE SERVICES INC.—See Arthur J. Gallagher & Co.; *U.S. Public*, pg. 207
PREMIUM 2000+ WARRANTIES; *U.S. Private*, pg. 3251
PRESERVATION RESOURCES—See Online Computer Library Center, Inc.; *U.S. Private*, pg. 3027
PRINTSTOCK PRODUCTS LIMITED—See The Marygold Companies, Inc.; *U.S. Public*, pg. 2112
PROFESSIONAL EXAMINATION SERVICE; *U.S. Private*, pg. 3275
P.T. CHORI INDONESIA—See Chori Co., Ltd.; *Int'l*, pg. 1583
PTI USA MANUFACTURING L.L.C.—See Oil States International, Inc.; *U.S. Public*, pg. 1565
PT NUNUKAN JAYA LESTARI—See Fima Corporation Berhad; *Int'l*, pg. 2664
PUBLIC INTEREST COMMUNICATION; *U.S. Private*, pg. 3299
QUALITY LOGO PRODUCTS, INC.; *U.S. Private*, pg. 3319
RACO WIRELESS LLC—See The Graham Group, Inc.; *U.S. Private*, pg. 4037
RAPISCAN SYSTEMS AUSTRALIA PTY LTD—See OSI Systems, Inc.; *U.S. Public*, pg. 1622
REDFLEX TRAFFIC SYSTEMS INDIA PRIVATE LIMITED—See Verra Mobility Corporation; *U.S. Public*, pg. 2287
REDFLEX TRAFFIC SYSTEMS LIMITED—See Verra Mobility Corporation; *U.S. Public*, pg. 2287
REDFLEX TRAFFIC SYSTEMS MALAYSIA SDN. BHD.—See Verra Mobility Corporation; *U.S. Public*, pg. 2287
REDFLEX TRAFFIC SYSTEMS PTY LTD—See Verra Mobility Corporation; *U.S. Public*, pg. 2287
RELOCATION MANAGEMENT RESOURCES, INC. - BUSINESS SOLUTIONS—See Relocation Management Resources, Inc.; *U.S. Private*, pg. 3395
RELOCATION MANAGEMENT RESOURCES, INC.; *U.S. Private*, pg. 3395
RESEARCH INSTITUTE FOR QUALITY LIVING CO., LTD.—See AEON Co., Ltd.; *Int'l*, pg. 178
REWARDSNOW, INC.; *U.S. Private*, pg. 3417
RHODE ISLAND CONVENTION CENTER AUTHORITY; *U.S. Private*, pg. 3422
ROBIMATIC LTD.—See Genuit Group plc; *Int'l*, pg. 2930
ROYAL DOCUMENT DESTRUCTION; *U.S. Private*, pg. 3492
SAFEHARBOR KNOWLEDGE SOLUTIONS—See Shackleton Equity Partners LLC; *U.S. Private*, pg. 3622
SAFER PRINTS INC.; *U.S. Private*, pg. 3524
SAI GLOBAL ITALIA SRL—See EQT AB; *Int'l*, pg. 2471
SAMUEL STEEL PICKLING COMPANY—See Worthington Industries, Inc.; *U.S. Public*, pg. 2382
SANOMA ENTERTAINMENT LTD.—See DPG Media Group NV; *Int'l*, pg. 2188
SBD ENTERPRISES, LLC—See Kainos Capital, LLC; *U.S. Private*, pg. 2255
SC DATA, INC.—See COR365 Information Solutions; *U.S. Private*, pg. 1046
SCHOTTENSTEIN/BERNSTEIN CAPITAL; *U.S. Private*, pg. 3569
SCI/STEELCON INC.; *U.S. Private*, pg. 3573
S.C. JOHNSON COMPANY LIMITED—See S.C. Johnson & Son, Inc.; *U.S. Private*, pg. 3517
SCORES LICENSING CORP.—See Scores Holding Company, Inc.; *U.S. Public*, pg. 1849
SCRIBE SOLUTIONS, INC.—See GEE Group Inc.; *U.S. Public*, pg. 910
SEA SUB SYSTEMS INC.—See GenNx360 Capital Partners, L.P.; *U.S. Private*, pg. 1672
SECOND STORY, INC.—See The Kroger Co.; *U.S. Public*, pg. 2109
SECURITY PRINTERS (M) SDN. BHD.—See Fima Corporation Berhad; *Int'l*, pg. 2664
SEIBU SERVICE CO., LTD.—See Hanwa Co., Ltd.; *Int'l*, pg. 3263
SHRED-IT GMBH—See Waste Management, Inc.; *U.S. Public*, pg. 2332
SIDIC TECHNOLOGY SDN. BHD.—See Edran Berhad; *Int'l*, pg. 2315
SIENNA GROUP, LLC—See Thoma Bravo, L.P.; *U.S. Private*, pg. 4146
SISTER'S SANITATION SERVICES, LLC—See Waste Management, Inc.; *U.S. Public*, pg. 2332
SKILLTECH CONSULTING SERVICES PTY LTD—See Downer EDI Limited; *Int'l*, pg. 2185
SMARTBASE SOLUTIONS LLC; *U.S. Private*, pg. 3691

SMILES FIDELIDADE SA—See Gol Linhas Aereas Inteligentes S.A.; *Int'l*, pg. 3023
SOPRA BANKING SOFTWARE—See Axway Software SA; *Int'l*, pg. 772
SOTHEBY'S HONG KONG LTD.—See Sotheby's; *U.S. Public*, pg. 1910
SOUTH DAKOTA STATE UNIVERSITY FOUNDATION; *U.S. Private*, pg. 3722
SOUTHERN COMPANY SERVICES, INC.—See The Southern Company; *U.S. Public*, pg. 2131
SOUTHWEST ARKANSAS DEVELOPMENT COUNCIL; *U.S. Private*, pg. 3738
THE SOUTHWESTERN COMPANY; *U.S. Private*, pg. 4119
SPECTRUM WINE AUCTIONS, LLC—See Spectrum Group International, Inc.; *U.S. Public*, pg. 1917
STACK'S-BOWERS NUMISMATICS, LLC—See Spectrum Group International, Inc.; *U.S. Public*, pg. 1917
STACK'S-BOWERS & PONTERIO, LTD.—See Spectrum Group International, Inc.; *U.S. Public*, pg. 1917
STEERS (PROPRIETARY) LIMITED—See Famous Brands Limited; *Int'l*, pg. 2612
STELLAR IT SOLUTIONS, LLC; *U.S. Private*, pg. 3799
STERILIZATION SERVICES OF TENNESSEE—See Altair Corporation; *U.S. Public*, pg. 86
ST. FRANCIS FOUNDATION—See Catholic Health Initiatives; *U.S. Private*, pg. 790
STONER & CO., INC.; *U.S. Private*, pg. 3830
SUMMIT FIRE & SECURITY—See BlackRock, Inc.; *U.S. Public*, pg. 346
SUNDEX CO., LTD.—See FTGroup Co Ltd.; *Int'l*, pg. 2800
SUSQUEHANNA VALLEY WATER CONDITIONING CO.—See Culligan Soft Water Service Co.; *U.S. Private*, pg. 1121
SWB MESSUNG UND ABRECHNUNG GMBH—See EWE Aktiengesellschaft; *Int'l*, pg. 2576
TELGIAN INC.; *U.S. Private*, pg. 3962
TONAQUINT DATA CENTERS, INC.; *U.S. Private*, pg. 4184
TRACE SERVICES INC.; *U.S. Private*, pg. 4200
TRANSFORMATION SYSTEMS, INC.; *U.S. Private*, pg. 4208
TTS MARINE INC.—See Cargotec Corporation; *Int'l*, pg. 1329
UNION PEN COMPANY; *U.S. Private*, pg. 4285
UNITED MOTOR CLUB OF AMERICA, INC.—See Tiptree Inc.; *U.S. Public*, pg. 2159
UNIVERSITY OF NEBRASKA FOUNDATION; *U.S. Private*, pg. 4309
UNIVERSITY OF NEW HAMPSHIRE FOUNDATION; *U.S. Private*, pg. 4309
UNTERSTUTZUNGSGESELLSCHAFT MBH DER DEUTZ AKTIENGESELLSCHAFT—See DEUTZ AG; *Int'l*, pg. 2086
USB TRADE SERVICES LIMITED—See U.S. Bancorp; *U.S. Public*, pg. 2213
U.S. UNDERWATER SERVICES, LLC—See Benford Capital Partners, LLC; *U.S. Private*, pg. 526
U.S. UNDERWATER SERVICES, LLC—See Coppermine Capital, LLC; *U.S. Private*, pg. 1045
V2X, INC.; *U.S. Public*, pg. 2270
V.A. ANDERSON ENTERPRISES, INC.—See Apax Partners LLP; *Int'l*, pg. 503
VAC-ALL SERVICE, INC.—See Republic Services, Inc.; *U.S. Public*, pg. 1788
VALMONT AUSTRALIA IRRIGATION PTY. LTD.—See Valmont Industries, Inc.; *U.S. Public*, pg. 2274
VANGUARD FIRE SYSTEMS, L.P.; *U.S. Private*, pg. 4343
VECTRUS FEDERAL SERVICES GMBH—See V2X, Inc.; *U.S. Public*, pg. 2270
VECTRUS SYSTEMS CORPORATION—See V2X, Inc.; *U.S. Public*, pg. 2270
VENNERS LTD.—See Christie Group plc; *Int'l*, pg. 1587
VERIDAS DIGITAL AUTHENTICATION SOLUTIONS S.L.—See Banco Bilbao Vizcaya Argentaria, S.A.; *Int'l*, pg. 818
VERIZON WIRELESS - JERSEY CITY—See Verizon Communications Inc.; *U.S. Public*, pg. 2284
VIA TRADING CORPORATION; *U.S. Private*, pg. 4375
VIGILENT CORPORATION; *U.S. Private*, pg. 4382
VISITING NURSE ASSOCIATION OF CENTRAL JERSEY—See Visiting Nurse Service of New York; *U.S. Private*, pg. 4393
VISITING NURSE ASSOCIATION OF STATEN ISLAND; *U.S. Private*, pg. 4393
VISUAL COMMUNICATIONS INC.; *U.S. Private*, pg. 4404
VOLUNTEERS FOR INTERAMERICAN DEVELOPMENT ASSISTANCE; *U.S. Private*, pg. 4411
VT GROUP (US) PLC—See Alvarez & Marsal, Inc.; *U.S. Private*, pg. 213
WAVETECH GLOBAL, INC.; *U.S. Private*, pg. 4458
WEICHERT WORKFORCE MOBILITY INC. BOSTON—See Weichert Co.; *U.S. Private*, pg. 4470
WEST SIDE SALVAGE, INC.—See West Side Unlimited Corporation; *U.S. Private*, pg. 4487
WILSONS TM LIMITED—See AVADA Group Limited; *Int'l*, pg. 734
THE WITTERN GROUP; *U.S. Private*, pg. 4138
WORLD TESTING INC.; *U.S. Private*, pg. 4567

WYNNE RESIDENTIAL CORPORATE HOUSING; *U.S. Private*, pg. 4578
XANDRION B.V.—See Compass Group PLC; *Int'l*, pg. 1752
YOUBET.COM, LLC—See Churchill Downs, Inc.; *U.S. Public*, pg. 494
ZANDHANDEL J. VAN VLIET B.V.—See HAL Trust N.V.; *Int'l*, pg. 3227
ZELOR TECHNOLOGY PTE LTD—See Frencken Group Limited; *Int'l*, pg. 2773
ZURN WATER, LLC—See Zurn Elkay Water Solutions Corporation; *U.S. Public*, pg. 2414

562111 — SOLID WASTE COLLECTION

1-800-PACK-RAT, LLC—See Waste Management, Inc.; *U.S. Public*, pg. 2330
A-1 DISPOSAL SERVICE, INC.—See Watts Trucking Service, Inc.; *U.S. Private*, pg. 4456
A2A AMBIENTE S.P.A.—See A2A S.p.A.; *Int'l*, pg. 29
ACCELERATED WASTE SOLUTIONS, LLC; *U.S. Private*, pg. 49
ADVANCED DISPOSAL SERVICES, INC.—See Waste Management, Inc.; *U.S. Public*, pg. 2330
ADVANCED WASTE SERVICES OF INDIANA, INC.—See EQT AB; *Int'l*, pg. 2473
AIMERI AMBIENTE SRL—See Biancamano S.p.A.; *Int'l*, pg. 1017
AMBIMED - GESTAO AMBIENTAL, LDA.—See Waste Management, Inc.; *U.S. Public*, pg. 2332
AMERICAN WASTE INDUSTRIES; *U.S. Private*, pg. 258
AMERICAN WASTE, LLC—See BC Partners LLP; *Int'l*, pg. 924
THE AMES COMPANIES UK LTD.—See Griffon Corporation; *U.S. Public*, pg. 969
ANDERSON LANDFILL, INC.—See Waste Management, Inc.; *U.S. Public*, pg. 2330
ARAKELIAN ENTERPRISES, INC.; *U.S. Private*, pg. 307
ASPEN WASTE SYSTEMS INC.; *U.S. Private*, pg. 352
AURUBIS BERANGO S.L.U.—See Aurubis AG; *Int'l*, pg. 714
BAY DISPOSAL INC.—See Schaubach Holdings Inc.; *U.S. Private*, pg. 3563
BIOCRUDE TECHNOLOGIES INC.; *Int'l*, pg. 1037
BION ENVIRONMENTAL TECHNOLOGIES, INC.; *U.S. Public*, pg. 338
BLACKHAWK WASTE DISPOSAL CO., INC.—See Watts Trucking Service, Inc.; *U.S. Private*, pg. 4456
BLOW BROS.—See Casella Waste Systems, Inc.; *U.S. Public*, pg. 445
BUDGET BINS LIMITED—See Capital Environment Holdings Limited; *Int'l*, pg. 1310
BUMI SEGAR INDAH SDN. BHD.—See Ann Joo Resources Berhad; *Int'l*, pg. 473
BURRTEC WASTE INDUSTRIES, INC.; *U.S. Private*, pg. 692
CALIFORNIA WASTE SOLUTIONS; *U.S. Private*, pg. 721
CALMET SERVICES INC.; *U.S. Private*, pg. 723
CAL SIERRA DISPOSAL—See Waste Management, Inc.; *U.S. Public*, pg. 2330
CASELLA WASTE MANAGEMENT, INC.—See Casella Waste Systems, Inc.; *U.S. Public*, pg. 446
CASELLA WASTE MANAGEMENT OF N.Y., INC. - DUNKIRK—See Casella Waste Systems, Inc.; *U.S. Public*, pg. 446
CENTRAL WASTE SYSTEMS, INC—See Watts Trucking Service, Inc.; *U.S. Private*, pg. 4456
CIA SANEAMENTO DO PARANA-SANEPAR; *Int'l*, pg. 1602
CLEANAWAY INDUSTRIES PTY LTD.—See Cleanaway Waste Management Limited; *Int'l*, pg. 1654
CLEAN EARTH OF WEST VIRGINIA, INC.—See Compass Diversified Holdings; *U.S. Public*, pg. 560
CLOSE THE LOOP LIMITED; *Int'l*, pg. 1661
CONCORD DISPOSAL SERVICE; *U.S. Private*, pg. 1009
CONSUMER PORTFOLIO SERVICES—See Consumer Portfolio Services, Inc.; *U.S. Public*, pg. 572
COVANTA NIAGARA I, LLC—See EQT AB; *Int'l*, pg. 2474
DAISEKI ECO. SOLUTION CO., LTD.; *Int'l*, pg. 1941
DELTA SANITATION, LLC—See Waste Pro USA, Inc.; *U.S. Private*, pg. 4450
EDCO DISPOSAL CORPORATION; *U.S. Private*, pg. 1332
E.J. HARRISON & SONS INC.; *U.S. Private*, pg. 1306
ELK RIVER LANDFILL, INC.—See Waste Management, Inc.; *U.S. Public*, pg. 2331
EQ ALABAMA, INC.—See Republic Services, Inc.; *U.S. Public*, pg. 1787
EQ DETROIT, INC.—See Republic Services, Inc.; *U.S. Public*, pg. 1787
ESE EUROPE SP. Z O.O.—See ESE Entertainment, Inc.; *Int'l*, pg. 2502
EUREC A/S—See BEWi ASA; *Int'l*, pg. 1004
FEATHER RIVER DISPOSAL, INC.—See Waste Management, Inc.; *U.S. Public*, pg. 2331
GARBAGEMAN CO; *U.S. Private*, pg. 1642
GARTRAN, L.L.C.—See Waste Management, Inc.; *U.S. Public*, pg. 2331
GEESINK NORBA LTD.—See Geesink Group B.V.; *Int'l*, pg. 2911
GEORGIA WASTE SYSTEMS, INC.—See Waste Management, Inc.; *U.S. Public*, pg. 2331
GOODE COMPANIES, INC.; *U.S. Private*, pg. 1739
GREEN SEAL ENVIRONMENTAL, INC.—See Teachers Insurance Association - College Retirement Fund; *U.S. Private*, pg. 3945
GREENWASTE RECOVERY INC.; *U.S. Private*, pg. 1780
GROUPE PIZZORNO ENVIRONNEMENT S.A.; *Int'l*, pg. 3109
HAWKEYE WASTE SYSTEMS, INC.—See Watts Trucking Service, Inc.; *U.S. Private*, pg. 4456
HOLZWARME GRINDELWALD AG—See BKW AG; *Int'l*, pg. 1055
IBOKIN CO., LTD.; *Int'l*, pg. 3576
IGS CAPITAL GROUP LTD.; *Int'l*, pg. 3603
INTEGRATED WASTE SOLUTIONS GROUP, LLC; *U.S. Private*, pg. 2101
LJP ENTERPRISES, INC.; *U.S. Private*, pg. 2474
L & M WASTE SYSTEMS, INC.—See Watts Trucking Service, Inc.; *U.S. Private*, pg. 4456
MARBORG INDUSTRIES INC.; *U.S. Private*, pg. 2570
MARIN SANITARY SERVICE INC.; *U.S. Private*, pg. 2574
MELTEC CO., LTD.—See Dowa Holdings Co., Ltd.; *Int'l*, pg. 2183
MIDWEST DISPOSALS LTD.—See Capital Environment Holdings Limited; *Int'l*, pg. 1310
MIE CHUO KAIHATSU CO., LTD.—See Daiei Kankyo Co., Ltd.; *Int'l*, pg. 1924
MONTE VISTA DISPOSAL, INC.—See Burrtec Waste Industries, Inc.; *U.S. Private*, pg. 692
NICHIWA SERVICE LTD.—See Hitachi, Ltd.; *Int'l*, pg. 3423
OAK RIDGE WASTE & RECYCLING OF CT LLC; *U.S. Private*, pg. 2984
OXFORD TRANSFER STATION, LLC—See Casella Waste Systems, Inc.; *U.S. Public*, pg. 446
PETSTAR, S.A. DE C.V.—See Arca Continental, S.A.B. de C.V.; *Int'l*, pg. 540
PINE GROVE LANDFILL, INC.—See Waste Management, Inc.; *U.S. Public*, pg. 2331
PLEASANT OAKS LANDFILL TX, LP—See Republic Services, Inc.; *U.S. Public*, pg. 1786
RANDY'S SANITATION, INC.; *U.S. Private*, pg. 3354
RECOLOGY CLEANSCAPES, INC.—See Arakelian Enterprises, Inc.; *U.S. Private*, pg. 307
RECOLOGY INC.—See Arakelian Enterprises, Inc.; *U.S. Private*, pg. 307
RENO DISPOSAL CO. - COMMERCIAL ROW FACILITY—See Waste Management, Inc.; *U.S. Public*, pg. 2332
RENO DISPOSAL CO.—See Waste Management, Inc.; *U.S. Public*, pg. 2332
REPUBLIC/CSC DISPOSAL AND LANDFILL, INC.—See Republic Services, Inc.; *U.S. Public*, pg. 1787
RESOURCE RECOVERY SYSTEMS, LLC—See Republic Services, Inc.; *U.S. Public*, pg. 1787
ROCKY MOUNTAIN SANITATION, LLC; *U.S. Private*, pg. 3469
SECHE TRANSPORTS SAS—See Groupe Seche SAS; *Int'l*, pg. 3110
SEKOPAC D.O.O.—See Ball Corporation; *U.S. Public*, pg. 268
SEPUR—See Fondations Capital SA; *Int'l*, pg. 2725
SOSO SMART ECO-COMPANY CO., LTD.—See Dowa Holdings Co., Ltd.; *Int'l*, pg. 2184
SOUTHERN WASTE SERVICES, L.L.C.—See Waste Management, Inc.; *U.S. Public*, pg. 2332
STERICYCLE HOKKAIDO GK—See Waste Management, Inc.; *U.S. Public*, pg. 2332
STREAM ENVIRONMENT (S) PTE. LTD.—See AWC Berhad; *Int'l*, pg. 752
SUBURBAN CARTING CORPORATION; *U.S. Private*, pg. 3848
SWIRE WASTE MANAGEMENT LIMITED—See Waste Management, Inc.; *U.S. Public*, pg. 2332
TAYLOR GARBAGE SERVICE, INC.—See Casella Waste Systems, Inc.; *U.S. Public*, pg. 446
TAYMAN INDUSTRIES, INC.—See Republic Services, Inc.; *U.S. Public*, pg. 1787
TEXAS DISPOSAL SYSTEMS INC.; *U.S. Private*, pg. 3975
TRANSIT WASTE, LLC—See BC Partners LLP; *Int'l*, pg. 924
TRANSPACIFIC CLEANAWAY PTY. LTD.—See Cleanaway Waste Management Limited; *Int'l*, pg. 1655
TRASHCO INC.—See Waste Management, Inc.; *U.S. Public*, pg. 2332
TRI-LINE DISPOSAL INC.—See BC Partners LLP; *Int'l*, pg. 924
TUCKER COUNTY SOLID WASTE AUTHORITY, INC.—See Tucker County Commission; *U.S. Private*, pg. 4256
TWIN BRIDGES GOLF CLUB, L.P.—See Waste Management, Inc.; *U.S. Public*, pg. 2332
URBASER, S.A.—See Platinum Equity, LLC; *U.S. Private*, pg. 3209
URBASER VENEZOLANA S.A.—See Platinum Equity, LLC; *U.S. Private*, pg. 3209
USA WASTE OF CALIFORNIA, INC.—See Waste Management, Inc.; *U.S. Public*, pg. 2332
VOGEL DISPOSAL SERVICE INC.; *U.S. Private*, pg. 4409
WASTE MANAGEMENT INC. OF FLORIDA - BRADENTON—See Waste Management, Inc.; *U.S. Public*, pg. 2333
WASTE MANAGEMENT INC. OF FLORIDA - HOBE SOUND—See Waste Management, Inc.; *U.S. Public*, pg. 2333
WASTE MANAGEMENT INC. OF FLORIDA - MELBOURNE—See Waste Management, Inc.; *U.S. Public*, pg. 2333
WASTE MANAGEMENT, INC. OF TENNESSEE - NASHVILLE—See Waste Management, Inc.; *U.S. Public*, pg. 2334
WASTE MANAGEMENT, INC.; *U.S. Public*, pg. 2330
WASTE MANAGEMENT OF ALAMEDA COUNTY, INC.—See Waste Management, Inc.; *U.S. Public*, pg. 2333
WASTE MANAGEMENT OF ARIZONA - PHOENIX SOUTH HAULING—See Waste Management, Inc.; *U.S. Public*, pg. 2333
WASTE MANAGEMENT OF CALIFORNIA - CASTROVILLE—See Waste Management, Inc.; *U.S. Public*, pg. 2333
WASTE MANAGEMENT OF CALIFORNIA - GOLD RIVER—See Waste Management, Inc.; *U.S. Public*, pg. 2333
WASTE MANAGEMENT OF CALIFORNIA - HEALTH SANITATION SERVICE—See Waste Management, Inc.; *U.S. Public*, pg. 2333
WASTE MANAGEMENT OF CALIFORNIA - SUN VALLEY HAULING—See Waste Management, Inc.; *U.S. Public*, pg. 2333
WASTE MANAGEMENT OF CANADA CORP. - BARRIE—See Waste Management, Inc.; *U.S. Public*, pg. 2333
WASTE MANAGEMENT OF CAROLINAS - GASTONIA—See Waste Management, Inc.; *U.S. Public*, pg. 2333
WASTE MANAGEMENT OF MISSISSIPPI - JACKSON HAULING—See Waste Management, Inc.; *U.S. Public*, pg. 2334
WASTE MANAGEMENT OF NEW YORK - ROCHESTER—See Waste Management, Inc.; *U.S. Public*, pg. 2334
WASTE MANAGEMENT OF PENNSYLVANIA - DUNMORE—See Waste Management, Inc.; *U.S. Public*, pg. 2334
WASTE MANAGEMENT OF SOUTH CAROLINA, INC.—See Waste Management, Inc.; *U.S. Public*, pg. 2334
WASTE MANAGEMENT OF WASHINGTON - KIRKLAND COLLECTIONS—See Waste Management, Inc.; *U.S. Public*, pg. 2334
WASTE PRO OF GEORGIA, INC.—See Waste Pro USA, Inc.; *U.S. Private*, pg. 4450
WATTS TRUCKING SERVICE, INC.; *U.S. Private*, pg. 4456
WEST OAHU AGGREGATE CO., INC.; *U.S. Private*, pg. 4486
WEST VALLEY RECYCLING & TRANSFER LLC—See Burrtec Waste Industries, Inc.; *U.S. Private*, pg. 692
WIND RIVER ENVIRONMENTAL LLC—See Gryphon Investors, LLC; *U.S. Private*, pg. 1800
WINTERS BROS WASTE SYSTEMS OF LONG ISLAND LLC; *U.S. Private*, pg. 4545
WM UNIVERSAL SOLUTIONS PRIVATE LIMITED—See Waste Management, Inc.; *U.S. Public*, pg. 2333
THE WOODLANDS OF VAN BUREN, INC.—See Waste Management, Inc.; *U.S. Public*, pg. 2332
ZOZZARO BROTHERS INC.; *U.S. Private*, pg. 4609

562112 — HAZARDOUS WASTE COLLECTION

ADVANCED CLEANUP TECHNOLOGIES; *U.S. Private*, pg. 88
A.S.A. ABFALL SERVICE WIENER NEUSTADT GMBH—See Fomento de Construcciones y Contratas, S.A.; *Int'l*, pg. 2722
AUGEAN NORTH SEA SERVICES LIMITED—See Ancala Partners LLP; *Int'l*, pg. 448
AUGEAN NORTH SEA SERVICES LIMITED—See Fiera Capital Corporation; *Int'l*, pg. 2659
BEE JOO INDUSTRIES PTE. LTD.—See ecoWise Holdings Limited; *Int'l*, pg. 2300
BOYLE TRANSPORTATION INC.; *U.S. Private*, pg. 628
CCI INDUSTRIAL SERVICES, LLC—See Bristol Bay Native Corporation; *U.S. Private*, pg. 656
CHEMICAL WASTE MANAGEMENT, INC.—See Waste Management, Inc.; *U.S. Public*, pg. 2330
CLEAN EARTH OF SOUTHERN FLORIDA, LLC—See Enviri Corporation; *U.S. Public*, pg. 780
CLEAN HARBORS ENERGY AND INDUSTRIAL SERVICES CORP.—See Clean Harbors, Inc.; *U.S. Public*, pg. 509
CLEAN HARBORS ENVIRONMENTAL SERVICES, INC.—See Clean Harbors, Inc.; *U.S. Public*, pg. 510
DIVERSIFIED SCIENTIFIC SERVICES, INC.—See Perma-Fix Environmental Services, Inc.; *U.S. Public*, pg. 1676
DRIMM SAS—See Groupe Seche SAS; *Int'l*, pg. 3110
ECODEAL-GESTAO INTEGRAL DE RESIDUOS INDUS-

562112 — HAZARDOUS WASTE COL...

TRIAIS, S.A.—See Fomento de Construcciones y Contratas, S.A.; *Int'l*, pg. 2722
ECO-SYSTEM JAPAN CO., LTD.—See Dowa Holdings Co., Ltd.; *Int'l*, pg. 2184
ECO-SYSTEM KOSAKA CO., LTD.—See Dowa Holdings Co., Ltd.; *Int'l*, pg. 2184
EGS INTERNATIONAL INC.; *U.S. Private*, pg. 1345
ENVIRONMENTAL ENTERPRISES INC.; *U.S. Private*, pg. 1407
ENVIROSERVE, INC.—See One Rock Capital Partners, LLC; *U.S. Private*, pg. 3022
ESPOSITO SERVIZI ECOLOGICI SRL—See I.M.G. 2 s.r.l.; *Int'l*, pg. 3566
FCC AMBITO, S.A.—See Fomento de Construcciones y Contratas, S.A.; *Int'l*, pg. 2722
FCC EKO-RADOMSKO SP. Z.O.O.—See Fomento de Construcciones y Contratas, S.A.; *Int'l*, pg. 2722
FCC ENVIRONMENT PORTUGAL, S.A.—See Fomento de Construcciones y Contratas, S.A.; *Int'l*, pg. 2723
HANGZHOU DADI HAIYANG ENVIRONMENTAL PROTECTION CO., LTD.; *Int'l*, pg. 3247
HIAP HUAT HOLDINGS BHD; *Int'l*, pg. 3382
INTERNATIONAL PETROLEUM CORPORATION OF DELAWARE—See J.F. Lehman & Company, Inc.; *U.S. Private*, pg. 2163
KENT ENVIROPOWER LIMITED—See Fomento de Construcciones y Contratas, S.A.; *Int'l*, pg. 2723
NAC INTERNATIONAL INC.—See Hitachi Zosen Corporation; *Int'l*, pg. 3411
NOVENT REFRIGERANT SERVICES, INC.—See BC Partners LLP; *Int'l*, pg. 923
NOVENT REFRIGERANT SERVICES, INC.—See EQT AB; *Int'l*, pg. 2482
NRC ENVIRONMENTAL SERVICES INC.—See AIP, LLC; *U.S. Private*, pg. 136
OPALE ENVIRONNEMENT—See Groupe Seche SAS; *Int'l*, pg. 3110
PANGEA GROUP; *U.S. Private*, pg. 3086
RAMKY CLEANTECH SERVICES PTE. LTD.—See KKR & Co. Inc.; *U.S. Public*, pg. 1263
RAMKY ENVIRO ENGINEERS MIDDLE EAST FZLLC—See KKR & Co. Inc.; *U.S. Public*, pg. 1263
RELIABLE ENVIRONMENTAL TRANSPORT, INC.—See Waste Management, Inc.; *U.S. Public*, pg. 2332
REPUBLIC SERVICES OF IOWA, LLC—See Republic Services, Inc.; *U.S. Public*, pg. 1787
RESTAURANT TECHNOLOGIES, INC.—See The Goldman Sachs Group, Inc.; *U.S. Public*, pg. 2080
SCI MEZEROLLES—See Groupe Seche SAS; *Int'l*, pg. 3110
SET ENVIRONMENTAL, INC.; *U.S. Private*, pg. 3617
THE S.M. STROLLER CORPORATION; *U.S. Private*, pg. 4113
SYQWEST, LLC—See CTS Corporation; *U.S. Public*, pg. 603
TREDI ARGENTINA—See Groupe Seche SAS; *Int'l*, pg. 3110
US ECOLOGY HOUSTON, INC.—See Republic Services, Inc.; *U.S. Public*, pg. 1788
WASTE MANAGEMENT NZ LIMITED—See Capital Environment Holdings Limited; *Int'l*, pg. 1310
WASTE MANAGEMENT OF CONNECTICUT, INC.—See Waste Management, Inc.; *U.S. Public*, pg. 2333
WASTE MANAGEMENT OF NORTH DAKOTA, INC.—See Waste Management, Inc.; *U.S. Public*, pg. 2334
WESTERN WASTE OF TEXAS, L.L.C.—See Waste Management, Inc.; *U.S. Public*, pg. 2334
WM CCP SOLUTIONS, LLC—See Waste Management, Inc.; *U.S. Public*, pg. 2332

562119 — OTHER WASTE COLLECTION

ADVANCED CIRCUITS, INC.—See Compass Diversified Holdings; *U.S. Public*, pg. 559
ALBA ELECTRONICS RECYCLING GMBH—See Alba SE; *Int'l*, pg. 292
ALBA EUROPE HOLDING PLC & CO. KG—See Alba SE; *Int'l*, pg. 292
ALBA HEILBRONN-FRANKEN PLC & CO. KG—See Alba SE; *Int'l*, pg. 292
ALIAXIS—See Aliaxis S.A./N.V.; *Int'l*, pg. 323
APRICA SPA—See A2A S.p.A.; *Int'l*, pg. 29
APS ALTPAPIER SERVICE SCHWEIZ AG—See CPH Chemie + Papier Holding AG; *Int'l*, pg. 1824
ARROW DISPOSAL SERVICE, LLC—See Waste Management, Inc.; *U.S. Public*, pg. 2330
A-SMART LIFE PTE LTD—See A-Smart Holdings Ltd.; *Int'l*, pg. 20
AVISTA OIL AG; *Int'l*, pg. 745
AVISTA OIL DANMARK A/S—See Avista Oil AG; *Int'l*, pg. 745
BANKA BIOLOO LIMITED; *Int'l*, pg. 850
BRAL RESTSTOFF-BEARBEITUNGS GMBH—See Alba SE; *Int'l*, pg. 293
CASCADES RECOVERY INC.—See Cascades Inc.; *Int'l*, pg. 1350
CASCADES RECOVERY U.S., INC.—See Cascades Inc.; *Int'l*, pg. 1350

CENTRAL DISPOSAL LLC—See Superior Waste Industries LLC; *U.S. Private*, pg. 3881
CISTOCA A.D.; *Int'l*, pg. 1618
CLEAN EARTH OF MICHIGAN, LLC—See Compass Diversified Holdings; *U.S. Public*, pg. 560
CLEAN HARBORS WICHITA, LLC—See Clean Harbors, Inc.; *U.S. Public*, pg. 510
COLEX ENVIRONMENTAL PTE LTD—See Bonvests Holdings Limited; *Int'l*, pg. 1110
COUNTY SANITATION DISTRICTS OF ORANGE COUNTY INC.; *U.S. Private*, pg. 1068
DAISEKI MCR CO., LTD.—See Daiseki Co. Ltd.; *Int'l*, pg. 1941
DELTA CONTAINER CORPORATION—See Republic Services, Inc.; *U.S. Public*, pg. 1786
ECOLOGIA Y TECNICAS SANITARIAS, S.L.—See ACS, Actividades de Construccion y Servicios, S.A.; *Int'l*, pg. 111
ECO-PAN LIMITED—See Concrete Pumping Holdings, Inc.; *U.S. Public*, pg. 566
ENVIRONMENT-ONE CORPORATION—See Berkshire Hathaway Inc.; *U.S. Public*, pg. 314
ERSECO, INC.—See Erving Industries, Inc.; *U.S. Private*, pg. 1424
ESTRE AMBIENTAL S.A.; *Int'l*, pg. 2518
FREEDOM WASTE SERVICE, LLC—See BC Partners LLP; *Int'l*, pg. 924
THE GARBAGE COMPANY INC.—See BC Partners LLP; *Int'l*, pg. 924
GREEN ENVIROTECH HOLDINGS CORP.; *U.S. Public*, pg. 963
HD RESOURCES MANAGEMENT CORPORATION—See CTCI Corporation; *Int'l*, pg. 1870
HIGH PLAINS DISPOSAL, INC.—See Superior Energy Services, Inc.; *U.S. Public*, pg. 3877
INVISIBLE WASTE SERVICES LLC—See GI Manager L.P.; *U.S. Private*, pg. 1694
ITALMACERO S.R.L.—See ACEA S.p.A.; *Int'l*, pg. 95
LA BI.CO DUE S.R.L.—See A2A S.p.A.; *Int'l*, pg. 29
LINEA AMBIENTE S.R.L.—See A2A S.p.A.; *Int'l*, pg. 29
LINEA GESTIONI S.R.L.—See A2A S.p.A.; *Int'l*, pg. 29
LMR DISPOSAL LLC—See Casella Waste Systems, Inc.; *U.S. Public*, pg. 446
LOADUP TECHNOLOGIES, LLC; *U.S. Private*, pg. 2476
LOMELLINA ENERGIA S.R.L.—See A2A S.p.A.; *Int'l*, pg. 29
LONESTAR SYLVAN INC.—See Clean Harbors, Inc.; *U.S. Public*, pg. 510
M&R ENVIRONMENTAL LTD.—See BC Partners LLP; *Int'l*, pg. 924
RECUP-OIL B.V.B.A.—See Avista Oil AG; *Int'l*, pg. 745
RECYDIA AS—See Cimentas Izmir Cimento Fabrikasi Turk A.S.; *Int'l*, pg. 1609
REFINING & TRADING HOLLAND N.V.—See Avista Oil AG; *Int'l*, pg. 745
ROSEMEAD OIL PRODUCTS, INC.—See Clean Harbors, Inc.; *U.S. Public*, pg. 510
SAV-TECH SOLVENT, INC—See J.F. Lehman & Company, Inc.; *U.S. Private*, pg. 2163
SLG RECYCLING—See Coller Capital Ltd.; *Int'l*, pg. 1699
SWB BELEUCHTUNG GMBH—See EWE Aktiengesellschaft; *Int'l*, pg. 2576
SYSTEM KIKOU CO., LTD.—See Daiseki Co. Ltd.; *Int'l*, pg. 1941
TAM INC.—See Casella Waste Systems, Inc.; *U.S. Public*, pg. 446
TEXAS COMMERCIAL WASTE—See M. Lipsitz & Co., Ltd.; *U.S. Private*, pg. 2527
TOKYO ECO RECYCLE CO., LTD.—See Hitachi, Ltd.; *Int'l*, pg. 3424
USA RECYCLING INDUSTRIES, INC.; *U.S. Public*, pg. 2267
USA WASTE OF TEXAS LANDFILLS, INC.—See Waste Management, Inc.; *U.S. Public*, pg. 2332
U.S. MICRO OPERATING COMPANY, LLC—See Arrow Electronics, Inc.; *U.S. Public*, pg. 200
VALET LIVING, LLC—See GI Manager L.P.; *U.S. Private*, pg. 1694
WUBBEN HANDELSMIJ B.V.—See Avista Oil AG; *Int'l*, pg. 745

562211 — HAZARDOUS WASTE TREATMENT AND DISPOSAL

ADVANCED STEEL RECOVERY LLC—See Commercial Metals Company; *U.S. Public*, pg. 545
ADVANTAGE DISPOSAL SOLUTIONS, INC.; *U.S. Private*, pg. 94
AEVITAS, INC.; *Int'l*, pg. 183
AFTERMATH SERVICES LLC—See ABRY Partners, LLC; *U.S. Private*, pg. 40
AKKHIE PRAKARN PUBLIC COMPANY LIMITED; *Int'l*, pg. 263
AKRON SPA—See Hera S.p.A.; *Int'l*, pg. 3356
ALABAMA DUMPSTER SERVICE, LLC—See BC Partners LLP; *Int'l*, pg. 923
ALLIED WASTE, INC.—See Republic Services, Inc.; *U.S. Public*, pg. 1785

ALPHA TECHNICAL SERVICES CORPORATION—See KKR & Co. Inc.; *U.S. Public*, pg. 1241
ALPINE WASTE & RECYCLING; *U.S. Private*, pg. 202
ALTAIR DISPOSAL SERVICES, LLC—See Clean Harbors, Inc.; *U.S. Public*, pg. 509
ALTEC UMWELTTECHNIK GMBH—See ALPINE Bau GmbH; *Int'l*, pg. 371
AMBIFACE & BUFFER SGPS LDA—See Waste Management, Inc.; *U.S. Public*, pg. 2332
AMERICAN ENVIRONMENTAL SERVICES, INC.—See Enviri Corporation; *U.S. Public*, pg. 780
ANHUI CHAOYUE ENVIRONMENTAL TECHNOLOGY CO., LTD.; *Int'l*, pg. 466
APLAS LTD.—See China Tianying Inc.; *Int'l*, pg. 1559
ATK ENERGY EU LIMITED—See AtkinsRealis Group Inc.; *Int'l*, pg. 673
ATKINS ENERGY GOVERNMENT GROUP, INC.—See AtkinsRealis Group Inc.; *Int'l*, pg. 673
AUGEAN TREATMENT LIMITED—See Ancala Partners LLP; *Int'l*, pg. 448
AUGEAN TREATMENT LIMITED—See Fiera Capital Corporation; *Int'l*, pg. 2659
AUTOMATED WASTE SERVICES LLC—See BC Partners LLP; *Int'l*, pg. 924
BATTERY SOLUTIONS, INC.—See Heritage Group; *U.S. Private*, pg. 1923
BAUER NIMR LLC—See BAUER Aktiengesellschaft; *Int'l*, pg. 893
BEARN ENVIRONNEMENT SA—See Groupe Seche SAS; *Int'l*, pg. 3110
BEE JOO ENVIRONMENTAL PTE. LTD.—See ecoWise Holdings Limited; *Int'l*, pg. 2300
BEIJING CAPITAL ECO-ENVIRONMENT PROTECTION GROUP CO., LTD.—See Beijing Capital Group Co., Ltd.; *Int'l*, pg. 947
BEIJING WATER BUSINESS DOCTOR CO., LTD.; *Int'l*, pg. 960
BFI WASTE SYSTEMS OF VIRGINIA, LLC—See Republic Services, Inc.; *U.S. Public*, pg. 1786
BIONOMICS INC—See Bionomics Limited; *Int'l*, pg. 1040
CAMBI ASA; *Int'l*, pg. 1268
CAPITOL ENVIRONMENTAL SERVICES, INC.; *U.S. Private*, pg. 743
CARAUSTAR INDUSTRIES, INC. - CLEVELAND RECYCLING PLANT—See Greif Inc.; *U.S. Public*, pg. 966
CASELLA WASTE SYSTEMS, INC.; *U.S. Public*, pg. 445
CCR TECHNOLOGIES LTD.—See CCR Technologies Limited; *Int'l*, pg. 1369
CENTRALISED WASTE TREATMENT PLANT SDN. BHD.—See Analabs Resources Berhad; *Int'l*, pg. 446
CENTRAL RESEARCH LABORATORIES—See Stabilus; *U.S. Private*, pg. 3774
CHINA INDUSTRIAL WASTE MANAGEMENT, INC.; *Int'l*, pg. 1510
CIVCO MEDICAL SOLUTIONS—See Roper Technologies, Inc.; *U.S. Public*, pg. 1810
CLEANAWAY COMPANY LIMITED; *Int'l*, pg. 1654
CLEAN EARTH OF ALABAMA, INC.—See Enviri Corporation; *U.S. Public*, pg. 780
CLEAN EARTH OF GEORGIA, LLC—See Enviri Corporation; *U.S. Public*, pg. 780
CLEAN HARBORS ARIZONA, LLC—See Clean Harbors, Inc.; *U.S. Public*, pg. 509
CLEAN HARBORS BDT, LLC—See Clean Harbors, Inc.; *U.S. Public*, pg. 509
CLEAN HARBORS BUTTONWILLOW, LLC—See Clean Harbors, Inc.; *U.S. Public*, pg. 509
CLEAN HARBORS CARIBE, INC.—See Clean Harbors, Inc.; *U.S. Public*, pg. 509
CLEAN HARBORS CATALYST SERVICES, LLC—See Clean Harbors, Inc.; *U.S. Public*, pg. 509
CLEAN HARBORS CATALYST SERVICES TRINIDAD LIMITED—See Clean Harbors, Inc.; *U.S. Public*, pg. 509
CLEAN HARBORS COFFEYVILLE, LLC—See Clean Harbors, Inc.; *U.S. Public*, pg. 509
CLEAN HARBORS COLFAX, LLC—See Clean Harbors, Inc.; *U.S. Public*, pg. 509
CLEAN HARBORS DEER TRAIL, LLC—See Clean Harbors, Inc.; *U.S. Public*, pg. 509
CLEAN HARBORS EL DORADO, LLC—See Clean Harbors, Inc.; *U.S. Public*, pg. 509
CLEAN HARBORS ENVIRONMENTAL SERVICES, INC.—See Clean Harbors, Inc.; *U.S. Public*, pg. 509
CLEAN HARBORS EXPLORATION SERVICES, INC.—See Clean Harbors, Inc.; *U.S. Public*, pg. 509
CLEAN HARBORS FLORIDA, LLC—See Clean Harbors, Inc.; *U.S. Public*, pg. 509
CLEAN HARBORS INDUSTRIAL SERVICES CANADA, INC.—See Clean Harbors, Inc.; *U.S. Public*, pg. 509
CLEAN HARBORS INDUSTRIAL SERVICES, INC.—See Clean Harbors, Inc.; *U.S. Public*, pg. 509
CLEAN HARBORS LODGING SERVICES LTD.—See Clean Harbors, Inc.; *U.S. Public*, pg. 509
CLEAN HARBORS LONE MOUNTAIN, LLC—See Clean Harbors, Inc.; *U.S. Public*, pg. 509
CLEAN HARBORS LOS ANGELES, LLC—See Clean Harbors, Inc.; *U.S. Public*, pg. 509

N.A.I.C.S. INDEX

562211 — HAZARDOUS WASTE TRE...

CLEAN HARBORS MERCIER, INC.—See Clean Harbors, Inc.; *U.S. Public*, pg. 509
CLEAN HARBORS OF BALTIMORE, INC.—See Clean Harbors, Inc.; *U.S. Public*, pg. 510
CLEAN HARBORS OF BRAINTREE, INC.—See Clean Harbors, Inc.; *U.S. Public*, pg. 510
CLEAN HARBORS OF CONNECTICUT, INC.—See Clean Harbors, Inc.; *U.S. Public*, pg. 510
CLEAN HARBORS RECYCLING SERVICES OF CHICAGO, LLC—See Clean Harbors, Inc.; *U.S. Public*, pg. 509
CLEAN HARBORS RECYCLING SERVICES OF OHIO LLC—See Clean Harbors, Inc.; *U.S. Public*, pg. 509
CLEAN HARBORS REIDSVILLE, LLC—See Clean Harbors, Inc.; *U.S. Public*, pg. 509
CLEAN HARBORS SAN LEON, INC.—See Clean Harbors, Inc.; *U.S. Public*, pg. 509
CLEAN HARBORS SERVICES, INC.—See Clean Harbors, Inc.; *U.S. Public*, pg. 509
CLEAN HARBORS SURFACE RENTALS LTD.—See Clean Harbors, Inc.; *U.S. Public*, pg. 509
CLEAN HARBORS TENNESSEE, LLC—See Clean Harbors, Inc.; *U.S. Public*, pg. 509
CLEAN HARBORS WESTMORLAND, LLC—See Clean Harbors, Inc.; *U.S. Public*, pg. 510
CLEAN HARBORS WHITE CASTLE, LLC—See Clean Harbors, Inc.; *U.S. Public*, pg. 510
CLEAN HARBORS WILMINGTON, LLC—See Clean Harbors, Inc.; *U.S. Public*, pg. 510
CLEAN TEQ WATER LIMITED; *Int'l*, pg. 1654
CLEANWAY DISPOSAL SERVICES PTE. LTD.—See Analabs Resources Berhad; *Int'l*, pg. 446
COUNTY WASTE SYSTEMS, INC.—See Watts Trucking Service, Inc.; *U.S. Private*, pg. 4456
COVANTA ENVIRONMENTAL SOLUTIONS—See EQT AB; *Int'l*, pg. 2473
CROSBY & OVERTON, INC.; *U.S. Private*, pg. 1103
THE CUROTTO-CAN, LLC—See Dover Corporation; *U.S. Public*, pg. 683
DAIEI AMET CO., LTD.—See Daiei Kankyo Co., Ltd.; *Int'l*, pg. 1924
DAIEI KANKYO CO., LTD.; *Int'l*, pg. 1924
DAIEI KANKYO RESEARCH INSTITUTE CO., LTD.—See Daiei Kankyo Co., Ltd.; *Int'l*, pg. 1924
DAISEKI CO. LTD. - CHIBA WORKS—See Daiseki Co. Ltd.; *Int'l*, pg. 1941
DAISEKI CO. LTD. - KANTO SECOND PLANT—See Daiseki Co. Ltd.; *Int'l*, pg. 1941
DELTA WASTE SYSTEMS, INC.—See Watts Trucking Service, Inc.; *U.S. Private*, pg. 4456
DFA - TRANSPORT UND LOGISTIK GMBH—See Aurelius Equity Opportunities SE & Co. KGaA; *Int'l*, pg. 708
DINS MIRAI CO., LTD.—See Daiei Kankyo Co., Ltd.; *Int'l*, pg. 1924
DOLOMATRIX PHILIPPINES INC.; *Int'l*, pg. 2159
DONGJIANG ENVIRONMENTAL COMPANY LIMITED; *Int'l*, pg. 2168
DOODYCALLS FRANCHISING, LLC—See Apax Partners LLP; *Int'l*, pg. 502
DOUBLE BARREL ENVIRONMENTAL SERVICES INCORPORATED; *U.S. Private*, pg. 1265
DRAMAR ANDALUCIA TRATAMIENTO DE MARPOLES, S.L.U.—See ACS, Actividades de Construccion y Servicios, S.A.; *Int'l*, pg. 111
DROP S.A.; *Int'l*, pg. 2206
DUNCAN DISPOSAL SYSTEMS LLC—See BC Partners LLP; *Int'l*, pg. 924
ECOLOGY CONTROL INDUSTRIES, INC—See Ecology Control Industries, Inc.; *U.S. Private*, pg. 1329
ECOPARC DE BARCELONA S.A.—See ACS, Actividades de Construccion y Servicios, S.A.; *Int'l*, pg. 111
ECOSERV LLC; *U.S. Private*, pg. 1330
EDAFOLOGIA Y RESTAURACION DEL ENTORNO GALLEGO, S.L.—See ACS, Actividades de Construccion y Servicios, S.A.; *Int'l*, pg. 111
EMERALD SERVICES INC.; *U.S. Private*, pg. 1380
ENVA UK LTD—See Exponent Private Equity LLP; *Int'l*, pg. 2589
ENVIRO CLEAN PRODUCTS & SERVICES—See Enviro Clean Services LLC; *U.S. Private*, pg. 1406
ENVIRO CLEAN PRODUCTS & SERVICES—See Enviro Clean Services LLC; *U.S. Private*, pg. 1406
ENVIRO CLEAN PRODUCTS & SERVICES—See Enviro Clean Services LLC; *U.S. Private*, pg. 1406
ENVIRONMENTAL CHEMICAL CORPORATION; *U.S. Private*, pg. 1407
ENVIRONMENTAL RESPONSE INC.—See Spray Systems Arizona Inc.; *U.S. Private*, pg. 3762
ENVIRONMENTAL SPECIALISTS, INC.—See ESI Contracting, Corp.; *U.S. Private*, pg. 1425
EQ FLORIDA, INC.—See Republic Services, Inc.; *U.S. Public*, pg. 1787
EQ INDUSTRIAL SERVICES INC. - INDIANAPOLIS—See Republic Services, Inc.; *U.S. Public*, pg. 1788
EQ NORTHEAST, INC.—See Republic Services, Inc.; *U.S. Public*, pg. 1788
EQ OKLAHOMA, INC.—See Republic Services, Inc.; *U.S. Public*, pg. 1788

EST ENERGETICS GMBH—See General Atomics; *U.S. Private*, pg. 1664
EUROPE TIANYING BVBA—See China Tianying Inc.; *Int'l*, pg. 1559
EUROPLASMA SA; *Int'l*, pg. 2557
FBSERWIS DOLNY SLASK SP. Z O.O—See Ferrovial S.A.; *Int'l*, pg. 2644
FBSERWIS KAMIENSK SP. Z O.O.—See Ferrovial S.A.; *Int'l*, pg. 2644
FBSERWIS KARPATIA SP. Z O.O.—See Ferrovial S.A.; *Int'l*, pg. 2644
FBSERWIS ODBIOR SP. Z O.O.—See Ferrovial S.A.; *Int'l*, pg. 2644
FBSERWIS SA—See Ferrovial S.A.; *Int'l*, pg. 2644
FBSERWIS WROCLAW SP. Z O.O.—See Ferrovial S.A.; *Int'l*, pg. 2644
FEDERAL SIGNAL ENVIRONMENTAL SOLUTIONS GROUP—See Federal Signal Corporation; *U.S. Public*, pg. 826
FIBRES INTERNATIONAL, INC.; *U.S. Private*, pg. 1502
FIBRES INTERNATIONAL, INC.—See Fibres International, Inc.; *U.S. Private*, pg. 1502
FLUOR IDAHO, LLC—See Fluor Corporation; *U.S. Public*, pg. 859
G-2 INTERNATIONAL—See Enviro Clean Services LLC; *U.S. Private*, pg. 1406
GAMMAFLUX INC.—See Barnes Group Inc.; *U.S. Public*, pg. 277
GENERAL DYNAMICS ORDNANCE AND TACTICAL SYSTEMS - MUNITION SERVICES—See General Dynamics Corporation; *U.S. Public*, pg. 914
GENERAL ENVIRONMENTAL CONSERVATION PUBLIC COMPANY LIMITED - MAP TAPHUT WASTE TREATMENT FACILITY—See General Environmental Conservation Public Company Limited; *Int'l*, pg. 2918
GENERAL ENVIRONMENTAL CONSERVATION PUBLIC COMPANY LIMITED - SAMAEDUM WASTE TREATMENT FACILITY—See General Environmental Conservation Public Company Limited; *Int'l*, pg. 2918
GEREP SAS—See Groupe Seche SAS; *Int'l*, pg. 3110
GIANT RESOURCE RECOVERY COMPANY, INC.—See Grupo Empresarial Kaluz S.A. de C.V.; *Int'l*, pg. 3127
GLOBAL INVESTMENT RECOVERY, INC.; *U.S. Private*, pg. 1715
GLYECO, INC.; *U.S. Private*, pg. 1721
GRANGER ASSOCIATES, INC.; *U.S. Private*, pg. 1754
GREEN FILL KOSAKA CO., LTD.—See Dowa Holdings Co., Ltd.; *Int'l*, pg. 2183
GRIZZCO CAMP SERVICES INC.—See Clean Harbors, Inc.; *U.S. Public*, pg. 510
GULF WASTE SYSTEMS, INC.—See Watts Trucking Service, Inc.; *U.S. Private*, pg. 4456
HEPACO INC.—See Gryphon Investors, LLC; *U.S. Private*, pg. 1798
HIM GMBH; *Int'l*, pg. 3395
HIRAM HOLLOW REGENERATION CORP.—See Casella Waste Systems, Inc.; *U.S. Public*, pg. 446
HITACHI ZOSEN INOVA AUSTRALIA PTY LTD—See Hitachi Zosen Corporation; *Int'l*, pg. 3411
HITACHI ZOSEN INOVA KRAFTWERKSTECHNIK GMBH—See Hitachi Zosen Corporation; *Int'l*, pg. 3411
HITACHI ZOSEN INOVA SLOVAKIA S.R.O.—See Hitachi Zosen Corporation; *Int'l*, pg. 3411
HITZ ENVIRONMENT SERVICE COMPANY LIMITED—See Hitachi Zosen Corporation; *Int'l*, pg. 3411
HOUSTON WASTE SOLUTIONS, LLC—See Fomento de Construcciones y Contratas, S.A.; *Int'l*, pg. 2723
HUNGAROPEC LTD.—See Groupe Seche SAS; *Int'l*, pg. 3110
HWAXIN ENVIRONMENTAL CO., LTD.; *Int'l*, pg. 3543
HYDROMET OPERATIONS LIMITED—See Hydromet Corporation Limited; *Int'l*, pg. 3548
IBERTREDI MEDIOAMBIENTAL S.A.—See Groupe Seche SAS; *Int'l*, pg. 3110
INTERNATIONAL POWER GROUP LTD.; *U.S. Public*, pg. 1158
J. FONS CO INC—See Priority Waste LLC; *U.S. Private*, pg. 3267
J. P. MASCARO & SONS; *U.S. Private*, pg. 2156
KLA SYSTEMS, INC.—See Sciens Capital Management LLC; *U.S. Private*, pg. 3574
KMG HAULING, INC.; *U.S. Private*, pg. 2321
LANCASTER OIL COMPANY—See Aurora Capital Group, LLC; *U.S. Private*, pg. 394
LIBERTY TIRE RECYCLING—See The Carlyle Group Inc.; *U.S. Public*, pg. 2048
LUBE-TECH LIQUID RECYCLING, INC.—See Lubrication Technologies, Inc.; *U.S. Private*, pg. 2510
MAKINOSATO AGRICULTURAL PRODUCERS COOPERATIVE CORPORATION—See Daiei Kankyo Co., Ltd.; *Int'l*, pg. 1924
MICHIGAN DISPOSAL, INC.—See Republic Services, Inc.; *U.S. Public*, pg. 1788
MP ENVIRONMENTAL SERVICES; *U.S. Private*, pg. 2803
NEALES WASTE MANAGEMENT LTD.—See Cementir Holding N.V.; *Int'l*, pg. 1397
NEGIBOZU AGRICULTURAL PRODUCERS' COOPERA-

TIVE CORPORATION—See Daiei Kankyo Co., Ltd.; *Int'l*, pg. 1924
NIHON SENKO CO., LTD.—See Godo Steel, Ltd.; *Int'l*, pg. 3020
NORTH DAVIDSON GARBAGE SERVICE, INC.—See BC Partners LLP; *Int'l*, pg. 924
OASIS AVIATION INC.; *U.S. Private*, pg. 2986
OASIS NUCLEAR INC.—See Oasis Aviation Inc.; *U.S. Private*, pg. 2986
OMIHACHIMAN ECO SERVICE CO., LTD.—See Daiei Kankyo Co., Ltd.; *Int'l*, pg. 1924
ONE STOP ENVIRONMENTAL, LLC—See Ambipar Participacoes e Empreendimentos SA; *Int'l*, pg. 414
PALO ALTO SANITATION COMPANY—See Waste Management, Inc.; *U.S. Public*, pg. 2331
PEORIA DISPOSAL COMPANY/AREA DISPOSAL SERVICE, INC.; *U.S. Private*, pg. 3143
PERMA-FIX ENVIRONMENTAL SERVICES, INC.; *U.S. Public*, pg. 1676
PERMA-FIX ENVIRONMENTAL SERVICES UK LIMITED—See Perma-Fix Environmental Services, Inc.; *U.S. Public*, pg. 1676
PERMA-FIX NORTHWEST, INC.—See Perma-Fix Environmental Services, Inc.; *U.S. Public*, pg. 1676
PERMA-FIX OF FLORIDA, INC.—See Perma-Fix Environmental Services, Inc.; *U.S. Public*, pg. 1676
PLAQUEMINE REMEDIATION SERVICES, LLC—See Clean Harbors, Inc.; *U.S. Public*, pg. 510
QINGYUAN DONGJIANG ENVIRONMENTAL TECHNOLOGIES COMPANY LIMITED—See Dongjiang Environmental Company Limited; *Int'l*, pg. 2168
RADIATION TECHNICAL SERVICES CO.; *U.S. Private*, pg. 3343
RANCHO DISPOSAL SERVICE, INC.—See Burrtec Waste Industries, Inc.; *U.S. Private*, pg. 692
RECYCLEBANK LLC—See Recycle Track Systems, Inc.; *U.S. Private*, pg. 3372
REPUBLIC SERVICES, INC.; *U.S. Public*, pg. 1785
RESIDUOS INDUSTRIALES DE ZARAGOZA, S.A.—See ACS, Actividades de Construccion y Servicios, S.A.; *Int'l*, pg. 116
RINCHEM COMPANY INCORPORATED; *U.S. Private*, pg. 3437
RINECO CHEMICAL INDUSTRIES—See EQT AB; *Int'l*, pg. 2482
RIZZO ENVIRONMENTAL SERVICES, INC.—See BC Partners LLP; *Int'l*, pg. 924
RMD TECHNOLOGIES, INC.; *U.S. Private*, pg. 3451
ROBBIE D. WOOD INC.; *U.S. Private*, pg. 3456
ROLLEX TRANSPORTATION INC—See Gestion Claude Robert Inc.; *Int'l*, pg. 2946
ROSS ENVIRONMENTAL SERVICES, INC.—See Ross Consolidated Corp.; *U.S. Private*, pg. 3485
SAFETY ISLAND CO., LTD.—See Daiei Kankyo Co., Ltd.; *Int'l*, pg. 1924
SAFETY-KLEEN DE MEXICO, S. DE R.L. DE C.V.—See Clean Harbors, Inc.; *U.S. Public*, pg. 510
SAFETY-KLEEN OF CALIFORNIA, INC.—See Clean Harbors, Inc.; *U.S. Public*, pg. 510
SAKAB AB—See E.ON SE; *Int'l*, pg. 2259
SANITHERM USA, INC.—See Clean Harbors, Inc.; *U.S. Public*, pg. 510
SANTEK ENVIRONMENTAL LLC; *U.S. Private*, pg. 3548
SANTEK WASTE SERVICES LLC—See Republic Services, Inc.; *U.S. Public*, pg. 1787
SECHE ALLIANCE SAS—See Groupe Seche SAS; *Int'l*, pg. 3110
SECHE ECO-SERVICES SAS—See Groupe Seche SAS; *Int'l*, pg. 3110
SERVICE CHEMICAL, LLC—See Clean Harbors, Inc.; *U.S. Public*, pg. 510
SHAOGUAN GREEN RECYCLING RESOURCE DEVELOPMENT CO LIMITED—See Dongjiang Environmental Company Limited; *Int'l*, pg. 2168
SHARPS ENVIRONMENTAL SERVICES, INC.—See Aurora Capital Group, LLC; *U.S. Private*, pg. 394
SK SERVICIOS AMBIENTALES ADMINISTRATIVOS, S. DE R.L. DE C.V.—See Clean Harbors, Inc.; *U.S. Public*, pg. 510
SOIL SAFE, INC.—See BC Partners LLP; *Int'l*, pg. 924
THE SOLVENTS RECOVERY SERVICE OF NEW JERSEY, INC.—See Clean Harbors, Inc.; *U.S. Public*, pg. 510
SOTREFI ETUPES—See Groupe Seche SAS; *Int'l*, pg. 3111
SOTRIS SPA—See Hera S.p.A.; *Int'l*, pg. 3356
SPECIALIZED RESPONSE SOLUTIONS, LP—See Republic Services, Inc.; *U.S. Public*, pg. 1788
SPEICHIM PROCESSING S.A.—See Groupe Seche SAS; *Int'l*, pg. 3110
SPEZIALTECHNIK DRESDEN GMBH—See General Atomics; *U.S. Private*, pg. 1663
SPREEWERK LUBBEN GMBH—See General Atomics; *U.S. Private*, pg. 1664
SPRING GROVE RESOURCE RECOVERY, INC.—See Clean Harbors, Inc.; *U.S. Public*, pg. 510
STERICARE ROMANIA—See Waste Management, Inc.; *U.S. Public*, pg. 2332
STERICYCLE ENVIRONMENTAL SOLUTIONS, INC.—See Enviri Corporation; *U.S. Public*, pg. 781

562211 — HAZARDOUS WASTE TRE...

STERICYCLE INTERNATIONAL, LLC—See Waste Management, Inc.; *U.S. Public*, pg. 2332
STERICYCLE JAPAN CO. LTD.—See Waste Management, Inc.; *U.S. Public*, pg. 2332
STERICYCLE KOREA CO LTD.—See Waste Management, Inc.; *U.S. Public*, pg. 2332
STERICYCLE PORTUGAL—See Waste Management, Inc.; *U.S. Public*, pg. 2332
STERICYCLE ROMANIA, SRL—See Waste Management, Inc.; *U.S. Public*, pg. 2332
STERICYCLE SPECIALTY WASTE SOLUTIONS, INC.—See Waste Management, Inc.; *U.S. Public*, pg. 2332
STERICYCLE ULC—See Waste Management, Inc.; *U.S. Public*, pg. 2332
SUNSET GARBAGE COLLECTION, INC.—See Arakelian Enterprises, Inc.; *U.S. Private*, pg. 307
SVO ECO-INDUSTRIES—See Groupe Seche SAS; *Int'l*, pg. 3110
SWB ENTSORGUNG GMBH & CO. KG—See EWE Aktiengesellschaft; *Int'l*, pg. 2576
TECHNOCHEM ENVIRONMENTAL COMPLEX PTE. LTD.—See Dowa Holdings Co., Ltd.; *Int'l*, pg. 2184
TERRACYCLE INC.; *U.S. Private*, pg. 3971
TEXAS MOLECULAR, LLC; *U.S. Public*, pg. 3976
TIRMADRID, S.A.—See ACS, Actividades de Construccion y Servicios, S.A.; *Int'l*, pg. 116
TOXCO INC.; *U.S. Private*, pg. 4198
TOX FREE (AUSTRALIA) PTY LTD—See Cleanaway Waste Management Limited; *Int'l*, pg. 1655
TOX FREE (HENDERSON) PTY LTD—See Cleanaway Waste Management Limited; *Int'l*, pg. 1655
TOX FREE (KWINANA) PTY LTD—See Cleanaway Waste Management Limited; *Int'l*, pg. 1655
TOX FREE (NEW SOUTH WALES) PTY LTD—See Cleanaway Waste Management Limited; *Int'l*, pg. 1655
TOX FREE (QUEENSLAND) PTY LTD—See Cleanaway Waste Management Limited; *Int'l*, pg. 1655
TRADEBE ENVIRONMENTAL SERVICES, LLC—See Grupo Tradebe Medioambiente S.L.; *Int'l*, pg. 3138
TRANSPACIFIC RECYCLING PTY LTD—See Cleanaway Waste Management Limited; *Int'l*, pg. 1655
TREDI SA—See Groupe Seche SAS; *Int'l*, pg. 3110
TRIADIS ETAMPES—See Groupe Seche SAS; *Int'l*, pg. 3111
TRIADIS SERVICES S.A.S.—See Groupe Seche SAS; *Int'l*, pg. 3111
TRI RINSE, INC.; *U.S. Private*, pg. 4220
TRI-S ENVIRONMENTAL SERVICES INC.; *U.S. Private*, pg. 4223
TRI-STAR WASTE SYSTEMS, INC.—See Watts Trucking Service, Inc.; *U.S. Private*, pg. 4456
TRI-VAX ENTERPRISES LTD.—See Clean Harbors, Inc.; *U.S. Public*, pg. 510
URBAMAR LEVANTE RESIDUOS INDUSTRIALES, S.L.—See ACS, Actividades de Construccion y Servicios, S.A.; *Int'l*, pg. 117
USA ENVIRONMENTAL, INC.; *U.S. Private*, pg. 4321
US ECOLOGY IDAHO, INC.—See Republic Services, Inc.; *U.S. Public*, pg. 1788
US ECOLOGY ILLINOIS, INC.—See Republic Services, Inc.; *U.S. Public*, pg. 1788
US ECOLOGY KARNES COUNTY DISPOSAL, LLC—See Republic Services, Inc.; *U.S. Public*, pg. 1788
US ECOLOGY MICHIGAN, INC.—See Republic Services, Inc.; *U.S. Public*, pg. 1788
US ECOLOGY NEVADA, INC.—See Republic Services, Inc.; *U.S. Public*, pg. 1788
US ECOLOGY TEXAS, INC.—See Republic Services, Inc.; *U.S. Public*, pg. 1788
US ECOLOGY WASHINGTON, INC.—See Republic Services, Inc.; *U.S. Public*, pg. 1788
US HYBRID CORPORATION—See Ideanomics, Inc.; *U.S. Public*, pg. 1088
U.S. PEROXIDE, LLC—See Danaher Corporation; *U.S. Public*, pg. 631
VIRIDOR LIMITED—See KKR & Co. Inc.; *U.S. Public*, pg. 1266
VISIONARY SOLUTIONS, LLC; *U.S. Private*, pg. 4392
WASTE CONTROL SPECIALISTS LLC—See J.F. Lehman & Company, Inc.; *U.S. Private*, pg. 2164
WASTE INDUSTRIES USA, INC.—See BC Partners LLP; *Int'l*, pg. 924
WASTE MANAGEMENT DISPOSAL SERVICES OF MAINE, INC.—See Waste Management, Inc.; *U.S. Public*, pg. 2333
WASTE MANAGEMENT DISPOSAL SERVICES OF OREGON - ARLINGTON HAZARDOUS WASTE FACILITY—See Waste Management, Inc.; *U.S. Public*, pg. 2333
WASTE MANAGEMENT OF ARKANSAS, INC.—See Waste Management, Inc.; *U.S. Public*, pg. 2333
WASTE MANAGEMENT OF OREGON, INC.—See Waste Management, Inc.; *U.S. Public*, pg. 2333
WASTE SERVICES AUSTRALIA PTY LTD—See Cleanaway Waste Management Limited; *Int'l*, pg. 1655
WAYNE DISPOSAL, INC.—See Republic Services, Inc.; *U.S. Public*, pg. 1788
WIGAND DISPOSAL COMPANY—See Peoria Disposal Company/Area Disposal Service, Inc.; *U.S. Private*, pg. 3143

562212 — SOLID WASTE LANDFILL

ABC DISPOSAL SERVICE, INC.; *U.S. Private*, pg. 35
AKHEA CONSORTIUM—See Hera S.p.A.; *Int'l*, pg. 3356
AMERICAN LANDFILL, INC.—See Waste Management, Inc.; *U.S. Public*, pg. 2330
AMERICAN LANDFILL MANAGEMENT, INC.—See Avalon Holdings Corporation; *U.S. Public*, pg. 239
ANTONY LARA ENVIRO SOLUTIONS PRIVATE LIMITED—See Antony Waste Handling Cell Limited; *Int'l*, pg. 485
ASA SPA—See Hera S.p.A.; *Int'l*, pg. 3356
ATLANTIC WASTE DISPOSAL, INC.—See Waste Management; Inc.; *U.S. Public*, pg. 2330
AUGEAN NORTH LIMITED—See Ancala Partners LLP; *Int'l*, pg. 448
AUGEAN NORTH LIMITED—See Fiera Capital Corporation; *Int'l*, pg. 2659
AUGEAN SOUTH LIMITED—See Ancala Partners LLP; *Int'l*, pg. 448
AUGEAN SOUTH LIMITED—See Fiera Capital Corporation; *Int'l*, pg. 2659
BIOCRUDE TECHNOLOGIES USA, INC.; *Int'l*, pg. 1037
BROADHURST ENVIRONMENTAL, INC.—See Republic Services, Inc.; *U.S. Public*, pg. 1786
CALIFORNIA ASBESTOS MONOFILL, INC.—See Waste Management, Inc.; *U.S. Public*, pg. 2330
CENTRAL DISPOSAL SYSTEMS, INC.—See Waste Management, Inc.; *U.S. Public*, pg. 2330
CENTRAL SANITARY LANDFILL, INC.—See Republic Services, Inc.; *U.S. Public*, pg. 1786
CHADWICK ROAD LANDFILL, INC.—See Waste Management, Inc.; *U.S. Public*, pg. 2330
CHINA BOQI ENVIRONMENTAL HOLDING CO., LTD.; *Int'l*, pg. 1487
CLINTON LANDFILL INC.—See Peoria Disposal Company/Area Disposal Service, Inc.; *U.S. Private*, pg. 3143
CONNECTICUT RESOURCES RECOVERY AUTHORITY; *U.S. Public*, pg. 1016
CUYAHOGA LANDFILL, INC.—See Waste Management, Inc.; *U.S. Public*, pg. 2331
DEER TRACK PARK LANDFILL, INC.—See Waste Management, Inc.; *U.S. Public*, pg. 2331
DEFFENBAUGH INDUSTRIES, INC.—See Waste Management, Inc.; *U.S. Public*, pg. 2331
DELAWARE RECYCLABLE PRODUCTS, INC.—See Waste Management, Inc.; *U.S. Public*, pg. 2331
DRAGON POLYMERS, INC.; *U.S. Private*, pg. 1271
EAGLE RIDGE LANDFILL, LLC—See BC Partners LLP; *Int'l*, pg. 924
EARTHMOVERS LANDFILL, LLC—See Waste Management, Inc.; *U.S. Public*, pg. 2331
EAST CAROLINA ENVIRONMENTAL, LLC—See Republic Services, Inc.; *U.S. Public*, pg. 1786
EASTERN ENVIRONMENT SOLUTIONS, CORP.; *Int'l*, pg. 2272
EASTERN SEABOARD ENVIRONMENTAL COMPLEX CO., LTD.—See Dowa Holdings Co., Ltd.; *Int'l*, pg. 2183
ECDC ENVIRONMENTAL L.C.; *U.S. Private*, pg. 1326
E.C. WASTE, INC.—See Post Capital Partners, LLC; *U.S. Private*, pg. 3234
ENTSORGA ENTSORGUNGS GMBH NFG KG—See Fomento de Construcciones y Contratas, S.A.; *Int'l*, pg. 2722
ENVIROSOLUTIONS, INC.; *U.S. Private*, pg. 1409
EPPERSON WASTE DISPOSAL, INC.—See Republic Services, Inc.; *U.S. Public*, pg. 1786
EVERGREEN RECYCLING AND DISPOSAL FACILITY, INC.—See Waste Management, Inc.; *U.S. Public*, pg. 2331
FORT BEND REGIONAL LANDFILL, LP—See BC Partners LLP; *Int'l*, pg. 924
FUJIKOH COMPANY., LIMITED; *Int'l*, pg. 2826
GALLEGOS SANITATION, INC.; *U.S. Private*, pg. 1639
GFL ENVIRONMENTAL INC. - SOLID WASTE TRANSFER DIVISION—See BC Partners LLP; *Int'l*, pg. 924
GLEN'S SANITARY LANDFILL, INC.—See Waste Management, Inc.; *U.S. Public*, pg. 2331
GRAND CENTRAL SANITARY LANDFILL, INC.—See Waste Management, Inc.; *U.S. Public*, pg. 2331
GRANGER WASTE MANAGEMENT CO.—See Granger Associates, Inc.; *U.S. Private*, pg. 1754
GREEN LINE POLYMERS, INC.—See Advanced Drainage Systems, Inc.; *U.S. Public*, pg. 46
HANSON LANDFILL SERVICES PTY LTD—See Heidelberg Materials AG; *Int'l*, pg. 3312
HILLSBORO LANDFILL INC.—See Waste Management, Inc.; *U.S. Public*, pg. 2331
HUNAN JUNXIN ENVIRONMENTAL PROTECTION CO., LTD.; *Int'l*, pg. 3533
IND.ECO S.R.L.—See Green Holding S.p.A.; *Int'l*, pg. 3071
JAY COUNTY LANDFILL, L.L.C.—See Waste Management, Inc.; *U.S. Public*, pg. 2331
K AND W LANDFILL INC.—See Waste Management, Inc.; *U.S. Public*, pg. 2331
KING GEORGE LANDFILL, INC.—See Waste Management, Inc.; *U.S. Public*, pg. 2331
LAUREL HIGHLANDS LANDFILL, INC.—See Waste Management, Inc.; *U.S. Public*, pg. 2331
LCS SERVICES LANDFILL, INC.—See Waste Management, Inc.; *U.S. Public*, pg. 2331
LIBERTY LANDFILL, L.L.C.—See Waste Management, Inc.; *U.S. Public*, pg. 2331
LONGLEAF C&D DISPOSAL FACILITY, INC.—See Waste Management, Inc.; *U.S. Public*, pg. 2331
MAHONING LANDFILL, INC.—See Waste Management, Inc.; *U.S. Public*, pg. 2331
METRO WASTE AUTHORITY; *U.S. Private*, pg. 2686
MODERN CORPORATION; *U.S. Private*, pg. 2760
MODERN LANDFILL INC.—See Modern Corporation; *U.S. Private*, pg. 2760
NATIONAL WASTE MANAGEMENT HOLDINGS, INC.; *U.S. Public*, pg. 1498
N.E. LAND FILL, LLC—See BC Partners LLP; *Int'l*, pg. 924
NOVAGO SP. Z O.O. - KOSINY PLANT—See China Everbright Group Limited; *Int'l*, pg. 1501
NOVAGO SP. Z O.O. - ROZANKI PLANT—See China Everbright Group Limited; *Int'l*, pg. 1501
NOVAGO SP. Z O.O.—See China Everbright Group Limited; *Int'l*, pg. 1501
NOVAGO SP. Z O.O. - ZLOTOW PLANT—See China Everbright Group Limited; *Int'l*, pg. 1501
NOVAGO SP. Z O.O. - ZNIN PLANT—See China Everbright Group Limited; *Int'l*, pg. 1501
OAKRIDGE LANDFILL, INC.—See Waste Management, Inc.; *U.S. Public*, pg. 2331
OAKWOOD LANDFILL, INC.—See Waste Management, Inc.; *U.S. Public*, pg. 2331
OKLAHOMA CITY LANDFILL, L.L.C.—See Republic Services, Inc.; *U.S. Public*, pg. 1786
OREG SITE WORK SERVICES, LLC; *U.S. Private*, pg. 3039
OZARK RIDGE LANDFILL, INC.—See Waste Management, Inc.; *U.S. Public*, pg. 2331
PAULS VALLEY LANDFILL, LLC—See BC Partners LLP; *Int'l*, pg. 924
PINE TREE ACRES, INC.—See Waste Management, Inc.; *U.S. Public*, pg. 2331
RAINBOW TRANSFER/RECYCLING, INC.—See Republic Services, Inc.; *U.S. Public*, pg. 1787
RAY'S TRASH SERVICE, INC.—See Waste Management, Inc.; *U.S. Public*, pg. 2331
RECOLOGY HAY ROAD—See Arakelian Enterprises, Inc.; *U.S. Private*, pg. 307
RED ROCK DISPOSAL LLC—See BC Partners LLP; *Int'l*, pg. 924
REDWOOD LANDFILL, INC.—See Waste Management, Inc.; *U.S. Public*, pg. 2331
REPUBLIC/MALOY LANDFILL & SANITATION—See Republic Services, Inc.; *U.S. Public*, pg. 1787
RIVERBEND LANDFILL CO.—See Waste Management, Inc.; *U.S. Public*, pg. 2332
RUMPKE SANITARY LANDFILL, INC.—See Rumpke Consolidated Companies, Inc.; *U.S. Private*, pg. 3503
S4 COLUMBIA RIDGE RECOVERY, LLC—See Waste Management, Inc.; *U.S. Public*, pg. 2332
SAFEGUARD LANDFILL MANAGEMENT LLC—See BC Partners LLP; *Int'l*, pg. 924
SHADE LANDFILL, INC.—See Waste Management, Inc.; *U.S. Public*, pg. 2332
SOONER LANDFILL—See BC Partners LLP; *Int'l*, pg. 924
SOUTHWEST DISPOSAL SERVICE, INC.—See Republic Services, Inc.; *U.S. Public*, pg. 1787
TRAIL RIDGE LANDFILL, INC.—See Waste Management, Inc.; *U.S. Public*, pg. 2332
WASTE CORPORATION OF KANSAS, INC.—See BC Partners LLP; *Int'l*, pg. 924
WASTE CORPORATION OF TEXAS, LP—See BC Partners LLP; *Int'l*, pg. 924
WASTE MANAGEMENT DISPOSAL SERVICES OF COLORADO, INC.—See Waste Management, Inc.; *U.S. Public*, pg. 2333
WASTE MANAGEMENT DISPOSAL SERVICES OF MASSACHUSETTS - HOLYOKE LANDFILL—See Waste Management, Inc.; *U.S. Public*, pg. 2333
WASTE MANAGEMENT DISPOSAL SERVICES OF OREGON - COLUMBIA RIDGE LANDFILL—See Waste Management, Inc.; *U.S. Public*, pg. 2333
WASTE MANAGEMENT HOLDINGS, INC.—See Waste Management, Inc.; *U.S. Public*, pg. 2333
WASTE MANAGEMENT OF CANADA CORP. - QUEBEC DIVISIONAL OFFICE-GMA—See Waste Management, Inc.; *U.S. Public*, pg. 2333
WASTE MANAGEMENT OF FLORIDA INC. - PINE RIDGE RECYCLING & DISPOSAL FACILITY—See Waste Management, Inc.; *U.S. Public*, pg. 2333
WASTE MANAGEMENT OF HAWAII, INC.—See Waste Management, Inc.; *U.S. Public*, pg. 2333
WASTE MANAGEMENT OF INDIANA, L.L.C.—See Waste Management, Inc.; *U.S. Public*, pg. 2334

N.A.I.C.S. INDEX

WASTE MANAGEMENT OF LOUISIANA, L.L.C.—See Waste Management, Inc.; *U.S. Public*, pg. 2334
WASTE MANAGEMENT OF MAINE, INC.—See Waste Management, Inc.; *U.S. Public*, pg. 2334
WASTE MANAGEMENT OF OKLAHOMA, INC.—See Waste Management, Inc.; *U.S. Public*, pg. 2334
WASTE MANAGEMENT RECYCLING AND DISPOSAL SERVICES OF CALIFORNIA, INC.—See Waste Management, Inc.; *U.S. Public*, pg. 2333
WCA OF OKLAHOMA, LLC—See BC Partners LLP; *Int'l*, pg. 924
WCA WASTE CORPORATION—See BC Partners LLP; *Int'l*, pg. 924
WESTERN WASTE INDUSTRIES—See Waste Management, Inc.; *U.S. Public*, pg. 2334
WHITE PINES CORPORATION—See J. P. Mascaro & Sons; *U.S. Private*, pg. 2156
WINNEBAGO RECLAMATION SERVICE INC.—See William Charles, Ltd.; *U.S. Private*, pg. 4523
WM GTL, INC.—See Waste Management, Inc.; *U.S. Public*, pg. 2333

562213 — SOLID WASTE COMBUSTORS AND INCINERATORS

ALLIED WASTE INDUSTRIES, INC—See Republic Services, Inc.; *U.S. Public*, pg. 1785
AVN ABFALLVERWERTUNG NIEDEROSTERREICH GMBH—See EVN AG; *Int'l*, pg. 2570
BEKKIHAYAMI ENVIRONMENT TECHNOLOGY CO., LTD.—See Hitachi Zosen Corporation; *Int'l*, pg. 3410
BIH HEATERS MALAYSIA SDN BHD—See Boustead Singapore Limited; *Int'l*, pg. 1120
BOUSTEAD INTERNATIONAL HEATERS CANADA LIMITED—See Boustead Singapore Limited; *Int'l*, pg. 1120
CLEAN BIOENERGY INC.; *Int'l*, pg. 1654
DYNAGREEN ENVIRONMENTAL PROTECTION GROUP CO., LTD.; *Int'l*, pg. 2239
FUJIMINO ECOWELLS CORPORATION—See Hitachi Zosen Corporation; *Int'l*, pg. 3410
GODAWARI POWER & ISPAT LTD.; *Int'l*, pg. 3018
GOTENBAOYAMA ENVIRONMENT TECHNOLOGY CO., LTD.—See Hitachi Zosen Corporation; *Int'l*, pg. 3410
GRANTS PASS SANITATION, INC.—See Republic Services, Inc.; *U.S. Public*, pg. 1786
HA-NA-IRO CO., LTD.—See Hitachi Zosen Corporation; *Int'l*, pg. 3412
HARBIN YIFENG ECO-ENVIRONMENT CO., LTD.—See EASTERN ENVIRONMENT SOLUTIONS, CORP.; *Int'l*, pg. 2272
HITACHI ZOSEN CHUGOKU CONSTRUCTION WORKS CO., LTD.—See Hitachi Zosen Corporation; *Int'l*, pg. 3410
HITZ ENVIRONMENT TAKAMATSU CO., LTD.—See Hitachi Zosen Corporation; *Int'l*, pg. 3411
ICHINOMIYA ENVIRONMENT TECHNOLOGY CO., LTD.—See Hitachi Zosen Corporation; *Int'l*, pg. 3411
INTERNATIONAL BALER CORP.; *U.S. Public*, pg. 1145
JONAN ENVIRONMENT TECHNOLOGY CO., LTD.—See Hitachi Zosen Corporation; *Int'l*, pg. 3411
KURASHIKI ENVIRONMENT TECHNOLOGY CO., LTD.—See Hitachi Zosen Corporation; *Int'l*, pg. 3411
LEADING ENERGY CORPORATION—See CTCI Corporation; *Int'l*, pg. 1870
MATSUYAMA ENVIRONMENT TECHNOLOGY CO., LTD.—See Hitachi Zosen Corporation; *Int'l*, pg. 3411
MURAKAMI ENVIRONMENT TECHNOLOGY CO., LTD.—See Hitachi Zosen Corporation; *Int'l*, pg. 3411
NAKAKITASORACHI ENVIRONMENT TECHNOLOGY CO., LTD.—See Hitachi Zosen Corporation; *Int'l*, pg. 3411
NETWORKS CENTRE B.V.—See Alcadon Group AB; *Int'l*, pg. 300
NICHIZO TECH INC.—See Hitachi Zosen Corporation; *Int'l*, pg. 3411
OYSTER BAY WIND FARM (RF) (PTY.) LTD.—See Enel S.p.A.; *Int'l*, pg. 2414
PT BOUSTEAD MAXITHERM INDUSTRIES—See Boustead Singapore Limited; *Int'l*, pg. 1121
ROSS CONSOLIDATED CORP.; *U.S. Private*, pg. 3485
ROSS INCINERATION SERVICES, INC.—See Ross Consolidated Corp.; *U.S. Private*, pg. 3485
SENERVAL—See Groupe Seche SAS; *Int'l*, pg. 3110
SHIKOKU ENVIRONMENT SERVICE CO., LTD.—See Hitachi Zosen Corporation; *Int'l*, pg. 3412
SINOMA ENERGY CONSERVATION LTD.—See China National Building Material Group Co., Ltd.; *Int'l*, pg. 1526
SKOGVIND AS—See Cloudberry Clean Energy ASA; *Int'l*, pg. 1662
TERMOELECTRICA JOSE DE SAN MARTIN S.A.—See Enel S.p.A.; *Int'l*, pg. 2415
TOYONAKA & ITAMI RECYCLE FOREST CO., LTD.—See Hitachi Zosen Corporation; *Int'l*, pg. 3412
TSUYAMA KEN-IKI ENVIRONMENT TECHNOLOGY CO., LTD.—See Hitachi Zosen Corporation; *Int'l*, pg. 3412

562219 — OTHER NONHAZARDOUS WASTE TREATMENT AND DISPOSAL

2TRG INC; *U.S. Private*, pg. 7
A CLEAN ENVIRONMENT CO., INC.; *U.S. Private*, pg. 18
A.C.R. THUKHACHANTHAR CO., LTD.—See Daiki Axis Co., Ltd.; *Int'l*, pg. 1932
AES ASSET ACQUISITION CORPORATION—See Compass Diversified Holdings; *U.S. Public*, pg. 559
ALL CYCLE WASTE, INC.—See Casella Waste Systems, Inc.; *U.S. Public*, pg. 445
ALLIED WASTE SERVICES OF CORVALLIS; *U.S. Private*, pg. 191
ALPHARETTA TRANSFER STATION, LLC—See Waste Management, Inc.; *U.S. Public*, pg. 2330
ALPHA WASTEWATER, INC.; *Int'l*, pg. 370
AMATA WATER CO. LTD.—See Amata Corporation Public Company Limited; *Int'l*, pg. 413
ANDERSON LANDFILL, INC.—See Waste Management, Inc.; *U.S. Public*, pg. 2330
ANTELOPE VALLEY RECYCLING AND DISPOSAL FACILITY, INC.—See Waste Management, Inc.; *U.S. Public*, pg. 2330
ARDEN LANDFILL, INC.—See Waste Management, Inc.; *U.S. Public*, pg. 2330
ASPEN WASTE SYSTEM OF MISSOURI—See Aspen Waste Systems Inc.; *U.S. Private*, pg. 352
AYR ENVIRONMENTAL SERVICES OPERATIONS LIMITED—See CK Hutchison Holdings Limited; *Int'l*, pg. 1637
BERKELEY SANITARY SERVICE, INC.—See Republic Services, Inc.; *U.S. Public*, pg. 1786
BIOSHAFT WATER TECHNOLOGY, INC.; *U.S. Public*, pg. 338
BIOTRAN INC.—See ProMed Waste Solutions LLC; *U.S. Private*, pg. 3282
BURNSVILLE SANITARY LANDFILL, INC.—See Waste Management, Inc.; *U.S. Public*, pg. 2330
CAPITOL DISPOSAL, INC.—See Waste Management, Inc.; *U.S. Public*, pg. 2330
CARBONMETA RESEARCH LTD.—See CARBONMETA TECHNOLOGIES, INC.; *U.S. Public*, pg. 433
CASELLA TRANSPORTATION, INC.—See Casella Waste Systems, Inc.; *U.S. Public*, pg. 446
CEDAR RIDGE LANDFILL, INC.—See Waste Management, Inc.; *U.S. Public*, pg. 2330
CELLPOINT B.V.—See Galapagos N.V.; *Int'l*, pg. 2870
CENTRAL JERSEY WASTE & RECYCLING, INC.—See Roark Capital Group Inc.; *U.S. Private*, pg. 3454
CENTRAL TEXAS REFUSE, INC.—See Integrated Waste Solutions Group, LLC; *U.S. Private*, pg. 2101
CENTRO DE TRANSFERENCIAS, S.A—See ACS, Actividades de Construccion y Servicios, S.A.; *Int'l*, pg. 110
CERTIFIED REFRIGERANT SERVICES, INC.—See A-Gas Limited; *Int'l*, pg. 19
CHAMBERS OF MISSISSIPPI, INC.—See Waste Management, Inc.; *U.S. Public*, pg. 2330
CHINA ECOTEK CORPORATION—See China Steel Corporation; *Int'l*, pg. 1555
CLAERH, S.A.—See ACS, Actividades de Construccion y Servicios, S.A.; *Int'l*, pg. 110
CLEAN EARTH OF CARTERET, LLC—See Enviri Corporation; *U.S. Public*, pg. 780
CLEAN EARTH OF CATERET, LLC—See Compass Diversified Holdings; *U.S. Public*, pg. 559
CLEAN EARTH OF GREATER WASHINGTON, LLC—See Enviri Corporation; *U.S. Public*, pg. 780
CLEAN EARTH OF MARYLAND, LLC—See Enviri Corporation; *U.S. Public*, pg. 780
CLEAN EARTH OF NEW CASTLE, LLC—See Enviri Corporation; *U.S. Public*, pg. 780
CLEAN EARTH OF NORTH JERSEY, INC.—See Enviri Corporation; *U.S. Public*, pg. 780
CLEAN EARTH OF PHILADELPHIA, LLC—See Enviri Corporation; *U.S. Public*, pg. 780
CLEAN EARTH OF SOUTHEAST PENNSYLVANIA, LLC—See Enviri Corporation; *U.S. Public*, pg. 780
CLEAN HARBORS BATON ROUGE, LLC—See Clean Harbors, Inc.; *U.S. Public*, pg. 509
CLEARFORD WATER SYSTEMS INC.; *Int'l*, pg. 1657
CNIM INSERTION—See CNIM Constructions Industrielles de la Mediterranee SA; *Int'l*, pg. 1677
CNIM OUEST ARMOR—See CNIM Constructions Industrielles de la Mediterranee SA; *Int'l*, pg. 1677
CNIM UK LTD—See CNIM Constructions Industrielles de la Mediterranee SA; *Int'l*, pg. 1677
CONPOREC, INC.; *Int'l*, pg. 1769
CONSHOHOCKEN RECYCLING & RAIL TRANSFER LLC—See 3i Group plc; *Int'l*, pg. 9
COUNTRYSIDE LANDFILL INC.—See Waste Management, Inc.; *U.S. Public*, pg. 2330
C.V. LANDFILL, INC.—See Casella Waste Systems, Inc.; *U.S. Public*, pg. 445
CWM CHEMICAL SERVICES, L.L.C.—See Waste Management, Inc.; *U.S. Public*, pg. 2330
DAFTER SANITARY LANDFILL, INC.—See Waste Management, Inc.; *U.S. Public*, pg. 2331

562219 — OTHER NONHAZARDOUS ...

DAISEKI CO. LTD.- KANTO FIRST PLANT—See Daiseki Co. Ltd.; *Int'l*, pg. 1941
DAISEKI CO. LTD. - KANTO THIRD PLANT—See Daiseki Co. Ltd.; *Int'l*, pg. 1941
DAISEKI CO. LTD. - KYUSHU UNIT—See Daiseki Co. Ltd.; *Int'l*, pg. 1941
DELMAR DISPOSAL—See TAS Environmental Services, L.P.; *U.S. Public*, pg. 3934
DOCTOR BRAMBLETT ROAD, LLC—See Waste Management, Inc.; *U.S. Public*, pg. 2331
EBARA ENVIRONMENTAL PLANT CO., LTD.—See Ebara Corporation; *Int'l*, pg. 2283
EL COQUI LANDFILL COMPANY, INC.—See Waste Management, Inc.; *U.S. Public*, pg. 2331
ENCYCLE/TEXAS, INC.—See Grupo Mexico, S.A.B. de C.V.; *Int'l*, pg. 3132
ENVA IRELAND LIMITED—See DCC plc; *Int'l*, pg. 1990
ENVIRITE OF ILLINOIS, INC.—See Republic Services, Inc.; *U.S. Public*, pg. 1788
ENVIRITE OF PENNSYLVANIA, INC.—See Republic Services, Inc.; *U.S. Public*, pg. 1788
EUROGREEN ITALIA S.R.L.—See BayWa AG; *Int'l*, pg. 917
EVOQUA WATER TECHNOLOGIES—See Xylem Inc.; *U.S. Public*, pg. 2393
EVOQUA WATER TECHNOLOGIES—See Xylem Inc.; *U.S. Public*, pg. 2394
EVOQUA WATER TECHNOLOGIES—See Xylem Inc.; *U.S. Public*, pg. 2394
FIRST AMERICAN SCIENTIFIC CORP.; *Int'l*, pg. 2681
FORTUNE ENERGY CORPORATION—See CTCI Corporation; *Int'l*, pg. 1870
FUTURE INDUSTRIAL SERVICES LTD—See Ancala Partners LLP; *Int'l*, pg. 448
FUTURE INDUSTRIAL SERVICES LTD—See Fiera Capital Corporation; *Int'l*, pg. 2659
GATEWAY TRANSFER STATION, LLC—See Waste Management, Inc.; *U.S. Public*, pg. 2331
GESTION Y PROTECCION AMBIENTAL, S.L.—See ACS, Actividades de Construccion y Servicios, S.A.; *Int'l*, pg. 112
GFL ENVIRONMENTAL INC. - LIQUID WASTE EAST DIVISION—See BC Partners LLP; *Int'l*, pg. 923
GFL ENVIRONMENTAL INC. - LIQUID WASTE WEST DIVISION—See BC Partners LLP; *Int'l*, pg. 923
G.I. INDUSTRIES—See Waste Management, Inc.; *U.S. Public*, pg. 2331
GLOBAL GREEN SOLUTIONS INC.; *Int'l*, pg. 2997
GREENSTAR MANAGED SERVICES - RLWM, LLC—See Waste Management, Inc.; *U.S. Public*, pg. 2331
GS ENVIROSERVICES, INC.—See GreenSource Corporation; *U.S. Private*, pg. 1780
HARLEY HOLLAN COMPANIES, INC.—See Superior Waste Industries LLC; *U.S. Private*, pg. 3881
HECKMANN WATER RESOURCES (CVR), INC.—See Select Water Solutions, Inc.; *U.S. Public*, pg. 1862
HERITAGE INTERACTIVE SERVICES, LLC—See EQT AB; *Int'l*, pg. 2482
HERITAGE-WTI, INC.—See EQT AB; *Int'l*, pg. 2482
HOMEBOY ELECTRONICS RECYCLING—See Homeboy Industries; *U.S. Private*, pg. 1972
HYDRODEC NORTH AMERICA LLP—See Hydrodec Group plc; *Int'l*, pg. 3547
HYDROMET CORPORATION PTY LIMITED - SOUTHERN, NSW—See Hydromet Corporation Limited; *Int'l*, pg. 3548
IMEX INTERNATIONAL CORP.; *U.S. Private*, pg. 2047
INOVATIVNI TECHNOLOGIE S.R.O.—See CHINO Corporation; *Int'l*, pg. 1571
INSTITUTIONAL CASEWORK INC.; *U.S. Private*, pg. 2094
INTERSTATE WASTE SERVICES, INC.; *U.S. Private*, pg. 2126
JAPAN ECOLOGY CORPORATION—See Daito Chemix Corporation; *Int'l*, pg. 1943
KTI BIO-FUELS, INC.—See Casella Waste Systems, Inc.; *U.S. Public*, pg. 446
LAB GMBH—See CNIM Constructions Industrielles de la Mediterranée SA; *Int'l*, pg. 1677
LIVING EARTH LIMITED—See Capital Environment Holdings Limited; *Int'l*, pg. 1310
MARMON WATER TREATMENT—See Berkshire Hathaway Inc.; *U.S. Public*, pg. 311
MATERIAL RECLAMATION, LLC—See BC Partners LLP; *Int'l*, pg. 924
MEADOWFILL LANDFILL, INC.—See Waste Management, Inc.; *U.S. Public*, pg. 2331
MIDLAND DAVIS CORPORATION—See Peoria Disposal Company/Area Disposal Service, Inc.; *U.S. Private*, pg. 3143
MINMET OPERATIONS PTY LIMITED—See Hydromet Corporation Limited; *Int'l*, pg. 3548
MSE MOBILE SCHLAMMENTWASSERUNGS GMBH—See EnBW Energie Baden-Wurttemberg AG; *Int'l*, pg. 2399
NATURE'S NEEDS, LLC—See Arakelian Enterprises, Inc.; *U.S. Private*, pg. 307
NECHES RIVER TREATMENT CORP.—See Exxon Mobil Corporation; *U.S. Public*, pg. 817
NEW ENGLAND WASTE SERVICES OF VERMONT, INC.—See Casella Waste Systems, Inc.; *U.S. Public*, pg. 446

562219 — OTHER NONHAZARDOUS ...

NEW MILFORD LANDFILL, L.L.C.—See Waste Management, Inc.; *U.S. Public*, pg. 2331
NEWS OF WORCESTER LLC—See Casella Waste Systems, Inc.; *U.S. Public*, pg. 446
NORTHERN SANITATION, INC.—See Casella Waste Systems, Inc.; *U.S. Public*, pg. 446
OAKLEAF WASTE MANAGEMENT, LLC—See Waste Management, Inc.; *U.S. Public*, pg. 2331
ONONDAGA COUNTY RESOURCE RECOVERY AGENCY; *U.S. Private*, pg. 3027
PEQUANNOCK DISPOSAL, INC.—See Interstate Waste Services, Inc.; *U.S. Private*, pg. 2126
PHOENIX RESOURCES, INC.—See Waste Management, Inc.; *U.S. Public*, pg. 2331
PINE TREE WASTE, INC.—See Casella Waste Systems, Inc.; *U.S. Public*, pg. 446
PLASTEKOL ORGANIZACJA ODZYSKU S.A.—See Grupa LOTOS S.A.; *Int'l*, pg. 3117
PONTICELLI S.R.L.—See Biancamano S.p.A.; *Int'l*, pg. 1017
PROMED WASTE SOLUTIONS LLC; *U.S. Private*, pg. 3282
RECOLOGY ASHLAND—See Arakelian Enterprises, Inc.; *U.S. Private*, pg. 307
RECOLOGY DEL NORTE, INC.—See Arakelian Enterprises, Inc.; *U.S. Private*, pg. 307
RECOLOGY ENVIRONMENTAL SOLUTIONS INC.—See Arakelian Enterprises, Inc.; *U.S. Private*, pg. 307
RECOLOGY MOUNTAIN VIEW—See Arakelian Enterprises, Inc.; *U.S. Private*, pg. 307
RECOLOGY OSTROM ROAD—See Arakelian Enterprises, Inc.; *U.S. Private*, pg. 307
RECOLOGY PORTLAND INC.—See Arakelian Enterprises, Inc.; *U.S. Private*, pg. 307
RECOLOGY SAN FRANCISCO—See Arakelian Enterprises, Inc.; *U.S. Private*, pg. 307
RECOLOGY VACAVILLE SOLANO—See Arakelian Enterprises, Inc.; *U.S. Private*, pg. 307
RECOLOGY YUBA-SUTTER—See Arakelian Enterprises, Inc.; *U.S. Private*, pg. 307
REFUSE, INC.—See Waste Management, Inc.; *U.S. Public*, pg. 2332
REFUSE SERVICES, INC.—See Waste Management, Inc.; *U.S. Public*, pg. 2331
RELIABLE LANDFILL, LLC—See Waste Management, Inc.; *U.S. Public*, pg. 2332
REPUBLIC WASTE SERVICES OF TEXAS LP, INC.—See Republic Services, Inc.; *U.S. Public*, pg. 1787
RETRAOIL, S.L.—See ACS, Actividades de Construccion y Servicios, S.A.; *Int'l*, pg. 116
REVERSE LOGISTICS GMBH—See Monitor Clipper Partners, LLC; *U.S. Private*, pg. 2771
RICHLAND COUNTY LANDFILL, INC.—See Waste Management, Inc.; *U.S. Public*, pg. 2332
RILTA ENVIRONMENTAL LTD—See Exponent Private Equity LLP; *Int'l*, pg. 2589
RUFFINO HILLS TRANSFER STATION, LP—See BC Partners LLP; *Int'l*, pg. 924
SAUR SA—See Ardian SAS; *Int'l*, pg. 556
SAUR SA—See Caisse des Depots et Consignations; *Int'l*, pg. 1258
SECHE ENVIRONNEMENT SA—See Groupe Seche SAS; *Int'l*, pg. 3110
SOUTHERN ALLEGHENIES LANDFILL, INC.—See Waste Management, Inc.; *U.S. Public*, pg. 2332
SPRINGFIELD RESOURCE RECOVERY, INC.—See Fluor Corporation; *U.S. Public*, pg. 859
SPRUCE RIDGE, INC.—See Waste Management, Inc.; *U.S. Public*, pg. 2332
STEREAU SAS—See Ardian SAS; *Int'l*, pg. 556
STEREAU SAS—See Caisse des Depots et Consignations; *Int'l*, pg. 1258
SYNAGRO TECHNOLOGIES, INC.—See EQT AB; *Int'l*, pg. 2481
SYSTECH ENVIRONMENTAL CORPORATION—See Holcim Ltd.; *Int'l*, pg. 3449
TECMED MAROC, S.A.R.L.—See ACS, Actividades de Construccion y Servicios, S.A.; *Int'l*, pg. 116
THERMORETEC CORP; *U.S. Private*, pg. 4143
TRADEBE SOLVENT RECYCLING LTD—See Grupo Tradebe Medioambiente S.L.; *Int'l*, pg. 3138
TRADEBE UK LIMITED—See Grupo Tradebe Medioambiente S.L.; *Int'l*, pg. 3138
TRADEBE USA HOLDINGS, INC—See Grupo Tradebe Medioambiente S.L.; *Int'l*, pg. 3138
TRINITY ENVIRONMENTAL SERVICES, L.L.C; *U.S. Private*, pg. 4233
TRINITY RECYCLERS LLC—See Green Tree Electronic Recycling, LLC; *U.S. Private*, pg. 1774
TX NEWCO, L.L.C.—See Waste Management, Inc.; *U.S. Public*, pg. 2332
USA VALLEY FACILITY, INC.—See Waste Management, Inc.; *U.S. Public*, pg. 2332
USA WASTE OF VIRGINIA LANDFILLS, INC.—See Waste Management, Inc.; *U.S. Public*, pg. 2332
US ECOLOGY ROMULUS, INC.—See Republic Services, Inc.; *U.S. Public*, pg. 1788
US ECOLOGY SULLIGENT, INC.—See Republic Services, Inc.; *U.S. Public*, pg. 1788
US ECOLOGY TAMPA, INC.—See Republic Services, Inc.; *U.S. Public*, pg. 1788
US ECOLOGY TULSA, INC.—See Republic Services, Inc.; *U.S. Public*, pg. 1788
US ECOLOGY WINNIE, LLC—See Republic Services, Inc.; *U.S. Public*, pg. 1788
VALICOR ENVIRONMENTAL SERVICES, LLC—See The Pritzker Group - Chicago, LLC; *U.S. Private*, pg. 4100
VALICOR ENVIRONMENTAL TECHNOLOGIES, LLC—See The Pritzker Group - Chicago, LLC; *U.S. Private*, pg. 4100
VALICOR, INC.; *U.S. Private*, pg. 4332
VICKERY ENVIRONMENTAL, INC.—See Waste Management, Inc.; *U.S. Public*, pg. 2332
VIRIDOR LONDON RECYCLING LIMITED—See KKR & Co. Inc.; *U.S. Public*, pg. 1266
VIRIDOR WASTE (GREATER MANCHESTER) LIMITED—See KKR & Co. Inc.; *U.S. Public*, pg. 1266
VIRIDOR WASTE (LANDFILL RESTORATION) LIMITED—See KKR & Co. Inc.; *U.S. Public*, pg. 1266
VIRIDOR WASTE (WEST SUSSEX) LIMITED—See KKR & Co. Inc.; *U.S. Public*, pg. 1266
WASTE MANAGEMENT COLLECTION AND RECYCLING, INC.—See Waste Management, Inc.; *U.S. Public*, pg. 2333
WASTE MANAGEMENT NATIONAL TRANSPORTATION SERVICES, INC.—See Waste Management, Inc.; *U.S. Public*, pg. 2333
WASTE MANAGEMENT OF IDAHO, INC.—See Waste Management, Inc.; *U.S. Public*, pg. 2334
WASTE MANAGEMENT OF IOWA, INC.—See Waste Management, Inc.; *U.S. Public*, pg. 2334
WASTE MANAGEMENT OF MARYLAND, INC.—See Waste Management, Inc.; *U.S. Public*, pg. 2334
WASTE MANAGEMENT OF MICHIGAN, INC.—See Waste Management, Inc.; *U.S. Public*, pg. 2334
WASTE MANAGEMENT OF MISSOURI, INC.—See Waste Management, Inc.; *U.S. Public*, pg. 2334
WASTE MANAGEMENT OF NEBRASKA, INC.—See Waste Management, Inc.; *U.S. Public*, pg. 2334
WASTE MANAGEMENT OF NEVADA, INC.—See Waste Management, Inc.; *U.S. Public*, pg. 2334
WASTE MANAGEMENT OF NEW MEXICO, INC.—See Waste Management, Inc.; *U.S. Public*, pg. 2334
WASTE MANAGEMENT OF NEW YORK - VARICK I TRANSFER STATION—See Waste Management, Inc.; *U.S. Public*, pg. 2334
WASTE MANAGEMENT OF RHODE ISLAND, INC.—See Waste Management, Inc.; *U.S. Public*, pg. 2334
WASTE MANAGEMENT OF WEST VIRGINIA, INC.—See Waste Management, Inc.; *U.S. Public*, pg. 2334
WASTE MANAGEMENT OF WISCONSIN, INC.—See Waste Management, Inc.; *U.S. Public*, pg. 2334
WASTE-STREAM, INC.—See Casella Waste Systems, Inc.; *U.S. Public*, pg. 446
WCA SHILOH LANDFILL, LLC—See BC Partners LLP; *Int'l*, pg. 924
WILLIMANTIC WASTE PAPER CO., INC.—See Casella Waste Systems, Inc.; *U.S. Public*, pg. 446
WINTERS BROTHERS, INC.—See Casella Waste Systems, Inc.; *U.S. Public*, pg. 446

562910 — REMEDIATION SERVICES

AAC CONTRACTING INC.; *U.S. Private*, pg. 30
ABITARE IN S.P.A.; *Int'l*, pg. 62
ABO GEOMET BV—See ABO-Group NV/SA; *Int'l*, pg. 66
ABO-MILIEUCONSULT BV—See ABO-Group NV/SA; *Int'l*, pg. 66
ABO NV—See ABO-Group NV/SA; *Int'l*, pg. 66
AGRICULTURAL SERVICES, INC.—See The Pritzker Group - Chicago, LLC; *U.S. Private*, pg. 4100
AMBIENTHESIS SPA; *Int'l*, pg. 414
AMERICAN TECHNOLOGIES, INC.; *U.S. Private*, pg. 256
AQUAVENTURE HOLDINGS LIMITED—See BDT Capital Partners, LLC; *U.S. Private*, pg. 502
ARC ABATEMENT, INC.; *U.S. Private*, pg. 309
ASPER BV—See ABO-Group NV/SA; *Int'l*, pg. 66
ASRC INDUSTRIAL SERVICES LLC—See Arctic Slope Regional Corporation; *U.S. Private*, pg. 316
AT ABATEMENT SERVICES, INC.—See AT Industries, Inc.; *U.S. Private*, pg. 363
AVISCO INC.; *U.S. Private*, pg. 408
AZIENDA SERVIZI VALTROMPIA S.P.A.—See A2A S.p.A.; *Int'l*, pg. 29
BELFOR (CANADA) INC.—See BELFOR USA Group, Inc.; *U.S. Private*, pg. 517
BIOLARGO WATER, INC.—See BioLargo, Inc.; *U.S. Public*, pg. 337
BOSKALIS DOLMAN B.V.—See HAL Trust N.V.; *Int'l*, pg. 3225
BRICE ENVIRONMENTAL SERVICES CORPORATION; *U.S. Public*, pg. 648
CBI EASTERN ANSTALT—See McDermott International, Inc.; *U.S. Public*, pg. 1405
CB&I—See McDermott International, Inc.; *U.S. Public*, pg. 1405
CBI VENEZOLANA, S.A.—See McDermott International, Inc.; *U.S. Public*, pg. 1405
CELTIC TECHNOLOGIES LTD.—See Colliers International Group Inc.; *Int'l*, pg. 1701
CENTRAL ENVIRONMENTAL INC.; *U.S. Private*, pg. 820
CLEAN HARBORS ENVIRONMENTAL SERVICES, INC.—See Clean Harbors, Inc.; *U.S. Public*, pg. 509
CLEAN VENTURE INC.; *U.S. Private*, pg. 931
COWLITZ CLEAN SWEEP—See Pacific Northern Environmental Corp; *U.S. Private*, pg. 3069
CROSS ENVIRONMENTAL SERVICES, INC.—See CES Synergies, Inc.; *U.S. Public*, pg. 476
CURRENT ENVIRONMENTAL SOLUTIONS LLC—See Tru-Arc Partners, L.P.; *U.S. Private*, pg. 4245
CUSTOM ENVIRONMENTAL SERVICES, INC.—See Ambipar Participacoes e Empreendimentos SA; *Int'l*, pg. 414
CYN OIL CORPORATION; *U.S. Private*, pg. 1134
DEC-TAM CORPORATION—See The White Oak Group, Inc.; *U.S. Private*, pg. 4135
DOWA ENVIRONMENTAL ENGINEERING (SUZHOU) CO., LTD.—See Dowa Holdings Co., Ltd.; *Int'l*, pg. 2183
ENTACT, LLC—See J.F. Lehman & Company, Inc.; *U.S. Private*, pg. 2163
ENVIRONMENTAL BIOTECH LIMITED—See Franchise Brands plc; *Int'l*, pg. 2760
ENVIROTECH LLC—See ITT Inc.; *U.S. Public*, pg. 1177
EURENCO BOFORS, INC.—See GIAT Industries S.A.; *Int'l*, pg. 2962
EXALCO FINANCE PLC; *Int'l*, pg. 2577
FILTA EUROPE B.V.—See Franchise Brands plc; *Int'l*, pg. 2760
FLUOR-B&W PORTSMOUTH LLC—See Fluor Corporation; *U.S. Public*, pg. 859
FLUOR FERNALD INC.—See Fluor Corporation; *U.S. Public*, pg. 859
FLUOR PORTSMOUTH LLC—See Fluor Corporation; *U.S. Public*, pg. 858
GARNER ENVIRONMENTAL SERVICES; *U.S. Private*, pg. 1645
GEO+ ENVIRONNEMENT SAS—See ABO-Group NV/SA; *Int'l*, pg. 66
GEOSONDA NETHERLANDS BV—See ABO-Group NV/SA; *Int'l*, pg. 66
GEOSONIC FRANCE SAS—See ABO-Group NV/SA; *Int'l*, pg. 66
GLOBAL DIVING & SALVAGE, INC.; *U.S. Private*, pg. 1713
GRADSKA CISTOCA A.D.; *Int'l*, pg. 3050
GRASSHOPPER ENVIRONMENTAL PTY. LTD.—See Cleanaway Waste Management Limited; *Int'l*, pg. 1655
GREENLEAF ENVIRONMENTAL GROUP, INC.; *U.S. Private*, pg. 1778
GRUPO NET SLU—See Derichebourg S.A.; *Int'l*, pg. 2042
GRUPO TRADEBE MEDIOAMBIENTE S.L.; *Int'l*, pg. 3138
GUANGZHOU GREAT WATER ENVIRONMENTAL PROTECTION CO., LTD.—See China TianYF Holdings Group Limited; *Int'l*, pg. 1559
IEP TECHNOLOGIES GMBH—See Sentinel Capital Partners, L.L.C.; *U.S. Private*, pg. 3609
IEP TECHNOLOGIES, LLC—See Sentinel Capital Partners, L.L.C.; *U.S. Private*, pg. 3609
INERTAM SAS—See Europlasma SA; *Int'l*, pg. 2557
INNOGEO SAS—See ABO-Group NV/SA; *Int'l*, pg. 66
IN SITU SOLUTIONS CO., LTD.—See EnBio Holdings Inc.; *Int'l*, pg. 2396
INTERSTATE RESTORATION GROUP, INC.; *U.S. Private*, pg. 2125
INTERSTATE RESTORATION HAWAII LLC—See Interstate Restoration Group, Inc.; *U.S. Private*, pg. 2126
KANKYOU BOUSAI CO., LTD.—See Founder's Consultants Holdings, Inc.; *Int'l*, pg. 2753
LAND CONCIERGE, INC.—See EnBio Holdings Inc.; *Int'l*, pg. 2396
LATA ENVIRONMENTAL SERVICES OF KENTUCKY, LLC—See Los Alamos Technical Associates, Inc.; *U.S. Private*, pg. 2496
LATA-KEMRON REMEDIATION, LLC—See Los Alamos Technical Associates, Inc.; *U.S. Private*, pg. 2496
LATA-SHARP REMEDIATION SERVICES, LLC—See Los Alamos Technical Associates, Inc.; *U.S. Private*, pg. 2496
LUSE COMPANIES, INC.—See Luse Holdings, Inc.; *U.S. Private*, pg. 2516
MARINE SPILL RESPONSE CORPORATION; *U.S. Private*, pg. 2575
MAXYMILLIAN TECHNOLOGIES INC.; *U.S. Private*, pg. 2620
MEDISOLUTION PTE. LTD.—See Boustead Singapore Limited; *Int'l*, pg. 1121
MERICO ABATEMENT CONTRACTORS, INC.; *U.S. Private*, pg. 2672
MILLER ENVIRONMENTAL GROUP, INC.—See GenNx360 Capital Partners, L.P.; *U.S. Private*, pg. 1672
THE NACHER CORPORATION—See Mistras Group, Inc.; *U.S. Public*, pg. 1451
NALCO JAPAN G.K.—See Ecolab Inc.; *U.S. Public*, pg. 716
NATIONAL RESPONSE CORPORATION (ANGOLA) LDA—See Republic Services, Inc.; *U.S. Public*, pg. 1788
NATIONAL RESPONSE CORPORATION (NRC) ENVIRON-

N.A.I.C.S. INDEX

562920 — MATERIALS RECOVERY ...

MENTAL SERVICES UAE L LC—See Republic Services, Inc.; *U.S. Public*, pg. 1788
NEO CORPORATION—See NRG Energy, Inc.; *U.S. Public*, pg. 1550
NORTH AMERICAN SITE DEVELOPERS, INC.—See Great Lakes Dredge & Dock Corporation; *U.S. Public*, pg. 962
NORTHSTAR CONTRACTING GROUP, INC.—See J.F. Lehman & Company, Inc.; *U.S. Private*, pg. 2164
NORTHSTAR CONTRACTING GROUP, INC.—See J.F. Lehman & Company, Inc.; *U.S. Private*, pg. 2164
NORTHSTAR DEMOLITION AND REMEDIATION, INC.—See J.F. Lehman & Company, Inc.; *U.S. Private*, pg. 2164
NORTHSTAR DEMOLITION AND REMEDIATION, INC.—See J.F. Lehman & Company, Inc.; *U.S. Private*, pg. 2164
NORTHSTAR DEMOLITION AND REMEDIATION, LP—See J.F. Lehman & Company, Inc.; *U.S. Private*, pg. 2164
NORTHSTAR DEMOLITION AND REMEDIATION, LP—See J.F. Lehman & Company, Inc.; *U.S. Private*, pg. 2164
NORTHSTAR DEMOLITION & REMEDIATION, INC.—See J.F. Lehman & Company, Inc.; *U.S. Private*, pg. 2164
NORTHSTAR DEMOLITION & REMEDIATION, LP—See J.F. Lehman & Company, Inc.; *U.S. Private*, pg. 2164
NRC ENVIRONMENTAL SERVICES (UK) LIMITED—See Republic Services, Inc.; *U.S. Public*, pg. 1788
ORM BERGOLD CHEMIE GMBH & CO.—See Clean Harbors, Inc.; *U.S. Public*, pg. 510
PERFORMANCE ABATEMENT SERVICES, INC.—See Performance Contracting Group; *U.S. Private*, pg. 3149
PINNACLE ENVIRONMENTAL CORPORATION; *U.S. Private*, pg. 3185
PRECISION ENVIRONMENTAL CO.; *U.S. Private*, pg. 3244
PRISM SPECTRUM HOLDINGS LLC—See The White Oak Group, Inc.; *U.S. Private*, pg. 4135
PSC ENVIRONMENTAL SERVICES, LLC—See Waste Management, Inc.; *U.S. Public*, pg. 2332
PSC INDUSTRIAL SERVICES, INC.—See Littlejohn & Co., LLC; *U.S. Private*, pg. 2471
RESOURCE ENVIRONMENTAL GROUP SERVICES, LLC—See Strategic Environmental & Energy Resources, Inc.; *U.S. Public*, pg. 1954
RESPONSE TEAM 1 LLC—See Franklin Resources, Inc.; *U.S. Public*, pg. 879
RESTEC CONTRACTORS INC.—See Anson Industries, Inc.; *U.S. Private*, pg. 286
RICK'S RESTORATIONS; *U.S. Private*, pg. 3431
SAFETY & ECOLOGY CORPORATION—See Perma-Fix Environmental Services, Inc.; *U.S. Public*, pg. 1676
SD - REKULTIVACE, A.S.—See CEZ, a.s.; *Int'l*, pg. 1428
SEALASKA ENVIRONMENTAL SERVICES, LLC—See Sealaska Corporation; *U.S. Public*, pg. 3585
SERVPRO OF BETHLEHEM; *U.S. Private*, pg. 3617
SEVENSON ENVIRONMENTAL SERVICES, INC.; *U.S. Private*, pg. 3619
SHANGHAI GREAT WATER ENVIRONMENTAL PROTECTION CO., LTD.—See China TianYF Holdings Group Limited; *Int'l*, pg. 1559
SIALTECH B.V.—See ABO-Group NV/SA; *Int'l*, pg. 66
SNYDER ENVIRONMENTAL, INC.; *U.S. Private*, pg. 3701
SPECPRO INC.—See Bristol Bay Native Corporation; *U.S. Private*, pg. 656
SPRAY SYSTEMS ARIZONA INC.; *U.S. Private*, pg. 3762
SSI SERVICES, LLC; *U.S. Private*, pg. 3769
SUPERIOR ENVIRONMENTAL SOLUTIONS, LLC—See Palladium Equity Partners, LLC; *U.S. Private*, pg. 3078
SWS ENVIRONMENTAL SERVICES; *U.S. Private*, pg. 3895
TBN ASSOCIATES INC.—See Thomas Rawlings Group Inc.; *U.S. Private*, pg. 4157
TERRA CONTRACTING SERVICES, LLC—See Great Lakes Dredge & Dock Corporation; *U.S. Public*, pg. 962
TERRATHERM, INC.—See TruArc Partners, L.P.; *U.S. Private*, pg. 4245
THERMATECH NORTHWEST, INC.—See Alliance Environmental Group, LLC; *U.S. Public*, pg. 182
TURNER MAINTENANCE CORPORATION—See Turner Industries Group, L.L.C.; *U.S. Private*, pg. 4261
TYREE ORGANIZATION, LTD; *U.S. Private*, pg. 4269
UNITEK INSULATION INC.—See Pacific Marine & Supply Co. Ltd. Inc.; *U.S. Private*, pg. 3068
USA ENVIRONMENT, L.P.—See J.F. Lehman & Company, Inc.; *U.S. Private*, pg. 2163
US ECOLOGY TAYLOR, INC.—See Republic Services, Inc.; *U.S. Public*, pg. 1788
VEIT & COMPANY, INC.; *U.S. Private*, pg. 4354
VENTURI RESTORATION - IRVINE—See Franklin Resources, Inc.; *U.S. Public*, pg. 879
VIETNAM GREAT WATER ENVIRONMENTAL PROTECTION CO., LTD.—See China TianYF Holdings Group Limited; *Int'l*, pg. 1559
YANKEE ENVIRONMENTAL SERVICES, LLC; *U.S. Private*, pg. 4585
YONKER ENVIRONMENTAL PROTECTION CO., LTD.—See Hunan Yonker Investment Group Co., Ltd.; *Int'l*, pg. 3534
YOUNG ENVIRONMENTAL CLEAN UP—See R.S. Young Excavating, Inc.; *U.S. Private*, pg. 3339

562920 — MATERIALS RECOVERY FACILITIES

A1 METAL RECYCLING LTD.—See Madison Dearborn Partners, LLC; *U.S. Private*, pg. 2541
ACN RECYCLING INDUSTRIES LLC—See America Chung Nam LLC; *U.S. Private*, pg. 220
ADVANTAGE METALS RECYCLING, LLC—See Nucor Corporation; *U.S. Public*, pg. 1554
AERC ACQUISITION CORPORATION—See Compass Diversified Holdings; *U.S. Public*, pg. 559
AERC RECYCLING SOLUTIONS—See Enviri Corporation; *U.S. Public*, pg. 780
AJ CATAGNUS INC.; *U.S. Private*, pg. 143
ALLAN COMPANY - ROLL DIVISION—See Allan Company; *U.S. Private*, pg. 174
ALL RECYCLING, INC.—See Metro Metals Northwest Inc.; *U.S. Private*, pg. 2686
ALT5 SIGMA CORPORATION; *U.S. Public*, pg. 85
ALUMEXX N.V.; *Int'l*, pg. 400
ALUMINUM SCRAP RECYCLE, L.L.C.—See Clayton, Dubilier & Rice, LLC; *U.S. Private*, pg. 921
AMERICAN COMMODITIES INC.; *U.S. Private*, pg. 227
AMPTHILL METAL COMPANY LTD.—See Madison Dearborn Partners, LLC; *U.S. Private*, pg. 2541
ANEL DOGA ENTEGRE GERI DONUSUM ENDUSTRI A.S.—See Anel Electrical Project Contracting Trade Inc.; *Int'l*, pg. 457
APOLLO WOOD RECOVERY INC.; *U.S. Private*, pg. 295
APOS A.D.; *Int'l*, pg. 519
ARCA CALIFORNIA—See ALT5 Sigma Corporation; *U.S. Public*, pg. 85
ARCA CANADA INC.—See ALT5 Sigma Corporation; *U.S. Public*, pg. 85
ARCA MINNESOTA—See ALT5 Sigma Corporation; *U.S. Public*, pg. 85
ASAHI INDUSTRIES CO., LTD. - SAITAMA PLANT—See Godo Steel, Ltd.; *Int'l*, pg. 3020
AUSTRIAN RECYCLING S.R.O.—See Heinzel Holding GmbH; *Int'l*, pg. 3325
AVALON HOLDINGS CORPORATION; *U.S. Public*, pg. 239
BAGUIO WASTE MANAGEMENT & RECYCLING LIMITED—See Baguio Green Group Limited; *Int'l*, pg. 799
BALCONES RECYCLING, INC. - DALLAS FACILITY—See Balcones Recycling, Inc.; *U.S. Private*, pg. 458
BALCONES RECYCLING, INC. - LITTLE ROCK FACILITY—See Balcones Recycling, Inc.; *U.S. Private*, pg. 458
BALCONES RECYCLING, INC.; *U.S. Private*, pg. 458
BASF METALS RECYCLING LTD.—See BASF SE; *Int'l*, pg. 880
BATLINER RECYCLING—See Pioneer Industries, Inc.; *U.S. Private*, pg. 3187
BATTERY RECYCLERS OF AMERICA, LLC; *U.S. Private*, pg. 488
BEFESA ALUMINIUM GERMANY GMBH—See Befesa S.A.; *Int'l*, pg. 940
BEFESA (CHINA) INVESTMENT CO., LTD.—See Befesa S.A.; *Int'l*, pg. 939
BEFESA MANAGEMENT SERVICES GMBH—See Befesa S.A.; *Int'l*, pg. 940
BEFESA MEDIO AMBIENTE, S.L.—See Befesa S.A.; *Int'l*, pg. 940
BEFESA SALT SLAGS, LTD.—See Befesa S.A.; *Int'l*, pg. 940
BEFESA S.A.; *Int'l*, pg. 939
BEFESA SCANDUST AB—See Befesa S.A.; *Int'l*, pg. 940
BEFESA SILVERMET ISKENDERUN CELIK TOZU GERI DONUSUMU, A.S.—See Befesa S.A.; *Int'l*, pg. 940
BEFESA STEEL SERVICES GMBH—See Befesa S.A.; *Int'l*, pg. 940
BEFESA VALERA, S.A.S.—See Befesa S.A.; *Int'l*, pg. 940
BEFESA ZINC COMERCIAL, S.A.—See Befesa S.A.; *Int'l*, pg. 940
BEFESA ZINC DUISBURG GMBH—See Befesa S.A.; *Int'l*, pg. 940
BEFESA ZINC FREIBERG GMBH & CO. KG—See Befesa S.A.; *Int'l*, pg. 940
BEFESA ZINC KOREA LTD.—See Befesa S.A.; *Int'l*, pg. 940
BEFESA ZINC OXIDO, S.A.—See Befesa S.A.; *Int'l*, pg. 940
BEST WAY OF INDIANA INC.; *U.S. Private*, pg. 543
BINDER+CO AG; *Int'l*, pg. 1033
BIOMAX ENVIRONMENTAL TECHNOLOGY (BEIJING) LIMITED—See Capital Environment Holdings Limited; *Int'l*, pg. 1310
BLT ENTERPRISES; *U.S. Private*, pg. 585
BLUESCOPE RECYCLING AND MATERIALS LLC—See BlueScope Steel Limited; *Int'l*, pg. 1073
BORO-WIDE RECYCLING CORP.; *U.S. Private*, pg. 619
BROTHER INDUSTRIES (SLOVAKIA) S.R.O.—See Brother Industries, Ltd.; *Int'l*, pg. 1197
BWXT GOVERNMENT GROUP, INC.—See BWX Technologies, Inc.; *U.S. Public*, pg. 413
CALGARY METAL RECYCLING INC.; *Int'l*, pg. 1263
CAN RECYCLING (S.A.) PTY LTD—See Coca-Cola Europacific Partners PLC; *Int'l*, pg. 1684
CANUSA HERSHMAN RECYCLING, LLC; *U.S. Private*, pg. 736
CARAUSTAR INDUSTRIES, INC. - CHARLOTTE RECYCLING PLANT—See Greif Inc.; *U.S. Public*, pg. 966
CARAUSTAR INDUSTRIES, INC. - CHATTANOOGA RECYCLING PLANT—See Greif Inc.; *U.S. Public*, pg. 966
CARBONLITE INDUSTRIES LLC—See HPC Industries LLC; *U.S. Private*, pg. 1996
CHANGYI ENERSAVE BIOMASS TO ENERGY CO., LTD.—See ecoWise Holdings Limited; *Int'l*, pg. 2300
CHIEMGAU RECYCLING GMBH—See Heinzel Holding GmbH; *Int'l*, pg. 3325
CHONGQING ECO-CTIG RUBBER TECHNOLOGY CO., LTD.—See ecoWise Holdings Limited; *Int'l*, pg. 2300
CLEAN EARTH DREDGING TECHNOLOGIES, LLC—See Enviri Corporation; *U.S. Public*, pg. 780
CLEAN HARBORS CHATTANOOGA, LLC—See Clean Harbors, Inc.; *U.S. Public*, pg. 509
CLEAN WATER LTD.—See OGM, Ltd.; *U.S. Private*, pg. 3003
CLEARCIRCLE ENVIRONMENTAL (NI) LTD—See Madison Dearborn Partners, LLC; *U.S. Private*, pg. 2541
CLEARCIRCLE METALS IRELAND LIMITED—See Madison Dearborn Partners, LLC; *U.S. Private*, pg. 2541
CLEARCIRCLE METALS (LIMERICK) LTD.—See Madison Dearborn Partners, LLC; *U.S. Private*, pg. 2541
CMC METAL RECYCLING (CAYCE)—See Commercial Metals Company; *U.S. Public*, pg. 546
CMC METAL RECYCLING (LEXINGTON)—See Commercial Metals Company; *U.S. Public*, pg. 546
CMC METAL RECYCLING (SEGUIN)—See Commercial Metals Company; *U.S. Public*, pg. 546
CMC RECYCLING—See Commercial Metals Company; *U.S. Public*, pg. 545
COMPAGNIE FRANCAISE ECO HUILE S.A.—See Aurea, S.A.; *Int'l*, pg. 707
CONSOLIDATED RESOURCE RECOVERY, INC.—See RFE Investment Partners; *U.S. Private*, pg. 3419
COOPER TANK & WELDING CORP; *U.S. Private*, pg. 1041
CORK METAL COMPANY LTD.—See Madison Dearborn Partners, LLC; *U.S. Private*, pg. 2541
COVANTA ABINGTON TRANSFER SOLUTIONS LLC—See EQT AB; *Int'l*, pg. 2473
COVANTA ALEXANDRIA/ARLINGTON, INC.—See EQT AB; *Int'l*, pg. 2473
COVANTA COMPANY OF SEMASS, LLC—See EQT AB; *Int'l*, pg. 2473
COVANTA ENERGY CORPORATION—See EQT AB; *Int'l*, pg. 2473
COVANTA HAVERHILL, INC.—See EQT AB; *Int'l*, pg. 2473
COVANTA HUNTSVILLE, INC.—See EQT AB; *Int'l*, pg. 2473
COVANTA KENT, INC.—See EQT AB; *Int'l*, pg. 2474
COVANTA LANCASTER, INC.—See EQT AB; *Int'l*, pg. 2474
COVANTA LONG BEACH RENEWABLE ENERGY CORP.—See EQT AB; *Int'l*, pg. 2474
COVANTA MARION, INC.—See EQT AB; *Int'l*, pg. 2474
COVANTA MONTGOMERY, INC.—See EQT AB; *Int'l*, pg. 2474
COVANTA NIAGARA, L.P.—See EQT AB; *Int'l*, pg. 2474
COVANTA PROJECTS OF WALLINGFORD, L.P.—See EQT AB; *Int'l*, pg. 2474
COVANTA RENEWABLE FUELS LLC—See EQT AB; *Int'l*, pg. 2474
COVANTA SOUTHEASTERN FLORIDA RENEWABLE ENERGY LLC—See EQT AB; *Int'l*, pg. 2474
COVANTA STANISLAUS, INC.—See EQT AB; *Int'l*, pg. 2474
COVANTA YORK RENEWABLE ENERGY LIMITED PARTNERSHIP—See EQT AB; *Int'l*, pg. 2474
CUMBERLAND RECYCLING CORPORATION OF SOUTH JERSEY; *U.S. Private*, pg. 1122
CUSTOM POLYMERS INC. - LATIN & SOUTH AMERICA—See Custom Polymers Inc.; *U.S. Private*, pg. 1129
CUSTOM POLYMERS INC.; *U.S. Private*, pg. 1129
DARPRO STORAGE SOLUTIONS LLC—See Darling Ingredients Inc.; *U.S. Public*, pg. 633
DATTO EUROPE LTD.—See Vista Equity Partners, LLC; *U.S. Private*, pg. 4396
DATTO, INC.—See Vista Equity Partners, LLC; *U.S. Private*, pg. 4396
DENSO SEIBI CO., LTD.—See Denso Corporation; *Int'l*, pg. 2030
DER GRUNE PUNKT - DUALES SYSTEM DEUTSCHLAND GMBH—See H.I.G. Capital, LLC; *U.S. Private*, pg. 1828
DEVENS RECYCLING CENTER, LLC—See Republic Services, Inc.; *U.S. Public*, pg. 1786
DIALOG ESECO SDN. BHD.—See Dialog Group Berhad; *Int'l*, pg. 2104
DORAVILLE RECYCLING PLANT—See Greif Inc.; *U.S. Public*, pg. 966
DS SMITH AMBALAJ A.S.—See DS Smith Plc; *Int'l*, pg. 2207
DS SMITH INOS PAPIR SERVIS D.O.O.—See DS Smith Plc; *Int'l*, pg. 2207
DS SMITH RECYCLING BENELUX B.V.—See DS Smith Plc; *Int'l*, pg. 2209
DS SMITH RECYCLING DEUTSCHLAND GMBH—See DS Smith Plc; *Int'l*, pg. 2209

562920 — MATERIALS RECOVERY ...

DS SMITH RECYCLING ITALIA SRL—See DS Smith Plc; *Int'l*, pg. 2209
DS SMITH RECYCLING SPAIN S.A.—See DS Smith Plc; *Int'l*, pg. 2209
DS SMITH UNIJAPAPIR CROATIA D.O.O.—See DS Smith Plc; *Int'l*, pg. 2209
DURO FELGUERA PLANTAS INDUSTRIALES, S.A.U.—See Duro Felguera, S.A.; *Int'l*, pg. 2228
EAGLE METAL PROCESSING & RECYCLING INC—See Eagle Manufacturing Group; *U.S. Private*, pg. 1309
EAST TENNESSEE MATERIALS AND ENERGY CORPORATION—See Perma-Fix Environmental Services, Inc.; *U.S. Public*, pg. 1676
ECO CENTRAL LTD—See Christchurch City Holdings Ltd.; *Int'l*, pg. 1586
ECONECOL INC.—See Envipro Holdings Inc.; *Int'l*, pg. 2454
ECOWISE HOLDINGS LIMITED - CO-GEN BIOMASS POWER PLANT—See ecoWise Holdings Limited; *Int'l*, pg. 2300
ECOWISE MARINA POWER PTE. LTD.—See ecoWise Holdings Limited; *Int'l*, pg. 2300
EFLUX SINGAPORE PTE LTD—See Hyflux Ltd; *Int'l*, pg. 3548
ELG CANADA, INC.—See Franz Haniel & Cie. GmbH; *Int'l*, pg. 2762
ELG CARBON FIBRE LTD.—See Franz Haniel & Cie. GmbH; *Int'l*, pg. 2762
ELG HANIEL METALS LTD—See Franz Haniel & Cie. GmbH; *Int'l*, pg. 2763
ELG INDIA PRIVATE LIMITED—See Franz Haniel & Cie. GmbH; *Int'l*, pg. 2763
ELG LEGIMA SPOL. S.R.O.—See Franz Haniel & Cie. GmbH; *Int'l*, pg. 2763
ELG METALS, INC.—See Franz Haniel & Cie. GmbH; *Int'l*, pg. 2763
ELG METALS, INC.—See Franz Haniel & Cie. GmbH; *Int'l*, pg. 2763
ELG METALS, INC. - SOUTHERN DIVISION—See Franz Haniel & Cie. GmbH; *Int'l*, pg. 2763
ELG METALS, INC. - WEST COAST DIVISION—See Franz Haniel & Cie. GmbH; *Int'l*, pg. 2763
ELG METALS TAIWAN CORPORATION—See Franz Haniel & Cie. GmbH; *Int'l*, pg. 2763
ELG RECYCLING PROCESSORS PTY LTD—See Franz Haniel & Cie. GmbH; *Int'l*, pg. 2763
ELG UTICA ALLOYS (HARTFORD), INC.—See Franz Haniel & Cie. GmbH; *Int'l*, pg. 2763
ELG UTICA ALLOYS LTD—See Franz Haniel & Cie. GmbH; *Int'l*, pg. 2763
ELLSIN ENVIRONMENTAL LTD. - ELLSIN PLANT 1—See Environmental Waste International Inc.; *Int'l*, pg. 2455
ELLSIN ENVIRONMENTAL LTD.—See Environmental Waste International Inc.; *Int'l*, pg. 2455
EL PASO IRON & METAL I, LTD.—See W. Silver Recycling, Inc.; *U.S. Private*, pg. 4418
EMPIRE RECYCLING CORP.; *U.S. Private*, pg. 1385
ENERGY ANSWERS INTERNATIONAL, INC.; *U.S. Private*, pg. 1393
ENVIPCO AUTOMATEN GMBH—See Envipco Holding N.V.; *Int'l*, pg. 2453
ENVIRO-METALS PTE LTD—See Enviro-Hub Holdings Ltd.; *Int'l*, pg. 2454
ENVIRONMENTAL RECYCLING TECHNOLOGIES; *U.S. Private*, pg. 1408
ENVIROSAFE SERVICES OF OHIO, INC.—See J.F. Lehman & Company, Inc.; *U.S. Private*, pg. 2163
EQ RESOURCE RECOVERY, INC.—See Republic Services, Inc.; *U.S. Public*, pg. 1788
E.R. JAPAN CORPORATION—See EDION Corporation; *Int'l*, pg. 2310
E-WASTE SYSTEMS, INC.; *U.S. Private*, pg. 1303
FACILITIES RESOURCE GROUP INC.; *U.S. Private*, pg. 1459
FAIRCHILD EQUIPMENT, INC.; *U.S. Private*, pg. 1462
FAIRWAY SALVAGE INC.—See Sims Limited; *U.S. Public*, pg. 1883
FCC RECYCLING (UK) LIMITED—See Fomento de Construccions y Contratas, S.A.; *Int'l*, pg. 2723
FDK ECOTEC CO., LTD.—See Fujitsu Limited; *Int'l*, pg. 2832
FERROCART S.R.L.—See ACEA S.p.A.; *Int'l*, pg. 95
FERROUS PROCESSING & TRADING CO. - FPT FT LAUDERDALE/SUNRISE RECYCLING FACILITY—See Soave Enterprises, LLC; *U.S. Private*, pg. 3702
FERROUS PROCESSING & TRADING CO. - FPT WYOMING AVE. FACILITY—See Soave Enterprises, LLC; *U.S. Private*, pg. 3702
FIELDING CHEMICAL TECHNOLOGIES INC.—See BC Partners LLP; *Int'l*, pg. 923
FPT CANTON, LLC—See Soave Enterprises, LLC; *U.S. Private*, pg. 3702
FPT CLEVELAND, LLC—See Soave Enterprises, LLC; *U.S. Private*, pg. 3702
FPT FLORIDA, LLC—See Cleveland-Cliffs, Inc.; *U.S. Public*, pg. 514
FPT PONTIAC DIVISION, LLC—See Soave Enterprises, LLC; *U.S. Private*, pg. 3702

FPT SCHLAFER DIVISION, LLC—See Soave Enterprises, LLC; *U.S. Private*, pg. 3702
FRIEDMAN RECYCLING COMPANY; *U.S. Private*, pg. 1611
GALWAY METAL COMPANY LTD.—See Madison Dearborn Partners, LLC; *U.S. Private*, pg. 2541
GEOCYCLE PTY. LTD.—See Heidelberg Materials AG; *Int'l*, pg. 3311
GEOCYCLE PTY. LTD.—See Holcim Ltd.; *Int'l*, pg. 3446
GERSHOW RECYCLING CORPORATION; *U.S. Private*, pg. 1688
GFL ENVIRONMENTAL INC. - MATERIAL RECYCLING FACILITY—See BC Partners LLP; *Int'l*, pg. 924
GFL ENVIRONMENTAL INC. - SAULT STE MARIE FACILITY—See BC Partners LLP; *Int'l*, pg. 924
GLASS RECYCLERS INC.; *U.S. Private*, pg. 1706
GLENCORE RECYCLING INC.—See Glencore plc; *Int'l*, pg. 2990
GLENCORE RECYCLING LLC—See Glencore plc; *Int'l*, pg. 2990
GLENDALE IRON & METAL CO.; *U.S. Private*, pg. 1710
GLOBAL ATOMIC CORPORATION; *Int'l*, pg. 2993
GOLDEN STATE METALS, INC.—See Sims Limited; *U.S. Public*, pg. 1883
GOPHER RESOURCE LLC—See Energy Capital Partners Management, LP; *U.S. Private*, pg. 1394
GRANDE PRAIRIE SALVAGE LTD—See A. B. C. Recycling Ltd; *Int'l*, pg. 21
GREAT VALLEY RECYCLING INC.—See J. P. Mascaro & Sons; *U.S. Private*, pg. 2156
GREEN AMERICA RECYCLING, LLC—See Summit Materials, Inc.; *U.S. Public*, pg. 1959
GREEN ARROWS CENTRAL CO., LTD.—See Daiseki Eco. Solution Co., Ltd.; *Int'l*, pg. 1941
GREEN ARROWS KANSAI CO., LTD.—See Daiei Kankyo Co., Ltd.; *Int'l*, pg. 1924
GREENSTAR ALLENTOWN, LLC—See Waste Management, Inc.; *U.S. Public*, pg. 2331
GREENSTAR MANAGED SERVICES - CONNECTICUT, LLC—See Waste Management, Inc.; *U.S. Public*, pg. 2331
GREENSTAR PATERSON, LLC—See Waste Management, Inc.; *U.S. Public*, pg. 2331
GREENTEC INTERNATIONAL INC.; *Int'l*, pg. 3076
GREEN VISION RECYCLING LIMITED—See Downer EDI Limited; *Int'l*, pg. 2186
GREYMART METAL COMPANY INC.; *U.S. Private*, pg. 1784
GRMEC A.D.; *Int'l*, pg. 3087
GULF RUBBER (MALAYSIA) SDN BHD—See ecoWise Holdings Limited; *Int'l*, pg. 2300
HAZER GROUP LIMITED; *Int'l*, pg. 3295
HKS SCRAP METALS B.V.—See Alfa Acciai SpA; *Int'l*, pg. 307
HKS SCRAP METALS B.V.—See CRONIMET Holding GmbH; *Int'l*, pg. 1855
HLS ELECTRONICS PTE LTD—See Enviro-Hub Holdings Ltd.; *Int'l*, pg. 2454
HORRY COUNTY SOLID WASTE AUTHORITY INC.; *U.S. Private*, pg. 1984
HUGO NEU RECYCLING, LLC—See Closed Loop Partners LLC; *U.S. Private*, pg. 946
HURON VALLEY STEEL CORP. - MAGNETICS DIVISION—See Huron Valley Steel Corp.; *U.S. Private*, pg. 2990
I.C.E. SERVICE GROUP, INC.; *U.S. Private*, pg. 2026
IHLE MAGYARORSZAG KFT.—See Compagnie Generale des Etablissements Michelin SCA; *Int'l*, pg. 1742
IHLE TIRES GMBH—See Compagnie Generale des Etablissements Michelin SCA; *Int'l*, pg. 1742
INLAND WATERS POLLUTION CONTROL INC.—See J.F. Lehman & Company, Inc.; *U.S. Private*, pg. 2163
INTERCON SOLUTIONS, INC.; *U.S. Private*, pg. 2109
THE INTERNATIONAL METALS RECLAMATION COMPANY, INC.—See Befesa S.A.; *Int'l*, pg. 939
INTERNATIONAL PAPER CO. - PHOENIX—See International Paper Company; *U.S. Public*, pg. 1156
JIANGXI DOWA ENVIRONMENTAL MANAGEMENT CO., LTD.—See Dowa Holdings Co., Ltd.; *Int'l*, pg. 2183
JOBU CO., LTD. - MATERIAL RECYCLING PLANT—See Godo Steel, Ltd.; *Int'l*, pg. 3020
JOSEPH SMITH & SONS, INC.—See European Metal Recycling Limited; *Int'l*, pg. 2556
JX NIPPON ENVIRONMENTAL SERVICES CO., LTD.—See ENEOS Holdings, Inc.; *Int'l*, pg. 2416
KEYWELL LLC - FALCONER PROCESSING FACILITY—See Keywell LLC; *U.S. Private*, pg. 2300
KEYWELL LLC - WEST MIFFLIN PROCESSING FACILITY—See Keywell LLC; *U.S. Private*, pg. 2300
KURODA RECYCLE CO., LTD.—See Envipro Holdings Inc.; *Int'l*, pg. 2454
LABNAC INC.—See Liston Brick Company of Corona Inc.; *U.S. Private*, pg. 2467
LIVING EARTH; *U.S. Private*, pg. 2474
LOOP PAPER RECYCLING INC.; *U.S. Private*, pg. 2494
LOUIS PADNOS IRON & METAL COMPANY - CADILLAC RECYCLING DIVISION—See Louis Padnos Iron & Metal Company; *U.S. Private*, pg. 2498
LOUIS PADNOS IRON & METAL COMPANY - HASTINGS DIVISION—See Louis Padnos Iron & Metal Company; *U.S. Private*, pg. 2498
LOUIS PADNOS IRON & METAL COMPANY - LANSING DIVISION—See Louis Padnos Iron & Metal Company; *U.S. Private*, pg. 2498
LOUIS PADNOS IRON & METAL COMPANY - PERE MARQUETTE DIVISION—See Louis Padnos Iron & Metal Company; *U.S. Private*, pg. 2498
MACOY RESOURCE CORPORATION—See Sims Limited; *U.S. Public*, pg. 1883
MELTEC IWAKI CO., LTD.—See Dowa Holdings Co., Ltd.; *Int'l*, pg. 2184
METAL MANAGEMENT NORTHEAST, INC.—See Sims Limited; *U.S. Public*, pg. 1883
METROPOLITAN PAPER RECYCLING INC.; *U.S. Private*, pg. 2689
MID-CITY IRON & METAL CORPORATION—See Sims Limited; *U.S. Public*, pg. 1883
MINERALPLUS GMBH—See Asterion Industrial Partners SGEIC SA; *Int'l*, pg. 654
MIREC B.V.—See Sims Limited; *U.S. Public*, pg. 1884
MOUNT KISCO TRANSFER STATION, INC.—See EQT AB; *Int'l*, pg. 2474
NEWELL RECYCLING OF ATLANTA, LLC—See Newell Recycling Southeast, LLC; *U.S. Private*, pg. 2914
NLR, INC.; *U.S. Private*, pg. 2931
ONE51 ES METALS (NORTH) LTD—See Madison Dearborn Partners, LLC; *U.S. Private*, pg. 2541
ONE MORE TIME INC.—See Baker Commodities, Inc.; *U.S. Private*, pg. 455
PACIFIC COAST RECYCLING, LLC—See Sims Limited; *U.S. Public*, pg. 1883
PET RECYCLING TEAM GMBH—See Alpla-Werke Alwin Lehner GmbH & Co. KG; *Int'l*, pg. 374
PHILLIPS SERVICES, LLC; *U.S. Private*, pg. 3171
PIONEER PAPER STOCK COMPANY—See Pioneer Industries, Inc.; *U.S. Private*, pg. 3187
PIONEER PAPER STOCK CO. OF TEXAS, INC.—See Pioneer Industries, Inc.; *U.S. Private*, pg. 3187
PLANET AID, INC.; *U.S. Private*, pg. 3195
PLASTIC RECYCLING, INC.; *U.S. Private*, pg. 3199
POTENTIAL INDUSTRIES INC.; *U.S. Private*, pg. 3235
PURFER SAS—See Derichebourg S.A.; *Int'l*, pg. 2041
RADIUS RECYCLING, INC.; *U.S. Public*, pg. 1760
R-B RECYCLING INC.—See Carlisle Companies Incorporated; *U.S. Public*, pg. 436
REPARCO NIJMEGEN B.V.—See H2 Equity Partners B.V.; *Int'l*, pg. 3199
REPARCO RANDSTAD B.V.—See H2 Equity Partners B.V.; *Int'l*, pg. 3199
REPARCO RENKUM B.V.—See H2 Equity Partners B.V.; *Int'l*, pg. 3199
RESOURCE MANAGEMENT ENTERPRISES INC.; *U.S. Private*, pg. 3407
RESOURCE MANAGEMENT ROCKFORD LLC—See Resource Management Enterprises Inc.; *U.S. Private*, pg. 3407
RICHMOND STEEL RECYCLING LIMITED—See Sims Limited; *U.S. Public*, pg. 1883
ROLL-GOM S.A.—See Aurea, S.A.; *Int'l*, pg. 707
ROUND2 INC.—See Avnet, Inc.; *U.S. Public*, pg. 254
RULO N.V.—See Aurea, S.A.; *Int'l*, pg. 707
RUMPKE RECYCLING—See Rumpke Consolidated Companies, Inc.; *U.S. Private*, pg. 3503
SAFETY-KLEEN ENVIROSYSTEMS CO.—See Clean Harbors, Inc.; *U.S. Public*, pg. 510
SAS CARBIOLICE—See Carbios SACA; *Int'l*, pg. 1320
SCHUPAN & SONS, INC.; *U.S. Private*, pg. 3571
SCI LCDL—See Groupe Seche SAS; *Int'l*, pg. 3110
SECHE ECO-INDUSTRIES SAS—See Groupe Seche SAS; *Int'l*, pg. 3110
SELF SERVE AUTO DISMANTLERS—See Sims Limited; *U.S. Public*, pg. 1883
SEM TREDI S.A. DE C.V.—See Groupe Seche SAS; *Int'l*, pg. 3110
SILOAM SPRINGS METAL RECYCLING INC.—See Yaffe Iron & Metal Company Inc.; *U.S. Private*, pg. 4584
SIMS ALUMINUM PTY. LIMITED—See Sims Limited; *U.S. Public*, pg. 1884
SIMS E-RECYCLING PTY. LTD.—See Sims Limited; *U.S. Public*, pg. 1884
SIMS METAL MANAGEMENT - STRATFORD-UPON-AVON—See Sims Limited; *U.S. Public*, pg. 1884
SIMS PACIFIC METALS LIMITED—See Sims Limited; *U.S. Public*, pg. 1884
SIMS RECYCLING SOLUTIONS - CHICAGO REFINING—See Sims Limited; *U.S. Public*, pg. 1884
SIMS RECYCLING SOLUTIONS, INC.—See Sims Limited; *U.S. Public*, pg. 1884
SIMS RECYCLING SOLUTIONS NV—See Sims Limited; *U.S. Public*, pg. 1884
SIMS RECYCLING SOLUTIONS UK LTD.—See Sims Limited; *U.S. Public*, pg. 1884
SIMS TYRECYCLE PTY. LTD.—See Sims Limited; *U.S. Public*, pg. 1884
SOREPLA INDUSTRIE S.A.—See Envipco Holding N.V.; *Int'l*, pg. 2453
SOUTHERN RECYCLING, LLC—See European Metal Re-

N.A.I.C.S. INDEX

cycling Limited; *Int'l*, pg. 2556
SSX, L.C.—See European Metal Recycling Limited; *Int'l*, pg. 2557
STAINLESS STEEL MIDWEST LLC; *U.S. Private*, pg. 3776
STRATEGIC MATERIALS, INC.—See Littlejohn & Co., LLC; *U.S. Private*, pg. 2471
STS ELECTRONICS RECYCLING, INC.; *U.S. Private*, pg. 3842
SUNRICH TYRE & AUTO PRODUCTS SDN BHD—See ecoWise Holdings Limited; *Int'l*, pg. 2300
SYNECO INC.—See Envipro Holdings Inc.; *Int'l*, pg. 2454
TALCO PLASTICS INC.; *U.S. Private*, pg. 3925
TERRAKOMP GMBH—See E.ON SE; *Int'l*, pg. 2259
TERRA RECYCLING SP. Z O.O.SP.K.—See Elemental Holding S.A.; *Int'l*, pg. 2358
TRG BERRYVILLE LLC—See Alter Trading Corporation; *U.S. Private*, pg. 207
TRG HARRISON, LLC—See Alter Trading Corporation; *U.S. Private*, pg. 207
TRG JONESBORO, LLC—See Alter Trading Corporation; *U.S. Private*, pg. 207
TRG ROGERS, LLC—See Alter Trading Corporation; *U.S. Private*, pg. 207
UMICORE ELECTRICAL MATERIALS USA INC.—See Trent Capital Partners, LLC; *U.S. Private*, pg. 4218
UNITED OIL RECOVERY, INC.—See Grupo Tradebe Medioambiente S.L.; *Int'l*, pg. 3138
UNIVERSAL RECYCLING TECHNOLOGIES, LLC—See Hendricks Holding Company, Inc.; *U.S. Private*, pg. 1915
UWHARRIE ENVIRONMENTAL—See Republic Services, Inc.; *U.S. Public*, pg. 1788
VALLS QUIMICA S.A.—See Groupe Seche SAS; *Int'l*, pg. 3111
VANTEC EUROPE LIMITED—See KKR & Co. Inc.; *U.S. Public*, pg. 1259
VIDEO INJECTION-INSITUFORM SAS—See New Mountain Capital, LLC; *U.S. Private*, pg. 2900
VIRIDOR POLYMER RECYCLING LIMITED—See KKR & Co. Inc.; *U.S. Public*, pg. 1266
VIRIDOR RESOURCE MANAGEMENT LIMITED—See KKR & Co. Inc.; *U.S. Public*, pg. 1266
VISTA INTERNATIONAL TECHNOLOGIES, INC.; *U.S. Private*, pg. 4403
VORTEX RECYCLING; *U.S. Private*, pg. 4413
WASTE MANAGEMENT OF COLORADO - DENVER-48TH AVENUE—See Waste Management, Inc.; *U.S. Public*, pg. 2333
WESTROCK RKT CO. - JACKSONVILLE RECYCLING CENTER—See WestRock Company; *U.S. Public*, pg. 2363
WISE RECYCLING LLC; *U.S. Private*, pg. 4550
WM RECYCLE AMERICA, LLC - PICO RIVERA—See Waste Management, Inc.; *U.S. Public*, pg. 2333
WM RECYCLE AMERICA, LLC—See Waste Management, Inc.; *U.S. Public*, pg. 2333
WM RECYCLE AMERICA, LLC - (SPRINGFIELD) ECYCLING SERVICES—See Waste Management, Inc.; *U.S. Public*, pg. 2333
WM RECYCLE AMERICA, LLC - SPRINGFIELD—See Waste Management, Inc.; *U.S. Public*, pg. 2333
WRR ENVIRONMENTAL SERVICES CO., INC.—See Caribou Corporation; *U.S. Private*, pg. 761
W. SILVER RECYCLING, INC. - DONNA FACILITY—See W. Silver Recycling, Inc.; *U.S. Private*, pg. 4418
W. SILVER RECYCLING, INC.; *U.S. Private*, pg. 4418
W. SILVER RECYCLING OF NEW MEXICO, INC.—See W. Silver Recycling, Inc.; *U.S. Private*, pg. 4418
ZALEV BROTHERS COMPANY—See Soave Enterprises, LLC; *U.S. Private*, pg. 3702

562991 — SEPTIC TANK AND RELATED SERVICES

ACE PIPE CLEANING, INC.—See Carylon Corporation; *U.S. Private*, pg. 777
ACTION CARTING ENVIRONMENTAL SERVICES, INC.—See Interstate Waste Services, Inc.; *U.S. Private*, pg. 2126
ANDY GUMP INC.; *U.S. Private*, pg. 281
CARYLON CORPORATION; *U.S. Private*, pg. 777
CHEM CAN SERVICES, INC.; *U.S. Private*, pg. 870
K2 INDUSTRIAL SERVICES, INC.—See Arctic Slope Regional Corporation; *U.S. Private*, pg. 316
K & D INDUSTRIAL SERVICES INC.; *U.S. Private*, pg. 2249
MOBILE DREDGING & PUMPING CO.—See Carylon Corporation; *U.S. Private*, pg. 777
MODERN PRECAST CONCRETE; *U.S. Private*, pg. 2762
NATIONAL PLANT SERVICES INC.—See Carylon Corporation; *U.S. Private*, pg. 777
ODESCO INDUSTRIAL SERVICES, INC.—See Carylon Corporation; *U.S. Private*, pg. 777
PARK ENERGY SERVICES, LLC—See Rock Hill Capital Group, LLC; *U.S. Private*, pg. 3464
ROBINSON PIPE CLEANING CO.—See Carylon Corporation; *U.S. Private*, pg. 777
ROBINSON PIPE SERVICES, INC.—See Carylon Corporation; *U.S. Private*, pg. 777

RUSSELL-WARNER INC.; *U.S. Private*, pg. 3507
SES PROPERTIES OF STANLEY, INC.—See Gryphon Investors, LLC; *U.S. Private*, pg. 1800
SOUTHERN CHAMPION CONSTRUCTION; *U.S. Private*, pg. 3730
UNITED SITE SERVICES, INC.—See Platinum Equity, LLC; *U.S. Private*, pg. 3209
VIDEO INDUSTRIAL SERVICE INC.—See Carylon Corporation; *U.S. Private*, pg. 777

562998 — ALL OTHER MISCELLANEOUS WASTE MANAGEMENT SERVICES

2PI SOLUTIONS; *U.S. Private*, pg. 7
ABFALLWIRTSCHAFTSZENTRUM MOSTVIERTEL GMBH—See Fomento de Construcciones y Contratas, S.A.; *Int'l*, pg. 2722
ACORN ENVIRONMENTAL SYSTEMS LIMITED—See Bord na Mona Plc; *Int'l*, pg. 1113
ACS, SERVICIOS COMUNICACIONES Y ENERGIA, S.L.—See ACS, Actividades de Construccion y Servicios, S.A.; *Int'l*, pg. 110
A&D ENVIRONMENTAL SERVICES, INC.—See Ross Consolidated Corp.; *U.S. Private*, pg. 3485
ADOLF ELLERMANN GMBH—See Georgsmarienhutte Holding GmbH; *Int'l*, pg. 2941
ADVANCED CHEMICAL TRANSPORT, INC.; *U.S. Private*, pg. 88
ADVANCED DISPOSAL SERVICES BLACKFOOT LANDFILL, INC.—See Waste Management, Inc.; *U.S. Public*, pg. 2330
ADVANCED DISPOSAL SERVICES BLUE RIDGE LANDFILL, INC.—See Waste Management, Inc.; *U.S. Public*, pg. 2330
ADVANCED DISPOSAL SERVICES CEDAR HILL LANDFILL, INC.—See Waste Management, Inc.; *U.S. Public*, pg. 2330
ADVANCED DISPOSAL SERVICES CRANBERRY CREEK LANDFILL, LLC—See Waste Management, Inc.; *U.S. Public*, pg. 2330
ADVANCED DISPOSAL SERVICES CYPRESS ACRES LANDFILL, INC.—See Waste Management, Inc.; *U.S. Public*, pg. 2330
ADVANCED DISPOSAL SERVICES EVERGREEN LANDFILL, INC.—See Waste Management, Inc.; *U.S. Public*, pg. 2330
ADVANCED DISPOSAL SERVICES JACKSON, LLC—See Waste Management, Inc.; *U.S. Public*, pg. 2330
ADVANCED DISPOSAL SERVICES LANCASTER LANDFILL, INC.—See Waste Management, Inc.; *U.S. Public*, pg. 2330
ADVANCED DISPOSAL SERVICES LITHONIA TRANSFER STATION, LLC—See Waste Management, Inc.; *U.S. Public*, pg. 2330
ADVANCED DISPOSAL SERVICES MACON, LLC—See Waste Management, Inc.; *U.S. Public*, pg. 2330
ADVANCED DISPOSAL SERVICES MAPLE HILL LANDFILL, INC.—See Waste Management, Inc.; *U.S. Public*, pg. 2330
ADVANCED DISPOSAL SERVICES MIDDLE GEORGIA, LLC—See Waste Management, Inc.; *U.S. Public*, pg. 2330
ADVANCED DISPOSAL SERVICES MOREHEAD LANDFILL, INC.—See Waste Management, Inc.; *U.S. Public*, pg. 2330
ADVANCED DISPOSAL SERVICES NORTH GEORGIA, LLC—See Waste Management, Inc.; *U.S. Public*, pg. 2330
ADVANCED DISPOSAL SERVICES ORCHARD HILLS LANDFILL, INC.—See Waste Management, Inc.; *U.S. Public*, pg. 2330
ADVANCED DISPOSAL SERVICES SELMA TRANSFER STATION, LLC—See Waste Management, Inc.; *U.S. Public*, pg. 2330
ADVANCED DISPOSAL SERVICES STAR RIDGE LANDFILL, INC.—See Waste Management, Inc.; *U.S. Public*, pg. 2330
ADVANCED DISPOSAL SERVICES VALLEY VIEW LANDFILL, INC.—See Waste Management, Inc.; *U.S. Public*, pg. 2330
AES ENVIRONMENTAL LLC—See Enviri Corporation; *U.S. Public*, pg. 780
AES PORTLAOISE—See Bord na Mona Plc; *Int'l*, pg. 1113
AES TULLAMORE—See Bord na Mona Plc; *Int'l*, pg. 1113
AFFILIATED WASTEWATER ENVIRONMENTAL SERVICES, LLC—See The Pritzker Group - Chicago, LLC; *U.S. Private*, pg. 4100
AFM RECYCLAGE S.A.—See Derichebourg S.A.; *Int'l*, pg. 2041
AFM TRANSPORT S.A.—See Derichebourg S.A.; *Int'l*, pg. 2041
AGC SUNSMILE, INC.—See AGC Inc.; *Int'l*, pg. 203
ALBA BERLIN GMBH—See Alba SE; *Int'l*, pg. 292
ALBA BRAUNSCHWEIG GMBH—See Alba SE; *Int'l*, pg. 292
ALBA CHINA RECYCLING SOLUTIONS LTD.—See Alba SE; *Int'l*, pg. 292
ALBA COTTBUS GMBH—See Alba SE; *Int'l*, pg. 292

ALBA DOLNY SLASK SP. Z O.O.—See Alba SE; *Int'l*, pg. 292
ALBA EKOPLUS SP. Z O.O.—See Alba SE; *Int'l*, pg. 292
ALBA FERROUS TRADING GMBH—See Alba SE; *Int'l*, pg. 292
ALBA INTEGRATED WASTE SOLUTIONS (HONG KONG) LIMITED—See Alba SE; *Int'l*, pg. 292
ALBA LOGISTIK GMBH—See Alba SE; *Int'l*, pg. 292
ALBA METALL NORD GMBH—See Alba SE; *Int'l*, pg. 292
ALBA METALL SUD FRANKEN GMBH—See Alba SE; *Int'l*, pg. 292
ALBA METALL SUD RHEIN-MAIN GMBH—See Alba SE; *Int'l*, pg. 292
ALBA MPGK SP. Z O.O.—See Alba SE; *Int'l*, pg. 292
ALBA MPO SP. Z O.O.—See Alba SE; *Int'l*, pg. 292
ALBA NIEDERSACHSEN-ANHALT GMBH—See Alba SE; *Int'l*, pg. 292
ALBA NORDBADEN GMBH—See Alba SE; *Int'l*, pg. 292
ALBA NORD GMBH—See Alba SE; *Int'l*, pg. 292
ALBA PGK SP. Z O.O.—See Alba SE; *Int'l*, pg. 292
ALBA POLUDNIE POLSKA SP. Z O.O.—See Alba SE; *Int'l*, pg. 292
ALBA PTS SP. Z O.O.—See Alba SE; *Int'l*, pg. 292
ALBA RISING GREEN FUEL (HONG KONG) LTD.—See Alba SE; *Int'l*, pg. 293
ALBA SACHSEN GMBH—See Alba SE; *Int'l*, pg. 293
ALBA SUD GMBH & CO. KG—See Alba SE; *Int'l*, pg. 293
ALBA SUPPLY CHAIN MANAGEMENT GMBH—See Alba SE; *Int'l*, pg. 293
ALBA TAV BETRIEBS GMBH—See Alba SE; *Int'l*, pg. 293
ALBA UCKERMARK GMBH—See Alba SE; *Int'l*, pg. 293
ALBA UTILITY SCRAP SOLUTIONS GMBH—See Alba SE; *Int'l*, pg. 293
ALBA WERTSTOFFMANAGEMENT GMBH—See Alba SE; *Int'l*, pg. 293
ALBA W&H SMART CITY PTE. LTD.—See Alba SE; *Int'l*, pg. 293
ALBA ZENICA D.O.O.—See Alba SE; *Int'l*, pg. 293
ALEX FRASER PTY LIMITED—See Heidelberg Materials AG; *Int'l*, pg. 3311
ALL ABFALL-LOGISTIK LEIPZIG GMBH—See Alba SE; *Int'l*, pg. 293
ALLIED WASTE SERVICES OF PAGE, INC.—See Republic Services, Inc.; *U.S. Public*, pg. 1785
ALLSTATE POWER VAC, INC.—See Republic Services, Inc.; *U.S. Public*, pg. 1787
ANTONY WASTE HANDLING CELL LIMITED; *Int'l*, pg. 485
AON INSURANCE MANAGERS (GUERNSEY) LTD.—See Aon plc; *Int'l*, pg. 494
APOTEFROTIRAS SA—See ELLAKTOR S.A.; *Int'l*, pg. 2364
AQUA-PURE VENTURES INC.; *Int'l*, pg. 527
.A.S.A. ABFALL SERVICE NEUNKIRCHEN GMBH—See Fomento de Construcciones y Contratas, S.A.; *Int'l*, pg. 2722
ASAHIKOUSEKI CO., LTD.—See Daiei Kankyo Co., Ltd.; *Int'l*, pg. 1924
A.S.A. HODMEZOVASARHELY KOZTLSZTASAGL KFT—See Fomento de Construcciones y Contratas, S.A.; *Int'l*, pg. 2722
ASHIYA JOSUI CO., LTD.—See Daiei Kankyo Co., Ltd.; *Int'l*, pg. 1924
ASMJ S.R.O.—See Fomento de Construcciones y Contratas, S.A.; *Int'l*, pg. 2722
ASSOCIATED OILS PTY LTD—See Cleanaway Waste Management Limited; *Int'l*, pg. 1655
ATAKA ASANO CO., LTD.—See Hitachi Zosen Corporation; *Int'l*, pg. 3410
ATLANTIC COAST FIBERS, INC.—See Casella Waste Systems, Inc.; *U.S. Public*, pg. 445
ATO ABFALLWIRTSCHAFT TORGAU-OSCHATZ GMBH—See Alba SE; *Int'l*, pg. 293
AUSTRALIAN POLLUTION ENGINEERING PTY LTD—See Cleanaway Waste Management Limited; *Int'l*, pg. 1654
AUSTRALIAN RESOURCE RECOVERY PTY LTD—See Cleanaway Waste Management Limited; *Int'l*, pg. 1655
AUSTRALIAN TERMINAL SERVICES PTY LTD—See Cleanaway Waste Management Limited; *Int'l*, pg. 1654
AVR-AFVALVERWERKING B.V.—See CK Hutchison Holdings Limited; *Int'l*, pg. 1636
AWISTA GESELLSCHAFT FUR ABFALLWIRTSCHAFT UND STADTREINIGUNG MBH—See EnBW Energie Baden-Wurttemberg AG; *Int'l*, pg. 2397
AWISTA LOGISTIK GMBH—See EnBW Energie Baden-Wurttemberg AG; *Int'l*, pg. 2398
AWS ENTSORGUNG GMBH—See BayWa AG; *Int'l*, pg. 915
AWU ABFALLWIRTSCHAFTS-UNION OBERHAVEL GMBH—See Alba SE; *Int'l*, pg. 293
AWU LOGISTIK OPR GMBH—See Alba SE; *Int'l*, pg. 293
AWU OSTPRIGNITZ-RUPPIN GMBH—See Alba SE; *Int'l*, pg. 293
AYR ENVIRONMENTAL SERVICES LIMITED—See CK Hutchison Holdings Limited; *Int'l*, pg. 1637
BANGPOO ENVIRONMENTAL COMPLEX LTD.—See Dowa Holdings Co., Ltd.; *Int'l*, pg. 2182
BARTIN RECYCLING GROUP S.A.S.—See Derichebourg S.A.; *Int'l*, pg. 2041
BAXTER BUSINESS PTY LTD—See Cleanaway Waste

562998 — ALL OTHER MISCELLAN...

Management Limited; *Int'l*, pg. 1654
BAXTER RECYCLERS PTY LTD—See Cleanaway Waste Management Limited; *Int'l*, pg. 1654
BEIJING ENTERPRISES URBAN RESOURCES GROUP LIMITED; *Int'l*, pg. 950
BETTER WORLD GREEN PUBLIC COMPANY LIMITED; *Int'l*, pg. 1003
BEYOND MEDICAL TECHNOLOGIES INC.; *Int'l*, pg. 1005
BIFFA WASTE SERVICES LIMITED—See Biffa Group Limited; *Int'l*, pg. 1020
BIO-NOMIC SERVICES, INC.—See Carylon Corporation; *U.S. Private*, pg. 777
BOLTON SARL—See Derichebourg S.A.; *Int'l*, pg. 2042
BORD NA MONA ENVIRONMENTAL LIMITED—See Bord na Mona Plc; *Int'l*, pg. 1113
BOSKALIS ENVIRONMENTAL B.V.—See HAL Trust N.V.; *Int'l*, pg. 3225
BOSKALIS TRANSPORT B.V.—See HAL Trust N.V.; *Int'l*, pg. 3225
BOUSTEAD MAXITHERM ENERGY PTE LTD—See Boustead Singapore Limited; *Int'l*, pg. 1120
BOUSTEAD SALCON WATER SOLUTIONS PTE LTD—See Boustead Singapore Limited; *Int'l*, pg. 1120
BYWATERS LTD; *Int'l*, pg. 1237
CANNON SLINE INDUSTRIAL, INC. - HOPEWELL DIVISION—See The Halifax Group LLC; *U.S. Private*, pg. 4042
CANNON SLINE INDUSTRIAL, INC. - MID ATLANTIC DIVISION—See The Halifax Group LLC; *U.S. Private*, pg. 4042
CANVEST ENVIRONMENTAL PROTECTION GROUP COMPANY LIMITED; *Int'l*, pg. 1300
CARBIOS SACA; *Int'l*, pg. 1320
CARTERSVILLE TRANSFER STATION, LLC—See Waste Management, Inc.; *U.S. Public*, pg. 2330
CASELLA WASTE MANAGEMENT OF PENNSYLVANIA, INC.—See Casella Waste Systems, Inc.; *U.S. Public*, pg. 446
CBP CARBON INDUSTRIES, INC.; *U.S. Private*, pg. 797
CERTIFIED RECYCLING, INC.—See Broadview Group Holdings, LLC; *U.S. Private*, pg. 660
CHALLENGER PROPERTY ASSET MANAGEMENT PTY LIMITED—See Challenger Limited; *Int'l*, pg. 1438
CHINA ENERGY RECOVERY INC.; *Int'l*, pg. 1500
CHINA ENVIRONMENT LTD.; *Int'l*, pg. 1500
CHINA EVERBRIGHT WATER LIMITED—See China Everbright Group Limited; *Int'l*, pg. 1501
CHINA WASTE CORPORATION LIMITED; *Int'l*, pg. 1562
CHONGQING SANFENG ENVIRONMENT GROUP CORP., LTD.; *Int'l*, pg. 1581
CHUTES INTERNATIONAL; *U.S. Private*, pg. 895
CIELO WASTE SOLUTIONS CORP.; *Int'l*, pg. 1605
CIMELIA RESOURCE RECOVERY PTE. LTD.—See Enviro-Hub Holdings Ltd.; *Int'l*, pg. 2454
CIRCON HOLDINGS, INC.—See EQT AB; *Int'l*, pg. 2473
CITIWASTE, LLC—See Aurora Capital Group, LLC; *U.S. Private*, pg. 394
CLEANAWAY DANIELS NSW PTY LTD—See Cleanaway Waste Management Limited; *Int'l*, pg. 1654
CLEANAWAY DANIELS VIC PTY LTD—See Cleanaway Waste Management Limited; *Int'l*, pg. 1654
CLEANAWAY WASTE MANAGEMENT LIMITED; *Int'l*, pg. 1654
CLEANEVENT INTERNATIONAL PTY LTD—See Downer EDI Limited; *Int'l*, pg. 2185
CLEAN HARBORS ENVIRONMENTAL SERVICES, INC.—See Clean Harbors, Inc.; *U.S. Public*, pg. 509
CLEAN HARBORS KIMBALL REALTY, LLC—See Clean Harbors, Inc.; *U.S. Public*, pg. 509
CLEAN R SIA; *Int'l*, pg. 1654
CLEANSCAPES, INC.; *U.S. Private*, pg. 931
CO2 SOLUTIONS, INC.; *Int'l*, pg. 1680
COLEX HOLDINGS LIMITED—See Bonvests Holdings Limited; *Int'l*, pg. 1110
COLONY MATERIALS, L.L.C.—See Haines & Kibblehouse Inc.; *U.S. Private*, pg. 1841
CONCORD BLUE ENGINEERING GMBH; *Int'l*, pg. 1764
CONCORD BLUE TECHNOLOGY LTD.—See Concord Blue Engineering GmbH; *Int'l*, pg. 1764
CONCORD BLUE USA, INC.—See Concord Blue Engineering GmbH; *Int'l*, pg. 1764
CONSENUR, S.A.—See ACS, Actividades de Construccion y Servicios, S.A.; *Int'l*, pg. 111
COREPA S.N.C.—See Derichebourg S.A.; *Int'l*, pg. 2042
CORTINA INTEGRATED WASTE MANAGEMENT INC.—See Earthworks Industries Inc.; *Int'l*, pg. 2269
COSERSA CONTRATAS Y SERVICIOS, S.A.—See ACS, Actividades de Construccion y Servicios, S.A.; *Int'l*, pg. 110
COUGAR LANDFILL, INC.—See Waste Management, Inc.; *U.S. Public*, pg. 2330
COVED—See Ardian SAS; *Int'l*, pg. 556
COVED—See Caisse des Depots et Consignations; *Int'l*, pg. 1258
CURRENT WATER TECHNOLOGIES INC.; *Int'l*, pg. 1879
CURTIS BAY ENERGY, INC.—See Aurora Capital Group, LLC; *U.S. Private*, pg. 393
DAIKI-USAFI LTD.—See Daiki Axis Co., Ltd.; *Int'l*, pg. 1932

DEEP GREEN WASTE & RECYCLING, INC.; *U.S. Public*, pg. 645
DENALI WATER SOLUTIONS LLC; *U.S. Private*, pg. 1204
DERICHEBOURG BELGIUM NV—See Derichebourg S.A.; *Int'l*, pg. 2041
DERICHEBOURG ENVIRONNEMENT—See Derichebourg S.A.; *Int'l*, pg. 2041
DERICHEBOURG S.A.; *Int'l*, pg. 2041
DGC ENVIRONMENTAL SERVICES, INC.—See DFW Capital Partners; *U.S. Private*, pg. 1221
DINS HOKKAIDO CO., LTD.—See Daiei Kankyo Co., Ltd.; *Int'l*, pg. 1924
DMC SWEEPING, LLC—See Warburg Pincus LLC; *U.S. Private*, pg. 4440
DORAVILLE TRANSFER STATION, LLC—See Waste Management, Inc.; *U.S. Public*, pg. 2331
DOWA ECO-SYSTEM CO., LTD.—See Dowa Holdings Co., Ltd.; *Int'l*, pg. 2182
EARTHWORKS INDUSTRIES INC.; *Int'l*, pg. 2269
EAST COAST LOT & PAVEMENT MAINTENANCE CORP.—See Cerberus Capital Management, L.P.; *U.S. Private*, pg. 839
ECOLOGY CONTROL INDUSTRIES, INC.; *U.S. Private*, pg. 1329
ECO-PAK, LLC—See The Townsend Corporation; *U.S. Private*, pg. 4127
ECO RECYCLING LIMITED.; *Int'l*, pg. 2292
ECOSPHERE TECHNOLOGIES, INC.; *U.S. Private*, pg. 1330
ECO-SYSTEM AKITA CO., LTD.—See Dowa Holdings Co., Ltd.; *Int'l*, pg. 2183
ECO-SYSTEM CHIBA CO., LTD.—See Dowa Holdings Co., Ltd.; *Int'l*, pg. 2184
ECO-SYSTEM HANAOKA CO., LTD.—See Dowa Holdings Co., Ltd.; *Int'l*, pg. 2184
ECOVATION, INC.—See Ecolab Inc.; *U.S. Public*, pg. 714
ECOWISE SOLUTIONS PTE. LTD.—See ecoWise Holdings Limited; *Int'l*, pg. 2300
EEC, INCORPORATED; *U.S. Private*, pg. 1343
EESTECH, INC.; *Int'l*, pg. 2317
EKOPARTNERIT TURKU OY—See Fortum Oyj; *Int'l*, pg. 2740
ELEMENTAL HOLDING S.A.; *Int'l*, pg. 2358
EMS MANAGEMENT, LLC—See KKR & Co. Inc.; *U.S. Public*, pg. 1251
ENBASYS GMBH—See BDI - BioEnergy International AG; *Int'l*, pg. 929
ENERGY ANSWERS INTERNATIONAL, LLC—See Energy Answers International, Inc.; *U.S. Private*, pg. 1393
ENTECH ENGINEERING INC.; *U.S. Private*, pg. 1402
ENVIROGUARD PTY LTD—See Cleanaway Waste Management Limited; *Int'l*, pg. 1655
ENVIROMETAL TECHNOLOGIES INC.; *Int'l*, pg. 2454
ENVIRONMENTAL WASTE INTERNATIONAL INC.; *Int'l*, pg. 2455
ENVIROWASTE SA PROPRIETARY LIMITED—See Groupe Seche SAS; *Int'l*, pg. 3110
ENVIROWASTE SERVICES LIMITED—See CK Hutchison Holdings Limited; *Int'l*, pg. 1637
EQ INDUSTRIAL SERVICES, INC.—See Republic Services, Inc.; *U.S. Public*, pg. 1788
EQ THE ENVIRONMENTAL QUALITY COMPANY—See Republic Services, Inc.; *U.S. Public*, pg. 1787
ERECO ZRT.—See Derichebourg S.A.; *Int'l*, pg. 2042
ERG RENEW S.P.A.—See ERG S.p.A.; *Int'l*, pg. 2491
E.R.N. ELEKTRO-RECYCLING NORD GMBH—See Aurubis AG; *Int'l*, pg. 715
ERS AUSTRALIA PTY LTD—See Cleanaway Waste Management Limited; *Int'l*, pg. 1655
ERS NEW ZEALAND LIMITED—See Capital Environment Holdings Limited; *Int'l*, pg. 1310
ERS SINGAPORE PTE LTD—See Cleanaway Waste Management Limited; *Int'l*, pg. 1655
ERV GMBH—See Alba SE; *Int'l*, pg. 293
ESKA S.A.S—See Derichebourg S.A.; *Int'l*, pg. 2041
E.V.A. GMBH—See Hochland SE; *Int'l*, pg. 3437
THE EVERGREEN GROUP, INC.—See Gryphon Investors, LLC; *U.S. Private*, pg. 1798
EVOQUA WATER TECHNOLOGIES LLC—See Xylem Inc.; *U.S. Public*, pg. 2393
EVOQUA WATER TECHNOLOGIES—See Xylem Inc.; *U.S. Public*, pg. 2393
FABTECH S.A. PTY. LTD.—See E&A Limited; *Int'l*, pg. 2247
FCC BEC S.R.O.—See Fomento de Construcciones y Contratas, S.A.; *Int'l*, pg. 2722
FCC BRATISLAVA S.R.O.—See Fomento de Construcciones y Contratas, S.A.; *Int'l*, pg. 2722
FCC BULGARIA E.O.O.D.—See Fomento de Construcciones y Contratas, S.A.; *Int'l*, pg. 2722
FCC CESKA REPUBLIKA S.R.O.—See Fomento de Construcciones y Contratas, S.A.; *Int'l*, pg. 2722
FCC CESKE BUDEJOVICE S.R.O.—See Fomento de Construcciones y Contratas, S.A.; *Int'l*, pg. 2722
FCC DACICE S.R.O.—See Fomento de Construcciones y Contratas, S.A.; *Int'l*, pg. 2722
FCC EKO D.O.O.—See Fomento de Construcciones y Contratas, S.A.; *Int'l*, pg. 2722
FCC EKO POLSKA SP. Z.O.O.—See Fomento de Construc-

ciones y Contratas, S.A.; *Int'l*, pg. 2722
FCC ENVIRONMENT ROMANIA S.R.L.—See Fomento de Construcciones y Contratas, S.A.; *Int'l*, pg. 2723
FCC ENVIRONMENT (UK) LIMITED—See Fomento de Construcciones y Contratas, S.A.; *Int'l*, pg. 2722
FCC FREISTADT ABFALL SERVICE GMBH—See Fomento de Construcciones y Contratas, S.A.; *Int'l*, pg. 2723
FCC HALBENRAIN ABFALL SERVICE GMBH & CO. NFG KG—See Fomento de Construcciones y Contratas, S.A.; *Int'l*, pg. 2723
FCC HP S.R.O.—See Fomento de Construcciones y Contratas, S.A.; *Int'l*, pg. 2723
FCC LIBEREC S.R.O.—See Fomento de Construcciones y Contratas, S.A.; *Int'l*, pg. 2723
FCC LUBLIENEC SP. Z.O.O.—See Fomento de Construcciones y Contratas, S.A.; *Int'l*, pg. 2723
FCC MAGYARORZAG KFT—See Fomento de Construcciones y Contratas, S.A.; *Int'l*, pg. 2723
FCC MOSTVIERTEL ABFALL SERVICE GMBH—See Fomento de Construcciones y Contratas, S.A.; *Int'l*, pg. 2723
FCC NERATOVICE S.R.O.—See Fomento de Construcciones y Contratas, S.A.; *Int'l*, pg. 2723
FCC NEUNKIRCHEN ABFALL SERVICE GMBH—See Fomento de Construcciones y Contratas, S.A.; *Int'l*, pg. 2723
FCC REGIOS AS—See Fomento de Construcciones y Contratas, S.A.; *Int'l*, pg. 2723
FCC SLOVENSKO S.R.O.—See Fomento de Construcciones y Contratas, S.A.; *Int'l*, pg. 2723
FCC TARNOBRZEG.SP. Z.O.O.—See Fomento de Construcciones y Contratas, S.A.; *Int'l*, pg. 2723
FCC TEXTIL2USE GMBH—See Fomento de Construcciones y Contratas, S.A.; *Int'l*, pg. 2723
FCC TRNAVA S.R.O.—See Fomento de Construcciones y Contratas, S.A.; *Int'l*, pg. 2723
FCC UHY S.R.O.—See Fomento de Construcciones y Contratas, S.A.; *Int'l*, pg. 2723
FCC UNANOV S.R.O.—See Fomento de Construcciones y Contratas, S.A.; *Int'l*, pg. 2723
FCC VRBAK D.O.O.—See Fomento de Construcciones y Contratas, S.A.; *Int'l*, pg. 2723
FCC WASTE SERVICES (UK) LIMITED—See Fomento de Construcciones y Contratas, S.A.; *Int'l*, pg. 2723
FCC ZABCICE S.R.O.—See Fomento de Construcciones y Contratas, S.A.; *Int'l*, pg. 2723
FCC ZABOVRESKY S.R.O.—See Fomento de Construcciones y Contratas, S.A.; *Int'l*, pg. 2723
FCC ZISTERDORF ABFALL SERVICE GMBH—See Fomento de Construcciones y Contratas, S.A.; *Int'l*, pg. 2723
FCC ZOHOR.S.R.O.—See Fomento de Construcciones y Contratas, S.A.; *Int'l*, pg. 2723
FERROTRADE SAS—See Derichebourg S.A.; *Int'l*, pg. 2041
FILTA ENVIRONMENTAL CANADA LIMITED—See Franchise Brands plc; *Int'l*, pg. 2760
FILTAFRY DEUTSCHLAND GMBH—See Franchise Brands plc; *Int'l*, pg. 2760
THE FILTA GROUP INCORPORATED—See Franchise Brands plc; *Int'l*, pg. 2760
THE FILTA GROUP LIMITED—See Franchise Brands plc; *Int'l*, pg. 2760
FORWARD WATER TECHNOLOGIES CORP; *Int'l*, pg. 2747
FRANKFURTER KANALREINIGUNGSGESELLSCHAFT MBH—See Fraport AG; *Int'l*, pg. 2764
FRICOM RECYCLING—See Derichebourg S.A.; *Int'l*, pg. 2041
FRONTIER CO., LTD.—See Hikari Tsushin, Inc.; *Int'l*, pg. 3390
GALILEO TECH LTD.; *Int'l*, pg. 2873
GANESHA ECOSPHERE LTD.; *Int'l*, pg. 2880
GARNEY COMPANIES, INC.—See Garney Holding Company, Inc.; *U.S. Private*, pg. 1645
GENERAL ENVIRONMENTAL CONSERVATION PUBLIC COMPANY LIMITED; *Int'l*, pg. 2918
GEOCYCLE S.A.—See Holcim Ltd.; *Int'l*, pg. 3446
GEORGE B. WITTMER ASSOCIATES, INC.—See QSAM Biosciences, Inc.; *U.S. Public*, pg. 1744
GFL ENVIRONMENTAL INC.—See BC Partners LLP; *Int'l*, pg. 923
GIF ENTERPRISES, INC.—See Apex Companies, LLC; *U.S. Private*, pg. 292
GLOBAL ARDOUR RECYCLING LIMITED—See Ardour World Limited; *Int'l*, pg. 557
GLOBAL ARDOUR RECYCLING LIMITED—See Global Metcorp Ltd; *Int'l*, pg. 2999
GMH RECYCLING SAAR GMBH—See Georgsmarienhutte Holding GmbH; *Int'l*, pg. 2940
GOLDEN DOWA ECO-SYSTEM MYANMAR COMPANY LIMITED—See Dowa Holdings Co., Ltd.; *Int'l*, pg. 2184
GOLD MEDAL SERVICES, LLC See Kinderhook Industries, LLC; *U.S. Private*, pg. 2307
GREENRISE TECHNOLOGIES, LLC—See Boyne Capital Management, LLC; *U.S. Private*, pg. 629
GREENTECH ENVIRONMENTAL CO., LTD.; *Int'l*, pg. 3076
GREEN TREE ELECTRONIC RECYCLING, LLC; *U.S. Private*, pg. 1774
GRINO ECOLOGIC, S.A.; *Int'l*, pg. 3087

N.A.I.C.S. INDEX
562998 — ALL OTHER MISCELLAN...

GRUNSKE METALL-RECYCLING GMBH & CO. KG—See Alba SE; *Int'l*, pg. 293
GULF WEST LANDFILL TX, LP—See Republic Services, Inc.; *U.S. Public*, pg. 1786
GUZZLER MANUFACTURING INC.—See Federal Signal Corporation; *U.S. Public*, pg. 826
H2O NATIONWIDE LIMITED—See Cap10 Partners LLP; *Int'l*, pg. 1301
HALL COUNTY TRANSFER STATION, LLC—See Waste Management, Inc.; *U.S. Public*, pg. 2331
HAMLETT ENGINEERING SALES COMPANY—See Brixey & Meyer, Inc.; *U.S. Private*, pg. 658
HAW HAVELLANDISCHE ABFALLWIRTSCHAFTSGESELLSCHAFT MBH—See Alba SE; *Int'l*, pg. 293
HC DURACLEAN SDN. BHD.—See Damansara Realty Berhad; *Int'l*, pg. 1955
HELECTOR CYPRUS—See ELLAKTOR S.A.; *Int'l*, pg. 2365
HELECTOR GMBH—See ELLAKTOR S.A.; *Int'l*, pg. 2365
HERHOF RECYCLING CENTER OSNABRUCK GMBH—See ELLAKTOR S.A.; *Int'l*, pg. 2365
HERITAGE-CRYSTAL CLEAN, INC.—See J.F. Lehman & Company, Inc.; *U.S. Private*, pg. 2163
HILLS WASTE SOLUTIONS LIMITED; *Int'l*, pg. 3393
HINKLE TRANSFER STATION, LLC—See Waste Management, Inc.; *U.S. Public*, pg. 2331
HYDROGEN UTOPIA INTERNATIONAL PLC; *Int'l*, pg. 3547
HYDROMET CORPORATION LIMITED; *Int'l*, pg. 3548
HYDROTEK PUBLIC COMPANY LIMITED; *Int'l*, pg. 3548
IFS BETEILIGUNGSGES MBH—See EQT AB; *Int'l*, pg. 2477
I.M.G. 2 S.R.L.; *Int'l*, pg. 3566
INAGRA, S.A.—See Ferrovial S.A.; *Int'l*, pg. 2644
INGENIUM; *U.S. Private*, pg. 2075
INLAND ENVIRONMENTAL RESOURCES, INC.—See Calix Limited; *Int'l*, pg. 1265
INOREC S.A.S.—See Derichebourg S.A.; *Int'l*, pg. 2041
INTEGRATED DISPLAY TECHNOLOGY LIMITED—See IDT International Limited; *Int'l*, pg. 3596
INTERSEROH AUSTRIA GMBH—See Alba SE; *Int'l*, pg. 293
INTERSEROH ORGANIZACJA ODZYSKU OPAKOWAN S.A.—See Alba SE; *Int'l*, pg. 293
INTERSEROH PRODUCT CYCLE GMBH—See Alba SE; *Int'l*, pg. 293
INTERSEROH SERVICE ITALIA S.R.L.—See Alba SE; *Int'l*, pg. 293
INTERSEROH SERVICES D. O. O.—See Alba SE; *Int'l*, pg. 293
INTERWASTE HOLDINGS LIMITED—See Groupe Seche SAS; *Int'l*, pg. 3110
INTER-WASTE PROPRIETARY LIMITED—See Groupe Seche SAS; *Int'l*, pg. 3110
INTERZERO D.O.O—See Alba SE; *Int'l*, pg. 293
JAEGER ET BOSSHARD SA—See HIAG Immobilen Holding AG; *Int'l*, pg. 3382
JET POLYMER RECYCLING, INC.—See Advanced Drainage Systems, Inc.; *U.S. Public*, pg. 46
KA INDUSTRIAL SERVICES, LLC—See The Halifax Group LLC; *U.S. Private*, pg. 4042
KETER ENVIRONMENTAL SERVICES, INC.—See TPG Capital, L.P.; *U.S. Public*, pg. 2174
KLINIKEN MUNCHEN PASING UND PERLACH GMBH—See Fresenius SE & Co. KGaA; *Int'l*, pg. 2779
KM INDUSTRIAL, INC. - BENICIA DIVISION—See The Halifax Group LLC; *U.S. Private*, pg. 4042
KM INDUSTRIAL, INC. - LAS VEGAS DIVISION—See The Halifax Group LLC; *U.S. Private*, pg. 4042
KM INDUSTRIAL, INC.—See The Halifax Group LLC; *U.S. Private*, pg. 4042
KM PLANT SERVICES, INC. - PEKIN DIVISION—See The Halifax Group LLC; *U.S. Private*, pg. 4042
KM PLANT SERVICES, INC.—See The Halifax Group LLC; *U.S. Private*, pg. 4042
KOBE PORT RECYCLE CO., LTD.—See Daiei Kankyo Co., Ltd.; *Int'l*, pg. 1924
KOHLER WASTE SERVICES INC.—See Interstate Waste Services, Inc.; *U.S. Private*, pg. 2126
KOWA SEIKO CO., LTD.—See Dowa Holdings Co., Ltd.; *Int'l*, pg. 2183
KVB KUNSTSTOFFVERWERTUNG BRANDENBURG GMBH—See Alba SE; *Int'l*, pg. 293
KYODOH DOBOKU CO., LTD.—See Daiei Kankyo Co., Ltd.; *Int'l*, pg. 1924
LCTH CORPORATION BHD—See Fu Yu Corporation Limited; *Int'l*, pg. 2801
LEGAL SHRED INC.; *U.S. Private*, pg. 2418
LEMONS LANDFILL, LLC—See Republic Services, Inc.; *U.S. Public*, pg. 1786
LEWISVILLE LANDFILL TX, LP—See Republic Services, Inc.; *U.S. Public*, pg. 1786
LIBERTY TIRE SERVICES, LLC—See The Carlyle Group Inc.; *U.S. Public*, pg. 2048
LIDRONE SPOL, S.R.O.—See CEZ, a.s.; *Int'l*, pg. 1429
LIMPIEZAS LAFUENTE, S.L.—See ACS, Actividades de Construccion y Servicios, S.A.; *Int'l*, pg. 115
LINEA GROUP HOLDING S.P.A.—See A2A S.p.A.; *Int'l*, pg. 29
LIQUID ENVIRONMENTAL SOLUTIONS OF TEXAS, LLC—See Audax Group, Limited Partnership; *U.S. Private*, pg. 388

L V RAWLINSON & ASSOCIATES PTY LTD—See Cleanaway Waste Management Limited; *Int'l*, pg. 1655
MACAU CAPITAL INVESTMENTS, INC.; *U.S. Public*, pg. 1351
MAJIC WHEELS, INC.; *U.S. Private*, pg. 2555
MAN IMPORTS PTY LTD—See Penske Automotive Group, Inc.; *U.S. Public*, pg. 1666
MARK DUNNING INDUSTRIES, INC.; *U.S. Private*, pg. 2577
MARX SPAENLIN SA—See Derichebourg S.A.; *Int'l*, pg. 2041
MBG HOLDINGS, INC.; *U.S. Public*, pg. 1403
MCCUTCHEON ENTERPRISES, INC.; *U.S. Private*, pg. 2631
MERIDIAN WASTE ACQUISITIONS, LLC—See Warren Equity Partners, LLC; *U.S. Private*, pg. 4443
MIEJSKIE PRZEDSIEBIORSTWO GOSPODARKI KOMUNALNEJ SP. Z.O.O.—See Fomento de Construcciones y Contratas, S.A.; *Int'l*, pg. 2723
MNH SUSTAINABLE CABIN SERVICES PTY SYDNEY - AUSTRALASIA—See Harwood Capital LLP; *Int'l*, pg. 3282
MODERN ASIA ENVIRONMENTAL HOLDINGS PTE. LTD.—See Dowa Holdings Co., Ltd.; *Int'l*, pg. 2184
MOSTOLLER LANDFILL, LLC—See Waste Management, Inc.; *U.S. Public*, pg. 2331
NATIONAL INDUSTRIAL MAINTENANCE, INC.—See Carylon Corporation; *U.S. Private*, pg. 777
NATIONAL POWER RODDING CORPORATION—See Carylon Corporation; *U.S. Private*, pg. 777
NATIONAL WASTE PARTNERS, LLC—See Bestige Holdings LLC; *U.S. Private*, pg. 544
NATIONWIDE OIL PTY LTD—See Cleanaway Waste Management Limited; *Int'l*, pg. 1655
NICOLL BELGIUM S.A.—See Aliaxis S.A./N.V.; *Int'l*, pg. 325
NICOLL SPA—See Aliaxis S.A./N.V.; *Int'l*, pg. 325
NICOLL S.R.L.—See Aliaxis S.A./N.V.; *Int'l*, pg. 325
NIKKEY COMPANY LIMITED—See Hibiya Engineering Ltd; *Int'l*, pg. 3383
NORDDEUTSCHE GESELLSCHAFT ZUR ABLAGERUNG VON MINERALSTOFFEN MBH—See E.ON SE; *Int'l*, pg. 2258
NORTHEAST OHIO REGIONAL SEWER DISTRICT; *U.S. Private*, pg. 2950
NORTHSTAR RECYCLING GROUP; *U.S. Private*, pg. 2958
NORTHUMBRIAN WATER PROJECTS LIMITED—See CK Hutchison Holdings Limited; *Int'l*, pg. 1637
NOVO ENVIROTECH (GUANGZHOU) CO. LTD—See CITIC Group Corporation; *Int'l*, pg. 1620
NQ RESOURCE RECOVERY PTY LTD—See Cleanaway Waste Management Limited; *Int'l*, pg. 1655
NW NATURAL WATER COMPANY, LLC—See Northwest Natural Holding Company; *U.S. Public*, pg. 1542
OCTEVA, S.A.S.—See ACS, Actividades de Construccion y Servicios, S.A.; *Int'l*, pg. 115
ONSITE CENTRAL LIMITED—See Arjun Infrastructure Partners Limited; *Int'l*, pg. 568
OOSTVLAAMS MILIEUBEHEER—See Eiffage S.A.; *Int'l*, pg. 2331
PALING INDUSTRIES SDN. BHD.—See Aliaxis S.A./N.V.; *Int'l*, pg. 325
PARALLEL PRODUCTS OF KENTUCKY, INC.; *U.S. Private*, pg. 3092
PELICAN WASTE & DEBRIS, LLC; *U.S. Private*, pg. 3131
PINE HILL FARMS LANDFILL TX, LP—See Republic Services, Inc.; *U.S. Public*, pg. 1786
PLATFORM WASTE SOLUTIONS, LLC—See Platform Capital, LLC; *U.S. Private*, pg. 3200
PORT CLINTON LANDFILL, INC.—See Republic Services, Inc.; *U.S. Public*, pg. 1786
PRIORITY WASTE LLC; *U.S. Private*, pg. 3267
P.T. PRASADHA PAMUNAH LIMBAH INDUSTRI—See Dowa Holdings Co., Ltd.; *Int'l*, pg. 2183
PUBLIC WORKS EQUIPMENT & SUPPLY, INC.—See Federal Signal Corporation; *U.S. Public*, pg. 826
QUAIL SPOL. S.R.O.—See Fomento de Construcciones y Contratas, S.A.; *Int'l*, pg. 2723
QUANTUM ENVIRONMENTAL SERVICES PTY LTD.—See Cleanaway Waste Management Limited; *Int'l*, pg. 1655
QUEST RESOURCE HOLDING CORPORATION; *U.S. Public*, pg. 1756
RAPID MICRO BIOSYSTEMS, INC.; *U.S. Public*, pg. 1763
RDB PLASTICS GMBH—See Alba SE; *Int'l*, pg. 293
RECONSERVE, INC.—See ReConserve, Inc.; *U.S. Private*, pg. 3371
RECYCLA S.P.A.—See Hera S.p.A.; *Int'l*, pg. 3356
RECYCLE TRACK SYSTEMS, INC.; *U.S. Private*, pg. 3372
RECYCLING & WASTE SOLUTIONS, LLC—See ATAR Capital, LLC; *U.S. Private*, pg. 365
RENOR AS—See Heidelberg Materials AG; *Int'l*, pg. 3319
REPASACK GMBH—See Alba SE; *Int'l*, pg. 293
REPUBLIC ENVIRONMENTAL TECHNOLOGIES, INC.—See Republic Services, Inc.; *U.S. Public*, pg. 1787
REPUBLIC SERVICES, INC. - GRANTS PASS—See Republic Services, Inc.; *U.S. Public*, pg. 1787
REPUBLIC SERVICES OF MURFREESBORO - ALLIED WASTE DIV—See Republic Services, Inc.; *U.S. Public*, pg. 1787

REPUBLIC SERVICES OF PENNSYLVANIA, LLC—See Republic Services, Inc.; *U.S. Public*, pg. 1787
RESTORATION + RECOVERY SERVICES, LLC—See DFW Capital Partners; *U.S. Private*, pg. 1221
RE SUSTAINABILITY LIMITED—See KKR & Co. Inc.; *U.S. Public*, pg. 1263
REVIVAL S.A.S.—See Derichebourg S.A.; *Int'l*, pg. 2041
ROHR SA—See Derichebourg S.A.; *Int'l*, pg. 2041
ROHSTOFF RECYCLING DORTMUND GMBH—See Georgsmarienhutte Holding GmbH; *Int'l*, pg. 2941
ROMRECYCLING SRL—See Derichebourg S.A.; *Int'l*, pg. 2042
ROTO-ROOTER GROUP, INC.—See Chemed Corporation; *U.S. Public*, pg. 484
ROW-CARE LLC—See The Townsend Corporation; *U.S. Private*, pg. 4127
RRO ROHSTOFF RECYCLING OSNABRUECK GMBH—See Georgsmarienhutte Holding GmbH; *Int'l*, pg. 2941
RUBUS HOLDINGS PTY LTD—See Cleanaway Waste Management Limited; *Int'l*, pg. 1655
RUMPKE OF INDIANA, INC.—See Rumpke Consolidated Companies, Inc.; *U.S. Private*, pg. 3503
RUMPKE OF KENTUCKY, INC.—See Rumpke Consolidated Companies, Inc.; *U.S. Private*, pg. 3503
RUMPKE OF OHIO, INC.—See Rumpke Consolidated Companies, Inc.; *U.S. Private*, pg. 3503
RUMPKE TRANSPORATION COMPANY, LLC—See Rumpke Consolidated Companies, Inc.; *U.S. Private*, pg. 3503
RUMPKE WASTE, INC.—See Rumpke Consolidated Companies, Inc.; *U.S. Private*, pg. 3503
SAGE SUSTAINABLE ELECTRONICS LLC—See Closed Loop Partners LLC; *U.S. Private*, pg. 946
SAKAB SELLBERGS AB—See E.ON SE; *Int'l*, pg. 2255
SANGAMON VALLEY LANDFILL, INC.—See Republic Services, Inc.; *U.S. Public*, pg. 1787
SAN SAC GROUP AB—See Accent Equity Partners AB; *Int'l*, pg. 81
SAS DU PETIT LAC—See Derichebourg S.A.; *Int'l*, pg. 2042
SCI QUAI DE NORVEGE—See Derichebourg S.A.; *Int'l*, pg. 2042
SCORPEX, INC.; *U.S. Private*, pg. 3575
SETCAR S.A.—See Directa Plus PLC; *Int'l*, pg. 2130
SETTSU SEIUN CO., LTD.—See Daiei Kankyo Co., Ltd.; *Int'l*, pg. 1924
SHAMROCK ENVIRONMENTAL CORPORATION—See CenterOak Partners LLC; *U.S. Private*, pg. 816
SHARPS COMPLIANCE CORP.—See Aurora Capital Group, LLC; *U.S. Private*, pg. 394
SINO ENVIRONMENTAL SERVICES CORP.—See CTCI Corporation; *Int'l*, pg. 1870
SLM FACILITY SOLUTIONS NATIONWIDE; *U.S. Private*, pg. 3689
SOCIETE POUR LE CONDITIONNEMENT DES DECHETS ET EFFLUENTS INDUSTRIELS—See Electricite de France S.A.; *Int'l*, pg. 2352
SOLUCORP INDUSTRIES LTD.; *U.S. Public*, pg. 1901
SONDERABFALL SERVICE SUDWEST - 3S GMBH—See Alba SE; *Int'l*, pg. 293
SOUTHEAST (OKC) LANDFILL—See Republic Services, Inc.; *U.S. Public*, pg. 1787
SOUTHERN OREGON SANITATION INC.; *U.S. Private*, pg. 3734
SOUTHWEST LANDFILL TX, LP—See Republic Services, Inc.; *U.S. Public*, pg. 1787
SPINNAKER RECYCLING CORP.—See Waste Management, Inc.; *U.S. Public*, pg. 2332
SPRINT ENERGY SERVICES—See Republic Services, Inc.; *U.S. Public*, pg. 1788
SR SERVICE GMBH—See Alba SE; *Int'l*, pg. 293
STERICYCLE, INC.—See Waste Management, Inc.; *U.S. Public*, pg. 2332
STERICYCLE, INC.—See Waste Management, Inc.; *U.S. Public*, pg. 2332
STRAP TRANSPORT S.A.S.—See Derichebourg S.A.; *Int'l*, pg. 2042
SYNERGY RECYCLING, LLC—See Clean Harbors, Inc.; *U.S. Public*, pg. 510
TALISMARK; *U.S. Private*, pg. 3926
TAS ENVIRONMENTAL SERVICES, L.P.; *U.S. Private*, pg. 3934
TOWNSEND TREE SERVICE—See The Townsend Corporation; *U.S. Private*, pg. 4127
T-PLUS GMBH—See EnBW Energie Baden-Wurttemberg AG; *Int'l*, pg. 2400
TRANSPACIFIC INDUSTRIES PTY LTD—See Cleanaway Waste Management Limited; *Int'l*, pg. 1655
TRANSPACIFIC PARAMOUNT SERVICES PTY LTD—See Cleanaway Waste Management Limited; *Int'l*, pg. 1655
TRANSPACIFIC RESOURCES PTY LTD—See Cleanaway Waste Management Limited; *Int'l*, pg. 1655
TRANSPACIFIC WASTE MANAGEMENT PTY LTD—See Cleanaway Waste Management Limited; *Int'l*, pg. 1655
TRANSWASTE TECHNOLOGIES PTY LTD—See Cleanaway Waste Management Limited; *Int'l*, pg. 1655
TRATAMIENTO INTEGRAL DE RESIDUOS DE CANTABRIA S.L.U.—See ACS, Actividades de Construccion y

562998 — ALL OTHER MISCELLAN...

Servicios, S.A.; *Int'l*, pg. 116
TREATMENT AND RECYCLING OF WISCONSIN, LLC—See Grupo Tradebe Medioambiente S.L.; *Int'l*, pg. 3138
TVF ALTWERT GMBH—See Alba SE; *Int'l*, pg. 293
UMWELT-SERVICE NORDSCHWARZWALD GMBH—See Alba SE; *Int'l*, pg. 293
URBASER ENVIRONNEMENT, S.A.S.—See Platinum Equity, LLC; *U.S. Private*, pg. 3209
URBASYS, S.A.S.—See ACS, Actividades de Construccion y Servicios, S.A.; *Int'l*, pg. 117
VALLONE S.R.L.—See Encavis AG; *Int'l*, pg. 2401
VALLORTIGARA SERVIZI AMBIENTALI S.P.A.—See Hera S.p.A.; *Int'l*, pg. 3357
VALME TECHNOLOGIES SAS—See Derichebourg S.A.; *Int'l*, pg. 2042
VALOREF SA—See Compagnie de Saint-Gobain SA; *Int'l*, pg. 1732
VALORIZA SERVICIOS MEDIOAMBIENTALES SA—See Morgan Stanley; *U.S. Public*, pg. 1473
VELOCITY DYNAMICS, LLC—See Baird Financial Group, Inc.; *U.S. Private*, pg. 453
VENEZOLANA DE LIMPIEZAS INDUSTRIALES, C.A.—See ACS, Actividades de Construccion y Servicios, S.A.; *Int'l*, pg. 117
VERANSA GROUP, INC.—See RFE Investment Partners; *U.S. Private*, pg. 3419
VIRIDOR WASTE (BRISTOL HOLDINGS) LIMITED—See KKR & Co. Inc.; *U.S. Public*, pg. 1266
VIRIDOR WASTE (BRISTOL) LIMITED—See KKR & Co. Inc.; *U.S. Public*, pg. 1266
VIRIDOR WASTE DISPOSAL LIMITED—See KKR & Co. Inc.; *U.S. Public*, pg. 1266
VIRIDOR WASTE KENT LIMITED—See KKR & Co. Inc.; *U.S. Public*, pg. 1266
VIRIDOR WASTE LIMITED—See KKR & Co. Inc.; *U.S. Public*, pg. 1266
VIRIDOR WASTE MANAGEMENT LTD.—See KKR & Co. Inc.; *U.S. Public*, pg. 1266
VIRIDOR WASTE (SHEFFIELD) LIMITED—See KKR & Co. Inc.; *U.S. Public*, pg. 1266
VLS RECOVERY SERVICES, LLC—See Aurora Capital Group, LLC; *U.S. Private*, pg. 394
WASATCH REGIONAL LANDFILL, INC.—See Republic Services, Inc.; *U.S. Public*, pg. 1788
WASTECH SERVICES LTD.—See Belkorp Industries, Inc.; *Int'l*, pg. 965
WASTECYCLE LTD.—See DCC plc; *Int'l*, pg. 1991
WASTE HARMONICS, LLC—See TPG Capital, L.P.; *U.S. Public*, pg. 2174
WASTE ITALIA S.P.A.—See Gruppo Waste Italia S.p.A.; *Int'l*, pg. 3141
WASTE MANAGEMENT OF CANADA CORPORATION—See Waste Management, Inc.; *U.S. Public*, pg. 2333
WASTE MANAGEMENT OF NEW JERSEY, INC.—See Waste Management, Inc.; *U.S. Public*, pg. 2334
WASTE MANAGEMENT SIAM LTD.—See Dowa Holdings Co., Ltd.; *Int'l*, pg. 2183
WASTE MANAGEMENT TECHNICAL SERVICES (NZ) LTD.—See Capital Environment Holdings Limited; *Int'l*, pg. 1310
WASTE SOLUTIONS LIMITED—See Downer EDI Limited; *Int'l*, pg. 2186
WILLIAM TRACEY LIMITED—See DCC plc; *Int'l*, pg. 1991
WM OF TEXAS, L.L.C.—See Waste Management, Inc.; *U.S. Public*, pg. 2333
WPO ALBA S.A.—See Alba SE; *Int'l*, pg. 293
WUHAN GEM RESOURCES RECYCLING CO., LTD—See GEM Co., Ltd.; *Int'l*, pg. 2914
ZENTRALDEPONIE HUBBELRATH GMBH—See EnBW Energie Baden-Wurttemberg AG; *Int'l*, pg. 2401

611110 — ELEMENTARY AND SECONDARY SCHOOLS

ACADEMEDIA GMBH—See AcadeMedia AB; *Int'l*, pg. 75
ACCESS INTERNATIONAL EDUCATION LTD.; *Int'l*, pg. 89
BENESSE BE STUDIO INC.—See EQT AB; *Int'l*, pg. 2467
CHARTERHOUSE PRIVATE SCHOOLS (PTY) LTD.—See ADvTECH Limited; *Int'l*, pg. 169
CHINA EDUCATION, INC.; *Int'l*, pg. 1499
CHINA MAPLE LEAF EDUCATIONAL SYSTEMS LIMITED; *Int'l*, pg. 1517
COGNITA SCHOOLS LIMITED; *Int'l*, pg. 1695
EDUCATIONAL SERVICES OF AMERICA; *U.S. Private*, pg. 1339
ENDEAVOR SCHOOLS, LLC; *U.S. Private*, pg. 1391
ESPIRA ARKJAER AS—See AcadeMedia AB; *Int'l*, pg. 75
ESPIRA AROLIA AS—See AcadeMedia AB; *Int'l*, pg. 75
ESPIRA AROSFJELLET AS—See AcadeMedia AB; *Int'l*, pg. 75
ESPIRA BAGGERODBANEN AS—See AcadeMedia AB; *Int'l*, pg. 75
ESPIRA BJORGENE AS—See AcadeMedia AB; *Int'l*, pg. 75
ESPIRA BLAKSTAD AS—See AcadeMedia AB; *Int'l*, pg. 75
ESPIRA BRADALSFJELLET AS—See AcadeMedia AB; *Int'l*, pg. 75
ESPIRA BRASTEINTUNET AS—See AcadeMedia AB; *Int'l*, pg. 75
ESPIRA DRAGERSKOGEN AS—See AcadeMedia AB; *Int'l*, pg. 75
ESPIRA DVERGSNES AS—See AcadeMedia AB; *Int'l*, pg. 75
ESPIRA EIKENGA AS—See AcadeMedia AB; *Int'l*, pg. 75
ESPIRA EIKENOTTA NATURBARNEHAGE AS—See AcadeMedia AB; *Int'l*, pg. 75
ESPIRA EVANGTUNET AS—See AcadeMedia AB; *Int'l*, pg. 75
ESPIRA EVENTYRSKOGEN AS—See AcadeMedia AB; *Int'l*, pg. 75
ESPIRA EVJE AS—See AcadeMedia AB; *Int'l*, pg. 75
ESPIRA FASANVEIEN AS—See AcadeMedia AB; *Int'l*, pg. 75
ESPIRA FENSTAD AS—See AcadeMedia AB; *Int'l*, pg. 75
ESPIRA FINNAS AS—See AcadeMedia AB; *Int'l*, pg. 75
ESPIRA GARHAUG AS—See AcadeMedia AB; *Int'l*, pg. 75
ESPIRA GARTNERLOKKA AS—See AcadeMedia AB; *Int'l*, pg. 75
ESPIRA GJEMBLE AS—See AcadeMedia AB; *Int'l*, pg. 75
ESPIRA GREFSEN AS—See AcadeMedia AB; *Int'l*, pg. 75
ESPIRA GRONNESTOLEN AS—See AcadeMedia AB; *Int'l*, pg. 75
ESPIRA GRUPPEN AS—See AcadeMedia AB; *Int'l*, pg. 75
ESPIRA GULLHELLA AS—See AcadeMedia AB; *Int'l*, pg. 75
ESPIRA HALSNOY KLOSTER AS—See AcadeMedia AB; *Int'l*, pg. 75
ESPIRA HELLDALSASEN AS—See AcadeMedia AB; *Int'l*, pg. 75
ESPIRA HOLBEKK IDRETTSBARNEHAGE AS—See AcadeMedia AB; *Int'l*, pg. 75
ESPIRA HOLLUND AS—See AcadeMedia AB; *Int'l*, pg. 75
ESPIRA HOLUM AS—See AcadeMedia AB; *Int'l*, pg. 75
ESPIRA HOVSMARKA AS—See AcadeMedia AB; *Int'l*, pg. 75
ESPIRA HUSEBYPARKEN AS—See AcadeMedia AB; *Int'l*, pg. 75
ESPIRA JELOY AS—See AcadeMedia AB; *Int'l*, pg. 75
ESPIRA JUBERG AS—See AcadeMedia AB; *Int'l*, pg. 75
ESPIRA KARMSUND AS—See AcadeMedia AB; *Int'l*, pg. 75
ESPIRA KLOVERENGA AS—See AcadeMedia AB; *Int'l*, pg. 75
ESPIRA KNERTEN AS—See AcadeMedia AB; *Int'l*, pg. 75
ESPIRA KNIVEASEN AS—See AcadeMedia AB; *Int'l*, pg. 75
ESPIRA KRYSTALLVEIEN AS—See AcadeMedia AB; *Int'l*, pg. 75
ESPIRA KULTURSTIEN AS—See AcadeMedia AB; *Int'l*, pg. 75
ESPIRA KUNNSKAPSBYEN AS—See AcadeMedia AB; *Int'l*, pg. 75
ESPIRA KUVENTRAE AS—See AcadeMedia AB; *Int'l*, pg. 75
ESPIRA KYSTAD GARD AS—See AcadeMedia AB; *Int'l*, pg. 76
ESPIRA LINDESNES AS—See AcadeMedia AB; *Int'l*, pg. 76
ESPIRA LITLASUND AS—See AcadeMedia AB; *Int'l*, pg. 76
ESPIRA LURA AS—See AcadeMedia AB; *Int'l*, pg. 76
ESPIRA MARIENFRYD AS—See AcadeMedia AB; *Int'l*, pg. 76
ESPIRA MARTHAHAUGEN AS—See AcadeMedia AB; *Int'l*, pg. 76
ESPIRA MOSTER AS—See AcadeMedia AB; *Int'l*, pg. 76
ESPIRA MURUVIK AS—See AcadeMedia AB; *Int'l*, pg. 76
ESPIRA MYRASKOGEN AS—See AcadeMedia AB; *Int'l*, pg. 76
ESPIRA NORDMO AS—See AcadeMedia AB; *Int'l*, pg. 76
ESPIRA NYKIRKE AS—See AcadeMedia AB; *Int'l*, pg. 76
ESPIRA OPAKER AS—See AcadeMedia AB; *Int'l*, pg. 76
ESPIRA OPSAHL AS—See AcadeMedia AB; *Int'l*, pg. 76
ESPIRA OREID AS—See AcadeMedia AB; *Int'l*, pg. 76
ESPIRA ORMDALEN AS—See AcadeMedia AB; *Int'l*, pg. 76
ESPIRA RA AS—See AcadeMedia AB; *Int'l*, pg. 76
ESPIRA RAMBJORA AS—See AcadeMedia AB; *Int'l*, pg. 76
ESPIRA REE AS—See AcadeMedia AB; *Int'l*, pg. 76
ESPIRA ROMHOLT AS—See AcadeMedia AB; *Int'l*, pg. 76
ESPIRA RUBBESTADNESET AS—See AcadeMedia AB; *Int'l*, pg. 76
ESPIRA SALAMONSKOGEN AS—See AcadeMedia AB; *Int'l*, pg. 76
ESPIRA SANDTOPPEN NATURBARNEHAGE AS—See AcadeMedia AB; *Int'l*, pg. 76
ESPIRA SANGEREIDASEN AS—See AcadeMedia AB; *Int'l*, pg. 76
ESPIRA SANUM AS—See AcadeMedia AB; *Int'l*, pg. 76
ESPIRA SCALA HUNDVAG AS—See AcadeMedia AB; *Int'l*, pg. 76
ESPIRA SCALA TASTA AS—See AcadeMedia AB; *Int'l*, pg. 76
ESPIRA SKAREDALEN AS—See AcadeMedia AB; *Int'l*, pg. 76
ESPIRA SKJERABERGET AS—See AcadeMedia AB; *Int'l*, pg. 76
ESPIRA SKOLEGATA AS—See AcadeMedia AB; *Int'l*, pg. 76
ESPIRA SLETTEN AS—See AcadeMedia AB; *Int'l*, pg. 76
ESPIRA SNURREFJELLET AS—See AcadeMedia AB; *Int'l*, pg. 76
ESPIRA SOLKNATTEN AS—See AcadeMedia AB; *Int'l*, pg. 76
ESPIRA SOLKROKEN AS—See AcadeMedia AB; *Int'l*, pg. 76
ESPIRA SPIREA AS—See AcadeMedia AB; *Int'l*, pg. 76
ESPIRA STEINSVIKEN AS—See AcadeMedia AB; *Int'l*, pg. 76
ESPIRA STJORDAL AS—See AcadeMedia AB; *Int'l*, pg. 76
ESPIRA SUNDBYFOSS AS—See AcadeMedia AB; *Int'l*, pg. 76
ESPIRA TAREMAREBY AS—See AcadeMedia AB; *Int'l*, pg. 76
ESPIRA TASTARUSTA AS—See AcadeMedia AB; *Int'l*, pg. 76
ESPIRA TAU AS—See AcadeMedia AB; *Int'l*, pg. 76
ESPIRA TJOSVOLL AS—See AcadeMedia AB; *Int'l*, pg. 76
ESPIRA TORSBERGSKOGEN AS—See AcadeMedia AB; *Int'l*, pg. 76
ESPIRA TORSHOVDALEN AS—See AcadeMedia AB; *Int'l*, pg. 76
ESPIRA TRISTILBAKKEN AS—See AcadeMedia AB; *Int'l*, pg. 76
ESPIRA TRYGSTAD AS—See AcadeMedia AB; *Int'l*, pg. 76
ESPIRA ULSETSKOGEN AS—See AcadeMedia AB; *Int'l*, pg. 76
ESPIRA ULVENVATNET AS—See AcadeMedia AB; *Int'l*, pg. 76
ESPIRA VANNVERKSDAMMEN AS—See AcadeMedia AB; *Int'l*, pg. 76
ESPIRA VEDDERHEIA AS—See AcadeMedia AB; *Int'l*, pg. 76
ESPIRA VELDETUN AS—See AcadeMedia AB; *Int'l*, pg. 76
EVOLVE EDUCATION GROUP LIMITED; *Int'l*, pg. 2572
FAMILY ADVOCACY SERVICES, LLC—See Centerbridge Partners, L.P.; *U.S. Private*, pg. 813
GAKKEN STUDY CO., LTD.—See Gakken Holdings Co., Ltd.; *Int'l*, pg. 2869
GULF OAKS THERAPEUTIC DAY SCHOOL, LLC—See Community Health Systems, Inc.; *U.S. Public*, pg. 553
HACKBRIGHT ACADEMY, INC.—See Strategic Education, Inc.; *U.S. Public*, pg. 1954
HAILIANG EDUCATION GROUP INC.; *Int'l*, pg. 3211
IMG ACADEMY, LLC—See Canada Pension Plan Investment Board; *Int'l*, pg. 1281
IMG ACADEMY, LLC—See EQT AB; *Int'l*, pg. 2470
KATHARINE GIBBS OF PHILADELPHIA, LLC—See Perdoceo Education Corporation; *U.S. Public*, pg. 1673
KTS VERWALTUNGS GMBH—See AcadeMedia AB; *Int'l*, pg. 77
MAPLE LEAF EDUCATION NORTH AMERICA LIMITED—See China Maple Leaf Educational Systems Limited; *Int'l*, pg. 1517
NAVE A VELA LTDA.—See Dragoneer Investment Group, LLC; *U.S. Private*, pg. 1272
NAVE A VELA LTDA.—See General Atlantic Service Company, L.P.; *U.S. Private*, pg. 1662
OCHANOMIZU SEMINAR CO., LTD.—See EQT AB; *Int'l*, pg. 2467
OXBRIDGE ACADEMY (PTY) LTD.—See ADvTECH Limited; *Int'l*, pg. 169
PLEK VOOR KINDEREN B.V.—See AcadeMedia AB; *Int'l*, pg. 77
PYSSLINGEN FORSKOLOR OCH SKOLOR AB—See AcadeMedia AB; *Int'l*, pg. 77
RISO KYOIKU CO., LTD.—See Hulic Co., Ltd.; *Int'l*, pg. 3528
SAE DIGITAL S.A.—See Dragoneer Investment Group, LLC; *U.S. Private*, pg. 1272
SAE DIGITAL S.A.—See General Atlantic Service Company, L.P.; *U.S. Private*, pg. 1662
SARASOTA MILITARY ACADEMY, INC.; *U.S. Private*, pg. 3549
SISTER CIRCLE LLC—See TEGNA Inc.; *U.S. Public*, pg. 1990
SKOGEN BARNEHAGE AS—See AcadeMedia AB; *Int'l*, pg. 77
STANDARD FOR SUCCESS, LLC—See Serent Capital Management Company, LLC; *U.S. Private*, pg. 3613
STEP KIDS EDUCATION GMBH—See AcadeMedia AB; *Int'l*, pg. 77
STEP KIDS KITAS GMBH—See AcadeMedia AB; *Int'l*, pg. 77
TOMM MURSTAD FRILUFTSBARNEHAGE AS—See AcadeMedia AB; *Int'l*, pg. 77
UNIVERSITY OF AFRICA LTD.—See ADvTECH Limited; *Int'l*, pg. 169
VITTRA AB—See Bure Equity AB; *Int'l*, pg. 1221

611210 — JUNIOR COLLEGES

ACADEMIES AUSTRALASIA INSTITUTE PTY. LIMITED—See Academies Australasia Group Limited; *Int'l*, pg. 77
CHINA EDUCATION GROUP HOLDINGS LIMITED; *Int'l*, pg. 1499
LINCOLN COLLEGE OF TECHNOLOGY—See Lincoln Educational Services Corporation; *U.S. Public*, pg. 1316

N.A.I.C.S. INDEX

611310 — COLLEGES, UNIVERSIT...

LINCOLN TECHNICAL INSTITUTE; *U.S. Private*, pg. 2459
SANFORD-BROWN COLLEGE - BOSTON—See Perdoceo Education Corporation; *U.S. Public*, pg. 1673
VOSTRO INSTITUTE OF TRAINING AUSTRALIA PTY. LIMITED—See Academies Australasia Group Limited; *Int'l*, pg. 77

611310 — COLLEGES, UNIVERSITIES, AND PROFESSIONAL SCHOOLS

ACADEMY OF ENGLISH PTY. LIMITED—See Academies Australasia Group Limited; *Int'l*, pg. 77
ACADEMY OF INFORMATION TECHNOLOGY PTY LTD—See iCollege Limited; *Int'l*, pg. 3582
ADTALEM GLOBAL EDUCATION INC.; *U.S. Public*, pg. 43
AEC BILINGUAL PTE LTD.—See AEC Education plc; *Int'l*, pg. 170
AEC COLLEGE PTE. LTD.—See AEC Education plc; *Int'l*, pg. 170
ALLIANT INTERNATIONAL UNIVERSITY-CAMPUS MEXICO, S.C.—See Bertelsmann SE & Co. KGaA; *Int'l*, pg. 990
AMERICAN DENTAL EDUCATION ASSOCIATION; *U.S. Private*, pg. 230
AMERICAN INTERCONTINENTAL UNIVERSITY, INC.—See Perdoceo Education Corporation; *U.S. Public*, pg. 1673
AMERICAN PUBLIC EDUCATION, INC.; *U.S. Public*, pg. 108
AMERICAN PUBLIC UNIVERSITY SYSTEM, INC.—See American Public Education, Inc.; *U.S. Public*, pg. 108
APRENDERE SKOLOR AB; *Int'l*, pg. 522
ARGOSY UNIVERSITY/ATLANTA—See Dream Center Foundation, a California Nonprofit Corp.; *U.S. Private*, pg. 1273
ARGOSY UNIVERSITY/CHICAGO—See Dream Center Foundation, a California Nonprofit Corp.; *U.S. Private*, pg. 1273
ARGOSY UNIVERSITY/DALLAS—See Dream Center Foundation, a California Nonprofit Corp.; *U.S. Private*, pg. 1273
ARGOSY UNIVERSITY/HONOLULU—See Dream Center Foundation, a California Nonprofit Corp.; *U.S. Private*, pg. 1273
ARGOSY UNIVERSITY/ORANGE COUNTY—See Dream Center Foundation, a California Nonprofit Corp.; *U.S. Private*, pg. 1273
ARGOSY UNIVERSITY/PHOENIX—See Dream Center Foundation, a California Nonprofit Corp.; *U.S. Private*, pg. 1273
ARGOSY UNIVERSITY/SARASOTA—See Dream Center Foundation, a California Nonprofit Corp.; *U.S. Private*, pg. 1273
ARGOSY UNIVERSITY/SCHAUMBURG—See Dream Center Foundation, a California Nonprofit Corp.; *U.S. Private*, pg. 1273
ARGOSY UNIVERSITY/SEATTLE—See Dream Center Foundation, a California Nonprofit Corp.; *U.S. Private*, pg. 1273
ARGOSY UNIVERSITY—See Dream Center Foundation, a California Nonprofit Corp.; *U.S. Private*, pg. 1272
ARGOSY UNIVERSITY/TAMPA—See Dream Center Foundation, a California Nonprofit Corp.; *U.S. Private*, pg. 1273
ARGOSY UNIVERSITY/TWIN CITIES—See Dream Center Foundation, a California Nonprofit Corp.; *U.S. Private*, pg. 1273
ARGOSY UNIVERSITY/WASHINGTON DC—See Dream Center Foundation, a California Nonprofit Corp.; *U.S. Private*, pg. 1273
ARIZONA STATE UNIVERSITY; *U.S. Private*, pg. 325
THE ART INSTITUTE ONLINE—See Dream Center Foundation, a California Nonprofit Corp.; *U.S. Private*, pg. 1274
THE ART INSTITUTES INTERNATIONAL LLC—See Dream Center Foundation, a California Nonprofit Corp.; *U.S. Private*, pg. 1274
ASHFORD UNIVERSITY LLC—See University of Arizona; *U.S. Private*, pg. 4308
ASPECT EDUCATION LIMITED—See Graham Holdings Company; *U.S. Public*, pg. 955
ASPEN UNIVERSITY INC—See Aspen Group, Inc.; *U.S. Public*, pg. 213
AVALON AVIATION ACADEMY PRIVATE LIMITED—See Aptech Limited; *Int'l*, pg. 523
BALL STATE UNIVERSITY; *U.S. Private*, pg. 460
BAY STATE COLLEGE—See Ambow Education Holding Ltd.; *Int'l*, pg. 415
BLOOMFIELD COLLEGE—See Montclair State University; *U.S. Private*, pg. 2775
BRIARCLIFFE COLLEGE—See Perdoceo Education Corporation; *U.S. Public*, pg. 1673
THE BRITISH INTERNATIONAL SCHOOL BRATISLAVA—See Canada Pension Plan Investment Board; *Int'l*, pg. 1281
THE BRITISH INTERNATIONAL SCHOOL BRATISLAVA—See EQT AB; *Int'l*, pg. 2470
THE BRITISH INTERNATIONAL SCHOOL BUDAPEST—See Canada Pension Plan Investment Board; *Int'l*, pg. 1281
THE BRITISH INTERNATIONAL SCHOOL BUDAPEST—See EQT AB; *Int'l*, pg. 2470
THE BRITISH INTERNATIONAL SCHOOL SHANGHAI—See Canada Pension Plan Investment Board; *Int'l*, pg. 1281
THE BRITISH INTERNATIONAL SCHOOL SHANGHAI—See EQT AB; *Int'l*, pg. 2470
CALIFORNIA INSTITUTE OF TECHNOLOGY; *U.S. Private*, pg. 719
CAMBRIDGE ARTS & SCIENCE LIMITED—See Bright Scholar Education Holdings Limited; *Int'l*, pg. 1161
CAMBRIDGE SCHOOL OF VISUAL & PERFORMING ARTS LIMITED—See Bright Scholar Education Holdings Limited; *Int'l*, pg. 1161
CAPELLA EDUCATION COMPANY—See Strategic Education, Inc.; *U.S. Public*, pg. 1953
CAPELLA UNIVERSITY, INC.—See Strategic Education, Inc.; *U.S. Public*, pg. 1954
CAREER QUEST LEARNING CENTERS, INC.—See Sverica Capital Management LP; *U.S. Private*, pg. 3888
CATS ACADEMY BOSTON INC.—See Bright Scholar Education Holdings Limited; *Int'l*, pg. 1161
CATS CANTERBURY LIMITED—See Bright Scholar Education Holdings Limited; *Int'l*, pg. 1161
CATS COLLEGE LONDON LIMITED—See Bright Scholar Education Holdings Limited; *Int'l*, pg. 1161
CATS COLLEGES HOLDINGS LIMITED—See Bright Scholar Education Holdings Limited; *Int'l*, pg. 1161
CENTRAL MICHIGAN UNIVERSITY; *U.S. Private*, pg. 822
CENTRO ESCOLAR UNIVERSITY; *Int'l*, pg. 1414
CHINA NEW HIGHER EDUCATION GROUP LIMITED; *Int'l*, pg. 1535
CHINA YUHUA EDUCATION CORPORATION LIMITED; *Int'l*, pg. 1565
THE COLLEGE FOR FINANCIAL PLANNING INSTITUTES CORPORATION—See Graham Holdings Company; *U.S. Public*, pg. 956
COLORADO TECHNICAL UNIVERSITY—See Perdoceo Education Corporation; *U.S. Public*, pg. 1673
CRESCENDO INTERNATIONAL COLLEGE SDN. BHD.—See Crescendo Corporation Berhad; *Int'l*, pg. 1839
DANIEL WEBSTER COLLEGE, INC.—See ITT Educational Services, Inc.; *U.S. Private*, pg. 2150
DASVE HOSPITALITY INSTITUTES LIMITED—See Hindustan Construction Co. Ltd; *Int'l*, pg. 3399
DELAWARE STATE UNIVERSITY; *U.S. Private*, pg. 1195
DENTAL IMPLANT TRAINING CENTER CORP.—See DENTSPLY SIRONA Inc.; *U.S. Public*, pg. 654
DEVRY/NEW YORK, INC.—See Adtalem Global Education Inc.; *U.S. Public*, pg. 43
DEVRY UNIVERSITY—See Adtalem Global Education Inc.; *U.S. Public*, pg. 43
DLORAH, INC.—See National American University Holdings, Inc.; *U.S. Public*, pg. 1493
DREXEL UNIVERSITY; *U.S. Private*, pg. 1276
DUKE UNIVERSITY; *U.S. Private*, pg. 1285
EDVANTAGE INSTITUTE AUSTRALIA PTY. LTD.—See Edvantage Group Holdings Limited; *Int'l*, pg. 2316
EDVANTAGE INSTITUTE (SINGAPORE) PTE. LTD.—See Edvantage Group Holdings Limited; *Int'l*, pg. 2316
EMBRY-RIDDLE AERONAUTICAL UNIVERSITY, ASIA LTD.—See Embry-Riddle Aeronautical University; *U.S. Private*, pg. 1379
EMBRY-RIDDLE AERONAUTICAL UNIVERSITY; *U.S. Private*, pg. 1378
ENGLISH INTERNATIONAL SCHOOL PRAGUE—See Canada Pension Plan Investment Board; *Int'l*, pg. 1281
ENGLISH INTERNATIONAL SCHOOL PRAGUE—See EQT AB; *Int'l*, pg. 2470
ERAU EXTENDED CAMPUS COLLEGE OF CAREER EDUCATION—See Embry-Riddle Aeronautical University; *U.S. Private*, pg. 1379
EUMECOM MEDIZIN INFORMATION FORTBILDING GMBH—See GSK plc; *Int'l*, pg. 3145
FIELMANN AKADEMIE SCHLOSS PLON, GEMEINNUTZIGE BILDUNGSSTATTE DER AUGENOPTIK GMBH—See Fielmann Group AG; *Int'l*, pg. 2658
FOUNDATION GLOBAL EDUCATION LIMITED—See Bright Scholar Education Holdings Limited; *Int'l*, pg. 1161
FPT UNIVERSITY CO. LTD.—See FPT Corporation; *Int'l*, pg. 2758
GAKKEN JUKU HOLDINGS CO., LTD.—See Gakken Holdings Co., Ltd.; *Int'l*, pg. 2869
GAKKEN MEDICAL SUPPORT CO., LTD.—See Gakken Holdings Co., Ltd.; *Int'l*, pg. 2869
GLOBAL BUSINESS COLLEGE OF AUSTRALIA PTY. LTD.—See Edvantage Group Holdings Limited; *Int'l*, pg. 2316
GLOBIS CORPORATION; *Int'l*, pg. 3007
GOG FOUNDATION, INC.; *U.S. Public*, pg. 1726
GO STUDY AUSTRALIA PTY LIMITED—See iCollege Limited; *Int'l*, pg. 3582
GRAND CANYON UNIVERSITY—See Grand Canyon Education, Inc.; *U.S. Public*, pg. 957
GREENWICH ENGLISH COLLEGE PTY LTD—See iCollege Limited; *Int'l*, pg. 3582
GSD EGITIM VAKFI BAHCELIEVLER ILKOKULU—See GSD Holding A.S.; *Int'l*, pg. 3144
HARRINGTON COLLEGE OF DESIGN—See Perdoceo Education Corporation; *U.S. Public*, pg. 1673
HARRINGTON INSTITUTE OF INTERIOR DESIGN, INC.—See Perdoceo Education Corporation; *U.S. Public*, pg. 1673
HMI INSTITUTE OF HEALTH SCIENCES PTE. LTD.—See EQT AB; *Int'l*, pg. 2475
HOLBORN COLLEGE LIMITED—See Graham Holdings Company; *U.S. Public*, pg. 955
IGB INTERNATIONAL SCHOOL SDN. BHD.—See IGB Berhad; *Int'l*, pg. 3601
INTERNATIONAL ACADEMY OF DESIGN AND TECHNOLOGY—See Perdoceo Education Corporation; *U.S. Public*, pg. 1673
INTERNATIONAL ACADEMY OF DESIGN & TECHNOLOGY DETROIT, INC.—See Perdoceo Education Corporation; *U.S. Public*, pg. 1673
INTERNATIONAL ACADEMY OF DESIGN & TECHNOLOGY-NASHVILLE, LLC—See Perdoceo Education Corporation; *U.S. Public*, pg. 1673
INTERNATIONAL ACADEMY OF DESIGN & TECHNOLOGY—See Perdoceo Education Corporation; *U.S. Public*, pg. 1673
INTERNATIONAL SCHOOL OF COLOUR & DESIGN PTY LTD—See iCollege Limited; *Int'l*, pg. 3582
INTERNATIONAL UNIVERSITY OF MONACO, SAM—See Perdoceo Education Corporation; *U.S. Public*, pg. 1673
IT GYMNASIET SVERIGE AB—See Bure Equity AB; *Int'l*, pg. 1221
JOHNS HOPKINS UNIVERSITY; *U.S. Private*, pg. 2226
JONES INTERNATIONAL UNIVERSITY; *U.S. Private*, pg. 2233
THE KATHARINE GIBBS CORPORATION-MELVILLE—See Perdoceo Education Corporation; *U.S. Public*, pg. 1673
KELLER GRADUATE SCHOOL OF MANAGEMENT—See Adtalem Global Education Inc.; *U.S. Public*, pg. 43
LAUREATE EDUCATION, INC.—See KKR & Co. Inc.; *U.S. Public*, pg. 1259
LE CORDON BLEU COLLEGE OF CULINARY ARTS—See Perdoceo Education Corporation; *U.S. Public*, pg. 1673
LE CORDON BLEU COLLEGE OF CULINARY ARTS—See Perdoceo Education Corporation; *U.S. Public*, pg. 1673
MANDER PORTMAN WOODWARD LIMITED—See Graham Holdings Company; *U.S. Public*, pg. 956
MASSACHUSETTS INSTITUTE OF TECHNOLOGY; *U.S. Private*, pg. 2604
MEDICAL UNIVERSITY OF SOUTH CAROLINA; *U.S. Private*, pg. 2656
MGH INSTITUTE OF HEALTH PROFESSIONS—See Partners HealthCare System, Inc.; *U.S. Private*, pg. 3102
MIAMI INTERNATIONAL UNIVERSITY OF ART & DESIGN—See Dream Center Foundation, a California Nonprofit Corp.; *U.S. Private*, pg. 1274
MICHIGAN PUBLIC HEALTH INSTITUTE; *U.S. Private*, pg. 2701
MONTCLAIR STATE UNIVERSITY; *U.S. Private*, pg. 2775
MOUNTAIN AREA HEALTH EDUCATION CENTER; *U.S. Private*, pg. 2798
MOUNT BACHELOR EDUCATIONAL CENTER, INC.—See Acadia Healthcare Company, Inc.; *U.S. Public*, pg. 29
NEW MILLENNIUM ACADEMY LLC—See NRG Energy, Inc.; *U.S. Public*, pg. 1550
NEW YORK INSTITUTE OF TECHNOLOGY; *U.S. Private*, pg. 2910
NORTHAMPTON COMMUNITY COLLEGE; *U.S. Private*, pg. 2948
NORTHWESTERN MEDICAL FACULTY FOUNDATION, INC.—See Northwestern Memorial HealthCare; *U.S. Private*, pg. 2963
OLD DOMINION UNIVERSITY; *U.S. Private*, pg. 3008
POPS ACADEMY AB—See AcadeMedia AB; *Int'l*, pg. 77
PREPNET; *U.S. Public*, pg. 3253
PRESIDENT AND FELLOWS OF HARVARD COLLEGE; *U.S. Private*, pg. 3254
PRIME EDUCATION, LLC—See Ziff Davis, Inc.; *U.S. Public*, pg. 2403
RASMUSSEN COLLEGE, LLC—See Renovus Capital Partners; *U.S. Private*, pg. 3399
RINGLING COLLEGE OF ART AND DESIGN, INC.; *U.S. Private*, pg. 3438
ROBERT MORRIS EXPERIENTIAL COLLEGE—See Roosevelt University; *U.S. Private*, pg. 3480
ROOSEVELT UNIVERSITY; *U.S. Private*, pg. 3480
SEVERN SCHOOL, INC; *U.S. Private*, pg. 3619
SOUTH UNIVERSITY - COLUMBIA—See Dream Center Foundation, a California Nonprofit Corp.; *U.S. Private*, pg. 1273
SOUTH UNIVERSITY - MONTGOMERY—See Dream Center Foundation, a California Nonprofit Corp.; *U.S. Private*, pg. 1273
SOUTH UNIVERSITY—See Dream Center Foundation, a California Nonprofit Corp.; *U.S. Private*, pg. 1273
SOUTH UNIVERSITY - WEST PALM BEACH—See Dream

611310 — COLLEGES, UNIVERSIT...

Center Foundation, a California Nonprofit Corp.; *U.S. Private*, pg. 1273
SPROTT SHAW COLLEGE CORP.—See Global Education Communities Corp; *Int'l*, pg. 2995
STAFFORD HOUSE SCHOOL OF ENGLISH LIMITED—See Bright Scholar Education Holdings Limited; *Int'l*, pg. 1162
STAFFORD HOUSE STUDY HOLIDAYS LIMITED—See Bright Scholar Education Holdings Limited; *Int'l*, pg. 1162
STRATEGIC EDUCATION, INC.; *U.S. Public*, pg. 1953
STRAYER UNIVERSITY—See Strategic Education, Inc.; *U.S. Public*, pg. 1954
SYOEI CO., LTD.—See Gakken Holdings Co., Ltd.; *Int'l*, pg. 2869
THOMAS SCIENTIFIC, LLC; *U.S. Private*, pg. 4157
THUNDERBIRD SCHOOL OF GLOBAL MANAGEMENT—See Arizona State University; *U.S. Private*, pg. 325
TIANJIN UNIVERSITY OF COMMERCE-BOUSTEAD INFORMATICS, LTD.—See Boustead Singapore Limited; *Int'l*, pg. 1121
TOKYO GLOBAL GATEWAY CO., LTD.—See Gakken Holdings Co., Ltd.; *Int'l*, pg. 2869
TRIBECA FLASHPOINT MEDIA ARTS ACADEMY; *U.S. Private*, pg. 4227
UNITED STATES UNIVERSITY, INC.—See Aspen Group, Inc.; *U.S. Public*, pg. 213
UNIVERSITY OF ARIZONA; *U.S. Private*, pg. 4308
UNIVERSITY OF CHICAGO; *U.S. Private*, pg. 4308
UNIVERSITY OF DREAMS, INC.; *U.S. Private*, pg. 4309
UNIVERSITY OF LOUISVILLE; *U.S. Private*, pg. 4309
UNIVERSITY OF MICHIGAN; *U.S. Private*, pg. 4309
THE UNIVERSITY OF OKLAHOMA COLLEGE OF MEDICINE; *U.S. Private*, pg. 4129
UNIVERSITY OF PHOENIX, INC.—See Apollo Global Management, Inc.; *U.S. Public*, pg. 146
UNIVERSITY OF PHOENIX, INC.—See The Vistria Group, LP; *U.S. Private*, pg. 4131
THE UNIVERSITY OF THE ROCKIES—See Zovio Inc.; *U.S. Public*, pg. 2411
WESLEY COLLEGE, INC.—See Delaware State University; *U.S. Private*, pg. 1195
WESTCLIFF UNIVERSITY; *U.S. Private*, pg. 4489
WESTERN STATE UNIVERSITY COLLEGE OF LAW—See Dream Center Foundation, a California Nonprofit Corp.; *U.S. Private*, pg. 1275
YALE UNIVERSITY PRESS; *U.S. Private*, pg. 4585
ZOVIO INC.; *U.S. Public*, pg. 2411

611410 — BUSINESS AND SECRETARIAL SCHOOLS

BRIGHTWOOD CAREER INSTITUTE—See Education Corporation of America; *U.S. Private*, pg. 1338
ENTERPRISE UNIVERSITY—See Enterprise Financial Services Corp; *U.S. Public*, pg. 778
HOLE-IN-THE-WALL EDUCATION LIMITED—See Coforge Ltd.; *Int'l*, pg. 1693
IMD INTERNATIONAL; *Int'l*, pg. 3623
THE KATHARINE GIBBS SCHOOL OF NORWALK, INC.—See Perdoceo Education Corporation; *U.S. Public*, pg. 1673
THE KATHARINE GIBBS SCHOOL OF PISCATAWAY, INC.—See Perdoceo Education Corporation; *U.S. Public*, pg. 1673
PENNSYLVANIA SCHOOL OF BUSINESS, INC.—See EVCI Career Colleges Holding Corp.; *U.S. Private*, pg. 1436
SANFORD-BROWN COLLEGE INC.—See Perdoceo Education Corporation; *U.S. Public*, pg. 1673

611420 — COMPUTER TRAINING

AGLSM SDN. BHD.—See Aptech Limited; *Int'l*, pg. 523
ALKHALEEJ TRAINING & EDUCATION COMPANY; *Int'l*, pg. 331
APTECH LIMITED; *Int'l*, pg. 523
ATLANTIC ASSOCIATES, INC.—See Poch Personnel, Inc.; *U.S. Private*, pg. 3219
AULDHOUSE COMPUTER TRAINING LIMITED—See AWN Holdings Limited; *Int'l*, pg. 753
AVANADE UK LTD.—See Accenture plc; *Int'l*, pg. 85
AWANBIRU TECHNOLOGY BERHAD; *Int'l*, pg. 751
BITS LTD.; *Int'l*, pg. 1050
CANTERBURY CONSULTING GROUP, INC.; *U.S. Private*, pg. 735
CBT NUGGETS, LLC; *U.S. Private*, pg. 797
CENTRE DE FORMATION EN HOMEOPATHIE LLC—See Boiron Group; *Int'l*, pg. 1101
CENTRE D ENSEIGNEMENT ET DE DEVELOPPEMENT DE L'HOMEOPATHIE LLC—See Boiron Group; *Int'l*, pg. 1101
COMPUTER TRAINING ASSOCIATES OF CHICAGO, INC.—See Camden Partners Holdings, LLC; *U.S. Private*, pg. 728
COMPUTER TRAINING SOURCE INC.; *U.S. Private*, pg. 1005

DDLS AUSTRALIA PTY LTD—See AWN Holdings Limited; *Int'l*, pg. 753
DPT CONSULTING GROUP, INC.; *U.S. Private*, pg. 1271
EDUCATION EXPERIENCES, INC.—See MidOcean Partners, LLP; *U.S. Private*, pg. 2716
EDUCOM CORPORATION—See EQT AB; *Int'l*, pg. 2467
EXITCERTIFIED CORP.—See Avnet, Inc.; *U.S. Public*, pg. 253
EXIT CERTIFIED LTD.—See Avnet, Inc.; *U.S. Public*, pg. 253
FUJI ELECTRIC IT CENTER CO., LTD.—See Fuji Electric Co., Ltd.; *Int'l*, pg. 2811
GLOBAL KNOWLEDGE TRAINING CENTER-VICTORIA—See MidOcean Partners, LLP; *U.S. Private*, pg. 2716
GLOBAL KNOWLEDGE TRAINING LLC—See MidOcean Partners, LLP; *U.S. Private*, pg. 2716
GROWEL SOFTECH LTD.—See Grauer & Weil India Limited; *Int'l*, pg. 3061
HERZING, INC.; *U.S. Private*, pg. 1927
INE, INC.; *U.S. Private*, pg. 2069
INEOQUEST TECHNOLOGIES DEUTSCHLAND GMBH—See Genstar Capital, LLC; *U.S. Private*, pg. 1679
INTERACTIVE STUDY SYSTEMS, INC.; *U.S. Private*, pg. 2108
ITC AUSTRALASIA PTY LTD—See ITC Learning Corp.; *U.S. Private*, pg. 2149
THE JAPAN INSTITUTE FOR EDUCATIONAL MEASUREMENT, INC.—See EduLab, Inc.; *Int'l*, pg. 2316
KOCHI SOFTWARE CENTER LTD.—See Computer Institute of Japan Ltd.; *Int'l*, pg. 1759
LANTEC OF LOUISIANA, LLC; *U.S. Private*, pg. 2391
LEARNING TREE INTERNATIONAL, INC.; *U.S. Public*, pg. 1298
LICENSE TECHNOLOGIES GROUP, INC.—See Dell Technologies Inc.; *U.S. Public*, pg. 650
LOGICAL OPERATIONS INC.; *U.S. Private*, pg. 2481
LUMIFY LEARN PTY. LTD.—See AWN Holdings Limited; *Int'l*, pg. 753
LURN INC.; *U.S. Private*, pg. 2516
MARLABS, INC.—See Marlabs, Inc.; *U.S. Private*, pg. 2583
MAX TECHNICAL TRAINING; *U.S. Private*, pg. 2617
MCAD DESIGN, INC.; *U.S. Private*, pg. 2625
METRON U.S., INC.—See Fortive Corporation; *U.S. Public*, pg. 871
MICROTEK; *U.S. Private*, pg. 2704
MONARCH MEDIA, INC.; *U.S. Private*, pg. 2769
N3K INFORMATIK GMBH—See DZ BANK AG Deutsche Zentral-Genossenschaftsbank; *Int'l*, pg. 2245
NEW HORIZONS COMPUTER LEARNING CENTER OF CLEVELAND, LLC—See Camden Partners Holdings, LLC; *U.S. Private*, pg. 728
NEW HORIZONS COMPUTER LEARNING CENTER OF METROPOLITAN NEW YORK, INC.—See Camden Partners Holdings, LLC; *U.S. Private*, pg. 728
NEW HORIZONS COMPUTER LEARNING CENTER OF SOUTHERN CALIFORNIA—See Camden Partners Holdings, LLC; *U.S. Private*, pg. 728
NIIT TECHNOLOGIES FZ LLC—See Coforge Ltd.; *Int'l*, pg. 1693
NIIT TECHNOLOGIES PTE LTD—See Coforge Ltd.; *Int'l*, pg. 1693
NIIT TECHNOLOGIES PTY LIMITED—See Coforge Ltd.; *Int'l*, pg. 1693
NXTDIGITAL LIMITED—See Hinduja Global Solutions Ltd.; *Int'l*, pg. 3398
ONCOURSE LEARNING CORPORATION—See Bertelsmann SE & Co. KGaA; *Int'l*, pg. 990
ONLINE CONSULTING, INC.; *U.S. Private*, pg. 3027
ORGANA TECHNOLOGIES GROUP INC.; *U.S. Public*, pg. 1615
PARITY TRAINING LIMITED—See ECS Limited; *Int'l*, pg. 2301
PC AGE, INC.; *U.S. Private*, pg. 3119
PREFERRED SOLUTIONS; *U.S. Private*, pg. 3248
QUADRATICA (UK) LIMITED—See OSI Systems, Inc.; *U.S. Public*, pg. 1622
QUASIUS INVESTMENT CORP.; *U.S. Private*, pg. 3324
QUICKSTART INTELLIGENCE, CORP.—See 360training.com, Inc.; *U.S. Private*, pg. 8
RAZORLEAF CORPORATION; *U.S. Private*, pg. 3360
REDVECTOR.COM, LLC—See Genstar Capital, LLC; *U.S. Private*, pg. 1679
SGC KNOWLEDGE TRANSFER LTD.—See Aerodrome Group Ltd.; *Int'l*, pg. 181
SMARTWORKS, LLC—See SharedLABS, Inc.; *U.S. Private*, pg. 3626
STRATEGIC SIMULATION & ANALYSIS LTD.—See Addnode Group AB; *Int'l*, pg. 130
SULLIVAN & COGLIANO TRAINING CENTERS INC.—See Sullivan & Cogliano Designers Inc.; *U.S. Private*, pg. 3850
TECHSKILLS, LLC; *U.S. Private*, pg. 3956
TIGER INFORMATION SYSTEMS INC.; *U.S. Private*, pg. 4169
TIPPING POINT SOLUTIONS, INC.; *U.S. Private*, pg. 4176
TOOLWIRE, INC.; *U.S. Private*, pg. 4186

TRAIN SIGNAL INC.; *U.S. Private*, pg. 4204
TRAVELING COACHES, INC; *U.S. Private*, pg. 4214
TREEHOUSE ISLAND INC.; *U.S. Private*, pg. 4217
UNITED GLOBAL RESOURCES LIMITED—See Emivest Berhad; *Int'l*, pg. 2383
VIDEO PROFESSOR INC.; *U.S. Private*, pg. 4380
WTT CAMPUSONE GMBH—See EnBW Energie Baden-Wurttemberg AG; *Int'l*, pg. 2400
XCHANGE SOFTWARE; *U.S. Private*, pg. 4580

611430 — PROFESSIONAL AND MANAGEMENT DEVELOPMENT TRAINING

30DC, INC.; *U.S. Private*, pg. 7
ACHIEVENEXT, LLC; *U.S. Private*, pg. 59
ACUMEN LEARNING, LLC; *U.S. Private*, pg. 71
ADAYANA INC.—See Comvest Group Holdings LLC; *U.S. Private*, pg. 1007
ADAYANA, INC.—See Comvest Group Holdings LLC; *U.S. Private*, pg. 1007
ADAYANA LEARNING SOLUTIONS PVT LTD—See Comvest Group Holdings LLC; *U.S. Private*, pg. 1007
ADVANCED BROADBAND NETWORK COMPANY LIMITED—See Advanced Info Service Plc; *Int'l*, pg. 159
ADVANCED LEARNING CENTERS, INC.; *U.S. Private*, pg. 90
ADVANTAGE PERFORMANCE GROUP—See BTS Group AB; *Int'l*, pg. 1205
AEROSIM, INC.—See Lincolnshire Management, Inc.; *U.S. Private*, pg. 2459
AIRT ACADEMY OF INFRARED TRAINING INC.—See Cantronic Systems Inc.; *Int'l*, pg. 1299
AKADEMIA UMIEJETNOSCI EUROCASH SP. Z O.O.—See Eurocash S.A.; *Int'l*, pg. 2533
ALLGEIER EDUCATION GMBH—See Allgeier SE; *Int'l*, pg. 336
ALTIOR CONSULTING & TRAINING LIMITED—See Leeds Equity Partners, LLC; *U.S. Private*, pg. 2414
AMERICAN ACADEMY OF DERMATOLOGY; *U.S. Private*, pg. 221
AMERICAN SOCIETY OF SAFETY ENGINEERS; *U.S. Private*, pg. 254
APOSPHARE GMBH—See IQVIA Holdings Inc.; *U.S. Public*, pg. 1168
ASSESSMENT TECHNOLOGIES INSTITUTE, LLC—See Blackstone Inc.; *U.S. Public*, pg. 348
ASSESSMENT TECHNOLOGIES INSTITUTE, LLC—See Canada Pension Plan Investment Board; *Int'l*, pg. 1279
AXIOS VALUATION SOLUTIONS, LLC—See Assurant, Inc.; *U.S. Public*, pg. 215
BEIJER REF ACADEMY LTD.—See Beijer Ref AB; *Int'l*, pg. 944
BERUFSBILDUNGSGESELLSCHAFT GEORGSMARIEN-HUTTE MBH—See Georgsmarienhutte Holding GmbH; *Int'l*, pg. 2940
BHARTI RESOURCES LTD.—See Bharti Enterprises Limited; *Int'l*, pg. 1013
BIGVISIBLE SOLUTIONS, INC.; *U.S. Private*, pg. 556
BLP TRAINING & SERVICES PTY. LTD.; *Int'l*, pg. 1065
BRISTOL MANAGEMENT CENTRE LIMITED—See KBR, Inc.; *U.S. Public*, pg. 1215
BTS BILBAO—See BTS Group AB; *Int'l*, pg. 1205
BTS BRUSSELS NV—See BTS Group AB; *Int'l*, pg. 1205
BTS CHICAGO LIMITED—See BTS Group AB; *Int'l*, pg. 1205
BTS CONSULTING (SHANGHAI) CO., LTD.—See BTS Group AB; *Int'l*, pg. 1205
BTS GROUP AB; *Int'l*, pg. 1205
BTS IN AMSTERDAM BV—See BTS Group AB; *Int'l*, pg. 1205
BTS MANAGEMENT SA—See BTS Group AB; *Int'l*, pg. 1205
BTS MEXICO—See BTS Group AB; *Int'l*, pg. 1205
BTS SCOTTSDALE—See BTS Group AB; *Int'l*, pg. 1205
BTS SEOUL—See BTS Group AB; *Int'l*, pg. 1205
BTS STAMFORD—See BTS Group AB; *Int'l*, pg. 1205
BTS STOCKHOLM—See BTS Group AB; *Int'l*, pg. 1205
BTS SVERIGE AB—See BTS Group AB; *Int'l*, pg. 1205
BTS TOKYO—See BTS Group AB; *Int'l*, pg. 1205
BTS UNITED STATES—See BTS Group AB; *Int'l*, pg. 1205
BTS USA, INC.—See BTS Group AB; *Int'l*, pg. 1205
BUILD-A-BEAR RETAIL MANAGEMENT, INC.—See Build-A-Bear Workshop, Inc.; *U.S. Public*, pg. 409
BUSINESS TRAINING LIBRARY; *U.S. Private*, pg. 695
BUSINESS TRAINING SOLUTIONS S.L.—See BTS Group AB; *Int'l*, pg. 1205
CADMES FRANCE S.A.S.—See Bechtle AG; *Int'l*, pg. 937
CAMBER CORPORATION—See Huntington Ingalls Industries, Inc.; *U.S. Public*, pg. 1072
CAREER BLAZERS LEARNING CENTER OF LOS ANGELES, INC.—See Deutsche Bank Aktiengesellschaft; *Int'l*, pg. 2055
CAREER PATH TRAINING CORP.; *U.S. Private*, pg. 752
CATALYSTS FOR PROFITABILITY AND GROWTH LTD—See BTS Group AB; *Int'l*, pg. 1205
CENTER FOR CREATIVE LEADERSHIP (CCL) PTE

611430 — PROFESSIONAL AND MA...

LTD—See Center for Creative Leadership Inc.; *U.S. Private*, pg. 810
CENTRE FOR EXCELLENCE IN RAIL TRAINING PTY. LTD.—See Engenco Limited; *Int'l*, pg. 2426
CENTUM LEARNING LIMITED—See Bharti Enterprises Limited; *Int'l*, pg. 1013
CGG TECHNOLOGY SERVICES (BEIJING) CO. LTD.—See CGG; *Int'l*, pg. 1432
CHEVIOT RECRUITMENT LTD—See MAXIMUS, Inc.; *U.S. Public*, pg. 1402
CHILDREN'S LITERACY INITIATIVE; *U.S. Private*, pg. 885
CHINA EXECUTIVE EDUCATION CORP.; *Int'l*, pg. 1501
CL EDUCATE LIMITED; *Int'l*, pg. 1640
CLICKSAFETY.COM, INC.—See Blackstone Inc.; *U.S. Public*, pg. 348
CLICKSAFETY.COM, INC.—See Canada Pension Plan Investment Board; *Int'l*, pg. 1279
CMI INTERNATIONAL—See Terex Corporation; *U.S. Public*, pg. 2018
COACH A CO., LTD; *Int'l*, pg. 1680
COACH U, INC.—See COACH A Co., Ltd; *Int'l*, pg. 1680
COLLECTIVE LEARNING AND DEVELOPMENT PTY LTD—See Collection House Limited; *Int'l*, pg. 1699
CONSEL CONSORZIO ELIS—See Corpay, Inc.; *U.S. Public*, pg. 579
CONSTRUCTION STUDY CENTRE LIMITED—See Costain Group PLC; *Int'l*, pg. 1814
CRITICAL INFORMATION NETWORK, LLC—See Comvest Group Holdings LLC; *U.S. Private*, pg. 1007
CS DISCO INDIA PRIVATE LTD.—See CS Disco, Inc.; *U.S. Public*, pg. 600
CSG SKILLS INSTITUTE PROPRIETARY LIMITED—See CSG Holdings Limited; *Int'l*, pg. 1864
CUX, INC.—See Udemy, Inc.; *U.S. Public*, pg. 2217
DALE CARNEGIE DENMARK—See Dale Carnegie & Associates, Inc.; *U.S. Private*, pg. 1148
THE DALLAS COUNTY LOCAL WORKFORCE DEVELOPMENT BOARD, INC.; *U.S. Private*, pg. 1504
DALLOZ FORMATION, SAS—See Editions Lefebvre Sarrut SA; *Int'l*, pg. 2311
DC BERLIN TRAINING GBR—See Dale Carnegie & Associates, Inc.; *U.S. Private*, pg. 1148
DCD TRAINING GMBH—See Dale Carnegie & Associates, Inc.; *U.S. Private*, pg. 1148
DEKRA AKADEMIE GMBH—See DEKRA e.V.; *Int'l*, pg. 2008
DEMOS (BEIJING) MANAGEMENT & TECHNICAL TRAINING CO., LTD.—See Demos S.A.; *Int'l*, pg. 2025
DEMOS BENELUX—See Demos S.A.; *Int'l*, pg. 2025
DEMOS GMBH—See Demos S.A.; *Int'l*, pg. 2025
DEMOS MIDDLE EAST FZ—See Demos S.A.; *Int'l*, pg. 2025
DEMOS POLSKA SP. Z O.O.—See Demos S.A.; *Int'l*, pg. 2026
DEMOS S.A.; *Int'l*, pg. 2025
DENSO E & TS TRAINING CENTER CORPORATION—See Denso Corporation; *Int'l*, pg. 2029
DIGITAL SPIRIT GMBH—See IDOX PLC; *Int'l*, pg. 3596
DIOREM—See Capgemini SE; *Int'l*, pg. 1305
DISTRIBUTIVE EDUCATION CLUBS OF AMERICA, INC.; *U.S. Private*, pg. 1239
DR. THOMAS + PARTNER GMBH & CO. KG; *Int'l*, pg. 2195
EAGLE EDUCATION & TRAINING LIMITED—See Graham Holdings Company; *U.S. Public*, pg. 954
EAGLE PRODUCTIVITY SOLUTIONS; *U.S. Private*, pg. 1310
E.C.P. LIMITED—See Edenred S.A.; *Int'l*, pg. 2307
EDIFIST LEARNING INC.—See Canon Inc.; *Int'l*, pg. 1296
EDSINC.; *U.S. Private*, pg. 1338
EDUCATE 360 LLC—See Morgan Stanley; *U.S. Public*, pg. 1474
EDUGRADE AB—See Hexatronic Group AB; *Int'l*, pg. 3370
ELEGIA FORMATION, SAS—See Editions Lefebvre Sarrut SA; *Int'l*, pg. 2311
THE EMMES COMPANY, LLC—See Behrman Brothers Management Corp.; *U.S. Private*, pg. 515
E.ON BUILDING SERVICES ACADEMY—See E.ON SE; *Int'l*, pg. 2252
EPATH LEARNING, INC.—See Welsh, Carson, Anderson & Stowe; *U.S. Private*, pg. 4479
E.R.J. INSURANCE GROUP, INC.—See The Allstate Corporation; *U.S. Public*, pg. 2033
ESB-GEMEINNUTZIGE GESELLSCHAFT FUR BERUFLICHE BILDUNG MBH—See Asklepios Kliniken GmbH & Co. KGaA; *Int'l*, pg. 624
ESSI SYSTEMS, INC.—See Accor S.A.; *Int'l*, pg. 91
EUROFINS CTC GMBH—See Eurofins Scientific S.E.; *Int'l*, pg. 2541
EUROMONEY TRAINING, INC.—See Astorg Partners S.A.S.; *Int'l*, pg. 656
EUROMONEY TRAINING, INC.—See Epiris Managers LLP; *Int'l*, pg. 2460
EXPLAY, INC.—See Gree Inc.; *Int'l*, pg. 3069
FACTS EDUCATION SOLUTIONS, LLC—See Nelnet, Inc.; *U.S. Public*, pg. 1504
FIERCE INC.; *U.S. Private*, pg. 1504
FORMADEMOS RABAT—See Demos S.A.; *Int'l*, pg. 2026
FORMENERG S.A.—See CNTEE TRANSELECTRICA SA; *Int'l*, pg. 1678
THE FORUM CORPORATION—See Providence Equity Partners L.L.C.; *U.S. Private*, pg. 3293
FORUM EUROPE LTD.—See Providence Equity Partners L.L.C.; *U.S. Private*, pg. 3294
FRANCIS LEFEBVRE FORMATION SAS—See Editions Lefebvre Sarrut SA; *Int'l*, pg. 2311
FUJI XEROX LEARNING INSTITUTE INC.—See FUJIFILM Holdings Corporation; *Int'l*, pg. 2826
THE G2G3 GROUP LTD.—See Capita plc; *Int'l*, pg. 1309
GALFAR TRAINING INSTITUTE LLC—See Galfar Engineering & Contracting SAOG; *Int'l*, pg. 2872
GENESYSWORKS; *U.S. Private*, pg. 1670
GENOVASI MALAYSIA SDN. BHD.—See Ancom Nylex Berhad; *Int'l*, pg. 449
GLK ENTERPRISES, INC.—See Francisco Partners Management, LP; *U.S. Private*, pg. 1588
GLOBAL EXPERIENCE SPECIALISTS (GES) LIMITED—See Viad Corp.; *U.S. Public*, pg. 2291
GLOBAL STRATEGIC MANAGEMENT INSTITUTE (GSMI); *U.S. Private*, pg. 1718
GORDON FRANKS TRAINING LTD.—See Hexatronic Group AB; *Int'l*, pg. 3370
GRACELAND COLLEGE CENTER FOR PROFESSIONAL DEVELOPMENT AND LIFELONG LEARNING, INC.; *U.S. Private*, pg. 1749
GROOVER SEMINARS, INC.; *U.S. Private*, pg. 1792
GSEVEN; *U.S. Private*, pg. 3144
HAYS SOCIAL CARE LIMITED—See Hays PLC; *Int'l*, pg. 3293
HEALTH CARE COMPLIANCE STRATEGIES, INC.—See HealthStream, Inc.; *U.S. Public*, pg. 1017
HELLIER NDT, INC.—See Rockwood Holdings Limited Partnership; *U.S. Private*, pg. 3468
HEMSLEY FRASER AUSTRALIA PTY LTD—See Demos S.A.; *Int'l*, pg. 2026
HEMSLEY FRASER GROUP LIMITED—See Demos S.A.; *Int'l*, pg. 2026
HEMSLEY FRASER US—See Demos S.A.; *Int'l*, pg. 2026
HITACHI ACADEMY CO., LTD.—See Hitachi, Ltd.; *Int'l*, pg. 3413
HOKUDEN PARTNER SERVICE INC.—See Hokuriku Electric Power Co.; *Int'l*, pg. 3445
HOOKS-YENSON LLC—See Parnassus Books LLC; *U.S. Private*, pg. 3099
HPTI HAMBURG PORT TRAINING INSTITUTE GMBH—See Hamburger Hafen und Logistik AG; *Int'l*, pg. 3236
HUTHWAITE INC.—See Providence Equity Partners L.L.C.; *U.S. Private*, pg. 3292
IDEATION TRAINING PTY LTD.; *Int'l*, pg. 3589
INDUSTRIAL TRAINING INTERNATIONAL, INC.—See Interplay Learning Inc.; *U.S. Private*, pg. 2123
INMEDIO SP. Z O.O.—See Eurocash S.A.; *Int'l*, pg. 2533
INTERNATIONAL INSTITUTE FOR LEARNING, INC.; *U.S. Private*, pg. 2118
INTERNATIONAL INSTITUTE FOR TRAUMA AND ADDICTION PROFESSIONALS; *U.S. Private*, pg. 2118
INTERNATIONAL UNION OF PAINTERS AND ALLIED TRADES; *U.S. Private*, pg. 2121
INTERPLAY LEARNING INC.; *U.S. Private*, pg. 2123
INTREPID LEARNING, INC.—See Ingram Industries, Inc.; *U.S. Private*, pg. 2076
INVISIBLE CLOSE; *U.S. Private*, pg. 2133
JHT, INC.; *U.S. Private*, pg. 2208
KAPLAN FINANCIAL LIMITED—See Graham Holdings Company; *U.S. Public*, pg. 955
KAPLAN HIGHER EDUCATION ACADEMY PTE. LTD.—See Graham Holdings Company; *U.S. Public*, pg. 955
KELLEHER ASSOCIATES, LLC—See AchieveNext, LLC; *U.S. Private*, pg. 59
KINGSLEY INTERNATIONAL SDN. BHD.—See China Maple Leaf Educational Systems Limited; *Int'l*, pg. 1517
KNOWLEDGE ANYWHERE, INC.; *U.S. Private*, pg. 2333
KONSULTBOLAG1 SYD AB—See AFRY AB; *Int'l*, pg. 194
KT ANDINA S.A.C.—See Kepner-Tregoe, Inc.; *U.S. Private*, pg. 2290
LANDER SIMULATION & TRAINING SOLUTIONS, S.A.—See Construcciones y Auxiliar de Ferrocarriles S.A.; *Int'l*, pg. 1777
LANDMARK EDUCATION SERVICES—See Irish Times; *U.S. Private*, pg. 2139
LANGUAGE TRAINING CENTER; *U.S. Private*, pg. 2390
LEARNING TREE INTERNATIONAL AB—See Learning Tree International, Inc.; *U.S. Public*, pg. 1298
LEARNING TREE INTERNATIONAL INC.—See Learning Tree International, Inc.; *U.S. Public*, pg. 1298
LEARNING TREE INTERNATIONAL, K.K.—See Learning Tree International, Inc.; *U.S. Public*, pg. 1298
LEARNING TREE INTERNATIONAL LTD.—See Learning Tree International, Inc.; *U.S. Public*, pg. 1298
LIUNA MIDWEST REGION; *U.S. Private*, pg. 2472
LOCKHEED MARTIN SIMULATION, TRAINING & SUPPORT—See Lockheed Martin Corporation; *U.S. Public*, pg. 1338
LOCKHEED MARTIN SIMULATION, TRAINING & SUPPORT—See Lockheed Martin Corporation; *U.S. Public*, pg. 1338
LOGISTICS & INFORMATION TECHNOLOGY (LOGIT) DIVISION—See Management Training & Consulting Inc.; *U.S. Private*, pg. 2561
MANAGEMENT CONSULTANCY INTERNATIONAL PTY LTD.—See Madison Dearborn Partners, LLC; *U.S. Private*, pg. 2540
THE MANAGEMENT EDGE, INC.; *U.S. Private*, pg. 4074
MANHATTAN REVIEW INC.; *U.S. Private*, pg. 2563
MARYLAND STATE EDUCATION ASSOCIATION; *U.S. Private*, pg. 2600
MCAFEE INSTITUTE, INC.; *U.S. Private*, pg. 2625
MENTORCLIQ, INC.; *U.S. Private*, pg. 2667
MENTOR MANAGEMENT, INC.—See Centerbridge Partners, L.P.; *U.S. Private*, pg. 814
MGE MANAGEMENT EXPERTS, INC.; *U.S. Private*, pg. 2694
THE MILES GROUP, LLC; *U.S. Private*, pg. 4079
MILLENNIUM COMMUNICATIONS GROUP LLC; *U.S. Private*, pg. 2731
MIRUCA CORPORATION—See DTS Corporation; *Int'l*, pg. 2217
MIS TRAINING INSTITUTE, LLC—See Astorg Partners S.A.S.; *Int'l*, pg. 656
MIS TRAINING INSTITUTE, LLC—See Epiris Managers LLP; *Int'l*, pg. 2460
MITT AUSTRALIA PTY. LTD.—See Atlassian Corporation; *Int'l*, pg. 686
THE MOSAIC COMPANY; *U.S. Private*, pg. 4081
MOTIVATING THE MASSES, INC.; *U.S. Public*, pg. 1477
MPIRICAL LIMITED—See Hexatronic Group AB; *Int'l*, pg. 3371
NAPW, INC.—See Professional Diversity Network, Inc.; *U.S. Public*, pg. 1724
NAR TRAINING, LLC—See Henry Schein, Inc.; *U.S. Public*, pg. 1027
NATIONAL ENVIRONMENTAL TRAINERS INC.—See Frontenac Company LLC; *U.S. Private*, pg. 1614
NATURAL CAPITALISM SOLUTIONS; *U.S. Private*, pg. 2867
NEXT STEP LEARNING INC.; *U.S. Private*, pg. 2920
NEXUM INC.; *U.S. Private*, pg. 2922
NIIT LEARNING LIMITED—See Car & General (Kenya) Limited; *Int'l*, pg. 1319
ORBIS OPERATIONS, LLC—See McNally Capital, LLC; *U.S. Private*, pg. 2643
PANYATARA CO., LTD.—See C.P. All Public Company Limited; *Int'l*, pg. 1244
PARADIGM LEARNING, INC.—See Hammond, Kennedy, Whitney & Company, Inc.; *U.S. Private*, pg. 1850
PERSONAL STRENGTHS PUBLISHING, INC.—See Leeds Equity Partners, LLC; *U.S. Private*, pg. 2415
PHARMACEUTICAL INSTITUTE, LLC—See Elliott Management Corporation; *U.S. Private*, pg. 1365
PHARMACEUTICAL INSTITUTE, LLC—See Patient Square Capital, L.P.; *U.S. Private*, pg. 3108
PHARMACEUTICAL INSTITUTE, LLC—See Veritas Capital Fund Management, LLC; *U.S. Private*, pg. 4365
POTOMAC RIVER GROUP, LLC; *U.S. Private*, pg. 3235
PRAGOEDUCA A.S.—See Demos S.A.; *Int'l*, pg. 2026
PROFESSIONAL CONVENTION MANAGEMENT ASSOCIATION; *U.S. Private*, pg. 3274
PT. LEARNING RESOURCES—See Empresaria Group Plc; *Int'l*, pg. 2389
QA LTD.—See COFRA Holding AG; *Int'l*, pg. 1693
RAYTHEON PROFESSIONAL SERVICES LLC—See RTX Corporation; *U.S. Public*, pg. 1825
REDROCK LEADERSHIP; *U.S. Private*, pg. 3379
REDVECTOR.COM, LLC—See Providence Equity Partners L.L.C.; *U.S. Private*, pg. 3294
RELIAS LEARNING LLC—See Bertelsmann SE & Co. KGaA; *Int'l*, pg. 991
THE ROCKET COMPANY; *U.S. Private*, pg. 4111
ROSEMOOR FOUNDATION, INC.; *U.S. Private*, pg. 3483
SAFETY SERVICES COMPANY; *U.S. Private*, pg. 2624
SALES OPTIMIZER LLC; *U.S. Private*, pg. 3532
SEMINUS GMBH—See Groupe Industriel Marcel Dassault S.A.; *Int'l*, pg. 3105
SHELL ROBERT TRAINING & CONFERENCE CENTER—See ConocoPhillips; *U.S. Public*, pg. 569
SINGER BUSINESS SCHOOL (PVT) LTD.—See Hayleys PLC; *Int'l*, pg. 3292
SMITH SYSTEM DRIVER IMPROVEMENT INSTITUTE INC.—See MidOcean Partners, LLP; *U.S. Private*, pg. 2717
STAFF DEVELOPMENT FOR EDUCATORS, INC.—See Highlights for Children, Inc.; *U.S. Private*, pg. 1940
STATISTICS.COM, LLC—See Elder Research Inc.; *U.S. Private*, pg. 1351
SUREHAND, INC.—See Stanley Black & Decker, Inc.; *U.S. Public*, pg. 1936
TALENTFIRST LLC; *U.S. Private*, pg. 3926
TEAM-CRUCIBLE, LLC; *U.S. Private*, pg. 3950
TEO TRAINING LIMITED—See Financial Index Australia Pty Ltd.; *Int'l*, pg. 2665
TERRA INFORMATION GROUP, INC (TIG)—See HR Path SAS; *Int'l*, pg. 3501
THINKETHBANK CO., LTD.—See Bain Capital, LP; *U.S. Private*, pg. 435
THE TRAINING ASSOCIATES (TTA); *U.S. Private*, pg. 4127

611430 — PROFESSIONAL AND MA...

TRAININGFOLKS; *U.S. Private*, pg. 4204
TTC INNOVATIONS; *U.S. Private*, pg. 4254
TTC TRAINING CENTER UNTERNEHMENSBERATUNG GMBH—See Assicurazioni Generali S.p.A.; *Int'l*, pg. 645
TURBINE INCUBATOR LIMITED—See ENL Limited; *Int'l*, pg. 2442
TWENTYEIGHTY, INC.—See Providence Equity Partners L.L.C.; *U.S. Private*, pg. 3294
UMBC TRAINING CENTERS; *U.S. Private*, pg. 4278
UNITED STATES SOCIETY ON DAMS; *U.S. Private*, pg. 4300
UNIVERSAL ACCOUNTING CENTER; *U.S. Private*, pg. 4303
VISTAGE FLORIDA—See Providence Equity Partners L.L.C.; *U.S. Private*, pg. 3294
VISUAL AWARENESS TECHNOLOGIES & CONSULTING, INC.; *U.S. Private*, pg. 4404
VISUALZ—See Vomela Specialty Company; *U.S. Private*, pg. 4412
VITALSMARTS LLC—See Leeds Equity Partners, LLC; *U.S. Private*, pg. 2415
VIZUAL LEARNING PLC—See Automatic Data Processing, Inc.; *U.S. Public*, pg. 230
WATERMARK LEARNING, INC.—See Morgan Stanley; *U.S. Public*, pg. 1474
WORK OPTIONS GROUP, INC.—See Bain Capital, LP; *U.S. Private*, pg. 437
XCELERATE MEDIA; *U.S. Private*, pg. 4580
XCEO, INC.; *U.S. Private*, pg. 4580

611511 — COSMETOLOGY AND BARBER SCHOOLS

BEAUTY BARRAGE, LLC; *U.S. Private*, pg. 508
B&H EDUCATION, INC.; *U.S. Private*, pg. 418
EUPHORIA ACQUISITION, LLC—See Lincoln Educational Services Corporation; *U.S. Public*, pg. 1316
LORAINE'S ACADEMY, INC.; *U.S. Private*, pg. 2494
MARINELLO SCHOOLS OF BEAUTY—See B&H Education, Inc.; *U.S. Private*, pg. 418
OGLE SCHOOL MANAGEMENT LLC—See The RLJ Companies, LLC; *U.S. Private*, pg. 4111
TRICOCI UNIVERSITY OF BEAUTY CULTURE—See NCK Capital LLC; *U.S. Private*, pg. 2876

611512 — FLIGHT TRAINING

AIRBALTIC TRAINING—See Air Baltic Corporation AS; *Int'l*, pg. 236
AIRBORNE TACTICAL ADVANTAGE COMPANY, LLC—See Textron Inc.; *U.S. Public*, pg. 2028
AIRBUS HELICOPTERS TRAINING SERVICES—See Airbus SE; *Int'l*, pg. 243
ALCHEMIST AVIATION PVT. LTD.—See Alchemist Ltd; *Int'l*, pg. 300
APFT BERHAD; *Int'l*, pg. 512
ASIAN AVIATION CENTRE OF EXCELLENCE SDN BHD—See AirAsia X Berhad; *Int'l*, pg. 241
AVIATION INSTITUTE OF MAINTENANCE- INDIANAPOLIS—See Centura College; *U.S. Private*, pg. 830
AVIATION INSTITUTE OF MAINTENANCE—See Centura College; *U.S. Private*, pg. 830
BABCOCK DEFENCE & SECURITY SERVICES—See Babcock International Group PLC; *Int'l*, pg. 792
BANGKOK AIR AVIATION TRAINING CENTER CO., LTD.—See Bangkok Airways Public Company Limited; *Int'l*, pg. 832
BOEING TRAINING & FLIGHT SERVICES AUSTRALIA PTY LTD—See The Boeing Company; *U.S. Public*, pg. 2040
BOEING TRAINING & FLIGHT SERVICES—See The Boeing Company; *U.S. Public*, pg. 2039
CAE AVIATION TRAINING PERU S.A.—See CAE Inc.; *Int'l*, pg. 1248
CAE BRUNEI MULTI PURPOSE TRAINING CENTRE SDN BHD—See CAE Inc.; *Int'l*, pg. 1248
CAE CENTER BRUSSELS N.V.—See CAE Inc.; *Int'l*, pg. 1248
CAE CENTRE COPENHAGEN A/S—See CAE Inc.; *Int'l*, pg. 1248
CAE CENTRE HONG KONG LIMITED—See CAE Inc.; *Int'l*, pg. 1248
CAE CENTRE OSLO AS—See CAE Inc.; *Int'l*, pg. 1248
CAE CENTRE STOCKHOLM AB—See CAE Inc.; *Int'l*, pg. 1248
CAE CIVIL AVIATION TRAINING SOLUTION, INC.; *U.S. Private*, pg. 713
CAE COLOMBIA FLIGHT TRAINING S.A.S.—See CAE Inc.; *Int'l*, pg. 1248
CAE DOSS AVIATION, INC.—See CAE Inc.; *Int'l*, pg. 1248
CAE ELEKTRONIK GMBH—See CAE Inc.; *Int'l*, pg. 1248
CAE FLIGHT TRAINING CENTER MEXICO, S.A. DE C.V.—See CAE Inc.; *Int'l*, pg. 1248
CAE FLIGHT TRAINING (INDIA) PRIVATE LIMITED—See CAE Inc.; *Int'l*, pg. 1248
CAE ICELANDAIR FLIGHT TRAINING EHF.—See Icelandair Group hf.; *Int'l*, pg. 3579
CAE KUALA LUMPUR SDN BHD—See CAE Inc.; *Int'l*, pg. 1249
CAE NORTH EAST TRAINING INC.—See CAE Inc.; *Int'l*, pg. 1249
CAE OXFORD AVIATION ACADEMY PHOENIX INC.—See CAE Inc.; *Int'l*, pg. 1249
CAE SINGAPORE (S.E.A.) PTE LTD.—See CAE Inc.; *Int'l*, pg. 1249
CAE TRAINING & SERVICES UK LTD.—See CAE Inc; *Int'l*, pg. 1249
CAE USA, INC.—See CAE Inc.; *Int'l*, pg. 1249
DEI SERVICES CORPORATION—See Kratos Defense & Security Solutions, Inc.; *U.S. Public*, pg. 1276
DIAMOND SIMULATION GMBH—See Diamond Aircraft Industries Gmbh; *Int'l*, pg. 2105
DISCOVERY AIR DEFENCE SERVICES INC.—See Clairvest Group Inc.; *Int'l*, pg. 1641
EMBRY-RIDDLE AERONAUTICAL UNIVERSITY - PRESCOTT—See Embry-Riddle Aeronautical University; *U.S. Private*, pg. 1379
ENDEAVOR EXPERIENCES, LLC—See Silver Lake Group, LLC; *U.S. Private*, pg. 3654
ERA TRAINING CENTER, LLC—See Bristow Group, Inc.; *U.S. Public*, pg. 388
ERA TRAINING CENTER, LLC—See Frasca International Inc.; *U.S. Private*, pg. 1599
EUROCOPTER DEUTSCHLAND GMBH—See Airbus SE; *Int'l*, pg. 243
FINNAIR FLIGHT ACADEMY OY—See Finnair Plc; *Int'l*, pg. 2676
FLIGHT SIMULATION COMPANY B.V.—See CAE Inc.; *Int'l*, pg. 1249
HELISIM—See Airbus SE; *Int'l*, pg. 244
KLM LUCHTVAARTSCHOOL B.V.—See Air France-KLM S.A.; *Int'l*, pg. 237
L3 COMMERCIAL TRAINING SOLUTIONS LIMITED—See L3Harris Technologies, Inc.; *U.S. Public*, pg. 1284
LEADING EDGE AVIATION, INC.; *U.S. Private*, pg. 2406
LUFTHANSA AVIATION TRAINING AUSTRIA GMBH—See Deutsche Lufthansa AG; *Int'l*, pg. 2068
LUFTHANSA AVIATION TRAINING BERLIN GMBH—See Deutsche Lufthansa AG; *Int'l*, pg. 2068
LUFTHANSA AVIATION TRAINING GERMANY GMBH—See Deutsche Lufthansa AG; *Int'l*, pg. 2068
LUFTHANSA AVIATION TRAINING GMBH—See Deutsche Lufthansa AG; *Int'l*, pg. 2068
LUFTHANSA AVIATION TRAINING OPERATIONS GERMANY GMBH—See Deutsche Lufthansa AG; *Int'l*, pg. 2068
LUFTHANSA AVIATION TRAINING USA INC.—See Deutsche Lufthansa AG; *Int'l*, pg. 2068
LUFTHANSA FLIGHT TRAINING VIENNA GMBH—See Deutsche Lufthansa AG; *Int'l*, pg. 2068
LUFTHANSA TECHNICAL TRAINING GMBH—See Deutsche Lufthansa AG; *Int'l*, pg. 2069
MASTERFLIGHT FOUNDATION INC.; *U.S. Private*, pg. 2608
NORTHWEST TRAINING CENTER—See Delta Air Lines, Inc.; *U.S. Public*, pg. 652
ONCORE TRAINING LLC; *U.S. Private*, pg. 3019
OXFORD AVIATION ACADEMY LIMITED—See CAE Inc.; *Int'l*, pg. 1249
PILOT TRAINING NETWORK GMBH—See Deutsche Lufthansa AG; *Int'l*, pg. 2068
PRESTOSIM, INC.—See CAE Inc.; *Int'l*, pg. 1249
PRESTOSIM, INC.—See Directional Capital LLC; *U.S. Private*, pg. 1236
ROTORSIM S.R.L.—See CAE Inc.; *Int'l*, pg. 1249
SIMCOM, INC.—See CAE Inc.; *Int'l*, pg. 1249
SIMCOM, INC.—See Directional Capital LLC; *U.S. Private*, pg. 1236
TEMPUS TRAINING SOLUTIONS LLC—See Tempus Applied Solutions Holdings, Inc.; *U.S. Public*, pg. 2000
ZHUHAI XIANG YI AVIATION TECHNOLOGY COMPANY LIMITED—See China Southern Airlines Co., Ltd.; *Int'l*, pg. 1553

611513 — APPRENTICESHIP TRAINING

CATERPILLAR OPERATOR TRAINING LTD.—See Caterpillar, Inc.; *U.S. Public*, pg. 451
FURSTENWALDER AUS- UND WEITERBILDUNGSZENTRUM GMBH—See AcadeMedia AB; *Int'l*, pg. 76
STUDYFLIX GMBH—See Bertelsmann SE & Co. KGaA; *Int'l*, pg. 996

611519 — OTHER TECHNICAL AND TRADE SCHOOLS

ABB TRAINING CENTER GMBH & CO. KG—See ABB Ltd.; *Int'l*, pg. 50
THE ACADEMY OF RADIO BROADCASTING, INC.; *U.S. Private*, pg. 3980
THE ACADEMY OF RADIO & TV—See The Academy of Radio Broadcasting, Inc.; *U.S. Private*, pg. 3981
ALGOL TECHNICS OY—See Algol Oy; *Int'l*, pg. 318
ALL-STATE CAREER, INC.—See JLL Partners, LLC; *U.S. Private*, pg. 2212
AMERICAN INSTITUTE OF TRUCKING, INC.—See Werner Enterprises, Inc.; *U.S. Public*, pg. 2349
AMERICAN SCHOOL OF CORRESPONDENCE; *U.S. Private*, pg. 246
ATI ENTERPRISES, INC.—See BC Partners LLP; *Int'l*, pg. 922
BAMBOOS EDUCATION- SCHOOL FOR TALENTS LIMITED—See Bamboos Health Care Holdings Limited; *Int'l*, pg. 813
BEIJING HUAFENG ELECTRONIC EQUIPMENT CO., LTD.—See Beijing Huafeng Test & Control Technology Co., Ltd.; *Int'l*, pg. 952
BRISTOW MANAGEMENT SERVICES PTY LIMITED—See Bristow Group, Inc.; *U.S. Public*, pg. 387
BROOKS INSTITUTE—See Perdoceo Education Corporation; *U.S. Public*, pg. 1673
BROWN COLLEGE—See Perdoceo Education Corporation; *U.S. Public*, pg. 1673
CANTERBURY MANAGEMENT GROUP, INC.—See Canterbury Consulting Group, Inc.; *U.S. Private*, pg. 735
CARRINGTON COLLEGE, INC.—See Adtalem Global Education Inc.; *U.S. Public*, pg. 43
CHARLES ATLAS, LTD.; *U.S. Private*, pg. 851
CHINA EDUCATION ALLIANCE, INC.; *Int'l*, pg. 1499
CHUBB COMPUTER SERVICES, INC.—See Chubb Limited; *Int'l*, pg. 1591
CLEVELAND INSTITUTE OF ELECTRONICS; *U.S. Private*, pg. 941
COLLIERY TRAINING COLLEGE (PTY) LIMITED—See Anglo American PLC; *Int'l*, pg. 461
COLLINS COLLEGE—See Perdoceo Education Corporation; *U.S. Public*, pg. 1673
CONCORDE CAREER COLLEGES, INC.—See Universal Technical Institute, Inc.; *U.S. Public*, pg. 2262
CONCURRENT TECHNOLOGIES CORPORATION—See Concurrent Technologies Corporation; *U.S. Private*, pg. 1011
CPF TRAINING CENTER CO., LTD.—See Charoen Pokphand Foods Public Company Limited; *Int'l*, pg. 1452
CUSTOM TRAINING GROUP, INC.—See Universal Technical Institute, Inc.; *U.S. Public*, pg. 2262
CYBERTEX INSTITUTE OF TECHNOLOGY; *U.S. Private*, pg. 1134
DECO INC.—See IDS International Government Services LLC; *U.S. Private*, pg. 2038
DEVRY/BECKER EDUCATIONAL DEVELOPMENT CORP.—See Adtalem Global Education Inc.; *U.S. Public*, pg. 43
DIMENSIONS TRAINING SOLUTIONS LTD.; *Int'l*, pg. 2126
DMG MORI ACADEMY GMBH—See DMG MORI Co., Ltd.; *Int'l*, pg. 2143
DRIVER TRAINING & SOLUTIONS, LLC.—See TransSystem Inc.; *U.S. Private*, pg. 4206
ECMK LIMITED—See Insight Venture Management, LLC; *U.S. Private*, pg. 2089
ECMK LIMITED—See Stone Point Capital LLC; *U.S. Private*, pg. 3822
EUREKA 4WD TRAINING PTY. LTD.—See Engenco Limited; *Int'l*, pg. 2427
EVERTHOUGHT EDUCATION PTY. LTD.—See AWN Holdings Limited; *Int'l*, pg. 753
FCNH, INC.—See Catterton Management Company, LLC; *U.S. Private*, pg. 794
FOLEY-BELSAW COMPANY; *U.S. Private*, pg. 1558
FORTIS COLLEGE—See JLL Partners, LLC; *U.S. Private*, pg. 2212
GCL CAPACITA SA—See Eurofins Scientific S.E.; *Int'l*, pg. 2550
GHETTO FILM SCHOOL, INC.; *U.S. Private*, pg. 1690
GRAND FORTUNE HIGH GRADE LIMITED; *Int'l*, pg. 3054
HEALTHCARE STAFFING, INC.—See Novation Companies, Inc.; *U.S. Public*, pg. 1548
HUMANAGEMENT PTY. LIMITED—See Academies Australasia Group Limited; *Int'l*, pg. 77
INCORPORATE MASSAGE CO.; *U.S. Private*, pg. 2054
INSTITUTE FOR HEALTHCARE COMMUNICATION, INC.; *U.S. Private*, pg. 2093
THE INSTITUTE OF CLASSICAL ARCHITECTURE; *U.S. Private*, pg. 4056
INSTITUTE OF DIGITAL MEDIA TECHNOLOGY (SHANGHAI) LIMITED—See Global Digital Creations Holdings Limited; *Int'l*, pg. 2994
ISTITUTO MARANGONI S.R.L.—See Providence Equity Partners L.L.C.; *U.S. Private*, pg. 3293
ITC LEARNING CORP.; *U.S. Private*, pg. 2149
KAPLAN PROFESSIONAL SCHOOLS, INC.—See Graham Holdings Company; *U.S. Public*, pg. 956
KITCHEN ACADEMY—See Perdoceo Education Corporation; *U.S. Public*, pg. 1673
LEARNING TREE INTERNATIONAL USA, INC.—See Learning Tree International, Inc.; *U.S. Public*, pg. 1298
MEDCERTS LLC; *U.S. Private*, pg. 2651
MERCY COLLEGE OF OHIO—See Catholic Healthcare Partners; *U.S. Private*, pg. 792
MISSOURI COLLEGE, INC.—See Perdoceo Education Cor-

N.A.I.C.S. INDEX

poration; *U.S. Public*, pg. 1673
MOVANT AB—See AcadeMedia AB; *Int'l*, pg. 77
NATIONAL AVIATION ACADEMY; *U.S. Private*, pg. 2847
NATIONAL COUNCIL OF STATE BOARDS OF NURSING; *U.S. Private*, pg. 2852
NH LEARNING SOLUTIONS CORPORATION—See Camden Partners Holdings, LLC; *U.S. Private*, pg. 728
NTI-SKOLAN AB—See AcadeMedia AB; *Int'l*, pg. 77
PETROSKILLS, LLC; *U.S. Private*, pg. 3163
PROCUREMENT INTERNATIONAL (PTY) LIMITED—See Marriott International, Inc.; *U.S. Public*, pg. 1371
REG LENNA CENTER FOR THE ARTS; *U.S. Private*, pg. 3385
RICH DAD EDUCATION, INC.; *U.S. Private*, pg. 3426
ROSS EDUCATION, LLC—See JLL Partners, LLC; *U.S. Private*, pg. 2213
SCIMEDICA GROUP; *U.S. Private*, pg. 3574
SPARTAN SCHOOL OF AERONAUTICS; *U.S. Private*, pg. 3746
STEINER EDUCATION GROUP, INC.—See Catterton Management Company, LLC; *U.S. Private*, pg. 794
ST. LAWRENCE-LEWIS BOCES; *U.S. Private*, pg. 3772
TECHNICAL CAREER INSTITUTES, INC.—See EVCI Career Colleges Holding Corp.; *U.S. Private*, pg. 1436
UNIVERSAL TECHNICAL INSTITUTE, INC.; *U.S. Public*, pg. 2262
UNIVERSAL TECHNICAL INSTITUTE OF ARIZONA, INC.—See Universal Technical Institute, Inc.; *U.S. Public*, pg. 2262
UNIVERSAL TECHNICAL INSTITUTE OF MASSACHUSETTS, INC.—See Universal Technical Institute, Inc.; *U.S. Public*, pg. 2262
UNIVERSAL TECHNICAL INSTITUTE OF PENNSYLVANIA, INC.—See Universal Technical Institute, Inc.; *U.S. Public*, pg. 2262
U.T.I. OF ILLINOIS, INC.—See Universal Technical Institute, Inc.; *U.S. Public*, pg. 2262
VALE NATIONAL TRAINING CENTER INC.—See The Carlyle Group Inc.; *U.S. Public*, pg. 2054
VIRGINIA MASSAGE THERAPY, INC.—See Catterton Management Company, LLC; *U.S. Private*, pg. 794
WORLD COLLEGE—See Cleveland Institute of Electronics; *U.S. Private*, pg. 941
WTI TRANSPORT, INC.—See Daseke, Inc.; *U.S. Private*, pg. 1162

611610 — FINE ARTS SCHOOLS

THE ART INSTITUTE OF ATLANTA, LLC—See Dream Center Foundation, a California Nonprofit Corp.; *U.S. Private*, pg. 1274
THE ART INSTITUTE OF CALIFORNIA - HOLLYWOOD, INC.—See Dream Center Foundation, a California Nonprofit Corp.; *U.S. Private*, pg. 1274
THE ART INSTITUTE OF CALIFORNIA - LOS ANGELES, INC.—See Dream Center Foundation, a California Nonprofit Corp.; *U.S. Private*, pg. 1274
THE ART INSTITUTE OF CALIFORNIA - ORANGE COUNTY, INC.—See Dream Center Foundation, a California Nonprofit Corp.; *U.S. Private*, pg. 1274
THE ART INSTITUTE OF CALIFORNIA - SUNNYVALE, INC.—See Dream Center Foundation, a California Nonprofit Corp.; *U.S. Private*, pg. 1274
THE ART INSTITUTE OF CHARLOTTE, LLC—See Dream Center Foundation, a California Nonprofit Corp.; *U.S. Private*, pg. 1274
THE ART INSTITUTE OF COLORADO, INC.—See Dream Center Foundation, a California Nonprofit Corp.; *U.S. Private*, pg. 1274
THE ART INSTITUTE OF DALLAS, INC.—See Dream Center Foundation, a California Nonprofit Corp.; *U.S. Private*, pg. 1274
THE ART INSTITUTE OF FORT LAUDERDALE, INC.—See Dream Center Foundation, a California Nonprofit Corp.; *U.S. Private*, pg. 1274
THE ART INSTITUTE OF HOUSTON, INC.—See Dream Center Foundation, a California Nonprofit Corp.; *U.S. Private*, pg. 1274
THE ART INSTITUTE OF LAS VEGAS, INC.—See Dream Center Foundation, a California Nonprofit Corp.; *U.S. Private*, pg. 1275
THE ART INSTITUTE OF NEW YORK CITY, INC.—See Dream Center Foundation, a California Nonprofit Corp.; *U.S. Private*, pg. 1274
THE ART INSTITUTE OF OHIO - CINCINNATI, INC.—See Dream Center Foundation, a California Nonprofit Corp.; *U.S. Private*, pg. 1275
THE ART INSTITUTE OF PHILADELPHIA LLC—See Dream Center Foundation, a California Nonprofit Corp.; *U.S. Private*, pg. 1274
THE ART INSTITUTE OF PITTSBURGH LLC—See Dream Center Foundation, a California Nonprofit Corp.; *U.S. Private*, pg. 1274
THE ART INSTITUTE OF PORTLAND, INC.—See Dream Center Foundation, a California Nonprofit Corp.; *U.S. Private*, pg. 1274
THE ART INSTITUTE OF SEATTLE, INC.—See Dream Center Foundation, a California Nonprofit Corp.; *U.S. Private*, pg. 1275
THE ART INSTITUTE OF TAMPA, INC.—See Dream Center Foundation, a California Nonprofit Corp.; *U.S. Private*, pg. 1275
THE ART INSTITUTE OF WASHINGTON, INC.—See Dream Center Foundation, a California Nonprofit Corp.; *U.S. Private*, pg. 1275
THE ART INSTITUTES INTERNATIONAL MINNESOTA, INC.—See Dream Center Foundation, a California Nonprofit Corp.; *U.S. Private*, pg. 1275
BLUE LAKE FINE ARTS CAMP; *U.S. Private*, pg. 589
FUTURE MEDIA CONCEPTS, INC.; *U.S. Private*, pg. 1627
HEARTFELT CREATIONS; *U.S. Private*, pg. 1899
THE ILLINOIS INSTITUTE OF ART AT SCHAUMBURG, INC.—See Dream Center Foundation, a California Nonprofit Corp.; *U.S. Private*, pg. 1275
THE ILLINOIS INSTITUTE OF ART, INC.—See Dream Center Foundation, a California Nonprofit Corp.; *U.S. Private*, pg. 1275
THE INSTITUTE OF POST-SECONDARY EDUCATION, INC.—See Dream Center Foundation, a California Nonprofit Corp.; *U.S. Private*, pg. 1275
THE NEW ENGLAND INSTITUTE OF ART, LLC—See Dream Center Foundation, a California Nonprofit Corp.; *U.S. Private*, pg. 1275
RYTMUS AB—See AcadeMedia AB; *Int'l*, pg. 77
STUDIODRAGON CORP.—See CJ Corporation; *Int'l*, pg. 1632
TAIC- SAN DIEGO, INC.—See Dream Center Foundation, a California Nonprofit Corp.; *U.S. Private*, pg. 1274
TAIC- SAN FRANCISCO, INC.—See Dream Center Foundation, a California Nonprofit Corp.; *U.S. Private*, pg. 1274

611620 — SPORTS AND RECREATION INSTRUCTION

ABOUTGOLF EUROPE LTD.—See AboutGolf Ltd.; *U.S. Private*, pg. 39
AMORIM SPORTS, LDA.—See CORTICEIRA AMORIM, S.G.P.S., S.A.; *Int'l*, pg. 1807
AVP, INC.; *U.S. Public*, pg. 254
BASEBALL FACTORY, INC.—See Ripken Baseball, Inc.; *U.S. Private*, pg. 3439
BAYER 04 LEVERKUSEN SPORTFORDERUNG GGMBH—See Bayer Aktiengesellschaft; *Int'l*, pg. 902
BLACK BEAR SPORTS GROUP, INC.—See Blackstreet Capital Holdings LLC; *U.S. Private*, pg. 576
BMI SPORTS INFO PROPRIETARY LIMITED—See Caxton and CTP Publishers and Printers Ltd.; *Int'l*, pg. 1363
CROYDON CLOCKTOWER; *Int'l*, pg. 1858
CRUZADOS S.A.D.P.; *Int'l*, pg. 1859
DOOSAN BEARS INC.—See Doosan Corporation; *Int'l*, pg. 2172
EAST PALO ALTO TENNIS & TUTORING; *U.S. Private*, pg. 1317
IFLY HOLDINGS, LLC; *U.S. Private*, pg. 2039
K2 CORPORATION OF CANADA—See Kohlberg & Company, LLC; *U.S. Private*, pg. 2338
MARUCCI ELITE TRAINING L.L.C.—See Compass Diversified Holdings; *U.S. Public*, pg. 560
NEW ERA FARMS, LLC—See Live Nation Entertainment, Inc.; *U.S. Public*, pg. 1330
PADI ASIA PACIFIC PTY LTD—See Capital Investments & Ventures Corp.; *U.S. Private*, pg. 741
PADI CANADA LIMITED—See Capital Investments & Ventures Corp.; *U.S. Private*, pg. 741
PADI JAPAN, INC.—See Capital Investments & Ventures Corp.; *U.S. Private*, pg. 741
PADI—See Lincolnshire Management, Inc.; *U.S. Private*, pg. 2459
REGAL DIVING AND TOURS LIMITED—See Cox & Kings Limited; *Int'l*, pg. 1823
RICHARD PETTY DRIVING EXPERIENCE, INC.—See BV Investment Partners, LLC; *U.S. Private*, pg. 699
SPORT1 GMBH—See Highlight Communications AG; *Int'l*, pg. 3388
USA GYMNASTICS; *U.S. Private*, pg. 4321
VARSITY SPIRIT LLC—See Bain Capital, LP; *U.S. Private*, pg. 452

611630 — LANGUAGE SCHOOLS

51TALK ONLINE EDUCATION GROUP; *Int'l*, pg. 12
ALPADIA S.A.—See Graham Holdings Company; *U.S. Public*, pg. 954
AMERICAN COUNCIL ON THE TEACHING OF FOREIGN LANGUAGES; *U.S. Private*, pg. 229
BIG LANGUAGE SOLUTIONS LLC—See MSouth Equity Partners, LLC; *U.S. Private*, pg. 2808
CEL LEP IDIOMAS—See H.I.G. Capital, LLC; *U.S. Private*, pg. 1828
EDO CULTURAL CENTER CO., LTD.—See Ichishin Holdings Co., Ltd.; *Int'l*, pg. 3581
EMC SCHOOL, LLC—See CIP Capital Fund, L.P.; *U.S. Private*, pg. 899
FIRST ENGLISH EDUCATION INSTITUTES LIMITED—See Aptech Limited; *Int'l*, pg. 523
LANGUAGE LINKS INTERNATIONAL PTY. LIMITED—See Academies Australasia Group Limited; *Int'l*, pg. 77
LEXICON MARKETING CORPORATION—See Golden Gate Capital Management II, LLC; *U.S. Private*, pg. 1731
LINGYOPHONE COMPANY LTD.—See Alkhaleej Training & Education Company; *Int'l*, pg. 331
MANGO LANGUAGES; *U.S. Private*, pg. 2563
SELC GROUP LTD.—See Xylem Inc.; *U.S. Public*, pg. 2394
UNITED LANGUAGE GROUP, INC.—See Leonard Green & Partners, L.P.; *U.S. Private*, pg. 2428
UNITED LANGUAGE GROUP, INC.—See TTCP Management Services, LLC; *U.S. Private*, pg. 4254
WALL STREET ENGLISH LIMITED LIABILITY COMPANY—See Asia Strategic Holdings Limited; *Int'l*, pg. 615

611691 — EXAM PREPARATION AND TUTORING

BECKER CONVISER PROFESSIONAL REVIEW—See Adtalem Global Education Inc.; *U.S. Public*, pg. 43
BLAKE ELEARNING PTY. LTD.—See 3P Learning Limited; *Int'l*, pg. 9
BRADAVERSE EDUCATION (INT'L) INVESTMENTS GROUP LIMITED; *Int'l*, pg. 1134
CERTIPORT, INC.; *U.S. Private*, pg. 842
CHUNGDAHM PHILIPPINES, INC.—See Chungdahm Learning, Inc.; *Int'l*, pg. 1597
DOMIA GROUP SA—See IK Investment Partners Limited; *Int'l*, pg. 3609
ELEARNING BROTHERS, LLC—See Fundos Group LLC; *U.S. Private*, pg. 1623
ELEARNING BROTHERS, LLC—See Trinity Private Equity Group, LLC; *U.S. Private*, pg. 4235
FANTAGIO CORP.; *Int'l*, pg. 2613
FIRST BOOK; *U.S. Private*, pg. 1514
GOLD STAR TUTORING SERVICES, INC.; *U.S. Private*, pg. 1728
GOLDWAY EDUCATION GROUP LIMITED; *Int'l*, pg. 3035
GROUP EXCELLENCE; *U.S. Private*, pg. 1793
INSPIRED ELEARNING, LLC—See Ziff Davis, Inc.; *U.S. Public*, pg. 2403
JUSTIN CRAIG EDUCATION LIMITED—See Graham Holdings Company; *U.S. Public*, pg. 955
LEARNOSITY LTD.; *U.S. Private*, pg. 2408
LEXIA LEARNING SYSTEMS, LLC—See Veritas Capital Fund Management, LLC; *U.S. Private*, pg. 4361
MONTGOMERY COALITION FOR ADULT ENGLISH LITERACY; *U.S. Private*, pg. 2776
PREPMATTERS; *U.S. Private*, pg. 3252
RAPID LEARNING DEPLOYMENT, LLC—See Tier 1 Performance Solutions, LLC; *U.S. Private*, pg. 4169
REVOLUTION PREP, LLC; *U.S. Private*, pg. 3416
SCHOOL TOMAS CO., LTD.—See Hulic Co., Ltd.; *Int'l*, pg. 3528
SHINGAKAI CO., LTD.—See Hulic Co., Ltd.; *Int'l*, pg. 3528
SOPHIA LEARNING, LLC—See Strategic Education, Inc.; *U.S. Public*, pg. 1954
STEUER-FACHSCHULE DR. ENDRISS GMBH & CO. KG—See Amadeus Fire AG; *Int'l*, pg. 405
STUDYPOINT, INC.; *U.S. Private*, pg. 3844
SUMMIT LEARNING SERVICES; *U.S. Private*, pg. 3855
SURE PREP LEARNING LLC; *U.S. Private*, pg. 3883
SYLVAN LEARNING, INC.—See Sterling Partners; *U.S. Private*, pg. 3807
TOKYO EDUCATIONAL INSTITUTE CO., LTD.—See EQT AB; *Int'l*, pg. 2467

611692 — AUTOMOBILE DRIVING SCHOOLS

123 FAHRSCHULE RHEIN-SIEG GMBH—See 123fahrschule SE; *Int'l*, pg. 2
123FAHRSCHULE SE; *Int'l*, pg. 2
ATLAS AUTOS (PRIVATE) LIMITED—See Atlas Group of Companies; *Int'l*, pg. 685
BUKIT BATOK DRIVING CENTRE LTD.—See Honda Motor Co., Ltd.; *Int'l*, pg. 3460
CENTER FOR TRANSPORTATION SAFETY, LLC—See Onity Group Inc.; *U.S. Public*, pg. 1605
CRVENI SIGNAL A.D.; *Int'l*, pg. 1859
CRVENI SIGNAL A.D.; *Int'l*, pg. 1859
DEKRA HOVEDSTADEN A/S—See DEKRA e.V.; *Int'l*, pg. 2006
DEKRA MIDTJYLLAND APS—See DEKRA e.V.; *Int'l*, pg. 2006
DEKRA SJAELLAND A/S—See DEKRA e.V.; *Int'l*, pg. 2010
DEKRA SYDJYLLAND A/S—See DEKRA e.V.; *Int'l*, pg. 2010
DRIVETECH (UK) LIMITED—See TowerBrook Capital Partners, L.P.; *U.S. Private*, pg. 4194
DRIVETECH (UK) LIMITED—See Warburg Pincus LLC; *U.S. Private*, pg. 4436
DUBAI INTERNATIONAL DRIVING CENTER (DIDC)—See

611692 — AUTOMOBILE DRIVING ...

Dubai Investments PJSC; *Int'l*, pg. 2219
EASTERN PIONEER DRIVING SCHOOL CO., LTD.; *Int'l*, pg. 2273
EMIRATES DRIVING COMPANY PJSC; *Int'l*, pg. 2381
RAINBOW MOTOR SCHOOL CO., LTD.—See Honda Motor Co., Ltd.; *Int'l*, pg. 3464
ROCKVILLE LUXURY IMPORTS, LLC—See AutoNation, Inc.; *U.S. Public*, pg. 237
TUC FYN APS—See DEKRA e.V.; *Int'l*, pg. 2010
TUC STRANDENS UDDANNELSES-CENTER APS—See DEKRA e.V.; *Int'l*, pg. 2010
UCPLUS A/S—See Deutsche Bahn AG; *Int'l*, pg. 2055

611699 — ALL OTHER MISCELLANEOUS SCHOOLS AND INSTRUCTION

ABRAKADOODLE INC.; *U.S. Private*, pg. 39
ACADEMIES AUSTRALASIA HAIR & BEAUTY PTY LIMITED—See Academies Australasia Group Limited; *Int'l*, pg. 77
ACCESS EVENT NETWORK, INC.—See MicroTek; *U.S. Private*, pg. 2704
A CLOUD GURU LTD.; *U.S. Private*, pg. 18
ADVANCED HEALTH EDUCATION CENTER, LTD.; *U.S. Private*, pg. 90
AEON DELIGHT ACADEMY CO., LTD.—See AEON Co., Ltd.; *Int'l*, pg. 176
AMERICAN COUNCIL FOR INTERNATIONAL STUDIES INC.—See American Institute for Foreign Study, Inc.; *U.S. Private*, pg. 237
APEX LEARNING, INC.—See The Vistria Group, LP; *U.S. Private*, pg. 4131
THE ARIEL GROUP LLC; *U.S. Private*, pg. 3988
ARTISTIC STUDIOS, LTD—See Irving Place Capital Management, L.P.; *U.S. Private*, pg. 2141
ASHWORTH COLLEGE—See IAC Inc.; *U.S. Public*, pg. 1083
ASL INTERPRETER REFERRAL SERVICE, INC.; *U.S. Private*, pg. 351
ASSETCO TECHNICAL RESCUE—See AssetCo plc; *Int'l*, pg. 643
BESHENICH MUIR & ASSOCIATES, LLC; *U.S. Private*, pg. 541
BETTER COMMUNICATIONS, INC—See The Ariel Group LLC; *U.S. Private*, pg. 3988
BEXCELLENT GROUP HOLDINGS LIMITED; *Int'l*, pg. 1004
BIBLE STUDY FELLOWSHIP; *U.S. Private*, pg. 550
BRISTOW ACADEMY, INC.—See Bristow Group, Inc.; *U.S. Public*, pg. 387
BROWN MACKIE COLLEGE-FORT WAYNE—See Dream Center Foundation, a California Nonprofit Corp.; *U.S. Private*, pg. 1273
THE BROWNSTONE SCHOOL; *U.S. Private*, pg. 4001
BUSINESS INDUSTRIAL NETWORK; *U.S. Private*, pg. 694
CAE HEALTHCARE INC.—See CAE Inc.; *Int'l*, pg. 1248
CAPITAL EDUCATION LLC—See Stride, Inc.; *U.S. Public*, pg. 1955
CARDEAN LEARNING GROUP, LLC; *U.S. Private*, pg. 749
CENTER FOR CREATIVE LEADERSHIP INC; *U.S. Private*, pg. 810
CENTRO DE FORMACAO DE EDUCADORES DA VILA LTDA.—See Bahema Educacao SA; *Int'l*, pg. 800
CHICAGO COMMONS ASSOCIATION; *U.S. Private*, pg. 877
CYBERVISTA LLC—See Graham Holdings Company; *U.S. Public*, pg. 954
DALE CARNEGIE & ASSOCIATES, INC.; *U.S. Private*, pg. 1148
DALE CARNEGIE INSTITUTE OF LONG ISLAND—See Dale Carnegie & Associates, Inc.; *U.S. Private*, pg. 1148
EMS SAFETY SERVICES INC.—See Waud Capital Partners LLC; *U.S. Private*, pg. 4457
FLIGHTSAFETY INTERNATIONAL, INC.—See Berkshire Hathaway Inc.; *U.S. Public*, pg. 304
FLIGHTSAFETY INTERNATIONAL SIMULATION SYSTEMS—See Berkshire Hathaway Inc.; *U.S. Public*, pg. 305
FLIGHTSAFETY INTERNATIONAL—See Berkshire Hathaway Inc.; *U.S. Public*, pg. 305
FLIGHTSAFETY SERVICES CORPORATION—See Berkshire Hathaway Inc.; *U.S. Public*, pg. 305
GAKKEN HOLDINGS CO., LTD.; *Int'l*, pg. 2869
GENEED, INC.—See Microsoft Corporation; *U.S. Public*, pg. 1439
GERSH ACADEMY, INC.; *U.S. Private*, pg. 1688
GLOBAL EDUCATION NETWORK—See Allen Holding Inc.; *U.S. Private*, pg. 179
GOLDFISH SWIM SCHOOL FRANCHISING LLC; *U.S. Private*, pg. 1735
GRAND CANYON EDUCATION, INC.; *U.S. Public*, pg. 956
HEALTH EDUCATION SERVICES, LLC—See Community Health Systems, Inc.; *U.S. Public*, pg. 553
HUMAN DIGICRAFTS (THAILAND) CO., LTD.—See Human Holdings Co., Ltd.; *Int'l*, pg. 3529
INSTITUTE FOR SUPPLY MANAGMENT; *U.S. Private*, pg. 2093
IPEXPERT, INC.; *U.S. Private*, pg. 2136
JEPPESEN SANDERSON, INC.—See The Boeing Company; *U.S. Public*, pg. 2039
KELBY MEDIA GROUP, INC.; *U.S. Private*, pg. 2274
KELBY TRAINING INC.—See Kelby Media Group, Inc.; *U.S. Private*, pg. 2274
KEYSTONE EDUCATION AND YOUTH SERVICES, LLC—See Universal Health Services, Inc.; *U.S. Public*, pg. 2258
KRIPALU CENTER FOR YOGA & HEALTH; *U.S. Private*, pg. 2351
LEARNDIRECT LIMITED—See Dimensions Training Solutions Ltd.; *Int'l*, pg. 2126
THE LEARNING ANNEX LLC—See Learning Annex Holdings, LLC; *U.S. Private*, pg. 2408
LE CORDON BLEU COLLEGE OF CULINARY ARTS IN CHICAGO—See Perdoceo Education Corporation; *U.S. Public*, pg. 1673
LE CORDON BLEU COLLEGE OF CULINARY ARTS—See Perdoceo Education Corporation; *U.S. Public*, pg. 1673
LIBERTY HIGHER EDUCATION, LLC—See Liberty Partners, L.P.; *U.S. Private*, pg. 2447
LINCOLN EDUCATIONAL SERVICES CORPORATION; *U.S. Public*, pg. 1316
THE LITTLE GYM INTERNATIONAL, INC.; *U.S. Private*, pg. 4071
LOGISTIC SERVICES INTERNATIONAL INC.; *U.S. Private*, pg. 2481
LUFTHANSA AVIATION TRAINING CREW ACADEMY GMBH—See Deutsche Lufthansa AG; *Int'l*, pg. 2068
MAPLE LEAF EDUCATION ASI PACIFIC LTD—See China Maple Leaf Educational Systems Limited; *Int'l*, pg. 1517
MARAGON PRIVATE SCHOOLS AVIANTO (PTY) LTD.—See ADvTECH Limited; *Int'l*, pg. 169
MARAGON PRIVATE SCHOOLS RUIMSIG (PTY) LTD.—See ADvTECH Limited; *Int'l*, pg. 169
MEDICAL EDUCATION TECHNOLOGIES, INC.—See CAE Inc.; *Int'l*, pg. 1248
NN ACQUISITION, LLC—See Lincoln Educational Services Corporation; *U.S. Public*, pg. 1316
O2B KIDS; *U.S. Private*, pg. 2982
OMEGA TRAINING GROUP, INC.—See Valiant Integrated Services LLC; *U.S. Private*, pg. 4331
OPTIONS UNIVERSITY; *U.S. Private*, pg. 3035
OUTREACH ORGANISATION LTD.—See Bergman & Beving AB; *Int'l*, pg. 980
PENN FOSTER, INC.—See IAC Inc.; *U.S. Public*, pg. 1083
THE PHARMACY DEVELOPMENT ACADEMY PROPRIETARY LIMITED—See Dis-Chem Pharmacies Ltd.; *Int'l*, pg. 2131
PROSPECT EDUCATION LLC; *U.S. Private*, pg. 3287
PUREWORKS, INC.—See Underwriters Laboratories Inc.; *U.S. Private*, pg. 4280
RINGLING COLLEGE LIFELONG LEARNING ACADEMY—See Ringling College of Art and Design, Inc.; *U.S. Private*, pg. 3438
ROZ MARKETING GROUP A CALIFORNIA CORPORATION; *U.S. Private*, pg. 3494
SEED CONSULTANTS INC.—See Corteva, Inc.; *U.S. Public*, pg. 584
SKY RANCH; *U.S. Private*, pg. 3684
SOUTHEAST KANSAS EDUCATION SERVICE CENTER, INC.; *U.S. Private*, pg. 3725
STAR SCHOOLS (PTY) LTD.—See ADvTECH Limited; *Int'l*, pg. 169
STUDENT ACHIEVEMENT PARTNERS; *U.S. Private*, pg. 3843
SWIMKIDS SWIM SCHOOLS; *U.S. Private*, pg. 3893
THERAPEUTIC RESEARCH CENTER LLC—See Levine Leichtman Capital Partners, LLC; *U.S. Private*, pg. 2436
TOKYO INDIVIDUALIZED EDUCATIONAL INSTITUTE, INC.—See EQT AB; *Int'l*, pg. 2467
TRIAGE FIRST INC.—See Emergency Nurses Association; *U.S. Private*, pg. 1380
UNZ & COMPANY, INC.; *U.S. Private*, pg. 4311
UTEC INC.—See Carrier Global Corporation; *U.S. Public*, pg. 444
WALLCUR, LLC—See J.H. Whitney & Co., LLC; *U.S. Private*, pg. 2166
YOGA WORKS, INC.; *U.S. Private*, pg. 4589

611710 — EDUCATIONAL SUPPORT SERVICES

ACADEMEDIA EDUCATION GMBH—See AcadeMedia AB; *Int'l*, pg. 75
ACADEMIES AUSTRALASIA COLLEGE PTE. LIMITED—See Academies Australasia Group Limited; *Int'l*, pg. 77
ACADEMIES AUSTRALASIA (MANAGEMENT) PTY LIMITED—See Academies Australasia Group Limited; *Int'l*, pg. 77
ACADEMIES AUSTRALASIA POLYTECHNIC PTY LIMITED—See Academies Australasia Group Limited; *Int'l*, pg. 77
ACADEMIES AUSTRALASIA PTY LIMITED—See Academies Australasia Group Limited; *Int'l*, pg. 77
ACADEMY FOR URBAN SCHOOL LEADERSHIP; *U.S. Private*, pg. 46
ACADEMY OF NURSING (M) SDN BHD—See Berjaya Corporation Berhad; *Int'l*, pg. 982
ACCESS (UK) EDUCATION LIMITED—See China Financial Services Holdings Limited; *Int'l*, pg. 1502
ACCREDITING COUNCIL FOR INDEPENDENT COLLEGES AND SCHOOLS; *U.S. Private*, pg. 54
ACE EDUTREND LTD.; *Int'l*, pg. 94
ACHIEVE 3000, INC.; *U.S. Private*, pg. 59
ACHIEVEFORUM (UK) LIMITED—See Korn Ferry; *U.S. Public*, pg. 1274
ACT EDUCATION SOLUTIONS (AUSTRALIA) PTY. LIMITED—See ACT Inc.; *U.S. Private*, pg. 66
ACT INC.; *U.S. Private*, pg. 66
ACT INFORMATION CONSULTING (SHANGHAI) CO., LTD.—See ACT Inc.; *U.S. Private*, pg. 66
ADVANCED; *U.S. Private*, pg. 87
ADVANTAGE ACADEMY OF MIAMI INC.; *U.S. Private*, pg. 93
ADVTECH LIMITED; *Int'l*, pg. 168
AEC EDUCATION PLC; *Int'l*, pg. 170
AEC EDU GROUP PTE LTD.—See AEC Education plc; *Int'l*, pg. 170
AEC RESOURCE DEVELOPMENT PTE LTD.—See AEC Education plc; *Int'l*, pg. 170
AEG HOLDING COMPANY, INC.; *U.S. Private*, pg. 116
AFAQ EDUCATIONAL SERVICES COMPANY—See Boubyan Petrochemical Co. KSC; *Int'l*, pg. 1119
AFTERCOLLEGE, INC.—See Jobcase, Inc.; *U.S. Private*, pg. 2217
AFTER SCHOOL MATTERS, INC.; *U.S. Private*, pg. 124
AFYA LIMITED; *Int'l*, pg. 196
AGILE EDUCATION GROUP—See Agile Group Holdings Limited; *Int'l*, pg. 209
AIR FORCE ACADEMY; *U.S. Private*, pg. 138
AKAD BILDUNGSGESELLSCHAFT MBH—See Galileo Global Education; *Int'l*, pg. 2873
AKADEMIE FUR INTERNATIONALE RECHNUNGSLEGUNG PROF. DR. LEIBFRIED GMBH—See Amadeus Fire AG; *Int'l*, pg. 405
AKANOVA GMBH—See AcadeMedia AB; *Int'l*, pg. 75
ALFIO BARDOLLA TRAINING GROUP SPA; *Int'l*, pg. 315
ALL HAPPENING LLC; *U.S. Private*, pg. 171
ALLIANT INTERNATIONAL UNIVERSITY, INC.—See Bertelsmann SE & Co. KGaA; *Int'l*, pg. 990
ALTERNATIVE SCHOOLS NETWORK; *U.S. Private*, pg. 207
AL-ZARQA EDUCATIONAL & INVESTMENT CO. P.L.C; *Int'l*, pg. 289
AMATA KWEG EDUCATION CO., LTD.—See Amata Corporation Public Company Limited; *Int'l*, pg. 412
AMBOW EDUCATION HOLDING LTD.; *Int'l*, pg. 415
AMERICA ACHIEVES; *U.S. Private*, pg. 220
AMERICA-MIDEAST EDUCATIONAL & TRAINING SERVICES, INC.; *U.S. Private*, pg. 221
AMERICAN ASSOCIATION OF STATE COLLEGES AND UNIVERSITIES; *U.S. Private*, pg. 223
AMERICAN COUNCIL OF LEARNED SOCIETIES; *U.S. Private*, pg. 229
AMERICAN COUNCILS FOR INTERNATIONAL EDUCATION; *U.S. Private*, pg. 229
AMERICAN EDUCATIONAL PRODUCTS LLC—See Geneve Holdings Corp.; *U.S. Private*, pg. 1671
AMERICAN EDUCATIONAL RESEARCH ASSOCIATION; *U.S. Private*, pg. 231
AMERICAN EDUCATION CENTER, INC.; *U.S. Public*, pg. 99
AMERICAN INSTITUTE FOR CHARTERED PROPERTY CASUALTY UNDERWRITERS; *U.S. Private*, pg. 237
AMERICAN INSTITUTE FOR FOREIGN STUDY COLLEGE DIVISION—See American Institute for Foreign Study, Inc.; *U.S. Private*, pg. 237
AMERICAN INSTITUTE FOR FOREIGN STUDY (DEUTSCHLAND) GMBH—See American Institute for Foreign Study, Inc.; *U.S. Private*, pg. 237
AMERICAN INSTITUTE FOR FOREIGN STUDY, INC.; *U.S. Private*, pg. 237
AMERICAN INSTITUTE FOR FOREIGN STUDY—See American Institute for Foreign Study, Inc.; *U.S. Private*, pg. 237
AMERICAN INSTITUTE OF FINANCIAL INTELLIGENCE LLC—See American Education Center, Inc.; *U.S. Public*, pg. 99
AMERICAN PLANNING ASSOCIATION; *U.S. Private*, pg. 243
AMERICA'S SCHOOLHOUSE COUNCIL, LLC—See Tetra Tech, Inc.; *U.S. Public*, pg. 2022
AMI EDUCATION SOLUTIONS LTD—See Constellation Software Inc.; *Int'l*, pg. 1773
ANHANGUERA EDUCACIONAL PARTICIPACOES S.A.—See Cogna Educacao S.A.; *Int'l*, pg. 1695
ANIMA HOLDING SA; *Int'l*, pg. 471
ANONYMOUS INTELLIGENCE COMPANY INC; *Int'l*, pg. 474
ANVIA HOLDINGS CORPORATION; *U.S. Public*, pg. 140
APLAYA CREATIONS LIMITED; *Int'l*, pg. 515
APOLLON HOCHSCHULE DER GESUND-

N.A.I.C.S. INDEX

611710 — EDUCATIONAL SUPPORT...

HEITSWIRTSCHAFT GMBH—See Ernst Klett AG; *Int'l*, pg. 2495
APPRENTICE & JOURNEYMEN TRAINING TRUST FUND OF THE SOUTHERN CALIFORNIA PLUMBING & PIPING INDUSTRY; *U.S. Private*, pg. 300
AQUA DATA INC.—See AtkinsRealis Group Inc.; *Int'l*, pg. 671
AQUA-REHAB, INC.—See Caisse de Depot et Placement du Quebec; *Int'l*, pg. 1255
ARAB INTERNATIONAL CO. FOR EDUCATION & INVESTMENT PLC; *Int'l*, pg. 530
ARDEO EDUCATION SOLUTIONS, LLC; *U.S. Private*, pg. 317
AREA COOPERATIVE EDUCATIONAL SERVICES; *U.S. Private*, pg. 317
ARGOSY EDUCATION GROUP, INC.—See Dream Center Foundation, a California Nonprofit Corp.; *U.S. Private*, pg. 1272
ARGOSY UNIVERSITY FAMILY CENTER, INC.—See Dream Center Foundation, a California Nonprofit Corp.; *U.S. Private*, pg. 1272
ARGOSY UNIVERSITY OF FLORIDA, INC.—See Dream Center Foundation, a California Nonprofit Corp.; *U.S. Private*, pg. 1272
ARIHANT INSTITUTE LIMITED; *Int'l*, pg. 564
ARKEO INC.—See Groupe Crit, S.A.; *Int'l*, pg. 3101
THE ART INSTITUTE OF AUSTIN, INC.—See Dream Center Foundation, a California Nonprofit Corp.; *U.S. Private*, pg. 1274
THE ART INSTITUTE OF CALIFORNIA - INLAND EMPIRE, INC.—See Dream Center Foundation, a California Nonprofit Corp.; *U.S. Private*, pg. 1274
THE ART INSTITUTE OF CALIFORNIA - SACRAMENTO, INC.—See Dream Center Foundation, a California Nonprofit Corp.; *U.S. Private*, pg. 1274
THE ART INSTITUTE OF CHARLESTON, INC.—See Dream Center Foundation, a California Nonprofit Corp.; *U.S. Private*, pg. 1274
THE ART INSTITUTE OF FORT WORTH, INC.—See Dream Center Foundation, a California Nonprofit Corp.; *U.S. Private*, pg. 1274
THE ART INSTITUTE OF INDIANAPOLIS, LLC—See Dream Center Foundation, a California Nonprofit Corp.; *U.S. Private*, pg. 1274
THE ART INSTITUTE OF JACKSONVILLE, INC.—See Dream Center Foundation, a California Nonprofit Corp.; *U.S. Private*, pg. 1274
THE ART INSTITUTE OF MICHIGAN, INC.—See Dream Center Foundation, a California Nonprofit Corp.; *U.S. Private*, pg. 1275
THE ART INSTITUTE OF RALEIGH-DURHAM, INC.—See Dream Center Foundation, a California Nonprofit Corp.; *U.S. Private*, pg. 1274
THE ART INSTITUTE OF SALT LAKE CITY, INC.—See Dream Center Foundation, a California Nonprofit Corp.; *U.S. Private*, pg. 1275
THE ART INSTITUTE OF SAN ANTONIO, INC.—See Dream Center Foundation, a California Nonprofit Corp.; *U.S. Private*, pg. 1275
THE ART INSTITUTE OF ST. LOUIS, INC.—See Dream Center Foundation, a California Nonprofit Corp.; *U.S. Private*, pg. 1274
THE ART INSTITUTE OF TENNESSEE - NASHVILLE, INC.—See Dream Center Foundation, a California Nonprofit Corp.; *U.S. Private*, pg. 1275
THE ART INSTITUTE OF TUCSON, INC.—See Dream Center Foundation, a California Nonprofit Corp.; *U.S. Private*, pg. 1275
THE ART INSTITUTE OF VIRGINIA BEACH LLC—See Dream Center Foundation, a California Nonprofit Corp.; *U.S. Private*, pg. 1274
THE ART INSTITUTE OF WASHINGTON - DULLES LLC—See Dream Center Foundation, a California Nonprofit Corp.; *U.S. Private*, pg. 1275
THE ART INSTITUTE OF WISCONSIN LLC—See Dream Center Foundation, a California Nonprofit Corp.; *U.S. Private*, pg. 1275
THE ART INSTITUTE OF YORK-PENNSYLVANIA LLC—See Dream Center Foundation, a California Nonprofit Corp.; *U.S. Private*, pg. 1275
THE ART INSTITUTES INTERNATIONAL - KANSAS CITY, INC.—See Dream Center Foundation, a California Nonprofit Corp.; *U.S. Private*, pg. 1275
ASIAMET EDUCATION GROUP BERHAD—See Creador Sdn. Bhd.; *Int'l*, pg. 1831
ASIAN AVIATION TRAINING CENTRE LTD.—See L3Harris Technologies, Inc.; *U.S. Public*, pg. 1280
ASPECT INTERNATIONALE SPRACHSCHULE GMBH—See Graham Holdings Company; *U.S. Public*, pg. 955
ASSESSMENT TECHNOLOGY, INC.—See Silver Lake Group, LLC; *U.S. Private*, pg. 3661
ASSOCIATION OF GOVERNING BOARDS OF UNIVERSITIES AND COLLEGES; *U.S. Private*, pg. 358
ASSOCIATION OF PRIVATE SECTOR COLLEGES AND UNIVERSITIES; *U.S. Private*, pg. 358
ASSOCIATION OF SCHOOLS AND PROGRAMS OF PUBLIC HEALTH; *U.S. Private*, pg. 359

ASSOCIATION OF TEXAS PROFESSIONAL EDUCATORS; *U.S. Private*, pg. 359
ATA CREATIVITY GLOBAL; *Int'l*, pg. 665
ATOS ORIGIN FORMATION S.A.—See Atos SE; *Int'l*, pg. 691
AUDITORY LEARNING FOUNDATION; *U.S. Private*, pg. 391
AUER VERLAG GMBH—See Ernst Klett AG; *Int'l*, pg. 2495
AU PAIR IN AMERICA—See American Institute for Foreign Study, Inc.; *U.S. Private*, pg. 237
AUSTRALIAN CAREERS NETWORK LIMITED; *Int'l*, pg. 721
AVENUE100 MEDIA SOLUTIONS INC.; *U.S. Private*, pg. 405
AVID CENTER; *U.S. Private*, pg. 406
BABCOCK EDUCATION & SKILLS LIMITED—See Babcock International Group PLC; *Int'l*, pg. 792
BAUER TRAINING CENTER GMBH—See BAUER Aktiengesellschaft; *Int'l*, pg. 893
BAY RIDGE PREP; *U.S. Private*, pg. 494
BBZ MITTE GMBH—See ATON GmbH; *Int'l*, pg. 688
BEIJING AMBOW SHIDA EDUCATION TECHNOLOGY CO., LTD.—See Ambow Education Holding Ltd.; *Int'l*, pg. 415
BEIJING CHINASOFT INTERNATIONAL EDUCATION TECHNOLOGY CO., LTD.—See Chinasoft International Ltd.; *Int'l*, pg. 1568
BEIJING JINGYEDA TECHNOLOGY CO., LTD.; *Int'l*, pg. 953
BENESSE I-CAREER, CO., LTD.—See EQT AB; *Int'l*, pg. 2467
BEO UK LIMITED—See Graham Holdings Company; *U.S. Public*, pg. 954
BERJAYA HIGHER EDUCATION SDN BHD—See Berjaya Corporation Berhad; *Int'l*, pg. 982
BHFS ONE LIMITED—See Bain Capital, LP; *U.S. Private*, pg. 436
BIBLIU LTD.; *Int'l*, pg. 1018
BIG NERD RANCH, LLC—See Amdocs Limited; *Int'l*, pg. 420
BIRCH FAMILY SERVICES, INC.; *U.S. Private*, pg. 564
BISK EDUCATION, INC.; *U.S. Private*, pg. 566
BJB CAREER EDUCATION COMPANY, LIMITED; *Int'l*, pg. 1053
BLACKBOARD (AUSTRALIA) PTY LTD.—See Class Technologies Inc.; *U.S. Private*, pg. 915
BLACKBOARD CZECH S.R.O.—See Class Technologies Inc.; *U.S. Private*, pg. 915
BLACKBOARD EDUCATIONAL (CANADA) CORPORATION—See Class Technologies Inc.; *U.S. Private*, pg. 915
BLACKBOARD GERMANY GMBH—See Class Technologies Inc.; *U.S. Private*, pg. 915
BLACKBOARD INTERNATIONAL B.V.—See Class Technologies Inc.; *U.S. Private*, pg. 915
BLACKBOARD JAPAN K.K.—See Class Technologies Inc.; *U.S. Private*, pg. 915
BLACK SPECTACLES, LLC; *U.S. Private*, pg. 573
BLUE C, LLC—See Comfort Systems USA, Inc.; *U.S. Public*, pg. 543
BOCA ENTERPRISE MANAGEMENT (SHANGHAI) CO., LTD.—See Korn Ferry; *U.S. Public*, pg. 1272
BOJUN EDUCATION COMPANY LIMITED; *Int'l*, pg. 1102
BOOTCAMP EDUCATION, INC.—See Graham Holdings Company; *U.S. Public*, pg. 955
BRIGHTON COMMERCIAL TRAINING CENTRE PTE LTD.—See AEC Education plc; *Int'l*, pg. 171
BRIGHT SCHOLAR EDUCATION HOLDINGS LIMITED; *Int'l*, pg. 1161
BRITUS INTERNATIONAL SCHOOL FOR SPECIAL EDUCATION W.L.L.—See GFH Financial Group B.S.C.; *Int'l*, pg. 2956
BROTHER'S BROTHER FOUNDATION; *U.S. Private*, pg. 665
BROWN MACKIE COLLEGE-ALBUQUERQUE LLC—See Dream Center Foundation, a California Nonprofit Corp.; *U.S. Private*, pg. 1273
BROWN MACKIE COLLEGE - ATLANTA/COLLEGE PARK, INC.—See Dream Center Foundation, a California Nonprofit Corp.; *U.S. Private*, pg. 1273
BROWN MACKIE COLLEGE-BIRMINGHAM LLC—See Dream Center Foundation, a California Nonprofit Corp.; *U.S. Private*, pg. 1273
BROWN MACKIE COLLEGE - BOISE, INC.—See Dream Center Foundation, a California Nonprofit Corp.; *U.S. Private*, pg. 1273
BROWN MACKIE COLLEGE - DALLAS/ FT. WORTH LLC—See Dream Center Foundation, a California Nonprofit Corp.; *U.S. Private*, pg. 1273
BROWN MACKIE COLLEGE-GREENVILLE, INC.—See Dream Center Foundation, a California Nonprofit Corp.; *U.S. Private*, pg. 1273
BROWN MACKIE COLLEGE-KANSAS CITY LLC—See Dream Center Foundation, a California Nonprofit Corp.; *U.S. Private*, pg. 1273
BROWN MACKIE COLLEGE - MIAMI, INC.—See Dream Center Foundation, a California Nonprofit Corp.; *U.S. Private*, pg. 1273
BROWN MACKIE COLLEGE-OKLAHOMA CITY LLC—See Dream Center Foundation, a California Nonprofit Corp.; *U.S. Private*, pg. 1273
BROWN MACKIE COLLEGE-PHOENIX, INC.—See Dream Center Foundation, a California Nonprofit Corp.; *U.S. Private*, pg. 1273
BROWN MACKIE COLLEGE-SALINA LLC—See Dream Center Foundation, a California Nonprofit Corp.; *U.S. Private*, pg. 1273
BROWN MACKIE COLLEGE - SAN ANTONIO LLC—See Dream Center Foundation, a California Nonprofit Corp.; *U.S. Private*, pg. 1273
BROWN MACKIE COLLEGE-ST. LOUIS, INC.—See Dream Center Foundation, a California Nonprofit Corp.; *U.S. Private*, pg. 1273
BROWN MACKIE COLLEGE-TUCSON, INC.—See Dream Center Foundation, a California Nonprofit Corp.; *U.S. Private*, pg. 1273
BROWN MACKIE COLLEGE - TULSA, INC.—See Dream Center Foundation, a California Nonprofit Corp.; *U.S. Private*, pg. 1273
BROWN MACKIE EDUCATION CORPORATION—See Dream Center Foundation, a California Nonprofit Corp.; *U.S. Private*, pg. 1273
BTI CONSULTANTS (INDIA) PRIVATE LIMITED—See Kelly Services, Inc.; *U.S. Public*, pg. 1219
BUNRI CO., LTD.—See Gakken Holdings Co., Ltd.; *Int'l*, pg. 2869
BURKE FOUNDATION; *U.S. Private*, pg. 688
BUSINESS BREAKTHROUGH, INC.; *Int'l*, pg. 1228
CAIRO INVESTMENT & REAL ESTATE DEVELOPMENT; *Int'l*, pg. 1253
CALIFORNIA SCHOOL EMPLOYEES ASSOCIATION; *U.S. Private*, pg. 720
CAMBIUM LEARNING GROUP, INC.—See Veritas Capital Fund Management, LLC; *U.S. Private*, pg. 4361
CAMP AMERICA—See American Institute for Foreign Study, Inc.; *U.S. Private*, pg. 237
CAPGEMINI EDUCATIONAL SERVICES B.V.—See Capgemini SE; *Int'l*, pg. 1306
CAPITA BUSINESS SERVICES LIMITED—See Capita plc; *Int'l*, pg. 1308
CAPPEX.COM LLC—See EAB Global, Inc.; *U.S. Private*, pg. 1308
CAPSTONE TECHNOLOGIES GROUP INC.; *Int'l*, pg. 1317
CARDIOPAPERS SOLUCOES DIGITAIS LTDA.—See Afya Limited; *Int'l*, pg. 196
CAREER DESIGN CENTER CO., LTD.; *Int'l*, pg. 1323
CAREER POINT LTD.; *Int'l*, pg. 1323
CAREER STEP, LLC—See Revelstoke Capital Partners LLC; *U.S. Private*, pg. 3413
CARSON-DELLOSA PUBLISHING GROUP, LLC—See IXL Learning, Inc.; *U.S. Private*, pg. 2152
CATHAY MEDIA & EDUCATION GROUP, INC.; *Int'l*, pg. 1360
CATHOLIC EDUCATION ARIZONA; *U.S. Private*, pg. 788
CCRES, INC.; *U.S. Private*, pg. 801
CEN CHINA EDUCATION NETWORK LTD.—See China Education Resources Inc.; *Int'l*, pg. 1499
CENTER FOR EDUCATIONAL INNOVATION - PUBLIC EDUCATION ASSOCIATION; *U.S. Private*, pg. 810
THE CENTER: RESOURCES FOR TEACHING AND LEARNING; *U.S. Private*, pg. 4006
CENTRO CARDIOLOGICO MONZINO S.P.A.; *Int'l*, pg. 1413
CENTRONIA; *U.S. Private*, pg. 830
CERIFI LLC—See Leeds Equity Partners, LLC; *U.S. Private*, pg. 2414
CERNET-BLACKBOARD INFORMATION TECHNOLOGY (BEIJING) CO. LTD—See Class Technologies Inc.; *U.S. Private*, pg. 915
CESBE S.R.L.—See CAD IT S.p.A.; *Int'l*, pg. 1247
CHAMBERLAIN UNIVERSITY LLC—See Adtalem Global Education Inc.; *U.S. Public*, pg. 43
CHANGEMAKER EDUCATIONS AB—See AcadeMedia AB; *Int'l*, pg. 75
CHARTER BOARD PARTNERS; *U.S. Private*, pg. 858
THE CHAUNCEY GROUP INTERNATIONAL LTD.—See Educational Testing Service Inc.; *U.S. Private*, pg. 1340
CHEGG INC.; *U.S. Public*, pg. 483
CHEGG INDIA PRIVATE LIMITED—See Chegg Inc.; *U.S. Public*, pg. 483
CHILDCRAFT EDUCATION CORPORATION—See School Specialty, Inc.; *U.S. Public*, pg. 1848
THE CHILDREN'S HOSPITAL OF PHILADELPHIA FOUNDATION; *U.S. Private*, pg. 4009
CHINA 21ST CENTURY EDUCATION GROUP LTD.; *Int'l*, pg. 1480
CHINA BESTSTUDY EDUCATION GROUP; *Int'l*, pg. 1486
CHINACAST EDUCATION CORPORATION; *Int'l*, pg. 1568
CHINA CHUNLAI EDUCATION GROUP CO., LTD.; *Int'l*, pg. 1488
CHINA DISTANCE EDUCATION LIMITED—See China Distance Education Holdings Limited; *Int'l*, pg. 1498
CHINA E-INFORMATION TECHNOLOGY GROUP LIMITED; *Int'l*, pg. 1498
CHINA GINGKO EDUCATION GROUP COMPANY LIMITED; *Int'l*, pg. 1504

611710 — EDUCATIONAL SUPPORT...   CORPORATE AFFILIATIONS

CHINA KEPEI EDUCATION GROUP LIMITED; *Int'l*, pg. 1514
CHINA VOCATIONAL EDUCATION HOLDINGS LIMITED; *Int'l*, pg. 1562
CHINA XINHUA EDUCATION GROUP LTD.; *Int'l*, pg. 1563
CHOICE FOUNDATION; *U.S. Private*, pg. 888
CHOICE SOLUTIONS, INC.—See Veritas Capital Fund Management, LLC; *U.S. Public*, pg. 4363
CHUANGLIAN HOLDINGS LIMITED; *Int'l*, pg. 1590
CHUNGDAHM LEARNING, INC.; *Int'l*, pg. 1597
CHUNGNAM NATIONAL UNIVERSITY; *Int'l*, pg. 1598
CJ EDUCATIONS CORPORATION—See CJ Corporation; *Int'l*, pg. 1632
CLASSES USA, INC.—See RockBridge Growth Equity, LLC; *U.S. Private*, pg. 3465
CLEVER INC.—See The Goldman Sachs Group, Inc.; *U.S. Public*, pg. 2082
CLIP CORPORATION; *Int'l*, pg. 1660
CLUB CONNECT LLC—See Dolphin Entertainment, Inc.; *U.S. Public*, pg. 673
CLUEY LIMITED; *Int'l*, pg. 1664
CMS EDU CO., LTD.—See Chungdahm Learning, Inc.; *Int'l*, pg. 1597
CODE.ORG; *U.S. Private*, pg. 960
COGNA EDUCACAO S.A.; *Int'l*, pg. 1695
COLEGIO BRITANICO SAINT MARGARET'S S.A.; *Int'l*, pg. 1697
COLEGIO INGLES CATOLICO DE LA SERENA S.A.; *Int'l*, pg. 1697
COLEGIO LA MAISONNETTE S.A.; *Int'l*, pg. 1698
THE COLLEGE OF HEALTH CARE PROFESSIONS; *U.S. Private*, pg. 4011
COLLEGE POSSIBLE NATIONAL; *U.S. Private*, pg. 968
COLLEGE TRACK; *U.S. Private*, pg. 968
COLLEGIS LLC; *U.S. Private*, pg. 968
THE COLORADO EDUCATION INITIATIVE; *U.S. Private*, pg. 4011
COLUMBUS CITIZENS FOUNDATION; *U.S. Private*, pg. 979
COMMON APPLICATION; *U.S. Private*, pg. 985
COMPLETE COLLEGE AMERICA INC.; *U.S. Private*, pg. 1000
COMPUTER ASSISTED TESTING SERVICE, INC.—See Educational Testing Service Inc.; *U.S. Private*, pg. 1340
CONDUENT EDUCATION SERVICES, LLC—See Conduent Incorporated; *U.S. Public*, pg. 566
CONDUENT GERMANY HOLDING GMBH—See Conduent Incorporated; *U.S. Public*, pg. 566
THE CONNECTING LINK, INC.—See Dream Center Foundation, a California Nonprofit Corp.; *U.S. Private*, pg. 1272
CONSORTIUM ON REACHING EXCELLENCE IN EDUCATION, INC.—See Korn Ferry; *U.S. Public*, pg. 1273
CONTACT ASSOCIATES LIMITED—See Capita plc; *Int'l*, pg. 1309
CORE CAREERS & SKILL DEVELOPMENTS LIMITED—See Core Education and Technologies Ltd.; *Int'l*, pg. 1797
CORE EDUCATION & CONSULTING SOLUTIONS FZ-LLC—See Core Education and Technologies Ltd.; *Int'l*, pg. 1797
CORE EDUCATION & CONSULTING SOLUTIONS, INC.—See Core Education and Technologies Ltd.; *Int'l*, pg. 1797
CORE EDUCATION & CONSULTING SOLUTIONS (UK) LTD.—See Core Education and Technologies Ltd.; *Int'l*, pg. 1797
CORPORATION FOR EDUCATION NETWORK INITIATIVES IN CALIFORNIA; *U.S. Private*, pg. 1056
CORTINA INSTITUTE OF LANGUAGES—See Cortina Learning International, Inc.; *U.S. Private*, pg. 1061
CORTINA LEARNING INTERNATIONAL, INC.; *U.S. Private*, pg. 1061
COUNCIL FOR CHRISTIAN COLLEGES & UNIVERSITIES; *U.S. Private*, pg. 1065
COUNCIL FOR OPPORTUNITY IN EDUCATION; *U.S. Private*, pg. 1065
COURSERA, INC.; *U.S. Public*, pg. 587
COVER CONCEPTS MARKETING SERVICES LLC—See The Walt Disney Company; *U.S. Public*, pg. 2139
CPM EDUCATIONAL PROGRAM; *U.S. Private*, pg. 1080
CRUCIAL INNOVATIONS, CORP.; *Int'l*, pg. 1859
CTM OVERSEAS EDUCATION CENTRE LIMITED—See Corporate Travel Management Limited; *Int'l*, pg. 1805
CUBIC ADVANCED LEARNING SOLUTIONS, INC.—See Elliott Management Corporation; *U.S. Private*, pg. 1367
CUBIC ADVANCED LEARNING SOLUTIONS, INC.—See Veritas Capital Fund Management, LLC; *U.S. Private*, pg. 4361
CURRO EDUCATION BOTSWANA (PTY) LTD.—See Curro Holdings Ltd.; *Int'l*, pg. 1879
CURRO EDUCATION NAMIBIA (PTY) LTD.—See Curro Holdings Ltd.; *Int'l*, pg. 1879
CYBERGYMNASIET MALMO AB—See AcadeMedia AB; *Int'l*, pg. 75
CYBERJAYA COLLEGE CENTRAL SDN. BHD.—See Cyberjaya Education Group Berhad; *Int'l*, pg. 1893

CYBERJAYA EDUCATION GROUP BERHAD; *Int'l*, pg. 1893
DADI EDUCATION HOLDINGS LIMITED; *Int'l*, pg. 1905
DAEKYO CO LTD; *Int'l*, pg. 1907
DAEKYO EYE LEVEL SINGAPORE PTE. LTD.—See Daekyo Co Ltd; *Int'l*, pg. 1907
DAEKYO MALAYSIA SND. BHD.—See Daekyo Co Ltd; *Int'l*, pg. 1907
DAEKYO VIETNAM CO., LTD.—See Daekyo Co Ltd; *Int'l*, pg. 1907
DALIAN UNIVERSITY OF TECHNOLOGY SCIENCE PARK CO., LTD—See Datang Huayin Electric Power Co., Ltd.; *Int'l*, pg. 1979
DEVELOPMENTAL STUDIES CENTER; *U.S. Private*, pg. 1218
DEVMOUNTAIN, LLC—See Strategic Education, Inc.; *U.S. Public*, pg. 1954
DEVOTEAM POLSKA SP. Z O.O.—See Devoteam SA; *Int'l*, pg. 2090
DEVOTEAM SA; *Int'l*, pg. 2089
DEVRY CANADA, LLC—See Adtalem Global Education Inc.; *U.S. Public*, pg. 43
DEVRY EDUCACIONAL DO BRASIL S/A—See Adtalem Global Education Inc.; *U.S. Public*, pg. 43
DHANADA EDUCATION PVT. LTD.—See DHANADA CORPORATION LIMITED; *Int'l*, pg. 2098
DHOFAR UNIVERSITY; *Int'l*, pg. 2100
DIEGO PLUS EDUCATION CORPORATION; *U.S. Private*, pg. 1228
DIGITAL DAESUNG CO., LTD.; *Int'l*, pg. 2121
DIGNITY SERVICES LTD.—See Dignity plc; *Int'l*, pg. 2124
DISCOVER ENGLISH PTY LTD—See Academies Australasia Group Limited; *Int'l*, pg. 77
DOCEBO NA INC.—See Docebo, Inc.; *Int'l*, pg. 2153
DOCEBO S.P.A—See Docebo, Inc.; *Int'l*, pg. 2153
DOCEBO UK LTD.—See Docebo, Inc.; *Int'l*, pg. 2153
DRAGONBOX FINLAND OY—See The Goldman Sachs Group, Inc.; *U.S. Public*, pg. 2082
DRISHA INSTITUTE FOR JEWISH EDUCATION, INC.; *U.S. Private*, pg. 1278
DRIVEITAWAY HOLDINGS, INC.; *U.S. Public*, pg. 688
DTCOM - DIRECT TO COMPANY S/A; *Int'l*, pg. 2216
THE DUBLIN BUSINESS SCHOOL LIMITED—See Graham Holdings Company; *U.S. Public*, pg. 956
DURO SALAJ A.D.; *Int'l*, pg. 2229
EARLY LEARNING COALITION OF DUVAL, INC.; *U.S. Private*, pg. 1313
EARLY LEARNING COALITION OF INDIAN RIVER, MARTIN & OKEECHOBEE COUNTIES, INC.; *U.S. Private*, pg. 1313
EARLY LEARNING COALITION OF MIAMI-DADE/MONROE; *U.S. Private*, pg. 1313
EAST BUY HOLDING LIMITED; *Int'l*, pg. 2269
EAST SIDE HOUSE, INC.; *U.S. Private*, pg. 1317
ECLC OF NEW JERSEY; *U.S. Private*, pg. 1328
ECO360, LLC—See RiskOn International, Inc.; *U.S. Public*, pg. 1799
ECOLOGY ACTION OF SANTA CRUZ; *U.S. Private*, pg. 1329
EC UTBILDNING AB—See AcadeMedia AB; *Int'l*, pg. 75
EDISON LEARNING, INC.—See Liberty Partners, L.P.; *U.S. Private*, pg. 2446
EDLOGICAL GROUP CORP.; *U.S. Private*, pg. 1337
EDMC MARKETING AND ADVERTISING, INC.—See Dream Center Foundation, a California Nonprofit Corp.; *U.S. Private*, pg. 1273
ED & TECH INTERNATIONAL LIMITED; *Int'l*, pg. 2302
EDTRIN GROUP LIMITED; *Int'l*, pg. 2315
EDUCARE GLOBAL ACADEMY PTE. LTD.—See Ascendo International Holdings Pte. Ltd.; *Int'l*, pg. 602
EDUCATE ONLINE, INC.—See Sterling Partners; *U.S. Private*, pg. 3807
EDUCATIONAL DEVELOPERS, INC.; *U.S. Private*, pg. 1339
EDUCATIONAL HOLDING GROUP K.S.C.P.—See Boubyan Petrochemical Co. KSC; *Int'l*, pg. 1119
EDUCATIONAL TECHNOLOGY ARABIA COMPANY LIMITED—See HAK Algahtani Group of Companies; *Int'l*, pg. 3219
EDUCATIONAL TESTING SERVICE INC.; *U.S. Private*, pg. 1339
EDUCATIONAL TREND SDN. BHD.—See HeiTech Padu Berhad; *Int'l*, pg. 3326
EDUCATIONCITY INC.—See The Vistria Group, LP; *U.S. Private*, pg. 4131
EDUCATION CONNECTION; *U.S. Private*, pg. 1338
EDUCATION HOLDINGS 1—See IAC Inc.; *U.S. Public*, pg. 1083
EDUCATION MANAGEMENT CORPORATION—See Dream Center Foundation, a California Nonprofit Corp.; *U.S. Private*, pg. 1272
EDUCATIONPARTNER CO LTD; *Int'l*, pg. 2315
EDUCATION PIONEERS; *U.S. Private*, pg. 1339
EDUCATION SERVICE CENTER REGION 12; *U.S. Private*, pg. 1339
EDUCATION SERVICE CENTER REGION II; *U.S. Private*, pg. 1339
THE EDUCATION TRUST; *U.S. Private*, pg. 4025

EDUCATIONWORKS; *U.S. Private*, pg. 1340
EDUCOMP SOLUTIONS, LTD.; *Int'l*, pg. 2315
EDUGRADE SE—See Hexatronic Group AB; *Int'l*, pg. 3370
EDULAB, INC.; *Int'l*, pg. 2316
EDUMATICS CORPORATION INC.—See Educomp Solutions, Ltd.; *Int'l*, pg. 2315
EDUNIVERSAL SA; *Int'l*, pg. 2316
EDU-PERFORMANCE CANADA INC.—See DGTL Holdings Inc.; *Int'l*, pg. 2097
EDU-PERFORMANCE EUROPE—See DGTL Holdings Inc.; *Int'l*, pg. 2097
EDU-PERFORMANCE MEXICO—See DGTL Holdings Inc.; *Int'l*, pg. 2097
EDUTAINMENTLIVE, LLC; *U.S. Private*, pg. 1340
EDVANTAGES; *U.S. Private*, pg. 1340
EDX, INC.—See 2U, Inc.; *U.S. Public*, pg. 3
E-FUTURE CO., LTD.; *Int'l*, pg. 2247
ELDERHOSTEL, INC.; *U.S. Private*, pg. 1351
ELENCO ELECTRONICS, INC.; *U.S. Private*, pg. 1357
ELITE LEGACY EDUCATION LTD.—See Legacy Education Alliance, Inc.; *U.S. Public*, pg. 1301
EMERGENT INDUSTRIAL SOLUTIONS LIMITED; *Int'l*, pg. 2378
EMERSON PROCESS MANAGEMENT—See Emerson Electric Co.; *U.S. Public*, pg. 746
EMIRATES DRIVING INSTITUTE—See Belhasa Group of Companies; *Int'l*, pg. 964
ERLEBNIS AKADEMIE AG; *Int'l*, pg. 2494
ESALEN INSTITUTE; *U.S. Private*, pg. 1424
ESTHETICS AND WELLNESS INTERNATIONAL SDN. BHD.—See Esthetics International Group Berhad; *Int'l*, pg. 2518
ET BUSINESS COLLEGE LIMITED—See Hong Kong Economic Times Holdings Ltd; *Int'l*, pg. 3465
EUROPAISCHE FERNHOCHSCHULE HAMBURG GMBH—See Ernst Klett AG; *Int'l*, pg. 2495
EVANGELICAL LUTHERAN CHURCH IN AMERICA; *U.S. Private*, pg. 1434
EVERONN EDUCATION LIMITED; *Int'l*, pg. 2568
EVERYBODY LOVES LANGUAGES CORP.; *Int'l*, pg. 2569
EXCELLIGENCE LEARNING CORPORATION—See Brentwood Associates; *U.S. Private*, pg. 645
EXCELSIOR EDUCATION MANAGEMENT SDN BHD—See Chip Eng Seng Corporation Ltd.; *Int'l*, pg. 1572
FAR EASTERN UNIVERSITY INC.; *Int'l*, pg. 2617
FENBI LTD.; *Int'l*, pg. 2633
FERDINAND PORSCHE FERNFH—See Ernst Klett AG; *Int'l*, pg. 2495
FERNAKADEMIE FUR ERWACHSENENBILDUNG GMBH—See Ernst Klett AG; *Int'l*, pg. 2495
FEU ALABANG, INC.—See Far Eastern University Inc.; *Int'l*, pg. 2617
FLIGHTSAFETY INTERNATIONAL COURSEWARE SUPPORT—See Berkshire Hathaway Inc.; *U.S. Public*, pg. 305
FLINT INT'L SERVICES, INC.; *Int'l*, pg. 2706
FOUNDATION FOR EDUCATIONAL SERVICES; *U.S. Private*, pg. 1580
FOUNDATION FOR EXCELLENCE IN EDUCATION; *U.S. Private*, pg. 1580
FOUNDATION FOR NEWARK'S FUTURE; *U.S. Private*, pg. 1580
FOUR SEASONS EDUCATION (CAYMAN) INC.; *Int'l*, pg. 2755
FPT EDUCATION COMPANY LIMITED—See FPT Corporation; *Int'l*, pg. 2757
THE FRANCE FOUNDATION—See SmithBucklin Corporation; *U.S. Private*, pg. 3697
FRANKLIN COVEY MIDDLE EAST COMPANY LTD.—See Alkhaleej Training & Education Company; *Int'l*, pg. 331
FRANKLYN SCHOLAR PTY LTD.—See Graham Holdings Company; *U.S. Public*, pg. 954
FUNDACION AES GENER—See The AES Corporation; *U.S. Public*, pg. 2031
FUTURE LEADERS OF AMERICA FOUNDATION, INC; *U.S. Private*, pg. 1627
GAKKEN EDUCATIONAL CO., LTD.—See Gakken Holdings Co., Ltd.; *Int'l*, pg. 2869
GAKKEN EDUCATION MALAYSIA SDN. BHD.—See Gakken Holdings Co., Ltd.; *Int'l*, pg. 2869
GAKKEN (HONG KONG) CO., LTD.—See Gakken Holdings Co., Ltd.; *Int'l*, pg. 2869
GAKKEN MEDICAL SHUJUNSHA CO., LTD.—See Gakken Holdings Co., Ltd.; *Int'l*, pg. 2869
GAKKEN PLUS CO., LTD.—See Gakken Holdings Co., Ltd.; *Int'l*, pg. 2869
GAKKEN PRODUCTS SUPPORT CO., LTD.—See Gakken Holdings Co., Ltd.; *Int'l*, pg. 2869
GAKKEN SMILEHEART CO., LTD.—See Gakken Holdings Co., Ltd.; *Int'l*, pg. 2869
GAKKEN STA:FUL CO., LTD.—See Gakken Holdings Co., Ltd.; *Int'l*, pg. 2869
GAKKYUSHA CO., LTD.; *Int'l*, pg. 2870
GAKUJO CO., LTD.; *Int'l*, pg. 2870
GALVANIZE INC.—See Stride, Inc.; *U.S. Public*, pg. 1955
GENIUS GROUP LIMITED; *Int'l*, pg. 2924
GEOTEXT TRANSLATIONS, INC.; *U.S. Private*, pg. 1685
GET EDUCATED INTERNATIONAL PROPRIETARY

N.A.I.C.S. INDEX 611710 — EDUCATIONAL SUPPORT...

LIMITED—See 2U, Inc.; *U.S. Public*, pg. 3
GETSMARTER ONLINE LIMITED—See 2U, Inc.; *U.S. Public*, pg. 3
GIFT USA INC.—See GIFT Holdings Inc.; *Int'l*, pg. 2970
THE GILDER LEHRMAN INSTITUTE OF AMERICAN HISTORY; *U.S. Private*, pg. 4033
GLOBAL EDUCATION ALLIANCE INC.—See Global Education Communities Corp; *Int'l*, pg. 2995
GLOBAL EDUCATION LIMITED; *Int'l*, pg. 2995
GLOBAL EXPERIENCES, INC.—See American Institute for Foreign Study, Inc.; *U.S. Private*, pg. 238
GLOBAL HEALTHCARE & EDUCATION MANAGEMENT, INC.; *U.S. Public*, pg. 942
GLOBALISE; *U.S. Private*, pg. 1719
GLOBEE INC.; *Int'l*, pg. 3007
GLOCAL EDUCATION SERVICES LIMITED—See Bexcellent Group Holdings Limited; *Int'l*, pg. 1005
GLYNLYON, INC.—See Silver Lake Group, LLC; *U.S. Private*, pg. 3661
GOLDEN CREST EDUCATION & SERVICES LIMITED; *Int'l*, pg. 3029
GOLDEN SUN HEALTH TECHNOLOGY GROUP LIMITED; *Int'l*, pg. 3032
GOLD&S CO., LTD.; *Int'l*, pg. 3026
GORMAN LEARNING CENTER, INC.; *U.S. Private*, pg. 1744
GRACE HILL, LLC—See Stone Point Capital LLC; *U.S. Private*, pg. 3825
GRAMMARLY, INC.; *U.S. Private*, pg. 1752
GRC ELEARNING LIMITED—See Bloom Equity Partners Management, LLC; *U.S. Private*, pg. 583
GREAAT SCHOOLS INC.; *U.S. Private*, pg. 1761
THE GREENE ORGANIZATION, INC.—See Kynetic LLC; *U.S. Private*, pg. 2360
GROLIER INTERNATIONAL, INC.—See Scholastic Corporation; *U.S. Public*, pg. 1847
GROLIER INTERNATIONAL PRIVATE LIMITED—See Scholastic Corporation; *U.S. Public*, pg. 1847
GROVO LEARNING INC.—See Clearlake Capital Group, L.P.; *U.S. Private*, pg. 934
G-TEC JAINX EDUCATION LTD.; *Int'l*, pg. 2863
GTG TRAINING LIMITED—See Arnold Clark Automobiles Limited; *Int'l*, pg. 576
GTT TRAINING LTD.—See Gaztransport Et Technigaz SA; *Int'l*, pg. 2892
HAF HAMBURGER AKADEMIE FUR FERNSTUDIEN GMBH—See Ernst Klett AG; *Int'l*, pg. 2495
HANDS ON EDUCATION CONSULTANTS CO., LTD.—See Graham Holdings Company; *U.S. Public*, pg. 955
HANOI EDUCATION DEVELOPMENT & INVESTMENT JSC; *Int'l*, pg. 3258
HANTANG CULTURE & EDUCATION HOLDING GROUP LIMITED; *Int'l*, pg. 3261
HAROLD GRINSPOON FOUNDATION; *U.S. Private*, pg. 1867
HAWKSMERE LIMITED—See Graham Holdings Company; *U.S. Public*, pg. 955
HEALTH PROFESSIONS EDUCATION FOUNDATION; *U.S. Private*, pg. 1894
HELIOS EDUCATION FOUNDATION; *U.S. Private*, pg. 1906
HEP-NOC VELIKA—See Hrvatska elektroprivreda d.d.; *Int'l*, pg. 3502
HERMODS AB—See AcadeMedia AB; *Int'l*, pg. 76
H-FARM SPA; *Int'l*, pg. 3194
H-FARM S.P.A.; *Int'l*, pg. 3194
HICA EDUCATION LOAN CORPORATION—See SLM Corporation; *U.S. Public*, pg. 1894
HIGH DESERT PARTNERSHIP IN ACADEMIC EXCELLENCE FOUNDATION, INC.; *U.S. Private*, pg. 1935
HIGHER EDUCATION SERVICES, INC.—See Dream Center Foundation, a California Nonprofit Corp; *U.S. Private*, pg. 1273
HIGHER EDUCATION & VOCATIONAL BOOK JSC; *Int'l*, pg. 3387
HIGHER LEARNING COMMISSION; *U.S. Private*, pg. 1937
HISPANIC ASSOCIATION OF COLLEGES AND UNIVERSITIES; *U.S. Private*, pg. 1951
HOPE EDUCATION GROUP CO., LTD.; *Int'l*, pg. 3473
HQ GLOBAL EDUCATION INC.; *Int'l*, pg. 3501
HSM DO BRASIL S.A.—See Anima Holding SA; *Int'l*, pg. 471
HUMAN ACADEMY CO., LTD.—See Human Holdings Co., Ltd.; *Int'l*, pg. 3529
HUMAN ACADEMY HIGH SCHOOL CO., LTD.—See Human Holdings Co., Ltd.; *Int'l*, pg. 3529
HUMAN ND CO., LTD.—See Human Holdings Co., Ltd.; *Int'l*, pg. 3529
HUMMING BIRD EDUCATION LTD.; *Int'l*, pg. 3531
IBKIMYOUNG CO., LTD.; *Int'l*, pg. 3576
IC NET LIMITED—See Gakken Holdings Co., Ltd.; *Int'l*, pg. 2869
ICOLLEGE LIMITED; *Int'l*, pg. 3582
IDP EDUCATION AUSTRALIA LIMITED; *Int'l*, pg. 3596
IEC EDUCATION LTD.; *Int'l*, pg. 3597
IECL PTY. LTD.—See GrowthOps Limited; *Int'l*, pg. 3113
ILA SOUTH PACIFIC LIMITED—See Graham Holdings Company; *U.S. Public*, pg. 955

ILLINOIS ASSOCIATION OF SCHOOL BOARDS; *U.S. Private*, pg. 2042
ILLINOIS HIGH SCHOOL ASSOCIATION; *U.S. Private*, pg. 2042
THE ILLINOIS INSTITUTE OF ART - TINLEY PARK LLC—See Dream Center Foundation, a California Nonprofit Corp.; *U.S. Private*, pg. 1275
INGENIUS, LLC; *U.S. Private*, pg. 2075
INSIDETRACK, INC.; *U.S. Private*, pg. 2085
INSTITUTE FOR BETTER EDUCATION; *U.S. Private*, pg. 2093
INSTITUTO EDUCACIONAL SANTO AGOSTINHO S.A.—See Afya Limited; *Int'l*, pg. 196
INSTRUCTIVISION, INC.; *U.S. Public*, pg. 1134
INTEL-ASSESS, INC.—See News Corporation; *U.S. Public*, pg. 1519
INTERNATIONAL ASSOCIATION FOR K-12 ONLINE LEARNING; *U.S. Private*, pg. 2114
INTERNATIONAL BACCALAUREATE; *U.S. Private*, pg. 2114
INTERNATIONAL CENTER FOR LEADERSHIP IN EDUCATION, INC.—See Veritas Capital Fund Management, LLC; *U.S. Private*, pg. 4363
INTERNATIONAL READING ASSOCIATION, INC.; *U.S. Private*, pg. 2119
INTERNATIONAL SCHOOL OF BERNE AG—See Stride, Inc.; *U.S. Public*, pg. 1955
INTERNATIONAL STUDENT VOLUNTEERS; *U.S. Private*, pg. 2121
INTERNATIONAL STUDIES ABROAD, INC.; *U.S. Private*, pg. 2121
INTERNATIONAL TEFL ACADEMY, INC.; *U.S. Private*, pg. 2121
INTERSERVE LEARNING EMPLOYMENT SERVICES LTD.—See Endless LLP; *Int'l*, pg. 2403
INVENT NOW, INC.; *U.S. Private*, pg. 2131
INVICTUS INTERNATIONAL SCHOOL (HONG KONG) LIMITED—See Chip Eng Seng Corporation Ltd.; *Int'l*, pg. 1572
INVICTUS INTERNATIONAL SCHOOL PTE. LTD.—See Chip Eng Seng Corporation Ltd.; *Int'l*, pg. 1572
INVICTUS JUNIOR SCHOOLS PTE. LTD.—See Chip Eng Seng Corporation Ltd.; *Int'l*, pg. 1572
INVICTUS SCHOOL (CHAI WAN) LIMITED—See Chip Eng Seng Corporation Ltd.; *Int'l*, pg. 1572
IOWA STATE EDUCATION ASSOCIATION; *U.S. Private*, pg. 2136
IOWA STUDENT LOAN LIQUIDITY CORPORATION; *U.S. Private*, pg. 2136
ISF INTERNATIONALE SCHULE FRANKFURT-RHEIN-MAIN GMBH & CO. KG—See General Motors Company; *U.S. Public*, pg. 927
ITHAKA; *U.S. Private*, pg. 2149
ITT EDUCATIONAL SERVICES, INC.; *U.S. Private*, pg. 2150
JAGGER BROWN, INC.; *U.S. Private*, pg. 2182
JAMPLAY LLC; *U.S. Private*, pg. 2186
KAPLAN BUSINESS SCHOOL AUSTRALIA PTY LTD—See Graham Holdings Company; *U.S. Public*, pg. 955
KAPLAN BUSINESS SCHOOL PTY LTD—See Graham Holdings Company; *U.S. Public*, pg. 955
KAPLAN CANADA INC.—See Graham Holdings Company; *U.S. Public*, pg. 955
KAPLAN FINANCIAL—See Graham Holdings Company; *U.S. Public*, pg. 956
KAPLAN GLOBAL SOLUTIONS, LLC—See Graham Holdings Company; *U.S. Public*, pg. 955
KAPLAN HIGHER EDUCATION, LLC—See Graham Holdings Company; *U.S. Public*, pg. 955
KAPLAN, INC.—See Graham Holdings Company; *U.S. Public*, pg. 955
KAPLAN INSTITUTE LIMITED—See Graham Holdings Company; *U.S. Public*, pg. 956
KAPLAN INTERNATIONAL COLLEGE LONDON LIMITED—See Graham Holdings Company; *U.S. Public*, pg. 956
KAPLAN INTERNATIONAL COLLEGES, C.A.—See Graham Holdings Company; *U.S. Public*, pg. 955
KAPLAN INTERNATIONAL COLLEGES U.K. LIMITED—See Graham Holdings Company; *U.S. Public*, pg. 956
KAPLAN INTERNATIONAL ENGLISH (AUSTRALIA) PTY LIMITED—See Graham Holdings Company; *U.S. Public*, pg. 955
KAPLAN INTERNATIONAL (MANLY) PTY LIMITED—See Graham Holdings Company; *U.S. Public*, pg. 956
KAPLAN LAW SCHOOL LIMITED—See Graham Holdings Company; *U.S. Public*, pg. 956
KAPLAN OPEN LEARNING (ESSEX) LIMITED—See Graham Holdings Company; *U.S. Public*, pg. 956
KAPLAN PROFESSIONAL—See Graham Holdings Company; *U.S. Public*, pg. 956
KAPLAN PUBLISHING LIMITED—See Graham Holdings Company; *U.S. Public*, pg. 956
KASHIN, INC.; *U.S. Public*, pg. 1214
THE KEHILLAH JEWISH EDUCATION FUND; *U.S. Private*, pg. 4064

KENTUCKY EDUCATION ASSOCIATION; *U.S. Private*, pg. 2288
KEY EDUCATION RESOURCES—See KeyCorp; *U.S. Public*, pg. 1225
KEYPATH EDUCATION INTERNATIONAL INC.—See Sterling Partners; *U.S. Private*, pg. 3806
KEYPATH EDUCATION LLC; *U.S. Private*, pg. 2294
KHAN ACADEMY, INC.; *U.S. Private*, pg. 2301
KIC INNOENERGY S.E.—See EnBW Energie Baden-Wurttemberg AG; *Int'l*, pg. 2399
KIDS IN NEED FOUNDATION; *U.S. Private*, pg. 2303
KIDS IN THE GAME LLC; *U.S. Private*, pg. 2303
KINGSLEY EDUGROUP LTD.—See China Maple Leaf Educational Systems Limited; *Int'l*, pg. 1517
KNOWLEDGECOM CORPORATION SDN. BHD.—See Censof Holdings Berhad; *Int'l*, pg. 1401
KOMPETENSUTVECKLINGSINSTITUTET SVERIGE AB—See AcadeMedia AB; *Int'l*, pg. 77
KORN FERRY CR S.R.L.—See Korn Ferry; *U.S. Public*, pg. 1273
KORN FERRY FUTURESTEP (THE PHILIPPINES) INC.—See Korn Ferry; *U.S. Public*, pg. 1273
KORN FERRY (SK) S.R.O.—See Korn Ferry; *U.S. Public*, pg. 1273
KYH AB—See AcadeMedia AB; *Int'l*, pg. 77
L-3 COMMUNICATIONS MAS (CANADA) INC.—See L3Harris Technologies, Inc.; *U.S. Public*, pg. 1282
THE LEADERSHIP INSTITUTE; *U.S. Private*, pg. 4068
LEARNIFY AB—See Grimaldi Industri AB; *Int'l*, pg. 3085
LEARNING EVOLUTION, LLC; *U.S. Private*, pg. 2408
LEARNING INTERNET INC.—See Educomp Solutions, Ltd.; *Int'l*, pg. 2315
LEARNING POOL LIMITED—See Marlin Equity Partners, LLC; *U.S. Private*, pg. 2584
LEARNING RESOURCES, INC.; *U.S. Private*, pg. 2408
LEARNLIVE TECHNOLOGIES; *U.S. Private*, pg. 2408
LE CORDON BLEU NORTH AMERICA, LLC—See Perdoceo Education Corporation; *U.S. Public*, pg. 1673
LEGACY EDUCATION ALLIANCE, INC.; *U.S. Public*, pg. 1301
LEGACY EDUCATION INC.; *U.S. Public*, pg. 1301
LOSCALZO ASSOCIATES, LTD.—See Graham Holdings Company; *U.S. Public*, pg. 956
MACKIN EDUCATIONAL RESOURCES; *U.S. Private*, pg. 2537
MAKEBOT ROBOTIC SOLUTIONS PRIVATE LIMITED—See Globalspace Technologies Limited; *Int'l*, pg. 3004
MANAGEMENT & TRAINING CORPORATION; *U.S. Private*, pg. 2560
MARITZ PERFORMANCE IMPROVEMENT COMPANY—See Maritz Holdings Inc.; *U.S. Private*, pg. 2577
MASSACHUSETTS INSTITUTE OF TECHNOLOGY; *U.S. Private*, pg. 2604
MATHEMATICAL ASSOCIATION OF AMERICA, INCORPORATED; *U.S. Private*, pg. 2610
MATH FOR AMERICA; *U.S. Private*, pg. 2610
MATHNASIUM LLC—See Roark Capital Group Inc.; *U.S. Private*, pg. 3455
MAXIPRINT GRAFICA E EDITORA LTDA—See Cogna Educacao S.A.; *Int'l*, pg. 1695
MAYO FOUNDATION FOR MEDICAL EDUCATION & RESEARCH; *U.S. Private*, pg. 2622
MCI INSTITUTE PTY LTD—See Madison Dearborn Partners, LLC; *U.S. Private*, pg. 2540
MCREL INTERNATIONAL; *U.S. Private*, pg. 2644
MEDIA DESIGN SCHOOL LIMITED—See Strategic Education, Inc.; *U.S. Public*, pg. 1954
MEDICAL TRANSCRIPTION EDUCATION CENTER, INC.—See Microsoft Corporation; *U.S. Public*, pg. 1442
MEDIOLANUM CORPORATE UNIVERSITY S.P.A.—See Banca Mediolanum S.p.A.; *Int'l*, pg. 815
MEMPHIS DEVELOPMENT FOUNDATION; *U.S. Private*, pg. 2664
METAMETRICS, INC.—See Pamlico Capital Management, L.P.; *U.S. Private*, pg. 3083
MICHIGAN EDUCATION ASSOCIATION; *U.S. Private*, pg. 2700
MIDDLEBURY INTERACTIVE LANGUAGES LLC—See Stride, Inc.; *U.S. Public*, pg. 1955
THE MILLENNIUM ALLIANCE LLC; *U.S. Private*, pg. 4079
MILLER HEIMAN GROUP (ASIA) PTE. LTD.—See Korn Ferry; *U.S. Public*, pg. 1275
MIND RESEARCH INSTITUTE; *U.S. Private*, pg. 2740
MINTRA LTD.—See Ferd AS; *Int'l*, pg. 2636
MINTRA TRAININGPORTAL AS—See Ferd AS; *Int'l*, pg. 2636
MLINK TECHNOLOGIES INC.—See Sweetview Partners, Inc.; *U.S. Private*, pg. 3892
MOODY'S ANALYTICS GLOBAL EDUCATION (CANADA) INC.—See Moody's Corporation; *U.S. Public*, pg. 1468
MORRIS COUNTY LIBRARY; *U.S. Private*, pg. 2787
MTS TESTING SYSTEMS (CANADA) LTD.—See Amphenol Corporation; *U.S. Public*, pg. 131
MYCOMPUTERCAREER INC.; *U.S. Private*, pg. 2823
MYCSP LIMITED—See Siris Capital Group, LLC; *U.S. Private*, pg. 3673

611710 — EDUCATIONAL SUPPORT...

NACEL OPEN DOOR, INC.; *U.S. Private*, pg. 2830
NAO TEXAS—See NAO, Inc.; *U.S. Private*, pg. 2834
NAPLES CHILDREN & EDUCATION FOUNDATION; *U.S. Private*, pg. 2834
NASCO MODESTO—See Geneve Holdings Corp.; *U.S. Private*, pg. 1671
NATIONAL ASSOCIATION OF COLLEGE AND UNIVERSITY BUSINESS OFFICERS; *U.S. Private*, pg. 2846
NATIONAL ASSOCIATION OF INDEPENDENT SCHOOLS, INC.; *U.S. Private*, pg. 2847
NATIONAL ASSOCIATION OF SECONDARY SCHOOL PRINCIPALS; *U.S. Private*, pg. 2847
NATIONAL ECONOMIC RESEARCH ASSOCIATES, INC.—See Marsh & McLennan Companies, Inc.; *U.S. Public*, pg. 1387
NATIONAL FFA FOUNDATION; *U.S. Private*, pg. 2853
NATIONAL MERIT SCHOLARSHIP CORP.; *U.S. Private*, pg. 2859
NATIONAL NETWORK DIGITAL SCHOOLS; *U.S. Private*, pg. 2859
NATIONAL SCHOOL BOARDS ASSOCIATION; *U.S. Private*, pg. 2862
NATIONAL STUDENT CLEARINGHOUSE; *U.S. Private*, pg. 2863
NELNET DIVERSIFIED SOLUTIONS, LLC—See Nelnet, Inc.; *U.S. Public*, pg. 1504
NETWORK FOR MEDICAL COMMUNICATION & RESEARCH, LLC—See Cencora, Inc.; *U.S. Public*, pg. 467
NETWORK FOR TEACHING ENTREPRENEURSHIP; *U.S. Private*, pg. 2889
NEVE YERUSHALAYIM INC.; *U.S. Private*, pg. 2891
NEW TEACHER CENTER; *U.S. Private*, pg. 2907
NEW VISIONS FOR PUBLIC SCHOOLS; *U.S. Private*, pg. 2907
THE NEW YORK INSTITUTE FOR SPECIAL EDUCATION; *U.S. Private*, pg. 4083
NEXTER TRAINING—See GIAT Industries S.A.; *Int'l*, pg. 2962
NIGHTINGALE-CONANT CORPORATION; *U.S. Private*, pg. 2927
NMCR ANALYTICS—See Cencora, Inc.; *U.S. Public*, pg. 467
NOGGINLABS, INC.; *U.S. Private*, pg. 2933
NORTH CLIFF CONSULTANTS, INC.—See GHO Capital Partners LLP; *Int'l*, pg. 2959
NORTH LOS ANGELES COUNTY REGIONAL CENTER INC.; *U.S. Private*, pg. 2945
NORTHRIDING COLLEGE (PTY) LTD.—See Curro Holdings Ltd.; *Int'l*, pg. 1879
NORTH SEATTLE COMMUNITY COLLEGE FOUNDATION; *U.S. Private*, pg. 2946
NORTHSTAR EDUCATION FINANCE, INC.; *U.S. Private*, pg. 2957
NORTHWEST EVALUATION ASSOCIATION—See Veritas Capital Fund Management, LLC; *U.S. Private*, pg. 4363
NORTHWEST HEALTH CAREERS, LLC; *U.S. Private*, pg. 2960
NP LIFE SCIENCES HEALTH INDUSTRY GROUP INC.; *U.S. Public*, pg. 1549
OBJECTIVE MANAGEMENT GROUP, INC.; *U.S. Private*, pg. 2987
OCL FINANCIAL SERVICES LLC—See Adtalem Global Education Inc.; *U.S. Public*, pg. 43
OHIO EDUCATION ASSOCIATION; *U.S. Private*, pg. 3004
ONE EXAM PREP LLC—See ProBility Media Corporation; *U.S. Public*, pg. 1723
ONEOK FOUNDATION, INC.—See ONEOK, Inc.; *U.S. Public*, pg. 1603
ORANGE COUNTY SCHOOL READINESS COALITION, INC.; *U.S. Private*, pg. 3037
ORBIS EDUCATION SERVICES, LLC—See Grand Canyon Education, Inc.; *U.S. Public*, pg. 957
OREGON EDUCATION ASSOCIATION; *U.S. Private*, pg. 3040
ORT AMERICA, INC.; *U.S. Private*, pg. 3045
OWL COMPANIES; *U.S. Private*, pg. 3055
PACIFIC LANGUAGE INSTITUTE, INC.—See Graham Holdings Company; *U.S. Public*, pg. 955
PALO ALTO VETERANS INSTITUTE FOR RESEARCH; *U.S. Private*, pg. 3082
PANHANDLE PLAINS MANAGEMENT AND SERVICING CORPORATION; *U.S. Private*, pg. 3086
PARENTHESIS, INC.; *U.S. Private*, pg. 3094
PATON - MILLER LLC—See H2I Group, Inc.; *U.S. Private*, pg. 1837
PCS EDVENTURES!.COM, INC.; *U.S. Public*, pg. 1658
PCT CO., LTD.—See Bain Capital, LP; *U.S. Private*, pg. 435
PEOPLELINK INC.—See Groupe Crit, S.A.; *Int'l*, pg. 3101
PERDOCEO EDUCATION CORPORATION; *U.S. Private*, pg. 1673
PERFEKT ZRT—See DPG Media Group NV; *Int'l*, pg. 2188
THE PERSE SCHOOL (SINGAPORE) PTE. LTD.—See Chip Eng Seng Corporation Ltd.; *Int'l*, pg. 1572
PIONEER VALLEY BOOKS; *U.S. Private*, pg. 3188
PIVOT LEARNING, LLC—See Korn Ferry; *U.S. Public*, pg. 1273
PORTABLE PRACTICAL EDUCATIONAL PREPARATION, INC; *U.S. Private*, pg. 3231

THE POSSE FOUNDATION, INC.; *U.S. Private*, pg. 4097
POWERSCHOOL GROUP LLC—See Vista Equity Partners, LLC; *U.S. Private*, pg. 4399
PRAGER UNIVERSITY FOUNDATION; *U.S. Private*, pg. 3242
PRAKTISKA SVERIGE AB—See FSN Capital Partners AS; *Int'l*, pg. 2799
PRAKTISKA SVERIGE AB—See FSN Capital Partners AS; *Int'l*, pg. 2799
PRAKTISKA SVERIGE AB—See FSN Capital Partners AS; *Int'l*, pg. 2799
PRAKTISKA SVERIGE AB—See FSN Capital Partners AS; *Int'l*, pg. 2799
PREMIER AGENDAS, INC.—See SDI Innovations, Inc.; *U.S. Private*, pg. 3581
THE PRINCETON REVIEW, INC.—See Charlesbank Capital Partners, LLC; *U.S. Private*, pg. 856
PROCIVITAS PRIVATA GYMNASIUM AB—See AcadeMedia AB; *Int'l*, pg. 77
PRODUCTION MANAGEMENT INSTITUTE OF SOUTH AFRICA (PTY) LIMITED—See Adcorp Holdings Limited; *Int'l*, pg. 127
PRO LINGUIS—See Graham Holdings Company; *U.S. Public*, pg. 955
PROMETRIC LLC—See Educational Testing Service Inc.; *U.S. Private*, pg. 1340
P.T. DAEKYO INDONESIA—See Daekyo Co Ltd; *Int'l*, pg. 1907
QC PLZEN S.R.O.—See DEKRA e.V.; *Int'l*, pg. 2010
QUALITY ASSIST, INC.—See Summit Partners, L.P.; *U.S. Private*, pg. 3856
QUESTAR ASSESSMENT, INC.—See Educational Testing Service Inc.; *U.S. Private*, pg. 1340
QUEST CE; *U.S. Private*, pg. 3325
RATEMYPROFESSORS.COM, LLC—See Altice USA, Inc.; *U.S. Public*, pg. 88
READING IS FUNDAMENTAL, INC.; *U.S. Private*, pg. 3366
READING PARTNERS; *U.S. Private*, pg. 3366
REAL FREEDOM INC.; *U.S. Private*, pg. 3367
REALLY GOOD STUFF, LLC—See Brentwood Associates; *U.S. Private*, pg. 646
REDBEAT ACADEMY SDN. BHD.—See Capital A Bhd; *Int'l*, pg. 1309
REEDLEY HIGH SCHOOL; *U.S. Private*, pg. 3383
REGION 13 EDUCATION SERVICE CENTER; *U.S. Private*, pg. 3388
REMOTE-LEARNER.NET, INC—See Marlin Equity Partners, LLC; *U.S. Private*, pg. 2584
RESPONSIVE INNOVATIONS, LLC—See Centre Lane Partners, LLC; *U.S. Private*, pg. 828
RESTAURANGAKDEMIEN AB—See Sysco Corporation; *U.S. Public*, pg. 1975
RICH DAD EDUCATION LTD.—See Legacy Education Alliance, Inc.; *U.S. Public*, pg. 1301
RTL JOURNALISTENSCHULE GMBH—See Bertelsmann SE & Co. KGaA; *Int'l*, pg. 996
SAFEBRIDGE CYPRUS LTD.—See Ferd AS; *Int'l*, pg. 2636
SAFEBRIDGE GMBH—See Ferd AS; *Int'l*, pg. 2636
SAFETY BUSINESS LEARNING LIMITED—See K1 Investment Management, LLC; *U.S. Private*, pg. 2252
SAINT VINCENT'S; *U.S. Private*, pg. 3530
SALLIE MAE BANK—See SLM Corporation; *U.S. Public*, pg. 1894
SANFORD-BROWN COLLEGE, LLC—See Perdoceo Education Corporation; *U.S. Public*, pg. 1673
SANGHAI DAEKYO CO., LTD.—See Daekyo Co Ltd; *Int'l*, pg. 1907
SATUSA CORPORATION; *U.S. Private*, pg. 3553
SAVVICA INC.—See Educomp Solutions, Ltd.; *Int'l*, pg. 2315
SCHOLARSFIRST LLC—See Pensler Capital Corporation; *U.S. Private*, pg. 3139
SCHOOL NUTRITION ASSOCIATION; *U.S. Private*, pg. 3568
SCHOOL TECH SUPPLY; *U.S. Private*, pg. 3568
SCHOOL YEAR ABROAD INC.; *U.S. Private*, pg. 3568
SCIENTIFIC LEARNING CORPORATION—See CIP Capital Fund, L.P.; *U.S. Private*, pg. 899
SCOLA; *U.S. Private*, pg. 3575
SCOTTISH BORDERS EDUCATION PARTNERSHIP LTD.—See Bilfinger SE; *Int'l*, pg. 1028
SCOYO GMBH—See Bertelsmann SE & Co. KGaA; *Int'l*, pg. 997
SELC AUSTRALIA PTY. LTD.—See Bain Capital, LP; *U.S. Private*, pg. 442
SELC CAREER COLLEGE CANADA LTD.—See Bain Capital, LP; *U.S. Private*, pg. 442
SELC ENGLISH LANGUAGE CENTRE CANADA LTD.—See Bain Capital, LP; *U.S. Private*, pg. 442
SHAKESPEARE SQUARED; *U.S. Private*, pg. 3623
SHANGHAI CHINASOFT RESOURCES INFORMATION TECHNOLOGY SERVICES LIMITED—See Chinasoft International Ltd.; *Int'l*, pg. 1569
THE SHELTERING ARMS; *U.S. Private*, pg. 4117
SHOWA BOSTON INSTITUTE FOR LANGUAGE AND CULTURE; *U.S. Private*, pg. 3643
SHT SCHWABISCH HALL TRAINING GMBH—See DZ BANK AG Deutsche Zentral-Genossenschaftsbank; *Int'l*, pg. 2244

SIBIL EDUCATION PRIVATE LIMITED—See Humming Bird Education Ltd.; *Int'l*, pg. 3531
SIEGFRIED VOGELE INSTITUT (SVI) - INTERNATIONALE GESELLSCHAFT FUR DIALOGMARKETING MBH—See Deutsche Post AG; *Int'l*, pg. 2082
SING-ED GLOBAL SCHOOLHOUSE PTE. LTD.—See Chip Eng Seng Corporation Ltd.; *Int'l*, pg. 1572
SIOUX FALLS CHRISTIAN SCHOOLS; *U.S. Private*, pg. 3671
SMR HR GROUP SDN. BHD.—See Cyberjaya Education Group Berhad; *Int'l*, pg. 1893
SOCIEDAD DE CAPACITACION STRUCTURALIA CHILE LIMITADA—See Graham Holdings Company; *U.S. Public*, pg. 956
SOHAR UNIVERSITY LLC—See Global Financial Investments Holding SAOG; *Int'l*, pg. 2996
SOUTH EDUCATION - TEXAS LLC—See Dream Center Foundation, a California Nonprofit Corp.; *U.S. Private*, pg. 1273
SOUTH UNIVERSITY, LLC—See Dream Center Foundation, a California Nonprofit Corp.; *U.S. Private*, pg. 1273
SOUTH UNIVERSITY OF ALABAMA, INC.—See Dream Center Foundation, a California Nonprofit Corp.; *U.S. Private*, pg. 1273
SOUTH UNIVERSITY OF ARIZONA LLC—See Dream Center Foundation, a California Nonprofit Corp.; *U.S. Private*, pg. 1273
SOUTH UNIVERSITY OF CAROLINA, INC.—See Dream Center Foundation, a California Nonprofit Corp.; *U.S. Private*, pg. 1274
SOUTH UNIVERSITY OF FLORIDA, INC.—See Dream Center Foundation, a California Nonprofit Corp.; *U.S. Private*, pg. 1274
SOUTH UNIVERSITY OF MICHIGAN, LLC—See Dream Center Foundation, a California Nonprofit Corp.; *U.S. Private*, pg. 1274
SOUTH UNIVERSITY OF NORTH CAROLINA LLC—See Dream Center Foundation, a California Nonprofit Corp.; *U.S. Private*, pg. 1274
SOUTH UNIVERSITY OF OHIO LLC—See Dream Center Foundation, a California Nonprofit Corp.; *U.S. Private*, pg. 1274
SOUTHWEST EDUCATIONAL DEVELOPMENT LABORATORY; *U.S. Private*, pg. 3739
STEP UP FOR STUDENTS, INC.; *U.S. Private*, pg. 3801
STRIDE, INC.; *U.S. Public*, pg. 1954
STUDENT ADVANTAGE LLC—See Roper Technologies, Inc.; *U.S. Public*, pg. 1813
STUDENT ALTERNATIVE PROGRAM, INC.; *U.S. Private*, pg. 3843
STUDENTSCOUT, LLC—See TrueBlue, Inc.; *U.S. Public*, pg. 2199
THE STUDY ABROAD FOUNDATION; *U.S. Private*, pg. 4123
STUDY GROUP AUSTRALIA PTY. LIMITED—See Providence Equity Partners L.L.C.; *U.S. Private*, pg. 3293
STUDY GROUP PTY. LIMITED—See Providence Equity Partners L.L.C.; *U.S. Private*, pg. 3293
STUDY GROUP UK LIMITED—See Ardian SAS; *Int'l*, pg. 556
STUDY GROUP USA, INC.—See Providence Equity Partners L.L.C.; *U.S. Private*, pg. 3293
SUNRISE OF PHILADELPHIA; *U.S. Private*, pg. 3870
SUSSMAN SALES COMPANY; *U.S. Private*, pg. 3886
SWALLOWS & AMAZONS PTE. LTD.—See Chip Eng Seng Corporation Ltd.; *Int'l*, pg. 1572
SWISS LEARNING HUB AG—See Constellation Software Inc.; *Int'l*, pg. 1772
TARGETX.COM LLC—See Liaison International, Inc.; *U.S. Private*, pg. 2442
TEACHERS ON CALL, INC.—See Kelly Services, Inc.; *U.S. Public*, pg. 1220
TEACHFORALL, INC.; *U.S. Private*, pg. 3948
TEACHING STRATEGIES, LLC—See Summit Partners, L.P.; *U.S. Private*, pg. 3856
TEAMWORKNET INC.; *U.S. Private*, pg. 3951
TECH ELEVATOR INC.—See Stride, Inc.; *U.S. Public*, pg. 1955
TECHNICAL EDUCATION RESEARCH CENTERS, INC.; *U.S. Private*, pg. 3954
TEXAS CMT INC.—See Gee Consultants, Inc.; *U.S. Private*, pg. 1655
THINK: COLLEGES PTY LTD—See Strategic Education, Inc.; *U.S. Public*, pg. 1954
THINK: EDUCATION GROUP PTY LIMITED—See KKR & Co. Inc.; *U.S. Public*, pg. 1259
THINK: EDUCATION SERVICES PTY LIMITED—See KKR & Co. Inc.; *U.S. Public*, pg. 1259
THINKFUL, INC.—See Chegg Inc.; *U.S. Public*, pg. 483
TOMAHAWK STRATEGIC SOLUTIONS LLC; *U.S. Private*, pg. 4183
TOP MEERHOUT NV—See Group de Cloedt SA; *Int'l*, pg. 3088
TOTAL RESOURCE MANAGEMENT, INC.; *U.S. Private*, pg. 4191
TPC TRAINING SYSTEMS, INC.—See Frontenac Company LLC; *U.S. Private*, pg. 1614

N.A.I.C.S. INDEX

TRC LIBRARY SERVICE INC.—See Dai Nippon Printing Co., Ltd.; *Int'l*, pg. 1916
TRIBAL NOVA, INC.—See Veritas Capital Fund Management, LLC; *U.S. Private*, pg. 4363
TRIBECA LEARNING PTY LIMITED—See Graham Holdings Company; *U.S. Private*, pg. 956
TRIUMPH HIGHER EDUCATION GROUP, LLC; *U.S. Private*, pg. 4239
TRUELEARN, LLC; *U.S. Private*, pg. 4248
TURNITIN, LLC—See Advance Publications, Inc.; *U.S. Private*, pg. 87
TWENTYEIGHTY STRATEGY EXECUTION (GERMANY) GMBH—See Korn Ferry; *U.S. Public*, pg. 1273
TWENTYEIGHTY STRATEGY EXECUTION, INC.—See Korn Ferry; *U.S. Public*, pg. 1273
TWENTYEIGHTY STRATEGY EXECUTION (UK) LTD.—See Korn Ferry; *U.S. Public*, pg. 1274
UA LOCAL UNION 669 ROAD SPRINKLER FITTERS; *U.S. Private*, pg. 4272
UJA FEDERATION OF NEW YORK; *U.S. Private*, pg. 4275
UNITED FOR RESPECT EDUCATION FUND; *U.S. Private*, pg. 4292
UNITED TEACHERS LOS ANGELES; *U.S. Private*, pg. 4301
THE UNITED TEACHERS OF DADE; *U.S. Private*, pg. 4129
UNIVERSIA BRASIL S.A.—See Banco Santander, S.A.; *Int'l*, pg. 828
UNIVERSITY INSTRUCTORS, INC.—See Public Consulting Group, Inc.; *U.S. Private*, pg. 3299
UNIVERSITY MEDICAL GROUP; *U.S. Private*, pg. 4308
UOC SDN. BHD.—See Cyberjaya Education Group Berhad; *Int'l*, pg. 1893
URBAN LAND INSTITUTE; *U.S. Private*, pg. 4314
URBAN PREP ACADEMIES; *U.S. Private*, pg. 4314
US-NOBEL PRIMARY EDUCATION DEVELOPMENT INT'L, INC.; *U.S. Private*, pg. 4320
UWORLD LLC; *U.S. Private*, pg. 4327
VARSITY TUTORS LLC; *U.S. Private*, pg. 4347
VECTORLEARNING.COM, INC.—See Providence Equity Partners L.L.C.; *U.S. Private*, pg. 3294
VERITAS PREP, LLC—See Varsity Tutors LLC; *U.S. Private*, pg. 4347
VIRGINIA MASON INSTITUTE; *U.S. Private*, pg. 4387
VISU ACADEMY LIMITED—See Ed & Tech International Limited; *Int'l*, pg. 2302
VIVALDI MUSIC ACADEMY, LLC; *U.S. Private*, pg. 4406
VKIDZ, INC.—See Veritas Capital Fund Management, LLC; *U.S. Private*, pg. 4361
VOYAGER LEARNING COMPANY—See Veritas Capital Fund Management, LLC; *U.S. Private*, pg. 4361
WASHINGTON EARLY LEARNING FUND; *U.S. Private*, pg. 4447
WATER ENVIRONMENT FEDERATION; *U.S. Private*, pg. 4451
WATERSTONE COLLEGE (PTY) LTD.—See Curro Holdings Ltd.; *Int'l*, pg. 1879
WEALTHCLASSES, LLC; *U.S. Private*, pg. 4462
WEA MIDSTATE; *U.S. Private*, pg. 4462
WEILL CORNELL MEDICINE; *U.S. Private*, pg. 4471
WESTERN SCHOOLS, INC.—See CITIC Group Corporation; *Int'l*, pg. 1619
WESTERN SCHOOLS, INC.—See Founders Equity, Inc.; *U.S. Private*, pg. 1581
WHITE LODGE BANGSAR SOUTH CHILDCARE CENTRE SDN. BHD.—See Chip Eng Seng Corporation Ltd.; *Int'l*, pg. 1572
WHITE LODGE, BUKIT TIMAH PTE. LTD.—See Chip Eng Seng Corporation Ltd.; *Int'l*, pg. 1572
WHITE LODGE KINDERGARTEN, EAST COAST PTE. LTD.—See Chip Eng Seng Corporation Ltd.; *Int'l*, pg. 1572
WHITE LODGE KINDERGARTEN, PHOENIX PARK PTE. LTD.—See Chip Eng Seng Corporation Ltd.; *Int'l*, pg. 1572
WHITE LODGE MONT KIARA CHILDCARE CENTRE SDN. BHD.—See Chip Eng Seng Corporation Ltd.; *Int'l*, pg. 1572
WHITE LODGE PRESCHOOL RIVER VALLEY PTE. LTD.—See Chip Eng Seng Corporation Ltd.; *Int'l*, pg. 1572
WHITE LODGE SCHOOL OF ARTS, LOEWEN GARDENS PTE. LTD.—See Chip Eng Seng Corporation Ltd.; *Int'l*, pg. 1572
WHITE LODGE, UPPER BUKIT TIMAH PTE. LTD.—See Chip Eng Seng Corporation Ltd.; *Int'l*, pg. 1572
WHITE LODGE, UPPER EAST COAST PTE. LTD.—See Chip Eng Seng Corporation Ltd.; *Int'l*, pg. 1572
WHITE LODGE, WEST COAST PTE. LTD.—See Chip Eng Seng Corporation Ltd.; *Int'l*, pg. 1572
WITH US CO., LTD.—See El.En. S.p.A.; *Int'l*, pg. 2342
WIZLEARN TECHNOLOGIES PTE LTD—See Educomp Solutions, Ltd.; *Int'l*, pg. 2315
WIZLEARN TECHNOLOGIES—See Educomp Solutions, Ltd.; *Int'l*, pg. 2315
WOODHILL COLLEGE PROPERTY HOLDINGS (PTY) LTD.—See Curro Holdings Ltd.; *Int'l*, pg. 1879
XANEDU PUBLISHING, INC.—See Frontenac Company LLC; *U.S. Private*, pg. 1614

YOUTH FOR UNDERSTANDING INC.; *U.S. Private*, pg. 4594
ZENKYOKEN CO., LTD.—See Gakken Holdings Co., Ltd.; *Int'l*, pg. 2870
ZENOSIS LIMITED—See Digital Learning Marketplace plc; *Int'l*, pg. 2122

621111 — OFFICES OF PHYSICIANS (EXCEPT MENTAL HEALTH SPECIALISTS)

21ST CENTURY ONCOLOGY, INC.—See Vestar Capital Partners, LLC; *U.S. Private*, pg. 4371
32ND STREET SURGERY CENTER, LLC—See KKR & Co. Inc.; *U.S. Public*, pg. 1244
AAC DALLAS OUTPATIENT CENTER, LLC—See AAC Holdings, Inc.; *U.S. Private*, pg. 30
AAC LAS VEGAS OUTPATIENT CENTER, LLC—See AAC Holdings, Inc.; *U.S. Private*, pg. 30
ACCESS HEALTH CARE, LLC; *U.S. Private*, pg. 51
ACCRELIST MEDICAL AESTHETICS (CENTRALACLARKE QUAY) PTE. LTD.—See Accrelist Ltd.; *Int'l*, pg. 93
ACCRELIST MEDICAL AESTHETICS (CM) PTE. LTD.—See Accrelist Ltd.; *Int'l*, pg. 93
ACCRELIST MEDICAL AESTHETICS (ORCHARD CENTRAL) PTE. LTD.—See Accrelist Ltd.; *Int'l*, pg. 93
ACCRELIST MEDICAL AESTHETICS (RAFFLES CITY) PTE. LTD.—See Accrelist Ltd.; *Int'l*, pg. 93
ADVANCED MEDICAL INSTITUTE INC.; *Int'l*, pg. 161
ADVANCED MEDICAL SPECIALTIES; *U.S. Private*, pg. 91
AESTHETIC MOBILE LASER SERVICES, INC.—See Sensus Healthcare, Inc.; *U.S. Public*, pg. 1868
AFFILIATED ENDOSCOPY SERVICES OF CLIFTON, LLC—See KKR & Co. Inc.; *U.S. Public*, pg. 1244
AIER EYE HOSPITAL GROUP CO., LTD.; *Int'l*, pg. 231
ALASKA SPINE CENTER, LLC—See HCA Healthcare, Inc.; *U.S. Public*, pg. 990
ALBUQUERQUE NEUROSCIENCE, INC.—See IMA Group Management Company, LLC; *U.S. Private*, pg. 2044
ALIANSALUD ENTIDAD PROMOTORA DE SALUD S.A.—See UnitedHealth Group Incorporated; *U.S. Public*, pg. 2238
ALLERGY & ASTHMA CARE NEW YORK PLLC—See Schweiger Dermatology Group; *U.S. Private*, pg. 3572
ALL WOMEN'S HEALTHCARE OF WEST BROWARD, INC.—See KKR & Co. Inc.; *U.S. Public*, pg. 1244
ALL WOMEN'S HEALTHCARE SERVICES, INC.—See KKR & Co. Inc.; *U.S. Public*, pg. 1244
ALPHAEON CORPORATION; *U.S. Private*, pg. 200
AMERICAN ACADEMY OF NEUROLOGY; *U.S. Private*, pg. 221
AMERICAN ANESTHESIOLOGY OF NAPLES, INC.—See MEDNAX, Inc.; *U.S. Public*, pg. 1413
THE AMERICAN BOARD OF PEDIATRICS; *U.S. Private*, pg. 3986
AMERICAN ONCOLOGY NETWORK, LLC—See American Oncology Network, Inc.; *U.S. Public*, pg. 108
ANESTHESIA ASSOCIATES OF PINELLAS COUNTY DIVISION, LLC—See KKR & Co. Inc.; *U.S. Public*, pg. 1244
ANESTHESIA SPECIAL OPERATIONS, LLC—See Blackstone Inc.; *U.S. Public*, pg. 359
AOI SURGICENTER, LLC—See HCA Healthcare, Inc.; *U.S. Public*, pg. 990
APIFIX LTD.—See OrthoPediatrics Corp.; *U.S. Public*, pg. 1619
APOLLO COSMETIC SURGICAL CENTRE PVT LIMITED—See Apollo Hospitals Enterprise Limited; *Int'l*, pg. 517
APOLLO KORAMANGALA CRADLE LIMITED—See Apollo Hospitals Enterprise Limited; *Int'l*, pg. 517
AQUA DERMATOLOGY MANAGEMENT, LLC—See Raj Patel, MD LLC; *U.S. Private*, pg. 3349
THE ARLINGTON EYE CENTER, INC.—See Centre Partners Management LLC; *U.S. Private*, pg. 828
ASCEND PLASTIC SURGERY PARTNERS; *U.S. Private*, pg. 346
ASCENSION SAINT THOMAS LEBANON SURGERY CENTER, LLC—See Tenet Healthcare Corporation; *U.S. Public*, pg. 2001
ASHLEY HOUSE PLC; *Int'l*, pg. 607
ASTER DM HEALTHCARE LTD.; *Int'l*, pg. 653
ATHWAL EYE ASSOCIATES PC—See Chicago Pacific Founders; *U.S. Private*, pg. 878
BALDWIN FAMILY HEALTH CARE, INC.; *U.S. Private*, pg. 458
BARD INDIA HEALTHCARE PVT. LTD.—See Becton, Dickinson & Company; *U.S. Public*, pg. 291
BARTOW HMA PHYSICIAN MANAGEMENT, LLC—See Community Health Systems, Inc.; *U.S. Public*, pg. 551
BASIL STREET PRACTICE LIMITED—See HCA Healthcare, Inc.; *U.S. Public*, pg. 991
BAXTER B.V.—See Baxter International Inc.; *U.S. Public*, pg. 280
BAXTER HEALTHCARE (THAILAND) COMPANY LIMITED—See Baxter International Inc.; *U.S. Public*, pg. 280
BAXTER MANUFACTURING (THAILAND) CO., LTD.—See Baxter International Inc.; *U.S. Public*, pg. 281

621111 — OFFICES OF PHYSICIA...

BAY AREA DERMATOLOGY ASSOCIATES—See Harvest Partners L.P.; *U.S. Private*, pg. 1876
BAY AREA HEART CENTER, INC.; *U.S. Private*, pg. 491
BELTON FAMILY PRACTICE CLINIC, LLC—See HCA Healthcare, Inc.; *U.S. Public*, pg. 991
BLOSSOMS HEALTHCARE LLP—See HCA Healthcare, Inc.; *U.S. Public*, pg. 991
BOUNTIFUL SURGERY CENTER, LLC—See HCA Healthcare, Inc.; *U.S. Public*, pg. 991
BOURKE STREET CLINIC PTY LTD—See Healius Limited; *Int'l*, pg. 3302
BOYNTON BEACH EFL IMAGING CENTER, LLC—See HCA Healthcare, Inc.; *U.S. Public*, pg. 991
BRASELTON ENDOSCOPY CENTER, LLC—See Tenet Healthcare Corporation; *U.S. Public*, pg. 2001
BRAVO HEALTH, LLC—See The Cigna Group; *U.S. Public*, pg. 2060
BRIGHAM & WOMEN'S PHYSICIANS ORGANIZATION—See Partners HealthCare System, Inc.; *U.S. Private*, pg. 3102
BROOKWOOD SPECIALTY CARE - ENDOCRINOLOGY, L.L.C.—See Tenet Healthcare Corporation; *U.S. Public*, pg. 2002
BROOKWOOD SPORTS AND ORTHOPEDICS, L.L.C.—See Tenet Healthcare Corporation; *U.S. Public*, pg. 2003
BSN RADIANTE SAS—See Essity Aktiebolag; *Int'l*, pg. 2516
CAMPBELL CLINIC ORTHOPAEDICS; *U.S. Private*, pg. 730
CANNA CLINICS PTY. LTD.—See Epsilon Healthcare Ltd.; *Int'l*, pg. 2466
CAPITAL DERMATOLOGY, LTD.—See Harvest Partners L.P.; *U.S. Private*, pg. 1876
CAPITOL PAIN INSTITUTE PA—See Iron Path Capital, L.P.; *U.S. Private*, pg. 2139
CARDIOLOGY CLINIC OF SAN ANTONIO, PLLC—See HCA Healthcare, Inc.; *U.S. Public*, pg. 992
CARDIOLOGY SPECIALISTS OF NORTH TEXAS, PLLC—See HCA Healthcare, Inc.; *U.S. Public*, pg. 992
CARDIOVASCULAR ASSOCIATES OF AMERICA, LLC—See Webster Equity Partners, LLC; *U.S. Private*, pg. 4467
CARDIOVASCULAR ASSOCIATES OF THE SOUTHEAST, L.L.C.—See Tenet Healthcare Corporation; *U.S. Public*, pg. 2003
CARE POINT MEDICAL CENTRES—See Canadian Back Institute Limited Partnership; *Int'l*, pg. 1282
CAROLINA EYE ASSOCIATES, P.A.; *U.S. Private*, pg. 768
CASCADE ENDOSCOPY CENTER, LLC—See KKR & Co. Inc.; *U.S. Public*, pg. 1245
CEDAR PARK SURGERY CENTER, LLC—See Community Health Systems, Inc.; *U.S. Public*, pg. 552
CEDARS-SINAI MEDICAL GROUP—See Cedars-Sinai Medical Center; *U.S. Private*, pg. 805
CENTER FOR EMERGENCY MEDICINE OF WESTERN PA INC.; *U.S. Private*, pg. 810
CENTER FOR RETINA AND MACULAR DISEASE; *U.S. Private*, pg. 811
CENTER FOR SIGHT, P.L.; *U.S. Private*, pg. 811
CENTER FOR VEIN RESTORATION—See Cortec Group Management Services, LLC; *U.S. Private*, pg. 1060
CENTERPOINT MEDICAL CENTER OF INDEPENDENCE, LLC—See HCA Healthcare, Inc.; *U.S. Public*, pg. 993
CHANGHUAT CORPORATION BERHAD; *Int'l*, pg. 1443
CHARLESTON AREA MEDICAL CENTER FOUNDATION INC.—See Charleston Area Medical Center Inc.; *U.S. Private*, pg. 856
CHIPPENHAM & JOHNSTON-WILLIS SPORTS MEDICINE, LLC—See HCA Healthcare, Inc.; *U.S. Public*, pg. 993
CHRISTIANSBURG INTERNAL MEDICINE, LLC—See HCA Healthcare, Inc.; *U.S. Public*, pg. 993
CITRIALS, INC.—See CenExel Clinical Research, Inc.; *U.S. Private*, pg. 809
CJW INFECTIOUS DISEASE, LLC—See HCA Healthcare, Inc.; *U.S. Public*, pg. 992
CLEARWATER PAIN MANAGEMENT ASSOCIATES DIVISION, LLC—See KKR & Co. Inc.; *U.S. Public*, pg. 1245
CLINICAL RESEARCH ATLANTA—See KKR & Co. Inc.; *U.S. Public*, pg. 1252
CLINICAL SERVICES OF RHODE ISLAND - GREENVILLE—See AAC Holdings, Inc.; *U.S. Private*, pg. 30
CLINIQUE BON SECOURS SAS—See Eurazeo SE; *Int'l*, pg. 2527
CLINIQUE DU JURA SAS—See Eurazeo SE; *Int'l*, pg. 2528
CLINIQUE DU PARC LYON SA—See Eurazeo SE; *Int'l*, pg. 2528
CLINIQUE DU RENAISON SAS—See Eurazeo SE; *Int'l*, pg. 2528
CLINIQUE NOUVELLE DU FOREZ SA—See Eurazeo SE; *Int'l*, pg. 2527
CLINIQUE SAINT MARTIN SA—See Eurazeo SE; *Int'l*, pg. 2527
COASTAL OCCUPATIONAL MEDICAL GROUP—See Kain Capital, LLC; *U.S. Private*, pg. 2254
COAST DERMATOLOGY & SKIN CANCER CENTER, P.A.—See Raj Patel, MD LLC; *U.S. Private*, pg. 3349
COLORADO INNOVATIVE PHYSICIAN SOLUTIONS,

621111 — OFFICES OF PHYSICIA...

INC.—See DaVita Inc.; *U.S. Public*, pg. 636
COLUMBIA ASSOCIATES PSYCHIATRY P.C.—See North-East Health Services, LLC; *U.S. Private*, pg. 2950
COLUMBIA/HCA OF NORTH TEXAS, INC.—See HCA Healthcare, Inc.; *U.S. Public*, pg. 994
COLUMBIA PLAZA MEDICAL CENTER OF FORT WORTH SUBSIDIARY, L.P.—See HCA Healthcare, Inc.; *U.S. Public*, pg. 994
COLUMBUS CYBERKNIFE, LLC—See Akumin, Inc.; *U.S. Public*, pg. 70
COMMONWEALTH PERINATAL SERVICES, LLC—See HCA Healthcare, Inc.; *U.S. Public*, pg. 994
COMPREHENSIVE MEDICAL CARE LTD., INC.—See Allina Health System, Inc.; *U.S. Private*, pg. 192
CONCENTRA MEDICAL CENTER—See Select Medical Holdings Corporation; *U.S. Public*, pg. 1857
CONCENTRA MEDICAL CENTER—See Welsh, Carson, Anderson & Stowe; *U.S. Private*, pg. 4479
CONCORDE TREATMENT CENTER, LLC—See AAC Holdings, Inc.; *U.S. Private*, pg. 30
CONGENITAL HEART SURGERY CENTER, PLLC—See HCA Healthcare, Inc.; *U.S. Public*, pg. 994
CONNECTICUT DERMATOLOGY GROUP—See Schweiger Dermatology Group; *U.S. Private*, pg. 3572
THE CONRAD / PEARSON CLINIC, P.C.—See Gauge Capital LLC; *U.S. Private*, pg. 1652
COOPER STREET CLINIC PTY LTD—See Healius Limited; *Int'l*, pg. 3302
CROSSROADS EYE CARE ASSOCIATES, LTD.—See Blue Sea Capital Management LLC; *U.S. Private*, pg. 592
CROSSROADS EYE CARE ASSOCIATES, LTD.—See Ophthalmic Consultants of Long Island; *U.S. Private*, pg. 3032
CYBERKNIFE CENTER OF PHILADELPHIA, LLC—See Akumin, Inc.; *U.S. Public*, pg. 70
DAVIDSON FAMILY MEDICINE, P.A.—See Alo Solutions, LLC; *U.S. Private*, pg. 195
DAYTONA HEART GROUP HOLDINGS, P.A.—See Webster Equity Partners, LLC; *U.S. Private*, pg. 4479
DEAN HEALTH SYSTEMS, INC.—See SSM Health Care Corporation; *U.S. Private*, pg. 3769
DEKALB MEDICAL DOWNTOWN DECATUR—See Dekalb Regional Healthcare System, Inc.; *U.S. Private*, pg. 1192
DELTA 9 LIFESTYLE CANNABIS CLINIC INC.—See Delta 9 Cannabis, Inc.; *Int'l*, pg. 2015
DERMATOLOGY ASSOCIATES OF CENTRAL TEXAS—See ABRY Partners, LLC; *U.S. Private*, pg. 42
DERMATOLOGY & LASER CENTER OF FORT WORTH—See ABRY Partners, LLC; *U.S. Private*, pg. 42
DERMATOLOGY & LASER-DEL MAR INC.—See West Dermatology Med Management, Inc.; *U.S. Private*, pg. 4485
DERMATOLOGY OF NORTHERN COLORADO, P.C.—See Harvest Partners L.P.; *U.S. Private*, pg. 1876
DIAGNOSTIC CLINIC—See GuideWell Mutual Holding Corporation; *U.S. Private*, pg. 1813
DIAGNOSTICS RESEARCH GROUP, LLC—See IMA Group Management Company, LLC; *U.S. Private*, pg. 2044
DLP CONEMAUGH MINERS MEDICAL CENTER, LLC—See Apollo Global Management, Inc.; *U.S. Public*, pg. 155
DLP CONEMAUGH PHYSICIAN PRACTICES, LLC—See Apollo Global Management, Inc.; *U.S. Public*, pg. 155
DLP FRYE REGIONAL MEDICAL CENTER, LLC—See Apollo Global Management, Inc.; *U.S. Public*, pg. 155
DLP MARQUETTE PHYSICIAN PRACTICES, INC.—See Apollo Global Management, Inc.; *U.S. Public*, pg. 155
DONALDSON PLASTIC SURGERY, LLC; *U.S. Private*, pg. 1260
DUBLIN SURGERY CENTER, LLC—See UnitedHealth Group Incorporated; *U.S. Public*, pg. 2240
EAGLE WELLNESS, LLC—See Eagle Publishing Inc.; *U.S. Private*, pg. 1310
EMERGENT MEDICAL ASSOCIATES; *U.S. Private*, pg. 1381
ENT PARTNERS LLC; *U.S. Private*, pg. 1402
ENVISION HEALTHCARE CLINICAL RESEARCH, INC.—See KKR & Co. Inc.; *U.S. Public*, pg. 1245
EPIPHANY DERMATOLOGY PA; *U.S. Private*, pg. 1413
ERGO SCIENCE CORP.; *U.S. Private*, pg. 1417
ESSITY CANADA INC.—See Essity Aktiebolag; *Int'l*, pg. 2516
ESSITY CHILE SA—See Essity Aktiebolag; *Int'l*, pg. 2516
ESSITY FRANCE SAS—See Essity Aktiebolag; *Int'l*, pg. 2517
ESSITY ITALY S.P.A.—See Essity Aktiebolag; *Int'l*, pg. 2517
ESSITY OPERATIONS POLAND SP. Z O.O.—See Essity Aktiebolag; *Int'l*, pg. 2517
ESSITY POLAND SP. Z O.O.—See Essity Aktiebolag; *Int'l*, pg. 2517
ESSITY PROFESSIONAL HYGIENE NORTH AMERICA LLC—See Essity Aktiebolag; *Int'l*, pg. 2517
EUREKA SPRINGS HOSPITAL, LLC—See UnitedHealth Group Incorporated; *U.S. Public*, pg. 2245
EU YAN SANG INTEGRATIVE HEALTH PTE. LTD.—See Eu Yan Sang International Ltd.; *Int'l*, pg. 2525
EXCELVIEW LASER EYE CENTRE SDN BHD—See Focus Point Holdings Berhad; *Int'l*, pg. 2719

EYE SPECIALIST OF MID FLORIDA P.A.; *U.S. Private*, pg. 1453
EYE SURGERY CENTER OF WESTERN OHIO, LLC—See KKR & Co. Inc.; *U.S. Public*, pg. 1245
FAMILY ALLERGY & ASTHMA; *U.S. Private*, pg. 1468
FAMILY CARE AT ARBOR WALK, LLC—See HCA Healthcare, Inc.; *U.S. Public*, pg. 996
FAMILY PHYSICIANS GROUP, INC.—See Humana, Inc.; *U.S. Public*, pg. 1069
FIRECREST CLINICAL LTD.—See ICON plc; *Int'l*, pg. 3584
FISHMAN CENTER FOR TOTAL EYE CARE—See Blue Sea Capital Management LLC; *U.S. Private*, pg. 592
FISHMAN CENTER FOR TOTAL EYE CARE—See Ophthalmic Consultants of Long Island; *U.S. Private*, pg. 3032
FITNESS TOGETHER; *U.S. Private*, pg. 1536
FLORIDA CANCER SPECIALISTS, P.L.; *U.S. Private*, pg. 1547
FLORIDA EYE SPECIALISTS, P.A.; *U.S. Private*, pg. 1548
FLORIDA GULF-TO-BAY ANESTHESIOLOGY ASSOCIATES, LLC—See Blackstone Inc.; *U.S. Public*, pg. 359
FLORIDA MEDICAL CLINIC P.A.; *U.S. Private*, pg. 1550
FORTERUS HEALTH CARE SERVICES, INC.—See AAC Holdings, Inc.; *U.S. Private*, pg. 30
FORTIS LA FEMME LIMITED—See Fortis Healthcare Limited; *Int'l*, pg. 2739
FOUNDATION FOR THE ELDERLY; *U.S. Private*, pg. 1580
FRESNO CA MULTI ASC, L.P.—See KKR & Co. Inc.; *U.S. Public*, pg. 1245
GASTROENTEROLOGY ASSOCIATES OF NORTHERN VIRGINIA, LLC—See Gastro Health, LLC; *U.S. Private*, pg. 1649
GASTRO HEALTH, LLC; *U.S. Private*, pg. 1649
GATEWAY RADIOLOGY CONSULTANTS, P.A.; *U.S. Private*, pg. 1651
GDS CLEVELAND—See Republic Services, Inc.; *U.S. Public*, pg. 1786
GENERAL SURGEONS OF PASADENA, PLLC—See HCA Healthcare, Inc.; *U.S. Public*, pg. 996
GLEN ENDOSCOPY CENTER, LLC—See KKR & Co. Inc.; *U.S. Public*, pg. 1245
GOPPERT-TRINITY FAMILY CARE, LLC—See HCA Healthcare, Inc.; *U.S. Public*, pg. 997
GORDIAN MEDICAL, INC.—See OEP Capital Advisors, L.P.; *U.S. Private*, pg. 2999
GORDIAN MEDICAL, INC.—See Silverfern Capital Management, LLC; *U.S. Private*, pg. 3663
GRACE FAMILY PRACTICE, LLC—See HCA Healthcare, Inc.; *U.S. Public*, pg. 997
GREATER FLORIDA ANESTHESIOLOGISTS, LLC—See KKR & Co. Inc.; *U.S. Public*, pg. 1245
GRIFFIN IMAGING, INC.—See Cypress Partners, LLC; *U.S. Private*, pg. 1135
GULF COAST DIVISION, INC.—See HCA Healthcare, Inc.; *U.S. Public*, pg. 997
GULF COAST HMA PHYSICIAN MANAGEMENT, LLC—See Community Health Systems, Inc.; *U.S. Public*, pg. 553
GULF COAST OBSTETRICS AND GYNECOLOGY OF SARASOTA, LLC; *U.S. Private*, pg. 1815
GULFCOAST SPINE INSTITUTE, PA; *U.S. Private*, pg. 1817
HAMILTON MEDICALLY ASSISTED TREATMENT ASSOCIATES, LLC—See AAC Holdings, Inc.; *U.S. Private*, pg. 31
HARBIN CLINIC LLC; *U.S. Private*, pg. 1858
HARLEY STREET CLINIC @ THE GROVES LLP—See HCA Healthcare, Inc.; *U.S. Public*, pg. 998
HEALTHAMERICA HEALTH INSURANCE—See CVS Health Corporation; *U.S. Public*, pg. 615
HEALTHCARE NETWORK OF SOUTHWEST FLORIDA; *U.S. Private*, pg. 1895
HEALTHCARE PARTNERS INVESTMENTS LLC; *U.S. Private*, pg. 1895
HEALTHGRADES OPERATING COMPANY, INC.—See Vestar Capital Partners, LLC; *U.S. Private*, pg. 4371
HEALTHONE CLINIC SERVICES - CANCER SPECIALTIES, LLC—See HCA Healthcare, Inc.; *U.S. Public*, pg. 998
HEALTHPOINT MEDICAL GROUP—See BayCare Health System Inc.; *U.S. Private*, pg. 495
HEARTLAND DERMATOLOGY AND SKIN CANCER CENTER, P.A.; *U.S. Private*, pg. 1899
HENDRICK CANCER CENTER—See Hendrick Health System; *U.S. Private*, pg. 1914
HENRICO RADIATION ONCOLOGY, LLC—See HCA Healthcare, Inc.; *U.S. Public*, pg. 998
HENRY SCHEIN, INC.-FLORIDA—See Henry Schein, Inc.; *U.S. Public*, pg. 1026
HILL PHYSICIANS MEDICAL GROUP, INC.—See Primed Management Consulting Services Inc.; *U.S. Private*, pg. 3262
HOPEWELL HEALTH CENTERS INC.; *U.S. Private*, pg. 1979
HORIZON HEALTH CARE, INC.; *U.S. Private*, pg. 1981
HOWARD COUNTY GASTROINTESTINAL DIAGNOSTIC CENTER, LLC—See Tenet Healthcare Corporation; *U.S. Public*, pg. 2004
HUMPHREY & PARTNERS MEDICAL SERVICES MAN-

CORPORATE AFFILIATIONS

AGEMENT LIMITED—See HKR International Limited; *Int'l*, pg. 3429
ICON CLINICAL RESEARCH (BEIJING) CO. LIMITED—See ICON plc; *Int'l*, pg. 3584
ICON CLINICAL RESEARCH LIMITED—See ICON plc; *Int'l*, pg. 3584
ICON CLINICAL RESEARCH LLC—See ICON plc; *Int'l*, pg. 3585
ICON CLINICAL RESEARCH—See ICON plc; *Int'l*, pg. 3584
IDANT LABORATORY—See Daxor Corporation; *U.S. Public*, pg. 644
ILLINOIS CYBERKNIFE, LLC—See Akumin, Inc.; *U.S. Public*, pg. 70
INLAND IMAGING ASSOCIATES, P.S.; *U.S. Private*, pg. 2078
INTEGRIS SOUTHWEST MEDICAL CENTER—See INTEGRIS Health, Inc.; *U.S. Private*, pg. 2102
INTERCOASTAL MEDICAL GROUP, INC.; *U.S. Private*, pg. 2109
INTERNATIONAL OCD FOUNDATION; *U.S. Private*, pg. 2119
THE IOWA CLINIC PC; *U.S. Private*, pg. 4057
JAMES RIVER INTERNISTS, LLC—See HCA Healthcare, Inc.; *U.S. Public*, pg. 999
JENNERSVILLE FAMILY MEDICINE, LLC—See Tower Health; *U.S. Private*, pg. 4193
JEWETT ORTHOPAEDIC CLINIC, P.A.; *U.S. Private*, pg. 2205
JOHNSON & JOHNSON SURGICAL VISION, INC.—See Johnson & Johnson; *U.S. Public*, pg. 1199
JORDAN FAMILY HEALTH, L.L.C.—See HCA Healthcare, Inc.; *U.S. Public*, pg. 999
JSA HEALTHCARE CORPORATION; *U.S. Private*, pg. 2241
JUPITER IMAGING ASSOCIATES, INC.—See KKR & Co. Inc.; *U.S. Public*, pg. 1245
KAISER PERMANENTE, HAWAII REGION—See Kaiser Permanente; *U.S. Private*, pg. 2256
KALAMAZOO DERMATOLOGY, P.C.—See Harvest Partners L.P.; *U.S. Private*, pg. 1876
KINDHEART, LLC—See Intuitive Surgical, Inc.; *U.S. Public*, pg. 1160
KINDRED NURSING CENTERS WEST, L.L.C.—See Apollo Global Management, Inc.; *U.S. Public*, pg. 156
KINGWOOD SURGERY CENTER, LLC—See HCA Healthcare, Inc.; *U.S. Public*, pg. 1000
LAKEVIEW HOSPITAL PHYSICIAN SERVICES, LLC—See HCA Healthcare, Inc.; *U.S. Public*, pg. 1000
LAKEVIEW INTERNAL MEDICINE, LLC—See HCA Healthcare, Inc.; *U.S. Public*, pg. 1000
LAKEVIEW NEUROSURGERY CLINIC, LLC—See HCA Healthcare, Inc.; *U.S. Public*, pg. 1000
LAYTON FAMILY PRACTICE, LLC—See HCA Healthcare, Inc.; *U.S. Public*, pg. 1000
LEWIS-GALE PHYSICIANS, LLC—See HCA Healthcare, Inc.; *U.S. Public*, pg. 1001
LIFESTAGES, SAMARITAN CENTERS FOR WOMEN, LTD.—See Catholic Health Initiatives; *U.S. Private*, pg. 790
LOWER MANHATTAN MEDICAL ASSOCIATES P.C.—See Schweiger Dermatology Group; *U.S. Private*, pg. 3572
LUNGENPRAXIS AM WORDEMANNSWEG GMBH—See Asklepios Kliniken GmbH & Co. KGaA; *Int'l*, pg. 623
LUTRONIC JAPAN CO., LTD.—See Hahn & Company; *Int'l*, pg. 3208
MANATEE SURGICAL CENTER, LLC—See KKR & Co. Inc.; *U.S. Public*, pg. 1246
MANHATTAN DERMATOLOGY PA—See Heartland Dermatology and Skin Cancer Center, P.A.; *U.S. Private*, pg. 1899
MARSHFIELD CLINIC; *U.S. Private*, pg. 2593
MARYHILL DISPENSARY LIMITED—See Walgreens Boots Alliance, Inc.; *U.S. Public*, pg. 2322
MASSACHUSETTS GENERAL PHYSICIANS ORGANIZATION, INC.—See Partners HealthCare System, Inc.; *U.S. Private*, pg. 3102
MATTHEW F MCCARTY M D PLLC—See Iron Path Capital, L.P.; *U.S. Private*, pg. 2139
MCIVER CLINIC; *U.S. Private*, pg. 2637
MD NOW MEDICAL CENTERS, INC.—See Brockway Moran & Partners, Inc.; *U.S. Private*, pg. 661
MEDCARE EQUIPMENT COMPANY, LLC; *U.S. Private*, pg. 2650
MEDICAL ANESTHESIA CONSULTANTS MEDICAL GROUP, INC.—See KKR & Co. Inc.; *U.S. Public*, pg. 1246
MEDICAL SPECIALTIES, INC.—See HCA Healthcare, Inc.; *U.S. Public*, pg. 1002
MEDICAL & WELFARE INFORMATION CENTER OF SHOWA-OTA INC.—See Business Brain Showa-Ota Inc.; *Int'l*, pg. 1228
MEDICUM HAMBURG MVZ GMBH—See Asklepios Kliniken GmbH & Co. KGaA; *Int'l*, pg. 624
MEDIKUMPPANI OY—See Empresaria Group Plc; *Int'l*, pg. 2389
MEDNAX, INC.; *U.S. Public*, pg. 1413
MEDNAX SERVICES, INC.—See MEDNAX, Inc.; *U.S. Public*, pg. 1413

N.A.I.C.S. INDEX

621111 — OFFICES OF PHYSICIA...

MEMORIAL HERMANN ENDOSCOPY CENTER NORTH FREEWAY, LLC—See Tenet Healthcare Corporation; *U.S. Public*, pg. 2011
MEMORIAL HERMANN SURGERY CENTER KINGSLAND, LLC—See Tenet Healthcare Corporation; *U.S. Public*, pg. 2011
MEMORIAL HERMANN SURGERY CENTER PINECROFT, LLC—See Tenet Healthcare Corporation; *U.S. Public*, pg. 2011
MEMORIAL HERMANN SURGERY CENTER SOUTHWEST, LLP—See Tenet Healthcare Corporation; *U.S. Public*, pg. 2011
MEMORIAL HERMANN SURGERY CENTER WOODLANDS PARKWAY, LLC—See Tenet Healthcare Corporation; *U.S. Public*, pg. 2011
MEMORIAL NEUROSURGERY GROUP, LLC—See HCA Healthcare, Inc.; *U.S. Public*, pg. 1002
MERCHANT MEDICINE, LLC—See Urgent Care Partners, Inc.; *U.S. Private*, pg. 4315
MERCY WESTSIDE HOSPITAL—See Catholic Health Initiatives; *U.S. Private*, pg. 789
METROPOLITAN CRANIOFACIAL CENTER, P.A.—See Riverside Oral Surgery; *U.S. Private*, pg. 3445
MH ANGEL MEDICAL CENTER, LLLP—See HCA Healthcare, Inc.; *U.S. Public*, pg. 1001
MH ECKERD LIVING CENTER, LLLP—See HCA Healthcare, Inc.; *U.S. Public*, pg. 1001
MH HIGHLANDS-CASHIERS MEDICAL CENTER, LLLP—See HCA Healthcare, Inc.; *U.S. Public*, pg. 1001
MH MISSION HOSPITAL, LLLP—See HCA Healthcare, Inc.; *U.S. Public*, pg. 1001
MH MISSION HOSPITAL MCDOWELL, LLLP—See HCA Healthcare, Inc.; *U.S. Public*, pg. 1001
MHS SURGERY CENTERS, L.P.—See HCA Healthcare, Inc.; *U.S. Public*, pg. 1002
MHS SURGERY CENTERS, L.P.—See Methodist Healthcare Ministries of South Texas, Inc.; *U.S. Private*, pg. 2683
MH TRANSYLVANIA REGIONAL HOSPITAL, LLLP—See HCA Healthcare, Inc.; *U.S. Public*, pg. 1001
MICHAEL G. HAAS, M.D., LLC—See Panorama Eye Care LLC; *U.S. Private*, pg. 3087
MICHIGAN SURGERY SPECIALISTS PC.; *U.S. Private*, pg. 2701
MID ATLANTIC ENDOSCOPY CENTER, LLC—See KKR & Co. Inc.; *U.S. Public*, pg. 1246
MID-MICHIGAN DERMATOLOGY, PLLC—See Harvest Partners L.P.; *U.S. Private*, pg. 1876
MID SOUTH RADIOLOGY PARTNERS, LLC; *U.S. Private*, pg. 2706
MIDWEST CARDIOVASCULAR & THORACIC SURGERY, LLC—See HCA Healthcare, Inc.; *U.S. Public*, pg. 1003
MIDWEST INFECTIOUS DISEASE SPECIALISTS, LLC—See HCA Healthcare, Inc.; *U.S. Public*, pg. 1003
MIDWEST PERINATAL ASSOCIATES, P.A.—See MEDNAX, Inc.; *U.S. Public*, pg. 1413
MILLENNIUM PHYSICIAN GROUP LLC; *U.S. Private*, pg. 2732
MINIMALLY INVASIVE SURGICENTER LLC—See Tenet Healthcare Corporation; *U.S. Public*, pg. 2004
MONTGOMERY CANCER CENTER, LLC—See HCA Healthcare, Inc.; *U.S. Public*, pg. 1003
MONTGOMERY SURGERY ASSOCIATES, LLC—See HCA Healthcare, Inc.; *U.S. Public*, pg. 1003
MONTGOMERY SURGERY CENTER—See UnitedHealth Group Incorporated; *U.S. Public*, pg. 2251
MOUNTAINSTAR BEHAVIORAL HEALTH, LLC—See HCA Healthcare, Inc.; *U.S. Public*, pg. 1003
MOUNTAINSTAR CARDIOVASCULAR SERVICES, LLC—See HCA Healthcare, Inc.; *U.S. Public*, pg. 1003
MOUNTAINSTAR OGDEN PEDIATRICS, LLC—See HCA Healthcare, Inc.; *U.S. Public*, pg. 1003
MOUNTAIN VIEW MEDICAL GROUP—See DaVita Inc.; *U.S. Public*, pg. 641
MOUNTAIN WEST SURGERY CENTER, LLC—See HCA Healthcare, Inc.; *U.S. Public*, pg. 1003
MOUNTCASTLE VEIN CENTERS INTERNATIONAL, INC.; *U.S. Private*, pg. 2801
MVH PROFESSIONAL SERVICES, LLC—See HCA Healthcare, Inc.; *U.S. Public*, pg. 1001
MVZ DAVITA AMBULANTES KARDIOLOGISCHES ZENTRUM PEINE GMBH—See DaVita Inc.; *U.S. Public*, pg. 640
MVZ DAVITA BAD AIBLING GMBH—See DaVita Inc.; *U.S. Public*, pg. 640
MVZ DAVITA CARDIO CENTRUM DUSSELDORF GMBH—See DaVita Inc.; *U.S. Public*, pg. 640
MVZ DAVITA DILLENBURG GMBH—See DaVita Inc.; *U.S. Public*, pg. 640
MVZ DAVITA GEILENKIRCHEN GMBH—See DaVita Inc.; *U.S. Public*, pg. 640
NANTONG HEMEIJIA OBSTETRICS & GYNECOLOGY HOSPITAL CO. LTD.—See Harbin Electric Corporation; *Int'l*, pg. 3270
NASSAU CROSSING ENDOSCOPY CENTER, LLC—See Tenet Healthcare Corporation; *U.S. Public*, pg. 2004
NEWHOPE IMAGING CENTER, INC.—See Tenet Healthcare Corporation; *U.S. Public*, pg. 2006

NEWQUEST, LLC—See The Cigna Group; *U.S. Public*, pg. 2061
NEXT STEP ORTHOPAEDICS, INC.—See Patient Square Capital, L.P.; *U.S. Private*, pg. 3107
NORTH FLORIDA ANESTHESIA CONSULTANTS, P.A.—See KKR & Co. Inc.; *U.S. Public*, pg. 1250
NORTH FLORIDA PERINATAL ASSOCIATES, INC.—See KKR & Co. Inc.; *U.S. Public*, pg. 1246
NORTH SHORE PHYSICIANS GROUP INC.—See Partners HealthCare System, Inc.; *U.S. Private*, pg. 3102
NORTHWESTERN MEMORIAL PHYSICIANS GROUP—See Northwestern Memorial HealthCare; *U.S. Private*, pg. 2963
OAKLAND DERMATOLOGY ASSOCIATES—See Harvest Partners L.P.; *U.S. Private*, pg. 1876
OAK LAWN IL ENDOSCOPY ASC, LLC—See KKR & Co. Inc.; *U.S. Public*, pg. 1246
OAKWOOD SURGERY CENTER, LTD., LLP—See HCA Healthcare, Inc.; *U.S. Public*, pg. 1005
OB HOSPITALIST GROUP, INC.—See Kohlberg & Company, LLC; *U.S. Private*, pg. 2338
OGDEN INTERNAL MEDICINE & UROLOGY, LLC—See HCA Healthcare, Inc.; *U.S. Public*, pg. 1005
OMNI HEALTHCARE INC.—See Lovell Minnick Partners LLC; *U.S. Private*, pg. 2503
ONCOLOGY/HEMATOLOGY CARE, INC.—See Bon Secours Mercy Health, Inc.; *U.S. Private*, pg. 612
OPHTHALMIC CONSULTANTS OF LONG ISLAND; *U.S. Private*, pg. 3032
ORANGE COUNTY RADIATION ONCOLOGY, LLC—See RadNet, Inc.; *U.S. Public*, pg. 1761
ORTHOTIC & PROSTHETIC TECHNOLOGIES, INC.—See Patient Square Capital, L.P.; *U.S. Private*, pg. 3107
PALM HARBOR DERMATOLOGY, P.A.; *U.S. Private*, pg. 3079
PARADIGM SPINE, LLC—See Surgalign Holdings, Inc.; *U.S. Public*, pg. 1967
PARALLAX CENTER, LLC—See AAC Holdings, Inc.; *U.S. Private*, pg. 30
PARK FAMILY PRACTICE SERVICES PTY LTD—See Healius Limited; *Int'l*, pg. 3303
PARTNERS COMMUNITY HEALTHCARE, INC.—See Partners HealthCare System, Inc.; *U.S. Private*, pg. 3101
PASADENA EYE CENTER; *U.S. Private*, pg. 3103
PATRICK T. OTTUSO, M.D., F.A.A.D., P.A.—See Harvest Partners L.P.; *U.S. Private*, pg. 1876
PEDIATRIC CARDIAC INTENSIVISTS OF NORTH TEXAS, PLLC—See HCA Healthcare, Inc.; *U.S. Public*, pg. 1006
PEDIATRIC HOSPITALISTS OF CONROE, PLLC—See HCA Healthcare, Inc.; *U.S. Public*, pg. 1006
PEDIATRIC SPECIALISTS OF CLEAR LAKE, PLLC—See HCA Healthcare, Inc.; *U.S. Public*, pg. 1006
PEDIATRIC THERAPEUTIC SERVICES, INC.—See Kelly Services, Inc.; *U.S. Public*, pg. 1220
PEDIATRIX MEDICAL GROUP, INC.—See MEDNAX, Inc.; *U.S. Public*, pg. 1413
PHM MULTIDISCIPLINARY CLINIC ARECIBO LLC—See Elevance Health, Inc.; *U.S. Public*, pg. 730
PHM MULTIDISCIPLINARY CLINIC CABO ROJO LLC—See Elevance Health, Inc.; *U.S. Public*, pg. 730
PHM MULTISALUD, LLC—See Elevance Health, Inc.; *U.S. Public*, pg. 730
PHYSICIAN OFFICE PARTNERS, INC.—See KKR & Co. Inc.; *U.S. Public*, pg. 1246
THE PHYSICIANS CLINIC LIMITED—See HCA Healthcare, Inc.; *U.S. Public*, pg. 1012
PHYSICIANS' EYE SURGERY CENTER, LLC—See KKR & Co. Inc.; *U.S. Public*, pg. 1246
PHYSICIAN'S PRACTICE ORGANIZATION INC.; *U.S. Private*, pg. 3175
PINNACLE DERMATOLOGY LLC; *U.S. Private*, pg. 3185
PIONEER MEDICAL GROUP, INC—See Presbyterian Intercommunity Hospital, Inc.; *U.S. Private*, pg. 3253
PLUS ONE HEALTH MANAGEMENT, INC.; *U.S. Private*, pg. 3215
POLYCLINIQUE DU PARC DREVON, SA—See Eurazeo SE; *Int'l*, pg. 2529
POLYCLINIQUE DU VAL DE SAONE SAS—See Eurazeo SE; *Int'l*, pg. 2529
POLYCLINIQUE SAINT-ODILON, SA—See Eurazeo SE; *Int'l*, pg. 2529
PRATT MEDICAL CENTER, LTD.—See Sentara Healthcare; *U.S. Private*, pg. 3608
PRESTIGE HEALTH CHOICE LLC—See GuideWell Mutual Holding Corporation; *U.S. Private*, pg. 1814
PRIMARY HEALTH GROUP, INC.—See HCA Healthcare, Inc.; *U.S. Public*, pg. 1006
PRINCE WILLIAM AMBULATORY SURGERY CENTER, LLC—See Tenet Healthcare Corporation; *U.S. Public*, pg. 2006
PROGRESSIVE MEDICAL ASSOCIATES, PLLC—See American Physician Partners, LLC; *U.S. Private*, pg. 243
PROSTHETIC LABORATORIES OF ROCHESTER, INC.—See Patient Square Capital, L.P.; *U.S. Private*, pg. 3107
PWH FOUNDATION INC.—See Novant Health, Inc.; *U.S. Private*, pg. 2967

QTC MANAGEMENT, INC.—See Lockheed Martin Corporation; *U.S. Public*, pg. 1339
R2 DERMATOLOGY INCORPORATED—See INNOVATE Corp.; *U.S. Public*, pg. 1126
RADIOLOGY REGIONAL CENTER, P.A.; *U.S. Private*, pg. 3344
RAJ PATEL, MD LLC; *U.S. Private*, pg. 3349
RETINA CONSULTANTS OF SOUTHWEST FLORIDA, INC.; *U.S. Private*, pg. 3412
RETINA CONSULTANTS OF WNY—See Ophthalmic Consultants of Long Island; *U.S. Private*, pg. 3032
RETREAT INTERNAL MEDICINE, LLC—See HCA Healthcare, Inc.; *U.S. Public*, pg. 1007
RIO GRANDE VALLEY CARDIOLOGY, PLLC—See HCA Healthcare, Inc.; *U.S. Public*, pg. 1007
RIVERCHASE DERMATOLOGY & COSMETIC SURGERY - PEMBROKE PINES—See GTCR LLC; *U.S. Private*, pg. 1806
RIVER PARISHES HOSPITAL, LLC—See Apollo Global Management, Inc.; *U.S. Public*, pg. 158
RIVERSIDE ORAL SURGERY; *U.S. Private*, pg. 3445
RIVERTON MEMORIAL HOSPITAL LLC—See Apollo Global Management, Inc.; *U.S. Public*, pg. 158
ROCKY MOUNTAIN HEALTH MAINTENANCE ORGANIZATION, INCORPORATED—See UnitedHealth Group Incorporated; *U.S. Public*, pg. 2250
ROODLANE MEDICAL LIMITED—See HCA Healthcare, Inc.; *U.S. Public*, pg. 1007
SAINT JOSEPH MERCY HEALTH SYSTEM—See Trinity Health Corporation; *U.S. Private*, pg. 4234
SAN FRANCISCO CYBERKNIFE, LLC—See Akumin, Inc.; *U.S. Public*, pg. 70
SCHEIN ERNST MISHRA EYE, P.C.—See Henry Schein, Inc.; *U.S. Public*, pg. 1027
SCHWEIGER DERMATOLOGY GROUP; *U.S. Private*, pg. 3572
SCOPE ORTHOTICS & PROSTHETICS, INC.—See Patient Square Capital, L.P.; *U.S. Private*, pg. 3107
SCOTTSDALE ENDOSCOPY ASC, LLC—See Tenet Healthcare Corporation; *U.S. Public*, pg. 2007
S.E.E.K ARIZONA; *U.S. Private*, pg. 3517
SHERIDAN ANESTHESIA SERVICES OF LOUISIANA, INC.—See KKR & Co. Inc.; *U.S. Public*, pg. 1246
SHIELDS ORTHOTIC PROSTHETIC SERVICES, INC.—See Patient Square Capital, L.P.; *U.S. Private*, pg. 3107
SINGER ISLAND RECOVERY CENTER LLC—See AAC Holdings, Inc.; *U.S. Private*, pg. 31
SKINSMART DERMATOLOGY; *U.S. Private*, pg. 3682
SKINTRUST DERMATOLOGY—See Harvest Partners L.P.; *U.S. Private*, pg. 1876
SKY RIDGE SURGERY CENTER, L.P.—See HCA Healthcare, Inc.; *U.S. Public*, pg. 1008
SOLANTIC CORPORATION—See Tenet Healthcare Corporation; *U.S. Public*, pg. 2014
THE SOUTH BEND CLINIC, LLP; *U.S. Private*, pg. 4119
SOUTHEAST PERINATAL ASSOCIATES, INC.—See KKR & Co. Inc.; *U.S. Public*, pg. 1246
SOUTHEAST QUADRANT MOBILE CRITICAL CARE UNIT INC.; *U.S. Private*, pg. 3726
SOUTHEAST VEIN & LASER CENTER, P.C.—See Cortec Group Management Services, LLC; *U.S. Private*, pg. 1060
SOUTHERN INDIANA ENT LLC—See ENT Partners LLC; *U.S. Private*, pg. 1402
SOUTH PALM AMBULATORY SURGERY CENTER, LLC—See Baptist Health South Florida, Inc.; *U.S. Private*, pg. 471
SOUTH PLAINS ENDOSCOPY ASSOCIATES, LLC—See Tenet Healthcare Corporation; *U.S. Public*, pg. 2007
SOUTHWEST MEDICAL ASSOCIATES—See UnitedHealth Group Incorporated; *U.S. Public*, pg. 2252
SPALDING REHABILITATION LLC—See HCA Healthcare, Inc.; *U.S. Public*, pg. 1010
SPECIALISTS IN UROLOGY, PA; *U.S. Private*, pg. 3748
SPECTRUM DERMATOLOGY, PLLC—See Pinnacle Dermatology LLC; *U.S. Private*, pg. 3185
SPECTRUM VISION PARTNERS LLC—See Blue Sea Capital Management LLC; *U.S. Public*, pg. 592
SPORT & SPINE REHAB; *U.S. Private*, pg. 3760
STATE OF FRANKLIN HEALTHCARE ASSOCIATES PLLC; *U.S. Private*, pg. 3792
ST. CLOUD SURGICAL CENTER, LLC—See UnitedHealth Group Incorporated; *U.S. Public*, pg. 2250
ST. DAVID'S CARDIOLOGY, PLLC—See HCA Healthcare, Inc.; *U.S. Public*, pg. 1010
ST. DAVID'S NORTH AUSTIN MEDICAL CENTER—See HCA Healthcare, Inc.; *U.S. Public*, pg. 1010
ST. DAVID'S ROUND ROCK MEDICAL CENTER—See HCA Healthcare, Inc.; *U.S. Public*, pg. 1010
ST. DAVID'S SPECIALIZED WOMENS SERVICES, PLLC—See HCA Healthcare, Inc.; *U.S. Public*, pg. 1010
ST. MARY'S HOSPITAL—See Ascension Health Alliance; *U.S. Private*, pg. 347
SUNRISE AMBULATORY SURGICAL CENTER, LLC—See KKR & Co. Inc.; *U.S. Public*, pg. 1246
SUNRISE MEDICAL GROUP II, L.L.C.—See Tenet Healthcare Corporation; *U.S. Public*, pg. 2004

621111 — OFFICES OF PHYSICIA...

SUN VALLEY HEALTH, LLC—See Empower Clinics Inc.; *Int'l*, pg. 2388
SURGCENTER TUCSON, LLC—See Tenet Healthcare Corporation; *U.S. Public*, pg. 2007
SURGERY CENTER OF ALLENTOWN, LLC—See KKR & Co. Inc.; *U.S. Public*, pg. 1247
SURGERY CENTER OF NORTHEAST TEXAS, LLC—See KKR & Co. Inc.; *U.S. Public*, pg. 1247
SURGERY SPECIALISTS OF BROWARD, INC.—See KKR & Co. Inc.; *U.S. Public*, pg. 1247
SURGICAL ELITE OF AVONDALE, L.L.C.—See Tenet Healthcare Corporation; *U.S. Public*, pg. 2005
SURGICARE OF DENVER MID-TOWN, INC.—See HCA Healthcare, Inc.; *U.S. Public*, pg. 1011
SURGICARE OF JACKSON, LLC—See UnitedHealth Group Incorporated; *U.S. Public*, pg. 2251
SUTTER ALHAMBRA SURGERY CENTER, L.P.—See UnitedHealth Group Incorporated; *U.S. Public*, pg. 2251
SWH HOLDINGS, INC.—See Centene Corporation; *U.S. Public*, pg. 469
TAMPA BAY ORTHOPAEDIC SPECIALISTS, PA; *U.S. Private*, pg. 3929
TEMECULA CA UNITED SURGERY, L.P.—See KKR & Co. Inc.; *U.S. Public*, pg. 1247
TENET FLORIDA PHYSICIAN SERVICES III, L.L.C.—See Tenet Healthcare Corporation; *U.S. Public*, pg. 2004
TLC VISION CORPORATION—See Charlesbank Capital Partners, LLC; *U.S. Private*, pg. 856
TRINITY HEALTH OF NEW ENGLAND/USP SURGERY CENTERS, L.L.C.—See Tenet Healthcare Corporation; *U.S. Public*, pg. 2009
TRISTAR FAMILY CARE, LLC—See HCA Healthcare, Inc.; *U.S. Public*, pg. 1012
TRISTAR MEDICAL GROUP - LEGACY HEALTH, LLC—See HCA Healthcare, Inc.; *U.S. Public*, pg. 1012
TUHC ANESTHESIOLOGY GROUP, LLC—See HCA Healthcare, Inc.; *U.S. Public*, pg. 1011
UNITED STATES STEEL CORP.—See United States Steel Corporation; *U.S. Public*, pg. 2237
UPDEGRAFF VISION; *U.S. Private*, pg. 4311
UROLOGY SPECIALISTS OF RICHMOND, LLC—See HCA Healthcare, Inc.; *U.S. Public*, pg. 1013
UROLOGY SURGERY CENTER OF COLORADO, LLC—See HCA Healthcare, Inc.; *U.S. Public*, pg. 1013
U.S. ORTHOPAEDIC PARTNERS—See FFL Partners, LLC; *U.S. Private*, pg. 1500
USP MARYLAND, INC.—See Tenet Healthcare Corporation; *U.S. Public*, pg. 2004
VALUEOPTIONS, INC.—See Beacon Health Holdings LLC; *U.S. Private*, pg. 504
VASCULAR SPECIALISTS OF CENTRAL FLORIDA, INC.; *U.S. Private*, pg. 4347
VISAGE DERMATOLOGY & LASER CENTER, LLC; *U.S. Private*, pg. 4389
WALKER CANCER CENTER—See Community Health Systems, Inc.; *U.S. Public*, pg. 551
WASHINGTON DERMATOLOGY CENTER—See Ridgemont Partners Management LLC; *U.S. Private*, pg. 3433
WELLSTAR MEDICAL GROUP INTERVENTIONAL NEUROLOGY—See WellStar Health System, Inc.; *U.S. Private*, pg. 4478
WEST CENTRAL OHIO GROUP, LTD.—See Catholic Healthcare Partners; *U.S. Private*, pg. 792
WEST DERMATOLOGY MED MANAGEMENT, INC.; *U.S. Private*, pg. 4485
WESTERN WYOMING DERMATOLOGY & SURGERY—See Harvest Partners L.P.; *U.S. Private*, pg. 1876
WEST ROXBURY MEDICAL GROUP INC.—See Partners HealthCare System, Inc.; *U.S. Private*, pg. 3102
WEST VALLEY IMAGING, LLC—See HCA Healthcare, Inc.; *U.S. Public*, pg. 1013
WHITTENLASEREYE, LLC—See Centre Partners Management LLC; *U.S. Private*, pg. 828
WOMAN'S HEALTH GROUP, PLLC—See HCA Healthcare, Inc.; *U.S. Public*, pg. 1014
WOMEN'S AND CHILDREN'S PROFESSIONAL MANAGEMENT, L.L.C.—See HCA Healthcare, Inc.; *U.S. Public*, pg. 1014
WOMEN'S CENTER AT BROOKSIDE, LLC—See HCA Healthcare, Inc.; *U.S. Public*, pg. 1014
WOMEN'S HEALTH CONNECTICUT, INC.; *U.S. Private*, pg. 4556
WOMENSLINK CENTER OF WYLIE - A MEDICAL CENTER OF PLANO FACILITY, LLC—See HCA Healthcare, Inc.; *U.S. Public*, pg. 1014

621112 — OFFICES OF PHYSICIANS, MENTAL HEALTH SPECIALISTS

ARC HEALTH HOLDINGS, LLC—See Thurston Group, LLC; *U.S. Private*, pg. 4166
ASIAMEDIC ASTIQUE THE AESTHETIC CLINIC PTE LTD—See AsiaMedic Ltd.; *Int'l*, pg. 616
ATAI LIFE SCIENCES US INC.—See ATAI Life Sciences N.V.; *Int'l*, pg. 665
BEHAVIORAL CONSULTING OF TAMPA BAY INC.; *U.S. Private*, pg. 514
BIOTECH MEDICS, INC.; *U.S. Public*, pg. 339
CENPATICO BEHAVIORAL HEALTH LLC—See Centene Corporation; *U.S. Public*, pg. 468
CENTENE UK LIMITED—See Centene Corporation; *U.S. Public*, pg. 468
CHCA WEST HOUSTON, L.P.—See HCA Healthcare, Inc.; *U.S. Public*, pg. 992
CHILDREN'S HOME OF BRADFORD, PA.; *U.S. Private*, pg. 884
CITRUS PRIMARY CARE, INC.—See HCA Healthcare, Inc.; *U.S. Public*, pg. 993
DETACH AB; *Int'l*, pg. 2047
DISCOVERY BEHAVIORAL HEALTH, INC; *U.S. Private*, pg. 1237
EMERGENCY ASSISTANCE BEIJING CO., LTD.—See Emergency Assistance Japan Co., Ltd.; *Int'l*, pg. 2378
THE ENDOSCOPY CENTER OF WEST CENTRAL OHIO, LLC—See Kelso & Company; *U.S. Private*, pg. 2279
HARLINGEN MEDICAL CENTER, LP—See Prime Healthcare Services, Inc.; *U.S. Public*, pg. 3261
HEALTH DELIVERY INC.; *U.S. Private*, pg. 1893
HORIZONS BEHAVIORAL HEALTH LLC—See Centegra Health System; *U.S. Public*, pg. 809
HUMANPROTECT CONSULTING GMBH—See DZ BANK AG Deutsche Zentral-Genossenschaftsbank; *Int'l*, pg. 2244
INLAND SURGERY CENTER, L.P.—See UnitedHealth Group Incorporated; *U.S. Public*, pg. 2250
INTERNIST ASSOCIATES OF HOUSTON, PLLC—See HCA Healthcare, Inc.; *U.S. Public*, pg. 999
IORA HEALTH, INC.—See Amazon.com, Inc.; *U.S. Public*, pg. 90
JULIAN ONG ENDOSCOPY & SURGERY PTE. LTD.—See HC Surgical Specialists Limited; *Int'l*, pg. 3297
KUYKENDAHL MEDICAL CENTER LLC—See Adeptus Health Inc.; *U.S. Private*, pg. 78
LAI BEC PTE. LTD.—See HC Surgical Specialists Limited; *Int'l*, pg. 3297
LONESTAR PROVIDER NETWORK—See HCA Healthcare, Inc.; *U.S. Public*, pg. 1001
MCALLEN MEDICAL CENTER—See Universal Health Services, Inc.; *U.S. Public*, pg. 2260
MEHRAVISTA HEALTH; *U.S. Private*, pg. 2660
MINDPATH CARE CENTERS PLLC; *U.S. Private*, pg. 2740
MISSOURI CARE, INC.—See Centene Corporation; *U.S. Public*, pg. 471
MONTCLAIR ROAD IMAGING, LLC—See US Radiology Specialists, Inc.; *U.S. Private*, pg. 4319
THE NATIONAL DEAF ACADEMY, LLC—See Universal Health Services, Inc.; *U.S. Public*, pg. 2260
NEURORESTORATIVE—See Centerbridge Partners, L.P.; *U.S. Private*, pg. 814
OCCUPATIONAL HEALTH CENTERS OF CALIFORNIA, A MEDICAL, CORP.; *U.S. Public*, pg. 2988
OPYS PHYSICIAN SERVICES, LLC; *U.S. Private*, pg. 3036
PROMEDICA ENDOSCOPY CENTER—See American Healthcare Systems Corp., Inc.; *U.S. Private*, pg. 236
PSYCHIATRIC CENTERS AT SAN DIEGO, INC.—See MindPath Care Centers PLLC; *U.S. Private*, pg. 2740
SACRAMENTO MIDTOWN ENDOSCOPY CENTER, LLC—See Tenet Healthcare Corporation; *U.S. Public*, pg. 2012
SAN GABRIEL VALLEY MEDICAL CENTER—See AHMC & AHMC Healthcare Inc.; *U.S. Private*, pg. 130
SHERMAN WAY CAMPUS—See Catholic Health Initiatives; *U.S. Private*, pg. 789
ST. ROSE DOMINICAN HOSPITAL—See Catholic Health Initiatives; *U.S. Private*, pg. 790
TEXAS SAN MARCOS TREATMENT CENTER, L.P.—See Universal Health Services, Inc.; *U.S. Public*, pg. 2259
TINY TOTS THERAPY INC.; *U.S. Private*, pg. 4175
UHS OF CENTENNIAL PEAKS, LLC—See Universal Health Services, Inc.; *U.S. Public*, pg. 2260
US EXP GROUP, INC.; *U.S. Private*, pg. 4318
VIA CHRISTI HEALTH PARTNERS, INC.; *U.S. Private*, pg. 4375
VIRTUAL THERAPEUTICS CORPORATION—See UnitedHealth Group Incorporated; *U.S. Public*, pg. 2252
WHATCOM COUNSELING & PSYCHIATRIC CLINIC—See Compass Health; *U.S. Private*, pg. 999
WORTHINGTON INDUSTRIES MEDICAL CENTER, INC.—See Worthington Industries, Inc.; *U.S. Public*, pg. 2383

621210 — OFFICES OF DENTISTS

1300 SMILES LIMITED—See BGH Capital Pty Ltd; *Int'l*, pg. 1007
ABSOLUTE DENTAL GROUP, LLC; *U.S. Private*, pg. 44
ACES DENTAL—See Absolute Dental Group, LLC; *U.S. Private*, pg. 44
A+ DENTAL CARE—See Gryphon Investors, LLC; *U.S. Private*, pg. 1799
A+ DENTAL CARE—See Gryphon Investors, LLC; *U.S. Private*, pg. 1799
AMERICAN ACADEMY OF PERIODONTOLOGY; *U.S. Private*, pg. 221
APPLEWHITE DENTAL LLC—See NMS Capital Services, LLC; *U.S. Private*, pg. 2931
AUCKLAND DENTAL GROUP—See BGH Capital Pty Ltd; *Int'l*, pg. 1008
AUGUSTA REGIONAL CLINIC; *U.S. Private*, pg. 392
BIOMET 3I DENTAL IBERICA SL—See Zimmer Biomet Holdings, Inc.; *U.S. Public*, pg. 2405
BIRNER DENTAL MANAGEMENT SERVICES, INC.—See New Mountain Capital, LLC; *U.S. Private*, pg. 2904
CASTLE DENTAL, INC.—See Gryphon Investors, LLC; *U.S. Private*, pg. 1799
CENTRAL PARK WEST DENTISTRY PC; *U.S. Private*, pg. 824
CHICAGO DENTAL SOCIETY; *U.S. Private*, pg. 877
CHRISTIAN MEDICAL & DENTAL ASSOCIATIONS; *U.S. Private*, pg. 891
COAST DENTAL SERVICES, INC.; *U.S. Private*, pg. 954
COMFORTABLE CARE DENTAL GROUP, INC.—See Huron Capital Partners LLC; *U.S. Private*, pg. 2012
DELAWARE VALLEY MANAGEMENT HOLDINGS, INC.—See Sun Capital Partners, Inc.; *U.S. Private*, pg. 3859
DELTA DENTAL OF SOUTH DAKOTA; *U.S. Private*, pg. 1199
DELTA DENTAL PLAN OF WYOMING; *U.S. Private*, pg. 1200
DELTA DENTAL PLANS ASSOCIATION; *U.S. Private*, pg. 1200
DENTALCARE PARTNERS INC.; *U.S. Private*, pg. 1206
DENTAL CORPORATION PUBLIC COMPANY LIMITED; *Int'l*, pg. 2033
DENTAL FOCUS (BENDEMEER) PTE. LTD.—See Clearbridge Health Limited; *Int'l*, pg. 1656
DENTAL FOCUS (PEOPLE'S PARK) PTE. LTD.—See Clearbridge Health Limited; *Int'l*, pg. 1656
DENTAL FOCUS (PIONEER) PTE. LTD.—See Clearbridge Health Limited; *Int'l*, pg. 1656
DENTAL PATIENT CARE AMERICA, INC.; *U.S. Public*, pg. 654
DIMENSIONAL MANAGEMENT CORP.—See Waud Capital Partners LLC; *U.S. Private*, pg. 4457
DYNAMIC DENTAL PARTNERS INC—See Huron Capital Partners LLC; *U.S. Private*, pg. 2012
ESPIRE DENTAL PRACTICE, LLC; *U.S. Private*, pg. 1427
GROVE CITY DENTAL; *U.S. Private*, pg. 1794
HEARTLAND DENTAL, LLC—See KKR & Co. Inc.; *U.S. Public*, pg. 1252
HILL MANAGEMENT SERVICES INC.—See The Home Sales Company; *U.S. Private*, pg. 4054
IDEAL IMPLANT, INC.—See Bimini Technologies, LLC; *U.S. Private*, pg. 560
IMPLANT & GENERAL DENTISTRY OF NORTHERN COLORADO; *U.S. Private*, pg. 2050
JAIMINI HEALTH, INC.—See Unum Group; *U.S. Public*, pg. 2263
LA COSTA DENTAL GROUP—See Espire Dental Practice, LLC; *U.S. Private*, pg. 1427
LASERDONTICS LIMITED—See Human Health Holdings Limited; *Int'l*, pg. 3529
LUMINO CARE DENTAL—See BGH Capital Pty Ltd; *Int'l*, pg. 1008
MADE YA SMILE DENTAL; *U.S. Private*, pg. 2539
MID-ATLANTIC DENTAL SERVICE HOLDINGS LLC—See New Mountain Capital, LLC; *U.S. Private*, pg. 2904
ORTHOSYNETICS, INC.; *U.S. Private*, pg. 3045
PACIFIC DENTAL SERVICES, INC.; *U.S. Private*, pg. 3067
PLAZA CENTRAL DENTISTS PTY. LTD.—See BGH Capital Pty Ltd; *Int'l*, pg. 1007
PREMIER ORTHODONTIC SPECIALISTS, PLLC; *U.S. Private*, pg. 3250
PROHEALTH/CAREMOUNT DENTAL MANAGEMENT, LLC—See UnitedHealth Group Incorporated; *U.S. Public*, pg. 2249
PROPOSAL SOFTWARE, INC.—See Camden Partners Holdings, LLC; *U.S. Private*, pg. 728
SAVE-ON DENTAL CARE—See CPF Dental, LLC; *U.S. Private*, pg. 1080
SETO & WAN DENTAL CENTRE LIMITED—See Human Health Holdings Limited; *Int'l*, pg. 3529
SIGNATURE SMILE—See CPF Dental, LLC; *U.S. Private*, pg. 1080
SIMON DENTISTRY LLC—See MB2 Dental Solutions LLC; *U.S. Private*, pg. 2624
SIX MONTH SMILES, INC.—See Huron Capital Partners LLC; *U.S. Private*, pg. 2012
SMILE BRANDS, INC.—See Gryphon Investors, LLC; *U.S. Private*, pg. 1799
TUZODENT S.A. DE C.V.—See DENTSPLY SIRONA Inc.; *U.S. Public*, pg. 655
WESTERN DENTAL SERVICES INC.—See New Mountain Capital, LLC; *U.S. Private*, pg. 2904
ZIMMER DENTAL ITALY SRL—See Zimmer Biomet Holdings, Inc.; *U.S. Public*, pg. 2407
ZIMMER DENTAL SWEDEN AB—See Zimmer Biomet Holdings, Inc.; *U.S. Public*, pg. 2407

N.A.I.C.S. INDEX

621310 — OFFICES OF CHIROPRACTORS

ACN GROUP OF CALIFORNIA, INC.—See UnitedHealth Group Incorporated; *U.S. Public*, pg. 2238
CARQUEST DISTRIBUTION CENTER CALIFORNIA—See Advance Auto Parts, Inc.; *U.S. Public*, pg. 45
CHIRO ONE WELLNESS CENTERS; *U.S. Private*, pg. 886
EXPRESSIONS CHIROPRACTIC & REHAB, P.A.—See Eco Innovation Group, Inc.; *U.S. Public*, pg. 712
HEALTHSOURCE; *U.S. Private*, pg. 1897
INTERNATIONAL DALECO CORPORATION; *U.S. Public*, pg. 1151
THE JOINT CORP.; *U.S. Public*, pg. 2107
KETTLEY & COMPANY REALTORS-SUGAR GROVE—See Kettley & Company Realtors Inc.; *U.S. Private*, pg. 2292
TRUE HEALTH STUDIO, INC.—See CARBON GREEN INC.; *Int'l*, pg. 1320

621320 — OFFICES OF OPTOMETRISTS

ASIAMEDIC EYE CENTRE PTE. LTD.—See AsiaMedic Ltd.; *Int'l*, pg. 616
CHESAPEAKE EYE CARE & LASER CENTER, LLC—See Centre Partners Management LLC; *U.S. Private*, pg. 828
COASTAL EYE ASSOCIATES PLLC; *U.S. Private*, pg. 956
EUROEYES APS—See EuroEyes International Eye Clinic Limited; *Int'l*, pg. 2535
EUROEYES AUGENLASERZENTRUM BERLIN GMBH—See EuroEyes International Eye Clinic Limited; *Int'l*, pg. 2535
EUROEYES AUGENLASERZENTRUM BREMEN GMBH—See EuroEyes International Eye Clinic Limited; *Int'l*, pg. 2535
EUROEYES AUGENLASERZENTRUM CITY HAMBURG GMBH—See EuroEyes International Eye Clinic Limited; *Int'l*, pg. 2535
EUROEYES AUGENLASERZENTRUM HANNOVER GMBH—See EuroEyes International Eye Clinic Limited; *Int'l*, pg. 2535
EUROEYES AUGENLASERZENTRUM STUTTGART GMBH—See EuroEyes International Eye Clinic Limited; *Int'l*, pg. 2535
EUROEYES DEUTSCHLAND HOLDING GMBH & CO. KG—See EuroEyes International Eye Clinic Limited; *Int'l*, pg. 2535
EUROEYES HONG KONG CO. LIMITED—See EuroEyes International Eye Clinic Limited; *Int'l*, pg. 2535
EYE CARE ASSOCIATES; *U.S. Private*, pg. 1453
EYEQ OPTOMETRISTS PTY. LTD.—See EYECARE PARTNERS LIMITED; *Int'l*, pg. 2592
FORTY FORT EYE ASSOCIATES; *U.S. Private*, pg. 1577
NORD FARM SP. Z O.O.—See Farmak JSC; *Int'l*, pg. 2619
PANORAMA EYE CARE LLC; *U.S. Private*, pg. 3087
PREMIER EYE CARE LLC—See H.I.G. Capital, LLC; *U.S. Private*, pg. 1833
RETINA HEALTH CENTER; *U.S. Private*, pg. 3412
ROCKVILLE EYE SURGERY CENTER, LLC—See UnitedHealth Group Incorporated; *U.S. Public*, pg. 2250
SCHULTZ EYE CLINIC—See Trilogy Eye Medical Group Inc.; *U.S. Private*, pg. 4232
SENIOR VISION SERVICES, INC.—See Serent Capital Management Company, LLC; *U.S. Private*, pg. 3613
SIGHT MEDICAL DOCTORS, PLLC—See Chicago Pacific Founders; *U.S. Private*, pg. 878
TOYOS CLINIC; *U.S. Private*, pg. 4198

621330 — OFFICES OF MENTAL HEALTH PRACTITIONERS (EXCEPT PHYSICIANS)

AVERTEST, LLC; *U.S. Private*, pg. 405
CAMELOT CARE CENTERS, INC—See ATAR Capital, LLC; *U.S. Private*, pg. 364
CAMELOT COMMUNITY CARE, INC.—See ModivCare, Inc.; *U.S. Public*, pg. 1455
CCRI, INC.—See DENTSPLY SIRONA Inc.; *U.S. Public*, pg. 654
CHILDREN'S BEHAVIORAL HEALTH, INC.—See ATAR Capital, LLC; *U.S. Private*, pg. 364
CHOICES GROUP, INC.—See ATAR Capital, LLC; *U.S. Private*, pg. 364
CLINIQUE LA METAIRE—See Apax Partners LLP; *Int'l*, pg. 502
CNLR HORIZONS LIMITED—See Madison Dearborn Partners, LLC; *U.S. Private*, pg. 2540
COMPREHENSIVE BEHAVIORAL HEALTH; *U.S. Private*, pg. 1002
DOCKSIDE SERVICES, INC—See ModivCare, Inc.; *U.S. Public*, pg. 1455
ELEMENTS BEHAVIORAL HEALTH, INC.; *U.S. Private*, pg. 1357
FAMILY PRESERVATION SERVICES, INC.—See ATAR Capital, LLC; *U.S. Private*, pg. 364
FAMILY PRESERVATION SERVICES OF NORTH CAROLINA, INC.—See ATAR Capital, LLC; *U.S. Private*, pg. 364
FAMILY PRESERVATION SERVICES OF WASHINGTON, D.C., INC.—See ATAR Capital, LLC; *U.S. Private*, pg. 364
FHC HEALTH SYSTEMS INC.; *U.S. Private*, pg. 1501
FIDES SERVIZI S.C.A R.L.—See Garofalo Health Care SpA; *Int'l*, pg. 2886
IMPULS GMBH—See H&M Hennes & Mauritz AB; *Int'l*, pg. 3192
LAGUNA TREATMENT HOSPITAL, LLC—See AAC Holdings, Inc.; *U.S. Private*, pg. 30
LEWISTOWN COMPREHENSIVE TREATMENT CENTER, LLC—See Acadia Healthcare Company, Inc.; *U.S. Public*, pg. 29
MAGELLAN HEALTH, INC.—See Centene Corporation; *U.S. Public*, pg. 469
MINDDISTRICT B.V.—See Asklepios Kliniken GmbH & Co. KGaA; *Int'l*, pg. 624
MINDDISTRICT GMBH—See Asklepios Kliniken GmbH & Co. KGaA; *Int'l*, pg. 624
MINDDISTRICT LTD.—See Asklepios Kliniken GmbH & Co. KGaA; *Int'l*, pg. 624
MYSTRENGTH, INC.—See Teladoc Health, Inc.; *U.S. Public*, pg. 1992
NEW DIRECTIONS BEHAVIORAL HEALTH LLC—See GuideWell Mutual Holding Corporation; *U.S. Private*, pg. 1814
OXFORD TREATMENT CENTER, LLC—See AAC Holdings, Inc.; *U.S. Private*, pg. 30
PATHWAYS COMMUNITY SERVICES LLC—See ATAR Capital, LLC; *U.S. Private*, pg. 364
PATHWAYS OF ARIZONA, INC.—See ATAR Capital, LLC; *U.S. Private*, pg. 364
PATHWAYS OF MAINE, INC.—See ATAR Capital, LLC; *U.S. Private*, pg. 364
PHOENIX HEALTH CARE INC.—See Constellation Healthcare Technologies, Inc.; *U.S. Private*, pg. 1023
PTPC PHYSICAL THERAPY & PERFORMANCE CENTER—See Confluent Health, LLC; *U.S. Private*, pg. 1013
RIO GRANDE BEHAVIORAL HEALTH SERVICES, INC—See ModivCare, Inc.; *U.S. Public*, pg. 1456
TELADOC HEALTH BRASIL - SERVICOS DE CONSULTORIA EM SAUDE LTDA—See Teladoc Health, Inc.; *U.S. Public*, pg. 1992
TELADOC HEALTH PORTUGAL, S.A.—See Teladoc Health, Inc.; *U.S. Public*, pg. 1992
VILLA VON SIEBENTHAL S.R.L.—See Garofalo Health Care SpA; *Int'l*, pg. 2886
WELLPOINT BEHAVIORAL HEALTH—See Elevance Health, Inc.; *U.S. Public*, pg. 730

621340 — OFFICES OF PHYSICAL, OCCUPATIONAL AND SPEECH THERAPISTS, AND AUDIOLOGISTS

1 ON 1 PHYSICAL THERAPY, LLC—See U.S. Physical Therapy, Inc.; *U.S. Public*, pg. 2213
ABILITY HEALTH SERVICES & REHABILITATION, L.P.—See U.S. Physical Therapy, Inc.; *U.S. Public*, pg. 2213
ABINGDON HEARING CARE—See Alpaca Audiology; *U.S. Private*, pg. 196
ACHIEVE PHYSICAL THERAPY, LIMITED PARTNERSHIP—See U.S. Physical Therapy, Inc.; *U.S. Public*, pg. 2213
ACHILLES THERAPEUTICS PLC; *Int'l*, pg. 103
ACS SLUCHMED SP. Z O.O.—See Demant A/S; *Int'l*, pg. 2022
ACTIVE PHYSICAL THERAPY, LIMITED PARTNERSHIP—See U.S. Physical Therapy, Inc.; *U.S. Public*, pg. 2213
THE ADVANCED CENTER FOR PHYSICAL THERAPY—See Audax Group, Limited Partnership; *U.S. Private*, pg. 389
ALBANY PHYSICAL THERAPY, PC—See Gryphon Investors, LLC; *U.S. Private*, pg. 1799
ALDRIDGE PHYSICAL THERAPY, LLC—See Audax Group, Limited Partnership; *U.S. Private*, pg. 389
ALPACA AUDIOLOGY; *U.S. Private*, pg. 196
ALTERITY THERAPEUTICS INC.—See Alterity Therapeutics Limited; *Int'l*, pg. 391
AMPLIFON INDIA PVT LTD.—See Amplifon S.p.A.; *Int'l*, pg. 435
AMPLIFON ITALIA S.P.A.—See Amplifon S.p.A.; *Int'l*, pg. 435
AMPLIFON MAGYARORSZAG LTD.—See Amplifon S.p.A.; *Int'l*, pg. 435
ARCH PHYSICAL THERAPY AND SPORTS MEDICINE, LIMITED PARTNERSHIP—See U.S. Physical Therapy, Inc.; *U.S. Public*, pg. 2213
ARKANSAS PHYSICAL THERAPY SERVICES OF CONWAY, LLC—See UnitedHealth Group Incorporated; *U.S. Public*, pg. 2244
ASB SANATORIY SOLNECHNY UE—See Belarusbank; *Int'l*, pg. 963
ASHLAND PHYSICAL THERAPY, LIMITED PARTNERSHIP—See U.S. Physical Therapy, Inc.; *U.S. Public*, pg. 2213
ATHLETICO LTD.; *U.S. Private*, pg. 368
ATLANTA PEDIATRIC THERAPY, INC.; *U.S. Private*, pg. 371
ATLANTICARE OCCUPATIONAL HEALTH—See Geisinger Health System; *U.S. Private*, pg. 1656
ATTUNE HEARING PTY. LTD.—See Amplifon S.p.A.; *Int'l*, pg. 435
AUCKLAND HEARING LTD.—See Amplifon S.p.A.; *Int'l*, pg. 435
AUDIGY GROUP LLC—See GN Store Nord A/S; *Int'l*, pg. 3016
AUDIKA AB—See Demant A/S; *Int'l*, pg. 2023
AUDIKA APS—See Demant A/S; *Int'l*, pg. 2023
AUDIOLOGY SERVICES COMPANY LLC—See Demant A/S; *Int'l*, pg. 2023
AUDIO SELECCION S.L.—See Demant A/S; *Int'l*, pg. 2023
AUDMET OY—See Demant A/S; *Int'l*, pg. 2023
BAY AUDIOLOGY LTD.—See Amplifon S.p.A.; *Int'l*, pg. 435
BAY AUDIO PTY. LTD.—See Amplifon S.p.A.; *Int'l*, pg. 435
BAYSIDE PHYSICAL THERAPY & SPORTS REHABILITATION, LIMITED PARTNERSHIP—See U.S. Physical Therapy, Inc.; *U.S. Public*, pg. 2214
BENCHMARK REHAB PARTNERS; *U.S. Private*, pg. 524
BERTIN IT SAS—See CNIM Constructions Industrielles de la Mediterranee SA; *Int'l*, pg. 1677
BIOCANCELL THERAPEUTICS ISRAEL LTD.—See Chemomab Therapeutics Ltd.; *Int'l*, pg. 1463
BLACK MOUNTAIN PHYSICAL THERAPY LLC—See Audax Group, Limited Partnership; *U.S. Private*, pg. 389
BRIDGING THE GAP PHYSICAL THERAPY LLC—See HealthLynked Corp.; *U.S. Public*, pg. 1016
CAROLINA PHYSICAL THERAPY & SPORTS MEDICINE, LIMITED PARTNERSHIP—See U.S. Physical Therapy, Inc.; *U.S. Public*, pg. 2214
CELLTRUST ANIMAL THERAPEUTICS CO., LTD.—See FUJIFILM Holdings Corporation; *Int'l*, pg. 2821
CLEAR LAKE REHABILITATION HOSPITAL, LLC—See Select Rehabilitation, LLC; *U.S. Private*, pg. 3601
COBB PEDIATRIC THERAPY SERVICES; *U.S. Private*, pg. 957
COMPLETE CARE PHYSICAL THERAPY—See U.S. Physical Therapy, Inc.; *U.S. Public*, pg. 2216
CONFLUENT HEALTH, LLC; *U.S. Private*, pg. 1013
CROWLEY PHYSICAL THERAPY CLINIC, INC.—See Select Medical Holdings Corporation; *U.S. Public*, pg. 1857
CUSTOM PHYSICAL THERAPY, LIMITED PARTNERSHIP—See U.S. Physical Therapy, Inc.; *U.S. Public*, pg. 2214
DECATUR HAND AND PHYSICAL THERAPY SPECIALISTS, LIMITED PARTNERSHIP—See U.S. Physical Therapy, Inc.; *U.S. Public*, pg. 2214
DEKALB COMPREHENSIVE PHYSICAL THERAPY, LIMITED PARTNERSHIP—See U.S. Physical Therapy, Inc.; *U.S. Public*, pg. 2214
DOUGLAS AVERY & ASSOCIATES, LTD.—See Select Medical Holdings Corporation; *U.S. Public*, pg. 1858
DOUGLASS ORTHOPEDIC & SPINE REHABILITATION, INC.; *U.S. Private*, pg. 1267
EASTGATE PHYSICAL THERAPY, LIMITED PARTNERSHIP—See U.S. Physical Therapy, Inc.; *U.S. Public*, pg. 2214
ENABLE, INC.; *U.S. Private*, pg. 1389
EVOFEM, INC—See Evofem Biosciences, Inc.; *U.S. Public*, pg. 804
FIVE RIVERS THERAPY SERVICES, LIMITED PARTNERSHIP—See U.S. Physical Therapy, Inc.; *U.S. Public*, pg. 2214
FLANNERY PHYSICAL THERAPY, LIMITED PARTNERSHIP—See U.S. Physical Therapy, Inc.; *U.S. Public*, pg. 2214
FREDERICKSBURG PHYSICAL THERAPY, LIMITED PARTNERSHIP—See U.S. Physical Therapy, Inc.; *U.S. Public*, pg. 2214
GEORGIA PHYSICAL THERAPY, INC.—See Select Medical Holdings Corporation; *U.S. Public*, pg. 1858
THE HALE HAND CENTER, LIMITED PARTNERSHIP—See U.S. Physical Therapy, Inc.; *U.S. Public*, pg. 2216
HAND THERAPY ASSOCIATES, INC.—See Select Medical Holdings Corporation; *U.S. Public*, pg. 1858
HARBOR PHYSICAL THERAPY, LIMITED PARTNERSHIP—See U.S. Physical Therapy, Inc.; *U.S. Public*, pg. 2214
HEARING HOLDING BELGIUM NV—See Demant A/S; *Int'l*, pg. 2023
HEARINGLIFE CANADA LTD.—See Demant A/S; *Int'l*, pg. 2023
HEARING SCREENING ASSOCIATES LLC—See Demant A/S; *Int'l*, pg. 2023
HH REHAB ASSOCIATES, INC.—See U.S. Physical Therapy, Inc.; *U.S. Public*, pg. 2214
HIDDEN HEARING LIMITED—See Demant A/S; *Int'l*, pg. 2024
HIDDEN HEARING (PORTUGAL), UNIPESSOAL LDA.—See Demant A/S; *Int'l*, pg. 2023
HIGHLANDS PHYSICAL THERAPY & SPORTS MEDICINE,

621340 — OFFICES OF PHYSICAL...

LIMITED PARTNERSHIP—See U.S. Physical Therapy, Inc.; *U.S. Public*, pg. 2214
HOMETOWN HEARING CENTRE INC.—See Amplifon S.p.A.; *Int'l*, pg. 435
INDIANAPOLIS PHYSICAL THERAPY AND SPORTS MEDICINE, INC.—See Select Medical Holdings Corporation; *U.S. Public*, pg. 1858
INHOME THERAPY INC.; *U.S. Private*, pg. 2077
INMED SP. Z O.O.—See Demant A/S; *Int'l*, pg. 2024
INTEGRATED REHAB GROUP, LIMITED PARTNERSHIP—See U.S. Physical Therapy, Inc.; *U.S. Public*, pg. 2214
INTERACTIVE THERAPY GROUP CONSULTANTS, INC.—See American Learning Corporation; *U.S. Private*, pg. 239
JOYNER SPORTSMEDICINE INSTITUTE, INC.—See Select Medical Holdings Corporation; *U.S. Public*, pg. 1858
JUNEAU PHYSICAL THERAPY, A PROFESSIONAL CORPORATION—See SouthEast Alaska Regional Health Consortium; *U.S. Private*, pg. 3724
KENTUCKY ORTHOPEDIC REHABILITATION, LLC—See Select Medical Holdings Corporation; *U.S. Public*, pg. 1858
KINGWOOD PHYSICAL THERAPY, LTD.—See U.S. Physical Therapy, Inc.; *U.S. Public*, pg. 2215
LAKE HOUSTON PHYSICAL THERAPY, LIMITED PARTNERSHIP—See U.S. Physical Therapy, Inc.; *U.S. Public*, pg. 2215
LAWRENCE PARK HEALTH & WELLNESS CLINIC INC.—See Empower Clinics Inc.; *Int'l*, pg. 2388
LEAP THERAPEUTICS, INC.; *U.S. Public*, pg. 1296
LIFE FITNESS PHYSICAL THERAPY, LLC—See U.S. Physical Therapy, Inc.; *U.S. Public*, pg. 2215
LIVING SOUNDS HEARING CENTRE LTD.—See Amplifon S.p.A.; *Int'l*, pg. 435
LOUISVILLE PHYSICAL THERAPY, P.S.C.—See Select Medical Holdings Corporation; *U.S. Public*, pg. 1858
MADISON PT OF NEW JERSEY, PC—See U.S. Physical Therapy, Inc.; *U.S. Public*, pg. 2215
MADISON SPINE, LIMITED PARTNERSHIP—See U.S. Physical Therapy, Inc.; *U.S. Public*, pg. 2215
MAPLEWOOD PHYSICAL THERAPY, LIMITED PARTNERSHIP—See U.S. Physical Therapy, Inc.; *U.S. Public*, pg. 2215
MARBURGER IONENSTRAHL-THERAPIE BETRIEBSGESELLSCHAFT MBH—See Asklepios Kliniken GmbH & Co. KGaA; *Int'l*, pg. 624
MAXIMUM IMPACT PHYSICAL THERAPY SERVICES, LLC—See Athletico Ltd.; *U.S. Private*, pg. 368
MEDTON LTD.—See Demant A/S; *Int'l*, pg. 2024
MISSISSIPPI PHYSICAL THERAPY SERVICES OF BILOXI, LLC—See UnitedHealth Group Incorporated; *U.S. Public*, pg. 2246
MUIR/DIABLO OCCUPATIONAL MEDICINE—See Community Health Systems, Inc.; *U.S. Public*, pg. 555
NATIONAL BOARD FOR CERTIFICATION IN OCCUPATIONAL THERAPY, INC.; *U.S. Private*, pg. 2848
NEBRASKA ORTHOTIC & PROSTHETIC SERVICES, INC.—See Patient Square Capital, L.P.; *U.S. Private*, pg. 3107
NEW HORIZONS PT, LIMITED PARTNERSHIP—See U.S. Physical Therapy, Inc.; *U.S. Public*, pg. 2215
NORTH SHORE PEDIATRIC THERAPY; *U.S. Private*, pg. 2947
NORTH SHORE SPORTS & PHYSICAL THERAPY, LIMITED PARTNERSHIP—See U.S. Physical Therapy, Inc.; *U.S. Public*, pg. 2215
NORTHWOODS PHYSICAL THERAPY, LIMITED PARTNERSHIP—See U.S. Physical Therapy, Inc.; *U.S. Public*, pg. 2215
NOUVELLE AUDITION SAS—See Amplifon S.p.A.; *Int'l*, pg. 435
NOVACARE REHABILITATION—See Select Medical Holdings Corporation; *U.S. Public*, pg. 1858
OTICON ITALIA S.R.L.—See Demant A/S; *Int'l*, pg. 2024
PEAK MEDICAL - BEAR CREEK CENTER—See Formation Capital, LLC; *U.S. Private*, pg. 1570
PHOENIX REHABILITATION & HEALTH SERVICES, INC.—See Audax Group, Limited Partnership; *U.S. Private*, pg. 389
THE PHYSICAL THERAPY CONNECTION, INC.—See Audax Group, Limited Partnership; *U.S. Private*, pg. 389
PHYSICAL THERAPY NORTHWEST, LIMITED PARTNERSHIP—See U.S. Physical Therapy, Inc.; *U.S. Public*, pg. 2215
PHYSIOTHERAPY ASSOCIATES, INC.—See Select Medical Holdings Corporation; *U.S. Public*, pg. 1858
PRECISION PHYSICAL THERAPY, LIMITED PARTNERSHIP—See U.S. Physical Therapy, Inc.; *U.S. Public*, pg. 2215
PRESTIGE PHYSICAL THERAPY, LIMITED PARTNERSHIP—See U.S. Physical Therapy, Inc.; *U.S. Public*, pg. 2215
PROACTIVE PHYSICAL THERAPY, LIMITED PARTNERSHIP—See U.S. Physical Therapy, Inc.; *U.S. Public*, pg. 2215
PRO ACTIVE THERAPY OF NORTH CAROLINA, INC.—See Select Medical Holdings Corporation; *U.S. Public*, pg. 1858
PRO ACTIVE THERAPY OF VIRGINIA, INC.—See Select Medical Holdings Corporation; *U.S. Public*, pg. 1858
PT NETWORK, LLC—See CI Capital Partners LLC; *U.S. Private*, pg. 895
QUAD CITY PHYSICAL THERAPY, LIMITED PARTNERSHIP—See U.S. Physical Therapy, Inc.; *U.S. Public*, pg. 2215
RAINDROP HEARING CLINICI INC.—See Amplifon S.p.A.; *Int'l*, pg. 436
RCI (MICHIGAN), INC.—See Select Medical Holdings Corporation; *U.S. Public*, pg. 1858
RCI (WRS), INC.—See Select Medical Holdings Corporation; *U.S. Public*, pg. 1858
REBUD OCCUPATIONAL & PHYSICAL THERAPY, LIMITED PARTNERSHIP—See U.S. Physical Therapy, Inc.; *U.S. Public*, pg. 2215
REHAB ASSOCIATES; *U.S. Private*, pg. 3389
REHABILITATION ASSOCIATES OF CENTRAL VIRGINIA, LIMITED PARTNERSHIP—See U.S. Physical Therapy, Inc.; *U.S. Public*, pg. 2216
REHABILITATION INSTITUTE OF DENTON, LLC—See Select Medical Holdings Corporation; *U.S. Public*, pg. 1859
REHAKLINIK DUSSNANG AG—See Fresenius SE & Co. KGaA; *Int'l*, pg. 2780
RIO RANCHO PHYSICAL THERAPY—See Gryphon Investors, LLC; *U.S. Private*, pg. 1799
SACO BAY ORTHOPAEDIC AND SPORTS PHYSICAL THERAPY, INC.—See Select Medical Holdings Corporation; *U.S. Public*, pg. 1859
SALT LAKE PHYSICAL THERAPY ASSOCIATES, INC.—See Select Rehabilitation, LLC; *U.S. Private*, pg. 3601
SAMARITAN PHYSICAL THERAPY—See UK HealthCare Good Samaritan Hospital; *U.S. Private*, pg. 4275
SEACOAST PHYSICAL THERAPY, LIMITED PARTNERSHIP—See U.S. Physical Therapy, Inc.; *U.S. Public*, pg. 2216
SELECT PHYSICAL THERAPY - AVON—See Select Medical Holdings Corporation; *U.S. Public*, pg. 1859
SELECT PHYSICAL THERAPY OF ALBUQUERQUE, LTD.—See Select Medical Holdings Corporation; *U.S. Public*, pg. 1859
SELECT PHYSICAL THERAPY OF BLUE SPRINGS LIMITED PARTNERSHIP—See Select Medical Holdings Corporation; *U.S. Public*, pg. 1859
SELECT PHYSICAL THERAPY OF COLORADO SPRINGS LIMITED PARTNERSHIP—See Select Medical Holdings Corporation; *U.S. Public*, pg. 1859
SELECT PHYSICAL THERAPY OF CONNECTICUT LIMITED PARTNERSHIP—See Select Medical Holdings Corporation; *U.S. Public*, pg. 1859
SELECT PHYSICAL THERAPY OF DENVER, LTD.—See Select Medical Holdings Corporation; *U.S. Public*, pg. 1859
SELECT PHYSICAL THERAPY OF KENDALL, LTD.—See Select Medical Holdings Corporation; *U.S. Public*, pg. 1859
SELECT PHYSICAL THERAPY OF LOUISVILLE, LTD.—See Select Medical Holdings Corporation; *U.S. Public*, pg. 1859
SELECT PHYSICAL THERAPY OF PORTOLA VALLEY LIMITED PARTNERSHIP—See Select Medical Holdings Corporation; *U.S. Public*, pg. 1859
SELECT PHYSICAL THERAPY OF ST. LOUIS LIMITED PARTNERSHIP—See Select Medical Holdings Corporation; *U.S. Public*, pg. 1859
SELECT PHYSICAL THERAPY OF WEST DENVER LIMITED PARTNERSHIP—See Select Medical Holdings Corporation; *U.S. Public*, pg. 1859
SELECT PHYSICAL THERAPY TEXAS LIMITED PARTNERSHIP—See Select Medical Holdings Corporation; *U.S. Public*, pg. 1859
SELECT REHABILITATION, LLC; *U.S. Private*, pg. 3601
SELECT SPECIALTY HOSPITAL-BOARDMAN, INC.—See Select Medical Holdings Corporation; *U.S. Public*, pg. 1860
SELECT SPECIALTY HOSPITAL-RICHMOND, INC.—See Select Medical Holdings Corporation; *U.S. Public*, pg. 1861
SIGNATURE LEARNING RESOURCES, INC.—See American Learning Corporation; *U.S. Private*, pg. 239
SNOHOMISH PHYSICAL THERAPY, LLC—See U.S. Physical Therapy, Inc.; *U.S. Public*, pg. 2216
SOONER PHYSICAL THERAPY, LIMITED PARTNERSHIP—See U.S. Physical Therapy, Inc.; *U.S. Public*, pg. 2216
SPEAR PHYSICAL THERAPY, PLLC; *U.S. Private*, pg. 3747
SPECTRUM PHYSICAL THERAPY, LIMITED PARTNERSHIP—See U.S. Physical Therapy, Inc.; *U.S. Public*, pg. 2216
SPINE & SPORT; *U.S. Private*, pg. 3757
SPORT & SPINE CLINIC OF AUBURNDALE, LIMITED PARTNERSHIP—See U.S. Physical Therapy, Inc.; *U.S. Public*, pg. 2216
STAR PHYSICAL THERAPY, LIMITED PARTNERSHIP—See U.S. Physical Therapy, Inc.; *U.S. Public*, pg. 2216
TERRACE HEARING CLINIC LTD.—See Amplifon S.p.A.; *Int'l*, pg. 436
TERRIO THERAPY-FITNESS, INC.; *U.S. Private*, pg. 3972
TEXAS JOINT INSTITUTE, PLLC—See HCA Healthcare, Inc.; *U.S. Public*, pg. 1011
TEXAS PHYSICAL THERAPY SPECIALISTS; *U.S. Private*, pg. 3976
THERAPY SOURCE, INC.; *U.S. Private*, pg. 4142
THIBODEAU PHYSICAL THERAPY, LIMITED PARTNERSHIP—See U.S. Physical Therapy, Inc.; *U.S. Public*, pg. 2216
THUNDER PHYSICAL THERAPY, LIMITED PARTNERSHIP—See U.S. Physical Therapy, Inc.; *U.S. Public*, pg. 2216
UDICARE S.R.L.—See Demant A/S; *Int'l*, pg. 2025
UNIVERSAL SMARTCOMP, LLC; *U.S. Private*, pg. 4306
U.S. PHYSICAL THERAPY, INC.; *U.S. Public*, pg. 2213
WESLACO REGIONAL REHABILITATION HOSPITAL, LLC—See Ernest Health, Inc.; *U.S. Private*, pg. 1421
WEST GABLES REHABILITATION HOSPITAL, LLC—See Select Medical Holdings Corporation; *U.S. Public*, pg. 1862
WIDEX HONG KONG HEARING & SPEECH CENTRE LTD.—See EQT AB; *Int'l*, pg. 2481
WIDEX MACAU HEARING & SPEECH CENTRE LIMITED—See EQT AB; *Int'l*, pg. 2481
YOUR HEARING NETWORK LLC—See Demant A/S; *Int'l*, pg. 2025
ZENITAS ONTRAC PTY LTD—See Adamantem Capital Management Pty Limited; *Int'l*, pg. 124

621391 — OFFICES OF PODIATRISTS

FOOT & ANKLE ASSOCIATES OF SOUTHWEST VIRGINIA, P.C.—See NMS Capital Services, LLC; *U.S. Private*, pg. 2932
HUMANA AB; *Int'l*, pg. 3529

621399 — OFFICES OF ALL OTHER MISCELLANEOUS HEALTH PRACTITIONERS

4M METALS, INC.—See Industrial Opportunity Partners, LLC; *U.S. Private*, pg. 2067
ACCESS 2 HEALTH CARE PHYSICIANS, LLC—See HCA Healthcare, Inc.; *U.S. Public*, pg. 990
ACCESS RESPIRATORY HOME CARE, LLC—See Quipt Home Medical Corp.; *U.S. Public*, pg. 1757
ACUSTICA SP. Z O.O.—See Demant A/S; *Int'l*, pg. 2023
AIRROSTI REHAB CENTERS, LLC; *U.S. Private*, pg. 142
ALLEGHENY HEALTH NETWORK; *U.S. Private*, pg. 176
ANNE ARUNDEL DERMATOLOGY P.A.—See NMS Capital Services, LLC; *U.S. Private*, pg. 2931
AOXIN Q & M DENTAL GROUP LIMITED; *Int'l*, pg. 498
APEX DENTAL PARTNERS, LP; *U.S. Private*, pg. 292
ARIZONA UROLOGY SPECIALISTS, P.L.L.C.—See Audax Group, Limited Partnership; *U.S. Private*, pg. 387
ATLANTIS OUTPATIENT CENTER—See HCA Healthcare, Inc.; *U.S. Public*, pg. 990
AUGUSTA SURGICAL CENTER—See HCA Healthcare, Inc.; *U.S. Public*, pg. 991
BACK IN MOTION PHYSICAL THERAPY—See GPB Capital Holdings, LLC; *U.S. Private*, pg. 1748
BALTIMORE EYE PHYSICIANS, LLC—See Centre Partners Management LLC; *U.S. Private*, pg. 828
BAYONET POINT SURGERY & ENDOSCOPY CENTER—See HCA Healthcare, Inc.; *U.S. Public*, pg. 991
BEIJING TONG REN TANG VANCOUVER HEALTHCARE CENTER CO., LTD.—See Beijing Tong Ren Tang Chinese Medicine Company Limited; *Int'l*, pg. 959
BELTON REGIONAL MEDICAL CENTER—See HCA Healthcare, Inc.; *U.S. Public*, pg. 991
BIOSCRIP PHARMACY SERVICES, INC.—See Option Care Health, Inc.; *U.S. Public*, pg. 1609
BITAC MAP S.L.U.—See IQVIA Holdings Inc.; *U.S. Public*, pg. 1168
BRADENTON OUTPATIENT SERVICES, LLC—See HCA Healthcare, Inc.; *U.S. Public*, pg. 991
BROWARD NEUROSURGEONS, LLC—See HCA Healthcare, Inc.; *U.S. Public*, pg. 992
BROWARD ONCOLOGY ASSOCIATES, P.A.—See The Oncology Institute, Inc.; *U.S. Public*, pg. 2118
CALIFORNIA FORENSIC MEDICAL GROUP, INC.; *U.S. Private*, pg. 719
CANADIAN BACK INSTITUTE LIMITED PARTNERSHIP; *Int'l*, pg. 1282
CAPE CORAL SURGERY CENTER, INC.—See HCA Healthcare, Inc.; *U.S. Public*, pg. 992
CAPITAL REGIONAL HEART ASSOCIATES LLC—See HCA Healthcare, Inc.; *U.S. Public*, pg. 992
CARENEX HEALTH SERVICES; *U.S. Private*, pg. 753
CARISK PARTNERS, INC.—See Elements Health Investors, LLC; *U.S. Private*, pg. 1357

621399 — OFFICES OF ALL OTHE...

CARISK PARTNERS, INC.—See Lee Equity Partners LLC; U.S. Private, pg. 2412
CEDAR CREEK MEDICAL GROUP, LLC—See HCA Healthcare, Inc.; U.S. Public, pg. 992
CEDARS HEALTHCARE GROUP, LTD.—See HCA Healthcare, Inc.; U.S. Public, pg. 992
CENTERPOINT AMBULATORY SURGERY CENTER—See HCA Healthcare, Inc.; U.S. Public, pg. 993
CENTERPOINT CARDIOLOGY SERVICES, LLC—See HCA Healthcare, Inc.; U.S. Public, pg. 993
CENTERPOINT HOSPITAL BASED PHYSICIANS, LLC—See HCA Healthcare, Inc.; U.S. Public, pg. 993
CENTERPOINT PHYSICIANS GROUP, LLC—See HCA Healthcare, Inc.; U.S. Public, pg. 993
CHINA MEDICAL & HEALTHCARE GROUP LIMITED; Int'l, pg. 1518
CLEMSON EYE, P.A.—See Independence Capital Partners, LLC; U.S. Private, pg. 2056
COHEN MEDICAL ASSOCIATES LLC—See Medical Specialists of The Palm Beaches, Inc.; U.S. Private, pg. 2656
COLLETON AMBULATORY SURGERY CENTER—See HCA Healthcare, Inc.; U.S. Public, pg. 993
COLOPLAST A/S; Int'l, pg. 1702
COLUMBIA HOSPITAL AT MEDICAL CITY DALLAS SUBSIDIARY, L.P.—See HCA Healthcare, Inc.; U.S. Public, pg. 994
COLUMBIA MEDICAL CENTER OF LEWISVILLE SUBSIDIARY, L.P.—See HCA Healthcare, Inc.; U.S. Public, pg. 994
COLUMBIA MEDICAL CENTER OF MCKINNEY SUBSIDIARY, L.P.—See HCA Healthcare, Inc.; U.S. Public, pg. 994
COLUMBIA MEDICAL CENTER OF PLANO SUBSIDIARY, L.P.—See HCA Healthcare, Inc.; U.S. Public, pg. 994
COLUMBIA MEDICAL GROUP - CENTENNIAL, INC.—See HCA Healthcare, Inc.; U.S. Public, pg. 994
COLUMBIA POLK GENERAL HOSPITAL, INC.—See HCA Healthcare, Inc.; U.S. Public, pg. 994
COMMONWEALTH SPECIALISTS OF KENTUCKY, LLC—See HCA Healthcare, Inc.; U.S. Public, pg. 994
CONCENTRA OPERATING CORPORATION—See Select Medical Holdings Corporation; U.S. Public, pg. 1857
CONCENTRA OPERATING CORPORATION—See Welsh, Carson, Anderson & Stowe; U.S. Private, pg. 4479
DENTAL INTELLIGENCE, INC.; U.S. Private, pg. 1206
DERMPATH DIAGNOSTICS—See Quest Diagnostics, Inc.; U.S. Public, pg. 1755
DEROSA MEDICAL PC—See Nobilis Health Corp.; U.S. Private, pg. 2932
DOCTORS HOSPITAL (CONROE), INC.—See HCA Healthcare, Inc.; U.S. Public, pg. 995
DOCTORS HOSPITAL OF AUGUSTA NEUROLOGY, LLC—See HCA Healthcare, Inc.; U.S. Public, pg. 995
EASTERN IDAHO REGIONAL MEDICAL CENTER—See HCA Healthcare, Inc.; U.S. Public, pg. 995
EAST FALLS FAMILY MEDICINE, LLC—See HCA Healthcare, Inc.; U.S. Public, pg. 995
EAST FLORIDA EMERGENCY PHYSICIAN GROUP, LLC—See HCA Healthcare, Inc.; U.S. Public, pg. 995
EAST FLORIDA HOSPITALISTS, LLC—See HCA Healthcare, Inc.; U.S. Public, pg. 995
EDMOND PODIATRY ASSOCIATES, LLC—See HCA Healthcare, Inc.; U.S. Public, pg. 995
ENVOLVE PHARMACY SOLUTIONS, INC.—See Centene Corporation; U.S. Public, pg. 468
FAMILY HEALTH MEDICAL GROUP OF OVERLAND PARK, LLC—See HCA Healthcare, Inc.; U.S. Public, pg. 996
FAMILY MEDICINE OF TERRE HAUTE, LLC—See HCA Healthcare, Inc.; U.S. Public, pg. 996
FLAMINGO SURGERY CENTER—See HCA Healthcare, Inc.; U.S. Public, pg. 996
FORT PIERCE ORTHOPAEDICS, LLC—See HCA Healthcare, Inc.; U.S. Public, pg. 996
FT. WALTON BEACH ANESTHESIA SERVICES, LLC—See HCA Healthcare, Inc.; U.S. Public, pg. 996
GALICHIA HEART HOSPITAL—See HCA Healthcare, Inc.; U.S. Public, pg. 996
GARDEN PARK HOSPITALIST PROGRAM, LLC—See HCA Healthcare, Inc.; U.S. Public, pg. 996
GENESIS CARE PTY. LTD.—See China Resources (Holdings) Co., Ltd.; Int'l, pg. 1548
GOLDEN DENTAL PLANS, INC.—See DENCAP Dental Plans, Inc.; U.S. Private, pg. 1204
GRANDE DUNES SURGERY CENTER—See HCA Healthcare, Inc.; U.S. Public, pg. 997
GRANDVIEW HEALTH CARE CLINIC, LLC—See HCA Healthcare, Inc.; U.S. Public, pg. 997
GRAYSON PRIMARY CARE, LLC—See HCA Healthcare, Inc.; U.S. Public, pg. 997
GREENVIEW REGIONAL HOSPITAL—See HCA Healthcare, Inc.; U.S. Public, pg. 997
GREENVIEW SPECIALTY ASSOCIATES, LLC—See HCA Healthcare, Inc.; U.S. Public, pg. 997
G. SCHNIDER, M.D., PLLC—See HCA Healthcare, Inc.; U.S. Public, pg. 996
H2U WELLNESS CENTERS - CONROE REGIONAL MEDICAL CENTER, PLLC—See HCA Healthcare, Inc.; U.S. Public, pg. 997
H2U WELLNESS CENTERS - DEL SOL MEDICAL CENTER, PLLC—See HCA Healthcare, Inc.; U.S. Public, pg. 997
HANGER, INC.—See Patient Square Capital, L.P.; U.S. Private, pg. 3106
HANGER PROSTHETICS & ORTHOTICS EAST, INC.—See Patient Square Capital, L.P.; U.S. Private, pg. 3107
HEALTH PARTNERS OF KANSAS, INC.—See HCA Healthcare, Inc.; U.S. Public, pg. 998
HEALTH SOLUTIONS, LLC; U.S. Private, pg. 1894
HEALTHWAYS HEALTH SUPPORT—See Stone Point Capital LLC; U.S. Private, pg. 3825
HEART OF AMERICA ASC, LLC—See HCA Healthcare, Inc.; U.S. Public, pg. 998
HERBALIFE (CAMBODIA) CO., LTD.—See Herbalife Nutrition Ltd.; Int'l, pg. 3359
HOMECHOICE PARTNERS, INC—See Option Care Health, Inc.; U.S. Public, pg. 1609
HOSPITALISTS AT FAIRVIEW PARK, LLC—See HCA Healthcare, Inc.; U.S. Public, pg. 998
HYGEA HOLDINGS CORP.; U.S. Private, pg. 2018
ICC HEALTHCARE, LLC—See HCA Healthcare, Inc.; U.S. Public, pg. 999
INDUSTRIAL PARAMEDIC SERVICES, LTD.—See DXP Enterprises, Inc.; U.S. Public, pg. 697
INFUSCIENCE, INC.—See Option Care Health, Inc.; U.S. Public, pg. 1609
INTEGRATED DERMATOLOGY OF PONCHATOULA LLC—See Integrated Dermatology Group; U.S. Private, pg. 2099
INTEGRATED PRACTICE SOLUTIONS, INC.—See Waud Capital Partners LLC; U.S. Private, pg. 4457
INTEGRITY URGENT CARE - EAST—See University of Colorado Health; U.S. Private, pg. 4308
INTERNATIONAL HEALTH GROUP INC.—See Dalrada Financial Corporation; U.S. Public, pg. 621
IVF CENTRE (HONG KONG) LIMITED—See First Shanghai Investments Limited; Int'l, pg. 2687
JACKSON COUNTY PULMONARY MEDICAL GROUP, LLC—See HCA Healthcare, Inc.; U.S. Public, pg. 999
JACKSONVILLE SPECIALISTS, LLC—See HCA Healthcare, Inc.; U.S. Public, pg. 999
JOHNSON COUNTY NEUROLOGY, LLC—See HCA Healthcare, Inc.; U.S. Public, pg. 999
KANSAS PULMONARY & SLEEP SPECIALISTS, LLC—See HCA Healthcare, Inc.; U.S. Public, pg. 1000
KANSAS TRAUMA & CRITICAL CARE SPECIALISTS, LLC—See HCA Healthcare, Inc.; U.S. Public, pg. 1000
KIRKSVILLE MISSOURI HOSPITAL COMPANY, LLC—See Community Health Systems, Inc.; U.S. Public, pg. 554
KPH-CONSOLIDATION, INC.—See HCA Healthcare, Inc.; U.S. Public, pg. 999
LAD IMAGING, LLC—See HCA Healthcare, Inc.; U.S. Public, pg. 1000
LAFAYETTE SURGERY CENTER LIMITED PARTNERSHIP—See HCA Healthcare, Inc.; U.S. Public, pg. 1000
LANDAUER-MEDSTAR—See Quadrant Management, Inc.; U.S. Private, pg. 3316
LAS COLINAS SURGERY CENTER, LTD.—See HCA Healthcare, Inc.; U.S. Public, pg. 1000
LEAVITT MEDICAL ASSOCIATES OF FLORIDA, INC.—See Harvest Partners L.P.; U.S. Private, pg. 1876
LEE'S SUMMIT MEDICAL CENTER—See HCA Healthcare, Inc.; U.S. Public, pg. 1001
THE LITTLE CLINIC OF OHIO LLC—See The Kroger Co.; U.S. Public, pg. 2109
LUDWICK EYE CENTER LTD.—See NMS Capital Services, LLC; U.S. Private, pg. 2931
MARIETTA OUTPATIENT SURGERY, LTD.—See HCA Healthcare, Inc.; U.S. Public, pg. 1001
MEDA HEALTH SALES IRELAND LTD—See Viatris Inc.; U.S. Public, pg. 2293
MEDA PHARMA HUNGARY KFT.—See Viatris Inc.; U.S. Public, pg. 2293
MEDBRIDGE HEALTHCARE, LLC—See Vicente Capital Partners, LLC; U.S. Private, pg. 4376
MEDICAL CENTER OF TRINITY—See HCA Healthcare, Inc.; U.S. Public, pg. 1002
MEDPHARMICS, LLC—See GHO Capital Partners LLP; Int'l, pg. 2959
MEMORIAL HEALTHCARE GROUP, INC.—See HCA Healthcare, Inc.; U.S. Public, pg. 1002
MEMORIAL HOSPITAL OF TAMPA—See HCA Healthcare, Inc.; U.S. Public, pg. 1002
MENORAH MEDICAL GROUP, LLC—See HCA Healthcare, Inc.; U.S. Public, pg. 1002
MERCY HOSPITAL, A CAMPUS OF PLANTATION GENERAL HOSPITAL—See HCA Healthcare, Inc.; U.S. Public, pg. 1006
METHODIST MEDICAL CENTER ASC, L.P.—See HCA Healthcare, Inc.; U.S. Public, pg. 1002
METHODIST MEDICAL CENTER ASC, L.P.—See Methodist Healthcare Ministries of South Texas, Inc.; U.S. Private, pg. 2683
METHODIST PHYSICIAN ALLIANCE—See HCA Healthcare, Inc.; U.S. Public, pg. 1002
METHODIST PHYSICIAN ALLIANCE—See Methodist Healthcare Ministries of South Texas, Inc.; U.S. Private, pg. 2683
METHODIST STONE OAK HOSPITAL—See HCA Healthcare, Inc.; U.S. Public, pg. 1002
METHODIST STONE OAK HOSPITAL—See Methodist Healthcare Ministries of South Texas, Inc.; U.S. Private, pg. 2683
METROPOLITAN METHODIST HOSPITAL—See HCA Healthcare, Inc.; U.S. Public, pg. 1002
METROPOLITAN METHODIST HOSPITAL—See Methodist Healthcare Ministries of South Texas, Inc.; U.S. Private, pg. 2684
MIAMI-DADE CARDIOLOGY CONSULTANTS, LLC—See HCA Healthcare, Inc.; U.S. Public, pg. 1002
MIAMI LAKES SURGERY CENTER, LTD.—See HCA Healthcare, Inc.; U.S. Public, pg. 1002
MIDAMERICA DIVISION, INC.—See HCA Healthcare, Inc.; U.S. Public, pg. 1003
MIDSTATE ORTHOPAEDIC AND SPORTS MEDICINE CENTER, INC.—See FFL Partners, LLC; U.S. Private, pg. 1500
MIDWEST DIVISION - ACH, LLC—See HCA Healthcare, Inc.; U.S. Public, pg. 1003
MIDWEST DIVISION - OPRMC, LLC—See HCA Healthcare, Inc.; U.S. Public, pg. 1003
MIDWEST HEART & VASCULAR SPECIALISTS, LLC—See HCA Healthcare, Inc.; U.S. Public, pg. 1003
MIDWEST PHARMACIES, INC.—See Tenet Healthcare Corporation; U.S. Public, pg. 2014
MISSOULA RADIOLOGY, P.C.—See Inland Imaging Associates, P.S.; U.S. Private, pg. 2078
MYCOTOPIA THERAPIES INC.—See Ehave, Inc.; U.S. Public, pg. 721
MYOGEM HEALTH COMPANY S.L.—See 1nKemia IUCT Group, S.A.; Int'l, pg. 3
NATIONAL PARTNERS IN HEALTHCARE, LLC—See Assured Guaranty Ltd.; Int'l, pg. 650
NEUROSCIENCE ASSOCIATES OF KANSAS CITY, LLC—See HCA Healthcare, Inc.; U.S. Public, pg. 1004
NEW HAVEN RADIOLOGY ASSOCIATES, P.C.—See Midstate Radiology Associates LLC; U.S. Private, pg. 2718
NEXTCARE, INC.—See NextCare Holdings, Inc.; U.S. Private, pg. 2920
NHC GROUP PTY. LTD.—See Amplifon S.p.A.; Int'l, pg. 435
NICEVILLE FAMILY PRACTICE, LLC—See HCA Healthcare, Inc.; U.S. Public, pg. 1004
NORMAN REGIONAL HEALTH SYSTEM; U.S. Private, pg. 2938
NORTH CENTRAL METHODIST ASC, L.P.—See HCA Healthcare, Inc.; U.S. Public, pg. 1004
NORTH COUNTY SURGICENTER—See HCA Healthcare, Inc.; U.S. Public, pg. 1004
NORTHEAST METHODIST HOSPITAL—See HCA Healthcare, Inc.; U.S. Public, pg. 1002
NORTHEAST METHODIST HOSPITAL—See Methodist Healthcare Ministries of South Texas, Inc.; U.S. Private, pg. 2684
NORTH FLORIDA ENDOSCOPY CENTER—See HCA Healthcare, Inc.; U.S. Public, pg. 1004
NORTH FLORIDA REGIONAL OTOLARYNGOLOGY, LLC—See HCA Healthcare, Inc.; U.S. Public, pg. 1004
NORTH TEXAS - MCA, LLC—See HCA Healthcare, Inc.; U.S. Public, pg. 1004
NORTH TRANSFER CENTER, LLC—See HCA Healthcare, Inc.; U.S. Public, pg. 1004
NUTRIO.COM, INC.; U.S. Private, pg. 2974
OCALA HEALTH TRAUMA, LLC—See HCA Healthcare, Inc.; U.S. Public, pg. 1005
OKALOOSA HOSPITAL, INC.—See HCA Healthcare, Inc.; U.S. Public, pg. 1005
ONE CALL CARE MANAGEMENT, INC.—See Apax Partners LLP; Int'l, pg. 505
ONE CALL CARE MANAGEMENT, INC.—See Apax Partners LLP; Int'l, pg. 505
ONPOINT ONCOLOGY, INC.—See RxVantage, Inc.; U.S. Private, pg. 3509
ON-SITE-SOLUTIONS, INC—See The Judge Group, Inc.; U.S. Private, pg. 4063
ORANGE PARK SURGERY CENTER—See HCA Healthcare, Inc.; U.S. Public, pg. 1005
OSCEOLA SURGICAL ASSOCIATES, LLC—See HCA Healthcare, Inc.; U.S. Public, pg. 1005
OVERLAND PARK MEDICAL SPECIALISTS, LLC—See HCA Healthcare, Inc.; U.S. Public, pg. 1005
OVERLAND PARK ORTHOPEDICS, LLC—See HCA Healthcare, Inc.; U.S. Public, pg. 1005
OVERLAND PARK REGIONAL MEDICAL CENTER—See HCA Healthcare, Inc.; U.S. Public, pg. 1003
OVERLAND PARK SURGERY CENTER—See HCA Healthcare, Inc.; U.S. Public, pg. 1005
OVIEDO MEDICAL CENTER, LLC—See HCA Healthcare, Inc.; U.S. Public, pg. 1005
PALACE GATE PRACTICE LIMITED—See HCA Healthcare, Inc.; U.S. Public, pg. 1005
PALMS OF PASADENA HOSPITAL—See HCA Healthcare, Inc.; U.S. Public, pg. 1005
PARKLAND ONCOLOGY, LLC—See HCA Healthcare, Inc.; U.S. Public, pg. 1006

621399 — OFFICES OF ALL OTHE...

PARKRIDGE EAST HOSPITAL—See HCA Healthcare, Inc.; *U.S. Public*, pg. 1012
PARKRIDGE VALLEY HOSPITAL—See HCA Healthcare, Inc.; *U.S. Public*, pg. 1012
PEDIATRIC SPECIALTY CLINIC LLC—See HCA Healthcare, Inc.; *U.S. Public*, pg. 1006
PHYSICAL THERAPY ETC.—See Audax Group, Limited Partnership; *U.S. Private*, pg. 389
PINNACLE TREATMENT CENTERS—See Linden LLC; *U.S. Private*, pg. 2460
THE POLYCLINIC—See UnitedHealth Group Incorporated; *U.S. Public*, pg. 2251
PONCE DE LEON FEDERAL BANK; *U.S. Private*, pg. 3227
PORT ST. LUCIE SURGERY CENTER, LTD.—See HCA Healthcare, Inc.; *U.S. Public*, pg. 1006
PRISM HEALTH CARE SERVICES, INC.; *U.S. Private*, pg. 3267
PROVIDACARE, LLC—See KKR & Co. Inc.; *U.S. Public*, pg. 1250
PUTNAM HOSPITAL, INC.—See HCA Healthcare, Inc.; *U.S. Public*, pg. 1006
QUIVIRA INTERNAL MEDICINE, INC.—See HCA Healthcare, Inc.; *U.S. Public*, pg. 1007
RAPIDES AFTER HOURS CLINIC, L.L.C.—See HCA Healthcare, Inc.; *U.S. Public*, pg. 1007
RAPIDES REGIONAL PHYSICIAN GROUP, LLC—See HCA Healthcare, Inc.; *U.S. Public*, pg. 1007
RAPIDES REGIONAL PHYSICIAN GROUP PRIMARY CARE, LLC—See HCA Healthcare, Inc.; *U.S. Public*, pg. 1007
RAPIDES REGIONAL PHYSICIAN GROUP SPECIALTY CARE, LLC—See HCA Healthcare, Inc.; *U.S. Public*, pg. 1007
REDMOND ANESTHESIA SERVICES, LLC—See HCA Healthcare, Inc.; *U.S. Public*, pg. 1007
REMEDY THERAPY STAFFING PLLC—See InHome Therapy Inc.; *U.S. Private*, pg. 2077
RESEARCH MEDICAL CENTER—See HCA Healthcare, Inc.; *U.S. Public*, pg. 1007
RESTORIXHEALTH LLC—See Sverica Capital Management LP; *U.S. Private*, pg. 3888
RISE MEDICAL STAFFING, LLC—See AMN Healthcare Services, Inc.; *U.S. Public*, pg. 125
RIVERCHASE DERMATOLOGY & COSMETIC SURGERY LLC—See GTCR LLC; *U.S. Private*, pg. 1806
THE ROSS CENTER FOR ANXIETY & RELATED DISORDERS, LLC—See Thurston Group, LLC; *U.S. Private*, pg. 4166
SAAD'S NURSING SERVICES INC.—See Saad's Healthcare Services, Inc.; *U.S. Private*, pg. 3519
SAN JOSE HEALTHCARE SYSTEM, LP—See HCA Healthcare, Inc.; *U.S. Public*, pg. 1008
SAN MARCOS SURGERY CENTER—See HCA Healthcare, Inc.; *U.S. Public*, pg. 1008
SIMPLEHEALTH, INC.; *U.S. Private*, pg. 3667
SIMPLY DENTAL MANAGEMENT, INC.; *U.S. Private*, pg. 3668
SLEEP SERVICES OF AMERICA, INC.—See Vicente Capital Partners, LLC; *U.S. Private*, pg. 4376
SOUTH DADE NEONATOLOGY, LLC—See MEDNAX, Inc.; *U.S. Public*, pg. 1413
SPRING HILL PHYSICIANS, LLC—See HCA Healthcare, Inc.; *U.S. Public*, pg. 1010
STATLAND MEDICAL GROUP, LLC—See HCA Healthcare, Inc.; *U.S. Public*, pg. 1010
STEPHENSON LASER CENTER, L.L.C.—See HCA Healthcare, Inc.; *U.S. Public*, pg. 1010
STILES ROAD IMAGING LLC—See HCA Healthcare, Inc.; *U.S. Public*, pg. 1010
STIRLING INSTITUTE OF AUSTRALIA PTY. LTD.—See MAXIMUS, Inc.; *U.S. Public*, pg. 1402
ST. LUCIE HOSPITALISTS, LLC—See HCA Healthcare, Inc.; *U.S. Public*, pg. 1010
SUNRISE FRANCE S.A.S.—See Vestar Capital Partners, LLC; *U.S. Private*, pg. 4372
SUNRISE MEDICAL AB—See Vestar Capital Partners, LLC; *U.S. Private*, pg. 4372
SUNRISE MEDICAL AS—See Vestar Capital Partners, LLC; *U.S. Private*, pg. 4372
SURGERY CENTER AT ST. ANDREWS—See HCA Healthcare, Inc.; *U.S. Public*, pg. 1011
SURGERY CENTER OF ROME, L.P.—See HCA Healthcare, Inc.; *U.S. Public*, pg. 1011
SURGICARE - UNIDADES DE SAUDE, S.A.—See Fosun International Limited; *Int'l*, pg. 2751
SYNERGY RADIOLOGY ASSOCIATES, P.A.—See MEDNAX, Inc.; *U.S. Public*, pg. 1413
TALLAHASSEE MEDICAL CENTER, INC.—See HCA Healthcare, Inc.; *U.S. Public*, pg. 1011
TLC VISION CORPORATION—See Charlesbank Capital Partners, LLC; *U.S. Private*, pg. 856
TRI-COUNTY SURGICAL SPECIALISTS, LLC—See HCA Healthcare, Inc.; *U.S. Public*, pg. 1012
TRIDENT BEHAVIORAL HEALTH SERVICES, LLC—See HCA Healthcare, Inc.; *U.S. Public*, pg. 1012
TRIDENT NEONATOLOGY SERVICES, LLC—See HCA Healthcare, Inc.; *U.S. Public*, pg. 1013
TRISTAR ASHLAND CITY MEDICAL CENTER—See HCA Healthcare, Inc.; *U.S. Public*, pg. 997
TRISTAR CENTENNIAL MEDICAL CENTER—See HCA Healthcare, Inc.; *U.S. Public*, pg. 997
TRISTAR GYNECOLOGY ONCOLOGY, LLC—See HCA Healthcare, Inc.; *U.S. Public*, pg. 1012
TRISTAR HENDERSONVILLE MEDICAL CENTER—See HCA Healthcare, Inc.; *U.S. Public*, pg. 1012
TRISTAR HORIZON MEDICAL CENTER—See HCA Healthcare, Inc.; *U.S. Public*, pg. 1012
TRISTAR SKYLINE MADISON CAMPUS—See HCA Healthcare, Inc.; *U.S. Public*, pg. 1012
TRISTAR SKYLINE MEDICAL CENTER—See HCA Healthcare, Inc.; *U.S. Public*, pg. 1012
TRISTAR SOUTHERN HILLS MEDICAL CENTER—See HCA Healthcare, Inc.; *U.S. Public*, pg. 997
TRISTAR STONECREST MEDICAL CENTER—See HCA Healthcare, Inc.; *U.S. Public*, pg. 997
TRISTAR SUMMIT MEDICAL CENTER—See HCA Healthcare, Inc.; *U.S. Public*, pg. 997
TUHC PHYSICIAN GROUP, LLC—See HCA Healthcare, Inc.; *U.S. Public*, pg. 1011
TULANE MEDICAL CENTER—See HCA Healthcare, Inc.; *U.S. Public*, pg. 1013
UMASS MEMORIAL HEALTH CARE, INC.; *U.S. Private*, pg. 4278
UNITYPOINT HEALTH; *U.S. Private*, pg. 4303
WALTERBORO COMMUNITY HOSPITAL, INC.—See HCA Healthcare, Inc.; *U.S. Public*, pg. 1013
WELLMED MEDICAL MANAGEMENT INC—See UnitedHealth Group Incorporated; *U.S. Public*, pg. 2240
WESTMED MEDICAL GROUP, P.C.—See Apposite Capital LLP; *Int'l*, pg. 522
WESTSIDE SURGERY CENTER, LTD.—See HCA Healthcare, Inc.; *U.S. Public*, pg. 1014
WHITEGLOVE HOUSE CALL HEALTH, INC.; *U.S. Private*, pg. 4511
WHITING CLINIC LASIK + EYE CARE—See Vision Group Holdings LLC; *U.S. Private*, pg. 4390
ZONEPERFECT NUTRITION COMPANY; *U.S. Private*, pg. 4608
ZOOM CARE P.C.—See PeaceHealth; *U.S. Private*, pg. 3123

621410 — FAMILY PLANNING CENTERS

ABANO HEALTHCARE GROUP LIMITED—See BGH Capital Pty Ltd; *Int'l*, pg. 1007
AMOENA GMBH & CO. KG—See Coloplast A/S; *Int'l*, pg. 1702
CALIFORNIA CRYOBANK STEM CELL SERVICES LLC—See Longitude Capital Management Co., LLC; *U.S. Private*, pg. 2492
CARESTEPS.COM—See Stone Point Capital LLC; *U.S. Private*, pg. 3825
CIGNA HEALTHCARE OF SOUTH CAROLINA, INC.—See The Cigna Group; *U.S. Public*, pg. 2060
CIVITAS SOLUTIONS, INC.—See Centerbridge Partners, L.P.; *U.S. Private*, pg. 813
COLOPLAST AB—See Coloplast A/S; *Int'l*, pg. 1703
COLOPLAST AG—See Coloplast A/S; *Int'l*, pg. 1703
COLOPLAST BETEILIGUNGS GMBH—See Coloplast A/S; *Int'l*, pg. 1703
COLOPLAST CANADA CORPORATION—See Coloplast A/S; *Int'l*, pg. 1703
COLOPLAST (CHINA) CO. LTD.—See Coloplast A/S; *Int'l*, pg. 1703
COLOPLAST DE ARGENTINA S.A.—See Coloplast A/S; *Int'l*, pg. 1704
COLOPLAST DE COSTA RICA S.A.—See Coloplast A/S; *Int'l*, pg. 1704
COLOPLAST DO BRASIL LTDA.—See Coloplast A/S; *Int'l*, pg. 1704
COLOPLAST GMBH—See Coloplast A/S; *Int'l*, pg. 1703
COLOPLAST GMBH—See Coloplast A/S; *Int'l*, pg. 1703
COLOPLAST HUNGARY KFT.—See Coloplast A/S; *Int'l*, pg. 1703
COLOPLAST K.K.—See Coloplast A/S; *Int'l*, pg. 1703
COLOPLAST NORGE AS—See Coloplast A/S; *Int'l*, pg. 1703
COLOPLAST N.V.—See Coloplast A/S; *Int'l*, pg. 1703
COLOPLAST PRODUCTOS MEDICOS S.A.—See Coloplast A/S; *Int'l*, pg. 1703
COLOPLAST PTY. LTD.—See Coloplast A/S; *Int'l*, pg. 1703
COLOPLAST S.P.A.—See Coloplast A/S; *Int'l*, pg. 1704
COLOPLAST SP.Z.O.O.—See Coloplast A/S; *Int'l*, pg. 1704
COLOPLAST UK LTD.—See Coloplast A/S; *Int'l*, pg. 1704
DKT INTERNATIONAL, INC.; *U.S. Private*, pg. 1247
ELITE SURGICAL AFFILIATES—See Nobilis Health Corp.; *U.S. Private*, pg. 2932
HAW PAR HEALTHCARE LIMITED—See Haw Par Corporation Limited; *Int'l*, pg. 3287
KOMALI FERTILITY CENTRE LLP—See Aster DM Healthcare Ltd; *Int'l*, pg. 654
LAMAZE INTERNATIONAL; *U.S. Private*, pg. 2379
LISTER FERTILITY AT PORTLAND HOSPITAL LIMITED—See HCA Healthcare, Inc.; *U.S. Public*, pg. 1001
MENTOR ABI GROUP—See Centerbridge Partners, L.P.; *U.S. Private*, pg. 813
MERCY HOSPITAL & HEALTH SERVICES—See Catholic Health Initiatives; *U.S. Private*, pg. 790
MERCY SOUTHWEST HOSPITAL—See Catholic Health Initiatives; *U.S. Private*, pg. 790
OAK VALLEY HOSPITAL DISTRICT—See Catholic Health Initiatives; *U.S. Private*, pg. 790
PLANNED PARENTHOOD GREAT PLAINS; *U.S. Private*, pg. 3196
PRANATAL-MEDIZIN MUNCHEN FRAUENARZTE UND HUMANGENETIKER MVZ GMBH—See Eurofins Scientific S.E.; *Int'l*, pg. 2551
ST. JOHN'S REGIONAL MEDICAL CENTER—See Catholic Health Initiatives; *U.S. Private*, pg. 789
ST. MARY'S MEDICAL CENTER—See Catholic Health Initiatives; *U.S. Private*, pg. 790
TRISTAR HEALTH SYSTEM—See HCA Healthcare, Inc.; *U.S. Public*, pg. 1012

621420 — OUTPATIENT MENTAL HEALTH AND SUBSTANCE ABUSE CENTERS

A BETTER WAY THERAPY LLC—See UnitedHealth Group Incorporated; *U.S. Public*, pg. 2238
ABS LINCS SC, INC.—See Universal Health Services, Inc.; *U.S. Public*, pg. 2255
ADCARE CRIMINAL JUSTICE SERVICES, INC.—See AAC Holdings, Inc.; *U.S. Private*, pg. 30
ADCARE RHODE ISLAND, INC.—See AAC Holdings, Inc.; *U.S. Private*, pg. 30
ADDICTION & MENTAL HEALTH SERVICES, LLC—See Lee Equity Partners LLC; *U.S. Private*, pg. 2412
AMERICANWORK, INC.—See ATAR Capital, LLC; *U.S. Private*, pg. 364
ARIZONA BIODYNE—See Centene Corporation; *U.S. Public*, pg. 469
ATLANTICARE BEHAVORIAL HEALTH, INC.—See Geisinger Health System; *U.S. Private*, pg. 1656
BALDWIN COUNTY MENTAL HEALTH-MENTAL RETARDATION SERVICES, INC.; *U.S. Private*, pg. 458
BAY AREA ADDICTION RESEARCH & TREATMENT, INC.—See Webster Equity Partners, LLC; *U.S. Private*, pg. 4466
BBH PBMC, LLC—See Tenet Healthcare Corporation; *U.S. Public*, pg. 2001
BBH SBMC, LLC—See Tenet Healthcare Corporation; *U.S. Public*, pg. 2001
BBH WBMC, LLC—See Tenet Healthcare Corporation; *U.S. Public*, pg. 2001
BEACON CENTER, LLC—See Saul Centers, Inc.; *U.S. Public*, pg. 1842
BEAR RIVER HEALTHCARE LLC—See The Pennant Group, Inc.; *U.S. Public*, pg. 2118
BEHAVIORAL HEALTHCARE CORPORATION; *U.S. Private*, pg. 515
BEHAVIORAL HEALTHCARE OPTIONS, INC.—See UnitedHealth Group Incorporated; *U.S. Public*, pg. 2252
BEHAVIORAL HEALTH SERVICES NORTH, INC.; *U.S. Private*, pg. 514
BERT NASH COMMUNITY MENTAL HEALTH CENTER, INC.; *U.S. Private*, pg. 539
BHC HERITAGE OAKS HOSPITAL, INC.—See Universal Health Services, Inc.; *U.S. Public*, pg. 2256
BIOCORRX INC.; *U.S. Public*, pg. 335
BLUE RIDGE BEHAVIORAL HEALTHCARE; *U.S. Private*, pg. 591
BOLEY CENTERS, INC.; *U.S. Private*, pg. 610
BRATTLEBORO RETREAT; *U.S. Private*, pg. 640
THE BRIEN CENTER; *U.S. Private*, pg. 4000
BROWARD BEHAVIORAL HEALTH COALITION, INC.; *U.S. Private*, pg. 666
BUTTERFLY EFFECTS INC; *U.S. Private*, pg. 698
THE CAMP RECOVERY CENTER, LLC—See Acadia Healthcare Company, Inc.; *U.S. Public*, pg. 30
CANVAS HEALTH; *U.S. Private*, pg. 736
THE CANYON AT SANTA MONICA, LLC—See Universal Health Services, Inc.; *U.S. Public*, pg. 2259
CARE PLUS NJ, INC.; *U.S. Private*, pg. 751
CCS/LANSING, INC.—See Universal Health Services, Inc.; *U.S. Public*, pg. 2256
CENTER FOR AUTISM AND RELATED DISORDERS, LLC—See Blackstone Inc.; *U.S. Public*, pg. 352
CENTERPOINT HEALTH INC; *U.S. Private*, pg. 817
CENTERSTONE OF AMERICA, INC.; *U.S. Private*, pg. 817
CHANGE POINT, INC. - MAIN OFFICE—See Change Point, Inc.; *U.S. Private*, pg. 848
CHANGE POINT, INC.; *U.S. Private*, pg. 848
CHILD GUIDANCE RESOURCE CENTERS; *U.S. Private*, pg. 882
COLLEGE COMMUNITY SERVICES—See ATAR Capital, LLC; *U.S. Private*, pg. 364
COMMUNITY HEALTHLINK INC.; *U.S. Private*, pg. 994
COMPASS HEALTH; *U.S. Private*, pg. 999
CONSUMER SERVICES, INC.; *U.S. Private*, pg. 1025
CORNELL INTERVENTIONS, INC.—See The GEO Group, Inc.; *U.S. Public*, pg. 2075

N.A.I.C.S. INDEX

621491 — HMO MEDICAL CENTERS

CORRECTIONAL PROPERTIES, LLC—See The GEO Group, Inc.; *U.S. Public*, pg. 2075
COUNSELING & RECOVERY SERVICES OF OKLAHOMA; *U.S. Private*, pg. 1065
CYGNET BEHAVIOURAL HEALTH—See Universal Health Services, Inc.; *U.S. Public*, pg. 2256
CYGNET CARE SERVICES LIMITED—See Universal Health Services, Inc.; *U.S. Public*, pg. 2256
CYGNET CLIFTON LIMITED—See Universal Health Services, Inc.; *U.S. Public*, pg. 2256
DICKINSON CENTER, INC.; *U.S. Private*, pg. 1227
DRUG ABUSE AND COMPREHENSIVE COORDINATING OFFICE, INC.; *U.S. Private*, pg. 1279
EASY DOES IT INC.; *U.S. Private*, pg. 1323
ECKER CENTER FOR BEHAVIORAL HEALTH; *U.S. Private*, pg. 1327
EDGEWATER SYSTEMS FOR BALANCED LIVING; *U.S. Private*, pg. 1335
EMPLOYEE ASSISTANCE SERVICES, INC.—See Centene Corporation; *U.S. Public*, pg. 469
ENGAGE BEHAVIORAL HEALTH; *U.S. Private*, pg. 1397
FOUNDATIONS ATLANTA, LLC—See Universal Health Services, Inc.; *U.S. Public*, pg. 2257
FOUNDATIONS RECOVERY NETWORK, LLC—See Universal Health Services, Inc.; *U.S. Public*, pg. 2257
FOUNDATIONS SAN DIEGO, LLC—See Universal Health Services, Inc.; *U.S. Public*, pg. 2257
FOUNTAIN HOUSE, INC.; *U.S. Private*, pg. 1581
FRN NASHVILLE, LLC—See Universal Health Services, Inc.; *U.S. Public*, pg. 2257
FRN OUTPATIENT, LLC—See Universal Health Services, Inc.; *U.S. Public*, pg. 2257
FRN SAN FRANCISCO, LLC—See Universal Health Services, Inc.; *U.S. Public*, pg. 2257
FRONTIER HEALTH; *U.S. Private*, pg. 1615
GATEWAYS HOSPITAL AND MENTAL HEALTH CENTER; *U.S. Private*, pg. 1651
GEO AMEY PECS, LTD.—See The GEO Group, Inc.; *U.S. Public*, pg. 2075
GEO AUSTRALIA MANAGEMENT SERVICES PTY, LTD.—See The GEO Group, Inc.; *U.S. Public*, pg. 2075
GEO CARE, INC.—See The GEO Group, Inc.; *U.S. Public*, pg. 2075
GEO CARE OF SOUTH CAROLINA, INC.—See The GEO Group, Inc.; *U.S. Public*, pg. 2075
GEO CORRECTIONS AND DETENTION, LLC—See The GEO Group, Inc.; *U.S. Public*, pg. 2075
GRAND LAKE MENTAL HEALTH CENTER, INC.; *U.S. Private*, pg. 1753
GREEN OAKS HOSPITAL—See HCA Healthcare, Inc.; *U.S. Public*, pg. 997
HALLMARK YOUTHCARE-RICHMOND, LLC—See Petra Capital Partners, LLC; *U.S. Private*, pg. 3161
HAMILTON CENTER, INC.; *U.S. Private*, pg. 1847
HEALTHONE MENTAL HEALTH THERAPY CENTER, LLC—See HCA Healthcare, Inc.; *U.S. Public*, pg. 998
HEALTHY PHARMS, INC.—See 4Front Ventures Corp.; *U.S. Public*, pg. 9
HOPEWELL HEALTH CENTERS INC.—See Hopewell Health Centers Inc.; *U.S. Private*, pg. 1979
INTERBOROUGH DEVELOPMENTAL AND CONSULTATION CENTER; *U.S. Private*, pg. 2109
JOURNEY MENTAL HEALTH CENTER; *U.S. Private*, pg. 2238
KEDREN COMMUNITY HEALTH CENTER, INC.; *U.S. Private*, pg. 2271
KIDSPEACE; *U.S. Private*, pg. 2303
LEE MENTAL HEALTH CENTER, INC.; *U.S. Private*, pg. 2413
LIVENGRIN FOUNDATION; *U.S. Private*, pg. 2473
LOWER EASTSIDE SERVICE CENTER, INC.; *U.S. Private*, pg. 2505
MAGELLAN HEALTH SERVICES—See Centene Corporation; *U.S. Public*, pg. 469
MAPLE STAR NEVADA, INC.—See ATAR Capital, LLC; *U.S. Private*, pg. 364
MCDERMOTT CENTER; *U.S. Private*, pg. 2631
MEDMARK SERVICES, INC.; *U.S. Private*, pg. 2658
MENTAL HEALTH ASSOCIATION OF CONNECTICUT INC.; *U.S. Private*, pg. 2667
MENTAL HEALTH ASSOCIATION OF NEW YORK CITY; *U.S. Private*, pg. 2667
THE MENTAL HEALTH CENTER OF GREATER MANCHESTER; *U.S. Private*, pg. 4078
MENTAL HEALTH PARTNERS; *U.S. Private*, pg. 2667
MINDWISE INNOVATIONS—See Riverside Community Care, Inc.; *U.S. Private*, pg. 3445
MONTGOMERY COUNTY EMERGENCY SERVICE, INC.; *U.S. Private*, pg. 2776
NATIONAL ALLIANCE ON MENTAL ILLNESS; *U.S. Private*, pg. 2839
NAVOS MENTAL HEALTH SOLUTIONS; *U.S. Private*, pg. 2873
NETCARE ACCESS; *U.S. Private*, pg. 2887
NEW HORIZON COUNSELING CENTER, INC.; *U.S. Private*, pg. 2897
NORTHEAST GUIDANCE CENTER; *U.S. Private*, pg. 2950

NORTHEAST HEALTH SERVICES, LLC; *U.S. Private*, pg. 2950
NORTHERN MAINE MEDICAL CENTER; *U.S. Private*, pg. 2953
NORTHERN MICHIGAN SUBSTANCE ABUSE SERVICES INC.; *U.S. Private*, pg. 2953
NORTHWESTERN COUNSELING & SUPPORT SERVICES, INC.; *U.S. Private*, pg. 2962
NORTHWOOD HEALTH SYSTEMS; *U.S. Private*, pg. 2963
ONTRAK, INC.; *U.S. Public*, pg. 1605
ORCHARD PORTMAN HOSPITAL LIMITED—See Universal Health Services, Inc.; *U.S. Public*, pg. 2258
PARENTERAL DRUG ASSOCIATION, INC.; *U.S. Private*, pg. 3094
PENNYROYAL REGIONAL MENTAL HEALTH, MENTAL RETARDATION BOARD, INC.; *U.S. Private*, pg. 3138
PROJECT RENEWAL; *U.S. Private*, pg. 3280
PROTON THERAPY PTE. LTD.—See Berjaya Corporation Berhad; *Int'l*, pg. 984
PROTOTYPES; *U.S. Private*, pg. 3290
THE RANCH AT DOVE TREE LLC—See FFL Partners, LLC; *U.S. Private*, pg. 1500
THE RANCH AT DOVE TREE LLC—See Lee Equity Partners LLC; *U.S. Private*, pg. 2412
RECOVERY FIRST OF FLORIDA, LLC—See AAC Holdings, Inc.; *U.S. Public*, pg. 30
REHABILITATION SUPPORT SERVICES, INC.; *U.S. Private*, pg. 3389
RESEARCH FOUNDATION FOR MENTAL HYGIENE, INC.; *U.S. Private*, pg. 3404
RICHMOND AREA ASSOCIATION FOR RETARDED CITIZENS; *U.S. Private*, pg. 3430
RIDGEVIEW INSTITUTE, INC.—See US Healthvest LLC; *U.S. Private*, pg. 4319
ROLLING HILLS HOSPITALS, INC.—See Acadia Healthcare Company, Inc.; *U.S. Public*, pg. 30
ROSECRANCE, INC.; *U.S. Private*, pg. 3482
SERVICENET, INC.; *U.S. Private*, pg. 3616
SOUTH AFRICAN CUSTODIAL MANAGEMENT PTY, LTD.—See The GEO Group, Inc.; *U.S. Public*, pg. 2075
SOUTH SHORE ASSOCIATION FOR INDEPENDENT LIVING, INC.; *U.S. Private*, pg. 3723
SPURWINK SERVICES INCORPORATED; *U.S. Private*, pg. 3765
STEINWAY CHILD AND FAMILY SERVICES, INC.; *U.S. Private*, pg. 3798
SUMMIT HEALTHCARE MANAGEMENT, LLC—See FFL Partners, LLC; *U.S. Private*, pg. 1500
SUMMIT HEALTHCARE MANAGEMENT, LLC—See Lee Equity Partners LLC; *U.S. Private*, pg. 2412
SUNDOWN M RANCH; *U.S. Private*, pg. 3866
SWOPE HEALTH SERVICES; *U.S. Private*, pg. 3895
SYRACUSE BRICK HOUSE, INC.; *U.S. Private*, pg. 3905
TERROS INC.; *U.S. Private*, pg. 3972
TOUCHSTONE BEHAVIORAL HEALTH; *U.S. Private*, pg. 4192
TRANSITIONAL SERVICES FOR NEW YORK, INC.; *U.S. Private*, pg. 4208
UNITED COUNSELING SERVICE; *U.S. Private*, pg. 4290
VALLEY HOPE ASSOCIATION; *U.S. Private*, pg. 4334
VENTURA CANNABIS AND WELLNESS CORP.; *U.S. Public*, pg. 2279
VESTA, INC.; *U.S. Private*, pg. 4371
WESTSIDE COMMUNITY MENTAL HEALTH CENTER; *U.S. Private*, pg. 4500

621491 — HMO MEDICAL CENTERS

ACCOUNTABLE CARE COALITION OF COMMUNITY HEALTH CENTERS, LLC—See Centene Corporation; *U.S. Public*, pg. 471
ACCOUNTABLE CARE COALITION OF DEKALB, LLC—See Centene Corporation; *U.S. Public*, pg. 471
ADC SURGICENTER, LLC—See HCA Healthcare, Inc.; *U.S. Public*, pg. 990
ADVANCE AB—See CompuGroup Medical SE & Co. KGaA; *Int'l*, pg. 1755
ADVANCED CORRECTIONAL HEALTHCARE; *U.S. Private*, pg. 89
ADVANCED SURGICAL HOSPITAL, LLC—See UnitedHealth Group Incorporated; *U.S. Public*, pg. 2238
ADVENTHEALTH SURGERY CENTER CELEBRATION, LLC—See Tenet Healthcare Corporation; *U.S. Public*, pg. 2009
AFFINITY CARDIO-THORACIC SPECIALISTS, LLC—See Community Health Systems, Inc.; *U.S. Public*, pg. 551
AFFINITY CARDIOVASCULAR SPECIALISTS, LLC—See Community Health Systems, Inc.; *U.S. Public*, pg. 551
AGAPE PHYSICAL THERAPY & SPORTS REHABILITATION, LIMITED PARTNERSHIP—See U.S. Physical Therapy, Inc.; *U.S. Public*, pg. 2213
AGENDIA INC.—See Agendia NV; *Int'l*, pg. 205
ALASKA SURGERY CENTER, INC.—See UnitedHealth Group Incorporated; *U.S. Public*, pg. 2238
ALLIANCE HEALTHCARE GROUP LIMITED; *Int'l*, pg. 339
ALLIANT HEALTH SOLUTIONS; *U.S. Private*, pg. 184

AMERICAN ELDERCARE, INC.—See Humana, Inc.; *U.S. Public*, pg. 1069
AMGEN S.A.S.—See Amgen Inc.; *U.S. Public*, pg. 123
ANCILLA SYSTEMS INCORPORATED; *U.S. Private*, pg. 274
ANTELOPE VALLEY SURGERY CENTER, L.P.—See UnitedHealth Group Incorporated; *U.S. Public*, pg. 2239
APPLIED PATHWAYS LLC—See Elevance Health, Inc.; *U.S. Public*, pg. 728
ARCHIV BUNEK S.R.O.—See Esperite N.V.; *Int'l*, pg. 2506
ARC PHYSICAL THERAPY PLUS, LIMITED PARTNERSHIP—See U.S. Physical Therapy, Inc.; *U.S. Public*, pg. 2213
ASIAN HEALTHCARE SPECIALISTS LIMITED—See Doctor Anywhere Pte Ltd.; *Int'l*, pg. 2153
BARREN RIDGE PHYSICAL THERAPY, LIMITED PARTNERSHIP—See U.S. Physical Therapy, Inc.; *U.S. Public*, pg. 2214
BAXTER DEUTSCHLAND HOLDING GMBH—See Baxter International Inc.; *U.S. Public*, pg. 280
BAXTER HEALTHCARE SA—See Baxter International Inc.; *U.S. Public*, pg. 280
BAXTER MEDICAL AB—See Baxter International Inc.; *U.S. Public*, pg. 280
BAYFRONT HEALTH IMAGING CENTER, LLC—See Community Health Systems, Inc.; *U.S. Public*, pg. 551
B. E. SMITH, LLC—See AMN Healthcare Services, Inc.; *U.S. Public*, pg. 125
BIRMINGHAM ORTHOPEDICS & SPORTS SPECIALISTS, LLC—See Community Health Systems, Inc.; *U.S. Public*, pg. 551
BRANDON PHYSICIAN MANAGEMENT, LLC—See Community Health Systems, Inc.; *U.S. Public*, pg. 551
BRAVO HEALTH OF PENNSYLVANIA, INC.—See The Cigna Group; *U.S. Public*, pg. 2060
CAC-FLORIDA MEDICAL CENTERS, LLC—See Humana, Inc.; *U.S. Public*, pg. 1069
CAC MEDICAL CENTER HOLDINGS, INC.—See Humana, Inc.; *U.S. Public*, pg. 1069
CAPITAL REGIONAL PSYCHIATRY ASSOCIATES, LLC—See HCA Healthcare, Inc.; *U.S. Public*, pg. 992
CAREFIRST BLUECROSS BLUESHIELD, CLAIMS CENTER—See CareFirst, Inc.; *U.S. Private*, pg. 753
CARE UK CLINICAL SERVICES LIMITED—See Bridgepoint Group Plc; *Int'l*, pg. 1154
THE CELL-FACTORY NV—See Esperite N.V.; *Int'l*, pg. 2506
CELLSURE, L3C—See Predictive Technology Group, Inc.; *U.S. Public*, pg. 1713
CENTRACARE HEALTH FOUNDATION; *U.S. Private*, pg. 818
CGM CLINICAL DEUTSCHLAND GMBH—See CompuGroup Medical SE & Co. KGaA; *Int'l*, pg. 1756
CHISWICK OUTPATIENT CENTRE LLP—See HCA Healthcare, Inc.; *U.S. Public*, pg. 993
CLARKSVILLE SURGICENTER, LLC—See HCA Healthcare, Inc.; *U.S. Public*, pg. 993
COLISEUM MEDICAL CENTER, LLC—See HCA Healthcare, Inc.; *U.S. Public*, pg. 993
COLLEGE PARK ENDOSCOPY CENTER, LLC—See HCA Healthcare, Inc.; *U.S. Public*, pg. 993
COLORADO SPRINGS HEALTH PARTNERS—See DaVita Inc.; *U.S. Public*, pg. 637
COMMUNITY CHARITY ADVANCEMENT, INC.; *U.S. Private*, pg. 990
COMPASS IMAGING, LLC—See Community Health Systems, Inc.; *U.S. Public*, pg. 552
COMPUGROUP MEDICAL DEUTSCHLAND AG GESCHAFTSBEREICH HIS—See CompuGroup Medical SE & Co. KGaA; *Int'l*, pg. 1756
COMPUGROUP MEDICAL SOUTH AFRICA (PTY) LTD.—See CompuGroup Medical SE & Co. KGaA; *Int'l*, pg. 1756
COMPUGROUP MEDICAL SWEDEN AB—See CompuGroup Medical SE & Co. KGaA; *Int'l*, pg. 1756
COMPUGROUP MEDICAL SWEDEN AB—See CompuGroup Medical SE & Co. KGaA; *Int'l*, pg. 1756
CONDUENT STATE HEALTHCARE, LLC—See Conduent Incorporated; *U.S. Public*, pg. 566
CONTINUCARE MDHC, LLC—See Humana, Inc.; *U.S. Public*, pg. 1069
CORPUS CHRISTI HEART CLINIC, PLLC—See HCA Healthcare, Inc.; *U.S. Public*, pg. 994
COVENTRY HEALTH CARE OF THE CAROLINAS, INC.—See CVS Health Corporation; *U.S. Public*, pg. 615
CRYO-SAVE AG—See Esperite N.V.; *Int'l*, pg. 2506
CRYO-SAVE ESPANA S.A.—See Esperite N.V.; *Int'l*, pg. 2506
CRYO-SAVE GMBH—See Esperite N.V.; *Int'l*, pg. 2506
CRYO-SAVE (PTY) LTD.—See Esperite N.V.; *Int'l*, pg. 2506
CULBERT HEALTHCARE SOLUTIONS; *U.S. Private*, pg. 1120
CURAPHAR B.V.—See Fagron NV; *Int'l*, pg. 2603
CY-FAIR MEDICAL CENTER HOSPITAL, LLC—See HCA Healthcare, Inc.; *U.S. Public*, pg. 995
DAVITA MEDICAL ACO CALIFORNIA, LLC—See DaVita Inc.; *U.S. Public*, pg. 637
DEKALB REGIONAL HEALTHCARE SYSTEM, INC.; *U.S. Private*, pg. 1192

621491 — HMO MEDICAL CENTERS

DENALI PHYSICAL THERAPY, LIMITED PARTNERSHIP—See U.S. Physical Therapy, Inc.; *U.S. Public*, pg. 2214
DENTAL PARTNERS PTY LIMITED—See BGH Capital Pty Ltd; *Int'l*, pg. 1008
DLP PERSON URGENT CARE, LLC—See Apollo Global Management, Inc.; *U.S. Public*, pg. 155
DOCTOR ANYWHERE PTE LTD.; *Int'l*, pg. 2153
DOCTORS EXCHANGE, INC.—See Ebix Inc.; *U.S. Public*, pg. 710
EAST FLORIDA CARENOW URGENT CARE, LLC—See HCA Healthcare, Inc.; *U.S. Public*, pg. 995
EASTSIDE HEART AND VASCULAR, LLC—See HCA Healthcare, Inc.; *U.S. Public*, pg. 995
EASTSIDE URGENT CARE LLC—See HCA Healthcare, Inc.; *U.S. Public*, pg. 995
EBOS GROUP PTY LIMITED—See EBOS Group Limited; *Int'l*, pg. 2285
EBOS HEALTH & SCIENCE PTY LIMITED—See EBOS Group Limited; *Int'l*, pg. 2285
ENVOLVE PEOPLECARE, INC.—See Centene Corporation; *U.S. Public*, pg. 468
EP-PHARMALINE CO., LTD—See EPS Holdings, Inc.; *Int'l*, pg. 2465
ESCORTS HEART AND SUPER SPECIALITY INSTITUTE LIMITED—See Fortis Healthcare Limited; *Int'l*, pg. 2739
ESCORTS HEART INSTITUTE AND RESEARCH CENTRE LIMITED—See Fortis Healthcare Limited; *Int'l*, pg. 2739
ESCORTS HOSPITAL AND RESEARCH CENTRE LIMITED—See Fortis Healthcare Limited; *Int'l*, pg. 2739
FAMILYCARE HEALTH PLANS, INC.; *U.S. Private*, pg. 1471
FAYETTEVILLE ARKANSAS HOSPITAL COMPANY, LLC—See Community Health Systems, Inc.; *U.S. Public*, pg. 553
FMG PRIMECARE, LLC—See Community Health Systems, Inc.; *U.S. Public*, pg. 553
FOCUS HAND SURGICENTER, LLC—See HCA Healthcare, Inc.; *U.S. Public*, pg. 996
GE BE PRIVATE LTD.—See GE HealthCare Technologies Inc.; *U.S. Public*, pg. 908
GE HEALTHCARE AB—See GE HealthCare Technologies Inc.; *U.S. Public*, pg. 908
GE HEALTHCARE ALGERIE SARL—See GE HealthCare Technologies Inc.; *U.S. Public*, pg. 908
GE HEALTHCARE BUCHLER GMBH & CO. KG—See GE HealthCare Technologies Inc.; *U.S. Public*, pg. 909
GE HEALTHCARE COTE D'IVOIRE SARL—See GE HealthCare Technologies Inc.; *U.S. Public*, pg. 909
GE HEALTHCARE DANMARK A/S—See GE HealthCare Technologies Inc.; *U.S. Public*, pg. 909
GE HEALTHCARE GMBH—See GE HealthCare Technologies Inc.; *U.S. Public*, pg. 909
GE HEALTHCARE HANDELS GMBH—See GE HealthCare Technologies Inc.; *U.S. Public*, pg. 909
GE HEALTHCARE KENYA LIMITED—See GE HealthCare Technologies Inc.; *U.S. Public*, pg. 909
GE HEALTHCARE KOREA, INC.—See GE HealthCare Technologies Inc.; *U.S. Public*, pg. 908
GE HEALTHCARE MAGYARORSZAG KFT.—See GE HealthCare Technologies Inc.; *U.S. Public*, pg. 909
GE HEALTHCARE SVERIGE AB—See GE HealthCare Technologies Inc.; *U.S. Public*, pg. 909
GE HEALTHCARE TUNISIA SARL—See GE HealthCare Technologies Inc.; *U.S. Public*, pg. 909
GE MEDICAL SYSTEMS LIMITED—See GE HealthCare Technologies Inc.; *U.S. Public*, pg. 909
GE MEDICAL SYSTEMS POLSKA SP. Z O.O.—See GE HealthCare Technologies Inc.; *U.S. Public*, pg. 909
GE MEDICAL SYSTEMS (SCHWEIZ) AG—See GE HealthCare Technologies Inc.; *U.S. Public*, pg. 909
GENOSPACE, LLC—See HCA Healthcare, Inc.; *U.S. Public*, pg. 997
GE VINGMED ULTRASOUND A/S—See GE HealthCare Technologies Inc.; *U.S. Public*, pg. 909
GLOBAL HEALTH LIMITED; *Int'l*, pg. 2997
GLOBAL HEALTH PARTNER SWE AB—See Apax Partners LLP; *Int'l*, pg. 502
GREEN COUNTRY PHYSICAL THERAPY, LIMITED PARTNERSHIP—See U.S. Physical Therapy, Inc.; *U.S. Public*, pg. 2214
HCG EKO ONCOLOGY LLP—See Healthcare Global Enterprises Limited; *Int'l*, pg. 3304
HEALTHCARE GLOBAL ENTERPRISES LIMITED; *Int'l*, pg. 3304
HEALTHCHAMPION PARTNERS LLC; *U.S. Private*, pg. 1895
HEALTH ITALIA S.P.A.; *Int'l*, pg. 3303
HEALTH NET ACCESS, INC.—See Centene Corporation; *U.S. Public*, pg. 469
HEALTH NET FEDERAL SERVICES, LLC—See Centene Corporation; *U.S. Public*, pg. 469
HEMAS DEVELOPMENTS (PTE) LTD—See Hemas Holdings PLC; *Int'l*, pg. 3340
HENDRICK PROVIDER NETWORK—See Hendrick Health System; *U.S. Private*, pg. 1914
HERITAGE HEALTHCARE INNOVATION FUND II, LP—See Community Health Systems, Inc.; *U.S. Public*, pg. 553

HIGH PERFORMANCE PHYSICAL THERAPY, LLC—See U.S. Physical Therapy, Inc.; *U.S. Public*, pg. 2214
HOSPITAL CORPORATION OF CHINA LIMITED; *Int'l*, pg. 3486
HUMANA BEHAVIORAL HEALTH, INC.—See Humana, Inc.; *U.S. Public*, pg. 1069
HUMAN HEALTH HOLDINGS LIMITED; *Int'l*, pg. 3528
INNOVACARE HEALTH, INC.—See UnitedHealth Group Incorporated; *U.S. Public*, pg. 2241
INTERMEDIX DEUTSCHLAND GMBH—See CompuGroup Medical SE & Co. KGaA; *Int'l*, pg. 1755
THE JACKSON CLINICS, LIMITED PARTNERSHIP—See U.S. Physical Therapy, Inc.; *U.S. Public*, pg. 2216
JACKSON HEALTH SYSTEM; *U.S. Private*, pg. 2176
JOHNSON & JOHNSON DEL PERU S.A.—See Kenvue Inc.; *U.S. Public*, pg. 1224
JOHNSON & JOHNSON HEALTH AND WELLNESS SOLUTIONS, INC.—See Johnson & Johnson; *U.S. Public*, pg. 1198
JOHNSON & JOHNSON MIDDLE EAST FZ-LLC—See Johnson & Johnson; *U.S. Public*, pg. 1199
LAKESIDE MEDICAL GROUP, INC.; *U.S. Private*, pg. 2378
LCA-VISION INC.; *U.S. Private*, pg. 2403
LETO S.A.—See DIAGNOSTIC AND THERAPEUTIC CENTER OF ATHENS-HYGEIA S.A.; *Int'l*, pg. 2103
LIFE STRIDES PHYSICAL THERAPY AND REHABILITATION, LIMITED PARTNERSHIP—See U.S. Physical Therapy, Inc.; *U.S. Public*, pg. 2215
LIMASSOL MEDICAL CENTRE 'ACHILLION' LTD—See DIAGNOSTIC AND THERAPEUTIC CENTER OF ATHENS-HYGEIA S.A.; *Int'l*, pg. 2103
LOGISTICS HEALTH, INC.—See UnitedHealth Group Incorporated; *U.S. Public*, pg. 2242
MASH HEALTH LIMITED—See Arsenal Capital Management LP; *U.S. Private*, pg. 338
MATERIAL.ONE AG—See adesso SE; *Int'l*, pg. 144
MCBEE ASSOCIATES INC.—See GI Manager L.P.; *U.S. Private*, pg. 1693
MCBEE ASSOCIATES INC.—See TA Associates, Inc.; *U.S. Private*, pg. 3916
MEDICAL NET SAS—See CompuGroup Medical SE & Co. KGaA; *Int'l*, pg. 1757
MEDIFAST (HONG KONG) LIMITED—See iKang Healthcare Group, Inc.; *Int'l*, pg. 3610
MEDI HUB CO., LTD.—See Birmingham Sports Holdings Limited; *Int'l*, pg. 1048
MEDXPERT HEALTHCARE SSOLUTIONS GMBH—See CompuGroup Medical SE & Co. KGaA; *Int'l*, pg. 1757
METCARE OF FLORIDA, INC.—See Humana, Inc.; *U.S. Public*, pg. 1070
MICHIGAN COMPLETE HEALTH—See Centene Corporation; *U.S. Public*, pg. 470
MID-ATLANTIC COLLABORATIVE CARE, LLC—See Centene Corporation; *U.S. Public*, pg. 471
MINDEN PHYSICIAN PRACTICES, LLC—See Apollo Global Management, Inc.; *U.S. Public*, pg. 158
MISSION REHABILITATION AND SPORTS MEDICINE LIMITED PARTNERSHIP—See U.S. Physical Therapy, Inc.; *U.S. Public*, pg. 2215
MITERA S.A.—See DIAGNOSTIC AND THERAPEUTIC CENTER OF ATHENS-HYGEIA S.A.; *Int'l*, pg. 2103
MOBILE HEARTBEAT, LLC—See HCA Healthcare, Inc.; *U.S. Public*, pg. 1003
MOLINA CENTER LLC—See Molina Healthcare, Inc.; *U.S. Public*, pg. 1458
MOMENTUM PHYSICAL & SPORTS REHABILITATION, LIMITED PARTNERSHIP—See U.S. Physical Therapy, Inc.; *U.S. Public*, pg. 2215
MOUNTAINSTAR MEDICAL GROUP TIMPANOGOS SPECIALTY CARE, LLC—See HCA Healthcare, Inc.; *U.S. Public*, pg. 1003
MVP HEALTH CARE INC.; *U.S. Private*, pg. 2821
MVP HEALTH CARE INC.—See MVP Health Care Inc.; *U.S. Private*, pg. 2822
MY FAMILY CLINIC (HOUGANG CENTRAL) PTE. LTD.—See Alliance Healthcare Group Limited; *Int'l*, pg. 340
MY FAMILY CLINIC (PN) PTE. LTD.—See Alliance Healthcare Group Limited; *Int'l*, pg. 340
MY FAMILY CLINIC (RV) PTE. LTD.—See Alliance Healthcare Group Limited; *Int'l*, pg. 340
MY FAMILY CLINIC (TPY) PTE. LTD.—See Alliance Healthcare Group Limited; *Int'l*, pg. 340
MYLAN HOSPITAL AS—See Viatris Inc.; *U.S. Public*, pg. 2294
NATIONAL BOARD OF MEDICAL EXAMINERS; *U.S. Private*, pg. 2849
NEBRASKA TOTAL CARE, INC.—See Centene Corporation; *U.S. Public*, pg. 470
NEPHROCARE ROSTOCK GMBH—See Fresenius Medical Care AG; *Int'l*, pg. 2776
NEPHROCARE SCHWANDORF-REGENSTAUF GMBH—See Fresenius Medical Care AG; *Int'l*, pg. 2776
NETWORK HEALTH PLAN—See Affinity Health System; *U.S. Private*, pg. 123
NEUROSURGERY ATLANTA, LLC—See HCA Healthcare, Inc.; *U.S. Public*, pg. 1004
NEUROSURGERY OF KINGWOOD, PLLC—See HCA Healthcare, Inc.; *U.S. Public*, pg. 1004

CORPORATE AFFILIATIONS

NIHON STERY, INC.—See H.U. Group Holdings, Inc.; *Int'l*, pg. 3197
NOTRE DAME INTERMEDICA PARTICIPACOES S.A.—See Hapvida Participacoes e Investimentos S.A.; *Int'l*, pg. 3269
NOVAMED SURGERY CENTER OF CHATTANOOGA, LLC—See Bain Capital, LP; *U.S. Private*, pg. 446
NOVAMED SURGERY CENTER OF SAN ANTONIO, L.P.—See Bain Capital, LP; *U.S. Private*, pg. 446
NOVUS MEDICAL DETOX CENTER OF PASCO COUNTY, LLC; *U.S. Private*, pg. 2968
OLD TOWNE PHYSICAL THERAPY, LIMITED PARTNERSHIP—See U.S. Physical Therapy, Inc.; *U.S. Public*, pg. 2215
O&M HALYARD FRANCE—See Owens & Minor, Inc.; *U.S. Public*, pg. 1626
O&M HALYARD JAPAN GK—See Owens & Minor, Inc.; *U.S. Public*, pg. 1626
OPTUMHEALTH INC.—See UnitedHealth Group Incorporated; *U.S. Public*, pg. 2248
OPTUM, INC.—See UnitedHealth Group Incorporated; *U.S. Public*, pg. 2243
PACIFIC PARTNERS MANAGEMENT SERVICES, INC.—See HCA Healthcare, Inc.; *U.S. Public*, pg. 1005
PALM POINT BEHAVIORAL HEALTH, LLC—See Universal Health Services, Inc.; *U.S. Public*, pg. 2259
PARTNERSHIP HEALTH GROUP LIMITED—See Bridgepoint Group Plc; *Int'l*, pg. 1154
PASTEUR MEDICAL CENTER, LLC—See Elevance Health, Inc.; *U.S. Public*, pg. 730
PATHWAYS OF MASSACHUSETTS, LLC—See ATAR Capital, LLC; *U.S. Private*, pg. 364
PENNS WOOD PHYSICAL THERAPY, LIMITED PARTNERSHIP—See U.S. Physical Therapy, Inc.; *U.S. Public*, pg. 2215
PHILADELPHIA FIGHT; *U.S. Private*, pg. 3169
PHYSICIANS PHARMACY ALLIANCE, INC.—See The Riverside Company; *U.S. Private*, pg. 4110
THE PRACTICE (GROUP) LIMITED—See Centene Corporation; *U.S. Public*, pg. 470
PRECISION SURGERY CENTER, LLC—See Community Health Systems, Inc.; *U.S. Public*, pg. 556
PRINCE WILLIAM HEALTH SYSTEMS INC.—See Novant Health, Inc.; *U.S. Private*, pg. 2967
PROFDOC SDN BHD—See CompuGroup Medical SE & Co. KGaA; *Int'l*, pg. 1757
PROVIDENCE HOSPITAL, LLC—See Apollo Global Management, Inc.; *U.S. Public*, pg. 158
PROVIDENCE IMAGING CENTER, LLC—See Apollo Global Management, Inc.; *U.S. Public*, pg. 158
RADTKE PHYSICAL THERAPY, LIMITED PARTNERSHIP—See U.S. Physical Therapy, Inc.; *U.S. Public*, pg. 2215
R. CLAIR PHYSICAL THERAPY, LIMITED PARTNERSHIP—See U.S. Physical Therapy, Inc.; *U.S. Public*, pg. 2215
REACTION PHYSICAL THERAPY, LLC—See U.S. Physical Therapy, Inc.; *U.S. Public*, pg. 2215
REDMOND RIDGE MANAGEMENT, LLC—See U.S. Physical Therapy, Inc.; *U.S. Public*, pg. 2216
RED RIVER VALLEY PHYSICAL THERAPY, LIMITED PARTNERSHIP—See U.S. Physical Therapy, Inc.; *U.S. Public*, pg. 2215
RTS EXCELSIOR CO., LTD.—See Excelsior Medical Co., Ltd.; *Int'l*, pg. 2579
SAFE PASSAGE NEUROMONITORING—See Globus Medical, Inc.; *U.S. Public*, pg. 947
SCOTT & WHITE HEALTH PLAN INC.; *U.S. Private*, pg. 3576
SENIORBRIDGE FAMILY COMPANIES (FL), INC.—See Humana, Inc.; *U.S. Public*, pg. 1070
SENIORBRIDGE FAMILY COMPANIES (MD), INC.—See Humana, Inc.; *U.S. Public*, pg. 1070
SENIORBRIDGE (NC), INC.—See Humana, Inc.; *U.S. Public*, pg. 1070
SIGNATURE PHYSICAL THERAPY, LIMITED PARTNERSHIP—See U.S. Physical Therapy, Inc.; *U.S. Public*, pg. 2216
SILVERSUMMIT HEALTHPLAN, INC.—See Centene Corporation; *U.S. Public*, pg. 470
SOLIS MAMMOGRAPHY AT MEDICAL CENTER OF MCKINNEY, LLC—See HCA Healthcare, Inc.; *U.S. Public*, pg. 1009
SRL, INC.—See H.U. Group Holdings, Inc.; *Int'l*, pg. 3197
SRL MEDISEARCH INC.—See H.U. Group Holdings, Inc.; *Int'l*, pg. 3197
STICHTING CRYO-SAVE—See Esperite N.V.; *Int'l*, pg. 2506
ST. JOSEPH'S HOSPITAL & MEDICAL CENTER—See Catholic Health Initiatives; *U.S. Private*, pg. 790
TABULA RASA HEALTHCARE, INC.—See Nautic Partners, LLC; *U.S. Private*, pg. 2871
TELEMED ONLINE SERVICE FUR HEILBERUFE GMBH—See CompuGroup Medical SE & Co. KGaA; *Int'l*, pg. 1757
TEPE INTERNATIONAL HEALTH INFORMATION SYSTEMS A.S.—See CompuGroup Medical SE & Co. KGaA; *Int'l*, pg. 1757

N.A.I.C.S. INDEX

THERAPYWORKS PHYSICAL THERAPY, LLC—See U.S. Physical Therapy, Inc.; *U.S. Public*, pg. 2216
TOTAL CAROLINA CARE, INC.—See Centene Corporation; *U.S. Public*, pg. 471
TRAUMA MEDICINE SERVICES OF TN, LLC—See HCA Healthcare, Inc.; *U.S. Public*, pg. 1012
UNITEDHEALTHCARE PLAN OF THE RIVER VALLEY, INC.—See UnitedHealth Group Incorporated; *U.S. Public*, pg. 2251
URGENT CARE MSO, LLC—See UnitedHealth Group Incorporated; *U.S. Public*, pg. 2252
U.S. PT ALLIANCE REHABILITATION SERVICES, INCITATION SERVICES—See U.S. Physical Therapy, Inc.; *U.S. Public*, pg. 2216
VANTAGE HEALTH PLAN INC.; *U.S. Private*, pg. 4345
VAUGHT, INC.; *U.S. Private*, pg. 4348
VICTORIA TEXAS HOME CARE SERVICES, LLC—See Community Health Systems, Inc.; *U.S. Public*, pg. 557
VICTORY PHYSICAL THERAPY, LIMITED PARTNERSHIP—See U.S. Physical Therapy, Inc.; *U.S. Public*, pg. 2216
VOYAGER THERAPEUTICS, INC.; *U.S. Public*, pg. 2312
WELLCARE HEALTH PLANS OF KENTUCKY, INC.—See Centene Corporation; *U.S. Public*, pg. 471
WEST TEXAS PHYSICAL THERAPY, LIMITED PARTNERSHIP—See U.S. Physical Therapy, Inc.; *U.S. Public*, pg. 2216
WINDSOR HEALTH GROUP, INC.—See Centene Corporation; *U.S. Public*, pg. 471
WORLD MEDICAL S.A.S.—See Biotronik GmbH & Co.; *Int'l*, pg. 1044
ZENITAS HEALTHCARE LIMITED—See Adamantem Capital Management Pty Limited; *Int'l*, pg. 124

621492 — KIDNEY DIALYSIS CENTERS

ABERDEEN DIALYSIS, LLC—See DaVita Inc.; *U.S. Public*, pg. 635
AFTON DIALYSIS, LLC—See DaVita Inc.; *U.S. Public*, pg. 635
AHERN DIALYSIS, LLC—See DaVita Inc.; *U.S. Public*, pg. 635
ALAMOSA DIALYSIS, LLC—See DaVita Inc.; *U.S. Public*, pg. 635
AMERICAN FORK DIALYSIS, LLC—See DaVita Inc.; *U.S. Public*, pg. 636
AMERICAN RENAL ASSOCIATES HOLDINGS, INC.—See Nautic Partners, LLC; *U.S. Private*, pg. 2868
AMERICAN RENAL TEXAS, L.P.—See Nautic Partners, LLC; *U.S. Private*, pg. 2869
AMERICAN SOCIETY OF NEPHROLOGY; *U.S. Private*, pg. 254
AMERICAN UNIVERSAL-HOCKESSIN, LLC—See Nautic Partners, LLC; *U.S. Private*, pg. 2869
AMERI-TECH KIDNEY CENTER- ARLINGTON, LLC—See Nautic Partners, LLC; *U.S. Private*, pg. 2869
AMERI-TECH KIDNEY CENTER- BEDFORD, LLC—See Nautic Partners, LLC; *U.S. Private*, pg. 2869
ANDREWS DIALYSIS, LLC—See DaVita Inc.; *U.S. Public*, pg. 636
ANIMAS DIALYSIS, LLC—See DaVita Inc.; *U.S. Public*, pg. 636
ARA-ADELPHI LLC—See Nautic Partners, LLC; *U.S. Private*, pg. 2869
ARA-AUGUSTA CLINIC LLC—See Nautic Partners, LLC; *U.S. Private*, pg. 2869
ARA-AVENTURA LLC—See Nautic Partners, LLC; *U.S. Private*, pg. 2869
ARA-BOCA RATON DIALYSIS LLC—See Nautic Partners, LLC; *U.S. Private*, pg. 2869
ARA-DAYTONA BEACH DIALYSIS LLC—See Nautic Partners, LLC; *U.S. Private*, pg. 2869
ARA DIALYSIS UNIT AT OHIO VALLEY HOSPITAL, LLC—See Nautic Partners, LLC; *U.S. Private*, pg. 2869
ARA-JOHNSTON DIALYSIS LLC—See Nautic Partners, LLC; *U.S. Private*, pg. 2869
ARA - LUDLOW DIALYSIS, LLC—See Nautic Partners, LLC; *U.S. Private*, pg. 2868
ARA-NAPLES DIALYSIS CENTER LLC—See Nautic Partners, LLC; *U.S. Private*, pg. 2869
ARA-NAPLES SOUTH DIALYSIS CENTER LLC—See Nautic Partners, LLC; *U.S. Private*, pg. 2869
ARA-ORANGE PARK LLC—See Nautic Partners, LLC; *U.S. Private*, pg. 2869
ARA-PROVIDENCE DIALYSIS LLC—See Nautic Partners, LLC; *U.S. Private*, pg. 2869
ARA-RHODE ISLAND DIALYSIS II LLC—See Nautic Partners, LLC; *U.S. Private*, pg. 2869
ARA-SOUTH LABURNUM DIALYSIS LLC—See Nautic Partners, LLC; *U.S. Private*, pg. 2869
ARA-TITUSVILLE DIALYSIS LLC—See Nautic Partners, LLC; *U.S. Private*, pg. 2869
ARA-TIVERTON DIALYSIS LLC—See Nautic Partners, LLC; *U.S. Private*, pg. 2869
ARA-WEST JACKSONVILLE LLC—See Nautic Partners, LLC; *U.S. Private*, pg. 2869
ARA-YUBA CITY DIALYSIS LLC—See Nautic Partners, LLC; *U.S. Private*, pg. 2869
ARGYLE DIALYSIS, LLC—See DaVita Inc.; *U.S. Public*, pg. 636
ARLINGTON DIALYSIS CENTER, LLC—See Nautic Partners, LLC; *U.S. Private*, pg. 2869
ARTESIA DIALYSIS, LLC—See DaVita Inc.; *U.S. Public*, pg. 636
ATHIO DIALYSIS, LLC—See DaVita Inc.; *U.S. Public*, pg. 636
ATLANTIC DIALYSIS, LLC—See DaVita Inc.; *U.S. Public*, pg. 636
BABLER DIALYSIS, LLC—See DaVita Inc.; *U.S. Public*, pg. 636
BAKER DIALYSIS, LLC—See DaVita Inc.; *U.S. Public*, pg. 636
BANNON DIALYSIS, LLC—See DaVita Inc.; *U.S. Public*, pg. 636
BASIN DIALYSIS, LLC—See DaVita Inc.; *U.S. Public*, pg. 636
BAY CITY DIALYSIS CENTER, LLP—See Nautic Partners, LLC; *U.S. Private*, pg. 2869
B. BRAUN AVITUM POLAND SP.Z.O.O.—See B. Braun Melsungen AG; *Int'l*, pg. 786
B. BRAUN AVITUM RUSSLAND OOO—See B. Braun Melsungen AG; *Int'l*, pg. 786
B. BRAUN AVITUM S.R.O.—See B. Braun Melsungen AG; *Int'l*, pg. 786
B. BRAUN AVITUM S.R.O.—See B. Braun Melsungen AG; *Int'l*, pg. 786
B. BRAUN AVITUM TURKEY SANAYI TICARET ANONIM SIRKETI—See B. Braun Melsungen AG; *Int'l*, pg. 786
B. BRAUN AVITUM UAB—See B. Braun Melsungen AG; *Int'l*, pg. 786
BEAR CREEK DIALYSIS, L.P.—See DaVita Inc.; *U.S. Public*, pg. 636
BEAUMONT-ARA DIALYSIS LLP—See Nautic Partners, LLC; *U.S. Private*, pg. 2869
BEDELL DIALYSIS, LLC—See DaVita Inc.; *U.S. Public*, pg. 636
BELFAIR DIALYSIS, LLC—See DaVita Inc.; *U.S. Public*, pg. 636
BELLE GLADE DIALYSIS CENTER, LLC—See Nautic Partners, LLC; *U.S. Private*, pg. 2869
BEVERLY HILLS DIALYSIS PARTNERSHIP—See DaVita Inc.; *U.S. Public*, pg. 636
BIDWELL DIALYSIS, LLC—See DaVita Inc.; *U.S. Public*, pg. 636
BIG LAKE KIDNEY CENTER LLC—See Nautic Partners, LLC; *U.S. Private*, pg. 2869
BIRCH DIALYSIS, LLC—See DaVita Inc.; *U.S. Public*, pg. 636
BLISS DIALYSIS, LLC—See DaVita Inc.; *U.S. Public*, pg. 636
BOARDMAN DIALYSIS CENTER LLC—See Nautic Partners, LLC; *U.S. Private*, pg. 2869
BOGACHIEL DIALYSIS, LLC—See DaVita Inc.; *U.S. Public*, pg. 636
BOLLINGER DIALYSIS, LLC—See DaVita Inc.; *U.S. Public*, pg. 636
BRACHE DIALYSIS, LLC—See DaVita Inc.; *U.S. Public*, pg. 636
BRADENTON DIALYSIS CENTER LLC—See Nautic Partners, LLC; *U.S. Private*, pg. 2869
BROCKTON DIALYSIS CENTER, LLC—See Nautic Partners, LLC; *U.S. Private*, pg. 2869
BROCKTON HEALTHCARE CLINIC, LLC—See Nautic Partners, LLC; *U.S. Private*, pg. 2869
BROOK DIALYSIS, LLC—See DaVita Inc.; *U.S. Public*, pg. 636
BROWNSVILLE KIDNEY CENTER, LTD—See DaVita Inc.; *U.S. Public*, pg. 636
BRUNO DIALYSIS, LLC—See The Ensign Group, Inc.; *U.S. Public*, pg. 2070
BUFORD DIALYSIS, LLC—See DaVita Inc.; *U.S. Public*, pg. 636
BUTANO DIALYSIS, LLC—See DaVita Inc.; *U.S. Public*, pg. 636
BUTLER-ARA, LLC—See Nautic Partners, LLC; *U.S. Private*, pg. 2869
CAGLES DIALYSIS, LLC—See DaVita Inc.; *U.S. Public*, pg. 636
CANYON SPRINGS DIALYSIS, LLC—See DaVita Inc.; *U.S. Public*, pg. 636
CAPE CORAL KIDNEY CENTER, LLC—See Nautic Partners, LLC; *U.S. Private*, pg. 2869
CAPITAL DIALYSIS PARTNERSHIP—See DaVita Inc.; *U.S. Public*, pg. 636
CARLSBAD DIALYSIS, LLC—See DaVita Inc.; *U.S. Public*, pg. 636
CAROLINA DIALYSIS LLC—See Nautic Partners, LLC; *U.S. Private*, pg. 2869
CARROLL COUNTY DIALYSIS FACILITY LIMITED PARTNERSHIP—See DaVita Inc.; *U.S. Public*, pg. 636
CARROLLTON REGIONAL DIALYSIS CENTER, LLC—See Nautic Partners, LLC; *U.S. Private*, pg. 2869
CASWELL DIALYSIS, LLC—See DaVita Inc.; *U.S. Public*, pg. 636

621492 — KIDNEY DIALYSIS CEN...

CENTENNIAL LV, LLC—See DaVita Inc.; *U.S. Public*, pg. 636
CENTERS FOR DIALYSIS CARE; *U.S. Private*, pg. 817
CENTRAL CAROLINA DIALYSIS CENTERS, LLC—See DaVita Inc.; *U.S. Public*, pg. 636
CENTRAL COLUMBIA KIDNEY CENTER, LLC—See Nautic Partners, LLC; *U.S. Private*, pg. 2869
CENTRAL KENTUCKY DIALYSIS CENTERS, LLC—See DaVita Inc.; *U.S. Public*, pg. 636
CENTRAL KITTANNING DIALYSIS CENTER LLC—See Nautic Partners, LLC; *U.S. Private*, pg. 2869
CENTRUM DIALIZA II SP. Z O.O.—See DaVita Inc.; *U.S. Public*, pg. 636
CERITO DIALYSIS PARTNERS, LLC—See DaVita Inc.; *U.S. Public*, pg. 636
CHADRON DIALYSIS, LLC—See DaVita Inc.; *U.S. Public*, pg. 636
CHAMPION DIALYSIS CENTER, LLC—See Nautic Partners, LLC; *U.S. Private*, pg. 2869
CHAMPIONS DIALYSIS, LLC—See DaVita Inc.; *U.S. Public*, pg. 636
CHERAW DIALYSIS, LLC—See DaVita Inc.; *U.S. Public*, pg. 636
CHICAGO HEIGHTS DIALYSIS, LLC—See DaVita Inc.; *U.S. Public*, pg. 636
CHIPETA DIALYSIS, LLC—See DaVita Inc.; *U.S. Public*, pg. 636
CHURCHILL DIALYSIS, LLC—See DaVita Inc.; *U.S. Public*, pg. 636
CIMARRON DIALYSIS, LLC—See DaVita Inc.; *U.S. Public*, pg. 636
CLARION DIALYSIS CENTER, LLC—See Nautic Partners, LLC; *U.S. Private*, pg. 2869
CLEBURNE DIALYSIS, LLC—See DaVita Inc.; *U.S. Public*, pg. 636
CLERMONT DIALYSIS CENTER LLC—See Nautic Partners, LLC; *U.S. Private*, pg. 2869
CLEWISTON DIALYSIS CENTER, LLC—See Nautic Partners, LLC; *U.S. Private*, pg. 2869
CLIFTON DIALYSIS CENTER, LLC—See Nautic Partners, LLC; *U.S. Private*, pg. 2869
CLIFTON DIALYSIS, LLC—See DaVita Inc.; *U.S. Public*, pg. 636
CLINICA MEDICA DAVITA LONDRINA SERVICOS DE NEFROLOGIA LTDA.—See DaVita Inc.; *U.S. Public*, pg. 636
CLINTON DIALYSIS CLINIC, LLC—See Nautic Partners, LLC; *U.S. Private*, pg. 2869
CLINTON TOWNSHIP DIALYSIS, LLC—See DaVita Inc.; *U.S. Public*, pg. 636
CLOUGH DIALYSIS, LLC—See DaVita Inc.; *U.S. Public*, pg. 636
CLOVER DIALYSIS, LLC—See DaVita Inc.; *U.S. Public*, pg. 636
COLUMBIA NORTHEAST KIDNEY CENTER, LLC—See Nautic Partners, LLC; *U.S. Private*, pg. 2869
COLUMBUS-RNA-DAVITA, LLC—See DaVita Inc.; *U.S. Public*, pg. 637
COMMERCE TOWNSHIP DIALYSIS CENTER, LLC—See DaVita Inc.; *U.S. Public*, pg. 637
COMPLETE DIALYSIS CARE, LLC—See Nautic Partners, LLC; *U.S. Private*, pg. 2869
CONTINENTAL DIALYSIS CENTER OF SPRINGFIELD-FAIRFAX, INC.—See DaVita Inc.; *U.S. Public*, pg. 637
CORAL DIALYSIS, LLC—See DaVita Inc.; *U.S. Public*, pg. 637
COWELL DIALYSIS, LLC—See DaVita Inc.; *U.S. Public*, pg. 637
CROFT DIALYSIS, LLC—See DaVita Inc.; *U.S. Public*, pg. 637
CURECANTI DIALYSIS, LLC—See DaVita Inc.; *U.S. Public*, pg. 637
DAMON DIALYSIS, LLC—See DaVita Inc.; *U.S. Public*, pg. 638
DAVIS DIALYSIS, LLC—See DaVita Inc.; *U.S. Public*, pg. 638
DAVITA AMERY DIALYSIS, LLC—See DaVita Inc.; *U.S. Public*, pg. 637
DAVITA AMHERST DIALYSIS CENTER—See DaVita Inc.; *U.S. Public*, pg. 637
DAVITA APAC HOLDING B.V.—See DaVita Inc.; *U.S. Public*, pg. 637
DAVITA BEVERLY DIALYSIS—See DaVita Inc.; *U.S. Public*, pg. 637
DAVITA CARE (INDIA) PRIVATE LIMITED—See DaVita Inc.; *U.S. Public*, pg. 637
DAVITA DAKOTA DIALYSIS CENTER, LLC—See DaVita Inc.; *U.S. Public*, pg. 637
DAVITA DESERT SPRINGS DIALYSIS—See DaVita Inc.; *U.S. Public*, pg. 637
DAVITA DEUTSCHLAND GMBH—See DaVita Inc.; *U.S. Public*, pg. 637
DAVITA DIALYSIS, LLC—See DaVita Inc.; *U.S. Public*, pg. 637
DAVITA EL PASO EAST, L.P.—See DaVita Inc.; *U.S. Public*, pg. 637
DAVITA INC.; *U.S. Public*, pg. 635

621492 — KIDNEY DIALYSIS CEN...

DAVITA KEY WEST DIALYSIS—See DaVita Inc.; *U.S. Public*, pg. 637
DAVITA KIDNEY CARE—See DaVita Inc.; *U.S. Public*, pg. 637
DAVITA MEDICAL CENTER—See DaVita Inc.; *U.S. Public*, pg. 637
DAVITA MEDICAL GROUP SOUTH FLORIDA, LLC—See UnitedHealth Group Incorporated; *U.S. Public*, pg. 2243
DAVITA NORTHWEST DIALYSIS CENTER—See DaVita Inc.; *U.S. Public*, pg. 637
DAVITA PASADENA FOOTHILLS DIALYSIS—See DaVita Inc.; *U.S. Public*, pg. 637
DAVITA PDI JOHNSTOWN—See DaVita Inc.; *U.S. Public*, pg. 637
DAVITA PRYOR DIALYSIS—See DaVita Inc.; *U.S. Public*, pg. 637
DAVITA RIDDLE DIALYSIS CENTER—See DaVita Inc.; *U.S. Public*, pg. 637
DAVITA-RIVERSIDE II, LLC—See DaVita Inc.; *U.S. Public*, pg. 638
DAVITA S.A.S.—See DaVita Inc.; *U.S. Public*, pg. 637
DAVITA SERVICOS DE NEFROLOGIA BOTAFOGO LTDA.—See DaVita Inc.; *U.S. Public*, pg. 637
DAVITA SERVICOS DE NEFROLOGIA DE ARARAQUARA LTDA.—See DaVita Inc.; *U.S. Public*, pg. 638
DAVITA SERVICOS DE NEFROLOGIA JARDIM DAS IMBUIAS LTDA.—See DaVita Inc.; *U.S. Public*, pg. 638
DAVITA SERVICOS DE NEFROLOGIA JOAO DIAS LTDA.—See DaVita Inc.; *U.S. Public*, pg. 638
DAVITA SERVICOS DE NEFROLOGIA PENHA LTDA.—See DaVita Inc.; *U.S. Public*, pg. 638
DAVITA SERVICOS DE NEFROLOGIA RECIFE LTDA.—See DaVita Inc.; *U.S. Public*, pg. 638
DAVITA SERVICOS DE NEFROLOGIA SANTOS LTDA.—See DaVita Inc.; *U.S. Public*, pg. 638
DAVITA TIDEWATER-VIRGINIA BEACH, LLC—See DaVita Inc.; *U.S. Public*, pg. 638
DAVITA TOWN & COUNTY WEST AT HOME—See DaVita Inc.; *U.S. Public*, pg. 638
DAVITA VILLAGEHEALTH OF OHIO, INC.—See DaVita Inc.; *U.S. Public*, pg. 638
DAWSON DIALYSIS, LLC—See DaVita Inc; *U.S. Public*, pg. 638
DEARBORN KIDNEY CENTER, LLC—See Nautic Partners, LLC; *U.S. Private*, pg. 2869
DELANO KIDNEY CENTER, LLC—See Nautic Partners, LLC; *U.S. Private*, pg. 2869
DELRAY BEACH DIALYSIS CENTER LLC—See Nautic Partners, LLC; *U.S. Private*, pg. 2869
DENTSVILLE KIDNEY CENTER, LLC—See Nautic Partners, LLC; *U.S. Private*, pg. 2869
DESOTO DIALYSIS, LLC—See DaVita Inc.; *U.S. Public*, pg. 638
DESOTO REGIONAL DIALYSIS CENTER LLC—See Nautic Partners, LLC; *U.S. Private*, pg. 2869
DIABLO DIALYSIS, LLC—See DaVita Inc.; *U.S. Public*, pg. 638
DIALYSE-ZENTRUM HAMBURG-OST GMBH—See DaVita Inc.; *U.S. Public*, pg. 638
DIALYSIS CARE CENTER OF PALM COAST LLC—See Nautic Partners, LLC; *U.S. Private*, pg. 2869
THE DIALYSIS CENTER OF ATTLEBORO, LLC—See Nautic Partners, LLC; *U.S. Private*, pg. 2871
THE DIALYSIS CENTER OF GARY - MERRILLVILLE, LLC—See Nautic Partners, LLC; *U.S. Private*, pg. 2871
THE DIALYSIS CENTER OF HAMMOND, LLC—See Nautic Partners, LLC; *U.S. Private*, pg. 2871
DIALYSIS CENTER OF MILLEDGEVILLE, LLC—See Nautic Partners, LLC; *U.S. Private*, pg. 2869
THE DIALYSIS CENTER OF NORTH PHILADELPHIA, LLC—See Nautic Partners, LLC; *U.S. Private*, pg. 2871
THE DIALYSIS CENTER OF PORTAGE, LLC—See Nautic Partners, LLC; *U.S. Private*, pg. 2871
THE DIALYSIS CENTER OF SCHERERVILLE, LLC—See Nautic Partners, LLC; *U.S. Private*, pg. 2871
DIALYSIS CENTER OF WAKEFIELD LLC—See Nautic Partners, LLC; *U.S. Private*, pg. 2869
DIALYSIS CENTER OF WESTERLY LLC—See Nautic Partners, LLC; *U.S. Private*, pg. 2869
DIALYSIS CENTER OF WESTERN MASSACHUSETTS LLC—See Nautic Partners, LLC; *U.S. Private*, pg. 2869
DIALYSIS CENTER OF WEST ORANGE LLC—See Nautic Partners, LLC; *U.S. Private*, pg. 2869
DIALYSIS CENTER OF WEST WARWICK LLC—See Nautic Partners, LLC; *U.S. Private*, pg. 2869
DIALYSIS CENTER OF WOONSOCKET LLC—See Nautic Partners, LLC; *U.S. Private*, pg. 2869
DIALYSIS CLINIC, INC.; *U.S. Private*, pg. 1222
DIALYSIS OF DES MOINES, LLC—See DaVita Inc.; *U.S. Public*, pg. 638
DIALYSIS SERVICES OF LONDON, LLC—See Nautic Partners, LLC; *U.S. Private*, pg. 2869
DIALYSIS SERVICES OF PINEVILLE, LLC—See Nautic Partners, LLC; *U.S. Private*, pg. 2870
DIALYSIS SPECIALISTS OF DALLAS, INC.—See DaVita Inc.; *U.S. Public*, pg. 638
THE DIALYSIS UNIT OF CENTER CITY PHILADELPHIA, LLC—See Nautic Partners, LLC; *U.S. Private*, pg. 2871

DIAVERUM AB—See Bridgepoint Group Plc; *Int'l*, pg. 1153
DOME DIALYSIS, LLC—See DaVita Inc.; *U.S. Public*, pg. 638
DOWNRIVER CENTERS, INC.—See DaVita Inc.; *U.S. Public*, pg. 638
DOWNTOWN HOUSTON DIALYSIS CENTER, L.P.—See DaVita Inc.; *U.S. Public*, pg. 638
DRESHER DIALYSIS, LLC—See DaVita Inc.; *U.S. Public*, pg. 638
DUBLIN DIALYSIS CENTER, LLC—See Nautic Partners, LLC; *U.S. Private*, pg. 2870
DURANGO DIALYSIS CENTER, LLC—See DaVita Inc.; *U.S. Public*, pg. 638
DVA HEALTHCARE OF MASSACHUSETTS, INC.—See DaVita Inc.; *U.S. Public*, pg. 637
DVA HEALTHCARE OF NEW LONDON, LLC—See DaVita Inc.; *U.S. Public*, pg. 637
DVA HEALTHCARE OF NORWICH, LLC—See DaVita Inc.; *U.S. Public*, pg. 637
DVA HEALTHCARE OF PENNSYLVANIA, INC.—See DaVita Inc.; *U.S. Public*, pg. 637
DVA HEALTHCARE OF TUSCALOOSA, LLC—See DaVita Inc.; *U.S. Public*, pg. 637
DVA HEALTHCARE RENAL CARE, INC.—See DaVita Inc.; *U.S. Public*, pg. 637
DVA RENAL HEALTHCARE, INC.—See DaVita Inc.; *U.S. Public*, pg. 637
DVA/WASHINGTON UNIVERSITY HEALTHCARE OF GREATER ST. LOUIS, LLC—See DaVita Inc.; *U.S. Public*, pg. 637
DV CARE NETHERLANDS B.V.—See DaVita Inc.; *U.S. Public*, pg. 637
DWORSHER DIALYSIS, LLC—See DaVita Inc.; *U.S. Public*, pg. 638
EAST END DIALYSIS CENTER, INC.—See DaVita Inc.; *U.S. Public*, pg. 638
EAST FT. LAUDERDALE, LLC—See DaVita Inc.; *U.S. Public*, pg. 638
EDISTO DIALYSIS, LLC—See DaVita Inc.; *U.S. Public*, pg. 638
EG HEALTHCARE, INC.—See Excelsior Medical Co., Ltd.; *Int'l*, pg. 2579
ELBERTON DIALYSIS FACILITY, INC.—See DaVita Inc.; *U.S. Public*, pg. 638
ELDRIST DIALYSIS, LLC—See DaVita Inc.; *U.S. Public*, pg. 638
ELK GROVE DIALYSIS CENTER, LLC—See DaVita Inc.; *U.S. Public*, pg. 638
ELLICOTT KIDNEY CENTER, LLC—See Nautic Partners, LLC; *U.S. Private*, pg. 2870
EL PASO HEALTH, LLC—See Nautic Partners, LLC; *U.S. Private*, pg. 2870
ESPECIALISTAS EN SALUD-ESENSA S.A.S.—See DaVita Inc.; *U.S. Public*, pg. 638
ESTRELLA MOUNTAIN DIALYSIS, LLC—See Nautic Partners, LLC; *U.S. Private*, pg. 2870
ETOWAH DIALYSIS, LLC—See DaVita Inc.; *U.S. Public*, pg. 638
EUFAULA DIALYSIS, LLC—See DaVita Inc.; *U.S. Public*, pg. 638
EVERETT MSO, INC.—See DaVita Inc.; *U.S. Public*, pg. 638
EVERGLADES DIALYSIS, LLC—See DaVita Inc.; *U.S. Public*, pg. 638
FALL RIVER KIDNEY CENTER, LLC—See Nautic Partners, LLC; *U.S. Private*, pg. 2870
FARRAGUT DIALYSIS, LLC—See DaVita Inc.; *U.S. Public*, pg. 638
FIVE STAR DIALYSIS, LLC—See DaVita Inc.; *U.S. Public*, pg. 638
FJORDS DIALYSIS, LLC—See DaVita Inc.; *U.S. Public*, pg. 638
FLAGLER DIALYSIS, LLC—See DaVita Inc.; *U.S. Public*, pg. 638
FLAMINGO PARK KIDNEY CENTER, INC.—See DaVita Inc.; *U.S. Public*, pg. 638
FLANDRAU DIALYSIS, LLC—See DaVita Inc.; *U.S. Public*, pg. 638
FLORIDA DIALYSIS CENTER OF CELEBRATION, LLC—See Nautic Partners, LLC; *U.S. Private*, pg. 2870
FLORIDA DIALYSIS CENTER OF ORLANDO, LLC—See Nautic Partners, LLC; *U.S. Private*, pg. 2870
FMC DIALIZIS CENTER KFT.—See Fresenius Medical Care AG; *Int'l*, pg. 2774
FMC MAGYARORSZAG EGESZSEGUGYI KORLATOLT FELELOSSEGU TARSASAG—See Fresenius Medical Care AG; *Int'l*, pg. 2775
FMC RENALCARE CORP.—See Fresenius Medical Care AG; *Int'l*, pg. 2775
FORT MYERS KIDNEY CENTER, LLC—See Nautic Partners, LLC; *U.S. Private*, pg. 2870
FORT VALLEY DIALYSIS CENTER, LLC—See Nautic Partners, LLC; *U.S. Private*, pg. 2870
FOSS DIALYSIS, LLC—See DaVita Inc.; *U.S. Public*, pg. 639
FRESENIUS MEDICAL CARE ARGENTINA S.A.—See Fresenius Medical Care AG; *Int'l*, pg. 2774
FRESENIUS MEDICAL CARE BH D.O.O.—See Fresenius Medical Care AG; *Int'l*, pg. 2774
FRESENIUS MEDICAL CARE COLOMBIA S.A.—See Fresenius Medical Care AG; *Int'l*, pg. 2775

CORPORATE AFFILIATIONS

FRESENIUS MEDICAL CARE DEL PERU S.A.—See Fresenius Medical Care AG; *Int'l*, pg. 2775
FRESENIUS MEDICAL CARE DE VENEZUELA C.A.—See Fresenius Medical Care AG; *Int'l*, pg. 2775
FRESENIUS MEDICAL CARE MAROC S.A.—See Fresenius Medical Care AG; *Int'l*, pg. 2775
FRESENIUS MEDICAL CARE NEPHROLOGICA DEUTSCHLAND GMBH—See CSL Limited; *Int'l*, pg. 1866
FRESENIUS MEDICAL CARE NORTH AMERICA—See Fresenius Medical Care AG; *Int'l*, pg. 2775
FRESENIUS MEDICAL CARE (SHANGHAI) CO., LTD.—See Fresenius Medical Care AG; *Int'l*, pg. 2774
FRESENIUS MEDICAL CARE SINGAPORE PTE. LTD.—See Fresenius Medical Care AG; *Int'l*, pg. 2775
FRESENIUS MEDICAL CARE SLOVENIJA D.O.O.—See Fresenius Medical Care AG; *Int'l*, pg. 2775
FRESENIUS MEDICAL CARE SLOVENSKO, SPOL. S.R.O.—See Fresenius Medical Care AG; *Int'l*, pg. 2775
FRESENIUS MEDICAL CARE SVERIGE AB—See Fresenius Medical Care AG; *Int'l*, pg. 2775
FRESENIUS MEDICAL CARE UKRAINE LLC—See Fresenius Medical Care AG; *Int'l*, pg. 2775
FRONTENAC DIALYSIS, LLC—See DaVita Inc.; *U.S. Public*, pg. 639
FRONTIER DIALYSIS, LLC—See DaVita Inc.; *U.S. Public*, pg. 639
FULLERTON DIALYSIS CENTER, LLC—See DaVita Inc.; *U.S. Public*, pg. 639
GERTRUDE DIALYSIS, LLC—See DaVita Inc.; *U.S. Public*, pg. 639
GEYSER DIALYSIS, LLC—See DaVita Inc.; *U.S. Public*, pg. 639
GIVHAN DIALYSIS, LLC—See DaVita Inc.; *U.S. Public*, pg. 639
GLASSLAND DIALYSIS, LLC—See DaVita Inc.; *U.S. Public*, pg. 639
GOLDENDALE DIALYSIS, LLC—See DaVita Inc.; *U.S. Public*, pg. 639
GOLIAD DIALYSIS, LLC—See DaVita Inc.; *U.S. Public*, pg. 639
GONZALES DIALYSIS CENTERS - SOUTHEAST, LP—See DaVita Inc.; *U.S. Public*, pg. 639
GOODALE DIALYSIS, LLC—See DaVita Inc.; *U.S. Public*, pg. 639
GRAND HOME DIALYSIS, LLC—See DaVita Inc.; *U.S. Public*, pg. 639
GRAND PRAIRIE DIALYSIS CENTER, LLC—See Nautic Partners, LLC; *U.S. Private*, pg. 2870
GREATER LAS VEGAS DIALYSIS, LLC—See DaVita Inc.; *U.S. Public*, pg. 639
GREATER LOS ANGELES DIALYSIS CENTERS, LLC—See DaVita Inc.; *U.S. Public*, pg. 639
GREAT FALLS DIALYSIS, LLC—See Nautic Partners, LLC; *U.S. Private*, pg. 2870
GREENACRES DIALYSIS CENTER, LLC—See Nautic Partners, LLC; *U.S. Private*, pg. 2870
GREENLEAF DIALYSIS, LLC—See DaVita Inc.; *U.S. Public*, pg. 639
GREENVILLE DIALYSIS CLINIC, LLC—See Nautic Partners, LLC; *U.S. Private*, pg. 2870
GREENWOOD DIALYSIS, LLC—See DaVita Inc.; *U.S. Public*, pg. 639
GRIFFIN DIALYSIS, LLC—See DaVita Inc.; *U.S. Public*, pg. 639
GRIFFS DIALYSIS, LLC—See DaVita Inc.; *U.S. Public*, pg. 639
GUNTERSVILLE DIALYSIS, LLC—See DaVita Inc.; *U.S. Public*, pg. 639
HAMMOND DIALYSIS CLINIC, LLC—See Nautic Partners, LLC; *U.S. Private*, pg. 2870
HANFORD DIALYSIS, LLC—See DaVita Inc.; *U.S. Public*, pg. 639
HARMONY DIALYSIS, LLC—See DaVita Inc.; *U.S. Public*, pg. 639
HARRIS DIALYSIS, LLC—See DaVita Inc.; *U.S. Public*, pg. 639
HAWAIIAN GARDENS DIALYSIS, LLC—See DaVita Inc.; *U.S. Public*, pg. 639
HAWTHORN KIDNEY CENTER, LLC—See Nautic Partners, LLC; *U.S. Private*, pg. 2870
HAZELTON DIALYSIS, LLC—See DaVita Inc.; *U.S. Public*, pg. 639
HEADLANDS DIALYSIS, LLC—See DaVita Inc.; *U.S. Public*, pg. 639
HEAVENER DIALYSIS, LLC—See DaVita Inc.; *U.S. Public*, pg. 639
HEIDECK DIALYSIS, LLC—See DaVita Inc.; *U.S. Public*, pg. 639
HELMER DIALYSIS, LLC—See DaVita Inc.; *U.S. Public*, pg. 639
HEMOTEK RENAL CENTER, INC.—See Euro-Med Laboratories Phil., Inc.; *Int'l*, pg. 2532
HERALD SQUARE DIALYSIS, LLC—See Nautic Partners, LLC; *U.S. Private*, pg. 2870
HERITAGE DIALYSIS CENTER LLC—See Nautic Partners, LLC; *U.S. Private*, pg. 2870

621492 — KIDNEY DIALYSIS CEN...

HEYBURN DIALYSIS, LLC—See DaVita Inc.; *U.S. Public*, pg. 639
HOCHATOWN DIALYSIS, LLC—See DaVita Inc.; *U.S. Public*, pg. 639
HOLIDAY DIALYSIS, LLC—See DaVita Inc.; *U.S. Public*, pg. 639
HOLTEN DIALYSIS, LLC—See DaVita Inc.; *U.S. Public*, pg. 639
HORTENSE & LOUIS RUBIN DIALYSIS CENTER, INC.; *U.S. Private*, pg. 1984
HOUSTON KIDNEY CENTER/TOTAL RENAL CARE INTEGRATED SERVICE NETWORK LIMITED PARTNERSHIP—See DaVita Inc.; *U.S. Public*, pg. 639
HOWARD UNIVERSITY DIALYSIS CENTER, LLC—See Nautic Partners, LLC; *U.S. Private*, pg. 2870
HUMBOLDT DIALYSIS, LLC—See DaVita Inc.; *U.S. Public*, pg. 639
HUMMER DIALYSIS, LLC—See DaVita Inc.; *U.S. Public*, pg. 639
HUNT COUNTY REGIONAL DIALYSIS CENTER LLC—See Nautic Partners, LLC; *U.S. Private*, pg. 2870
HUNTINGTON ARTIFICIAL KIDNEY CENTER, LTD.—See DaVita Inc.; *U.S. Public*, pg. 639
HUNTINGTON PARK DIALYSIS, LLC—See DaVita Inc.; *U.S. Public*, pg. 639
HYDE DIALYSIS, LLC—See DaVita Inc.; *U.S. Public*, pg. 639
INDIAN RIVER DIALYSIS CENTER, LLC—See DaVita Inc.; *U.S. Public*, pg. 639
INNOVATIVE RENAL CARE LLC—See Nautic Partners, LLC; *U.S. Private*, pg. 2868
IONIA DIALYSIS, LLC—See DaVita Inc.; *U.S. Public*, pg. 639
IROQUOIS DIALYSIS, LLC—See DaVita Inc.; *U.S. Public*, pg. 640
JASPER-ARA DIALYSIS L.L.P.—See Nautic Partners, LLC; *U.S. Private*, pg. 2870
JEDBURG DIALYSIS, LLC—See DaVita Inc.; *U.S. Public*, pg. 640
JIATE EXCELSIOR CO., LTD.—See Fresenius Medical Care AG; *Int'l*, pg. 2775
JOSHUA DIALYSIS, LLC—See DaVita Inc.; *U.S. Public*, pg. 640
JSC FRESENIUS SP—See Fresenius Medical Care AG; *Int'l*, pg. 2776
JUPITER KIDNEY CENTER LLC—See Nautic Partners, LLC; *U.S. Private*, pg. 2870
KAMAKEE DIALYSIS, LLC—See DaVita Inc.; *U.S. Public*, pg. 640
KAMIAH DIALYSIS, LLC—See DaVita Inc.; *U.S. Public*, pg. 640
KAVETT DIALYSIS, LLC—See DaVita Inc.; *U.S. Public*, pg. 640
KERMAN DIALYSIS CENTER, LLC—See Nautic Partners, LLC; *U.S. Private*, pg. 2870
KERRICHER DIALYSIS, LLC—See DaVita Inc.; *U.S. Public*, pg. 640
KIDNEY CARE CENTERS OF CAMBRIDGE OHIO, LLC—See Nautic Partners, LLC; *U.S. Private*, pg. 2870
KIDNEY CARE CENTERS OF COSHOCTON OHIO, LLC—See Nautic Partners, LLC; *U.S. Private*, pg. 2870
KIDNEY CENTER OF ARVADA LLC—See Nautic Partners, LLC; *U.S. Private*, pg. 2870
KIDNEY CENTER OF BEAR CREEK, LLC—See Nautic Partners, LLC; *U.S. Private*, pg. 2870
KIDNEY CENTER OF BEXLEY, LLC—See Nautic Partners, LLC; *U.S. Private*, pg. 2870
KIDNEY CENTER OF LAFAYETTE LLC—See Nautic Partners, LLC; *U.S. Private*, pg. 2870
KIDNEY CENTER OF LAKEWOOD LLC—See Nautic Partners, LLC; *U.S. Private*, pg. 2870
KIDNEY CENTER OF LONGMONT LLC—See Nautic Partners, LLC; *U.S. Private*, pg. 2870
KIDNEY CENTER OF NORTH DENVER, LLC—See Nautic Partners, LLC; *U.S. Private*, pg. 2870
THE KIDNEY CENTER OF SOUTH PHILADELPHIA, LLC—See Nautic Partners, LLC; *U.S. Private*, pg. 2871
KIDNEY CENTER OF WESTMINSTER LLC—See Nautic Partners, LLC; *U.S. Private*, pg. 2870
THE KIDNEY CENTER ON MAIN, LLC—See Nautic Partners, LLC; *U.S. Private*, pg. 2871
KIDNEY CENTERS OF MICHIGAN, LLC—See DaVita Inc.; *U.S. Public*, pg. 640
KIDNEY HOME CENTER, LLC—See DaVita Inc.; *U.S. Public*, pg. 640
KNICKERBOCKER DIALYSIS, INC.—See DaVita Inc.; *U.S. Public*, pg. 640
KOBUK DIALYSIS, LLC—See DaVita Inc.; *U.S. Public*, pg. 640
LAKE GRAY DIALYSIS CENTER LLC—See Nautic Partners, LLC; *U.S. Private*, pg. 2870
LANGHORNE DIALYSIS LLC—See Nautic Partners, LLC; *U.S. Private*, pg. 2870
LAPHAM DIALYSIS, LLC—See DaVita Inc.; *U.S. Public*, pg. 640
LAS OLAS DE SEQUOIA, LLC—See DaVita Inc.; *U.S. Public*, pg. 640
LASSEN DIALYSIS, LLC—See DaVita Inc.; *U.S. Public*, pg. 640
LAS VEGAS PEDIATRIC DIALYSIS, LLC—See DaVita Inc.; *U.S. Public*, pg. 640
LATHROP DIALYSIS, LLC—See DaVita Inc.; *U.S. Public*, pg. 640
LATROBE DIALYSIS, LLC—See DaVita Inc.; *U.S. Public*, pg. 640
LAWRENCEBURG DIALYSIS, LLC—See DaVita Inc.; *U.S. Public*, pg. 640
LAWTON DIALYSIS CENTER, LLC—See Nautic Partners, LLC; *U.S. Private*, pg. 2870
LEES DIALYSIS, LLC—See DaVita Inc.; *U.S. Public*, pg. 640
LEHIGH ACRES DIALYSIS CENTER, LLC—See Nautic Partners, LLC; *U.S. Private*, pg. 2870
LEWIS-CLARK KIDNEY CENTER, LLC—See Nautic Partners, LLC; *U.S. Private*, pg. 2870
LEXINGTON KIDNEY CENTER, LLC—See Nautic Partners, LLC; *U.S. Private*, pg. 2870
LIFELINE PENSACOLA, LLC—See DaVita Inc.; *U.S. Public*, pg. 640
LIFELINE VASCULAR CENTER- ALBANY, LLC—See DaVita Inc.; *U.S. Public*, pg. 640
LIFELINE VASCULAR CENTER OF SOUTH ORLANDO, LLC—See DaVita Inc.; *U.S. Public*, pg. 640
LIFELINE VASCULAR CENTER - ORLANDO, LLC—See DaVita Inc.; *U.S. Public*, pg. 640
LINCOLN PARK DIALYSIS SERVICES, INC.—See DaVita Inc.; *U.S. Public*, pg. 640
LINCOLN PARK KIDNEY CENTER, LLC—See Nautic Partners, LLC; *U.S. Private*, pg. 2870
LINCOLNTON DIALYSIS, LLC—See DaVita Inc.; *U.S. Public*, pg. 640
LITTLE ROCK DIALYSIS CENTERS, LLC—See DaVita Inc.; *U.S. Public*, pg. 640
LLANO DIALYSIS, LLC—See DaVita Inc.; *U.S. Public*, pg. 640
LOCKHART DIALYSIS, LLC—See DaVita Inc.; *U.S. Public*, pg. 640
LONG BEACH DIALYSIS CENTER, LLC—See DaVita Inc.; *U.S. Public*, pg. 640
LONGWORTH DIALYSIS, LLC—See DaVita Inc.; *U.S. Public*, pg. 640
LORD BALTIMORE DIALYSIS, LLC—See DaVita Inc.; *U.S. Public*, pg. 640
LOUP DIALYSIS, LLC—See DaVita Inc.; *U.S. Public*, pg. 640
LOURDES DIALYSIS, LLC—See DaVita Inc.; *U.S. Public*, pg. 640
MADERA KIDNEY CENTER, LLC—See Nautic Partners, LLC; *U.S. Private*, pg. 2870
MADIGAN DIALYSIS, LLC—See DaVita Inc.; *U.S. Public*, pg. 640
MAGNOLIA DIALYSIS, LLC—See DaVita Inc.; *U.S. Public*, pg. 641
MAGOFFIN DIALYSIS, LLC—See DaVita Inc.; *U.S. Public*, pg. 641
MAHONEY DIALYSIS, LLC—See DaVita Inc.; *U.S. Public*, pg. 641
MAMMOTH DIALYSIS, LLC—See DaVita Inc.; *U.S. Public*, pg. 641
MANCHESTER DIALYSIS, LLC—See DaVita Inc.; *U.S. Public*, pg. 641
MANITO DIALYSIS, LLC—See DaVita Inc.; *U.S. Public*, pg. 641
MANZANO DIALYSIS, LLC—See DaVita Inc.; *U.S. Public*, pg. 641
MAPLES DIALYSIS, LLC—See DaVita Inc.; *U.S. Public*, pg. 641
MARLTON DIALYSIS CENTER, LLC—See DaVita Inc.; *U.S. Public*, pg. 641
MARYSVILLE DIALYSIS CENTER, LLC—See DaVita Inc.; *U.S. Public*, pg. 641
MAZONIA DIALYSIS, LLC—See DaVita Inc.; *U.S. Public*, pg. 641
MEADOWS DIALYSIS, LLC—See DaVita Inc.; *U.S. Public*, pg. 641
MEESA DIALYSIS, LLC—See DaVita Inc.; *U.S. Public*, pg. 641
MEMORIAL DIALYSIS CENTER, L.P.—See DaVita Inc.; *U.S. Public*, pg. 641
MENA DIALYSIS CENTER, LLC—See DaVita Inc.; *U.S. Public*, pg. 641
MENDOCINO DIALYSIS, LLC—See DaVita Inc.; *U.S. Public*, pg. 641
MESILLA DIALYSIS, LLC—See DaVita Inc.; *U.S. Public*, pg. 641
METRO ST. LOUIS DIALYSIS - FLORISSANT, LLC—See Nautic Partners, LLC; *U.S. Private*, pg. 2870
MIAMI-ARA LLC—See Nautic Partners, LLC; *U.S. Private*, pg. 2870
MIAMI REGIONAL DIALYSIS CENTER WEST, LLC—See Nautic Partners, LLC; *U.S. Private*, pg. 2870
MINAM DIALYSIS, LLC—See DaVita Inc.; *U.S. Public*, pg. 641
MISSION DIALYSIS SERVICES, LLC—See DaVita Inc.; *U.S. Public*, pg. 641
MOCCA DIALYSIS, LLC—See DaVita Inc.; *U.S. Public*, pg. 641
MOHAWK VALLEY DIALYSIS CENTER, INC.—See Nautic Partners, LLC; *U.S. Private*, pg. 2870
MONCRIEF DIALYSIS CENTER/TOTAL RENAL CARE LIMITED PARTNERSHIP—See DaVita Inc.; *U.S. Public*, pg. 641
MONTAUK DIALYSIS, LLC—See DaVita Inc.; *U.S. Public*, pg. 641
MORAINE DIALYSIS, LLC—See DaVita Inc.; *U.S. Public*, pg. 641
MULGEE DIALYSIS, LLC—See DaVita Inc.; *U.S. Public*, pg. 641
MUSKOGEE DIALYSIS, LLC—See DaVita Inc.; *U.S. Public*, pg. 641
MVZ DAVITA ALZEY GMBH—See DaVita Inc.; *U.S. Public*, pg. 640
MVZ DAVITA DINKELSBUHL GMBH—See DaVita Inc.; *U.S. Public*, pg. 640
MVZ DAVITA EMDEN GMBH—See DaVita Inc.; *U.S. Public*, pg. 640
MVZ DAVITA GERA GMBH—See DaVita Inc.; *U.S. Public*, pg. 640
MVZ DAVITA NEUSS GMBH—See DaVita Inc.; *U.S. Public*, pg. 640
MVZ DAVITA NIERENZENTRUM BERLIN-BRITZ GMBH—See DaVita Inc.; *U.S. Public*, pg. 640
MVZ DAVITA RHEIN-AHR GMBH—See DaVita Inc.; *U.S. Public*, pg. 640
MVZ DAVITA RHEIN RUHR GMBH—See DaVita Inc.; *U.S. Public*, pg. 640
MVZ DAVITA SALZGITTER-SEESEN GMBH—See DaVita Inc.; *U.S. Public*, pg. 640
MVZ DAVITA VIERSEN GMBH—See DaVita Inc.; *U.S. Public*, pg. 640
MVZ GELSENKIRCHEN-BUER GMBH—See Fresenius Medical Care AG; *Int'l*, pg. 2776
MYRTLE DIALYSIS, LLC—See DaVita Inc.; *U.S. Public*, pg. 641
NATIONAL MEDICAL CARE OF SPAIN, S.A.—See Fresenius Medical Care AG; *Int'l*, pg. 2776
NATOMAS DIALYSIS, LLC—See DaVita Inc.; *U.S. Public*, pg. 641
NAVARRO DIALYSIS, LLC—See DaVita Inc.; *U.S. Public*, pg. 641
NAVILLE DIALYSIS, LLC—See DaVita Inc.; *U.S. Public*, pg. 641
NEFF DIALYSIS, LLC—See DaVita Inc.; *U.S. Public*, pg. 641
NEFRODIAL D.O.O.—See Fresenius Medical Care AG; *Int'l*, pg. 2775
NEPHROCARE AHRENSBURG GMBH—See Fresenius Medical Care AG; *Int'l*, pg. 2776
NEPHROCARE BERLIN-WEISSENSEE GMBH—See Fresenius Medical Care AG; *Int'l*, pg. 2776
NEPHROCARE BETZDORF GMBH—See Fresenius Medical Care AG; *Int'l*, pg. 2776
NEPHROCARE BIELEFELD GMBH—See Fresenius Medical Care AG; *Int'l*, pg. 2776
NEPHROCARE BUCHHOLZ GMBH—See Fresenius Medical Care AG; *Int'l*, pg. 2776
NEPHROCARE DAUN GMBH—See Fresenius Medical Care AG; *Int'l*, pg. 2776
NEPHROCARE DEUTSCHLAND GMBH—See Fresenius Medical Care AG; *Int'l*, pg. 2776
NEPHROCARE DOBELN GMBH—See Fresenius Medical Care AG; *Int'l*, pg. 2776
NEPHROCARE DORTMUND GMBH—See Fresenius Medical Care AG; *Int'l*, pg. 2776
NEPHROCARE FRIEDBERG GMBH—See Fresenius Medical Care AG; *Int'l*, pg. 2776
NEPHROCARE GREVENBROICH GMBH—See Fresenius Medical Care AG; *Int'l*, pg. 2776
NEPHROCARE HAGEN GMBH—See Fresenius Medical Care AG; *Int'l*, pg. 2776
NEPHROCARE HAMBURG-ALTONA GMBH—See Fresenius Medical Care AG; *Int'l*, pg. 2776
NEPHROCARE HAMBURG-BARMBEK GMBH—See Fresenius Medical Care AG; *Int'l*, pg. 2776
NEPHROCARE INGOLSTADT GMBH—See Fresenius Medical Care AG; *Int'l*, pg. 2776
NEPHROCARE KAUFERING GMBH—See Fresenius Medical Care AG; *Int'l*, pg. 2776
NEPHROCARE KREFELD GMBH—See Fresenius Medical Care AG; *Int'l*, pg. 2776
NEPHROCARE LAHR GMBH—See Fresenius Medical Care AG; *Int'l*, pg. 2776
NEPHROCARE LEVERKUSEN GMBH—See Fresenius Medical Care AG; *Int'l*, pg. 2776
NEPHROCARE LUDWIGSHAFEN GMBH—See Fresenius Medical Care AG; *Int'l*, pg. 2776
NEPHROCARE METTMANN GMBH—See Fresenius Medical Care AG; *Int'l*, pg. 2776
NEPHROCARE MUHLHAUSEN GMBH—See Fresenius Medical Care AG; *Int'l*, pg. 2776
NEPHROCARE MVZ AALEN GMBH—See Fresenius Medical Care AG; *Int'l*, pg. 2776
NEPHROCARE OBERHAUSEN GMBH—See Fresenius Medical Care AG; *Int'l*, pg. 2776
NEPHROCARE PAPENBURG GMBH—See Fresenius Medical Care AG; *Int'l*, pg. 2776
NEPHROCARE PIRMASENS GMBH—See Fresenius Medical Care AG; *Int'l*, pg. 2776

621492 — KIDNEY DIALYSIS CEN...

NEPHROCARE PUTTLINGEN GMBH—See Fresenius Medical Care AG; *Int'l*, pg. 2776
NEPHROCARE RECKLINGHAUSEN GMBH—See Fresenius Medical Care AG; *Int'l*, pg. 2776
NEPHROCARE SALZGITTER GMBH—See Fresenius Medical Care AG; *Int'l*, pg. 2776
NEPHROCARE SCHROBENHAUSEN GMBH—See Fresenius Medical Care AG; *Int'l*, pg. 2776
NEPHROCARE WETZLAR GMBH—See Fresenius Medical Care AG; *Int'l*, pg. 2776
NEPHROCARE WITTEN GMBH—See Fresenius Medical Care AG; *Int'l*, pg. 2776
NEPHROLOGISCH-INTERNISTISCHE VERSORGUNG INGOLSTADT GMBH—See Fresenius Medical Care AG; *Int'l*, pg. 2776
NEPHROLOGY CENTER OF DETROIT, LLC—See Nautic Partners, LLC; *U.S. Private*, pg. 2870
NEPHROLOGY FOUNDATION OF BROOKLYN; *U.S. Private*, pg. 2885
NEPHROLOGY MEDICAL ASSOCIATES OF GEORGIA, LLC—See DaVita Inc.; *U.S. Public*, pg. 641
NEW BAY DIALYSIS, LLC—See DaVita Inc.; *U.S. Public*, pg. 641
NOLIA DIALYSIS, LLC—See DaVita Inc.; *U.S. Public*, pg. 641
NORTE DIALYSIS, LLC—See DaVita Inc.; *U.S. Public*, pg. 641
NORTH COLORADO SPRINGS DIALYSIS, LLC—See DaVita Inc.; *U.S. Public*, pg. 641
NORTHEAST PHILADELPHIA DIALYSIS CENTER, LLC—See Nautic Partners, LLC; *U.S. Private*, pg. 2870
NORTH MAIN KIDNEY CENTER, LLC—See Nautic Partners, LLC; *U.S. Private*, pg. 2870
NOSTER DIALYSIS, LLC—See DaVita Inc.; *U.S. Public*, pg. 641
NXSTAGE KIDNEY CARE, INC.—See Fresenius Medical Care AG; *Int'l*, pg. 2777
OASIS DIALYSIS, LLC—See DaVita Inc.; *U.S. Public*, pg. 641
OIL CITY DIALYSIS CENTER, LLC—See Nautic Partners, LLC; *U.S. Private*, pg. 2870
OKANOGAN DIALYSIS, LLC—See DaVita Inc.; *U.S. Public*, pg. 641
OLIVE DIALYSIS, LLC—See DaVita Inc.; *U.S. Public*, pg. 641
ORANGE DIALYSIS, LLC—See DaVita Inc.; *U.S. Public*, pg. 641
OSAGE DIALYSIS, LLC—See DaVita Inc.; *U.S. Public*, pg. 641
OWYHEE DIALYSIS, LLC—See DaVita Inc.; *U.S. Public*, pg. 641
PACHECO DIALYSIS, LLC—See DaVita Inc.; *U.S. Public*, pg. 641
PALMETTO DIALYSIS, LLC—See DaVita Inc.; *U.S. Public*, pg. 641
PALOMAR DIALYSIS, LLC—See DaVita Inc.; *U.S. Public*, pg. 641
PARKER DIALYSIS, LLC—See DaVita Inc.; *U.S. Public*, pg. 641
PARKER KIDNEY CENTER, LLC—See Nautic Partners, LLC; *U.S. Private*, pg. 2870
PARKSIDE DIALYSIS, LLC—See DaVita Inc.; *U.S. Public*, pg. 641
PATIENT PATHWAYS, LLC—See DaVita Inc.; *U.S. Public*, pg. 641
PATOKA DIALYSIS, LLC—See DaVita Inc.; *U.S. Public*, pg. 642
PEARL DIALYSIS, LLC—See DaVita Inc.; *U.S. Public*, pg. 642
PEDERNALES DIALYSIS, LLC—See DaVita Inc.; *U.S. Public*, pg. 642
PEKIN DIALYSIS, LLC—See DaVita Inc.; *U.S. Public*, pg. 642
PENDSTER DIALYSIS, LLC—See DaVita Inc.; *U.S. Public*, pg. 642
PERCHA DIALYSIS, LLC—See DaVita Inc.; *U.S. Public*, pg. 642
PHILADELPHIA-CAMDEN INTEGRATED KIDNEY CARE, LLC.—See DaVita Inc.; *U.S. Public*, pg. 642
PHYSICIANS CHOICE DIALYSIS, LLC—See DaVita Inc.; *U.S. Public*, pg. 642
PHYSICIANS DIALYSIS OF LANCASTER, LLC—See DaVita Inc.; *U.S. Public*, pg. 642
PIBLE DIALYSIS, LLC—See DaVita Inc.; *U.S. Public*, pg. 642
PICKAWAY DIALYSIS CENTER LLC—See Nautic Partners, LLC; *U.S. Private*, pg. 2870
PITTSBURG DIALYSIS PARTNERS, LLC—See DaVita Inc.; *U.S. Public*, pg. 642
PLAINE DIALYSIS, LLC—See DaVita Inc.; *U.S. Public*, pg. 642
PLATTE DIALYSIS, LLC—See DaVita Inc.; *U.S. Public*, pg. 642
PLURIBUS DIALISE - BENFICA, S.A.—See DaVita Inc.; *U.S. Public*, pg. 642
PLURIBUS DIALISE - CASCAIS, S.A.—See DaVita Inc.; *U.S. Public*, pg. 642
POKAGON DIALYSIS, LLC—See DaVita Inc.; *U.S. Public*, pg. 642
PONCA DIALYSIS, LLC—See DaVita Inc.; *U.S. Public*, pg. 642
PORTOLA DIALYSIS, LLC—See DaVita Inc.; *U.S. Public*, pg. 642
POWERTON DIALYSIS, LLC—See DaVita Inc.; *U.S. Public*, pg. 642
PRAIRIE DIALYSIS, LLC—See DaVita Inc.; *U.S. Public*, pg. 642
PRIDAY DIALYSIS, LLC—See DaVita Inc.; *U.S. Public*, pg. 642
QUALITY DIALYSIS CARE SDN. BHD.—See DaVita Inc.; *U.S. Public*, pg. 642
RANCHO DIALYSIS, LLC—See DaVita Inc.; *U.S. Public*, pg. 642
REDCLIFF DIALYSIS, LLC—See DaVita Inc.; *U.S. Public*, pg. 642
RED WILLOW DIALYSIS, LLC—See DaVita Inc.; *U.S. Public*, pg. 642
REEF DIALYSIS, LLC—See DaVita Inc.; *U.S. Public*, pg. 642
REGIONAL DIALYSIS CENTER OF LANCASTER LLC—See Nautic Partners, LLC; *U.S. Private*, pg. 2870
REGIONAL DIALYSIS CENTER OF MESQUITE LLC—See Nautic Partners, LLC; *U.S. Private*, pg. 2870
RENAL CENTER OF FLOWER MOUND, LLC—See DaVita Inc.; *U.S. Public*, pg. 642
RENAL CENTER OF FRISCO, LLC—See DaVita Inc.; *U.S. Public*, pg. 642
RENAL CENTER OF LEWISVILLE, LLC—See DaVita Inc.; *U.S. Public*, pg. 642
RENAL CENTER OF NEDERLAND, LLC—See DaVita Inc.; *U.S. Public*, pg. 642
RENAL CENTER OF NORTH DENTON, L.L.L.P.—See DaVita Inc.; *U.S. Public*, pg. 642
RENAL CENTER OF PORT ARTHUR, LLC—See DaVita Inc.; *U.S. Public*, pg. 642
RENAL CENTER OF STORM LAKE, LLC—See DaVita Inc.; *U.S. Public*, pg. 642
RENAL LIFE LINK, INC.—See DaVita Inc.; *U.S. Public*, pg. 642
RENAL TREATMENT CENTERS-CALIFORNIA, INC.—See DaVita Inc.; *U.S. Public*, pg. 642
RENAL TREATMENT CENTERS - HAWAII, INC.—See DaVita Inc.; *U.S. Public*, pg. 642
RENAL TREATMENT CENTERS-ILLINOIS, INC.—See DaVita Inc.; *U.S. Public*, pg. 642
RENAL TREATMENT CENTERS-MID-ATLANTIC, INC.—See DaVita Inc.; *U.S. Public*, pg. 642
RENAL TREATMENT CENTERS-WEST, INC.—See DaVita Inc.; *U.S. Public*, pg. 642
RICHMOND REGIONAL DIALYSIS, LLC—See Nautic Partners, LLC; *U.S. Private*, pg. 2871
RIO DIALYSIS, LLC—See DaVita Inc.; *U.S. Public*, pg. 642
RIPLEY DIALYSIS, LLC—See DaVita Inc.; *U.S. Public*, pg. 642
RITA RANCH DIALYSIS, LLC—See DaVita Inc.; *U.S. Public*, pg. 642
RIVER VALLEY DIALYSIS, LLC—See DaVita Inc.; *U.S. Public*, pg. 642
RNA-DAVITA DIALYSIS, LLC—See DaVita Inc.; *U.S. Public*, pg. 642
ROBINSON DIALYSIS, LLC—See DaVita Inc.; *U.S. Public*, pg. 642
ROUSHE DIALYSIS, LLC—See DaVita Inc.; *U.S. Public*, pg. 642
RUSSELL DIALYSIS, LLC—See DaVita Inc.; *U.S. Public*, pg. 642
RYE DIALYSIS, LLC—See DaVita Inc.; *U.S. Public*, pg. 642
SADDLEBACK DIALYSIS, LLC—See DaVita Inc.; *U.S. Public*, pg. 642
SANDUSKY DIALYSIS, LLC—See DaVita Inc.; *U.S. Public*, pg. 643
SAN MARCOS DIALYSIS, LLC—See DaVita Inc.; *U.S. Public*, pg. 643
SANTA FE SPRINGS DIALYSIS, LLC—See DaVita Inc.; *U.S. Public*, pg. 643
SANTIAM DIALYSIS, LLC—See DaVita Inc.; *U.S. Public*, pg. 643
SEASONS DIALYSIS, LLC—See DaVita Inc.; *U.S. Public*, pg. 643
SEMINOLE DIALYSIS, LLC—See DaVita Inc.; *U.S. Public*, pg. 643
SENECA DIALYSIS CENTER, LLC—See Nautic Partners, LLC; *U.S. Private*, pg. 2871
SENECA DIALYSIS, LLC—See DaVita Inc.; *U.S. Public*, pg. 643
SHADOW DIALYSIS, LLC—See DaVita Inc.; *U.S. Public*, pg. 643
SHAWANO DIALYSIS, LLC—See DaVita Inc.; *U.S. Public*, pg. 643
SHAYANO DIALYSIS, LLC—See DaVita Inc.; *U.S. Public*, pg. 643
SHELBY DIALYSIS, LLC—See DaVita Inc.; *U.S. Public*, pg. 643
SHELLING DIALYSIS, LLC—See DaVita Inc.; *U.S. Public*, pg. 643
SHINING STAR DIALYSIS, INC.—See DaVita Inc.; *U.S. Public*, pg. 643
SHOALS DIALYSIS, LLC—See DaVita Inc.; *U.S. Public*, pg. 643
SHONE DIALYSIS, LLC—See DaVita Inc.; *U.S. Public*, pg. 643
SHOSHONE DIALYSIS, LLC—See DaVita Inc.; *U.S. Public*, pg. 643
SIENA DIALYSIS CENTER, LLC—See DaVita Inc.; *U.S. Public*, pg. 643
SILVERWOOD DIALYSIS, LLC—See DaVita Inc.; *U.S. Public*, pg. 643
SMITHGALL DIALYSIS, LLC—See DaVita Inc.; *U.S. Public*, pg. 643
SOLEDAD DIALYSIS CENTER, LLC—See DaVita Inc.; *U.S. Public*, pg. 643
SOMERVILLE DIALYSIS CENTER, LLC—See DaVita Inc.; *U.S. Public*, pg. 643
SOUTH ARLINGTON DIALYSIS CENTER, LLC—See Nautic Partners, LLC; *U.S. Private*, pg. 2871
SOUTH AUGUSTA DIALYSIS CLINIC, LLC—See Nautic Partners, LLC; *U.S. Private*, pg. 2871
SOUTH CENTRAL FLORIDA DIALYSIS PARTNERS, LLC—See DaVita Inc.; *U.S. Public*, pg. 643
SOUTHCREST DIALYSIS, LLC—See DaVita Inc.; *U.S. Public*, pg. 643
SOUTHEASTERN KIDNEY COUNCIL, INC.; *U.S. Private*, pg. 3728
SOUTHERN HILLS DIALYSIS CENTER, LLC—See DaVita Inc.; *U.S. Public*, pg. 643
SOUTH FLORIDA INTEGRATED KIDNEY CARE, LLC—See DaVita Inc.; *U.S. Public*, pg. 643
SOUTH SHORE DIALYSIS CENTER. L.P.—See DaVita Inc.; *U.S. Public*, pg. 643
SOUTHWEST ATLANTA DIALYSIS CENTERS, LLC—See DaVita Inc.; *U.S. Public*, pg. 643
SOUTHWEST INDIANA DIALYSIS, LLC—See DaVita Inc.; *U.S. Public*, pg. 643
SOUTHWEST JACKSONVILLE DIALYSIS CENTER LLC—See Nautic Partners, LLC; *U.S. Private*, pg. 2871
SPACE CITY DIALYSIS CENTER, LLC—See Nautic Partners, LLC; *U.S. Private*, pg. 2871
SPARTANBURG DIALYSIS, LLC—See Nautic Partners, LLC; *U.S. Private*, pg. 2871
STAR DIALYSIS, LLC—See DaVita Inc.; *U.S. Public*, pg. 643
STARKS DIALYSIS, LLC—See DaVita Inc.; *U.S. Public*, pg. 643
STEARNS DIALYSIS, LLC—See DaVita Inc.; *U.S. Public*, pg. 643
STEWART DIALYSIS, LLC—See DaVita Inc.; *U.S. Public*, pg. 643
STINES DIALYSIS, LLC—See DaVita Inc.; *U.S. Public*, pg. 643
STOCKTON DIALYSIS, LLC—See DaVita Inc.; *U.S. Public*, pg. 643
STORRIE DIALYSIS, LLC—See DaVita Inc.; *U.S. Public*, pg. 643
ST. PETERSBURG KIDNEY CARE SOUTH, LLC—See Nautic Partners, LLC; *U.S. Private*, pg. 2871
STRONGSVILLE DIALYSIS, LLC—See DaVita Inc.; *U.S. Public*, pg. 643
SUGARLOAF DIALYSIS, LLC—See DaVita Inc.; *U.S. Public*, pg. 643
SUMMIT DIALYSIS CENTER, L.P.—See DaVita Inc.; *U.S. Public*, pg. 643
SUN CITY DIALYSIS CENTER, LLC—See DaVita Inc.; *U.S. Public*, pg. 643
SUN CITY WEST DIALYSIS CENTER LLC—See DaVita Inc.; *U.S. Public*, pg. 643
SUN DESERT DIALYSIS, LLC—See DaVita Inc.; *U.S. Public*, pg. 643
SUNSET DIALYSIS, LLC—See DaVita Inc.; *U.S. Public*, pg. 643
SWAINSBORO DIALYSIS CLINIC, LLC—See Nautic Partners, LLC; *U.S. Private*, pg. 2871
TAUNTON HEALTHCARE CLINIC, LLC—See Nautic Partners, LLC; *U.S. Private*, pg. 2871
TAYLOR DIALYSIS, LLC—See DaVita Inc.; *U.S. Public*, pg. 643
TENNESSEE VALLEY DIALYSIS CENTER, LLC—See DaVita Inc.; *U.S. Public*, pg. 643
THORNTON KIDNEY CENTER, LLC—See Nautic Partners, LLC; *U.S. Private*, pg. 2871
TONKA BAY DIALYSIS, LLC—See DaVita Inc.; *U.S. Public*, pg. 643
TORTUGAS DIALYSIS, LLC—See DaVita Inc.; *U.S. Public*, pg. 643
TOTAL RENAL CARE/EATON CANYON DIALYSIS CENTER PARTNERSHIP—See DaVita Inc.; *U.S. Public*, pg. 643
TOTAL RENAL CARE NORTH CAROLINA, LLC—See DaVita Inc.; *U.S. Public*, pg. 643
TOWNSEND DIALYSIS, LLC—See DaVita Inc.; *U.S. Public*, pg. 644
TRAILSTONE DIALYSIS, LLC—See DaVita Inc.; *U.S. Public*, pg. 644
TRANSMOUNTAIN DIALYSIS, L.P.—See DaVita Inc.; *U.S. Public*, pg. 644

TRC-FOUR CORNERS DIALYSIS CLINICS, LLC—See DaVita Inc.; *U.S. Public*, pg. 643
TRC - INDIANA, LLC—See DaVita Inc.; *U.S. Public*, pg. 643
TRC OF NEW YORK, INC.—See DaVita Inc.; *U.S. Public*, pg. 643
TRC WEST, INC.—See DaVita Inc.; *U.S. Public*, pg. 643
TREE CITY DIALYSIS, LLC—See DaVita Inc.; *U.S. Public*, pg. 644
TROSS DIALYSIS, LLC—See DaVita Inc.; *U.S. Public*, pg. 644
TULSA DIALYSIS, LLC—See DaVita Inc.; *U.S. Public*, pg. 644
TUNNEL DIALYSIS, LLC—See DaVita Inc.; *U.S. Public*, pg. 644
TURLOCK DIALYSIS CENTER, LLC—See DaVita Inc.; *U.S. Public*, pg. 644
TUSTIN DIALYSIS CENTER, LLC—See DaVita Inc.; *U.S. Public*, pg. 644
TYLER DIALYSIS, LLC—See DaVita Inc.; *U.S. Public*, pg. 644
UKIAH DIALYSIS, LLC—See DaVita Inc.; *U.S. Public*, pg. 644
UNICOI DIALYSIS, LLC—See DaVita Inc.; *U.S. Public*, pg. 644
UNITED VASCULAR OF HUNTSVILLE, LLC—See Community Health Systems, Inc.; *U.S. Public*, pg. 557
UNIVERSAL DIALYSIS CENTER, LLC—See Nautic Partners, LLC; *U.S. Private*, pg. 2871
UNIVERSITY DIALYSIS CENTER, LLC—See DaVita Inc.; *U.S. Public*, pg. 644
UNIVERSITY KIDNEY CENTER BLUEGRASS, LLC—See Nautic Partners, LLC; *U.S. Private*, pg. 2871
UPPER VALLEY DIALYSIS, L.P.—See DaVita Inc.; *U.S. Public*, pg. 644
USC-DAVITA DIALYSIS CENTER, LLC—See DaVita Inc.; *U.S. Public*, pg. 644
U.S. RENAL CARE, INC.; *U.S. Private*, pg. 4272
UT SOUTHWESTERN DVA HEALTHCARE, LLP—See DaVita Inc.; *U.S. Public*, pg. 644
VALLEY SPRINGS DIALYSIS, LLC—See DaVita Inc.; *U.S. Public*, pg. 644
VICTORY DIALYSIS, LLC—See DaVita Inc.; *U.S. Public*, pg. 644
VOLO DIALYSIS, LLC—See DaVita Inc.; *U.S. Public*, pg. 644
WAKONI DIALYSIS, LLC—See DaVita Inc.; *U.S. Public*, pg. 644
WALCOTT DIALYSIS, LLC—See DaVita Inc.; *U.S. Public*, pg. 644
WALLINGFORD DIALYSIS CARE, LLC—See Nautic Partners, LLC; *U.S. Private*, pg. 2871
WALTHAM DIALYSIS LLC—See Nautic Partners, LLC; *U.S. Private*, pg. 2871
WALTON DIALYSIS, LLC—See DaVita Inc.; *U.S. Public*, pg. 644
WARREN DIALYSIS CENTER LLC—See Nautic Partners, LLC; *U.S. Private*, pg. 2871
WAUSEON DIALYSIS, LLC—See DaVita Inc.; *U.S. Public*, pg. 644
WELDON DIALYSIS, LLC—See DaVita Inc.; *U.S. Public*, pg. 644
WELLESLEY DIALYSIS LLC—See Nautic Partners, LLC; *U.S. Private*, pg. 2871
WESLEY CHAPEL DIALYSIS, LLC—See DaVita Inc.; *U.S. Public*, pg. 644
WEST BLOOMFIELD DIALYSIS, LLC—See DaVita Inc.; *U.S. Public*, pg. 644
WEST ELK GROVE DIALYSIS, LLC—See DaVita Inc.; *U.S. Public*, pg. 644
WESTERN COMMUNITY DIALYSIS CENTER, LLC—See Nautic Partners, LLC; *U.S. Private*, pg. 2871
WESTHAMPTON REGIONAL DIALYSIS, LLC—See Nautic Partners, LLC; *U.S. Private*, pg. 2871
WESTON DIALYSIS CENTER, LLC—See DaVita Inc.; *U.S. Public*, pg. 644
WEST SACRAMENTO DIALYSIS, LLC—See DaVita Inc.; *U.S. Public*, pg. 644
WHARTON DIALYSIS CARE, L.L.P.—See Nautic Partners, LLC; *U.S. Private*, pg. 2871
WILLOWBROOK DIALYSIS CENTER, L.P.—See DaVita Inc.; *U.S. Public*, pg. 644
WINDS DIALYSIS, LLC—See DaVita Inc.; *U.S. Public*, pg. 644
WOOD DIALYSIS, LLC—See DaVita Inc.; *U.S. Public*, pg. 644
WOODHAVEN DIALYSIS CENTER, LLC—See Nautic Partners, LLC; *U.S. Private*, pg. 2871
WOODLAND PARK DIALYSIS CENTER, LLC—See Nautic Partners, LLC; *U.S. Private*, pg. 2871
WYANDOTTE CENTRAL DIALYSIS, LLC—See DaVita Inc.; *U.S. Public*, pg. 644
YARGOL DIALYSIS, LLC—See DaVita Inc.; *U.S. Public*, pg. 644
YBOR CITY DIALYSIS, LLC—See DaVita Inc.; *U.S. Public*, pg. 644
YOUNGSTOWN-WARREN HOME DIALYSIS, LLC—See Nautic Partners, LLC; *U.S. Private*, pg. 2871
YUCAIPA DIALYSIS, LLC—See DaVita Inc.; *U.S. Public*, pg. 644
ZENTRUM FUR NIEREN- UND HOCHDRUCKKRANKHEITEN BENSHEIM GMBH—See Fresenius Medical Care AG; *Int'l*, pg. 2777
ZEPHYRHILLS DIALYSIS CENTER, LLC—See DaVita Inc.; *U.S. Public*, pg. 644

621493 — FREESTANDING AMBULATORY SURGICAL AND EMERGENCY CENTERS

ABQ HEALTH PARTNERS ENDOSCOPY CENTER, LLC—See DaVita Inc.; *U.S. Public*, pg. 635
ACUFOCUS, INC.—See Bausch Health Companies Inc.; *Int'l*, pg. 895
ADEPTUS HEALTH LLC—See Adeptus Health Inc.; *U.S. Private*, pg. 78
ADVANCED AMBULATORY SURGICAL CARE, L.P.—See Tenet Healthcare Corporation; *U.S. Public*, pg. 2009
ADVANCED PSYCHIATRIC GROUP, P.A—See Thurston Group, LLC; *U.S. Private*, pg. 4166
ADVANCED REGIONAL SURGERY CENTER, LLC—See Tenet Healthcare Corporation; *U.S. Public*, pg. 2001
ADVANCED SURGERY CENTER OF BETHESDA, LLC—See Tenet Healthcare Corporation; *U.S. Public*, pg. 2001
ADVANCED SURGERY CENTER OF SARASOTA, LLC—See Tenet Healthcare Corporation; *U.S. Public*, pg. 2001
ADVANCED SURGERY CENTER OF TAMPA, LLC—See Tenet Healthcare Corporation; *U.S. Public*, pg. 2001
ADVANCED SURGICAL CARE OF ST LOUIS, LLC—See Tenet Healthcare Corporation; *U.S. Public*, pg. 2001
ADVANCED SURGICAL CONCEPTS, LLC—See Tenet Healthcare Corporation; *U.S. Public*, pg. 2009
AJNH MEDICAL CENTER LLC—See Adeptus Health Inc.; *U.S. Private*, pg. 78
ALLEN BETHANY MEDICAL CENTER LLC—See Adeptus Health Inc.; *U.S. Private*, pg. 78
ALLIANCE SURGICAL CENTER, LLC—See UnitedHealth Group Incorporated; *U.S. Public*, pg. 2238
THE ALTAMONTE SPRINGS FL ENDOSCOPY ASC, LLC—See KKR & Co. Inc.; *U.S. Public*, pg. 1247
ALVIN MEDICAL CENTER LLC—See Adeptus Health Inc.; *U.S. Private*, pg. 78
AMBULATORY ENDOSCOPY CLINIC OF DALLAS, LTD.—See HCA Healthcare, Inc.; *U.S. Public*, pg. 990
AMBULATORY SURGICAL ASSOCIATES, LLC—See Tenet Healthcare Corporation; *U.S. Public*, pg. 2009
AMBULATORY SURGICAL CENTER OF SOMERVILLE, LLC—See Tenet Healthcare Corporation; *U.S. Public*, pg. 2009
AMERICAN HEALTHWAYS SERVICES, INC.—See Stone Point Capital LLC; *U.S. Private*, pg. 3825
AMSURG BURBANK, INC.—See KKR & Co. Inc.; *U.S. Public*, pg. 1244
AMSURG CORP. - CENTRAL REGIONAL OFFICE—See KKR & Co. Inc.; *U.S. Public*, pg. 1244
AMSURG EL PASO, INC.—See KKR & Co. Inc.; *U.S. Public*, pg. 1244
AMSURG ST. GEORGE ANESTHESIA, LLC—See KKR & Co. Inc.; *U.S. Public*, pg. 1246
ANIMAS SURGICAL HOSPITAL, LLC—See Bain Capital, LP; *U.S. Private*, pg. 446
ATHENS SURGERY CENTER, LLC—See Apollo Global Management, Inc.; *U.S. Public*, pg. 154
ATLANTIC COAST SURGICAL SUITES, LLC—See Tenet Healthcare Corporation; *U.S. Public*, pg. 2001
AUSTIN HEART, PLLC—See HCA Healthcare, Inc.; *U.S. Public*, pg. 991
BAPTIST SURGERY CENTER, L.P.—See Tenet Healthcare Corporation; *U.S. Public*, pg. 2009
BEAR CREEK SURGERY CENTER, LLC—See Tenet Healthcare Corporation; *U.S. Public*, pg. 2001
BETHLEHEM ENDOSCOPE CENTER; *U.S. Private*, pg. 546
BLUE CHIP SURGICAL CENTER PARTNERS, LLC—See Nueterra Capital Management, LLC; *U.S. Private*, pg. 2972 .
BLUE RIDGE SURGERY CENTER—See HCA Healthcare, Inc.; *U.S. Public*, pg. 1007
BLUE RIDGE SURGICAL CENTER, LLC—See Bain Capital, LP; *U.S. Private*, pg. 445
THE BOCA RATON OPHTHALMOLOGY ASC, LLC—See KKR & Co. Inc.; *U.S. Public*, pg. 1247
BON SECOURS SURGERY CENTER AT HARBOUR VIEW, LLC—See Tenet Healthcare Corporation; *U.S. Public*, pg. 2009
BON SECOURS SURGERY CENTER AT VIRGINIA BEACH, LLC—See Tenet Healthcare Corporation; *U.S. Public*, pg. 2009
BOULDERS AMBULATORY SURGERY CENTER—See HCA Healthcare, Inc.; *U.S. Public*, pg. 991
BRANDON AMBULATORY SURGERY CENTER, LLC—See UnitedHealth Group Incorporated; *U.S. Public*, pg. 2239
B.R.A.S.S. PARTNERSHIP IN COMMENDAM—See UnitedHealth Group Incorporated; *U.S. Public*, pg. 2239
BRENTWOOD SURGERY CENTER, LLC—See Bain Capital, LP; *U.S. Private*, pg. 445
BRIAR FOREST-ELDRIDGE MEDICAL CENTER LLC—See Adeptus Health Inc.; *U.S. Private*, pg. 78
CAMP LOWELL SURGERY CENTER, L.L.C.—See Tenet Healthcare Corporation; *U.S. Public*, pg. 2009
THE CAPE CORAL/FT. MYERS ENDOSCOPY ASC, LLC—See KKR & Co. Inc.; *U.S. Public*, pg. 1247
CAPITAL AREA PROVIDERS—See HCA Healthcare, Inc.; *U.S. Public*, pg. 992
CARMEL SPECIALTY SURGERY CENTER, LLC—See Tenet Healthcare Corporation; *U.S. Public*, pg. 2001
CASCADE SPINE CENTER, LLC—See Tenet Healthcare Corporation; *U.S. Public*, pg. 2009
THE CATARACT SPECIALTY SURGICAL CENTER, LLC—See Bain Capital, LP; *U.S. Private*, pg. 447
CEDAR PARK SURGERY CENTER, L.L.P.—See Tenet Healthcare Corporation; *U.S. Public*, pg. 2009
THE CENTER FOR AMBULATORY SURGICAL TREATMENT, L.P.—See Tenet Healthcare Corporation; *U.S. Public*, pg. 2013
THE CENTER FOR SPECIALIZED SURGERY, LP—See Bain Capital, LP; *U.S. Private*, pg. 447
THE CENTER FOR SPECIAL SURGERY, LLC—See Bain Capital, LP; *U.S. Private*, pg. 447
CENTER STREET DP MEDICAL CENTER LLC—See Adeptus Health Inc.; *U.S. Private*, pg. 78
CENTRAL JERSEY SURGERY CENTER, LLC—See Tenet Healthcare Corporation; *U.S. Public*, pg. 2009
CENTRAL PARK SURGERY CENTER—See HCA Healthcare, Inc.; *U.S. Public*, pg. 992
CENTRAL VIRGINIA SURGI-CENTER, L.P.—See Tenet Healthcare Corporation; *U.S. Public*, pg. 2009
CENTRE MEDICO-CHIRURGICAL DES EAUX-VIVES SA—See AEVIS VICTORIA SA; *Int'l*, pg. 183
CENTROMED QUILPUE S.A.—See UnitedHealth Group Incorporated; *U.S. Public*, pg. 2239
CHANNEL ISLANDS SURGICENTER, L.P.—See UnitedHealth Group Incorporated; *U.S. Public*, pg. 2239
CHESAPEAKE UROLOGY ASSOCIATES PA—See Audax Group, Limited Partnership; *U.S. Private*, pg. 387
CHESTERFIELD AMBULATORY SURGERY CENTER, L.P.—See Tenet Healthcare Corporation; *U.S. Public*, pg. 2009
CHICO SURGERY CENTER, L.P.—See Tenet Healthcare Corporation; *U.S. Public*, pg. 2009
THE CHRIST HOSPITAL SPINE SURGERY CENTER, LLC—See Tenet Healthcare Corporation; *U.S. Public*, pg. 2013
CHRISTUS CABRINI SURGERY CENTER, L.L.C.—See Tenet Healthcare Corporation; *U.S. Public*, pg. 2009
CITRUS REGIONAL SURGERY CENTER, L.P.—See UnitedHealth Group Incorporated; *U.S. Public*, pg. 2240
CLARKSTON ASC PARTNERS, LLC—See Tenet Healthcare Corporation; *U.S. Public*, pg. 2010
CLARKSVILLE SURGERY CENTER, LLC—See Tenet Healthcare Corporation; *U.S. Public*, pg. 2010
CLINICA CENTRAL DO BONFIM S.A—See DaVita Inc.; *U.S. Public*, pg. 636
CLINICA DEL COUNTRY S.A.—See UnitedHealth Group Incorporated; *U.S. Public*, pg. 2239
CLISA - CLINICA DE SANTO ANTONIO, S.A.—See UnitedHealth Group Incorporated; *U.S. Public*, pg. 2239
CMO - CENTRO MEDICO DE OFTALMOLOGIA S/S LTDA.—See UnitedHealth Group Incorporated; *U.S. Public*, pg. 2239
COAST SURGERY CENTER, L.P.—See Tenet Healthcare Corporation; *U.S. Public*, pg. 2010
COLONIAL HEIGHTS SURGERY CENTER—See HCA Healthcare, Inc.; *U.S. Public*, pg. 994
COLONIAL OUTPATIENT SURGERY CENTER, LLC—See UnitedHealth Group Incorporated; *U.S. Public*, pg. 2240
THE COLUMBIA MD ORTHOPAEDIC ASC, LLC—See KKR & Co. Inc.; *U.S. Public*, pg. 1247
CONNECTICUT EYE SURGERY CENTER SOUTH, LLC—See KKR & Co. Inc.; *U.S. Public*, pg. 1249
CONNECTICUT SURGERY CENTER, LIMITED PARTNERSHIP—See UnitedHealth Group Incorporated; *U.S. Public*, pg. 2240
COPPERWOOD MEDICAL CENTER LLC—See Adeptus Health Inc.; *U.S. Private*, pg. 78
CORPUS CHRISTI ENDOSCOPY CENTER, L.L.P.—See UnitedHealth Group Incorporated; *U.S. Public*, pg. 2240
CP SURGERY CENTER, LLC—See HCA Healthcare, Inc.; *U.S. Public*, pg. 992
CREEKWOOD SURGERY CENTER, L.P.—See Tenet Healthcare Corporation; *U.S. Public*, pg. 2010
CROWN POINT SURGERY CENTER, LLC—See Tenet Healthcare Corporation; *U.S. Public*, pg. 2010
CYPRESS SURGERY CENTER, LLC—See Bain Capital, LP; *U.S. Private*, pg. 446
DAROGA DIALYSIS, LLC—See DaVita Inc.; *U.S. Public*, pg. 638
DAVITA HEALTHCARE PARTNERS PLAN, INC.—See DaVita Inc.; *U.S. Public*, pg. 637
DAVITA MEDICAL GROUP HEALTH INFORMATION MANAGEMENT—See UnitedHealth Group Incorporated; *U.S. Public*, pg. 2243

621493 — FREESTANDING AMBULA... CORPORATE AFFILIATIONS

N.A.I.C.S. Index

DAVITA NEPHROLIFE (INDIA) PRIVATE LIMITED—See DaVita Inc.; *U.S. Public*, pg. 637
DAY SURGERY CENTER AT DENTON REGIONAL MEDICAL CENTER—See HCA Healthcare, Inc.; *U.S. Public*, pg. 995
DELAWARE OUTPATIENT CENTER FOR SURGERY, LLC—See Bain Capital, LP; *U.S. Private*, pg. 446
DELRAY BEACH ASC, LLC—See Tenet Healthcare Corporation; *U.S. Public*, pg. 2002
DENVILLE SURGERY CENTER, LLC—See Tenet Healthcare Corporation; *U.S. Public*, pg. 2010
DERRY SURGICAL CENTER, LLC—See UnitedHealth Group Incorporated; *U.S. Public*, pg. 2240
DESERT RIDGE OUTPATIENT SURGERY, LLC—See Tenet Healthcare Corporation; *U.S. Public*, pg. 2010
DESTIN SURGERY CENTER, LLC—See Tenet Healthcare Corporation; *U.S. Public*, pg. 2010
DIGESTIVE ENDOSCOPY CENTER, LLC—See KKR & Co. Inc.; *U.S. Public*, pg. 1245
DIGESTIVE HEALTH CENTER, LLC—See KKR & Co. Inc.; *U.S. Public*, pg. 1245
DOCTORS PARK SURGERY CENTER, LLC—See KKR & Co. Inc.; *U.S. Public*, pg. 1245
DRY CREEK SURGERY CENTER, LLC—See UnitedHealth Group Incorporated; *U.S. Public*, pg. 2240
DTC SURGERY CENTER, LLC—See UnitedHealth Group Incorporated; *U.S. Public*, pg. 2240
EAGLE EYE SURGERY AND LASER CENTER, LLC—See KKR & Co. Inc.; *U.S. Public*, pg. 1245
EAST BRUNSWICK SURGERY CENTER, LLC—See UnitedHealth Group Incorporated; *U.S. Public*, pg. 2240
EAST PFLUGERVILLE MEDICAL CENTER LLC—See Adeptus Health Inc.; *U.S. Private*, pg. 78
EAST PORTLAND SURGERY CENTER, LLC—See Tenet Healthcare Corporation; *U.S. Public*, pg. 2010
EAST VALLEY ENDOSCOPY, LLC—See KKR & Co. Inc.; *U.S. Public*, pg. 1245
EAST WEST SURGERY CENTER, L.P.—See Tenet Healthcare Corporation; *U.S. Public*, pg. 2010
ECC WEST TENNESSEE MC, LLC—See Anderson Regional Health System; *U.S. Private*, pg. 277
EFFINGHAM SURGICAL PARTNERS, LLC—See Tenet Healthcare Corporation; *U.S. Public*, pg. 2010
EL PASO SURGERY CENTERS, L.P.—See HCA Healthcare, Inc.; *U.S. Public*, pg. 995
EMERGENCY PROFESSIONAL SERVICES, PC—See KKR & Co. Inc.; *U.S. Public*, pg. 1245
ENCINITAS ENDOSCOPY CENTER, LLC—See Tenet Healthcare Corporation; *U.S. Public*, pg. 2010
ENCLARA PHARMACIA, INC.—See Humana, Inc.; *U.S. Public*, pg. 1069
ENDOSCOPY CENTER OF HACKENSACK, LLC—See Tenet Healthcare Corporation; *U.S. Public*, pg. 2010
ENDOSCOPY CENTER OF LAKE COUNTY LLC—See Tenet Healthcare Corporation; *U.S. Public*, pg. 2002
THE ENDOSCOPY CENTER OF ST. THOMAS, L.P.—See KKR & Co. Inc.; *U.S. Public*, pg. 1247
E STREET ENDOSCOPY, LLC—See UnitedHealth Group Incorporated; *U.S. Public*, pg. 2240
EURODIAL-CENTRO DE NEFROLOGIA E DIALISE DE LEIRIA, S.A.—See DaVita Inc.; *U.S. Public*, pg. 638
EXECUTIVE SURGERY CENTER, LLC—See UnitedHealth Group Incorporated; *U.S. Public*, pg. 2240
EXTRACORP AKTIENGESELLSCHAFT—See DaVita Inc.; *U.S. Public*, pg. 638
EYECARE CONSULTANTS SURGERY CENTER, LLC—See KKR & Co. Inc.; *U.S. Public*, pg. 1245
EYE SURGERY CENTER OF NASHVILLE, LLC—See Tenet Healthcare Corporation; *U.S. Public*, pg. 2010
FAIRFAX SURGICAL CENTER, L.P.—See HCA Healthcare, Inc.; *U.S. Public*, pg. 996
FAMILY ER + URGENT CARE; *U.S. Private*, pg. 1469
FANNIN SURGICARE—See HCA Healthcare, Inc.; *U.S. Public*, pg. 996
FAST PACE MEDICAL CLINIC, PLLC—See Revelstoke Capital Partners LLC; *U.S. Private*, pg. 3413
FIRST CHOICE ER, LLC—See Adeptus Health Inc.; *U.S. Private*, pg. 78
FIRST HEALTH SYSTEM INCORPORATED—See Universal Health Services, Inc.; *U.S. Public*, pg. 2257
FLATIRONS SURGERY CENTER, LLC—See Tenet Healthcare Corporation; *U.S. Public*, pg. 2010
FRANKLIN SURGICAL CENTER, LLC—See UnitedHealth Group Incorporated; *U.S. Public*, pg. 2240
FRITZ CLINIC, LLC—See Webster Equity Partners, LLC; *U.S. Private*, pg. 4466
FRONTENAC AMBULATORY SURGERY & SPINE CARE CENTER, L.P.—See Tenet Healthcare Corporation; *U.S. Public*, pg. 2010
GADSDEN SURGERY CENTER, LLC—See UnitedHealth Group Incorporated; *U.S. Public*, pg. 2241
GADSDEN SURGERY CENTER, LTD.—See UnitedHealth Group Incorporated; *U.S. Public*, pg. 2241
GENEOHM SCIENCES CANADA INC.—See Becton, Dickinson & Company; *U.S. Public*, pg. 292
GENESIS ASC PARTNERS, LLC—See Tenet Healthcare Corporation; *U.S. Public*, pg. 2010
GENEVA SURGICAL SUITES, LLC—See Tenet Healthcare Corporation; *U.S. Public*, pg. 2002
GILBERT MEDICAL CENTER LLC—See Adeptus Health Inc.; *U.S. Private*, pg. 78
GILEAD SCIENCES RUSSIA LLC—See Gilead Sciences, Inc.; *U.S. Public*, pg. 937
GILEAD SCIENCES S.R.O.—See Gilead Sciences, Inc.; *U.S. Public*, pg. 937
GLENDALE OPHTHALMOLOGY ASC, L.P.—See KKR & Co. Inc.; *U.S. Public*, pg. 1245
GLEN ECHO SURGERY CENTER, LLC—See Tenet Healthcare Corporation; *U.S. Public*, pg. 2002
GLENWOOD SURGICAL CENTER, L.P.—See UnitedHealth Group Incorporated; *U.S. Public*, pg. 2241
GOLDEN TRIANGLE SURGICENTER, L.P.—See UnitedHealth Group Incorporated; *U.S. Public*, pg. 2241
GRANTS PASS SURGERY CENTER, LLC—See UnitedHealth Group Incorporated; *U.S. Public*, pg. 2241
GREAT LAKES SURGICAL SUITES, LLC—See Tenet Healthcare Corporation; *U.S. Public*, pg. 2002
GREENSPRING STATION ENDOSCOPY, LLC—See KKR & Co. Inc.; *U.S. Public*, pg. 1245
GREENVILLE SURGERY CENTER, LLC—See UnitedHealth Group Incorporated; *U.S. Public*, pg. 2241
GREENWAY SURGICAL SUITES, LLC—See UnitedHealth Group Incorporated; *U.S. Public*, pg. 2241
GREENWOOD ASC, LLC—See Tenet Healthcare Corporation; *U.S. Public*, pg. 2010
GROVE PLACE SURGERY CENTER, LLC—See UnitedHealth Group Incorporated; *U.S. Public*, pg. 2241
HACIENDA OUTPATIENT SURGERY CENTER, LLC—See Tenet Healthcare Corporation; *U.S. Public*, pg. 2010
HAGERSTOWN SURGERY CENTER, LLC—See Tenet Healthcare Corporation; *U.S. Public*, pg. 2002
THE HANOVER NJ ENDOSCOPY ASC, LLC—See KKR & Co. Inc.; *U.S. Public*, pg. 1247
HARBOR HEIGHTS SURGERY CENTER, LLC—See Tenet Healthcare Corporation; *U.S. Public*, pg. 2002
HARVARD PARK SURGERY CENTER, LLC—See Tenet Healthcare Corporation; *U.S. Public*, pg. 2010
HAYMARKET SURGERY CENTER, LLC—See Tenet Healthcare Corporation; *U.S. Public*, pg. 2002
HCA HOUSTON ER 24/7 - CYPRESS FAIRBANKS—See HCA Healthcare, Inc.; *U.S. Public*, pg. 998
HEARTLAND HEART & VASCULAR, LLC—See UnitedHealth Group Incorporated; *U.S. Public*, pg. 2241
HERSHEY OUTPATIENT SURGERY CENTER, L.P.—See Tenet Healthcare Corporation; *U.S. Public*, pg. 2010
HOSPITAL DE CLINICAS DE JACAREPAGUA LTDA.—See UnitedHealth Group Incorporated; *U.S. Public*, pg. 2241
HOSPITAL SAMARITANO DE SAO PAULO LTDA.—See UnitedHealth Group Incorporated; *U.S. Public*, pg. 2241
HOUSTON AMBULATORY SURGICAL ASSOCIATES, L.P.—See Tenet Healthcare Corporation; *U.S. Public*, pg. 2010
HUMBLE KINGWOOD ENDOSCOPY CENTER—See HCA Healthcare, Inc.; *U.S. Public*, pg. 1000
INOV8 SURGICAL AT MEMORIAL CITY, LLC—See UnitedHealth Group Incorporated; *U.S. Public*, pg. 2241
INTEGRATED DERMATOLOGY OF HICKORY PLLC—See Integrated Dermatology Group; *U.S. Private*, pg. 2099
INTEGRATED ONCOLOGY NETWORK LLC—See Silver Oak Services Partners, LLC; *U.S. Private*, pg. 3661
INTRACOASTAL SURGERY CENTER, LLC—See Tenet Healthcare Corporation; *U.S. Public*, pg. 2004
J. MICHAEL MALONEY, M.D., P.C.—See Epiphany Dermatology PA; *U.S. Private*, pg. 1413
JOLIET SURGERY CENTER LIMITED PARTNERSHIP—See UnitedHealth Group Incorporated; *U.S. Public*, pg. 2242
KATY ER CENTER LLC—See Adeptus Health Inc.; *U.S. Private*, pg. 78
KHS AMBULATORY SURGERY CENTER LLC—See Tenet Healthcare Corporation; *U.S. Public*, pg. 2010
THE KISSIMMEE FL ENDOSCOPY ASC, LLC—See KKR & Co. Inc.; *U.S. Public*, pg. 1247
LAKEVIEW SURGERY CENTER, LLC—See Ventas, Inc.; *U.S. Public*, pg. 2278
LANCASTER EMERGENCY MEDICAL SERVICES ASSOCIATION—See Community Health Systems, Inc.; *U.S. Public*, pg. 554
LANCASTER SPECIALTY SURGERY CENTER, LLC—See Tenet Healthcare Corporation; *U.S. Public*, pg. 2004
LA PORTE MEDICAL CENTER LLC—See Adeptus Health Inc.; *U.S. Private*, pg. 78
LARGO MEDICAL CENTER-INDIAN ROCKS RD. CAMPUS—See Largo Medical Center; *U.S. Private*, pg. 2392
LASIK GERMANY GMBH—See EuroEyes International Eye Clinic Limited; *Int'l*, pg. 2535
LA VETA SURGICAL CENTER—See Encompass Health Corporation; *U.S. Public*, pg. 758
LAWRENCEVILLE SURGERY CENTER, L.L.C.—See Tenet Healthcare Corporation; *U.S. Public*, pg. 2011
LEONARDTOWN SURGERY CENTER, LLC—See Tenet Healthcare Corporation; *U.S. Public*, pg. 2004
THE LITTLE CLINIC OF ARIZONA LLC—See The Kroger Co.; *U.S. Public*, pg. 2109
LONGLEAF SURGERY CENTER, LLC—See Tenet Healthcare Corporation; *U.S. Public*, pg. 2004
LOUISVILLE S.C., LTD.—See UnitedHealth Group Incorporated; *U.S. Public*, pg. 2242
LOYOLA AMBULATORY SURGERY CENTER AT OAKBROOK, INC.—See UnitedHealth Group Incorporated; *U.S. Public*, pg. 2242
MANCHESTER AMBULATORY SURGERY CENTER, LP—See Tenet Healthcare Corporation; *U.S. Public*, pg. 2011
MAPLE LAWN SURGERY CENTER, LLC—See Tenet Healthcare Corporation; *U.S. Public*, pg. 2004
MARIN ENDOSCOPY CENTER, LLC—See KKR & Co. Inc.; *U.S. Public*, pg. 1246
MARION SURGERY CENTER, LLC—See Tenet Healthcare Corporation; *U.S. Public*, pg. 2004
MARSHLAND EMERGENCY PHYSICIANS, LLC—See HCA Healthcare, Inc.; *U.S. Public*, pg. 1001
MARYLAND ENDOSCOPY CENTER LIMITED LIABILITY COMPANY—See KKR & Co. Inc.; *U.S. Public*, pg. 1246
MARYLAND SURGERY CENTER FOR WOMEN, LLC—See KKR & Co. Inc.; *U.S. Public*, pg. 1249
MASSACHUSETTS AVENUE SURGERY CENTER, LLC—See UnitedHealth Group Incorporated; *U.S. Public*, pg. 2242
MATLOCK MEDICAL CENTER LLC—See Adeptus Health Inc.; *U.S. Private*, pg. 78
MAY STREET SURGI CENTER, LLC—See KKR & Co. Inc.; *U.S. Public*, pg. 1246
MEDICAL CITY DALLAS AMBULATORY SURGERY CENTER—See HCA Healthcare, Inc.; *U.S. Public*, pg. 1002
MEDICAL CITY SURGERY CENTER OF ALLEN, LLC—See HCA Healthcare, Inc.; *U.S. Public*, pg. 1002
MEDICAL MANAGEMENT RESOURCES, INC.—See Blackstone Inc.; *U.S. Public*, pg. 359
MEMORIAL HERMANN BAY AREA ENDOSCOPY CENTER, LLC—See Tenet Healthcare Corporation; *U.S. Public*, pg. 2011
MEMORIAL SURGERY CENTER, LLC—See Tenet Healthcare Corporation; *U.S. Public*, pg. 2011
METHODIST AMBULATORY SURGERY HOSPITAL - NORTHWEST—See HCA Healthcare, Inc.; *U.S. Public*, pg. 1002
METHODIST AMBULATORY SURGERY HOSPITAL - NORTHWEST—See Methodist Healthcare Ministries of South Texas, Inc.; *U.S. Private*, pg. 2683
METROPOLITAN MEDICAL PARTNERS, LLC—See UnitedHealth Group Incorporated; *U.S. Public*, pg. 2242
METROPOLITAN NEW JERSEY, LLC—See Tenet Healthcare Corporation; *U.S. Public*, pg. 2011
METRO SPECIALTY SURGERY CENTER, LLC—See Tenet Healthcare Corporation; *U.S. Public*, pg. 2004
METRO SURGERY CENTER, LLC—See Tenet Healthcare Corporation; *U.S. Public*, pg. 2011
MIAMI SURGICAL SUITES, LLC—See Tenet Healthcare Corporation; *U.S. Public*, pg. 2004
MIDLAND TEXAS SURGICAL CENTER, LLC—See Tenet Healthcare Corporation; *U.S. Public*, pg. 2011
MID RIVERS AMBULATORY SURGERY CENTER, L.P.—See Tenet Healthcare Corporation; *U.S. Public*, pg. 2011
MIDTOWN SURGERY CENTER J.V.—See Campbell Clinic Orthopaedics; *U.S. Private*, pg. 730
MIDWEST CENTER FOR DAY SURGERY, LLC—See UnitedHealth Group Incorporated; *U.S. Public*, pg. 2242
MILE HIGH SURGICENTER, LLC—See UnitedHealth Group Incorporated; *U.S. Public*, pg. 2242
MILLENNIUM SURGICAL CENTER, LLC—See Tenet Healthcare Corporation; *U.S. Public*, pg. 2011
MISSISSIPPI COAST ENDOSCOPY AND AMBULATORY SURGERY CENTER, INC.—See KKR & Co. Inc.; *U.S. Public*, pg. 1250
MOHAWK SURGERY CENTER, LLC—See UnitedHealth Group Incorporated; *U.S. Public*, pg. 2242
MONMOUTH-OCEAN HOSPITAL SERVICE CORPORATION; *U.S. Private*, pg. 2771
MONOCACY SURGERY CENTER, LLC—See Tenet Healthcare Corporation; *U.S. Public*, pg. 2004
MSD PHARMA (SINGAPORE) PTE. LTD.—See Merck & Co., Inc.; *U.S. Public*, pg. 1418
MT. OGDEN SURGICAL CENTER—See HCA Healthcare, Inc.; *U.S. Public*, pg. 1003
MT. PLEASANT SURGERY CENTER, L.P.—See UnitedHealth Group Incorporated; *U.S. Public*, pg. 2242
MUNSTER SPECIALTY SURGERY CENTER, LLC—See Tenet Healthcare Corporation; *U.S. Public*, pg. 2004
NEBRASKA LASER EYE ASSOCIATES—See Vance Thompson Vision Clinic Prof LLC; *U.S. Private*, pg. 4342
NEW HORIZONS SURGERY CENTER, LLC—See Tenet Healthcare Corporation; *U.S. Public*, pg. 2011
NORTH ATLANTIC SURGICAL SUITES, LLC—See Tenet Healthcare Corporation; *U.S. Public*, pg. 2005
NORTH DALLAS TOLLWAY MEDICAL CENTER LLC—See Adeptus Health Inc.; *U.S. Private*, pg. 78
NORTHERN MONMOUTH REGIONAL SURGERY CENTER, L.L.C.—See Tenet Healthcare Corporation; *U.S. Public*, pg. 2011

N.A.I.C.S. INDEX 621493 — FREESTANDING AMBULA...

NORTH HILLS SURGICARE, L.P.—See HCA Healthcare, Inc.; *U.S. Public*, pg. 1004
NORTHPOINTE SURGICAL SUITES, LLC—See Tenet Healthcare Corporation; *U.S. Public*, pg. 2005
NORTH SHORE SURGICAL SUITES, LLC—See Tenet Healthcare Corporation; *U.S. Public*, pg. 2005
NORTHSIDE GASTROENTEROLOGY ENDOSCOPY CENTER, LLC—See KKR & Co. Inc.; *U.S. Public*, pg. 1246
NORTH VALLEY ENDOSCOPY CENTER, LLC—See KKR & Co. Inc.; *U.S. Public*, pg. 1246
NORTHWEST AMBULATORY SURGERY CENTER, LLC—See Tenet Healthcare Corporation; *U.S. Public*, pg. 2012
NORTHWEST GEORGIA ORTHOPAEDIC SURGERY CENTER, LLC—See Tenet Healthcare Corporation; *U.S. Public*, pg. 2012
NORTHWEST REGIONAL ASC, LLC—See Tenet Healthcare Corporation; *U.S. Public*, pg. 2012
NORTHWEST REGIONAL SURGERY CENTER, LLC—See Tenet Healthcare Corporation; *U.S. Public*, pg. 2005
NOVAMED SURGERY CENTER OF CLEVELAND, LLC—See Bain Capital, LP; *U.S. Private*, pg. 446
NOVAMED SURGERY CENTER OF COLORADO SPRINGS, LLC—See Bain Capital, LP; *U.S. Private*, pg. 446
NOVAMED SURGERY CENTER OF DENVER, LLC—See Bain Capital, LP; *U.S. Private*, pg. 446
NOVAMED SURGERY CENTER OF MADISON, LIMITED PARTNERSHIP—See Bain Capital, LP; *U.S. Private*, pg. 446
NOVAMED SURGERY CENTER OF NASHUA, LLC—See Bain Capital, LP; *U.S. Private*, pg. 446
NOVAMED SURGERY CENTER OF OAK LAWN, LLC—See Bain Capital, LP; *U.S. Private*, pg. 446
NOVAMED SURGERY CENTER OF ORLANDO, LLC—See Bain Capital, LP; *U.S. Private*, pg. 446
NOVAMED SURGERY CENTER OF RIVER FOREST, LLC—See Bain Capital, LP; *U.S. Private*, pg. 446
NOVAMED SURGERY CENTER OF SANDUSKY, LLC—See Bain Capital, LP; *U.S. Private*, pg. 446
NOVAMED SURGERY CENTER OF ST. PETERS, LLC—See Bain Capital, LP; *U.S. Private*, pg. 446
NOVAMED SURGERY CENTER OF WARRENSBURG, LLC—See Bain Capital, LP; *U.S. Private*, pg. 446
OCEAN SPRINGS SURGICAL AND ENDOSCOPY CENTER, LLC—See KKR & Co. Inc.; *U.S. Public*, pg. 1250
OLD TESSON SURGERY CENTER, L.P.—See Tenet Healthcare Corporation; *U.S. Public*, pg. 2012
OLOL PONTCHARTRAIN SURGERY CENTER, LLC—See Tenet Healthcare Corporation; *U.S. Public*, pg. 2012
ORANGE CITY SURGERY CENTER, LLC—See Bain Capital, LP; *U.S. Private*, pg. 446
PACIFIC ENDO-SURGICAL CENTER, L.P.—See Tenet Healthcare Corporation; *U.S. Public*, pg. 2012
PALOS HEALTH SURGERY CENTER, LLC—See Tenet Healthcare Corporation; *U.S. Public*, pg. 2006
PARAMEDICS PLUS LLC—See Alvarez & Marsal, Inc.; *U.S. Private*, pg. 213
PARK CENTRAL SURGICAL CENTER, LTD.—See HCA Healthcare, Inc.; *U.S. Public*, pg. 1006
PARKCREEK ASC, LLC—See Tenet Healthcare Corporation; *U.S. Public*, pg. 2006
PARKWAY SURGERY CENTER, LLC—See Tenet Healthcare Corporation; *U.S. Public*, pg. 2012
PARKWEST SURGERY CENTER, L.P.—See Tenet Healthcare Corporation; *U.S. Public*, pg. 2012
PATIENT EDUCATION CONCEPTS, INC—See Bain Capital, LP; *U.S. Private*, pg. 446
PATIENT PARTNERS, LLC—See Tenet Healthcare Corporation; *U.S. Public*, pg. 2012
PEACEHEALTH; *U.S. Private*, pg. 3123
PEARLAND AMBULATORY SURGERY CENTER, LP—See Tenet Healthcare Corporation; *U.S. Public*, pg. 2012
PEARLAND SUNRISE MEDICAL CENTER LLC—See Adeptus Health Inc.; *U.S. Private*, pg. 78
PEDIATRICS & ADOLESCENT MEDICINE, PC—See American Medical Administrators, Inc.; *U.S. Private*, pg. 241
PHOENIX ENDOSCOPY, L.L.C.—See KKR & Co. Inc.; *U.S. Public*, pg. 1246
THE PHOENIX OPHTHALMOLOGY ASC, LLC—See KKR & Co. Inc.; *U.S. Public*, pg. 1248
PHYSICIANS SURGERY CENTER AT GOOD SAMARITAN, LLC—See Tenet Healthcare Corporation; *U.S. Public*, pg. 2012
PHYSICIANS SURGERY CENTER, LLC; *U.S. Private*, pg. 3175
PHYSICIAN'S SURGERY CENTER OF KNOXVILLE, LLC—See Tenet Healthcare Corporation; *U.S. Public*, pg. 2012
PHYSICIANS SURGICAL CARE, INC—See Bain Capital, LP; *U.S. Private*, pg. 446
PICCARD SURGERY CENTER, LLC—See Tenet Healthcare Corporation; *U.S. Public*, pg. 2006
PLANO ER CARE CENTER LLC—See Adeptus Health Inc.; *U.S. Private*, pg. 78
PONTE VEDRA PLASTIC SURGERY—See Ascend Plastic Surgery Partners; *U.S. Private*, pg. 346
POTOMAC VIEW SURGERY CENTER, LLC—See Tenet Healthcare Corporation; *U.S. Public*, pg. 2006
PREMIER ORTHOPAEDIC SURGERY CENTER—See HCA Healthcare, Inc.; *U.S. Public*, pg. 1006
PSHS ALPHA PARTNERS, LTD.—See Bain Capital, LP; *U.S. Private*, pg. 446
PSHS BETA PARTNERS, LTD.—See Bain Capital, LP; *U.S. Private*, pg. 446
P.T. HICLEARANCE MEDICAL INDONESIA—See Hi-Clearance, Inc.; *Int'l*, pg. 3380
RED CEDAR SURGERY CENTER, LLC—See Tenet Healthcare Corporation; *U.S. Public*, pg. 2006
RESEARCH SURGICAL CENTER, LLC—See UnitedHealth Group Incorporated; *U.S. Public*, pg. 2250
RESURGENS SURGERY CENTER, LLC—See Tenet Healthcare Corporation; *U.S. Public*, pg. 2012
RETINA ASSOCIATES OF NEW JERSEY, P.A.—See Quad-C Management, Inc.; *U.S. Private*, pg. 3315
RHN CLARK MEMORIAL PHYSICIAN PRACTICES, LLC—See Apollo Global Management, Inc.; *U.S. Public*, pg. 158
RIDGELINE ENDOSCOPY CENTER—See HCA Healthcare, Inc.; *U.S. Public*, pg. 1007
RIVA ROAD SURGERY CENTER, LLC—See Tenet Healthcare Corporation; *U.S. Public*, pg. 2006
RIVERBEND MEDICAL GROUP—See Trinity Health Corporation; *U.S. Private*, pg. 4234
RIVERSIDE AMBULATORY SURGERY CENTER, LLC—See Tenet Healthcare Corporation; *U.S. Public*, pg. 2012
RIVERSIDE SURGICAL CENTER OF MEADOWLANDS, LLC—See UnitedHealth Group Incorporated; *U.S. Public*, pg. 2250
ROCKVILLE SURGICAL SUITES, LLC—See Tenet Healthcare Corporation; *U.S. Public*, pg. 2006
ROSWELL SURGERY CENTER, L.L.C.—See Tenet Healthcare Corporation; *U.S. Public*, pg. 2012
SAN ANTONIO NACOGDOCHES MEDICAL CENTER LLC—See Adeptus Health Inc.; *U.S. Private*, pg. 78
SAN GABRIEL VALLEY SURGICAL CENTER, L.P.—See Tenet Healthcare Corporation; *U.S. Public*, pg. 2012
SANTA CLARITA SURGERY CENTER, L.P.—See Tenet Healthcare Corporation; *U.S. Public*, pg. 2012
SARASOTA AMBULATORY SURGERY CENTER, LTD.—See Bain Capital, LP; *U.S. Private*, pg. 446
SCA-DORAL, LLC—See UnitedHealth Group Incorporated; *U.S. Public*, pg. 2250
SCA PREMIER SURGERY CENTER OF LOUISVILLE, LLC—See UnitedHealth Group Incorporated; *U.S. Public*, pg. 2250
SCA-SAN LUIS OBISPO, LLC—See UnitedHealth Group Incorporated; *U.S. Public*, pg. 2250
SCA-WESTOVER HILLS, LLC—See UnitedHealth Group Incorporated; *U.S. Public*, pg. 2250
SEASIDE SURGERY CENTER, LLC—See Tenet Healthcare Corporation; *U.S. Public*, pg. 2007
SELECT SPECIALTY HOSPITAL-CLEVELAND, LLC—See Select Medical Holdings Corporation; *U.S. Public*, pg. 1860
SELECT SPECIALTY HOSPITAL-KALAMAZOO, INC.—See Select Medical Holdings Corporation; *U.S. Public*, pg. 1860
SENTRY ANESTHESIA MANAGEMENT, LLC—See Bain Capital, LP; *U.S. Private*, pg. 446
SEQUOIA SURGICAL CENTER, L.P.—See Bain Capital, LP; *U.S. Private*, pg. 445
SHELBY BAPTIST AMBULATORY SURGERY CENTER, LLC—See Tenet Healthcare Corporation; *U.S. Public*, pg. 2007
SHORE OUTPATIENT SURGICENTER, L.L.C.—See Tenet Healthcare Corporation; *U.S. Public*, pg. 2012
THE SIDNEY ASC, LLC—See KKR & Co. Inc.; *U.S. Public*, pg. 1248
SILICON VALLEY SURGERY CENTER, L.P.—See HCA Healthcare, Inc.; *U.S. Public*, pg. 1008
SKINVET CLINIC, LLC—See Percheron Investment Management LP; *U.S. Private*, pg. 3146
SKY RIDGE SURGICAL CENTER—See HCA Healthcare, Inc.; *U.S. Public*, pg. 1008
SKYWAY SURGERY CENTER, LLC—See Bain Capital, LP; *U.S. Private*, pg. 445
SOUTH AUSTIN SURGERY CENTER, LTD.—See HCA Healthcare, Inc.; *U.S. Public*, pg. 1010
SOUTH COUNTY OUTPATIENT ENDOSCOPY SERVICES, L.P.—See Tenet Healthcare Corporation; *U.S. Public*, pg. 2012
SOUTHEASTERN PHYSICIAN ASSOCIATES, LLC—See Blackstone Inc.; *U.S. Public*, pg. 359
SOUTH PORTLAND SURGICAL CENTER, LLC—See KKR & Co. Inc.; *U.S. Public*, pg. 1250
SOUTHWESTERN AMBULATORY SURGERY CENTER, LLC—See Tenet Healthcare Corporation; *U.S. Public*, pg. 2012
SOUTHWEST FLORIDA EMERGENCY MANAGEMENT, LLC—See Blackstone Inc.; *U.S. Public*, pg. 359
SPACE COAST SURGERY CENTER LLC—See Bain Capital, LP; *U.S. Private*, pg. 446
SPECIALTY SURGICAL CENTER, LLC—See Bain Capital, LP; *U.S. Private*, pg. 446
SPINAL DIAGNOSTICS AND TREATMENT CENTERS, L.L.C.—See Tenet Healthcare Corporation; *U.S. Public*, pg. 2013
SSH MEDICAL CENTER LLC—See Adeptus Health Inc.; *U.S. Private*, pg. 78
ST. FRANCIS AFFILIATED SERVICES, LLC—See Apollo Global Management, Inc.; *U.S. Public*, pg. 158
ST. FRANCIS PHYSICIAN PRACTICES, LLC—See Apollo Global Management, Inc.; *U.S. Public*, pg. 159
ST. GEORGE ENDOSCOPY CENTER, LLC—See KKR & Co. Inc.; *U.S. Public*, pg. 1246
ST. LOUIS SURGICAL CENTER, LC—See Tenet Healthcare Corporation; *U.S. Public*, pg. 2013
ST. LOUIS WOMEN'S SURGERY CENTER, LLC—See Bain Capital, LP; *U.S. Private*, pg. 446
ST. MARKS PHYSICIAN BILLING, LLC—See HCA Healthcare, Inc.; *U.S. Public*, pg. 1010
ST. MARY'S AMBULATORY SURGERY CENTER, LLC—See Tenet Healthcare Corporation; *U.S. Public*, pg. 2013
STOCKTON OUTPATIENT SURGERY CENTER, LLC—See Tenet Healthcare Corporation; *U.S. Public*, pg. 2013
STONEGATE SURGERY CENTER, L.P.—See UnitedHealth Group Incorporated; *U.S. Public*, pg. 2250
STONE OAK SURGICENTER, LLC—See HCA Healthcare, Inc.; *U.S. Public*, pg. 1010
SUBURBAN ENDOSCOPY CENTER, LLC—See Tenet Healthcare Corporation; *U.S. Public*, pg. 2013
SUMMERWOOD MEDICAL CENTER LLC—See Adeptus Health Inc.; *U.S. Private*, pg. 78
SUMMIT VIEW SURGERY CENTER, LLC—See Tenet Healthcare Corporation; *U.S. Public*, pg. 2013
SURGCENTER AT PARADISE VALLEY, LLC—See Tenet Healthcare Corporation; *U.S. Public*, pg. 2007
SURGCENTER CAMELBACK, LLC—See Tenet Healthcare Corporation; *U.S. Public*, pg. 2007
SURGCENTER NORTHEAST, LLC—See Tenet Healthcare Corporation; *U.S. Public*, pg. 2007
SURGCENTER OF GREATER JACKSONVILLE, LLC—See Tenet Healthcare Corporation; *U.S. Public*, pg. 2007
SURGCENTER OF NORTHERN BALTIMORE, LLC—See Tenet Healthcare Corporation; *U.S. Public*, pg. 2007
SURGCENTER OF PALM BEACH GARDENS, LLC—See Tenet Healthcare Corporation; *U.S. Public*, pg. 2007
SURGCENTER OF SILVER SPRING, LLC—See Tenet Healthcare Corporation; *U.S. Public*, pg. 2007
SURGCENTER OF SOUTHERN MARYLAND, LLC—See Tenet Healthcare Corporation; *U.S. Public*, pg. 2007
SURGCENTER OF ST. LUCIE, LLC—See Tenet Healthcare Corporation; *U.S. Public*, pg. 2007
SURGCENTER OF WHITE MARSH, LLC—See Tenet Healthcare Corporation; *U.S. Public*, pg. 2007
SURGCENTER PINELLAS, LLC—See Tenet Healthcare Corporation; *U.S. Public*, pg. 2007
SURGE CENTER OF GLEN BURNIE LLC—See Tenet Healthcare Corporation; *U.S. Public*, pg. 2007
SURGERY CENTER AT CHERRY CREEK, LLC—See UnitedHealth Group Incorporated; *U.S. Public*, pg. 2250
SURGERY CENTER AT KISSING CAMELS, LLC—See UnitedHealth Group Incorporated; *U.S. Public*, pg. 2250
THE SURGERY CENTER, L.L.C.—See Bain Capital, LP; *U.S. Private*, pg. 447
SURGERY CENTER OF ATHENS, LLC—See UnitedHealth Group Incorporated; *U.S. Public*, pg. 2250
SURGERY CENTER OF CANFIELD, LLC—See Tenet Healthcare Corporation; *U.S. Public*, pg. 2013
SURGERY CENTER OF CLARKSVILLE, L.P.—See UnitedHealth Group Incorporated; *U.S. Public*, pg. 2250
SURGERY CENTER OF COLUMBIA, L.P.—See Tenet Healthcare Corporation; *U.S. Public*, pg. 2013
SURGERY CENTER OF DES MOINES, LLC—See UnitedHealth Group Incorporated; *U.S. Public*, pg. 2250
SURGERY CENTER OF FREMONT, LLC—See Bain Capital, LP; *U.S. Private*, pg. 446
SURGERY CENTER OF GILBERT, L.L.C.—See Tenet Healthcare Corporation; *U.S. Public*, pg. 2013
SURGERY CENTER OF LEBANON, LP—See Bain Capital, LP; *U.S. Private*, pg. 446
SURGERY CENTER OF LEXINGTON, LLC—See UnitedHealth Group Incorporated; *U.S. Public*, pg. 2250
SURGERY CENTER OF PEORIA, L.L.C.—See Tenet Healthcare Corporation; *U.S. Public*, pg. 2013
SURGERY CENTER OF ROCKVILLE, LLC—See UnitedHealth Group Incorporated; *U.S. Public*, pg. 2250
SURGERY CENTER OF SCOTTSDALE, LLC—See Tenet Healthcare Corporation; *U.S. Public*, pg. 2013
SURGERY CENTER OF TEMPE, LLC—See Tenet Healthcare Corporation; *U.S. Public*, pg. 2013
SURGERY CENTER OF VOLUSIA, LLC—See KKR & Co. Inc.; *U.S. Public*, pg. 1247
SURGERY CENTER PARTNERS, LLC—See Bain Capital, LP; *U.S. Private*, pg. 446
SURGERY CENTERS OF DES MOINES, LTD.—See UnitedHealth Group Incorporated; *U.S. Public*, pg. 2250
SURGICAL CENTER AT MILLBURN, LLC—See KKR & Co. Inc.; *U.S. Public*, pg. 1250
SURGICAL CENTER OF SOUTH JERSEY, LIMITED

N.A.I.C.S. Index

621493 — FREESTANDING AMBULA...

PARTNERSHIP—See UnitedHealth Group Incorporated; *U.S. Public*, pg. 2251

THE SURGICAL CENTER OF THE TREASURE COAST, LLC—See UnitedHealth Group Incorporated; *U.S. Public*, pg. 2251

SURGICAL PROCESS INSTITUTE DEUTSCHLAND GMBH—See Johnson & Johnson; *U.S. Public*, pg. 1200

SURGICAL SPECIALTY CENTER OF NORTHEASTERN PENNSYLVANIA, LLC—See KKR & Co. Inc.; *U.S. Public*, pg. 1250

SURGICARE OF CENTRAL PARK SURGERY CENTER, LLC—See HCA Healthcare, Inc.; *U.S. Public*, pg. 1011

SURGICARE OF MOBILE, LLC—See UnitedHealth Group Incorporated; *U.S. Public*, pg. 2251

SURGICENTER OF BALTIMORE, LLP—See Tenet Healthcare Corporation; *U.S. Public*, pg. 2013

SURGICENTER OF KANSAS CITY, L.L.C.—See HCA Healthcare, Inc.; *U.S. Public*, pg. 1011

TAMPA BAY JOINT & SPINE, LLC—See Tenet Healthcare Corporation; *U.S. Public*, pg. 2007

TERRE HAUTE SURGICAL CENTER, LLC—See Tenet Healthcare Corporation; *U.S. Public*, pg. 2013

TEXAS EMERGENCY CARE CENTERS, LLC—See Family ER + Urgent Care; *U.S. Private*, pg. 1469

TEXAS HEALTH SURGERY CENTER CHISHOLM TRAIL, LLC—See UnitedHealth Group Incorporated; *U.S. Public*, pg. 2251

THOMAS JOHNSON SURGERY CENTER, LLC—See UnitedHealth Group Incorporated; *U.S. Public*, pg. 2251

TIMONIUM SURGERY CENTER, LLC—See Tenet Healthcare Corporation; *U.S. Public*, pg. 2009

TOPS SPECIALTY HOSPITAL, LTD.—See Tenet Healthcare Corporation; *U.S. Public*, pg. 2013

TRAILS EDGE SURGERY CENTER, LLC—See UnitedHealth Group Incorporated; *U.S. Public*, pg. 2251

TRIANGLE ENDOSCOPY CENTER, LLC—See KKR & Co. Inc.; *U.S. Public*, pg. 1249

TRISTAR CARDIOVASCULAR SURGERY, LLC—See HCA Healthcare, Inc.; *U.S. Public*, pg. 1012

TUCSON ARIZONA SURGICAL CENTER, LLC—See UnitedHealth Group Incorporated; *U.S. Public*, pg. 2251

TUSCAN SURGERY CENTER AT LAS COLINAS, LLC—See Tenet Healthcare Corporation; *U.S. Public*, pg. 2013

TWIN CITIES AMBULATORY SURGERY CENTER, L.P.—See Tenet Healthcare Corporation; *U.S. Public*, pg. 2013

UNDERWOOD SURGERY CENTER, LLC—See Tenet Healthcare Corporation; *U.S. Public*, pg. 2014

UPPER BAY SURGERY CENTER, LLC—See Tenet Healthcare Corporation; *U.S. Public*, pg. 2014

UTICA ASC PARTNERS, LLC—See Tenet Healthcare Corporation; *U.S. Public*, pg. 2014

VANCE THOMPSON VISION CLINIC PROF LLC; *U.S. Private*, pg. 4342

VIRTUA SURGICAL GROUP; *U.S. Private*, pg. 4388

VIVERE HEALTH LLC—See Prelude Fertility, Inc.; *U.S. Private*, pg. 3249

THE VOORHEES NJ ENDOSCOPY ASC, LLC—See KKR & Co. Inc.; *U.S. Public*, pg. 1248

WACO GASTROENTEROLOGY ENDOSCOPY CENTER, LLC—See KKR & Co. Inc.; *U.S. Public*, pg. 1249

WARNER PARK SURGERY CENTER, L.P.—See Tenet Healthcare Corporation; *U.S. Public*, pg. 2014

WASATCH FRONT SURGERY CENTER, LLC—See HCA Healthcare, Inc.; *U.S. Public*, pg. 1013

WATERSIDE MEDICAL CENTER LLC—See Adeptus Health Inc.; *U.S. Private*, pg. 78

WAUWATOSA SURGERY CENTER, LIMITED PARTNERSHIP—See UnitedHealth Group Incorporated; *U.S. Public*, pg. 2252

WAVERLY SURGERY CENTER, LLC—See KKR & Co. Inc.; *U.S. Public*, pg. 1250

WCB MEDICAL CENTER LLC—See Adeptus Health Inc.; *U.S. Private*, pg. 78

WELLINGTON ENDO, LLC—See Tenet Healthcare Corporation; *U.S. Public*, pg. 2015

WESTCHASE SURGERY CENTER, LTD.—See Bain Capital, LP; *U.S. Public*, pg. 447

WEST COAST ENDOSCOPY HOLDINGS, LLC—See UnitedHealth Group Incorporated; *U.S. Public*, pg. 2253

WESTERN CONNECTICUT ORTHOPEDIC SURGICAL CENTER, LLC—See UnitedHealth Group Incorporated; *U.S. Public*, pg. 2253

WESTGATE SURGERY CENTER, LLC—See Tenet Healthcare Corporation; *U.S. Public*, pg. 2015

WILMINGTON ASC, LLC—See UnitedHealth Group Incorporated; *U.S. Public*, pg. 2253

WILMINGTON HEALTH ASSOCIATES, PA.; *U.S. Private*, pg. 4529

WILTON SURGERY CENTER, LLC—See KKR & Co. Inc.; *U.S. Public*, pg. 1249

WINCHESTER ENDOSCOPY, LLC—See UnitedHealth Group Incorporated; *U.S. Public*, pg. 2253

WISCONSIN SPECIALTY SURGERY CENTER, LLC—See Tenet Healthcare Corporation; *U.S. Public*, pg. 2015

WOMEN'S AND CHILDREN'S SPECIALISTS, LLC—See HCA Healthcare, Inc.; *U.S. Public*, pg. 1014

621498 — ALL OTHER OUTPATIENT CARE CENTERS

ABBOTT HEALTHCARE CONNECTIONS LIMITED—See Abbott Laboratories; *U.S. Public*, pg. 18

ABBOTT RAPID DIAGNOSTICS BV—See Abbott Laboratories; *U.S. Public*, pg. 18

ACUTE BEHAVIORAL HEALTH, LLC—See Petra Capital Partners, LLC; *U.S. Private*, pg. 3161

ADAMS COUNTY PHYSICAL THERAPY, LIMITED PARTNERSHIP—See U.S. Physical Therapy, Inc.; *U.S. Public*, pg. 2213

ADVENTHEALTH SURGERY CENTER DAVENPORT, LLC—See Tenet Healthcare Corporation; *U.S. Public*, pg. 2001

ALERE PHILIPPINES, INC.—See Abbott Laboratories; *U.S. Public*, pg. 18

ALLEN CREEK HEALTHCARE, INC.—See The Ensign Group, Inc.; *U.S. Public*, pg. 2069

ALOHACARE; *U.S. Private*, pg. 195

ALPHACARE OF NEW YORK, INC.—See Centene Corporation; *U.S. Public*, pg. 469

ALPOWA HEALTHCARE, INC.—See The Ensign Group, Inc.; *U.S. Public*, pg. 2070

AMBULATORY SURGERY CENTER GROUP, LTD.—See HCA Healthcare, Inc.; *U.S. Public*, pg. 990

AMERICAN ACADEMY OF SLEEP MEDICINE; *U.S. Private*, pg. 221

AMERICAN SUBSTANCE ABUSE PROFESSIONALS, INC.; *U.S. Private*, pg. 256

AMICUS THERAPEUTICS B.V.—See Amicus Therapeutics, Inc.; *U.S. Public*, pg. 124

AMICUS THERAPEUTICS GMBH—See Amicus Therapeutics, Inc.; *U.S. Public*, pg. 124

AMICUS THERAPEUTICS SAS—See Amicus Therapeutics, Inc.; *U.S. Public*, pg. 124

AMICUS THERAPEUTICS S.L.—See Amicus Therapeutics, Inc.; *U.S. Public*, pg. 124

AMICUS THERAPEUTICS S.R.L.—See Amicus Therapeutics, Inc.; *U.S. Public*, pg. 124

ANKENY PHYSICAL & SPORTS THERAPY, LIMITED PARTNERSHIP—See U.S. Physical Therapy, Inc.; *U.S. Public*, pg. 2213

ANZA HEALTHCARE, INC.—See The Ensign Group, Inc.; *U.S. Public*, pg. 2070

THE ARCADIA CA ENDOSCOPY ASC, L.P.—See KKR & Co. Inc.; *U.S. Public*, pg. 1247

ARIEL CLINICAL SERVICES; *U.S. Private*, pg. 322

ARRIVA MEDICAL PHILIPPINES, INC.—See Abbott Laboratories; *U.S. Public*, pg. 19

ARROW PHYSICAL THERAPY, LIMITED PARTNERSHIP—See U.S. Physical Therapy, Inc.; *U.S. Public*, pg. 2213

ATLANTIS GLORY INC.; *U.S. Public*, pg. 223

AUBURN COMMUNITY HOSPITAL; *U.S. Private*, pg. 385

AUDUBON PHYSICAL THERAPY, LIMITED PARTNERSHIP—See U.S. Physical Therapy, Inc.; *U.S. Public*, pg. 2214

AXELACARE HOLDINGS, INC.—See Harvest Partners L.P.; *U.S. Private*, pg. 1876

THE BALTIMORE ENDOSCOPY ASC, LLC—See KKR & Co. Inc.; *U.S. Public*, pg. 1247

BANGKOK HOSPITAL SAMUI CO., LTD.—See Bangkok Dusit Medical Services Public Company Limited; *Int'l*, pg. 834

BAPTIST MEDICAL & DENTAL MISSION INTERNATIONAL, INC.; *U.S. Private*, pg. 471

BAPTIST OUTPATIENT SERVICES—See Baptist Health South Florida, Inc.; *U.S. Private*, pg. 470

BAYSIDE HEALTHCARE, INC.—See The Ensign Group, Inc.; *U.S. Public*, pg. 2070

B. BRAUN AVITUM ITALY S.P.A.—See B. Braun Melsungen AG; *Int'l*, pg. 786

B. BRAUN TRAVACARE GMBH—See B. Braun Melsungen AG; *Int'l*, pg. 787

BEACON HILL HEALTHCARE, INC.—See The Ensign Group, Inc.; *U.S. Public*, pg. 2070

BEAUFORT PHYSICAL THERAPY, LIMITED PARTNERSHIP—See U.S. Physical Therapy, Inc.; *U.S. Public*, pg. 2214

BEHAVIORAL HEALTH SERVICES—See Northwestern Memorial HealthCare; *U.S. Private*, pg. 2962

BELLEAIR SURGERY CENTER, LTD.—See HCA Healthcare, Inc.; *U.S. Public*, pg. 991

BETHESDA CHEVY CHASE SURGERY CENTER, LLC—See Tenet Healthcare Corporation; *U.S. Public*, pg. 2001

BETHESDA OUTPATIENT SURGERY CENTER, LLC—See KKR & Co. Inc.; *U.S. Public*, pg. 1245

BIG PASS S.A.—See Edenred S.A.; *Int'l*, pg. 2307

BIOPLUS SPECIALTY PHARMACY SERVICES, LLC; *U.S. Private*, pg. 562

BIOSYMM PTY LTD.—See Madison Dearborn Partners, LLC; *U.S. Private*, pg. 2540

BLANCHARD VALLEY HEALTH SYSTEM; *U.S. Private*, pg. 579

BNH MEDICAL CENTER CO., LTD.—See Bangkok Dusit Medical Services Public Company Limited; *Int'l*, pg. 833

BOSQUE RIVER PHYSICAL THERAPY & REHABILITATION, LIMITED PARTNERSHIP—See U.S. Physical Therapy, Inc.; *U.S. Public*, pg. 2214

BOW PHYSICAL THERAPY & SPINE CENTER, LIMITED PARTNERSHIP—See U.S. Physical Therapy, Inc.; *U.S. Public*, pg. 2214

BRADLEY COUNTY MEDICAL CENTER; *U.S. Private*, pg. 632

BRAZOS VALLEY PHYSICAL THERAPY, LIMITED PARTNERSHIP—See U.S. Physical Therapy, Inc.; *U.S. Public*, pg. 2214

BRECKINRIDGE HEALTH, INC.; *U.S. Private*, pg. 644

BRICK HAND & REHABILITATIVE SERVICES, LIMITED PARTNERSHIP—See U.S. Physical Therapy, Inc.; *U.S. Public*, pg. 2214

THE BRIDGE INC.; *U.S. Private*, pg. 4000

BROOKDALE BEND OR, LLC—See Brookdale Senior Living Inc.; *U.S. Public*, pg. 393

BY THE BAY HEALTH—See University of California San Francisco Medical Center; *U.S. Private*, pg. 4308

CALIFORNIA FAMILY HEALTH COUNCIL; *U.S. Private*, pg. 719

CALIFORNIA RURAL INDIAN HEALTH BOARD, INC.; *U.S. Private*, pg. 720

CAMARENA HEALTH; *U.S. Private*, pg. 725

CANTERBURY-ON-THE-LAKE; *U.S. Private*, pg. 735

CAPE COD HAND THERAPY, LIMITED PARTNERSHIP—See U.S. Physical Therapy, Inc.; *U.S. Public*, pg. 2214

CAPITAL HAND & PHYSICAL THERAPY, LIMITED PARTNERSHIP—See U.S. Physical Therapy, Inc.; *U.S. Public*, pg. 2214

CAREGIVER, INC.; *U.S. Private*, pg. 753

CAREOREGON, INC.; *U.S. Private*, pg. 754

CARING PARTNERS INTERNATIONAL; *U.S. Private*, pg. 761

CARLE FOUNDATION; *U.S. Private*, pg. 763

CARSON TAHOE REGIONAL HEALTHCARE; *U.S. Private*, pg. 774

CENTER FOR DIAGNOSTIC IMAGING, INC.—See Wellspring Capital Management LLC; *U.S. Private*, pg. 4477

CENTRAL MONTANA MEDICAL CENTER; *U.S. Private*, pg. 822

CENTRO INMUNOLOGICA DE LA COMUNIDAD VALENCIANA, S.L.—See Centene Corporation; *U.S. Public*, pg. 468

CHAPTERS HEALTH SYSTEM, INC.; *U.S. Private*, pg. 850

CHARLES B. WANG COMMUNITY HEALTH CENTER, INC.; *U.S. Private*, pg. 851

THE CHATTANOOGA ENDOSCOPY ASC, LLC—See KKR & Co. Inc.; *U.S. Public*, pg. 1247

CHATTANOOGA PAIN MANAGEMENT CENTER, LLC—See Tenet Healthcare Corporation; *U.S. Public*, pg. 2009

THE CHEVY CHASE ASC, LLC—See KKR & Co. Inc.; *U.S. Public*, pg. 1247

CHILDREN'S HEALTH COUNCIL; *U.S. Private*, pg. 883

CHOPTANK COMMUNITY HEALTH SYSTEM, INC.; *U.S. Private*, pg. 888

CHRIST COMMUNITY HEALTH SERVICES; *U.S. Private*, pg. 890

THE CHRIST HOSPITAL; *U.S. Private*, pg. 4009

CHRISTIAN HEALTH CARE CENTER; *U.S. Private*, pg. 891

CINCINNATI HEALTH NETWORK; *U.S. Private*, pg. 898

CLAYDELLE HEALTHCARE, INC.—See The Ensign Group, Inc.; *U.S. Public*, pg. 2070

CLINICA SANTO DOMINGO DE LUGO, S.L.—See Centene Corporation; *U.S. Public*, pg. 468

CME MEDICAL (UK) LIMITED—See Becton, Dickinson & Company; *U.S. Public*, pg. 291

COBRE VALLEY REGIONAL MEDICAL CENTER; *U.S. Private*, pg. 958

COLUMBUS SPECIALTY SURGERY CENTER LLC—See Tenet Healthcare Corporation; *U.S. Public*, pg. 2002

COMMONWEALTH CARE ALLIANCE, INC.; *U.S. Private*, pg. 986

COMMUNITY HEALTH CENTERS OF THE CENTRAL COAST, INC.; *U.S. Private*, pg. 993

COMMUNITY HEALTH CENTER; *U.S. Private*, pg. 993

COMMUNITY HEALTH CONNECTIONS, INC.; *U.S. Private*, pg. 993

COMMUNITY HEALTH GROUP; *U.S. Private*, pg. 993

COMMUNITY HEALTH OF SOUTH FLORIDA, INC.; *U.S. Private*, pg. 994

COMMUNITY HEALTH PROGRAMS, INC.; *U.S. Private*, pg. 994

COMMUNITY HEALTH SERVICES, INC.; *U.S. Private*, pg. 994

COMMUNITYHEALTH; *U.S. Private*, pg. 997

COMMUNITY HOSPICE, INC.; *U.S. Private*, pg. 994

COMMUNITY HOSPITAL, INC.; *U.S. Private*, pg. 994

COMMUNITY MEDICAL CENTERS, INC.; *U.S. Private*, pg. 995

COMMUNITY MEMORIAL HEALTHCARE, INC.; *U.S. Private*, pg. 995

COMPAGNIE STEPHANOISE DE SANTE SA—See Bridgepoint Group Plc; *Int'l*, pg. 1154

N.A.I.C.S. INDEX

621498 — ALL OTHER OUTPATIEN...

COMPREHENSIVE HAND & PHYSICAL THERAPY, LIMITED PARTNERSHIP—See U.S. Physical Therapy, Inc.; *U.S. Public*, pg. 2214

CONCILIO DE SALUD INTEGRAL DE LOIZA, INC.; *U.S. Private*, pg. 1009

COPE COMMUNITY SERVICES, INC.; *U.S. Private*, pg. 1044

COPLEY PROFESSIONAL SERVICES GROUP, INC.; *U.S. Private*, pg. 1045

COPPELL SPINE & SPORTS REHAB, LIMITED PARTNERSHIP—See U.S. Physical Therapy, Inc.; *U.S. Public*, pg. 2214

CORAL SPRINGS SURGI-CENTER, LTD.—See HCA Healthcare, Inc.; *U.S. Public*, pg. 994

CORNERSTONE CARE, INC.; *U.S. Private*, pg. 1051

CORTLAND REGIONAL MEDICAL CENTER; *U.S. Private*, pg. 1061

COUNTRYSIDE SURGERY CENTER, LTD.—See HCA Healthcare, Inc.; *U.S. Public*, pg. 994

CRAWFORD PHYSICAL THERAPY, LIMITED PARTNERSHIP—See U.S. Physical Therapy, Inc.; *U.S. Public*, pg. 2214

CROSS CREEK PHYSICAL THERAPY, LIMITED PARTNERSHIP—See U.S. Physical Therapy, Inc.; *U.S. Public*, pg. 2214

DALLAS REGIONAL MEDICAL CENTER - WOUND CARE & HYPERBARIC CENTER—See Prime Healthcare Services, Inc.; *U.S. Public*, pg. 3261

DELAWARE VALLEY COMMUNITY HEALTH, INC.; *U.S. Private*, pg. 1196

DERMATOLOGY & SKIN SURGERY CENTER; *U.S. Private*, pg. 1209

DIABETES SELF-MANAGEMENT CENTER, INC.—See UnitedHealth Group Incorporated; *U.S. Public*, pg. 2244

DISTRICT OF COLUMBIA PRIMARY CARE ASSOCIATION; *U.S. Private*, pg. 1239

DOCTORS OUTPATIENT CENTER FOR SURGERY, LLC—See Tenet Healthcare Corporation; *U.S. Public*, pg. 2002

DOCTORS SAME DAY SURGERY CENTER, INC.—See HCA Healthcare, Inc.; *U.S. Public*, pg. 995

DR. PARK AVE.; *U.S. Private*, pg. 1271

DS WELLNESS & HEALTH MANAGEMENT LIMITED—See Feiyang International Holdings Group Limited; *Int'l*, pg. 2632

EAGLE HARBOR HEALTHCARE, INC.—See The Ensign Group, Inc.; *U.S. Public*, pg. 2070

EDENSLEEP NEW ZEALAND LIMITED—See ResMed Inc.; *U.S. Public*, pg. 1790

EDGAR P BENJAMIN HEALTHCARE CENTER, INC.; *U.S. Private*, pg. 1333

EDGE PHYSICAL THERAPY, LIMITED PARTNERSHIP—See U.S. Physical Therapy, Inc.; *U.S. Public*, pg. 2214

EDUCATION-PLUS, INC.; *U.S. Private*, pg. 1339

EMBLEM HEALTHCARE, INC.—See The Ensign Group, Inc.; *U.S. Public*, pg. 2070

EMPIRECARE HEALTH ASSOCIATES, INC.—See The Ensign Group, Inc.; *U.S. Public*, pg. 2070

THE ENDOSCOPY CENTER OF EL PASO, L.P.—See KKR & Co. Inc.; *U.S. Public*, pg. 1247

THE ENDOSCOPY CENTER OF SANTA FE, L.P.—See KKR & Co. Inc.; *U.S. Public*, pg. 1247

THE ENDOSCOPY CENTER OF SOUTHEAST TEXAS, L.P.—See KKR & Co. Inc.; *U.S. Public*, pg. 1247

THE ENDOSCOPY CENTER OF THE SOUTH BAY, L.P.—See KKR & Co. Inc.; *U.S. Public*, pg. 1247

THE ENDOSCOPY CENTER OF TOPEKA, L.P.—See KKR & Co. Inc.; *U.S. Public*, pg. 1247

THE ENDOSCOPY CENTER OF WASHINGTON D.C., L.P.—See KKR & Co. Inc.; *U.S. Public*, pg. 1247

THE ENGLEWOOD ASC, LLC—See KKR & Co. Inc.; *U.S. Public*, pg. 1247

EPISCOPAL HEALTH FOUNDATION; *U.S. Private*, pg. 1413

EQHEALTH SOLUTIONS, LLC—See Apax Partners LLP; *Int'l*, pg. 504

ERIE FAMILY HEALTH CENTER; *U.S. Private*, pg. 1420

ESCREEN CANADA ULC—See Abbott Laboratories; *U.S. Public*, pg. 19

FACHKLINIK ZWIESELBERG GMBH—See Asklepios Kliniken GmbH & Co. KGaA; *Int'l*, pg. 623

FAMILY HEALTH CENTERS OF SOUTHWEST FLORIDA INC.; *U.S. Private*, pg. 1470

FAMILY HEALTH CENTER; *U.S. Private*, pg. 1470

FAMILY HEALTH SERVICES CORPORATION; *U.S. Private*, pg. 1470

FAMILY PHYSICIANS OF WINTER PARK, INC.—See Humana, Inc.; *U.S. Public*, pg. 1069

THE FELLOWSHIP HOUSE—See Centerstone of America, Inc.; *U.S. Private*, pg. 817

FINDLAY SURGERY CENTER, LTD.—See Blanchard Valley Health System; *U.S. Private*, pg. 579

FIRST CHOICE COMMUNITY HEALTHCARE, INC.; *U.S. Private*, pg. 1515

THE FLORHAM PARK ENDOSCOPY ASC, LLC—See KKR & Co. Inc.; *U.S. Public*, pg. 1247

FOCUS POINT HOLDINGS BERHAD; *Int'l*, pg. 2719

FOCUS RX INC.—See UnitedHealth Group Incorporated; *U.S. Public*, pg. 2247

FOOTHILL COMMUNITY HEALTH CENTER—See Bay Area Community Health; *U.S. Private*, pg. 491

FOREST CITY PHYSICAL THERAPY, LIMITED PARTNERSHIP—See U.S. Physical Therapy, Inc.; *U.S. Public*, pg. 2214

FRANKLIN ENDOSCOPY CENTER, LLC—See Tenet Healthcare Corporation; *U.S. Public*, pg. 2010

FRANKLIN PRIMARY HEALTH CENTER, INC.; *U.S. Private*, pg. 1597

FRIEND FAMILY HEALTH CENTER, INC.; *U.S. Private*, pg. 1611

FRISCO PHYSICAL THERAPY, LIMITED PARTNERSHIP—See U.S. Physical Therapy, Inc.; *U.S. Public*, pg. 2214

FUNCTIONAL PATHWAYS, LLC.; *U.S. Private*, pg. 1622

FURUSATO. CO., LTD.—See Haseko Corporation; *Int'l*, pg. 3283

GHP SPECIALTY CARE AB—See Apax Partners LLP; *Int'l*, pg. 502

GLOBAL DIAGNOSTICS IRELAND LIMITED—See IK Investment Partners Limited; *Int'l*, pg. 3609

GOSHEN HOSPITAL & HEALTH CARE FOUNDATION INC.; *U.S. Private*, pg. 1744

GRACE HEALTH; *U.S. Private*, pg. 1749

GRAND RAPIDS SURGICAL SUITES, LLC—See Tenet Healthcare Corporation; *U.S. Public*, pg. 2002

GRASSLAND HEALTHCARE AND REHABILITATION, INC.—See The Ensign Group, Inc.; *U.S. Public*, pg. 2071

THE GREATER FAIRBANKS COMMUNITY HOSPITAL FOUNDATION, INCORPORATED; *U.S. Private*, pg. 4038

GREEN OAKS PHYSICAL THERAPY, LIMITED PARTNERSHIP—See U.S. Physical Therapy, Inc.; *U.S. Public*, pg. 2214

THE GREENSBORO OPTHALMOLOGY ASC, LLC—See KKR & Co. Inc.; *U.S. Public*, pg. 1247

GROUP HEALTH COOPERATIVE OF EAU CLAIRE; *U.S. Private*, pg. 1793

GSI HEALTH, LLC—See Health Care Service Corporation; *U.S. Private*, pg. 1892

GVNA HEALTHCARE, INC.; *U.S. Private*, pg. 1821

HACKLEY COMMUNITY CARE; *U.S. Private*, pg. 1838

HAMILTON PHYSICAL THERAPY, LIMITED PARTNERSHIP—See U.S. Physical Therapy, Inc.; *U.S. Public*, pg. 2214

HANGER PROSTHETIC & ORTHOTICS, INC.—See Patient Square Capital, L.P.; *U.S. Private*, pg. 3107

HARBOR BEACH COMMUNITY HOSPITAL, INC.; *U.S. Private*, pg. 1858

HAUSLICHE KRANKENPFLEGE CHARLOTTE KONIG GMBH & CO.—See Clariane SE; *Int'l*, pg. 1643

HEALTH AFFILIATES MAINE; *U.S. Private*, pg. 1892

HEALTHCREST SURGICAL PARTNERS, LLC; *U.S. Private*, pg. 1896

HEALTHFIRST BLUEGRASS; *U.S. Private*, pg. 1896

HEALTH NETWORK ONE, INC.—See H.I.G. Capital, LLC; *U.S. Private*, pg. 1833

HEALTHREACH COMMUNITY HEALTH CENTERS; *U.S. Private*, pg. 1897

HEALTH SHARE OF OREGON; *U.S. Private*, pg. 1894

HEALTHSOURCE OF OHIO; *U.S. Private*, pg. 1897

THE HEART GROUP OF LANCASTER GENERAL HEALTH; *U.S. Private*, pg. 4049

HENRY J. AUSTIN HEALTH CENTER, INC.; *U.S. Private*, pg. 1918

HIGH PLAINS PHYSICAL THERAPY, LIMITED PARTNERSHIP—See U.S. Physical Therapy, Inc.; *U.S. Public*, pg. 2214

HITCHCOCK HEALTHCARE, INC.—See Universal Health Services, Inc.; *U.S. Public*, pg. 2258

HOEPPNER PHYSICAL THERAPY, LIMITED PARTNERSHIP—See U.S. Physical Therapy, Inc.; *U.S. Public*, pg. 2214

HOMEDALE HEALTHCARE, INC.—See The Ensign Group, Inc.; *U.S. Public*, pg. 2071

HOME MEDICAL SERVICES LLC; *U.S. Private*, pg. 1971

HOSPICE OF THE PIEDMONT, INC.; *U.S. Private*, pg. 1986

HOUSTON AREA COMMUNITY SERVICES; *U.S. Private*, pg. 1992

HUDSON HEADWATERS HEALTH NETWORK; *U.S. Private*, pg. 2001

HYDE PARK SURGERY CENTER, LLC—See Tenet Healthcare Corporation; *U.S. Public*, pg. 2005

INFUSION SOLUTIONS OF PUERTO RICO, LLC—See The Kroger Co.; *U.S. Public*, pg. 2108

INLAND NORTHWEST HEALTH SERVICES; *U.S. Private*, pg. 2078

INSTITUTE FOR POPULATION HEALTH; *U.S. Private*, pg. 2093

INTEGRATED BEHAVIORAL HEALTH, INC.; *U.S. Private*, pg. 2099

INTEGRIS JIM THORPE REHABILITATION CENTER—See INTEGRIS Health, Inc.; *U.S. Private*, pg. 2102

INTERFACE CLINICAL SERVICES LTD.—See IQVIA Holdings Inc.; *U.S. Public*, pg. 1169

INTERMOUNTAIN PHYSICAL THERAPY, LIMITED PARTNERSHIP—See U.S. Physical Therapy, Inc.; *U.S. Public*, pg. 2214

INTERNATIONAL COMMUNITY HEALTH SERVICES; *U.S. Private*, pg. 2115

IQVIA NEDERLAND—See IQVIA Holdings Inc.; *U.S. Public*, pg. 1170

JEFFERSON HEALTH CARE, INC.—See The Ensign Group, Inc.; *U.S. Public*, pg. 2071

JEFFERSON MANOR HEALTH CENTER; *U.S. Private*, pg. 2198

JESSIE TRICE COMMUNITY HEALTH CENTER, INC.; *U.S. Private*, pg. 2203

JEWISH RENAISSANCE MEDICAL CENTER INC.; *U.S. Private*, pg. 2206

JOHNSON REGIONAL MEDICAL CENTER; *U.S. Private*, pg. 2228

JOSEPH M. SMITH COMMUNITY HEALTH CENTER, INC.; *U.S. Private*, pg. 2237

JOSEPH P. ADDABBO FAMILY HEALTH CENTER, INC.; *U.S. Private*, pg. 2237

JOURNEYCARE, INC.—See Addus HomeCare Corporation; *U.S. Public*, pg. 40

JOURNEY FORWARD; *U.S. Private*, pg. 2238

JULIE EMOND PHYSICAL THERAPY, LIMITED PARTNERSHIP—See U.S. Physical Therapy, Inc.; *U.S. Public*, pg. 2214

KALEIDA HEALTH; *U.S. Private*, pg. 2257

KDI KLINIKSERVICE GMBH—See Fresenius SE & Co. KGaA; *Int'l*, pg. 2779

KEYSTONE CENTER—See Universal Health Services, Inc.; *U.S. Public*, pg. 2260

THE LA JOLLA ENDOSCOPY CENTER, L.P.—See KKR & Co. Inc.; *U.S. Public*, pg. 1247

THE LANCASTER PA ENDOSCOPY ASC, L.P.—See KKR & Co. Inc.; *U.S. Public*, pg. 1247

LANDMARK SURGICAL SUITES, LLC—See Tenet Healthcare Corporation; *U.S. Public*, pg. 2004

LAUREL RIDGE HEALTH CARE CENTER—See Athena Health Care Systems; *U.S. Private*, pg. 367

LEADER PHYSICAL THERAPY, LIMITED PARTNERSHIP—See U.S. Physical Therapy, Inc.; *U.S. Public*, pg. 2215

LEARN IT SYSTEMS LLC—See Gryphon Investors, LLC; *U.S. Private*, pg. 1799

LINDENGROVE, INC.; *U.S. Private*, pg. 2460

LOWER VALLEY HOSPITAL ASSOCIATION; *U.S. Private*, pg. 2506

MAGELLAN HEALTHCARE, INC.—See Centene Corporation; *U.S. Public*, pg. 469

MAGELLAN HEALTHCARE PROVIDER GROUP, INC.—See Centene Corporation; *U.S. Public*, pg. 469

MAGELLAN METHOD, LLC—See Centene Corporation; *U.S. Public*, pg. 470

MAINE PHYSICAL THERAPY, LIMITED PARTNERSHIP—See U.S. Physical Therapy, Inc.; *U.S. Public*, pg. 2215

MANSFIELD PHYSICAL THERAPY, LIMITED PARTNERSHIP—See U.S. Physical Therapy, Inc.; *U.S. Public*, pg. 2215

MARGARET MARY COMMUNITY HOSPITAL; *U.S. Private*, pg. 2573

MARKET BAYOU HEALTHCARE, INC.—See The Ensign Group, Inc.; *U.S. Public*, pg. 2071

MARLETTE REGIONAL HOSPITAL; *U.S. Private*, pg. 2583

MARTIN LUTHER KING, JR. COMMUNITY HEALTH FOUNDATION; *U.S. Private*, pg. 2595

MEDEXPRESS URGENT CARE—See General Atlantic Service Company, L.P.; *U.S. Private*, pg. 1663

MEDEXPRESS URGENT CARE—See Sequoia Capital Operations, LLC; *U.S. Public*, pg. 3612

MEDICAL TEAMS INTERNATIONAL; *U.S. Private*, pg. 2656

MEDICLIN THERAPIE GMBH—See Asklepios Kliniken GmbH & Co. KGaA; *Int'l*, pg. 623

MEMORIAL HERMANN ENDOSCOPY & SURGERY CENTER NORTH HOUSTON, L.L.C.—See Tenet Healthcare Corporation; *U.S. Public*, pg. 2011

MEMORIAL HERMANN SURGERY CENTER MEMORIAL CITY, L.L.C.—See Tenet Healthcare Corporation; *U.S. Public*, pg. 2011

MEMORIAL HERMANN SURGERY CENTER RICHMOND, LLC—See Tenet Healthcare Corporation; *U.S. Public*, pg. 2011

MERCER COUNTY SURGERY CENTER, LLC—See KKR & Co. Inc.; *U.S. Public*, pg. 1246

MERRILL PHYSICAL THERAPY, LIMITED PARTNERSHIP—See U.S. Physical Therapy, Inc.; *U.S. Public*, pg. 2215

METRO WELLNESS AND COMMUNITY CENTERS; *U.S. Private*, pg. 2687

MICHIGAN OUTPATIENT SURGICAL SOLUTIONS, LLC—See Tenet Healthcare Corporation; *U.S. Public*, pg. 2004

MILESTONE CENTERS, INC.; *U.S. Private*, pg. 2728

MILFORD REGIONAL MEDICAL CENTER, INC.; *U.S. Private*, pg. 2729

MILFORD REGIONAL PHYSICIAN GROUP; *U.S. Private*, pg. 2729

621498 — ALL OTHER OUTPATIEN... CORPORATE AFFILIATIONS

THE MINNEAPOLIS OPHTHALMOLOGY ASC, LLC—See KKR & Co. Inc.; *U.S. Public*, pg. 1248
MINNESOTA VISITING NURSE AGENCY; *U.S. Private*, pg. 2744
MISSION TRAILS HEALTHCARE, INC.—See The Ensign Group, Inc.; *U.S. Public*, pg. 2071
MISSOURI SLOPE LUTHERAN CARE CENTER; *U.S. Private*, pg. 2749
MOBILE SPINE & REHABILITATION, LIMITED PARTNERSHIP—See U.S. Physical Therapy, Inc.; *U.S. Public*, pg. 2215
MODERN MEDICAL GROUP PTY LTD—See Adamantem Capital Management Pty Limited; *Int'l*, pg. 124
MONTGOMERY EYE SURGERY CENTER, LLC—See KKR & Co. Inc.; *U.S. Public*, pg. 1246
MOTHER ANGELINE MCCRORY MANOR; *U.S. Private*, pg. 2795
MOUNTAIN PARK HEALTH CENTER; *U.S. Private*, pg. 2799
MOUNT PLEASANT OUTPATIENT SURGERY CENTER, LLC—See Tenet Healthcare Corporation; *U.S. Public*, pg. 2004
MRI & IMAGING OF GEORGIA—See Novant Health, Inc.; *U.S. Private*, pg. 2967
NAPLES WOMENS CENTER—See HealthLynked Corp.; *U.S. Public*, pg. 1016
NATIONAL HEALTHCARE OF NEWPORT, INC.—See Unity Health - White County Medical Center; *U.S. Private*, pg. 4303
NATIVE AMERICAN HEALTH CENTER; *U.S. Private*, pg. 2866
NAUTILUS HEALTHCARE, INC.—See The Ensign Group, Inc.; *U.S. Public*, pg. 2071
NAVEN HEALTH, INC.—See Option Care Health, Inc.; *U.S. Public*, pg. 1610
NEIGHBORCARE HEALTH; *U.S. Private*, pg. 2881
NEWARK COMMUNITY HEALTH CENTERS, INC.; *U.S. Private*, pg. 2913
NEXTGEN HEALTHCARE INDIA PVT. LTD.—See Thoma Bravo, L.P.; *U.S. Private*, pg. 4150
NORMAN PHYSICAL THERAPY, LIMITED PARTNERSHIP—See U.S. Physical Therapy, Inc.; *U.S. Public*, pg. 2215
NORTHEAST VALLEY HEALTH CORPORATION; *U.S. Private*, pg. 2951
NORTHERN MICHIGAN SURGICAL SUITES, LLC—See Tenet Healthcare Corporation; *U.S. Public*, pg. 2005
NORTHERN NECK PHYSICAL THERAPY, LIMITED PARTNERSHIP—See U.S. Physical Therapy, Inc.; *U.S. Public*, pg. 2215
NORTH SHORE COMMUNITY HEALTH CENTER, INC.; *U.S. Private*, pg. 2946
THE NORTH WARD CENTER, INC.; *U.S. Private*, pg. 4084
NOVACARE REHABILITATION—See Select Medical Holdings Corporation; *U.S. Public*, pg. 1859
OPTUM INFUSION SERVICES 100, INC.—See UnitedHealth Group Incorporated; *U.S. Public*, pg. 2243
ORANGE HEALTH CARE CENTER—See Apollo Global Management, Inc.; *U.S. Public*, pg. 157
OREGON SPINE & PHYSICAL THERAPY, LIMITED PARTNERSHIP—See U.S. Physical Therapy, Inc.; *U.S. Public*, pg. 2215
ORLANDO OUTPATIENT CENTER FOR SURGERY, LLC—See Tenet Healthcare Corporation; *U.S. Public*, pg. 2006
ORO VALLEY SURGICAL SUITES, LLC—See Tenet Healthcare Corporation; *U.S. Public*, pg. 2006
OUTPATIENT SURGERY CENTER OF HILTON HEAD, LLC—See UnitedHealth Group Incorporated; *U.S. Public*, pg. 2249
OUTREACH COMMUNITY HEALTH CENTERS, INC.; *U.S. Private*, pg. 3051
PACK HEALTH, LLC—See Quest Diagnostics, Inc.; *U.S. Public*, pg. 1755
PAOLO MEDIC CO., LTD.—See Bangkok Dusit Medical Services Public Company Limited; *Int'l*, pg. 834
PARAGON HEALTHCARE, INC.—See Elevance Health, Inc.; *U.S. Public*, pg. 730
PARKSIDE HEALTHCARE, INC.—See The Ensign Group, Inc.; *U.S. Public*, pg. 2072
PARKSIDE SURGERY CENTER, INC.—See HCA Healthcare, Inc.; *U.S. Public*, pg. 1006
PARTNERS CONTINUING CARE, INC.—See Partners HealthCare System, Inc.; *U.S. Private*, pg. 3101
PARTNERS IN HEALTH; *U.S. Private*, pg. 3102
PATHWAYS HOSPICE; *U.S. Private*, pg. 3106
PEAK VISTA COMMUNITY HEALTH CENTERS; *U.S. Private*, pg. 3124
PELICAN STATE PHYSICAL THERAPY, LIMITED PARTNERSHIP—See U.S. Physical Therapy, Inc.; *U.S. Public*, pg. 2215
PEMBROOKE OCCUPATIONAL HEALTH, INC.—See Abbott Laboratories; *U.S. Public*, pg. 19
PENINSULA COMMUNITY HEALTH SERVICES OF ALASKA, INC.; *U.S. Private*, pg. 3133
PENINSULA COMMUNITY HEALTH SERVICES; *U.S. Private*, pg. 3133

PEOPLE OF COLOR NETWORK, INC.; *U.S. Private*, pg. 3140
PFLEGE AUS EINER HAND GMBH—See Clariane SE; *Int'l*, pg. 1643
PHARMMD SOLUTIONS, LLC—See The Riverside Company; *U.S. Private*, pg. 4110
PHYSICAL THERAPY & SPINE INSTITUTE, LIMITED PARTNERSHIP—See U.S. Physical Therapy, Inc.; *U.S. Public*, pg. 2215
PIONEER PHYSICAL THERAPY, LIMITED PARTNERSHIP—See U.S. Physical Therapy, Inc.; *U.S. Public*, pg. 2215
PLYMOUTH PHYSICAL THERAPY SPECIALISTS, LIMITED PARTNERSHIP—See U.S. Physical Therapy, Inc.; *U.S. Public*, pg. 2215
POPULATION SERVICES INTERNATIONAL; *U.S. Private*, pg. 3229
PORT CITY PHYSICAL THERAPY, LIMITED PARTNERSHIP—See U.S. Physical Therapy, Inc.; *U.S. Public*, pg. 2215
PORT ORANGE PHYSICAL THERAPY, LIMITED PARTNERSHIP—See U.S. Physical Therapy, Inc.; *U.S. Public*, pg. 2215
PORTSIDE HEALTHCARE, INC.—See The Ensign Group, Inc.; *U.S. Public*, pg. 2072
PRAIRIE CENTER HEALTH SYSTEMS, INC.—See Centerstone of America, Inc.; *U.S. Private*, pg. 817
PREMIER AT EXTON SURGERY CENTER LLC—See Tenet Healthcare Corporation; *U.S. Public*, pg. 2006
PRINCE FREDERICK SURGERY CENTER, LLC—See Tenet Healthcare Corporation; *U.S. Public*, pg. 2006
PRO ACTIVE THERAPY OF SOUTH CAROLINA, INC.—See Select Medical Holdings Corporation; *U.S. Public*, pg. 1858
THE PROMPTCARE COMPANIES, INC.—See The Halifax Group LLC; *U.S. Private*, pg. 4042
RED CLIFFS HEALTHCARE, INC.—See The Ensign Group, Inc.; *U.S. Public*, pg. 2072
RED ROCK HEALTHCARE, INC.—See The Ensign Group, Inc.; *U.S. Public*, pg. 2072
REGENERATIVE MEDICINE SOLUTIONS LLC; *U.S. Private*, pg. 3386
REGIONAL PHYSICAL THERAPY CENTER, LIMITED PARTNERSHIP—See U.S. Physical Therapy, Inc.; *U.S. Public*, pg. 2216
REHABCARE GROUP, INC.—See Select Rehabilitation, LLC; *U.S. Private*, pg. 3601
RICE REHABILITATION ASSOCIATES, LIMITED PARTNERSHIP—See U.S. Physical Therapy, Inc.; *U.S. Public*, pg. 2216
RIVA ROAD SURGICAL CENTER, L.L.C.—See Tenet Healthcare Corporation; *U.S. Public*, pg. 2006
RIVERVIEW PHYSICAL THERAPY, LIMITED PARTNERSHIP—See U.S. Physical Therapy, Inc.; *U.S. Public*, pg. 2216
THE ROCKLEDGE FL ENDOSCOPY ASC, LLC—See KKR & Co. Inc.; *U.S. Public*, pg. 1248
ROEPKE PHYSICAL THERAPY, LIMITED PARTNERSHIP—See U.S. Physical Therapy, Inc.; *U.S. Public*, pg. 2216
SAGINAW VALLEY SPORT & SPINE, LIMITED PARTNERSHIP—See U.S. Physical Therapy, Inc.; *U.S. Public*, pg. 2216
SAMITIVEJ INTERNATIONAL CO., LTD.—See Bangkok Dusit Medical Services Public Company Limited; *Int'l*, pg. 834
THE SAN LUIS OBISPO CA ENDOSCOPY ASC, L.P.—See KKR & Co. Inc.; *U.S. Public*, pg. 1248
THE SARASOTA ENDOSCOPY ASC, LLC—See KKR & Co. Inc.; *U.S. Public*, pg. 1248
SELECT PHYSICIANS SURGERY CENTER, LLC—See Tenet Healthcare Corporation; *U.S. Public*, pg. 2007
THE SENECA PA ASC, LLC—See KKR & Co. Inc.; *U.S. Public*, pg. 1248
SHASTA COMMUNITY HEALTH CENTER; *U.S. Private*, pg. 3627
SILVER CROSS/USP SURGERY CENTER, LLC—See Tenet Healthcare Corporation; *U.S. Public*, pg. 2007
THE SILVER SPRING MD ENDOSCOPY ASC, LLC—See KKR & Co. Inc.; *U.S. Public*, pg. 1248
SIXTEENTH STREET COMMUNITY HEALTH CENTER; *U.S. Private*, pg. 3677
SKIN, A MEDICAL SPA—See MD Esthetics, LLC; *U.S. Private*, pg. 2646
SKYLINE MEDICAL GROUP, LLC—See HCA Healthcare, Inc.; *U.S. Public*, pg. 1008
SKYLINE NEUROSCIENCE ASSOCIATES, LLC—See HCA Healthcare, Inc.; *U.S. Public*, pg. 1008
SODEXO HEALTHCARE SUPPORT SERVICE (THAILAND) CO., LTD.—See Bangkok Dusit Medical Services Public Company Limited; *Int'l*, pg. 834
SONA MEDSPA INTERNATIONAL, INC.—See Pharos Capital Group, LLC; *U.S. Private*, pg. 3166
SOUTH BAY FAMILY HEALTH CARE—See Venice Family Clinic; *U.S. Private*, pg. 4356
SOUTHERN IDAHO AMBULATORY SURGERY CENTER, LLC—See KKR & Co. Inc.; *U.S. Public*, pg. 1246

SOUTHSIDE HEALTHCARE, INC.—See The Ensign Group, Inc.; *U.S. Public*, pg. 2072
SOUTH TULSA PHYSICAL THERAPY, LIMITED PARTNERSHIP—See U.S. Physical Therapy, Inc.; *U.S. Public*, pg. 2216
SPARROW HOSPITAL - ST. LAWRENCE CAMPUS—See University of Michigan; *U.S. Private*, pg. 4309
SPAULDING REHABILITATION HOSPITAL CORPORATION—See Partners HealthCare System, Inc.; *U.S. Private*, pg. 3101
SPECIALCARE HOSPITAL MANAGEMENT CORPORATION—See Webster Equity Partners, LLC; *U.S. Private*, pg. 4467
SPICEWOOD SURGERY CENTER LLC—See Tenet Healthcare Corporation; *U.S. Public*, pg. 2007
SPINE & SPORT PHYSICAL THERAPY, LIMITED PARTNERSHIP—See U.S. Physical Therapy, Inc.; *U.S. Public*, pg. 2216
SPOONER HEALTH SYSTEM; *U.S. Private*, pg. 3760
SPORT & SPINE CLINIC, L.P.—See U.S. Physical Therapy, Inc.; *U.S. Public*, pg. 2216
SPRACKLEN PHYSICAL THERAPY, LP—See U.S. Physical Therapy, Inc.; *U.S. Public*, pg. 2216
STEALTHCO, INC.—See Wellness Center USA, Inc.; *U.S. Public*, pg. 2343
STODDARD BAPTIST GLOBAL CARE, INC.; *U.S. Private*, pg. 3815
SUMMERSVILLE REGIONAL MEDICAL CENTER; *U.S. Private*, pg. 3853
SUMMIT HEALTH, INC.—See Quest Diagnostics, Inc.; *U.S. Public*, pg. 1756
SUNSET COMMUNITY HEALTH CENTER; *U.S. Private*, pg. 3871
THE SURGERY CENTER OF MIDDLE TENNESSEE, LLC—See KKR & Co. Inc.; *U.S. Public*, pg. 1248
SURGERY PARTNERS OF PARK PLACE, LLC—See Bain Capital, LP; *U.S. Private*, pg. 447
SURGICARE OF CLARKSVILLE, LLC—See HCA Healthcare, Inc.; *U.S. Public*, pg. 1011
SWISS MEDICAL CENTERS NETWORK S.A.—See AEVIS VICTORIA SA; *Int'l*, pg. 183
SYRACUSE COMMUNITY HEALTH CENTER, INC.; *U.S. Private*, pg. 3905
TAMPA PAIN RELIEF CENTER, INC.—See Bain Capital, LP; *U.S. Private*, pg. 447
THE TEMECULA CA ENDOSCOPY CENTER ASC, L.P.—See KKR & Co. Inc.; *U.S. Public*, pg. 1248
TEXAS ONCOLOGY - SAN ANTONIO NORTHEAST—See Texas Oncology, PA; *U.S. Private*, pg. 3976
TEXSTAR PHYSICAL THERAPY, LIMITED PARTNERSHIP—See U.S. Physical Therapy, Inc.; *U.S. Public*, pg. 2216
THAI MEDICAL CENTER PCL.—See Bangkok Dusit Medical Services Public Company Limited; *Int'l*, pg. 834
THEDACARE INC.—See Froedtert Memorial Lutheran Hospital, Inc.; *U.S. Private*, pg. 1613
THOMAS HAND & REHABILITATION SPECIALISTS, LIMITED PARTNERSHIP—See U.S. Physical Therapy, Inc.; *U.S. Public*, pg. 2216
THREE LOWER COUNTIES COMMUNITY SERVICES, INC.; *U.S. Private*, pg. 4164
THYROCARE TECHNOLOGIES LIMITED—See Docon Technologies Private Limited; *Int'l*, pg. 2153
TOTAL SPECTRUM, LLC—See Gryphon Investors, LLC; *U.S. Private*, pg. 1799
TOWN & COUNTRY PHYSICAL THERAPY, LTD.—See U.S. Physical Therapy, Inc.; *U.S. Public*, pg. 2216
TOWSON SURGICAL CENTER, LLC—See KKR & Co. Inc.; *U.S. Public*, pg. 1249
TRI-COUNTY MENTAL HEALTH SERVICES—See Spurwink Services Incorporated; *U.S. Private*, pg. 3765
TRS BEHAVIORAL CARE, INC.—See Elements Behavioral Health, Inc.; *U.S. Private*, pg. 1357
TRU COMMUNITY CARE; *U.S. Private*, pg. 4244
TRUVERIS, INC.; *U.S. Private*, pg. 4251
TUALITY HEALTHCARE; *U.S. Private*, pg. 4255
UNION HILL HEALTHCARE, INC.—See The Ensign Group, Inc.; *U.S. Public*, pg. 2072
UNITY HEALTH - WHITE COUNTY MEDICAL CENTER; *U.S. Private*, pg. 4303
UNIVERSITY PHYSICAL THERAPY, LIMITED PARTNERSHIP—See U.S. Physical Therapy, Inc.; *U.S. Public*, pg. 2216
URBAN HEALTH PLAN, INC.; *U.S. Private*, pg. 4314
U.S. HEALTHWORKS MEDICAL GROUP, PROF. CORP.—See Catholic Health Initiatives; *U.S. Private*, pg. 790
US PT THERAPY SERVICES INC.—See U.S. Physical Therapy, Inc.; *U.S. Public*, pg. 2216
US PT THERAPY SERVICES INC.—See U.S. Physical Therapy, Inc.; *U.S. Public*, pg. 2216
US PT THERAPY SERVICES INC.—See U.S. Physical Therapy, Inc.; *U.S. Public*, pg. 2216
US PT THERAPY SERVICES INC.—See U.S. Physical Therapy, Inc.; *U.S. Public*, pg. 2216
US PT THERAPY SERVICES INC.—See U.S. Physical Therapy, Inc.; *U.S. Public*, pg. 2216
US PT THERAPY SERVICES INC.—See U.S. Physical

N.A.I.C.S. INDEX

621511 — MEDICAL LABORATORIE...

Therapy, Inc.; *U.S. Public*, pg. 2216
U.S. STEM CELL CLINIC OF THE VILLAGES LLC—See U.S. Stem Cell, Inc.; *U.S. Public*, pg. 2217
U.S. THERAPY, INC.—See Advent International Corporation; *U.S. Private*, pg. 96
VALIR REHABILITATION HOSPITAL OF OKC, LLC—See Valir Health; *U.S. Private*, pg. 4332
THE VALLEY ENDOSCOPY CENTER, L.P.; *U.S. Private*, pg. 4130
VALUEOPTIONS, INC.—See Beacon Health Holdings LLC; *U.S. Private*, pg. 504
VARIETY CARE; *U.S. Private*, pg. 4346
VENTURA ENDOSCOPY CENTER PARTNERS, LLC—See Tenet Healthcare Corporation; *U.S. Public*, pg. 2015
VESPER HEALTHCARE, INC.—See The Ensign Group, Inc.; *U.S. Public*, pg. 2072
VIENNA AIRPORT HEALTH CENTER GMBH—See Flughafen Wien Aktiengesellschaft; *Int'l*, pg. 2713
VIEWPOINT HEALTHCARE, INC.—See The Ensign Group, Inc.; *U.S. Public*, pg. 2072
VILLAGECARE; *U.S. Private*, pg. 4384
VILLAGE SURGICENTER, LIMITED PARTNERSHIP—See Bain Capital, LP; *U.S. Private*, pg. 447
VINE INTERNATIONAL; *U.S. Private*, pg. 4385
VISITING NURSE SERVICE AT ST. FRANCIS, INC.; *U.S. Private*, pg. 4393
VNS HOMECARE INC.; *U.S. Private*, pg. 4408
WALGREENS SPECIALTY CARE CENTERS, LLC—See Walgreens Boots Alliance, Inc.; *U.S. Public*, pg. 2324
WEIRTON MEDICAL CENTER; *U.S. Private*, pg. 4472
WELLBE, INC.—See Orbita, Inc.; *U.S. Private*, pg. 3038
WELLNESS POINTE; *U.S. Private*, pg. 4476
WEST CHESTER SURGICAL SUITES, LLC—See Tenet Healthcare Corporation; *U.S. Public*, pg. 2015
WESTERN NORTH CAROLINA COMMUNITY HEALTH SERVICES, INC.; *U.S. Private*, pg. 4495
WESTMINSTER SURGERY CENTER, LLC—See Tenet Healthcare Corporation; *U.S. Public*, pg. 2015
WICKENBURG COMMUNITY HOSPITAL; *U.S. Private*, pg. 4515

621511 — MEDICAL LABORATORIES

ABBOTT DIAGNOSTICS KOREA, INC.—See Abbott Laboratories; *U.S. Public*, pg. 14
ABBOTT DIAGNOSTICS TECHNOLOGIES AS—See Abbott Laboratories; *U.S. Public*, pg. 14
ABBOTT LABORATORIES LIMITED—See Abbott Laboratories; *U.S. Public*, pg. 16
ABBOTT LABORATORIOS, S.A.—See Abbott Laboratories; *U.S. Public*, pg. 16
ABBOTT PATHOLOGY PTY LTD—See Healius Limited; *Int'l*, pg. 3302
ABBOTT RAPID DIAGNOSTICS AB—See Abbott Laboratories; *U.S. Public*, pg. 17
ABBOTT RAPID DIAGNOSTICS AS—See Abbott Laboratories; *U.S. Public*, pg. 17
ABBOTT RAPID DIAGNOSTICS AUSTRIA GMBH—See Abbott Laboratories; *U.S. Public*, pg. 17
ABBOTT RAPID DIAGNOSTICS GERMANY GMBH—See Abbott Laboratories; *U.S. Public*, pg. 17
ABBOTT RAPID DIAGNOSTICS LDA—See Abbott Laboratories; *U.S. Public*, pg. 17
ABBOTT RAPID DIAGNOSTICS OY AB—See Abbott Laboratories; *U.S. Public*, pg. 17
ABBOTT RAPID DIAGNOSTICS S.A.S—See Abbott Laboratories; *U.S. Public*, pg. 17
ABBOTT RAPID DIAGNOSTICS—See Abbott Laboratories; *U.S. Public*, pg. 17
ABBOTT RAPID DIAGNOSTICS S.R.L.—See Abbott Laboratories; *U.S. Public*, pg. 17
ABBOTT RAPID DIAGNOSTICS ULC—See Abbott Laboratories; *U.S. Public*, pg. 18
ABBOTT RAPID DX INTERNATIONAL LIMITED—See Abbott Laboratories; *U.S. Public*, pg. 17
ACCUGENIX, INC.—See Charles River Laboratories International, Inc.; *U.S. Public*, pg. 479
ACOUSORT AB; *Int'l*, pg. 108
ACTIVE HEALTHCARE, INC.; *U.S. Private*, pg. 69
ADDICTION LABS OF AMERICA, LLC—See AAC Holdings, Inc.; *U.S. Private*, pg. 30
ADVANTAR LABORATORIES, INC.—See Eurofins Scientific S.E.; *Int'l*, pg. 2548
AFFILIATED LABORATORY, INC.—See Eastern Maine Healthcare Systems; *U.S. Private*, pg. 1320
AGEACARE SWITZERLAND S.A.—See Eurofins Scientific S.E.; *Int'l*, pg. 2535
ALEAFIA HEALTH INC.; *Int'l*, pg. 305
ALMAC DIAGNOSTICS—See Almac Sciences Group Ltd.; *Int'l*, pg. 362
ALPHA MEDICAL, S.R.O.—See Apax Partners LLP; *Int'l*, pg. 507
ALS TESTING SERVICES INDIA PRIVATE LIMITED—See ALS Limited; *Int'l*, pg. 377
ALTASCIENCES CLINICAL LOS ANGELES, INC.—See Altasciences Company Inc.; *Int'l*, pg. 387

ALTHEADX, INC.—See Castle Biosciences, Inc.; *U.S. Public*, pg. 447
ALTRA D.D.; *Int'l*, pg. 397
AMEDES HOLDING GMBH—See BNP Paribas SA; *Int'l*, pg. 1093
AMERICAN INSTITUTE OF TOXICOLOGY, INC.; *U.S. Private*, pg. 238
AMERICAN SHARED HOSPITAL SERVICES; *U.S. Public*, pg. 109
AMERICAN SHARED RADIOSURGERY SERVICES—See American Shared Hospital Services; *U.S. Public*, pg. 109
AMERIPATH CONSOLIDATED LABS, INC.—See Quest Diagnostics, Inc.; *U.S. Public*, pg. 1755
AMERIPATH CONSULTING PATHOLOGY SERVICES, P.A.—See Quest Diagnostics, Inc.; *U.S. Public*, pg. 1755
AMERIPATH, INC.—See Quest Diagnostics, Inc.; *U.S. Public*, pg. 1755
AMERIPATH INDIANAPOLIS, P.C.—See Quest Diagnostics, Inc.; *U.S. Public*, pg. 1755
AMERIPATH PITTSBURGH, P.C.—See Quest Diagnostics, Inc.; *U.S. Public*, pg. 1755
ANAHEIM HILLS MEDICAL IMAGING, L.L.C.—See UCI Health; *U.S. Public*, pg. 4274
ANALYTICAL INSTRUMENTS SA—See HORIBA Ltd; *Int'l*, pg. 3474
ANTISEPTICA CHEM.-PHARM PRODUKTE GMBH; *Int'l*, pg. 483
AOTEA PATHOLOGY LIMITED—See BGH Capital Pty Ltd; *Int'l*, pg. 1007
ARCPOINT GROUP LLC—See ARCpoint Inc.; *U.S. Public*, pg. 186
ARCPOINT INC.; *U.S. Public*, pg. 186
ARIS TELERADIOLOGY, LLC—See Great Point Partners, LLC; *U.S. Private*, pg. 1767
ARLINGTON PATHOLOGY ASSOCIATION 5.01(A) CORPORATION—See Quest Diagnostics, Inc.; *U.S. Public*, pg. 1755
ASPIRA PATHLAB & DIAGNOSTICS LIMITED; *Int'l*, pg. 630
ASSOCIATED CLINICAL LABORATORIES—See Quest Diagnostics, Inc.; *U.S. Public*, pg. 1755
ASSOCIATION OF PUBLIC HEALTH LABORATORIES; *U.S. Private*, pg. 358
ASTELLAS RESEARCH INSTITUTE OF AMERICA LLC—See Astellas Pharma Inc.; *Int'l*, pg. 653
ATEB CANADA LTD.—See Omnicell, Inc.; *U.S. Public*, pg. 1572
ATHEROTECH, INC.—See Behrman Brothers Management Corp.; *U.S. Private*, pg. 515
AUREON BIOSCIENCES, INC; *U.S. Private*, pg. 393
AXIOM VETERINARY LABORATORIES LIMITED—See CVS Group Plc; *Int'l*, pg. 1890
AXON LAB B.V.—See HORIBA Ltd; *Int'l*, pg. 3475
BERKELEY HEARTLAB, INC.—See Quest Diagnostics, Inc.; *U.S. Public*, pg. 1755
BETAGRO SCIENCE CENTER COMPANY LIMITED—See Betagro Public Company Limited; *Int'l*, pg. 1002
BILCARE LTD.—See Bilcare Limited; *Int'l*, pg. 1023
BILCARE MARKETING AMERICA LATINA LTDA.—See Bilcare Limited; *Int'l*, pg. 1023
BILCARE RESEARCH GMBH—See Bilcare Limited; *Int'l*, pg. 1023
BILCARE SINGAPORE PTE. LTD.—See Bilcare Limited; *Int'l*, pg. 1023
BIOCEPT, INC.; *U.S. Public*, pg. 335
BIOCLINICA, INC.—See Astorg Partners S.A.S.; *Int'l*, pg. 657
BIOMEDICAL SYSTEMS PTY LIMITED—See CVC Limited; *Int'l*, pg. 1889
BIORA THERAPEUTICS, INC.; *U.S. Public*, pg. 338
BIO-REFERENCE LABORATORIES, INC.—See OPKO Health, Inc.; *U.S. Public*, pg. 1608
BIOTAGE SINGAPORE PTE. LTD.—See Biotage AB; *Int'l*, pg. 1042
BIOTECNET I MAS D S.A.—See FAES Farma, S.A.; *Int'l*, pg. 2601
BIOTHERANOSTICS, INC.—See Hologic, Inc.; *U.S. Public*, pg. 1044
BOJI MEDICAL TECHNOLOGY CO., LTD.; *Int'l*, pg. 1101
BOSTON HEART DIAGNOSTICS CORPORATION—See Eurofins Scientific S.E.; *Int'l*, pg. 2535
BOSTWICK LABORATORIES, INC.—See Poplar Healthcare, PLLC; *U.S. Private*, pg. 3228
BRAINLAB AG—See Intel Corporation; *U.S. Public*, pg. 1138
CAN B CORP; *U.S. Public*, pg. 428
CANNAMM LIMITED PARTNERSHIP—See Laboratory Corporation of America Holdings; *U.S. Public*, pg. 1285
CARDIOLABS, INC.—See Alive Cor Inc.; *U.S. Private*, pg. 169
CAROLINA FOREST IMAGING CENTER, LLC—See HCA Healthcare, Inc.; *U.S. Public*, pg. 992
CELERA CORPORATION—See Quest Diagnostics, Inc.; *U.S. Public*, pg. 1755
CELLNETIX PATHOLOGY & LABORATORIES, LLC; *U.S. Private*, pg. 807
CENEXEL CLINICAL RESEARCH, INC.; *U.S. Private*, pg. 809
CENTER FOR DISEASE DETECTION, LLC—See Laboratory Corporation of America Holdings; *U.S. Public*, pg. 1285
CEPHEID UK—See Danaher Corporation; *U.S. Public*, pg. 625
CHOICE GENETICS ARGENTINA—See Groupe Grimaud La Corbiere SA; *Int'l*, pg. 3103
CHOICE GENETICS BRASIL LTDA—See Groupe Grimaud La Corbiere SA; *Int'l*, pg. 3103
CHOICE GENETICS CANADA INC.—See Groupe Grimaud La Corbiere SA; *Int'l*, pg. 3103
CHOICE GENETICS DEUTSCHLAND GMBH—See Groupe Grimaud La Corbiere SA; *Int'l*, pg. 3103
CHOICE GENETICS POLSKA SP Z O.O.—See Groupe Grimaud La Corbiere SA; *Int'l*, pg. 3103
CHOICE GENETICS SAS—See Groupe Grimaud La Corbiere SA; *Int'l*, pg. 3103
CHOICE GENETICS VIETNAM—See Groupe Grimaud La Corbiere SA; *Int'l*, pg. 3103
CHRISTIE MEDICAL HOLDINGS, INC.—See CAREstream Medical Ltd.; *Int'l*, pg. 1325
CITOXLAB SCANTOX A/S—See Charles River Laboratories International, Inc.; *U.S. Public*, pg. 480
CLEARBRIDGE HEALTH LIMITED; *Int'l*, pg. 1656
CLEARBRIDGE LIFESTYLE PTE. LTD.—See Clearbridge Health Limited; *Int'l*, pg. 1656
CLEARBRIDGE MEDICAL GROUP PTE. LTD.—See Clearbridge Health Limited; *Int'l*, pg. 1656
CLEARBRIDGE MEDICAL HONG KONG CORPORATION LIMITED—See Clearbridge Health Limited; *Int'l*, pg. 1656
CLEAR GENETICS, INC.—See Invitae Corporation; *U.S. Public*, pg. 1165
CLEARSTONE CENTRAL LABORATORIES (CANADA) INC.—See Laboratory Corporation of America Holdings; *U.S. Public*, pg. 1285
CLEVELAND SKIN PATHOLOGY LABORATORY INC.—See Aurora Diagnostics Holdings, LLC; *U.S. Private*, pg. 394
CLINICAL LABORATORIES PTY. LTD.—See Crescent Capital Partners Ltd.; *Int'l*, pg. 1839
CLINICAL LABORATORY PARTNERS, LLC—See Hartford HealthCare Corporation; *U.S. Private*, pg. 1873
CLINICAL REFERENCE LABORATORY, INC.; *U.S. Private*, pg. 944
CLINILAB LABORATORIO CLINICO HUELVA, S.L.U.—See Eurofins Scientific S.E.; *Int'l*, pg. 2535
CLINISYS SCOTLAND LIMITED—See Roper Technologies, Inc.; *U.S. Public*, pg. 1810
CLL CHEMNITZER LABORLEISTUNGS GMBH—See Eurofins Scientific S.E.; *Int'l*, pg. 2535
COAST ENVIRONMENTAL, INC.—See Alliance Environmental Group, LLC; *U.S. Public*, pg. 182
COLA, INC.; *U.S. Private*, pg. 965
COLORADO PATHOLOGY CONSULTANTS, P.C.—See Quest Diagnostics, Inc.; *U.S. Public*, pg. 1755
COMEF SP. Z O.O. SP.K.—See HORIBA Ltd; *Int'l*, pg. 3475
COMPUGROUP MEDICAL LAB AB—See CompuGroup Medical SE & Co. KGaA; *Int'l*, pg. 1756
COMPUNET CLINICAL LABORATORIES, INC.; *U.S. Private*, pg. 1004
COOMEVA ENTIDAD PROMOTORA DE SALUD SA; *Int'l*, pg. 1789
CORAL LABORATORIES LTD.; *Int'l*, pg. 1794
CORDLIFE GROUP LIMITED; *Int'l*, pg. 1796
COVANCE CENTRAL LABORATORY SERVICES, INC.—See Laboratory Corporation of America Holdings; *U.S. Public*, pg. 1285
COVANCE CLINICAL RESEARCH UNIT, INC.—See Laboratory Corporation of America Holdings; *U.S. Public*, pg. 1286
COVANCE KOREA SERVICES LIMITED—See Laboratory Corporation of America Holdings; *U.S. Public*, pg. 1286
COVANCE LABORATORIES KOREA COMPANY LIMITED—See Laboratory Corporation of America Holdings; *U.S. Public*, pg. 1286
COVANCE MEXICO SERVICES, S. DE R. L. DE C.V.—See Laboratory Corporation of America Holdings; *U.S. Public*, pg. 1286
COVANCE PERU SERVICES S.A.—See Laboratory Corporation of America Holdings; *U.S. Public*, pg. 1286
COVANCE PRECLINICAL SERVICES GMBH—See Laboratory Corporation of America Holdings; *U.S. Public*, pg. 1286
COVANCE SERVICES (THAILAND) LIMITED—See Laboratory Corporation of America Holdings; *U.S. Public*, pg. 1286
COVANCE TAIWAN SERVICES LIMITED—See Laboratory Corporation of America Holdings; *U.S. Public*, pg. 1286
CRYOCORD SDN. BHD.—See Cryocord Holdings Sdn. Bhd.; *Int'l*, pg. 1859
CRYO-SAVE (INDIA) PVT. LTD.; *Int'l*, pg. 1859
CTI-VIENNA GESELLSCHAFT ZUR PRUFUNG ELEKTROTECHNISCHER INDUSTRIEPRODUKTE GMBH—See Eaton Corporation plc; *Int'l*, pg. 2277
CYCLOPHARM LIMITED; *Int'l*, pg. 1894
CYTOPATH, P.C.—See Aurora Diagnostics Holdings, LLC; *U.S. Private*, pg. 394

621511 — MEDICAL LABORATORIE... CORPORATE AFFILIATIONS

DAIICHI CLINICAL LABORATORIES, INC.—See BML, Inc.; *Int'l*, pg. 1076
DAKO NETHERLANDS B.V.—See Agilent Technologies, Inc.; *U.S. Public*, pg. 61
DECHRA LABORATORY SERVICES—See Patterson Companies, Inc.; *U.S. Public*, pg. 1654
DEVYSER GMBH—See Devyser Diagnostics AB; *Int'l*, pg. 2091
DIAGNOSTIC LABORATORY OF OKLAHOMA LLC—See Quest Diagnostics, Inc.; *U.S. Public*, pg. 1755
DIAGNOSTICOS DA AMERICA S.A.; *Int'l*, pg. 2103
DIAGNOSTIC PATHOLOGY SERVICES, P.C.—See Quest Diagnostics, Inc.; *U.S. Public*, pg. 1755
DIAMED HOLDING AG—See Bio-Rad Laboratories, Inc.; *U.S. Public*, pg. 333
DIANON SYSTEMS, INC.—See Laboratory Corporation of America Holdings; *U.S. Public*, pg. 1286
DIANON SYSTEMS, INC.—See Laboratory Corporation of America Holdings; *U.S. Public*, pg. 1286
DIANON SYSTEMS, INC.—See Laboratory Corporation of America Holdings; *U.S. Public*, pg. 1286
DIATHERIX LABORATORIES, LLC—See Eurofins Scientific S.E.; *Int'l*, pg. 2536
DIGIPATH LABS, INC.—See Hypha Labs, Inc.; *U.S. Public*, pg. 1079
DISCOVERYBIOMED INC.—See Eurofins Scientific S.E.; *Int'l*, pg. 2536
DISTRICT MEDICAL GROUP INC.; *U.S. Private*, pg. 1239
DNA DIRECT, INC.—See The Cigna Group; *U.S. Public*, pg. 2062
DNA LABORATORIES SDN. BHD.—See Revvity, Inc.; *U.S. Public*, pg. 1794
DYNACARE CANADA INC.—See Laboratory Corporation of America Holdings; *U.S. Public*, pg. 1286
DYNACARE COMPANY—See Laboratory Corporation of America Holdings; *U.S. Public*, pg. 1286
DYNACARE NORTHWEST INC.—See Laboratory Corporation of America Holdings; *U.S. Public*, pg. 1286
DYNALIFEDX—See Laboratory Corporation of America Holdings; *U.S. Public*, pg. 1286
EGL GENETIC DIAGNOSTICS LLC—See Eurofins Scientific S.E.; *Int'l*, pg. 2536
EMPOWERDX, INC.—See Eurofins Scientific S.E.; *Int'l*, pg. 2536
ENZO BIOCHEM INC.; *U.S. Public*, pg. 782
ENZO CLINICAL LABS INC.—See Enzo Biochem Inc.; *U.S. Public*, pg. 782
EPS GLOBAL RESEARCH PTE. LTD.—See EPS Holdings, Inc.; *Int'l*, pg. 2465
ESCREEN, INC.—See Abbott Laboratories; *U.S. Public*, pg. 19
ESOTERIX GENETIC COUNSELING, LLC—See Laboratory Corporation of America Holdings; *U.S. Public*, pg. 1286
ESOTERIX GENETIC LABORATORIES, LLC—See Laboratory Corporation of America Holdings; *U.S. Public*, pg. 1286
ESSILOR LABORATORIES OF AMERICA, INC.—See EssilorLuxottica SA; *Int'l*, pg. 2513
EUROFINS ANALYSES POUR LE BATIMENT NORD-OUEST CEBAT S.A.S.—See Eurofins Scientific S.E.; *Int'l*, pg. 2537
EUROFINS BIOMNIS UK LIMITED—See Eurofins Scientific S.E.; *Int'l*, pg. 2538
EUROFINS BIOPHARMA PRODUCT TESTING COLUMBIA, INC.—See Eurofins Scientific S.E.; *Int'l*, pg. 2538
EUROFINS CHEMTEST LIMITED—See Eurofins Scientific S.E.; *Int'l*, pg. 2539
EUROFINS CLINICAL GENETICS INDIA PVT LTD—See Eurofins Scientific S.E.; *Int'l*, pg. 2539
EUROFINS COUNTY PATHOLOGY LIMITED—See Eurofins Scientific S.E.; *Int'l*, pg. 2539
EUROFINS CRL COSMETICS, INC.—See Eurofins Scientific S.E.; *Int'l*, pg. 2538
EUROFINS CRL INC.—See Eurofins Scientific S.E.; *Int'l*, pg. 2538
EUROFINS EAG MATERIALS SCIENCE NETHERLANDS B.V.—See Eurofins Scientific S.E.; *Int'l*, pg. 2540
EUROFINS ENVIRO-WORKS, INC.—See Eurofins Scientific S.E.; *Int'l*, pg. 2540
EUROFINS EPK BUILT ENVIRONMENT TESTING, LLC—See Eurofins Scientific S.E.; *Int'l*, pg. 2540
EUROFINS FOOD CONTROL SERVICES GMBH—See Eurofins Scientific S.E.; *Int'l*, pg. 2541
EUROFINS FOOD & FEED TESTING LEIPZIG GMBH—See Eurofins Scientific S.E.; *Int'l*, pg. 2541
EUROFINS INSTITUT DR. APPELT HILTER GMBH—See Eurofins Scientific S.E.; *Int'l*, pg. 2544
EUROFINS LABORATORIO DE CASTILLA Y LEON, SL—See Eurofins Scientific S.E.; *Int'l*, pg. 2545
EUROFINS LABORATORIO PREFASI SL—See Eurofins Scientific S.E.; *Int'l*, pg. 2545
EUROFINS LEBENSMITTELANALYTIK OSTERREICH GMBH—See Eurofins Scientific S.E.; *Int'l*, pg. 2545
EUROFINS MEDINET INC.—See Eurofins Scientific S.E.; *Int'l*, pg. 2548
EUROFINS MEDINET SAS—See Eurofins Scientific S.E.; *Int'l*, pg. 2543

EUROFINS MITOX FOPSE S.A.R.L.—See Eurofins Scientific S.E.; *Int'l*, pg. 2545
EUROFINS MUNUERA, S.L.U.—See Eurofins Scientific S.E.; *Int'l*, pg. 2546
EUROFINS RESERVOIRS ENVIRONMENTAL, INC.—See Eurofins Scientific S.E.; *Int'l*, pg. 2547
EUROFINS VIRACOR, INC.—See Eurofins Scientific S.E.; *Int'l*, pg. 2549
EUROFINS VRL, INC.—See Eurofins Scientific S.E.; *Int'l*, pg. 2549
EUROIMMUN JAPAN CO. LTD.—See Revvity, Inc.; *U.S. Public*, pg. 1794
EUROIMMUN TURKEY TIBBI LABORATUAR TESHISLERI A.S.—See Revvity, Inc.; *U.S. Public*, pg. 1794
EUROPA APOTHEEK SERVICE VENLO B.V.—See Europa Apotheek Venlo BV; *Int'l*, pg. 2555
EVERLYWELL, INC.; *U.S. Private*, pg. 1440
EXACT SCIENCES DEUTSCHLAND GMBH—See Exact Sciences Corporation; *U.S. Public*, pg. 805
EXACT SCIENCES LABORATORIES LLC—See Exact Sciences Corporation; *U.S. Public*, pg. 805
EXACT SCIENCES UK, LTD.—See Exact Sciences Corporation; *U.S. Public*, pg. 805
EXAMONE CANADA, INC.—See Quest Diagnostics, Inc.; *U.S. Public*, pg. 1755
FALCO HOLDINGS CO., LTD.; *Int'l*, pg. 2610
FLEXSITE DIAGNOSTICS, INC.—See Geonostics, Inc.; *U.S. Private*, pg. 1681
FOCUS DIAGNOSTICS, INC.—See DiaSorin S.p.A.; *Int'l*, pg. 2106
FOLTENE LABS S.P.A.—See Gerolymatos Group of Companies; *Int'l*, pg. 2943
FORENSIC FLUIDS LABORATORIES, INC.; *U.S. Private*, pg. 1566
FORMOSA LABORATORIES, INC.; *Int'l*, pg. 2735
GALA PHARMACEUTICAL, INC.; *U.S. Private*, pg. 1636
GEMOSCAN CANADA, INC.; *Int'l*, pg. 2916
GENETICS & IVF INSTITUTE, INC.—See Amulet Capital Partners, L.P.; *U.S. Private*, pg. 268
GENNEX LABORATORIES LTD.; *Int'l*, pg. 2925
GENOMIC HEALTH ITALIA S.R.L.—See Exact Sciences Corporation; *U.S. Public*, pg. 805
GENOMICTREE, INC.; *Int'l*, pg. 2925
GENOMIC VISION SA; *Int'l*, pg. 2925
GENOVA DIAGNOSTICS, INC.—See Levine Leichtman Capital Partners, LLC; *U.S. Private*, pg. 2436
GEONOSTICS, INC.; *U.S. Private*, pg. 1681
GEORGIA HEALTHCARE GROUP PLC—See Georgia Capital PLC; *Int'l*, pg. 2939
GEROLPHARM S.A.—See Gerolymatos Group of Companies; *Int'l*, pg. 2943
GETINGE UK LTD.—See Getinge AB; *Int'l*, pg. 2950
GLAXOSMITHKLINE—See GSK plc; *Int'l*, pg. 3146
GLOBAL CORD BLOOD CORPORATION; *Int'l*, pg. 2994
GLOBAL GREEN, INC.—See Nutritional Health Institute Laboratories, LLC; *U.S. Private*, pg. 2974
GLOBAL PHYSICS SOLUTIONS, INC.—See Fortive Corporation; *U.S. Public*, pg. 871
GOLD STANDARD DIAGNOSTICS CORP, INC.—See Eurofins Scientific S.E.; *Int'l*, pg. 2550
GOODGENE INC.—See Bit Computer Co., Ltd.; *Int'l*, pg. 1049
GOOD START GENETICS, INC.—See Invitae Corporation; *U.S. Public*, pg. 1165
GX SCIENCES, LLC—See Fagron NV; *Int'l*, pg. 2603
GYOGYSZERIPARI ELLENORZO ES FEJLESTO LABORATORIUM—See Gedeon Richter Plc.; *Int'l*, pg. 2910
HAEMATOLOGIC TECHNOLOGIES, LLC—See Edgewater Capital Partners, L.P.; *U.S. Private*, pg. 1335
HAROL BROTHERS LLC; *U.S. Private*, pg. 1866
H.A. SHAR & SONS LTD.—See HORIBA Ltd; *Int'l*, pg. 3475
HDM ELQUITECNICA CIA LTDA.—See HORIBA Ltd; *Int'l*, pg. 3477
HEALIUS PATHOLOGY PTY. LTD.—See Healius Limited; *Int'l*, pg. 3302
HEALTH DIAGNOSTICS MANAGEMENT, LLC—See FONAR Corporation; *U.S. Public*, pg. 863
HEMAGEN DIAGNOSTICS, INC.; *U.S. Public*, pg. 1025
HEMOCUE HOLDING AB—See Quest Diagnostics, Inc.; *U.S. Public*, pg. 1755
HLB PANAGENE CO., LTD.; *Int'l*, pg. 3430
IATRIKI TECHNIKI S.A.—See Athens Medical Centers SA; *Int'l*, pg. 670
IDX PATHOLOGY, INC.—See Laboratory Corporation of America Holdings; *U.S. Public*, pg. 1287
IMAGING CORE LAB LLC—See Cinven Limited; *Int'l*, pg. 1612
IMPACT GENETICS CORPORATION—See Laboratory Corporation of America Holdings; *U.S. Public*, pg. 1287
IMPACT GENETICS, INC.—See Laboratory Corporation of America Holdings; *U.S. Public*, pg. 1287
INSIGHT HEALTH CORP.—See Black Diamond Capital Holdings, LLC; *U.S. Private*, pg. 570
INSTACLUSTR PTY. LTD.—See NetApp, Inc.; *U.S. Public*, pg. 1507
INSTITUT FUR MEDIZINISCHE UND CHEMISCHE LABORDIAGNOSTIK GMBH—See Cinven Limited; *Int'l*, pg. 1614
INSTITUTO HERMES PARDINI S.A.—See Fleury S.A.; *Int'l*, pg. 2701
INTEGRATED REGIONAL LABORATORIES; *U.S. Private*, pg. 2101
INTERLAB SUPPLY; *U.S. Private*, pg. 2111
INTERSOCIETAL ACCREDITATION COMMISSION; *U.S. Private*, pg. 2123
INVITAE CORPORATION; *U.S. Public*, pg. 1165
INVITRO INTERNATIONAL; *U.S. Public*, pg. 1165
IQVIA RDS EAST ASIA PTE LTD.—See IQVIA Holdings Inc.; *U.S. Public*, pg. 1170
ISS INTERNATIONAL SCIENTIFIC SERVICES CO.—See HORIBA Ltd; *Int'l*, pg. 3477
JEWISH HEALTHCARE CENTER; *U.S. Private*, pg. 2206
KAILOS GENETICS, INC.—See HealthOme Inc.; *U.S. Private*, pg. 1897
KAI MEDICAL LABORATORY, LLC—See Empower Clinics Inc.; *Int'l*, pg. 2388
KOSSODO S.A.C.—See HORIBA Ltd; *Int'l*, pg. 3477
LABCORP BVBA—See Laboratory Corporation of America Holdings; *U.S. Public*, pg. 1287
LABCORP CLINICAL TRIALS—See Laboratory Corporation of America Holdings; *U.S. Public*, pg. 1287
LABCORP JAPAN, G.K.—See Laboratory Corporation of America Holdings; *U.S. Public*, pg. 1287
LAB DEPOT S.A.—See HORIBA Ltd; *Int'l*, pg. 3477
LABIMEX SRO—See HORIBA Ltd; *Int'l*, pg. 3477
LAB LOGISTICS LLC—See Atlantic Street Capital Management LLC; *U.S. Private*, pg. 374
LAB MASTER SDN. BHD.—See Hiap Huat Holdings Bhd; *Int'l*, pg. 3382
LABORATOIRES COLOPLAST—See Coloplast A/S; *Int'l*, pg. 1704
LABORATORIO SAO LUCAS LTDA.—See Eurofins Scientific S.E.; *Int'l*, pg. 2550
LABORATORIOS MONTORO BOTELLA SL—See Eurofins Scientific S.E.; *Int'l*, pg. 2551
LABORATORIOS VERIS S.A.—See FAES Farma, S.A.; *Int'l*, pg. 2601
LABORATORIO SYNTHESIS S.A.S.—See Abbott Laboratories; *U.S. Public*, pg. 20
LABORDIAGNOSZTIKA KFT.—See HORIBA Ltd; *Int'l*, pg. 3477
LABOTEC, INC.—See BML, Inc.; *Int'l*, pg. 1076
LABTESTS LIMITED—See Brookfield Corporation; *Int'l*, pg. 1176
LGC LIMITED—See KKR & Co. Inc.; *U.S. Public*, pg. 1258
LIFEDNA, INC.—See Nu Skin Enterprises, Inc.; *U.S. Public*, pg. 1551
LILLY RESEARCH LABORATORIES—See Eli Lilly & Company; *U.S. Public*, pg. 733
LIMAGRAIN GENETICS INTERNATIONAL—See Groupe Limagrain Holding SA; *Int'l*, pg. 3107
LINEAGEN, INC.—See Bionano Genomics, Inc.; *U.S. Public*, pg. 338
LOTOS LAB SP. Z O.O.—See Grupa LOTOS S.A.; *Int'l*, pg. 3117
LUCID DIAGNOSTICS INC.—See PAVmed Inc.; *U.S. Public*, pg. 1655
M2GEN—See H. Lee Moffitt Cancer Center & Research Institute; *U.S. Private*, pg. 1825
THE MAASTRICHT FORENSIG INSTITUTE B.V.—See Eurofins Scientific S.E.; *Int'l*, pg. 2552
MAIN STREET CLINICAL LABORATORY, INC.—See Schryver Medical Sales; *U.S. Private*, pg. 3570
MAKO MEDICAL LABORATORIES, LLC; *U.S. Private*, pg. 2556
MANAGED LAB SERVICES INC.—See Flagship Facility Services, Inc.; *U.S. Private*, pg. 1539
MATSUDO MEDICAL LABORATORIES, INC.—See BML, Inc.; *Int'l*, pg. 1076
MEDEXIS S.A—See Gerolymatos Group of Companies; *Int'l*, pg. 2943
MED FUSION, LLC—See Quest Diagnostics, Inc.; *U.S. Public*, pg. 1755
MEDICAL LABORATORY WELLINGTON—See BGH Capital Pty Ltd; *Int'l*, pg. 1008
MEDILYS LABORGESELLSCHAFT MBH—See Asklepios Kliniken GmbH & Co. KGaA; *Int'l*, pg. 623
MEDPACE REFERENCE LABORATORIES LLC—See Cinven Limited; *Int'l*, pg. 1612
MEDTOX SCIENTIFIC, INC.—See Laboratory Corporation of America Holdings; *U.S. Public*, pg. 1287
MERIDIEN RESEARCH; *U.S. Private*, pg. 2674
MESA OMAHA (OMF) BIOLOGICAL INDICATOR MANUFACTURING FACILITY—See Mesa Laboratories, Inc.; *U.S. Public*, pg. 1426
METAMETRIX, INC.—See Levine Leichtman Capital Partners, LLC; *U.S. Private*, pg. 2436
MIPS—See Roper Technologies, Inc.; *U.S. Public*, pg. 1810
MVZ HANSE HISTOLOGIKUM GMBH—See Asklepios Kliniken GmbH & Co. KGaA; *Int'l*, pg. 623
NATERA, INC.; *U.S. Public*, pg. 1492
NATIONAL VETERINARY SERVICES LIMITED—See Patterson Companies, Inc.; *U.S. Public*, pg. 1654

N.A.I.C.S. INDEX

621512 — DIAGNOSTIC IMAGING ...

NELSON DIAGNOSTIC LABORATORY—See BGH Capital Pty Ltd; *Int'l*, pg. 1008
NEOGENIX LABORATOIRE SDN. BHD.—See Hong Seng Consolidated Berhad; *Int'l*, pg. 3469
NEOGENOMICS, INC.; *U.S. Public*, pg. 1505
NEUROWAVE MONITORING INC.—See Calder Development Associates, Inc.; *U.S. Private*, pg. 716
NEW BRIGHTON BUSINESS CENTER, LLC—See Laboratory Corporation of America Holdings; *U.S. Public*, pg. 1287
NEW ENGLAND MEDICAL TRANSCRIPTION; *U.S. Private*, pg. 2894
NEW-ROAD AGENCIES LTD.—See HORIBA Ltd; *Int'l*, pg. 3477
NIKKEN IGAKU, INC.—See BML, Inc.; *Int'l*, pg. 1076
NORTHLAND PATHOLOGY LABORATORY LIMITED—See Brookfield Corporation; *Int'l*, pg. 1176
NUCLEAR DIAGNOSIS, INC.—See HCA Healthcare, Inc.; *U.S. Public*, pg. 1005
NUTRITIONAL HEALTH INSTITUTE LABORATORIES, LLC; *U.S. Private*, pg. 2974
OMNICELL B.V.—See Omnicell, Inc.; *U.S. Public*, pg. 1572
OMNICELL, INC.; *U.S. Public*, pg. 1572
OMNICELL LTD.—See Omnicell, Inc.; *U.S. Public*, pg. 1572
OMNICELL PTY LTD—See Omnicell, Inc.; *U.S. Public*, pg. 1572
OMNICELL S.R.L.—See Omnicell, Inc.; *U.S. Public*, pg. 1573
OPGEN, INC.; *U.S. Public*, pg. 1607
ORALDNA LABS, INC.—See Access Genetics, LLC; *U.S. Private*, pg. 51
ORCHID CELLMARK ULC—See Laboratory Corporation of America Holdings; *U.S. Public*, pg. 1287
ORGENTEC DIAGNOSTIKA GMBH—See Caisse de Depot et Placement du Quebec; *Int'l*, pg. 1255
ORGENTEC DIAGNOSTIKA GMBH—See CVC Capital Partners SICAV-FIS S.A.; *Int'l*, pg. 1884
PASSPORT HEALTH; *U.S. Private*, pg. 3104
PATHGROUP; *U.S. Private*, pg. 3106
PATHOLOGY CONSULTANTS, INC.—See PathGroup; *U.S. Private*, pg. 3106
PCL JAPAN, INC.—See BML, Inc.; *Int'l*, pg. 1076
PEE DEE PATHOLOGY ASSOCIATES, INC.—See Laboratory Corporation of America Holdings; *U.S. Public*, pg. 1287
PERFORMANCE VALIDATION, INC.; *U.S. Private*, pg. 3150
PERKINELMER GENOMICS, INC.—See Revvity, Inc.; *U.S. Public*, pg. 1794
PHARMACOLOGY DISCOVERY SERVICES TAIWAN, LTD.—See Eurofins Scientific S.E.; *Int'l*, pg. 2551
PHC MEDICAL DIAGNOSTIC CENTRE LIMITED—See China Biotech Services Holdings Limited; *Int'l*, pg. 1487
PHENOPATH LABORATORIES, PLLC—See Quest Diagnostics, Inc.; *U.S. Public*, pg. 1755
PLUTON BIOSCIENCES LLC; *U.S. Private*, pg. 3215
PREDICTIVE LABORATORIES, INC.—See Predictive Technology Group, Inc.; *U.S. Public*, pg. 1714
PRELUDE FERTILITY, INC.; *U.S. Private*, pg. 3249
PREVENTIONGENETICS LLC—See Exact Sciences Corporation; *U.S. Public*, pg. 805
PROGENE MOLECULAR DIAGNOSTIC CENTER LIMITED—See China Biotech Services Holdings Limited; *Int'l*, pg. 1487
P.T. ANGLER BIOCHEM LAB LTD.—See Eurofins Scientific S.E.; *Int'l*, pg. 2551
PURE HARVEST CORPORATION GROUP, INC.; *U.S. Public*, pg. 1738
QIS RESEARCH LABORATORY SDN. BHD.—See Hai-O Enterprise Berhad; *Int'l*, pg. 3209
Q SQUARED SOLUTIONS (BEIJING) CO. LTD.—See IQVIA Holdings Inc.; *U.S. Public*, pg. 1170
Q SQUARED SOLUTIONS K.K.—See IQVIA Holdings Inc.; *U.S. Public*, pg. 1170
Q SQUARED SOLUTIONS LIMITED—See IQVIA Holdings Inc.; *U.S. Public*, pg. 1170
Q SQUARED SOLUTIONS PTE. LTD.—See IQVIA Holdings Inc.; *U.S. Public*, pg. 1170
Q SQUARED SOLUTIONS (SHANGHAI) CO. LTD.—See IQVIA Holdings Inc.; *U.S. Public*, pg. 1170
QUEST DIAGNOSTICS CLINICAL LABORATORIES, INC.—See Quest Diagnostics, Inc.; *U.S. Public*, pg. 1755
QUEST DIAGNOSTICS - HOUSTON—See Quest Diagnostics, Inc.; *U.S. Public*, pg. 1755
QUEST DIAGNOSTICS, INC.; *U.S. Public*, pg. 1755
QUEST DIAGNOSTICS IRELAND LIMITED—See Quest Diagnostics, Inc.; *U.S. Public*, pg. 1756
QUEST DIAGNOSTICS - LENEXA—See Quest Diagnostics, Inc.; *U.S. Public*, pg. 1755
QUEST DIAGNOSTICS LIMITED—See Quest Diagnostics, Inc.; *U.S. Public*, pg. 1756
QUEST DIAGNOSTICS - NASHVILLE—See Quest Diagnostics, Inc.; *U.S. Public*, pg. 1755
QUEST DIAGNOSTICS NICHOLS INSTITUTE, INC.—See Quest Diagnostics, Inc.; *U.S. Public*, pg. 1756
QUEST DIAGNOSTICS NICHOLS INSTITUTE—See Quest Diagnostics, Inc.; *U.S. Public*, pg. 1756
QUEST DIAGNOSTICS - SAN ANTONIO—See Quest Diagnostics, Inc.; *U.S. Public*, pg. 1755

QUEST DIAGNOSTICS - SCHAUMBERG—See Quest Diagnostics, Inc.; *U.S. Public*, pg. 1755
QUEST DIAGNOSTICS - SEATTLE—See Quest Diagnostics, Inc.; *U.S. Public*, pg. 1755
QUEST DIAGNOSTICS - SYOSSET—See Quest Diagnostics, Inc.; *U.S. Public*, pg. 1755
QUEST DIAGNOSTICS - WEST HILLS—See Quest Diagnostics, Inc.; *U.S. Public*, pg. 1755
QUEST LABORATORIES PTE. LTD.—See Brookfield Corporation; *Int'l*, pg. 1176
REGIONAL TOXICOLOGY SERVICES, LLC—See Waud Capital Partners LLC; *U.S. Private*, pg. 4457
SAGENEX DIAGNOSTICS LABORATORY, LLC—See AAC Holdings, Inc.; *U.S. Private*, pg. 31
SAM LABORATORY PTE. LTD.—See Clearbridge Health Limited; *Int'l*, pg. 1656
SCIL ANIMAL CARE COMPANY GMBH—See Mars, Incorporated; *U.S. Private*, pg. 2589
SEDIA BIOSCIENCES CORPORATION; *U.S. Public*, pg. 3597
SEQUENOM CENTER FOR MOLECULAR MEDICINE, LLC—See Laboratory Corporation of America Holdings; *U.S. Public*, pg. 1287
SHARP CLINICAL SERVICES, INC.—See Clayton, Dubilier & Rice, LLC; *U.S. Private*, pg. 928
SIGNATURE GENOMIC LABORATORIES, LLC; *U.S. Private*, pg. 3650
SINCLAIR RESEARCH CENTER, LLC; *U.S. Private*, pg. 3669
SINGULEX, INC.; *U.S. Private*, pg. 3670
SINTESY PHARMA S.R.L.—See Glenmark Pharmaceuticals Limited; *Int'l*, pg. 2992
SKIN PATHOLOGY ASSOCIATES INC.—See Harvest Partners L.P.; *U.S. Private*, pg. 1876
SLEEPMED INC. - SLEEP THERAPY SERVICES OPERATIONS CENTER—See SleepMed Inc; *U.S. Private*, pg. 3688
SLEEPMED INC; *U.S. Private*, pg. 3688
SOURCE BIOSCIENCE LIMITED—See Harwood Capital LLP; *Int'l*, pg. 3282
SOUTHEASTERN PATHOLOGY ASSOCIATES—See PathGroup; *U.S. Private*, pg. 3106
SOUTHERN COMMUNITY LABORATORIES LTD.—See Brookfield Corporation; *Int'l*, pg. 1176
SPECIALTY LABORATORIES, INC.—See Quest Diagnostics, Inc.; *U.S. Public*, pg. 1755
SPECION SRO—See HORIBA Ltd; *Int'l*, pg. 3478
SPECTRUM SOLUTIONS L.L.C.; *U.S. Private*, pg. 3753
STEMCYTE, INC.; *U.S. Private*, pg. 3801
STEMTECH INTERNATIONAL SDN. BHD.—See Cryocord Holdings Sdn. Bhd.; *Int'l*, pg. 1859
ST. LUKE'S PATHOLOGY ASSOCIATES, P.A.—See Quest Diagnostics, Inc.; *U.S. Public*, pg. 1756
SUMMIT IMAGING, LLC; *U.S. Private*, pg. 3854
SUPER RELIGARE LABORATORIES INTERNATIONAL FZ LLC—See Fortis Healthcare Limited; *Int'l*, pg. 2739
SYNLAB HOLDING DEUTSCHLAND GMBH—See Cinven Limited; *Int'l*, pg. 1614
SYNLAB LABORATORY SERVICES LIMITED—See Cinven Limited; *Int'l*, pg. 1614
SYNTERACT CORP.—See Elliott Management Corporation; *U.S. Private*, pg. 1366
SYNTERACT CORP.—See Patient Square Capital, L.P.; *U.S. Private*, pg. 3108
SYNTERACT CORP.—See Veritas Capital Fund Management, LLC; *U.S. Private*, pg. 4365
TELEMEDX CORP.—See Ancor Holdings, L.P.; *U.S. Private*, pg. 275
TESTAMERICA DENVER—See H.I.G. Capital, LLC; *U.S. Private*, pg. 1831
THERMO FISHER IRELAND LTD.—See Thermo Fisher Scientific Inc.; *U.S. Public*, pg. 2152
THYROCARE BANGLADESH LIMITED—See Docon Technologies Private Limited; *Int'l*, pg. 2153
TOKYO KOSHUEISEI LABORATORIES, INC.—See BML, Inc.; *Int'l*, pg. 1076
TOTAL RENAL LABORATORIES, INC.—See DaVita Inc.; *U.S. Public*, pg. 644
TRI-CITIES LABORATORY, LLC—See Laboratory Corporation of America Holdings; *U.S. Public*, pg. 1287
TRICORE REFERENCE LABORATORIES; *U.S. Private*, pg. 4229
TRISONICS, INC.—See Avista Capital Partners, L.P.; *U.S. Private*, pg. 409
TURLOCK IMAGING SERVICES, LLC—See Tenet Healthcare Corporation; *U.S. Public*, pg. 2003
UNITED BIOMEDICAL, INC.; *U.S. Private*, pg. 4288
UNITED ESOTERIC CORP.; *U.S. Private*, pg. 4291
UPSCIENCE ITALIA S.R.L.—See Archer-Daniels-Midland Company; *U.S. Public*, pg. 185
US RADIOLOGY SPECIALISTS, INC.; *U.S. Private*, pg. 4319
VERACYTE, INC.; *U.S. Public*, pg. 2279
VHS UNIVERSITY LABORATORIES, INC.—See Tenet Healthcare Corporation; *U.S. Public*, pg. 2015
VIRACOR-IBT LABORATORIES, INC.—See Eurofins Scientific S.E.; *Int'l*, pg. 2549

VISTA CLINICAL DIAGNOSTICS, LLC; *U.S. Private*, pg. 4393
VIVOPHARM EUROPE, LTD.—See Vyant Bio, Inc.; *U.S. Public*, pg. 2315
VIVOPHARM PTY, LTD.—See Vyant Bio, Inc.; *U.S. Public*, pg. 2315
VTGTE INC.—See Kelso & Company, L.P.; *U.S. Private*, pg. 2278
VYANT BIO, INC.; *U.S. Public*, pg. 2314
WEB INDUSTRIES—See Web Industries Inc.; *U.S. Private*, pg. 4464
WEST PHYSICS CONSULTING LLC; *U.S. Private*, pg. 4486
ZINSSER ANALYTIC GMBH—See Ingersoll Rand Inc.; *U.S. Public*, pg. 1120

621512 — DIAGNOSTIC IMAGING CENTERS

ADVANCED DIAGNOSTIC GROUP, LLC—See Akumin, Inc.; *U.S. Public*, pg. 69
ADVANCED MEDICAL IMAGING, LLC—See Franciscan Health System; *U.S. Private*, pg. 1587
ADVANCED RADIOLOGY, LLC—See RadNet, Inc.; *U.S. Public*, pg. 1760
AFFIDEA B.V.—See B-FLEXION Group Holdings SA; *Int'l*, pg. 785
ALLIANCE HEALTHCARE SERVICES, INC.—See Akumin, Inc.; *U.S. Public*, pg. 69
AMBER DIAGNOSTICS, INC.; *U.S. Private*, pg. 217
AMERICAN IMAGING MANAGEMENT, INC.—See Elevance Health, Inc.; *U.S. Public*, pg. 728
AMERICAN RADIOLOGY SERVICES, LLC—See RadNet, Inc.; *U.S. Public*, pg. 1760
AMERICAN RADIOLOGY SERVICES OF DELAWARE, INC.—See RadNet, Inc.; *U.S. Public*, pg. 1760
ANIMALSCAN MRI-NC SCHOOL OF VETERINARY MEDICINE—See AnimalScan; *U.S. Private*, pg. 283
ANIMALSCAN MRI—See AnimalScan; *U.S. Private*, pg. 283
ANIMALSCAN MRI—See AnimalScan; *U.S. Private*, pg. 283
ANIMALSCAN MRI—See AnimalScan; *U.S. Private*, pg. 283
ANIMALSCAN; *U.S. Private*, pg. 283
APELEM SAS—See Diagnostic Medical Systems S.A.; *Int'l*, pg. 2103
ARES GENETICS GMBH—See OpGen, Inc.; *U.S. Public*, pg. 1607
ASIAMEDIC PET/CT CENTRE PTE LTD—See AsiaMedic Ltd.; *Int'l*, pg. 616
BAKORP L.L.C.—See The Ensign Group, Inc.; *U.S. Public*, pg. 2070
THE BIRTH COMPANY LIMITED—See HCA Healthcare, Inc.; *U.S. Public*, pg. 1011
BLUEPRINT GENETICS OY—See Quest Diagnostics, Inc.; *U.S. Public*, pg. 1755
BREAST DIAGNOSTICS OF NORTH TEXAS, P A—See Solis Women's Health, Inc.; *U.S. Private*, pg. 3709
BRIT SYSTEMS, LLC—See KKR & Co. Inc.; *U.S. Public*, pg. 1249
BROOKWOOD BAPTIST IMAGING, LLC—See Tenet Healthcare Corporation; *U.S. Public*, pg. 2001
BROOKWOOD WOMEN'S DIAGNOSTIC CENTER, LLC—See Tenet Healthcare Corporation; *U.S. Public*, pg. 2009
BUMRUNGRAD MYANMAR CO., LTD.—See Bumrungrad Hospital Public Company Limited; *Int'l*, pg. 1215
BUTTERFLY NETWORK, INC.; *U.S. Public*, pg. 413
CAMPBELLTOWN MRI PTY LTD—See Healius Limited; *Int'l*, pg. 3302
CAPITAL RADIOLOGY WA PTY LTD—See Capitol Health Limited; *Int'l*, pg. 1314
CAPITOL HEALTH LIMITED; *Int'l*, pg. 1314
CARESTREAM DENTAL, LLC—See Clayton, Dubilier & Rice, LLC; *U.S. Private*, pg. 920
CARISK SPECIALTY SERVICES, INC.—See Elements Health Investors, LLC; *U.S. Private*, pg. 1357
CARISK SPECIALTY SERVICES, INC.—See Lee Equity Partners LLC; *U.S. Public*, pg. 2412
CARROLL COUNTY RADIOLOGY, LLC—See RadNet, Inc.; *U.S. Public*, pg. 1760
CENTRO DE IMAGEM DIAGNOSTICOS S.A.; *Int'l*, pg. 1413
CENTRO DIAGNOSTICO ITALIANO S.P.A.—See Bracco S.p.A.; *Int'l*, pg. 1134
CHANDLER ENDOSCOPY AMBULATORY SURGERY CENTER, LLC—See Tenet Healthcare Corporation; *U.S. Public*, pg. 2009
CHATTANOOGA DIAGNOSTIC ASSOCIATES, LLC—See HCA Healthcare, Inc.; *U.S. Public*, pg. 993
CHELSEA OUTPATIENT CENTRE LLP—See HCA Healthcare, Inc.; *U.S. Public*, pg. 993
CHRISTIE INNOMED, INC.; *Int'l*, pg. 1587
COMBIMATRIX MOLECULAR DIAGNOSTICS, INC.—See Invitae Corporation; *U.S. Public*, pg. 1165
CONCORD MEDICAL SERVICES HOLDINGS LIMITED; *Int'l*, pg. 1765
CRYSTALVUE MEDICAL CORPORATION; *Int'l*, pg. 1860
CT PRESOV S.R.O.—See Centene Corporation; *U.S. Public*, pg. 468
DEVONSHIRE DIAGNOSTIC CENTRE LIMITED—See HCA

621512 — DIAGNOSTIC IMAGING ...

Healthcare, Inc.; *U.S. Public*, pg. 995
DIAGNOSTIC GROUP LLC—See Demant A/S; *Int'l*, pg. 2023
DIAGNOSTIC IMAGING ASSOCIATES—See RadNet, Inc.; *U.S. Public*, pg. 1761
DIAGNOSTIC PATHOLOGY SERVICES, INC.—See Quest Diagnostics, Inc.; *U.S. Public*, pg. 1755
DIAGNOSTIC REFERENCE SERVICES INC.—See Quest Diagnostics, Inc.; *U.S. Public*, pg. 1755
DIAN DIAGNOSTICS GROUP CO., LTD.; *Int'l*, pg. 2106
DIASORIN ITALIA S.P.A.—See DiaSorin S.p.A.; *Int'l*, pg. 2106
DOLPHIN IMAGING SYSTEMS, LLC—See Patterson Companies, Inc.; *U.S. Public*, pg. 1653
DYNAMIC MOBILE IMAGING; *U.S. Private*, pg. 1298
EAST BERGEN IMAGING, LLC—See RadNet, Inc.; *U.S. Public*, pg. 1761
EUROFINS ADVANTAR LABORATORIES, INC.—See Eurofins Scientific S.E.; *Int'l*, pg. 2536
EUROFINS CLINICAL DIAGNOSTICS KORTRIJK N.V.—See Eurofins Scientific S.E.; *Int'l*, pg. 2539
EUROFINS DIATHERIX LABORATORIES, LLC—See Eurofins Scientific S.E.; *Int'l*, pg. 2539
EUROFINS GELRE B.V.—See Eurofins Scientific S.E.; *Int'l*, pg. 2543
EUROFINS GENETECH KK—See Eurofins Scientific S.E.; *Int'l*, pg. 2543
EXAMWORKS GROUP, INC.—See GIC Pte. Ltd.; *Int'l*, pg. 2964
EXAMWORKS GROUP, INC.—See Leonard Green & Partners, L.P.; *U.S. Private*, pg. 2425
FAMILY CARE HOSPITALS LTD.; *Int'l*, pg. 2612
FEEDBACK MEDICAL LIMITED—See Feedback plc; *Int'l*, pg. 2632
GARDEN STATE RADIOLOGY NETWORK, LLC—See RadNet, Inc.; *U.S. Public*, pg. 1761
GATEWAY ENDOSCOPY CENTER, L.P.—See Tenet Healthcare Corporation; *U.S. Public*, pg. 2010
GENETIC LAB CO., LTD.—See Eurofins Scientific S.E.; *Int'l*, pg. 2550
GENETICS GENERATION ADVANCEMENT CORP.; *Int'l*, pg. 2922
GENOLYTIC DIAGNOSTIK GMBH—See Eurofins Scientific S.E.; *Int'l*, pg. 2550
GEORGIA ENDOSCOPY CENTER, LLC—See Tenet Healthcare Corporation; *U.S. Public*, pg. 2010
G MEDICAL DIAGNOSTIC SERVICES, INC.—See G Medical Innovations Holdings Ltd.; *Int'l*, pg. 2861
GME MEDICAL SUPPLY, INC.—See AdaptHealth Corp.; *U.S. Public*, pg. 38
GREATER SPRINGFIELD MRI, LP—See Akumin, Inc.; *U.S. Public*, pg. 70
HEALTECH S.R.L.—See GPI S.p.A.; *Int'l*, pg. 3046
HEALTHCARE IMAGING SERVICES PTY LTD—See Healius Limited; *Int'l*, pg. 3302
HEALTHCARE IMAGING SERVICES (VICTORIA) PTY LTD—See Healius Limited; *Int'l*, pg. 3302
HOLOGIC, INC. - BREAST IMAGING SOLUTIONS—See Hologic, Inc.; *U.S. Public*, pg. 1045
HTG MOLECULAR DIAGNOSTICS, INC.; *U.S. Public*, pg. 1065
IMAGEONE CO., LTD.; *Int'l*, pg. 3618
IMPACT MEDICAL IMAGING CENTRE COMPANY LIMITED—See Human Health Holdings Limited; *Int'l*, pg. 3529
IMRIS (EUROPE) SPRL—See IMRIS Inc.; *U.S. Public*, pg. 1114
IMRIS SINGAPORE PTE. LTD.—See IMRIS Inc.; *U.S. Public*, pg. 1114
INGLEWOOD IMAGING CENTER LLC; *U.S. Private*, pg. 2076
INJURY QED LIMITED—See AnaCap Financial Partners LLP; *Int'l*, pg. 445
INSIGHT RADIOLOGY LIMITED—See BGH Capital Pty Ltd; *Int'l*, pg. 1008
IPPOKRATIS MAGNETIC TOMOGRAPHY S.A.—See AXON Holdings S.A.; *Int'l*, pg. 770
IRJB INSTITUT DE RADIOLOGIE DU JURA BERNOIS SA—See AEVIS VICTORIA SA; *Int'l*, pg. 183
JUNEAU BIOSCIENCES, LLC; *U.S. Private*, pg. 2244
JUSTESA IMAGEN MEXICANA, S.A.—See Bracco S.p.A.; *Int'l*, pg. 1134
LABCORP - BATON ROUGE—See Laboratory Corporation of America Holdings; *U.S. Public*, pg. 1287
LABONE CANADA, INC.—See Quest Diagnostics, Inc.; *U.S. Public*, pg. 1755
LED DENTAL INC—See Level Equity Management, LLC; *U.S. Private*, pg. 2434
LIME AVENUE RADIOLOGY PTY LTD—See Capitol Health Limited; *Int'l*, pg. 1314
LOC AT THE HARBORNE HOSPITAL LIMITED—See HCA Healthcare, Inc.; *U.S. Public*, pg. 1000
THE LONDON BREAST INSTITUTE UK LTD—See HCA Healthcare, Inc.; *U.S. Public*, pg. 1012
LONDON RADIOTHERAPY CENTRE LTD.—See HCA Healthcare, Inc.; *U.S. Public*, pg. 1001
LONE STAR ENDOSCOPY CENTER, LLC—See Tenet Healthcare Corporation; *U.S. Public*, pg. 2011

MAGNETIC RESONANCE IMAGING OF SAN LUIS OBISPO, INC.—See Tenet Healthcare Corporation; *U.S. Public*, pg. 2008
MCKESSON MEDICAL IMAGING GROUP—See McKesson Corporation; *U.S. Public*, pg. 1408
MED CELL MEDICAL CO. K.S.C.C.—See Al-Mazaya Holding Company K.S.C.P.; *Int'l*, pg. 287
MEDICAL IMAGING CORP.; *U.S. Public*, pg. 1411
MEDRISK, LLC—See The Carlyle Group Inc.; *U.S. Public*, pg. 2049
MERCY GENERAL HOSPITAL—See Catholic Health Initiatives; *U.S. Private*, pg. 790
METROWEST IMAGING CENTER, LLC—See Akumin, Inc.; *U.S. Public*, pg. 70
MID ROCKLAND IMAGING PARTNERS, INC.—See RadNet, Inc.; *U.S. Public*, pg. 1761
MIDSTATE RADIOLOGY ASSOCIATES LLC; *U.S. Private*, pg. 2718
MOBILE CARDIAC IMAGING, LLC; *U.S. Private*, pg. 2757
MODESTO RADIOLOGY IMAGING, INC.—See Tenet Healthcare Corporation; *U.S. Public*, pg. 2003
MONTGOMERY COMMUNITY MAGNETIC IMAGING CENTER LIMITED PARTNERSHIP—See RadNet, Inc.; *U.S. Public*, pg. 1761
MOUNT AIRY IMAGING CENTER, LLC—See RadNet, Inc.; *U.S. Public*, pg. 1761
MT. BAKER PETCT, LLC—See Akumin, Inc.; *U.S. Public*, pg. 70
NATIONAL DENTEX CORPORATION—See Cerberus Capital Management, L.P.; *U.S. Private*, pg. 839
NEUROSKELETAL IMAGING, LLC—See Community Health Systems, Inc.; *U.S. Public*, pg. 555
NEW JERSEY IMAGING NETWORK, LLC—See RadNet, Inc.; *U.S. Public*, pg. 1761
NIGHTHAWK RADIOLOGY, INC.—See MEDNAX, Inc.; *U.S. Public*, pg. 1413
NOVOCELLUS LIMITED—See ANGLE plc; *Int'l*, pg. 461
OPKO BIOLOGICS, LTD—See OPKO Health, Inc.; *U.S. Public*, pg. 1608
OPKO LAB, LLC—See OPKO Health, Inc.; *U.S. Public*, pg. 1608
OPKO RENAL, LLC—See OPKO Health, Inc.; *U.S. Public*, pg. 1608
OPTIMAL IMX, INC.—See Great Point Partners, LLC; *U.S. Private*, pg. 1767
THE ORCHARD IMAGING CENTRE PTE LTD—See Asia-Medic Ltd.; *Int'l*, pg. 617
ORIGIO A/S—See The Cooper Companies, Inc.; *U.S. Public*, pg. 2066
ORIGIO FRANCE SARL—See The Cooper Companies, Inc.; *U.S. Public*, pg. 2066
ORIGIO LTD.—See The Cooper Companies, Inc.; *U.S. Public*, pg. 2066
PARTNERS IMAGING CENTER OF CHARLOTTE, LLC—See Medical Imaging Corp.; *U.S. Public*, pg. 1411
PARTNERS IMAGING CENTER OF NAPLES, LLC—See Medical Imaging Corp.; *U.S. Public*, pg. 1412
PARTNERS IMAGING CENTER OF VENICE, LLC—See Medical Imaging Corp.; *U.S. Public*, pg. 1412
PERKINELMER MEDICAL IMAGING, LLC—See Varex Imaging Corporation; *U.S. Public*, pg. 2275
PHYSICIANS ENDOSCOPY CENTER—See HCA Healthcare, Inc.; *U.S. Public*, pg. 1006
PHYSICIANS SPECIALTY HOSPITAL, LLC—See Community Health Systems, Inc.; *U.S. Public*, pg. 556
PLEASANTON DIAGNOSTIC IMAGING, INC.—See Tenet Healthcare Corporation; *U.S. Public*, pg. 2003
PREVENTIVE DIAGNOSTICS, INC.; *U.S. Private*, pg. 3257
PREVILAB ANALISES CLINICAS LTDA—See Diagnosticos da America S.A.; *Int'l*, pg. 2103
PRICESPECTIVE LLC—See ICON plc; *Int'l*, pg. 3586
THE PROSTATE CENTRE LIMITED—See HCA Healthcare, Inc.; *U.S. Public*, pg. 1012
PSYCHEMEDICS CORPORATION; *U.S. Public*, pg. 1734
QT IMAGING HOLDINGS, INC.; *U.S. Public*, pg. 1744
QUALITY ELECTRODYNAMICS LLC—See Canon Inc.; *Int'l*, pg. 1298
QUALITY MOBILE X RAY SERVICES, INC.—See Schryver Medical Sales; *U.S. Private*, pg. 3570
QUEENSLAND DIAGNOSTIC IMAGING PTY LTD—See Healius Limited; *Int'l*, pg. 3302
QUEST DIAGNOSTICS INCORPORATED—See Quest Diagnostics, Inc.; *U.S. Public*, pg. 1755
QUEST DIAGNOSTICS INCORPORATED—See Quest Diagnostics, Inc.; *U.S. Public*, pg. 1756
QUEST DIAGNOSTICS INCORPORATED—See Quest Diagnostics, Inc.; *U.S. Public*, pg. 1756
RADIATION PHYSICS, INC.—See Preventive Diagnostics, Inc.; *U.S. Private*, pg. 3257
RADIOLOGY ALLIANCE DELIVERY SYSTEM, LLC—See RadNet, Inc.; *U.S. Public*, pg. 1761
RADMD INC.—See IK Investment Partners Limited; *Int'l*, pg. 3609
RADNET, INC.; *U.S. Public*, pg. 1760
RADNET MANAGED IMAGING SERVICES, INC.—See RadNet, Inc.; *U.S. Public*, pg. 1761
REIMED, SCRL—See Bracco S.p.A.; *Int'l*, pg. 1134

REPERTOIRE GENESIS CO., LTD.—See Eurofins Scientific S.E.; *Int'l*, pg. 2551
RMIS IMAGING SERVICES, INC.—See RadNet, Inc.; *U.S. Public*, pg. 1761
ROLLING OAKS RADIOLOGY, INC.—See RadNet, Inc.; *U.S. Public*, pg. 1761
SCHUYLKILL OPEN MRI, INC.—See Medical Imaging Corp.; *U.S. Public*, pg. 1412
SCIL ANIMAL CARE COMPANY—See Mars, Incorporated; *U.S. Private*, pg. 2589
SHIEL MEDICAL LABORATORY, INC.—See Quest Diagnostics, Inc.; *U.S. Public*, pg. 1756
SITEC LABS PVT. LTD.—See Cipla Ltd.; *Int'l*, pg. 1617
SOLIS MAMMOGRAPHY AT CLEAR LAKE REGIONAL MEDICAL CENTER, LLC—See HCA Healthcare, Inc.; *U.S. Public*, pg. 1008
SOLIS MAMMOGRAPHY AT CONROE REGIONAL MEDICAL CENTER, LLC—See HCA Healthcare, Inc.; *U.S. Public*, pg. 1009
SOLIS MAMMOGRAPHY AT DENTON REGIONAL MEDICAL CENTER, LLC—See HCA Healthcare, Inc.; *U.S. Public*, pg. 1009
SOLIS MAMMOGRAPHY AT HCA HOUSTON TOMBALL, LLC—See HCA Healthcare, Inc.; *U.S. Public*, pg. 1009
SOLIS MAMMOGRAPHY AT KINGWOOD MEDICAL CENTER, LLC—See HCA Healthcare, Inc.; *U.S. Public*, pg. 1009
SOLIS MAMMOGRAPHY AT LAS COLINAS MEDICAL CENTER, LLC—See HCA Healthcare, Inc.; *U.S. Public*, pg. 1009
SOLIS MAMMOGRAPHY AT MEDICAL CENTER ALLIANCE, LLC—See HCA Healthcare, Inc.; *U.S. Public*, pg. 1009
SOLIS MAMMOGRAPHY AT MEDICAL CENTER ARLINGTON, LLC—See HCA Healthcare, Inc.; *U.S. Public*, pg. 1009
SOLIS MAMMOGRAPHY AT MEDICAL CITY DALLAS, LLC—See HCA Healthcare, Inc.; *U.S. Public*, pg. 1009
SOLIS MAMMOGRAPHY AT OGDEN REGIONAL MEDICAL CENTER, LLC—See HCA Healthcare, Inc.; *U.S. Public*, pg. 1009
SOLIS MAMMOGRAPHY AT PEARLAND MEDICAL CENTER, LLC—See HCA Healthcare, Inc.; *U.S. Public*, pg. 1009
SOLIS MAMMOGRAPHY AT ROSE MEDICAL CENTER, LLC—See HCA Healthcare, Inc.; *U.S. Public*, pg. 1009
SOLIS MAMMOGRAPHY AT SKYLINE MEDICAL CENTER, LLC—See HCA Healthcare, Inc.; *U.S. Public*, pg. 1009
SOLIS MAMMOGRAPHY AT ST. DAVID'S MEDICAL CENTER, LLC—See HCA Healthcare, Inc.; *U.S. Public*, pg. 1009
SOLIS MAMMOGRAPHY AT ST. MARK'S HOSPITAL, LLC—See HCA Healthcare, Inc.; *U.S. Public*, pg. 1009
SOLIS MAMMOGRAPHY AT STONECREST MEDICAL CENTER, LLC—See HCA Healthcare, Inc.; *U.S. Public*, pg. 1009
SOLIS MAMMOGRAPHY AT TIMPANOGOS REGIONAL HOSPITAL, LLC—See HCA Healthcare, Inc.; *U.S. Public*, pg. 1009
SOLIS MAMMOGRAPHY AT WEST HOUSTON MEDICAL CENTER, LLC—See HCA Healthcare, Inc.; *U.S. Public*, pg. 1009
SOLIS MAMMOGRAPHY AT WOMANS HOSPITAL OF TEXAS, LLC—See HCA Healthcare, Inc.; *U.S. Public*, pg. 1009
SOLIS MAMMOGRAPHY OF CEDAR HILL, LLC—See HCA Healthcare, Inc.; *U.S. Public*, pg. 1009
SOLIS MAMMOGRAPHY OF CYFAIR, LLC—See HCA Healthcare, Inc.; *U.S. Public*, pg. 1009
SOLIS MAMMOGRAPHY OF FLOWER MOUND, LLC—See HCA Healthcare, Inc.; *U.S. Public*, pg. 1009
SOLIS MAMMOGRAPHY OF FRISCO, LLC—See HCA Healthcare, Inc.; *U.S. Public*, pg. 1009
SOLIS MAMMOGRAPHY OF GARLAND, LLC—See HCA Healthcare, Inc.; *U.S. Public*, pg. 1009
SOLIS MAMMOGRAPHY OF GRAND PRAIRIE, LLC—See HCA Healthcare, Inc.; *U.S. Public*, pg. 1009
SOLIS MAMMOGRAPHY OF HOUSTON NW, LLC—See HCA Healthcare, Inc.; *U.S. Public*, pg. 1009
SOLIS MAMMOGRAPHY OF KATY, LLC—See HCA Healthcare, Inc.; *U.S. Public*, pg. 1009
SOLIS MAMMOGRAPHY OF MAINLAND, LLC—See HCA Healthcare, Inc.; *U.S. Public*, pg. 1009
SOLIS MAMMOGRAPHY OF MANSFIELD, LLC—See HCA Healthcare, Inc.; *U.S. Public*, pg. 1009
SOLIS MAMMOGRAPHY OF MESQUITE, LLC—See HCA Healthcare, Inc.; *U.S. Public*, pg. 1009
SOLIS MAMMOGRAPHY OF MONTGOMERY, LLC—See HCA Healthcare, Inc.; *U.S. Public*, pg. 1009
SOLIS MAMMOGRAPHY OF NORTH CYPRESS, LLC—See HCA Healthcare, Inc.; *U.S. Public*, pg. 1009
SOLIS MAMMOGRAPHY OF RED OAK, LLC—See HCA Healthcare, Inc.; *U.S. Public*, pg. 1009
SOLIS MAMMOGRAPHY OF RIVER OAKS, LLC—See HCA Healthcare, Inc.; *U.S. Public*, pg. 1009
SOLIS MAMMOGRAPHY OF ROWLETT, LLC—See HCA Healthcare, Inc.; *U.S. Public*, pg. 1009
SOLIS MAMMOGRAPHY OF SOUTHWEST FORT WORTH,

N.A.I.C.S. INDEX

621610 — HOME HEALTH CARE SE...

LLC—See HCA Healthcare, Inc.; *U.S. Public*, pg. 1009
SOLIS MAMMOGRAPHY OF SUGAR LAND, LLC—See HCA Healthcare, Inc.; *U.S. Public*, pg. 1009
SOLIS MAMMOGRAPHY OF TOWNE LAKE, LLC—See HCA Healthcare, Inc.; *U.S. Public*, pg. 1010
SOLIS MAMMOGRAPHY OF WEST PLANO, LLC—See HCA Healthcare, Inc.; *U.S. Public*, pg. 1010
SOLIS MAMMOGRAPHY OF WOMANS PLACE, LLC—See HCA Healthcare, Inc.; *U.S. Public*, pg. 1010
SOLIS WOMEN'S HEALTH, INC.; *U.S. Private*, pg. 3709
SONODEPOT, INC.—See Avista Capital Partners, L.P.; *U.S. Private*, pg. 408
SOUTH BAY IMAGING, LLC—See HCA Healthcare, Inc.; *U.S. Public*, pg. 1010
SUMMIT RESEARCH NETWORK, INC.—See KKR & Co. Inc.; *U.S. Public*, pg. 1252
SXR MEDICAL, LLC—See KKR & Co. Inc.; *U.S. Public*, pg. 1250
SYWEST MEDICAL TECHNOLOGIES INC.—See Merry X-Ray Corporation; *U.S. Public*, pg. 2676
TEMPLETON IMAGING, INC.—See Adventist Health System; *U.S. Private*, pg. 108
TOOWOOMBA DIAGNOSTIC IMAGING PTY. LTD.—See Healius Limited; *Int'l*, pg. 3303
TRI CITY PETCT LLC—See Akumin, Inc.; *U.S. Public*, pg. 70
UNILABS AB—See Apax Partners LLP; *Int'l*, pg. 507
UNILABS S.A.—See Apax Partners LLP; *Int'l*, pg. 507
U.S. LABORATORIES; *U.S. Private*, pg. 4271
UVAXX PTE. LTD.—See Barramundi Group Ltd.; *Int'l*, pg. 867
VALLEY IMAGING PARTNERS INC.—See RadNet, Inc.; *U.S. Public*, pg. 1761
VHS SAN ANTONIO IMAGING PARTNERS, L.P.—See Tenet Healthcare Corporation; *U.S. Public*, pg. 2014
VIRTUAL RADIOLOGIC CORPORATION—See MEDNAX, Inc.; *U.S. Public*, pg. 1413
VISTA IMAGING SERVICES, INC.; *U.S. Private*, pg. 4403
WASATCH ENDOSCOPY CENTER—See HCA Healthcare, Inc.; *U.S. Public*, pg. 1013
WELLINGTON DIAGNOSTIC SERVICES LLP—See HCA Healthcare, Inc.; *U.S. Public*, pg. 1013
WESTERN MASSACHUSETTS PET/CT IMAGING CENTER LLC—See Akumin, Inc.; *U.S. Public*, pg. 70
WHITSUNDAY RADIOLOGY PTY. LTD.—See Healius Limited; *Int'l*, pg. 3303
WOODLAND DIAGNOSTIC IMAGING, LLC—See Akumin, Inc.; *U.S. Public*, pg. 70
ZICIX CORP.; *U.S. Public*, pg. 2403
ZIEHM IMAGING FINNLAND (OY)—See ATON GmbH; *Int'l*, pg. 689
ZIEHM IMAGING GMBH—See ATON GmbH; *Int'l*, pg. 689
ZIEHM IMAGING INC.—See ATON GmbH; *Int'l*, pg. 689
ZIEHM IMAGING SARL—See ATON GmbH; *Int'l*, pg. 689
ZIEHM IMAGING SA—See ATON GmbH; *Int'l*, pg. 689
ZIEHM IMAGING SINGAPORE PTE. LTD.—See ATON GmbH; *Int'l*, pg. 689
ZIEHM MEDICAL DO BRASIL—See ATON GmbH; *Int'l*, pg. 689
ZIEHM MEDICAL LLC—See ATON GmbH; *Int'l*, pg. 689
ZIEHM MEDICAL (SHANGHAI) CO. LTD.—See ATON GmbH; *Int'l*, pg. 689

621610 — HOME HEALTH CARE SERVICES

123 HOME CARE SERVICES, LLC; *U.S. Private*, pg. 2
1LIFE HEALTHCARE, INC.—See Amazon.com, Inc.; *U.S. Public*, pg. 90
1ST AVENUE PHARMACY, INC.—See UnitedHealth Group Incorporated; *U.S. Public*, pg. 2238
24HR HOMECARE; *U.S. Private*, pg. 6
3M GULF LTD.—See 3M Company; *U.S. Public*, pg. 6
3M INNOVATION SINGAPORE PTE LTD.—See 3M Company; *U.S. Public*, pg. 6
3M ITALIA SRL—See 3M Company; *U.S. Public*, pg. 6
3M ROMANIA S.R.L.—See 3M Company; *U.S. Public*, pg. 7
3M TECHNOLOGIES PRIVATE LIMITED—See 3M Company; *U.S. Public*, pg. 7
AAA HOME HEALTH INC.—See UnitedHealth Group Incorporated; *U.S. Public*, pg. 2243
ABBA HOME HEALTH, L.P.—See Encompass Health Corporation; *U.S. Public*, pg. 754
ABBOTT BIOTECHNOLOGY DEUTSCHLAND GMBH—See Abbott Laboratories; *U.S. Public*, pg. 15
ABBOTT DEUTSCHLAND GMBH—See Abbott Laboratories; *U.S. Public*, pg. 15
ABBOTT DIABETES CARE LIMITED—See Abbott Laboratories; *U.S. Public*, pg. 14
ABBOTT HEALTHCARE PRIVATE LIMITED—See Abbott Laboratories; *U.S. Public*, pg. 17
ABBOTT HEALTHCARE PRODUCTS LTD.—See Abbott Laboratories; *U.S. Public*, pg. 16
ABBOTT INFORMATICS EUROPE LIMITED—See Abbott Laboratories; *U.S. Public*, pg. 20
ABBOTT LABORATORIES INC; *U.S. Private*, pg. 35
ABBOTT LABORATORIES INTERNATIONAL CO.—See Abbott Laboratories; *U.S. Public*, pg. 15
ABBOTT LABORATORIES TRADING (SHANGHAI) CO., LTD.—See Abbott Laboratories; *U.S. Public*, pg. 16
ABBOTT NEDERLAND C.V.—See Abbott Laboratories; *U.S. Public*, pg. 14
A & B HOMECARE SOLUTIONS, LLC—See Encompass Health Corporation; *U.S. Public*, pg. 754
ABLE HEALTH LLC—See Health Catalyst, Inc.; *U.S. Public*, pg. 1014
ABLE HOME HEALTH, INC.—See UnitedHealth Group Incorporated; *U.S. Public*, pg. 2243
ACADIA MALIBU, INC.; *U.S. Private*, pg. 46
ACADIAN HOMECARE, LLC—See UnitedHealth Group Incorporated; *U.S. Public*, pg. 2243
ACADIAN PHYSICAL THERAPY SERVICES, LLC—See UnitedHealth Group Incorporated; *U.S. Public*, pg. 2243
ACCELERO HEALTH PARTNERS, LLC—See Zimmer Biomet Holdings, Inc.; *U.S. Public*, pg. 2405
ACCESS COMMUNITY HEALTH LIMITED—See Green Cross Health Limited; *Int'l*, pg. 3070
ACCESS HOSPICE, LLC—See UnitedHealth Group Incorporated; *U.S. Public*, pg. 2243
ACCESS QUALITY CARE SERVICES—See Chenega Corporation; *U.S. Private*, pg. 872
ACCREDITED HEALTH SERVICES, INC.—See Blue Wolf Capital Partners LLC; *U.S. Private*, pg. 595
ACCREDO CARE NETWORK, INC.—See The Cigna Group; *U.S. Public*, pg. 2062
ACCUFIX RESEARCH INSTITUTE INC.—See Ansell Limited; *Int'l*, pg. 478
ACCUHEALTH TECHNOLOGIES LLC—See Sunstone Partners Management LLC; *U.S. Private*, pg. 3873
ACCURATE HOME CARE, LLC; *U.S. Private*, pg. 55
ACF MEDICAL SERVICES, INC.—See Encore Capital Group, Inc.; *U.S. Public*, pg. 759
ACHYUT HEALTHCARE LTD.; *Int'l*, pg. 104
ACRUX LIMITED; *Int'l*, pg. 109
ACTICA OMSORG AB—See Apax Partners LLP; *Int'l*, pg. 502
ACTIVE HEALTH MANAGEMENT, INC.—See CVS Health Corporation; *U.S. Public*, pg. 614
ADAPTOGENICS HEALTH CORP.; *Int'l*, pg. 125
ADDUS HEALTHCARE (DELAWARE), INC.—See Addus HomeCare Corporation; *U.S. Public*, pg. 40
ADDUS HEALTHCARE (IDAHO), INC.—See Addus HomeCare Corporation; *U.S. Public*, pg. 40
ADDUS HEALTHCARE, INC.—See Addus HomeCare Corporation; *U.S. Public*, pg. 40
ADDUS HEALTHCARE (NEVADA), INC.—See Addus HomeCare Corporation; *U.S. Public*, pg. 40
ADDUS HEALTHCARE (SOUTH CAROLINA), INC.—See Addus HomeCare Corporation; *U.S. Public*, pg. 40
ADDUS HOMECARE CORPORATION; *U.S. Public*, pg. 40
ADORA FERTILITY PTY LTD—See Healius Limited; *Int'l*, pg. 3302
ADULT DAY CARE OF AMERICA, INC.—See UnitedHealth Group Incorporated; *U.S. Public*, pg. 2243
ADVANCED CARE MANAGEMENT, INC.—See Bain Capital, LP; *U.S. Private*, pg. 431
ADVANCED CARE PARTNERS, LLC; *U.S. Private*, pg. 88
ADVANCED CARE SCRIPTS, INC.—See CVS Health Corporation; *U.S. Public*, pg. 613
ADVANCED HEALTH CARE CORPORATION—See Larry H. Miller Group of Companies; *U.S. Private*, pg. 2392
ADVANCED HOME CARE INC.—See AdaptHealth Corp.; *U.S. Public*, pg. 38
ADVANCED HOMECARE MANAGEMENT, INC.—See Encompass Health Corporation; *U.S. Public*, pg. 754
ADVANTAGE MEDICAL GROUP, LLC—See Elevance Health, Inc.; *U.S. Public*, pg. 728
ADVANTAGE RISK MANAGEMENT CO.,LTD.; *Int'l*, pg. 164
ADVANZ PHARMA CORP. LIMITED; *Int'l*, pg. 166
ADVENTIST HEALTH/HOME CARE & HOSPICE SERVICES - MENDOCINO COUNTY—See Adventist Health System; *U.S. Private*, pg. 108
ADVOCATE AURORA ENTERPRISES, INC.—See Advocate Health Care Network; *U.S. Private*, pg. 111
ADVOCATE HOME CARE SERVICES; *U.S. Private*, pg. 111
AETNA BETTER HEALTH OF MICHIGAN INC.—See CVS Health Corporation; *U.S. Public*, pg. 614
AETNA GLOBAL BENEFITS (MIDDLE EAST) LLC—See CVS Health Corporation; *U.S. Public*, pg. 613
AETNA GLOBAL BENEFITS (UK) LIMITED—See CVS Health Corporation; *U.S. Public*, pg. 614
AETNA (SHANGHAI) ENTERPRISE SERVICES CO. LTD.—See CVS Health Corporation; *U.S. Public*, pg. 614
AGILON HEALTH, INC.; *U.S. Public*, pg. 62
AGRIPHAR SARL—See Element Solutions Inc.; *U.S. Public*, pg. 725
AINO HEALTH AB; *Int'l*, pg. 234
ALABAMA HOMECARE OF VESTAVIA HILLS—See UnitedHealth Group Incorporated; *U.S. Public*, pg. 2243
ALACARE HOME HEALTH SERVICES, INC.—See Encompass Health Corporation; *U.S. Public*, pg. 754
ALCURA UK LIMITED—See Walgreens Boots Alliance, Inc.; *U.S. Public*, pg. 2321
AL-DAWAA MEDICAL SERVICES COMPANY; *Int'l*, pg. 284
ALERE HEALTH SYSTEMS, INC.—See UnitedHealth Group Incorporated; *U.S. Public*, pg. 2248
ALIO HEALTH SERVICES INC.—See Calian Group Ltd.; *Int'l*, pg. 1263
ALIVI; *U.S. Private*, pg. 169
ALLEGAN GENERAL HOSPITAL; *U.S. Private*, pg. 175
ALLIANCE HEALTHCARE FRANCE SA—See Walgreens Boots Alliance, Inc.; *U.S. Public*, pg. 2321
ALLIANCE HEALTHCARE ROMANIA SRL—See Walgreens Boots Alliance, Inc.; *U.S. Public*, pg. 2322
ALLIANCE HEALTHCARE S.R.O.—See Walgreens Boots Alliance, Inc.; *U.S. Public*, pg. 2322
ALLIANCE HOME SERVICES INC; *U.S. Private*, pg. 183
ALLIANCE PHARMACEUTICALS GMBH—See Alliance Pharma PLC; *Int'l*, pg. 340
ALLIED CORP.; *Int'l*, pg. 357
ALLIED HEALTHCARE GROUP LIMITED—See Charterhouse Capital Partners LLP; *Int'l*, pg. 1455
ALLIED HEALTHCARE GROUP LIMITED—See CVC Capital Partners SICAV-FIS S.A.; *Int'l*, pg. 1882
ALL METRO HEALTH CARE; *U.S. Private*, pg. 171
ALLSCRIPTS (INDIA) PRIVATE LIMITED—See Veradigm Inc.; *U.S. Public*, pg. 2279
ALMOST FAMILY PC OF FT. LAUDERDALE, LLC—See UnitedHealth Group Incorporated; *U.S. Public*, pg. 2243
ALMOST FAMILY PC OF KENTUCKY, LLC—See UnitedHealth Group Incorporated; *U.S. Public*, pg. 2243
ALMOST FAMILY PC OF SW FLORIDA, LLC—See UnitedHealth Group Incorporated; *U.S. Public*, pg. 2243
ALMOST FAMILY PC OF WEST PALM, LLC—See UnitedHealth Group Incorporated; *U.S. Public*, pg. 2243
ALO SOLUTIONS, LLC; *U.S. Private*, pg. 195
ALPHEIDE-SENIORENZENTRUM GMBH—See Clariane SE; *Int'l*, pg. 1642
ALTEN-PFLEGEHEIM VEITSBRONN GMBH—See Clariane SE; *Int'l*, pg. 1642
ALTERNATE SOLUTIONS HOMECARE; *U.S. Private*, pg. 207
ALTHEA PARK LIMITED—See Bridgepoint Group Plc; *Int'l*, pg. 1154
ALTRUISTA HEALTH, INC.—See Blackstone Inc.; *U.S. Public*, pg. 354
AMBERCARE CORPORATION—See Addus HomeCare Corporation; *U.S. Public*, pg. 40
AMEDISYS ARIZONA, L.L.C.—See Amedisys, Inc.; *U.S. Public*, pg. 93
AMEDISYS DELAWARE, L.L.C.—See Amedisys, Inc.; *U.S. Public*, pg. 93
AMEDISYS FLORIDA, L.L.C.—See Amedisys, Inc.; *U.S. Public*, pg. 93
AMEDISYS HOME HEALTH CARE - GASTONIA—See Amedisys, Inc.; *U.S. Public*, pg. 93
AMEDISYS HOME HEALTH CARE—See Amedisys, Inc.; *U.S. Public*, pg. 93
AMEDISYS HOME HEALTH CARE - WHEELING—See Amedisys, Inc.; *U.S. Public*, pg. 93
AMEDISYS HOME HEALTH, INC. OF ALABAMA—See Amedisys, Inc.; *U.S. Public*, pg. 93
AMEDISYS HOME HEALTH, INC. OF SOUTH CAROLINA—See Amedisys, Inc.; *U.S. Public*, pg. 93
AMEDISYS HOME HEALTH OF NEBRASKA, L.L.C.—See Amedisys, Inc.; *U.S. Public*, pg. 93
AMEDISYS, INC.; *U.S. Public*, pg. 93
AMEDISYS NEW HAMPSHIRE, L.L.C.—See Amedisys, Inc.; *U.S. Public*, pg. 93
AMEDISYS NEW JERSEY, L.L.C.—See Amedisys, Inc.; *U.S. Public*, pg. 93
AMEDISYS NORTH CAROLINA, L.L.C.—See Amedisys, Inc.; *U.S. Public*, pg. 93
AMEDISYS OKLAHOMA, L.L.C.—See Amedisys, Inc.; *U.S. Public*, pg. 93
AMEDISYS SPECIALIZED MEDICAL SERVICES, INC.—See Amedisys, Inc.; *U.S. Public*, pg. 93
AMEDISYS SP-IN, L.L.C.—See Amedisys, Inc.; *U.S. Public*, pg. 93
AMEDISYS SP-KY, L.L.C.—See Amedisys, Inc.; *U.S. Public*, pg. 93
AMEDISYS SP-OH, L.L.C.—See Amedisys, Inc.; *U.S. Public*, pg. 93
AMEDISYS TENNESSEE, L.L.C.—See Amedisys, Inc.; *U.S. Public*, pg. 93
AMENITY HEALTH, INC.; *U.S. Private*, pg. 218
AMERICAN HOSPICE LLC—See The Riverside Company; *U.S. Private*, pg. 4107
AMERICAN MEDICAL RESPONSE MID-ATLANTIC, INC.—See KKR & Co. Inc.; *U.S. Public*, pg. 1251
AMERICAN MEDICAL RESPONSE OF CONNECTICUT, INC.—See KKR & Co. Inc.; *U.S. Public*, pg. 1251
AMERICAN NURSING CARE INC.—See Catholic Health Initiatives; *U.S. Private*, pg. 789
AMERICAN OUTCOMES MANAGEMENT, L.P.—See Ridgemont Partners Management LLC; *U.S. Private*, pg. 3433
AMERICAN RETIREMENT CORPORATION—See Brookdale Senior Living Inc.; *U.S. Public*, pg. 393
AMERICAN SENIOR SERVICES, INC.; *U.S. Private*, pg. 253
AMERIMED, INC.—See Catholic Health Initiatives; *U.S. Private*, pg. 789
AMERITA, INC.—See KKR & Co. Inc.; *U.S. Public*, pg. 1262
AMIDA CARE INC.; *U.S. Private*, pg. 263

621610 — HOME HEALTH CARE SE...

AMISUB (SFH), INC.—See Tenet Healthcare Corporation; *U.S. Public*, pg. 2007
AMSURG GREENSBORO ANESTHESIA, LLC—See KKR & Co. Inc.; *U.S. Public*, pg. 1244
AMSURG TOLEDO ANESTHESIA, LLC—See KKR & Co. Inc.; *U.S. Public*, pg. 1244
ANDROSCOGGIN HOME HEALTH SERVICES, INC.; *U.S. Private*, pg. 280
ANGELES HOME HEALTH CARE, INC.—See The Ensign Group, Inc.; *U.S. Public*, pg. 2070
ANGEL'S TOUCH HOME CARE, INC.—See Formation Capital, LLC; *U.S. Private*, pg. 1571
ANGEL WATCH HOME CARE, L.L.C.—See Amedisys, Inc.; *U.S. Public*, pg. 93
ANMED ENCOMPASS HEALTH REHABILITATION HOSPITAL, LLC—See Encompass Health Corporation; *U.S. Public*, pg. 754
ANOVA HEALTHCARE SERVICES, INC.; *U.S. Private*, pg. 285
APEX HOSPICE LLC—See Encompass Health Corporation; *U.S. Public*, pg. 754
APISMELLIS HOMECARE LLC—See The Ensign Group, Inc.; *U.S. Public*, pg. 2070
A PLUS HEALTH CARE, INC.—See Addus HomeCare Corporation; *U.S. Public*, pg. 40
APOLLO GLENEAGLES PET-CT LIMITED—See Apollo Hospitals Enterprise Limited; *Int'l*, pg. 935
APPLE HOME HEALTH CARE LTD—See Addus HomeCare Corporation; *U.S. Public*, pg. 40
APPLIED HEALTH CARE, LTD.—See Option Care Health, Inc.; *U.S. Public*, pg. 1609
APRIA HEALTHCARE GROUP INC.—See Blackstone Inc.; *U.S. Public*, pg. 348
ARBOUR ELDER SERVICES, INC.—See Universal Health Services, Inc.; *U.S. Public*, pg. 2255
ARCHE DE VIE SA—See Clariane SE; *Int'l*, pg. 1642
ARKANSAS EXTENDED CARE, LLC—See UnitedHealth Group Incorporated; *U.S. Public*, pg. 2244
ARKANSAS HOMECARE OF FULTON, LLC—See UnitedHealth Group Incorporated; *U.S. Public*, pg. 2244
ARKANSAS HOME HOSPICE, LLC—See UnitedHealth Group Incorporated; *U.S. Public*, pg. 2244
ARMC, L.P.—See Community Health Systems, Inc.; *U.S. Public*, pg. 550
ARTEMIS MEDICARE SERVICES LIMITED; *Int'l*, pg. 582
ASCEND GENE AND CELL THERAPIES GMBH; *Int'l*, pg. 601
ASCENSION ST JOHN FOUNDATION; *U.S. Private*, pg. 348
ASCOTT SALES INTEGRATION PTY. LTD.—See IQVIA Holdings Inc.; *U.S. Public*, pg. 1168
ASIAN AMERICAN HOME CARE, INC.—See Humana, Inc.; *U.S. Public*, pg. 1069
ASKLEPIOS MEDI TOP PFLEGEDIENST & SERVICE GMBH—See Asklepios Kliniken GmbH & Co. KGaA; *Int'l*, pg. 623
ASPEN FRANCE SAS—See Aspen Pharmacare Holdings Limited; *Int'l*, pg. 629
ASPEN HEALTHCARE FZ LLC—See Aspen Pharmacare Holdings Limited; *Int'l*, pg. 629
ASPEN HEALTHCARE SERVICES; *U.S. Private*, pg. 352
ASPIRE HEALTH, INC.—See Elevance Health, Inc.; *U.S. Public*, pg. 729
ASSOCIATED EYE SURGICAL CENTER, LLC—See KKR & Co. Inc.; *U.S. Public*, pg. 1249
ASSOCIATED HOME CARE, LLC—See Amedisys, Inc.; *U.S. Public*, pg. 93
ASSURED HEALTH CARE, INC.—See Regional Health Properties, Inc.; *U.S. Public*, pg. 1775
ASSURED HEALTHCARE PARTNERS LLC—See Assured Guaranty Ltd.; *Int'l*, pg. 650
ASSURE HOME HEALTHCARE—See Bain Capital, LP; *U.S. Private*, pg. 439
ASTRAZENECA D.O.O.—See AstraZeneca PLC; *Int'l*, pg. 661
ASTRAZENECA VENEZUELA S.A.—See AstraZeneca PLC; *Int'l*, pg. 661
ASTRAZENECA VIETNAM COMPANY LIMITED—See AstraZeneca PLC; *Int'l*, pg. 661
A & T HEALTH CARE LLC; *U.S. Private*, pg. 18
ATHENS-LIMESTONE HOMECARE, LLC—See UnitedHealth Group Incorporated; *U.S. Public*, pg. 2244
AT MEDICS HOLDINGS LLP—See Centene Corporation; *U.S. Public*, pg. 467
ATRIUM CENTERS, LLC; *U.S. Private*, pg. 382
AUGMEDIX, INC.—See HCA Healthcare, Inc.; *U.S. Public*, pg. 994
AUGUSTA CYBERKNIFE, LLC—See HCA Healthcare, Inc.; *U.S. Public*, pg. 991
AURORA COMMUNITY SERVICES; *U.S. Private*, pg. 394
AUSTIN ENDOSCOPY CENTER I, LP—See KKR & Co. Inc.; *U.S. Public*, pg. 1244
AVALANCHE HEALTHCARE, INC.—See The Ensign Group, Inc.; *U.S. Public*, pg. 2070
AVALON HEALTH SERVICES, LLC; *U.S. Private*, pg. 403
AVALON HOSPICE IOWA, LLC—See Humana, Inc.; *U.S. Public*, pg. 1069

AVALON HOSPICE MINNESOTA, LLC—See Humana, Inc.; *U.S. Public*, pg. 1069
AVALON HOSPICE MISSOURI, LLC—See Humana, Inc.; *U.S. Public*, pg. 1069
AVALON HOSPICE OHIO, LLC—See Humana, Inc.; *U.S. Public*, pg. 1069
AVOW HOSPICE, INC.; *U.S. Private*, pg. 410
B4HEALTH, LLC—See AMN Healthcare Services, Inc.; *U.S. Public*, pg. 125
BADGER ACQUISITION OF ORLANDO LLC—See CVS Health Corporation; *U.S. Public*, pg. 616
BAMBOOS PROFESSIONAL NURSING SERVICES LIMITED—See Bamboos Health Care Holdings Limited; *Int'l*, pg. 813
BARNABAS HEALTH MEDICAL GROUP; *U.S. Private*, pg. 476
BAYADA HOME HEALTH CARE, INC.; *U.S. Private*, pg. 495
BAYSHORE HEALTH & HOMEMAKER SERVICES, INC.; *U.S. Private*, pg. 496
BEACON HEALTH OPTIONS OF PENNSYLVANIA, INC.—See Elevance Health, Inc.; *U.S. Public*, pg. 729
BEACON HOSPICE, INC.—See Amedisys, Inc.; *U.S. Public*, pg. 93
BEAUTY FARM MEDICAL & HEALTH INDUSTRY INC.; *Int'l*, pg. 935
BECKMAN COULTER SAUDI ARABIA CO.LTD—See Danaher Corporation; *U.S. Public*, pg. 624
BEDRIJFSARTSENGROEP HOLDING B.V.—See ASR Nederland N.V.; *Int'l*, pg. 632
BEHAVIORAL HEALTH NETWORK, INC.—See Elevance Health, Inc.; *U.S. Public*, pg. 729
BEHAVIORAL HEALTH WELLNESS CENTER, LLC—See HCA Healthcare, Inc.; *U.S. Public*, pg. 991
BELLEVUE SA—See Clariane SE; *Int'l*, pg. 1642
BENDCARE, LLC; *U.S. Private*, pg. 524
BENEFIT ADMINISTRATION FOR THE SELF EMPLOYED, L.L.C.—See UnitedHealth Group Incorporated; *U.S. Public*, pg. 2239
BENEFITS ASSURANCE CO., INC.—See Addus HomeCare Corporation; *U.S. Public*, pg. 40
BENESSE MCM CORP.—See EQT AB; *Int'l*, pg. 2467
BENESSE SENIOR SUPPORT CO., LTD.—See EQT AB; *Int'l*, pg. 2467
BERCHTOLD GMBH & CO KG—See Stryker Corporation; *U.S. Public*, pg. 1955
BERGEN REGIONAL MEDICAL CENTER; *U.S. Private*, pg. 530
BEST HOME CARE LP—See Encompass Health Corporation; *U.S. Public*, pg. 754
BESTPRACTICES, INC.—See KKR & Co. Inc.; *U.S. Public*, pg. 1249
BETH ISRAEL LAHEY HEALTH INC; *U.S. Private*, pg. 545
BIG BEND HOME CARE SERVICES, LLC—See Community Health Systems, Inc.; *U.S. Public*, pg. 551
BIOMET MEDIKAL DRUNJER DADYTYM PAZARLAMA YHRACAT VE DYS TICARET LTD. STI.—See Zimmer Biomet Holdings, Inc.; *U.S. Public*, pg. 2406
BIOMET US INC.—See Zimmer Biomet Holdings, Inc.; *U.S. Public*, pg. 2406
BIONEXUS GENE LAB CORP.; *Int'l*, pg. 1040
BIOSCRIP INFUSION SERVICES, LLC—See Option Care Health, Inc.; *U.S. Public*, pg. 1609
BLACK STONE OPERATIONS, LLC—See UnitedHealth Group Incorporated; *U.S. Public*, pg. 2243
BLUE RIDGE HOSPICE; *U.S. Private*, pg. 591
BLYTHE AMBULANCE SERVICE—See KKR & Co. Inc.; *U.S. Public*, pg. 1251
BOND PHARMACY, INC.; *U.S. Private*, pg. 613
BON SECOURS MERCY HEALTH, INC.; *U.S. Private*, pg. 612
BOOTS HEARINGCARE LIMITED—See Walgreens Boots Alliance, Inc.; *U.S. Public*, pg. 2322
BOOTS RETAIL (IRELAND) LIMITED—See Walgreens Boots Alliance, Inc.; *U.S. Public*, pg. 2322
BRADEN PARTNERS L.P.; *U.S. Private*, pg. 631
BRAVO WELLNESS, LLC—See Medical Mutual of Ohio; *U.S. Private*, pg. 2655
BRCH HOME HEALTH SERVICE INC.—See BRRH Corporation; *U.S. Private*, pg. 670
BRETHREN HOME COMMUNITY WINDBER; *U.S. Private*, pg. 646
BREVARD HMA HOME HEALTH, LLC—See Community Health Systems, Inc.; *U.S. Public*, pg. 551
BREVARD HMA HOSPICE, LLC—See Community Health Systems, Inc.; *U.S. Public*, pg. 551
BREVARD HMA NURSING HOME, LLC—See Community Health Systems, Inc.; *U.S. Public*, pg. 551
BRIDGEWAY HEALTH SERVICES, LLC—See Merit Capital Partners; *U.S. Private*, pg. 2674
BRIOVARX INFUSION SERVICES 101, INC.—See UnitedHealth Group Incorporated; *U.S. Public*, pg. 2239
BRIOVARX INFUSION SERVICES 102, INC.—See UnitedHealth Group Incorporated; *U.S. Public*, pg. 2239
BRIOVARX INFUSION SERVICES 103, INC.—See UnitedHealth Group Incorporated; *U.S. Public*, pg. 2239
BRIOVARX INFUSION SERVICES 200, INC.—See UnitedHealth Group Incorporated; *U.S. Public*, pg. 2239
BRIOVARX INFUSION SERVICES 201, INC.—See United-

Health Group Incorporated; *U.S. Public*, pg. 2239
BRIOVARX INFUSION SERVICES 202, INC.—See UnitedHealth Group Incorporated; *U.S. Public*, pg. 2239
BRIOVARX INFUSION SERVICES 203, INC.—See UnitedHealth Group Incorporated; *U.S. Public*, pg. 2239
BRIOVARX INFUSION SERVICES 207, INC.—See UnitedHealth Group Incorporated; *U.S. Public*, pg. 2239
BRIOVARX INFUSION SERVICES 208, INC.—See UnitedHealth Group Incorporated; *U.S. Public*, pg. 2239
BRIOVARX INFUSION SERVICES 302, LLC—See UnitedHealth Group Incorporated; *U.S. Public*, pg. 2239
BRIOVARX INFUSION SERVICES 308, LLC—See UnitedHealth Group Incorporated; *U.S. Public*, pg. 2239
BRIOVARX INFUSION SERVICES 402, LLC—See UnitedHealth Group Incorporated; *U.S. Public*, pg. 2239
BRIOVARX INFUSION SERVICES 403, LLC—See UnitedHealth Group Incorporated; *U.S. Public*, pg. 2239
BRIOVARX INFUSION SERVICES 404, LLC—See UnitedHealth Group Incorporated; *U.S. Public*, pg. 2239
BRIOVARX OF MAINE, INC.—See UnitedHealth Group Incorporated; *U.S. Public*, pg. 2247
BROADREACH MEDICAL RESOURCES, INC.; *U.S. Private*, pg. 659
BROKERAGE CONCEPTS INC.; *U.S. Private*, pg. 662
BROOKSVILLE HMA PHYSICIAN MANAGEMENT, LLC—See Community Health Systems, Inc.; *U.S. Public*, pg. 551
BROOKWOOD PRIMARY CARE CAHABA HEIGHTS, L.L.C.—See Tenet Healthcare Corporation; *U.S. Public*, pg. 2002
BRUUSH ORAL CARE, INC.; *Int'l*, pg. 1201
BWB SUNBELT HOME HEALTH SERVICES, LLC—See Apollo Global Management, Inc.; *U.S. Public*, pg. 156
B-XII BILLERICA LLC—See Welltower Inc.; *U.S. Public*, pg. 2347
B-XII SHREWSBURY LLC—See Welltower Inc.; *U.S. Public*, pg. 2347
CAJANUKSENTIENKOTI OY—See Humana AB; *Int'l*, pg. 3529
CALDER IMMEDIATE CARE, PLLC—See HCA Healthcare, Inc.; *U.S. Public*, pg. 992
CALEA LTD.—See Fresenius SE & Co. KGaA; *Int'l*, pg. 2777
CALGARY CO-OP HOME HEALTH CARE LIMITED—See Calgary Co-operative Association Limited; *Int'l*, pg. 1263
CALIFORNIA NURSES ASSOCIATION; *U.S. Private*, pg. 720
CALMARK SWEDEN AB; *Int'l*, pg. 1265
CAMDEN HOMECARE, LLC—See UnitedHealth Group Incorporated; *U.S. Public*, pg. 2244
CANCER TREATMENT HOLDINGS, INC.; *U.S. Public*, pg. 428
CANO HEALTH, LLC—See Cano Health, Inc.; *U.S. Public*, pg. 430
CAPE FEAR VALLEY HOMECARE AND HOSPICE, LLC—See UnitedHealth Group Incorporated; *U.S. Public*, pg. 2244
CAPE MEDICAL SUPPLY, INC.—See AdaptHealth Corp.; *U.S. Public*, pg. 39
CARDINAL HEALTH 414, LLC—See Cardinal Health, Inc.; *U.S. Public*, pg. 433
CARE ADVANTAGE, INC.—See Searchlight Capital Partners, L.P.; *U.S. Private*, pg. 3586
CARE CONNECTION OF CINCINNATI, LLC—See KKR & Co. Inc.; *U.S. Public*, pg. 1249
CARECYCLE SOLUTIONS, LLC—See Kelso & Company, L.P.; *U.S. Private*, pg. 2278
CARE FINANCIAL OF TEXAS, LLC—See The Allstate Corporation; *U.S. Public*, pg. 2033
CAREHERE, LLC; *U.S. Private*, pg. 753
CARE HOTEL MANAGEMENT CO., LTD.—See Biken Techno Corporation Ltd.; *Int'l*, pg. 1023
CAREKINESIS, INC.—See Nautic Partners, LLC; *U.S. Private*, pg. 2871
CAREMETX, LLC—See General Atlantic Service Company, L.P.; *U.S. Private*, pg. 1662
CARE PHARMACEUTICALS PTY LIMITED—See Prestige Consumer Healthcare Inc.; *U.S. Public*, pg. 1716
CARETENDERS OF CLEVELAND, INC.—See UnitedHealth Group Incorporated; *U.S. Public*, pg. 2244
CARETENDERS VISITING SERVICES OF GAINESVILLE, LLC—See UnitedHealth Group Incorporated; *U.S. Public*, pg. 2244
CARETENDERS VISITING SERVICES OF KENTUCKIANA, LLC—See UnitedHealth Group Incorporated; *U.S. Public*, pg. 2244
CARETENDERS VISITING SERVICES OF ORLANDO, LLC—See UnitedHealth Group Incorporated; *U.S. Public*, pg. 2244
CARETENDERS VISITING SERVICES OF SOUTHERN ILLINOIS, LLC—See UnitedHealth Group Incorporated; *U.S. Public*, pg. 2244
CARETENDERS VS OF BOSTON, LLC—See UnitedHealth Group Incorporated; *U.S. Public*, pg. 2243
CARETENDERS VS OF LINCOLN TRAIL, LLC—See UnitedHealth Group Incorporated; *U.S. Public*, pg. 2243
CARETENDERS VS OF LOUISVILLE, LLC—See UnitedHealth Group Incorporated; *U.S. Public*, pg. 2243
CARETENDERS VS OF NORTHERN KY, LLC—See Unit-

N.A.I.C.S. INDEX

621610 — HOME HEALTH CARE SE...

edHealth Group Incorporated; *U.S. Public*, pg. 2243
CARETENDERS VS OF OHIO, LLC—See UnitedHealth Group Incorporated; *U.S. Public*, pg. 2243
CARETENDERS VS OF SE OHIO, LLC—See UnitedHealth Group Incorporated; *U.S. Public*, pg. 2243
CARETENDERS VS OF WESTERN KY, LLC—See UnitedHealth Group Incorporated; *U.S. Public*, pg. 2243
CARETRACKER, INC.—See Constellation Software Inc.; *Int'l*, pg. 1773
CARE UK COMMUNITY PARTNERSHIPS GROUP LIMITED—See Bridgepoint Group Plc; *Int'l*, pg. 1154
CARE UNLIMITED, INC.—See Bain Capital, LP; *U.S. Private*, pg. 439
CAREWATCH CARE SERVICES LTD.—See Horizon Capital LLP; *Int'l*, pg. 3479
CARING SENIOR SERVICE; *U.S. Private*, pg. 761
CASA REHA SENIORENPFLEGEHEIM GMBH—See Clariane SE; *Int'l*, pg. 1642
CATHOLIC HOME CARE—See Catholic Health Services of Long Island; *U.S. Private*, pg. 791
CAUCASUS MEDICAL CENTER, LLC—See Georgia Capital PLC; *Int'l*, pg. 2939
CBR SYSTEMS, INC.—See GI Manager L.P.; *U.S. Private*, pg. 1691
CCS JAPAN—See Azenta, Inc.; *U.S. Public*, pg. 258
CELTIC COMMUNITY SERVICES OF NE OHIO, INC.—See Graham Holdings Company; *U.S. Public*, pg. 954
CELTIC HEALTHCARE, INC.—See Graham Holdings Company; *U.S. Public*, pg. 954
CELTIC HEALTHCARE OF CARLISLE, INC.—See Graham Holdings Company; *U.S. Public*, pg. 954
CELTIC HEALTHCARE OF E. MO, LLC—See Graham Holdings Company; *U.S. Public*, pg. 954
CELTIC HEALTHCARE OF NC PA, LLC—See Graham Holdings Company; *U.S. Public*, pg. 954
CELTIC HEALTHCARE OF NE OHIO, INC.—See Graham Holdings Company; *U.S. Public*, pg. 954
CELTIC REHABILITATION, INC.—See Graham Holdings Company; *U.S. Public*, pg. 954
CENGILD G.I. MEDICAL CENTRE; *Int'l*, pg. 1401
CENTENNIAL HEART, LLC—See HCA Healthcare, Inc.; *U.S. Public*, pg. 992
CENTENNIAL NEUROSCIENCE, LLC—See HCA Healthcare, Inc.; *U.S. Public*, pg. 992
CENTER FOR HOSPICE CARE; *U.S. Private*, pg. 810
CENTER FOR OCCUPATIONAL MEDICINE, LLC—See HCA Healthcare, Inc.; *U.S. Public*, pg. 992
CENTRAL VERMONT HOME HEALTH AND HOSPICE; *U.S. Private*, pg. 826
CENTRE HBP SERVICES, LLC—See Quorum Health Corporation; *U.S. Private*, pg. 3329
CENTRE HOSPITAL CORPORATION—See Quorum Health Corporation; *U.S. Private*, pg. 3329
CENTRO MEDICO SPECIALISTICO SRL—See Clariane SE; *Int'l*, pg. 1642
CENTURION OF NEW HAMPSHIRE, LLC—See Centene Corporation; *U.S. Public*, pg. 468
CENTURION OF PENNSYLVANIA, LLC—See Centene Corporation; *U.S. Public*, pg. 468
CENTURY LIFE CO., LTD.—See Haseko Corporation; *Int'l*, pg. 3282
CERIDIAN CARES U.S.—See Dayforce, Inc.; *U.S. Public*, pg. 645
CERNER CORPORATION PTY LIMITED—See Oracle Corporation; *U.S. Public*, pg. 1610
CERNER EGYPT L.L.C.—See Oracle Corporation; *U.S. Public*, pg. 1610
CERNER IBERIA, S.L.—See Oracle Corporation; *U.S. Public*, pg. 1610
CERNER IRELAND LIMITED—See Oracle Corporation; *U.S. Public*, pg. 1610
CERNER LIMITED—See Oracle Corporation; *U.S. Public*, pg. 1610
CERNER MIDDLE EAST FZ-LLC—See Oracle Corporation; *U.S. Public*, pg. 1610
CHABIOTECH CO., LTD.; *Int'l*, pg. 1436
CHAPEL VALLEY HOUSING II LLC—See Kimberly-Clark Corporation; *U.S. Public*, pg. 1229
CHILDRENS HOSPITAL FOUNDATION; *Int'l*, pg. 1478
CHILDRENS HOSPITAL OF WISCONSIN; *U.S. Private*, pg. 885
CHILDREN'S HOSPITAL TRUST; *Int'l*, pg. 1478
CHOICE HEALTH AT HOME, LLC—See Coltala Holdings, LLC; *U.S. Private*, pg. 976
CHOICE THERAPEUTICS, INC.—See Adynxx, Inc.; *U.S. Public*, pg. 50
CHRISTIAN HOSPITAL FOUNDATION; *U.S. Private*, pg. 891
CHRISTUS HOMECARE-ST. MICHAEL, LLC—See UnitedHealth Group Incorporated; *U.S. Public*, pg. 2244
CHS-NAPOLEON—See CHS INC.; *U.S. Public*, pg. 492
CIC SERVICES LLC—See CVS Health Corporation; *U.S. Public*, pg. 616
CIGNA WORLDWIDE GENERAL INSURANCE COMPANY LIMITED—See The Cigna Group; *U.S. Public*, pg. 2060
CISEN PHARMACEUTICALS INDIA PRIVATE LIMITED—See Cisen Pharmaceutical Co., Ltd.; *Int'l*, pg. 1618

CITRUS HOMEHEALTH, INC.—See HCA Healthcare, Inc.; *U.S. Public*, pg. 993
CITRUS VALLEY HEALTH PARTNERS; *U.S. Private*, pg. 905
CLAIMSECURE INC.; *Int'l*, pg. 1641
CLAIRE DE VIE SPRL—See Clariane SE; *Int'l*, pg. 1642
CLARKSVILLE HOME CARE SERVICES, LLC—See Community Health Systems, Inc.; *U.S. Public*, pg. 552
CLARVIEW REST HOME INC.; *U.S. Private*, pg. 915
CLAY COUNTY HOSPITAL HOMECARE, LLC—See UnitedHealth Group Incorporated; *U.S. Public*, pg. 2244
CLAY HOME MEDICAL, INC.—See AdaptHealth Corp.; *U.S. Public*, pg. 38
CLEVELAND HOME CARE SERVICES, LLC—See Community Health Systems, Inc.; *U.S. Public*, pg. 552
CLINICA BAVIERA S.A.—See Aier Eye Hospital Group Co., Ltd.; *Int'l*, pg. 231
CLINICAL RESOURCE NETWORK, LLC; *U.S. Public*, pg. 944
CLINICA SAN FRANCESCO S.R.L.—See Garofalo Health Care SpA; *Int'l*, pg. 2886
CLINLAB, INC.—See Rennova Health, Inc.; *U.S. Public*, pg. 1783
CLINPSYCH PSYCHOLOGY SERVICES PTY. LTD.—See Madison Dearborn Partners, LLC; *U.S. Private*, pg. 2540
CMAX CLINICAL RESEARCH PTY LTD—See I'rom Group Co., Ltd.; *Int'l*, pg. 3562
CMAX JAPAN CO., LTD.—See I'rom Group Co., Ltd.; *Int'l*, pg. 3562
COLLETON DIAGNOSTIC CENTER, LLC—See HCA Healthcare, Inc.; *U.S. Public*, pg. 993
COLORADO HEALTH & REHAB, LLC; *U.S. Public*, pg. 974
COLORADO IN-HOME PARTNER-I, LLC—See UnitedHealth Group Incorporated; *U.S. Public*, pg. 2244
COLUMBIA HEALTHCARE CENTER, LLC—See National HealthCare Corporation; *U.S. Public*, pg. 1495
COLUMBUS HOSPICE; *U.S. Public*, pg. 979
COMMUNITY ANCILLARY SERVICES, INC.; *U.S. Private*, pg. 989
COMMUNITY CARE COMPANIONS INC.; *U.S. Private*, pg. 990
COMMUNITY CARE HEALTH NETWORK, INC.—See Frazier & Company, Inc.; *U.S. Private*, pg. 1599
COMMUNITY CARE HEALTH NETWORK, INC.—See ModivCare, Inc.; *U.S. Public*, pg. 1455
COMMUNITY HEALTH CENTERS OF THE RUTLAND REGION; *U.S. Private*, pg. 993
COMMUNITY HOME CARE OF VANCE COUNTY, LLC—See Humana, Inc.; *U.S. Public*, pg. 1069
COMMUNITY HOME HEALTH & HOSPICE; *U.S. Private*, pg. 994
COMMUNITY HOME HEALTH SERVICES, INC.; *U.S. Private*, pg. 994
THE COMMUNITY HOSPICE, INC.; *U.S. Private*, pg. 4012
COMMUNITY HOSPICE OF TEXAS; *U.S. Private*, pg. 994
COMMUNITY NURSING SERVICE OF DU PAGE COUNTY; *U.S. Private*, pg. 996
COMPASSIONATE CARE AT HOME LLC—See Guardian Angels HomeCare, LLC; *U.S. Private*, pg. 1809
COMPASSIONATE CARE HOSPICE OF BRYAN TEXAS, LLC—See Amedisys, Inc.; *U.S. Public*, pg. 93
COMPASSIONATE CARE HOSPICE OF CLIFTON, LLC—See Amedisys, Inc.; *U.S. Public*, pg. 93
COMPASSIONATE CARE HOSPICE OF HOUSTON, LLC—See Amedisys, Inc.; *U.S. Public*, pg. 93
COMPASSIONATE CARE HOSPICE OF ILLINOIS, LLC—See Amedisys, Inc.; *U.S. Public*, pg. 93
COMPASSIONATE CARE HOSPICE OF KANSAS, LLC—See Amedisys, Inc.; *U.S. Public*, pg. 93
COMPASSIONATE CARE HOSPICE OF MICHIGAN, LLC—See Amedisys, Inc.; *U.S. Public*, pg. 93
COMPASSIONATE CARE HOSPICE OF MINNESOTA, LLC—See Amedisys, Inc.; *U.S. Public*, pg. 93
COMPASSIONATE CARE HOSPICE OF PITTSBURG, LLC—See Amedisys, Inc.; *U.S. Public*, pg. 93
COMPASSIONATE CARE HOSPICE OF THE MIDWEST, LLC—See Amedisys, Inc.; *U.S. Public*, pg. 93
COMPASSIONATE CARE HOSPICE OF WISCONSIN, LLC—See Amedisys, Inc.; *U.S. Public*, pg. 93
CONCEPTUS MEDICAL LIMITED—See Bayer Aktiengesellschaft; *Int'l*, pg. 905
CONNECTICUT HOSPICE INC.; *U.S. Public*, pg. 1016
CONSOLIDATED HEALTH SERVICES INC.—See Catholic Health Initiatives; *U.S. Public*, pg. 789
CONTESSA HEALTH OF TENNESSEE, LLC—See Amedisys, Inc.; *U.S. Public*, pg. 93
CONTINENTAL HOME CARE, INC.—See Encompass Health Corporation; *U.S. Public*, pg. 755
CONTIN-U-CARE HOME HEALTH SERVICES—See Erlanger Health System; *U.S. Private*, pg. 1421
CONTINUCARE MSO, INC.—See Humana, Inc.; *U.S. Public*, pg. 1070
CONTROL BIONICS LIMITED; *Int'l*, pg. 1785
COOPERATIVE HOME HEALTH CARE OF ATLANTIC COUNTY INC.; *U.S. Private*, pg. 1042
COORDINATED CARE CORP.; *U.S. Private*, pg. 1043
COOSA VALLEY HOMECARE, LLC—See UnitedHealth Group Incorporated; *U.S. Public*, pg. 2244

CORAM SPECIALTY INFUSION SERVICES—See Blackstone Inc.; *U.S. Public*, pg. 348
CORNERSTONE HEALTHCARE, INC.—See The Pennant Group, Inc.; *U.S. Public*, pg. 2118
CORNERSTONE PALLIATIVE AND HOSPICE, LLC—See UnitedHealth Group Incorporated; *U.S. Public*, pg. 2244
COTTAGE HOME OPTIONS, L.L.C.—See Community Health Systems, Inc.; *U.S. Public*, pg. 552
COVENTRY HEALTH CARE OF KANSAS, INC.—See CVS Health Corporation; *U.S. Public*, pg. 615
CRESCENT HEALTHCARE, INC.—See Walgreens Boots Alliance, Inc.; *U.S. Public*, pg. 2323
CRITICAL CARE SYSTEMS OF NEW YORK, INC.—See The Cigna Group; *U.S. Public*, pg. 2062
CRITICAL HOMECARE SOLUTIONS, INC.—See Option Care Health, Inc.; *U.S. Public*, pg. 1609
CROCE DI MALTA SRL—See Clariane SE; *Int'l*, pg. 1642
CROTHALL HEALTHCARE INC.—See Compass Group PLC; *Int'l*, pg. 1751
CSL BATESVILLE, LLC—See Sonida Senior Living, Inc.; *U.S. Public*, pg. 1903
CSL CE CORPUS, LLC—See Sonida Senior Living, Inc.; *U.S. Public*, pg. 1903
CSL CE STEPHENVILLE, LLC—See Sonida Senior Living, Inc.; *U.S. Public*, pg. 1903
CSL CHARLESTOWN, LLC—See Sonida Senior Living, Inc.; *U.S. Public*, pg. 1903
CSL COLUMBUS, LLC—See Sonida Senior Living, Inc.; *U.S. Public*, pg. 1903
CSL FITCHBURG MANAGEMENT, LLC—See Sonida Senior Living, Inc.; *U.S. Public*, pg. 1903
CSL SUMMIT, LLC—See Sonida Senior Living, Inc.; *U.S. Public*, pg. 1903
C STREET HEALTH ASSOCIATES LLC—See The Ensign Group, Inc.; *U.S. Public*, pg. 2070
CT ASSIST LLC; *U.S. Private*, pg. 1118
CUMBERLAND MEDICAL CENTER, INC.—See HCA Healthcare, Inc.; *U.S. Public*, pg. 995
CURA PARTNERS, LLC—See Addus HomeCare Corporation; *U.S. Public*, pg. 40
CURO HEALTH SERVICES, LLC—See Apollo Global Management, Inc.; *U.S. Public*, pg. 156
DAYBYDAY STAFF RELIEF, INC.—See Encompass Health Corporation; *U.S. Public*, pg. 755
DBMOTION, LTD.—See Veradigm Inc.; *U.S. Public*, pg. 2280
DEACONESS HOMECARE, LLC—See UnitedHealth Group Incorporated; *U.S. Public*, pg. 2244
DECATUR MORGAN HOMECARE—See UnitedHealth Group Incorporated; *U.S. Public*, pg. 2244
DE NOOTELAER PLC—See Clariane SE; *Int'l*, pg. 1642
THE DENVER HOSPICE AND OPTIO HEALTH SERVICES; *U.S. Private*, pg. 4020
DHANVANTRI JEEVAN REKHA LTD.; *Int'l*, pg. 2098
DIAMOND HEALTHCARE CORPORATION—See Markel Group Inc.; *U.S. Public*, pg. 1368
DINGDANG HEALTH TECHNOLOGY GROUP LIMITED; *Int'l*, pg. 2127
DIRECTMED PARTS & SERVICE LLC—See NMS Capital Services, LLC; *U.S. Private*, pg. 2931
DISARM THERAPEUTICS INC.—See Eli Lilly & Company; *U.S. Public*, pg. 731
DIVERSICARE THERAPY SERVICES, LLC—See Diversicare Healthcare Services, Inc.; *U.S. Public*, pg. 669
DLP CARDIOLOGY ASSOCIATES, LLC—See Apollo Global Management, Inc.; *U.S. Public*, pg. 155
DLP CENTRAL CAROLINA FAMILY MEDICINE, LLC—See Apollo Global Management, Inc.; *U.S. Public*, pg. 155
DLP CONEMAUGH MEMORIAL MEDICAL CENTER, LLC—See Apollo Global Management, Inc.; *U.S. Public*, pg. 155
DLP HARRIS REGIONAL HOSPITAL, LLC—See Apollo Global Management, Inc.; *U.S. Public*, pg. 155
DLP MARQUETTE GENERAL HOSPITAL, LLC—See Apollo Global Management, Inc.; *U.S. Public*, pg. 155
DLP RUTHERFORD PHYSICIAN PRACTICES, LLC—See Apollo Global Management, Inc.; *U.S. Public*, pg. 155
DLP RUTHERFORD REGIONAL HEALTH SYSTEM, LLC—See Apollo Global Management, Inc.; *U.S. Public*, pg. 155
DLP SWAIN COUNTY HOSPITAL, LLC—See Apollo Global Management, Inc.; *U.S. Public*, pg. 155
DLP WESTERN CAROLINA PHYSICIAN PRACTICES, LLC—See Apollo Global Management, Inc.; *U.S. Public*, pg. 155
DLP WILSON PHYSICIAN PRACTICES, LLC—See Apollo Global Management, Inc.; *U.S. Public*, pg. 155
DOCTOR CARE ANYWHERE GROUP PLC; *Int'l*, pg. 2153
DOCTOR'S CHOICE HOME CARE, INC.; *U.S. Private*, pg. 1251
THE DOCTORS (HASTINGS) LIMITED—See Green Cross Health Limited; *Int'l*, pg. 3070
DOCTORS HOSPITAL NORTH AUGUSTA IMAGING CENTER, LLC—See HCA Healthcare, Inc.; *U.S. Public*, pg. 995
THE DOCTORS (HUAPAI) LIMITED—See Green Cross Health Limited; *Int'l*, pg. 3070

621610 — HOME HEALTH CARE SE...

THE DOCTORS (NEW LYNN) LIMITED—See Green Cross Health Limited; *Int'l*, pg. 3070
THE DOCTORS (WHANGAPARAOA) LIMITED—See Green Cross Health Limited; *Int'l*, pg. 3070
DOLPHIN MEDICAL SERVICES LTD.; *Int'l*, pg. 2159
DOMUS NOVA S.P.A.—See Garofalo Health Care SpA; *Int'l*, pg. 2886
DOSEOLOGY SCIENCES INC.; *Int'l*, pg. 2180
DOSIK, INC.—See Encompass Health Corporation; *U.S. Public*, pg. 755
DOUGLAS HEALTH SERVICE LLC—See Silverhawk Capital Partners, LLC; *U.S. Private*, pg. 3663
DOXIMITY, INC.; *U.S. Public*, pg. 686
DRC HEALTH SYSTEMS, L.P.—See Encompass Health Corporation; *U.S. Public*, pg. 755
DR MAGNET S.R.O.—See Centene Corporation; *U.S. Public*, pg. 468
DRURY SURGERY LIMITED—See Green Cross Health Limited; *Int'l*, pg. 3070
DUEARITY AB; *Int'l*, pg. 2223
DUNN & BERGER, INC.—See Aveanna Healthcare Holdings Inc.; *U.S. Public*, pg. 242
DYNEON GMBH—See 3M Company; *U.S. Public*, pg. 8
E4E HEALTHCARE SERVICES PVT. LTD.—See e4e Inc.; *U.S. Private*, pg. 1308
EARLY START AUSTRALIA PTY LTD.—See Madison Dearborn Partners, LLC; *U.S. Private*, pg. 2540
EAST ALABAMA MEDICAL CENTER HOMECARE, LLC—See UnitedHealth Group Incorporated; *U.S. Public*, pg. 2244
EAST COOPER COASTAL FAMILY PHYSICIANS, L.L.C.—See Tenet Healthcare Corporation; *U.S. Public*, pg. 2003
EASYSCRIPTS CUTLER BAY, LLC—See Elevance Health, Inc.; *U.S. Public*, pg. 729
EASYSCRIPTS HIALEAH LLC—See Elevance Health, Inc.; *U.S. Public*, pg. 729
EASYSCRIPTS WESTCHESTER, LLC—See Elevance Health, Inc.; *U.S. Public*, pg. 729
EC HEALTHCARE; *Int'l*, pg. 2287
EDGEMODE, INC.; *U.S. Public*, pg. 717
EHHI HOLDINGS, INC.—See Encompass Health Corporation; *U.S. Public*, pg. 755
EK HEALTH SERVICES, INC.; *U.S. Private*, pg. 1348
ELDER HOME OPTIONS, L.L.C.—See Amedisys, Inc.; *U.S. Public*, pg. 93
ELEKTA MEDICAL SYSTEMS SRL—See Elekta AB; *Int'l*, pg. 2356
ELITE HOME HEALTH OF HOLIDAY ISLAND—See UnitedHealth Group Incorporated; *U.S. Public*, pg. 2245
ELK VALLEY HEALTH SERVICES, LLC—See UnitedHealth Group Incorporated; *U.S. Public*, pg. 2244
ELK VALLEY PROFESSIONAL AFFILIATES, INC.—See UnitedHealth Group Incorporated; *U.S. Public*, pg. 2244
ELLISON NURSING GROUP, LLC; *U.S. Private*, pg. 1374
ELMS ENDOSCOPY CENTER, LLC—See KKR & Co. Inc.; *U.S. Public*, pg. 1245
EMED, LLC; *U.S. Private*, pg. 1379
EMERALD HEALTHCARE, INC.—See The Ensign Group, Inc.; *U.S. Public*, pg. 2070
EMFI SAS—See 3M Company; *U.S. Public*, pg. 8
ENCOMPASS HEALTH DEACONESS REHABILITATION HOSPITAL, LLC—See Encompass Health Corporation; *U.S. Public*, pg. 755
ENCOMPASS HEALTH REHABILITATION HOSPITAL OF ALBUQUERQUE, LLC—See Encompass Health Corporation; *U.S. Public*, pg. 755
ENCOMPASS HEALTH REHABILITATION HOSPITAL OF ALTAMONTE SPRINGS, LLC—See Encompass Health Corporation; *U.S. Public*, pg. 755
ENCOMPASS HEALTH REHABILITATION HOSPITAL OF BAKERSFIELD, LLC—See Encompass Health Corporation; *U.S. Public*, pg. 755
ENCOMPASS HEALTH REHABILITATION HOSPITAL OF BLUFFTON, LLC—See Encompass Health Corporation; *U.S. Public*, pg. 755
ENCOMPASS HEALTH REHABILITATION HOSPITAL OF BRAINTREE, LLC—See Encompass Health Corporation; *U.S. Public*, pg. 755
ENCOMPASS HEALTH REHABILITATION HOSPITAL OF CARDINAL HILL, LLC—See Encompass Health Corporation; *U.S. Public*, pg. 755
ENCOMPASS HEALTH REHABILITATION HOSPITAL OF CINCINNATI, LLC—See Encompass Health Corporation; *U.S. Public*, pg. 755
ENCOMPASS HEALTH REHABILITATION HOSPITAL OF DAYTON, LLC—See Encompass Health Corporation; *U.S. Public*, pg. 755
ENCOMPASS HEALTH REHABILITATION HOSPITAL OF EAST VALLEY, LLC—See Encompass Health Corporation; *U.S. Public*, pg. 755
ENCOMPASS HEALTH REHABILITATION HOSPITAL OF ERIE, LLC—See Encompass Health Corporation; *U.S. Public*, pg. 755
ENCOMPASS HEALTH REHABILITATION HOSPITAL OF FORT SMITH, LLC—See Encompass Health Corporation; *U.S. Public*, pg. 755
ENCOMPASS HEALTH REHABILITATION HOSPITAL OF FRANKLIN, LLC—See Encompass Health Corporation; *U.S. Public*, pg. 755
ENCOMPASS HEALTH REHABILITATION HOSPITAL OF GULFPORT, LLC—See Encompass Health Corporation; *U.S. Public*, pg. 755
ENCOMPASS HEALTH REHABILITATION HOSPITAL OF KINGSPORT, LLC—See Encompass Health Corporation; *U.S. Public*, pg. 755
ENCOMPASS HEALTH REHABILITATION HOSPITAL OF LAKEVIEW, LLC—See Encompass Health Corporation; *U.S. Public*, pg. 755
ENCOMPASS HEALTH REHABILITATION HOSPITAL OF LAS VEGAS, LLC—See Encompass Health Corporation; *U.S. Public*, pg. 755
ENCOMPASS HEALTH REHABILITATION HOSPITAL OF MODESTO, LLC—See Encompass Health Corporation; *U.S. Public*, pg. 755
ENCOMPASS HEALTH REHABILITATION HOSPITAL OF MONTGOMERY, INC.—See Encompass Health Corporation; *U.S. Public*, pg. 755
ENCOMPASS HEALTH REHABILITATION HOSPITAL OF NEW ENGLAND, LLC—See Encompass Health Corporation; *U.S. Public*, pg. 755
ENCOMPASS HEALTH REHABILITATION HOSPITAL OF NORTHERN KENTUCKY, LLC—See Encompass Health Corporation; *U.S. Public*, pg. 755
ENCOMPASS HEALTH REHABILITATION HOSPITAL OF OCALA, LLC—See Encompass Health Corporation; *U.S. Public*, pg. 755
ENCOMPASS HEALTH REHABILITATION HOSPITAL OF ROCK HILL, LLC—See Encompass Health Corporation; *U.S. Public*, pg. 755
ENCOMPASS HEALTH REHABILITATION HOSPITAL OF SAVANNAH, LLC—See Encompass Health Corporation; *U.S. Public*, pg. 755
ENCOMPASS HEALTH REHABILITATION HOSPITAL OF SHELBY COUNTY, LLC—See Encompass Health Corporation; *U.S. Public*, pg. 755
ENCOMPASS HEALTH REHABILITATION HOSPITAL OF SUNRISE, LLC—See Encompass Health Corporation; *U.S. Public*, pg. 756
ENCOMPASS HEALTH REHABILITATION HOSPITAL OF TOLEDO, LLC—See Encompass Health Corporation; *U.S. Public*, pg. 756
ENCOMPASS HEALTH REHABILITATION HOSPITAL OF TUSTIN, L.P.—See Encompass Health Corporation; *U.S. Public*, pg. 756
ENCOMPASS HEALTH REHABILITATION HOSPITAL OF WESTERN MASSACHUSETTS, LLC—See Encompass Health Corporation; *U.S. Public*, pg. 756
ENCOMPASS HEALTH REHABILITATION HOSPITAL OF WESTERVILLE, LLC—See Encompass Health Corporation; *U.S. Public*, pg. 756
ENCOMPASS HEALTH REHABILITATION HOSPITAL OF YORK, LLC—See Encompass Health Corporation; *U.S. Public*, pg. 756
ENCOMPASS HOME HEALTH OF AUSTIN, LLC—See Encompass Health Corporation; *U.S. Public*, pg. 756
ENCOMPASS HOME HEALTH OF COLORADO, LLC—See Encompass Health Corporation; *U.S. Public*, pg. 756
ENCOMPASS HOME HEALTH OF DFW, LLC—See Encompass Health Corporation; *U.S. Public*, pg. 756
ENCOMPASS HOME HEALTH OF THE MID ATLANTIC, LLC—See Encompass Health Corporation; *U.S. Public*, pg. 756
ENCOMPASS HOME HEALTH OF THE SOUTHEAST, LLC—See Encompass Health Corporation; *U.S. Public*, pg. 756
ENCOMPASS HOME HEALTH OF THE WEST, LLC—See Encompass Health Corporation; *U.S. Public*, pg. 756
ENCOMPASS HOSPICE OF THE WEST, LLC—See Encompass Health Corporation; *U.S. Public*, pg. 756
ENCOMPASS OF FORT WORTH, LP—See Encompass Health Corporation; *U.S. Public*, pg. 756
ENCOMPASS OF WEST TEXAS, LP—See Encompass Health Corporation; *U.S. Public*, pg. 756
ENCOMPASS REHABILITATION HOSPITAL OF ABILENE, LLC—See Encompass Health Corporation; *U.S. Public*, pg. 756
ENCOMPASS REHABILITATION HOSPITAL OF DALLAS, LLC—See Encompass Health Corporation; *U.S. Public*, pg. 756
ENCOMPASS REHABILITATION HOSPITAL OF PEARLAND, LLC—See Encompass Health Corporation; *U.S. Public*, pg. 756
ENCOMPASS REHABILITATION HOSPITAL OF RICHARDSON, LLC—See Encompass Health Corporation; *U.S. Public*, pg. 756
ENCOMPASS REHABILITATION HOSPITAL OF ROUND ROCK, LLC—See Encompass Health Corporation; *U.S. Public*, pg. 756
ENCOMPASS REHABILITATION HOSPITAL OF THE MID-CITIES, LLC—See Encompass Health Corporation; *U.S. Public*, pg. 756
ENCOMPASS REHABILITATION HOSPITAL OF THE WOODLANDS, INC.—See Encompass Health Corporation; *U.S. Public*, pg. 756
ENCOMPASS REHABILITATION HOSPITAL THE VINTAGE, LLC—See Encompass Health Corporation; *U.S. Public*, pg. 756
ENDO MANAGEMENT LIMITED—See Endo International plc; *Int'l*, pg. 2404
ENDO U.S. INC.—See Endo International plc; *Int'l*, pg. 2404
ENHABIT, INC.; *U.S. Public*, pg. 768
ENTREPRENEUR UNIVERSE BRIGHT GROUP; *U.S. Public*, pg. 779
ENVISION MEDICAL SOLUTIONS, LLC—See New Rite Aid, LLC; *U.S. Private*, pg. 2905
EPIC REFERENCE LABS, INC.—See TPT Global Tech, Inc.; *U.S. Public*, pg. 2178
EPINEX DIAGNOSTICS LABORATORIES, INC.—See Rennova Health, Inc.; *U.S. Public*, pg. 1783
EQUIAN, LLC—See UnitedHealth Group Incorporated; *U.S. Public*, pg. 2240
ESSITY SWITZERLAND AG—See Essity Aktiebolag; *Int'l*, pg. 2517
ESUMEDICA - PRESTACAO DE CUIDADOS MEDICOS, S.A.—See Fosun International Limited; *Int'l*, pg. 2751
ETAO INTERNATIONAL CO., LTD.; *U.S. Public*, pg. 796
EUDA HEALTH LTD.—See EUDA Health Holdings Limited; *Int'l*, pg. 2526
EUKEDOS S.P.A.; *Int'l*, pg. 2526
EUREKA SPRINGS HOSPITAL HOSPICE, LLC—See UnitedHealth Group Incorporated; *U.S. Public*, pg. 2245
EUROEYES INTERNATIONAL EYE CLINIC LIMITED; *Int'l*, pg. 2534
EUROMEDICA SA; *Int'l*, pg. 2554
EURO REGISTRATIE COLLECTIEF B.V.—See Walgreens Boots Alliance, Inc.; *U.S. Public*, pg. 2322
EVERGREEN PFLEGE- UND BETREUUNGSZENTRUM BERGNEUSTADT GMBH—See Clariane SE; *Int'l*, pg. 1642
EVERGREEN PFLEGE- UND BETREUUNGSZENTRUM BUTZBACH GMBH—See Clariane SE; *Int'l*, pg. 1642
EVERGREEN PFLEGE- UND BETREUUNGSZENTRUM LANDSCHEID GMBH—See Clariane SE; *Int'l*, pg. 1642
EVERGREEN PFLEGE- UND BETREUUNGSZENTRUM PADERBORN GMBH—See Clariane SE; *Int'l*, pg. 1642
EVERGREEN PFLEGE- UND BETREUUNGSZENTRUM RECKLINGHAUSEN GMBH—See Clariane SE; *Int'l*, pg. 1642
EVERGREEN PFLEGE- UND BETREUUNGSZENTRUM SAARBURG GMBH—See Clariane SE; *Int'l*, pg. 1642
EVERGREEN PFLEGEZENTRUM AM ALTEN POSTSTADION GMBH—See Clariane SE; *Int'l*, pg. 1642
EVERSIDE HEALTH GROUP, INC.; *U.S. Public*, pg. 801
EVOLUTION HEALTH, LLC—See Amedisys, Inc.; *U.S. Public*, pg. 93
EXCELLA HOME HEALTH AGENCY, LLC—See Encompass Health Corporation; *U.S. Public*, pg. 756
EXECUTIVE HEALTH MANAGEMENT BV—See Air France-KLM S.A.; *Int'l*, pg. 237
EXPERITY, INC.—See Warburg Pincus LLC; *U.S. Private*, pg. 4438
EXPRESS SCRIPTS CANADA CO.—See The Cigna Group; *U.S. Public*, pg. 2061
EXTENDED FAMILY, LLC—See HouseWorks, LLC; *U.S. Private*, pg. 1992
EXTENDICARE, INC.—See Extendicare Inc.; *Int'l*, pg. 2591
EYE LOVE LLC; *U.S. Private*, pg. 1453
FAITH REGIONAL HEALTH SERVICES; *U.S. Private*, pg. 1465
FAMILY HEALTH CARE SERVICES—See UnitedHealth Group Incorporated; *U.S. Public*, pg. 2252
FAMILY HOME HEALTH CARE, INC.—See Amedisys, Inc.; *U.S. Public*, pg. 94
FAMILY HOME HEALTH SERVICES, INC.; *U.S. Private*, pg. 1470
FAMILY HOME HOSPICE, INC.—See UnitedHealth Group Incorporated; *U.S. Public*, pg. 2252
FAMILY MEDICINE ASSOCIATES OF EDMOND, LLC—See HCA Healthcare, Inc.; *U.S. Public*, pg. 996
FARNACIAS BENAVIDES S.A.B. DE C.V.—See Walgreens Boots Alliance, Inc.; *U.S. Public*, pg. 2322
FAYETTE MEDICAL CENTER HOMECARE, LLC—See UnitedHealth Group Incorporated; *U.S. Public*, pg. 2245
FELICIANA HOME HEALTH—See UnitedHealth Group Incorporated; *U.S. Public*, pg. 2245
FELICIANA HOME HEALTH SOUTH—See UnitedHealth Group Incorporated; *U.S. Public*, pg. 2245
FELICIANA PHYSICAL THERAPY SERVICES, LLC—See UnitedHealth Group Incorporated; *U.S. Public*, pg. 2245
FEMTEC HEALTH, INC.; *U.S. Private*, pg. 1494
FIGS, INC.; *U.S. Public*, pg. 834
FINGERPAINT MEDICAL COMMUNICATIONS—See Knox Lane LP; *U.S. Private*, pg. 2324
FINN WELLNESS KFT.—See Honkarakenne Oyj; *Int'l*, pg. 3471
FIRST CHOICE CHILDREN'S HOMECARE, LP—See Encompass Health Corporation; *U.S. Public*, pg. 756
FIRST-CHOICE HOME CARE, INC.; *U.S. Private*, pg. 1531
FIRST CHOICE HOME HEALTH—See The Pennant Group, Inc.; *U.S. Public*, pg. 2118
THE FIRST STRING HEALTHCARE, INC.—See AMN Healthcare Services, Inc.; *U.S. Public*, pg. 125
FISHER-TITUS MEDICAL CENTER; *U.S. Private*, pg. 1535

N.A.I.C.S. INDEX

621610 — HOME HEALTH CARE SE...

FLEMING MEDICAL CENTER, LLC—See Apollo Global Management, Inc.; *U.S. Public*, pg. 155

FLOYD HOMECARE, LLC—See UnitedHealth Group Incorporated; *U.S. Public*, pg. 2245

FMC DEL PERU S.A.—See Fresenius Medical Care AG; *Int'l*, pg. 2774

FMC ESPANA, S.A.U.—See Fresenius Medical Care AG; *Int'l*, pg. 2774

FMC HOLDINGS, INC.—See Fresenius Medical Care AG; *Int'l*, pg. 2774

FMC HONG KONG LTD.—See Fresenius Medical Care AG; *Int'l*, pg. 2774

FMC JAPAN K.K.—See Fresenius Medical Care AG; *Int'l*, pg. 2774

FMC LTDA.—See Fresenius Medical Care AG; *Int'l*, pg. 2774

FMC LTD.—See Fresenius Medical Care AG; *Int'l*, pg. 2774

FMC ROMANIA S.R.L.—See Fresenius Medical Care AG; *Int'l*, pg. 2774

FMC (SCHWEIZ) AG—See Fresenius Medical Care AG; *Int'l*, pg. 2774

FMC (SHANGHAI) CO., LTD.—See Fresenius Medical Care AG; *Int'l*, pg. 2774

FMC SUOMI OY—See Fresenius Medical Care AG; *Int'l*, pg. 2774

FMC (U.K.) LTD.—See Fresenius Medical Care AG; *Int'l*, pg. 2774

FMC VIETNAM LLC—See Fresenius Medical Care AG; *Int'l*, pg. 2774

FOOTHILL NURSING COMPANY PARTNERSHIP—See Apollo Global Management, Inc.; *U.S. Public*, pg. 156

FORT PAYNE HOME CARE CORPORATION—See Community Health Systems, Inc.; *U.S. Public*, pg. 553

FORT SMITH HMA, LLC—See Community Health Systems, Inc.; *U.S. Public*, pg. 553

FOX HILL VILLAGE PARTNERSHIP—See Apollo Global Management, Inc.; *U.S. Public*, pg. 156

FRANKLIN HOME CARE SERVICES, LLC—See Community Health Systems, Inc.; *U.S. Public*, pg. 553

FUNDAMENTAL LONG TERM CARE HOLDINGS; *U.S. Private*, pg. 1623

FUSION HEALTH TECHNOLOGIES CORPORATION; *U.S. Private*, pg. 1625

GADSDEN HOME CARE SERVICES, LLC—See Community Health Systems, Inc.; *U.S. Public*, pg. 553

GALESBURG HOME CARE CORPORATION—See Community Health Systems, Inc.; *U.S. Public*, pg. 553

GC LABTECH, INC.—See GC Biopharma Corp.; *Int'l*, pg. 2893

GE HEALTHCARE TECHNOLOGIES INC.; *U.S. Public*, pg. 908

GEM CITY HOME CARE, LLC—See KKR & Co. Inc.; *U.S. Public*, pg. 1249

GENERTEC UNIVERSAL MEDICAL GROUP COMPANY LIMITED; *Int'l*, pg. 2921

GENE-TRAK, INC.—See Abbott Laboratories; *U.S. Public*, pg. 20

GENEVA WOODS PHARMACY, LLC—See CVS Health Corporation; *U.S. Public*, pg. 616

GENTIVA HEALTH SERVICES, INC.—See Apollo Global Management, Inc.; *U.S. Public*, pg. 156

GENTIVA HOSPICE—See Apollo Global Management, Inc.; *U.S. Public*, pg. 156

GEORGIA HOMECARE OF HARRIS, LLC—See UnitedHealth Group Incorporated; *U.S. Public*, pg. 2245

GESUNDHEITSWELT CHIEMGAU AG; *Int'l*, pg. 2946

GIAN LIFE CARE LIMITED; *Int'l*, pg. 2961

GILCHRIST HOSPICE CARE INC.; *U.S. Private*, pg. 1699

GLOBAL LONGLIFE HOSPITAL & RESEARCH LIMITED; *Int'l*, pg. 2999

GOLDEN HOUSE LTD.; *Int'l*, pg. 3029

GOLDEN MORGEN BVBA—See Clariane SE; *Int'l*, pg. 1642

GRACE HOSPICE; *U.S. Private*, pg. 1749

GRAHAM HEALTHCARE CAPITAL, LLC—See Graham Holdings Company; *U.S. Public*, pg. 954

GRAHAM HEALTHCARE GROUP, INC.—See Graham Holdings Company; *U.S. Public*, pg. 954

GRAND STRAND SURGICAL SPECIALISTS, LLC—See HCA Healthcare, Inc.; *U.S. Public*, pg. 997

GRANDVIEW PHARMACY, LLC—See CVS Health Corporation; *U.S. Public*, pg. 616

GRANITE CITY HOME CARE SERVICES, LLC—See Community Health Systems, Inc.; *U.S. Public*, pg. 553

GREAT FALLS HEALTH CARE - BUTTE CENTER—See Formation Capital, LLC; *U.S. Public*, pg. 1570

GREAT FALLS HEALTH CARE - DEER LODGE—See Formation Capital, LLC; *U.S. Private*, pg. 1570

GREAT FALLS HEALTH CARE - MISSOURI RIVER CENTER—See Formation Capital, LLC; *U.S. Private*, pg. 1570

GREAT LAKES HOME HEALTH SERVICES, INC.—See Blue Wolf Capital Partners LLC; *U.S. Private*, pg. 594

GREAT PLAINS HEALTHCARE, INC.—See The Ensign Group, Inc.; *U.S. Public*, pg. 2071

GREEN CROSS HEALTH LIMITED; *Int'l*, pg. 3070

GREENVILLE CLINIC CORP.—See Quorum Health Corporation; *U.S. Public*, pg. 3330

GRISWOLD HOME CARE; *U.S. Private*, pg. 1790

GROUP HEALTH INC.—See EmblemHealth, Inc.; *U.S. Private*, pg. 1378

GUARDIAN ANGELS HOMECARE, LLC; *U.S. Private*, pg. 1809

GUARDIAN HEALTH SERVICES, L.L.C.—See Apollo Global Management, Inc.; *U.S. Public*, pg. 155

GUARDIAN HOME CARE, INC.—See Encompass Health Corporation; *U.S. Public*, pg. 756

GUINNESS NORTHERN COUNTIES LTD; *Int'l*, pg. 3174

THE GURWIN JEWISH GERIATRIC CENTER; *U.S. Private*, pg. 4040

HALCYON HOSPICE OF AIKEN, LLC—See UnitedHealth Group Incorporated; *U.S. Public*, pg. 2245

HALCYON HOSPICE—See UnitedHealth Group Incorporated; *U.S. Public*, pg. 2245

HALEON PLC; *Int'l*, pg. 3228

THE HAMISTER GROUP, INC.; *U.S. Private*, pg. 4042

HANG CHI HOLDINGS LIMITED; *Int'l*, pg. 3244

HAPBEE TECHNOLOGIES INC.; *Int'l*, pg. 3268

HARMONY HOME HEALTH, LLC; *U.S. Private*, pg. 1866

HARTWELL HEALTH HOLDINGS LLC—See The Ensign Group, Inc.; *U.S. Public*, pg. 2071

HASEKO SENIOR HOLDINGS CO., LTD.—See Haseko Corporation; *Int'l*, pg. 3283

HAUS AMSELHOF SENIORENRESIDENZ GMBH—See Clariane SE; *Int'l*, pg. 1643

HAVEN HOSPICE—See SantaFe Healthcare, Inc.; *U.S. Private*, pg. 3547

HB MANAGEMENT GROUP, INC.; *U.S. Private*, pg. 1886

HEALTH ACQUISITION CORP—See Blue Wolf Capital Partners LLC; *U.S. Private*, pg. 595

HEALTH AT HOME—See LCS Holdings Inc.; *U.S. Private*, pg. 2404

HEALTHCARE AT HOME LTD.; *Int'l*, pg. 3303

HEALTH CARE CONCEPT GMBH—See Asklepios Kliniken GmbH & Co. KGaA; *Int'l*, pg. 623

HEALTHCARE CORPORATION OF AMERICA; *U.S. Public*, pg. 1015

HEALTHCARE INNOVATIONS OF OKLAHOMA, L.L.C.—See Encompass Health Corporation; *U.S. Public*, pg. 756

HEALTHCARE INNOVATIONS OF WESTERN OKLAHOMA, L.L.C.—See Encompass Health Corporation; *U.S. Public*, pg. 756

HEALTHCARE INNOVATIONSTRAVERTINE HEALTH SERVICES, L.L.C.—See Encompass Health Corporation; *U.S. Public*, pg. 756

HEALTHCARE MANAGEMENT OF AMERICA, INC.—See Healthcare Realty Trust Incorporated; *U.S. Public*, pg. 1015

HEALTHCARE PARTNERS COLORADO, LLC—See DaVita Inc.; *U.S. Public*, pg. 639

HEALTHCARE ROYALTY, INC.; *U.S. Public*, pg. 1015

HEALTHCARE SOLUTIONS HOLDING, LLC—See Cardinal Health, Inc.; *U.S. Public*, pg. 434

HEALTHCARE SUPPORT SERVICES, LLC—See HCA Healthcare, Inc.; *U.S. Public*, pg. 998

HEALTHCARE TRIANGLE, INC.; *U.S. Public*, pg. 1015

HEALTHCHANNELS, INC.; *U.S. Private*, pg. 1895

HEALTHCONN CORP.; *Int'l*, pg. 3304

HEALTH DATA & MANAGEMENT SOLUTIONS, INC.—See CVS Health Corporation; *U.S. Public*, pg. 615

HEALTHDRIVE CORPORATION—See Cressey & Company, LP; *U.S. Private*, pg. 1095

HEALTHFIELD HOME HEALTH, LLC—See Humana, Inc.; *U.S. Public*, pg. 1069

HEALTHFLEX HOME HEALTH SERVICES; *U.S. Private*, pg. 1896

HEALTH MANAGEMENT LIMITED—See MAXIMUS, Inc.; *U.S. Public*, pg. 1402

HEALTHONE COLORADO CARE PARTNERS ACO LLC—See HCA Healthcare, Inc.; *U.S. Public*, pg. 998

HEALTHPOINT OF NORTH CAROLINA, L.L.C.—See Tenet Healthcare Corporation; *U.S. Public*, pg. 2003

HEALTH RECOVERY SOLUTIONS INC.; *U.S. Private*, pg. 1894

HEALTH SERVICES MANAGEMENT, INC.; *U.S. Private*, pg. 1894

HEALTH SERVICES OF NORTHERN NEW YORK, INC.—See The Hamister Group, Inc.; *U.S. Private*, pg. 4042

HEALTHSOUTH CLINICAL TECHNOLOGIES, LLC—See Encompass Health Corporation; *U.S. Public*, pg. 756

HEALTHSOUTH EAST VALLEY REHABILITATION HOSPITAL, LLC—See Encompass Health Corporation; *U.S. Public*, pg. 756

HEALTHSOUTH LITTLETON REHABILITATION, LLC—See Encompass Health Corporation; *U.S. Public*, pg. 756

HEALTHSOUTH MIDDLETOWN REHABILITATION HOSPITAL, LLC—See Encompass Health Corporation; *U.S. Public*, pg. 756

HEALTHSOUTH OF PHENIX CITY, INC.—See Encompass Health Corporation; *U.S. Public*, pg. 758

HEALTHSOUTH PLANO REHABILITATION HOSPITAL, LLC—See Encompass Health Corporation; *U.S. Public*, pg. 756

HEALTHSOUTH REHABILITATION HOSPITAL OF AUSTIN, INC.—See Encompass Health Corporation; *U.S. Public*, pg. 756

HEALTHSOUTH REHABILITATION HOSPITAL OF BEAUMONT, LLC—See Encompass Health Corporation; *U.S. Public*, pg. 756

HEALTHSOUTH REHABILITATION HOSPITAL OF CHARLESTON, LLC—See Encompass Health Corporation; *U.S. Public*, pg. 757

HEALTHSOUTH REHABILITATION HOSPITAL OF FORT WORTH, LLC—See Encompass Health Corporation; *U.S. Public*, pg. 757

HEALTHSOUTH REHABILITATION HOSPITAL OF HENDERSON, LLC—See Encompass Health Corporation; *U.S. Public*, pg. 757

HEALTHSOUTH REHABILITATION HOSPITAL OF HUMBLE, LLC—See Encompass Health Corporation; *U.S. Public*, pg. 757

HEALTHSOUTH REHABILITATION HOSPITAL OF JONESBORO, LLC—See Encompass Health Corporation; *U.S. Public*, pg. 757

HEALTHSOUTH REHABILITATION HOSPITAL OF LARGO, LLC—See Encompass Health Corporation; *U.S. Public*, pg. 757

HEALTHSOUTH REHABILITATION HOSPITAL OF MARTIN COUNTY, LLC—See Encompass Health Corporation; *U.S. Public*, pg. 757

HEALTHSOUTH REHABILITATION HOSPITAL OF MIDLAND/ODESSA, LLC—See Encompass Health Corporation; *U.S. Public*, pg. 757

HEALTHSOUTH REHABILITATION HOSPITAL OF NEWNAN, LLC—See Encompass Health Corporation; *U.S. Public*, pg. 757

HEALTHSOUTH REHABILITATION HOSPITAL OF NORTH HOUSTON, LP—See Encompass Health Corporation; *U.S. Public*, pg. 757

HEALTHSOUTH REHABILITATION HOSPITAL OF READING, LLC—See Encompass Health Corporation; *U.S. Public*, pg. 757

HEALTHSOUTH REHABILITATION HOSPITAL OF SARASOTA, LLC—See Encompass Health Corporation; *U.S. Public*, pg. 757

HEALTHSOUTH REHABILITATION HOSPITAL OF SEMINOLE COUNTY, LLC—See Encompass Health Corporation; *U.S. Public*, pg. 757

HEALTHSOUTH REHABILITATION HOSPITAL OF TALLAHASSEE, LLC—See Encompass Health Corporation; *U.S. Public*, pg. 757

HEALTHSOUTH REHABILITATION HOSPITAL OF TEXARKANA, INC.—See Encompass Health Corporation; *U.S. Public*, pg. 757

HEALTHSOUTH REHABILITATION HOSPITAL OF UTAH, LLC—See Encompass Health Corporation; *U.S. Public*, pg. 757

HEALTHSOUTH REHABILITATION HOSPITAL THE WOODLANDS, INC.—See Encompass Health Corporation; *U.S. Public*, pg. 756

HEALTHSOUTH REHABILITATION INSTITUTE OF SAN ANTONIO (RIOSA), INC.—See Encompass Health Corporation; *U.S. Public*, pg. 757

HEALTHSOUTH SUNRISE REHABILITATION HOSPITAL, LLC—See Encompass Health Corporation; *U.S. Public*, pg. 757

HEALTHSOUTH WALTON REHABILITATION HOSPITAL, LLC—See Encompass Health Corporation; *U.S. Public*, pg. 757

HEALTHSUN HEALTH PLANS, INC.—See Elevance Health, Inc.; *U.S. Public*, pg. 730

HEALTH UNION, LLC; *U.S. Private*, pg. 1894

HEARTLAND REHABILITATION SERVICES, LLC—See American Healthcare Systems Corp., Inc.; *U.S. Private*, pg. 236

HELP AT HOME, LLC—See Centerbridge Partners, L.P.; *U.S. Public*, pg. 815

HELP AT HOME, LLC—See The Vistria Group, LP; *U.S. Private*, pg. 4131

HELVITA SENIORENZENTREN GMBH—See Clariane SE; *Int'l*, pg. 1643

HENRY STREET SETTLEMENT; *U.S. Private*, pg. 1919

HEYDEVELD BVBA—See Clariane SE; *Int'l*, pg. 1643

HIGH TECH HOME CARE AG—See Healthcare at Home Ltd.; *Int'l*, pg. 3304

HIKARI HEIGHTS-VARUS CO., LTD.; *Int'l*, pg. 3389

HILL-ROM CANADA RESPIRATORY, LTD.—See Baxter International Inc.; *U.S. Public*, pg. 283

HILLSIDE HOSPITAL, LLC—See Apollo Global Management, Inc.; *U.S. Public*, pg. 155

HILTON HEAD HEALTH SYSTEM, L.P.—See Tenet Healthcare Corporation; *U.S. Public*, pg. 2008

HIP & JOINT SPECIALISTS OF NORTH TEXAS, PLLC—See HCA Healthcare, Inc.; *U.S. Public*, pg. 998

HMC HOME HEALTH, LLC—See UnitedHealth Group Incorporated; *U.S. Public*, pg. 2245

HOAG HOSPITAL FOUNDATION; *U.S. Private*, pg. 1957

HOLY NAME MEDICAL CENTER; *U.S. Private*, pg. 1969

HOMECALL OF FREDERICK—See UnitedHealth Group Incorporated; *U.S. Public*, pg. 2245

HOME CARE ASSISTANCE CORPORATION; *U.S. Private*, pg. 1970

621610 — HOME HEALTH CARE SE...

HOME CARE CONNECTIONS, INC.—See UnitedHealth Group Incorporated; *U.S. Public*, pg. 2245
HOME CARE CONNECT LLC; *U.S. Private*, pg. 1970
HOMECARE HEALTH SOLUTIONS, INC.—See Humana, Inc.; *U.S. Public*, pg. 1069
HOME CARE PHARMACY, LLC—See CVS Health Corporation; *U.S. Public*, pg. 616
HOMECARE PREFERRED CHOICE, INC.—See Amedisys, Inc.; *U.S. Public*, pg. 94
HOME GROUP LIMITED; *Int'l*, pg. 3454
HOME HEALTH OF ALEXANDRIA, L.L.C.—See Amedisys, Inc.; *U.S. Public*, pg. 94
HOME HEALTH OF RURAL TEXAS, INC.—See Apollo Global Management, Inc.; *U.S. Public*, pg. 156
HOME HELPERS OF TAMPA; *U.S. Private*, pg. 1971
HOME RESIDENCE DU PLATEAU SPRL—See Clariane SE; *Int'l*, pg. 1643
HOME SERVICES SYSTEMS INC; *U.S. Private*, pg. 1972
HOMEWATCH INTERNATIONAL, INC.—See Apax Partners LLP; *Int'l*, pg. 502
HONLIV HEALTHCARE MANAGEMENT GROUP COMPANY LIMITED; *Int'l*, pg. 3471
HOOD MEDICAL GROUP—See Community Health Systems, Inc.; *U.S. Public*, pg. 553
HOPE HOSPICE AND COMMUNITY SERVICES INC.; *U.S. Private*, pg. 1979
HOPE HOSPICE INC.—See University of California San Francisco Medical Center; *U.S. Public*, pg. 4308
HOPEWELL HEALTHCARE, INC.—See The Ensign Group, Inc.; *U.S. Public*, pg. 2071
HOSPARUS INC.; *U.S. Private*, pg. 1985
HOSPICE AND PALLIATIVE CARE CENTER OF ALAMANCE-CASWELL; *U.S. Private*, pg. 1985
HOSPICE AT GREENSBORO, INC.; *U.S. Private*, pg. 1985
HOSPICE AUSTIN; *U.S. Private*, pg. 1985
HOSPICE BUFFALO; *U.S. Private*, pg. 1985
HOSPICE CARE OF SOUTHWEST MICHIGAN; *U.S. Private*, pg. 1985
HOSPICE EL PASO; *U.S. Private*, pg. 1985
HOSPICE OF CENTRAL ARKANSAS, LLC—See UnitedHealth Group Incorporated; *U.S. Public*, pg. 2245
HOSPICE OF CITRUS COUNTY, INC.—See Chemed Corporation; *U.S. Public*, pg. 484
HOSPICE OF DAYTON, INC.; *U.S. Private*, pg. 1986
HOSPICE OF EAST TEXAS; *U.S. Private*, pg. 1986
HOSPICE OF LAURENS COUNTY, INC.; *U.S. Private*, pg. 1986
HOSPICE OF MARION COUNTY; *U.S. Private*, pg. 1986
HOSPICE OF MESILLA VALLEY, LLC—See Humana, Inc.; *U.S. Public*, pg. 1069
HOSPICE OF NORTHWEST OHIO; *U.S. Private*, pg. 1986
HOSPICE OF RUTHERFORD COUNTY, INC.; *U.S. Private*, pg. 1986
HOSPICE OF THE COMFORTER, INC.; *U.S. Private*, pg. 1986
HOSPICE OF THE RED RIVER VALLEY; *U.S. Private*, pg. 1986
HOSPICE OF THE SACRED HEART; *U.S. Private*, pg. 1986
HOSPICE OF THE VALLEY; *U.S. Private*, pg. 1986
HOSPICE OF THE WESTERN RESERVE, INC.; *U.S. Private*, pg. 1987
HOSPICE & PALLIATIVE CARECENTER; *U.S. Private*, pg. 1985
HOSPITAL POLUSA, S.A.—See Centene Corporation; *U.S. Public*, pg. 469
HOSPITAL POVISA, S.A.—See Centene Corporation; *U.S. Public*, pg. 469
HOST HEALTHCARE, INC.—See TPG Capital, L.P; *U.S. Public*, pg. 2176
HOUSEWORKS, LLC; *U.S. Private*, pg. 1992
HOUSTON HEART, PLLC—See HCA Healthcare, Inc.; *U.S. Public*, pg. 999
HUAXIA EYE HOSPITAL GROUP CO., LTD.; *Int'l*, pg. 3515
HUIZE PHILEMON & BAUCIS WZC—See Ackermans & van Haaren NV; *Int'l*, pg. 106
HUMANA AT HOME (DALLAS), INC.—See Humana, Inc.; *U.S. Public*, pg. 1069
HUMANA AT HOME (HOUSTON), INC.—See Humana, Inc.; *U.S. Public*, pg. 1069
HUMANA INSURANCE OF PUERTO RICO, INC.—See Humana, Inc.; *U.S. Public*, pg. 1070
HUMAN DEVELOPMENT ASSOCIATION; *U.S. Private*, pg. 2005
HUMAN LIFE CARE CO., LTD.—See Human Holdings Co., Ltd.; *Int'l*, pg. 3529
H.U. WELLNESS, INC.—See H.U. Group Holdings, Inc.; *Int'l*, pg. 3197
HUYSE ELCKERLYC NV—See Clariane SE; *Int'l*, pg. 1643
HYGEIA HEALTHCARE HOLDINGS COMPANY LIMITED; *Int'l*, pg. 3549
ICARES MEDICUS, INC.; *Int'l*, pg. 3578
IDAHO HOME HEALTH AND HOSPICE INC.—See UnitedHealth Group Incorporated; *U.S. Public*, pg. 2245
IEC GROUP, INC.—See Elevance Health, Inc.; *U.S. Public*, pg. 730
IGEAMED SPA; *Int'l*, pg. 3602
IHS ACQUISITION XXX, INC.—See Cencora, Inc.; *U.S. Public*, pg. 467

ILLINOIS LIV, LLC—See UnitedHealth Group Incorporated; *U.S. Public*, pg. 2245
I.M.E. 2016 B.V.—See Asahi Kasei Corporation; *Int'l*, pg. 597
IMMEDIATE CARE, INC.; *U.S. Private*, pg. 2047
IMMEUBLE JAZZ LONGUEUIL, SOCIETE EN COMMANDITE—See Welltower Inc.; *U.S. Public*, pg. 2348
IMMUNOCLIN CORPORATION; *U.S. Private*, pg. 2047
IMPERIUM HEALTH MANAGEMENT, LLC—See UnitedHealth Group Incorporated; *U.S. Public*, pg. 2244
IMV MEDICAL INFORMATION DIVISION, INC.—See Bio-Rad Laboratories, Inc.; *U.S. Public*, pg. 334
INDIVIDUAL CENTRICITY CORPORATION; *U.S. Private*, pg. 2064
INFINITY HOME CARE, L.L.C.—See Amedisys, Inc.; *U.S. Public*, pg. 94
INFIRMARY HOME HEALTH AGENCY, INC.—See UnitedHealth Group Incorporated; *U.S. Public*, pg. 2245
INFUSERVE AMERICA, INC.; *U.S. Private*, pg. 2075
INFUSIONCARE—See Option Care Health, Inc.; *U.S. Public*, pg. 1610
INFUSION PARTNERS, LLC—See Option Care Health, Inc.; *U.S. Public*, pg. 1610
INFUSIONS SOLUTIONS CORP.—See Option Care Health, Inc.; *U.S. Public*, pg. 1610
INNOMAR STRATEGIES, INC.—See Cencora, Inc.; *U.S. Public*, pg. 467
THE INNOVATION INSTITUTE; *U.S. Private*, pg. 4056
INOVA HEALTH SYSTEM FOUNDATION; *U.S. Private*, pg. 2084
INSPIRIS OF NEW YORK MANAGEMENT, INC.—See UnitedHealth Group Incorporated; *U.S. Public*, pg. 2241
INSTANT CARE OF ARIZONA LLC—See Coltala Holdings, LLC; *U.S. Private*, pg. 976
INSTITUTE FOR WOMEN'S HEALTH AND BODY, LLC—See HCA Healthcare, Inc.; *U.S. Public*, pg. 999
INTEGRACARE OF ABILENE, LLC—See Apollo Global Management, Inc.; *U.S. Public*, pg. 156
INTEGRACARE OF ALBANY, LLC—See Apollo Global Management, Inc.; *U.S. Public*, pg. 156
INTEGRACARE OF GRANBURY, LLC—See Apollo Global Management, Inc.; *U.S. Public*, pg. 156
INTEGRACARE OF OLNEY HOME HEALTH, LLC—See Apollo Global Management, Inc.; *U.S. Public*, pg. 156
INTEGRACARE OF WICHITA FALLS, LLC—See Apollo Global Management, Inc.; *U.S. Public*, pg. 156
INTEGRA PARTNERS LLC; *U.S. Private*, pg. 2098
INTEGRATED MEDICAL SOLUTIONS, LLC; *U.S. Private*, pg. 2100
THE INTEGRATIVE MEDICAL CENTRE (PTY) LTD—See Ascendis Health Limited; *Int'l*, pg. 601
INTEGRIUS, LLC—See U.S. Physical Therapy, Inc.; *U.S. Public*, pg. 2214
INTERNATIONAL MARKETING VENTURES, LIMITED—See Bio-Rad Laboratories, Inc.; *U.S. Public*, pg. 334
INTERNATIONAL PHYSICIANS NETWORK, L.L.C.—See Cencora, Inc.; *U.S. Public*, pg. 467
INTERNATIONAL TECHNOLOGIES, LLC—See Rennova Health, Inc.; *U.S. Public*, pg. 1783
INTREPID USA HEALTHCARE SERVICES—See Patriarch Partners, LLC; *U.S. Private*, pg. 3109
INVACARE AUSTRALIA PTY LIMITED—See Invacare Corporation; *U.S. Private*, pg. 2130
INVACARE B.V.—See Invacare Corporation; *U.S. Private*, pg. 2130
INVACARE CANADA LP—See Invacare Corporation; *U.S. Private*, pg. 2130
INVACARE LDA.—See Invacare Corporation; *U.S. Private*, pg. 2131
INVACARE NV—See Invacare Corporation; *U.S. Private*, pg. 2131
INVISALIGN AUSTRALIA PTY LTD—See Align Technology, Inc.; *U.S. Public*, pg. 77
IOWA HOSPICE, L.L.C.—See Humana, Inc.; *U.S. Public*, pg. 1070
IOWA LABORERS DISTRICT COUNCIL HEALTH & WELFARE PLAN; *U.S. Private*, pg. 2134
IQVIA QUALITY METRIC INC.—See IQVIA Holdings Inc.; *U.S. Public*, pg. 1169
I'ROM CO., LTD.—See I'rom Group Co., Ltd.; *Int'l*, pg. 3562
I'ROM CS CO., LTD.—See I'rom Group Co., Ltd.; *Int'l*, pg. 3562
I'ROM EC CO., LTD.—See I'rom Group Co., Ltd.; *Int'l*, pg. 3562
I'ROM NA CO., LTD.—See I'rom Group Co., Ltd.; *Int'l*, pg. 3562
ISLANDS HOSPICE, INC.; *U.S. Private*, pg. 2145
ITAMAR MEDICAL, INC.—See Asahi Kasei Corporation; *Int'l*, pg. 597
IVX HEALTH, INC.; *U.S. Private*, pg. 2151
JACKSON COUNTY HOME HEALTH, LLC—See UnitedHealth Group Incorporated; *U.S. Public*, pg. 2245
JACKSON SURGICAL CENTER, LLC—See Tenet Healthcare Corporation; *U.S. Public*, pg. 2010
JEFFERSON REGIONAL HOMECARE, LLC—See UnitedHealth Group Incorporated; *U.S. Public*, pg. 2245
JELF WELLBEING LIMITED—See Marsh & McLennan Companies, Inc.; *U.S. Public*, pg. 1378
JELLICO MEDICAL CENTER, INC.—See Rennova Health, Inc.; *U.S. Public*, pg. 1783
JOHN XXIII HOME; *U.S. Private*, pg. 2225
JOKILAAKSON PERHEKODIT OY—See Humana AB; *Int'l*, pg. 3530
JOURDANTON HOME CARE SERVICES, LLC—See Community Health Systems, Inc.; *U.S. Public*, pg. 554
JUST LIKE FAMILY HOME CARE, LLC; *U.S. Private*, pg. 2245
KABAFUSION - MICHIGAN—See The Pritzker Group - Chicago, LLC; *U.S. Private*, pg. 4099
KAISER FOUNDATION HEALTH PLAN OF WASHINGTON—See Kaiser Permanente; *U.S. Private*, pg. 2255
KAISER PERMANENTE, NORTHWEST REGION—See Kaiser Permanente; *U.S. Private*, pg. 2256
KANSAS CITY HOME CARE, INC.; *U.S. Private*, pg. 2260
KANSAS CITY HOSPICE & PALLIATIVE CARE; *U.S. Private*, pg. 2260
KANSAS CITY PULMONOLOGY PRACTICE, LLC—See HCA Healthcare, Inc.; *U.S. Public*, pg. 1000
KAREN SPRL—See Clariane SE; *Int'l*, pg. 1643
KAY COUNTY CLINIC COMPANY, LLC—See Community Health Systems, Inc.; *U.S. Public*, pg. 554
KENTUCKY HOMECARE OF HENDERSON, LLC—See UnitedHealth Group Incorporated; *U.S. Public*, pg. 2245
KENTUCKY LV, LLC—See UnitedHealth Group Incorporated; *U.S. Public*, pg. 2245
KENTUCKY RIVER HBP, LLC—See Quorum Health Corporation; *U.S. Private*, pg. 3330
KINDERHORT SALZBURGER LEITE GGMBH—See Asklepios Kliniken GmbH & Co. KGaA; *Int'l*, pg. 624
KINDLY MD, INC.; *U.S. Public*, pg. 1234
KINDRED HOSPICE MISSOURI, LLC—See Humana, Inc.; *U.S. Public*, pg. 1070
KINETIKA SARDEGNA SRL—See Clariane SE; *Int'l*, pg. 1643
KNOXVILLE EYE ANESTHESIA, LLC—See KKR & Co. Inc.; *U.S. Public*, pg. 1249
KURTZ AMBULANCE SERVICE, INC.—See KKR & Co. Inc.; *U.S. Public*, pg. 1251
LA AMISTAD RESIDENTIAL TREATMENT CENTER, LLC—See Universal Health Services, Inc.; *U.S. Public*, pg. 2258
LAFAYETTE HEALTH CARE CENTER, INC.—See Apollo Global Management, Inc.; *U.S. Public*, pg. 157
LAKESHORE SYSTEM SERVICES OF FLORIDA, INC.—See Encompass Health Corporation; *U.S. Public*, pg. 758
LASALLE AMBULANCE, INC.—See KKR & Co. Inc.; *U.S. Public*, pg. 1249
LAS VEGAS SOLARI HOSPICE CARE, LLC—See DaVita Inc.; *U.S. Public*, pg. 640
LEAF RIVER HOME HEALTH CARE, LLC—See UnitedHealth Group Incorporated; *U.S. Public*, pg. 2245
LE COLVERT SPRL—See Clariane SE; *Int'l*, pg. 1643
LEGACY COMMUNITY HEALTH; *U.S. Private*, pg. 2416
LEIDOS HEALTH, LLC—See ManpowerGroup Inc.; *U.S. Public*, pg. 1362
LES CHARMILLES SA—See Clariane SE; *Int'l*, pg. 1643
LES RECOLLETS SA—See Clariane SE; *Int'l*, pg. 1643
LES SITELLES SA—See Clariane SE; *Int'l*, pg. 1643
LHCG CVIII, LLC—See UnitedHealth Group Incorporated; *U.S. Public*, pg. 2245
LHCG CX, LLC—See UnitedHealth Group Incorporated; *U.S. Public*, pg. 2245
LHCG CXV, LLC—See UnitedHealth Group Incorporated; *U.S. Public*, pg. 2245
LHCG CXXI, LLC—See UnitedHealth Group Incorporated; *U.S. Public*, pg. 2245
LHCG LIX, LLC—See UnitedHealth Group Incorporated; *U.S. Public*, pg. 2245
LHCG LVII, LLC—See UnitedHealth Group Incorporated; *U.S. Public*, pg. 2245
LHCG LXIII, LLC—See UnitedHealth Group Incorporated; *U.S. Public*, pg. 2245
LHCG LXXIX, LLC—See UnitedHealth Group Incorporated; *U.S. Public*, pg. 2245
LHCG LXX, LLC—See UnitedHealth Group Incorporated; *U.S. Public*, pg. 2245
LHC GROUP, INC.—See UnitedHealth Group Incorporated; *U.S. Public*, pg. 2243
LHC GROUP PHARMACEUTICAL SERVICES, LLC—See UnitedHealth Group Incorporated; *U.S. Public*, pg. 2245
LHCG-VI, LLC—See UnitedHealth Group Incorporated; *U.S. Public*, pg. 2245
LHCG-V, L.L.C.—See UnitedHealth Group Incorporated; *U.S. Public*, pg. 2245
LHCG XVII, LLC—See UnitedHealth Group Incorporated; *U.S. Public*, pg. 2245
LHCG XXI, LLC—See UnitedHealth Group Incorporated; *U.S. Public*, pg. 2245
LHCG XXXVII, LLC—See UnitedHealth Group Incorporated; *U.S. Public*, pg. 2245
LHC HOMECARE OF TENNESSEE, LLC—See UnitedHealth Group Incorporated; *U.S. Public*, pg. 2245

N.A.I.C.S. INDEX 621610 — HOME HEALTH CARE SE...

LIFECARE ALLIANCE—See Central Ohio Diabetes Association; *U.S. Private*, pg. 824

LIFE CARE HOME HEALTH SERVICES CORP—See LCS Holdings Inc.; *U.S. Private*, pg. 2404

LIFEFLEET SOUTHEAST, INC.—See KKR & Co. Inc.; *U.S. Public*, pg. 1251

LIFELINE HOME HEALTH CARE OF BOWLING GREEN, LLC—See UnitedHealth Group Incorporated; *U.S. Public*, pg. 2245

LIFELINE HOME HEALTH CARE OF FULTON, LLC—See UnitedHealth Group Incorporated; *U.S. Public*, pg. 2245

LIFELINE HOME HEALTH CARE OF HOPKINSVILLE, LLC—See UnitedHealth Group Incorporated; *U.S. Public*, pg. 2245

LIFELINE HOME HEALTH CARE OF LEXINGTON, LLC—See UnitedHealth Group Incorporated; *U.S. Public*, pg. 2245

LIFELINE HOME HEALTH CARE OF RUSSELLVILLE, LLC—See UnitedHealth Group Incorporated; *U.S. Public*, pg. 2246

LIFELINE HOME HEALTH CARE OF SOMERSET, LLC—See UnitedHealth Group Incorporated; *U.S. Public*, pg. 2246

LIFELINE HOME HEALTH CARE OF SPRINGFIELD, LLC—See UnitedHealth Group Incorporated; *U.S. Public*, pg. 2246

LIFELINE OF WEST TENNESSEE, LLC—See UnitedHealth Group Incorporated; *U.S. Public*, pg. 2246

LIFELINE PRIVATE DUTY SERVICES OF KENTUCKY, LLC—See UnitedHealth Group Incorporated; *U.S. Public*, pg. 2246

LIFELINE ROCKCASTLE HOME HEALTH, LLC—See UnitedHealth Group Incorporated; *U.S. Public*, pg. 2246

LIFEMARK HEALTH CORPORATION—See George Weston Limited; *Int'l*, pg. 2939

LIFEMATTERS; *U.S. Private*, pg. 2450

LIFEMATTERS—See Lifematters; *U.S. Private*, pg. 2450

LIFESPAN HOME MEDICAL—See Lifespan Corp.; *U.S. Private*, pg. 2451

LITHA HEALTHCARE GROUP LIMITED—See Endo International plc; *Int'l*, pg. 2404

LIVEWELL CLINIC, LLC; *U.S. Private*, pg. 2473

LONG TERM SOLUTIONS INC.—See UnitedHealth Group Incorporated; *U.S. Public*, pg. 2244

LOS ANGELES/INGLEWOOD ENDOSCOPY ASC, LP—See KKR & Co. Inc.; *U.S. Public*, pg. 1249

LOUISIANA EXTENDED CARE HOSPITAL OF KENNER, LLC—See UnitedHealth Group Incorporated; *U.S. Public*, pg. 2246

LOUISIANA HEALTH CARE GROUP, LLC—See UnitedHealth Group Incorporated; *U.S. Public*, pg. 2246

LOUISIANA HOMECARE OF AMITE, LLC—See UnitedHealth Group Incorporated; *U.S. Public*, pg. 2246

LOUISIANA HOMECARE OF DELHI, LLC—See UnitedHealth Group Incorporated; *U.S. Public*, pg. 2246

LOUISIANA HOMECARE OF KENNER, LLC—See UnitedHealth Group Incorporated; *U.S. Public*, pg. 2246

LOUISIANA HOMECARE OF MISS-LOU, LLC—See UnitedHealth Group Incorporated; *U.S. Public*, pg. 2246

LOUISIANA HOMECARE OF MONROE, LLC—See UnitedHealth Group Incorporated; *U.S. Public*, pg. 2246

LOUISIANA HOMECARE OF NORTHWEST LOUISIANA, LLC—See UnitedHealth Group Incorporated; *U.S. Public*, pg. 2246

LOUISIANA HOMECARE OF RACELAND, LLC—See UnitedHealth Group Incorporated; *U.S. Public*, pg. 2246

LOUISIANA HOMECARE OF SLIDELL, LLC—See UnitedHealth Group Incorporated; *U.S. Public*, pg. 2246

LUMIERE CHILDREN'S THERAPY, INC.; *U.S. Private*, pg. 2514

LUNG BIOTECHNOLOGY INC.—See United Therapeutics Corporation; *U.S. Public*, pg. 2238

LUOTSIMAJA OY—See Humana AB; *Int'l*, pg. 3530

MAIDS MORETON OPERATIONS LIMITED—See Welltower Inc.; *U.S. Public*, pg. 2348

MAIN LINE MEDIA NEWS—See Alden Global Capital LLC; *U.S. Private*, pg. 156

MAISON DE XX AOUT SA—See Clariane SE; *Int'l*, pg. 1643

MANCHESTER HEALTH SERVICES—See VNA & Hospice of the Southwest Region, Inc.; *U.S. Private*, pg. 4408

MANGOCEUTICALS, INC.; *U.S. Public*, pg. 1356

MANIPAL CIGNA HEALTH INSURANCE COMPANY LIMITED—See The Cigna Group; *U.S. Public*, pg. 2062

MANOIR ARCHER INC.—See Welltower Inc.; *U.S. Public*, pg. 2348

MARIETTA HOME HEALTH AND HOSPICE, L.L.C.—See Amedisys, Inc.; *U.S. Public*, pg. 94

MARION REGIONAL HOMECARE, LLC—See UnitedHealth Group Incorporated; *U.S. Public*, pg. 2246

MARLBORO HUDSON AMBULANCE & WHEELCHAIR SERVICE, INC.—See KKR & Co. Inc.; *U.S. Public*, pg. 1249

MARPAI, INC; *U.S. Public*, pg. 1370

MARTIN HEALTH SERVICES, LLC—See CVS Health Corporation; *U.S. Public*, pg. 616

MARYLAND ENDOSCOPY ANESTHESIA, LLC—See KKR & Co. Inc.; *U.S. Public*, pg. 1249

MASONIC HOME OF VIRGINIA; *U.S. Private*, pg. 2602

MASSACHUSETTS BEHAVIORAL HEALTH PARTNERSHIP, LLP—See Elevance Health, Inc.; *U.S. Public*, pg. 730

MASS GENERAL BRIGHAM INCORPORATED; *U.S. Private*, pg. 2603

MATRIX MEDICAL NETWORK OF ARIZONA, L.L.C.—See Frazier & Company, Inc.; *U.S. Private*, pg. 1599

MATRIX MEDICAL NETWORK OF ARIZONA, L.L.C.—See ModivCare, Inc.; *U.S. Public*, pg. 1455

MAVEC CORPORATION—See Merck & Co., Inc.; *U.S. Public*, pg. 1418

MAXIMUS HEALTH & HUMAN SERVICES LIMITED—See MAXIMUS, Inc.; *U.S. Public*, pg. 1402

MAX SOLUTIONS PTY LIMITED—See MAXIMUS, Inc.; *U.S. Public*, pg. 1402

MB2 DENTAL SOLUTIONS LLC; *U.S. Private*, pg. 2624

MCDOWELL HOME HEALTH AGENCY—See Ephraim McDowell Health, Inc.; *U.S. Private*, pg. 1412

MCKINNIS CONSULTING SERVICES, LLC—See Bain Capital, LP; *U.S. Private*, pg. 432

MED-CARE MANAGEMENT, INC.—See Medical Cost Management Corp.; *U.S. Private*, pg. 2654

MEDDIUS, LLC—See Premier, Inc.; *U.S. Public*, pg. 1715

MEDERI CARETENDERS VS OF BROWARD, LLC—See UnitedHealth Group Incorporated; *U.S. Public*, pg. 2244

MEDERI CARETENDERS VS OF SE FL, LLC—See UnitedHealth Group Incorporated; *U.S. Public*, pg. 2244

MEDERI CARETENDERS VS OF SW FL, LLC—See UnitedHealth Group Incorporated; *U.S. Public*, pg. 2244

MEDICAL BILLING CHOICES, INC.—See Rennova Health, Inc.; *U.S. Public*, pg. 1783

MEDICAL BILLING SOLUTIONS, LLC—See Bain Capital, LP; *U.S. Private*, pg. 445

MEDICAL CENTER ALLIANCE—See HCA Healthcare, Inc.; *U.S. Public*, pg. 1004

MEDICAL CENTER HOME HEALTH, LLC—See UnitedHealth Group Incorporated; *U.S. Public*, pg. 2246

MEDICAL CENTERS HOMECARE, LLC—See UnitedHealth Group Incorporated; *U.S. Public*, pg. 2246

MEDICAL COST MANAGEMENT CORP.; *U.S. Private*, pg. 2654

MEDICAL GURADIAN, LLC—See Water Street Healthcare Partners, LLC; *U.S. Private*, pg. 4452

MEDICAL MIME, INC.—See Rennova Health, Inc.; *U.S. Public*, pg. 1783

MEDICAL NOTE, INC.—See Aflac Incorporated; *U.S. Public*, pg. 57

MEDICAL ONCOLOGY ASSOCIATES, LLC—See HCA Healthcare, Inc.; *U.S. Public*, pg. 1002

MEDICAL SERVICES OF AMERICA, INC.; *U.S. Private*, pg. 2655

MEDICINA NOVE ZAMKY S.R.O.—See Centene Corporation; *U.S. Public*, pg. 470

MEDICS EMERGENCY SERVICES OF PALM BEACH COUNTY, INC.—See KKR & Co. Inc.; *U.S. Public*, pg. 1250

MEDLIANCE, LLC—See Nautic Partners, LLC; *U.S. Private*, pg. 2871

MEDPAGE TODAY, LLC—See Ziff Davis, Inc.; *U.S. Public*, pg. 2404

MEDRAVE SOFTWARE AB—See Carasent ASA; *Int'l*, pg. 1319

MEDRAVE SOFTWARE AS—See Carasent ASA; *Int'l*, pg. 1319

MEDSTREAM ANESTHESIA PLLC—See Assured Guaranty Ltd.; *Int'l*, pg. 650

MEDTECH SERVICES OF DADE, INC.—See Apollo Global Management, Inc.; *U.S. Public*, pg. 157

MED TECH SERVICES OF PALM BEACH, INC.—See Apollo Global Management, Inc.; *U.S. Public*, pg. 157

MED. TECH. SERVICES OF SOUTH FLORIDA, INC.—See Apollo Global Management, Inc.; *U.S. Public*, pg. 157

MFI FEO, LLC—See Platform Partners LLC; *U.S. Private*, pg. 3200

MERCK CANADA INC.—See Merck & Co., Inc.; *U.S. Public*, pg. 1419

MERCK SHARP & DOHME (AUSTRALIA) PTY. LIMITED—See Merck & Co., Inc.; *U.S. Public*, pg. 1419

MERCK SHARP & DOHME DE ESPANA SAU—See Merck & Co., Inc.; *U.S. Public*, pg. 1420

METHODIST HOSPITAL FOUNDATION; *U.S. Private*, pg. 2684

METHODIST HOSPITAL OF SOUTHERN CALIFORNIA; *U.S. Private*, pg. 2684

METHODIST INPATIENT MANAGEMENT GROUP—See HCA Healthcare, Inc.; *U.S. Public*, pg. 1002

METHODIST INPATIENT MANAGEMENT GROUP—See Methodist Healthcare Ministries of South Texas, Inc.; *U.S. Private*, pg. 2683

METODIKA AB—See Carasent ASA; *Int'l*, pg. 1319

THE METROHEALTH FOUNDATION, INC.; *U.S. Private*, pg. 4078

METROPOLITAN JEWISH HEALTH SYSTEM; *U.S. Private*, pg. 2688

METROPOLITAN METHODIST HOSPITAL, A METHODIST HOSPITAL FACILITY—See HCA Healthcare, Inc.; *U.S. Public*, pg. 1002

METROPOLITAN METHODIST HOSPITAL, A METHODIST HOSPITAL FACILITY—See Methodist Healthcare Ministries of South Texas, Inc.; *U.S. Private*, pg. 2684

METRO THERAPY, INC.—See Revelstoke Capital Partners LLC; *U.S. Private*, pg. 3413

METROWEST HOMECARE & HOSPICE, LLC—See Tenet Healthcare Corporation; *U.S. Public*, pg. 2004

MIDWEST PALLIATIVE & HOSPICE CARECENTER; *U.S. Private*, pg. 2722

MILLENIUM HOME HEALTH CARE, INC.—See Formation Capital, LLC; *U.S. Private*, pg. 1571

MILLICANSOLUTIONS, LLC—See AMN Healthcare Services, Inc.; *U.S. Public*, pg. 125

MILLS MEDICAL PRACTICES, LLC—See Apollo Global Management, Inc.; *U.S. Public*, pg. 157

MIRACLE CITY HOSPICE, LLC—See Addus HomeCare Corporation; *U.S. Public*, pg. 40

MISSISSIPPI HOMECARE, LLC—See UnitedHealth Group Incorporated; *U.S. Public*, pg. 2246

MISSOURI HOMECARE LLC—See UnitedHealth Group Incorporated; *U.S. Public*, pg. 2246

MIZELL MEMORIAL HOSPITAL HOMECARE, LLC—See UnitedHealth Group Incorporated; *U.S. Public*, pg. 2246

MMC ENCOMPASS HEALTH REHABILITATION HOSPITAL, LLC—See Encompass Health Corporation; *U.S. Public*, pg. 758

MMM HEALTHCARE, LLC—See Elevance Health, Inc.; *U.S. Public*, pg. 730

MOBILITY AUSTRALIA PTY LTD.—See Madison Dearborn Partners, LLC; *U.S. Private*, pg. 2540

MOLINA HEALTHCARE OF CALIFORNIA—See Molina Healthcare, Inc.; *U.S. Public*, pg. 1458

MOLINA HEALTHCARE OF FLORIDA, INC.—See Molina Healthcare, Inc.; *U.S. Public*, pg. 1459

MOLINA HEALTHCARE OF KENTUCKY, INC.—See Molina Healthcare, Inc.; *U.S. Public*, pg. 1459

MOLINA HEALTHCARE OF MISSISSIPPI, INC.—See Molina Healthcare, Inc.; *U.S. Public*, pg. 1459

MOLINA HEALTHCARE OF NEVADA, INC.—See Molina Healthcare, Inc.; *U.S. Public*, pg. 1459

MOLINA HEALTHCARE OF TEXAS INSURANCE COMPANY—See Molina Healthcare, Inc.; *U.S. Public*, pg. 1459

MOLINA HEALTHCARE OF VIRGINIA, INC.—See Molina Healthcare, Inc.; *U.S. Public*, pg. 1459

MOLINA HEALTHCARE OF WISCONSIN, INC.—See Molina Healthcare, Inc.; *U.S. Public*, pg. 1459

MONTGOMERY HOSPICE, INC.; *U.S. Private*, pg. 2777

MONTROSE MEMORIAL HOSPITAL; *U.S. Private*, pg. 2777

MORGANTOWN HOSPICE, LLC.—See Amedisys, Inc.; *U.S. Public*, pg. 94

MORNING GLORY HEALTHCARE, INC.—See The Ensign Group, Inc.; *U.S. Public*, pg. 2071

MOSAIC LIFE CARE; *U.S. Private*, pg. 2792

MOSSO'S MEDICAL SUPPLY COMPANY; *U.S. Private*, pg. 2795

MOTION PT GROUP, INC.—See Confluent Health, LLC; *U.S. Private*, pg. 1013

MOUNTAIN DIVISION - CVH, LLC—See HCA Healthcare, Inc.; *U.S. Public*, pg. 1003

MOUNTAINEER HOMECARE, LLC—See UnitedHealth Group Incorporated; *U.S. Public*, pg. 2246

MOUNTAINSTAR CARE PARTNERS ACO, LLC—See HCA Healthcare, Inc.; *U.S. Public*, pg. 1003

MOUNTAINSTAR CARE PARTNERS, LLC—See HCA Healthcare, Inc.; *U.S. Public*, pg. 1003

MOUNTAINSTAR SPECIALTY SERVICES, LLC—See HCA Healthcare, Inc.; *U.S. Public*, pg. 1003

MOUNTAIN VIEW HOSPITAL—See HCA Healthcare, Inc.; *U.S. Public*, pg. 1003

MOUNTAIN VIEW PHYSICIAN PRACTICE, INC.—See Rennova Health, Inc.; *U.S. Public*, pg. 1783

MOUNTAINVIEW REGIONAL HOME HEALTH—See Community Health Systems, Inc.; *U.S. Public*, pg. 555

MOUNTAIN WEST ENDOSCOPY CENTER—See HCA Healthcare, Inc.; *U.S. Public*, pg. 991

MOUNT NITTANY MEDICAL CENTER; *U.S. Private*, pg. 2798

THE MPB GROUP, LLC—See Waste Management, Inc.; *U.S. Public*, pg. 2332

MR POPRAD S.R.O.—See Centene Corporation; *U.S. Public*, pg. 469

MR ZILINA S.R.O.—See Centene Corporation; *U.S. Public*, pg. 469

MSP RECOVERY, INC.; *U.S. Public*, pg. 1484

MUNROE REGIONAL HOMECARE, LLC—See UnitedHealth Group Incorporated; *U.S. Public*, pg. 2246

MVZ SOBERNHEIM GMBH—See Asklepios Kliniken GmbH & Co. KGaA; *Int'l*, pg. 623

MY HEALTH DIRECT, INC.—See Experian plc; *Int'l*, pg. 2588

MYNEXUS, INC.—See Elevance Health, Inc.; *U.S. Public*, pg. 731

MYRTLE BEACH REHABILITATION HOSPITAL, LLC—See Encompass Health Corporation; *U.S. Public*, pg. 758

MYRTLE HILLIARD DAVIS COMPREHENSIVE HEALTH CENTERS, INC.; *U.S. Private*, pg. 2826

NASHVILLE GASTROINTESTINAL SPECIALISTS,

LLC—See KKR & Co. Inc.; *U.S. Public*, pg. 1250
NATIONAL HEALTHCARE CORPORATION—See National HealthCare Corporation; *U.S. Public*, pg. 1496
NATIONAL HEALTHCARE CORPORATION—See National HealthCare Corporation; *U.S. Public*, pg. 1496
NATIONAL HEALTHCARE LOGISTICS, INC.; *U.S. Public*, pg. 1497
NATIONAL HEALTH INFUSION—See Option Care Health, Inc.; *U.S. Public*, pg. 1610
NATIONAL HOME HEALTH CARE CORP.—See Blue Wolf Capital Partners LLC; *U.S. Private*, pg. 595
NATIONAL MARROW DONOR PROGRAM, INC.; *U.S. Private*, pg. 2859
NAVARRO HOSPITAL, L.P.—See Community Health Systems, Inc.; *U.S. Public*, pg. 552
NCCN FOUNDATION—See National Comprehensive Cancer Network; *U.S. Private*, pg. 2851
NCH MANAGEMENT SYSTEMS, INC.—See Evolent Health, Inc.; *U.S. Public*, pg. 804
NEW ENGLAND HOME CARE, INC.—See Blue Wolf Capital Partners LLC; *U.S. Private*, pg. 595
NEW ENGLAND HOME THERAPIES INC.—See Option Care Health, Inc.; *U.S. Public*, pg. 1610
NEW YORK HEALTH CARE, INC.; *U.S. Private*, pg. 2909
NEXERA, LLC—See Premier, Inc.; *U.S. Public*, pg. 1715
NEXTTCARE PTY LTD—See Adamantem Capital Management Pty Limited; *Int'l*, pg. 124
NHC FARRAGUT MEMORY CARE, LLC—See National HealthCare Corporation; *U.S. Public*, pg. 1495
NHC HEALTHCARE/ATHENS, LLC—See National HealthCare Corporation; *U.S. Public*, pg. 1495
NHC HEALTHCARE/BLUFFTON, LLC—See National HealthCare Corporation; *U.S. Public*, pg. 1495
NHC HEALTHCARE-CHARLESTON, LLC—See National HealthCare Corporation; *U.S. Public*, pg. 1495
NHC HEALTHCARE/CLINTON, LLC—See National HealthCare Corporation; *U.S. Public*, pg. 1495
NHC HEALTHCARE/COLUMBIA, LLC—See National HealthCare Corporation; *U.S. Public*, pg. 1495
NHC HEALTHCARE/JOPLIN, LLC—See National HealthCare Corporation; *U.S. Public*, pg. 1495
NHC HEALTHCARE/LEXINGTON, LLC—See National HealthCare Corporation; *U.S. Public*, pg. 1496
NHC HEALTHCARE/MILAN, LLC—See National HealthCare Corporation; *U.S. Public*, pg. 1496
NHC HEALTHCARE/NORTH AUGUSTA, LLC—See National HealthCare Corporation; *U.S. Public*, pg. 1496
NHC HEALTHCARE/ROSSVILLE, LLC—See National HealthCare Corporation; *U.S. Public*, pg. 1496
NHC HEALTHCARE/SOMERVILLE, LLC—See National HealthCare Corporation; *U.S. Public*, pg. 1496
NHC HEALTHCARE-SPRINGFIELD MISSOURI, LLC—See National HealthCare Corporation; *U.S. Public*, pg. 1495
NHC HEALTHCARE/ST. CHARLES, LLC—See National HealthCare Corporation; *U.S. Public*, pg. 1496
NHC HOMECARE-SOUTH CAROLINA, LLC—See National HealthCare Corporation; *U.S. Public*, pg. 1496
NHC/OP, L.P.—See National HealthCare Corporation; *U.S. Public*, pg. 1496
NHC/OP, L.P.—See National HealthCare Corporation; *U.S. Public*, pg. 1496
NHC/OP, L.P.—See National HealthCare Corporation; *U.S. Public*, pg. 1496
NHC/OP, L.P.—See National HealthCare Corporation; *U.S. Public*, pg. 1496
NHC/OP, L.P.—See National HealthCare Corporation; *U.S. Public*, pg. 1496
NHC/OP, L.P.—See National HealthCare Corporation; *U.S. Public*, pg. 1496
NHC/OP, L.P.—See National HealthCare Corporation; *U.S. Public*, pg. 1496
NHC PLACE AT THE TRACE, LLC—See National HealthCare Corporation; *U.S. Public*, pg. 1496
NHC PLACE/LAKE ST. CHARLES, LLC—See National HealthCare Corporation; *U.S. Public*, pg. 1496
NHC PLACE MERRITT ISLAND, LLC—See National HealthCare Corporation; *U.S. Public*, pg. 1496
NICHIIGAKKAN CO., LTD.—See Bain Capital, LP; *U.S. Private*, pg. 442
NINE PALMS 1, LP—See Amedisys, Inc.; *U.S. Public*, pg. 94
NINE PALMS 2, LLP—See Amedisys, Inc.; *U.S. Public*, pg. 94
NO/AIDS TASK FORCE; *U.S. Private*, pg. 2932
NORTHAMPTON HOME CARE, LLC—See Community Health Systems, Inc.; *U.S. Public*, pg. 555
NORTH ARKANSAS HOMECARE—See UnitedHealth Group Incorporated; *U.S. Public*, pg. 2246
NORTH CAROLINA IN-HOME PARTNER-IV, LLC—See UnitedHealth Group Incorporated; *U.S. Public*, pg. 2246
NORTH CAROLINA IN-HOME PARTNER-V, LLC—See UnitedHealth Group Incorporated; *U.S. Public*, pg. 2246
NORTHEAST ENDOSCOPY CENTER, LLC—See KKR & Co. Inc.; *U.S. Public*, pg. 1250
NORTHEAST WASHINGTON HOME HEALTH, INC.—See UnitedHealth Group Incorporated; *U.S. Public*, pg. 2246
NORTH JERSEY GASTROENTEROLOGY & ENDOSCOPY CENTER, PA—See KKR & Co. Inc.; *U.S. Public*, pg. 1250

NORTHLAND LTACH, LLC—See Apollo Global Management, Inc.; *U.S. Public*, pg. 157
NORTHWEST ARKANSAS REHABILITATION ASSOCIATES—See Encompass Health Corporation; *U.S. Public*, pg. 758
NORTHWESTERN MEMORIAL HOME HEALTH CARE—See Northwestern Memorial HealthCare; *U.S. Private*, pg. 2963
NORTHWEST HEALTHCARE ALLIANCE, INC.—See UnitedHealth Group Incorporated; *U.S. Public*, pg. 2246
NORTHWEST PHYSICIANS, LLC—See Community Health Systems, Inc.; *U.S. Public*, pg. 555
NOVA HOME HEALTH CARE INC.—See Searchlight Capital Partners, L.P.; *U.S. Private*, pg. 3586
NOVAMED EYE SURGERY CENTER OF MARYVILLE, LLC—See Bain Capital, LP; *U.S. Private*, pg. 445
NOVAMED EYE SURGERY CENTER OF NORTH COUNTY, LLC—See Bain Capital, LP; *U.S. Private*, pg. 445
NOVANT HEALTH REHABILITATION HOSPITAL OF WINSTON-SALEM, LLC—See Encompass Health Corporation; *U.S. Public*, pg. 758
NURSE ON CALL HOME HEALTHCARE; *U.S. Private*, pg. 2973
NURSE-ON-CALL OF SOUTH FLORIDA, INC.—See Brookdale Senior Living Inc.; *U.S. Public*, pg. 395
OAK SHADOWS OF JENNINGS, LLC—See UnitedHealth Group Incorporated; *U.S. Public*, pg. 2246
OAK STREET HEALTH, INC.—See CVS Health Corporation; *U.S. Public*, pg. 616
OASIS MEDICAL SOLUTIONS LIMITED—See Veradigm Inc.; *U.S. Public*, pg. 2280
OB CARE S.R.O.—See Centene Corporation; *U.S. Public*, pg. 470
OB KLINIKA A.S.—See Centene Corporation; *U.S. Public*, pg. 470
ODYSSEY HEALTHCARE OF SOUTH TEXAS, LLC—See Apollo Global Management, Inc.; *U.S. Public*, pg. 156
OKLAHOMA SURGICARE, INC.—See HCA Healthcare, Inc.; *U.S. Public*, pg. 1005
OMNI HOME HEALTH - DISTRICT 1, LLC—See UnitedHealth Group Incorporated; *U.S. Public*, pg. 2244
OMNI HOME HEALTH - DISTRICT 4, LLC—See UnitedHealth Group Incorporated; *U.S. Public*, pg. 2244
OMNI HOME HEALTH - JACKSONVILLE, LLC—See UnitedHealth Group Incorporated; *U.S. Public*, pg. 2244
ONAFHANKELIJKE THUISZORG VLAANDEREN CVBA—See Clariane SE; *Int'l*, pg. 1643
ONE HOMECARE SOLUTIONS, LLC—See Humana, Inc.; *U.S. Public*, pg. 1070
OPEN SYSTEMS HEALTHCARE, INC.—See Centerbridge Partners, L.P.; *U.S. Private*, pg. 815
OPEN SYSTEMS HEALTHCARE, INC.—See The Vistria Group, LP; *U.S. Private*, pg. 4132
OPEROSE HEALTH LTD.—See Centene Corporation; *U.S. Public*, pg. 470
OPTAVIA (HONG KONG) LIMITED—See Medifast, Inc.; *U.S. Public*, pg. 1412
OPTAVIA, LLC—See Medifast, Inc.; *U.S. Public*, pg. 1412
OPTAVIA (SINGAPORE) PTE. LTD.—See Medifast, Inc.; *U.S. Public*, pg. 1412
OPTIMUS HEALTHCARE SERVICES, INC.; *U.S. Public*, pg. 1609
OPTION CARE ENTERPRISES, INC.—See Option Care Health, Inc.; *U.S. Public*, pg. 1610
OPTION CARE HOME HEALTH, L.L.C.—See Option Care Health, Inc.; *U.S. Public*, pg. 1610
OPTION CARE, INC.—See Option Care Health, Inc.; *U.S. Public*, pg. 1610
OPTION CARE OF NEW YORK, INC.—See Option Care Health, Inc.; *U.S. Public*, pg. 1610
OPTION HEALTH, LTD.—See Option Care Health, Inc.; *U.S. Public*, pg. 1610
OPTIONS SERVICES, INC.—See Addus HomeCare Corporation; *U.S. Public*, pg. 40
OPTUM INFUSION SERVICES 301, LP—See UnitedHealth Group Incorporated; *U.S. Public*, pg. 2243
OPTUM PERKS LLC—See UnitedHealth Group Incorporated; *U.S. Public*, pg. 2243
ORGANON GMBH—See Organon & Co.; *U.S. Public*, pg. 1616
ORIGIO, INC.—See The Cooper Companies, Inc.; *U.S. Public*, pg. 2066
ORMCO EUROPE BV—See Danaher Corporation; *U.S. Public*, pg. 629
ORSINI NURSING AGENCY, INC.; *U.S. Private*, pg. 3045
OSF HEALTHCARE SYSTEM—See The Sisters of the Third Order of St. Francis; *U.S. Private*, pg. 4118
OTT HYDROMET CORP.—See Danaher Corporation; *U.S. Public*, pg. 629
OUTREACH HEALTH SERVICES OF NORTH TEXAS, LLC—See Apollo Global Management, Inc.; *U.S. Public*, pg. 157
OWENS & MINOR GLOBAL SERVICES—See Owens & Minor, Inc.; *U.S. Public*, pg. 1626
P4 HEALTHCARE, LLC—See Cardinal Health, Inc.; *U.S. Public*, pg. 434
PARTNERS HOME CARE INC.—See Partners HealthCare System, Inc.; *U.S. Private*, pg. 3101

PARTNERS IN CARE; *U.S. Private*, pg. 3102
PARTNERS IN HEALTHCARE, INC.; *U.S. Private*, pg. 3102
PATHWAYS; *U.S. Private*, pg. 3106
PATIENT CARE, INC.—See UnitedHealth Group Incorporated; *U.S. Public*, pg. 2244
PATIENT CARE MEDICAL SERVICES, INC.—See UnitedHealth Group Incorporated; *U.S. Public*, pg. 2244
PATIENT CARE NEW JERSEY, INC.—See UnitedHealth Group Incorporated; *U.S. Public*, pg. 2244
PATIENT CARE PENNSYLVANIA, INC.—See UnitedHealth Group Incorporated; *U.S. Public*, pg. 2244
PATIENT'S CHOICE HOSPICE, LLC—See UnitedHealth Group Incorporated; *U.S. Public*, pg. 2246
PATIENTYS SAS—See Concentrix Corporation; *U.S. Public*, pg. 565
PD-RX PHARMACEUTICALS, INC.; *U.S. Public*, pg. 1658
PEARL STREET HEALTHCARE CENTER, LLC—See National HealthCare Corporation; *U.S. Public*, pg. 1496
PEDIATRIC HOME RESPIRATORY SERVICES, LLC—See InTandem Capital Partners, LLC; *U.S. Public*, pg. 2097
PEDIATRIC SERVICES OF AMERICA, INC.—See Bain Capital, LP; *U.S. Private*, pg. 439
PEDIATRICS OF GREATER HOUSTON, PLLC—See HCA Healthcare, Inc.; *U.S. Public*, pg. 1006
PENNSYLVANIA HEALTH & WELLNESS, INC.—See Centene Corporation; *U.S. Public*, pg. 470
PENTEC HEALTH, INC.—See Wellspring Capital Management LLC; *U.S. Private*, pg. 4477
PEOPLEFIRST HOMECARE & HOSPICE OF INDIANA, LLC—See Apollo Global Management, Inc.; *U.S. Public*, pg. 157
PEOPLEFIRST HOMECARE & HOSPICE OF OHIO, LLC—See Apollo Global Management, Inc.; *U.S. Public*, pg. 157
PEOPLEFIRST VIRGINIA, LLC—See Apollo Global Management, Inc.; *U.S. Public*, pg. 157
PEOPLESCOUT LIMITED—See TrueBlue, Inc.; *U.S. Public*, pg. 2198
PERSONAL-TOUCH HOME CARE, INC.; *U.S. Private*, pg. 3155
PERSONAL TOUCH HOME CARE OF BALTIMORE INC.—See Personal-Touch Home Care, Inc.; *U.S. Private*, pg. 3155
PERSONAL TOUCH HOME CARE OF VA. INC.—See Personal-Touch Home Care, Inc.; *U.S. Private*, pg. 3155
PFLEGEN & WOHNEN HAMBURG GMBH—See Deutsche Wohnen SE; *Int'l*, pg. 2085
PHARMDATA S.R.O.—See Walgreens Boots Alliance, Inc.; *U.S. Public*, pg. 2322
PHOENIX CHILDREN'S FOUNDATION; *U.S. Private*, pg. 3172
PHOENIX EMERGENCY SERVICES OF INVERNESS, LLC—See KKR & Co. Inc.; *U.S. Public*, pg. 1250
PHONIX-HAUS AM STEINSGRABEN SENIOREN- UND PFLEGEZENTRUM GMBH—See Clariane SE; *Int'l*, pg. 1643
PHONIX - HAUS ROGGENBERG - PFLEGEHEIM GMBH—See Clariane SE; *Int'l*, pg. 1643
PHONIX-HAUS ROSMARIN SENIOREN- UND PFLEGEZENTRUM GMBH—See Clariane SE; *Int'l*, pg. 1643
PHONIX - HAUS SILBERDISTEL - ALTEN- U.PFLEGEHEIM GMBH—See Clariane SE; *Int'l*, pg. 1643
PHONIX-SENIORENRESIDENZ AM TEICHBERG GMBH—See Clariane SE; *Int'l*, pg. 1643
PHONIX SENIORENRESIDENZ ELSTERTALBLICK GMBH—See Clariane SE; *Int'l*, pg. 1643
PHONIX-SENIORENZENTRUM AHORNHOF GMBH—See Clariane SE; *Int'l*, pg. 1643
PHONIX-SENIORENZENTRUM AM BODENSEERING GMBH—See Clariane SE; *Int'l*, pg. 1643
PHONIX-SENIORENZENTRUM AM MUPPBERG GMBH—See Clariane SE; *Int'l*, pg. 1643
PHONIX-SENIORENZENTRUM AM SCHLOSSTEICH GMBH—See Clariane SE; *Int'l*, pg. 1643
PHONIX-SENIORENZENTRUM EVERGREEN GMBH—See Clariane SE; *Int'l*, pg. 1643
PHONIX-SENIORENZENTRUM EVERGREEN MAXHUTTE GMBH—See Clariane SE; *Int'l*, pg. 1644
PHONIX-SENIORENZENTRUM GARTENSTADT GMBH—See Clariane SE; *Int'l*, pg. 1644
PHONIX - SENIORENZENTRUM GRAF TILLY GMBH—See Clariane SE; *Int'l*, pg. 1643
PHONIX-SENIORENZENTRUM HERZOG ALBRECHT GMBH—See Clariane SE; *Int'l*, pg. 1644
PHONIX - SENIORENZENTRUM HESSENALLEE GMBH—See Clariane SE; *Int'l*, pg. 1643
PHONIX-SENIORENZENTRUM IM BRUHL GMBH—See Clariane SE; *Int'l*, pg. 1644
PHONIX-SENIORENZENTRUM MAINPARKSEE GMBH—See Clariane SE; *Int'l*, pg. 1644
PHONIX-SENIORENZENTRUM NEUPERLACH GMBH—See Clariane SE; *Int'l*, pg. 1644
PHONIX-SENIORENZENTRUM ST HEDWIG GMBH—See Clariane SE; *Int'l*, pg. 1644
PHONIX-SENIORENZENTRUM TAUNUSBLICK GMBH—See Clariane SE; *Int'l*, pg. 1644

N.A.I.C.S. INDEX

621610 — HOME HEALTH CARE SE...

PHONIX-SENIORENZENTRUM ULMENHOF GMBH—See Clariane SE; *Int'l*, pg. 1644
PHONIX-SENIORENZENTRUM ZWEI LINDEN GMBH—See Clariane SE; *Int'l*, pg. 1644
PHONIX SOZIALZENTRUM WINDSBACH GMBH—See Clariane SE; *Int'l*, pg. 1643
PHYSICIANS DEVELOPMENT GROUP LLC; *U.S. Private*, pg. 3175
PHYSMED INC.—See Pharos Capital Group, LLC; *U.S. Private*, pg. 3166
PICAYUNE HOMECARE, LLC—See UnitedHealth Group Incorporated; *U.S. Public*, pg. 2246
PIRTAKOTI OY—See Humana AB; *Int'l*, pg. 3530
THE PLATINUM MEDICAL CENTRE—See HCA Healthcare, Inc.; *U.S. Public*, pg. 1012
PMDCA, LLC—See The Ensign Group, Inc.; *U.S. Public*, pg. 2071
POORT VAN WIJK BV—See Clariane SE; *Int'l*, pg. 1644
PRECISION HEALTH CARE SERVICES LIMITED—See China Biotech Services Holdings Limited; *Int'l*, pg. 1487
PREFERRED HOME HEALTH, L.P.—See Encompass Health Corporation; *U.S. Public*, pg. 758
PREMIER HEALTH CARE SERVICES, LLC—See Blackstone Inc.; *U.S. Public*, pg. 359
PREMIER HEALTHCARE SOLUTIONS INC—See Premier, Inc.; *U.S. Public*, pg. 1715
PREMIER PHYSICIAN SERVICES, INC.—See Blackstone Inc.; *U.S. Public*, pg. 359
PRESBYTERIAN HEALTHCARE FOUNDATION; *U.S. Private*, pg. 3253
PRESTON MEMORIAL HOMECARE, LLC—See UnitedHealth Group Incorporated; *U.S. Public*, pg. 2246
PRIMARY CARE AT HOME OF LOUISIANA II, LLC—See UnitedHealth Group Incorporated; *U.S. Public*, pg. 2246
PRIMARY CARE AT HOME OF MARYLAND, LLC—See UnitedHealth Group Incorporated; *U.S. Public*, pg. 2246
PRIMARY HEALTH, INC.—See HCA Healthcare, Inc.; *U.S. Public*, pg. 1006
PRINCETON COMMUNITY HOMECARE, LLC—See UnitedHealth Group Incorporated; *U.S. Public*, pg. 2246
PRIORITY HOME HEALTH CARE, INC.—See Addus HomeCare Corporation; *U.S. Public*, pg. 40
PRIVIA HEALTH GROUP, INC.; *U.S. Public*, pg. 1722
PROCTER & GAMBLE NEUILLY S.A.S.—See The Procter & Gamble Company; *U.S. Public*, pg. 2121
PROFESSIONAL HEALTHCARE RESOURCES, INC.; *U.S. Private*, pg. 3275
PROFESSIONAL HOME CARE SERVICES, INC.—See Option Care Health, Inc.; *U.S. Public*, pg. 1610
PROFESSIONAL MEDICAL TRANSPORT, INC.—See KKR & Co. Inc.; *U.S. Public*, pg. 1252
PROFESSIONAL RELIABLE NURSING SERVICE INC.—See Addus HomeCare Corporation; *U.S. Public*, pg. 40
PROGRESSIVE HEALTH GROUP, LLC; *U.S. Private*, pg. 3279
PROGRESS MEDICAL A.S.—See Centene Corporation; *U.S. Public*, pg. 470
PROGYNY, INC.; *U.S. Public*, pg. 1726
PRO RTG S.R.O—See Centene Corporation; *U.S. Public*, pg. 470
PROTOM INTERNATIONAL, INC.; *U.S. Private*, pg. 3290
PSI PREMIER SPECIALTIES, INC.; *U.S. Private*, pg. 3297
PSYCHIATRY SERVICES OF OSCEOLA, LLC—See HCA Healthcare, Inc.; *U.S. Public*, pg. 1006
PT. AETNA GLOBAL BENEFITS INDONESIA—See CVS Health Corporation; *U.S. Public*, pg. 616
PT FMC INDONESIA—See Fresenius Medical Care AG; *Int'l*, pg. 2777
PURCHASE CLINIC, LLC—See HCA Healthcare, Inc.; *U.S. Public*, pg. 1006
PURPOSECARE HOMECARE LLC—See Lorient Capital Management LLC; *U.S. Private*, pg. 2495
QOLEAD, LIMITED—See Dai-ichi Life Holdings, Inc.; *Int'l*, pg. 1918
QUALCARE; *U.S. Private*, pg. 3317
QUALITY CARE SERVICES LIMITED—See Graphite Capital Management LLP; *Int'l*, pg. 3060
QUALITY CARE SITTER SERVICE, INC.; *U.S. Private*, pg. 3318
QUANTUM CARE (UK) LIMITED—See Acadia Healthcare Company, Inc.; *U.S. Public*, pg. 29
QUEEN CITY HOSPICE, LLC—See Addus HomeCare Corporation; *U.S. Public*, pg. 40
QUILLEN REHABILITATION HOSPITAL OF JOHNSON CITY, LLC—See Encompass Health Corporation; *U.S. Public*, pg. 758
RADIOLOGY ASSOCIATES OF HOLLYWOOD, INC.—See KKR & Co. Inc.; *U.S. Public*, pg. 1250
RADIOMETER K.K.—See Danaher Corporation; *U.S. Public*, pg. 631
RAYMORE MEDICAL GROUP, LLC—See HCA Healthcare, Inc.; *U.S. Public*, pg. 1007
READYNURSE STAFFING SERVICES—See ShiftMed, LLC; *U.S. Private*, pg. 3636
RED BUD HOME CARE SERVICES, LLC—See Community Health Systems, Inc.; *U.S. Public*, pg. 556

REEVES-SAIN DRUG STORE, INC.—See Fred's Inc.; *U.S. Public*, pg. 884
REHABILITATION HOSPITAL OF BRISTOL, LLC—See Encompass Health Corporation; *U.S. Public*, pg. 758
REM OHIO II, LLC—See Centerbridge Partners, L.P.; *U.S. Private*, pg. 814
RENAVATIO HEALTHCARE COMMUNICATIONS LLC; *U.S. Private*, pg. 3397
RESIDENCE AU BON VIEUX TEMPS PLC—See Clariane SE; *Int'l*, pg. 1644
RESIDENCE AUX DEUX PARCS SA—See Clariane SE; *Int'l*, pg. 1644
RESIDENCE LA PASSERINETTE SA—See Clariane SE; *Int'l*, pg. 1644
RESIDENCE LE PROGRES PLC—See Clariane SE; *Int'l*, pg. 1644
RESIDENCE MELOPEE PLC—See Clariane SE; *Int'l*, pg. 1644
RESIDENCE REINE ASTRID SA—See Clariane SE; *Int'l*, pg. 1644
RESIDENCE RY DU CHEVREUIL SPRL—See Clariane SE; *Int'l*, pg. 1644
RESIDENCE SEIGNEURIE DU VAL SA—See Clariane SE; *Int'l*, pg. 1644
RESIDENTIAL HOSPICE, LLC—See Graham Holdings Company; *U.S. Public*, pg. 956
RESIDENTIE BONEPUT PLC—See Clariane SE; *Int'l*, pg. 1644
RESIDENTIE EDELWEIS PLC—See Clariane SE; *Int'l*, pg. 1644
RESIDENTIE PALOKE NV—See Clariane SE; *Int'l*, pg. 1644
RESIDENTIE PRINSENPARK NV—See Clariane SE; *Int'l*, pg. 1644
RESIDENZA VILLA CARLA SRL—See Clariane SE; *Int'l*, pg. 1644
RESPIRATORY CARE AFRICA (PTY) LTD—See Ascendis Health Limited; *Int'l*, pg. 601
RESTON SURGERY CENTER—See HCA Healthcare, Inc.; *U.S. Public*, pg. 1007
RESTORE REHAB SERVICES, LLC; *U.S. Private*, pg. 3410
REVINT SOLUTIONS—See New Mountain Capital, LLC; *U.S. Private*, pg. 2904
RHHC LLC—See Robert Half Inc.; *U.S. Public*, pg. 1803
RICHARDSON MEDICAL CENTER HOMECARE, LLC—See UnitedHealth Group Incorporated; *U.S. Public*, pg. 2246
RICHMOND HOME NEED SERVICES INC; *U.S. Private*, pg. 3430
RIDGEVIEW MEDICAL CENTER; *U.S. Private*, pg. 3433
RIGHT AT HOME, INC.; *U.S. Private*, pg. 3435
RIVER DRIVE SURGERY CENTER, LLC—See KKR & Co. Inc.; *U.S. Public*, pg. 1250
RIVERWALK HEALTHCARE, INC.—See The Ensign Group, Inc.; *U.S. Public*, pg. 2072
RLDATIX LIMITED—See TA Associates, Inc.; *U.S. Private*, pg. 3917
ROANE HOMECARE, LLC—See UnitedHealth Group Incorporated; *U.S. Public*, pg. 2247
ROCHESTER PRIMARY CARE NETWORK, INC.; *U.S. Private*, pg. 3463
ROCKAWAY HOME ATTENDANT SERVICES INC.; *U.S. Private*, pg. 3465
ROCKY MOUNTAIN CARE; *U.S. Private*, pg. 3468
ROOIERHEIDE NV—See Clariane SE; *Int'l*, pg. 1644
ROTECH HEALTHCARE, INC.; *U.S. Private*, pg. 3486
RSA FRATESOLE SRL—See Clariane SE; *Int'l*, pg. 1644
RUSK REHABILITATION CENTER, LLC—See Encompass Health Corporation; *U.S. Public*, pg. 759
RUSTOORD DE VLAAMSE ARDENNEN LLC—See Clariane SE; *Int'l*, pg. 1644
RVT DELLEBRON BVBA—See Clariane SE; *Int'l*, pg. 1644
SAAD'S MEDICAL MANAGEMENT INC.—See Saad's Healthcare Services, Inc.; *U.S. Private*, pg. 3519
SAGEBRUSH HEALTHCARE, INC.—See The Ensign Group, Inc.; *U.S. Public*, pg. 2072
SALEM AREA VISITING NURSE ASSOCIATION; *U.S. Private*, pg. 3531
SALEM HOME CARE, LLC—See UnitedHealth Group Incorporated; *U.S. Public*, pg. 2247
SALEM HOME CARE SERVICES, LLC—See Community Health Systems, Inc.; *U.S. Public*, pg. 556
SALEM SURGERY CENTER, LIMITED PARTNERSHIP—See HCA Healthcare, Inc.; *U.S. Public*, pg. 1008
SAMARITAN HEALTHCARE & HOSPICE; *U.S. Private*, pg. 3536
SAND LILY HEALTHCARE, INC.—See The Ensign Group, Inc.; *U.S. Public*, pg. 2072
SAN JOAQUIN GENERAL HOSPITAL; *U.S. Private*, pg. 3541
SANTA BARBARA SPECIALTY PHARMACY, LLC—See Elevance Health, Inc.; *U.S. Public*, pg. 730
SANTA ROSA CONSULTING, INC.; *U.S. Private*, pg. 3547
SAUFLON CL LTD—See The Cooper Companies, Inc.; *U.S. Public*, pg. 2066
SCHAUINSLAND PFLEGEBETRIEB GMBH—See Clariane SE; *Int'l*, pg. 1644

SCOTT-WILSON, INC.—See UnitedHealth Group Incorporated; *U.S. Public*, pg. 2244
SEGESTA SPA—See Clariane SE; *Int'l*, pg. 1644
SEIKATSU KAGAKU UN-EI CO., LTD.—See Haseko Corporation; *Int'l*, pg. 3283
SENIORBRIDGE CARE MANAGEMENT, INC.—See Humana, Inc.; *U.S. Public*, pg. 1070
SENIORBRIDGE FAMILY COMPANIES, INC.—See Humana, Inc.; *U.S. Public*, pg. 1070
SENIORBRIDGE FAMILY COMPANIES (NY), INC.—See Humana, Inc.; *U.S. Public*, pg. 1070
SENIORBRIDGE-FLORIDA, LLC—See Humana, Inc.; *U.S. Public*, pg. 1070
SENIOREN-DOMIZIL FAMILIE WOHNSIEDLER GMBH—See Clariane SE; *Int'l*, pg. 1644
SENIORENPFLEGE HASSLOCH GMBH—See Clariane SE; *Int'l*, pg. 1644
SENIORENRESIDENZ DETTELBACH GMBH—See Clariane SE; *Int'l*, pg. 1644
SENIOREN- UND FACHPFLEGEZENTRUM GMBH—See Clariane SE; *Int'l*, pg. 1644
SENIORENWOHNANLAGE OETTINGEN GMBH—See Clariane SE; *Int'l*, pg. 1644
SENIORHEIM AN DER PAAR GMBH—See Clariane SE; *Int'l*, pg. 1644
SENIOR HOME CARE, INC.—See Apollo Global Management, Inc.; *U.S. Public*, pg. 157
SENIORIE DE MARETAK NV—See Clariane SE; *Int'l*, pg. 1644
SENIOR LIVING GROUP NV—See Clariane SE; *Int'l*, pg. 1644
SENIORS HOME CARE LLC; *U.S. Private*, pg. 3607
SENTINEL HEALTHCARE SERVICES, LLC—See KKR & Co. Inc.; *U.S. Public*, pg. 1250
SENTIVO EITORF GMBH—See Clariane SE; *Int'l*, pg. 1644
SENTIVO MONCHENGLADBACH GMBH—See Clariane SE; *Int'l*, pg. 1644
SENTIVO RHONDORF GMBH—See Clariane SE; *Int'l*, pg. 1644
SENTIVO SOLINGEN GMBH—See Clariane SE; *Int'l*, pg. 1644
SEQUOIA HOME HEALTH—See The Ensign Group, Inc.; *U.S. Public*, pg. 2072
SERENITY PALLIATIVE CARE & HOSPICE, LLC—See Addus HomeCare Corporation; *U.S. Public*, pg. 40
SHANGHAI LIONTOWN HOSPITAL LOGISTICS MANAGEMENT CO., LTD—See Anxian Yuan China Holdings Limited; *Int'l*, pg. 486
SHIFTMED, LLC; *U.S. Private*, pg. 3636
SHIFTWISE, INC.—See AMN Healthcare Services, Inc.; *U.S. Public*, pg. 125
S-H OPCO CARLSBAD, LLC—See Brookdale Senior Living Inc.; *U.S. Public*, pg. 395
S-H OPCO CLIFF VIEW, LLC—See Brookdale Senior Living Inc.; *U.S. Public*, pg. 395
S-H OPCO COTTAGE VILLAGE, LLC—See Brookdale Senior Living Inc.; *U.S. Public*, pg. 395
S-H OPCO DARTMOUTH VILLAGE, LLC—See Brookdale Senior Living Inc.; *U.S. Public*, pg. 395
S-H OPCO FOX RIVER, LLC—See Brookdale Senior Living Inc.; *U.S. Public*, pg. 395
S-H OPCO LINCOLN HEIGHTS, LLC—See Brookdale Senior Living Inc.; *U.S. Public*, pg. 395
S-H OPCO NORTHPARK PLACE, LLC—See Brookdale Senior Living Inc.; *U.S. Public*, pg. 395
S-H OPCO SPICEWOOD SPRINGS, LLC—See Brookdale Senior Living Inc.; *U.S. Public*, pg. 395
S-H OPCO SPRING CREEK GARDENS, LLC—See Brookdale Senior Living Inc.; *U.S. Public*, pg. 395
S-H OPCO SPRING POINTE, LLC—See Brookdale Senior Living Inc.; *U.S. Public*, pg. 395
S-H OPCO SPRING VILLAGE, LLC—See Brookdale Senior Living Inc.; *U.S. Public*, pg. 395
S-H OPCO WILSON MOUNTAIN, LLC—See Brookdale Senior Living Inc.; *U.S. Public*, pg. 395
SIBLEY NURSING PERSONNEL SERVICE, INC.—See The Lifetime Healthcare Companies; *U.S. Private*, pg. 4070
SIGNALLAMP HEALTH INC.—See Sunstone Partners Management LLC; *U.S. Private*, pg. 3873
SILAS CREEK MANOR—See Apollo Global Management, Inc.; *U.S. Public*, pg. 157
SILVER LAKE HEALTHCARE, INC.—See The Ensign Group, Inc.; *U.S. Public*, pg. 2072
SILVERSHEET INC.—See AMN Healthcare Services, Inc.; *U.S. Public*, pg. 125
SILVER STATE ACO, LLC—See Apollo Global Management, Inc.; *U.S. Public*, pg. 157
SILVERSTREAM HEALTH CENTRE LIMITED—See Green Cross Health Limited; *Int'l*, pg. 3070
SMERALDA RSA DI PADRU SRL—See Clariane SE; *Int'l*, pg. 1644
SNC-LAVALIN HEALTH—See AtkinsRealis Group Inc.; *Int'l*, pg. 673
SOCIAL CONCERN COMMUNITY DEVELOPMENT CORP; *U.S. Private*, pg. 3703
SOLIS MAMMOGRAPHY AT ST. DAVID'S ROUND ROCK MEDICAL CENTER, LLC—See HCA Healthcare, Inc.; *U.S. Public*, pg. 1009

621610 — HOME HEALTH CARE SE...

SOLUTIONHEALTH; *U.S. Private*, pg. 3711
SOTERA HEALTH COMPANY; *U.S. Public*, pg. 1909
SOUTHEAST ALABAMA HOMECARE, LLC—See UnitedHealth Group Incorporated; *U.S. Public*, pg. 2247
SOUTHERN CHARM HEALTHCARE, INC.—See The Ensign Group, Inc.; *U.S. Public*, pg. 2071
SOUTHERN HOME CARE SERVICES, INC.-MICHIGAN—See KKR & Co. Inc.; *U.S. Public*, pg. 1263
SOUTHERN HOME CARE SERVICES, INC.—See KKR & Co. Inc.; *U.S. Public*, pg. 1262
SOUTHERN NEVADA HOME HEALTH CARE, INC.—See The Nathan Adelson Hospice; *U.S. Private*, pg. 4081
SOUTHERN PINES HEALTHCARE LLC—See The Pennant Group, Inc.; *U.S. Public*, pg. 2118
SOUTHERN UTAH HOME OXYGEN—See Apollo Global Management, Inc.; *U.S. Public*, pg. 157
SOUTH SHORE HOME HEALTH SERVICES, INC.—See Addus HomeCare Corporation; *U.S. Public*, pg. 40
SOUTHWEST ARKANSAS HOMECARE, LLC—See UnitedHealth Group Incorporated; *U.S. Public*, pg. 2247
SOZIALKONZEPT BARBARAHOF GMBH—See Clariane SE; *Int'l*, pg. 1644
SOZIALKONZEPT CACILIENHOF MBH—See Clariane SE; *Int'l*, pg. 1644
SOZIALKONZEPT DOROTHEENHOF GMBH—See Clariane SE; *Int'l*, pg. 1644
SOZIALKONZEPT FRIEDERIKENHOF GMBH—See Clariane SE; *Int'l*, pg. 1645
SOZIALKONZEPT HELENENHOF GMBH—See Clariane SE; *Int'l*, pg. 1645
SOZIALKONZEPT IM ROSENPARK GMBH—See Clariane SE; *Int'l*, pg. 1645
SOZIALKONZEPT KATHARINENHOF MBH—See Clariane SE; *Int'l*, pg. 1645
SOZIALKONZEPT LORETTAHOF GMBH—See Clariane SE; *Int'l*, pg. 1645
SOZIALKONZEPT LUISENHOF GMBH—See Clariane SE; *Int'l*, pg. 1645
SOZIALKONZEPT MAGDALENENHOF MBH—See Clariane SE; *Int'l*, pg. 1645
SOZIALKONZEPT MARIENHOF GMBH—See Clariane SE; *Int'l*, pg. 1645
SOZIALKONZEPT MARIETTENHOF GMBH—See Clariane SE; *Int'l*, pg. 1645
SOZIALKONZEPT SCHULZE-KATHRINHOF GMBH—See Clariane SE; *Int'l*, pg. 1645
SOZIALKONZEPT SOPHIENHOF GMBH—See Clariane SE; *Int'l*, pg. 1645
SPARROW COMMUNITY CARE—See University of Michigan; *U.S. Private*, pg. 4309
SPARROW SPECIALTY HOSPITAL—See University of Michigan; *U.S. Private*, pg. 4309
SPA STRATEGY LIMITED—See Walgreens Boots Alliance, Inc.; *U.S. Public*, pg. 2323
SPECIALTY EXTENDED CARE HOSPITAL OF MONROE, LLC—See UnitedHealth Group Incorporated; *U.S. Public*, pg. 2247
THE SPECIALTY HOSPITAL, L.L.C.—See Apollo Global Management, Inc.; *U.S. Public*, pg. 157
SPITS B.V.—See Walgreens Boots Alliance, Inc.; *U.S. Public*, pg. 2323
SPRINGVILLE PHARMACY INFUSION THERAPY, INC.—See Walgreens Boots Alliance, Inc.; *U.S. Public*, pg. 2323
STAFF BUILDERS HOME HEALTH—See Amedisys, Inc.; *U.S. Public*, pg. 94
STA-HOME HEALTH & HOSPICE, INC.—See Advent International Corporation; *U.S. Private*, pg. 97
STARR FARM PARTNERSHIP—See Apollo Global Management, Inc.; *U.S. Public*, pg. 157
ST. CLOUD PHYSICIAN MANAGEMENT, LLC—See Community Health Systems, Inc.; *U.S. Public*, pg. 557
STEM CELL AUTHORITY, LTD.; *U.S. Public*, pg. 1944
STERLING HEALTHCARE SERVICES, INC.—See CVS Health Corporation; *U.S. Public*, pg. 616
STIMIT AG—See Draegerwerk AG & Co. KGaA; *Int'l*, pg. 2198
ST. JOHN ENCOMPASS HEALTH REHABILITATION HOSPITAL, LLC—See Encompass Health Corporation; *U.S. Public*, pg. 759
ST. JOSEPH ENCOMPASS HEALTH REHABILITATION HOSPITAL, LLC—See Encompass Health Corporation; *U.S. Public*, pg. 759
ST. JOSEPH'S HEALTH CENTRE—See Laboratory Corporation of America Holdings; *U.S. Public*, pg. 1287
ST. LUKE'S REHABILITATION HOSPITAL, LLC—See Apollo Global Management, Inc.; *U.S. Public*, pg. 157
ST. MARY'S MEDICAL CENTER HOME HEALTH SERVICES, LLC—See UnitedHealth Group Incorporated; *U.S. Public*, pg. 2247
STRETCH ZONE FRANCHISING, LLC; *U.S. Private*, pg. 3839
STRYKER CHINA LIMITED—See Stryker Corporation; *U.S. Public*, pg. 1956
STRYKER COLOMBIA SAS—See Stryker Corporation; *U.S. Public*, pg. 1956
STRYKER GMBH & CO. KG—See Stryker Corporation; *U.S. Public*, pg. 1956
STRYKER ITALIA SRL—See Stryker Corporation; *U.S. Public*, pg. 1957
STRYKER NEDERLAND BV—See Stryker Corporation; *U.S. Public*, pg. 1957
STRYKER OSTEONICS AG—See Stryker Corporation; *U.S. Public*, pg. 1957
STRYKER PORTUGAL - PRODUTOS MEDICOS UNIPESSOAL, LDA.—See Stryker Corporation; *U.S. Public*, pg. 1957
STRYKER ROMANIA SRL—See Stryker Corporation; *U.S. Public*, pg. 1957
SUMMIT HEALTHCARE, INC.—See The Ensign Group, Inc.; *U.S. Public*, pg. 2072
SUMMIT WALK-IN CLINIC, LLC—See HCA Healthcare, Inc.; *U.S. Public*, pg. 1011
SUNCREST HEALTHCARE, INC.—See UnitedHealth Group Incorporated; *U.S. Public*, pg. 2244
SUNRISE OF CUPERTINO PROPCO, LLC—See Welltower Inc.; *U.S. Public*, pg. 2349
SUNRISE OF REDMOND PROPCO, LLC—See Welltower Inc.; *U.S. Public*, pg. 2349
SUPERIOR HEALTHPLAN COMMUNITY SOLUTIONS, INC.—See Centene Corporation; *U.S. Public*, pg. 470
SVAN CARE AB—See AddLife AB; *Int'l*, pg. 130
SYMBOL HEALTHCARE, INC.—See The Ensign Group, Inc.; *U.S. Public*, pg. 2072
SYMBOL HEALTH SOLUTIONS, LLC—See Community Health Systems, Inc.; *U.S. Public*, pg. 557
SYMMEDRX, LLC—See Premier, Inc.; *U.S. Public*, pg. 1715
SYNERGY HOME CARE CAPITOL REGION, INC.—See Apollo Global Management, Inc.; *U.S. Public*, pg. 157
SYNERGY HOME CARE CENTRAL REGION, INC.—See Apollo Global Management, Inc.; *U.S. Public*, pg. 157
SYNERGY HOMECARE FRANCHISING LLC; *U.S. Private*, pg. 3904
SYNERGY HOME CARE NORTHEASTERN REGION, INC.—See Apollo Global Management, Inc.; *U.S. Public*, pg. 157
SYNERGY HOME CARE NORTHSHORE REGION, INC.—See Apollo Global Management, Inc.; *U.S. Public*, pg. 158
SYNERGY HOME CARE NORTHWESTERN REGION, INC.—See Apollo Global Management, Inc.; *U.S. Public*, pg. 158
SYNERGY HOME CARE SOUTHEASTERN REGION, INC.—See Apollo Global Management, Inc.; *U.S. Public*, pg. 158
TAIHE GROUP, INC.; *U.S. Public*, pg. 1978
TAKE CARE PRIVATE DUTY HOME HEALTH CARE; *U.S. Private*, pg. 3925
TALKSPACE, INC.; *U.S. Public*, pg. 1979
TCG INTERESTS, LTD.—See Elm Creek Partners; *U.S. Private*, pg. 1375
TEAM NURSE, INC.—See Searchlight Capital Partners, L.P.; *U.S. Private*, pg. 3587
TECHE REGIONAL PHYSICIAN PRACTICES, LLC—See Apollo Global Management, Inc.; *U.S. Public*, pg. 159
TENDER LOVING CARE HEALTH CARE SERVICES OF ERIE NIAGARA, LLC—See Amedisys, Inc.; *U.S. Public*, pg. 94
TENDER LOVING CARE HEALTH CARE SERVICES OF GEORGIA, LLC—See Amedisys, Inc.; *U.S. Public*, pg. 94
TENDER LOVING CARE HEALTH CARE SERVICES OF LONG ISLAND, LLC—See Amedisys, Inc.; *U.S. Public*, pg. 94
TENNESSEE IN-HOME PARTNER-II, LLC—See UnitedHealth Group Incorporated; *U.S. Public*, pg. 2247
TEN PRINS PLC—See Clariane SE; *Int'l*, pg. 1645
TETON HEALTHCARE, INC.—See The Ensign Group, Inc.; *U.S. Public*, pg. 2072
TEXAS HEALTH CARE GROUP, LLC—See UnitedHealth Group Incorporated; *U.S. Public*, pg. 2247
TEXAS INSTITUTE OF PEDIATRICS, PLLC—See HCA Healthcare, Inc.; *U.S. Public*, pg. 1011
TEXAS NHI INVESTORS, LLC—See National Health Investors, Inc.; *U.S. Public*, pg. 1495
TEXAS VISITING NURSE LTD.; *U.S. Private*, pg. 3978
THE THERAPY GROUP, INC.—See Apollo Global Management, Inc.; *U.S. Public*, pg. 158
THOMAS HOME HEALTH, LLC—See UnitedHealth Group Incorporated; *U.S. Public*, pg. 2247
THOMAS ROAD SENIOR HOUSING, INC.—See The Ensign Group, Inc.; *U.S. Public*, pg. 2072
THOMPSON MEDICAL & CHIROPRACTIC LLC—See Atlantic Health System Inc.; *U.S. Private*, pg. 373
THORNE HEALTHTECH, INC.—See Catterton Management Company, LLC; *U.S. Private*, pg. 794
THREE RIVERS HOMECARE, LLC—See UnitedHealth Group Incorporated; *U.S. Public*, pg. 2247
TIDEWELL HOSPICE INC.; *U.S. Private*, pg. 4168
TLC PLUS OF TEXAS, INC.—See Humana, Inc.; *U.S. Public*, pg. 1070
TNI MEDICAL AG—See Masimo Corporation; *U.S. Public*, pg. 1392
TOMBALL TEXAS HOME CARE SERVICES, LLC—See Community Health Systems, Inc.; *U.S. Public*, pg. 557
TORREVIEJA SALUD S.L.U.—See Centene Corporation; *U.S. Public*, pg. 470
TOTAL HOME HEALTH CARE, INC.—See Capitol Partners LLC; *U.S. Private*, pg. 744
TOWNSEND; *U.S. Private*, pg. 4198
TRANSCARE SERVICE GMBH—See B. Braun Melsungen AG; *Int'l*, pg. 788
TRANSITIONAL SERVICES, LLC—See Centerbridge Partners, L.P.; *U.S. Private*, pg. 814
TRI-CITIES HOME HEALTH, LLC—See Amedisys, Inc.; *U.S. Public*, pg. 94
TRINITYCARE L.L.C.—See Catholic Health Initiatives; *U.S. Private*, pg. 789
TRINITY HOMECARE LLC—See Walgreens Boots Alliance, Inc.; *U.S. Public*, pg. 2323
TRINITY HOSPICE OF TEXAS, LLC—See Apollo Global Management, Inc.; *U.S. Public*, pg. 158
TRI-PARISH COMMUNITY HOMECARE, LLC—See UnitedHealth Group Incorporated; *U.S. Public*, pg. 2247
TRIPLE-S ADVANTAGE, INC.—See Triple-S Management Corp.; *U.S. Public*, pg. 2195
TRISTAR JOINT REPLACEMENT INSTITUTE, LLC—See HCA Healthcare, Inc.; *U.S. Public*, pg. 1012
TRIUMPH HOSPITAL NORTHWEST INDIANA, LLC—See Apollo Global Management, Inc.; *U.S. Public*, pg. 157
TWIN LAKES HOME HEALTH AGENCY, LLC—See UnitedHealth Group Incorporated; *U.S. Public*, pg. 2247
UBC LATE STAGE, INC.—See The Cigna Group; *U.S. Public*, pg. 2062
UBC SCIENTIFIC SOLUTIONS, LIMITED—See The Cigna Group; *U.S. Public*, pg. 2062
UCI HEALTH; *U.S. Private*, pg. 4273
UNICARE HEALTH PLAN OF WEST VIRGINIA, INC.—See Elevance Health, Inc.; *U.S. Public*, pg. 730
UNIQUE HOME HEALTH CARE LIMITED—See Apollo Hospitals Enterprise Limited; *Int'l*, pg. 518
UNITED CLAIM SOLUTIONS, LLC; *U.S. Private*, pg. 4289
UNITED COMPANY OF PHARMACISTS SAE—See Walgreens Boots Alliance, Inc.; *U.S. Public*, pg. 2323
UNITED HOME CARE SERVICES INC.; *U.S. Private*, pg. 4293
UNITY HEALTH HOSPICE—See Enhabit, Inc.; *U.S. Public*, pg. 768
UNIVERSITY OF CALIFORNIA SAN FRANCISCO MEDICAL CENTER; *U.S. Private*, pg. 4308
UNIVERSITY OF TN MEDICAL CENTER HOME CARE SERVICES, LLC—See UnitedHealth Group Incorporated; *U.S. Public*, pg. 2247
UPJOHN MIDDLE EAST FZ-LLC—See Viatris Inc.; *U.S. Public*, pg. 2294
UPLAND OUTPATIENT SURGICAL CENTER, L.P.—See UnitedHealth Group Incorporated; *U.S. Public*, pg. 2252
UROLOGY AMERICA, LLC—See Gauge Capital LLC; *U.S. Private*, pg. 1652
USMD CANCER TREATMENT CENTERS, LLC—See UnitedHealth Group Incorporated; *U.S. Public*, pg. 2240
USMD INC.—See UnitedHealth Group Incorporated; *U.S. Public*, pg. 2240
UVA ENCOMPASS HEALTH REHABILITATION HOSPITAL, LLC—See Encompass Health Corporation; *U.S. Public*, pg. 759
VALLEY VIEW HEALTH SERVICES, INC.—See The Ensign Group, Inc.; *U.S. Public*, pg. 2072
VALUE HEALTH CARE SERVICES, LLC—See CVS Health Corporation; *U.S. Public*, pg. 616
VAMED LEBEN AM ROSENBERG KRONACH GMBH—See Fresenius SE & Co. KGaA; *Int'l*, pg. 2779
VANGUARD HOME CARE, LLC—See Tenet Healthcare Corporation; *U.S. Public*, pg. 2015
VETERANS HOME CARE LLC; *U.S. Private*, pg. 4374
VICTORIA HEALTHCARE, INC.—See Select Medical Holdings Corporation; *U.S. Public*, pg. 1862
VIDEOJET ITALIA SRL—See Danaher Corporation; *U.S. Public*, pg. 631
VIDEOJET TECHNOLOGIES EUROPE B.V.—See Danaher Corporation; *U.S. Public*, pg. 632
VIDEOJET TECHNOLOGIES (SHANGHAI) CO., LTD.—See Danaher Corporation; *U.S. Public*, pg. 632
VIDEOJET TECHNOLOGIES (S) PTE. LTD.—See Danaher Corporation; *U.S. Public*, pg. 631
VIEMED HEALTHCARE, INC.; *U.S. Public*, pg. 2297
VII VOYES SPRL—See Clariane SE; *Int'l*, pg. 1645
VILLA ASTRA BV—See Clariane SE; *Int'l*, pg. 1645
VILLA CREST HEALTHCARE CENTER, LLC—See National HealthCare Corporation; *U.S. Public*, pg. 1497
VILLA DE HORSTING BV—See Clariane SE; *Int'l*, pg. 1645
VILLA DELLE TERME SPA—See Clariane SE; *Int'l*, pg. 1645
VILLAGE HEALTH WORKS; *U.S. Private*, pg. 4383
VILLAGE PRACTICE MANAGEMENT COMPANY, LLC—See Four Corners Property Trust, Inc.; *U.S. Public*, pg. 875
VILLA OOSTERVELD BV—See Clariane SE; *Int'l*, pg. 1645
VILLA SAN CLEMENTE SRL—See Clariane SE; *Int'l*, pg. 1645
VILLA SILVANA SPA—See Clariane SE; *Int'l*, pg. 1645
VILLA SPES NOSTRA BV—See Clariane SE; *Int'l*, pg. 1645
VIP HEALTH CARE SERVICES, INC.—See Addus HomeCare Corporation; *U.S. Public*, pg. 40
VIRGINIA IN-HOME PARTNER-VIII, LLC—See UnitedHealth Group Incorporated; *U.S. Public*, pg. 2247

N.A.I.C.S. INDEX

621991 — BLOOD AND ORGAN BAN...

VIRGINIA IN-HOME PARTNER-V, LLC—See UnitedHealth Group Incorporated; *U.S. Public*, pg. 2247
VIRGINIA LEAGUE FOR PLANNED PARENTHOOD INC.; *U.S. Private*, pg. 4387
VIRGINIA MASON HEALTH SYSTEM—See Franciscan Health System; *U.S. Private*, pg. 1587
VISITING NURSE ASSOCIATION OF SOMERSET HILLS INC.; *U.S. Private*, pg. 4393
VISITING NURSE ASSOCIATION OF SOUTH CENTRAL CONNECTICUT; *U.S. Private*, pg. 4393
VISITING NURSE SERVICE OF NEW YORK; *U.S. Private*, pg. 4393
VISITING NURSE SERVICES IN WESTCHESTER, INC.; *U.S. Private*, pg. 4393
VITALS; *U.S. Private*, pg. 4405
VITAS HEALTHCARE CORPORATION OF CALIFORNIA—See Chemed Corporation; *U.S. Public*, pg. 484
VITAS HEALTHCARE CORPORATION OF GEORGIA—See Chemed Corporation; *U.S. Public*, pg. 484
VITAS HEALTHCARE CORPORATION OF OHIO—See Chemed Corporation; *U.S. Public*, pg. 484
VITAS SOLUTIONS, INC.—See Chemed Corporation; *U.S. Public*, pg. 484
VIVIFY HEALTH, INC.—See UnitedHealth Group Incorporated; *U.S. Public*, pg. 2252
VIZIENT, INC.; *U.S. Private*, pg. 4407
VNA OF RHODE ISLAND; *U.S. Private*, pg. 4408
VORTEX MEDICAL—See AngioDynamics, Inc.; *U.S. Public*, pg. 137
WALGREENS HOME CARE, INC.—See Option Care Health, Inc.; *U.S. Public*, pg. 1610
WATERTOWN MEDICAL CENTER, LLC—See Apollo Global Management, Inc.; *U.S. Public*, pg. 159
WATERTOWN PHYSICIAN PRACTICES, LLC—See Apollo Global Management, Inc.; *U.S. Public*, pg. 159
WAUKEGAN HOSPICE, LLC—See Community Health Systems, Inc.; *U.S. Public*, pg. 557
WEBMEDX INC.—See Microsoft Corporation; *U.S. Public*, pg. 1443
WELLCARE, INC.—See Encompass Health Corporation; *U.S. Public*, pg. 759
WELLMED MEDICAL MANAGEMENT OF FLORIDA, INC.—See UnitedHealth Group Incorporated; *U.S. Public*, pg. 2252
WELLPOINT FEDERAL CORPORATION—See Elevance Health, Inc.; *U.S. Public*, pg. 730
WELLPOINT TENNESSEE, INC.—See Elevance Health, Inc.; *U.S. Public*, pg. 730
WEST TENNESSEE REHABILITATION HOSPITAL, LLC—See Encompass Health Corporation; *U.S. Public*, pg. 759
WETZEL COUNTY HOMECARE, LLC—See UnitedHealth Group Incorporated; *U.S. Public*, pg. 2247
WHIRLPOOL MANAGEMENT SERVICES SAGL—See Whirlpool Corporation; *U.S. Public*, pg. 2368
WHIRLPOOL NEDERLAND B.V.—See Whirlpool Corporation; *U.S. Public*, pg. 2368
WHISPERING PINES HOME CARE, LLC—See UnitedHealth Group Incorporated; *U.S. Public*, pg. 2247
WILCOX MEDICAL, INC.—See Option Care Health, Inc.; *U.S. Public*, pg. 1610
WILLCARE, INC. - NEWBURGH—See UnitedHealth Group Incorporated; *U.S. Public*, pg. 2244
WILLCARE, INC. - OLEAN—See UnitedHealth Group Incorporated; *U.S. Public*, pg. 2244
WILLCARE, INC.—See UnitedHealth Group Incorporated; *U.S. Public*, pg. 2244
WILLCARE, INC. - TRUMBULL—See UnitedHealth Group Incorporated; *U.S. Public*, pg. 2244
THE WILMSLOW HOSPITAL—See HCA Healthcare, Inc.; *U.S. Public*, pg. 990
WOHN- UND PFLEGEWELT LAHNBLICK GMBH—See Deutsche Wohnen SE; *Int'l*, pg. 2085
WOMEN SPECIALISTS OF CLEAR LAKE, PLLC—See HCA Healthcare, Inc.; *U.S. Public*, pg. 1014
X-RITE ASIA PACIFIC LIMITED—See Danaher Corporation; *U.S. Public*, pg. 632
YOUTHFUL AGING HOME HEALTH, INC.; *U.S. Private*, pg. 4594
ZENITAS CARING CHOICE PTY LTD—See Adamantem Capital Management Pty Limited; *Int'l*, pg. 124
ZIMMER BIOMET SWEDEN AB—See Zimmer Biomet Holdings, Inc.; *U.S. Public*, pg. 2407
ZIMMER DO BRASIL COMERCIO LTDA.—See Zimmer Biomet Holdings, Inc.; *U.S. Public*, pg. 2408
ZIMMER KNEE CREATIONS, INC.—See Zimmer Biomet Holdings, Inc.; *U.S. Public*, pg. 2407
ZYDUS HOSPIRA ONCOLOGY PRIVATE LIMITED—See Pfizer Inc.; *U.S. Public*, pg. 1683

621910 — AMBULANCE SERVICES

ACADIAN AMBULANCE SERVICE INC.; *U.S. Private*, pg. 47
ACTION AMBULANCE SERVICE INC.; *U.S. Private*, pg. 67
ADVANCED MEDICAL TRANSPORT OF CENTRAL ILLINOIS; *U.S. Private*, pg. 91
AGAPE LUXURY CORP.; *U.S. Private*, pg. 126
AIR MEDICAL LTD.—See KKR & Co. Inc.; *U.S. Public*, pg. 1251
ALERT AMBULANCE SERVICE, INC.; *U.S. Private*, pg. 162
ALLEGIANCE MOBILE HEALTH; *U.S. Private*, pg. 176
AMBULANCE SERVICES OF DYERSBURG, INC.—See Community Health Systems, Inc.; *U.S. Public*, pg. 551
AMBULANCE SERVICES OF MCNAIRY, INC.—See Community Health Systems, Inc.; *U.S. Public*, pg. 551
AMERICAN MEDICAL RESPONSE, INC.—See KKR & Co. Inc.; *U.S. Public*, pg. 1251
AMERICAN MEDICAL RESPONSE NORTHWEST, INC.—See KKR & Co. Inc.; *U.S. Public*, pg. 1251
AMERICAN MEDICAL RESPONSE OF COLORADO, INC.—See KKR & Co. Inc.; *U.S. Public*, pg. 1251
AMERICAN MEDICAL RESPONSE OF INLAND EMPIRE—See KKR & Co. Inc.; *U.S. Public*, pg. 1251
AMERICAN MEDICAL RESPONSE OF NEW YORK, LLC—See KKR & Co. Inc.; *U.S. Public*, pg. 1251
AMERIPRO HEALTH LLC; *U.S. Private*, pg. 260
AMSURG CITRUS ANESTHESIA, LLC—See KKR & Co. Inc.; *U.S. Public*, pg. 1244
AMSURG FRESNO CA, INC.—See KKR & Co. Inc.; *U.S. Public*, pg. 1244
AS AMBULANCES SERVICES SA—See AEVIS VICTORIA SA; *Int'l*, pg. 183
ASCEND MANAGEMENT INNOVATIONS LLC; *U.S. Private*, pg. 346
BANGKOK HELICOPTER SERVICES CO., LTD.—See Bangkok Dusit Medical Services Public Company Limited; *Int'l*, pg. 834
BEAUMONT MOBILE MEDICINE—See Beaumont Health; *U.S. Private*, pg. 508
BH TRANS COMPANY, LLC—See Community Health Systems, Inc.; *U.S. Public*, pg. 551
COMMUNITY EMERGENCY MEDICAL SERVICE, INC.—See Beaumont Health; *U.S. Private*, pg. 508
COMMUNITY EMS, INC.—See KKR & Co. Inc.; *U.S. Public*, pg. 1249
COMTRANS, INC.—See KKR & Co. Inc.; *U.S. Public*, pg. 1251
COSHOCTON COUNTY EMS LLC—See Ohio Medical Transportation; *U.S. Private*, pg. 3004
CVS TRANSPORTATION, LLC—See CVS Health Corporation; *U.S. Public*, pg. 615
ECON AMBULANCE SERVICES PTE LTD—See China Healthcare Limited; *Int'l*, pg. 1507
EMERGENCY MEDICAL FOUNDATION; *U.S. Private*, pg. 1380
EMERGENCY MEDICAL TRANSPORT, INC.—See KKR & Co. Inc.; *U.S. Public*, pg. 1249
EMERGYCARE, INC.; *U.S. Private*, pg. 1381
EMPRESS AMBULANCE SERVICE INC.; *U.S. Private*, pg. 1388
GATEWAY AMBULANCE SERVICE LLC—See Interlock Industries, Inc.; *U.S. Public*, pg. 2111
GLOBAL MEDICAL RESPONSE, INC.—See KKR & Co. Inc.; *U.S. Public*, pg. 1251
GOLD CROSS AMBULANCE SERVICES, INC.—See KKR & Co. Inc.; *U.S. Public*, pg. 1249
GOLD CROSS SERVICES INC.; *U.S. Private*, pg. 1727
HARRIS COUNTY EMERGENCY CORPS; *U.S. Private*, pg. 1869
HEALTHLIFT MEDICAL TRANSPORTATION, INC.—See The Ensign Group, Inc.; *U.S. Public*, pg. 2071
HUNTSVILLE EMERGENCY MEDICAL SERVICES INC; *U.S. Private*, pg. 2011
INTERNATIONAL LIFE SUPPORT, INC.—See KKR & Co. Inc.; *U.S. Public*, pg. 1251
IRHYTHM TECHNOLOGIES LIMITED—See iRhythm Technologies, Inc.; *U.S. Public*, pg. 1171
LIFECARE AMBULANCE, INC.; *U.S. Private*, pg. 2449
LIFECARE MEDICAL SERVICES, INC.; *U.S. Private*, pg. 2449
LIFEGUARD AIR AMBULANCE, INC.; *U.S. Private*, pg. 2450
LIFEGUARD TRANSPORTATION SERVICE, INC.; *U.S. Private*, pg. 2450
LIFEGUARD TRANSPORTATION SERVICE, INC.—See Lifeguard Transportation Service, Inc.; *U.S. Private*, pg. 2450
LIFELINE AMBULANCE SERVICE, INC.—See KKR & Co. Inc.; *U.S. Public*, pg. 1249
LIFENET, INC.; *U.S. Private*, pg. 2450
LIFESTAR AMBULANCE, INC.—See Catholic Healthcare Partners; *U.S. Private*, pg. 792
LONG BEACH SURGERY CENTER, L.P.—See KKR & Co. Inc.; *U.S. Public*, pg. 1246
MEDCARE AMBULANCE—See Ohio Medical Transportation; *U.S. Private*, pg. 3004
MEDIC WEST AMBULANCE, INC.—See KKR & Co. Inc.; *U.S. Public*, pg. 1251
MERCY FLIGHTS INC.; *U.S. Private*, pg. 2671
METROPOLITAN HEALTH CARE, INC.; *U.S. Private*, pg. 2688
MSC ANESTHESIA, INC.—See KKR & Co. Inc.; *U.S. Public*, pg. 1246
NATIONAL MEDTRANS, LLC—See ModivCare, Inc.; *U.S. Public*, pg. 1455
NAZARETH VOLUNTEER AMBULANCE CORPS; *U.S. Private*, pg. 2874
NEW ENGLAND MEDICAL TRANSPORTATION, INC.—See The Ensign Group, Inc.; *U.S. Public*, pg. 2071
NEW WINDSOR VOLUNTEER AMBULANCE CORPS INC.; *U.S. Private*, pg. 2908
NORTHERN BERKSHIRE EMS, INC.; *U.S. Private*, pg. 2952
OHIO MEDICAL TRANSPORTATION; *U.S. Private*, pg. 3004
PATIENTCARE EMS SOLUTIONS—See Alvarez & Marsal, Inc.; *U.S. Private*, pg. 213
PATRIOT CARE, INC.—See Patriot National, Inc.; *U.S. Private*, pg. 3110
PHI AIR MEDICAL, L.L.C.—See PHI, Inc.; *U.S. Public*, pg. 3168
PICKAWAY PLAINS AMBULANCE SERVICE, INC.—See Source Capital, LLC; *U.S. Private*, pg. 3718
THE PINELLAS COUNTY EMERGENCY MEDICAL SERVICES AUTHORITY; *U.S. Private*, pg. 4095
PRN AMBULANCE, LLC—See ProTransport-1; *U.S. Private*, pg. 3290
PUCKETT AMBULANCE SERVICE, INC.—See KKR & Co. Inc.; *U.S. Public*, pg. 1251
REACH AIR MEDICAL SERVICES, LLC—See KKR & Co. Inc.; *U.S. Public*, pg. 1252
REGIONAL EMERGENCY MEDICAL SERVICES AUTHORITY; *U.S. Private*, pg. 3388
RICHMOND AMBULANCE AUTHORITY; *U.S. Private*, pg. 3430
ROYAL AMBULANCE; *U.S. Private*, pg. 3491
RURAL/METRO OF NORTHERN OHIO, INC.—See KKR & Co. Inc.; *U.S. Public*, pg. 1252
SCHAEFER AMBULANCE SERVICE; *U.S. Private*, pg. 3563
SOUTHERN BERKS REGIONAL EMERGENCY MEDICAL SERVICES, INC.—See Tower Health; *U.S. Private*, pg. 4193
SUNRISE HANDICAP TRANSPORT CORP.—See KKR & Co. Inc.; *U.S. Public*, pg. 1251
SUPERIOR AMBULANCE SERVICE, INC.; *U.S. Private*, pg. 3875
SYMONS AMBULANCE; *U.S. Private*, pg. 3899
TRANSCARE NEW YORK INC.; *U.S. Private*, pg. 4207
TRANSCARE OF MARYLAND INC—See Transcare New York Inc.; *U.S. Private*, pg. 4207
UNIVERSAL MACOMB AMBULANCE SERVICE, INC.; *U.S. Private*, pg. 4305
VILLAGE AMBULANCE SERVICE, INC.—See Northern Berkshire EMS, Inc.; *U.S. Private*, pg. 2952
WCA HOSPITAL; *U.S. Private*, pg. 4461
WCA SERVICES CORP.—See WCA Hospital; *U.S. Private*, pg. 4461
WESTMED AMBULANCE SERVICE, INC.—See KKR & Co. Inc.; *U.S. Public*, pg. 1250
WHITE KNIGHT LIMOUSINE INC.; *U.S. Private*, pg. 4509

621991 — BLOOD AND ORGAN BANKS

ARKANSAS REGIONAL ORGAN RECOVERY AGENCY; *U.S. Private*, pg. 326
BIO-BLOOD COMPONENTS, INC.—See Grifols, S.A.; *Int'l*, pg. 3085
BIOMAT USA, INC.—See Grifols, S.A.; *Int'l*, pg. 3084
BLOOD BANK OF HAWAII; *U.S. Private*, pg. 583
THE BLOOD & TISSUE CENTER OF CENTRAL TEXAS; *U.S. Private*, pg. 3995
CALIFORNIA CRYOBANK LLC—See GI Manager L.P.; *U.S. Private*, pg. 1691
CARTER BLOODCARE; *U.S. Private*, pg. 775
CELL CARE AUSTRALIA PTY. LTD.—See The Cooper Companies, Inc.; *U.S. Public*, pg. 2066
CELLUMED CO., LTD; *Int'l*, pg. 1395
THE COMMUNITY BLOOD CENTER, INC.; *U.S. Private*, pg. 4012
COMMUNITY BLOOD CENTER OF THE CAROLINAS, INC.—See OneBlood, Inc.; *U.S. Private*, pg. 3024
COMMUNITY BLOOD CENTER OF THE OZARKS; *U.S. Private*, pg. 990
COMMUNITY BLOOD CENTER; *U.S. Private*, pg. 990
COMMUNITY BLOOD COUNCIL OF NEW JERSEY, INC.; *U.S. Private*, pg. 990
CORAL BLOOD SERVICES—See Charles River Laboratories International, Inc.; *U.S. Public*, pg. 480
CORDLIFE (HONG KONG) LIMITED—See Cordlife Group Limited; *Int'l*, pg. 1796
CORDLIFE MEDICAL PHILS., INC.—See Cordlife Group Limited; *Int'l*, pg. 1796
CORDLIFE SCIENCES (INDIA) PVT. LTD.—See Cordlife Group Limited; *Int'l*, pg. 1796
CSL PLASMA INC.—See CSL Limited; *Int'l*, pg. 1865
CU BLOOD, INC.—See CRYO-CELL International, Inc.; *U.S. Public*, pg. 600

621991 — BLOOD AND ORGAN BAN...

DCI BIOLOGICALS INC.; *U.S. Private,* pg. 1179
DONOR ALLIANCE, INC.; *U.S. Private,* pg. 1261
DONOR NETWORK OF ARIZONA; *U.S. Private,* pg. 1261
FAMILY HOME HEALTH SERVICES LLC; *U.S. Private,* pg. 1470
GENERATE LIFE SCIENCES, INC.—See The Cooper Companies, Inc.; *U.S. Public,* pg. 2066
GIFT OF HOPE ORGAN & TISSUE DONOR NETWORK; *U.S. Private,* pg. 1697
HAEMA AG—See Grifols, S.A.; *Int'l,* pg. 3085
HEALTHBABY BIOTECH (MACAU) CO., LIMITED—See Cordlife Group Limited; *Int'l,* pg. 1796
HEARTLAND BLOOD CENTERS; *U.S. Private,* pg. 1899
HEMACARE CORPORATION—See Charles River Laboratories International, Inc.; *U.S. Public,* pg. 480
HOUCHIN COMMUNITY BLOOD BANK; *U.S. Private,* pg. 1990
INDIANA DONOR NETWORK; *U.S. Private,* pg. 2062
INTERMOUNTAIN DONOR SERVICES; *U.S. Private,* pg. 2113
INTERSTATE BLOOD BANK, INC.—See Grifols, S.A.; *Int'l,* pg. 3085
IOWA DONOR NETWORK; *U.S. Private,* pg. 2134
KENTUCKY ORGAN DONOR AFFILIATES; *U.S. Private,* pg. 2288
LIFECENTER NORTHWEST; *U.S. Private,* pg. 2449
LIFELINK FOUNDATION, INC.; *U.S. Private,* pg. 2450
LIFESERVE BLOOD CENTER; *U.S. Private,* pg. 2451
LIFESHARE COMMUNITY BLOOD SERVICES; *U.S. Private,* pg. 2451
LIFESTREAM; *U.S. Private,* pg. 2451
LOUISIANA ORGAN PROCUREMENT AGENCY; *U.S. Private,* pg. 2500
MIDWEST TRANSPLANT NETWORK; *U.S. Private,* pg. 2723
MISSISSIPPI BLOOD SERVICES; *U.S. Private,* pg. 2748
MISSISSIPPI ORGAN RECOVERY AGENCY; *U.S. Private,* pg. 2748
MUSCULOSKELETAL TRANSPLANT FOUNDATION; *U.S. Private,* pg. 2817
NEW ENGLAND ORGAN BANK; *U.S. Private,* pg. 2894
NEW YORK BLOOD CENTER, INC.; *U.S. Private,* pg. 2908
NJ SHARING NETWORK; *U.S. Private,* pg. 2930
ONEBLOOD, INC.; *U.S. Private,* pg. 3024
ORGAN PROCUREMENT AGENCY OF MICHIGAN; *U.S. Private,* pg. 3041
PLASMADIENST TIROL GMBH—See Biotest AG; *Int'l,* pg. 1043
PLASMA SERVICE EUROPE GMBH—See Biotest AG; *Int'l,* pg. 1043
PT. CORDLIFE PERSADA—See Cordlife Group Limited; *Int'l,* pg. 1796
RHODE ISLAND BLOOD CENTER; *U.S. Private,* pg. 3422
SHEPEARD COMMUNITY BLOOD CENTER; *U.S. Private,* pg. 3632
SIGYN THERAPEUTICS, INC.; *U.S. Public,* pg. 1878
SOUTHERN CORD INC.—See GI Manager L.P.; *U.S. Private,* pg. 1691
SOUTHWEST TRANSPLANT ALLIANCE, INC.; *U.S. Private,* pg. 3741
STEMLIFE BERHAD—See Cordlife Group Limited; *Int'l,* pg. 1796
TISSUE BANKS INTERNATIONAL; *U.S. Private,* pg. 4176
UPPER MIDWEST ORGAN PROCUREMENT ORGANIZATION, INC.; *U.S. Private,* pg. 4312
VISION SHARE; *U.S. Private,* pg. 4391
WASHINGTON REGIONAL TRANSPLANT COMMUNITY; *U.S. Private,* pg. 4449

621999 — ALL OTHER MISCELLANEOUS AMBULATORY HEALTH CARE SERVICES

101 MOBILITY, LLC; *U.S. Private,* pg. 2
154TH STREET MEDICAL PLAZA, INC.—See Humana, Inc.; *U.S. Public,* pg. 1069
54TH STREET MEDICAL PLAZA, INC.—See Humana, Inc.; *U.S. Public,* pg. 1069
ABBOTT RAPID DIAGNOSTICS PTY, LTD.—See Abbott Laboratories; *U.S. Public,* pg. 17
ABBOTT SAUDI ARABIA FOR TRADING—See Abbott Laboratories; *U.S. Public,* pg. 18
ABCO INDIA PRIVATE LIMITED—See UnitedHealth Group Incorporated; *U.S. Public,* pg. 2238
ACA SALUD—See Asociacion de Cooperativas Argentinas C.L.; *Int'l,* pg. 628
ACCORDANT HEALTH SERVICES, INC.—See CVS Health Corporation; *U.S. Public,* pg. 613
ACCUMEN, INC.—See Arsenal Capital Management LP; *U.S. Private,* pg. 337
ACO HEALTH PARTNERS LLC—See HealthLynked Corp.; *U.S. Public,* pg. 1016
ACTIVE ASSISTANCE—See August Equity LLP; *Int'l,* pg. 703
ACUTECARE TELEMEDICINE, LLC—See Teladoc Health, Inc.; *U.S. Public,* pg. 1992
ADAPTHEALTH PATIENT CARE SOLUTIONS, INC.—See AdaptHealth Corp.; *U.S. Public,* pg. 38

ADMERA HEALTH, LLC; *U.S. Private,* pg. 80
AETNA BETTER HEALTH, INC.—See CVS Health Corporation; *U.S. Public,* pg. 614
AETNA BETTER HEALTH, INC.—See CVS Health Corporation; *U.S. Public,* pg. 614
AETNA BETTER HEALTH, INC.—See CVS Health Corporation; *U.S. Public,* pg. 614
AETNA BETTER HEALTH, INC.—See CVS Health Corporation; *U.S. Public,* pg. 614
AETNA BETTER HEALTH, INC.—See CVS Health Corporation; *U.S. Public,* pg. 614
AETNA BETTER HEALTH, INC.—See CVS Health Corporation; *U.S. Public,* pg. 614
AETNA BETTER HEALTH, INC.—See CVS Health Corporation; *U.S. Public,* pg. 614
AETNA BETTER HEALTH OF CALIFORNIA INC.—See CVS Health Corporation; *U.S. Public,* pg. 614
AETNA BETTER HEALTH OF FLORIDA INC.—See CVS Health Corporation; *U.S. Public,* pg. 613
AETNA BETTER HEALTH OF KANSAS INC.—See CVS Health Corporation; *U.S. Public,* pg. 614
AETNA BETTER HEALTH OF KENTUCKY INSURANCE COMPANY—See CVS Health Corporation; *U.S. Public,* pg. 614
AETNA HEALTH OF IOWA INC.—See CVS Health Corporation; *U.S. Public,* pg. 614
AFC HEALTH LTD.—See Active Fine Chemicals Limited; *Int'l,* pg. 120
AFFIMED GMBH—See Affimed N.V.; *Int'l,* pg. 186
AFTER HOURS PEDIATRICS, INC.—See Blackstone Inc.; *U.S. Public,* pg. 359
AGFA HEALTHCARE EQUIPMENTS PORTUGAL LDA.—See Agfa-Gevaert N.V.; *Int'l,* pg. 208
AGFA HEALTHCARE FRANCE S.A.—See Agfa-Gevaert N.V.; *Int'l,* pg. 208
AGFA HEALTHCARE IT UK LIMITED—See Agfa-Gevaert N.V.; *Int'l,* pg. 208
AGFA HEALTHCARE KAZAKHSTAN LLP—See Agfa-Gevaert N.V.; *Int'l,* pg. 208
AGFA HEALTHCARE MIDDLE EAST FZ-LLC—See Agfa-Gevaert N.V.; *Int'l,* pg. 208
AGFA HEALTHCARE SAUDI ARABIA COMPANY LIMITED LLC—See Agfa-Gevaert N.V.; *Int'l,* pg. 208
AGFA HEALTHCARE UKRAINE LLC—See Agfa-Gevaert N.V.; *Int'l,* pg. 208
AGFA HEALTHCARE VIETNAM CO. LTD.—See Agfa-Gevaert N.V.; *Int'l,* pg. 208
AGFA SP. Z.O.O.—See Agfa-Gevaert N.V.; *Int'l,* pg. 208
AHN TARGET HOLDINGS, LLC—See UnitedHealth Group Incorporated; *U.S. Public,* pg. 2238
AIDIAN DENMARK APS—See Axcel Management A/S; *Int'l,* pg. 762
AIDIAN GERMANY GMBH—See Axcel Management A/S; *Int'l,* pg. 762
AIDIAN OY—See Axcel Management A/S; *Int'l,* pg. 762
AIICO MULTISHIELD LIMITED—See AIICO Insurance PLC; *Int'l,* pg. 232
AIKCHOL HOSPITAL PUBLIC COMPANY LIMITED; *Int'l,* pg. 232
AINO HEALTH MANAGEMENT OY—See Aino Health AB; *Int'l,* pg. 234
AJAL MEDICAL SPECIALTY COMPANY LTD.—See Eurofins Scientific S.E.; *Int'l,* pg. 2535
AKESO MEDICAL HOLDINGS, LLC—See Kain Capital, LLC; *U.S. Private,* pg. 2254
AKUMIN, INC.; *U.S. Public,* pg. 69
ALABAMA DIGESTIVE HEALTH ENDOSCOPY CENTER, L.L.C.—See Tenet Healthcare Corporation; *U.S. Public,* pg. 2007
ALABAMA HAND AND SPORTS MEDICINE, L.L.C.—See Tenet Healthcare Corporation; *U.S. Public,* pg. 2002
ALERE HEALTHCARE CONNECTIONS LIMITED—See Abbott Laboratories; *U.S. Public,* pg. 18
ALERE HEALTH, LLC—See UnitedHealth Group Incorporated; *U.S. Public,* pg. 2248
ALERT MARKETING, INC.—See The Wicks Group of Companies, LLC; *U.S. Private,* pg. 4135
ALLCARE PLUS PHARMACY LLC—See IQVIA Holdings Inc.; *U.S. Public,* pg. 1168
ALLIANCE MEDINET PTE. LTD.—See Alliance Healthcare Group Limited; *Int'l,* pg. 339
ALLONE HEALTH RESOURCES, INC.—See Highmark Health; *U.S. Private,* pg. 1940
ALMEDA, A.S.—See Fresenius SE & Co. KGaA; *Int'l,* pg. 2777
ALR TECHNOLOGIES INC.; *U.S. Public,* pg. 85
ALS LEASING, INC.—See Brookdale Senior Living Inc.; *U.S. Public,* pg. 393
ALTERNATIVE LIVING SERVICES HOME CARE, INC.—See Brookdale Senior Living Inc.; *U.S. Public,* pg. 393
ALVIVA AB—See AB Volvo; *Int'l,* pg. 42
ALZHEIMER'S ASSOCIATION; *U.S. Private,* pg. 214
AMBU (DEUTSCHLAND) GMBH—See Ambu A/S; *Int'l,* pg. 416
AMBULANTA ZDRAVJE, ZDRAVSTVENE STORITVE, D.O.O.—See Assicurazioni Generali S.p.A.; *Int'l,* pg. 643
AMBULATORY CARE SOLUTIONS OF OHIO LLC—See Humana, Inc.; *U.S. Public,* pg. 1069
AMBULATORY SERVICES OF AMERICA, INC.—See U.S. Renal Care, Inc.; *U.S. Private,* pg. 4272
AMBULATORY SURGERY CENTER OF COOL SPRINGS, LLC—See Bain Capital, LP; *U.S. Public,* pg. 446
AMBULATORY SURGICAL CENTER OF AIKEN, L.L.C.—See Universal Health Services, Inc.; *U.S. Public,* pg. 2255
AMCAD BIOMED CORPORATION; *Int'l,* pg. 416
AMC/NORTH FULTON URGENT CARE #1, L.L.C.—See Tenet Healthcare Corporation; *U.S. Public,* pg. 2005
AMC/NORTH FULTON URGENT CARE #5, L.L.C.—See Tenet Healthcare Corporation; *U.S. Public,* pg. 2005
AMERICAN HEALTHCARE SYSTEMS CORP., INC.; *U.S. Private,* pg. 236
AMERICAN INDIAN HEALTH & SERVICES CORP.—See KKR & Co. Inc.; *U.S. Public,* pg. 1239
AMERICAN MEDICAL ADMINISTRATORS, INC.; *U.S. Private,* pg. 241
AMERICAN MEDICAL GROUP LLC; *U.S. Private,* pg. 241
AMERICAN PARA PROFESSIONAL SYSTEMS, INC.; *U.S. Private,* pg. 243
AMERICAN PHYSICIAN PARTNERS, LLC; *U.S. Private,* pg. 243
AMERICAN UTILITY MANAGEMENT, INC.—See Thoma Bravo, L.P.; *U.S. Private,* pg. 4152
AMERICHOICE CORPORATION—See UnitedHealth Group Incorporated; *U.S. Public,* pg. 2238
AMERIGROUP DISTRICT OF COLUMBIA, INC.—See Elevance Health, Inc.; *U.S. Public,* pg. 728
AMERIGROUP IOWA, INC.—See Elevance Health, Inc.; *U.S. Public,* pg. 728
AMPHIVENA THERAPEUTICS INC.—See Affimed N.V.; *Int'l,* pg. 186
ANALCLINIC SA—See Eurofins Scientific S.E.; *Int'l,* pg. 2535
ANGIOLOGIKUM GMBH—See Asklepios Kliniken GmbH & Co. KGaA; *Int'l,* pg. 622
APAACO, INC.—See Astrana Health Inc.; *U.S. Public,* pg. 217
APOLLO CVHF LIMITED—See Apollo Hospitals Enterprise Limited; *Int'l,* pg. 517
APOLLO HEALTH AND LIFESTYLE LIMITED—See Apollo Hospitals Enterprise Limited; *Int'l,* pg. 517
APOLLOMED ACCOUNTABLE CARE ORGANIZATION, INC.—See Astrana Health Inc.; *U.S. Public,* pg. 217
APOLLO SUGAR CLINICS LIMITED—See Apollo Hospitals Enterprise Limited; *Int'l,* pg. 517
APPLECARE MEDICAL MANAGEMENT, LLC—See UnitedHealth Group Incorporated; *U.S. Public,* pg. 2239
APPLEGATE RECOVERY, LLC—See Webster Equity Partners, LLC; *U.S. Private,* pg. 4466
APPLING HEALTHCARE SYSTEM; *U.S. Private,* pg. 300
APRICA HEALTHCARE PRIVATE LIMITED—See Eris Lifesciences Limited; *Int'l,* pg. 2493
ARBOUR FOUNDATION, INC.—See Universal Health Services, Inc.; *U.S. Public,* pg. 2255
ARC BAY PINES INC—See Brookdale Senior Living Inc.; *U.S. Public,* pg. 393
ARC BOYNTON BEACH LLC—See Brookdale Senior Living Inc.; *U.S. Public,* pg. 393
ARC BRADENTON HC, INC.—See Brookdale Senior Living Inc.; *U.S. Public,* pg. 393
ARC BRANDYWINE, LP—See Brookdale Senior Living Inc.; *U.S. Public,* pg. 393
ARC COCONUT CREEK LLC—See Brookdale Senior Living Inc.; *U.S. Public,* pg. 393
ARC COUNTRYSIDE LLC—See Brookdale Senior Living Inc.; *U.S. Public,* pg. 393
ARC FREEDOM SQUARE LLC—See Brookdale Senior Living Inc.; *U.S. Public,* pg. 393
ARC GALLERIA WOODS INC—See Brookdale Senior Living Inc.; *U.S. Public,* pg. 393
ARC GREENWOOD VILLAGE INC—See Brookdale Senior Living Inc.; *U.S. Public,* pg. 393
ARC PARKLANE INC—See Brookdale Senior Living Inc.; *U.S. Public,* pg. 393
ARC RICHMOND PLACE INC—See Brookdale Senior Living Inc.; *U.S. Public,* pg. 393
ARIZONA CARE NETWORK - NEXT, LLC—See Tenet Healthcare Corporation; *U.S. Public,* pg. 2001
ASA SRL—See El.En. S.p.A.; *Int'l,* pg. 2341
ASCENDIS HEALTH LIMITED; *Int'l,* pg. 601
ASKLEPIOS MVZ BAYERN GMBH—See Asklepios Kliniken GmbH & Co. KGaA; *Int'l,* pg. 622
ASTRIA HEALTH; *U.S. Public,* pg. 361
ASURIS NORTHWEST HEALTH—See Cambia Health Solutions, Inc.; *U.S. Private,* pg. 726
ATRYS HEALTH SA; *Int'l,* pg. 694
AUDIKA GROUPE SA—See Demant A/S; *Int'l,* pg. 2023
AUGUSTA PRIMARY CARE SERVICES, LLC—See HCA Healthcare, Inc.; *U.S. Public,* pg. 991
AVENTURA HOSPITAL & MEDICAL CENTER—See HCA Healthcare, Inc.; *U.S. Public,* pg. 991
AVENUES HEALTHCARE, INC.—See The Ensign Group, Inc.; *U.S. Public,* pg. 2070
AVIACODE INCORPORATED—See ChrysCapital Management Co.; *Int'l,* pg. 1588
BALTIMORE MEDICAL SYSTEM INC.; *U.S. Private,* pg. 462

N.A.I.C.S. INDEX

621999 — ALL OTHER MISCELLAN...

BASELINE HEALTHCARE, INC.—See The Ensign Group, Inc.; *U.S. Public*, pg. 2070
BAYLOR SCOTT & WHITE HEALTH—See Baylor Scott & White Holdings; *U.S. Private*, pg. 496
BAYMARK HEALTH SERVICES, INC.—See Webster Equity Partners, LLC; *U.S. Private*, pg. 4466
BAYSIDE ENDOSCOPY CENTER, LLC—See Bain Capital, LP; *U.S. Private*, pg. 446
BELL MEDICAL SOLUTIONS INC.—See Bain Capital, LP; *U.S. Private*, pg. 436
BILLING CENTER LAKE POINTE MEDICAL, L.L.C.—See Tenet Healthcare Corporation; *U.S. Public*, pg. 2006
BIOLIFE REMEDIES, INC.; *Int'l*, pg. 1039
BIOMEDICAL SYSTEMS CORP.—See Astorg Partners S.A.S.; *Int'l*, pg. 657
BIOS S.P.A.; *Int'l*, pg. 1041
BIRMINGHAM SURGERY CENTER, LLC—See Bain Capital, LP; *U.S. Private*, pg. 446
BLC GABLES MONROVIA LP—See Brookdale Senior Living Inc.; *U.S. Public*, pg. 393
BLOMENBURG HOLDING GMBH—See Asklepios Kliniken GmbH & Co. KGaA; *Int'l*, pg. 623
BLOOMIOS, INC.; *U.S. Public*, pg. 363
BLUE RIDGE CHINA; *Int'l*, pg. 1069
BLUE SPRIG PEDIATRICS, INC.; *U.S. Private*, pg. 593
BLUFFTON OKATIE SURGERY CENTER, L.L.C.—See Tenet Healthcare Corporation; *U.S. Public*, pg. 2005
BML FOOD SCIENCE SOLUTIONS, INC.—See BML, Inc.; *Int'l*, pg. 1076
BNR UDYOG LTD.; *Int'l*, pg. 1093
BON SECOURS HEALTH SYSTEM LTD—See Bon Secours Mercy Health, Inc.; *U.S. Private*, pg. 612
BONUM HEALTH, LLC—See Scienture Holdings, Inc.; *U.S. Public*, pg. 1849
BOSQUE MEDICAL CENTER S.A.—See UnitedHealth Group Incorporated; *U.S. Public*, pg. 2239
BREATHE FREE LANKA (PRIVATE) LIMITED—See Cipla Ltd.; *Int'l*, pg. 1616
BRIOTIX HEALTH, LIMITED PARTNERSHIP—See U.S. Physical Therapy, Inc.; *U.S. Public*, pg. 2214
BROOKDALE EAU GALLIE—See Brookdale Senior Living Inc.; *U.S. Public*, pg. 393
BROOKDALE GARDENS INC—See Brookdale Senior Living Inc.; *U.S. Public*, pg. 394
BROOKDALE HOME HEALTH—See Brookdale Senior Living Inc.; *U.S. Public*, pg. 394
BROOKDALE SENIOR LIVING INC. - JACKSONVILLE—See Brookdale Senior Living Inc.; *U.S. Public*, pg. 394
BROOKWOOD HOME HEALTH, LLC—See Tenet Healthcare Corporation; *U.S. Public*, pg. 2008
BROOKWOOD MEDICAL PARTNERS - ENT, L.L.C.—See Tenet Healthcare Corporation; *U.S. Public*, pg. 2002
BROOKWOOD PRIMARY CARE HOOVER, L.L.C.—See Tenet Healthcare Corporation; *U.S. Public*, pg. 2002
BROOKWOOD PRIMARY CARE - INVERNESS, L.L.C.—See Tenet Healthcare Corporation; *U.S. Public*, pg. 2002
BROOKWOOD PRIMARY CARE - MOUNTAIN BROOK, L.L.C.—See Tenet Healthcare Corporation; *U.S. Public*, pg. 2002
BROOKWOOD PRIMARY CARE - OAK MOUNTAIN, L.L.C.—See Tenet Healthcare Corporation; *U.S. Public*, pg. 2002
BROOKWOOD PRIMARY CARE THE NARROWS, L.L.C.—See Tenet Healthcare Corporation; *U.S. Public*, pg. 2002
BUCKEYE COMMUNITY HEALTH PLAN INC.—See Centene Corporation; *U.S. Public*, pg. 468
BUCKLEY HEALTHCARE CENTER, LLC—See National HealthCare Corporation; *U.S. Public*, pg. 1495
BURNSIDE WAR MEMORIAL HOSPITAL INC.; *Int'l*, pg. 1226
BURNT CHURCH PRIMARY & URGENT CARE, L.L.C.—See Tenet Healthcare Corporation; *U.S. Public*, pg. 2008
BWP ASSOCIATES, LTD.—See Tenet Healthcare Corporation; *U.S. Public*, pg. 2008
CAE HEALTHCARE INC.—See Madison Industries Holdings LLC; *U.S. Private*, pg. 2543
CALLOWAY CREEK SURGERY CENTER, L.P.—See HCA Healthcare, Inc.; *U.S. Public*, pg. 992
CAMPION AMBULANCE SERVICE, INC.; *U.S. Private*, pg. 731
CANNON ST. (H.C.C.) LIMITED—See Co-operative Group Limited; *Int'l*, pg. 1679
CAPIO PROXIMITY CARE—See Apax Partners LLP; *Int'l*, pg. 502
CAPITAL RADIOLOGY PTY LTD—See Capitol Health Limited; *Int'l*, pg. 1314
CARDIAC NETWORK, INC.; *U.S. Private*, pg. 749
CARDIOLOGY PHYSICIANS ASSOCIATES, L.L.C.—See Tenet Healthcare Corporation; *U.S. Public*, pg. 2003
CARDIOVASCULAR CARE GROUP, INC.; *U.S. Private*, pg. 751
CARE MANAGEMENT GROUP, LLC—See Security National Financial Corporation; *U.S. Public*, pg. 1856

CARE NETWORK—See Managed Care of America Inc.; *U.S. Private*, pg. 2559
CARESPOT OF OVERLAND PARK (W. 151ST STREET), LLC—See HCA Healthcare, Inc.; *U.S. Public*, pg. 992
CARESPOT—See Tenet Healthcare Corporation; *U.S. Public*, pg. 2013
CARLTON LIFE - RESIDENCIAS E SERVICOS S.A.—See UnitedHealth Group Incorporated; *U.S. Public*, pg. 2239
CARL ZEISS MEDITEC CO., LTD.—See Carl-Zeiss-Stiftung; *Int'l*, pg. 1334
CARTERSVILLE OCCUPATIONAL MEDICINE CENTER, LLC—See HCA Healthcare, Inc.; *U.S. Public*, pg. 992
CCBH PSYCHIATRIC HOSPITALISTS, LLC—See HCA Healthcare, Inc.; *U.S. Public*, pg. 992
CD DIAGNOSTICS, INC.—See Zimmer Biomet Holdings, Inc.; *U.S. Public*, pg. 2406
CDS OF NEVADA, INC.—See Catholic Health Initiatives; *U.S. Public*, pg. 789
CEDARCARE, INC.—See HCA Healthcare, Inc.; *U.S. Public*, pg. 992
CEDAR HILL PRIMARY CARE, L.L.C.—See Tenet Healthcare Corporation; *U.S. Public*, pg. 2003
CEGEDIM RX SRL—See Cegedim S.A.; *Int'l*, pg. 1390
CELLECTIS THERAPEUTICS—See Cellectis S.A.; *Int'l*, pg. 1393
CENTENNIAL PRIMARY CARE, LLC—See HCA Healthcare, Inc.; *U.S. Public*, pg. 992
CENTENNIAL PSYCHIATRIC ASSOCIATES, LLC—See HCA Healthcare, Inc.; *U.S. Public*, pg. 992
CENTENNIAL SURGERY CENTER, L.P.—See HCA Healthcare, Inc.; *U.S. Public*, pg. 992
CENTENNIAL SURGICAL ASSOCIATES, LLC—See HCA Healthcare, Inc.; *U.S. Public*, pg. 992
CENTER FOR ADVANCED DIAGNOSTICS LLC—See HCA Healthcare, Inc.; *U.S. Public*, pg. 992
CENTERPOINT CLINIC OF BLUE SPRINGS, LLC—See HCA Healthcare, Inc.; *U.S. Public*, pg. 993
CENTERPOINT ORTHOPEDICS, LLC—See HCA Healthcare, Inc.; *U.S. Public*, pg. 993
CENTRAL CAROLINA-CIM, L.L.C.—See Apollo Global Management, Inc.; *U.S. Public*, pg. 155
CENTRAL CAROLINA-IMA, L.L.C.—See Apollo Global Management, Inc.; *U.S. Public*, pg. 155
CENTRAL FLORIDA REGIONAL HOSPITAL, INC.—See HCA Healthcare, Inc.; *U.S. Public*, pg. 993
CENTRAL HEALTH PLAN OF CALIFORNIA, INC.—See Molina Healthcare, Inc.; *U.S. Public*, pg. 1458
CENTRIFYHEALTH, LLC—See UnitedHealth Group Incorporated; *U.S. Public*, pg. 2239
CENTRUM SURGERY CENTER, LTD.—See HCA Healthcare, Inc.; *U.S. Public*, pg. 993
CENTRUS PREMIER HOMECARE, INC.—See Maxim Healthcare Services, Inc.; *U.S. Private*, pg. 2618
CERNER MULTUM, INC.—See Oracle Corporation; *U.S. Public*, pg. 1610
CGH HOSPITAL, LTD.—See Tenet Healthcare Corporation; *U.S. Public*, pg. 2006
CHA HOLLYWOOD MEDICAL CENTER, L.P.—See Chabiotech Co., Ltd.; *Int'l*, pg. 1436
CHARLESTON HOLDING HMBH—See Compagnia Finanziaria de Benedetti S.p.A.; *Int'l*, pg. 1722
CHARTER HEALTH CARE GROUP LLC—See Pharos Capital Group, LLC; *U.S. Private*, pg. 3166
CHARTLOGIC, INC.—See Medsphere Systems Corp.; *U.S. Private*, pg. 2658
CHATEAU JULIA HEALTHCARE, INC.—See The Ensign Group, Inc.; *U.S. Public*, pg. 2070
CHEM NUT, INC.; *U.S. Private*, pg. 870
CHILL N OUT CRYOTHERAPY, INC.; *U.S. Public*, pg. 489
CHINA HEALTH MANAGEMENT CORP.; *U.S. Public*, pg. 489
CHIU HO (CHINA) MEDICAL TECHNOLOGY CO., LTD.—See CHC Healthcare Group; *Int'l*, pg. 1458
CIPLA HEALTH LIMITED—See Cipla Ltd.; *Int'l*, pg. 1617
CIPLA KENYA LIMITED—See Cipla Ltd.; *Int'l*, pg. 1617
CITIUSTECH INC.; *U.S. Private*, pg. 901
CLARKSVILLE TREATMENT CENTER, LLC—See Acadia Healthcare Company, Inc.; *U.S. Public*, pg. 28
CLEARBRIDGE MEDICAL PHILIPPINES, INC.—See Clearbridge Health Limited; *Int'l*, pg. 1656
CLEARBRIDGE MEDICA SDN BHD—See Clearbridge Health Limited; *Int'l*, pg. 1656
CLEOPATRA HOSPITALS; *Int'l*, pg. 1658
CLINICA BIO BIO S.A.—See UnitedHealth Group Incorporated; *U.S. Public*, pg. 2240
CLINICA CIUDAD DEL MAR S.A.—See UnitedHealth Group Incorporated; *U.S. Public*, pg. 2240
CLINICA DAVILA Y SERVICIOS MEDICOS S.A.—See UnitedHealth Group Incorporated; *U.S. Public*, pg. 2240
CLINICA DE MARLY SA; *Int'l*, pg. 1659
CLINICAL LASERTHERMIA SYSTEMS AMERICAS INC.—See Clinical Laserthermia Systems AB; *Int'l*, pg. 1660
CLINICA MEDICO CIRURGICA DE SANTA TECLA, S.A.—See UnitedHealth Group Incorporated; *U.S. Public*, pg. 2240
CLINICA SAN BORJA—See UnitedHealth Group Incorporated; *U.S. Public*, pg. 2240

CLINICA SANCHEZ FERRER S.A.—See UnitedHealth Group Incorporated; *U.S. Public*, pg. 2240
CLINICA SAN FELIPE S.A.—See UnitedHealth Group Incorporated; *U.S. Public*, pg. 2240
CLINICA SANTA MARIA S.A.—See UnitedHealth Group Incorporated; *U.S. Public*, pg. 2240
CLINICA VESPUCIO S.A.—See UnitedHealth Group Incorporated; *U.S. Public*, pg. 2240
CLINIQUE GENERALE-BEAULIEU SA—See AEVIS VICTORIA SA; *Int'l*, pg. 183
CLINTEC INTERNATIONAL, INC.—See IQVIA Holdings Inc.; *U.S. Public*, pg. 1168
CLINTEC INTERNATIONAL LTD.—See IQVIA Holdings Inc.; *U.S. Public*, pg. 1168
CLIPPER CARDIOVASCULAR ASSOCIATES, INC.—See HCA Healthcare, Inc.; *U.S. Public*, pg. 993
CMIC ASIA-PACIFIC (AUSTRALIA) PTY LTD—See CMIC Holdings Co., Ltd.; *Int'l*, pg. 1670
CMIC ASIA-PACIFIC (HONG KONG) LIMITED—See CMIC Holdings Co., Ltd.; *Int'l*, pg. 1670
CMIC DATA SCIENCE VIETNAM COMPANY LIMITED—See CMIC Holdings Co., Ltd.; *Int'l*, pg. 1670
CMMP SURGICAL CENTER, L.L.C.—See Bain Capital, LP; *U.S. Private*, pg. 446
COASTAL CAROLINA MEDICAL CENTER, INC.—See Tenet Healthcare Corporation; *U.S. Public*, pg. 2008
COGSTATE HEALTHCARE LLC—See CogState Limited; *Int'l*, pg. 1695
COKER GROUP HOLDINGS, LLC—See Trinity Hunt Management, L.P.; *U.S. Private*, pg. 4234
COLLIN COUNTY DIAGNOSTIC ASSOCIATES, PLLC—See HCA Healthcare, Inc.; *U.S. Public*, pg. 994
COLOPLAST B.V.—See Coloplast A/S; *Int'l*, pg. 1703
COLOPLAST TAIWAN CO., LTD.—See Coloplast A/S; *Int'l*, pg. 1704
COLOPLAST TURKIYE MEDIKAL GERECLER SAN. VE TIC. A.S.—See Coloplast A/S; *Int'l*, pg. 1704
COLUMBIA HOSPITAL (PALM BEACHES) LIMITED PARTNERSHIP—See HCA Healthcare, Inc.; *U.S. Public*, pg. 994
COLUMBIA MEDICAL CENTER OF ARLINGTON SUBSIDIARY, L.P.—See HCA Healthcare, Inc.; *U.S. Public*, pg. 994
COMCARE MEDICAL B.V.—See Adenia Partners Ltd; *Int'l*, pg. 143
COMPLETE HEALTHCARE INTERNATIONAL PTE LTD—See AsiaMedic Ltd.; *Int'l*, pg. 617
COMPREHENSIVE HEALTH SERVICES, INC.; *U.S. Private*, pg. 1003
CONCENTRIC HEALTH EXPERIENCE LIMITED—See Stagwell, Inc.; *U.S. Public*, pg. 1926
CONCEPT EFL IMAGING CENTER, LLC—See HCA Healthcare, Inc.; *U.S. Public*, pg. 994
CONIFER HEALTH SOLUTIONS, LLC—See Tenet Healthcare Corporation; *U.S. Public*, pg. 2002
CONIFER VALUE-BASED CARE, LLC—See Tenet Healthcare Corporation; *U.S. Public*, pg. 2002
CONMED, INC.—See H.I.G. Capital, LLC; *U.S. Private*, pg. 1829
CONSTELLATION HEALTHCARE TECHNOLOGIES, INC.; *U.S. Public*, pg. 1023
COOK FAMILY HEALTH CENTER INC.—See Cook Group Incorporated; *U.S. Private*, pg. 1037
CORAL RIDGE OUTPATIENT CENTER, LLC—See Tenet Healthcare Corporation; *U.S. Public*, pg. 2005
CORNERSTONE HEALTHCARE PARTNERS, LLC—See Summit Healthcare REIT, Inc.; *U.S. Private*, pg. 3854
COVENANT HEALTH, INC.; *U.S. Private*, pg. 1071
COVENANT PHYSICIAN PARTNERS, INC.—See KKR & Co. Inc.; *U.S. Public*, pg. 1243
COVENTRY HEALTH CARE OF TEXAS, INC.—See CVS Health Corporation; *U.S. Public*, pg. 615
CROATIA POLIKLINIKA—See Adris Grupa d.d.; *Int'l*, pg. 153
CROWN HEALTH CARE LAUNDRY SERVICES—See The Pritzker Organization, LLC; *U.S. Private*, pg. 4100
CSE-HEALTHCARE SYSTEMS LIMITED—See CSE Global Ltd.; *Int'l*, pg. 1863
CYNOSURE KOREA LIMITED—See El.En. S.p.A.; *Int'l*, pg. 2341
CYNOSURE SPAIN S.L.—See El.En. S.p.A.; *Int'l*, pg. 2341
CYPRESS CREEK HEALTHCARE, INC.—See The Ensign Group, Inc.; *U.S. Public*, pg. 2070
DAVITA AGUAS CLARAS SERVICOS DE NEFROLOGIA LTDA.—See DaVita Inc.; *U.S. Public*, pg. 637
DAVITA BAURU SERVICOS DE NEFROLOGIA LTDA.—See DaVita Inc.; *U.S. Public*, pg. 637
DAVITA CEILANDIA SERVICOS DE NEFROLOGIA LTDA.—See DaVita Inc.; *U.S. Public*, pg. 637
DAVITA SERVICOS DE NEFROLOGIA BOA VISTA LTDA.—See DaVita Inc.; *U.S. Public*, pg. 637
DAVITA SERVICOS DE NEFROLOGIA CAMPO GRANDE LTDA.—See DaVita Inc.; *U.S. Public*, pg. 638
DAVITA SERVICOS DE NEFROLOGIA CUIABA LTDA.—See DaVita Inc.; *U.S. Public*, pg. 638
DAVITA SERVICOS DE NEFROLOGIA PACINI LTDA.—See DaVita Inc.; *U.S. Public*, pg. 638
DAVITA SERVICOS DE NEFROLOGIA SANTOS DUMONT LTDA.—See DaVita Inc.; *U.S. Public*, pg. 638

621999 — ALL OTHER MISCELLAN...

DAVITA SERVICOS DE NEFROLOGIA SUMARE LTDA.—See DaVita Inc.; *U.S. Public*, pg. 638
DELTA REGIONAL MEDICAL CENTER; *U.S. Private*, pg. 1201
DENTAL BENEFIT PROVIDERS, INC.—See UnitedHealth Group Incorporated; *U.S. Public*, pg. 2240
DESERT REGIONAL MEDICAL CENTER, INC.—See Tenet Healthcare Corporation; *U.S. Public*, pg. 2003
DEUTSCHE INTENSIVPFLEGE HOLDING B.V.—See Groupe Bruxelles Lambert SA; *Int'l*, pg. 3099
DGS BUSINESS SERVICES SP. Z O.O.—See Demant A/S; *Int'l*, pg. 2964
DIGITAL INFUSION GMBH—See Asklepios Kliniken GmbH & Co. KGaA; *Int'l*, pg. 623
DIGNITY HEALTH MEDICAL GROUP NEVADA, LLC—See Catholic Health Initiatives; *U.S. Private*, pg. 789
DIRECT IME CORP.—See GIC Pte. Ltd.; *Int'l*, pg. 2964
DIRECT IME CORP.—See Leonard Green & Partners, L.P.; *U.S. Private*, pg. 2426
DISA GLOBAL SOLUTIONS, INC.—See Audax Group, Limited Partnership; *U.S. Private*, pg. 387
DIVERSIFIED CLINICAL SERVICES, INC.; *U.S. Private*, pg. 1241
DIVURGENT; *U.S. Private*, pg. 1244
DMC CARDIOVASCULAR INSTITUTE—See Tenet Healthcare Corporation; *U.S. Public*, pg. 2015
DMC EDUCATION & RESEARCH—See Tenet Healthcare Corporation; *U.S. Public*, pg. 2015
DMC IMAGING, L.L.C.—See Tenet Healthcare Corporation; *U.S. Public*, pg. 2003
DOCAVENUE SASU—See Cegedim S.A.; *Int'l*, pg. 1390
DOCTOR CARE ANYWHERE LIMITED—See Doctor Care Anywhere Group PLC; *Int'l*, pg. 2153
DOGUS SAGLIKLI YASAM VE DANISMANLIK HIZMETLERI TICARET A.S.—See Dogus Holding AS; *Int'l*, pg. 2154
THE DOHMEN COMPANY FOUNDATION—See Dohmen Co.; *U.S. Private*, pg. 1254
DOMINION FERTILITY—See Webster Equity Partners, LLC; *U.S. Private*, pg. 4467
DR. AGARWAL'S EYE HOSPITAL LIMITED; *Int'l*, pg. 2190
DR LALCHANDANI LABS LTD.; *Int'l*, pg. 2189
DR. LAL PATHLABS LTD.; *Int'l*, pg. 2194
DR. SULAIMAN AL HABIB MEDICAL SERVICES GROUP COMPANY; *Int'l*, pg. 2195
DUBLIN INTERNAL MEDICINE PC—See St. Luke's Health Network, Inc.; *U.S. Private*, pg. 3773
E4 SERVICES, LLC—See McLarty Capital Partners UK LLP; *U.S. Private*, pg. 2640
EAST COOPER COMMUNITY HOSPITAL, INC.—See Tenet Healthcare Corporation; *U.S. Public*, pg. 2008
EAST COOPER HYPERBARICS, L.L.C.—See Tenet Healthcare Corporation; *U.S. Public*, pg. 2003
EAST COOPER OBGYN, L.L.C.—See Tenet Healthcare Corporation; *U.S. Public*, pg. 2003
EAST COOPER PRIMARY CARE PHYSICIANS, L.L.C.—See Tenet Healthcare Corporation; *U.S. Public*, pg. 2003
EAST FLORIDA PRIMARY CARE, LLC—See HCA Healthcare, Inc.; *U.S. Public*, pg. 995
EAST POINTE HOSPITAL, INC.—See HCA Healthcare, Inc.; *U.S. Public*, pg. 995
EATING RECOVERY CENTER; *U.S. Private*, pg. 1323
E+CANCERCARE—See Kohlberg & Company, LLC; *U.S. Private*, pg. 2339
ECLINIX HOLDINGS LIMITED—See Aidigong Maternal & Child Health Limited; *Int'l*, pg. 231
ECLUSIVE LLC—See Nautic Partners, LLC; *U.S. Private*, pg. 2872
ECON CARESKILL TRAINING CENTRE PTE LTD—See China Healthcare Limited; *Int'l*, pg. 1507
EDMOND GENERAL SURGERY, LLC—See HCA Healthcare, Inc.; *U.S. Public*, pg. 995
EDMOND PHYSICIAN SERVICES, LLC—See HCA Healthcare, Inc.; *U.S. Public*, pg. 995
EHE, INC.—See UM Holdings Limited; *U.S. Private*, pg. 4278
ELITE HEARING LLC—See Amplifon S.p.A.; *Int'l*, pg. 435
ELITE ORTHOPAEDICS OF EL PASO, PLLC—See HCA Healthcare, Inc.; *U.S. Public*, pg. 995
ELITE ORTHOPAEDICS OF IRVING, PLLC—See HCA Healthcare, Inc.; *U.S. Public*, pg. 995
ELITE ORTHOPAEDICS PTE. LTD.—See Alliance Healthcare Group Limited; *Int'l*, pg. 340
EL MIRADOR SURGERY CENTER, L.L.C.—See Tenet Healthcare Corporation; *U.S. Public*, pg. 2005
EL PASO DAY SURGERY, LLC—See Tenet Healthcare Corporation; *U.S. Public*, pg. 2005
EMBEDDED HEALTH SOLUTIONS PTY. LTD.—See Careteq Limited; *Int'l*, pg. 1325
EMBLEM CORP.—See Aleafia Health Inc.; *Int'l*, pg. 305
EMED HUMAN RESOURCES INDIA PRIVATE LIMITED—See Aster DM Healthcare Ltd.; *Int'l*, pg. 654
EMEIS BELGIUM—See Emeis SA; *Int'l*, pg. 2376
EMERGENCY PSYCHIATRIC MEDICINE, PLLC—See HCA Healthcare, Inc.; *U.S. Public*, pg. 995
ENCOMPASS HEALTH REHABILITATION HOSPITAL OF IOWA CITY, LLC—See Encompass Health Corporation; *U.S. Public*, pg. 755
ENCOUNTERCARE SOLUTIONS, INC.; *U.S. Public*, pg. 760
ENDOSCOPY CONSULTANTS, LLC—See WellStar Health System, Inc.; *U.S. Private*, pg. 4478
ENDOSCOPY OF PLANO, L.P.—See HCA Healthcare, Inc.; *U.S. Public*, pg. 995
EPHRAIM MCDOWELL HEALTH, INC.; *U.S. Private*, pg. 1412
EQUINITI 360 CLINICAL LIMITED—See Siris Capital Group, LLC; *U.S. Private*, pg. 3673
ESHO - EMPRESA DE SERVICOS HOSPITALARES S.A.—See UnitedHealth Group Incorporated; *U.S. Public*, pg. 2240
ESTHELOGUE SRL—See El.En. S.p.A.; *Int'l*, pg. 2342
EUROFINS LGS MEGALAB ANALISIS VETERINARIOS SLU—See Eurofins Scientific S.E.; *Int'l*, pg. 2545
EUROHEALTH SYSTEMS FZ LLC—See Aster DM Healthcare Ltd.; *Int'l*, pg. 654
EVANS SURGERY CENTER—See HCA Healthcare, Inc.; *U.S. Public*, pg. 996
EVICORE HEALTHCARE MSI, LLC—See The Cigna Group; *U.S. Public*, pg. 2062
EXCELLION SERVICOS BIOMEDICOS S.A.—See UnitedHealth Group Incorporated; *U.S. Public*, pg. 2240
EXECUTIVE HEALTH RESOURCES, INC.—See UnitedHealth Group Incorporated; *U.S. Public*, pg. 2240
FARMAFORCE LIMITED; *Int'l*, pg. 2619
FASTMED URGENT CARE—See ABRY Partners, LLC; *U.S. Private*, pg. 41
FEDERATION OF STATE BOARDS OF PHYSICAL THERAPY; *U.S. Private*, pg. 1492
FEELGOOD SVENSKA AB; *Int'l*, pg. 2632
FINLEY TRI-STATES HEALTH GROUP, INC.—See UnityPoint Health; *U.S. Private*, pg. 4303
FLEET LABORATORIES—See Prestige Consumer Healthcare Inc.; *U.S. Public*, pg. 1716
FLEURY S.A.; *Int'l*, pg. 2701
FLEXMINDER, INC.—See The Jellyvision Lab, Inc.; *U.S. Private*, pg. 4058
FMC (JIANGSU) CO. LTD.—See Fresenius Medical Care AG; *Int'l*, pg. 2774
FOR HEALTH OF ARIZONA, INC.—See UnitedHealth Group Incorporated; *U.S. Public*, pg. 2240
FORMATIV HEALTH—See Northwell Health, Inc.; *U.S. Private*, pg. 2958
FRESENIUS KABI AUSTRALIA PTY LIMITED—See Fresenius SE & Co. KGaA; *Int'l*, pg. 2778
FRESENIUS KABI BIDIPHAR JSC—See Fresenius SE & Co. KGaA; *Int'l*, pg. 2778
FRESENIUS KABI BRASIL LTDA.—See Fresenius SE & Co. KGaA; *Int'l*, pg. 2778
FRESENIUS KABI BULGARIA EOOD—See Fresenius SE & Co. KGaA; *Int'l*, pg. 2778
FRESENIUS KABI CHILE LTDA.—See Fresenius SE & Co. KGaA; *Int'l*, pg. 2778
FRESENIUS KABI (CHINA) CO., LTD.—See Fresenius SE & Co. KGaA; *Int'l*, pg. 2777
FRESENIUS KABI COLOMBIA S.A.S.—See Fresenius SE & Co. KGaA; *Int'l*, pg. 2778
FRESENIUS KABI DANMARK A / S—See Fresenius SE & Co. KGaA; *Int'l*, pg. 2778
FRESENIUS KABI D.O.O.—See Fresenius SE & Co. KGaA; *Int'l*, pg. 2778
FRESENIUS KABI HONG KONG LIMITED—See Fresenius SE & Co. KGaA; *Int'l*, pg. 2778
FRESENIUS KABI HUNGARY KFT.—See Fresenius SE & Co. KGaA; *Int'l*, pg. 2778
FRESENIUS KABI ILAC SAN. VE TIC. LTD. STI.—See Fresenius SE & Co. KGaA; *Int'l*, pg. 2778
FRESENIUS KABI INDIA PVT. LTD.—See Fresenius SE & Co. KGaA; *Int'l*, pg. 2778
FRESENIUS KABI JAPAN K.K.—See Fresenius SE & Co. KGaA; *Int'l*, pg. 2778
FRESENIUS KABI MALAYSIA SDN. BHD.—See Fresenius SE & Co. KGaA; *Int'l*, pg. 2778
FRESENIUS KABI NEDERLAND B.V.—See Fresenius SE & Co. KGaA; *Int'l*, pg. 2778
FRESENIUS KABI NEW ZEALAND LIMITED—See Fresenius SE & Co. KGaA; *Int'l*, pg. 2778
FRESENIUS KABI NORWAY AS—See Fresenius SE & Co. KGaA; *Int'l*, pg. 2778
FRESENIUS KABI NV/SA—See Fresenius SE & Co. KGaA; *Int'l*, pg. 2778
FRESENIUS KABI PHARMA PORTUGAL, LDA.—See Fresenius SE & Co. KGaA; *Int'l*, pg. 2778
FRESENIUS KABI PHILIPPINES, INC.—See Fresenius SE & Co. KGaA; *Int'l*, pg. 2778
FRESENIUS KABI S.A.—See Fresenius SE & Co. KGaA; *Int'l*, pg. 2778
FRESENIUS KABI SCIENTIFIC OFFICE EGYPT, LDA.—See Fresenius SE & Co. KGaA; *Int'l*, pg. 2778
FRESENIUS KABI (SINGAPORE) PTE. LTD.—See Fresenius SE & Co. KGaA; *Int'l*, pg. 2777
FRESENIUS KABI S.R.O.—See Fresenius SE & Co. KGaA; *Int'l*, pg. 2778

CORPORATE AFFILIATIONS

FRESENIUS KABI (THAILAND) LTD.—See Fresenius SE & Co. KGaA; *Int'l*, pg. 2777
FRESENIUS MEDICAL CARE (IRELAND) LIMITED—See Fresenius Medical Care AG; *Int'l*, pg. 2774
FRONTIERMEDEX CANADA LIMITED—See UnitedHealth Group Incorporated; *U.S. Public*, pg. 2241
FRYECARE VALDESE, L.L.C.—See Tenet Healthcare Corporation; *U.S. Public*, pg. 2003
FRYECARE WATAUGA, L.L.C.—See Tenet Healthcare Corporation; *U.S. Public*, pg. 2003
GABATHER AB; *Int'l*, pg. 2867
GALEN HOSPITAL ALASKA, INC.—See HCA Healthcare, Inc.; *U.S. Public*, pg. 996
GATEWAY HEALTH ALLIANCE, INC.—See Apollo Global Management, Inc.; *U.S. Public*, pg. 155
GCAM, INC.—See GC Biopharma Corp.; *Int'l*, pg. 2893
GCE SOLUTIONS, GMBH—See IQVIA Holdings Inc.; *U.S. Public*, pg. 1168
GCSA AMBULATORY SURGERY CENTER, LLC—See Tenet Healthcare Corporation; *U.S. Public*, pg. 2005
GEDEON RICHTER VIETNAM LTD.—See Chemical Works of Gedeon Richter Plc; *Int'l*, pg. 1462
GENAE AMERICAS, INC.—See IQVIA Holdings Inc.; *U.S. Public*, pg. 1170
GENAE ASSOCIATES NV—See IQVIA Holdings Inc.; *U.S. Public*, pg. 1170
GENBOOK, INC.—See Booksy Inc.; *U.S. Private*, pg. 616
GENERAL HOSPITAL CAMPUS OF ST. JOSEPH HOSPITAL—See Saint Joseph Hospital; *U.S. Private*, pg. 3529
GENERALI ZAKRILA HEALTH INSURANCE AD—See Assicurazioni Generali S.p.A.; *Int'l*, pg. 644
GENERALI ZAKRILA MEDICAL & DENTAL CENTRE EOOD—See Assicurazioni Generali S.p.A.; *Int'l*, pg. 647
GENERAL MILLS INTERNATIONAL BUSINESSES, INC.—See General Mills, Inc.; *U.S. Public*, pg. 921
GENERATIONS BEHAVIORAL HEALTH, LLC—See Acadia Healthcare Company, Inc.; *U.S. Public*, pg. 29
GENESIS HC LLC—See Welltower Inc.; *U.S. Public*, pg. 2348
GENETIC TECHNOLOGIES CORPORATION PTY. LTD.—See Genetic Technologies Limited; *Int'l*, pg. 2922
GENOA TELEPSYCHIATRY, INC.—See UnitedHealth Group Incorporated; *U.S. Public*, pg. 2241
GLAXOSMITHKLINE CONSUMER HEALTHCARE B.V.—See GSK plc; *Int'l*, pg. 3147
GLOBAL ACCESS HEALTH NETWORK SARL—See Discovery Limited; *Int'l*, pg. 2134
GLOBAL CARE S.R.L.—See Gruppo MutuiOnline S.p.A; *Int'l*, pg. 3141
GNOSCO AB—See Barco N.V.; *Int'l*, pg. 864
GOLDBELT GLACIER HEALTH SERVICES, LLC—See Gold Belt Incorporated; *U.S. Private*, pg. 1727
GOLDEN DEVELOPING SOLUTIONS, INC.; *U.S. Public*, pg. 950
GOLDEN GATE HEALTHCARE CENTER—See Apollo Global Management, Inc.; *U.S. Public*, pg. 156
GOOD SAMARITAN HOSPITAL, LOS ANGELES—See Presbyterian Intercommunity Hospital, Inc.; *U.S. Private*, pg. 3253
GOOOGREEN, INC.; *U.S. Public*, pg. 952
GRACE MEDICAL HOME, INC.; *U.S. Private*, pg. 1749
GRAND STRAND SENIOR HEALTH CENTER, LLC—See HCA Healthcare, Inc.; *U.S. Public*, pg. 997
GRAND STRAND SPECIALTY ASSOCIATES, LLC—See HCA Healthcare, Inc.; *U.S. Public*, pg. 997
GREATER GWINNETT INTERNAL MEDICINE ASSOCIATES, LLC—See HCA Healthcare, Inc.; *U.S. Public*, pg. 997
GREATER NORTHWEST HOUSTON ENTERPRISES—See Tenet Healthcare Corporation; *U.S. Public*, pg. 2003
GREENBROOK TMS, INC.; *Int'l*, pg. 3073
GREEN CROSS I-MED—See GC Biopharma Corp.; *Int'l*, pg. 2894
GREEN CROSS PROPERTY LIMITED—See Co-operative Group Limited; *Int'l*, pg. 1679
GREENLANE IMAGING LTD—See BGH Capital Pty Ltd; *Int'l*, pg. 1008
GREYSTONE INTERNAL MEDICINE - BROOKWOOD, L.L.C.—See Tenet Healthcare Corporation; *U.S. Public*, pg. 2003
GUANGZHOU KINGMED DIAGNOSTICS GROUP CO., LTD.; *Int'l*, pg. 3166
GULF COAST MEDICAL CENTER PRIMARY CARE, LLC—See HCA Healthcare, Inc.; *U.S. Public*, pg. 997
HARBOR MEDICAL ASSOCIATES P.C.—See Partners HealthCare System, Inc.; *U.S. Private*, pg. 3101
HARLEY STREET MEDICAL CENTRE LLC—See Aster DM Healthcare Ltd.; *Int'l*, pg. 654
HARLINGEN PHYSICIAN NETWORK, INC.—See Tenet Healthcare Corporation; *U.S. Public*, pg. 2014
HAYES LOCUMS LLC; *U.S. Private*, pg. 1884
HCA HEALTH SERVICES OF OKLAHOMA, INC.—See HCA Healthcare, Inc.; *U.S. Public*, pg. 997
HCENTIVE, INC.—See UnitedHealth Group Incorporated; *U.S. Public*, pg. 2253
HCSC INSURANCE SERVICES COMPANY—See Health Care Service Corporation; *U.S. Private*, pg. 1892

N.A.I.C.S. INDEX

621999 — ALL OTHER MISCELLAN...

HC SURGICAL SPECIALISTS LIMITED; *Int'l*, pg. 3297
HEALTHCARE GATEWAY LIMITED—See EMIS Group plc; *Int'l*, pg. 2383
HEALTHCARE PARTNERS ASC-LB, LLC—See DaVita Inc.; *U.S. Public*, pg. 639
HEALTHCARE PARTNERS, LLC—See DaVita Inc.; *U.S. Public*, pg. 639
HEALTHCARE PARTNERS SOUTH FLORIDA, LLC—See DaVita Inc.; *U.S. Public*, pg. 639
HEALTHCARE RESOURCE NETWORK LLC; *U.S. Private*, pg. 1895
HEALTHCARE SERVICES GROUP, INC.; *U.S. Public*, pg. 1015
HEALTHCARE SOLUTIONS TEAM, LLC—See The Allstate Corporation; *U.S. Public*, pg. 2033
HEALTHCARESOURCE HR, INC.—See Clearlake Capital Group, L.P.; *U.S. Private*, pg. 937
HEALTHCARESOURCE HR, INC.—See SkyKnight Capital LLC; *U.S. Private*, pg. 3685
HEALTHCARE STRATEGY GROUP, LLC; *U.S. Private*, pg. 1895
HEALTHCLICK CO., LTD.—See CMIC Holdings Co., Ltd.; *Int'l*, pg. 1670
HEALTH COMPLEX MEDICAL, INC.—See AdaptHealth Corp.; *U.S. Public*, pg. 39
HEALTH FITNESS CONCEPTS RN, LLC—See Cardiac Imaging Solutions, LLC; *U.S. Private*, pg. 749
HEALTHIX, INC.; *U.S. Private*, pg. 1896
HEALTHLOGIC SYSTEMS CORPORATION—See Bank of America Corporation; *U.S. Public*, pg. 271
HEALTH-LYNX, INC.—See The Cigna Group; *U.S. Public*, pg. 2061
HEALTHONE CLINIC SERVICES - PRIMARY CARE, LLC—See HCA Healthcare, Inc.; *U.S. Public*, pg. 998
HEALTHONE HEART CARE LLC—See HCA Healthcare, Inc.; *U.S. Public*, pg. 998
HEALTH PARTNERS, INC.; *U.S. Private*, pg. 1894
HEALTH SMART LIMITED—See Hong Kong Economic Times Holdings Ltd; *Int'l*, pg. 3465
HEALTHSPRING OF FLORIDA, INC.—See The Cigna Group; *U.S. Public*, pg. 2061
HEALTHSTAT, INC.—See New Enterprise Associates, LLC; *U.S. Private*, pg. 2895
HEALTHWAYS WHOLEHEALTH NETWORKS, INC.—See Stone Point Capital LLC; *U.S. Private*, pg. 3825
THE HEART AND VASCULAR CLINIC, L.L.C.—See Tenet Healthcare Corporation; *U.S. Public*, pg. 2008
HEART MEDICAL CARE CO., LTD.—See EQT AB; *Int'l*, pg. 2467
HEART & VASCULAR CENTER OF ARIZONA, PLLC—See Webster Equity Partners, LLC; *U.S. Private*, pg. 4467
HEART & VASCULAR INSTITUTE OF MICHIGAN—See Tenet Healthcare Corporation; *U.S. Public*, pg. 2015
HELIOS KLINIKUM PIRNA GMBH—See Fresenius SE & Co. KGaA; *Int'l*, pg. 2778
HEMOSONICS, LLC—See Diagnostica Stago S.A.S.; *Int'l*, pg. 2103
HENDERSONVILLE HOSPITAL CORPORATION—See HCA Healthcare, Inc.; *U.S. Public*, pg. 998
HENDERSONVILLE OB/GYN, LLC—See HCA Healthcare, Inc.; *U.S. Public*, pg. 998
HERITAGE MEDICAL GROUP OF HILTON HEAD, L.L.C.—See Tenet Healthcare Corporation; *U.S. Public*, pg. 2008
HERMED INGENIERIA CLINICA ESPANA, S.L.—See Fresenius SE & Co. KGaA; *Int'l*, pg. 2780
HERMED MEDIZINTECHNIK SCHWEIZ AG—See Fresenius SE & Co. KGaA; *Int'l*, pg. 2780
HERMED MEDROTT MEDICAL BVBA—See Fresenius SE & Co. KGaA; *Int'l*, pg. 2780
HERMED MEDROTT MEDICAL B.V.—See Fresenius SE & Co. KGaA; *Int'l*, pg. 2780
HERMED TECHNISCHE BERATUNGS GMBH—See Fresenius SE & Co. KGaA; *Int'l*, pg. 2780
HERMITAGE PRIMARY CARE, LLC—See HCA Healthcare, Inc.; *U.S. Public*, pg. 998
HIGHWAY TO HEALTH, INC.; *U.S. Private*, pg. 1942
HILLROM BELGIUM B.V.—See Baxter International Inc.; *U.S. Public*, pg. 283
HMO MISSOURI, INC.—See Elevance Health, Inc.; *U.S. Public*, pg. 730
HOA LAM-SHANGRI-LA HEALTHCARE LTD. LIABILITY CO—See Aseana Properties Ltd.; *Int'l*, pg. 605
HO KOK SUN COLORECTAL PTE. LTD.—See Alliance Healthcare Group Limited; *Int'l*, pg. 340
HOKUSHIN CLINICAL LABORATORY, INC.—See H.U. Group Holdings, Inc.; *Int'l*, pg. 3197
HOLISTIC CARE HOME HEALTH AGENCY, INC.—See Astrana Health Inc.; *U.S. Public*, pg. 217
HOLYOKE HEALTHCARE CENTER, LLC—See National HealthCare Corporation; *U.S. Public*, pg. 1495
HORIZON CSA LLC—See Cressey & Company, LP; *U.S. Private*, pg. 1095
HORIZON CSA LLC—See Health Enterprise Partners LLC; *U.S. Private*, pg. 1893
HOSPITAL ALVORADA DE TAGUATINGA LTDA.—See UnitedHealth Group Incorporated; *U.S. Public*, pg. 2241
HOSPITAL MONTE KLINIKUM S/S LTDA.—See United-Health Group Incorporated; *U.S. Public*, pg. 2241
HOUSE CALLS OF NEW MEXICO, LLC—See Addus HomeCare Corporation; *U.S. Public*, pg. 40
HOUSTON SPECIALTY HOSPITAL, INC.—See Tenet Healthcare Corporation; *U.S. Public*, pg. 2008
HPP A.C.E.—See UnitedHealth Group Incorporated; *U.S. Public*, pg. 2241
HPP ALGARVE, S.A.—See UnitedHealth Group Incorporated; *U.S. Public*, pg. 2241
HPP BOAVISTA, S.A.—See UnitedHealth Group Incorporated; *U.S. Public*, pg. 2241
HPP - HOSPITAIS PRIVADOS DE PORTUGAL, SGPS, S.A.—See UnitedHealth Group Incorporated; *U.S. Public*, pg. 2241
HPP SAUDE - PARCERIAS CASCAIS, S.A.—See UnitedHealth Group Incorporated; *U.S. Public*, pg. 2241
H.U. GROUP RESEARCH INSTITUTE G.K.—See H.U. Group Holdings, Inc.; *Int'l*, pg. 3197
HUMMINGBIRD COACHING SYSTEMS LLC—See Humana, Inc.; *U.S. Public*, pg. 1070
ICECURE MEDICAL INC.—See Icecure Medical Ltd.; *Int'l*, pg. 3579
IGB INTEGRATIVES GESUNDHEITSZENTRUM BOIZENBURG GMBH—See Asklepios Kliniken GmbH & Co. KGaA; *Int'l*, pg. 624
IMAX CORPORATION—See Imax Corporation; *Int'l*, pg. 3620
IMEDICAL EQUIPMENT & SERVICES LLC; *U.S. Private*, pg. 2046
IMPLANT CONCIERGE, LLC—See Zimmer Biomet Holdings, Inc.; *U.S. Public*, pg. 2406
INCARNUS MALAYSIA SDN. BHD.—See IQVIA Holdings Inc.; *U.S. Public*, pg. 1169
INFOLYTX BANGLADESH LIMITED—See Advanced Chemical Industries Limited; *Int'l*, pg. 158
INFUSYSTEMS HOLDINGS, INC.; *U.S. Private*, pg. 2075
INGRAM & ASSOCIATES, LLC—See UnitedHealth Group Incorporated; *U.S. Public*, pg. 2241
INSIGHT GENETICS, INC.—See OncoCyte Corporation; *U.S. Public*, pg. 1601
INSIGNIA HEALTH, LLC—See Phreesia, Inc.; *U.S. Public*, pg. 1689
INSITE-INTERVENTIONS GMBH—See Asklepios Kliniken GmbH & Co. KGaA; *Int'l*, pg. 623
INTEGRATED DERMATOLOGY GROUP; *U.S. Private*, pg. 2099
INTEGRIS CARDIOVASCULAR PHYSICIANS LLC—See INTEGRIS Health, Inc.; *U.S. Private*, pg. 2102
INTERACTIVE HEALTH, INC.—See CI Capital Partners LLC; *U.S. Private*, pg. 895
INTERIM HOUSE WEST FACILITIES, INC.—See Public Health Management Corporation; *U.S. Private*, pg. 3299
INTERNATIONAL PLANT NUTRITION INSTITUTE; *U.S. Private*, pg. 2119
INTERRA HEALTH, INC.; *U.S. Private*, pg. 2123
INTRA-OP MONITORING SERVICES, LLC—See HealthEdge Investment Partners, LLC; *U.S. Private*, pg. 1896
INZETBAAR BV—See Allied Universal Manager LLC; *U.S. Private*, pg. 190
IOWA TOTAL CARE, INC.—See Centene Corporation; *U.S. Public*, pg. 469
IQVIA AG—See IQVIA Holdings Inc.; *U.S. Public*, pg. 1168
IQVIA SOLUTIONS ASIA PTE. LTD.—See IQVIA Holdings Inc.; *U.S. Public*, pg. 1168
IQVIA SOLUTIONS DO BRASIL LTDA.—See IQVIA Holdings Inc.; *U.S. Public*, pg. 1169
IQVIA SOLUTIONS (NZ) LIMITED—See IQVIA Holdings Inc.; *U.S. Public*, pg. 1168
IQVIA SOLUTIONS PAKISTAN (PRIVATE) LIMITED—See IQVIA Holdings Inc.; *U.S. Public*, pg. 1169
IQVIA SOLUTIONS PHILIPPINES INC.—See IQVIA Holdings Inc.; *U.S. Public*, pg. 1168
IQVIA TECHNOLOGY AND SERVICES AG—See IQVIA Holdings Inc.; *U.S. Public*, pg. 1169
IQVIA (THAILAND) CO. LTD.—See IQVIA Holdings Inc.; *U.S. Public*, pg. 1169
IVY VENTURES, LLC—See ABRY Partners, LLC; *U.S. Private*, pg. 41
JACKSON MEDICAL CENTER, L.L.C.—See Tenet Healthcare Corporation; *U.S. Public*, pg. 2003
JACKSONVILLE BEACH SURGERY CENTER, LLC—See Bain Capital, LP; *U.S. Private*, pg. 446
JAGER HEALTH KOLN GMBH—See IQVIA Holdings Inc.; *U.S. Public*, pg. 1169
JANSSEN-CILAG PTY. LIMITED—See Johnson & Johnson; *U.S. Public*, pg. 1197
JAPAN CLINICAL LABORATORIES, INC.—See H.U. Group Holdings, Inc.; *Int'l*, pg. 3197
JENNY CRAIG OPERATIONS, INC.—See H.I.G. Capital, LLC; *U.S. Private*, pg. 1830
JN-INTERNATIONAL MEDICAL CORPORATION; *U.S. Private*, pg. 2216
JOHN ADAMS HEALTHCARE CENTER, LLC—See National HealthCare Corporation; *U.S. Public*, pg. 1495
JORDAN HEALTH SERVICES, INC.—See Kelso & Company, L.P.; *U.S. Private*, pg. 2278
JOURNEY HOME HEALTHCARE OF SAN ANTONIO, LLC—See Tenet Healthcare Corporation; *U.S. Public*, pg. 2014
JSA P5 NEVADA, LLC.—See DaVita Inc.; *U.S. Public*, pg. 640
KANSAS CITY VASCULAR & GENERAL SURGERY GROUP, LLC—See HCA Healthcare, Inc.; *U.S. Public*, pg. 1000
KANTAR HEALTH—See Oracle Corporation; *U.S. Public*, pg. 1611
KARSONS PHARMACY LIMITED—See Bestway (Holdings) Limited; *Int'l*, pg. 1001
KBBM, INC.—See H.U. Group Holdings, Inc.; *Int'l*, pg. 3197
KEYSTONE PEER REVIEW ORGANIZATION, INC.—See Apax Partners LLP; *Int'l*, pg. 504
KIDZ TEETH LIMITED—See BGH Capital Pty Ltd; *Int'l*, pg. 1008
KIOSK MEDICINE KENTUCKY, LLC—See The Kroger Co.; *U.S. Public*, pg. 2108
KLINIK HILDESHEIMER LAND GMBH—See Fresenius SE & Co. KGaA; *Int'l*, pg. 2779
KLINIKUM GIFHORN GMBH—See Fresenius SE & Co. KGaA; *Int'l*, pg. 2779
KLM HEALTH SERVICES B.V.—See Air France-KLM S.A.; *Int'l*, pg. 237
KOS SPA—See Compagnia Finanziaria de Benedetti S.p.A.; *Int'l*, pg. 1722
KYODO IGAKU LABORATORIES, INC.—See BML, Inc.; *Int'l*, pg. 1076
LABCORP EMPLOYER SERVICES, INC.—See Laboratory Corporation of America Holdings; *U.S. Public*, pg. 1287
LAKE WALES HOSPITAL CORPORATION—See Adventist Health System Sunbelt Healthcare Corporation; *U.S. Private*, pg. 109
LAS ENCINAS HOSPITAL—See HCA Healthcare, Inc.; *U.S. Public*, pg. 1000
LAS VEGAS SURGERY CENTER—See HCA Healthcare, Inc.; *U.S. Public*, pg. 1000
LAWNWOOD CARDIOVASCULAR SURGERY, LLC—See HCA Healthcare, Inc.; *U.S. Public*, pg. 1000
LAWNWOOD PAVILION PHYSICIAN SERVICES, LLC—See HCA Healthcare, Inc.; *U.S. Public*, pg. 1000
LEHIGH VALLEY HEALTH NETWORK EMS—See Lehigh Valley Health Network, Inc.; *U.S. Private*, pg. 2419
LIBERTY RC, INC.—See DaVita Inc.; *U.S. Public*, pg. 640
LIM JIT FONG COLORECTAL PTE. LTD.—See Alliance Healthcare Group Limited; *Int'l*, pg. 340
LIQUIDAGENTS HEALTHCARE, LLC; *U.S. Private*, pg. 2466
THE LITTLE CLINIC OF COLORADO LLC—See The Kroger Co.; *U.S. Public*, pg. 2109
THE LITTLE CLINIC OF IN LLC—See The Kroger Co.; *U.S. Public*, pg. 2109
LIVHOME, INC.—See Bain Capital, LP; *U.S. Private*, pg. 431
LLOYDS PHARMACY CLINICAL HOMECARE LIMITED—See McKesson Corporation; *U.S. Public*, pg. 1408
LMT SURGICAL PTY LTD—See EBOS Group Limited; *Int'l*, pg. 2285
LOGISITICS HEALTH, INC.—See UnitedHealth Group Incorporated; *U.S. Public*, pg. 2242
LOS ANGELES CARDIOLOGY & ASSOCIATES—See Presbyterian Intercommunity Hospital, Inc.; *U.S. Private*, pg. 3253
LUX MED SP. Z.O.O—See Abris Capital Partners Sp. z o.o.; *Int'l*, pg. 69
MADISON INTERNAL MEDICINE, LLC—See HCA Healthcare, Inc.; *U.S. Public*, pg. 1001
MALARIA RESEARCH COMPANY PTY LTD—See Arovella Therapeutics Limited; *Int'l*, pg. 578
MANAGED HEALTH NETWORK, LLC—See Centene Corporation; *U.S. Public*, pg. 470
THE MANAGEMENT GROUP LLC—See Centene Corporation; *U.S. Public*, pg. 470
MARCH VISION CARE, INC.—See UnitedHealth Group Incorporated; *U.S. Public*, pg. 2242
MARIENIA SA—See Clariane SE; *Int'l*, pg. 1643
MARYLAND COLLABORATIVE CARE TRANSFORMATION ORGANIZATION, INC.—See Centene Corporation; *U.S. Public*, pg. 471
MAXIM HOME HEALTH RESOURCES, INC.—See Maxim Healthcare Services, Inc.; *U.S. Private*, pg. 2618
MCMC LLC; *U.S. Public*, pg. 2642
MEDASCEND LLC—See The Advanced Group of Companies; *U.S. Private*, pg. 3982
MEDECIN DIRECT—See Teladoc Health, Inc.; *U.S. Public*, pg. 1992
MEDEXPRESS URGENT CARE OF BOYNTON BEACH, LLC—See UnitedHealth Group Incorporated; *U.S. Public*, pg. 2242
MEDGATE DEUTSCHLAND GMBH—See Asklepios Kliniken GmbH & Co. KGaA; *Int'l*, pg. 624
MEDI24 AG—See Allianz SE; *Int'l*, pg. 354
THE MEDICAL CENTER OF CENTRAL GEORGIA, INC.—See Central Georgia Health System Inc.; *U.S. Private*, pg. 821
MEDICAL PREPARATORY SCHOOL OF ALLIED HEALTH, LLC—See UnitedHealth Group Incorporated; *U.S. Public*, pg. 2242

621999 — ALL OTHER MISCELLAN... CORPORATE AFFILIATIONS

N.A.I.C.S. Index

MEDICAL STAFFING OPTIONS—See Health Carousel, LLC; *U.S. Private*, pg. 1893
MEDICLIN MVZ ACHERN GMBH—See Asklepios Kliniken GmbH & Co. KGaA; *Int'l*, pg. 624
MEDICOLEGAL SERVICES, LLC—See GIC Pte. Ltd.; *Int'l*, pg. 2964
MEDICOLEGAL SERVICES, LLC—See Leonard Green & Partners, L.P.; *U.S. Private*, pg. 2425
MEDISCAN DIAGNOSTIC SERVICES, LLC—See Cross Country Healthcare, Inc.; *U.S. Public*, pg. 595
MEDITERRA - SEDLCANY, S.R.O.—See Fresenius SE & Co. KGaA; *Int'l*, pg. 2780
MEDIWARE CONSULTING & ANALYTICS—See Leonard Green & Partners, L.P.; *U.S. Private*, pg. 2430
MEDIWARE CONSULTING & ANALYTICS—See TPG Capital, L.P.; *U.S. Public*, pg. 2177
MEDPLEX OUTPATIENT SURGERY CENTER, LTD.—See Tenet Healthcare Corporation; *U.S. Public*, pg. 2008
MEDSHOP GARDEN PHARMACY LLC—See Aster DM Healthcare Ltd.; *Int'l*, pg. 654
MEDSYS GROUP CONSULTING; *U.S. Private*, pg. 2659
MEMPHIS URGENT CARE #2, L.L.C.—See Tenet Healthcare Corporation; *U.S. Public*, pg. 2005
MES SOLUTIONS—See GIC Pte. Ltd.; *Int'l*, pg. 2964
MES SOLUTIONS—See Leonard Green & Partners, L.P.; *U.S. Private*, pg. 2425
METANOMICS HEALTH GMBH—See BIOCRATES Life Sciences AG; *Int'l*, pg. 1037
METRO AVIATION, INC.; *U.S. Private*, pg. 2685
METRO MEDICAL CENTER L.L.C.—See Aster DM Healthcare Ltd.; *Int'l*, pg. 654
MICHAEL B. BAYLESS & ASSOCIATES, LLC—See Centene Corporation; *U.S. Public*, pg. 470
MICROPHONICS, INC.; *U.S. Public*, pg. 1438
MID-AMERICA SURGERY CENTER, LLC—See HCA Healthcare, Inc.; *U.S. Public*, pg. 1002
MID-ATLANTIC HOME HEALTH NETWORK, INC.; *U.S. Public*, pg. 1445
MID-ISLAND PRIMARY & URGENT CARE, L.L.C.—See Tenet Healthcare Corporation; *U.S. Public*, pg. 2008
MIDWEST CARDIOVASCULAR & THORACIC SURGEONS OF KANSAS, LLC—See HCA Healthcare, Inc.; *U.S. Public*, pg. 1003
MIDWEST CARDIOVASCULAR & THORACIC SURGERY, LLC—See HCA Healthcare, Inc.; *U.S. Public*, pg. 1003
MISSION HEALTH PARTNERS, INC.—See HCA Healthcare, Inc.; *U.S. Public*, pg. 1003
MK PROSTHETIC & ORTHOTIC SERVICES INC.—See Patient Square Capital, L.P.; *U.S. Private*, pg. 3107
MLS GROUP OF COMPANIES, LLC—See GIC Pte. Ltd.; *Int'l*, pg. 2964
MLS GROUP OF COMPANIES, LLC—See Leonard Green & Partners, L.P.; *U.S. Private*, pg. 2425
M&M MORTGAGE SERVICES, INC.—See American Securities LLC; *U.S. Private*, pg. 250
MODERN DAR AL SHIFA PHARMACY LLC—See Aster DM Healthcare Ltd.; *Int'l*, pg. 654
MODESTO ON-CALL SERVICES, L.L.C.—See Tenet Healthcare Corporation; *U.S. Public*, pg. 2003
MONTE KLINIKUM DIAGNOSTICO POR IMAGEM LTDA.—See UnitedHealth Group Incorporated; *U.S. Public*, pg. 2242
MORRISON MANAGEMENT SPECIALISTS, INC.—See Compass Group PLC; *Int'l*, pg. 1751
MORROW FAMILY MEDICINE, LLC; *U.S. Private*, pg. 2790
MPLT HEALTHCARE, LLC; *U.S. Private*, pg. 2804
MPT OF ST. LUKE'S LEAWOOD, LLC—See Medical Properties Trust, Inc.; *U.S. Public*, pg. 1412
MPT OF ST. LUKE'S OLATHE, LLC—See Medical Properties Trust, Inc.; *U.S. Public*, pg. 1412
MPT OF ST. LUKE'S PARALLEL PARKWAY, LLC—See Medical Properties Trust, Inc.; *U.S. Public*, pg. 1412
MPT OF ST. LUKE'S ROELAND PARK, LLC—See Medical Properties Trust, Inc.; *U.S. Public*, pg. 1412
MPT OF ST. LUKE'S SHAWNEE, LLC—See Medical Properties Trust, Inc.; *U.S. Public*, pg. 1412
MPT OF ST VINCENT AVON, LLC—See Medical Properties Trust, Inc.; *U.S. Public*, pg. 1412
MPT OF ST VINCENT BROWNSBURG, LLC—See Medical Properties Trust, Inc.; *U.S. Public*, pg. 1412
MPT OF ST VINCENT CASTLETON, LLC—See Medical Properties Trust, Inc.; *U.S. Public*, pg. 1412
MPT OF ST VINCENT INDIANAPOLIS SOUTH, LLC—See Medical Properties Trust, Inc.; *U.S. Public*, pg. 1412
MPT OF ST VINCENT NOBLESVILLE SOUTH, LLC—See Medical Properties Trust, Inc.; *U.S. Public*, pg. 1412
MPT OF ST VINCENT PLAINFIELD, LLC—See Medical Properties Trust, Inc.; *U.S. Public*, pg. 1412
MUNCIE TREATMENT CENTER, LLC—See Acadia Healthcare Company, Inc.; *U.S. Public*, pg. 29
MURDOCK AMBULATORY SURGICAL CENTER, LLC—See Tenet Healthcare Corporation; *U.S. Public*, pg. 2005
MUTUAL HEALTH SERVICES—See Medical Mutual of Ohio; *U.S. Private*, pg. 2655
MVZ BAD NEUSTADT/ SAALE GMBH—See Asklepios Kliniken GmbH & Co. KGaA; *Int'l*, pg. 624
MVZ DRESDEN BETRIEBS GMBH—See DaVita Inc.; *U.S. Public*, pg. 640
MVZ MANAGEMENT GMBH ATTENDORN—See Fresenius SE & Co. KGaA; *Int'l*, pg. 2779
MY FAMILY CLINIC (ANGSANA BREEZE@YISHUN) PTE. LTD.—See Alliance Healthcare Group Limited; *Int'l*, pg. 340
MY FAMILY CLINIC (CCK) PTE. LTD.—See Alliance Healthcare Group Limited; *Int'l*, pg. 340
MY FAMILY CLINIC (CLEMENTI 325) PTE. LTD.—See Alliance Healthcare Group Limited; *Int'l*, pg. 340
MY FAMILY CLINIC (CLEMENTI) PTE. LTD.—See Alliance Healthcare Group Limited; *Int'l*, pg. 340
MY FAMILY CLINIC (PUNGGOL CENTRAL) PTE. LTD.—See Alliance Healthcare Group Limited; *Int'l*, pg. 340
MY FAMILY CLINIC (SEGAR) PTE. LTD.—See Alliance Healthcare Group Limited; *Int'l*, pg. 340
MY FAMILY CLINIC (SJ) PTE. LTD.—See Alliance Healthcare Group Limited; *Int'l*, pg. 340
MY FAMILY CLINIC (ST GEORGE) PTE. LTD.—See Alliance Healthcare Group Limited; *Int'l*, pg. 340
MY FAMILY CLINIC (TH) PTE. LTD.—See Alliance Healthcare Group Limited; *Int'l*, pg. 340
MY FAMILY CLINIC (WD) PTE. LTD.—See Alliance Healthcare Group Limited; *Int'l*, pg. 340
MY FAMILY CLINIC (WOODLANDS GLEN) PTE. LTD.—See Alliance Healthcare Group Limited; *Int'l*, pg. 340
MY HEALTH SERVICES (THAILAND) CO., LTD.—See Allianz Ayudhya Capital Public Company Limited; *Int'l*, pg. 341
NATIONAL DECISION SUPPORT COMPANY, LLC—See UnitedHealth Group Incorporated; *U.S. Public*, pg. 2248
NATIONAL DIAGNOSTIC IMAGING CENTERS, INC.—See Tenet Healthcare Corporation; *U.S. Public*, pg. 2004
NATIONAL HOLDING INVESTMENT CO.—See National Presto Industries, Inc; *U.S. Public*, pg. 1497
NAVICUS; *U.S. Private*, pg. 2872
NEPHROCARE PORTUGAL S.A.—See Fresenius Medical Care AG; *Int'l*, pg. 2776
NESTOR PRIMECARE SERVICES LTD.—See Charterhouse Capital Partners LLP; *Int'l*, pg. 1454
NESTOR PRIMECARE SERVICES LTD.—See CVC Capital Partners SICAV-FIS S.A.; *Int'l*, pg. 1882
NETIMPACT HOLDINGS, INC.; *U.S. Public*, pg. 1508
NEUSOFT CHC MEDICAL SERVICE CO., LTD.—See CHC Healthcare Group; *Int'l*, pg. 1458
NEW ALBANY OUTPATIENT SURGERY, LLC—See Bain Capital, LP; *U.S. Private*, pg. 447
NEW WORLD HEALTH BRANDS, INC.—See SPARTA COMMERCIAL SERVICES, INC.; *U.S. Public*, pg. 1914
NHC HEALTHCARE/KINGSPORT, LLC—See National HealthCare Corporation; *U.S. Public*, pg. 1496
NHC HEALTHCARE-SUMNER, LLC—See National HealthCare Corporation; *U.S. Public*, pg. 1495
NHC HEALTHCARE/TULLAHOMA, LLC—See National HealthCare Corporation; *U.S. Public*, pg. 1496
NHC-MAURY REGIONAL TRANSITIONAL CARE CENTER, LLC—See National HealthCare Corporation; *U.S. Public*, pg. 1496
NOBEL BIOCARE PROCERA SERVICES INC.—See Danaher Corporation; *U.S. Public*, pg. 629
NOCTURNA SLEEP CENTER, LLC—See Foundation Healthcare, Inc.; *U.S. Private*, pg. 1580
NOCTURNA SLEEP THERAPY, LP—See Foundation Healthcare, Inc.; *U.S. Private*, pg. 1580
NOLAND HEALTH SERVICES, INC.; *U.S. Private*, pg. 2934
NORTH AMERICAN MEDICAL MANAGEMENT - ILLINOIS, INC.—See UnitedHealth Group Incorporated; *U.S. Public*, pg. 2242
NORTHERN NEVADA MEDICAL GROUP, LLC—See Universal Health Services, Inc.; *U.S. Public*, pg. 2258
NORTH SHORE LIJ HEALTH SYSTEMS; *U.S. Private*, pg. 2946
NORTHWEST PERMANENTE P.C.—See Kaiser Permanente; *U.S. Private*, pg. 2256
NORTHWEST TEXAS SURGICAL HOSPITAL, L.L.C.—See Universal Health Services, Inc.; *U.S. Public*, pg. 2258
NOVO INTEGRATED SCIENCES, INC.; *U.S. Public*, pg. 1549
NOVU, INC.; *U.S. Private*, pg. 2968
NUCH OF TEXAS—See Tenet Healthcare Corporation; *U.S. Public*, pg. 2005
OAK PLAINS ACADEMY OF TENNESSEE, INC.—See Universal Health Services, Inc.; *U.S. Public*, pg. 2258
OB HEALTHCARE CORPORATION—See InfuSystem Holdings, Inc.; *U.S. Public*, pg. 1118
OCALA BEHAVIORAL HEALTH, LLC—See Universal Health Services, Inc.; *U.S. Public*, pg. 2258
OKLAHOMA CITY HOME CARE SERVICES, LLC—See Community Health Systems, Inc.; *U.S. Public*, pg. 555
OLFACTORY BIOSCIENCES CORP.; *U.S. Public*, pg. 1570
ONCOLOGICS, INC.—See Kohlberg & Company, LLC; *U.S. Private*, pg. 2339
ONCURE MEDICAL CORPORATION—See Vestar Capital Partners, LLC; *U.S. Private*, pg. 4371
ONE CALL CARE TRANSPORT + TRANSLATE ENTERPRISES, LLC—See Apax Partners LLP; *Int'l*, pg. 505
ONSITE OCCUPATIONAL HEALTH & SAFETY, INC.; *U.S. Private*, pg. 3028
ON TARGET HEALTH, LLC; *U.S. Private*, pg. 3018
O OLIVE OIL, LLC—See Lifecore Biomedical, Inc.; *U.S. Public*, pg. 1312
OPTIMUM CONTACT LIMITED—See IQVIA Holdings Inc.; *U.S. Public*, pg. 1170
OPTUM360, LLC—See UnitedHealth Group Incorporated; *U.S. Public*, pg. 2247
OPTUM (FRANCE) SAS—See UnitedHealth Group Incorporated; *U.S. Public*, pg. 2243
OPTUM HEALTH SOLUTIONS (UK) LIMITED—See UnitedHealth Group Incorporated; *U.S. Public*, pg. 2243
OPTUM (SPAIN) S.A.U.—See UnitedHealth Group Incorporated; *U.S. Public*, pg. 2243
ORPEA DEUTSCHLAND GMBH—See Emeis SA; *Int'l*, pg. 2376
ORPEA IBERICA S.A.U—See Emeis SA; *Int'l*, pg. 2376
ORPEA POLSKA SP. Z O. O—See Emeis SA; *Int'l*, pg. 2376
ORTHOCENTER GOTEBORG AB—See Apax Partners LLP; *Int'l*, pg. 502
THE ORTHOPAEDIC CENTRE (FARRER) PTE. LTD.—See Doctor Anywhere Pte Ltd.; *Int'l*, pg. 2153
THE ORTHOPAEDIC CENTRE (GLENEAGLES) PTE. LTD.—See Doctor Anywhere Pte Ltd.; *Int'l*, pg. 2153
THE ORTHOPAEDIC CENTRE (NOVENA) PTE. LTD.—See Doctor Anywhere Pte Ltd.; *Int'l*, pg. 2153
THE ORTHOPAEDIC CENTRE (ORCHARD) PTE. LTD.—See Doctor Anywhere Pte Ltd.; *Int'l*, pg. 2153
ORTHOPAEDIC SURGERY CENTER OF ASHEVILLE, L.P.—See Bain Capital, LP; *U.S. Private*, pg. 447
OTTO HEALTH, LLC—See Thoma Bravo, L.P.; *U.S. Private*, pg. 4150
OU FRESENIUS MEDICAL CARE ESTONIA—See Fresenius Medical Care AG; *Int'l*, pg. 2777
OUR HEALTHY CIRCLE—See Quorum Health Corporation; *U.S. Private*, pg. 3330
PACIFIC ENDOSCOPY & SURGERY CENTER, LLC—See Tenet Healthcare Corporation; *U.S. Public*, pg. 2005
PACIFIC MEDICAL CENTRES PTY LTD—See Healius Limited; *Int'l*, pg. 3303
PACIV, INC.—See Blackford Capital LLC; *U.S. Private*, pg. 574
PALMETTO BEHAVIORAL HEALTH SYSTEM, L.L.C.—See Universal Health Services, Inc.; *U.S. Public*, pg. 2259
PALMETTO PEE DEE BEHAVIORAL HEALTH, L.L.C.—See Universal Health Services, Inc.; *U.S. Public*, pg. 2259
PALMS WEST SURGICENTER—See HCA Healthcare, Inc.; *U.S. Public*, pg. 1005
PANCREATIC CANCER ACTION NETWORK; *U.S. Private*, pg. 3085
PAPERFREE MEDICAL SOLUTIONS, INC.; *U.S. Public*, pg. 1636
PARADIGM MANAGEMENT SERVICES, LLC—See Summit Partners, L.P.; *U.S. Private*, pg. 3855
PARK PLAZA HOSPITAL BILLING CENTER, L.L.C.—See HCA Healthcare, Inc.; *U.S. Public*, pg. 1006
PARTNERMD, LLC—See Markel Group Inc.; *U.S. Public*, pg. 1369
PARTNERS HEALTHCARE SYSTEM, INC.; *U.S. Private*, pg. 3101
PARTNERS IN CARE INC.—See Visiting Nurse Service of New York; *U.S. Private*, pg. 4393
PARTNERS IN CARE MARYLAND, INC.—See Visiting Nurse Service of New York; *U.S. Private*, pg. 4393
PATIENT PLATFORM LIMITED—See EMIS Group plc; *Int'l*, pg. 2383
PEACHTREE SURGICAL & BARIATRIC, PC—See WellStar Health System, Inc.; *U.S. Private*, pg. 4478
PEAK BEHAVIORAL HEALTH SERVICES, LLC—See Universal Health Services, Inc.; *U.S. Public*, pg. 2259
PEDIATRIC SURGERY CENTER - ODESSA, LLC—See Tenet Healthcare Corporation; *U.S. Public*, pg. 2005
PEDIATRIC SURGERY CENTERS, LLC—See Tenet Healthcare Corporation; *U.S. Public*, pg. 2005
PERMANENTE DENTAL ASSOCIATES, PC—See Kaiser Permanente; *U.S. Private*, pg. 2256
THE PERMANENTE MEDICAL GROUP, INC.—See Kaiser Permanente; *U.S. Private*, pg. 2256
PERSONIFILRX, LLC—See Nautic Partners, LLC; *U.S. Private*, pg. 2871
PHARMASITE RESEARCH INC.—See KKR & Co. Inc.; *U.S. Public*, pg. 1252
PHOENIX HEALTH PLANS, INC.—See Tenet Healthcare Corporation; *U.S. Public*, pg. 2014
PHYSICIAN ALLIANCE OF THE ROCKIES, LLC—See UnitedHealth Group Incorporated; *U.S. Public*, pg. 2249
PHYSICIAN CARE PARTNERS, INC.—See UnitedHealth Group Incorporated; *U.S. Public*, pg. 2249
PHYSICIAN PERFORMANCE NETWORK OF GEORGIA, L.L.C.—See Tenet Healthcare Corporation; *U.S. Public*, pg. 2008
PHYSICIANS MEDICAL CENTER, LLC—See Bain Capital, LP; *U.S. Private*, pg. 447
PICMONIC, INC.—See TrueLearn, LLC; *U.S. Private*, pg. 4248
PIONEER HEALTH RESOURCES—See ATAR Capital, LLC; *U.S. Private*, pg. 364

N.A.I.C.S. INDEX

621999 — ALL OTHER MISCELLAN...

PLANIT, INCORPORATED—See Dohmen Co.; *U.S. Private*, pg. 1254
PLATINUM HEALTHCARE PTY. LTD.—See ComfortDelGro Corporation Limited; *Int'l*, pg. 1713
PLAZA SURGERY CENTER, LIMITED PARTNERSHIP—See Universal Health Services, Inc.; *U.S. Public*, pg. 2259
PLURIBUS DIALISE - SACAVEM, S.A.—See DaVita Inc.; *U.S. Public*, pg. 642
PM PEDIATRICS; *U.S. Private*, pg. 3216
POBELLO DIALYSIS, LLC—See DaVita Inc.; *U.S. Public*, pg. 642
POSTGRADUATE HEALTHCARE EDUCATION, LLC—See The Wicks Group of Companies, LLC; *U.S. Private*, pg. 4135
PPJ HEALTHCARE ENTERPRISES, INC.; *U.S. Public*, pg. 1711
PRACTICE PARTNERS IN HEALTHCARE, LLC—See UnitedHealth Group Incorporated; *U.S. Public*, pg. 2249
PREFERRED CARE PARTNERS MEDICAL GROUP, INC.—See UnitedHealth Group Incorporated; *U.S. Public*, pg. 2249
PREMIER MEDICAL GROUP LIMITED—See Capita plc; *Int'l*, pg. 1309
PREMIER MEDICAL SPECIALISTS, L.L.C.—See Tenet Healthcare Corporation; *U.S. Public*, pg. 2003
PRESBYTERIAN INTERCOMMUNITY HOSPITAL, INC.; *U.S. Private*, pg. 3253
PRESS GANEY ASSOCIATES, INC.—See Ares Management Corporation; *U.S. Public*, pg. 190
PRESS GANEY ASSOCIATES, INC.—See Leonard Green & Partners, L.P.; *U.S. Private*, pg. 2427
PRIDE INSTITUTE, INC.—See Universal Health Services, Inc.; *U.S. Public*, pg. 2259
PRIMECARE MEDICAL NETWORK, INC.—See UnitedHealth Group Incorporated; *U.S. Public*, pg. 2249
PRIMECARE OF CITRUS VALLEY, INC.—See UnitedHealth Group Incorporated; *U.S. Public*, pg. 2249
PRIMECARE OF CORONA, INC.—See UnitedHealth Group Incorporated; *U.S. Public*, pg. 2249
PRIMECARE OF HEMET VALLEY, INC.—See UnitedHealth Group Incorporated; *U.S. Public*, pg. 2249
PRIMECARE OF INLAND VALLEY, INC.—See UnitedHealth Group Incorporated; *U.S. Public*, pg. 2249
PRIMECARE OF MORENO VALLEY, INC.—See UnitedHealth Group Incorporated; *U.S. Public*, pg. 2249
PRIMECARE OF REDLANDS, INC.—See UnitedHealth Group Incorporated; *U.S. Public*, pg. 2249
PRIMECARE OF RIVERSIDE, INC.—See UnitedHealth Group Incorporated; *U.S. Public*, pg. 2249
PRIMECARE OF SAN BERNARDINO, INC.—See UnitedHealth Group Incorporated; *U.S. Public*, pg. 2249
PRIMECARE OF SUN CITY, INC.—See UnitedHealth Group Incorporated; *U.S. Public*, pg. 2249
PRIMECARE OF TEMECULA, INC.—See UnitedHealth Group Incorporated; *U.S. Public*, pg. 2249
PRIORITY HEALTH MANAGED BENEFITS, INC.—See Spectrum Health Continuing Care Group, Inc.; *U.S. Private*, pg. 3752
PRIVACY ANALYTICS INC.—See IQVIA Holdings Inc.; *U.S. Public*, pg. 1170
PRIVATPATH DIAGNOSTICS, INC.; *U.S. Private*, pg. 3268
PROCE INC.; *U.S. Private*, pg. 3271
PROFESSIONAL PROBATION SERVICES, INC.—See Universal Health Services, Inc.; *U.S. Public*, pg. 2259
PROFICIO, INC.; *U.S. Private*, pg. 3276
PROGRESSIVEHEALTH COMPANIES, LLC—See U.S. Physical Therapy, Inc.; *U.S. Public*, pg. 2215
PROGRESSIVE HEALTH SYSTEMS INC; *U.S. Private*, pg. 3279
PROHEALTH INC.—See Progressive Health Systems Inc.; *U.S. Private*, pg. 3279
PROVIDIGM, LLC—See HealthStream, Inc.; *U.S. Public*, pg. 1017
PROVO CANYON SCHOOL, INC.—See Universal Health Services, Inc.; *U.S. Public*, pg. 2259
PSJ ACQUISITION, LLC—See Universal Health Services, Inc.; *U.S. Public*, pg. 2258
PT CHC MEDIKA INDONESIA—See CHC Healthcare Group; *Int'l*, pg. 1458
PT GEVAERT-AGFA HEALTHCARE INDONESIA—See Agfa-Gevaert N.V.; *Int'l*, pg. 209
THE PUBLIC HEALTH MANAGEMENT SERVICES CORPORATION—See Public Health Management Corporation; *U.S. Private*, pg. 3299
PULSE8, LLC—See Veradigm Inc.; *U.S. Public*, pg. 2280
QIAN YUAN BAIXING, INC.; *U.S. Public*, pg. 1743
QOL MEDS, LLC—See Genoa Healthcare LLC; *U.S. Private*, pg. 1673
QUARTERS AT DES PERES, LLC—See National HealthCare Corporation; *U.S. Public*, pg. 1496
RAM TECHNOLOGIES, INC.; *U.S. Private*, pg. 3351
RAULERSON GYN, LLC—See HCA Healthcare, Inc.; *U.S. Public*, pg. 1007
RAYLIFE SRL—See El.En. S.p.A.; *Int'l*, pg. 2342
RAZOR GENOMICS, INC.—See OncoCyte Corporation; *U.S. Public*, pg. 1601
RDG OUTPATIENT COUNSELING, L.L.C.—See Universal Health Services, Inc.; *U.S. Public*, pg. 2259
REAL APPEAL, INC.—See UnitedHealth Group Incorporated; *U.S. Public*, pg. 2250
RECOVER HEALTH, INC.; *U.S. Private*, pg. 3372
RED ROCKS RADIATION & ONCOLOGY, LLC—See HCA Healthcare, Inc.; *U.S. Public*, pg. 1007
REGENERON FRANCE SAS—See Regeneron Pharmaceuticals, Inc.; *U.S. Public*, pg. 1775
REGENERON ITALY S.R.L.—See Regeneron Pharmaceuticals, Inc.; *U.S. Public*, pg. 1775
REGENERON JAPAN KK—See Regeneron Pharmaceuticals, Inc.; *U.S. Public*, pg. 1775
REGENEUS ANIMAL HEALTH PTY LTD—See Cambium Bio Limited; *Int'l*, pg. 1269
REGENTYS CORPORATION—See Generex Biotechnology Corporation; *U.S. Public*, pg. 930
RELIAS LLC—See Bertelsmann SE & Co. KGaA; *Int'l*, pg. 996
REMEDY HEALTHCARE GROUP PTY LTD—See Australian Unity Limited; *Int'l*, pg. 723
REM RAMSEY, INC.—See Centerbridge Partners, L.P.; *U.S. Private*, pg. 814
RENAISSANCE SURGERY CENTER, LLC—See Tenet Healthcare Corporation; *U.S. Public*, pg. 2006
RESOLUTE HEALTH PHYSICIANS NETWORK, INC.—See Tenet Healthcare Corporation; *U.S. Public*, pg. 2014
RESPICARDIA, INC.—See Asahi Kasei Corporation; *Int'l*, pg. 597
RH BOPHELO LTD.—See Public Investment Corporation; *U.S. Private*, pg. 3299
RHON-CATERINGGESELLSCHAFT MBH—See Asklepios Kliniken GmbH & Co. KGaA; *Int'l*, pg. 624
RICHMOND PEDIATRIC SURGEONS, LLC—See HCA Healthcare, Inc.; *U.S. Public*, pg. 1007
RIGHTSMILE, INC.; *U.S. Public*, pg. 1798
RIVER OAKS, INC.—See Universal Health Services, Inc.; *U.S. Public*, pg. 2259
RMS LIFELINE, INC.—See DaVita Inc.; *U.S. Public*, pg. 642
ROCKET PHARMACEUTICALS, INC.; *U.S. Public*, pg. 1805
ROCKY MOUNTAIN PEDIATRIC HEMATOLOGY ONCOLOGY, LLC—See HCA Healthcare, Inc.; *U.S. Public*, pg. 1007
ROLLING HILLS HOSPITAL, LLC—See Universal Health Services, Inc.; *U.S. Public*, pg. 2259
ROSE SURGICAL CENTER—See HCA Healthcare, Inc.; *U.S. Public*, pg. 1008
RS OCCUPATIONAL HEALTH LTD—See Audax Group, Limited Partnership; *U.S. Private*, pg. 387
RXVANTAGE, INC.; *U.S. Private*, pg. 3509
SAINT FRANCIS HOSPITAL BILLING CENTER, L.L.C.—See Tenet Healthcare Corporation; *U.S. Public*, pg. 2007
SAINT FRANCIS HOSPITAL MEDICARE ACO, LLC—See Tenet Healthcare Corporation; *U.S. Public*, pg. 2006
SAINT FRANCIS HOSPITAL PRO FEE BILLING, L.L.C.—See Tenet Healthcare Corporation; *U.S. Public*, pg. 2003
SAINT FRANCIS SURGICAL ASSOCIATES, L.L.C.—See Tenet Healthcare Corporation; *U.S. Public*, pg. 2003
SAINT VINCENT PHYSICIAN SERVICES, INC.—See Tenet Healthcare Corporation; *U.S. Public*, pg. 2014
SALVE WOHNGRUPPEN GMBH—See ResMed Inc.; *U.S. Public*, pg. 1791
SAMITIVEJ PUBLIC COMPANY LIMITED—See Bangkok Dusit Medical Services Public Company Limited; *Int'l*, pg. 834
SAMUDRA HEALTHCARE ENTERPRISES LIMITED—See Apollo Hospitals Enterprise Limited; *Int'l*, pg. 518
SAN RAMON SURGERY CENTER, LLC—See Tenet Healthcare Corporation; *U.S. Public*, pg. 2003
SANTA CRUZ ENDOSCOPY CENTER, LLC—See UnitedHealth Group Incorporated; *U.S. Public*, pg. 2250
SAPIEN BIOSCIENCES PRIVATE LIMITED—See Apollo Hospitals Enterprise Limited; *Int'l*, pg. 518
SARL CLINIQUE MAISON BLANCHE—See Clariane SE; *Int'l*, pg. 1644
SARL RESIDENCE DE BALBIGNY—See Emeis SA; *Int'l*, pg. 2374
SC FRESENIUS KABI ROMANIA SRL—See Fresenius SE & Co. KGaA; *Int'l*, pg. 2781
SCHECK & SIRESS PROSTHETICS, INC.—See Patient Square Capital, L.P.; *U.S. Public*, pg. 3107
SEASHORE SURGICAL INTITUTE, LLC—See UnitedHealth Group Incorporated; *U.S. Public*, pg. 2251
SEASIDE HEALTH PLAN—See Memorial Health Services; *U.S. Private*, pg. 2664
SEKUNJALO MEDICAL SERVICES (PTY) LTD—See African Equity Empowerment Investmts Limited; *Int'l*, pg. 191
SELECT SPECIALTY HOSPITAL-MIDTOWN ATLANTA, LLC—See Select Medical Holdings Corporation; *U.S. Public*, pg. 1861
SELMA CARLSON, INC.—See Tenet Healthcare Corporation; *U.S. Public*, pg. 2005
SELMESTA CO., LTD.—See H.U. Group Holdings, Inc.; *Int'l*, pg. 3199
SENEVITA AG—See Emeis SA; *Int'l*, pg. 2376
SENIORBRIDGE FAMILY COMPANIES (IL), INC.—See Humana, Inc.; *U.S. Public*, pg. 1070
SENIORBRIDGE FAMILY COMPANIES (PA), INC.—See Humana, Inc.; *U.S. Public*, pg. 1070
SENIOR CARE PARTNERS, INC.—See UnitedHealth Group Incorporated; *U.S. Public*, pg. 2250
SENTINEL HEALTHCARE LLC—See The Pennant Group, Inc.; *U.S. Public*, pg. 2118
SERVICIOS DE SALUD IPS SURAMERICANA S.A.—See Grupo de Inversiones Suramericana S.A.; *Int'l*, pg. 3126
SERVISOURCE HEALTHCARE LIMITED—See Bain Capital, LP; *U.S. Private*, pg. 434
SETO HOLDINGS, INC.; *U.S. Public*, pg. 1872
SEVENBAR AVIATION, LLC—See KKR & Co. Inc.; *U.S. Public*, pg. 1252
SHADOW MOUNTAIN BEHAVIORAL HEALTH SYSTEM, LLC—See Universal Health Services, Inc.; *U.S. Public*, pg. 2259
SHANNON HEALTH SYSTEM; *U.S. Private*, pg. 3625
SHINDAGHA PHARMACY LLC—See Aster DM Healthcare Ltd.; *Int'l*, pg. 654
SIERRA PROVIDENCE HEALTH NETWORK, INC.—See Tenet Healthcare Corporation; *U.S. Public*, pg. 2003
SIGNIFY HEALTH LLC; *U.S. Private*, pg. 3651
SINFONIARX, INC.—See Vora Ventures LLC; *U.S. Private*, pg. 4412
SITTERS ETC.; *U.S. Private*, pg. 3677
SLH PHYSICIANS, L.L.C.—See Tenet Healthcare Corporation; *U.S. Public*, pg. 2006
SLUH ANESTHESIA PHYSICIANS, L.L.C.—See Tenet Healthcare Corporation; *U.S. Public*, pg. 2006
SOLAR GOLD LTD.; *U.S. Public*, pg. 1899
SOMERSET, INCORPORATED—See Universal Health Services, Inc.; *U.S. Public*, pg. 2259
SOMNICARE, INC.—See Foundation Healthcare, Inc.; *U.S. Private*, pg. 1580
SONDERMIND, INC.; *U.S. Private*, pg. 3712
SOUTH CAROLINA SEWEE FAMILY MEDICINE, L.L.C.—See Tenet Healthcare Corporation; *U.S. Public*, pg. 2003
SOUTHEAST ALASKA REGIONAL HEALTH CONSORTIUM; *U.S. Private*, pg. 3724
THE SOUTHEASTERN SPINE INSTITUTE SURGERY CENTER, L.L.C.—See Tenet Healthcare Corporation; *U.S. Public*, pg. 2008
SOUTHERN HILLS HOSPITAL & MEDICAL CENTER—See HCA Healthcare, Inc.; *U.S. Public*, pg. 1010
SOUTHERN HILLS NEUROLOGY CONSULTANTS, LLC—See HCA Healthcare, Inc.; *U.S. Public*, pg. 1010
SOUTHERN IDAHO REGIONAL LABORATORY—See Laboratory Corporation of America Holdings; *U.S. Public*, pg. 1287
SOUTH FLORIDA AMBULATORY SURGICAL CENTER, LLC—See Tenet Healthcare Corporation; *U.S. Public*, pg. 2005
SOUTH SUBURBAN SURGICAL SUITES, LLC—See Tenet Healthcare Corporation; *U.S. Public*, pg. 2007
SPACE COAST SURGICAL CENTER, LTD.—See HCA Healthcare, Inc.; *U.S. Public*, pg. 1010
SPALDING REGIONAL URGENT CARE CENTER AT HERON BAY, L.L.C.—See Tenet Healthcare Corporation; *U.S. Public*, pg. 2005
SP BEHAVIORAL, LLC—See Universal Health Services, Inc.; *U.S. Public*, pg. 2259
SPECIALTY SURGERY CENTER AT FOUNTAIN VALLEY REGIONAL HOSPITAL, L.L.C.—See UCI Health; *U.S. Private*, pg. 4274
SPECIALTY SURGERY CENTER—See HCA Healthcare, Inc.; *U.S. Public*, pg. 1010
SPECIALTY SURGICAL CENTER OF ARCADIA, LLC—See Bain Capital, LP; *U.S. Private*, pg. 447
SPECIALTY SURGICAL CENTER OF BEVERLY HILLS, L.P.—See Bain Capital, LP; *U.S. Private*, pg. 447
SPECIALTY SURGICAL CENTER OF ENCINO, LLC—See Bain Capital, LP; *U.S. Private*, pg. 447
SPECIALTY SURGICAL CENTER OF IRVINE, LLC—See Bain Capital, LP; *U.S. Private*, pg. 447
SPORTSMED SA HOSPITALS PTY LTD—See Burnside War Memorial Hospital Inc.; *Int'l*, pg. 1226
SPRIG HEALTH, INC.—See Cambia Health Solutions, Inc.; *U.S. Private*, pg. 726
SRL INTERNATIONAL, INC.—See H.U. Group Holdings, Inc.; *Int'l*, pg. 3197
SRL KITAKANTO LABORATORY, INC.—See H.U. Group Holdings, Inc.; *Int'l*, pg. 3197
SRL & SHIZUOKA CANCER CENTER COLLABORATIVE LABORATORIES, INC.—See H.U. Group Holdings, Inc.; *Int'l*, pg. 3197
STAR MULTI CARE SERVICES OF FLORIDA, INC—See Star Multi Care Services Inc.; *U.S. Private*, pg. 3785
ST. CHRISTOPHER'S PEDIATRIC URGENT CARE CENTER, L.L.C.—See Drexel University; *U.S. Private*, pg. 1276
ST. CHRISTOPHER'S PEDIATRIC URGENT CARE CENTER, L.L.C.—See Tower Health; *U.S. Private*, pg. 4193
STERILIZATION SERVICES OF GEORGIA—See Altair Corporation; *U.S. Public*, pg. 86
STERLING PRIMARY CARE ASSOCIATES, LLC—See HCA

621999 — ALL OTHER MISCELLAN...

Healthcare, Inc.; *U.S. Public*, pg. 1010
ST. JAKOB-APOTHEKE AG—See CSL Limited; *Int'l*, pg. 1866
ST. LOUIS URGENT CARE #2, L.L.C.—See Tenet Healthcare Corporation; *U.S. Public*, pg. 2005
ST. LUKE'S HEALTH SYSTEM, INC.—See UnityPoint Health; *U.S. Private*, pg. 4303
ST. LUKE'S PHYSICIAN GROUP, INC.—See St. Luke's Health Network, Inc.; *U.S. Private*, pg. 3773
ST. MARIEN KRANKENHAUS LAMPERTHEIM GMBH—See Eurofins Scientific S.E.; *Int'l*, pg. 2551
STOCKHOLM ARRHYTHMIA CENTER AB—See Apax Partners LLP; *Int'l*, pg. 502
SUMMERLIN HOSPITAL MEDICAL CENTER LLC—See Universal Health Services, Inc.; *U.S. Public*, pg. 2259
SUNRISE MEDICAL GROUP I, L.L.C.—See Tenet Healthcare Corporation; *U.S. Public*, pg. 2004
SURGAID MEDICAL (XIAMEN) CO., LTD.—See Double Medical Technology Inc.; *Int'l*, pg. 2181
THE SURGERY CENTER, LLC—See Bain Capital, LP; *U.S. Private*, pg. 447
SURGERY CENTER OF CHATTANOOGA, L.P.—See HCA Healthcare, Inc.; *U.S. Public*, pg. 1011
THE SURGERY CENTER OF OCALA, LLC—See Bain Capital, LP; *U.S. Private*, pg. 447
SURGERY CENTER OF OKEECHOBEE, LLC—See Tenet Healthcare Corporation; *U.S. Public*, pg. 2005
SURGERY CENTER OF PEMBROKE PINES, L.L.C.—See Tenet Healthcare Corporation; *U.S. Public*, pg. 2005
SURGERY CENTER OF THE ROCKIES, LLC—See HCA Healthcare, Inc.; *U.S. Public*, pg. 1011
SURGICAL ASSOCIATES OF THE NEW RIVER VALLEY, LLC—See HCA Healthcare, Inc.; *U.S. Public*, pg. 1011
SURGICAL SOLUTIONS, LLC; *U.S. Private*, pg. 3884
SURGICARE OF MIRAMAR, L.L.C.—See Tenet Healthcare Corporation; *U.S. Public*, pg. 2008
SWEDISH MEDICAL CENTER—See HCA Healthcare, Inc.; *U.S. Public*, pg. 998
SYMBION PTY LTD—See EBOS Group Limited; *Int'l*, pg. 2286
TBJ BEHAVIORAL CENTER, LLC—See Universal Health Services, Inc.; *U.S. Public*, pg. 2259
TECNOLOGIAS DE INFORMACION EN SALUD S.A.—See UnitedHealth Group Incorporated; *U.S. Public*, pg. 2251
TELADOC HEALTH, INC.; *U.S. Public*, pg. 1991
TENET FLORIDA, INC.—See Tenet Healthcare Corporation; *U.S. Public*, pg. 2004
TENET FLORIDA PHYSICIAN SERVICES, L.L.C.—See Tenet Healthcare Corporation; *U.S. Public*, pg. 2004
TENET FRISCO, LTD—See Tenet Healthcare Corporation; *U.S. Public*, pg. 2004
TENET HILTON HEAD HEART, L.L.C.—See Tenet Healthcare Corporation; *U.S. Public*, pg. 2008
TENNESSEE BLOOD SERVICES CORP.—See BioIVT, LLC; *U.S. Private*, pg. 562
TENNESSEE CLINICAL SCHOOLS, LLC—See Universal Health Services, Inc.; *U.S. Public*, pg. 2259
TEXARKANA SURGERY CENTER GP, LLC—See Bain Capital, LP; *U.S. Private*, pg. 447
TEXOMACARE—See Universal Health Services, Inc.; *U.S. Public*, pg. 2259
THEDA OAKS GASTROENTEROLOGY & ENDOSCOPY CENTER, LLC—See Tenet Healthcare Corporation; *U.S. Public*, pg. 2005
THUNDER HEALTHCARE, INC.—See The Ensign Group, Inc.; *U.S. Public*, pg. 2072
TIDEPOOL PROJECT; *U.S. Private*, pg. 4168
TOTAL RENAL CARE TEXAS LIMITED PARTNERSHIP—See DaVita Inc.; *U.S. Public*, pg. 643
TRC-PETERSBURG, LLC—See DaVita Inc.; *U.S. Public*, pg. 643
TRENDCO HAIR SUPPLIES CO., LTD—See Aderans Co., Ltd.; *Int'l*, pg. 144
TRICITY PAIN ASSOCIATES PA—See Spindletop Capital Management LLC; *U.S. Private*, pg. 3757
TRINITY HEALTH SYSTEMS, INC.—See UnityPoint Health; *U.S. Private*, pg. 4303
UHS MIDWEST CENTER FOR YOUTH AND FAMILIES, LLC—See Universal Health Services, Inc.; *U.S. Public*, pg. 2260
UHS OF PARKWOOD, INC.—See Universal Health Services, Inc.; *U.S. Public*, pg. 2260
UHS OF PHOENIX, LLC—See Universal Health Services, Inc.; *U.S. Public*, pg. 2260
UHS OF ROCKFORD, LLC—See Universal Health Services, Inc.; *U.S. Public*, pg. 2260
UHS OF SPRINGWOODS, L.L.C.—See Universal Health Services, Inc.; *U.S. Public*, pg. 2260
UNITEDHEALTHCARE BENEFITS OF TEXAS, INC.—See UnitedHealth Group Incorporated; *U.S. Public*, pg. 2251
UNITEDHEALTHCARE INDIA PRIVATE LIMITED—See UnitedHealth Group Incorporated; *U.S. Public*, pg. 2251
UNITEDHEALTH GROUP GLOBAL HEALTHCARE SERVICES LIMITED—See UnitedHealth Group Incorporated; *U.S. Public*, pg. 2251
UNITEDHEALTH GROUP GLOBAL SERVICES, INC.—See UnitedHealth Group Incorporated; *U.S. Public*, pg. 2251

UNITED MEDICAL SYSTEMS (DE), INC.; *U.S. Private*, pg. 4294
UNIVERSAL CARE, INC.—See Molina Healthcare, Inc.; *U.S. Public*, pg. 1459
UPMC WESTERN MARYLAND CORPORATION—See University of Pittsburgh Medical Center; *U.S. Public*, pg. 4310
URAC; *U.S. Private*, pg. 4313
URGENT CARE CENTERS OF ARIZONA, LLC—See Tenet Healthcare Corporation; *U.S. Public*, pg. 2005
US FOOT & ANKLE SPECIALISTS, LLC—See NMS Capital Services, LLC; *U.S. Private*, pg. 2932
U.S. HEALTHWORKS MEDICAL GROUP, PROF. CORP.—See Select Medical Holdings Corporation; *U.S. Public*, pg. 1857
U.S. HEALTHWORKS MEDICAL GROUP, PROF. CORP.—See Welsh, Carson, Anderson & Stowe; *U.S. Private*, pg. 4479
VALLEY AMBULATORY SURGERY CENTER, L.P.—See Bain Capital, LP; *U.S. Private*, pg. 447
VALLEY HEALTH CARE NETWORK—See Tenet Healthcare Corporation; *U.S. Public*, pg. 2015
VALLEY PHYSICIANS NETWORK, INC.—See UnitedHealth Group Incorporated; *U.S. Public*, pg. 2252
VALLEY SURGICAL CENTER, LTD.—See Bain Capital, LP; *U.S. Private*, pg. 447
VALUEHEALTH LLC—See Nueterra Capital Management, LLC; *U.S. Private*, pg. 2972
VAMED SERVICE- UND BETEILIGUNGSGES MBH—See Fresenius SE & Co. KGaA; *Int'l*, pg. 2781
VAMED UKK PROJEKTGESELLSCHAFT M.B.H.—See Fresenius SE & Co. KGaA; *Int'l*, pg. 2781
VHS ACQUISITION PARTNERSHIP NUMBER 2, L.P.—See Tenet Healthcare Corporation; *U.S. Public*, pg. 2014
VIDANT EDGECOMBE HOSPITAL—See HCA Healthcare, Inc.; *U.S. Public*, pg. 1013
VIGIL HEALTH SOLUTIONS INC.—See ASSA ABLOY AB; *Int'l*, pg. 641
VIIV HEALTHCARE PTY LTD—See GSK plc; *Int'l*, pg. 3150
VIIV HEALTHCARE SAS—See GSK plc; *Int'l*, pg. 3150
VIIV HEALTHCARE S.R.L.—See GSK plc; *Int'l*, pg. 3150
VIIV HEALTHCARE ULC—See GSK plc; *Int'l*, pg. 3150
VILLAGEHEALTH DM, LLC—See DaVita Inc.; *U.S. Public*, pg. 644
VILLAGES OF JACKSON CREEK, LLC—See National HealthCare Corporation; *U.S. Public*, pg. 1497
VILLAGES OF JACKSON CREEK MEMORY CARE, LLC—See National HealthCare Corporation; *U.S. Public*, pg. 1497
VILLAGES OF ST. PETERS, LLC—See National HealthCare Corporation; *U.S. Public*, pg. 1497
VISION GROUP HOLDINGS LLC; *U.S. Private*, pg. 4390
VITA BARIATRIC CLINICS STOCKHOLM AB—See Apax Partners LLP; *Int'l*, pg. 502
VITA CLINICS UK LTD—See Apax Partners LLP; *Int'l*, pg. 502
VITALLIFE CORPORATION LTD.—See Bumrungrad Hospital Public Company Limited; *Int'l*, pg. 1215
VITERION TELEHEALTHCARE LLC—See Bayer Aktiengesellschaft; *Int'l*, pg. 902
VITREOSHEALTH, INC.—See Veritas Capital Fund Management, LLC; *U.S. Private*, pg. 4362
VIZION HEALTH LLC; *U.S. Private*, pg. 4407
VNSNY CHOICE—See Visiting Nurse Service of New York; *U.S. Private*, pg. 4393
WALKER STREET IMAGING CARE, INC.—See Tenet Healthcare Corporation; *U.S. Public*, pg. 2005
WATERWAY PRIMARY CARE, LLC—See HCA Healthcare, Inc.; *U.S. Public*, pg. 1013
WELLSTAR MEDICAL GROUP CARDIOVASCULAR MEDICINE—See WellStar Health System, Inc.; *U.S. Private*, pg. 4478
WELLSTAR MEDICAL GROUP FAMILY MEDICINE—See WellStar Health System, Inc.; *U.S. Private*, pg. 4478
WELLSTAR MEDICAL GROUP RHEUMATOLOGY—See WellStar Health System, Inc.; *U.S. Private*, pg. 4478
WELLSTAR NORTH FULTON HOSPITAL—See WellStar Health System, Inc.; *U.S. Private*, pg. 4478
WESTERN PLAINS CAPITAL, INC.—See HCA Healthcare, Inc.; *U.S. Public*, pg. 1014
WEST FLORIDA INTERNAL MEDICINE, LLC—See HCA Healthcare, Inc.; *U.S. Public*, pg. 1013
WEST HILLS SURGICAL CENTER, LTD.—See HCA Healthcare, Inc.; *U.S. Public*, pg. 1013
WESTON OUTPATIENT SURGICAL CENTER, LTD.—See KKR & Co. Inc.; *U.S. Public*, pg. 1249
WFM MEDICAL & WELLNESS CENTERS, INC.—See Amazon.com, Inc.; *U.S. Public*, pg. 91
WHO ARE YOU LTD.—See Intelli Centrics Inc.; *U.S. Private*, pg. 2105
WILMINGTON SURGERY CENTER, L.P.—See Bain Capital, LP; *U.S. Private*, pg. 447
WINTER HAVEN AMBULATORY SURGICAL CENTER, L.L.C.—See Tenet Healthcare Corporation; *U.S. Public*, pg. 2005
WORCESTER CENTER, L.P.—See Tenet Healthcare Corporation; *U.S. Public*, pg. 2005
WORKING SYSTEMS SOLUTIONS PTY. LTD.—See Global Health Limited; *Int'l*, pg. 2997
WORK-LOSS DATA INSTITUTE, LLC—See The Hearst Corporation; *U.S. Public*, pg. 4045
XSOLIS, INC.; *U.S. Private*, pg. 4582
XTREME HEALTHCARE CORPORATION; *U.S. Private*, pg. 4583
Y-PHARMA S.A.—See DIAGNOSTIC AND THERAPEUTIC CENTER OF ATHENS-HYGEIA S.A.; *Int'l*, pg. 2103
ZAO FRESENIUS SP—See Fresenius Medical Care AG; *Int'l*, pg. 2777
ZYTER, INC.; *U.S. Private*, pg. 4611

622110 — GENERAL MEDICAL AND SURGICAL HOSPITALS

52 ALDERLEY ROAD LLP—See HCA Healthcare, Inc.; *U.S. Public*, pg. 990
AASHKA HOSPITALS LTD.; *Int'l*, pg. 38
ABBOTT AMBULANCE, INC.—See KKR & Co. Inc.; *U.S. Public*, pg. 1251
ABRAZO MEDICAL GROUP URGENT CARE, LLC—See Tenet Healthcare Corporation; *U.S. Public*, pg. 2014
ABS LINCS VA, INC.—See Universal Health Services, Inc.; *U.S. Public*, pg. 2255
ACADIAN HOMECARE OF NEW IBERIA, LLC—See UnitedHealth Group Incorporated; *U.S. Public*, pg. 2243
ACCESS HEALTH CARE PHYSICIANS, LLC—See HCA Healthcare, Inc.; *U.S. Public*, pg. 990
ACCURA S.R.L.—See GPI S.p.A.; *Int'l*, pg. 3046
ACQUISITION BELL HOSPITAL, LLC—See Apollo Global Management, Inc.; *U.S. Public*, pg. 154
ACUCORT AB; *Int'l*, pg. 121
ACUTE KIDS URGENT CARE OF MEDICAL CITY CHILDREN'S HOSPITAL, PLLC—See HCA Healthcare, Inc.; *U.S. Public*, pg. 990
ADAGIO HEALTH; *U.S. Private*, pg. 72
ADAIR COUNTY HOSPITAL DISTRICT; *U.S. Private*, pg. 73
ADENA HEALTH SYSTEM; *U.S. Private*, pg. 78
ADULT & PEDIATRIC DERMATOLOGY, PC; *U.S. Private*, pg. 83
ADVANCED CENTER FOR SURGERY - VERO BEACH, LLC—See Tenet Healthcare Corporation; *U.S. Public*, pg. 2001
ADVANCED SPINE CENTER OF WISCONSIN, LLC—See Tenet Healthcare Corporation; *U.S. Public*, pg. 2001
ADVANCED SURGERY CENTER OF CLIFTON, LLC—See UnitedHealth Group Incorporated; *U.S. Public*, pg. 2238
ADVANCED SURGERY CENTER OF METAIRIE, LLC—See Tenet Healthcare Corporation; *U.S. Public*, pg. 2001
ADVANCED SURGERY CENTER OF NORTHERN LOUISIANA, LLC—See Tenet Healthcare Corporation; *U.S. Public*, pg. 2001
ADVANCED SURGICAL CARE OF CLEARWATER, LLC—See Tenet Healthcare Corporation; *U.S. Public*, pg. 2001
ADVANCED TREATMENT SYSTEMS, INC.—See Acadia Healthcare Company, Inc.; *U.S. Public*, pg. 28
ADVANCE MEDICAL HEALTH CARE MANAGEMENT SERVICES CHILE S.A.—See Teladoc Health, Inc.; *U.S. Public*, pg. 1992
ADVANCE MEDICAL HEALTH-CARE MANAGEMENT SERVICES, S.A.—See Teladoc Health, Inc.; *U.S. Public*, pg. 1992
ADVANCE MEDICAL, INC.—See Teladoc Health, Inc.; *U.S. Public*, pg. 1992
ADVENTHEALTH HEART OF FLORIDA—See Adventist Health System Sunbelt Healthcare Corporation; *U.S. Private*, pg. 108
ADVENTHEALTH OCALA—See Community Health Systems, Inc.; *U.S. Public*, pg. 550
ADVENTHEALTH SURGERY CENTER MILLS PARK, LLC—See Tenet Healthcare Corporation; *U.S. Public*, pg. 2001
ADVENTHEALTH SURGERY CENTER WELLSWOOD, LLC—See Tenet Healthcare Corporation; *U.S. Public*, pg. 2001
ADVENTIST GLENOAKS HOSPITAL—See Adventist Health System Sunbelt Healthcare Corporation; *U.S. Private*, pg. 109
ADVENTIST HINSDALE HOSPITAL—See Adventist Health System Sunbelt Healthcare Corporation; *U.S. Private*, pg. 109
ADVOCATE SHERMAN HOSPITAL, L.P.—See Community Health Systems, Inc.; *U.S. Public*, pg. 550
AESCULAPIO S.R.L.—See Garofalo Health Care SpA; *Int'l*, pg. 2886
AFFINITY HEALTH ALLIANCE, INC.—See Christiana Care Health System, Inc.; *U.S. Private*, pg. 891
AFFINITY HEALTH SYSTEMS, LLC—See Community Health Systems, Inc.; *U.S. Public*, pg. 551
AFFINITY HOSPITAL, LLC—See Community Health Systems, Inc.; *U.S. Public*, pg. 551
AFFINITY HOSPITALS HOLDING LIMITED—See Acadia Healthcare Company, Inc.; *U.S. Public*, pg. 28
AFFINITY ORTHOPEDIC SERVICES, LLC—See Community Health Systems, Inc.; *U.S. Public*, pg. 551
AFRICAN MEDICAL INVESTMENT PLC; *Int'l*, pg. 192

N.A.I.C.S. INDEX

622110 — GENERAL MEDICAL AND...

AGAPE CARE GROUP—See Ridgemont Partners Management LLC; *U.S. Private*, pg. 3432
AGENCY FOR COMMUNITY TREATMENT SERVICES, INC.; *U.S. Private*, pg. 126
AHMC & AHMC HEALTHCARE INC.; *U.S. Private*, pg. 130
AHS OKLAHOMA HEALTH SYSTEM, LLP—See Ventas, Inc.; *U.S. Public*, pg. 2277
AIDS RESOURCE CENTER OF WISCONSIN; *U.S. Private*, pg. 132
AIKEN REGIONAL MEDICAL CENTERS, LLC—See Universal Health Services, Inc.; *U.S. Public*, pg. 2255
AITKIN COMMUNITY HOSPITAL; *U.S. Private*, pg. 143
AKG KLINIK HOHWALD GMBH—See Asklepios Kliniken GmbH & Co. KGaA; *Int'l*, pg. 622
AKG KLINIK PARCHIM GMBH—See Asklepios Kliniken GmbH & Co. KGaA; *Int'l*, pg. 622
ALAMO HEIGHTS SURGICARE, L.P.—See Tenet Healthcare Corporation; *U.S. Public*, pg. 2009
ALASKA REGIONAL HOSPITAL—See HCA Healthcare, Inc.; *U.S. Public*, pg. 990
ALASKA REGIONAL MEDICAL GROUP, LLC—See HCA Healthcare, Inc.; *U.S. Public*, pg. 990
ALBANY DAY HOSPITAL PTY LTD—See Healius Limited; *Int'l*, pg. 3302
ALBANY FAMILY PRACTICE, LLC—See HCA Healthcare, Inc.; *U.S. Public*, pg. 990
AL-BILAD MEDICAL SERVICES CO.; *Int'l*, pg. 284
THE ALEXANDRIA OPHTHALMOLOGY ASC, LLC—See KKR & Co. Inc.; *U.S. Public*, pg. 1247
AL HAMMADI HOLDING COMPANY; *Int'l*, pg. 278
ALLAMANDA PRIVATE HOSPITAL PTY. LTD.—See Brookfield Corporation; *Int'l*, pg. 1176
ALLCARE CLINICAL ASSOCIATES, PLLC—See Bain Capital, LP; *U.S. Private*, pg. 445
ALL CHILDREN'S HOSPITAL INC.; *U.S. Private*, pg. 170
ALLEGHANY HOSPITALISTS, LLC—See HCA Healthcare, Inc.; *U.S. Public*, pg. 990
ALLERVIE HEALTH PROFESSIONAL CORPORATION; *U.S. Private*, pg. 180
ALLIANCE COMMUNITY HOSPITAL; *U.S. Private*, pg. 181
ALLIANCE HEALTH CENTER, INC.—See Universal Health Services, Inc.; *U.S. Public*, pg. 2255
ALLINA HEALTH SYSTEM, INC.; *U.S. Private*, pg. 192
ALLIUM HEALTHCARE (SINGAPORE) PTE LTD—See G. K. Goh Holdings Limited; *Int'l*, pg. 2864
ALL WOMEN'S HEALTHCARE OF SAWGRASS, INC.—See KKR & Co. Inc.; *U.S. Public*, pg. 1244
AL MOUWASAT MEDICAL SERVICES COMPANY; *Int'l*, pg. 281
ALPHA HOSPITALS (NW) LIMITED—See Universal Health Services, Inc.; *U.S. Public*, pg. 2255
AL-SHOROUK HOSPITAL COMPANY S.A.E—See Cleopatra Hospitals; *Int'l*, pg. 1658
ALTA BATES SUMMIT MEDICAL CENTER—See Sutter Health; *U.S. Private*, pg. 3887
ALTAMED HEALTH SERVICES CORPORATION; *U.S. Private*, pg. 204
ALTRU HEALTH SYSTEM; *U.S. Private*, pg. 210
ALVARADO HOSPITAL, LLC—See UC San Diego Health; *U.S. Private*, pg. 4273
ALVARADO REGIONAL MEDICAL CENTER, INC.—See UC San Diego Health; *U.S. Private*, pg. 4273
AMBULANCE SERVICES OF LEXINGTON, INC.—See Quorum Health Corporation; *U.S. Private*, pg. 3329
AMBULANCE SERVICES OF MCKENZIE, INC.—See Quorum Health Corporation; *U.S. Private*, pg. 3329
AMBULATORY ANESTHESIA ASSOCIATES INC.—See KKR & Co. Inc.; *U.S. Public*, pg. 1244
AMERICAN ACADEMY OF OTOLARYNGOLOGY-HEAD AND NECK SURGERY; *U.S. Private*, pg. 221
AMERICAN ASSOCIATION FOR THE STUDY OF LIVER DISEASES; *U.S. Private*, pg. 223
AMERICAN BURN ASSOCIATION; *U.S. Private*, pg. 226
AMERICAN COLLEGE OF GASTROENTEROLOGY; *U.S. Private*, pg. 227
AMERICAN CURRENT CARE OF ARIZONA, P.A.—See Select Medical Holdings Corporation; *U.S. Public*, pg. 1857
AMERICAN CURRENT CARE OF ARKANSAS, P.A.—See Select Medical Holdings Corporation; *U.S. Public*, pg. 1857
AMERICAN CURRENT CARE OF MASSACHUSETTS, P.C.—See Select Medical Holdings Corporation; *U.S. Public*, pg. 1857
AMERICAN CURRENT CARE OF MICHIGAN, P.C.—See Select Medical Holdings Corporation; *U.S. Public*, pg. 1857
AMERICAN CURRENT CARE OF NEBRASKA, P.C.—See Select Medical Holdings Corporation; *U.S. Public*, pg. 1857
AMERICAN CURRENT CARE OF NEW JERSEY PA—See Select Medical Holdings Corporation; *U.S. Public*, pg. 1857
AMERICAN CURRENT CARE OF NORTH CAROLINA, P.C.—See Select Medical Holdings Corporation; *U.S. Public*, pg. 1857
AMERICAN OSTEOPATHIC ASSOCIATION; *U.S. Private*, pg. 242

AMERICAN SOCIETY FOR GASTROINTESTINAL ENDOSCOPY; *U.S. Private*, pg. 253
AMERICAN SOCIETY OF RADIOLOGIC TECHNOLOGISTS; *U.S. Private*, pg. 254
AMERY REGIONAL MEDICAL CENTER; *U.S. Private*, pg. 261
AMG-LIVINGSTON, LLC—See Apollo Global Management, Inc.; *U.S. Public*, pg. 154
AMG-SOUTHERN TENNESSEE, LLC—See Apollo Global Management, Inc.; *U.S. Public*, pg. 154
AMMED CANCER CENTER (CENTRAL) LIMITED—See HKR International Limited; *Int'l*, pg. 3429
AMORY HMA, LLC—See Curae Health, Inc.; *U.S. Private*, pg. 1124
AMS ADVANCED MEDICAL SERVICES GMBH; *Int'l*, pg. 438
AMSURG CINCINNATI ANESTHESIA, LLC—See KKR & Co. Inc.; *U.S. Public*, pg. 1244
AMSURG CORP.—See KKR & Co. Inc.; *U.S. Public*, pg. 1244
AMSURG HERMITAGE ANESTHESIA, LLC—See KKR & Co. Inc.; *U.S. Public*, pg. 1244
AMSURG KENTUCKY OPHTHALMOLOGY, LLC—See KKR & Co. Inc.; *U.S. Public*, pg. 1244
AMSURG LOUISVILLE GI, LLC—See KKR & Co. Inc.; *U.S. Public*, pg. 1244
AMSURG NORTHERN KENTUCKY GI, LLC—See KKR & Co. Inc.; *U.S. Public*, pg. 1244
AMSURG ROCKLEDGE FL ANESTHESIA, LLC—See KKR & Co. Inc.; *U.S. Public*, pg. 1244
AMSURG TAMPA BAY ANESTHESIA, LLC—See KKR & Co. Inc.; *U.S. Public*, pg. 1244
ANAHEIM REGIONAL MEDICAL CENTER—See AHMC & AHMC Healthcare Inc.; *U.S. Private*, pg. 130
ANCHORAGE SURGICENTER, LLC—See HCA Healthcare, Inc.; *U.S. Public*, pg. 990
ANDERSON REGIONAL HEALTH SYSTEM; *U.S. Private*, pg. 277
ANDERSON REGIONAL MEDICAL CENTER—See Anderson Regional Health System; *U.S. Private*, pg. 277
ANDROSCOGGIN VALLEY HOSPITAL; *U.S. Private*, pg. 280
ANESTHESIOLOGISTS OF GREATER ORLANDO, INC.—See KKR & Co. Inc.; *U.S. Public*, pg. 1244
ANESTHESIOLOGY ASSOCIATES OF TALLAHASSEE, INC.—See KKR & Co. Inc.; *U.S. Public*, pg. 1244
ANESTHESIOLOGY PROFESSIONAL SERVICES, INC.—See Bain Capital, LP; *U.S. Private*, pg. 445
ANMED HEALTH MEDICAL CENTER—See AnMed Health; *U.S. Private*, pg. 284
ANMED HEALTH; *U.S. Private*, pg. 284
ANNA CLINIC CORP.—See Quorum Health Corporation; *U.S. Private*, pg. 3329
ANNA HOSPITAL CORPORATION—See Quorum Health Corporation; *U.S. Private*, pg. 3329
ANNE ARUNDEL DERMATOLOGY MANAGEMENT LLC—See Ridgemont Partners Management LLC; *U.S. Private*, pg. 3433
ANNISTON HMA, LLC—See The Health Care Authority of the City of Anniston; *U.S. Private*, pg. 4043
ANN & ROBERT H. LURIE CHILDREN'S HOSPITAL OF CHICAGO; *U.S. Private*, pg. 284
ANTELOPE MEMORIAL HOSPITAL; *U.S. Private*, pg. 287
AO CAPITAL PARTNERS, LLC—See Azalea Health Innovations, Inc.; *U.S. Private*, pg. 415
APOLLO CARE CONNECT, INC.—See Astrana Health Inc.; *U.S. Public*, pg. 217
APOLLO HOSPITALS ENTERPRISE LIMITED; *Int'l*, pg. 517
APOLLO LAVASA HEALTH CORPORATION LIMITED—See Apollo Hospitals Enterprise Limited; *Int'l*, pg. 517
APOLLOMD, INC.; *U.S. Private*, pg. 295
APOLLO MEDICAL MANAGEMENT, INC.—See Astrana Health Inc.; *U.S. Public*, pg. 217
APOLLO NELLORE HOSPITAL LIMITED—See Apollo Hospitals Enterprise Limited; *Int'l*, pg. 517
APOLLO RAJSHREE HOSPITALS PRIVATE LIMITED—See Apollo Hospitals Enterprise Limited; *Int'l*, pg. 517
APPALACHIAN REGIONAL HEALTHCARE, INC.; *U.S. Private*, pg. 295
APPLEDORE MEDICAL GROUP, INC.—See HCA Healthcare, Inc.; *U.S. Public*, pg. 990
APPLEDORE MEDICAL GROUP, INC.—See HCA Healthcare, Inc.; *U.S. Public*, pg. 990
APPOMATTOX IMAGING, LLC—See HCA Healthcare, Inc.; *U.S. Public*, pg. 990
ARAPAHOE SURGICENTER, LLC—See HCA Healthcare, Inc.; *U.S. Public*, pg. 990
ARC OF GEORGIA, LLC—See Bain Capital, LP; *U.S. Private*, pg. 445
ARC WORCESTER CENTER L.P.—See Tenet Healthcare Corporation; *U.S. Public*, pg. 2009
ARIZONA HEALTH PARTNERS, LLC—See Tenet Healthcare Corporation; *U.S. Public*, pg. 2014
ARIZONA SPINE AND JOINT HOSPITAL LLC—See Bain Capital, LP; *U.S. Private*, pg. 445
ARKANSAS CHILDREN'S HOSPITAL; *U.S. Private*, pg. 325

ARKANSAS FOUNDATION FOR MEDICAL CARE, INC.; *U.S. Private*, pg. 326
ARKANSAS METHODIST MEDICAL CENTER; *U.S. Private*, pg. 326
ARLINGTON ORTHOPEDIC AND SPINE HOSPITAL, LLC—See Tenet Healthcare Corporation; *U.S. Public*, pg. 2009
ARMENIA AMBULATORY SURGERY CENTER, LLC—See Bain Capital, LP; *U.S. Private*, pg. 445
ARMSTRONG COUNTY MEMORIAL HOSPITAL; *U.S. Private*, pg. 331
ARROWHEAD ENDOSCOPY AND PAIN MANAGEMENT CENTER, LLC—See Tenet Healthcare Corporation; *U.S. Public*, pg. 2009
ARTHRITIS SPECIALISTS OF NASHVILLE, INC.—See HCA Healthcare, Inc.; *U.S. Public*, pg. 990
ASCENSION BORGESS LEE HOSPITAL—See Ascension Health Alliance; *U.S. Private*, pg. 346
ASHLEY VALLEY MEDICAL CENTER, LLC—See Apollo Global Management, Inc.; *U.S. Public*, pg. 154
ASIAN AMERICAN MEDICAL GROUP LIMITED; *Int'l*, pg. 617
ASIAN HEALTH SERVICES; *U.S. Private*, pg. 351
ASIAN PACIFIC HEALTH CARE VENTURE, INC.; *U.S. Private*, pg. 351
ASKLEPIOS - ASB KRANKENHAUS RADEBERG GMBH—See Asklepios Kliniken GmbH & Co. KGaA; *Int'l*, pg. 622
ASKLEPIOS HARZKLINIKEN GMBH—See Asklepios Kliniken GmbH & Co. KGaA; *Int'l*, pg. 622
ASKLEPIOS KLINIK ALTONA—See Asklepios Kliniken GmbH & Co. KGaA; *Int'l*, pg. 622
ASKLEPIOS KLINIK BAD SALZUNGEN GMBH—See Asklepios Kliniken GmbH & Co. KGaA; *Int'l*, pg. 622
ASKLEPIOS KLINIK BARMBEK GMBH—See Asklepios Kliniken GmbH & Co. KGaA; *Int'l*, pg. 622
ASKLEPIOS KLINIK DR. WALB HOMBERG/OHM—See Asklepios Kliniken GmbH & Co. KGaA; *Int'l*, pg. 622
ASKLEPIOS KLINIKEN GMBH & CO. KGAA; *Int'l*, pg. 622
ASKLEPIOS KLINIKEN VERWALTUNGS - GESELLSCHAFT MBH - MEDICINE & SCIENCE DIVISION—See Asklepios Kliniken GmbH & Co. KGaA; *Int'l*, pg. 622
ASKLEPIOS KLINIK GAUTING GMBH—See Asklepios Kliniken GmbH & Co. KGaA; *Int'l*, pg. 622
ASKLEPIOS KLINIK LICH GMBH—See Asklepios Kliniken GmbH & Co. KGaA; *Int'l*, pg. 622
ASKLEPIOS KLINIK LINDAU GMBH—See Asklepios Kliniken GmbH & Co. KGaA; *Int'l*, pg. 622
ASKLEPIOS KLINIK NORD GMBH—See Asklepios Kliniken GmbH & Co. KGaA; *Int'l*, pg. 622
ASKLEPIOS KLINIK PASEWALK GMBH—See Asklepios Kliniken GmbH & Co. KGaA; *Int'l*, pg. 622
ASKLEPIOS KLINIK SANKT AUGUSTIN GMBH—See Asklepios Kliniken GmbH & Co. KGaA; *Int'l*, pg. 622
ASKLEPIOS KLINIKUM HARBURG—See Asklepios Kliniken GmbH & Co. KGaA; *Int'l*, pg. 622
ASKLEPIOS MVZ BRANDENBURG GMBH—See Asklepios Kliniken GmbH & Co. KGaA; *Int'l*, pg. 622
ASKLEPIOS MVZ HESSEN GMBH—See Asklepios Kliniken GmbH & Co. KGaA; *Int'l*, pg. 622
ASKLEPIOS MVZ MITTELDEUTSCHLAND GMBH—See Asklepios Kliniken GmbH & Co. KGaA; *Int'l*, pg. 622
ASKLEPIOS MVZ NIEDERSACHSEN GMBH—See Asklepios Kliniken GmbH & Co. KGaA; *Int'l*, pg. 622
ASKLEPIOS MVZ NORD SCHLESWIG HOLSTEIN GMBH—See Asklepios Kliniken GmbH & Co. KGaA; *Int'l*, pg. 622
ASKLEPIOS MVZ SACHSEN-ANHALT GMBH—See Asklepios Kliniken GmbH & Co. KGaA; *Int'l*, pg. 622
ASKLEPIOS NORDSEEKLINIK WESTERLAND GMBH—See Asklepios Kliniken GmbH & Co. KGaA; *Int'l*, pg. 622
ASKLEPIOS POLAND SP. Z O.O.—See Asklepios Kliniken GmbH & Co. KGaA; *Int'l*, pg. 622
ASKLEPIOS REHAKLINIK BAD OLDESLOE GMBH—See Asklepios Kliniken GmbH & Co. KGaA; *Int'l*, pg. 622
ASKLEPIOS SCHWALM-EDER-KLINIKEN GMBH—See Asklepios Kliniken GmbH & Co. KGaA; *Int'l*, pg. 622
ASKLEPIOS STADTKLINIK BAD TOLZ GMBH—See Asklepios Kliniken GmbH & Co. KGaA; *Int'l*, pg. 623
ASKLEPIOS SUDPFALZKLINIKEN GMBH—See Asklepios Kliniken GmbH & Co. KGaA; *Int'l*, pg. 623
ASKLEPIOS THERAPIE GMBH—See Asklepios Kliniken GmbH & Co. KGaA; *Int'l*, pg. 623
ASPEN EDUCATION GROUP, INC.—See Acadia Healthcare Company, Inc.; *U.S. Public*, pg. 28
ASPEN YOUTH, INC.—See Acadia Healthcare Company, Inc.; *U.S. Public*, pg. 28
ASPIRE SCOTLAND LIMITED.—See Acadia Healthcare Company, Inc.; *U.S. Public*, pg. 28
ASSOCIATED HEALTH SERVICES INC; *U.S. Private*, pg. 356
ASSOCIATES IN MEDICAL PHYSICS, LLC; *U.S. Private*, pg. 358
ASSOCIATION OF WOMEN'S HEALTH, OBSTETRIC & NEONATAL NURSES; *U.S. Private*, pg. 359
ASTRANA HEALTH INC.; *U.S. Public*, pg. 216

622110 — GENERAL MEDICAL AND... CORPORATE AFFILIATIONS

N.A.I.C.S. Index

ASTRIA REGIONAL MEDICAL CENTER—See Astria Health; *U.S. Private*, pg. 361
ASTRIA SUNNYSIDE HOSPITAL—See Astria Health; *U.S. Private*, pg. 361
ASTRIA TOPPENISH HOSPITAL—See Astria Health; *U.S. Private*, pg. 361
ATHAS HEALTH, LLC—See Nobilis Health Corp.; *U.S. Private*, pg. 2932
ATHENS MEDICAL CENTERS SA; *Int'l*, pg. 670
ATHENS SURGERY CENTER PARTNER, LLC—See Apollo Global Management, Inc.; *U.S. Public*, pg. 154
ATLANTA OUTPATIENT SURGERY CENTER—See HCA Healthcare, Inc.; *U.S. Public*, pg. 990
ATLANTA SURGERY CENTER, LTD.—See HCA Healthcare, Inc.; *U.S. Public*, pg. 991
ATLANTICARE REGIONAL MEDICAL CENTER, INC.—See Geisinger Health System; *U.S. Private*, pg. 1656
ATLANTIC HEALTH SYSTEM INC.; *U.S. Private*, pg. 373
ATLANTIC SHORES HOSPITAL, LLC—See Universal Health Services, Inc.; *U.S. Public*, pg. 2256
ATLANTIS OUTPATIENT CENTER—See HCA Healthcare, Inc.; *U.S. Public*, pg. 991
ATRIUS HEALTH, INC.; *U.S. Private*, pg. 382
ATS OF DELAWARE, INC.—See Acadia Healthcare Company, Inc.; *U.S. Public*, pg. 27
AUBURN REGIONAL MEDICAL CENTER—See Universal Health Services, Inc.; *U.S. Public*, pg. 2260
AUGUSTA HEALTH SYSTEM, LLC—See Quorum Health Corporation; *U.S. Private*, pg. 3329
AUGUSTA PHYSICIAN SERVICES, LLC—See Quorum Health Corporation; *U.S. Private*, pg. 3329
AUKAMM KLINIK FUR OPERATIVE RHEUMATOLOGIE UND ORTHOPADIE GMBH—See Fresenius SE & Co. KGaA; *Int'l*, pg. 2778
AURORA HEALTH CARE, INC.—See Advocate Health Care Network; *U.S. Private*, pg. 111
AUSTIN CENTER FOR OUTPATIENT SURGERY, L.P.—See UnitedHealth Group Incorporated; *U.S. Public*, pg. 2239
THE AUSTIN DIAGNOSTIC CLINIC, PLLC—See HCA Healthcare, Inc.; *U.S. Public*, pg. 1011
AUSTIN UROGYNECOLOGY, PLLC—See HCA Healthcare, Inc.; *U.S. Public*, pg. 991
AUSTRALIAN HOSPITAL CARE (COMO) PTY. LTD.—See Brookfield Corporation; *Int'l*, pg. 1176
AUSTRALIAN HOSPITAL CARE (KNOX) PTY. LTD.—See Brookfield Corporation; *Int'l*, pg. 1176
AUSTRALIAN ORTHOPAEDIC FIXATIONS PTY LTD—See Austofix Group Limited; *Int'l*, pg. 718
AVENTURA HEALTHCARE SPECIALISTS LLC—See HCA Healthcare, Inc.; *U.S. Public*, pg. 991
AVITA HEALTH SYSTEM; *U.S. Private*, pg. 409
AVOYELLES HOSPITAL—See Progressive Acute Care LLC; *U.S. Private*, pg. 3278
A WOMAN'S PLACE, LLC—See Community Health Systems, Inc.; *U.S. Public*, pg. 550
AZURE ACRES TREATMENT CENTER, LLC—See Acadia Healthcare Company, Inc.; *U.S. Public*, pg. 28
BACON COUNTY HEALTH SERVICES, LNC.; *U.S. Private*, pg. 423
BAILEY SQUARE AMBULATORY SURGICAL CENTER, LTD.—See HCA Healthcare, Inc.; *U.S. Public*, pg. 991
BAILEY SQUARE SURGERY CENTER—See HCA Healthcare, Inc.; *U.S. Public*, pg. 991
BAKERSFIELD MEMORIAL HOSPITAL—See Catholic Health Initiatives; *U.S. Private*, pg. 789
BANGKOK HOSPITAL CHIANGMAI CO., LTD.—See Bangkok Dusit Medical Services Public Company Limited; *Int'l*, pg. 834
BANGKOK HOSPITAL CHIANGRAI CO., LTD.—See Bangkok Dusit Medical Services Public Company Limited; *Int'l*, pg. 834
BANGKOK HOSPITAL HAT YAI CO., LTD.—See Bangkok Dusit Medical Services Public Company Limited; *Int'l*, pg. 834
BANGKOK HOSPITAL MEDICAL CENTER—See Bangkok Dusit Medical Services Public Company Limited; *Int'l*, pg. 834
BANGKOK HOSPITAL PATTAYA CO., LTD.—See Bangkok Dusit Medical Services Public Company Limited; *Int'l*, pg. 834
BANGKOK HOSPITAL PHUKET CO., LTD.—See Bangkok Dusit Medical Services Public Company Limited; *Int'l*, pg. 834
BANGKOK HOSPITAL PRAPADAENG CO., LTD.—See Bangkok Dusit Medical Services Public Company Limited; *Int'l*, pg. 834
BANGKOK HOSPITAL RATCHASIMA CO., LTD.—See Bangkok Dusit Medical Services Public Company Limited; *Int'l*, pg. 834
BANGKOK HOSPITAL SURAT CO., LTD.—See Bangkok Dusit Medical Services Public Company Limited; *Int'l*, pg. 834
BANGKOK HOSPITAL TRAT CO., LTD.—See Bangkok Dusit Medical Services Public Company Limited; *Int'l*, pg. 834
BANGKOK KHON KAEN HOSPITAL CO., LTD.—See Bangkok Dusit Medical Services Public Company Limited; *Int'l*, pg. 834
BANGKOK PATTAYA HOSPITAL CO., LTD.—See Bangkok Dusit Medical Services Public Company Limited; *Int'l*, pg. 834
BANGKOK PHUKET HOSPITAL CO., LTD.—See Bangkok Dusit Medical Services Public Company Limited; *Int'l*, pg. 834
BANGKOK RATCHASIMA HOSPITAL CO., LTD.—See Bangkok Dusit Medical Services Public Company Limited; *Int'l*, pg. 834
BANGKOK RAYONG HOSPITAL CO., LTD.—See Bangkok Dusit Medical Services Public Company Limited; *Int'l*, pg. 834
BANGKOK SAMUI HOSPITAL CO., LTD.—See Bangkok Dusit Medical Services Public Company Limited; *Int'l*, pg. 834
BANNER HEALTH WEST—See Banner Health System; *U.S. Private*, pg. 469
BAPTIST HEALTH ENTERPRISES—See Baptist Health South Florida, Inc.; *U.S. Private*, pg. 470
BAPTIST HEALTH MEDICAL CENTER; *U.S. Private*, pg. 470
BAPTIST HEALTH SOUTH FLORIDA, INC.; *U.S. Private*, pg. 470
BAPTIST HOSPITAL OF MIAMI—See Baptist Health South Florida, Inc.; *U.S. Private*, pg. 470
BAPTIST HOSPITALS OF SOUTHEAST TEXAS; *U.S. Private*, pg. 471
BAPTIST PLAZA SURGICARE, L.P.—See Tenet Healthcare Corporation; *U.S. Public*, pg. 2009
BARBERTON HEALTH SYSTEM, LLC—See Community Health Systems, Inc.; *U.S. Public*, pg. 551
BARNES-KASSON HOSPITAL; *U.S. Private*, pg. 477
BARNESVILLE HOSPITAL; *U.S. Private*, pg. 477
BARRANCA SURGERY CENTER, LLC—See UnitedHealth Group Incorporated; *U.S. Public*, pg. 2239
BARTOW REGIONAL MEDICAL CENTER INC.—See BayCare Health System Inc.; *U.S. Private*, pg. 495
BATESVILLE HMA MEDICAL GROUP, LLC—See Curae Health, Inc.; *U.S. Private*, pg. 1124
BATH COMMUNITY HOSPITAL; *U.S. Private*, pg. 487
BATON ROUGE TREATMENT CENTER, INC.—See Acadia Healthcare Company, Inc.; *U.S. Public*, pg. 28
BAXTER HEALTHCARE LIMITED—See Baxter International Inc.; *U.S. Public*, pg. 281
BAXTER PHARMACEUTICALS INDIA PVT. LTD.—See Baxter International Inc.; *U.S. Public*, pg. 281
BAY AREA ANESTHESIA, LLC—See KKR & Co. Inc.; *U.S. Public*, pg. 1245
BAY AREA COMMUNITY HEALTH; *U.S. Private*, pg. 491
BAY AREA HEALTHCARE GROUP, LTD.—See HCA Healthcare, Inc.; *U.S. Public*, pg. 991
BAY AREA HOUSTON ENDOSCOPY CENTER—See HCA Healthcare, Inc.; *U.S. Public*, pg. 991
BAY AREA SURGICARE CENTER, INC.—See HCA Healthcare, Inc.; *U.S. Public*, pg. 991
BAYCARE ALLIANT HOSPITAL—See BayCare Health System Inc.; *U.S. Private*, pg. 495
BAYCARE HEALTH SYSTEM INC.; *U.S. Private*, pg. 495
BAYER ZYDUS PHARMA PRIVATE LIMITED—See Bayer Aktiengesellschaft; *Int'l*, pg. 906
BAYFRONT AMBULATORY SURGICAL CENTER, LLC—See Community Health Systems, Inc.; *U.S. Public*, pg. 551
BAYFRONT HEALTH BROOKSVILLE—See Community Health Systems, Inc.; *U.S. Public*, pg. 551
BAYFRONT HEALTH PORT CHARLOTTE—See Community Health Systems, Inc.; *U.S. Public*, pg. 551
BAYFRONT HEALTH SPRING HILL—See Community Health Systems, Inc.; *U.S. Public*, pg. 551
BAYFRONT HEALTH ST. PETERSBURG—See Orlando Health, Inc.; *U.S. Private*, pg. 3043
BAYFRONT HEALTH SYSTEM, INC.—See Community Health Systems, Inc.; *U.S. Public*, pg. 551
BAYFRONT HMA CONVENIENT CARE, LLC—See Community Health Systems, Inc.; *U.S. Public*, pg. 551
BAYFRONT HMA MEDICAL CENTER, LLC—See Community Health Systems, Inc.; *U.S. Public*, pg. 551
BAYFRONT HMA PHYSICIAN MANAGEMENT, LLC—See Community Health Systems, Inc.; *U.S. Public*, pg. 551
BAY HOSPITAL, INC.—See HCA Healthcare, Inc.; *U.S. Public*, pg. 991
BAYLOR HEALTH CARE SYSTEM; *U.S. Private*, pg. 496
BAYLOR SURGICARE AT ENNIS, LLC—See Tenet Healthcare Corporation; *U.S. Public*, pg. 2009
BAYLOR SURGICARE AT GRANBURY, LLC—See Tenet Healthcare Corporation; *U.S. Public*, pg. 2009
BAYLOR SURGICARE AT MANSFIELD, LLC—See Tenet Healthcare Corporation; *U.S. Public*, pg. 2009
BAYLOR SURGICARE AT NORTH DALLAS, LLC—See Tenet Healthcare Corporation; *U.S. Public*, pg. 2009
BAYLOR SURGICARE AT PLANO PARKWAY, LLC—See Tenet Healthcare Corporation; *U.S. Public*, pg. 2009
BAYONET POINT SURGERY AND ENDOSCOPY CENTER—See HCA Healthcare, Inc.; *U.S. Public*, pg. 991
BAYSIDE MARIN, INC.—See Acadia Healthcare Company, Inc.; *U.S. Public*, pg. 28
BAYSTATE MEDICAL EDUCATION & RESEARCH FOUNDATION INC.—See Baystate Health System, Inc.; *U.S. Private*, pg. 497
BDMS WELLNESS CLINIC CO., LTD.—See Bangkok Dusit Medical Services Public Company Limited; *Int'l*, pg. 833
BEACON INTERNATIONAL SPECIALIST CENTRE SDN. BHD.; *Int'l*, pg. 932
BEAUMONT SURGICAL AFFILIATES, LTD.—See Tenet Healthcare Corporation; *U.S. Public*, pg. 2009
BEAVER DAM COMMUNITY HOSPITALS, INC.; *U.S. Private*, pg. 509
BECKLEY TREATMENT CENTER, LLC—See Acadia Healthcare Company, Inc.; *U.S. Public*, pg. 28
BEEBE MEDICAL CENTER; *U.S. Private*, pg. 513
BEHAVIORAL HEALTH MANAGEMENT, LLC—See Universal Health Services, Inc.; *U.S. Public*, pg. 2256
BEIJING UNITED FAMILY HOSPITAL CO., LTD.—See TPG Capital, L.P.; *U.S. Public*, pg. 2169
BELLAIRE OUTPATIENT SURGERY CENTER, L.L.P.—See Tenet Healthcare Corporation; *U.S. Public*, pg. 2009
BELLAIRE SURGICAL HOSPITAL HOLDINGS, LLC—See Nobilis Health Corp.; *U.S. Private*, pg. 2932
BELL PHYSICIAN PRACTICES, INC.—See Apollo Global Management, Inc.; *U.S. Public*, pg. 154
BELMONT BEHAVIORAL HOSPITAL, LLC—See Acadia Healthcare Company, Inc.; *U.S. Public*, pg. 28
BELOIT HEALTH SYSTEM, INC.; *U.S. Private*, pg. 521
BENCHMARK BEHAVIORAL HEALTH SYSTEM, INC.—See Universal Health Services, Inc.; *U.S. Public*, pg. 2256
BERJAYA HOSPITALITY SERVICES SDN BHD—See Berjaya Corporation Berhad; *Int'l*, pg. 983
BERWICK HOSPITAL COMPANY, LLC—See Community Health Systems, Inc.; *U.S. Public*, pg. 551
BEST DOCTORS CANADA INC.—See Teladoc Health, Inc.; *U.S. Public*, pg. 1992
BEST DOCTORS PORTUGAL LTD.—See Teladoc Health, Inc.; *U.S. Public*, pg. 1992
BETHANY HOSPICE AND PALLIATIVE CARE—See Apollo Global Management, Inc.; *U.S. Public*, pg. 156
BETHESDA ANESTHESIA ASSOCIATES, INC.—See KKR & Co. Inc.; *U.S. Public*, pg. 1245
BETHESDA HEALTHCARE INC.—See Catholic Health Initiatives; *U.S. Private*, pg. 790
BETHESDA HOSPITAL—See Fairview Health Services; *U.S. Private*, pg. 1464
BETH ISRAEL DEACONESS MEDICAL CENTER—See CareGroup, Inc.; *U.S. Private*, pg. 753
BETTY JEAN KERR PEOPLES HEALTH CENTERS; *U.S. Private*, pg. 547
BGI OF BRANDYWINE, INC.—See Acadia Healthcare Company, Inc.; *U.S. Public*, pg. 28
BHC ALHAMBRA HOSPITAL, INC.—See Universal Health Services, Inc.; *U.S. Public*, pg. 2256
BHC FOX RUN HOSPITAL, INC.—See Universal Health Services, Inc.; *U.S. Public*, pg. 2256
BHC HEALTH SERVICES OF NEVADA, INC.—See Universal Health Services, Inc.; *U.S. Public*, pg. 2256
BIG SPRING HOSPITAL CORPORATION—See Quorum Health Corporation; *U.S. Private*, pg. 3329
BILOXI HMA, INC.—See Community Health Systems, Inc.; *U.S. Public*, pg. 551
BINGHAM MEMORIAL HOSPITAL; *U.S. Private*, pg. 560
BIOMEDICA D.O.O.—See AddLife AB; *Int'l*, pg. 129
BIOMEDICAL RESEARCH INSTITUTE OF NEW MEXICO; *U.S. Private*, pg. 562
BIOMET 3I DO BRASIL COMERCIO DE APARELHOS MEDICOS LTDA.—See Zimmer Biomet Holdings, Inc.; *U.S. Public*, pg. 2405
BIRMINGHAM HOME CARE SERVICES, LLC—See Community Health Systems, Inc.; *U.S. Public*, pg. 551
BIRMINGHAM OUTPATIENT SURGERY CENTER, LTD.—See UnitedHealth Group Incorporated; *U.S. Public*, pg. 2239
BLACK CREEK MEDICAL CONSULTANTS LLC—See Community Health Systems, Inc.; *U.S. Public*, pg. 551
BLACK RIVER MEMORIAL HOSPITAL; *U.S. Private*, pg. 573
BLACKWELL HMA, LLC—See Community Health Systems, Inc.; *U.S. Public*, pg. 551
BLAINE MN MULTI-SPECIALTY ASC, LLC—See KKR & Co. Inc.; *U.S. Public*, pg. 1245
BLAKE MEDICAL CENTER—See HCA Healthcare, Inc.; *U.S. Public*, pg. 991
BLUEFIELD CLINIC COMPANY, LLC—See Community Health Systems, Inc.; *U.S. Public*, pg. 551
BLUEFIELD HBP MEDICAL GROUP, LLC—See Community Health Systems, Inc.; *U.S. Public*, pg. 551
BLUEFIELD HOSPITAL COMPANY, LLC—See Princeton Community Hospital; *U.S. Private*, pg. 3264
BLUE ISLAND CLINIC COMPANY, LLC—See Quorum Health Corporation; *U.S. Private*, pg. 3329
BLUE ISLAND HOME CARE SERVICES, LLC—See Community Health Systems, Inc.; *U.S. Public*, pg. 551
THE BLUE RIDGE/CLEMSON ORTHOPAEDIC ASC, LLC—See KKR & Co. Inc.; *U.S. Public*, pg. 1247
BLUE RIDGE MOUNTAIN RECOVERY CENTER, LLC—See Acadia Healthcare Company, Inc.; *U.S. Public*, pg. 28
BLUFFTON HEALTH SYSTEM, LLC—See Community

N.A.I.C.S. INDEX 622110 — GENERAL MEDICAL AND...

N.A.I.C.S. Index

Health Systems, Inc.; *U.S. Public*, pg. 551
BLUFFTON OKATIE PRIMARY CARE, L.L.C.—See Tenet Healthcare Corporation; *U.S. Public*, pg. 2007
BMI HEALTHCARE LIMITED—See Centene Corporation; *U.S. Public*, pg. 468
BMI SOUTHEND PRIVATE HOSPITAL LTD.—See Centene Corporation; *U.S. Public*, pg. 468
BMI SYON CLINIC LTD.—See Centene Corporation; *U.S. Public*, pg. 468
BMI THE EDGBASTON HOSPITAL—See Centene Corporation; *U.S. Public*, pg. 468
BMI THE HUDDERSFIELD HOSPITAL—See Centene Corporation; *U.S. Public*, pg. 468
BMI THE LANCASTER HOSPITAL—See Centene Corporation; *U.S. Public*, pg. 468
BOCA ANESTHESIA SERVICE, INC.—See KKR & Co. Inc.; *U.S. Public*, pg. 1245
BOCA RATON REGIONAL HOSPITAL, INC.—See Baptist Health South Florida, Inc.; *U.S. Private*, pg. 470
BOLIVAR MEDICAL CENTER—See Apollo Global Management, Inc.; *U.S. Public*, pg. 154
BOND COMMUNITY HEALTH CENTER, INC.; *U.S. Private*, pg. 613
BON SECOURS HEALTH SYSTEM, INC.—See Bon Secours Mercy Health, Inc.; *U.S. Private*, pg. 612
BOONE MEMORIAL HOSPITAL; *U.S. Private*, pg. 616
BORGESS MEDICAL CENTER—See Ascension Health Alliance; *U.S. Private*, pg. 346
BOSTON ENDOSCOPY CENTER, LLC—See KKR & Co. Inc.; *U.S. Public*, pg. 1245
BOSTON HEALTH CARE FOR THE HOMELESS PROGRAM; *U.S. Private*, pg. 621
BOSTON OUT-PATIENT SURGICAL SUITES, L.L.C.—See KKR & Co. Inc.; *U.S. Public*, pg. 1245
BOSTON SCIENTIFIC HELLAS S.A.—See Boston Scientific Corporation; *U.S. Public*, pg. 374
BOULCOTT HOSPITAL LIMITED—See Evolution Healthcare Pty. Ltd.; *Int'l*, pg. 2572
BOULDER CITY HOSPITAL; *U.S. Private*, pg. 623
BOULDER SPINE CENTER, LLC—See Bain Capital, LP; *U.S. Private*, pg. 445
BOURBON COMMUNITY HOSPITAL, LLC—See Apollo Global Management, Inc.; *U.S. Public*, pg. 154
BOWLING GREEN INN OF PENSACOLA, INC.—See Acadia Healthcare Company, Inc.; *U.S. Public*, pg. 28
BRANDON HMA, LLC—See Community Health Systems, Inc.; *U.S. Public*, pg. 551
BRANDON REGIONAL HOSPITAL—See HCA Healthcare, Inc.; *U.S. Public*, pg. 991
BRIARCLIFF AMBULATORY SURGERY CENTER, L.P.—See Tenet Healthcare Corporation; *U.S. Public*, pg. 2009
BRIDGEWAY HEALTH SOLUTIONS OF ARIZONA LLC—See Centene Corporation; *U.S. Public*, pg. 468
BRIDGTON HOSPITAL; *U.S. Private*, pg. 650
BRIGHAM CITY COMMUNITY HOSPITAL, INC.—See HCA Healthcare, Inc.; *U.S. Public*, pg. 991
THE BRIGHAM & WOMEN'S FAULKNER HOSPITAL—See Partners HealthCare System, Inc.; *U.S. Private*, pg. 3102
THE BRIGHAM & WOMEN'S HOSPITAL—See Partners HealthCare System, Inc.; *U.S. Private*, pg. 3102
BRIGHT HEALTH MANAGEMENT, INC.—See NeueHealth, Inc.; *U.S. Public*, pg. 1510
BRIGHTON COMMUNITY HOSPITAL ASSOCIATION; *U.S. Private*, pg. 652
BRIGHTPOINT HEALTH, INC.—See Hudson River HealthCare, Inc.; *U.S. Private*, pg. 2002
BRISBANE PRIVATE HOSPITAL PTY. LTD.—See Brookfield Corporation; *Int'l*, pg. 1176
BRISBANE WATERS EQUITIES PTY. LTD.—See Brookfield Corporation; *Int'l*, pg. 1176
BRISTOL SPINE CENTER, LLC—See Bain Capital, LP; *U.S. Private*, pg. 445
BROAD RIVER PRIMARY CARE, L.L.C.—See Tenet Healthcare Corporation; *U.S. Public*, pg. 2007
BROCKTON NEIGHBORHOOD HEALTH CENTER; *U.S. Private*, pg. 660
BRONSON BATTLE CREEK HOSPITAL—See Bronson Healthcare Group, Inc.; *U.S. Private*, pg. 662
BRONSON HEALTHCARE GROUP, INC.; *U.S. Private*, pg. 662
BROOKS MEMORIAL HOSPITAL; *U.S. Private*, pg. 664
BROOKWOOD CENTER DEVELOPMENT CORPORATION—See Tenet Healthcare Corporation; *U.S. Public*, pg. 2007
BROOKWOOD HEALTH SERVICES, INC.—See Tenet Healthcare Corporation; *U.S. Public*, pg. 2008
BROOKWOOD - MATERNAL FETAL MEDICINE, L.L.C.—See Tenet Healthcare Corporation; *U.S. Public*, pg. 2002
BROOKWOOD PRIMARY CARE - GRAND RIVER, L.L.C.—See Tenet Healthcare Corporation; *U.S. Public*, pg. 2001
BROOKWOOD WOMEN'S CARE, L.L.C.—See Tenet Healthcare Corporation; *U.S. Public*, pg. 2003
BROWARD HEALTH; *U.S. Private*, pg. 666
BROWNSVILLE HOSPITAL CORPORATION—See Community Health Systems, Inc.; *U.S. Public*, pg. 551
BROWNSVILLE SURGICAL SPECIALISTS, PLLC—See HCA Healthcare, Inc.; *U.S. Public*, pg. 992
BROWNWOOD HOSPITAL, L.P.—See Community Health Systems, Inc.; *U.S. Public*, pg. 551
BRYAN LGH MEDICAL CENTER INC.; *U.S. Private*, pg. 673
BUFORD ROAD IMAGING, L.L.C.—See HCA Healthcare, Inc.; *U.S. Public*, pg. 992
BULLHEAD CITY CLINIC CORP.—See Community Health Systems, Inc.; *U.S. Public*, pg. 551
BULLHEAD CITY HOSPITAL CORPORATION—See Community Health Systems, Inc.; *U.S. Public*, pg. 551
BUMRUNGRAD HOSPITAL PUBLIC COMPANY LIMITED; *Int'l*, pg. 1215
BUMRUNGRAD MEDICAL CENTER LTD. (BMC)—See Bumrungrad Hospital Public Company Limited; *Int'l*, pg. 1215
THE BURBANK OPHTHALMOLOGY ASC, L.P.—See KKR & Co. Inc.; *U.S. Public*, pg. 1247
BURNETT MEDICAL CENTER; *U.S. Private*, pg. 689
BURNEY DIALYSIS, LLC—See DaVita Inc.; *U.S. Public*, pg. 636
CABELL HUNTINGTON HOSPITAL, INC.; *U.S. Private*, pg. 710
CAC INDIA PRIVATE LIMITED—See CAC Holdings Corporation; *Int'l*, pg. 1247
CAHABA ORTHOPEDICS, LLC—See Community Health Systems, Inc.; *U.S. Public*, pg. 552
CALAIS REGIONAL HOSPITAL; *U.S. Private*, pg. 716
CALDWELL COUNTY HOSPITAL, INC.; *U.S. Private*, pg. 716
CALHOUN LIBERTY HOSPITAL; *U.S. Private*, pg. 717
CALIFORNIA HEALTH & WELLNESS PLAN—See Centene Corporation; *U.S. Public*, pg. 468
CALIFORNIA HOSPITAL MEDICAL CENTER—See Catholic Health Initiatives; *U.S. Private*, pg. 789
CALIFORNIA PACIFIC MEDICAL CENTER—See Sutter Health; *U.S. Private*, pg. 3887
CALIFORNIA REHABILITATION INSTITUTE, LLC—See Select Medical Holdings Corporation; *U.S. Public*, pg. 1857
CALIFORNIA TREATMENT SERVICES—See Acadia Healthcare Company, Inc.; *U.S. Public*, pg. 28
CALVARY HOSPITAL, INC.; *U.S. Private*, pg. 724
CAMBRIDGE HEALTH ALLIANCE; *U.S. Private*, pg. 727
CAMCARE HEALTH CORPORATION; *U.S. Private*, pg. 727
CAMC CANCER CENTERS, LLC—See Akumin, Inc.; *U.S. Public*, pg. 70
CAMPBELL COUNTY HMA, LLC—See Community Health Systems, Inc.; *U.S. Public*, pg. 552
THE CAMP RECOVERY CENTERS, L.P.—See Acadia Healthcare Company, Inc.; *U.S. Public*, pg. 30
CAMPUS SURGERY CENTER, LLC—See KKR & Co. Inc.; *U.S. Public*, pg. 1245
CANBERRA PRIVATE HOSPITAL PTY. LTD.—See Evolution Healthcare Pty. Ltd.; *Int'l*, pg. 2572
CANCER CARE, INC.; *U.S. Private*, pg. 733
CANTON-POTSDAM HOSPITAL; *U.S. Private*, pg. 735
CANYON RIDGE HOSPITAL, INC.—See Universal Health Services, Inc.; *U.S. Public*, pg. 2256
CANYON VISTA MEDICAL CENTER; *U.S. Private*, pg. 737
CAPE CORAL AMBULATORY SURGERY CENTER, LLC—See Bain Capital, LP; *U.S. Private*, pg. 445
CAPE CORAL SURGERY CENTER, INC.—See HCA Healthcare, Inc.; *U.S. Public*, pg. 992
CAPIO AB—See Apax Partners LLP; *Int'l*, pg. 502
CAPITAL AREA PRIMARY CARE PROVIDERS—See HCA Healthcare, Inc.; *U.S. Public*, pg. 992
CAPITAL HEALTH SYSTEMS INC.; *U.S. Private*, pg. 740
CAPITAL HOSPICE; *U.S. Private*, pg. 740
CAPITAL MEDICAL CENTER—See Apollo Global Management, Inc.; *U.S. Public*, pg. 154
CAPITAL REGIONAL MEDICAL CENTER—See HCA Healthcare, Inc.; *U.S. Public*, pg. 992
CAPITAL REGION MEDICAL CENTER INC.—See Curators of the University of Missouri; *U.S. Private*, pg. 1124
CARDIAC SURGICAL ASSOCIATES, LLC—See HCA Healthcare, Inc.; *U.S. Public*, pg. 992
CARDIOLOGY PHYSICIANS CORPORATION, L.L.C.—See Tenet Healthcare Corporation; *U.S. Public*, pg. 2003
CARDIO VASCULAR SURGEONS OF NORTH TEXAS, PLLC—See HCA Healthcare, Inc.; *U.S. Public*, pg. 992
CAREGROUP, INC.; *U.S. Private*, pg. 753
CARELONRX, INC.—See Elevance Health, Inc.; *U.S. Public*, pg. 729
CARERX CORPORATION; *Int'l*, pg. 1325
CARESOURCE; *U.S. Private*, pg. 754
CARESPOT OF ORLANDO/HSI URGENT CARE, LLC—See Tenet Healthcare Corporation; *U.S. Public*, pg. 2001
CARILION HEALTH SYSTEM; *U.S. Private*, pg. 761
CARITAS REHAB SERVICES, LLC—See Select Medical Holdings Corporation; *U.S. Public*, pg. 1857
CARLINVILLE AREA HOSPITAL; *U.S. Private*, pg. 764
CARLSBAD MEDICAL CENTER, LLC—See Community Health Systems, Inc.; *U.S. Public*, pg. 552
CARO COMMUNITY HOSPITAL; *U.S. Private*, pg. 766
CAROLINAS HEALTHCARE SYSTEM; *U.S. Private*, pg. 769
CARONDELET HEALTH NETWORK—See Ascension Health Alliance; *U.S. Private*, pg. 347
CARONDELET ST. MARY'S-NORTHWEST, L.L.C.—See Tenet Healthcare Corporation; *U.S. Public*, pg. 2001
CARROLL COUNTY MEMORIAL HOSPITAL; *U.S. Private*, pg. 773
CARTERSVILLE CENTER, INC.—See Acadia Healthcare Company, Inc.; *U.S. Public*, pg. 28
CARTERSVILLE MEDICAL CENTER, LLC—See HCA Healthcare, Inc.; *U.S. Public*, pg. 992
CARTHAGE AREA HOSPITAL, INC.; *U.S. Private*, pg. 776
CASA DI CURA PROF. NOBILI S.P.A.—See Garofalo Health Care SpA; *Int'l*, pg. 2886
CASA DI CURA VILLA GARDA S.P.A.—See Garofalo Health Care SpA; *Int'l*, pg. 2886
CASA GRANDE REGIONAL MEDICAL CENTER; *U.S. Private*, pg. 778
CASCADE BEHAVIORAL HOSPITAL, LLC—See Acadia Healthcare Company, Inc.; *U.S. Public*, pg. 28
CASTLE ROCK SURGERY CENTER, LLC—See Tenet Healthcare Corporation; *U.S. Public*, pg. 2009
CASTLE ROCK SURGICENTER, LLC—See UnitedHealth Group Incorporated; *U.S. Public*, pg. 2239
CASTLEVIEW HOSPITAL, LLC—See Apollo Global Management, Inc.; *U.S. Public*, pg. 154
CATAWBA-PIEDMONT CARDIOTHORACIC SURGERY, L.L.C.—See Tenet Healthcare Corporation; *U.S. Public*, pg. 2008
CATHOLIC HEALTHCARE PARTNERS; *U.S. Private*, pg. 791
CATHOLIC MEDICAL CENTER; *U.S. Private*, pg. 792
CAT SEATTLE, LLC—See Universal Health Services, Inc.; *U.S. Public*, pg. 2256
CATSKILL REGIONAL MEDICAL CENTER; *U.S. Private*, pg. 792
CAYUGA MEDICAL CENTER AT ITHACA; *U.S. Private*, pg. 795
CBHSP ARIZONA, INC.—See Centene Corporation; *U.S. Public*, pg. 468
CDH-DELNOR HEALTH SYSTEM, INC.—See Northwestern Memorial HealthCare; *U.S. Private*, pg. 2962
CEDAR CREST CLINIC—See Acadia Healthcare Company, Inc.; *U.S. Public*, pg. 29
CEDAR PARK HEALTH SYSTEM, L.P.—See Community Health Systems, Inc.; *U.S. Public*, pg. 552
CEDARS-SINAI MEDICAL CENTER; *U.S. Private*, pg. 805
CENTEGRA HEALTH SYSTEM; *U.S. Private*, pg. 809
CENTENNIAL ASC, L.P.—See Tenet Healthcare Corporation; *U.S. Public*, pg. 2002
CENTENNIAL MEDICAL CENTER—See HCA Healthcare, Inc.; *U.S. Public*, pg. 992
CENTENNIAL MEDICAL GROUP INC; *U.S. Private*, pg. 809
CENTENNIAL SURGICAL CLINIC, LLC—See HCA Healthcare, Inc.; *U.S. Public*, pg. 992
CENTER FOR ADULT HEALTHCARE, LLC—See Community Health Systems, Inc.; *U.S. Public*, pg. 552
CENTER FOR AIDS RESEARCH, EDUCATION AND SERVICES; *U.S. Private*, pg. 809
CENTER FOR AMBULATORY SURGERY, LLC—See KKR & Co. Inc.; *U.S. Public*, pg. 1245
THE CENTER FOR COMPREHENSIVE CARE & DIAGNOSIS OF INHERITED BLOOD DISORDERS; *U.S. Private*, pg. 4006
CENTER FOR MEDICAL INTEROPERABILITY, INC.—See Community Health Systems, Inc.; *U.S. Public*, pg. 552
THE CENTER FOR SPECIAL SURGERY AT TCA—See HCA Healthcare, Inc.; *U.S. Public*, pg. 1008
CENTER FOR SPECIAL SURGERY—See HCA Healthcare, Inc.; *U.S. Public*, pg. 993
CENTERLIGHT HEALTH SYSTEM; *U.S. Private*, pg. 816
CENTERPOINTE COMMUNITY BASED SERVICES, LLC—See Acadia Healthcare Company, Inc.; *U.S. Public*, pg. 28
CENTRAK, INC.—See Halma plc; *Int'l*, pg. 3231
CENTRAL CAROLINA AMBULATORY SURGERY CENTER, LLC—See Apollo Global Management, Inc.; *U.S. Public*, pg. 155
CENTRAL CITY COMMUNITY HEALTH CENTER; *U.S. Private*, pg. 819
CENTRAL DUPAGE HOSPITAL ASSOCIATION—See Northwestern Memorial HealthCare; *U.S. Private*, pg. 2962
CENTRAL FLORIDA FAMILY HEALTH CENTER, INC.; *U.S. Private*, pg. 820
CENTRAL FLORIDA REGIONAL HOSPITAL—See HCA Healthcare, Inc.; *U.S. Public*, pg. 993
CENTRAL GEORGIA HEALTH SYSTEM INC.; *U.S. Private*, pg. 821
CENTRAL MINNESOTA DIAGNOSTIC INC.; *U.S. Private*, pg. 822
CENTRAL SHARED SERVICES, LLC—See HCA Healthcare, Inc.; *U.S. Public*, pg. 993
CENTRAL TEXAS COMMUNITY HEALTH CENTERS; *U.S. Private*, pg. 825
CENTRE CLINIC CORP.—See Quorum Health Corporation; *U.S. Private*, pg. 3329
CENTRO MEDICO SAN BIAGIO S.R.L.—See Garofalo Health Care SpA; *Int'l*, pg. 2886
CENTRO MEDICO UNIVERSITA CASTRENSE S.R.L.—See

622110 — GENERAL MEDICAL AND...   CORPORATE AFFILIATIONS

Garofalo Health Care SpA; *Int'l*, pg. 2886
CENTRUM LE CBY POHYBOVEHO APARATU, S.R.O.—See Fresenius SE & Co. KGaA; *Int'l*, pg. 2777
CENTRUM MEDYCZNE ENEL-MED S.A.; *Int'l*, pg. 1415
CENTRUM SURGICAL CENTER—See HCA Healthcare, Inc.; *U.S. Public*, pg. 993
CENTURION LLC—See Centene Corporation; *U.S. Public*, pg. 468
CENTURION OF INDIANA, LLC—See Centene Corporation; *U.S. Public*, pg. 468
CGH MEDICAL CENTER; *U.S. Private*, pg. 844
CHAMPION SPORTS MEDICINE BIRMINGHAM, LLC—See Community Health Systems, Inc.; *U.S. Public*, pg. 552
CHARLESTON AREA MEDICAL CENTER INC.; *U.S. Private*, pg. 856
CHARLESTON TREATMENT CENTER, LLC—See Acadia Healthcare Company, Inc.; *U.S. Public*, pg. 28
CHARLEVOIX AREA HOSPITAL; *U.S. Private*, pg. 857
CHARLOTTE ENDOSCOPIC SURGERY CENTER, LLC—See Tenet Healthcare Corporation; *U.S. Public*, pg. 2002
CHARTER OAK HEALTH CENTER, INC.; *U.S. Private*, pg. 858
CHASE BREXTON HEALTH SERVICES, INC.; *U.S. Private*, pg. 859
CHATUGE REGIONAL HOSPITAL; *U.S. Private*, pg. 868
CHEROKEE REGIONAL MEDICAL CENTER; *U.S. Private*, pg. 873
CHESTERFIELD GENERAL HOSPITAL—See McLeod Health; *U.S. Private*, pg. 2641
CHESTERFIELD IMAGING, LLC—See HCA Healthcare, Inc.; *U.S. Public*, pg. 993
CHESTERFIELD IMAGING, LLC—See HCA Healthcare, Inc.; *U.S. Public*, pg. 993
CHESTER HMA, INC.—See Medical University Of South Carolina; *U.S. Private*, pg. 2656
CHESTERTON SURGERY CENTER, LLC—See Community Health Systems, Inc.; *U.S. Public*, pg. 552
CHESTNUT HEALTH SYSTEMS, INC.; *U.S. Private*, pg. 875
CHHS HOSPITAL COMPANY, LLC—See Tower Health; *U.S. Private*, pg. 4193
CHIANG MAI RAM MEDICAL BUSINESS PCL; *Int'l*, pg. 1476
CHI HEALTH CREIGHTON UNIVERSITY MEDICAL CENTER - BERGAN MERCY—See Catholic Health Initiatives; *U.S. Private*, pg. 789
CHILDREN'S CARE HOSPITAL & SCHOOL; *U.S. Private*, pg. 883
CHILDREN'S HEALTHCARE OF ATLANTA; *U.S. Private*, pg. 883
CHILDREN'S HOSPITAL LOS ANGELES; *U.S. Private*, pg. 884
CHILDREN'S HOSPITAL MEDICAL CENTER OF AKRON; *U.S. Private*, pg. 884
CHILDREN'S HOSPITAL & MEDICAL CENTER; *U.S. Private*, pg. 884
CHILDREN'S HOSPITAL MEDICAL PRACTICE CORPORATION; *U.S. Private*, pg. 884
CHILDREN'S HOSPITAL OF NEW JERSEY—See Barnabas Health, Inc.; *U.S. Private*, pg. 476
CHILDREN'S HOSPITAL PEDIATRIC ASSOCIATES, INC.; *U.S. Private*, pg. 884
CHILDREN'S HOSPITAL; *U.S. Private*, pg. 884
THE CHILDRENS MERCY HOSPITAL; *U.S. Private*, pg. 4009
CHILDREN'S POPULATION HEALTH; *U.S. Private*, pg. 885
CHINA RESOURCES MEDICAL HOLDINGS CO., LTD.; *Int'l*, pg. 1549
CHINA SHESAYS MEDICAL COSMETOLOGY INC.; *Int'l*, pg. 1551
CHINO VALLEY MEDICAL CENTER—See Prime Healthcare Services, Inc.; *U.S. Private*, pg. 3261
CHIPPENHAM & JOHNSTON-WILLIS HOSPITALS, INC.—See HCA Healthcare, Inc.; *U.S. Public*, pg. 993
CHIPPENHAM PEDIATRIC SPECIALISTS, LLC—See HCA Healthcare, Inc.; *U.S. Public*, pg. 993
CHRISTIANA CARE CORPORATION; *U.S. Private*, pg. 891
CHRISTIANA CARE HEALTH SYSTEM, INC.; *U.S. Private*, pg. 891
CHRISTIAN COMMUNITY HEALTH CENTER; *U.S. Private*, pg. 891
CHRISTIAN HEALTHCARE MINISTRIES, INC.; *U.S. Private*, pg. 891
THE CHRISTIE CLINIC LLP—See HCA Healthcare, Inc.; *U.S. Public*, pg. 1012
CHRISTUS HEALTH; *U.S. Private*, pg. 892
CHRISTUS LAKE AREA HOSPITAL—See CHRISTUS Health; *U.S. Private*, pg. 892
CHRYSSAFILIOTISSA PUBLIC LTD—See DIAGNOSTIC AND THERAPEUTIC CENTER OF ATHENS-HYGEIA S.A.; *Int'l*, pg. 2103
CHS/COMMUNITY HEALTH SYSTEMS, INC.—See Community Health Systems, Inc.; *U.S. Public*, pg. 551
CHSPSC, LLC—See Community Health Systems, Inc.; *U.S. Public*, pg. 551
CHULARAT HOSPITAL PUBLIC COMPANY LIMITED; *Int'l*, pg. 1596

CHW/MERCY HOSPITAL BAKERSFIELD—See Catholic Health Initiatives; *U.S. Private*, pg. 789
CIRCLE HEALTH 1 LTD.—See Centene Corporation; *U.S. Public*, pg. 468
CIRCLE HEALTH LIMITED—See Centene Corporation; *U.S. Public*, pg. 468
CIRCLE HOME, INC.; *U.S. Private*, pg. 899
CITRUS HEALTH NETWORK, INC.; *U.S. Private*, pg. 904
CITRUS HMA, INC.—See Community Health Systems, Inc.; *U.S. Public*, pg. 553
CITRUS MEMORIAL HOSPITAL, INC.—See HCA Healthcare, Inc.; *U.S. Public*, pg. 993
CITY OF HOPE NATIONAL MEDICAL CENTER; *U.S. Private*, pg. 906
CJ PHARMACEUTICAL ENTERPRISES LIMITED—See Dis-Chem Pharmacies Ltd.; *Int'l*, pg. 2130
CJW MEDICAL CENTER—See HCA Healthcare, Inc.; *U.S. Public*, pg. 992
CKH (MT A) PTE. LTD.—See HC Surgical Specialists Limited; *Int'l*, pg. 3297
CLARA BARTON HOSPITAL; *U.S. Private*, pg. 910
CLARA MAASS MEDICAL CENTER—See Barnabas Health, Inc.; *U.S. Private*, pg. 476
CLAREMONT HOSPITAL LLP—See Tenet Healthcare Corporation; *U.S. Public*, pg. 2002
CLAREMORE ANESTHESIA, LLC—See Community Health Systems, Inc.; *U.S. Public*, pg. 552
CLAREMORE INTERNAL MEDICINE, LLC—See Community Health Systems, Inc.; *U.S. Public*, pg. 552
CLARION HOSPITAL; *U.S. Private*, pg. 911
CLARK REGIONAL PHYSICIAN PRACTICES, LLC—See Apollo Global Management, Inc.; *U.S. Public*, pg. 155
CLARKSBURG TREATMENT CENTER, LLC—See Acadia Healthcare Company, Inc.; *U.S. Public*, pg. 28
CLARKSDALE HMA, LLC—See Curae Health, Inc.; *U.S. Private*, pg. 1124
CLARKSVILLE MEDICAL CENTER, G.P.—See Community Health Systems, Inc.; *U.S. Public*, pg. 552
CLAXTON-HEPBURN MEDICAL CENTER; *U.S. Private*, pg. 917
CLEAR CREEK SURGERY CENTER, LLC—See HCA Healthcare, Inc.; *U.S. Public*, pg. 993
CLEAR LAKE FAMILY PHYSICIANS, PLLC—See HCA Healthcare, Inc.; *U.S. Public*, pg. 993
CLEAR LAKE REGIONAL MEDICAL CENTER, INC.—See HCA Healthcare, Inc.; *U.S. Public*, pg. 993
CLEVELAND CLINIC REHABILITATION HOSPITALS, LLC—See Select Medical Holdings Corporation; *U.S. Public*, pg. 1857
CLEVELAND HOSPITAL CORPORATION—See Community Health Systems, Inc.; *U.S. Public*, pg. 552
CLEVELAND MEDICAL CLINIC, INC.—See Community Health Systems, Inc.; *U.S. Public*, pg. 552
CLEVELAND TENNESSEE HOSPITAL COMPANY, LLC—See Hamilton Health Care System, Inc.; *U.S. Private*, pg. 1848
CLINCH VALLEY MEDICAL CENTER, INC.—See Apollo Global Management, Inc.; *U.S. Public*, pg. 155
CLINCH VALLEY PHYSICIANS ASSOCIATES, LLC—See Apollo Global Management, Inc.; *U.S. Public*, pg. 155
CLINICA LAS CONDES S.A.; *Int'l*, pg. 1659
CLINICAL GRAPHICS BV—See Zimmer Biomet Holdings, Inc.; *U.S. Public*, pg. 2406
CLINICAL RADIOLOGY FOUNDATION; *U.S. Private*, pg. 944
CLINICA SABEDOTTI LTDA.—See Centro de Imagem Diagnosticos S.A.; *Int'l*, pg. 1413
CLINICAS DEL CAMINO REAL, INC.; *U.S. Private*, pg. 944
CLINICAS DE SALUD DEL PUEBLO, INC.; *U.S. Private*, pg. 944
CLINTON COUNTY HOSPITAL, INC.; *U.S. Private*, pg. 944
CLINTON HMA, LLC—See Community Health Systems, Inc.; *U.S. Public*, pg. 552
CLINTON HOSPITAL CORPORATION—See Quorum Health Corporation; *U.S. Private*, pg. 3329
CLIPPER CARDIOVASCULAR ASSOCIATES, INC.—See HCA Healthcare, Inc.; *U.S. Public*, pg. 993
CLIRIA - HOSPITAL PRIVADO DE AVEIRO, S.A.—See Fosun International Limited; *Int'l*, pg. 2751
CLOUD COUNTY HEALTH CENTER; *U.S. Private*, pg. 946
CLUBHOUSE MEDIA GROUP, INC.; *U.S. Public*, pg. 515
CMC HOME HEALTH AND HOSPICE, LLC—See UnitedHealth Group Incorporated; *U.S. Public*, pg. 2244
CML-CHICAGO MARKET LABS, INC.—See Tenet Healthcare Corporation; *U.S. Public*, pg. 2014
CMSC, LLC—See Bain Capital, LP; *U.S. Public*, pg. 445
C.M.S.R. VENETO MEDICA S.R.L.—See Garofalo Health Care SpA; *Int'l*, pg. 2886
COA ASC OF FRANKLIN COUNTY, LLC—See KKR & Co. Inc.; *U.S. Public*, pg. 1245
COALITION OF CANCER COOPERATIVE GROUPS; *U.S. Private*, pg. 954
COASTAL FAMILY HEALTH CENTER; *U.S. Private*, pg. 956
COASTAL HEALTHCARE SERVICES, INC.—See HCA Healthcare, Inc.; *U.S. Public*, pg. 993
COASTAL INPATIENT PHYSICIANS, LLC—See HCA Healthcare, Inc.; *U.S. Public*, pg. 993

COASTAL MEDICAL ASSOCIATES INC; *U.S. Private*, pg. 956
COAST PLAZA DOCTORS HOSPITAL INC.; *U.S. Private*, pg. 954
COATESVILLE HOSPITAL CORPORATION—See Tower Health; *U.S. Private*, pg. 4193
COCKE COUNTY HMA, LLC—See Community Health Systems, Inc.; *U.S. Public*, pg. 552
COFFEE REGIONAL MEDICAL CENTER, INC.; *U.S. Private*, pg. 961
COFFEYVILLE REGIONAL MEDICAL CENTER; *U.S. Private*, pg. 961
COGENT HMG, INC.; *U.S. Private*, pg. 962
COLISEUM HEALTH GROUP, LLC—See HCA Healthcare, Inc.; *U.S. Public*, pg. 993
COLISEUM HEALTH SYSTEM—See HCA Healthcare, Inc.; *U.S. Public*, pg. 993
COLISEUM NORTHSIDE HOSPITAL, LLC—See HCA Healthcare, Inc.; *U.S. Public*, pg. 993
COLLEGE STATION HOSPITAL, L.P.—See Community Health Systems, Inc.; *U.S. Public*, pg. 552
COLLEGE STATION RHC COMPANY, LLC—See Community Health Systems, Inc.; *U.S. Public*, pg. 552
COLLETON MEDICAL CENTER—See HCA Healthcare, Inc.; *U.S. Public*, pg. 993
COLLIER HMA NEUROLOGICAL VASCULAR MEDICAL GROUP, LLC—See Community Health Systems, Inc.; *U.S. Public*, pg. 552
COLORADO PLAINS PHYSICIAN PRACTICES, LLC—See Apollo Global Management, Inc.; *U.S. Public*, pg. 155
COLORADO UROLOGIC SURGERY CENTER, LLC—See Tenet Healthcare Corporation; *U.S. Public*, pg. 2002
COLTON CA MULTI ASC, L.P.—See KKR & Co. Inc.; *U.S. Public*, pg. 1245
COLUMBIA/ALLEGHANY REGIONAL HOSPITAL, INCORPORATED—See HCA Healthcare, Inc.; *U.S. Public*, pg. 994
THE COLUMBIA ASC, LLC—See KKR & Co. Inc.; *U.S. Public*, pg. 1247
THE COLUMBIA ASC NORTHWEST, LLC—See KKR & Co. Inc.; *U.S. Public*, pg. 1247
COLUMBIA/HCA RETREAT HOSPITAL, INC.—See HCA Healthcare, Inc.; *U.S. Public*, pg. 994
COLUMBIA HOSPITAL CORPORATION OF SOUTH BROWARD—See HCA Healthcare, Inc.; *U.S. Public*, pg. 994
COLUMBIA MEDICAL CENTER OF DENTON SUBSIDIARY, L.P.—See HCA Healthcare, Inc.; *U.S. Public*, pg. 994
COLUMBIA MEDICAL CENTER OF LAS COLINAS, INC.—See HCA Healthcare, Inc.; *U.S. Public*, pg. 994
COLUMBIA MEMORIAL HOSPITAL; *U.S. Private*, pg. 977
COLUMBIA NORTH HILLS HOSPITAL SUBSIDIARY, L.P.—See HCA Healthcare, Inc.; *U.S. Public*, pg. 994
COLUMBIA ST. MARY'S INC.—See Ascension Health Alliance; *U.S. Private*, pg. 347
COMANCHE COUNTY MEDICAL CENTER; *U.S. Private*, pg. 980
COMMONSPIRIT HEALTH; *U.S. Private*, pg. 986
COMMONWEALTH HEALTH CANCER NETWORK, LLC—See Community Health Systems, Inc.; *U.S. Public*, pg. 552
COMMONWEALTH PHYSICIAN NETWORK, LLC—See Community Health Systems, Inc.; *U.S. Public*, pg. 552
COMMUNITY CARE CHANNING WAY, LLC—See Bain Capital, LP; *U.S. Private*, pg. 445
COMMUNITY CARE WEST SIDE, LLC—See Bain Capital, LP; *U.S. Private*, pg. 445
COMMUNITY HEALTH CARE; *U.S. Private*, pg. 993
COMMUNITY HEALTH CENTER, INC.; *U.S. Private*, pg. 993
COMMUNITY HEALTH CENTER OF SOUTHEAST KANSAS; *U.S. Private*, pg. 993
COMMUNITY HEALTH NETWORK OF CONNECTICUT, INC.; *U.S. Private*, pg. 994
COMMUNITY HEALTH SERVICES OF GEORGIA; *U.S. Private*, pg. 994
COMMUNITY HOSPICE & PALLIATIVE CARE; *U.S. Private*, pg. 994
COMMUNITY HOSPITAL OF SAN BERNARDINO—See Catholic Health Initiatives; *U.S. Private*, pg. 789
COMMUNITY HOSPITALS AND WELLNESS CENTERS; *U.S. Private*, pg. 994
COMMUNITY MEDICAL CENTER, INC.—See Apollo Global Management, Inc.; *U.S. Public*, pg. 154
COMMUNITY MEDICAL CENTER—See Barnabas Health, Inc.; *U.S. Private*, pg. 476
COMMUNITY MEMORIAL HEALTHCENTER; *U.S. Private*, pg. 996
COMMUNITY MEMORIAL HEALTH SYSTEM; *U.S. Private*, pg. 995
COMMUNITY REHABILITATION SERVICES, INC.; *U.S. Private*, pg. 996
COMPREHENSIVE RADIOLOGY MANAGEMENT SERVICES, LTD.—See HCA Healthcare, Inc.; *U.S. Public*, pg. 994
CONCENTRA PRIMARY CARE OF NEW JERSEY PA—See Select Medical Holdings Corporation; *U.S. Public*, pg. 1857

N.A.I.C.S. INDEX 622110 — GENERAL MEDICAL AND...
N.A.I.C.S. Index

CONIFER HOLDINGS, INC.—See Tenet Healthcare Corporation; *U.S. Public*, pg. 2002
CONIFER REVENUE CYCLE SOLUTIONS, LLC—See Tenet Healthcare Corporation; *U.S. Public*, pg. 2002
CONNECTICUT CHILDREN'S MEDICAL CENTER—See Connecticut Children's Medical Center Corporation, Inc.; *U.S. Private*, pg. 1015
CONNECTICUT PEER REVIEW ORGANIZATION, INC.; *U.S. Private*, pg. 1016
CONQUEST CARE HOMES (SOHAM) LIMITED—See Acadia Healthcare Company, Inc.; *U.S. Public*, pg. 28
CONROE REGIONAL MEDICAL CENTER—See HCA Healthcare, Inc.; *U.S. Public*, pg. 994
CONSEJO DE SALUD DE PUERTO RICO, INC.; *U.S. Private*, pg. 1019
CONSOLIDATED HEALTH SYSTEMS INC; *U.S. Private*, pg. 1021
CONSULTANTS IN PAIN MEDICINE, LLC—See Bain Capital, LP; *U.S. Private*, pg. 445
CONVERSE MEDICAL CENTER LLC—See Adeptus Health Inc.; *U.S. Private*, pg. 78
CONWAY BEHAVIORAL HEALTH, LLC—See Acadia Healthcare Company, Inc.; *U.S. Public*, pg. 28
COOPER HEALTH SYSTEMS; *U.S. Private*, pg. 1041
CORAL GABLES HOSPITAL, INC.—See Tenet Healthcare Corporation; *U.S. Public*, pg. 2006
CORAL SPRINGS AMBULATORY SURGERY CENTER, LLC—See KKR & Co. Inc.; *U.S. Public*, pg. 1245
CORDENTAL GROUP MANAGEMENT, LLC—See NMS Capital Services, LLC; *U.S. Private*, pg. 2931
CORIZON HEALTH, INC.—See Flacks Homes LLC; *U.S. Private*, pg. 1538
CORIZON HEALTH, INC.—See Flacks Homes LLC; *U.S. Private*, pg. 1539
CORNELL SCOTT-HILL HEALTH CENTER; *U.S. Private*, pg. 1051
CORNERSTONE SURGERY CENTER, LLC—See UnitedHealth Group Incorporated; *U.S. Public*, pg. 2240
CORPUS CHRISTI MEDICAL CENTER—See HCA Healthcare, Inc.; *U.S. Public*, pg. 994
CORPUS CHRISTI SURGICARE, LTD.—See Tenet Healthcare Corporation; *U.S. Public*, pg. 2010
CORRY MEMORIAL HOSPITAL; *U.S. Private*, pg. 1059
COSSMA INC.; *U.S. Private*, pg. 1062
COTTAGE HOSPITAL; *U.S. Private*, pg. 1063
COUNTRYSIDE SURGERY CENTER—See HCA Healthcare, Inc.; *U.S. Public*, pg. 994
COVANCE CHILE SERVICES LIMITADA—See Laboratory Corporation of America Holdings; *U.S. Public*, pg. 1285
COVANCE CLASSIC LABORATORY SERVICES INC.—See Laboratory Corporation of America Holdings; *U.S. Public*, pg. 1286
COVANCE CLINICAL PRODUCT DEVELOPMENTS LTD.—See Laboratory Corporation of America Holdings; *U.S. Public*, pg. 1286
COVANCE HONG KONG SERVICES LIMITED—See Laboratory Corporation of America Holdings; *U.S. Public*, pg. 1286
COVANCE INDIA PHARMACEUTICAL SERVICES PRIVATE LIMITED—See Laboratory Corporation of America Holdings; *U.S. Public*, pg. 1286
COVENANT MEDICAL CENTER INC; *U.S. Private*, pg. 1071
CRAIG HOSPITAL; *U.S. Private*, pg. 1082
CRANE CREEK SURGICAL PARTNERS, LLC—See Community Health Systems, Inc.; *U.S. Public*, pg. 552
CRANEWARE US HOLDINGS, INC.—See Craneware plc; *Int'l*, pg. 1828
CRC HEALTH, LLC—See Acadia Healthcare Company, Inc.; *U.S. Public*, pg. 28
CRC HEALTH TREATMENT CLINICS, LLC—See Acadia Healthcare Company, Inc.; *U.S. Public*, pg. 28
CRC WISCONSIN RD, LLC—See Acadia Healthcare Company, Inc.; *U.S. Public*, pg. 28
CRESTWOOD HOSPITAL, LLC—See Community Health Systems, Inc.; *U.S. Public*, pg. 552
CRESTWOOD PHYSICIAN SERVICES, LLC—See Community Health Systems, Inc.; *U.S. Public*, pg. 552
CREWE OUTPATIENT IMAGING, LLC—See HCA Healthcare, Inc.; *U.S. Public*, pg. 995
CRITICAL CARE SERVICES, INC.; *U.S. Private*, pg. 1101
CROCKETT HOSPITAL, LLC—See Apollo Global Management, Inc.; *U.S. Public*, pg. 155
CROSSING RIVERS HEALTH; *U.S. Private*, pg. 1106
CROSSINGS HEALTHCARE SOLUTIONS, INC.—See Universal Health Services, Inc.; *U.S. Public*, pg. 2256
CROSSROADS HOME CARE SERVICES, LLC—See Community Health Systems, Inc.; *U.S. Public*, pg. 552
CROSSROADS PHYSICIAN CORP.—See Quorum Health Corporation; *U.S. Private*, pg. 3329
CROSSROADS REGIONAL HOSPITAL, LLC—See Acadia Healthcare Company, Inc.; *U.S. Public*, pg. 28
THE CRYSTAL RIVER ENDOSCOPY ASC, L.P.—See KKR & Co. Inc.; *U.S. Public*, pg. 1247
CSPC HEALTHCARE INC.—See CSPC Pharmaceutical Group Limited; *Int'l*, pg. 1867
CSRA HOLDINGS, LLC—See Quorum Health Corporation; *U.S. Private*, pg. 3329
CTCUE B.V.—See IQVIA Holdings Inc.; *U.S. Public*, pg. 1168
CUBA MEMORIAL HOSPITAL, INC.; *U.S. Private*, pg. 1119
CULEMBORG PHARMACY PROPRIETARY LIMITED—See Dis-Chem Pharmacies Ltd.; *Int'l*, pg. 2130
CULLMAN REGIONAL MEDICAL CENTER; *U.S. Private*, pg. 1121
CUMBERLAND COUNTY HOSPITAL ASSOCIATION INC.; *U.S. Private*, pg. 1122
CUMBERLAND HOSPITAL, LLC—See Universal Health Services, Inc.; *U.S. Public*, pg. 2256
CURATORS OF THE UNIVERSITY OF MISSOURI; *U.S. Private*, pg. 1124
CURTIS V. COOPER PRIMARY HEALTH CARE, INC.; *U.S. Private*, pg. 1127
CYGNET 2000 LIMITED—See Universal Health Services, Inc.; *U.S. Public*, pg. 2256
CYSTIC FIBROSIS FOUNDATION; *U.S. Private*, pg. 1135
DADE PROSTHETICS & ORTHOTICS, INC.—See Select Medical Holdings Corporation; *U.S. Public*, pg. 1857
DALLAH HEALTH COMPANY; *Int'l*, pg. 1954
DALLAS COUNTY INDIGENT CARE CORPORATION; *U.S. Private*, pg. 1149
DALLAS MEDICAL SPECIALISTS, PLLC—See HCA Healthcare, Inc.; *U.S. Public*, pg. 995
DALLAS SURGICAL PARTNERS, L.L.P.—See Tenet Healthcare Corporation; *U.S. Public*, pg. 2014
D'AMBROSIO EYE CARE, INC.; *U.S. Private*, pg. 1138
DAMERON HOSPITAL ASSOCIATION; *U.S. Private*, pg. 1151
DANVILLE DIAGNOSTIC IMAGING CENTER, LLC—See Apollo Global Management, Inc.; *U.S. Public*, pg. 155
DANVILLE PHYSICIAN PRACTICES, LLC—See Apollo Global Management, Inc.; *U.S. Public*, pg. 155
DANVILLE REGIONAL MEDICAL CENTER, LLC—See Apollo Global Management, Inc.; *U.S. Public*, pg. 155
DANVILLE REGIONAL MEDICAL CENTER SCHOOL OF HEALTH PROFESSIONS, LLC—See Apollo Global Management, Inc.; *U.S. Public*, pg. 155
DARWIN PRIVATE HOSPITAL PTY. LTD.—See Brookfield Corporation; *Int'l*, pg. 1176
DAUTERIVE HOSPITAL—See HCA Healthcare, Inc.; *U.S. Public*, pg. 995
DAVITA HIGHLAND RANCH DIALYSIS CENTER—See DaVita Inc.; *U.S. Public*, pg. 637
DAYTON CHILDRENS HOSPITAL; *U.S. Private*, pg. 1177
DAYTON HEART & VASCULAR HOSPITAL—See Catholic Health Initiatives; *U.S. Private*, pg. 790
DEACONESS PHYSICIAN SERVICES, LLC—See Community Health Systems, Inc.; *U.S. Public*, pg. 552
DEARBORN COUNTY HOSPITAL; *U.S. Private*, pg. 1185
DELAWARE HOSPICE, INC.; *U.S. Private*, pg. 1194
DELF (UK) LIMITED—See Neogen Corporation; *U.S. Public*, pg. 1505
DELNOR-COMMUNITY HOSPITAL—See Northwestern Memorial HealthCare; *U.S. Private*, pg. 2962
DELRAY MEDICAL CENTER, INC.—See Tenet Healthcare Corporation; *U.S. Public*, pg. 2003
DEL SOL MEDICAL CENTER—See HCA Healthcare, Inc.; *U.S. Public*, pg. 995
DELTA HEALTH ALLIANCE; *U.S. Private*, pg. 1200
DEMING HOSPITAL CORPORATION—See Quorum Health Corporation; *U.S. Private*, pg. 3329
DENTON SURGICARE PARTNERS, LTD.—See Tenet Healthcare Corporation; *U.S. Public*, pg. 2010
DENVER MID-TOWN SURGERY CENTER, LTD.—See HCA Healthcare, Inc.; *U.S. Public*, pg. 995
DENVER SURGICENTER, LLC—See HCA Healthcare, Inc.; *U.S. Public*, pg. 995
DERMA HEALTH; *U.S. Private*, pg. 1209
DESMED, LLC—See Universal Health Realty Income Trust; *U.S. Public*, pg. 2255
DESOTO HOSPITAL ASSOCIATION; *U.S. Private*, pg. 1215
DESOTO SURGICARE PARTNERS, LTD.—See Tenet Healthcare Corporation; *U.S. Public*, pg. 2010
DETAR HOSPITAL, LLC—See Community Health Systems, Inc.; *U.S. Public*, pg. 552
DETROIT BEHAVIORAL INSTITUTE, INC.—See Acadia Healthcare Company, Inc.; *U.S. Public*, pg. 28
DETROIT MEDICAL CENTER—See Tenet Healthcare Corporation; *U.S. Public*, pg. 2015
DEWITT HOSPITAL & NURSING HOME; *U.S. Private*, pg. 1219
DEXTER HOSPITAL LLC—See Southeast Missouri Hospital Association; *U.S. Private*, pg. 3726
DIAGNOSTIC AND THERAPEUTIC CENTER OF ATHENS-HYGEIA S.A.; *Int'l*, pg. 2103
DIAGNOSTIC CLINIC OF LONGVIEW—See Community Health Systems, Inc.; *U.S. Public*, pg. 552
DIAGNOSTIC ENDOSCOPY CENTER, LLC—See KKR & Co. Inc.; *U.S. Public*, pg. 1245
DIAGNOSTIC IMAGING OF BRANDYWINE VALLEY, LP—See Community Health Systems, Inc.; *U.S. Public*, pg. 552
DIGNITY HEALTH—See Catholic Health Initiatives; *U.S. Private*, pg. 789
DIGNITY HEALTH - SOUTHERN CALIFORNIA—See Catholic Health Initiatives; *U.S. Private*, pg. 789
DIMENSIONS HEALTHCARE CORPORATION; *U.S. Private*, pg. 1233
DIMMIT REGIONAL HOSPITAL; *U.S. Private*, pg. 1233
DIS-CHEM AIRPORT JUNCTION PROPRIETARY LIMITED—See Dis-Chem Pharmacies Ltd.; *Int'l*, pg. 2130
DIS-CHEM BALLITO JUNCTION PROPRIETARY LIMITED—See Dis-Chem Pharmacies Ltd.; *Int'l*, pg. 2130
DIS-CHEM BALLITO LIFESTYLE PROPRIETARY LIMITED—See Dis-Chem Pharmacies Ltd.; *Int'l*, pg. 2131
DIS-CHEM FERNDALE PROPRIETARY LIMITED—See Dis-Chem Pharmacies Ltd.; *Int'l*, pg. 2131
DIS-CHEM FESTIVAL MALL PROPRIETARY LIMITED—See Dis-Chem Pharmacies Ltd.; *Int'l*, pg. 2131
DIS-CHEM FLAMEWOOD VALUE CENTRE PROPRIETARY LIMITED—See Dis-Chem Pharmacies Ltd.; *Int'l*, pg. 2131
DIS-CHEM GLEN FAIR PROPRIETARY LIMITED—See Dis-Chem Pharmacies Ltd.; *Int'l*, pg. 2131
DIS-CHEM GOODWOOD PROPRIETARY LIMITED—See Dis-Chem Pharmacies Ltd.; *Int'l*, pg. 2131
DIS-CHEM JUBILEE PROPRIETARY LIMITED—See Dis-Chem Pharmacies Ltd.; *Int'l*, pg. 2131
DIS-CHEM KRUGERSDORP PROPRIETARY LIMITED—See Dis-Chem Pharmacies Ltd.; *Int'l*, pg. 2131
DIS-CHEM MAMS MALL PROPRIETARY LIMITED—See Dis-Chem Pharmacies Ltd.; *Int'l*, pg. 2131
DIS-CHEM MAPONYA PROPRIETARY LIMITED—See Dis-Chem Pharmacies Ltd.; *Int'l*, pg. 2131
DIS-CHEM MEGA MALL PROPRIETARY LIMITED—See Dis-Chem Pharmacies Ltd.; *Int'l*, pg. 2131
DIS-CHEM SWAKOPMUND PROPRIETARY LIMITED—See Dis-Chem Pharmacies Ltd.; *Int'l*, pg. 2131
DIS-CHEM THE GALLERIA AMANZIMTOTI PROPRIETARY LIMITED—See Dis-Chem Pharmacies Ltd.; *Int'l*, pg. 2131
DIS-CHEM THREE RIVERS PROPRIETARY LIMITED—See Dis-Chem Pharmacies Ltd.; *Int'l*, pg. 2131
DIS-CHEM TLC DE WIEKUS PROPRIETARY LIMITED—See Dis-Chem Pharmacies Ltd.; *Int'l*, pg. 2131
DIS-CHEM WALVIS BAY PROPRIETARY LIMITED—See Dis-Chem Pharmacies Ltd.; *Int'l*, pg. 2131
DIS-CHEM WERNHILL PROPRIETARY LIMITED—See Dis-Chem Pharmacies Ltd.; *Int'l*, pg. 2131
DIS-CHEM WORCESTER PROPRIETARY LIMITED—See Dis-Chem Pharmacies Ltd.; *Int'l*, pg. 2131
DISCOVERY CLINICAL RESEARCH, INC.—See KKR & Co. Inc.; *U.S. Public*, pg. 1245
DISCOVERY HOUSE-LT, INC.—See Acadia Healthcare Company, Inc.; *U.S. Public*, pg. 28
DISCOVERY HOUSE TV, INC.—See Acadia Healthcare Company, Inc.; *U.S. Public*, pg. 28
DISCOVERY HOUSE-UC, INC.—See Acadia Healthcare Company, Inc.; *U.S. Public*, pg. 28
DISCOVERY HOUSE WC, INC.—See Acadia Healthcare Company, Inc.; *U.S. Public*, pg. 28
DIVERSICARE AFTON OAKS, LLC—See Diversicare Healthcare Services, Inc.; *U.S. Public*, pg. 669
DIVERSICARE BRIARCLIFF, LLC—See Diversicare Healthcare Services, Inc.; *U.S. Public*, pg. 669
DIVERSICARE CLINTON, LLC—See Diversicare Healthcare Services, Inc.; *U.S. Public*, pg. 669
DIVERSICARE ESTATES, LLC—See Diversicare Healthcare Services, Inc.; *U.S. Public*, pg. 669
DIVERSICARE HARTFORD, LLC—See Diversicare Healthcare Services, Inc.; *U.S. Public*, pg. 669
DIVERSICARE HILLCREST, LLC—See Diversicare Healthcare Services, Inc.; *U.S. Public*, pg. 669
DIVERSICARE HUMBLE, LLC—See Diversicare Healthcare Services, Inc.; *U.S. Public*, pg. 669
DIVERSICARE KATY, LLC—See Diversicare Healthcare Services, Inc.; *U.S. Public*, pg. 669
DIVERSICARE MANAGEMENT SERVICES CO.—See Diversicare Healthcare Services, Inc.; *U.S. Public*, pg. 669
DIVERSICARE NORMANDY TERRACE, LLC—See Diversicare Healthcare Services, Inc.; *U.S. Public*, pg. 669
DIVERSICARE OF CHATEAU, LLC—See Diversicare Healthcare Services, Inc.; *U.S. Public*, pg. 669
DIVERSICARE OF MANSFIELD, LLC—See Diversicare Healthcare Services, Inc.; *U.S. Public*, pg. 669
DIVERSICARE OF RIVERSIDE, LLC—See Diversicare Healthcare Services, Inc.; *U.S. Public*, pg. 670
DIVERSICARE OF SENECA PLACE, LLC—See Diversicare Healthcare Services, Inc.; *U.S. Public*, pg. 670
DIVERSICARE TREEMONT, LLC—See Diversicare Healthcare Services, Inc.; *U.S. Public*, pg. 669
DIVERSICARE WINDSOR HOUSE, LLC—See Diversicare Healthcare Services, Inc.; *U.S. Public*, pg. 669
DIVERSICARE YORKTOWN, LLC—See Diversicare Healthcare Services, Inc.; *U.S. Public*, pg. 669
DLP CARDIAC PARTNERS, LLC—See Apollo Global Man-

agement, Inc.; *U.S. Public*, pg. 155
DLP MARIA PARHAM MEDICAL CENTER, LLC—See Apollo Global Management, Inc.; *U.S. Public*, pg. 155
DLP MARIA PARHAM PHYSICIAN PRACTICES, LLC—See Apollo Global Management, Inc.; *U.S. Public*, pg. 155
DLT RESOLUTION INC.; *U.S. Public*, pg. 670
DMC-MEMPHIS, INC.—See Acadia Healthcare Company, Inc.; *U.S. Public*, pg. 28
DMC SURGERY HOSPITAL—See Tenet Healthcare Corporation; *U.S. Public*, pg. 2015
DOCASAP, INC.—See UnitedHealth Group Incorporated; *U.S. Public*, pg. 2240
DOCTORS HOSPITAL OF AUGUSTA, LLC—See HCA Healthcare, Inc.; *U.S. Public*, pg. 995
DOCTORS HOSPITAL OF MANTECA, INC.—See Tenet Healthcare Corporation; *U.S. Public*, pg. 2003
DOCTORS HOSPITAL OF SARASOTA—See HCA Healthcare, Inc.; *U.S. Public*, pg. 995
DOCTORS HOSPITAL PHYSICIAN SERVICES, LLC—See Quorum Health Corporation; *U.S. Private*, pg. 3329
DOCTORS HOSPITAL—See Baptist Health South Florida, Inc.; *U.S. Private*, pg. 471
DOCTORS MEDICAL CENTER OF MODESTO, INC.—See Tenet Healthcare Corporation; *U.S. Public*, pg. 2003
DOCTORS' MEMORIAL HOSPITAL INC.; *U.S. Private*, pg. 1251
DOCTORS OUTPATIENT SURGICENTER, LTD.—See Tenet Healthcare Corporation; *U.S. Public*, pg. 2010
DOMINICAN HOSPITAL—See Catholic Health Initiatives; *U.S. Private*, pg. 789
DOMINICAN SISTERS FAMILY HEALTH SERVICE; *U.S. Private*, pg. 1256
DOMINION HOSPITAL—See HCA Healthcare, Inc.; *U.S. Public*, pg. 995
DOMINION HOSPITAL—See HCA Healthcare, Inc.; *U.S. Public*, pg. 995
DONALSONVILLE HOSPITAL, INC.; *U.S. Private*, pg. 1260
DORCHESTER HOUSE MULTI-SERVICE CENTER; *U.S. Private*, pg. 1262
THE DOVER OPHTHALMOLOGY ASC, LLC—See KKR & Co. Inc.; *U.S. Public*, pg. 1247
DOWN EAST COMMUNITY HOSPITAL; *U.S. Private*, pg. 1269
DRS. ELLIS, ROJAS, ROSS & DEBS, INC.—See KKR & Co. Inc.; *U.S. Public*, pg. 1245
DUBUIS HEALTH SYSTEM, INC.; *U.S. Private*, pg. 1283
DUFFYS NAPA VALLEY REHAB, LLC—See Acadia Healthcare Company, Inc.; *U.S. Public*, pg. 28
DUKES PHYSICIAN SERVICES, LLC—See Community Health Systems, Inc.; *U.S. Private*, pg. 552
DUNCAN REGIONAL HOSPITAL; *U.S. Private*, pg. 1287
DURANT H.M.A., LLC—See Community Health Systems, Inc.; *U.S. Public*, pg. 552
DURDANS HOSPITAL; *Int'l*, pg. 2228
DVH HOSPITAL ALLIANCE, LLC—See Universal Health Services, Inc.; *U.S. Public*, pg. 2257
D.W. MCMILLAN MEMORIAL HOSPITAL—See UnitedHealth Group Incorporated; *U.S. Public*, pg. 2244
DYERSBURG HOSPITAL CORPORATION—See Community Health Systems, Inc.; *U.S. Public*, pg. 553
EAGLEVILLE HOSPITAL; *U.S. Private*, pg. 1312
EARL & LORAINE MILLER CHILDREN'S HOSPITAL—See Memorial Health Services; *U.S. Private*, pg. 2663
EAST BOSTON NEIGHBORHOOD HEALTH CENTER CORP.; *U.S. Private*, pg. 1315
EAST EL PASO PHYSICIANS' MEDICAL CENTER, LLC—See Tenet Healthcare Corporation; *U.S. Public*, pg. 2010
EASTERN LONG ISLAND HOSPITAL; *U.S. Private*, pg. 1320
EASTERN MAINE HEALTHCARE SYSTEMS; *U.S. Private*, pg. 1320
EASTERN NIAGARA HEALTH SERVICES; *U.S. Private*, pg. 1320
EASTERN ORTHODOX MANAGEMENT CORP.; *U.S. Private*, pg. 1320
EAST GEORGIA REGIONAL MEDICAL CENTER, LLC—See Community Health Systems, Inc.; *U.S. Public*, pg. 553
EAST HARLEM COUNCIL FOR HUMAN SERVICES, INC.; *U.S. Private*, pg. 1316
EAST INDIANA TREATMENT CENTER, LLC—See Acadia Healthcare Company, Inc.; *U.S. Public*, pg. 28
EAST JEFFERSON GENERAL HOSPITAL AUXILIARY, INC.; *U.S. Private*, pg. 1316
EAST ORANGE GENERAL HOSPITAL—See Leonard Green & Partners, L.P.; *U.S. Private*, pg. 2428
EASTSIDE MEDICAL CENTER—See HCA Healthcare, Inc.; *U.S. Public*, pg. 1012
EAST TENNESSEE CHILDREN'S HOSPITAL; *U.S. Private*, pg. 1318
EAST TENNESSEE CLINIC CORP.—See Community Health Systems, Inc.; *U.S. Public*, pg. 553
EBENEZER MEDICAL OUTREACH, INC.; *U.S. Private*, pg. 1324
ECHO LOCUM TENENS, INC.—See UnitedHealth Group Incorporated; *U.S. Public*, pg. 2240

EDEN MEDICAL CENTER—See Sutter Health; *U.S. Private*, pg. 3887
EDGERTON HOSPITAL AND HEALTH SERVICES INC.; *U.S. Private*, pg. 1334
EDINBURGH MEDICAL SERVICES LIMITED—See Tenet Healthcare Corporation; *U.S. Public*, pg. 2002
EDWARD HOSPITAL INC.—See Edward Hospital & Health Services; *U.S. Private*, pg. 1341
EDWARD M. KENNEDY COMMUNITY HEALTH CENTER, INC.; *U.S. Private*, pg. 1341
EDWARDSVILLE AMBULATORY SURGERY CENTER, L.L.C.—See Quorum Health Corporation; *U.S. Private*, pg. 3329
EDWARD W. SPARROW HOSPITAL ASSOCIATION—See University of Michigan; *U.S. Private*, pg. 4309
EINSTEIN MONTGOMERY SURGERY CENTER, LLC—See Tenet Healthcare Corporation; *U.S. Public*, pg. 2010
EKACHAI MEDICAL CARE PCL; *Int'l*, pg. 2338
ELECTRONIC HEALTHCARE NETWORK ACCREDITATION COMMISSION; *U.S. Public*, pg. 1355
ELK REGIONAL HEALTH CENTER; *U.S. Private*, pg. 1362
ELLENVILLE REGIONAL HOSPITAL; *U.S. Private*, pg. 1363
ELMHURST MEMORIAL HEALTHCARE; *U.S. Private*, pg. 1376
THE EL PASO ASC, L.P.—See KKR & Co. Inc.; *U.S. Public*, pg. 1247
EL PASO CENTER FOR GASTROINTESTINAL ENDOSCOPY, LLC—See Tenet Healthcare Corporation; *U.S. Public*, pg. 2002
EL PASO HEALTHCARE SYSTEM, LTD.—See HCA Healthcare, Inc.; *U.S. Public*, pg. 995
EL PASO SPECIALTY HOSPITAL, LTD.—See Bain Capital, LP; *U.S. Private*, pg. 445
EL RIO SANTA CRUZ NEIGHBORHOOD HEALTH CENTER, INC.; *U.S. Private*, pg. 1349
EMERGENCY PHYSICIAN SOLUTIONS OF SOUTH FLORIDA, LLC—See KKR & Co. Inc.; *U.S. Public*, pg. 1245
EMERSON HOSPITAL; *U.S. Private*, pg. 1382
EMORY JOHNS CREEK HOSPITAL—See HCA Healthcare, Inc.; *U.S. Public*, pg. 995
EMPORIA HOME CARE SERVICES, LLC—See Community Health Systems, Inc.; *U.S. Public*, pg. 553
EMPORIA HOSPITAL CORPORATION—See Bon Secours Mercy Health, Inc.; *U.S. Private*, pg. 612
ENDION MEDICAL HEALTHCARE, P.C.—See UnitedHealth Group Incorporated; *U.S. Public*, pg. 2240
ENDLESS MOUNTAINS HEALTH SYSTEMS; *U.S. Private*, pg. 1391
ENDOSCOPY ASC OF MIDDLE GEORGIA, LLC—See Tenet Healthcare Corporation; *U.S. Public*, pg. 2002
THE ENDOSCOPY CENTER OF KNOXVILLE, L.P.—See KKR & Co. Inc.; *U.S. Public*, pg. 1247
ENDOSCOPY CENTER OF SOUTH SACRAMENTO, LLC—See Tenet Healthcare Corporation; *U.S. Public*, pg. 2002
ENGLEWOOD COMMUNITY HOSPITAL, INC.—See HCA Healthcare, Inc.; *U.S. Public*, pg. 996
ENGLEWOOD COMMUNITY HOSPITAL—See HCA Healthcare, Inc.; *U.S. Public*, pg. 996
ENHANCECORP LIMITED—See HCA Healthcare, Inc.; *U.S. Public*, pg. 996
ENVISION HEALTHCARE CORPORATION—See KKR & Co. Inc.; *U.S. Public*, pg. 1244
ENVISION PHYSICIAN SERVICES, LLC—See KKR & Co. Inc.; *U.S. Public*, pg. 1249
EPIC DEVELOPMENT, INC.—See HCA Healthcare, Inc.; *U.S. Public*, pg. 995
EPIC PROPERTIES, INC.—See HCA Healthcare, Inc.; *U.S. Public*, pg. 995
EPIC SURGERY CENTERS, INC.—See HCA Healthcare, Inc.; *U.S. Public*, pg. 995
ERLANGER HEALTH SYSTEM; *U.S. Private*, pg. 1421
ESPERANZA HEALTH CENTER; *U.S. Private*, pg. 1426
ESPIRITO SANTO - UNIDADES DE SAUDE E DE APOIO A TERCEIRA IDADE, S.A.—See Fosun International Limited; *Int'l*, pg. 2751
ESSENTIA HEALTH; *U.S. Private*, pg. 1427
ETHEMA HEALTH CORPORATION; *U.S. Public*, pg. 797
EUROMEDICA PALAIOU FALIROU S.A.—See AXON Holdings S.A.; *Int'l*, pg. 770
EVANSTON CLINIC CORP.—See Quorum Health Corporation; *U.S. Private*, pg. 3329
EVANSTON HOSPITAL CORPORATION—See Quorum Health Corporation; *U.S. Public*, pg. 3329
EVANSTON HOSPITAL—See NorthShore University HealthSystem; *U.S. Private*, pg. 2957
EVANSVILLE TREATMENT CENTER, LLC—See Acadia Healthcare Company, Inc.; *U.S. Public*, pg. 28
EVERSIDE HEALTH, LLC—See New Enterprise Associates, LLC; *U.S. Private*, pg. 2895
EVOLUTION HURSTVILLE PTY. LTD.—See Evolution Healthcare Pty. Ltd.; *Int'l*, pg. 2572
EYE SURGERY CENTER, LLC—See KKR & Co. Inc.; *U.S. Public*, pg. 1245

EZRAS CHOILIM HEALTH CENTER INC.; *U.S. Private*, pg. 1454
FACHKLINIK RHEIN/RUHR FUR HERZ/KREISLAUF- UND BEWEGUNGSSYSTEM GMBH & CO. KG—See Asklepios Kliniken GmbH & Co. KGaA; *Int'l*, pg. 623
FACHKLINIKUM WIESEN GMBH—See Asklepios Kliniken GmbH & Co. KGaA; *Int'l*, pg. 623
FACHKRANKENHAUS FUR PSYCHIATRIE UND NEUROLOGIE HILDBURGHAUSEN GMBH—See Fresenius SE & Co. KGaA; *Int'l*, pg. 2778
FAIRFAX SURGICAL CENTER—See HCA Healthcare, Inc.; *U.S. Public*, pg. 996
FAIRFIELD DIALYSIS, LLC—See DaVita Inc.; *U.S. Public*, pg. 638
FAIRFIELD MEDICAL CENTER; *U.S. Private*, pg. 1463
FAIR HAVEN COMMUNITY HEALTH CENTER; *U.S. Private*, pg. 1462
FAIRVIEW HEALTH SERVICES; *U.S. Private*, pg. 1464
FAIRVIEW PARK HOSPITAL—See HCA Healthcare, Inc.; *U.S. Public*, pg. 996
FALLBROOK HOSPITAL CORPORATION—See Community Health Systems, Inc.; *U.S. Public*, pg. 553
FALLON HEALTH; *U.S. Private*, pg. 1468
FALL RIVER HEALTH SYSTEM; *U.S. Private*, pg. 1467
FALLS COMMUNITY HOSPITAL & CLINIC; *U.S. Private*, pg. 1468
FAMILY CARE OF E. JACKSON COUNTY, LLC—See HCA Healthcare, Inc.; *U.S. Public*, pg. 996
FAMILY CARE PARTNERS, LLC—See HCA Healthcare, Inc.; *U.S. Public*, pg. 996
FAMILY HEALTHCARE; *U.S. Private*, pg. 1470
FAMILY HEALTH CENTER INC.; *U.S. Private*, pg. 1470
FAMILY HEALTH CENTERS, INC.; *U.S. Private*, pg. 1470
FAMILY HEALTH MEDICAL GROUP OF OVERLAND PARK, LLC—See HCA Healthcare, Inc.; *U.S. Public*, pg. 996
FAMILY HEALTH SPECIALISTS OF LEE'S SUMMIT, LLC—See HCA Healthcare, Inc.; *U.S. Public*, pg. 996
FAMILY MEDICINE OF BLACKSBURG, LLC—See HCA Healthcare, Inc.; *U.S. Public*, pg. 996
FANNIN SURGICARE—See HCA Healthcare, Inc.; *U.S. Public*, pg. 996
FARMERS UNION HOSPITAL ASSOCIATION; *U.S. Private*, pg. 1479
FAULKNER HOSPITAL INC.—See Partners HealthCare System, Inc.; *U.S. Private*, pg. 3102
FAUQUIER MEDICAL CENTER, LLC—See Apollo Global Management, Inc.; *U.S. Public*, pg. 155
FAWCETT MEMORIAL HOSPITAL, INC.—See HCA Healthcare, Inc.; *U.S. Public*, pg. 996
FAWCETT MEMORIAL HOSPITAL—See HCA Healthcare, Inc.; *U.S. Public*, pg. 996
FAYETTE MEMORIAL HOSPITAL ASSOCIATION INC; *U.S. Private*, pg. 1484
FENWAY HEALTH; *U.S. Private*, pg. 1495
FIRST CARE MEDICAL SERVICES; *U.S. Private*, pg. 1515
FIRST CHOICE HEALTH PLAN OF MISSISSIPPI, LLC—See Community Health Systems, Inc.; *U.S. Public*, pg. 553
FIRSTHEALTH MOORE REGIONAL HOSPITAL—See FirstHealth of the Carolinas, Inc.; *U.S. Private*, pg. 1532
FIRST TEXAS HOSPITAL CARROLLTON LLC—See Adeptus Health Inc.; *U.S. Private*, pg. 78
FISHERMEN'S COMMUNITY HOSPITAL, INC.—See Baptist Health South Florida, Inc.; *U.S. Private*, pg. 471
FIVE RIVERS MEDICAL CENTER INC; *U.S. Private*, pg. 1537
FLAMINGO ANESTHESIA ASSOCIATES, INC.—See KKR & Co. Inc.; *U.S. Public*, pg. 1245
FLETCHER ALLEN HEALTH CARE, INC; *U.S. Private*, pg. 1542
FLORENCE HOSPITAL AT ANTHEM, LLC—See Gilbert Hospital LLC; *U.S. Private*, pg. 1699
FLORIDA ENDOSCOPY AND SURGERY CENTER, LLC—See Community Health Systems, Inc.; *U.S. Public*, pg. 553
FLORIDA HEALTHY KIDS CORPORATION; *U.S. Private*, pg. 1548
FLORIDA HOSPITAL DADE CITY, INC.—See Adventist Health System Sunbelt Healthcare Corporation; *U.S. Private*, pg. 109
FLORIDA HOSPITAL HEARTLAND MEDICAL CENTER—See Adventist Health System Sunbelt Healthcare Corporation; *U.S. Private*, pg. 109
FLORIDA HOSPITAL WATERMAN, INC.—See Adventist Health System Sunbelt Healthcare Corporation; *U.S. Private*, pg. 109
FLORIDA SPRINGS SURGERY CENTER, LLC—See Tenet Healthcare Corporation; *U.S. Public*, pg. 2002
FLUSHING HOSPITAL MEDICAL CENTER; *U.S. Private*, pg. 1553
FMC COLOMBIA S.A.—See Fresenius Medical Care AG; *Int'l*, pg. 2774
FMH HEALTH SERVICES, LLC—See HCA Healthcare, Inc.; *U.S. Public*, pg. 996
FOLEY HOSPITAL CORPORATION—See Community Health Systems, Inc.; *U.S. Public*, pg. 553
FOLSOM OUTPATIENT SURGERY CENTER, L.P.—See Tenet Healthcare Corporation; *U.S. Public*, pg. 2010

N.A.I.C.S. INDEX 622110 — GENERAL MEDICAL AND...
N.A.I.C.S. Index

FORREST CITY ARKANSAS HOSPITAL COMPANY, LLC—See Quorum Health Corporation; *U.S. Private*, pg. 3329
FORREST CITY CLINIC COMPANY, LLC—See Quorum Health Corporation; *U.S. Private*, pg. 3329
FORT DUNCAN MEDICAL CENTER, INC.—See Universal Health Services, Inc.; *U.S. Public*, pg. 2257
FORTIS HEALTHCARE LIMITED; *Int'l*, pg. 2739
FORTIS MALAR HOSPITALS LIMITED—See Fortis Healthcare Limited; *Int'l*, pg. 2739
FORT NORFOLK RETIREMENT COMMUNITY INC.; *U.S. Private*, pg. 1574
FORT PAYNE HOSPITAL CORPORATION—See Quorum Health Corporation; *U.S. Private*, pg. 3330
FORT PAYNE RHC CORP.—See Quorum Health Corporation; *U.S. Private*, pg. 3330
FORT SANDERS REGIONAL MEDICAL CENTER; *U.S. Private*, pg. 1575
FORT WALTON BEACH MEDICAL CENTER, INC.—See HCA Healthcare, Inc.; *U.S. Public*, pg. 996
FORT WORTH SURGICARE PARTNERS, LTD.—See Tenet Healthcare Corporation; *U.S. Public*, pg. 2010
FOUNDATION BARIATRIC HOSPITAL OF SAN ANTONIO, LLC—See Foundation Healthcare, Inc.; *U.S. Private*, pg. 1580
FOUNDATION FOR EMBRYONIC COMPETENCE; *U.S. Private*, pg. 1580
FOUNDATION SURGICAL HOSPITAL MANAGEMENT, LLC—See Foundation Healthcare, Inc.; *U.S. Private*, pg. 1580
FOUNDERS RX LLC—See The Ensign Group, Inc.; *U.S. Public*, pg. 2071
FOUNTAIN VALLEY REGIONAL HOSPITAL & MEDICAL CENTER, INC.—See UCI Health; *U.S. Private*, pg. 4274
FOUNTAIN VALLEY SURGERY CENTER, LLC—See Tenet Healthcare Corporation; *U.S. Public*, pg. 2005
FRANCES MAHON DEACONESS HOSPITAL; *U.S. Private*, pg. 1586
FRANCISCAN ALLIANCE, INC.; *U.S. Private*, pg. 1587
FRANCISCAN HOSPITAL FOR CHILDREN; *U.S. Private*, pg. 1587
FRANKFORT REGIONAL MEDICAL CENTER—See HCA Healthcare, Inc.; *U.S. Public*, pg. 996
FRANKLIN CLINIC CORP.—See Community Health Systems, Inc.; *U.S. Public*, pg. 553
FRANKLIN HOSPITAL CORPORATION—See Bon Secours Mercy Health, Inc.; *U.S. Private*, pg. 612
FRASERS HOSPITALITY PTE. LTD.—See Frasers Property Limited; *Int'l*, pg. 2766
FREDERICK MEMORIAL HOSPITAL, INC.; *U.S. Private*, pg. 1602
FREMONT-RIDEOUT HEALTH GROUP; *U.S. Private*, pg. 1608
FRESNO CA ENDOSCOPY ASC, L.P.—See KKR & Co. Inc.; *U.S. Public*, pg. 1245
FRIO REGIONAL HOSPITAL; *U.S. Private*, pg. 1612
FRISCO MEDICAL CENTER, L.L.P.—See Tenet Healthcare Corporation; *U.S. Public*, pg. 2010
FROEDTERT MEMORIAL LUTHERAN HOSPITAL, INC.; *U.S. Private*, pg. 1613
FRONTLINE RESIDENTIAL TREATMENT CENTER, LLC—See Universal Health Services, Inc.; *U.S. Public*, pg. 2257
FRYECARE PHYSICIANS, L.L.C.—See Tenet Healthcare Corporation; *U.S. Public*, pg. 2003
FRYE REGIONAL MEDICAL CENTER, INC.—See Apollo Global Management, Inc.; *U.S. Public*, pg. 155
FSHC, LLC—See Mahwah Bergen Retail Group, Inc.; *U.S. Private*, pg. 2550
FULTON COUNTY MEDICAL CENTER; *U.S. Private*, pg. 1621
GADSDEN REGIONAL MEDICAL CENTER, LLC—See Community Health Systems, Inc.; *U.S. Public*, pg. 553
GADSDEN REGIONAL PRIMARY CARE, LLC—See Community Health Systems, Inc.; *U.S. Public*, pg. 553
GAFFNEY HMA, INC.—See Spartanburg Regional Health Services District, Inc.; *U.S. Private*, pg. 3747
GAINESVILLE ENDOSCOPY CENTER, LLC—See Tenet Healthcare Corporation; *U.S. Public*, pg. 2002
GAINESVILLE FAMILY PHYSICIANS—See HCA Healthcare, Inc.; *U.S. Public*, pg. 996
GALESBURG HOSPITAL CORPORATION—See Quorum Health Corporation; *U.S. Private*, pg. 3330
GAMBRO HOSPAL S.P.A.—See Baxter International Inc.; *U.S. Public*, pg. 281
GAMMA SURGERY CENTER, LLC—See Tenet Healthcare Corporation; *U.S. Public*, pg. 2010
GARDENDALE SURGICAL ASSOCIATES, LLC—See Tenet Healthcare Corporation; *U.S. Public*, pg. 2002
GARDEN PARK COMMUNITY HOSPITAL LIMITED PARTNERSHIP—See HCA Healthcare, Inc.; *U.S. Public*, pg. 996
GARDEN PARK MEDICAL CENTER—See HCA Healthcare, Inc.; *U.S. Public*, pg. 996
GARDEN PARK PHYSICIAN GROUP, INC.—See HCA Healthcare, Inc.; *U.S. Public*, pg. 996
GARDENS EFL IMAGING CENTER, LLC—See HCA Healthcare, Inc.; *U.S. Public*, pg. 996
GARDENS REGIONAL HOSPITAL & MEDICAL CENTER; *U.S. Private*, pg. 1643
GARFIELD PARK HOSPITAL, LLC—See Universal Health Services, Inc.; *U.S. Public*, pg. 2257
GARLAND SURGICARE PARTNERS, LTD.—See Tenet Healthcare Corporation; *U.S. Public*, pg. 2010
GASTROENTEROLOGY SPECIALISTS OF MIDDLE TENNESSEE, LLC—See HCA Healthcare, Inc.; *U.S. Public*, pg. 996
GATEWAY HEALTH SYSTEM—See Community Health Systems, Inc.; *U.S. Public*, pg. 552
GAYLORD HOSPITAL; *U.S. Private*, pg. 1652
GAY MEN'S HEALTH CRISIS, INC.; *U.S. Private*, pg. 1652
GEISINGER - BLOOMSBURG HOSPITAL—See Geisinger Health System; *U.S. Private*, pg. 1656
GENERAL GERMAN AGED PEOPLE'S HOME OF BALTIMORE; *U.S. Private*, pg. 1665
GENERAL HEALTHCARE GROUP LTD; *Int'l*, pg. 2918
GENERAL HEALTHCARE RESOURCES, LLC—See Platform Partners LLC; *U.S. Private*, pg. 3200
GENERAL JOHN J PERSHING MEMORIAL HOSPITAL ASSOCIATION; *U.S. Private*, pg. 1665
GENERAL MEDICAL CLINICS LIMITED—See HCA Healthcare, Inc.; *U.S. Public*, pg. 996
GENERAL SURGERY OF JUPITER MEDICAL SPECIALISTS, LLC—See KKR & Co. Inc.; *U.S. Public*, pg. 1245
GENOA HEALTHCARE, INC.—See UnitedHealth Group Incorporated; *U.S. Public*, pg. 2241
GENOLIER SWISS MEDICAL NETWORK SA—See AEVIS VICTORIA SA; *Int'l*, pg. 183
GEORGETOWN COMMUNITY HOSPITAL, LLC—See Apollo Global Management, Inc.; *U.S. Public*, pg. 155
GEORGIA NORTHSIDE EAR, NOSE AND THROAT, L.L.C.—See Tenet Healthcare Corporation; *U.S. Public*, pg. 2002
GEORGIA SPINE SURGERY CENTER, LLC—See Tenet Healthcare Corporation; *U.S. Public*, pg. 2002
GETINGE ITALIA S.R.L.—See Getinge AB; *Int'l*, pg. 2950
GI ASSOCIATES OF LEWISVILLE, PLLC—See HCA Healthcare, Inc.; *U.S. Public*, pg. 996
GIFFORD STREET WELLNESS CENTER, LLC—See Acadia Healthcare Company, Inc.; *U.S. Public*, pg. 29
GILBERT HOSPITAL LLC; *U.S. Private*, pg. 1699
GKB KLINIKBETRIEBE GMBH—See Asklepios Kliniken GmbH & Co. KGaA; *Int'l*, pg. 623
GLENBROOK HOSPITAL—See NorthShore University HealthSystem; *U.S. Private*, pg. 2957
GLENCOE REGIONAL HEALTH SERVICES; *U.S. Private*, pg. 1709
GLENDIVE MEDICAL CENTER; *U.S. Private*, pg. 1710
THE GLENDORA CA ENDOSCOPY ASC, L.P.—See KKR & Co. Inc.; *U.S. Public*, pg. 1247
GLOBAL SURGICAL PARTNERS, INC.—See KKR & Co. Inc.; *U.S. Public*, pg. 1245
GLOBUS RELIEF; *U.S. Private*, pg. 1720
THE GOG FOUNDATION, INC.; *U.S. Private*, pg. 4033
GOLDEN SUN BEAR, LLC—See DaVita Inc.; *U.S. Public*, pg. 639
THE GOOD CLINIC, LLC—See Mitesco, Inc.; *U.S. Public*, pg. 1452
GOOD SAMARITAN HOSPITAL, LLC—See HCA Healthcare, Inc.; *U.S. Public*, pg. 997
GOOD SAMARITAN HOSPITAL, L.P.—See HCA Healthcare, Inc.; *U.S. Public*, pg. 997
GOOD SAMARITAN HOSPITAL MEDICAL CENTER—See Catholic Health Services of Long Island; *U.S. Private*, pg. 791
GOOD SAMARITAN HOSPITAL—See Catholic Health Initiatives; *U.S. Private*, pg. 790
GOOD SAMARITAN MEDICAL CENTER, INC.—See Tenet Healthcare Corporation; *U.S. Public*, pg. 2008
GOOD SHEPHERD HEALTH CARE SYSTEM; *U.S. Private*, pg. 1738
GOOD SHEPHERD HOSPICE—See Catholic Health Services of Long Island; *U.S. Private*, pg. 791
GOSHEN MEDICAL CENTER, INC.; *U.S. Private*, pg. 1744
GRACE HOSPITAL; *U.S. Private*, pg. 1749
GRAFTON CITY HOSPITAL; *U.S. Private*, pg. 1751
GRAMERCY OUTPATIENT SURGERY CENTER—See HCA Healthcare, Inc.; *U.S. Public*, pg. 997
GRANBURY HOSPITAL CORPORATION—See Community Health Systems, Inc.; *U.S. Public*, pg. 553
GRAND ITASCA CLINIC & HOSPITAL—See Fairview Health Services; *U.S. Private*, pg. 1464
GRAND STRAND REGIONAL MEDICAL CENTER—See HCA Healthcare, Inc.; *U.S. Public*, pg. 997
GRANDVIEW SURGERY CENTER, LTD.—See UnitedHealth Group Incorporated; *U.S. Public*, pg. 2250
GRANDY ENVIRONMENTAL (H.K.) LIMITED—See Good Fellow Healthcare Holdings Limited; *Int'l*, pg. 3038
GRANITE CITY CLINIC CORP.—See Quorum Health Corporation; *U.S. Private*, pg. 3330
GRANITE CITY ILLINOIS HOSPITAL COMPANY, LLC—See Quorum Health Corporation; *U.S. Private*, pg. 3330
GRANITE CITY ORTHOPEDIC PHYSICIANS COMPANY, LLC—See Quorum Health Corporation; *U.S. Private*, pg. 3330
GRANITE CITY PHYSICIANS CORP.—See Quorum Health Corporation; *U.S. Private*, pg. 3330
GRANT CENTER HOSPITAL OF OCALA, INC.—See HCA Healthcare, Inc.; *U.S. Public*, pg. 997
GRANT MEMORIAL HOSPITAL; *U.S. Private*, pg. 1756
GRAPEVINE SURGICARE PARTNERS, LTD.—See Tenet Healthcare Corporation; *U.S. Public*, pg. 2010
GRASS VALLEY OUTPATIENT SURGERY CENTER, L.P.—See Tenet Healthcare Corporation; *U.S. Public*, pg. 2010
GREATER LAWRENCE FAMILY HEALTH CENTER, INC.; *U.S. Private*, pg. 1769
GREATER PEORIA SPECIALTY HOSPITAL, LLC—See Apollo Global Management, Inc.; *U.S. Public*, pg. 157
GREATER PHILADELPHIA HEALTH ACTION; *U.S. Private*, pg. 1770
GREATER TAMPA BAY PHYSICIAN NETWORK, LLC—See HCA Healthcare, Inc.; *U.S. Public*, pg. 997
GREATER TAMPA BAY PHYSICIAN SPECIALISTS, LLC—See HCA Healthcare, Inc.; *U.S. Public*, pg. 997
GREATER TAMPA BAY PHYSICIANS - PINELLAS, LLC—See HCA Healthcare, Inc.; *U.S. Public*, pg. 997
GREAT FALLS CLINIC SURGERY CENTER, LLC—See Bain Capital, LP; *U.S. Private*, pg. 445
GREAT LAKES SPECIALTY HOSPITAL-HACKLEY, LLC—See Select Medical Holdings Corporation; *U.S. Public*, pg. 1858
GREENBRIER REALTY, L.L.C.—See Acadia Healthcare Company, Inc.; *U.S. Public*, pg. 29
GREEN CLINIC, LLC—See Community Health Systems, Inc.; *U.S. Public*, pg. 553
GREENLEAF CENTER, LLC—See Acadia Healthcare Company, Inc.; *U.S. Public*, pg. 29
THE GREENSBORO NC ENDOSCOPY ASC, LLC—See KKR & Co. Inc.; *U.S. Public*, pg. 1247
THE GREENVILLE ASC, LLC—See KKR & Co. Inc.; *U.S. Public*, pg. 1247
GREENVILLE HOSPITAL CORPORATION—See Quorum Health Corporation; *U.S. Private*, pg. 3330
GREENVILLE HOSPITAL SYSTEM INC.; *U.S. Private*, pg. 1780
GREENVILLE REGIONAL HOSPITAL; *U.S. Private*, pg. 1780
GRIFFIN HEALTH SERVICES CORPORATION; *U.S. Private*, pg. 1788
GRITMAN MEDICAL CENTER; *U.S. Private*, pg. 1791
GROUP HEALTH COOPERATIVE OF SOUTH CENTRAL WISCONSIN; *U.S. Private*, pg. 1793
GROVE CITY MEDICAL CENTER—See Allegheny Health Network; *U.S. Private*, pg. 176
G. ROWE, M.D. , PLLC—See HCA Healthcare, Inc.; *U.S. Public*, pg. 996
GRUPO HIMA-SAN PABLO, INC.—See Metro Pavia Health System, Inc.; *U.S. Private*, pg. 2686
GUANGDONG KANGHUA HEALTHCARE CO., LTD.; *Int'l*, pg. 3157
GUARDIAN HEALTH CARE, INC.—See KKR & Co. Inc.; *U.S. Public*, pg. 1249
GULF COAST MEDICAL CENTER, LLC—See Community Health Systems, Inc.; *U.S. Public*, pg. 553
GULF COAST MEDICAL CENTER—See Lee Memorial Health System; *U.S. Private*, pg. 2413
GULF COAST PHYSICIAN ADMINISTRATORS, INC.—See HCA Healthcare, Inc.; *U.S. Public*, pg. 997
GULF COAST SURGERY CENTER—See HCA Healthcare, Inc.; *U.S. Public*, pg. 997
GULF MEDICAL PROJECTS COMPANY PJSC; *Int'l*, pg. 3181
GULF POINTE SURGERY CENTER—See HCA Healthcare, Inc.; *U.S. Public*, pg. 997
GULFSHORE ENDOSCOPY CENTER, LLC—See Tenet Healthcare Corporation; *U.S. Public*, pg. 2002
GULF SOUTH SURGERY CENTER, LLC—See Community Health Systems, Inc.; *U.S. Public*, pg. 553
GUNDERSEN LUTHERAN HEALTH SYSTEMS, INC.; *U.S. Private*, pg. 1818
THE GUTHRIE CLINIC; *U.S. Private*, pg. 4040
GW HEALTH NETWORK, LLC—See Universal Health Services, Inc.; *U.S. Public*, pg. 2257
GWINNETT HOSPITAL SYSTEM, INC.; *U.S. Private*, pg. 1821
GYNECOLOGIC ONCOLOGY ASSOCIATES, INC.—See KKR & Co. Inc.; *U.S. Public*, pg. 1245
H2U WELLNESS CENTERS, LLC—See HCA Healthcare, Inc.; *U.S. Public*, pg. 997
HACKENSACK UNIVERSITY MEDICAL CENTER—See Hackensack Meridian Health, Inc.; *U.S. Private*, pg. 1838
HACKETTSTOWN MEDICAL CENTER—See Atlantic Health System Inc.; *U.S. Private*, pg. 373
HAINES CITY HMA URGENT CARE, LLC—See Community Health Systems, Inc.; *U.S. Public*, pg. 553
HALIFAX MEDICAL CENTER; *U.S. Private*, pg. 1843
HAMILTON HEALTH CARE SYSTEM, INC.; *U.S. Private*, pg. 1848
HAMILTON MEMORIAL HOSPITAL, INC.—See HCA Healthcare, Inc.; *U.S. Public*, pg. 998
HANGZHOU JIUZHOU GRAND PHARMACY CHAIN CO., LTD.—See CHINA JO-JO DRUGSTORES, INC.; *Int'l*, pg. 1513

622110 — GENERAL MEDICAL AND...   CORPORATE AFFILIATIONS

THE HARLEY STREET CLINIC—See HCA Healthcare, Inc.; *U.S. Public*, pg. 1012
THE HARLEY STREET CLINIC—See HCA Healthcare, Inc.; *U.S. Public*, pg. 998
HARRINGTON HEALTHCARE SYSTEM; *U.S. Private*, pg. 1868
HARRIS MEDICAL CLINICS, INC.—See Community Health Systems, Inc.; *U.S. Public*, pg. 553
HARRISON COMMUNITY HOSPITAL, INC.—See Wheeling Hospital, Inc.; *U.S. Private*, pg. 4506
HARRISON ENDO SURGICAL CENTER, LLC—See UnitedHealth Group Incorporated; *U.S. Public*, pg. 2241
HARRISON HMA, INC.—See Community Health Systems, Inc.; *U.S. Public*, pg. 553
HARRISON MEDICAL CENTER—See Franciscan Health System; *U.S. Private*, pg. 1587
THE HARTFORD DISPENSARY; *U.S. Private*, pg. 4043
HARTSVILLE HMA, INC.—See Apollo Global Management, Inc.; *U.S. Public*, pg. 154
HAVASU REGIONAL MEDICAL CENTER, LLC—See Apollo Global Management, Inc.; *U.S. Public*, pg. 155
HAVASU SURGERY CENTER, INC.—See Apollo Global Management; Inc.; *U.S. Public*, pg. 155
HAYS MEDICAL CENTER; *U.S. Private*, pg. 1885
HAZEN MEMORIAL HOSPITAL ASSOCIATION; *U.S. Private*, pg. 1886
HCA FLORIDA WEST TAMPA HOSPITAL—See HCA Healthcare, Inc.; *U.S. Public*, pg. 997
HCA GULF COAST DIVISION—See HCA Healthcare, Inc.; *U.S. Public*, pg. 997
HCA HEALTHCARE MISSION FUND, LLC—See HCA Healthcare, Inc.; *U.S. Public*, pg. 997
HCA HEALTHCARE UK LIMITED—See HCA Healthcare, Inc.; *U.S. Public*, pg. 998
HCA-HEALTHONE, LLC—See HCA Healthcare, Inc.; *U.S. Public*, pg. 998
HCA HEALTH SERVICES OF TENNESSEE, INC.—See HCA Healthcare, Inc.; *U.S. Public*, pg. 997
HCA HEALTH SERVICES OF VIRGINIA—See HCA Healthcare, Inc.; *U.S. Public*, pg. 997
HCA HOUSTON HEALTHCARE-MAINLAND—See HCA Healthcare, Inc.; *U.S. Public*, pg. 998
HCA HOUSTON HEALTHCARE - SOUTHEAST—See HCA Healthcare, Inc.; *U.S. Public*, pg. 998
HCA HOUSTON HEALTHCARE TOMBALL—See HCA Healthcare, Inc.; *U.S. Public*, pg. 998
HCA HOUSTON HEALTHCARE WEST—See HCA Healthcare, Inc.; *U.S. Public*, pg. 998
HCA INTERNATIONAL HOLDINGS LIMITED—See HCA Healthcare, Inc.; *U.S. Public*, pg. 998
HCA INTERNATIONAL LIMITED—See HCA Healthcare, Inc.; *U.S. Public*, pg. 998
HCA - RALEIGH COMMUNITY HOSPITAL, INC.—See HCA Healthcare, Inc.; *U.S. Public*, pg. 997
HCA RICHMOND CARDIAC CLINICAL CO-MANAGEMENT COMPANY, LLC—See HCA Healthcare, Inc.; *U.S. Public*, pg. 998
HCI CARE SERVICES; *U.S. Private*, pg. 1888
HDH THORACIC SURGEONS, LLC—See HCA Healthcare, Inc.; *U.S. Public*, pg. 998
HEALIUS LIMITED; *Int'l*, pg. 3302
HEALOGICS, INC.—See Clayton, Dubilier & Rice, LLC; *U.S. Private*, pg. 924
HEALTH ACCESS NETWORK; *U.S. Private*, pg. 1892
HEALTH CARE FOR THE HOMELESS; *U.S. Private*, pg. 1892
HEALTH CARE FOUNDATION OF GREATER KANSAS CITY; *U.S. Private*, pg. 1892
HEALTH & CARE GROUP LIMITED—See HKR International Limited; *Int'l*, pg. 3429
HEALTHCARE NETWORK HOSPITALS, INC.—See Tenet Healthcare Corporation; *U.S. Public*, pg. 2004
HEALTHCARE PARTNERS HOLDINGS LLC—See DaVita Inc.; *U.S. Public*, pg. 639
HEALTHEAST CARE SYSTEM—See Fairview Health Services; *U.S. Private*, pg. 1464
HEALTHEAST ST. JOHN'S HOSPITAL—See Fairview Health Services; *U.S. Private*, pg. 1464
HEALTH FEDERATION OF PHILADELPHIA; *U.S. Private*, pg. 1893
HEALTHFIRST NETWORK; *U.S. Private*, pg. 1896
HEALTH GRID, LLC—See Veradigm Inc.; *U.S. Public*, pg. 2280
HEALTH IMPERATIVES, INC.; *U.S. Private*, pg. 1893
HEALTHLINC, INC.; *U.S. Private*, pg. 1897
HEALTH MANAGEMENT ASSOCIATES OF WEST VIRGINIA, INC.—See Community Health Systems, Inc.; *U.S. Public*, pg. 553
HEALTH MANAGEMENT INTERNATIONAL LTD.—See EQT AB; *Int'l*, pg. 2475
HEALTHNET, INC.; *U.S. Private*, pg. 1897
HEALTHONE OF DENVER, INC.—See HCA Healthcare, Inc.; *U.S. Public*, pg. 998
HEALTHONE RIDGE VIEW ENDOSCOPY CENTER, LLC—See HCA Healthcare, Inc.; *U.S. Public*, pg. 998
HEALTHPOINT; *U.S. Private*, pg. 1897
HEALTH QUEST SYSTEMS, INC.; *U.S. Private*, pg. 1894

HEALTH RESOURCES NORTHWEST; *U.S. Private*, pg. 1894
HEALTHRIGHT 360; *U.S. Private*, pg. 1897
HEALTH SCIENCES SOUTH CAROLINA; *U.S. Private*, pg. 1894
HEALTHSCOPE OPERATIONS PTY. LTD.—See Brookfield Corporation; *Int'l*, pg. 1176
HEALTHSCOPE (TASMANIA) PTY. LTD.—See Brookfield Corporation; *Int'l*, pg. 1176
HEALTH SERVICES NETWORK HOSPITALS, INC.—See Tenet Healthcare Corporation; *U.S. Public*, pg. 2002
HEALTHTRUST EUROPE COMPANY LIMITED—See HCA Healthcare, Inc.; *U.S. Public*, pg. 998
HEALTHTRUST PURCHASING GROUP, L.P.—See HCA Healthcare, Inc.; *U.S. Public*, pg. 1005
THE HEALTH TRUST; *U.S. Public*, pg. 4044
HEALTH & WELLNESS SURGERY CENTER, L.P.—See Tenet Healthcare Corporation; *U.S. Public*, pg. 2003
HEART HOSPITAL OF AUSTIN, A CAMPUS OF ST. DAVIDS MEDICAL CENTER—See HCA Healthcare, Inc.; *U.S. Public*, pg. 998
HEARTLAND RURAL HEALTHCARE, LLC—See Quorum Health Corporation; *U.S. Private*, pg. 3330
HEART OF FLORIDA SURGERY CENTER, LLC—See Adventist Health System Sunbelt Healthcare Corporation; *U.S. Private*, pg. 108
HEART TO HEART INTERNATIONAL INC.; *U.S. Private*, pg. 1899
HEART & VASCULAR INSTITUTE OF TEXAS, INC.—See Tenet Healthcare Corporation; *U.S. Public*, pg. 2014
HEATHROW INTERNAL MEDICINE, LLC—See HCA Healthcare, Inc.; *U.S. Public*, pg. 998
HELIOS AGNES-KARLL KRANKENHAUS GMBH—See Fresenius SE & Co. KGaA; *Int'l*, pg. 2779
HELIOS FACHKLINIKEN HILDBURGHAUSEN GMBH—See Fresenius SE & Co. KGaA; *Int'l*, pg. 2779
HELIOS FRANKENWALDKLINIK KRONACH GMBH—See Fresenius SE & Co. KGaA; *Int'l*, pg. 2779
HELIOS HANSEKLINIKUM STRALSUND GMBH—See Fresenius SE & Co. KGaA; *Int'l*, pg. 2779
HELIOS KLINIK BLEICHERODE GMBH—See Fresenius SE & Co. KGaA; *Int'l*, pg. 2779
HELIOS KLINIKEN MANSFELD-SUDHARZ GMBH—See Fresenius SE & Co. KGaA; *Int'l*, pg. 2779
HELIOS KLINIKEN MITTELWESER GMBH—See Fresenius SE & Co. KGaA; *Int'l*, pg. 2779
HELIOS KLINIK JERICHOWER LAND GMBH—See Fresenius SE & Co. KGaA; *Int'l*, pg. 2779
HELIOS KLINIK KOTHEN GMBH—See Fresenius SE & Co. KGaA; *Int'l*, pg. 2779
HELIOS KLINIK LENGERICH GMBH—See Fresenius SE & Co. KGaA; *Int'l*, pg. 2779
HELIOS KLINIK ROTTWEIL GMBH—See Fresenius SE & Co. KGaA; *Int'l*, pg. 2779
HELIOS KLINIK SCHLESWIG GMBH—See Fresenius SE & Co. KGaA; *Int'l*, pg. 2779
HELIOS KLINIKUM AUE GMBH—See Fresenius SE & Co. KGaA; *Int'l*, pg. 2780
HELIOS KLINIKUM BAD SAAROW GMBH—See Fresenius SE & Co. KGaA; *Int'l*, pg. 2780
HELIOS KLINIKUM ERFURT GMBH—See Fresenius SE & Co. KGaA; *Int'l*, pg. 2780
HELIOS KLINIKUM GIFHORN GMBH—See Fresenius SE & Co. KGaA; *Int'l*, pg. 2780
HELIOS KLINIKUM MEININGEN GMBH—See Fresenius SE & Co. KGaA; *Int'l*, pg. 2780
HELIOS KLINIKUM PFORZHEIM GMBH—See Fresenius SE & Co. KGaA; *Int'l*, pg. 2778
HELIOS KLINIKUM SIEGBURG GMBH—See Fresenius SE & Co. KGaA; *Int'l*, pg. 2780
HELIOS KLINIKUM UELZEN GMBH—See Fresenius SE & Co. KGaA; *Int'l*, pg. 2780
HELIOS KLINIKUM WARBURG GMBH—See Fresenius SE & Co. KGaA; *Int'l*, pg. 2778
HELIOS KLINIK WESERMARSCH GMBH—See Fresenius SE & Co. KGaA; *Int'l*, pg. 2779
HELIOS KLINIK WIPPERFURTH GMBH—See Fresenius SE & Co. KGaA; *Int'l*, pg. 2779
HELIOS ST. MARIENBERG KLINIK HELMSTEDT GMBH—See Fresenius SE & Co. KGaA; *Int'l*, pg. 2780
HELIOS VERSORGUNGSZENTREN GMBH—See Fresenius SE & Co. KGaA; *Int'l*, pg. 2780
HELIOS WEISSERITZTAL-KLINIKEN GMBH—See Fresenius SE & Co. KGaA; *Int'l*, pg. 2778
HEMAS HOSPITALS (PVT) LTD.—See Hemas Holdings PLC; *Int'l*, pg. 3340
HEMOPHILIA CENTER OF WESTERN NEW YORK, INC.; *U.S. Private*, pg. 1913
HEMOPHILIA SERVICES CONSORTIUM, INC.; *U.S. Private*, pg. 1913
HENDERSONVILLE MEDICAL CENTER—See HCA Healthcare, Inc.; *U.S. Public*, pg. 998
HENNEPIN HEALTHCARE SYSTEM, INC.; *U.S. Private*, pg. 1916
HENRICO DOCTORS' HOSPITAL—See HCA Healthcare, Inc.; *U.S. Public*, pg. 997
HENRY COUNTY HOSPITAL; *U.S. Private*, pg. 1917
HENRY FORD ALLEGIANCE HEALTH—See Henry Ford Health System; *U.S. Private*, pg. 1918

HERITAGE HEALTH AND HOUSING; *U.S. Private*, pg. 1923
HERITAGE PARK SURGICAL HOSPITAL, LLC—See Tenet Healthcare Corporation; *U.S. Public*, pg. 2010
HERMANN DRIVE SURGICAL HOSPITAL, LP—See Nobilis Health Corp.; *U.S. Private*, pg. 2932
HERNANDO HMA, INC.—See Community Health Systems, Inc.; *U.S. Public*, pg. 553
HERNANDO HMA, INC.—See Community Health Systems, Inc.; *U.S. Public*, pg. 553
HERZZENTRUM LAHR/BADEN GMBH & CO. KG—See Asklepios Kliniken GmbH & Co. KGaA; *Int'l*, pg. 623
HERZZENTRUM LEIPZIG GMBH—See Fresenius SE & Co. KGaA; *Int'l*, pg. 2778
HESPERIA HOSPITAL MODENA S.P.A.—See Garofalo Health Care SpA; *Int'l*, pg. 2886
HEYWOOD HOSPITAL; *U.S. Private*, pg. 1928
HHC FOCUS FLORIDA, INC.—See Universal Health Services, Inc.; *U.S. Public*, pg. 2257
HHC SOUTH CAROLINA, INC.—See Universal Health Services, Inc.; *U.S. Public*, pg. 2257
HIALEAH HOSPITAL, INC.—See Tenet Healthcare Corporation; *U.S. Public*, pg. 2003
HIAWATHA COMMUNITY HOSPITAL; *U.S. Private*, pg. 1932
HIDALGO COUNTY CLINICAL SERVICES INC.; *U.S. Private*, pg. 1934
HIGHGATE HOSPITAL LLP—See Tenet Healthcare Corporation; *U.S. Public*, pg. 2004
HIGHLAND PARK HOSPITAL—See NorthShore University HealthSystem; *U.S. Private*, pg. 2957
HILL COUNTRY SURGERY CENTER, LLC—See Tenet Healthcare Corporation; *U.S. Public*, pg. 2004
HILLCREST HEALTHCARE SYSTEM—See Ventas, Inc.; *U.S. Public*, pg. 2279
THE HILLMONT ASC, L.P.—See KKR & Co, Inc.; *U.S. Public*, pg. 1247
HILL REGIONAL CLINIC CORP.—See Community Health Systems, Inc.; *U.S. Public*, pg. 553
HILLS AND DALES GENERAL HOSPITAL; *U.S. Private*, pg. 1947
HILLSBORO AREA HOSPITAL; *U.S. Private*, pg. 1947
HILTON HEAD REGIONAL OB/GYN PARTNERS, L.L.C.—See Tenet Healthcare Corporation; *U.S. Public*, pg. 2008
HILTON HEAD REGIONAL PHYSICIAN NETWORK - GEORGIA, LLC—See Tenet Healthcare Corporation; *U.S. Public*, pg. 2004
HINSDALE SURGICAL CENTER, LLC—See Tenet Healthcare Corporation; *U.S. Public*, pg. 2010
HMA SANTA ROSA MEDICAL CENTER, INC.—See Community Health Systems, Inc.; *U.S. Public*, pg. 553
HMIH CEDAR CREST, LLC—See Acadia Healthcare Company, Inc.; *U.S. Public*, pg. 29
HNMC, INC.—See Tenet Healthcare Corporation; *U.S. Public*, pg. 2002
HOBART PRIVATE HOSPITAL—See Brookfield Corporation; *Int'l*, pg. 1176
HOLSTON VALLEY AMBULATORY SURGERY CENTER, LLC—See Tenet Healthcare Corporation; *U.S. Public*, pg. 2004
HOLTON COMMUNITY HOSPITAL; *U.S. Private*, pg. 1969
HOLY CROSS HEALTH SYSTEM—See Trinity Health Corporation; *U.S. Private*, pg. 4233
HOLY CROSS HOSPITAL—See Ascension Health Alliance; *U.S. Private*, pg. 347
HOLZER HEALTH SYSTEM; *U.S. Private*, pg. 1969
HOMESTEAD HOSPITAL—See Baptist Health South Florida, Inc.; *U.S. Private*, pg. 471
HONOLULU SPINE CENTER, LLC—See Bain Capital, LP; *U.S. Private*, pg. 445
HOOD HOME HEALTH SERVICE, LLC—See UnitedHealth Group Incorporated; *U.S. Public*, pg. 2245
HOPEDALE MEDICAL FOUNDATION; *U.S. Private*, pg. 1979
HOPEHEALTH, INC.; *U.S. Private*, pg. 1979
HORIZON HEALTH SERVICES, INC.; *U.S. Private*, pg. 1981
HORIZON RIDGE SURGERY CENTER, LLC—See Tenet Healthcare Corporation; *U.S. Public*, pg. 2004
HOSPICE HAWAII; *U.S. Private*, pg. 1985
HOSPICE & PALLIATIVE CARE CHARLOTTE REGION—See Hospice of Laurens County, Inc.; *U.S. Private*, pg. 1986
HOSPICE SAVANNAH, INC.; *U.S. Private*, pg. 1987
HOSPICIO Y HOME CARE SAN LUCAS; *U.S. Private*, pg. 1987
HOSPITAL ANA COSTA S.A.—See UnitedHealth Group Incorporated; *U.S. Public*, pg. 2241
HOSPITAL BUEN SAMARITANO, INC.; *U.S. Private*, pg. 1987
HOSPITAL DA ARRABIDA - GAIA, S.A.—See Fosun International Limited; *Int'l*, pg. 2751
HOSPITAL DA LUZ, S.A.—See Fosun International Limited; *Int'l*, pg. 2751
HOSPITAL DE LA CONCEPCION; *U.S. Private*, pg. 1987
HOSPITAL DE MAJADAHONDA, S.A.—See DIF Manage-

4966

N.A.I.C.S. INDEX

622110 — GENERAL MEDICAL AND...

ment Holding B.V.; *Int'l*, pg. 2118
HOSPITAL DEVELOPMENT OF WEST PHOENIX, INC.—See Tenet Healthcare Corporation; *U.S. Public*, pg. 2014
HOSPITAL E MATERNIDADE SAMARITANO LTDA.—See Hapvida Participacoes e Investimentos S.A.; *Int'l*, pg. 3269
HOSPITAL FOR SPECIAL CARE; *U.S. Private*, pg. 1987
HOSPITALISTS AT STONECREST, LLC—See HCA Healthcare, Inc.; *U.S. Public*, pg. 999
HOSPITALISTS OF NORTHERN MICHIGAN; *U.S. Private*, pg. 1987
HOSPITAL OF BARSTOW, INC.—See Quorum Health Corporation; *U.S. Private*, pg. 3330
HOSPITAL OF FULTON, INC.—See Community Health Systems, Inc.; *U.S. Public*, pg. 553
HOSPITAL OF LOUISA, INC.—See Quorum Health Corporation; *U.S. Private*, pg. 3330
HOSPITAL OF MORRISTOWN, INC.—See Community Health Systems, Inc.; *U.S. Public*, pg. 553
HOSPITAL SAN CARLOS BORROMEO; *U.S. Private*, pg. 1987
HOSPITAL SANTA HELENA S.A.—See UnitedHealth Group Incorporated; *U.S. Public*, pg. 2241
HOSPOR - HOSPITAIS PORTUGUESES, S.A.—See Fosun International Limited; *Int'l*, pg. 2751
HOT SPRINGS COUNTY MEMORIAL HOSPITAL; *U.S. Private*, pg. 1989
HOULTON REGIONAL HOSPITAL; *U.S. Private*, pg. 1990
HOUSE RESEARCH INSTITUTE; *U.S. Private*, pg. 1992
HOUSTON METRO ORTHO AND SPINE SURGERY CENTER, LLC—See Nobilis Health Corp.; *U.S. Private*, pg. 2932
HOUSTON NORTHWEST MEDICAL CENTER, INC.—See HCA Healthcare, Inc.; *U.S. Public*, pg. 999
HOUSTON NORTHWEST OPERATING COMPANY, L.L.C.—See HCA Healthcare, Inc.; *U.S. Public*, pg. 999
HOUSTON PEDIATRIC SPECIALTY GROUP, PLLC—See HCA Healthcare, Inc.; *U.S. Public*, pg. 999
HOUSTON UROLOGIC SURGICENTER, LLC—See HCA Healthcare, Inc.; *U.S. Public*, pg. 999
HOWARD BROWN HEALTH CENTER; *U.S. Private*, pg. 1994
HOWARD MEMORIAL HOSPITAL; *U.S. Private*, pg. 1995
HPG SOLUTIONS, LLC—See HCA Healthcare, Inc.; *U.S. Public*, pg. 998
HSS SYSTEMS, LLC—See HCA Healthcare, Inc.; *U.S. Public*, pg. 998
HUDSON CROSSING SURGERY CENTER, LLC—See KKR & Co. Inc.; *U.S. Public*, pg. 1245
HUDSON RIVER HEALTHCARE, INC.; *U.S. Private*, pg. 2002
HUNTINGTON TREATMENT CENTER, LLC—See Acadia Healthcare Company, Inc.; *U.S. Public*, pg. 29
HUTCHINSON HEALTH; *U.S. Private*, pg. 2014
HUTZEL WOMEN'S HOSPITAL—See Tenet Healthcare Corporation; *U.S. Public*, pg. 2015
HWCA, PLLC—See HCA Healthcare, Inc.; *U.S. Public*, pg. 998
HYUNDAI ADM BIO INC; *Int'l*, pg. 3555
IDA COUNTY, IOWA COMMUNITY HOSPITAL; *U.S. Private*, pg. 2034
IDENTITY HEALTHCARE LTD.; *Int'l*, pg. 3592
IHA HEALTH SERVICES CORPORATION; *U.S. Private*, pg. 2040
IKANG HEALTHCARE GROUP, INC.; *Int'l*, pg. 3610
IMAGING CENTER AT BAXTER VILLAGE, L.L.C.—See Tenet Healthcare Corporation; *U.S. Public*, pg. 2008
IMAGING SERVICES OF LOUISIANA, LLC—See HCA Healthcare, Inc.; *U.S. Public*, pg. 999
IMA WORLD HEALTH; *U.S. Private*, pg. 2044
IMPERIAL HOSPITAL & RESEARCH CENTRE LIMITED—See Apollo Hospitals Enterprise Limited; *Int'l*, pg. 518
IMPULSE MONITORING, INC.—See Globus Medical, Inc.; *U.S. Public*, pg. 947
INDEPENDENCE HEALTHCARE CORPORATION—See ModivCare, Inc.; *U.S. Public*, pg. 1455
INDEPENDENCE REGIONAL MEDICAL GROUP, LLC—See HCA Healthcare, Inc.; *U.S. Public*, pg. 999
THE INDIANA HEMOPHILIA & THROMBOSIS CENTER, INC.; *U.S. Private*, pg. 4055
INDIANAPOLIS TREATMENT CENTER, LLC—See Acadia Healthcare Company, Inc.; *U.S. Public*, pg. 29
INDIANA REGIONAL MEDICAL CENTER; *U.S. Private*, pg. 2063
INDIAN HEALTH COUNCIL, INC.; *U.S. Private*, pg. 2061
INDIAN PATH HOSPITAL, INC.—See HCA Healthcare, Inc.; *U.S. Public*, pg. 999
INFECTIOUS DISEASES SOCIETY OF AMERICA; *U.S. Private*, pg. 2070
INFORM DIAGNOSTICS, INC.—See Fulgent Genetics, Inc.; *U.S. Public*, pg. 892
INGALLS HEALTH SYSTEM INC—See University of Chicago; *U.S. Private*, pg. 4308
INNOVATIONS SURGERY CENTER, LLC—See Community Health Systems, Inc.; *U.S. Public*, pg. 553

INOVA ALEXANDRIA HOSPITAL—See Inova Health System; *U.S. Private*, pg. 2084
INOVA HEALTH SYSTEM; *U.S. Private*, pg. 2084
THE INSTITUTE FOR FAMILY HEALTH; *U.S. Private*, pg. 4056
THE INSTITUTE FOR HEALTHCARE IMPROVEMENT; *U.S. Private*, pg. 4056
INSTITUTE OF ADVANCED ENT SURGERY, LLC—See HCA Healthcare, Inc.; *U.S. Public*, pg. 999
INSTITUTO DO RADIUM DE CAMMPINAS LTDA—See UnitedHealth Group Incorporated; *U.S. Public*, pg. 2241
INSTRUCLEAN GMBH—See Fresenius SE & Co. KGaA; *Int'l*, pg. 2780
INTECARE, INC.; *U.S. Private*, pg. 2097
INTEGRATED REGIONAL LAB, LLC—See HCA Healthcare, Inc.; *U.S. Public*, pg. 999
INTEGRATED REGIONAL LABORATORIES PATHOLOGY SERVICES, LLC—See HCA Healthcare, Inc.; *U.S. Public*, pg. 999
INTEGRIS BASS BAPTIST HEALTH CENTER—See INTEGRIS Health, Inc.; *U.S. Private*, pg. 2102
INTEGRIS HEALTH, INC.; *U.S. Private*, pg. 2102
INTEGRIS RURAL HEALTHCARE OF OKLAHOMA, INC.—See INTEGRIS Health, Inc.; *U.S. Private*, pg. 2102
INTERFAITH MEDICAL CENTER; *U.S. Private*, pg. 2110
INTERMOUNTAIN HEALTHCARE INC.; *U.S. Private*, pg. 2113
INTERMOUNTAIN MEDICAL GROUP, INC.—See Community Health Systems, Inc.; *U.S. Public*, pg. 553
INTERNAL MEDICINE ASSOCIATES OF SOUTHERN HILLS, LLC—See HCA Healthcare, Inc.; *U.S. Public*, pg. 999
INTERNAL MEDICINE OF BLACKSBURG, LLC—See HCA Healthcare, Inc.; *U.S. Public*, pg. 999
INTERNAL MEDICINE OF PASADENA, PLLC—See HCA Healthcare, Inc.; *U.S. Public*, pg. 999
INTERNATIONAL FALLS MEMORIAL HOSPITAL ASSOCIATION; *U.S. Private*, pg. 2116
INTERNATIONAL MEDICAL CENTRE (HONG KONG) LIMITED—See First Shanghai Investments Limited; *Int'l*, pg. 2687
INTERNATIONAL MEDICAL CENTRES LIMITED—See CIEL Ltd.; *Int'l*, pg. 1605
INVIVOLINK, INC.—See HCA Healthcare, Inc.; *U.S. Public*, pg. 999
I. OLA LAHUI INC.; *U.S. Private*, pg. 2026
IRVINE REGIONAL HOSPITAL & MEDICAL CENTER—See Tenet Healthcare Corporation; *U.S. Public*, pg. 2008
ISD CANTON, LLC—See DaVita Inc.; *U.S. Public*, pg. 639
ISD KANSAS CITY, LLC—See DaVita Inc.; *U.S. Public*, pg. 639
ISD KENDALLVILLE, LLC—See DaVita Inc.; *U.S. Public*, pg. 639
ISIS HEALTH CARE INDIA PRIVATE LIMITED—See Apollo Hospitals Enterprise Limited; *Int'l*, pg. 517
ISLAND PEER REVIEW ORGANIZATION, INC.; *U.S. Private*, pg. 2145
JACKSON HB MEDICAL SERVICES, LLC—See Community Health Systems, Inc.; *U.S. Public*, pg. 554
JACKSON HMA, LLC—See Community Health Systems, Inc.; *U.S. Public*, pg. 554
JACKSON HOSPITAL CORPORATION—See Quorum Health Corporation; *U.S. Private*, pg. 3330
JACKSON HOSPITAL; *U.S. Private*, pg. 2177
JACKSON MEDICAL MALL FOUNDATION; *U.S. Private*, pg. 2177
JACKSON PHYSICIAN CORP.—See Quorum Health Corporation; *U.S. Private*, pg. 3330
JACKSON, TENNESSEE HOSPITAL COMPANY, LLC—See Community Health Systems, Inc.; *U.S. Public*, pg. 554
JACKSONVILLE BEACHES ANESTHESIA ASSOCIATES, INC.—See KKR & Co. Inc.; *U.S. Public*, pg. 1245
JACKSONVILLE CARENOW URGENT CARE, LLC—See HCA Healthcare, Inc.; *U.S. Public*, pg. 999
JACKSONVILLE ENDOSCOPY CENTERS, LLC—See Tenet Healthcare Corporation; *U.S. Public*, pg. 2004
JACKSONVILLE MULTISPECIALTY SERVICES, LLC—See HCA Healthcare, Inc.; *U.S. Public*, pg. 999
JACKSONVILLE ORTHOPEDIC INSTITUTE—See Baptist Health Medical Center; *U.S. Private*, pg. 470
JACKSONVILLE SURGERY CENTER, LTD.—See HCA Healthcare, Inc.; *U.S. Public*, pg. 999
JAMAICA HOSPITAL MEDICAL CENTER; *U.S. Private*, pg. 2182
JAMES A. HALEY VETERANS' HOSPITAL; *U.S. Private*, pg. 2183
JAMES RIVER INTERNISTS, LLC—See HCA Healthcare, Inc.; *U.S. Public*, pg. 999
JANE TODD CRAWFORD MEMORIAL HOSP., INC.; *U.S. Private*, pg. 2186
JEFFERSON COUNTY HMA, LLC—See Community Health Systems, Inc.; *U.S. Public*, pg. 554
JEFFERSON HEALTH SYSTEM, INC.; *U.S. Private*, pg. 2197
JEFFERSON REGIONAL MEDICAL CENTER; *U.S. Private*, pg. 2198

JENNIE M. MELHAM MEMORIAL MEDICAL CENTER; *U.S. Private*, pg. 2200
JENNINGS AMERICAN LEGION HOSPITAL; *U.S. Private*, pg. 2200
JERSEY HEALTH CONNECT; *U.S. Private*, pg. 2202
JERSEY SHORE HOSPITAL; *U.S. Private*, pg. 2203
JFK MEDICAL CENTER—See HCA Healthcare, Inc.; *U.S. Public*, pg. 999
JFK MEMORIAL HOSPITAL, INC.—See Tenet Healthcare Corporation; *U.S. Public*, pg. 2003
JFK NORTH SURGICENTER, LLC—See HCA Healthcare, Inc.; *U.S. Public*, pg. 999
JOHN RANDOLPH MEDICAL CENTER—See HCA Healthcare, Inc.; *U.S. Public*, pg. 999
JOHN RANDOLPH OB/GYN, LLC—See HCA Healthcare, Inc.; *U.S. Public*, pg. 999
JOHNS HOPKINS HEALTH SYSTEM; *U.S. Private*, pg. 2226
JOHNSON COUNTY NEUROLOGY, LLC—See HCA Healthcare, Inc.; *U.S. Public*, pg. 999
JOHN T. MATHER MEMORIAL HOSPITAL; *U.S. Private*, pg. 2225
JONES MEMORIAL HOSPITAL; *U.S. Private*, pg. 2233
JPS HEALTH NETWORK; *U.S. Private*, pg. 2239
JUPITER ANESTHESIA ASSOCIATES, LLC—See KKR & Co. Inc.; *U.S. Public*, pg. 1245
JUPITER EFL IMAGING CENTER, LLC—See HCA Healthcare, Inc.; *U.S. Public*, pg. 999
JWCH INSTITUTE, INC.; *U.S. Private*, pg. 2246
KADLEC REGIONAL MEDICAL CENTER; *U.S. Private*, pg. 2253
KAISER FOUNDATION HOSPITALS—See Kaiser Permanente; *U.S. Private*, pg. 2256
KALIHI-PALAMA HEALTH CENTER; *U.S. Private*, pg. 2257
KANAWHA HOSPICE CARE, INC.; *U.S. Private*, pg. 2259
KANDY PRIVATE HOSPITALS LTD—See Central Finance Company PLC; *Int'l*, pg. 1406
KANSAS CITY GASTROENTEROLOGY & HEPATOLOGY PHYSICIANS GROUP, LLC—See HCA Healthcare, Inc.; *U.S. Public*, pg. 999
KANSAS CITY NEUROLOGY ASSOCIATES, LLC—See HCA Healthcare, Inc.; *U.S. Public*, pg. 999
KANSAS PULMONARY AND SLEEP SPECIALISTS, LLC—See HCA Healthcare, Inc.; *U.S. Public*, pg. 1000
KARKKILAN LAAKARIKESKUS OY—See Componenta Corporation; *Int'l*, pg. 1753
KATHY L. SUMMERS, M.D., PLLC—See HCA Healthcare, Inc.; *U.S. Public*, pg. 1000
KAY COUNTY OKLAHOMA HOSPITAL COMPANY, LLC—See Community Health Systems, Inc.; *U.S. Public*, pg. 552
KB KRANKENHAUSBETEILIGUNGSGESELLSCHAFT MBH & CO. KG—See Asklepios Kliniken GmbH & Co. KGaA; *Int'l*, pg. 623
KEARN DIALYSIS, LLC—See DaVita Inc.; *U.S. Public*, pg. 640
KENDALL REGIONAL MEDICAL CENTER, LLC—See HCA Healthcare, Inc.; *U.S. Public*, pg. 1000
KENDALL REGIONAL URGENT CARE, LLC—See HCA Healthcare, Inc.; *U.S. Public*, pg. 1000
KENMORE MERCY HOSPITAL—See Catholic Health System, Inc.; *U.S. Private*, pg. 791
KENNEDALE PRIMARY CARE PLLC—See HCA Healthcare, Inc.; *U.S. Public*, pg. 1000
KENNEDY HEALTH SYSTEM; *U.S. Private*, pg. 2285
KENNETT HMA, INC.—See Community Health Systems, Inc.; *U.S. Public*, pg. 554
KENTMERE REHABILITATION AND HEALTHCARE CENTER; *U.S. Private*, pg. 2288
KENTUCKIANA MEDICAL CENTER, LLC—See Lennar Corporation; *U.S. Public*, pg. 1306
KENTUCKYONE HEALTH, INC.—See University of Louisville; *U.S. Private*, pg. 4309
KENTUCKY PHYSICIAN SERVICES, INC.—See Apollo Global Management, Inc.; *U.S. Public*, pg. 155
KENTUCKY REHABILITATION SERVICES, INC.—See Select Medical Holdings Corporation; *U.S. Public*, pg. 1858
KENWOOD ASC, LLC—See KKR & Co. Inc.; *U.S. Public*, pg. 1245
KESSLER INSTITUTE FOR REHABILITATION, INC.—See Select Medical Holdings Corporation; *U.S. Public*, pg. 1858
KETTERING ADVENTIST HEALTHCARE; *U.S. Private*, pg. 2292
KEY POINT HEALTH SERVICES, INC.; *U.S. Private*, pg. 2293
KEY WEST HMA, INC.—See Community Health Systems, Inc.; *U.S. Public*, pg. 554
KIDS BEHAVIORAL HEALTH OF MONTANA, INC.—See Acadia Healthcare Company, Inc.; *U.S. Public*, pg. 29
KIDS BEHAVIORAL HEALTH OF UTAH, INC.—See Universal Health Services, Inc.; *U.S. Public*, pg. 2258
KIMBALL MEDICAL CENTER—See Barnabas Health, Inc.; *U.S. Private*, pg. 476
KINDRED HOSPITAL - CLEVELAND—See Apollo Global Management, Inc.; *U.S. Public*, pg. 156
KINDRED HOSPITAL PALM BEACH, L.L.C.—See Apollo Global Management, Inc.; *U.S. Public*, pg. 156

N.A.I.C.S. Index

622110 — GENERAL MEDICAL AND... CORPORATE AFFILIATIONS

KINDRED HOSPITAL-PITTSBURGH-NORTH SHORE, L.L.C.—See Apollo Global Management, Inc.; *U.S. Public*, pg. 156
KINDRED HOSPITAL TUCSON—See Apollo Global Management, Inc.; *U.S. Public*, pg. 156
KING CITY PHYSICIAN COMPANY, LLC—See Quorum Health Corporation; *U.S. Private*, pg. 3330
KINGFISHER REGIONAL HOSPITAL; *U.S. Private*, pg. 2311
KINGMAN HOSPITAL, INC.; *U.S. Private*, pg. 2311
KINGMAN REGIONAL MEDICAL CENTER; *U.S. Private*, pg. 2311
KINGSBROOK JEWISH MEDICAL CENTER; *U.S. Private*, pg. 2311
KINGWOOD MEDICAL CENTER—See HCA Healthcare, Inc.; *U.S. Public*, pg. 1000
KIRBY MEDICAL CENTER; *U.S. Private*, pg. 2314
KIRKSVILLE ACADEMIC MEDICINE, LLC—See Community Health Systems, Inc.; *U.S. Public*, pg. 554
KIRKSVILLE CLINIC CORP.—See Community Health Systems, Inc.; *U.S. Public*, pg. 554
KIRKSVILLE PHYSICAL THERAPY SERVICES, LLC—See Community Health Systems, Inc.; *U.S. Public*, pg. 554
KLINIKEN HERZBERG UND OSTERODE GMBH—See Fresenius SE & Co. KGaA; *Int'l*, pg. 2779
KLINIK FEUERBERG GMBH—See Asklepios Kliniken GmbH & Co. KGaA; *Int'l*, pg. 624
KLINIK FUR HERZCHIRURGIE DER HERZ- UND GEFASS-KLINIK GMBH—See Asklepios Kliniken GmbH & Co. KGaA; *Int'l*, pg. 624
KLINIK HAUS FRANKEN GMBH—See Asklepios Kliniken GmbH & Co. KGaA; *Int'l*, pg. 624
KLINIKUM FRANKFURT (ODER) GMBH—See Asklepios Kliniken GmbH & Co. KGaA; *Int'l*, pg. 624
KLINIKUM MEININGEN GMBH—See Fresenius SE & Co. KGaA; *Int'l*, pg. 2779
KLINIKUM SALZGITTER GMBH—See Fresenius SE & Co. KGaA; *Int'l*, pg. 2779
KLINIKUM UELZEN GMBH—See Fresenius SE & Co. KGaA; *Int'l*, pg. 2779
KMI ACQUISITION, LLC—See Universal Health Services, Inc.; *U.S. Public*, pg. 2258
KNOX CLINIC CORP.—See Quorum Health Corporation; *U.S. Private*, pg. 3330
KNOX COMMUNITY HOSPITAL; *U.S. Private*, pg. 2324
KNOXVILLE HB MEDICAL SERVICES, LLC—See Community Health Systems, Inc.; *U.S. Public*, pg. 554
KNOXVILLE HMA CARDIOLOGY PPM, LLC—See Community Health Systems, Inc.; *U.S. Public*, pg. 554
KNOXVILLE HMA PHYSICIAN MANAGEMENT, LLC—See Community Health Systems, Inc.; *U.S. Public*, pg. 554
KNOXVILLE HOME CARE SERVICES, LLC—See Community Health Systems, Inc.; *U.S. Public*, pg. 554
KNOXVILLE HOSPITAL & CLINICS; *U.S. Private*, pg. 2324
KRAICHGAU-KLINIK AKTIENGESELLSCHAFT—See Asklepios Kliniken GmbH & Co. KGaA; *Int'l*, pg. 623
KRANKENHAUS CUXHAVEN GMBH—See Asklepios Kliniken GmbH & Co. KGaA; *Int'l*, pg. 624
KRANKENHAUS KOTHEN GMBH—See Fresenius SE & Co. KGaA; *Int'l*, pg. 2779
KRANKENHAUS ST. BARBARA ATTENDORN GMBH—See Fresenius SE & Co. KGaA; *Int'l*, pg. 2779
KREISKRANKENHAUS GIFHORN GMBH—See Asklepios Kliniken GmbH & Co. KGaA; *Int'l*, pg. 624
KUNMING TONGREN HOSPITAL CO., LTD.—See China Medical & HealthCare Group Limited; *Int'l*, pg. 1518
LABETTE HEALTH; *U.S. Private*, pg. 2370
LABORATORIO DE ANALISES CLINICAS SAO LUCAS LTDA.—See Centro de Imagem Diagnosticos S.A.; *Int'l*, pg. 1413
LACKEY MEMORIAL HOSPITAL; *U.S. Private*, pg. 2371
LA CLINICA DE LA RAZA INC.; *U.S. Private*, pg. 2368
LAFAYETTE GENERAL HEALTH SYSTEM; *U.S. Private*, pg. 2372
LAFAYETTE OB HOSPITALISTS, LLC—See HCA Healthcare, Inc.; *U.S. Public*, pg. 1000
LAFAYETTE REGIONAL HEALTH CENTER—See HCA Healthcare, Inc.; *U.S. Public*, pg. 1000
LAFAYETTE SURGICARE, INC.—See HCA Healthcare, Inc.; *U.S. Public*, pg. 1000
LAHEY CLINIC; *U.S. Private*, pg. 2373
LAKE AREA PHYSICIAN SERVICES, LLC—See Community Health Systems, Inc.; *U.S. Public*, pg. 554
LAKE CITY IMAGING, LLC—See HCA Healthcare, Inc.; *U.S. Public*, pg. 1000
LAKE CITY MEDICAL CENTER—See HCA Healthcare, Inc.; *U.S. Public*, pg. 1000
LAKE CITY REGIONAL MEDICAL GROUP, LLC—See HCA Healthcare, Inc.; *U.S. Public*, pg. 1000
LAKE CUMBERLAND CARDIOLOGY ASSOCIATES, LLC—See Apollo Global Management, Inc.; *U.S. Public*, pg. 158
LAKE CUMBERLAND REGIONAL HOSPITAL, LLC—See Apollo Global Management, Inc.; *U.S. Public*, pg. 158
LAKE CUMBERLAND SURGERY CENTER, LP—See Apollo Global Management, Inc.; *U.S. Public*, pg. 158
LAKE ENDOSCOPY CENTER, LLC—See Tenet Healthcare Corporation; *U.S. Public*, pg. 2004
LAKEFRONT MEDICAL ASSOCIATES, LLC—See Tenet Healthcare Corporation; *U.S. Public*, pg. 2014
LAKE GRANBURY HOSPITAL-BASED PROFESSIONAL SERVICES—See Community Health Systems, Inc.; *U.S. Public*, pg. 554
LAKE HOSPITAL SYSTEM, INC.; *U.S. Private*, pg. 2375
LAKELAND BEHAVIORAL HEALTH SYSTEM—See Acadia Healthcare Company, Inc.; *U.S. Public*, pg. 29
LAKELAND COMMUNITY HOSPITAL, INC.—See Curae Health, Inc.; *U.S. Private*, pg. 1124
LAKELAND HOME CARE SERVICES, LLC—See Community Health Systems, Inc.; *U.S. Public*, pg. 554
LAKE LANSING ASC PARTNERS, LLC—See Tenet Healthcare Corporation; *U.S. Public*, pg. 2011
LAKE MARY SURGERY CENTER, L.L.C.—See Bain Capital, LP; *U.S. Private*, pg. 445
LAKE NONA EMERGENCY PHYSICIANS, LLC—See HCA Healthcare, Inc.; *U.S. Public*, pg. 1000
LAKE NONA INPATIENT SERVICES, LLC—See HCA Healthcare, Inc.; *U.S. Public*, pg. 1000
LAKE POINTE OPERATING COMPANY, L.L.C.—See Tenet Healthcare Corporation; *U.S. Public*, pg. 2006
LAKE POINTE PARTNERS, LTD.—See Tenet Healthcare Corporation; *U.S. Public*, pg. 2006
LAKE REGION HEALTHCARE; *U.S. Private*, pg. 2376
LAKESIDE WOMEN'S HOSPITAL—See INTEGRIS Health, Inc.; *U.S. Private*, pg. 2102
LAKEVIEW ENDOSCOPY CENTER—See HCA Healthcare, Inc.; *U.S. Public*, pg. 1000
LAKEVIEW HOSPITAL—See HCA Healthcare, Inc.; *U.S. Public*, pg. 1000
LAKEVIEW MEDICAL CENTER, LLC—See HCA Healthcare, Inc.; *U.S. Public*, pg. 1000
LAKEVIEW REGIONAL PHYSICIAN GROUP, LLC—See HCA Healthcare, Inc.; *U.S. Public*, pg. 1000
LAKE WALES CLINIC CORP.—See Community Health Systems, Inc.; *U.S. Public*, pg. 554
LAKEWAY REGIONAL HOSPITAL—See Community Health Systems, Inc.; *U.S. Public*, pg. 554
LAKEWOOD REGIONAL MEDICAL CENTER, INC.—See UCI Health; *U.S. Private*, pg. 4274
LAKEWOOD SURGERY CENTER, LLC—See Tenet Healthcare Corporation; *U.S. Public*, pg. 2011
LAMPREY HEALTH CARE; *U.S. Private*, pg. 2381
LANCASTER BEHAVIORAL HEALTH HOSPITAL, LLC—See Universal Health Services, Inc.; *U.S. Public*, pg. 2258
LANCASTER CLINIC CORP.—See Community Health Systems, Inc.; *U.S. Public*, pg. 554
LANCASTER GENERAL HEALTH; *U.S. Private*, pg. 2381
LANCASTER HOME CARE SERVICES, LLC—See Community Health Systems, Inc.; *U.S. Public*, pg. 554
LANCASTER HOSPITAL CORPORATION—See Universal Health Services, Inc.; *U.S. Public*, pg. 2258
LANCASTER IMAGING CENTER, LLC—See Community Health Systems, Inc.; *U.S. Public*, pg. 554
LANCASTER MEDICAL GROUP, LLC—See Community Health Systems, Inc.; *U.S. Public*, pg. 554
LANCASTER OUTPATIENT IMAGING, LLC—See Community Health Systems, Inc.; *U.S. Public*, pg. 554
LANDER VALLEY PHYSICIAN PRACTICES, LLC—See Apollo Global Management, Inc.; *U.S. Public*, pg. 158
LANDMARK HEALTH, LLC—See UnitedHealth Group Incorporated; *U.S. Public*, pg. 2242
LANDMARK HEALTH OF CALIFORNIA, LLC—See UnitedHealth Group Incorporated; *U.S. Public*, pg. 2242
LANDMARK HEALTH OF NORTH CAROLINA, LLC—See UnitedHealth Group Incorporated; *U.S. Public*, pg. 2242
LANDMARK HEALTH OF OREGON, LLC—See UnitedHealth Group Incorporated; *U.S. Public*, pg. 2242
LANDMARK HEALTH OF PENNSYLVANIA, LLC—See UnitedHealth Group Incorporated; *U.S. Public*, pg. 2242
LANDMARK HEALTH OF WASHINGTON, LLC—See UnitedHealth Group Incorporated; *U.S. Public*, pg. 2242
LANDMARK HEALTH TECHNOLOGIES PRIVATE LIMITED—See UnitedHealth Group Incorporated; *U.S. Public*, pg. 2242
LANDMARK MEDICAL CENTER—See Prime Healthcare Services, Inc.; *U.S. Private*, pg. 3261
LANDMARK MEDICAL OF MASSACHUSETTS, PLLC—See UnitedHealth Group Incorporated; *U.S. Public*, pg. 2242
LA PALMA INTERCOMMUNITY HOSPITAL—See Prime Healthcare Services, Inc.; *U.S. Private*, pg. 3261
LA PAZ REGIONAL HOSPITAL; *U.S. Private*, pg. 2369
LAPORTE MEDICAL GROUP SURGICAL CENTER, LLC—See Community Health Systems, Inc.; *U.S. Public*, pg. 554
LA RABIDA CHILDREN'S HOSPITAL; *U.S. Private*, pg. 2369
LAREDO FED JV1, LLC—See Universal Health Services, Inc.; *U.S. Public*, pg. 2258
LAREDO REGIONAL MEDICAL CENTER, L.P.—See Universal Health Services, Inc.; *U.S. Public*, pg. 2258
LARGO ENDOSCOPY CENTER, L.P.—See Bain Capital, LP; *U.S. Private*, pg. 445
LARGO PHYSICIAN GROUP, LLC—See HCA Healthcare, Inc.; *U.S. Public*, pg. 1000
LARGO SURGERY, LLC—See Bain Capital, LP; *U.S. Private*, pg. 445
LAS CRUCES MEDICAL CENTER, LLC—See Community Health Systems, Inc.; *U.S. Public*, pg. 554
LAS CRUCES PHYSICIAN SERVICES, LLC—See Community Health Systems, Inc.; *U.S. Public*, pg. 554
LAS CRUCES SURGERY CENTER - TELSHOR, LLC—See Community Health Systems, Inc.; *U.S. Public*, pg. 554
LAS ENCINAS HOSPITAL—See HCA Healthcare, Inc.; *U.S. Public*, pg. 1000
LASER AND OUTPATIENT SURGERY CENTER, LLC—See Bain Capital, LP; *U.S. Private*, pg. 445
LASER SPINE INSTITUTE, LLC; *U.S. Private*, pg. 2395
LAS PALMAS DEL SOL HEALTHCARE—See HCA Healthcare, Inc.; *U.S. Public*, pg. 1000
THE LAS VEGAS EAST OPHTHALMOLOGY ASC, LLC—See KKR & Co. Inc.; *U.S. Public*, pg. 1247
LAS VEGAS MEDICAL GROUP, LLC—See Universal Health Services, Inc.; *U.S. Public*, pg. 2258
LAUGHLIN MEMORIAL HOSPITAL—See Mountain States Health Alliance; *U.S. Private*, pg. 2800
LAUREL OAKS BEHAVIORAL HEALTH CENTER, INC.—See Universal Health Services, Inc.; *U.S. Public*, pg. 2258
LAWNWOOD REGIONAL MEDICAL CENTER—See HCA Healthcare, Inc.; *U.S. Public*, pg. 1000
LAWRENCE COUNTY MEMORIAL HOSPITAL; *U.S. Private*, pg. 2401
LCMC HEALTH HOLDINGS, INC.; *U.S. Private*, pg. 2403
LEADERS IN ONCOLOGY CARE LIMITED—See HCA Healthcare, Inc.; *U.S. Public*, pg. 1000
LEBANON ENDOSCOPY CENTER, LLC—See Tenet Healthcare Corporation; *U.S. Public*, pg. 2011
LEBANON HMA, INC.—See Community Health Systems, Inc.; *U.S. Public*, pg. 554
LEBANON HMA SURGERY CENTER, LLC—See Community Health Systems, Inc.; *U.S. Public*, pg. 554
LEBANON SURGERY CENTER, LLC—See Community Health Systems, Inc.; *U.S. Public*, pg. 554
LEE MEMORIAL HEALTH SYSTEM; *U.S. Private*, pg. 2413
LEGACY EMANUEL HOSPITAL & HEALTH CENTER—See Legacy Health System; *U.S. Private*, pg. 2416
LEGACY GOOD SAMARITAN HOSPITAL & MEDICAL CENTER—See Legacy Health System; *U.S. Private*, pg. 2416
LEGACY HEALTH SYSTEM; *U.S. Private*, pg. 2416
LEGACY MERIDIAN PARK HOSPITAL—See Legacy Health System; *U.S. Private*, pg. 2416
LEGACY MOUNT HOOD MEDICAL CENTER—See Legacy Health System; *U.S. Private*, pg. 2416
LEGACY SALMON CREEK HOSPITAL—See Legacy Health System; *U.S. Private*, pg. 2416
LEHIGH HMA, LLC—See Prime Healthcare Services, Inc.; *U.S. Private*, pg. 3261
LEON MEDICAL CENTERS, INC.; *U.S. Private*, pg. 2423
LEON SULLIVAN HEALTH CARE CENTER; *U.S. Private*, pg. 2423
LEWIS COUNTY PRIMARY CARE CENTER; *U.S. Private*, pg. 2438
LEWISGALE HOSPITAL ALLEGHANY—See HCA Healthcare, Inc.; *U.S. Public*, pg. 1001
LEWISGALE HOSPITAL ALLEGHANY—See HCA Healthcare, Inc.; *U.S. Public*, pg. 1001
LEWIS-GALE HOSPITAL, INCORPORATED—See HCA Healthcare, Inc.; *U.S. Public*, pg. 1001
LEWISGALE HOSPITAL MONTGOMERY—See HCA Healthcare, Inc.; *U.S. Public*, pg. 1001
LEWISGALE HOSPITAL MONTGOMERY—See HCA Healthcare, Inc.; *U.S. Public*, pg. 1003
LEWISGALE HOSPITAL-PULASKI—See HCA Healthcare, Inc.; *U.S. Public*, pg. 1001
LEWIS-GALE MEDICAL CENTER, LLC—See HCA Healthcare, Inc.; *U.S. Public*, pg. 1001
LEWISVILLE MEDICAL CENTER LLC—See Adeptus Health Inc.; *U.S. Private*, pg. 78
LEXINGTON FAMILY PHYSICIANS, LLC—See Quorum Health Corporation; *U.S. Private*, pg. 3330
LEXINGTON HOSPITAL CORPORATION—See Quorum Health Corporation; *U.S. Private*, pg. 3330
LEXINGTON MEMORIAL HOSPITAL INC.—See Davidson Health Care, Inc.; *U.S. Private*, pg. 1171
LEXINGTON SURGERY CENTER, LTD.—See UnitedHealth Group Incorporated; *U.S. Public*, pg. 2242
LHCG XLII, LLC.—See UnitedHealth Group Incorporated; *U.S. Public*, pg. 2245
LHCG XL, LLC—See UnitedHealth Group Incorporated; *U.S. Public*, pg. 2245
LHCG XLVII, LLC—See UnitedHealth Group Incorporated; *U.S. Public*, pg. 2245
LHCG XXXIII, LLC—See UnitedHealth Group Incorporated; *U.S. Public*, pg. 2245
LIBERTY AMBULATORY SURGERY CENTER, LLC—See Tenet Healthcare Corporation; *U.S. Public*, pg. 2011
LIBERTY AMBULATORY SURGERY CENTER, L.P.—See Tenet Healthcare Corporation; *U.S. Public*, pg. 2011
LIBERTY HOSPITAL; *U.S. Private*, pg. 2444
LIBERTY POINT BEHAVIORAL HEALTHCARE, LLC—See Universal Health Services, Inc.; *U.S. Public*, pg. 2258

N.A.I.C.S. INDEX
622110 — GENERAL MEDICAL AND...

LIFEBRIDGE HEALTH; *U.S. Private*, pg. 2449
LIFECARE HOSPITAL—See Post Acute Medical, LLC; *U.S. Private*, pg. 3234
LIFECARE MEDICAL CENTER; *U.S. Private*, pg. 2449
LIFELONG; *U.S. Private*, pg. 2450
LIFENET HEALTH, INC.; *U.S. Private*, pg. 2450
LIFEPOINT OF LAKE CUMBERLAND, LLC—See Apollo Global Management, Inc.; *U.S. Public*, pg. 158
LIFESHARE MANAGEMENT GROUP, LLC—See Centene Corporation; *U.S. Public*, pg. 469
LIFE WORKS COMMUNITY LIMITED—See Acadia Healthcare Company, Inc.; *U.S. Public*, pg. 29
LIMESTONE MEDICAL CENTER, LLC—See UnitedHealth Group Incorporated; *U.S. Public*, pg. 2242
LINCOLN SURGERY CENTER, LLC—See HCA Healthcare, Inc.; *U.S. Public*, pg. 1001
LISTER HOSPITAL—See HCA Healthcare, Inc.; *U.S. Public*, pg. 1001
THE LITTLE CLINIC OF TENNESSEE LLC—See The Kroger Co.; *U.S. Public*, pg. 2109
LITTLETON REGIONAL HEALTHCARE; *U.S. Private*, pg. 2472
LIVE OAK HMA, LLC—See Community Health Systems, Inc.; *U.S. Public*, pg. 554
LIVE OAK IMMEDIATE CARE CENTER, LLC—See HCA Healthcare, Inc.; *U.S. Public*, pg. 1001
LIVINGSTON HOSPITAL & HEALTHCARE SERVICES, INC.; *U.S. Private*, pg. 2474
LIVINGSTON REGIONAL HOSPITAL, LLC—See Apollo Global Management, Inc.; *U.S. Public*, pg. 158
THE LOCAL CHOICE PROPRIETARY LIMITED—See Dis-Chem Pharmacies Ltd.; *Int'l*, pg. 2131
LOCK HAVEN HOME CARE SERVICES, LLC—See Community Health Systems, Inc.; *U.S. Public*, pg. 554
LOGAN GENERAL HOSPITAL, LLC—See Apollo Global Management, Inc.; *U.S. Public*, pg. 158
LOGAN HEALTH; *U.S. Private*, pg. 2480
LONDON BRIDGE HOSPITAL—See HCA Healthcare, Inc.; *U.S. Public*, pg. 1001
LONDON BRIDGE HOSPITAL—See HCA Healthcare, Inc.; *U.S. Public*, pg. 1001
LONE PEAK HOSPITAL, INC.—See HCA Healthcare, Inc.; *U.S. Public*, pg. 1001
LONE STAR CIRCLE OF CARE; *U.S. Private*, pg. 2484
LONE STAR HMA, L.P.—See Prime Healthcare Services, Inc.; *U.S. Private*, pg. 3261
LONGMONT UNITED HOSPITAL; *U.S. Private*, pg. 2492
LONGVIEW REGIONAL MEDICAL CENTER—See Community Health Systems, Inc.; *U.S. Public*, pg. 554
LORING HOSPITAL; *U.S. Private*, pg. 2495
LOS ALAMITOS MEDICAL CENTER, INC.—See UCI Health; *U.S. Private*, pg. 4274
LOS ROBLES REGIONAL MEDICAL CENTER—See HCA Healthcare, Inc.; *U.S. Public*, pg. 1001
LOS ROBLES SURGICENTER, LLC—See HCA Healthcare, Inc.; *U.S. Public*, pg. 1001
LOTTEN-EYES OFTALMOLOGIA CLINICA E CIRURGICA LTDA.—See UnitedHealth Group Incorporated; *U.S. Public*, pg. 2242
LOUETTA MEDICAL CENTER LLC—See Adeptus Health Inc.; *U.S. Private*, pg. 78
LOUISA HOME CARE SERVICES, LLC—See Community Health Systems, Inc.; *U.S. Public*, pg. 554
LOUISBURG HMA, INC.—See Community Health Systems, Inc.; *U.S. Public*, pg. 554
LOUISIANA HEALTH CARE CONNECTIONS, INC.—See Centene Corporation; *U.S. Public*, pg. 469
LOUISIANA PHYSICAL THERAPY, LLC—See UnitedHealth Group Incorporated; *U.S. Public*, pg. 2246
LOUISIANA PUBLIC HEALTH INSTITUTE; *U.S. Private*, pg. 2500
LOURDES HEALTH NETWORK—See Ascension Health Alliance; *U.S. Private*, pg. 347
LOURDES MEDICAL CENTER—See Ascension Health Alliance; *U.S. Private*, pg. 347
LOWER BUCKS HOSPITAL; *U.S. Private*, pg. 2505
LOWRY SURGERY CENTER, LLC—See HCA Healthcare, Inc.; *U.S. Public*, pg. 1001
LOYOLA UNIVERSITY MEDICAL CENTER—See Trinity Health Corporation; *U.S. Private*, pg. 4233
LUBBOCK HEART HOSPITAL, LLC—See Bain Capital, LP; *U.S. Private*, pg. 445
LUTHERAN MEDICAL GROUP, LLC—See Community Health Systems, Inc.; *U.S. Public*, pg. 554
MACNEAL HEALTH PROVIDERS, INC.—See Tenet Healthcare Corporation; *U.S. Public*, pg. 2014
MACNEAL HOSPITAL—See Trinity Health Corporation; *U.S. Private*, pg. 4233
MACON PSYCHIATRIC HOSPITALISTS, LLC—See HCA Healthcare, Inc.; *U.S. Public*, pg. 1001
MADISON COMMUNITY HOSPITAL INC; *U.S. Private*, pg. 2540
MADISON HMA, LLC—See Community Health Systems, Inc.; *U.S. Public*, pg. 555
MADISON LUTHERAN HOME; *U.S. Private*, pg. 2544
MADISON RIVER OAKS MEDICAL CENTER—See Community Health Systems, Inc.; *U.S. Public*, pg. 556
MAGEE GENERAL HOSPITAL; *U.S. Private*, pg. 2545

MAGNOLIA CREEK—See Nautic Partners, LLC; *U.S. Private*, pg. 2871
MAGNOLIA SURGERY CENTER LIMITED PARTNERSHIP—See Tenet Healthcare Corporation; *U.S. Public*, pg. 2014
MAGRUDER HOSPITAL; *U.S. Private*, pg. 2549
MAINE COAST REGIONAL HEALTH FACILITIES INC.; *U.S. Private*, pg. 2552
MAINEGENERAL HEALTH INC.; *U.S. Private*, pg. 2552
MAINEGENERAL MEDICAL CENTER—See MaineGeneral Health Inc.; *U.S. Private*, pg. 2552
MAINLAND PRIMARY CARE PHYSICIANS, PLLC—See HCA Healthcare, Inc.; *U.S. Public*, pg. 1001
MAIN LINE SPINE SURGERY CENTER, LLC—See UnitedHealth Group Incorporated; *U.S. Public*, pg. 2242
MANATEE CARDIOLOGY ASSOCIATES, LLC—See Universal Health Services, Inc.; *U.S. Public*, pg. 2258
MANATEE MEMORIAL HOSPITAL & HEALTH SYSTEM—See Universal Health Services, Inc.; *U.S. Public*, pg. 2260
MANATEE SURGICARE, LTD.—See HCA Healthcare, Inc.; *U.S. Public*, pg. 1001
MANET COMMUNITY HEALTH CENTER, INC.; *U.S. Private*, pg. 2563
MANNING REGIONAL HEALTHCARE CENTER; *U.S. Private*, pg. 2565
THE MANOR CLINIC LIMITED—See Acadia Healthcare Company, Inc.; *U.S. Public*, pg. 30
MAPLE GROVE HOSPITAL; *U.S. Private*, pg. 2568
MARCUS DALY MEMORIAL HOSPITAL; *U.S. Private*, pg. 2572
MARIETTA AREA HEALTH CARE, INC.; *U.S. Private*, pg. 2574
MARIETTA SURGICAL CENTER, INC.—See HCA Healthcare, Inc.; *U.S. Public*, pg. 1001
MARINERS HOSPITAL—See Baptist Health South Florida, Inc.; *U.S. Private*, pg. 471
MARIN GENERAL HOSPITAL—See Marin Healthcare District; *U.S. Private*, pg. 2574
MARION GENERAL HOSPITAL, INC; *U.S. Private*, pg. 2576
MARION HOSPITAL CORPORATION—See Quorum Health Corporation; *U.S. Public*, pg. 3330
MARION PHYSICIAN SERVICES, LLC—See Community Health Systems, Inc.; *U.S. Public*, pg. 555
MARK COLLEGE LIMITED—See Acadia Healthcare Company, Inc.; *U.S. Public*, pg. 29
MARK TWAIN MEDICAL CENTER—See Catholic Health Initiatives; *U.S. Private*, pg. 790
MARLBORO PARK HOSPITAL—See McLeod Health; *U.S. Private*, pg. 2641
MARSHALL COUNTY HMA, LLC—See Community Health Systems, Inc.; *U.S. Public*, pg. 555
MARSHALL COUNTY HMPN, LLC—See Community Health Systems, Inc.; *U.S. Public*, pg. 555
MARSHALL COUNTY HOSPITAL; *U.S. Private*, pg. 2592
MARSHALL MEDICAL CENTER NORTH—See Marshall Medical Center; *U.S. Private*, pg. 2593
MARSHALL MEDICAL CENTER; *U.S. Private*, pg. 2592
MARSHALLTOWN MEDICAL & SURGICAL CENTER; *U.S. Private*, pg. 2593
MARTHA'S VINEYARD HOSPITAL INC.—See Partners HealthCare System, Inc.; *U.S. Private*, pg. 3102
MARTIN CLINIC CORP.—See Community Health Systems, Inc.; *U.S. Public*, pg. 555
MARTIN HEALTH SYSTEM; *U.S. Private*, pg. 2595
MARTIN HOSPITAL COMPANY, LLC—See Community Health Systems, Inc.; *U.S. Public*, pg. 555
MARY BLACK HEALTH SYSTEM LLC—See Spartanburg Regional Health Services District, Inc.; *U.S. Private*, pg. 3747
MARY IMMACULATE AMBULATORY SURGERY CENTER, LLC—See Tenet Healthcare Corporation; *U.S. Public*, pg. 2011
MARY RUTAN HOSPITAL; *U.S. Private*, pg. 2599
THE MARYVILLE ASC, L.P.—See KKR & Co. Inc.; *U.S. Public*, pg. 1248
THE MASSACHUSETTS GENERAL HOSPITAL—See Partners HealthCare System, Inc.; *U.S. Private*, pg. 3102
MASSACHUSETTS LEAGUE OF COMMUNITY HEALTH CENTERS; *U.S. Private*, pg. 2604
MAYES COUNTY HMA, LLC—See Community Health Systems, Inc.; *U.S. Public*, pg. 555
MAYES COUNTY HMPN, LLC—See Community Health Systems, Inc.; *U.S. Public*, pg. 555
MAYFIELD SPINE SURGERY CENTER, LLC—See Tenet Healthcare Corporation; *U.S. Public*, pg. 2004
MAYO CLINIC ARIZONA—See Mayo Clinic; *U.S. Private*, pg. 2622
MAYO CLINIC FLORIDA—See Mayo Clinic; *U.S. Private*, pg. 2622
MAYO CLINIC; *U.S. Private*, pg. 2622
MCALLEN HEART HOSPITAL, L.P.—See Universal Health Services, Inc.; *U.S. Public*, pg. 2258
MCCALLUM GROUP, LLC—See Acadia Healthcare Company, Inc.; *U.S. Public*, pg. 29
MCCULLOUGH HYDE MEMORIAL HOSPITAL, INC.—See Catholic Health Initiatives; *U.S. Private*, pg. 790

MCCURTAIN MEMORIAL MEDICAL MANAGEMENT, INC.; *U.S. Private*, pg. 2631
MCKENZIE MEMORIAL HOSPITAL; *U.S. Private*, pg. 2638
MCKENZIE PHYSICIAN SERVICES, LLC—See Quorum Health Corporation; *U.S. Public*, pg. 3330
MCKENZIE-WILLAMETTE REGIONAL MEDICAL CENTER ASSOCIATES, LLC—See Quorum Health Corporation; *U.S. Public*, pg. 3330
MCKINNEY SURGEONS, PLLC—See HCA Healthcare, Inc.; *U.S. Public*, pg. 1001
MCNAIRY HOSPITAL CORPORATION—See Community Health Systems, Inc.; *U.S. Public*, pg. 555
MCSA, L.L.C.—See Community Health Systems, Inc.; *U.S. Public*, pg. 554
MDSINE, LLC—See KKR & Co. Inc.; *U.S. Public*, pg. 1246
MEADOWS SURGERY CENTER, LLC—See KKR & Co. Inc.; *U.S. Public*, pg. 1246
MEADVILLE MEDICAL CENTER; *U.S. Private*, pg. 2647
MEASE COUNTRYSIDE HOSPITAL—See BayCare Health System Inc.; *U.S. Private*, pg. 495
MEASE DUNEDIN HOSPITAL—See BayCare Health System Inc.; *U.S. Private*, pg. 495
MEDAXIO INSURANCE MEDICAL SERVICES LP—See Laboratory Corporation of America Holdings; *U.S. Public*, pg. 1287
MEDEX HEALTHCARE, INC.—See PACIFIC HEALTH CARE ORGANIZATION, INC.; *U.S. Public*, pg. 1632
MEDICAL CENTER ENTERPRISE—See Community Health Systems, Inc.; *U.S. Public*, pg. 552
MEDICAL CENTER OF ARLINGTON—See HCA Healthcare, Inc.; *U.S. Public*, pg. 1001
THE MEDICAL CENTER OF AURORA—See HCA Healthcare, Inc.; *U.S. Public*, pg. 1012
MEDICAL CENTER OF BATON ROUGE, INC.—See HCA Healthcare, Inc.; *U.S. Public*, pg. 1001
MEDICAL CENTER OF GARDEN GROVE, INC.—See Tenet Healthcare Corporation; *U.S. Public*, pg. 2004
MEDICAL CENTER OF LEWISVILLE—See HCA Healthcare, Inc.; *U.S. Public*, pg. 1001
MEDICAL CENTER OF MCKINNEY—See HCA Healthcare, Inc.; *U.S. Public*, pg. 1001
MEDICAL CENTER OF PLANO—See HCA Healthcare, Inc.; *U.S. Public*, pg. 1001
MEDICAL CENTER OF SANTA ROSA, INC.—See HCA Healthcare, Inc.; *U.S. Public*, pg. 1001
MEDICAL CITY HOSPITAL—See HCA Healthcare, Inc.; *U.S. Public*, pg. 1002
MEDICAL CITY SURGERY CENTER OF ALLIANCE, LLC—See HCA Healthcare, Inc.; *U.S. Public*, pg. 1002
MEDICAL CITY SURGERY CENTER OF FRISCO, LLC—See HCA Healthcare, Inc.; *U.S. Public*, pg. 1002
THE MEDICAL GROUP OF KANSAS CITY, LLC—See HCA Healthcare, Inc.; *U.S. Public*, pg. 1012
MEDICAL GROUP - SOUTHERN HILLS OF BRENTWOOD, LLC—See HCA Healthcare, Inc.; *U.S. Public*, pg. 1002
MEDICAL GROUP - STONECREST, INC.—See HCA Healthcare, Inc.; *U.S. Public*, pg. 1002
MEDICAL IMAGING CENTER OF OCALA, LLP—See Community Health Systems, Inc.; *U.S. Public*, pg. 555
MEDICAL PARK DIAGNOSTIC CENTER—See HCA Healthcare, Inc.; *U.S. Public*, pg. 1002
MEDICAL PARK TOWER SURGERY CENTER, LLC—See Tenet Healthcare Corporation; *U.S. Public*, pg. 2011
MEDICAL SPECIALISTS OF THE PALM BEACHES, INC.; *U.S. Private*, pg. 2655
MEDICLIN AKTIENGESELLSCHAFT—See Asklepios Kliniken GmbH & Co. KGaA; *Int'l*, pg. 623
MEDICLIN GESCHAFTSFUHRUNGS-GMBH—See Asklepios Kliniken GmbH & Co. KGaA; *Int'l*, pg. 623
MEDICLIN KRAKENHAUS AM CRIVITZER SEE—See Asklepios Kliniken GmbH & Co. KGaA; *Int'l*, pg. 623
MEDICLIN MEDIZINISCHES VERSORGUNGSZENTRUM GMBH—See Asklepios Kliniken GmbH & Co. KGaA; *Int'l*, pg. 624
MEDICLIN MURITZ-KLINIKUM GMBH & CO. KG—See Asklepios Kliniken GmbH & Co. KGaA; *Int'l*, pg. 623
MEDICLIN PFLEGE GMBH—See Asklepios Kliniken GmbH & Co. KGaA; *Int'l*, pg. 623
MEDICREDIT, INC.—See HCA Healthcare, Inc.; *U.S. Public*, pg. 1001
MEDICS AMBULANCE SERVICE, INC.—See KKR & Co. Inc.; *U.S. Public*, pg. 1249
MEDIVISION, INC.—See HCA Healthcare, Inc.; *U.S. Public*, pg. 1001
MEDLINE HEALTHCARE GROUP—See ESAS Holding A.S.; *Int'l*, pg. 2501
MEDPARTNERS HIM, LLC—See AMN Healthcare Services, Inc.; *U.S. Public*, pg. 125
MEDPRO GROUP INC—See Berkshire Hathaway Inc.; *U.S. Public*, pg. 312
MEDSTAR HEALTH; *U.S. Private*, pg. 2659
MEDSTAT, LLC—See Community Health Systems, Inc.; *U.S. Public*, pg. 554
MEDWISH INTERNATIONAL; *U.S. Private*, pg. 2659
THE MELBOURNE ASC, L.P.—See KKR & Co. Inc.; *U.S. Public*, pg. 1248
MEMORIAL COMMUNITY HEALTH, INC.; *U.S. Private*, pg. 2663

622110 — GENERAL MEDICAL AND...

MEMORIAL HEALTH CARE SYSTEMS; *U.S. Private*, pg. 2663
MEMORIAL HERMANN HEALTHCARE SYSTEM; *U.S. Private*, pg. 2664
MEMORIAL HERMANN SPECIALTY HOSPITAL KINGWOOD, L.L.C.—See Tenet Healthcare Corporation; *U.S. Public*, pg. 2011
MEMORIAL HERMANN SURGERY CENTER KATY, LLP—See Tenet Healthcare Corporation; *U.S. Public*, pg. 2011
MEMORIAL HERMANN SURGERY CENTER SUGAR LAND, LLP—See Tenet Healthcare Corporation; *U.S. Public*, pg. 2011
MEMORIAL HERMANN SURGERY CENTER TEXAS MEDICAL CENTER, LLP—See Tenet Healthcare Corporation; *U.S. Public*, pg. 2004
MEMORIAL HERMANN SURGERY CENTER - THE WOODLANDS, LLP—See Tenet Healthcare Corporation; *U.S. Public*, pg. 2011
MEMORIAL HERMANN TEXAS INTERNATIONAL ENDOSCOPY CENTER, LLC—See Tenet Healthcare Corporation; *U.S. Public*, pg. 2011
MEMORIAL HOSPITAL, INC.; *U.S. Private*, pg. 2664
MEMORIAL HOSPITAL OF MARTINSVILLE & HENRY COUNTY AMBULATORY SURGERY CENTER, LLC—See Apollo Global Management, Inc.; *U.S. Public*, pg. 158
MEMORIAL HOSPITAL—See HCA Healthcare, Inc.; *U.S. Public*, pg. 1002
MEMORIAL MANAGEMENT, INC.—See Quorum Health Corporation; *U.S. Private*, pg. 3330
MEMORIAL REGIONAL HOSPITAL SOUTH—See South Broward Hospital District; *U.S. Private*, pg. 3720
MEMORIAL SATILLA SPECIALISTS, LLC—See HCA Healthcare, Inc.; *U.S. Public*, pg. 1002
MEMORIAL SPECIALTY HOSPITAL; *U.S. Private*, pg. 2664
MENA MEDICAL CENTER HOME HEALTH, LLC—See UnitedHealth Group Incorporated; *U.S. Public*, pg. 2246
MENNONITE GENERAL HOSPITAL, INC.; *U.S. Private*, pg. 2666
MENTAL HEALTH CONNECTICUT, INC.; *U.S. Private*, pg. 2667
MENTIS NEURO EL PASO, LLC—See Centerbridge Partners, L.P.; *U.S. Private*, pg. 813
MENTIS NEURO HOUSTON, LLC—See Centerbridge Partners, L.P.; *U.S. Private*, pg. 813
MENTIS NEURO SAN ANTONIO, LLC—See Centerbridge Partners, L.P.; *U.S. Private*, pg. 813
MERCED AMBULATORY SURGERY CENTER, LLC—See Tenet Healthcare Corporation; *U.S. Public*, pg. 2004
MERCY HEALTHCARE SACRAMENTO INC.—See Catholic Health Initiatives; *U.S. Private*, pg. 790
MERCY HEALTH SERVICES; *U.S. Private*, pg. 2671
MERCY HOSPITAL OF BUFFALO—See Catholic Health System, Inc.; *U.S. Private*, pg. 791
MERCY HOSPITAL OF FOLSOM—See Catholic Health Initiatives; *U.S. Private*, pg. 790
MERCY MEDICAL CENTER MT. SHASTA—See Catholic Health Initiatives; *U.S. Private*, pg. 790
MERCY MEDICAL CENTER - NORTH IOWA—See Trinity Health Corporation; *U.S. Private*, pg. 4233
MERCY MEDICAL CENTER REDDING—See Catholic Health Initiatives; *U.S. Private*, pg. 790
MERCY MEDICAL CENTER—See Catholic Health Services of Long Island; *U.S. Private*, pg. 791
MERCY MEMORIAL HOSPITAL SYSTEM; *U.S. Private*, pg. 2671
MERCY SAN JUAN HOSPITAL—See Catholic Health Initiatives; *U.S. Private*, pg. 790
MERIDIAN HEALTH SERVICES; *U.S. Private*, pg. 2673
MERRIDELL ACHIEVEMENT CENTER, INC.—See Universal Health Services, Inc.; *U.S. Public*, pg. 2258
MERRITT ISLAND ASC, LLC—See Community Health Systems, Inc.; *U.S. Public*, pg. 555
MERRITT ISLAND SURGERY CENTER—See HCA Healthcare, Inc.; *U.S. Public*, pg. 1002
MESA VIEW PT, LLC—See Quorum Health Corporation; *U.S. Private*, pg. 3330
METHODIST AMBULATORY SURGERY CENTER OF LANDMARK, LLC—See HCA Healthcare, Inc.; *U.S. Public*, pg. 1002
METHODIST HEALTHCARE; *U.S. Private*, pg. 2683
METHODIST HEALTHCARE SYSTEM OF SAN ANTONIO, LTD.—See HCA Healthcare, Inc.; *U.S. Public*, pg. 1002
METHODIST HEALTHCARE SYSTEM OF SAN ANTONIO, LTD.—See Methodist Healthcare Ministries of South Texas, Inc.; *U.S. Private*, pg. 2683
METHODIST HEALTH SYSTEM; *U.S. Private*, pg. 2683
METHODIST HOSPITAL HILL COUNTRY—See HCA Healthcare, Inc.; *U.S. Public*, pg. 1002
METHODIST HOSPITAL HILL COUNTRY—See Methodist Healthcare Ministries of South Texas, Inc.; *U.S. Private*, pg. 2683
METHODIST HOSPITAL OF SACRAMENTO—See Catholic Health Initiatives; *U.S. Private*, pg. 790
THE METHODIST HOSPITALS, INC; *U.S. Private*, pg. 4078
METHODIST HOSPITAL; *U.S. Private*, pg. 2684

METHODIST HOSPITAL—See HCA Healthcare, Inc.; *U.S. Public*, pg. 1002
METHODIST HOSPITAL SOUTH—See HCA Healthcare, Inc.; *U.S. Public*, pg. 1002
METHODIST HOSPITAL SOUTH—See Methodist Healthcare Ministries of South Texas, Inc.; *U.S. Private*, pg. 2683
METHODIST HOSPITAL UNION COUNTY—See Methodist Hospital; *U.S. Private*, pg. 2684
METHODIST PHYSICIAN PRACTICES, PLLC—See HCA Healthcare, Inc.; *U.S. Public*, pg. 1002
METHODIST SOUTHLAKE HOSPITAL, LLC—See Methodist Health System; *U.S. Private*, pg. 2683
METROCREST SURGERY CENTER, L.P.—See Tenet Healthcare Corporation; *U.S. Public*, pg. 2011
METRO KNOXVILLE HMA, LLC—See Community Health Systems, Inc.; *U.S. Public*, pg. 555
METROPLEX SURGICARE PARTNERS, LTD.—See Tenet Healthcare Corporation; *U.S. Public*, pg. 2011
METROPOLITAN MEDICAL PRACTICE PLAN PC; *U.S. Private*, pg. 2688
MEXIA PRINCIPAL HEALTHCARE LIMITED PARTNERSHIP—See Apollo Global Management, Inc.; *U.S. Public*, pg. 158
MIAMI BEACH COMMUNITY HEALTH CENTER, INC.; *U.S. Private*, pg. 2696
MICHIGAN COMMUNITY DENTAL CLINICS, INC.; *U.S. Private*, pg. 2700
MICHIGAN PIONEER ACO, LLC—See Tenet Healthcare Corporation; *U.S. Public*, pg. 2015
MIDAMERICA ONCOLOGY, LLC—See HCA Healthcare, Inc.; *U.S. Public*, pg. 1003
MIDAMERICA ONCOLOGY, LLC—See HCA Healthcare, Inc.; *U.S. Public*, pg. 1003
MID-AMERICA SURGERY INSTITUTE, LLC—See HCA Healthcare, Inc.; *U.S. Public*, pg. 1002
MID COAST HOSPITAL—See MaineHealth; *U.S. Private*, pg. 2553
MIDDLE TENNESSEE AMBULATORY SURGERY CENTER, L.P.—See Tenet Healthcare Corporation; *U.S. Public*, pg. 2011
THE MIDDLETOWN ENDOSCOPY ASC, LLC—See KKR & Co. Inc.; *U.S. Public*, pg. 1248
MIDLAND CARE CONNECTION, INC.; *U.S. Private*, pg. 2715
MIDLANDS ORTHOPAEDICS SURGERY CENTER, LLC; *U.S. Private*, pg. 2715
MID-STATE ENDOSCOPY CENTER, LLC—See Tenet Healthcare Corporation; *U.S. Public*, pg. 2011
MIDWEST DIGESTIVE HEALTH CENTER, LLC—See Tenet Healthcare Corporation; *U.S. Public*, pg. 2011
MIDWEST HOLDINGS, INC.—See HCA Healthcare, Inc.; *U.S. Public*, pg. 1003
MIDWEST METROPOLITAN PHYSICIANS GROUP, LLC—See HCA Healthcare, Inc.; *U.S. Public*, pg. 1003
MIDWEST ONCOLOGY ASSOCIATES, LLC—See HCA Healthcare, Inc.; *U.S. Public*, pg. 1003
MIDWEST REGIONAL MEDICAL CENTER, LLC—See Community Health Systems, Inc.; *U.S. Public*, pg. 555
MIDWEST SPECIALTY SURGERY CENTER, LLC—See Tenet Healthcare Corporation; *U.S. Public*, pg. 2004
MILLENIA SURGERY CENTER, L.L.C.—See Bain Capital, LP; *U.S. Private*, pg. 445
MILLS-PENINSULA MEDICAL CENTER—See Sutter Health; *U.S. Private*, pg. 3887
THE MILTON S. HERSHEY MEDICAL CENTER—See Penn State Health; *U.S. Private*, pg. 3135
MILWAUKEE REGIONAL MEDICAL CENTER, INC.; *U.S. Private*, pg. 2739
MINIMALLY INVASIVE SURGERY CENTER OF NE, LLC—See Tenet Healthcare Corporation; *U.S. Public*, pg. 2004
MINIMALLY INVASIVE SURGICENTER OF DELRAY, LLC—See Tenet Healthcare Corporation; *U.S. Public*, pg. 2004
MINNIE HAMILTON HEALTH CARE CENTER INC.; *U.S. Private*, pg. 2744
MISSISSIPPI HMA DME, LLC—See Community Health Systems, Inc.; *U.S. Public*, pg. 555
MISSISSIPPI HMA HOSPITALISTS, LLC—See Community Health Systems, Inc.; *U.S. Public*, pg. 555
MISSOURI DELTA MEDICAL CENTER; *U.S. Private*, pg. 2749
MITTELWESER KLINIKEN GMBH KRANKENHAUS HOYA—See Asklepios Kliniken GmbH & Co. KGaA; *Int'l*, pg. 624
MITTELWESER KLINIKEN GMBH NIENBURG HOYA STOLZENAU—See Asklepios Kliniken GmbH & Co. KGaA; *Int'l*, pg. 624
MMC OF NEVADA, LLC—See Quorum Health Corporation; *U.S. Private*, pg. 3330
MOAB REGIONAL HOSPITAL; *U.S. Private*, pg. 2756
MOBERLY HBP MEDICAL GROUP, LLC—See Community Health Systems, Inc.; *U.S. Public*, pg. 555
MOBERLY MEDICAL CLINICS, INC.—See Community Health Systems, Inc.; *U.S. Public*, pg. 555
MOBILE-SC, LTD.—See UnitedHealth Group Incorporated; *U.S. Public*, pg. 2242

CORPORATE AFFILIATIONS

MONOCACY HEALTH PARTNERS; *U.S. Private*, pg. 2771
MONROE CLINIC; *U.S. Private*, pg. 2773
MONROE HMA, INC.—See Quorum Health Corporation; *U.S. Private*, pg. 3330
MONTGOMERY BAPTIST OUTREACH SERVICES CORPORATION; *U.S. Private*, pg. 2776
MONTGOMERY GENERAL HOSPITAL, INC.; *U.S. Private*, pg. 2777
MONTGOMERY REGIONAL HOSPITAL, INC.—See HCA Healthcare, Inc.; *U.S. Public*, pg. 1003
MONTSERRAT DH PTY LTD—See Healius Limited; *Int'l*, pg. 3303
MONTVALE PET/CT, LLC—See Akumin, Inc.; *U.S. Public*, pg. 70
MONUMENT HEALTH, LLC—See UnitedHealth Group Incorporated; *U.S. Public*, pg. 2242
MOORESTOWN VISITING NURSE ASSOCIATION; *U.S. Private*, pg. 2780
MOORESVILLE HOSPITAL MANAGEMENT ASSOCIATES, INC.—See Community Health Systems, Inc.; *U.S. Public*, pg. 555
MORRIS HEIGHTS HEALTH CENTER, INC.; *U.S. Private*, pg. 2787
MORRO DIALYSIS, LLC—See DaVita Inc.; *U.S. Public*, pg. 641
MORTON COMPREHENSIVE HEALTH SERVICES, INC.; *U.S. Private*, pg. 2792
MORTON PLANT HOSPITAL—See BayCare Health System Inc.; *U.S. Private*, pg. 495
MORTON PLANT MEASE HEALTH CARE—See BayCare Health System Inc.; *U.S. Private*, pg. 495
MORTON PLANT NORTH BAY HOSPITAL—See BayCare Health System Inc.; *U.S. Private*, pg. 495
MOTT CHILDREN'S HEALTH CENTER; *U.S. Private*, pg. 2797
MOUNTAIN EMPIRE SURGERY CENTER, L.P.—See Tenet Healthcare Corporation; *U.S. Public*, pg. 2011
MOUNTAINSTAR CARDIOLOGY ST. MARKS, LLC—See HCA Healthcare, Inc.; *U.S. Public*, pg. 1003
MOUNTAINSTAR INTENSIVIST SERVICES, LLC—See HCA Healthcare, Inc.; *U.S. Public*, pg. 1003
MOUNTAINSTAR MEDICAL GROUP - CACHE VALLEY, LLC—See HCA Healthcare, Inc.; *U.S. Public*, pg. 1003
MOUNTAINSTAR MEDICAL GROUP NEUROSURGERY - ST. MARKS, LLC—See HCA Healthcare, Inc.; *U.S. Public*, pg. 1003
MOUNTAINSTAR URGENT CARE, LLC—See HCA Healthcare, Inc.; *U.S. Public*, pg. 1003
MOUNTAIN STATES HEALTH ALLIANCE; *U.S. Private*, pg. 2800
MOUNTAIN VIEW HOSPITAL, INC.—See HCA Healthcare, Inc.; *U.S. Public*, pg. 1003
MOUNTAIN VIEW HOSPITAL, LLC—See Bain Capital, LP; *U.S. Private*, pg. 445
MOUNTAINVIEW HOSPITAL (PAYSON UT)—See HCA Healthcare, Inc.; *U.S. Public*, pg. 1003
MOUNTAINVIEW HOSPITAL—See HCA Healthcare, Inc.; *U.S. Public*, pg. 1003
MOUNT DORA OPHTHALMOLOGY ASC, LLC—See KKR & Co. Inc.; *U.S. Public*, pg. 1246
MOUNT NITTANY HEALTH SYSTEM; *U.S. Private*, pg. 2798
MOUNT SINAI MEDICAL CENTER; *U.S. Private*, pg. 2798
MOUNT ST. MARY'S HOSPITAL OF NIAGARA FALLS; *U.S. Private*, pg. 2798
MT. GRAHAM REGIONAL MEDICAL CENTER; *U.S. Private*, pg. 2808
MT. OGDEN UTAH SURGICAL CENTER, LLC—See HCA Healthcare, Inc.; *U.S. Public*, pg. 1003
MUHLENBERG COMMUNITY HOSPITAL; *U.S. Private*, pg. 2811
MULTICARE HEALTH SYSTEM; *U.S. Private*, pg. 2812
MULTICULTURAL HOME CARE, INC.—See ModivCare, Inc.; *U.S. Public*, pg. 1455
MUSKINGUM VALLEY HEALTH CENTERS; *U.S. Private*, pg. 2818
MV ONCOLOGY, LLC—See Bain Capital, LP; *U.S. Private*, pg. 445
MVZ ASKLEPIOS KLINIK SELIGENSTADT GMBH—See Asklepios Kliniken GmbH & Co. KGaA; *Int'l*, pg. 623
MVZ AUGENARZTLICHES DIAGNOSTIK- UND THERAPIEZENTRUM DUSSELDORF GMBH—See Asklepios Kliniken GmbH & Co. KGaA; *Int'l*, pg. 624
MVZ CAMPUS GIFHORN GMBH—See Fresenius SE & Co. KGaA; *Int'l*, pg. 2780
MVZ MANAGEMENT GMBH BADEN-WURTTEMBERG—See Fresenius SE & Co. KGaA; *Int'l*, pg. 2779
MVZ MANAGEMENT GMBH SUD—See Fresenius SE & Co. KGaA; *Int'l*, pg. 2779
MVZ MEDICLIN BONN GMBH—See Asklepios Kliniken GmbH & Co. KGaA; *Int'l*, pg. 623
MVZ UNIVERSITATSKLINIKUM MARBURG GMBH—See Asklepios Kliniken GmbH & Co. KGaA; *Int'l*, pg. 624
NANJING TONGREN HOSPITAL CO., LTD.—See China Medical & HealthCare Group Limited; *Int'l*, pg. 1518
NANTUCKET COTTAGE HOSPITAL—See Partners HealthCare System, Inc.; *U.S. Private*, pg. 3102

N.A.I.C.S. INDEX 622110 — GENERAL MEDICAL AND...
N.A.I.C.S. Index

NAPLES HMA, INC.—See Community Health Systems, Inc.; *U.S. Public*, pg. 555
NASH HEALTH CARE SYSTEMS INC.; *U.S. Private*, pg. 2835
THE NASHVILLE TN OPHTHALMOLOGY ASC, LLC—See KKR & Co. Inc.; *U.S. Public*, pg. 1248
NASON HOSPITAL—See Apollo Global Management, Inc.; *U.S. Public*, pg. 158
NASON PHYSICIAN PRACTICES, LLC—See Apollo Global Management, Inc.; *U.S. Public*, pg. 158
NATCHEZ HOSPITAL COMPANY, LLC—See Community Health Systems, Inc.; *U.S. Public*, pg. 555
NATHAN LITTAUER HOSPITAL & NURSING HOME; *U.S. Private*, pg. 2838
NATIONAL BOARD OF OSTEOPATHIC MEDICAL EXAMINERS, INC.; *U.S. Private*, pg. 2849
THE NATIONAL CANCER COALITION, INC.; *U.S. Private*, pg. 4082
NATIONAL CONSORTIUM OF BREAST CENTERS INC.; *U.S. Private*, pg. 2851
NATIONAL HEALTHCARE OF LEESVILLE, INC.—See Community Health Systems, Inc.; *U.S. Public*, pg. 555
NATIONAL HEALTHCARE OF MT. VERNON, INC.—See Quorum Health Corporation; *U.S. Private*, pg. 3330
NATIONAL IMAGING OF CARTERVILLE, LLC—See Quorum Health Corporation; *U.S. Private*, pg. 3330
NATIONAL IMAGING OF MOUNT VERNON, LLC—See Quorum Health Corporation; *U.S. Private*, pg. 3330
NATIONAL PAIN CENTERS, INC.—See Wellness Center USA, Inc.; *U.S. Public*, pg. 2342
NATIONAL PATIENT ACCOUNT SERVICES, INC.—See HCA Healthcare, Inc.; *U.S. Public*, pg. 1004
NATIONAL SPECIALTY CLINICS, LLC—See Acadia Healthcare Company, Inc.; *U.S. Public*, pg. 29
NATIONAL TRAIL DIALYSIS, LLC—See DaVita Inc.; *U.S. Public*, pg. 641
NAVARRE FAMILY CARE, LLC—See HCA Healthcare, Inc.; *U.S. Public*, pg. 1004
NAVARRO REGIONAL, LLC—See Community Health Systems, Inc.; *U.S. Public*, pg. 552
NEIGHBORHOOD HEALTH CENTER CORPORATION; *U.S. Private*, pg. 2881
NEIGHBORHOOD HEALTH CLINICS; *U.S. Private*, pg. 2881
NEMOCNICE TANVALD, S.R.O.—See Fresenius SE & Co. KGaA; *Int'l*, pg. 2781
NEOSPINE PUYALLUP SPINE CENTER, LLC—See Bain Capital, LP; *U.S. Private*, pg. 445
NEPHROCARE HAMBURG-SUDERELBE GMBH—See Fresenius Medical Care AG; *Int'l*, pg. 2776
NEPHROCARE MUNSTER GMBH—See Fresenius Medical Care AG; *Int'l*, pg. 2776
NEPHROCARE (THAILAND) CO., LTD.—See Fresenius Medical Care AG; *Int'l*, pg. 2776
THE NEUROHEALTH SCIENCES CENTER, LLC—See HCA Healthcare, Inc.; *U.S. Public*, pg. 1012
NEUROLOGISCHES THERAPIEZENTRUM KAPFENBERG GMBH—See Fresenius SE & Co. KGaA; *Int'l*, pg. 2780
NEVADA PREFERRED HEALTHCARE PROVIDERS, LLC—See Universal Health Services, Inc.; *U.S. Public*, pg. 2258
THE NEWARK ENDOSCOPY ASC, LLC—See KKR & Co. Inc.; *U.S. Public*, pg. 1248
NEW DIRECTIONS (ST. LEONARDS ON SEA) LIMITED—See Acadia Healthcare Company, Inc.; *U.S. Public*, pg. 29
NEW GULF COAST SURGERY CENTER, LLC—See Community Health Systems, Inc.; *U.S. Public*, pg. 555
NEW HORIZONS HEALTH SYSTEMS, INC.; *U.S. Private*, pg. 2897
NEW MEXICO ORTHOPAEDIC SURGERY CENTER, L.P.—See Tenet Healthcare Corporation; *U.S. Public*, pg. 2011
NEW ORLEANS REGIONAL PHYSICIAN HOSPITAL ORGANIZATION, LLC—See UnitedHealth Group Incorporated; *U.S. Public*, pg. 2242
NEW PORT RICHEY SURGERY CENTER AT TRINITY—See HCA Healthcare, Inc.; *U.S. Public*, pg. 1004
NEW TAMPA SURGERY CENTER, LLC—See Bain Capital, LP; *U.S. Private*, pg. 445
NEWTON HEALTHCARE CORPORATION; *U.S. Private*, pg. 2918
NEWTON-WELLESLEY HOSPITAL—See Partners HealthCare System, Inc.; *U.S. Private*, pg. 3101
NEW WEST PHYSICIANS, INC.—See UnitedHealth Group Incorporated; *U.S. Public*, pg. 2242
NEW YORK EHEALTH COLLABORATIVE, INC.; *U.S. Private*, pg. 2909
NEW YORK-PRESBYTERIAN HEALTHCARE SYSTEM, INC.; *U.S. Private*, pg. 2912
NEXT GENERATION BEHAVIORAL HEALTH, LLC—See Acadia Healthcare Company, Inc.; *U.S. Public*, pg. 29
NHCI OF HILLSBORO, INC.—See Community Health Systems, Inc.; *U.S. Public*, pg. 555
NH CLINICAL SERVICES, PLLC—See Nobilis Health Corp.; *U.S. Private*, pg. 2932
NIAGARA FALLS MEMORIAL MEDICAL CENTER; *U.S. Private*, pg. 2924
NME REHABILITATION PROPERTIES, INC.—See Tenet Healthcare Corporation; *U.S. Public*, pg. 2004
NOBILIS HEALTH CORP.; *U.S. Private*, pg. 2932
NOOR AL SHEFA CLINIC LLC—See Aster DM Healthcare Ltd.; *Int'l*, pg. 654
NORTH AMERICAN MEDICAL MANAGEMENT CALIFORNIA, INC.—See UnitedHealth Group Incorporated; *U.S. Public*, pg. 2242
NORTHAMPTON CLINIC COMPANY, LLC—See Community Health Systems, Inc.; *U.S. Public*, pg. 555
NORTH ANAHEIM SURGERY CENTER, LLC—See Tenet Healthcare Corporation; *U.S. Public*, pg. 2005
NORTH ANAHEIM SURGICENTER, LTD.—See Tenet Healthcare Corporation; *U.S. Public*, pg. 2014
NORTH AURORA MEDICAL CENTER LLC—See Adeptus Health Inc.; *U.S. Private*, pg. 78
NORTH AUSTIN SURGERY CENTER—See HCA Healthcare, Inc.; *U.S. Public*, pg. 1004
NORTHBAY HEALTHCARE; *U.S. Private*, pg. 2948
NORTH CAMPUS SURGERY CENTER, LLC—See Tenet Healthcare Corporation; *U.S. Public*, pg. 2005
NORTH CAROLINA HMA REGIONAL SERVICE CENTER, LLC—See Community Health Systems, Inc.; *U.S. Public*, pg. 555
NORTH CAROLINA SPECIALTY HOSPITAL, LLC—See Bain Capital, LP; *U.S. Private*, pg. 445
NORTH CENTRAL SURGICAL CENTER, L.L.P.—See Tenet Healthcare Corporation; *U.S. Public*, pg. 2005
NORTH COUNTRY HOSPITAL; *U.S. Private*, pg. 2944
NORTH COUNTY HEALTH PROJECT, LNC.; *U.S. Private*, pg. 2944
NORTHCREST MEDICAL CENTER; *U.S. Private*, pg. 2949
NORTH DAKOTA SURGERY CENTER, LLC—See Bain Capital, LP; *U.S. Private*, pg. 445
NORTHEAST GEORGIA HEALTH SYSTEM INC.; *U.S. Private*, pg. 2950
THE NORTHEAST HEALTH GROUP INC; *U.S. Private*, pg. 4084
NORTHEAST HOSPITAL CORPORATION; *U.S. Private*, pg. 2950
NORTHEAST METHODIST SURGICARE, LTD.—See HCA Healthcare, Inc.; *U.S. Public*, pg. 1004
NORTHEAST MONTANA HEALTH SERVICES; *U.S. Private*, pg. 2950
NORTHEAST OHIO NEIGHBORHOOD HEALTH SERVICES, INC.; *U.S. Private*, pg. 2950
NORTHEAST PHO, INC.—See HCA Healthcare, Inc.; *U.S. Public*, pg. 1004
NORTHERN ARIZONA HEALTHCARE CORPORATION; *U.S. Private*, pg. 2951
NORTHERN COCHISE COMMUNITY HOSPITAL, INC.; *U.S. Private*, pg. 2952
NORTHERN MONTANA HEALTH CARE; *U.S. Private*, pg. 2953
NORTHERN NEVADA CARDIOLOGY PC—See Universal Health Services, Inc.; *U.S. Public*, pg. 2258
NORTHERN NEVADA MEDICAL CENTER—See Universal Health Services, Inc.; *U.S. Public*, pg. 2260
THE NORTHERN NV ENDOSCOPY ASC, LLC—See KKR & Co. Inc.; *U.S. Public*, pg. 1248
NORTHERN ROCKIES SURGICENTER, INC.—See UnitedHealth Group Incorporated; *U.S. Public*, pg. 2242
NORTHERN UTAH HEALTHCARE CORPORATION—See HCA Healthcare, Inc.; *U.S. Public*, pg. 1004
NORTHERN UTAH IMAGING, LLC—See HCA Healthcare, Inc.; *U.S. Public*, pg. 1004
NORTH FLORIDA CANCER CENTER LAKE CITY, LLC—See HCA Healthcare, Inc.; *U.S. Public*, pg. 1004
NORTH FLORIDA ENDOSCOPY CENTER—See HCA Healthcare, Inc.; *U.S. Public*, pg. 1004
NORTH FLORIDA OUTPATIENT IMAGING CENTER, LTD.—See HCA Healthcare, Inc.; *U.S. Public*, pg. 1004
NORTH FLORIDA RADIATION ONCOLOGY, LLC—See HCA Healthcare, Inc.; *U.S. Public*, pg. 1004
NORTH FLORIDA REGIONAL MEDICAL CENTER, INC.—See HCA Healthcare, Inc.; *U.S. Public*, pg. 1004
NORTH FLORIDA SURGICAL ASSOCIATES, LLC—See HCA Healthcare, Inc.; *U.S. Public*, pg. 1004
NORTH FLORIDA SURGICAL ASSOCIATES, LLC—See HCA Healthcare, Inc.; *U.S. Public*, pg. 1004
NORTH GARLAND SURGERY CENTER, L.L.P.—See Tenet Healthcare Corporation; *U.S. Public*, pg. 2011
NORTH HAVEN SURGERY CENTER, LLC—See Tenet Healthcare Corporation; *U.S. Public*, pg. 2011
NORTH IDAHO DAY SURGERY, LLC—See Bain Capital, LP; *U.S. Private*, pg. 445
NORTH METRO MEDICAL CENTER; *U.S. Private*, pg. 2945
NORTH MIAMI BEACH SURGERY CENTER LIMITED PARTNERSHIP—See HCA Healthcare, Inc.; *U.S. Public*, pg. 1004
NORTH MIAMI BEACH SURGICAL CENTER, LLC—See HCA Healthcare, Inc.; *U.S. Public*, pg. 1004
NORTH OKALOOSA CLINIC CORP.—See Community Health Systems, Inc.; *U.S. Public*, pg. 555
NORTH RICHLAND HILLS ENDOSCOPY CENTER, LLC—See KKR & Co. Inc.; *U.S. Public*, pg. 1246
NORTHRIDGE HOSPITAL MEDICAL CENTER—See Catholic Health Initiatives; *U.S. Private*, pg. 789
NORTHRIDGE SURGERY CENTER, L.P.—See Tenet Healthcare Corporation; *U.S. Public*, pg. 2012
NORTHSHORE EXTENDED CARE HOSPITAL, LLC—See UnitedHealth Group Incorporated; *U.S. Public*, pg. 2246
NORTH SHORE MEDICAL CENTER INC.—See Partners HealthCare System, Inc.; *U.S. Private*, pg. 3102
NORTH SHORE MEDICAL CENTER, INC.—See Tenet Healthcare Corporation; *U.S. Public*, pg. 2005
NORTH SHORE SAME DAY SURGERY, L.L.C.—See Tenet Healthcare Corporation; *U.S. Public*, pg. 2011
NORTHSIDE HOSPITAL AND HEART INSTITUTE—See HCA Healthcare, Inc.; *U.S. Public*, pg. 1004
NORTHSIDE HOSPITAL; *U.S. Private*, pg. 2957
NORTH SPRING BEHAVIORAL HEALTHCARE, INC.—See Universal Health Services, Inc.; *U.S. Public*, pg. 2258
NORTH SUBURBAN MEDICAL CENTER—See HCA Healthcare, Inc.; *U.S. Public*, pg. 1004
NORTH TEXAS HEART SURGERY CENTER, PLLC—See HCA Healthcare, Inc.; *U.S. Public*, pg. 1004
NORTH TEXAS INTERNAL MEDICINE SPECIALISTS, PLLC—See HCA Healthcare, Inc.; *U.S. Public*, pg. 1004
NORTH TEXAS MEDICAL CENTER, INC.—See HCA Healthcare, Inc.; *U.S. Public*, pg. 1004
NORTH TEXAS PULMONARY CRITICAL CARE, PLLC—See HCA Healthcare, Inc.; *U.S. Public*, pg. 1004
NORTH VALLEY HOSPITAL; *U.S. Private*, pg. 2948
NORTHWEST ALLIED PHYSICIANS, LLC—See Community Health Systems, Inc.; *U.S. Public*, pg. 555
NORTHWEST AMBULATORY SURGERY SERVICES, LLC—See Bain Capital, LP; *U.S. Private*, pg. 445
NORTHWEST ARKANSAS HOSPITALS, LLC—See Community Health Systems, Inc.; *U.S. Public*, pg. 555
NORTHWEST BENTON COUNTY PHYSICIAN SERVICES, LLC—See Community Health Systems, Inc.; *U.S. Public*, pg. 555
NORTHWEST COMMUNITY CARE NETWORK; *U.S. Private*, pg. 2959
NORTHWEST COMMUNITY HEALTHCARE CORPORATION—See NorthShore University HealthSystem; *U.S. Private*, pg. 2957
NORTHWESTERN MEDICAL CENTER, INC.; *U.S. Private*, pg. 2962
NORTHWESTERN MEMORIAL HEALTHCARE; *U.S. Private*, pg. 2962
NORTHWESTERN MEMORIAL HOSPITAL—See Northwestern Memorial HealthCare; *U.S. Private*, pg. 2963
NORTHWEST FLORIDA COMMUNITY HOSPITAL; *U.S. Private*, pg. 2960
NORTHWEST FLORIDA MULTISPECIALTY PHYSICIANS, LLC—See HCA Healthcare, Inc.; *U.S. Public*, pg. 1004
NORTHWEST FLORIDA PRIMARY CARE, LLC—See HCA Healthcare, Inc.; *U.S. Public*, pg. 1004
NORTHWEST HOSPITAL, LLC—See Community Health Systems, Inc.; *U.S. Public*, pg. 552
NORTHWEST KIDNEY CENTERS; *U.S. Private*, pg. 2961
NORTHWEST MEDICAL CENTER, INC.—See Curae Health, Inc.; *U.S. Private*, pg. 1124
NORTHWEST SURGERY CENTER, LLP—See Tenet Healthcare Corporation; *U.S. Public*, pg. 2012
NORTHWEST SURGERY CENTER, LTD—See Tenet Healthcare Corporation; *U.S. Public*, pg. 2005
NORTHWEST SURGICARE, LLC—See UnitedHealth Group Incorporated; *U.S. Public*, pg. 2243
NORTHWEST SURGICARE, LTD.—See UnitedHealth Group Incorporated; *U.S. Public*, pg. 2243
NORTHWEST TEXAS HEALTHCARE SYSTEM, INC.—See Universal Health Services, Inc.; *U.S. Public*, pg. 2258
NORTHWEST TEXAS PHYSICIAN GROUP—See Universal Health Services, Inc.; *U.S. Public*, pg. 2258
NORTHWEST TEXAS WYATT CLINIC, PLLC—See Universal Health Services, Inc.; *U.S. Public*, pg. 2258
NORTHWEST TUCSON DIALYSIS, LLC—See DaVita Inc.; *U.S. Public*, pg. 641
NORTON HEALTHCARE, INC.; *U.S. Private*, pg. 2963
NORTON HMA, INC.—See Community Health Systems, Inc.; *U.S. Public*, pg. 555
NOTAMI HOSPITALS OF FLORIDA, INC.—See HCA Healthcare, Inc.; *U.S. Public*, pg. 1004
NOTAMI, LLC—See HCA Healthcare, Inc.; *U.S. Public*, pg. 1005
NOTRE DAME HEALTH CARE CENTER, INC.; *U.S. Private*, pg. 2965
NOVACARE REHABILITATION SERVICES, INC.—See Select Medical Holdings Corporation; *U.S. Public*, pg. 1858
NOVAMED EYE SURGERY CENTER OF NEW ALBANY, L.L.C.—See Bain Capital, LP; *U.S. Private*, pg. 445
NOVAMED EYE SURGERY CENTER OF OVERLAND PARK, LLC—See Bain Capital, LP; *U.S. Private*, pg. 445
NOVAMED MANAGEMENT SERVICES, LLC—See Bain Capital, LP; *U.S. Private*, pg. 445
NOVAMED SURGERY CENTER OF BATON ROUGE, LLC—See Bain Capital, LP; *U.S. Private*, pg. 445
NOVAMED SURGERY CENTER OF CHICAGO-NORTHSHORE, LLC—See Bain Capital, LP; *U.S. Private*, pg. 446
NOVAMED SURGERY CENTER OF JONESBORO,

622110 — GENERAL MEDICAL AND...

LLC—See Bain Capital, LP; *U.S. Private*, pg. 446
NOVAMED SURGERY CENTER OF TYLER, L.P.—See Bain Capital, LP; *U.S. Private*, pg. 446
NOVAMED SURGERY CENTER OF WHITTIER, LLC—See Bain Capital, LP; *U.S. Private*, pg. 446
NOVASYS HEALTH, INC.—See Centene Corporation; *U.S. Public*, pg. 470
NOVO HEALTHNET LIMITED—See Novo Integrated Sciences, Inc.; *U.S. Public*, pg. 1549
NUESTRA CLINICA DEL VALLE, INC.; *U.S. Private*, pg. 2972
NUFFIELD HOSPITAL HARROGATE—See Centene Corporation; *U.S. Public*, pg. 468
N.V. STRYKER SA—See Stryker Corporation; *U.S. Public*, pg. 1956
NWMC-WINFIELD ANESTHESIA PHYSICIANS, LLC—See Apollo Global Management, Inc.; *U.S. Public*, pg. 158
NWTX PHYSICIAN NETWORK, PLLC—See Universal Health Services, Inc.; *U.S. Public*, pg. 2258
OAKDALE COMMUNITY HOSPITAL—See Progressive Acute Care LLC; *U.S. Private*, pg. 3278
OAK HILL CLINIC CORP.—See Community Health Systems, Inc.; *U.S. Public*, pg. 555
OAK HILL HOSPITAL CORPORATION—See Community Health Systems, Inc.; *U.S. Public*, pg. 555
OAK HILL HOSPITAL—See HCA Healthcare, Inc.; *U.S. Public*, pg. 1005
OAKHURST MEDICAL CENTERS, INC.; *U.S. Private*, pg. 2984
THE OAKLAND CA ENDOSCOPY ASC, L.P.—See KKR & Co. Inc.; *U.S. Public*, pg. 1248
OBSTETRIX MEDICAL GROUP—See MEDNAX, Inc.; *U.S. Public*, pg. 1413
THE OCALA ENDOSCOPY ASC, L.P.—See KKR & Co. Inc.; *U.S. Public*, pg. 1248
OCALA HEALTH IMAGING SERVICES, LLC—See HCA Healthcare, Inc.; *U.S. Public*, pg. 1005
OCALA HEALTH SURGICAL GROUP, LLC—See HCA Healthcare, Inc.; *U.S. Public*, pg. 1005
OCALA REGIONAL MEDICAL CENTER—See HCA Healthcare, Inc.; *U.S. Public*, pg. 1005
OCCSPECIALISTS CORP., A MEDICAL CORPORATION—See Select Medical Holdings Corporation; *U.S. Public*, pg. 1858
OCCUPATIONAL AND FAMILY MEDICINE OF SOUTH TEXAS—See HCA Healthcare, Inc.; *U.S. Public*, pg. 1005
OCCUPATIONAL HEALTH CENTERS OF CALIFORNIA, A MEDICAL CORPORATION—See Select Medical Holdings Corporation; *U.S. Public*, pg. 1858
OCCUPATIONAL HEALTH CENTERS OF MICHIGAN, P.C.—See Select Medical Holdings Corporation; *U.S. Public*, pg. 1858
OCCUPATIONAL HEALTH CENTERS OF NEBRASKA, P.C.—See Select Medical Holdings Corporation; *U.S. Public*, pg. 1858
OCCUPATIONAL HEALTH CENTERS OF OHIO, P.A., CO.—See Select Medical Holdings Corporation; *U.S. Public*, pg. 1858
OCCUPATIONAL HEALTH CENTERS OF THE SOUTHWEST, P.A.—See Select Medical Holdings Corporation; *U.S. Public*, pg. 1858
OCEAN ENDOSURGERY CENTER—See KKR & Co. Inc.; *U.S. Public*, pg. 1246
OCEAN MEDICAL CENTER—See Hackensack Meridian Health, Inc.; *U.S. Private*, pg. 1838
OCHIN, INC.; *U.S. Private*, pg. 2992
OCHSNER-ACADIA, LLC—See Acadia Healthcare Company, Inc.; *U.S. Public*, pg. 29
OCHSNER HEALTH SYSTEM; *U.S. Private*, pg. 2992
OCHSNER MEDICAL CENTER-NORTH SHORE LLC—See Ochsner Health System; *U.S. Private*, pg. 2992
O'CONNOR HOSPITAL—See Daughters of Charity Health System; *U.S. Private*, pg. 1167
ODA PRIMARY HEALTH CARE NETWORK; *U.S. Private*, pg. 2993
ODESSA REGIONAL MEDICAL CENTER—See Steward Health Care System LLC; *U.S. Private*, pg. 3810
OGDEN REGIONAL MEDICAL CENTER—See HCA Healthcare, Inc.; *U.S. Public*, pg. 1005
OHIO COUNTY HOSPITAL CORPORATION; *U.S. Private*, pg. 3004
THE OHIO HOSPITAL ASSOCIATION; *U.S. Private*, pg. 4088
OHIO HOSPITAL FOR PSYCHIATRY, LLC—See Acadia Healthcare Company, Inc.; *U.S. Public*, pg. 29
OHIO VALLEY HEALTH SERVICES AND EDUCATION; *U.S. Private*, pg. 3005
OKATIE SURGICAL PARTNERS, L.L.C.—See Tenet Healthcare Corporation; *U.S. Public*, pg. 2008
OKLAHOMA CENTER FOR ORTHOPEDIC AND MULTI-SPECIALTY SURGERY, LLC—See Tenet Healthcare Corporation; *U.S. Public*, pg. 2005
OKLAHOMA STATE UNIVERSITY MEDICAL CENTER—See Oklahoma State University Medical Center Trust; *U.S. Private*, pg. 3007
OLD TOWN ENDOSCOPY CENTER, LLC—See KKR & Co. Inc.; *U.S. Public*, pg. 1246

O&M HALYARD HEALTH INDIA PRIVATE LIMITED—See Owens & Minor, Inc.; *U.S. Public*, pg. 1626
ONSITE OCCMED, P.A.—See Select Medical Holdings Corporation; *U.S. Public*, pg. 1858
ONYX & PEARL SURGICAL SUITES, LLC—See Tenet Healthcare Corporation; *U.S. Public*, pg. 2005
OPEN HAND; *U.S. Private*, pg. 3029
OPHTHALMOLOGY SURGERY CENTER OF ORLANDO, LLC—See Tenet Healthcare Corporation; *U.S. Public*, pg. 2005
OPTIMUM SPINE CENTER, LLC—See Tenet Healthcare Corporation; *U.S. Public*, pg. 2005
OPTIMUS HEALTH CARE; *U.S. Private*, pg. 3035
OPTIONS TREATMENT CENTER ACQUISITION CORPORATION—See Acadia Healthcare Company, Inc.; *U.S. Public*, pg. 29
ORANGE PARK ENDOSCOPY CENTER, LLC—See Tenet Healthcare Corporation; *U.S. Public*, pg. 2006
ORANGE PARK MEDICAL CENTER, INC.—See HCA Healthcare, Inc.; *U.S. Public*, pg. 1005
OREGON OUTPATIENT SURGERY CENTER, LLC—See UnitedHealth Group Incorporated; *U.S. Public*, pg. 2251
THE ORLANDO FL ENDOSCOPY ASC, LLC—See KKR & Co. Inc.; *U.S. Public*, pg. 1248
ORLANDO HEALTH, INC.; *U.S. Private*, pg. 3043
THE ORLANDO/MILLS FL ENDOSCOPY ASC, LLC—See KKR & Co. Inc.; *U.S. Public*, pg. 1248
ORLANDO OUTPATIENT SURGICAL CENTER, INC.—See HCA Healthcare, Inc.; *U.S. Public*, pg. 1005
ORNDA HOSPITAL CORPORATION—See Tenet Healthcare Corporation; *U.S. Public*, pg. 2005
ORTHOARIZONA SURGERY CENTER GILBERT, LLC—See Tenet Healthcare Corporation; *U.S. Public*, pg. 2006
ORTHOLOGY INC.—See UnitedHealth Group Incorporated; *U.S. Public*, pg. 2249
ORTHOPAEDIC HOSPITAL; *U.S. Private*, pg. 3045
ORTHOPEDIC ASSOCIATES OF THE LOWCOUNTRY, L.L.C.—See Tenet Healthcare Corporation; *U.S. Public*, pg. 2006
ORTHOPEDIC & SPINE SURGICAL HOSPITAL OF SOUTH TEXAS LP—See Bain Capital, LP; *U.S. Private*, pg. 445
ORTHOPEDICS SPECIALISTS, LLC—See HCA Healthcare, Inc.; *U.S. Public*, pg. 1005
OSCEOLA REGIONAL MEDICAL CENTER—See HCA Healthcare, Inc.; *U.S. Public*, pg. 1005
OSCEOLA SURGICAL ASSOCIATES, LLC—See HCA Healthcare, Inc.; *U.S. Public*, pg. 1005
OSLER HMA MEDICAL GROUP, LLC—See Community Health Systems, Inc.; *U.S. Public*, pg. 555
OSPEDALI PRIVATI RIUNITI S.R.L.—See Garofalo Health Care SpA; *Int'l*, pg. 2886
OSR LOUISIANA, LLC—See Select Medical Holdings Corporation; *U.S. Public*, pg. 1858
OTSEGO MEMORIAL HOSPITAL ASSOCIATION; *U.S. Private*, pg. 3049
OTTUMWA REGIONAL HEALTH CENTER, INC.—See Apollo Global Management, Inc.; *U.S. Public*, pg. 159
OU MEDICAL CENTER EDMOND—See HCA Healthcare, Inc.; *U.S. Public*, pg. 1005
OU MEDICAL CENTER—See HCA Healthcare, Inc.; *U.S. Public*, pg. 1005
OUTPATIENT SURGICAL SERVICES, LTD.—See HCA Healthcare, Inc.; *U.S. Public*, pg. 1005
OVERLAKE HOSPITAL MEDICAL CENTER; *U.S. Private*, pg. 3053
THE OVERLAND PARK KS ENDOSCOPY ASC, LLC—See KKR & Co. Inc.; *U.S. Public*, pg. 1248
OVERLAND PARK SURGICAL SPECIALTIES, LLC—See HCA Healthcare, Inc.; *U.S. Public*, pg. 1005
OWASSO DIALYSIS, LLC—See DaVita Inc.; *U.S. Public*, pg. 641
PACIFIC ALLIANCE MEDICAL CENTER, INC.—See PAMC, Ltd.; *U.S. Private*, pg. 3083
PACIFIC BUSINESS GROUP ON HEALTH; *U.S. Private*, pg. 3065
PACIFIC CARDIOVASCULAR ASSOCIATES MEDICAL GROUP, INC.—See UnitedHealth Group Incorporated; *U.S. Public*, pg. 2249
PACIFIC MEDICAL CENTERS; *U.S. Private*, pg. 3068
THE PADUCAH OPHTHALMOLOGY ASC, LLC—See KKR & Co. Inc.; *U.S. Public*, pg. 1248
PAIN DIAGNOSTIC AND TREATMENT CENTER, L.P.—See Tenet Healthcare Corporation; *U.S. Public*, pg. 2012
PAIN TREATMENT CENTERS OF MICHIGAN, LLC—See Tenet Healthcare Corporation; *U.S. Public*, pg. 2012
PAINTSVILLE HMA PHYSICIAN MANAGEMENT, LLC—See Quorum Health Corporation; *U.S. Private*, pg. 3330
PAINTSVILLE HOSPITAL COMPANY, LLC—See Quorum Health Corporation; *U.S. Private*, pg. 3330
PALISADES MEDICAL CENTER—See New York-Presbyterian Healthcare System, Inc.; *U.S. Private*, pg. 2913
PALLIATIVE CARECENTER & HOSPICE OF CATAWBA VALLEY, INC.; *U.S. Private*, pg. 3079
PALM BEACH GARDENS COMMUNITY HOSPITAL, INC.—See Tenet Healthcare Corporation; *U.S. Public*, pg. 2008

PALM BEACH HOSPITALISTS PROGRAM, LLC—See HCA Healthcare, Inc.; *U.S. Public*, pg. 1005
PALM BEACH INTERNATIONAL SURGERY CENTER, LLC—See Tenet Healthcare Corporation; *U.S. Public*, pg. 2006
PALMETTO HEALTH BAPTIST EASLEY—See Palmetto Health; *U.S. Private*, pg. 3081
PALMETTO HEALTH; *U.S. Private*, pg. 3081
PALMETTO TRI-COUNTY MEDICAL SPECIALISTS, LLC—See Community Health Systems, Inc.; *U.S. Public*, pg. 555
PALMS WEST HOSPITAL—See HCA Healthcare, Inc.; *U.S. Public*, pg. 1005
PALOS COMMUNITY HOSPITAL; *U.S. Private*, pg. 3082
PANA COMMUNITY HOSPITAL; *U.S. Private*, pg. 3084
PANAMA CITY SURGERY CENTER, LLC—See UnitedHealth Group Incorporated; *U.S. Public*, pg. 2249
PANCARE OF FLORIDA, INC.; *U.S. Private*, pg. 3085
PARAGON SURGERY CENTERS OF TEXAS, INC.—See HCA Healthcare, Inc.; *U.S. Public*, pg. 1005
PARALLON BUSINESS SOLUTIONS, LLC—See HCA Healthcare, Inc.; *U.S. Public*, pg. 1005
PARAMUS ENDOSCOPY, LLC—See Tenet Healthcare Corporation; *U.S. Public*, pg. 2012
PARHAM DOCTORS' HOSPITAL—See HCA Healthcare, Inc.; *U.S. Public*, pg. 997
PARITY HEALTHCARE, INC.—See KKR & Co. Inc.; *U.S. Public*, pg. 1246
PARK CITIES SURGERY CENTER, LLC—See Tenet Healthcare Corporation; *U.S. Public*, pg. 2012
PARKER JEWISH INSTITUTE FOR HEALTH CARE & REHABILITATION; *U.S. Private*, pg. 3097
PARKERSBURG TREATMENT CENTER, LLC—See Acadia Healthcare Company, Inc.; *U.S. Public*, pg. 29
PARK-KRANKENHAUS LEIPZIG-SUDOST GMBH—See Asklepios Kliniken GmbH & Co. KGaA; *Int'l*, pg. 624
PARKLAND MEDICAL CENTER—See HCA Healthcare, Inc.; *U.S. Public*, pg. 1006
PARKLAND PHYSICIAN SERVICES, INC.—See HCA Healthcare, Inc.; *U.S. Public*, pg. 1006
PARK RIDGE HEALTH; *U.S. Private*, pg. 3096
PARKRIDGE MEDICAL CENTER, INC.—See HCA Healthcare, Inc.; *U.S. Public*, pg. 1012
PARK RIDGE SURGERY CENTER, LLC—See HCA Healthcare, Inc.; *U.S. Public*, pg. 1006
PARKRIDGE WEST HOSPITAL—See HCA Healthcare, Inc.; *U.S. Public*, pg. 1012
PARK VENTURA ENDOSCOPY CENTER, LLC—See KKR & Co. Inc.; *U.S. Public*, pg. 1246
PARKVIEW COMMUNITY HOSPITAL MEDICAL CENTER; *U.S. Private*, pg. 3098
PARKVIEW MEDICAL CENTER, INC.—See University of Colorado Health; *U.S. Public*, pg. 4308
PARKWAY RECOVERY CARE CENTER, LLC—See Tenet Healthcare Corporation; *U.S. Public*, pg. 2006
PARKWAY REGIONAL MEDICAL CLINIC, INC.—See Community Health Systems, Inc.; *U.S. Public*, pg. 555
PARK WEST HEALTH SYSTEM; *U.S. Private*, pg. 3097
PARKWEST MEDICAL CENTER; *U.S. Private*, pg. 3099
PARTNERSHIPS IN CARE LIMITED—See Acadia Healthcare Company, Inc.; *U.S. Public*, pg. 29
PASSAVANT MEMORIAL HOSPITAL ASSOCIATION; *U.S. Private*, pg. 3104
PATIENT ACCESS NETWORK FOUNDATION; *U.S. Private*, pg. 3106
PATIENT CARE ASSOCIATES, L.L.C.—See UnitedHealth Group Incorporated; *U.S. Public*, pg. 2249
THE PAVILION AT HEALTHPARK, LLC—See Acadia Healthcare Company, Inc.; *U.S. Public*, pg. 31
PAWNEE VALLEY COMMUNITY HOSPITAL INC.; *U.S. Private*, pg. 3115
PAYSON HOSPITAL CORPORATION—See Banner Health System; *U.S. Private*, pg. 469
PEACH TREE HEALTH; *U.S. Private*, pg. 3123
PECKVILLE HOSPITAL COMPANY, LLC—See Community Health Systems, Inc.; *U.S. Public*, pg. 555
PECOS VALLEY OF NEW MEXICO, LLC—See Community Health Systems, Inc.; *U.S. Public*, pg. 555
PEDIATRIC ACADEMIC ASSOCIATION INC.; *U.S. Private*, pg. 3128
PEDIATRIC INTENSIVIST GROUP, LLC—See HCA Healthcare, Inc.; *U.S. Public*, pg. 1006
PEKIN HOSPITAL—See Progressive Health Systems Inc.; *U.S. Private*, pg. 3279
PELLA REGIONAL HEALTH CENTER; *U.S. Private*, pg. 3131
PEMBINA COUNTY MEMORIAL HOSPITAL; *U.S. Private*, pg. 3131
PEMISCOT MEMORIAL HEALTH SYSTEMS; *U.S. Private*, pg. 3132
PENINSULA EYE SURGERY CENTER, LLC—See UnitedHealth Group Incorporated; *U.S. Public*, pg. 2249
PENN HIGHLANDS BROOKVILLE—See Penn Highlands Healthcare; *U.S. Private*, pg. 3134
PENN HIGHLANDS HEALTHCARE; *U.S. Private*, pg. 3134
PENNINGTON GAP HMA, INC.—See Community Health Systems, Inc.; *U.S. Public*, pg. 555
PENSLOW MEDICAL CENTER—See Wilmington Health

N.A.I.C.S. INDEX — 622110 — GENERAL MEDICAL AND...

Associates, Pa.; *U.S. Private*, pg. 4529
PERHAM PHYSICAL THERAPY, LTD.—See UnitedHealth Group Incorporated; *U.S. Public*, pg. 2249
PERIMETER ROAD SURGICAL HOSPITAL, LLC—See Nobilis Health Corp.; *U.S. Private*, pg. 2932
PERRY COUNTY HEALTH SYSTEM; *U.S. Private*, pg. 3153
PETERSBURG CLINIC COMPANY, LLC—See Community Health Systems, Inc.; *U.S. Public*, pg. 555
PETERSBURG HOSPITAL COMPANY, LLC—See Bon Secours Mercy Health, Inc.; *U.S. Private*, pg. 612
PHC-FORT MOHAVE, INC.—See Apollo Global Management, Inc.; *U.S. Public*, pg. 158
PHC-LOS ALAMOS, INC.—See Apollo Global Management, Inc.; *U.S. Public*, pg. 158
PHC MEADOWWOOD, LLC—See Acadia Healthcare Company, Inc.; *U.S. Public*, pg. 29
PHC-MINDEN, L.P.—See Apollo Global Management, Inc.; *U.S. Public*, pg. 158
PHC OF MICHIGAN, INC.—See Acadia Healthcare Company, Inc.; *U.S. Public*, pg. 29
PHC OF NEVADA, INC.—See Acadia Healthcare Company, Inc.; *U.S. Public*, pg. 29
PHC OF UTAH, INC.—See Acadia Healthcare Company, Inc.; *U.S. Public*, pg. 29
PHC OF VIRGINIA, INC.—See Acadia Healthcare Company, Inc.; *U.S. Public*, pg. 29
PH COPPER COUNTRY APOTHECARIES, LLC—See Apollo Global Management, Inc.; *U.S. Public*, pg. 158
PHELPS MEMORIAL HEALTH CENTER; *U.S. Private*, pg. 3167
PHELPS MEMORIAL HOSPITAL CENTER; *U.S. Private*, pg. 3167
PHILADELPHIA CRISIS RESPONSE CENTER, LLC—See Acadia Healthcare Company, Inc.; *U.S. Public*, pg. 29
PHILLIPS CLINIC CORP.—See Quorum Health Corporation; *U.S. Private*, pg. 3330
PHILLIPS HOSPITAL CORPORATION—See Quorum Health Corporation; *U.S. Private*, pg. 3330
PHOENIX ORTHOPAEDIC AMBULATORY CENTER, L.L.C.—See KKR & Co. Inc.; *U.S. Public*, pg. 1246
PHOENIX SURGERY CENTER, LLC—See Nobilis Health Corp.; *U.S. Private*, pg. 2932
PHOENIXVILLE HOSPITAL COMPANY, LLC—See Tower Health; *U.S. Private*, pg. 4193
PHS PHYSICAL THERAPY, LLC—See Select Medical Holdings Corporation; *U.S. Public*, pg. 1858
PHYATHAI 1 HOSPITAL CO., LTD.—See Bangkok Dusit Medical Services Public Company Limited; *Int'l*, pg. 834
THE PHYA THAI II HOSPITAL CO., LTD.—See Bangkok Dusit Medical Services Public Company Limited; *Int'l*, pg. 834
PHYSICIAN PRACTICE SUPPORT, INC.—See Community Health Systems, Inc.; *U.S. Public*, pg. 555
THE PHYSICIANS' CENTER, L.P.—See Tenet Healthcare Corporation; *U.S. Public*, pg. 2013
PHYSICIANS DAY SURGERY CENTER, LLC—See UnitedHealth Group Incorporated; *U.S. Public*, pg. 2249
PHYSICIANS ENDOSCOPY CENTER—See HCA Healthcare, Inc.; *U.S. Public*, pg. 1006
PHYSICIANS PAVILION, L.P.—See Tenet Healthcare Corporation; *U.S. Public*, pg. 2012
PHYSICIANS REGIONAL MARCO ISLAND, LLC—See Community Health Systems, Inc.; *U.S. Public*, pg. 556
PHYSICIAN'S SURGERY CENTER OF CHATTANOOGA, L.L.C.—See Tenet Healthcare Corporation; *U.S. Public*, pg. 2006
PHYSICIANS SURGERY CENTER OF TEMPE, LLC—See Tenet Healthcare Corporation; *U.S. Public*, pg. 2006
PIEDMONT BEHAVIORAL MEDICINE ASSOCIATES, L.L.C.—See Tenet Healthcare Corporation; *U.S. Public*, pg. 2008
PIEDMONT CAROLINA OB/GYN OF YORK COUNTY, L.L.C.—See Tenet Healthcare Corporation; *U.S. Public*, pg. 2008
PIEDMONT/CAROLINA—See Tenet Healthcare Corporation; *U.S. Public*, pg. 2008
PIEDMONT/CAROLINAS RADIATION THERAPY, LLC—See Tenet Healthcare Corporation; *U.S. Public*, pg. 2006
PIEDMONT EAST URGENT CARE CENTER, L.L.C.—See Tenet Healthcare Corporation; *U.S. Public*, pg. 2008
PIEDMONT FAMILY PRACTICE AT ROCK HILL, L.L.C.—See Tenet Healthcare Corporation; *U.S. Public*, pg. 2008
PIEDMONT FAMILY PRACTICE AT TEGA CAY, L.L.C.—See Tenet Healthcare Corporation; *U.S. Public*, pg. 2008
PIEDMONT HEALTHCARE, INC.; *U.S. Private*, pg. 3177
PIEDMONT HEALTH, INC.; *U.S. Private*, pg. 3177
PIEDMONT NEWNAN HOSPITAL; *U.S. Private*, pg. 3177
PIEDMONT PHYSICIAN NETWORK, LLC—See Tenet Healthcare Corporation; *U.S. Public*, pg. 2006
PIEDMONT REGIONAL HEALTH; *U.S. Private*, pg. 3178
PIEDMONT SURGICAL CENTER OF EXCELLENCE, LLC—See Community Health Systems, Inc.; *U.S. Public*, pg. 556
PIEDMONT URGENT CARE CENTER AT BAXTER VILLAGE, LLC—See Tenet Healthcare Corporation; *U.S. Public*, pg. 2008

PIEDMONT WEST URGENT CARE CENTER LLC—See Tenet Healthcare Corporation; *U.S. Public*, pg. 2008
PIH HEALTH HOSPITAL - DOWNEY—See Presbyterian Intercommunity Hospital, Inc.; *U.S. Private*, pg. 3253
THE PIKESVILLE MD ENDOSCOPY ASC, LLC—See KKR & Co. Inc.; *U.S. Public*, pg. 1248
PINES HEALTH SERVICES; *U.S. Private*, pg. 3183
PINNACLE PHYSICIAN NETWORK, LLC—See HCA Healthcare, Inc.; *U.S. Public*, pg. 1006
PIONEER VALLEY SURGICENTER, LLC—See KKR & Co. Inc.; *U.S. Public*, pg. 1246
PKS PRIVATKLINIK SALZBURG GMBH & CO KG—See Fresenius SE & Co. KGaA; *Int'l*, pg. 2780
PLACENTIA-LINDA HOSPITAL, INC.—See UCI Health; *U.S. Private*, pg. 4274
PLANI JACAREI DIAGNOSTICOS MEDICOS LTDA.—See Centro de Imagem Diagnosticos S.A.; *Int'l*, pg. 1413
PLANTATION GENERAL HOSPITAL—See HCA Healthcare, Inc.; *U.S. Public*, pg. 1006
PLAZA MEDICAL CENTER OF FORT WORTH—See HCA Healthcare, Inc.; *U.S. Public*, pg. 1006
PLAZA MEDICAL SPECIALISTS, PLLC—See HCA Healthcare, Inc.; *U.S. Public*, pg. 1006
PLAZA SURGERY CENTER II—See HCA Healthcare, Inc.; *U.S. Public*, pg. 1006
PLAZA TRANSPLANT CENTER, PLLC—See HCA Healthcare, Inc.; *U.S. Public*, pg. 1006
PLEASANT VALLEY HOSPITAL, INC.—See Cabell Huntington Hospital, Inc.; *U.S. Private*, pg. 710
PLICO, INC.—See Berkshire Hathaway Inc.; *U.S. Public*, pg. 313
PLUSHCARE, INC.—See Accolade, Inc.; *U.S. Public*, pg. 33
PMC PHYSICIAN NETWORK, L.L.C.—See Tenet Healthcare Corporation; *U.S. Public*, pg. 2008
PMM, INC.—See HCA Healthcare, Inc.; *U.S. Public*, pg. 1005
POCONO AMBULATORY SURGERY CENTER, LIMITED—See UnitedHealth Group Incorporated; *U.S. Public*, pg. 2249
POINTE DIALYSIS, LLC—See DaVita Inc.; *U.S. Public*, pg. 642
POLIAMBULATORIO DALLA ROSA PRATI S.R.L.—See Garofalo Health Care SpA; *Int'l*, pg. 2886
POLK MEDICAL CENTER—See HCA Healthcare, Inc.; *U.S. Public*, pg. 1006
POMONA VALLEY HOSPITAL MEDICAL CENTER; *U.S. Private*, pg. 3227
PONCA CITY HOME CARE SERVICES, INC.—See Community Health Systems, Inc.; *U.S. Public*, pg. 556
POPLAR BLUFF REGIONAL MEDICAL CENTER, INC.—See Community Health Systems, Inc.; *U.S. Public*, pg. 556
PORTSMOUTH REGIONAL AMBULATORY SURGERY CENTER, LLC—See HCA Healthcare, Inc.; *U.S. Public*, pg. 1006
PORTSMOUTH REGIONAL HOSPITAL—See HCA Healthcare, Inc.; *U.S. Public*, pg. 1006
POTOMAC PHYSICIANS PRACTICE ASSOCIATION—See CareFirst, Inc.; *U.S. Private*, pg. 753
POTRANCO MEDICAL CENTER LLC—See Adeptus Health Inc.; *U.S. Private*, pg. 78
POTTSTOWN HOSPITAL COMPANY, LLC—See Tower Health; *U.S. Private*, pg. 4193
THE POTTSVILLE PA ENDOSCOPY ASC, L.P.—See KKR & Co. Inc.; *U.S. Public*, pg. 1248
POWELL VALLEY HEALTHCARE; *U.S. Private*, pg. 3237
PREFERRED CARE NETWORK, INC.—See UnitedHealth Group Incorporated; *U.S. Public*, pg. 2249
PREFERRED IMAGING OF AMARILLO, LLC—See Akumin, Inc.; *U.S. Public*, pg. 70
PREFERRED IMAGING OF AUSTIN, LLC—See Akumin, Inc.; *U.S. Public*, pg. 70
PREFERRED IMAGING OF CORINTH, LLC—See Akumin, Inc.; *U.S. Public*, pg. 70
PREFERRED IMAGING OF DENTON, LLC—See Akumin, Inc.; *U.S. Public*, pg. 70
PREFERRED IMAGING OF FORT WORTH, LLC—See Akumin, Inc.; *U.S. Public*, pg. 70
PREFERRED IMAGING OF FRISCO, LLC—See Akumin, Inc.; *U.S. Public*, pg. 70
PREFERRED IMAGING OF GRAPEVINE/COLLEYVILLE, LLC—See Akumin, Inc.; *U.S. Public*, pg. 70
PREFERRED IMAGING OF IRVING, LLC—See Akumin, Inc.; *U.S. Public*, pg. 70
PREFERRED IMAGING OF MCKINNEY, LLC—See Akumin, Inc.; *U.S. Public*, pg. 70
PREFERRED IMAGING OF MESQUITE, LLC—See Akumin, Inc.; *U.S. Public*, pg. 70
PREFERRED IMAGING ON PLANO PARKWAY, LLC—See Akumin, Inc.; *U.S. Public*, pg. 70
PREMIER ACO PHYSICIANS NETWORK, LLC—See Tenet Healthcare Corporation; *U.S. Public*, pg. 2006
PREMIERCARE OF NORTHWEST ARKANSAS, LLC—See Community Health Systems, Inc.; *U.S. Public*, pg. 556
PREMIER ENDOSCOPY ASC, LLC—See Tenet Healthcare Corporation; *U.S. Public*, pg. 2006
PREMIER HEALTH PARTNERS—See Catholic Health Initiatives; *U.S. Private*, pg. 790

PRESBYTERIAN COMMUNITY HOSPITAL INC; *U.S. Private*, pg. 3253
PRESBYTERIAN HEALTHCARE SERVICES; *U.S. Private*, pg. 3253
PRESBYTERIAN/ST. LUKE'S MEDICAL CENTER—See HCA Healthcare, Inc.; *U.S. Public*, pg. 998
PRESENCE HEALTH—See Ascension Health Alliance; *U.S. Private*, pg. 347
PRESTON MEMORIAL HOSPITAL; *U.S. Private*, pg. 3256
PRHC-ALABAMA, LLC—See Apollo Global Management, Inc.; *U.S. Public*, pg. 158
PRIMARY CARE AT HOME OF WEST VIRGINIA, LLC—See UnitedHealth Group Incorporated; *U.S. Public*, pg. 2246
PRIMARY CARE HEALTH SERVICES, INC.; *U.S. Private*, pg. 3260
PRIMARY CARE OF WEST END, LLC—See HCA Healthcare, Inc.; *U.S. Public*, pg. 1006
PRIMARY CARE PHYSICIANS CENTER, LLC—See Tenet Healthcare Corporation; *U.S. Public*, pg. 2014
PRIMARY HEALTH CARE INC.; *U.S. Private*, pg. 3260
PRIME HEALTHCARE FOUNDATION-COSHOCTON, LLC—See Prime Healthcare Services, Inc.; *U.S. Private*, pg. 3261
PRINCESS GRACE HOSPITAL—See HCA Healthcare, Inc.; *U.S. Public*, pg. 1006
PRINCETON COMMUNITY HOSPITAL; *U.S. Private*, pg. 3264
THE PRIORY GROUP LIMITED—See Acadia Healthcare Company, Inc.; *U.S. Public*, pg. 31
PROGRESS ADULT SERVICES LIMITED—See Acadia Healthcare Company, Inc.; *U.S. Public*, pg. 29
PROGRESSIVE ACUTE CARE LLC; *U.S. Private*, pg. 3278
PROHEALTH MEDICAL GROUP—See Progressive Health Systems Inc.; *U.S. Private*, pg. 3279
PRO IMAGEM LTDA.—See Centro de Imagem Diagnosticos S.A.; *Int'l*, pg. 1413
PROMEDICA HEALTH SYSTEM, INC.—See American Healthcare Systems Corp., Inc.; *U.S. Private*, pg. 236
PROMISE HOSPITAL OF EAST LOS ANGELES, L.P.—See Apollo Global Management, Inc.; *U.S. Public*, pg. 157
PROVIDENCE HOSPITAL; *U.S. Private*, pg. 3294
PROVIDENCE MEDICAL CENTER; *U.S. Private*, pg. 3294
PROVIDENCE TARZANA MEDICAL CENTER—See Providence St. Joseph Health; *U.S. Private*, pg. 3295
PROVIVERE GMBH—See Asklepios Kliniken GmbH & Co. KGaA; *Int'l*, pg. 624
PSYCHOSOMATISCHE KLINIK—See Asklepios Kliniken GmbH & Co. KGaA; *Int'l*, pg. 624
PTSMA, INC.—See Select Medical Holdings Corporation; *U.S. Public*, pg. 1858
PULASKI COMMUNITY HOSPITAL, INC.—See HCA Healthcare, Inc.; *U.S. Public*, pg. 1006
PUNTA GORDA HMA, INC.—See Community Health Systems, Inc.; *U.S. Public*, pg. 556
PUNTA GORDA HMA PHYSICIAN MANAGEMENT, LLC—See Community Health Systems, Inc.; *U.S. Public*, pg. 556
PURE HEALTH HOLDING LLC—See Alpha Dhabi Holding PJSC; *Int'l*, pg. 367
PUTNAM COMMUNITY MEDICAL CENTER, LLC—See Apollo Global Management, Inc.; *U.S. Public*, pg. 158
PUTNAM RADIATION ONCOLOGY, LLC—See HCA Healthcare, Inc.; *U.S. Public*, pg. 1006
PUTNAM SURGICAL GROUP, LLC—See HCA Healthcare, Inc.; *U.S. Public*, pg. 1006
PUYALLUP TRIBAL HEALTH AUTHORITY; *U.S. Private*, pg. 3308
QHG OF ENTERPRISE, INC.—See Community Health Systems, Inc.; *U.S. Public*, pg. 556
QHG OF FORT WAYNE COMPANY, LLC—See Community Health Systems, Inc.; *U.S. Public*, pg. 556
QHG OF HATTIESBURG, INC.—See Community Health Systems, Inc.; *U.S. Public*, pg. 556
QHG OF SOUTH CAROLINA, INC.—See Community Health Systems, Inc.; *U.S. Public*, pg. 556
QHG OF SPRINGDALE, INC.—See Community Health Systems, Inc.; *U.S. Public*, pg. 556
QRX MEDICAL MANAGEMENT, LLC—See KKR & Co. Inc.; *U.S. Public*, pg. 1250
QUAIL SURGICAL AND PAIN MANAGEMENT CENTER, LLC—See Universal Health Services, Inc.; *U.S. Public*, pg. 2259
QUALIGENICS MEDICAL LIMITED—See HKR International Limited; *Int'l*, pg. 3429
QUALITY ADDICTION MANAGEMENT INC.—See Acadia Healthcare Company, Inc.; *U.S. Public*, pg. 29
QUARTERLINE CONSULTING SERVICES, LLC—See Planned Systems International, Inc.; *U.S. Private*, pg. 3196
THE QUEEN'S HEALTH SYSTEMS; *U.S. Private*, pg. 4101
QUIVIRA INTERNAL MEDICINE, INC.—See HCA Healthcare, Inc.; *U.S. Public*, pg. 1006
QUORUM HEALTH RESOURCES, LLC—See Grant Avenue Capital, LLC; *U.S. Private*, pg. 1756
QUORUM SOLUTIONS, LLC—See Quorum Health Corporation; *U.S. Private*, pg. 3330
RADFORD FAMILY MEDICINE, LLC—See HCA Healthcare, Inc.; *U.S. Public*, pg. 1007

622110 — GENERAL MEDICAL AND... CORPORATE AFFILIATIONS

N.A.I.C.S. Index

RADIOLOGY SERVICES OF JUPITER MEDICAL SPECIALISTS, LLC—See KKR & Co. Inc.; *U.S. Public*, pg. 1246
RADSOURCE, LLC—See Tenet Healthcare Corporation; *U.S. Public*, pg. 2006
RALEIGH GENERAL HOSPITAL, LLC—See Apollo Global Management, Inc.; *U.S. Public*, pg. 158
THE RALEIGH NC ENDOSCOPY ASC, LLC—See KKR & Co. Inc.; *U.S. Public*, pg. 1248
RAPIDES REGIONAL MEDICAL CENTER—See HCA Healthcare, Inc.; *U.S. Public*, pg. 1007
RAPIDES REGIONAL PHYSICIAN GROUP, LLC—See HCA Healthcare, Inc.; *U.S. Public*, pg. 1007
RAULERSON HOSPITAL—See HCA Healthcare, Inc.; *U.S. Public*, pg. 1007
READING HOSPITAL—See Tower Health; *U.S. Private*, pg. 4193
REAGAN STREET SURGERY CENTER, L.L.C.—See Tenet Healthcare Corporation; *U.S. Public*, pg. 2006
REBEKAH REHAB & EXTENDED CARE CENTER; *U.S. Private*, pg. 3370
RECOVERY HEALTH SERVICES; *U.S. Private*, pg. 3372
REDBIRD SQUARE ENDOSCOPY CENTER, LLC—See KKR & Co. Inc.; *U.S. Public*, pg. 1246
RED BUD CLINIC CORP.—See Quorum Health Corporation; *U.S. Private*, pg. 3330
RED BUD ILLINOIS HOSPITAL COMPANY, LLC—See Quorum Health Corporation; *U.S. Private*, pg. 3330
RED BUD REGIONAL CLINIC COMPANY, LLC—See Quorum Health Corporation; *U.S. Private*, pg. 3330
REDICLINIC LLC—See New Rite Aid, LLC; *U.S. Private*, pg. 2905
REDINGTON-FAIRVIEW GENERAL HOSPITAL; *U.S. Private*, pg. 3379
REDMOND REGIONAL MEDICAL CENTER—See HCA Healthcare, Inc.; *U.S. Public*, pg. 1007
RED RIVER HOLDING COMPANY, LLC—See Acadia Healthcare Company, Inc.; *U.S. Public*, pg. 29
RED RIVER HOSPITAL, LLC—See Acadia Healthcare Company, Inc.; *U.S. Public*, pg. 29
RED ROCK AT SMOKE RANCH, LLC—See HCA Healthcare, Inc.; *U.S. Public*, pg. 1007
RED ROCKS SURGERY CENTER, LLC—See HCA Healthcare, Inc.; *U.S. Public*, pg. 1007
THE REFUGE, A HEALING PLACE, LLC—See Acadia Healthcare Company, Inc.; *U.S. Public*, pg. 31
THE REFUGE-THE NEST, LLC—See Acadia Healthcare Company, Inc.; *U.S. Public*, pg. 31
REGENCE HEALTH NETWORK, INC.; *U.S. Private*, pg. 3386
REGENCY HOSPITAL OF FORT WORTH, LLLP—See Select Medical Holdings Corporation; *U.S. Public*, pg. 1859
REGENCY SPECIALIST HOSPITAL SDN.BHD.—See EQT AB; *Int'l*, pg. 2475
REGIONAL CANCER TREATMENT CENTER, LTD.—See Community Health Systems, Inc.; *U.S. Public*, pg. 556
REGIONAL EMPLOYEE ASSISTANCE PROGRAM—See Community Health Systems, Inc.; *U.S. Public*, pg. 556
REGIONAL MEDICAL CENTER BAYONET POINT—See HCA Healthcare, Inc.; *U.S. Public*, pg. 1007
REGIONAL MEDICAL CENTER OF SAN JOSE—See HCA Healthcare, Inc.; *U.S. Public*, pg. 1007
REGIONAL ONE HEALTH; *U.S. Private*, pg. 3388
REHABILITATION CENTERS, INC.—See Acadia Healthcare Company, Inc.; *U.S. Public*, pg. 30
REHA-KLINIK GMBH & CO. KG—See Asklepios Kliniken GmbH & Co. KGaA; *Int'l*, pg. 623
REHOBOTH MCKINLEY CHRISTIAN HEALTH CARE SERVICES; *U.S. Private*, pg. 3389
REIMBURSEMENT TECHNOLOGIES, INC.—See KKR & Co. Inc.; *U.S. Public*, pg. 1249
RELIANT HOME HEALTH, INC.—See Merit Capital Partners; *U.S. Private*, pg. 2674
RENOWN HEALTH; *U.S. Private*, pg. 3399
RENOWN NETWORK SERVICES; *U.S. Private*, pg. 3399
RESOLUTE ACQUISITION CORPORATION—See Acadia Healthcare Company, Inc.; *U.S. Public*, pg. 30
RESOLUTE HEALTH FAMILY URGENT CARE, INC.—See Tenet Healthcare Corporation; *U.S. Public*, pg. 2014
RESOURCE OPTIMIZATION & INNOVATION, L.L.C.—See HCA Healthcare, Inc.; *U.S. Public*, pg. 1007
RESTON HOSPITAL CENTER—See HCA Healthcare, Inc.; *U.S. Public*, pg. 1007
RESTON SURGERY CENTER, L.P.—See HCA Healthcare, Inc.; *U.S. Public*, pg. 1007
RESURGENS EAST SURGERY CENTER, LLC—See Tenet Healthcare Corporation; *U.S. Public*, pg. 2006
RESURGENS FAYETTE SURGERY CENTER, LLC—See Tenet Healthcare Corporation; *U.S. Public*, pg. 2006
RETREAT DOCTORS' HOSPITAL—See HCA Healthcare, Inc.; *U.S. Public*, pg. 997
RHN CLARK MEMORIAL HOSPITAL, LLC—See Apollo Global Management, Inc.; *U.S. Public*, pg. 158
RHN SCOTT PHYSICIAN PRACTICES, LLC—See Apollo Global Management, Inc.; *U.S. Public*, pg. 158
THE RHODE ISLAND QUALITY INSTITUTE; *U.S. Private*, pg. 4106
RICHMOND TREATMENT CENTER, LLC—See Acadia Healthcare Company, Inc.; *U.S. Public*, pg. 30
RIDGE OUTPATIENT COUNSELING, L.L.C.—See Universal Health Services, Inc.; *U.S. Public*, pg. 2259
RIO GRANDE REGIONAL HOSPITAL, INC.—See HCA Healthcare, Inc.; *U.S. Public*, pg. 1007
RISE HEALTH, INC.—See Teladoc Health, Inc.; *U.S. Public*, pg. 1992
RITE AID LEASE MANAGEMENT COMPANY—See New Rite Aid, LLC; *U.S. Private*, pg. 2905
RIVEREDGE HOSPITAL, INC.—See Universal Health Services, Inc.; *U.S. Public*, pg. 2259
RIVER MEDICAL INCORPORATED—See KKR & Co. Inc.; *U.S. Public*, pg. 1249
RIVER NORTH SAME DAY SURGERY, L.L.C.—See Tenet Healthcare Corporation; *U.S. Public*, pg. 2012
RIVER OAKS HOSPITAL, INC.—See Community Health Systems, Inc.; *U.S. Public*, pg. 556
RIVER PARISHES PHYSICIAN PRACTICES, LLC—See Apollo Global Management, Inc.; *U.S. Public*, pg. 158
RIVERPARK ASC, LLC—See Community Health Systems, Inc.; *U.S. Public*, pg. 556
RIVERPARK COMMUNITY CATH LAB, LLC—See Community Health Systems, Inc.; *U.S. Public*, pg. 556
RIVERSIDE COMMUNITY HOSPITAL—See HCA Healthcare, Inc.; *U.S. Public*, pg. 1007
RIVERSIDE HOSPITAL, INC.—See HCA Healthcare, Inc.; *U.S. Public*, pg. 1007
RIVERSIDE-SAN BERNARDINO COUNTY INDIAN HEALTH, INC.; *U.S. Private*, pg. 3446
RIVER TO RIVER HEART GROUP, LLC—See Quorum Health Corporation; *U.S. Private*, pg. 3330
RIVER VALLEY ASC, LLC—See UnitedHealth Group Incorporated; *U.S. Public*, pg. 2250
RIVERVIEW BEHAVIORAL HEALTH, LLC—See Acadia Healthcare Company, Inc.; *U.S. Public*, pg. 30
RIVERVIEW MEDICAL CENTER, LLC—See Apollo Global Management, Inc.; *U.S. Public*, pg. 158
RIVERVIEW MEDICAL CENTER—See Hackensack Meridian Health, Inc.; *U.S. Private*, pg. 1838
RIVERVIEW REGIONAL MEDICAL CENTER, LLC—See Prime Healthcare Services, Inc.; *U.S. Private*, pg. 3261
RIVERWALK ASC, LLC—See HCA Healthcare, Inc.; *U.S. Public*, pg. 1007
RIVERWALK SURGERY CENTER—See HCA Healthcare, Inc.; *U.S. Public*, pg. 1007
RIVERWOODS BEHAVIORAL HEALTH, LLC—See Acadia Healthcare Company, Inc.; *U.S. Public*, pg. 30
RK KLINIK BETRIEBS GMBH NR. 31—See Asklepios Kliniken GmbH & Co. KGaA; *Int'l*, pg. 624
RMCA PROFESSIONALS MGMT, LLC—See HCA Healthcare, Inc.; *U.S. Public*, pg. 1007
RML HEALTH PROVIDERS LIMITED PARTNERSHIP; *U.S. Private*, pg. 3452
ROANE MEDICAL CENTER; *U.S. Private*, pg. 3453
ROANOKE SURGERY CENTER, L.P.—See HCA Healthcare, Inc.; *U.S. Public*, pg. 1007
ROBERT F. KENNEDY MEDICAL CENTER—See Daughters of Charity Health System; *U.S. Private*, pg. 1167
ROBERT WOOD JOHNSON UNIVERSITY HOSPITAL RAHWAY—See Barnabas Health Medical Group; *U.S. Private*, pg. 476
ROBESON HEALTH CARE CORPORATION; *U.S. Private*, pg. 3460
ROCK BRIDGE SURGICAL INSTITUTE, L.L.C.—See Tenet Healthcare Corporation; *U.S. Public*, pg. 2003
ROCKCASTLE REGIONAL HOSPITAL AND RESPIRATORY CARE CENTER, INC.; *U.S. Private*, pg. 3465
THE ROCKVILLE/ESC-NORTH MD ENDOSCOPY ASC, LLC—See KKR & Co. Inc.; *U.S. Public*, pg. 1248
ROCKWALL AMBULATORY SURGERY CENTER, L.L.P.—See Tenet Healthcare Corporation; *U.S. Public*, pg. 2012
ROCKWALL/HEATH SURGERY CENTER, L.L.P.—See Tenet Healthcare Corporation; *U.S. Public*, pg. 2012
ROCKY MOUNTAIN SURGERY CENTER, LLC—See HCA Healthcare, Inc.; *U.S. Public*, pg. 1007
ROCKY MOUNTAIN SURGERY CENTER, LLC—See HCA Healthcare, Inc.; *U.S. Public*, pg. 1007
THE ROGERS AR OPHTHALMOLOGY ASC, LLC—See KKR & Co. Inc.; *U.S. Public*, pg. 1248
ROH, LLC—See Community Health Systems, Inc.; *U.S. Public*, pg. 556
ROSELAND COMMUNITY HOSPITAL; *U.S. Private*, pg. 3482
ROSE MEDICAL CENTER INC.—See HCA Healthcare, Inc.; *U.S. Public*, pg. 1008
ROSE SURGICAL CENTER—See HCA Healthcare, Inc.; *U.S. Public*, pg. 1008
ROSEVILLE SURGERY CENTER, L.P.—See Tenet Healthcare Corporation; *U.S. Public*, pg. 2012
ROSSENDALE SCHOOL LIMITED—See Acadia Healthcare Company, Inc.; *U.S. Public*, pg. 30
ROSWELL GEORGIA SURGERY CENTER, L.L.C.—See WellStar Health System, Inc.; *U.S. Private*, pg. 4478
ROSWELL HOSPITAL CORPORATION—See Community Health Systems, Inc.; *U.S. Public*, pg. 556
ROUND ROCK HOSPITAL, INC.—See HCA Healthcare, Inc.; *U.S. Public*, pg. 1008
ROUND ROCK MEDICAL CENTER—See HCA Healthcare, Inc.; *U.S. Public*, pg. 1008
ROUND ROCK TRAUMA SURGEONS, PLLC—See HCA Healthcare, Inc.; *U.S. Public*, pg. 1008
RUGANI HOSPITAL S.R.L.—See Garofalo Health Care SpA; *Int'l*, pg. 2886
RUSH-COPLEY MEDICAL CENTER—See Advent International Corporation; *U.S. Private*, pg. 96
RUSH OAK BROOK SURGERY CENTER, LLC—See UnitedHealth Group Incorporated; *U.S. Public*, pg. 2250
RUSH OAK PARK HOSPITAL—See Wheaton Franciscan Services Inc.; *U.S. Private*, pg. 4505
RUSSELLVILLE HOSPITAL, INC.—See Curae Health, Inc.; *U.S. Private*, pg. 1124
RUSTON CLINIC COMPANY, LLC—See Community Health Systems, Inc.; *U.S. Public*, pg. 556
RUSTON LOUISIANA HOSPITAL COMPANY, LLC—See Community Health Systems, Inc.; *U.S. Public*, pg. 556
RYDER MEMORIAL HOSPITAL; *U.S. Private*, pg. 3511
RYNFIELD TERRACE PROPRIETARY LIMITED—See Dis-Chem Pharmacies Ltd.; *Int'l*, pg. 2131
SACO BAY ORTHOPEDIC AND SPORTS PHYSICAL THERAPY, INC.—See Select Medical Holdings Corporation; *U.S. Public*, pg. 1859
SACRED HEART HEALTHCARE SYSTEM—See UnityPoint Health; *U.S. Private*, pg. 4303
SACRED HEART HEALTH SYSTEM—See Ascension Health Alliance; *U.S. Private*, pg. 347
SADCO SAMI DANDAN & CO.—See Dar Al Dawa Development & Investment Co.; *Int'l*, pg. 1971
SADDLEBACK MEMORIAL AT SAN CLEMENTE—See Memorial Health Services; *U.S. Private*, pg. 2664
SAHARA SURGERY CENTER—See HCA Healthcare, Inc.; *U.S. Public*, pg. 1008
SAINT ANTHONY HOSPITAL; *U.S. Private*, pg. 3529
SAINT FRANCIS CENTER FOR SURGICAL WEIGHT LOSS, L.L.C.—See Tenet Healthcare Corporation; *U.S. Public*, pg. 2003
SAINT FRANCIS HOSPITAL-BARTLETT, INC.—See Tenet Healthcare Corporation; *U.S. Public*, pg. 2008
SAINT FRANCIS HOSPITAL INPATIENT PHYSICIANS, L.L.C.—See Tenet Healthcare Corporation; *U.S. Public*, pg. 2003
SAINT FRANCIS MEDICAL CENTER; *U.S. Private*, pg. 3529
SAINT FRANCIS MEDICAL PARTNERS, EAST, L.L.C.—See Tenet Healthcare Corporation; *U.S. Public*, pg. 2003
SAINT FRANCIS SURGERY CENTER, L.L.C.—See Tenet Healthcare Corporation; *U.S. Public*, pg. 2007
SAINT JOSEPH HOSPITAL; *U.S. Private*, pg. 3529
SAINT LOUISE REGIONAL HOSPITAL—See Daughters of Charity Health System; *U.S. Private*, pg. 1167
SAINT LOUIS REGIONAL HEALTH COMMISSION; *U.S. Private*, pg. 3530
SAINT LUKE'S HEALTH SYSTEM, INC.—See BJC Health System; *U.S. Private*, pg. 568
SAINT THOMAS CAMPUS SURGICARE, L.P.—See Tenet Healthcare Corporation; *U.S. Public*, pg. 2012
SAINT THOMAS HIGHLANDS HOSPITAL, LLC—See Ascension Health Alliance; *U.S. Private*, pg. 347
SAINT THOMAS MIDTOWN HOSPITAL—See Ascension Health Alliance; *U.S. Private*, pg. 347
SAINT THOMAS STONES RIVER HOSPITAL, LLC—See Ascension Health Alliance; *U.S. Private*, pg. 347
SAINT VINCENT HOSPITAL, L.L.C.—See Tenet Healthcare Corporation; *U.S. Public*, pg. 2006
SALEM COMMUNITY HOSPITAL; *U.S. Private*, pg. 3531
SALEM HOSPITAL CORPORATION—See Community Health Systems, Inc.; *U.S. Public*, pg. 556
SALEM SURGERY CENTER, LLC—See UnitedHealth Group Incorporated; *U.S. Public*, pg. 2250
SALINA REGIONAL HEALTH CENTER; *U.S. Private*, pg. 3532
SALINE COUNTY MEDICAL CENTER; *U.S. Private*, pg. 3532
SALMON SURGERY CENTER, LLC—See Tenet Healthcare Corporation; *U.S. Public*, pg. 2006
SALUD INTEGRAL EN LA MONTANA, INC.; *U.S. Private*, pg. 3534
SALUD PARA LA GENTE; *U.S. Private*, pg. 3534
SAMARITAN HEALTH SERVICES, INC.; *U.S. Private*, pg. 3536
SAMARITAN REGIONAL HEALTH SYSTEM; *U.S. Private*, pg. 3536
SAME DAY SC OF CENTRAL NJ, LLC—See Tenet Healthcare Corporation; *U.S. Public*, pg. 2007
SAMITIVEJ CHONBURI CO., LTD.—See Bangkok Dusit Medical Services Public Company Limited; *Int'l*, pg. 834
SAMITIVEJ SRIRACHA CO., LTD.—See Bangkok Dusit Medical Services Public Company Limited; *Int'l*, pg. 834
SAN ANGELO COMMUNITY MEDICAL CENTER, LLC—See Community Health Systems, Inc.; *U.S. Public*, pg. 556
SAN ANGELO HOSPITAL, L.P.—See Community Health Systems, Inc.; *U.S. Public*, pg. 552
SAN ANTONIO ASC, LP—See KKR & Co. Inc.; *U.S. Public*, pg. 1246
SAN ANTONIO ENDOSCOPY, L.P.—See Tenet Healthcare

Corporation; *U.S. Public*, pg. 2012
SAN ANTONIO SURGICENTER, LLC—See HCA Healthcare, Inc.; *U.S. Public*, pg. 1008
THE SAN ANTONIO TX ENDOSCOPY ASC, L.P.—See KKR & Co. Inc.; *U.S. Public*, pg. 1248
THE SAN DIEGO CA MULTI-SPECIALTY ASC, LLC—See KKR & Co. Inc.; *U.S. Public*, pg. 1248
SAN DIEGO HEALTH ALLIANCE—See Acadia Healthcare Company, Inc.; *U.S. Public*, pg. 30
SAN DIMAS COMMUNITY HOSPITAL—See Prime Healthcare Services, Inc.; *U.S. Private*, pg. 3262
SAND LAKE SURGICENTER, LLC—See UnitedHealth Group Incorporated; *U.S. Public*, pg. 2250
SAN FERNANDO VALLEY SURGERY CENTER, L.P.—See Tenet Healthcare Corporation; *U.S. Public*, pg. 2007
SAN JUAN CAPESTRANO HOSPITAL, INC.—See Acadia Healthcare Company, Inc.; *U.S. Public*, pg. 30
SAN JUAN REGIONAL MEDICAL CENTER; *U.S. Private*, pg. 3541
SAN MARCOS ASC, LLC—See HCA Healthcare, Inc.; *U.S. Public*, pg. 1008
SAN MARTIN SURGERY CENTER, LLC—See Tenet Healthcare Corporation; *U.S. Public*, pg. 2012
SAN MIGUEL CLINIC CORP.—See Quorum Health Corporation; *U.S. Private*, pg. 3330
SAN RAMON REGIONAL MEDICAL CENTER, INC.—See Tenet Healthcare Corporation; *U.S. Public*, pg. 2003
SANTA BARBARA OUTPATIENT SURGERY CENTER, LLC—See Tenet Healthcare Corporation; *U.S. Public*, pg. 2007
SARAH BUSH LINCOLN HEALTH CENTER; *U.S. Private*, pg. 3549
SARAH CANNON RESEARCH INSTITUTE, LLC—See HCA Healthcare, Inc.; *U.S. Public*, pg. 1008
SARASOTA DOCTORS HOSPITAL, INC.—See HCA Healthcare, Inc.; *U.S. Public*, pg. 1008
SARASOTA PHYSICIANS SURGICAL CENTER, LLC—See KKR & Co. Inc.; *U.S. Public*, pg. 1246
SARATOGA HOSPITAL; *U.S. Private*, pg. 3549
SARRELL DENTAL; *U.S. Private*, pg. 3550
SAUK PRAIRIE HEALTHCARE; *U.S. Private*, pg. 3554
SCANMED S.A.—See Abris Capital Partners Sp. z o.o.; *Int'l*, pg. 69
SCHC PEDIATRIC ANESTHESIA ASSOCIATES, L.L.C.—See Drexel University; *U.S. Private*, pg. 1276
SCHC PEDIATRIC ANESTHESIA ASSOCIATES, L.L.C.—See Tower Health; *U.S. Private*, pg. 4193
SCHC PEDIATRIC ASSOCIATES, LLC—See Drexel University; *U.S. Private*, pg. 1276
SCHC PEDIATRIC ASSOCIATES, LLC—See Tower Health; *U.S. Private*, pg. 4193
SCOTT COUNTY HMA, LLC—See Community Health Systems, Inc.; *U.S. Public*, pg. 556
SCRANTON CLINIC COMPANY, LLC—See Community Health Systems, Inc.; *U.S. Public*, pg. 556
SCRANTON EMERGENCY PHYSICIAN SERVICES, LLC—See Community Health Systems, Inc.; *U.S. Public*, pg. 556
SCRANTON HOSPITALIST PHYSICIAN SERVICES, LLC—See Community Health Systems, Inc.; *U.S. Public*, pg. 556
SCRANTON QUINCY AMBULANCE, LLC—See Community Health Systems, Inc.; *U.S. Public*, pg. 556
SCRANTON QUINCY CLINIC COMPANY, LLC—See Community Health Systems, Inc.; *U.S. Public*, pg. 556
SCRANTON QUINCY HOSPITAL COMPANY, LLC—See Community Health Systems, Inc.; *U.S. Public*, pg. 556
SCRIBEAMERICA; *U.S. Private*, pg. 3579
SCRIPPS ENCINITAS SURGERY CENTER, LLC—See Tenet Healthcare Corporation; *U.S. Public*, pg. 2012
SCRIPPS MERCY HOSPITAL—See Scripps Health; *U.S. Private*, pg. 3580
SEBRING HOSPITAL MANAGEMENT ASSOCIATES, LLC—See HCA Healthcare, Inc.; *U.S. Public*, pg. 1008
SELECTHEALTH, INC.; *U.S. Private*, pg. 3601
SELECT SPECIALTY-DOWNRIVER, LLC—See Select Medical Holdings Corporation; *U.S. Public*, pg. 1861
SELECT SPECIALTY HOSPITAL-AKRON, LLC—See Select Medical Holdings Corporation; *U.S. Public*, pg. 1859
SELECT SPECIALTY HOSPITAL-ANN ARBOR, INC.—See Select Medical Holdings Corporation; *U.S. Public*, pg. 1859
SELECT SPECIALTY HOSPITAL-ARIZONA, INC.—See Select Medical Holdings Corporation; *U.S. Public*, pg. 1859
SELECT SPECIALTY HOSPITAL-AUGUSTA, INC.—See Select Medical Holdings Corporation; *U.S. Public*, pg. 1859
SELECT SPECIALTY HOSPITAL-BELHAVEN, LLC—See Select Medical Holdings Corporation; *U.S. Public*, pg. 1860
SELECT SPECIALTY HOSPITAL-CENTRAL PENNSYLVANIA, L.P.—See Select Medical Holdings Corporation; *U.S. Public*, pg. 1860
SELECT SPECIALTY HOSPITAL-CHARLESTON, INC.—See Select Medical Holdings Corporation; *U.S. Public*, pg. 1860
SELECT SPECIALTY HOSPITAL-COLORADO SPRINGS, INC.—See Select Medical Holdings Corporation; *U.S. Public*, pg. 1860
SELECT SPECIALTY HOSPITAL-COLUMBUS, INC.—See Select Medical Holdings Corporation; *U.S. Public*, pg. 1860
SELECT SPECIALTY HOSPITAL-DALLAS, INC.—See Select Medical Holdings Corporation; *U.S. Public*, pg. 1860
SELECT SPECIALTY HOSPITAL-DANVILLE, INC.—See Select Medical Holdings Corporation; *U.S. Public*, pg. 1860
SELECT SPECIALTY HOSPITAL - DAYTONA BEACH, INC.—See Select Medical Holdings Corporation; *U.S. Public*, pg. 1859
SELECT SPECIALTY HOSPITAL-DENVER, INC.—See Select Medical Holdings Corporation; *U.S. Public*, pg. 1860
SELECT SPECIALTY HOSPITAL-DES MOINES, INC.—See Select Medical Holdings Corporation; *U.S. Public*, pg. 1860
SELECT SPECIALTY HOSPITAL-DURHAM, INC.—See Select Medical Holdings Corporation; *U.S. Public*, pg. 1860
SELECT SPECIALTY HOSPITAL-ERIE INC.—See Select Medical Holdings Corporation; *U.S. Public*, pg. 1860
SELECT SPECIALTY HOSPITAL-EVANSVILLE, INC.—See Select Medical Holdings Corporation; *U.S. Public*, pg. 1860
SELECT SPECIALTY HOSPITAL-EVANSVILLE, LLC—See Select Medical Holdings Corporation; *U.S. Public*, pg. 1860
SELECT SPECIALTY HOSPITAL-FLINT, INC.—See Select Medical Holdings Corporation; *U.S. Public*, pg. 1860
SELECT SPECIALTY HOSPITAL-FORT MYERS, INC.—See Select Medical Holdings Corporation; *U.S. Public*, pg. 1860
SELECT SPECIALTY HOSPITAL-FORT SMITH, INC.—See Select Medical Holdings Corporation; *U.S. Public*, pg. 1860
SELECT SPECIALTY HOSPITAL-FORT WAYNE, INC.—See Select Medical Holdings Corporation; *U.S. Public*, pg. 1860
SELECT SPECIALTY HOSPITAL-GAINESVILLE, INC.—See Select Medical Holdings Corporation; *U.S. Public*, pg. 1860
SELECT SPECIALTY HOSPITAL-GREENSBORO, INC.—See Select Medical Holdings Corporation; *U.S. Public*, pg. 1860
SELECT SPECIALTY HOSPITAL-GROSSE POINTE, INC.—See Select Medical Holdings Corporation; *U.S. Public*, pg. 1860
SELECT SPECIALTY HOSPITAL-GULF COAST, INC.—See Select Medical Holdings Corporation; *U.S. Public*, pg. 1860
SELECT SPECIALTY HOSPITAL-HOUSTON, L.P.—See Select Medical Holdings Corporation; *U.S. Public*, pg. 1860
SELECT SPECIALTY HOSPITAL-JACKSON, INC.—See Select Medical Holdings Corporation; *U.S. Public*, pg. 1860
SELECT SPECIALTY HOSPITAL-JOHNSTOWN, INC.—See Select Medical Holdings Corporation; *U.S. Public*, pg. 1860
SELECT SPECIALTY HOSPITAL-KANSAS CITY, INC.—See Select Medical Holdings Corporation; *U.S. Public*, pg. 1860
SELECT SPECIALTY HOSPITAL-KNOXVILLE, INC.—See Select Medical Holdings Corporation; *U.S. Public*, pg. 1860
SELECT SPECIALTY HOSPITAL-LAUREL HIGHLANDS, INC.—See Select Medical Holdings Corporation; *U.S. Public*, pg. 1860
SELECT SPECIALTY HOSPITAL-LEXINGTON, INC.—See Select Medical Holdings Corporation; *U.S. Public*, pg. 1860
SELECT SPECIALTY HOSPITAL-LINCOLN, INC.—See Select Medical Holdings Corporation; *U.S. Public*, pg. 1860
SELECT SPECIALTY HOSPITAL-LITTLE ROCK, INC.—See Select Medical Holdings Corporation; *U.S. Public*, pg. 1860
SELECT SPECIALTY HOSPITAL-LONGVIEW, INC.—See Select Medical Holdings Corporation; *U.S. Public*, pg. 1860
SELECT SPECIALTY HOSPITAL-MACOMB COUNTY, INC.—See Select Medical Holdings Corporation; *U.S. Public*, pg. 1860
SELECT SPECIALTY HOSPITAL-MADISON, INC.—See Select Medical Holdings Corporation; *U.S. Public*, pg. 1860
SELECT SPECIALTY HOSPITAL-MCKEESPORT, INC.—See Select Medical Holdings Corporation; *U.S. Public*, pg. 1860
SELECT SPECIALTY HOSPITAL-MEMPHIS, INC.—See Select Medical Holdings Corporation; *U.S. Public*, pg. 1860
SELECT SPECIALTY HOSPITAL-MIAMI LAKES, INC.—See Select Medical Holdings Corporation; *U.S. Public*, pg. 1860
SELECT SPECIALTY HOSPITAL-MIDLAND, INC.—See Select Medical Holdings Corporation; *U.S. Public*, pg. 1860
SELECT SPECIALTY HOSPITAL-MILWAUKEE, INC.—See Select Medical Holdings Corporation; *U.S. Public*, pg. 1861
SELECT SPECIALTY HOSPITAL-NASHVILLE, INC.—See Select Medical Holdings Corporation; *U.S. Public*, pg. 1861
SELECT SPECIALTY HOSPITAL-NORTHEAST NEW JERSEY, INC.—See Select Medical Holdings Corporation; *U.S. Public*, pg. 1861
SELECT SPECIALTY HOSPITAL-NORTHEAST OHIO, INC.—See Select Medical Holdings Corporation; *U.S. Public*, pg. 1861
SELECT SPECIALTY HOSPITAL-NORTHERN KENTUCKY, LLC—See Select Medical Holdings Corporation; *U.S. Public*, pg. 1861
SELECT SPECIALTY HOSPITAL-NORTH KNOXVILLE, INC.—See Select Medical Holdings Corporation; *U.S. Public*, pg. 1861
SELECT SPECIALTY HOSPITAL-NORTHWEST DETROIT, INC.—See Select Medical Holdings Corporation; *U.S. Public*, pg. 1861
SELECT SPECIALTY HOSPITAL-OKLAHOMA CITY, INC.—See Select Medical Holdings Corporation; *U.S. Public*, pg. 1861
SELECT SPECIALTY HOSPITAL-OMAHA, INC.—See Select Medical Holdings Corporation; *U.S. Public*, pg. 1861
SELECT SPECIALTY HOSPITAL-PALM BEACH, INC.—See Select Medical Holdings Corporation; *U.S. Public*, pg. 1861
SELECT SPECIALTY HOSPITAL-PANAMA CITY, INC.—See Select Medical Holdings Corporation; *U.S. Public*, pg. 1861
SELECT SPECIALTY HOSPITAL-PENSACOLA, INC.—See Select Medical Holdings Corporation; *U.S. Public*, pg. 1861
SELECT SPECIALTY HOSPITAL-PHOENIX, INC.—See Select Medical Holdings Corporation; *U.S. Public*, pg. 1861
SELECT SPECIALTY HOSPITAL-PITTSBURGH/UPMC, INC.—See Select Medical Holdings Corporation; *U.S. Public*, pg. 1861
SELECT SPECIALTY HOSPITAL-PONTIAC, INC.—See Select Medical Holdings Corporation; *U.S. Public*, pg. 1861
SELECT SPECIALTY HOSPITAL-QUAD CITIES, INC.—See Select Medical Holdings Corporation; *U.S. Public*, pg. 1861
SELECT SPECIALTY HOSPITAL-SAGINAW, INC.—See Select Medical Holdings Corporation; *U.S. Public*, pg. 1861
SELECT SPECIALTY HOSPITAL-SAN ANTONIO, INC.—See Select Medical Holdings Corporation; *U.S. Public*, pg. 1861
SELECT SPECIALTY HOSPITAL-SAVANNAH, INC.—See Select Medical Holdings Corporation; *U.S. Public*, pg. 1861
SELECT SPECIALTY HOSPITAL-SIOUX FALLS, INC.—See Select Medical Holdings Corporation; *U.S. Public*, pg. 1861
SELECT SPECIALTY HOSPITAL - SPECTRUM HEALTH—See Select Medical Holdings Corporation; *U.S. Public*, pg. 1859
SELECT SPECIALTY HOSPITAL-SPRINGFIELD, INC.—See Select Medical Holdings Corporation; *U.S. Public*, pg. 1861
SELECT SPECIALTY HOSPITAL-TALLAHASSEE, INC.—See Select Medical Holdings Corporation; *U.S. Public*, pg. 1861
SELECT SPECIALTY HOSPITAL-THE VILLAGES, INC.—See Select Medical Holdings Corporation; *U.S. Public*, pg. 1861
SELECT SPECIALTY HOSPITAL-TRICITIES, INC.—See Select Medical Holdings Corporation; *U.S. Public*, pg. 1861
SELECT SPECIALTY HOSPITAL - TUCSON, LLC—See Community Health Systems, Inc.; *U.S. Public*, pg. 556
SELECT SPECIALTY HOSPITAL-TULSA, INC.—See Select Medical Holdings Corporation; *U.S. Public*, pg. 1861
SELECT SPECIALTY HOSPITAL-TULSA/MIDTOWN, LLC—See Select Medical Holdings Corporation; *U.S. Public*, pg. 1861
SELECT SPECIALTY HOSPITAL-WESTERN MISSOURI, INC.—See Select Medical Holdings Corporation; *U.S. Public*, pg. 1861
SELECT SPECIALTY HOSPITAL-WICHITA, INC.—See Select Medical Holdings Corporation; *U.S. Public*, pg. 1861
SELECT SPECIALTY HOSPITAL-WILMINGTON, INC.—See Select Medical Holdings Corporation; *U.S. Public*, pg. 1861
SELECT SPECIALTY HOSPITAL-WINSTON-SALEM, INC.—See Select Medical Holdings Corporation; *U.S. Public*, pg. 1861
SELECT SPECIALTY HOSPITAL-YOUNGSTOWN, INC.—See Select Medical Holdings Corporation; *U.S. Public*, pg. 1861
SELECT SPECIALTY HOSPITAL-ZANESVILLE, INC.—See Select Medical Holdings Corporation; *U.S. Public*, pg. 1861
SELECT SYNERGOS, INC.—See Select Medical Holdings Corporation; *U.S. Public*, pg. 1861
SEMINOLE HMA, LLC—See Community Health Systems, Inc.; *U.S. Public*, pg. 556
SENIOR CARE CEDAR HILLS, LLC—See Diversicare Healthcare Services, Inc.; *U.S. Public*, pg. 670
SENIOR CARE GROUP INC; *U.S. Private*, pg. 3606

622110 — GENERAL MEDICAL AND... CORPORATE AFFILIATIONS

SENIOR HEALTH ASSOCIATES, LLC—See HCA Healthcare, Inc.; *U.S. Public*, pg. 1008
SENTARA HEALTHCARE; *U.S. Private*, pg. 3608
SEQUOIA HOSPITAL—See Catholic Health Initiatives; *U.S. Private*, pg. 790
SERENITY KNOLLS—See Acadia Healthcare Company, Inc.; *U.S. Public*, pg. 30
SERVICE ACCESS AND MANAGEMENT, INC.; *U.S. Private*, pg. 3614
SERVICE ORGANIZATION OF CONCHO VALLEY; *U.S. Private*, pg. 3615
SERVICIOS MEDICOS UNIVERSITARIOS INC; *U.S. Private*, pg. 3617
SETON MEDICAL CENTER COASTSIDE—See Daughters of Charity Health System; *U.S. Private*, pg. 1167
SETON MEDICAL CENTER—See Daughters of Charity Health System; *U.S. Private*, pg. 1167
SEVEN HILLS HOSPITAL, INC.—See Acadia Healthcare Company, Inc.; *U.S. Public*, pg. 29
S. FISHER AND S. THOMAS, INC.—See KKR & Co. Inc.; *U.S. Public*, pg. 1249
SFMPE - CRITTENDEN, L.L.C.—See Tenet Healthcare Corporation; *U.S. Public*, pg. 2006
SHAKER CLINIC, LLC—See Acadia Healthcare Company, Inc.; *U.S. Public*, pg. 30
SHANNON MEDICAL CENTER—See Shannon Health System; *U.S. Private*, pg. 3625
SHARON CLINIC COMPANY, LLC—See Community Health Systems, Inc.; *U.S. Public*, pg. 556
SHARON HOME CARE SERVICES, LLC—See Community Health Systems, Inc.; *U.S. Public*, pg. 556
SHARON REGIONAL HEALTH SYSTEM, INC.—See Community Health Systems, Inc.; *U.S. Public*, pg. 556
SHARP HEALTHCARE—See Blackstone Inc.; *U.S. Public*, pg. 359
SHC-KPH, LP—See Universal Health Services, Inc.; *U.S. Public*, pg. 2259
SHELBYVILLE CLINIC CORP.—See Community Health Systems, Inc.; *U.S. Public*, pg. 556
SHELBYVILLE HOME CARE SERVICES, LLC—See Community Health Systems, Inc.; *U.S. Public*, pg. 556
SHELBYVILLE HOSPITAL CORPORATION—See Community Health Systems, Inc.; *U.S. Public*, pg. 556
SHEPHERD CENTER, INC.; *U.S. Private*, pg. 3632
SHERIDAN RADIOLOGY SERVICES OF CENTRAL FLORIDA, INC.—See KKR & Co. Inc.; *U.S. Public*, pg. 1246
SHERIDAN RADIOLOGY SERVICES OF KENTUCKY, INC.—See KKR & Co. Inc.; *U.S. Public*, pg. 1246
SHERIDAN RADIOLOGY SERVICES OF PINELLAS, INC.—See KKR & Co. Inc.; *U.S. Public*, pg. 1246
SHERIDAN RADIOLOGY SERVICES OF VIRGINIA, INC.—See KKR & Co. Inc.; *U.S. Public*, pg. 1246
SHIJI INFORMATION TECHNOLOGY SPAIN, S.A.—See Beijing Shiji Information Technology Co., Ltd.; *Int'l*, pg. 956
SHONAN ROBO CARE CENTER CO., LTD.—See Cyberdyne Inc.; *Int'l*, pg. 1893
SHORELINE SURGERY CENTER, LLP—See Tenet Healthcare Corporation; *U.S. Public*, pg. 2012
SHORT GROUND LIMITED—See Universal Health Services, Inc.; *U.S. Public*, pg. 2259
SHORT HILLS SURGERY CENTER, LLC—See KKR & Co. Inc.; *U.S. Public*, pg. 1246
SHREWSBURY SURGERY CENTER, LLC—See Tenet Healthcare Corporation; *U.S. Public*, pg. 2012
SHUI JUN NURSING CENTRE (YAU TONG) COMPANY LIMITED—See Hang Chi Holdings Limited; *Int'l*, pg. 3244
SHUI ON NURSING CENTRE (KWAI SHING E.) CO., LIMITED—See Hang Chi Holdings Limited; *Int'l*, pg. 3244
SICAT GMBH & CO. KG—See DENTSPLY SIRONA Inc.; *U.S. Public*, pg. 655
SIDNEY HEALTH CENTER; *U.S. Private*, pg. 3646
SID PETERSON MEMORIAL HOSPITAL; *U.S. Private*, pg. 3645
SIERRA NEVADA MEMORIAL HOSPITAL—See Catholic Health Initiatives; *U.S. Private*, pg. 790
SIERRA TUCSON INC.—See Acadia Healthcare Company, Inc.; *U.S. Public*, pg. 30
SIERRA VISTA HOSPITAL, INC.—See Adventist Health System; *U.S. Private*, pg. 108
SIGHTLINE HEALTH; *U.S. Private*, pg. 3648
SILVER CREEK MRI, LLC—See Community Health Systems, Inc.; *U.S. Public*, pg. 557
SILVER CROSS AMBULATORY SURGERY CENTER, LLC—See Tenet Healthcare Corporation; *U.S. Public*, pg. 2007
SILVER HILL HOSPITAL, INC.; *U.S. Private*, pg. 3653
SILVERTON HEALTH; *U.S. Private*, pg. 3664
SINAI HEALTH SYSTEM; *U.S. Private*, pg. 3669
SINGAPORE INSTITUTE OF ADVANCED MEDICINE HOLDINGS PTE LTD—See Berjaya Corporation Berhad; *Int'l*, pg. 984
SISTERS OF CHARITY HOSPITAL OF BUFFALO, NEW YORK—See Catholic Health System, Inc.; *U.S. Private*, pg. 791
SISTERS OF CHARITY HOSPITAL - ST. JOSEPH CAMPUS—See Catholic Health System, Inc.; *U.S. Private*, pg. 791
SISTERS OF CHARITY OF LEAVENWORTH HEALTH SYSTEM—See Intermountain Healthcare Inc.; *U.S. Private*, pg. 2113
SKYLINE MEDICAL CENTER—See HCA Healthcare, Inc.; *U.S. Public*, pg. 1008
SKYRIDGE CLINICAL ASSOCIATES, LLC—See Community Health Systems, Inc.; *U.S. Public*, pg. 557
SKY RIDGE MEDICAL CENTER—See HCA Healthcare, Inc.; *U.S. Public*, pg. 1008
SKYWAY HOUSE, LLC—See Acadia Healthcare Company, Inc.; *U.S. Public*, pg. 30
SLH VISTA, INC.—See Tenet Healthcare Corporation; *U.S. Public*, pg. 2006
SMMC MEDICAL GROUP—See Quorum Health Corporation; *U.S. Private*, pg. 3330
SOBER LIVING BY THE SEA, INC.—See Acadia Healthcare Company, Inc.; *U.S. Public*, pg. 30
SOCIEDADE GESTORA DO HOSPITAL DE LOURES, S.A.—See Fosun International Limited; *Int'l*, pg. 2751
SOC TELEMED, INC.—See Patient Square Capital, L.P.; *U.S. Private*, pg. 3107
SOLIS MAMMOGRAPHY AT MEDICAL CENTER OF PLANO, LLC—See HCA Healthcare, Inc.; *U.S. Public*, pg. 1009
SOMERSET OUTPATIENT SURGERY, LLC—See UnitedHealth Group Incorporated; *U.S. Public*, pg. 2250
SONIMED DIAGNOSTICOS LTDA.—See Centro de Imagem Diagnosticos S.A.; *Int'l*, pg. 1414
SONORA BEHAVIORAL HEALTH HOSPITAL, LLC—See Acadia Healthcare Company, Inc.; *U.S. Public*, pg. 30
SOTERIA KLINIK LEIPZIG GMBH—See Asklepios Kliniken GmbH & Co, KGaA; *Int'l*, pg. 624
SOTTO INTERNATIONAL, INC.; *U.S. Private*, pg. 3716
SOUND SHORE MEDICAL CENTER OF WESTCHESTER; *U.S. Private*, pg. 3717
SOUTH ARKANSAS PHYSICIAN SERVICES, LLC—See Community Health Systems, Inc.; *U.S. Public*, pg. 557
SOUTH BAY HOSPITAL—See HCA Healthcare, Inc.; *U.S. Public*, pg. 1010
THE SOUTH BEND IN ENDOSCOPY ASC, LLC—See KKR & Co. Inc.; *U.S. Public*, pg. 1248
SOUTH BOSTON COMMUNITY HEALTH CENTER; *U.S. Private*, pg. 3720
SOUTH BROWARD HOSPITAL DISTRICT; *U.S. Private*, pg. 3720
SOUTH DAVIS COMMUNITY HOSPITAL; *U.S. Private*, pg. 3722
SOUTHEAST MICHIGAN SURGICAL HOSPITAL, LLC—See Bain Capital, LP; *U.S. Private*, pg. 445
SOUTHEAST MISSOURI HOSPITAL ASSOCIATION; *U.S. Private*, pg. 3726
SOUTHEAST OHIO SURGICAL SUITES, LLC—See Tenet Healthcare Corporation; *U.S. Public*, pg. 2007
SOUTH END COMMUNITY HEALTH CENTER—See East Boston Neighborhood Health Center Corp.; *U.S. Private*, pg. 1315
SOUTHERN CRESCENT ANESTHESIOLOGY, PC—See Bain Capital, LP; *U.S. Private*, pg. 446
SOUTHERN CRESCENT NURSE ANESTHESIA, LLC—See Bain Capital, LP; *U.S. Private*, pg. 446
SOUTHERN HEALTH CORPORATION OF DAHLONGEA, INC.—See SunLink Health Systems, Inc.; *U.S. Public*, pg. 1964
SOUTHERN HEALTH CORPORATION OF ELLIJAY, INC.—See SunLink Health Systems, Inc.; *U.S. Public*, pg. 1964
SOUTHERN HEALTH CORPORATION OF HOUSTON, INC.—See SunLink Health Systems, Inc.; *U.S. Public*, pg. 1964
SOUTHERN HILLS MEDICAL CENTER—See HCA Healthcare, Inc.; *U.S. Public*, pg. 1010
SOUTHERN ILLINOIS HEALTHCARE FOUNDATION; *U.S. Private*, pg. 3732
SOUTHERN ILLINOIS MEDICAL CARE ASSOCIATES, LLC—See Quorum Health Corporation; *U.S. Private*, pg. 3330
SOUTHERN INDIANA TREATMENT CENTER, LLC—See Acadia Healthcare Company, Inc.; *U.S. Public*, pg. 30
SOUTHERN KENTUCKY MEDICINE ASSOCIATES, LLC—See HCA Healthcare, Inc.; *U.S. Public*, pg. 1010
SOUTHERN MAINE HEALTH CARE; *U.S. Private*, pg. 3733
SOUTHERN OCEAN MEDICAL CENTER—See Hackensack Meridian Health, Inc.; *U.S. Private*, pg. 1838
SOUTHERN ORTHOPEDICS AND SPORTS MEDICINE, L.L.C.—See Tenet Healthcare Corporation; *U.S. Public*, pg. 2003
SOUTHERN REGIONAL HEALTH SYSTEM—See Prime Healthcare Services, Inc.; *U.S. Private*, pg. 3262
SOUTHERN TENNESSEE REGIONAL HEALTH SYSTEM—See Apollo Global Management, Inc.; *U.S. Public*, pg. 158
SOUTH FLORIDA BAPTIST HOSPITAL—See BayCare Health System Inc.; *U.S. Private*, pg. 496
SOUTH LAKES SURGICENTER, LLC—See HCA Healthcare, Inc.; *U.S. Public*, pg. 1010
SOUTH MIAMI HOSPITAL—See Baptist Health South Florida, Inc.; *U.S. Private*, pg. 471
SOUTH SHORE HOSPITAL; *U.S. Private*, pg. 3723
SOUTH SHORE HOSPITAL—See Partners HealthCare System, Inc.; *U.S. Private*, pg. 3102
SOUTHSIDE MEDICAL CENTER INC; *U.S. Private*, pg. 3738
SOUTHSTONE BEHAVIORAL HEALTHCARE CENTER, LLC—See Acadia Healthcare Company, Inc.; *U.S. Public*, pg. 30
SOUTH TEXAS ACO CLINICAL PARTNERS, LLC—See Universal Health Services, Inc.; *U.S. Public*, pg. 2259
SOUTHWEST COMMUNITY HEALTH CENTER, INC.; *U.S. Private*, pg. 3738
SOUTHWEST ENDOSCOPY, LLC—See Tenet Healthcare Corporation; *U.S. Public*, pg. 2007
SOUTHWESTERN CHILDREN'S HEALTH SERVICES, INC.—See Acadia Healthcare Company, Inc.; *U.S. Public*, pg. 30
SOUTHWESTERN ILLINOIS HEALTH FACILITIES, INC.; *U.S. Private*, pg. 3741
SOUTHWESTERN MEDICAL CENTER—See Apollo Global Management, Inc.; *U.S. Public*, pg. 159
SOUTHWEST FREEWAY SURGERY CENTER MANAGEMENT, LLC—See Nobilis Health Corp.; *U.S. Private*, pg. 2932
SOUTHWEST HEALTHCARE SERVICES; *U.S. Private*, pg. 3739
SOUTHWEST HEALTHCARE SYSTEM—See Universal Health Services, Inc.; *U.S. Public*, pg. 2260
SOUTHWEST HEALTH CENTER; *U.S. Private*, pg. 3739
SOUTHWEST HEALTH SYSTEM, INC.; *U.S. Private*, pg. 3739
SOUTHWEST LOUISIANA HOSPITAL ASSOCIATION; *U.S. Private*, pg. 3739
SOUTHWEST MEDICAL CENTER; *U.S. Private*, pg. 3740
SOUTHWEST MEDICAL CENTER SURGICAL GROUP, LLC—See HCA Healthcare, Inc.; *U.S. Public*, pg. 1010
SOUTHWOOD PSYCHIATRIC HOSPITAL, INC.—See Acadia Healthcare Company, Inc.; *U.S. Public*, pg. 30
SPARKS FAMILY HOSPITAL, INC.—See Universal Health Services, Inc.; *U.S. Public*, pg. 2259
SPARKS PREMIERCARE, L.L.C.—See Community Health Systems, Inc.; *U.S. Public*, pg. 557
SPARROW CARSON HOSPITAL—See University of Michigan; *U.S. Private*, pg. 4309
SPARROW CLINTON HOSPITAL—See University of Michigan; *U.S. Private*, pg. 4309
SPARROW EATON HOSPITAL—See University of Michigan; *U.S. Private*, pg. 4309
SPARROW IONIA HOSPITAL—See University of Michigan; *U.S. Private*, pg. 4309
SPARTANBURG MEDICAL CENTER—See Spartanburg Regional Health Services District, Inc.; *U.S. Private*, pg. 3747
SPECIALISTS ON CALL, INC.—See Patient Square Capital, L.P.; *U.S. Private*, pg. 3107
SPECIALTY ASSOCIATES OF WEST HOUSTON, PLLC—See HCA Healthcare, Inc.; *U.S. Public*, pg. 1010
SPECIALTY HEALTHCARE SERVICES, INC.—See Apollo Global Management, Inc.; *U.S. Public*, pg. 157
SPECIALTY THERAPEUTIC CARE, GP, LLC—See Centene Corporation; *U.S. Public*, pg. 470
SPOKANE VALLEY WASHINGTON HOSPITAL COMPANY, LLC—See Community Health Systems, Inc.; *U.S. Public*, pg. 557
SPOTSYLVANIA MULTI-SPECIALTY GROUP, LLC—See HCA Healthcare, Inc.; *U.S. Public*, pg. 1010
SPOTSYLVANIA REGIONAL MEDICAL CENTER—See HCA Healthcare, Inc.; *U.S. Public*, pg. 1010
SPOTSYLVANIA REGIONAL MEDICAL CENTER—See HCA Healthcare, Inc.; *U.S. Public*, pg. 1010
SPRINGFIELD PARK VIEW HOSPITAL, L.L.C.—See Apollo Global Management, Inc.; *U.S. Public*, pg. 157
SPRINGHILL HOSPITALS, INC.—See Southern Medical Health Systems Inc.; *U.S. Private*, pg. 3733
SPRING HILL IMAGING, LLC—See HCA Healthcare, Inc.; *U.S. Public*, pg. 1010
SPRINGHILL MEDICAL SERVICES, INC.; *U.S. Private*, pg. 3764
SPRING VIEW HOSPITAL, LLC—See Apollo Global Management, Inc.; *U.S. Public*, pg. 158
SRL, INC. - HACHINOHE SALES DIVISION—See H.U. Group Holdings, Inc.; *Int'l*, pg. 3197
SRL, INC. - IWAKI SALES DIVISION—See H.U. Group Holdings, Inc.; *Int'l*, pg. 3197
SRL, INC. - KAWAGOE SALES DIVISION I—See H.U. Group Holdings, Inc.; *Int'l*, pg. 3197
SRL, INC. - KITAMI SALES DIVISION—See H.U. Group Holdings, Inc.; *Int'l*, pg. 3197
SRL, INC. - KOBE SALES DIVISION V—See H.U. Group Holdings, Inc.; *Int'l*, pg. 3197
SRL, INC. - KUSHIRO SALES DIVISION—See H.U. Group Holdings, Inc.; *Int'l*, pg. 3198
SRL, INC. - SAKATA SALES DIVISION—See H.U. Group Holdings, Inc.; *Int'l*, pg. 3198
SRL, INC. - SHIMANE SALES DIVISION—See H.U. Group Holdings, Inc.; *Int'l*, pg. 3198
SRL, INC. - TOMAKOMAI SALES DIVISION—See H.U.

N.A.I.C.S. INDEX 622110 — GENERAL MEDICAL AND...

N.A.I.C.S. Index

Group Holdings, Inc.; *Int'l*, pg. 3198
SRL, INC. - YAMAGUCHI SALES DIVISION—See H.U. Group Holdings, Inc.; *Int'l*, pg. 3199
SRL LABORATORIES CREATE, INC.—See H.U. Group Holdings, Inc.; *Int'l*, pg. 3197
SSM SELECT REHAB ST. LOUIS, LLC—See Select Medical Holdings Corporation; *U.S. Public*, pg. 1859
SSM ST. CLARE SURGICAL CENTER, L.L.C.—See Tenet Healthcare Corporation; *U.S. Public*, pg. 2012
ST. AGNES MEDICAL CENTER—See Trinity Health Corporation; *U.S. Private*, pg. 4234
ST. ALEXIUS MEDICAL CENTER; *U.S. Private*, pg. 3770
ST. ALPHONSUS REGIONAL MEDICAL CENTER—See Trinity Health Corporation; *U.S. Private*, pg. 4234
ST. ANNE'S MATERNITY HOME; *U.S. Private*, pg. 3770
ST. ANTHONY REGIONAL HOSPITAL & NURSING HOME; *U.S. Private*, pg. 3770
ST. ANTHONY'S HOSPITAL—See BayCare Health System Inc.; *U.S. Private*, pg. 495
ST. ANTHONY'S MEDICAL CENTER; *U.S. Private*, pg. 3770
STARK AMBULATORY SURGERY CENTER, LLC—See Tenet Healthcare Corporation; *U.S. Public*, pg. 2007
STARLITE RECOVERY CENTER, LLC—See Acadia Healthcare Company, Inc.; *U.S. Public*, pg. 30
STATESBORO HMA, INC.—See Community Health Systems, Inc.; *U.S. Public*, pg. 557
STATESVILLE HMA, INC.—See Community Health Systems, Inc.; *U.S. Public*, pg. 557
STAT HEALTH, LLC—See Teladoc Health, Inc.; *U.S. Public*, pg. 1992
STATLAND MEDICAL GROUP, LLC—See HCA Healthcare, Inc.; *U.S. Public*, pg. 1010
ST. AUGUSTINE ENDOSCOPY CENTER, LLC—See Tenet Healthcare Corporation; *U.S. Public*, pg. 2007
STAYWELL HEALTH CARE, INC.; *U.S. Private*, pg. 3794
ST. BERNARDS HEALTHCARE, INC.; *U.S. Private*, pg. 3771
ST. CATHERINE OF SIENA MEDICAL CENTER—See Catholic Health Services of Long Island; *U.S. Private*, pg. 791
ST. CHARLES HOSPITAL—See Catholic Health Services of Long Island; *U.S. Private*, pg. 791
ST. CHRISTOPHER'S HOSPITAL FOR CHILDREN, LLC—See Drexel University; *U.S. Private*, pg. 1276
ST. CHRISTOPHER'S HOSPITAL FOR CHILDREN, LLC—See Tower Health; *U.S. Private*, pg. 4193
ST. CLAIR DARDEN HEALTH SYSTEM; *U.S. Private*, pg. 3770
ST. CLAIR SHORES MI OPHTHALMOLOGY ASC, LLC—See KKR & Co. Inc.; *U.S. Public*, pg. 1246
THE ST. CLOUD MN OPHTHALMOLOGY ASC, LLC—See KKR & Co. Inc.; *U.S. Public*, pg. 1248
ST. DAVID'S GEORGETOWN HOSPITAL—See HCA Healthcare, Inc.; *U.S. Public*, pg. 1010
ST. DAVID'S MEDICAL CENTER—See HCA Healthcare, Inc.; *U.S. Public*, pg. 1010
ST. DAVID'S SOUTH AUSTIN MEDICAL CENTER—See HCA Healthcare, Inc.; *U.S. Public*, pg. 1010
ST. DAVIS'S SOUTH AUSTIN MEDICAL CENTER—See HCA Healthcare, Inc.; *U.S. Public*, pg. 1010
ST. ELISABETH-KRANKENHAUS GMBH—See Fresenius SE & Co. KGaA; *Int'l*, pg. 2779
ST. ELIZABETH COMMUNITY HOSPITAL—See Catholic Health Initiatives; *U.S. Private*, pg. 789
STERLING RIDGE MEDICAL CENTER LLC—See Adeptus Health Inc.; *U.S. Private*, pg. 78
STERN CARDIOVASCULAR FOUNDATION; *U.S. Private*, pg. 3807
STEVENS COMMUNITY MEDICAL CENTER; *U.S. Private*, pg. 3809
STEWARD EASTON HOSPITAL, INC.—See Steward Health Care System LLC; *U.S. Private*, pg. 3810
STEWARD HEALTH CARE SYSTEM LLC; *U.S. Private*, pg. 3810
STEWARD MELBOURNE HOSPITAL, INC.—See Steward Health Care System LLC; *U.S. Private*, pg. 3810
STEWARD ROCKLEDGE HOSPITAL, INC.—See Steward Health Care System LLC; *U.S. Private*, pg. 3810
STEWARD SEBASTIAN RIVER MEDICAL CENTER, INC.—See Steward Health Care System LLC; *U.S. Private*, pg. 3810
STEWARD SHARON REGIONAL HEALTH SYSTEM, INC.—See Steward Health Care System LLC; *U.S. Private*, pg. 3810
STEWARD TRUMBULL MEMORIAL HOSPITAL, INC.—See Steward Health Care System LLC; *U.S. Private*, pg. 3810
ST. FRANCIS HEALTH, LLC—See Apollo Global Management, Inc.; *U.S. Public*, pg. 159
ST. FRANCIS HOSPITAL—See Catholic Health Services of Long Island; *U.S. Private*, pg. 791
ST. FRANCIS MEDICAL CENTER—See Daughters of Charity Health System; *U.S. Private*, pg. 1167
STIFTUNG DEUTSCHE KLINIK FUR DIAGNOSTIK GMBH—See Fresenius SE & Co. KGaA; *Int'l*, pg. 2779
ST. JOHN CONNER CREEK VILLAGE—See Ascension Health Alliance; *U.S. Private*, pg. 347
ST. JOHN HEALTH SYSTEM INC.; *U.S. Private*, pg. 3771
ST. JOHN HOSPITAL & MEDICAL CENTER—See Ascension Health Alliance; *U.S. Private*, pg. 347
ST. JOHN MACOMB HOSPITAL—See Ascension Health Alliance; *U.S. Private*, pg. 347
ST. JOHN OAKLAND HOSPITAL—See Ascension Health Alliance; *U.S. Private*, pg. 347
ST. JOHN PROVIDENCE HEALTH SYSTEM—See Ascension Health Alliance; *U.S. Private*, pg. 347
ST. JOHN RIVER DISTRICT HOSPITAL—See Ascension Health Alliance; *U.S. Private*, pg. 347
ST. JOHN'S HOSPITAL OF THE HOSPITAL SISTERS OF THE THIRD ORDER OF ST. FRANCIS-SPRINGFIELD—See Hospital Sisters Health System; *U.S. Private*, pg. 1987
ST. JOHN'S MERCY HEALTH CARE—See Sisters of Mercy Health System; *U.S. Private*, pg. 3676
ST. JOHN'S PLEASANT VALLEY HOSPITAL—See Catholic Health Initiatives; *U.S. Private*, pg. 789
ST. JOSEPH HOSPITAL—See Catholic Health Services of Long Island; *U.S. Private*, pg. 791
ST. JOSEPH MANOR HEALTH CARE INC.; *U.S. Private*, pg. 3772
ST. JOSEPH MEDICAL CENTER—See Prime Healthcare Services, Inc.; *U.S. Private*, pg. 3262
ST. JOSEPH MERCY OAKLAND—See Trinity Health Corporation; *U.S. Private*, pg. 4234
ST. JOSEPH MERCY PORT HURON—See Trinity Health Corporation; *U.S. Private*, pg. 4234
ST. JOSEPH REGIONAL HEALTH NETWORK—See Penn State Health; *U.S. Private*, pg. 3134
ST. JOSEPH REGIONAL MEDICAL CENTER—See Ascension Health Alliance; *U.S. Private*, pg. 347
ST. JOSEPH'S-BAPTIST HEALTH CARE—See BayCare Health System Inc.; *U.S. Private*, pg. 495
ST. JOSEPH'S BEHAVIORAL HEALTH CENTER—See Catholic Health Initiatives; *U.S. Private*, pg. 790
ST. JOSEPH'S/CANDLER; *U.S. Private*, pg. 3772
ST. JOSEPH'S CHILDREN'S HOSPITAL—See BayCare Health System Inc.; *U.S. Private*, pg. 496
ST. JOSEPH'S HOSPITAL-NORTH—See BayCare Health System Inc.; *U.S. Private*, pg. 496
ST. JOSEPH'S HOSPITAL—See Ascension Health Alliance; *U.S. Private*, pg. 347
ST. JOSEPH'S HOSPITAL—See BayCare Health System Inc.; *U.S. Private*, pg. 496
ST. JOSEPHS MEDICAL CENTER—See Catholic Health Initiatives; *U.S. Private*, pg. 790
ST. JOSEPH'S OUTPATIENT SURGERY CENTER, LLC—See Tenet Healthcare Corporation; *U.S. Public*, pg. 2013
ST. JOSEPH'S SURGERY CENTER, L.P.—See Tenet Healthcare Corporation; *U.S. Public*, pg. 2013
ST. JOSEPH'S WOMEN'S HOSPITAL—See BayCare Health System Inc.; *U.S. Private*, pg. 496
THE ST. LOUIS MO ORTHOPAEDIC ASC, LLC—See KKR & Co. Inc.; *U.S. Public*, pg. 1248
ST. LOUIS SPECIALTY SURGICAL CENTER, LLC—See UnitedHealth Group Incorporated; *U.S. Public*, pg. 2250
ST. LUCIE MEDICAL CENTER—See HCA Healthcare, Inc.; *U.S. Public*, pg. 1010
ST. LUCIE MEDICAL SPECIALISTS, LLC—See HCA Healthcare, Inc.; *U.S. Public*, pg. 1010
ST. LUKE'S CORNWALL HOSPITAL—See Montefiore Medical Center; *U.S. Private*, pg. 2776
ST. LUKE'S DES PERES HOSPITAL—See St. Luke's Hospital; *U.S. Private*, pg. 3773
ST. LUKE'S FREE MEDICAL CLINIC; *U.S. Private*, pg. 3772
ST. LUKE'S HOSPITAL; *U.S. Private*, pg. 3773
ST. MARK'S HOSPITAL—See HCA Healthcare, Inc.; *U.S. Public*, pg. 1010
ST. MARY MEDICAL CENTER—See Catholic Health Initiatives; *U.S. Private*, pg. 789
ST. MARY'S HEALTH CARE SYSTEM; *U.S. Private*, pg. 3773
ST. MARY'S HOSPITAL—See Ascension Health Alliance; *U.S. Private*, pg. 347
ST. MARY'S MEDICAL CENTER, INC.—See Cabell Huntington Hospital, Inc.; *U.S. Private*, pg. 710
ST. MARY'S MEDICAL CENTER, INC.—See Tenet Healthcare Corporation; *U.S. Public*, pg. 2008
ST. MARY'S MEDICAL CENTER—See Prime Healthcare Services, Inc.; *U.S. Private*, pg. 3262
ST. MARY'S MEDICAL PARK PHARMACY, INC.—See Select Medical Holdings Corporation; *U.S. Public*, pg. 1861
ST. MARY'S SURGICAL CENTER, LLC—See Tenet Healthcare Corporation; *U.S. Public*, pg. 2013
STONECREST MEDICAL GROUP - FAMILY PRACTICE OF MURFREESBORO, LLC—See HCA Healthcare, Inc.; *U.S. Public*, pg. 1010
ST. PETERSBURG GENERAL HOSPITAL—See HCA Healthcare, Inc.; *U.S. Public*, pg. 1010
STRATHMORE COLLEGE LIMITED—See Acadia Healthcare Company, Inc.; *U.S. Public*, pg. 30
STURDY MEMORIAL HOSPITAL; *U.S. Private*, pg. 3844
ST. VINCENT HOSPITAL; *U.S. Private*, pg. 3773
ST. VINCENT MEDICAL CENTER—See The Chan Soon-Shiong Family Foundation; *U.S. Private*, pg. 4007
ST. VINCENT'S HEALTHCARE—See Ascension Health Alliance; *U.S. Private*, pg. 347
ST. VINCENT'S MEDICAL CENTER RIVERSIDE—See Ascension Health Alliance; *U.S. Private*, pg. 348
ST. VINCENT'S MEDICAL CENTER SOUTHSIDE—See Ascension Health Alliance; *U.S. Private*, pg. 348
SUCCESS ACQUISITION CORPORATION—See Acadia Healthcare Company, Inc.; *U.S. Public*, pg. 30
SUGARITE DIALYSIS, LLC—See DaVita Inc.; *U.S. Public*, pg. 643
SUGAR LAND SURGERY CENTER, LTD.—See HCA Healthcare, Inc.; *U.S. Public*, pg. 1011
SUMMIT AMBULATORY SURGICAL CENTER, L.L.C.—See Tenet Healthcare Corporation; *U.S. Public*, pg. 2007
SUMMIT MEDICAL CENTER—See HCA Healthcare, Inc.; *U.S. Public*, pg. 1012
SUMMIT OAKS HOSPITAL, INC.—See Universal Health Services, Inc.; *U.S. Public*, pg. 2259
SUMMIT SURGERY CENTER, L.P.—See HCA Healthcare, Inc.; *U.S. Public*, pg. 1011
SUMNER REGIONAL MEDICAL CENTER, LLC—See Apollo Global Management, Inc.; *U.S. Public*, pg. 159
SUNBURY CLINIC COMPANY, LLC—See Quorum Health Corporation; *U.S. Private*, pg. 3330
THE SUNCOAST ENDOSCOPY ASC, L.P.—See KKR & Co. Inc.; *U.S. Public*, pg. 1248
SUNCOAST SPECIALTY SURGERY CENTER, LLLP—See Bain Capital, LP; *U.S. Private*, pg. 446
SUN HEALTH SERVICES; *U.S. Private*, pg. 3863
SUNLINK HEALTHCARE LLC—See SunLink Health Systems, Inc.; *U.S. Public*, pg. 1964
SUNLINK HEALTH SYSTEMS, INC.; *U.S. Public*, pg. 1964
SUNRISE HOSPITAL AND MEDICAL CENTER, LLC—See HCA Healthcare, Inc.; *U.S. Public*, pg. 1011
SUNRISE HOSPITAL & MEDICAL CENTER—See HCA Healthcare, Inc.; *U.S. Public*, pg. 1011
SUNRISE TRAUMA SERVICES, LLC—See HCA Healthcare, Inc.; *U.S. Public*, pg. 1011
SUN VIEW IMAGING, L.L.C.—See Tenet Healthcare Corporation; *U.S. Public*, pg. 2004
SURGCENTER OF GLEN BURNIE, LLC—See Tenet Healthcare Corporation; *U.S. Public*, pg. 2007
SURGCENTER OF PLANO, LLC—See Tenet Healthcare Corporation; *U.S. Public*, pg. 2007
SURGCENTER OF THE POTOMAC, LLC—See Tenet Healthcare Corporation; *U.S. Public*, pg. 2007
SURGERY ASSOCIATES OF NTX, PLLC—See HCA Healthcare, Inc.; *U.S. Public*, pg. 1011
SURGERY CENTER AT COTTONWOOD, LLC—See UnitedHealth Group Incorporated; *U.S. Public*, pg. 2250
THE SURGERY CENTER AT JENSEN BEACH, LLC—See Tenet Healthcare Corporation; *U.S. Public*, pg. 2009
THE SURGERY CENTER AT WILLIAMSON, LLC—See Tenet Healthcare Corporation; *U.S. Public*, pg. 2013
SURGERY CENTER OF ATLANTA, LLC—See Tenet Healthcare Corporation; *U.S. Public*, pg. 2013
SURGERY CENTER OF AVENTURA, LTD.—See HCA Healthcare, Inc.; *U.S. Public*, pg. 1011
SURGERY CENTER OF KALAMAZOO, LLC—See Bain Capital, LP; *U.S. Private*, pg. 446
SURGERY CENTER OF KEY WEST, LLC—See Community Health Systems, Inc.; *U.S. Public*, pg. 557
SURGERY CENTER OF LANCASTER, LLC—See Nueterra Capital Management, LLC; *U.S. Private*, pg. 2972
SURGERY CENTER OF MIDWEST CITY, LLC—See Community Health Systems, Inc.; *U.S. Public*, pg. 557
SURGERY CENTER OF PORT CHARLOTTE, LTD.—See HCA Healthcare, Inc.; *U.S. Public*, pg. 1011
SURGERY CENTER OF SOUTH CENTRAL KANSAS—See KKR & Co. Inc.; *U.S. Public*, pg. 1247
SURGERY CENTRE OF SW FLORIDA, LLC—See Tenet Healthcare Corporation; *U.S. Public*, pg. 2007
SURGERY PARTNERS HOLDINGS LLC—See Bain Capital, LP; *U.S. Private*, pg. 446
SURGERY PARTNERS, INC.—See Bain Capital, LP; *U.S. Private*, pg. 444
SURGERY SPECIALTY HOSPITALS OF AMERICA (SSHA)—See Dynacq Healthcare, Inc.; *U.S. Private*, pg. 1297
SURGICAL AND MEDICAL SUPPLIES PTY. LTD.—See EBOS Group Limited; *Int'l*, pg. 2286
SURGICAL CENTER OF EL PASO—See HCA Healthcare, Inc.; *U.S. Public*, pg. 1011
SURGICAL HOSPITAL OF AUSTIN, L.P.—See Bain Capital, LP; *U.S. Private*, pg. 447
SURGICAL HOSPITAL OF OKLAHOMA, LLC—See UnitedHealth Group Incorporated; *U.S. Public*, pg. 2251
SURGICAL INSTITUTE OF READING, LLC—See Tenet Healthcare Corporation; *U.S. Public*, pg. 2013
SURGICAL PARK CENTER, LTD.—See HCA Healthcare, Inc.; *U.S. Public*, pg. 1011
SURGICAL SPECIALISTS AT PRINCETON, LLC—See Tenet Healthcare Corporation; *U.S. Public*, pg. 2013
SURGICAL SPECIALISTS OF CLEAR LAKE, PLLC—See HCA Healthcare, Inc.; *U.S. Public*, pg. 1011
SURGICAL SPECIALTY CENTER OF MID-ATLANTIC, LLC—See Tenet Healthcare Corporation; *U.S. Public*, pg. 2007

SURGICARE OF CENTRAL JERSEY, LLC—See United-Health Group Incorporated; *U.S. Public*, pg. 2251
SURGICARE OF CORPUS CHRISTI, LLC—See HCA Healthcare, Inc.; *U.S. Public*, pg. 1011
SURGICARE OF COUNTRYSIDE, INC.—See HCA Healthcare, Inc.; *U.S. Public*, pg. 1011
SURGICARE OF SALEM, LLC—See HCA Healthcare, Inc.; *U.S. Public*, pg. 1011
SURGICARE OF SOUTH AUSTIN, INC.—See HCA Healthcare, Inc.; *U.S. Public*, pg. 1011
SURGICARE OF SOUTH AUSTIN—See HCA Healthcare, Inc.; *U.S. Public*, pg. 1011
SURGICARE OF SOUTHERN HILLS, INC.—See HCA Healthcare, Inc.; *U.S. Public*, pg. 1011
SURGICARE OF WASATCH FRONT, LLC—See HCA Healthcare, Inc.; *U.S. Public*, pg. 1011
SURGICARE OF WICHITA, LLC—See HCA Healthcare, Inc.; *U.S. Public*, pg. 1011
SURGICARE OUTPATIENT CENTER OF LAKE CHARLES, INC.—See Community Health Systems, Inc.; *U.S. Public*, pg. 557
SURGICENTER OF JOHNSON COUNTY, LTD.—See HCA Healthcare, Inc.; *U.S. Public*, pg. 1011
SURGICENTER OF JOHNSON COUNTY—See HCA Healthcare, Inc.; *U.S. Public*, pg. 1003
SUTTER AMADOR HOSPITAL—See Sutter Health; *U.S. Private*, pg. 3887
SUTTER DAVIS HOSPITAL—See Sutter Health; *U.S. Private*, pg. 3887
SUTTER DELTA MEDICAL CENTER—See Sutter Health; *U.S. Private*, pg. 3887
SUTTER LAKESIDE HOSPITAL—See Sutter Health; *U.S. Private*, pg. 3887
SUTTER MEDICAL CENTER, SACRAMENTO—See Sutter Health; *U.S. Private*, pg. 3887
SUWS OF THE CAROLINAS, INC.—See Acadia Healthcare Company, Inc.; *U.S. Public*, pg. 30
SWEDISHAMERICAN HEALTH SYSTEM; *U.S. Private*, pg. 3891
SWEETWATER HOSPITAL ASSOCIATION; *U.S. Private*, pg. 3892
SWIFT RIVER ACADEMY, L.L.C.—See Acadia Healthcare Company, Inc.; *U.S. Public*, pg. 30
SWISS MEDICAL NETWORK SA—See AEVIS VICTORIA SA; *Int'l*, pg. 183
SYCAMORE SHOALS HOSPITAL, INC.—See HCA Healthcare, Inc.; *U.S. Public*, pg. 1011
TALLAHASSEE MEMORIAL HEALTHCARE; *U.S. Private*, pg. 3927
TALLAHASSEE OUTPATIENT SURGERY CENTER—See HCA Healthcare, Inc.; *U.S. Public*, pg. 1011
TAMARAC SURGERY CENTER, LLC—See Tenet Healthcare Corporation; *U.S. Public*, pg. 2013
TAMPA EYE & SPECIALTY SURGERY CENTER—See HCA Healthcare, Inc.; *U.S. Public*, pg. 1011
TARRANT COUNTY INDIGENT CARE CORPORATION; *U.S. Private*, pg. 3934
TARRANT COUNTY SURGERY CENTER, L.P.—See HCA Healthcare, Inc.; *U.S. Public*, pg. 1011
TASK FORCE FOR GLOBAL HEALTH, INC.; *U.S. Private*, pg. 3934
TECHE ACTION BOARD INC; *U.S. Private*, pg. 3952
TELERHYTHMICS, LLC—See G Medical Innovations Holdings Ltd.; *Int'l*, pg. 2861
TEMECULA VALLEY HOSPITAL, INC.—See Universal Health Services, Inc.; *U.S. Public*, pg. 2259
TEN BROECK TAMPA, LLC—See Acadia Healthcare Company, Inc.; *U.S. Public*, pg. 30
TENET HEALTHCARE CORPORATION; *U.S. Public*, pg. 2001
TENET HEALTHSYSTEM HAHNEMANN, LLC—See Paladin Healthcare Capital, LLC; *U.S. Private*, pg. 3076
TENET HEALTHSYSTEM MEDICAL, INC.—See Tenet Healthcare Corporation; *U.S. Public*, pg. 2007
TENET SOUTH CAROLINA ISLAND MEDICAL, L.L.C.—See Tenet Healthcare Corporation; *U.S. Public*, pg. 2008
TENET SOUTH CAROLINA LOWCOUNTRY OB/GYN, L.L.C.—See Tenet Healthcare Corporation; *U.S. Public*, pg. 2008
TENET UNIFOUR URGENT CARE CENTER, L.L.C.—See Tenet Healthcare Corporation; *U.S. Public*, pg. 2004
TEN LAKES CENTER, LLC—See Acadia Healthcare Company, Inc.; *U.S. Public*, pg. 30
TENNESSEE HEALTHCARE MANAGEMENT, INC.—See HCA Healthcare, Inc.; *U.S. Public*, pg. 1011
TERRE HAUTE REGIONAL HOSPITAL—See HCA Healthcare, Inc.; *U.S. Public*, pg. 1011
TETON OUTPATIENT SERVICES, LLC—See Tenet Healthcare Corporation; *U.S. Public*, pg. 2013
TETON VALLEY HEALTH CARE, INC.; *U.S. Private*, pg. 3973
TEXAN AMBULATORY SURGERY CENTER, L.P.—See Tenet Healthcare Corporation; *U.S. Public*, pg. 2013
TEXARKANA BEHAVIORAL ASSOCIATES, L.C.—See Acadia Healthcare Company, Inc.; *U.S. Public*, pg. 30
TEXAS ENDOSCOPY CENTERS, LLC—See Tenet Healthcare Corporation; *U.S. Public*, pg. 2008

TEXAS HEALTH RESOURCES; *U.S. Private*, pg. 3975
TEXAS INSTITUTE OF MEDICINE & SURGERY—See HCA Healthcare, Inc.; *U.S. Public*, pg. 1011
TEXAS MEDICAL CENTER CORP.; *U.S. Private*, pg. 3976
TEXAS ORTHOPEDIC HOSPITAL—See HCA Healthcare, Inc.; *U.S. Public*, pg. 1011
TEXAS PANHANDLE CLINICAL PARTNERS ACO, LLC—See Universal Health Services, Inc.; *U.S. Public*, pg. 2259
TEXAS SCOTTISH RITE HOSPITAL FOR CHILDREN; *U.S. Private*, pg. 3977
TEXAS SPINE AND JOINT HOSPITAL, LLC—See Tenet Healthcare Corporation; *U.S. Public*, pg. 2009
TEXOMACARE SPECIALTY PHYSICIANS—See Universal Health Services, Inc.; *U.S. Public*, pg. 2259
THOMAS H. BOYD MEMORIAL HOSPITAL; *U.S. Private*, pg. 4155
THREE RIVERS MEDICAL CLINICS, INC.—See Quorum Health Corporation; *U.S. Private*, pg. 3330
THREE SHIRES HOSPITAL LP—See Centene Corporation; *U.S. Public*, pg. 470
TIMPANOGOS REGIONAL HOSPITAL—See HCA Healthcare, Inc.; *U.S. Public*, pg. 1012
TITUSVILLE CENTER FOR SURGICAL EXCELLENCE, LLC—See Tenet Healthcare Corporation; *U.S. Public*, pg. 2013
TK BEHAVIORAL, LLC—See Acadia Healthcare Company, Inc.; *U.S. Public*, pg. 30
TLC HEALTH NETWORK; *U.S. Private*, pg. 4178
TLC MEDIPARK PROPRIETARY LIMITED—See Dis-Chem Pharmacies Ltd.; *Int'l*, pg. 2131
TMF HEALTH QUALITY INSTITUTE; *U.S. Private*, pg. 4179
THE TOLEDO ENDOSCOPY ASC, LLC—See KKR & Co. Inc.; *U.S. Public*, pg. 1248
TOMS RIVER SURGERY CENTER, L.L.C.—See Tenet Healthcare Corporation; *U.S. Public*, pg. 2013
TOOELE CLINIC CORP.—See Quorum Health Corporation; *U.S. Private*, pg. 3330
THE TORRANCE CA MULTI-SPECIALTY ASC, LLC—See KKR & Co. Inc.; *U.S. Public*, pg. 1248
TOTAL CARE; *U.S. Private*, pg. 4190
TOTAL IMAGING - PARSONS, LLC—See HCA Healthcare, Inc.; *U.S. Public*, pg. 1012
TOTAL JOINT CENTER OF THE NORTHLAND, LLC—See Tenet Healthcare Corporation; *U.S. Public*, pg. 2009
TOTAL RENAL CARE/CRYSTAL RIVER DIALYSIS, L.C.—See DaVita Inc.; *U.S. Public*, pg. 643
TOUCHETTE REGIONAL HOSPITAL; *U.S. Private*, pg. 4192
TOWNER COUNTY MEDICAL CENTER; *U.S. Private*, pg. 4198
TOWN PLAZA FAMILY PRACTICE, LLC—See HCA Healthcare, Inc.; *U.S. Public*, pg. 1012
TOWN PLAZA FAMILY PRACTICE, LLC—See HCA Healthcare, Inc.; *U.S. Public*, pg. 1012
TRANSCULTURAL HEALTH DEVELOPMENT, INC.—See Acadia Healthcare Company, Inc.; *U.S. Public*, pg. 31
TRANSFORM HOSPITAL GROUP LTD.—See Aurelius Equity Opportunities SE & Co. KGaA; *Int'l*, pg. 710
TRANSYLVANIA COMMUNITY HOSPITAL, INC.; *U.S. Private*, pg. 4212
TREASURE COAST BEHAVIORAL HEALTH, LLC—See Universal Health Services, Inc.; *U.S. Public*, pg. 2260
TREATMENT ASSOCIATES, INC.—See Acadia Healthcare Company, Inc.; *U.S. Public*, pg. 31
THE TRESANTI SURGICAL CENTER, LLC—See Tenet Healthcare Corporation; *U.S. Public*, pg. 2005
TRIAD OF ALABAMA, LLC—See Community Health Systems, Inc.; *U.S. Public*, pg. 557
TRIDENT HEALTH SYSTEM—See HCA Healthcare, Inc.; *U.S. Public*, pg. 1012
TRIDENT MEDICAL CENTER, LLC—See HCA Healthcare, Inc.; *U.S. Public*, pg. 1013
TRIHEALTH INC.—See Catholic Health Initiatives; *U.S. Private*, pg. 790
TRILOGY EYE MEDICAL GROUP INC.; *U.S. Private*, pg. 4232
TRINIDAD AREA HEALTH ASSOCIATION; *U.S. Private*, pg. 4233
TRINITAS REGIONAL MEDICAL CENTER; *U.S. Private*, pg. 4233
TRINITY PARK SURGERY CENTER—See HCA Healthcare, Inc.; *U.S. Public*, pg. 1013
TRISTAR BONE MARROW TRANSPLANT, LLC—See HCA Healthcare, Inc.; *U.S. Public*, pg. 1012
TRISTAR GREENVIEW REGIONAL HOSPITAL—See HCA Healthcare, Inc.; *U.S. Public*, pg. 1012
TRISTAR RADIATION ONCOLOGY, LLC—See HCA Healthcare, Inc.; *U.S. Public*, pg. 1012
TRISTAR TENNESSEE HEART AND VASCULAR, LLC—See HCA Healthcare, Inc.; *U.S. Public*, pg. 1012
TRI-STATE MEMORIAL HOSPITAL & MEDICAL CAMPUS; *U.S. Private*, pg. 4224
TROPHY CLUB MEDICAL CENTER, L.P.—See Tenet Healthcare Corporation; *U.S. Public*, pg. 2013
TROUSDALE MEDICAL CENTER, LLC—See Apollo Global Management, Inc.; *U.S. Public*, pg. 159
TRUSTPOINT HOSPITAL, LLC—See Acadia Healthcare Company, Inc.; *U.S. Public*, pg. 31

TUBA CITY REGIONAL HEALTH CARE CORPORATION; *U.S. Private*, pg. 4255
TULLAHOMA HMA, INC.—See Community Health Systems, Inc.; *U.S. Public*, pg. 557
THE TULSA OK OPHTHALMOLOGY ASC, LLC—See KKR & Co. Inc.; *U.S. Public*, pg. 1248
TUNKHANNOCK CLINIC COMPANY, LLC—See Community Health Systems, Inc.; *U.S. Public*, pg. 557
TWIN CITIES COMMUNITY HOSPITAL, INC.—See Adventist Health System; *U.S. Private*, pg. 108
TWIN CITIES HOSPITAL—See HCA Healthcare, Inc.; *U.S. Public*, pg. 1013
TWO RIVERS PHYSICIAN PRACTICES, LLC—See Apollo Global Management, Inc.; *U.S. Public*, pg. 159
UCHEALTH BROOMFIELD HOSPITAL LLC—See Adeptus Health Inc.; *U.S. Private*, pg. 78
UCHICAGO MEDICINE INGALLS MEMORIAL—See University of Chicago; *U.S. Private*, pg. 4308
UC SAN DIEGO HEALTH; *U.S. Private*, pg. 4273
UCSF MEDICAL CENTER; *U.S. Private*, pg. 4274
UHS IMAGING LLC—See Universal Health Services, Inc.; *U.S. Public*, pg. 2260
UINTAH BASIN MEDICAL CENTER; *U.S. Private*, pg. 4275
UK HEALTHCARE GOOD SAMARITAN HOSPITAL; *U.S. Private*, pg. 4275
UNION COMMUNITY HEALTH CENTER; *U.S. Private*, pg. 4284
UNION HEALTH CENTER; *U.S. Private*, pg. 4284
UNION HOSPITAL; *U.S. Private*, pg. 4284
UNION HOSPITAL—See Barnabas Health, Inc.; *U.S. Private*, pg. 477
UNITED COM-SERVE; *U.S. Private*, pg. 4289
UNITED FAMILY PRACTICE HEALTH CENTER; *U.S. Private*, pg. 4292
UNITED MEDICAL PARK ASC, LLC—See UnitedHealth Group Incorporated; *U.S. Public*, pg. 2251
UNITED SURGICAL PARTNERS INTERNATIONAL, INC.—See Tenet Healthcare Corporation; *U.S. Public*, pg. 2013
UNITY HEALTH CARE, INC.; *U.S. Private*, pg. 4303
UNIVERSAL HEALTH SERVICES, INC.; *U.S. Public*, pg. 2255
UNIVERSITATSKLINIKUM GIEBEN UND MARBURG GMBH—See Asklepios Kliniken GmbH & Co. KGaA; *Int'l*, pg. 624
UNIVERSITATSKLINIKUM GIESSEN UND MARBURG GMBH—See Asklepios Kliniken GmbH & Co. KGaA; *Int'l*, pg. 624
UNIVERSITY HEALTH SYSTEM; *U.S. Private*, pg. 4308
UNIVERSITY HOSPITAL, LTD.—See HCA Healthcare, Inc.; *U.S. Public*, pg. 1013
UNIVERSITY HOSPITAL & MEDICAL CENTER—See HCA Healthcare, Inc.; *U.S. Public*, pg. 1013
UNIVERSITY OF CHICAGO MEDICINE—See University of Chicago; *U.S. Private*, pg. 4308
UNIVERSITY OF COLORADO HEALTH; *U.S. Private*, pg. 4308
UNIVERSITY OF PITTSBURGH MEDICAL CENTER; *U.S. Private*, pg. 4309
UNIVERSITY SURGERY CENTER, LTD.—See Tenet Healthcare Corporation; *U.S. Public*, pg. 2014
UNIVERSITY CITY SURGICENTER, LLC—See HCA Healthcare, Inc.; *U.S. Public*, pg. 1013
UPLAND HILLS HEALTH, INC.; *U.S. Private*, pg. 4312
UPMC JAMESON—See University of Pittsburgh Medical Center; *U.S. Private*, pg. 4309
UPMC PINNACLE CARLISLE—See University of Pittsburgh Medical Center; *U.S. Private*, pg. 4310
UPMC PINNACLE LANCASTER—See University of Pittsburgh Medical Center; *U.S. Private*, pg. 4310
UPMC PINNACLE LITITZ—See University of Pittsburgh Medical Center; *U.S. Private*, pg. 4310
UPMC PINNACLE MEMORIAL—See University of Pittsburgh Medical Center; *U.S. Private*, pg. 4310
UPMC SOMERSET—See University of Pittsburgh Medical Center; *U.S. Private*, pg. 4310
UPPER CONNECTICUT VALLEY HOSPITAL; *U.S. Private*, pg. 4312
UPPER CUMBERLAND PHYSICIANS' SURGERY CENTER, LLC—See Tenet Healthcare Corporation; *U.S. Public*, pg. 2014
UPSON REGIONAL MEDICAL CENTER; *U.S. Private*, pg. 4312
URGENT CARE PARTNERS, INC.; *U.S. Private*, pg. 4315
UROLOGY SPECIALISTS OF KINGWOOD, PLLC—See HCA Healthcare, Inc.; *U.S. Public*, pg. 1013
U.S. CENTER FOR SPORTS MEDICINE, L.L.C.—See Tenet Healthcare Corporation; *U.S. Public*, pg. 2009
US-CHINA BIOMEDICAL TECHNOLOGY, INC.; *U.S. Private*, pg. 4320
USMD HOSPITAL AT ARLINGTON, L.P.—See UnitedHealth Group Incorporated; *U.S. Public*, pg. 2240
USMD HOSPITAL AT FT. WORTH, L.P.—See UnitedHealth Group Incorporated; *U.S. Public*, pg. 2240
U.S. MEDGROUP OF ILLINOIS, P.C.—See Select Medical Holdings Corporation; *U.S. Public*, pg. 1862
U.S. MEDGROUP OF KANSAS, P.A.—See Select Medical

N.A.I.C.S. INDEX 622110 — GENERAL MEDICAL AND...
N.A.I.C.S. Index

Holdings Corporation; *U.S. Public*, pg. 1862
U.S. MEDGROUP OF MICHIGAN, P.C.—See Select Medical Holdings Corporation; *U.S. Public*, pg. 1862
U.S. MEDGROUP, P.A.—See Select Medical Holdings Corporation; *U.S. Public*, pg. 1862
U.S. REGIONAL OCCUPATIONAL HEALTH II OF NJ, P.C.—See Select Medical Holdings Corporation; *U.S. Public*, pg. 1862
U.S. REGIONAL OCCUPATIONAL HEALTH II, P.C.—See Select Medical Holdings Corporation; *U.S. Public*, pg. 1862
UTAH SURGICAL CENTER—See HCA Healthcare, Inc.; *U.S. Public*, pg. 1013
VALLEY BAPTIST LAB SERVICES, LLC—See Tenet Healthcare Corporation; *U.S. Public*, pg. 2015
VALLEY BEHAVIORAL HEALTH SYSTEM, LLC—See Acadia Healthcare Company, Inc.; *U.S. Public*, pg. 31
VALLEY HOSPITAL ASSOCIATION; *U.S. Private*, pg. 4334
VALLEY HOSPITAL MEDICAL CENTER—See Universal Health Services, Inc.; *U.S. Public*, pg. 2260
VALLEY REGIONAL MEDICAL CENTER—See HCA Healthcare, Inc.; *U.S. Public*, pg. 1013
VALLEY VIEW HOSPITAL; *U.S. Private*, pg. 4336
VAL VERDE HOSPITAL CORPORATION; *U.S. Private*, pg. 4329
VANDERBILT-INGRAM CANCER CENTER AT TENNOVA HEALTHCARE-CLARKSVILLE—See Community Health Systems, Inc.; *U.S. Public*, pg. 557
VANGUARD HEALTH SYSTEMS, INC.—See Tenet Healthcare Corporation; *U.S. Public*, pg. 2014
VAN WERT COUNTY HOSPITAL; *U.S. Private*, pg. 4341
VAUGHAN REGIONAL MEDICAL CENTER, LLC—See Apollo Global Management, Inc.; *U.S. Public*, pg. 159
VBOA ASC PARTNERS, L.P.—See Tenet Healthcare Corporation; *U.S. Public*, pg. 2015
VENICE FAMILY CLINIC; *U.S. Private*, pg. 4356
VENICE HMA, INC.—See Community Health Systems, Inc.; *U.S. Public*, pg. 557
VENTANA SURGICAL CENTER, LLC—See Tenet Healthcare Corporation; *U.S. Public*, pg. 2015
VERITYSTREAM, INC.—See HealthStream, Inc.; *U.S. Public*, pg. 1017
VERMILION HOSPITAL, LLC—See Acadia Healthcare Company, Inc.; *U.S. Public*, pg. 31
VHS ACQUISITION SUBSIDIARY NUMBER 1, INC.—See Tenet Healthcare Corporation; *U.S. Public*, pg. 2014
VHS ACQUISITION SUBSIDIARY NUMBER 3, INC.—See Tenet Healthcare Corporation; *U.S. Public*, pg. 2014
VHS ACQUISITION SUBSIDIARY NUMBER 4, INC.—See Tenet Healthcare Corporation; *U.S. Public*, pg. 2014
VHS ACQUISITION SUBSIDIARY NUMBER 7, INC.—See Tenet Healthcare Corporation; *U.S. Public*, pg. 2014
VHS ACQUISITION SUBSIDIARY NUMBER 9, INC.—See Tenet Healthcare Corporation; *U.S. Public*, pg. 2014
VHS ARIZONA HEART INSTITUTE, INC.—See Tenet Healthcare Corporation; *U.S. Public*, pg. 2014
VHS BROWNSVILLE HOSPITAL COMPANY, LLC—See Tenet Healthcare Corporation; *U.S. Public*, pg. 2015
VHS CHILDREN'S HOSPITAL OF MICHIGAN, INC.—See Tenet Healthcare Corporation; *U.S. Public*, pg. 2015
VHS DETROIT RECEIVING HOSPITAL, INC.—See Tenet Healthcare Corporation; *U.S. Public*, pg. 2015
VHS HARLINGEN HOSPITAL COMPANY, LLC—See Tenet Healthcare Corporation; *U.S. Public*, pg. 2015
VHS HARPER-HUTZEL HOSPITAL, INC.—See Tenet Healthcare Corporation; *U.S. Public*, pg. 2015
VHS HURON VALLEY-SINAI HOSPITAL, INC.—See Tenet Healthcare Corporation; *U.S. Public*, pg. 2015
VHS OF MICHIGAN, INC.—See Tenet Healthcare Corporation; *U.S. Public*, pg. 2015
VHS OF PHOENIX, INC.—See Tenet Healthcare Corporation; *U.S. Public*, pg. 2014
VHS OF SOUTH PHOENIX, INC.—See Tenet Healthcare Corporation; *U.S. Public*, pg. 2014
VHS OUTPATIENT CLINICS, INC.—See Tenet Healthcare Corporation; *U.S. Public*, pg. 2014
VHS SINAI-GRACE HOSPITAL, INC.—See Tenet Healthcare Corporation; *U.S. Public*, pg. 2015
VHS VALLEY HEALTH SYSTEM, LLC—See Tenet Healthcare Corporation; *U.S. Public*, pg. 2015
VHS WESTLAKE HOSPITAL, INC.—See Tenet Healthcare Corporation; *U.S. Public*, pg. 2015
VIBRA HOSPITAL OF SAN DIEGO, LLC—See Select Medical Holdings Corporation; *U.S. Public*, pg. 1862
VICKSBURG HEALTHCARE, LLC—See Community Health Systems, Inc.; *U.S. Public*, pg. 557
VICTORIA AMBULATORY SURGERY CENTER, L.P.—See Tenet Healthcare Corporation; *U.S. Public*, pg. 2014
VICTORIA OF TEXAS, L.P.—See Community Health Systems, Inc.; *U.S. Public*, pg. 557
VIEWMONT SURGERY CENTER, L.L.C.—See Apollo Global Management, Inc.; *U.S. Public*, pg. 155
VILA LUSITANO - UNIDADES DE SAUDE, S.A.—See Fosun International Limited; *Int'l*, pg. 2751
VILLAGE BEHAVIORAL HEALTH, LLC—See Acadia Healthcare Company, Inc.; *U.S. Public*, pg. 31
VIRGINIA GYNECOLOGIC ONCOLOGY, LLC—See HCA Healthcare, Inc.; *U.S. Public*, pg. 1013
VIRGINIA GYNECOLOGIC ONCOLOGY, LLC—See HCA Healthcare, Inc.; *U.S. Public*, pg. 1013
VIRGINIA HEMATOLOGY & ONCOLOGY ASSOCIATES, INC.—See HCA Healthcare, Inc.; *U.S. Public*, pg. 1013
VIRGINIA HOSPITALISTS, INC.—See HCA Healthcare, Inc.; *U.S. Public*, pg. 1013
VISION CONSULTING GROUP LLC—See HCA Healthcare, Inc.; *U.S. Public*, pg. 1013
VISTA PHYSICIAN GROUP—See Quorum Health Corporation; *U.S. Private*, pg. 3330
VITAL CARE; *U.S. Private*, pg. 4405
VITALISKLINIK VERWALTUNGS-GMBH—See Asklepios Kliniken GmbH & Co. KGaA; *Int'l*, pg. 623
VITA NOVA, LLC—See Acadia Healthcare Company, Inc.; *U.S. Public*, pg. 31
VOLUNTEER TREATMENT CENTER, INC.—See Acadia Healthcare Company, Inc.; *U.S. Public*, pg. 31
VPAY BENEFITS CORPORATION—See UnitedHealth Group Incorporated; *U.S. Public*, pg. 2252
VTR AMS, INC.—See Ventas, Inc.; *U.S. Public*, pg. 2278
WAIHI MEDICAL CENTRE LIMITED—See Green Cross Health Limited; *Int'l*, pg. 3070
WAKE COUNTY MEDICAL SOCIETY; *U.S. Private*, pg. 4427
WAKEMED; *U.S. Private*, pg. 4427
THE WALDORF ENDOSCOPY ASC, LLC—See KKR & Co. Inc.; *U.S. Public*, pg. 1248
WALKER COUNTY HOSPITAL CORPORATION; *U.S. Private*, pg. 4429
WAR MEMORIAL HOSPITAL; *U.S. Private*, pg. 4436
THE WASATCH ENDOSCOPY CENTER, LTD.—See HCA Healthcare, Inc.; *U.S. Public*, pg. 1012
WA-SPOK DH CRNA, LLC—See Community Health Systems, Inc.; *U.S. Public*, pg. 557
WA-SPOK MEDICAL CARE, LLC—See Community Health Systems, Inc.; *U.S. Public*, pg. 557
WA-SPOK PRIMARY CARE, LLC—See Community Health Systems, Inc.; *U.S. Public*, pg. 557
WA-SPOK PULMONARY & CRITICAL CARE, LLC—See Community Health Systems, Inc.; *U.S. Public*, pg. 557
WA-SPOK VH CRNA, LLC—See Community Health Systems, Inc.; *U.S. Public*, pg. 557
WATAUGA MEDICAL CENTER; *U.S. Private*, pg. 4451
WATERBURY HOSPITAL; *U.S. Private*, pg. 4452
WATSONVILLE HOSPITAL CORPORATION; *U.S. Private*, pg. 4456
WAUKEGAN ILLINOIS HOSPITAL COMPANY, LLC—See Quorum Health Corporation; *U.S. Private*, pg. 3330
WAYNE COUNTY HOSPITAL, INC.; *U.S. Private*, pg. 4459
WCHS, INC.—See Acadia Healthcare Company, Inc.; *U.S. Public*, pg. 31
WEATHERFORD TEXAS HOSPITAL COMPANY, LLC—See HCA Healthcare, Inc.; *U.S. Public*, pg. 1013
WEBSTER WELLNESS PROFESSIONALS, LLC—See Acadia Healthcare Company, Inc.; *U.S. Public*, pg. 31
WEEKS MEDICAL CENTER; *U.S. Private*, pg. 4469
THE WELLINGTON HOSPITAL—See HCA Healthcare, Inc.; *U.S. Public*, pg. 1012
WELLINGTON REGIONAL MEDICAL CENTER—See Universal Health Services, Inc.; *U.S. Public*, pg. 2260
WELLPLACE, INC.—See Acadia Healthcare Company, Inc.; *U.S. Public*, pg. 31
WELLSTAR ATLANTA MEDICAL CENTER, INC.—See WellStar Health System, Inc.; *U.S. Private*, pg. 4478
WELLSTAR ATLANTA MEDICAL CENTER SOUTH—See WellStar Health System, Inc.; *U.S. Private*, pg. 4478
WELLSTAR HEALTH SYSTEM, INC.; *U.S. Private*, pg. 4478
WELLSTAR NORTH FULTON HOSPITAL, INC.—See WellStar Health System, Inc.; *U.S. Private*, pg. 4478
WELLSTAR SYLVAN GROVE HOSPITAL, INC.—See WellStar Health System, Inc.; *U.S. Private*, pg. 4478
WESLEY HEALTH SYSTEM, LLC—See Community Health Systems, Inc.; *U.S. Public*, pg. 557
WESLEY MEDICAL CENTER, LLC—See HCA Healthcare, Inc.; *U.S. Public*, pg. 1013
WEST BANK SURGERY CENTER, LLC—See KKR & Co. Inc.; *U.S. Public*, pg. 1249
WEST BOCA MEDICAL CENTER, INC.—See Tenet Healthcare Corporation; *U.S. Public*, pg. 2004
WEST BOYNTON BEACH OPEN IMAGING CENTER, LLC—See HCA Healthcare, Inc.; *U.S. Public*, pg. 1013
WEST BRIDGEWATER MA ENDOSCOPY ASC, LLC—See KKR & Co. Inc.; *U.S. Public*, pg. 1249
WEST CENTRAL KANSAS ASSOCIATION, INC.; *U.S. Private*, pg. 4484
WEST CHURCH PARTNERSHIP—See Universal Health Services, Inc.; *U.S. Public*, pg. 2261
WEST COUNTY HEALTH CENTERS, INC.; *U.S. Private*, pg. 4484
WESTERN PLAINS MEDICAL COMPLEX—See Apollo Global Management, Inc.; *U.S. Public*, pg. 159
WESTERN RESERVE HEALTH EDUCATION, INC.—See Community Health Systems, Inc.; *U.S. Public*, pg. 557
WEST FLORIDA BEHAVIORAL HEALTH, INC.—See HCA Healthcare, Inc.; *U.S. Public*, pg. 1013
WEST FLORIDA CARDIOLOGY NETWORK, LLC—See HCA Healthcare, Inc.; *U.S. Public*, pg. 1013
WEST FLORIDA DIVISION, INC.—See HCA Healthcare, Inc.; *U.S. Public*, pg. 1013
WEST FLORIDA PHYSICIAN NETWORK, LLC—See HCA Healthcare, Inc.; *U.S. Public*, pg. 1013
WEST FLORIDA REGIONAL MEDICAL CENTER—See HCA Healthcare, Inc.; *U.S. Public*, pg. 1013
THE WESTGLEN ENDOSCOPY CENTER, LLC—See KKR & Co. Inc.; *U.S. Public*, pg. 1249
WEST GROVE HOSPITAL COMPANY, LLC—See Tower Health; *U.S. Private*, pg. 4193
WESTHEALTH SURGERY CENTER, LLC—See UnitedHealth Group Incorporated; *U.S. Public*, pg. 2253
WEST HILLS HOSPITAL & MEDICAL CENTER—See HCA Healthcare, Inc.; *U.S. Public*, pg. 1013
WEST HILLS SURGICAL CENTER, LTD.—See HCA Healthcare, Inc.; *U.S. Public*, pg. 1013
WEST HOUSTON SURGICARE, INC.—See HCA Healthcare, Inc.; *U.S. Public*, pg. 1013
WEST HOUSTON SURGICARE, INC.—See HCA Healthcare, Inc.; *U.S. Public*, pg. 1013
WEST KENDALL BAPTIST HOSPITAL—See Baptist Health South Florida, Inc.; *U.S. Private*, pg. 471
WEST LOUISIANA HEALTH SERVICES INC; *U.S. Private*, pg. 4486
WEST PALM OUTPATIENT SURGERY & LASER CENTER, LTD—See KKR & Co. Inc.; *U.S. Public*, pg. 1249
WEST POINT HOSPITAL PTE LTD—See China Healthcare Limited; *Int'l*, pg. 1507
WESTSIDE FAMILY HEALTHCARE; *U.S. Private*, pg. 4500
WEST VALLEY MEDICAL CENTER—See HCA Healthcare, Inc.; *U.S. Public*, pg. 1013
WEST VALLEY MEDICAL GROUP, LLC—See HCA Healthcare, Inc.; *U.S. Public*, pg. 1014
WHEATON FRANCISCAN HEALTHCARE; *U.S. Private*, pg. 4504
WHEELING HOSPITAL, INC.; *U.S. Private*, pg. 4506
WHEELING TREATMENT CENTER, LLC—See Acadia Healthcare Company, Inc.; *U.S. Public*, pg. 31
WHITE DEER RUN, INC.—See Acadia Healthcare Company, Inc.; *U.S. Public*, pg. 31
WHITE FENCE SURGICAL SUITES, LLC—See Tenet Healthcare Corporation; *U.S. Public*, pg. 2015
WHITMAN-WALKER CLINIC, INC.; *U.S. Private*, pg. 4513
WHITNEY M. YOUNG, JR. HEALTH CENTER; *U.S. Private*, pg. 4513
THE WICHITA ORTHOPAEDIC ASC, LLC—See KKR & Co. Inc.; *U.S. Public*, pg. 1249
WICHITA TREATMENT CENTER INC.—See Acadia Healthcare Company, Inc.; *U.S. Public*, pg. 31
WILKES-BARRE ACADEMIC MEDICINE, LLC—See Community Health Systems, Inc.; *U.S. Public*, pg. 557
WILKES-BARRE HOME CARE SERVICES, LLC—See Community Health Systems, Inc.; *U.S. Public*, pg. 557
WILKES-BARRE HOSPITAL COMPANY, LLC—See Community Health Systems, Inc.; *U.S. Public*, pg. 557
WILKES-BARRE SKILLED NURSING SERVICES, LLC—See Community Health Systems, Inc.; *U.S. Public*, pg. 557
WILLIAM NEWTON HOSPITAL; *U.S. Private*, pg. 4524
WILLIAMSON TREATMENT CENTER, LLC—See Acadia Healthcare Company, Inc.; *U.S. Public*, pg. 31
WILLIAMSTON HBP SERVICES, LLC—See Quorum Health Corporation; *U.S. Private*, pg. 3331
THE WILLOUGHBY ASC, LLC—See KKR & Co. Inc.; *U.S. Public*, pg. 1249
WINDBER HOSPITAL INC; *U.S. Private*, pg. 4537
WINDER HMA, LLC—See Northeast Georgia Health System Inc.; *U.S. Private*, pg. 2950
WINDSOR MILL SURGERY CENTER, LLC—See Tenet Healthcare Corporation; *U.S. Public*, pg. 2015
WINN PARISH MEDICAL CENTER—See Progressive Acute Care LLC; *U.S. Private*, pg. 3278
WINSTON COUNTY MEDICAL FOUNDATION; *U.S. Private*, pg. 4544
THE WINTER HAVEN/SEBRING FL OPHTHALMOLOGY ASC, LLC—See KKR & Co. Inc.; *U.S. Public*, pg. 1249
WISCONSIN HEALTH FUND; *U.S. Private*, pg. 4548
WOMAN'S CHRISTIAN ASSOCIATION—See WCA Hospital; *U.S. Private*, pg. 4461
THE WOMAN'S HOSPITAL OF TEXAS—See HCA Healthcare, Inc.; *U.S. Public*, pg. 1012
THE WOMEN'S CANCER CENTRE LIMITED—See Advanced Oncotherapy plc; *Int'l*, pg. 161
WOMEN'S HEALTH AND WELLNESS OF JUPITER MEDICAL SPECIALISTS, LLC—See KKR & Co. Inc.; *U.S. Public*, pg. 1249
WOMEN'S HEALTH PARTNERS, LLC—See Community Health Systems, Inc.; *U.S. Public*, pg. 557
WOMENS HEALTH PARTNERS, LLC—See Community Health Systems, Inc.; *U.S. Public*, pg. 557
WOMENS HEALTH SPECIALISTS OF BIRMINGHAM, INC.—See Community Health Systems, Inc.; *U.S. Public*, pg. 557
WOMENS HEALTH SPECIALISTS OF CARLISLE, LLC—See Community Health Systems, Inc.; *U.S. Public*, pg. 557
WOMEN SPECIALISTS OF MAINLAND, PLLC—See HCA Healthcare, Inc.; *U.S. Public*, pg. 1014

N.A.I.C.S. Index

622110 — GENERAL MEDICAL AND... CORPORATE AFFILIATIONS

WOOD COUNTY HOSPITAL; *U.S. Private*, pg. 4556
WOODLAND HEALTHCARE—See Catholic Health Initiatives; *U.S. Private*, pg. 790
WOODLAND HEIGHTS MEDICAL CENTER, LLC—See Community Health Systems, Inc.; *U.S. Public*, pg. 552
WOODWARD HEALTH SYSTEM, LLC—See Community Health Systems, Inc.; *U.S. Public*, pg. 557
WOODWARD HOME CARE SERVICES, LLC—See Community Health Systems, Inc.; *U.S. Public*, pg. 557
WORLD LUNG FOUNDATION; *U.S. Private*, pg. 4566
WOUND CARE ADVANTAGE; *U.S. Private*, pg. 4570
WYCKOFF HEIGHTS MEDICAL CENTER; *U.S. Private*, pg. 4575
WYOMING MEDICAL CENTER; *U.S. Private*, pg. 4579
WYTHE COUNTY COMMUNITY HOSPITAL, LLC—See Apollo Global Management, Inc.; *U.S. Public*, pg. 159
XRAY ONE S.R.L.—See Garofalo Health Care SpA; *Int'l*, pg. 2886
YAKIMA VALLEY MEMORIAL HOSPITAL; *U.S. Private*, pg. 4584
YAMPA VALLEY MEDICAL CENTER; *U.S. Private*, pg. 4585
YAVAPAI COMMUNITY HOSPITAL ASSOCIATION; *U.S. Private*, pg. 4587
YORK ANESTHESIOLOGY PHYSICIAN SERVICES, LLC—See Community Health Systems, Inc.; *U.S. Public*, pg. 557
YORK CLINIC COMPANY, LLC—See Community Health Systems, Inc.; *U.S. Public*, pg. 557
YORK HOME CARE SERVICES, LLC—See Community Health Systems, Inc.; *U.S. Public*, pg. 557
YORK HOSPITAL; *U.S. Private*, pg. 4590
YOUNGSTOWN OHIO PHYSICIAN SERVICES COMPANY, LLC—See Steward Health Care System LLC; *U.S. Private*, pg. 3811
YOUTH CARE OF UTAH, INC.—See Acadia Healthcare Company, Inc.; *U.S. Public*, pg. 31
YOUTH & FAMILY CENTERED SERVICES OF NEW MEXICO, INC.—See Acadia Healthcare Company, Inc.; *U.S. Public*, pg. 31
YUMA ADVANCED SURGICAL SUITES, LLC—See Tenet Healthcare Corporation; *U.S. Public*, pg. 2015
ZENTRALKLINIK BAD BERKA GMBH—See Asklepios Kliniken GmbH & Co. KGaA; *Int'l*, pg. 624
ZIT ZENTRALINSTITUT FUR TRANSFUSIONSMEDIZIN GMBH—See Asklepios Kliniken GmbH & Co. KGaA; *Int'l*, pg. 624
ZUFALL HEALTH; *U.S. Private*, pg. 4610

622210 — PSYCHIATRIC AND SUBSTANCE ABUSE HOSPITALS

ACADIA MONTANA, INC.—See Acadia Healthcare Company, Inc.; *U.S. Public*, pg. 27
ACADIANA ADDICTION CENTER, LLC—See Acadia Healthcare Company, Inc.; *U.S. Public*, pg. 27
AMERICAN ADDICTION CENTERS, INC.—See AAC Holdings, Inc.; *U.S. Private*, pg. 30
AMERICAN PSYCHOLOGICAL ASSOCIATION; *U.S. Private*, pg. 244
THE ARBOUR HOSPITAL—See Universal Health Services, Inc.; *U.S. Public*, pg. 2260
ARBOUR-HRI HOSPITAL—See Universal Health Services, Inc.; *U.S. Public*, pg. 2260
ARROWHEAD BEHAVIORAL HEALTH, LLC—See Universal Health Services, Inc.; *U.S. Public*, pg. 2256
ASKLEPIOS FACHKLINIKUM STADTRODA GMBH—See Asklepios Kliniken GmbH & Co. KGaA; *Int'l*, pg. 622
ASPIRATIONS CARE LTD.—See Elysian Capital LLP; *Int'l*, pg. 2372
AUSTEN RIGGS CENTER; *U.S. Private*, pg. 395
BEACON LIGHT BEHAVIORAL HEALTH SYSTEMS—See Children's Home of Bradford, PA.; *U.S. Private*, pg. 884
BEHAVIORAL HEALTH CONNECTIONS, INC.—See Universal Health Services, Inc.; *U.S. Public*, pg. 2256
BEHAVIOR ANALYSIS CENTER FOR AUTISM—See Gryphon Investors, LLC; *U.S. Private*, pg. 1799
BHC BELMONT PINES HOSPITAL, INC.—See Universal Health Services, Inc.; *U.S. Public*, pg. 2256
BHC FREMONT HOSPITAL, INC.—See Universal Health Services, Inc.; *U.S. Public*, pg. 2256
BHC INTERMOUNTAIN HOSPITAL, INC.—See Universal Health Services, Inc.; *U.S. Public*, pg. 2256
BHC MESILLA VALLEY HOSPITAL, LLC—See Universal Health Services, Inc.; *U.S. Public*, pg. 2256
BHC PINNACLE POINTE HOSPITAL, INC.—See Universal Health Services, Inc.; *U.S. Public*, pg. 2256
BOWLING GREEN INN OF SOUTH DAKOTA, INC.—See Acadia Healthcare Company, Inc.; *U.S. Public*, pg. 28
BRENTWOOD ACQUISITION, INC.—See Universal Health Services, Inc.; *U.S. Public*, pg. 2256
BRENTWOOD HOSPITAL—See Universal Health Services, Inc.; *U.S. Public*, pg. 2256
THE BRIDGEWAY HOSPITAL—See Universal Health Services, Inc.; *U.S. Public*, pg. 2260
BRIDGEWAY REHABILITATION SERVICES; *U.S. Private*, pg. 650
BROOKHAVEN HOSPITAL, INC.—See Vizion Health LLC; *U.S. Private*, pg. 4407
BRYNN MARR HOSPITAL, INC.—See Universal Health Services, Inc.; *U.S. Public*, pg. 2256
CALVARY CENTER, INC.—See Universal Health Services, Inc.; *U.S. Public*, pg. 2256
THE CANYON AT PEACE PARK, LLC—See Universal Health Services, Inc.; *U.S. Public*, pg. 2259
CANYON RDG HOSPITAL, INC.—See Universal Health Services, Inc.; *U.S. Public*, pg. 2256
CANYON VISTA RECOVERY CENTER—See AAC Holdings, Inc.; *U.S. Private*, pg. 30
CARRIER CLINIC—See Hackensack Meridian Health, Inc.; *U.S. Private*, pg. 1838
CAZENOVIA RECOVERY SYSTEMS, INC.; *U.S. Private*, pg. 796
CENTERSTONE OF FLORIDA, INC.—See Centerstone of America, Inc.; *U.S. Private*, pg. 817
CENTERSTONE OF INDIANA, INC.—See Centerstone of America, Inc.; *U.S. Private*, pg. 817
CHILDREN'S BEHAVIORAL SOLUTIONS, LLC—See Acadia Healthcare Company, Inc.; *U.S. Public*, pg. 28
CHILDREN'S CRISIS TREATMENT CENTER; *U.S. Private*, pg. 883
CLARITY CHILD GUIDANCE CENTER; *U.S. Private*, pg. 911
COASTAL HARBOR TREATMENT CENTER—See Universal Health Services, Inc.; *U.S. Public*, pg. 2260
COLUMBUS HOSPITAL, LLC—See Universal Health Services, Inc.; *U.S. Public*, pg. 2256
COOPERRIIS HEALING COMMUNITY, INC.; *U.S. Private*, pg. 1043
CORAL SHORES BEHAVIORAL HEALTH, LLC—See Universal Health Services, Inc.; *U.S. Public*, pg. 2256
COUNSELING CENTER & BLANK PSYCHIATRY—See UnityPoint Health; *U.S. Private*, pg. 4303
COVENANT HEALTH; *U.S. Private*, pg. 1071
CRI LIFETREE—See ICON plc; *Int'l*, pg. 3585
CYGNET HEALTH CARE LTD.—See Universal Health Services, Inc.; *U.S. Public*, pg. 2256
DEL AMO HOSPITAL—See Universal Health Services, Inc.; *U.S. Public*, pg. 2260
THE DERBYSHIRE LEICESTERSHIRE NOTTINGHAMSHIRE & RUTLAND COMMUNITY REHABILITATION COMPANY LIMITED—See ModivCare, Inc.; *U.S. Public*, pg. 1456
EL PASO BEHAVIORAL HEALTH SYSTEM—See Universal Health Services, Inc.; *U.S. Public*, pg. 2257
EMERALD COAST BEHAVIORAL HOSPITAL, LLC—See Universal Health Services, Inc.; *U.S. Public*, pg. 2257
ERLANGER BEHAVIORAL HEALTH, LLC—See Acadia Healthcare Company, Inc.; *U.S. Public*, pg. 28
FIRST HOSPITAL PANAMERICANO, INC.—See Universal Health Services, Inc.; *U.S. Public*, pg. 2257
FOREST VIEW PSYCHIATRIC HOSPITAL—See Universal Health Services, Inc.; *U.S. Public*, pg. 2260
FOUNDATIONS VIRGINIA, LLC—See Universal Health Services, Inc.; *U.S. Public*, pg. 2257
FOX RUN CENTER FOR CHILDREN & ADOLESCENTS—See Universal Health Services, Inc.; *U.S. Public*, pg. 2257
FRIENDS BEHAVIORAL HEALTH SYSTEM, L.P.—See Universal Health Services, Inc.; *U.S. Public*, pg. 2257
FRONTLINE HOSPITAL, LLC—See Universal Health Services, Inc.; *U.S. Public*, pg. 2257
GALAX TREATMENT CENTER, INC.—See Acadia Healthcare Company, Inc.; *U.S. Public*, pg. 28
GARLAND BEHAVIORAL HOSPITAL, INC.—See Universal Health Services, Inc.; *U.S. Public*, pg. 2257
GAUDENZIA, INC.; *U.S. Private*, pg. 1652
GLEN OAKS HOSPITAL—See Universal Health Services, Inc.; *U.S. Public*, pg. 2260
GREAT PLAINS HOSPITAL, INC.—See Universal Health Services, Inc.; *U.S. Public*, pg. 2257
GREENHOUSE TREATMENT CENTER, LLC—See AAC Holdings, Inc.; *U.S. Private*, pg. 30
HABILITATION CENTER, INC.—See Acadia Healthcare Company, Inc.; *U.S. Public*, pg. 30
HARBOR POINT BEHAVIORAL HEALTH CENTER, INC.—See Universal Health Services, Inc.; *U.S. Public*, pg. 2257
HAVENWYCK HOSPITAL INC.—See Universal Health Services, Inc.; *U.S. Public*, pg. 2257
H.C. PARTNERSHIP—See Universal Health Services, Inc.; *U.S. Public*, pg. 2257
HHC AUGUSTA, INC.—See Universal Health Services, Inc.; *U.S. Public*, pg. 2257
HHC INDIANA, INC.—See Universal Health Services, Inc.; *U.S. Public*, pg. 2257
HHC POPLAR SPRINGS, INC.—See Universal Health Services, Inc.; *U.S. Public*, pg. 2257
HHC RIVER PARK, INC.—See Universal Health Services, Inc.; *U.S. Public*, pg. 2257
HHC S CAROLINA, INC.—See Universal Health Services, Inc.; *U.S. Public*, pg. 2257
HHC ST. SIMONS, INC.—See Universal Health Services, Inc.; *U.S. Public*, pg. 2257
HICKORY TRAIL HOSPITAL, L.P.—See Universal Health Services, Inc.; *U.S. Public*, pg. 2258
HOLLY HILL HOSPITAL, LLC—See Universal Health Services, Inc.; *U.S. Public*, pg. 2258
HORIZON BEHAVIORAL SERVICES, INC.—See CVS Health Corporation; *U.S. Public*, pg. 615
HORIZON HEALTH CORPORATION—See Universal Health Services, Inc.; *U.S. Public*, pg. 2258
HRI HOSPITAL, INC.—See Universal Health Services, Inc.; *U.S. Public*, pg. 2257
INDIAN RIVER BEHAVIORAL HEALTH, LLC—See Universal Health Services, Inc.; *U.S. Public*, pg. 2258
INSIGHT TELEPSYCHIATRY LLC—See Harbour Point Management LLC; *U.S. Private*, pg. 1861
KEYSTONE CHARLOTTE LLC—See Universal Health Services, Inc.; *U.S. Public*, pg. 2258
KEYSTONE NEWPORT NEWS, LLC—See Universal Health Services, Inc.; *U.S. Public*, pg. 2258
LA AMISTAD BEHAVIORAL HEALTH SERVICES—See Universal Health Services, Inc.; *U.S. Public*, pg. 2260
LAKEVIEW HEALTH SYSTEMS, L.L.C.—See Lee Equity Partners LLC; *U.S. Private*, pg. 2412
LIBERATION PROGRAMS INC.; *U.S. Private*, pg. 2442
LOURDES COUNSELING CENTER—See Ascension Health Alliance; *U.S. Private*, pg. 347
LOYOLA RECOVERY FOUNDATION; *U.S. Private*, pg. 2506
MADISON BEHAVIORAL HEALTH, LLC—See HCA Healthcare, Inc.; *U.S. Public*, pg. 1001
MAGELLAN BEHAVIORAL HEALTH, INC.—See Centene Corporation; *U.S. Public*, pg. 469
MAGELLAN BEHAVIORAL HEALTH OF FLORIDA, INC.—See Centene Corporation; *U.S. Public*, pg. 469
MAGELLAN BEHAVIORAL HEALTH OF PENNSYLVANIA, INC.—See Centene Corporation; *U.S. Public*, pg. 469
MARYLAND HEIGHTS CENTER FOR BEHAVIORAL HEALTH, LLC—See National HealthCare Corporation; *U.S. Public*, pg. 1495
MAYHILL BEHAVIORAL HEALTH, LLC—See Universal Health Services, Inc.; *U.S. Public*, pg. 2258
THE MCLEAN HOSPITAL CORPORATION—See Partners HealthCare System, Inc.; *U.S. Private*, pg. 3102
MIDWESTERN CONNECTICUT COUNCIL OF ALCOHOLISM; *U.S. Private*, pg. 2724
MILLCREEK MANAGEMENT CORPORATION—See Acadia Healthcare Company, Inc.; *U.S. Public*, pg. 29
MILLWOOD HOSPITAL—See Universal Health Services, Inc.; *U.S. Public*, pg. 2258
MMO BEHAVIORAL HEALTH SYSTEMS LLC—See Acadia Healthcare Company, Inc.; *U.S. Public*, pg. 29
MSO NASH INC.—See Nash Health Care Systems Inc.; *U.S. Private*, pg. 2835
NATIONAL CENTER FOR MISSING & EXPLOITED CHILDREN; *U.S. Private*, pg. 2850
NEURO INSTITUTE OF AUSTIN, L.P.—See Universal Health Services, Inc.; *U.S. Public*, pg. 2258
NEW JERSEY ADDICTION TREATMENT CENTER, LLC—See AAC Holdings, Inc.; *U.S. Private*, pg. 30
NEW LEAF ACADEMY, INC.—See Acadia Healthcare Company, Inc.; *U.S. Public*, pg. 29
PARTHENON PAVILION INC.—See HCA Healthcare, Inc.; *U.S. Public*, pg. 992
PASSAGES TO RECOVERY, LLC—See Acadia Healthcare Company, Inc.; *U.S. Public*, pg. 29
PINEWOOD HEALTHCARE REALTY, L.P.—See Acadia Healthcare Company, Inc.; *U.S. Public*, pg. 29
PSYCH ASSOCIATES OF MARYLAND, LLC—See Comprehensive Behavioral Health; *U.S. Private*, pg. 1002
PYRAMID HEALTH CARE LP; *U.S. Private*, pg. 3310
RAMSAY YOUTH SERVICES OF GEORGIA, INC.—See Universal Health Services, Inc.; *U.S. Public*, pg. 2259
RECOVERY PHYSICIANS GROUP OF GEORGIA, LLC—See Universal Health Services, Inc.; *U.S. Public*, pg. 2259
RECOVERY PHYSICIANS GROUP OF TENNESSEE, LLC—See Universal Health Services, Inc.; *U.S. Public*, pg. 2259
RIVER CREST HOSPITAL—See Universal Health Services, Inc.; *U.S. Public*, pg. 2260
RIVER OAKS HOSPITAL—See Universal Health Services, Inc.; *U.S. Public*, pg. 2260
SALT LAKE BEHAVIORAL HEALTH, LLC—See Universal Health Services, Inc.; *U.S. Public*, pg. 2259
SAN DIEGO ADDICTION TREATMENT CENTER, INC.—See AAC Holdings, Inc.; *U.S. Private*, pg. 31
SAN DIEGO TREATMENT SERVICES—See Acadia Healthcare Company, Inc.; *U.S. Public*, pg. 30
SHORELINE, INC.—See Vizion Health LLC; *U.S. Private*, pg. 4407
THE STAFFORDSHIRE AND WEST MIDLANDS COMMUNITY REHABILITATION COMPANY LIMITED—See ModivCare, Inc.; *U.S. Public*, pg. 1456
SUNDANCE BEHAVIORAL HEALTHCARE SYSTEM; *U.S. Private*, pg. 3866
TEXAS CYPRESS CREEK HOSPITAL, L.P.—See Universal Health Services, Inc.; *U.S. Public*, pg. 2259
TEXAS LAUREL RIDGE HOSPITAL, L.P.—See Universal Health Services, Inc.; *U.S. Public*, pg. 2259
TURNING POINT HOSPITAL—See Universal Health Ser-

vices, Inc.; *U.S. Public*, pg. 2260
TWO RIVERS PSYCHIATRIC HOSPITAL—See Universal Health Services, Inc.; *U.S. Public*, pg. 2260
UBH OF OREGON, LLC—See Universal Health Services, Inc.; *U.S. Public*, pg. 2260
UBH OF PHOENIX, LLC—See Universal Health Services, Inc.; *U.S. Public*, pg. 2260
UHP, LP—See Universal Health Services, Inc.; *U.S. Public*, pg. 2260
UHS OF TUCSON, LLC—See Universal Health Services, Inc.; *U.S. Public*, pg. 2260
VIRGINIA TREATMENT CENTER, INC.—See Acadia Healthcare Company, Inc.; *U.S. Public*, pg. 31
VISTA BEHAVIORAL HEALTH, LLC—See Acadia Healthcare Company, Inc.; *U.S. Public*, pg. 31
VISTA HEALTH—See Centene Corporation; *U.S. Public*, pg. 470
WISCONSIN AVENUE PSYCHIATRIC CENTER, INC.,—See Universal Health Services, Inc.; *U.S. Public*, pg. 2261
WOODRIDGE BEHAVIORAL CARE—See Ridgemont Partners Management LLC; *U.S. Private*, pg. 3433
WP ACQUISITION SUB, LLC—See Acadia Healthcare Company, Inc.; *U.S. Public*, pg. 31
YARROW LODGE, LLC—See Universal Health Services, Inc.; *U.S. Public*, pg. 2261

622310 — SPECIALTY (EXCEPT PSYCHIATRIC AND SUBSTANCE ABUSE) HOSPITALS

2CUREX AB; *Int'l*, pg. 4
360 MED CARE PTY. LTD.—See Enovis Corporation; *U.S. Public*, pg. 770
THE ABILENE EYE ASC, L.P.—See KKR & Co. Inc.; *U.S. Public*, pg. 1247
ADMINISTRADORA CLINICA LA COLINA S.A.S.—See UnitedHealth Group Incorporated; *U.S. Public*, pg. 2238
AESTHETIC MEDICAL CENTRE PTE LTD—See AsiaMedic Ltd.; *Int'l*, pg. 616
ALEXIAN BROTHERS HEALTH SYSTEM, INC.—See Ascension Health Alliance; *U.S. Private*, pg. 346
THE AMERICAN ACADEMY OF PEDIATRICS; *U.S. Private*, pg. 3985
AMERICAN FAMILY CARE, INC.; *U.S. Private*, pg. 233
AMERICAN SOCIETY OF CATARACT AND REFRACTIVE SURGERY; *U.S. Private*, pg. 254
APEX HCG ONCOLOGY HOSPITALS LLP—See Healthcare Global Enterprises Limited; *Int'l*, pg. 3304
ARIZONA HEART HOSPITAL, LLC—See Tenet Healthcare Corporation; *U.S. Public*, pg. 2014
ASCELIA PHARMA INC.—See Ascelia Pharma AB; *Int'l*, pg. 601
ASIAMEDIC LTD.; *Int'l*, pg. 616
ASKLEPIOS FACHKLINIKEN BRANDENBURG GMBH—See Asklepios Kliniken GmbH & Co. KGaA; *Int'l*, pg. 622
ASKLEPIOS GESUNDHEITSZENTRUM BAD TOLZ GMBH—See Asklepios Kliniken GmbH & Co. KGaA; *Int'l*, pg. 622
ASKLEPIOS KLINIK ALSBACH GMBH—See Asklepios Kliniken GmbH & Co. KGaA; *Int'l*, pg. 622
ASKLEPIOS KLINIK AM KURPARK BAD SCHWARTAU—See Asklepios Kliniken GmbH & Co. KGaA; *Int'l*, pg. 622
ASKLEPIOS KLINIK BAD GRIESBACH GMBH & CIE OHG—See Asklepios Kliniken GmbH & Co. KGaA; *Int'l*, pg. 622
ASKLEPIOS KLINIK BAD WILDUNGEN GMBH—See Asklepios Kliniken GmbH & Co. KGaA; *Int'l*, pg. 622
ASKLEPIOS KLINIKEN LANGEN-SELIGENSTADT GMBH—See Asklepios Kliniken GmbH & Co. KGaA; *Int'l*, pg. 622
ASKLEPIOS KLINIKEN WEISSENFELS - HOHENMOLSEN GMBH—See Asklepios Kliniken GmbH & Co. KGaA; *Int'l*, pg. 622
ASKLEPIOS KLINIK LENGGRIES GMBH—See Asklepios Kliniken GmbH & Co. KGaA; *Int'l*, pg. 622
ASKLEPIOS KLINIK LINDENLOHE GMBH—See Asklepios Kliniken GmbH & Co. KGaA; *Int'l*, pg. 622
ASKLEPIOS KLINIK SCHAUFLING GMBH—See Asklepios Kliniken GmbH & Co. KGaA; *Int'l*, pg. 622
ASKLEPIOS KLINIK SOBERNHEIM GMBH—See Asklepios Kliniken GmbH & Co. KGaA; *Int'l*, pg. 622
ASKLEPIOS KLINIK ST. GEORG—See Asklepios Kliniken GmbH & Co. KGaA; *Int'l*, pg. 622
ASKLEPIOS KLINIKUM BAD ABBACH GMBH—See Asklepios Kliniken GmbH & Co. KGaA; *Int'l*, pg. 622
ASKLEPIOS KLINIKUM UCKERMARK GMBH—See Asklepios Kliniken GmbH & Co. KGaA; *Int'l*, pg. 622
ASKLEPIOS KLINIK WANDSBEK—See Asklepios Kliniken GmbH & Co. KGaA; *Int'l*, pg. 622
ASKLEPIOS KLINIK WIESBADEN GMBH—See Asklepios Kliniken GmbH & Co. KGaA; *Int'l*, pg. 622
ASKLEPIOS PSYCHIATRIE NIEDERSACHSEN GMBH—See Asklepios Kliniken GmbH & Co. KGaA; *Int'l*, pg. 622
ASKLEPIOS WESERBERGLAND-KLINIK GMBH—See Asklepios Kliniken GmbH & Co. KGaA; *Int'l*, pg. 623
ASKLEPIOS WESTKLINIKUM HAMBURG GMBH—See Asklepios Kliniken GmbH & Co. KGaA; *Int'l*, pg. 623
AUSTRALIAN HOSPITAL CARE (DORSET) PTY. LTD.—See Brookfield Corporation; *Int'l*, pg. 1176
BAKERSFIELD HEART HOSPITAL—See Cardiovascular Care Group, Inc.; *U.S. Private*, pg. 751
BAY STATE PHYSICAL THERAPY; *U.S. Private*, pg. 494
B. BRAUN AVITUM AUSTERLITZ S.R.O.—See B. Braun Melsungen AG; *Int'l*, pg. 786
BE HEALTH SPECIALIST LIMITED—See Human Health Holdings Limited; *Int'l*, pg. 3529
BEIJING C-MER DENNIS LAM EYE HOSPITAL CO., LTD.—See C-Mer Eye Care Holdings Inc.; *Int'l*, pg. 1239
BELOIT REGIONAL HOSPICE—See Beloit Health System, Inc.; *U.S. Private*, pg. 521
BIOLOGICS, INC.—See McKesson Corporation; *U.S. Public*, pg. 1407
BJC/HEALTHSOUTH REHABILITATION CENTER, L.L.C.—See Encompass Health Corporation; *U.S. Public*, pg. 754
BLIND INDUSTRIES & SERVICES OF MARYLAND; *U.S. Private*, pg. 581
BLYTHEDALE CHILDREN'S HOSPITAL; *U.S. Private*, pg. 600
THE BREAST CANCER CHARITIES OF AMERICA; *U.S. Private*, pg. 4000
THE BREAST CANCER SOCIETY, INC.; *U.S. Private*, pg. 4000
THE CANCER CARE CENTER OF NORTH FLORIDA, LLC—See HCA Healthcare, Inc.; *U.S. Public*, pg. 1012
CANCER CARE KENYA LIMITED—See Healthcare Global Enterprises Limited; *Int'l*, pg. 3304
CANCER CENTERS OF SOUTHWEST OKLAHOMA; *U.S. Private*, pg. 733
CANCER CENTRE LONDON LLP—See Tenet Healthcare Corporation; *U.S. Public*, pg. 2001
CANCER TREATMENT CENTERS OF AMERICA—See City of Hope National Medical Center; *U.S. Private*, pg. 906
CAREMERIDIAN, LLC—See Centerbridge Partners, L.P.; *U.S. Private*, pg. 813
CARMEL MOUNTAIN REHABILITATION AND HEALTHCARE CENTER—See The Ensign Group, Inc.; *U.S. Public*, pg. 2070
CAROL MILGARD BREAST CENTER; *U.S. Private*, pg. 766
CENTRAL ARKANSAS RADIATION THERAPY INSTITUTE INC; *U.S. Private*, pg. 818
CENTRAL ARKANSAS REHABILITATION ASSOCIATES, L.P.—See Encompass Health Corporation; *U.S. Public*, pg. 754
CENTRAL LOUISIANA REHAB ASSOCIATES, L.P.—See Encompass Health Corporation; *U.S. Public*, pg. 755
CENTRAL PARK ENDOSCOPY CENTER, LLC—See KKR & Co. Inc.; *U.S. Public*, pg. 1245
CENTRAL TEXAS ENDOSCOPY CENTER, LLC—See KKR & Co. Inc.; *U.S. Public*, pg. 1245
CHENGDU BRIGHT EYE HOSPITAL CO., LTD.; *Int'l*, pg. 1467
CHENNAI MEENAKSHI MULTISPECIALITY HOSPITAL LIMITED; *Int'l*, pg. 1470
THE CHILDREN'S HOSPITAL OF PHILADELPHIA; *U.S. Private*, pg. 4009
CHILDREN'S MEDICAL CENTER DALLAS; *U.S. Private*, pg. 885
CINEOLIA SAS—See Econocom Group SA; *Int'l*, pg. 2297
CIVCO MEDICAL SOLUTIONS B.V.—See Roper Technologies, Inc.; *U.S. Public*, pg. 1810
CLEVELAND HEARTLAB, INC.—See Quest Diagnostics, Inc.; *U.S. Public*, pg. 1755
CMS REHAB OF WF, L.P.—See Encompass Health Corporation; *U.S. Public*, pg. 754
COLUMBIA HOSPITAL CORPORATION OF CORPUS CHRISTI—See HCA Healthcare, Inc.; *U.S. Public*, pg. 994
COMMUNITY DENTAL CARE; *U.S. Private*, pg. 991
COMPLETERX, LTD.; *U.S. Private*, pg. 1001
CONCORD HEALTHCARE SINGAPORE PTE. LTD.—See Concord Medical Services Holdings Limited; *Int'l*, pg. 1765
CORPORACION DERMOESTETICA, S.A.; *Int'l*, pg. 1803
CORPUS CHRISTI RADIATION ONCOLOGY, PLLC—See HCA Healthcare, Inc.; *U.S. Public*, pg. 994
C-RAD AUSTRALIA & NEW ZEALAND PTY. LTD.—See C-RAD AB; *Int'l*, pg. 1239
CURE 4 THE KIDS FOUNDATION; *U.S. Private*, pg. 1124
CURE STARTS NOW; *U.S. Private*, pg. 1124
DAVIE MEDICAL CENTER, LLC—See HCA Healthcare, Inc.; *U.S. Public*, pg. 995
DM HEALTHCARE MANAGEMENT SERVICES LLC; *Int'l*, pg. 2142
DOCTORS' HOSPITAL OF SHREVEPORT—See Universal Health Services, Inc.; *U.S. Public*, pg. 2260
DYNACQ HEALTHCARE, INC.; *U.S. Private*, pg. 1297
DYNATRONICS CORPORATION; *U.S. Public*, pg. 700
E & J HEALTH CARE, LLC—See Centerbridge Partners, L.P.; *U.S. Private*, pg. 813
END STAGE RENAL DISEASE NETWORK OF TEXAS, INC.—See Alliant Health Solutions; *U.S. Private*, pg. 184
FOUR CIRCLES RECOVERY CENTER, LLC—See Acadia Healthcare Company, Inc.; *U.S. Public*, pg. 28
FRANKENWALDKLINIK KRONACH GMBH—See Fresenius SE & Co. KGaA; *Int'l*, pg. 2778
GRUPPO VENETO DIAGNOSTICA E RIABILITAZIONE S.R.L.—See Garofalo Health Care SpA; *Int'l*, pg. 2886
HAUS SAALETAL GMBH—See Asklepios Kliniken GmbH & Co. KGaA; *Int'l*, pg. 624
HEALTHSOUTH HARMARVILLE REHABILITATION HOSPITAL, LLC—See Encompass Health Corporation; *U.S. Public*, pg. 756
HEALTHSOUTH MESA REHABILITATION HOSPITAL, LLC—See Encompass Health Corporation; *U.S. Public*, pg. 756
HEALTHSOUTH OF AUSTIN, INC.—See Encompass Health Corporation; *U.S. Public*, pg. 757
HEALTHSOUTH OF DOTHAN, INC.—See Encompass Health Corporation; *U.S. Public*, pg. 758
HEALTHSOUTH OF EAST TENNESSEE, LLC—See Encompass Health Corporation; *U.S. Public*, pg. 758
HEALTHSOUTH OF HOUSTON, INC.—See Encompass Health Corporation; *U.S. Public*, pg. 758
HEALTHSOUTH OF LARGO LIMITED PARTNERSHIP—See Encompass Health Corporation; *U.S. Public*, pg. 758
HEALTHSOUTH OF MIDLAND, INC.—See Encompass Health Corporation; *U.S. Public*, pg. 758
HEALTHSOUTH OF READING, LLC—See Encompass Health Corporation; *U.S. Public*, pg. 758
HEALTHSOUTH OF SAN ANTONIO, INC.—See Encompass Health Corporation; *U.S. Public*, pg. 758
HEALTHSOUTH OF SEA PINES LIMITED PARTNERSHIP—See Encompass Health Corporation; *U.S. Public*, pg. 758
HEALTHSOUTH OF SOUTH CAROLINA, INC.—See Encompass Health Corporation; *U.S. Public*, pg. 758
HEALTHSOUTH OF SPRING HILL, INC.—See Encompass Health Corporation; *U.S. Public*, pg. 758
HEALTHSOUTH OF TEXARKANA, INC.—See Encompass Health Corporation; *U.S. Public*, pg. 758
HEALTHSOUTH OF TEXAS, INC.—See Encompass Health Corporation; *U.S. Public*, pg. 758
HEALTHSOUTH OF TOMS RIVER, LLC—See Encompass Health Corporation; *U.S. Public*, pg. 758
HEALTHSOUTH OF TREASURE COAST, INC.—See Encompass Health Corporation; *U.S. Public*, pg. 758
HEALTHSOUTH OF UTAH, INC.—See Encompass Health Corporation; *U.S. Public*, pg. 758
HEALTHSOUTH REHABILITATION CENTER, INC.—See Encompass Health Corporation; *U.S. Public*, pg. 756
HEALTHSOUTH REHABILITATION CENTER OF NEW HAMPSHIRE, INC.—See Encompass Health Corporation; *U.S. Public*, pg. 756
HEALTHSOUTH REHABILITATION HOSPITAL OF ARLINGTON, LLC—See Encompass Health Corporation; *U.S. Public*, pg. 756
HEALTHSOUTH REHABILITATION HOSPITAL OF CYPRESS, LLC—See Encompass Health Corporation; *U.S. Public*, pg. 757
HEALTHSOUTH REHABILITATION HOSPITAL OF DESERT CANYON, LLC—See Encompass Health Corporation; *U.S. Public*, pg. 757
HEALTHSOUTH REHABILITATION HOSPITAL OF MANATI, INC.—See Encompass Health Corporation; *U.S. Public*, pg. 757
HEALTHSOUTH REHABILITATION HOSPITAL OF MECHANICSBURG, LLC—See Encompass Health Corporation; *U.S. Public*, pg. 757
HEALTHSOUTH REHABILITATION HOSPITAL OF NEW MEXICO, INC.—See Encompass Health Corporation; *U.S. Public*, pg. 757
HEALTHSOUTH REHABILITATION HOSPITAL OF PETERSBURG, LLC—See Encompass Health Corporation; *U.S. Public*, pg. 757
HEALTHSOUTH REHABILITATION HOSPITAL OF SAN JUAN, INC.—See Encompass Health Corporation; *U.S. Public*, pg. 757
HEALTHSOUTH REHABILITATION HOSPITAL OF SEWICKLEY, LLC—See Encompass Health Corporation; *U.S. Public*, pg. 757
HEALTHSOUTH REHABILITATION HOSPITAL OF SOUTH JERSEY, LLC—See Encompass Health Corporation; *U.S. Public*, pg. 757
HEALTHSOUTH REHABILITATION INSTITUTE OF TUCSON, LLC—See Encompass Health Corporation; *U.S. Public*, pg. 757
HEALTHSOUTH SCOTTSDALE REHABILITATION HOSPITAL, LLC—See Encompass Health Corporation; *U.S. Public*, pg. 757
HEALTHSOUTH VALLEY OF THE SUN REHABILITATION HOSPITAL, LLC—See Encompass Health Corporation; *U.S. Public*, pg. 757
HEART HOSPITAL OF NEW MEXICO, LLC—See Ventas, Inc.; *U.S. Public*, pg. 2278
HELIOS KLINIK LEEZEN GMBH—See Fresenius SE & Co. KGaA; *Int'l*, pg. 2779

622310 — SPECIALTY (EXCEPT P...

HELIOS KLINIK LEISNIG GMBH—See Fresenius SE & Co. KGaA; *Int'l*, pg. 2779
HERZ-UND GEFASS-KLINIK GMBH—See Asklepios Kliniken GmbH & Co. KGaA; *Int'l*, pg. 624
H. LEE MOFFITT CANCER CENTER & RESEARCH INSTITUTE; *U.S. Private*, pg. 1824
HOSPICE CARE INC.—See Chemed Corporation; *U.S. Public*, pg. 484
IASO S.A.—See Brookfield Corporation; *Int'l*, pg. 1182
INSIGHT MEDICAL SYSTEMS, INC.—See Enovis Corporation; *U.S. Public*, pg. 773
INTEGRITY PHYSICAL THERAPY, INC.—See Select Medical Holdings Corporation; *U.S. Public*, pg. 1858
KANSAS CITY WOMEN'S CLINIC GROUP, LLC—See HCA Healthcare, Inc.; *U.S. Public*, pg. 1000
KANSAS REHABILITATION HOSPITAL, INC.—See Encompass Health Corporation; *U.S. Public*, pg. 758
KINDRED HOSPITAL - ATLANTA—See Apollo Global Management, Inc.; *U.S. Public*, pg. 156
KINDRED HOSPITAL - SAN DIEGO—See Apollo Global Management, Inc.; *U.S. Public*, pg. 156
KPC PROMISE HOSPITAL OF BATON ROUGE, LLC—See KPC Healthcare Holdings, Inc.; *U.S. Private*, pg. 2346
KPC PROMISE HOSPITAL OF DALLAS, LLC—See KPC Healthcare Holdings, Inc.; *U.S. Private*, pg. 2346
KPC PROMISE HOSPITAL OF OVERLAND PARK, LLC—See KPC Healthcare Holdings, Inc.; *U.S. Private*, pg. 2346
KPC PROMISE HOSPITAL OF PHOENIX, LLC—See KPC Healthcare Holdings, Inc.; *U.S. Private*, pg. 2346
KPC PROMISE HOSPITAL OF SALT LAKE, LLC—See KPC Healthcare Holdings, Inc.; *U.S. Private*, pg. 2346
KPC PROMISE HOSPITAL OF VICKSBURG, LLC—See KPC Healthcare Holdings, Inc.; *U.S. Private*, pg. 2346
KPC PROMISE HOSPITAL OF WICHITA FALLS, LLC—See KPC Healthcare Holdings, Inc.; *U.S. Private*, pg. 2346
KRAICHGAU-KLINIK BAD RAPPENAU GMBH & CO. KG—See Asklepios Kliniken GmbH & Co. KGaA; *Int'l*, pg. 623
THE LAKELAND FL ENDOSCOPY ASC, LLC—See KKR & Co. Inc.; *U.S. Public*, pg. 1247
LARGO MEDICAL CENTER; *U.S. Private*, pg. 2392
THE LAUREL MD ENDOSCOPY ASC, LLC—See KKR & Co. Inc.; *U.S. Public*, pg. 1248
LEGACY EMANUEL CHILDREN'S HOSPITAL—See Legacy Health System; *U.S. Private*, pg. 2416
L'EREMO DI MIAZZINA S.R.L.—See Garofalo Health Care SpA; *Int'l*, pg. 2886
LIFECARE HOLDINGS, INC.—See The Carlyle Group Inc.; *U.S. Public*, pg. 2048
LIMA FRANCE S.A.S.—See Enovis Corporation; *U.S. Public*, pg. 773
LIMA IMPLANTES S.L.U.—See Enovis Corporation; *U.S. Public*, pg. 773
LIMA ORTHOPAEDICS CANADA INC.—See Enovis Corporation; *U.S. Public*, pg. 773
LIVESTRONG FOUNDATION; *U.S. Private*, pg. 2473
LOC AT CHELSEA LLP—See HCA Healthcare, Inc.; *U.S. Public*, pg. 1000
THE LONDON GAMMA KNIFE CENTRE LLP—See HCA Healthcare, Inc.; *U.S. Public*, pg. 1012
LOUISIANA HEART HOSPITAL, LLC—See Cardiovascular Care Group, Inc.; *U.S. Private*, pg. 751
LOUISIANA HOSPICE AND PALLIATIVE CARE, LLC—See UnitedHealth Group Incorporated; *U.S. Public*, pg. 2246
LOUISIANA HOSPICE & PALLIATIVE CARE—See UnitedHealth Group Incorporated; *U.S. Public*, pg. 2246
LUNG BIOTECHNOLOGY PBC—See United Therapeutics Corporation; *U.S. Public*, pg. 2238
THE MAIN LINE PA ENDOSCOPY ASC, L.P.—See KKR & Co. Inc.; *U.S. Public*, pg. 1248
MARIANJOY REHABILITATION HOSPITAL—See Wheaton Franciscan Services Inc.; *U.S. Private*, pg. 4504
MARY BIRD PERKINS CANCER CENTER; *U.S. Private*, pg. 2598
MEDICA GROUP PLC—See IK Investment Partners Limited; *Int'l*, pg. 3609
MEDICLIN GMBH & CO. KG—See Asklepios Kliniken GmbH & Co. KGaA; *Int'l*, pg. 623
MEDICLIN KRANKENHAUS AM CRIVITZER SEE GMBH—See Asklepios Kliniken GmbH & Co. KGaA; *Int'l*, pg. 623
MEMORIAL SLOAN-KETTERING CANCER CENTER INC.; *U.S. Private*, pg. 2664
METHODIST REHABILITATION CENTER; *U.S. Private*, pg. 2684
METRO PAVIA HEALTH SYSTEM, INC.; *U.S. Private*, pg. 2686
MIAMI CHILDREN'S HOSPITAL; *U.S. Private*, pg. 2696
MID-ATLANTIC ENDOSCOPY, LLC—See KKR & Co. Inc.; *U.S. Public*, pg. 1250
MIDDLE TENNESSEE NEUROLOGY LLC—See HCA Healthcare, Inc.; *U.S. Public*, pg. 1003
NATIONAL SPINE & PAIN CENTERS, LLC—See Avista Capital Partners, L.P.; *U.S. Private*, pg. 408
NEUROLOGICAL SPECIALISTS OF MCKINNEY, PLLC—See HCA Healthcare, Inc.; *U.S. Public*, pg. 1004
NEUROLOGISCHE KLINIK GMBH—See Asklepios Kliniken GmbH & Co. KGaA; *Int'l*, pg. 624
NEUROSURGICAL ASSOCIATES OF NORTH TEXAS, PLLC—See HCA Healthcare, Inc.; *U.S. Public*, pg. 1004
NEUROSURGICAL SPECIALISTS OF EL PASO, PLLC—See HCA Healthcare, Inc.; *U.S. Public*, pg. 1004
NEUROSURGICAL SPECIALISTS OF NORTH TEXAS, PLLC—See HCA Healthcare, Inc.; *U.S. Public*, pg. 1004
NEURO TEXAS, PLLC—See HCA Healthcare, Inc.; *U.S. Public*, pg. 1004
NEW ENGLAND REHABILITATION SERVICES OF CENTRAL MASSACHUSETTS, INC.—See Encompass Health Corporation; *U.S. Public*, pg. 758
NOVACARE OCCUPATIONAL HEALTH SERVICES, INC.—See Select Medical Holdings Corporation; *U.S. Public*, pg. 1858
NOVACARE OUTPATIENT REHABILITATION, INC.—See Select Medical Holdings Corporation; *U.S. Public*, pg. 1858
NOVACARE REHABILITATION OF OHIO, INC.—See Select Medical Holdings Corporation; *U.S. Public*, pg. 1858
OKLAHOMA CYBERKNIFE, LLC—See Akumin, Inc.; *U.S. Public*, pg. 70
ONCOLOGY NURSING SOCIETY; *U.S. Private*, pg. 3019
ORTHONET LLC—See UnitedHealth Group Incorporated; *U.S. Public*, pg. 2248
ORTHOPEDIC AND SURGICAL SPECIALTY COMPANY, LLC—See Tenet Healthcare Corporation; *U.S. Public*, pg. 2012
ORTHOPEDIC SOUTH SURGICAL PARTNERS, LLC—See Tenet Healthcare Corporation; *U.S. Public*, pg. 2012
ORTHOPY HEALTH GMBH—See Enovis Corporation; *U.S. Public*, pg. 773
OSR PHYSICAL THERAPY, LIMITED PARTNERSHIP—See U.S. Physical Therapy, Inc.; *U.S. Public*, pg. 2215
OUR LADY OF LOURDES WOMEN'S & CHILDREN'S HOSPITAL—See HCA Healthcare, Inc.; *U.S. Public*, pg. 1005
PACIFIC CANCER INSTITUTE, LLC—See Akumin, Inc.; *U.S. Public*, pg. 70
PAM REHABILITATION HOSPITAL OF BEAUMONT—See Post Acute Medical, LLC; *U.S. Private*, pg. 3234
PATIENT PORTAL TECHNOLOGIES, INC.; *U.S. Public*, pg. 1652
PENN CENTER INC.—See UnityPoint Health; *U.S. Private*, pg. 4303
PHYSIO AT HAMMONDS CENTRE, LLC—See Select Medical Holdings Corporation; *U.S. Public*, pg. 1858
PHYSIOTHERAPY ASSOCIATES NRH REHAB, LLC—See Select Medical Holdings Corporation; *U.S. Public*, pg. 1858
POST ACUTE MEDICAL, LLC; *U.S. Private*, pg. 3234
PROFESSIONAL REHABILITATION HOSPITAL, LLC—See SentryCare, Inc.; *U.S. Private*, pg. 3611
REHAB ASSOCIATES OF JACKSON HOSPITAL, LLC—See Select Medical Holdings Corporation; *U.S. Public*, pg. 1859
THE REHAB CENTER—See Select Medical Holdings Corporation; *U.S. Public*, pg. 1861
REHABILITATION HOSPITAL CORPORATION OF AMERICA, LLC—See Encompass Health Corporation; *U.S. Public*, pg. 758
REHABILITATION HOSPITAL OF COLORADO SPRINGS, INC.—See Encompass Health Corporation; *U.S. Public*, pg. 758
REHABILITATION HOSPITAL OF NEVADA-LAS VEGAS, L.P.—See Encompass Health Corporation; *U.S. Public*, pg. 758
REHABILITATION HOSPITAL OF PHENIX CITY, L.L.C.—See Encompass Health Corporation; *U.S. Public*, pg. 758
REHABILITATIONSZENTRUM GERNSBACH/SCHWARZWALD GMBH & CO. KG—See Asklepios Kliniken GmbH & Co. KGaA; *Int'l*, pg. 623
REHAB XCEL, LLC—See Select Medical Holdings Corporation; *U.S. Public*, pg. 1859
THE RENFREW CENTERS INC.; *U.S. Private*, pg. 4104
RENO CYBERKNIFE, LLC—See Akumin, Inc.; *U.S. Public*, pg. 70
SACHSISCHE SCHWEIZ KLINIKEN GMBH—See Asklepios Kliniken GmbH & Co. KGaA; *Int'l*, pg. 624
SAINT BARNABAS / HEALTHSOUTH REHABILITATION CENTER LLC—See Encompass Health Corporation; *U.S. Public*, pg. 759
THE SALEM OR OPHTHALMOLOGY ASC, LLC—See KKR & Co. Inc.; *U.S. Public*, pg. 1248
SARAH CANNON DEVELOPMENT INNOVATIONS, LLC—See HCA Healthcare, Inc.; *U.S. Public*, pg. 1008
SARAH CANNON RESEARCH INSTITUTE UK LIMITED—See HCA Healthcare, Inc.; *U.S. Public*, pg. 1008
THE SARASOTA OPHTHALMOLOGY ASC, LLC—See KKR & Co. Inc.; *U.S. Public*, pg. 1248
SELECT MEDICAL CORPORATION—See Select Medical Holdings Corporation; *U.S. Public*, pg. 1859
SELECT PHYSICAL THERAPY OF CHICAGO, INC.—See Select Medical Holdings Corporation; *U.S. Public*, pg. 1859
SERENITY HOSPICE CARE LLC—See Ridgemont Partners Management LLC; *U.S. Private*, pg. 3432
SHRINERS HOSPITALS FOR CHILDREN; *U.S. Private*, pg. 3643
SIGHTLIFE; *U.S. Private*, pg. 3648
SIRTEX GLOBAL PTY. LTD.—See CDH China Management Company Limited; *Int'l*, pg. 1371
SIRTEX MEDICAL EUROPE GMBH—See CDH China Management Company Limited; *Int'l*, pg. 1371
SIRTEX MEDICAL PRODUCTS PTY. LTD.—See CDH China Management Company Limited; *Int'l*, pg. 1371
SIRTEX TECHNOLOGY PTY. LTD.—See CDH China Management Company Limited; *Int'l*, pg. 1371
SIRTEX WILMINGTON LLC—See CDH China Management Company Limited; *Int'l*, pg. 1371
SOLIS MAMMOGRAPHY AT MEDICAL CENTER OF LEWISVILLE, LLC—See HCA Healthcare, Inc.; *U.S. Public*, pg. 1009
SOLUTIONS TREATMENT CENTER, LLC—See AAC Holdings, Inc.; *U.S. Private*, pg. 31
SOUTHERN ARIZONA REGIONAL REHABILITATION HOSPITAL, L.P.—See Encompass Health Corporation; *U.S. Public*, pg. 759
SPECIAL CARE HOSPITAL, LLC—See Select Medical Holdings Corporation; *U.S. Public*, pg. 1861
SPECIALTYCARE, INC.—See Kohlberg & Company, LLC; *U.S. Private*, pg. 2339
STEWARD HILLSIDE REHABILITATION HOSPITAL, INC.—See Steward Health Care System LLC; *U.S. Private*, pg. 3810
ST. HELENS PRIVATE HOSPITAL—See Brookfield Corporation; *Int'l*, pg. 1176
ST. LANDRY EXTENDED CARE HOSPITAL, LLC—See UnitedHealth Group Incorporated; *U.S. Public*, pg. 2247
ST. LOUIS CYBERKNIFE, LLC—See Akumin, Inc.; *U.S. Public*, pg. 70
ST. LUKE'S CATARACT & LASER INSTITUTE; *U.S. Private*, pg. 3772
SUPERIOR CARE PHARMACY, INC.—See CVS Health Corporation; *U.S. Public*, pg. 616
SURGERY CENTER AT UNIVERSITY PARK, LLC—See Tenet Healthcare Corporation; *U.S. Public*, pg. 2013
SWANSON ORTHOTIC AND PROSTHETIC CENTER, INC.—See Select Medical Holdings Corporation; *U.S. Public*, pg. 1861
TARRANT COUNTY REHABILITATION HOSPITAL, INC.—See Encompass Health Corporation; *U.S. Public*, pg. 759
TEXAS ONCOLOGY, PA; *U.S. Private*, pg. 3976
TEXAS ORTHOPEDIC HOSPITAL—See HCA Healthcare, Inc.; *U.S. Public*, pg. 1011
TEXAS ORTHOPEDICS SURGERY CENTER, LLC—See Tenet Healthcare Corporation; *U.S. Public*, pg. 2013
THROMBODX BV—See Illumina, Inc.; *U.S. Public*, pg. 1112
TORRANCE SURGERY CENTER, L.P.—See KKR & Co. Inc.; *U.S. Public*, pg. 1249
TUCSON HEART HOSPITAL—See Ascension Health Alliance; *U.S. Private*, pg. 347
TULSA SPECIALTY HOSPITAL, LLC—See Select Rehabilitation, LLC; *U.S. Private*, pg. 3601
TYLER REHABILITATION HOSPITAL, INC.—See Encompass Health Corporation; *U.S. Public*, pg. 759
UROLOGY ASSOCIATES OF NORTH TEXAS, PLLC—See UnitedHealth Group Incorporated; *U.S. Public*, pg. 2240
U.S. HEALTHWORKS, INC.—See Select Medical Holdings Corporation; *U.S. Public*, pg. 1862
U.S. HEALTHWORKS MEDICAL GROUP OF KANSAS CITY, P.A.—See Select Medical Holdings Corporation; *U.S. Public*, pg. 1861
U.S. HEALTHWORKS MEDICAL GROUP OF MAINE, INC.—See Select Medical Holdings Corporation; *U.S. Public*, pg. 1861
U.S. HEALTHWORKS MEDICAL GROUP OF MINNESOTA, P.C.—See Select Medical Holdings Corporation; *U.S. Public*, pg. 1862
U.S. HEALTHWORKS MEDICAL GROUP OF NORTH CAROLINA, P.C.—See Select Medical Holdings Corporation; *U.S. Public*, pg. 1862
U.S. HEALTHWORKS MEDICAL GROUP OF OHIO, INC.—See Select Medical Holdings Corporation; *U.S. Public*, pg. 1862
U.S. HEALTHWORKS MEDICAL GROUP OF TENNESSEE, P.C.—See Select Medical Holdings Corporation; *U.S. Public*, pg. 1862
U.S. HEALTHWORKS MEDICAL GROUP OF WASHINGTON, P.S.—See Select Medical Holdings Corporation; *U.S. Public*, pg. 1862
U.S. HEALTHWORKS OF INDIANA, INC.—See Select Medical Holdings Corporation; *U.S. Public*, pg. 1862
U.S. HEALTHWORKS OF WASHINGTON, INC.—See Select Medical Holdings Corporation; *U.S. Public*, pg. 1862
U.S. HEALTHWORKS PROVIDER NETWORK OF COLORADO, INC.—See Select Medical Holdings Corporation; *U.S. Public*, pg. 1862
US ONCOLOGY, INC.—See McKesson Corporation; *U.S. Public*, pg. 1408
VALLEY MOUNTAIN REGIONAL CENTER INC.; *U.S. Private*, pg. 4334

VAN MATRE REHABILITATION CENTER LLC—See Encompass Health Corporation; *U.S. Public*, pg. 759
VHS REHABILITATION INSTITUTE OF MICHIGAN, INC.—See Tenet Healthcare Corporation; *U.S. Public*, pg. 2015
VIBRA HEALTHCARE, LLC; *U.S. Private*, pg. 4376
VIBRA HOSPITAL OF CHARLESTON—See Vibra Healthcare, LLC; *U.S. Private*, pg. 4376
THE VICTORIAN REHABILITATION CENTRE PTY. LTD.—See Brookfield Corporation; *Int'l*, pg. 1176
VITAS, CORP.—See Chemed Corporation; *U.S. Public*, pg. 484
VITAS HEALTHCARE CORPORATION—See Chemed Corporation; *U.S. Public*, pg. 484
VITAS HEALTHCARE, INC.—See Chemed Corporation; *U.S. Public*, pg. 484
VITAS HEALTHCARE, INC.—See Chemed Corporation; *U.S. Public*, pg. 484
VITAS HEALTHCARE—See Chemed Corporation; *U.S. Public*, pg. 484
VITAS HME SOLUTIONS, INC.—See Chemed Corporation; *U.S. Public*, pg. 484
VITAS HOSPICE CARE—See Chemed Corporation; *U.S. Public*, pg. 484
VITAS HOSPICE SERVICES, LLC—See Chemed Corporation; *U.S. Public*, pg. 484
VITAS, INC.—See Chemed Corporation; *U.S. Public*, pg. 484
VITAS, INC.—See Chemed Corporation; *U.S. Public*, pg. 484
VITAS INNOVATIVE HOSPICE CARE—See Chemed Corporation; *U.S. Public*, pg. 484
VITAS—See Chemed Corporation; *U.S. Public*, pg. 484
VITAS—See Chemed Corporation; *U.S. Public*, pg. 484
WATSON CLINIC LLP; *U.S. Private*, pg. 4455
WELLNESS ASSESSMENT CENTRE PTE LTD—See Asia-Medic Ltd.; *Int'l*, pg. 617
WELLSPRING CANCER CENTER PLC; *U.S. Private*, pg. 4477
WELLSTAR MEDICAL GROUP NEUROSURGERY—See WellStar Health System, Inc.; *U.S. Private*, pg. 4478
WELLSTAR MEDICAL GROUP NORTHSIDE ENT—See WellStar Health System, Inc.; *U.S. Private*, pg. 4478
WEST LPN FORT WORTH ONCOLOGY, PLLC—See HCA Healthcare, Inc.; *U.S. Public*, pg. 1013
THE WEST ORANGE NJ ENDOSCOPY ASC, LLC—See KKR & Co. Inc.; *U.S. Public*, pg. 1248
YUMA REHABILITATION HOSPITAL, LLC—See Encompass Health Corporation; *U.S. Public*, pg. 759

623110 — NURSING CARE FACILITIES (SKILLED NURSING FACILITIES)

3030 PARK HEALTH SYSTEMS INC.; *U.S. Private*, pg. 7
ACADEMY NURSING HOME, INC.—See Welltower Inc.; *U.S. Public*, pg. 2347
ADAMSPLACE, LLC—See National HealthCare Corporation; *U.S. Public*, pg. 1495
ADAPTIVE NURSING & HEALTHCARE SERVICES, INC.; *U.S. Private*, pg. 76
ADK LUMBER CITY OPERATOR, LLC—See Regional Health Properties, Inc.; *U.S. Public*, pg. 1775
ADK OCEANSIDE OPERATOR, LLC—See Regional Health Properties, Inc.; *U.S. Public*, pg. 1775
ADK POWDER SPRINGS OPERATOR, LLC—See Regional Health Properties, Inc.; *U.S. Public*, pg. 1775
ADL PLC; *Int'l*, pg. 150
ADVANTAGE REHABILITATION CLINICS, INC.—See Select Medical Holdings Corporation; *U.S. Public*, pg. 1857
AEGIS ASSISTED LIVING PROPERTIES LLC; *U.S. Private*, pg. 116
ALASTREAN CARE HOME ABOYNE—See Balhousie Holdings Limited; *Int'l*, pg. 808
ALC OPERATING, LLC—See TPG Capital, L.P.; *U.S. Public*, pg. 2168
ALIVE HOSPICE; *U.S. Private*, pg. 169
ALLIANCE FOUNDATION OF FLORIDA, INC.; *U.S. Private*, pg. 182
ALLIANCE HEALTH, INC.; *U.S. Private*, pg. 183
ALLIES INC.; *U.S. Private*, pg. 191
ALPS CARE HEART CORPORATION—See Altech Corporation; *Int'l*, pg. 389
ALTEN-UND PFLEGEHEIM SIEGLAR GMBH—See Clariane SE; *Int'l*, pg. 1643
ANTIQUARY CARE HOME ARBROATH—See Balhousie Holdings Limited; *Int'l*, pg. 808
APPLE HEALTH CARE INC.; *U.S. Private*, pg. 296
ARC RICHMOND HEIGHTS LLC—See Brookdale Senior Living Inc.; *U.S. Public*, pg. 393
ARC SANTA CATALINA INC—See Brookdale Senior Living Inc.; *U.S. Public*, pg. 393
ARISTOCRAT BEREA SKILLED NURSING AND REHABILITATION CENTER—See Communicare, Inc.; *U.S. Private*, pg. 988
ARKANSAS HOSPICE, INC.; *U.S. Private*, pg. 326
ARVADA CARE & REHABILITATION CENTER—See The Ensign Group, Inc.; *U.S. Public*, pg. 2070
ASPEN COURT, LLC—See TPG Capital, L.P.; *U.S. Public*, pg. 2168
ASSISTED LIVING PROPERTIES INC—See Brookdale Senior Living Inc.; *U.S. Public*, pg. 393
ASSOCIATION OF PERIOPERATIVE REGISTERED NURSES; *U.S. Private*, pg. 358
THE ASSUMPTION VILLAGE—See Catholic Healthcare Partners; *U.S. Private*, pg. 792
ATLANTA ASSOCIATION FOR CONVALESCENT AGED PERSONS INC.; *U.S. Private*, pg. 370
ATLANTIC MEMORIAL HEALTHCARE ASSOCIATES, INC.—See The Ensign Group, Inc.; *U.S. Public*, pg. 2070
AUCHTERARDER CARE HOME—See Balhousie Holdings Limited; *Int'l*, pg. 808
AUTUMN CORPORATION—See Saber Healthcare Group LLC; *U.S. Private*, pg. 3520
AVERA TYLER HOSPITAL—See Avera Health; *U.S. Private*, pg. 405
AVERY HEALTHCARE GROUP LIMITED—See Welltower Inc.; *U.S. Public*, pg. 2347
AVERY MANOR NURSING, L.L.C.—See Apollo Global Management, Inc.; *U.S. Public*, pg. 156
AWBREY HOUSE, LLC—See TPG Capital, L.P.; *U.S. Public*, pg. 2168
AZALEA GARDENS OF MOBILE—See Management Seven, LLC; *U.S. Private*, pg. 2561
AZTEC HEALTHCARE, INC.—See The Ensign Group, Inc.; *U.S. Public*, pg. 2070
BANNER HEALTH SYSTEM; *U.S. Private*, pg. 469
BAPTIST HOME HEALTH, LLC—See UnitedHealth Group Incorporated; *U.S. Public*, pg. 2244
BAPTIST ST. ANTHONY—See Ventas, Inc.; *U.S. Public*, pg. 2278
BARKLEY CENTER—See Formation Capital, LLC; *U.S. Private*, pg. 1569
BAY TREE CENTER—See Formation Capital, LLC; *U.S. Private*, pg. 1569
BENTON NURSING, LLC—See Regional Health Properties, Inc.; *U.S. Public*, pg. 1775
BIOSCRIP NURSING SERVICES, LLC—See Option Care Health, Inc.; *U.S. Public*, pg. 1609
BLC ATRIUM-JACKSONVILLE, LLC—See Brookdale Senior Living Inc.; *U.S. Public*, pg. 393
BLC FOXWOOD SPRINGS LLC—See Brookdale Senior Living Inc.; *U.S. Public*, pg. 393
BLC RAMSEY LLC—See Brookdale Senior Living Inc.; *U.S. Public*, pg. 393
BLC TAMPA GC LLC—See Brookdale Senior Living Inc.; *U.S. Public*, pg. 393
BOSTONIAN WHOLESALE DIVISION—See C&J Clark Limited; *Int'l*, pg. 1239
BRADFORD SQUARE NURSING, LLC—See Formation Capital, LLC; *U.S. Private*, pg. 1569
BRAKELEY PARK CENTER—See Formation Capital, LLC; *U.S. Private*, pg. 1569
BRANDYWINE HALL CARE CENTER—See Formation Capital, LLC; *U.S. Private*, pg. 1569
BREA ATLANTA COURT LLC—See Brookdale Senior Living Inc.; *U.S. Public*, pg. 393
BREA ROANOKE LLC—See Brookdale Senior Living Inc.; *U.S. Public*, pg. 393
BREA SARASOTA LLC—See Brookdale Senior Living Inc.; *U.S. Public*, pg. 393
BRIDGESTONE LIVING LLC—See The Ensign Group, Inc.; *U.S. Public*, pg. 2070
BRINTON MANOR, INC.—See Welltower Inc.; *U.S. Public*, pg. 2348
BRISTOL HOSPICE, LLC—See Webster Equity Partners, LLC; *U.S. Private*, pg. 4467
BROAD ACRES NURSING HOME ASSOCIATION; *U.S. Private*, pg. 658
BROOKDALE LEAWOOD—See Brookdale Senior Living Inc.; *U.S. Public*, pg. 394
BROOKDALE PLACE OF ANN ARBOR, LLC—See Brookdale Senior Living Inc.; *U.S. Public*, pg. 394
BROOKDALE PLACE OF BATH, LLC—See Brookdale Senior Living Inc.; *U.S. Public*, pg. 394
BROWNSVILLE CARE ASSOCIATES, INC.—See The Ensign Group, Inc.; *U.S. Public*, pg. 2070
BUENA VISTA HOSPICE CARE, INC.—See The Ensign Group, Inc.; *U.S. Public*, pg. 2070
BURLINGTON WOODS CARE CENTER—See Formation Capital, LLC; *U.S. Private*, pg. 1570
BURLINGTON WOODS CONVALESCENT CENTER, INC.—See Welltower Inc.; *U.S. Public*, pg. 2348
B-X NORTH ANDOVER LLC—See Welltower Inc.; *U.S. Public*, pg. 2347
CABS NURSING HOME COMPANY INC.; *U.S. Private*, pg. 711
THE CALVERT COUNTY NURSING CENTER, INC.; *U.S. Private*, pg. 4003
CAMARILLO COMMUNITY CARE, INC.—See The Ensign Group, Inc.; *U.S. Public*, pg. 2070
CANTERBURY OF SHEPHERDSTOWN LIMITED PARTNERSHIP—See Welltower Inc.; *U.S. Public*, pg. 2348
CAPITAL SENIOR LIVING ILM-B, INC.—See Sonida Senior Living, Inc.; *U.S. Public*, pg. 1903
CARE CENTER OF ROSSMOOR, L.L.C.—See Apollo Global Management, Inc.; *U.S. Public*, pg. 156
CAREERSTAFF UNLIMITED, INC.—See ShiftMed, LLC; *U.S. Private*, pg. 3636
CARE PARTNER CO LTD—See Daito Trust Construction Co., Ltd.; *Int'l*, pg. 1943
CARE SERVICE CO., LTD.; *Int'l*, pg. 1323
CARE TWENTYONE CORPORATION; *Int'l*, pg. 1323
CARIS HEALTHCARE L.P.—See National HealthCare Corporation; *U.S. Public*, pg. 1496
CARONDELET MANOR—See Ascension Health Alliance; *U.S. Private*, pg. 347
CARRIAGE HOUSE ASSISTED LIVING, INC.—See TPG Capital, L.P.; *U.S. Public*, pg. 2168
CARROLLTON HEIGHTS HEALTHCARE, INC.—See The Ensign Group, Inc.; *U.S. Public*, pg. 2070
CASA DI CURA VILLA BERICA S.P.A.—See Garofalo Health Care SpA; *Int'l*, pg. 2886
CASSENA CARE LLC; *U.S. Private*, pg. 784
CEDAR CO., LTD.; *Int'l*, pg. 1388
CENTRE CARE INC.; *U.S. Private*, pg. 827
CGI MANAGEMENT, INC.—See Sonida Senior Living, Inc.; *U.S. Public*, pg. 1903
CHELSEA PLACE CARE CENTER, LLC; *U.S. Private*, pg. 870
CHELSEA SENIOR LIVING LLC; *U.S. Private*, pg. 870
CHEROKEE HEALTHCARE, INC.—See The Ensign Group, Inc.; *U.S. Public*, pg. 2071
CIRCLE OF LIFE HOSPICE; *U.S. Private*, pg. 900
CLARIANE SE; *Int'l*, pg. 1642
CLEMENT PARK CARE HOME DUNDEE—See Balhousie Holdings Limited; *Int'l*, pg. 808
CLINICAL SERVICES, INC.; *U.S. Private*, pg. 944
CLINIC MANAGEMENT SERVICES, INC.—See Blackstone Inc.; *U.S. Public*, pg. 359
CLIPPER HARBOR CENTER—See Formation Capital, LLC; *U.S. Private*, pg. 1570
CMCP MONTROSE LLC—See Brookdale Senior Living Inc.; *U.S. Public*, pg. 394
COLONIAL HILL CENTER—See Formation Capital, LLC; *U.S. Private*, pg. 1570
COLONY HOUSE NURSING AND REHABILITATION CENTER—See Apollo Global Management, Inc.; *U.S. Public*, pg. 156
COMMUNICARE, INC.; *U.S. Private*, pg. 987
COMPANION MANAGEMENT GROUP, LLC—See Webster Equity Partners, LLC; *U.S. Private*, pg. 4467
COMPASS HOSPICE, INC—See Apollo Global Management, Inc.; *U.S. Public*, pg. 156
CONNECTED HEALTHCARE, INC.—See The Ensign Group, Inc.; *U.S. Public*, pg. 2070
CONTINUING CARE INC; *U.S. Private*, pg. 1031
COOPER RIVER WEST—See Formation Capital, LLC; *U.S. Private*, pg. 1570
COOSA NURSING ADK, LLC—See Regional Health Properties, Inc.; *U.S. Public*, pg. 1775
CORNERSTONE LIVING SKILLS, INC.—See Centerbridge Partners, L.P.; *U.S. Private*, pg. 813
COUPAR ANGUS CARE HOME—See Balhousie Holdings Limited; *Int'l*, pg. 808
CRESTVIEW CENTER—See Formation Capital, LLC; *U.S. Private*, pg. 1570
CRESTVIEW CONVALESCENT HOME, INC.—See Welltower Inc.; *U.S. Public*, pg. 2348
CRESTVIEW NORTH, INC.—See Welltower Inc.; *U.S. Public*, pg. 2348
CRIEFF CARE HOME—See Balhousie Holdings Limited; *Int'l*, pg. 808
CSL KEYSTONE WOODS, LLC—See Sonida Senior Living, Inc.; *U.S. Public*, pg. 1903
CSL LAURELHURST NC, LLC—See Sonida Senior Living, Inc.; *U.S. Public*, pg. 1903
CSL MIRACLE HILLS LLC—See Sonida Senior Living, Inc.; *U.S. Public*, pg. 1903
CSL VAN DORN, LLC—See Sonida Senior Living, Inc.; *U.S. Public*, pg. 1903
CURANUM AG—See Clariane SE; *Int'l*, pg. 1643
CURANUM BAD HERSFELD GMBH—See Clariane SE; *Int'l*, pg. 1643
CURANUM FRANZISKUSHAUS GMBH—See Clariane SE; *Int'l*, pg. 1643
CURANUM SENIORENPFLEGEZENTRUM AM SPESSART—See Clariane SE; *Int'l*, pg. 1643
CURANUM WESTFALEN GMBH—See Clariane SE; *Int'l*, pg. 1643
CYPRESS HEALTH CARE MANAGEMENT—See The Schwartzberg Companies; *U.S. Private*, pg. 4115
CYPRESS POINT REHABILITATION & HEALTH CARE CENTER—See Apollo Global Management, Inc.; *U.S. Public*, pg. 156
DAIWA HOUSE LIFE SUPPORT CO., LTD.—See Daiwa House Industry Co., Ltd.; *Int'l*, pg. 1945
THE DALGUISE CENTRE CARE HOME PERTH—See Balhousie Holdings Limited; *Int'l*, pg. 808
DA VINCI HEALTHCARE, INC.—See The Ensign Group, Inc.; *U.S. Public*, pg. 2070
D&B WELLNESS, LLC—See Acreage Holdings, Inc.; *U.S. Public*, pg. 36

623110 — NURSING CARE FACILI... CORPORATE AFFILIATIONS
N.A.I.C.S. Index

DEVELOPING EXCELLENCE PTY. LIMITED—See Academies Australasia Group Limited; *Int'l*, pg. 77
DEWITT REHABILITATION & NURSING CENTER, INC.—See Cassena Care LLC; *U.S. Private*, pg. 784
DIVERSICARE HEALTHCARE SERVICES, INC.; *U.S. Public*, pg. 669
DIVERSICARE OF ARAB, LLC—See Diversicare Healthcare Services, Inc.; *U.S. Public*, pg. 669
DIVERSICARE OF BATESVILLE, LLC—See Diversicare Healthcare Services, Inc.; *U.S. Public*, pg. 669
DIVERSICARE OF BESSEMER, LLC—See Diversicare Healthcare Services, Inc.; *U.S. Public*, pg. 669
DIVERSICARE OF BIG SPRINGS, LLC—See Diversicare Healthcare Services, Inc.; *U.S. Public*, pg. 669
DIVERSICARE OF BOAZ, LLC—See Diversicare Healthcare Services, Inc.; *U.S. Public*, pg. 669
DIVERSICARE OF BRADFORD PLACE, LLC—See Diversicare Healthcare Services, Inc.; *U.S. Public*, pg. 669
DIVERSICARE OF BROOKHAVEN, LLC—See Diversicare Healthcare Services, Inc.; *U.S. Public*, pg. 669
DIVERSICARE OF CHANUTE, LLC—See Diversicare Healthcare Services, Inc.; *U.S. Public*, pg. 669
DIVERSICARE OF COUNCIL GROVE, LLC—See Diversicare Healthcare Services, Inc.; *U.S. Public*, pg. 669
DIVERSICARE OF EUPORA, LLC—See Diversicare Healthcare Services, Inc.; *U.S. Public*, pg. 669
DIVERSICARE OF FOLEY, LLC—See Diversicare Healthcare Services, Inc.; *U.S. Public*, pg. 669
DIVERSICARE OF HAYSVILLE, LLC—See Diversicare Healthcare Services, Inc.; *U.S. Public*, pg. 669
DIVERSICARE OF HUEYTOWN, LLC—See Diversicare Healthcare Services, Inc.; *U.S. Public*, pg. 669
DIVERSICARE OF HUTCHINSON, LLC—See Diversicare Healthcare Services, Inc.; *U.S. Public*, pg. 669
DIVERSICARE OF LANETT, LLC—See Diversicare Healthcare Services, Inc.; *U.S. Public*, pg. 669
DIVERSICARE OF LARNED, LLC—See Diversicare Healthcare Services, Inc.; *U.S. Public*, pg. 669
DIVERSICARE OF MERIDIAN, LLC—See Diversicare Healthcare Services, Inc.; *U.S. Public*, pg. 669
DIVERSICARE OF MONTGOMERY, LLC—See Diversicare Healthcare Services, Inc.; *U.S. Public*, pg. 669
DIVERSICARE OF NICHOLASVILLE, LLC—See Diversicare Healthcare Services, Inc.; *U.S. Public*, pg. 669
DIVERSICARE OF ONEONTA, LLC—See Diversicare Healthcare Services, Inc.; *U.S. Public*, pg. 669
DIVERSICARE OF OXFORD, LLC—See Diversicare Healthcare Services, Inc.; *U.S. Public*, pg. 669
DIVERSICARE OF PELL CITY, LLC—See Diversicare Healthcare Services, Inc.; *U.S. Public*, pg. 669
DIVERSICARE OF PROVIDENCE, LLC—See Diversicare Healthcare Services, Inc.; *U.S. Public*, pg. 669
DIVERSICARE OF RIPLEY, LLC—See Diversicare Healthcare Services, Inc.; *U.S. Public*, pg. 670
DIVERSICARE OF RIVERCHASE, LLC—See Diversicare Healthcare Services, Inc.; *U.S. Public*, pg. 670
DIVERSICARE OF SEDGWICK, LLC—See Diversicare Healthcare Services, Inc.; *U.S. Public*, pg. 670
DIVERSICARE OF SELMA, LLC—See Diversicare Healthcare Services, Inc.; *U.S. Public*, pg. 670
DIVERSICARE OF SIENA WOODS, LLC—See Diversicare Healthcare Services, Inc.; *U.S. Public*, pg. 670
DIVERSICARE OF ST. JOSEPH, LLC—See Diversicare Healthcare Services, Inc.; *U.S. Public*, pg. 670
DIVERSICARE OF ST. THERESA, LLC—See Diversicare Healthcare Services, Inc.; *U.S. Public*, pg. 670
DIVERSICARE OF TUPELO, LLC—See Diversicare Healthcare Services, Inc.; *U.S. Public*, pg. 670
DIVERSICARE OF TYLERTOWN, LLC—See Diversicare Healthcare Services, Inc.; *U.S. Public*, pg. 670
DIVERSICARE OF WINFIELD, LLC—See Diversicare Healthcare Services, Inc.; *U.S. Public*, pg. 670
DIXIE WHITE HOUSE NURSING HOME, LLC—See Omega Healthcare Investors, Inc.; *U.S. Public*, pg. 1571
DLP WILMED NURSING CARE AND REHABILITATION CENTER, LLC—See Apollo Global Management, Inc.; *U.S. Public*, pg. 155
DOVER REHABILITATION & LIVING CENTER—See Apollo Global Management, Inc.; *U.S. Public*, pg. 156
DOWNEY CARE CENTER CORP.—See The Ensign Group, Inc.; *U.S. Public*, pg. 2070
EAGLEWOOD VILLAGE, LLC—See Regional Health Properties, Inc.; *U.S. Public*, pg. 1775
EC KNOXVILLE REALTY, LLC—See Ventas, Inc.; *U.S. Public*, pg. 2278
ECON HEALTHCARE (M) SDN BHD—See China Healthcare Limited; *Int'l*, pg. 1507
ECON MEDICARE CENTRE PTE LTD—See China Healthcare Limited; *Int'l*, pg. 1507
ECON MEDICARE CENTRE SDN BHD—See China Healthcare Limited; *Int'l*, pg. 1507
EMBRACE (UK) LIMITED—See D. E. Shaw & Co., L.P.; *U.S. Private*, pg. 1139
EMBRACE (UK) LIMITED—See Varde Partners, Inc.; *U.S. Private*, pg. 4346
EMBRACING HOSPICE—See The Riverside Company; *U.S. Private*, pg. 4107
EMEIS SA; *Int'l*, pg. 2376
EMERI-SKY SC LLC—See Brookdale Senior Living Inc.; *U.S. Public*, pg. 394
EMERITUSMERCED INC.—See Brookdale Senior Living Inc.; *U.S. Public*, pg. 394
EMPRES AT ROCK SPRINGS, LLC—See Apollo Global Management, Inc.; *U.S. Public*, pg. 156
EMVIA LIVING GMBH—See Chequers SA; *Int'l*, pg. 1471
ENCARE OF PENNYPACK, INC.—See Welltower Inc.; *U.S. Public*, pg. 2348
ENCINITAS HERITAGE PARTNERS, LLC—See AlerisLife Inc.; *U.S. Private*, pg. 160
ENCOMPASS HEALTH CORPORATION; *U.S. Public*, pg. 754
ENCOMPASS HEALTH REHABILITATION HOSPITAL OF ALTOONA, LLC—See Encompass Health Corporation; *U.S. Public*, pg. 755
ENCOMPASS HEALTH REHABILITATION HOSPITAL OF FREDERICKSBURG, LLC—See Encompass Health Corporation; *U.S. Public*, pg. 755
ENCOMPASS HEALTH REHABILITATION HOSPITAL OF GADSDEN, LLC—See Encompass Health Corporation; *U.S. Public*, pg. 755
ENCOMPASS HEALTH REHABILITATION HOSPITAL OF MIAMI, LLC—See Encompass Health Corporation; *U.S. Public*, pg. 755
ENCOMPASS HEALTH REHABILITATION HOSPITAL OF NORTHERN VIRGINIA, LLC—See Encompass Health Corporation; *U.S. Public*, pg. 755
ENCOMPASS HEALTH REHABILITATION HOSPITAL OF SUGAR LAND, LLC—See Encompass Health Corporation; *U.S. Public*, pg. 755
ENCORE REHABILITATION SERVICES LLC—See Revelstoke Capital Partners LLC; *U.S. Private*, pg. 3413
ENSIGN CLOVERDALE LLC—See The Ensign Group, Inc.; *U.S. Public*, pg. 2070
THE ENSIGN GROUP, INC.; *U.S. Public*, pg. 2069
ENSIGN MONTGOMERY LLC—See The Ensign Group, Inc.; *U.S. Public*, pg. 2070
ENSIGN PLEASANTON LLC—See The Ensign Group, Inc.; *U.S. Public*, pg. 2071
ENSIGN SANTA ROSA LLC—See The Ensign Group, Inc.; *U.S. Public*, pg. 2071
ENSIGN SONOMA LLC—See The Ensign Group, Inc.; *U.S. Public*, pg. 2071
ENSIGN WHITTIER WEST LLC—See The Ensign Group, Inc.; *U.S. Public*, pg. 2071
ENSIGN WILLITS LLC—See The Ensign Group, Inc.; *U.S. Public*, pg. 2071
ESTAUGH; *U.S. Private*, pg. 1428
EXTENDICARE (CANADA), INC.—See Extendicare Inc.; *Int'l*, pg. 2591
EXTENDICARE HEALTH SERVICES INC.—See Extendicare Inc.; *Int'l*, pg. 2591
EXTENDICARE INC.; *Int'l*, pg. 2591
FAIRVIEW CARE CENTER OF BETHLEHEM PIKE—See Formation Capital, LLC; *U.S. Private*, pg. 1570
FAIRVIEW CARE CENTER OF PAPER MILL ROAD—See Formation Capital, LLC; *U.S. Private*, pg. 1570
FAUQUIER LONG-TERM CARE, LLC—See Apollo Global Management, Inc.; *U.S. Public*, pg. 155
FIVE STAR ASPENWOOD LLC—See AlerisLife Inc.; *U.S. Private*, pg. 160
FIVE STAR CARY HEARTFIELDS LLC—See AlerisLife Inc.; *U.S. Private*, pg. 160
FIVE STAR CORAL OAKS LLC—See AlerisLife Inc.; *U.S. Private*, pg. 160
FIVE STAR DESERT HARBOR LLC—See AlerisLife Inc.; *U.S. Private*, pg. 160
FIVE STAR EASTON HEARTFIELDS LLC—See AlerisLife Inc.; *U.S. Private*, pg. 161
FIVE STAR ELLICOTT CITY LLC—See AlerisLife Inc.; *U.S. Private*, pg. 161
FIVE STAR FOULK MANOR NORTH LLC—See AlerisLife Inc.; *U.S. Private*, pg. 161
FIVE STAR FREDERICK HEARTFIELDS LLC—See AlerisLife Inc.; *U.S. Private*, pg. 161
FIVE STAR HOME HEALTH, INC.—See AlerisLife Inc.; *U.S. Private*, pg. 161
FIVE STAR INSURANCE, INC.—See AlerisLife Inc.; *U.S. Private*, pg. 161
FIVE STAR KNIGHTSBRIDGE LLC—See AlerisLife Inc.; *U.S. Private*, pg. 161
FIVE STAR LINCOLN HEIGHTS LLC—See AlerisLife Inc.; *U.S. Private*, pg. 161
FIVE STAR MEMORIAL WOODS LLC—See AlerisLife Inc.; *U.S. Private*, pg. 161
FIVE STAR MONTEBELLO LLC—See AlerisLife Inc.; *U.S. Private*, pg. 161
FIVE STAR MORNINGSIDE BELLGRADE LLC—See AlerisLife Inc.; *U.S. Private*, pg. 161
FIVE STAR MORNINGSIDE CHARLOTTESVILLE LLC—See AlerisLife Inc.; *U.S. Private*, pg. 161
FIVE STAR NEWPORT NEWS LLC—See AlerisLife Inc.; *U.S. Private*, pg. 161
FIVE STAR NORTHSHORE LLC—See AlerisLife Inc.; *U.S. Private*, pg. 161
FIVE STAR OVERLAND PARK LLC—See AlerisLife Inc.; *U.S. Private*, pg. 161
FIVE STAR QUALITY CARE-CA, LLC—See AlerisLife Inc.; *U.S. Private*, pg. 161
FIVE STAR QUALITY CARE-GA, LLC—See AlerisLife Inc.; *U.S. Private*, pg. 161
FIVE STAR QUALITY CARE-GHV, LLC—See AlerisLife Inc.; *U.S. Private*, pg. 161
FIVE STAR QUALITY CARE-IA, INC.—See AlerisLife Inc.; *U.S. Private*, pg. 161
FIVE STAR QUALITY CARE-IL, LLC—See AlerisLife Inc.; *U.S. Private*, pg. 161
FIVE STAR QUALITY CARE-IN, LLC—See AlerisLife Inc.; *U.S. Private*, pg. 161
FIVE STAR QUALITY CARE-KS, LLC—See AlerisLife Inc.; *U.S. Private*, pg. 161
FIVE STAR QUALITY CARE-MS, LLC—See AlerisLife Inc.; *U.S. Private*, pg. 161
FIVE STAR QUALITY CARE-NJ, LLC—See AlerisLife Inc.; *U.S. Private*, pg. 161
FIVE STAR QUALITY CARE-SAVANNAH, LLC—See AlerisLife Inc.; *U.S. Private*, pg. 161
FIVE STAR QUALITY CARE-WY, LLC—See AlerisLife Inc.; *U.S. Private*, pg. 161
FIVE STAR REHABILITATION AND WELLNESS SERVICES, LLC—See AlerisLife Inc.; *U.S. Private*, pg. 161
FIVE STAR REMINGTON CLUB LLC—See AlerisLife Inc.; *U.S. Private*, pg. 161
FIVE STAR RIO LAS PALMAS LLC—See AlerisLife Inc.; *U.S. Private*, pg. 161
FIVE STAR SEVERNA PARK LLC—See AlerisLife Inc.; *U.S. Private*, pg. 161
FIVE STAR TUCSON FORUM LLC—See AlerisLife Inc.; *U.S. Private*, pg. 161
FLEXIBILITY & CO., LLC; *U.S. Private*, pg. 1544
FLORIDA HOSPITAL MEDICINE SERVICES, LLC—See Blackstone Inc.; *U.S. Public*, pg. 359
FLORIDA LIVING NURSING CENTER; *U.S. Private*, pg. 1549
FOREST HAVEN, INC.—See Mid-Atlantic Health Care, LLC; *U.S. Private*, pg. 2707
FORESTVIEW NURSING, L.L.C.—See Apollo Global Management, Inc.; *U.S. Public*, pg. 156
FORTHVIEW CARE HOME—See Balhousie Holdings Limited; *Int'l*, pg. 808
THE FORUM AT THE WOODLANDS, INC.—See AlerisLife Inc.; *U.S. Private*, pg. 162
FRANKLIN SKILLED NURSING & REHABILITATION CENTER—See Apollo Global Management, Inc.; *U.S. Public*, pg. 156
FRESNO HERITAGE PARTNERS, A CALIFORNIA LIMITED PARTNERSHIP—See AlerisLife Inc.; *U.S. Private*, pg. 161
FRONTIER HOSPICE—See The Riverside Company; *U.S. Private*, pg. 4107
FS LEISURE PARK TENANT TRUST—See AlerisLife Inc.; *U.S. Private*, pg. 160
FS LEXINGTON TENANT TRUST—See AlerisLife Inc.; *U.S. Private*, pg. 160
FSQC-AL, LLC—See AlerisLife Inc.; *U.S. Private*, pg. 160
FVE EC LLC—See AlerisLife Inc.; *U.S. Private*, pg. 160
FVE SE HOME PLACE NEW BERN LLC—See AlerisLife Inc.; *U.S. Private*, pg. 160
GAKKEN COCOFUMP NURSERY CO., LTD.—See Gakken Holdings Co., Ltd.; *Int'l*, pg. 2869
GALEN HEALTH INSTITUTES, INC.—See HCA Healthcare, Inc.; *U.S. Public*, pg. 996
GATE THREE HEALTHCARE LLC—See The Ensign Group, Inc.; *U.S. Public*, pg. 2071
GENESIS ELDERCARE CENTERS - HARSTON, INC.—See Welltower Inc.; *U.S. Public*, pg. 2348
GENESIS ELDERCARE NATIONAL CENTERS, INC.—See Welltower Inc.; *U.S. Public*, pg. 2348
GENESIS HEALTHCARE CORPORATION—See Formation Capital, LLC; *U.S. Private*, pg. 1569
GENESIS HEALTHCARE CORPORATION - WESTERN DIVISION—See Formation Capital, LLC; *U.S. Private*, pg. 1570
GENESIS HEALTHCARE, LLC- SILVER LAKE CENTER—See Welltower Inc.; *U.S. Public*, pg. 2348
GENESIS HEALTHCARE-PHILLIPSBURG CENTER—See Formation Capital, LLC; *U.S. Private*, pg. 1570
GENESIS HEALTH VENTURES OF WILKES-BARRE, INC.—See Welltower Inc.; *U.S. Public*, pg. 2348
GENESIS MAGNOLIA RIDGE—See Formation Capital, LLC; *U.S. Private*, pg. 1570
GLENMARK ASSOCIATES, INC.—See Welltower Inc.; *U.S. Public*, pg. 2348
GLENS CARE HOME BRECHIN—See Balhousie Holdings Limited; *Int'l*, pg. 808
GMA-MADISON, INC.—See Welltower Inc.; *U.S. Public*, pg. 2348
GOOD SAMARITAN NURSING HOME, INC.—See Catholic Health Services of Long Island; *U.S. Private*, pg. 791
GPT-WEBSTER GREEN, LLC—See Equity Residential; *U.S. Public*, pg. 792
GRACE HEALTHCARE, LLC; *U.S. Private*, pg. 1749
THE GRAND HEALTHCARE SYSTEM; *U.S. Private*, pg. 4037
THE GRAND REHABILITATION AND NURSING AT RIVER

N.A.I.C.S. INDEX

623110 — NURSING CARE FACILI...

VALLEY—See The Grand Healthcare System; *U.S. Private*, pg. 4037

GRAND VILLA PHX, INC.—See The Ensign Group, Inc.; *U.S. Public*, pg. 2071

THE GRANGE CARE HOME PERTH—See Balhousie Holdings Limited; *Int'l*, pg. 808

GREAT BARRINGTON REHABILITATION AND NURSING CENTER—See Apollo Global Management, Inc.; *U.S. Public*, pg. 156

GREENBRIAR OPERATIONS, LLC—See Apollo Global Management, Inc.; *U.S. Public*, pg. 156

GREENFIELDS ASSISTED LIVING LLC—See The Ensign Group, Inc.; *U.S. Public*, pg. 156

GREENFIELD SENIOR LIVING INC.; *U.S. Private*, pg. 1778

GUARDIAN CARE OF AHOSKIE—See Apollo Global Management, Inc.; *U.S. Public*, pg. 156

GUARDIAN CARE OF ROANOKE RAPIDS—See Apollo Global Management, Inc.; *U.S. Public*, pg. 156

GYPSUM CREEK HEALTHCARE, INC.—See The Ensign Group, Inc.; *U.S. Public*, pg. 2071

HALE MAKUA; *U.S. Private*, pg. 1842

HAMILTON ARMS CENTER—See Formation Capital, LLC; *U.S. Private*, pg. 1570

HARBOR VIEW BEHAVIORAL HEALTH CENTER—See Formation Capital, LLC; *U.S. Private*, pg. 1570

HARLINGEN HEALTHCARE, INC.—See The Ensign Group, Inc.; *U.S. Public*, pg. 2071

HASEKO SENIOR WELL DESIGN CO., LTD.—See Haseko Corporation; *Int'l*, pg. 3283

HC-ONE LIMITED—See Court Cavendish Limited; *Int'l*, pg. 1819

THE HEALTH CENTER OF HERMITAGE, LLC—See National HealthCare Corporation; *U.S. Public*, pg. 1496

HEALTH RESOURCES OF EMERY, L.L.C.—See Welltower Inc.; *U.S. Public*, pg. 2348

HEALTH RESOURCES OF GLASTONBURY, INC.—See Welltower Inc.; *U.S. Public*, pg. 2348

HEALTHSOUTH OF NITTANY VALLEY, INC.—See Encompass Health Corporation; *U.S. Public*, pg. 758

HEARTH & CARE OF GREENFIELD, LLC—See Regional Health Properties, Inc.; *U.S. Public*, pg. 1775

HEARTLAND VILLA CENTER—See Formation Capital, LLC; *U.S. Private*, pg. 1570

THE HELLENIC WOMEN'S BENEVOLENT ASSOCIATION, INC.; *U.S. Private*, pg. 4051

HIGHLAND HEALTHCARE LLC—See The Ensign Group, Inc.; *U.S. Public*, pg. 2071

HIGLEY HEALTHCARE, INC.—See The Ensign Group, Inc.; *U.S. Public*, pg. 2071

HILLCREST CENTER—See Formation Capital, LLC; *U.S. Private*, pg. 1570

HLTC INC; *U.S. Public*, pg. 1954

HOMESTEAD NURSING, LLC—See Regional Health Properties, Inc.; *U.S. Public*, pg. 1776

HOPKINS CENTER—See Formation Capital, LLC; *U.S. Private*, pg. 1570

HOPKINS MANOR LTD.—See Tryko Partners, LLC; *U.S. Private*, pg. 4251

HOQUIAM HEALTHCARE, INC.—See The Ensign Group, Inc.; *U.S. Public*, pg. 2071

HORIZON HOSPICE AND PALLIATIVE CARE; *U.S. Private*, pg. 1981

HOSPICE OF AMERICA, INC.—See Dorilton Capital Advisors LLC; *U.S. Private*, pg. 1263

HOSPICE OF ARIZONA—See The Riverside Company; *U.S. Private*, pg. 4107

HOSPICE OF CENTRAL PENNSYLVANIA; *U.S. Private*, pg. 1985

HOSPICE OF MICHIGAN INC.; *U.S. Private*, pg. 1986

HOSPICE OF NEW JERSEY—See The Riverside Company; *U.S. Private*, pg. 4107

HOSPICE OF SOUTHERN ILLINOIS, INC.; *U.S. Private*, pg. 1986

HOSPICE OF THE BLUEGRASS; *U.S. Private*, pg. 1986

HOSPICE OF VIRGINIA—See The Riverside Company; *U.S. Private*, pg. 4107

HOSPICE OF WAKE COUNTY; *U.S. Private*, pg. 1987

THE HOUSE OF CAMPBELL, INC.—See Welltower Inc.; *U.S. Public*, pg. 2349

HUENEME HEALTHCARE, INC.—See The Ensign Group, Inc.; *U.S. Public*, pg. 2071

HUMILITY HOUSE—See Catholic Healthcare Partners; *U.S. Private*, pg. 792

HUNTINGTON PLACE LIMITED PARTNERSHIP—See Formation Capital, LLC; *U.S. Private*, pg. 1571

INDIANAPOLIS JEWISH HOME, INC.; *U.S. Private*, pg. 2063

INNOVATIVE SENIOR CARE HOME HEALTH OF NASHVILLE LLC—See Brookdale Senior Living Inc.; *U.S. Public*, pg. 394

INSTITUTE FOR FAMILY CENTERED SERVICES, INC.—See Centerbridge Partners, L.P.; *U.S. Private*, pg. 813

IROQUOIS NURSING HOME, INC.; *U.S. Private*, pg. 2140

J & B PARTNERSHIP LLP—See The Royal Health Group LLC; *U.S. Private*, pg. 4112

JRT HEALTHCARE, INC.—See The Ensign Group, Inc.; *U.S. Public*, pg. 2071

JUKEIKAI CO., LTD.—See Daiwa House Industry Co., Ltd.; *Int'l*, pg. 1947

KATHARINENHOF SENIOREHWOHN- UND PFLEGEANLAGE BETRIEBS-GMBH—See Deutsche Wohnen SE; *Int'l*, pg. 2085

KESSLER ORTHOTIC & PROSTHETIC SERVICES, INC.—See Select Medical Holdings Corporation; *U.S. Public*, pg. 1858

KESSLER REHAB CENTERS, INC.—See Select Medical Holdings Corporation; *U.S. Public*, pg. 1858

KEYSTONE NURSING HOME, INC.—See Welltower Inc.; *U.S. Public*, pg. 2348

KINDRED HEALTHCARE, LLC—See Apollo Global Management, Inc.; *U.S. Public*, pg. 156

KINDRED HEALTHCARE OF ELIZABETH CITY—See Apollo Global Management, Inc.; *U.S. Public*, pg. 156

KINDRED HOSPITAL - BAY AREA - TAMPA—See Apollo Global Management, Inc.; *U.S. Public*, pg. 156

KINDRED HOSPITAL - LOUISVILLE—See Apollo Global Management, Inc.; *U.S. Public*, pg. 156

KINDRED NURSING AND REHABILITATION - BRAINTREE—See Apollo Global Management, Inc.; *U.S. Public*, pg. 157

KINDRED NURSING CENTERS LIMITED PARTNERSHIP—See Apollo Global Management, Inc.; *U.S. Public*, pg. 156

KINDRED NURSING CENTERS WEST, LLC—See Apollo Global Management, Inc.; *U.S. Public*, pg. 156

KORT REHABILITATION AT HOME, LLC—See Select Medical Holdings Corporation; *U.S. Public*, pg. 1858

KPC PROMISE SKILLED NURSING FACILITY OF OVERLAND PARK, LLC—See KPC Healthcare Holdings, Inc.; *U.S. Private*, pg. 2346

KPC PROMISE SKILLED NURSING FACILITY OF WICHITA FALLS, LLC—See KPC Healthcare Holdings, Inc.; *U.S. Private*, pg. 2346

KRANKENHEIM RUHESITZ AM WANNSEE-SENIORENHEIMSTATT GMBH—See Clariane SE; *Int'l*, pg. 1643

KRESSON VIEW CENTER—See Formation Capital, LLC; *U.S. Private*, pg. 1571

LAFAYETTE SPECIALTY HOSPITAL, LLC—See Apollo Global Management, Inc.; *U.S. Public*, pg. 157

LA JOLLA SKILLED, INC.—See The Ensign Group, Inc.; *U.S. Public*, pg. 2071

LAKES REGION VISITING NURSE ASSOCIATION; *U.S. Private*, pg. 2376

LARKIN CHASE CENTER—See Formation Capital, LLC; *U.S. Private*, pg. 1571

LAS VEGAS HEALTHCARE AND REHABILITATION CENTER—See Apollo Global Management, Inc.; *U.S. Public*, pg. 157

LAUREL HEALTH RESOURCES, INC.—See Welltower Inc.; *U.S. Public*, pg. 2348

LEDGEWOOD HEALTH CARE CORPORATION—See Apollo Global Management, Inc.; *U.S. Public*, pg. 157

LEDGEWOOD REHABILITATION AND SKILLED NURSING CENTER—See Apollo Global Management, Inc.; *U.S. Public*, pg. 157

LIFE CARE CENTER OF CARROLLTON; *U.S. Private*, pg. 2448

LIFE CARE CENTERS OF AMERICA; *U.S. Private*, pg. 2448

LINDAHL HEALTHCARE, INC.—See The Ensign Group, Inc.; *U.S. Public*, pg. 2071

LISDEN CARE HOME KIRRIEMUIR—See Balhousie Holdings Limited; *Int'l*, pg. 808

LIVINGSTON CARE ASSOCIATES, INC.—See The Ensign Group, Inc.; *U.S. Public*, pg. 2071

LONG BEACH MEMORIAL NURSING HOME; *U.S. Private*, pg. 2490

LOYDS LIBERTY HOMES, INC.—See Centerbridge Partners, L.P.; *U.S. Private*, pg. 813

LUNCARTY CARE HOME—See Balhousie Holdings Limited; *Int'l*, pg. 808

LUTHERAN FAMILY SERVICES IN THE CAROLINAS; *U.S. Private*, pg. 2517

LUTHERAN HOME FOR THE AGED; *U.S. Private*, pg. 2517

LYCOMING COMMUNITY CARE INC; *U.S. Private*, pg. 2519

LYNNWOOD HEALTH SERVICES, INC.—See The Ensign Group, Inc.; *U.S. Public*, pg. 2071

MADISON REHABILITATION CENTER, INC.—See Select Medical Holdings Corporation; *U.S. Public*, pg. 1858

MAGNOLIA VILLAGE—See Formation Capital, LLC; *U.S. Private*, pg. 1571

MAINE ASSISTED LIVING, L.L.C.—See Apollo Global Management, Inc.; *U.S. Public*, pg. 157

MAIN PULZE, INC.; *U.S. Private*, pg. 2551

MANAGEMENT SEVEN, LLC; *U.S. Private*, pg. 2561

MANOR PARK HEALTHCARE LLC—See The Ensign Group, Inc.; *U.S. Public*, pg. 2071

MARIA REGINA RESIDENCE; *U.S. Private*, pg. 2573

MARIETTA CENTER—See Formation Capital, LLC; *U.S. Private*, pg. 1571

MARY ANN MORSE HEALTHCARE CENTER; *U.S. Private*, pg. 2598

MASHPEE ACQUISITION LLC—See The Royal Health Group LLC; *U.S. Private*, pg. 4113

MASSACHUSETTS MENTOR, LLC—See Centerbridge Partners, L.P.; *U.S. Private*, pg. 813

MATULAITIS NURSING HOME; *U.S. Private*, pg. 2614

MAYWOOD ACRES HEALTHCARE—See Apollo Global Management, Inc.; *U.S. Public*, pg. 157

THE MCGUIRE GROUP, INC.; *U.S. Private*, pg. 4077

MEDICAL CARE SERVICE CO., LTD.—See Gakken Holdings Co., Ltd.; *Int'l*, pg. 2869

MENTOR ABI, LLC—See Centerbridge Partners, L.P.; *U.S. Private*, pg. 814

MENTOR MARYLAND, INC.—See Centerbridge Partners, L.P.; *U.S. Private*, pg. 814

METHVEN CARE HOME PERTH—See Balhousie Holdings Limited; *Int'l*, pg. 808

MID-ATLANTIC HEALTH CARE, LLC; *U.S. Private*, pg. 2707

MILESTONE HEALTH SYSTEMS, LLC—See American Healthcare Systems Corp., Inc.; *U.S. Private*, pg. 236

MINERAL SPRINGS CENTER—See Formation Capital, LLC; *U.S. Private*, pg. 1571

MJM ASSOCIATES, LLC; *U.S. Private*, pg. 2753

MOMENCE MEADOWS REALTY, LLC—See Strawberry Fields REIT, Inc.; *U.S. Public*, pg. 1954

MONKBARNS CARE HOME ARBROATH—See Balhousie Holdings Limited; *Int'l*, pg. 808

MONROE HEALTHCARE, INC.—See The Ensign Group, Inc.; *U.S. Public*, pg. 2071

MONTEBELLO WELLNESS CENTER—See The Ensign Group, Inc.; *U.S. Public*, pg. 2071

MORNINGSIDE OF ANDERSON, L.P.—See AlerisLife Inc.; *U.S. Private*, pg. 161

MORNINGSIDE OF BELMONT, LLC—See AlerisLife Inc.; *U.S. Private*, pg. 161

MORNINGSIDE OF BOWLING GREEN, LLC—See AlerisLife Inc.; *U.S. Private*, pg. 161

MORNINGSIDE OF CAMDEN, LLC—See AlerisLife Inc.; *U.S. Private*, pg. 161

MORNINGSIDE OF CLEVELAND, LLC—See AlerisLife Inc.; *U.S. Private*, pg. 161

MORNINGSIDE OF COLUMBUS, L.P.—See AlerisLife Inc.; *U.S. Private*, pg. 161

MORNINGSIDE OF CONYERS, LLC—See AlerisLife Inc.; *U.S. Private*, pg. 161

MORNINGSIDE OF COOKEVILLE, LLC—See AlerisLife Inc.; *U.S. Private*, pg. 161

MORNINGSIDE OF CULLMAN, LLC—See AlerisLife Inc.; *U.S. Private*, pg. 161

MORNINGSIDE OF DECATUR, L.P.—See AlerisLife Inc.; *U.S. Private*, pg. 161

MORNINGSIDE OF EVANS, LIMITED PARTNERSHIP—See AlerisLife Inc.; *U.S. Private*, pg. 161

MORNINGSIDE OF FRANKLIN, LLC—See AlerisLife Inc.; *U.S. Private*, pg. 161

MORNINGSIDE OF GAINESVILLE, LLC—See AlerisLife Inc.; *U.S. Private*, pg. 162

MORNINGSIDE OF GALLATIN, LLC—See AlerisLife Inc.; *U.S. Private*, pg. 162

MORNINGSIDE OF GASTONIA, LLC—See AlerisLife Inc.; *U.S. Private*, pg. 162

MORNINGSIDE OF GREENWOOD, L.P.—See AlerisLife Inc.; *U.S. Private*, pg. 162

MORNINGSIDE OF HARTSVILLE, LLC—See AlerisLife Inc.; *U.S. Private*, pg. 162

MORNINGSIDE OF HOPKINSVILLE, LIMITED PARTNERSHIP—See AlerisLife Inc.; *U.S. Private*, pg. 162

MORNINGSIDE OF JACKSON, LLC—See AlerisLife Inc.; *U.S. Private*, pg. 162

MORNINGSIDE OF LEXINGTON, LLC—See AlerisLife Inc.; *U.S. Private*, pg. 162

MORNINGSIDE OF ORANGEBURG, LLC—See AlerisLife Inc.; *U.S. Private*, pg. 162

MORNINGSIDE OF PADUCAH, LLC—See AlerisLife Inc.; *U.S. Private*, pg. 162

MORNINGSIDE OF PARIS, LLC—See AlerisLife Inc.; *U.S. Private*, pg. 162

MORNINGSIDE OF RALEIGH, LLC—See AlerisLife Inc.; *U.S. Private*, pg. 162

MORNINGSIDE OF SKIPWITH-RICHMOND, LLC—See AlerisLife Inc.; *U.S. Private*, pg. 162

MORNINGSIDE OF SOUTH CAROLINA, L.P.—See AlerisLife Inc.; *U.S. Private*, pg. 162

MORNINGSIDE OF SUMTER—See AlerisLife Inc.; *U.S. Private*, pg. 162

MORNINGSIDE OF WILLIAMSBURG, LLC—See AlerisLife Inc.; *U.S. Private*, pg. 162

MOUNTAIN VIEW NURSING, LLC—See Regional Health Properties, Inc.; *U.S. Public*, pg. 1776

MOYNESS CARE HOME DUNDEE—See Balhousie Holdings Limited; *Int'l*, pg. 808

NATIONAL HEALTHCARE CENTER OF FORT OGLETHORPE, L.P.—See National HealthCare Corporation; *U.S. Public*, pg. 1496

NATIONAL LEAGUE FOR NURSING; *U.S. Private*, pg. 2858

NEIGHBORCARE OF VIRGINIA, LLC—See CVS Health

623110 — NURSING CARE FACILI... CORPORATE AFFILIATIONS

N.A.I.C.S. Index

Corporation; *U.S. Public*, pg. 616
NEVILLE CENTER AT FRESH POND; *U.S. Private*, pg. 2891
NEWARK HERITAGE PARTNERS I, LLC—See AlerisLife Inc.; *U.S. Private*, pg. 162
NEW HAVEN CENTER—See Formation Capital, LLC; *U.S. Private*, pg. 1571
NEW MARTINSVILLE CENTER—See Formation Capital, LLC; *U.S. Private*, pg. 1571
NEXION HEALTH, INC.; *U.S. Private*, pg. 2919
NHC HEALTHCARE/ANDERSON, LLC—See National HealthCare Corporation; *U.S. Public*, pg. 1495
NHC HEALTHCARE/ANNISTON, LLC—See National HealthCare Corporation; *U.S. Public*, pg. 1495
NHC HEALTHCARE/CHATTANOOGA, LLC—See National HealthCare Corporation; *U.S. Public*, pg. 1495
NHC HEALTHCARE/COOL SPRINGS, LLC—See National HealthCare Corporation; *U.S. Public*, pg. 1495
NHC HEALTHCARE/DESLOGE, LLC—See National HealthCare Corporation; *U.S. Public*, pg. 1495
NHC HEALTHCARE/DICKSON, LLC—See National HealthCare Corporation; *U.S. Public*, pg. 1495
NHC HEALTHCARE/FARRAGUT, LLC—See National HealthCare Corporation; *U.S. Public*, pg. 1495
NHC HEALTHCARE/FRANKLIN, LLC—See National HealthCare Corporation; *U.S. Public*, pg. 1495
NHC HEALTHCARE/GARDEN CITY, LLC—See National HealthCare Corporation; *U.S. Public*, pg. 1495
NHC HEALTHCARE/GLASGOW, LLC—See National HealthCare Corporation; *U.S. Public*, pg. 1495
NHC HEALTHCARE/GREENVILLE, LLC—See National HealthCare Corporation; *U.S. Public*, pg. 1495
NHC HEALTHCARE/GREENWOOD, LLC—See National HealthCare Corporation; *U.S. Public*, pg. 1495
NHC HEALTHCARE/HENDERSONVILLE, LLC—See National HealthCare Corporation; *U.S. Public*, pg. 1495
NHC HEALTHCARE/HOLSTON HILLS, LLC—See National HealthCare Corporation; *U.S. Public*, pg. 1495
NHC HEALTHCARE/JOHNSON CITY, LLC—See National HealthCare Corporation; *U.S. Public*, pg. 1495
NHC HEALTHCARE/KENNETT, LLC—See National HealthCare Corporation; *U.S. Public*, pg. 1496
NHC HEALTHCARE/KNOXVILLE, LLC—See National HealthCare Corporation; *U.S. Public*, pg. 1496
NHC HEALTHCARE/LAURENS, LLC—See National HealthCare Corporation; *U.S. Public*, pg. 1496
NHC HEALTHCARE-MACON, LLC—See National HealthCare Corporation; *U.S. Public*, pg. 1495
NHC HEALTHCARE/MADISONVILLE, LLC—See National HealthCare Corporation; *U.S. Public*, pg. 1496
NHC HEALTHCARE/MARYLAND HEIGHTS, LLC—See National HealthCare Corporation; *U.S. Public*, pg. 1496
NHC HEALTHCARE/MAULDIN, LLC—See National HealthCare Corporation; *U.S. Public*, pg. 1496
NHC HEALTHCARE/MCMINNVILLE, LLC—See National HealthCare Corporation; *U.S. Public*, pg. 1496
NHC HEALTHCARE/MOULTON, LLC—See National HealthCare Corporation; *U.S. Public*, pg. 1496
NHC HEALTHCARE/OAKWOOD, LLC—See National HealthCare Corporation; *U.S. Public*, pg. 1496
NHC HEALTHCARE-OSAGE BEACH, LLC—See National HealthCare Corporation; *U.S. Public*, pg. 1495
NHC HEALTHCARE/PENSACOLA, INC.—See National HealthCare Corporation; *U.S. Public*, pg. 1496
NHC HEALTHCARE/PULASKI, LLC—See National HealthCare Corporation; *U.S. Public*, pg. 1496
NHC HEALTHCARE/SCOTT, LLC—See National HealthCare Corporation; *U.S. Public*, pg. 1496
NHC HEALTHCARE/SMITHVILLE, LLC—See National HealthCare Corporation; *U.S. Public*, pg. 1496
NHC HEALTHCARE/SPARTA, LLC—See National HealthCare Corporation; *U.S. Public*, pg. 1496
NHC HEALTHCARE/SPRINGFIELD, LLC—See National HealthCare Corporation; *U.S. Public*, pg. 1496
NHC HEALTHCARE/TOWN & COUNTRY—See National HealthCare Corporation; *U.S. Public*, pg. 1496
NHC HOMECARE MISSOURI, LLC—See National HealthCare Corporation; *U.S. Public*, pg. 1496
NHC HOMECARE - SOUTH CAROLINA, LLC—See National HealthCare Corporation; *U.S. Public*, pg. 1496
NHC PLACE/ANNISTON, LLC—See National HealthCare Corporation; *U.S. Public*, pg. 1496
NORTHERN OAKS HEALTHCARE, INC.—See The Ensign Group, Inc.; *U.S. Public*, pg. 2071
NORTH GROVE CARE HOME PERTH—See Balhousie Holdings Limited; *Int'l*, pg. 808
NORTH INCH CARE HOME PERTH—See Balhousie Holdings Limited; *Int'l*, pg. 808
NURSE ON CALL, INC.—See Brookdale Senior Living Inc.; *U.S. Public*, pg. 395
NURSING AND RETIREMENT CENTER OF THE ANDOVERS, INC.—See Welltower Inc.; *U.S. Public*, pg. 2348
NUTMEG PAVILION HEALTHCARE—See Apollo Global Management, Inc.; *U.S. Public*, pg. 157
OCEANVIEW HEALTHCARE, INC.—See The Ensign Group, Inc.; *U.S. Public*, pg. 2071
OHIO MENTOR, INC.—See Centerbridge Partners, L.P.; *U.S. Private*, pg. 814
OLIVE VISTA BEHAVIORAL HEALTH CENTER—See Formation Capital, LLC; *U.S. Private*, pg. 1570
OPTION CARE ENTERPRISES, INC.—See Madison Dearborn Partners, LLC; *U.S. Private*, pg. 2542
ORCHARD RIDGE CARE & REHABILITATION CENTER—See Formation Capital, LLC; *U.S. Private*, pg. 1571
OWENTON CENTER—See Formation Capital, LLC; *U.S. Private*, pg. 1571
OZANAM HALL OF QUEENS NURSING HOME; *U.S. Private*, pg. 3057
PACIFIC COAST CARE CENTER, L.L.C.—See Apollo Global Management, Inc.; *U.S. Public*, pg. 157
THE PALMETTOS OF PARKLANE, LLC—See National HealthCare Corporation; *U.S. Public*, pg. 1497
PALOMAR VISTA HEALTHCARE CENTER—See The Ensign Group, Inc.; *U.S. Public*, pg. 2071
PANAMA CITY NURSING CENTER LLC—See Omega Healthcare Investors, Inc.; *U.S. Public*, pg. 1571
PARKHURST HOUSE, LLC—See TPG Capital, L.P.; *U.S. Public*, pg. 2168
PARKVIEW - SKILLED NURSING, INC.—See Omega Healthcare Investors, Inc.; *U.S. Public*, pg. 1571
PARK WAVERLY HEALTHCARE LLC—See The Ensign Group, Inc.; *U.S. Public*, pg. 2071
PARKWAY PAVILION HEALTHCARE—See Apollo Global Management, Inc.; *U.S. Public*, pg. 157
PATIENT'S CHOICE HOSPICE AND PALLIATIVE CARE OF LOUISIANA, LLC—See UnitedHealth Group Incorporated; *U.S. Public*, pg. 2246
THE PAVILION CARE CENTER, LLC—See Regional Health Properties, Inc.; *U.S. Public*, pg. 1776
PAVILLION NURSING CENTER NORTH, INC.—See Omega Healthcare Investors, Inc.; *U.S. Public*, pg. 1571
PEAK MEDICAL IDAHO OPERATIONS, INC.—See Formation Capital, LLC; *U.S. Private*, pg. 1570
PEAK MEDICAL - MCKINLEY CENTER—See Formation Capital, LLC; *U.S. Private*, pg. 1570
PEAK MEDICAL OF IDAHO, INC.—See Formation Capital, LLC; *U.S. Private*, pg. 1570
PEAK MEDICAL - PIKES PEAK CENTER—See Formation Capital, LLC; *U.S. Private*, pg. 1570
PENACOOK PLACE; *U.S. Private*, pg. 3132
PERSONACARE OF OHIO, LLC—See Apollo Global Management, Inc.; *U.S. Public*, pg. 157
PETERSEN HEALTH CARE, INC.; *U.S. Private*, pg. 3159
PETERSEN HEALTH CARE - PALM TERRACE OF MATTOON—See Petersen Health Care, Inc.; *U.S. Private*, pg. 3159
PETTIGREW REHABILITATION & HEALTHCARE CENTER—See Apollo Global Management, Inc.; *U.S. Public*, pg. 157
PHILADELPHIA AVENUE ASSOCIATES—See Welltower Inc.; *U.S. Public*, pg. 2349
PHNTUS PINEHURST LLC—See Brookdale Senior Living Inc.; *U.S. Public*, pg. 395
PINEBROOK CARE & REHABILITATION CENTER—See Formation Capital, LLC; *U.S. Private*, pg. 1571
PINE CARE GROUP LIMITED—See Chinachem Group; *Int'l*, pg. 1568
PINES OF SARASOTA, INC.; *U.S. Private*, pg. 3184
PINEY LUFKIN HEALTHCARE, INC.—See The Ensign Group, Inc.; *U.S. Public*, pg. 2072
PINNACLE HEALTH CARE; *U.S. Private*, pg. 3185
PITLOCHRY CARE HOME—See Balhousie Holdings Limited; *Int'l*, pg. 808
PLUM HEALTHCARE GROUP, LLC; *U.S. Private*, pg. 3214
POINT PLACE CENTER—See Formation Capital, LLC; *U.S. Private*, pg. 1571
POMAC, LLC—See Lennar Corporation; *U.S. Public*, pg. 1307
POMPTON CARE, L.L.C.—See Welltower Inc.; *U.S. Public*, pg. 2349
PRESCOTT NURSING HOME, INC.—See Welltower Inc.; *U.S. Public*, pg. 2349
PRESIDENTIAL CENTER—See Formation Capital, LLC; *U.S. Private*, pg. 1571
PRESIDIO HEALTH ASSOCIATES LLC—See The Ensign Group, Inc.; *U.S. Public*, pg. 2072
PRICE HEALTHCARE, INC.—See The Ensign Group, Inc.; *U.S. Public*, pg. 2072
PRIME HOME CARE, INC.—See TPG Capital, L.P.; *U.S. Public*, pg. 2168
PROGRESS PHARMACY LTD—See AlerisLife Inc.; *U.S. Private*, pg. 162
PROMEDICA SENIOR CARE—See American Healthcare Systems Corp., Inc.; *U.S. Private*, pg. 236
QUINCE HOLDINGS, LLC—See Apollo Global Management, Inc.; *U.S. Public*, pg. 157
RADIANT HILLS HEALTH ASSOCIATES LLC—See The Ensign Group, Inc.; *U.S. Public*, pg. 2072
REDMOND CARE & REHABILITATION CENTER—See The Ensign Group, Inc.; *U.S. Public*, pg. 2072
REGENCY HOSPITAL COMPANY OF MACON, LLC—See Select Medical Holdings Corporation; *U.S. Public*, pg. 1858
REGENCY HOSPITAL COMPANY OF MERIDIAN, L.L.C.—See Select Medical Holdings Corporation; *U.S. Public*, pg. 1858
REGENCY HOSPITAL COMPANY OF SOUTH ATLANTA, L.L.C.—See Select Medical Holdings Corporation; *U.S. Public*, pg. 1858
REGENCY HOSPITAL COMPANY OF SOUTH CAROLINA, L.L.C.—See Select Medical Holdings Corporation; *U.S. Public*, pg. 1858
REGENCY HOSPITAL OF CINCINNATI, LLC—See Select Medical Holdings Corporation; *U.S. Public*, pg. 1858
REGENCY HOSPITAL OF COLUMBUS, LLC—See Select Medical Holdings Corporation; *U.S. Public*, pg. 1858
REGENCY HOSPITAL OF COVINGTON, LLC—See Select Medical Holdings Corporation; *U.S. Public*, pg. 1858
REGENCY HOSPITAL OF GREENVILLE, LLC—See Select Medical Holdings Corporation; *U.S. Public*, pg. 1859
REGENCY HOSPITAL OF JACKSON, LLC—See Select Medical Holdings Corporation; *U.S. Public*, pg. 1859
REGENCY HOSPITAL OF MINNEAPOLIS, LLC—See Select Medical Holdings Corporation; *U.S. Public*, pg. 1859
REGENCY HOSPITAL OF NORTH CENTRAL OHIO, LLC—See Select Medical Holdings Corporation; *U.S. Public*, pg. 1859
REGENCY HOSPITAL OF NORTHWEST ARKANSAS, LLC—See Select Medical Holdings Corporation; *U.S. Public*, pg. 1859
REGENCY HOSPITAL OF NORTHWEST INDIANA, LLC—See Select Medical Holdings Corporation; *U.S. Public*, pg. 1859
REGENCY HOSPITAL OF SOUTHERN MISSISSIPPI, LLC—See Select Medical Holdings Corporation; *U.S. Public*, pg. 1859
REHABCLINICS (SPT), INC.—See Select Medical Holdings Corporation; *U.S. Public*, pg. 1859
REHABILITATION CENTER OF WASHINGTON, D.C., INC.—See Select Medical Holdings Corporation; *U.S. Public*, pg. 1859
REHABILITATION HOSPITAL OF NORTH ALABAMA, LLC—See Encompass Health Corporation; *U.S. Public*, pg. 758
REHABILITATION HOSPITAL OF THE CAPE AND ISLANDS—See Partners HealthCare System, Inc.; *U.S. Private*, pg. 3101
REHAB PROVIDER NETWORK-EAST I, INC.—See Select Medical Holdings Corporation; *U.S. Public*, pg. 1859
REHAB PROVIDER NETWORK-MICHIGAN, INC.—See Select Medical Holdings Corporation; *U.S. Public*, pg. 1859
REHAB PROVIDER NETWORK-PENNSYLVANIA, INC.—See Select Medical Holdings Corporation; *U.S. Public*, pg. 1859
REM ARROWHEAD, INC.—See Centerbridge Partners, L.P.; *U.S. Private*, pg. 814
REM CENTRAL LAKES, INC.—See Centerbridge Partners, L.P.; *U.S. Private*, pg. 814
REM COMMUNITY OPTIONS, LLC—See Centerbridge Partners, L.P.; *U.S. Private*, pg. 814
REM CONNECTICUT COMMUNITY SERVICES, INC.—See Centerbridge Partners, L.P.; *U.S. Private*, pg. 814
REM DEVELOPMENTAL SERVICES, INC.—See Centerbridge Partners, L.P.; *U.S. Private*, pg. 814
REM EAST, LLC—See Centerbridge Partners, L.P.; *U.S. Private*, pg. 814
REM HEARTLAND, INC.—See Centerbridge Partners, L.P.; *U.S. Private*, pg. 814
REM HENNEPIN, INC.—See Centerbridge Partners, L.P.; *U.S. Private*, pg. 814
REM INDIANA COMMUNITY SERVICES, INC.—See Centerbridge Partners, L.P.; *U.S. Private*, pg. 814
REM INDIANA, INC.—See Centerbridge Partners, L.P.; *U.S. Private*, pg. 814
REM IOWA COMMUNITY SERVICES, INC.—See Centerbridge Partners, L.P.; *U.S. Private*, pg. 814
REM IOWA, INC.—See Centerbridge Partners, L.P.; *U.S. Private*, pg. 814
REM MINNESOTA COMMUNITY SERVICES, INC.—See Centerbridge Partners, L.P.; *U.S. Private*, pg. 814
REM MINNESOTA, INC.—See Centerbridge Partners, L.P.; *U.S. Private*, pg. 814
REM NEVADA, INC.—See Centerbridge Partners, L.P.; *U.S. Private*, pg. 814
REM NORTH DAKOTA, INC.—See Centerbridge Partners, L.P.; *U.S. Private*, pg. 814
REM NORTH STAR, INC.—See Centerbridge Partners, L.P.; *U.S. Private*, pg. 814
REM OCCAZIO, INC.—See Centerbridge Partners, L.P.; *U.S. Private*, pg. 814
REM OHIO, INC.—See Centerbridge Partners, L.P.; *U.S. Private*, pg. 814
REM OHIO WAIVERED SERVICES, INC.—See Centerbridge Partners, L.P.; *U.S. Private*, pg. 814
REM RIVER BLUFFS, INC.—See Centerbridge Partners, L.P.; *U.S. Private*, pg. 814
REM SOUTH CENTRAL SERVICES, INC.—See Centerbridge Partners, L.P.; *U.S. Private*, pg. 814
REM SOUTHWEST SERVICES, INC.—See Centerbridge Partners, L.P.; *U.S. Private*, pg. 814

N.A.I.C.S. INDEX

623210 — RESIDENTIAL INTELLE...

REM WEST VIRGINIA, LLC—See Centerbridge Partners, L.P.; *U.S. Private*, pg. 814
REM WISCONSIN III, INC.—See Centerbridge Partners, L.P.; *U.S. Private*, pg. 814
REM WISCONSIN, INC.—See Centerbridge Partners, L.P.; *U.S. Private*, pg. 814
REM WOODVALE, INC.—See Centerbridge Partners, L.P.; *U.S. Private*, pg. 814
RENAISSANCE TERRACE CARE & REHABILITATION CENTER—See Formation Capital, LLC; *U.S. Private*, pg. 1571
RESIDENZ LOBBERICH GMBH—See Clariane SE; *Int'l*, pg. 1643
REU LIVING SDN. BHD.—See IGB Berhad; *Int'l*, pg. 3601
RHA SULLIVAN INC; *U.S. Private*, pg. 3421
RICHMOND SENIOR SERVICES, INC.—See The Ensign Group, Inc.; *U.S. Public*, pg. 2072
RIGIFA CARE HOME PERTH—See Balhousie Holdings Limited; *Int'l*, pg. 808
RIVERDALE PLACE CARE & REHABILITATION CENTER—See Formation Capital, LLC; *U.S. Private*, pg. 1571
RIVER OAKS—See Stonerise Healthcare LLC; *U.S. Private*, pg. 3830
RIVER'S EDGE REHABILITATION & LIVING CENTER—See The Ensign Group, Inc.; *U.S. Public*, pg. 2072
RIVER STREET ASSOCIATES—See Welltower Inc.; *U.S. Public*, pg. 2349
RIVERVIEW HEALTH & REHAB CENTER INC.; *U.S. Private*, pg. 3448
ROCK HILL HEALTHCARE, INC.—See The Ensign Group, Inc.; *U.S. Public*, pg. 2071
ROHM SERVICES, CORP.; *U.S. Private*, pg. 3473
ROSE PARK HEALTHCARE ASSOCIATES, INC.—See The Ensign Group, Inc.; *U.S. Public*, pg. 2072
RUMBLING BRIDGE CARE HOME KINROSS—See Balhousie Holdings Limited; *Int'l*, pg. 808
SABER HEALTHCARE GROUP LLC; *U.S. Private*, pg. 3520
SALADO CREEK SENIOR CARE, INC.—See The Ensign Group, Inc.; *U.S. Public*, pg. 2072
SALEM CARE & REHABILITATION CENTER—See Formation Capital, LLC; *U.S. Private*, pg. 1571
SAND HOLLOW HEALTHCARE, INC.—See The Ensign Group, Inc.; *U.S. Public*, pg. 2072
SANKEI BUILDING WELL CARE CO., LTD.—See Fuji Media Holdings, Inc.; *Int'l*, pg. 2814
SAN SIMEON BY THE SOUND NURSING & REHABILITATION; *U.S. Private*, pg. 3542
SANTA CRUZ HEALTHCARE CENTER—See Apollo Global Management, Inc.; *U.S. Public*, pg. 157
SARAH BRAYTON GENERAL PARTNERSHIP—See Welltower Inc.; *U.S. Public*, pg. 2349
SAVA SENIOR CARE LLC; *U.S. Private*, pg. 3555
SAVOY HEALTHCARE, INC.—See The Ensign Group, Inc.; *U.S. Public*, pg. 2072
SELECT MEDICAL OF MARYLAND, INC.—See Select Medical Holdings Corporation; *U.S. Public*, pg. 1859
SENIORENZENTRUM HENNEF GMBH—See Clariane SE; *Int'l*, pg. 1643
SENIOR LIVING OPTIONS INC.; *U.S. Private*, pg. 3607
SHAUGHNESSY KAPLAN REHABILITATION HOSPITAL—See Partners HealthCare System, Inc.; *U.S. Private*, pg. 3101
SIGNATURE HEALTHCARE AT TOWER ROAD—See Signature HealthCARE LLC; *U.S. Private*, pg. 3650
SIGNATURE HEALTHCARE LLC; *U.S. Private*, pg. 3650
SIGNATURE HEALTHCARE OF COSHOCTON—See Signature HealthCARE LLC; *U.S. Private*, pg. 3650
SILVERADO SENIOR LIVING DALLAS, INC.—See Welltower Inc.; *U.S. Public*, pg. 2349
SILVERADO SENIOR LIVING, INC.—See Welltower Inc.; *U.S. Public*, pg. 2349
SILVERADO SENIOR LIVING SCOTTSDALE, INC.—See Welltower Inc.; *U.S. Public*, pg. 2349
THE SILVERCREST CENTER FOR NURSING AND REHABILITATION; *U.S. Private*, pg. 4118
SILVER LAKE CENTER, INC.; *U.S. Private*, pg. 3653
SILVER STREAM CENTER—See Formation Capital, LLC; *U.S. Private*, pg. 1571
SKYLARK CARE SERVICE CO., LTD.—See Bain Capital, LP; *U.S. Private*, pg. 444
SLOVAK AMERICAN CHARITABLE ASSOCIATION; *U.S. Private*, pg. 3689
SMITH RANCH CARE CENTER, L.L.C.—See Apollo Global Management, Inc.; *U.S. Public*, pg. 157
SOMERFORD HOUSE FREDERICK—See AlerisLife Inc.; *U.S. Private*, pg. 162
SOMERFORD PLACE LLC—See AlerisLife Inc.; *U.S. Private*, pg. 162
SOMERTON CENTER—See Formation Capital, LLC; *U.S. Private*, pg. 1571
SONIDA SENIOR LIVING, INC.; *U.S. Public*, pg. 1903
SOUTH CAROLINA MENTOR, INC.—See Centerbridge Partners, L.P.; *U.S. Private*, pg. 814
SOUTH CENTRAL WYOMING HEALTHCARE & REHABILITATION—See Apollo Global Management, Inc.; *U.S. Public*, pg. 157
SOUTHERN ASSISTED LIVING, LLC—See Brookdale Senior Living Inc.; *U.S. Public*, pg. 395
SOUTHERN CALIFORNIA SPECIALTY CARE, LLC—See Apollo Global Management, Inc.; *U.S. Public*, pg. 157
SOUTHERN OAKS HEALTHCARE, INC.—See The Ensign Group, Inc.; *U.S. Public*, pg. 2072
SOUTH VALLEY HEALTHCARE, INC.—See The Ensign Group, Inc.; *U.S. Public*, pg. 2072
SPAULDING HOSPITAL - CAMBRIDGE INC.—See Partners HealthCare System, Inc.; *U.S. Private*, pg. 3101
SPECTRUM HEALTH CONTINUING CARE GROUP, INC.; *U.S. Private*, pg. 3752
STANDIFER PLACE PROPERTIES, LLC—See National HealthCare Corporation; *U.S. Public*, pg. 1496
STANTON LAKE HEALTHCARE, INC.—See The Ensign Group, Inc.; *U.S. Public*, pg. 2071
ST. CAMILLUS CENTER—See Formation Capital, LLC; *U.S. Private*, pg. 1571
ST. CATHERINE LABOURE MANOR, INC.—See Ascension Health Alliance; *U.S. Private*, pg. 348
STEERE HOUSE; *U.S. Private*, pg. 3797
ST. JOSEPH'S CENTER—See Formation Capital, LLC; *U.S. Private*, pg. 1571
ST. MARY'S MANOR—See Ascension Health Alliance; *U.S. Private*, pg. 347
STONERISE HEALTHCARE LLC; *U.S. Private*, pg. 3830
STONEY HILL HEALTHCARE, INC.—See The Ensign Group, Inc.; *U.S. Public*, pg. 2071
STORMONT CARE HOME BLAIRGOWRIE—See Balhousie Holdings Limited; *Int'l*, pg. 808
ST. PATRICK'S MANOR SKILLED NURSING AND SHORT TERM REHABILITATION CENTER; *U.S. Private*, pg. 3773
ST. PATRICK'S RESIDENCE; *U.S. Private*, pg. 3773
SUMMERVILLE AT PRINCE WILLIAM, INC.—See Brookdale Senior Living Inc.; *U.S. Public*, pg. 395
SUMMERVILLE AT WEKIWA SPRINGS LLC—See Brookdale Senior Living Inc.; *U.S. Public*, pg. 395
SUNBRIDGE BRITTANY REHABILITATION CENTER, INC.—See Formation Capital, LLC; *U.S. Private*, pg. 1570
SUNBRIDGE CARE ENTERPRISES WEST, INC.—See Formation Capital, LLC; *U.S. Private*, pg. 1570
SUNBRIDGE CARMICHAEL REHABILITATION CENTER, INC.—See Formation Capital, LLC; *U.S. Private*, pg. 1570
SUNBRIDGE HALLMARK HEALTH SERVICES, INC.—See Formation Capital, LLC; *U.S. Private*, pg. 1570
SUN COAST NURSING CENTERS INC; *U.S. Private*, pg. 3862
SUNDANCE SERVICES CORPORATION—See Formation Capital, LLC; *U.S. Private*, pg. 1570
SUNNYVILLE NURSING HOME (1996) PTE LTD—See China Healthcare Limited; *Int'l*, pg. 1507
SUNSET POINT CARE & REHABILITATION CENTER - CLEARWATER—See Formation Capital, LLC; *U.S. Private*, pg. 1571
SUSQUE-VIEW HOME, INC.; *U.S. Private*, pg. 3885
SUTHERLAND CARE CENTER—See AlerisLife Inc.; *U.S. Private*, pg. 162
SWAN HOME HEALTH, LLC—See TPG Capital, L.P.; *U.S. Public*, pg. 2168
TENDERCARE, INC.—See Extendicare Inc.; *Int'l*, pg. 2591
THOMPSON PEAK HEALTHCARE LLC—See The Ensign Group, Inc.; *U.S. Public*, pg. 2072
TORREY PINES CARE CENTER—See Apollo Global Management, Inc.; *U.S. Public*, pg. 158
TORTOLITA HEALTHCARE, INC—See The Ensign Group, Inc.; *U.S. Public*, pg. 2072
TOWN EAST HEALTHCARE, INC.—See The Ensign Group, Inc.; *U.S. Public*, pg. 2072
TRINITY TOWERS LIMITED PARTNERSHIP—See Brookdale Senior Living Inc.; *U.S. Public*, pg. 395
TRIUMPH REHABILITATION HOSPITAL OF NORTHEAST HOUSTON, LLC—See Apollo Global Management, Inc.; *U.S. Public*, pg. 157
TRUMP PAVILION FOR NURSING AND REHABILITATION; *U.S. Private*, pg. 4250
TUCKER NURSING CENTER, LLC—See Apollo Global Management, Inc.; *U.S. Public*, pg. 158
TWIN RIVERS CENTER—See Formation Capital, LLC; *U.S. Private*, pg. 1571
TWIN TOWERS; *U.S. Private*, pg. 4266
ULTIMATE NURSING SERVICES OF IOWA, INC.; *U.S. Private*, pg. 4277
UNLIMITED QUEST, INC.—See Centerbridge Partners, L.P.; *U.S. Private*, pg. 814
UPLAND COMMUNITY CARE, INC.—See The Ensign Group, Inc.; *U.S. Public*, pg. 2072
VALLEY RIVER NURSING, LLC—See Regional Health Properties, Inc.; *U.S. Public*, pg. 1776
VANGUARD HEALTHCARE SERVICES LLC; *U.S. Private*, pg. 4343
VICTORIA NURSING & REHABILITATION CENTER, INC.; *U.S. Private*, pg. 4378
VICTORIA VENTURA HEALTHCARE LLC—See The Ensign Group, Inc.; *U.S. Public*, pg. 2072
VILLA MARIA HEALTHCARE CENTER, LLC—See The Ensign Group, Inc.; *U.S. Public*, pg. 2072
VILLA SAINT JOSEPH—See Ascension Health Alliance; *U.S. Private*, pg. 347
VISITING NURSE SERVICE & HOSPICE OF SUFFOLK, INC.; *U.S. Private*, pg. 4393
VISITING NURSE SERVICES OF NEWPORT AND BRISTOL COUNTIES; *U.S. Private*, pg. 4393
VISTA WOODS HEALTH ASSOCIATES LLC—See The Ensign Group, Inc.; *U.S. Public*, pg. 2072
VNA & HOSPICE OF THE SOUTHWEST REGION, INC.; *U.S. Private*, pg. 4408
VNA HOSPICE & PALLIATIVE CARE OF SOUTHERN CALIFORNIA; *U.S. Private*, pg. 4408
VTA MANAGEMENT SERVICES, LLC—See Apollo Global Management, Inc.; *U.S. Public*, pg. 158
WASATCH VALLEY REHABILITATION—See Apollo Global Management, Inc.; *U.S. Public*, pg. 158
WATSON WOODS HEALTHCARE, INC.—See The Ensign Group, Inc.; *U.S. Public*, pg. 2072
WAYNE NURSING & REHABILITATION CENTER, INC.; *U.S. Private*, pg. 4460
WEATHERFORD HOME CARE SERVICES, LLC—See Community Health Systems, Inc.; *U.S. Public*, pg. 557
WEBSTER AT RYE; *U.S. Private*, pg. 4466
WEBSTER HOUSE; *U.S. Private*, pg. 4467
WELLINGTON HEALTHCARE, INC.—See The Ensign Group, Inc.; *U.S. Public*, pg. 2072
THE WELLSTEAD OF ROGERS DIAMONDCREST SENIOR LIVING—See AlerisLife Inc.; *U.S. Private*, pg. 162
WEST BAY OF TAMPA—See Formation Capital, LLC; *U.S. Private*, pg. 1571
WHEATLANDS CARE HOME BONNYBRIDGE—See Balhousie Holdings Limited; *Int'l*, pg. 808
WILDCREEK HEALTHCARE, INC.—See The Ensign Group, Inc.; *U.S. Public*, pg. 2072
WILLIAMSVILLE SUBURBAN, LLC—See Safire Rehabilitation of Amherst, LLC; *U.S. Private*, pg. 3525
WILLOWBANK CARE HOME CARNOUSTIE—See Balhousie Holdings Limited; *Int'l*, pg. 808
WILLOW MANOR NURSING HOME, INC.—See Welltower Inc.; *U.S. Public*, pg. 2349
WILLOW RIDGE CENTER—See Formation Capital, LLC; *U.S. Private*, pg. 1571
WIND RIVER HEALTH CARE & REHABILITATION CENTER—See Apollo Global Management, Inc.; *U.S. Public*, pg. 158
WINDSOR HEALTH AND REHAB CENTER; *U.S. Private*, pg. 4539
WNR INC.—See Partners HealthCare System, Inc.; *U.S. Private*, pg. 3102
WOODARD CREEK HEALTHCARE, INC.—See The Ensign Group, Inc.; *U.S. Public*, pg. 2072
YELLOWWOOD ACRES INC; *U.S. Private*, pg. 4588
YOUNGTOWN HEALTH, INC.—See The Ensign Group, Inc.; *U.S. Public*, pg. 2073

623210 — RESIDENTIAL INTELLECTUAL AND DEVELOPMENTAL DISABILITY FACILITIES

ABLE2 ENHANCING POTENTIAL; *U.S. Private*, pg. 39
ADEC INC.; *U.S. Private*, pg. 77
ALTERNATIVE RESIDENCES TWO INC.; *U.S. Private*, pg. 207
ALTERNATIVE SERVICES INC.; *U.S. Private*, pg. 207
ANN STORCK CENTER, INC.; *U.S. Private*, pg. 284
ARIZONA BEHAVIORAL HEALTH CORPORATION; *U.S. Private*, pg. 323
ASPIRE OF WESTERN NEW YORK, INC.; *U.S. Private*, pg. 352
ASSOCIATION FOR THE DEVELOPMENTALLY DISABLED; *U.S. Private*, pg. 358
THE AUTISM PROGRAM OF VIRGINIA, INC.; *U.S. Private*, pg. 3990
BAKERSFIELD ARC; *U.S. Private*, pg. 457
BENHAVEN, INC.; *U.S. Private*, pg. 526
BLUEGRASS.ORG, INC.; *U.S. Private*, pg. 597
BUCKINGHAM'S CHICAGO, LLC—See Park Hotels & Resorts Inc.; *U.S. Public*, pg. 1638
BUSHWICK STUYVESANT HEIGHTS HOME ATTENDANTS, INC.; *U.S. Private*, pg. 694
CAMP VENTURE, INC.; *U.S. Private*, pg. 730
CAPE ABILITIES INC.; *U.S. Private*, pg. 737
CARE FOCUS, INC.—See Maxim Healthcare Services, Inc.; *U.S. Private*, pg. 2618
CARE UK PLC—See Bridgepoint Group Plc; *Int'l*, pg. 1154
CENTER FOR SOCIAL CHANGE; *U.S. Private*, pg. 811
CHARLES RIVER ASSOCIATION FOR RETARDED CITIZENS INC.; *U.S. Private*, pg. 853
CHEAHA REGIONAL MENTAL HEALTH CENTER—See Baldwin County Mental Health-Mental Retardation Services, Inc.; *U.S. Public*, pg. 458
CHILD GUIDANCE & FAMILY SOLUTIONS; *U.S. Private*, pg. 882
CHRISTIAN OPPORTUNITY CENTER; *U.S. Private*, pg. 891

623210 — RESIDENTIAL INTELLE...

COALITION TO SALUTE AMERICA'S HEROES; *U.S. Private*, pg. 954
COMMUNITY SERVICES FOR THE DEVELOPMENTALLY DISABLED, INC.; *U.S. Private*, pg. 997
COOPERATIVE PRODUCTION, INC.; *U.S. Private*, pg. 1042
COUNSELING ASSOCIATES, INC.; *U.S. Private*, pg. 1065
CRYSTAL RUN VILLAGE, INC.; *U.S. Private*, pg. 1115
CURATIVE CARE NETWORK, INC.; *U.S. Private*, pg. 1124
CURO CARE LIMITED—See Horizon Capital LLP; *Int'l*, pg. 3479
DAWN OF HOPE, INC.; *U.S. Private*, pg. 1175
DAY SPRING, INC.; *U.S. Private*, pg. 1176
DELMARVA COMMUNITY SERVICES, INC.; *U.S. Private*, pg. 1197
DELTA PROJECTS, INC.; *U.S. Private*, pg. 1201
DEVELOPMENTAL PATHWAYS, INC.; *U.S. Private*, pg. 1217
DEVELOPMENTAL SERVICES OF NORTHWEST KANSAS, INC.; *U.S. Private*, pg. 1218
DEVEREUX FLORIDA—See The Devereux Foundation, Inc.; *U.S. Private*, pg. 4020
DISABILITY RIGHTS TEXAS; *U.S. Private*, pg. 1237
D&S RESIDENTIAL SERVICES, LP—See Comvest Group Holdings LLC; *U.S. Private*, pg. 1007
EMERITOL GRAND TERRACE LLC—See Brookdale Senior Living Inc.; *U.S. Public*, pg. 394
ENVISION UNLIMITED; *U.S. Private*, pg. 1410
EXCEPTIONAL CHILDREN'S FOUNDATION; *U.S. Private*, pg. 1446
FAMILY RESIDENCES AND ESSENTIAL ENTERPRISES INC.; *U.S. Private*, pg. 1471
FRANKLIN COUNTY RESIDENTIAL SERVICES, INC.; *U.S. Private*, pg. 1597
FRONTIER COMMUNITY SERVICES; *U.S. Private*, pg. 1615
GENESIS REHABILITATION HOSPITAL, INC.—See Genesis Health, Inc.; *U.S. Private*, pg. 1669
GENTLEBROOK, INC.; *U.S. Private*, pg. 1679
GREYSTONE PROGRAMS, INC.; *U.S. Private*, pg. 1786
HEINZERLING FOUNDATION; *U.S. Private*, pg. 1905
HOPEWELL INDUSTRIES INC.; *U.S. Private*, pg. 1979
HUGHES CENTER, LLC—See Universal Health Services, Inc.; *U.S. Public*, pg. 2258
HUMAN CARE SERVICES FOR FAMILIES AND CHILDREN, INC.; *U.S. Private*, pg. 2005
ICDC II, LLC—See National Storage Affiliates Trust; *U.S. Public*, pg. 1498
INDEPENDENT SUPPORT SERVICES INC.; *U.S. Private*, pg. 2061
INNOVATIVE SERVICES, INC.; *U.S. Private*, pg. 2083
INSTITUTE FOR COMMUNITY LIVING; *U.S. Private*, pg. 2093
THE INSTITUTE OF PROFESSIONAL PRACTICE, INC.; *U.S. Private*, pg. 4056
JEWISH FOUNDATION FOR GROUP HOMES; *U.S. Private*, pg. 2206
JOSINA LOTT RESIDENTIAL & COMMUNITY SERVICES; *U.S. Private*, pg. 2237
JUDGE ROTENBERG EDUCATIONAL CENTER; *U.S. Private*, pg. 2242
KENNEDY-DONOVAN CENTER, INC.; *U.S. Private*, pg. 2285
KREIDER SERVICES, INC.; *U.S. Private*, pg. 2350
LAKE SHORE BEHAVIORAL HEALTH, INC.; *U.S. Private*, pg. 2376
LAMBS FARM, INC.; *U.S. Private*, pg. 2380
LIFESKILLS, INC.—See Pennyroyal Regional Mental Health, Mental Retardation Board, Inc.; *U.S. Private*, pg. 3138
LIFEWORKS SERVICES INC.; *U.S. Private*, pg. 2452
LITTLE FRIENDS, INC.; *U.S. Private*, pg. 2468
LIVING WELL DISABILITY SERVICES; *U.S. Private*, pg. 2474
MAT-SU SERVICES FOR CHILDREN AND ADULTS INC.; *U.S. Private*, pg. 2608
MAY INSTITUTE, INC.; *U.S. Private*, pg. 2620
MICHAEL DUNN CENTER; *U.S. Private*, pg. 2697
MISERICORDIA; *U.S. Private*, pg. 2746
MONARCH NC; *U.S. Private*, pg. 2769
OCEAN STATE COMMUNITY RESOURCES, INC.; *U.S. Private*, pg. 2990
OHI MAINE; *U.S. Private*, pg. 3003
THE OLD DEANERY CARE VILLAGE—See August Equity LLP; *Int'l*, pg. 703
OPEN ARMS CARE CORPORATION; *U.S. Private*, pg. 3029
OPPORTUNITY ENTERPRISES, INC.; *U.S. Private*, pg. 3033
OPPORTUNITY PARTNERS, INC.; *U.S. Private*, pg. 3033
PATHFINDER, INC.; *U.S. Private*, pg. 3105
PRIMECARE, INC.; *U.S. Private*, pg. 3262
RELIANCE HOUSE INC.; *U.S. Private*, pg. 3394
SKILLS, INC.; *U.S. Private*, pg. 3682
SOUTHEAST FLORIDA BEHAVIORAL HEALTH NETWORK, INC.; *U.S. Private*, pg. 3725
SOUTHEAST KANSAS INDEPENDENT LIVING RESOURCE CENTER, INC.; *U.S. Private*, pg. 3725
SPRINGBROOK; *U.S. Private*, pg. 3763
STARKEY, INC.; *U.S. Private*, pg. 3787
ST. CHRISTOPHER'S, INC.; *U.S. Private*, pg. 3771
ST. JOSEPH'S CENTER; *U.S. Private*, pg. 3772
ST. LOUIS ARC, INC.; *U.S. Private*, pg. 3772
STONE MOUNTAIN SCHOOL, INC.—See Acadia Healthcare Company, Inc.; *U.S. Public*, pg. 30
TRI-COUNTIES ASSOCIATION FOR THE DEVELOPMENTALLY DISABLED; *U.S. Private*, pg. 4222
VINE VILLAGE, INC.; *U.S. Private*, pg. 4385
WESTMORELAND CASEMANAGEMENT AND SUPPORTS, INC.; *U.S. Private*, pg. 4499
WHOLE LIFE, INC; *U.S. Private*, pg. 4514
WOODHAVEN LEARNING CENTER; *U.S. Private*, pg. 4558
WOOD LANE RESIDENTIAL SERVICES, INC.; *U.S. Private*, pg. 4557

623220 — RESIDENTIAL MENTAL HEALTH AND SUBSTANCE ABUSE FACILITIES

12 & 12, INC.—See Grand Lake Mental Health Center, Inc.; *U.S. Private*, pg. 1753
ACHIEVEMENT CENTER, INC.; *U.S. Private*, pg. 59
ADCARE HOSPITAL OF WORCESTER, INC.—See AAC Holdings, Inc.; *U.S. Private*, pg. 30
ADULT AND CHILD; *U.S. Private*, pg. 83
ALTERNATIVE REHABILITATION COMMUNITIES, INC.; *U.S. Private*, pg. 207
ALZHEIMER'S RESOURCE CENTER OF CONNECTICUT, INC.; *U.S. Private*, pg. 214
AMBROSIA SUBSTANCE ABUSE TREATMENT CENTER; *U.S. Private*, pg. 218
A NEW LEAF; *U.S. Private*, pg. 18
ANKA BEHAVIORAL HEALTH, INC.; *U.S. Private*, pg. 284
API BETRIEBS GEMEINNUTZIGE GMBH—See Fresenius SE & Co. KGaA; *Int'l*, pg. 2777
ARIZONA'S CHILDREN ASSOCIATION; *U.S. Private*, pg. 325
ASIAN AMERICAN DRUG ABUSE PROGRAM; *U.S. Private*, pg. 351
ASIAN COUNSELING & REFERRAL SERVICE; *U.S. Private*, pg. 351
ASPIRE HEALTH PARTNERS - FERNPARK FACILITY—See Aspire Health Partners, Inc.; *U.S. Private*, pg. 352
ASPIRE HEALTH PARTNERS, INC.; *U.S. Private*, pg. 352
ASPIRE HEALTH PARTNERS - PRINCETON PLAZA—See Aspire Health Partners, Inc.; *U.S. Private*, pg. 352
ATHENS BEHAVIORAL HEALTH CLINIC—See Hopewell Health Centers Inc.; *U.S. Private*, pg. 1979
BEHAVIORAL CONNECTIONS OF WOOD COUNTY, INC.—See Harbor Corp.; *U.S. Private*, pg. 1858
BEHAVIORAL HEALTHCARE PARTNERS OF CENTRAL OHIO, INC.; *U.S. Private*, pg. 515
BEHAVIORAL HEALTH GROUP; *U.S. Private*, pg. 514
BELLEFAIRE JCB; *U.S. Private*, pg. 520
THE BETTY FORD CENTER—See Hazelden Betty Ford Foundation; *U.S. Private*, pg. 1886
BHC FAIRFAX HOSPITAL, INC.—See Universal Health Services, Inc.; *U.S. Public*, pg. 2256
BHC SIERRA VISTA HOSPITAL, INC.—See Universal Health Services, Inc.; *U.S. Public*, pg. 2256
BHC STREAMWOOD HOSPITAL, INC.—See Universal Health Services, Inc.; *U.S. Public*, pg. 2256
BLOOMINGTON MEADOWS, GENERAL PARTNERSHIP—See Universal Health Services, Inc.; *U.S. Public*, pg. 2256
BRIDGEVIEW COMMUNITY MENTAL HEALTH CENTER—See Bethany for Children & Families; *U.S. Private*, pg. 545
BROOK LANE; *U.S. Private*, pg. 663
BURRELL CENTER; *U.S. Private*, pg. 691
CAL RIPKEN, SR. FOUNDATION; *U.S. Private*, pg. 715
CAMERON CARE, LLC—See Jackson House; *U.S. Private*, pg. 2177
CAREY COUNSELING CENTER, INC.; *U.S. Private*, pg. 754
CCS/LANSING, INC.—See Universal Health Services, Inc.; *U.S. Public*, pg. 2256
CENTERSTONE OF ILLINOIS, INC.—See Centerstone of America, Inc.; *U.S. Private*, pg. 817
CENTRAL FLORIDA BEHAVIORAL HEALTH NETWORK INC; *U.S. Private*, pg. 820
CENTRAL FLORIDA CARES HEALTH SYSTEM, INC.; *U.S. Private*, pg. 820
CHESTNUT RIDGE COUNSELING SERVICES, INC.; *U.S. Private*, pg. 875
CHILDREN'S CENTER FOR DEVELOPMENTAL ENRICHMENT; *U.S. Private*, pg. 883
CHILDREN'S CENTER FOR TREATMENT AND EDUCATION; *U.S. Private*, pg. 883
THE CHILDREN'S CENTER OF HAMDEN, INC.; *U.S. Private*, pg. 4008
CHILDRENS SERVICE CENTER OF WYOMING VALLEY, INC.; *U.S. Private*, pg. 885
COASTAL BEHAVIORAL HEALTHCARE, INC.; *U.S. Private*, pg. 955

CODAC BEHAVIORAL HEALTH SERVICES, INC.; *U.S. Private*, pg. 960
COLUMBIA RIVER MENTAL HEALTH SERVICES; *U.S. Private*, pg. 977
COMMUNITY ANTI-DRUG COALITIONS OF AMERICA; *U.S. Private*, pg. 989
COMMUNITY BEHAVIORAL HEALTH; *U.S. Private*, pg. 990
COMMUNITY COUNSELING CENTERS, INC.; *U.S. Private*, pg. 991
COMMUNITY COUNSELING OF BRISTOL COUNTY, INC.; *U.S. Private*, pg. 991
COMMUNITY COUNSELING SERVICES, INC.; *U.S. Private*, pg. 991
COMMUNITY HEALTH RESOURCES; *U.S. Private*, pg. 994
COMMUNITY INVOLVEMENT PROGRAMS; *U.S. Private*, pg. 995
COMMUNITY PARTNERSHIP OF SOUTHERN ARIZONA; *U.S. Private*, pg. 996
COMMUNITY PARTNERS; *U.S. Private*, pg. 996
COMPREHENSIVE BEHAVIORAL HEALTHCARE, INC.; *U.S. Private*, pg. 1002
COMPREHENSIVE OPTIONS FOR DRUG ABUSERS; *U.S. Private*, pg. 1003
THE COUNSELING SERVICE OF ADDISON COUNTY, INC.; *U.S. Private*, pg. 4015
CREOKS BEHAVIORAL HEALTH SERVICES; *U.S. Private*, pg. 1092
CUMBERLAND COUNTY GUIDANCE CENTER; *U.S. Private*, pg. 1122
DENALI FAMILY SERVICES; *U.S. Private*, pg. 1204
DEPAUL COMMUNITY SERVICES, INC.; *U.S. Private*, pg. 1208
DETROIT RESCUE MISSION MINISTRIES; *U.S. Private*, pg. 1216
DOUGLAS GARDENS COMMUNITY MENTAL HEALTH CENTER OF MIAMI BEACH; *U.S. Private*, pg. 1267
DR WARREN E SMITH COMMUNITY MENTAL HEALTH MENTAL RETARDATION & SUBSTANCE ABUSE CENTERS; *U.S. Private*, pg. 1271
EDGEWOOD CENTER FOR CHILDREN AND FAMILIES; *U.S. Private*, pg. 1335
FAMILY & CHILDRENS SERVICES; *U.S. Private*, pg. 1468
FAMILY GUIDANCE CENTERS, INC.; *U.S. Private*, pg. 1470
FHCHS OF PUERTO RICO, INC.—See Universal Health Services, Inc.; *U.S. Public*, pg. 2257
FRIENDSHIP HOUSE; *U.S. Private*, pg. 1612
FRONTIER BEHAVIORAL HEALTH; *U.S. Private*, pg. 1614
GANDARA MENTAL HEALTH CENTER, INC.; *U.S. Private*, pg. 1641
GEORGE WEST MENTAL HEALTH FOUNDATION; *U.S. Private*, pg. 1683
GRACE BEHAVIORAL HEALTH, LLC—See KKR & Co. Inc.; *U.S. Public*, pg. 1249
GRACIE SQUARE HOSPITAL; *U.S. Private*, pg. 1749
GRAND PRAIRIE SERVICES; *U.S. Private*, pg. 1753
GRANT-BLACKFORD MENTAL HEALTH, INC.; *U.S. Private*, pg. 1757
HABILITATIVE SERVICES, INC.—See Centerbridge Partners, L.P.; *U.S. Private*, pg. 813
HAZELDEN/NEW YORK—See Hazelden Betty Ford Foundation; *U.S. Private*, pg. 1886
HAZELDEN—See Hazelden Betty Ford Foundation; *U.S. Private*, pg. 1886
HEALTH CARE AND REHABILITATION SERVICES; *U.S. Private*, pg. 1892
HELIOS KLINIK BAD BERLEBURG GMBH—See Fresenius SE & Co. KGaA; *Int'l*, pg. 2779
HELIOS KLINIK BAD EMS GMBH—See Fresenius SE & Co. KGaA; *Int'l*, pg. 2779
HELIOS REHAKLINIKEN BAD BERLEBURG GMBH—See Fresenius SE & Co. KGaA; *Int'l*, pg. 2780
HIGHLANDS HOSPITAL; *U.S. Private*, pg. 1940
HOGAR CREA INC.; *U.S. Private*, pg. 1961
HOSPICE OF HOPE; *U.S. Private*, pg. 1986
HUMAN DEVELOPMENT CENTER; *U.S. Private*, pg. 2005
HUMAN SERVICES CENTER; *U.S. Private*, pg. 2006
INSIGHT HUMAN SERVICES; *U.S. Private*, pg. 2086
INTEGRITY HOUSE, INC.; *U.S. Private*, pg. 2103
THE JED FOUNDATION; *U.S. Private*, pg. 4058
KIDSPEACE CORPORATION; *U.S. Private*, pg. 2303
LIFESTREAM BEHAVIORAL CENTER; *U.S. Private*, pg. 2451
LIFEWELL BEHAVIORAL WELLNESS; *U.S. Private*, pg. 2452
LOS ANGELES CHILD GUIDANCE CLINIC; *U.S. Private*, pg. 2496
LOS ANGELES MISSION, INC.; *U.S. Private*, pg. 2496
MARYHAVEN, INC.; *U.S. Private*, pg. 2599
MCLEOD ADDICTIVE DISEASE CENTER, INC.; *U.S. Private*, pg. 2641
MENTAL HEALTH SERVICES FOR CLARK AND MADISON COUNTIES, INC.; *U.S. Private*, pg. 2667
MERIDELL ACHIEVEMENT CENTER—See Universal Health Services, Inc.; *U.S. Public*, pg. 2260
MERIDIAN BEHAVIORAL HEALTHCARE, INC.; *U.S. Private*, pg. 2672

N.A.I.C.S. INDEX

623311 — CONTINUING CARE RET...

MINNESOTA TEEN CHALLENGE INC; *U.S. Private*, pg. 2743
NARCO FREEDOM, INC.; *U.S. Private*, pg. 2835
NATIONAL COUNCIL FOR BEHAVIORAL HEALTH; *U.S. Private*, pg. 2852
NATIONAL MENTOR HEALTHCARE, LLC—See Centerbridge Partners, L.P.; *U.S. Private*, pg. 814
NATIONAL MENTOR HOLDINGS, INC—See Centerbridge Partners, L.P.; *U.S. Private*, pg. 814
NEUROLOGISCHES THERAPIEZENTRUM GMUNDNERBERG GMBH—See Fresenius SE & Co. KGaA; *Int'l*, pg. 2780
NEWBRIDGE SERVICES INC.; *U.S. Private*, pg. 2914
NEW HORIZONS OF THE TREASURE COAST AND OKEECHOBEE; *U.S. Private*, pg. 2897
NEXUS; *U.S. Private*, pg. 2922
THE NORD CENTER; *U.S. Private*, pg. 4084
NORTHEAST BEHAVIORAL HEALTH CORPORATION; *U.S. Private*, pg. 2949
NORTHERN ARIZONA BEHAVIORAL HEALTH AUTHORITY, INC.; *U.S. Private*, pg. 2951
NUECES COUNTY MHMR COMMUNITY CENTER; *U.S. Private*, pg. 2972
ODYSSEY HOUSE; *U.S. Private*, pg. 2994
PALMER CONTINUUM OF CARE, INC.; *U.S. Private*, pg. 3080
PALM SPRINGS TREATMENT CENTERS, LLC—See Universal Health Services, Inc.; *U.S. Public*, pg. 2259
PATH, INC.; *U.S. Private*, pg. 3105
PATHWAYS COMMUNITY HEALTH; *U.S. Private*, pg. 3106
PENNDEL MENTAL HEALTH CENTER, INC.; *U.S. Private*, pg. 3135
PENNSYLVANIA PSYCHIATRIC INSTITUTE; *U.S. Private*, pg. 3137
PEOPLES CARE, INC.; *U.S. Private*, pg. 3141
PERSONAL ENRICHMENT THROUGH MENTAL HEALTH SERVICES; *U.S. Private*, pg. 3155
PHOENIX HOUSE FOUNDATION, INC.; *U.S. Private*, pg. 3173
PINELANDS GROUP HOMES, INC.—See Bain Capital, LP; *U.S. Private*, pg. 431
PMHCC INC; *U.S. Private*, pg. 3218
PORTAGE PATH BEHAVIORAL HEALTH; *U.S. Private*, pg. 3231
POSTGRADUATE CENTER FOR MENTAL HEALTH; *U.S. Private*, pg. 3235
PRESTERA CENTER; *U.S. Private*, pg. 3255
PROGRESSIVE LIFE CENTER; *U.S. Private*, pg. 3279
RECOVERY CENTERS OF AMERICA OPERATIONS, LLC; *U.S. Private*, pg. 3372
RECOVERY SERVICES OF NEW JERSEY, INC.—See Recovery Centers of America Operations, LLC; *U.S. Private*, pg. 3372
REDISCOVER; *U.S. Private*, pg. 3379
REHABILITATIONSKLINIK IM MONTAFON BETRIEBSGMBH—See Fresenius SE & Co. KGaA; *Int'l*, pg. 2780
REHABILITATIONSZENTRUM KITZBUHEL BETRIEBSGMBH—See Fresenius SE & Co. KGaA; *Int'l*, pg. 2780
REHABILITATIONSZENTRUM OBERNDORF BETRIEBSGMBH & CO KG—See Fresenius SE & Co. KGaA; *Int'l*, pg. 2780
REHAKLINIK WIEN BAUMGARTEN BETRIEBSGMBH—See Fresenius SE & Co. KGaA; *Int'l*, pg. 2780
REHAKLINIK ZIHLSCHLACHT AG—See Fresenius SE & Co. KGaA; *Int'l*, pg. 2781
REHA SEEWIS AG—See Fresenius SE & Co. KGaA; *Int'l*, pg. 2780
REHAZENTRUM HARBURG GMBH—See Fresenius SE & Co. KGaA; *Int'l*, pg. 2781
REHAZENTRUM LUBECK GMBH—See Fresenius SE & Co. KGaA; *Int'l*, pg. 2781
REHAZENTRUM NORDERSTEDT GMBH—See Fresenius SE & Co. KGaA; *Int'l*, pg. 2781
RHA NORTH CAROLINA MR INC; *U.S. Private*, pg. 3421
SAMARITAN BEHAVIORAL HEALTH, INC.; *U.S. Private*, pg. 3536
SEABROOK HOUSE, INC.; *U.S. Private*, pg. 3583
SOUND MENTAL HEALTH; *U.S. Private*, pg. 3717
SOUTHEAST, INC.; *U.S. Private*, pg. 3727
SOUTHEAST MENTAL HEALTH CENTER; *U.S. Private*, pg. 3726
SOUTHERN HIGHLANDS COMMUNITY MENTAL HEALTH CENTER; *U.S. Private*, pg. 3732
SPECTRUM HEALTH SYSTEMS; *U.S. Private*, pg. 3752
SPRINGSTONE, INC.—See Apollo Global Management, Inc.; *U.S. Public*, pg. 158
STAIRWAYS BEHAVIORAL HEALTH—See Children's Home of Bradford, PA; *U.S. Private*, pg. 884
STANLEY STREET TREATMENT & RESOURCES; *U.S. Private*, pg. 3783
ST. ANN'S HOME, INC.; *U.S. Private*, pg. 3770
STATEN ISLAND MENTAL HEALTH SOCIETY, INC.; *U.S. Private*, pg. 3793
SUNRISE COMMUNITY, INC.; *U.S. Private*, pg. 3869
SUNRISE DETOX; *U.S. Private*, pg. 3869
SUNRISE MEDICAL AG—See Vestar Capital Partners, LLC; *U.S. Private*, pg. 4372
SUNRISE MEDICAL PTY. LTD.—See Vestar Capital Partners, LLC; *U.S. Private*, pg. 4372
SUNRISE MEDICAL S.R.L.—See Vestar Capital Partners, LLC; *U.S. Private*, pg. 4372
TOCCA LIFE HOLDINGS, INC.; *U.S. Public*, pg. 2161
TOWNSEND RECOVERY CENTER NEW ORLEANS, LLC—See AAC Holdings, Inc.; *U.S. Private*, pg. 31
TURQUOISE HEALTH & WELLNESS, INC.; *U.S. Private*, pg. 4262
UNITED SERVICES INC.; *U.S. Private*, pg. 4297
UNITY HOUSE OF CAYUGA COUNTY, INC.; *U.S. Private*, pg. 4303
US HEALTHVEST LLC; *U.S. Private*, pg. 4319
USR HOLDINGS, LLC—See Akumin, Inc.; *U.S. Public*, pg. 70
VALEO BEHAVIORAL HEALTH CARE; *U.S. Private*, pg. 4331
VALIR HEALTH; *U.S. Private*, pg. 4332
VAMED GESUNDHEIT HOLDING DEUTSCHLAND GMBH—See Fresenius SE & Co. KGaA; *Int'l*, pg. 2781
THE VILLAGE NETWORK; *U.S. Private*, pg. 4131
VINFEN CORPORATION; *U.S. Private*, pg. 4385
VISTA DEL MAR CHILD AND FAMILY SERVICES; *U.S. Private*, pg. 4394
WEST PHILADELPHIA COMMUNITY MENTAL HEALTH CONSORTIUM, INC.; *U.S. Private*, pg. 4486
WHITE'S RESIDENTIAL & FAMILY SERVICES OF NORTHWEST INDIANA—See White's Residential & Family Services, Inc.; *U.S. Private*, pg. 4510
WOODWARD YOUTH CORPORATION; *U.S. Private*, pg. 4561

623311 — CONTINUING CARE RETIREMENT COMMUNITIES

9994165 CANADA INC.—See Extendicare Inc.; *Int'l*, pg. 2591
ACCENTCARE, INC.—See Advent International Corporation; *U.S. Private*, pg. 97
ACTIVE RETIREMENT COMMUNITY INC.; *U.S. Private*, pg. 70
AHC SOUTHLAND-MELBOURNE, LLC—See Brookdale Senior Living Inc.; *U.S. Public*, pg. 393
AHC SOUTHLAND-ORMOND BEACH, LLC—See Brookdale Senior Living Inc.; *U.S. Public*, pg. 393
AIR FORCE RETIRED OFFICERS COMMUNITY; *U.S. Private*, pg. 138
ALAMANCE EXTENDED CARE, INC.; *U.S. Private*, pg. 149
ALLEGRO SENIOR LIVING, LLC—See Love Real Estate Company; *U.S. Private*, pg. 2501
ALPINE TERRACE—See Sava Senior Care LLC; *U.S. Private*, pg. 3555
ALTA VISTA HEALTHCARE—See Apollo Global Management, Inc.; *U.S. Public*, pg. 156
AMERICAN SENIORS FOUNDATION INC; *U.S. Private*, pg. 253
AMSTERDAM HOUSE CONTINUING CARE RETIREMENT COMMUNITY, INC.; *U.S. Private*, pg. 268
ARBUTUS PARK RETIREMENT COMMUNITY; *U.S. Private*, pg. 309
ARVADA MERIDIAN, LLC—See Brookdale Senior Living Inc.; *U.S. Public*, pg. 393
ARVIDA GROUP LIMITED; *Int'l*, pg. 587
ASBURY COMMUNITIES, INC.; *U.S. Private*, pg. 345
ATHERTON BAPTIST HOMES; *U.S. Private*, pg. 368
ATRIA GUILDERLAND—See Atria Senior Living, Inc.; *U.S. Private*, pg. 382
ATRIA HUNTINGTON—See Atria Senior Living, Inc.; *U.S. Private*, pg. 382
ATRIA PALM DESERT—See Atria Senior Living, Inc.; *U.S. Private*, pg. 382
ATRIA SENIOR LIVING, INC.; *U.S. Private*, pg. 382
AUGUSTA RESOURCE CENTER ON AGING, INC.—See Life Care Companies, LLC; *U.S. Private*, pg. 2448
AVEO HEALTHCARE LIMITED—See Brookfield Corporation; *Int'l*, pg. 1186
THE BAPTIST HOME OF PHILADELPHIA; *U.S. Private*, pg. 3991
BELMONT NURSING & REHABILITATION CENTER—See Health Dimensions Group; *U.S. Private*, pg. 1893
BENCHMARK SENIOR LIVING, LLC; *U.S. Private*, pg. 524
BETH SHOLOM LIFECARE COMMUNITY; *U.S. Private*, pg. 545
BLAKEFORD AT GREEN HILLS; *U.S. Private*, pg. 578
BLUEBERRY HILL HEALTHCARE NURSING HOME—See Apollo Global Management, Inc.; *U.S. Public*, pg. 156
BOULEVARD MANOR NURSING CENTER—See Sava Senior Care LLC; *U.S. Private*, pg. 3555
BREA BOYNTON BEACH LLC—See Brookdale Senior Living Inc.; *U.S. Public*, pg. 393
BREA DENVER LLC—See Brookdale Senior Living Inc.; *U.S. Public*, pg. 393
BREA EAST MESA LLC—See Brookdale Senior Living Inc.; *U.S. Public*, pg. 393
BREA PEORIA LLC—See Brookdale Senior Living Inc.; *U.S. Public*, pg. 393
BREA RENO LLC—See Brookdale Senior Living Inc.; *U.S. Public*, pg. 393
BRETHREN RETIREMENT COMMUNITY; *U.S. Private*, pg. 646
BRETHREN VILLAGE; *U.S. Private*, pg. 646
BRIARWOOD CONTINUING CARE RETIREMENT COMMUNITY; *U.S. Private*, pg. 648
BROOKDALE SENIOR LIVING INC.; *U.S. Public*, pg. 392
BROOKDALE SENIOR LIVING, INC.—See Brookdale Senior Living Inc.; *U.S. Public*, pg. 394
BROOKDALE ST. AUGUSTINE LLC—See Brookdale Senior Living Inc.; *U.S. Public*, pg. 394
BROOKDALE YORKTOWNE—See Brookdale Senior Living Inc.; *U.S. Public*, pg. 394
BSLC II; *U.S. Private*, pg. 675
BUENA VIDA CONTINUING CARE & REHABILITATION CENTER; *U.S. Private*, pg. 680
CALIFORNIA-NEVADA METHODIST HOMES—See Pacifica Companies, LLC; *U.S. Private*, pg. 3072
CALVARY FELLOWSHIP HOMES; *U.S. Private*, pg. 724
CAPITAL MANOR; *U.S. Private*, pg. 741
CAROLINA MEADOWS, INC.; *U.S. Private*, pg. 768
CASCADIA HEALTHCARE LLC; *U.S. Private*, pg. 781
CATHEDRAL VILLAGE; *U.S. Private*, pg. 788
CA TINTON FALLS, LLC—See Chelsea Senior Living LLC; *U.S. Private*, pg. 870
THE CEDARS RETIREMENT COMMUNITY; *U.S. Private*, pg. 4006
CHRISTWOOD; *U.S. Private*, pg. 892
CHURCH OF GOD HOME; *U.S. Private*, pg. 894
CLARK RETIREMENT COMMUNITY; *U.S. Private*, pg. 913
COLONIAL INC.; *U.S. Private*, pg. 971
COMMUNITY SENIOR LIFE INC; *U.S. Private*, pg. 997
CONGREGATIONAL HOMES INC; *U.S. Private*, pg. 1013
THE CONGREGATIONAL HOME; *U.S. Private*, pg. 4014
CORNWALL MANOR; *U.S. Private*, pg. 1053
COVENANT CARE, LLC—See Centre Partners Management LLC; *U.S. Private*, pg. 828
CSH NORTH RICHLAND HILLS LLC—See Brookdale Senior Living Inc.; *U.S. Public*, pg. 394
CSH ROUND ROCK LLC—See Brookdale Senior Living Inc.; *U.S. Public*, pg. 394
CSH SAN MARCOS LLC—See Brookdale Senior Living Inc.; *U.S. Public*, pg. 394
CYPRESS COVE AT HEALTHPARK FLORIDA; *U.S. Private*, pg. 1134
DALLAS RETIREMENT VILLAGE; *U.S. Private*, pg. 1150
DAMAR SERVICES, INC.; *U.S. Private*, pg. 1151
DAUGHTERS OF SARAH SENIOR COMMUNITY; *U.S. Private*, pg. 1167
DEACONESS ABUNDANT LIFE COMMUNITIES; *U.S. Private*, pg. 1182
DEERFIELD EPISCOPAL RETIREMENT COMMUNITY, INC.; *U.S. Private*, pg. 1190
DEKALB AREA RETIREMENT CENTER; *U.S. Private*, pg. 1192
DIRIGO PINES RETIREMENT COMMUNITY LLC—See Chicago Pacific Founders; *U.S. Private*, pg. 878
DOMINICAN OAKS CORPORATION—See Catholic Health Initiatives; *U.S. Private*, pg. 789
DUNCASTER LIFECARE COMMUNITY; *U.S. Private*, pg. 1288
DUNWOODY VILLAGE; *U.S. Private*, pg. 1291
EASTSIDE RETIREMENT ASSOCIATION; *U.S. Private*, pg. 1322
EDGEWOOD LIFECARE COMMUNITY; *U.S. Private*, pg. 1335
ELDER SERVICES OF CAPE COD & THE ISLANDS, INC.; *U.S. Private*, pg. 1351
ELMCROFT OF FLORENCE, LP—See Senior Care, Inc.; *U.S. Private*, pg. 3606
EMERICARE SKYLYN PLACE LLC—See Brookdale Senior Living Inc.; *U.S. Public*, pg. 394
EMERITUS CORPORATION—See Brookdale Senior Living Inc.; *U.S. Public*, pg. 394
EPISCOPAL CHURCH HOME & AFFILIATES LIFE CARE COMMUNITY INC.; *U.S. Private*, pg. 1413
ESKATON; *U.S. Private*, pg. 1426
THE ESTATES AT CARPENTERS; *U.S. Private*, pg. 4027
EVERGREEN; *U.S. Private*, pg. 1438
FAHRNEY-KEEDY HOME & VILLAGE; *U.S. Private*, pg. 1461
FAIRHAVEN CHRISTIAN RETIREMENT CENTER; *U.S. Private*, pg. 1464
FAMILY HEALTH & HOUSING FOUNDATION INC.; *U.S. Private*, pg. 1470
FIFTH AVENUE HEALTHCARE CENTER—See Apollo Global Management, Inc.; *U.S. Public*, pg. 156
FLORIDA LIVING OPTIONS INC; *U.S. Private*, pg. 1549
THE FOREST AT DUKE, INC.; *U.S. Private*, pg. 4029
THE FOUNTAINS AT FRANKLIN—See The Fountains, Inc.; *U.S. Private*, pg. 4030
THE FOUNTAINS, INC.; *U.S. Private*, pg. 4030
THE FOUNTAINS—See Rohm Services, Corp.; *U.S. Private*, pg. 3473
FOXDALE VILLAGE CORPORATION; *U.S. Private*, pg. 1585
FREDERICK LIVING; *U.S. Private*, pg. 1602
FREEDOM VILLAGE OF BRADENTON, LLC—See Brookdale Senior Living Inc.; *U.S. Public*, pg. 394

623311 — CONTINUING CARE RET...

FRIENDS RETIREMENT CONCEPTS, INC.—See LCS Holdings Inc.; *U.S. Private*, pg. 2404
GALLOWAY RIDGE, INC.; *U.S. Private*, pg. 1640
GOLDEN AGE INC.; *U.S. Private*, pg. 1730
GOLDEN LIVING—See Fillmore Capital Partners, LLC; *U.S. Private*, pg. 1506
GOODWILL RETIREMENT COMMUNITY; *U.S. Private*, pg. 1741
GRACE HEALTHCARE OF TUCKER—See Grace Healthcare, LLC; *U.S. Private*, pg. 1749
GREEN HILL INC.; *U.S. Private*, pg. 1773
HARBOR RETIREMENT ASSOCIATES, LLC; *U.S. Private*, pg. 1859
HARROGATE, INC.; *U.S. Private*, pg. 1871
HEALTHTIQUE DURHAM LLC—See Healthtique Group LLC; *U.S. Private*, pg. 1898
HEALTHTIQUE GROUP LLC; *U.S. Private*, pg. 1898
HEALTHTIQUE WINSTON SALEM LLC—See Healthtique Group LLC; *U.S. Private*, pg. 1898
HEARTH & HOME OF URBANA, LLC—See Regional Health Properties, Inc.; *U.S. Public*, pg. 1775
HEARTH & HOME OF VANDALIA, INC.—See Regional Health Properties, Inc.; *U.S. Public*, pg. 1776
HEARTH & HOME OF VAN WERT, LLC—See Regional Health Properties, Inc.; *U.S. Public*, pg. 1776
HEARTHSTONE; *U.S. Private*, pg. 1899
HEATH VILLAGE RETIREMENT COMMUNITY; *U.S. Private*, pg. 1902
HENRY FORD VILLAGE; *U.S. Private*, pg. 1918
THE HIGHLANDS AT WYOMISSING; *U.S. Private*, pg. 4052
HILLTOP VILLAGE—See Sava Senior Care LLC; *U.S. Private*, pg. 3555
IMPERIAL HEALTH CARE CENTER—See Sava Senior Care LLC; *U.S. Private*, pg. 3555
INDIANA MASONIC HOME, INC.; *U.S. Private*, pg. 2062
INGLESIDE AT ROCK CREEK; *U.S. Private*, pg. 2076
JENNER'S POND; *U.S. Private*, pg. 2200
JEWISH HOME OF CINCINNATI; *U.S. Private*, pg. 2206
JOHN KNOX VILLAGE OF FLORIDA, INC.; *U.S. Private*, pg. 2222
KAHALA SENIOR LIVING COMMUNITY, INC.; *U.S. Private*, pg. 2254
LAKE PARK OF MADISON LLC—See Healthtique Group LLC; *U.S. Private*, pg. 1898
LAMBETH HOUSE, INC.; *U.S. Private*, pg. 2380
LAWTON HEALTHCARE CENTER—See Apollo Global Management, Inc.; *U.S. Public*, pg. 157
LES HAUTS DE GENOLIER SA—See AEVIS VICTORIA SA; *Int'l*, pg. 183
LIBBY CARE CENTER OF CASCADIA—See Cascadia Healthcare LLC; *U.S. Private*, pg. 781
LIFE CARE COMPANIES, LLC; *U.S. Private*, pg. 2448
LIFECIRCLES; *U.S. Private*, pg. 2449
LIFESPACE COMMUNITIES; *U.S. Private*, pg. 2451
LOURDES-NOREEN MCKEEN RESIDENCE; *U.S. Private*, pg. 2500
LUTHERAN HOMES OF OCONOMOWOC; *U.S. Private*, pg. 2517
LYTTON GARDENS INC.; *U.S. Private*, pg. 2522
MARYFIELD, INC.; *U.S. Private*, pg. 2599
MENNONITE FRIENDSHIP COMMUNITIES; *U.S. Private*, pg. 2666
MERRITT ISLAND RHF HOUSING INC; *U.S. Private*, pg. 2676
METHODIST HOME OF THE DISTRICT OF COLUMBIA; *U.S. Private*, pg. 2684
MIKEVA OY—See Attendo AB; *Int'l*, pg. 696
MILLENNIUM VENTURES LIMITED PARTNERSHIP, L.L.P.—See The Goodman Group, Inc.; *U.S. Private*, pg. 4034
THE MONTEBELLO ON ACADEMY—See AlerisLife Inc.; *U.S. Private*, pg. 162
MONTGOMERY PLACE RETIREMENT COMMUNITY; *U.S. Private*, pg. 2777
THE MOORINGS, INC.; *U.S. Private*, pg. 4080
MOORINGS PARK INSTITUTE INC.; *U.S. Private*, pg. 2781
MORAVIAN HOME INCORPORATED; *U.S. Private*, pg. 2782
MORAVIAN MANORS, INC.; *U.S. Private*, pg. 2782
MORAVIAN VILLAGE OF BETHLEHEM; *U.S. Private*, pg. 2782
MULDER HEALTH CARE FACILITY, INC.; *U.S. Private*, pg. 2811
THE NATHAN ADELSON HOSPICE; *U.S. Private*, pg. 4081
NATIONAL HEALTHCARE CORPORATION; *U.S. Public*, pg. 1495
NAVAL CONTINUING CARE RETIREMENT FOUNDATION, INC.; *U.S. Private*, pg. 2872
NAZARETH LIVING CENTER; *U.S. Private*, pg. 2874
THE OSBORN; *U.S. Private*, pg. 4089
OTTERBEIN SENIOR LIFESTYLE CHOICES; *U.S. Private*, pg. 3049
PACIFICA SENIOR LIVING; *U.S. Private*, pg. 3072
PARKVIEW ACRES CURE & REHABILITATION CENTER—See Apollo Global Management, Inc.; *U.S. Public*, pg. 157
PEOPLE CREATING SUCCESS, INC.; *U.S. Private*, pg. 3140
PEOPLE INC.; *U.S. Private*, pg. 3140
THE PHILADELPHIA PROTESTANT HOME; *U.S. Private*, pg. 4094
PLEASANT VIEW RETIREMENT COMMUNITY; *U.S. Private*, pg. 3213
PLYMOUTH HARBOR INC.; *U.S. Private*, pg. 3216
PLYMOUTH PLACE INC.; *U.S. Private*, pg. 3216
PRESBYTERIAN HOMES OF TENNESSEE, INC.; *U.S. Private*, pg. 3253
QUALIFIED PLANS, LLC—See Aquiline Capital Partners LLC; *U.S. Private*, pg. 304
QUALIFIED PLANS, LLC—See Genstar Capital, LLC; *U.S. Private*, pg. 1675
QUARRYVILLE PRESBYTERIAN RETIREMENT COMMUNITY; *U.S. Private*, pg. 3324
RAISER SENIOR SERVICES LLC; *U.S. Private*, pg. 3348
RAPPAHANNOCK WESTMINSTER-CANTERBURY, INC.; *U.S. Private*, pg. 3356
REDSTONE PRESBYTERIAN SENIORCARE; *U.S. Private*, pg. 3380
REGION II COMMISSION ON SERVICES TO THE AGING; *U.S. Private*, pg. 3388
REGION VII AREA AGENCY ON AGING; *U.S. Private*, pg. 3388
RIDDLE VILLAGE; *U.S. Private*, pg. 3431
RIDGELINE MANAGEMENT COMPANY; *U.S. Private*, pg. 3432
RIO RICO PROPERTIES INC.—See Brookfield Corporation; *Int'l*, pg. 1183
SAN DIEGO HEBREW HOMES; *U.S. Private*, pg. 3539
SARASOTA MANATEE JEWISH HOUSING COUNCIL, INC.; *U.S. Private*, pg. 3549
SCOTTSDALE NURSING CENTER—See Sava Senior Care LLC; *U.S. Private*, pg. 3555
SEASONS RETIREMENT COMMUNITY—See Senior Lifestyle Corporation; *U.S. Private*, pg. 3607
SENIOR CARE, INC.; *U.S. Private*, pg. 3606
SENIOR LIVING PROPERTIES, LLC; *U.S. Private*, pg. 3607
SENIOR MANAGEMENT ADVISORS, INC.; *U.S. Private*, pg. 3607
SHARON TOWERS; *U.S. Private*, pg. 3626
SHELL POINT RETIREMENT COMMUNITY—See Christian and Missionary Alliance Foundation, Inc.; *U.S. Private*, pg. 890
SHENANDOAH VALLEY WESTMINSTER-CANTERBURY; *U.S. Private*, pg. 3632
SILVER CREEK MANOR NURSING CENTER—See Sava Senior Care LLC; *U.S. Private*, pg. 3555
SIMPSON HOUSE; *U.S. Private*, pg. 3668
SKYLER BOYINGTON, INC.—See Omega Healthcare Investors, Inc.; *U.S. Public*, pg. 1571
SOLVANG LUTHERAN HOME, INC.; *U.S. Private*, pg. 3711
SOUTHFARM LP—See Benchmark Senior Living, LLC; *U.S. Private*, pg. 524
SOUTH HAVEN MANOR NURSING HOME—See Sava Senior Care LLC; *U.S. Private*, pg. 3555
SOUTHLAND NURSING HOME—See Sava Senior Care LLC; *U.S. Private*, pg. 3555
SOUTHMINSTER; *U.S. Private*, pg. 3737
SPANISH COVE HOUSING AUTHORITY; *U.S. Private*, pg. 3745
SPIRITRUST LUTHERAN; *U.S. Private*, pg. 3758
SPRINGMOOR LIFE CARE RETIREMENT COMMUNITY; *U.S. Private*, pg. 3764
STANLEY TOTAL LIVING CENTER, INC.; *U.S. Private*, pg. 3783
ST. ANNE'S RETIREMENT COMMUNITY, INC.; *U.S. Private*, pg. 3770
ST. JOHN OF GOD RETIREMENT AND CARE CENTER; *U.S. Private*, pg. 3770
STONEBRIDGE HEALTHCARE, INC—See The Ensign Group, Inc.; *U.S. Public*, pg. 2072
SUMMERVILLE AT NORTH HILLS LLC—See Brookdale Senior Living Inc.; *U.S. Public*, pg. 395
SUMMERVILLE AT OUTLOOK MANOR LLC—See Brookdale Senior Living Inc.; *U.S. Public*, pg. 395
SUMMERVILLE AT RIDGEWOOD GARDENS LLC—See Brookdale Senior Living Inc.; *U.S. Public*, pg. 395
SUMMERVILLE AT ROSEVILLE GARDENS LLC—See Brookdale Senior Living Inc.; *U.S. Public*, pg. 395
SUMMERVILLE AT VOORHEES, LLC—See Brookdale Senior Living Inc.; *U.S. Public*, pg. 395
SUMMERVILLE AT WESTMINSTER, LLC—See Brookdale Senior Living Inc.; *U.S. Public*, pg. 395
SUNSET RETIREMENT COMMUNITIES; *U.S. Private*, pg. 3871
SUNWEST MANAGEMENT, INC.; *U.S. Private*, pg. 3874
TACOMA LUTHERAN RETIREMENT COMMUNITY; *U.S. Private*, pg. 3921
TEMPE LIFE CARE VILLAGE INC; *U.S. Private*, pg. 3963
THE TEMPLE FOUNDATION; *U.S. Private*, pg. 4126
THE TERRACES AT BONITA SPRINGS—See SantaFe Healthcare, Inc.; *U.S. Private*, pg. 3548
TOWN VILLAGE STERLING HEIGHTS, LLC—See Chicago Pacific Founders; *U.S. Private*, pg. 878
TOWN VILLAGE VESTAVIA HILLS, LLC—See Chicago Pacific Founders; *U.S. Private*, pg. 878
UNITED CHURCH OF CHRIST HOMES, INC.; *U.S. Private*, pg. 4289
VALLEY VIEW HAVEN, INC.; *U.S. Private*, pg. 4336
THE VILLAGE AT MORRISONS COVE; *U.S. Private*, pg. 4131
VILLAGE SHALOM, INC.; *U.S. Private*, pg. 4384
VINTAGE PARK AT LENEXA, LLC—See Chicago Pacific Founders; *U.S. Private*, pg. 878
VISTA GRANDE VILLA; *U.S. Private*, pg. 4403
VITALITY SENIOR LIVING MANAGEMENT, LLC; *U.S. Private*, pg. 4405
WELL SPRING RETIREMENT COMMUNITY; *U.S. Private*, pg. 4474
WESTMINSTER PRESBYTERIAN RETIREMENT COMMUNITY, INC.; *U.S. Private*, pg. 4499
WHITE HORSE VILLAGE; *U.S. Private*, pg. 4509
WHITE RIVER AREA AGENCY ON AGING INC; *U.S. Private*, pg. 4509
WILLAMETTE VIEW, INC.; *U.S. Private*, pg. 4521
WILLOW VALLEY COMMUNITIES; *U.S. Private*, pg. 4529

623312 — ASSISTED LIVING FACILITIES FOR THE ELDERLY

ACTS RETIREMENT-LIFE COMMUNITIES, INC.; *U.S. Private*, pg. 70
AGEOPTIONS; *U.S. Private*, pg. 127
AGESPAN, INC.; *U.S. Private*, pg. 127
AGRI-TRADE HOLDINGS LIMITED; *Int'l*, pg. 216
AI DREAM LIFE SUPPORT CO., LTD.—See AISIN Corporation; *Int'l*, pg. 251
AL I/EAST BRUNSWICK SENIOR HOUSING, LLC—See Ventas, Inc.; *U.S. Public*, pg. 2277
ALLITY PTY LTD—See Archer Capital Pty. Ltd.; *Int'l*, pg. 547
A.L. WIZARD, INC.—See Thoma Bravo, L.P.; *U.S. Private*, pg. 4152
ANIMA NV—See Ackermans & van Haaren NV; *Int'l*, pg. 104
ARARAT HOME OF LOS ANGELES, INC.; *U.S. Private*, pg. 307
THE ARCHWAY PROGRAMS, INC.; *U.S. Private*, pg. 3987
AREA AGENCY ON AGING OF WESTERN ARKANSAS, INC.; *U.S. Private*, pg. 317
AREA AGENCY ON AGING, PSA2; *U.S. Private*, pg. 317
AREA AGENCY ON AGING REGION 9, INC.; *U.S. Private*, pg. 317
ASSISTED LIVING CONCEPTS, LLC—See TPG Capital, L.P.; *U.S. Public*, pg. 2168
ATRIUM AT WESTON PLACE, LLC—See Ventas, Inc.; *U.S. Public*, pg. 2278
AUTUMN SENIOR LIVING, LLC; *U.S. Private*, pg. 402
THE BAPTIST HOME, INC.; *U.S. Private*, pg. 3991
BARTELS LUTHERAN RETIREMENT COMMUNITY; *U.S. Private*, pg. 482
BARUCH SLS, INC.; *U.S. Private*, pg. 484
BAY VILLAGE OF SARASOTA, INC.; *U.S. Private*, pg. 495
BELMONT VILLAGE BUFFALO GROVE, L.L.C.—See Welltower Inc.; *U.S. Public*, pg. 2347
BELMONT VILLAGE CAROL STREAM, L.L.C.—See Welltower Inc.; *U.S. Public*, pg. 2347
BELMONT VILLAGE OAK PARK, L.L.C.—See Welltower Inc.; *U.S. Public*, pg. 2348
BELMONT VILLAGE RANCHO PALOS VERDES TENANT, LLC—See Welltower Inc.; *U.S. Public*, pg. 2348
BELMONT VILLAGE SAN JOSE, LLC—See Welltower Inc.; *U.S. Public*, pg. 2348
BELMONT VILLAGE ST. MATTHEWS, L.L.C.—See Welltower Inc.; *U.S. Public*, pg. 2348
BELMONT VILLAGE SUNNYVALE, LLC—See Welltower Inc.; *U.S. Public*, pg. 2348
BETHANY HOME SOCIETY OF SAN JOAQUIN COUNTY, INC.; *U.S. Private*, pg. 545
BETHANY ST. JOSEPH CORPORATION; *U.S. Private*, pg. 545
BETHESDA FOUNDATION; *U.S. Private*, pg. 545
BETHLEN HOME OF THE HUNGARIAN REFORMED FEDERATION OF AMERICA; *U.S. Private*, pg. 546
BHI SENIOR LIVING, INC.; *U.S. Private*, pg. 549
BICKFORD OF ALPHARETTA, LLC—See Bickford Senior Living Group, LLC; *U.S. Private*, pg. 550
BKD BELLE MEADE, LLC—See Brookdale Senior Living Inc.; *U.S. Public*, pg. 393
BKD COLLEGE PLACE, LLC—See Brookdale Senior Living Inc.; *U.S. Public*, pg. 393
BKD JONES FARM, LLC—See Brookdale Senior Living Inc.; *U.S. Public*, pg. 393
BKD LAWRENCEVILLE, LLC—See Brookdale Senior Living Inc.; *U.S. Public*, pg. 393
BKD LODI, LLC—See Brookdale Senior Living Inc.; *U.S. Public*, pg. 393
BKD MURRAY, LLC—See Brookdale Senior Living Inc.; *U.S. Public*, pg. 393
BKD NEWNAN, LLC—See Brookdale Senior Living Inc.; *U.S. Public*, pg. 393
BKD NORTH GILBERT, LLC—See Brookdale Senior Living Inc.; *U.S. Public*, pg. 393
BKD NORTH GLENDALE, LLC—See Brookdale Senior Living Inc.; *U.S. Public*, pg. 393

N.A.I.C.S. INDEX 623312 — ASSISTED LIVING FAC...

N.A.I.C.S. Index

BKD OAK PARK, LLC—See Brookdale Senior Living Inc.; *U.S. Public*, pg. 393
BKD PARKPLACE, LLC—See Brookdale Senior Living Inc.; *U.S. Public*, pg. 393
BKD SOUTH BAY, LLC—See Brookdale Senior Living Inc.; *U.S. Public*, pg. 393
BKD TANQUE VERDE, LLC—See Brookdale Senior Living Inc.; *U.S. Public*, pg. 393
BKD TULLAHOMA, LLC—See Brookdale Senior Living Inc.; *U.S. Public*, pg. 393
BKD WEKIWA SPRINGS, LLC—See Brookdale Senior Living Inc.; *U.S. Public*, pg. 393
BKD WILSONVILLE,LLC—See Brookdale Senior Living Inc.; *U.S. Public*, pg. 393
BLEU RESIDENCE LORMONT SCI—See Groupe BPCE; *Int'l*, pg. 3092
BOLTON MILLS RETIREMENT COMMUNITY INC.—See Extendicare Inc.; *Int'l*, pg. 2591
BRANDMAN CENTERS FOR SENIOR CARE; *U.S. Private*, pg. 637
BREA WEST ORANGE,LLC—See Brookdale Senior Living Inc.; *U.S. Public*, pg. 393
BRENWOOD PARK SENIOR LIVING, INC.—See The Ensign Group, Inc.; *U.S. Public*, pg. 2070
BROMPTON HEIGHTS, INC.—See The Hamister Group, Inc.; *U.S. Private*, pg. 4042
BROOKDALE LIVING COMMUNITIES OF NEW JERSEY, LLC—See Ventas, Inc.; *U.S. Public*, pg. 2278
BROOKDALE LIVING COMMUNITIES OF NORTH CAROLINA, INC.—See Brookdale Senior Living Inc.; *U.S. Public*, pg. 394
BROOKDALE MCMINNVILLE WESTSIDE, LLC—See Brookdale Senior Living Inc.; *U.S. Public*, pg. 394
BROOKDALE PLACE AT FALL CREEK, LLC—See Brookdale Senior Living Inc.; *U.S. Public*, pg. 394
BROOKDALE PLACE AT KENWOOD, LLC—See Brookdale Senior Living Inc.; *U.S. Public*, pg. 394
BROOKDALE PLACE AT OAKWOOD, LLC—See Brookdale Senior Living Inc.; *U.S. Public*, pg. 394
BROOKDALE PLACE AT WILLOW LAKE, LLC—See Brookdale Senior Living Inc.; *U.S. Public*, pg. 394
BROOKDALE PLACE OF AUGUSTA, LLC—See Brookdale Senior Living Inc.; *U.S. Public*, pg. 394
BROOKDALE PLACE OF ENGLEWOOD, LLC—See Brookdale Senior Living Inc.; *U.S. Public*, pg. 394
BROOKDALE PLACE OF WEST HARTFORD, LLC—See Brookdale Senior Living Inc.; *U.S. Public*, pg. 394
BROOKDALE PLACE OF WOOSTER, LLC—See Brookdale Senior Living Inc.; *U.S. Public*, pg. 394
BROOKDALE WELLINGTON, INC.—See Brookdale Senior Living Inc.; *U.S. Public*, pg. 394
BROWN ROAD SENIOR HOUSING LLC—See The Ensign Group, Inc.; *U.S. Public*, pg. 2070
BURLINGTON MANOR, LLC—See Brookdale Senior Living Inc.; *U.S. Public*, pg. 394
B-X PROVIDENCE LLC—See Welltower Inc.; *U.S. Public*, pg. 2347
CARE INITIATIVES; *U.S. Private*, pg. 751
CAREPATROL FRANCHISE SYSTEMS, LLC—See Riverside Partners, LLC; *U.S. Private*, pg. 3445
CAROLINA HOUSE OF CHAPEL HILL, LLC—See Brookdale Senior Living Inc.; *U.S. Public*, pg. 394
CAROLINA HOUSE OF DURHAM, LLC—See Brookdale Senior Living Inc.; *U.S. Public*, pg. 394
CAROLINA HOUSE OF FOREST CITY, LLC—See Brookdale Senior Living Inc.; *U.S. Public*, pg. 394
CAROLINA HOUSE OF LEXINGTON, LLC—See Brookdale Senior Living Inc.; *U.S. Public*, pg. 394
CAROLINA HOUSE OF MOREHEAD CITY, LLC—See Brookdale Senior Living Inc.; *U.S. Public*, pg. 394
CAROLINA HOUSE OF SMITHFIELD, LLC—See Brookdale Senior Living Inc.; *U.S. Public*, pg. 394
CATHOLIC ELDERCARE; *U.S. Private*, pg. 788
CB SENIORENRESIDENZ ARMBRUSTERGASSE GMBH—See Clariane SE; *Int'l*, pg. 1643
CC3 ACQUISITION, LLC—See Welltower Inc.; *U.S. Public*, pg. 2348
CCRC - FREEDOM POINTE AT THE VILLAGES, LLC—See Brookdale Senior Living Inc.; *U.S. Public*, pg. 394
CCRC - REGENCY OAKS, LLC—See Brookdale Senior Living Inc.; *U.S. Public*, pg. 394
CEDAR CROSSING RETIREMENT COMMUNITY INC.—See Extendicare Inc.; *Int'l*, pg. 2591
CENTER FOR ELDERS' INDEPENDENCE; *U.S. Private*, pg. 810
CENTRAL BAPTIST VILLAGE; *U.S. Private*, pg. 819
CHINA HEALTHCARE LIMITED; *Int'l*, pg. 1507
CHINA SENIOR LIVING INDUSTRY INTERNATIONAL HOLDING CORPORATION; *Int'l*, pg. 1550
THE CHURCH AID OF THE PROTESTANT EPISCOPAL CHURCH; *U.S. Private*, pg. 4009
CIJ WAVE LTD.—See Computer Institute of Japan Ltd.; *Int'l*, pg. 1759
CLACKAMAS WOODS ASSISTED LIVING, LLC—See Ventas, Inc.; *U.S. Public*, pg. 2278
COAST TO COAST ASSISTED LIVING REALTY, LLC—See Ventas, Inc.; *U.S. Public*, pg. 2278
COGEDIM RESIDENCES SERVICES SNC—See Altarea SCA; *Int'l*, pg. 385
CONSULATE HEALTH CARE, LLC; *U.S. Private*, pg. 1025
COSTA VICTORIA HEALTHCARE LLC—See The Ensign Group, Inc.; *U.S. Public*, pg. 2070
COTTAGE GROVE PLACE; *U.S. Private*, pg. 1063
COUNCIL ON AGING OF SOUTHWESTERN OHIO; *U.S. Private*, pg. 1065
CPF SENIOR LIVING ACQUISITIONS LLC—See Chicago Pacific Founders; *U.S. Private*, pg. 878
CREST VIEW CORPORATION; *U.S. Private*, pg. 1096
CRSA—See LCS Holdings Inc.; *U.S. Private*, pg. 2404
CRYSTAL OAKS; *U.S. Private*, pg. 1115
CSH LAKE ORIENTA LLC—See Brookdale Senior Living Inc.; *U.S. Public*, pg. 394
CSH PORT ST. LUCIE LLC—See Brookdale Senior Living Inc.; *U.S. Public*, pg. 394
CSL RIVERBEND IN, LLC—See Sonida Senior Living, Inc.; *U.S. Public*, pg. 1903
CSL TOWNE CENTRE, LLC—See Sonida Senior Living, Inc.; *U.S. Public*, pg. 1903
CSL WHITCOMB HOUSE, LLC—See Sonida Senior Living, Inc.; *U.S. Public*, pg. 1903
DAUGHTERS OF MIRIAM CENTER; *U.S. Private*, pg. 1167
DENMARK SENIOR LIVING, INC.—See The Ensign Group, Inc.; *U.S. Public*, pg. 2070
DEPAUL; *U.S. Private*, pg. 1208
THE DOMAIN RETIREMENT COUNTRY CLUB PTY. LTD.—See Brookfield Corporation; *Int'l*, pg. 1186
DOMINION VILLAGE AT CHESAPEAKE—See AlerisLife Inc.; *U.S. Private*, pg. 160
DOUGLAS CROSSING RETIREMENT COMMUNITY INC.—See Extendicare Inc.; *Int'l*, pg. 2591
EDEN RETIREMENT CENTER INC.; *U.S. Private*, pg. 1333
E-KURASHI CO., LTD.—See Chubu Electric Power Co., Inc.; *Int'l*, pg. 1593
ELDERSERVE, INC.; *U.S. Private*, pg. 1351
ELDERWOOD AT TONAWANDA—See Post Acute Partners, LLC; *U.S. Private*, pg. 3234
ELISA SENIORENSTIFT ASCHAFFENBURG GMBH—See Clariane SE; *Int'l*, pg. 1643
ELISA SENIORENSTIFT GMBH—See Clariane SE; *Int'l*, pg. 1643
EMERIWEG DEERFIELD LLC—See Brookdale Senior Living Inc.; *U.S. Public*, pg. 394
EMPIRE CROSSING RETIREMENT COMMUNITY INC.—See Extendicare Inc.; *Int'l*, pg. 2591
ENCORE SENIOR LIVING, LLC—See LCS Holdings Inc.; *U.S. Private*, pg. 2404
ENGLEWOOD MERIDIAN LLC—See Brookdale Senior Living Inc.; *U.S. Public*, pg. 394
ENSIGN PANORAMA LLC—See The Ensign Group, Inc.; *U.S. Public*, pg. 2071
ESTIA HEALTH LIMITED—See Bain Capital, LP; *U.S. Private*, pg. 431
FREEDOM VILLAGE OF HOLLAND MICHIGAN—See Brookdale Senior Living Inc.; *U.S. Public*, pg. 394
THE FRESHWATER GROUP, INC.—See The Fountains, Inc.; *U.S. Private*, pg. 4030
FRIENDSHIP HAVEN, INC.; *U.S. Private*, pg. 1612
GATEWAYS INDUSTRIES; *U.S. Private*, pg. 1651
GENESIS HEALTHCARE LOPATCONG CENTER—See Formation Capital, LLC; *U.S. Private*, pg. 1570
GERIATRIC SERVICES, INC.; *U.S. Private*, pg. 1686
GLENMEADOW, INC.; *U.S. Private*, pg. 1710
GOVERNMENTAL & EDUCATIONAL ASSISTANCE CORPORATION; *U.S. Private*, pg. 1746
GRACE LUTHERAN FOUNDATION; *U.S. Private*, pg. 1749
GREATER LYNN SENIOR SERVICES, INC.; *U.S. Private*, pg. 1769
GREAT FALLS HEALTH CARE COMPANY, L.L.C.—See Formation Capital, LLC; *U.S. Private*, pg. 1570
GREENSBORO MANOR, LP—See Brookdale Senior Living Inc.; *U.S. Public*, pg. 394
HARVEST RETIREMENT COMMUNITY INC.—See Extendicare Inc.; *Int'l*, pg. 2591
HEATHER HEIGHTS OF PITTSFORD, INC.—See The Hamister Group, Inc.; *U.S. Private*, pg. 4042
HIGH POINT MANOR, LP—See Brookdale Senior Living Inc.; *U.S. Public*, pg. 394
HOMEPLACE OF BURLINGTON—See AlerisLife Inc.; *U.S. Private*, pg. 161
HOMEWOOD AT BROOKMONT TERRACE, LLC—See Brookdale Senior Living Inc.; *U.S. Public*, pg. 394
HOOSIER CARE PROPERTIES, INC.; *U.S. Private*, pg. 1978
HORIZON HOUSE; *U.S. Private*, pg. 1981
HOSPICE INC.; *U.S. Private*, pg. 1985
HOSPICE OF CHATTANOOGA, INC.; *U.S. Private*, pg. 1985
JEROME HOME; *U.S. Private*, pg. 2201
JEWISH HOME LIFECARE; *U.S. Private*, pg. 2206
THE JEWISH HOME OF EASTERN PENNSYLVANIA; *U.S. Private*, pg. 4059
JEWISH SENIOR SERVICES OF FAIRFIELD COUNTY INC.; *U.S. Private*, pg. 2206
KENOSHA SENIOR LIVING, INC.—See The Ensign Group, Inc.; *U.S. Public*, pg. 2070
KEYSTONE COMMUNITIES OF EAGAN, LLC—See Welltower Inc.; *U.S. Public*, pg. 2348
KEYSTONE COMMUNITIES OF PRIOR LAKE, LLC—See Welltower Inc.; *U.S. Public*, pg. 2348
LAKE JAMES LODGE; *U.S. Private*, pg. 2375
LAKE SEMINOLE SQUARE, LLC—See Brookdale Senior Living Inc.; *U.S. Public*, pg. 395
LAKEWOOD MERIDIAN LLC—See Brookdale Senior Living Inc.; *U.S. Public*, pg. 395
LEGACY SENIOR SERVICES; *U.S. Private*, pg. 2417
LH ASSISTED LIVING, LLC—See Brookdale Senior Living Inc.; *U.S. Public*, pg. 394
LIFESTREAM COMPLETE SENIOR LIVING; *U.S. Private*, pg. 2451
LOOMIS COMMUNITIES, INC.; *U.S. Private*, pg. 2494
LOS ANGELES JEWISH HOME; *U.S. Private*, pg. 2496
THE LUTHERAN HOME, INC.; *U.S. Private*, pg. 4073
LUTHERCARE; *U.S. Private*, pg. 2518
LYNDE CREEK MANOR RETIREMENT COMMUNITY INC.—See Extendicare Inc.; *Int'l*, pg. 2591
MADISON SENIOR LIVING, INC.—See The Ensign Group, Inc.; *U.S. Public*, pg. 2070
MANITOWOC SENIOR LIVING, INC.—See The Ensign Group, Inc.; *U.S. Public*, pg. 2070
MASONIC HOMES OF CALIFORNIA, INC.; *U.S. Private*, pg. 2602
MCCREADY FOUNDATION, INC.; *U.S. Private*, pg. 2631
MENORAH MANOR; *U.S. Private*, pg. 2666
MERRILL GARDENS LLC—See RD Merrill Company; *U.S. Private*, pg. 3362
METHODIST HOMES OF ALABAMA & NORTHWEST FLORIDA; *U.S. Private*, pg. 2684
METSUN JACKSON NJ SENIOR LIVING, LLC—See Welltower Inc.; *U.S. Public*, pg. 2348
METSUN LEAWOOD KS SENIOR LIVING, LLC—See Welltower Inc.; *U.S. Public*, pg. 2348
MID-FLORIDA AREA AGENCY ON AGING, INC.; *U.S. Private*, pg. 2708
MOHAVE HEALTHCARE, INC.—See The Ensign Group, Inc.; *U.S. Public*, pg. 2071
MONTECITO RETIREMENT ASSOCIATION; *U.S. Private*, pg. 2775
MORNINGSIDE MINISTRIES; *U.S. Private*, pg. 2785
MOUNTAIN VISTA SENIOR LIVING, INC.—See The Ensign Group, Inc.; *U.S. Public*, pg. 2070
NHC HEALTHCARE/HEARTLAND, LLC—See National HealthCare Corporation; *U.S. Public*, pg. 1495
NORTHERN CALIFORNIA CONGREGATIONAL RETIREMENT HOMES, INC.; *U.S. Private*, pg. 2952
OAKMONT OF CAMARILLO OPCO, LLC—See Healthpeak Properties, Inc.; *U.S. Public*, pg. 1016
OAKMONT OF CONCORD LLC—See Healthpeak Properties, Inc.; *U.S. Public*, pg. 1016
OAKMONT OF FAIR OAKS LLC—See Healthpeak Properties, Inc.; *U.S. Public*, pg. 1016
OAKMONT OF MARINER POINT LLC—See Healthpeak Properties, Inc.; *U.S. Public*, pg. 1016
OAKMONT OF PACIFIC BEACH OPCO, LLC—See Healthpeak Properties, Inc.; *U.S. Public*, pg. 1016
OAKMONT OF RIVERPARK OPCO, LLC—See Healthpeak Properties, Inc.; *U.S. Public*, pg. 1016
ODD FELLOWS HOME OF PENNSYLVANIA; *U.S. Private*, pg. 2993
ORCHARD HEIGHTS, INC.—See The Hamister Group, Inc.; *U.S. Private*, pg. 4042
OTAY TENANT LLC—See Welltower Inc.; *U.S. Public*, pg. 2349
OUR HOSPICE OF SOUTH CENTRAL INDIANA, INC.; *U.S. Private*, pg. 3050
PHNTUS CREEKSIDE LLC—See Brookdale Senior Living Inc.; *U.S. Public*, pg. 395
PHNTUS QUAIL RIDGE LLC—See Brookdale Senior Living Inc.; *U.S. Public*, pg. 395
PHOENIX HOUSES OF LOS ANGELES, INC.; *U.S. Private*, pg. 3173
PICKERSGILL RETIREMENT COMMUNITY; *U.S. Private*, pg. 3176
THE PINES AT WHITING; *U.S. Private*, pg. 4095
PINNACLE SENIOR LIVING LLC—See The Pennant Group, Inc.; *U.S. Public*, pg. 2118
PLEASANT RIDGE MANOR; *U.S. Private*, pg. 3213
PRESBYTERIAN HOMES OF GEORGIA; *U.S. Private*, pg. 3253
PRESBYTERIAN SENIORCARE; *U.S. Private*, pg. 3253
PSC COMMUNITY SERVICES INC; *U.S. Private*, pg. 3297
RAIN HOME ATTENDANT SERVICES INC; *U.S. Private*, pg. 3347
REGENCY PARK SENIOR LIVING, INC.—See Fish Construction Company; *U.S. Private*, pg. 1533
REGINA COMMUNITY NURSING CENTER; *U.S. Private*, pg. 3388
RETIREMENT LIVING, INC.; *U.S. Private*, pg. 3412
THE REUTLINGER COMMUNITY FOR JEWISH LIVING; *U.S. Private*, pg. 4106
RITTENHOUSE SENIOR LIVING OF INDIANAPOLIS LLC—See Rittenhouse Senior Living; *U.S. Private*, pg. 3442
RIVERBEND CROSSING RETIREMENT COMMUNITY

623312 — ASSISTED LIVING FAC...

INC.—See Extendicare Inc.; *Int'l*, pg. 2591
RIVERVIEW VILLAGE SENIOR LIVING, INC.—See The Ensign Group, Inc.; *U.S. Public*, pg. 2070
SANTAFE SENIOR LIVING—See SantaFe Healthcare, Inc.; *U.S. Private*, pg. 3547
SCOTTSDALE RESIDENTIAL CARE INVESTORS—See Pacifica Senior Living; *U.S. Private*, pg. 3072
SCOTT STREET SENIOR HOUSING COMPLEX INC; *U.S. Private*, pg. 3577
SELFHELP COMMUNITY SERVICES, INC; *U.S. Private*, pg. 3602
SENIOR CARE NURSING HOME LIMITED—See DreamEast Group Limited; *Int'l*, pg. 2203
SENIORENZENTRUM ST. CORONA AM SCHOPFL BETRIEBSGESELLSCHAFT M.B.H.—See Fresenius SE & Co. KGaA; *Int'l*, pg. 2781
SENIOR FRIENDSHIP CENTERS, INC.; *U.S. Private*, pg. 3606
SENIOR-LIVING.COM, INC.—See Thoma Bravo, L.P.; *U.S. Private*, pg. 4153
SENIORS HOUSING INVESTMENT III REIT INC.—See Welltower Inc.; *U.S. Public*, pg. 2349
S-H OPCO EAST BAY MANOR, LLC—See Brookdale Senior Living Inc.; *U.S. Public*, pg. 395
S-H OPCO GREENWICH BAY MANOR, LLC—See Brookdale Senior Living Inc.; *U.S. Public*, pg. 395
S-H OPCO PROSPERITY OAKS, LLC—See Brookdale Senior Living Inc.; *U.S. Public*, pg. 395
S-H THIRTY-FIVE OPCO - POCASSET, LLC—See Brookdale Senior Living Inc.; *U.S. Public*, pg. 395
S-H THIRTY-FIVE OPCO - WILLOWWOOD, LLC—See Brookdale Senior Living Inc.; *U.S. Public*, pg. 395
SILVERADO SENIOR LIVING ALHAMBRA, INC.—See Welltower Inc.; *U.S. Public*, pg. 2349
SILVERADO SENIOR LIVING SALT LAKE CITY, INC.—See Welltower Inc.; *U.S. Public*, pg. 2349
SILVER LAKE ASSISTED LIVING, LLC—See Brookdale Senior Living Inc.; *U.S. Public*, pg. 395
SKIDAWAY HEALTH AND LIVING SERVICES, INC.; *U.S. Private*, pg. 3681
SOMMERSET ASSISTED LIVING RESIDENCE LLC—See Haverland Carter Lifestyle Group; *U.S. Private*, pg. 1880
SOURCEWISE; *U.S. Private*, pg. 3719
SPRINGS AT CLACKAMAS WOODS, LLC—See Ventas, Inc.; *U.S. Public*, pg. 2278
ST. EDWARD HOME; *U.S. Private*, pg. 3771
STELLA ORTON HOME CARE AGENCY; *U.S. Private*, pg. 3799
STEVENS POINT SENIOR LIVING, INC.—See The Ensign Group, Inc.; *U.S. Public*, pg. 2070
ST. JOSEPH'S REHABILITATION & RESIDENCE; *U.S. Private*, pg. 3770
ST. MARGARET'S AT MERCY; *U.S. Private*, pg. 3773
STONEBRIDGE CROSSING RETIREMENT COMMUNITY INC.—See Extendicare Inc.; *Int'l*, pg. 2591
STOUGHTON SENIOR LIVING, INC.—See The Ensign Group, Inc.; *U.S. Public*, pg. 2070
SUMMERVILLE AT STAFFORD, LLC—See Brookdale Senior Living Inc.; *U.S. Public*, pg. 395
SUN CITY HILTON HEAD—See PulteGroup, Inc.; *U.S. Public*, pg. 1737
SUN CITY HUNTLEY—See PulteGroup, Inc.; *U.S. Public*, pg. 1737
SUN CITY TEXAS—See PulteGroup, Inc.; *U.S. Public*, pg. 1737
SYMMES LIFE CARE INC.; *U.S. Private*, pg. 3899
SZR COLUMBIA LLC—See Ventas, Inc.; *U.S. Public*, pg. 2278
SZR NORTH HILLS LLC—See Ventas, Inc.; *U.S. Public*, pg. 2278
SZR OLD TAPPAN ASSISTED LIVING, L.L.C.—See Ventas, Inc.; *U.S. Public*, pg. 2278
TERRACE COURT SENIOR LIVING, INC.—See The Ensign Group, Inc.; *U.S. Public*, pg. 2070
TRINITY CONTINUING CARE SERVICES—See Trinity Health Corporation; *U.S. Private*, pg. 4234
TRUEWOOD—See RD Merrill Company; *U.S. Private*, pg. 3362
UNION TOWNSHIP ADULT COMMUNITY DEVELOPMENT CORPORATION; *U.S. Private*, pg. 4285
UNITED LUTHERAN PROGRAM FOR THE AGING, INC.; *U.S. Private*, pg. 4293
UNITED METHODIST RETIREMENT COMMUNITIES; *U.S. Private*, pg. 4294
VILLA CHICOUTIMI INC.—See Welltower Inc.; *U.S. Public*, pg. 2349
VIRGIN RIVER HEALTHCARE, INC.—See The Ensign Group, Inc.; *U.S. Public*, pg. 2072
VISITING NURSE & HOSPICE OF FAIRFIELD COUNTY; *U.S. Private*, pg. 4392
WASHINGTON CARE CENTER; *U.S. Private*, pg. 4446
WESLEY GARDENS; *U.S. Private*, pg. 4483
WESTERN HOME COMMUNITIES INC.; *U.S. Private*, pg. 4493
WEST PARK CROSSING RETIREMENT COMMUNITY INC.—See Extendicare Inc.; *Int'l*, pg. 2591
WEST VALLEY NURSING HOMES, INC.; *U.S. Private*, pg. 4487

WILLOW CREEK SENIOR LIVING, INC.—See The Ensign Group, Inc.; *U.S. Public*, pg. 2070
WILLOW VALLEY ASSOCIATES INC.; *U.S. Private*, pg. 4528
WISCONSIN RAPIDS SENIOR LIVING, INC.—See The Ensign Group, Inc.; *U.S. Public*, pg. 2070
WOLFEBORO BAY CENTER—See Formation Capital, LLC; *U.S. Private*, pg. 1571
YORKTON CROSSING RETIREMENT COMMUNITY INC.—See Extendicare Inc.; *Int'l*, pg. 2591

623990 — OTHER RESIDENTIAL CARE FACILITIES

ARMCO CAPITAL INC.; *Int'l*, pg. 574
ARMS ACRES INC.—See Liberty Management Group, Inc.; *U.S. Private*, pg. 2444
ARNON CORPORATION; *Int'l*, pg. 577
BETHANNA INC.; *U.S. Private*, pg. 545
BRAILLE INSTITUTE OF AMERICA; *U.S. Private*, pg. 634
BROADSTEP BEHAVIORAL HEALTH—See Bain Capital, LP; *U.S. Private*, pg. 431
BUTTERFIELD YOUTH SERVICES, INC.—See Great Circle; *U.S. Private*, pg. 1762
CA MONTESSORI CHILDREN'S CENTER, INC.—See Broadcom Inc.; *U.S. Public*, pg. 389
CA MONTESSORI CHILDREN'S CENTER, INC.—See Broadcom Inc.; *U.S. Public*, pg. 389
CA MONTESSORI CHILDREN'S CENTER, INC.—See Broadcom Inc.; *U.S. Public*, pg. 389
CA MONTESSORI CHILDREN'S CENTER, INC.—See Broadcom Inc.; *U.S. Public*, pg. 389
CANTERBURY TOWERS, INC.; *U.S. Private*, pg. 735
CAP SERVICES, INC.; *U.S. Private*, pg. 737
CHANDLER HALL HEALTH SERVICES, INC.; *U.S. Private*, pg. 848
CHARITABLE ASSISTANCE TO COMMUNITY'S HOMELESS (CATCH), INC.; *U.S. Private*, pg. 851
CHARM CARE CORPORATION K.K.; *Int'l*, pg. 1450
THE CHICAGO LIGHTHOUSE FOR PEOPLE WHO ARE BLIND OR VISUALLY IMPAIRED; *U.S. Private*, pg. 4008
COLORADO DENTAL SERVICE, INC.; *U.S. Private*, pg. 973
COLUMBIA CARE SERVICE, INC; *U.S. Private*, pg. 976
COMMUNITY ACCESS UNLIMITED, INC.; *U.S. Private*, pg. 989
COMMUNITY INITIATIVES DEVELOPMENT CORPORATION; *U.S. Private*, pg. 995
CORECIVIC, INC. - FOX FACILITY—See Corecivic, Inc.; *U.S. Public*, pg. 577
CORRECT CARE SOLUTIONS, LLC—See H.I.G. Capital, LLC; *U.S. Private*, pg. 1829
CSL GREEN BAY, LLC—See Sonida Senior Living, Inc.; *U.S. Public*, pg. 1903
CSL VIRGINIA BEACH, LLC—See Sonida Senior Living, Inc.; *U.S. Public*, pg. 1903
CSL WHISPERING PINES, LLC—See Sonida Senior Living, Inc.; *U.S. Public*, pg. 1903
DISMAS CHARITIES, INC.; *U.S. Private*, pg. 1238
EAST ORLANDO HEALTH & REHAB CENTER INC; *U.S. Private*, pg. 1317
EATON RESIDENCES MANAGEMENT LIMITED—See Great Eagle Holdings Limited; *Int'l*, pg. 3064
ELEMENT CARE; *U.S. Private*, pg. 1357
GENERAL ISRAEL ORPHAN HOME FOR GIRLS JERUSALEM; *U.S. Private*, pg. 1665
G&L SENIOR CARE PROPERTIES, LLC—See G&L Realty Corp.; *U.S. Private*, pg. 1629
GRASSHOPPERS EARLY LEARNING CENTRE PTY. LTD.—See G8 Education Ltd.; *Int'l*, pg. 2867
GULF COAST TREATMENT CENTER, INC.—See Universal Health Services, Inc.; *U.S. Public*, pg. 2257
HARMONY HEALTHCARE INTERNATIONAL, INC.; *U.S. Private*, pg. 1866
HEARTLANDS ASSISTED LIVING AT SEVERNA PARK—See AlerisLife Inc.; *U.S. Private*, pg. 161
HOMESTEAD CENTER—See Formation Capital, LLC; *U.S. Private*, pg. 1570
INTERIM HOUSE INC.—See Public Health Management Corporation; *U.S. Private*, pg. 3299
JUNIPER ASSISTED LIVING RESIDENCE I, LLC—See LTC Properties, Inc.; *U.S. Public*, pg. 1344
KEEPING KIDS SAFE INC.; *U.S. Private*, pg. 2273
KEYSTONE RICHLAND CENTER LLC—See Universal Health Services, Inc.; *U.S. Public*, pg. 2258
KORIAN LES OLIVIERS JSC—See Clariane SE; *Int'l*, pg. 1643
KORIAN LES TROIS TOURS JSC—See Clariane SE; *Int'l*, pg. 1643
LES FLOTS LLC—See Clariane SE; *Int'l*, pg. 1643
LONG BEACH AFFORDABLE HOUSING COALITION; *U.S. Private*, pg. 2490
MATTHEW 25 MINISTRIES, INC; *U.S. Private*, pg. 2613
NEW BEGINNINGS TREATMENT CENTER INC.—See Corecivic, Inc.; *U.S. Public*, pg. 577

NORTHERN MANOR MULTICARE CENTER; *U.S. Private*, pg. 2953
OUTLOOK NEBRASKA, INC.; *U.S. Private*, pg. 3051
PIERCE MEMORIAL BAPTIST HOME, INC.; *U.S. Private*, pg. 3178
PINE STREET INN INC.; *U.S. Private*, pg. 3183
RAYSTOWN DEVELOPMENTAL SERVICES, INC.—See ATAR Capital, LLC; *U.S. Private*, pg. 364
REM MARYLAND, INC.—See Centerbridge Partners, L.P.; *U.S. Private*, pg. 814
RES-CARE, INC.—See KKR & Co. Inc.; *U.S. Public*, pg. 1262
SANDSTONE SENIOR LIVING, INC.—See The Ensign Group, Inc.; *U.S. Public*, pg. 2070
SCI KORIAN LE GRAND PARC IMMOBILIER—See Clariane SE; *Int'l*, pg. 1644
SCI KORIAN LES CATALAUNES IMMOBILIER—See Clariane SE; *Int'l*, pg. 1644
SCI KORIAN MORNAY IMMOBILIER—See Clariane SE; *Int'l*, pg. 1644
SENIOR WESLEYAN LIVING; *U.S. Private*, pg. 3607
SOUTH MIDDLESEX OPPORTUNITY COUNCIL, INC.; *U.S. Private*, pg. 3723
VISIONSPRING; *U.S. Private*, pg. 4392

624110 — CHILD AND YOUTH SERVICES

ABILITYFIRST; *U.S. Private*, pg. 38
ADELBROOK, INC.; *U.S. Private*, pg. 77
ALEXANDER YOUTH NETWORK; *U.S. Private*, pg. 164
AMIKIDS, INC.; *U.S. Private*, pg. 263
AMIT CHILDREN, INC.; *U.S. Private*, pg. 263
ANGLATROLL AB—See Egmont Fonden; *Int'l*, pg. 2325
ASSOCIATED RECREATION COUNCIL; *U.S. Private*, pg. 357
AZLEWAY, INC.; *U.S. Private*, pg. 415
THE BABY FOLD; *U.S. Private*, pg. 3990
BERKSHIRE FARM CENTER AND SERVICES FOR YOUTH; *U.S. Private*, pg. 533
BIENVENIDOS; *U.S. Private*, pg. 551
BIG BROTHERS BIG SISTERS OF AMERICA; *U.S. Private*, pg. 552
BONA VISTA PROGRAMS, INC.; *U.S. Private*, pg. 613
CHAI LIFELINE; *U.S. Private*, pg. 845
CHILD AND FAMILY CENTER; *U.S. Private*, pg. 881
CHILD CARE ASSOCIATES; *U.S. Private*, pg. 881
CHILDCAREGROUP; *U.S. Private*, pg. 882
CHILDCARE LEARNING CENTERS, INC.; *U.S. Private*, pg. 882
CHILD CARE RESOURCE CENTER; *U.S. Private*, pg. 882
CHILD DEVELOPMENT INC.; *U.S. Private*, pg. 882
CHILD & FAMILY SERVICES; *U.S. Private*, pg. 881
CHILDHAVEN—See Children'S Home Society Of Washington; *U.S. Private*, pg. 884
CHILDNET; *U.S. Private*, pg. 882
CHILD-PARENT CENTERS, INC.; *U.S. Private*, pg. 882
CHILDREN & FAMILIES OF IOWA; *U.S. Private*, pg. 883
CHILDREN & FAMILY SERVICES, CORP.—See KKR & Co. Inc.; *U.S. Public*, pg. 1262
CHILDRENS BUREAU, INC.; *U.S. Private*, pg. 885
CHILDREN'S CHOICE, INC.; *U.S. Private*, pg. 883
CHILDREN'S COUNCIL SAN FRANCISCO; *U.S. Private*, pg. 883
CHILDREN'S DEFENSE FUND; *U.S. Private*, pg. 883
CHILDREN'S FRIEND; *U.S. Private*, pg. 883
CHILDREN'S HOME + AID; *U.S. Private*, pg. 883
THE CHILDREN'S HOME OF PITTSBURGH & LEMIEUX FAMILY CENTER; *U.S. Private*, pg. 4008
CHILDREN'S HOME SOCIETY OF CALIFORNIA; *U.S. Private*, pg. 884
CHILDREN'S HOME SOCIETY OF FLORIDA; *U.S. Private*, pg. 884
CHILDREN'S HOME SOCIETY OF NORTH CAROLINA, INC.; *U.S. Private*, pg. 884
CHILDREN'S HOME SOCIETY OF WASHINGTON; *U.S. Private*, pg. 884
CHILDREN'S HOPE ALLIANCE FOUNDATION—See Children's Hope Alliance; *U.S. Private*, pg. 884
CHILDREN'S HOPE ALLIANCE; *U.S. Private*, pg. 884
THE CHILDREN'S INSTITUTE; *U.S. Private*, pg. 4009
CHILD TRENDS, INC.; *U.S. Private*, pg. 882
COALITION FOR HISPANIC FAMILY SERVICES; *U.S. Private*, pg. 953
COMMUNITY BASED CARE OF CENTRAL FLORIDA, INC.; *U.S. Private*, pg. 990
COMMUNITY CHILD CARE COUNCIL OF SANTA CLARA COUNTY, INC.; *U.S. Private*, pg. 990
COMMUNITY PARTNERSHIP FOR CHILDREN; *U.S. Private*, pg. 996
COMPASS FOSTERING—See August Equity LLP; *Int'l*, pg. 703
COOK INLET TRIBAL COUNCIL, INC.; *U.S. Private*, pg. 1038
CORA SERVICES, INC.; *U.S. Private*, pg. 1046
COUNSELING & RESEARCH ASSOCIATES; *U.S. Private*, pg. 1065
CREATIVE CHILD CARE, INC.; *U.S. Private*, pg. 1088

N.A.I.C.S. INDEX

624120 — SERVICES FOR THE EL...

CRYSTAL STAIRS, INC.; *U.S. Private*, pg. 1116
CUNNINGHAM CHILDREN'S HOME; *U.S. Private*, pg. 1123
DREW CHILD DEVELOPMENT CORPORATION; *U.S. Private*, pg. 1276
EARLY LEARNING COALITION OF BROWARD COUNTY, INC.; *U.S. Private*, pg. 1313
THE EARLY LEARNING COALITION OF FLAGLER AND VOLUSIA COUNTIES, INC.; *U.S. Private*, pg. 4024
EARLY LEARNING COALITION OF LAKE COUNTY; *U.S. Private*, pg. 1313
EARLY LEARNING COALITION OF MANATEE COUNTY, INC.; *U.S. Private*, pg. 1313
EARLY LEARNING COALITION OF NORTHWEST FLORIDA, INC.; *U.S. Private*, pg. 1313
EARLY LEARNING COALITION OF OSCEOLA COUNTY, INC.; *U.S. Private*, pg. 1313
EARLY LEARNING COALITION OF PALM BEACH COUNTY, INC.; *U.S. Private*, pg. 1313
EARLY LEARNING COALITION OF PINELLAS COUNTY, INC.; *U.S. Private*, pg. 1313
EARLY LEARNING COALITION OF SOUTHWEST FLORIDA, INC.; *U.S. Private*, pg. 1313
EARLY LEARNING COALITION OF THE NATURE COAST, INC.; *U.S. Private*, pg. 1313
ELIADA HOMES, INC.; *U.S. Private*, pg. 1360
ENVIRONMENTAL ALTERNATIVES; *U.S. Private*, pg. 1407
EVANGELICAL CHILDREN'S HOME; *U.S. Private*, pg. 1434
FAITHBRIDGE GROUP LLC.; *U.S. Private*, pg. 1466
FAMILY CENTRAL INC.; *U.S. Private*, pg. 1469
FLORIDA UNITED METHODIST CHILDREN'S HOME; *U.S. Private*, pg. 1551
FOREVER CHANGED INTERNATIONAL; *U.S. Private*, pg. 1567
FOUR OAKS FAMILY & CHILDREN'S SERVICES; *U.S. Private*, pg. 1582
FRIENDS CHILD CARE CENTER; *U.S. Private*, pg. 1611
FRIENDS OF YOUTH; *U.S. Private*, pg. 1611
GEORGE H & IRENE L WALKER HOME FOR CHILDREN INCORPORATED; *U.S. Private*, pg. 1682
GIVE KIDS THE WORLD, INC.; *U.S. Private*, pg. 1703
GLOBAL BRIGADES, INC.; *U.S. Private*, pg. 1712
GLOBAL OPERATIONS AND DEVELOPMENT; *U.S. Private*, pg. 1716
GREATER RIDGEWOOD YOUTH COUNCIL INC.; *U.S. Private*, pg. 1770
GREEN CHIMNEYS CHILDREN'S SERVICES, INC.; *U.S. Private*, pg. 1772
GUILFORD CHILD DEVELOPMENT; *U.S. Private*, pg. 1814
HEARTLAND FAMILY SERVICE; *U.S. Private*, pg. 1900
HEARTLAND FOR CHILDREN; *U.S. Private*, pg. 1900
HILLEL: THE FOUNDATION FOR JEWISH CAMPUS LIFE; *U.S. Private*, pg. 1946
HOLLY CITY DEVELOPMENT CORPORATION; *U.S. Private*, pg. 1966
HOLT INTERNATIONAL CHILDREN'S SERVICES; *U.S. Private*, pg. 1968
THE ICLA DA SILVA FOUNDATION; *U.S. Private*, pg. 4055
ILLINOIS ACTION FOR CHILDREN; *U.S. Private*, pg. 2042
INMED PARTNERSHIPS FOR CHILDREN; *U.S. Private*, pg. 2080
INTERGENERATIONAL LIVING AND HEALTH CARE, INC.; *U.S. Private*, pg. 2110
INTERNATIONAL YOUTH FOUNDATION; *U.S. Private*, pg. 2122
JACK & JILL OF AMERICA, INC.; *U.S. Private*, pg. 2173
JACKSON HOUSE; *U.S. Private*, pg. 2177
J. ARTHUR TRUDEAU MEMORIAL CENTER; *U.S. Private*, pg. 2155
JEWISH COUNCIL FOR YOUTH SERVICES; *U.S. Private*, pg. 2205
JONATHAN'S PLACE; *U.S. Private*, pg. 2231
JOURNEY HOUSE, INC.; *U.S. Private*, pg. 2238
JOY FOR OUR YOUTH INC.; *U.S. Private*, pg. 2238
JULIETTE FOWLER HOMES INC.; *U.S. Private*, pg. 2243
JUSTICEWORKS YOUTHCARE INC.; *U.S. Private*, pg. 2246
KAMAAINA KIDS; *U.S. Private*, pg. 2258
KANSAS CHILDREN'S SERVICE LEAGUE; *U.S. Private*, pg. 2260
KOINONIA FOSTER HOMES, INC.; *U.S. Private*, pg. 2340
LATIN AMERICAN YOUTH CENTER INC.; *U.S. Private*, pg. 2397
LEAKE & WATTS SERVICES INC.; *U.S. Private*, pg. 2407
LIFELINE YOUTH & FAMILY SERVICES, INC.; *U.S. Private*, pg. 2450
MAKE-A-WISH FOUNDATION OF AMERICA; *U.S. Private*, pg. 2556
MARTHA & MARY LUTHERAN SERVICES; *U.S. Private*, pg. 2594
MASSACHUSETTS SOCIETY FOR THE PREVENTION OF CRUELTY TO CHILDREN; *U.S. Private*, pg. 2606
MERCY MEDICAL CENTER - SIOUX CITY—See Trinity Health Corporation; *U.S. Private*, pg. 4233
MIAMI VALLEY CHILD DEVELOPMENT CENTERS, INC.; *U.S. Private*, pg. 2697
MISSISSIPPI CHILDREN'S HOME SERVICES; *U.S. Private*, pg. 2748

NATIONAL CHILDREN'S CENTER, INC.; *U.S. Private*, pg. 2850
NATIONAL SAFE PLACE; *U.S. Private*, pg. 2862
NEW YORK CENTER FOR CHILD DEVELOPMENT; *U.S. Private*, pg. 2908
THE NORTH CAROLINA PARTNERSHIP FOR CHILDREN, INC.; *U.S. Private*, pg. 4084
NORTHERN CHILDRENS SERVICES; *U.S. Private*, pg. 2952
NORTHSIDE CENTER FOR CHILD DEVELOPMENT; *U.S. Private*, pg. 2957
NUORISOKOTI VALOKKI OY—See Humana AB; *Int'l*, pg. 3530
OREGON CHILD DEVELOPMENT COALITION, INC.; *U.S. Private*, pg. 3040
PAT'S PLACE CHILD ADVOCACY CENTER INC.; *U.S. Private*, pg. 3105
PLAN INTERNATIONAL USA; *U.S. Private*, pg. 3195
PLAN USA, INC.; *U.S. Private*, pg. 3195
THE POINT COMMUNITY DEVELOPMENT CORPORATION; *U.S. Private*, pg. 4097
PRICELESS PARENTING, LLC; *U.S. Private*, pg. 3259
QUIET ANGEL FOUNDATION; *U.S. Private*, pg. 3327
REBEKAH CHILDREN'S SERVICES.; *U.S. Private*, pg. 3370
THE REDONDO BEACH EDUCATIONAL FOUNDATION; *U.S. Private*, pg. 4103
ROBERT F. KENNEDY CHILDREN'S ACTION CORPS; *U.S. Private*, pg. 3457
RONALD MCDONALD HOUSE CHARITIES, INC.—See McDonald's Corporation; *U.S. Public*, pg. 1406
SAFE SPACE NYC INC.; *U.S. Private*, pg. 3524
SCALA BIO CENTER AALBORG APS—See Egmont Fonden; *Int'l*, pg. 2326
SCHOOL-TO-SCHOOL INTERNATIONAL; *U.S. Private*, pg. 3568
SCOPE EDUCATION SERVICES; *U.S. Private*, pg. 3575
SEMINOLE COUNTY COALITION FOR SCHOOL READINESS, INC.; *U.S. Private*, pg. 3604
SIERRA VISTA CHILD AND FAMILY SERVICES; *U.S. Private*, pg. 3648
SOLVIK BARNEVERN AS—See Humana AB; *Int'l*, pg. 3530
SOUTH ARKANSAS YOUTH, SERVICES, INC.; *U.S. Private*, pg. 3719
SPORTS HUMANITARIAN GROUP INC.; *U.S. Private*, pg. 3761
SQUARE ONE; *U.S. Private*, pg. 3766
SUPPORTING FAMILIES TOGETHER ASSOCIATION; *U.S. Private*, pg. 3882
THERAPEUTIC FAMILY LIFE; *U.S. Private*, pg. 4142
THOMPSON CHILD & FAMILY FOCUS; *U.S. Private*, pg. 4159
TICKETS FOR KIDS CHARITIES; *U.S. Private*, pg. 4167
TRUECORE BEHAVIORAL SOLUTIONS, LLC; *U.S. Private*, pg. 4248
VALLEY YOUTH HOUSE; *U.S. Private*, pg. 4336
VENUEPOINT AB—See Egmont Fonden; *Int'l*, pg. 2326
VENUEPOINT AS—See Egmont Fonden; *Int'l*, pg. 2326
VERITAS ADVISORY GROUP, INC.—See Cobepa S.A.; *Int'l*, pg. 1683
WARD HOME, INC.—See Auberle; *U.S. Private*, pg. 385
WASHBURN CENTER FOR CHILDREN; *U.S. Private*, pg. 4445
WHITE'S RESIDENTIAL & FAMILY SERVICES, INC.; *U.S. Private*, pg. 4510
WISCONSIN EARLY CHILDHOOD ASSOCIATION; *U.S. Private*, pg. 4548
WORLD VISION INC.; *U.S. Private*, pg. 4567
YOUNG MARINES OF THE MARINE CORPS LEAGUE; *U.S. Private*, pg. 4593
YOUTH CO-OP, INC.; *U.S. Private*, pg. 4594
YOUTH IN NEED, INC.; *U.S. Private*, pg. 4594

624120 — SERVICES FOR THE ELDERLY AND PERSONS WITH DISABILITIES

AABR; *U.S. Private*, pg. 30
ABILIS, INC.; *U.S. Private*, pg. 38
ABILITY CONNECTION TEXAS; *U.S. Private*, pg. 38
ACCRA CARE; *U.S. Private*, pg. 54
ACTIVE DAY INC.—See Audax Group, Limited Partnership; *U.S. Private*, pg. 389
ACTIVE DAY OF RANDALLSTOWN—See Audax Group, Limited Partnership; *U.S. Private*, pg. 389
ADAPTIVE SPORTS USA, INC.; *U.S. Private*, pg. 76
ADULT DAY HEALTH, INC.—See Centerbridge Partners, L.P.; *U.S. Private*, pg. 813
A.G. RHODES HEALTH & REHAB; *U.S. Private*, pg. 25
AIM SERVICES, INC.; *U.S. Private*, pg. 133
ALBANY ADVOCACY RESOURCE CENTER, INC.; *U.S. Private*, pg. 151
ALLEGHENY LUTHERAN SOCIAL MINISTRIES; *U.S. Private*, pg. 176
AMERICAN BAPTIST HOMES OF THE MIDWEST; *U.S. Private*, pg. 224
AMERICAN EAGLE LIFECARE CORPORATION; *U.S. Private*, pg. 231

ANDELCARE, INC.; *U.S. Private*, pg. 275
THE ARC MERCER, INC.; *U.S. Private*, pg. 3987
ARC OF GREATER NEW ORLEANS; *U.S. Private*, pg. 309
ARC OF THE UNITED STATES; *U.S. Private*, pg. 309
AREA AGENCY ON AGING FOR SOUTHWEST FLORIDA INC.; *U.S. Private*, pg. 317
AREA AGENCY ON AGING OF CENTRAL FLORIDA; *U.S. Private*, pg. 317
AREA AGENCY ON AGING OF PALM BEACH/TREASURE COAST, INC.; *U.S. Private*, pg. 317
AREA FIVE AGENCY ON AGING & COMMUNITY SERVICES, INC.; *U.S. Private*, pg. 317
AREAWIDE COUNCIL ON AGING OF BROWARD COUNTY, INC.; *U.S. Private*, pg. 318
ARKANSAS ELDER OUTREACH OF LITTLE ROCK, INC.; *U.S. Private*, pg. 325
ARROWHEAD WEST, INC.; *U.S. Private*, pg. 336
ASSYRIAN UNIVERSAL ALLIANCE FOUNDATION, INC.; *U.S. Private*, pg. 360
ASTOCO INC.—See Envipro Holdings Inc.; *Int'l*, pg. 2454
ATLANTIC HOUSING FOUNDATION, INC.; *U.S. Private*, pg. 373
AVIV CENTERS FOR LIVING; *U.S. Private*, pg. 409
BABCOCK CENTER, INC.; *U.S. Private*, pg. 421
BAPTIST HOMES SOCIETY; *U.S. Private*, pg. 471
BARC DEVELOPMENTAL SERVICES; *U.S. Private*, pg. 472
BATEMAN SENIOR MEALS—See Compass Group PLC; *Int'l*, pg. 1750
BAY HUMAN SERVICES; *U.S. Private*, pg. 493
BECOMING INDEPENDENT; *U.S. Private*, pg. 512
BENESSE PALETTE CO., LTD.—See EQT AB; *Int'l*, pg. 2467
BENESSE STYLE CARE CO., LTD.—See EQT AB; *Int'l*, pg. 2467
BERKS COUNTY CENTER FOR INDEPENDENT LIVING; *U.S. Private*, pg. 533
BEVERLY J. SEARLES FOUNDATION; *U.S. Private*, pg. 547
BLOCK INSTITUTE; *U.S. Private*, pg. 583
BOST, INC.; *U.S. Private*, pg. 620
THE BRETHREN HOME COMMUNITY; *U.S. Private*, pg. 4000
THE BRIDGE OF CENTRAL MASSACHUSETTS, INC.; *U.S. Private*, pg. 4000
BRIDGEWELL INC.; *U.S. Private*, pg. 650
CALIFORNIA COMMUNICATIONS ACCESS FOUNDATION; *U.S. Private*, pg. 718
CALIFORNIA MENTOR FAMILY HOME AGENCY, LLC—See Centerbridge Partners, L.P.; *U.S. Private*, pg. 813
CARE MANAGEMENT NETWORK INC.—See Assicurazioni Generali S.p.A.; *Int'l*, pg. 643
CARE WISCONSIN FIRST, INC.; *U.S. Private*, pg. 752
CATHOLIC RESIDENTIAL SERVICES, INC.; *U.S. Private*, pg. 792
CATHOLIC SENIOR HOUSING & HEALTHCARE SERVICES, INC.; *U.S. Private*, pg. 792
CATTARAUGUS REHABILITATION CENTER, INC.; *U.S. Private*, pg. 792
CEDAR FALLS LUTHERAN HOME; *U.S. Private*, pg. 804
CEDAR VALLEY SERVICES, INC.; *U.S. Private*, pg. 805
CENTER FOR DISABILITY SERVICES, INC.; *U.S. Private*, pg. 810
THE CENTER FOR FAMILY SUPPORT; *U.S. Private*, pg. 4006
CENTER FOR INDEPENDENCE OF THE DISABLED, NEW YORK; *U.S. Private*, pg. 810
CENTER FOR INDEPENDENT LIVING; *U.S. Private*, pg. 810
CENTRAL WV AGING SERVICES, INC.; *U.S. Private*, pg. 826
CEREBRAL PALSY OF NORTH JERSEY; *U.S. Private*, pg. 840
CEREBRAL PALSY OF WESTCHESTER, INC.; *U.S. Private*, pg. 840
CHALLENGE UNLIMITED, INC.; *U.S. Private*, pg. 845
CHAPIN HOME FOR THE AGING; *U.S. Private*, pg. 849
CHARLESTON TRANSITIONAL FACILITY; *U.S. Private*, pg. 857
CHI CENTERS, INC.; *U.S. Private*, pg. 876
CHILD-ADULT RESOURCE SERVICES, INC.; *U.S. Private*, pg. 882
CHILDREN AND ADULT DISABILITY AND EDUCATIONAL SERVICES; *U.S. Private*, pg. 883
THE CHILDREN'S GUILD INC.; *U.S. Private*, pg. 4008
CHRISTIAN HORIZONS; *U.S. Private*, pg. 891
CHS OF WALTHAM INC.; *U.S. Private*, pg. 893
THE CHURCH STREET CORPORATION; *U.S. Private*, pg. 4009
CICOA AGING & IN-HOME SOLUTIONS; *U.S. Private*, pg. 896
COASTAL DEVELOPMENTAL SERVICES FOUNDATION; *U.S. Private*, pg. 956
COAST HEALTHCARE MANAGEMENT, LLC—See Tenet Healthcare Corporation; *U.S. Public*, pg. 2003
COASTLINE ELDERLY SERVICE, INC.; *U.S. Private*, pg. 957

624120 — SERVICES FOR THE EL...

COMMUNITY INTERACTIONS, INC.; *U.S. Private*, pg. 995
COMMUNITY LIVING ALLIANCE, INC.; *U.S. Private*, pg. 995
COMMUNITY LIVING AND SUPPORT SERVICES; *U.S. Private*, pg. 995
COMMUNITY RESOURCES FOR INDEPENDENCE; *U.S. Private*, pg. 996
COMMUNITY SYSTEMS, INC.; *U.S. Private*, pg. 997
COMMUNITY, WORK & INDEPENDENCE, INC.; *U.S. Private*, pg. 997
COTTONWOOD INCORPORATED; *U.S. Private*, pg. 1064
CREATIVE CARE FOR REACHING INDEPENDENCE; *U.S. Private*, pg. 1088
DALE ROGERS TRAINING CENTER, INC.; *U.S. Private*, pg. 1149
DEUTSCHES ALTENHEIM, INC.; *U.S. Private*, pg. 1217
DEVELOPMENT HOMES, INC.; *U.S. Private*, pg. 1217
DIDLAKE, INC.; *U.S. Private*, pg. 1228
DISABILITY RIGHTS CALIFORNIA; *U.S. Private*, pg. 1237
DISABILITY SERVICES OF THE SOUTHWEST; *U.S. Private*, pg. 1237
DISABLED SPORTS USA, INC.—See Adaptive Sports USA, Inc.; *U.S. Private*, pg. 76
DISABLED VETERANS NATIONAL FOUNDATION; *U.S. Private*, pg. 1237
DULUTH REGIONAL CARE CENTER; *U.S. Private*, pg. 1286
EAST ARKANSAS AREA AGENCY ON AGING; *U.S. Private*, pg. 1315
EASTER SEALS CENTRAL TEXAS; *U.S. Private*, pg. 1319
ECHOING HILLS VILLAGE, INC.; *U.S. Private*, pg. 1327
ECUMEN; *U.S. Private*, pg. 1331
ELDERSOURCE; *U.S. Private*, pg. 1351
ELIZA BRYANT VILLAGE; *U.S. Private*, pg. 1362
EMERGE, INC.; *U.S. Private*, pg. 1380
ERIE COUNTY CARE MANAGEMENT, INC.; *U.S. Private*, pg. 1420
ERIE HOMES FOR CHILDREN AND ADULTS, INC.; *U.S. Private*, pg. 1420
EVANGELICAL HOMES OF MICHIGAN; *U.S. Private*, pg. 1434
EVERGREEN LIFE SERVICES; *U.S. Private*, pg. 1439
EVERGREEN LIVING INNOVATIONS, INC.; *U.S. Private*, pg. 1439
EXCEL COMPANION CARE, INC.—See Centerbridge Partners, L.P.; *U.S. Private*, pg. 815
EXCEL COMPANION CARE, INC.—See The Vistria Group, LP; *U.S. Private*, pg. 4131
FAMILY EMPOWERMENT COUNCIL, INC.; *U.S. Private*, pg. 1469
FAR NORTHERN COORDINATING COUNCIL ON DEVELOPMENTAL DISABILITIES, INC.; *U.S. Private*, pg. 1473
FELLOWSHIP SENIOR LIVING; *U.S. Private*, pg. 1494
FIELDHOME; *U.S. Private*, pg. 1504
FIRST STEP, INC.; *U.S. Private*, pg. 1529
FIRST STEP INDEPENDENT LIVING PROGRAM, INC.—See Centerbridge Partners, L.P.; *U.S. Private*, pg. 813
FLORIDA ARF; *U.S. Private*, pg. 1547
FRANZISKA RACKER CENTERS; *U.S. Private*, pg. 1599
FREDA H. GORDON HOSPICE & PALLIATIVE CARE OF TIDEWATER—See UnitedHealth Group Incorporated; *U.S. Public*, pg. 2245
FRIENDSHIP COMMUNITY; *U.S. Private*, pg. 1612
FRIENDS LIFE CARE; *U.S. Private*, pg. 1611
FRONTIER COMMUNITY SERVICES; *U.S. Private*, pg. 1615
FULL LIFE CARE; *U.S. Private*, pg. 1620
GALT FOUNDATION; *U.S. Private*, pg. 1640
GARDEN SPOT VILLAGE; *U.S. Private*, pg. 1643
GARTEN SERVICES, INC.; *U.S. Private*, pg. 1646
GLACIER HILLS SENIOR LIVING COMMUNITY; *U.S. Private*, pg. 1704
GLENCROFT; *U.S. Private*, pg. 1709
GOLDEN STATE MEDICARE HEALTH PLAN; *U.S. Private*, pg. 1733
THE GOOD SAMARITAN HOME OF QUINCY; *U.S. Private*, pg. 4034
GRACELAND SENIOR LIVING, INC—See The Ensign Group, Inc.; *U.S. Public*, pg. 2071
GREATER HARLEM NURSING HOME & REHABILITATION CENTER INC.; *U.S. Private*, pg. 1769
GUIDING EYES FOR THE BLIND, INC.; *U.S. Private*, pg. 1814
THE GUILD FOR EXCEPTIONAL CHILDREN, INC.; *U.S. Private*, pg. 4040
THE GUILD FOR HUMAN SERVICES, INC.; *U.S. Private*, pg. 4040
HAMASPIK OF ROCKLAND COUNTY, INC.; *U.S. Private*, pg. 1847
HARBOR DEVELOPMENTAL DISABILITIES FOUNDATION, INC.; *U.S. Private*, pg. 1859
HASC CENTER INC.; *U.S. Private*, pg. 1878
HAVERLAND CARTER LIFESTYLE GROUP; *U.S. Private*, pg. 1880
HEAD INJURY ASSOCIATION, INC.; *U.S. Private*, pg. 1891
THE HEBREW HOME AT RIVERDALE; *U.S. Private*, pg. 4050
THE HELP GROUP; *U.S. Private*, pg. 4051
HELPING HAND CENTER; *U.S. Private*, pg. 1912
HELPING RESTORE ABILITY; *U.S. Private*, pg. 1912
HERITAGE CHRISTIAN SERVICES, INC.; *U.S. Private*, pg. 1922
HILLCREST EDUCATIONAL CENTERS, INC.; *U.S. Private*, pg. 1946
HILLCREST; *U.S. Private*, pg. 1946
HIRAYAMA LACC CO., LTD.—See Hirayama Holdings Co., Ltd.; *Int'l*, pg. 3404
HIT, INC.; *U.S. Private*, pg. 1952
HOME ATTENDANT SERVICE OF HYDE PARK; *U.S. Private*, pg. 1970
HOME OF HOPE, INC; *U.S. Private*, pg. 1972
HUDSON COMMUNITY ENTERPRISES; *U.S. Private*, pg. 2001
HUMANIM, INC.; *U.S. Private*, pg. 2006
IDA SERVICES, INC.—See Crossroads of Western Iowa, Inc.; *U.S. Private*, pg. 1108
ILLINOIS MENTOR, INC.—See Centerbridge Partners, L.P.; *U.S. Private*, pg. 813
INDEPENDENCE CARE SYSTEM; *U.S. Private*, pg. 2058
INDEPENDENCEFIRST; *U.S. Private*, pg. 2058
INDEPENDENCE RESIDENCES, INC.; *U.S. Private*, pg. 2058
INDEPENDENT GROUP HOME LIVING PROGRAM INC.; *U.S. Private*, pg. 2059
INDEPENDENT LIVING, INC.; *U.S. Private*, pg. 2059
INDEPENDENT LIVING SYSTEMS, LLC.; *U.S. Private*, pg. 2059
INLAND REGIONAL CENTER; *U.S. Private*, pg. 2079
IN-PACT, INC.; *U.S. Private*, pg. 2052
INTEGRATED CARE PTY LTD.—See Madison Dearborn Partners, LLC; *U.S. Private*, pg. 2540
ISABELLE RIDGWAY CARE CENTER; *U.S. Private*, pg. 2142
ISLAND REHABILITATION AND NURSING CENTER INC; *U.S. Private*, pg. 2145
JAMES L. MAHER CENTER; *U.S. Private*, pg. 2184
JAWONIO; *U.S. Private*, pg. 2191
JENNINGS CENTER FOR OLDER ADULTS; *U.S. Private*, pg. 2200
JEWISH FAMILY SERVICE ASSOCIATION OF CLEVELAND; *U.S. Private*, pg. 2205
JONI AND FRIENDS; *U.S. Private*, pg. 2234
JUDSON SERVICES, INC.; *U.S. Private*, pg. 2242
KALIX; *U.S. Private*, pg. 2257
KANSAS ELKS TRAINING CENTER FOR THE HANDICAPPED, INC.; *U.S. Private*, pg. 2261
KERN REGIONAL CENTER; *U.S. Private*, pg. 2291
LANDMARK SCHOOL, INC.; *U.S. Private*, pg. 2385
LIFEDESIGNS; *U.S. Private*, pg. 2449
LIFELONG MEDICAL CARE; *U.S. Private*, pg. 2450
LIFEPATH; *U.S. Private*, pg. 2450
LIFESPAN INCORPORATED; *U.S. Private*, pg. 2451
LIFE'S WORC; *U.S. Private*, pg. 2449
LIFETIME ASSISTANCE INC.; *U.S. Private*, pg. 2451
LIGHTHOUSE LOUISIANA; *U.S. Private*, pg. 2453
LYCOMING-CLINTON JOINDER BOARD; *U.S. Private*, pg. 2519
MACOMB-OAKLAND REGIONAL CENTER; *U.S. Private*, pg. 2538
MANKATO REHABILITATION CENTER, INC.; *U.S. Private*, pg. 2564
MARKLUND CHILDREN'S HOME; *U.S. Private*, pg. 2582
MATHENY MEDICAL AND EDUCATIONAL CENTER; *U.S. Private*, pg. 2610
MATHER LIFEWAYS; *U.S. Private*, pg. 2610
MEDIGOLD; *U.S. Private*, pg. 2656
MENORAH CAMPUS, INC.; *U.S. Private*, pg. 2666
MENORAH PARK CENTER FOR SENIOR LIVING; *U.S. Private*, pg. 2667
METROPOLITAN AREA AGENCY ON AGING, INC.; *U.S. Private*, pg. 2687
MISSION HEALTH SERVICES; *U.S. Private*, pg. 2747
MOKA CORPORATION; *U.S. Private*, pg. 2766
MON YOUGH COMMUNITY SERVICES, INC.; *U.S. Private*, pg. 2768
MOUNT OLIVET ROLLING ACRES; *U.S. Private*, pg. 2798
MYSTIC VALLEY ELDER SERVICES, INC.; *U.S. Private*, pg. 2826
THE NATIONAL ASSOCIATION FOR HISPANIC ELDERLY; *U.S. Private*, pg. 4082
NATIONAL FEDERATION OF THE BLIND; *U.S. Private*, pg. 2853
NEW AVENUES TO INDEPENDENCE, INC.; *U.S. Private*, pg. 2892
THE NEWCOURTLAND LIFE PROGRAM; *U.S. Private*, pg. 4083
NEW HORIZONS REHABILITATION SERVICES, INC.; *U.S. Private*, pg. 2897
NORTHEAST SENIOR HEALTH CORPORATION; *U.S. Private*, pg. 2951
NORTH HILL NEEDHAM, INC.; *U.S. Private*, pg. 2945
NORTH METRO COMMUNITY SERVICES, INC.; *U.S. Private*, pg. 2945
NORTHWEST CENTER; *U.S. Private*, pg. 2959
NUPATH, INC.; *U.S. Private*, pg. 2973
OAKLAND LIVINGSTON HUMAN SERVICE AGENCY; *U.S. Private*, pg. 2984
OAKWOOD LUTHERAN HOMES ASSOCIATION, INC.; *U.S. Private*, pg. 2985
OCCUPATIONAL TRAINING CENTER OF BURLINGTON COUNTY, INC.; *U.S. Private*, pg. 2988
OLD COLONY ELDER SERVICES; *U.S. Private*, pg. 3008
OPEN DOOR FAMILY MEDICAL CENTER, INC.; *U.S. Private*, pg. 3029
ORANGE COUNTY ADULT ACHIEVEMENT CENTER; *U.S. Private*, pg. 3037
ORC INDUSTRIES, INC.; *U.S. Private*, pg. 3038
OUR LADY OF CONSOLATION NURSING & REHABILITATIVE CARE CENTER—See Catholic Health Services of Long Island; *U.S. Private*, pg. 791
PACE ORGANIZATION OF RHODE ISLAND; *U.S. Private*, pg. 3063
PACESETTERS, INC; *U.S. Private*, pg. 3065
PARC, INC.; *U.S. Private*, pg. 3094
PASSAVANT MEMORIAL HOMES; *U.S. Private*, pg. 3104
PATINA WELLNESS LIMITED—See Chinachem Group; *Int'l*, pg. 1568
PENN-MAR ORGANIZATION, INC.; *U.S. Private*, pg. 3135
PENN-MAR ORGANIZATION, INC.—See Penn-Mar Organization, Inc.; *U.S. Private*, pg. 3135
PHILLIPS LIFT SYSTEMS, INC.—See Homecare Products, Inc.; *U.S. Private*, pg. 1973
PHI; *U.S. Private*, pg. 3167
PINE TREE SOCIETY FOR HANDICAPPED CHILDREN AND ADULTS, INC.; *U.S. Private*, pg. 3183
PRIMROSE WELLNESS GROUP, LLC—See Clearday, Inc.; *U.S. Public*, pg. 512
PROGRESS INDUSTRIES; *U.S. Private*, pg. 3278
PROGRESSIVE ELDERCARE SERVICES - DREW INC.; *U.S. Private*, pg. 3279
PROGRESSIVE ELDERCARE SERVICES MORRILTON INC.; *U.S. Private*, pg. 3279
PROSPECTUS BERCO; *U.S. Private*, pg. 3288
PROVIDENCE LIFE SERVICES; *U.S. Private*, pg. 3294
PROVIDENCE REST; *U.S. Private*, pg. 3294
QUALITY SERVICES FOR THE AUTISM COMMUNITY; *U.S. Private*, pg. 3321
REDMOND HEIGHTS SENIOR LIVING—See The Ensign Group, Inc.; *U.S. Public*, pg. 2072
RED RIVER HUMAN SERVICES FOUNDATION; *U.S. Private*, pg. 3375
REDWOOD COAST DEVELOPMENTAL SERVICES CORPORATION; *U.S. Private*, pg. 3380
REGIONAL CENTER OF THE EAST BAY; *U.S. Private*, pg. 3388
RELAY RESOURCES; *U.S. Private*, pg. 3393
RESOURCE CENTER FOR INDEPENDENT LIVING, INC.; *U.S. Private*, pg. 3406
RESOURCES FOR HUMAN DEVELOPMENT; *U.S. Private*, pg. 3407
RESTHAVEN CARE COMMUNITY; *U.S. Private*, pg. 3408
RISE, INC.; *U.S. Private*, pg. 3440
RIVERFRONT ACTIVITY CENTER, INC.; *U.S. Private*, pg. 3444
ROCKY MOUNTAIN HUMAN SERVICES; *U.S. Private*, pg. 3469
ROESER HOUSING DEVELOPMENT CORPORATION; *U.S. Private*, pg. 3470
ROMAN EAGLE REHABILITATION AND HEALTH CARE CENTER, INC.; *U.S. Private*, pg. 3475
ROSE-MARY CENTER; *U.S. Private*, pg. 3482
SAINT DOMINIC'S HOME; *U.S. Private*, pg. 3529
SAINT JOHN'S COMMUNITIES, INC.; *U.S. Private*, pg. 3529
SAN DIEGO-IMPERIAL COUNTIES DEVELOPMENTAL SERVICES INC.; *U.S. Private*, pg. 3540
SENIOR CARE CENTERS OF AMERICA, INC.—See Audax Group, Limited Partnership; *U.S. Private*, pg. 389
SENIOR CARE ELDERLY LIMITED—See DreamEast Group Limited; *Int'l*, pg. 2203
SENIORCARE, INC.; *U.S. Private*, pg. 3607
SENIOR CONNECTION CENTER, INC.; *U.S. Private*, pg. 3606
THE SENIOR LIVING FOUNDATION INC; *U.S. Private*, pg. 4116
SENIOR SERVICES, INC.; *U.S. Private*, pg. 3607
SENIOR SERVICES OF SNOHOMISH COUNTY; *U.S. Private*, pg. 3607
SERTOMA CENTRE, INC.; *U.S. Private*, pg. 3614
SERVICE COORDINATION, INC.; *U.S. Private*, pg. 3615
SHADOWFAX CORPORATION; *U.S. Private*, pg. 3622
SHADY LANE, INC.; *U.S. Private*, pg. 3623
SHANGRI-LA; *U.S. Private*, pg. 3625
SKILLS OF CENTRAL PENNSYLVANIA, INC.; *U.S. Private*, pg. 3682
SKOOKUM SERVICES, LLC; *U.S. Private*, pg. 3683
SOLIVITA AT POINCIANA, INC.—See Brookfield Corporation; *Int'l*, pg. 1183
SOUTHEAST COMMUNITY WORK CENTER, INC.; *U.S. Private*, pg. 3725
SOUTHERN INDIANA REHABILITATION HOSPITAL—See Omega Healthcare Investors, Inc.; *U.S. Public*, pg. 1571
SRVS; *U.S. Private*, pg. 3768

N.A.I.C.S. INDEX

624190 — OTHER INDIVIDUAL AN...

STARPOINT; *U.S. Private*, pg. 3787
STAVROS CENTER FOR INDEPENDENT LIVING, INC.; *U.S. Private*, pg. 3794
ST. CATHERINE OF SIENA NURSING & REHABILITATION CARE CENTER—See Catholic Health Services of Long Island; *U.S. Private*, pg. 791
STEP BY STEP, INC.; *U.S. Private*, pg. 3801
ST. NICHOLAS HUMAN SUPPORT CORPORATION; *U.S. Private*, pg. 3770
ST. PATRICKS HOME; *U.S. Private*, pg. 3773
SUBURBAN ADULT SERVICES INC.; *U.S. Private*, pg. 3847
SUNNYHILL, INC.; *U.S. Private*, pg. 3868
THRESHOLD REHABILITATION SERVICES, INC.; *U.S. Private*, pg. 4164
TRAINING TOWARD SELF-RELIANCE, INC.; *U.S. Private*, pg. 4204
THE TREATMENT AND LEARNING CENTERS, INC.; *U.S. Private*, pg. 4128
TREE OF LIFE FOUNDATION NPO—See Bank of Georgia Group PLC; *Int'l*, pg. 843
UNIQUESOURCE; *U.S. Private*, pg. 4286
UNITED CHURCH HOMES AND SERVICES; *U.S. Private*, pg. 4288
UPARC, INC.; *U.S. Private*, pg. 4311
VALLEYLIFE; *U.S. Private*, pg. 4336
VARIETY CHILD LEARNING CENTER; *U.S. Private*, pg. 4347
THE VIRGINIA HOME; *U.S. Private*, pg. 4131
VITALIA AT TRADITION, LLC—See Brookfield Corporation; *Int'l*, pg. 1183
VOCATIONAL DEVELOPMENT CENTER; *U.S. Private*, pg. 4408
VOCATIONAL INDEPENDENCE PROGRAM INC; *U.S. Private*, pg. 4409
VOICES FOR INDEPENDENCE; *U.S. Private*, pg. 4409
VTC ENTERPRISES; *U.S. Private*, pg. 4415
WABASH CENTER INC.; *U.S. Private*, pg. 4423
WAVERLY HEIGHTS LTD.; *U.S. Private*, pg. 4458
WENDELL FOSTER'S CAMPUS FOR DEVELOPMENTAL DISABILITIES; *U.S. Private*, pg. 4480
WESLEY COMMUNITY SERVICES; *U.S. Private*, pg. 4482
WESTCHESTER INSTITUTE FOR HUMAN DEVELOPMENT; *U.S. Private*, pg. 4489
WESTERN RESERVE AREA AGENCY ON AGING; *U.S. Private*, pg. 4496
WESTSIDE HABILITATION CENTER, INC.; *U.S. Private*, pg. 4501
WEXNER HERITAGE VILLAGE; *U.S. Private*, pg. 4502
WHEEL CHAIR HOME, INC.; *U.S. Private*, pg. 4505
THE WHOLE PERSON, INC.; *U.S. Private*, pg. 4135
WILLIAMSBURG LANDING, INC.; *U.S. Private*, pg. 4527
WORK, INC.; *U.S. Private*, pg. 4563
WORK SERVICES CORPORATION; *U.S. Private*, pg. 4563
WORK TRAINING CENTER, INC; *U.S. Private*, pg. 4563
YOUNG ADULT INSTITUTE, INC.; *U.S. Private*, pg. 4592

624190 — OTHER INDIVIDUAL AND FAMILY SERVICES

ABANDONED CHILDREN'S FUND; *U.S. Private*, pg. 34
ABBOTT LABORATORIES D.O.O. HRK—See Abbott Laboratories; *U.S. Public*, pg. 16
ABBOTT MEDICAL CANADA CO.—See Abbott Laboratories; *U.S. Public*, pg. 17
ABILITY BEYOND DISABILITY; *U.S. Private*, pg. 38
ACCION SOCIAL DE PUERTO RICO, INC.; *U.S. Private*, pg. 53
ACI SUPPORT SPECIALISTS, INC.—See Dungarvin, Inc.; *U.S. Private*, pg. 1289
ACTION FOR BOSTON COMMUNITY DEVELOPMENT, INC.; *U.S. Private*, pg. 67
ACTION FOR BRIDGEPORT COMMUNITY DEVELOPMENT, INC.; *U.S. Private*, pg. 67
ADVANCING NATIVE MISSIONS; *U.S. Private*, pg. 93
AEGIS THERAPIES—See Fillmore Capital Partners, LLC; *U.S. Private*, pg. 1506
AFRICARE; *U.S. Private*, pg. 124
AGRACE HOSPICECARE, INC.; *U.S. Private*, pg. 128
THE AGRICULTURAL & LABOR PROGRAM INC; *U.S. Private*, pg. 3983
AGUDATH ISREAL OF AMERICA COMMUNITY SERVICES INC; *U.S. Private*, pg. 130
A KID'S PLACE OF TAMPA BAY, INC.; *U.S. Private*, pg. 18
ALCOHOL & DRUG RECOVERY CENTERS, INC.; *U.S. Private*, pg. 154
ALTERNATIVE FAMILY SERVICES; *U.S. Private*, pg. 207
ALTERNATIVES, INC.; *U.S. Private*, pg. 208
ALVIS, INC.; *U.S. Private*, pg. 214
AMAZING GRACE OUTREACH MINISTRIES & US FOOD RESCUE INC; *U.S. Private*, pg. 216
AMERICAN ACTION NETWORK; *U.S. Private*, pg. 221
AMERICAN INTERNATIONAL HEALTH ALLIANCE; *U.S. Private*, pg. 238
AMERICAN LEARNING CORPORATION; *U.S. Private*, pg. 239

AMERICAN NICARAGUA FOUNDATION; *U.S. Private*, pg. 242
AMERICA'S CHARITIES; *U.S. Private*, pg. 221
APARTMENT LIFE; *U.S. Private*, pg. 290
A PLACE FOR MOM, INC.—See General Atlantic Service Company, L.P.; *U.S. Private*, pg. 1662
A PLACE FOR MOM, INC.—See Silver Lake Group, LLC; *U.S. Private*, pg. 3655
ARAPAHOE HOUSE; *U.S. Private*, pg. 307
ARGENTINE BETTERMENT CORPORATION; *U.S. Private*, pg. 320
ARUNDEL COMMUNITY DEVELOPMENT SERVICES, INC.; *U.S. Private*, pg. 344
THE ASIA FOUNDATION; *U.S. Private*, pg. 3989
ASOCIACION PUERTORRIQUENOS EN MARCHA FOR EVERYONE; *U.S. Private*, pg. 351
ASPENPOINTE; *U.S. Private*, pg. 352
ASPIRANET; *U.S. Private*, pg. 352
ASPIRE CHICAGO; *U.S. Private*, pg. 352
AUBERLE; *U.S. Private*, pg. 384
AUTISM SERVICES, INC.; *U.S. Private*, pg. 396
AVEDIS FOUNDATION; *U.S. Private*, pg. 405
BATON ROUGE AREA FOUNDATION; *U.S. Private*, pg. 487
BAY AREA COMMUNITY RESOURCES INC.; *U.S. Private*, pg. 491
BAY COVE HUMAN SERVICES, INC.; *U.S. Private*, pg. 492
BETHANY CHRISTIAN SERVICES; *U.S. Private*, pg. 545
BETHANY FOR CHILDREN & FAMILIES; *U.S. Private*, pg. 545
BETHESDA MINISTRIES; *U.S. Private*, pg. 546
BLACK FAMILY DEVELOPMENT, INC.; *U.S. Private*, pg. 572
BREVARD FAMILY PARTNERSHIP; *U.S. Private*, pg. 646
BRISTOL COMMUNITY ORGANIZATION, INC.—See Human Resources Agency of New Britain, Inc.; *U.S. Private*, pg. 2006
CAMPUS RESEARCH CORPORATION; *U.S. Private*, pg. 732
CAPITAL AREA COMMUNITY ACTION AGENCY, INC.; *U.S. Private*, pg. 738
CAPITAL AREA COMMUNITY SERVICES, INC.; *U.S. Private*, pg. 738
CAPITAL IMPACT PARTNERS; *U.S. Private*, pg. 740
CAPSTONE COMMUNITY ACTION; *U.S. Private*, pg. 746
CARE.COM EUROPE GMBH—See IAC Inc.; *U.S. Public*, pg. 1082
CARE.COM SWITZERLAND AG—See IAC Inc.; *U.S. Public*, pg. 1082
CARE DIMENSIONS; *U.S. Private*, pg. 751
CARELINK COMMUNITY SUPPORT SERVICES; *U.S. Private*, pg. 753
CARMEL CITY CENTER COMMUNITY DEVELOPMENT CORPORATION; *U.S. Private*, pg. 766
CARSON VALLEY CHILDREN'S AID; *U.S. Private*, pg. 774
CASA CENTRAL CORPORATION; *U.S. Private*, pg. 775
CASA PACIFICA CENTERS FOR CHILDREN & FAMILIES; *U.S. Private*, pg. 778
CATHOLIC CHARITIES COMMUNITY SERVICES; *U.S. Private*, pg. 788
CATHOLIC CHARITIES OF FAIRFIELD COUNTY INC.; *U.S. Private*, pg. 788
CATHOLIC CHARITIES OF SOUTHERN NEVADA; *U.S. Private*, pg. 788
CATHOLIC COMMUNITY SERVICES OF SOUTHERN ARIZONA, INC.; *U.S. Private*, pg. 788
CATHOLIC HOLY FAMILY SOCIETY; *U.S. Private*, pg. 792
CATHOLIC SOCIAL SERVICES; *U.S. Private*, pg. 792
CDS MONARCH, INC.; *U.S. Private*, pg. 803
C.E.F.S. ECONOMIC OPPORTUNITY CORPORATION; *U.S. Private*, pg. 706
CENTER FOR AMERICAN PROGRESS; *U.S. Private*, pg. 809
CENTER FOR PEOPLE IN NEED, INC.; *U.S. Private*, pg. 811
THE CENTERS FOR FAMILIES AND CHILDREN; *U.S. Private*, pg. 4006
CENTERS FOR YOUTH & FAMILIES, INC.; *U.S. Private*, pg. 817
CENTRAL CITY CONCERN; *U.S. Private*, pg. 819
CENTRAL INDIANA COMMUNITY FOUNDATION; *U.S. Private*, pg. 821
CENTRAL UNION MISSION; *U.S. Private*, pg. 825
CENTRAL WYOMING COUNSELING CENTER; *U.S. Private*, pg. 826
CENTRO DE SALUD DE LARES, INC.; *U.S. Private*, pg. 830
CHAMPIONS FOR CHILDREN, INC.; *U.S. Private*, pg. 847
CHARLOTTESVILLE AREA COMMUNITY FOUNDATION; *U.S. Private*, pg. 858
CHICAGOLAND ENTREPRENEURIAL CENTER; *U.S. Private*, pg. 879
THE CHICANO FEDERATION, INC.; *U.S. Private*, pg. 4008
CHICANOS POR LA CAUSA, INC.; *U.S. Private*, pg. 880
CHILD AND FAMILY GUIDANCE CENTER; *U.S. Private*, pg. 881
CHILD AND FAMILY SERVICES; *U.S. Private*, pg. 881
CHILD CARE LINKS; *U.S. Private*, pg. 881

CHILD & FAMILY; *U.S. Private*, pg. 881
CHILDREN AND FAMILIES FIRST DELAWARE INC; *U.S. Private*, pg. 883
CHILDREN'S AID & FAMILY SERVICES, INC.; *U.S. Private*, pg. 883
THE CHILDREN'S CLINIC, "SERVING CHILDREN AND THEIR FAMILIES"; *U.S. Private*, pg. 4008
CHILDREN'S HOME OF WYOMING CONFERENCE; *U.S. Private*, pg. 884
THE CHILDREN'S HOME SOCIETY OF NEW JERSEY; *U.S. Private*, pg. 4008
CHILDREN'S HOME SOCIETY OF SOUTH DAKOTA; *U.S. Private*, pg. 884
CHILDREN'S HOSPITALS AND CLINICS OF MINNESOTA; *U.S. Private*, pg. 885
CHOR YOUTH AND FAMILY SERVICES, INC.; *U.S. Private*, pg. 888
CITIZENS FOR CITIZENS, INC.; *U.S. Private*, pg. 903
CLEAN THE WORLD FOUNDATION, INC.; *U.S. Private*, pg. 931
COASTAL COMMUNITY FOUNDATION; *U.S. Private*, pg. 955
COASTAL ENTERPRISES, INC.; *U.S. Private*, pg. 956
COLORADO NONPROFIT DEVELOPMENT CENTER; *U.S. Private*, pg. 974
COLUMBUS DOWNTOWN DEVELOPMENT CORPORATION; *U.S. Private*, pg. 979
COMBINED JEWISH PHILANTHROPIES OF GREATER BOSTON, INC.; *U.S. Private*, pg. 980
COMMUNITIES FOR PEOPLE, INC.; *U.S. Private*, pg. 989
COMMUNITY AND ECONOMIC DEVELOPMENT ASSOCIATION OF COOK COUNTY, INCORPORATED; *U.S. Private*, pg. 989
COMMUNITY ASSOCIATIONS INSTITUTE; *U.S. Private*, pg. 989
COMMUNITY BASED SERVICES INC.; *U.S. Private*, pg. 990
COMMUNITY COUNCIL OF IDAHO, INC.; *U.S. Private*, pg. 991
COMMUNITY FIRST SOLUTIONS; *U.S. Private*, pg. 991
COMMUNITY FOUNDATION FOR GREATER BUFFALO; *U.S. Private*, pg. 992
COMMUNITY FOUNDATION FOR PALM BEACH AND MARTIN COUNTIES; *U.S. Private*, pg. 992
THE COMMUNITY FOUNDATION OF FREDERICK COUNTY, MD, INC; *U.S. Private*, pg. 4012
COMMUNITY FOUNDATION OF GREATER MEMPHIS; *U.S. Private*, pg. 992
COMMUNITY FOUNDATION OF KANKAKEE RIVER VALLEY; *U.S. Private*, pg. 992
COMMUNITY FOUNDATION OF NORTHERN COLORADO; *U.S. Private*, pg. 993
COMMUNITY FOUNDATION OF NORTHWEST CONNECTICUT, INC.; *U.S. Private*, pg. 993
COMMUNITY FOUNDATION OF WEST GEORGIA, INC.; *U.S. Private*, pg. 993
THE COMMUNITY FOUNDATION SERVING BOULDER COUNTY; *U.S. Private*, pg. 4012
COMMUNITY LIVING OPPORTUNITIES; *U.S. Private*, pg. 995
COMMUNITY OF CARING; *U.S. Private*, pg. 996
COMMUNITY OF HOPE; *U.S. Private*, pg. 996
COMMUNITY RENEWAL TEAM, INC.; *U.S. Private*, pg. 996
COMMUNITY SERVICE NETWORK INC; *U.S. Private*, pg. 997
COMMUNITY SERVICES AND EMPLOYMENT TRAINING, INC.; *U.S. Private*, pg. 997
COMMUNITY SPECIALISTS CORPORATION; *U.S. Private*, pg. 997
COMMUNITY SUPPORT SERVICES, INC.; *U.S. Private*, pg. 997
COMPREHENSIVE COMMUNITY ACTION PROGRAM; *U.S. Private*, pg. 1002
CONFERENCE ON JEWISH MATERIAL CLAIMS AGAINST GERMANY, INC.; *U.S. Private*, pg. 1013
CONNECTICUT COMMUNITY CARE, INC.; *U.S. Private*, pg. 1015
CONNECTICUT FOOD BANK INC.; *U.S. Private*, pg. 1016
THE CONNECTION, INC.; *U.S. Private*, pg. 4014
CONSULTANT CONNECT LIMITED—See Teladoc Health, Inc.; *U.S. Public*, pg. 1992
CONTINUUM OF CARE, INC.; *U.S. Private*, pg. 1031
CORPORATION TO DEVELOP COMMUNITIES OF TAMPA, INC.; *U.S. Private*, pg. 1058
COUNCIL ON RURAL SERVICES; *U.S. Private*, pg. 1065
CREATIVE ALTERNATIVES, INC.; *U.S. Private*, pg. 1087
CROSSROADS YOUTH & FAMILY SERVICES, INC.; *U.S. Private*, pg. 1108
DAYSPRING INTERNATIONAL; *U.S. Private*, pg. 1177
DEFY VENTURES INC.; *U.S. Private*, pg. 1191
DELLA LAMB COMMUNITY SERVICES; *U.S. Private*, pg. 1197
EAC NETWORK; *U.S. Private*, pg. 1308
EAST BALTIMORE DEVELOPMENT INC.; *U.S. Private*, pg. 1315
EAST BAY COMMUNITY FOUNDATION; *U.S. Private*, pg. 1315
EAST BAY INTEGRATED CARE; *U.S. Private*, pg. 1315

624190 — OTHER INDIVIDUAL AN...

EAST LAKE FOUNDATION; *U.S. Private*, pg. 1316
EAST TEXAS SUPPORT SERVICES, INC.; *U.S. Private*, pg. 1318
ECONOMIC OPPORTUNITY AUTHORITY FOR SAVANNAH-CHATHAM COUNTY, INC.; *U.S. Private*, pg.1330
EDWIN GOULD SERVICES FOR CHILDREN AND FAMILIES; *U.S. Private*, pg. 1342
EIGHT NORTHERN INDIAN PUEBLOS COUNCIL, INC.; *U.S. Private*, pg. 1347
THE EMBARRAS RIVER BASIN AGENCY, INC.; *U.S. Private*, pg. 4025
EMPIRE STATE RELIEF FUND; *U.S. Private*, pg. 1386
EMPLOYEE & FAMILY RESOURCES INC.; *U.S. Private*, pg. 1386
EPG COMMUNICATION HOLDINGS LIMITED—See IQVIA Holdings Inc.; *U.S. Public*, pg. 1168
EPISCOPAL COMMUNITIES & SERVICES; *U.S. Private*, pg. 1413
EPISCOPAL RELIEF & DEVELOPMENT; *U.S. Private*, pg. 1413
ESCAMBIA COUNTY SCHOOL READINESS COALITION, INC.; *U.S. Private*, pg. 1424
EUROPEAN AMERICAN ASSOCIATION; *U.S. Private*, pg. 1434
FAMILJEHEMSBANKEN AB—See Byggfakta Group Nordic HoldCo AB; *Int'l*, pg. 1234
FAMILY CENTERS, INC.; *U.S. Private*, pg. 1469
FAMILY & CHILDREN'S ASSOCIATION; *U.S. Private*, pg. 1468
FAMILY & CHILDREN'S CENTER; *U.S. Private*, pg. 1468
FAMILY & COMMUNITY SERVICES, INC.; *U.S. Private*, pg. 1468
THE FAMILY CONSERVANCY; *U.S. Private*, pg. 4027
FAMILY FOCUS, INC.; *U.S. Private*, pg. 1470
FAMILYLINKS; *U.S. Private*, pg. 1471
FAMILY RESEARCH COUNCIL; *U.S. Private*, pg. 1471
FAMILY SERVICE ASSOCIATION; *U.S. Private*, pg. 1471
FAMILY SERVICE OF RHODE ISLAND, INC.; *U.S. Private*, pg. 1471
FAMILY SERVICES OF WESTCHESTER; *U.S. Private*, pg. 1471
FEDERATION OF ORGANIZATIONS; *U.S. Private*, pg. 1492
FIRETREE, LTD.; *U.S. Private*, pg. 1512
FIVE ACRES - THE BOYS' AND GIRLS' AID SOCIETY OF LOS ANGELES COUNTY; *U.S. Private*, pg. 1537
FLEXSTEEL RIVERSIDE DIVISION—See Flexsteel Industries, Inc.; *U.S. Public*, pg. 853
FOCUS IN CHINUCH INC.; *U.S. Private*, pg. 1556
THE FORTUNE SOCIETY; *U.S. Private*, pg. 4030
FRANKLIN/GLENBURN HOME, INC.; *U.S. Private*, pg. 1598
FRED FINCH YOUTH CENTER; *U.S. Private*, pg. 1600
FRESNO ECONOMIC OPPORTUNITIES COMMISSION; *U.S. Private*, pg. 1610
FUNDACION PARA EL DESAROLLO DEL HOGAR PROPIO, INC; *U.S. Private*, pg. 1622
GATEWAY-LONGVIEW, INC.; *U.S. Private*, pg. 1651
GATEWAY REHABILITATION CENTER; *U.S. Private*, pg. 1651
GENERATIONS FAMILY HEALTH CENTER, INC.; *U.S. Private*, pg. 1668
GILEAD COMMUNITY SERVICES, INC.; *U.S. Private*, pg. 1699
GOLDEN GATE REGIONAL CENTER INC.; *U.S. Private*, pg. 1732
GOOD SHEPHERD SERVICES; *U.S. Private*, pg. 1738
GREATER LAWRENCE COMMUNITY ACTION COUNCIL, INC.; *U.S. Private*, pg. 1769
GRIST MAGAZINE, INC.; *U.S. Private*, pg. 1790
GULF COAST SOCIAL SERVICES; *U.S. Private*, pg. 1815
HANAC, INC.; *U.S. Private*, pg. 1852
HARBOR CORP.; *U.S. Private*, pg. 1858
HARBOR-UCLA FACULTY PRACTICE PLAN, A MEDICAL GROUP, INC.—See Harbor-UCLA Medical Foundation, Inc.; *U.S. Private*, pg. 1859
HARLEM CHILDREN'S ZONE, INC.; *U.S. Private*, pg. 1865
HARRISTOWN DEVELOPMENT CORPORATION; *U.S. Private*, pg. 1871
HCS HEAD START, INC.; *U.S. Private*, pg. 1890
HEALTHWELL FOUNDATION; *U.S. Private*, pg. 1898
HENRY LEE WILLIS COMMUNITY CENTER INC; *U.S. Private*, pg. 1918
H.E.R.O.E.S. CARE; *U.S. Private*, pg. 1826
THE H GROUP; *U.S. Private*, pg. 4040
HIAS INC.; *U.S. Private*, pg. 1932
HIGHBRIDGE ADVISORY COUNCIL FAMILY SERVICES, INC.; *U.S. Private*, pg. 1937
HIGHLANDS RANCH COMMUNITY ASSOCIATION, INC.; *U.S. Private*, pg. 1940
HILL COUNTRY COMMUNITY ACTION ASSOCIATION, INC.; *U.S. Private*, pg. 1945
HINDS COUNTY HUMAN RESOURCE AGENCY; *U.S. Private*, pg. 1948
HOCKING ATHENS PERRY COMMUNITY ACTION; *U.S. Private*, pg. 1959
HOLSTON UNITED METHODIST HOME FOR CHILDREN; *U.S. Private*, pg. 1968
HOMECARE & HOSPICE OF THE VALLEY; *U.S. Private*, pg. 1973
HOME INSTRUCTION FOR PARENTS OF PRESCHOOL YOUNGSTERS (HIPPY); *U.S. Private*, pg. 1971
HOPE OF LIFE INTERNATIONAL; *U.S. Private*, pg. 1979
HOPE WORLDWIDE, LTD.; *U.S. Private*, pg. 1979
HOSPICE & COMMUNITY CARE; *U.S. Private*, pg. 1985
HOSPICE OF THE PIEDMONT; *U.S. Private*, pg. 1986
HUMANA ASSISTANS AB—See Humana AB; *Int'l*, pg. 3530
HUMANAN KALLIO OY—See Humana AB; *Int'l*, pg. 3530
HUMAN ARC CORPORATION—See ABRY Partners, LLC; *U.S. Private*, pg. 41
HUMAN CARE BO AS—See Humana AB; *Int'l*, pg. 3530
HUMAN CARE HOLDING AS—See Humana AB; *Int'l*, pg. 3530
HUMANKIND; *U.S. Private*, pg. 2006
HUMAN RESOURCES AGENCY OF NEW BRITAIN, INC.; *U.S. Private*, pg. 2006
ILOVE GMBH—See freenet AG; *Int'l*, pg. 2770
INDIANHEAD COMMUNITY ACTION AGENCY, INC.; *U.S. Private*, pg. 2063
INDTAI INC.; *U.S. Private*, pg. 2064
INSPIRE DEVELOPMENT CENTERS; *U.S. Private*, pg. 2092
INTER-LAKES COMMUNITY ACTION PARTNERSHIP; *U.S. Private*, pg. 2107
INTERNATIONAL CITY/COUNTY MANAGEMENT ASSOCIATION; *U.S. Private*, pg. 2115
INTERNATIONAL HOUSE PHILADELPHIA; *U.S. Private*, pg. 2117
INTERNATIONAL LONGSHOREMEN'S ASSOCIATION, AFL-CIO; *U.S. Private*, pg. 2118
INTERNATIONAL PARTNERSHIP FOR HUMAN DEVELOPMENT; *U.S. Private*, pg. 2119
INTERNATIONAL RESCUE COMMITTEE, INC.; *U.S. Private*, pg. 2119
INTERNATIONAL RESEARCH AND EXCHANGES BOARD; *U.S. Private*, pg. 2120
JEWISH CHILD & FAMILY SERVICES; *U.S. Private*, pg. 2205
JEWISH COMMUNITY CENTER OF SAN FRANCISCO; *U.S. Private*, pg. 2205
JEWISH COMMUNITY CENTERS OF GREATER BOSTON, INC.; *U.S. Private*, pg. 2205
JEWISH COMMUNITY SERVICES; *U.S. Private*, pg. 2205
JEWISH FAMILY AND CHILDREN'S SERVICES OF SAN FRANCISCO, THE PENINSULA, MARIN AND SONOMA COUNTIES; *U.S. Private*, pg. 2205
JEWISH FAMILY & CHILDREN'S SERVICE; *U.S. Private*, pg. 2205
JEWISH FAMILY SERVICE OF LOS ANGELES; *U.S. Private*, pg. 2205
JOHN H. BONER COMMUNITY CENTER; *U.S. Private*, pg. 2222
J/P HAITIAN RELIEF ORGANIZATION; *U.S. Private*, pg. 2172
JULIA DYCKMAN ANDRUS MEMORIAL, INC.; *U.S. Private*, pg. 2243
JUSTICE RESOURCE INSTITUTE INC; *U.S. Private*, pg. 2246
KANSAS MASONIC HOME; *U.S. Private*, pg. 2261
KATZMAN FAMILY SUPPORT FOUNDATION; *U.S. Private*, pg. 2265
KCEOC COMMUNITY ACTION PARTNERSHIP, INC.; *U.S. Private*, pg. 2269
KEY PROGRAM INCORPORATED; *U.S. Private*, pg. 2293
KIAWAH ISLAND COMMUNITY ASSOCIATION, INC.; *U.S. Private*, pg. 2302
KIDZMATTER INC.; *U.S. Private*, pg. 2303
KINGS COMMUNITY ACTION ORGANIZATION; *U.S. Private*, pg. 2311
THE KINTOCK GROUP; *U.S. Private*, pg. 4065
LADERA RANCH MAINTENANCE CORP.; *U.S. Private*, pg. 2372
LAKEMARY CENTER INC.; *U.S. Private*, pg. 2376
LAKESHORE ESTATES INC; *U.S. Private*, pg. 2377
LAKEWOOD RESOURCE & REFERRAL CENTER; *U.S. Private*, pg. 2379
LA PALOMA TREATMENT CENTER, LLC—See Universal Health Services, Inc.; *U.S. Public*, pg. 2258
LASTENSUOJELUYKSIKKO PIHAKOIVU OY—See Humana AB; *Int'l*, pg. 3530
LEADING THE WAY WITH DR. MICHAEL YOUSSEF; *U.S. Private*, pg. 2406
LIBERTY RESOURCES, INC.; *U.S. Private*, pg. 2447
L.I. CHILD & FAMILY DEVELOPMENT SERVICES, INC.; *U.S. Private*, pg. 2366
LIFE FOR RELIEF & DEVELOPMENT; *U.S. Private*, pg. 2448
LIFESPAN, INC.—See Community First Solutions; *U.S. Private*, pg. 991
LIFEWORKS NW; *U.S. Private*, pg. 2452
LOGAN COMMUNITY RESOURCES, INC.; *U.S. Private*, pg. 2480
LOWELL COMMUNITY HEALTH CENTER, INC.; *U.S. Private*, pg. 2505
LUK CRISIS CENTER, INC.; *U.S. Private*, pg. 2512
LUK, INC.; *U.S. Private*, pg. 2512
LUTHERAN FAMILY SERVICES OF VIRGINIA, INC.; *U.S. Private*, pg. 2517
LYNN ECONOMIC OPPORTUNITY, INC.; *U.S. Private*, pg. 2521
MAGELLAN HEALTH SERVICES—See Centene Corporation; *U.S. Public*, pg. 469
MANIILAQ ASSOCIATION; *U.S. Private*, pg. 2564
MARTHA'S TABLE; *U.S. Private*, pg. 2594
MARYHAVEN CENTER OF HOPE—See Catholic Health Services of Long Island; *U.S. Private*, pg. 791
MASTERS MANNA INC.; *U.S. Private*, pg. 2608
MATTER; *U.S. Private*, pg. 2613
MEDIQ MEDISOURCE B.V.—See Advent International Corporation; *U.S. Private*, pg. 104
MEDSANA SRL—See Athens Medical Centers SA; *Int'l*, pg. 670
THE MENTOR NETWORK; *U.S. Private*, pg. 4078
MERAGE JEWISH COMMUNITY CENTER OF ORANGE COUNTY; *U.S. Private*, pg. 2668
MERCY MARICOPA INTEGRATED CARE; *U.S. Private*, pg. 2671
METROPOLITAN COMMITTEE ON ANTI-POVERTY OF SAN DIEGO COUNTY, INC.; *U.S. Private*, pg. 2687
MEXICAN AMERICAN OPPORTUNITY FOUNDATION; *U.S. Private*, pg. 2692
THE MICHAEL-ANN RUSSELL JEWISH COMMUNITY CENTER; *U.S. Private*, pg. 4079
MICHIGAN COMMUNITY ACTION AGENCY ASSOCIATION; *U.S. Private*, pg. 2700
MICHIGAN FAMILY RESOURCES; *U.S. Private*, pg. 2700
MID-COLUMBIA MEDICAL CENTER; *U.S. Private*, pg. 2707
MID-VALLEY COMMUNITY ACTION AGENCY; *U.S. Private*, pg. 2709
MIDVALLEY HEALTHCARE; *U.S. Private*, pg. 2718
MIDWEST CENTER FOR STRESS & ANXIETY, LLC—See Transom Capital Group, LLC; *U.S. Private*, pg. 4209
MONTACHUSETT OPPORTUNITY COUNCIL, INC.; *U.S. Private*, pg. 2774
MULTI SERVICE CENTER; *U.S. Private*, pg. 2812
NATIONAL ASSOCIATION OF COUNTY AND CITY HEALTH OFFICIALS; *U.S. Private*, pg. 2846
NATIONAL COMMUNITY REINVESTMENT COALITION, INC.; *U.S. Private*, pg. 2851
NATIONAL CONGRESS OF PARENTS AND TEACHERS; *U.S. Private*, pg. 2851
NATIONAL EMPLOYEE ASSISTANCE SERVICES INC.—See ProHealth Care, Inc.; *U.S. Private*, pg. 3280
NATIONAL SLOVAK SOCIETY; *U.S. Private*, pg. 2863
NATIONAL YOUTH ADVOCATE PROGRAM; *U.S. Private*, pg. 2865
NAVIHEALTH, INC.—See Cardinal Health, Inc.; *U.S. Public*, pg. 434
NEBRASKA FAMILIES COLLABORATIVE; *U.S. Private*, pg. 2878
NECCO; *U.S. Private*, pg. 2879
NEIGHBORHOOD VISITING NURSE ASSOCIATION; *U.S. Private*, pg. 2881
NEIGHBORIMPACT; *U.S. Private*, pg. 2881
NEIGHBORS IN NEED OF SERVICES, INC.; *U.S. Private*, pg. 2881
NEUMANN FAMILY SERVICES; *U.S. Private*, pg. 2890
NEVINS FAMILY OF SERVICES; *U.S. Private*, pg. 2891
NEW CHARLOTTE CORPORATION; *U.S. Private*, pg. 2893
NEW DIRECTIONS COUNSELING SERVICES, LLC—See NorthEast Health Services, LLC; *U.S. Private*, pg. 2950
NEW ENGLAND FARM WORKERS COUNCIL INC.; *U.S. Private*, pg. 2894
NEW HOPE COMMUNITY, INC.; *U.S. Private*, pg. 2897
NEW HOPE COUNSELING—See Crystal Cathedral Ministries Inc.; *U.S. Private*, pg. 1115
NEW MOMS, INC.—See Parenthesis, Inc.; *U.S. Private*, pg. 3094
NHS HUMAN SERVICES, INC.; *U.S. Private*, pg. 2924
NINTH DISTRICT OPPORTUNITY, INC.; *U.S. Private*, pg. 2928
NORTH COAST OPPORTUNITIES, INC.; *U.S. Private*, pg. 2944
NORTHEAST MICHIGAN COMMUNITY SERVICE AGENCY, INC.; *U.S. Private*, pg. 2950
NORTHEAST PARENT & CHILD SOCIETY, INC.; *U.S. Private*, pg. 2951
NORTHWEST NEW JERSEY COMMUNITY ACTION PROGRAM; *U.S. Private*, pg. 2961
OHIOGUIDESTONE; *U.S. Private*, pg. 3005
OORAH, INC.; *U.S. Private*, pg. 3028
OPERATION PAR, INC.; *U.S. Private*, pg. 3032
OPERATION THRESHOLD; *U.S. Private*, pg. 3032
OPPORTUNITIES INDUSTRIALIZATION CENTERS INTERNATIONAL; *U.S. Private*, pg. 3033
THE OPPORTUNITY ALLIANCE; *U.S. Private*, pg. 4088
OPPORTUNITY INTERNATIONAL, INC.; *U.S. Private*, pg. 3033
OPTIONS FOR COMMUNITY LIVING, INC.; *U.S. Private*, pg. 3035

N.A.I.C.S. INDEX

624210 — COMMUNITY FOOD SERV...

ORANGE COUNTY HEAD START, INC.; *U.S. Private*, pg. 3037
THE OSBORNE ASSOCIATION, INC.; *U.S. Private*, pg. 4089
OUR CITY READING; *U.S. Private*, pg. 3050
OUR KIDS OF MIAMI-DADE/MONROE, INC.; *U.S. Private*, pg. 3050
PACES, INC.; *U.S. Private*, pg. 3064
PACIFIC SOUTHWEST COMMUNITY DEVELOPMENT CORPORATION; *U.S. Private*, pg. 3070
PACT; *U.S. Private*, pg. 3073
PALLADIA, INC.; *U.S. Private*, pg. 3077
PANHANDLE COMMUNITY SERVICES; *U.S. Private*, pg. 3086
PARTNERSHIP FOR CHILDREN OF CUMBERLAND COUNTY, INC.; *U.S. Private*, pg. 3103
PARTNERSHIP FOR STRONG FAMILIES, INC.; *U.S. Private*, pg. 3103
PATHSTONE CORPORATION; *U.S. Private*, pg. 3106
PATHWAYS HEALTH AND COMMUNITY SUPPORT LLC—See ATAR Capital, LLC; *U.S. Private*, pg. 364
PEARL RIVER VALLEY OPPORTUNITY, INC.; *U.S. Private*, pg. 3125
PEOPLE'S EQUAL ACTION AND COMMUNITY EFFORT, INC.; *U.S. Private*, pg. 3141
THE PHILADELPHIA FOUNDATION; *U.S. Private*, pg. 4094
PHILADELPHIA PARENT CHILD CENTER; *U.S. Private*, pg. 3169
PINELLAS OPPORTUNITY COUNCIL INC; *U.S. Private*, pg. 3183
THE PINES AT DAVIDSON; *U.S. Private*, pg. 4095
PINNACLE SERVICES, INC.; *U.S. Private*, pg. 3185
PIONEER CENTER FOR HUMAN SERVICES; *U.S. Private*, pg. 3186
THE PLANNING COUNCIL; *U.S. Private*, pg. 4096
PORTER-LEATH; *U.S. Private*, pg. 3232
PRESENCELEARNING, INC.—See Genstar Capital, LLC; *U.S. Private*, pg. 1679
PRO ACTION OF STEUBEN & YATES, INC.; *U.S. Private*, pg. 3269
PROJECT FOR PRIDE IN LIVING, INC.; *U.S. Private*, pg. 3280
PROJECT NOW, INC.; *U.S. Private*, pg. 3280
PROXIMITY DESIGN; *U.S. Private*, pg. 3295
PSCH, INC.; *U.S. Private*, pg. 3297
PUBLIC INTEREST REGISTRY; *U.S. Private*, pg. 3299
PUERTO RICAN ACTION BOARD; *U.S. Private*, pg. 3302
PUERTO RICAN FAMILY INSTITUTE, INC.; *U.S. Private*, pg. 3302
QUAD AREA COMMUNITY ACTION AGENCY INC.; *U.S. Private*, pg. 3314
REACH COMMUNITY DEVELOPMENT, INC.; *U.S. Private*, pg. 3365
REBUILD NORTHWEST FLORIDA, INC.; *U.S. Private*, pg. 3370
RELIEF INTERNATIONAL; *U.S. Private*, pg. 3395
RESTORE NEIGHBORHOODS LA, INC.; *U.S. Private*, pg. 3410
RETAIL IN MOTION MEXICO S. DE R.L. DE C.V.—See Deutsche Lufthansa AG; *Int'l*, pg. 2070
RIVERSIDE COMMUNITY CARE, INC.; *U.S. Private*, pg. 3445
ROCKY MOUNTAIN DEVELOPMENT COUNCIL; *U.S. Private*, pg. 3468
RS EDEN; *U.S. Private*, pg. 3496
SACRAMENTO REGION COMMUNITY FOUNDATION; *U.S. Private*, pg. 3522
SACRED HEART COMMUNITY SERVICE; *U.S. Private*, pg. 3522
SAFEKONT GMBH—See E.ON SE; *Int'l*, pg. 2259
SCO FAMILY OF SERVICES; *U.S. Private*, pg. 3574
SCRANTON-LACKAWANNA HUMAN DEVELOPMENT AGENCY, INC.; *U.S. Private*, pg. 3579
SEAMEN'S SOCIETY FOR CHILDREN AND FAMILIES; *U.S. Private*, pg. 3585
SELF HELP, INC.; *U.S. Private*, pg. 3602
SELF STORAGE GROUP ASA—See Teachers Insurance Association - College Retirement Fund; *U.S. Private*, pg. 3945
SENECA FAMILY OF AGENCIES; *U.S. Private*, pg. 3606
SEQUEL YOUTH AND FAMILY SERVICES, LLC; *U.S. Private*, pg. 3612
SERVICES FOR THE UNDERSERVED, INC.; *U.S. Private*, pg. 3616
SERVICES TO ENHANCE POTENTIAL; *U.S. Private*, pg. 3616
SEVEN HILLS FOUNDATION; *U.S. Private*, pg. 3618
SHAKLEE RESEARCH CENTER—See Activated Holdings LLC; *U.S. Private*, pg. 69
SHAKLEE RESEARCH CENTER—See Ripplewood Holdings LLC; *U.S. Private*, pg. 3439
SHALOM PARK; *U.S. Private*, pg. 3623
SHIELDS FOR FAMILIES, INC.; *U.S. Private*, pg. 3636
SHORE UP! INC.; *U.S. Private*, pg. 3641
SKIP-A-LONG FAMILY AND COMMUNITY SERVICES; *U.S. Private*, pg. 3682
SOLANO COUNTY COMMUNITY HOUSING CORPORATION; *U.S. Private*, pg. 3706

SOLES4SOULS; *U.S. Private*, pg. 3709
SOUTH CENTRAL HUMAN RESOURCE AGENCY; *U.S. Private*, pg. 3721
SOUTH DELTA PLANNING & DEVELOPMENT DISTRICT, INC.; *U.S. Private*, pg. 3722
SOUTHEAST BRONX NEIGHBORHOOD CENTERS, INC.; *U.S. Private*, pg. 3725
SOUTHERN MARYLAND TRI-COUNTY COMMUNITY ACTION COMMITTEE, INC.; *U.S. Private*, pg. 3733
SOUTH PUGET INTERTRIBAL PLANNING AGENCY; *U.S. Private*, pg. 3723
SOUTH SHORE COMMUNITY ACTION COUNCIL, INC.; *U.S. Private*, pg. 3723
SOUTHWESTERN COMMUNITY SERVICES, INC.; *U.S. Private*, pg. 3741
SOUTHWEST GEORGIA COMMUNITY ACTION COUNCIL, INC.; *U.S. Private*, pg. 3739
SOUTHWEST KEY PROGRAMS; *U.S. Private*, pg. 3739
SPECIAL SERVICE FOR GROUPS; *U.S. Private*, pg. 3748
SPRINGFIELD URBAN LEAGUE, INC.; *U.S. Private*, pg. 3764
THE STARFISH FOUNDATION; *U.S. Private*, pg. 4121
START TREATMENT & RECOVERY CENTERS; *U.S. Private*, pg. 3788
ST.NICKS ALLIANCE; *U.S. Private*, pg. 3774
THE ST. PETERSBURG FREE CLINIC, INC.; *U.S. Private*, pg. 4120
STRATEGIC CRISIS ADVISORS LLC—See AIP, LLC; *U.S. Private*, pg. 137
ST. VINCENT DE PAUL SOCIETY OF LANE COUNTY, INC.; *U.S. Private*, pg. 3773
ST. VINCENT DE PAUL VILLAGE, INC.; *U.S. Private*, pg. 3773
SUCCESS 4 KIDS & FAMILIES, INC.; *U.S. Private*, pg. 3848
SUMMIT BHC SEVIERVILLE, LLC—See FFL Partners, LLC; *U.S. Private*, pg. 1500
SUMMIT BHC SEVIERVILLE, LLC—See Lee Equity Partners LLC; *U.S. Private*, pg. 2412
SUNBELT HEALTH AND REHAB CENTER APOPKA; *U.S. Private*, pg. 3865
SUNCOAST CENTER INC; *U.S. Private*, pg. 3865
SUPREME COUNCIL OF THE ROYAL ARCANUM; *U.S. Private*, pg. 3882
SWLA CENTER FOR HEALTH SERVICES, INC.; *U.S. Private*, pg. 3895
TALBERT HOUSE; *U.S. Private*, pg. 3925
TENDER LOVING CARE OF DULUTH—See Centerbridge Partners, L.P.; *U.S. Private*, pg. 814
TIDES; *U.S. Private*, pg. 4168
THE TODAY SHOW CHARITABLE FOUNDATION INC.; *U.S. Private*, pg. 4127
TOTAL COMMUNITY ACTION, INC.; *U.S. Private*, pg. 4190
TRAINING AND RESEARCH FOUNDATION; *U.S. Private*, pg. 4204
TRANSITIONAL FAMILY SERVICES, INC.—See ATAR Capital, LLC; *U.S. Private*, pg. 365
TRANSITION HOUSE; *U.S. Private*, pg. 4208
TRI COUNTY COMMUNITY ACTION AGENCY, INC.; *U.S. Private*, pg. 4220
TRILLIUM FAMILY SERVICES; *U.S. Private*, pg. 4231
TWIN OAKS COMMUNITY SERVICES INC.; *U.S. Private*, pg. 4265
UNITED COMMUNITY ACTION NETWORK; *U.S. Private*, pg. 4289
UNITED COMMUNITY CENTER, INC.; *U.S. Private*, pg. 4290
UNITED METHODIST FAMILY SERVICES OF VIRGINIA, INC.; *U.S. Private*, pg. 4294
UNITED MIGRANT OPPORTUNITY SERVICES, INC.; *U.S. Private*, pg. 4294
UNITED MUSLIM RELIEF; *U.S. Private*, pg. 4294
UNITED PLANNING ORGANIZATION; *U.S. Private*, pg. 4295
UNITY HOUSE OF TROY, INC.; *U.S. Private*, pg. 4303
UNIVERSITY AREA COMMUNITY DEVELOPMENT CORPORATION, INC.; *U.S. Private*, pg. 4307
UPCAP SERVICES, INC.; *U.S. Private*, pg. 4311
UPPER DES MOINES OPPORTUNITY, INC.; *U.S. Private*, pg. 4312
UPPER EAST TENNESSEE HUMAN DEVELOPMENT AGENCY, INC.; *U.S. Private*, pg. 4312
UPSTATE CEREBRAL PALSY; *U.S. Private*, pg. 4313
URBAN HABITAT; *U.S. Private*, pg. 4314
U.S. GREEN BUILDING COUNCIL, INC.; *U.S. Private*, pg. 4270
U.S. NATIONAL WHITEWATER CENTER, INC.; *U.S. Private*, pg. 4271
VALLEY HOSPICE, INC.; *U.S. Private*, pg. 4334
VALLEY VISTA CARE CORPORATION; *U.S. Private*, pg. 4336
VANDERHEYDEN HALL, INC.; *U.S. Private*, pg. 4343
VANTAGE AGING; *U.S. Private*, pg. 4344
THE VERMONT COMMUNITY FOUNDATION; *U.S. Private*, pg. 4130
VILLA ESPERANZA SERVICES; *U.S. Private*, pg. 4383
VILLAGE FAMILY SERVICE CENTER; *U.S. Private*, pg. 4383
THE VILLAGE FAMILY SERVICES; *U.S. Private*, pg. 4131

THE VILLAGE FOR FAMILIES & CHILDREN, INC.; *U.S. Private*, pg. 4131
THE VILLAGES; *U.S. Private*, pg. 4131
WAYSIDE YOUTH & FAMILY SUPPORT NETWORK; *U.S. Private*, pg. 4460
THE WAY TO HAPPINESS FOUNDATION INTERNATIONAL; *U.S. Private*, pg. 4134
WELLNESS NETWORKS INC; *U.S. Private*, pg. 4476
WELLPOINT IOWA, INC.—See Elevance Health, Inc.; *U.S. Public*, pg. 730
WESLEY SPECTRUM SERVICES; *U.S. Private*, pg. 4483
WEST CENTRAL MISSOURI COMMUNITY ACTION AGENCY; *U.S. Private*, pg. 4484
WESTCHESTER COUNTY ASSOCIATION, INC.—See Hudson Valley Economic Development Corporation; *U.S. Private*, pg. 2002
WESTERN CAROLINA COMMUNITY ACTION, INC.; *U.S. Private*, pg. 4491
WESTERN PIEDMONT COUNCIL OF GOVERNMENTS; *U.S. Private*, pg. 4495
WFD CONSULTING, INC.; *U.S. Private*, pg. 4503
WHEELER CLINIC, INC.; *U.S. Private*, pg. 4505
WISBY ASSISTANS AB—See Humana AB; *Int'l*, pg. 3530
WOMEN'S HOUSING & ECONOMIC DEVELOPMENT CORPORATION; *U.S. Private*, pg. 4556
YAMHILL COMMUNITY CARE ORGANIZATION; *U.S. Private*, pg. 4585
YELED V'YALDA EARLY CHILDHOOD CENTER INC; *U.S. Private*, pg. 4587
YORK COUNTY COMMUNITY ACTION CORPORATION; *U.S. Private*, pg. 4590
YOUTH OPPORTUNITIES UPHELD, INC.—See Seven Hills Foundation; *U.S. Private*, pg. 3618

624210 — COMMUNITY FOOD SERVICES

ALAMEDA COUNTY COMMUNITY FOOD BANK; *U.S. Private*, pg. 149
THE ANDERSONS CANADA LIMITED—See The Andersons Incorporated; *U.S. Public*, pg. 2034
ARKANSAS RICE DEPOT, INC.; *U.S. Private*, pg. 326
BIOGAIA AB; *Int'l*, pg. 1037
BLUE APRON HOLDINGS, INC.—See Wonder Group, Inc.; *U.S. Private*, pg. 4556
BONDUELLE EUROPE LONG LIFE SAS—See Bonduelle SAS; *Int'l*, pg. 1106
BONDUELLE NORTHERN EUROPE NV—See Bonduelle SAS; *Int'l*, pg. 1106
BONDUELLE USA INC.—See Bonduelle SAS; *Int'l*, pg. 1106
CALIFORNIA EMERGENCY FOODLINK; *U.S. Private*, pg. 719
CAPITAL AREA FOOD BANK; *U.S. Private*, pg. 738
CHATTANOOGA AREA FOOD BANK; *U.S. Private*, pg. 868
CHEFMOD LLC—See Ark Restaurants Corp.; *U.S. Public*, pg. 193
CHILDREN'S HUNGER FUND; *U.S. Private*, pg. 885
CHOICELUNCH; *U.S. Private*, pg. 888
CITYMEALS-ON-WHEELS; *U.S. Private*, pg. 907
COMMUNITY CENTER OF NORTHERN WESTCHESTER; *U.S. Private*, pg. 990
COMMUNITY FOOD BANK OF EASTERN OKLAHOMA, INC.; *U.S. Private*, pg. 991
COMMUNITY HARVEST FOOD BANK OF NORTHEAST INDIANA, INC.; *U.S. Private*, pg. 993
COMPASS GROUP HONG KONG LTD.—See Compass Group PLC; *Int'l*, pg. 1750
CONVOY OF HOPE, INC.; *U.S. Private*, pg. 1036
EDESIA INC.; *U.S. Private*, pg. 1333
EMERGENCY FOOD NETWORK; *U.S. Private*, pg. 1380
EMPAKK AS—See Christian Berner Tech Trade AB; *Int'l*, pg. 1586
FEED AMERICA FIRST; *U.S. Private*, pg. 1492
FEEDING SOUTH FLORIDA; *U.S. Private*, pg. 1492
FOOD BANK OF CONTRA COSTA AND SOLANO; *U.S. Private*, pg. 1560
THE FOOD BANK OF NORTHEAST GEORGIA; *U.S. Private*, pg. 4029
FOOD BANK OF SAN LUIS OBISPO COUNTY; *U.S. Private*, pg. 1560
FOODBANK OF SOUTHEASTERN VIRGINIA AND THE EASTERN SHORE; *U.S. Private*, pg. 1561
FOOD BANK OF THE ROCKIES; *U.S. Private*, pg. 1560
THE FOOD BANK OF WESTERN MASSACHUSETTS; *U.S. Private*, pg. 4029
FOOD EXPORT ASSOCIATION OF THE MIDWEST USA; *U.S. Private*, pg. 1560
FOOD FOR LANE COUNTY; *U.S. Private*, pg. 1560
FOOD FOR THE POOR, INC.; *U.S. Private*, pg. 1560
FOOD OPPORTUNITIES ORGANIZATION &. DISTRIBUTION INC.; *U.S. Private*, pg. 1561
FORGOTTEN HARVEST, INC.; *U.S. Private*, pg. 1568
GLOBAL HUNGER PROJECT; *U.S. Private*, pg. 1714
GLYNWOOD CENTER, INC.; *U.S. Private*, pg. 1721
GOLDEN HARVEST FOOD BANK; *U.S. Private*, pg. 1732
GREATER BATON ROUGE FOOD BANK; *U.S. Private*, pg. 1769
GREATER BERKS FOOD BANK; *U.S. Private*, pg. 1769

624210 — COMMUNITY FOOD SERV...

GREATER CHICAGO FOOD DEPOSITORY; *U.S. Private*, pg. 1769
HARVESTERS - THE COMMUNITY FOOD NETWORK; *U.S. Private*, pg. 1877
THE HAWAII FOODBANK; *U.S. Private*, pg. 4043
HELPING HAND FOR RELIEF & DEVELOPMENT; *U.S. Private*, pg. 1912
INSTITUTE OF FOOD TECHNOLOGISTS; *U.S. Private*, pg. 2093
INTERNATIONAL FOOD POLICY RESEARCH INSTITUTE; *U.S. Private*, pg. 2116
ISLAMIC FOOD AND NUTRITION COUNCIL OF AMERICA; *U.S. Private*, pg. 2144
LEJI INTERMEDIACAO S.A.—See Companhia Brasileira de Distribuicao; *Int'l*, pg. 1746
LOWCOUNTRY FOOD BANK INC.; *U.S. Private*, pg. 2504
MARION-POLK FOOD SHARE; *U.S. Private*, pg. 2576
MIDWEST FOOD BANK; *U.S. Private*, pg. 2721
ONE ACRE FUND; *U.S. Private*, pg. 3020
PINES INTERNATIONAL, INC.; *U.S. Private*, pg. 3183
PROJECT HOSPITALITY, INC.; *U.S. Private*, pg. 3280
THE REDWOOD EMPIRE FOOD BANK; *U.S. Private*, pg. 4103
REGIONAL FOOD BANK OF OKLAHOMA; *U.S. Private*, pg. 3388
RHODE ISLAND COMMUNITY FOOD BANK; *U.S. Private*, pg. 3422
RISE AGAINST HUNGER; *U.S. Private*, pg. 3440
SAMARITAN CENTER; *U.S. Private*, pg. 3536
SECOND HARVEST OF SOUTH GEORGIA, INC.; *U.S. Private*, pg. 3593
SENIOR GLEANERS INC.; *U.S. Private*, pg. 3607
SHARE OUR STRENGTH; *U.S. Private*, pg. 3626
THE SOCIETY OF SAINT ANDREW, INC.; *U.S. Private*, pg. 4119
SOL CARE SERVICES, INC.; *U.S. Private*, pg. 3706
ST. LOUIS AREA FOODBANK, INC.; *U.S. Private*, pg. 3772
TABLE TO TABLE; *U.S. Private*, pg. 3920
WAYSIDE CHRISTIAN MISSION; *U.S. Private*, pg. 4460
WORCESTER COUNTY FOOD BANK; *U.S. Private*, pg. 4562
WORLD EMERGENCY RELIEF; *U.S. Private*, pg. 4565

624221 — TEMPORARY SHELTERS

BETHLEHEM HAVEN—See Pittsburgh Mercy Health System, Inc.; *U.S. Private*, pg. 3191
CRS TEMPORARY HOUSING—See GenNx360 Capital Partners, L.P.; *U.S. Private*, pg. 1672
FAMILIES FORWARD PHILADELPHIA; *U.S. Private*, pg. 1468
GROWING IN VOICES; *U.S. Private*, pg. 1795
HDT EXPEDITIONARY SYSTEMS, INC.—See Metalmark Capital Holdings LLC; *U.S. Private*, pg. 2681
HIGHMARK CARING PLACE—See Highmark Health; *U.S. Private*, pg. 1940
JOSEPH'S HOUSE OF CAMDEN; *U.S. Private*, pg. 2237
MEN'S SHELTER OF CHARLOTTE, INC.—See Urban Ministry Center; *U.S. Private*, pg. 4314
NEW HORIZONS FOR NEW HAMPSHIRE—See FIT/NHNH, INC.; *U.S. Private*, pg. 1535
SHELTER PARTNERSHIP, INC.; *U.S. Private*, pg. 3631
SO OTHERS MIGHT EAT; *U.S. Private*, pg. 3702
TEMPORARY HOUSING DIRECTORY, INC.; *U.S. Private*, pg. 3964
UNION GOSPEL MISSION; *U.S. Private*, pg. 4284

624229 — OTHER COMMUNITY HOUSING SERVICES

ACTION-HOUSING, INC.; *U.S. Private*, pg. 68
AEON; *U.S. Private*, pg. 117
AHC INC.; *U.S. Private*, pg. 130
ALLEN & O'HARA EDUCATION SERVICES, INC.—See Greystar Real Estate Partners, LLC; *U.S. Private*, pg. 1785
ALLIES & ROSS MANAGEMENT AND DEVELOPMENT CORPORATION; *U.S. Private*, pg. 191
ALMA METALS LIMITED; *Int'l*, pg. 362
AMERICAN OPPORTUNITY FOR HOUSING, INC.; *U.S. Private*, pg. 242
ARIZONA HOUSING, INC.; *U.S. Private*, pg. 324
ASPEN WALK (EIGHT ASH GREEN) MANAGEMENT COMPANY LIMITED—See Bellway plc; *Int'l*, pg. 967
ASSISTANS PA GOTLAND AB—See Humana AB; *Int'l*, pg. 3529
AUSTRALIAN RETIREMENT HOMES LIMITED—See Brookfield Corporation; *Int'l*, pg. 1185
BCCU INC.; *U.S. Private*, pg. 499
B C HOUSING MANAGEMENT COMMISSION; *Int'l*, pg. 783
BEECHCROFT DEVELOPMENTS LTD.; *Int'l*, pg. 939
BELLWAY HOUSING TRUST LIMITED—See Bellway plc; *Int'l*, pg. 968
BELLWEST MANAGEMENT CORPORATION; *U.S. Private*, pg. 520
BELMONT HOUSING RESOURCES FOR WNY; *U.S. Private*, pg. 520
BICKERDIKE REDEVELOPMENT CORPORATION; *U.S. Private*, pg. 550
BLVD SUITES CORPORATE HOUSING, INC.; *U.S. Private*, pg. 600
BOISE HOUSING CORPORATION; *U.S. Private*, pg. 609
BOWERY RESIDENTS' COMMITTEE, INC.; *U.S. Private*, pg. 625
BROOKLAWN INC.; *U.S. Private*, pg. 663
THE BURTON FOUNDATION; *U.S. Private*, pg. 4003
CAMILLUS HOUSE, INC.; *U.S. Private*, pg. 729
CARITAS CORPORATION; *U.S. Private*, pg. 761
CATHEDRAL ARMS INC.; *U.S. Private*, pg. 788
CATHOLIC CHARITIES HEALTH & HUMAN SERVICES; *U.S. Private*, pg. 788
CELSIUM SERWIS SP. Z O.O.—See E.ON SE; *Int'l*, pg. 2251
CELSIUM SP. Z O.O.—See E.ON SE; *Int'l*, pg. 2251
CENTURY HOUSING; *U.S. Private*, pg. 833
THE CESAR CHAVEZ FOUNDATION; *U.S. Private*, pg. 4007
CHURCHILL CORPORATE SERVICES; *U.S. Private*, pg. 894
CLEVELAND GARDENS PTY. LTD.—See Brookfield Corporation; *Int'l*, pg. 1186
CLEVELAND HOUSING NETWORK; *U.S. Private*, pg. 941
COACHELLA VALLEY HOUSING COALITION; *U.S. Private*, pg. 953
COAST & COUNTRY HOUSING LTD.; *Int'l*, pg. 1681
COMMUNITY HOUSING CONCEPTS, INC.; *U.S. Private*, pg. 994
COMMUNITY HOUSING DEVELOPMENT CORPORATION; *U.S. Private*, pg. 994
COMMUNITY HOUSING INNOVATIONS, INC.; *U.S. Private*, pg. 994
COMPASS HOUSING ALLIANCE; *U.S. Private*, pg. 999
COPPERHOUSE GREEN MANAGEMENT COMPANY LIMITED—See Bellway plc; *Int'l*, pg. 968
CORPORATION FOR ENTERPRISE DEVELOPMENT CFED; *U.S. Private*, pg. 1056
CORVALLIS NEIGHBORHOOD HOUSING SERVICES, INC.; *U.S. Private*, pg. 1061
CRITTENDEN BOULEVARD HOUSING COMPANY, INC.; *U.S. Private*, pg. 1102
CROSSROADS HOUSING DEVELOPMENT CORP; *U.S. Private*, pg. 1108
DD HAPPYHOMES RESIDENTIAL CENTERS INC.—See DoubleDragon Corporation; *Int'l*, pg. 2181
DEL WEBB COMMUNITIES OF VIRGINIA, INC.—See PulteGroup, Inc.; *U.S. Public*, pg. 1737
DIGITAALINEN ASUNTOKAUPPA DIAS OY—See Alma Media Corporation; *Int'l*, pg. 362
EDUCATIONAL HOUSING SERVICES; *U.S. Private*, pg. 1339
ELIM PARK BAPTIST HOME INC.; *U.S. Private*, pg. 1360
EMERGENCY ASSISTANCE JAPAN (SINGAPORE), PTE. LTD—See Emergency Assistance Japan Co., Ltd.; *Int'l*, pg. 2378
EMERGENCY ASSISTANCE JAPAN (U.S.A), INC.—See Emergency Assistance Japan Co., Ltd.; *Int'l*, pg. 2378
EMERGENCY ASSISTANCE THAILAND CO., LTD—See Emergency Assistance Japan Co., Ltd.; *Int'l*, pg. 2378
EMPLOY-ABILITY UNLIMITED INC.; *U.S. Private*, pg. 1386
ENERGY OUTREACH COLORADO; *U.S. Private*, pg. 1395
ENTERPRISE COMMUNITY PARTNERS, INC.; *U.S. Private*, pg. 1403
EQR-NOTCH LLC—See Equity Residential; *U.S. Public*, pg. 791
EQR-RESERVE AT EISENHOWER LLC—See Equity Residential; *U.S. Public*, pg. 791
EVENTIDE SENIOR LIVING COMMUNITIES; *U.S. Private*, pg. 1437
FATHER BILL'S & MAINSPRING; *U.S. Private*, pg. 1483
FIRST COLONY COMMUNITY ASSOCIATION; *U.S. Private*, pg. 1516
FIT/NHNH, INC.; *U.S. Private*, pg. 1535
FOREST PLACE MANAGEMENT LIMITED—See Brookfield Corporation; *Int'l*, pg. 1186
FOUNDATION COMMUNITIES; *U.S. Private*, pg. 1579
GULF COAST RENAISSANCE CORPORATION; *U.S. Private*, pg. 1815
HAVEN FOR HOPE OF BEXAR COUNTY; *U.S. Private*, pg. 1880
HAZEL FOLD RESIDENTS MANAGEMENT COMPANY LIMITED—See Bellway plc; *Int'l*, pg. 968
THE HEAT AND WARMTH FUND; *U.S. Private*, pg. 4050
HIGHLANDS MUTUAL HOUSING CORPORATION, INC.; *U.S. Private*, pg. 1940
HINXHILL PARK (ASHFORD) MANAGEMENT COMPANY LIMITED—See Bellway plc; *Int'l*, pg. 968
HOME/LIFE SERVICES, INC.; *U.S. Private*, pg. 1972
HOMESTRONGUSA; *U.S. Private*, pg. 1975
HOUSING ASSISTANCE COUNCIL; *U.S. Private*, pg. 1992
HOUSING NETWORK OF HAMILTON COUNTY INC.; *U.S. Private*, pg. 1992
THE HOUSING PARTNERSHIP NETWORK; *U.S. Private*, pg. 4054
HOUSING TRUST SILICON VALLEY; *U.S. Private*, pg. 1992
HUMANA DANMARK APS—See Humana AB; *Int'l*, pg. 3530
INSPIRICA, INC.; *U.S. Private*, pg. 2092
INTERFAITH HOUSING FOUNDATION; *U.S. Private*, pg. 2110
IRVINE COMMUNITY LAND TRUST; *U.S. Private*, pg. 2141
JOLIET AREA COMMUNITY HOSPICE; *U.S. Private*, pg. 2230
LONG ACRE (SHINFIELD) MANAGEMENT COMPANY LIMITED—See Bellway plc; *Int'l*, pg. 968
MADRID HOME COMMUNITIES; *U.S. Private*, pg. 2544
MERCY SENIOR HOUSING, INC.—See Catholic Health Initiatives; *U.S. Private*, pg. 790
MIDPEN HOUSING CORPORATION; *U.S. Private*, pg. 2717
MULTICULTURAL COMMUNITY SERVICES OF THE PIONEER VALLEY, INC.; *U.S. Private*, pg. 2812
NATIONAL CORPORATE HOUSING; *U.S. Private*, pg. 2851
NAVIGATE AFFORDABLE HOUSING PARTNERS, INC.; *U.S. Private*, pg. 2873
NEHEMIAH HOUSING DEVELOPMENT FUND; *U.S. Private*, pg. 2880
NEIGHBORHOOD HOUSING SERVICES OF SOUTH FLORIDA; *U.S. Private*, pg. 2881
NRG HOME SERVICES LLC—See NRG Energy, Inc.; *U.S. Public*, pg. 1550
OHIO CAPITAL CORPORATION FOR HOUSING; *U.S. Private*, pg. 3004
OREGON AFFORDABLE HOUSING ASSISTANCE CORPORATION; *U.S. Private*, pg. 3039
PHIPPS HOUSES; *U.S. Private*, pg. 3172
PREFERRED CORPORATE HOUSING; *U.S. Private*, pg. 3247
PRESBYTERIAN HOMES & SERVICES OF KENTUCKY, INC.; *U.S. Private*, pg. 3253
PRESBYTERIAN HOMES; *U.S. Private*, pg. 3253
PRESERVATION NON-PROFIT HOUSING CORPORATION; *U.S. Private*, pg. 3254
PRESERVATION OF AFFORDABLE HOUSING, INC.; *U.S. Private*, pg. 3254
REPARALIA DIRECT SL—See Brookfield Corporation; *Int'l*, pg. 1188
REPARALIA S.A.—See Brookfield Corporation; *Int'l*, pg. 1188
RESCUE MISSION MINISTRIES, INC.; *U.S. Private*, pg. 3403
RESIDENTIAL REALTY GROUP I INC.; *U.S. Private*, pg. 3405
RESTORATION DESIGN LLC—See NRG Energy, Inc.; *U.S. Public*, pg. 1551
R.I.K. ASSISTANS AKTIEBOLAG—See Humana AB; *Int'l*, pg. 3530
ROLLESTON MANOR MANAGEMENT COMPANY LIMITED—See Bellway plc; *Int'l*, pg. 968
ROXBURY TENANTS OF HARVARD; *U.S. Private*, pg. 3490
SPARTA ECUMENICAL COUNCIL ON SENIOR CITIZEN HOUSING INC.; *U.S. Private*, pg. 3746
SRO HOUSING CORPORATION; *U.S. Private*, pg. 3768
STILTON GATE MANAGEMENT COMPANY LIMITED—See Bellway plc; *Int'l*, pg. 968
ST. MARY CATHOLIC HOUSING CORPORATION—See Catholic Health Initiatives; *U.S. Private*, pg. 790
ST. PATRICK CENTER; *U.S. Private*, pg. 3773
TLINGIT-HAIDA REGIONAL HOUSING AUTHORITY; *U.S. Private*, pg. 4179
TRINITY MANOR INC.; *U.S. Private*, pg. 4235
VERMONT HOUSING FINANCE AGENCY; *U.S. Private*, pg. 4367
WESTHAB; *U.S. Private*, pg. 4498
WESTMINSTER VILLAGE NORTH; *U.S. Private*, pg. 4499
WILLAMETTE NEIGHBORHOOD HOUSING SERVICES—See Corvallis Neighborhood Housing Services, Inc.; *U.S. Private*, pg. 1061
XI S&D, INC.—See GS Holdings Corp.; *Int'l*, pg. 3142

624230 — EMERGENCY AND OTHER RELIEF SERVICES

ABRACADABRA RESTORATION, INC.—See Kustom US, Inc.; *U.S. Private*, pg. 2358
AMAANAH REFUGEE SERVICES; *U.S. Private*, pg. 215
ASI GLOBAL, LLC—See UnitedHealth Group Incorporated; *U.S. Public*, pg. 2241
ASPLUNDH ENVIRONMENTAL SERVICES, INC.—See Asplundh Tree Expert Co.; *U.S. Private*, pg. 353
ASSETCO UAE—See AssetCo plc; *Int'l*, pg. 643
BEARTOOTH BILLINGS CLINIC; *U.S. Private*, pg. 507
CARE CANADA; *Int'l*, pg. 1323
CHRISTIAN EMERGENCY RELIEF TEAMS INTERNATIONAL; *U.S. Private*, pg. 891
COMPASSION COALITION, INC.; *U.S. Private*, pg. 999
CSKTS INC.—See Atlas Copco AB; *Int'l*, pg. 681
DAMAGE CONTROL, LLC; *U.S. Private*, pg. 1150
DENVER RESCUE MISSION; *U.S. Private*, pg. 1207
DIVERSIFIED SECURITY SOLUTIONS, INC.—See Kratos Defense & Security Solutions, Inc.; *U.S. Public*, pg. 1276

N.A.I.C.S. INDEX

EMERGENCY ASSISTANCE JAPAN CO., LTD.; *Int'l*, pg. 2378
ETHIOPIAN COMMUNITY DEVELOPMENT COUNCIL, INC.; *U.S. Private*, pg. 1431
EXECUTIVE PROTECTION SYSTEMS LLC; *U.S. Private*, pg. 1448
FEED THE CHILDREN, INC.; *U.S. Private*, pg. 1492
FRONTIER MEDEX LIMITED—See UnitedHealth Group Incorporated; *U.S. Public*, pg. 2241
GOD'S PIT CREW; *U.S. Private*, pg. 1724
HOMESERVE MEMBERSHIP LIMITED—See Brookfield Corporation; *Int'l*, pg. 1188
HOPE RESTORATION MINISTRIES, INC.; *U.S. Private*, pg. 1979
IMMIGRANT AND REFUGEE COMMUNITY ORGANIZATION; *U.S. Private*, pg. 2047
INCIDENT RESPONSE TECHNOLOGIES, INC.—See The Riverside Company; *U.S. Private*, pg. 4109
KENYON INTERNATIONAL EMERGENCY SERVICES, INC.—See Wheels Up Experience Inc.; *U.S. Public*, pg. 2366
LUTHERAN IMMIGRATION AND REFUGEE SERVICE; *U.S. Private*, pg. 2517
MAKE THE ROAD NEW YORK; *U.S. Private*, pg. 2556
MC ENDEAVORS, INC.; *U.S. Private*, pg. 1403
MIDATLANTIC MEDEVAC, L.L.C.—See KKR & Co. Inc.; *U.S. Public*, pg. 1252
MOBILEHELP, LLC—See Water Street Healthcare Partners, LLC; *U.S. Private*, pg. 4452
NATIONAL RESPONSE CORPORATION—See Republic Services, Inc.; *U.S. Public*, pg. 1788
NEW YORK DISASTER INTERFAITH SERVICES; *U.S. Private*, pg. 2909
NEXT STEP DOMESTIC VIOLENCE PROJECT; *U.S. Private*, pg. 2920
REZEK EQUIPMENT; *U.S. Private*, pg. 3419
SALAMANDER TECHNOLOGIES; *U.S. Private*, pg. 3530
SERVPRO INDUSTRIES, LLC—See Blackstone Inc.; *U.S. Public*, pg. 357

624310 — VOCATIONAL REHABILITATION SERVICES

ALUE CO., LTD.; *Int'l*, pg. 400
THE ARKANSAS LIGHTHOUSE FOR THE BLIND—See Winston-Salem Industries for The Blind, Inc.; *U.S. Private*, pg. 4544
ASPIRE OF ILLINOIS; *U.S. Private*, pg. 352
ATI PHYSICAL THERAPY, INC.—See Advent International Corporation; *U.S. Private*, pg. 96
CAPITAL VOCATIONAL SPECIALISTS—See GIC Pte. Ltd.; *Int'l*, pg. 2964
CAPITAL VOCATIONAL SPECIALISTS—See Leonard Green & Partners, L.P.; *U.S. Private*, pg. 2425
CAREER SERVICES GROUP, INC.—See Talent, Inc.; *U.S. Private*, pg. 3926
CENTER FOR EMPLOYMENT TRAINING INC.; *U.S. Private*, pg. 810
CHANGE, INC.—See Penn-Mar Organization, Inc.; *U.S. Private*, pg. 3135
CLAREMONT BEHAVIORAL SERVICES, INC.—See Integrated Behavioral Health, Inc.; *U.S. Private*, pg. 2099
COMMUNITY ENTERPRISES, INC.; *U.S. Private*, pg. 991
CONSORTIUM FOR WORKER EDUCATION INC.; *U.S. Private*, pg. 1023
CORNERSTONE FIRST FINANCIAL—See Fathom Holdings Inc.; *U.S. Public*, pg. 824
CRC SERVICES, LLC—See California Resources Corporation; *U.S. Public*, pg. 423
DBM VIRCON SERVICES (NZ) LTD.—See INNOVATE Corp.; *U.S. Public*, pg. 1126
DBM VIRCON SERVICES (PHILIPPINES) INC.—See INNOVATE Corp.; *U.S. Public*, pg. 1126
DBM VIRCON SERVICES (THAILAND) CO., LTD.—See INNOVATE Corp.; *U.S. Public*, pg. 1126
DEVELOPMENT CORP.—See Synergis Technologies Group; *U.S. Private*, pg. 3903
THE DIRECTIONS GROUP, LLC—See EK Health Services, Inc.; *U.S. Private*, pg. 1348
DISABILITY SERVICES, INC.—See Dungarvin, Inc.; *U.S. Private*, pg. 1289
DON MILLS SURGICAL UNIT LTD.—See CareRx Corporation; *Int'l*, pg. 1325
DOWNER PIPETECH PTY. LIMITED—See Downer EDI Limited; *Int'l*, pg. 2186
EMPLOYMENT DEVELOPMENT, INC.; *U.S. Private*, pg. 1387
EXPERIENCE WORKS, INC.; *U.S. Private*, pg. 1449
GEISINGER HEALTHSOUTH REHABILITATION HOSPITAL—See Encompass Health Corporation; *U.S. Public*, pg. 756
GEISINGER HEALTHSOUTH REHABILITATION HOSPITAL—See Geisinger Health System; *U.S. Private*, pg. 1656
GOLD FIELDS EXTERNAL TRAINING SERVICES (PTY) LIMITED—See Adcorp Holdings Limited; *Int'l*, pg. 127

GOODWILL INDUSTRIES OF KANAWHA VALLEY, INC.; *U.S. Private*, pg. 1740
ICD INSTITUTE FOR CAREER DEVELOPMENT; *U.S. Private*, pg. 2030
INNOVATIVE TRAINING & RECRUITMENT PTY LTD.—See Madison Dearborn Partners, LLC; *U.S. Private*, pg. 2540
JACKSON RECOVERY CENTERS, INC.—See Rosecrance, Inc.; *U.S. Private*, pg. 3482
JOBWORKS, INC.; *U.S. Private*, pg. 2217
KNOWLGY CORPORATION; *U.S. Private*, pg. 2324
MCCALL LIMITED—See Empresaria Group Plc; *Int'l*, pg. 2389
MERS/MISSOURI GOODWILL INDUSTRIES; *U.S. Private*, pg. 2677
MINACT INC.; *U.S. Private*, pg. 2740
NATIONAL TRAINING INSTITUTE LLC—See Babcock International Group PLC; *Int'l*, pg. 793
NORTH BAY REGIONAL CENTER; *U.S. Private*, pg. 2942
PRISON REHABILITATIVE INDUSTRIES AND DIVERSIFIED ENTERPRISES, INC.; *U.S. Private*, pg. 3267
RELIANT REHABILITATION HOLDINGS, INC.—See H.I.G. Capital, LLC; *U.S. Private*, pg. 1831
ROSS INNOVATIVE EMPLOYMENT SOLUTIONS CORP.—See ModivCare, Inc.; *U.S. Public*, pg. 1456
SACRAMENTO EMPLOYMENT & TRAINING AGENCY; *U.S. Private*, pg. 3522
THE SALES BOARD, INC.—See RFE Investment Partners; *U.S. Private*, pg. 3419
SUNRISE MEDICAL BENELUS—See Vestar Capital Partners, LLC; *U.S. Private*, pg. 4372
SVRC INDUSTRIES, INC.; *U.S. Private*, pg. 3889
SW RESOURCES, INC.—See Goodwill Industries of Kanawha Valley, Inc.; *U.S. Private*, pg. 1740
TENCO INDUSTRIES, INC.—See Alamo Group Inc.; *U.S. Public*, pg. 71
THE VOCATIONAL DEVELOPMENT FOUNDATION; *U.S. Private*, pg. 4132
VOCATIONAL GUIDANCE SERVICES; *U.S. Private*, pg. 4409
THE WINIFRED MASTERSON BURKE REHABILITATION HOSPITAL, INC.; *U.S. Private*, pg. 4137
WINSTON-SALEM INDUSTRIES FOR THE BLIND, INC.; *U.S. Private*, pg. 4544
WORK ABLE CENTRES INC.—See CareRx Corporation; *Int'l*, pg. 1325
WORK ABLE CENTRES NORTH YORK INC.—See CareRx Corporation; *Int'l*, pg. 1325

624410 — CHILD CARE SERVICES

ADA S. MCKINLEY COMMUNITY SERVICES, INC.; *U.S. Private*, pg. 72
AFFINITY EDUCATION GROUP LIMITED—See Anchorage Capital Partners Pty. Limited; *Int'l*, pg. 448
AIAI CHILD CARE CO., LTD.—See AIAI Group Corporation; *Int'l*, pg. 227
ALBINA HEAD START, INC.; *U.S. Private*, pg. 153
BABYSTEPS LIMITED—See Cornerstone Financial Holdings Limited; *Int'l*, pg. 1801
BEEHIVE DAY NURSERIES LIMITED—See Bain Capital, LP; *U.S. Private*, pg. 437
BFK FRANCHISE COMPANY, LLC—See DriveItAway Holdings, Inc.; *U.S. Public*, pg. 688
BRECKENRIDGE SKI RESORT—See Vail Resorts, Inc.; *U.S. Public*, pg. 2272
BRIGHT HORIZONS CHILDREN'S CENTERS LLC—See Bain Capital, LP; *U.S. Private*, pg. 437
BRIGHT HORIZONS FAMILY SOLUTIONS CALIFORNIA REGIONAL OFFICE—See Bain Capital, LP; *U.S. Private*, pg. 436
BRIGHT HORIZONS FAMILY SOLUTIONS CHICAGO REGIONAL OFFICE—See Bain Capital, LP; *U.S. Private*, pg. 436
BRIGHT HORIZONS FAMILY SOLUTIONS FLORIDA REGIONAL OFFICE—See Bain Capital, LP; *U.S. Private*, pg. 436
BRIGHT HORIZONS FAMILY SOLUTIONS, INC.—See Bain Capital, LP; *U.S. Private*, pg. 436
BRIGHT HORIZONS FAMILY SOLUTIONS IRELAND—See Bain Capital, LP; *U.S. Private*, pg. 436
BRIGHT HORIZONS FAMILY SOLUTIONS LIMITED—See Bain Capital, LP; *U.S. Private*, pg. 437
BRIGHT HORIZONS FAMILY SOLUTIONS LLC—See Bain Capital, LP; *U.S. Private*, pg. 436
BRIGHT HORIZONS FAMILY SOLUTIONS MARYLAND REGIONAL OFFICE—See Bain Capital, LP; *U.S. Private*, pg. 437
BRIGHT HORIZONS FAMILY SOLUTIONS NASHVILLE REGIONAL OFFICE—See Bain Capital, LP; *U.S. Private*, pg. 437
BRIGHT HORIZONS FAMILY SOLUTIONS SCOTLAND REGIONAL OFFICE—See Bain Capital, LP; *U.S. Private*, pg. 437
BRIGHT HORIZONS FAMILY SOLUTIONS TEXAS REGIONAL OFFICE—See Bain Capital, LP; *U.S. Private*, pg. 437
BRIGHT HORIZONS FAMILY SOLUTIONS UNITED KINGDOM—See Bain Capital, LP; *U.S. Private*, pg. 437

624410 — CHILD CARE SERVICES

BRIGHT HORIZONS LIVINGSTON LTD.—See Bain Capital, LP; *U.S. Private*, pg. 437
BRIGHT HORIZONS LLC—See Bain Capital, LP; *U.S. Private*, pg. 436
CAMBIUM EDUCATION, INC.—See Veritas Capital Fund Management, LLC; *U.S. Private*, pg. 4361
CAPE FEAR TUTORING, INC.; *U.S. Private*, pg. 737
CENTRAL CALIFORNIA CHILD DEVELOPMENT SERVICES, INC.; *U.S. Private*, pg. 819
CHILD DEVELOPMENT SCHOOLS, INC.—See Glencoe Capital LLC; *U.S. Private*, pg. 1709
CHILD FOCUS, INC.; *U.S. Private*, pg. 882
CHILDREN'S CHOICE LEARNING CENTERS, INC.—See Bain Capital, LP; *U.S. Private*, pg. 437
CHILD START INC.; *U.S. Private*, pg. 882
CREATIVE KIDS, INC.—See American Securities LLC; *U.S. Private*, pg. 249
CUMMINS CHILD DEVELOPMENT CENTER, INC.—See Cummins Inc.; *U.S. Public*, pg. 605
DAISIES DAY NURSERIES LIMITED—See Bain Capital, LP; *U.S. Private*, pg. 437
DALEVILLE CHRISTIAN CHURCH DAY CARE CENTER; *U.S. Private*, pg. 1149
DOLPHIN NURSERIES (TOOTING) LTD.—See Bain Capital, LP; *U.S. Private*, pg. 437
DUSSMANN KULTURKINDERGARTEN GEMEINNUTZIGE GMBH—See Dussmann Stiftung & Co. KGaA; *Int'l*, pg. 2234
EARLY LEARNING COALITION OF ALACHUA COUNTY; *U.S. Private*, pg. 1313
EARLY LEARNING COALITION OF BREVARD COUNTY, INC.; *U.S. Private*, pg. 1313
EARLY LEARNING COALITION OF THE BIG BEND REGION; *U.S. Private*, pg. 1313
EVANCIA SAS; *Int'l*, pg. 2560
FAMILY LEAGUE OF BALTIMORE CITY, INC.; *U.S. Private*, pg. 1470
FAMILY LEGACY MISSIONS INTERNATIONAL; *U.S. Private*, pg. 1471
G8 EDUCATION LTD.; *Int'l*, pg. 2867
GLOBAL KIDS COMPANY CORP.; *Int'l*, pg. 2998
GODDARD SYSTEMS, INC.—See Wind River Holdings, L.P.; *U.S. Private*, pg. 4536
GROWING ROOM INC.; *U.S. Private*, pg. 1795
INGLEWOOD DAY NURSERY AND COLLEGE LTD.—See Bain Capital, LP; *U.S. Private*, pg. 437
INSTITUTE OF COMMUNITY SERVICES, INC.; *U.S. Private*, pg. 2093
KINDERGARDEN NEDERLAND B.V.—See Bain Capital, LP; *U.S. Private*, pg. 437
LA MAISON BLEUE SA—See Activa Capital S.A.S.; *Int'l*, pg. 119
LASTENSUOJELUYKSIKKO LEPPALINTU OY—See Humana AB; *Int'l*, pg. 3530
LEARNING CARE GROUP, INC.—See American Securities LLC; *U.S. Private*, pg. 249
LE CHAPERON ROUGE; *U.S. Private*, pg. 2405
LIMHAMNS FORSKOLA AB—See AcadeMedia AB; *Int'l*, pg. 77
LIPTON CORPORATE CHILDCARE, INC.—See Bain Capital, LP; *U.S. Private*, pg. 437
THE LITTLE RED SCHOOL HOUSE, INC.—See Rainbow Rascals Learning Center, Inc.; *U.S. Private*, pg. 3347
LITTLE SPROUTS LLC—See Evancia SAS; *Int'l*, pg. 2560
LOLLIPOPS EDUCARE (BIRKENHEAD) LIMITED—See Evolve Education Group Limited; *Int'l*, pg. 2573
LUZERNE COUNTY HEAD START, INC.; *U.S. Private*, pg. 2518
MARYVALE; *U.S. Private*, pg. 2600
MONTESSORI ACADEMY GROUP HOLDINGS PTY LTD.—See Dalian Thermal Power Co., Ltd.; *Int'l*, pg. 1952
NEW HORIZON KIDS QUEST, INC.; *U.S. Private*, pg. 2897
NEW HORIZONS IN CHILD DEVELOPMENT—See Measured Progress Inc.; *U.S. Private*, pg. 2648
NEWTON-WELLESLEY CHILDREN'S CORNER INC.—See Partners HealthCare System, Inc.; *U.S. Private*, pg. 3101
NORTHRIDGE ACADEMY, LLC; *U.S. Private*, pg. 2957
OPTIONS FOR LEARNING; *U.S. Private*, pg. 3035
PALISADES CHILD CARE CENTER INC.—See New York-Presbyterian Healthcare System, Inc.; *U.S. Private*, pg. 2913
PARENTS IN COMMUNITY ACTION, INC.; *U.S. Private*, pg. 3094
PATHWAYS OF WASHINGTON, INC.—See ATAR Capital, LLC; *U.S. Private*, pg. 364
PONZANO CHILDREN S.R.L.—See Edizione S.r.l.; *Int'l*, pg. 2312
QUALITY CARE FOR CHILDREN, INC.; *U.S. Private*, pg. 3318
RAINBOW RASCALS LEARNING CENTER, INC.; *U.S. Private*, pg. 3347
RAINBOW STATION INC.; *U.S. Private*, pg. 3347
R'CLUB CHILD CARE, INC.; *U.S. Private*, pg. 3333
SEEKINGSITTERS INC.; *U.S. Private*, pg. 3598
SEI FINANCIAL SERVICES COMPANY—See SEI Investments Company; *U.S. Public*, pg. 1857

624410 — CHILD CARE SERVICES

SOUTH CAROLINA FIRST STEPS TO SCHOOL READINESS; *U.S. Private*, pg. 3720
SPRINGFIELD LODGE DAY NURSERY (DARTFORD) LTD.—See Bain Capital, LP; *U.S. Private*, pg. 437
SPRINGFIELD LODGE DAY NURSERY (SWANSCOMBE) LTD.—See Bain Capital, LP; *U.S. Private*, pg. 437
STORYBOOK COTTAGE DAYCARE CENTER, LLC; *U.S. Private*, pg. 3832
TEDDIES CHILDCARE PROVISION LIMITED—See Bain Capital, LP; *U.S. Private*, pg. 437
TRUSTED LABS, INC.—See IAC Inc.; *U.S. Public*, pg. 1082
U-GRO LEARNING CENTRES, INC.—See American Securities LLC; *U.S. Private*, pg. 249
WAKE COUNTY SMARTSTART, INC.; *U.S. Private*, pg. 4427
WEE FOLK ROCKFORD CHILD CENTER, INC.—See Byrne Electrical Specialists, Inc.; *U.S. Private*, pg. 701
ZERO TO THREE: NATIONAL CENTER FOR INFANTS, TODDLERS AND FAMILIES; *U.S. Private*, pg. 4602

711110 — THEATER COMPANIES AND DINNER THEATERS

AMBASSADOR FOOD SERVICES CORP.; *U.S. Private*, pg. 217
AMERICAN CONSERVATORY THEATRE; *U.S. Private*, pg. 228
ATLANTIC THEATER COMPANY; *U.S. Private*, pg. 374
BLUE MAN PRODUCTIONS, INC.—See TPG Capital, L.P.; *U.S. Public*, pg. 2169.
BROADWAY ACROSS AMERICA - MINNEAPOLIS—See Key Brand Entertainment, Inc.; *U.S. Private*, pg. 2292
BROADWAY ACROSS AMERICA - SEATTLE—See Key Brand Entertainment, Inc.; *U.S. Private*, pg. 2292
CENTER THEATRE GROUP OF LOS ANGELES, INC.; *U.S. Private*, pg. 811
CIRQUE DU SOLEIL INC.—See TPG Capital, L.P.; *U.S. Public*, pg. 2169
CIRQUE DU SOLEIL ORLANDO INC.—See TPG Capital, L.P.; *U.S. Public*, pg. 2169
CIVIC LIGHT OPERA ASSOCIATION OF PITTSBURGH; *U.S. Private*, pg. 908
CJ CGV CO., LTD.; *Int'l*, pg. 1631
DAVID A. STRAZ JR. CENTER FOR THE PERFORMING ARTS; *U.S. Private*, pg. 1169
DISNEY THEATRICAL PRODUCTIONS—See The Walt Disney Company; *U.S. Public*, pg. 2139
GERMAINE'S LUAU, INC.—See Zippy's, Inc.; *U.S. Private*, pg. 4606
THE GOODMAN THEATRE; *U.S. Private*, pg. 4034
HOUSTON GRAND OPERA ASSOCIATION; *U.S. Private*, pg. 1993
KONA GRILL INC.—See The ONE Group Hospitality, Inc.; *U.S. Public*, pg. 2118
LINCOLN CENTER FOR THE PERFORMING ARTS, INC.; *U.S. Private*, pg. 2457
MANHATTAN THEATRE CLUB, INC.; *U.S. Private*, pg. 2564
MAYO PERFORMING ARTS CENTER; *U.S. Private*, pg. 2622
MEDIEVAL DINNER & TOURNAMENT, INC.; *U.S. Private*, pg. 2656
MEDIEVAL TIMES MANAGEMENT INC.—See Medieval Dinner & Tournament, Inc.; *U.S. Private*, pg. 2656
MILWAUKEE SYMPHONY ORCHESTRA INC.; *U.S. Private*, pg. 2739
MIRACLE ENTERTAINMENT, INC.; *U.S. Public*, pg. 1450
THE NATIONAL THEATRE CORPORATION; *U.S. Private*, pg. 4082
THE NEW 42ND STREET, INC; *U.S. Private*, pg. 4082
NEW YORK CITY BALLET; *U.S. Private*, pg. 2909
NEW YORK CITY OPERA INC.; *U.S. Private*, pg. 2909
THE OLD GLOBE; *U.S. Private*, pg. 4088
OLYMPUS THEATRICALS, LLC—See Olympus Holdings, LLC; *U.S. Private*, pg. 3013
OREGON SHAKESPEARE FESTIVAL; *U.S. Private*, pg. 3040
PALAZZO PRODUCTIES B.V.—See CTS Eventim AG & Co. KGaA; *Int'l*, pg. 1873
PALAZZO PRODUKTIONEN BERLIN GMBH—See CTS Eventim AG & Co. KGAA; *Int'l*, pg. 1873
PALAZZO PRODUKTIONEN GMBH—See CTS Eventim AG & Co. KGaA; *Int'l*, pg. 1873
PASADENA PLAYHOUSE; *U.S. Private*, pg. 3103
PERFECT MARKETING CORPORATION; *U.S. Private*, pg. 3148
PLAYHOUSE SQUARE FOUNDATION; *U.S. Private*, pg. 3212
THE PUBLIC THEATER; *U.S. Private*, pg. 4101
SCHAUMBURG CASTLE INC.—See Medieval Dinner & Tournament, Inc.; *U.S. Private*, pg. 2656
SETH CHILDS 12 OF KANSAS L.L.C.—See Dalian Wanda Group Corporation Ltd.; *Int'l*, pg. 1953
SOUTHERN THEATRES, LLC; *U.S. Private*, pg. 3735
START MEDIA LLC—See Dalian Wanda Group Corporation Ltd.; *Int'l*, pg. 1953

THEATER COMPANY HIKOSEN INC.—See Bushiroad, Inc.; *Int'l*, pg. 1227
THEATERMANIA.COM, INC.—See AudienceView Ticketing Corporation; *Int'l*, pg. 701
THEATRE FOR A NEW AUDIENCE; *U.S. Private*, pg. 4141
UTAH SYMPHONY & OPERA; *U.S. Private*, pg. 4324
VENUE OF SCOTTSDALE; *U.S. Private*, pg. 4358
VICTORIA THEATRE ASSOCIATION; *U.S. Private*, pg. 4378
WALNUT STREET THEATRE CORPORATION; *U.S. Private*, pg. 4432
WORCESTER CENTER FOR PERFORMING ARTS; *U.S. Private*, pg. 4562

711120 — DANCE COMPANIES

BALLET THEATRE FOUNDATION, INC.; *U.S. Private*, pg. 461
BOSTON BALLET INC.; *U.S. Private*, pg. 621
HOUSTON BALLET FOUNDATION INC.; *U.S. Private*, pg. 1993
MIAMI CITY BALLET, INC.; *U.S. Private*, pg. 2696
ORLANDO BALLET, INC.; *U.S. Private*, pg. 3043
PENNSYLVANIA BALLET; *U.S. Private*, pg. 3136

711130 — MUSICAL GROUPS AND ARTISTS

8BALL MUSIC B.V.—See Bertelsmann SE & Co. KGaA; *Int'l*, pg. 989
ACADIANA SYMPHONY ASSOCIATION; *U.S. Private*, pg. 47
THE ACTORS FUND; *U.S. Private*, pg. 3981
AEG PRESENTS LLC—See The Anschutz Corporation; *U.S. Private*, pg. 3986
AUGUSTA SYMPHONY INC.; *U.S. Private*, pg. 392
AVEX HONG KONG LTD.—See Avex Inc.; *Int'l*, pg. 740
BAD BOY RECORDS—See Access Industries, Inc.; *U.S. Private*, pg. 52
BAD BOY RECORDS—See Bad Boy Worldwide Entertainment Group; *U.S. Private*, pg. 423
BAD BOY WORLDWIDE ENTERTAINMENT GROUP; *U.S. Private*, pg. 423
BBC SYMPHONY ORCHESTRA—See British Broadcasting Corporation; *Int'l*, pg. 1169
BELLEVUE PHILHARMONIC ORCHESTRA INC.; *U.S. Private*, pg. 520
BERKELEY SYMPHONY ORCHESTRA; *U.S. Private*, pg. 532
BEYOND FRAMES ENTERTAINMENT AB; *Int'l*, pg. 1005
BOULDER PHILHARMONIC ORCHESTRA; *U.S. Private*, pg. 623
B-SHARP MUSICAL PRODUCTIONS; *U.S. Private*, pg. 419
CINCINNATI SYMPHONY ORCHESTRA; *U.S. Private*, pg. 898
COLORADO SYMPHONY ASSOCIATION INC.; *U.S. Private*, pg. 975
CONSTANTIN FILM UND ENTERTAINMENT AG—See Highlight Communications AG; *Int'l*, pg. 3388
CORD WORLDWIDE LTD.—See Canada Pension Plan Investment Board; *Int'l*, pg. 1280
CORD WORLDWIDE LTD.—See EQT AB; *Int'l*, pg. 2482
DALLAS SYMPHONY ASSOCIATION INC.; *U.S. Private*, pg. 1150
DCINY; *U.S. Private*, pg. 1180
DENTSU MUSIC AND ENTERTAINMENT INC.—See Dentsu Group Inc.; *Int'l*, pg. 2038
DES MOINES SYMPHONY ASSOCIATION; *U.S. Private*, pg. 1210
DETROIT SYMPHONY ORCHESTRA, INC.; *U.S. Private*, pg. 1216
EDEL MEDIA & ENTERTAINMENT GMBH—See Edel SE & Co. KGaA; *Int'l*, pg. 2305
ENGLISH NATIONAL OPERA; *Int'l*, pg. 2435
ENTERTAINMENT FOR ALL, LLC—See Comcast Corporation; *U.S. Public*, pg. 538
ERIE PHILHARMONIC; *U.S. Private*, pg. 1420
ESM PRODUCTIONS, LLC—See Live Nation Entertainment, Inc.; *U.S. Public*, pg. 1328
FAIRBANKS SYMPHONY ASSOCIATION; *U.S. Private*, pg. 1462
FARGO-MOORHEAD SYMPHONY; *U.S. Private*, pg. 1473
FKP AREA ONE GMBH—See CTS Eventim AG & Co. KGaA; *Int'l*, pg. 1873
GAITHER MANAGEMENT GROUP; *U.S. Private*, pg. 1635
GRAND RAPIDS SYMPHONY SOCIETY; *U.S. Private*, pg. 1753
HARTFORD SYMPHONY ORCHESTRA INC.; *U.S. Private*, pg. 1873
HEADSUP ENTERTAINMENT INTERNATIONAL, INC.; *Int'l*, pg. 3301
HIGHLIGHT EVENT AG—See Highlight Event & Entertainment AG; *Int'l*, pg. 3388
HIGH NOON SALOON LLC—See Live Nation Entertainment, Inc.; *U.S. Public*, pg. 1329
INDIANAPOLIS CHAMBER ORCHESTRA; *U.S. Private*, pg. 2063

CORPORATE AFFILIATIONS

LINCOLN SYMPHONY ORCHESTRA; *U.S. Private*, pg. 2459
LIVE NATION BEC-TERO ENTERTAINMENT CO., LTD—See Live Nation Entertainment, Inc.; *U.S. Public*, pg. 1329
LIVE NATION FINLAND OY—See Live Nation Entertainment, Inc.; *U.S. Public*, pg. 1329
LOS ANGELES OPERA; *U.S. Private*, pg. 2496
LOUISVILLE ORCHESTRA, INC.; *U.S. Private*, pg. 2500
LUBBOCK SYMPHONY ORCHESTRA; *U.S. Private*, pg. 2510
MIFAH CO. LTD.—See GMM Grammy Public Company Limited; *Int'l*, pg. 3013
MOJO CONCERTS BV—See Live Nation Entertainment, Inc.; *U.S. Public*, pg. 1330
MORGAN PARK SUMMER MUSIC FESTIVAL ASSOCIATION INC.; *U.S. Private*, pg. 2784
MUSICAL ARTS ASSOCIATION; *U.S. Private*, pg. 2818
NASHVILLE SYMPHONY ASSOCIATION; *U.S. Private*, pg. 2836
NORTH CAROLINA OPERA; *U.S. Private*, pg. 2943
NORTH CAROLINA SYMPHONY; *U.S. Private*, pg. 2943
PETER NERO & THE PHILLY POPS—See The Philadelphia Orchestra Association; *U.S. Private*, pg. 4094
THE PHILADELPHIA ORCHESTRA ASSOCIATION; *U.S. Private*, pg. 4094
THE PHILADELPHIA ORCHESTRA—See The Philadelphia Orchestra Association; *U.S. Private*, pg. 4094
PITTSBURGH OPERA; *U.S. Private*, pg. 3191
PONY CANYON MUSIC INC.—See Fuji Media Holdings, Inc.; *Int'l*, pg. 2814
QUEENS SYMPHONY ORCHESTRA; *U.S. Private*, pg. 3325
RACINE SYMPHONY ORCHESTRA ASSOCIATION INC.; *U.S. Private*, pg. 3342
RAINIER SYMPHONY; *U.S. Private*, pg. 3348
REVERB, INC.—See Etsy, Inc.; *U.S. Public*, pg. 797
RHODE ISLAND PHILHARMONIC ORCHESTRA INC.; *U.S. Private*, pg. 3422
SAN DIEGO SYMPHONY ORCHESTRA ASSOCIATION; *U.S. Private*, pg. 3539
SAN FRANCISCO SYMPHONY; *U.S. Private*, pg. 3541
SOUTH CAROLINA PHILHARMONIC ASSOCIATION INC.; *U.S. Private*, pg. 3720
SPOKANE SYMPHONY ORCHESTRA; *U.S. Private*, pg. 3760
SYRACUSE SYMPHONY ORCHESTRA; *U.S. Private*, pg. 3905
TOLEDO SYMPHONY; *U.S. Private*, pg. 4181
TUCSON SYMPHONY ORCHESTRA; *U.S. Private*, pg. 4256
VERMONT SYMPHONY ORCHESTRA; *U.S. Private*, pg. 4367
VIACOM INTERNATIONAL MEDIA NETWORKS—See National Amusements, Inc.; *U.S. Private*, pg. 2842
VIRGINIA SYMPHONY ORCHESTRA; *U.S. Private*, pg. 4388
WESTERN PIEDMONT SYMPHONY; *U.S. Private*, pg. 4495
WOLFSON ENTERTAINMENT, INC.—See Live Nation Entertainment, Inc.; *U.S. Public*, pg. 1331

711190 — OTHER PERFORMING ARTS COMPANIES

BEST PARTY CONCEPTS, LLC—See Vinco Ventures, Inc.; *U.S. Public*, pg. 2298
BOOT RANCH CIRCLE LLC—See Terra Verde Group, LLC; *U.S. Private*, pg. 3970
BOOT RANCH CIRCLE LLC—See Wheelock Street Capital L.L.C.; *U.S. Private*, pg. 4506
CHINA HEAVEN CREATION INTERNATIONAL PERFORMING ARTS CO., LTD.—See China Travel International Investment Hong Kong Ltd; *Int'l*, pg. 1560
EVENT MARKETING SERVICE GMBH; *Int'l*, pg. 2562
FELD ENTERTAINMENT, INC.; *U.S. Private*, pg. 1493
FM PRODUCTION SERVICES LLC—See Comcast Corporation; *U.S. Public*, pg. 538
INNERCEPT MANAGEMENT CORPORATION; *U.S. Private*, pg. 2080
NBCUNIVERSAL ENTERTAINMENT JAPAN LLC—See Comcast Corporation; *U.S. Public*, pg. 539
NICK AT NITE'S TV LAND RETROMERCIALS INC.—See National Amusements, Inc.; *U.S. Private*, pg. 2842
RED MOUNTAIN ENTERTAINMENT, LLC—See Live Nation Entertainment, Inc.; *U.S. Public*, pg. 1330
RINGLING BROS., BARNUM & BAILEY COMBINED SHOWS, INC.—See Feld Entertainment, Inc.; *U.S. Private*, pg. 1493
RUSH COMMUNICATIONS, INC.; *U.S. Private*, pg. 3505
TIHATI PRODUCTIONS LTD., INC.; *U.S. Private*, pg. 4170

711211 — SPORTS TEAMS AND CLUBS

AALBORG BOLDSPILKLUB A/S; *Int'l*, pg. 36
ADMIRALS CLUB, INC.—See American Airlines Group Inc.; *U.S. Public*, pg. 95

N.A.I.C.S. INDEX

711211 — SPORTS TEAMS AND CL...

AGF A S; *Int'l*, pg. 206
AIK FOTBOLL AB; *Int'l*, pg. 232
ALTOONA CURVE BASEBALL CLUB—See Lozinak Professional Baseball LLC; *U.S. Private*, pg. 2507
AMERICAN BASKETBALL ASSOCIATION, INC.; *U.S. Public*, pg. 97
THE AMERICAN JUNIOR GOLF ASSOCIATION; *U.S. Private*, pg. 3986
AMERICAN POOLPLAYERS ASSOCIATION INC.; *U.S. Private*, pg. 244
AMERICAN YOUTH SOCCER ORGANIZATION; *U.S. Private*, pg. 258
ANAHEIM AMATEUR HOCKEY ASSOCIATION; *U.S. Private*, pg. 271
ANAHEIM DUCKS HOCKEY CLUB, LLC; *U.S. Private*, pg. 271
ANGELS BASEBALL, L.P.; *U.S. Private*, pg. 282
ARIZONA CARDINALS FOOTBALL CLUB, INC.; *U.S. Private*, pg. 323
ARIZONA DIAMONDBACKS; *U.S. Private*, pg. 324
ARIZONA PROFESSIONAL BASEBALL LTD PARTNERSHIP—See Pinnacle West Capital Corporation; *U.S. Public*, pg. 1692
A.S. ROMA S.P.A—See The Friedkin Group, Inc.; *U.S. Private*, pg. 4031
ASSOCIAZIONE CALCIO MILAN S.P.A.—See RedBird Capital Partners L.P.; *U.S. Private*, pg. 3377
ASTON VILLA FOOTBALL CLUB LIMITED—See Aston Villa Limited; *Int'l*, pg. 655
ASTON VILLA LIMITED; *Int'l*, pg. 655
ASTRALIS A/S; *Int'l*, pg. 658
ATLANTA BRAVES, INC.—See Atlanta Braves Holdings, Inc.; *U.S. Public*, pg. 222
ATLANTA FALCONS FOOTBALL CLUB, LLC; *U.S. Private*, pg. 370
ATLANTA HAWKS, L.P.; *U.S. Private*, pg. 370
ATLANTA NATIONAL LEAGUE BASEBALL CLUB, LLC—See Atlanta Braves Holdings, Inc.; *U.S. Public*, pg. 222
AUSTRALIAN GRAND PRIX CORPORATION PTY. LTD.; *Int'l*, pg. 721
AUSTRALIAN RUGBY UNION; *Int'l*, pg. 722
AZUL AZUL SA; *Int'l*, pg. 781
BALTIMORE ORIOLES, L.P.; *U.S. Private*, pg. 462
BALTIMORE RAVENS LIMITED PARTNERSHIP; *U.S. Private*, pg. 462
THE BASEBALL CLUB OF SEATTLE, L.P.; *U.S. Private*, pg. 3992
BASEBALL HEAVEN INC.—See Steel Partners Holdings L.P.; *U.S. Public*, pg. 1942
BEC-TERO ARSENAL CO., LTD.—See BEC World Public Company Limited; *Int'l*, pg. 936
BEC-TERO SASANA CO., LTD—See BEC World Public Company Limited; *Int'l*, pg. 936
BENETTON RUGBY TREVISO S.R.L.—See Edizione S.r.l.; *Int'l*, pg. 2312
BESIKTAS FUTBOL YATIRIMLARI SANAYI VE TICARET AS; *Int'l*, pg. 998
BIRMINGHAM BARONS, LLC; *U.S. Private*, pg. 564
BIRMINGHAM CITY FOOTBALL CLUB PLC—See Birmingham Sports Holdings Limited; *Int'l*, pg. 1048
BISON BASEBALL, INC.—See Rich Holdings, Inc.; *U.S. Private*, pg. 3426
BLACKHEATH & BROMLEY HARRIERS AC; *Int'l*, pg. 1061
BORUSSIA DORTMUND GMBH & CO. KGAA; *Int'l*, pg. 1115
BOSTON CELTICS LIMITED PARTNERSHIP—See Boston Basketball Partners LLC; *U.S. Private*, pg. 621
BOSTON PROFESSIONAL HOCKEY ASSOCIATION, INC.; *U.S. Private*, pg. 622
BOSTON RED SOX BASEBALL CLUB LIMITED PARTNERSHIP—See Fenway Sports Group Holdings, LLC; *U.S. Private*, pg. 1496
BRISBANE BRONCOS RUGBY LEAGUE CLUB PTY. LTD.—See News Corporation; *U.S. Private*, pg. 1520
BROENDBYERNES IF FODBOLD A/S; *Int'l*, pg. 1173
BUCCANEERS LIMITED PARTNERSHIP; *U.S. Private*, pg. 676
BUFFALO BILLS, INC.; *U.S. Private*, pg. 680
BVB MERCHANDISING GMBH—See Borussia Dortmund GmbH & Co. KGaA; *Int'l*, pg. 1115
BVB STADION GMBH—See Borussia Dortmund GmbH & Co. KGaA; *Int'l*, pg. 1115
BVB STADIONMANAGEMENT GMBH—See Borussia Dortmund GmbH & Co. KGaA; *Int'l*, pg. 1115
CALGARY FLAMES LIMITED PARTNERSHIP; *Int'l*, pg. 1263
CELTIC F.C.—See Celtic plc; *Int'l*, pg. 1396
CELTIC PLC; *Int'l*, pg. 1396
CHAMPIONSHIP PRODUCTIONS INC.—See National Amusements, Inc.; *U.S. Private*, pg. 2841
CHELSEA FOOTBALL CLUB LIMITED—See Clearlake Capital Group, L.P.; *U.S. Private*, pg. 933
CHICAGO BEARS FOOTBALL CLUB, INC.; *U.S. Private*, pg. 877
CHICAGO BLACKHAWK HOCKEY TEAM, INC.—See Wirtz Corporation; *U.S. Private*, pg. 4547

CHICAGO NATIONAL LEAGUE BALL CLUB, LLC; *U.S. Private*, pg. 878
CHICAGO PROFESSIONAL SPORTS LIMITED PARTNERSHIP; *U.S. Private*, pg. 878
CHICAGO WHITE SOX LTD.; *U.S. Private*, pg. 879
CHINA SPORTS INDUSTRY GROUP CO., LTD.; *Int'l*, pg. 1553
CHIP GANASSI RACING TEAMS, INC. - INDYCAR—See Chip Ganassi Racing Teams, Inc.; *U.S. Private*, pg. 886
CHIP GANASSI RACING WITH FELIX SABATES, LLC—See Chip Ganassi Racing Teams, Inc.; *U.S. Private*, pg. 886
CHUNICHI DRAGONS CO., INC.—See Chunichi Shimbun Co., Ltd.; *Int'l*, pg. 1598
CINCINNATI BENGALS, INC.; *U.S. Private*, pg. 897
CLEVELAND BROWNS FOOTBALL COMPANY LLC; *U.S. Private*, pg. 940
CLEVELAND CAVALIERS/QUICKEN LOANS ARENA—See Cavaliers Operating Company, LLC; *U.S. Private*, pg. 795
CLEVELAND INDIANS BASEBALL COMPANY, INC.; *U.S. Private*, pg. 941
CLUB DE HOCKEY CANADIEN, INC.; *Int'l*, pg. 1664
COLORADO AVALANCHE, LLC—See Kroenke Sports & Entertainment, LLC; *U.S. Private*, pg. 2352
COLORADO ROCKIES BASEBALL CLUB, LTD.; *U.S. Private*, pg. 974
CORPUS CHRISTI BASEBALL CLUB, L.P.—See Ryan Sanders Baseball, L.P.; *U.S. Private*, pg. 3510
COYOTES HOCKEY, LLC—See Renaissance Sports & Entertainment, LLC; *U.S. Private*, pg. 3397
DALE EARNHARDT, INC.; *U.S. Private*, pg. 1148
DALLAS COWBOYS FOOTBALL CLUB, LTD.; *U.S. Private*, pg. 1149
DALLAS MAVERICKS; *U.S. Private*, pg. 1150
DALLAS STARS L.P.—See Hicks Holdings, LLC; *U.S. Private*, pg. 1934
DEMPO SPORTS CLUB PVT. LTD.—See Goa Carbon Ltd.; *Int'l*, pg. 3018
DENVER BRONCOS FOOTBALL CLUB—See Bowlen Sports, Inc.; *U.S. Private*, pg. 626
THE DENVER NUGGETS LIMITED PARTNERSHIP—See Kroenke Sports & Entertainment, LLC; *U.S. Private*, pg. 2352
THE DETROIT LIONS, INC.; *U.S. Private*, pg. 4020
DETROIT PISTONS BASKETBALL COMPANY—See Platinum Equity, LLC; *U.S. Private*, pg. 3206
DETROIT TIGERS BASEBALL CLUB, INC.—See Ilitch Holdings, Inc.; *U.S. Private*, pg. 2041
THE DURHAM BULLS BASEBALL CLUB, INC.—See Capitol Broadcasting Company, Inc.; *U.S. Private*, pg. 743
EAGLE FOOTBALL GROUP; *Int'l*, pg. 2264
EBARA SHOHNAN SPORTS CENTER INC.—See Ebara Corporation; *Int'l*, pg. 2282
ELIZABETHTON TWINS BASEBALL CLUB—See Pohlad Companies; *U.S. Private*, pg. 3221
EXTRA INNINGS FRANCHISE COMPANY; *U.S. Private*, pg. 1452
FIFA TRANSFER MATCHING SYSTEM GMBH—See Federation Internationale de Football Association; *Int'l*, pg. 2631
FLORIDA EVERBLADES; *U.S. Private*, pg. 1548
FLORIDA MARLINS, L.P.; *U.S. Private*, pg. 1549
FLORIDA PANTHERS HOCKEY CLUB, LTD.—See Sunrise Sports & Entertainment LLLP; *U.S. Private*, pg. 3870
FOOTBALL CLUB DES GIRONDINS DE BORDEAUX—See B. Riley Financial, Inc.; *U.S. Public*, pg. 261
FORT MYERS MIRACLE PROFESSIONAL BASEBALL—See Pohlad Companies; *U.S. Private*, pg. 3221
FUTEBOL CLUBE DO PORTO; *Int'l*, pg. 2852
GENERAL SPORTS & ENTERTAINMENT, LLC; *U.S. Private*, pg. 1667
GOLDEN STATE WARRIORS, LLC; *U.S. Private*, pg. 1733
GRAND RAPIDS GRIFFINS—See DP Fox Ventures, LLC; *U.S. Private*, pg. 1270
GREEN BAY PACKERS, INC.; *U.S. Private*, pg. 1771
GS SPORTS CORPORATION—See GS Holdings Corp.; *Int'l*, pg. 3142
HANSHIN TIGERS BASEBALL CLUB—See Hankyu Hanshin Holdings Inc.; *Int'l*, pg. 3256
HARLEM GLOBETROTTERS INTERNATIONAL, INC.—See Herschend Family Entertainment Corp.; *U.S. Private*, pg. 1926
HENDRICK MOTORSPORTS, LLC—See The Hendrick Companies, LLC; *U.S. Private*, pg. 4051
HIBERNIAN FOOTBALL CLUB LTD.; *Int'l*, pg. 3383
HIROSHIMA TOYO CARP, K.K.; *Int'l*, pg. 3405
HITACHI KASHIWA REYSOL CO., LTD.—See Hitachi, Ltd.; *Int'l*, pg. 3420
HOCKEY WESTERN NEW YORK, LLC; *U.S. Private*, pg. 1958
HORNETS BASKETBALL, LLC; *U.S. Private*, pg. 1984
HOUSTON ASTROS, LLC—See Houston Baseball Partners LLC; *U.S. Private*, pg. 1993
HOUSTON TEXANS, L.P.; *U.S. Private*, pg. 1994
HUMAN PLANNING CO., LTD.—See Human Holdings Co., Ltd.; *Int'l*, pg. 3529

HURRICANES HOCKEY LIMITED PARTNERSHIP—See Hurricanes Holdings, LLC; *U.S. Private*, pg. 2013
HYLTE JAKT & LANTMAN AB—See BHG Group AB; *Int'l*, pg. 1015
I9 SPORTS CORPORATION; *U.S. Private*, pg. 2027
IMPULSORA DEL DEPORTIVO NECAXA, S.A. DE C.V.—See Grupo Televisa, S.A.B.; *Int'l*, pg. 3136
INDIANAPOLIS COLTS, INC.; *U.S. Private*, pg. 2063
IP-AGENCY FINLAND OY—See BHG Group AB; *Int'l*, pg. 1015
JACKSONVILLE JAGUARS, LLC; *U.S. Private*, pg. 2179
JAZZ BASKETBALL INVESTORS, INC.; *U.S. Private*, pg. 2192
JEONBUK HYUNDAI MOTORS FC CO., LTD.—See Hyundai Motor Company; *Int'l*, pg. 3560
JOE GIBBS RACING INC.; *U.S. Private*, pg. 2218
JUVENTUS FOOTBALL CLUB S.P.A—See Giovanni Agnelli B.V.; *Int'l*, pg. 2978
K2 GAMER (PVT) LTD.—See Gamer Pakistan Inc.; *U.S. Public*, pg. 895
KANSAS CITY CHIEFS FOOTBALL CLUB, INC.; *U.S. Private*, pg. 2260
KANSAS CITY ROYALS BASEBALL CORPORATION; *U.S. Private*, pg. 2260
KSA INDUSTRIES INC.; *U.S. Private*, pg. 2354
LA CLIPPERS LLC; *U.S. Private*, pg. 2368
THE LAS VEGAS GOLDEN KNIGHTS—See Black Knight Sports & Entertainment LLC; *U.S. Private*, pg. 572
LIGHTNING HOCKEY LP—See Tampa Bay Sports & Entertainment LLC; *U.S. Private*, pg. 3929
LIVERPOOL FOOTBALL CLUB & ATHLETIC GROUNDS LTD.—See Fenway Sports Group Holdings, LLC; *U.S. Private*, pg. 1496
LOS ANGELES DODGERS LLC—See Guggenheim Baseball Management, L.P.; *U.S. Private*, pg. 1811
LOS ANGELES KINGS HOCKEY CLUB L.P.—See The Anschutz Corporation; *U.S. Private*, pg. 3987
THE LOS ANGELES LAKERS, INC.; *U.S. Private*, pg. 4072
MADISON SQUARE GARDEN, L.P.—See Madison Square Garden Sports Corp.; *U.S. Public*, pg. 1354
MAGIC SPORTS MEDIA GMBH—See Highlight Communications AG; *Int'l*, pg. 3388
MAJOR LEAGUE FOOTBALL, INC.; *U.S. Public*, pg. 1355
MEMPHIS BASKETBALL, LLC; *U.S. Private*, pg. 2664
MIAMI DOLPHINS, LTD.—See Dolphins Enterprises, LLC; *U.S. Private*, pg. 1255
MIAMI HEAT LIMITED PARTNERSHIP—See FBA II, Inc.; *U.S. Private*, pg. 1485
MILWAUKEE BREWERS BASEBALL CLUB, INC.; *U.S. Private*, pg. 2739
MILWAUKEE BUCKS, INC.; *U.S. Private*, pg. 2739
MINNESOTA TIMBERWOLVES BASKETBALL LIMITED PARTNERSHIP; *U.S. Private*, pg. 2744
MINNESOTA TWINS, LLC—See Pohlad Companies; *U.S. Private*, pg. 3221
MINNESOTA VIKINGS FOOTBALL LLC; *U.S. Private*, pg. 2744
MINNESOTA WILD HOCKEY CLUB, LP—See Minnesota Hockey Ventures Group, LP; *U.S. Private*, pg. 2743
MSG NETWORKS INC.—See Sphere Entertainment Co.; *U.S. Public*, pg. 1918
MYRTLE BEACH PELICANS BASEBALL CLUB—See Greenberg Sports Group Inc.; *U.S. Private*, pg. 1775
NATIONAL COLLEGIATE ATHLETIC ASSOCIATION; *U.S. Private*, pg. 2850
NATURALS BASEBALL, INC.—See Rich Holdings, Inc.; *U.S. Private*, pg. 3426
NC ELITE VOLLEYBALL CLUB; *U.S. Private*, pg. 2875
NEW BRITAIN BASEBALL CLUB, INC.—See Pohlad Companies; *U.S. Private*, pg. 3221
NEW ENGLAND PATRIOTS FOOTBALL CLUB, INC.—See The Kraft Group LLC; *U.S. Private*, pg. 4066
NEW JERSEY DEVILS LLC—See Devils Holdings, LLC; *U.S. Private*, pg. 1218
NEWMAN/HAAS RACING, LLC; *U.S. Private*, pg. 2916
NEW ORLEANS PELICANS NBA, LLC; *U.S. Private*, pg. 2904
NEW ORLEANS SAINTS L.P.; *U.S. Private*, pg. 2904
NEW YORK FOOTBALL GIANTS, INC.; *U.S. Private*, pg. 2909
NEW YORK ISLANDERS HOCKEY CLUB, L.P.; *U.S. Private*, pg. 2910
NEW YORK JETS FOOTBALL CLUB, INC.; *U.S. Private*, pg. 2910
NEW YORK KNICKS, LLC—See Madison Square Garden Sports Corp.; *U.S. Public*, pg. 1354
NEW YORK RANGERS, LLC—See Madison Square Garden Sports Corp.; *U.S. Public*, pg. 1354
NEW YORK YANKEES—See New York Yankees Partnership; *U.S. Private*, pg. 2912
NFL MANAGEMENT COUNCIL—See National Football League; *U.S. Private*, pg. 2854
NORTH TEXAS STATE SOCCER ASSOCIATION, INC.; *U.S. Private*, pg. 2948
OAKLAND ATHLETICS LIMITED PARTNERSHIP—See Athletics Investment Group, LLC; *U.S. Private*, pg. 368
THE OAKLAND RAIDERS, L.P.; *U.S. Private*, pg. 4087
OKLAHOMA CITY THUNDER—See The Professional Bas-

711211 — SPORTS TEAMS AND CL...

ketball Club, LLC; *U.S. Private*, pg. 4100
ORLANDO MAGIC, LTD.—See RDV Corporation; *U.S. Private*, pg. 3364
OTTAWA SENATORS HOCKEY CLUB—See Capital Sports Group of Companies; *Int'l*, pg. 1312
PACERS BASKETBALL, LLC; *U.S. Private*, pg. 3064
PADRES L.P.; *U.S. Private*, pg. 3074
PANTHERS FOOTBALL, LLC; *U.S. Private*, pg. 3087
PHANTOMS HOCKEY, LLC—See Comcast Corporation; *U.S. Public*, pg. 538
PHILADELPHIA 76ERS, L.P.; *U.S. Private*, pg. 3168
PHILADELPHIA EAGLES FOOTBALL CLUB, INC.; *U.S. Private*, pg. 3168
PHILADELPHIA FLYERS, L.P.—See Comcast Corporation; *U.S. Public*, pg. 538
PHILADELPHIA SKATING CLUB & HUMANE SOCIETY; *U.S. Private*, pg. 3169
THE PHILLIES, L.P.; *U.S. Private*, pg. 4095
PHOENIX MERCURY—See Suns Legacy Partners, LLC; *U.S. Private*, pg. 3871
PHOENIX SUNS—See Suns Legacy Partners, LLC; *U.S. Private*, pg. 3870
PITTSBURGH BASEBALL PARTNERSHIP—See The Nutting Company, Inc.; *U.S. Private*, pg. 4086
PITTSBURGH PENGUINS LLC—See Lemieux Group L.P.; *U.S. Private*, pg. 2421
PITTSBURGH STEELERS SPORTS INC.; *U.S. Private*, pg. 3191
PORTLAND TRAIL BLAZERS—See Vulcan Inc.; *U.S. Private*, pg. 4416
RADIO CITY PRODUCTIONS LLC—See Madison Square Garden Entertainment Corp.; *U.S. Public*, pg. 1353
THE RAMS FOOTBALL COMPANY, LLC—See The Los Angeles Rams, LLC; *U.S. Private*, pg. 4072
RANGERS BASEBALL EXPRESS LLC; *U.S. Private*, pg. 3355
RANGERS BASEBALL LLC—See Rangers Baseball Express LLC; *U.S. Private*, pg. 3355
REAL SALT LAKE—See SCP Worldwide; *U.S. Private*, pg. 3579
REDS BASEBALL PARTNERS, LLC; *U.S. Private*, pg. 3379
RICHARD PETTY MOTORSPORTS INC.—See Booth Creek Management Corporation; *U.S. Private*, pg. 616
RICHARD PETTY MOTORSPORTS LLC—See BV Investment Partners, LLC; *U.S. Private*, pg. 699
RIPKEN BASEBALL, INC.; *U.S. Private*, pg. 3439
ROCHESTER COMMUNITY BASEBALL, INC.; *U.S. Public*, pg. 1804
ROCKETS PARTNER LP; *U.S. Private*, pg. 3466
ROUND ROCK BASEBALL CLUB, L.P.—See Ryan Sanders Baseball, L.P.; *U.S. Private*, pg. 3510
ROUSH CORPORATION—See Fenway Sports Group Holdings, LLC; *U.S. Private*, pg. 1496
ROUSH CORPORATION—See Roush Enterprises, Inc.; *U.S. Private*, pg. 3489
ROYAL CHALLENGERS SPORTS PRIVATE LIMITED—See Diageo plc; *Int'l*, pg. 2103
SACRAMENTO KINGS LIMITED PARTNERSHIP—See Ranadive Group; *U.S. Private*, pg. 3352
SAGA HISAMITSU SPRINGS CO., LTD.—See Hisamitsu Pharmaceutical Co., Inc.; *Int'l*, pg. 3406
SAINT LOUIS CARDINALS, L.P.; *U.S. Private*, pg. 3529
SALT LAKE BEES—See Angels Baseball, L.P.; *U.S. Private*, pg. 282
SAN ANTONIO SPURS, LLC—See Spurs Sports & Entertainment; *U.S. Private*, pg. 3765
SAN DIEGO CHARGERS FOOTBALL CO.; *U.S. Private*, pg. 3539
SAN FRANCISCO FORTY NINERS, LTD.—See DeBartolo Corporation; *U.S. Private*, pg. 1186
SAN FRANCISCO GIANTS BASEBALL CLUB—See San Francisco Baseball Associates, L.P.; *U.S. Private*, pg. 3540
SAN JOSE SHARKS, LLC; *U.S. Private*, pg. 3541
SARASOTA POLO CLUB—See Schroeder-Manatee Ranch, Inc.; *U.S. Private*, pg. 3569
SEATTLE MARINERS BASEBALL CLUB; *U.S. Private*, pg. 3592
SEATTLE SEAHAWKS—See Vulcan Inc.; *U.S. Private*, pg. 4416
SIGNING DAY SPORTS, INC.; *U.S. Public*, pg. 1878
STATE COLLEGE SPIKES BASEBALL CLUB—See Greenberg Sports Group Inc.; *U.S. Private*, pg. 1775
STERLING METS, L.P.—See Sterling Equities, Inc.; *U.S. Private*, pg. 3805
ST. LOUIS BLUES HOCKEY CLUB, LLC—See SCP Worldwide; *U.S. Private*, pg. 3579
SWB YANKEES, LLC—See Mandalay Entertainment Group; *U.S. Private*, pg. 2562
SWB YANKEES, LLC—See New York Yankees Partnership; *U.S. Private*, pg. 2912
SWB YANKEES, LLC—See Seaport Capital, LLC; *U.S. Private*, pg. 3586
TAMPA BAY RAYS BASEBALL, LTD.; *U.S. Private*, pg. 3929
TAMPA SPORTS AUTHORITY; *U.S. Private*, pg. 3930
TENNESSEE FOOTBALL, INC.; *U.S. Private*, pg. 3907

TORONTO MAPLE LEAFS HOCKEY CLUB INC.—See BCE Inc.; *Int'l*, pg. 927
TORONTO RAPTORS BASKETBALL CLUB INC.—See BCE Inc.; *Int'l*, pg. 927
TRI-VALLEY MINOR HOCKEY ASSOCIATION; *U.S. Private*, pg. 4224
UK ELITE SOCCER INC.—See Steel Partners Holdings L.P.; *U.S. Public*, pg. 1943
THE UNITED STATES PONY CLUBS INC.; *U.S. Private*, pg. 4129
VANCOUVER CANUCKS—See Aquilini Investment Group; *Int'l*, pg. 528
WASHINGTON CAPITALS—See Lincoln Holdings LLC; *U.S. Private*, pg. 2457
WASHINGTON FOOTBALL, INC.; *U.S. Private*, pg. 4447
WASHINGTON MYSTICS—See Lincoln Holdings LLC; *U.S. Private*, pg. 2457
WASHINGTON NATIONALS, L.P.; *U.S. Private*, pg. 4448
WASHINGTON WIZARDS—See Lincoln Holdings LLC; *U.S. Private*, pg. 2457
WEST VIRGINIA BLACK BEARS BASEBALL, INC.—See Rich Holdings, Inc.; *U.S. Private*, pg. 3426
WNBA ENTERPRISES, LLC—See National Basketball Association; *U.S. Private*, pg. 2848
WOLVERHAMPTON WANDERERS FOOTBALL CLUB (1986) LIMITED—See Fosun International Limited; *Int'l*, pg. 2752
WTA TOUR, INC.; *U.S. Private*, pg. 4574
THE YOKOHAMA BAYSTARS BASEBALL CLUB, INC.—See DeNA Co., Ltd.; *Int'l*, pg. 2026
ZAKSA S.A.—See Grupa Azoty S.A.; *Int'l*, pg. 3116

711212 — RACETRACKS

ALPHA MONTICELLO, INC.—See Empire Resorts, Inc.; *U.S. Private*, pg. 1385
ARLINGTON PARK—See Churchill Downs, Inc.; *U.S. Public*, pg. 493
ATLANTA MOTOR SPEEDWAY, INC.—See Sonic Financial Corporation; *U.S. Private*, pg. 3713
AUSTRALIAN TURF CLUB (ATC); *Int'l*, pg. 722
AUTO CLUB SPEEDWAY—See National Association for Stock Car Auto Racing, Inc.; *U.S. Private*, pg. 2845
AXCIS INFORMATION NETWORK INC.—See Equibase Company LLC; *U.S. Private*, pg. 1415
BRAINERD INTERNATIONAL RACEWAY—See BIR Holdings, LLC; *U.S. Private*, pg. 564
BRISTOL MOTOR SPEEDWAY—See Sonic Financial Corporation; *U.S. Private*, pg. 3713
CALDER RACE COURSE, INC.—See Churchill Downs, Inc.; *U.S. Public*, pg. 493
CALL NOW, INC.; *U.S. Private*, pg. 721
CANTERBURY PARK ENTERTAINMENT LLC—See Canterbury Park Holding Corporation; *U.S. Public*, pg. 430
CCR PENNSYLVANIA RACING, INC.—See PENN Entertainment, Inc.; *U.S. Public*, pg. 1662
CHARLOTTE MOTOR SPEEDWAY, LLC—See Sonic Financial Corporation; *U.S. Private*, pg. 3713
CHURCHILL DOWNS, INC.; *U.S. Public*, pg. 493
CHURCHILL DOWNS MANAGEMENT COMPANY, LLC—See Churchill Downs, Inc.; *U.S. Public*, pg. 493
CLUB HIPICO DE SANTIAGO S.A.; *Int'l*, pg. 1664
COLONIAL DOWNS HOLDINGS, INC.—See Jacobs Entertainment, Inc.; *U.S. Private*, pg. 2180
DARLINGTON RACEWAY OF SOUTH CAROLINA, LLC—See National Association for Stock Car Auto Racing, Inc.; *U.S. Private*, pg. 2845
DAYTONA INTERNATIONAL SPEEDWAY, LLC—See National Association for Stock Car Auto Racing, Inc.; *U.S. Private*, pg. 2845
DELAWARE NORTH COMPANIES GAMING & ENTERTAINMENT—See Delaware North Companies, Inc.; *U.S. Private*, pg. 1194
DELAWARE RACING ASSOCIATION; *U.S. Private*, pg. 1195
DOVER INTERNATIONAL SPEEDWAY, INC.—See Sonic Financial Corporation; *U.S. Private*, pg. 3713
EQUIBASE COMPANY LLC; *U.S. Private*, pg. 1415
FAIR GROUNDS CORPORATION—See Churchill Downs, Inc.; *U.S. Public*, pg. 493
FINGER LAKES RACING ASSOCIATION INC.—See Delaware North Companies, Inc.; *U.S. Private*, pg. 1194
FLAMBORO DOWNS LIMITED—See Great Canadian Gaming Corporation; *Int'l*, pg. 3063
FULL THROTTLE INDOOR KART RACING INC.; *U.S. Private*, pg. 1621
GEORGIAN DOWNS LIMITED—See Great Canadian Gaming Corporation; *Int'l*, pg. 3063
GLOBAL GAMING RP, LLC—See Global Gaming Solutions, LLC; *U.S. Private*, pg. 1714
HARRAH'S BOSSIER CITY MANAGEMENT COMPANY, LLC—See Caesars Entertainment, Inc.; *U.S. Public*, pg. 419
HIALEAH INCORPORATED; *U.S. Private*, pg. 1932
HOMESTEAD-MIAMI SPEEDWAY, LLC—See National Association for Stock Car Auto Racing, Inc.; *U.S. Private*, pg. 2845

HOOSIER PARK, LLC—See Caesars Entertainment, Inc.; *U.S. Public*, pg. 420
INDIANAPOLIS MOTOR SPEEDWAY, LLC—See Penske Corporation; *U.S. Private*, pg. 3138
IOWA SPEEDWAY, LLC; *U.S. Private*, pg. 2135
ISC.COM, LLC—See National Association for Stock Car Auto Racing, Inc.; *U.S. Private*, pg. 2845
ISC PUBLICATIONS, INC.—See National Association for Stock Car Auto Racing, Inc.; *U.S. Private*, pg. 2845
ISM RACEWAY—See National Association for Stock Car Auto Racing, Inc.; *U.S. Private*, pg. 2845
KANSAS SPEEDWAY CORPORATION—See National Association for Stock Car Auto Racing, Inc.; *U.S. Private*, pg. 2845
KENTUCKY RACEWAY, LLC—See Sonic Financial Corporation; *U.S. Private*, pg. 3713
KEYSTONE TURF CLUB, INC.—See International Turf Investment Co., Inc.; *U.S. Private*, pg. 2121
LAS VEGAS MOTOR SPEEDWAY—See Sonic Financial Corporation; *U.S. Private*, pg. 3713
LEXINGTON TROTS BREEDERS ASSOCIATION; *U.S. Private*, pg. 2440
LONE STAR RACE PARK, LTD.—See Global Gaming Solutions, LLC; *U.S. Private*, pg. 1714
MARTINSVILLE INTERNATIONAL, INC.—See National Association for Stock Car Auto Racing, Inc.; *U.S. Private*, pg. 2845
MAYWOOD PARK TROTTING ASSOCIATION, INC.; *U.S. Private*, pg. 2623
MICHIGAN INTERNATIONAL SPEEDWAY, INC.—See National Association for Stock Car Auto Racing, Inc.; *U.S. Private*, pg. 2845
MOTORSPORTS ACCEPTANCE CORPORATION—See National Association for Stock Car Auto Racing, Inc.; *U.S. Private*, pg. 2846
NASHVILLE SPEEDWAY, USA, INC.—See Sonic Financial Corporation; *U.S. Private*, pg. 3713
NEVADA SPEEDWAY, LLC—See Sonic Financial Corporation; *U.S. Private*, pg. 3713
NEW HAMPSHIRE MOTOR SPEEDWAY, INC.—See Sonic Financial Corporation; *U.S. Private*, pg. 3713
NEW JERSEY SPORTS & EXPOSITION AUTHORITY; *U.S. Private*, pg. 2898
NEW YORK RACING ASSOCIATION, INC.; *U.S. Private*, pg. 2912
OAKLAWN JOCKEY CLUB, INC.; *U.S. Private*, pg. 2985
OCEAN DOWNS LLC—See Churchill Downs, Inc.; *U.S. Public*, pg. 494
THE OLD EVANGELINE DOWNS, LLC—See Boyd Gaming Corporation; *U.S. Public*, pg. 378
PARK JEFFERSON SPEEDWAY INC.—See Heroes, Inc.; *U.S. Private*, pg. 1926
PENNSYLVANIA NATIONAL TURF CLUB, LLC—See PENN Entertainment, Inc.; *U.S. Public*, pg. 1662
PINNACLE RETAMA PARTNERS, LLC—See PENN Entertainment, Inc.; *U.S. Public*, pg. 1662
QUARTER HORSE RACING INC.; *U.S. Private*, pg. 3324
RACEWAY ASSOCIATES, LLC—See National Association for Stock Car Auto Racing, Inc.; *U.S. Private*, pg. 2846
RACING ASSOCIATION OF CENTRAL IOWA; *U.S. Private*, pg. 3342
RICHMOND INTERNATIONAL RACEWAY, INC.—See National Association for Stock Car Auto Racing, Inc.; *U.S. Private*, pg. 2846
ROUTE 66 RACEWAY, LLC—See National Association for Stock Car Auto Racing, Inc.; *U.S. Private*, pg. 2846
RUIDOSO DOWNS RACING INC.; *U.S. Private*, pg. 3503
SARATOGA HARNESS RACING INC.; *U.S. Private*, pg. 3549
SCIOTO DOWNS, INC.—See Caesars Entertainment, Inc.; *U.S. Public*, pg. 420
SOKC, LLC—See PENN Entertainment, Inc.; *U.S. Public*, pg. 1662
SPEEDWAY SONOMA LLC—See Sonic Financial Corporation; *U.S. Private*, pg. 3713
TALLADEGA SUPERSPEEDWAY, LLC—See National Association for Stock Car Auto Racing, Inc.; *U.S. Private*, pg. 2846
TBC TELETHEATRE B.C. LTD.—See Great Canadian Gaming Corporation; *Int'l*, pg. 3063
TEXAS MOTOR SPEEDWAY—See Sonic Financial Corporation; *U.S. Private*, pg. 3713
THISTLEDOWN RACETRACK, LLC—See Caesars Entertainment, Inc.; *U.S. Public*, pg. 420
TP RACING L.L.L.P.; *U.S. Private*, pg. 4199
TURFWAY PARK, LLC—See Churchill Downs, Inc.; *U.S. Public*, pg. 494
WATKINS GLEN INTERNATIONAL, INC.—See National Association for Stock Car Auto Racing, Inc.; *U.S. Private*, pg. 2846

711219 — OTHER SPECTATOR SPORTS

AFC AJAX NV; *Int'l*, pg. 185
ASSOCIATED OUTDOOR CLUBS, INC.; *U.S. Private*, pg. 356

N.A.I.C.S. INDEX

711310 — PROMOTERS OF PERFOR...

ATP EUROPE BVBA—See ATP Tour, Inc.; *U.S. Private*, pg. 381
ATP INTERNATIONAL GROUP—See ATP Tour, Inc.; *U.S. Private*, pg. 381
CBS MAXPREPS INC.—See National Amusements, Inc.; *U.S. Private*, pg. 2840
DAIWA CORMORAN SPORTARTIKEL-VERTRIEBS GMBH—See Globeride, Inc.; *Int'l*, pg. 3007
DAIWA (H.K) CO., LTD—See Globeride, Inc.; *Int'l*, pg. 3007
DAIWA SPORTS LTD—See Globeride, Inc.; *Int'l*, pg. 3007
FANTASY SPORTS SHARK, LLC—See Bally's Corporation; *U.S. Public*, pg. 268
FISHING WORLD, INC.—See Globeride, Inc.; *Int'l*, pg. 3007
FRONT ROW MOTORSPORTS, INC.; *U.S. Private*, pg. 1613
HORSEMEN'S QUARTER HORSE RACING ASSOCIATION, INC.—See Quarter Horse Racing Inc.; *U.S. Private*, pg. 3324
NASU DAIWA, INC.—See Globeride, Inc.; *Int'l*, pg. 3007
NATIONAL THOROUGHBRED RACING ASSOCIATION; *U.S. Private*, pg. 2864
PENSKE RACING, INC.—See Penske Corporation; *U.S. Private*, pg. 3138
PHOENIX AIR RACING INC—See Phoenix Air Group Inc.; *U.S. Private*, pg. 3172
PLAYERS HEALTH COVER USA INC.; *U.S. Private*, pg. 3212
PLAYFLY SPORTS PROPERTIES, LLC; *U.S. Private*, pg. 3212
PNGI CHARLES TOWN GAMING, LLC—See PENN Entertainment, Inc.; *U.S. Public*, pg. 1662
RC-1, INC.; *U.S. Private*, pg. 3361
SAM HOUSTON RACE PARK LLC; *U.S. Private*, pg. 3535
SPORTS INTERACTIVE LTD.—See Entain PLC; *Int'l*, pg. 2450
UNDERWATER WORLD PATTAYA LTD.—See Haw Par Corporation Limited; *Int'l*, pg. 3287
USA TRIATHLON; *U.S. Private*, pg. 4321
WATERFORD SPEED BOWL; *U.S. Private*, pg. 4453
WORLD SPORTS, INC.—See Globeride, Inc.; *Int'l*, pg. 3007
XFL, LLC—See RedBird Capital Partners L.P.; *U.S. Private*, pg. 3377
YANKEE GREYHOUND RACING INC.; *U.S. Private*, pg. 4585
ZUFFA, LLC—See Silver Lake Group, LLC; *U.S. Private*, pg. 3654

711310 — PROMOTERS OF PERFORMING ARTS, SPORTS, AND SIMILAR EVENTS WITH FACILITIES

ACT ENTERTAINMENT AG—See CTS Eventim AG & Co. KGAA; *Int'l*, pg. 1872
THE ADRIENNE ARSHT CENTER FOR THE PERFORMING ARTS OF MIAMI-DADE COUNTY, INC.; *U.S. Private*, pg. 3982
THE AIR CANADA CENTRE—See BCE Inc.; *Int'l*, pg. 927
ALLEY THEATRE; *U.S. Private*, pg. 180
ALL IN ONE COMMUNICATION AG—See CTS Eventim AG & Co. KGAA; *Int'l*, pg. 1872
ALLSTATE SUGAR BOWL; *U.S. Private*, pg. 193
AMALIE ARENA—See Tampa Bay Sports & Entertainment LLC; *U.S. Private*, pg. 3929
AMERICAN REPERTORY THEATER; *U.S. Private*, pg. 246
AMERICAN SMALL BUSINESS ALLIANCE, INC.; *U.S. Private*, pg. 253
AMOEBA CULTURE CO., LTD.—See CJ Corporation; *Int'l*, pg. 1631
ANSCHUTZ ENTERTAINMENT GROUP—See The Anschutz Corporation; *U.S. Private*, pg. 3986
ARCADIA LIVE GMBH—See CTS Eventim AG & Co. KGAA; *Int'l*, pg. 1872
ARENA BERLIN BETRIEBS GMBH—See CTS Eventim AG & Co. KGAA; *Int'l*, pg. 1872
ARENA ONE GMBH—See E.ON SE; *Int'l*, pg. 2251
ARENA OPERATIONS, LLC—See Atlanta Hawks, L.P.; *U.S. Private*, pg. 370
ARENA STAGE; *U.S. Private*, pg. 318
ARTSQUEST; *U.S. Private*, pg. 344
ASHTON GARDENS HOUSTON; *U.S. Private*, pg. 350
ATLANTIC 10 CONFERENCE; *U.S. Private*, pg. 371
ATLANTIC COAST CONFERENCE; *U.S. Private*, pg. 372
ATLANTIC WHARF JV LLC—See Boston Properties, Inc.; *U.S. Public*, pg. 373
AUDIENCEVIEW TICKETING CORPORATION; *Int'l*, pg. 701
AVA GALLERY & ART CENTER; *U.S. Private*, pg. 402
AZOFF MSG ENTERTAINMENT LLC—See Azoff Music Management; *U.S. Private*, pg. 415
AZOFF MSG ENTERTAINMENT LLC—See Madison Square Garden Sports Corp.; *U.S. Public*, pg. 1354
BARRACUDA MUSIC GMBH—See CTS Eventim AG & Co. KGAA; *Int'l*, pg. 1872
BEATS AT SEA, LLC—See Live Nation Entertainment, Inc.; *U.S. Public*, pg. 1328
BE-AT VENUES N.V.—See Live Nation Entertainment, Inc.; *U.S. Public*, pg. 1328

BECORE; *U.S. Private*, pg. 512
BEIJING GEHUA CULTURE CENTER CO., LTD.—See Beijing Gehua Cultural Development Group Co., Ltd.; *Int'l*, pg. 950
BELLATOR SPORT WORLDWIDE LLC—See National Amusements, Inc.; *U.S. Private*, pg. 2839
BETHEL WOODS CENTER FOR THE ARTS, INC.; *U.S. Private*, pg. 545
BIG NIGHT ENTERTAINMENT GROUP; *U.S. Private*, pg. 553
BILL EDWARDS PRESENTS, INC.; *U.S. Private*, pg. 557
BILLETLUGEN A/S—See Egmont Fonden; *Int'l*, pg. 2325
BLACK KNIGHT SPORTS ARENA LLC—See Black Knight Sports & Entertainment LLC; *U.S. Private*, pg. 572
BLACK PAGE CONCESSIONS, LLC—See Live Nation Entertainment, Inc.; *U.S. Public*, pg. 1328
BLACKTIE LLC; *U.S. Private*, pg. 577
BLACKTIE-SAN ANTONIO—See Blacktie LLC; *U.S. Private*, pg. 577
BLUE NOTE SPA—See Casta Diva Group; *Int'l*, pg. 1355
BLUMENTHAL PERFORMING ARTS; *U.S. Private*, pg. 599
BOBCATS BASKETBALL CENTER, LLC—See MJ Basketball Holdings, LLC; *U.S. Private*, pg. 2752
THE BOWERY PRESENTS, LLC—See The Anschutz Corporation; *U.S. Private*, pg. 3987
BOXOFFICETICKETSALES.COM; *U.S. Private*, pg. 626
BRAG FZ-LLC—See Live Nation Entertainment, Inc.; *U.S. Public*, pg. 1328
BROADWAY ACROSS AMERICA - SALT LAKE CITY—See Key Brand Entertainment, Inc.; *U.S. Private*, pg. 2292
BROOKLYN ACADEMY OF MUSIC, INC.; *U.S. Private*, pg. 663
THE BUFFALO FINE ARTS ACADEMY; *U.S. Private*, pg. 4002
CANADIAN TIRE CENTRE—See Capital Sports Group of Companies; *Int'l*, pg. 1312
CARAMOOR CENTER FOR MUSIC & THE ARTS, INC.; *U.S. Private*, pg. 748
CARLISLE EVENTS SERVICES LIMITED—See HFBG Holding B.V.; *Int'l*, pg. 3374
CARRIAGE HOUSE EVENT CENTER INC.; *U.S. Public*, pg. 439
CEO EVENT MEDYA AS; *Int'l*, pg. 1420
CERESPO CO., LTD.; *Int'l*, pg. 1422
CINCINNATI ARTS ASSOCIATION; *U.S. Private*, pg. 897
CITI PERFORMING ARTS CENTER, INC.; *U.S. Private*, pg. 901
CITY CENTER OF MUSIC AND DRAMA INC.; *U.S. Private*, pg. 905
CITYNEON HOLDINGS LIMITED; *Int'l*, pg. 1629
CLASSICAL KING FM 98.1; *U.S. Private*, pg. 917
CLASSIC COMMUNICATIONS, INC.—See Altice USA, Inc.; *U.S. Public*, pg. 88
CMIC INTERNATIONAL EXHIBITION CO., LTD.—See China Machinery Engineering Corporation; *Int'l*, pg. 1516
COASTAL LUXURY MANAGEMENT; *U.S. Private*, pg. 956
COCO TOURS VERANSTALTUNGS GMBH—See DEAG Deutsche Entertainment AG; *Int'l*, pg. 1998
CONCERT CONCEPT VERANSTALTUNGS-GMBH—See DEAG Deutsche Entertainment AG; *Int'l*, pg. 1997
THE CONTEMPORARY ART MUSEUM; *U.S. Private*, pg. 4014
CORPORACION INTERAMERICANA DE ENTRETENIMIENTO, S. A. B. DE C. V.; *Int'l*, pg. 1804
COSMOPOP GMBH—See Live Nation Entertainment, Inc.; *U.S. Public*, pg. 1328
COURTS FOR KIDS; *U.S. Private*, pg. 1070
THE COWLES CENTER; *U.S. Private*, pg. 4015
CSM EVENTS LIMITED—See Wasserman Media Group, LLC; *U.S. Private*, pg. 4450
CSM PRODUCTION—See Wasserman Media Group, LLC; *U.S. Private*, pg. 4450
CTS EVENTIM ISRAEL LTD.—See CTS Eventim AG & Co. KGAA; *Int'l*, pg. 1872
CTS EVENTIM RU O.O.O.—See CTS Eventim AG & Co. KGAA; *Int'l*, pg. 1872
CUFFE AND TAYLOR LIMITED—See Live Nation Entertainment, Inc.; *U.S. Public*, pg. 1328
CULTURAL DATA PROJECT; *U.S. Private*, pg. 1122
CYCLONE SPORTS PROPERTIES, LLC—See Atairos Group, Inc.; *U.S. Private*, pg. 363
THE CYNTHIA WOODS MITCHELL PAVILION; *U.S. Private*, pg. 4017
DALLAS FAN FARES, INC.; *U.S. Private*, pg. 1149
DEAG CLASSICS AG—See DEAG Deutsche Entertainment AG; *Int'l*, pg. 1997
DEAG CONCERTS GMBH—See DEAG Deutsche Entertainment AG; *Int'l*, pg. 1997
DEKRA EVENT & LOGISTIC SERVICES GMBH—See DEKRA e.V.; *Int'l*, pg. 2008
DENTSU SPORTS ASIA, PTE. LTD.—See Dentsu Group Inc.; *Int'l*, pg. 2037
DENTSU SPORTS PARTNERS INC.—See Dentsu Group Inc.; *Int'l*, pg. 2038
DENVER CENTER FOR THE PERFORMING ARTS INC.; *U.S. Private*, pg. 1207
DERTICKETSERVICE DE GMBH & CO. KG—See CTS Eventim AG & Co. KGAA; *Int'l*, pg. 1872

DEVILS ARENA ENTERTAINMENT LLC—See Devils Holdings, LLC; *U.S. Private*, pg. 1218
DIAMOND SPORTS GROUP, LLC—See Sinclair, Inc.; *U.S. Public*, pg. 1885
DICK'S SPORTING GOODS PARK—See Kroenke Sports & Entertainment, LLC; *U.S. Private*, pg. 2352
DIVERSIFIED EXHIBITIONS AUSTRALIA—See Diversified Communications; *U.S. Private*, pg. 1241
DREAMHAUS GMBH—See CTS Eventim AG & Co. KGAA; *Int'l*, pg. 1872
DUTCHESS COUNTY AGRICULTURAL SOCIETY, INC.; *U.S. Private*, pg. 1294
ELBKLASSIK KONZERTE GMBH—See DEAG Deutsche Entertainment AG; *Int'l*, pg. 1998
EM EVENT MARKETING AG—See DEAG Deutsche Entertainment AG; *Int'l*, pg. 1998
ES GLOBAL LTD; *Int'l*, pg. 2500
ETHNOMETRICS INC.—See Viad Corp.; *U.S. Public*, pg. 2291
EVENKO—See Club de hockey Canadien, Inc.; *Int'l*, pg. 1664
EVENTA ENTERTAINMENT GROUP LTD.; *Int'l*, pg. 2562
EVENT CINEMAS LIMITED—See Event Hospitality & Entertainment Limited; *Int'l*, pg. 2562
EVENTIKO INC.; *Int'l*, pg. 2562
EVENTIM MARKETING UND SPONSORING GMBH—See CTS Eventim AG & Co. KGAA; *Int'l*, pg. 1872
EVENTIM POPKURS HAMBURG GEMEINNUTZIGE GMBH—See CTS Eventim AG & Co. KGAA; *Int'l*, pg. 1872
EVENTS SOCIAL MARKETING AND PRODUCTIONS AFRIKA (PTY) LTD—See African Equity Empowerment Investmts Limited; *Int'l*, pg. 191
EXG, INC.—See Viad Corp.; *U.S. Public*, pg. 2290
EXHIBITIONS AND TRADE FAIRS PTY LIMITED—See Freeman Decorating Co.; *U.S. Private*, pg. 1605
FEDERALCONFERENCE.COM; *U.S. Private*, pg. 1491
FERIAS Y EXPOSICIONES S.A.—See Grupo Clarin S.A.; *Int'l*, pg. 3125
FESTIVAL HALL VENUE MANAGEMENT PTY. LTD.—See Live Nation Entertainment, Inc.; *U.S. Public*, pg. 1328
FILM SOCIETY OF LINCOLN CENTER, INC.; *U.S. Private*, pg. 1506
FINANCIAL STABILITY INSTITUTE—See Bank for International Settlements; *Int'l*, pg. 838
FIRST FLEET CONCERTS, LLC—See Live Nation Entertainment, Inc.; *U.S. Public*, pg. 1328
FKP SCORPIO BELGIUM B.V.—See CTS Eventim AG & Co. KGAA; *Int'l*, pg. 1873
FKP SCORPIO POLAND SP. Z O.O.—See CTS Eventim AG & Co. KGAA; *Int'l*, pg. 1873
FKP SHOW CREATIONS GMBH—See CTS Eventim AG & Co. KGAA; *Int'l*, pg. 1873
FOUNDERS ENTERTAINMENT, LLC—See Live Nation Entertainment, Inc.; *U.S. Public*, pg. 1328
FOX PERFORMING ARTS CHARITABLE FOUNDATION; *U.S. Private*, pg. 1584
THE FRIST CENTER FOR THE VISUAL ARTS, INC.; *U.S. Private*, pg. 4031
FULL PRODUCTION OY—See Live Nation Entertainment, Inc.; *U.S. Public*, pg. 1328
FULLSTEAM AGENCY OY—See CTS Eventim AG & Co. KGAA; *Int'l*, pg. 1873
FUNDACION OCESA ENTRETENIMIENTO, A.C.—See Live Nation Entertainment, Inc.; *U.S. Public*, pg. 1328
GADGET ABC ENTERTAINMENT GROUP AG—See CTS Eventim AG & Co. KGAA; *Int'l*, pg. 1873
GALE FORCE SPORTS & ENTERTAINMENT, LLC—See Gale Force Holdings, LP; *U.S. Private*, pg. 1636
GEMINI INSURANCE COMPANY—See W.R. Berkley Corporation; *U.S. Public*, pg. 2318
GERRY WEBER MANAGEMENT & EVENT OHG—See GERRY WEBER International AG; *Int'l*, pg. 2944
GET ME IN! LTD.—See Live Nation Entertainment, Inc.; *U.S. Public*, pg. 1331
GIMA INTERNATIONAL EXHIBITION GROUP GMBH & CO. KG—See Providence Equity Partners L.L.C.; *U.S. Private*, pg. 3292
GIMA INTERNATIONAL EXHIBITION GROUP GMBH & CO. KG—See Searchlight Capital Partners, L.P.; *U.S. Private*, pg. 3587
GLOBAL CONCERTS GMBH—See DEAG Deutsche Entertainment AG; *Int'l*, pg. 1998
GLOBAL CONCERTS TOURING GMBH—See DEAG Deutsche Entertainment AG; *Int'l*, pg. 1998
GOODLIVE ARTISTS GMBH & CO. KG—See Live Nation Entertainment, Inc.; *U.S. Public*, pg. 1329
GOODLIVE GMBH—See Live Nation Entertainment, Inc.; *U.S. Public*, pg. 1329
GOTA LEJON LIVE AB—See Live Nation Entertainment, Inc.; *U.S. Public*, pg. 1329
THE GREATER UNION ORGANISATION PTY LIMITED—See Event Hospitality & Entertainment Limited; *Int'l*, pg. 2562
HANDWERKER PROMOTION E. GMBH—See DEAG Deutsche Entertainment AG; *Int'l*, pg. 1998
HAWTHORNE DIRECT INC.; *U.S. Private*, pg. 1884

711310 — PROMOTERS OF PERFOR...

HITCHED WEDDINGS & EVENTS LLC—See Minted LLC.; *U.S. Private*, pg. 2745
HOI PRODUCTIONS GERMANY GMBH—See CTS Eventim AG & Co. KGAA; *Int'l*, pg. 1873
HOLIDAY ON ICE PRODUCTIONS B.V.—See CTS Eventim AG & Co. KGAA; *Int'l*, pg. 1873
HOLLYWOOD FOREIGN PRESS ASSOCIATION; *U.S. Private*, pg. 1966
HOPSCOTCH GROUPE S.A.; *Int'l*, pg. 3474
HOUSE OF BLUES CONCERTS, INC.—See Live Nation Entertainment, Inc.; *U.S. Public*, pg. 1329
HOUSTON LIVESTOCK SHOW AND RODEO; *U.S. Private*, pg. 1993
HT MUSIC AND ENTERTAINMENT COMPANY LIMITED—See HT Media Limited; *Int'l*, pg. 3508
IMG MEDIA LIMITED—See Silver Lake Group, LLC; *U.S. Private*, pg. 3654
IMMOBILIERE LES FONTAINES S.A.R.L.—See Capgemini SE; *Int'l*, pg. 1306
INFRONT AUSTRIA GMBH—See Dalian Wanda Group Corporation Ltd.; *Int'l*, pg. 1953
INFRONT FINLAND OY—See Dalian Wanda Group Corporation Ltd.; *Int'l*, pg. 1953
INFRONT FRANCE SAS—See Dalian Wanda Group Corporation Ltd.; *Int'l*, pg. 1953
INFRONT NETHERLANDS BV—See Dalian Wanda Group Corporation Ltd.; *Int'l*, pg. 1953
INFRONT PAN-ASIA PTE. LTD.—See Dalian Wanda Group Corporation Ltd.; *Int'l*, pg. 1953
INFRONT SPORTIF PAZARLAMA ANONIM SIRKETI—See Dalian Wanda Group Corporation Ltd.; *Int'l*, pg. 1953
INFRONT SPORTS & MEDIA AG—See Dalian Wanda Group Corporation Ltd.; *Int'l*, pg. 1953
INFRONT SPORTS & MEDIA (CHINA) CO., LTD—See Dalian Wanda Group Corporation Ltd.; *Int'l*, pg. 1953
INTERNATIONAL POLO CLUB PALM BEACH—See Wellington Equestrian Partners, LLC; *U.S. Private*, pg. 4475
ITECA ALATOO—See Providence Equity Partners L.L.C.; *U.S. Private*, pg. 3293
ITECA ALATOO—See Searchlight Capital Partners, L.P.; *U.S. Private*, pg. 3588
ITECA KAZAKHSTAN—See Providence Equity Partners L.L.C.; *U.S. Private*, pg. 3293
ITECA KAZAKHSTAN—See Searchlight Capital Partners, L.P.; *U.S. Private*, pg. 3588
ITE CHINA—See Providence Equity Partners L.L.C.; *U.S. Private*, pg. 3292
ITE CHINA—See Searchlight Capital Partners, L.P.; *U.S. Private*, pg. 3587
ITE GULF FZ LLC—See Providence Equity Partners L.L.C.; *U.S. Private*, pg. 3292
ITE GULF FZ LLC—See Searchlight Capital Partners, L.P.; *U.S. Private*, pg. 3588
ITE LLC MOSCOW—See Providence Equity Partners L.L.C.; *U.S. Private*, pg. 3292
ITE LLC MOSCOW—See Searchlight Capital Partners, L.P.; *U.S. Private*, pg. 3588
ITE NORTH AMERICA INC.—See Providence Equity Partners L.L.C.; *U.S. Private*, pg. 3293
ITE NORTH AMERICA INC.—See Searchlight Capital Partners, L.P.; *U.S. Private*, pg. 3588
ITE POLAND SP. Z O.O.—See Providence Equity Partners L.L.C.; *U.S. Private*, pg. 3293
ITE POLAND SP. Z O.O.—See Searchlight Capital Partners, L.P.; *U.S. Private*, pg. 3588
ITE TURKEY—See Providence Equity Partners L.L.C.; *U.S. Private*, pg. 3293
ITE TURKEY—See Searchlight Capital Partners, L.P.; *U.S. Private*, pg. 3588
ITE UZBEKISTAN—See Providence Equity Partners L.L.C.; *U.S. Private*, pg. 3293
ITE UZBEKISTAN—See Searchlight Capital Partners, L.P.; *U.S. Private*, pg. 3588
JAMES GRANT SPORTS MANAGEMENT—See Formation Group PLC; *Int'l*, pg. 2734
JEANNE B. MCCOY COMMUNITY CENTER FOR THE ARTS; *U.S. Private*, pg. 2196
JEB CO., LTD.—See Dentsu Group Inc.; *Int'l*, pg. 2039
JEWISH MUSEUM; *U.S. Private*, pg. 2206
JJLA LLC; *U.S. Private*, pg. 2211
JOHN F. KENNEDY CENTER FOR THE PERFORMING ARTS; *U.S. Private*, pg. 2221
JUST MARKETING INTERNATIONAL LTD.—See Providence Equity Partners L.L.C.; *U.S. Private*, pg. 3291
KBK KONZERT- UND KUNSTLERAGENTUR GMBH—See DEAG Deutsche Entertainment AG; *Int'l*, pg. 1998
KEY BRAND ENTERTAINMENT, INC.; *U.S. Private*, pg. 2292
KROENKE ARENA COMPANY, LLC—See Kroenke Sports & Entertainment, LLC; *U.S. Private*, pg. 2352
KULTUR- UND KONGRESSZENTRUM JAHRHUNDERTHALLE GMBH—See DEAG Deutsche Entertainment AG; *Int'l*, pg. 1998
L'ARENA DES CANADIENS, INC.—See Club de hockey Canadien, Inc.; *Int'l*, pg. 1664
LES QUATRE GLACES (1994) INC—See Canlan Ice Sports Corporation; *Int'l*, pg. 1291
LIVE MUSIC PRODUCTION SA—See DEAG Deutsche Entertainment AG; *Int'l*, pg. 1998
LIVE NATION - MIDWEST DIVISION—See Live Nation Entertainment, Inc.; *U.S. Public*, pg. 1329
LOCKPORT ICE ARENA; *U.S. Private*, pg. 2478
THE LONG NOW FOUNDATION; *U.S. Private*, pg. 4072
LOSBERGER UK LTD.—See Gilde Buy Out Partners B.V.; *Int'l*, pg. 2975
LUTHER BURBANK MEMORIAL FOUNDATION; *U.S. Private*, pg. 2516
MAIN EVENT ENTERTAINMENT LP—See Keystone Group, L.P.; *U.S. Private*, pg. 2297
MARCUS CENTER FOR THE PERFORMING ARTS; *U.S. Private*, pg. 2572
MAREK LIEBERBERG KONZERTAGENTUR GMBH & CO. KG—See CTS Eventim AG & Co. KGAA; *Int'l*, pg. 1873
THE MEADOWS STANDARDBRED OWNERS ASSOCIATION; *U.S. Private*, pg. 4077
MICHAEL HYATT & COMPANY LLC; *U.S. Private*, pg. 2698
MILFORD ICE PAVILION—See Blackstreet Capital Holdings LLC; *U.S. Private*, pg. 576
MISSISSIPPI ARTS AND ENTERTAINMENT CENTER; *U.S. Private*, pg. 2748
MTOUCH SRL—See IQVIA Holdings Inc.; *U.S. Public*, pg. 1169
NANTUCKET DREAMLAND FOUNDATION; *U.S. Private*, pg. 2833
NEW AGE MEDIA VENTURES LLC; *U.S. Private*, pg. 2892
NEW JERSEY PERFORMING ARTS CENTER; *U.S. Private*, pg. 2898
NFL VENTURES, INC.—See National Football League; *U.S. Private*, pg. 2854
NIELSEN ADMOSPHERE BULGARIA JSC.—See Brookfield Corporation; *Int'l*, pg. 1179
NIELSEN ADMOSPHERE BULGARIA JSC.—See Elliott Management Corporation; *U.S. Private*, pg. 1371
NIELSEN SPORTS BELGIUM SA—See Brookfield Corporation; *Int'l*, pg. 1179
NIELSEN SPORTS BELGIUM SA—See Elliott Management Corporation; *U.S. Private*, pg. 1372
NORTHFIELD PARK ASSOCIATES LLC—See MGM Resorts International; *U.S. Public*, pg. 1435
NORWAY HOUSE; *U.S. Private*, pg. 2964
OAK VIEW GROUP, LLC—See Silver Lake Group, LLC; *U.S. Private*, pg. 3658
OKLAHOMA STATE FAIR, INC.; *U.S. Private*, pg. 3007
OLYMPIA ENTERTAINMENT, INC.—See Ilitch Holdings, Inc.; *U.S. Private*, pg. 2042
OMAHA PERFORMING ARTS; *U.S. Private*, pg. 3014
THE OMAHA THEATER COMPANY; *U.S. Private*, pg. 4088
ON LOCATION EVENTS, LLC—See Silver Lake Group, LLC; *U.S. Private*, pg. 3654
OPADE ORGANIZAC. Y PROMOC DE ACTIVIDADES DEPORTIVAS, S.A.—See ACS, Actividades de Construccion y Servicios, S.A.; *Int'l*, pg. 115
THE OPERA HOUSE INC.—See Live Nation Entertainment, Inc.; *U.S. Public*, pg. 1331
PALAZZO PRODUKTIONEN GMBH—See CTS Eventim AG & Co. KGAA; *Int'l*, pg. 1873
PALLACANESTRO TREVISO SOCIETA SPORTIVA DILETTANTISTICA A R.L.—See Edizione S.r.l.; *Int'l*, pg. 2312
THE PEACH FOUNDATION; *U.S. Private*, pg. 4091
PEOPLEFORBIKES FOUNDATION—See PeopleForBikes Coalition LLC; *U.S. Private*, pg. 3141
PGM PROMOTERS GROUP MUNICH KONZERTAGENTUR GMBH—See CTS Eventim AG & Co. KGAA; *Int'l*, pg. 1873
PGM PROMOTORS GROUP MUNICH KONZERTAGENTUR GMBH—See CTS Eventim AG & Co. KGAA; *Int'l*, pg. 1873
PHOENIX ARENA GP, LLC—See Suns Legacy Partners, LLC; *U.S. Private*, pg. 3870
PITTSBURGH ARENA OPERATING LP—See Sports & Exhibition Authority of Pittsburgh & Allegheny County; *U.S. Private*, pg. 3761
PITTSBURGH CULTURAL TRUST; *U.S. Private*, pg. 3191
POP WARNER LITTLE SCHOLARS INC.; *U.S. Private*, pg. 3228
PPC EVENT SERVICES, LLC; *U.S. Private*, pg. 3240
PREMIERE EVENTS; *U.S. Private*, pg. 3251
PREMIER EXPO—See Providence Equity Partners L.L.C.; *U.S. Private*, pg. 3293
PREMIER EXPO—See Searchlight Capital Partners, L.P.; *U.S. Private*, pg. 3588
PRG HOLDINGS, LLC—See The Jordan Company, L.P.; *U.S. Private*, pg. 4061
PRG K.K.—See The Jordan Company, L.P.; *U.S. Private*, pg. 4061
PRIMEXPO—See Providence Equity Partners L.L.C.; *U.S. Private*, pg. 3293
PRIMEXPO—See Searchlight Capital Partners, L.P.; *U.S. Private*, pg. 3588
PRO EM OPERATIONS, LLC; *U.S. Private*, pg. 3269
PROVIDENCE PERFORMING ARTS CENTER; *U.S. Private*, pg. 3294
PSSI STADIUM CORPORATION—See Pittsburgh Steelers Sports Inc.; *U.S. Private*, pg. 3191
QUEST EVENTS, LLC; *U.S. Private*, pg. 3325
QUINTEVENTS LLC—See Liberty Media Corporation; *U.S. Public*, pg. 1311
RACEWIRE LLC—See Genstar Capital, LLC; *U.S. Private*, pg. 1678
REVIVAL EVENT VENUE INC.—See Live Nation Entertainment, Inc.; *U.S. Public*, pg. 1330
RIVER CONCERTS GMBH—See DEAG Deutsche Entertainment AG; *Int'l*, pg. 1998
ROCK WORLD LISBOA S.A.—See Live Nation Entertainment, Inc.; *U.S. Public*, pg. 1330
ROYAL HILLS CO., LTD.—See Alpen Co., Ltd.; *Int'l*, pg. 366
RWS & ASSOCIATES ENTERTAINMENT, INC.; *U.S. Private*, pg. 3509
SALLE WAGRAM—See Altarea SCA; *Int'l*, pg. 385
SAN ANTONIO STOCK SHOW & RODEO; *U.S. Private*, pg. 3539
SAN FRANCISCO BALLET; *U.S. Private*, pg. 3540
SARVIK CORP.; *U.S. Private*, pg. 3551
SCOTTSDALE CULTURAL COUNCIL; *U.S. Private*, pg. 3578
SEASIDE FESTIVAL AG—See CTS Eventim AG & Co. KGAA; *Int'l*, pg. 1873
SECRET SOUNDS GROUP SERVICES PTY LTD—See Live Nation Entertainment, Inc.; *U.S. Public*, pg. 1330
SEEKERS EVENT GMBH—See CTS Eventim AG & Co. KGAA; *Int'l*, pg. 1873
SEGERSTROM CENTER FOR THE ARTS; *U.S. Private*, pg. 3598
SHEN YUN PERFORMING ARTS INC.; *U.S. Private*, pg. 3632
SHORENSTEIN HAYS-NEDERLANDER THEATRES LLC; *U.S. Private*, pg. 3641
SHOW IMAGING, INC.; *U.S. Private*, pg. 3643
SIBERIAN FAIR LLC—See Providence Equity Partners L.L.C.; *U.S. Private*, pg. 3293
SIBERIAN FAIR LLC—See Searchlight Capital Partners, L.P.; *U.S. Private*, pg. 3588
SKIRBALL CULTURAL CENTER; *U.S. Private*, pg. 3682
SKYLINE DFW EXHIBITS & EVENTS; *U.S. Private*, pg. 3685
THE SMITH CENTER; *U.S. Private*, pg. 4118
STADIUM AUSTRALIA GROUP LTD.—See Foresight Group Holdings Limited; *Int'l*, pg. 2731
STAGE IT CORP.—See VNUE, Inc.; *U.S. Public*, pg. 2308
STOREFRONT FOR ART & ARCHITECTURE; *U.S. Private*, pg. 3831
THE SUN BELT CONFERENCE; *U.S. Private*, pg. 4125
SUN LIFE STADIUM—See Dolphins Enterprises, LLC; *U.S. Private*, pg. 1255
SUNSHINE CINEMAS PTY LIMITED—See Event Hospitality & Entertainment Limited; *Int'l*, pg. 2562
SUNTEC SINGAPORE INTERNATIONAL CONVENTION & EXHIBITION SERVICES PTE. LTD.—See ESR Group Limited; *Int'l*, pg. 2508
SUPERBLOOM FESTIVAL GMBH & CO. KG—See Live Nation Entertainment, Inc.; *U.S. Public*, pg. 1330
SWISS GADGET ENTERTAINMENT AG—See CTS Eventim AG & Co. KGAA; *Int'l*, pg. 1873
TAMPA THEATRE, INC.; *U.S. Private*, pg. 3930
TEKEYAN CULTURAL ASSOCIATION INC.; *U.S. Private*, pg. 3958
TICKETCORNER AG—See CTS Eventim AG & Co. KGAA; *Int'l*, pg. 1874
TIX CORPORATION; *U.S. Public*, pg. 2161
TOURNAMENT GOLF FOUNDATION; *U.S. Private*, pg. 4193
TRAVERSE CITY FILM FESTIVAL; *U.S. Private*, pg. 4214
THE TRIFFID PTY. LTD.—See Live Nation Entertainment, Inc.; *U.S. Public*, pg. 1331
TULSA ROUTE 66 MARATHON INC.; *U.S. Private*, pg. 4258
UFA SPORTS GMBH—See Bertelsmann SE & Co. KGaA; *Int'l*, pg. 995
UNIPUBLIC S.A.—See Atresmedia Corporacion de Medios de Comunicacion, S.A.; *Int'l*, pg. 693
UNITED STATES HANG GLIDING & PARAGLIDING ASSOCIATION, INC.; *U.S. Private*, pg. 4299
USA HOCKEY, INC.; *U.S. Private*, pg. 4321
V8 SUPERCARS AUSTRALIA PTY LTD—See Archer Capital Pty. Ltd.; *Int'l*, pg. 547
VERDE SPORT S.P.A.—See Edizione S.r.l.; *Int'l*, pg. 2312
VERIZON CENTER—See Lincoln Holdings LLC; *U.S. Private*, pg. 2457
VERTIGO S.R.L.—See CTS Eventim AG & Co. KGAA; *Int'l*, pg. 1874
THE VIVIAN BEAUMONT THEATER, INC.; *U.S. Private*, pg. 4132
WEPROMOTE ENTERTAINMENT GROUP SWITZERLAND AG—See CTS Eventim AG & Co. KGAA; *Int'l*, pg. 1874
WHEEL SPORT MANAGEMENT SDN. BHD.—See Ancom Nylex Berhad; *Int'l*, pg. 449
WORLD GOLF FOUNDATION; *U.S. Private*, pg. 4565
WORLDTEK EVENTS, LLC—See InteleTravel.com; *U.S. Private*, pg. 2104
YOU ARE SPECIAL EVENTS AG—See CTS Eventim AG & Co. KGAA; *Int'l*, pg. 1874

N.A.I.C.S. INDEX

711410 — AGENTS AND MANAGERS...

711320 — PROMOTERS OF PERFORMING ARTS, SPORTS, AND SIMILAR EVENTS WITHOUT FACILITIES

ALL ARTISTS AGENCY GMBH—See CTS Eventim AG & Co. KGAA; *Int'l*, pg. 1872
ANTWERPS SPORTPALEIS N.V.—See Live Nation Entertainment, Inc.; *U.S. Public*, pg. 1328
ATHLETX SPORTS GROUP, LLC; *U.S. Private*, pg. 368
AVEX ASIA PTE. LTD.—See Avex Inc.; *Int'l*, pg. 740
AVEX CLASSICS INTERNATIONAL INC.—See Avex Inc.; *Int'l*, pg. 740
AVEX MARKETING INC.—See Avex Inc.; *Int'l*, pg. 740
BAHAMAS BILLFISH CHAMPIONSHIP, INC.—See Active Interest Media, Inc.; *U.S. Private*, pg. 69
BANDAI NAMCO ARTS INC.—See BANDAI NAMCO Holdings Inc.; *Int'l*, pg. 828
BEIJING POLY ARTIST MANAGEMENT CO., LTD.—See China Poly Group Corporation; *Int'l*, pg. 1540
BERGEN LIVE AS—See Live Nation Entertainment, Inc.; *U.S. Public*, pg. 1328
BIG BREAK PRODUCTIONS, INC.—See Bertelsmann SE & Co. KGaA; *Int'l*, pg. 991
BOARDWALK INC.—See Dentsu Group Inc.; *Int'l*, pg. 2034
BROADWAY ACROSS AMERICA—See Key Brand Entertainment, Inc.; *U.S. Private*, pg. 2292
BROOKLYN BOWL LAS VEGAS, LLC—See Live Nation Entertainment, Inc.; *U.S. Public*, pg. 1328
C3 PRESENTS, LLC—See Live Nation Entertainment, Inc.; *U.S. Public*, pg. 1328
CARDENAS MARKETING NETWORK INC.; *U.S. Private*, pg. 749
CLIPPER VENTURES PLC; *Int'l*, pg. 1660
COMCERTO SRL—See Live Nation Entertainment, Inc.; *U.S. Public*, pg. 1328
COMPETITOR GROUP, INC.—See Dalian Wanda Group Corporation Ltd.; *Int'l*, pg. 1953
CROWDCARE B.V.—See Live Nation Entertainment, Inc.; *U.S. Public*, pg. 1328
CSM MOTORSPORTS, INC.—See Providence Equity Partners L.L.C.; *U.S. Private*, pg. 3291
CVENT EUROPE LTD.—See Blackstone Inc.; *U.S. Public*, pg. 353
CVENT INDIA PRIVATE LIMITED—See Blackstone Inc.; *U.S. Public*, pg. 353
DESTINATION CONCEPTS, INC.; *U.S. Private*, pg. 1215
DONE & DUSTED GROUP LIMITED; *Int'l*, pg. 2163
DONE & DUSTED PRODUCTIONS, INC.—See Done & Dusted Group Limited; *Int'l*, pg. 2163
EQUITY DISTRIBUTION LLC—See Live Nation Entertainment, Inc.; *U.S. Public*, pg. 1328
ESPN REGIONAL TELEVISION, INC.—See The Walt Disney Company; *U.S. Public*, pg. 2138
EVENT STAGING DIVISION—See KVL Audio Visual Services; *U.S. Private*, pg. 2359
EXPO LOGIC; *U.S. Private*, pg. 1450
FELD MOTOR SPORTS, INC.—See Feld Entertainment, Inc.; *U.S. Private*, pg. 1493
FIRST CLASS EDUCATORS (FCE)—See Pasch Consulting Group, LLC; *U.S. Private*, pg. 3103
GAMER PAKISTAN INC.; *U.S. Public*, pg. 895
GATEHOUSE LIVE, LLC—See Gannett Co., Inc.; *U.S. Public*, pg. 901
GETGO CONSULTING GMBH—See CTS Eventim AG & Co. KGAA; *Int'l*, pg. 1874
GUANGZHOU POLY SOUTHEN CULTURE PROMULGATION CO., LTD—See China Poly Group Corporation; *Int'l*, pg. 1541
HANSHIN CONTENTS LINK CORPORATION—See Hankyu Hanshin Holdings Inc.; *Int'l*, pg. 3255
IMG UNIVERSE LLC—See Silver Lake Group, LLC; *U.S. Private*, pg. 3657
IMG UNIVERSE LLC—See William Morris Endeavor Entertainment, LLC; *U.S. Private*, pg. 4524
I-MOTION GMBH—See DEAG Deutsche Entertainment AG; *Int'l*, pg. 1998
I-MOTION GMBH—See LiveStyle, Inc.; *U.S. Private*, pg. 2473
INTERNATIONAL HOT ROD ASSOCIATION—See Feld Entertainment, Inc.; *U.S. Private*, pg. 1493
KINGDOM OF MIND, LLC—See Live Nation Entertainment, Inc.; *U.S. Public*, pg. 1329
LIVE NATION BRAND PARTNERSHIP & MEDIA GMBH—See Live Nation Entertainment, Inc.; *U.S. Public*, pg. 1329
LIVE NATION ENTERTAINMENT, INC. - TIMES SQUARE OFFICE—See Live Nation Entertainment, Inc.; *U.S. Public*, pg. 1329
LIVE NATION - SOUTHERN DIVISION—See Live Nation Entertainment, Inc.; *U.S. Public*, pg. 1329
LIVESTYLE, INC.; *U.S. Private*, pg. 2473
LOS ANGELES PHILHARMONIC ASSOCIATION; *U.S. Private*, pg. 2496
MAGNOLIA ENTERTAINMENT LLC; *U.S. Private*, pg. 2548
MAINLAND MUSIC AG—See Live Nation Entertainment, Inc.; *U.S. Public*, pg. 1330
MCD PRODUCTIONS LIMITED—See Live Nation Entertainment, Inc.; *U.S. Public*, pg. 1330
MISS UNIVERSE, L.P.—See Silver Lake Group, LLC; *U.S. Private*, pg. 3657
MISS UNIVERSE, L.P.—See William Morris Endeavor Entertainment, LLC; *U.S. Private*, pg. 4524
MOJO WORKS B.V.—See Live Nation Entertainment, Inc.; *U.S. Public*, pg. 1330
NBA PROPERTIES, INC.—See National Basketball Association; *U.S. Private*, pg. 2848
NIELSEN SPORTS ASIA PTE. LTD.—See Brookfield Corporation; *Int'l*, pg. 1179
NIELSEN SPORTS ASIA PTE. LTD.—See Elliott Management Corporation; *U.S. Private*, pg. 1372
NIELSEN SPORTS ESPANA S.L.U.—See Brookfield Corporation; *Int'l*, pg. 1179
NIELSEN SPORTS ESPANA S.L.U.—See Elliott Management Corporation; *U.S. Private*, pg. 1372
NIELSEN SPORTS ITALIA SRL—See Brookfield Corporation; *Int'l*, pg. 1179
NIELSEN SPORTS ITALIA SRL—See Elliott Management Corporation; *U.S. Private*, pg. 1372
NIELSEN SPORTS JAPAN K.K.—See Brookfield Corporation; *Int'l*, pg. 1179
NIELSEN SPORTS JAPAN K.K.—See Elliott Management Corporation; *U.S. Private*, pg. 1372
NIELSEN SPORTS KOREA LLC—See Brookfield Corporation; *Int'l*, pg. 1179
NIELSEN SPORTS KOREA LLC—See Elliott Management Corporation; *U.S. Private*, pg. 1372
NIELSEN SPORTS NEDERLAND B.V.—See Brookfield Corporation; *Int'l*, pg. 1180
NIELSEN SPORTS NEDERLAND B.V.—See Elliott Management Corporation; *U.S. Private*, pg. 1372
NIELSEN SPORTS UK & IRELAND LIMITED—See Brookfield Corporation; *Int'l*, pg. 1180
NIELSEN SPORTS UK & IRELAND LIMITED—See Elliott Management Corporation; *U.S. Private*, pg. 1372
OCTAGON—See The Interpublic Group of Companies, Inc.; *U.S. Public*, pg. 2103
PDH MUSIC A/S—See Live Nation Entertainment, Inc.; *U.S. Public*, pg. 1330
PHILHARMONIC SYMPHONY SOCIETY OF NEW YORK INC.; *U.S. Private*, pg. 3169
PIERS 92/94 LLC—See Vornado Realty Trust; *U.S. Public*, pg. 2310
THE PROFESSIONAL GOLFERS ASSOCIATION OF AMERICA; *U.S. Private*, pg. 4100
PROMOWEST PRODUCTIONS, INC.—See The Anschutz Corporation; *U.S. Private*, pg. 3986
QUINCY SYMPHONY ORCHESTRA ASSOCIATION; *U.S. Private*, pg. 3328
RED FROG EVENTS, LLC; *U.S. Private*, pg. 3374
SCHEME ENGINE, LLC—See Live Nation Entertainment, Inc.; *U.S. Public*, pg. 1330
SCHOLASTIC BOOK FAIRS, INC.—See Scholastic Corporation; *U.S. Public*, pg. 1847
SEA OTTER CLASSIC, INC.—See Lifetime, Inc.; *U.S. Private*, pg. 2451
SEINAJOKI FESTIVALS OY—See CTS Eventim AG & Co. KGAA; *Int'l*, pg. 1873
SIX FLAGS ENTERTAINMENT CORPORATION; *U.S. Public*, pg. 1890
SMG EUROPE—See Northlane Capital Partners, LLC; *U.S. Private*, pg. 2956
SMG NETWORK, INC.—See Northlane Capital Partners, LLC; *U.S. Private*, pg. 2956
SONICBIDS CORPORATION—See Guggenheim Partners, LLC; *U.S. Private*, pg. 1811
SPOHN RANCH, INC.; *U.S. Private*, pg. 3759
SWEDEN ROCK FESTIVAL AB—See Live Nation Entertainment, Inc.; *U.S. Public*, pg. 1331
TELEDEPORTES S.A.—See Grupo Clarin S.A.; *Int'l*, pg. 3125
TELE RED IMAGEN S.A.—See Grupo Clarin S.A.; *Int'l*, pg. 3125
TICKETZOOM.COM; *U.S. Private*, pg. 4167
TOTALLY TICKETS INC.; *U.S. Private*, pg. 4192
TOUGH MUDDER LLC; *U.S. Private*, pg. 4193
TREAT ENTERTAINMENT INC.; *U.S. Private*, pg. 4216
THE UTICA SYMPHONY ORCHESTRA; *U.S. Private*, pg. 4130
VEEPS INC.—See Live Nation Entertainment, Inc.; *U.S. Public*, pg. 1331
WOLFTRAP FOUNDATION FOR THE PERFORMING ARTS; *U.S. Private*, pg. 4554
WORLD TRIATHLON CORPORATION—See Dalian Wanda Group Corporation Ltd.; *Int'l*, pg. 1953
WWE CANADA, CO.—See Silver Lake Group, LLC; *U.S. Private*, pg. 3654
WWE GERMANY GMBH—See Silver Lake Group, LLC; *U.S. Private*, pg. 3654

711410 — AGENTS AND MANAGERS FOR ARTISTS, ATHLETES, ENTERTAINERS, AND OTHER PUBLIC FIGURES

19 ENTERTAINMENT LIMITED—See Apollo Global Management, Inc.; *U.S. Public*, pg. 148
ANGELS MODEL MANAGEMENT SARL—See Elite World S.A.; *Int'l*, pg. 2362
ATHLETIC CLUB AJACCIEN ACA FOOTBALL; *Int'l*, pg. 670
A U L CORP.—See Dai-ichi Life Holdings, Inc.; *Int'l*, pg. 1917
AVEX MANAGEMENT INC.—See Avex Inc.; *Int'l*, pg. 740
AZEAL INC.—See Amuse Inc.; *Int'l*, pg. 442
AZOFF MUSIC MANAGEMENT; *U.S. Private*, pg. 415
BAND REP MANAGEMENT, INC.; *Int'l*, pg. 828
BETA MUSIC GROUP, INC.; *U.S. Private*, pg. 545
BLACK ROCK ARTS FOUNDATION—See Burning Man Project; *U.S. Private*, pg. 689
CAA SPORTS—See TPG Capital, L.P.; *U.S. Public*, pg. 2170
CAA SPORTS—See TPG Capital, L.P.; *U.S. Public*, pg. 2170
CAVE INTERACTIVE CO., LTD.; *Int'l*, pg. 1361
CJ ENTERTAINMENT AMERICA CORP.—See CJ Corporation; *Int'l*, pg. 1631
COLUMBIA ARTISTS MANAGEMENT LLC; *U.S. Private*, pg. 976
CONVENTION MODELS & TALENT, INC; *U.S. Private*, pg. 1035
CONVERGE MEDIA GROUP, LLC—See Zealot Networks, Inc.; *U.S. Private*, pg. 4599
CREATIVE ARTISTS AGENCY, LLC—See TPG Capital, L.P.; *U.S. Public*, pg. 2170
CREATIVE ARTISTS AGENCY, LLC - ST. LOUIS OFFICE—See TPG Capital, L.P.; *U.S. Public*, pg. 2170
CREATIVE ARTISTS AGENCY UK LIMITED—See TPG Capital, L.P.; *U.S. Public*, pg. 2170
DNA MODEL MANAGEMENT LLC; *U.S. Private*, pg. 1249
ELITE LICENSING COMPANY S.A.—See Elite World S.A.; *Int'l*, pg. 2362
ELITE MANAGEMENT S.A.—See Elite World S.A.; *Int'l*, pg. 2362
ELITE MODEL MANAGEMENT AMSTERDAM B.V.—See Elite World S.A.; *Int'l*, pg. 2362
ELITE MODEL MANAGEMENT BRATISLAVA SRO.—See Elite World S.A.; *Int'l*, pg. 2362
ELITE MODEL MANAGEMENT COPENHAGEN—See Elite World S.A.; *Int'l*, pg. 2362
ELITE MODEL MANAGEMENT CORPORATION; *U.S. Private*, pg. 1361
ELITE MODEL MANAGEMENT LONDON LTD.—See Elite World S.A.; *Int'l*, pg. 2362
ELITE MODEL MANAGEMENT PRAGUE SRO—See Elite World S.A.; *Int'l*, pg. 2362
ELITE MODEL MANAGEMENT SARL—See Elite World S.A.; *Int'l*, pg. 2363
ELITE MODEL MANAGEMENT SARL—See Elite World S.A.; *Int'l*, pg. 2363
THE ENDEAVOR AGENCY LLC—See The Interpublic Group of Companies, Inc.; *U.S. Public*, pg. 2104
ENVIRONMENTAL MANAGEMENT ALTERNATIVES, INC.—See Gryphon Investors, LLC; *U.S. Private*, pg. 1798
EPITAPH RECORDS; *U.S. Private*, pg. 1413
EVO ENTERTAINMENT GROUP, LLC; *U.S. Private*, pg. 1442
FORD MODELS INC.; *U.S. Private*, pg. 1564
FOX BASEBALL HOLDINGS, INC.—See Fox Corporation; *U.S. Public*, pg. 875
GREENLIGHT MEDIA & MARKETING, LLC—See Live Nation Entertainment, Inc.; *U.S. Public*, pg. 1329
GROWEST INC.; *U.S. Private*, pg. 1795
HOME ACCESS HEALTH CORPORATION—See Everlywell, Inc.; *U.S. Private*, pg. 1440
ICON INTERNATIONAL MODEL MANAGEMENT LIMITED—See Emperor Culture Group Limited; *Int'l*, pg. 2386
IERVOLINO & LADY BACARDI ENTERTAINMENT S.P.A.; *Int'l*, pg. 3597
INDEPENDENT TALENT GROUP LTD.—See The Yucaipa Companies LLC; *U.S. Private*, pg. 4140
INTERNATIONAL CREATIVE MANAGEMENT, INC. - NEW YORK—See TPG Capital, L.P.; *U.S. Public*, pg. 2170
INTERNATIONAL CREATIVE MANAGEMENT, INC.—See TPG Capital, L.P.; *U.S. Public*, pg. 2170
JANKLOW & NESBIT ASSOCIATES; *U.S. Private*, pg. 2187
KELLY & PARTNERS, INC.—See Keystone Digital Imaging, Incorporated; *U.S. Private*, pg. 2296
KING OCEAN SERVICES LIMITED; *U.S. Private*, pg. 2309
THE LEGACY AGENCY, INC. - NEWPORT BEACH—See Gatemore Capital Management LLP; *Int'l*, pg. 2889
THE LEGACY AGENCY, INC. - NEW YORK—See Gatemore Capital Management LLP; *Int'l*, pg. 2889
LEXINGTON GROUP, INC.; *U.S. Private*, pg. 2440
MANTI RESOURCES, INC.; *U.S. Private*, pg. 2567
METAWORKS PLATFORMS, INC.; *U.S. Public*, pg. 1428
NEXT MANAGEMENT, LLC; *U.S. Private*, pg. 2920
ONE MODEL MANAGEMENT LLC; *U.S. Private*, pg. 3020
OPUS 3 ARTISTS GMBH—See Opus 3 Artists LLC; *U.S. Private*, pg. 3036
OPUS 3 ARTISTS LLC - LOS ANGELES—See Opus 3 Artists LLC; *U.S. Private*, pg. 3036
OPUS 3 ARTISTS LLC; *U.S. Private*, pg. 3036
PHARMAFORCE INTERNATIONAL INC.—See Northlane Capital Partners, LLC; *U.S. Private*, pg. 2956

711410 — AGENTS AND MANAGERS...

PLAYER ONE AMUSEMENT GROUP INC.—See OpenGate Capital Management, LLC; *U.S. Private*, pg. 3031
PREMIER SPORTS & ENTERTAINMENT, INC.—See Zealot Networks, Inc.; *U.S. Private*, pg. 4599
Q MODEL MANAGEMENT INC.; *U.S. Private*, pg. 3312
RADLER FINANCIAL INC.—See Radler Enterprises Inc.; *U.S. Private*, pg. 3345
SCENE MODEL MANAGEMENT PTY LTD.—See BKM Management Limited; *Int'l*, pg. 1054
SCENE MODEL MANAGEMENT PTY LTD.—See BKM Management Limited; *Int'l*, pg. 1054
SCENE MODEL MANAGEMENT PTY LTD.—See BKM Management Limited; *Int'l*, pg. 1054
SEITRACK USA, LLC—See Live Nation Entertainment, Inc.; *U.S. Public*, pg. 1330
SHOW-FACTORY ENTERTAINMENT GMBH—See CTS Eventim AG & Co. KGAA; *Int'l*, pg. 1873
SKYDANCE MEDIA LLC—See RedBird Capital Partners L.P.; *U.S. Private*, pg. 3377
SOLIX, INC.; *U.S. Private*, pg. 3709
SPECTRA360, INC.; *U.S. Private*, pg. 3751
SPORTSTRUST ADVISORS, LLC; *U.S. Private*, pg. 3761
STORM MODEL MANAGEMENT LTD.—See Apollo Global Management, Inc.; *U.S. Public*, pg. 148
TALENT BANG LIMITED—See Emperor Culture Group Limited; *Int'l*, pg. 2386
TEXTRON AVIATION DEFENSE LLC—See Textron Inc.; *U.S. Public*, pg. 2028
UNITED TALENT AGENCY, INC.; *U.S. Private*, pg. 4301
VIAN ENTERPRISES, INC.—See Crane Company; *U.S. Public*, pg. 589
WILHELMINA NEW YORK—See Wilhelmina International, Inc.; *U.S. Public*, pg. 2370
WILLIAM MORRIS AGENCY, LLC - NEW YORK OFFICE—See William Morris Endeavor Entertainment, LLC; *U.S. Private*, pg. 4524
WILLIAM MORRIS AGENCY, LLC—See William Morris Endeavor Entertainment, LLC; *U.S. Private*, pg. 4524
WME IMG, LLC—See William Morris Endeavor Entertainment, LLC; *U.S. Private*, pg. 4524
WORLDFLIX, INC.; *U.S. Public*, pg. 2382

711510 — INDEPENDENT ARTISTS, WRITERS, AND PERFORMERS

ARGUS MEDIA, INC. - WASHINGTON, D.C.—See General Atlantic Service Company, L.P.; *U.S. Private*, pg. 1662
ARGUS MEDIA, INC. - WASHINGTON, D.C.—See HgCapital Trust plc; *Int'l*, pg. 3376
A-SKETCH INC.—See Amuse Inc.; *Int'l*, pg. 442
THE ASSOCIATED PRESS AB—See The Associated Press; *U.S. Private*, pg. 3989
BAMYAN MEDIA; *U.S. Private*, pg. 464
CARA COMMUNICATIONS LLC—See Clarion Capital Partners, LLC; *U.S. Private*, pg. 911
CINEWORLD CINEMA PROPERTIES LIMITED—See Cineworld Group plc; *Int'l*, pg. 1610
CROSSFIT, INC.—See Berkshire Partners LLC; *U.S. Private*, pg. 534
THE CURTIS PUBLISHING COMPANY; *U.S. Private*, pg. 4017
GEORGE WASHINGTON'S MOUNT VERNON; *U.S. Private*, pg. 1683
HEDGEBROOK; *U.S. Private*, pg. 1903
HNA INTERNATIONAL INVESTMENT HOLDINGS LIMITED; *Int'l*, pg. 3433
THE INTERNATIONAL SPY MUSEUM; *U.S. Private*, pg. 4057
JOURNALISTENSCHULE AXEL SPRINGER—See Axel Springer SE; *Int'l*, pg. 766
THE J. PAUL GETTY TRUST; *U.S. Private*, pg. 4058
LW1, INC.—See Wilhelmina International, Inc.; *U.S. Public*, pg. 2370
MUSEUM OF NEW MEXICO FOUNDATION; *U.S. Private*, pg. 2817
OTHER ART FAIRS LTD—See Graham Holdings Company; *U.S. Public*, pg. 956
PACIFIC COAST FIELD SERVICES, INC.—See New Mountain Capital, LLC; *U.S. Private*, pg. 2900
PACIFIC SYMPHONY; *U.S. Private*, pg. 3071
RICOCHET LIMITED—See Warner Bros. Discovery, Inc.; *U.S. Public*, pg. 2329
STERN.DE GMBH—See Bertelsmann SE & Co. KGaA; *Int'l*, pg. 997
TALENT PLUS INC.; *U.S. Private*, pg. 3926
TRACK ENTERTAINMENT; *U.S. Private*, pg. 4201
TWENTY TWENTY PRODUCTIONS LIMITED—See Warner Bros. Discovery, Inc.; *U.S. Public*, pg. 2329
WILHELMINA INTERNATIONAL, LTD.—See Wilhelmina International, Inc.; *U.S. Public*, pg. 2370
WILHELMINA LONDON LIMITED—See Wilhelmina International, Inc.; *U.S. Public*, pg. 2370
WILHELMINA-MIAMI, INC.—See Wilhelmina International, Inc.; *U.S. Public*, pg. 2370
WILHELMINA WEST, INC.—See Wilhelmina International, Inc.; *U.S. Public*, pg. 2370

712110 — MUSEUMS

THE ADLER PLANETARIUM & ASTRONOMY MUSEUM; *U.S. Private*, pg. 3982
AMAZEUM; *U.S. Private*, pg. 216
AMERICAN PHILOSOPHICAL SOCIETY; *U.S. Private*, pg. 243
AMERICAN SOCIETY FOR YAD VASHEM; *U.S. Private*, pg. 254
AMON CARTER MUSEUM OF AMERICAN ART; *U.S. Private*, pg. 264
AMUSE EDUTAINMENT INC.—See Amuse Inc.; *Int'l*, pg. 442
ATLANTA HISTORY CENTER; *U.S. Private*, pg. 370
THE BALTIMORE MUSEUM OF ART; *U.S. Private*, pg. 3991
BISHOP MUSEUM; *U.S. Private*, pg. 565
BROOKLYN CHILDREN'S MUSEUM INC.; *U.S. Private*, pg. 663
BROOKLYN INSTITUTE OF ARTS AND SCIENCES; *U.S. Private*, pg. 664
BUFFALO BILL MEMORIAL ASSOCIATION; *U.S. Private*, pg. 680
CENTER FOR MAINE CONTEMPORARY ART; *U.S. Private*, pg. 810
CHALK & VERMILLION FINE ARTS & MARTIN LAWRENCE GALLERIES; *U.S. Private*, pg. 845
CHICAGO HISTORY MUSEUM; *U.S. Private*, pg. 878
CHILDREN'S MUSEUM OF HOUSTON; *U.S. Private*, pg. 885
THE CHILDREN'S MUSEUM OF INDIANAPOLIS; *U.S. Private*, pg. 4009
CHRYSLER MUSEUM OF ART; *U.S. Private*, pg. 893
CINCINNATI ART MUSEUM; *U.S. Private*, pg. 897
CLEVELAND MUSEUM OF ART; *U.S. Private*, pg. 941
CLEVELAND MUSEUM OF NATURAL HISTORY; *U.S. Private*, pg. 941
COLORADO MUSEUM OF NATURAL HISTORY; *U.S. Private*, pg. 974
CONNER PRAIRIE MUSEUM, INC.; *U.S. Private*, pg. 1017
COUNTRY MUSIC FOUNDATION, INC.; *U.S. Private*, pg. 1067
CREATION EVIDENCE MUSEUM OF TEXAS; *U.S. Private*, pg. 1087
CROCKER ART MUSEUM ASSOCIATION; *U.S. Private*, pg. 1102
DAVID O'KEEFE STUDIOS INC.; *U.S. Private*, pg. 1171
DELAWARE MUSEUM OF NATURAL HISTORY; *U.S. Private*, pg. 1194
DENVER ART MUSEUM; *U.S. Private*, pg. 1207
DISCOVERY PLACE, INC.; *U.S. Private*, pg. 1238
ELVIS PRESLEY ENTERPRISES, INC.—See Apollo Global Management, Inc.; *U.S. Public*, pg. 148
ERIE COUNTY HISTORICAL SOCIETY; *U.S. Private*, pg. 1420
THE FARMERS' MUSEUM, INC.; *U.S. Private*, pg. 4027
FERNBANK MUSEUM OF NATURAL HISTORY; *U.S. Private*, pg. 1497
THE FIELD MUSEUM; *U.S. Private*, pg. 4028
FINCA MUSEUM S.L.—See Baron de Ley, S.A.; *Int'l*, pg. 867
FINE ARTS MUSEUMS OF SAN FRANCISCO; *U.S. Private*, pg. 1509
FORT WORTH MUSEUM OF SCIENCE AND HISTORY; *U.S. Private*, pg. 1575
THE FRICK COLLECTION; *U.S. Private*, pg. 4031
GEORGIA MUSEUMS, INC.; *U.S. Private*, pg. 1684
THE GETTYSBURG FOUNDATION; *U.S. Private*, pg. 4033
HENRY FORD MUSEUM AND GREENFIELD VILLAGE; *U.S. Private*, pg. 1918
INDIANA HISTORICAL SOCIETY; *U.S. Private*, pg. 2062
INDIANAPOLIS MUSEUM OF ART; *U.S. Private*, pg. 2063
ISABELLA STEWART GARDNER MUSEUM; *U.S. Private*, pg. 2142
LIBERTY SCIENCE CENTER, INC.; *U.S. Private*, pg. 2447
LONG ISLAND CHILDREN'S MUSEUM; *U.S. Private*, pg. 2490
LOS ANGELES COUNTY MUSEUM OF NATURAL HISTORY FOUNDATION; *U.S. Private*, pg. 2496
MAYMONT FOUNDATION; *U.S. Private*, pg. 2622
THE METROPOLITAN MUSEUM OF ART; *U.S. Private*, pg. 4078
MICHIGAN HISTORIC PRESERVATION NETWORK; *U.S. Private*, pg. 2700
MINNESOTA HISTORICAL SOCIETY; *U.S. Private*, pg. 2743
MUSEE GREVIN SA—See Compagnie des Alpes S.A.; *Int'l*, pg. 1738
MUSEUM OF AMERICAN FINANCE; *U.S. Private*, pg. 2817
THE MUSEUM OF CONTEMPORARY ART, LOS ANGELES; *U.S. Private*, pg. 4081
MUSEUM OF FINE ARTS OF ST. PETERSBURG FLORIDA INC.; *U.S. Private*, pg. 2817
MUSEUM OF FLIGHT FOUNDATION; *U.S. Private*, pg. 2817
MUSEUM OF HISTORY & INDUSTRY; *U.S. Private*, pg. 2817
THE MUSEUM OF MODERN ART; *U.S. Private*, pg. 4081
MUSEUM OF PHOTOGRAPHIC ARTS—See The San Diego Museum of Art; *U.S. Private*, pg. 4113

CORPORATE AFFILIATIONS

MUSEUM OF SCIENCE AND INDUSTRY; *U.S. Private*, pg. 2817
MUSEUM OF SCIENCE & HISTORY OF JACKSONVILLE, INC.; *U.S. Private*, pg. 2817
NATIONAL BLUES MUSEUM; *U.S. Private*, pg. 2848
THE NATIONAL CORVETTE MUSEUM; *U.S. Private*, pg. 4082
NATIONAL FOOTBALL MUSEUM, INC.; *U.S. Private*, pg. 2854
NATIONAL RAILWAY HISTORICAL SOCIETY.; *U.S. Private*, pg. 2861
THE NEW CHILDRENS MUSEUM; *U.S. Private*, pg. 4083
NEW ORLEANS MUSEUM OF ART; *U.S. Private*, pg. 2904
NEW YORK HALL OF SCIENCE; *U.S. Private*, pg. 2909
OHIO HISTORY CONNECTION; *U.S. Private*, pg. 3004
THE OREGON HISTORICAL SOCIETY; *U.S. Private*, pg. 4089
OWLS HEAD TRANSPORTATION MUSEUM; *U.S. Private*, pg. 3055
THE PALEY CENTER FOR MEDIA; *U.S. Private*, pg. 4090
THE PEABODY ESSEX MUSEUM; *U.S. Private*, pg. 4091
PHILADELPHIA MUSEUM OF ART; *U.S. Private*, pg. 3169
PITTSBURGH HISTORY & LANDMARKS FOUNDATION; *U.S. Private*, pg. 3191
PLANETARIO ALFA—See ALFA, S.A.B. de C.V.; *Int'l*, pg. 313
PORTLAND ART MUSEUM; *U.S. Private*, pg. 3232
SALVADOR DALI MUSEUM, INC.; *U.S. Private*, pg. 3535
SAN ANTONIO CHILDREN'S MUSEUM; *U.S. Private*, pg. 3538
THE SAN DIEGO MUSEUM OF ART; *U.S. Private*, pg. 4113
SAN FRANCISCO MUSEUM OF MODERN ART; *U.S. Private*, pg. 3540
SCIENCE MUSEUM OKLAHOMA; *U.S. Private*, pg. 3573
SEMINARY RIDGE HISTORIC PRESERVATION FOUNDATION; *U.S. Private*, pg. 3604
THE SPEED ART MUSEUM; *U.S. Private*, pg. 4120
THE STRONG; *U.S. Private*, pg. 4123
TOLEDO MUSEUM OF ART; *U.S. Private*, pg. 4181
TUBE DUDE, LLC; *U.S. Private*, pg. 4255
USS MIDWAY MUSEUM; *U.S. Private*, pg. 4324
U.S. SPACE & ROCKET CENTER; *U.S. Private*, pg. 4272
UTAH ZOOLOGICAL SOCIETY; *U.S. Private*, pg. 4324
VERMONT HISTORICAL SOCIETY; *U.S. Private*, pg. 4367
VERO BEACH MUSEUM OF ART, INC.; *U.S. Private*, pg. 4368
WADSWORTH ATHENEUM MUSEUM OF ART; *U.S. Private*, pg. 4425

712120 — HISTORICAL SITES

HISTORIC HUDSON VALLEY; *U.S. Private*, pg. 1951
THE MOUNT VERNON LADIES' ASSOCIATION OF THE UNION; *U.S. Private*, pg. 4081
NATIONAL TRUST FOR HISTORIC PRESERVATION; *U.S. Private*, pg. 2864
THE NATIONAL UNDERGROUND RAILROAD FREEDOM CENTER; *U.S. Private*, pg. 4082
THOMAS JEFFERSON FOUNDATION INC.; *U.S. Private*, pg. 4157
WORLD MONUMENTS FUND, INC.; *U.S. Private*, pg. 4566

712130 — ZOOS AND BOTANICAL GARDENS

AH-TRADING GMBH—See BHG Group AB; *Int'l*, pg. 1014
AQUARIUM GEANT DE SAINT MALO SAS—See Compagnie des Alpes S.A.; *Int'l*, pg. 1737
ATLANTA BOTANICAL GARDEN, INC.; *U.S. Private*, pg. 370
AUDUBON NATURE INSTITUTE; *U.S. Private*, pg. 391
AUSTRALIA ZOO PTY LTD; *Int'l*, pg. 720
BROOKLYN BOTANIC GARDEN CORPORATION; *U.S. Private*, pg. 663
CHICAGO HORTICULTURAL SOCIETY; *U.S. Private*, pg. 878
CHICAGO ZOOLOGICAL SOCIETY, INC.; *U.S. Private*, pg. 879
CLEARWATER MARINE AQUARIUM, INC.; *U.S. Private*, pg. 939
COLUMBUS ZOOLOGICAL PARK ASSOCIATION; *U.S. Private*, pg. 979
COMMONWEALTH ZOOLOGICAL CORPORATION; *U.S. Private*, pg. 987
DENVER BOTANIC GARDENS; *U.S. Private*, pg. 1207
DENVER ZOOLOGICAL FOUNDATION; *U.S. Private*, pg. 1208
EAST BAY ZOOLOGICAL SOCIETY; *U.S. Private*, pg. 1315
THE FLORIDA AQUARIUM, INC.; *U.S. Private*, pg. 4029
FRESNO CHAFFEE ZOO; *U.S. Private*, pg. 1610
JOHN G. SHEDD AQUARIUM; *U.S. Private*, pg. 2221
LINCOLN PARK ZOO; *U.S. Private*, pg. 2458
LOWRY PARK ZOOLOGICAL SOCIETY OF TAMPA INC.; *U.S. Private*, pg. 2506
THE MARITIME AQUARIUM AT NORWALK; *U.S. Private*, pg. 4074

N.A.I.C.S. INDEX

MARYLAND ZOOLOGICAL SOCIETY, INC.; *U.S. Private*, pg. 2600
MISSOURI BOTANICAL GARDEN; *U.S. Private*, pg. 2749
MONTEREY BAY AQUARIUM FOUNDATION; *U.S. Private*, pg. 2776
MOTE MARINE LABORATORY, INC.; *U.S. Private*, pg. 2795
NASHVILLE ZOO AT GRASSMERE; *U.S. Private*, pg. 2837
NATIONAL AQUARIUM IN BALTIMORE INC.; *U.S. Private*, pg. 2845
NEW ENGLAND AQUARIUM; *U.S. Private*, pg. 2894
THE NEW YORK BOTANICAL GARDEN; *U.S. Private*, pg. 4083
OKLAHOMA CITY ZOOLOGICAL PARK; *U.S. Private*, pg. 3007
OMAHA ZOOLOGICAL SOCIETY; *U.S. Private*, pg. 3014
PHOENIX ZOO; *U.S. Private*, pg. 3174
THE POLLY HILL ARBORETUM; *U.S. Private*, pg. 4097
SAN ANTONIO ZOO; *U.S. Private*, pg. 3539
SEA RESEARCH FOUNDATION INC.; *U.S. Private*, pg. 3582
SEDGWICK COUNTY ZOO; *U.S. Private*, pg. 3597
SOUTH CAROLINA AQUARIUM; *U.S. Private*, pg. 3720
TETRA (UK) LIMITED—See Spectrum Brands Holdings, Inc.; *U.S. Public*, pg. 1917
THE TOLEDO ZOOLOGICAL SOCIETY; *U.S. Private*, pg. 4127
UNDERWATER WORLD LANGKAWI SDN. BHD.—See Eden Inc. Berhad; *Int'l*, pg. 2306
WOODLAND PARK ZOOLOGICAL SOCIETY; *U.S. Private*, pg. 4559
ZOOLOGICAL SOCIETY OF BUFFALO; *U.S. Private*, pg. 4608
ZOOLOGICAL SOCIETY OF CINCINNATI; *U.S. Private*, pg. 4608
ZOOLOGICAL SOCIETY OF PHILADELPHIA; *U.S. Private*, pg. 4608
ZOOLOGICAL SOCIETY OF PITTSBURGH; *U.S. Private*, pg. 4608
ZOOLOGICAL SOCIETY OF SAN DIEGO; *U.S. Private*, pg. 4608

712190 — NATURE PARKS AND OTHER SIMILAR INSTITUTIONS

21ST CENTURY PARKS INC.; *U.S. Private*, pg. 5
ALPHA PARK—See LAZ Parking Ltd, LLC; *U.S. Private*, pg. 2402
AMERICAN BIRD CONSERVANCY; *U.S. Private*, pg. 224
CARIBBEAN DISCOVERY, S.A. DE C.V.; *Int'l*, pg. 1330
CINCINNATI PARKS FOUNDATION; *U.S. Private*, pg. 898
COCA-COLA TRADING COMPANY—See The Coca-Cola Company; *U.S. Public*, pg. 2065
DEATH VALLEY CONSERVANCY; *U.S. Private*, pg. 1185
DIXIE STAMPEDE LP; *U.S. Private*, pg. 1245
FOREST PARK FOREVER; *U.S. Private*, pg. 1567
FOREVER RESORTS, LLC; *U.S. Private*, pg. 1567
HOUSE OF WYOMING VALLEY INC.; *U.S. Private*, pg. 1992
LAND TRUST ALLIANCE; *U.S. Private*, pg. 2384
MILITARY PARK PARTNERSHIP; *U.S. Private*, pg. 2729
NATURAL LANDS TRUST, INC.; *U.S. Private*, pg. 2867
POLYNESIAN CULTURAL CENTER; *U.S. Private*, pg. 3226
SAVE THE CHIMPS; *U.S. Private*, pg. 3556
WEEKI WACHEE SPRINGS STATE PARK; *U.S. Private*, pg. 4469
YOSEMITE FOUNDATION; *U.S. Private*, pg. 4591

713110 — AMUSEMENT AND THEME PARKS

ADVENTURE ISLAND—See United Parks & Resorts Inc.; *U.S. Public*, pg. 2234
ADVENTURE LANDS OF AMERICA, INC.; *U.S. Private*, pg. 109
AL-MOSUL FOR FUNFAIRS; *Int'l*, pg. 287
AMAT MUHIBAH SDN BHD—See Berjaya Corporation Berhad; *Int'l*, pg. 982
APEX PARKS GROUP, LLC—See Edgewater Services, LLC; *U.S. Private*, pg. 1335
AQUATICA—See United Parks & Resorts Inc.; *U.S. Public*, pg. 2234
BELPARK BV—See Compagnie des Alpes S.A.; *Int'l*, pg. 1737
BERJAYA TIMES SQUARE THEME PARK SDN BHD—See Berjaya Assets Berhad; *Int'l*, pg. 981
BLACKPOOL PLEASURE BEACH LTD.; *Int'l*, pg. 1061
BUSCH GARDENS TAMPA BAY—See United Parks & Resorts Inc.; *U.S. Public*, pg. 2234
BUSCH GARDENS WILLIAMSBURG—See United Parks & Resorts Inc.; *U.S. Public*, pg. 2234
CANADA'S WONDERLAND COMPANY—See Six Flags Entertainment Corporation; *U.S. Public*, pg. 1890
CAROWINDS—See Six Flags Entertainment Corporation; *U.S. Public*, pg. 1890
CDA-DS SAS—See Compagnie des Alpes S.A.; *Int'l*, pg. 1737
CEDAR POINT PARK LLC—See Six Flags Entertainment Corporation; *U.S. Public*, pg. 1890
CEDAR POINT—See Six Flags Entertainment Corporation; *U.S. Public*, pg. 1890
DAM SEN WATER PARK CORPORATION; *Int'l*, pg. 1955
DISCOVERY COVE—See United Parks & Resorts Inc.; *U.S. Public*, pg. 2234
DISNEY DESTINATIONS, LLC—See The Walt Disney Company; *U.S. Public*, pg. 2138
DORNEY PARK & WILDWATER KINGDOM—See Six Flags Entertainment Corporation; *U.S. Public*, pg. 1890
DXB ENTERTAINMENTS PJSC; *Int'l*, pg. 2237
ECOBIOGESTION SAS—See Compagnie des Alpes S.A.; *Int'l*, pg. 1738
EURO DISNEY ASSOCIES SCA—See The Walt Disney Company; *U.S. Public*, pg. 2139
E-WORLD CO., LTD.; *Int'l*, pg. 2249
FAMILYPARK GMBH INC.—See Compagnie des Alpes S.A.; *Int'l*, pg. 1738
FIESTA TEXAS, INC.—See Six Flags Entertainment Corp.; *U.S. Public*, pg. 1890
FLYOVER CANADA, INC.—See Viad Corp.; *U.S. Public*, pg. 2290
FRANCE MINIATURE SAS—See Compagnie des Alpes S.A.; *Int'l*, pg. 1738
FUJI KYUKO CO., LTD.; *Int'l*, pg. 2813
FUN SPOT OF FLORIDA, INC.; *U.S. Private*, pg. 1622
FUN TOWN SPLASH TOWN USA; *U.S. Private*, pg. 1622
GEAUGA LAKE & WILDWATER KINGDOM—See Six Flags Entertainment Corporation; *U.S. Public*, pg. 1890
GODWIN'S GATORLAND, INC.; *U.S. Private*, pg. 1725
GOLD REEF CITY THEME PARK—See Hosken Consolidated Investments Limited; *Int'l*, pg. 3485
GRAND OLE OPRY, LLC—See Ryman Hospitality Properties, Inc.; *U.S. Public*, pg. 1829
GREAT AMERICA—See Six Flags Entertainment Corporation; *U.S. Public*, pg. 1890
GREENLAND RESORT COMPANY LIMITED; *Int'l*, pg. 3075
GREVIN & CIE TOURAINE SAS—See Compagnie des Alpes S.A.; *Int'l*, pg. 1738
GREVIN DEUTSCHLAND GMBH—See Compagnie des Alpes S.A.; *Int'l*, pg. 1738
HELLENDOORN AVONTUREN PARK BV—See Compagnie des Alpes S.A.; *Int'l*, pg. 1738
HERSCHEND FAMILY ENTERTAINMENT CORP.; *U.S. Private*, pg. 1926
HERSHEY ENTERTAINMENT & RESORTS COMPANY; *U.S. Private*, pg. 1926
HONG KONG DISNEYLAND MANAGEMENT LIMITED—See The Walt Disney Company; *U.S. Public*, pg. 2139
HURRICANE HARBOR GP LLC—See Six Flags Entertainment Corp.; *U.S. Public*, pg. 1890
IMAGICAAWORLD ENTERTAINMENT LTD.; *Int'l*, pg. 3619
KERRVILLE CAMP-RESORT, LLC—See Sun Communities, Inc.; *U.S. Public*, pg. 1961
KINGS DOMINION LLC—See Six Flags Entertainment Corporation; *U.S. Public*, pg. 1890
KINGS ISLAND COMPANY—See Six Flags Entertainment Corporation; *U.S. Public*, pg. 1890
KINGS ISLAND PARK LLC—See Six Flags Entertainment Corporation; *U.S. Public*, pg. 1890
KNOTT'S BERRY FARM LLC—See Six Flags Entertainment Corporation; *U.S. Public*, pg. 1890
KOCH DEVELOPMENT CORPORATION; *U.S. Private*, pg. 2326
LAGUNA TEN BOSCH CO., LTD.—See H.I.S. Co., Ltd.; *Int'l*, pg. 3195
THE LOST PARADISE OF DILMUN WATER PARK BSC—See GFH Financial Group B.S.C.; *Int'l*, pg. 2957
MARTIN'S FANTASY ISLAND—See Edgewater Services, LLC; *U.S. Private*, pg. 1335
MICHIGAN'S ADVENTURE—See Six Flags Entertainment Corporation; *U.S. Public*, pg. 1890
MOBILITYLAND CORPORATION—See Honda Motor Co., Ltd.; *Int'l*, pg. 3463
MOREY'S PIERS INCORPORATED; *U.S. Private*, pg. 2782
MULLIGAN LTD.; *U.S. Private*, pg. 2811
PAN INDIA PARYATAN LIMITED—See Essel Corporate Resources Pvt. Ltd.; *Int'l*, pg. 2509
PARC ASTERIX SAS—See Compagnie des Alpes S.A.; *Int'l*, pg. 1738
PARKS! AMERICA, INC.; *U.S. Public*, pg. 1650
PEDRO LAND INC.—See The Schafer Company Inc.; *U.S. Private*, pg. 4114
PLEASUREWOOD HILLS LTD—See Compagnie des Alpes S.A.; *Int'l*, pg. 1738
SAFARI AFRICAIN DE PORT SAINT PERE SA—See Compagnie des Alpes S.A.; *Int'l*, pg. 1738
SANTA CRUZ SEASIDE COMPANY; *U.S. Private*, pg. 3547
SEAWORLD CALIFORNIA—See United Parks & Resorts Inc.; *U.S. Public*, pg. 2234
SEA WORLD OF FLORIDA LLC—See United Parks & Resorts Inc.; *U.S. Public*, pg. 2234
SEA WORLD OF TEXAS LLC—See United Parks & Resorts Inc.; *U.S. Public*, pg. 2234
SEAWORLD PARKS & ENTERTAINMENT LLC—See United Parks & Resorts Inc.; *U.S. Public*, pg. 2234
SESAME PLACE—See United Parks & Resorts Inc.; *U.S. Public*, pg. 2234
SIX FLAGS AMERICA LP—See Six Flags Entertainment Corp.; *U.S. Public*, pg. 1890
SIX FLAGS DISCOVERY KINGDOM—See Six Flags Entertainment Corp.; *U.S. Public*, pg. 1890
SIX FLAGS ENTERTAINMENT CORP.; *U.S. Public*, pg. 1890
SIX FLAGS GREAT ADVENTURE LLC—See Six Flags Entertainment Corp.; *U.S. Public*, pg. 1890
SIX FLAGS GREAT AMERICA, INC.—See Six Flags Entertainment Corp.; *U.S. Public*, pg. 1890
SIX FLAGS HURRICANE HARBOR—See Six Flags Entertainment Corp.; *U.S. Public*, pg. 1890
SIX FLAGS MAGIC MOUNTAIN & HURRICANE HARBOR—See Six Flags Entertainment Corp.; *U.S. Public*, pg. 1890
SIX FLAGS MEXICO S.A. DE C.V.—See Six Flags Entertainment Corp.; *U.S. Public*, pg. 1890
SIX FLAGS OVER GEORGIA, INC.—See Six Flags Entertainment Corp.; *U.S. Public*, pg. 1890
SIX FLAGS OVER TEXAS & HURRICANE HARBOR—See Six Flags Entertainment Corp.; *U.S. Public*, pg. 1890
SIX FLAGS OVER TEXAS, INC.—See Six Flags Entertainment Corp.; *U.S. Public*, pg. 1890
SIX FLAGS ST. LOUIS LLC—See Six Flags Entertainment Corp.; *U.S. Public*, pg. 1890
SIX FLAGS THEME PARKS INC.—See Six Flags Entertainment Corp.; *U.S. Public*, pg. 1890
SOUTH OF THE BORDER RESTAURANT INC.—See The Schafer Company Inc.; *U.S. Private*, pg. 4114
SPARKY'S OCEANICA AMUSEMENT TOYS LLC—See Abdul Mohsen Al-Hokair Group for Tourism and Development Company; *Int'l*, pg. 58
STAR COIN INC.—See United Gaming, LLC; *U.S. Private*, pg. 4293
STOCKTON DELTA RESORT, LLC—See Sun Communities, Inc.; *U.S. Public*, pg. 1963
SUZUKA CIRCUITLAND CO., LTD.—See Honda Motor Co., Ltd.; *Int'l*, pg. 3464
UNITED PARKS & RESORTS INC.; *U.S. Public*, pg. 2234
UNIVERSAL CITY DEVELOPMENT PARTNERS, LTD.—See Comcast Corporation; *U.S. Public*, pg. 540
UNIVERSAL PARKS & RESORTS MANAGEMENT SERVICES LLC—See Comcast Corporation; *U.S. Public*, pg. 540
UNIVERSAL STUDIOS HOLLYWOOD—See Comcast Corporation; *U.S. Public*, pg. 541
UNIVERSITY CIRCLE INCORPORATED; *U.S. Private*, pg. 4307
USJ LLC—See Comcast Corporation; *U.S. Public*, pg. 540
VALLEYFAIR—See Six Flags Entertainment Corporation; *U.S. Public*, pg. 1890
WALIBI HOLLAND BV—See Compagnie des Alpes S.A.; *Int'l*, pg. 1738
WALT DISNEY HOLDINGS (HONG KONG) LIMITED—See The Walt Disney Company; *U.S. Public*, pg. 2140
WALT DISNEY PARKS & RESORTS U.S., INC.—See The Walt Disney Company; *U.S. Public*, pg. 2138
WATER COUNTRY USA—See United Parks & Resorts Inc.; *U.S. Public*, pg. 2234
WET 'N WILD ORLANDO—See Comcast Corporation; *U.S. Public*, pg. 541
WILD ADVENTURES, INC.; *U.S. Private*, pg. 4518
WILD ANIMAL, INC.—See Parks! America, Inc.; *U.S. Public*, pg. 1650
WILD ANIMAL SAFARI, INC.—See Parks! America, Inc.; *U.S. Public*, pg. 1650
WORLDS OF FUN—See Six Flags Entertainment Corporation; *U.S. Public*, pg. 1890

713120 — AMUSEMENT ARCADES

AEON FANTASY CO., LTD.—See AEON Co., Ltd.; *Int'l*, pg. 177
AMERICAN AMUSEMENTS LLC—See Trive Capital Inc.; *U.S. Private*, pg. 4240
AM/PM PROPERTY MANAGEMENT, INC.—See Trive Capital Inc.; *U.S. Private*, pg. 4240
AMUSEMENT SALES & SERVICE INC.—See United Gaming, LLC; *U.S. Private*, pg. 4293
CAPCOM USA, INC.—See Capcom Co., Ltd.; *Int'l*, pg. 1302
COLLINS ENTERTAINMENT INC.; *U.S. Private*, pg. 969
FERNANDEZ ENTERTAINMENT; *U.S. Private*, pg. 1497
FUN FACTORY INC.—See Fernandez Entertainment; *U.S. Private*, pg. 1497
GRAVITY GAME ARISE CO., LTD.—See Gravity Co., Ltd.; *Int'l*, pg. 3062
INSPIRED GAMING (UK) LIMITED—See Inspired Entertainment Inc; *U.S. Public*, pg. 1131
MCDONALD'S AMUSEMENTS INC.; *U.S. Private*, pg. 2632
NAMCO ENTERPRISES ASIA LTD.—See BANDAI NAMCO Holdings Inc.; *Int'l*, pg. 829
NAMCO OPERATIONS SPAIN S.L.—See BANDAI NAMCO Holdings Inc.; *Int'l*, pg. 829
NICKELS & DIMES INC.; *U.S. Private*, pg. 2926

PRIMETIME AMUSEMENTS OF SOUTH FLORIDA LLC; *U.S. Private*, pg. 3263
REGAL AMUSEMENT MACHINE SALES LTD.—See Light & Wonder, Inc.; *U.S. Public*, pg. 1314
ROCK SOLID AMUSEMENTS, LLC—See Boyd Gaming Corporation; *U.S. Public*, pg. 378
UNITED LABEL S.A.—See CI GAMES S.A.; *Int'l*, pg. 1601
WMS GAMING AFRICA (PTY) LTD.—See Light & Wonder, Inc.; *U.S. Public*, pg. 1315
WMS GAMING AUSTRALIA PTY LTD.—See Light & Wonder, Inc.; *U.S. Public*, pg. 1315
WMS GAMING INTERNATIONAL, S.L.—See Light & Wonder, Inc.; *U.S. Public*, pg. 1315
WMS GAMING MEXICO, S. DE R.L. DE C.V.—See Light & Wonder, Inc.; *U.S. Public*, pg. 1315
WMS GAMING SERVICES EUROPE, S.L.—See Light & Wonder, Inc.; *U.S. Public*, pg. 1315
ZONE X LEISURE PTE LTD—See Aspial Corporation Limited; *Int'l*, pg. 630
ZONE X LEISURE PTE LTD—See Fragrance Group Limited; *Int'l*, pg. 2758

713210 — CASINOS (EXCEPT CASINO HOTELS)

A.G. TRUCANO, SON & GRANDSONS, INC.—See Maverick Gold LLC; *U.S. Private*, pg. 2616
ALTON CASINO, LLC—See PENN Entertainment, Inc.; *U.S. Public*, pg. 1662
AMERICAN CONTRACT BRIDGE LEAGUE, INC.; *U.S. Private*, pg. 228
ARISTOCRAT PROPERTIES PTY LTD—See Aristocrat Leisure Limited; *Int'l*, pg. 566
BAYMOUNT INCORPORATED; *Int'l*, pg. 914
BELLE OF ORLEANS, LLC—See Boyd Gaming Corporation; *U.S. Public*, pg. 377
BELLE OF SIOUX CITY, L.P.—See PENN Entertainment, Inc.; *U.S. Public*, pg. 1662
BET-AT-HOME.COM AG; *Int'l*, pg. 1001
BICYCLE CASINO; *U.S. Private*, pg. 551
BLUBERI GAMING TECHNOLOGIES INC.—See Callidus Capital Corporation; *Int'l*, pg. 1265
BTN, LLC—See PENN Entertainment, Inc.; *U.S. Public*, pg. 1662
CAESARS ENTERTAINMENT UK LTD.—See Caesars Entertainment, Inc.; *U.S. Public*, pg. 420
CAESARS RIVERBOAT CASINO, LLC—See Caesars Entertainment, Inc.; *U.S. Public*, pg. 419
CASINOS AUSTRIA AG; *Int'l*, pg. 1352
CASINOS AUSTRIA INTERNATIONAL GMBH—See Casinos Austria AG; *Int'l*, pg. 1352
CASINOS POLAND LTD.—See Century Casinos, Inc.; *U.S. Public*, pg. 474
CENTRAL OHIO GAMING VENTURES, LLC—See PENN Entertainment, Inc.; *U.S. Public*, pg. 1662
CENTURY CASINO BATH, LTD.—See Century Casinos, Inc.; *U.S. Public*, pg. 474
CENTURY CASINOS, INC.; *U.S. Public*, pg. 474
CENTURY CASINO ST. ALBERT, INC.—See Century Casinos, Inc.; *U.S. Public*, pg. 474
CENTURY RESORTS MANAGEMENT GMBH—See Century Casinos, Inc.; *U.S. Public*, pg. 474
CLERMONT LEISURE (UK) LIMITED; *Int'l*, pg. 1658
CODERE S.A.; *Int'l*, pg. 1688
COLORADO GRANDE ENTERPRISES, INC.—See Maverick Gold LLC; *U.S. Private*, pg. 2616
CONGRESS CASINO BADEN GMBH—See Casinos Austria AG; *Int'l*, pg. 1353
CUBUS LUX D.O.O—See Cubus Lux Plc; *Int'l*, pg. 1876
DERBY CITY GAMING, LLC—See Churchill Downs, Inc.; *U.S. Public*, pg. 493
DIAMOND JO, LLC—See Boyd Gaming Corporation; *U.S. Public*, pg. 377
DIAMOND JO WORTH, LLC—See Boyd Gaming Corporation; *U.S. Public*, pg. 377
ELYS GAME TECHNOLOGY, CORP.; *Int'l*, pg. 2371
EMPHASIS SERVICES LIMITED—See AsianLogic Limited; *Int'l*, pg. 620
EVERGREEN ENTERTAINMENT CORPORATION—See Maverick Gold LLC; *U.S. Private*, pg. 2616
GHOTEL GMBH—See Art-Invest Real Estate Management GmbH & Co. KG; *Int'l*, pg. 580
GOLDEN MARDI GRAS CASINO—See Bally's Corporation; *U.S. Public*, pg. 268
GREENWOOD GAMING & ENTERTAINMENT, INC.—See International Turf Investment Co., Inc.; *U.S. Private*, pg. 2121
GROUPE PARTOUCHE S.A.; *Int'l*, pg. 3109
HARRODS CASINO—See Harrods Ltd.; *Int'l*, pg. 3279
HIGHSTREET CRUISES & ENTERTAINMENT PRIVATE LIMITED—See Delta Corp Ltd.; *Int'l*, pg. 2016
ICELANDAIR HOTELS EHF.—See Berjaya Corporation Berhad; *Int'l*, pg. 983
JEAN METZ S.A.S.—See Groupe Partouche S.A.; *Int'l*, pg. 3109
KANSAS STAR CASINO, LLC—See Boyd Gaming Corporation; *U.S. Public*, pg. 377
LAKES GAMING & RESORTS, LLC—See Golden Entertainment, Inc.; *U.S. Public*, pg. 950
LONDON CLUBS LSQ LIMITED—See Caesars Entertainment, Inc.; *U.S. Public*, pg. 420
LONDON CLUBS SOUTHEND LIMITED—See Caesars Entertainment, Inc.; *U.S. Public*, pg. 420
THE MISSOURI GAMING COMPANY, LLC—See PENN Entertainment, Inc.; *U.S. Public*, pg. 1662
MOHEGAN COMMERCIAL VENTURES-PA, LLC—See Mohegan Tribal Gaming Authority; *U.S. Private*, pg. 2765
NEVADA GOLD BVR, L.L.C.—See Maverick Gold LLC; *U.S. Private*, pg. 2616
PENN CECIL MARYLAND, INC.—See PENN Entertainment, Inc.; *U.S. Public*, pg. 1662
PRAIRIE ISLAND INDIAN COMMUNITY; *U.S. Private*, pg. 3242
RIH ACQUISITIONS MS II, LLC—See PENN Entertainment, Inc.; *U.S. Public*, pg. 1662
RUSH STREET INTERACTIVE, INC.; *U.S. Public*, pg. 1827
SEMINOLE CASINO HOLLYWOOD—See Seminole Tribe of Florida, Inc.; *U.S. Private*, pg. 3604
SOUTHWEST CASINO CORP.; *U.S. Private*, pg. 3738
THE SPORTSMAN CLUB LIMITED—See Caesars Entertainment, Inc.; *U.S. Public*, pg. 420
STRIKE LUCKY GAMES LTD—See DM plc; *Int'l*, pg. 2142
TOLEDO GAMING VENTURES, LLC—See PENN Entertainment, Inc.; *U.S. Public*, pg. 1663
WASHINGTON GOLD CASINOS LLC—See Maverick Gold LLC; *U.S. Private*, pg. 2616

713290 — OTHER GAMBLING INDUSTRIES

AGTECH HOLDINGS LIMITED—See Alibaba Group Holding Limited; *Int'l*, pg. 326
ALFABET S.A.S.—See evoke plc; *Int'l*, pg. 2572
ANGLER GAMING PLC; *Int'l*, pg. 461
APUESTAS INTERNACIONALES, S.A. DE C.V.—See Grupo Televisa, S.A.B.; *Int'l*, pg. 3136
ASIANLOGIC LIMITED; *Int'l*, pg. 619
AVIATOR LLC—See Flutter Entertainment plc; *Int'l*, pg. 2715
BALLY TECHNOLOGIES INDIA PRIVATE LIMITED—See Light & Wonder, Inc.; *U.S. Public*, pg. 1314
BERJAYA ASSETS BERHAD; *Int'l*, pg. 981
BERJAYA PHILIPPINES, INC.—See Berjaya Corporation Berhad; *Int'l*, pg. 983
BEST OF THE BEST PLC; *Int'l*, pg. 999
BET365 GROUP LIMITED; *Int'l*, pg. 1001
BET-AT-HOME.COM ENTERTAINMENT GMBH—See bet-at-home.com AG; *Int'l*, pg. 1001
BET-AT-HOME.COM ENTERTAINMENT LTD.—See bet-at-home.com AG; *Int'l*, pg. 1001
BETFAIR LIMITED—See Flutter Entertainment plc; *Int'l*, pg. 2715
BETMAKERS TECHNOLOGY GROUP LTD.; *Int'l*, pg. 1002
BETTER COLLECTIVE D.O.O.—See Better Collective A/S; *Int'l*, pg. 1003
BETTER COLLECTIVE GREECE P.C.—See Better Collective A/S; *Int'l*, pg. 1003
BETTER COLLECTIVE SAS—See Better Collective A/S; *Int'l*, pg. 1003
BIG RED KENO LTD.; *U.S. Private*, pg. 553
BIG VALLEY RANCHERIA; *U.S. Private*, pg. 555
BILIBILI CO., LTD.—See Bilibili Inc.; *Int'l*, pg. 1029
BLUE SQUARE LTD.—See Flutter Entertainment plc; *Int'l*, pg. 2715
CAPITAL DISTRICT REGIONAL OFF-TRACK BETTING CORPORATION; *U.S. Private*, pg. 739
CARTAMUNDI - DIGITAL NV—See Cartamundi N.V.; *Int'l*, pg. 1348
CASINOS DU TOUQUET S.A.S.—See Groupe Partouche S.A.; *Int'l*, pg. 3109
THE CATSKILL REGIONAL OFF-TRACK BETTING CORPORATION; *U.S. Private*, pg. 4006
CENTURY ENTERTAINMENT INTERNATIONAL HOLDINGS LIMITED; *Int'l*, pg. 1418
CENTURY GAMING TECHNOLOGIES; *U.S. Private*, pg. 833
CG TECHNOLOGY, L.P.—See Cantor Fitzgerald, L.P.; *U.S. Private*, pg. 736
CODERE ARGENTINA S.A.—See Codere S.A.; *Int'l*, pg. 1688
CODERE COLOMBIA S.A.—See Codere S.A.; *Int'l*, pg. 1688
CODERE DO BRASIL ENTRETENIMENTO LTDA—See Codere S.A.; *Int'l*, pg. 1688
CODERE ITALIA SPA—See Codere S.A.; *Int'l*, pg. 1688
CODERE MEXICO, S.A.—See Codere S.A.; *Int'l*, pg. 1688
CODERE PANAMA, S.A.—See Codere S.A.; *Int'l*, pg. 1688
CODERE URUGUAY S.A.—See Codere S.A.; *Int'l*, pg. 1688
THE CORPORATE COMMISSION OF MILLE LACS BAND OJIBWE INDIANS; *U.S. Private*, pg. 4015
COUNTRYWIDE TRUCK INSURANCE AGENCY; *U.S. Private*, pg. 1068
DELTATECH GAMING LIMITED—See Delta Corp Ltd.; *Int'l*, pg. 2016
DON BEST SPORTS CORPORATION—See Light & Wonder, Inc.; *U.S. Public*, pg. 1314
DOVER DOWNS GAMING & ENTERTAINMENT, INC.—See Bally's Corporation; *U.S. Public*, pg. 268
DUBUQUE RACING ASSOCIATION LTD.; *U.S. Private*, pg. 1283
EMPIRE GLOBAL GAMING, INC.; *U.S. Public*, pg. 753
ESPORTS ENTERTAINMENT GROUP, INC.; *Int'l*, pg. 2506
EUROBET ITALIA SRL—See Entain PLC; *Int'l*, pg. 2450
EUROPEBET LLC—See Betsson AB; *Int'l*, pg. 1003
FANSUNITE ENTERTAINMENT, INC.; *Int'l*, pg. 2613
FORTUNA SAZKOVA KANCELAR, A.S.; *Int'l*, pg. 2743
GAMENET GROUP S.P.A.; *Int'l*, pg. 2877
GAMING ENTERTAINMENT INTERNATIONAL, INC.; *U.S. Private*, pg. 1640
GAMING INNOVATION GROUP INC.; *U.S. Public*, pg. 896
GAMING LABORATORIES INTERNATIONAL LLC; *U.S. Private*, pg. 1640
GAMING VC CORPORATION LIMITED—See Entain PLC; *Int'l*, pg. 2449
GAUSELMANN AG; *Int'l*, pg. 2890
GRAND VISION GAMING LLC—See Century Gaming Technologies; *U.S. Private*, pg. 833
GREEK ORGANISATION OF FOOTBALL PROGNOSTICS S.A.; *Int'l*, pg. 3069
GRUPO NUEVA COMERCIAL TB, S.A. DE C.V.—See Grupo Televisa, S.A.B.; *Int'l*, pg. 3136
GUYANA LOTTERY COMPANY LIMITED—See Canadian Bank Note Company Limited; *Int'l*, pg. 1282
GVC CORPORATION B.V.—See Entain PLC; *Int'l*, pg. 2449
INTERACTIVE SPORTS (CI) LIMITED—See Entain PLC; *Int'l*, pg. 2450
INTERSARE S.A.—See Codere S.A.; *Int'l*, pg. 1688
INTER-TRACK PARTNERS LLC; *U.S. Private*, pg. 2107
INTERTRONIC LIMITED—See Entain PLC; *Int'l*, pg. 2450
KEWEENAW BAY INDIAN COMMUNITY; *U.S. Private*, pg. 2292
LADBROKES BETTING & GAMING LIMITED—See Entain PLC; *Int'l*, pg. 2450
LATTNER ENTERTAINMENT GROUP ILLINOIS, LLC—See Boyd Gaming Corporation; *U.S. Public*, pg. 377
LOTTERY.COM INC.; *U.S. Public*, pg. 1342
LOUISIANA CASINO CRUISES, INC.—See Gaming and Leisure Properties, Inc.; *U.S. Public*, pg. 896
THE MAJESTIC STAR CASINO II, INC.—See Majestic Star Casino & Hotel; *U.S. Private*, pg. 2554
MAVERICK GOLD LLC; *U.S. Private*, pg. 2616
MCINTYRE DODD MARKETING LTD—See DM plc; *Int'l*, pg. 2142
MERKUR INTERACTIVE SERVICES GMBH—See Gauselmann AG; *Int'l*, pg. 2890
MULTIGIOCO SRL—See Elys Game Technology, Corp.; *Int'l*, pg. 2371
MULTIMEDIA GAMES, INC.—See Everi Holdings Inc.; *U.S. Public*, pg. 801
NANOTECH GAMING, INC.; *U.S. Public*, pg. 1490
NASSAU REGIONAL OFF-TRACK BETTING; *U.S. Private*, pg. 2837
NATURAL AVENUE SDN. BHD.—See Berjaya Assets Berhad; *Int'l*, pg. 981
NATURAL AVENUE SDN. BHD.—See Berjaya Assets Berhad; *Int'l*, pg. 981
NATURAL AVENUE SDN. BHD.—See Berjaya Assets Berhad; *Int'l*, pg. 981
NATURAL AVENUE SDN. BHD.—See Berjaya Assets Berhad; *Int'l*, pg. 982
NEW YORK CITY OFF-TRACK BETTING CORPORATION; *U.S. Private*, pg. 2909
ON LINE LOTTERY SERVICES (PROPRIETARY) LIMITED—See CONDUIT CAPITAL LIMITED; *Int'l*, pg. 1766
OPAP SERVICES S.A.—See Greek Organisation of Football Prognostics S.A.; *Int'l*, pg. 3069
PACIFIC ONLINE SYSTEMS CORPORATION—See Belle Corporation; *Int'l*, pg. 966
PECHANGA RESORTS & CASINOS; *U.S. Private*, pg. 3126
PENN ENTERTAINMENT, INC.; *U.S. Public*, pg. 1661
RACEBETS INTERNATIONAL GAMING LTD.—See Betsson AB; *Int'l*, pg. 1003
RAIL CITY CASINO—See Truckee Gaming LLC; *U.S. Private*, pg. 4246
RATIONAL ENTERTAINMENT ENTERPRISES LIMITED—See Flutter Entertainment plc; *Int'l*, pg. 2715
RED LAKE GAMING INC.; *U.S. Private*, pg. 3375
SCIENTIFIC GAMES (CHINA) COMPANY LIMITED—See Light & Wonder, Inc.; *U.S. Public*, pg. 1314
SCIENTIFIC GAMES GERMANY GMBH—See Light & Wonder, Inc.; *U.S. Public*, pg. 1314
SCIENTIFIC GAMES WORLDWIDE LIMITED—See Light & Wonder, Inc.; *U.S. Public*, pg. 1315
SISAL S.P.A.—See Flutter Entertainment plc; *Int'l*, pg. 2715
SMEETS COMMUNICATIONS GMBH—See Azerion Group N.V.; *Int'l*, pg. 778
SMSC ENTERPRISES; *U.S. Private*, pg. 3699
SPORTSBET PTY LIMITED—See Flutter Entertainment plc; *Int'l*, pg. 2715
SPORTS TOTO BERHAD—See Berjaya Corporation Berhad; *Int'l*, pg. 983
SPRINGFIELD GAMING AND REDEVELOPMENT, LLC—See PENN Entertainment, Inc.; *U.S. Public*, pg. 1662

N.A.I.C.S. INDEX

STOCKMAN'S CASINO—See Full House Resorts, Inc.; *U.S. Public*, pg. 892
SUFFOLK REGIONAL OFF-TRACK BETTING; *U.S. Private*, pg. 3849
SULAKE OY—See Azerion Group N.V.; *Int'l*, pg. 778
SUMMIT AMUSEMENT & DISTRIBUTING LTD.—See AMCON Distributing Company; *U.S. Public*, pg. 93
TAIWAN LOTTERY CO., LTD.—See CTBC Financial Holding Co., Ltd.; *Int'l*, pg. 1869
TOTALIZATOR ENGINEERING LIMITED—See Fujitsu Limited; *Int'l*, pg. 2834
TOTOLOTEK S.A.—See Gauselmann AG; *Int'l*, pg. 2890
TRUCKEE GAMING LLC; *U.S. Private*, pg. 4246
TULALIP CASINO—See Tulalip Tribes; *U.S. Private*, pg. 4257
UNITED GAMING, LLC; *U.S. Private*, pg. 4292
UNITED TOTE CANADA, INC.—See Churchill Downs, Inc.; *U.S. Public*, pg. 494
WILLIAM HILL LATVIA SIA—See evoke plc; *Int'l*, pg. 2572
WORLD POKER STORE, INC.; *U.S. Public*, pg. 2381
YONKERS RACING CORPORATION—See MGM Resorts International; *U.S. Public*, pg. 1435

713910 — GOLF COURSES AND COUNTRY CLUBS

ADANI AIRPORT HOLDINGS LIMITED—See Adani Enterprises Limited; *Int'l*, pg. 124
ADVANCED TURF TECHNOLOGIES LTD.—See Stanley Black & Decker, Inc.; *U.S. Public*, pg. 1931
ALISO VIEJO COUNTRY CLUB—See Apollo Global Management, Inc.; *U.S. Public*, pg. 149
ALPINE COUNTRY CLUB; *U.S. Private*, pg. 201
AMERICAN GOLF CORPORATION; *U.S. Private*, pg. 235
ANANTI INC.; *Int'l*, pg. 447
ANGEL PARK GOLF, LLC; *U.S. Private*, pg. 281
ANSLEY GOLF CLUB; *U.S. Private*, pg. 286
ANTHEM GOLF & COUNTRY CLUB—See Apollo Global Management, Inc.; *U.S. Public*, pg. 149
APAWAMIS CLUB; *U.S. Private*, pg. 290
ARNOLD PALMER'S BAY HILL CLUB & LODGE; *U.S. Private*, pg. 333
ASOLO GOLF CLUB S.R.L.—See Edizione S.r.l.; *Int'l*, pg. 2312
ASPEN GLEN CLUB—See Apollo Global Management, Inc.; *U.S. Public*, pg. 149
AVALON COUNTRY CLUB AT SHARON, INC.—See Avalon Holdings Corporation; *U.S. Public*, pg. 239
AVALON GOLF AND COUNTRY CLUB, INC.—See Avalon Holdings Corporation; *U.S. Public*, pg. 239
AVALON LAKES GOLF, INC.—See Avalon Holdings Corporation; *U.S. Public*, pg. 239
AWBREY GLEN GOLF CLUB, INC.—See Brooks Resources Corporation; *U.S. Private*, pg. 664
A. WILBERT'S SONS ISLAND, LLC—See A. Wilbert's Sons, LLC; *U.S. Private*, pg. 24
BAILEYS GYM, INC.—See Rachas Inc.; *U.S. Private*, pg. 3341
BALLENISLES COUNTRY CLUB; *U.S. Private*, pg. 461
BALTIMORE COUNTRY CLUB; *U.S. Private*, pg. 462
BAYOU GOLF CLUB—See Fore Golf Services, LP; *U.S. Private*, pg. 1565
BELMONT COUNTRY CLUB—See Apollo Global Management, Inc.; *U.S. Public*, pg. 149
BERJAYA GOLF RESORT BERHAD—See Berjaya Corporation Berhad; *Int'l*, pg. 983
BETHESDA COUNTRY CLUB; *U.S. Private*, pg. 545
BIG SKY GOLF AND COUNTRY CLUB—See Belkorp Industries, Inc.; *Int'l*, pg. 965
BLACK DIAMOND RANCH—See Escalante Golf, Inc.; *U.S. Private*, pg. 1424
BLACKHAWK COUNTRY CLUB; *U.S. Private*, pg. 575
BLACKHAWK GOLF CLUB—See OnCourse Strategies; *U.S. Private*, pg. 3019
BOCA WEST COUNTRY CLUB INC.; *U.S. Private*, pg. 607
BONITA BAY CLUB; *U.S. Private*, pg. 614
BRAEMAR COUNTRY CLUB—See Apollo Global Management, Inc.; *U.S. Public*, pg. 149
BRIER CREEK COUNTRY CLUB—See Apollo Global Management, Inc.; *U.S. Public*, pg. 149
BROKEN SOUND CLUB, INC.; *U.S. Private*, pg. 661
BROOKHAVEN COUNTRY CLUB—See Apollo Global Management, Inc.; *U.S. Public*, pg. 149
BUCKINGHAMSHIRE GOLF COMPANY, LTD.—See Arora Hotels Limited; *Int'l*, pg. 577
BUKIT KIARA RESORT BERHAD—See Berjaya Corporation Berhad; *Int'l*, pg. 983
CANYON CREEK COUNTRY CLUB—See Apollo Global Management, Inc.; *U.S. Public*, pg. 149
CANYON CREST COUNTRY CLUB—See Apollo Global Management, Inc.; *U.S. Public*, pg. 149
CANYON GATE COUNTRY CLUB—See Apollo Global Management, Inc.; *U.S. Public*, pg. 149
CAPITAL CITY CLUB INC.; *U.S. Private*, pg. 739
CARMEL COUNTRY CLUB; *U.S. Private*, pg. 766
CAROLINA COUNTRY CLUB; *U.S. Private*, pg. 767

CENTRAL COAST LEAGUES CLUB LIMITED; *Int'l*, pg. 1405
CHARLOTTE COUNTRY CLUB; *U.S. Private*, pg. 857
CHENAL COUNTRY CLUB—See PotlatchDeltic Corporation; *U.S. Public*, pg. 1704
CITY SPORTS AND RECREATION PUBLIC COMPANY LIMITED; *Int'l*, pg. 1628
CLAREMONT COUNTRY CLUB; *U.S. Private*, pg. 910
THE CLUB AT BOCA POINTE; *U.S. Private*, pg. 4010
THE CLUB AT EAGLEBROOKE; *U.S. Private*, pg. 4010
THE CLUB AT FALCON POINT—See Apollo Global Management, Inc.; *U.S. Public*, pg. 150
THE CLUB AT GRAND HAVEN—See Escalante Golf, Inc.; *U.S. Private*, pg. 1424
THE CLUB AT LAS CAMPANAS, INC.; *U.S. Private*, pg. 4010
THE CLUB AT PRADERA, INC.—See D.R. Horton, Inc.; *U.S. Public*, pg. 620
CLUB AT SEABROOK ISLAND INC.; *U.S. Private*, pg. 948
THE CLUB AT TREASURE ISLAND—See Bill Edwards Presents, Inc.; *U.S. Private*, pg. 557
CLUBCORP USA, INC.—See Apollo Global Management, Inc.; *U.S. Public*, pg. 149
CLUB DE POLO Y EQUITACION SAN CRISTOBAL; *Int'l*, pg. 1664
CNGC MATRIX INC.—See Matrix Development Group Inc.; *U.S. Private*, pg. 2612
COLONIAL COUNTRY CLUB; *U.S. Private*, pg. 970
COMMONWEALTH MATRIX LP—See Matrix Development Group Inc.; *U.S. Private*, pg. 2612
CONCERT GOLF PARTNERS, LLC; *U.S. Private*, pg. 1009
THE CONCESSION GOLF CLUB LLC; *U.S. Private*, pg. 4013
CONESTOGA GOLF CLUB LLC—See PulteGroup, Inc.; *U.S. Public*, pg. 1737
CONGRESSIONAL COUNTRY CLUB; *U.S. Private*, pg. 1014
COSMOS CLUB; *U.S. Private*, pg. 1062
THE COUNTRY CLUB AT WOODMORE—See Concert Golf Partners, LLC; *U.S. Private*, pg. 1009
COUNTRY CLUB OF ASHEVILLE—See McConnell Golf LLC; *U.S. Private*, pg. 2629
COUNTRY CLUB OF BIRMINGHAM; *U.S. Private*, pg. 1066
COUNTRY CLUB OF HILTON HEAD—See Apollo Global Management, Inc.; *U.S. Public*, pg. 149
COUNTRY CLUB OF THE NORTH—See Escalante Golf, Inc.; *U.S. Private*, pg. 1424
THE COUNTRY CLUB OF WINTER HAVEN; *U.S. Private*, pg. 4015
THE COUNTRY CLUB; *U.S. Private*, pg. 4015
CRESTVIEW COUNTRY CLUB—See Concert Golf Partners, LLC; *U.S. Private*, pg. 1009
CROOKED TREE GOLF CLUB INC.—See Boyne USA Resorts Inc.; *U.S. Private*, pg. 629
THE CROSBY CLUB—See Escalante Golf, Inc.; *U.S. Private*, pg. 1424
CROWN GOLF PROPERTIES, LP—See Henry Crown & Company; *U.S. Private*, pg. 1918
CUMBERLAND TRAIL GOLF COURSE, LLC—See Huntington Bancshares Incorporated; *U.S. Public*, pg. 1071
CYPRESS LAKE COUNTRY CLUB INC.; *U.S. Private*, pg. 1135
DAIMAN GOLF BERHAD—See Daiman Development Berhad; *Int'l*, pg. 1938
DAIWA ROYAL GOLF CO., LTD.—See Daiwa House Industry Co., Ltd.; *Int'l*, pg. 1946
DALLAS COUNTRY CLUB; *U.S. Private*, pg. 1149
DARULAMAN GOLF RESORT BEHARD—See Bina Darulaman Berhad; *Int'l*, pg. 1032
DEACON'S LODGE GOLF COURSE—See Whitebirch Enterprises, Inc.; *U.S. Private*, pg. 4511
DEBARY GOLF & COUNTRY CLUB—See Apollo Global Management, Inc.; *U.S. Public*, pg. 149
DEERCREEK COUNTRY CLUB—See Apollo Global Management, Inc.; *U.S. Public*, pg. 149
DESERT MOUNTAIN CLUB, INC.; *U.S. Private*, pg. 1213
DOMINION VALLLEY COUNTRY CLUB—See Apollo Global Management, Inc.; *U.S. Public*, pg. 149
DRIVE SHACK ORLANDO LLC—See Drive Shack Inc.; *U.S. Public*, pg. 688
DUVINE ADVENTURES, INC.—See Lindblad Expeditions Holdings, Inc.; *U.S. Public*, pg. 1319
ECHO FARMS GOLF & COUNTRY CLUB, INC.—See Matrix Development Group Inc.; *U.S. Private*, pg. 2612
ELMWOOD COUNTRY CLUB, INC.—See Ridgewood Real Estate Partners, LLC; *U.S. Private*, pg. 3434
ESCALANTE GOLF, INC.; *U.S. Private*, pg. 1424
EUPE GOLF MANAGEMENT BHD.—See Eupe Corporation Berhad; *Int'l*, pg. 2526
FARMINGTON COUNTRY CLUB; *U.S. Private*, pg. 1480
FIRESTONE COUNTRY CLUB—See Apollo Global Management, Inc.; *U.S. Public*, pg. 149
FORE GOLF SERVICES, LP; *U.S. Private*, pg. 1565
FOREST CREEK GOLF CLUB—See OnCourse Strategies; *U.S. Private*, pg. 3019
FOUNTAINS COUNTRY CLUB; *U.S. Private*, pg. 1581
FREEDOM BOAT CLUB LLC—See Brunswick Corporation; *U.S. Public*, pg. 407

713910 — GOLF COURSES AND CO...

FRENCHMAN'S RESERVE COUNTRY CLUB, INC.—See Toll Brothers, Inc.; *U.S. Public*, pg. 2161
FRESH MEADOW COUNTRY CLUB; *U.S. Private*, pg. 1610
FUKUCHIYAMA GOLF CO., LTD.—See Daiei Kankyo Co., Ltd.; *Int'l*, pg. 1924
FULL HOUSE RESORTS, INC.; *U.S. Public*, pg. 892
GLENEAGLES COUNTRY CLUB—See Apollo Global Management, Inc.; *U.S. Public*, pg. 149
GLEN OAK COUNTRY CLUB; *U.S. Private*, pg. 1709
GLEN OAKS CLUB; *U.S. Private*, pg. 1709
GLOBAL ACQUISITIONS CORPORATION; *U.S. Public*, pg. 940
GOLDEN BEAR GOLF CLUB AT INDIGO RUN—See Apollo Global Management, Inc.; *U.S. Public*, pg. 149
GOLF CARD INTERNATIONAL, LLC—See Camping World Holdings, Inc.; *U.S. Public*, pg. 428
THE GOLF CLUB AT DOVE MOUNTAIN—See Escalante Golf, Inc.; *U.S. Private*, pg. 1424
THE GOLF CLUB OF AMELIA ISLAND—See Concert Golf Partners, LLC; *U.S. Private*, pg. 1009
GOLF DO CO., LTD.; *Int'l*, pg. 3035
GOLFPLATZ EGGEBERG GMBH & CO. ANLAGEN KG—See GERRY WEBER International AG; *Int'l*, pg. 2945
GOLFTEC INTELLECTUAL PROPERTY, LLC—See Golf Digest Online Inc.; *Int'l*, pg. 3035
GOLFWALKER PTE LTD; *Int'l*, pg. 3035
GRANADILLA COUNTRY CLUB S.A.; *Int'l*, pg. 3054
GRANITE BAY GOLF CLUB—See Apollo Global Management, Inc.; *U.S. Public*, pg. 149
GRAY PLANTATION GOLF CLUB AND THE SPORT CLUB AT GRAYWOOD—See Escalante Golf, Inc.; *U.S. Private*, pg. 1424
GREENFIELD GOLF, L.L.C.; *U.S. Private*, pg. 1777
GREENSBORO COUNTRY CLUB; *U.S. Private*, pg. 1780
GREENVILLE COUNTRY CLUB; *U.S. Private*, pg. 1780
GREY OAKS COUNTRY CLUB INC.—See Barron Collier Company, Ltd.; *U.S. Private*, pg. 480
HAMPTON HALL CLUB, INC.—See Toll Brothers, Inc.; *U.S. Public*, pg. 2161
HASENTREE—See Apollo Global Management, Inc.; *U.S. Public*, pg. 149
HEATHROW COUNTRY CLUB—See Concert Golf Partners, LLC; *U.S. Private*, pg. 1009
HERITAGE GOLF GROUP LLC—See KSL Capital Partners, LLC; *U.S. Private*, pg. 2355
HERITAGE HILLS GOLF COURSE—See Orscheln Group; *U.S. Private*, pg. 3045
HERITAGE PALMS GOLF & COUNTRY CLUB INC.; *U.S. Private*, pg. 1924
HERSHEY'S MILL GOLF CLUB INC.—See Wooldridge Construction Co., Inc.; *U.S. Private*, pg. 4562
HIDDEN VALLEY RESORT—See The Nutting Company, Inc.; *U.S. Private*, pg. 4086
HILLCREST GOLF & COUNTRY CLUB, LTD.—See PulteGroup, Inc.; *U.S. Public*, pg. 1737
HILL TOP COUNTRY CLUB LIMITED—See ENM Holdings Limited; *Int'l*, pg. 2442
HILLWOOD COUNTRY CLUB; *U.S. Private*, pg. 1947
HOBE SOUND GOLF CLUB, INC.; *U.S. Private*, pg. 1958
HONOURS GOLF COMPANY, LLC—See Troon Golf L.L.C.; *U.S. Private*, pg. 4242
HORSESHOE BAY RESORT LTD.; *U.S. Private*, pg. 1984
HOUSTON GOLF ASSOCIATION; *U.S. Private*, pg. 1993
THE HOUSTONIAN GOLF & COUNTRY CLUB—See The Redstone Companies, L.P.; *U.S. Private*, pg. 4103
HUB CO., LTD.; *Int'l*, pg. 3516
HUNTER'S GREEN COUNTRY CLUB—See Apollo Global Management, Inc.; *U.S. Public*, pg. 149
IBIS WEST PALM PARTNERS LP; *U.S. Private*, pg. 2028
INDAH CORPORATION BERHAD—See Berjaya Corporation Berhad; *Int'l*, pg. 983
INDIGO GOLF PARTNERS, LLC—See Troon Golf L.L.C.; *U.S. Private*, pg. 4242
INDIGO INTERNATIONAL INC.—See CTO Realty Growth, Inc.; *U.S. Public*, pg. 602
INNIS ARDEN GOLF CLUB; *U.S. Private*, pg. 2080
JACKSON HOLE GOLF & TENNIS CLUB, INC.—See Vail Resorts, Inc.; *U.S. Public*, pg. 2271
JOHN'S ISLAND CLUB, INC.; *U.S. Private*, pg. 2225
JUNIOR SPORTS CORPORATION—See The Riverside Company; *U.S. Private*, pg. 4109
JUPITER COUNTRY CLUB, INC.—See Apollo Global Management, Inc.; *U.S. Public*, pg. 149
KDE RECREATION BERHAD—See Berjaya Corporation Berhad; *Int'l*, pg. 983
KEMPER SPORTS, INC.; *U.S. Private*, pg. 2282
KINGWOOD COVE GOLF CLUB—See OnCourse Strategies; *U.S. Private*, pg. 3019
LA CALA GOLF CLUB S.L.—See Farmer Business Developments plc; *Int'l*, pg. 2619
LAKE NONA GOLF & COUNTRY CLUB, LLC—See Tavistock Group; *U.S. Private*, pg. 3937
LAKESIDE COUNTRY CLUB; *U.S. Private*, pg. 2377
LAKEWOOD RANCH GOLF & COUNTRY CLUB; *U.S. Private*, pg. 2379
LEROY SPRINGS & COMPANY INC.; *U.S. Private*, pg. 2431

713910 — GOLF COURSES AND CO...

LINKS AT SPRUCE CREEK SOUTH—See Heritage Management Corp.; *U.S. Private*, pg. 1924
LINKSCORP LLC; *U.S. Private*, pg. 2462
LONE PALM GOLF CLUB, LLC—See Publix Super Markets, Inc.; *U.S. Private*, pg. 3301
LPGA INTERNATIONAL GIRLS GOLF CLUB, INC.—See Fore Golf Services, LP; *U.S. Private*, pg. 1565
MADERAS COUNTRY CLUB LLC—See Sunroad Holding Corporation; *U.S. Private*, pg. 3870
MAIDSTONE CLUB INC; *U.S. Private*, pg. 2551
MATRIX GOLF & HOSPITALITY—See Matrix Development Group Inc.; *U.S. Private*, pg. 2612
MCCONNELL GOLF LLC; *U.S. Private*, pg. 2629
MCHENRY METALS GOLF CORP.; *U.S. Public*, pg. 1407
MEDALIST VILLAGE CLUB, INC.—See Great White Shark Enterprises, Inc.; *U.S. Private*, pg. 1768
MEDINA GOLF & COUNTRY CLUB—See Apollo Global Management, Inc.; *U.S. Public*, pg. 150
MELBOURNE GOLF ACADEMY PTY LTD—See Blackstone Inc.; *U.S. Public*, pg. 353
METROPOLITAN CLUB; *U.S. Private*, pg. 2688
MIAMI BEACH GOLF CLUB—See Professional Course Management, Inc.; *U.S. Private*, pg. 3274
MIAMI SHORES COUNTRY CLUB—See Professional Course Management, Inc.; *U.S. Private*, pg. 3274
MIRA VISTA GOLF CLUB, L.C.—See Goff Capital, Inc.; *U.S. Private*, pg. 1726
MISSION HILLS COUNTRY CLUB—See Apollo Global Management, Inc.; *U.S. Public*, pg. 150
MISSION INN RESORTS INC.; *U.S. Private*, pg. 2747
MONTCLAIR GOLF CLUB; *U.S. Private*, pg. 2775
MONTEREY PENINSULA COUNTRY CLUB; *U.S. Private*, pg. 2776
MOUNTAIN VIEW COUNTRY CLUB, INC.—See Toll Brothers, Inc.; *U.S. Public*, pg. 2162
MYERS PARK COUNTRY CLUB; *U.S. Private*, pg. 2824
NATIONAL GOLF CLUB, INC.—See Pinehurst, LLC; *U.S. Private*, pg. 3183
THE NEWPORT BEACH COUNTRY CLUB—See Eagle Four Equities LLC; *U.S. Private*, pg. 1309
THE NEWPORT BEACH COUNTRY CLUB—See Pacific Hospitality Group, Inc.; *U.S. Private*, pg. 3067
NEW SEABURY GOLF CLUB LLC—See Icahn Enterprises L.P.; *U.S. Public*, pg. 1084
NORBECK COUNTRY CLUB, INC.—See Apollo Global Management, Inc.; *U.S. Public*, pg. 150
NORMANDY SHORES GOLF CLUB—See Professional Course Management, Inc.; *U.S. Private*, pg. 3275
NORTH AMERICAN MEMBERSHIP GROUP, INC.—See Pilot Group, LLC; *U.S. Private*, pg. 3181
NORTH RANCH COUNTRY CLUB; *U.S. Private*, pg. 2946
OAK CREEK GOLF CLUB—See Apollo Global Management, Inc.; *U.S. Public*, pg. 150
OAK HILL GOLF RANGE—See OnCourse Strategies; *U.S. Private*, pg. 3019
OAKHURST GOLF CLUB—See OnCourse Strategies; *U.S. Private*, pg. 3019
OLD WESTBURY GOLF & COUNTRY CLUB; *U.S. Private*, pg. 3009
OLYMPIC CLUB; *U.S. Private*, pg. 3012
ONCOURSE STRATEGIES; *U.S. Private*, pg. 3019
ORANGE COUNTY NATIONAL GOLF CENTER & LODGE; *U.S. Private*, pg. 3037
ORANGE LAKE COUNTRY CLUB, INC.—See Kemmons Wilson, Inc.; *U.S. Private*, pg. 2281
ORO VALLEY COUNTRY CLUB, INC.—See Apollo Global Management, Inc.; *U.S. Public*, pg. 150
PAPER VALLEY CORPORATION—See The Boldt Group Inc.; *U.S. Private*, pg. 3996
PARKLAND GOLF CLUB, INC.—See Toll Brothers, Inc.; *U.S. Public*, pg. 2162
PELICAN MARSH GOLF CLUB—See Lennar Corporation; *U.S. Public*, pg. 1307
PERSIMMON GOLF CLUB LLC—See Drive Shack Inc.; *U.S. Public*, pg. 688
PHILADELPHIA COUNTRY CLUB; *U.S. Private*, pg. 3168
PHILADELPHIA CRICKET CLUB; *U.S. Private*, pg. 3168
PINE CREEK GOLF CLUB—See Escalante Golf, Inc.; *U.S. Private*, pg. 1424
PINEHURST, LLC; *U.S. Private*, pg. 3183
PIPING ROCK CLUB; *U.S. Private*, pg. 3190
THE PLAZA CLUB; *U.S. Private*, pg. 4096
POPE GOLF, LLC; *U.S. Private*, pg. 3228
THE PRESIDENT COUNTRY CLUB INC.; *U.S. Private*, pg. 4098
PRESTONWOOD GOLF CLUB LLC—See Apollo Global Management, Inc.; *U.S. Public*, pg. 150
PRINCETON CLUB OF NEW YORK; *U.S. Private*, pg. 3264
PROFESSIONAL COURSE MANAGEMENT, INC.; *U.S. Private*, pg. 3274
PT BATAMINDO EXECUTIVE VILLAGE—See Gallant Venture Ltd.; *Int'l*, pg. 2874
RAIN BIRD CORPORATION - RAIN BIRD GOLF DIVISION—See Rain Bird Corporation; *U.S. Private*, pg. 3347
RAINBOW PROPERTIES SDN BHD—See GSH Corporation Limited; *Int'l*, pg. 3144

THE RAVEN AT THREE PEAKS—See Escalante Golf, Inc.; *U.S. Private*, pg. 1424
RAVINIA GREEN COUNTRY CLUB—See Apollo Global Management, Inc.; *U.S. Public*, pg. 150
REDUS FREDERICA CLUB, LLC—See Wells Fargo & Company; *U.S. Public*, pg. 2345
REYNOLDS PLANTATION, INC.—See MetLife, Inc.; *U.S. Public*, pg. 1431
THE RIDGES AT MOUNTAIN HARBOUR, LLC—See Wells Fargo & Company; *U.S. Public*, pg. 2345
RIDGEWOOD LAKES GOLF & COUNTRY CLUB, INC.; *U.S. Private*, pg. 3434
RIVERSIDE GOLF COURSE—See OnCourse Strategies; *U.S. Private*, pg. 3020
RIVERWOOD GOLF CLUB—See Coral Hospitality, LLC; *U.S. Private*, pg. 1046
ROLLING HILLS COUNTRY CLUB; *U.S. Private*, pg. 3475
ROLLING ROCK CLUB; *U.S. Private*, pg. 3475
THE SANDS REGENT, LLC—See Jacobs Entertainment, Inc.; *U.S. Private*, pg. 2180
SANT'ANNA GOLF S.R.L.—See BPER BANCA S.p.A; *Int'l*, pg. 1132
SARA BAY COUNTRY CLUB, INC; *U.S. Private*, pg. 3549
SAUCON VALLEY COUNTRY CLUB; *U.S. Private*, pg. 3554
SCRATCH GOLF COMPANY—See The United Company; *U.S. Private*, pg. 4129
SEDONA GOLF RESORT LC—See Pinnacle West Capital Corporation; *U.S. Public*, pg. 1692
SERENOA GOLF CLUB—See OnCourse Strategies; *U.S. Private*, pg. 3020
SEVILLE GOLF & COUNTRY CLUB—See Apollo Global Management, Inc.; *U.S. Public*, pg. 150
SHADOWOOD GOLF INC.—See Kocolene Marketing, LLC; *U.S. Private*, pg. 2335
SHADOW WOOD COUNTRY CLUB, INC.; *U.S. Private*, pg. 3622
SKYTOP LODGE; *U.S. Public*, pg. 1892
SOLIVITA AT POINCIANA GOLF CLUB, INC.—See Brookfield Corporation; *Int'l*, pg. 1183
SONOMA GOLF CLUB, LLC—See Goff Capital, Inc.; *U.S. Private*, pg. 1726
SOUTHWOOD GOLF CLUB—See The St. Joe Company; *U.S. Public*, pg. 2131
SPANISH WELLS COUNTRY CLUB—See Escalante Golf, Inc.; *U.S. Private*, pg. 1424
STAFFIELD COUNTRY RESORT BERHAD—See Berjaya Corporation Berhad; *Int'l*, pg. 984
ST. ANDREWS COUNTRY CLUB, INC.; *U.S. Private*, pg. 3770
THE STANWICH CLUB, INC.; *U.S. Private*, pg. 4120
STONERIDGE GOLF COURSE, LLC—See Pinnacle West Capital Corporation; *U.S. Public*, pg. 1692
STONEYBROOK GOLF CLUB, INC.—See Lennar Corporation; *U.S. Public*, pg. 1307
SUNBELT GOLF CORPORATION; *U.S. Private*, pg. 3864
SUNRIDGE CANYON, LLC—See Pinnacle West Capital Corporation; *U.S. Public*, pg. 1692
TAGAYTAY HIGHLANDS INTERNATIONAL GOLF CLUB, INC.—See Belle Corporation; *Int'l*, pg. 966
TAGAYTAY MIDLANDS GOLF CLUB, INC.—See Belle Corporation; *Int'l*, pg. 966
TARA GOLF & COUNTRY CLUB; *U.S. Private*, pg. 3933
TARPON COVE YACHT AND RACQUET CLUB—See Escalante Golf, Inc.; *U.S. Private*, pg. 1424
THANA CITY GOLF & SPORTS CLUB CO., LTD.—See BTS Group Holdings Public Company Limited; *Int'l*, pg. 1206
TOLL OAK CREEK GOLF LLC—See Toll Brothers, Inc.; *U.S. Public*, pg. 2162
TOPGOLF INTERNATIONAL, INC.—See Topgolf Callaway Brands Corp.; *U.S. Public*, pg. 2164
TRIPOLI COUNTRY CLUB, INC.—See University Club of Milwaukee; *U.S. Private*, pg. 4307
TRUMP INTERNATIONAL GOLF CLUB, INC.—See The Trump Organization, Inc.; *U.S. Private*, pg. 4128
TRUMP NATIONAL GOLF CLUB, LLC—See The Trump Organization, Inc.; *U.S. Private*, pg. 4128
URBANA COUNTRY CLUB; *U.S. Private*, pg. 4315
UZUMINE COUNTRY CLUB CO., LTD.—See Dai Nippon Printing Co., Ltd.; *Int'l*, pg. 1916
VENICE GOLF ASSOCIATION, INC.; *U.S. Private*, pg. 4356
WAIKELE GOLF CLUB INC.—See Walton Street Capital, LLC; *U.S. Private*, pg. 4435
WEE BURN COUNTRY CLUB; *U.S. Private*, pg. 4468
WELLESLEY COUNTRY CLUB; *U.S. Private*, pg. 4475
WESTCHESTER COUNTRY CLUB INC.; *U.S. Private*, pg. 4489
WILMINGTON COUNTRY CLUB; *U.S. Private*, pg. 4529
WILSON RESORT MANAGEMENT CORP—See Kemmons Wilson, Inc.; *U.S. Private*, pg. 2281
WINDROSE GOLF CLUB—See OnCourse Strategies; *U.S. Private*, pg. 3020
WOODMONT COUNTRY CLUB; *U.S. Private*, pg. 4559
WOODWAY COUNTRY CLUB, INC.; *U.S. Private*, pg. 4561
WORLD GOLF TOUR—See Topgolf Callaway Brands Corp.; *U.S. Public*, pg. 2164
WORLD WOODS CORPORATION; *U.S. Private*, pg. 4568

713920 — SKIING FACILITIES

ARAPAHOE BASIN SKI AREA—See KSL Capital Partners, LLC; *U.S. Private*, pg. 2354
ATTITASH MOUNTAIN RESORT—See Vail Resorts, Inc.; *U.S. Public*, pg. 2271
BIG BEAR MOUNTAIN RESORT—See KSL Capital Partners, LLC; *U.S. Private*, pg. 2354
BLUE MOUNTAIN RESORTS LIMITED PARTNERSHIP—See KSL Capital Partners, LLC; *U.S. Private*, pg. 2354
CAMELBACK SKI CORPORATION; *U.S. Private*, pg. 728
CHANGCHUN JINGYUETAN SKIING GROUND LTD.—See Huangshan Tourism Development Co., Ltd.; *Int'l*, pg. 3513
COMPAGNIE DU MONT BLANC - SA; *Int'l*, pg. 1740
DEER VALLEY RESORT COMPANY, LLC—See KSL Capital Partners, LLC; *U.S. Private*, pg. 2354
DELTRECS, INC.—See Vail Resorts, Inc.; *U.S. Public*, pg. 2271
GRAND MASSIF DOMAINES SKIABLES SA—See Compagnie des Alpes S.A.; *Int'l*, pg. 1738
HIDDEN VALLEY GOLF AND SKI, INC.—See Vail Resorts, Inc.; *U.S. Public*, pg. 2271
HOMEWOOD MOUNTAIN RESORT—See JMA Ventures, LLC; *U.S. Private*, pg. 2214
HUNTER MOUNTAIN SKI BOWL, INC.—See Vail Resorts, Inc.; *U.S. Public*, pg. 2271
INTRAWEST/WINTER PARK OPERATIONS CORPORATION—See KSL Capital Partners, LLC; *U.S. Private*, pg. 2354
KILLINGTON RESORT—See Powdr Corp.; *U.S. Private*, pg. 3236
KIRKWOOD MOUNTAIN RESORTS, LLC—See Vail Resorts, Inc.; *U.S. Public*, pg. 2271
MAMMOTH MOUNTAIN SKI AREA, LLC—See KSL Capital Partners, LLC; *U.S. Private*, pg. 2354
MONT TREMBLANT RESORTS & COMPANY, LIMITED PARTNERSHIP—See KSL Capital Partners, LLC; *U.S. Private*, pg. 2354
MOONLIGHT BASIN LLC—See Lehman Brothers Holdings Inc. Plan Trust; *U.S. Private*, pg. 2419
MOUNTAIN CREEK RESORT, INC.—See Crystal Springs Resort; *U.S. Private*, pg. 1115
MOUNT CRANMORE SKI RESORT, INC.—See Booth Creek Management Corporation; *U.S. Private*, pg. 616
REMONTEES MECANIQUES CRANS MONTANA AMINONA (CMA) SA—See Vail Resorts, Inc.; *U.S. Public*, pg. 2271
SNOWSHOE MOUNTAIN, INC.—See KSL Capital Partners, LLC; *U.S. Private*, pg. 2354
SOLITUDE MOUNTAIN RESORT, LLC—See KSL Capital Partners, LLC; *U.S. Private*, pg. 2354
SPRING MOUNTAIN ADVENTURE CORP.; *U.S. Private*, pg. 3763
THE STRATTON CORPORATION—See KSL Capital Partners, LLC; *U.S. Private*, pg. 2354
SUGARLOAF/USA—See Boyne USA Resorts Inc.; *U.S. Private*, pg. 629
SUNDAY RIVER SKI RESORT; *U.S. Private*, pg. 3866
SUNDAY RIVER SKIWAY CORP—See Boyne USA Resorts Inc.; *U.S. Private*, pg. 629
WATERVILLE VALLEY SKI RESORT, INC.; *U.S. Private*, pg. 4454
WILMOT MOUNTAIN, INC.—See Vail Resorts, Inc.; *U.S. Public*, pg. 2272

713930 — MARINAS

ACI D.D.; *Int'l*, pg. 104
AMERICAN SHIPYARD CO., LLC—See Sun Communities, Inc.; *U.S. Public*, pg. 1963
ATHENS MARINA S.A.—See Avax S.A.; *Int'l*, pg. 737
BONITA BAY MARINA—See Bonita Bay Properties, Inc.; *U.S. Public*, pg. 614
BURNT STORE MARINA, INC.—See PGI Incorporated; *U.S. Public*, pg. 1684
CHULA VISTA MARINA/RV PARK, LTD.—See Sun Communities, Inc.; *U.S. Public*, pg. 1963
COASTAL MARINA MANAGEMENT LLC; *U.S. Private*, pg. 956
CRACKER BOY BOAT WORKS, INC.—See Jamco Inc.; *U.S. Private*, pg. 2182
EPPING FOREST YACHT CLUB—See Gate Petroleum Company; *U.S. Private*, pg. 1649
FANAUTIC CLUB, S.L.—See Brunswick Corporation; *U.S. Public*, pg. 408
FINCANTIERI MARINE REPAIR LLC—See Fincantieri S.p.A.; *Int'l*, pg. 2671
FINCANTIERI MARINE SYSTEMS LLC—See Fincantieri S.p.A.; *Int'l*, pg. 2671
GRAND HARBOUR MARINA P.L.C.; *Int'l*, pg. 3055
HAP O'NEILL, INC.; *U.S. Private*, pg. 1857
HARBORAGE MARINA, LLC—See International Marina Group, LP; *U.S. Private*, pg. 2118
HODGDON YACHT SERVICES, LLC—See Hodgdon Yachts, Inc.; *U.S. Private*, pg. 1959

IKM MOORING SERVICES AS—See IKM Gruppen AS; *Int'l*, pg. 3611
INTERNATIONAL MARINA GROUP, LP; *U.S. Private*, pg. 2118
LAKE LAS VEGAS MARINA LLC—See Centerbridge Partners, L.P.; *U.S. Private*, pg. 815
LANDS END MARINA—See Lands End Marina Holding Company, Inc.; *U.S. Private*, pg. 2387
LIGHTHOUSE POINT MARINA—See Marina Investment Management Inc.; *U.S. Private*, pg. 2574
LIGHTHOUSE POINT MARINA—See Miller Yacht Sales, Inc.; *U.S. Private*, pg. 2736
LOGGERHEAD MARINA—See Seven Kings Holdings, Inc.; *U.S. Private*, pg. 3618
LONGBOAT KEY CLUB MOORINGS—See Ocean Properties, Ltd.; *U.S. Private*, pg. 2989
MAKER 1 MARINA—See Coastal Marina Management LLC; *U.S. Private*, pg. 956
MARINA JACK, INC.—See Jack Graham Inc.; *U.S. Private*, pg. 2174
THE MARINA LIMITED PARTNERSHIP; *U.S. Private*, pg. 4074
MAXIMO MARINA; *U.S. Private*, pg. 2618
NAUTICUS ROBOTICS HOLDINGS, INC.—See Nauticus Robotics, Inc.; *U.S. Public*, pg. 1500
NAUTICUS ROBOTICS, INC.; *U.S. Public*, pg. 1500
NEW HOPE MARINE INC.—See Family Federation for World Peace & Unification; *U.S. Private*, pg. 1469
PORTLAND YACHT SERVICES, INC.; *U.S. Private*, pg. 3233
PORT MILFORD LLC—See Sun Communities, Inc.; *U.S. Public*, pg. 1961
RIVIERA DUNES MARINA—See Riviera Dunes Marina Condominium Association, Inc.; *U.S. Private*, pg. 3448
SAFE HARBOR MARINAS LLC—See Sun Communities, Inc.; *U.S. Public*, pg. 1963
SEABULK TOWING HOLDINGS INC.—See AIP, LLC; *U.S. Private*, pg. 137
SHIP AHOY LLC—See CMG Holdings Group, Inc.; *U.S. Public*, pg. 518
STATEN ISLAND YACHT CLUB, INC.—See Germain Motor Company; *U.S. Private*, pg. 1687
SUNTEX MARINAS INVESTORS LLC—See Centerbridge Partners, L.P.; *U.S. Private*, pg. 815
SUPER YACHT MANAGEMENT S.A.S.—See MarineMax, Inc.; *U.S. Public*, pg. 1367
SWEETWATER LANDING—See Bonita Bay Properties, Inc.; *U.S. Private*, pg. 614
TARPON LANDING MARINA—See East Lake, LLC; *U.S. Private*, pg. 1316
TIERRE VERDE MARINA—See HCI Group, Inc.; *U.S. Public*, pg. 1014
TRADER'S COVE—See Miller Yacht Sales, Inc.; *U.S. Private*, pg. 2736
TRIDENT MARITIME SYSTEMS, LLC—See J.F. Lehman & Company, Inc.; *U.S. Private*, pg. 2164
TWIN DOLPHIN MARINA—See Miller Enterprises of Manatee, Inc.; *U.S. Private*, pg. 2734
THE VIKING YACHTING CENTER INC—See Viking Yacht Company; *U.S. Private*, pg. 4383

713940 — FITNESS AND RECREATIONAL SPORTS CENTERS

24 HOUR FITNESS USA, INC.—See AEA Investors LP; *U.S. Private*, pg. 113
ABSOLUTE HEALTH & FITNESS, INC.; *U.S. Public*, pg. 27
ADVANTAGE TRAVEL LLC; *U.S. Private*, pg. 95
AGAIN FASTER LLC; *U.S. Private*, pg. 125
ALERE WELLBEING INC.—See UnitedHealth Group Incorporated; *U.S. Public*, pg. 2248
THE ALLUVIAN SPA, LLC—See The Middleby Corporation; *U.S. Public*, pg. 2115
AMERICAN FITNESS PROFESSIONALS & ASSOCIATES, LLC—See Moelis Asset Management LP; *U.S. Private*, pg. 2764
ANDACOR S.A.; *Int'l*, pg. 449
ANYTIME FITNESS LLC—See Self Esteem Brands LLC; *U.S. Private*, pg. 3602
ARAGON ENTERTAINMENT CENTER, INC.—See Live Nation Entertainment, Inc.; *U.S. Public*, pg. 1328
ATHLETES' PERFORMANCE, INC.; *U.S. Private*, pg. 368
ATHLETIC CLUB AT ONE CLEVELAND—See Walton Street Capital, LLC; *U.S. Private*, pg. 4435
AUSSIEFIT; *U.S. Private*, pg. 395
BALLY TOTAL FITNESS CORPORATION—See Harbert Management Corporation; *U.S. Private*, pg. 1858
BALLY TOTAL FITNESS HOLDINGS CORPORATION—See Harbert Management Corporation; *U.S. Private*, pg. 1858
BAY CLUB AMERICA, INC.—See KKR & Co. Inc.; *U.S. Public*, pg. 1264
BAY CLUB GOLDEN GATEWAY, INC.—See KKR & Co. Inc.; *U.S. Public*, pg. 1264
BAY CLUB MARIN—See KKR & Co. Inc.; *U.S. Public*, pg. 1264
THE BAY CLUBS COMPANY, LLC—See KKR & Co. Inc.; *U.S. Public*, pg. 1264

BAYER 04 LEVERKUSEN FUSSBALL GMBH—See Bayer Aktiengesellschaft; *Int'l*, pg. 901
BAY HARBOR GOLF CLUB INC.—See Boyne USA Resorts Inc.; *U.S. Private*, pg. 629
BE CLIMBING, INC.—See TOCCA Life Holdings, Inc.; *U.S. Public*, pg. 2161
BENEFIT SYSTEMS BULGARIA EOOD—See Benefit Systems SA; *Int'l*, pg. 972
BENEFIT SYSTEMS D. O. O.—See Benefit Systems SA; *Int'l*, pg. 972
BENEFIT SYSTEMS GREECE MIKE—See Benefit Systems SA; *Int'l*, pg. 972
BENEFIT SYSTEMS SLOVAKIA S.R.O.—See Benefit Systems SA; *Int'l*, pg. 972
BLANCO Y NEGRO SA; *Int'l*, pg. 1062
BLUE DECK CO., LTD.—See Ananda Development Public Company Limited; *Int'l*, pg. 447
BODYBUILDING.COM, LLC—See Qurate Retail, Inc.; *U.S. Public*, pg. 1757
BOXUNION HOLDINGS LLC; *U.S. Private*, pg. 627
THE BRIDGES AT RANCHO SANTA FE SALES COMPANY, INC.—See Lennar Corporation; *U.S. Public*, pg. 1307
BRONSON ATHLETIC CLUB—See Bronson Healthcare Group, Inc.; *U.S. Private*, pg. 662
CALIFORNIA FAMILY HEALTH LLC—See Perpetual Capital, LLC; *U.S. Private*, pg. 3152
CANLAN ICE SPORTS CORPORATION; *Int'l*, pg. 1291
CAPE CLUB OF BREVARD—See The Goldfield Corporation; *U.S. Public*, pg. 2075
CARDPOINT LIMITED—See NCR Voyix Corporation.; *U.S. Public*, pg. 1501
CARGILL—See Cargill, Inc.; *U.S. Private*, pg. 758
CENTER ICE DELMONT, LLC—See Blackstreet Capital Holdings LLC; *U.S. Private*, pg. 576
CENTRAL SPORTS CO., LTD.; *Int'l*, pg. 1410
CHELSEA PIERS LP; *U.S. Private*, pg. 870
CI:Z.LABO CO., LTD.—See Kenvue Inc.; *U.S. Public*, pg. 1223
CLARK OIL CO. INC.; *U.S. Private*, pg. 913
CLIFF DRYSDALE MANAGEMENT, LLC—See Troon Golf L.L.C.; *U.S. Private*, pg. 4242
CLUB 24 CONCEPT GYMS, LTD.; *U.S. Private*, pg. 948
CLUB ONE INC.; *U.S. Private*, pg. 948
CLUB PILATES LLC; *U.S. Private*, pg. 948
COBRA-UDISPORT CONDE DE GUADALHORCE, S.L—See ACS, Actividades de Construccion y Servicios, S.A.; *Int'l*, pg. 110
COLUMBUS BLUE JACKETS; *U.S. Private*, pg. 979
CONTOURS EXPRESS, INC.; *U.S. Private*, pg. 1031
COREPOWER YOGA, LLC—See TSG Consumer Partners LLC; *U.S. Private*, pg. 4253
COURTSIDE CLUB—See KKR & Co. Inc.; *U.S. Public*, pg. 1264
CRUNCH NEW MONTGOMERY, LLC—See TPG Capital, L.P.; *U.S. Public*, pg. 2176
CURVES JAPAN CO., LTD.—See Curves Holdings Co., Ltd.; *Int'l*, pg. 1880
D1 SPORTS HOLDINGS, LLC—See Athletes' Performance, Inc.; *U.S. Private*, pg. 368
DAIMAN JOHOR JAYA SPORTS COMPLEX BERHAD—See Daiman Development Berhad; *Int'l*, pg. 1938
DARTMOUTH CLUB PROPERTIES INC.—See Healthtrax Inc.; *U.S. Private*, pg. 1898
DECATHLON CLUB—See KKR & Co. Inc.; *U.S. Public*, pg. 1264
DEPORTES CLUB GOLF SANTIAGO SA; *Int'l*, pg. 2041
DRIVE SHACK INC.; *U.S. Public*, pg. 688
EDISON FITNESS GROUP LLC—See Planet Fitness, Inc.; *U.S. Public*, pg. 1697
EDWARD HOSPITAL & HEALTH SERVICES; *U.S. Private*, pg. 1341
ELEMENTS FOR WOMEN, INC.; *U.S. Private*, pg. 1357
ELLENTON ICE & SPORTS COMPLEX, LLC; *U.S. Private*, pg. 1363
ENFIELD HEALTHTRAX FITNESS & WELLNESS—See Healthtrax Inc.; *U.S. Private*, pg. 1898
ENJOY WELLNESS, S.L.—See Espiga Capital Gestion S.G.E.C.R, S.A.; *Int'l*, pg. 2506
ERGO-FIT GMBH & CO. KG; *Int'l*, pg. 2491
EUROFINS MEGALAB SA—See Eurofins Scientific S.E.; *Int'l*, pg. 2546
EVERGREEN ALLIANCE GOLF LTD—See Arcis Equity Partners LLC; *U.S. Private*, pg. 312
EXHALE ENTERPRISES, LLC—See Hyatt Hotels Corporation; *U.S. Public*, pg. 1077
FAST FITNESS JAPAN, INC.; *Int'l*, pg. 2621
FESTIVAL FUNPARKS LLC; *U.S. Private*, pg. 1499
FIT AFTER FIFTY, INC.; *U.S. Private*, pg. 1535
FITCORP PRIVATE FITNESS CENTERS—See Town Sports International Holdings, Inc.; *U.S. Private*, pg. 4197
FIT FABRIC SP. Z O.O.—See Benefit Systems SA; *Int'l*, pg. 972
FITGENES AUSTRALIA PTY LTD.; *Int'l*, pg. 2695
FITNESS ANYWHERE LLC; *U.S. Private*, pg. 1536
FITNESS CONNECTION—See Roark Capital Group Inc.; *U.S. Private*, pg. 3455
FITNESS CONSULTING GROUP; *U.S. Private*, pg. 1536

FITNESS INTERNATIONAL, LLC—See CIVC Partners LLC; *U.S. Private*, pg. 907
FITNESS INTERNATIONAL, LLC—See Madison Dearborn Partners, LLC; *U.S. Private*, pg. 2541
FITNESS INTERNATIONAL, LLC—See The Seidler Company, LLC; *U.S. Private*, pg. 4116
FITNESS ONBOARD; *U.S. Private*, pg. 1536
FITWORKS HOLDING LLC; *U.S. Private*, pg. 1536
FKP SCORPIO ENTERTAINMENT LTD.—See CTS Eventim AG & Co. KGAA; *Int'l*, pg. 1873
FLEET FEET SPORTS, LLC—See Investors Management Corporation; *U.S. Private*, pg. 2132
FLEX RESORTS & REAL ESTATE COMPANY K.S.C.; *Int'l*, pg. 2704
FLYERS SKATE ZONE, L.P.—See Comcast Corporation; *U.S. Public*, pg. 538
GALATASARAY SPORTIF SINAI VETICARI YATIRIMLAR AS; *Int'l*, pg. 2871
GDO SPORTS, INC.—See Golf Digest Online Inc.; *Int'l*, pg. 3035
GET IN SHAPE FOR WOMEN, INC.; *U.S. Private*, pg. 1688
GMM FITNESS CLUB CO., LTD.—See GMM Grammy Public Company Limited; *Int'l*, pg. 3012
GRUPO SPORTS WORLD, S. A. B. DE C. V.; *Int'l*, pg. 3135
GUNZE SPORTS CO., LTD.—See Gunze Limited; *Int'l*, pg. 3186
HANMAN FIT LIMITED; *Int'l*, pg. 3256
HARTFORD WOLFPACK, LLC—See Madison Square Garden Sports Corp.; *U.S. Public*, pg. 1354
HEALING TOUCH HOLDINGS, INC.; *Int'l*, pg. 3302
HEALTHCITY LUXEMBOURG S.A.—See Basic-Fit NV; *Int'l*, pg. 886
HEALTHTRACK SPORTS & WELLNESS, LLC—See Northwestern Memorial HealthCare; *U.S. Private*, pg. 2962
HEALTHTRACK SPORTS & WELLNESS, LLC—See Wheaton-Oaks Sport Center, Inc.; *U.S. Private*, pg. 4505
HEALTHTRAX INC.; *U.S. Private*, pg. 1898
HEALTHTRAX INTERNATIONAL INC.—See Healthtrax Inc.; *U.S. Private*, pg. 1898
H&H SHOOTING SPORTS COMPLEX; *U.S. Private*, pg. 1823
HIGHSTANDARD CO., LTD.—See Curves Holdings Co., Ltd.; *Int'l*, pg. 1880
HOLMES PLACE INTERNATIONAL LTD.; *Int'l*, pg. 3453
HOUSE OF BODS FITNESS, INC.; *U.S. Private*, pg. 1991
ICE LAND ASSOCIATES, LP—See Blackstreet Capital Holdings LLC; *U.S. Private*, pg. 576
ICE SPECIALTY ENTERTAINMENT INC.; *U.S. Private*, pg. 2031
IDAHO ATHLETIC CLUB, INC.—See TPG Capital, L.P.; *U.S. Public*, pg. 2176
IMAGINE SWIMMING, INC.; *U.S. Private*, pg. 2045
IMAXSHIFT, LLC—See Imax Corporation; *Int'l*, pg. 3620
IMPACT FITNESS—See Morgan Stanley; *U.S. Public*, pg. 1474
INCHES FITNESS; *U.S. Private*, pg. 2053
INGESPORT—See Corpfin Capital SA; *Int'l*, pg. 1802
INSPIRE FITNESS—See HighPost Capital, LLC; *U.S. Private*, pg. 1941
INTEGRATED HEALTH 21 LLC—See Cardiac Imaging Solutions, LLC; *U.S. Private*, pg. 749
ISLAND TENNIS LP; *U.S. Private*, pg. 2145
JACKSON HOLE MOUNTAIN RESORT; *U.S. Private*, pg. 2177
JSC PRIME FITNESS—See Bank of Georgia Group PLC; *Int'l*, pg. 843
KINGWOOD ATHLETIC CLUB INC.—See Starmark Management Holdings LLC; *U.S. Private*, pg. 3787
LAACO, LTD.—See CubeSmart; *U.S. Public*, pg. 604
LADY FITNESS INC.—See AEA Investors LP; *U.S. Private*, pg. 113
LA JOLLA BEACH & TENNIS CLUB INC.; *U.S. Private*, pg. 2368
LAKESHORE MANAGEMENT GROUP; *U.S. Private*, pg. 2377
LANDINGS CLUB INC.; *U.S. Private*, pg. 2385
LEISURE SPORTS INC.; *U.S. Private*, pg. 2420
LET'S PLAY SPORTS, INC.; *U.S. Private*, pg. 2433
LIFE TIME FITNESS - BLOOMINGDALE—See Leonard Green & Partners, L.P.; *U.S. Private*, pg. 2426
LIFE TIME FITNESS - BLOOMINGDALE—See TPG Capital, L.P.; *U.S. Public*, pg. 2174
LIFE TIME FITNESS - CHANHASSEN—See Leonard Green & Partners, L.P.; *U.S. Private*, pg. 2426
LIFE TIME FITNESS - CHANHASSEN—See TPG Capital, L.P.; *U.S. Public*, pg. 2174
LONG ISLAND TENNIS TIME INC.—See Island Tennis LP; *U.S. Private*, pg. 2145
MACD LLC—See The Macerich Company; *U.S. Public*, pg. 2110
MANDARA SPA ASIA LIMITED—See Catterton Management Company, LLC; *U.S. Private*, pg. 794
MANDARA SPA LLC—See Catterton Management Company, LLC; *U.S. Private*, pg. 794
MEIJI SPORTS PLAZA CO., LTD.—See Central Sports Co., Ltd.; *Int'l*, pg. 1410
MEPPS SNC—See Sheldons' Inc.; *U.S. Private*, pg. 3631
MISSOURI ATHLETIC CLUB; *U.S. Private*, pg. 2749

713940 — FITNESS AND RECREAT... CORPORATE AFFILIATIONS

N.A.I.C.S. Index

MSG SPORTS & ENTERTAINMENT, LLC—See Madison Square Garden Sports Corp.; *U.S. Public*, pg. 1353
MSG VENTURES, LLC—See Sphere Entertainment Co.; *U.S. Public*, pg. 1918
MULTNOMAH ATHLETIC CLUB; *U.S. Private*, pg. 2813
MY SPORTS DREAMS; *U.S. Private*, pg. 2823
NATIONAL COUNCIL YMCA OF THE USA; *U.S. Private*, pg. 2852
NATIONAL SCOUTING REPORT INC.; *U.S. Private*, pg. 2863
NATURAL WELLNESS CORPORATION LTD.—See Essel Corporate Resources Pvt. Ltd.; *Int'l*, pg. 2509
NENE WHITEWATER CENTRE LTD.—See AssetCo plc; *Int'l*, pg. 643
NEWINGTON HEALTH & WELLNESS CENTER—See Healthtrax Inc.; *U.S. Private*, pg. 1898
NEW YORK ATHLETIC CLUB; *U.S. Private*, pg. 2908
NEW YORK HEALTH CLUB INC.; *U.S. Private*, pg. 2909
NEW YORK LIBERTY, LLC—See Madison Square Garden Sports Corp.; *U.S. Public*, pg. 1354
NIPPON ATHLETIC SERVICE CO., LTD.—See Daiwa House Industry Co., Ltd.; *Int'l*, pg. 1947
NPE, LLC; *U.S. Private*, pg. 2969
O2 FITNESS; *U.S. Private*, pg. 2981
OVERTON ENTERPRISES, LLC; *U.S. Private*, pg. 3054
PACIFIC ATHLETIC CLUB - SAN DIEGO—See KKR & Co. Inc.; *U.S. Public*, pg. 1264
PACIFIC ATHLETIC CLUB—See KKR & Co. Inc.; *U.S. Public*, pg. 1264
PALM BEACH SPORTS CLUB, LLC—See Town Sports International Holdings, Inc.; *U.S. Private*, pg. 4197
PF DERRY LLC—See Planet Fitness, Inc.; *U.S. Public*, pg. 1697
PF ERIE LLC—See Planet Fitness, Inc.; *U.S. Public*, pg. 1697
PF GREENSBURG LLC—See Planet Fitness, Inc.; *U.S. Public*, pg. 1697
PF VALLEJO, LLC—See Planet Fitness, Inc.; *U.S. Public*, pg. 1697
PHYSIQUE 57; *U.S. Private*, pg. 3175
PLANET FITNESS, INC.; *U.S. Public*, pg. 1697
POTOMAC VALLEY PROPERTIES INC.; *U.S. Private*, pg. 3235
PREVENTURE, LLC—See Marlin Equity Partners, LLC; *U.S. Private*, pg. 2585
PROFESSIONAL RECREATION ORGANIZATION INC.—See KKR & Co. Inc.; *U.S. Public*, pg. 1264
PROFILE DEVELOPMENT, LLC; *U.S. Private*, pg. 3277
PUNE FOOTBALL CLUB LIMITED—See Ashok Piramal Group; *Int'l*, pg. 608
PURE GYM LIMITED—See Leonard Green & Partners, L.P.; *U.S. Private*, pg. 2428
PUTT-PUTT, LLC; *U.S. Private*, pg. 3308
RACHAS INC.; *U.S. Private*, pg. 3341
RDV SPORTSPLEX—See RDV Corporation; *U.S. Private*, pg. 3364
RECREATION CENTERS OF SUN CITY WEST, INC.; *U.S. Private*, pg. 3372
RIVALHEALTH, LLC—See Global Behavioral Solutions LLC; *U.S. Private*, pg. 1712
SAFETY HARBOR SPA SPRINGS, INC.—See S.H.S. Resort, LLC; *U.S. Private*, pg. 3517
SAN FRANCISCO BAY CLUB, INC.—See KKR & Co. Inc.; *U.S. Public*, pg. 1264
SARL THERMES DE CONTREXEVILLE—See Groupe Partouche S.A.; *Int'l*, pg. 3109
SELF ESTEEM BRANDS LLC; *U.S. Private*, pg. 3602
SHOCKOE COMMERCE GROUP, LLC.; *U.S. Private*, pg. 3639
SKATENATION PLUS; *U.S. Private*, pg. 3681
SLICK WILLIE'S FAMILY POOL HALL; *U.S. Private*, pg. 3688
SNAP FITNESS, INC.; *U.S. Private*, pg. 3699
SOCCERZONE, INC.—See Let's Play Sports, Inc.; *U.S. Private*, pg. 2433
SOPRATICO CO., LTD.—See Bushiroad, Inc.; *Int'l*, pg. 1227
SOULCYCLE INC.; *U.S. Private*, pg. 3717
SPA CHAKRA, INC.—See Hercules Capital, Inc.; *U.S. Public*, pg. 1028
SPARE TIME INC.; *U.S. Private*, pg. 3745
SPECTRUM CLUBS INC.; *U.S. Private*, pg. 3752
SPORT & HEALTH CLUBS, L.C.; *U.S. Private*, pg. 3760
SPORTS CLUB NAS CO., LTD.—See Daiwa House Industry Co., Ltd.; *Int'l*, pg. 1947
STEINER LEISURE LIMITED—See Catterton Management Company, LLC; *U.S. Private*, pg. 794
TBC INTERNATIONAL LLC—See BoxUnion Holdings LLC; *U.S. Private*, pg. 627
TEXAS FAMILY FITNESS LLC—See Topspin Partners, L.P.; *U.S. Private*, pg. 4188
TOWN SPORTS INTERNATIONAL, LLC—See Town Sports International Holdings, Inc.; *U.S. Private*, pg. 4197
TRUFUSION, LLC; *U.S. Private*, pg. 4249
TSI 1231 3RD AVENUE, LLC—See Town Sports International Holdings, Inc.; *U.S. Private*, pg. 4197
TSI 30 BROAD STREET, LLC—See Town Sports International Holdings, Inc.; *U.S. Private*, pg. 4197
TSI 555 6TH AVENUE, LLC—See Town Sports International Holdings, Inc.; *U.S. Private*, pg. 4197
TSI ALEXANDRIA, LLC—See Town Sports International Holdings, Inc.; *U.S. Private*, pg. 4198
TSI ARDMORE, LLC—See Town Sports International Holdings, Inc.; *U.S. Private*, pg. 4198
TSI ASTOR PLACE, LLC—See Town Sports International Holdings, Inc.; *U.S. Private*, pg. 4197
TSI BRADFORD, LLC—See Town Sports International Holdings, Inc.; *U.S. Private*, pg. 4197
TSI CLARENDON, LLC—See Town Sports International Holdings, Inc.; *U.S. Private*, pg. 4198
TSI EAST 86, LLC—See Town Sports International Holdings, Inc.; *U.S. Private*, pg. 4198
TSI HELL'S KITCHEN, LLC—See Town Sports International Holdings, Inc.; *U.S. Private*, pg. 4197
TSI-LIV CONDADO, LLC—See Town Sports International Holdings, Inc.; *U.S. Private*, pg. 4197
TSI-LIV GUAYNABO, LLC—See Town Sports International Holdings, Inc.; *U.S. Private*, pg. 4197
TSI - LUCILLE 38TH AVENUE, LLC—See Town Sports International Holdings, Inc.; *U.S. Private*, pg. 4197
TSI - LUCILLE 42ND STREET, LLC—See Town Sports International Holdings, Inc.; *U.S. Private*, pg. 4197
TSI - LUCILLE 89TH STREET, LLC—See Town Sports International Holdings, Inc.; *U.S. Private*, pg. 4197
TSI - LUCILLE ASTORIA, LLC—See Town Sports International Holdings, Inc.; *U.S. Private*, pg. 4197
TSI - LUCILLE AUSTIN STREET, LLC—See Town Sports International Holdings, Inc.; *U.S. Private*, pg. 4197
TSI - LUCILLE BAYSHORE, LLC—See Town Sports International Holdings, Inc.; *U.S. Private*, pg. 4197
TSI - LUCILLE BRONX, LLC—See Town Sports International Holdings, Inc.; *U.S. Private*, pg. 4197
TSI - LUCILLE CLIFTON, LLC—See Town Sports International Holdings, Inc.; *U.S. Private*, pg. 4197
TSI - LUCILLE COMMACK, LLC—See Town Sports International Holdings, Inc.; *U.S. Private*, pg. 4197
TSI - LUCILLE HOLBROOK, LLC—See Town Sports International Holdings, Inc.; *U.S. Private*, pg. 4197
TSI - LUCILLE JERSEY CITY, LLC—See Town Sports International Holdings, Inc.; *U.S. Private*, pg. 4197
TSI - LUCILLE KINGS HIGHWAY, LLC—See Town Sports International Holdings, Inc.; *U.S. Private*, pg. 4197
TSI - LUCILLE RALPH AVENUE, LLC—See Town Sports International Holdings, Inc.; *U.S. Private*, pg. 4197
TSI - LUCILLE ROCKVILLE CENTRE, LLC—See Town Sports International Holdings, Inc.; *U.S. Private*, pg. 4197
TSI - LUCILLE ST. NICHOLAS AVENUE, LLC—See Town Sports International Holdings, Inc.; *U.S. Private*, pg. 4197
TSI - LUCILLE VALLEY STREAM, LLC—See Town Sports International Holdings, Inc.; *U.S. Private*, pg. 4197
TSI MAHWAH, LLC—See Town Sports International Holdings, Inc.; *U.S. Private*, pg. 4198
TSI METHUEN, LLC—See Town Sports International Holdings, Inc.; *U.S. Private*, pg. 4197
TSI - NORTHRIDGE, LLC—See Town Sports International Holdings, Inc.; *U.S. Private*, pg. 4197
TSI PEABODY, LLC—See Town Sports International Holdings, Inc.; *U.S. Private*, pg. 4197
TSI - PEACOCK, PORT ST. LUCIE, LLC—See Town Sports International Holdings, Inc.; *U.S. Private*, pg. 4197
TSI - PLACENTIA, LLC—See Town Sports International Holdings, Inc.; *U.S. Private*, pg. 4197
TSI PRINCETON, LLC—See Town Sports International Holdings, Inc.; *U.S. Private*, pg. 4198
TSI SALISBURY, LLC—See Town Sports International Holdings, Inc.; *U.S. Private*, pg. 4197
TSI - SAN JOSE, LLC—See Town Sports International Holdings, Inc.; *U.S. Private*, pg. 4197
TSI SPRINGFIELD, LLC—See Town Sports International Holdings, Inc.; *U.S. Private*, pg. 4198
TSI - STUDIO CITY, LLC—See Town Sports International Holdings, Inc.; *U.S. Private*, pg. 4197
TSI - TOPANGA, LLC—See Town Sports International Holdings, Inc.; *U.S. Private*, pg. 4197
TSI - TORRANCE, LLC—See Town Sports International Holdings, Inc.; *U.S. Private*, pg. 4197
TSI - US HIGHWAY, JUPITER, LLC—See Town Sports International Holdings, Inc.; *U.S. Private*, pg. 4197
TSI - VALENCIA, LLC—See Town Sports International Holdings, Inc.; *U.S. Private*, pg. 4197
TSI WEST CALDWELL, LLC—See Town Sports International Holdings, Inc.; *U.S. Private*, pg. 4198
TSI - WESTLAKE, LLC—See Town Sports International Holdings, Inc.; *U.S. Private*, pg. 4197
TWIN PONDS EAST ARENA—See Blackstreet Capital Holdings LLC; *U.S. Private*, pg. 576
UFA SPORTS ASIA PTE LTD—See Bertelsmann SE & Co. KGaA; *Int'l*, pg. 995
UFA SPORTS SLOVAKIA S.R.O—See Bertelsmann SE & Co. KGaA; *Int'l*, pg. 995
USA SWIMMING; *U.S. Private*, pg. 4321
VIRGIN ACTIVE LIMITED—See Brait S.E.; *Int'l*, pg. 1137
WASHINGTON ATHLETIC CLUB; *U.S. Private*, pg. 4446
WELLBRIDGE CLUB MANAGEMENT INC.—See Starmark Management Holdings LLC; *U.S. Private*, pg. 3787
WELLNESS HANSHIN INC.—See Hankyu Hanshin Holdings Inc.; *Int'l*, pg. 3256
WESTCHESTER KNICKS, LLC—See Madison Square Garden Sports Corp.; *U.S. Public*, pg. 1354
WEST SPRINGFIELD PROPERTIES—See Healthtrax Inc.; *U.S. Private*, pg. 1898
WHEATON-OAKS SPORT CENTER, INC.; *U.S. Private*, pg. 4505
WINDY CITY FIELDHOUSE; *U.S. Private*, pg. 4540
XPONENTIAL FITNESS, INC.; *U.S. Public*, pg. 2392
YOU FIT, INC.; *U.S. Private*, pg. 4592
ZODIAK KIDS—See De Agostini S.p.A.; *Int'l*, pg. 1994

713950 — BOWLING CENTERS

AMF BOWLING CENTERS, INC.—See Bowlero Corp; *U.S. Public*, pg. 376
AMF BOWLING WORLDWIDE, INC.—See Bowlero Corp; *U.S. Public*, pg. 376
BOWL AMERICA INCORPORATED—See Bowlero Corp; *U.S. Public*, pg. 376
BOWL AMERICA SHIRLEY INC.—See Bowlero Corp; *U.S. Public*, pg. 376
BOWLERO CORP; *U.S. Public*, pg. 376
BOWL NEW ENGLAND INC.; *U.S. Private*, pg. 625
BRUNSWICK INDOOR RECREATION GROUP—See Brunswick Corporation; *U.S. Public*, pg. 407
CLOVERLANES, INC.—See Great Lakes Realty Corp.; *U.S. Private*, pg. 1765
DAIMAN BOWL SDN. BHD.—See Daiman Development Berhad; *Int'l*, pg. 1938
DOUBLE DECKER LANES—See Bowlero Corp; *U.S. Public*, pg. 376
FAIRLANES BOWL, INC.—See Great Lakes Realty Corp.; *U.S. Private*, pg. 1765
FALLS CHURCH BOWL INC.—See Bowlero Corp; *U.S. Public*, pg. 376
GREAT LAKES REALTY CORP.; *U.S. Private*, pg. 1765
HOLLYWOOD BOWL GROUP PLC; *Int'l*, pg. 3452
MANATEE LANES—See Bowlero Corp; *U.S. Public*, pg. 376
SCHUMAKER & CO. INC.; *U.S. Private*, pg. 3571
SHERIDAN LANES, INC.—See Bowlero Corp; *U.S. Public*, pg. 376
STRIKES UNLIMITED, INC.—See Bowlero Corp; *U.S. Public*, pg. 376
TEN ENTERTAINMENT GROUP PLC—See Trive Capital Inc.; *U.S. Private*, pg. 4240
VOIGHT ENTERPRISES, INC.; *U.S. Private*, pg. 4409
WEST PARK BOWLING LANES INC.—See Drury Inn Inc.; *U.S. Private*, pg. 1280
YPSI-ARBOR LANES—See Great Lakes Realty Corp.; *U.S. Private*, pg. 1765

713990 — ALL OTHER AMUSEMENT AND RECREATION INDUSTRIES

62NORD AS—See Flakk Holding AS; *Int'l*, pg. 2697
ACE ADVENTURE RESORT; *U.S. Private*, pg. 56
AC ENTERTAINMENT, LLC—See Live Nation Entertainment, Inc.; *U.S. Public*, pg. 1328
ACTION NETWORK INC.—See Better Collective A/S; *Int'l*, pg. 1003
ADVENTURES UNLIMITED CANOE RENTAL & SALES, INC.; *U.S. Private*, pg. 109
AJWA FUN WORLD & RESORT LIMITED; *Int'l*, pg. 258
AMBASSADAIR TRAVEL CLUB, INC.—See Grueninger Tours & Cruises Inc.; *U.S. Private*, pg. 1797
AMERICAN EXHIBITIONS, INC.; *U.S. Private*, pg. 232
AMUSEMENTS OF AMERICA INC.; *U.S. Private*, pg. 269
AN POST NATIONAL LOTTERY CO.—See An Post LLC; *Int'l*, pg. 443
APPLE SEEDS; *U.S. Private*, pg. 297
ARCHON CORPORATION; *U.S. Public*, pg. 185
AUSTRALIA SKYDIVE PTY. LTD.—See Experience Co Limited; *Int'l*, pg. 2588
BLUE GRASS SHOWS, INC.; *U.S. Private*, pg. 589
BLUE RIDGE ARSENAL INC.; *U.S. Private*, pg. 591
BLUE RIDGE REAL ESTATE COMPANY; *U.S. Public*, pg. 365
BUCK HILL FALLS CO.; *U.S. Public*, pg. 409
BUGGY BUS INC.—See Historic Tours of America Inc.; *U.S. Private*, pg. 1952
CABIN PLAZA CO., LTD.—See Dynam Japan Holdings, Co., Ltd.; *Int'l*, pg. 2239
CALEIDO GROUP S.P.A.; *Int'l*, pg. 1263
CAMP RICHARD CAMPERS ASSOCIATION, INC.; *U.S. Private*, pg. 729
CATAMARAN EXPRESS INC.—See Pacific Marine & Supply Co. Ltd. Inc.; *U.S. Private*, pg. 3068
CELEBI NAS AIRPORT SERVICES INDIA PVT. LTD.—See Celebi Hava Servisi AS; *Int'l*, pg. 1391
CHANCE RIDES MANUFACTURING, INC.—See Permanent Equity Management, LLC; *U.S. Private*, pg. 3152
CHILCO RIVER HOLDINGS, INC.; *U.S. Private*, pg. 881
THE CIRCUS ARTS CONSERVATORY, INC.; *U.S. Private*, pg. 4010
CIRCUSTRIX LLC; *U.S. Private*, pg. 900
CKP LEISURE LIMITED; *Int'l*, pg. 1639

N.A.I.C.S. INDEX

721110 — HOTELS (EXCEPT CASI...

COMPAGNIE DES ALPES S.A.; *Int'l*, pg. 1737
CONCH TOUR TRAIN—See Historic Tours of America Inc.; *U.S. Private*, pg. 1952
COPPER MOUNTAIN, INC.—See Powdr Corp.; *U.S. Private*, pg. 3236
CORAL STADIA LIMITED—See Entain PLC; *Int'l*, pg. 2450
CRYSTAL MOUNTAIN, INC.—See KSL Capital Partners, LLC; *U.S. Private*, pg. 2354
CTS EVENTIM AG & CO. KGAA; *Int'l*, pg. 1872
DELAWARE NORTH COMPANIES INTERNATIONAL LTD—See Delaware North Companies, Inc.; *U.S. Private*, pg. 1194
DG MEDIOS SPA—See Live Nation Entertainment, Inc.; *U.S. Public*, pg. 1328
DIGITAL TURBINE, INC.; *U.S. Public*, pg. 663
THE DOMINION GOLF GROUP—See Arcis Equity Partners LLC; *U.S. Private*, pg. 312
DOWN 2 FISH CHARTERS, LLC—See Arvana Inc.; *U.S. Public*, pg. 208
DREAM T ENTERTAINMENT CO., LTD.; *Int'l*, pg. 2203
DYNAM CO., LTD.—See Dynam Japan Holdings, Co., Ltd.; *Int'l*, pg. 2239
EA PHENOMIC—See Electronic Arts Inc.; *U.S. Public*, pg. 724
EDINBURGH BUTTERFLY & INSECT WORLD—See Hattington Capital LLP; *Int'l*, pg. 3285
ELK GROVE PARK DISTRICT; *U.S. Private*, pg. 1362
ELUM MUSIC COMPANY; *U.S. Private*, pg. 1377
EMPIRE RESORTS, INC.; *U.S. Private*, pg. 1385
ENBW MAINFRANKENPARK GMBH—See EnBW Energie Baden-Wurttemberg AG; *Int'l*, pg. 2398
ENTERTAINMENT MAGPIE LIMITED; *Int'l*, pg. 2452
EVERYTICKET.COM; *U.S. Private*, pg. 1441
EXPERIENCE CO LIMITED; *Int'l*, pg. 2588
EXPERIMENTAL AIRCRAFT ASSOCIATION; *U.S. Private*, pg. 1449
FACILITY MERCHANDISING, INC.; *U.S. Private*, pg. 1460
FACULTY PRODUCTIONS, LLC—See Live Nation Entertainment, Inc.; *U.S. Public*, pg. 1328
FISHER ISLAND CLUB, INC.; *U.S. Private*, pg. 1534
FJORD1 ASA—See Havila Holding AS; *Int'l*, pg. 3287
FJORD1 ASA—See Vision Ridge Partners, LLC; *U.S. Private*, pg. 4391
FRANCE BILLET S.A.—See Groupe Fnac S.A.; *Int'l*, pg. 3103
FRHUG FESTIVAL GMBH & CO. KG—See Live Nation Entertainment, Inc.; *U.S. Public*, pg. 1328
FURYU CORPORATION; *Int'l*, pg. 2848
FUTURE KID ENTERTAINMENT AND REAL ESTATE CO. K.S.C.C.; *Int'l*, pg. 2856
GALA INTERACTIVE (GIBRALTAR) LIMITED—See Entain PLC; *Int'l*, pg. 2450
GALAXY GAMING INC.; *U.S. Public*, pg. 894
GIANT INTERACTIVE GROUP INC—See Giant Network Group Co., Ltd.; *Int'l*, pg. 2962
GIBSON GUITAR CORP. - ENTERTAINMENT RELATIONS—See Gibson Brands, Inc.; *U.S. Private*, pg. 1696
GIBSON GUITAR CORP. - ENTERTAINMENT RELATIONS—See Gibson Brands, Inc.; *U.S. Private*, pg. 1696
GIBSON GUITAR CORP. - ENTERTAINMENT RELATIONS—See Gibson Brands, Inc.; *U.S. Private*, pg. 1696
GIBSON GUITAR CORP. - ENTERTAINMENT RELATIONS—See Gibson Brands, Inc.; *U.S. Private*, pg. 1696
GOLDEN NUGGET ONLINE GAMING, INC.—See DraftKings Inc.; *U.S. Public*, pg. 687
GOLDEN NUGGET ONLINE GAMING, LLC—See DraftKings Inc.; *U.S. Public*, pg. 687
GREENSTONE ENTERTAINMENT GP LIMITED—See Live Nation Entertainment, Inc.; *U.S. Public*, pg. 1329
GHEVIN & CIE—See Compagnie des Alpes S.A.; *Int'l*, pg. 1738
GUILD ESPORTS PLC; *Int'l*, pg. 3173
GYMBOGLOBAL CORPORATION; *U.S. Private*, pg. 1821
HANWHA RESORT CO., LTD.—See Hanwha Group; *Int'l*, pg. 3266
HIGH DESERT HUNT CLUB LLC—See Tejon Ranch Company; *U.S. Public*, pg. 1991
HISTORIC TOURS OF AMERICA INC.; *U.S. Private*, pg. 1952
HITECH STAGES LTD.; *Int'l*, pg. 3425
HOFFMAN ESTATES PARK DISTRICT; *U.S. Private*, pg. 1960
HONEY LAKE PLANTATION RESORT & SPA; *U.S. Private*, pg. 1976
HUNTMOUNTAIN RESOURCES LTD.; *U.S. Private*, pg. 2010
INTEGRAL AP TRZIC DD—See I Squared Capital Advisors (US) LLC; *U.S. Private*, pg. 2024
IRONMAN SOUND INDUSTRIES, LLC—See Markeys Audio Visual Inc.; *U.S. Private*, pg. 2581
ISLE OF CAPRI CASINOS, INC.—See Bally's Corporation; *U.S. Public*, pg. 268
JAI DINING SERVICES (HARLINGEN), INC.—See RCI Hospitality Holdings, Inc.; *U.S. Public*, pg. 1767

KAMAN'S ART SHOPPES INC.; *U.S. Private*, pg. 2258
KIDVILLE, INC.; *U.S. Public*, pg. 1228
KL OUTDOOR LLC; *U.S. Private*, pg. 2317
LITTLEFIELD CORPORATION; *U.S. Public*, pg. 1327
LITTLEFIELD ENTERTAINMENT—See Littlefield Corporation; *U.S. Public*, pg. 1327
LOS ANGELES COUNTY FAIR ASSOCIATION; *U.S. Private*, pg. 2496
MAJOR LEAGUE SOCCER LLC; *U.S. Private*, pg. 2555
MAMA & COMPANY LIMITED—See Live Nation Entertainment, Inc.; *U.S. Public*, pg. 1330
MODERN ROUND ENTERTAINMENT CORPORATION—See Trutankless Inc.; *U.S. Public*, pg. 2202
MOUNTAIN HIGH LLC—See General Mills, Inc.; *U.S. Public*, pg. 922
MOWLA PTY. LTD—See AMP Limited; *Int'l*, pg. 433
MUMMIES OF THE WORLD TOURING COMPANY INC.—See American Exhibitions, Inc.; *U.S. Public*, pg. 232
MYSTIC SEAPORT; *U.S. Private*, pg. 2826
MYTICKETIN.COM; *U.S. Private*, pg. 2826
NAMCO LTD.—See BANDAI NAMCO Holdings Inc.; *Int'l*, pg. 829
NAPERVILLE PARK DISTRICT; *U.S. Private*, pg. 2834
NEP GROUP, INC.—See The Carlyle Group Inc.; *U.S. Public*, pg. 2049
NEW ORLEANS JAZZ AND HERITAGE FOUNDATION; *U.S. Private*, pg. 2904
NEW SEABURY BEACH CLUB LLC—See Icahn Enterprises L.P.; *U.S. Public*, pg. 1084
OLD TOWN TROLLEY TOURS OF WASHINGTON INC.—See Historic Tours of America Inc.; *U.S. Private*, pg. 1952
ONE REEL INC.; *U.S. Private*, pg. 3020
ORANGEVILLE RACEWAY LIMITED—See Great Canadian Gaming Corporation; *Int'l*, pg. 3063
OVATION MUSIC & STUDIOS, INC.; *U.S. Private*, pg. 3052
PAYSON PARK THOROUGHBRED TRAINING CENTER INC.; *U.S. Private*, pg. 3117
PGA TOUR, INC.; *U.S. Private*, pg. 3165
PLEASURE CAST CO., LTD.—See BANDAI NAMCO Holdings Inc.; *Int'l*, pg. 829
PREMIER EXHIBITIONS, INC.; *U.S. Public*, pg. 1714
PROFESSIONAL BULL RIDERS, LLC—See Silver Lake Group, LLC; *U.S. Private*, pg. 3654
PROFESSIONAL CONCESSIONS, INC.; *U.S. Private*, pg. 3274
RACEWAY PARK, INC.—See PENN Entertainment, Inc.; *U.S. Public*, pg. 1662
RANCHO SIMI RECREATION PARK DISTRICT; *U.S. Private*, pg. 3352
RENAISSANCE ENTERTAINMENT CORP.—See Renaissance Entertainment Productions; *U.S. Private*, pg. 3397
RENAISSANCE ENTERTAINMENT PRODUCTIONS; *U.S. Private*, pg. 3397
RIVERBOAT CORPORATION OF MISSISSIPPI—See Bally's Corporation; *U.S. Public*, pg. 268
THE RIVER'S EDGE OUTFITTERS, LLC—See Vista Outdoor Inc.; *U.S. Public*, pg. 2305
RMS TITANIC INC—See Premier Exhibitions, Inc.; *U.S. Public*, pg. 1714
ROCKIN' JUMP HOLDINGS LLC—See CircusTrix LLC; *U.S. Private*, pg. 900
ROMFORD STADIUM LIMITED—See Entain PLC; *Int'l*, pg. 2450
ROVINJTURIST D.D.—See Adris Grupa d.d.; *Int'l*, pg. 153
RVP DEVELOPMENT CORPORATION; *U.S. Private*, pg. 3508
SALLY CORPORATION; *U.S. Private*, pg. 3533
SAN MANUEL INDIAN BINGO & CASINO; *U.S. Private*, pg. 3541
SAXONIA ENTERTAINMENT GMBH—See Bavaria Film GmbH; *Int'l*, pg. 899
SECRET SOUNDS GROUP PTY LTD—See Live Nation Entertainment, Inc.; *U.S. Public*, pg. 1330
SISSETON-WAHPETON SIOUX TRIBE; *U.S. Private*, pg. 3675
SPACE ADVENTURES LTD.; *U.S. Private*, pg. 3743
STEVENS PASS MOUNTAIN RESORT, LLC—See Vail Resorts, Inc.; *U.S. Public*, pg. 2271
STRATES ENTERPRISES INC.; *U.S. Private*, pg. 3836
STRIKE HOLDINGS LLC—See Bowlero Corp; *U.S. Public*, pg. 376
SUPER LEAGUE ENTERPRISE, INC.; *U.S. Public*, pg. 1966
SUTTER'S PLACE INC.; *U.S. Private*, pg. 3887
TEJON HOUNDS, LLC.—See Tejon Ranch Company; *U.S. Public*, pg. 1991
THANKSGIVING POINT; *U.S. Private*, pg. 3980
THREE SIX ZERO GROUP, INC.—See Live Nation Entertainment, Inc.; *U.S. Public*, pg. 1331
TICKETMASTER B.V.—See Live Nation Entertainment, Inc.; *U.S. Public*, pg. 1331
TOMMY BARTLETT, INC.; *U.S. Private*, pg. 4184
TOM'S AMUSEMENT COMPANY INC.—See Accel Entertainment, Inc.; *U.S. Public*, pg. 32
TRADETEC SKYLINE; *U.S. Private*, pg. 4202

TRENTHAM LEISURE LIMITED—See Blackstone Inc.; *U.S. Public*, pg. 358
UAB ECONOMUS—See City Service SE; *Int'l*, pg. 1628
US YOUTH SOCCER; *U.S. Private*, pg. 4320
VALIC CO., LTD.—See AOKI Holdings Inc.; *Int'l*, pg. 488
VCG HOLDING CORP.; *U.S. Public*, pg. 4349
VENUE DRIVER, LLC—See Sphere Entertainment Co.; *U.S. Public*, pg. 1918
VERTICAL VENTURES PARTNERS, INC.; *U.S. Private*, pg. 4370
WHEATON PARK DISTRICT; *U.S. Private*, pg. 4505
WHISTLER BLACKCOMB CORPORATION—See Vail Resorts, Inc.; *U.S. Public*, pg. 2272
WHITEFISH MOUNTAIN RESORT—See Winter Sports, Inc.; *U.S. Public*, pg. 4545
WHITEWATER EXPRESS, INC.; *U.S. Private*, pg. 4512
WILDERNESS RIVER ADVENTURES, LLC—See Aramark; *U.S. Public*, pg. 178
THE WOLF BOOKINGS B.V.—See Live Nation Entertainment, Inc.; *U.S. Public*, pg. 1331
WORLDWIDE LICENSING & MERCHANDISING, INC.—See Premier Exhibitions, Inc.; *U.S. Public*, pg. 1715
WTS INTERNATIONAL, INC.—See CI Capital Partners LLC; *U.S. Private*, pg. 896
WYNDHAM OCEAN RIDGE—See Travel & Leisure Co.; *U.S. Public*, pg. 2186
XTC CABARET (DALLAS), INC.—See RCI Hospitality Holdings, Inc.; *U.S. Public*, pg. 1767
XTC CABARET, INC.—See RCI Hospitality Holdings, Inc.; *U.S. Public*, pg. 1767

721110 — HOTELS (EXCEPT CASINO HOTELS) AND MOTELS

17402 HIDDEN VALLEY LLC—See Vail Resorts, Inc.; *U.S. Public*, pg. 2271
1859 HISTORIC HOTELS, LTD.—See Gal-Tex Hotel Corporation; *U.S. Private*, pg. 1635
21C MUSEUM HOTELS LLC—See Accor S.A.; *Int'l*, pg. 91
3385434 CANADA INC.—See Hyatt Hotels Corporation; *U.S. Public*, pg. 1076
ABC SP. Z O.O.—See Eurocash S.A.; *Int'l*, pg. 2533
ABDUL MOHSEN AL-HOKAIR GROUP FOR TOURISM AND DEVELOPMENT COMPANY; *Int'l*, pg. 58
ABERDEEN HOTEL LTD. PARTNERSHIP; *U.S. Private*, pg. 38
ABHOTEL CO., LTD.; *Int'l*, pg. 61
ABU DHABI NATIONAL HOTELS PJSC; *Int'l*, pg. 72
ACADEMIE ACCOR SA—See Accor S.A.; *Int'l*, pg. 91
ACADEMY HOTEL, LLC—See Silver Lake Group, LLC; *U.S. Private*, pg. 3654
ACCOR AUSTRIA AG—See Accor S.A.; *Int'l*, pg. 91
ACCOR BUSINESS & LEISURE NORTH AMERICA INC.—See Accor S.A.; *Int'l*, pg. 91
ACCOR CANADA INC.—See Accor S.A.; *Int'l*, pg. 91
ACCOR CENTRE DE CONTACTS CLIENTS—See Accor S.A.; *Int'l*, pg. 91
ACCOR GESTION MAROC SA—See Accor S.A.; *Int'l*, pg. 91
ACCOR HOSPITALITY ARGENTINA SA—See Accor S.A.; *Int'l*, pg. 91
ACCOR HOSPITALITY GERMANY GMBH—See Accor S.A.; *Int'l*, pg. 91
ACCOR HOSPITALITY NEDERLAND B.V.—See Accor S.A.; *Int'l*, pg. 91
ACCOR HOTELS BELGIUM NV—See Accor S.A.; *Int'l*, pg. 91
ACCOR HOTELS ROMANIA S.R.L.—See Accor S.A.; *Int'l*, pg. 91
ACCOR NORTH AMERICA INC.—See Accor S.A.; *Int'l*, pg. 91
ACCOR UK ECONOMY HOTELS LIMITED—See Accor S.A.; *Int'l*, pg. 91
ACKERMAN INVESTMENT COMPANY; *U.S. Private*, pg. 60
ACTION HOTELS PLC—See Action Group Holdings Company K.S.C.C.; *Int'l*, pg. 119
ADMIRAL COVE DEVELOPMENT SDN BHD—See Avillion Berhad; *Int'l*, pg. 743
ADMIRAL MARINA BERHAD—See Avillion Berhad; *Int'l*, pg. 743
ADOLPHUS HOTEL—See Crescent Hotels & Resorts; *U.S. Private*, pg. 1094
ADVANI HOTELS & RESORTS (INDIA) LIMITED; *Int'l*, pg. 164
AFFORDABLE SUITES OF AMERICA, INC.—See Goldberg Lindsay & Co., LLC; *U.S. Private*, pg. 1729
AFRICA ISRAEL HOTELS LTD.—See Africa Israel Investments Ltd.; *Int'l*, pg. 190
AFRICAN SUN ZIMBABWE (PRIVATE) LIMITED—See African Sun Limited; *Int'l*, pg. 192
AGGIE GREY'S HOTEL & BUNGALOWS; *Int'l*, pg. 209
AGORA HOSPITALITY GROUP CO., LTD.; *Int'l*, pg. 212
AGROEXPORT PROIZVODNJA I PROMET A.D.; *Int'l*, pg. 218

721110 — HOTELS (EXCEPT CASI...

AGROS DEVELOPMENT COMPANY PROODOS PUBLIC LTD.; *Int'l*, pg. 220
AI BATNAH HOTELS COMPANY SAOG; *Int'l*, pg. 226
AIRLANE HOTEL & CONFERENCE CENTRE THUNDER BAY—See Clarke Inc.; *Int'l*, pg. 1650
AITKEN SPENCE HOTEL HOLDINGS PLC—See Aitken Spence PLC; *Int'l*, pg. 254
AITKEN SPENCE HOTEL MANAGEMENTS (PVT) LTD.—See Aitken Spence PLC; *Int'l*, pg. 254
ALANGKA-SUKA HOTELS & RESORTS SDN. BHD.—See Advance Synergy Berhad; *Int'l*, pg. 156
ALBENA TOUR LTD; *Int'l*, pg. 293
ALBION RIVER INN, INC.—See Soul Community Planet, Inc.; *U.S. Private*, pg. 3717
ALBUQUERQUE SUITE HOSPITALITY LLC—See InnSuites Hospitality Trust; *U.S. Public*, pg. 1128
ALDEN ENTERPRISES, INC.; *U.S. Private*, pg. 155
AL FAISALIAH HOTEL—See Chow Tai Fook Enterprises Limited; *Int'l*, pg. 1585
ALILA HOTELS & RESORTS PTE. LTD.—See Hyatt Hotels Corporation; *U.S. Public*, pg. 1076
ALLGAU RESORT GMBH—See Fresenius SE & Co. KGaA; *Int'l*, pg. 2777
ALLIED DON VALLEY HOTEL INC.—See Allied Holdings Ltd.; *Int'l*, pg. 357
ALL SEASONS HOTELS—See Accor S.A.; *Int'l*, pg. 91
THE ALLUVIAN, LLC—See The Middleby Corporation; *U.S. Public*, pg. 2115
ALOR SETAR HOLIDAY VILLA SDN. BHD.—See Advance Synergy Berhad; *Int'l*, pg. 156
AL-SADEER HOTEL; *Int'l*, pg. 288
ALSIP HOTEL INVESTORS INC.; *U.S. Private*, pg. 202
ALTIN YUNUS TURISTIK TESISLER A.S.; *Int'l*, pg. 393
AMANA-NORDSTROM MOTEL CO.—See Amana Society, Inc.; *U.S. Private*, pg. 216
AMANOHASHIDATE HOTEL CO., LTD.—See Hankyu Hanshin Holdings Inc.; *Int'l*, pg. 3255
AMANRESORTS LIMITED—See DLF Limited; *Int'l*, pg. 2141
AMARA HOSPITALITY (THAILAND) CO., LTD.—See Amara Holdings Ltd.; *Int'l*, pg. 411
AMARA HOTEL PROPERTIES PTE LTD—See Amara Holdings Ltd.; *Int'l*, pg. 411
AMARA INTERNATIONAL HOTELS & RESORTS PTE LTD—See Amara Holdings Ltd.; *Int'l*, pg. 411
AMARA SENTOSA INVESTMENTS PTE LTD—See Amara Holdings Ltd.; *Int'l*, pg. 411
AMATHUS HOTELS LTD.—See Amathus Public Limited; *Int'l*, pg. 413
AMATHUS PUBLIC LIMITED; *Int'l*, pg. 413
AMELIA ISLAND COMPANY; *U.S. Private*, pg. 218
AMERICAN LEISURE HOLDINGS, INC.; *U.S. Public*, pg. 108
AMERIHOST FRANCHISE SYSTEMS, INC.—See Travel & Leisure Co.; *U.S. Public*, pg. 2185
AMERITEL INNS INCORPORATED; *U.S. Private*, pg. 261
ANADOLU JAPAN TURIZM A.S.—See Fiba Holding A.S.; *Int'l*, pg. 2651
ANDAZ AMSTERDAM PRINSENGRACHT—See Hyatt Hotels Corporation; *U.S. Public*, pg. 1076
ANDAZ LIVERPOOL STREET—See Hyatt Hotels Corporation; *U.S. Public*, pg. 1076
THE ANGLER'S BOUTIQUE RESORT—See Coral Hospitality, LLC; *U.S. Private*, pg. 1046
ANSA HOTEL KL SDN BHD—See Berjaya Corporation Berhad; *Int'l*, pg. 982
ANTARA HOLIDAY VILLAS SDN. BHD.—See Advance Synergy Berhad; *Int'l*, pg. 156
APARTMENT EXPRESS CORPORATE HOUSING INC.; *U.S. Private*, pg. 290
AP COMPANY USA, INC.—See AP Holdings Co., Ltd; *Int'l*, pg. 499
APPLIED DEVELOPMENT HOLDINGS LIMITED; *Int'l*, pg. 521
AQUA-ASTON HOSPITALITY, LLC—See Marriott Vacations Worldwide Corporation; *U.S. Public*, pg. 1373
AQUIS ENTERTAINMENT LIMITED; *Int'l*, pg. 528
ARAB INTERNATIONAL HOTELS PLC.; *Int'l*, pg. 530
ARGENTAL S.A.R.L.—See Danish Crown AmbA; *Int'l*, pg. 1964
ARIA HOTELS AND CONSULTANCY SERVICES PVT. LTD.—See Asian Hotels (West) Limited; *Int'l*, pg. 618
ARIA RESORT & CASINO, LLC—See MGM Resorts International; *U.S. Public*, pg. 1435
ARIMA VIEW HOTEL CO., LTD.—See Hankyu Hanshin Holdings Inc.; *Int'l*, pg. 3255
THE ARLINGTON RESORT HOTEL & SPA; *U.S. Private*, pg. 3988
ARO PALACE S.A.; *Int'l*, pg. 577
ARORA HOTELS LIMITED; *Int'l*, pg. 577
ARRABELLE AT VAIL SQUARE, LLC—See Vail Resorts, Inc.; *U.S. Public*, pg. 2271
ARUNA HOTELS LTD.; *Int'l*, pg. 586
ASHFORD ANCHORAGE LP—See Ashford Hospitality Trust, Inc.; *U.S. Public*, pg. 211
ASHFORD PITTSBURGH WATERFRONT LP—See Ashford Hospitality Trust, Inc.; *U.S. Public*, pg. 211
ASHFORD TRS FLAGSTAFF LLC—See Ashford Hospitality Trust, Inc.; *U.S. Public*, pg. 211

ASHFORD TRS FORT TOWER I LLC—See Ashford Hospitality Trust, Inc.; *U.S. Public*, pg. 211
ASHFORD TRS LE PAVILLON LLC—See Ashford Hospitality Trust, Inc.; *U.S. Public*, pg. 211
ASHFORD TRS MINNEAPOLIS AIRPORT LLC—See Ashford Hospitality Trust, Inc.; *U.S. Public*, pg. 211
ASHFORD TRS PIER HOUSE LLC—See Braemar Hotels & Resorts, Inc.; *U.S. Public*, pg. 379
ASHFORD TRS PITTSBURGH SOUTHPOINTE LLC—See Ashford Hospitality Trust, Inc.; *U.S. Public*, pg. 211
ASHFORD TRS POOL C1 LLC—See Ashford Hospitality Trust, Inc.; *U.S. Public*, pg. 211
ASHFORD TRS SIX LLC—See Ashford Hospitality Trust, Inc.; *U.S. Public*, pg. 211
ASHFORD TRS WICHITA LLC—See Ashford Hospitality Trust, Inc.; *U.S. Public*, pg. 211
ASIA AIRPORT HOTEL CO., LTD.—See Asia Hotel Public Company Limited; *Int'l*, pg. 613
ASIA HOTEL PUBLIC COMPANY LIMITED; *Int'l*, pg. 613
ASIAN HOTELS (WEST) LIMITED; *Int'l*, pg. 617
ASIA PATTAYA HOTEL CO., LTD.—See Asia Hotel Public Company Limited; *Int'l*, pg. 613
ASIA STANDARD HOTEL GROUP LIMITED—See Asia Standard International Group Limited; *Int'l*, pg. 615
ASPEN SKIING COMPANY, LLC—See Henry Crown & Company; *U.S. Private*, pg. 1917
ASTON HOTELS & RESORTS; *U.S. Private*, pg. 360
THE ASTOR CROWNE PLAZA NEW ORLEANS; *U.S. Private*, pg. 3989
ASTORIA A.D.; *Int'l*, pg. 657
ATHENEE PALACE HILTON BUCHAREST HOTEL; *Int'l*, pg. 670
ATLANTICA HOTELS & RESORTS LTD; *Int'l*, pg. 676
ATLIFIC INC.—See Ocean Properties, Ltd.; *U.S. Private*, pg. 2989
ATOS CONSUMER PRODUCTS PTE LTD—See Fitgenes Australia Pty Ltd.; *Int'l*, pg. 2695
ATOS WELLNESS PTE LTD—See Fitgenes Australia Pty Ltd.; *Int'l*, pg. 2695
ATRIA DANMARK A/S—See Atria Plc; *Int'l*, pg. 693
ATRIUM HOTEL, L.L.C—See Hyatt Hotels Corporation; *U.S. Public*, pg. 1076
A. TSOKKOS HOTELS PUBLIC LTD.; *Int'l*, pg. 22
AUBERGEDUSOLEIL; *U.S. Private*, pg. 384
AUBURN INVESTMENTS INC.—See Drury Inn Inc.; *U.S. Private*, pg. 1280
AUSTRIA HOTELS INTERNATIONAL BETRIEBS-GMBH; *Int'l*, pg. 723
AVALA A.D.; *Int'l*, pg. 734
AVA PACIFIC BEACH SOLAR, LLC—See AvalonBay Communities, Inc.; *U.S. Public*, pg. 240
AWAY RESORTS LTD.—See COFRA Holding AG; *Int'l*, pg. 1693
AZAR INCORPORATED; *U.S. Private*, pg. 415
BABYLON HOTEL; *Int'l*, pg. 793
BAC GOURMET HOUSE CO., LTD.—See Bangkok Airways Public Company Limited; *Int'l*, pg. 832
BAGATELLE HOTEL OPERATION LIMITED—See ENL Limited; *Int'l*, pg. 2441
BAGATELLE HOTEL OPERATIONS COMPANY LIMITED—See ENL Limited; *Int'l*, pg. 2441
BAHIA SUR RESORT S.C—See Banco Bilbao Vizcaya Argentaria, S.A.; *Int'l*, pg. 817
BAHRAIN TOURISM COMPANY B.S.C.—See Gulf Hotels Group B.S.C.; *Int'l*, pg. 3180
BAIYUN HOTEL, HUANGSHAN TOURISM DEVELOPMENT CO., LTD.—See Huangshan Tourism Development Co., Ltd.; *Int'l*, pg. 3513
THE BALBOA BAY CLUB & RESORT—See Eagle Four Equities LLC; *U.S. Private*, pg. 1309
THE BALBOA BAY CLUB & RESORT—See Pacific Hospitality Group, Inc.; *U.S. Private*, pg. 3067
BANADER HOTELS COMPANY BSC; *Int'l*, pg. 814
BANANA BAY WATERFRONT MOTEL; *U.S. Private*, pg. 464
BANAT ESTIVAL 2002 SA; *Int'l*, pg. 814
BANDAR BOTANIC RESORT BERHAD—See Gamuda Berhad; *Int'l*, pg. 2879
BANGLADESH SERVICES LIMITED; *Int'l*, pg. 836
BANJA LAKTASI A.D.; *Int'l*, pg. 836
BANYAN TREE HOTELS & RESORTS KOREA LIMITED—See Banyan Tree Holdings Ltd.; *Int'l*, pg. 855
BANYAN TREE HOTELS & RESORTS PTE. LTD.—See Banyan Tree Holdings Ltd.; *Int'l*, pg. 855
BANYAN TREE RESORTS & SPAS (THAILAND) COMPANY LIMITED—See Banyan Tree Holdings Ltd.; *Int'l*, pg. 855
BARCELO CONDAL HOTELES, S.A.—See Barcelo Corporacion Empresarial S.A.; *Int'l*, pg. 859
BARCELO CORPORACION EMPRESARIAL S.A.; *Int'l*, pg. 858
BARCELO GESTION HOTELES ITALIA, SRL—See Barcelo Corporacion Empresarial S.A.; *Int'l*, pg. 859
BARCELO PYRAMIDS LLC—See Barcelo Corporacion Empresarial S.A.; *Int'l*, pg. 859
BARCELO TURIZM OTELCILIK LIMITED—See Barcelo Corporacion Empresarial S.A.; *Int'l*, pg. 859
BAUHINIA HOTELS LIMITED—See Century City International Holdings Ltd; *Int'l*, pg. 1417

CORPORATE AFFILIATIONS

BAYER GASTRONOMIE GMBH—See Bayer Aktiengesellschaft; *Int'l*, pg. 904
BAY INN, INC.; *U.S. Private*, pg. 493
BAYSTAR HOTEL GROUP, LLC; *U.S. Private*, pg. 497
BDB HOTELS SDN. BHD.—See Bina Darulaman Berhad; *Int'l*, pg. 1032
BDL HOTEL GROUP; *Int'l*, pg. 929
THE BEACH HOTEL—See Gooderson Leisure Corporation; *Int'l*, pg. 3040
BEAU RIVAGE RESORTS, INC—See MGM Resorts International; *U.S. Public*, pg. 1435
BEIHAI HOTEL, HUANGSHAN TOURISM DEVELOPMENT CO., LTD.—See Huangshan Tourism Development Co., Ltd.; *Int'l*, pg. 3513
BEIJING INTERNATIONAL CLUB CO. LTD.—See Marriott International, Inc.; *U.S. Public*, pg. 1370
BEIJING OCEAN HOTEL CO., LTD.—See China COSCO Shipping Corporation Limited; *Int'l*, pg. 1492
BELLASERA—See SunStream, Inc.; *U.S. Private*, pg. 3873
BELVEDERE HOTEL PARTNERSHIP—See Probity International Corporation; *U.S. Private*, pg. 3271
BENNETT ENTERPRISES INC.; *U.S. Private*, pg. 527
THE BENTLEY HOTEL & BEACH CLUB—See Menin Hotels, Inc.; *U.S. Private*, pg. 2666
BERCHTESGADEN INTERNATIONAL RESORT BETRIEBS GMBH—See BayernLB Holding AG; *Int'l*, pg. 913
BERJAYA BEAU VALLON BAY BEACH RESORT LIMITED—See Berjaya Corporation Berhad; *Int'l*, pg. 982
BERJAYA CORPORATION BERHAD; *Int'l*, pg. 982
BERJAYA HILLS BERHAD—See Berjaya Corporation Berhad; *Int'l*, pg. 982
BERJAYA HOTELS & RESORTS (M) SDN BHD—See Berjaya Corporation Berhad; *Int'l*, pg. 984
BERJAYA HOTELS & RESORTS (SINGAPORE) PTE LTD—See Berjaya Corporation Berhad; *Int'l*, pg. 983
BERJAYA LAND BERHAD—See Berjaya Corporation Berhad; *Int'l*, pg. 982
BERJAYA LANGKAWI BEACH RESORT SDN BHD—See Berjaya Corporation Berhad; *Int'l*, pg. 983
BERJAYA PENANG HOTEL SDN BHD.—See Berjaya Corporation Berhad; *Int'l*, pg. 983
BERJAYA PRASLIN LIMITED—See Berjaya Corporation Berhad; *Int'l*, pg. 984
BERJAYA RESORT MANAGEMENT SERVICES SDN BHD—See Berjaya Corporation Berhad; *Int'l*, pg. 983
BEST EASTERN HOTELS LTD.; *Int'l*, pg. 999
BEST WESTERN - DENVER INTERNATIONAL AIRPORT—See Stonebridge Realty Advisors, Inc.; *U.S. Private*, pg. 3827
BEST WESTERN VILLAGE PARK INN; *Int'l*, pg. 999
THE BEVERLY HILLS HOTEL—See Dorchester Group of Companies; *Int'l*, pg. 2175
BHG S.A. - BRAZIL HOSPITALITY GROUP—See GTIS Partners LP; *U.S. Private*, pg. 1807
BIA ACQUISITION LTD—See Grupo Posadas S.A.B. de C.V.; *Int'l*, pg. 3134
BIG CEDAR LODGE; *U.S. Private*, pg. 552
BIG SKY RESORT—See Boyne USA Resorts Inc.; *U.S. Private*, pg. 629
BILMAR BEACH RESORT; *U.S. Private*, pg. 559
THE BIRCHWOOD; *U.S. Private*, pg. 3995
BIRMINGHAM JEFFERSON CONVENTION COMPLEX; *U.S. Private*, pg. 565
BLOCK47 EATS LLP—See Global Food Creators Co., Ltd.; *Int'l*, pg. 2997
BLUE COAST HOTELS LIMITED; *Int'l*, pg. 1067
BLUEGREEN VACATIONS UNLIMITED, INC.—See Hilton Grand Vacations Inc.; *U.S. Public*, pg. 1039
BLUE HARBOR RESORT & CONVENTION CENTER—See Centerbridge Partners, L.P.; *U.S. Private*, pg. 814
BLUESTAR RESORT & GOLF LLC—See J.F. Shea Co., Inc.; *U.S. Private*, pg. 2164
BOAVISTA GOLF & SPA RESORT EMPREENDIMENTOS TUR ISTICOS, SA—See Emerson Developments (Holdings) Limited; *Int'l*, pg. 2379
BOCA RESORTS, INC.—See Blackstone Inc.; *U.S. Public*, pg. 352
BODY CONTOURS PTE LTD—See Fitgenes Australia Pty Ltd.; *Int'l*, pg. 2695
BON BELTA CO., LTD.—See AEON Co., Ltd.; *Int'l*, pg. 177
BOOKING.COM B.V.—See Booking Holdings, Inc.; *U.S. Public*, pg. 368
BORNEO HIGHLANDS HORNBILL GOLF & JUNGLE CLUB BERHAD—See Country Heights Holdings Berhad; *Int'l*, pg. 1819
BOSTON HOTEL COMPANY, L.L.C.—See Hyatt Hotels Corporation; *U.S. Public*, pg. 1076
BOULDERS RESORT & GOLDEN DOOR SPA—See Blackstone Inc.; *U.S. Public*, pg. 351
BOULEVARD HOLDINGS, INC.; *Int'l*, pg. 1119
BOULEVARD MOTEL CORP.—See Sunburst Hospitality Corporation; *U.S. Private*, pg. 3865
BOYNE HIGHLANDS RESORT—See Boyne USA Resorts Inc.; *U.S. Private*, pg. 629
BOYNE MOUNTAIN RESORT—See Boyne USA Resorts Inc.; *U.S. Private*, pg. 629
BOYNE USA RESORTS INC.; *U.S. Private*, pg. 629

N.A.I.C.S. INDEX
721110 — HOTELS (EXCEPT CASI...

BRAMPTON ISLAND PTY LIMITED—See GPT Group; *Int'l*, pg. 3047
BREAKERS PALM BEACH INC.—See Flagler System Inc.; *U.S. Private*, pg. 1539
BRIGADE HOSPITALITY SERVICES LIMITED—See Brigade Enterprises Ltd.; *Int'l*, pg. 1160
BRIGHTON SKI RESORT—See Boyne USA Resorts Inc.; *U.S. Private*, pg. 629
BRISBANE LODGING, L.P.—See Stonebridge Realty Advisors, Inc.; *U.S. Private*, pg. 3827
BROADMOOR HOTEL, INC.—See The Anschutz Corporation; *U.S. Private*, pg. 3987
BROWN PALACE HOTEL ASSOCIATES L.P.; *U.S. Private*, pg. 668
BROWNS BEACH HOTELS PLC; *Int'l*, pg. 1198
BRUTGER EQUITIES, INC.; *U.S. Private*, pg. 673
BUDGET MOTELS INC.; *U.S. Private*, pg. 679
BUENA PARK SUITE HOSPITALITY LLC—See InnSuites Hospitality Trust; *U.S. Public*, pg. 1128
BUENA VISTA HOSPITALITY GROUP; *U.S. Private*, pg. 680
BUENA VISTA PALACE—See Blackstone Inc.; *U.S. Public*, pg. 351
BUFFALO LODGING ASSOCIATES, LLC; *U.S. Private*, pg. 680
BUGGSI, INC.; *U.S. Private*, pg. 681
BULGARI HOTELS AND RESORTS MILANO, S.R.L.—See Marriott International, Inc.; *U.S. Public*, pg. 1370
BUNKHOUSE GROUP LLC—See Hyatt Hotels Corporation; *U.S. Public*, pg. 1078
BUSHLANDS GAME LODGE—See Gooderson Leisure Corporation; *Int'l*, pg. 3039
BUTLIN'S LIMITED—See Blackstone Inc.; *U.S. Public*, pg. 352
BWI DENMARK, INC.—See Best Western International, Inc.; *U.S. Private*, pg. 544
CAL HOTEL CO. LTD.—See China Airlines Ltd.; *Int'l*, pg. 1482
CAMELBACK COUNTRY CLUB INC.—See Marriott International, Inc.; *U.S. Public*, pg. 1370
CAMPBELL LODGING INC.; *U.S. Private*, pg. 730
CANDLEWOOD HOTEL COMPANY, INC.; *U.S. Private*, pg. 428
CANEEL BAY—See Chow Tai Fook Enterprises Limited; *Int'l*, pg. 1585
CAPITOL HILL HOTEL—See Marriott International, Inc.; *U.S. Public*, pg. 1371
CAPSTAR SAN FRANCISCO COMPANY, LLC—See Acron AG; *Int'l*, pg. 109
CARINTHIA GROUP 1, L.P.—See Vail Resorts, Inc.; *U.S. Public*, pg. 2271
CARLSON HOTELS MANAGEMENT CORPORATION—See Carlson Companies Inc.; *U.S. Private*, pg. 764
CARLSON REZIDOR HOTEL GROUP - ASIA PACIFIC—See Carlson Companies Inc.; *U.S. Private*, pg. 764
CARNEGIE HOTELS, LLC—See Summit Hotel Properties, Inc.; *U.S. Public*, pg. 1959
CASA DEL MAR BEACH RESORT N.V.; *Int'l*, pg. 1349
CASA MADRONA HOTEL & SPA—See MetWest Realty Advisors LLC; *U.S. Private*, pg. 2691
CASA MONICA HOTEL—See The Kessler Enterprise Inc.; *U.S. Private*, pg. 4065
CASTLE HOSPITALITY GROUP; *U.S. Public*, pg. 447
CASTLE RESORTS & HOTELS, INC.—See Castle Hospitality Group; *U.S. Public*, pg. 447
CAVALIER HOTEL CORP—See Kyanite Mining Corporation; *U.S. Private*, pg. 2360
C.C.C. TOURIST ENTERPRISES PUBLIC COMPANY LIMITED—See G.S. Galatariotis & Sons Ltd.; *Int'l*, pg. 2866
CEDAR CAPITAL PARTNERS LIMITED; *Int'l*, pg. 1388
CENTARA VILLAS PHUKET—See Central Plaza Hotel Public Company Limited; *Int'l*, pg. 1409
CENTRAL A.D.; *Int'l*, pg. 1403
CENTRAL KRABI BAY RESORT—See Central Plaza Hotel Public Company Limited; *Int'l*, pg. 1409
CENTRAL MAE SOT HILL HOTEL CO LTD—See Central Plaza Hotel Public Company Limited; *Int'l*, pg. 1409
CENTRAL MULTISERVICIOS S.R.L.—See Aramark; *U.S. Public*, pg. 177
CENTRAL RESTAURANTS GROUP CO., LTD—See Central Plaza Hotel Public Company Limited; *Int'l*, pg. 1409
CENTRAL SAMUI BEACH RESORT CO., LTD.—See Central Plaza Hotel Public Company Limited; *Int'l*, pg. 1409
CENTRAL SAMUI VILLAGE CO., LTD.—See Central Plaza Hotel Public Company Limited; *Int'l*, pg. 1409
CENTRAL WORLD HOTEL CO., LTD.—See Central Plaza Hotel Public Company Limited; *Int'l*, pg. 1409
CENTURION STUDENT SERVICES PTY. LTD.—See Centurion Corporation Limited; *Int'l*, pg. 1417
CENTURION STUDENT SERVICES (UK) LTD.—See Centurion Corporation Limited; *Int'l*, pg. 1417
CEYLON HOTELS CORPORATION PLC; *Int'l*, pg. 1426
CHALET HOTELS LTD.; *Int'l*, pg. 1437
CHARLES GROUP HOTELS, INC.; *U.S. Private*, pg. 852

CHATEAU ELAN LTD.—See Fountainhead Development, LLC; *U.S. Private*, pg. 1581
CHATEAU ELAN WINERY & RESORT—See Fountainhead Development, LLC; *U.S. Private*, pg. 1581
CHATEAU INTERNATIONAL DEVELOPMENT CO., LTD.; *Int'l*, pg. 1457
CHATTANOOGA CHOO-CHOO HOLIDAY INN—See Choo Choo Partners L.P.; *U.S. Private*, pg. 888
CHERATING HOLIDAY VILLA BERHAD—See Advance Synergy Berhad; *Int'l*, pg. 156
CHERRY HILL PARK, LLC—See Century Communities, Inc.; *U.S. Public*, pg. 475
CHICAGO HILTON LLC—See Park Hotels & Resorts Inc.; *U.S. Public*, pg. 1638
CHICO HOT SPRINGS RESORT, INC.—See DiamondRock Hospitality Company; *U.S. Public*, pg. 659
THE CHIMO HOTEL—See Clarke Inc.; *Int'l*, pg. 1650
CHINA NUCLEAR ENERGY TECHNOLOGY CORPORATION LIMITED; *Int'l*, pg. 1536
CHINA TOURISM AND CULTURE INVESTMENT GROUP CO., LTD.; *Int'l*, pg. 1560
CHL LIMITED; *Int'l*, pg. 1575
CHOICE HOTELS AUSTRALASIA PTY. LTD.—See Choice Hotels International, Inc.; *U.S. Public*, pg. 489
CHOICE HOTELS CANADA, INC.—See Choice Hotels International, Inc.; *U.S. Public*, pg. 489
CHOICE HOTELS FRANCE, S.A.S—See Choice Hotels International, Inc.; *U.S. Public*, pg. 490
CHOICE HOTELS FRANCHISE, GMBH—See Choice Hotels International, Inc.; *U.S. Public*, pg. 490
CHOICE HOTELS INTERNATIONAL, INC.; *U.S. Public*, pg. 489
CHOICE HOTELS LIMITED—See Choice Hotels International, Inc.; *U.S. Public*, pg. 490
CHOICE VACATION RENTALS LLC—See Choice Hotels International, Inc.; *U.S. Public*, pg. 490
CHONGDE LOU HOTEL CO.—See Huangshan Tourism Development Co., Ltd.; *Int'l*, pg. 3513
CHROMA HOSPITALITY, INC.—See Filinvest Development Corporation; *Int'l*, pg. 2662
CITITEL HOTEL MANAGEMENT SDN. BHD.—See IGB Berhad; *Int'l*, pg. 3601
CITRUS LEISURE PLC; *Int'l*, pg. 1626
CITYCON ESTONIA OU—See Citycon Oyj; *Int'l*, pg. 1629
CITY LODGE HOTELS LIMITED; *Int'l*, pg. 1627
CLARIDGE PUBLIC LIMITED; *Int'l*, pg. 1648
CLASSIC HOTELS & RESORTS—See Grossman Company Properties, Inc.; *U.S. Private*, pg. 1792
C LAZY U RANCH, INC.; *U.S. Private*, pg. 701
CLEANBNB SPA; *Int'l*, pg. 1655
THE CLIFFS COMMUNITIES, INC.; *U.S. Private*, pg. 4010
CLUB MED AUSTRALIA & NEW ZEALAND—See Fosun International Limited; *Int'l*, pg. 2750
CLUB MED—See Fosun International Limited; *Int'l*, pg. 2750
COAST HOTELS LTD.—See APA Holdings Co., Ltd.; *Int'l*, pg. 500
COAST INTERNATIONAL INN—See Tanadgusix Corp.; *U.S. Private*, pg. 3930
COCRE8 PTE. LTD.—See Hong Fok Corporation Limited; *Int'l*, pg. 3465
THE COEUR D'ALENE RESORT—See The Hagadone Corporation; *U.S. Private*, pg. 4041
COLLIER DEVELOPMENT CO. INC.; *U.S. Private*, pg. 969
COLOGNE MH OPERATING COMPANY GMBH—See Marriott International, Inc.; *U.S. Public*, pg. 1370
COLUMBIA PROPERTIES LAUGHLIN, LLC—See Caesars Entertainment, Inc.; *U.S. Public*, pg. 421
COLUMBIA SUSSEX CORPORATION; *U.S. Private*, pg. 978
COMFORT INN—See Tramz Hotels Inc.; *U.S. Private*, pg. 4205
COMMUNE HOTELS & RESORTS ASIA PTE. LTD.—See Commune Hotels & Resorts, LLC; *U.S. Private*, pg. 987
COMO HOTELS & RESORTS (ASIA) PTE. LTD.; *Int'l*, pg. 1721
COMO HOTELS & RESORTS LTD.—See COMO Hotels & Resorts (Asia) Pte. Ltd.; *Int'l*, pg. 1721
COMO HOTELS & RESORTS USA—See COMO Hotels & Resorts (Asia) Pte. Ltd.; *Int'l*, pg. 1721
COMPAGNIE INTERNATIONALE DES WAGONS LITS ET DU TOURISME S.A.—See Accor S.A.; *Int'l*, pg. 91
CONRAD CHICAGO HOTEL—See DiamondRock Hospitality Company; *U.S. Public*, pg. 659
CONRAD HOTELS & RESORTS—See Hilton Worldwide Holdings Inc.; *U.S. Public*, pg. 1040
CONRAD INTERNATIONAL HOTELS (HK) LIMITED—See Hilton Worldwide Holdings Inc.; *U.S. Public*, pg. 1040
THE CONSERVATION CORPORATION SA LIMITED—See Hollard Insurance Company Ltd; *Int'l*, pg. 3451
CONSTANCE HOTELS SERVICES LIMITED; *Int'l*, pg. 1772
CONSTANTINOU BROS HOTELS LTD; *Int'l*, pg. 1772
CONTINENTAL FOODS CO., LTD.—See Hotel Okura Co., Ltd.; *Int'l*, pg. 3488
CORDIS HONG KONG LIMITED—See Great Eagle Holdings Limited; *Int'l*, pg. 3064
CORINTHIA HOTELS INTERNATIONAL; *Int'l*, pg. 1801
CORINTHIA PALACE HOTEL COMPANY LIMITED; *Int'l*, pg. 1801

COSMOPOLITAN HOTEL LIMITED—See Far East Consortium International Limited; *Int'l*, pg. 2615
COSMOS HOTEL MANAGEMENT CO., LTD.—See Daiwa House Industry Co., Ltd.; *Int'l*, pg. 1945
COTSWOLD INNS & HOTELS LIMITED—See Fuller, Smith & Turner PLC; *Int'l*, pg. 2842
THE COUNTRY CLUB AT TAGAYTAY HIGHLANDS, INC.—See Belle Corporation; *Int'l*, pg. 966
COUNTRY CLUB HOSPITALITY & HOLIDAYS LIMITED; *Int'l*, pg. 1818
COURTYARD ALBUQUERQUE AIRPORT OPERATOR LLC—See W.P. Carey Inc.; *U.S. Public*, pg. 2315
COURTYARD BALTIMORE WASHINGTON AIRPORT OPERATOR LLC—See W.P. Carey Inc.; *U.S. Public*, pg. 2315
COURTYARD BY MARRIOTT - EWING HOPEWELL—See KSL Capital Partners, LLC; *U.S. Private*, pg. 2355
COURTYARD BY MARRIOTT - MIAMI BEACH-SOUTH BEACH—See Robert Finvarb Companies, LLC; *U.S. Private*, pg. 3458
COURTYARD BY MARRIOTT - MIAMI COCONUT GROVE—See Robert Finvarb Companies, LLC; *U.S. Private*, pg. 3458
COURTYARD BY MARRIOTT - SAN DIEGO OLD TOWN—See Westbrook Real Estate Partners, LLC; *U.S. Private*, pg. 4488
COURTYARD CHICAGO OHARE OPERATOR LLC—See W.P. Carey Inc.; *U.S. Public*, pg. 2315
COURTYARD INDIANAPOLIS AIRPORT OPERATOR LLC—See W.P. Carey Inc.; *U.S. Public*, pg. 2315
COURTYARD IRVINE JOHN WAYNE AIRPORT OPERATOR LLC—See W.P. Carey Inc.; *U.S. Public*, pg. 2315
COURTYARD LOUISVILLE EAST OPERATOR LLC—See W.P. Carey Inc.; *U.S. Public*, pg. 2315
COURTYARD MARRIOTT-VACAVILLE INC.—See Marriott International, Inc.; *U.S. Public*, pg. 1370
COURTYARD NEWARK LIBERTY INTERNATIONAL AIRPORT OPERATOR LLC—See W.P. Carey Inc.; *U.S. Public*, pg. 2315
COURTYARD ORLANDO AIRPORT OPERATOR LLC—See W.P. Carey Inc.; *U.S. Public*, pg. 2315
COURTYARD ORLANDO INTERNATIONAL DRIVE CONVENTION CENTER OPERATOR LLC—See W.P. Carey Inc.; *U.S. Public*, pg. 2315
COURTYARD SPOKANE DOWNTOWN OPERATOR LLC—See W.P. Carey Inc.; *U.S. Public*, pg. 2315
COVE HAVEN ENTERTAINMENT RESORTS—See Mcsam Hotel Group LLC; *U.S. Private*, pg. 2644
CPI HOTELS, A.S.—See CPI Property Group, S.A.; *Int'l*, pg. 1825
CPI HOTELS SLOVAKIA, S.R.O.—See CPI Property Group, S.A.; *Int'l*, pg. 1825
CP LAUGHLIN REALTY, LLC—See Caesars Entertainment, Inc.; *U.S. Public*, pg. 420
CRE BUSHKILL GROUP, LLC—See Cerberus Capital Management, L.P.; *U.S. Private*, pg. 837
CRESCENT HOTELS & RESORTS; *U.S. Private*, pg. 1094
CRESTA MARAKANELO (PVT) LTD—See Botswana Development Corporation Limited; *Int'l*, pg. 1118
CRESTED BUTTE MOUNTAIN RESORT, INC.—See Vail Resorts, Inc.; *U.S. Public*, pg. 2271
CRESTLINE HOTELS & RESORTS, LLC—See Barcelo Corporacion Empresarial S.A.; *Int'l*, pg. 859
THE CROCKETT HOTEL—See Gal-Tex Hotel Corporation; *U.S. Private*, pg. 1635
THE CROWNE PLAZA TIMES SQUARE MANHATTAN; *U.S. Public*, pg. 4017
CROWN PLAZA LTD—See Africa Israel Investments Ltd.; *Int'l*, pg. 190
CROWN RESORTS, LTD.; *U.S. Private*, pg. 1112
CROWN SYDNEY PTY LTD—See Blackstone Inc.; *U.S. Public*, pg. 352
CRYSTAL PALMS BEACH RESORT; *U.S. Public*, pg. 1115
CRYSTAL SPRINGS RESORT; *U.S. Private*, pg. 1115
CSL STUDENT LIVING BENIKEA KP LTD—See Centurion Corporation Limited; *Int'l*, pg. 1416
CSL STUDENT LIVING (SELEGIE) PTE. LTD.—See Centurion Corporation Limited; *Int'l*, pg. 1416
CTF HOLDINGS INC.; *U.S. Private*, pg. 1118
CUBUS LUX PLC; *Int'l*, pg. 1876
CUSCADEN PROPERTIES PTE LTD—See Allgreen Properties Ltd.; *Int'l*, pg. 338
DAITO ASIA DEVELOPMENT (MALAYSIA) SDN. BHD.—See Daito Trust Construction Co., Ltd.; *Int'l*, pg. 1943
DAIWA RESORT CO., LTD.—See Daiwa House Industry Co., Ltd.; *Int'l*, pg. 1946
DAIWA ROYAL HOTEL CITY CO., LTD.—See Daiwa House Industry Co., Ltd.; *Int'l*, pg. 1946
DALATA HOTEL GROUP PLC; *Int'l*, pg. 1950
DALIAN NEW WORLD HOTEL CO., LTD.—See Chow Tai Fook Enterprises Limited; *Int'l*, pg. 1585
DAN HOTELS LTD.; *Int'l*, pg. 1957
DAYS INNS WORLDWIDE, INC.—See Travel & Leisure Co.; *U.S. Public*, pg. 2185
DC SIX LESSEE, L.L.C.—See Pebblebrook Hotel Trust; *U.S. Public*, pg. 1660

721110 — HOTELS (EXCEPT CASI...

DEAUVILLE HOTEL MANAGEMENT, LLC; *U.S. Private*, pg. 1185
DELTA INN INC.; *U.S. Private*, pg. 1201
DENIHAN HOSPITALITY GROUP, LLC; *U.S. Private*, pg. 1205
DEOGYUSAN RESORT CO., LTD.; *Int'l*, pg. 2040
DERDAP TURIST A.D.; *Int'l*, pg. 2041
THE DESMOND ALBANY HOTEL & CONFERENCE CENTER—See Delta Holdings, Inc.; *U.S. Private*, pg. 1200
THE DESMOND GREAT VALLEY HOTEL & CONFERENCE CENTER—See Delta Holdings, Inc.; *U.S. Private*, pg. 1200
DESTINATION HOTELS AND RESORTS, INC.—See Commune Hotels & Resorts, LLC; *U.S. Private*, pg. 987
DESTINATION RESIDENCES HAWAII LLC—See Hyatt Hotels Corporation; *U.S. Public*, pg. 1077
DESTINATION RESIDENCES LLC—See Hyatt Hotels Corporation; *U.S. Public*, pg. 1077
DEVELOPPEMENTS IMMOBILIERS ET COMMERCIAUX S.A.—See Accor S.A.; *Int'l*, pg. 91
DHANADA CORPORATION LIMITED; *Int'l*, pg. 2098
THE DHARMAWANGSA—See Chow Tai Fook Enterprises Limited; *Int'l*, pg. 1585
DH CAROLINA MANAGEMENT LLC—See Hyatt Hotels Corporation; *U.S. Public*, pg. 1076
DH DBHL MANAGEMENT LLC—See Hyatt Hotels Corporation; *U.S. Public*, pg. 1077
DH DEL MAR MANAGEMENT LLC—See Hyatt Hotels Corporation; *U.S. Public*, pg. 1077
DH KIRKLAND MANAGEMENT LLC—See Hyatt Hotels Corporation; *U.S. Public*, pg. 1077
DH MISSION BAY MANAGEMENT LLC—See Hyatt Hotels Corporation; *U.S. Public*, pg. 1077
DH MISSION PALMS MANAGEMENT LLC—See Hyatt Hotels Corporation; *U.S. Public*, pg. 1077
DH RICHMOND MANAGEMENT LLC—See Hyatt Hotels Corporation; *U.S. Public*, pg. 1077
DH ROSLYN MANAGEMENT LLC—See Hyatt Hotels Corporation; *U.S. Public*, pg. 1077
DH RSC MANAGEMENT LLC—See Hyatt Hotels Corporation; *U.S. Public*, pg. 1077
DH SAN ANTONIO MANAGEMENT LLC—See Hyatt Hotels Corporation; *U.S. Public*, pg. 1077
DH SCOTTSDALE MANAGEMENT LLC—See Hyatt Hotels Corporation; *U.S. Public*, pg. 1077
DH SEATTLE MANAGEMENT LLC—See Hyatt Hotels Corporation; *U.S. Public*, pg. 1077
DH SJ MANAGEMENT LLC—See Hyatt Hotels Corporation; *U.S. Public*, pg. 1077
DH STOWE MANAGEMENT LLC—See Hyatt Hotels Corporation; *U.S. Public*, pg. 1077
DH SUNRIVER MANAGEMENT LLC—See Hyatt Hotels Corporation; *U.S. Public*, pg. 1077
DH TAHOE MANAGEMENT LLC—See Hyatt Hotels Corporation; *U.S. Public*, pg. 1077
DH WASHINGTON MANAGEMENT LLC—See Hyatt Hotels Corporation; *U.S. Public*, pg. 1077
DH WEST LOOP MANAGEMENT LLC—See Hyatt Hotels Corporation; *U.S. Public*, pg. 1077
DH WILD DUNES MANAGEMENT LLC—See Hyatt Hotels Corporation; *U.S. Public*, pg. 1077
DIAMONDHEAD BEACH RESORT—See SunStream, Inc.; *U.S. Private*, pg. 3873
DIAMOND RESORTS CORPORATION—See Apollo Global Management, Inc.; *U.S. Public*, pg. 150
DIAMOND RESORTS CORPORATION—See Reverence Capital Partners LLC; *U.S. Private*, pg. 3415
DIAMONDROCK DC M STREET TENANT, LLC—See DiamondRock Hospitality Company; *U.S. Public*, pg. 659
DIAMONDROCK SAN DIEGO TENANT, LLC—See DiamondRock Hospitality Company; *U.S. Public*, pg. 659
DIMENSION DEVELOPMENT COMPANY; *U.S. Private*, pg. 1232
DIPLOMAT HOTEL CORPORATION; *U.S. Private*, pg. 1234
DISNEYLAND HOTELS—See The Walt Disney Company; *U.S. Public*, pg. 2138
DISNEY VACATION CLUB—See The Walt Disney Company; *U.S. Public*, pg. 2138
DIVI ARUBA BEACH RESORT; *Int'l*, pg. 2137
DIVI HOTELS, INC.; *U.S. Private*, pg. 1244
DKN HOTEL LLC; *U.S. Private*, pg. 1247
DOLPHIN HOTELS PLC; *Int'l*, pg. 2159
DOME INVESTMENTS PUBLIC COMPANY LTD.—See A. Tsokkos Hotels Public Ltd.; *Int'l*, pg. 22
DOM VILLE SERVICES; *Int'l*, pg. 2159
DON CESAR RESORT HOTEL LTD.—See Loews Corporation; *U.S. Public*, pg. 1340
DON'T LOOK BACK LESSEE, LLC—See Pebblebrook Hotel Trust; *U.S. Public*, pg. 1660
DORSETT BUKIT BINTANG SDN. BHD.—See Far East Consortium International Limited; *Int'l*, pg. 2615
DORSETT HOSPITALITY INTERNATIONAL LIMITED—See Far East Consortium International Limited; *Int'l*, pg. 2615
DORSETT HOSPITALITY INTERNATIONAL (SINGAPORE) PTE. LIMITED—See Far East Consortium International Limited; *Int'l*, pg. 2615
DORSETT REGENCY HOTEL (M) SDN. BHD.—See Far East Consortium International Limited; *Int'l*, pg. 2615
DOUBLETREE BY HILTON METROPOLITAN-NEW YORK CITY.—See Highgate Hotels, L.P.; *U.S. Private*, pg. 1938
DOUBLETREE BY HILTON - SOUTH BEND—See Hotel Group International, Inc.; *U.S. Private*, pg. 1989
DOUBLETREE HOTEL DENVER/BOULDER—See Hilton Worldwide Holdings Inc.; *U.S. Public*, pg. 1040
DOUBLETREE HOTEL WILMINGTON—See Hilton Worldwide Holdings Inc.; *U.S. Public*, pg. 1040
DOUBLETREE SPOKANE CITY CENTER LLC—See Park Hotels & Resorts Inc.; *U.S. Public*, pg. 1638
THE DOW HOTEL COMPANY LLC; *U.S. Private*, pg. 4023
DOWNTOWN MARRIOTT HOTEL—See Raphael Hotel Group; *U.S. Private*, pg. 3355
DOYLE HOTELS (HOLDINGS) LIMITED; *Int'l*, pg. 2187
DRAKENSBERG GARDENS GOLF & SPA RESORT—See Gooderson Leisure Corporation; *Int'l*, pg. 3039
DREAMWORLD LIMITED; *Int'l*, pg. 2203
DRIFTWOOD HOSPITALITY MANAGEMENT, LLC; *U.S. Private*, pg. 1277
THE DRUKER COMPANY, LTD.; *U.S. Private*, pg. 4023
DRURY HOTELS COMPANY, LLC.—See Drury Inn Inc.; *U.S. Private*, pg. 1280
DRURY INN INC.; *U.S. Private*, pg. 1280
DRURY INN POPLAR BLUFF INC.—See Drury Inn Inc.; *U.S. Private*, pg. 1280
DRURY INNS INC.—See Drury Inn Inc.; *U.S. Private*, pg. 1280
DRURY INN & SUITES STADIUM—See Drury Inn Inc.; *U.S. Private*, pg. 1280
DRURY SOUTH, INC.—See Drury Inn Inc.; *U.S. Private*, pg. 1280
DRURY SOUTHWEST, INC.—See Drury Inn Inc.; *U.S. Private*, pg. 1280
DUC LONG GIA LAI GROUP JSC; *Int'l*, pg. 2222
DUMAZULU LODGE & TRADITIONAL VILLAGE—See Gooderson Leisure Corporation; *Int'l*, pg. 3039
DUR HOSPITALITY CO.; *Int'l*, pg. 2227
DUSIT THANI PHILIPPINES, INC.—See Dusit Thani Public Company Limited; *Int'l*, pg. 2234
DUSIT THANI PUBLIC COMPANY LIMITED; *Int'l*, pg. 2234
DWELL ADELAIDE STUDENT LIVING PTY. LTD.—See Centurion Corporation Limited; *Int'l*, pg. 1481
DYNASTY HOTEL OF HAWAII, INC—See China Airlines Ltd.; *Int'l*, pg. 1481
EAGLE RIDGE RESORT, LLC; *U.S. Private*, pg. 1310
EASTERN & ORIENTAL HOTEL SDN. BHD.—See Eastern & Oriental Berhad; *Int'l*, pg. 2271
EAST SHORE RESORT; *U.S. Private*, pg. 1317
EAST SIDE HOTEL SERVICES, INC.—See Marriott International, Inc.; *U.S. Public*, pg. 1370
EASYHOTEL FRANCE SAS—See easyHotel plc; *Int'l*, pg. 2276
EASYHOTEL PLC; *Int'l*, pg. 2276
EASYHOTEL SPAIN S.L.U.—See easyHotel plc; *Int'l*, pg. 2276
EDL HOTELS SCA—See The Walt Disney Company; *U.S. Public*, pg. 2139
EGYPTIAN RESORTS COMPANY; *Int'l*, pg. 2327
EIGHTEEN SEVENTY STRAND CORP.; *U.S. Private*, pg. 1347
EIH ASSOCIATED HOTELS LIMITED; *Int'l*, pg. 2332
ELBIT IMAGING LTD.; *Int'l*, pg. 2344
EL CONQUISTADOR MAH II LLC—See MetLife, Inc.; *U.S. Public*, pg. 1430
EL CONQUISTADOR RESORT—See Blackstone Inc.; *U.S. Public*, pg. 351
ELEMENT LEXINGTON—See Marriott International, Inc.; *U.S. Public*, pg. 1372
EL GEZIRAH HOTELS TOURISM—See Accor S.A.; *Int'l*, pg. 91
ELITE HAVENS LTD.—See Dusit Thani Public Company Limited; *Int'l*, pg. 2234
ELSCINT LIMITED—See Elbit Imaging Ltd.; *Int'l*, pg. 2344
EL SHAMS PYRAMIDS CO. FOR HOTELS & TOURISTIC PROJECTS S.A.E.; *Int'l*, pg. 2341
EMAAR HOTELS & RESORTS LLC—See Emaar Properties PJSC; *Int'l*, pg. 2372
EMBASSY SUITES CASINO SAN JUAN—See Hilton Worldwide Holdings Inc.; *U.S. Public*, pg. 1040
EMBASSY SUITES CHICAGO O'HARE-ROSEMONT—See The Dow Hotel Company LLC; *U.S. Private*, pg. 4023
EMBASSY SUITES PHOENIX AIRPORT LLC—See Park Hotels & Resorts Inc.; *U.S. Public*, pg. 1638
THE EMPEROR HOTEL LIMITED—See Emperor International Holdings Limited; *Int'l*, pg. 2386
EMPORIO ACAPULCO, S.A. DE C.V.—See Emporio Hotels & Resorts S.A. de C.V.; *Int'l*, pg. 2387
EMPORIO HOTELS & RESORTS S.A. DE C.V.; *Int'l*, pg. 2387
EMPORIO IXTAPA S.A. DE C.V., LIC.—See Emporio Hotels & Resorts S.A. de C.V.; *Int'l*, pg. 2387
EMPORIO MAZATLAN, S.A. DE C.V.—See Emporio Hotels & Resorts S.A. de C.V.; *Int'l*, pg. 2387
EMPORIO VERACRUZ S.A. DE C.V.—See Emporio Hotels & Resorts S.A. de C.V.; *Int'l*, pg. 2387
EMPORIO ZACATECAS, S.A. DE C.V.—See Emporio Hotels & Resorts S.A. de C.V.; *Int'l*, pg. 2387

EQUALITY HOTEL MANAGEMENT SDN. BHD.—See HL Global Enterprises Limited; *Int'l*, pg. 3429
EQUATORIAL HOTEL MANAGEMENT PTE. LTD.—See HL Global Enterprises Limited; *Int'l*, pg. 3430
THE ERIN COMPANY; *U.S. Private*, pg. 4026
ESPRIT DE FRANCE SAS—See Compagnie Lebon SA; *Int'l*, pg. 91
ETAP HOTELS LTD—See Accor S.A.; *Int'l*, pg. 91
EUROCRETA S.A.—See Creta Farm S.A.; *Int'l*, pg. 1842
EURO-SUITES HOTEL—See Seven Kings Holdings, Inc.; *U.S. Private*, pg. 3618
EVANS HOTELS CORPORATION; *U.S. Private*, pg. 1435
EXCELSIOR HOTEL BEOGRAD; *Int'l*, pg. 2579
EXCLUSIVE RESORTS, LLC—See Revolution, LLC; *U.S. Private*, pg. 3417
EXEL USA INC.—See Exel Composites Oyj; *Int'l*, pg. 2582
EXTENDED STAY AMERICA, INC.—See Blackstone Inc.; *U.S. Public*, pg. 350
EXTENDED STAY AMERICA, INC.—See Starwood Capital Group Global I, LLC; *U.S. Public*, pg. 3789
EXTENDED STAY HOTELS LLC—See Centerbridge Partners, L.P.; *U.S. Private*, pg. 814
E-Z-8 MOTEL INC.; *U.S. Private*, pg. 1303
FABER KOMPLEKS SDN. BHD.—See Hotel Royal Limited; *Int'l*, pg. 3489
FAIRFIELD FMC, LLC—See Marriott International, Inc.; *U.S. Public*, pg. 1370
FAIRFIELD WILLIAMSBURG—See Travel & Leisure Co.; *U.S. Public*, pg. 2185
FAIRMONT HOTELS & RESORTS INC.—See Accor S.A.; *Int'l*, pg. 91
THE FAIRMONT SONOMA MISSION INN & SPA—See Accor S.A.; *Int'l*, pg. 91
FAIRWAYS INC.—See Sunburst Hospitality Corporation; *U.S. Private*, pg. 3865
THE FAIRWAYS RESORTS OF PALM AIRE—See Travel & Leisure Co.; *U.S. Public*, pg. 2186
FAR GLORY HOTEL CO., LTD.; *Int'l*, pg. 2617
FATTAL HOTELS LTD.—See Fattal Holdings (1998) Ltd.; *Int'l*, pg. 2623
FBD HOTELS (IRELAND) LIMITED—See Farmer Business Developments plc; *Int'l*, pg. 2619
FDC INTERNATIONAL HOTELS CORPORATION; *Int'l*, pg. 2628
FIBRAHOTEL; *Int'l*, pg. 2653
FIBRA INN; *Int'l*, pg. 2652
FIELD HOTEL ASSOCIATES; *U.S. Private*, pg. 1503
FIESTA INN INC.—See Rushlake Hotels USA Inc.; *U.S. Private*, pg. 3505
FIRST CHOICE PROPERTIES CORP.—See Sunburst Hospitality Corporation; *U.S. Private*, pg. 3865
FIRST HOTELS AB; *Int'l*, pg. 2684
FIRST SERVE HOSPITALITY GROUP; *U.S. Private*, pg. 1527
FLAGLER SYSTEM INC.; *U.S. Private*, pg. 1539
FOCUS HOSPITALITY SERVICES, LLC—See Focus Enterprises Inc.; *U.S. Private*, pg. 1556
FOMENTO RESORTS & HOTELS LTD; *Int'l*, pg. 2724
FONTAINEBLEAU HOTEL; *U.S. Private*, pg. 1559
FORBES HAMILTON MANAGEMENT COMPANY; *U.S. Private*, pg. 1562
FORGES THERMAL S.A.—See Groupe Partouche S.A.; *Int'l*, pg. 3109
FORMULA1 PTY—See Accor S.A.; *Int'l*, pg. 91
FORT LAUDERDALE HOSPITAL, INC.—See Universal Health Services, Inc.; *U.S. Public*, pg. 2257
FORTYSEVEN PARK STREET LIMITED—See Marriott Vacations Worldwide Corporation; *U.S. Public*, pg. 1373
FORWARD LODGING—See Forward Corporation; *U.S. Private*, pg. 1577
FOSHAN FORTUNA HOTEL COMPANY LIMITED—See Capital Estate Limited; *Int'l*, pg. 1310
FOSUN TOURISM GROUP.—See Fosun International Limited; *Int'l*, pg. 2751
FOUNTAINHEAD DEVELOPMENT INC.; *U.S. Private*, pg. 1581
FOUNTAINHEAD DEVELOPMENT, LLC; *U.S. Private*, pg. 1581
FOUR POINTS BY SHERATON - PHILADELPHIA AIRPORT—See Marriott International, Inc.; *U.S. Public*, pg. 1372
FOUR POINTS BY SHERATON PORTLAND EAST—See Marriott International, Inc.; *U.S. Public*, pg. 1372
FOUR POINTS BY SHERATON—See Marriott International, Inc.; *U.S. Public*, pg. 1372
FOUR POINTS BY SHERATON SUITES TAMPA AIRPORT WESTSHORE—See Marriott International, Inc.; *U.S. Public*, pg. 1372
FOUR POINTS BY SHERATON WAKEFIELD BOSTON HOTEL & CONFERENCE CENTER—See Marriott International, Inc.; *U.S. Public*, pg. 1372
FOUR SEASONS HOTEL ATLANTA—See Cascade Investment LLC; *U.S. Private*, pg. 779
FOUR SEASONS HOTEL AUSTIN—See Cascade Investment LLC; *U.S. Private*, pg. 779
FOUR SEASONS HOTEL BOSTON—See Cascade Investment LLC; *U.S. Private*, pg. 779
FOUR SEASONS HOTEL CHICAGO—See Cascade Invest-

N.A.I.C.S. INDEX

721110 — HOTELS (EXCEPT CASI...

ment LLC; *U.S. Private*, pg. 779
FOUR SEASONS HOTEL HOUSTON—See Cascade Investment LLC; *U.S. Private*, pg. 779
FOUR SEASONS HOTEL ISTANBUL—See Cascade Investment LLC; *U.S. Private*, pg. 779
FOUR SEASONS HOTEL LAS VEGAS—See Cascade Investment LLC; *U.S. Private*, pg. 779
FOUR SEASONS HOTEL LONDON—See Cascade Investment LLC; *U.S. Private*, pg. 779
FOUR SEASONS HOTEL LOS ANGELES AT BEVERLY HILLS—See Cascade Investment LLC; *U.S. Private*, pg. 779
FOUR SEASONS HOTEL MEXICO, D.F.—See Cascade Investment LLC; *U.S. Private*, pg. 779
FOUR SEASONS HOTEL MILANO—See Cascade Investment LLC; *U.S. Private*, pg. 779
FOUR SEASONS HOTEL NEW YORK—See Cascade Investment LLC; *U.S. Private*, pg. 779
FOUR SEASONS HOTEL PHILADELPHIA—See Cascade Investment LLC; *U.S. Private*, pg. 779
FOUR SEASONS HOTEL RITZ LISBON—See Cascade Investment LLC; *U.S. Private*, pg. 779
FOUR SEASONS HOTELS INC.—See Cascade Investment LLC; *U.S. Private*, pg. 779
FOUR SEASONS HOTEL SINGAPORE—See Cascade Investment LLC; *U.S. Private*, pg. 779
FOUR SEASONS HOTELS & RESORTS—See Cascade Investment LLC; *U.S. Private*, pg. 780
FOUR SEASONS HOTEL TORONTO—See Cascade Investment LLC; *U.S. Private*, pg. 780
FOUR SEASONS HOTEL VANCOUVER—See Cascade Investment LLC; *U.S. Private*, pg. 780
FOUR SEASONS HOTEL WASHINGTON, DC—See Cascade Investment LLC; *U.S. Private*, pg. 780
FOUR SEASONS RESORT AVIARA—See Cascade Investment LLC; *U.S. Private*, pg. 780
FOUR SEASONS RESORT BALI—See Cascade Investment LLC; *U.S. Private*, pg. 780
FOUR SEASONS RESORT & CLUB DALLAS—See Cascade Investment LLC; *U.S. Private*, pg. 780
FOUR SEASONS RESORT HUALALAI—See Cascade Investment LLC; *U.S. Private*, pg. 780
FOUR SEASONS RESORT MAUI—See Cascade Investment LLC; *U.S. Private*, pg. 780
FOUR SEASONS RESORT NEVIS—See Cascade Investment LLC; *U.S. Private*, pg. 780
FOUR SEASONS RESORT PALM BEACH—See Cascade Investment LLC; *U.S. Private*, pg. 780
FOUR SEASONS RESORT SANTA BARBARA—See Cascade Investment LLC; *U.S. Private*, pg. 780
FOUR SEASONS RESORT SCOTTSDALE AT TROON NORTH—See Braemar Hotels & Resorts, Inc.; *U.S. Public*, pg. 379
FRAGRANCE HOTEL MANAGEMENT PTE LTD—See Fragrance Group Limited; *Int'l*, pg. 2758
FRANKFURT MARRIOTT HOTELMANAGEMENT GMBH—See Marriott International, Inc.; *U.S. Public*, pg. 1370
FRANTOUR GROUP—See Accor S.A.; *Int'l*, pg. 91
FRIDAYS HOLDINGS, INC.—See Boulevard Holdings, Inc.; *Int'l*, pg. 1119
FUJIO FOOD SYSTEM U.S.A. CO., LTD.—See Fujio Food Group Inc.; *Int'l*, pg. 2830
FUJITA KANKO INC.; *Int'l*, pg. 2831
FX HOTELS GROUP, INC.; *Int'l*, pg. 2859
GAI BEACH HOTEL; *Int'l*, pg. 2868
GALADARI HOTELS (LANKA) PLC; *Int'l*, pg. 2870
GALAXY HOTEL SYSTEMS LLC—See Marriott International, Inc.; *U.S. Public*, pg. 1371
GALE SOUTH BEACH & REGENT HOTEL—See Menin Hotels, Inc.; *U.S. Private*, pg. 2666
GARDEN CITY HOTEL INC.; *U.S. Private*, pg. 1643
GARDEN HOTEL SHANGHAI; *Int'l*, pg. 2884
GASPARILLA INN, INC.; *U.S. Private*, pg. 1648
GATHER WORKSPACES, LLC; *U.S. Private*, pg. 1651
GCV SERVICES LIMITED; *Int'l*, pg. 2895
GEMSTONE HOTELS & RESORTS, LLC—See Benchmark Hospitality International Inc.; *U.S. Private*, pg. 524
GENERAL HOTEL MANAGEMENT LTD.; *Int'l*, pg. 2918
GENESAR INC.; *U.S. Private*, pg. 1668
GENO-HAUS STUTTGART GMBH & CO. KG VERWALTUNGSGESELLSCHAFT—See DZ BANK AG Deutsche Zentral-Genossenschaftsbank; *Int'l*, pg. 2244
GENTING INTERNATIONAL JAPAN CO. LTD—See Genting Berhad; *Int'l*, pg. 2928
GENTING MALAYSIA BERHAD—See Genting Berhad; *Int'l*, pg. 2928
THE GEORGIAN HOTEL—See BLVD Companies; *U.S. Private*, pg. 600
THE GEORGIAN HOTEL—See ESI Ventures LLC; *U.S. Private*, pg. 1426
THE GEORGIAN HOTEL—See Global Mutual Properties Limited; *Int'l*, pg. 2999
GERRY WEBER SPORTPARK HOTEL GMBH & CO. KG—See GERRY WEBER International AG; *Int'l*, pg. 2944
GHO CRETEIL LE LAC SAS—See Eurazeo SE; *Int'l*, pg. 2528

GHO GRENOBLE NORD VOREPPE SAS—See Eurazeo SE; *Int'l*, pg. 2529
GHO REIMS PARC DES EXPOSITIONS SAS—See Eurazeo SE; *Int'l*, pg. 2529
GHOTEL DEUTSCHLAND GMBH—See Art-Invest Real Estate Management GmbH & Co. KG; *Int'l*, pg. 580
GHOTEL GERMANY GMBH—See Art-Invest Real Estate Management GmbH & Co. KG; *Int'l*, pg. 580
GHOTEL HOTEL UND BOARDINGHAUS DEUTSCHLAND GMBH—See Art-Invest Real Estate Management GmbH & Co. KG; *Int'l*, pg. 580
GHO VITRY SUR SEINE A86 BORDS DE SEINE SAS—See Eurazeo SE; *Int'l*, pg. 2529
GINZA RENOIR CO., LTD.; *Int'l*, pg. 2977
GLACIER PARK, INC.—See Viad Corp.; *U.S. Public*, pg. 2291
GLEN COVE MANSION HOTEL & CONFERENCE CENTER—See Montclair Hotel Investors, Inc.; *U.S. Private*, pg. 2775
GLENWOOD PROPERTIES, INC.—See Fidelity Financial Corporation; *U.S. Private*, pg. 1503
GLH HOTELS LIMITED—See Hong Leong Investment Holdings Pte. Ltd.; *Int'l*, pg. 3468
GLH HOTELS MANAGEMENT (UK) LIMITED—See Hong Leong Investment Holdings Pte. Ltd.; *Int'l*, pg. 3468
GLOBAL PREMIUM HOTELS LIMITED; *Int'l*, pg. 3000
GOLDEN COAST COMPANY; *Int'l*, pg. 3028
GOLDEN HOTEL LIMITED PARTNERSHIP; *U.S. Private*, pg. 1732
GOLDEN PYRAMIDS PLAZA; *Int'l*, pg. 3031
GOLDEN TULIP WARSAW CENTRE HOTEL—See Starwood Capital Group Global I, LLC; *U.S. Private*, pg. 3789
GOLD HILL HOTEL, INC.—See COMSTOCK INC.; *U.S. Public*, pg. 562
GOLD KEY/PHR, LLC; *U.S. Private*, pg. 1728
GOOD-NITE INN INC.; *U.S. Private*, pg. 1738
GRANAT SA; *Int'l*, pg. 3054
GRAND AMERICA HOTELS & RESORTS—See HF Sinclair Corporation; *U.S. Public*, pg. 1034
GRAND CENTRAL (K.L.) SDN. BHD.—See Grand Central Enterprises Bhd.; *Int'l*, pg. 3054
GRAND ELY LODGE LLC; *U.S. Private*, pg. 1752
GRAND ELY LODGE—See Grand Ely Lodge LLC; *U.S. Private*, pg. 1752
GRAND EMPEROR ENTERTAINMENT & HOTEL (MACAU) LIMITED—See Emperor Entertainment Hotel Limited; *Int'l*, pg. 2386
GRAND GENEVA, LLC—See The Marcus Corporation; *U.S. Public*, pg. 2112
GRAND HARBOR MANAGEMENT, LLC—See Icahn Enterprises L.P.; *U.S. Public*, pg. 1084
GRAND HERITAGE HOTEL GROUP, LLC; *U.S. Private*, pg. 1752
GRAND HOLIDAY VILLA KHARTOUM CO. LTD.; *Int'l*, pg. 3055
GRAND HOTEL BUCHAREST SA; *Int'l*, pg. 3055
GRAND HOTEL INTER-CONTINENTAL PARIS SNC; *Int'l*, pg. 3055
GRAND HOTEL, LLC; *U.S. Private*, pg. 1752
GRAND HOTEL - MACKINAC ISLAND—See FAM AB; *Int'l*, pg. 2611
GRAND HOTEL UNION D.D.; *Int'l*, pg. 3055
GRAND HOTEL VICTORIA-JUNGFRAU AG—See AEVIS VICTORIA SA; *Int'l*, pg. 183
GRAND HYATT BERLIN GMBH—See Hyatt Hotels Corporation; *U.S. Public*, pg. 1077
GRAND HYATT SAN ANTONIO, L.L.C.—See Hyatt Hotels Corporation; *U.S. Public*, pg. 1077
GRAND HYATT SEOUL—See Hyatt Hotels Corporation; *U.S. Public*, pg. 1077
GRAND HYATT SF, L.L.C.—See Hyatt Hotels Corporation; *U.S. Public*, pg. 1077
GRAND HYATT SINGAPORE (PTE.) LIMITED—See Hyatt Hotels Corporation; *U.S. Public*, pg. 1077
GRAND ISLAND HOTEL (LANGKAWI) SDN. BHD.—See Grand Central Enterprises Bhd.; *Int'l*, pg. 3054
GRAND PLAZA HOTEL CORPORATION; *Int'l*, pg. 3056
GRAND TETON LODGE COMPANY, INC.—See Vail Resorts, Inc.; *U.S. Public*, pg. 2271
GRAND TORONTO VENTURE, L.P.—See Hyatt Hotels Corporation; *U.S. Public*, pg. 1077
GRAN OPERADORA POSADAS, S.A. DE C.V.—See Grupo Posadas S.A.B. de C.V.; *Int'l*, pg. 3134
GRAVISS HOSPITALITY LIMITED; *Int'l*, pg. 3061
GRAYSHOTT HALL LIMITED—See G. R. (Holdings) plc; *Int'l*, pg. 2864
GREAT CANADIAN CASINOS INC.—See Great Canadian Gaming Corporation; *U.S. Public*, pg. 3063
GREAT EAGLE HOTELS (AUCKLAND) LIMITED—See Great Eagle Holdings Limited; *Int'l*, pg. 3064
GREAT EAGLE HOTELS (CANADA) LIMITED—See Great Eagle Holdings Limited; *Int'l*, pg. 3064
GREAT EAGLE HOTELS (NEW ZEALAND) LIMITED—See Great Eagle Holdings Limited; *Int'l*, pg. 3064
GREATER BAY AREA DYNAMIC GROWTH HOLDINGS LIMITED; *Int'l*, pg. 3067
GREATER BELOIT PUBLISHING CO., INC.—See The Hagadone Corporation; *U.S. Private*, pg. 4041

GREAT WOLF LODGE GRAND MOUND—See Centerbridge Partners, L.P.; *U.S. Public*, pg. 815
GREAT WOLF LODGE OF GRAPEVINE, LLC—See Centerbridge Partners, L.P.; *U.S. Public*, pg. 815
GREAT WOLF LODGE OF KANSAS CITY, LLC—See Centerbridge Partners, L.P.; *U.S. Public*, pg. 815
GREAT WOLF LODGE OF THE CAROLINAS, LLC—See Centerbridge Partners, L.P.; *U.S. Public*, pg. 815
GREAT WOLF LODGE OF TRAVERSE CITY, LLC—See Centerbridge Partners, L.P.; *U.S. Public*, pg. 815
THE GREENBRIER—See Justice Family Group, LLC; *U.S. Private*, pg. 2246
GREEN LAKE RESORT, LLC—See The Marcus Corporation; *U.S. Public*, pg. 2112
GREENLINKS GOLF VILLAS; *U.S. Private*, pg. 1779
GREEN OAKS HOTEL—See Hostmark Hospitality Group; *U.S. Private*, pg. 1988
GREENS CO., LTD.; *Int'l*, pg. 3076
GREENTREE HOSPITALITY GROUP LTD.; *Int'l*, pg. 3077
GREEN WORLD HOTELS; *Int'l*, pg. 3073
GROW ON DEVELOPMENT LIMITED—See Great Eagle Holdings Limited; *Int'l*, pg. 3064
GRUPO HOTELERO SANTA FE, S.A.B. DE C.V.; *Int'l*, pg. 3130
GRUPO POSADAS S.A.B. DE C.V.; *Int'l*, pg. 3134
GRUPO REAL TURISMO S.A. DE C.V.; *Int'l*, pg. 3134
GRZA TURIST A.D.; *Int'l*, pg. 3141
GUAM REEF HOTEL, INC.—See H.I.S. Co., Ltd.; *Int'l*, pg. 3195
GUANGDONG (INTERNATIONAL) HOTEL MANAGEMENT HOLDINGS LIMITED—See GDH Limited; *Int'l*, pg. 2896
GUANGZHOU AGILE HOTEL CO., LTD.—See Agile Group Holdings Limited; *Int'l*, pg. 209
GUANGZHOU LINGNAN GROUP HOLDINGS COMPANY LIMITED; *Int'l*, pg. 3166
GUDOU HOLDINGS LIMITED; *Int'l*, pg. 3171
GUEST SERVICES, INC.; *U.S. Private*, pg. 1810
GUJARAT HOTELS LIMITED; *Int'l*, pg. 3176
GULF COURT HOTEL BUSINESS BAY LLC—See Gulf Hotels Group B.S.C.; *Int'l*, pg. 3180
GULF HOTELS GROUP B.S.C.; *Int'l*, pg. 3180
GULF HOTELS (OMAN) COMPANY LIMITED SAOG; *Int'l*, pg. 3180
GULLWING BEACH RESORT—See SunStream, Inc.; *U.S. Private*, pg. 3873
GUNSTOCK RECREATION AREA; *U.S. Private*, pg. 1818
GUOMAN HOTEL MANAGEMENT (UK) LIMITED—See Hong Leong Investment Holdings Pte. Ltd.; *Int'l*, pg. 3468
GW HOTEL INC.—See Hilton Worldwide Holdings Inc.; *U.S. Public*, pg. 1040
HAGADONE HOSPITALITY INC.—See The Hagadone Corporation; *U.S. Private*, pg. 4041
HAINAN DADONGHAI TOURISM CENTRE (HOLDINGS) CO., LTD.; *Int'l*, pg. 3211
HAKODATE KOKUSAI HOTEL, CO., LTD.; *Int'l*, pg. 3219
HAMBURG MARRIOTT HOTELMANAGEMENT GMBH—See Marriott International, Inc.; *U.S. Public*, pg. 1370
HAMILTON HOTEL PARTNERS LTD—See Pyramid Hotels & Resorts, Inc.; *U.S. Private*, pg. 3310
HAMPTON INN - FOOTHILL RANCH—See Stonebridge Realty Advisors, Inc.; *U.S. Private*, pg. 3827
HAMPTON INN - LAKEWOOD—See Stonebridge Realty Advisors, Inc.; *U.S. Private*, pg. 3827
HAMPTON INN & SUITES - CHERRY CREEK—See Stonebridge Realty Advisors, Inc.; *U.S. Private*, pg. 3827
HANDLERY HOTELS INC.; *U.S. Private*, pg. 1853
HANKYU HANSHIN HOTELS CO., LTD.—See Hankyu Hanshin Holdings Inc.; *Int'l*, pg. 3255
HANWHA DEVELOPMENT CO., LTD.—See Hanwha Group; *Int'l*, pg. 3265
HANWHA HOTELS & RESORTS CO., LTD.—See Hanwha Group; *Int'l*, pg. 3266
HARBOUR GRAND HONG KONG LIMITED—See CK Asset Holdings Limited; *Int'l*, pg. 1635
HARBOUR PLAZA 8 DEGREES LIMITED—See CK Hutchison Holdings Limited; *Int'l*, pg. 1637
HARBOUR PLAZA CHONGQING COMPANY LIMITED—See CK Asset Holdings Limited; *Int'l*, pg. 1635
HARBOUR PLAZA DEGREES LIMITED—See CK Asset Holdings Limited; *Int'l*, pg. 1635
HARBOUR PLAZA HOTEL MANAGEMENT LIMITED—See CK Asset Holdings Limited; *Int'l*, pg. 1635
HARBOUR PLAZA METROPOLIS LIMITED—See CK Asset Holdings Limited; *Int'l*, pg. 1635
HARBOUR PLAZA RESORT CITY LIMITED—See CK Asset Holdings Limited; *Int'l*, pg. 1635
HARDAGE HOTELS V LLC—See Hardage Investments, Inc.; *U.S. Private*, pg. 1862
HARDAGE INVESTMENTS, INC.; *U.S. Private*, pg. 1862
HARRAH'S COUNCIL BLUFFS LLC—See VICI Properties Inc.; *U.S. Public*, pg. 2295
HARRAH'S JOLIET LANDCO LLC—See VICI Properties Inc.; *U.S. Public*, pg. 2295
HARRAH'S LAKE TAHOE LLC—See VICI Properties Inc.; *U.S. Public*, pg. 2295
HARRINGTON HOUSE BEACHFRONT BED & BREAKFAST INN; *U.S. Private*, pg. 1868

721110 — HOTELS (EXCEPT CASI...

HARRIS RANCH INN & RESTAURANT—See Harris Farms, Inc.; *U.S. Private*, pg. 1869
HARRY E. FERRYMAN ENTERPRISES; *U.S. Private*, pg. 1871
HARVEST STAR INTERNATIONAL LIMITED—See Great Eagle Holdings Limited; *Int'l*, pg. 3064
HAWAII PRINCE HOTEL WAIKIKI—See *U.S. Private*, pg. 1881
HAYLEYS LEISURE PLC; *Int'l*, pg. 3291
HBE ADAM'S RIB—See HBE Corporation; *U.S. Private*, pg. 1887
HBE CORPORATION; *U.S. Private*, pg. 1887
HDG ASSOCIATES—See Hyatt Hotels Corporation; *U.S. Public*, pg. 1077
HD HOTEL LLC—See Meyer Jabara Hotels, LLC; *U.S. Private*, pg. 2692
HEARTLAND HOTEL CORP.; *U.S. Private*, pg. 1900
HEI HOSPITALITY, LLC; *U.S. Private*, pg. 1904
THE HELMSLEY SANDCASTLE—See Helmsley Enterprises, Inc.; *U.S. Private*, pg. 1912
HELNAN INTERNATIONAL HOTELS A/S; *Int'l*, pg. 3338
HEMSTREET DEVELOPMENT CORP.; *U.S. Private*, pg. 1913
HENGYI INTERNATIONAL INDUSTRIES GROUP, INC.; *Int'l*, pg. 3347
HERSHA HOSPITALITY MANAGEMENT CO.—See Hersha Enterprises, Ltd.; *U.S. Private*, pg. 1926
HETMOS MOSTAR HOTELI D.D.; *Int'l*, pg. 3365
HHC TRS BALTIMORE II LLC—See Ashford Hospitality Trust, Inc.; *U.S. Public*, pg. 211
HHLP BRIDGEWATER ASSOCIATES, LLC—See KSL Capital Partners, LLC; *U.S. Private*, pg. 2355
HHLP PRESCOTT ASSOCIATES, LLC—See KSL Capital Partners, LLC; *U.S. Private*, pg. 2355
HHLP WHITE PLAINS ASSOCIATES, LLC—See KSL Capital Partners, LLC; *U.S. Private*, pg. 2355
HHR HOLDINGS PTY LTD.—See Host Hotels & Resorts, Inc.; *U.S. Public*, pg. 1055
HICKEL INVESTMENT COMPANY INC.; *U.S. Private*, pg. 1933
HI DEVELOPMENT CORPORATION; *U.S. Private*, pg. 1931
HIHCL HP AMSTERDAM AIRPORT B.V.—See Hyatt Hotels Corporation; *U.S. Public*, pg. 1077
HIKKADUWA BEACH RESORT PLC—See Citrus Leisure PLC; *Int'l*, pg. 1626
HILTON CANADA INC.—See Hilton Worldwide Holdings Inc.; *U.S. Public*, pg. 1040
HILTON DENVER INVERNESS—See Commune Hotels & Resorts, LLC; *U.S. Private*, pg. 987
HILTON EL CONQUISTADOR GOLF & TENNIS RESORT—See Hilton Worldwide Holdings Inc.; *U.S. Public*, pg. 1041
HILTON GARDEN INN - ANCHORAGE—See Stonebridge Realty Advisors, Inc.; *U.S. Private*, pg. 3827
HILTON GARDEN INN - CHERRY CREEK—See Stonebridge Realty Advisors, Inc.; *U.S. Private*, pg. 3827
HILTON GARDEN INN - GARDEN GROVE—See Stonebridge Realty Advisors, Inc.; *U.S. Private*, pg. 3827
THE HILTON GARDEN INN—See Hilton Worldwide Holdings Inc.; *U.S. Public*, pg. 1041
HILTON HAWAIIAN VILLAGE—See Hilton Worldwide Holdings Inc.; *U.S. Public*, pg. 1041
HILTON HOTELS OF AUSTRALIA (MELBOURNE) PTY. LTD.—See Hilton Worldwide Holdings Inc.; *U.S. Public*, pg. 1040
HILTON HOTELS OF AUSTRALIA PTY. LTD.—See Hilton Worldwide Holdings Inc.; *U.S. Public*, pg. 1040
HILTON HOUSTON HOBBY AIRPORT HOTEL—See Gal-Tex Hotel Corporation; *U.S. Private*, pg. 1635
HILTON INTERNATIONAL HOTELS (UK) LIMITED—See Hilton Worldwide Holdings Inc.; *U.S. Public*, pg. 1040
HILTON INTERNATIONAL (SWITZERLAND) GMBH—See Hilton Worldwide Holdings Inc.; *U.S. Public*, pg. 1041
HILTON INTERNATIONAL WIEN GMBH—See Hilton Worldwide Holdings Inc.; *U.S. Public*, pg. 1041
HILTON LONDON—See Clarke Inc.; *Int'l*, pg. 1650
HILTON MALTA LIMITED—See Hilton Worldwide Holdings Inc.; *U.S. Public*, pg. 1041
HILTON MCLEAN TYSONS CORNER—See Hilton Worldwide Holdings Inc.; *U.S. Public*, pg. 1041
HILTON MIAMI DOWNTOWN—See Argent Ventures, LLC; *U.S. Private*, pg. 320
HILTON MUNICH AIRPORT HOTEL MANAGE GMBH—See Hilton Worldwide Holdings Inc.; *U.S. Public*, pg. 1041
HILTON NAIROBI LIMITED—See Hilton Worldwide Holdings Inc.; *U.S. Public*, pg. 1041
HILTON NEW YORK—See Hilton Worldwide Holdings Inc.; *U.S. Public*, pg. 1041
HILTON OF PANAMA LIMITED—See Hilton Worldwide Holdings Inc.; *U.S. Public*, pg. 1041
HILTON ON THE PARK MELBOURNE—See Brookfield Corporation; *Int'l*, pg. 1189
HILTON PALM SPRINGS HOTEL & RESORT—See Hilton Worldwide Holdings Inc.; *U.S. Public*, pg. 1041
HILTON SAN DIEGO LLC—See Hilton Worldwide Holdings Inc.; *U.S. Public*, pg. 1041
HILTON SINGER ISLAND OCEANFRONT/PALM BEACHES RESORT—See Hilton Worldwide Holdings Inc.; *U.S. Public*, pg. 1041

HILTON VIENNA DANUBE—See Hilton Worldwide Holdings Inc.; *U.S. Public*, pg. 1041
H.I.S. HOTEL HOLDINGS CO., LTD.—See H.I.S. Co., Ltd.; *Int'l*, pg. 3195
THE HISTORIC CRAGS LODGE—See Apollo Global Management, Inc.; *U.S. Public*, pg. 150
THE HISTORIC CRAGS LODGE—See Reverence Capital Partners LLC; *U.S. Private*, pg. 3415
HLV LTD.; *Int'l*, pg. 3431
HMC GATEWAY, INC.—See Host Hotels & Resorts, Inc.; *U.S. Public*, pg. 1055
HMC NGL LP—See Host Hotels & Resorts, Inc.; *U.S. Public*, pg. 1055
HOANG KIM TAY NGUYEN GROUP JOINT STOCK COMPANY; *Int'l*, pg. 3436
HOBBS & CURRY FAMILY LIMITED PARTNERSHIP; *U.S. Private*, pg. 1958
HOI AN TOURIST SERVICE JOINT STOCK COMPANY; *Int'l*, pg. 3442
HOLIDAY INN AUSTIN MIDTOWN—See Jones Lang LaSalle Incorporated; *U.S. Public*, pg. 1204
HOLIDAY INN EXPRESS BOSTON—See KSL Capital Partners, LLC; *U.S. Private*, pg. 2355
HOLIDAY INN EXPRESS - DENVER INTERNATIONAL AIRPORT—See Stonebridge Realty Advisors, Inc.; *U.S. Private*, pg. 3827
HOLIDAY INN OAKVILLE CENTRE HOTEL—See Clarke Inc.; *Int'l*, pg. 1650
HOLIDAY ISLE RESORT & MARINA; *U.S. Private*, pg. 1963
HOMEINNS HOTEL GROUP; *Int'l*, pg. 3455
HOMEWOOD SUITES - ANCHORAGE—See Stonebridge Realty Advisors, Inc.; *U.S. Private*, pg. 3827
HOMEWOOD SUITES BY HILTON—See Hilton Worldwide Holdings Inc.; *U.S. Public*, pg. 1041
HONG KONG COSCO HOTEL MANAGEMENT CO., LTD.—See China COSCO Shipping Corporation Limited; *Int'l*, pg. 1492
HORIZON HOTELS LTD.; *U.S. Private*, pg. 1981
HORSESHOE BOSSIER CITY PROP LLC—See VICI Properties Inc.; *U.S. Public*, pg. 2295
HORSESHOE COUNCIL BLUFFS LLC—See VICI Properties Inc.; *U.S. Public*, pg. 2295
HORSESHOE TUNICA LLC—See VICI Properties Inc.; *U.S. Public*, pg. 2295
HORSKY HOTEL TATRA, SPOL. S.R.O.—See Terex Corporation; *U.S. Public*, pg. 2019
HOSHINO RESORTS INC.; *Int'l*, pg. 3483
HOSHINO RESORTS OMO7 ASAHIKAWA HOTEL—See Hoshino Resorts Inc.; *Int'l*, pg. 3483
HOSPITALITY MARKETING CONCEPTS, INC.—See Hospitality Marketing Concepts, Inc.; *U.S. Private*, pg. 1987
HOSPITALITY PARTNERS; *U.S. Private*, pg. 1987
HOSPITALITY SPECIALISTS, INC.; *U.S. Private*, pg. 1988
HOTEIS OTHON S.A.; *Int'l*, pg. 3487
HOTEL 101 MANAGEMENT CORPORATION—See DoubleDragon Corporation; *Int'l*, pg. 2181
HOTEL AL KHOZAMA—See Chow Tai Fook Enterprises Limited; *Int'l*, pg. 1585
HOTEL ARCTIC A/S—See Air Greenland A/S; *Int'l*, pg. 238
HOTEL ARTS BARCELONA—See Marriott International, Inc.; *U.S. Public*, pg. 1371
HOTEL BELA LADA A.D.; *Int'l*, pg. 3487
HOTELBIRD GMBH—See 029 Group SE; *Int'l*, pg. 1
HOTEL BOSNA A.D. BANJA LUKA; *Int'l*, pg. 3487
HOTEL CAMPOS DE GUADALMINA S.L.—See Barcelo Corporacion Empresarial S.A.; *Int'l*, pg. 859
HOTEL CHANCELLOR @ ORCHARD PTE. LTD.—See Hotel Grand Central Limited; *Int'l*, pg. 3487
HOTEL CHINZANSO TOKYO—See Fujita Kanko Inc.; *Int'l*, pg. 2831
HOTEL CLUB ESTIVAL 2002 SA; *Int'l*, pg. 3487
HOTEL CORPORATION OF INDIA LIMITED—See Air India Limited; *Int'l*, pg. 238
HOTEL CRESCENT COURT—See Chow Tai Fook Enterprises Limited; *Int'l*, pg. 1585
HOTEL DEL CORONADO—See KSL Capital Partners, LLC; *U.S. Private*, pg. 2355
HOTEL DEVELOPERS (LANKA) PLC; *Int'l*, pg. 3487
HOTEL DU PONT COMPANY—See The Buccini/Pollin Group, Inc.; *U.S. Private*, pg. 4002
HOTELERA ADMINISTRADORA DE MONTERREY, S.A. DE C. V.—See Grupo Posadas S.A.B. de C.V.; *Int'l*, pg. 3134
HOTELERA INMOBILIARIA DE MONCLOVA, S.A. DE C.V.—See Grupo Posadas S.A.B. de C.V.; *Int'l*, pg. 3134
HOTELES BESTPRICE S.A.; *Int'l*, pg. 3489
HOTELES CITY EXPRESS, S.A.B. DE C.V.; *Int'l*, pg. 3489
HOTEL FLORA A.S.; *Int'l*, pg. 3487
HOTEL FUERTEVENTURA PLAYA, S.L—See Barcelo Corporacion Empresarial S.A.; *Int'l*, pg. 859
HOTEL GOLUBACKI GRAD A.D.; *Int'l*, pg. 3487
HOTEL GRAND CENTRAL LIMITED; *Int'l*, pg. 3487
HOTEL GRAND CHANCELLOR (ADELAIDE) PTY. LIMITED—See Hotel Grand Central Limited; *Int'l*, pg. 3487
HOTEL GRAND CHANCELLOR (AUCKLAND CITY) LIMITED—See Hotel Grand Central Limited; *Int'l*, pg. 3487
HOTEL GRAND CHANCELLOR (BRISBANE) PTY.

LIMITED—See Hotel Grand Central Limited; *Int'l*, pg. 3487
HOTEL GRAND CHANCELLOR (HOBART) PTY. LIMITED—See Hotel Grand Central Limited; *Int'l*, pg. 3487
HOTEL GRAND CHANCELLOR (LAUNCESTON) PTY. LIMITED—See Hotel Grand Central Limited; *Int'l*, pg. 3487
HOTEL GRAND CHANCELLOR (MELBOURNE) PTY. LIMITED—See Hotel Grand Central Limited; *Int'l*, pg. 3488
HOTEL GRAND CHANCELLOR (PALM COVE) PTY. LIMITED—See Hotel Grand Central Limited; *Int'l*, pg. 3488
HOTEL GRAND CHANCELLOR (TOWNSVILLE) PTY. LIMITED—See Hotel Grand Central Limited; *Int'l*, pg. 3488
HOTEL GROUP INTERNATIONAL, INC.; *U.S. Private*, pg. 1989
HOTEL HDC CO., LTD.—See HDC Hyundai Development Company; *Int'l*, pg. 3300
HOTEL HOLIDAY GARDEN; *Int'l*, pg. 3488
HOTEL HUM D.O.O.—See Adris Grupa d.d.; *Int'l*, pg. 153
HOTEL HYUNDAI CO., LTD.—See Hahn & Company; *Int'l*, pg. 3208
HOTEL HYUNDAI ULSAN—See Hahn & Company; *Int'l*, pg. 3208
HOTELI BERNARDIN D.D.; *Int'l*, pg. 3489
HOTELI DUBROVACKA RIVIJERA D.D.—See Adris Grupa d.d.; *Int'l*, pg. 153
HOTELI MAESTRAL D.D; *Int'l*, pg. 3489
HOTELI-METROPOL AD—See Fersped A.D.; *Int'l*, pg. 2646
HOTEL INTERNATIONAL DE LYON S.A.; *Int'l*, pg. 3488
HOTELI VODICE D.D.; *Int'l*, pg. 3489
HOTEL MANAGEMENT INTERNATIONAL CO., LTD.; *Int'l*, pg. 3488
HOTEL MAX; *U.S. Private*, pg. 1989
HOTEL METROPOLE SAM; *Int'l*, pg. 3488
HOTEL METROPOLITAN NAGANO CO., LTD.—See East Japan Railway Company; *Int'l*, pg. 2270
HOTEL METROPOLITAN TOKYO—See East Japan Railway Company; *Int'l*, pg. 2270
HOTEL MOSKVA BELGRADE; *Int'l*, pg. 3488
HOTEL NARVIK A.D.; *Int'l*, pg. 3488
HOTEL NEWGRAND CO., LTD.; *Int'l*, pg. 3488
HOTEL NEW HANKYU KOCHI CO., LTD.—See Hankyu Hanshin Holdings Inc.; *Int'l*, pg. 3255
HOTEL NEWMARKET PTY LTD—See Reading International, Inc.; *U.S. Public*, pg. 1768
THE HOTEL OF LAN KWAI FONG LIMITED—See Far East Consortium International Limited; *Int'l*, pg. 2615
HOTEL OKURA ENTERPRISE CO., LTD.—See Hotel Okura Co., Ltd.; *Int'l*, pg. 3488
HOTEL OKURA FUKUOKA—See Hotel Okura Co., Ltd.; *Int'l*, pg. 3488
HOTEL OKURA KOBE—See Hotel Okura Co., Ltd.; *Int'l*, pg. 3488
HOTEL OKURA NIIGATA—See Hotel Okura Co., Ltd.; *Int'l*, pg. 3488
HOTEL OKURA SAPPORO—See Hotel Okura Co., Ltd.; *Int'l*, pg. 3488
HOTEL OKURA TOKYO—See Hotel Okura Co., Ltd.; *Int'l*, pg. 3488
HOTELOPIA SL—See Canada Pension Plan Investment Board; *Int'l*, pg. 1279
HOTELOPIA SL—See Cinven Limited; *Int'l*, pg. 1612
HOTEL PALAS A.D. BANJA LUKA; *Int'l*, pg. 3488
HOTEL POLANA LTDA—See Aga Khan Development Network; *Int'l*, pg. 199
HOTEL PRAG A.D.; *Int'l*, pg. 3488
HOTEL PRIJEDOR A.D.; *Int'l*, pg. 3488
HOTEL REGINA PARIS S.A.; *Int'l*, pg. 3489
HOTEL ROUGE—See Pebblebrook Hotel Trust; *U.S. Public*, pg. 1660
HOTEL ROYAL @ QUEENS (SINGAPORE) PTE LTD—See Hotel Royal Limited; *Int'l*, pg. 3489
HOTELS FOR HOPE, INC.—See Liberty Media Corporation; *U.S. Public*, pg. 1311
HOTELS MANAGEMENT COMPANY INTERNATIONAL SAOG; *Int'l*, pg. 3489
HOTEL UNION SQUARE—See Engage Hospitality LLC; *U.S. Private*, pg. 1397
HOTEL U PARKU, S.R.O.—See CPI Property Group, S.A.; *Int'l*, pg. 1825
HOTEL WASHINGTON, INC.—See Dubai World Corporation; *Int'l*, pg. 2222
HOTEL YOUNTVILLE—See Braemar Hotels & Resorts, Inc.; *U.S. Public*, pg. 379
HOTUSA HOTELS SA; *Int'l*, pg. 3490
HOUSTON HOTEL ASSOCIATES L.P., L.L.P—See Sotherly Hotels Inc.; *U.S. Public*, pg. 1910
HOWARD HOTELS LTD.; *Int'l*, pg. 3493
HOYA RESORT HOTEL GROUP; *Int'l*, pg. 3498
HPL HOTELS & RESORTS PTE LTD—See Hotel Properties Limited; *Int'l*, pg. 3488
HR MC HOTEL COMPANY, S. DE R.L. DE C.V.—See Hyatt Hotels Corporation; *U.S. Public*, pg. 1077
H.S. INDIA LTD.; *Int'l*, pg. 3196

N.A.I.C.S. INDEX 721110 — HOTELS (EXCEPT CASI...

N.A.I.C.S. Index

HT-315 TRUMBULL STREET ASSOCIATES, LLC—See KSL Capital Partners, LLC; *U.S. Private*, pg. 2355
HTH CORPORATION; *U.S. Private*, pg. 1999
HTP FONTANA A.D.; *Int'l*, pg. 3508
HTP OREBIC D.D.; *Int'l*, pg. 3509
H.T.U.P. PARK A.D.; *Int'l*, pg. 3196
HUANGSHAN XIHAI HOTEL CO., LTD.—See Huangshan Tourism Development Co., Ltd.; *Int'l*, pg. 3513
HUANGSHAN YUCHENG CROWNE PLAZA HOTELS & RESORTS LTD.—See Huangshan Tourism Development Co., Ltd.; *Int'l*, pg. 3513
HUATIAN HOTEL GROUP CO., LTD.; *Int'l*, pg. 3514
HUDSON LEASECO LLC—See SBEEG Holdings, LLC; *U.S. Private*, pg. 3559
HUNAS HOLDINGS PLC; *Int'l*, pg. 3534
HUNT VALLEY COURTYARD, INC.—See Marriott International, Inc.; *U.S. Public*, pg. 1370
HUP BALKAN A.D.; *Int'l*, pg. 3537
HUP-ZAGREB INC; *Int'l*, pg. 3538
HUT ADUNA D.D.; *Int'l*, pg. 3540
HUTCHISON HOTEL HONG KONG LIMITED—See CK Asset Holdings Limited; *Int'l*, pg. 1635
HV GLOBAL GROUP, INC.—See Marriott Vacations Worldwide Corporation; *U.S. Public*, pg. 1373
H WORLD GROUP LIMITED; *Int'l*, pg. 3191
HYATT ARCADE, L.L.C.—See Hyatt Hotels Corporation; *U.S. Public*, pg. 1077
HYATT CRYSTAL CITY, L.L.C.—See Hyatt Hotels Corporation; *U.S. Public*, pg. 1077
HYATT HOTELS CORPORATION OF MARYLAND—See Hyatt Hotels Corporation; *U.S. Public*, pg. 1077
HYATT HOTELS CORPORATION; *U.S. Public*, pg. 1076
HYATT HOTELS OF CANADA, INC.—See Hyatt Hotels Corporation; *U.S. Public*, pg. 1077
HYATT INTERNATIONAL (EUROPE AFRICA MIDDLE EAST) LLC—See Hyatt Hotels Corporation; *U.S. Public*, pg. 1078
HYATT INTERNATIONAL (OSAKA) CORPORATION—See Hyatt Hotels Corporation; *U.S. Public*, pg. 1078
HYATT INTERNATIONAL - SOUTHWEST ASIA, LIMITED—See Hyatt Hotels Corporation; *U.S. Public*, pg. 1078
HYATT MINNEAPOLIS, LLC—See Hyatt Hotels Corporation; *U.S. Public*, pg. 1078
HYATT REGENCY CAMBRIDGE—See Hyatt Hotels Corporation; *U.S. Public*, pg. 1078
HYATT REGENCY COLOGNE GMBH—See Hyatt Hotels Corporation; *U.S. Public*, pg. 1078
HYATT REGENCY COLUMBUS; *U.S. Private*, pg. 2016
HYATT REGENCY ORLANDO—See Ares Management Corporation; *U.S. Public*, pg. 191
HYATT REGENCY ORLANDO—See RIDA Development Corp.; *U.S. Private*, pg. 3431
HYATT REGENCY OSAKA—See Hoshino Resorts Inc.; *Int'l*, pg. 3483
HYATT SERVICES GMBH—See Hyatt Hotels Corporation; *U.S. Public*, pg. 1078
IA LODGING DENVER CITY CENTER, L.L.C.—See XENIA HOTELS & RESORTS, INC.; *U.S. Public*, pg. 2386
IA LODGING GARDEN GROVE HARBOR L.L.C.—See XENIA HOTELS & RESORTS, INC.; *U.S. Public*, pg. 2386
IA LODGING PITTSBURGH PENN TRS DST—See XENIA HOTELS & RESORTS, INC.; *U.S. Public*, pg. 2386
IA URBAN HOTELS HOUSTON TRS LIMITED PARTNERSHIP—See XENIA HOTELS & RESORTS, INC.; *U.S. Public*, pg. 2386
IA URBAN HOTELS WASHINGTON DC FRANKLIN TRS, L.L.C.—See XENIA HOTELS & RESORTS, INC.; *U.S. Public*, pg. 2386
ICAHN NEVADA MANAGEMENT CORP.—See Icahn Enterprises L.P.; *U.S. Public*, pg. 1084
ICON BOROVEC EOOD—See Gek Terna Societe Anonyme Holdings Real Estate Constructions; *Int'l*, pg. 2913
IDA CASON CALLAWAY FOUNDATION; *U.S. Private*, pg. 2034
ILIRIJA D.D.; *Int'l*, pg. 3614
IMPERIAL HOTELS AUSTRIA AG—See Marriott International, Inc.; *U.S. Public*, pg. 1371
INMOBILIARIA HOTELERA DE TOLUCA, S.A. DE C.V.—See Grupo Posadas S.A.B. de C.V.; *Int'l*, pg. 3134
THE INN AT WILDERNESS ROAD, LLC—See UTG, Inc.; *U.S. Public*, pg. 2267
INNER HARMONY PTE LTD—See Fitgenes Australia Pty Ltd.; *Int'l*, pg. 2695
INN HOTEL MACAU LIMITED—See Emperor Entertainment Hotel Limited; *Int'l*, pg. 2386
INNISFREE HOTELS, INC.; *U.S. Private*, pg. 2080
INN OF LAKE CITY INC.; *U.S. Private*, pg. 2080
INN OF NAPLES, LLC; *U.S. Private*, pg. 2080
THE INN ON FIFTH—See Hybridge Commercial Real Estate; *U.S. Private*, pg. 2016
INNS OF AMERICA; *U.S. Private*, pg. 2084
INNSUITES HOTELS, INC.—See InnSuites Hospitality Trust; *U.S. Public*, pg. 1127
INTERCITY HOTEL GMBH—See H World Group Limited; *Int'l*, pg. 3191
INTERNATIONAL GARDEN HOTEL NARITA—See Alpine Grove Partners LLP; *U.S. Private*, pg. 201
INTERNATIONAL GARDEN HOTEL NARITA—See Hoshino Resorts Inc.; *Int'l*, pg. 3483
INTERNATIONAL HOTEL INVESTMENTS P.L.C.—See Corinthia Palace Hotel Company Limited; *Int'l*, pg. 1801
INTERVAL INTERNATIONAL GMBH—See Marriott Vacations Worldwide Corporation; *U.S. Public*, pg. 1373
INVESTACOR - SOCIEDADE GESTORA DE PARTICIPACOES SOCIAIS, S A—See Banco Santander, S.A.; *Int'l*, pg. 825
IONIAN HOTEL ENTERPRISES S.A.—See Alpha Services and Holdings S.A.; *Int'l*, pg. 369
ISLAND INN CO. INC.; *U.S. Private*, pg. 2145
ISLAND LIVING LTD.—See ENL Limited; *Int'l*, pg. 2442
IWATA GRAND HOTEL INC.—See Hamamatsu Photonics K.K.; *Int'l*, pg. 3235
IWF SAN SIMEON PINES, L.P.—See Invest West Financial Corporation; *U.S. Private*, pg. 2131
IZMIR ENTERNASYONAL OTELCILIK ANONIM SIRKETI—See Hilton Worldwide Holdings Inc.; *U.S. Public*, pg. 1041
JADE HOMES RESORT BERHAD—See Gamuda Berhad; *Int'l*, pg. 2879
JADE RESORTS PRIVATE LIMITED—See Country Club Hospitality & Holidays Limited; *Int'l*, pg. 1818
JAZ HOTEL GMBH—See H World Group Limited; *Int'l*, pg. 3191
JHM ENTERPRISES INC.; *U.S. Private*, pg. 2207
JLM VERWALTUNGS GMBH—See Marsh & McLennan Companies, Inc.; *U.S. Public*, pg. 1376
JOHN Q. HAMMONS HOTELS INC.; *U.S. Private*, pg. 2223
JOIE DE VIVRE HOSPITALITY, LLC—See Commune Hotels & Resorts, LLC; *U.S. Private*, pg. 987
JOINT VENTURE ITALKYR CLOSED JOINT STOCK COMPANY—See Hyatt Hotels Corporation; *U.S. Public*, pg. 1078
JR TOKAI HOTELS CO., LTD.—See Central Japan Railway Company; *Int'l*, pg. 1408
JUMBA BAY—See Chow Tai Fook Enterprises Limited; *Int'l*, pg. 1585
JUMEIRAH GROUP LLC—See Dubai Holding LLC; *Int'l*, pg. 2218
JUMEIRAH INTERNATIONAL LLC—See Dubai Holding LLC; *Int'l*, pg. 2218
JUPITER BEACH RESORT & SPA—See Ocean Properties, Ltd.; *U.S. Private*, pg. 2989
JUSTICE FAMILY GROUP, LLC; *U.S. Private*, pg. 2246
JUST SLEEP HUALIEN ZHONGZHENG CO., LTD.—See Formosa International Hotels Corp.; *Int'l*, pg. 2734
JUST SLEEP KAOHSIUNG STATION CO., LTD.—See Formosa International Hotels Corp.; *Int'l*, pg. 2734
JUST SLEEP KAOHSIUNG ZHONGZHENG CO., LTD.—See Formosa International Hotels Corp.; *Int'l*, pg. 2734
JUST SLEEP OSAKA SHINSAIBASHI CO., LTD.—See Formosa International Hotels Corp.; *Int'l*, pg. 2734
JUST SLEEP TAINAN HUSHAN CO., LTD.—See Formosa International Hotels Corp.; *Int'l*, pg. 2734
JUST SLEEP TAIPEI NTU CO., LTD.—See Formosa International Hotels Corp.; *Int'l*, pg. 2734
JUST SLEEP TAIPEI SANCHONG CO., LTD.—See Formosa International Hotels Corp.; *Int'l*, pg. 2734
JUST SLEEP TAIPEI XIMENDING CO., LTD.—See Formosa International Hotels Corp.; *Int'l*, pg. 2734
JUST SLEEP YILAN JIAOXI CO., LTD.—See Formosa International Hotels Corp.; *Int'l*, pg. 2734
KAANAPALI BEACH PROPERTIES, INC.—See KSL Capital Partners, LLC; *U.S. Private*, pg. 2355
KARON PHUKET HOTEL CO., LTD.—See Central Plaza Hotel Public Company Limited; *Int'l*, pg. 1409
KASTEEL VAN BRASSCHAAT NV—See Compass Group PLC; *Int'l*, pg. 1752
KATERINSKA HOTELS S.R.O—See Accor S.A.; *Int'l*, pg. 91
KBHL LLC; *U.S. Private*, pg. 2268
KENNETH M. SEATON ENTERPRISES—See Family Inns of America, Inc.; *U.S. Private*, pg. 1470
KENSINGTON PARK HOTEL—See Engage Hospitality LLC; *U.S. Private*, pg. 1397
KERMIA HOTELS LTD—See Atlantica Hotels & Resorts Ltd; *Int'l*, pg. 676
THE KESSLER ENTERPRISE INC.; *U.S. Private*, pg. 4065
KEY CLUB MIAMI LLC—See Live Nation Entertainment, Inc.; *U.S. Public*, pg. 1329
KIAWAH ISLAND GOLF RESORTS; *U.S. Private*, pg. 2302
KIAWAH PARTNERS; *U.S. Private*, pg. 2302
KING PACIFIC LODGE—See Chow Tai Fook Enterprises Limited; *Int'l*, pg. 1585
THE KINGSBURY PLC—See Hayleys PLC; *Int'l*, pg. 3292
KINSETH HOSPITALITY COMPANY; *U.S. Private*, pg. 2313
KITANO ARMS CORPORATION; *U.S. Private*, pg. 2316
KOHL'S RANCH LODGE—See Apollo Global Management, Inc.; *U.S. Public*, pg. 150
KOHL'S RANCH LODGE—See Reverence Capital Partners LLC; *U.S. Private*, pg. 3415
KOVALAM RESORT PRIVATE LIMITED—See HLV Ltd.; *Int'l*, pg. 3431
THE KOWLOON HOTEL LIMITED—See CK Asset Holdings Limited; *Int'l*, pg. 1635
KRGP INC.—See The Kroger Co.; *U.S. Public*, pg. 2108
KTC KOMMUNIKATIONS- UND TRAININGS-CENTER KONIGSTEIN GMBH—See Commerzbank AG; *Int'l*, pg. 1718
KUWAIT CONTINENTAL HOTEL CO.—See Fouad Alghanim & Sons Group of Companies; *Int'l*, pg. 2753
L1 BAL HARBOUR LLC—See Fosun International Limited; *Int'l*, pg. 2751
LA CHARTREUSE—See Carrefour SA; *Int'l*, pg. 1345
LAFAYETTE PARK HOTEL CORP.—See Woodside Hotels & Resorts; *U.S. Private*, pg. 4560
LAGO MAR PROPERTIES, INC.; *U.S. Private*, pg. 2373
LAGUARDIA ASSOCIATES; *U.S. Private*, pg. 2373
LAGUNA RESORTS & HOTELS PUBLIC COMPANY LIMITED—See Banyan Tree Holdings Ltd.; *Int'l*, pg. 855
LA MADELEINE DE CORPS, INC.—See Holding Le Duff SA; *Int'l*, pg. 3450
LA MANSION DEL RIO INC.; *U.S. Private*, pg. 2369
LANGHAM HOSPITALITY GROUP LIMITED—See Great Eagle Holdings Limited; *Int'l*, pg. 3064
LANGHAM HOTELS INTERNATIONAL LIMITED—See Great Eagle Holdings Limited; *Int'l*, pg. 3064
THE LANGHAM MELBOURNE—See Great Eagle Holdings Limited; *Int'l*, pg. 3064
LANGKAWI HOLIDAY VILLA SDN. BHD.—See Advance Synergy Berhad; *Int'l*, pg. 156
LARKEN INC.; *U.S. Private*, pg. 2392
LARKSPUR RESTAURANT & BAR, LLC—See Vail Resorts, Inc.; *U.S. Public*, pg. 2271
LARRY BLUMBERG & ASSOCIATES; *U.S. Private*, pg. 2392
LASALLE VENTURES ONE LTD.—See Lasalle International Partner; *U.S. Private*, pg. 2395
LASALLE WASHINGTON ONE LESSEE, INC.—See Pebblebrook Hotel Trust; *U.S. Public*, pg. 1660
LAS VEGAS SANDS, LLC—See Las Vegas Sands Corp.; *U.S. Public*, pg. 1293
LAS VENTANAS AL PARAISO—See JTL Capital, LLC; *U.S. Private*, pg. 2242
THE LEADING HOTELS OF THE WORLD, LTD.; *U.S. Private*, pg. 4068
LEATHERSTOCKING CORP.; *U.S. Private*, pg. 2409
LEGALL HOLDINGS, INC.; *U.S. Private*, pg. 2418
LEGENDARY HOLDING, INC.; *U.S. Private*, pg. 2418
LE MERIDIEN ATLANTA PERIMETER—See Marriott International, Inc.; *U.S. Public*, pg. 1371
LE MERIDIEN NEW ORLEANS—See Marriott International, Inc.; *U.S. Public*, pg. 1372
L'ENFANT DC HOTEL LLC—See Stanford Hotels Corporation; *U.S. Private*, pg. 3782
LEON CO.—See Central Security Patrols Co., Ltd.; *Int'l*, pg. 1410
LES VILLAS DE BEL OMBRE LTEE—See ENL Limited; *Int'l*, pg. 2442
LHO ALEXIS LESSEE, L.L.C.—See Pebblebrook Hotel Trust; *U.S. Public*, pg. 1660
LHO VIKING HOTEL, L.L.C.—See Pebblebrook Hotel Trust; *U.S. Public*, pg. 1660
LIDO BEACH RESORT; *U.S. Private*, pg. 2448
LIGHTHOUSE PROPERTIES, LLC—See Blue Beacon International, Inc.; *U.S. Private*, pg. 585
LIMITED LIABILITY COMPANY CYBM VOZNESENKIY HOTEL LEASING—See Marriott International, Inc.; *U.S. Public*, pg. 1370
LIMITED LIABILITY COMPANY "CY GRIBOEDOVA HOTEL LEASING"—See Marriott International, Inc.; *U.S. Public*, pg. 1370
LINCHRIS HOTEL CORP.; *U.S. Private*, pg. 2457
LITTLE AMERICA HOTELS—See HF Sinclair Corporation; *U.S. Public*, pg. 1034
LITTLE DIX BAY—See Chow Tai Fook Enterprises Limited; *Int'l*, pg. 1585
LITTLE PALM ISLAND ASSOCIATES, LTD.—See Noble House Hotels & Resorts, Ltd.; *U.S. Private*, pg. 2932
LIUHUA HOTEL GROUP COMPANY LTD.—See Guangzhou Lingnan Group Holdings Company Limited; *Int'l*, pg. 3166
LJC DEVELOPMENT CORP.—See Loews Corporation; *U.S. Public*, pg. 1340
LLI MANAGEMENT COMPANY, LLC; *U.S. Private*, pg. 2475
LN GARDEN HOTEL COMPANY LTD.—See Guangzhou Lingnan Group Holdings Company Limited; *Int'l*, pg. 3166
THE LODGE AT VAIL—See Vail Resorts, Inc.; *U.S. Public*, pg. 2271
LODGING ENTERPRISES INC.; *U.S. Private*, pg. 2479
LODGING ENTERPRISES, LLC—See American Hotel Income Properties REIT LP; *Int'l*, pg. 422
LODGING RESOURCES, INC.; *U.S. Private*, pg. 2479
LOEWS ANNAPOLIS HOTEL CORP.; *U.S. Private*, pg. 2480
LOEWS HOTELS HOLDING CORPORATION—See Loews Corporation; *U.S. Public*, pg. 1340
LOEWS SANTA MONICA BEACH HOTEL—See Loews Corporation; *U.S. Public*, pg. 1340
LOEWS VANDERBILT PLAZA HOTEL—See Loews Corporation; *U.S. Public*, pg. 1340
THE LONDON WEST HOLLYWOOD HOTEL—See Blackstone Inc.; *U.S. Public*, pg. 351

721110 — HOTELS (EXCEPT CASI...

LONE PINE HOTEL (C) SDN. BHD.—See Eastern & Oriental Berhad; *Int'l*, pg. 2271
LONG BEACH RESORT LTD.—See CIEL Ltd.; *Int'l*, pg. 1605
LOS ABRIGADOS RESORT & SPA—See Apollo Global Management, Inc.; *U.S. Public*, pg. 150
LOS ABRIGADOS RESORT & SPA—See Reverence Capital Partners LLC; *U.S. Private*, pg. 3415
LOST PINES BEVERAGE, LLC—See Hyatt Hotels Corporation; *U.S. Public*, pg. 1078
LOWE HOSPITALITY GROUP—See Lowe Enterprises, Inc.; *U.S. Private*, pg. 2504
LUFTHANSA SEEHEIM GMBH—See Deutsche Lufthansa AG; *Int'l*, pg. 2069
LUFTHANSA TRAINING & CONFERENCE CENTER GMBH—See Deutsche Lufthansa AG; *Int'l*, pg. 2070
LUITPOLDPARK-HOTEL BETRIEBS- UND VERMIETUNGSGESELLSCHAFT MBH—See Erste Group Bank AG; *Int'l*, pg. 2499
LUNA SERVICE S.R.L.—See Gruppo MutuiOnline S.p.A; *Int'l*, pg. 3141
LUXURY HOTELS INTERNATIONAL OF SPAIN S.L.U.—See Marriott International, Inc.; *U.S. Public*, pg. 1371
LVCUT ASSOCIATES, LLC—See Las Vegas Sands Corp.; *U.S. Public*, pg. 1293
LYNNWOOD INNS, INC.—See Hilton Worldwide Holdings Inc.; *U.S. Public*, pg. 1041
MAC CHARLES (INDIA) LIMITED—See Blackstone Inc.; *U.S. Public*, pg. 350
MAGNOLIA HOTELS; *U.S. Private*, pg. 2548
MAGNUSON HOTELS; *U.S. Private*, pg. 2549
MAINSAIL SUITES HOTEL & CONFERENCE CENTER TAMPA—See Mainsail Lodging & Development, LLC; *U.S. Private*, pg. 2553
MAISTRA D.D.—See Adris Grupa d.d.; *Int'l*, pg. 153
MANCHESTER GRAND RESORTS, INC.—See Host Hotels & Resorts, Inc.; *U.S. Public*, pg. 1055
MANTRA GROUP OPERATIONS PTY. LTD.—See Accor S.A.; *Int'l*, pg. 92
MARARA SA—See Accor S.A.; *Int'l*, pg. 92
MARCO BEACH OCEAN RESORT MANAGEMENT INC.; *U.S. Private*, pg. 2571
THE MARCUS CORPORATION; *U.S. Public*, pg. 2111
MARCUS CORPORATION—See The Marcus Corporation; *U.S. Public*, pg. 2112
MARCUS HOTELS ASSOCIATES, INC.—See The Marcus Corporation; *U.S. Public*, pg. 2112
MARCUS MADISON, LLC—See The Marcus Corporation; *U.S. Public*, pg. 2112
MARCUS MANAGEMENT LAS VEGAS, LLC—See The Marcus Corporation; *U.S. Public*, pg. 2112
MARCUS NORTHSTAR, INC.—See The Marcus Corporation; *U.S. Public*, pg. 2112
MARINA BAY SANDS PTE. LTD.—See Las Vegas Sands Corp.; *U.S. Public*, pg. 1293
MARIPOSA MEDSPA; *U.S. Private*, pg. 2576
MARRIOTT HOTEL-BETRIEBSGESELLSCHAFT, MBH—See Marriott International, Inc.; *U.S. Public*, pg. 1371
MARRIOTT HOTEL HOLDING GMBH—See Marriott International, Inc.; *U.S. Public*, pg. 1371
MARRIOTT HOTELS AND RESORTS OF CANADA—See Marriott International, Inc.; *U.S. Public*, pg. 1371
MARRIOTT HOTEL SERVICES, INC.—See Marriott International, Inc.; *U.S. Public*, pg. 1371
MARRIOTT HOTELS INTERNATIONAL B.V.—See Marriott International, Inc.; *U.S. Public*, pg. 1371
MARRIOTT HOTELS INTERNATIONAL LIMITED—See Marriott International, Inc.; *U.S. Public*, pg. 1371
MARRIOTT HOTELS LIMITED—See Marriott International, Inc.; *U.S. Public*, pg. 1371
MARRIOTT HOTELS MANAGEMENT FRANCE SAS—See Marriott International, Inc.; *U.S. Public*, pg. 1371
MARRIOTT HOTELS OF AMSTERDAM, B.V.—See Marriott International, Inc.; *U.S. Public*, pg. 1371
MARRIOTT INTERNATIONAL, INC.; *U.S. Public*, pg. 1370
MATRICA LIMITED—See CK Asset Holdings Limited; *Int'l*, pg. 1635
MAXX HOTEL GMBH—See H World Group Limited; *Int'l*, pg. 3191
MAYFLOWER INN & SPA; *U.S. Private*, pg. 2622
MCARDLE LTD.; *U.S. Private*, pg. 2625
MCCAMLY PLAZA HOTEL—See Grand Heritage Hotel Group, LLC; *U.S. Private*, pg. 1752
MCHD CYPRESS CREEK CORP.—See Sunburst Hospitality Corporation; *U.S. Private*, pg. 3865
MCHD FORT LAUDERDALE CORP.—See Sunburst Hospitality Corporation; *U.S. Private*, pg. 3865
MCH MANAGEMENT INC.—See Sunburst Hospitality Corporation; *U.S. Private*, pg. 3865
MCKIBBON HOTEL MANAGEMENT, INC.; *U.S. Private*, pg. 2638
MCR DEVELOPMENT LLC; *U.S. Private*, pg. 2644
MENGER HOTEL—See Gal-Tex Hotel Corporation; *U.S. Private*, pg. 1635
MENIN HOTELS, INC.; *U.S. Private*, pg. 2666
MENNA DEVELOPMENT & MANAGEMENT, INC.; *U.S. Private*, pg. 2666

MERCURE—See Accor S.A.; *Int'l*, pg. 92
MESA VERDE COMPANY—See Aramark; *U.S. Public*, pg. 176
METRO 29TH STREET ASSOCIATES, LLC—See KSL Capital Partners, LLC; *U.S. Private*, pg. 2355
MEYER JABARA HOTELS, LLC; *U.S. Private*, pg. 2692
MGM GRAND (INTERNATIONAL), PTE—See MGM Resorts International; *U.S. Public*, pg. 1435
MGM GRAND (MACAO) LIMITED—See MGM Resorts International; *U.S. Public*, pg. 1435
MGM RESORTS INTERNATIONAL MARKETING, LTD—See MGM Resorts International; *U.S. Public*, pg. 1435
MHI HOTELS LLC; *U.S. Private*, pg. 2695
MILLENNIUM & COPTHORNE HOTELS LIMITED—See Hong Leong Investment Holdings Pte. Ltd.; *Int'l*, pg. 3468
MILWAUKEE CITY CENTER, LLC—See The Marcus Corporation; *U.S. Public*, pg. 2112
MIRAMAR HOTEL AND INVESTMENT COMPANY, LIMITED—See Henderson Land Development Co. Ltd.; *Int'l*, pg. 3345
MIRAVAL GROUP, LLC—See Hyatt Hotels Corporation; *U.S. Public*, pg. 1078
MIRAVAL RESORT ARIZONA, LLC—See Hyatt Hotels Corporation; *U.S. Public*, pg. 1078
MMI HOTEL GROUP INC.; *U.S. Private*, pg. 2754
THE MONARCH HOTEL & CONFERENCE CENTER; *U.S. Private*, pg. 4080
MONDRIAN LOS ANGELES—See SBEEG Holdings, LLC; *U.S. Private*, pg. 3559
MONTCLAIR HOTEL INVESTORS, INC.; *U.S. Private*, pg. 2775
MONTECASTILLO SPORT CATERING, S.L—See Barcelo Corporacion Empresarial S.A.; *Int'l*, pg. 859
MONTEREY PLAZA HOTEL; *U.S. Private*, pg. 2776
MORGANS HOTEL GROUP CO. LLC—See SBEEG Holdings, LLC; *U.S. Private*, pg. 3559
MOTEL 6 OPERATING L.P.—See Blackstone Inc.; *U.S. Public*, pg. 353
MOUNTAIN LAKE HOTEL—See Gal-Tex Hotel Corporation; *U.S. Private*, pg. 1635
MOUNTAIN MAN RESORTS INC.—See Moore Holdings Inc.; *U.S. Private*, pg. 2780
MOVENPICK HOTELS & RESORTS AG—See Accor S.A.; *Int'l*, pg. 92
MOVENPICK HOTELS & RESORTS MANAGEMENT AG—See Accor S.A.; *Int'l*, pg. 92
MPH HOTELS, INC.; *U.S. Private*, pg. 2804
MRG ATX HOLDINGS, LLC—See Hyatt Hotels Corporation; *U.S. Public*, pg. 1078
MRG CRW HOLDINGS, LLC—See Hyatt Hotels Corporation; *U.S. Public*, pg. 1078
MTUNZINI FOREST LODGE—See Gooderson Leisure Corporation; *Int'l*, pg. 3040
MUNICH AIRPORT MARRIOTT HOTELMANAGEMENT GMBH—See Marriott International, Inc.; *U.S. Public*, pg. 1371
MURANOWSKA SP. Z O.O.—See Accor S.A.; *Int'l*, pg. 92
MURPHCO OF FLORIDA INC.; *U.S. Private*, pg. 2815
MUSSELMAN BROTHERS INC.; *U.S. Private*, pg. 2818
MVCI ASIA PACIFIC PTE. LTD.—See Marriott Vacations Worldwide Corporation; *U.S. Public*, pg. 1374
MVCI HOLIDAYS, S.L.—See Marriott Vacations Worldwide Corporation; *U.S. Public*, pg. 1374
MWH PRESERVATION LTD. PARTNER; *U.S. Private*, pg. 2822
MYSTIC DUNES RESORT & GOLF CLUB—See Apollo Global Management, Inc.; *U.S. Public*, pg. 150
MYSTIC DUNES RESORT & GOLF CLUB—See Reverence Capital Partners LLC; *U.S. Private*, pg. 3415
NAOSHIMA BENESSE—See EQT AB; *Int'l*, pg. 2467
NAOSHIMA CULTURAL VILLAGE CO., LTD.—See EQT AB; *Int'l*, pg. 2467
NAPLES BEACH HOTEL & GOLF CLUB; *U.S. Private*, pg. 2834
NAPLES GRANDE RESORT AND CLUB—See Blackstone Inc.; *U.S. Public*, pg. 352
NATADOLA BAY RESORT LIMITED—See Fiji National Provident Fund; *Int'l*, pg. 2661
NESTOR HOTEL OBJEKT LUDWIGSBURG GMBH—See Aurelius Equity Opportunities SE & Co. KGaA; *Int'l*, pg. 710
NESTOR HOTEL OBJEKT NECKARSULM GMBH—See Aurelius Equity Opportunities SE & Co. KGaA; *Int'l*, pg. 710
NEW CASTLE HOTELS, LLC; *U.S. Private*, pg. 2893
NEW GALAXY ENTERTAINMENT COMPANY LIMITED—See Galaxy Entertainment Group Limited; *Int'l*, pg. 2871
NEW GRAND HOTEL AB—See FAM AB; *Int'l*, pg. 2611
NEW HARRAH'S NORTH KANSAS CITY LLC—See VICI Properties Inc.; *U.S. Public*, pg. 2296
NEW HAVEN HOTEL LLC—See Noble Investment Group, LLC; *U.S. Private*, pg. 2933
NEW HORSESHOE HAMMOND LLC—See VICI Properties Inc.; *U.S. Public*, pg. 2296
NEW LIFE HIKING SPA, INC.; *U.S. Private*, pg. 2898
NEWPORT HARBOR CORPORATION—See Deutsche Bank Aktiengesellschaft; *Int'l*, pg. 2061
NEW SUNCADIA, LLC—See Commune Hotels & Resorts, LLC; *U.S. Private*, pg. 987
NEW WORLD HOTEL MANAGEMENT LIMITED—See Chow Tai Fook Enterprises Limited; *Int'l*, pg. 1585
NICKLAUS OF FLORIDA, INC.; *U.S. Private*, pg. 2926
NIMITZ PARTNERS, INC. BEST WESTERN PLAZA HOTEL; *U.S. Private*, pg. 2927
NIPPON VIEW HOTEL CO., LTD.—See Hulic Co., Ltd.; *Int'l*, pg. 3528
NISHIWAKI ROYAL HOTEL CO., LTD.—See Daiwa House Industry Co., Ltd.; *Int'l*, pg. 1947
NOBLE HOUSE HOTELS & RESORTS, LTD.; *U.S. Private*, pg. 2932
NORGANI FINLAND HOLDING OY—See Eiendomsspar ASA; *Int'l*, pg. 2329
NORGANI HOTELS ASA—See Eiendomsspar ASA; *Int'l*, pg. 2329
NORTHEAST HOTEL ASSOCIATES—See AVR Realty Company, LLC; *U.S. Private*, pg. 410
NOVOTEL ATHENS S.A.—See Accor S.A.; *Int'l*, pg. 92
NOVOTEL GOTEBORG AB—See Accor S.A.; *Int'l*, pg. 92
NOVOTEL PACIFIC BAY COFFS HARBOUR RESORT—See Brookfield Corporation; *Int'l*, pg. 1189
NOVOTEL—See Accor S.A.; *Int'l*, pg. 92
NYLO DALLAS SOUTH SIDE—See NYLO Hotels LLC; *U.S. Private*, pg. 2976
NYLO HOTELS LLC; *U.S. Private*, pg. 2976
NYLO IRVING/LAS COLINAS—See NYLO Hotels LLC; *U.S. Private*, pg. 2976
NYLO NEW YORK CITY—See NYLO Hotels LLC; *U.S. Private*, pg. 2976
NYLO PLANO/LEGACY—See NYLO Hotels LLC; *U.S. Private*, pg. 2976
NYLO PROVIDENCE/WARWICK—See NYLO Hotels LLC; *U.S. Private*, pg. 2976
OCEANA RESORTS, LLC—See Travel & Leisure Co.; *U.S. Public*, pg. 2185
OCEAN CENTURY INVESTMENTS LIMITED—See CK Asset Holdings Limited; *Int'l*, pg. 1635
OCEAN DUNES RESORT & VILLAS; *U.S. Private*, pg. 2989
OCEAN KEY RESORT & SPA—See Noble House Hotels & Resorts, Ltd.; *U.S. Private*, pg. 2932
OCEAN PROPERTIES, LTD.; *U.S. Private*, pg. 2989
OCEAN REEF CLUB INC.; *U.S. Private*, pg. 2989
OETKER HOTEL MANAGEMENT COMPANY GMBH—See Dr. August Oetker KG; *Int'l*, pg. 2190
OGLE HAUS, LLC—See PENN Entertainment, Inc.; *U.S. Public*, pg. 1662
OJAI VALLEY INN & SPA; *U.S. Private*, pg. 3006
OKURA ACT CITY HOTEL HAMAMATSU—See Hotel Okura Co., Ltd.; *Int'l*, pg. 3488
OKURA AKADEMIA PARK HOTEL, CHIBA—See Hotel Okura Co., Ltd.; *Int'l*, pg. 3488
OKURA CHIBA HOTEL—See Hotel Okura Co., Ltd.; *Int'l*, pg. 3488
OKURA FRONTIER HOTEL EBINA—See Hotel Okura Co., Ltd.; *Int'l*, pg. 3488
OKURA FRONTIER HOTEL TSUKUBA—See Hotel Okura Co., Ltd.; *Int'l*, pg. 3488
OKURA GARDEN HOTEL SHANGHAI—See Hotel Okura Co., Ltd.; *Int'l*, pg. 3488
OLD COLORADO INN HOTEL; *U.S. Private*, pg. 3008
OLD KEY WEST RESORT—See The Walt Disney Company; *U.S. Public*, pg. 2138
OLY/METRO NEW MEXICO LP—See Olympus Real Estate Corp.; *U.S. Private*, pg. 3014
OLYMPUS REAL ESTATE CORP.; *U.S. Private*, pg. 3014
OMAHA MAGNOLIA HOTEL—See Magnolia Hotels; *U.S. Private*, pg. 2548
OMNI BARTON CREEK, INC.—See TRT Holdings, Inc.; *U.S. Private*, pg. 4244
OMNI GROVE PARK, LLC—See TRT Holdings, Inc.; *U.S. Private*, pg. 4244
OMNI HOMESTEAD, INC.—See TRT Holdings, Inc.; *U.S. Private*, pg. 4244
OMNI LA COSTA RESORT & SPA, LLC—See TRT Holdings, Inc.; *U.S. Private*, pg. 4244
OMNI RANCHO LAS PALMAS, LLC—See TRT Holdings, Inc.; *U.S. Private*, pg. 4244
ONE SKI HILL PLACE, LLC—See Vail Resorts, Inc.; *U.S. Public*, pg. 2271
ONPEAK LLC—See Viad Corp.; *U.S. Public*, pg. 2291
ONTARIO HOSPITALITY PROPERTIES LIMITED PARTNERSHIP—See InnSuites Hospitality Trust; *U.S. Public*, pg. 1128
ORBIS S.A.—See Accor S.A.; *Int'l*, pg. 92
ORIENT ESCAPE TRAVEL SDN. BHD.—See Advance Synergy Berhad; *Int'l*, pg. 156
OSAKA MARUBIRU CO., LTD.—See Daiwa House Industry Co., Ltd.; *Int'l*, pg. 1947
OSTAR GRUPO HOTELERO—See Grupo Carso, S.A.B. de C.V.; *Int'l*, pg. 3123
OSTSEE RESORT DAMP GMBH—See Fresenius SE & Co. KGaA; *Int'l*, pg. 2780
OU TLG HOTELL—See AS Infortar; *Int'l*, pg. 590
PACIFICA HOST HOTELS—See Pacifica Companies, LLC; *U.S. Private*, pg. 3072

PACIFIC BEACH HOTEL—See HTH Corporation; *U.S. Private*, pg. 1999
PACIFIC HOSPITALITY GROUP, INC.; *U.S. Private*, pg. 3067
PANALI CO., LTD.—See Hotel Royal Limited; *Int'l*, pg. 3489
PANDOX AB—See Eiendomsspar ASA; *Int'l*, pg. 2329
PANNONIA HOTELS RT—See Accor S.A.; *Int'l*, pg. 92
PAOLI PEAKS INC.—See Vail Resorts, Inc.; *U.S. Public*, pg. 2271
PARADISE STREAM RESORT—See Mcsam Hotel Group LLC; *U.S. Private*, pg. 2644
PARAMOUNT HOTEL GROUP, LLC; *U.S. Private*, pg. 3093
PARAMOUNT HOTELS LLC; *U.S. Private*, pg. 3093
PARK CENTRAL HOTEL SAN FRANCISCO—See Pebblebrook Hotel Trust; *U.S. Public*, pg. 1660
PARK HYATT HAMBURG GMBH—See Hyatt Hotels Corporation; *U.S. Public*, pg. 1078
PARK HYATT HOTEL GMBH—See Hyatt Hotels Corporation; *U.S. Public*, pg. 1078
PARK HYATT WATER TOWER ASSOCIATES, L.L.C.—See Hyatt Hotels Corporation; *U.S. Public*, pg. 1078
PARK INN HOTELS—See Carlson Companies Inc.; *U.S. Private*, pg. 764
PARK LANE DRIVE HOTEL DEVELOPMENT, LLC—See Choice Hotels International, Inc.; *U.S. Public*, pg. 490
PARK MANAGEMENT GROUP—See J.E. Robert Company; *U.S. Private*, pg. 2162
PARK PLACE HOTEL; *U.S. Private*, pg. 3096
PARK PLAZA BLOOMINGTON—See Carlson Companies Inc.; *U.S. Private*, pg. 764
PARK SHORE RESORT—See SunStream, Inc.; *U.S. Private*, pg. 3873
PARK SUNSET, LLC—See Pebblebrook Hotel Trust; *U.S. Public*, pg. 1660
PARNAS HOTEL CO., LTD.—See GS Holdings Corp.; *Int'l*, pg. 3142
PATRICIA GRAND RESORT, LLC—See Travel & Leisure Co.; *U.S. Public*, pg. 2185
PEABODY HOTEL GROUP, INC.—See Belz Enterprises; *U.S. Private*, pg. 522
PEBBLE BEACH COMPANY; *U.S. Private*, pg. 3126
PEGASUS HOTELS OF CEYLON PLC—See Carson Cumberbatch PLC; *Int'l*, pg. 1347
PEPPERS LEISURE PTY. LTD.—See Accor S.A.; *Int'l*, pg. 92
THE PERRY SOUTH BEACH HOTEL—See Coral Hospitality, LLC; *U.S. Private*, pg. 1046
PERSONALITY HOTELS INC.; *U.S. Private*, pg. 3155
THE PFISTER HOTEL—See The Marcus Corporation; *U.S. Public*, pg. 2112
PFISTER, LLC—See The Marcus Corporation; *U.S. Public*, pg. 2112
PGA RESORTS LTD; *U.S. Private*, pg. 3165
PHC HOTELS SDN. BHD.—See Aspial Corporation Limited; *Int'l*, pg. 630
PHOENICIAN OPERATING LLC—See Host Hotels & Resorts, Inc.; *U.S. Public*, pg. 1055
THE PHOENICIAN—See Marriott International, Inc.; *U.S. Public*, pg. 1372
PHU QUOC INVESTMENT & DEVELOPMENT JSC—See C.E.O Group Joint Stock Company; *Int'l*, pg. 1240
PILLO HOTELS LIMITED—See Dalata Hotel Group plc; *Int'l*, pg. 1950
PINK SHELL BEACH RESORT & MARINA—See Boykin Management Company, LLC; *U.S. Private*, pg. 628
PLAINVILLE GAMING AND REDEVELOPMENT, LLC—See PENN Entertainment, Inc.; *U.S. Public*, pg. 1662
PLATENO GROUP CO. LTD.—See CDC Group plc; *Int'l*, pg. 1370
PLATENO GROUP CO. LTD.—See Sequoia Capital Operations, LLC; *U.S. Private*, pg. 3612
PLATENO GROUP CO. LTD.—See The Carlyle Group Inc.; *U.S. Public*, pg. 2052
POCONO MANOR GOLF RESORT & SPA; *U.S. Private*, pg. 3219
POCONO PALACE, INC.—See Mcsam Hotel Group LLC; *U.S. Private*, pg. 2644
POINTE HILTON TAPATIO CLIFFS RESORT—See Hilton Worldwide Holdings Inc.; *U.S. Public*, pg. 1041
POLSERV S.A. DE C.V.—See Host Hotels & Resorts, Inc.; *U.S. Public*, pg. 1055
PONTE VEDRA BEACH INN & CLUB—See Gate Petroleum Company; *U.S. Private*, pg. 1649
PONTE VEDRA LODGE & CLUB—See Gate Petroleum Company; *U.S. Private*, pg. 1649
POSADAS DE MEXICO, S.A. DE C.V.—See Grupo Posadas S.A.B. de C.V.; *Int'l*, pg. 3134
POSTCARD INN ON THE BEACH; *U.S. Private*, pg. 3235
PRADOTEL SAS—See Accor S.A.; *Int'l*, pg. 92
PREMIERE CLASSE HOTEL—See Starwood Capital Group Global I, LLC; *U.S. Private*, pg. 3789
PREMIER LODGE SOUTH AFRICA—See Accor S.A.; *Int'l*, pg. 92
PRINCE-BUSH INVESTMENTS; *U.S. Private*, pg. 3264
PRINCE OCALA, LTD.—See Best Western International, Inc.; *U.S. Private*, pg. 544
PRISM HOSPITALITY, LP—See Advent International Corporation; *U.S. Private*, pg. 97

PRISM HOTEL COMPANY, INC.—See Advent International Corporation; *U.S. Private*, pg. 97
PRITIKIN LONGEVITY CENTER & SPA; *U.S. Private*, pg. 3268
PROFIT MANAGEMENT CORP.—See Family Inns of America, Inc.; *U.S. Private*, pg. 1470
PROMOCIONES MARRIOTT, S.A. DE C.V.—See Marriott Vacations Worldwide Corporation; *U.S. Public*, pg. 1374
PROVIDENCE LEASING LLC—See Kimberly-Clark Corporation; *U.S. Public*, pg. 1231
PROVISIONS—See Carlson Companies Inc.; *U.S. Private*, pg. 764
P.T. AMANRESORTS INDONESIA—See DLF Limited; *Int'l*, pg. 2141
PT BALI GIRIKENCANA—See Hotel Properties Limited; *Int'l*, pg. 3488
P.T. DIWANGKARA HOLIDAY VILLA BAL—See Advance Synergy Berhad; *Int'l*, pg. 156
PT GUTHRIE JAYA INDAH ISLAND RESORT—See Guthrie GTS Limited; *Int'l*, pg. 3189
PUEBLO BONITO EMERALD BAY—See Pueblo Bonito Hotels & Resorts; *U.S. Private*, pg. 3301
PUEBLO BONITO HOTELS & RESORTS; *U.S. Private*, pg. 3301
PUEBLO BONITO LOS CABOS—See Pueblo Bonito Hotels & Resorts; *U.S. Private*, pg. 3301
PUEBLO BONITO MAZATLAN—See Pueblo Bonito Hotels & Resorts; *U.S. Private*, pg. 3302
PUEBLO BONITO PACIFICA HOLISTIC RETREAT AND SPA—See Pueblo Bonito Hotels & Resorts; *U.S. Private*, pg. 3302
PUEBLO BONITO ROSE—See Pueblo Bonito Hotels & Resorts; *U.S. Private*, pg. 3302
PUEBLO BONITO SUNSET BEACH—See Pueblo Bonito Hotels & Resorts; *U.S. Private*, pg. 3302
PULLMAN INTERNATIONAL HOTELS—See Accor S.A.; *Int'l*, pg. 92
PYRAMID HOTEL GROUP LLC—See Pyramid Advisors LLC; *U.S. Private*, pg. 3310
PYRAMID RESORT GROUP—See Pyramid Advisors LLC; *U.S. Private*, pg. 3310
QT HOTELS & RESORTS PTY LIMITED—See Event Hospitality & Entertainment Limited; *Int'l*, pg. 2562
QUAINTANCE-WEAVER INC.; *U.S. Private*, pg. 3316
RADISSON HOTELS & RESORTS—See Carlson Companies Inc.; *U.S. Private*, pg. 764
RAFFAELLO CHICAGO HOTEL—See Menin Hotels, Inc.; *U.S. Private*, pg. 2666
RAFFLES INTERNATIONAL LTD—See Accor S.A.; *Int'l*, pg. 91
RAHN BAHIA MAR, LLC—See Hilton Worldwide Holdings Inc.; *U.S. Public*, pg. 1041
RALEIGH ENTERPRISES; *U.S. Private*, pg. 3349
THE RALEIGH HOTEL—See SBEEG Holdings, LLC; *U.S. Private*, pg. 3559
RAMADA WAIKIKI—See China Airlines Ltd.; *Int'l*, pg. 1481
RAMADA WORLDWIDE INC.—See Travel & Leisure Co.; *U.S. Public*, pg. 2185
RANDASH INVESTMENT LIMITED—See CK Asset Holdings Limited; *Int'l*, pg. 1635
THE RAPHAEL HOTEL—See Blue Beacon International, Inc.; *U.S. Private*, pg. 585
R-C SPAIN, S.L.—See Marriott International, Inc.; *U.S. Public*, pg. 1371
RECORD STREET BREWING COMPANY—See UPD Holding Corp.; *U.S. Public*, pg. 2264
THE REDBURY HOTEL—See SBEEG Holdings, LLC; *U.S. Private*, pg. 3559
RED LION ANAHEIM, LLC—See The RMR Group Inc.; *U.S. Public*, pg. 2126
RED LION HOTELS CORP.—See The RMR Group Inc.; *U.S. Public*, pg. 2126
REGAL HOTELS INTERNATIONAL HOLDINGS LIMITED—See Century City International Holdings Ltd; *Int'l*, pg. 1418
REGAL RIVERSIDE HOTEL LIMITED—See Century City International Holdings Ltd; *Int'l*, pg. 1418
REGENT TAIPEI CO., LTD.—See Formosa International Hotels Corp.; *Int'l*, pg. 2734
RENAISSANCE DO BRASIL HOTELERIA LTDA.—See Marriott International, Inc.; *U.S. Public*, pg. 1371
THE RENAISSANCE WAILEA BEACH RESORT—See Marriott International, Inc.; *U.S. Public*, pg. 1373
RESIDENCE INN BY MARRIOTT, LLC—See Marriott International, Inc.; *U.S. Public*, pg. 1371
RESIDENCE INN DALLAS RICHARDSON—See Marriott International, Inc.; *U.S. Public*, pg. 1371
THE RESIDENCE MAURITIUS—See Bonvests Holdings Limited; *Int'l*, pg. 1110
RESIDENSEA; *U.S. Private*, pg. 3405
THE RESORT COMPANY—See Tonka Bay Equity Partners LLC; *U.S. Private*, pg. 4185
RESORT HOSPITALITY ENTERPRISES LTD.; *U.S. Private*, pg. 3406
RESORTS WORLD AT SENTOSA PTE. LTD.—See Genting Berhad; *Int'l*, pg. 2929
RESORTS WORLD LAS VEGAS LLC—See Genting Berhad; *Int'l*, pg. 2929

RICHFIELD HOSPITALITY, INC.; *U.S. Private*, pg. 3429
THE RITZ-CARLTON CHICAGO—See Cascade Investment LLC; *U.S. Private*, pg. 780
THE RITZ-CARLTON HOTEL COMPANY (BERLIN) GMBH—See W.P. Carey Inc.; *U.S. Public*, pg. 2316
THE RITZ-CARLTON HOTEL COMPANY LLC—See W.P. Carey Inc.; *U.S. Public*, pg. 2316
THE RITZ-CARLTON HOTEL COMPANY OF CANADA LIMITED—See W.P. Carey Inc.; *U.S. Public*, pg. 2316
THE RITZ-CARLTON HOTEL COMPANY OF JAMAICA LIMITED—See W.P. Carey Inc.; *U.S. Public*, pg. 2316
THE RITZ-CARLTON HOTEL COMPANY OF MEXICO, S.A. DE C.V.—See W.P. Carey Inc.; *U.S. Public*, pg. 2316
THE RITZ-CARLTON HOTEL COMPANY OF SINGAPORE PTE LTD.—See W.P. Carey Inc.; *U.S. Public*, pg. 2316
RIVERVIEW HOTEL; *U.S. Private*, pg. 3448
THE RIVETT GROUP LLC; *U.S. Private*, pg. 4110
RLJ LODGING TRUST L.P.—See The RLJ Companies, LLC; *U.S. Private*, pg. 4111
RLK & COMPANY; *U.S. Private*, pg. 3450
ROBERT M. GOFF & ASSOCIATES; *U.S. Private*, pg. 3458
ROBSON DENTON DEVELOPMENT, LP.—See Robson Communities, Inc.; *U.S. Private*, pg. 3463
ROBUST HOTELS PRIVATE LIMITED—See Asian Hotels (East) Limited; *Int'l*, pg. 617
ROCHESTER RESORTS INC.; *U.S. Private*, pg. 3464
ROCKY GAP CASINO RESORT—See Golden Entertainment, Inc.; *U.S. Public*, pg. 950
ROGER SMITH HOTELS CORP.; *U.S. Private*, pg. 3471
ROSEDALE HOTEL GROUP LIMITED—See Greater Bay Area Dynamic Growth Holdings Limited; *Int'l*, pg. 3067
ROSEDALE HOTEL KOWLOON LIMITED—See Greater Bay Area Dynamic Growth Holdings Limited; *Int'l*, pg. 3067
ROSEDALE HOTEL SHENYANG COMPANY LIMITED—See Greater Bay Area Dynamic Growth Holdings Limited; *Int'l*, pg. 3067
ROSEDALE PARK LIMITED—See Greater Bay Area Dynamic Growth Holdings Limited; *Int'l*, pg. 3067
ROSEMONT PROJECT MANAGEMENT, LLC—See Hyatt Hotels Corporation; *U.S. Public*, pg. 1078
ROSEN CENTRE HOTEL—See Rosen Hotels & Resorts, Inc.; *U.S. Private*, pg. 3483
ROSEN PLAZA HOTEL—See Rosen Hotels & Resorts, Inc.; *U.S. Private*, pg. 3483
ROSEWOOD HOTELS & RESORTS LLC—See Chow Tai Fook Enterprises Limited; *Int'l*, pg. 1585
ROSS HAMMOCK RANCH, INC.; *U.S. Private*, pg. 3485
ROTATE BLACK, INC.; *U.S. Public*, pg. 1815
ROYAL PLACE OWNER, LLC—See Hilton Worldwide Holdings Inc.; *U.S. Public*, pg. 1041
ROYAL SONESTA NEW ORLEANS—See The RMR Group Inc.; *U.S. Public*, pg. 2126
ROYAL STREET CORPORATION; *U.S. Private*, pg. 3493
ROYAL STREET LAND CO.—See Royal Street Corporation; *U.S. Private*, pg. 3493
ROYAL STREET OF UTAH INC.—See Royal Street Corporation; *U.S. Private*, pg. 3493
ROYALTON, LLC—See MCR Development LLC; *U.S. Private*, pg. 2644
RRF LIMITED PARTNERSHIP—See InnSuites Hospitality Trust; *U.S. Public*, pg. 1128
RUSHLAKE HOTELS USA INC.; *U.S. Private*, pg. 3505
RUSH ONTARIO, LLC—See The Marcus Corporation; *U.S. Public*, pg. 2112
RYDGES BANKSTOWN PTY LIMITED—See Event Hospitality & Entertainment Limited; *Int'l*, pg. 2562
RYDGES CRONULLA PTY LIMITED—See Event Hospitality & Entertainment Limited; *Int'l*, pg. 2562
RYDGES HOBART HOTEL PTY LIMITED—See Event Hospitality & Entertainment Limited; *Int'l*, pg. 2562
RYDGES ROTORUA HOTEL LIMITED—See Event Hospitality & Entertainment Limited; *Int'l*, pg. 2562
SADDLEBROOK RESORTS, INC.—See Saddlebrook Holdings, Inc.; *U.S. Private*, pg. 3523
SAGAMORE HOTEL; *U.S. Private*, pg. 3525
SAGE HOSPITALITY RESOURCES, LLP—See Sage Investment Holdings; *U.S. Private*, pg. 3526
SAINT JAMES HOTEL—See Red Wing Shoe Company, Inc.; *U.S. Private*, pg. 3376
SALAMANDER INNISBROOK, LLC; *U.S. Private*, pg. 3530
SA LOISEAU DES VIGNES—See Bernard Loiseau SA; *Int'l*, pg. 986
SA LOISEAU RIVE GAUCHE—See Bernard Loiseau SA; *Int'l*, pg. 986
SAMBA VALLARTA—See Emporio Hotels & Resorts S.A. de C.V.; *Int'l*, pg. 2387
SANCTUARY HOTEL AND SPA—See Menin Hotels, Inc.; *U.S. Private*, pg. 2666
SANDALS RESORTS INTERNATIONAL; *U.S. Private*, pg. 3542
SANDESTIN GOLF & BEACH RESORT; *U.S. Private*, pg. 3543
SAN FERNANDO SHERATON CORPORATION—See Marriott International, Inc.; *U.S. Public*, pg. 1371
THE SAN LUIS RESORT, SPA & CONFERENCE CENTER—See Fertitta Entertainment, Inc.; *U.S. Private*, pg. 1499

721110 — HOTELS (EXCEPT CASI...

SANTA MARIA SUITES RESORT—See Forbes Hamilton Management Company; *U.S. Private*, pg. 1562
SAO PAULO INVESTMENT COMPANY INC.—See Hyatt Hotels Corporation; *U.S. Public*, pg. 1078
SARL LOISEAU DES DUCS—See Bernard Loiseau SA; *Int'l*, pg. 986
S.A.R.L. ROOM SERVICE—See Delivery Hero SE; *Int'l*, pg. 2013
SAS LA VILLA DU PARC—See Clariane SE; *Int'l*, pg. 1644
SAS LOISEAU DES SENS—See Bernard Loiseau SA; *Int'l*, pg. 986
SAV HOSPITALITY LIMITED—See Chuang's Consortium International Limited; *Int'l*, pg. 1590
THE SAVOY HOTEL—See Coral Hospitality, LLC; *U.S. Private*, pg. 1046
SAWMILL CREEK RESORT, LTD.—See Six Flags Entertainment Corporation; *U.S. Public*, pg. 1890
SBE ENTERTAINMENT GROUP, LLC; *U.S. Private*, pg. 3559
S & B MOTELS, INC.; *U.S. Private*, pg. 3511
SCANDIC HOTEL DEUTSCHLAND GMBH—See EQT AB; *Int'l*, pg. 2479
SCANDIC HOTELS AB—See EQT AB; *Int'l*, pg. 2479
SCANDIC HOTELS AS—See EQT AB; *Int'l*, pg. 2479
SCANDIC HOTELS A/S—See EQT AB; *Int'l*, pg. 2479
SCANDIC HOTELS OY—See EQT AB; *Int'l*, pg. 2479
THE SCOTT RESORT & SPA—See Grossman Company Properties, Inc.; *U.S. Private*, pg. 1792
SCOTTSDALE PLAZA RESORT LLC; *U.S. Private*, pg. 3578
SEA GARDENS BEACH & TENNIS RESORT—See Travel & Leisure Co.; *U.S. Public*, pg. 2186
THE SEAGATE HOTEL & SPA; *U.S. Private*, pg. 4115
SEA ISLAND COMPANY; *U.S. Private*, pg. 3582
SEA MIST INC.; *U.S. Private*, pg. 3582
SEAPEARL HOTELS PRIVATE LIMITED—See Chalet Hotels Ltd.; *Int'l*, pg. 1437
SEA PINES RESORT, LLC—See The Riverstone Group, LLC; *U.S. Private*, pg. 4110
SEASIDE HOTEL (THAILAND) CO, LTD—See Hotel Properties Limited; *Int'l*, pg. 3488
SEAWAY HOTELS CORPORATION; *U.S. Private*, pg. 3592
SELECT HOTELS GROUP, L.L.C.—See Hyatt Hotels Corporation; *U.S. Public*, pg. 1078
SELECT INN; *U.S. Private*, pg. 3600
SERENDIB LEISURE MANAGEMENT LTD.—See Hemas Holdings PLC; *Int'l*, pg. 3341
SERVICIOS ADMINISTRATIVOS LOS CABOS, S.A. DE C.V.—See Grupo Posadas S.A.B. de C.V.; *Int'l*, pg. 3134
SERVICIOS HOTELEROS DE MANZANILLO SRL DE CV—See Barcelo Corporacion Empresarial S.A.; *Int'l*, pg. 859
SETAI HOTEL LLC; *U.S. Private*, pg. 3617
SEVEN SPRINGS MOUNTAIN RESORT, INC.—See The Nutting Company, Inc.; *U.S. Private*, pg. 4086
SHAMIN HOTELS INC.; *U.S. Private*, pg. 3623
SHANER CORP.; *U.S. Private*, pg. 3625
SHANGRI-LA INTERNATIONAL HOTEL MARKETING LTD.—See China Rare Earth Resources And Technology Co., Ltd.; *Int'l*, pg. 1546
SHELBORNE SOUTH BEACH HOTEL—See Cedar Capital Partners Limited; *Int'l*, pg. 1388
SHELBORNE SOUTH BEACH HOTEL—See King Street Real Estate GP, L.L.C; *U.S. Private*, pg. 2310
SHEPHARD'S BEACH RESORT, INC.; *U.S. Private*, pg. 3632
SHERATON BALTIMORE WASHINGTON AIRPORT HOTEL - BWI—See Marriott International, Inc.; *U.S. Public*, pg. 1372
SHERATON CENTRE TORONTO HOTEL—See Marriott International, Inc.; *U.S. Public*, pg. 1372
SHERATON COLLEGE PARK NORTH HOTEL—See Marriott International, Inc.; *U.S. Public*, pg. 1372
THE SHERATON CORPORATION—See Marriott International, Inc.; *U.S. Public*, pg. 1372
SHERATON DENVER TECH CENTER HOTEL—See Marriott International, Inc.; *U.S. Public*, pg. 1372
SHERATON EDISON HOTEL—See Marriott International, Inc.; *U.S. Public*, pg. 1372
SHERATON GRAND PHOENIX LLC—See Marriott International, Inc.; *U.S. Public*, pg. 1371
SHERATON INDIANAPOLIS HOTEL—See Marriott International, Inc.; *U.S. Public*, pg. 1372
SHERATON INTERNATIONAL, LLC—See Marriott International, Inc.; *U.S. Public*, pg. 1372
SHERATON MILWAUKEE BROOKFIELD HOTEL—See Marriott International, Inc.; *U.S. Public*, pg. 1372
SHERATON OPERATING CORPORATION—See Marriott International, Inc.; *U.S. Public*, pg. 1371
SHERATON OVERSEAS MANAGEMENT CORPORATION—See Marriott International, Inc.; *U.S. Public*, pg. 1372
SHERATON PROVIDENCE AIRPORT HOTEL—See Marriott International, Inc.; *U.S. Public*, pg. 1372
SHERATON SAN DIEGO HOTEL & MARINA—See Marriott International, Inc.; *U.S. Public*, pg. 1372
SHERATON SKYLINE HOTEL LONDON HEATHROW—See Marriott International, Inc.; *U.S. Public*, pg. 1372
SHERATON SUITES WILMINGTON DOWTOWN—See Marriott International, Inc.; *U.S. Public*, pg. 1372
SHERATON TOWERS SINGAPORE—See Bonvests Holdings Limited; *Int'l*, pg. 1110
SHERATON TYSONS HOTEL—See Marriott International, Inc.; *U.S. Public*, pg. 1372
SHERATON VISTANA RESORT—See Marriott International, Inc.; *U.S. Public*, pg. 1372
SHERATON WEST PORT INC.; *U.S. Private*, pg. 3633
SHILIN HOTEL OF HUANGSHAN TOURISM DEVELOPMENT CO., LTD.—See Huangshan Tourism Development Co., Ltd.; *Int'l*, pg. 3513
SHIMODA AQUA SERVICE INC.—See Fujita Kanko Inc.; *Int'l*, pg. 2831
SHIRE HOTELS LIMITED—See Daniel Thwaites PLC; *Int'l*, pg. 1962
SHORE CLUB SOUTH BEACH—See SBEEG Holdings, LLC; *U.S. Private*, pg. 3559
S.H.S. RESORT, LLC; *U.S. Private*, pg. 3517
SHULAR COMPANY; *U.S. Private*, pg. 3644
SIA TLG HOTELL LALVIJA—See AS Infortar; *Int'l*, pg. 590
SILK ROAD RESTAURANTS INTERNATIONAL PTE LTD—See Amara Holdings Ltd.; *Int'l*, pg. 411
SILKS CLUB CO., LTD.—See Formosa International Hotels Corp.; *Int'l*, pg. 2734
SILKS PLACE TAINAN CO., LTD.—See Formosa International Hotels Corp.; *Int'l*, pg. 2734
SILKS PLACE TAROKO CO., LTD.—See Formosa International Hotels Corp.; *Int'l*, pg. 2734
SILKS PLACE YILAN CO., LTD.—See Formosa International Hotels Corp.; *Int'l*, pg. 2734
SILKY OAKS PTY LIMITED—See GPT Group; *Int'l*, pg. 3047
SILVER CLOUD INNS & HOTELS; *U.S. Private*, pg. 3653
SINO CHINA ENTERPRISES LIMITED—See CK Asset Holdings Limited; *Int'l*, pg. 1635
SKIINFO.FR S.A.R.L.—See Vail Resorts, Inc.; *U.S. Public*, pg. 2271
SKI LIBERTY OPERATING CORP.—See Vail Resorts, Inc.; *U.S. Public*, pg. 2271
SKYTOP LODGE CORP.; *U.S. Public*, pg. 1893
SLEEP INN HOTELS—See Choice Hotels International, Inc.; *U.S. Public*, pg. 490
SLIM CHICKENS DEVELOPMENT CO.; *U.S. Private*, pg. 3688
SNC NMP FRANCE—See Accor S.A.; *Int'l*, pg. 92
SNOWBASIN RESORT COMPANY—See HF Sinclair Corporation; *U.S. Public*, pg. 1034
SNOW KING RESORT, INC.; *U.S. Private*, pg. 3700
SOCIETE ABIDJANAISE—See Accor S.A.; *Int'l*, pg. 92
SOCIETE D'EXPLOITATION D'ACTIVITES TOURISTIQUES—See Danone; *Int'l*, pg. 1968
SOCIETE DU CASINO DE SAINT AMAND S.A.S.—See Groupe Partouche S.A.; *Int'l*, pg. 3109
SOCIETE DU LOUVRE SA—See Starwood Capital Group Global I, LLC; *U.S. Private*, pg. 3789
SOCIETE FRANCAISE DE PROMOTION TOURISTIQUE ET HOTELIERE SA—See Accor S.A.; *Int'l*, pg. 92
SOCIETE HOTELIERE 61 QUAI DE GRENELLE—See Accor S.A.; *Int'l*, pg. 92
SOCIETE HOTELIERE PARIS VANVES—See Accor S.A.; *Int'l*, pg. 92
SOCIETE INTERNATIONALE DES HOTELS NOVOTEL—See Accor S.A.; *Int'l*, pg. 92
SOCIETE PARISIENNE DES HOTELS ECONOMIQUES—See Accor S.A.; *Int'l*, pg. 92
SOFITEL CENTRAL HUA HIN RESORT—See Central Plaza Hotel Public Company Limited; *Int'l*, pg. 1409
SOFITEL LUXURY HOTELS FRANCE SAS—See Accor S.A.; *Int'l*, pg. 92
SO LUXURY HMC SARL—See Accor S.A.; *Int'l*, pg. 92
SONESTA BAYFRONT HOTEL COCONUT GROVE—See The RMR Group Inc.; *U.S. Public*, pg. 2126
SONNENALP PROPERTIES INC.; *U.S. Private*, pg. 3714
SONNENALP REAL ESTATE—See Sonnenalp Properties Inc.; *U.S. Private*, pg. 3714
SOTHERLY HOTELS LP—See Sotherly Hotels Inc.; *U.S. Public*, pg. 1910
SOUL COMMUNITY PLANET, INC.; *U.S. Private*, pg. 3716
SOUTHERN SUN HOTELS (PTY) LIMITED—See Hosken Consolidated Investments Limited; *Int'l*, pg. 3485
SOUTHINGTON SUITES, LLC—See KSL Capital Partners, LLC; *U.S. Private*, pg. 2355
SOUTH SHORE HARBOUR RESORT & CONFERENCE CENTER—See Gal-Tex Hotel Corporation; *U.S. Private*, pg. 1635
SPACE SHUTTLE INN—See Best Western International, Inc.; *U.S. Private*, pg. 544
SPIRE HOSPITALITY, LLC—See Winston Harton Holdings, LLC; *U.S. Private*, pg. 4544
SPREE HOTELS AND REAL ESTATE PRIVATE LIMITED—See Easy Trip Planners Limited; *Int'l*, pg. 2276
SPRINGHILL SUITES (BY MARRIOTT) - CONVENTION CENTER/INTERNATIONAL DRIVE AREA—See Marriott International, Inc.; *U.S. Public*, pg. 1371
SPRINGHILL SUITES (BY MARRIOTT) - TARRYTOWN GREENBURGH—See Marriott International, Inc.; *U.S. Public*, pg. 1371
SRI PANWA MANAGEMENT CO., LTD.—See Charn Issara Development Public Company Limited; *Int'l*, pg. 1451
STANDARD HOTEL HOLLYWOOD—See Hyatt Hotels Corporation; *U.S. Public*, pg. 1078
STANDARD INTERNATIONAL MANAGEMENT LLC—See Hyatt Hotels Corporation; *U.S. Public*, pg. 1078
STANFORD HOTELS CORPORATION; *U.S. Private*, pg. 3782
STAR TOWER S.A.L.—See Al-Massaleh Real Estate Company K.S.C.C.; *Int'l*, pg. 287
STARWOOD ASIA PACIFIC HOTELS & RESORTS PTE LTD.—See Marriott International, Inc.; *U.S. Public*, pg. 1371
STARWORLD HOTEL COMPANY LIMITED—See Galaxy Entertainment Group Limited; *Int'l*, pg. 2871
STATEK BLATINY, S.R.O.—See CPI Property Group, S.A.; *Int'l*, pg. 1825
STEIGENBERGER HOTELS AKTIENGESELLSCHAFT—See H World Group Limited; *Int'l*, pg. 3191
STEIGENBERGER SPA GMBH—See H World Group Limited; *Int'l*, pg. 3191
ST. GILES-THE TUSCANY HOTEL; *U.S. Private*, pg. 3771
THE ST. REGIS ASPEN RESORT—See Marriott International, Inc.; *U.S. Public*, pg. 1372
THE ST. REGIS HOTEL - HOUSTON—See Marriott International, Inc.; *U.S. Public*, pg. 1372
THE ST. REGIS - NEW YORK—See Marriott International, Inc.; *U.S. Public*, pg. 1372
ST. REGIS SAN FRANCISCO HOTEL LLC—See Marriott International, Inc.; *U.S. Public*, pg. 1371
STUBB'S AUSTIN RESTAURANT COMPANY, LC—See Live Nation Entertainment, Inc.; *U.S. Public*, pg. 1330
SUMMER BAY RESORT; *U.S. Private*, pg. 3853
SUMMIT GROUP INC.; *U.S. Private*, pg. 3854
THE SUNAPEE DIFFERENCE LLC—See Vail Resorts, Inc.; *U.S. Public*, pg. 2271
SUNBURST HOSPITALITY CORPORATION; *U.S. Private*, pg. 3865
SUNDIAL BEACH AND GOLF RESORT—See CoreStates Capital Advisors, LLC; *U.S. Private*, pg. 1049
SUNSET BEACH CLUB S.A.—See Farmer Business Developments plc; *Int'l*, pg. 2619
SUNSTREAM, INC.; *U.S. Private*, pg. 3873
SUN VALLEY COMPANY—See HF Sinclair Corporation; *U.S. Public*, pg. 1034
SUPER 8 MOTEL TIMMINS—See Clarke Inc.; *Int'l*, pg. 1650
SUPER VISTA SDN BHD—See Hotel Properties Limited; *Int'l*, pg. 3488
SYBARIS CLUBS INTERNATIONAL INC.; *U.S. Private*, pg. 3895
SYCAMORE LAKE, INC.—See Vail Resorts, Inc.; *U.S. Public*, pg. 2271
SYDELL GROUP LTD.—See Hilton Worldwide Holdings Inc.; *U.S. Public*, pg. 1041
TAAMEER HQSPITALITY-S.A.L.—See Al-Massaleh Real Estate Company K.S.C.C.; *Int'l*, pg. 287
TANADGUSIX CORP.; *U.S. Private*, pg. 3930
TANGQUAN HOTEL OF HUANGSHAN TOURISM DEVELOPMENT CO., LTD.—See Huangshan Tourism Development Co., Ltd.; *Int'l*, pg. 3513
TEMPLE SQUARE HOSPITALITY CORPORATION—See Deseret Management Corporation; *U.S. Private*, pg. 1212
THAI WAH PLAZA LIMITED—See Banyan Tree Holdings Ltd.; *Int'l*, pg. 855
THANYING RESTAURANT SINGAPORE PTE. LTD.—See Amara Holdings Ltd.; *Int'l*, pg. 411
THISTLE HOTELS LIMITED—See Hong Leong Investment Holdings Pte. Ltd.; *Int'l*, pg. 3468
THOMPSON HOTELS LLC—See Commune Hotels & Resorts, LLC; *U.S. Private*, pg. 987
TIBURON GOLF VENTURES LIMITED PARTNERSHIP—See Host Hotels & Resorts, Inc.; *U.S. Public*, pg. 1055
TIJUANA PARTNERS, S. DE R.L. DE C.V.—See Hyatt Hotels Corporation; *U.S. Public*, pg. 1078
TIOMAN ISLAND RESORT BERHAD—See Berjaya Corporation Berhad; *Int'l*, pg. 983
TISHMAN HOTEL CORPORATION—See AECOM; *U.S. Public*, pg. 52
TOLBERT ENTERPRISES INC.; *U.S. Private*, pg. 4181
TORGERSON PROPERTIES INC.; *U.S. Private*, pg. 4188
TORONTO MARRIOTT DOWNTOWN CENTRE HOTEL—See Marriott International, Inc.; *U.S. Public*, pg. 1373
TOWN & COUNTRY HOTEL, LLC—See Atlas Hotels, Inc.; *U.S. Private*, pg. 378
TRADEWINDS ISLANDS RESORTS ON SAINT PETE BEACH—See Resort Inns of America Inc.; *U.S. Private*, pg. 3406
TRAMZ HOTELS INC.; *U.S. Private*, pg. 4205
TRANS INNS MANAGEMENT INC.; *U.S. Private*, pg. 4205
TRANS WORLD HOTELS AUSTRIA GMBH—See Far East Consortium International Limited; *Int'l*, pg. 2616
TRAPP FAMILY LODGE, INC.; *U.S. Private*, pg. 4212

N.A.I.C.S. INDEX

TRAVELODGE BARRIE ON BAYFIELD—See Clarke Inc.; *Int'l*, pg. 1650
TRAVELODGE HOTEL BELLEVILLE—See Clarke Inc.; *Int'l*, pg. 1650
TRAVELODGE HOTELS, INC.—See Travel & Leisure Co.; *U.S. Public*, pg. 2185
TRAVELODGE OTTAWA WEST—See Clarke Inc.; *Int'l*, pg. 1650
TRAVELODGE TIMMINS—See Clarke Inc.; *Int'l*, pg. 1650
TR BIG SUR MANAGEMENT LLC—See Hyatt Hotels Corporation; *U.S. Public*, pg. 1078
TR CAMINO MANAGEMENT LLC—See Hyatt Hotels Corporation; *U.S. Public*, pg. 1078
TR EXCELSIOR MANAEMENT LLC—See Hyatt Hotels Corporation; *U.S. Public*, pg. 1078
TRIANON HOTEL CO.; *U.S. Private*, pg. 4227
TRINIDAD RESORT & CLUB, LLC—See Apex Oil Company, Inc.; *U.S. Private*, pg. 293
TR LAKESHORE MANAGEMENT LLC—See Hyatt Hotels Corporation; *U.S. Public*, pg. 1078
TR NEW YORK MANAGEMENT LLC—See Hyatt Hotels Corporation; *U.S. Public*, pg. 1078
TROPICANA HOTEL - GOLDEN MILE—See Gooderson Leisure Corporation; *Int'l*, pg. 3040
TR PARK SOUTH MANAGEMENT LLC—See Hyatt Hotels Corporation; *U.S. Public*, pg. 1078
TR POST MANAGEMENT LLC—See Hyatt Hotels Corporation; *U.S. Public*, pg. 1078
TR PRESIDIO MANAGEMENT LLC—See Hyatt Hotels Corporation; *U.S. Public*, pg. 1078
TR SANTA CLARA MANAGEMENT LLC—See Hyatt Hotels Corporation; *U.S. Public*, pg. 1078
TR SEATTLE MANAGEMENT LLC—See Hyatt Hotels Corporation; *U.S. Public*, pg. 1078
TR SEDONA MANAGEMENT LLC—See Hyatt Hotels Corporation; *U.S. Public*, pg. 1078
TR SUNNYVALE MANAGEMENT LLC—See Hyatt Hotels Corporation; *U.S. Public*, pg. 1078
TRUE NORTH HOTEL GROUP, INC.; *U.S. Private*, pg. 4248
TRUMP CENTRAL PARK WEST CORP.—See The Trump Organization, Inc.; *U.S. Private*, pg. 4128
TRUST HOSPITALITY LLC; *U.S. Private*, pg. 4250
TUCSON HOSPITALITY PROPERTIES, LTD—See InnSuites Hospitality Trust; *U.S. Public*, pg. 1128
TUCSON ST. MARY'S SUITE HOSPITALITY LLC—See InnSuites Hospitality Trust; *U.S. Public*, pg. 1128
TURNBERRY ISLE RESORT & SPA—See Turnberry, Ltd.; *U.S. Private*, pg. 4260
TWIN TIER HOSPITALITY, LLC; *U.S. Private*, pg. 4266
UNION HOTELS D.D.—See Grand Hotel Union d.d.; *Int'l*, pg. 3055
UNIVERSAL PARAGON CORPORATION; *U.S. Private*, pg. 4306
URGO HOTELS LP; *U.S. Private*, pg. 4315
U.S. FRANCHISE SYSTEMS, INC.—See Travel & Leisure Co.; *U.S. Public*, pg. 2185
VACATION ASIA (HK) LIMITED—See Avillion Berhad; *Int'l*, pg. 743
VAGABOND FRANCHISE SYSTEM, INC.; *U.S. Private*, pg. 4329
VAIL MOUNTAIN LODGE & SPA—See KSL Capital Partners, LLC; *U.S. Private*, pg. 2355
VAIL RESORTS, INC.; *U.S. Public*, pg. 2270
VAIL SUMMIT RESORTS, INC.—See Vail Resorts, Inc.; *U.S. Public*, pg. 2272
VAN DON TOURISM DEVELOPMENT & INVESTMENT JOINT STOCK COMPANY—See C.E.O Group Joint Stock Company; *Int'l*, pg. 1240
VARSITY CLUBS OF AMERICA - SOUTH BEND—See Apollo Global Management, Inc.; *U.S. Public*, pg. 150
VARSITY CLUBS OF AMERICA - SOUTH BEND—See Reverence Capital Partners LLC; *U.S. Private*, pg. 3415
VARSITY CLUBS OF AMERICA - TUCSON—See Apollo Global Management, Inc.; *U.S. Public*, pg. 150
VARSITY CLUBS OF AMERICA - TUCSON—See Reverence Capital Partners LLC; *U.S. Private*, pg. 3415
VDARA CONDO HOTEL, LLC—See MGM Resorts International; *U.S. Public*, pg. 1435
VENETIAN CASINO RESORT, LLC—See Las Vegas Sands Corp.; *U.S. Public*, pg. 1293
VENETIAN MARKETING SERVICES LIMITED—See Las Vegas Sands Corp.; *U.S. Public*, pg. 1293
VENTURA BEACH MARRIOTT—See Brighton Management LLC; *U.S. Private*, pg. 652
VICEROY HOTEL MANAGEMENT, LLC; *U.S. Private*, pg. 4376
THE VICTORIA FALLS HOTEL—See African Sun Limited; *Int'l*, pg. 192
VICTORIA-JUNGFRAU COLLECTION AG—See AEVIS VICTORIA SA; *Int'l*, pg. 183
THE VINOY RENAISSANCE ST. PETERSBURG RESORT & GOLF CLUB—See Marriott International, Inc.; *U.S. Public*, pg. 1373
VJC-MANAGEMENT AG—See AEVIS VICTORIA SA; *Int'l*, pg. 183
VOYAGES HOTEL & RESORTS LTD.—See GPT Group; *Int'l*, pg. 3047

VOYAGES HOTELS & RESORTS PTY LIMITED—See GPT Group; *Int'l*, pg. 3047
WALL STREET MANAGER, LLC—See Hyatt Hotels Corporation; *U.S. Public*, pg. 1078
WALT DISNEY WORLD SWAN & DOLPHIN RESORTS—See AECOM; *U.S. Public*, pg. 52
WASHINGTON HILTON, L.L.C.—See Hilton Worldwide Holdings Inc.; *U.S. Public*, pg. 1041
WATERCOLOR INN & RESORT—See Noble House Hotels & Resorts, Ltd.; *U.S. Private*, pg. 2932
WATERFORD HOTEL GROUP, INC.—See Waterford Group, LLC; *U.S. Private*, pg. 4453
THE WATERMARK HOTEL NAGASAKI CO., LTD.—See H.I.S. Co., Ltd.; *Int'l*, pg. 3196
W ATLANTA BUCKHEAD BEVERAGE LLC—See Marriott International, Inc.; *U.S. Public*, pg. 1373
W ATLANTA - DOWNTOWN HOTEL—See Marriott International, Inc.; *U.S. Public*, pg. 1372
W CHICAGO - CITY CENTER HOTEL—See Marriott International, Inc.; *U.S. Public*, pg. 1372
WELLSPRING BY SILKS CO., LTD.—See Formosa International Hotels Corp.; *Int'l*, pg. 2735
WEST COAST LODGING, L.P.—See Stonebridge Realty Advisors, Inc.; *U.S. Private*, pg. 3827
THE WESTGATE HOTEL—See HF Sinclair Corporation; *U.S. Public*, pg. 1034
WEST GLACIER MERCANTILE, INC.—See Viad Corp.; *U.S. Public*, pg. 2291
THE WESTIN DENVER DOWNTOWN—See Marriott International, Inc.; *U.S. Public*, pg. 1372
THE WESTIN GALLERIA HOUSTON—See Marriott International, Inc.; *U.S. Public*, pg. 1372
THE WESTIN INDIANAPOLIS—See Marriott International, Inc.; *U.S. Public*, pg. 1372
WESTIN INTERNATIONAL (MALTA) LTD.—See Marriott International, Inc.; *U.S. Public*, pg. 1373
THE WESTIN LOS ANGELES AIRPORT—See Marriott International, Inc.; *U.S. Public*, pg. 1373
THE WESTIN NEW YORK AT TIMES SQUARE—See Marriott International, Inc.; *U.S. Public*, pg. 1373
THE WESTIN PHILADELPHIA—See Marriott International, Inc.; *U.S. Public*, pg. 1373
THE WESTIN PRINCETON AT FORRESTAL VILLAGE HOTEL—See Marriott International, Inc.; *U.S. Public*, pg. 1373
WESTIN SAN ANTONIO RESORT COMPANY—See Marriott International, Inc.; *U.S. Public*, pg. 1373
THE WESTIN SAN FRANCISCO AIRPORT—See Marriott International, Inc.; *U.S. Public*, pg. 1373
WESTIN SAVANNAH HOLDINGS, LLC—See Marriott International, Inc.; *U.S. Public*, pg. 1373
THE WESTIN SEATTLE—See Marriott International, Inc.; *U.S. Public*, pg. 1373
THE WESTIN SOUTH COAST PLAZA, COSTA MESA—See Marriott International, Inc.; *U.S. Public*, pg. 1373
THE WESTIN ST. FRANCIS SAN FRANCISCO ON UNION SQUARE—See Marriott International, Inc.; *U.S. Public*, pg. 1373
THE WESTIN ST. JOHN RESORT VILLAS—See Marriott International, Inc.; *U.S. Public*, pg. 1373
THE WESTIN WALTHAM BOSTON—See Marriott International, Inc.; *U.S. Public*, pg. 1373
WESTLITE DORMITORY (BUKIT MINYAK) SDN. BHD.—See Centurion Corporation Limited; *Int'l*, pg. 1417
WESTLITE DORMITORY (JB TECHPARK) SDN. BHD.—See Centurion Corporation Limited; *Int'l*, pg. 1417
WESTLITE DORMITORY (PASIR GUDANG) SDN. BHD.—See Centurion Corporation Limited; *Int'l*, pg. 1417
WESTLITE DORMITORY (SENAI) SDN. BHD.—See Centurion Corporation Limited; *Int'l*, pg. 1417
WESTLITE DORMITORY (SN II) SDN. BHD.—See Centurion Corporation Limited; *Int'l*, pg. 1417
WESTLITE DORMITORY (TAMPOI) SDN. BHD.—See Centurion Corporation Limited; *Int'l*, pg. 1417
WESTLITE DORMITORY (TEBRAU) SDN. BHD.—See Centurion Corporation Limited; *Int'l*, pg. 1417
WESTMARK HOTELS, ALASKA—See Carnival Corporation; *U.S. Public*, pg. 438
WESTMARK HOTELS OF CANADA, LTD.—See Carnival Corporation; *U.S. Public*, pg. 438
WHITEBIRCH, INC.—See Whitebirch Enterprises, Inc.; *U.S. Private*, pg. 4511
W HOTELS REAL ESTATE, LLC—See Marriott International, Inc.; *U.S. Public*, pg. 1372
WILLIAMS INVESTMENT COMPANY; *U.S. Private*, pg. 4526
WILSON HOTEL MANAGEMENT COMPANY, INC.—See Kemmons Wilson, Inc.; *U.S. Private*, pg. 2281
WINDJAMMER LANDING VILLA BEACH RESORT & SPA—See EllisDon Corporation; *Int'l*, pg. 2367
WINEGARDNER & HAMMONS, INC.; *U.S. Private*, pg. 4540
WINGATE INNS INTERNATIONAL, INC.—See Travel & Leisure Co.; *U.S. Public*, pg. 2185
WIN-SUM SKI CORPORATION; *U.S. Private*, pg. 4533
WINTER SPORTS, INC.; *U.S. Private*, pg. 4545
W LEICESTER SQUARE LTD.—See Marriott International, Inc.; *U.S. Public*, pg. 1373

W NEW ORLEANS - FRENCH QUARTER HOTEL—See Marriott International, Inc.; *U.S. Public*, pg. 1372
WOODFIN SUITE HOTELS—See Hardage Investments, Inc.; *U.S. Private*, pg. 1862
WOODLOCH PINES INC.; *U.S. Private*, pg. 4559
WOODSIDE HOTELS & RESORTS; *U.S. Private*, pg. 4560
WPH AIRPORT ASSOCIATES; *U.S. Private*, pg. 4571
W SEATTLE HOTEL—See Marriott International, Inc.; *U.S. Public*, pg. 1372
W.W. LEISURE, INC.; *U.S. Private*, pg. 4423
W.W. LODGING, INC.—See W.W. Leisure, Inc.; *U.S. Private*, pg. 4423
WYNDHAM GOVERNOR'S GREEN—See Travel & Leisure Co.; *U.S. Public*, pg. 2185
WYNDHAM HOTELS & RESORTS, INC.; *U.S. Public*, pg. 2384
WYNDHAM HOTELS & RESORTS, LLC—See Travel & Leisure Co.; *U.S. Public*, pg. 2185
WYNDHAM KINGSGATE—See Travel & Leisure Co.; *U.S. Public*, pg. 2185
WYNDHAM RESORT AT FAIRFIELD MOUNTAINS—See Travel & Leisure Co.; *U.S. Public*, pg. 2186
WYNDHAM ROYAL VISTA—See Travel & Leisure Co.; *U.S. Public*, pg. 2186
WYNDHAM SANTA BARBARA RESORT & YACHT CLUB—See Travel & Leisure Co.; *U.S. Public*, pg. 2186
WYNDHAM WESTWINDS—See Travel & Leisure Co.; *U.S. Public*, pg. 2186
WYNYARD PROPERTIES PTY LIMITED—See Brookfield Corporation; *Int'l*, pg. 1189
XANTERRA PARKS & RESORTS, INC.—See The Anschutz Corporation; *U.S. Private*, pg. 3987
XUANYUAN INTERNATIONAL HOTEL OF HUANGSHAN TOURISM DEVELOPMENT CO., LTD.—See Huangshan Tourism Development Co., Ltd.; *Int'l*, pg. 3513
YELLOWKNIFE INN—See Clarke Inc.; *Int'l*, pg. 1650
YOCO STAYS PVT. LTD.—See Global Education Limited; *Int'l*, pg. 2995
Y.O. RANCH RESORT HOTEL & CONFERENCE CENTER—See Gal-Tex Hotel Corporation; *U.S. Private*, pg. 1635
YOSEMITE MANAGEMENT GROUP LLC; *U.S. Private*, pg. 4591
YUMA HOSPITALITY PROPERTIES, LTD.—See InnSuites Hospitality Trust; *U.S. Public*, pg. 1128
YUPINGLOU HOTEL OF HUANGSHAN TOURISM DEVELOPMENT CO., LTD.—See Huangshan Tourism Development Co., Ltd.; *Int'l*, pg. 3513

721120 — CASINO HOTELS

49'S LIMITED—See Entain PLC; *Int'l*, pg. 2449
ABRH, LLC—See Cannae Holdings, Inc.; *U.S. Public*, pg. 429
ACCOR CASINOS—See Accor S.A.; *Int'l*, pg. 91
AFFINITY GAMING—See Z Capital Group, LLC; *U.S. Private*, pg. 4595
AFRICAN SUN LIMITED; *Int'l*, pg. 192
AKANI EGOLI (PTY) LIMITED—See Hosken Consolidated Investments Limited; *Int'l*, pg. 3485
AKANI MSUNDUZI (PTY) LTD.—See Hosken Consolidated Investments Limited; *Int'l*, pg. 3485
ALIANTE GAMING, LLC—See Boyd Gaming Corporation; *U.S. Public*, pg. 377
AL WATHBA A LUXURY COLLECTION DESERT RESORT & SPA - SOLE PROPRIETORSHIP LLC—See Alpha Dhabi Holding PJSC; *Int'l*, pg. 367
AMERISTAR CASINO BLACK HAWK, LLC—See PENN Entertainment, Inc.; *U.S. Public*, pg. 1662
AMERISTAR CASINO COUNCIL BLUFFS, LLC—See PENN Entertainment, Inc.; *U.S. Public*, pg. 1662
AMERISTAR CASINO EAST CHICAGO, LLC—See PENN Entertainment, Inc.; *U.S. Public*, pg. 1662
AMERISTAR CASINO KANSAS CITY, LLC—See Boyd Gaming Corporation; *U.S. Public*, pg. 377
AMERISTAR CASINO ST. CHARLES, LLC—See Boyd Gaming Corporation; *U.S. Public*, pg. 377
AMERISTAR CASINO VICKSBURG, LLC—See PENN Entertainment, Inc.; *U.S. Public*, pg. 1662
APACHE CASINO HOTEL—See Fort Sill Apache Tribe of Oklahoma; *U.S. Public*, pg. 1575
THE ARAGON GROUP—See Boyd Gaming Corporation; *U.S. Public*, pg. 378
ASHFORD TRS FIVE LLC—See Ashford Hospitality Trust, Inc.; *U.S. Public*, pg. 211
ASHFORD TRS POOL A LLC—See Ashford Hospitality Trust, Inc.; *U.S. Public*, pg. 211
ASIAN HOTELS (NORTH) LIMITED; *Int'l*, pg. 617
AVALON RESORTS, INC.—See Avalon Holdings Corporation; *U.S. Public*, pg. 239
BALLY'S ATLANTIC CITY LLC—See Bally's Corporation; *U.S. Public*, pg. 268
BALLY'S LAKE TAHOE—See Caesars Entertainment, Inc.; *U.S. Public*, pg. 420
BALLY'S LAS VEGAS—See Caesars Entertainment, Inc.; *U.S. Public*, pg. 420

721120 — CASINO HOTELS

CORPORATE AFFILIATIONS

BARDEN DEVELOPMENT, INC.—See Barden Companies, Inc.; *U.S. Private*, pg. 474
BARDEN MISSISSIPPI GAMING, LLC—See Majestic Star Casino & Hotel; *U.S. Private*, pg. 2554
BARONA VALLEY RANCH RESORT & CASINO; *U.S. Private*, pg. 478
BBCV RECEIVABLES-Q 2010 LLC—See Hilton Grand Vacations, Inc.; *U.S. Public*, pg. 1039
BB DEVELOPMENT, LLC—See Churchill Downs, Inc.; *U.S. Public*, pg. 493
BELLAGIO, LLC—See MGM Resorts International; *U.S. Public*, pg. 1435
BELTERRA RESORT INDIANA, LLC—See Boyd Gaming Corporation; *U.S. Public*, pg. 377
BERJAYA LOTTERY MANAGEMENT (HK) LTD.—See Berjaya Corporation Berhad; *Int'l*, pg. 983
BERJAYA WATERFRONT SDN. BHD.—See Berjaya Assets Berhad; *Int'l*, pg. 981
BHCMC, LLC—See Butler National Corporation; *U.S. Public*, pg. 413
BLUE CHIP CASINO, LLC—See Boyd Gaming Corporation; *U.S. Public*, pg. 377
BLUEGREEN/BIG CEDAR VACATIONS, LLC—See Hilton Grand Vacations Inc.; *U.S. Public*, pg. 1039
BLUEGREEN COMMUNITIES, LLC—See Hilton Grand Vacations, Inc.; *U.S. Public*, pg. 1039
BOOMTOWN, LLC—See PENN Entertainment, Inc.; *U.S. Public*, pg. 1662
BORGATA HOTEL CASINO & SPA, LLC—See MGM Resorts International; *U.S. Public*, pg. 1435
BOSSIER CASINO VENTURE, LLC—See PENN Entertainment, Inc.; *U.S. Public*, pg. 1662
BOYD BILOXI, LLC—See Boyd Gaming Corporation; *U.S. Public*, pg. 377
BOYD RACING, L.L.C.—See Boyd Gaming Corporation; *U.S. Public*, pg. 377
BOYD SHARED SERVICES INC.—See Boyd Gaming Corporation; *U.S. Public*, pg. 377
BOYD TUNICA, INC.—See Boyd Gaming Corporation; *U.S. Public*, pg. 377
BWIN LATAM S.A.S.—See Entain PLC; *Int'l*, pg. 2449
CACTUS PETE'S, LLC—See PENN Entertainment, Inc.; *U.S. Public*, pg. 1662
CAESARS GROWTH BALLY'S LV, LLC—See Caesars Entertainment, Inc.; *U.S. Public*, pg. 420
CAESARS NEW JERSEY, INC.—See Caesars Entertainment, Inc.; *U.S. Public*, pg. 419
CAESARS PALACE CORPORATION—See Caesars Entertainment, Inc.; *U.S. Public*, pg. 419
CALIFORNIA HOTEL & CASINO—See Boyd Gaming Corporation; *U.S. Public*, pg. 377
THE CANNERY HOTEL & CASINO, LLC—See Boyd Gaming Corporation; *U.S. Public*, pg. 378
CASABLANCA RESORTS, LLC—See Mesquite Gaming, LLC; *U.S. Private*, pg. 2679
CASINO CANBERRA LIMITED—See Aquis Entertainment Limited; *Int'l*, pg. 528
CASINO MAGIC NEUQUEN SA—See PENN Entertainment, Inc.; *U.S. Public*, pg. 1662
CASINO NOVA SCOTIA—See Great Canadian Gaming Corporation; *Int'l*, pg. 3063
CASINO ONE CORPORATION—See Caesars Entertainment, Inc.; *U.S. Public*, pg. 420
CASINO QUEEN, INC.; *U.S. Private*, pg. 783
CC-RENO, LLC—See Caesars Entertainment, Inc.; *U.S. Public*, pg. 419
CENTAUR ACQUISITION, LLC—See Caesars Entertainment, Inc.; *U.S. Public*, pg. 420
CENTURY CASINO CALGARY INC.—See Century Casinos, Inc.; *U.S. Public*, pg. 474
CENTURY CASINOS AFRICA (PTY) LTD.—See Century Casinos, Inc.; *U.S. Public*, pg. 474
CENTURY CASINOS CALEDON (PTY) LTD.—See Century Casinos, Inc.; *U.S. Public*, pg. 474
CENTURY CASINOS CRIPPLE CREEK, INC.—See Century Casinos, Inc.; *U.S. Public*, pg. 474
CENTURY CASINOS EUROPE GMBH—See Century Casinos, Inc.; *U.S. Public*, pg. 474
CENTURY RESORTS ALBERTA, INC.—See Century Casinos, Inc.; *U.S. Public*, pg. 474
CGE ASSETS, INC.—See Maverick Gold LLC; *U.S. Private*, pg. 2616
CHEROKEE NATION ENTERTAINMENT—See Cherokee Nation Businesses; *U.S. Private*, pg. 873
CINDRELLA HOTELS LTD.; *Int'l*, pg. 1610
CIRCUS CIRCUS CASINOS, INC.—See MGM Resorts International; *U.S. Public*, pg. 1435
CIRCUS & ELDORADO JOINT VENTURE, LLC—See Caesars Entertainment, Inc.; *U.S. Public*, pg. 420
COAST CASINOS, INC.—See Boyd Gaming Corporation; *U.S. Public*, pg. 377
COAST HOTELS & CASINOS, INC.—See Boyd Gaming Corporation; *U.S. Public*, pg. 377
COLORADO BELLE HOTEL & CASINO—See Marnell Corrao Associates, Inc.; *U.S. Private*, pg. 2586
COQUILLE ECONOMIC DEVELOPMENT; *U.S. Private*, pg. 1046
CORNER INVESTMENT COMPANY, LLC—See Caesars Entertainment, Inc.; *U.S. Public*, pg. 420
THE CROMWELL (LAS VEGAS) HOTEL & CASINO—See Caesars Entertainment, Inc.; *U.S. Public*, pg. 420
CROWN MELBOURNE LIMITED—See Blackstone Inc.; *U.S. Public*, pg. 352
CROWN PERTH—See Blackstone Inc.; *U.S. Public*, pg. 352
CROWN RESORTS LIMITED—See Blackstone Inc.; *U.S. Public*, pg. 352
DEERFOOT INN & CASINO INC.—See Gamehost Inc.; *Int'l*, pg. 2877
DETROIT ENTERTAINMENT, LLC—See Ilitch Holdings, Inc.; *U.S. Private*, pg. 2041
DGMB CASINO, LLC; *U.S. Public*, pg. 1221
DIAMONDHEAD CASINO CORPORATION; *U.S. Public*, pg. 659
DIAMOND JACKS CASINO & HOTEL—See The Cordish Companies; *U.S. Private*, pg. 4015
DISCOVERY WORLD CORPORATION; *Int'l*, pg. 2134
DONACO INTERNATIONAL LIMITED; *Int'l*, pg. 2162
DOUBLE BOGEY, LLC—See PENN Entertainment, Inc.; *U.S. Public*, pg. 1662
DOVER DOWNS, INC—See Bally's Corporation; *U.S. Public*, pg. 268
EDGEWATER HOTEL & CASINO—See Marnell Corrao Associates, Inc.; *U.S. Private*, pg. 2586
ELDORADO, INC.—See Boyd Gaming Corporation; *U.S. Public*, pg. 377
ELDORADO RESORTS LLC—See Caesars Entertainment, Inc.; *U.S. Public*, pg. 420
ELGIN RIVERBOAT RESORT—See Caesars Entertainment, Inc.; *U.S. Public*, pg. 420
EMERALD SAFARI RESORT (PTY) LIMITED—See Caesars Entertainment, Inc.; *U.S. Public*, pg. 420
EVERGREEN GAMING CORPORATION—See Maverick Gold LLC; *U.S. Private*, pg. 2616
FALCON'S BEYOND GLOBAL, INC.; *U.S. Public*, pg. 820
FESTIVA RESORTS LLC; *U.S. Private*, pg. 1499
FIRST HOTEL COMPANY LTD.; *Int'l*, pg. 2684
FLAMINGO LAS VEGAS OPERATING COMPANY, LLC—See Caesars Entertainment, Inc.; *U.S. Public*, pg. 420
FORT MOJAVE TRIBAL COUNCIL; *U.S. Private*, pg. 1574
FOXWOODS RESORT CASINO—See Mashantucket Pequot Gaming Enterprise Inc.; *U.S. Private*, pg. 2601
FREEHOLD RACEWAY OFF TRACK LLC—See PENN Entertainment, Inc.; *U.S. Public*, pg. 1662
GAMEHOST INC.; *Int'l*, pg. 2877
GAMING VENTURES OF LAS VEGAS, INC.—See Maverick Gold LLC; *U.S. Private*, pg. 2616
GARDEN ROUTE CASINO (PTY) LTD.—See Hosken Consolidated Investments Limited; *Int'l*, pg. 3485
GENTING SINGAPORE LIMITED—See Genting Berhad; *Int'l*, pg. 2929
GLP CAPITAL, L.P.—See Gaming and Leisure Properties, Inc.; *U.S. Public*, pg. 896
GOLDEN GAMING, LLC—See Golden Entertainment, Inc.; *U.S. Public*, pg. 950
GOLDEN NUGGET HOTEL & CASINO - ATLANTIC CITY—See Fertitta Entertainment, Inc.; *U.S. Private*, pg. 1499
GOLDEN NUGGET HOTEL & CASINO - LAS VEGAS—See Fertitta Entertainment, Inc.; *U.S. Private*, pg. 1499
GOLDEN NUGGET HOTEL & CASINO - LAUGHLIN—See Fertitta Entertainment, Inc.; *U.S. Private*, pg. 1499
GOLDEN PAHRUMP NUGGET, LLC—See Golden Entertainment, Inc.; *U.S. Public*, pg. 950
GOLDEN PAHRUMP TOWN, LLC—See Golden Entertainment, Inc.; *U.S. Public*, pg. 950
GOLDEN ROAD MOTOR INN, INC.—See Monarch Casino & Resort, Inc.; *U.S. Public*, pg. 1460
GOLDEN ROUTE OPERATIONS LLC—See Golden Entertainment, Inc.; *U.S. Public*, pg. 950
GOLDFIELDS CASINO & ENTERTAINMENT CENTRE (PTY) LTD.—See Hosken Consolidated Investments Limited; *Int'l*, pg. 3485
GRAND CASINOS OF BILOXI, LLC—See Caesars Entertainment, Inc.; *U.S. Public*, pg. 419
GRAND KOREA LEISURE CO.LTD; *Int'l*, pg. 3055
GREAT AMERICAN GAMING CORPORATION—See Maverick Gold LLC; *U.S. Private*, pg. 2616
GREAT CANADIAN GAMING CORPORATION; *Int'l*, pg. 3063
GREEKTOWN CASINO HOTEL—See PENN Entertainment, Inc.; *U.S. Public*, pg. 1662
GREEKTOWN HOLDINGS, LLC; *U.S. Private*, pg. 1770
GROUPE LUCIEN BARRIERE S.A.; *Int'l*, pg. 3108
GROUPE PARTOUCHE INTERNATIONAL S.A.—See Groupe Partouche S.A.; *Int'l*, pg. 3109
HARD ROCK CAFE INTERNATIONAL UNIVERSAL CITY—See Seminole Tribe of Florida, Inc.; *U.S. Private*, pg. 3605
HARD ROCK CAFE INTERNATIONAL USA—See Seminole Tribe of Florida, Inc.; *U.S. Private*, pg. 3605
HARRAH'S ARIZONA CORPORATION—See Caesars Entertainment, Inc.; *U.S. Public*, pg. 419
HARRAH'S ATLANTIC CITY OPERATING COMPANY, LLC—See Caesars Entertainment, Inc.; *U.S. Public*, pg. 420
HARRAH'S ILLINOIS CORPORATION—See Caesars Entertainment, Inc.; *U.S. Public*, pg. 419
HARRAH'S LAS VEGAS, LLC—See Caesars Entertainment, Inc.; *U.S. Public*, pg. 420
HARRAH'S LAUGHLIN, LLC—See Caesars Entertainment, Inc.; *U.S. Public*, pg. 420
HARRAH'S RENO—See Caesars Entertainment, Inc.; *U.S. Public*, pg. 419
HARVEYS TAHOE MANAGEMENT COMPANY, INC.—See Caesars Entertainment, Inc.; *U.S. Public*, pg. 419
HAZEL LESSEE LLC—See Pebblebrook Hotel Trust; *U.S. Public*, pg. 1660
HC AURORA, LLC—See PENN Entertainment, Inc.; *U.S. Public*, pg. 1662
HC BANGOR, LLC—See PENN Entertainment, Inc.; *U.S. Public*, pg. 1662
HORSESHOE ENTERTAINMENT, INC.—See Caesars Entertainment, Inc.; *U.S. Public*, pg. 420
THE HORSESHU HOTEL & CASINO—See PENN Entertainment, Inc.; *U.S. Public*, pg. 1662
HWCC-TUNICA, LLC—See PENN Entertainment, Inc.; *U.S. Public*, pg. 1662
HYATT REGENCY LAKE TAHOE RESORT & CASINO—See Hyatt Hotels Corporation; *U.S. Public*, pg. 1078
IKE GAMING, INC.; *U.S. Private*, pg. 2041
INDIANA GAMING COMPANY, LLC—See PENN Entertainment, Inc.; *U.S. Public*, pg. 1662
IOC-CARUTHERSVILLE, LLC—See Century Casinos, Inc.; *U.S. Public*, pg. 474
IOC-KANSAS CITY, INC.—See Bally's Corporation; *U.S. Public*, pg. 268
ISLE OF CAPRI BETTENDORF, L.C.—See Bally's Corporation; *U.S. Public*, pg. 268
ISLE OF CAPRI BLACK HAWK, LLC—See Bally's Corporation; *U.S. Public*, pg. 268
JACKPOT JUNCTION CASINO HOTEL; *U.S. Private*, pg. 2175
JAZZ CASINO COMPANY, LLC—See Caesars Entertainment, Inc.; *U.S. Public*, pg. 420
JEAN DEVELOPMENT COMPANY, LLC—See MGM Resorts International; *U.S. Public*, pg. 1435
JOHN ASCUAGA'S NUGGET; *U.S. Private*, pg. 2220
LAGUNA HOLIDAY CLUB LIMITED—See Banyan Tree Holdings Ltd.; *Int'l*, pg. 855
LAS VEGAS ARENA MANAGEMENT, LLC—See MGM Resorts International; *U.S. Public*, pg. 1435
LAS VEGAS SANDS CORP.; *U.S. Public*, pg. 1293
THE LINQ HOTEL & CASINO—See Caesars Entertainment, Inc.; *U.S. Public*, pg. 420
LVGV, LLC—See PENN Entertainment, Inc.; *U.S. Public*, pg. 1662
MAHONEY'S SILVER NUGGET INC.; *U.S. Private*, pg. 2550
MANDALAY CORP.—See MGM Resorts International; *U.S. Public*, pg. 1435
MARTINGALE MALTA 2 LIMITED—See Entain PLC; *Int'l*, pg. 2450
MASHANTUCKET PEQUOT GAMING ENTERPRISE INC.; *U.S. Private*, pg. 2601
MAWARID HOTELS AND HOSPITALITY LLC—See Alpha Dhabi Holding PJSC; *Int'l*, pg. 367
MERKUR CASINO LIMITED—See Gauselmann AG; *Int'l*, pg. 2890
MERKUR SPIELBANKEN SACHSEN-ANHALT GMBH, & CO. KG—See Gauselmann AG; *Int'l*, pg. 2890
MERKUR SPORTWETTEN GMBH—See Gauselmann AG; *Int'l*, pg. 2890
MGM CHINA HOLDINGS LIMITED—See MGM Resorts International; *U.S. Public*, pg. 1435
MGM FINANCE CORP.—See MGM Resorts International; *U.S. Public*, pg. 1435
MGM GRAND DETROIT, LLC—See MGM Resorts International; *U.S. Public*, pg. 1435
MGM GRAND HOTEL, LLC—See MGM Resorts International; *U.S. Public*, pg. 1435
MGM GROWTH PROPERTIES LLC—See VICI Properties Inc.; *U.S. Public*, pg. 2295
MGM NATIONAL HARBOR, LLC—See MGM Resorts International; *U.S. Public*, pg. 1435
MGM RESORTS MISSISSIPPI, INC.—See Cherokee Nation Businesses; *U.S. Private*, pg. 873
MGM SPRINGFIELD, LLC—See MGM Resorts International; *U.S. Public*, pg. 1435
MIAMI VALLEY GAMING & RACING, LLC—See Churchill Downs, Inc.; *U.S. Public*, pg. 493
MIRAGE RESORTS INCORPORATED—See MGM Resorts International; *U.S. Public*, pg. 1435
MOHEGAN TRIBAL GAMING AUTHORITY; *U.S. Private*, pg. 2765
MONARCH BLACK HAWK, INC.—See Monarch Casino & Resort, Inc.; *U.S. Public*, pg. 1460
MONTREIGN OPERATING COMPANY, LLC—See Empire Resorts, Inc.; *U.S. Public*, pg. 1385
MOORETOWN RANCHERIA; *U.S. Private*, pg. 2781
MOUNTAINEER PARK, INC.—See Century Casinos, Inc.; *U.S. Public*, pg. 474
MSP MUNZSPIELPARTNER GMBH & CO. KG—See Gauselmann AG; *Int'l*, pg. 2891

N.A.I.C.S. INDEX

721199 — ALL OTHER TRAVELER ...

NEVADA GOLD & CASINOS, INC.—See Maverick Gold LLC; *U.S. Private*, pg. 2616
NEVADA PALACE, LLC—See Boyd Gaming Corporation; *U.S. Public*, pg. 378
NEVADA PROPERTY 1 LLC—See Deutsche Bank Aktiengesellschaft; *Int'l*, pg. 2061
NEW CASTLE CORP.—See MGM Resorts International; *U.S. Public*, pg. 1435
NEW YORK-NEW YORK HOTEL & CASINO, LLC—See MGM Resorts International; *U.S. Public*, pg. 1435
NP FIESTA LLC—See Red Rock Resorts, Inc.; *U.S. Public*, pg. 1770
NP PALACE LLC—See Red Rock Resorts, Inc.; *U.S. Public*, pg. 1770
NP RANCHO LLC—See Red Rock Resorts, Inc.; *U.S. Public*, pg. 1770
NP RED ROCK LLC—See Red Rock Resorts, Inc.; *U.S. Public*, pg. 1770
NP SANTA FE LLC—See Red Rock Resorts, Inc.; *U.S. Public*, pg. 1770
NP SUNSET LLC—See Red Rock Resorts, Inc.; *U.S. Public*, pg. 1770
NP TEXAS LLC—See Red Rock Resorts, Inc.; *U.S. Public*, pg. 1770
PAR-A-DICE GAMING CORPORATION—See Boyd Gaming Corporation; *U.S. Public*, pg. 378
PARIS LAS VEGAS OPERATING COMPANY, LLC—See Caesars Entertainment, Inc.; *U.S. Public*, pg. 420
PCI GAMING AUTHORITY; *U.S. Public*, pg. 3120
PEPPERMILL CASINOS, INC.; *U.S. Private*, pg. 3145
PEPPERMILL HOTEL CASINO—See Peppermill Casinos, Inc.; *U.S. Private*, pg. 3145
PHW LAS VEGAS, LLC—See Caesars Entertainment, Inc.; *U.S. Public*, pg. 420
PIONEER GROUP, INC.—See Full House Resorts, Inc.; *U.S. Public*, pg. 892
PIONEER HOTEL INC.—See Archon Corporation; *U.S. Public*, pg. 185
PORT AVENTURA ENTERTAINMENT, S.A.U.—See BI-Invest Advisors S.A.; *Int'l*, pg. 1017
POSADAS DE SAN JUAN ASSOCIATES—See Blackstone Inc.; *U.S. Public*, pg. 357
PPI, INC.—See Bally's Corporation; *U.S. Public*, pg. 268
PREMIER ENTERTAINMENT BILOXI, LLC—See Bally's Corporation; *U.S. Public*, pg. 268
PRESCOTT RESORT & CONVENTION CENTER L.P.—See W.M. Grace Development Company; *U.S. Private*, pg. 4422
PRESQUE ISLE DOWNS, INC.—See Churchill Downs, Inc.; *U.S. Public*, pg. 494
PRIMM VALLEY CASINO RESORTS—See Z Capital Group, LLC; *U.S. Private*, pg. 4595
RAILROAD PASS INVESTMENT GROUP—See MGM Resorts International; *U.S. Public*, pg. 1435
RAINBOW CASINO-VICKSBURG PARTNERSHIP, L.P.—See Bally's Corporation; *U.S. Public*, pg. 268
RED RIVER ENTERTAINMENT OF SHREVEPORT, LLC—See Boyd Gaming Corporation; *U.S. Public*, pg. 378
RED ROCK RESORT—See Red Rock Resorts, Inc.; *U.S. Public*, pg. 1770
RESORT SOLUTIONS LIMITED—See Marriott Vacations Worldwide Corporation; *U.S. Public*, pg. 1374
ROYAL CASINO DGB GMBH—See Gauselmann AG; *Int'l*, pg. 2890
SANDS BETHWORKS GAMING LLC—See PCI Gaming Authority; *U.S. Private*, pg. 3120
SANDS REGENCY CASINO HOTEL—See Jacobs Entertainment, Inc.; *U.S. Private*, pg. 2180
SHOWBOAT ATLANTIC CITY OPERATING COMPANY, LLC—See Caesars Entertainment, Inc.; *U.S. Public*, pg. 419
SILVER HERITAGE GROUP LIMITED—See HatchAsia Inc.; *Int'l*, pg. 3284
SILVER SLIPPER CASINO VENTURE, LLC—See Full House Resorts, Inc.; *U.S. Public*, pg. 892
SILVERSTAR CASINO (PTY) LTD.—See Hosken Consolidated Investments Limited; *Int'l*, pg. 3485
SOUTHERN ILLINOIS RIVERBOAT/CASINO CRUISES, INC.—See Caesars Entertainment, Inc.; *U.S. Public*, pg. 420
STIRLING HOTELS & RESORTS, INC.; *U.S. Private*, pg. 3813
ST. LOUIS GAMING VENTURES, LLC—See PENN Entertainment, Inc.; *U.S. Public*, pg. 1662
STRATOSPHERE GAMING LLC—See Golden Entertainment, Inc.; *U.S. Public*, pg. 950
STRATOSPHERE LLC—See Golden Entertainment, Inc.; *U.S. Public*, pg. 950
ST. REGIS SAADIYAT ISLAND RESORT - ABU DHABI—See Alpha Dhabi Holding PJSC; *Int'l*, pg. 368
TELAL RESORT LLC—See Alpha Dhabi Holding PJSC; *Int'l*, pg. 368
TOURIST COMPANY OF NIGERIA PLC.—See Ikeja Hotel Plc; *Int'l*, pg. 3610
TRANS WORLD CORPORATION—See Far East Consortium International Limited; *Int'l*, pg. 2616
TRANS WORLD HOTELS & ENTERTAINMENT A.S.—See Far East Consortium International Limited; *Int'l*, pg. 2616
TRANS WORLD HOTELS GERMANY GMBH—See Far East Consortium International Limited; *Int'l*, pg. 2616
TREASURE CHEST CASINO, L.L.C.—See Boyd Gaming Corporation; *U.S. Public*, pg. 378
TREASURE CHEST, LLC—See Boyd Gaming Corporation; *U.S. Public*, pg. 378
TREASURE ISLAND CORP.; *U.S. Private*, pg. 4216
TROPICANA ENTERTAINMENT INC.—See Caesars Entertainment, Inc.; *U.S. Public*, pg. 420
TROPICANA LAS VEGAS, INC.—See PENN Entertainment, Inc.; *U.S. Public*, pg. 1663
TSOGO SUN EMONTI (PTY) LTD.—See Hosken Consolidated Investments Limited; *Int'l*, pg. 3485
TSOGO SUN GAMING (PTY) LIMTED—See Hosken Consolidated Investments Limited; *Int'l*, pg. 3485
TSOGO SUN KWAZULU-NATAL (PTY) LTD.—See Hosken Consolidated Investments Limited; *Int'l*, pg. 3485
TUNICA GOLF COURSE, LLC—See Boyd Gaming Corporation; *U.S. Public*, pg. 378
TURTLE MOUNTAIN BAND OF CHIPPEWA INDIANS INC.; *U.S. Private*, pg. 4262
TWIN RIVER - TIVERTON, LLC—See Bally's Corporation; *U.S. Public*, pg. 268
UTGR, INC.—See Bally's Corporation; *U.S. Public*, pg. 268
VACATION VILLAGE, INC.—See Golden Entertainment, Inc.; *U.S. Public*, pg. 950
VALLEY FORGE CONVENTION CENTER PARTNERS, LLC—See Boyd Gaming Corporation; *U.S. Public*, pg. 378
VCAT, LLC; *U.S. Private*, pg. 4349
VERNON DOWNS CASINO & HOTEL; *U.S. Private*, pg. 4368
VIRGIN RIVER CASINO CORPORATION—See Mesquite Gaming, LLC; *U.S. Private*, pg. 2679
WATERFORD GROUP, LLC; *U.S. Private*, pg. 4453
WEST COAST LEISURE (PTY) LTD.—See Hosken Consolidated Investments Limited; *Int'l*, pg. 3485
WILD ROSE CASINO & RESORT; *U.S. Private*, pg. 4518
WINDSOR CASINO LIMITED—See Caesars Entertainment, Inc.; *U.S. Public*, pg. 420
WMCK-VENTURE CORP.—See Century Casinos, Inc.; *U.S. Public*, pg. 474
WYNN LAS VEGAS, LLC—See Wynn Resorts Limited; *U.S. Public*, pg. 2384
WYNN MACAU, LIMITED—See Wynn Resorts Limited; *U.S. Public*, pg. 2385
WYNN RESORTS LIMITED; *U.S. Public*, pg. 2384
ZALANTA RESORT AT THE VILLAGE, LLC—See Waterfall Asset Management LLC; *U.S. Private*, pg. 4453

721191 — BED-AND-BREAKFAST INNS

ARC SUN CITY WEST, LLC—See Welltower Inc.; *U.S. Public*, pg. 2347
GREATER PARK CITY COMPANY INC.—See Powdr Corp.; *U.S. Private*, pg. 3236
JAMESON INNS, Inc.—See J.E. Robert Company; *U.S. Private*, pg. 2162
PIERPONT INN, INC.—See DKN Hotel LLC; *U.S. Private*, pg. 1247
ROARING LLC—See Fitzpatrick Companies Inc.; *U.S. Private*, pg. 1536
WEST MONTGOMERY HOTEL HOLDINGS INC.—See Sunburst Hospitality Corporation; *U.S. Private*, pg. 3865

721199 — ALL OTHER TRAVELER ACCOMMODATION

305 DEGREES LLC; *U.S. Private*, pg. 7
ACCOR BRASIL SA—See Accor S.A.; *Int'l*, pg. 91
ACCOR GMBH—See Accor S.A.; *Int'l*, pg. 91
ADMIRAL STRAND FERIEHUSE APS—See Axel Springer SE; *Int'l*, pg. 766
ADVENTURE INC.; *Int'l*, pg. 167
ALLIED ARABIA.—See Allied International Ltd.; *Int'l*, pg. 357
ALPINE HOLDING COMPANY; *U.S. Private*, pg. 201
ALSTONS TRAVEL LIMITED—See ANSA McAL Limited; *Int'l*, pg. 477
AMIVAC S.A.S—See HomeToGo SE; *Int'l*, pg. 3455
ARRIVIA—See 3i Group plc; *Int'l*, pg. 8
ATRAVEO GMBH—See HomeToGo SE; *Int'l*, pg. 3456
AYALA HOTELS, INC.—See Ayala Corporation; *Int'l*, pg. 774
BAREFOOT LODGE & HIKER HOSTEL, LLC—See Barefoot Luxury, Inc.; *U.S. Private*, pg. 474
BEAVER CREEK RESORT—See Vail Resorts, Inc.; *U.S. Public*, pg. 2272
BECK COMPANY; *U.S. Private*, pg. 510
BOREAL RIDGE CORP—See Powdr Corp.; *U.S. Private*, pg. 3236
BOURNE LEISURE GROUP LTD.—See Blackstone Inc.; *U.S. Public*, pg. 352
BRIDGESTREET ACCOMMODATIONS LONDON LTD.—See Independence Capital Partners, LLC; *U.S. Private*, pg. 2057
BRIDGESTREET WORLDWIDE INC.—See Independence Capital Partners, LLC; *U.S. Private*, pg. 2057
CANYON RANCH MANAGEMENT, LLC; *U.S. Private*, pg. 736
CASAMUNDO GMBH—See HomeToGo SE; *Int'l*, pg. 3456
CFS INVESTMENT AND IMPORT EXPORT TRADING JSC; *Int'l*, pg. 1430
CLUB MEDITERRANEE ITALIA S.P.A.—See Fosun International Limited; *Int'l*, pg. 2750
CLUB MEDITERRANEE SAS—See Fosun International Limited; *Int'l*, pg. 2750
CLUB MEDITERRANEE U.K. LTD.—See Fosun International Limited; *Int'l*, pg. 2750
DH YORK MANAGEMENT LLC—See Hyatt Hotels Corporation; *U.S. Public*, pg. 1077
E-DOMIZIL AG—See HomeToGo SE; *Int'l*, pg. 3456
E-DOMIZIL GMBH—See HomeToGo SE; *Int'l*, pg. 3456
ELDORA MOUNTAIN RESORT—See Powdr Corp.; *U.S. Private*, pg. 3236
EQUITY LIFESTYLE PROPERTIES, INC.; *U.S. Public*, pg. 790
FERIES S.R.L.—See HomeToGo SE; *Int'l*, pg. 3456
THE GLENEAGLES HOTEL—See Diageo plc; *Int'l*, pg. 2103
GLOBAIR HUNGARY KFT.—See Marriott International, Inc.; *U.S. Public*, pg. 1370
GLOBAL EDUCATION CITY HOLDINGS INC.—See Global Education Communities Corp; *Int'l*, pg. 2995
GREAT CEDAR HOTEL—See Mashantucket Pequot Gaming Enterprise Inc.; *U.S. Private*, pg. 2601
THE HEIGHTS PTY LTD—See Bonatla Property Holdings Limited; *Int'l*, pg. 1105
THE HELMSLEY CARLTON HOUSE—See Helmsley Enterprises, Inc.; *U.S. Private*, pg. 1912
HIATUS SPA & RETREAT; *U.S. Private*, pg. 1932
HOMEEXCHANGE.COM INC.; *U.S. Private*, pg. 1973
HOSEASONS HOLIDAYS LIMITED—See Travel & Leisure Co.; *U.S. Public*, pg. 2185
HOSTELLING INTERNATIONAL USA; *U.S. Private*, pg. 1988
HOTEL MAJESTIC LLC—See Kennedy-Wilson Holdings, Inc.; *U.S. Public*, pg. 1223
HTP KORCULA D.D.; *Int'l*, pg. 3509
INNS OF UGANDA—See Alam Group of Companies; *Int'l*, pg. 289
INTRAWEST HOSPITALITY MANAGEMENT, LLC—See KSL Capital Partners, LLC; *U.S. Private*, pg. 2354
LAKE AUSTIN SPA RESORT; *U.S. Private*, pg. 2374
LANCASTER HOST RESORT & CONFERENCE CENTER; *U.S. Private*, pg. 2381
LODGIAN INC.—See Lone Star Global Acquisitions, LLC; *U.S. Private*, pg. 2489
MOUNT BACHELOR VILLAGE DRIVE—See Brooks Resources Corporation; *U.S. Private*, pg. 664
MOUNT SNOW, LTD.—See Vail Resorts, Inc.; *U.S. Public*, pg. 2271
NEXTPLAY TECHNOLOGIES, INC.; *U.S. Public*, pg. 1527
NOVOTEL AMSTERDAM CITY—See Accor S.A.; *Int'l*, pg. 92
ORA RESORT CO., LTD.—See Daelim Industrial Co., Ltd.; *Int'l*, pg. 1908
PEDDLER'S VILLAGE, INC.; *U.S. Private*, pg. 3127
PEEK'N PEAK RECREATION INC.; *U.S. Private*, pg. 3128
POSADAS USA INC.—See Grupo Posadas S.A.B. de C.V.; *Int'l*, pg. 3134
RED ROOF INNS, INC.; *U.S. Private*, pg. 3375
THE REGENCY HOTEL—See Loews Corporation; *U.S. Public*, pg. 1340
THE RITZ-CARLTON HOTEL COMPANY OF QATAR LIMITED—See Marriott International, Inc.; *U.S. Public*, pg. 1373
THE RITZ HOTEL (LONDON) LIMITED—See Ellerman Investments Ltd.; *Int'l*, pg. 2365
ROUNDTOP MOUNTAIN RESORT—See Vail Resorts, Inc.; *U.S. Public*, pg. 2271
SAMALAJU PROPERTIES SDN BHD—See Cahya Mata Sarawak Berhad; *Int'l*, pg. 1251
SAS LE CHATEAU D'EBBLINGHEM—See Cox & Kings Limited; *Int'l*, pg. 1823
SHERATON BOSTON HOTEL—See Marriott International, Inc.; *U.S. Public*, pg. 1372
SHERATON SUITES PHILADELPHIA AIRPORT—See Marriott International, Inc.; *U.S. Public*, pg. 1372
SNOW TIME, INC.—See Vail Resorts, Inc.; *U.S. Public*, pg. 2271
SNOW VALLEY LLC—See KSL Capital Partners, LLC; *U.S. Private*, pg. 2354
TOPNOTCH RESORT & SPA—See Winston Harton Holdings, LLC; *U.S. Private*, pg. 4544
TRAVIAUSTRIA GMBH—See Deutsche Lufthansa AG; *Int'l*, pg. 2071
TUTHILL CORP; *U.S. Private*, pg. 4262
TWO TREES INN—See Mashantucket Pequot Gaming Enterprise Inc.; *U.S. Private*, pg. 2601
VACATION RESORTS INTERNATIONAL, LLC—See Marriott Vacations Worldwide Corporation; *U.S. Public*, pg. 1374
VACATIONROOST GROUP INC.; *U.S. Private*, pg. 4329
VISAHQ.COM INC.; *U.S. Private*, pg. 4389
WARNER LEISURE LTD.—See Blackstone Inc.; *U.S. Public*, pg. 352

721199 — ALL OTHER TRAVELER ...

W CHICAGO - LAKESHORE HOTEL—See Park Hotels & Resorts Inc.; *U.S. Public*, pg. 1638
THE WESTIN FORT LAUDERDALE—See Marriott International, Inc.; *U.S. Public*, pg. 1372
WESTIN HOTEL MANAGEMENT, LP—See Marriott International, Inc.; *U.S. Public*, pg. 1372
WYNDHAM EXCHANGE AND RENTALS, INC.—See Travel & Leisure Co.; *U.S. Public*, pg. 2185

721211 — RV (RECREATIONAL VEHICLE) PARKS AND CAMPGROUNDS

CAREFREE RV RESORTS; *U.S. Private*, pg. 753
EASTGATE STORAGE, LLC—See CBL & Associates Properties, Inc.; *U.S. Public*, pg. 458
HAVEN LEISURE LTD.—See Blackstone Inc.; *U.S. Public*, pg. 352
HOMAIR VACANCES SA—See The Carlyle Group Inc.; *U.S. Public*, pg. 2047
NACO CORP.—See Equity LifeStyle Properties, Inc.; *U.S. Public*, pg. 790
PISMO COAST VILLAGE, INC.; *U.S. Private*, pg. 3190
POUGHKEEPSIE-HIGHLAND RAILROAD BRIDGE CO. INC.; *U.S. Private*, pg. 3236
SUWANNEE RIVER RENDEZVOUS RESORT & CAMPGROUND; *U.S. Private*, pg. 3887
VICTORY RANCH; *U.S. Private*, pg. 4379
VIRGINIA LANDING CORPORATION—See Equity LifeStyle Properties, Inc.; *U.S. Public*, pg. 790
WINDROCK PARK, LLC—See Windrock Land Company; *U.S. Public*, pg. 2373

721214 — RECREATIONAL AND VACATION CAMPS (EXCEPT CAMPGROUNDS)

AFTON ALPS INC.; *U.S. Private*, pg. 124
BELAMBRA VVF SNC—See Caravelle SA; *Int'l*, pg. 1320
BERJAYA VACATION CLUB BERHAD—See Berjaya Corporation Berhad; *Int'l*, pg. 983
CAMPGROUP LLC; *U.S. Private*, pg. 731
CAMPING IN COMFORT B.V.—See Cox & Kings Limited; *Int'l*, pg. 1822
CAMP MANAGEMENT INC.; *U.S. Private*, pg. 729
CAMP WAHANOWIN; *Int'l*, pg. 1274
CAROLINA LANDING CORPORATION—See Equity LifeStyle Properties, Inc.; *U.S. Public*, pg. 790
CASTLE HILL RSL CLUB LTD.; *Int'l*, pg. 1357
CULLUM & MAXEY CAMPING CENTER, INC.—See Camping World Holdings, Inc.; *U.S. Public*, pg. 427
EASYCAMP B.V.—See Cox & Kings Limited; *Int'l*, pg. 1822
ECAMP GMBH—See Cox & Kings Limited; *Int'l*, pg. 1822
EUROCAMP TRAVEL AG—See Cox & Kings Limited; *Int'l*, pg. 1822
EUROCAMP TRAVEL B.V.—See Cox & Kings Limited; *Int'l*, pg. 1822
GBR HELICOPTERS PTY. LTD.—See Experience Co Limited; *Int'l*, pg. 2588
GRAND VACATIONS SERVICES LLC—See Hilton Grand Vacations Inc.; *U.S. Public*, pg. 1040
GUIDED DISCOVERIES INC.; *U.S. Private*, pg. 1813
HOST-PLUS PTY. LIMITED; *Int'l*, pg. 3486
INDIAN LAKES WILDERNESS PRESERVE CORPORATION—See Equity LifeStyle Properties, Inc.; *U.S. Public*, pg. 790
KAMPGROUNDS OF AMERICA, INC.—See KOA Holdings Inc.; *U.S. Private*, pg. 2325
KEYCAMP HOLIDAYS (IRELAND) LIMITED—See Cox & Kings Limited; *Int'l*, pg. 1822
KOSCIUSZKO THREDBO PTY LIMITED—See Event Hospitality & Entertainment Limited; *Int'l*, pg. 2562
LAKE MINDEN RESORT—See Equity LifeStyle Properties, Inc.; *U.S. Public*, pg. 790
LANDSEA CAMP AND CATERING SERVICES LTD.—See Aramark; *U.S. Public*, pg. 178
LITTLE DIAMOND RV RESORT—See Equity LifeStyle Properties, Inc.; *U.S. Public*, pg. 790
THE LONE MOUNTAIN RANCH, INC.—See Makar Properties, LLC; *U.S. Private*, pg. 2556
MEADOWKIRK RETREAT DELTA FARM; *U.S. Private*, pg. 2647
NANTAHALA OUTDOOR CENTER; *U.S. Private*, pg. 2833
NATURAL RETREATS US LLC; *U.S. Private*, pg. 2867
PARK CITY MOUNTAIN RESORT—See Vail Resorts, Inc.; *U.S. Public*, pg. 2271
PARKDEAN HOLIDAYS LIMITED—See Alchemy Partners LLP; *Int'l*, pg. 300
PARKDEAN RESORTS UK LIMITED—See Alchemy Partners LLP; *Int'l*, pg. 300
PGL ADVENTURE LIMITED—See Cox & Kings Limited; *Int'l*, pg. 1823
RCI, LLC—See Travel & Leisure Co.; *U.S. Public*, pg. 2185
RCI MID-AMERICAN OFFICE—See Travel & Leisure Co.; *U.S. Public*, pg. 2185
REEF MAGIC CRUISES PTY. LTD.—See Experience Co Limited; *Int'l*, pg. 2588
RESTON ASSOCIATION; *U.S. Private*, pg. 3409

SEDONA SOUL ADVENTURES, INC.; *U.S. Private*, pg. 3597
SILVER DOLLAR GOLF & TRAP CLB—See National Home Communities LLC; *U.S. Public*, pg. 2856
SKYDIVE QUEENSTOWN LIMITED—See Experience Co Limited; *Int'l*, pg. 2588
SKYDIVE WANAKA LIMITED—See Experience Co Limited; *Int'l*, pg. 2588
SKYHAWKS SPORTS ACADEMY, INC.—See Genstar Capital, LLC; *U.S. Private*, pg. 1678
THOUSAND TRAILS LP—See Equity LifeStyle Properties, Inc.; *U.S. Public*, pg. 790
TRIPLE D OF BREVARD INC—See Outdoor Resorts of America; *U.S. Private*, pg. 3051
TURNKEY VACATION RENTALS LLC—See Vacasa, Inc.; *U.S. Public*, pg. 2270
TURTLE BEACH PRESERVE—See Equity LifeStyle Properties, Inc.; *U.S. Public*, pg. 790
THE UNITED SERVICE ORGANIZATIONS, INC.; *U.S. Private*, pg. 4129
THE WELK GROUP INC.; *U.S. Private*, pg. 4134
WILDERNESS LAKES—See Equity LifeStyle Properties, Inc.; *U.S. Public*, pg. 790

721310 — ROOMING AND BOARDING HOUSES, DORMITORIES, AND WORKERS&APOS; CAMPS

138 STUDENT LIVING JAMAICA LIMITED; *Int'l*, pg. 2
319 BRAGG STUDENT HOUSING AUBURN AL LLC—See Greystar Real Estate Partners, LLC; *U.S. Private*, pg. 1785
EDUCATION REALTY TRUST, INC.—See Greystar Real Estate Partners, LLC; *U.S. Private*, pg. 1785
EMERALD PARK SDN. BHD.—See Gromutual Berhad; *Int'l*, pg. 3087
FRASERS HOSPITALITY JAPAN KABUSHIKI KAISHA—See Frasers Property Limited; *Int'l*, pg. 2766
GEORGETOWN RETIREMENT RESIDENCE—See Holladay Corporation; *U.S. Private*, pg. 1963
THE GROUCHO CLUB LTD.—See Graphite Capital Management LLP; *Int'l*, pg. 3061
INTERMOTEL LEASING, INC.—See Corpay, Inc.; *U.S. Public*, pg. 580
INTERNATIONAL HOUSE; *U.S. Private*, pg. 2117
KAPPA KAPPA GAMMA; *U.S. Private*, pg. 2262
KENSINGTON STUDENT SERVICES LIMITED—See Graham Holdings Company; *U.S. Public*, pg. 956
LJK COMPANIES INC.—See Corpay, Inc.; *U.S. Public*, pg. 580
POINTE ESTERO BEACH RESORT—See SunStream, Inc.; *U.S. Private*, pg. 3873
SWITCHPLACE; *U.S. Private*, pg. 3894

722310 — FOOD SERVICE CONTRACTORS

AAS CATERING CO., LTD.—See Gourmet Kineya Co., Ltd.; *Int'l*, pg. 3044
ABB WIRTSCHAFTSBETRIEBE GMBH—See ABB Ltd.; *Int'l*, pg. 50
ACORN SERVICES INC.; *U.S. Private*, pg. 64
ALADDIN FOOD MANAGEMENT SERVICES, LLC—See Charterhouse Capital Partners LLP; *Int'l*, pg. 1455
ALLERGY RESEARCH GROUP LLC—See WM Partners LP; *U.S. Private*, pg. 4552
AMAZE CO., LTD.; *Int'l*, pg. 413
AMC GROUP, INC.—See ICV Partners, LLC; *U.S. Private*, pg. 2034
AMERIQUAL GROUP, LLC—See Harlan Bakeries LLC; *U.S. Private*, pg. 1865
AMERISERVE FOOD MANAGEMENT SERVICES—See Charterhouse Capital Partners LLP; *Int'l*, pg. 1455
AQUIMISA S.L.—See ALS Limited; *Int'l*, pg. 377
ARAMARK AMERICAN FOOD SERVICES, LLC—See Aramark; *U.S. Public*, pg. 176
ARAMARK FHC BUSINESS SERVICES, LLC—See Aramark; *U.S. Public*, pg. 176
ARAMARK HARRISON LODGING—See Aramark; *U.S. Public*, pg. 176
ARAMARK HEALTHCARE SUPPORT SERVICES, LLC—See Aramark; *U.S. Public*, pg. 176
ARAMARK REMOTE WORKPLACE SERVICES LTD.—See Aramark; *U.S. Public*, pg. 177
ARAMARK RESTAURATIONS GMBH—See Aramark; *U.S. Public*, pg. 176
ARAMARK SERVICIOS INTEGRALES, S.A.—See Aramark; *U.S. Public*, pg. 177
ARAMARK SERVICIOS SRL—See Aramark; *U.S. Public*, pg. 177
ASAHI CALPIS WELLNESS CO., LTD.—See Asahi Group Holdings Ltd.; *Int'l*, pg. 593
A TABLE MATSUYA CO., LTD.—See ALPICO Holdings Co., Ltd.; *Int'l*, pg. 371
AURIC PACIFIC MARKETING PTE LTD—See Diethelm Keller Holding Limited; *Int'l*, pg. 2116

AUTOGRILL CATERING UK LIMITED—See Avolta AG; *Int'l*, pg. 749
AUTOGRILL IBERIA S.L.U.—See Avolta AG; *Int'l*, pg. 749
A'VIANDS, LLC—See Charterhouse Capital Partners LLP; *Int'l*, pg. 1455
BASSIAN FARMS, INC.—See The Chefs' Warehouse, Inc.; *U.S. Public*, pg. 2058
BERLI JUCKER FOODS LIMITED—See Berli Jucker Public Co. Ltd.; *Int'l*, pg. 985
BESTWAY WHOLESALE LIMITED—See Bestway (Holdings) Limited; *Int'l*, pg. 1001
BONANZA FOODS & PROVISIONS INC.; *U.S. Private*, pg. 613
BON-FOOD PTE LTD—See Bonvests Holdings Limited; *Int'l*, pg. 1110
BONFRESH PTE LTD—See Bonvests Holdings Limited; *Int'l*, pg. 1110
BRAKE BROS LTD. - THORPE DEPOT—See Sysco Corporation; *U.S. Public*, pg. 1973
BRAKES FOODSERVICE NI LIMITED—See Sysco Corporation; *U.S. Public*, pg. 1973
BROCK & COMPANY INC.; *U.S. Private*, pg. 660
BVB EVENT & CATERING GMBH—See Borussia Dortmund GmbH & Co. KGaA; *Int'l*, pg. 1115
CAMPBELL CATERING (BELFAST) LTD.—See Aramark; *U.S. Public*, pg. 177
CANTEEN SERVICES INC.; *U.S. Private*, pg. 735
CANTERBURY PARK CONCESSIONS, INC.—See Canterbury Park Holding Corporation; *U.S. Public*, pg. 430
CANTU SERVICES INC.; *U.S. Private*, pg. 736
CHARTWELLS USA—See Compass Group PLC; *Int'l*, pg. 1751
CJ FOODVILLE USA INC.—See CJ Corporation; *Int'l*, pg. 1632
CJ QINGDAO FOODS CO., LTD.—See CJ Corporation; *Int'l*, pg. 1633
THE COASTAL COMPANIES—See Continental Grain Company; *U.S. Private*, pg. 1029
COMPASS CATERING Y SERVICIOS CHILE LIMITADA—See Compass Group PLC; *Int'l*, pg. 1750
COMPASS GROUP BELGILUX S.A.—See Compass Group PLC; *Int'l*, pg. 1750
COMPASS GROUP FS FINLAND OY—See Compass Group PLC; *Int'l*, pg. 1750
COMPASS GROUP SERVICES COLOMBIA S.A.—See Compass Group PLC; *Int'l*, pg. 1751
COMPASS GROUP SWEDEN AB—See Compass Group PLC; *Int'l*, pg. 1751
COMPASS INDIA SUPPORT SERVICES PRIVATE LIMITED—See Compass Group PLC; *Int'l*, pg. 1751
CONSUMER PRODUCT DISTRIBUTORS, INC.; *U.S. Private*, pg. 1025
CONVINI SVERIGE AB; *Int'l*, pg. 1787
CORPORATE CHEFS INC.—See Charterhouse Capital Partners LLP; *Int'l*, pg. 1455
COUNTRY KITCHEN INTERNATIONAL, INC.—See Kitchen Investment Group; *U.S. Private*, pg. 2316
CREMONINI CHEF IBERICA S.A.—See Cremonini S.p.A.; *Int'l*, pg. 1838
CSG FOOD SOLUTIONS PROPRIETARY LIMITED—See CSG Holdings Limited; *Int'l*, pg. 1864
CULINAIRE DES PAYS DE L'ADOUR SAS—See Compass Group PLC; *Int'l*, pg. 1751
CULINART, INC.—See Compass Group PLC; *Int'l*, pg. 1751
CULT FOOD SCIENCE CORP.; *Int'l*, pg. 1877
DDFOODSOLUTIONS; *U.S. Private*, pg. 1181
DELAWARE NORTH COMPANIES, INC.; *U.S. Private*, pg. 1194
DELKA S.A.—See Floridienne SA; *Int'l*, pg. 2708
DFO, LLC—See Denny's Corporation; *U.S. Public*, pg. 654
DO & CO POLAND SP. Z O.O.—See DO & CO Aktiengesellschaft; *Int'l*, pg. 2152
DOMINO'S PIZZA GERMANY GMBH—See Domino's Pizza Group plc; *Int'l*, pg. 2162
EISHOKU-MEDIX, INC.—See Compass Group PLC; *Int'l*, pg. 1751
ELMER'S RESTAURANTS, INC.; *U.S. Private*, pg. 1376
ESASLIGRUP—See ESAS Holding A.S.; *Int'l*, pg. 2501
EUREST BREMEN GMBH—See Compass Group PLC; *Int'l*, pg. 1751
EUREST PROPER MEALS DE MEXICO S.A. DE C.V.—See Compass Group PLC; *Int'l*, pg. 1751
EUREST RESTAURATIONSBETRIEBSGESELLSCHAFT M.B.H—See Compass Group PLC; *Int'l*, pg. 1752
EUREST UK LIMITED—See Compass Group PLC; *Int'l*, pg. 1752
FAMOUS BRANDS INTERNATIONAL; *U.S. Private*, pg. 1471
FEEDR LIMITED—See Compass Group PLC; *Int'l*, pg. 1752
FITZ, VOGT & ASSOCIATES, LTD.—See Charterhouse Capital Partners LLP; *Int'l*, pg. 1455
FLIK INTERNATIONAL—See Compass Group PLC; *Int'l*, pg. 1751
FLINCKHEUVEL BV—See Compass Group PLC; *Int'l*, pg. 1752
FOODGUYS; *U.S. Private*, pg. 1561
THE FRESH DIET INC.; *U.S. Private*, pg. 4031
THE FRUITGUYS; *U.S. Private*, pg. 4031

N.A.I.C.S. INDEX

722320 — CATERERS

FTA FOOD SOLUTIONS PTY LTD; *Int'l*, pg. 2800
GIDASER GIDA DAGITIM SANAYI VE TICARET A.S.—See ESAS Holding A.S.; *Int'l*, pg. 2501
GODDARD CATERING GROUP BOGOTA LTDA.—See Goddard Enterprises Limited; *Int'l*, pg. 3019
GOOD SOURCE SOLUTIONS, INC.—See Alvarez & Marsal, Inc.; *U.S. Private*, pg. 213
GOOD SOURCE SOLUTIONS, INC.—See Highview Capital, LLC; *U.S. Private*, pg. 1942
GOOD SOURCE SOLUTIONS—See Alvarez & Marsal, Inc.; *U.S. Private*, pg. 213
GOOD SOURCE SOLUTIONS—See Highview Capital, LLC; *U.S. Private*, pg. 1942
GORDON FOOD SERVICE INC.; *U.S. Private*, pg. 1743
GREAT WESTERN DINING SERVICE, INC., *U.S. Private*, pg. 1768
GRILL CONCEPTS, INC.; *U.S. Private*, pg. 1789
GSL SOLUTIONS, INC.—See Becton, Dickinson & Company; *U.S. Public*, pg. 292
GUANGZHOU NANLAND AIR CATERING COMPANY LIMITED—See China Southern Airlines Co., Ltd.; *Int'l*, pg. 1553
H.J. HEINZ FOODSERVICE—See 3G Capital Inc.; *U.S. Private*, pg. 10
H.J. HEINZ FOODSERVICE—See Berkshire Hathaway Inc.; *U.S. Public*, pg. 317
HJS CONDIMENTS LIMITED—See Hayleys PLC; *Int'l*, pg. 3291
HMSHOST CORPORATION—See Avolta AG; *Int'l*, pg. 749
HORMEL FOODS CORP. - FOODSERVICE DIVISION—See Hormel Foods Corporation; *U.S. Public*, pg. 1054
HYUNDAI GF HOLDINGS CO., LTD.; *Int'l*, pg. 3556
INDOGUNA LORDLY COMPANY LIMITED—See C.P. All Public Company Limited; *Int'l*, pg. 1244
INDOGUNA (SINGAPORE) PTE. LTD.—See C.P. All Public Company Limited; *Int'l*, pg. 1244
INDOGUNA VINA FOOD SERVICE COMPANY LIMITED—See C.P. All Public Company Limited; *Int'l*, pg. 1244
INSTITUTIONAL PROCESSING SERVICES, LLC—See Aramark; *U.S. Public*, pg. 177
J&M CATERING SERVICES NV—See Compass Group PLC; *Int'l*, pg. 1752
JM SWANK, LLC—See Platinum Equity, LLC; *U.S. Private*, pg. 3205
KANNE CAFE GMBH—See Compass Group PLC; *Int'l*, pg. 1752
LA RECETTA SOLUCIONES GASTRONOMICAS INTEGRADAS S.A.S.—See Grupo Nutresa S.A.; *Int'l*, pg. 3133
LEGEND FOOD SERVICE LLC; *U.S. Private*, pg. 2418
LEONARDI GMBH & CO. KG—See Compass Group PLC; *Int'l*, pg. 1752
LEONARDI HPM GMBH—See Compass Group PLC; *Int'l*, pg. 1752
LEONARDI SVM GMBH—See Compass Group PLC; *Int'l*, pg. 1752
LESSINGS INC.; *U.S. Private*, pg. 2432
LINDLEY FOOD SERVICE CORPORATION—See Charterhouse Capital Partners LLP; *Int'l*, pg. 1455
MAXZI THE GOOD FOOD RESTAURANT & CAFE L.L.C.—See C.P. All Public Company Limited; *Int'l*, pg. 1244
MBM CORPORATION; *U.S. Private*, pg. 2624
MEDUSPLUS GMBH—See Asklepios Kliniken GmbH & Co. KGaA; *Int'l*, pg. 623
NEWK'S FRANCHISE COMPANY; *U.S. Private*, pg. 2915
NEXT LEVEL HOSPITALITY SERVICES, LLC—See Aramark; *U.S. Public*, pg. 178
NUTRITION INC.; *U.S. Private*, pg. 2974
NUTRITION MANAGEMENT SERVICES COMPANY; *U.S. Public*, pg. 1556
OCCITANIE RESTAURATION SAS—See Compass Group PLC; *Int'l*, pg. 1752
OCEANE DE RESTAURATION SAS—See Compass Group PLC; *Int'l*, pg. 1752
OPAA FOOD MANAGEMENT INC.; *U.S. Private*, pg. 3028
PEDUS FOOD SERVICES INC.—See Dussmann Stiftung & Co. KGaA; *Int'l*, pg. 2235
POPMAIL.COM, INC.; *U.S. Private*, pg. 3228
PREFERRED MARKETING SOLUTIONS, INC.—See T Enterprises, Inc.; *U.S. Private*, pg. 3909
PREFERRED MEALS, INC.—See Charterhouse Capital Partners LLP; *Int'l*, pg. 1455
RED ROBIN FREDERICK COUNTY, LLC—See Red Robin Gourmet Burgers, Inc.; *U.S. Public*, pg. 1769
RED ROBIN OF BALTIMORE COUNTY, INC.—See Red Robin Gourmet Burgers, Inc.; *U.S. Public*, pg. 1769
RED ROBIN OF CHARLES COUNTY, INC.—See Red Robin Gourmet Burgers, Inc.; *U.S. Public*, pg. 1769
REINHART FOODSERVICE, LLC - BURLINGTON DIVISION—See Performance Food Group Company; *U.S. Public*, pg. 1675
REINHART FOODSERVICE, LLC - CLEVELAND DIVISION—See Performance Food Group Company; *U.S. Public*, pg. 1675
REINHART FOODSERVICE, LLC - RICHMOND DIVISION—See Performance Food Group Company; *U.S. Public*, pg. 1675
REINHART FOODSERVICE, LLC - SHREVEPORT DIVISION—See Performance Food Group Company; *U.S. Public*, pg. 1676
REINHART FOODSERVICE, LLC - SPRINGFIELD DIVISION—See Performance Food Group Company; *U.S. Public*, pg. 1676
REINHART FOODSERVICE, LLC - TIDEWATER DIVISION—See Performance Food Group Company; *U.S. Public*, pg. 1676
REINHART FOODSERVICE, LLC - TWIN CITIES DIVISION—See Performance Food Group Company; *U.S. Public*, pg. 1676
REVOLUTION FOODS, INC.; *U.S. Private*, pg. 3416
THE RK GROUP, LLC; *U.S. Private*, pg. 4110
ROISUM ELITE SALES & MARKETING COMPANY INC.; *U.S. Private*, pg. 3473
SANKEI KAIKAN CO., LTD.—See Fuji Media Holdings, Inc.; *Int'l*, pg. 2814
SEABOARD FOODS LLC—See Seaboard Corporation; *U.S. Public*, pg. 1851
SEA HARVEST CORPORATION LIMITED—See Brimstone Investment Corporation Ltd.; *Int'l*, pg. 1164
SEIYO FOOD-COMPASS GROUP, INC.—See Compass Group PLC; *Int'l*, pg. 1752
SIAM FLIGHT SERVICES LTD.—See Deutsche Lufthansa AG; *Int'l*, pg. 2067
SIFA YEMEK VE GIDA URETIM TESISLERI TIC. A.S.—See Ihlas Holding A.S.; *Int'l*, pg. 3606
SKOR CULINARY CONCEPTS INC.—See Colabor Group Inc.; *Int'l*, pg. 1697
SMG FOOD & BEVERAGE, LLC—See Northlane Capital Partners, LLC; *U.S. Private*, pg. 2956
SMITH & SONS FOODS, INC.—See Metz Enterprises Inc.; *U.S. Private*, pg. 2691
SPARTAN SHOPS INC.; *U.S. Private*, pg. 3746
SPECTRUM CATERING—See Silver Lake Group, LLC; *U.S. Private*, pg. 3658
SUD EST TRAITEUR SAS—See Compass Group PLC; *Int'l*, pg. 1752
SYSCO ATLANTIC CANADA—See Sysco Corporation; *U.S. Public*, pg. 1975
SYSCO KNOXVILLE, LLC—See Sysco Corporation; *U.S. Public*, pg. 1976
SYSTEMS SERVICES OF AMERICA, INC.—See US Foods Holding Corp.; *U.S. Public*, pg. 2266
SYSTM FOODS INC.—See SYSTM Brands, LLC; *U.S. Private*, pg. 3908
TALOCA GMBH—See Mondelez International, Inc.; *U.S. Public*, pg. 1463
TEA AVENUE (PRIVATE) LIMITED—See Food Empire Holdings Limited; *Int'l*, pg. 2727
TOOLS FOR SCHOOLS, INC.—See Alvarez & Marsal, Inc.; *U.S. Private*, pg. 213
TOOLS FOR SCHOOLS, INC.—See Highview Capital, LLC; *U.S. Private*, pg. 1942
TRIBE MEDITERRANEAN FOODS INC—See Lakeview Farms LLC; *U.S. Private*, pg. 2378
TRINITY SERVICES GROUP, INC.—See H.I.G. Capital, LLC; *U.S. Private*, pg. 1832
TRIPLE F HOLDINGS, LLC—See Bain Capital, LP; *U.S. Private*, pg. 441
UAB CAMARGO—See Floridienne SA; *Int'l*, pg. 2708
UNIDINE CORPORATION; *U.S. Private*, pg. 4282
UNIVERSAL YUMS LLC; *U.S. Private*, pg. 4307
VALLEY SERVICES, INC.—See Charterhouse Capital Partners LLP; *Int'l*, pg. 1455
VAN EERDEN FOODSERVICE COMPANY; *U.S. Private*, pg. 4340
WHITSONS FOOD SERVICE CORP.; *U.S. Private*, pg. 4513
WILSON VALE CATERING MANAGEMENT LIMITED—See Aramark; *U.S. Public*, pg. 178
XANDRION BELGIE BVBA—See Compass Group PLC; *Int'l*, pg. 1752
YK FOOD SERVICE CO., LTD.—See Dong Won Fisheries Co., Ltd.; *Int'l*, pg. 2164

722320 — CATERERS

1ST & FRESH, LLC—See Aramark; *U.S. Public*, pg. 176
28 VILLAGES PTY LTD.—See Compass Group PLC; *Int'l*, pg. 1750
7000 SET MEAL SAS—See Compass Group PLC; *Int'l*, pg. 1750
AIRO CATERING SERVICES EESTI OU—See Deutsche Lufthansa AG; *Int'l*, pg. 2067
AIRO CATERING SERVICES LATVIJA SIA—See Deutsche Lufthansa AG; *Int'l*, pg. 2067
AIRO CATERING SERVICES - UKRAINE—See Deutsche Lufthansa AG; *Int'l*, pg. 2066
AIRPORT CATER SERVICE GMBH—See Fraport AG; *Int'l*, pg. 2764
ALAM FOOD INDUSTRIES (M) SDN. BHD.—See Alam Maritim Resources Berhad; *Int'l*, pg. 290
APLEONA AHR CARECATERING GMBH—See EQT AB; *Int'l*, pg. 2468
APLEONA HSG CULINARESS GMBH—See EQT AB; *Int'l*, pg. 2468
APOLLO SINDOORI HOTELS LIMITED; *Int'l*, pg. 518
ARAMARK CATERING LIMITED—See Aramark; *U.S. Public*, pg. 176
ARAMARK COLOMBIA SAS—See Aramark; *U.S. Public*, pg. 177
ARAMARK CO. LTD.—See Aramark; *U.S. Public*, pg. 177
ARAMARK LIMITED—See Aramark; *U.S. Public*, pg. 176
ARAMARK MANAGEMENT GMBH—See Aramark; *U.S. Public*, pg. 177
ARAMARK PERU, S.A.C.—See Aramark; *U.S. Public*, pg. 177
ARAMARK SARL—See Aramark; *U.S. Public*, pg. 177
ARAMARK SERVICIOS DE CATERING, S.L.—See Aramark; *U.S. Public*, pg. 177
ARAMARK, S.R.O.—See Aramark; *U.S. Public*, pg. 177
ARAMARK WORKPLACE SOLUTIONS (UK) LTD.—See Aramark; *U.S. Public*, pg. 177
ATESCO INDUSTRIAL CARTERING JOINT STOCK COMPANY; *Int'l*, pg. 668
ATLANTIC QUEST CATERING COMPANY—See LM Restaurants, Inc.; *U.S. Private*, pg. 2476
AVENANCE ITALIA S.P.A—See Charterhouse Capital Partners LLP; *Int'l*, pg. 1455
BANGKOK AIR CATERING CO., LTD.—See Bangkok Airways Public Company Limited; *Int'l*, pg. 832
BANGKOK AIR CATERING PHUKET CO., LTD.—See Bangkok Airways Public Company Limited; *Int'l*, pg. 832
BANGKOK AIR CATERING SAMUI CO., LTD.—See Bangkok Airways Public Company Limited; *Int'l*, pg. 832
BARRACK'S CATER INN BANQUET CENTER & CATERING; *U.S. Private*, pg. 479
B & B BETRIEBSRESTAURANTS GMBH—See DO & CO Aktiengesellschaft; *Int'l*, pg. 2151
BEHIND THE SCENES, INC; *U.S. Private*, pg. 515
BIMAN FLIGHT CATERING CENTRE LTD—See Biman Bangladesh Airlines; *Int'l*, pg. 1032
BORENSTEIN CATERERS, INC.—See El Al Airlines Ltd.; *Int'l*, pg. 2340
BY WORD OF MOUTH LIMITED—See Aramark; *U.S. Public*, pg. 178
CAISSA TOSUN DEVELOPMENT CO., LTD.; *Int'l*, pg. 1253
CAMPBELL CATERING LIMITED—See Campbells/Bewley Group; *Int'l*, pg. 1274
CAM RANH INTERNATIONAL AIRPORT SERVICES JSC; *Int'l*, pg. 1266
CAMST-COOPERATIVA ALBERGO MENSA SPETTACOLO E TURISMO, SOC. COOP. A.R.L.; *Int'l*, pg. 1275
CARLE PLACE RESTAURANT INC.—See Scotto's Holding Corp.; *U.S. Private*, pg. 3578
CATERING BY ROSEMARY, INC.—See The RK Group, LLC; *U.S. Private*, pg. 4110
CATERING INTERNATIONAL & SERVICES S.A.; *Int'l*, pg. 1359
CATHAY PACIFIC CATERING SERVICES (H.K.) LTD.—See Cathay Pacific Airways Limited; *Int'l*, pg. 1360
CELEBRATION CATERING & EVENTS, LLP—See Brigade Enterprises Ltd.; *Int'l*, pg. 1160
CENTRAL DE RESTAURANTES ARAMARK LIMITADA—See Aramark; *U.S. Public*, pg. 177
CHARTWELLS HIGHER EDUCATION DINING SERVICES—See Compass Group PLC; *Int'l*, pg. 1750
CHEWSE, INC.; *U.S. Private*, pg. 876
CIS BRAZIL LTDA—See Catering International & Services S.A.; *Int'l*, pg. 1359
CJ FRESHWAY CORPORATION; *Int'l*, pg. 1634
CLS CATERING SERVICES LTD.—See Deutsche Lufthansa AG; *Int'l*, pg. 2067
COMISARIATO DE BAJA CALIFORNIA, SA. DE C.V.—See Deutsche Lufthansa AG; *Int'l*, pg. 2067
COMPASS GROUP (AUSTRALIA) PTY LTD—See Compass Group PLC; *Int'l*, pg. 1750
COMPASS GROUP CANADA LTD.—See Compass Group PLC; *Int'l*, pg. 1750
COMPASS GROUP CZECH REPUBLIC S.R.O.—See Compass Group PLC; *Int'l*, pg. 1750
COMPASS GROUP DANMARK A/S—See Compass Group PLC; *Int'l*, pg. 1750
COMPASS GROUP DEUTSCHLAND GMBH—See Compass Group PLC; *Int'l*, pg. 1750
COMPASS GROUP FRANCE SAS—See Compass Group PLC; *Int'l*, pg. 1750
COMPASS GROUP ITALIA S.P.A—See Compass Group PLC; *Int'l*, pg. 1750
COMPASS GROUP NEDERLAND BV—See Compass Group PLC; *Int'l*, pg. 1750
COMPASS GROUP NEW ZEALAND LIMITED—See Compass Group PLC; *Int'l*, pg. 1750
COMPASS GROUP POLAND SP. Z O.O.—See Compass Group PLC; *Int'l*, pg. 1751
COMPASS GROUP SLOVAKIA S. R. O.—See Compass Group PLC; *Int'l*, pg. 1751
COMPASS GROUP, UK & IRELAND LIMITED—See Compass Group PLC; *Int'l*, pg. 1751
CONTINENTAL DISTRIBUTORS, INC.; *U.S. Private*, pg. 1028
CONTINENTAL HOSTS LTD.; *U.S. Private*, pg. 1030

722320 — CATERERS

CONTINENTAL SERVICES, INC.; *U.S. Private*, pg. 1031
CONTINENTAL SERVICES INC.—See New Heritage Capital LLC; *U.S. Private*, pg. 2896
COSMOPOLITAN CATERING, LLC—See Compass Group PLC; *Int'l*, pg. 1751
CREMONINI RESTAURATION S.A.S.—See Cremonini S.p.A.; *Int'l*, pg. 1838
CULINART GROUP, INC.—See Compass Group PLC; *Int'l*, pg. 1751
CULINARY EYE, INC; *U.S. Private*, pg. 1120
DAMAC AL JAZEIRA CATERING WLL—See DAMAC Group; *Int'l*, pg. 1955
DB GASTRONOMIE GMBH—See Deutsche Bahn AG; *Int'l*, pg. 2050
DD MAPEX MAGLAJ; *Int'l*, pg. 1993
DEVELOPMENT WORKS FOOD CO; *Int'l*, pg. 2088
DINE CONTRACT CATERING LIMITED—See Compass Group PLC; *Int'l*, pg. 1751
DO & CO AIRLINE CATERING AUSTRIA GMBH—See DO & CO Aktiengesellschaft; *Int'l*, pg. 2151
DO & CO AKTIENGESELLSCHAFT; *Int'l*, pg. 2151
DO & CO ALBERTINA GMBH—See DO & CO Aktiengesellschaft; *Int'l*, pg. 2152
DO & CO BERLIN GMBH—See DO & CO Aktiengesellschaft; *Int'l*, pg. 2152
DO & CO CATERING-CONSULT & BETEILIGUNGS GMBH—See DO & CO Aktiengesellschaft; *Int'l*, pg. 2152
DO & CO CATERING & LOGISTICS AUSTRIA GMBH—See DO & CO Aktiengesellschaft; *Int'l*, pg. 2152
DO & CO CHICAGO CATERING, INC.—See DO & CO Aktiengesellschaft; *Int'l*, pg. 2152
DO & CO EVENT & AIRLINE CATERING LTD—See DO & CO Aktiengesellschaft; *Int'l*, pg. 2152
DO & CO EVENT AUSTRIA GMBH—See DO & CO Aktiengesellschaft; *Int'l*, pg. 2152
DO & CO FRANKFURT GMBH—See DO & CO Aktiengesellschaft; *Int'l*, pg. 2152
DO & CO GASTRONOMIE GMBH—See DO & CO Aktiengesellschaft; *Int'l*, pg. 2152
DO & CO IM HAAS HAUS RESTAURANTBETRIEBS GMBH—See DO & CO Aktiengesellschaft; *Int'l*, pg. 2152
DO & CO INTERNATIONAL CATERING LTD—See DO & CO Aktiengesellschaft; *Int'l*, pg. 2152
DO & CO KYIV LLC—See DO & CO Aktiengesellschaft; *Int'l*, pg. 2152
DO & CO LOS ANGELES, INC.—See DO & CO Aktiengesellschaft; *Int'l*, pg. 2152
DO & CO LOUNGE GMBH—See DO & CO Aktiengesellschaft; *Int'l*, pg. 2152
DO & CO MUNCHEN GMBH—See DO & CO Aktiengesellschaft; *Int'l*, pg. 2152
DO & CO MUSEUM CATERING LTD—See DO & CO Aktiengesellschaft; *Int'l*, pg. 2152
DO & CO NEW YORK CATERING, INC.—See DO & CO Aktiengesellschaft; *Int'l*, pg. 2152
DO & CO PARTY-SERVICE & CATERING GMBH—See DO & CO Aktiengesellschaft; *Int'l*, pg. 2152
DO & CO PASTRY GMBH—See DO & CO Aktiengesellschaft; *Int'l*, pg. 2152
DO & CO SALZBURG RESTAURANTS & BETRIEBS GMBH—See DO & CO Aktiengesellschaft; *Int'l*, pg. 2152
DO & CO SERVICE GMBH—See DO & CO Aktiengesellschaft; *Int'l*, pg. 2152
DONGWON HOME FOOD CO., LTD.—See Dongwon Enterprise Co., Ltd.; *Int'l*, pg. 2170
EAST COAST CATERING LIMITED—See Compass Group PLC; *Int'l*, pg. 1751
EAST COAST CATERING (NS) LIMITED—See Compass Group PLC; *Int'l*, pg. 1751
EDEN CATERING SDN. BHD.—See Eden Inc. Berhad; *Int'l*, pg. 2306
EDIBLES REX; *U.S. Private*, pg. 1336
ELDOON LIMITED—See Cafe de Coral Holdings Limited; *Int'l*, pg. 1250
ELIOR SCA—See Charterhouse Capital Partners LLP; *Int'l*, pg. 1455
E-LUNCH SRL—See Edenred S.A.; *Int'l*, pg. 2307
EPICURE CATERING CO., LTD.—See Dusit Thani Public Company Limited; *Int'l*, pg. 2234
EUREST COLECTIVIDADES SA—See Compass Group PLC; *Int'l*, pg. 1751
EUREST DEUTSCHLAND GMBH—See Compass Group PLC; *Int'l*, pg. 1751
EUREST ETTEREMUZEMELTETO KORLATOLT FELELOSSEGU TARSASAG—See Compass Group PLC; *Int'l*, pg. 1751
EUREST LUXEMBOURG S.A.—See Compass Group PLC; *Int'l*, pg. 1751
EUREST NEDERLAND BV—See Compass Group PLC; *Int'l*, pg. 1751
EUREST ROM SRL—See Compass Group PLC; *Int'l*, pg. 1752
FAMOUS FLAVOURS B.V.—See Compass Group PLC; *Int'l*, pg. 1752
FINNAIR CATERING OY—See Deutsche Lufthansa AG; *Int'l*, pg. 2067
FLYING FOOD FARE, INC.—See Flying Food Group, LLC; *U.S. Private*, pg. 1553

FLYING FOOD GROUP, LLC; *U.S. Private*, pg. 1553
FOODBUY LLC—See Compass Group PLC; *Int'l*, pg. 1751
FRESH IDEAS MANAGEMENT, LLC—See Compass Group PLC; *Int'l*, pg. 1750
GCG GROUP—See Goddard Enterprises Limited; *Int'l*, pg. 3019
GEMEAZ CUSIN S.P.A.—See Charterhouse Capital Partners LLP; *Int'l*, pg. 1455
GODDARD CATERING GROUP (ANTIGUA) LIMITED—See Goddard Enterprises Limited; *Int'l*, pg. 3019
GODDARD CATERING GROUP CARACAS S.A.—See Goddard Enterprises Limited; *Int'l*, pg. 3019
GODDARD CATERING GROUP CURACAO, N.V.—See Goddard Enterprises Limited; *Int'l*, pg. 3019
GODDARD CATERING GROUP EL SALVADOR, S.A. DE C.V.—See Goddard Enterprises Limited; *Int'l*, pg. 3019
GODDARD CATERING GROUP (GUATEMALA) S.A.—See Goddard Enterprises Limited; *Int'l*, pg. 3019
GODDARD CATERING GROUP GUAYAQUIL S.A.—See Goddard Enterprises Limited; *Int'l*, pg. 3019
GODDARD CATERING GROUP (JAMAICA) LTD.—See Goddard Enterprises Limited; *Int'l*, pg. 3019
GODDARD CATERING GROUP URUGUAY S.A.—See Goddard Enterprises Limited; *Int'l*, pg. 3019
GOODIES FROM GOODMAN, INC.; *U.S. Private*, pg. 1739
GRAVISS HOTELS & RESORTS LIMITED—See GRAVISS HOSPITALITY LIMITED; *Int'l*, pg. 3062
GREAT PERFORMANCES/ARTISTS AS WAITRESSES, INC.; *U.S. Private*, pg. 1766
GTB GASTRO TEAM BREMEN GMBH—See Aramark; *U.S. Public*, pg. 177
GTH CATERING A.S.—See Genesis Capital s.r.o.; *Int'l*, pg. 2921
HEIDELBERG CATERING SERVICES GMBH—See Heidelberger Druckmaschinen AG; *Int'l*, pg. 3321
INFLIGHT CATERING SERVICES LIMITED—See Deutsche Lufthansa AG; *Int'l*, pg. 2067
INNOVATIVE GOURMET, LLC—See Innovative Food Holdings, Inc.; *U.S. Public*, pg. 1127
JET CHEF—See Air France-KLM S.A.; *Int'l*, pg. 237
KLM CATERING SERVICES SCHIPHOL B.V.—See Air France-KLM S.A.; *Int'l*, pg. 237
KUWAIT PEARLS CATERING CO.—See Ali Abdullah Al Tamimi Company; *Int'l*, pg. 319
LSG CATERING CHINA LTD—See Deutsche Lufthansa AG; *Int'l*, pg. 2067
LSG CATERING (THAILAND) LTD.—See Deutsche Lufthansa AG; *Int'l*, pg. 2067
LSG HOLDING ASIA LTD.—See Deutsche Lufthansa AG; *Int'l*, pg. 2067
LSG LUFTHANSA SERVICE CAPE TOWN (PTY) LTD—See Deutsche Lufthansa AG; *Int'l*, pg. 2067
LSG LUFTHANSA SERVICE CATERING- UND DIENSTLEISTUNGSGESELLSCHAFT MBH—See Deutsche Lufthansa AG; *Int'l*, pg. 2067
LSG LUFTHANSA SERVICE HONG KONG LTD.—See Deutsche Lufthansa AG; *Int'l*, pg. 2067
LSG SKY CHEFS BELGIUM N.V.—See Deutsche Lufthansa AG; *Int'l*, pg. 2067
LSG SKY CHEFS DEUTSCHLAND GMBH—See Deutsche Lufthansa AG; *Int'l*, pg. 2067
LSG SKY CHEFS DE VENEZUELA C.A.—See Deutsche Lufthansa AG; *Int'l*, pg. 2068
LSG SKY CHEFS/GCC LTD.—See Deutsche Lufthansa AG; *Int'l*, pg. 2068
LSG SKY CHEFS HAVACILIK HIZMETLERI A.S.—See Deutsche Lufthansa AG; *Int'l*, pg. 2067
LSG SKY CHEFS (INDIA) PVT. LTD.—See Deutsche Lufthansa AG; *Int'l*, pg. 2067
LSG SKY CHEFS KOREA CO LTD.—See Deutsche Lufthansa AG; *Int'l*, pg. 2067
LSG SKY CHEFS LOUNGE GMBH—See Deutsche Lufthansa AG; *Int'l*, pg. 2067
LSG SKY CHEFS NEW ZEALAND LIMITED—See Deutsche Lufthansa AG; *Int'l*, pg. 2067
LSG SKY CHEFS NORGE AS—See Deutsche Lufthansa AG; *Int'l*, pg. 2067
LSG SKY CHEFS SCHWEIZ AG—See Deutsche Lufthansa AG; *Int'l*, pg. 2067
LSG SKY CHEFS SOLUTIONS ASIA LIMITED—See Deutsche Lufthansa AG; *Int'l*, pg. 2067
LSG SKY CHEFS SOUTH AFRICA (PTY) LTD.—See Deutsche Lufthansa AG; *Int'l*, pg. 2067
LSG SKY CHEFS SUPPLY CHAIN SOLUTIONS, INC.—See Deutsche Lufthansa AG; *Int'l*, pg. 2067
LSG SKY CHEFS SVERIGE AB—See Deutsche Lufthansa AG; *Int'l*, pg. 2068
LSG SKY CHEFS USA, INC.—See Deutsche Lufthansa AG; *Int'l*, pg. 2067
MAIN EVENT CATERERS; *U.S. Private*, pg. 2551
MARTINS INC.; *U.S. Private*, pg. 2597
MAZZONE HOSPITALITY, LLC—See Compass Group PLC; *Int'l*, pg. 1752
MAZZONE MANAGEMENT GROUP LTD, INC.; *U.S. Private*, pg. 2623
MEDICLIN CATERING GMBH—See Asklepios Kliniken GmbH & Co. KGaA; *Int'l*, pg. 623

MEDIREST GMBH & CO OHG—See Compass Group PLC; *Int'l*, pg. 1750
METROPOLITAN CENTRAL KITCHEN LIMITED—See Century City International Holdings Ltd; *Int'l*, pg. 1418
MICHAEL LEWIS COMPANY; *U.S. Private*, pg. 2698
MOBILE MEALS; *U.S. Private*, pg. 2757
MURRAY CATERING COMPANY LIMITED—See Four Seas Mercantile Holdings Limited; *Int'l*, pg. 2755
NEWREST WAGONS-LITS S.A.S.—See Accor S.A.; *Int'l*, pg. 92
OPEN KITCHENS INC.; *U.S. Private*, pg. 3029
OUTBACK CATERING, INC.—See Bloomin' Brands, Inc.; *U.S. Public*, pg. 363
PACE PAPARAZZI CATERING & EVENT GMBH—See Axel Springer SE; *Int'l*, pg. 766
PROM MANAGEMENT GROUP, INC.—See Compass Group PLC; *Int'l*, pg. 1751
PROOF OF THE PUDDING—See Bruin Capital Holdings, LLC; *U.S. Private*, pg. 671
PUFF N STUFF CATERING, LLC; *U.S. Private*, pg. 3302
RECIPE UNLIMITED CORPORATION—See Fairfax Financial Holdings Limited; *Int'l*, pg. 2608
RESTORAMA AG—See Compass Group PLC; *Int'l*, pg. 1750
RIB CRIB BBQ INC.; *U.S. Private*, pg. 3424
RICHTER SZOLGALTATO KFT—See Gedeon Richter Plc.; *Int'l*, pg. 2910
THE RK GROUP WEST, LLC—See The RK Group, LLC; *U.S. Private*, pg. 4110
R+V DIENSTLEISTUNGS GMBH—See DZ BANK AG Deutsche Zentral-Genossenschaftsbank; *Int'l*, pg. 2244
SANTA BARBARA CATERING COMPANY; *U.S. Private*, pg. 3547
SARL CIEPTAL—See Catering International & Services S.A.; *Int'l*, pg. 1360
SCOLAREST - ZARIZENI SKOLNIHO STRAVOVANI SPOL. S.R.O—See Compass Group PLC; *Int'l*, pg. 1752
SCOTTO BROTHERS WESTBURY RESTAURANT INC.—See Scotto's Holding Corp.; *U.S. Private*, pg. 3578
SCOTTO'S HOLDING CORP.; *U.S. Private*, pg. 3578
SENTRY CENTERS HOLDINGS LLC; *U.S. Private*, pg. 3610
SERVICIOS RENOVADOS DE ALIMENTACION, S.A.U.—See Compass Group PLC; *Int'l*, pg. 1752
SGS-SCHWARZHEIDER GASTRONOMIE UND SERVICE GMBH—See BASF SE; *Int'l*, pg. 884
SHENZHEN CAFE DE CORAL CATERING COMPANY LIMITED—See Cafe de Coral Holdings Limited; *Int'l*, pg. 1250
SHING HIN CATERING GROUP LTD.—See Compass Group PLC; *Int'l*, pg. 1752
SHOGA GMBH—See ManpowerGroup Inc.; *U.S. Public*, pg. 1362
SINGER'S GETRANKE SHOP GMBH & CO. KG—See Live Nation Entertainment, Inc.; *U.S. Public*, pg. 1330
SKY CHEFS DE MEXICO, S.A. DE C.V.—See Deutsche Lufthansa AG; *Int'l*, pg. 2068
SKY CHEFS DE PANAMA, S.A.—See Deutsche Lufthansa AG; *Int'l*, pg. 2068
SKY GOURMET - AIRLINE CATERING AND LOGISTICS GMBH—See DO & CO Aktiengesellschaft; *Int'l*, pg. 2152
SOFRA YEMEK URETIM VE HIZMET A.S.—See Compass Group PLC; *Int'l*, pg. 1752
SPOTLESS SERVICES (NZ) LTD.—See Downer EDI Limited; *Int'l*, pg. 2185
TASTY CATERING, INC.; *U.S. Private*, pg. 3935
TRAVERS FOOD SERVICE LTD.—See Aramark; *U.S. Public*, pg. 176
TRIPLE A SERVICES INC.; *U.S. Private*, pg. 4236
UAB AIRO CATERING SERVICES LIETUVA—See Deutsche Lufthansa AG; *Int'l*, pg. 2068
WORD OF MOUTH FINE CATERING; *U.S. Private*, pg. 4562
ZAO AEROMAR—See Deutsche Lufthansa AG; *Int'l*, pg. 2068

722330 — MOBILE FOOD SERVICES

ABL MANAGEMENT INC.; *U.S. Private*, pg. 39
AGF SUZUKA CO., LTD.—See Mondelez International, Inc.; *U.S. Public*, pg. 1461
AJINOMOTO GENERAL FOODS, INC.—See Ajinomoto Company, Inc.; *Int'l*, pg. 256
AJINOMOTO GENERAL FOODS, INC.—See Mondelez International, Inc.; *U.S. Public*, pg. 1461
ALADDIN TEMP-RITE CANADA—See Ali Holding S.r.l; *Int'l*, pg. 320
ALADDIN TEMP-RITE PUERTO RICO—See Ali Holding S.r.l; *Int'l*, pg. 320
AMERICAN PATRIOT BRANDS, INC.; *U.S. Private*, pg. 243
AMWAY DE PANAMA S.A.—See Alticor Inc.; *U.S. Private*, pg. 209
AMWAY (EUROPE) LTD.—See Alticor Inc.; *U.S. Private*, pg. 208
AMWAY HONG KONG LTD.—See Alticor Inc.; *U.S. Private*, pg. 209
AMWAY (SCHWEIZ) AG—See Alticor Inc.; *U.S. Private*, pg. 208

N.A.I.C.S. INDEX

AMWAY TAIWAN, LTD.—See Alticor Inc.; *U.S. Private*, pg. 209
AMWAY (U.K.) LIMITED—See Alticor Inc.; *U.S. Private*, pg. 208
ARAMARK REFRESHMENT SERVICES, LLC—See Aramark; *U.S. Public*, pg. 176
AVON LAKE ENVIRONMENTAL REDEVELOPMENT GROUP, LLC—See SER Capital Partners LLC; *U.S. Private*, pg. 3612
CADBURY ADAMS MEXICO, S. DE R.L. DE C.V.—See Mondelez International, Inc.; *U.S. Public*, pg. 1460
CADBURY ADAMS MIDDLE EAST S.A.L.—See Mondelez International, Inc.; *U.S. Public*, pg. 1460
CADBURY ADAMS (THAILAND) LIMITED—See Mondelez International, Inc.; *U.S. Public*, pg. 1460
CADBURY CONFECTIONERY SALES (M) SDN. BHD.—See Mondelez International, Inc.; *U.S. Public*, pg. 1460
CADBURY ENTERPRISES PTE. LTD.—See Mondelez International, Inc.; *U.S. Public*, pg. 1460
CADBURY MARKETING SERVICES PTY LIMITED—See Mondelez International, Inc.; *U.S. Public*, pg. 1461
CARLTON LEBENSMITTEL VERTRIEBS GMBH—See Mondelez International, Inc.; *U.S. Public*, pg. 1462
CHINA PACIFIC CATERING SERVICES LTD.—See China Airlines Ltd.; *Int'l*, pg. 1482
ERNEST JACKSON & CO LIMITED—See Mondelez International, Inc.; *U.S. Public*, pg. 1462
FLAVOR PRODUCERS, LLC—See Glanbia Co-Operative Society Limited; *Int'l*, pg. 2987
GEA FOOD SOLUTIONS CHILE COMERCIALIZADORA LTDA.—See GEA Group Aktiengesellschaft; *Int'l*, pg. 2899
GENERALE BISCUIT SAS—See Mondelez International, Inc.; *U.S. Public*, pg. 1463
KRAFT FOODS CEEMA GMBH—See Mondelez International, Inc.; *U.S. Public*, pg. 1462
KRAFT FOODS COSTA RICA, S.A.—See Mondelez International, Inc.; *U.S. Public*, pg. 1461
KRAFT FOODS DE NICARAGUA S.A.—See Mondelez International, Inc.; *U.S. Public*, pg. 1461
KRAFT FOODS EESTI Osauhing—See Mondelez International, Inc.; *U.S. Public*, pg. 1462
KRAFT FOODS EGYPT L.L.C.—See Mondelez International, Inc.; *U.S. Public*, pg. 1461
KRAFT FOODS FINLAND PRODUCTION OY—See Mondelez International, Inc.; *U.S. Public*, pg. 1462
KRAFT FOODS FRANCE INTELLECTUAL PROPERTY S.A.S.—See Mondelez International, Inc.; *U.S. Public*, pg. 1463
KRAFT FOODS GROUP PUERTO RICO, LLC—See 3G Capital Inc.; *U.S. Private*, pg. 10
KRAFT FOODS GROUP PUERTO RICO, LLC—See Berkshire Hathaway Inc.; *U.S. Public*, pg. 318
KRAFT FOODS (MIDDLE EAST & AFRICA) LTD.—See Mondelez International, Inc.; *U.S. Public*, pg. 1462
KRAFT GIDA SANAYI VE TICARET A. S.—See Mondelez International, Inc.; *U.S. Public*, pg. 1461
MONDELEZ BAHRAIN W.L.L.—See Mondelez International, Inc.; *U.S. Public*, pg. 1462
MONDELEZ BELGIUM PRODUCTION BVBA—See Mondelez International, Inc.; *U.S. Public*, pg. 1463
MONDELEZ CZECH REPUBLIC S.R.O.—See Mondelez International, Inc.; *U.S. Public*, pg. 1463
MONDELEZ CZECH REPUBLIC S.R.O.—See Mondelez International, Inc.; *U.S. Public*, pg. 1463
MONDELEZ ESPANA SERVICES, S.L.U.—See Mondelez International, Inc.; *U.S. Public*, pg. 1463
MONDELEZ EUROPE GMBH—See Mondelez International, Inc.; *U.S. Public*, pg. 1462
MONDELEZ FINLAND OY—See Mondelez International, Inc.; *U.S. Public*, pg. 1463
MONDELEZ IRELAND LIMITED—See Mondelez International, Inc.; *U.S. Public*, pg. 1463
MONDELEZ PORTUGAL IBERIA PRODUCTION, S.A.—See Mondelez International, Inc.; *U.S. Public*, pg. 1463
MONDELEZ STRASBOURG PRODUCTION S.N.C.—See Mondelez International, Inc.; *U.S. Public*, pg. 1463
THE NATURAL CONFECTIONERY CO. PTY LTD—See Mondelez International, Inc.; *U.S. Public*, pg. 1462
OVATIONS FOOD SERVICES LP; *U.S. Private*, pg. 3052
PADDINGTON—See Mondelez International, Inc.; *U.S. Public*, pg. 1464
P.T. KRAFT ULTRAJAYA INDONESIA—See Mondelez International, Inc.; *U.S. Public*, pg. 1462
SNAPFINGER, INC.; *U.S. Private*, pg. 3700
TALOCA CAFE LTDA.—See Mondelez International, Inc.; *U.S. Public*, pg. 1463
VEND FOOD SERVICES INC.; *U.S. Private*, pg. 4356

722410 — DRINKING PLACES (ALCOHOLIC BEVERAGES)

ADMIRAL TAVERNS LTD.—See C&C Group Plc; *Int'l*, pg. 1238
ADMIRAL TAVERNS LTD.—See Proprium Capital Partners, L.P.; *U.S. Private*, pg. 3286
A-HEAD FOR PROFITS LLC; *U.S. Private*, pg. 22
ANDERSON HILL INSURANCE LIMITED—See PepsiCo, Inc.; *U.S. Public*, pg. 1668
ARADHANA FOODS AND JUICES PRIVATE LIMITED—See PepsiCo, Inc.; *U.S. Public*, pg. 1668
AUX INTERNATIONAL HOLDINGS LIMITED; *Int'l*, pg. 732
BACARDI AB—See Bacardi Limited; *Int'l*, pg. 793
BACARDI CHINA LIMITED—See Bacardi Limited; *Int'l*, pg. 793
BACARDI MARTINI PATRON INTERNATIONAL GMBH—See Bacardi Limited; *Int'l*, pg. 794
BACARDI-MARTINI POLSKA SP Z O.O.—See Bacardi Limited; *Int'l*, pg. 794
BACARDI NORGE AS—See Bacardi Limited; *Int'l*, pg. 794
BACARDI RUS LLC—See Bacardi Limited; *Int'l*, pg. 794
BAR PACIFIC GROUP HOLDINGS LIMITED; *Int'l*, pg. 857
BARTECH SYSTEMS INTERNATIONAL INC.; *U.S. Private*, pg. 482
BEOGRAD A.D.; *Int'l*, pg. 978
BIG BUCK BREWERY & STEAKHOUSE, INC.; *U.S. Private*, pg. 552
BITBURGER HOLDING GMBH; *Int'l*, pg. 1049
BORDER PROPERTIES, INC.—See PepsiCo, Inc.; *U.S. Public*, pg. 1668
BRUNNING AND PRICE LIMITED—See Apollo Global Management, Inc.; *U.S. Public*, pg. 164
CHURCH STREET ENTERTAINMENT; *U.S. Private*, pg. 894
CINETOPIA, LLC—See Dalian Wanda Group Corporation Ltd.; *Int'l*, pg. 1953
CLUB ONYX HOUSTON—See RCI Hospitality Holdings, Inc.; *U.S. Public*, pg. 1767
COMPACT SENSATION SDN. BHD.—See 9R Limited; *Int'l*, pg. 17
COUNT'S VAMP'D; *U.S. Private*, pg. 1066
DRAKE & MORGAN LIMITED; *U.S. Private*, pg. 2200
DUYVIS PRODUCTION B.V.—See PepsiCo, Inc.; *U.S. Public*, pg. 1668
ELECTROPURA, S.R.L. DE C.V.—See PepsiCo, Inc.; *U.S. Public*, pg. 1668
THE END ZONE, INC.—See RCI Hospitality Holdings, Inc.; *U.S. Public*, pg. 1767
FADO PUBS INC.; *U.S. Private*, pg. 1461
FINE ENTERTAINMENT CO.; *U.S. Private*, pg. 1509
FLANIGAN'S ENTERPRISES, INC. OF GEORGIA—See Flanigan's Enterprises, Inc.; *U.S. Public*, pg. 852
FOUR CORNERS BREWING CO.—See Constellation Brands, Inc.; *U.S. Public*, pg. 571
FRITO-LAY GIDA SANAYI VE TICARET A.S.—See PepsiCo, Inc.; *U.S. Public*, pg. 1670
FRITO-LAY NETHERLANDS HOLDING B.V.—See PepsiCo, Inc.; *U.S. Public*, pg. 1670
FRITO LAY SP.Z.O.O.—See PepsiCo, Inc.; *U.S. Public*, pg. 1670
FRUKO MESRUBAT SANAYI, LTD. STI.—See PepsiCo, Inc.; *U.S. Public*, pg. 1668
FULL THROTTLE SALOON; *U.S. Private*, pg. 1621
GENERAL MILLS—See General Mills, Inc.; *U.S. Public*, pg. 921
GREENE KING RETAILING LIMITED—See CK Asset Holdings Limited; *Int'l*, pg. 1635
GRUPO SABRITAS, S. DE R.L. DE C.V.—See PepsiCo, Inc.; *U.S. Public*, pg. 1668
HARRY'S HOLDINGS LTD.—See Everstone Capital Advisors Pvt. Ltd.; *Int'l*, pg. 2569
HENNESSEY'S TAVERN, INC.; *U.S. Private*, pg. 1916
HILLEBRAND KENYA LIMITED—See Deutsche Post AG; *Int'l*, pg. 2080
HOUSE OF BLUES MYRTLE BEACH RESTAURANT CORP.—See Live Nation Entertainment, Inc.; *U.S. Public*, pg. 1329
ILLINOIS CORN PROCESSING, LLC—See Alto Ingredients, Inc.; *U.S. Public*, pg. 88
INTERBEV AS—See Altia Oyj; *Int'l*, pg. 392
INTERNATIONAL RESTAURANT SERVICES; *U.S. Private*, pg. 2120
JAI DINING SERVICES (EDINBURG), INC.—See RCI Hospitality Holdings, Inc.; *U.S. Public*, pg. 1767
J.F. HILLEBRAND BENELUX B.V.—See Deutsche Post AG; *Int'l*, pg. 2081
JF HILLEBRAND LIMITED—See Deutsche Post AG; *Int'l*, pg. 2081
J.F. HILLEBRAND SVERIGE AB—See Deutsche Post AG; *Int'l*, pg. 2081
KLONDIKE CHEESE COMPANY; *U.S. Private*, pg. 2320
KRAGNES FARMERS ELEVATOR CO.; *U.S. Private*, pg. 2349
LATVIAN SNACKS SIA—See PepsiCo, Inc.; *U.S. Public*, pg. 1669
LEVY RESTAURANTS—See Compass Group PLC; *Int'l*, pg. 1751
MARBO D.O.O. LAKTASI—See PepsiCo, Inc.; *U.S. Public*, pg. 1669
MIAMI GARDENS SQUARE ONE, INC.—See RCI Hospitality Holdings, Inc.; *U.S. Public*, pg. 1767
MOON MANAGEMENT, INC.; *U.S. Private*, pg. 2778
NATIONAL PROCESSORS LTD.—See GraceKennedy Limited; *Int'l*, pg. 3049
PA PUBS INC.; *U.S. Private*, pg. 3062
RCI DINING SERVICES (16328 I-35), INC.—See RCI Hospitality Holdings, Inc.; *U.S. Public*, pg. 1767
RCI DINING SERVICES (37TH STREET), INC.—See RCI Hospitality Holdings, Inc.; *U.S. Public*, pg. 1767
RCI DINING SERVICES (AIRPORT FREEWAY), INC.—See RCI Hospitality Holdings, Inc.; *U.S. Public*, pg. 1767
RCI DINING SERVICES (GLENWOOD), INC.—See RCI Hospitality Holdings, Inc.; *U.S. Public*, pg. 1767
RCI DINING SERVICES (NEW YORK), INC.—See RCI Hospitality Holdings, Inc.; *U.S. Public*, pg. 1767
RCI DINING SERVICES (ROUND ROCK), INC.—See RCI Hospitality Holdings, Inc.; *U.S. Public*, pg. 1767
RCI DINING SERVICES (SULPHUR), INC.—See RCI Hospitality Holdings, Inc.; *U.S. Public*, pg. 1767
RCI ENTERTAINMENT (FORT WORTH), INC.—See RCI Hospitality Holdings, Inc.; *U.S. Public*, pg. 1767
RCI ENTERTAINMENT (MINNESOTA), INC.—See RCI Hospitality Holdings, Inc.; *U.S. Public*, pg. 1767
RCI ENTERTAINMENT (SAN ANTONIO), INC.—See RCI Hospitality Holdings, Inc.; *U.S. Public*, pg. 1767
RESTAURANT BUSINESS INC.; *U.S. Private*, pg. 3408
ROADHOUSE GRILL ITALIA S.R.L.—See Cremonini S.p.A.; *Int'l*, pg. 1838
S.A. BACARDI-MARTINI BELGIUM N.V.—See Bacardi Limited; *Int'l*, pg. 794
SEVILLE OPERATIONS LLC—See RCI Hospitality Holdings, Inc.; *U.S. Public*, pg. 1767
SOUTH JERSEY PUBS INC—See Metz Enterprises Inc.; *U.S. Private*, pg. 2691
TILTED KILT PUB & EATERY!; *U.S. Private*, pg. 4171
T.J.'S SPORTS GARDEN RESTAURANT—See Boury Enterprises; *U.S. Private*, pg. 624
TOP SHELF ENTERTAINMENT, LLC—See RCI Hospitality Holdings, Inc.; *U.S. Public*, pg. 1767
VOP BERRY PARK, LLC—See Ventas, Inc.; *U.S. Public*, pg. 2278
WFKR INC.; *U.S. Private*, pg. 4503
WINKING LIZARD INC.; *U.S. Private*, pg. 4542
WORLD OF BEER FRANCHISING, INC.; *U.S. Private*, pg. 4566

722511 — FULL-SERVICE RESTAURANTS

1501 BROADWAY RESTAURANT CORP.—See TPG Capital, L.P.; *U.S. Public*, pg. 2167
1957 & CO. (HOSPITALITY) LIMITED; *Int'l*, pg. 3
99 RESTAURANTS, LLC—See Fidelity National Financial, Inc.; *U.S. Public*, pg. 830
ABU DHABI UNITED HOSPITALITY - SOLE PROPRIETORSHIP LLC—See Alpha Dhabi Holding PJSC; *Int'l*, pg. 367
ADASTRIA EAT CREATIONS CO., LTD.—See Adastria Co., Ltd.; *Int'l*, pg. 126
AEON EAHEART CO., LTD.—See AEON Co., Ltd.; *Int'l*, pg. 176
AHC GROUP, INC.; *Int'l*, pg. 222
AHM LIFESTYLES-CREATIVE HOSPITALITY JOINT STOCK COMPANY—See Charoen Pokphand Foods Public Company Limited; *Int'l*, pg. 1451
AID RESTAURANT, INC.—See Dream Center Foundation, a California Nonprofit Corp.; *U.S. Private*, pg. 1274
AIRPORT RESTAURANTS (1996) LIMITED—See Goddard Enterprises Limited; *Int'l*, pg. 3018
AL AHLIA RESTAURANTS CO.—See Adeptio LLC; *Int'l*, pg. 143
ALBUQUERQUE HOOTERS, INC.—See Restaurants of America, Inc.; *U.S. Private*, pg. 3408
ALE HOUSE MANAGEMENT, INC.; *U.S. Private*, pg. 160
ALIMENTOS LATINOAMERICANOS VENEZUELA ALV, C.A.—See Arcos Dorados Holdings Inc.; *Int'l*, pg. 550
ALOHA RESTAURANTS, INC.; *U.S. Private*, pg. 195
AL SAFAT UNITED FOOD COMPANY K.S.C.—See Al-Safwa Group Holding Co. K.P.S.C.; *Int'l*, pg. 288
AMARATHAI RESTAURANT PTE LTD—See Amara Holdings Ltd.; *Int'l*, pg. 411
AMC BURGERS, INC.—See ICV Partners, LLC; *U.S. Private*, pg. 2034
AMERGENT HOSPITALITY GROUP, INC.; *U.S. Public*, pg. 95
AMERICANA RESTAURANTS INTERNATIONAL PLC; *Int'l*, pg. 423
AMERICAN PARK 'N SWAP—See Delaware North Companies, Inc.; *U.S. Private*, pg. 1194
AMERICAN RESTAURANT GROUP, INC.; *U.S. Private*, pg. 246
AMERICAN ROADSIDE BURGERS SMITHTOWN, INC.—See Sonnet BioTherapeutics Holdings, Inc.; *U.S. Public*, pg. 1903
AMERICAN SEAFOOD PARTNERS LP—See American Pizza Partners LP; *U.S. Private*, pg. 243
AMERICA'S INCREDIBLE PIZZA COMPANY; *U.S. Private*, pg. 221
AMERIGO RESTAURANT CORPORATION; *U.S. Private*, pg. 259
AMIYAKI TEI CO., LTD.; *Int'l*, pg. 428

722511 — FULL-SERVICE RESTAU...

AMREST COFFEE SP. Z O. O.—See Starbucks Corporation; *U.S. Public*, pg. 1939
AMREST COFFEE S.R.O.—See Starbucks Corporation; *U.S. Public*, pg. 1939
AMREST, LLC—See AmRest Holdings SE; *Int'l*, pg. 437
AMREST PIZZA GMBH—See AmRest Holdings SE; *Int'l*, pg. 437
AMWAY GRAND PLAZA HOTEL—See Alticor Inc.; *U.S. Private*, pg. 209
ANADOLU RESTORAN ISLETMELERI LIMITED SIRKETI—See AG Anadolu Grubu Holding A.S.; *Int'l*, pg. 197
ANDY M. CAMACHO INC.; *U.S. Private*, pg. 281
ANNAPOLIS OUTBACK, INC.—See Bloomin' Brands, Inc.; *U.S. Public*, pg. 362
ANRAKUTEI CO., LTD.; *Int'l*, pg. 475
ANTHONY PARASSON INC.; *U.S. Private*, pg. 287
ANTHONY'S COAL FIRED PIZZA; *U.S. Private*, pg. 288
ANTHONY'S FISH GROTTO; *U.S. Private*, pg. 288
APPLEBEE'S FRANCHISOR LLC—See Dine Brands Global, Inc.; *U.S. Public*, pg. 666
APPLEBEE'S INTERNATIONAL, INC.—See Dine Brands Global, Inc.; *U.S. Public*, pg. 666
APPLEBEE'S RESTAURANTS NORTH, LLC—See Dine Brands Global, Inc.; *U.S. Public*, pg. 666
APPLEBEE'S RESTAURANTS TEXAS, LLC—See Dine Brands Global, Inc.; *U.S. Public*, pg. 666
APPLEBEE'S RESTAURANTS VERMONT, INC.—See Dine Brands Global, Inc.; *U.S. Public*, pg. 667
APPLE CORE ENTERPRISES INC.; *U.S. Private*, pg. 296
APPLEJAM OF TX INC.—See Applejam Inc.; *U.S. Private*, pg. 297
APPLE METRO INC.; *U.S. Private*, pg. 297
APPLE SAUCE, INC.; *U.S. Private*, pg. 297
ARAMARK EDUCATIONAL GROUP, LLC—See Aramark; *U.S. Public*, pg. 176
ARAMARK FHC, LLC—See Aramark; *U.S. Public*, pg. 176
ARBY'S CANADA, INC.—See Roark Capital Group Inc.; *U.S. Private*, pg. 3455
ARCLAND SERVICE HOLDINGS CO., LTD.—See Arclands Corp; *Int'l*, pg. 549
ARCOS DORADOS ARUBA N.V.—See Arcos Dorados Holdings Inc.; *Int'l*, pg. 550
ARCOS DORADOS COLOMBIA S.A.S—See Arcos Dorados Holdings Inc.; *Int'l*, pg. 550
ARCOS DORADOS COSTA RICA ADCR, S.A.—See Arcos Dorados Holdings Inc.; *Int'l*, pg. 550
ARCOS DORADOS PUERTO RICO, LLC—See Arcos Dorados Holdings Inc.; *Int'l*, pg. 550
ARCOS DOURADOS COMERCIO DE ALIMENTOS LTDA.—See Arcos Dorados Holdings Inc.; *Int'l*, pg. 550
ARCOS MENDOCINOS S.A.—See Arcos Dorados Holdings Inc.; *Int'l*, pg. 550
ARCOS SERCAL INMOBILIARIA, S. DE R.L. DE C.V.—See Arcos Dorados Holdings Inc.; *Int'l*, pg. 550
ARK AC BURGER BAR LLC—See Ark Restaurants Corp.; *U.S. Public*, pg. 192
ARK ATLANTIC CITY CORP.—See Ark Restaurants Corp.; *U.S. Public*, pg. 192
ARK ATLANTIC CITY RESTAURANT CORP.—See Ark Restaurants Corp.; *U.S. Public*, pg. 192
ARK BRYANT PARK CORP.—See Ark Restaurants Corp.; *U.S. Public*, pg. 192
ARK BRYANT PARK SOUTHWEST LLC—See Ark Restaurants Corp.; *U.S. Public*, pg. 192
ARK CONNECTICUT BRANCHES CORP.—See Ark Restaurants Corp.; *U.S. Public*, pg. 192
ARK D.C. KIOSK, INC.—See Ark Restaurants Corp.; *U.S. Public*, pg. 192
ARK ISLAND BEACH RESORT LLC—See Ark Restaurants Corp.; *U.S. Public*, pg. 192
ARK JUPITER RI, LLC—See Ark Restaurants Corp.; *U.S. Public*, pg. 192
ARK LAS VEGAS RESTAURANT CORP.—See Ark Restaurants Corp.; *U.S. Public*, pg. 192
ARK MEADOWLANDS LLC—See Ark Restaurants Corp.; *U.S. Public*, pg. 192
ARK OPERATING CORP.—See Ark Restaurants Corp.; *U.S. Public*, pg. 192
ARK OYSTER HOUSE GULF SHORES I, LLC—See Ark Restaurants Corp.; *U.S. Public*, pg. 192
ARK POTOMAC CORPORATION—See Ark Restaurants Corp.; *U.S. Public*, pg. 192
ARK SOUTHWEST D.C. CORP.—See Ark Restaurants Corp.; *U.S. Public*, pg. 192
ARK UNION STATION, INC.—See Ark Restaurants Corp.; *U.S. Public*, pg. 192
ARNIES RESTAURANT; *U.S. Private*, pg. 332
ARNIS INC.; *U.S. Private*, pg. 332
ASAHI GROUP FOODS, LTD.—See Asahi Group Holdings Ltd.; *Int'l*, pg. 593
ASAKUMA CO., LTD.; *Int'l*, pg. 599
ASIAN HOTELS (EAST) LIMITED; *Int'l*, pg. 617
ASIATIQUE RIVERFRONT CO., LTD.—See Asset World Corp Public Company Limited; *Int'l*, pg. 643
ATASEHIR RESTORAN ISLETMELERI GIDA TURIZM TICARET A.S.—See Dogus Holding AS; *Int'l*, pg. 2154

THE ATLANTA PALM—See Palm Restaurant Group; *U.S. Private*, pg. 3080
THE ATLANTIC CITY PALM—See Palm Restaurant Group; *U.S. Private*, pg. 3080
ATOM CORPORATION; *Int'l*, pg. 687
AUNT SARAH'S LLC; *U.S. Private*, pg. 393
AUTOGRILL SCHWEIZ A.G.—See Edizione S.r.l.; *Int'l*, pg. 2311
AUTOGRILL VFS F&B CO. LTD.—See Edizione S.r.l.; *Int'l*, pg. 2311
AXXE REISEGASTRONOMIE GMBH—See Abu Dhabi Investment Authority; *Int'l*, pg. 71
AXXE REISEGASTRONOMIE GMBH—See Allianz SE; *Int'l*, pg. 351
AZTECA RESTAURANT ENTERPRISES; *U.S. Private*, pg. 416
BAB SYSTEMS, INC.—See BAB, Inc.; *U.S. Public*, pg. 262
BAGATELLE LITTLE WEST 12TH, LLC—See The ONE Group Hospitality, Inc.; *U.S. Public*, pg. 2118
BAGGER DAVE'S BURGER TAVERN, INC.; *U.S. Public*, pg. 264
BAHAMA BREEZE—See Darden Restaurants, Inc.; *U.S. Public*, pg. 632
BAHRAIN FAMILY LEISURE COMPANY B.S.C.; *Int'l*, pg. 800
BAKERS SQUARE—See Fidelity National Financial, Inc.; *U.S. Public*, pg. 830
BALEA ESTIVAL 2002 S.A.; *Int'l*, pg. 807
BALNIBARBI CO., LTD.; *Int'l*, pg. 810
BAL TURIZM VE GIDA PAZARLAMA A.S.—See Dogus Holding AS; *Int'l*, pg. 2154
BANDANA'S BAR B Q; *U.S. Private*, pg. 465
BARCELONA SONO; *U.S. Private*, pg. 473
BARGERBURGER INC.; *U.S. Private*, pg. 474
BAR HARBOR LOBSTER COMPANY, INC.; *U.S. Private*, pg. 471
BARLEYCORN'S; *U.S. Private*, pg. 476
BARUNSON CO., LTD.; *Int'l*, pg. 870
BASCOM'S CHOP HOUSE; *U.S. Private*, pg. 484
BATARD—See Myriad Restaurant Group; *U.S. Private*, pg. 2825
BATTLEGROUND RESTAURANT GROUP INC.; *U.S. Private*, pg. 490
BAYANGOL HOTEL JOINT STOCK COMPANY; *Int'l*, pg. 901
BBQ BLUES TEXAS LTD.; *U.S. Private*, pg. 498
BCI GROUP HOLDINGS LIMITED; *Int'l*, pg. 928
BD FOODS LTD.—See AAK AB; *Int'l*, pg. 32
BEAU DELICIOUS! INTERNATIONAL LLC; *U.S. Private*, pg. 507
BECKER & K LLP; *Int'l*, pg. 938
BEL AIR OUTBACK, INC.—See Bloomin' Brands, Inc.; *U.S. Public*, pg. 362
BELMONT CHASE, LLC—See Regency Centers Corporation; *U.S. Public*, pg. 1774
BENIHANA BETHESDA CORP.—See TPG Capital, L.P.; *U.S. Public*, pg. 2167
BENIHANA BROOMFIELD CORP.—See TPG Capital, L.P.; *U.S. Public*, pg. 2167
BENIHANA CARLSBAD CORP.—See TPG Capital, L.P.; *U.S. Public*, pg. 2167
BENIHANA CHANDLER CORP.—See TPG Capital, L.P.; *U.S. Public*, pg. 2167
BENIHANA COLUMBUS CORP.—See TPG Capital, L.P.; *U.S. Public*, pg. 2167
BENIHANA CORAL SPRINGS CORP.—See TPG Capital, L.P.; *U.S. Public*, pg. 2167
BENIHANA ENCINO CORP.—See TPG Capital, L.P.; *U.S. Public*, pg. 2167
BENIHANA LAS COLINAS CORP.—See TPG Capital, L.P.; *U.S. Public*, pg. 2167
BENIHANA LOMBARD CORP.—See TPG Capital, L.P.; *U.S. Public*, pg. 2167
BENIHANA MARINA CORP.—See TPG Capital, L.P.; *U.S. Public*, pg. 2167
BENIHANA NATIONAL OF FLORIDA CORP.—See TPG Capital, L.P.; *U.S. Public*, pg. 2167
BENIHANA OF PUENTE HILLS CORP.—See TPG Capital, L.P.; *U.S. Public*, pg. 2167
BENIHANA ONTARIO CORP.—See TPG Capital, L.P.; *U.S. Public*, pg. 2167
BENIHANA ORLANDO CORP.—See TPG Capital, L.P.; *U.S. Public*, pg. 2167
BENIHANA PLANO CORP.—See TPG Capital, L.P.; *U.S. Public*, pg. 2167
BENIHANA PLYMOUTH MEETING CORP.—See TPG Capital, L.P.; *U.S. Public*, pg. 2167
BENIHANA SUNRISE CORP.—See TPG Capital, L.P.; *U.S. Public*, pg. 2167
BENIHANA WESTBURY CORP.—See TPG Capital, L.P.; *U.S. Public*, pg. 2167
BENIHANA WHEELING CORP.—See TPG Capital, L.P.; *U.S. Public*, pg. 2167
BENIHANA WOODLANDS CORP.—See TPG Capital, L.P.; *U.S. Public*, pg. 2167
BERICE LLC—See Charoen Pokphand Foods Public Company Limited; *Int'l*, pg. 1451
BERJAYA FOOD SUPREME SDN BHD—See Berjaya Cor-

CORPORATE AFFILIATIONS

poration Berhad; *Int'l*, pg. 982
BERJAYA FOOD TRADING SDN BHD—See Berjaya Corporation Berhad; *Int'l*, pg. 982
BERJAYA HOTELS & RESORTS VIETNAM SDN BHD—See Berjaya Corporation Berhad; *Int'l*, pg. 982
BERJAYA KRISPY KREME DOUGHNUTS MALAYSIA SDN BHD—See Berjaya Corporation Berhad; *Int'l*, pg. 984
BERJAYA MOUNT ROYAL BEACH HOTEL LIMITED—See Berjaya Corporation Berhad; *Int'l*, pg. 982
BERJAYA ROASTERS (M) SDN BHD—See Berjaya Corporation Berhad; *Int'l*, pg. 984
BERNARD LOISEAU SA; *Int'l*, pg. 986
BERTUCCI'S CORPORATION—See Earl Enterprises; *U.S. Private*, pg. 1312
B&G FOOD ENTERPRISES INC.; *U.S. Private*, pg. 418
BGR ANNAPOLIS, LLC—See Sonnet BioTherapeutics Holdings, Inc.; *U.S. Public*, pg. 1904
BGR COLUMBIA, LLC—See Sonnet BioTherapeutics Holdings, Inc.; *U.S. Public*, pg. 1904
BGR MOSAIC, LLC—See Sonnet BioTherapeutics Holdings, Inc.; *U.S. Public*, pg. 1904
BGR TYSONS, LLC—See Sonnet BioTherapeutics Holdings, Inc.; *U.S. Public*, pg. 1904
BGR TYSONS, LLC—See Sonnet BioTherapeutics Holdings, Inc.; *U.S. Public*, pg. 1904
BGR WASHINGTONIAN, LLC—See Sonnet BioTherapeutics Holdings, Inc.; *U.S. Public*, pg. 1904
BHTT ENTERTAINMENT, INC.—See J.H. Whitney & Co.; *U.S. Private*, pg. 2166
BICKFORD'S FAMILY RESTAURANTS; *U.S. Private*, pg. 550
BIG BOY RESTAURANTS INTERNATIONAL, LLC; *U.S. Private*, pg. 552
BIGLARI HOLDINGS INC.; *U.S. Public*, pg. 331
BIKINIS SPORTS BAR & GRILL; *U.S. Private*, pg. 556
BILL JOHNSONS RESTAURANT; *U.S. Private*, pg. 557
BISTRO MANAGEMENT; *U.S. Private*, pg. 566
BJ'S RESTAURANT OPERATIONS COMPANY—See BJ'S RESTAURANTS, INC.; *U.S. Public*, pg. 340
BJ'S RESTAURANTS, INC.; *U.S. Public*, pg. 340
BLACK-EYED PEA RESTAURANTS INC.—See Dynamic Management Company LLC; *U.S. Private*, pg. 1298
BLOOMCHEER LIMITED—See Cafe de Coral Holdings Limited; *Int'l*, pg. 1249
BLOOM NO.2 LIMITED—See Bloomin' Brands, Inc.; *U.S. Public*, pg. 362
BL RESTAURANT OPERATIONS, LLC—See Sun Capital Partners, Inc.; *U.S. Private*, pg. 3858
BLUBECKERS LIMITED—See Apollo Global Management, Inc.; *U.S. Public*, pg. 164
BLUE BAKER; *U.S. Private*, pg. 585
BLUES SEAFOOD RESTAURANT LLC—See DAMAC Group; *Int'l*, pg. 1955
BMB DINING SERVICES (STEMMONS), INC.—See RCI Hospitality Holdings, Inc.; *U.S. Public*, pg. 1767
BMJ FOODS PR INC.; *U.S. Private*, pg. 601
THE BOATHOUSE RESTAURANTS OF CANADA, INC.—See Fertitta Entertainment, Inc.; *U.S. Private*, pg. 1499
BOB EVANS RESTAURANTS, LLC—See Golden Gate Capital Management II, LLC; *U.S. Private*, pg. 1731
BODDIE-NOELL ENTERPRISES, INC.; *U.S. Private*, pg. 607
BOGOTA LATIN BISTRO; *U.S. Private*, pg. 609
BOLOCO; *U.S. Private*, pg. 611
BOMBAY PALACE COMPANY; *U.S. Private*, pg. 612
BONANZA RESTAURANTS—See Fog Cutter Capital Group Inc.; *U.S. Private*, pg. 1557
BON APPETIT MANAGEMENT CO—See Compass Group PLC; *Int'l*, pg. 1750
BONEFISH/CENTREVILLE, LIMITED PARTNERSHIP—See Bloomin' Brands, Inc.; *U.S. Public*, pg. 362
BONEFISH/CRESCENT SPRINGS, LIMITED PARTNERSHIP—See Bloomin' Brands, Inc.; *U.S. Public*, pg. 362
BONEFISH/FREDERICKSBURG, LIMITED PARTNERSHIP—See Bloomin' Brands, Inc.; *U.S. Public*, pg. 362
BONEFISH/GREENSBORO, LIMITED PARTNERSHIP—See Bloomin' Brands, Inc.; *U.S. Public*, pg. 362
BONEFISH GRILL, LLC—See Bloomin' Brands, Inc.; *U.S. Public*, pg. 362
BONEFISH GRILL OF FLORIDA, LLC—See Bloomin' Brands, Inc.; *U.S. Public*, pg. 362
BONEFISH/HYDE PARK, LIMITED PARTNERSHIP—See Bloomin' Brands, Inc.; *U.S. Public*, pg. 362
BONEFISH/NEWPORT NEWS, LIMITED PARTNERSHIP—See Bloomin' Brands, Inc.; *U.S. Public*, pg. 362
BONEFISH OF BEL AIR, LLC—See Bloomin' Brands, Inc.; *U.S. Public*, pg. 362
BONEFISH OF GAITHERSBURG, INC.—See Bloomin' Brands, Inc.; *U.S. Public*, pg. 362
BONEFISH/RICHMOND, LIMITED PARTNERSHIP—See Bloomin' Brands, Inc.; *U.S. Public*, pg. 362
BONEFISH/TALLAHASSEE, LIMITED

N.A.I.C.S. INDEX

722511 — FULL-SERVICE RESTAU...

PARTNERSHIP—See Bloomin' Brands, Inc.; *U.S. Public*, pg. 362
BONEFISH/VIRGINIA, LIMITED PARTNERSHIP—See Bloomin' Brands, Inc.; *U.S. Public*, pg. 363
BOOKATABLE GMBH & CO. KG.—See TripAdvisor, Inc.; *U.S. Public*, pg. 2195
BORDER GRILL; *U.S. Private*, pg. 617
BORICI A.D.; *Int'l*, pg. 1114
BOSTON RESTAURANT ASSOCIATES, INC.; *U.S. Private*, pg. 622
BOTTLE LAB TECHNOLOGIES PRIVATE LIMITED—See Compass Group PLC; *Int'l*, pg. 1750
BOW AND ARROW MANOR INC.; *U.S. Private*, pg. 625
BRC SEHER A.D.; *Int'l*, pg. 1143
THE BRIAD GROUP; *U.S. Private*, pg. 4000
BRICKTOWN RESTAURANT GROUP, INC.; *U.S. Private*, pg. 648
THE BRIGANTINE RESTAURANT CORP.; *U.S. Private*, pg. 4000
BRINKER INTERNATIONAL, INC.; *U.S. Public*, pg. 384
BRINKER RESTAURANT CORPORATION—See Brinker International, Inc.; *U.S. Public*, pg. 384
BRIOCHE DOREE—See Holding Le Duff SA; *Int'l*, pg. 3450
BRIO FREEHOLD, LLC—See GP Investments, Ltd.; *Int'l*, pg. 3045
BRIO MARLTON, LLC—See GP Investments, Ltd.; *Int'l*, pg. 3045
BRIO TUSCAN GRILLE OF CHEROKEE, LLC—See GP Investments, Ltd.; *Int'l*, pg. 3045
BRIO TUSCAN GRILLE OF MARYLAND, INC.—See GP Investments, Ltd.; *Int'l*, pg. 3045
BRONCO BILLY CO., LTD.; *Int'l*, pg. 1174
B. SMITH ENTERPRISES LTD.; *U.S. Private*, pg. 420
BUBBA GUMP SHRIMP CO. RESTAURANTS, INC.—See Fertitta Entertainment, Inc.; *U.S. Private*, pg. 1499
BUCA DI BEPPO MINNEAPOLIS—See Planet Hollywood International, Inc.; *U.S. Private*, pg. 3196
BUCA, INC.—See Planet Hollywood International, Inc.; *U.S. Private*, pg. 3196
BUDI IMPIAN SDN BHD—See Berjaya Corporation Berhad; *Int'l*, pg. 983
BUFFALO GRILL S.A.—See ABENEX Capital S.A.; *Int'l*, pg. 59
BUKE TURIZM VE LOKANTACILIK TICARET A.S.—See Dogus Holding AS; *Int'l*, pg. 2154
BURGERBUSTERS INC.; *U.S. Private*, pg. 686
CABANA GRILL, INC.—See Garnett Station Partners, LLC; *U.S. Private*, pg. 1645
CAFE CENTRO—See Delaware North Companies, Inc.; *U.S. Private*, pg. 1195
CAFE DE CORAL FAST FOOD LIMITED—See Cafe de Coral Holdings Limited; *Int'l*, pg. 1250
CAFE DE CORAL GROUP LIMITED—See Cafe de Coral Holdings Limited; *Int'l*, pg. 1250
CAFE ENTERPRISES, INC.—See Milestone Partners Ltd.; *U.S. Private*, pg. 2728
CAFE PINOT—See Delaware North Companies, Inc.; *U.S. Private*, pg. 1195
CALIFORNIA BANQUET CORPORATION; *U.S. Private*, pg. 718
CALIFORNIA BEACH RESTAURANTS; *U.S. Private*, pg. 718
CALIFORNIA CAFE; *U.S. Private*, pg. 718
CALIFORNIA PIZZA KITCHEN INC.—See Golden Gate Capital Management II, LLC; *U.S. Private*, pg. 1731
CALIFORNIA SULLIVAN'S, INC.—See Catterton Management Company, LLC; *U.S. Private*, pg. 793
CAMERON MITCHELL RESTAURANTS, LLC; *U.S. Private*, pg. 729
CAMPOS, INC.; *U.S. Private*, pg. 732
C.A. MUER CORPORATION—See Fertitta Entertainment, Inc.; *U.S. Private*, pg. 1499
CAPITAL HOTELS PLC.; *Int'l*, pg. 1311
CAPITAL RESTAURANT CONCEPTS, LTD.; *U.S. Private*, pg. 742
CAPITOL BURGER, LLC—See Sonnet BioTherapeutics Holdings, Inc.; *U.S. Public*, pg. 1904
CAPPUCCINO'S—See The Copper Cellar Corporation; *U.S. Private*, pg. 4014
CAREY HILLIARDS DRIVE-IN RESTAURANT; *U.S. Private*, pg. 754
CARIBBEAN FOOD DELIGHTS; *U.S. Private*, pg. 760
CARMEN ANTHONY FISHHOUSE LLC—See Carmen Anthony Restaurant Group, LLC; *U.S. Private*, pg. 766
CARRABBA'S/COOL SPRINGS, LIMITED PARTNERSHIP—See Bloomin' Brands, Inc.; *U.S. Public*, pg. 363
CARRABBA'S/DEERFIELD TOWNSHIP, LIMITED PARTNERSHIP—See Bloomin' Brands, Inc.; *U.S. Public*, pg. 363
CARRABBA'S/GREEN HILLS, LIMITED PARTNERSHIP—See Bloomin' Brands, Inc.; *U.S. Public*, pg. 363
CARRABBA'S ITALIAN GRILL, LLC—See Bloomin' Brands, Inc.; *U.S. Public*, pg. 363
CARRABBA'S ITALIAN GRILL OF HOWARD COUNTY, INC.—See Bloomin' Brands, Inc.; *U.S. Public*, pg. 363
CARRABBA'S ITALIAN GRILL OF OVERLEA, INC.—See Bloomin' Brands, Inc.; *U.S. Public*, pg. 363
CARRABBA'S/LEXINGTON, LIMITED PARTNERSHIP—See Bloomin' Brands, Inc.; *U.S. Public*, pg. 363
CARRABBA'S/MIAMI BEACH, LIMITED PARTNERSHIP—See Bloomin' Brands, Inc.; *U.S. Public*, pg. 363
CARRABBA'S OF GERMANTOWN, INC.—See Bloomin' Brands, Inc.; *U.S. Public*, pg. 363
CARRABBA'S OF OCEAN CITY, INC.—See Bloomin' Brands, Inc.; *U.S. Public*, pg. 363
CARRABBA'S OF PASADENA, INC.—See Bloomin' Brands, Inc.; *U.S. Public*, pg. 363
CARRABBA'S OF WALDORF, INC.—See Bloomin' Brands, Inc.; *U.S. Public*, pg. 363
CARRIANNA (CHIU CHOW) RESTAURANT LIMITED—See Carrianna Group Holdings Company Limited; *Int'l*, pg. 1346
CASK 'N CLEAVER—See C&C Organization Inc.; *U.S. Private*, pg. 702
CASK 'N CLEAVER—See C&C Organization Inc.; *U.S. Private*, pg. 702
CASK 'N CLEAVER—See C&C Organization Inc.; *U.S. Private*, pg. 702
CASUAL DINING GROUP LTD—See Epiris Managers LLP; *Int'l*, pg. 2460
CATER CHAIN FOODSERVICES (PTY) LTD.—See Famous Brands Limited; *Int'l*, pg. 2612
CATTLE BARON RESTAURANTS INC.; *U.S. Private*, pg. 794
CBK HOLDINGS LIMITED; *Int'l*, pg. 1365
CBOCS, INC.—See Cracker Barrel Old Country Store, Inc.; *U.S. Public*, pg. 589
CBOCS TEXAS, LLC—See Cracker Barrel Old Country Store, Inc.; *U.S. Public*, pg. 589
CEDAR CREEK INN CORPORATION; *U.S. Private*, pg. 804
CENTER CUT HOSPITALITY, INC.—See Catterton Management Company, LLC; *U.S. Private*, pg. 793
CENTRICO—See Myriad Restaurant Group; *U.S. Private*, pg. 2825
CERULEAN AT THE BLUEBIRD, LLC—See UTG, Inc.; *U.S. Public*, pg. 2267
CFL PIZZA, LLC; *U.S. Private*, pg. 843
THE CHAR GRILL INC.; *U.S. Private*, pg. 4007
CHARLIO'S—See The Riese Organization; *U.S. Private*, pg. 4107
THE CHARLOTTE PALM—See Palm Restaurant Group; *U.S. Private*, pg. 3080
CHATEAU RESTAURANT OF WALTHAM INC.; *U.S. Private*, pg. 860
CHEDDAR'S SCRATCH KITCHEN—See Darden Restaurants, Inc.; *U.S. Public*, pg. 633
CHEESEBURGER IN PARADISE OF ANNE ARUNDEL COUNTY, INC.—See Luby's, Inc.; *U.S. Public*, pg. 1345
CHEESEBURGER OF SOUTHPORT, LLC—See Luby's, Inc.; *U.S. Public*, pg. 1345
CHEESECAKE FACTORY INCORPORATED; *U.S. Public*, pg. 483
THE CHEESECAKE FACTORY RESTAURANTS, INC.—See Cheesecake Factory Incorporated; *U.S. Public*, pg. 483
CHEESECAKE FACTORY RESTAURANTS OF KANSAS LLC—See Cheesecake Factory Incorporated; *U.S. Public*, pg. 483
CHEF JON MOLNAR—See Suarez Corporation Industries; *U.S. Private*, pg. 3846
CHEF'S HALL, INC.—See Compass Group PLC; *Int'l*, pg. 1750
CHEF'S INTERNATIONAL, INC.; *U.S. Private*, pg. 869
CHELDA, INC.; *U.S. Private*, pg. 870
CHEROKEE GRILL—See The Copper Cellar Corporation; *U.S. Private*, pg. 4014
CHESAPEAKE'S—See The Copper Cellar Corporation; *U.S. Private*, pg. 4014
CHICAGO DIVERSIFIED FOODS INC.; *U.S. Private*, pg. 877
THE CHICAGO PALM—See Palm Restaurant Group; *U.S. Private*, pg. 3080
CHICAGO PIZZA & BREWERY, LP—See BJ'S RESTAURANTS, INC.; *U.S. Public*, pg. 340
CHIKARANOMOTO HOLDINGS CO., LTD.; *Int'l*, pg. 1478
CHILI'S, INC.—See Brinker International, Inc.; *U.S. Public*, pg. 384
CHILI'S OF SALISBURY, LLC—See Brinker International, Inc.; *U.S. Public*, pg. 384
CHINA INN RESTAURANTS, INC.—See Cafe de Coral Holdings Limited; *Int'l*, pg. 1250
CHINA QUANJUDE (GROUP) CO., LTD.; *Int'l*, pg. 1542
CHIPOTLE MEXICAN GRILL CANADA CORP.—See Chipotle Mexican Grill, Inc.; *U.S. Public*, pg. 489
CHIPOTLE MEXICAN GRILL GERMANY GMBH—See Chipotle Mexican Grill, Inc.; *U.S. Public*, pg. 489
CHIPOTLE MEXICAN GRILL, INC.; *U.S. Public*, pg. 489
CHIPOTLE MEXICAN GRILL OF BERWYN HEIGHTS, LLC—See Chipotle Mexican Grill, Inc.; *U.S. Public*, pg. 489
CHIPOTLE MEXICAN GRILL OF COLORADO, LLC—See Chipotle Mexican Grill, Inc.; *U.S. Public*, pg. 489
CHIPOTLE MEXICAN GRILL SERVICE CO., LLC—See Chipotle Mexican Grill, Inc.; *U.S. Public*, pg. 489
CHIQUITO LIMITED—See Apollo Global Management, Inc.; *U.S. Public*, pg. 164
CHOUSHIMARU CO., LTD.; *Int'l*, pg. 1584
CHOZEN HOLDINGS LTD.—See Charoen Pokphand Foods Public Company Limited; *Int'l*, pg. 1452
CHS CABIN AND HANDLING SERVICE BAYERN GMBH—See Air Berlin PLC & Co. Luftverkehrs KG; *Int'l*, pg. 236
CICI ENTERPRISES, LP—See Continental Grain Company; *U.S. Private*, pg. 1029
CIGI BEVERAGES OF TEXAS, LLC—See Bloomin' Brands, Inc.; *U.S. Public*, pg. 363
CITE GOURMANDE—See Holding Le Duff SA; *Int'l*, pg. 3450
CITRUS LLC—See Kinder Morgan, Inc.; *U.S. Public*, pg. 1232
CITY CENTER ANNEX TENANT CORPORATION—See Marriott International, Inc.; *U.S. Public*, pg. 1370
CITY CENTRE RESTAURANTS (UK) LIMITED—See Apollo Global Management, Inc.; *U.S. Public*, pg. 164
CITY PUB GROUP PLC; *Int'l*, pg. 1627
CJ FOODVILLE CORP.—See CJ Corporation; *Int'l*, pg. 1632
CKE RESTAURANTS HOLDINGS, INC.—See Roark Capital Group Inc.; *U.S. Private*, pg. 3454
CLABUCET ESTIVAL 2002 S.A.; *Int'l*, pg. 1641
CLARION HIGHLANDER HOTEL AND CONFERENCE CENTER; *U.S. Private*, pg. 911
CLASSIC FOODS LTD.; *U.S. Private*, pg. 916
CLASSIFIED GROUP; *Int'l*, pg. 1653
CLOUD LIVE TECHNOLOGY GROUP CO., LTD.; *Int'l*, pg. 1662
CLYDE ARK LLC—See Ark Restaurants Corp.; *U.S. Public*, pg. 193
CLYDE, INC.; *U.S. Private*, pg. 949
CLYDE'S AT MARK CENTER, LLC—See Graham Holdings Company; *U.S. Public*, pg. 954
CLYDE'S OF CHEVY CHASE, LLC—See Graham Holdings Company; *U.S. Public*, pg. 954
CLYDE'S TOWER OAKS LODGE, LLC—See Graham Holdings Company; *U.S. Public*, pg. 954
COCO PAZZO OF ILLINOIS LLC; *U.S. Private*, pg. 959
COLLIS FOODS INC.; *U.S. Private*, pg. 969
COLONIAL ICE CREAM INC.; *U.S. Private*, pg. 971
COLORADO SPRINGS HOOTERS, INC.—See Restaurants of America, Inc.; *U.S. Private*, pg. 3408
COLOWIDE ASIA CO., LTD.—See Colowide Co., Ltd.; *Int'l*, pg. 1705
COLOWIDE CO., LTD.; *Int'l*, pg. 1704
COLOWIDE MD CO., LTD.—See Colowide Co., Ltd.; *Int'l*, pg. 1705
COLOWIDE VIETNAM., JSC.—See Colowide Co., Ltd.; *Int'l*, pg. 1705
COLTON'S RESTAURANT GROUP, INC.; *U.S. Private*, pg. 976
COLUMBIA RESTAURANT GROUP; *U.S. Private*, pg. 977
COMPASS CATERING SERVICES, IRELAND LIMITED—See Compass Group PLC; *Int'l*, pg. 1750
COMPASS GROUP AB—See Compass Group PLC; *Int'l*, pg. 1750
COMPASS GROUP FS NORWAY A/S—See Compass Group PLC; *Int'l*, pg. 1750
COMPASS GROUP PROCUREMENT LTD—See Compass Group PLC; *Int'l*, pg. 1751
COMPASS GROUP RUS OOO—See Compass Group PLC; *Int'l*, pg. 1751
COMPASS GROUP (SCHWEIZ) AG—See Compass Group PLC; *Int'l*, pg. 1750
COMPASS GROUP SOUTHERN AFRICA (PTY) LTD—See Compass Group PLC; *Int'l*, pg. 1751
COMPTOIR GROUP PLC; *Int'l*, pg. 1754
CONCORD HOSPITALITY INC; *U.S. Private*, pg. 1010
CONCORD NEIGHBORHOOD CORP.—See Concord Hospitality Inc.; *U.S. Private*, pg. 1010
CONNOR CONCEPTS INCORPORATED; *U.S. Private*, pg. 1018
CONRAD J. FREEMAN INC.; *U.S. Private*, pg. 1019
CONSOLIDATED RESTAURANT OPERATIONS, INC.—See Cracken, Harkey & Co., LLC; *U.S. Private*, pg. 1081
COOPER'S HAWK WINERY & RESTAURANT, LLC—See Ares Management Corporation; *U.S. Public*, pg. 189
COPELANDS OF NEW ORLEANS INC.; *U.S. Private*, pg. 1044
THE COPPER CELLAR CORPORATION; *U.S. Private*, pg. 4014
CORDIA CORP.; *U.S. Public*, pg. 575
COREAL SA; *Int'l*, pg. 1798
CORKY'S BAR-B-Q; *U.S. Private*, pg. 1050
CORPORATE RESTAURANT CONCEPTS, INC.; *U.S. Public*, pg. 580
COSI, INC.; *U.S. Private*, pg. 1062
COSTA VIDA MANAGEMENT, INC.; *U.S. Private*, pg. 1063
COTTON PATCH CAFE INC.—See Altamont Capital Partners; *U.S. Private*, pg. 205
CPF DISTRIBUTION GMBH—See Charoen Pokphand Foods Public Company Limited; *Int'l*, pg. 1452

N.A.I.C.S. Index
722511 — FULL-SERVICE RESTAU... CORPORATE AFFILIATIONS

C.P. FOOD PRODUCTS CO., LTD.—See Charoen Pokphand Foods Public Company Limited; *Int'l*, pg. 1452
CP HILAI HARBOUR CO., LTD.—See Charoen Pokphand Foods Public Company Limited; *Int'l*, pg. 1452
CRACKER BARREL OLD COUNTRY STORE, INC.; *U.S. Public*, pg. 589
CREATE DINING INC.—See create restaurants holdings inc.; *Int'l*, pg. 1832
CREATE RESTAURANTS ASIA PTE.LTD.—See create restaurants holdings inc.; *Int'l*, pg. 1832
CREATE RESTAURANTS HOLDINGS INC.; *Int'l*, pg. 1832
CREATE RESTAURANTS HONG KONG LTD.—See create restaurants holdings inc.; *Int'l*, pg. 1832
CREATE RESTAURANTS INC.—See create restaurants holdings inc.; *Int'l*, pg. 1832
CREATE RESTAURANTS TAIWAN CO., LTD.—See create restaurants holdings inc.; *Int'l*, pg. 1832
CREATE SPORTS & LEISURE INC.—See create restaurants holdings inc.; *Int'l*, pg. 1832
CREMONINI RAIL IBERICA S.A.—See Cremonini S.p.A.; *Int'l*, pg. 1838
C&R STEAKS INC.; *U.S. Private*, pg. 703
CUKURAMBAR LOKANTACILIK GIDA TURIZM A.S—See Dogus Holding AS; *Int'l*, pg. 2154
CULINARY ADVENTURES, INC.—See Culinary Holdings Inc.; *U.S. Private*, pg. 1120
CULINARY HOLDINGS INC.; *U.S. Private*, pg. 1120
CULVER FRANCHISING SYSTEM, INC.; *U.S. Private*, pg. 1122
THE CUMBERLAND GRILL—See The Copper Cellar Corporation; *U.S. Private*, pg. 4014
CYPRESS GROVE CHEVRE, INC.—See Emmi AG; *Int'l*, pg. 2384
DAI BAI DANG RESTAURANTS INC—See Cafe de Coral Holdings Limited; *Int'l*, pg. 1250
DAISYO CORPORATION; *Int'l*, pg. 1943
D'AMICO & SONS INC.; *U.S. Private*, pg. 1138
DARDEN RESTAURANTS, INC.; *U.S. Public*, pg. 632
DATZ; *U.S. Private*, pg. 1167
DAVE & BUSTER'S ENTERTAINMENT, INC.—See Keystone Group, L.P.; *U.S. Private*, pg. 2297
DAVE & BUSTER'S, INC.—See Keystone Group, L.P.; *U.S. Private*, pg. 2297
D&D SALADS—See Hy-Vee, Inc.; *U.S. Private*, pg. 2016
DEA COMMUNICATIONS SA—See De Agostini S.p.A.; *Int'l*, pg. 1995
DELAWARE NORTH COMPANIES (AUSTRALIA) PTY. LTD.—See Delaware North Companies, Inc.; *U.S. Private*, pg. 1194
DELAWARE NORTH COMPANIES PARKS & RESORTS—See Delaware North Companies, Inc.; *U.S. Private*, pg. 1194
DEL FRISCO'S - DALLAS, L.P.—See Catterton Management Company, LLC; *U.S. Private*, pg. 793
DEL FRISCO'S DOUBLE EAGLE STEAK HOUSE—See Fertitta Entertainment, Inc.; *U.S. Private*, pg. 1499
DEL FRISCO'S - FORT WORTH, L.P.—See Catterton Management Company, LLC; *U.S. Private*, pg. 793
DEL FRISCO'S GRILLE OF ATLANTA, LLC—See Catterton Management Company, LLC; *U.S. Private*, pg. 793
DEL FRISCO'S GRILLE OF NEW YORK, LLC—See Catterton Management Company, LLC; *U.S. Private*, pg. 793
DEL FRISCO'S GRILLE OF PHOENIX, LLC—See Catterton Management Company, LLC; *U.S. Private*, pg. 793
DEL FRISCO'S GRILLE OF WASHINGTON DC, LLC—See Catterton Management Company, LLC; *U.S. Private*, pg. 793
DEL FRISCO'S OF BOSTON, LLC—See Catterton Management Company, LLC; *U.S. Private*, pg. 793
DEL FRISCO'S OF CHICAGO, LLC—See Catterton Management Company, LLC; *U.S. Private*, pg. 793
DEL FRISCO'S OF COLORADO, INC.—See Catterton Management Company, LLC; *U.S. Private*, pg. 793
DEL FRISCO'S OF NEVADA, INC.—See Catterton Management Company, LLC; *U.S. Private*, pg. 793
DEL FRISCO'S OF NEW YORK, LLC—See Catterton Management Company, LLC; *U.S. Private*, pg. 793
DEL FRISCO'S OF NORTH CAROLINA, INC.—See Catterton Management Company, LLC; *U.S. Private*, pg. 793
DEL FRISCO'S OF PHILADELPHIA, INC.—See Catterton Management Company, LLC; *U.S. Private*, pg. 793
DEL FRISCO'S RESTAURANT GROUP, INC.—See Catterton Management Company, LLC; *U.S. Private*, pg. 793
DENNY'S CORPORATION; *U.S. Public*, pg. 653
DENNY'S, INC.—See Denny's Corporation; *U.S. Public*, pg. 654
THE DENVER PALM—See Palm Restaurant Group; *U.S. Private*, pg. 3080
DEROSA CORPORATION; *U.S. Private*, pg. 1210
DEVYANI INTERNATIONAL LIMITED; *Int'l*, pg. 2090
DIAMOND DINING CO., LTD.—See DD Holdings Co., Ltd.; *Int'l*, pg. 1993
DICK CLARK RESTAURANTS, INC.—See Valence Media Group; *U.S. Private*, pg. 4331
DICKEY'S BARBECUE RESTAURANTS, INC.; *U.S. Private*, pg. 1227
DIM SUM LESSEE, INC.—See Pebblebrook Hotel Trust; *U.S. Public*, pg. 1660
DINEOUT SA LTD.; *Int'l*, pg. 2127
DINNG CREATIVE, INC.—See LifeVantage Corporation; *U.S. Public*, pg. 1313
DIVERSIFIED RESTAURANT HOLDINGS, INC.—See ICV Partners, LLC; *U.S. Private*, pg. 2034
DIXIE RESTAURANTS INC.; *U.S. Private*, pg. 1245
DO & CO HOTEL MUNCHEN GMBH—See DO & CO Aktiengesellschaft; *Int'l*, pg. 2152
DO & CO IM PLATINUM RESTAURANTBETRIEBS GMBH—See DO & CO Aktiengesellschaft; *Int'l*, pg. 2152
DOHERTY ENTERPRISES, INC.; *U.S. Private*, pg. 1253
DON HUMBERTO SPA—See The AES Corporation; *U.S. Public*, pg. 2031
DOOLITTLES RESTAURANTS; *U.S. Private*, pg. 1261
DOS GRINGOS INC.; *U.S. Private*, pg. 1264
DOUBLE DOWN HOLDINGS INC.; *U.S. Private*, pg. 1265
DP PIZZA LIMITED—See DP Poland PLC; *Int'l*, pg. 2187
DPP RESTAURANTS LIMITED—See Apollo Global Management, Inc.; *U.S. Public*, pg. 164
DRAGON KING GROUP HOLDINGS LIMITED; *Int'l*, pg. 2199
DRAIEH GENERA TRADING CO. WLL—See DAMAC Group; *Int'l*, pg. 1955
DRD NORTHWEST LLC; *U.S. Private*, pg. 1272
DRIFTWOOD CATERING, LLC; *U.S. Private*, pg. 1277
DUFFY'S SPORTS GRILL—See Duffy's Holdings Inc.; *U.S. Private*, pg. 1285
DUTCHMAN HOSPITALITY GROUP, INC.; *U.S. Private*, pg. 1294
DYNAMIC MANAGEMENT COMPANY LLC; *U.S. Private*, pg. 1298
DZINE FOOD SOLUTIONS CO., LTD.—See Charoen Pokphand Foods Public Company Limited; *Int'l*, pg. 1452
EATERIES, INC.; *U.S. Private*, pg. 1323
EAT HERE BRANDS, LLC; *U.S. Private*, pg. 1323
EAT&HOLDINGS CO.,LTD; *Int'l*, pg. 2277
EAT'N PARK HOSPITALITY GROUP, INC.; *U.S. Private*, pg. 1323
EAT WALK CO., LTD—See create restaurants holdings inc.; *Int'l*, pg. 1832
EAT WELL INC.; *U.S. Private*, pg. 1323
EB-RESTAURANTSBETRIEBE GES.M.B.H.—See Erste Group Bank AG; *Int'l*, pg. 2498
EDENRED HONG-KONG LIMITED—See Edenred S.A.; *Int'l*, pg. 2307
EDENRED LIBAN—See Edenred S.A.; *Int'l*, pg. 2308
EDENRED MAROC SAS—See Edenred S.A.; *Int'l*, pg. 2308
EDENRED POLSKA SP. Z O.O—See Edenred S.A.; *Int'l*, pg. 2308
EDENRED SHANGHAI (CHINA)—See Edenred S.A.; *Int'l*, pg. 2308
EDENRED SLOVAKIA, S.R.O—See Edenred S.A.; *Int'l*, pg. 2308
EDENRED SUISSE SA—See Edenred S.A.; *Int'l*, pg. 2308
ED'S EASY DINER GROUP LIMITED; *Int'l*, pg. 2303
EGGSMART CORPORATION—See Chairman's Brands Corporation; *Int'l*, pg. 1437
EIGHTYTHREE CORPORATION—See Hibino Corporation; *Int'l*, pg. 3383
EL FENIX CORPORATION; *U.S. Private*, pg. 1349
EL TORITO RESTAURANTS, INC.—See Z Capital Group, LLC; *U.S. Private*, pg. 4596
EMINENT PEDESTAL SDN. BHD—See Eastern & Oriental Berhad; *Int'l*, pg. 2271
THE EPICUREAN GROUP; *U.S. Private*, pg. 4026
ERIK'S DELICAFE, INC.; *U.S. Private*, pg. 1421
ESS MOBILE OFFSHORE UNITS A/S—See Compass Group PLC; *Int'l*, pg. 1751
E-STATION GREEN TECHNOLOGY GROUP CO., LIMITED; *Int'l*, pg. 2249
EUREST (PORTUGAL) - SOCIEDADE EUROPEIA DE RESTAURANTES, LDA.—See Compass Group PLC; *Int'l*, pg. 1751
EUREST SERVICES GMBH—See Compass Group PLC; *Int'l*, pg. 1751
EUROFINS LABORATORIO MEDICANTABRIA SL—See Eurofins Scientific S.E.; *Int'l*, pg. 2545
EVN BUSINESS SERVICE GMBH—See EVN AG; *Int'l*, pg. 2571
EXO ENTERPRISES LIMITED—See Cafe de Coral Holdings Limited; *Int'l*, pg. 1250
FAIRWOOD FAST FOOD LIMITED—See Fairwood Holdings Limited; *Int'l*, pg. 2609
FAIRWOOD HOLDINGS LIMITED; *Int'l*, pg. 2609
FAMIGLIA - DEBARTOLO, LLC—See DeBartolo Holdings, LLC; *U.S. Private*, pg. 1186
FAMILY RESTAURANTS INC.; *U.S. Private*, pg. 1471
FAMILY SPORTS CONCEPTS, INC.; *U.S. Private*, pg. 1471
FAMOUS-AMOS RESTAURANTS INC.; *U.S. Private*, pg. 1472
FAMOUS BRANDS CHEESE COMPANY (PTY) LTD.—See Famous Brands Limited; *Int'l*, pg. 2612
FAMOUS BRANDS COFFEE COMPANY (PTY) LTD.—See Famous Brands Limited; *Int'l*, pg. 2612
FAT BRANDS INC.—See Fog Cutter Capital Group Inc.; *U.S. Private*, pg. 1556
FAT PATTY'S—See ARC Group, Inc.; *U.S. Public*, pg. 179
FATTAL HOLDINGS (1998) LTD.; *Int'l*, pg. 2623
FAZOLI'S SYSTEM MANAGEMENT, LLC—See Sentinel Capital Partners, L.L.C.; *U.S. Private*, pg. 3609
FAZ RESTAURANT INC.; *U.S. Private*, pg. 1484
FB GROUP ENTERPRISES MANAGEMENT COMPANY LIMITED—See Future Bright Holdings Limited; *Int'l*, pg. 2852
FERME DES LOGES SARL—See Holding Le Duff SA; *Int'l*, pg. 3450
FERRARO FOODS INC.—See Kelso & Company, L.P.; *U.S. Private*, pg. 2278
FIELMANN SCHLOSS PLON HOTEL- UND CATERING GMBH—See Fielmann Group AG; *Int'l*, pg. 2658
FIFTH GROUP RESTAURANTS; *U.S. Private*, pg. 1505
FIGARO COFFEE GROUP INCORPORATED; *Int'l*, pg. 2660
FIRST KITCHEN LTD—See The Wendy's Company; *U.S. Public*, pg. 2141
FIRST WATCH RESTAURANTS, INC.—See Advent International Corporation; *U.S. Private*, pg. 101
FIVE ELEVEN INC.—See Premier Ventures, Inc.; *U.S. Private*, pg. 3251
FIVE STAR RESTAURANT LLC; *U.S. Private*, pg. 1538
FLANIGAN'S ENTERPRISES, INC.; *U.S. Public*, pg. 852
FLANIGAN'S ENTERPRISES, INC.—See Flanigan's Enterprises, Inc.; *U.S. Public*, pg. 852
FLANIGAN'S ENTERPRISES, INC.—See Flanigan's Enterprises, Inc.; *U.S. Public*, pg. 852
FLANIGAN'S ENTERPRISES, INC. - SURFSIDE—See Flanigan's Enterprises, Inc.; *U.S. Public*, pg. 852
FLEMING'S OF BALTIMORE, LLC—See Bloomin' Brands, Inc.; *U.S. Public*, pg. 363
FLEMING'S PRIME STEAKHOUSE & WINE BAR—See Bloomin' Brands, Inc.; *U.S. Public*, pg. 363
FLIXENTERTAINMENT LLC; *U.S. Private*, pg. 1546
FLO JAPON CO., LTD.—See Bain Capital, LP; *U.S. Private*, pg. 444
FLORIDA TEXAS RESTAURANT GROUP—See Pacesetter Capital Group; *U.S. Private*, pg. 3064
FLORIDA WEST COAST CRUISES, INC.; *U.S. Private*, pg. 1551
FLYING GARDEN CO., LTD.; *Int'l*, pg. 2716
FOGO DE CHAO (HOLDINGS) INC.—See Thomas H. Lee Partners, L.P.; *U.S. Private*, pg. 4156
FOLKS RESTAURANTS, LTD.; *U.S. Private*, pg. 1559
FOOD AFFAIRS GMBH—See Compass Group PLC; *Int'l*, pg. 1752
FOOD CONCEPTS INTERNATIONAL; *U.S. Private*, pg. 1560
FOODIO CONCEPTS SP. Z O.O.—See Agora S.A.; *Int'l*, pg. 212
FOOD & LIFE COMPANIES LTD.; *Int'l*, pg. 2727
FOOD MASTERS INC.; *U.S. Private*, pg. 1561
FOOD REPUBLIC PTE LTD—See BreadTalk Group Pte Ltd.; *Int'l*, pg. 1143
FOOD SERVICE OF TALLAHASSEE; *U.S. Private*, pg. 1561
FOOD SERVICE PROJECT, SL—See Alsea, S.A.B. de C.V.; *Int'l*, pg. 379
FOODS NORTH LLC; *U.S. Private*, pg. 1562
FOOD SPECIALISTS INC.; *U.S. Private*, pg. 1561
FORMULA BREWING, LLC; *U.S. Private*, pg. 1572
FOUR FOODS GROUP HOLDINGS; *U.S. Private*, pg. 1582
FOX RESTAURANT CONCEPTS, LLC—See Cheesecake Factory Incorporated; *U.S. Public*, pg. 483
FRANKENMUTH BAVARIAN INN, INC.; *U.S. Private*, pg. 1596
FRANKFURT RH OPERATING COMPANY GMBH—See Marriott International, Inc.; *U.S. Public*, pg. 1370
FRANKIE & BENNYS S.L.—See Apollo Global Management, Inc.; *U.S. Public*, pg. 164
FREDERICK OUTBACK, INC.—See Bloomin' Brands, Inc.; *U.S. Public*, pg. 363
FREEWAY FOODS INC.; *U.S. Private*, pg. 1607
FRESCA'S MEXICAN GRILL, INC.—See American Restaurant Holdings, Inc.; *U.S. Private*, pg. 246
FRESHII, INC.—See Foodtastic Inc.; *Int'l*, pg. 2728
FR FREIRAUM GASTRONOMIE GMBH—See DO & CO Aktiengesellschaft; *Int'l*, pg. 2152
FRIENDLY CORPORATION; *Int'l*, pg. 2792
FRIENDLY ICE CREAM CORPORATION—See Sun Capital Partners, Inc.; *U.S. Private*, pg. 3859
FRISCH INDIANA LLC—See NRD Capital Management, LLC; *U.S. Private*, pg. 2969
FRISCH KENTUCKY LLC—See NRD Capital Management, LLC; *U.S. Private*, pg. 2969
FRISCH OHIO LLC—See NRD Capital Management, LLC; *U.S. Private*, pg. 2969
FRONT BURNER BRANDS, INC.; *U.S. Private*, pg. 1613
FUJINO CLUB CO., LTD.—See Amada Holdings Co., Ltd.; *Int'l*, pg. 404
FUJIO FOOD GROUP INC.; *Int'l*, pg. 2829
FULLFILLMENT SYSTEMS, INC.; *U.S. Private*, pg. 1621
FULUM FOOD (INTERNATIONAL) LIMITED—See Fulum Group Holdings Limited; *Int'l*, pg. 2844
GAN KHERLEN JOINT STOCK COMPANY; *Int'l*, pg. 2880
GARDEN FRESH RESTAURANT LLC—See Cerberus Capital Management, L.P.; *U.S. Private*, pg. 838
GARDUNOS RESTAURANT; *U.S. Private*, pg. 1644

N.A.I.C.S. INDEX

722511 — FULL-SERVICE RESTAU...

GARFIELD BEACH CVS, L.L.C.—See CVS Health Corporation; *U.S. Public*, pg. 616
GASHO OF JAPAN INTERNATIONAL LTD.; *U.S. Private*, pg. 1648
GASHO OF JAPAN LONG ISLAND—See Gasho of Japan International Ltd.; *U.S. Private*, pg. 1648
GASTRONOMY INC.; *U.S. Private*, pg. 1649
GBK RESTAURANTS LIMITED—See Famous Brands Limited; *Int'l*, pg. 2612
GC PARTNERS INC.; *U.S. Private*, pg. 1653
GENGHIS GRILL; *U.S. Private*, pg. 1671
GENKI SUSHI HONG KONG LIMITED—See Genki Global Dining Concepts Corporation; *Int'l*, pg. 2924
GENKI SUSHI USA INC.—See Genki Global Dining Concepts Corporation; *Int'l*, pg. 2924
GEN RESTAURANT GROUP, INC.; *U.S. Public*, pg. 911
GEORGIA WORLD CONGRESS CENTER AUTHORITY; *U.S. Private*, pg. 1685
GINGER BEEF EXPRESS LTD.—See Ginger Beef Corporation; *Int'l*, pg. 2977
GLACIER RESTAURANT GROUP LLC; *U.S. Private*, pg. 1704
GLOBAL DINING, INC.; *Int'l*, pg. 2994
GLOBAL-DINING, INC.—See Global Dining, Inc.; *Int'l*, pg. 2994
GLOBEAT JAPAN INC.—See Fullcast Holdings Co., Ltd.; *Int'l*, pg. 2842
GLORY DAYS GRILL; *U.S. Private*, pg. 1720
GODFATHER'S PIZZA, INC.; *U.S. Private*, pg. 1724
GOLDEN ARCHES RESTAURANTS SDN. BHD.—See McDonald's Corporation; *U.S. Public*, pg. 1406
GOLDEN PARTNERS INC.—See Brentwood Associates; *U.S. Private*, pg. 646
GONPACHI RESTAURANT LIMITED—See 1957 & Co. (Hospitality) Limited; *Int'l*, pg. 3
GOOD EARTH RESTAURANTS OF MINNESOTA—See Parasole Restaurant Holdings, Inc.; *U.S. Private*, pg. 3093
GOODE-COOK INC.; *U.S. Private*, pg. 1739
GOODERSON LEISURE CORPORATION; *Int'l*, pg. 3039
GOOD TIMES DRIVE-THRU, INC.—See Good Times Restaurants, Inc.; *U.S. Public*, pg. 951
GOURMET BRANDS COMPANY INC.—See create restaurants holdings inc.; *Int'l*, pg. 1832
GOURMET DINING, LLC—See Compass Group PLC; *Int'l*, pg. 1752
GOURMET KINEYA CO., LTD.; *Int'l*, pg. 3044
GRAND LUX CAFE LLC—See Cheesecake Factory Incorporated; *U.S. Public*, pg. 483
GRANDMA'S RESTAURANT CO.; *U.S. Private*, pg. 1754
GREAT AMERICAN FOOD CHAIN, INC.; *U.S. Public*, pg. 961
GREAT AMERICAN FOODS CORP.; *U.S. Private*, pg. 1762
GREAT AMERICAN RESTAURANTS, INC.; *U.S. Private*, pg. 1762
THE GREENE TURTLE FRANCHISING CORPORATION—See Stone-Goff Partners, LLC; *U.S. Private*, pg. 3826
GRILL CONCEPTS-D.C., INC.—See Grill Concepts, Inc.; *U.S. Private*, pg. 1789
GRILLIT, INC.; *U.S. Public*, pg. 969
GRINGO'S MEXICAN KITCHEN; *U.S. Private*, pg. 1790
GRISANTI, INC.; *U.S. Private*, pg. 1790
GROOT HOSPITALITY LLC—See Live Nation Entertainment, Inc.; *U.S. Public*, pg. 1329
GROUPE BERTRAND SARL; *Int'l*, pg. 3092
GROUPE FLO SA—See Groupe Bertrand SARL; *Int'l*, pg. 3092
GROUPE ST-HUBERT INC.—See Fairfax Financial Holdings Limited; *Int'l*, pg. 2608
GROWTH MANAGEMENT CORPORATION; *U.S. Private*, pg. 1796
GULF AND ARAB WORLD RESTAURANTS CO.—See Adeptio LLC; *Int'l*, pg. 143
GULLEY ENTERPRISES INC.; *U.S. Private*, pg. 1818
GUNAYDIN ET SANAYI VE TICARET A.S.—See Dogus Holding AS; *Int'l*, pg. 2155
G-VISION INTERNATIONAL (HOLDINGS) LIMITED; *Int'l*, pg. 2864
THE HABIT RESTAURANTS, INC.—See Yum! Brands, Inc.; *U.S. Public*, pg. 2400
HADDAD SPECIALTY RESTAURANTS, INC.—See Haddad Restaurant Group, Inc.; *U.S. Private*, pg. 1839
HAGERSTOWN OUTBACK, INC.—See Bloomin' Brands, Inc.; *U.S. Public*, pg. 363
HAIWAN INTERNATIONAL DEVELOPMENT CO., LTD.; *Int'l*, pg. 3218
HAKKASAN LTD.; *Int'l*, pg. 3219
HALLS DRIVE INS INC.; *U.S. Private*, pg. 1845
HALPERN'S STEAK & SEAFOOD CO.; *U.S. Private*, pg. 1846
HAL SMITH RESTAURANT GROUP, INC.; *U.S. Private*, pg. 1841
HAMAYUU CO., LTD.; *Int'l*, pg. 3236
HANGOOK MCDONALD'S CO. LTD.—See McDonald's Corporation; *U.S. Public*, pg. 1406
HANKYU HANSHIN RESTAURANTS CO., LTD.—See Hankyu Hanshin Holdings Inc.; *Int'l*, pg. 3255

HANSHIN HOTEL SYSTEMS CO., LTD.—See Hankyu Hanshin Holdings Inc.; *Int'l*, pg. 3255
HAPPY CHEF SYSTEMS, INC.; *U.S. Private*, pg. 1857
HAPPY DAY CORPORATION; *U.S. Private*, pg. 1857
HARD ROCK CAFE INTERNATIONAL CHICAGO—See Seminole Tribe of Florida, Inc.; *U.S. Private*, pg. 3604
HARD ROCK CAFE INTERNATIONAL INC. GEORGIA—See Seminole Tribe of Florida, Inc.; *U.S. Private*, pg. 3605
HARD ROCK CAFE INTERNATIONAL, INC.—See Seminole Tribe of Florida, Inc.; *U.S. Private*, pg. 3604
HARD ROCK CAFE INTERNATIONAL LA JOLLA—See Seminole Tribe of Florida, Inc.; *U.S. Private*, pg. 3605
HARD ROCK CAFE INTERNATIONAL LAS VEGAS—See Seminole Tribe of Florida, Inc.; *U.S. Private*, pg. 3605
HARD ROCK CAFE INTERNATIONAL MAUI—See Seminole Tribe of Florida, Inc.; *U.S. Private*, pg. 3605
HARD ROCK CAFE INTERNATIONAL MIAMI—See Seminole Tribe of Florida, Inc.; *U.S. Private*, pg. 3605
HARD ROCK CAFE INTERNATIONAL NEW JERSEY—See Seminole Tribe of Florida, Inc.; *U.S. Private*, pg. 3605
HARD ROCK CAFE INTERNATIONAL NEWPORT BEACH—See Seminole Tribe of Florida, Inc.; *U.S. Private*, pg. 3605
HARD ROCK CAFE INTERNATIONAL NEW YORK—See Seminole Tribe of Florida, Inc.; *U.S. Private*, pg. 3605
HARD ROCK CAFE INTERNATIONAL SAN ANTONIO—See Seminole Tribe of Florida, Inc.; *U.S. Private*, pg. 3605
HARD ROCK CAFE INTERNATIONAL—See Seminole Tribe of Florida, Inc.; *U.S. Private*, pg. 3604
HARD ROCK CAFE INTERNATIONAL—See Seminole Tribe of Florida, Inc.; *U.S. Private*, pg. 3604
HARD ROCK CAFE INTERNATIONAL SOUTH CAROLINA—See Seminole Tribe of Florida, Inc.; *U.S. Private*, pg. 3605
HARD ROCK CAFE INTERNATIONAL TENNESSEE—See Seminole Tribe of Florida, Inc.; *U.S. Private*, pg. 3605
HARD ROCK CAFE INTERNATIONAL TEXAS—See Seminole Tribe of Florida, Inc.; *U.S. Private*, pg. 3605
HARD ROCK CAFE KEY WEST—See Seminole Tribe of Florida, Inc.; *U.S. Private*, pg. 3605
HARD ROCK CAFE PUERTO RICO—See Seminole Tribe of Florida, Inc.; *U.S. Private*, pg. 3605
HARRY S ESPLANADE PTE. LTD.—See Everstone Capital Advisors Pvt. Ltd.; *Int'l*, pg. 2569
HARRY S INTERNATIONAL PTE. LTD—See Everstone Capital Advisors Pvt. Ltd.; *Int'l*, pg. 2569
HARRY'S OF AMERICA INC.; *U.S. Private*, pg. 1872
HARU AMSTERDAM AVENUE CORP.—See TPG Capital, L.P.; *U.S. Public*, pg. 2167
HARU GRAMERCY PARK CORP.—See TPG Capital, L.P.; *U.S. Public*, pg. 2167
HARU THIRD AVENUE CORP.—See TPG Capital, L.P.; *U.S. Public*, pg. 2167
HARU WALL STREET CORP.—See TPG Capital, L.P.; *U.S. Public*, pg. 2167
HAUS KURFURST GMBH—See ATON GmbH; *Int'l*, pg. 689
HAVANA YAYINCILIK TURIZM VE GIDA PAZARLAMA TICARET A.S.—See Dogus Holding AS; *Int'l*, pg. 2155
HAWAIIAN PACIFIC RESTAURANT GROUP, INC.; *U.S. Private*, pg. 1882
HEILBAD SAUERBRUNN BETRIEBSGESELLSCHAFT M.B.H.—See Fresenius SE & Co. KGaA; *Int'l*, pg. 2779
HEIRLOOM RESTAURANT GROUP; *U.S. Private*, pg. 1905
HEKI CO., LTD.; *Int'l*, pg. 3327
HENRY THE ART OF LIVING GMBH—See DO & CO Aktiengesellschaft; *Int'l*, pg. 2152
HERSHEY'S MILL RESTAURANT SERVICE INC.—See Wooldridge Construction Co., Inc.; *U.S. Private*, pg. 4562
HEYDE COMPANIES; *U.S. Private*, pg. 1928
HH HOLDINGS INC.; *U.S. Private*, pg. 1931
HIDA JAPANESE RESTAURANT—See Gasho of Japan International Ltd.; *U.S. Private*, pg. 1648
HIDAY HIDAKA CORP.; *Int'l*, pg. 3384
HIGASHI-MATSUYAMA SKYLARK—See Bain Capital, LP; *U.S. Private*, pg. 444
HIGHLINE INTERNATIONAL LTD.—See BRF S.A.; *Int'l*, pg. 1151
HI-LAI FOODS CO., LTD.; *Int'l*, pg. 3380
HIRAMATSU INC.; *Int'l*, pg. 3403
HMR ACQUISITION COMPANY INC.; *U.S. Private*, pg. 1955
HOF'S HUT RESTAURANTS INC.; *U.S. Private*, pg. 1959
HOKKOKU CO., LTD.; *Int'l*, pg. 3443
HOLIDAY INN DOWNTOWN BEIJING COMPANY LIMITED—See Beijing Properties (Holdings) Limited; *Int'l*, pg. 955
HOME MEAL REPLACEMENT SA; *Int'l*, pg. 3455
HOMESTYLE DINING, LLC—See Fog Cutter Capital Group Inc.; *U.S. Private*, pg. 1557
HOOT AUSTRALIA PTY LTD—See Sonnet BioTherapeutics Holdings, Inc.; *U.S. Public*, pg. 1904
HOOTERS BRAZIL—See Sonnet BioTherapeutics Holdings, Inc.; *U.S. Public*, pg. 1904
HOOTERS MANAGEMENT CORPORATION; *U.S. Private*, pg. 1978
HOOTERS OF CAPE CORAL, INC.—See LTP Management Group, Inc.; *U.S. Private*, pg. 2510

HOOTERS OF CRYSTAL LAKE, INC.—See LTP Management Group, Inc.; *U.S. Private*, pg. 2510
HOOTERS OF CYPRESS CREEK, INC.—See LTP Management Group, Inc.; *U.S. Private*, pg. 2510
HOOTERS OF DORAL, INC.—See LTP Management Group, Inc.; *U.S. Private*, pg. 2510
HOOT PARRAMATTA PTY LTD—See Sonnet BioTherapeutics Holdings, Inc.; *U.S. Public*, pg. 1904
HORII FOODSERVICE CO., LTD.; *Int'l*, pg. 3478
HOSS'S STEAK & SEA HOUSE, INC.; *U.S. Private*, pg. 1988
HOSTMORE PLC; *Int'l*, pg. 3486
HOTELS ILIDZA D.D. ILIDZA; *Int'l*, pg. 3489
HOTLAND CO., LTD.; *Int'l*, pg. 3489
HOULE RESTAURATION; *Int'l*, pg. 3490
HOULIHAN'S RESTAURANTS, INC.—See Fertitta Entertainment, Inc.; *U.S. Private*, pg. 1499
HOUSE OF BLUES NEW ORLEANS RESTAURANT CORP.—See Live Nation Entertainment, Inc.; *U.S. Public*, pg. 1329
THE HOUSTON CHEESECAKE FACTORY CORPORATION—See Cheesecake Factory Incorporated; *U.S. Public*, pg. 483
THE HOUSTON PALM—See Palm Restaurant Group; *U.S. Private*, pg. 3080
HOUSTON'S RESTAURANTS INC.; *U.S. Private*, pg. 1994
HRM ENTERPRISES INC.; *U.S. Private*, pg. 1998
HUDDLE HOUSE, INC.; *U.S. Private*, pg. 2001
HUHOT MONGOLIAN GRILLS, LLC; *U.S. Private*, pg. 2004
HUMAP JAPAN CO., LTD.—See Dynam Japan Holdings, Co., Ltd.; *Int'l*, pg. 2239
HURRICANE AMT, LLC—See Fog Cutter Capital Group Inc.; *U.S. Private*, pg. 1557
HYATT GTLD, L.L.C.—See Hyatt Hotels Corporation; *U.S. Public*, pg. 1077
HYATT HOTELS OF FLORIDA, INC.—See Hyatt Hotels Corporation; *U.S. Public*, pg. 1077
IBC HOTELS, LLC—See InnSuites Hospitality Trust; *U.S. Public*, pg. 1127
IBERSOL S.G.P.S., S.A.; *Int'l*, pg. 3574
ICCHOU INC.—See create restaurants holdings inc.; *Int'l*, pg. 1832
ICHIBANYA CO., LTD. - SAGA PLANT—See House Foods Group Inc.; *Int'l*, pg. 3490
ICHIBANYA CO., LTD.—See House Foods Group Inc.; *Int'l*, pg. 3490
ICHIBANYA CO., LTD. - TOCHIGI PLANT—See House Foods Group Inc.; *Int'l*, pg. 3490
ICHIBANYA HONG KONG LIMITED—See House Foods Group Inc.; *Int'l*, pg. 3490
ICHIBANYA USA—See House Foods Group Inc.; *Int'l*, pg. 3490
ICHIROKUDO CO., LTD.; *Int'l*, pg. 3581
IDEAL RESTAURANT GROUP, INC.; *U.S. Private*, pg. 2036
IGNITE RESTAURANT GROUP, INC.—See J.H. Whitney & Co., LLC; *U.S. Private*, pg. 2166
IGNITE RESTAURANTS-NEW JERSEY, INC.—See J.H. Whitney & Co., LLC; *U.S. Private*, pg. 2166
IHOP FRANCHISOR, LLC—See Dine Brands Global, Inc.; *U.S. Public*, pg. 667
IHOP RESTAURANTS, LLC—See Dine Brands Global, Inc.; *U.S. Public*, pg. 667
IKEJA HOTEL PLC; *Int'l*, pg. 3610
IKKA DINING PROJECT CO., LTD.; *Int'l*, pg. 3611
IL FORNAIO (AMERICA) CORPORATION—See create restaurants holdings inc.; *Int'l*, pg. 1832
THE INDIGO ROAD HOSPITALITY GROUP, LLC; *U.S. Private*, pg. 4055
INTERNATIONAL HOTEL LICENSING COMPANY S.AR.L. LUXEMBOURG—See Marriott International, Inc.; *U.S. Public*, pg. 1370
INTERNATIONAL HOUSE OF PANCAKES, INC.—See Dine Brands Global, Inc.; *U.S. Public*, pg. 667
INVENTURE RESTAURANTES LTDA.—See Yum! Brands, Inc.; *U.S. Public*, pg. 2400
IRISH TIMES; *U.S. Private*, pg. 2138
ISAAC'S RESTAURANT & DELI INC.; *U.S. Private*, pg. 2142
ITAL-AMERICAS FOODS CORP.; *U.S. Private*, pg. 2148
IVARS INC.; *U.S. Private*, pg. 2150
J&B RESTAURANT PARTNERS INC.; *U.S. Private*, pg. 2153
JCS MONMOUTH MALL-NJ, LLC—See J.H. Whitney & Co., LLC; *U.S. Private*, pg. 2166
JD RESTAURANTS, INC.; *U.S. Private*, pg. 2195
JERRY'S FAMOUS DELI, INC.; *U.S. Private*, pg. 2202
JH SERVICES INC.; *U.S. Private*, pg. 2207
JLC FOOD SYSTEMS INC.; *U.S. Private*, pg. 2212
JOE'S CRAB SHACK-ABINGDON MD, INC.—See J.H. Whitney & Co., LLC; *U.S. Private*, pg. 2166
JOE'S CRAB SHACK-ALABAMA PRIVATE CLUB INC.—See J.H. Whitney & Co., LLC; *U.S. Private*, pg. 2166
JOE'S CRAB SHACK-ANNE ARUNDEL MD, INC.—See J.H. Whitney & Co., LLC; *U.S. Private*, pg. 2166
JOE'S CRAB SHACK-HUNT VALLEY MD, INC.—See J.H. Whitney & Co., LLC; *U.S. Private*, pg. 2166
JOE'S CRAB SHACK-KANSAS, INC.—See J.H. Whitney &

722511 — FULL-SERVICE RESTAU...

Co., LLC; *U.S. Private*, pg. 2166
JOE'S CRAB SHACK-MARYLAND, INC.—See J.H. Whitney & Co., LLC; *U.S. Private*, pg. 2166
JOE'S CRAB SHACK-REDONDO BEACH, INC.—See J.H. Whitney & Co., LLC; *U.S. Private*, pg. 2166
JOE'S CRAB SHACK-SAN DIEGO INC.—See J.H. Whitney & Co., LLC; *U.S. Private*, pg. 2166
JOE'S CRAB SHACK—See J.H. Whitney & Co., LLC; *U.S. Private*, pg. 2166
JOE'S CRAB SHACK-TEXAS, INC.—See J.H. Whitney & Co., LLC; *U.S. Private*, pg. 2166
JOHN HARVARD'S BREWHOUSE LLC; *U.S. Private*, pg. 2222
THE JOHNNY ROCKETS GROUP, INC.—See Fog Cutter Capital Group Inc.; *U.S. Private*, pg. 1557
JOJO'S PIZZA KITCHEN INC.—See American Restaurant Holdings, Inc.; *U.S. Private*, pg. 246
JOLLIBEAN FOODS PTE LTD.—See Berjaya Corporation Berhad; *Int'l*, pg. 984
JOMAR INVESTMENTS LC; *U.S. Private*, pg. 2230
JONAS & CO., LTD.—See Bain Capital, LP; *U.S. Private*, pg. 444
J.S. VENTURES, INC.; *U.S. Private*, pg. 2171
J. THOMAS & CO. INC; *U.S. Private*, pg. 2157
KATECH INGREDIENT SOLUTIONS GMBH—See Ingredion Incorporated; *U.S. Public*, pg. 1124
KATECH INGREDIENT SOLUTIONS LTD.—See Ingredion Incorporated; *U.S. Public*, pg. 1124
KATECH INGREDIENT SOLUTIONS SP. Z O.O.—See Ingredion Incorporated; *U.S. Public*, pg. 1124
KATER INTERNATIONAL LIMITED—See Cafe de Coral Holdings Limited; *Int'l*, pg. 1250
KAVANAUGH, INC.; *U.S. Private*, pg. 2265
K-BOB'S USA INC.; *U.S. Private*, pg. 2250
KENDALL'S BRASSERIE & BAR—See Delaware North Companies, Inc.; *U.S. Private*, pg. 1195
KENTUCKY FRIED CHICKEN (GREAT BRITAIN) SERVICES LIMITED—See Yum! Brands, Inc.; *U.S. Public*, pg. 2400
KENTUCKY FRIED CHICKEN LIMITED—See Yum! Brands, Inc.; *U.S. Public*, pg. 2400
KER, INC.; *U.S. Private*, pg. 2290
KESSLER GROUP INCORPORATED; *U.S. Private*, pg. 2291
KEYSTONE RESORT PROPERTY MANAGEMENT COMPANY—See Vail Resorts, Inc.; *U.S. Public*, pg. 2271
KFC (PTY) LTD.—See Yum! Brands, Inc.; *U.S. Public*, pg. 2400
KFC RESTAURANTS SPAIN S.L.—See Yum! Brands, Inc.; *U.S. Public*, pg. 2400
KICKAPOO TRIBE IN KANSAS; *U.S. Private*, pg. 2302
KING CANNON, INC; *U.S. Private*, pg. 2309
KINGFISH INC.; *U.S. Private*, pg. 2310
KING'S FAMILY RESTAURANTS INC; *U.S. Private*, pg. 2310
KING'S HAWAIIAN RETAIL, INC.—See King's Hawaiian Holding Company, Inc.; *Int'l*, pg. 2310
KING'S RESTAURANT & SUPERMARKET, INC.; *U.S. Private*, pg. 2310
KINGS SEAFOOD COMPANY; *U.S. Private*, pg. 2311
KISSES FROM ITALY, INC.; *U.S. Public*, pg. 1236
KITCHEN FAIR—See Towncraft Homewares, LLC; *U.S. Private*, pg. 4198
KMG ENTERPRISES INC.; *U.S. Private*, pg. 2321
KOBE JAPANESE STEAK HOUSE LLC—See Yamada Group USA Ltd.; *U.S. Private*, pg. 4585
KONA SUSHI, INC.—See The ONE Group Hospitality, Inc.; *U.S. Public*, pg. 2118
KONA TEXAS RESTAURANTS, INC.—See The ONE Group Hospitality, Inc.; *U.S. Public*, pg. 2118
KR HOLDINGS CORPORATION—See create restaurants holdings inc.; *Int'l*, pg. 1832
KYROS KEBAB SDN BHD—See Cab Cakaran Corporation Berhad; *Int'l*, pg. 1245
LABA ROYALTY SUB LLC—See Innoviva, Inc.; *U.S. Public*, pg. 1127
LA MADELEINE INC.; *U.S. Private*, pg. 2368
LA MADELEINE OF MARYLAND, INC.—See La Madeleine Inc.; *U.S. Private*, pg. 2369
LAMBERTS BAY FOODS (PTY) LTD.—See Famous Brands Limited; *Int'l*, pg. 2612
LA PRIMA CATERING; *U.S. Private*, pg. 2369
LASCO ENTERPRISES; *U.S. Private*, pg. 2395
LASTING IMPRESSIONS FOOD CO., LTD.—See DO & CO Aktiengesellschaft; *Int'l*, pg. 2152
LAS VEGAS AMERICA CORP.—See Ark Restaurants Corp.; *U.S. Public*, pg. 193
LAS VEGAS FESTIVAL FOOD CORP.—See Ark Restaurants Corp.; *U.S. Public*, pg. 193
THE LAS VEGAS PALM—See Palm Restaurant Group; *U.S. Private*, pg. 3080
LAS VEGAS VENICE DELI CORP.—See Ark Restaurants Corp.; *U.S. Public*, pg. 193
LATITUDE 360, INC.; *U.S. Private*, pg. 2397
LAURIER ENTERPRISES INC.; *U.S. Private*, pg. 2400
LAWRY'S RESTAURANTS, INC.; *U.S. Private*, pg. 2402
LC3S INC.; *U.S. Private*, pg. 2403

LE BISON GOURMAND SARL—See Derichebourg S.A.; *Int'l*, pg. 2042
LEEANN CHIN, INC.; *U.S. Private*, pg. 2414
LEGAL SEA FOODS INC.—See PPX Hospitality Brands Inc.; *U.S. Private*, pg. 3241
LE NOIR CAFE - SOLE PROPRIETORSHIP LLC—See Alpha Dhabi Holding PJSC; *Int'l*, pg. 367
LEON DE BRUXELLES SA—See Eurazeo SE; *Int'l*, pg. 2529
LE ROUGE AB—See Frontier Digital Ventures Limited; *Int'l*, pg. 2795
LETNES RESTAURANT INC.; *U.S. Private*, pg. 2433
LETTUCE ENTERTAIN YOU ENTERPRISES, INC.; *U.S. Private*, pg. 2433
LETTUCE SOUPRISE YOU, INC.; *U.S. Private*, pg. 2433
LEVY RESTAURANTS FRANCE SAS—See Compass Group PLC; *Int'l*, pg. 1752
LEVY RESTAURANTS, INC.—See Compass Group PLC; *Int'l*, pg. 1751
LG&EW INC.—See create restaurants holdings inc.; *Int'l*, pg. 1832
LHOBERGE LESSEE, INC.—See Pebblebrook Hotel Trust; *U.S. Public*, pg. 1660
LIFEWORKS RESTAURANT GROUP, LLC—See Aramark; *U.S. Public*, pg. 178
LIVE VENTURES INCORPORATED—See Live Ventures Incorporated; *U.S. Public*, pg. 1332
LIZARD'S THICKET INC.; *U.S. Private*, pg. 2474
LM RESTAURANTS, INC.; *U.S. Private*, pg. 2476
LONE STAR STEAKHOUSE—See Day Star Restaurant Holdings, LLC; *U.S. Private*, pg. 1176
LOUIS PAPPAS RESTAURANT GROUP, LLC; *U.S. Private*, pg. 2499
LOWE WILD DUNES INVESTORS LP; *U.S. Private*, pg. 2505
LT ACQUISITION CORP.; *U.S. Private*, pg. 2509
LUBCO, INC.—See Luby's, Inc.; *U.S. Public*, pg. 1345
LUBY'S BEVCO, INC.—See Luby's, Inc.; *U.S. Public*, pg. 1345
LUBY'S FUDDRUCKERS RESTAURANTS, LLC; *U.S. Private*, pg. 2510
LUBY'S, INC.; *U.S. Public*, pg. 1344
LUBY'S LIMITED PARTNER, INC.—See Luby's, Inc.; *U.S. Public*, pg. 1345
LUBY'S MANAGEMENT, INC.—See Luby's, Inc.; *U.S. Public*, pg. 1345
LUBY'S RESTAURANTS LP; *U.S. Private*, pg. 2510
LUXURY HOTEL MANAGEMENT OF CZECH REPUBLIC S.R.O.—See Marriott International, Inc.; *U.S. Public*, pg. 1370
LZ-CATERING GMBH—See Deutsche Lufthansa AG; *Int'l*, pg. 2068
MAALI RESTAURANT INC.—See Maali Enterprises Inc.; *U.S. Private*, pg. 2530
MACAYO RESTAURANTS LLC; *U.S. Private*, pg. 2534
MAC FOOD SERVICES (MALAYSIA) SDN. BHD.—See Tyson Foods, Inc.; *U.S. Public*, pg. 2210
MAD ANTHONY'S INCORPORATED; *U.S. Private*, pg. 2538
MAGGARD ENTERPRISES INC.; *U.S. Private*, pg. 2545
MAKAMER HOLDINGS, INC.; *U.S. Public*, pg. 1355
MAMA DEVECHIO'S PIZZERIA, LLC—See UTG, Inc.; *U.S. Public*, pg. 2267
MAMA FU'S—See Raving Brands, Inc.; *U.S. Private*, pg. 3357
MAMMA ILARDO'S CORP.; *U.S. Private*, pg. 2559
MANGO TREE (HK) LIMITED—See 1957 & Co. (Hospitality) Limited; *Int'l*, pg. 3
THE MANSION ON TURTLE CREEK—See Chow Tai Fook Enterprises Limited; *Int'l*, pg. 1585
MARIE CALLENDER PIE SHOPS, LLC—See Marie Callender's, Inc.; *U.S. Private*, pg. 2574
MARKET CAFE—See Delaware North Companies, Inc.; *U.S. Private*, pg. 1195
MARMALADE LLC; *U.S. Private*, pg. 2586
MARRIOTT CURACAO N.V.—See Marriott International, Inc.; *U.S. Public*, pg. 1371
MARRIOTT EUROPEAN HOTEL OPERATING COMPANY LIMITED—See Marriott International, Inc.; *U.S. Public*, pg. 1371
MARRIOTT HOTELMANAGEMENT GMBH—See Marriott International, Inc.; *U.S. Public*, pg. 1371
MARRIOTT HOTELS OF CANADA LTD.—See Marriott International, Inc.; *U.S. Public*, pg. 1371
MARRIOTT INTERNATIONAL CAPITAL CORPORATION—See Marriott International, Inc.; *U.S. Public*, pg. 1371
MARYS PIZZA SHACK; *U.S. Private*, pg. 2600
MASCOTT CORPORATION; *U.S. Private*, pg. 2601
MAX & ERMA'S RESTAURANTS, INC.—See Glacier Restaurant Group LLC; *U.S. Private*, pg. 1704
MAZZARO'S ITALIAN MARKET, LLC; *U.S. Private*, pg. 2623
MAZZIO'S PIZZA—See Mazzio's Corporation; *U.S. Private*, pg. 2623
MCALISTER'S CORPORATION—See Roark Capital Group Inc.; *U.S. Private*, pg. 3455
MCCORMICK & SCHMICK'S SEAFOOD RESTAURANTS,

INC.—See Fertitta Entertainment, Inc.; *U.S. Private*, pg. 1499
MCDONALD'S AUSTRALIA LIMITED—See McDonald's Corporation; *U.S. Public*, pg. 1406
MCDONALD'S COMPANY (JAPAN), LTD.—See McDonald's Corporation; *U.S. Public*, pg. 1406
MCDONALD'S DEUTSCHLAND GMBH—See McDonald's Corporation; *U.S. Public*, pg. 1406
MCDONALD'S FRANCE SA—See McDonald's Corporation; *U.S. Public*, pg. 1406
MCDONALD'S FRANCE SERVICES SARL—See McDonald's Corporation; *U.S. Public*, pg. 1406
MCDONALD'S FRANCHISE GMBH (AUSTRIA)—See McDonald's Corporation; *U.S. Public*, pg. 1406
MCDONALD'S ITALIA S.R.L.—See McDonald's Corporation; *U.S. Public*, pg. 1406
MCDONALD'S LIEGENSCHAFTSVERWALTUNGS GESELLSCHAFT M.B.H.—See McDonald's Corporation; *U.S. Public*, pg. 1406
MCDONALD'S NEDERLAND B.V.—See McDonald's Corporation; *U.S. Public*, pg. 1406
MCDONALD'S PANAMA—See McDonald's Corporation; *U.S. Public*, pg. 1406
MCDONALD'S POLSKA SP. Z O.O—See McDonald's Corporation; *U.S. Public*, pg. 1406
MCDONALD'S RESTAURANTS (HONG KONG) LTD.—See McDonald's Corporation; *U.S. Public*, pg. 1406
MCDONALD'S RESTAURANTS (NEW ZEALAND) LIMITED—See McDonald's Corporation; *U.S. Public*, pg. 1406
MCDONALD'S RESTAURANTS (NEW ZEALAND) LIMITED—See McDonald's Corporation; *U.S. Public*, pg. 1406
MCDONALD'S RESTAURANTS OF CANADA LTD.—See McDonald's Corporation; *U.S. Public*, pg. 1406
MCDONALD'S RESTAURANTS OF IRELAND LIMITED (IRELAND)—See McDonald's Corporation; *U.S. Public*, pg. 1406
MCDONALD'S RESTAURANTS PTE., LTD.—See McDonald's Corporation; *U.S. Public*, pg. 1406
MCDONALD'S USA, LLC—See McDonald's Corporation; *U.S. Public*, pg. 1406
MCGRATH'S PUBLICK FISH HOUSE; *U.S. Private*, pg. 2635
MCGUFFEY'S RESTAURANTS, INC.; *U.S. Private*, pg. 2636
MCKEY FOOD SERVICES LIMITED—See Tyson Foods, Inc.; *U.S. Public*, pg. 2210
MCKEY FOOD SERVICES (THAILAND) LIMITED—See Tyson Foods, Inc.; *U.S. Public*, pg. 2210
MCL RESTAURANT & BAKERY; *U.S. Private*, pg. 2639
MCMENAMINS INC.; *U.S. Private*, pg. 2642
MEAL WORKS CO., LTD.—See Arclands Corp.; *Int'l*, pg. 549
MEATHEADS; *U.S. Private*, pg. 2648
MEB ON FIRST, INC.—See Ark Restaurants Corp.; *U.S. Public*, pg. 193
THE MELTING POT RESTAURANTS INC.—See Front Burner Brands, Inc.; *U.S. Private*, pg. 1613
METROPOLITAN METRO ASIA (MA ON SHAN) LIMITED—See Century City International Holdings Ltd; *Int'l*, pg. 1417
METZ ENTERPRISES INC.; *U.S. Private*, pg. 2691
MEXICAN RESTAURANTS, INC.—See Williston Holding Co., Inc.; *U.S. Public*, pg. 2372
THE MEXICO CITY PALM—See Palm Restaurant Group; *U.S. Private*, pg. 3080
MFM WINTER PARK, LLC—See Fertitta Entertainment, Inc.; *U.S. Private*, pg. 1499
MID-AMERICAN RESTAURANTS INC.; *U.S. Private*, pg. 2707
MIDWAY INC.; *U.S. Private*, pg. 2718
MILLER'S ALE HOUSE, INC.—See Ale House Management, Inc.; *U.S. Private*, pg. 160
MING CORPORATION; *U.S. Private*, pg. 2742
MITCHCO INTERNATIONAL INC.; *U.S. Private*, pg. 2750
MMI DINING SYSTEMS—See MMI Hotel Group Inc.; *U.S. Private*, pg. 2755
MOE'S SOUTHWEST GRILL, LLC—See Roark Capital Group Inc.; *U.S. Private*, pg. 3454
MONGOLIAN OPERATING CO. LLC—See Kinderhook Industries, LLC; *U.S. Private*, pg. 2307
MORTON'S OF CHICAGO, INC.—See Morton's Restaurant Group, Inc.; *U.S. Private*, pg. 2792
MOUNTAIN RANGE RESTAURANT LLC; *U.S. Private*, pg. 2799
MTC INC.; *U.S. Private*, pg. 2809
MUGG & BEAN FRANCHISING (PTY) LTD.—See Famous Brands Limited; *Int'l*, pg. 2612
MULLIGAN'S BEACH HOUSE BAR & GRILL—See J.P.B. Enterprises, Inc.; *U.S. Private*, pg. 2170
MULTISYSTEMS RESTAURANTS INC.; *U.S. Private*, pg. 2813
MUNICH OPCO GMBH—See Hyatt Hotels Corporation; *U.S. Public*, pg. 1078
MURRAY'S LIC LLC—See The Kroger Co.; *U.S. Public*, pg. 2108
MYRIAD RESTAURANT GROUP; *U.S. Private*, pg. 2825
NAKED RESTAURANTS, INC.; *U.S. Private*, pg. 2831

N.A.I.C.S. INDEX

722511 — FULL-SERVICE RESTAU...

NATHAN'S FAMOUS OF YONKERS, INC.—See Nathan's Famous Inc.; *U.S. Public*, pg. 1493
NATIONAL RESTAURANT MANAGEMENT, INC.—See The Riese Organization; *U.S. Private*, pg. 4107
NEIGHBORHOOD RESTAURANTS INC.; *U.S. Private*, pg. 2881
NEW BOSTON GARDEN CORP.—See Delaware North Companies, Inc.; *U.S. Public*, pg. 1194
THE NEW YORK PALM TOO—See Palm Restaurant Group; *U.S. Private*, pg. 3080
NEXT LEVEL BURGER COMPANY, INC.; *U.S. Private*, pg. 2920
NEXUS ENERGY SERVICES, INC.; *U.S. Public*, pg. 1527
NICK & STEF'S STEAKHOUSE—See Delaware North Companies, Inc.; *U.S. Private*, pg. 1195
NIECO CORPORATION—See The Middleby Corporation; *U.S. Public*, pg. 2115
NILAX CO., LTD.—See Bain Capital, LP; *U.S. Private*, pg. 444
NINFA'S HOLDINGS, L.P.; *U.S. Private*, pg. 2928
NOBLE RESTAURANT GROUP INC.; *U.S. Private*, pg. 2933
NOBU FIFTY SEVEN—See Myriad Restaurant Group; *U.S. Private*, pg. 2825
NOBU LONDON—See Myriad Restaurant Group; *U.S. Private*, pg. 2825
NOBU NEW YORK—See Myriad Restaurant Group; *U.S. Private*, pg. 2825
NOBU NEXT DOOR—See Myriad Restaurant Group; *U.S. Private*, pg. 2825
NOODLES & COMPANY—See Catterton Management Company, LLC; *U.S. Private*, pg. 793
NORMS RESTAURANTS; *U.S. Private*, pg. 2939
NORTH BELT RESTAURANT, INC.—See Louisiana Fine Food Companies, Inc.; *U.S. Private*, pg. 2499
THE NORTHBROOK PALM—See Palm Restaurant Group; *U.S. Private*, pg. 3080
NORTHCOTT HOSPITALITY INTERNATIONAL, LLC; *U.S. Private*, pg. 2949
NORTH TOWNE GRILL & SEAFOOD; *U.S. Private*, pg. 2948
NPC RESTAURANT HOLDINGS, LLC; *U.S. Private*, pg. 2969
OCEAN CITY OUTBACK, INC.—See Bloomin' Brands, Inc.; *U.S. Public*, pg. 363
O'CHARLEY'S INC.—See Fidelity National Financial, Inc.; *U.S. Public*, pg. 830
OLD SPAGHETTI FACTORY (CANADA) LTD.—See Cracken, Harkey & Co., LLC; *U.S. Private*, pg. 1081
OLE RED GATLINBURG, LLC—See Ryman Hospitality Properties, Inc.; *U.S. Public*, pg. 1829
OLGA'S KITCHEN INC.—See Robert B. Solomon Holding Company, Inc.; *U.S. Private*, pg. 3457
OLIVE GARDEN ITALIAN RESTAURANT—See Darden Restaurants, Inc.; *U.S. Public*, pg. 633
ONTARIO HOSPITALITY PROPERTIES L.L.L.P.—See InnSuites Hospitality Trust; *U.S. Public*, pg. 1128
ONTARIO MILLS—See Simon Property Group, Inc.; *U.S. Public*, pg. 1882
OPERACIONES ARCOS DORADOS DE PERU, S.A.—See Arcos Dorados Holdings Inc.; *Int'l*, pg. 550
OREGON RESTAURANT SERVICES, INC.; *U.S. Private*, pg. 3040
THE ORLANDO PALM—See Palm Restaurant Group; *U.S. Private*, pg. 3080
OSF INTERNATIONAL, INC.; *U.S. Private*, pg. 3047
OSI/FLEMING'S, LLC—See Bloomin' Brands, Inc.; *U.S. Public*, pg. 363
OSTERIA GAMBERONI SDN. BHD.—See Advance Synergy Berhad; *Int'l*, pg. 157
OTG EXP, INC.; *U.S. Private*, pg. 3049
OUTBACK KANSAS LLC—See Bloomin' Brands, Inc.; *U.S. Public*, pg. 363
OUTBACK OF ASPEN HILL, INC.—See Bloomin' Brands, Inc.; *U.S. Public*, pg. 363
OUTBACK OF GERMANTOWN, INC.—See Bloomin' Brands, Inc.; *U.S. Public*, pg. 363
OUTBACK OF LA PLATA, INC.—See Bloomin' Brands, Inc.; *U.S. Public*, pg. 363
OUTBACK OF WALDORF, INC.—See Bloomin' Brands, Inc.; *U.S. Public*, pg. 363
OUTBACK/SOUTHFIELD, LIMITED PARTNERSHIP—See Bloomin' Brands, Inc.; *U.S. Public*, pg. 363
OUTBACK STEAKHOUSE INTERNATIONAL, LLC—See Bloomin' Brands, Inc.; *U.S. Public*, pg. 363
OUTBACK STEAKHOUSE JAPAN CO., LTD.—See Bloomin' Brands, Inc.; *U.S. Public*, pg. 363
OUTBACK STEAKHOUSE KOREA, LTD.—See Bloomin' Brands, Inc.; *U.S. Public*, pg. 363
OUTBACK STEAKHOUSE OF BOWIE, INC.—See Bloomin' Brands, Inc.; *U.S. Public*, pg. 363
OUTBACK STEAKHOUSE OF CANTON, INC.—See Bloomin' Brands, Inc.; *U.S. Public*, pg. 363
OUTBACK STEAKHOUSE OF HOWARD COUNTY, INC.—See Bloomin' Brands, Inc.; *U.S. Public*, pg. 363
OUTBACK STEAKHOUSE OF JONESBORO, INC.—See Bloomin' Brands, Inc.; *U.S. Public*, pg. 363
OUTBACK STEAKHOUSE OF ST. MARY'S COUNTY, INC.—See Bloomin' Brands, Inc.; *U.S. Public*, pg. 363
OUTBACK STEAKHOUSE WEST VIRGINIA, INC.—See Bloomin' Brands, Inc.; *U.S. Public*, pg. 363
OVATION BRANDS, INC.—See Food Management Partners, Inc.; *U.S. Private*, pg. 1561
OZARK WAFFLES LLC; *U.S. Private*, pg. 3058
PACIFIC COAST RESTAURANTS, INC.—See Sun Capital Partners, Inc.; *U.S. Private*, pg. 3860
THE PALM AT THE HUNTTING INN—See Palm Restaurant Group; *U.S. Private*, pg. 3080
THE PALM RESTAURANT—See Palm Restaurant Group; *U.S. Private*, pg. 3080
THE PALM RESTAURANT—See Palm Restaurant Group; *U.S. Private*, pg. 3080
PAPAGO BREWING CO. INC.—See Huss Brewing Co. LLC; *U.S. Private*, pg. 2014
PAPPAS PARTNERS LP; *U.S. Private*, pg. 3088
PAPPAS RESTAURANTS INC.—See Pappas Partners LP; *U.S. Private*, pg. 3088
PARK AVENUE BBQ & GRILLE INC.; *U.S. Private*, pg. 3095
PARKER RD. HOOTERS, INC.—See Restaurants of America, Inc.; *U.S. Private*, pg. 3408
THE PASTA HOUSE CO.; *U.S. Private*, pg. 4091
PATINA RESTAURANT GROUP LLC—See Delaware North Companies, Inc.; *U.S. Public*, pg. 1195
PATINA—See Delaware North Companies, Inc.; *U.S. Private*, pg. 1195
PATXI'S PIZZA; *U.S. Private*, pg. 3112
PB&J RESTAURANTS INC.; *U.S. Private*, pg. 3118
PEI WEI ASIAN DINER, LLC; *U.S. Private*, pg. 3130
PEI WEI ASIAN DINER TWO (DALLAS) LLP—See Pei Wei Asian Diner, LLC; *U.S. Private*, pg. 3130
PEI WEI HOUSTON, INC.—See Pei Wei Asian Diner, LLC; *U.S. Private*, pg. 3130
PEPPER DINING INC.—See Brinker International, Inc.; *U.S. Public*, pg. 384
PEPPER MILL INC.; *U.S. Private*, pg. 3144
PERFORMANCE INDUSTRIES INC.; *U.S. Private*, pg. 3149
PERKINS LLC—See Huddle House, Inc.; *U.S. Private*, pg. 2001
PERRY HALL OUTBACK, INC.—See Bloomin' Brands, Inc.; *U.S. Public*, pg. 363
PETER PIPER, INC.—See Apollo Global Management, Inc.; *U.S. Public*, pg. 148
PFCCB EQUIPMENT LLC—See Centerbridge Partners, L.P.; *U.S. Private*, pg. 815
PFC HAWAII LLC—See Centerbridge Partners, L.P.; *U.S. Private*, pg. 815
THE PHILADELPHIA PALM—See Palm Restaurant Group; *U.S. Private*, pg. 3080
PHILLIPS FOODS ASIA CO., LTD.—See Phillips Foods Inc.; *U.S. Private*, pg. 3171
PHILLIPS FOODS INC.; *U.S. Private*, pg. 3171
PHILLIPS SEAFOOD RESTAURANT—See Phillips Foods Inc.; *U.S. Private*, pg. 3171
PHOENIX HOOTERS, INC.—See Restaurants of America, Inc.; *U.S. Private*, pg. 3408
PH VICTORIA JUNCTION (PTY) LTD—See Marriott International, Inc.; *U.S. Public*, pg. 1371
PICK UP STIX—See West Coast Capital LLC; *U.S. Private*, pg. 4484
PINCHERS CRAB SHACK, INC.; *U.S. Private*, pg. 3181
PINNACLE RESTAURANT GROUP LLC; *U.S. Private*, pg. 3185
PINOT PROVENCE—See Delaware North Companies, Inc.; *U.S. Private*, pg. 1195
PLANET HOLLYWOOD INTERNATIONAL, INC.; *U.S. Private*, pg. 3196
PONDEROSA STEAKHOUSE—See Fog Cutter Capital Group Inc.; *U.S. Private*, pg. 1557
PONDEROSA STEAKHOUSE—See Fog Cutter Capital Group Inc.; *U.S. Private*, pg. 1557
PORTLAND SEAFOOD COMPANY—See Sun Capital Partners, Inc.; *U.S. Private*, pg. 3860
POSADOS CAFE INC.; *U.S. Private*, pg. 3233
POTTER'S MILL, INC.—See Apollo Global Management, Inc.; *U.S. Public*, pg. 150
POTTER'S MILL, INC.—See Reverence Capital Partners LLC; *U.S. Private*, pg. 3415
PPX HOSPITALITY BRANDS INC.; *U.S. Private*, pg. 3241
PREMIUM DINING RESTAURANTS & PUBS LIMITED—See CK Asset Holdings Limited; *Int'l*, pg. 1635
PRIME RESTAURANTS INC.—See Fairfax Financial Holdings Limited; *Int'l*, pg. 2608
PULIDO ASSOCIATES INC.; *U.S. Private*, pg. 3303
PULSE—See Myriad Restaurant Group; *U.S. Private*, pg. 2825
PUY DU FOU RESTAURATION SAS—See Compass Group PLC; *Int'l*, pg. 1752
QUAKER STEAK & LUBE—See BP plc; *Int'l*, pg. 1127
QUALITY DINING, INC.; *U.S. Private*, pg. 3318
QUALITY IS OUR RECIPE, LLC—See The Wendy's Company; *U.S. Public*, pg. 2141
QUALITY RESTAURANT CONCEPTS; *U.S. Private*, pg. 3321
QUEEN CITY TELEVISION SERVICE CO. INC.; *U.S. Private*, pg. 3325
RAFFERTY'S INC.; *U.S. Private*, pg. 3345
RAINFOREST CAFE, INC.—See Fertitta Entertainment, Inc.; *U.S. Private*, pg. 1499
RAISING CANE'S USA, LLC; *U.S. Private*, pg. 3348
RAM INTERNATIONAL LTD.; *U.S. Private*, pg. 3351
RASA SAYANG VILLAGE PTE. LTD.—See GS Holdings Limited; *Int'l*, pg. 3143
RA SCOTTSDALE CORP.—See TPG Capital, L.P.; *U.S. Public*, pg. 2167
RA SUSHI ATLANTA MIDTOWN CORP.—See TPG Capital, L.P.; *U.S. Public*, pg. 2167
RA SUSHI BALTIMORE CORP.—See TPG Capital, L.P.; *U.S. Public*, pg. 2167
RA SUSHI CHICAGO CORP.—See TPG Capital, L.P.; *U.S. Public*, pg. 2167
RA SUSHI CHINO HILLS CORP.—See TPG Capital, L.P.; *U.S. Public*, pg. 2167
RA SUSHI CITY CENTER CORP.—See TPG Capital, L.P.; *U.S. Public*, pg. 2167
RA SUSHI CORONA CORP.—See TPG Capital, L.P.; *U.S. Public*, pg. 2167
RA SUSHI FORT WORTH CORP.—See TPG Capital, L.P.; *U.S. Public*, pg. 2167
RA SUSHI GLENVIEW CORP.—See TPG Capital, L.P.; *U.S. Public*, pg. 2167
RA SUSHI HUNTINGTON BEACH CORP.—See TPG Capital, L.P.; *U.S. Public*, pg. 2167
RA SUSHI LAS VEGAS CORP.—See TPG Capital, L.P.; *U.S. Public*, pg. 2167
RA SUSHI LEAWOOD CORP.—See TPG Capital, L.P.; *U.S. Public*, pg. 2167
RA SUSHI LOMBARD CORP.—See TPG Capital, L.P.; *U.S. Public*, pg. 2167
RA SUSHI MESA CORP.—See TPG Capital, L.P.; *U.S. Public*, pg. 2167
RA SUSHI PALM BEACH GARDENS CORP.—See TPG Capital, L.P.; *U.S. Public*, pg. 2167
RA SUSHI PEMBROKE PINES CORP.—See TPG Capital, L.P.; *U.S. Public*, pg. 2167
RA SUSHI PLANO CORP.—See TPG Capital, L.P.; *U.S. Public*, pg. 2167
RA SUSHI SAN DIEGO CORP.—See TPG Capital, L.P.; *U.S. Public*, pg. 2167
RA SUSHI SOUTH MIAMI CORP.—See TPG Capital, L.P.; *U.S. Public*, pg. 2168
RA SUSHI TORRANCE CORP.—See TPG Capital, L.P.; *U.S. Public*, pg. 2168
RA SUSHI TUCSON CORP.—See TPG Capital, L.P.; *U.S. Public*, pg. 2168
RA SUSHI TUSTIN CORP.—See TPG Capital, L.P.; *U.S. Public*, pg. 2168
RAVE RESTAURANT GROUP, INC.; *U.S. Public*, pg. 1763
RAVING BRANDS, INC.; *U.S. Private*, pg. 3357
RAZZOOS INC.; *U.S. Private*, pg. 3360
RCSH OPERATIONS, LLC—See Darden Restaurants, Inc.; *U.S. Public*, pg. 633
RDE, INC.; *U.S. Public*, pg. 1767
REAL FF PTY LTD—See Ampol Limited; *Int'l*, pg. 436
REAL GRANDY VALLEY PIZZA HUT, LLC; *U.S. Private*, pg. 3367
REDEYE COFFEE ROASTING, LLC; *U.S. Private*, pg. 3378
RED HOT & BLUE RESTAURANTS, INC.; *U.S. Private*, pg. 3375
RED LOBSTER HOSPITALITY LLC—See Golden Gate Capital Management II, LLC; *U.S. Private*, pg. 1731
RED ROBIN GOURMET BURGERS, INC.; *U.S. Public*, pg. 1769
RED ROBIN INTERNATIONAL, INC.—See Red Robin Gourmet Burgers, Inc.; *U.S. Public*, pg. 1769
RED ROBIN WEST, INC.—See Red Robin Gourmet Burgers, Inc.; *U.S. Public*, pg. 1769
REINS INTERNATIONAL (SINGAPORE) PTE. LTD.—See Colowide Co., Ltd.; *Int'l*, pg. 1705
REM GLOBAL, INC.; *U.S. Private*, pg. 3395
RENAISSANCE HAMBURG HOTELMANAGEMENT GMBH—See Marriott International, Inc.; *U.S. Public*, pg. 1371
RESERVAS DE RESTAURANTES, SL—See TripAdvisor, Inc.; *U.S. Public*, pg. 2195
RESTAURANT ASSOCIATES (AUSTRALIA) PTY LTD—See Compass Group PLC; *Int'l*, pg. 1752
RESTAURANT ASSOCIATES CORPORATION—See Compass Group PLC; *Int'l*, pg. 1751
RESTAURANT BRANDS AUSTRALIA PTY LIMITED—See Grupo Finaccess S.A.P.I. de C.V.; *Int'l*, pg. 3129
RESTAURANT BRANDS LIMITED—See Grupo Finaccess S.A.P.I. de C.V.; *Int'l*, pg. 3129
RESTAURANTES MCDONALD'S S.A.—See McDonald's Corporation; *U.S. Public*, pg. 1406
THE RESTAURANT GROUP PLC—See Apollo Global Management, Inc.; *U.S. Public*, pg. 164
RESTAURANT MANAGEMENT OF SOUTH CAROLINA INC.; *U.S. Private*, pg. 3408
RESTAURANTS NO LIMIT, INC.; *U.S. Private*, pg. 3408
RESTAURANTS UNLIMITED, INC.—See Sun Capital Partners, Inc.; *U.S. Private*, pg. 3860
RESTO BELLE EPINE SNC—See Eurazeo SE; *Int'l*, pg. 2529

722511 — FULL-SERVICE RESTAU...

RESTO CLERMONT-FERRAND SNC—See Eurazeo SE; *Int'l*, pg. 2529
RESTO LES HALLES SNC—See Eurazeo SE; *Int'l*, pg. 2529
RESTO L'ISLE ADAM SNC—See Eurazeo SE; *Int'l*, pg. 2529
RESTO MAREUIL SNC—See Eurazeo SE; *Int'l*, pg. 2529
RESTO MONTLHERY SNC—See Eurazeo SE; *Int'l*, pg. 2529
RESTO PESSAC SNC—See Eurazeo SE; *Int'l*, pg. 2529
RESTO ROSNY SNC—See Eurazeo SE; *Int'l*, pg. 2529
RESTO SAINT-GERMAIN SNC—See Eurazeo SE; *Int'l*, pg. 2529
RESTO TOURS SNC—See Eurazeo SE; *Int'l*, pg. 2529
RESTO TRAPPES SNC—See Eurazeo SE; *Int'l*, pg. 2529
RESTO VELIZY SNC—See Eurazeo SE; *Int'l*, pg. 2529
RESTO VILLIERS SNC—See Eurazeo SE; *Int'l*, pg. 2529
RESTO WASQUEHAL SNC—See Eurazeo SE; *Int'l*, pg. 2529
RIB CITY GRILL, INC.; *U.S. Private*, pg. 3424
RICHARD'S RESTAURANTS INC.; *U.S. Private*, pg. 3428
RIP'S COUNTRY INN; *U.S. Private*, pg. 3439
THE RITZ-CARLTON HOTEL MANAGEMENT GMBH—See W.P. Carey Inc.; *U.S. Public*, pg. 2316
RMH FRANCHISE CORPORATION; *U.S. Private*, pg. 3452
ROADCHEF MOTORWAYS LTD—See BNP Paribas SA; *Int'l*, pg. 1082
ROASTERS ASIA PACIFIC (M) SDN BHD—See Berjaya Corporation Berhad; *Int'l*, pg. 984
ROBERT B. SOLOMON HOLDING COMPANY, INC.; *U.S. Private*, pg. 3457
ROBERT BUGATTO ENTERPRISES, INC.; *U.S. Private*, pg. 3457
ROD FRASER ENTERPRISES INC.; *U.S. Private*, pg. 3469
ROMACORP, INC.; *U.S. Private*, pg. 3475
ROMULUS INC.; *U.S. Private*, pg. 3477
ROTELLI PIZZA & PASTA; *U.S. Private*, pg. 3486
ROUTE 9G INC.—See create restaurants holdings inc.; *Int'l*, pg. 1832
ROYAL BUSINESS RESTAURANTS GMBH—See Compass Group PLC; *Int'l*, pg. 1752
ROYAL ZOUTE GOLF CLUB SA—See Compagnie Het Zoute NV; *Int'l*, pg. 1745
ROY'S OF BALTIMORE, LLC—See United Ohana, LLC; *U.S. Private*, pg. 4295
RREAL TACOS SANDY SPRINGS LLC; *U.S. Private*, pg. 3496
RSR DEVELOPMENT CORP.; *U.S. Private*, pg. 3497
R TO FIFTH, INC.; *U.S. Private*, pg. 3331
RUBICON—See Myriad Restaurant Group; *U.S. Private*, pg. 2825
RUBIO'S RESTAURANTS, INC.—See Mill Road Capital Management LLC; *U.S. Private*, pg. 2730
RUBY'S INN INC.; *U.S. Private*, pg. 3500
RUBY'S RESTAURANT GROUP; *U.S. Private*, pg. 3500
RUBY TUESDAY, INC,—See NRD Capital Management, LLC; *U.S. Private*, pg. 2969
RUBY TUESDAY LONG ISLAND; *U.S. Private*, pg. 3500
RUBY TUESDAY OF ANDERSON, INC.—See NRD Capital Management, LLC; *U.S. Private*, pg. 2969
RUBY TUESDAY OF ARVADA, INC.—See NRD Capital Management, LLC; *U.S. Private*, pg. 2969
RUBY TUESDAY OF COLUMBIA, INC.—See NRD Capital Management, LLC; *U.S. Private*, pg. 2969
RUBY TUESDAY OF DEERWOOD, INC.—See NRD Capital Management, LLC; *U.S. Private*, pg. 2969
RUBY TUESDAY OF FREDERICK, INC.—See NRD Capital Management, LLC; *U.S. Private*, pg. 2969
RUBY TUESDAY OF LINTHICUM, INC.—See NRD Capital Management, LLC; *U.S. Private*, pg. 2969
RUBY TUESDAY OF MARLEY STATION, INC.—See NRD Capital Management, LLC; *U.S. Private*, pg. 2969
RUBY TUESDAY OF POCOMOKE CITY, INC.—See NRD Capital Management, LLC; *U.S. Private*, pg. 2969
RUBY TUESDAY OF RUSSELLVILLE, INC.—See NRD Capital Management, LLC; *U.S. Private*, pg. 2969
RUBY TUESDAY OF SALISBURY, INC.—See NRD Capital Management, LLC; *U.S. Private*, pg. 2969
RUBY TUESDAY OF SOUTHCASE, INC.—See NRD Capital Management, LLC; *U.S. Private*, pg. 2969
RUBY TUESDAY TAMPA FRANCHISE LP; *U.S. Private*, pg. 3500
RUSSO'S NEW YORK PIZZERIA; *U.S. Private*, pg. 3507
RWS ENTERPRISES; *U.S. Private*, pg. 3509
SADLER'S BAR-B-QUE SALES, LTD.; *U.S. Private*, pg. 3523
SAGE RESTAURANT GROUP—See Sage Investment Holdings; *U.S. Private*, pg. 3526
SAKE NO HANA LTD.—See Sphere Entertainment Co.; *U.S. Public*, pg. 1918
SALTGRASS INC.—See Fertitta Entertainment, Inc.; *U.S. Private*, pg. 1499
SAS AMIENS GLISY—See Eurazeo SE; *Int'l*, pg. 2529
SAS LYON MEZIEU—See Eurazeo SE; *Int'l*, pg. 2529
SAS RESTO BESANCON—See Eurazeo SE; *Int'l*, pg. 2529
SAS RESTO DEV LEON 6 - ARRAS—See Eurazeo SE; *Int'l*, pg. 2529
SAS RESTO METZ—See Eurazeo SE; *Int'l*, pg. 2529
SAS RESTO NANTES—See Eurazeo SE; *Int'l*, pg. 2529

SAXTON PIERCE RESTAURANT CORP; *U.S. Private*, pg. 3558
SB SUPPLIES & LOGISTICS SDN. BHD.—See Borneo Oil Berhad; *Int'l*, pg. 1114
SCHWARTZ BROTHERS RESTAURANTS; *U.S. Private*, pg. 3572
SCOTTO BROTHERS ENTERPRISES, INC.—See Scotto's Holding Corp.; *U.S. Private*, pg. 3578
SCOTTO BROTHERS WOODBURY RESTAURANT INC.—See Scotto's Holding Corp.; *U.S. Private*, pg. 3578
SEATTLE CRAB CO.; *U.S. Private*, pg. 3591
SELECT RESTAURANTS, INC.—See Select Management Holdings, Inc.; *U.S. Private*, pg. 3600
SEMOLINA INC.—See Taste Buds, Inc.; *U.S. Private*, pg. 3935
SER VEGANO SDN. BHD.—See Berjaya Corporation Berhad; *Int'l*, pg. 984
SEVEN CORNERS CENTER, LLC—See Saul Centers, Inc.; *U.S. Public*, pg. 1842
SHAKE SHACK ENTERPRISES, LLC—See Shake Shack Inc.; *U.S. Public*, pg. 1873
SHAKEY'S USA, INC.—See Jacmar Companies, Inc.; *U.S. Private*, pg. 2179
SHANDONG KEYSTONE CHINWHIZ FOODS CO. LTD.—See Tyson Foods, Inc.; *U.S. Public*, pg. 2210
SHANE'S RIB SHACK—See Petrus Brands, Inc; *U.S. Private*, pg. 3163
SHANGHAI HOUSE CURRY COCO ICHIBANYA RESTAURANT, INC.—See House Foods Group Inc.; *Int'l*, pg. 3490
SHARI'S MANAGEMENT CORPORATION—See Capital-Spring LLC; *U.S. Private*, pg. 742
THE SHIPYARD COMMUNITIES RETAIL OPERATOR, LLC—See Lennar Corporation; *U.S. Public*, pg. 1307
SHONEY'S NORTH AMERICA CORP—See Royal Hospitality Corp.; *U.S. Private*, pg. 3492
SHONEY'S OF KNOXVILLE INC.; *U.S. Private*, pg. 3639
SHONEY'S OF RICHMOND INC.; *U.S. Private*, pg. 3639
SHONEY'S RESTAURANT—See Royal Hospitality Corp.; *U.S. Private*, pg. 3492
SIGN OF THE BEEFCARVER INC.; *U.S. Private*, pg. 3649
SILVER DINER, INC.; *U.S. Private*, pg. 3653
SILVER P LESSEE, LLC—See Pebblebrook Hotel Trust; *U.S. Public*, pg. 1660
SILVERWATER CAFE; *U.S. Private*, pg. 3664
SIMA MARINE SALES INC.; *U.S. Private*, pg. 3665
SIMPLY SOUTHERN RESTAURANT GROUP LLC—See Brentwood Associates; *U.S. Private*, pg. 646
SISTEMAS CENTRAL AMERICA, S.A.—See Arcos Dorados Holdings Inc.; *Int'l*, pg. 550
SISTEMAS MCDONALD'S PORTUGAL LDA—See McDonald's Corporation; *U.S. Public*, pg. 1406
SIX PENN KITCHEN—See Eat'n Park Hospitality Group, Inc.; *U.S. Private*, pg. 1323
SIZZLER USA, INC.; *U.S. Private*, pg. 3678
SIZZLING PLATTER LLC; *U.S. Private*, pg. 3678
SKIPPERS INC.—See Seattle Crab Co.; *U.S. Private*, pg. 3591
SKYCHEF LTD—See Air France-KLM S.A.; *Int'l*, pg. 238
SKYLARK HOLDINGS CO., LTD.—See Bain Capital, LP; *U.S. Private*, pg. 444
SKYLINE CHILI, INC.; *U.S. Private*, pg. 3685
SLAYMAKER RESTAURANT GROUP INC.; *U.S. Private*, pg. 3688
THE SMITH & WOLLENSKY RESTAURANT GROUP, INC.—See Danu Investment Partners Ltd.; *Int'l*, pg. 1969
SMOKEY BONES, LLC—See Fog Cutter Capital Group Inc.; *U.S. Private*, pg. 1557
SMOKY MOUNTAIN BREWERY—See The Copper Cellar Corporation; *U.S. Private*, pg. 4014
SNC RESTO CHARTRES—See Eurazeo SE; *Int'l*, pg. 2529
SOCIETE DE RESTAURATION MONTPARNASSE SAS—See Eurazeo SE; *Int'l*, pg. 2529
SOLO CUP COMPANY—See Dart Container Corporation; *U.S. Private*, pg. 1160
SOME SEVIT CORPORATION—See Hyosung TNC Co. Ltd.; *Int'l*, pg. 3552
SONNY'S FRANCHISE COMPANY INC.; *U.S. Private*, pg. 3714
SONNY'S REAL PIT BAR-B-QUE; *U.S. Private*, pg. 3714
SOPREGIM SAS—See Compass Group PLC; *Int'l*, pg. 1752
SOUTHERN CONCEPTS RESTAURANT GROUP, INC.; *U.S. Public*, pg. 1911
SOUTHERN MULTIFOODS INC.; *U.S. Private*, pg. 3734
SPACE NEEDLE CORPORATION; *U.S. Private*, pg. 3744
SPAGHETTI WAREHOUSE, INC.—See Cracken, Harkey & Co., LLC; *U.S. Private*, pg. 1081
SPECIALTY RESTAURANT GROUP LLC; *U.S. Private*, pg. 3750
SPECIALTY RESTAURANTS CORPORATION; *U.S. Private*, pg. 3750
SPECIALTY'S CAFE AND BAKERY; *U.S. Private*, pg. 3751
SPFS INC.; *U.S. Private*, pg. 3756
SPIRES RESTAURANTS INC.; *U.S. Private*, pg. 3758
SPRINGHILL SMC, LLC—See Marriott International, Inc.; *U.S. Public*, pg. 1371
STANDARD CORP.—See Brother Industries, Ltd.; *Int'l*, pg. 1198

STARBUCKS COFFEE SWITZERLAND A.G.—See Starbucks Corporation; *U.S. Public*, pg. 1939
STAR BUFFET, INC.; *U.S. Public*, pg. 1937
STEAK N SHAKE ALAMO RANCH, LLC—See Biglari Holdings Inc.; *U.S. Public*, pg. 331
STEAK N SHAKE ENTERPRISES, INC.—See Biglari Holdings Inc.; *U.S. Public*, pg. 331
STEAK N SHAKE, LLC—See Biglari Holdings Inc.; *U.S. Public*, pg. 331
STEAK N SHAKE OPERATIONS, INC.—See Biglari Holdings Inc.; *U.S. Public*, pg. 331
STEINMAN PARK RESTAURANT INC.—See Lancaster Newspapers Inc.; *U.S. Private*, pg. 2381
STK ATLANTA, LLC—See The ONE Group Hospitality, Inc.; *U.S. Public*, pg. 2118
STK CHICAGO, LLC—See The ONE Group Hospitality, Inc.; *U.S. Public*, pg. 2118
STK DC, LLC—See The ONE Group Hospitality, Inc.; *U.S. Public*, pg. 2118
STK IBIZA, LLC—See The ONE Group Hospitality, Inc.; *U.S. Public*, pg. 2118
STK-LA, LLC—See The ONE Group Hospitality, Inc.; *U.S. Public*, pg. 2118
STK-LAS VEGAS, LLC—See The ONE Group Hospitality, Inc.; *U.S. Public*, pg. 2118
STK MIAMI, LLC—See The ONE Group Hospitality, Inc.; *U.S. Public*, pg. 2118
STK MIDTOWN, LLC—See The ONE Group Hospitality, Inc.; *U.S. Public*, pg. 2118
STK NASHVILLE, LLC—See The ONE Group Hospitality, Inc.; *U.S. Public*, pg. 2118
STK ORLANDO, LLC—See The ONE Group Hospitality, Inc.; *U.S. Public*, pg. 2118
STOCKADE COMPANIES, INC.; *U.S. Private*, pg. 3814
STRANG CORPORATION; *U.S. Private*, pg. 3833
STUART ANDERSON'S BLACK ANGUS & CATTLE COMPANY RESTAURANTS—See American Restaurant Group, Inc.; *U.S. Private*, pg. 246
SULLIVAN'S - AUSTIN, L.P.—See Catterton Management Company, LLC; *U.S. Private*, pg. 793
SULLIVAN'S OF ARIZONA, INC.—See Catterton Management Company, LLC; *U.S. Private*, pg. 793
SULLIVAN'S OF DELAWARE, INC.—See Catterton Management Company, LLC; *U.S. Private*, pg. 793
SULLIVAN'S OF ILLINOIS, INC.—See Catterton Management Company, LLC; *U.S. Private*, pg. 793
SULLIVAN'S OF KANSAS, INC.—See Catterton Management Company, LLC; *U.S. Private*, pg. 793
SULLIVAN'S OF NORTH CAROLINA, INC.—See Catterton Management Company, LLC; *U.S. Private*, pg. 793
SULLIVAN'S OF OHIO, INC.—See Catterton Management Company, LLC; *U.S. Private*, pg. 793
SULLIVAN'S OF WASHINGTON, LLC—See Catterton Management Company, LLC; *U.S. Private*, pg. 793
SULLIVAN'S RESTAURANTS OF NEBRASKA, INC.—See Catterton Management Company, LLC; *U.S. Private*, pg. 793
SUNSET CITY, LLC—See Pebblebrook Hotel Trust; *U.S. Public*, pg. 1660
SUN WEST RESTAURANT CONCEPTS; *U.S. Private*, pg. 3864
SUSHI LYON 64 SAS—See AmRest Holdings SE; *Int'l*, pg. 437
SUSHIRO KOREA, INC.—See Food & Life Companies Ltd.; *Int'l*, pg. 2727
SUSHI SHOP AMIENS SARL—See AmRest Holdings SE; *Int'l*, pg. 437
SUSHI SHOP ANGERS SARL—See AmRest Holdings SE; *Int'l*, pg. 437
SUSHI SHOP CAEN SARL—See AmRest Holdings SE; *Int'l*, pg. 437
SUSHI SHOP CAUDERAN SAS—See AmRest Holdings SE; *Int'l*, pg. 437
SUSHI SHOP COURCELLES SARL—See AmRest Holdings SE; *Int'l*, pg. 437
SUSHI SHOP GENEVE SA—See AmRest Holdings SE; *Int'l*, pg. 437
SUSHI SHOP LA ROCHELLE SARL—See AmRest Holdings SE; *Int'l*, pg. 437
SUSHI SHOP LAUSANNE SARL—See AmRest Holdings SE; *Int'l*, pg. 437
SUSHI SHOP LE MANS SARL—See AmRest Holdings SE; *Int'l*, pg. 438
SUSHI SHOP LEPIC SARL—See AmRest Holdings SE; *Int'l*, pg. 438
SUSHI SHOP LEVALLOIS SARL—See AmRest Holdings SE; *Int'l*, pg. 437
SUSHI SHOP LILLE CENTRE SAS—See AmRest Holdings SE; *Int'l*, pg. 438
SUSHI SHOP LOUISE SA—See AmRest Holdings SE; *Int'l*, pg. 438
SUSHI SHOP MARTYRS SARL—See AmRest Holdings SE; *Int'l*, pg. 438
SUSHI SHOP NYON SARL—See AmRest Holdings SE; *Int'l*, pg. 438
SUSHI SHOP RENNES NEMOURS SARL—See AmRest Holdings SE; *Int'l*, pg. 438

N.A.I.C.S. INDEX

722513 — LIMITED-SERVICE RES...

SUSHI SHOP ROUEN SAS—See AmRest Holdings SE; *Int'l*, pg. 438
SUSHI SHOP SECRETAN SARL—See AmRest Holdings SE; *Int'l*, pg. 438
SUSHI SHOP ST DOMINIQUE SARL—See AmRest Holdings SE; *Int'l*, pg. 438
SUSHI SHOP TOULOUSE 3 SARL—See AmRest Holdings SE; *Int'l*, pg. 438
SUSHI SHOP TOURS SARL—See AmRest Holdings SE; *Int'l*, pg. 438
SUSHI SHOP VINCENNES SARL—See AmRest Holdings SE; *Int'l*, pg. 438
SUSHI SHOP ZURICH GMBH—See AmRest Holdings SE; *Int'l*, pg. 438
SW34 GASTRO GMBH—See GFT Technologies SE; *Int'l*, pg. 2957
SWEET BABY RAY'S BARBECUE WOOD DALE LLC—See SBR Events Group; *U.S. Private*, pg. 3560
SWEETGREEN, INC.; *U.S. Public*, pg. 1968
SWEETHEART CUP COMPANY INC.—See Dart Container Corporation; *U.S. Private*, pg. 1160
SWH FREDERICK MARYLAND, INC.—See Holding Le Duff SA; *Int'l*, pg. 3450
SWH HOWARD MARYLAND, INC.—See Holding Le Duff SA; *Int'l*, pg. 3450
TACO ALOHA, INC.—See Grupo Finaccess S.A.P.I. de C.V.; *Int'l*, pg. 3129
TAHOE JOE'S FAMOUS STEAKHOUSE, INC.—See Food Management Partners, Inc.; *U.S. Private*, pg. 1561
THE TAMPA BAY PALM—See Palm Restaurant Group; *U.S. Private*, pg. 3080
THE TAMPA CLUB; *U.S. Private*, pg. 4126
TANAKA OF TOKYO RESTAURANTS; *U.S. Private*, pg. 3930
TARRANT COUNTY CONCESSIONS, LLC—See Aramark; *U.S. Public*, pg. 178
TASTE BUDS, INC.; *U.S. Private*, pg. 3935
TASTEFULLY SIMPLE INC.; *U.S. Private*, pg. 3935
TASTER FOOD PTE LTD—See BreadTalk Group Pte Ltd.; *Int'l*, pg. 1143
TAVERN ON THE GREEN LP; *U.S. Private*, pg. 3936
T-BIRD RESTAURANT GROUP, INC.—See H.I.G. Capital, LLC; *U.S. Private*, pg. 1831
TEL AVIV HILTON LIMITED—See Hilton Worldwide Holdings Inc.; *U.S. Public*, pg. 1041
TEPPAN RESTAURANTS LTD.—See TPG Capital, L.P.; *U.S. Public*, pg. 2168
TEXAS LAND & CATTLE; *U.S. Private*, pg. 3976
TEXAS LAND & CATTLE STEAKHOUSE—See Day Star Restaurant Holdings, LLC; *U.S. Private*, pg. 1176
TEXAS ROADHOUSE DELAWARE LLC—See Texas Roadhouse, Inc.; *U.S. Public*, pg. 2027
TEXAS ROADHOUSE HOLDINGS LLC—See Texas Roadhouse, Inc.; *U.S. Public*, pg. 2027
TEXAS ROADHOUSE, INC.; *U.S. Public*, pg. 2027
TEXAS ROADHOUSE OF AUSTIN, LTD.—See Texas Roadhouse, Inc.; *U.S. Public*, pg. 2027
TEXAS ROADHOUSE OF AUSTIN-NORTH, LTD.—See Texas Roadhouse, Inc.; *U.S. Public*, pg. 2027
TEXAS ROADHOUSE OF BAKERSFIELD, LLC—See Texas Roadhouse, Inc.; *U.S. Public*, pg. 2027
TEXAS ROADHOUSE OF BAYTOWN, TX, LLC—See Texas Roadhouse, Inc.; *U.S. Public*, pg. 2027
TEXAS ROADHOUSE OF CEDAR FALLS, LLC—See Texas Roadhouse, Inc.; *U.S. Public*, pg. 2027
TEXAS ROADHOUSE OF CHEYENNE, LLC—See Texas Roadhouse, Inc.; *U.S. Public*, pg. 2027
TEXAS ROADHOUSE OF CONWAY, INC.—See Texas Roadhouse, Inc.; *U.S. Public*, pg. 2027
TEXAS ROADHOUSE OF CORONA, CA LLC—See Texas Roadhouse, Inc.; *U.S. Public*, pg. 2027
TEXAS ROADHOUSE OF ELYRIA, LLC—See Texas Roadhouse, Inc.; *U.S. Public*, pg. 2027
TEXAS ROADHOUSE OF FORT WAYNE, LLC—See Texas Roadhouse, Inc.; *U.S. Public*, pg. 2027
TEXAS ROADHOUSE OF GRAND JUNCTION, LLC—See Texas Roadhouse, Inc.; *U.S. Public*, pg. 2027
TEXAS ROADHOUSE OF HENDERSONVILLE, DE NOVO, LLC—See Texas Roadhouse, Inc.; *U.S. Public*, pg. 2027
TEXAS ROADHOUSE OF HUBER HEIGHTS, LLC—See Texas Roadhouse, Inc.; *U.S. Public*, pg. 2027
TEXAS ROADHOUSE OF JACKSONVILLE, NC LLC—See Texas Roadhouse, Inc.; *U.S. Public*, pg. 2027
TEXAS ROADHOUSE OF KANSAS, LLC—See Texas Roadhouse, Inc.; *U.S. Public*, pg. 2027
TEXAS ROADHOUSE OF LANCASTER, LLC—See Texas Roadhouse, Inc.; *U.S. Public*, pg. 2027
TEXAS ROADHOUSE OF LANCASTER OH, LLC—See Texas Roadhouse, Inc.; *U.S. Public*, pg. 2027
TEXAS ROADHOUSE OF LANSING, LLC—See Texas Roadhouse, Inc.; *U.S. Public*, pg. 2027
TEXAS ROADHOUSE OF LYNCHBURG, LLC—See Texas Roadhouse, Inc.; *U.S. Public*, pg. 2027
TEXAS ROADHOUSE OF MANSFIELD, LTD.—See Texas Roadhouse, Inc.; *U.S. Public*, pg. 2027
TEXAS ROADHOUSE OF MENIFEE, CA LLC—See Texas Roadhouse, Inc.; *U.S. Public*, pg. 2027
TEXAS ROADHOUSE OF PARKER—See Texas Roadhouse, Inc.; *U.S. Public*, pg. 2027

TEXAS ROADHOUSE OF RENO, NV, LLC—See Texas Roadhouse, Inc.; *U.S. Public*, pg. 2027
TEXAS ROADHOUSE OF RICHMOND, LLC—See Texas Roadhouse, Inc.; *U.S. Public*, pg. 2027
TEXAS ROADHOUSE OF ROSEVILLE, LLC—See Texas Roadhouse, Inc.; *U.S. Public*, pg. 2027
TEXAS ROADHOUSE OF STILLWATER, OK, LLC—See Texas Roadhouse, Inc.; *U.S. Public*, pg. 2027
TEXAS ROADHOUSE OF WARWICK, LLC—See Texas Roadhouse, Inc.; *U.S. Public*, pg. 2027
THAI HACHIBAN CO., LTD.—See HACHI-BAN CO., LTD.; *Int'l*, pg. 3203
THOMAS E. STRAUSS INC.; *U.S. Private*, pg. 4155
THOMAS & KING INC.; *U.S. Private*, pg. 4154
THOMPSON HOSPITALITY INC.; *U.S. Private*, pg. 4159
TICKFAW PIT STOP INC.—See Amar Oil Co. Inc.; *U.S. Private*, pg. 216
TIKI RESTAURANT, LOUNGE & MARINA, INC.; *U.S. Private*, pg. 4170
T&J RESTAURANTS LLC; *U.S. Private*, pg. 3909
TK LAS VEGAS, LLC—See Las Vegas Sands Corp.; *U.S. Public*, pg. 1293
TODAI FRANCHISING LLC; *U.S. Private*, pg. 4180
TOKYO BAY HILTON CO. LTD.—See Hilton Worldwide Holdings Inc.; *U.S. Public*, pg. 1041
TOMS KITCHEN LTD—See Dogus Holding AS; *Int'l*, pg. 2155
TOOJAY'S MANAGEMENT CORP.; *U.S. Private*, pg. 4185
TOPAZ HOTEL—See Pebblebrook Hotel Trust; *U.S. Public*, pg. 1660
TOUCHPOINT SUPPORT SERVICES, LLC—See Compass Group PLC; *Int'l*, pg. 1752
TOWNGAS ENTERPRISE LIMITED—See Henderson Land Development Co. Ltd.; *Int'l*, pg. 3344
TRANS PAPA LOGISTICS, INC.—See Papa John's International, Inc.; *U.S. Public*, pg. 1636
TRAVAGLINI ENTERPRISES, INC.; *U.S. Private*, pg. 4212
T R FOODS, INC.; *U.S. Private*, pg. 3909
TRIBECA GRILL—See Myriad Restaurant Group; *U.S. Private*, pg. 2825
TRP RESTAURANT ENTERPRISES, INC.; *U.S. Private*, pg. 4244
TRUDY'S TEXAS STAR INC.; *U.S. Private*, pg. 4247
TRUE WORLD FOODS-ALASKA—See Family Federation for World Peace & Unification; *U.S. Private*, pg. 1469
TRUFOODS LLC; *U.S. Private*, pg. 4249
TUMBLEWEED, INC.; *U.S. Private*, pg. 4258
TURKENT GIDA VE TURIZM SANAYI VE TICARET A.S.—See Yum! Brands, Inc.; *U.S. Public*, pg. 2400
TWO ROADS LAS VEGAS, LLC—See Las Vegas Sands Corp.; *U.S. Public*, pg. 1293
TYP RESTAURANT GROUP INC.; *U.S. Private*, pg. 4268
UFOOD RESTAURANT GROUP, INC.; *U.S. Private*, pg. 4274
UNCLE JULIO'S CORPORATION—See Catterton Management Company, LLC; *U.S. Public*, pg. 794
UNITED OHANA, LLC; *U.S. Private*, pg. 4295
UNO RESTAURANT HOLDINGS CORPORATION—See Centre Partners Management LLC; *U.S. Private*, pg. 829
URBN 640 OSTERIA LLC—See Urban Outfitters, Inc.; *U.S. Public*, pg. 2265
URBN CALLOWHILL LLC—See Urban Outfitters, Inc.; *U.S. Public*, pg. 2265
URBN CHANCELLOR LLC—See Urban Outfitters, Inc.; *U.S. Public*, pg. 2265
URBN NVY LOSP LLC—See Urban Outfitters, Inc.; *U.S. Public*, pg. 2265
URBN WAVERLY AMIS LLC—See Urban Outfitters, Inc.; *U.S. Public*, pg. 2265
USA RESTAURANTS, INC.; *U.S. Private*, pg. 4321
US RESTAURANTS INC.; *U.S. Private*, pg. 4319
VAIL FOOD SERVICES INC.—See Vail Resorts, Inc.; *U.S. Public*, pg. 2271
VAL INC.; *U.S. Private*, pg. 4329
VEGGIE GRILL, INC.—See Next Level Burger Company, Inc.; *U.S. Private*, pg. 2920
VETRI RESTAURANT CORP.—See Vetri Holdings LLC; *U.S. Private*, pg. 4374
VICTORIA STATION INC.—See A.S. Management Corporation; *U.S. Private*, pg. 28
VILLA DUBROVNIK D.D.—See Dogus Holding AS; *Int'l*, pg. 2155
VILLAGE INN RESTAURANTS—See Fidelity National Financial, Inc.; *U.S. Public*, pg. 830
VISION FS INC.; *U.S. Private*, pg. 4390
V&J NATIONAL ENTERPRISES LLC; *U.S. Private*, pg. 4327
VOODOO BBQ & GRILL; *U.S. Private*, pg. 4412
WAEN INTERNATIONAL LIMITED—See Hotland Co., Ltd.; *Int'l*, pg. 3489
WAFFLE HOUSE, INCORPORATED; *U.S. Private*, pg. 4425
WALL STREET DELI, INC.—See TruFoods LLC; *U.S. Private*, pg. 4249
WALRUS CORPORATION—See Clyde, Inc.; *U.S. Private*, pg. 949
WATERSTREET, LTD.; *U.S. Private*, pg. 4454

WEATHERVANE SEAFOOD COMPANY; *U.S. Private*, pg. 4463
WEAVER ENTERPRISES LTD.; *U.S. Private*, pg. 4463
WEBER ENTERPRISES INC.; *U.S. Private*, pg. 4465
WENDY'S OF DENVER, INC.—See The Wendy's Company; *U.S. Public*, pg. 2141
WENDY'S OF N.E. FLORIDA, INC.—See The Wendy's Company; *U.S. Public*, pg. 2141
WENDY'S OLD FASHIONED HAMBURGERS OF NEW YORK, INC.—See The Wendy's Company; *U.S. Public*, pg. 2141
WENDY'S RESTAURANTS—See The Wendy's Company; *U.S. Public*, pg. 2141
WESTERN SIZZLIN CORPORATION—See Biglari Holdings Inc.; *U.S. Public*, pg. 331
THE WESTIN LONG BEACH—See Marriott International, Inc.; *U.S. Public*, pg. 1372
WESTMINSTER HOOTERS, INC.—See Restaurants of America, Inc.; *U.S. Public*, pg. 3408
WHEATSTONE RESTAURANT GROUP LLC—See Northcott Hospitality International, LLC; *U.S. Public*, pg. 2949
THE WHITE BUFFALO SALOON, LLC; *U.S. Private*, pg. 4134
WHIT-MART INC.; *U.S. Private*, pg. 4507
WIND & SEA RESTAURANTS INC.; *U.S. Private*, pg. 4533
WINGSTOP RESTAURANTS, INC.—See Roark Capital Group Inc.; *U.S. Public*, pg. 3456
WORLD OF GOOD TASTES, INC.; *U.S. Private*, pg. 4566
WR RESTAURANTS MANAGEMENT LLC; *U.S. Private*, pg. 4571
XPERIENCE XRG RESTAURANT GROUP—See Z Capital Group, LLC; *U.S. Private*, pg. 4596
YABOO, INC.; *U.S. Private*, pg. 4584
YADAV ENTERPRISES, INC.; *U.S. Private*, pg. 4584
YALLA MEDITERRANEAN FRANCHISING COMPANY, LLC—See Fog Cutter Capital Group Inc.; *U.S. Private*, pg. 1557
YARD HOUSE IRVINE SPECTRUM, LLC—See Darden Restaurants, Inc.; *U.S. Public*, pg. 633
THE YARD HOUSE, L.P.—See Darden Restaurants, Inc.; *U.S. Public*, pg. 633
YARD HOUSE RANCHO MIRAGE, LLC—See Darden Restaurants, Inc.; *U.S. Public*, pg. 633
YARD HOUSE SAN DIEGO, LLC—See Darden Restaurants, Inc.; *U.S. Public*, pg. 633
YARD HOUSE TRIANGLE SQUARE, LLC—See Darden Restaurants, Inc.; *U.S. Public*, pg. 633
YOSHIHARU GLOBAL CO.; *U.S. Public*, pg. 2399
YOUNG & ASSOCIATES INC.; *U.S. Private*, pg. 4592
YUK CUISINE LIMITED—See Echo International Holdings Group Limited; *Int'l*, pg. 2289
YUMI YUMI CATERERS LIMITED—See Cafe de Coral Holdings Limited; *Int'l*, pg. 1250
YUNARI CO., LTD.—See create restaurants holdings inc.; *Int'l*, pg. 1832
YUZURU INC.—See create restaurants holdings inc.; *Int'l*, pg. 1832
ZEHNDERS OF FRANKENMUTH INC.; *U.S. Private*, pg. 4599
ZERODIX SARL—See CPI Property Group, S.A.; *Int'l*, pg. 1825
ZETTON, INC.—See Adastria Co., Ltd.; *Int'l*, pg. 126
ZOCALO L.C.—See Rreal Tacos Sandy Springs LLC; *U.S. Private*, pg. 3496
ZOE'S KITCHEN, INC.—See Cava Group, Inc.; *U.S. Public*, pg. 454
Z-TEJAS INC.; *U.S. Private*, pg. 4596

722513 — LIMITED-SERVICE RESTAURANTS

241 PIZZA (2006) LTD.—See Chairman's Brands Corporation; *Int'l*, pg. 1437
2JR PIZZA ENTERPRISES, LLC; *U.S. Private*, pg. 7
5 DEVELOPMENT CORP.; *U.S. Private*, pg. 15
AARSAND & COMPANY, INC.; *U.S. Private*, pg. 33
ABBYS INC.; *U.S. Private*, pg. 35
A&B ENTERPRISES INC.; *U.S. Private*, pg. 19
ACW CORP.; *U.S. Private*, pg. 71
ADAMS TRI CITIES ENTERPRISES; *U.S. Private*, pg. 75
AFSCO INC.; *U.S. Private*, pg. 124
AKWEN LLC; *U.S. Private*, pg. 147
ALIA CORP.; *U.S. Private*, pg. 166
ALIVE & KICKIN—See Port City Bakery Inc.; *U.S. Private*, pg. 3230
ALTES LLC; *U.S. Private*, pg. 208
AMERICAN DINING CORPORATION; *U.S. Private*, pg. 230
AMERICAN HUTS INC.; *U.S. Private*, pg. 237
AMERICAN PIZZA PARTNERS LP; *U.S. Private*, pg. 243
AMREST HOLDINGS SE; *Int'l*, pg. 437
AMREST KFT—See AmRest Holdings SE; *Int'l*, pg. 437
AMREST SP. Z O.O.—See AmRest Holdings SE; *Int'l*, pg. 437
AMREST S.R.O.—See AmRest Holdings SE; *Int'l*, pg. 437
ANDY'S RESTAURANTS, INC.; *U.S. Private*, pg. 281
ANOTHER BROKEN EGG OF AMERICA LLC—See The Beekman Group; *U.S. Private*, pg. 3992

722513 — LIMITED-SERVICE RES...   CORPORATE AFFILIATIONS

APEX RESTAURANT MANAGEMENT, INC.; *U.S. Private*, pg. 293
APPLEJAM INC.; *U.S. Private*, pg. 297
APPLEJAM OF GA INC.—See Applejam Inc.; *U.S. Private*, pg. 297
ARBICO EAST LLC; *U.S. Private*, pg. 308
ARCOS DORADOS HOLDINGS INC.; *Int'l*, pg. 550
ARCTIC CIRCLE RESTAURANTS, INC.—See Artic Circle, Inc.; *U.S. Private*, pg. 342
A&R FOODS INC.; *U.S. Private*, pg. 20
ARTIC CIRCLE, INC.; *U.S. Private*, pg. 342
THE ATLANTA BREAD COMPANY; *U.S. Private*, pg. 3990
ATLANTIC COAST FOODS, INC.; *U.S. Private*, pg. 372
ATLANTIC SERVICES; *U.S. Private*, pg. 374
A&W RESTAURANTS, INC.; *U.S. Private*, pg. 21
BAD DADDY'S INTERNATIONAL, LLC—See Good Times Restaurants, Inc.; *U.S. Public*, pg. 951
BAIM ENTERPRISES INC.; *U.S. Private*, pg. 426
BARTLETT MANAGEMENT SERVICES; *U.S. Private*, pg. 483
BART RICH ENTERPRISES INC.; *U.S. Private*, pg. 482
BAY FOODS INC.; *U.S. Private*, pg. 492
BEATON INC.; *U.S. Private*, pg. 507
BEEF CORPORATION OF AMERICA; *U.S. Private*, pg. 514
BEIJING PIZZA HUT CO., LTD.—See Yum China Holdings, Inc.; *U.S. Public*, pg. 2399
BENTON ENTERPRISES INCORPORATED; *U.S. Private*, pg. 529
BERJAYA PIZZA COMPANY SDN BHD—See Berjaya Corporation Berhad; *Int'l*, pg. 982
BERNARD KARCHER INVESTMENTS INC.; *U.S. Private*, pg. 536
BETTER FOOD SYSTEMS INCORPORATION; *U.S. Private*, pg. 546
BF SOUTH INC.; *U.S. Private*, pg. 548
B&G DIVERSIFIED CONCEPTS LLC—See B&G Food Enterprises Inc.; *U.S. Private*, pg. 418
B&G FOOD ENTERPRISES TEXAS LLC—See B&G Food Enterprises Inc.; *U.S. Private*, pg. 418
BILL BARNES; *U.S. Private*, pg. 556
BIRCHWOOD MALL, LLC—See Brookfield Corporation; *Int'l*, pg. 1185
BISCUITVILLE, INC.; *U.S. Private*, pg. 565
BLAKE'S LOTABURGER LLC; *U.S. Private*, pg. 578
BLIMPIE INTERNATIONAL INC.; *U.S. Private*, pg. 581
BLIMPIE SUBS & SALADS—See Blimpie International Inc.; *U.S. Private*, pg. 581
BOBBY COX COMPANIES, INC.; *U.S. Private*, pg. 606
BOJANGLES', INC.—See Durational Capital Management, LP; *U.S. Private*, pg. 1293
BOJANGLES', INC.—See The Jordan Company, L.P.; *U.S. Private*, pg. 4060
BOJANGLES' RESTAURANTS, INC.—See Durational Capital Management, LP; *U.S. Private*, pg. 1293
BOJANGLES' RESTAURANTS, INC.—See The Jordan Company, L.P.; *U.S. Private*, pg. 4060
BORDER FOODS, INC.; *U.S. Private*, pg. 617
BOSS ENTERPRISES INC.; *U.S. Private*, pg. 620
BOSTON MARKET CORPORATION; *U.S. Private*, pg. 621
BOULEVARD MALL, LLC—See Brookfield Corporation; *Int'l*, pg. 1185
BRANDICORP; *U.S. Private*, pg. 637
BR ASSOCIATES, INC.; *U.S. Private*, pg. 630
BRAVO RESTAURANTS INC.; *U.S. Private*, pg. 641
BRAZIL FAST FOOD CORP; *Int'l*, pg. 1142
BRIDGEMAN'S RESTAURANTS INC.; *U.S. Private*, pg. 649
BROOKS RESTAURANTS INC.; *U.S. Private*, pg. 664
BROS MANAGEMENT INC.; *U.S. Private*, pg. 665
BROWN'S CHICKEN & PASTA, INC.; *U.S. Private*, pg. 669
BRUMIT RESTAURANT GROUP; *U.S. Private*, pg. 672
BRYANT RESTAURANTS INC.; *U.S. Private*, pg. 673
BULLARD RESTAURANTS INC.; *U.S. Private*, pg. 684
BURGER KING FRANCE SAS—See Groupe Bertrand SARL; *Int'l*, pg. 3092
BURGER STREET INCORPORATED; *U.S. Private*, pg. 686
BURGERVILLE USA—See The Holland, Inc.; *U.S. Private*, pg. 4054
BVI DOUBLE DRIVE-THRU INC.; *U.S. Private*, pg. 700
CAFE EXPRESS LLC; *U.S. Private*, pg. 714
CAFE RIO, INC.; *U.S. Private*, pg. 714
CALIFORNIA GRILL LLC—See RCI Hospitality Holdings, Inc.; *U.S. Public*, pg. 1767
CAM/RB INC—See CAM Consultants, Inc.; *U.S. Private*, pg. 725
CAPTAIN D'S, LLC—See Sentinel Capital Partners, L.L.C.; *U.S. Private*, pg. 3608
CARL KARCHER ENTERPRISES, INC.—See Roark Capital Group Inc.; *U.S. Private*, pg. 3454
CAROLINA CHICKEN INC.; *U.S. Private*, pg. 767
CAROLINA QUALITY INC.; *U.S. Private*, pg. 768
CAROLINA RESTAURANT GROUP; *U.S. Private*, pg. 768
CASINO CAFETERIA SAS—See Finatis SA; *Int'l*, pg. 2670
CASPERS COMPANY; *U.S. Private*, pg. 783
THE CASPIAN INTERNATIONAL RESTAURANTS COMPANY, LLP—See Adeptio LLC; *Int'l*, pg. 143
CASSANO'S INC.; *U.S. Private*, pg. 783
CEDAR OF NEW ENGLAND, LTD.—See Cedar Enterprises Inc.; *U.S. Private*, pg. 804

CEF ENTERPRISES INC.; *U.S. Private*, pg. 805
CENTURY FAST FOODS INC.; *U.S. Private*, pg. 832
CHAIRMAN'S BRANDS CORPORATION; *Int'l*, pg. 1437
CHAT INC.; *U.S. Private*, pg. 860
CHECKERS DRIVE-IN RESTAURANTS, INC.—See Keystone Group, L.P.; *U.S. Private*, pg. 2299
CHICK-FIL-A, INC.; *U.S. Private*, pg. 880
CHI POLSKA S.A.—See The Coca-Cola Company; *U.S. Public*, pg. 2065
CHURCH'S CHICKEN, INC.—See Arcapita Group Holdings Limited; *Int'l*, pg. 542
CITY LUMBER INC.; *U.S. Private*, pg. 906
CLK, INC.; *U.S. Private*, pg. 945
CLP CORPORATION; *U.S. Private*, pg. 948
COFFEE TIME DONUTS INCORPORATED—See Chairman's Brands Corporation; *Int'l*, pg. 1437
COLLINS FOODS LIMITED; *Int'l*, pg. 1702
COLOMEX INC.; *U.S. Private*, pg. 970
COLUMBIA BASIN PIZZA HUT INC.; *U.S. Private*, pg. 976
COMPETITIVE FOODS AUSTRALIA PTY. LTD.; *Int'l*, pg. 1753
CONCESSIONS INTERNATIONAL INC.; *U.S. Private*, pg. 1009
CONSOLIDATED INVESTMENT CORPORATION; *U.S. Private*, pg. 1021
CONSOLIDATED RESTAURANTS OF CALIFORNIA; *U.S. Private*, pg. 1022
COOPER PETROLEUM INC.; *U.S. Private*, pg. 1041
COTTI FOODS CORPORATION; *U.S. Private*, pg. 1063
COUGH INC.; *U.S. Private*, pg. 1064
COUNTRY STYLE COOKING RESTAURANT CHAIN CO., LTD.; *Int'l*, pg. 1819
COUSINS SUBMARINES, INC.; *U.S. Private*, pg. 1071
COVELLI ENTERPRISES LLC; *U.S. Private*, pg. 1071
COWABUNGA INC.; *U.S. Private*, pg. 1073
CREATIVE FOODS CORP.; *U.S. Private*, pg. 1088
CRISPERS, LLC—See Boyne Capital Management, LLC; *U.S. Private*, pg. 629
CRT PARTNERS INC.; *U.S. Private*, pg. 1113
CRUISERS GRILL; *U.S. Private*, pg. 1114
CSRWIRE, LLC—See 3BL Media LLC; *U.S. Private*, pg. 8
CURRY UP NOW; *U.S. Private*, pg. 1126
DAKOTA KING INC.; *U.S. Private*, pg. 1147
DALAND CORPORATION; *U.S. Private*, pg. 1148
DALIAN KFC CO., LTD.—See Yum China Holdings, Inc.; *U.S. Public*, pg. 2399
DAMON'S INTERNATIONAL INC.—See Alliance Development Group; *U.S. Private*, pg. 182
DAR-MEL INC.; *U.S. Private*, pg. 1158
DAVCO RESTAURANTS LLC—See DavCo Acquisition Holding Inc.; *U.S. Private*, pg. 1168
DAVID J. STANTON AND ASSOCIATES; *U.S. Private*, pg. 1170
DAY ENTERPRISES INC.; *U.S. Private*, pg. 1176
D. CARR INVESTMENTS INC.; *U.S. Private*, pg. 1139
DEBONAIRS PIZZA (PTY) LTD.—See Famous Brands Limited; *Int'l*, pg. 2612
DELAWARE NORTH COMPANIES INTERNATIONAL, LTD.—See Delaware North Companies, Inc.; *U.S. Private*, pg. 1194
DELAWARE NORTH COMPANIES SPORTSERVICE—See Delaware North Companies, Inc.; *U.S. Private*, pg. 1194
DELAWARE NORTH COMPANIES TRAVEL HOSPITALITY SERVICES—See Delaware North Companies, Inc.; *U.S. Private*, pg. 1194
DELI MANAGEMENT INC.; *U.S. Private*, pg. 1196
DEL TACO LLC—See Jack in the Box Inc.; *U.S. Public*, pg. 1183
DELTON RESTAURANTS INC.; *U.S. Private*, pg. 1202
DIPASQUA ENTERPRISES, INC.; *U.S. Private*, pg. 1234
DISTRIBUIDORA E IMPORTADORA ALSEA, S. A. DE C. V.—See Alsea, S.A.B. de C.V.; *Int'l*, pg. 379
DOMINO'S PIZZA DISTRIBUTION LLC—See Domino's Pizza, Inc.; *U.S. Public*, pg. 675
DOMINO'S PIZZA ENTERPRISES LTD.; *Int'l*, pg. 2162
DOMINO'S PIZZA GROUP LIMITED—See Domino's Pizza Group plc; *Int'l*, pg. 2162
DOMINO'S PIZZA INTERNATIONAL LLC—See Domino's Pizza, Inc.; *U.S. Public*, pg. 675
DOMINO'S PIZZA LLC—See Domino's Pizza, Inc.; *U.S. Public*, pg. 675
DOMINO'S PIZZA NEDERLAND B.V.—See Domino's Pizza Enterprises Ltd.; *Int'l*, pg. 2162
DONATOS PIZZERIA CORPORATION; *U.S. Private*, pg. 1260
DONGGUAN KFC CO., LTD.—See Yum China Holdings, Inc.; *U.S. Public*, pg. 2399
DOUBLE CHEESE CORPORATION; *U.S. Private*, pg. 1265
DPFC S.A.R.L.—See Domino's Pizza Enterprises Ltd.; *Int'l*, pg. 2162
DP POLAND PLC; *Int'l*, pg. 2187
DRM INC.; *U.S. Private*, pg. 1278
DSW RESTAURANTS INC.—See Drury Inn Inc.; *U.S. Private*, pg. 1280
DUCKREY ENTERPRISES INC.; *U.S. Private*, pg. 1284
DUTCH BROS. COFFEE, LLC; *U.S. Private*, pg. 1294
DWELL US STUDENT LIVING LLC—See Centurion Corporation Limited; *Int'l*, pg. 1417

EEGEES INC.—See Eastbridge Group; *Int'l*, pg. 2271
ELITE PIZZA TEXAS, LLC; *U.S. Private*, pg. 1361
ELLIS HOLDING CO.; *U.S. Private*, pg. 1374
EL POLLO LOCO INC.—See Trimaran Capital Partners, LLC; *U.S. Private*, pg. 4232
EMERALD FOODS INC.; *U.S. Private*, pg. 1379
E.M. THOMAS MANAGEMENT INC.; *U.S. Private*, pg. 1306
ERIE COUNTY INVESTMENT CO.; *U.S. Private*, pg. 1420
ES-O-EN CORP; *U.S. Private*, pg. 1424
ESPECIALISTAS EN RESTAURANTES DE COMIDA ESTILO ASIATICA, S. A. DE C. V.—See Alsea, S.A.B. de C.V.; *Int'l*, pg. 379
EXCALIBUR PIZZA LLC; *U.S. Private*, pg. 1445
EXELCO INC.; *U.S. Private*, pg. 1448
FALCON HOLDINGS, LLC; *U.S. Private*, pg. 1466
FAMOUS BRANDS LIMITED; *Int'l*, pg. 2612
FAMOUS TOASTERY OF CONCORD, LLC; *U.S. Private*, pg. 1472
F AND F CONCESSIONS, INC.—See Live Nation Entertainment, Inc.; *U.S. Public*, pg. 1328
FAST FOOD ENTERPRISES; *U.S. Private*, pg. 1482
FAST FOOD SUDAMERICANA, S. A.—See Alsea, S.A.B. de C.V.; *Int'l*, pg. 379
FATBURGER CORPORATION—See Fog Cutter Capital Group Inc.; *U.S. Private*, pg. 1557
FATBURGER NORTH AMERICA, INC.—See Fog Cutter Capital Group Inc.; *U.S. Private*, pg. 1557
FCH ENTERPRISES INC.; *U.S. Private*, pg. 1485
F&D HUEBNER LLC; *U.S. Private*, pg. 1454
FFC LIMITED PARTNERSHIP; *U.S. Private*, pg. 1500
FIGTREE COMPANY, LLC—See Fifth Third Bancorp; *U.S. Public*, pg. 833
FIRST SUN MANAGEMENT CORPORATION; *U.S. Private*, pg. 1529
FIVE GUYS ENTERPRISES, LLC; *U.S. Private*, pg. 1537
FLYING PIE PIZZARIA, INC.; *U.S. Private*, pg. 1553
FOOD SERVICES UNLIMITED, INC.; *U.S. Private*, pg. 1561
FOODTASTIC INC.; *Int'l*, pg. 2727
FOSTER DOLAN ENTERPRISES INC.; *U.S. Private*, pg. 1578
FOSTERS FREEZE, LLC; *U.S. Private*, pg. 1579
FOUR CROWN INC.; *U.S. Private*, pg. 1582
FOURJAY LLC; *U.S. Private*, pg. 1583
FOWLER FOODS INC.; *U.S. Private*, pg. 1583
FRANCHISE OPERATIONS INC.; *U.S. Private*, pg. 1587
FRESH ENTERPRISES, LLC; *U.S. Private*, pg. 1609
FRIGOSCANDIA AB—See Dachser GmbH & Co.; *Int'l*, pg. 1904
FRONTIER ENTERPRISES, INC.; *U.S. Private*, pg. 1615
FURMAN'S, INC.; *U.S. Private*, pg. 1624
GALADCO INC.; *U.S. Private*, pg. 1636
GALAXY CLOUD KITCHENS LIMITED; *Int'l*, pg. 2871
GARDENBURGER, LLC—See Kellanova; *U.S. Public*, pg. 1218
GENKI GLOBAL DINING CONCEPTS CORPORATION; *Int'l*, pg. 2924
GENXMEX FOODS, INC.; *U.S. Private*, pg. 1680
GEORGIA NORTH FOODS INC.; *U.S. Private*, pg. 1684
GIFFORDS FAMOUS ICE CREAM; *U.S. Private*, pg. 1697
GIGGLES N HUGS, INC.; *U.S. Public*, pg. 1697
GILCHRIST ENTERPRISES; *U.S. Private*, pg. 1699
GIORDANO'S ENTERPRISES, INC.; *U.S. Private*, pg. 1702
GOLDEN ARCH ENTERPRISES; *U.S. Private*, pg. 1730
GOLDEN M CO. INC.; *U.S. Private*, pg. 1732
GOLDEN STATE SERVICE INDUSTRIES, INC.—See Golden State Foods Corp.; *U.S. Private*, pg. 1733
GOLDEN TRIANGLE DAIRY QUEENS, INC.; *U.S. Private*, pg. 1734
GOOD EARTH RESTAURANTS OF MINNESOTA—See Parasole Restaurant Holdings, Inc.; *U.S. Private*, pg. 3093
GOOD TIMES RESTAURANTS, INC.; *U.S. Public*, pg. 951
GOSH ENTERPRISES, INC.; *U.S. Private*, pg. 1744
GRANDY'S—See Sentinel Capital Partners, L.L.C.; *U.S. Private*, pg. 3609
GREAT AMERICAN DELI, INC.—See The H.T. Hackney Company; *U.S. Private*, pg. 4041
GREEN BEANS COFFEE COMPANY, INC.; *U.S. Private*, pg. 1771
GROTTO PIZZA INC.; *U.S. Private*, pg. 1793
GUANGZHOU RESTAURANT GROUP CO., LTD.; *Int'l*, pg. 3167
GUMBY'S PIZZA SYSTEMS INC.; *U.S. Private*, pg. 1818
GZK INC.; *U.S. Private*, pg. 1822
HACHI-BAN CO., LTD.; *Int'l*, pg. 3203
HAKIMIANPOUR RESTAURANT GROUP; *U.S. Private*, pg. 1841
HALJOHN INC.; *U.S. Private*, pg. 1843
HALJOHN-SAN ANTONIO, INC.—See Haljohn Inc.; *U.S. Private*, pg. 1843
HANNON'S KENTUCKY FRIED CHICKEN, INC.; *U.S. Private*, pg. 1855
HAPPY JOE'S PIZZA AND ICE CREAM PARLOR, INC.; *U.S. Private*, pg. 1857
HARDEE'S FOOD SYSTEMS, INC.—See Roark Capital Group Inc.; *U.S. Private*, pg. 3454
HARDEES SOUTHWEST MISSOURI INC.; *U.S. Private*, pg. 1862

N.A.I.C.S. INDEX

722513 — LIMITED-SERVICE RES...

HAWAII PIZZA HUT, INC.—See Grupo Finaccess S.A.P.I. de C.V.; *Int'l*, pg. 3129
HB BOYS, LLC; *U.S. Private*, pg. 1886
HEARTLAND FOOD SERVICES INC.; *U.S. Private*, pg. 1900
HILLCREST FOODS INC.; *U.S. Private*, pg. 1946
THE HOLLAND, INC.; *U.S. Private*, pg. 4054
HONEY DEW ASSOCIATES, INC.; *U.S. Private*, pg. 1976
HOSPITALITY USA INVESTMENT GROUP, INC.; *U.S. Private*, pg. 1988
HOSPITALITY WEST LLC; *U.S. Private*, pg. 1988
HOUSE OF BLUES ORLANDO RESTAURANT CORP.—See Live Nation Entertainment, Inc.; *U.S. Public*, pg. 1329
HOUSTON PIZZA VENTURE LP; *U.S. Private*, pg. 1993
H. SALT OF SOUTHERN CALIFORNIA, INC.; *U.S. Private*, pg. 1825
HUNGRY HOWIE'S PIZZA & SUBS INC.; *U.S. Private*, pg. 2007
HURRICANE FOODS INC.; *U.S. Private*, pg. 2012
IN-N-OUT BURGERS, INC.; *U.S. Private*, pg. 2052
INTERNATIONAL TOURISTIC PROJECTS LEBANESE COMPANY—See Adeptio LLC; *Int'l*, pg. 143
ISLANDS RESTAURANTS LP; *U.S. Private*, pg. 2146
JACK IN THE BOX INC.; *U.S. Public*, pg. 1183
JACK MARSHALL FOODS INC.; *U.S. Private*, pg. 2174
JACK'S FAMILY RESTAURANTS INC.—See AEA Investors LP; *U.S. Private*, pg. 114
JAMBA JUICE COMPANY—See Roark Capital Group Inc.; *U.S. Private*, pg. 3454
JAMES CONEY ISLAND INC.; *U.S. Private*, pg. 2183
JAMES E. BARNES ENTERPRISES INC.; *U.S. Private*, pg. 2183
THE JAN COMPANIES; *U.S. Private*, pg. 4058
JERSEY MIKE'S FRANCHISE SYSTEMS, INC.; *U.S. Private*, pg. 2203
JOHN NEWCOMB ENTERPRISES INC.; *U.S. Private*, pg. 2223
JOHNSON PARTNERS INC.; *U.S. Private*, pg. 2228
JOHNSTONE FOODS INC.; *U.S. Private*, pg. 2230
JONATHAN'S CO., LTD.—See Bain Capital, LP; *U.S. Private*, pg. 444
JPL MANAGEMENT INC.; *U.S. Private*, pg. 2239
JRC PIZZA LLC; *U.S. Private*, pg. 2240
KADES CORP.; *U.S. Private*, pg. 2253
KAZI FOODS CORP. OF HAWAII—See Kazi Foods Inc.; *U.S. Private*, pg. 2267
KAZI FOODS INC.; *U.S. Private*, pg. 2267
KB OF BALTIMORE INC.; *U.S. Private*, pg. 2268
KC BELL, INC.; *U.S. Private*, pg. 2269
KDE INC.; *U.S. Private*, pg. 2270
KEKE'S BREAKFAST CAFE INC.—See Denny's Corporation; *U.S. Public*, pg. 654
KELSEYS INTERNATIONAL, INC.—See Fairfax Financial Holdings Limited; *Int'l*, pg. 2608
KENTUCKY FRIED CHICKEN CANADA COMPANY—See Yum! Brands, Inc.; *U.S. Public*, pg. 2400
KENTUCKY FRIED CHICKEN (GREAT BRITAIN) LIMITED—See Yum! Brands, Inc.; *U.S. Public*, pg. 2400
KENTUCKY FRIED CHICKEN PTY. LTD.—See Yum! Brands, Inc.; *U.S. Public*, pg. 2400
KFC CHAMNORD SAS—See Yum! Brands, Inc.; *U.S. Public*, pg. 2400
KFC CORPORATION—See Yum! Brands, Inc.; *U.S. Public*, pg. 2400
KFC RESTAURANTS ASIA PTE., LTD.—See Yum! Brands, Inc.; *U.S. Public*, pg. 2400
KING OF STERLING HEIGHTS INC.—See Michigan Multi-King Inc.; *U.S. Private*, pg. 2701
KING TACO RESTAURANT INC.; *U.S. Private*, pg. 2310
KING VENTURE INC.; *U.S. Private*, pg. 2310
KLEIN-KAUFMAN CORP.; *U.S. Private*, pg. 2319
KOHR BROTHERS, INC.; *U.S. Private*, pg. 2340
KONING RESTAURANTS INTERNATIONAL, LTD.; *U.S. Private*, pg. 2342
KOSTKA ENTERPRISES INC.; *U.S. Private*, pg. 2345
KURANI INCORPORATED; *U.S. Private*, pg. 2357
KUWAIT FOOD COMPANY (AMERICANA) S.A.K.—See Adeptio LLC; *Int'l*, pg. 143
KUWAIT FOOD COMPANY (UAE)—See Adeptio LLC; *Int'l*, pg. 143
LAMKONE RESTAURANTS INC.; *U.S. Private*, pg. 2380
LA PIZZA LOCA, INC.—See Meruelo Group LLC; *U.S. Private*, pg. 2677
LA SALSA, INC.—See Fresh Enterprises, LLC; *U.S. Private*, pg. 1609
LAS-CAL CORPORATION; *U.S. Private*, pg. 2394
LAURINBURG KFC TAKE HOME INC.—See ZV Pate Inc.; *U.S. Private*, pg. 4610
LDF FOOD GROUP; *U.S. Private*, pg. 2404
LEE'S FAMOUS RECIPES INC.; *U.S. Private*, pg. 2414
LEONA'S PIZZERIA INC.; *U.S. Private*, pg. 2423
LETTUCE FEED YOU INC.; *U.S. Private*, pg. 2433
LEWIS FOODS INC.; *U.S. Private*, pg. 2439
LITTLE CAESAR ENTERPRISES, INC.—See Ilitch Holdings, Inc.; *U.S. Private*, pg. 2041
LITTLE CAESARS ENTERPRISES, INC.—See Ilitch Holdings, Inc.; *U.S. Private*, pg. 2042

LONG JOHN SILVER'S LLC; *U.S. Private*, pg. 2490
LUIHN FOOD SYSTEMS INC.; *U.S. Private*, pg. 2512
LUNAN CORPORATION; *U.S. Private*, pg. 2515
LWD INC.; *U.S. Private*, pg. 2519
MACADOS INC.; *U.S. Private*, pg. 2531
MACKINAW FOOD SERVICE CORP.—See Daland Corporation; *U.S. Private*, pg. 1148
MAGGIANO'S, INC.—See Brinker International, Inc.; *U.S. Public*, pg. 384
MALLARD HOLDING COMPANY LLC; *U.S. Private*, pg. 2557
MARCO'S PIZZA, INC.—See Highland Ventures, Ltd.; *U.S. Private*, pg. 1939
MARTINS RESTAURANT SYSTEMS INC.; *U.S. Private*, pg. 2597
MASTORAN RESTAURANT INC.; *U.S. Private*, pg. 2608
MAUI WOWI FRANCHISING, INC.; *U.S. Private*, pg. 2615
MB FOOD SERVICE INC.; *U.S. Private*, pg. 2623
MCDONALD'S CORPORATION; *U.S. Public*, pg. 1405
MCDONALD'S GMBH—See McDonald's Corporation; *U.S. Public*, pg. 1406
MCDONALD'S IMMOBILIEN GMBH—See McDonald's Corporation; *U.S. Public*, pg. 1406
MCDONALDS OF CALHOUN INC.; *U.S. Private*, pg. 2632
MCDONALDS OF SCOTTSDALE; *U.S. Private*, pg. 2632
MCDONALDS OF SIOUX CITY; *U.S. Private*, pg. 2632
MCDONALD'S RESTAURANTS LIMITED—See McDonald's Corporation; *U.S. Public*, pg. 1406
MCDONALD'S RESTAURANTS OF ILLINOIS, INC.—See McDonald's Corporation; *U.S. Public*, pg. 1406
MCDONALD'S RESTAURANTS OF MARYLAND, INC.—See McDonald's Corporation; *U.S. Public*, pg. 1406
MCDONALD'S SUISSE FRANCHISE SARL—See McDonald's Corporation; *U.S. Public*, pg. 1406
MCESSY INVESTMENTS CO.; *U.S. Private*, pg. 2633
MCMANGA FOODS, INC.; *U.S. Private*, pg. 2642
MCTHAI COMPANY LTD.—See McDonald's Corporation; *U.S. Public*, pg. 1406
MELTON MANAGEMENT INC.; *U.S. Private*, pg. 2663
MERITAGE HOSPITALITY GROUP INC.; *U.S. Public*, pg. 1425
MIAMI SUBS CORPORATION—See Miami Subs Capital Partners I, Inc.; *U.S. Private*, pg. 2697
MIAMI SUBS USA, INC.—See Miami Subs Capital Partners I, Inc.; *U.S. Private*, pg. 2697
MICHIGAN MULTI-KING INC.; *U.S. Private*, pg. 2701
MICHIGAN PIZZA HUT INC.; *U.S. Private*, pg. 2701
MID AMERICA CORP.; *U.S. Private*, pg. 2705
MIDAMERICA HOTELS CORPORATION; *U.S. Private*, pg. 2710
MIDLAND FOOD SERVICES; *U.S. Private*, pg. 2715
MID-SOUTH RESTAURANTS INC.; *U.S. Private*, pg. 2709
MIRABILE INVESTMENT CORP.; *U.S. Private*, pg. 2745
MJG CORPORATION; *U.S. Private*, pg. 2753
M&J MANAGEMENT CORPORATION; *U.S. Private*, pg. 2524
MOD SUPER FAST PIZZA, LLC; *U.S. Private*, pg. 2759
MONTY MEX CORP.; *U.S. Private*, pg. 2777
MOOYAH FRANCHISING, LLC—See Balmoral Funds LLC; *U.S. Private*, pg. 461
MOOYAH FRANCHISING, LLC—See Gala Capital Partners, LLC; *U.S. Private*, pg. 1635
MORGAN'S FOODS, INC.—See Apex Restaurant Management, Inc.; *U.S. Private*, pg. 293
MR. GATTI'S, L.P.—See Sovrano LLC; *U.S. Private*, pg. 3743
NABEEL'S CAFE & MARKET; *U.S. Private*, pg. 2829
NATHAN'S FAMOUS INC.; *U.S. Public*, pg. 1493
NATH COMPANIES INCORPORATED; *U.S. Private*, pg. 2838
NATH FLORIDA FRANCHISE GROUP—See Nath Companies Incorporated; *U.S. Private*, pg. 2838
NATH MINNESOTA FRANCHISE GROUP—See Nath Companies Incorporated; *U.S. Private*, pg. 2838
NATIONAL CONEY ISLAND INC.; *U.S. Private*, pg. 2851
NETWORK MEDICS, INC.—See Tonka Bay Equity Partners LLC; *U.S. Private*, pg. 4185
NEW KING INC.; *U.S. Private*, pg. 2898
NEWPORT CREAMERY LLC—See The Jan Companies; *U.S. Private*, pg. 4058
NIPPON RESTAURANT SYSTEM, INC.—See Doutor-Nichires Holdings Co., Ltd.; *Int'l*, pg. 2182
NOBLE ROMAN'S, INC.; *U.S. Public*, pg. 1531
NOR-CAL FOODS, INC.; *U.S. Private*, pg. 2935
NORTHERN EMPIRE PIZZA INCORPORATED; *U.S. Private*, pg. 2952
NORTHWEST RESTAURANTS; *U.S. Private*, pg. 2961
NORTHWIND INVESTMENTS INC.; *U.S. Private*, pg. 2963
NPC INTERNATIONAL, INC.—See Olympus Partners; *U.S. Private*, pg. 3013
NRD HOLDINGS, LLC—See National Restaurant Development, Inc.; *U.S. Private*, pg. 2862
OERTHER FOODS, INC.; *U.S. Private*, pg. 3000
OISHI JAPANESE PIZZA PTE LTD—See ABR Holdings, Ltd.; *Int'l*, pg. 67
OKLAHOMA MAGIC LP; *U.S. Private*, pg. 3007
OLD WEST PROPERTIES LLC; *U.S. Private*, pg. 3009

OOO AMREST—See AmRest Holdings SE; *Int'l*, pg. 437
OPERADORA DE FRANQUICIAS ALSEA, S. A. DE C. V.—See Alsea, S.A.B. de C.V.; *Int'l*, pg. 379
ORANGE FOOD COURT—See AEON Co., Ltd.; *Int'l*, pg. 178
ORANGE JULIUS OF AMERICA—See Berkshire Hathaway Inc.; *U.S. Public*, pg. 308
PACIFIC ALTERNATIVE ASSET MANAGEMENT COMPANY, LLC—See PAAMCO Prisma Holdings, LLC; *U.S. Private*, pg. 3062
PANDA EXPRESS INC.—See Panda Restaurant Group, Inc.; *U.S. Private*, pg. 3085
PAPA JOHN'S INTERNATIONAL, INC.; *U.S. Public*, pg. 1636
PAPA JOHN'S OF IOWA LLC; *U.S. Private*, pg. 3087
PAPOULI'S GREEK GRILL RESTAURANTS; *U.S. Private*, pg. 3088
PARK OF HOLDING INC.; *U.S. Private*, pg. 3096
PASCHEN MANAGEMENT CORPORATION; *U.S. Private*, pg. 3104
PDM COMPANY INC.; *U.S. Private*, pg. 3122
PENGUIN POINT FRANCHISE SYSTEMS INC; *U.S. Private*, pg. 3133
PERU PIZZA CO. INC.—See Daland Corporation; *U.S. Private*, pg. 1148
PETER-DE FRIES INCORPORATED; *U.S. Private*, pg. 3159
PETROTEX; *U.S. Private*, pg. 3163
PEZOLD MANAGEMENT ASSOCIATES; *U.S. Private*, pg. 3164
PHIDEB PARTNERSHIP; *U.S. Private*, pg. 3168
PITA PIT USA, INC.; *U.S. Private*, pg. 3190
PIZZACO INC.; *U.S. Private*, pg. 3193
PIZZA HUT, INC.—See Yum! Brands, Inc.; *U.S. Public*, pg. 2400
PIZZA HUT OF AMERICA, INC.—See Yum! Brands, Inc.; *U.S. Public*, pg. 2400
PIZZA HUT OF ARIZONA INC.; *U.S. Private*, pg. 3193
PIZZA HUT OF IDAHO INC.; *U.S. Private*, pg. 3193
PIZZA HUT OF MARYLAND INC.; *U.S. Private*, pg. 3193
PIZZA HUT OF PUERTO RICO INC.—See Encanto Restaurants, Inc; *U.S. Private*, pg. 1389
PIZZA OF SCOTLAND INC.—See ZV Pate Inc.; *U.S. Private*, pg. 4610
PIZZA VENTURE SAN ANTONIO LLC; *U.S. Private*, pg. 3193
PIZZA VENTURES WEST TEXAS LLC—See Pizza Venture San Antonio LLC; *U.S. Private*, pg. 3193
PLAMONDON ENTERPRISES INC.; *U.S. Private*, pg. 3195
POLLO OPERATIONS, INC.—See Garnett Station Partners, LLC; *U.S. Private*, pg. 1645
POLLY'S INC.—See EDD Investment Co.; *U.S. Private*, pg. 1332
PONTCHARTRAIN FOODS INC.; *U.S. Private*, pg. 3227
POPEYES LIMITED PARTNERSHIP I; *U.S. Private*, pg. 3228
PORTILLOS HOT DOGS INCORPORATED; *U.S. Private*, pg. 3232
PORT OF SUBS INC.; *U.S. Private*, pg. 3230
POTBELLY SANDWICH WORKS, LLC—See Potbelly Corporation; *U.S. Public*, pg. 1704
PRIMARY AIM, LLC; *U.S. Private*, pg. 3260
PSB CO.—See White Castle System, Inc.; *U.S. Private*, pg. 4508
QATAR FOOD COMPANY—See Adeptio LLC; *Int'l*, pg. 143
QDOBA MEXICAN GRILL INC.—See Jack in the Box Inc.; *U.S. Public*, pg. 1183
QUALITY DISTRIBUTING COMPANY; *U.S. Private*, pg. 3318
QUICK QUALITY RESTAURANT INC.; *U.S. Private*, pg. 3326
"B"ING THE BEST, INC.; *U.S. Private*, pg. 1
RAHE INC.; *U.S. Private*, pg. 3346
RAMEN PLAY PTE. LTD.—See BreadTalk Group Pte Ltd.; *Int'l*, pg. 1143
REDARHCS INC.; *U.S. Private*, pg. 3377
RED BRICK PIZZA LLC—See BRIX Holdings, LLC; *U.S. Private*, pg. 657
RED INC.; *U.S. Private*, pg. 3375
REE INC.; *U.S. Private*, pg. 3381
RESTAURANT BRANDS NEW ZEALAND LIMITED—See Grupo Finaccess S.A.P.I. de C.V.; *Int'l*, pg. 3129
RESTAURANT MANAGEMENT CORP.; *U.S. Private*, pg. 3408
RESTAURANT MANAGEMENT INC.; *U.S. Private*, pg. 3408
RESTAURANT SYSTEMS INC.; *U.S. Private*, pg. 3408
RICE GARDEN INC.—See Arbor Private Investment Company, LLC; *U.S. Private*, pg. 309
RICKEY'S RESTAURANT & LOUNGE, INC.; *U.S. Private*, pg. 3431
ROBEKS CORPORATION; *U.S. Private*, pg. 3457
ROBINS DONUTS—See Chairman's Brands Corporation; *Int'l*, pg. 1437
ROCHELLE HOLDING COMPANY; *U.S. Private*, pg. 3463
ROCKY ROCOCO CORPORATION; *U.S. Private*, pg. 3469
RO HO HO INC.; *U.S. Private*, pg. 3453
ROTTINGHAUS CO. INC.; *U.S. Private*, pg. 3487

722513 — LIMITED-SERVICE RES...

ROUND TABLE PIZZA—See Fog Cutter Capital Group Inc.; U.S. Private, pg. 1557
ROYAL FORK RESTAURANT CORP; U.S. Private, pg. 3492
RPM PIZZA INC.; U.S. Private, pg. 3495
RUBBER CITY ARCHES, LLC; U.S. Private, pg. 3499
RUNZA DRIVE-INNS OF AMERICA INC.; U.S. Private, pg. 3504
SACCA CORPORATION; U.S. Private, pg. 3521
SAILORMEN INC.—See Interfoods of America, Inc.; U.S. Private, pg. 2110
SALADWORKS, LLC—See Centre Lane Partners, LLC; U.S. Private, pg. 827
SANDYS ASSOCIATES INC.; U.S. Private, pg. 3545
SANWECO INC.; U.S. Private, pg. 3548
SAVANNAH RESTAURANTS CORP.; U.S. Private, pg. 3556
SBARRO LLC; U.S. Private, pg. 3559
SCHLOTZSKY'S, LTD.—See Roark Capital Group Inc.; U.S. Private, pg. 3455
SCHUSTER ENTERPRISES INC.; U.S. Private, pg. 3571
SCOTT M & A CORPORATION; U.S. Private, pg. 3577
SEAGATE FOODS INC.; U.S. Private, pg. 3584
SEATTLE'S BEST COFFEE INTERNATIONAL—See Roark Capital Group Inc.; U.S. Private, pg. 3455
SEAWEND LTD.—See Cedar Enterprises Inc.; U.S. Private, pg. 804
SENSOR ENTERPRISES INC.; U.S. Private, pg. 3608
SHAKE SHACK INC.; U.S. Public, pg. 1873
SHAMROCK CO.; U.S. Private, pg. 3624
SHANGHAI KFC CO., LTD.—See Yum China Holdings, Inc.; U.S. Public, pg. 2399
SHANGHAI PIZZA HUT CO., LTD.—See Yum China Holdings, Inc.; U.S. Public, pg. 2399
S&H INCORPORATED; U.S. Private, pg. 3513
SHORTY'S MEXICAN ROADHOUSE; U.S. Private, pg. 3643
SIMMONDS RESTAURANT MANAGEMENT; U.S. Private, pg. 3665
SINGLER-ERNSTER INC.; U.S. Private, pg. 3670
SISCO ENTERPRISES INC.; U.S. Private, pg. 3675
SKYPORT COMPANIES LLC; U.S. Private, pg. 3686
SMB RESTAURANTS LLC; U.S. Private, pg. 3693
SONIC CORPORATION—See Roark Capital Group Inc.; U.S. Private, pg. 3455
SONIC INDUSTRIES, INC.—See Roark Capital Group Inc.; U.S. Private, pg. 3455
SONIC MANAGEMENT; U.S. Private, pg. 3713
SONIC MERRITTED GROUP; U.S. Private, pg. 3713
SOUPER SALAD, LLC—See BRIX Holdings, LLC; U.S. Private, pg. 658
SOUTH AMERICAN RESTAURANTS CORP.; U.S. Private, pg. 3719
SOUTHEAST FOOD SERVICES CORP; U.S. Private, pg. 3725
SOUTHERN MANAGEMENT CORPORATION; U.S. Private, pg. 3733
SOUTHLAND MALL, L.P.—See Brookfield Corporation; Int'l, pg. 1185
SOUTHWEST TRADERS INCORPORATED; U.S. Private, pg. 3741
SPANGLES INC.; U.S. Private, pg. 3745
SP DELTA FOODS INC.—See SPFS Inc.; U.S. Private, pg. 3756
SPOKANE FOOD SERVICES, INC.; U.S. Private, pg. 3759
STONEFIRE GRILL INC.—See Goode Partners, LLC; U.S. Private, pg. 1739
STRAW HAT RESTAURANTS, INC.; U.S. Private, pg. 3837
SUBWAY RESTAURANTS—See Doctor's Associates Inc.; U.S. Private, pg. 1251
SUNSHINE RESTAURANT PARTNERS, LLC; U.S. Private, pg. 3872
SUTHERLAND MANAGEMENT COMPANY; U.S. Private, pg. 3886
SVENSKA MCDONALD'S AB—See McDonald's Corporation; U.S. Public, pg. 1406
SWITCHGRASS HOLDINGS, LLC—See BOK Financial Corporation; U.S. Public, pg. 367
TACALA, LLC; U.S. Private, pg. 3920
TACALA LLC—See Altamont Capital Partners; U.S. Private, pg. 205
TACO BELL CORP.—See Yum! Brands, Inc.; U.S. Public, pg. 2400
TACO BUENO RESTAURANTS, L.P.—See TPG Capital, L.P.; U.S. Public, pg. 2177
TACO CABANA, INC.—See Yadav Enterprises, Inc.; U.S. Private, pg. 4584
TACO DEL MAR FRANCHISING CORP.; U.S. Private, pg. 3920
TACOMA INC.; U.S. Private, pg. 3921
TACO MAYO FRANCHISE SYSTEMS, INC.; U.S. Private, pg. 3920
TAIWAN SKYLARK CO., LTD.—See Bain Capital, LP; U.S. Private, pg. 444
TANDEM INC.; U.S. Private, pg. 3930
TAR HEEL CAPITAL CORPORATION NO. 2; U.S. Private, pg. 3933
TASTEE FREEZ LLC—See Galardi Group, Inc; U.S. Private, pg. 1636
TCH RESTAURANT GROUP INC.; U.S. Private, pg. 3942
TEAM WASHINGTON, INC.; U.S. Private, pg. 3950
TEN D. ENTERPRISES, INC.; U.S. Private, pg. 3964
TEXAS SUBS; U.S. Private, pg. 3977
TEX-BEST TRAVEL CENTERS INC.; U.S. Private, pg. 3974
THAI SKYLARK CO., LTD.—See Bain Capital, LP; U.S. Private, pg. 444
TIDEWATER PIZZA TIME INC.; U.S. Private, pg. 4168
TMC FOODS LLC; U.S. Private, pg. 4179
TOM + CHEE; U.S. Private, pg. 4182
TREFZ & TREFZ INC.; U.S. Private, pg. 4217
TRI CITY FOODS INC.; U.S. Private, pg. 4220
TRICON RESTAURANT INTERNATIONAL (PR), INC.—See Encanto Restaurants, Inc; U.S. Private, pg. 1389
TRIDENT FOODS, LTD.—See Cedar Enterprises Inc.; U.S. Private, pg. 804
TROPICAL SMOOTHIE FRANCHISE DEVELOPMENT CORP.—See BIP Opportunities Fund, LP; U.S. Private, pg. 563
TUBBY'S SUB SHOPS, INC.; U.S. Private, pg. 4255
TWENTY FIRST CENTURY LP; U.S. Private, pg. 4264
TWM INDUSTRIES; U.S. Private, pg. 4266
TWOTON INC.; U.S. Private, pg. 4267
UNIQUE FOODS CORP.; U.S. Public, pg. 2227
UNITED STATES BEEF CORPORATION; U.S. Private, pg. 4298
UPCHURCH MANAGEMENT CO. INC.; U.S. Private, pg. 4311
US PIZZA COMPANY; U.S. Private, pg. 4319
VALLEY MANAGEMENT, INC.; U.S. Private, pg. 4334
VILLA ENTERPRISES MANAGEMENT LTD., INC.; U.S. Private, pg. 4383
VINEYARD INDUSTRIES INC.; U.S. Private, pg. 4385
VIRGINIA PIZZA CO., INC.—See Daland Corporation; U.S. Private, pg. 1148
VLBF CORP.; U.S. Private, pg. 4407
VOCELLI PIZZA; U.S. Private, pg. 4409
WADE-CARY ENTERPRISES INC.; U.S. Private, pg. 4424
WARMEL CORP.; U.S. Private, pg. 4442
WATERMARK DONUT COMPANY; U.S. Private, pg. 4454
WEN-ALABAMA INC; U.S. Private, pg. 4480
WENDCO CORP.; U.S. Private, pg. 4480
WENDCO OF PUERTO RICO INC.; U.S. Private, pg. 4480
WENDY'S BOWLING GREEN INC.; U.S. Private, pg. 4481
WENDY'S INTERNATIONAL, INC.—See The Wendy's Company; U.S. Public, pg. 2141
WENDY'S OF COLORADO SPRINGS, INC.—See WCS, Inc.; U.S. Private, pg. 4462
WENDY'S OF LAS VEGAS, INC.—See Cedar Enterprises Inc.; U.S. Private, pg. 804
WENDY'S OF MISSOURI INC.; U.S. Private, pg. 4481
WENDY'S OF MONTANA INC.; U.S. Private, pg. 4481
WENDY'S OF SAN ANTONIO, INC.—See Cedar Enterprises Inc.; U.S. Private, pg. 804
WENDY'S RESTAURANTS OF CANADA, INC.—See The Wendy's Company; U.S. Public, pg. 2141
WENDY'S RESTAURANTS OF ROCHESTER, INC.; U.S. Private, pg. 4481
WESFAM RESTAURANTS INC.; U.S. Private, pg. 4482
WESTERN RESERVE RESTAURANT MANAGEMENT; U.S. Private, pg. 4496
WESTERN RESTAURANTS INC.; U.S. Private, pg. 4496
WEST QUALITY FOOD SERVICE INC.; U.S. Private, pg. 4487
WESTWIND INC.; U.S. Private, pg. 4501
WHATABURGER, INC.; U.S. Private, pg. 4504
WHATABURGER OF MESQUITE INC.; U.S. Private, pg. 4504
WHITE CASTLE SYSTEM, INC.; U.S. Private, pg. 4508
WINGSTREET, LLC—See Yum! Brands, Inc.; U.S. Public, pg. 2400
WIT GROUP INC.; U.S. Private, pg. 4550
WUXI KFC CO., LTD.—See Yum China Holdings, Inc.; U.S. Public, pg. 2399
WYNDALL'S ENTERPRISES INC.; U.S. Private, pg. 4576
WYVERN RESTAURANTS INC.; U.S. Private, pg. 4579
WZ FRANCHISE CORP.; U.S. Private, pg. 4579
XIAMEN KFC CO., LTD.—See Yum China Holdings, Inc.; U.S. Public, pg. 2399
YAMATO FOODS CO., LTD.—See CSS Holdings, Ltd.; Int'l, pg. 1867
YUM! RESTAURANTS AUSTRALIA PTY. LIMITED—See Yum! Brands, Inc.; U.S. Public, pg. 2400
YUM! RESTAURANTS CHINA HOLDINGS LIMITED—See Yum China Holdings, Inc.; U.S. Public, pg. 2399
YUM! RESTAURANTS CONSULTING (SHANGHAI) CO., LTD.—See Yum China Holdings, Inc.; U.S. Public, pg. 2400
YUM! RESTAURANTS EUROPE LIMITED—See Yum! Brands, Inc.; U.S. Public, pg. 2400
YUM! RESTAURANTS (SHENZHEN) CO., LTD.—See Yum China Holdings, Inc.; U.S. Public, pg. 2400
YUM! RESTAURANTS (XIAN) CO., LTD.—See Yum China Holdings, Inc.; U.S. Public, pg. 2400
ZAXBY'S FRANCHISING, INC.; U.S. Private, pg. 4598
ZIPPY'S, INC.; U.S. Private, pg. 4606

722514 — CAFETERIAS, GRILL BUFFETS, AND BUFFETS

AZTEC SHOPS LTD. INC.; U.S. Private, pg. 416
CORPORATE CULINARY SERVICE INC.; U.S. Private, pg. 1054
GO GASTSTATTENBETRIEBS GMBH; Int'l, pg. 3017
GOLDEN CORRAL CORPORATION—See Investors Management Corporation; U.S. Private, pg. 2132
GOURMET SERVICES INC.; U.S. Private, pg. 1746
GUEST SERVICES COMPANY OF VIRGINIA—See Guest Services, Inc.; U.S. Private, pg. 1811
HEART DINING INC—See H2O Retailing Corp.; Int'l, pg. 3200
J&S CAFETERIA INC.; U.S. Private, pg. 2155
KELLY'S CAJUN GRILL FRANCHISE; U.S. Private, pg. 2277
K&W CAFETERIAS INC.; U.S. Private, pg. 2250
MEDICLIN A LA CARTE GMBH—See Asklepios Kliniken GmbH & Co. KGaA; Int'l, pg. 623
NORTHERN GC, LLC—See WCS, Inc.; U.S. Private, pg. 4462
PICCADILLY RESTAURANTS, LLC—See The Yucaipa Companies LLC; U.S. Private, pg. 4140
SAGE DINING SERVICES INC.; U.S. Private, pg. 3526
SOUTHERN FOODSERVICE MANAGEMENT INC.; U.S. Private, pg. 3732
TAHER INC; U.S. Private, pg. 3922
TREAT AMERICA FOOD SERVICES, INC.; U.S. Private, pg. 4216

722515 — SNACK AND NONALCOHOLIC BEVERAGE BARS

AFTER YOU PCL; Int'l, pg. 196
AMREST COFFEE DEUTSCHLAND SP. Z O.O. & CO. KG—See AmRest Holdings SE; Int'l, pg. 437
AQUATERRA CORPORATION—See Primo Water Corporation; U.S. Public, pg. 1718
BASKIN-ROBBINS LLC—See Roark Capital Group Inc.; U.S. Private, pg. 3455
BERJAYA STARBUCKS COFFEE COMPANY SDN. BHD.—See Berjaya Corporation Berhad; Int'l, pg. 982
BERJAYA STARBUCKS COFFEE COMPANY SDN. BHD.—See Starbucks Corporation; U.S. Public, pg. 1938
BEVERAGES, FOODS & SERVICE INDUSTRIES, INC.—See PepsiCo, Inc.; U.S. Public, pg. 1668
CATALINA CAFE—See RedEye Coffee Roasting, LLC; U.S. Private, pg. 3378
CHIULISTA SERVICES, INC.; U.S. Private, pg. 887
COFFEE DAY GLOBAL LIMITED—See Affirma Capital Limited; Int'l, pg. 187
COFFEE DAY GLOBAL LTD. - CAFE COFFEE DAY DIVISION—See Affirma Capital Limited; Int'l, pg. 187
COFFEE REPUBLIC (UK) LIMITED—See Coffee Republic Trading Ltd.; Int'l, pg. 1692
COLD STONE CREAMERY, INC.—See Kahala Corp.; U.S. Private, pg. 2254
COMERCIALIZADORA SNACKS, S.R.L.—See PepsiCo, Inc.; U.S. Public, pg. 1668
ESPRESSO PARTNERS INC.—See Wind Point Advisors LLC; U.S. Private, pg. 4536
FES INDUSTRIES SDN BHD—See Food Empire Holdings Limited; Int'l, pg. 2727
GLOBAL SCIENCES HOLDINGS, INC.—See CBD Global Sciences, Inc.; U.S. Public, pg. 455
HALO FOODS LTD.—See Peak Rock Capital LLC; U.S. Private, pg. 3124
HAS LIFESTYLE LIMITED; Int'l, pg. 3282
HDOS ENTERPRISES—See Fog Cutter Capital Group Inc.; U.S. Private, pg. 1557
HOME BISTRO, INC.; U.S. Public, pg. 1045
HYUNGKUK F&B CO.,LTD; Int'l, pg. 3561
KOUFU GROUP LIMITED—See Dominus Capital, L.P.; U.S. Private, pg. 1256
LE DUFF AMERICA, INC.—See Holding Le Duff SA; Int'l, pg. 3450
MULTI FLOW INDUSTRIES, LLC—See Falconhead Capital, LLC; U.S. Private, pg. 1467
QINGDAO AMERICAN STARBUCKS COFFEE COMPANY LIMITED—See Starbucks Corporation; U.S. Public, pg. 1938
RACHELLI ITALIA S.R.L.—See Emmi AG; Int'l, pg. 2385
RED MANGO—See BRIX Holdings, LLC; U.S. Private, pg. 657
SCI EUROPE I, INC.—See Starbucks Corporation; U.S. Public, pg. 1938
SEATTLE'S BEST COFFEE LLC—See Starbucks Corporation; U.S. Public, pg. 1938
THE SMOOTHIE FACTORY, INC.—See BRIX Holdings, LLC; U.S. Private, pg. 658
SMOOTHIES KOREA INC—See Affirma Capital Limited; Int'l, pg. 187
SOUTHERN ICE CREAM SPECIALTIES INC—See The Kroger Co.; U.S. Public, pg. 2109
SPARTAN FOODS OF AMERICA INC—See B&G Foods, Inc.; U.S. Public, pg. 260

N.A.I.C.S. INDEX

SPLASH BEVERAGE GROUP, INC.; *U.S. Public*, pg. 1919
STARBUCKS BRASIL COMERCIO DE CAFES LTDA.—See Starbucks Corporation; *U.S. Public*, pg. 1938
STARBUCKS CARD EUROPE LIMITED—See Starbucks Corporation; *U.S. Public*, pg. 1939
STARBUCKS (CHINA) COMPANY LIMITED—See Starbucks Corporation; *U.S. Public*, pg. 1938
STARBUCKS COFFEE ARGENTINA S.R.L.—See Alsea, S.A.B. de C.V.; *Int'l*, pg. 379
STARBUCKS COFFEE ASIA PACIFIC LIMITED—See Starbucks Corporation; *U.S. Public*, pg. 1938
STARBUCKS COFFEE AUSTRIA GMBH—See Starbucks Corporation; *U.S. Public*, pg. 1939
STARBUCKS COFFEE CANADA, INC.—See Starbucks Corporation; *U.S. Public*, pg. 1939
STARBUCKS COFFEE COMPANY AUSTRALIA PTY. LTD.—See Starbucks Corporation; *U.S. Public*, pg. 1938
STARBUCKS COFFEE ESPANA S.L.—See Alsea, S.A.B. de C.V.; *Int'l*, pg. 379
STARBUCKS COFFEE FRANCE S.A.S.—See Starbucks Corporation; *U.S. Public*, pg. 1939
STARBUCKS COFFEE INTERNATIONAL, INC.—See Starbucks Corporation; *U.S. Public*, pg. 1938
STARBUCKS COFFEE JAPAN, LTD.—See Starbucks Corporation; *U.S. Public*, pg. 1939
STARBUCKS COFFEE SINGAPORE PTE. LTD.—See Starbucks Corporation; *U.S. Public*, pg. 1939
STARBUCKS COFFEE (THAILAND) CO., LTD.—See Starbucks Corporation; *U.S. Public*, pg. 1938
TASTI D-LITE LLC—See Kahala Corp.; *U.S. Private*, pg. 2254
TATA STARBUCKS PRIVATE LIMITED—See Starbucks Corporation; *U.S. Public*, pg. 1939
TEAVANA CORPORATION—See Starbucks Corporation; *U.S. Public*, pg. 1939
TORREFAZIONE ITALIA LLC—See Starbucks Corporation; *U.S. Public*, pg. 1939
U-SWIRL INTERNATIONAL, INC.—See Rocky Mountain Chocolate Factory, Inc.; *U.S. Public*, pg. 1807
YUM YUM DONUT SHOPS, INC.; *U.S. Private*, pg. 4595

811111 — GENERAL AUTOMOTIVE REPAIR

ABBYLAND TRUCKING, INC.—See Abbyland Foods, Inc.; *U.S. Private*, pg. 35
ACCIDENT REPAIR MANAGEMENT PTY LTD—See AMA Group Limited; *Int'l*, pg. 403
ACTIA GROUP SA - ACTIA MULLER (FRANCE) DIVISION—See Actia Group SA; *Int'l*, pg. 118
A&D MAINTENANCE LEASING & REPAIRS, INC.—See Custom Truck One Source, Inc.; *U.S. Public*, pg. 612
ALBERT'S TRUCK SERVICE & SUPPLY, INC.—See American Securities LLC; *U.S. Private*, pg. 248
ALLBILDELAR I HUDDINGE AB—See Bilia AB; *Int'l*, pg. 1029
ALLIED LUBE INC.; *U.S. Private*, pg. 186
AMERIT FLEET SOLUTIONS, INC.—See Brightstar Capital Partners, L.P.; *U.S. Private*, pg. 652
AN COLLISION CENTER OF SARASOTA, INC.—See AutoNation, Inc.; *U.S. Public*, pg. 231
ASA PSS D.O.O—See ASA Holding d.o.o.; *Int'l*, pg. 591
ATHLON HOLDING N.V.—See Cooperatieve Centrale Raiffeisen-Boerenleenbank B.A.; *Int'l*, pg. 1791
ATRACCO AUTO AB—See LKQ Corporation; *U.S. Public*, pg. 1333
AUDI CORAL SPRINGS—See Lithia Motors, Inc.; *U.S. Public*, pg. 1321
AUTEX INC.; *U.S. Private*, pg. 396
AUTOKORAN A.D.; *Int'l*, pg. 727
AUTO KUCA 21. MAJ A.D.; *Int'l*, pg. 725
AUTO KUCA VOZDOVAC A.D.; *Int'l*, pg. 725
AUTO KUCA ZEMUN A.D.; *Int'l*, pg. 725
AUTONATION FLEET SERVICES, LLC—See AutoNation, Inc.; *U.S. Public*, pg. 232
AUTO TAG OF AMERICA LLC—See Verra Mobility Corporation; *U.S. Public*, pg. 2286
BARON BMW—See Group 1 Automotive, Inc.; *U.S. Public*, pg. 970
BARON MINI—See Group 1 Automotive, Inc.; *U.S. Public*, pg. 970
BARRETT MOTOR CARS; *U.S. Private*, pg. 480
BASF COATINGS SERVICES PTY. LTD.—See BASF SE; *Int'l*, pg. 873
BEACON MOTORS, INC.—See AutoNation, Inc.; *U.S. Public*, pg. 233
BILIA VERSTRAETEN NV—See Bilia AB; *Int'l*, pg. 1029
BILSALONGEN AS—See Bilia AB; *Int'l*, pg. 1029
BLACKBIRD HERITAGE MOTORWORKS LIMITED—See CCT Fortis Holdings Limited; *Int'l*, pg. 1369
BLACKHAWK S.A.S.—See Snap-on Incorporated; *U.S. Public*, pg. 1897
BLUETORINO SRL—See Financiere de L'Odet; *Int'l*, pg. 2666
BMW OF STRATHAM—See Group 1 Automotive, Inc.; *U.S. Public*, pg. 970
BODEN BRUSSELS NV—See General Motors Company; *U.S. Public*, pg. 923

BODYTECHNICS LIMITED—See Berjaya Corporation Berhad; *Int'l*, pg. 984
THE BOYD GROUP (U.S.) INC.—See Boyd Group Services Inc.; *Int'l*, pg. 1124
BRAEGER FORD INC.—See Braeger Company of Wisconsin Inc.; *U.S. Private*, pg. 633
BRAKE-O-RAMA INC.; *U.S. Private*, pg. 634
BRAKE-O-RAMA—See Brake-O-Rama Inc.; *U.S. Private*, pg. 635
BRIDGESTONE RETAIL OPERATIONS, LLC—See Bridgestone Corporation; *Int'l*, pg. 1156
BUESO & FORMAN, INC.; *U.S. Private*, pg. 680
BUMPERDOC INC.; *U.S. Private*, pg. 685
CAMPINE FRANCE S.A.S—See Campine N.V.; *Int'l*, pg. 1275
CAPITAL S.M.A.R.T. REPAIRS AUSTRALIA PTY LTD—See AMA Group Limited; *Int'l*, pg. 403
CAPITAL S.M.A.R.T. REPAIRS NEW ZEALAND PTY LTD—See AMA Group Limited; *Int'l*, pg. 403
CAPRICORN SOCIETY LIMITED; *Int'l*, pg. 1317
CAR CARE CLINIC, INC.; *U.S. Private*, pg. 747
CARMAX AUTO SUPERSTORES SERVICES, INC.—See CarMax, Inc.; *U.S. Public*, pg. 437
CDMDATA, INC.—See Cox Enterprises, Inc.; *U.S. Private*, pg. 1076
CEDAR RIVER INTERNATIONAL TRUCKS INC.; *U.S. Private*, pg. 805
CHANDLERS (HAILSHAM) LIMITED—See Group 1 Automotive, Inc.; *U.S. Public*, pg. 971
CHRISTIAN BROTHERS AUTOMOTIVE CORPORATION; *U.S. Private*, pg. 890
CLASS EIGHT TRUCK REPAIR INC.—See The Mennel Milling Company; *U.S. Private*, pg. 4077
CMH AUTOGAS PRODUCTS (PTY) LTD—See Combined Motor Holdings Limited; *Int'l*, pg. 1709
COACH BUILDERS—See Peter Pan Bus Lines, Inc.; *U.S. Private*, pg. 3159
CONRAD'S TIRE SERVICE INC.; *U.S. Private*, pg. 1019
CORPUS CHRISTI COLLISION CENTER, INC.—See AutoNation, Inc.; *U.S. Public*, pg. 234
DALLAS SERVICE CENTER, INC.—See Ryder System, Inc.; *U.S. Public*, pg. 1828
DAVID MCDAVID ACURA—See David McDavid Automotive Group; *U.S. Private*, pg. 1170
DB FAHRZEUGINSTANDHALTUNG GMBH—See Deutsche Bahn AG; *Int'l*, pg. 2050
DB FERNVERKEHR AKTIENGESELLSCHAFT—See Deutsche Bahn AG; *Int'l*, pg. 2050
DB FUHRPARKSERVICE GMBH—See Deutsche Bahn AG; *Int'l*, pg. 2050
DEACON JONES AUTO PARK; *U.S. Private*, pg. 1181
DEALER-FX NORTH AMERICA GROUP INC.—See Snap-on Incorporated; *U.S. Public*, pg. 1897
DESERT FLEET-SERV, INC.—See OEP Capital Advisors, L.P.; *U.S. Private*, pg. 3000
DIAMOND/TRIUMPH AUTO GLASS INC.; *U.S. Private*, pg. 1224
DICKINSON FLEET SERVICES LLC—See Cox Enterprises, Inc.; *U.S. Private*, pg. 1075
DIESEL FORWARD, INC.; *U.S. Private*, pg. 1228
DIVINE CORPORATION; *U.S. Private*, pg. 1244
D.W. CAMPBELL-COBB PKWY, INC.—See D.W. Campbell, Inc.; *U.S. Private*, pg. 1143
D.W. CAMPBELL OF ATLANTA, INC.—See D.W. Campbell, Inc.; *U.S. Private*, pg. 1143
D.W. CAMPBELL OF DUNWOODY, INC.—See D.W. Campbell, Inc.; *U.S. Private*, pg. 1143
D.W. CAMPBELL OF KENNESAW, INC.—See D.W. Campbell, Inc.; *U.S. Private*, pg. 1143
D.W. CAMPBELL OF MARIETTA, INC.—See D.W. Campbell, Inc.; *U.S. Private*, pg. 1143
EASTERN NOVA CO., LTD.—See Honda Motor Co., Ltd.; *Int'l*, pg. 3460
ECONO LUBE N' TUNE INC.—See Roark Capital Group Inc.; *U.S. Private*, pg. 3454
EFFICIENT DRIVETRAINS INC.—See Cummins Inc.; *U.S. Public*, pg. 607
EL MONTE AUTO SERVICES LLC—See Car Pros Automotive Group, Inc.; *U.S. Private*, pg. 747
ELMS STANSTED LIMITED—See Group 1 Automotive, Inc.; *U.S. Public*, pg. 971
ENSING TRUCK SERVICE INC—See En-Way Enterprises Inc.; *U.S. Private*, pg. 1389
EUROFIX; *U.S. Private*, pg. 1433
E-Z-GO CANADA LIMITED—See Textron Inc.; *U.S. Public*, pg. 2028
FAULTLESS RECOVERY SERVICES PTY. LTD.—See Butn Limited; *Int'l*, pg. 1229
FERNDALE COLLISION, LLC—See Lithia Motors, Inc.; *U.S. Public*, pg. 1322
FIDELITY WARRANTY SERVICES, INC.—See JM Family Enterprises Inc.; *U.S. Private*, pg. 2214
FLEETNET AMERICA, INC.—See Cox Enterprises, Inc.; *U.S. Private*, pg. 1076
FLUOR-BWXT PORTSMOUTH LLC—See Fluor Corporation; *U.S. Public*, pg. 859
FORMEX PRESSINGS (PROPRIETARY) LIMITED—See E Media Holdings Limited; *Int'l*, pg. 2246

811111 — GENERAL AUTOMOTIVE ...

FRAME SERVICE INC.—See American Securities LLC; *U.S. Private*, pg. 248
G1R MASS, LLC—See Group 1 Automotive, Inc.; *U.S. Public*, pg. 971
GA-CC COLUMBUS, INC.—See AutoNation, Inc.; *U.S. Public*, pg. 235
GASAN ZAMMIT MOTORS CO., LTD.—See Honda Motor Co., Ltd.; *Int'l*, pg. 3460
GATES AUTOMOTIVE CENTER; *U.S. Private*, pg. 1650
GEA S.R.L.—See CogenInfra SpA; *Int'l*, pg. 1694
GE HONDA AERO ENGINES LLC—See Honda Motor Co., Ltd.; *Int'l*, pg. 3460
GERBER COLLISION & GLASS (KANSAS), INC.—See Boyd Group Services Inc.; *Int'l*, pg. 1125
GILBERT BODY SHOP, INC.—See AutoNation, Inc.; *U.S. Public*, pg. 235
GPI FL-H, LLC—See Group 1 Automotive, Inc.; *U.S. Public*, pg. 971
GPI GA-CGM, LLC—See Group 1 Automotive, Inc.; *U.S. Public*, pg. 971
GPI TX-EPGM, INC.—See Group 1 Automotive, Inc.; *U.S. Public*, pg. 971
GPI TX-SKII, INC.—See Group 1 Automotive, Inc.; *U.S. Public*, pg. 971
GPI TX-SVIII INC.—See Group 1 Automotive, Inc.; *U.S. Public*, pg. 971
GRUPA AZOTY TRANSTECH SP. Z O.O.—See Grupa Azoty S.A.; *Int'l*, pg. 3116
HJS MOTOREN GMBH—See 2G Energy AG; *Int'l*, pg. 5
HKS TECHNICAL FACTORY CO., LTD.—See HKS CO., LTD.; *Int'l*, pg. 3429
HODGSON AUTOMOTIVE LIMITED—See Group 1 Automotive, Inc.; *U.S. Public*, pg. 971
HONDA AUTOMOBILE WESTERN AFRICA LTD.—See Honda Motor Co., Ltd.; *Int'l*, pg. 3460
HONDA CARS CEBU, INC.—See Ayala Corporation; *Int'l*, pg. 774
H&V COLLISION CENTER; *U.S. Private*, pg. 1824
JACK BYRNE FORD & MERCURY, INC.; *U.S. Private*, pg. 2173
JENSEN TIRE & AUTO CO.; *U.S. Private*, pg. 2201
JUKONSKI TRUCK SALES AND SERVICE; *U.S. Private*, pg. 2243
JUST CAR CLINICS—See The Carlyle Group Inc.; *U.S. Public*, pg. 2050
KAIN AUTOMOTIVE, INC.—See NCM Associates, Inc.; *U.S. Private*, pg. 2876
KANSAS AVIATION OF INDEPENDENCE, L.L.C.—See VSE Corporation; *U.S. Public*, pg. 2313
KAUL GMBH—See Freudenberg SE; *Int'l*, pg. 2789
KENT FRANCE SAS—See Berner SE; *Int'l*, pg. 988
KENT INDUSTRI DANMARK APS—See Berner SE; *Int'l*, pg. 988
KENT ITALIA S.R.L.—See Berner SE; *Int'l*, pg. 988
KENT NEDERLAND B.V.—See Berner SE; *Int'l*, pg. 988
KENT UK LTD.—See Berner SE; *Int'l*, pg. 988
KEYSTONE TURBINE SERVICES LLC—See M International Inc.; *U.S. Private*, pg. 2523
KOOL AUTOMOTIVE; *U.S. Private*, pg. 2343
LAKESIDE INTERNATIONAL LLC—See Lakeside International Trucks Inc.; *U.S. Private*, pg. 2378
LAMB'S TIRE & AUTOMOTIVE CENTERS; *U.S. Private*, pg. 2379
LEGACY AUTOMOTIVE GROUP; *U.S. Private*, pg. 2416
LEGACY FORD-MERCURY INC.—See Legacy Automotive Group; *U.S. Private*, pg. 2416
LETZIGRABEN GARAGE AG—See Honda Motor Co., Ltd.; *Int'l*, pg. 3463
LEWISVILLE COLLISION, INC.—See AutoNation, Inc.; *U.S. Public*, pg. 236
LOGISTIC LEASING, LLC; *U.S. Private*, pg. 2481
MADAGASCAR AUTOMOBILE SA—See Honda Motor Co., Ltd.; *Int'l*, pg. 3463
MANAGED MOBILE, INC.—See Epika Fleet Services, Inc.; *U.S. Private*, pg. 1413
MAPLE GROVE AUTO SERVICE, INC.—See O2 Investment Partners, LLC; *U.S. Private*, pg. 2982
MASTERRACKCROWN—See Leggett & Platt, Incorporated; *U.S. Public*, pg. 1303
MCNICOLL VEHICLE HIRE LTD.—See Avis Budget Group, Inc.; *U.S. Public*, pg. 249
MEINEKE CAR CARE CENTERS, INC.—See Roark Capital Group Inc.; *U.S. Private*, pg. 3454
MESA COLLISION, INC.—See AutoNation, Inc.; *U.S. Public*, pg. 236
MESSMER GMBH—See LKQ Corporation; *U.S. Public*, pg. 1335
MIDAMERICAN TRUCK MAINTENANCE—See Murphy-Hoffman Company; *U.S. Private*, pg. 2816
MIDAS AUSTRALIA PTY LTD—See Bapcor Limited; *Int'l*, pg. 857
MID ATLANTIC COLLISION CENTER—See R.F. Inc.; *U.S. Private*, pg. 3336
MINUTEMAN TRUCKS, INC.—See Allegiance Trucks, LLC; *U.S. Private*, pg. 176
MOBILE FLEET SERVICE INC.; *U.S. Private*, pg. 2757
MODERN AUTOMOBILE COMPANY LIMITED—See Baguio Green Group Limited; *Int'l*, pg. 799

811111 — GENERAL AUTOMOTIVE ...

MONRO, INC.; *U.S. Public,* pg. 1465
MORTIMER COLLISION, LLC—See AutoNation, Inc.; *U.S. Public,* pg. 236
MOTOR TRUCKS INC.; *U.S. Private,* pg. 2797
MOUNTAIN VIEW TIRE & SERVICE CO; *U.S. Private,* pg. 2800
MR. WHEELS SOLUTIONS, LLC—See AutoNation, Inc.; *U.S. Public,* pg. 236
MT DRUITT AUTOBODY REPAIRS PTY LTD—See AMA Group Limited; *Int'l,* pg. 403
MTR FLEET SERVICES, LLC—See American Securities LLC; *U.S. Private,* pg. 248
MT TECHNOLOGIES GMBH—See Callista Private Equity GmbH & Co. KG; *Int'l,* pg. 1265
NATIONAL TRUCK REPAIR—See American Securities LLC; *U.S. Private,* pg. 248
NATIONWIDE ACCIDENT REPAIR SERVICES LTD.—See The Carlyle Group Inc.; *U.S. Public,* pg. 2050
NATIONWIDE NETWORK SERVICES LTD—See The Carlyle Group Inc.; *U.S. Public,* pg. 2050
NORTH TEXAS FLEET SERVICES LLC—See Merx Truck & Trailer, Inc.; *U.S. Private,* pg. 2677
O2 AUTO SERVICE MIDCO, LLC—See O2 Investment Partners, LLC; *U.S. Private,* pg. 2982
OHMATSU SERVICES CO., LTD.—See Hirayama Holdings Co., Ltd.; *Int'l,* pg. 3404
ORANGE VEHICLE SALES LLC—See Tesla, Inc.; *U.S. Public,* pg. 2021
OVERLAND INC; *U.S. Private,* pg. 3053
P.A.M. DEDICATED SERVICES, INC.—See P.A.M. Transportation Services, Inc.; *U.S. Public,* pg. 1630
PERRY'S AUTO PARTS & SERVICE; *U.S. Private,* pg. 3154
PIT-STOP AUTO SERVICE GMBH—See BLUO SICAV-SIF; *Int'l,* pg. 1075
PLANO COLLISION, INC.—See AutoNation, Inc.; *U.S. Public,* pg. 237
POWERS TRUCK AND TRAILER SALES LLC—See American Securities LLC; *U.S. Private,* pg. 248
PRECISION AUTO CARE, INC.—See Icahn Enterprises L.P.; *U.S. Public,* pg. 1085
PRECISION TUNE AUTO CARE, INC.—See Icahn Enterprises L.P.; *U.S. Public,* pg. 1085
PRIMEPOWER QUEENSLAND PTY LTD—See Babylon Pump & Power Limited; *Int'l,* pg. 793
PROGRESS RAIL SERVICES DE MEXICO S.A. DE C.V.—See Caterpillar, Inc.; *U.S. Public,* pg. 453
PRO STOP TRUCK SERVICE INC.—See Dart Transit Company; *U.S. Private,* pg. 1160
R.A. JOHNSON INC.; *U.S. Private,* pg. 3334
RAMONA AUTO SERVICES INC.; *U.S. Private,* pg. 3351
REPAIRSMITH, INC.—See AutoNation, Inc.; *U.S. Public,* pg. 237
THE ROADSTER SHOP; *U.S. Private,* pg. 4111
ROSEVILLE-C, INC.—See Lithia Motors, Inc.; *U.S. Public,* pg. 1326
RUGE'S AUTOMOTIVE; *U.S. Private,* pg. 3502
RUSH TRUCK CENTERS OF CALIFORNIA INC.—See Rush Enterprises, Inc.; *U.S. Public,* pg. 1826
RV REPAIR & SALES INC.—See Pollard Enterprises Inc.; *U.S. Private,* pg. 3224
SACRAMENTO COLLISION, INC.—See AutoNation, Inc.; *U.S. Public,* pg. 237
SOUTHEAST POWER SYSTEMS OF TAMPA—See Southeast Power Systems of Orlando, Inc.; *U.S. Private,* pg. 3726
SOUTHERN CALIFORNIA FLEET SERVICES, INC.—See Velocity Vehicle Group; *U.S. Private,* pg. 4355
SPEEDY FRANCE SAS—See Bridgestone Corporation; *Int'l,* pg. 1159
STERLING MCCALL HONDA—See Group 1 Automotive, Inc.; *U.S. Public,* pg. 972
STERLING SERVICE INC.; *U.S. Private,* pg. 3807
STEUBENVILLE TRUCK CENTER, INC.—See American Securities LLC; *U.S. Private,* pg. 248
STORK GEARS & SERVICES ASIA PTE. LTD.—See Fluor Corporation; *U.S. Public,* pg. 859
STORK TURBO BLADING B.V.—See Fluor Corporation; *U.S. Public,* pg. 860
STYLINE DIESEL SERVICE CENTER INC.—See Styline Industries Inc.; *U.S. Private,* pg. 3846
SUN DEVIL AUTO PARTS INC.—See Greenbriar Equity Group, L.P.; *U.S. Private,* pg. 1776
SUN-ELECTRIC AUSTRIA GESELLSCHAFT M.B.H—See Snap-on Incorporated; *U.S. Public,* pg. 1899
TAM TRUCK & TRAILER SERVICES LLC—See American Securities LLC; *U.S. Private,* pg. 248
TED WIENS TIRE & AUTO CENTERS; *U.S. Private,* pg. 3957
TERRY WYNTER AUTO SERVICE CENTER, INC.; *U.S. Private,* pg. 3972
THOUSAND OAKS-S, INC.—See Lithia Motors, Inc.; *U.S. Public,* pg. 1326
TK SERVICES, INC.—See Sonsray, Inc.; *U.S. Private,* pg. 3714
TRACTION—See Genuine Parts Company; *U.S. Public,* pg. 932
TRANSAFRICA MOTORS LTD.—See Honda Motor Co., Ltd.; *Int'l,* pg. 3464
TREELINE DIESEL CENTER LLC—See Legend Oil and Gas, Ltd.; *U.S. Public,* pg. 1301
TROY-CJD, LLC—See Lithia Motors, Inc.; *U.S. Public,* pg. 1326
TRUE2FORM COLLISION REPAIR CENTERS, INC.—See Boyd Group Services Inc.; *Int'l,* pg. 1125
TX-CC DALLAS, INC.—See AutoNation, Inc.; *U.S. Public,* pg. 238
TX-CC GALLERIA, INC.—See AutoNation, Inc.; *U.S. Public,* pg. 238
TX-CC SPRING, INC.—See AutoNation, Inc.; *U.S. Public,* pg. 238
U-GO STATIONS INC.—See Blink Charging Co.; *U.S. Public,* pg. 361
VALLEY AUTOMOTIVE GROUP; *U.S. Private,* pg. 4332
VAN HORN AUTOMOTIVE GROUP, INC.; *U.S. Private,* pg. 4340
THE VEHICLE CONVERTERS LLC—See Ilustrato Pictures International Inc.; *Int'l,* pg. 3617
VEHICLE DATA SERVICES LIMITED—See LKQ Corporation; *U.S. Public,* pg. 1337
VERIZON WIRELESS - FALLS CHURCH—See Verizon Communications Inc.; *U.S. Public,* pg. 2284
VZ BUTSURYU CORPORATION—See KKR & Co. Inc.; *U.S. Public,* pg. 1259
WARREN TIRE SERVICE CENTER, INC.; *U.S. Private,* pg. 4444
W.B. MCCARTNEY OIL COMPANY; *U.S. Private,* pg. 4419
WESTERN SYDNEY REPAIR CENTRE PTY LTD—See ComfortDelGro Corporation Limited; *Int'l,* pg. 1713
WESTMONT COLLISION, INC.—See AutoNation, Inc.; *U.S. Public,* pg. 238
WIDELLS BILPLAT EFTR AB—See LKQ Corporation; *U.S. Public,* pg. 1337
WPB COLLISION, INC.—See AutoNation, Inc.; *U.S. Public,* pg. 238
YOUR LOCATION LUBRICATION, LLC—See Get Spiffy, Inc.; *U.S. Private,* pg. 1688
YUBA CITY-CJD, INC.—See Lithia Motors, Inc.; *U.S. Public,* pg. 1326

811114 — SPECIALIZED AUTOMOTIVE REPAIR

AAMCO TRANSMISSIONS, INC.—See Ares Management Corporation; *U.S. Public,* pg. 187
ALLANNIC FRERES SA; *Int'l,* pg. 333
ALLIED EXHAUST SYSTEMS—See Allied Manufacturing Inc.; *U.S. Private,* pg. 186
ALPS ELECTRIC (NORTH AMERICA), INC.—See Alps Alpine Co., Ltd.; *Int'l,* pg. 376
A. RAYMOND & CIE SCS; *Int'l,* pg. 21
AUNDE ACHTER & EBELS GMBH; *Int'l,* pg. 705
AUTO CENTER SA; *Int'l,* pg. 724
AUTOSHOP SOLUTIONS INC.; *U.S. Private,* pg. 401
AUTOTEHNA A.D.; *Int'l,* pg. 732
BIZJET INTERNATIONAL SALES & SUPPORT, INC.—See Deutsche Lufthansa AG; *Int'l,* pg. 2069
BRAKES PLUS CORPORATION; *U.S. Private,* pg. 635
BRIDGEWATER CHEVROLET, INC.—See General Motors Company; *U.S. Public,* pg. 923
BROOKS MUFFLER & BRAKE CENTER; *U.S. Private,* pg. 664
CAR-O-LINER DEUTSCHLAND GMBH—See Snap-on Incorporated; *U.S. Public,* pg. 1897
CARTER THERMO KING INC.; *U.S. Private,* pg. 776
CAR-X ASSOCIATES CORP.—See Tuffy Associates Corporation; *U.S. Private,* pg. 4257
CAR-X AUTO SERVICE, INC.—See Tuffy Associates Corporation; *U.S. Private,* pg. 4257
CDTI SWEDEN AB—See CDTi Advanced Materials, Inc.; *U.S. Public,* pg. 462
CERTIFIED TRANSMISSION REBUILDERS INC.; *U.S. Private,* pg. 842
CHEVAL TECHNOLOGY CO. LTD.—See Blackstone Inc.; *U.S. Public,* pg. 354
COLEMAN-TAYLOR AUTOMATIC TRANSMISSION COMPANY, INC.; *U.S. Private,* pg. 967
COMMERCIAL TIRE INC.; *U.S. Private,* pg. 984
CORSA PERFORMANCE EXHAUSTS; *U.S. Private,* pg. 1059
COTTMAN TRANSMISSION SYSTEMS, LLC; *U.S. Private,* pg. 1063
CREWS ELECTRICAL TESTING, INC.—See Blue Sea Capital Management LLC; *U.S. Private,* pg. 592
CROSSWIND TRANSMISSION, LLC—See NRG Energy, Inc.; *U.S. Public,* pg. 1549
CUMMINS BRIDGEWAY LLC—See Cummins Inc.; *U.S. Public,* pg. 605
DAIDO REBUILD SERVICES INC.—See Daido Metal Corporation; *Int'l,* pg. 1921
DALLAS MECHANICAL GROUP, LLC—See EMCOR Group, Inc.; *U.S. Public,* pg. 736
DANCO TRANSMISSION; *U.S. Private,* pg. 1153
DAU DRAXLMAIER AUTOMOTIVE UK LTD.—See Draxlmaier Gruppe; *Int'l,* pg. 2198
DINARA SERVIS AD; *Int'l,* pg. 2127
DIXIE ELECTRIC LTD.—See Motorcar Parts of America, Inc.; *U.S. Public,* pg. 1477
DURAND SERVICES; *Int'l,* pg. 2228
EAGLEBURGMANN (WUXI) CO. LTD.—See Freudenberg SE; *Int'l,* pg. 2783
El AUTOSERVIS A.D.; *Int'l,* pg. 2328
ENERGOREMONT BOBOV DOL EAD—See Dietsmann N.V.; *Int'l,* pg. 2117
FIRST VEHICLE SERVICES—See FirstGroup plc; *Int'l,* pg. 2689
FLUIDDRIVE HOLDINGS PTY LTD—See AMA Group Limited; *Int'l,* pg. 403
FOX VALLEY BUICK-GMC, INC.—See General Motors Company; *U.S. Public,* pg. 924
FRIMO INC.—See Deutsche Beteiligungs AG; *Int'l,* pg. 2062
GENERAL MOTORS ASIA PACIFIC (PTE) LTD.—See General Motors Company; *U.S. Public,* pg. 924
GENERAL MOTORS GLOBAL SERVICE OPERATIONS, INC.—See General Motors Company; *U.S. Public,* pg. 925
GLOBAL PERFORMANCE; *U.S. Private,* pg. 1716
HAMPSON PRECISION AUTOMOTIVE (INDIA) PRIVATE LIMITED—See Hampson Industries PLC; *Int'l,* pg. 3239
HANG XANH MOTORS SERVICE JOINT STOCK COMPANY; *Int'l,* pg. 3245
HUSKY SPRING; *U.S. Private,* pg. 2014
ING SOLUTIONS LLC; *U.S. Private,* pg. 2075
JIANGSU FUJITSU TELECOMMUNICATIONS TECHNOLOGY CO., LTD.—See Fujitsu Limited; *Int'l,* pg. 2835
MAGNETECH INDUSTRIAL SERVICES, INC.—See IES Holdings, Inc.; *U.S. Public,* pg. 1094
MANHEIM PITTSBURGH—See Cox Enterprises, Inc.; *U.S. Private,* pg. 1077
MARLAND CLUTCH PRODUCTS—See Regal Rexnord Corporation; *U.S. Public,* pg. 1772
MARTIN AUTOMOTIVE, INC.—See General Motors Company; *U.S. Public,* pg. 926
MAX AUTO SUPPLY CO.; *U.S. Private,* pg. 2617
MICHIGAN TRAILER SERVICE INC.—See Trudell Trailers of Grand Rapids, Inc.; *U.S. Private,* pg. 4247
MIDAS AUTO SYSTEMS EXPERTS INC.; *U.S. Private,* pg. 2710
MIDWAY TRAILERS, INC.; *U.S. Private,* pg. 2719
MISSOURI GREAT DANE—See Midway Trailers, Inc.; *U.S. Private,* pg. 2719
MONRO SERVICE CORPORATION—See Monro, Inc.; *U.S. Public,* pg. 1465
MONSTER TRANSMISSION & PERFORMANCE; *U.S. Private,* pg. 2774
M.T.I . SAS—See Figeac-Aero SA; *Int'l,* pg. 2660
NORTHCUTT INC.; *U.S. Private,* pg. 2949
NORTHWEST FUEL INJECTION SERVICE, INC.; *U.S. Private,* pg. 2960
NORTHWEST FUEL INJECTION SERVICE OF INDIANA, L.L.C.—See Northwest Fuel Injection Service, Inc.; *U.S. Private,* pg. 2960
NORTHWEST FUEL INJECTION SERVICE OF MICHIGAN, LLC—See Northwest Fuel Injection Service, Inc.; *U.S. Private,* pg. 2960
PALMER JOHNSON ENTERPRISES, INC.; *U.S. Private,* pg. 3081
PALMER JOHNSON POWER SYSTEMS LLC—See Palmer Johnson Enterprises, Inc.; *U.S. Private,* pg. 3081
PETERSON SPRING-COMMONWEALTH PLANT—See MiddleGround Management, LP; *U.S. Private,* pg. 2712
PEVETO COMPANIES LTD.; *U.S. Private,* pg. 3163
RAC LTD.—See The Carlyle Group Inc.; *U.S. Public,* pg. 2052
REPAIR CENTER, LLC; *U.S. Private,* pg. 3400
RING & PINION SERVICE INC.—See Linsalata Capital Partners, Inc.; *U.S. Private,* pg. 2463
ROADCLIPPER ENTERPRISES INC.; *U.S. Private,* pg. 3453
SAFE AIR AUSTRALIA PTY LIMITED—See Airbus SE; *Int'l,* pg. 247
SEMI SERVICE, INC.—See J.B. Poindexter & Co., Inc.; *U.S. Private,* pg. 2159
SENECA CORPORATION; *U.S. Private,* pg. 3606
SESCO ELECTRICAL SERVICES GROUP; *U.S. Private,* pg. 3617
SMOG 'N GO, LLC; *U.S. Private,* pg. 3698
SNAP-ON EQUIPMENT LTD.—See Snap-on Incorporated; *U.S. Public,* pg. 1898
SNOW-NABSTEDT POWER TRANSMISSIONS—See Allard Nazarian Group Inc.; *U.S. Private,* pg. 175
SPANISH POWER, S.L.—See Banco de Sabadell, S.A.; *Int'l,* pg. 821
SPEED-O-TACH, INC.; *U.S. Private,* pg. 3753
TECHNI-CAR INC.; *U.S. Private,* pg. 3953
THE THOMPSON COMPANY; *U.S. Private,* pg. 4126
TRI-STAR SEMI TRUCK & TRAILER SERVICES, LLC; *U.S. Private,* pg. 4223
TWIN CITY TRAILER SALES & SERVICE, INC.; *U.S. Private,* pg. 4265
U-PULL U-SAVE AUTO PARTS—See Stellex Capital Management LP; *U.S. Private,* pg. 3800
VCE MONTAZE, A.S.—See CEZ, a.s.; *Int'l,* pg. 1429

N.A.I.C.S. INDEX

811192 — CAR WASHES

WESMOR CRYOGENIC LLC—See Trinity Industries, Inc.; *U.S. Public*, pg. 2194
YUNCHENG BAOZEN AUTOMOBILE SALES AND SERVICES CO., LTD.—See China Yongda Automobiles Services Holdings Limited; *Int'l*, pg. 1565
ZAPADOCESKA ENERGETIKA, A.S.—See CEZ, a.s.; *Int'l*, pg. 1429

811121 — AUTOMOTIVE BODY, PAINT, AND INTERIOR REPAIR AND MAINTENANCE

3 D BODY WORKS, INC.; *U.S. Private*, pg. 7
3M AUTOMOTIVE AFTERMARKET DIVISION—See 3M Company; *U.S. Public*, pg. 5
ABRA AUTOMOTIVE SYSTEMS LP—See Hellman & Friedman LLC; *U.S. Private*, pg. 1907
ACS CARSTAR; *U.S. Private*, pg. 66
AUTOPLEX BMW—See Autoplex Automotive LP; *U.S. Private*, pg. 401
BARNSCO FLEET MAINTENANCE, INC.—See Kodiak Building Partners LLC; *U.S. Private*, pg. 2336
BILLION CC, INC.—See Billion Motors, Inc.; *U.S. Private*, pg. 559
B & M PAINTING CO., INC.—See ATL Partners, LLC; *U.S. Private*, pg. 369
B & M PAINTING CO., INC.—See British Columbia Investment Management Corp.; *Int'l*, pg. 1170
BRANDYWINE COACH WORKS, INC.—See Susquehanna International Group, LLP; *U.S. Private*, pg. 3885
BULLWELL TRAILER SOLUTIONS LIMITED—See Ryder System, Inc.; *U.S. Public*, pg. 1828
CALIBER BODYWORKS OF TEXAS, INC.—See Hellman & Friedman LLC; *U.S. Private*, pg. 1907
CAPITOL BODY SHOP INC.; *U.S. Private*, pg. 743
CARS COLLISION CENTER, LLC—See Boyd Group Services Inc.; *Int'l*, pg. 1125
CARSTAR FRANCHISE SYSTEMS, INC.—See Roark Capital Group Inc.; *U.S. Private*, pg. 3454
CASA AUTOPLEX—See Casa Auto Group; *U.S. Private*, pg. 777
CCRO, LLC—See Susquehanna International Group, LLP; *U.S. Private*, pg. 3885
CENTRAL AUTO BODY REBUILDERS, INC.; *U.S. Private*, pg. 818
CLARKSTOWN INTERNATIONAL COLLISION, INC.; *U.S. Private*, pg. 915
COLLEX COLLISION EXPERTS, INC.—See Boyd Group Services Inc.; *Int'l*, pg. 1124
COLLISIONMAX OF CINNAMINSON—See CSI Holdings Inc.; *U.S. Private*, pg. 1117
COLLISION REVISION 13081 INC.—See Collision Revision, Inc.; *U.S. Private*, pg. 969
COLLISION REVISION, INC.; *U.S. Private*, pg. 969
COLLISION SERVICES INTERNATIONAL INC.—See CSI Holdings Inc.; *U.S. Private*, pg. 1117
COLLISION WORKS, INC.; *U.S. Private*, pg. 969
CONTROLAUTO - CONTROLO TECNICO AUTOMOVEL, S.A.—See APG Asset Management NV; *Int'l*, pg. 512
COOK'S COLLISION; *U.S. Private*, pg. 1038
DENT WIZARD GMBH—See Gridiron Capital, LLC; *U.S. Private*, pg. 1786
DENT WIZARD INTERNATIONAL CORP.—See Gridiron Capital, LLC; *U.S. Private*, pg. 1786
D.T. CARSON ENTERPRISES INC.; *U.S. Private*, pg. 1142
DURR SYSTEMS S.A.S.—See Durr AG; *Int'l*, pg. 2231
EAST COAST FLEET SERVICE CORPORATION—See CSI Holdings Inc.; *U.S. Private*, pg. 1117
EBRAHIM K. KANOO COMPANY B.S.C - AUTO PAINT DIVISION—See Ebrahim K. Kanoo Company B.S.C.; *Int'l*, pg. 2286
EQUIPEMENTS PIERRE CHAMPIGNY LTEE; *Int'l*, pg. 2485
EUROMASTER GMBH—See Compagnie Generale des Etablissements Michelin SCA; *Int'l*, pg. 1742
FAIRWAY AUTO BODY REPAIR—See Fairway Ford, Inc.; *U.S. Private*, pg. 1465
FIRST AND TEN INC.—See CSI Holdings Inc.; *U.S. Private*, pg. 1117
FOREST RIVER INC.—See Berkshire Hathaway Inc.; *U.S. Public*, pg. 305
GAMBOAS BODY & FRAME INC.; *U.S. Private*, pg. 1640
GERBER COLLISION & GLASS - DENVER—See Boyd Group Services Inc.; *Int'l*, pg. 1125
GKN DRIVELINE SERVICE LTD—See GKN plc; *Int'l*, pg. 2984
GLASER'S COLLISION CENTER; *U.S. Private*, pg. 1706
HENDERSON COLLISION, INC.—See AutoNation, Inc.; *U.S. Public*, pg. 235
HOLMES BODY SHOP INC.; *U.S. Private*, pg. 1967
H&V COLLISION CENTER - CLIFTON PARK—See H&V Collision Center; *U.S. Private*, pg. 1824
HYDUKE ENERGY SERVICES INC. - BIG RIG SANDBLASTING, PAINTING AND REPAIR DIVISION—See Hyduke Energy Services Inc.; *Int'l*, pg. 3548
IDENS DETAILING INC—See Pacific Northwest Capital Corp.; *U.S. Private*, pg. 3069
JX GRAPHICS—See JX Enterprises Inc.; *U.S. Private*, pg. 2247
KANAZU MFG. CO., LTD.—See Hitachi Astemo, Ltd.; *Int'l*, pg. 3408
KEIHIN CORPORATION - SAYAMA PLANT—See Hitachi Astemo, Ltd.; *Int'l*, pg. 3409
KEIHIN CORPORATION - SUZUKA PLANT—See Hitachi Astemo, Ltd.; *Int'l*, pg. 3409
KEIHIN SOGYO CO., LTD.—See Hitachi Astemo, Ltd.; *Int'l*, pg. 3409
LDV INC.; *U.S. Private*, pg. 2404
LEAR CORPORATION SWEDEN AB—See Lear Corporation; *U.S. Public*, pg. 1297
LLC JV O'ZAUTO-AUSTEM—See Austem Co., Ltd.; *Int'l*, pg. 717
LUFTHANSA TECHNIK TURBINE SHANNON LIMITED—See Deutsche Lufthansa AG; *Int'l*, pg. 2070
MAGNUSSEN'S CAR WEST AUTO BODY; *U.S. Private*, pg. 2549
MAG SPECIALTY VEHICLES—See Mid Western Automotive LLC; *U.S. Private*, pg. 2707
MARCO'S AUTO BODY, INC.—See Blackstone Inc.; *U.S. Public*, pg. 356
NALLEY COLLISION CENTER - ROSWELL BODY SHOP—See Asbury Automotive Group, Inc.; *U.S. Public*, pg. 210
NEVADA CLASSICS, INC.; *U.S. Private*, pg. 2891
NU-LOOK COLLISION, INC.—See Boyd Group Services Inc.; *Int'l*, pg. 1125
OLDHAM COLLISION CENTER—See Glaser's Collision Center; *U.S. Private*, pg. 1706
PACIFIC AUTO BODY; *U.S. Private*, pg. 3065
PARAMOUNT CENTRE, INC.—See Susquehanna International Group, LLP; *U.S. Private*, pg. 3885
PPG COATINGS (SUZHOU) COMPANY LTD.—See PPG Industries, Inc.; *U.S. Public*, pg. 1708
PPG MEXICO, S.A. DE C.V.—See PPG Industries, Inc.; *U.S. Public*, pg. 1709
RAINES IMPORTS, INC.; *U.S. Private*, pg. 3347
RED MOUNTAIN COLLISION—See Boyd Group Services Inc.; *Int'l*, pg. 1124
RIDE-AWAY HANDICAP EQUIPMENT; *U.S. Private*, pg. 3432
RIFLED AIR CONDITIONING—See The Matthews Group Inc.; *U.S. Private*, pg. 4076
RUDY LUTHERS HOPKINS HONDA—See Luther Holding Company; *U.S. Private*, pg. 2517
SALINAS VALLEY FORD; *U.S. Private*, pg. 3532
SCHAEFER AUTOBODY CENTERS—See Susquehanna International Group, LLP; *U.S. Private*, pg. 3886
SERVICE KING PAINT & BODY, LLC—See Blackstone Inc.; *U.S. Public*, pg. 357
SHINHANG DURR INC.—See Durr AG; *Int'l*, pg. 2233
SPECTRUM VERF B.V.—See LKQ Corporation; *U.S. Public*, pg. 1336
STOOPS AUTOMOTIVE GROUP, INC.; *U.S. Private*, pg. 3830
SUN AUTO TIRE & SERVICE, INC.—See Greenbriar Equity Group, L.P.; *U.S. Private*, pg. 1776
SYNERGIS TECHNOLOGIES GROUP; *U.S. Private*, pg. 3903
TOTAL CAR FRANCHISING CORP.; *U.S. Private*, pg. 4190
TREW AUTO BODY, INC.—See Susquehanna International Group, LLP; *U.S. Private*, pg. 3886
TRITEX CORPORATION—See AMETEK, Inc.; *U.S. Public*, pg. 122
TRUE2FORM COLLISION REPAIR CENTERS, LLC—See Boyd Group Services Inc.; *Int'l*, pg. 1125
TUFFY ASSOCIATES CORPORATION; *U.S. Private*, pg. 4257
UAG FAIRFIELD CM, LLC—See Penske Automotive Group, Inc.; *U.S. Public*, pg. 1666
VERIND S.P.A.—See Durr AG; *Int'l*, pg. 2233
ZAK PRODUCTS INC.; *U.S. Private*, pg. 4597

811122 — AUTOMOTIVE GLASS REPLACEMENT SHOPS

AGC AUTOMOTIVE PHILIPPINES INC.—See AGC Inc.; *Int'l*, pg. 201
ALL STAR GLASS CO. INC.; *U.S. Private*, pg. 172
AUTO GLASS SERVICE LLC.; *U.S. Private*, pg. 397
BINSWANGER ENTERPRISES, LLC—See Wingate Partners, LLP; *U.S. Private*, pg. 4541
CARGLASS YAMATO CO.,LTD.—See AGC Inc.; *Int'l*, pg. 204
CASCADE AUTOGLASS INCORPORATED; *U.S. Private*, pg. 778
CENTRAL SAINT-GOBAIN CO., LTD.—See Central Glass Co., Ltd.; *Int'l*, pg. 1407
CENTRAL SAINT-GOBAIN CO., LTD.—See Compagnie de Saint-Gobain SA; *Int'l*, pg. 1722
COOPER GLASS COMPANY, LLC—See TopBuild Corp.; *U.S. Public*, pg. 2163
DIVERSIFIED GLASS SERVICES; *U.S. Private*, pg. 1242
GLASS AMERICA, INC.—See Boyd Group Services Inc.; *Int'l*, pg. 1125
THE J.N. PHILLIPS GLASS CO. INC.; *U.S. Private*, pg. 4058
K & K GLASS, INC.—See Driven Brands Holdings Inc.; *U.S. Public*, pg. 688
MIKE'S AUTO GLASS INC.; *U.S. Private*, pg. 2726
PGW AUTO GLASS, LLC—See OEP Capital Advisors, L.P.; *U.S. Private*, pg. 2999
PROTEX CANADA INC.—See XPEL, Inc.; *U.S. Public*, pg. 2391
SYNERGISTIC INTERNATIONAL LLC—See Harvest Partners L.P.; *U.S. Private*, pg. 1877
TECHNA GLASS, INC.; *U.S. Private*, pg. 3953
WHALLEY GLASS CO., INC.; *U.S. Private*, pg. 4503

811191 — AUTOMOTIVE OIL CHANGE AND LUBRICATION SHOPS

AMERICAN LUBEFAST LLC—See MidOcean Partners, LLP; *U.S. Private*, pg. 2716
CAROLINA LUBES INC.—See Lucor, Inc.; *U.S. Private*, pg. 2512
CENLUB INDUSTRIES LTD.; *Int'l*, pg. 1401
DHR FINLAND OY—See Danaher Corporation; *U.S. Public*, pg. 625
EBRAHIM K. KANOO COMPANY B.S.C - OILS & LUBRICANTS DIVISION—See Ebrahim K. Kanoo Company B.S.C.; *Int'l*, pg. 2286
EXPRESS OIL CHANGE LLC—See Golden Gate Capital Management II, LLC; *U.S. Private*, pg. 1731
GAGAN GASES LTD.; *Int'l*, pg. 2868
GALENA ASSOCIATES, LLC; *U.S. Private*, pg. 1637
GREASE MONKEY INTERNATIONAL, LLC—See MidOcean Partners, LLP; *U.S. Private*, pg. 2716
GULF OIL LUBRICANTS INDIA LIMITED—See Hinduja Group Ltd.; *Int'l*, pg. 3399
HENLEY ENTERPRISES, INC.; *U.S. Private*, pg. 1916
LUBE MANAGEMENT CORPORATION—See Greenbriar Equity Group, L.P.; *U.S. Private*, pg. 1776
THE LUBE STOP, INC.—See Argonne Capital Group, LLC; *U.S. Private*, pg. 321
LUCOR, INC.; *U.S. Private*, pg. 2511
MOLUB-ALLOY AB—See Aspo Oyj; *Int'l*, pg. 631
OIL CHANGER INC.—See Greenbriar Equity Group, L.P.; *U.S. Private*, pg. 1776
OILWELL INC.; *U.S. Private*, pg. 3006
PEPPER TREE INC.; *U.S. Private*, pg. 3144
RELADYNE LLC—See AIP, LLC; *U.S. Private*, pg. 135
SILICONE SPECIALTIES, INC.; *U.S. Private*, pg. 3652
SOUTH LUBES INC.; *U.S. Private*, pg. 3723
SPEEDCO INC.—See Love's Travel Stops & Country Stores, Inc.; *U.S. Private*, pg. 2501
SPEED LUBE LLC; *U.S. Private*, pg. 3753
TAKE 5 OIL CHANGE, LLC—See Roark Capital Group Inc.; *U.S. Private*, pg. 3454
TOYOTA BOSHOKU FILTRATION SYSTEM (THAILAND) CO., LTD.—See Denso Corporation; *Int'l*, pg. 2033
VALVOLINE LLC—See Valvoline Inc.; *U.S. Public*, pg. 2274

811192 — CAR WASHES

4 SEASONS CAR WASH—See Splash Car Wash, Inc.; *U.S. Private*, pg. 3759
AP FORMULATORS—See Highlander Partners, LP.; *U.S. Private*, pg. 1939
BAIRD BROTHERS EXPRESS CAR WASH—See Roark Capital Group Inc.; *U.S. Private*, pg. 3454
BLUE BEACON INTERNATIONAL, INC.; *U.S. Private*, pg. 585
CARAMBA BREMEN GMBH—See Berner SE; *Int'l*, pg. 988
CARAMBA NEDERLANDS B.V.—See Berner SE; *Int'l*, pg. 988
CARNETT'S MANAGEMENT COMPANY; *U.S. Private*, pg. 766
CAR WASH EXPRESS—See Car Wash Partners, Inc.; *U.S. Private*, pg. 747
CAR WASH PARTNERS, INC.; *U.S. Private*, pg. 747
DISCOUNT CAR WASH INC.; *U.S. Private*, pg. 1237
ELRING KLINGER MOTORTECHNIK GMBH—See ElringKlinger AG; *Int'l*, pg. 2369
FLEETWASH, INC.—See ACON Investments, LLC; *U.S. Private*, pg. 62
GET SPIFFY, INC.; *U.S. Private*, pg. 1688
HALLIM MACHINERY CO., LTD.—See Daifuku Co., Ltd.; *Int'l*, pg. 1926
IMO AUTOPFLEGE GMBH—See Roark Capital Group Inc.; *U.S. Private*, pg. 3455
IMO CAR WASH GROUP LTD.—See Roark Capital Group Inc.; *U.S. Private*, pg. 3455
IMO LAVAGE—See Roark Capital Group Inc.; *U.S. Private*, pg. 3455
JERRY'S EXPRESS CARWASH—See Whitewater Express, Inc.; *U.S. Private*, pg. 4512
KRYSTAL KLEAN USA INC.—See ACON Investments, LLC; *U.S. Private*, pg. 62
LARK AVE CAR WASH CORPORATION; *U.S. Private*, pg. 2392
MAMMOTH HOLDINGS, LLC—See Red Dog Equity LLC; *U.S. Private*, pg. 3374

811192 — CAR WASHES

MARC1 CARWASH—See Red Dog Equity LLC; *U.S. Private*, pg. 3374
MISTER CAR WASH, INC.; *U.S. Public*, pg. 1450
MISTER CAR WASH—See Car Wash Partners, Inc.; *U.S. Private*, pg. 747
MISTER CAR WASH—See Car Wash Partners, Inc.; *U.S. Private*, pg. 748
MR. MAGIC CAR WASH INC.—See Incline MGMT Corp.; *U.S. Private*, pg. 2053
NEW WAVE INDUSTRIES, LTD.—See New Mountain Capital, LLC; *U.S. Private*, pg. 2904
REV CAR WASH, LLC—See WhiteWater Holding Company, LLC; *U.S. Private*, pg. 4512
ROUTE 12 WASH 'N' GAS INC.; *U.S. Private*, pg. 3489
SPLASH CAR WASH, INC.; *U.S. Private*, pg. 3759
SUPERSONIC CAR WASH INC.; *U.S. Private*, pg. 3881
SUPERSONIC CAR WASH—See Supersonic Car Wash Inc.; *U.S. Private*, pg. 3881
TRIANGLE CAR WASH INC.; *U.S. Private*, pg. 4226
TRUCKOMAT CORPORATION—See Iowa 80 Group, Inc.; *U.S. Private*, pg. 2134
WASH DEPOT HOLDINGS, INC.; *U.S. Private*, pg. 4445
WASH ME FAST, LLC—See Red Dog Equity LLC; *U.S. Private*, pg. 3374
THE WASH TUB; *U.S. Private*, pg. 4133
WHITEWATER HOLDING COMPANY, LLC; *U.S. Private*, pg. 4512
WIGGY WASH, LLC—See Red Dog Equity LLC; *U.S. Private*, pg. 3374

811198 — ALL OTHER AUTOMOTIVE REPAIR AND MAINTENANCE

AAPICO HITECH PARTS CO., LTD—See AAPICO Hitech plc; *Int'l*, pg. 37
ABT SPORTSLINE GMBH; *Int'l*, pg. 70
ACCIDENT EXCHANGE GROUP PLC; *Int'l*, pg. 90
ACTIVE AERO MOTOR CARRIER, LLC—See Roadrunner Transportation Systems, Inc.; *U.S. Public*, pg. 1802
ACTIVE AERO SERVICES, LLC—See Roadrunner Transportation Systems, Inc.; *U.S. Public*, pg. 1802
ADROIT INSPECTION SERVICES PRIVATE LIMITED—See CarTrade Tech Ltd.; *Int'l*, pg. 1348
ADTRANS AUSTRALIA PTY LTD—See Eagers Automotive Limited; *Int'l*, pg. 2263
ADTRANS TRUCKS PTY LTD—See Eagers Automotive Limited; *Int'l*, pg. 2263
AERO MAINTENANCE GROUP LLC—See Air France-KLM S.A.; *Int'l*, pg. 236
AEROMARITIME AMERICA INC.—See Bain Capital, LP; *U.S. Private*, pg. 433
AIDA ENGINEERING DE MEXICO, S. DE R. L. DE C.V.—See AIDA Engineering, Ltd.; *Int'l*, pg. 230
AISIN MAINTENANCE CO., LTD.—See AISIN Corporation; *Int'l*, pg. 252
AKATSUKI EAZIMA CO., LTD.; *Int'l*, pg. 260
ALLOY WHEEL REPAIR SPECIALIST, INC.—See Soundcore Capital Partners, LLC; *U.S. Private*, pg. 3717
AMERICAN SUNROOF CORPORATION; *U.S. Private*, pg. 256
ANSA AUTOMOTIVE LIMITED—See ANSA McAL Limited; *Int'l*, pg. 477
APPLUS ARGENTINA, S.A.—See I Squared Capital Advisors (US) LLC; *U.S. Private*, pg. 2021
APPLUS CAR TESTING SERVICE, LTD.—See I Squared Capital Advisors (US) LLC; *U.S. Private*, pg. 2021
APPLUS CHILE, S.A.—See I Squared Capital Advisors (US) LLC; *U.S. Private*, pg. 2021
APPLUS DANMARK, A/S—See I Squared Capital Advisors (US) LLC; *U.S. Private*, pg. 2021
APPLUS INDIA PRIVATE LIMITED—See I Squared Capital Advisors (US) LLC; *U.S. Private*, pg. 2021
APPLUS INGENIERIA Y CONSULTORIA, SAS—See I Squared Capital Advisors (US) LLC; *U.S. Private*, pg. 2021
APPLUS ITEUVE GALICIA, S.L.U.—See I Squared Capital Advisors (US) LLC; *U.S. Private*, pg. 2021
APPLUS JAPAN KK.—See I Squared Capital Advisors (US) LLC; *U.S. Private*, pg. 2022
APPLUS KAZAKHSTAN LLC—See I Squared Capital Advisors (US) LLC; *U.S. Private*, pg. 2022
APPLUS MEXICO, S.A. DE C.V.—See I Squared Capital Advisors (US) LLC; *U.S. Private*, pg. 2022
APPLUS MONGOLIA, LLC—See I Squared Capital Advisors (US) LLC; *U.S. Private*, pg. 2022
APPLUS NORCONTROL GUATEMALA, S.A.—See I Squared Capital Advisors (US) LLC; *U.S. Private*, pg. 2022
APPLUS PANAMA, S.A.—See I Squared Capital Advisors (US) LLC; *U.S. Private*, pg. 2022
APPLUS PNG LIMITED—See I Squared Capital Advisors (US) LLC; *U.S. Private*, pg. 2022
APPLUS RTD DEUTSCHLAND INSPEKTIONSGESELL-SCHAFT, GMBH—See I Squared Capital Advisors (US) LLC; *U.S. Private*, pg. 2022
APPLUS RTD PTE, LTD.—See I Squared Capital Advisors (US) LLC; *U.S. Private*, pg. 2022

APPLUS RTD USA, INC.—See I Squared Capital Advisors (US) LLC; *U.S. Private*, pg. 2022
APPLUS TURKEY GOZETIM HIZMETLERI LIMITED SIRKETI—See I Squared Capital Advisors (US) LLC; *U.S. Private*, pg. 2022
APPLUS URUGUAY, S.A.—See I Squared Capital Advisors (US) LLC; *U.S. Private*, pg. 2022
APPLUS VELOSI SA (PTY) LTD.—See I Squared Capital Advisors (US) LLC; *U.S. Private*, pg. 2022
ARNOTT, INC.—See MidOcean Partners, LLP; *U.S. Private*, pg. 2716
ASSURANT FRANCE—See Assurant, Inc.; *U.S. Public*, pg. 215
ASSURED QUALITY TESTING SERVICES, LLC—See LKQ Corporation; *U.S. Public*, pg. 1333
ATS EUROMASTER LIMITED—See Compagnie Generale des Etablissements Michelin SCA; *Int'l*, pg. 1741
AUDATEX POLSKA SP. Z.O.O.—See Vista Equity Partners, LLC; *U.S. Private*, pg. 4400
AUSTRIAN AIRLINES TECHNIK-BRATISLAVA, S.R.O.—See Deutsche Lufthansa AG; *Int'l*, pg. 2066
AUTOBACS VENTURE SINGAPORE PTE. LTD.—See Autobacs Seven Co., Ltd.; *Int'l*, pg. 726
AUTOCLIK BY ACG COMPANY LIMITED—See Autocorp Holding Public Company Limited; *Int'l*, pg. 726
AUTOGATOR, INC.; *U.S. Private*, pg. 398
AUTOKUCA RAKETA AD; *Int'l*, pg. 727
AUTOLIV ELECTRONICS, PONTOISE—See Autoliv, Inc.; *Int'l*, pg. 728
AUTOMOTIVE CONCEPTS OF NORTH AMERICA; *U.S. Private*, pg. 400
AUTOMOTIVE TESTING AND DEVELOPMENT SERVICES, INC.; *U.S. Private*, pg. 401
AUTOPARTES WALKER, S. DE R.L. DE C.V—See Apollo Global Management, Inc.; *U.S. Public*, pg. 163
AUTO RECYCLERS LLC; *U.S. Private*, pg. 397
AUTOTEST-TOUR S.R.O.—See DEKRA e.V.; *Int'l*, pg. 2007
AUTO WAREHOUSING COMPANY; *U.S. Private*, pg. 397
AUTOWORKS MARKHAM, LP—See Lithia Motors, Inc.; *U.S. Public*, pg. 1321
AWQUIS JAPAN CO., LTD...—See AISIN Corporation; *Int'l*, pg. 253
BACS BOOTS CO., LTD.—See Autobacs Seven Co., Ltd.; *Int'l*, pg. 726
BAGHDAD MOTOR CARS SERVICING CO.; *Int'l*, pg. 799
BEAUTECH POWER SYSTEMS, LLC; *U.S. Private*, pg. 508
BELHASA AUTOMOTIVE SERVICE CENTER & SPARE PARTS—See Belhasa Group of Companies; *Int'l*, pg. 963
BENZ CONNECTION OF NAPLES INC.; *U.S. Private*, pg. 529
BLACK FOREST INDUSTRIES; *U.S. Private*, pg. 572
BOB HOWARD AUTOMOTIVE-EAST, INC.—See Group 1 Automotive, Inc.; *U.S. Public*, pg. 971
BOLS MOTOREN B.V.—See LKQ Corporation; *U.S. Public*, pg. 1334
BOLTON OIL CO. LTD; *U.S. Private*, pg. 611
THE BOYD GROUP INC.—See Boyd Group Services Inc.; *Int'l*, pg. 1124
BRUNN GMBH—See LKQ Corporation; *U.S. Public*, pg. 1334
B&T EXACT GMBH; *Int'l*, pg. 784
BUSINESS ELECTRONICS SOLDERING TECHNOLOGIES; *U.S. Private*, pg. 694
BYSTRONIC DO BRASIL LTDA—See Bystronic AG; *Int'l*, pg. 1236
CANADA POWER TECHNOLOGY LIMITED; *Int'l*, pg. 1282
CARCARE COLLISION CENTERS, INC.; *U.S. Private*, pg. 748
CAR-O-LINER GROUP AB—See Snap-on Incorporated; *U.S. Public*, pg. 1897
CARTAGZ INC.; *U.S. Private*, pg. 775
CERTIFIED AUTOMOTIVE PARTS ASSOCIATION; *U.S. Private*, pg. 841
CHU KAI PUBLIC COMPANY LIMITED; *Int'l*, pg. 1589
CLIFF WALL AUTOMOTIVE LLC—See Bergstrom Corp.; *U.S. Public*, pg. 531
COMPETENT AUTOMOBILES CO. LTD.; *Int'l*, pg. 1753
COSWORTH RACING INC.—See Ford Motor Company; *U.S. Public*, pg. 864
CRMA SARL—See Air France-KLM S.A.; *Int'l*, pg. 237
CURRENT TECH CENTER CO., LTD.—See Current Motor Corporation; *Int'l*, pg. 1879
DALES TIRE & RETREADING INC.; *U.S. Private*, pg. 1149
DCM TOOLS NV—See LKQ Corporation; *U.S. Public*, pg. 1334
DEFTECH UNMANNED SYSTEMS SDN. BHD.—See DRB-HICOM Berhad; *Int'l*, pg. 2201
DEKRA AMERICA, INC.—See DEKRA e.V.; *Int'l*, pg. 2008
DEKRA AUTOMOTIVE LTD.—See DEKRA e.V.; *Int'l*, pg. 2006
DEKRA AUTOMOTIVE PTY. LTD.—See DEKRA e.V.; *Int'l*, pg. 2006
DEKRA AUTOMOTIVE S.A R.L.—See DEKRA e.V.; *Int'l*, pg. 2006
DEKRA AUTOMOTIVE SOLUTIONS ITALY S.R.L.—See DEKRA e.V.; *Int'l*, pg. 2007
DEKRA CANADA INC.—See DEKRA e.V.; *Int'l*, pg. 2007

CORPORATE AFFILIATIONS

DEKRA CARIBBEAN B.V.—See DEKRA e.V.; *Int'l*, pg. 2007
DEKRA EXPERT LTD—See DEKRA e.V.; *Int'l*, pg. 2009
DEKRA FYN APS—See DEKRA e.V.; *Int'l*, pg. 2006
DEKRA (INDIA) PVT. LTD.—See DEKRA e.V.; *Int'l*, pg. 2006
DEKRA INDUSTRIAL (GUANGZHOU) CO., LTD.—See DEKRA e.V.; *Int'l*, pg. 2006
DEKRA INDUSTRIAL OY—See DEKRA e.V.; *Int'l*, pg. 2008
DEKRA INDUSTRIAL RSA.—See DEKRA e.V.; *Int'l*, pg. 2009
DEKRA INSPECOES PORTUGAL - UNIPESSOAL LDA—See DEKRA e.V.; *Int'l*, pg. 2006
DEKRA IST RELIABILITY SERVICES INC.—See DEKRA e.V.; *Int'l*, pg. 2010
DEKRA IST RELIABILITY SERVICES LIMITED—See DEKRA e.V.; *Int'l*, pg. 2010
DEKRA MIDDLE EAST FZE—See DEKRA e.V.; *Int'l*, pg. 2006
DEKRA NORDJYLLAND A/S—See DEKRA e.V.; *Int'l*, pg. 2006
DEKRA ORGANISATIONAL RELIABILITY LTD.—See DEKRA e.V.; *Int'l*, pg. 2006
DEKRA QUALITY MANAGEMENT AB—See DEKRA e.V.; *Int'l*, pg. 2006
DEKRA RAIL B.V.—See DEKRA e.V.; *Int'l*, pg. 2006
DEKRA SLOVENSKO S.R.O.—See DEKRA e.V.; *Int'l*, pg. 2010
DEKRA TEST CENTER S.A.—See DEKRA e.V.; *Int'l*, pg. 2009
DEKRA TESTING & CERTIFICATION CO., LTD.—See DEKRA e.V.; *Int'l*, pg. 2010
DEKRA TESTING & CERTIFICATION LTDA.—See DEKRA e.V.; *Int'l*, pg. 2010
DEKRA TESTING & CERTIFICATION, S.A.U—See DEKRA e.V.; *Int'l*, pg. 2010
DEKRA TESTING & CERTIFICATION (SHANGHAI) LTD.—See DEKRA e.V.; *Int'l*, pg. 2010
DEKRA TESTING & CERTIFICATION (SUZHOU) CO., LTD.—See DEKRA e.V.; *Int'l*, pg. 2010
DEKRA UK LTD.—See DEKRA e.V.; *Int'l*, pg. 2010
DELEHANTY FORD INC.—See LaFontaine Automotive Group, LLC; *U.S. Private*, pg. 2373
DENSO HOKKAIDO CORPORATION—See Denso Corporation; *Int'l*, pg. 2029
DENSO KANSAI CORPORATION—See Denso Corporation; *Int'l*, pg. 2029
DENSO KYUSHU CORPORATION—See Denso Corporation; *Int'l*, pg. 2029
DENSO SERVICE NISHISAITAMA CO., LTD.—See Denso Corporation; *Int'l*, pg. 2030
DENSO SERVICE OKINAWA CO., LTD.—See Denso Corporation; *Int'l*, pg. 2030
DENSO TOHOKU CORPORATION—See Denso Corporation; *Int'l*, pg. 2031
DENSO TOKYO CORPORATION—See Denso Corporation; *Int'l*, pg. 2031
DEUTZ FRANCE S.A.—See DEUTZ AG; *Int'l*, pg. 2086
DRIVELINES NW, INC.—See Platinum Equity, LLC; *U.S. Private*, pg. 3209
DRIVETRAIN PHILIPPINES INC.—See Engenco Limited; *Int'l*, pg. 2427
DRIVETRAIN POWER AND PROPULSION PTY. LTD.—See Engenco Limited; *Int'l*, pg. 2427
DSPACE INC.—See dSPACE GmbH; *Int'l*, pg. 2210
DSPACE JAPAN K.K.—See dSPACE GmbH; *Int'l*, pg. 2210
DSPACE LTD.—See dSPACE GmbH; *Int'l*, pg. 2210
DSPACE MECHATRONIC CONTROL TECHNOLOGY (SHANGHAI) CO., LTD.—See dSPACE GmbH; *Int'l*, pg. 2210
DSPACE SARL—See dSPACE GmbH; *Int'l*, pg. 2210
DSU RENTAL—See DSU Peterbilt & GMC Truck, Inc.; *U.S. Private*, pg. 1282
DURR ASSEMBLY PRODUCTS GMBH—See Durr AG; *Int'l*, pg. 2231
EASTERN IOWA TIRE CO. INC.; *U.S. Private*, pg. 1320
EBAY MOTORS INDIA PRIVATE LIMITED—See eBay Inc.; *U.S. Public*, pg. 709
ECHO AUTOMOTIVE, INC.; *U.S. Private*, pg. 1327
EMILAB, SRL.—See I Squared Capital Advisors (US) LLC; *U.S. Private*, pg. 2022
ENVIRONMENTAL SYSTEM PRODUCTS HOLDING; *U.S. Private*, pg. 1408
EURO GARAGE SOLUTIONS LTD—See LKQ Corporation; *U.S. Public*, pg. 1334
EUROMASTER CESKA REPUBLIKA S.R.O.—See Compagnie Generale des Etablissements Michelin SCA; *Int'l*, pg. 1742
EUROMASTER FRANCE S.N.C—See Compagnie Generale des Etablissements Michelin SCA; *Int'l*, pg. 1742
EUROMASTER ITALIA S.R.L.—See Compagnie Generale des Etablissements Michelin SCA; *Int'l*, pg. 1742
EUROMASTER LASTIK VE SERVIS LIMITED SIRKETI—See Compagnie Generale des Etablissements Michelin SCA; *Int'l*, pg. 1742
EUROMASTER POLSKA SP. Z.O.O.—See Compagnie Generale des Etablissements Michelin SCA; *Int'l*, pg. 1742
EUROMASTER REIFENSERVICE GMBH—See Compagnie

N.A.I.C.S. INDEX

811210 — ELECTRONIC AND PREC...

Generale des Etablissements Michelin SCA; *Int'l*, pg. 1742
EUROMASTER TYRE & SERVICES ROMANIA S.A.—See Compagnie Generale des Etablissements Michelin SCA; *Int'l*, pg. 1742
EXACT SYSTEMS S.A.—See CVI Dom Maklerski sp. z o.o.; *Int'l*, pg. 1889
FASTLIGN LLC—See Searchlight Capital Partners, L.P.; *U.S. Private*, pg. 3590
FINANCIERE SNOP DUNOIS SA; *Int'l*, pg. 2669
FIX AUTO CANADA, INC.; *Int'l*, pg. 2696
FLETCHER'S TIRE AND AUTO SERVICE; *U.S. Private*, pg. 1543
FORMIDO B.V.—See KKR & Co. Inc.; *U.S. Public*, pg. 1261
FREE SERVICE TIRE COMPANY, INC.; *U.S. Private*, pg. 1602
FT TECHNO EUROPE GMBH—See AISIN Corporation; *Int'l*, pg. 253
FT TECHNO INC.—See AISIN Corporation; *Int'l*, pg. 253
GARAGE DU BOIS VERT; *Int'l*, pg. 2883
GARAGE LAMERAIN S.A.S; *Int'l*, pg. 2883
GAS MONKEY GARAGE; *U.S. Private*, pg. 1647
GEMBALLA GMBH—See GEMBALLA Holding SE; *Int'l*, pg. 2915
GKK GUTACHTERZENTRALE GMBH—See DEKRA e.V.; *Int'l*, pg. 2009
GLOBAL INDUSTRIAL CANADA INC.—See Global Industrial Company; *U.S. Public*, pg. 942
GORDON-DARBY INC.; *U.S. Private*, pg. 1743
GRANINGER & MAYR GESELLSCHAFT M.B.H—See BayWa AG; *Int'l*, pg. 918
GREAT WALL BUILDERS LTD.; *Int'l*, pg. 3065
HAASZ AUTO MALL, LLC—See Sarchione Automotive Group; *U.S. Private*, pg. 3550
HH-CDJR MOTORS, INC.—See AutoNation, Inc.; *U.S. Public*, pg. 235
HH-COLLISION, INC.—See AutoNation, Inc.; *U.S. Public*, pg. 235
HILLCREST AUTOMOTIVE SERVICES; *U.S. Private*, pg. 1946
HONDA RACING DEVELOPMENT LTD.—See Honda Motor Co., Ltd.; *Int'l*, pg. 3462
HORIBA MIRA LTD.—See HORIBA Ltd; *Int'l*, pg. 3476
HUNTER AEROSPACE CORPORATION PTY LIMITED—See BAE Systems plc; *Int'l*, pg. 798
HUPER OPTIK INTERNATIONAL PTE. LTD.—See Eastman Chemical Company; *U.S. Public*, pg. 705
HUPER OPTIK U.S.A., L.P.—See Eastman Chemical Company; *U.S. Public*, pg. 705
HUTTER AUFZUGE GMBH—See Otis Worldwide Corporation; *U.S. Public*, pg. 1623
HYDRACO INDUSTRIES INC.; *Int'l*, pg. 3546
IB MOTORS PTY. LTD.—See Eagers Automotive Limited; *Int'l*, pg. 2264
ICIN CO., LTD.—See Current Motor Corporation; *Int'l*, pg. 1879
IDEALEASE SERVICES, INC.—See Idealease, Inc.; *U.S. Private*, pg. 2037
IDIADA AUTOMOTIVE TECHNOLOGY INDIA PVT, LTD.—See I Squared Capital Advisors (US) LLC; *U.S. Private*, pg. 2022
IDIADA AUTOMOTIVE TECHNOLOGY MEXICO S DE RL DE CV.—See I Squared Capital Advisors (US) LLC; *U.S. Private*, pg. 2022
IDIADA AUTOMOTIVE TECHNOLOGY RUS, LLC—See I Squared Capital Advisors (US) LLC; *U.S. Private*, pg. 2022
IDIADA AUTOMOTIVE TECHNOLOGY UK, LTD.—See I Squared Capital Advisors (US) LLC; *U.S. Private*, pg. 2022
IDIADA FAHRZEUGTECHNIK, GMBH—See I Squared Capital Advisors (US) LLC; *U.S. Private*, pg. 2022
IMPERIAL GROUP (PTY) LIMITED—See Dubai World Corporation; *Int'l*, pg. 2221
INDUSTRIEPARK NIENBURG GMBH—See Eastman Chemical Company; *U.S. Public*, pg. 705
INSPECCIO TECNICA DE VEHICLES I SERVEIS, S.A.—See I Squared Capital Advisors (US) LLC; *U.S. Private*, pg. 2022
INTERTEC SPOL. S R.O.—See Agrofert Holding, a.s.; *Int'l*, pg. 219
ITW GLOBAL TIRE REPAIR INC.—See Illinois Tool Works Inc.; *U.S. Public*, pg. 1106
JAMES W. HALTERMAN, INC.—See ARR Investments, LLC; *U.S. Private*, pg. 334
JIM CLICK COLLISION CENTER EASTSIDE—See Jim Click, Inc.; *U.S. Private*, pg. 2208
K1 KASASTAJAT, OY—See I Squared Capital Advisors (US) LLC; *U.S. Private*, pg. 2023
KALMAR TURKEY YUK TASIMA SISTEMLERI ANONIM SIRKETI—See Cargotec Corporation; *Int'l*, pg. 1328
KLM UK ENGINEERING LIMITED—See Air France-KLM S.A.; *Int'l*, pg. 237
KNOWLES ON SITE REPAIR, INC.—See American Securities LLC; *U.S. Private*, pg. 248
LIBERTY RAILWAY SERVICES, INC.—See ERS Industries Inc.; *U.S. Private*, pg. 1423

LIQUID RESINS INTERNATIONAL, LTD.; *U.S. Private*, pg. 2466
LOCO, INC.; *U.S. Private*, pg. 2479
LUFTHANSA TECHNIK AERO ALZEY GMBH—See Deutsche Lufthansa AG; *Int'l*, pg. 2070
LUFTHANSA TECHNIK AIRMOTIVE IRELAND LTD.—See Deutsche Lufthansa AG; *Int'l*, pg. 2070
LUFTHANSA TECHNIK BRUSSELS N.V.—See Deutsche Lufthansa AG; *Int'l*, pg. 2070
LUFTHANSA TECHNIK COMPONENT SERVICES LLC—See Deutsche Lufthansa AG; *Int'l*, pg. 2070
LUFTHANSA TECHNIK MAINTENANCE INTERNATIONAL GMBH—See Deutsche Lufthansa AG; *Int'l*, pg. 2070
LUFTHANSA TECHNIK SERVICES INDIA PRIVATE LIMITED—See Deutsche Lufthansa AG; *Int'l*, pg. 2070
LUFTHANSA TECHNIK SWITZERLAND GMBH—See Deutsche Lufthansa AG; *Int'l*, pg. 2070
LYON MAINTENANCE—See Air France-KLM S.A.; *Int'l*, pg. 238
MAXEY LOGISTICS, INC; *U.S. Private*, pg. 2617
MCCARTHY FORD INC.—See Harold Zeigler Auto Group, Inc.; *U.S. Private*, pg. 1867
MERX TRUCK & TRAILER, INC.; *U.S. Private*, pg. 2677
MIRACLE PARTNERS, INC.—See Icahn Enterprises L.P.; *U.S. Public*, pg. 1085
MONROE MEXICO S.A. DE C.V.—See Apollo Global Management, Inc.; *U.S. Public*, pg. 163
MOTORXCHANGE S.A.R.L.—See LKQ Corporation; *U.S. Public*, pg. 1335
MOTRAC HANDLING & CLEANING N.V.-S.A.—See KKR & Co. Inc.; *U.S. Public*, pg. 1255
MOTRAC HANDLING & CLEANING N.V.-S.A.—See The Goldman Sachs Group, Inc.; *U.S. Public*, pg. 2079
MRT-ENGINES B.V.—See LKQ Corporation; *U.S. Public*, pg. 1335
M.R.T. POLSKA SP. Z O.O.—See LKQ Corporation; *U.S. Public*, pg. 1335
NATIONAL AUTO CARE CORPORATION—See Lovell Minnick Partners LLC; *U.S. Private*, pg. 2503
NORCONTROL CHILE, S.A.—See I Squared Capital Advisors (US) LLC; *U.S. Private*, pg. 2023
NORCONTROL NICARAGUA, S.A.—See I Squared Capital Advisors (US) LLC; *U.S. Private*, pg. 2023
OPTARE GROUP LTD.—See Hinduja Group Ltd.; *Int'l*, pg. 3398
OPUS INSPECTION INC.—See Searchlight Capital Partners, L.P.; *U.S. Private*, pg. 3590
PARRISH TIRE COMPANY, INC. - COMMERCIAL DIVISION—See Parrish Tire Company, Inc.; *U.S. Private*, pg. 3100
PASCALE SERVICE CORPORATION—See Platinum Equity, LLC; *U.S. Private*, pg. 3209
PENSKE COMMERCIAL VEHICLES NZ—See Penske Automotive Group, Inc.; *U.S. Public*, pg. 1665
PIRELLI PERSONAL SERVICE GMBH—See China National Chemical Corporation; *Int'l*, pg. 1528
PRAXIS—See KKR & Co. Inc.; *U.S. Public*, pg. 1261
PRIME AUTO CARE INC.—See Kingsway Financial Services Inc.; *U.S. Public*, pg. 1235
PUERTO SECO SANTANDER-EBRO, S.A.—See ACS, Actividades de Construccion y Servicios, S.A.; *Int'l*, pg. 115
THE PULLMAN COMPANY—See Apollo Global Management, Inc.; *U.S. Public*, pg. 163
PURCELL TIRE & RUBBER COMPANY INC.; *U.S. Private*, pg. 3304
PURCELL TIRE & RUBBER COMPANY—See Purcell Tire & Rubber Company Inc.; *U.S. Private*, pg. 3305
PUSPAKOM SDN. BHD.—See DRB-HICOM Berhad; *Int'l*, pg. 2202
PYROBAN ENVIROSAFE LIMITED—See Caterpillar, Inc.; *U.S. Public*, pg. 453
QSL OF AUSTINTOWN OHIO LLC—See BP plc; *Int'l*, pg. 1127
RALPH SELLERS MOTOR CO.; *U.S. Private*, pg. 3350
RCG LOGISTICS LLC—See Tailwind Capital Group, LLC; *U.S. Private*, pg. 3924
REVISIONES TECNICAS APPLUS DEL ECUADOR APPLUSITEUVE, S.A.—See I Squared Capital Advisors (US) LLC; *U.S. Private*, pg. 2023
RISK-AKTIV VERSICHERUNGSSERVICE GMBH—See Assicurazioni Generali S.p.A.; *Int'l*, pg. 646
RITEVE SYC, S.A.—See I Squared Capital Advisors (US) LLC; *U.S. Private*, pg. 2023
SAVELYS GROUP—See ENGIE SA; *Int'l*, pg. 2434
SELLERS 3 PROPERTIES, LLC—See Ralph Sellers Motor Co.; *U.S. Private*, pg. 3350
SERVICE TIRE TRUCK CENTERS, INC.; *U.S. Private*, pg. 3616
SERVICIOS Y ASISTENCIA OK24, S.L.—See Compagnie Generale des Etablissements Michelin SCA; *Int'l*, pg. 1745
SHAKEN-BANKIN DEPOT INC.—See Autobacs Seven Co., Ltd.; *Int'l*, pg. 726
SHANGAI IDIADA AUTOMOTIVE TECHNOLOGY SERVICES CO., LTD.—See I Squared Capital Advisors (US) LLC; *U.S. Private*, pg. 2023
SIRA ENVIRONMENTAL LIMITED—See CSA Group; *Int'l*, pg. 1861

SK AUTOMOBILE PTE. LTD.—See Autobacs Seven Co., Ltd.; *Int'l*, pg. 726
SLOWBOY RACING, INC.; *U.S. Private*, pg. 3689
SNA EUROPE (CZECH REPUBLIC) S.R.O.—See Snap-on Incorporated; *U.S. Public*, pg. 1898
SOUTHWEST FUEL SYSTEMS LLC—See M International Inc.; *U.S. Private*, pg. 2523
SPEEDEMISSIONS, INC.; *U.S. Public*, pg. 1917
STAHLGRUBER GES. M.B.H—See LKQ Corporation; *U.S. Public*, pg. 1336
STATE TIRE & SERVICE—See Complete General Construction Co. Inc.; *U.S. Private*, pg. 1000
STEEPLETON TIRE CO.; *U.S. Private*, pg. 3797
STEPGRADES MOTOR ACCESSORIES LTD.—See Halfords Group plc; *Int'l*, pg. 3229
STK SLAVKOV S.R.O.—See DEKRA e.V.; *Int'l*, pg. 2009
STK - STANICE TECHNICKO KOITROLY S.R.O.—See DEKRA e.V.; *Int'l*, pg. 2009
SUPERIOR SPRING COMPANY—See Illinois Tool Works Inc.; *U.S. Public*, pg. 1111
SUPERIOR VAN & MOBILITY, LLC.; *U.S. Private*, pg. 3881
TAGROS D.O.O.—See Cargotec Corporation; *Int'l*, pg. 1329
TENNECO AUTOMOTIVE ITALIA S.R.L.—See Apollo Global Management, Inc.; *U.S. Public*, pg. 163
TENNECO AUTOMOTIVE OPERATING COMPANY INC—See Apollo Global Management, Inc.; *U.S. Public*, pg. 163
TENNECO CANADA INC—See Apollo Global Management, Inc.; *U.S. Public*, pg. 163
THERMAL SOLUTIONS MANUFACTURING, INC.—See Altus Capital Partners, Inc.; *U.S. Private*, pg. 211
THORN VALLEY ENTERPRISES—See Norman-Spencer Agency, Inc.; *U.S. Private*, pg. 2938
TIRES PLUS TOTAL CAR CARE—See Bridgestone Corporation; *Int'l*, pg. 1157
TOMMY HOUSE TIRE COMPANY; *U.S. Private*, pg. 4184
TRAC INTERSTAR LLC—See Stonepeak Partners L.P.; *U.S. Private*, pg. 3829
TROY COLLISION, LLC—See Lithia Motors, Inc.; *U.S. Public*, pg. 1326
TWIN RIDGE AUTO AND LIGHT TRUCK SERVICE, INC.—See Bueso & Forman, Inc.; *U.S. Private*, pg. 680
UAB DEKRA INDUSTRIAL—See DEKRA e.V.; *Int'l*, pg. 2010
VADOTECH JAPAN KK—See AB Dynamics plc; *Int'l*, pg. 39
VEHICLE TESTING NEW ZEALAND LTD.—See DEKRA e.V.; *Int'l*, pg. 2010
VELOSI BAHRAIN WLL.—See I Squared Capital Advisors (US) LLC; *U.S. Private*, pg. 2023
VELOSI LLC—See I Squared Capital Advisors (US) LLC; *U.S. Private*, pg. 2023
VELOSI UGANDA LTD.—See I Squared Capital Advisors (US) LLC; *U.S. Private*, pg. 2024
VOLVO MAKEDONIJA LTD.—See AB Volvo; *Int'l*, pg. 45
VOSSLOH LOCOMOTIVES FRANCE SAS—See CRRC Corporation Limited; *Int'l*, pg. 1859
VULCO TRUCK SERVICES—See The Goodyear Tire & Rubber Company; *U.S. Public*, pg. 2085
WENTWORTH TIRE SERVICE INC.; *U.S. Private*, pg. 4481
WEST COAST CUSTOMS, INC.; *U.S. Private*, pg. 4484
WEST HERR TOYOTA OF ROCHESTER—See West Herr Automotive Group, Inc.; *U.S. Private*, pg. 4485
YB VEHICLE SERVICES—See Younger Brothers Group Inc.; *U.S. Private*, pg. 4593
ZYNIT CHINA CO., LTD.—See AB Dynamics plc; *Int'l*, pg. 39
ZYX METROLOGY S.L.U.—See I Squared Capital Advisors (US) LLC; *U.S. Private*, pg. 2024

811210 — ELECTRONIC AND PRECISION EQUIPMENT REPAIR AND MAINTENANCE

1026128 ALBERTA LTD—See ITT Inc.; *U.S. Public*, pg. 1177
4K S.R.L.—See CompuGroup Medical SE & Co. KGaA; *Int'l*, pg. 1755
AC6 METROLOGIA, S.L.—See I Squared Capital Advisors (US) LLC; *U.S. Private*, pg. 2021
ACCRAM INC.; *U.S. Private*, pg. 54
ACCUSERVE INC.—See Electrical Test Instrument, LLC; *U.S. Private*, pg. 1353
ACOUSTIC METROLOGY LIMITED—See Demant A/S; *Int'l*, pg. 2022
ACROPOLIS COMPUTERS, INC.—See IT Solutions Consulting LLC; *U.S. Private*, pg. 2148
ACUTECH NETWORK SERVICES INC—See Integritek LLC; *U.S. Private*, pg. 2102
ADAMS REMCO INC.; *U.S. Private*, pg. 75
ADVANCED CAE (ME) CONTROL SYSTEM L.L.C.—See Advanced Holdings Ltd.; *Int'l*, pg. 159
ADVANCED ELECTRONIC SERVICES, INC.; *U.S. Private*, pg. 89
ADVANCED MICROELECTRONICS, INC.; *U.S. Private*, pg. 91
ADVANCED TECHNICAL SOLUTIONS, INC.; *U.S. Private*, pg. 93
AEC SAS—See Draegerwerk AG & Co. KGaA; *Int'l*, pg. 2196
AEM LIMITED—See AMETEK, Inc.; *U.S. Public*, pg. 116
AER TECHNOLOGIES, INC.; *U.S. Private*, pg. 117
AFEX INTERNATIONAL (HK) LIMITED—See AMCO United

811210 — ELECTRONIC AND PREC...

Holding Limited; *Int'l*, pg. 416
THE AFTERMARKET GROUP, INC.—See Invacare Corporation; *U.S. Private*, pg. 2131
AGFA DE MEXICO S.A. DE C.V.—See Agfa-Gevaert N.V.; *Int'l*, pg. 207
AGFA HEALTHCARE HUNGARY KFT.—See Agfa-Gevaert N.V.; *Int'l*, pg. 207
AHEARN & SOPER INC.—See Ahearn & Soper Inc.; *Int'l*, pg. 222
AHEARN & SOPER INC.—See Ahearn & Soper Inc.; *Int'l*, pg. 222
AHEARN & SOPER INC.—See Ahearn & Soper Inc.; *Int'l*, pg. 223
ALFRED CONHAGEN INCORPORATED; *U.S. Private*, pg. 165
ALLCOMM WIRELESS, INC.—See Sentinel Capital Partners, L.L.C.; *U.S. Private*, pg. 3609
ALLIANCE OFFICE SYSTEMS; *U.S. Private*, pg. 183
ALPHA AUTOMATION INC.—See United Salt Corporation; *U.S. Private*, pg. 4297
ALPHA SOLUTIONS AG—See Bechtle AG; *Int'l*, pg. 937
AMERICAN WATER TREATMENT, INC.—See Nolan Capital, Inc.; *U.S. Private*, pg. 2934
ANALYTICAL MAINTENANCE SERVICES, INC.—See CBRE Group, Inc.; *U.S. Public*, pg. 460
ANDRITZ INC. - GLEN FALLS—See ANDRITZ AG; *Int'l*, pg. 453
A NOVO POLSKA SP.Z0.O.—See Hainan Traffic Administration Holding Co., Ltd.; *Int'l*, pg. 3213
ANOVO S.A.—See Hainan Traffic Administration Holding Co., Ltd.; *Int'l*, pg. 3213
ARKOS FIELD SERVICES, LP—See Burckhardt Compression Holding AG; *Int'l*, pg. 1220
ARRC TECHNOLOGY; *U.S. Private*, pg. 334
ARTEMIS ELECTRONICS LLC.; *U.S. Private*, pg. 341
ARTIFICIAL INTELLIGENCE TECHNOLOGY SOLUTIONS INC.; *U.S. Public*, pg. 208
ARVATO SERVICES K.S.—See Bertelsmann SE & Co. KGaA; *Int'l*, pg. 990
ASHLAND HOME NET—See Jefferson Public Radio; *U.S. Private*, pg. 2198
ASSURED QUALITY TECHNOLOGY, LTD.—See Atlas Fibre Company; *U.S. Private*, pg. 376
AUCNET MEDICAL INC.—See Aucnet Inc.; *Int'l*, pg. 700
AUDIO PIXELS HOLDINGS LIMITED; *Int'l*, pg. 701
AUGWIND ENERGY TECH STORAGE LTD.; *Int'l*, pg. 704
AVI-SPL, INC. - DALLAS—See Marlin Equity Partners, LLC; *U.S. Private*, pg. 2583
BARFIELD, INC.—See Air France-KLM S.A.; *Int'l*, pg. 236
B&E GROUP, LLC—See Arlington Capital Partners LLC; *U.S. Private*, pg. 327
BEIER RADIO LLC; *U.S. Private*, pg. 516
BEIJING COMTECH EF DATA EQUIPMENT REPAIR SERVICE, CO., LTD.—See Comtech Telecommunications Corp.; *U.S. Public*, pg. 562
BELAIR INSTRUMENT COMPANY LLC; *U.S. Private*, pg. 516
BIGSTON CORPORATION USA; *U.S. Private*, pg. 556
BIOTEK SERVICES, INC.—See Transcat, Inc.; *U.S. Public*, pg. 2179
BMHIOL INDUSTRIES—See Hiolle Industries S.A.; *Int'l*, pg. 3401
BOCA THEATER & AUTOMATION, INC.; *U.S. Private*, pg. 607
BRACING SYSTEMS INC.; *U.S. Private*, pg. 630
BRAINS II INC.; *Int'l*, pg. 1137
BRAVAS LLC—See Presidio Investors LLC; *U.S. Private*, pg. 3255
BRAVAS MINNEAPOLIS—See Presidio Investors LLC; *U.S. Private*, pg. 3255
BRITT METAL PROCESSING, INC.—See Jets MRO, LLC; *U.S. Private*, pg. 2204
BUDUCNOST HLADENJE SLAP A.D.; *Int'l*, pg. 1211
BUFFALO'S EXPERT SERVICE TECHNICIANS, INC.; *U.S. Private*, pg. 681
CADY LIFTERS—See Columbus McKinnon Corporation; *U.S. Public*, pg. 535
CALL2RECYCLE, INC.; *U.S. Private*, pg. 721
CANON ECOLOGY INDUSTRY INC.—See Canon Inc.; *Int'l*, pg. 1293
CANON INFORMATION TECHNOLOGY SERVICES INC.—See Canon Inc.; *Int'l*, pg. 1297
CAPITAL AVIONICS, INC.; *U.S. Private*, pg. 738
CARDIO DINAMICA LTDA.—See Halma plc; *Int'l*, pg. 3231
CAROLINA BUSINESS EQUIPMENT, INC.—See Perpetual Capital, LLC; *U.S. Private*, pg. 3153
CARSON GRAVITY METER & INSTRUMENTATION COMPANY INC.—See Carson Helicopters Inc.; *U.S. Private*, pg. 774
CARTER BROTHERS ARAMARK INTEGRATED FACILITIES MANAGEMENT, LLC—See Aramark; *U.S. Public*, pg. 177
CARTRIDGE TECHNOLOGIES, LLC—See CenterGate Capital, LP; *U.S. Private*, pg. 816
CARWOOD (REWIND) YEOVIL LTD—See Carwood Motor Units Ltd; *Int'l*, pg. 1349
CASCADE ASSET MANAGEMENT, LLC.; *U.S. Private*, pg. 778

CATERPILLAR PROPULSION NAMIBIA (PROPRIETARY) LIMITED—See Caterpillar, Inc.; *U.S. Public*, pg. 451
CENTECH GROUP INC.; *U.S. Private*, pg. 809
CENTRINET CORP; *U.S. Private*, pg. 830
CE POWER SOLUTIONS, LLC—See New Mountain Capital, LLC; *U.S. Private*, pg. 2903
CHROMALLOY GAS TURBINE LLC—See Veritas Capital Fund Management, LLC; *U.S. Private*, pg. 4364
CINIX 1 PTY. LTD.—See HeiTech Padu Berhad; *Int'l*, pg. 3326
CLICKAWAY CORPORATION; *U.S. Private*, pg. 942
CNA GROUP LTD.; *Int'l*, pg. 1673
COMDOC INC.—See Xerox Holdings Corporation; *U.S. Public*, pg. 2389
COMMUNICATION CONCEPTS INC.; *U.S. Private*, pg. 988
COMMUNICATIONS BROKERS, INC.—See Keystone Group, L.P.; *U.S. Private*, pg. 2297
COMMUNICATIONS BROKERS, INC.—See Pamlico Capital Management, L.P.; *U.S. Private*, pg. 3083
COMMUNICATIONS TEST DESIGN INC.; *U.S. Private*, pg. 989
COMMUNICATION TECHNOLOGY SERVICES; *U.S. Private*, pg. 988
COMPU-FIX, INC.—See Harvest Partners L.P.; *U.S. Private*, pg. 1877
COMPUTER AGE ELECTRONICS, INC.; *U.S. Private*, pg. 1004
COMPUTER AIDED PRODUCTS, INC.; *U.S. Private*, pg. 1004
COMPUTER DATA SOURCE, INC.—See New State Capital Partners LLC; *U.S. Private*, pg. 2906
COMPUTER WORLD, INC.—See VC3, Inc.; *U.S. Private*, pg. 4349
COMPUTER WORLD SERVICES CORP.; *U.S. Private*, pg. 1005
COMSONICS, INC. - CALIFORNIA REPAIR FACILITY—See ComSonics, Inc.; *U.S. Public*, pg. 1006
CONSENSYS IMAGING SERVICE, INC.—See Galen Partners, L.P.; *U.S. Private*, pg. 1637
CONTEC HOLDINGS, LLC—See Bain Capital, LP; *U.S. Private*, pg. 438
CONVANO, INC.; *Int'l*, pg. 1786
CPR STRONGSVILLE LLC—See Assurant, Inc.; *U.S. Public*, pg. 215
CSL MOBILE CARE (M) SDN. BHD.—See Digilife Technologies Limited; *Int'l*, pg. 2119
CSM COMPRESSOR INC.—See Burckhardt Compression Holding AG; *Int'l*, pg. 1221
CSU LLC; *U.S. Private*, pg. 1118
CUBIC WORLDWIDE TECHNICAL SERVICES, INC.—See Elliott Management Corporation; *U.S. Private*, pg. 1368
CUBIC WORLDWIDE TECHNICAL SERVICES, INC.—See Veritas Capital Fund Management, LLC; *U.S. Private*, pg. 4362
CULLITON BROTHERS LIMITED; *Int'l*, pg. 1877
CUSTOM HARDWARE ENGINEERING & CONSULTING, INC.—See Charlesbank Capital Partners, LLC; *U.S. Private*, pg. 856
CUSTOM HARDWARE ENGINEERING & CONSULTING, INC.—See GTCR LLC; *U.S. Private*, pg. 1806
CYBER-TEST, INC.—See Bain Capital, LP; *U.S. Private*, pg. 444
DAIDONG ENGINEERING MALAYSIA SDN BHD—See Daidong Electronics Co., Ltd.; *Int'l*, pg. 1924
DAISHINKU (DEUTSCHLAND) GMBH—See Daishinku Corp.; *Int'l*, pg. 1942
DATA EXCHANGE CORPORATION; *U.S. Private*, pg. 1162
DATA NETWORK SERVICES INC.—See Cloud Equity Group, LLC; *U.S. Private*, pg. 946
DAY MANAGEMENT CORP.; *U.S. Private*, pg. 1176
DBA SAS—See Eurazeo SE; *Int'l*, pg. 2528
DBK CONCEPTS INC.—See Sole Source Capital LLC; *U.S. Private*, pg. 3708
DEFTECH SYSTEMS INTEGRATION SDN. BHD.—See DRB-HICOM Berhad; *Int'l*, pg. 2201
DEPOT INTERNATIONAL INC.; *U.S. Private*, pg. 1209
DIAGNOSYS FERNDOWN LIMITED—See Astronics Corporation; *U.S. Public*, pg. 217
DIAGNOSYS GMBH—See Astronics Corporation; *U.S. Public*, pg. 217
DIEBOLD INFORMATION AND SECURITY SYSTEMS, LLC—See Diebold Nixdorf, Inc.; *U.S. Public*, pg. 660
DIGITEK ELECTRONICS LTD.—See Jabil Inc.; *U.S. Public*, pg. 1180
DIGITEST ELEKTRONIK SERVICE GMBH; *Int'l*, pg. 2124
DISNEY WORLDWIDE SERVICES, INC.—See The Walt Disney Company; *U.S. Public*, pg. 2139
DOCUMENT ESSENTIALS LLC—See Doceo Office Solutions, LLC; *U.S. Private*, pg. 1251
DOORMATION, INC.; *U.S. Private*, pg. 1262
DS TECHNOLOGIES INC.—See Densan System Co., Ltd.; *Int'l*, pg. 2028
EBARA FIELD TECH. CORPORATION—See Ebara Corporation; *Int'l*, pg. 2283
EBARA PRECISION MACHINERY EUROPE GMBH—See Ebara Corporation; *Int'l*, pg. 2283
ECMM SERVICES INC.—See Hon Hai Precision Industry Co., Ltd.; *Int'l*, pg. 3456

ECONOCOM MANAGED SERVICES SAS—See Econocom Group SA; *Int'l*, pg. 2297
ECO-RECYCLE CO., LTD.—See Dowa Holdings Co., Ltd.; *Int'l*, pg. 2184
E-CYCLE LLC; *U.S. Private*, pg. 1302
EIZO SUPPORT NETWORK CORPORATION—See EIZO Corporation; *Int'l*, pg. 2337
ELECTRICAL RELIABILITY SERVICES, INC.—See Emerson Electric Co.; *U.S. Public*, pg. 746
ELECTRICAL RELIABILITY SERVICES, INC.—See Emerson Electric Co.; *U.S. Public*, pg. 746
ELECTRICAL RELIABILITY SERVICES, INC.—See Emerson Electric Co.; *U.S. Public*, pg. 746
ELECTRICAL RELIABILITY SERVICES, INC.—See Emerson Electric Co.; *U.S. Public*, pg. 746
ELECTRICAL RELIABILITY SERVICES, INC.—See Emerson Electric Co.; *U.S. Public*, pg. 746
ELECTRICAL TEST INSTRUMENT, LLC; *U.S. Private*, pg. 1353
ELECTRONIC DRIVES & CONTROLS; *U.S. Private*, pg. 1355
ELECTRONIC MAINTENANCE COMPANY INCORPORATED; *U.S. Private*, pg. 1355
ELECTRONIC RECYCLERS INTERNATIONAL, INC.; *U.S. Private*, pg. 1356
ELECTROSERVICE AB—See AB Electrolux; *Int'l*, pg. 41
ELEKTROSERVIS A.D.; *Int'l*, pg. 2357
ELEMENTAL USA INC.—See Elemental Holding S.A.; *Int'l*, pg. 2358
ELITE TECHNOLOGY INC.; *U.S. Private*, pg. 1361
ELTEK MONTAGE GMBH—See Delta Electronics, Inc.; *Int'l*, pg. 2017
EMERGING MARKETS COMMUNICATIONS LLC—See PAR Capital Management, Inc.; *U.S. Private*, pg. 3089
EMERSON INSTRUMENT & VALVE SERVICE—See Emerson Electric Co.; *U.S. Public*, pg. 748
EMERSON INSTRUMENT & VALVE SERVICES—See Emerson Electric Co.; *U.S. Public*, pg. 746
EMERSON NETWORK POWER, LIEBERT SERVICES, INC. - EDISON—See Vertiv Holdings Co; *U.S. Public*, pg. 2289
EMERSON NETWORK POWER, LIEBERT SERVICES, INC.—See Vertiv Holdings Co; *U.S. Public*, pg. 2289
EMERSON PROCESS MANAGEMENT INSTRUMENT & VALVE SERVICES—See Emerson Electric Co.; *U.S. Public*, pg. 744
EMPIRE POWER SYSTEMS—See Empire Southwest LLC; *U.S. Private*, pg. 1385
EMPIRE PRECISION MACHINING—See Empire Southwest LLC; *U.S. Private*, pg. 1385
ENCOMPASS GROUP AFFILIATES, INC.—See Bain Capital, LP; *U.S. Private*, pg. 444
ENERGETICKE OPRAVNY, A.S.—See CEZ, a.s.; *Int'l*, pg. 1427
ENGENT, INC.—See H.B. Fuller Company; *U.S. Public*, pg. 977
ENTRUST TECHNOLOGY CONSULTING SERVICES—See The Aldridge Company; *U.S. Private*, pg. 3983
EUROFINS ELECTRICAL & ELECTRONIC UK LIMITED—See Eurofins Scientific S.E.; *Int'l*, pg. 2540
EUROFINS LAMM S.R.L.—See Eurofins Scientific S.E.; *Int'l*, pg. 2545
EYECARE PARTNERS LIMITED; *Int'l*, pg. 2592
FABRYKA WAGONOW GNIEWCZYNA SA; *Int'l*, pg. 2600
FANDOTECH, LLC—See Cooperative Systems, LLC; *U.S. Private*, pg. 1043
FANUC AMERICA CORPORATION - MIDWEST—See FANUC Corporation; *Int'l*, pg. 2614
FITZGERALD EQUIPMENT COMPANY INCORPORATED; *U.S. Private*, pg. 1536
FIXATION UK LTD.—See Aurelius Equity Opportunities SE & Co. KGaA; *Int'l*, pg. 708
FLEXTRON GLOBAL SERVICES—See Flex Ltd.; *Int'l*, pg. 2703
FLEXTRONICS INTERNATIONAL KFT.—See Flex Ltd.; *Int'l*, pg. 2702
FLIGHT SYSTEMS, INC.; *U.S. Private*, pg. 1545
FLOWSERVE CORP.—See Flowserve Corporation; *U.S. Public*, pg. 855
FLY BN LIMITED—See B-N Group Limited; *Int'l*, pg. 785
FPA TECHNOLOGY SERVICES INC.—See VC3, Inc.; *U.S. Private*, pg. 4349
FR AVIATION LIMITED—See Advent International Corporation; *U.S. Private*, pg. 99
FUJI FESTEC CO., LTD.—See Fuji Electric Co., Ltd.; *Int'l*, pg. 2812
FUJIFILM MEDICAL TECHNICAL SERVICE (SHANGHAI) CO., LTD.—See FUJIFILM Holdings Corporation; *Int'l*, pg. 2824
FUJIFILM OPTICAL DEVICES EUROPE GMBH—See FUJIFILM Holdings Corporation; *Int'l*, pg. 2824
FUJIFILM TECHNO SERVICE CO., LTD.—See FUJIFILM Holdings Corporation; *Int'l*, pg. 2825
FUNAI SERVICE CO., LTD.—See Funai Electric Co., Ltd.; *Int'l*, pg. 2845
FURMANITE WORLDWIDE, INC.—See Team, Inc.; *U.S. Public*, pg. 1987
FUSO DENTSU CO., LTD.; *Int'l*, pg. 2850

N.A.I.C.S. INDEX

811210 — ELECTRONIC AND PREC...

GADGET REPAIR SOLUTIONS LIMITED—See Stone Point Capital LLC; *U.S. Private*, pg. 3821
GD USA, INC.—See Coesia S.p.A.; *Int'l*, pg. 1690
GENCO INC.; *U.S. Private*, pg. 1660
GENERAL PARTS, LLC—See Berkshire Partners LLC; *U.S. Private*, pg. 535
GENSERVE INC.—See GenNx360 Capital Partners, L.P.; *U.S. Private*, pg. 1672
GE POWER SYSTEMS GMBH—See General Electric Company; *U.S. Public*, pg. 917
GESSNER INDUSTRIES INC.; *U.S. Private*, pg. 1688
GIJIMA GROUP LIMITED—See Guma Group; *Int'l*, pg. 3183
GMS MINE REPAIR & MAINTENANCE; *U.S. Private*, pg. 1723
GREEN HOME SOLUTIONS LLC—See Grupe Holding Company; *U.S. Private*, pg. 1797
GREEN REMANUFACTURING LLC—See Progressive Green Solutions, Inc.; *U.S. Public*, pg. 1726
GREENWICH, INC.—See Berkshire Partners LLC; *U.S. Private*, pg. 535
GRUBER TECHNICAL INC.—See Gruber Industries Inc.; *U.S. Private*, pg. 1796
GSL ELECTRIC—See Great Salt Lake Electric Incorporated; *U.S. Private*, pg. 1768
HADER INC.—See Hader Industries Inc.; *U.S. Private*, pg. 1839
HANDPIECE HEADQUARTERS CORP.—See Henry Schein, Inc.; *U.S. Public*, pg. 1025
HEICO COMPONENT REPAIR GROUP—See HEICO Corporation; *U.S. Public*, pg. 1019
HIGH VOLTAGE MAINTENANCE CORPORATION—See Emerson Electric Co.; *U.S. Public*, pg. 748
HIGH VOLTAGE MAINTENANCE CORP.—See Emerson Electric Co.; *U.S. Public*, pg. 748
HIGH VOLTAGE MAINTENANCE CORP.—See Emerson Electric Co.; *U.S. Public*, pg. 748
HIGH VOLTAGE MAINTENANCE CORP.—See Emerson Electric Co.; *U.S. Public*, pg. 748
HKE HOLDINGS LTD.; *Int'l*, pg. 3428
HOH WATER TECHNOLOGY A/S—See BWT Aktiengesellschaft; *Int'l*, pg. 1233
HONEYWELL AEROSPACE—See Honeywell International Inc.; *U.S. Public*, pg. 1047
HYLAN DATACOM & ELECTRICAL, LLC; *U.S. Private*, pg. 2018
IBM CHINA COMPANY LIMITED—See International Business Machines Corporation; *U.S. Public*, pg. 1146
IBM CROATIA LTD.—See International Business Machines Corporation; *U.S. Public*, pg. 1146
IBM DEL URUGUAY, S.A.—See International Business Machines Corporation; *U.S. Public*, pg. 1149
IBM EAST AFRICA LIMITED—See International Business Machines Corporation; *U.S. Public*, pg. 1146
IBM EAST EUROPE/ASIA LTD.—See International Business Machines Corporation; *U.S. Public*, pg. 1146
IBM ESTONIA OU—See International Business Machines Corporation; *U.S. Public*, pg. 1146
IBM INDIA PRIVATE LIMITED—See International Business Machines Corporation; *U.S. Public*, pg. 1147
IBM (INTERNATIONAL BUSINESS MACHINES) TURK LTD SIRKETI—See International Business Machines Corporation; *U.S. Public*, pg. 1145
IBM ITALIA S.P.A. - CYPRUS—See International Business Machines Corporation; *U.S. Public*, pg. 1147
IBM ITALIA S.P.A.—See International Business Machines Corporation; *U.S. Public*, pg. 1147
IBM LIETUVA—See International Business Machines Corporation; *U.S. Public*, pg. 1147
IBM MALAYSIA SDN. BHD.—See International Business Machines Corporation; *U.S. Public*, pg. 1147
IBM ROMANIA SRL—See International Business Machines Corporation; *U.S. Public*, pg. 1148
IBM SCHWEIZ AG—See International Business Machines Corporation; *U.S. Public*, pg. 1146
IBM SLOVENIJA D.O.O.—See International Business Machines Corporation; *U.S. Public*, pg. 1148
IBM SLOVENSKO SPOL. S.R.O.—See International Business Machines Corporation; *U.S. Public*, pg. 1148
IBM SOUTH AFRICA (PTY) LTD.—See International Business Machines Corporation; *U.S. Public*, pg. 1148
IBM TRINIDAD & TOBAGO—See International Business Machines Corporation; *U.S. Public*, pg. 1148
IBM TUNISIE—See International Business Machines Corporation; *U.S. Public*, pg. 1145
IBM VIETNAM COMPANY—See International Business Machines Corporation; *U.S. Public*, pg. 1149
IBOPE ERATINGS.COM MEXICO—See Brookfield Corporation; *Int'l*, pg. 1178
IBOPE ERATINGS.COM MEXICO—See Elliott Management Corporation; *U.S. Private*, pg. 1371
IFCO SYSTEMS US, LLC—See Audax Group, Limited Partnership; *U.S. Public*, pg. 386
IFIXIT, INC.—See Apple Inc.; *U.S. Public*, pg. 169
ILLINOIS AUTO CENTRAL DIVISION—See Illinois Auto Electric Co.; *U.S. Private*, pg. 2042
IMAGETEC L.P.; *U.S. Private*, pg. 2045
IMPELLER REPAIR SERVICE—See ITT Inc.; *U.S. Public*, pg. 1178

INDUSTRIAL CONTROL REPAIR, INC.; *U.S. Private*, pg. 2065
INDUSTRIAL VALVE SALES & SERVICE; *U.S. Private*, pg. 2069
INGRAM MICRO SERVICES LTD.—See Hainan Traffic Administration Holding Co., Ltd.; *Int'l*, pg. 3215
INTEGRATION TECHNOLOGIES GROUP, INC.; *U.S. Private*, pg. 2101
INTELLISITE CORPORATION; *U.S. Private*, pg. 2106
IOWA REBUILDERS, INC.—See Mestek, Inc.; *U.S. Public*, pg. 1426
JABIL CIRCUIT AUTOMOTIVE, SAS—See Jabil Inc.; *U.S. Public*, pg. 1181
JABIL CIRCUIT (SINGAPORE) PTE. LTD.—See Jabil Inc.; *U.S. Public*, pg. 1181
JABIL CIRCUIT U.K., LIMITED—See Jabil Inc.; *U.S. Public*, pg. 1181
JABIL GLOBAL SERVICES DE MEXICO, S.A. DE C.V.—See Jabil Inc.; *U.S. Public*, pg. 1181
J&B MASKINTEKNIK AB—See Searchlight Capital Partners, L.P.; *U.S. Private*, pg. 3590
JINPAN INTERNATIONAL (USA) LTD.—See Forebright Capital Management Ltd.; *Int'l*, pg. 2731
KELLER ELECTRICAL INDUSTRIES, INC.; *U.S. Private*, pg. 2274
KEYTRONICEMS COMPUTER PERIPHERAL CO.—See Key Tronic Corporation; *U.S. Public*, pg. 1225
KEY TRONIC JUAREZ S.A. DE CV—See Key Tronic Corporation; *U.S. Public*, pg. 1225
KEY TRONIC REYNOSA, S.A. DE CV—See Key Tronic Corporation; *U.S. Public*, pg. 1225
THE KEYW CORPORATION—See Jacobs Engineering Group, Inc.; *U.S. Public*, pg. 1186
KIDDE FIRE TRAINERS, INC.—See Carrier Global Corporation; *U.S. Public*, pg. 440
KIMBALL ELECTRONICS POLAND SP. Z O.O—See Kimball Electronics, Inc.; *U.S. Public*, pg. 1228
KINGS III OF AMERICA, LLC—See Arcline Investment Management LP; *U.S. Private*, pg. 314
KOCH-GLITSCH FIELD SERVICE—See Koch Industries, Inc.; *U.S. Private*, pg. 2332
KOSSE PARTNERS I, LLC—See Vspeed Capital, LLC; *U.S. Private*, pg. 4415
K&S SERVICES INC.; *U.S. Private*, pg. 2250
LASER SYSTEMS, INC.—See Loffler Companies, Inc.; *U.S. Private*, pg. 2480
LH MARTHINUSEN (PTY.) LTD.—See ACTOM (Pty) Ltd.; *Int'l*, pg. 120
LIEBERT CORPORATION—See Vertiv Holdings Co; *U.S. Public*, pg. 2289
LONG ISLAND EDUCATIONAL TV COUNCIL, INC.—See WNET; *U.S. Private*, pg. 4553
LONGO ELECTRICAL-MECHANICAL INC.; *U.S. Private*, pg. 2492
LOUISIANA LIFT & EQUIPMENT INC.; *U.S. Private*, pg. 2499
L & R PALLET SERVICE, INC.—See Freeman Spogli & Co. Incorporated; *U.S. Private*, pg. 1606
MAGNETIC PRODUCTS & SERVICES, INC.; *U.S. Private*, pg. 2547
MAHR U.K. PLC.—See Carl Mahr Holding GmbH; *Int'l*, pg. 1333
MARS AIRCRAFT SERVICES CO. OF NEW JERSEY—See AAR Corp.; *U.S. Public*, pg. 13
MARSHALL SCIENTIFIC LLC; *U.S. Private*, pg. 2593
MARSTON TECHNICAL SERVICES—See Belair Instrument Company LLC; *U.S. Private*, pg. 516
MARTHINUSEN & COUTTS (PTY.) LTD.—See ACTOM (Pty) Ltd.; *Int'l*, pg. 120
MATRIX COMMUNICATIONS INC.; *U.S. Private*, pg. 2611
MCA COMMUNICATIONS INC.; *U.S. Private*, pg. 2625
METROFUSER LLC; *U.S. Private*, pg. 2687
METTLER-TOLEDO (ALBSTADT) GMBH—See Mettler-Toledo International, Inc.; *U.S. Public*, pg. 1432
METTLER-TOLEDO GES.M.B.H.—See Mettler-Toledo International, Inc.; *U.S. Public*, pg. 1432
METTLER-TOLEDO GMBH—See Mettler-Toledo International, Inc.; *U.S. Public*, pg. 1432
METTLER-TOLEDO LTD.—See Mettler-Toledo International, Inc.; *U.S. Public*, pg. 1433
METTLER-TOLEDO LTD.—See Mettler-Toledo International, Inc.; *U.S. Public*, pg. 1433
METTLER-TOLEDO PHILIPPINES INC.—See Mettler-Toledo International, Inc.; *U.S. Public*, pg. 1433
METTLER-TOLEDO PROCESS ANALYTICS, INC.—See Mettler-Toledo International, Inc.; *U.S. Public*, pg. 1433
METTLER-TOLEDO S.A.S.—See Mettler-Toledo International, Inc.; *U.S. Public*, pg. 1433
METTLER-TOLEDO S.P.A.—See Mettler-Toledo International, Inc.; *U.S. Public*, pg. 1433
MFS, INC.; *U.S. Private*, pg. 2693
MID SOUTH ENGINE & POWER SYSTEMS, LLC—See Atlas Copco AB; *Int'l*, pg. 683
MIDWESTERN MACHINE & HYDRAULICS, INC.; *U.S. Private*, pg. 2724
MINELAB AMERICAS INC.—See Codan Limited; *Int'l*, pg. 1688

MINELAB INTERNATIONAL LTD—See Codan Limited; *Int'l*, pg. 1688
MINILEC SERVICE INCORPORATED; *U.S. Private*, pg. 2742
MINING MACHINERY INC.; *U.S. Private*, pg. 2742
MINT TURBINES LLC—See M International Inc.; *U.S. Private*, pg. 2523
MISYS INTERNATIONAL BANKING SYSTEMS (RISK) LLC—See Vista Equity Partners, LLC; *U.S. Private*, pg. 4397
MITEL BUSINESS SYSTEMS, INC.—See Searchlight Capital Partners, L.P.; *U.S. Private*, pg. 3589
MITUTOYO AMERICA CORPORATION; *U.S. Private*, pg. 2752
MOBILE INSTRUMENT SERVICE & REPAIR, INC.—See Thomas H. Lee Partners, L.P.; *U.S. Private*, pg. 4156
MOGAS INDUSTRIES PTY LTD—See Flowserve Corporation; *U.S. Public*, pg. 857
MOHAWK LTD.; *U.S. Private*, pg. 2765
MOLEX SERVICES GMBH—See Koch Industries, Inc.; *U.S. Private*, pg. 2334
MPW CONTAINER MANAGEMENT CORP.—See MPW Industrial Services Group, Inc.; *U.S. Private*, pg. 2804
MR. ELECTRIC LLC—See Harvest Partners L.P.; *U.S. Private*, pg. 1877
THE MUNDY COMPANIES; *U.S. Private*, pg. 4081
NATIONAL COMMUNICATIONS SERVICES, INC.—See Affinitech, Inc.; *U.S. Private*, pg. 122
NATIONAL STEEL COMPANY LIMITED—See Al-Tuwairqi Group; *Int'l*, pg. 289
NAVHOUSE CORPORATION—See Reliance Aerotech Inc.; *U.S. Private*, pg. 3394
NDS SOLUTION CO., LTD.—See COMSYS Holdings Corporation; *Int'l*, pg. 1762
NERDS ON CALL; *U.S. Private*, pg. 2885
NET ACTIVITY, INC.—See Custom Computer Specialists, LLC; *U.S. Private*, pg. 1128
NEW ENGLAND SYSTEMS, INC.; *U.S. Private*, pg. 2894
NEXICORE SERVICES, LLC—See Avnet, Inc.; *U.S. Public*, pg. 253
NICKERSON BUSINESS SYSTEMS, INC.; *U.S. Private*, pg. 2926
NIFTY CORPORATION—See Fujitsu Limited; *Int'l*, pg. 2837
N.V. METTLER-TOLEDO S.A.—See Mettler-Toledo International, Inc.; *U.S. Public*, pg. 1433
OFFSHORE INLAND SERVICES INC.; *U.S. Private*, pg. 3002
OPENREACH—See BT Group plc; *Int'l*, pg. 1203
OPTOMA CANADA—See Coretronic Corporation; *Int'l*, pg. 1800
ORACLE ELEVATOR COMPANY - TORRINGTON—See L Squared Capital Management LP; *U.S. Private*, pg. 2362
ORANGE COUNTY SPEAKER, INC.; *U.S. Private*, pg. 3037
PACIFIC POWER SERVICES CORP.—See Andrews Group; *U.S. Private*, pg. 280
PACKARD BELL (UK) LTD.—See Acer Incorporated; *Int'l*, pg. 100
PARAGON TECHNOLOGIES INC.; *U.S. Private*, pg. 3092
THE PARKER GROUP, INC.—See Diploma PLC; *Int'l*, pg. 2129
PDSI SINGAPORE PTE. LTD.—See Avnet, Inc.; *U.S. Public*, pg. 253
PENTAIR VALVES & CONTROLS, INC. - BRIDGEPORT—See Emerson Electric Co.; *U.S. Public*, pg. 751
PENTAX MEDICAL BULGARIA EOOD—See Hoya Corporation; *Int'l*, pg. 3495
PERIPHERAL COMPUTER SUPPORT, INC.—See Lincolnshire Management, Inc.; *U.S. Private*, pg. 2459
PHILLIPS KILN SERVICES LTD.—See FLSmidth & Co. A/S; *Int'l*, pg. 2712
PHILLIPS MACHINE SERVICE INC.; *U.S. Private*, pg. 3171
PIKES PEAK DISTRIBUTORS LLC; *U.S. Private*, pg. 3180
PINEAPPLE HOUSE OF BREVARD, INC.—See The Goldfield Corporation; *U.S. Public*, pg. 2075
PIONEER SERVICE NETWORK CORP—See EQT AB; *Int'l*, pg. 2471
PIPETTE CALIBRATION SERVICES, INC.—See Mettler-Toledo International, Inc.; *U.S. Public*, pg. 1433
PLANETBIDS INC—See The CapStreet Group LLC; *U.S. Private*, pg. 4005
POWER SERVICE GMBH—See Ceconomy AG; *Int'l*, pg. 1385
PRATT & WHITNEY ENGINE SERVICES, INC.—See RTX Corporation; *U.S. Public*, pg. 1823
PRECISION COPIER SERVICE, INC.—See Xerox Holdings Corporation; *U.S. Public*, pg. 2388
PRECISION ELECTRIC MOTOR WORKS, INC.—See Odyssey Investment Partners, LLC; *U.S. Private*, pg. 2995
PROFESSIONAL AIRCRAFT ACCESSORIES, INC.—See Greenwich AeroGroup, Inc.; *U.S. Private*, pg. 1781
PROTO SCRIPT PHARMACEUTICAL CORP.; *U.S. Public*, pg. 1730
PT AMTEK PRECISION COMPONENTS BATAM—See Blackstone Inc.; *U.S. Public*, pg. 355
PT IBM INDONESIA—See International Business Machines Corporation; *U.S. Public*, pg. 1149
PTR BALER & COMPACTOR SERVICE INC.—See Komar

811210 — ELECTRONIC AND PREC...

Industries, LLC; *U.S. Private,* pg. 2342
QUALITY QUICKLY, INC.—See Docugraphics, LLC; *U.S. Private,* pg. 1252
RADON MEDICAL IMAGING CORP; *U.S. Private,* pg. 3345
RAYMOND V. DAMADIAN M.D. MR SCANNING CENTER MANAGEMENT COMPANY—See FONAR Corporation; *U.S. Public,* pg. 863
REGENERSIS (BUCHAREST) SRL—See Francisco Partners Management, LP; *U.S. Private,* pg. 1588
REGENERSIS (CZECH) S.R.O—See Francisco Partners Management, LP; *U.S. Private,* pg. 1588
REGENERSIS (GLENROTHES) LTD.—See Francisco Partners Management, LP; *U.S. Private,* pg. 1588
REGENERSIS INC.—See Francisco Partners Management, LP; *U.S. Private,* pg. 1588
REGENERSIS ISTANBUL TEKNOLOJI DANISMANLIGI LIMITED SIRKETI—See Francisco Partners Management, LP; *U.S. Private,* pg. 1588
REGENERSIS MEXICO S.A.DE C.V.—See Francisco Partners Management, LP; *U.S. Private,* pg. 1588
REGENERSIS (PORTUGAL) LTD—See Francisco Partners Management, LP; *U.S. Private,* pg. 1588
REGENERSIS RUS O.O.O—See Francisco Partners Management, LP; *U.S. Private,* pg. 1588
REGENERSIS (SOMMERDA) GMBH—See Francisco Partners Management, LP; *U.S. Private,* pg. 1588
REGENERSIS (SOUTH AFRICA) (PTY) LTD—See Francisco Partners Management, LP; *U.S. Private,* pg. 1588
REGENERSIS (WARSAW) SP.Z.O.O.—See Francisco Partners Management, LP; *U.S. Private,* pg. 1588
REID & MITCHELL (PTY.) LTD.—See ACTOM (Pty) Ltd.; *Int'l,* pg. 120
RELIABLE TURBINE SERVICES LLC—See Fuji Electric Co., Ltd.; *Int'l,* pg. 2812
THE REMI GROUP, LLC; *U.S. Private,* pg. 4104
REVERTECH SOLUTIONS—See Leading Ridge Management, LLC; *U.S. Private,* pg. 2406
REXCO EQUIPMENT INC.; *U.S. Private,* pg. 3417
RMS OMEGA TECHNOLOGIES GROUP, INC.; *U.S. Private,* pg. 3452
ROUND ROCK COPIER, LLC—See Stargel Office Systems, Inc.; *U.S. Private,* pg. 3786
RSG AVIATION—See Trinity Hunt Management, L.P.; *U.S. Private,* pg. 4235
SABIEDRIBA AR IROBEZOTU ATBILDIBU IBM LATVIJA—See International Business Machines Corporation; *U.S. Public,* pg. 1150
SC ELECTRONIC SERVICE GMBH—See Hormann KG Verkaufsgesellschaf; *Int'l,* pg. 3481
SEALCO LLC—See Angeles Equity Partners, LLC; *U.S. Private,* pg. 282
SENTINEL POWER SERVICES, INC.—See Techpro Power Group, Inc.; *U.S. Private,* pg. 3956
SENTINEL TECHNOLOGIES, INC.; *U.S. Private,* pg. 3610
SERVICE EXPRESS, LLC—See Harvest Partners L.P.; *U.S. Private,* pg. 1877
SERVICE SUPPLY CORPORATION—See Stephenson Equipment, Inc.; *U.S. Private,* pg. 3803
SERVO SOUTH, INC.—See Wynnchurch Capital, L.P.; *U.S. Private,* pg. 4577
SETCO GREAT LAKES SERVICE CENTER—See Holden Industries, Inc.; *U.S. Private,* pg. 1962
SHANGHAI EBARA PRECISION MACHINERY CO., LTD.—See the Ebara Corporation; *Int'l,* pg. 2284
SHARP SUPPORT & SERVICE CORPORATION—See Hon Hai Precision Industry Co., Ltd.; *Int'l,* pg. 3459
SHENZHEN ZHONGWEI TECHNOLOGY CO., LTD.—See American Education Center, Inc.; *U.S. Public,* pg. 99
SIGMA ENERGO, S.R.O.—See CEZ, a.s.; *Int'l,* pg. 1428
SIGNATURE TECHNOLOGY GROUP, INC.—See TD Synnex Corp; *U.S. Public,* pg. 1986
SOF S.P.A.—See Fincantieri S.p.A.; *Int'l,* pg. 2671
SOHNEN ENTERPRISES INC.; *U.S. Private,* pg. 3706
SOUTH PLAINS BIOMEDICAL SERVICES, INC.; *U.S. Private,* pg. 3723
SPARTAN INDUSTRIAL INC.; *U.S. Private,* pg. 3746
SPHEREA TEST & SERVICES S.A.S.—See Andera Partners SCA; *Int'l,* pg. 450
SPHEREA TEST & SERVICES S.A.S.—See Coller Capital Ltd.; *Int'l,* pg. 1699
STANLEY SECURITY SOLUTIONS EUROPE LTD.—See Stanley Black & Decker, Inc.; *U.S. Public,* pg. 1935
STAN'S - LPS MIDWEST; *U.S. Private,* pg. 3777
STARFIRE SYSTEMS, INC.—See The Riverside Company; *U.S. Private,* pg. 4108
STEPHENSON EQUIPMENT, INC.; *U.S. Private,* pg. 3803
STORK GEARS & SERVICES B.V.—See Fluor Corporation; *U.S. Public,* pg. 860
STREAMLINE TECHNICAL SERVICES, INC.; *U.S. Private,* pg. 3838
TAJIMA USA, INC.—See Hirsch International Corp.; *U.S. Private,* pg. 1950
TANGENT INDUSTRIES LTD.—See Esquire Radio & Electronics Inc.; *U.S. Private,* pg. 1427
TEAM INDUSTRIAL SERVICES, INC.—See Team, Inc.; *U.S. Public,* pg. 1988
TEAM INDUSTRIAL SERVICES—See Team, Inc.; *U.S. Public,* pg. 1988

TECH DATA DELAWARE, INC.—See TD Synnex Corp; *U.S. Public,* pg. 1986
TECHNOLOGY UNLIMITED INC.; *U.S. Private,* pg. 3956
TECHTRENDS, INC.—See Nuvera Communications, Inc.; *U.S. Public,* pg. 1556
TEKNOSER A.S.—See Hitay Investment Holdings A.S.; *Int'l,* pg. 3425
TELEPHONE SERVICES INC.; *U.S. Private,* pg. 3961
TELEPLAN CENTRAL EUROPE HOLDING B.V.—See Clover Wireless; *U.S. Private,* pg. 948
TELEPLAN COLCHESTER LTD.—See Clover Wireless; *U.S. Private,* pg. 948
TELEPLAN COMMUNICATIONS B.V.—See Clover Wireless; *U.S. Private,* pg. 948
TELEPLAN ELECTRONIC TECHNOLOGY (SHANGHAI) CO. LTD.—See Clover Wireless; *U.S. Private,* pg. 948
TELEPLAN GERMANY GMBH—See Clover Wireless; *U.S. Private,* pg. 948
TELEPLAN INTERNATIONAL N.V.—See Clover Wireless; *U.S. Private,* pg. 947
TELEPLAN RHEIN-MAIN GMBH—See Clover Wireless; *U.S. Private,* pg. 948
TELEPLAN TECHNOLOGY SERVICES SDN BHD—See Clover Wireless; *U.S. Private,* pg. 948
TELEPLAN VIDEOCOM SOLUTIONS, INC.—See Clover Wireless; *U.S. Private,* pg. 948
TELEPLAN & WHITE ELECTRONICS B.V.—See Clover Wireless; *U.S. Private,* pg. 947
TELMAR NETWORK TECHNOLOGY B.V.—See Jabil Inc.; *U.S. Public,* pg. 1182
TELMAR NETWORK TECHNOLOGY CO., LTD.—See Jabil Inc.; *U.S. Public,* pg. 1182
TELMAR NETWORK TECHNOLOGY SDN BHD—See Jabil Inc.; *U.S. Public,* pg. 1182
TELMAR NETWORK TECHNOLOGY S.R.L.—See Jabil Inc.; *U.S. Public,* pg. 1182
TEL-NT BRAZIL COMERCIO DE EQUIPAMENTOS DE TELECOMUNICAOES LTDA.—See Jabil Inc.; *U.S. Public,* pg. 1182
TEXAS POS, INC.—See NCR Voyix Corporation.; *U.S. Public,* pg. 1503
TOSHIBA MEDICAL SYSTEMS CORPORATION—See Canon Inc.; *Int'l,* pg. 1298
TOTAL TELCO SPECIALIST INC.; *U.S. Private,* pg. 4191
TRIAD ELECTRIC & CONTROLS INC.—See The Newtron Group Inc.; *U.S. Private,* pg. 4084
TRIAD, INC.; *U.S. Private,* pg. 4225
TRIDENT CONTRACT MANAGEMENT; *U.S. Private,* pg. 4229
TRIMEDX INTERNATIONAL, LLC—See Ascension Health Alliance; *U.S. Private,* pg. 346
TRIUMPH INSTRUMENTS-BURBANK, INC.—See Triumph Group, Inc.; *U.S. Public,* pg. 2197
TRS GLOBAL SERVICES, LLC—See Knox Capital Holdings, LLC; *U.S. Private,* pg. 2324
TSI INSTRUMENTS LTD.—See TSI Incorporated; *U.S. Private,* pg. 4253
TSUKEN CORPORATION—See COMSYS Holdings Corporation; *Int'l,* pg. 1762
TURBO MACHINERY REPAIR, INC.—See DXP Enterprises, Inc.; *U.S. Public,* pg. 698
TYLER TECHNOLOGIES, INC.—See Tyler Technologies, Inc.; *U.S. Public,* pg. 2209
UBEO, LLC—See Sentinel Capital Partners, L.L.C.; *U.S. Private,* pg. 3609
UBREAKIFIX—See Asurion LLC; *U.S. Private,* pg. 363
ULTRA SOLUTIONS—See E&A Industries, LLC; *U.S. Private,* pg. 1301
UNITED RADIO INC.; *U.S. Private,* pg. 4296
UPRIGHT TECHNOLOGIES LLC—See DEVsource Technology Solutions, LLC; *U.S. Private,* pg. 1219
UTILITIES & INDUSTRIES—See BSI Diversified LLC; *U.S. Private,* pg. 675
V2 SYSTEMS, INC.; *U.S. Private,* pg. 4328
VANDER-BEND MANUFACTURING, LLC—See Aterian Investment Management, L.P.; *U.S. Private,* pg. 367
VIRTUAL ACCESS (IRELAND) LTD.—See Ependion AB; *Int'l,* pg. 2459
VITRON ELECTRONIC SERVICES, INC.—See Omega Electronics Manufacturing Services; *U.S. Private,* pg. 3015
WABM-TV—See Sinclair, Inc.; *U.S. Public,* pg. 1886
WALBAR INC.—See RTX Corporation; *U.S. Public,* pg. 1822
WALLIS NOMINEES (COMPUTING) PTY. LTD.—See DWS Limited; *Int'l,* pg. 2236
WELLINGTON TECHNOLOGIES, INC.; *U.S. Private,* pg. 4475
WENCO INTERNATIONAL MINING SYSTEMS LTD.—See Hitachi, Ltd.; *Int'l,* pg. 3424
WILM-TV—See Capitol Broadcasting Company, Inc.; *U.S. Private,* pg. 743
WILSON UTILITY EQUIPMENT CO.—See Wilson Construction Co., Inc.; *U.S. Private,* pg. 4530
WINKLE INDUSTRIES, INC.—See Groupe R.Y. Beaudoin, Inc.; *Int'l,* pg. 3110
WIRELESS ELECTRONICS, INC.; *U.S. Private,* pg. 4547
WIRELESS TECHNOLOGY EQUIPMENT COMPANY,

INC.—See Motorola Solutions, Inc.; *U.S. Public,* pg. 1479
WOODWARD, INC. - LOVES PARK—See Woodward, Inc.; *U.S. Public,* pg. 2378
WOODWARD INTERNATIONAL, INC. - GLOUCESTER PLANT—See Woodward, Inc.; *U.S. Public,* pg. 2378
WOODWARD POWER SOLUTIONS GMBH—See Woodward, Inc.; *U.S. Public,* pg. 2378
WUSA-TV—See TEGNA Inc.; *U.S. Public,* pg. 1991
WUXI CAS PHOTONICS CO., LTD.—See Focused Photonics (Hangzhou), Inc.; *Int'l,* pg. 2720
XERXES COMPUTER COMPANY, LLC—See PosNavitas Retail Services, Inc.; *U.S. Private,* pg. 3234

811310 — COMMERCIAL AND INDUSTRIAL MACHINERY AND EQUIPMENT (EXCEPT AUTOMOTIVE AND ELECTRONIC) REPAIR AND MAINTENANCE

3PHASE ELEVATOR CORP; *U.S. Private,* pg. 13
ABB BAILEY BEIJING ENGINEERING CO. LTD.—See ABB Ltd.; *Int'l,* pg. 49
ABB SERVICE GMBH—See ABB Ltd.; *Int'l,* pg. 50
ACCESSORY TECHNOLOGIES CORPORATION—See HEICO Corporation; *U.S. Public,* pg. 1021
ACS AIRCONTAINER SERVICES GESELLSCHAFT M.B.H.—See Deutsche Lufthansa AG; *Int'l,* pg. 2066
ADEX ZONEX PTE. LTD.—See Caterpillar, Inc.; *U.S. Public,* pg. 449
ADVANCED DOCUMENT SOLUTIONS, INC.; *U.S. Private,* pg. 89
ADVANCED TECHNOLOGY SERVICES, INC.—See WestView Capital Partners, L.P.; *U.S. Private,* pg. 4501
AEGION COATING SERVICES, LLC—See Voyager Interests, LLC; *U.S. Private,* pg. 4414
AEGION CORPORATION—See New Mountain Capital, LLC; *U.S. Private,* pg. 2899
AERO CONTROLS INC.; *U.S. Private,* pg. 118
AERO PRECISION & REPAIR OVERHAUL COMPANY INC.—See Groupe Industriel Marcel Dassault S.A.; *Int'l,* pg. 3105
AEROREPAIR CORP.—See GenNx360 Capital Partners, L.P.; *U.S. Private,* pg. 1672
AEROSPACE & COMMERCIAL TECHNOLOGIES, LLC—See HEICO Corporation; *U.S. Public,* pg. 1021
AEROSPACE PRECISION INC.—See Aerospace Distributors Inc.; *U.S. Private,* pg. 119
AGP CORPORATION; *Int'l,* pg. 213
AGRI SERVICE INCORPORATED; *U.S. Private,* pg. 129
AIRBASE SERVICES INC.—See Regent Aerospace Corporation; *U.S. Private,* pg. 3387
AIRCRAFT TECHNOLOGY, INC.—See HEICO Corporation; *U.S. Public,* pg. 1019
AIR FRAME STRAIGHTENING; *U.S. Private,* pg. 138
AIR & HYDRAULIC POWER CENTRE—See Baker & Provan Pty. Ltd.; *Int'l,* pg. 805
AIRTEC LIMITED—See Ingersoll Rand Inc.; *U.S. Public,* pg. 1120
AKITA ENGINEERING CO., LTD.—See Dowa Holdings Co., Ltd.; *Int'l,* pg. 2182
ALAMO GROUP THE NETHERLANDS B.V.—See Alamo Group Inc.; *U.S. Public,* pg. 71
ALAMO GROUP THE NETHERLANDS MIDDELBURG B.V.—See Alamo Group Inc.; *U.S. Public,* pg. 71
ALCOMET AD; *Int'l,* pg. 302
ALTECH ENGINEERING CO., LTD.—See Altech Co., Ltd.; *Int'l,* pg. 388
AMERAMEX INTERNATIONAL, INC.; *U.S. Public,* pg. 94
AMERICAN COOLER SERVICE, LLC—See JLL Partners, LLC; *U.S. Private,* pg. 2212
AMERICON EQUIPMENT SERVICES, INC.—See Babcock & Wilcox Enterprises, Inc.; *U.S. Public,* pg. 262
AMKO SERVICE COMPANY—See FIBA Technologies Inc.; *U.S. Private,* pg. 1501
ANIXTER AUSTRALIA PTY. LTD.—See WESCO International, Inc.; *U.S. Public,* pg. 2350
ANMAR CONSTRUCTION AFRICA (PTY) LTD—See Anmar Mechanical and Electrical Contractors Ltd.; *Int'l,* pg. 473
APM TERMINALS VALENCIA S.A.—See A.P. Moller-Maersk A/S; *Int'l,* pg. 25
APPULSE CORPORATION; *Int'l,* pg. 522
APS RESOURCES—See ASSA ABLOY AB; *Int'l,* pg. 633
AQUAMARINE SUBSEA STAVANGER AS—See HitecVision AS; *Int'l,* pg. 3426
AQUILEX ARABIA, LTD.—See Ali Abdullah Al Tamimi Company; *Int'l,* pg. 319
AQUILEX SPECIALTY REPAIR & OVERHAUL INC.—See AZZ, Inc.; *U.S. Public,* pg. 259
AQUILEX WELDING SERVICES, B.V.—See AZZ, Inc.; *U.S. Public,* pg. 259
AQUILEX WELDING SERVICES POLAND SP. Z O.O.—See AZZ, Inc.; *U.S. Public,* pg. 259
AQUILEX WSI NUCLEAR SERVICES—See AZZ, Inc.; *U.S. Public,* pg. 259
ASM SERVICES AND SUPPORT ISRAEL LTD—See ASM INTERNATIONAL N.V.; *Int'l,* pg. 626
ATELIER P.V. HYDRAULIQUE 2004 INC.—See Applied In-

N.A.I.C.S. INDEX

811310 — COMMERCIAL AND INDU...

dustrial Technologies, Inc.; *U.S. Public*, pg. 170
ATLAS COPCO KOMPRESSORTEKNIKK AS—See Atlas Copco AB; *Int'l*, pg. 677
ATLAS COPCO S.R.O.—See Atlas Copco AB; *Int'l*, pg. 681
ATOMENERGOREMONT PLC; *Int'l*, pg. 687
AUSTIN ENGINEERING LTD.; *Int'l*, pg. 718
AVERY BERKEL FRANCE SAS—See Illinois Tool Works Inc.; *U.S. Public*, pg. 1101
AZZ GALVANIZING - VIRGINIA LLC—See AZZ, Inc.; *U.S. Public*, pg. 259
AZZ SMS LLC—See CenterGate Capital, LP; *U.S. Private*, pg. 816
AZZ WSI B.V.—See AZZ, Inc.; *U.S. Public*, pg. 259
AZZ WSI CANADA, ULC—See AZZ, Inc.; *U.S. Public*, pg. 259
AZZ WSI DO BRASIL LTDA.—See AZZ, Inc.; *U.S. Public*, pg. 259
AZZ WSI, INC.—See AZZ, Inc.; *U.S. Public*, pg. 259
BABCOCK & WILCOX DE MONTERREY, S.A. DE C.V.—See Babcock & Wilcox Enterprises, Inc.; *U.S. Public*, pg. 263
BARNES AEROSPACE - EAST GRANBY—See Barnes Group Inc.; *U.S. Public*, pg. 276
BARTLETT HOLDINGS, INC.—See Bernhard Capital Partners Management, LP; *U.S. Private*, pg. 537
BEARING INSPECTION INC.—See The Timken Company; *U.S. Public*, pg. 2132
BEPCO IBERICA SA—See Group Thermote & Vanhalst; *Int'l*, pg. 3089
BGR ENERGY SYSTEMS LIMITED; *Int'l*, pg. 1008
BILFINGER DANMARK A/S—See Bilfinger SE; *Int'l*, pg. 1027
BILFINGER EMV B.V.—See Bilfinger SE; *Int'l*, pg. 1027
BILFINGER ENGINEERING & MAINTENANCE GMBH—See Bilfinger SE; *Int'l*, pg. 1027
BILFINGER INDUSTRIAL SERVICES AUSTRIA GMBH—See Bilfinger SE; *Int'l*, pg. 1027
BILFINGER INDUSTRIAL SERVICES POLSKA SP. Z O.O.—See Bilfinger SE; *Int'l*, pg. 1027
BILFINGER INDUSTRIAL SERVICES SCHWEIZ AG—See Bilfinger SE; *Int'l*, pg. 1026
BILFINGER NORDICS AS—See Bilfinger SE; *Int'l*, pg. 1027
BILFINGER NORTH AMERICA INC.—See Bilfinger SE; *Int'l*, pg. 1027
BIOSAR AMERICA LLC—See ELLAKTOR S.A.; *Int'l*, pg. 2364
BIOSAR AUSTRALIA PTY LTD—See ELLAKTOR S.A.; *Int'l*, pg. 2364
BIOSAR BRASIL - ENERGIA RENOVAVEL LTDA—See ELLAKTOR S.A.; *Int'l*, pg. 2365
BIOSAR CHILE SPA—See ELLAKTOR S.A.; *Int'l*, pg. 2365
BIOSAR ENERGY (UK) LTD—See ELLAKTOR S.A.; *Int'l*, pg. 2365
BIOSAR HOLDINGS LTD.—See ELLAKTOR S.A.; *Int'l*, pg. 2365
BIOSAR PANAMA INC.—See ELLAKTOR S.A.; *Int'l*, pg. 2365
BIS CZECH S.R.O.—See Bilfinger SE; *Int'l*, pg. 1025
BIS HUNGARY KFT.—See Bilfinger SE; *Int'l*, pg. 1025
BIS ROB ZEELAND B.V.—See Bilfinger SE; *Int'l*, pg. 1025
BIS SALAMIS INC.—See Bilfinger SE; *Int'l*, pg. 1026
BIS TSG INDUSTRIESERVICE GMBH—See Bilfinger SE; *Int'l*, pg. 1026
BLAIR PARK SERVICES, LLC—See Dycom Industries, Inc.; *U.S. Public*, pg. 698
BLOOM ELECTRIC SERVICES, INC.; *U.S. Private*, pg. 583
BLUDWORTH MARINE, LLC; *U.S. Private*, pg. 585
BOASSO AMERICA - CHANNELVIEW—See Apax Partners LLP; *Int'l*, pg. 505
BOASSO AMERICA - CHARLESTON—See Apax Partners LLP; *Int'l*, pg. 505
BOASSO AMERICA - CHESAPEAKE—See Apax Partners LLP; *Int'l*, pg. 505
BOASSO AMERICA - CHICAGO—See Apax Partners LLP; *Int'l*, pg. 505
BOASSO AMERICA CORPORATION—See Apax Partners LLP; *Int'l*, pg. 505
BOASSO AMERICA - DETROIT—See Apax Partners LLP; *Int'l*, pg. 505
BOASSO AMERICA - GARDEN CITY—See Apax Partners LLP; *Int'l*, pg. 505
BOASSO AMERICA - JACKSONVILLE—See Apax Partners LLP; *Int'l*, pg. 505
BOASSO AMERICA - WEST MEMPHIS—See Apax Partners LLP; *Int'l*, pg. 505
BOUSTEAD MEDICAL CARE HOLDINGS PTE. LTD.—See Boustead Singapore Limited; *Int'l*, pg. 1120
BRANDON & CLARK INC.; *U.S. Private*, pg. 638
BRIGGS & STRATTON CZ, S.R.O.—See Briggs & Stratton Corporation; *U.S. Private*, pg. 651
BTREN MANTENIMIENTO FERROVIARIO S.A.—See Alstom S.A.; *Int'l*, pg. 383
BUCHER HYDRAULICS CORPORATION—See Bucher Industries AG; *Int'l*, pg. 1207
BUIMA ENERGY INC.—See Buima Group, Inc.; *Int'l*, pg. 1212
CABLECOM, LLC—See Dycom Industries, Inc.; *U.S. Public*, pg. 698

CABLECOM OF CALIFORNIA, INC.—See Dycom Industries, Inc.; *U.S. Public*, pg. 698
CABNET M&E SDN. BHD.—See Cabnet Holding Berhad; *Int'l*, pg. 1246
CAMEXIP S.A.; *Int'l*, pg. 1272
C&B OPERATIONS LLC; *U.S. Private*, pg. 702
C&C MECHANICAL LTD.—See Absolent Air Care Group AB; *Int'l*, pg. 70
CENTRE D'ESSAIS FERROVIAIRES SAS—See Alstom S.A.; *Int'l*, pg. 383
CEZ ENERGOSERVIS SPOL, S.R.O.—See CEZ, a.s.; *Int'l*, pg. 1426
CH MURPHY/CLARK-ULLMAN INC.; *U.S. Private*, pg. 844
CHROMALLOY POWER SERVICES CORP.—See Veritas Capital Fund Management, LLC; *U.S. Private*, pg. 4364
CHROMALLOY SAN DIEGO CORPORATION—See Veritas Capital Fund Management, LLC; *U.S. Private*, pg. 4364
CIEM S.P.A.; *Int'l*, pg. 1605
CIRUS CONTROL LLC—See Brinkmere Capital Partners LLC; *U.S. Private*, pg. 655
CKD FIELD ENGINEERING CORPORATION—See CKD Corporation; *Int'l*, pg. 1639
CN ASIA CORPORATION BHD.; *Int'l*, pg. 1672
COLEMAN HYDRAULICS LIMITED—See Westinghouse Air Brake Technologies Corporation; *U.S. Public*, pg. 2357
COLT ATLANTIC SERVICES, INC.; *U.S. Private*, pg. 975
COMERCIAL INGERSOLL-RAND (CHILE) LIMITADA—See Ingersoll Rand Inc.; *U.S. Public*, pg. 1118
COMMERCIAL ARMATURE WORKS; *U.S. Private*, pg. 983
COMPLETE INDUSTRIAL ENTERPRISES; *U.S. Private*, pg. 1001
CONNECTED WIND SERVICES A/S—See EnBW Energie Baden-Wurttemberg AG; *Int'l*, pg. 2398
CONSULTANTS F.DRAPEAU INC.; *Int'l*, pg. 1778
CONTINENTAL CYLINDER INC.—See Corrosion & Abrasion Solutions Ltd.; *Int'l*, pg. 1806
COPERION INTERNATIONAL TRADING (SHANGHAI) CO. LTD.—See Hillenbrand, Inc.; *U.S. Public*, pg. 1036
COPERION MACHINERY & SYSTEMS (SHANGHAI) CO. LTD.—See Hillenbrand, Inc.; *U.S. Public*, pg. 1036
COSCO SHIPPING LINES AMERICAS, INC.—See COSCO Shipping Holdings Co., Ltd.; *Int'l*, pg. 1810
COSCO SHIPPING LINES (BRAZIL) S.A.—See COSCO Shipping Holdings Co., Ltd.; *Int'l*, pg. 1810
CROTONE CRUISE PORT S.R.L.—See Global Yatirim Holding A.S.; *Int'l*, pg. 3002
CUBE AIRE—See Freeman Spogli & Co. Incorporated; *U.S. Private*, pg. 1606
CYBEM SERVICES PTY LTD.—See Aquirian Limited; *Int'l*, pg. 528
DAEBO MAGNETIC CO., LTD.; *Int'l*, pg. 1905
DAIKIN AIR-CONDITIONING TECHNOLOGY (BEIJING), LTD.—See Daikin Industries, Ltd.; *Int'l*, pg. 1933
DAIO PRINTING CORPORATION—See Daio Paper Corporation; *Int'l*, pg. 1939
DAIWA LIFECOSMO CO., LTD.—See Daiwa House Industry Co., Ltd.; *Int'l*, pg. 1945
DALDRUP BOHRTECHNIK AG—See Daldrup & Sohne AG; *Int'l*, pg. 1950
DAYA BUMIMAJU SDN. BHD.; *Int'l*, pg. 1985
DEMPO SHIPBUILDING & ENGINEERING PVT. LTD.—See Goa Carbon Ltd.; *Int'l*, pg. 3018
DENEL AERONAUTICS—See Denel SOC Ltd.; *Int'l*, pg. 2026
DESTINI PRIMA SDN. BHD.—See Destini Berhad; *Int'l*, pg. 2046
DEUTSCHE BABCOCK MIDDLE EAST FZE—See Bilfinger SE; *Int'l*, pg. 1028
DF MOMPRESA, S.A.U.—See Duro Felguera, S.A.; *Int'l*, pg. 2228
DIGITAL CHARGING SOLUTIONS GMBH—See Bayerische Motoren Werke Aktiengesellschaft; *Int'l*, pg. 912
DISCO HI-TEC (VIETNAM) CO., LTD.—See Disco Corporation; *Int'l*, pg. 2131
DISTRIBUIDORA CUMMINS CENTROAMERICA GUATEMALA, LTDA.—See Cummins Inc.; *U.S. Public*, pg. 607
DJK FACTORY SOLUTIONS (PHILIPPINES), INC.—See Daiichi Jitsugyo Co. Ltd.; *Int'l*, pg. 1927
D.N.K. CO., LTD.—See Dai Nippon Printing Co., Ltd.; *Int'l*, pg. 1914
DOOSAN MECATEC CO., LTD.—See Doosan Corporation; *Int'l*, pg. 2173
DRIVETRAIN AUSTRALIA PTY. LTD.—See Engenco Limited; *Int'l*, pg. 2427
DRIVETRAIN SINGAPORE PTE. LTD.—See Engenco Limited; *Int'l*, pg. 2427
DUNCAN AVIATION INC.; *U.S. Private*, pg. 1287
DURASERV CORP; *U.S. Private*, pg. 1293
DYNAMIC CERTIFICATION LABORATORIES—See Vibration Mountings & Controls, Inc.; *U.S. Private*, pg. 4376
DYNAPAR CORPORATION—See Fortive Corporation; *U.S. Public*, pg. 870
EASY ICE, LLC—See Freeman Spogli & Co. Incorporated; *U.S. Private*, pg. 1606
ECOFYS WTTS B.V.—See Bain Capital, LP; *U.S. Private*, pg. 432
ELECTRIC MELTING SERVICES COMPANY, LTD.—See Indel, Inc.; *U.S. Private*, pg. 2055

ELECTRIC SERVICE & SALES, INC.—See Tencarva Machinery Company, LLC; *U.S. Private*, pg. 3965
ELEKTROREMONT D.D.; *Int'l*, pg. 2357
ELITE LINE SERVICES, INC.—See Daifuku Co., Ltd.; *Int'l*, pg. 1925
EMERSON PROFESSIONAL TOOLS (SHANGHAI) CO., LTD.—See Emerson Electric Co.; *U.S. Public*, pg. 749
EMMEGI S.P.A.—See Cifin S.r.l.; *Int'l*, pg. 1605
ENDEL SAS—See ENGIE SA; *Int'l*, pg. 2431
ENDOSCOPY DEVELOPMENT COMPANY LLC—See RoundTable Healthcare Management, Inc.; *U.S. Private*, pg. 3489
ENERGOREMONT RUSE AD—See Dietsmann N.V.; *Int'l*, pg. 2117
ENESERVE CORPORATION—See Daiwa House Industry Co., Ltd.; *Int'l*, pg. 1946
ENVITEC SERVICE GMBH—See EnviTec Biogas AG; *Int'l*, pg. 2456
E.ON ANLAGENSERVICE GMBH—See E.ON SE; *Int'l*, pg. 2252
EPIROC TRADING CO., LTD.—See Epiroc AB; *Int'l*, pg. 2462
EQUIPEMENTS & SERVICES NIAMEY—See BIA Overseas S.A.; *Int'l*, pg. 1017
EQUIPSYSTEMS, LLC.; *U.S. Private*, pg. 1415
E/S STYROMATIC AB—See Bravida Holding AB; *Int'l*, pg. 1142
EUROPEAN PNEUMATIC COMPONENT OVERHAUL & REPAIR (EPCOR) BV—See Air France-KLM S.A.; *Int'l*, pg. 237
EUTECTIC DO BRASIL LTDA—See Enovis Corporation; *U.S. Public*, pg. 772
EVERGREEN SHIPPING AGENCY PHILIPPINES CORPORATION—See Evergreen Marine Corporation (Taiwan) Ltd.; *Int'l*, pg. 2566
FANUC FA DEUTSCHLAND GMBH—See FANUC Corporation; *Int'l*, pg. 2614
FANUC FA FRANCE S.A.S.—See FANUC Corporation; *Int'l*, pg. 2614
FANUC FA HUNGARY KFT—See FANUC Corporation; *Int'l*, pg. 2614
FANUC FA IBERIA S.A.U.—See FANUC Corporation; *Int'l*, pg. 2614
FANUC FA NORDIC AB—See FANUC Corporation; *Int'l*, pg. 2614
FANUC FA SATIS VE SERVIS TICARET LTD.—See FANUC Corporation; *Int'l*, pg. 2614
FANUC FA SWITZERLAND GMBH—See FANUC Corporation; *Int'l*, pg. 2614
FANUC KOREA SERVICE CORPORATION—See FANUC Corporation; *Int'l*, pg. 2614
FANUC POLSKA SP. Z O.O.—See FANUC Corporation; *Int'l*, pg. 2614
FANUC VIETNAM LIMITED—See FANUC Corporation; *Int'l*, pg. 2614
FAR EAST MAJU ENGINEERING WORKS SDN BHD—See Far East Group Limited; *Int'l*, pg. 2616
F&E AIRCRAFT MAINTENANCE; *U.S. Private*, pg. 1454
FE & B ENGINEERING (M) SDN. BHD.—See Far East Group Limited; *Int'l*, pg. 2616
FEMCO HOLDINGS, LLC; *U.S. Private*, pg. 1494
FEMCO MACHINE COMPANY—See Saugatuck Capital Company; *U.S. Private*, pg. 3554
FENNER DUNLOP CONVEYOR SERVICES, LLC—See Compagnie Generale des Etablissements Michelin SCA; *Int'l*, pg. 1744
FESTO E.U.R.L.—See Festo AG & Co. KG; *Int'l*, pg. 2647
FLANDERS ELECTRIC MOTOR SERVICE INC.; *U.S. Private*, pg. 1540
FLEXTRONICS INTERNATIONAL JAPAN CO., LTD.—See Flex Ltd.; *Int'l*, pg. 2702
FLSMIDTH USA INC.—See FLSmidth & Co. A/S; *Int'l*, pg. 2712
FOCKE DO BRASIL LTDA—See Focke & Co. (GmbH & Co.) Verpackungsmaschinen; *Int'l*, pg. 2718
FOKKER AIRCRAFT SERVICES B.V.—See GKN plc; *Int'l*, pg. 2983
FORCE EQUIPMENT PTY LTD—See Emeco Holdings Limited; *Int'l*, pg. 2376
FORKLIFTS OF MINNESOTA, INC. - FORKLIFTS OF WISCONSIN DIVISION—See Forklifts of Minnesota, Inc.; *U.S. Private*, pg. 1569
FOSBEL, INC.—See Ares Management Corporation; *U.S. Public*, pg. 189
FRANKLIN EQUIPMENT LLC—See United Rentals, Inc.; *U.S. Public*, pg. 2235
FRIEDRICH EISEN GMBH—See Bilfinger SE; *Int'l*, pg. 1028
FRONTIER SERVICE PARTNERS—See Apex Service Partners LLC; *U.S. Private*, pg. 293
FRONTKEN CORPORATION BERHAD; *Int'l*, pg. 2796
FUJI ELECTRIC FA SERVICE CO., LTD.—See Fuji Electric Co., Ltd.; *Int'l*, pg. 2811
FUJI ELECTRIC RETAIL SEVICE CO., LTD.—See Fuji Electric Co., Ltd.; *Int'l*, pg. 2811
FURMANITE A/S—See Team, Inc.; *U.S. Public*, pg. 1987
FUTURE AVIATION, INC.—See HEICO Corporation; *U.S. Public*, pg. 1019
GAMMERLER GMBH—See Blue Cap AG; *Int'l*, pg. 1067

811310 — COMMERCIAL AND INDU... CORPORATE AFFILIATIONS

GBW RAILCAR SERVICES, LLC—See Kinder Morgan, Inc.; *U.S. Public*, pg. 1233
GBW RAILCAR SERVICES, LLC—See The Greenbrier Companies, Inc.; *U.S. Public*, pg. 2085
GEA GRENCO IRELAND LTD.—See GEA Group Aktiengesellschaft; *Int'l*, pg. 2899
GEA REFRIGERATION CANADA INC.—See GEA Group Aktiengesellschaft; *Int'l*, pg. 2902
GE ENGINE SERVICES, INC.—See General Electric Company; *U.S. Public*, pg. 919
GIA (SHANGHAI) MINING EQUIPMENT CO., LTD.—See Epiroc AB; *Int'l*, pg. 2462
GILBARCO AUTOTANK AS—See Vontier Corporation; *U.S. Public*, pg. 2308
GOODTECH ENVIRONMENT AB—See Goodtech ASA; *Int'l*, pg. 3041
GRABENER PRESSENSYSTEME GMBH & CO. KG—See ANDRITZ AG; *Int'l*, pg. 456
GRAFTECH HONG KONG LIMITED—See Brookfield Corporation; *U.S. Public*, pg. 1187
GRAND CENTRAL ENTERPRISES (SARAWAK) SDN. BHD.—See Grand Central Enterprises Bhd.; *Int'l*, pg. 3054
G REEKIE GROUP LTD; *Int'l*, pg. 2861
GRODSKY SERVICE, INC.—See Harry Grodsky & Co., Inc.; *U.S. Private*, pg. 1871
GROUPE AG3I SA; *Int'l*, pg. 3091
GUANGZHOU KINTE MATERIAL TECHNOLOGY CO., LTD.—See China National Electric Apparatus Research Institute Co., Ltd.; *Int'l*, pg. 1531
GXP AUTOMATION LLC.—See Huron Capital Partners LLC; *U.S. Private*, pg. 2011
HAHN GROUP GMBH; *Int'l*, pg. 3208
HAINAN HITACHI ELEVATOR SERVICE CO., LTD.—See Hitachi, Ltd.; *Int'l*, pg. 3416
HAMILTON POWER SOLUTIONS—See Palmer Johnson Enterprises, Inc.; *U.S. Private*, pg. 3081
HANWA STEEL SERVICE LTD.—See Hanwa Co., Ltd.; *Int'l*, pg. 3262
HARTER AEROSPACE, LLC—See HEICO Corporation; *U.S. Public*, pg. 1020
HDW BV—See Group Thermote & Vanhalst; *Int'l*, pg. 3089
HEARTLAND SERVICES, INC.; *U.S. Private*, pg. 1900
HEAVYMECH PTY. LTD.—See E&A Limited; *Int'l*, pg. 2247
HENNESSY INDUSTRIES CANADA—See Vontier Corporation; *U.S. Public*, pg. 2309
H.G.S. GMBH & CO. KG—See ENGIE SA; *Int'l*, pg. 2429
HIGHLINES CONSTRUCTION COMPANY, INC.—See Asplundh Tree Expert Co.; *U.S. Private*, pg. 353
HITACHI CONSTRUCTION MACHINERY SALES AND SERVICE FRANCE S.A.S.—See Hitachi, Ltd.; *Int'l*, pg. 3416
HITACHI-MYCOM MAINTENANCE & SOLUTIONS LTDA.—See Hitachi, Ltd.; *Int'l*, pg. 3422
HITACHI PLANT CONSTRUCTION, LTD.—See Hitachi, Ltd.; *Int'l*, pg. 3420
H. JESSEN JURGENSEN AB—See Beijer Ref AB; *Int'l*, pg. 944
HMI ELECTRIC—See Heavy Machines, Inc.; *U.S. Private*, pg. 1902
HOLMGRENS TRUCK-MOTOR AB—See Bilia AB; *Int'l*, pg. 1029
HONG WEI ELECTRICAL INDUSTRY CO., LTD.; *Int'l*, pg. 3469
HOWDEN UK LIMITED - CARCROFT DIVISION—See Chart Industries, Inc.; *U.S. Public*, pg. 482
HOWDEN UK LIMITED - CONSTRUCTION & MAINTENANCE DIVISION—See Chart Industries, Inc.; *U.S. Public*, pg. 482
HRD AERO SYSTEMS, INC.; *U.S. Private*, pg. 1998
HRI, INC.—See Apollo Global Management, Inc.; *U.S. Public*, pg. 166
HUDSON TECHNOLOGIES, INC.; *U.S. Public*, pg. 1068
HYDRAULIC REPAIR AND DESIGN, INC.—See Clearlake Capital Group, L.P.; *U.S. Private*, pg. 933
ICHIKAWA CO. LTD.; *Int'l*, pg. 3580
IES INFRASTRUCTURE SOLUTIONS, LLC—See IES Holdings, Inc.; *U.S. Public*, pg. 1094
IMA NORTH AMERICA INC.—See I.M.A. Industria Macchine Automatiche S.p.A.; *Int'l*, pg. 3565
INDUSTRIAL POWERTRAIN PTY. LTD.—See Engenco Limited; *Int'l*, pg. 2427
INDUSTRIAL SERVICE SOLUTIONS LLC—See Wynnchurch Capital, L.P.; *U.S. Private*, pg. 4577
INERTIAL AEROSPACE SERVICES—See HEICO Corporation; *U.S. Public*, pg. 1020
INSITUFORM A/S—See New Mountain Capital, LLC; *U.S. Private*, pg. 2899
INTEGRATED POWER SERVICES LLC—See Odyssey Investment Partners, LLC; *U.S. Private*, pg. 2995
IRS INTERNATIONAL PTY. LTD.—See Daikin Industries, Ltd.; *Int'l*, pg. 1935
ITRON CZECH REPUBLIC S.R.O.—See Itron, Inc.; *U.S. Public*, pg. 1176
JAMES ELECTRIC MOTOR SERVICES LTD.—See Ferguson plc; *Int'l*, pg. 2638
JASPER ELECTRIC MOTORS INC.—See Jasper Engine & Transmission Exchange Inc.; *U.S. Private*, pg. 2190

J. CHRISTOF E & P SERVICES S.R.L.—See Christof Holding AG; *Int'l*, pg. 1587
JEUMONT ELECTRIC MAINTENANCE—See Altawest Group; *Int'l*, pg. 388
JIMCO MAINTENANCE, INC.; *U.S. Private*, pg. 2210
KALMAR BELGIUM NV/SA—See Cargotec Corporation; *Int'l*, pg. 1327
KALMAR EQUIPMENT (AUSTRALIA) PTY. LTD.—See Cargotec Corporation; *Int'l*, pg. 1327
KALMAR GERMANY GMBH—See Cargotec Corporation; *Int'l*, pg. 1328
KEC CORPORATION—See Electric Power Development Co., Ltd.; *Int'l*, pg. 2349
KIEMLE-HANKINS COMPANY; *U.S. Private*, pg. 2303
KITO CORPORATION—See The Carlyle Group Inc.; *U.S. Public*, pg. 2054
KOCH-GLITSCH ITALIA S.R.L.—See Koch Industries, Inc.; *U.S. Private*, pg. 2332
KREMLIN REXSON PTE LTD—See Exel Industries SA; *Int'l*, pg. 2583
LAMAR TECHNOLOGIES CORPORATION—See Aeries Enterprises, LLC; *U.S. Private*, pg. 117
LAND & SEA INSTRUMENTATION LTD—See Black & McDonald Limited; *Int'l*, pg. 1056
LAUING HEATEC CO., LTD.—See Bilfinger SE; *Int'l*, pg. 1028
LOCKHEED MARTIN AERONAUTICS COMPANY—See Lockheed Martin Corporation; *U.S. Public*, pg. 1338
LOTOS SERWIS SP. Z O.O.—See Grupa LOTOS S.A.; *Int'l*, pg. 3117
LOUISIANA VALVE SOURCE INC.—See MiddleGround Management, LP; *U.S. Private*, pg. 2712
LUCAS PRECISION LLC—See FERMAT Group, a.s.; *Int'l*, pg. 2639
MANT. AYUDA A LA EXPLOT. Y SERVICIOS, S.A—See ACS, Actividades de Construccion y Servicios, S.A.; *Int'l*, pg. 115
MANTENIMIENTO Y MONTAJES INDUSTRIALES, S.A—See ACS, Actividades de Construccion y Servicios, S.A.; *Int'l*, pg. 115
MASA ALGECIRAS, S.A.—See ACS, Actividades de Construccion y Servicios, S.A.; *Int'l*, pg. 115
MASA GALICIA, S.A.—See ACS, Actividades de Construccion y Servicios, S.A.; *Int'l*, pg. 115
MASA HUELVA, S.A.—See ACS, Actividades de Construccion y Servicios, S.A.; *Int'l*, pg. 115
MASA NORTE, S.A.—See ACS, Actividades de Construccion y Servicios, S.A.; *Int'l*, pg. 115
MASA PUERTOLLANO, S.A.—See ACS, Actividades de Construccion y Servicios, S.A.; *Int'l*, pg. 115
MASA SERVICIOS, S.A.—See ACS, Actividades de Construccion y Servicios, S.A.; *Int'l*, pg. 115
MASA TENERIFE, S.A.—See ACS, Actividades de Construccion y Servicios, S.A.; *Int'l*, pg. 115
MATECO LOCATION DE NACELLES SA—See Group Thermote & Vanhalst; *Int'l*, pg. 3089
MAXXIM REBUILD COMPANY, INC.—See The Brink's Company; *U.S. Private*, pg. 2043
MCCLAIN INTERNATIONAL, INC.—See HEICO Corporation; *U.S. Public*, pg. 1020
MEDIMAX ONLINE GMBH—See ElectronicPartner Handel SE; *Int'l*, pg. 2354
MEGTEC SYSTEMS AB—See Durr AG; *Int'l*, pg. 2231
MEGTEC SYSTEMS AUSTRALIA, INC.—See Durr AG; *Int'l*, pg. 2231
MIAMI DIVER LLC—See GenNx360 Capital Partners, L.P.; *U.S. Private*, pg. 1672
MIDCON COMPRESSION, L.L.C—See Rock Hill Capital Group, LLC; *U.S. Private*, pg. 3464
MIDSTATE AIR COMPRESSOR, INC.—See Atlas Copco AB; *Int'l*, pg. 680
MINER FLEET MANAGEMENT GROUP—See On-Point Group, LLC; *U.S. Private*, pg. 3019
MING FUNG CONTAINER LIMITED—See Eng Kong Holdings Pte Ltd.; *Int'l*, pg. 2426
MODEST INFRASTRUCTURE PVT. LTD.—See Goa Carbon Ltd.; *Int'l*, pg. 3018
MONCOBRA, S.A.—See ACS, Actividades de Construccion y Servicios, S.A.; *Int'l*, pg. 115
MOTOR PROPANE SERVICE, INC.—See Ferrellgas Partners, L.P.; *U.S. Public*, pg. 829
MOWREY ELEVATOR CO., INC.; *U.S. Private*, pg. 2802
MPW INDUSTRIAL SERVICES, LTD.—See MPW Industrial Services Group, Inc.; *U.S. Private*, pg. 2804
MPW INDUSTRIAL SERVICES OF INDIANA, LLC—See MPW Industrial Services Group, Inc.; *U.S. Private*, pg. 2804
MTS ENVIRONMENTAL GMBH—See Babcock & Wilcox Enterprises, Inc.; *U.S. Public*, pg. 263
MULTI-SERVICE SUPPLY—See The Buncher Company; *U.S. Private*, pg. 4002
MULTI TEC CO., LTD.—See Bain Capital, LP; *U.S. Private*, pg. 434
MVV ENSERVIS A.S.—See Groupe BPCE; *Int'l*, pg. 3094
NANJING CML GRANDLINK LOGISTICS CO., LTD.—See China Master Logistics Co., Ltd.; *Int'l*, pg. 1517
NATIONAL ENGINEERING INDUSTRIES LTD—See CK Birla Group; *Int'l*, pg. 1636

NATIONAL WATER MAIN CLEANING CO.—See Carylon Corporation; *U.S. Private*, pg. 777
NCH COLOMBIA, S.A.—See NCH Corporation; *U.S. Private*, pg. 2875
NCH D.O.O. LJUBLJANA—See NCH Corporation; *U.S. Private*, pg. 2876
NCH ECUADOR S A.—See NCH Corporation; *U.S. Private*, pg. 2875
NCH ITALIA SRL—See NCH Corporation; *U.S. Private*, pg. 2876
NCH PERU, S.A.—See NCH Corporation; *U.S. Private*, pg. 2876
NCH SLOVAKIA S. R. O.—See NCH Corporation; *U.S. Private*, pg. 2876
NIACC-AVITECH TECHNOLOGIES INC.—See HEICO Corporation; *U.S. Public*, pg. 1020
NIIGATA POWER SYSTEMS PHILIPPINES, INC.—See IHI Corporation; *Int'l*, pg. 3606
NMC TECHNOLOGIES—See Nebraska Machinery Company Inc.; *U.S. Private*, pg. 2878
NORBAR TORQUE TOOLS INDIA PRIVATE LIMITED—See Snap-on Incorporated; *U.S. Public*, pg. 1898
NORD COFFRAGE S.A.—See Hiolle Industries S.A.; *Int'l*, pg. 3401
NORTH FLORIDA SHIPYARDS INC.; *U.S. Private*, pg. 2945
NUCLEAR LOGISTICS LLC—See Paragon Energy Solutions, LLC; *U.S. Private*, pg. 3091
OBBCO SAFETY & SUPPLY, INC.—See Genuine Parts Company; *U.S. Public*, pg. 933
ODESSA PUMPS AND EQUIPMENT INC.—See DNOW Inc.; *U.S. Public*, pg. 671
OHMSTEDE INDUSTRIAL SERVICES—See EMCOR Group, Inc.; *U.S. Public*, pg. 738
OMEGA ENVIRONMENTAL, INC.—See Arcline Investment Management LP; *U.S. Private*, pg. 314
P/A BRASIL LTDA—See P/A Industries, Inc.; *U.S. Private*, pg. 3061
PALM BEACH RESOURCE RECOVERY CORPORATION—See EQT AB; *Int'l*, pg. 2474
PANA R&D CO., LTD.—See Altech Corporation; *Int'l*, pg. 389
PANHANDLE VALVE, FABRICATION & MACHINE—See D.E. Rice Construction Co., Inc.; *U.S. Private*, pg. 1142
PAPE MATERIAL HANDLING—See The Pape Group, Inc.; *U.S. Private*, pg. 4090
PARTS ADVANTAGE, LLC—See HEICO Corporation; *U.S. Public*, pg. 1019
PBBS EQUIPMENT CORPORATION; *U.S. Private*, pg. 3118
PEAK OILFIELD SERVICES COMPANY—See Cook Inlet Region, Inc.; *U.S. Private*, pg. 1038
PEI GROUP, LLC—See Electricite de France S.A.; *Int'l*, pg. 2352
PENGATE HANDLING SYSTEMS INC.; *U.S. Private*, pg. 3132
PERFORMANCE AVIATION (NEW ZEALAND) LIMITED—See Experience Co Limited; *Int'l*, pg. 2588
PETROCHEMICAL SERVICES INC.; *U.S. Private*, pg. 3162
PHASOR ENGINEERING INC.—See Quanta Services, Inc.; *U.S. Public*, pg. 1753
PLANT MAINTENANCE SERVICE CORPORATION - FIELD CONSTRUCTION DIVISION—See Plant Maintenance Service Corporation; *U.S. Private*, pg. 3197
PLASTSVEIS AS—See Egersund Group AS; *Int'l*, pg. 2324
PLATFORM SERVICE AND REPAIR LIMITED—See Terex Corporation; *U.S. Public*, pg. 2019
POWERSCREEN INTERNATIONAL DISTRIBUTION LIMITED—See Terex Corporation; *U.S. Public*, pg. 2020
PROFESSIONAL TELECONCEPTS, INC.—See Dycom Industries, Inc.; *U.S. Public*, pg. 699
PROGRESS RAIL MANUFACTURING CORPORATION—See Caterpillar, Inc.; *U.S. Public*, pg. 453
PROPULSION CONTROLS ENGINEERING; *U.S. Private*, pg. 3286
PT. FANUC INDONESIA—See FANUC Corporation; *Int'l*, pg. 2615
PT. HOWASKA MESIN INDONESIA—See Howa Machinery, Ltd.; *Int'l*, pg. 3493
QUALAWASH HOLDINGS, LLC—See KKR & Co. Inc.; *U.S. Public*, pg. 1241
REGIONAL JET CENTER BV—See Air France-KLM S.A.; *Int'l*, pg. 238
RELIABLE JET MAINTENANCE LLC; *U.S. Private*, pg. 3394
RESOLVE MARINE SERVICES, INC.; *U.S. Private*, pg. 3406
R&M FASSADENTECHNIK SUDWEST GMBH—See Bilfinger SE; *Int'l*, pg. 1028
ROTORCRAFT SERVICES GROUP, INC.—See Trinity Hunt Management, L.P.; *U.S. Private*, pg. 4235
RUSHLIFT LTD.—See Doosan Corporation; *Int'l*, pg. 2174
SALEM INVESTMENT CAPITAL LLC; *U.S. Private*, pg. 3531
SANMINA-SCI EMS HAUKIPUDAS OY—See Sanmina Corporation; *U.S. Public*, pg. 1840
SANMINA-SCI ENCLOSURE SYSTEMS (ASIA) LTD.—See Sanmina Corporation; *U.S. Public*, pg. 1840
SCA SERVICE CENTER ALTENWERDER GMBH—See Hamburger Hafen und Logistik AG; *Int'l*, pg. 3237

N.A.I.C.S. INDEX

811412 — APPLIANCE REPAIR AN...

SC DINAFIT SRL—See Christof Holding AG; *Int'l*, pg. 1587
SELF LEVELING MACHINES, INC.—See Team, Inc.—*U.S. Public*, pg. 1988
SEMO TANK/BAKER EQUIPMENT CO.; *U.S. Private*, pg. 3605
SENSENICH PROPELLER MANUFACTURING CO., INC.—See The Philadelphia Bourse, Inc.; *U.S. Private*, pg. 4094
SENSENICH WOOD PROPELLER CO., INC.—See The Philadelphia Bourse, Inc.; *U.S. Private*, pg. 4094
SERVICIOS DE ADMINISTRACION DE LOCOMOTORAS, S. DE R.L. DE C.V.—See Westinghouse Air Brake Technologies Corporation; *U.S. Public*, pg. 2359
SETCO WESTERN SERVICE CENTER—See Holden Industries, Inc.; *U.S. Private*, pg. 1962
SHANGHAI SMART COLD SCM CO., LTD.—See China Master Logistics Co., Ltd.; *Int'l*, pg. 1518
SHICK ESTEVE—See Hillenbrand, Inc.; *U.S. Public*, pg. 1037
SHORTS MARINE INC.; *U.S. Private*, pg. 3643
SISTEMAS INTEGRALES DE MANTENIMIENTO, S.A.—See ACS, Actividades de Construccion y Servicios, S.A.; *Int'l*, pg. 116
SKAFF CRYOGENICS, INC.—See Chart Industries, Inc.; *U.S. Public*, pg. 482
SKIPPER BUDS OF ILLINOIS INC.; *U.S. Private*, pg. 3682
SMITH SERVICES INC.—See The Timken Company; *U.S. Public*, pg. 2133
SOLES ELECTRIC COMPANY INC.; *U.S. Private*, pg. 3709
SOUTH COAST ELECTRIC SYSTEMS, LLC.—See Beier Radio LLC; *U.S. Private*, pg. 516
SOUTHERN CHUTE, INC.; *U.S. Private*, pg. 3730
SOUTHERN INDUSTRIAL SALES AND SERVICES, INC.—See IES Holdings, Inc.; *U.S. Public*, pg. 1094
SOUTHWEST ELECTRIC CO. INC.; *U.S. Private*, pg. 3739
STAMBAUGH AVIATION, INC.—See Stambaugh's Air Service, Inc.; *U.S. Private*, pg. 3776
STAMBAUGH'S AIR SERVICE, INC.; *U.S. Private*, pg. 3776
STORK - ELECTRIC EQUIPMENT SERVICES - REGENSBURG—See Fluor Corporation; *U.S. Public*, pg. 860
STORK - ESLOO—See Fluor Corporation; *U.S. Public*, pg. 860
SULLIVAN WELDING—See Quanta Services, Inc.; *U.S. Public*, pg. 1751
TAMPA ARMATURE WORKS INC.; *U.S. Private*, pg. 3928
TARDIEU TECHNICAL SUPPORT LTD.—See Forges Tardieu Ltd; *Int'l*, pg. 2733
TAT HONG HEAVY EQUIPMENT (PTE.) LTD.—See Affirma Capital Limited; *Int'l*, pg. 187
TAW INC.—See Tampa Armature Works Inc.; *U.S. Private*, pg. 3928
TAW—See Tampa Armature Works Inc.; *U.S. Private*, pg. 3928
TEAM TURBO MACHINES JSC—See Hiolle Industries S.A.; *Int'l*, pg. 3401
TEAM VALVE AND ROTATING SERVICES LIMITED—See Team, Inc.; *U.S. Public*, pg. 1988
TECHNIPLUS S.A.R.L.—See Hili Ventures Ltd; *Int'l*, pg. 3391
TEXSUN SWIMMING POOLS & SPAS, INC.; *U.S. Private*, pg. 3978
THYSSENKRUPP ELEVATOR ALMOAYYED W.L.L.—See Advent International Corporation; *U.S. Private*, pg. 106
THYSSENKRUPP ELEVATOR ALMOAYYED W.L.L.—See Cinven Limited; *Int'l*, pg. 1615
THYSSENKRUPP ELEVATOR ASIA PACIFIC LTD.—See Advent International Corporation; *U.S. Private*, pg. 107
THYSSENKRUPP ELEVATOR ASIA PACIFIC LTD.—See Cinven Limited; *Int'l*, pg. 1615
THYSSENKRUPP ELEVATOR HOLDING FRANCE S.A.S.—See Advent International Corporation; *U.S. Private*, pg. 107
THYSSENKRUPP ELEVATOR HOLDING FRANCE S.A.S.—See Cinven Limited; *Int'l*, pg. 1615
THYSSENKRUPP ELEVATORI D.O.O.—See Advent International Corporation; *U.S. Private*, pg. 107
THYSSENKRUPP ELEVATORI D.O.O.—See Cinven Limited; *Int'l*, pg. 1615
THYSSENKRUPP ELEVATOR MALAYSIA SDN. BHD.—See Advent International Corporation; *U.S. Private*, pg. 107
THYSSENKRUPP ELEVATOR MALAYSIA SDN. BHD.—See Cinven Limited; *Int'l*, pg. 1615
THYSSENKRUPP ELEVATOR SAUDI CO. LTD.—See Advent International Corporation; *U.S. Private*, pg. 107
THYSSENKRUPP ELEVATOR SAUDI CO. LTD.—See Cinven Limited; *Int'l*, pg. 1615
THYSSENKRUPP ELEVATOR SP. Z O.O.—See Advent International Corporation; *U.S. Private*, pg. 107
THYSSENKRUPP ELEVATOR SP. Z O.O.—See Cinven Limited; *Int'l*, pg. 1615
TQC QUANTUM QUALITY, S.A. DE C.V.—See Dover Corporation; *U.S. Public*, pg. 682
TRACKWORK & SUPPLIES SDN. BHD.—See AWC Berhad; *Int'l*, pg. 752
TRICOOL REEFER SDN BHD—See Eng Kong Holdings Pte Ltd; *Int'l*, pg. 2426

TRI COUNTY FARMERS EQUIPMENT; *U.S. Private*, pg. 4220
TRINITY INDUSTRIES—See Trinity Industries, Inc.; *U.S. Public*, pg. 2194
TRI-STATE ELECTRIC OF CORINTH—See Tri-State Armature & Electric Works, Inc.; *U.S. Private*, pg. 4223
TRI-STATE GRINDING—See Colter & Peterson Inc.; *U.S. Private*, pg. 976
TSF POWER PTY LTD—See EVZ Limited; *Int'l*, pg. 2574
TURBINE GENERATOR MAINTENANCE, INC.; *U.S. Private*, pg. 4259
TURBOGENERADORES DEL PERU, S.A.C.—See Duro Felguera, S.A.; *Int'l*, pg. 2229
TWIN CITY CRANE & HOIST INC.—See Balance Point Capital Advisors, LLC; *U.S. Private*, pg. 457
UNITED TECHNICAL SERVICES—See Mechanical Equipment Company Inc.; *U.S. Private*, pg. 2648
VACOM TECHNOLOGIES LLC—See BITZER SE; *Int'l*, pg. 1052
VALMEC LIMITED—See Altrad Investment Authority SAS; *Int'l*, pg. 398
VCI CONSTRUCTION, INC.—See Dycom Industries, Inc.; *U.S. Public*, pg. 699
VIASTAR SERVICES, LP—See Roper Technologies, Inc.; *U.S. Public*, pg. 1814
VMR SERVICE—See Handl-It Inc.; *U.S. Private*, pg. 1852
WATCO MECHANICAL SERVICES, LLC - CUDAHY—See Kinder Morgan, Inc.; *U.S. Public*, pg. 1233
WATCO MECHANICAL SERVICES, LLC - CUDAHY—See The Greenbrier Companies, Inc.; *U.S. Public*, pg. 2085
WATCO MECHANICAL SERVICES, LLC - JACKSONVILLE—See Kinder Morgan, Inc.; *U.S. Public*, pg. 1233
WATCO MECHANICAL SERVICES, LLC - JACKSONVILLE—See The Greenbrier Companies, Inc.; *U.S. Public*, pg. 2085
WESTERN TECHNOLOGY SERVICES INC.—See Austin Engineering Ltd.; *Int'l*, pg. 718
WGE SAS—See Concentrix Corporation; *U.S. Public*, pg. 565
WHA DUN BUILDING MANAGEMENT SERVICE CO., LTD.—See Chung-Hsin Electric & Machinery Manufacturing Corp.; *Int'l*, pg. 1597
WHITING EQUIPMENT SERVICES CO. LTD.—See GK Enterprises, Inc.; *U.S. Private*, pg. 1703
WHITING SERVICES INC.—See GK Enterprises, Inc.; *U.S. Private*, pg. 1703
WINDSOR AIRMOTIVE ASIA PTE. LTD.—See Barnes Group Inc.; *U.S. Public*, pg. 276
WINDY CITY EQUIPMENT SERVICE, INC.; *U.S. Private*, pg. 4540
WITTENBACH BUSINESS SYSTEMS, INC.—See Argosy Capital Group, LLC; *U.S. Private*, pg. 321
WITT GALVANIZING - CINCINNATI, LLC—See AZZ, Inc.; *U.S. Public*, pg. 260
WITT GALVANIZING - PLYMOUTH, LLC—See AZZ, Inc.; *U.S. Public*, pg. 260
WRG SERVICES, INC.; *U.S. Private*, pg. 4572
YOWN'S BOILER & FURNACE SERVICE, INC.—See Audax Group, Limited Partnership; *U.S. Private*, pg. 390
ZAO ATLAS COPCO—See Atlas Copco AB; *Int'l*, pg. 684

811411 — HOME AND GARDEN EQUIPMENT REPAIR AND MAINTENANCE

AEROGROW INTERNATIONAL, INC.—See The Scotts Miracle-Gro Company; *U.S. Public*, pg. 2127
AM SERVICES, INC.—See A-Mark Precious Metals, Inc.; *U.S. Public*, pg. 10
ARMADILLO CONSTRUCTION COMPANY, LTD.; *U.S. Private*, pg. 329
CHING FENG HOME FASHIONS CO., LTD.; *Int'l*, pg. 1570
GREEN GROUP HOLDINGS LLC; *U.S. Private*, pg. 1773
GRIFFIN CATERING SERVICES LIMITED—See Fuller, Smith & Turner PLC; *Int'l*, pg. 2842
HOMESERVE SPAIN SLU—See Brookfield Corporation; *Int'l*, pg. 1188
HOMESERVE USA ENERGY SERVICES LLC—See Brookfield Corporation; *Int'l*, pg. 1188
HOMESERVE USA REPAIR MANAGEMENT CORP.—See Brookfield Corporation; *Int'l*, pg. 1188
ID ENERGIES SAS—See Brookfield Corporation; *Int'l*, pg. 1188
MOW POWER, INC.—See Teamshares Inc.; *U.S. Private*, pg. 3951
NATURE'S FOOTPRINT, INC.; *U.S. Private*, pg. 2867
OSCAGAS HOGAR SLU—See Brookfield Corporation; *Int'l*, pg. 1188
ROUSSIN ENERGIES SAS—See Brookfield Corporation; *Int'l*, pg. 1188
SERVICE LINE WARRANTIES OF CANADA INC.—See Brookfield Corporation; *Int'l*, pg. 1188
SIGNODE PACKAGING ESPANA, S.L.—See Illinois Tool Works Inc.; *U.S. Public*, pg. 1110
TRUDELA PARTNERS LLC—See Coltala Holdings, LLC; *U.S. Private*, pg. 976
UNDER PRESSURE WASHING, LLC—See ACON Investments, LLC; *U.S. Private*, pg. 62
US TOOL GRINDING INC.; *U.S. Public*, pg. 4320
VETTED LIMITED—See Brookfield Corporation; *Int'l*, pg. 1189

811412 — APPLIANCE REPAIR AND MAINTENANCE

ABANS ELECTRICALS PLC; *Int'l*, pg. 48
AIR TEMP MECHANICAL SERVICES, INC.—See United Mechanical, Inc.; *U.S. Private*, pg. 4294
ALFA LAVAL (CHINA) LTD.—See Alfa Laval AB; *Int'l*, pg. 308
AROUND THE CLOCK A/C SERVICE, LLC; *U.S. Private*, pg. 334
BARIDI BARIDI TANZANIA LTD.—See Daikin Industries, Ltd.; *Int'l*, pg. 1932
B&B AIR CONDITIONING & HEATING SERVICE COMPANY; *U.S. Private*, pg. 417
BELHASA ACTIONCRETE INTERNATIONAL—See Belhasa Group of Companies; *Int'l*, pg. 963
BRADY TRANE SERVICE, INC.; *U.S. Private*, pg. 633
BURCKHARDT COMPRESSION (CANADA) INC.—See Burckhardt Compression Holding AG; *Int'l*, pg. 1220
CFU COME LIMITED—See C Cheng Holdings Limited; *Int'l*, pg. 1237
CHILLER SYSTEMS SERVICE, INC.—See The Arcticom Group, LLC; *U.S. Private*, pg. 3987
CHILLER TECHNOLOGY, INC.; *U.S. Private*, pg. 885
CONTROLLED SYSTEMS OF WISCONSIN, INC.; *U.S. Private*, pg. 1034
DAIKIN AIRCONDITIONING SAUDI ARABIA LLC—See Daikin Industries, Ltd.; *Int'l*, pg. 1933
DAIKIN AIRTECHNOLOGY & ENGINEERING CO., LTD.—See Daikin Industries, Ltd.; *Int'l*, pg. 1933
DAIKIN AR CONDICIONADO BRASIL LTDA.—See Daikin Industries, Ltd.; *Int'l*, pg. 1934
DAIKIN INDUSTRIES CZECH REPUBLIC S.R.O.—See Daikin Industries, Ltd.; *Int'l*, pg. 1934
DATA PROCESSING AIR CORP.; *U.S. Private*, pg. 1163
DUROCRAFT DESIGN MANUFACTURING INC.—See Craftmade International, Inc.; *U.S. Private*, pg. 1082
EBAJITSU CO., LTD.—See Ebara Jitsugyo Co., Ltd.; *Int'l*, pg. 2284
ELECTRICAL ENGINEERING & SERVICE CO., INC.—See ABB Ltd.; *Int'l*, pg. 56
FRESCHI SERVICE EXPERTS—See Lennox International Inc.; *U.S. Public*, pg. 1307
FRONTDOOR, INC.; *U.S. Public*, pg. 886
GAMBETTI KENOLOGIA SRL; *Int'l*, pg. 2877
HERD ENTERPRISES INC.; *U.S. Private*, pg. 1921
HITACHI OPERATION & MAINTENANCE - EGYPT S.A.E.—See Hitachi, Ltd.; *Int'l*, pg. 3420
HORIS SAS—See Illinois Tool Works Inc.; *U.S. Public*, pg. 1104
INDOOR CLIMATE MANAGEMENT S.L.—See I Squared Capital Advisors (US) LLC; *U.S. Private*, pg. 2022
INDY CONNECTION ELECTRICAL CONTRACTORS, INC.; *U.S. Private*, pg. 2069
LONE STAR A/C & APPLIANCE REPAIR, LLC—See NRG Energy, Inc.; *U.S. Public*, pg. 1550
LUEDERS ENVIRONMENTAL, INC.; *U.S. Private*, pg. 2512
MAR-CONE APPLIANCE PARTS CO.; *U.S. Private*, pg. 2569
MILLER'S VANGUARD LTD.—See Ali Holding S.r.l; *Int'l*, pg. 322
MR. APPLIANCE LLC—See Harvest Partners L.P.; *U.S. Private*, pg. 1877
NCS INDUSTRIES, INC.—See Leveling 8, Inc.; *U.S. Private*, pg. 2434
NORTH SHORE REFRIGERATION CO. INC.; *U.S. Private*, pg. 2947
PALM HARBOR HEATING & AIR CONDITIONING, INC.—See Northside Services, Inc.; *U.S. Private*, pg. 2957
PIERATTS INC.; *U.S. Private*, pg. 3178
PIVOTAL HOME SOLUTIONS, LLC—See American Water Works Company, Inc.; *U.S. Public*, pg. 112
PRO-AIR SERVICES; *U.S. Private*, pg. 3270
PT DAIWABO SHEETEC INDONESIA—See Daiwabo Holdings Co., Ltd.; *Int'l*, pg. 1950
RENA WARE DE CHILE, S.A.I.C.—See Rena-Ware Distributors Inc.; *U.S. Private*, pg. 3397
SERVICE 7000 AG—See Coop-Gruppe Genossenschaft; *Int'l*, pg. 1790
SERVICECARE, INC.—See Dominion Energy, Inc.; *U.S. Public*, pg. 674
SERVICE EXPERTS LLC—See Brookfield Infrastructure Partners L.P.; *Int'l*, pg. 1190
SERVICELINE—See Ali Holding S.r.l; *Int'l*, pg. 322
SMC SYSTEMS, INC.—See Gallant Capital Partners, LLC; *U.S. Private*, pg. 1639
SOCIETE DE SERVICES DE MAINTENANCE INDUSTRIELS—See Electronic Business System; *Int'l*, pg. 2354
SOURCE REFRIGERATION & HVAC, INC.—See Audax Group, Limited Partnership; *U.S. Private*, pg. 389
TOTAL APPLIANCE & AIR CONDITIONING REPAIRS,

811412 — APPLIANCE REPAIR AN...

INC.; *U.S. Private*, pg. 4190
TRANSPORT REFRIGERATION OF SOUTH DAKOTA INC.; *U.S. Private*, pg. 4210
TURBINE DIAGNOSTIC SERVICES, INC.; *U.S. Private*, pg. 4258
UTILITIES PLUS ENERGY SERVICES—See New Mountain Capital, LLC; *U.S. Private*, pg. 2903
VACUUM SYSTEMS INTERNATIONAL, INC.—See Lakewood Capital, LLC; *U.S. Private*, pg. 2379
WILLIAM A. HARRISON INC.; *U.S. Private*, pg. 4522

811420 — REUPHOLSTERY AND FURNITURE REPAIR

ARIZONA OFFICE TECHNOLOGIES—See Xerox Holdings Corporation; *U.S. Public*, pg. 2389
CALSPAN AIR SERVICES, LLC—See TransDigm Group Incorporated; *U.S. Public*, pg. 2180
CASCO MANUFACTURING SOLUTIONS, INC.; *U.S. Private*, pg. 781
COVERCRAFT DIRECT, LLC; *U.S. Private*, pg. 1072
DREAM POLISHERS, INC.; *U.S. Private*, pg. 1275
FURNITURE MEDIC LIMITED PARTNERSHIP—See EMP Management, LLC; *U.S. Private*, pg. 1384
GT COVERS—See Covercraft Direct, LLC; *U.S. Private*, pg. 1072
J.M. MURRAY CENTER INC.; *U.S. Private*, pg. 2169
UPHOLSTERY INTERNATIONAL, INC.; *U.S. Private*, pg. 4311

811430 — FOOTWEAR AND LEATHER GOODS REPAIR

MCDAVID, INC.—See Wells Fargo & Company; *U.S. Public*, pg. 2344
MINIT ASIA PACIFIC CO., LTD.—See AOYAMA TRADING Co. Ltd.; *Int'l*, pg. 498
MINIT AUSTRALIA PTY LIMITED—See AOYAMA TRADING Co. Ltd.; *Int'l*, pg. 498

811490 — OTHER PERSONAL AND HOUSEHOLD GOODS REPAIR AND MAINTENANCE

ACM ELEVATOR CO.—See Otis Worldwide Corporation; *U.S. Public*, pg. 1623
ADVANCED SERVICE SOLUTIONS, INC.—See Lincolnshire Management, Inc.; *U.S. Private*, pg. 2459
ALL AMERICAN SPORTS CORPORATION—See Fenway Partners, LLC; *U.S. Private*, pg. 1495
AMERICAN SCALE CO. LLC—See Rotunda Capital Partners LLC; *U.S. Private*, pg. 3487
AMERICAN VENDING MACHINES, INC.—See Vendors Exchange International, Inc.; *U.S. Private*, pg. 4356
AMERICAN VISION WINDOWS, INC.; *U.S. Private*, pg. 258
ARTISTS' FRAME SERVICE, INC.; *U.S. Private*, pg. 343
ASTRO-TEK INDUSTRIES INC.—See White Wolf Capital LLC; *U.S. Private*, pg. 4510
B. HANEY & SONS, INC.—See The Davey Tree Expert Company; *U.S. Private*, pg. 4018
CLEAN HARBORS KANSAS, LLC—See Clean Harbors, Inc.; *U.S. Public*, pg. 509
COZZINI BROS., INC.—See Birch Hill Equity Partners Management Inc.; *Int'l*, pg. 1046
C&W FACILITY SERVICES, INC.—See TPG Capital, L.P.; *U.S. Public*, pg. 2171
E.E. NEWCOMER ENTERPRISES INC.; *U.S. Private*, pg. 1305
ELEKTRO INDUSTRIJSKA SERVISNA MREZA A.D.; *Int'l*, pg. 2357
FLINT HILLS MUSIC, INC.—See Ernie Williamson, Inc.; *U.S. Private*, pg. 1422
HAYES WELDING INC.; *U.S. Private*, pg. 1884
HOMESERVE PLC—See Brookfield Corporation; *Int'l*, pg. 1188
ICEE-USA CORP.—See J&J Snack Foods Corporation; *U.S. Public*, pg. 1179
KALMAR NETHERLANDS B.V.—See Cargotec Corporation; *Int'l*, pg. 1328
KALMAR PORTUGAL, S.A.—See Cargotec Corporation; *Int'l*, pg. 1328
KIMBERLY-CLARK (CHINA) COMPANY LTD.—See Kimberly-Clark Corporation; *U.S. Public*, pg. 1229
KTI, INC.; *U.S. Private*, pg. 2355
LIFT TRUCK SPECIALISTS, INC.—See Fairchild Equipment, Inc.; *U.S. Private*, pg. 1462
MACGREGOR BELGIUM N.V.—See Cargotec Corporation; *Int'l*, pg. 1328
MACGREGOR POLAND SP. Z O.O.—See Cargotec Corporation; *Int'l*, pg. 1329
MAXIMET—See Karsten Manufacturing Corporation; *U.S. Private*, pg. 2263
MESOS GESTION Y SERVICIOS S.L.—See Brookfield Corporation; *Int'l*, pg. 1188
MOCHEM—See Momar, Inc.; *U.S. Private*, pg. 2768
MODERN SUPPLY CO., INC.—See Modern Welding Company, Inc.; *U.S. Private*, pg. 2762
NORTH ATLANTIC ENERGY SERVICE CORPORATION—See Eversource Energy; *U.S. Public*, pg. 801
NVH ACQUISITION HOLDINGS LLC—See Angeles Equity Partners, LLC; *U.S. Private*, pg. 282
OSW EQUIPMENT & REPAIR, LLC—See Federal Signal Corporation; *U.S. Public*, pg. 826
PINMAR USA, INC.—See GYG plc; *Int'l*, pg. 3191
PRO ELEVATOR SERVICES INC—See Champion Elevator Corp.; *U.S. Private*, pg. 846
PTRC, INC.—See People's Jewelry Company, Inc.; *U.S. Private*, pg. 3141
SCHUMACHER ELEVATOR CO. INC.; *U.S. Private*, pg. 3571
TOLEDO ELEVATOR & MACHINE, CO.—See Carroll Capital LLC; *U.S. Private*, pg. 773
TRANSEL ELEVATOR & ELECTRIC INC.—See Analogue Holdings Limited; *Int'l*, pg. 446
TRAVERTINE, INC.; *U.S. Private*, pg. 4214
TREADMILLDOCTOR.COM, INC.; *U.S. Private*, pg. 4216
THE VIKING YACHT SERVICE CENTER—See Viking Yacht Company; *U.S. Private*, pg. 4383
VORTEX INDUSTRIES INC.; *U.S. Private*, pg. 4413
WEIGHING & CONTROL, INC.—See Tannehill International Industries; *U.S. Private*, pg. 3931
WELDMENTS, INC.—See Precision Metal Fabrication, Inc.; *U.S. Private*, pg. 3245
X-CELL TOOL & MOLD, INC.—See Crestview Partners, L.P.; *U.S. Private*, pg. 1099

812111 — BARBER SHOPS

AMERICAN LASER CENTERS; *U.S. Private*, pg. 239
BIRDS BARBERSHOP; *U.S. Private*, pg. 564
THE CENTER AT SLATTEN RANCH, LLC—See Regency Centers Corporation; *U.S. Public*, pg. 1774
GENTS PLACE MEN'S FINE GROOM—See Massage Heights; *U.S. Private*, pg. 2606
GINO MORENA ENTERPRISES, LLC; *U.S. Private*, pg. 1702
HAIRGROUP AG; *Int'l*, pg. 3216
INDIQUE HAIR, LLC.; *U.S. Private*, pg. 2064
SPORT CLIPS, INC.; *U.S. Private*, pg. 3760

812112 — BEAUTY SALONS

ARD INC.; *U.S. Private*, pg. 317
ARTE STRAITS HOLDINGS PTE. LTD.—See ARTE Salon Holdings, Inc.; *Int'l*, pg. 581
ASH CO., LTD.—See ARTE Salon Holdings, Inc.; *Int'l*, pg. 581
ASN TANFORAN CROSSING II LLC—See AvalonBay Communities, Inc.; *U.S. Public*, pg. 240
ASTERSPRING INTERNATIONAL SDN. BHD.—See Esthetics International Group Berhad; *Int'l*, pg. 2518
AVI SPA SDN BHD—See Avillion Berhad; *Int'l*, pg. 743
THE BEAUTIFUL GROUP MANAGEMENT, LLC—See Regent, LLC; *U.S. Private*, pg. 3388
BEAUTY BAZAR INC.; *U.S. Private*, pg. 508
BEAUTY GARAGE INC.; *Int'l*, pg. 935
BEAUTY MANAGEMENT INCORPORATED; *U.S. Private*, pg. 509
THE BEAUTY SOLUTION, LLC—See XCel Brands, Inc.; *U.S. Public*, pg. 2385
BOOKSY INC.; *U.S. Private*, pg. 616
CHARLES PENZONE INC.; *U.S. Private*, pg. 853
CLEOPATRA INTERNATIONAL GROUP, INC.; *Int'l*, pg. 1658
COLE'S SALON INC; *U.S. Private*, pg. 966
COLORPROOF HAIRCARE LLC—See Cosway Co Inc.; *U.S. Private*, pg. 1063
COSMEDICAL SPA—See Apollo Med Innovations LLC; *U.S. Private*, pg. 295
CUTTING LOOSE SALON AND SPA; *U.S. Private*, pg. 1132
DELLARIA SALONS; *U.S. Private*, pg. 1197
DERMATOLOGY PROFESSIONALS, INC.—See Adult & Pediatric Dermatology, PC; *U.S. Private*, pg. 83
DERMICUS AB—See Barco N.V.; *Int'l*, pg. 864
DESIGN ON STAGE HAIR, INC.; *U.S. Private*, pg. 1213
DESSANGE INTERNATIONAL SA—See Eurazeo SE; *Int'l*, pg. 2528
EDGE SYSTEMS INTERMEDIATE, LLC—See The Beauty Health Company; *U.S. Public*, pg. 2038
ESTHETICS INTERNATIONAL GROUP BERHAD; *Int'l*, pg. 2518
EUROPEAN WAX CENTER INC.; *U.S. Public*, pg. 799
EWC AVENTURA, LLC—See European Wax Center Inc.; *U.S. Public*, pg. 799
FAMEGLOW HOLDINGS LTD.; *Int'l*, pg. 2611
FANTASTIC SAMS INTERNATIONAL CORPORATION—See Eurazeo SE; *Int'l*, pg. 2528
FEKKAI BRANDS, LLC—See LUXE Brands, Inc.; *U.S. Private*, pg. 2518
FIESTA SALONS, INC.—See Regis Corporation; *U.S. Public*, pg. 1777
FIRST CHOICE HAIRCUTTERS, LTD—See Regis Corporation; *U.S. Public*, pg. 1777
FREDERIC FEKKAI DALLAS, LLC—See LUXE Brands, Inc.; *U.S. Private*, pg. 2518
FREDERIC FEKKAI GREENWICH, LLC—See LUXE Brands, Inc.; *U.S. Private*, pg. 2518
FREDERIC FEKKAI (MARK NY), LLC—See LUXE Brands, Inc.; *U.S. Private*, pg. 2518
FREDERIC FEKKAI NEW YORK, LLC—See LUXE Brands, Inc.; *U.S. Private*, pg. 2518
FRIKA WEAVE (PTY) LTD—See Godrej & Boyce Mfg. Co. Ltd.; *Int'l*, pg. 3020
GADABOUT INC.; *U.S. Private*, pg. 1633
GENE JUAREZ SALONS LLC—See Transom Capital Group, LLC; *U.S. Private*, pg. 4209
GINGER BAY SALON GROUP, LTD.; *U.S. Private*, pg. 1701
GMO BEAUTY INC—See GMO Internet Group, Inc.; *Int'l*, pg. 3013
GREAT CLIPS, INC.; *U.S. Private*, pg. 1762
GREEN ENDEAVORS, INC.; *U.S. Private*, pg. 1772
HAIR CLUB FOR MEN, LLC—See Aderans Co., Ltd.; *Int'l*, pg. 143
THE HAIR CUTTERY—See The Ratner Companies; *U.S. Private*, pg. 4102
HAIRSTYLISTS MANAGEMENT SYSTEMS; *U.S. Private*, pg. 1841
HEADQUARTERS LIMITED—See Century Legend Holdings Ltd; *Int'l*, pg. 1418
THE HYDRAFACIAL COMPANY IBERIA, S.L.U.—See The Beauty Health Company; *U.S. Public*, pg. 2038
THE HYDRAFACIAL COMPANY JAPAN K.K.—See The Beauty Health Company; *U.S. Public*, pg. 2038
THE HYDRAFACIAL COMPANY MX, S. DE R.L. DE C.V.—See The Beauty Health Company; *U.S. Public*, pg. 2038
HYDRAFACIAL UK LIMITED—See The Beauty Health Company; *U.S. Public*, pg. 2038
J.CON SALON & SPA; *U.S. Private*, pg. 2160
LEONARD DRAKE (HK) LTD.—See Esthetics International Group Berhad; *Int'l*, pg. 2518
MAIMU CO., LTD.—See BELLUNA CO. LTD.; *Int'l*, pg. 967
MASSAGE THERAPY CONNECTIONS LLC; *U.S. Private*, pg. 2606
MILK + HONEY DAY SPA; *U.S. Private*, pg. 2729
MITCHELLS SALON & DAY SPA; *U.S. Private*, pg. 2751
PHENIX SALON LLC; *U.S. Private*, pg. 3167
PHENIX SALON SUITES FRANCHISING LLC—See Phenix Salon LLC; *U.S. Private*, pg. 3167
PHILIP PELUSI SALONS; *U.S. Private*, pg. 3169
PIIDEA CANADA LTD.—See Henkel AG & Co. KGaA; *Int'l*, pg. 3354
PLANET BEACH FRANCHISING CORPORATION; *U.S. Private*, pg. 3195
PROCTER & GAMBLE CANADA HOLDING B.V.—See The Procter & Gamble Company; *U.S. Public*, pg. 2121
PRO-CUTS, INC.—See Regis Corporation; *U.S. Public*, pg. 1777
PROVALLIANCE, SAS—See Core Equity Holdings SA; *Int'l*, pg. 1798
THE RATNER COMPANIES - COLORWORKS DIVISION—See The Ratner Companies; *U.S. Private*, pg. 4102
THE RATNER COMPANIES; *U.S. Private*, pg. 4102
REGIS CORPORATION; *U.S. Public*, pg. 1776
RUMORS SALON & SPA; *U.S. Private*, pg. 3503
SALON DEVELOPMENT CORP.; *U.S. Private*, pg. 3533
SAND DOLLAR CORPORATION; *U.S. Private*, pg. 3542
SCHWARZKOPF & HENKEL GMBH—See Henkel AG & Co. KGaA; *Int'l*, pg. 3354
SCHWARZKOPF S.A.—See Henkel AG & Co. KGaA; *Int'l*, pg. 3354
SEATTLE SUN TAN; *U.S. Private*, pg. 3592
SENSIA SALON, INC.; *U.S. Private*, pg. 3607
SHEAR ART SALON & SPA; *U.S. Private*, pg. 3629
SKIN SCIENCES, INC.—See FibroGen, Inc.; *U.S. Public*, pg. 830
SMARTSTYLE FAMILY HAIR SALONS—See Regis Corporation; *U.S. Public*, pg. 1777
STATE BEAUTY SUPPLY OF ST. LOUIS; *U.S. Private*, pg. 3791
STUDIO 921 SALON & DAY SPA; *U.S. Private*, pg. 3843
STUDIO RK SALON; *U.S. Private*, pg. 3843
STYLE INDUSTRIES LIMITED—See Godrej & Boyce Mfg. Co. Ltd.; *Int'l*, pg. 3021
SUDDENLY SLENDER INTERNATIONAL, INC.; *U.S. Private*, pg. 3849
SUN TAN CITY; *U.S. Private*, pg. 3864
SUPERCUTS CORPORATE SHOPS, INC.—See Regis Corporation; *U.S. Public*, pg. 1777
SUPERCUTS, INC.—See Regis Corporation; *U.S. Public*, pg. 1777
TONI & GUY USA, INC.; *U.S. Private*, pg. 4184
URBAN NIRVANA; *U.S. Private*, pg. 4314
VISIBLE CHANGES; *U.S. Private*, pg. 4390
WELLQUEST MEDICAL & WELLNESS CORPORATION; *U.S. Public*, pg. 2343
ZOGI SRL—See The Procter & Gamble Company; *U.S. Public*, pg. 2124

N.A.I.C.S. INDEX

812210 — FUNERAL HOMES AND F...

812113 — NAIL SALONS

DASHING DIVA INTERNATIONAL CO., LTD.—See Human Holdings Co., Ltd.; *Int'l*, pg. 3529
FRENCHIES MODERN NAIL CARE—See The Riverside Company; *U.S. Private*, pg. 4108
PROFUSS GMBH—See Asklepios Kliniken GmbH & Co. KGaA; *Int'l*, pg. 624
VALLEY NAILS LLC—See Hudson Blvd. Group LLC; *U.S. Private*, pg. 2001

812191 — DIET AND WEIGHT REDUCING CENTERS

ADVANCED WEIGHT LOSS CLINICS; *U.S. Private*, pg. 93
BAR METHOD INC.—See Self Esteem Brands LLC; *U.S. Private*, pg. 3602
BLUE SKY MD; *U.S. Private*, pg. 593
BLUE SKY MD—See Blue Sky MD; *U.S. Private*, pg. 593
DIET CENTER WORLDWIDE, INC.—See The Health Management Group, Inc.; *U.S. Private*, pg. 4043
FIT AMERICA INC.; *U.S. Private*, pg. 1535
HF HEALTHCARE LIMITED—See Walgreens Boots Alliance, Inc.; *U.S. Public*, pg. 2322
JENNY CRAIG WEIGHT LOSS CENTRES (CANADA) COMPANY—See H.I.G. Capital, LLC; *U.S. Private*, pg. 1830
JENNY CRAIG WEIGHT LOSS CENTRES, INC.—See H.I.G. Capital, LLC; *U.S. Private*, pg. 1830
JENNY CRAIG WEIGHT LOSS CENTRES (NZ) LTD—See H.I.G. Capital, LLC; *U.S. Private*, pg. 1830
JENNY CRAIG WEIGHT LOSS CENTRES PTY. LTD.—See H.I.G. Capital, LLC; *U.S. Private*, pg. 1830
KURBO, INC.—See WW International, Inc.; *U.S. Public*, pg. 2384
MEDI IP, LLC; *U.S. Private*, pg. 2651
MINILUXE, INC.—See MiniLuxe Holding Corp.; *U.S. Public*, pg. 1449
NUTRISYSTEM, INC.—See Kainos Capital, LLC; *U.S. Private*, pg. 2255
PHYSICIANS WEIGHT LOSS CENTERS, INC.—See The Health Management Group, Inc.; *U.S. Private*, pg. 4043
SLIM & TONE—See Kainos Capital, LLC; *U.S. Private*, pg. 2255
STRUCTURE HOUSE, LLC—See Acadia Healthcare Company, Inc.; *U.S. Public*, pg. 30
VAEGTKONSULENTERNE A/S—See Egmont Fonden; *Int'l*, pg. 2326
WEIGHTWATCHERS.COM, INC.—See WW International, Inc.; *U.S. Public*, pg. 2384
WEIGHT WATCHERS DENMARK APS—See WW International, Inc.; *U.S. Public*, pg. 2384
WEIGHT WATCHERS (DEUTSCHLAND) GMBH—See WW International, Inc.; *U.S. Public*, pg. 2384
WEIGHTWATCHERS.FR S.A.R.L—See WW International, Inc.; *U.S. Public*, pg. 2384
WEIGHT WATCHERS INTERNATIONAL PTY. LTD—See WW International, Inc.; *U.S. Public*, pg. 2384
WEIGHTWATCHERS.NL B.V.—See WW International, Inc.; *U.S. Public*, pg. 2384
WEIGHT WATCHERS OPERATIONS SPAIN S.L.—See WW International, Inc.; *U.S. Public*, pg. 2384
WEIGHT WATCHERS POLSKA SPZ.O.O.—See WW International, Inc.; *U.S. Public*, pg. 2384
WEIGHT WATCHERS SERVICES PTY LTD—See WW International, Inc.; *U.S. Public*, pg. 2384
WEIGHT WATCHERS SWEDEN VIKTVAKTARNA AKIEBOLAG—See WW International, Inc.; *U.S. Public*, pg. 2384
WEIGHT WATCHERS (U.K.) LIMITED—See WW International, Inc.; *U.S. Public*, pg. 2384
WW BELGIUM NV—See WW International, Inc.; *U.S. Public*, pg. 2384
WW.COM, LLC—See WW International, Inc.; *U.S. Public*, pg. 2384
WW.FR SARL—See WW International, Inc.; *U.S. Public*, pg. 2384
WW GROUP INC.; *U.S. Private*, pg. 4575
WW (SWITZERLAND) SA—See WW International, Inc.; *U.S. Public*, pg. 2384

812199 — OTHER PERSONAL CARE SERVICES

ADERANS (SHANGHAI) TRADING CO., LTD—See Aderans Co., Ltd.; *Int'l*, pg. 143
ADKM, INC.; *U.S. Private*, pg. 80
AFFINITY PHYSICIAN SERVICES, LLC—See Community Health Systems, Inc.; *U.S. Public*, pg. 551
AIRSCULPT TECHNOLOGIES, INC.; *U.S. Public*, pg. 68
ALMOST HEAVEN SAUNAS LLC—See Harvia Oyj; *Int'l*, pg. 3281
ALWAYS SUMMER LLC; *U.S. Private*, pg. 214
AMERICAN CORRECTIONAL SOLUTIONS, INC.; *U.S. Private*, pg. 228

A PLACE TO CALL HOME, INC.—See KKR & Co. Inc.; *U.S. Public*, pg. 1262
ARIA BAY RETIREMENT VILLAGE LIMITED—See Arvida Group Limited; *Int'l*, pg. 587
ARIA GARDENS LIMITED—See Arvida Group Limited; *Int'l*, pg. 587
ARIA PARK RETIREMENT VILLAGE LIMITED—See Arvida Group Limited; *Int'l*, pg. 587
ASALEO CARE LIMITED—See Essity Aktiebolag; *Int'l*, pg. 2516
ASHWOOD PARK RETIREMENT VILLAGE LIMITED—See Arvida Group Limited; *Int'l*, pg. 587
BABYLISS SA—See American Securities LLC; *U.S. Private*, pg. 247
BAINLEA HOUSE (2013) LIMITED—See Arvida Group Limited; *Int'l*, pg. 587
BAINSWOOD HOUSE REST HOME LIMITED—See Arvida Group Limited; *Int'l*, pg. 587
BDMS SILVER CO., LTD.—See Bangkok Dusit Medical Services Public Company Limited; *Int'l*, pg. 834
BEAUTY HEALTH GROUP LIMITED; *Int'l*, pg. 935
BETHLEHEM COUNTRY CLUB VILLAGE LIMITED—See Arvida Group Limited; *Int'l*, pg. 587
THE CASCADES RETIREMENT RESORT LIMITED—See Arvida Group Limited; *Int'l*, pg. 587
COLOMBIANA KIMBERLY COLPAPEL S.A.—See Kimberly-Clark Corporation; *U.S. Public*, pg. 1229
COMPLETELY BARE SPA, INC.; *U.S. Private*, pg. 1001
CONTINENTAL CONAIR, LTD.—See American Securities LLC; *U.S. Private*, pg. 248
COPPER CREST RETIREMENT VILLAGE LIMITED—See Arvida Group Limited; *Int'l*, pg. 587
CROSSROADS OF WESTERN IOWA, INC.; *U.S. Private*, pg. 1108
DEVARANA SPA CO., LTD.—See Dusit Thani Public Company Limited; *Int'l*, pg. 2234
DOMO WELLNESS ROMANIA SRL—See Harvia Oyj; *Int'l*, pg. 3281
EDGEWELL PERSONAL CARE, LLC—See Edgewell Personal Care Company; *U.S. Public*, pg. 718
EXHALE ENTERPRISES III, INC.—See Hyatt Hotels Corporation; *U.S. Public*, pg. 1077
EXHALE ENTERPRISES II, LLC—See Hyatt Hotels Corporation; *U.S. Public*, pg. 1077
EXHALE ENTERPRISES IV, LLC—See Hyatt Hotels Corporation; *U.S. Public*, pg. 1077
EXHALE ENTERPRISES VIII, INC.—See Hyatt Hotels Corporation; *U.S. Public*, pg. 1077
EXHALE ENTERPRISES V, LLC—See Hyatt Hotels Corporation; *U.S. Public*, pg. 1077
EXHALE ENTERPRISES XIV, LLC—See Hyatt Hotels Corporation; *U.S. Public*, pg. 1077
EXHALE ENTERPRISES XIX, LLC—See Hyatt Hotels Corporation; *U.S. Public*, pg. 1077
EXHALE ENTERPRISES XVIII, LLC—See Hyatt Hotels Corporation; *U.S. Public*, pg. 1077
EXHALE ENTERPRISES XVI, LLC—See Hyatt Hotels Corporation; *U.S. Public*, pg. 1077
EXHALE ENTERPRISES XXI, LLC—See Hyatt Hotels Corporation; *U.S. Public*, pg. 1077
EXHALE ENTERPRISES XXIV, LLC—See Hyatt Hotels Corporation; *U.S. Public*, pg. 1077
EXHALE ENTERPRISES XX, LLC—See Hyatt Hotels Corporation; *U.S. Public*, pg. 1077
EXHALE ENTERPRISES XXVIII, LLC—See Hyatt Hotels Corporation; *U.S. Public*, pg. 1077
EXHALE ENTERPRISES XXVI, LLC—See Hyatt Hotels Corporation; *U.S. Public*, pg. 1077
EXHALE ENTERPRISES XXXII, LLC—See Hyatt Hotels Corporation; *U.S. Public*, pg. 1077
EXHALE ENTERPRISES XXXI, LLC—See Hyatt Hotels Corporation; *U.S. Public*, pg. 1077
FRANKFURTER BETEILIGUNGS-TREUHAND GMBH—See Deutsche Bank Aktiengesellschaft; *Int'l*, pg. 2062
FREDERIC, LLC—See The Procter & Gamble Company; *U.S. Public*, pg. 2120
FUREASU CO., LTD.; *Int'l*, pg. 2846
GLENBRAE REST HOME & HOSPITAL LIMITED—See Arvida Group Limited; *Int'l*, pg. 587
HAIR CLUB FOR MEN, LTD., INC.—See Aderans Co., Ltd.; *Int'l*, pg. 143
HAIR CLUB FOR MEN, LTD., INC.—See Aderans Co., Ltd.; *Int'l*, pg. 143
HEALTH SPAS GUIDE (PTY) LTD.—See Caxton and CTP Publishers and Printers Ltd.; *Int'l*, pg. 1363
HENGAN INTERNATIONAL GROUP CO. LTD.; *Int'l*, pg. 3345
HENKEL & CIE AG - LAESSER KLEBSTOFFE DIVISION—See Henkel AG & Co. KGaA; *Int'l*, pg. 3348
HENKEL WASCH- UND REINIGUNGSMITTEL GMBH—See Henkel AG & Co. KGaA; *Int'l*, pg. 3352
IDEAL IMAGE DEVELOPMENT, INC.—See Catterton Management Company, LLC; *U.S. Private*, pg. 794
INPATIENT MEDICAL SERVICES, INC.; *U.S. Private*, pg. 2084
KUSATEK GMBH—See Harvia Oyj; *Int'l*, pg. 3281

LANSDOWNE PARK VILLAGE LIMITED—See Arvida Group Limited; *Int'l*, pg. 587
LAURISTON PARK RETIREMENT VILLAGE LIMITED—See Arvida Group Limited; *Int'l*, pg. 587
LEGACY MEDICAL, LLC—See AdaptHealth Corp.; *U.S. Public*, pg. 39
MANDARA SPA ARUBA N.V.—See OneSpaWorld Holdings Limited; *U.S. Public*, pg. 1604
MANDARA SPA (BAHAMAS) LIMITED—See OneSpaWorld Holdings Limited; *U.S. Public*, pg. 1604
MANDARA SPA PALAU—See OneSpaWorld Holdings Limited; *U.S. Public*, pg. 1604
MANDARA SPA PUERTO RICO, INC.—See OneSpaWorld Holdings Limited; *U.S. Public*, pg. 1604
MASSAGE ENVY FRANCHISING, LLC; *U.S. Private*, pg. 2606
MASSAGE ENVY LIMITED, LLC—See Roark Capital Group Inc.; *U.S. Private*, pg. 3455
MASSAGE HEIGHTS; *U.S. Private*, pg. 2606
MCKINNEY TRAILERS & CONTAINERS—See Mckinney Trailers & Containers; *U.S. Private*, pg. 2639
MD ESTHETICS, LLC; *U.S. Private*, pg. 2646
MIELLE ORGANICS, LLC—See The Procter & Gamble Company; *U.S. Public*, pg. 2120
NU SKIN ENTERPRISES PHILIPPINES LLC—See Nu Skin Enterprises, Inc.; *U.S. Public*, pg. 1552
OU HERA SALONGID—See AS Infortar; *Int'l*, pg. 590
PALM BEACH TAN, INC.; *U.S. Private*, pg. 3079
PARK LANE RETIREMENT VILLAGE LIMITED—See Arvida Group Limited; *Int'l*, pg. 587
PETITS-FILS DEVELOPPEMENT JSC—See Clariane SE; *Int'l*, pg. 1643
PIVOT HEALTH SOLUTIONS—See Athletico Ltd.; *U.S. Private*, pg. 368
PROCTER & GAMBLE FINLAND OY—See The Procter & Gamble Company; *U.S. Public*, pg. 2121
PROSKIN LLC—See Bausch Health Companies Inc.; *Int'l*, pg. 897
PT MANDARA SPA INDONESIA—See OneSpaWorld Holdings Limited; *U.S. Public*, pg. 1604
RADIANCY, INC.—See Gadsden Properties, Inc.; *U.S. Public*, pg. 894
RESIDENCIAS FAMILIARES PARA MAYORES SL—See Clariane SE; *Int'l*, pg. 1644
RIRAKU CO., LTD.—See Advantage Partners LLP; *Int'l*, pg. 164
SENTIOTEC GMBH—See Harvia Oyj; *Int'l*, pg. 3282
TRANSCOM NORGE AS—See Altor Equity Partners AB; *Int'l*, pg. 396
TRANSCOM WORLDWIDE S.P.A.—See Altor Equity Partners AB; *Int'l*, pg. 396
VESPYR BRANDS LLC—See Aurobindo Pharma Ltd.; *Int'l*, pg. 713
WELLNESS ARENA CORPORATION—See Hulic Co., Ltd.; *Int'l*, pg. 3528
XYNMANAGAMENT, INC.—See CareDx, Inc.; *U.S. Public*, pg. 435

812210 — FUNERAL HOMES AND FUNERAL SERVICES

A.B. COLEMAN MORTUARY, INC.—See Service Corporation International; *U.S. Public*, pg. 1869
AFFORDABLE FUNERALS AND CREMATIONS OF AMERICA, INC.—See Security National Financial Corporation; *U.S. Public*, pg. 1856
ALLNUTT FUNERAL SERVICE, INC.—See Service Corporation International; *U.S. Public*, pg. 1870
ALTAVISTA MEMORIAL PARK LLC—See Axar Capital Management L.P.; *U.S. Private*, pg. 411
ANDERSON-MCQUEEN COMPANY; *U.S. Private*, pg. 278
AUMAN'S, INC.—See Service Corporation International; *U.S. Public*, pg. 1871
AVALON MORTUARY SERVICE CORP.—See The John P. Brooks Family Corporation; *U.S. Private*, pg. 4059
BARNETT, DEMROW & ERNST, INC—See Carriage Services, Inc.; *U.S. Public*, pg. 439
BATESVILLE CASKET COMPANY, INC.—See LongRange Capital LLC; *U.S. Private*, pg. 2493
BATESVILLE CASKET DE MEXICO, S.A. DE C.V.—See Hillenbrand, Inc.; *U.S. Public*, pg. 1035
BATESVILLE MANUFACTURING, INC.—See Hillenbrand, Inc.; *U.S. Public*, pg. 1035
BATESVILLE SERVICES, INC.—See Hillenbrand, Inc.; *U.S. Public*, pg. 1035
THE BAUE FUNERAL HOME CO.—See Birch Hill Equity Partners Management Inc.; *Int'l*, pg. 1046
THE BAUE FUNERAL HOME CO.—See Homesteaders Life Co. Inc.; *U.S. Private*, pg. 1974
BRIDGFORD & SONS LIMITED—See Co-operative Group Limited; *Int'l*, pg. 1679
BURGEE-HENSS-SEITZ FUNERAL HOME, INC.—See Service Corporation International; *U.S. Public*, pg. 1869
CALLAWAY JONES FUNERAL HOME—See Birch Hill Equity Partners Management Inc.; *Int'l*, pg. 1046
CALLAWAY JONES FUNERAL HOME—See Homesteaders Life Co. Inc.; *U.S. Private*, pg. 1974

N.A.I.C.S. Index

812210 — FUNERAL HOMES AND F... CORPORATE AFFILIATIONS

CAMELLIA MEMORIAL LAWN, INC.—See Service Corporation International; *U.S. Public*, pg. 1869
CARL BARNES FUNERAL HOME, INC.—See Service Corporation International; *U.S. Public*, pg. 1869
CARRIAGE FUNERAL HOLDINGS INC.—See Carriage Services, Inc.; *U.S. Public*, pg. 439
CARRIAGE SERVICES, INC.; *U.S. Public*, pg. 439
CASDORPH & CURRY FUNERAL HOME, INC.—See Service Corporation International; *U.S. Public*, pg. 1871
CATAUDELLA FUNERAL HOME, INC.—See Carriage Services, Inc.; *U.S. Public*, pg. 439
CATHOLIC FUNERALS NEWCASTLE PTY LIMITED—See TPG Capital, L.P.; *U.S. Public*, pg. 2174
CEDAR HILL FUNERAL HOME, INC.—See Axar Capital Management L.P.; *U.S. Private*, pg. 411
CHAPEL HILL FUNERAL HOME, INC.—See Axar Capital Management L.P.; *U.S. Private*, pg. 411
CHAPEL OF THE VALLEY FUNERAL HOME, INC.—See Service Corporation International; *U.S. Public*, pg. 1871
CHARLES S. ZEILER & SON, INC.—See Service Corporation International; *U.S. Public*, pg. 1869
CHAS. PETER NAGEL, LLC—See Service Corporation International; *U.S. Public*, pg. 1869
CHICAGO CEMETERY CORPORATION—See Service Corporation International; *U.S. Public*, pg. 1869
CHRISTY SMITH FUNERAL HOMES, INC.—See Birch Hill Equity Partners Management Inc.; *Int'l*, pg. 1046
CHRISTY SMITH FUNERAL HOMES, INC.—See Homesteaders Life Co. Inc.; *U.S. Private*, pg. 1974
CLINCH VALLEY MEMORIAL CEMETERY, INC.—See Axar Capital Management L.P.; *U.S. Private*, pg. 411
CLOVERDALE PARK, INC.—See Carriage Services, Inc.; *U.S. Public*, pg. 439
COCHRANE'S CHAPEL OF THE ROSES, INC.—See Carriage Services, Inc.; *U.S. Public*, pg. 439
COCHRANE—See Carriage Services, Inc.; *U.S. Public*, pg. 439
COCOLONET CO., LTD.; *Int'l*, pg. 1687
COLLEGE PARK CEMETERY, INC.—See Service Corporation International; *U.S. Public*, pg. 1869
CO-OPERATIVE FUNERALCARE LIMITED—See Co-operative Group Limited; *Int'l*, pg. 1679
CO-OPERATIVE GROUP LIMITED; *Int'l*, pg. 1679
COTTONWOOD MORTUARY, INC.—See Security National Financial Corporation; *U.S. Public*, pg. 1856
CREST LAWN MEMORIAL GARDENS, INC.—See Service Corporation International; *U.S. Public*, pg. 1871
CREST LAWN MEMORIAL PARK, INC.—See Service Corporation International; *U.S. Public*, pg. 1869
CRYSTAL ROSE FUNERAL HOME, INC.—See Security National Financial Corporation; *U.S. Public*, pg. 1856
CSI FUNERAL SERVICES OF MASSACHUSETTS, INC.—See Carriage Services, Inc.; *U.S. Public*, pg. 439
CYPRESS FAIRBANKS FUNERAL HOME—See Carriage Services, Inc.; *U.S. Public*, pg. 439
DALE-RIGGS FUNERAL HOME, INC.—See Service Corporation International; *U.S. Public*, pg. 1869
DANZANSKY-GOLDBERG MEMORIAL CHAPELS, INC.—See Service Corporation International; *U.S. Public*, pg. 1869
DESERET MEMORIAL, INC.—See Security National Financial Corporation; *U.S. Public*, pg. 1856
DIGNITY CARING FUNERAL SERVICES—See Dignity plc; *Int'l*, pg. 2124
DIGNITY FUNERALS LIMITED—See Dignity plc; *Int'l*, pg. 2124
DIGNITY PLC; *Int'l*, pg. 2124
DK-FH INC.—See DraftKings Inc.; *U.S. Public*, pg. 687
DRUID RIDGE CEMETERY—See Service Corporation International; *U.S. Public*, pg. 1871
DUNBAR FUNERAL HOME—See Service Corporation International; *U.S. Public*, pg. 1871
D.W. NEWCOMER'S SONS FUNERAL HOMES—See Service Corporation International; *U.S. Public*, pg. 1871
EAST LAWN PALMS MORTUARY & CEMETERY—See Service Corporation International; *U.S. Public*, pg. 1869
ECONET LIFE (PRIVATE) LIMITED—See EcoCash Holdings Zimbabwe Limited; *Int'l*, pg. 2294
EDWARD SAGEL FUNERAL DIRECTION, INC.—See Service Corporation International; *U.S. Public*, pg. 1869
ELOISE B. KYPER FUNERAL HOME, INC.—See Axar Capital Management L.P.; *U.S. Private*, pg. 411
EMERALD HILLS FUNERAL HOME & MEMORIAL PARK—See Service Corporation International; *U.S. Public*, pg. 1871
EUBANK FUNERAL HOME, INC.—See Service Corporation International; *U.S. Public*, pg. 1870
FAIRFAX MEMORIAL FUNERAL HOME, LLC—See Carriage Services, Inc.; *U.S. Public*, pg. 439
THE FAIRWAYS PARTNERSHIP LIMITED—See Co-operative Group Limited; *Int'l*, pg. 1679
FAMILY MEMORIALS INC.; *Int'l*, pg. 2612
FARRIS FUNERAL SERVICE, INC.—See Birch Hill Equity Partners Management Inc.; *Int'l*, pg. 1046
FARRIS FUNERAL SERVICE, INC.—See Homesteaders Life Co. Inc.; *U.S. Private*, pg. 1974
FIDELITY LIFE ASSET MANAGEMENT COMPANY (PRIVATE) LIMITED—See Fidelity Life Assurance Limited; *Int'l*, pg. 2654
FIDELITY LIFE ASSURANCE LIMITED; *Int'l*, pg. 2654
FIDELITY LIFE FINANCIAL SERVICES (PRIVATE) LIMITED—See Fidelity Life Assurance Limited; *Int'l*, pg. 2654
FLANNER & BUCHANAN, INC.; *U.S. Private*, pg. 1540
FORASTIERE FAMILY FUNERAL SERVICES, INC.—See Carriage Services, Inc.; *U.S. Public*, pg. 439
FOREST LAWN MEMORIAL CHAPEL, INC.—See Axar Capital Management L.P.; *U.S. Private*, pg. 411
FOREST LAWN MEMORY GARDENS, INC.—See Axar Capital Management L.P.; *U.S. Private*, pg. 411
FORT LINCOLN CEMETERY, INC.—See Service Corporation International; *U.S. Public*, pg. 1871
FRANKLIN-STRICKLAND FUNERAL HOME, INC.—See Service Corporation International; *U.S. Public*, pg. 1869
FUNERAL SERVICES NORTHERN IRELAND LIMITED—See Co-operative Group Limited; *Int'l*, pg. 1679
GARY L. KAUFMAN FUNERAL HOME AT MEADOWRIDGE MEMORIAL PARK, INC.—See Service Corporation International; *U.S. Public*, pg. 1869
GEORGE WASHINGTON CEMETERY COMPANY, LLC—See Service Corporation International; *U.S. Public*, pg. 1869
GILMARTIN FUNERAL HOME AND CREMATION CO., INC.—See H.E. Turner & Co., Inc.; *U.S. Private*, pg. 1826
GRACELAND CEMETERY DEVELOPMENT CO.—See Service Corporation International; *U.S. Public*, pg. 1869
GRACELAWN MEMORIAL PARK, INC—See Service Corporation International; *U.S. Public*, pg. 1869
GREENLAWN FUNERAL HOMES, INC.—See Carriage Services, Inc.; *U.S. Public*, pg. 439
GREER-WILSON FUNERAL HOME, INC.—See Security National Financial Corporation; *U.S. Public*, pg. 1856
GRIFFIN-LEGGETT HEALEY & ROTH FUNERAL HOME—See Service Corporation International; *U.S. Public*, pg. 1871
GRUPA KLEPSYDRA SA; *Int'l*, pg. 3117
GUARDIAN FUNERAL HOME—See Service Corporation International; *U.S. Public*, pg. 1871
HAMILTON FUNERAL CHAPEL, INC.—See Service Corporation International; *U.S. Public*, pg. 1869
HAWAIIAN MEMORIAL LIFE PLAN, LTD.—See Service Corporation International; *U.S. Public*, pg. 1869
HEAVEN'S PETS AT LAKELAWN METAIRIE, LLC—See Service Corporation International; *U.S. Public*, pg. 1869
HENLOPEN MEMORIAL PARK LLC—See Axar Capital Management L.P.; *U.S. Private*, pg. 411
H.E. TURNER & CO., INC.; *U.S. Private*, pg. 1826
H GOODWIN & SON (NEWCASTLE) LIMITED—See Co-operative Group Limited; *Int'l*, pg. 1679
H H BIRCH & SON LIMITED—See Co-operative Group Limited; *Int'l*, pg. 1679
HINES-RINALDI FUNERAL HOME, INC.—See Service Corporation International; *U.S. Public*, pg. 1871
HOLLADAY MEMORIAL PARK, INC.—See Security National Financial Corporation; *U.S. Public*, pg. 1856
HOLMES FUNERAL DIRECTORS, INC.—See Service Corporation International; *U.S. Public*, pg. 1869
H. P. BRANDT FUNERAL HOME, INC.—See Service Corporation International; *U.S. Public*, pg. 1869
I. J. MORRIS, LLC—See Service Corporation International; *U.S. Public*, pg. 1869
INTEGRITY FUNERAL CARE—See Birch Hill Equity Partners Management Inc.; *Int'l*, pg. 1046
INTEGRITY FUNERAL CARE—See Homesteaders Life Co. Inc.; *U.S. Private*, pg. 1974
INVOCARE LIMITED—See TPG Capital, L.P.; *U.S. Public*, pg. 2174
JOHN M. TAYLOR FUNERAL HOME, INC.—See Service Corporation International; *U.S. Public*, pg. 1871
THE JOHN P. BROOKS FAMILY CORPORATION; *U.S. Private*, pg. 4059
KENNEDY MEMORIAL GARDENS, INC.—See Service Corporation International; *U.S. Public*, pg. 1869
KER-WESTERLUND FUNERAL HOME, INC.—See Service Corporation International; *U.S. Public*, pg. 1869
KIRK & NICE, INC.—See Axar Capital Management L.P.; *U.S. Private*, pg. 411
KIRK & NICE SUBURBAN CHAPEL, INC.—See Axar Capital Management L.P.; *U.S. Private*, pg. 411
KLINGEL-CARPENTER MORTUARY, INC.—See Service Corporation International; *U.S. Public*, pg. 1871
KOWLOON FUNERAL PARLOUR COMPANY LIMITED—See Grand Peace Group Holdings Limited; *Int'l*, pg. 3056
LAKE VIEW MEMORIAL GARDENS, INC.—See Service Corporation International; *U.S. Public*, pg. 1869
LAVENIA SMITH & SUMMERS HOME FOR FUNERALS—See Flanner & Buchanan, Inc.; *U.S. Private*, pg. 1540
LEMMON FUNERAL HOME OF DULANEY VALLEY, INC.—See Service Corporation International; *U.S. Public*, pg. 1869
LIBERTY FUNERALS PTY LIMITED—See TPG Capital, L.P.; *U.S. Public*, pg. 2174
LIFE CORPORATION SERVICES (S) PTE. LTD.—See Global Cord Blood Corporation; *Int'l*, pg. 2994
LINCOLN FUNERAL HOME, INC.—See Service Corporation International; *U.S. Public*, pg. 1870
LINCOLN MEMORIAL PARK—See Service Corporation International; *U.S. Public*, pg. 1870
LOMBARDO FUNERAL HOME—See Carriage Services, Inc.; *U.S. Public*, pg. 439
LOUDON PARK FUNERAL HOME, INC.—See Service Corporation International; *U.S. Public*, pg. 1871
LSC MICHIGAN CORP.—See LSC Acquisition Corporation; *U.S. Private*, pg. 2508
MAINLAND FUNERAL HOME, INC.—See Service Corporation International; *U.S. Public*, pg. 1870
MATTHEWS INTERNATIONAL SARL—See Matthews International Corporation; *U.S. Public*, pg. 1400
MCHUGH FUNERAL HOME, INC.—See Service Corporation International; *U.S. Public*, pg. 1870
MCKENNA FUNERALS LIMITED—See Co-operative Group Limited; *Int'l*, pg. 1679
MCLAURIN'S FUNERAL HOME, LLC—See Service Corporation International; *U.S. Public*, pg. 1871
MEMORA SERVICIOS FUNERARIOS S.L.—See 3i Group plc; *Int'l*, pg. 9
MEMORIAL ESTATES, INC.—See Security National Financial Corporation; *U.S. Public*, pg. 1856
MEMORIAL GUARDIAN PLAN PTY LIMITED—See TPG Capital, L.P.; *U.S. Public*, pg. 2174
MEMORIAL PARK CEMETERY ASSOCIATION OF MISSOURI, INC.—See Birch Hill Equity Partners Management Inc.; *Int'l*, pg. 1046
MEMORIAL PARK CEMETERY ASSOCIATION OF MISSOURI, INC.—See Homesteaders Life Co. Inc.; *U.S. Private*, pg. 1974
MILLER-DIPPEL FUNERAL HOME, INC.—See Service Corporation International; *U.S. Public*, pg. 1870
MILLER ENTERPRISES, INC.; *U.S. Private*, pg. 2734
M. J. EDWARDS FUNERAL HOME, INC.—See Service Corporation International; *U.S. Public*, pg. 1870
MONTLAWN MEMORIAL PARK, INC.—See Axar Capital Management L.P.; *U.S. Private*, pg. 411
MORRIS-BATES FUNERAL HOME, INC.—See Service Corporation International; *U.S. Public*, pg. 1870
MOUNT VERNON MEMORIAL PARK & MORTUARY—See Service Corporation International; *U.S. Public*, pg. 1870
MOURNING GLORY FUNERAL SERVICES INC.—See Service Corporation International; *U.S. Public*, pg. 1870
NATIONAL CREMATION SERVICE, INC.—See Service Corporation International; *U.S. Public*, pg. 1870
NATIONAL HARMONY MEMORIAL PARK, INC.—See Service Corporation International; *U.S. Public*, pg. 1871
NEPTUNE SOCIETY INC.; *U.S. Private*, pg. 2885
NEW YORK FUNERAL CHAPELS, LLC—See Service Corporation International; *U.S. Public*, pg. 1870
NORTHSTAR MEMORIAL GROUP, LLC; *U.S. Private*, pg. 2958
OAKLAWN CEMETERY ASSOCIATION—See Service Corporation International; *U.S. Public*, pg. 1870
OAKMONT MEMORIAL PARK & MORTUARY—See Carriage Services, Inc.; *U.S. Public*, pg. 439
OAKWOOD FUNERALS PTY LIMITED—See TPG Capital, L.P.; *U.S. Public*, pg. 2174
OAK WOODS MANAGEMENT COMPANY—See Service Corporation International; *U.S. Public*, pg. 1870
PAGE THEUS FUNERAL HOME—See NorthStar Memorial Group, LLC; *U.S. Private*, pg. 2958
PALM MORTUARY INC.—See Service Corporation International; *U.S. Public*, pg. 1870
PARADISE CHAPEL FUNERAL HOME, INC.—See Security National Financial Corporation; *U.S. Public*, pg. 1856
PARADISE FUNERAL HOME, INC.—See Service Corporation International; *U.S. Public*, pg. 1870
PARK LAWN CORPORATION—See Birch Hill Equity Partners Management Inc.; *Int'l*, pg. 1046
PARK LAWN CORPORATION—See Homesteaders Life Co. Inc.; *U.S. Private*, pg. 1974
THE PARKWOOD CEMETERY COMPANY—See Service Corporation International; *U.S. Public*, pg. 1871
PASADENA FUNERAL HOME, INC.—See Service Corporation International; *U.S. Public*, pg. 1871
PHOENIX MEMORIAL PARK ASSOCIATION—See Service Corporation International; *U.S. Public*, pg. 1870
PINEVIEW MEMORIAL PARK, INC.—See Service Corporation International; *U.S. Public*, pg. 1870
PITCHER AND LE QUESNE LIMITED—See Dignity plc; *Int'l*, pg. 2124
RABENHORST FUNERAL HOME INC.; *U.S. Private*, pg. 3341
RESOMATION LIMITED—See Co-operative Group Limited; *Int'l*, pg. 1679
REST HAVEN FUNERAL HOME, INC.—See Carriage Services, Inc.; *U.S. Public*, pg. 440
RIDGEWOOD CEMETERY COMPANY, INC.—See Service Corporation International; *U.S. Public*, pg. 1870
ROBERT L. HENDRICKS FUNERAL HOME, INC.—See Service Corporation International; *U.S. Public*, pg. 1870
ROHLAND FUNERAL HOME—See Service Corporation International; *U.S. Public*, pg. 1870

N.A.I.C.S. INDEX

812320 — DRYCLEANING AND LAU...

ROLLING HILLS MEMORIAL PARK—See Carriage Services, Inc.; *U.S. Public*, pg. 440
ROSEDALE CEMETERY COMPANY—See Service Corporation International; *U.S. Public*, pg. 1870
SAUL-GABAUER FUNERAL HOME, INC.—See Service Corporation International; *U.S. Public*, pg. 1870
SCHIMUNEK FUNERAL HOME, INC.—See Service Corporation International; *U.S. Public*, pg. 1870
SCI ALABAMA FUNERAL SERVICES, LLC—See Service Corporation International; *U.S. Public*, pg. 1870
SCI COLORADO FUNERAL SERVICES, LLC—See Service Corporation International; *U.S. Public*, pg. 1870
SCI LOUISIANA FUNERAL SERVICES, INC.—See Service Corporation International; *U.S. Public*, pg. 1870
SCI MISSOURI FUNERAL SERVICES, INC.—See Service Corporation International; *U.S. Public*, pg. 1870
SCI OHIO FUNERAL SERVICES, INC.—See Service Corporation International; *U.S. Public*, pg. 1870
SCI OKLAHOMA FUNERAL SERVICES, INC.—See Service Corporation International; *U.S. Public*, pg. 1870
SCI PENNSYLVANIA FUNERAL SERVICES, INC.—See Service Corporation International; *U.S. Public*, pg. 1870
SCI SOUTH CAROLINA FUNERAL SERVICES, INC.—See Service Corporation International; *U.S. Public*, pg. 1870
SCI TEXAS FUNERAL SERVICES, INC.—See Service Corporation International; *U.S. Public*, pg. 1870
SCI WEST VIRGINIA FUNERAL SERVICES, INC.—See Service Corporation International; *U.S. Public*, pg. 1870
SCI WISCONSIN FUNERAL SERVICES, INC.—See Service Corporation International; *U.S. Public*, pg. 1870
SFS CARE PTE LTD—See Global Cord Blood Corporation; *Int'l*, pg. 2994
SHERWOOD MEMORIAL PARK & MAUSOLEUM, INC.—See Service Corporation International; *U.S. Public*, pg. 1870
SIMPLE TRIBUTE FUNERAL AND CREMATION CENTER—See Service Corporation International; *U.S. Public*, pg. 1871
SINGAPORE CASKET COMPANY (PRIVATE) LIMITED—See TPG Capital, L.P.; *U.S. Public*, pg. 2174
SOUTHERN FUNERAL HOME, INC.—See Service Corporation International; *U.S. Public*, pg. 1871
SPEAKS CHAPELS LLC—See Birch Hill Equity Partners Management Inc.; *Int'l*, pg. 1046
SPEAKS CHAPELS LLC—See Homesteaders Life Co. Inc.; *U.S. Private*, pg. 1974
STEPHEN R. HAKY FUNERAL HOME, INC.—See Axar Capital Management L.P.; *U.S. Private*, pg. 412
STERLING-ASHTON-SCHWAB FUNERAL HOME, INC—See Service Corporation International; *U.S. Public*, pg. 1871
STERLING-ASHTON-SCHWAB-WITZKE FUNERAL HOME OF CATONSVILLE, INC.—See Service Corporation International; *U.S. Public*, pg. 1871
ST. LAURENT FUNERAL HOME, INC.—See Service Corporation International; *U.S. Public*, pg. 1870
STONEMOR INC.—See Axar Capital Management L.P.; *U.S. Private*, pg. 411
STONEMOR PUERTO RICO LLC—See Axar Capital Management L.P.; *U.S. Private*, pg. 412
SUNSET MEMORIAL PARK COMPANY—See Service Corporation International; *U.S. Public*, pg. 1871
THEO. C. AUMAN, INC—See Service Corporation International; *U.S. Public*, pg. 1871
THOMAS AMM GMBH—See Service Corporation International; *U.S. Public*, pg. 1871
THOMAS M. QUINN & SONS, LLC—See Service Corporation International; *U.S. Public*, pg. 1871
THOMPSON FUNERAL HOME, INC.—See Service Corporation International; *U.S. Public*, pg. 1871
TRADITIONAL SERVICE COMPANY, LLC—See Traditional Service Corporation; *U.S. Private*, pg. 4203
VANCOUVER FUNERAL CHAPEL, INC.—See Service Corporation International; *U.S. Public*, pg. 1871
VAN ZANDT COUNTY HAVEN OF MEMORIES, INC.—See Service Corporation International; *U.S. Public*, pg. 1870
WACO MEMORIAL PARK, INC.—See Service Corporation International; *U.S. Public*, pg. 1871
WARFORD-WALKER MORTUARY, INC.—See Service Corporation International; *U.S. Public*, pg. 1871
WEERTS FUNERAL HOME, INC.—See Service Corporation International; *U.S. Public*, pg. 1871
WESTMINSTER GARDENS, INC.—See Service Corporation International; *U.S. Public*, pg. 1871
WFG-CRISTO REY FUNERAL HOME, INC.—See Service Corporation International; *U.S. Public*, pg. 1871
WFG-FULLER FUNERALS, INC.—See Service Corporation International; *U.S. Public*, pg. 1871
WFG-LOCKWOOD FUNERAL HOME, INC.—See Service Corporation International; *U.S. Public*, pg. 1871
WFH, INC—See Birch Hill Equity Partners Management Inc.; *Int'l*, pg. 1046
WFH, INC—See Homesteaders Life Co. Inc.; *U.S. Private*, pg. 1974
WIEN & WIEN, INC.—See Service Corporation International; *U.S. Public*, pg. 1871
WILSON FUNERAL HOME, INC.—See Service Corporation International; *U.S. Public*, pg. 1871
WILSON & KRATZER MORTUARIES INC.—See Carriage Services, Inc.; *U.S. Public*, pg. 440
WOODLAND BURIAL PARKS GROUP LTD.—See Bibby Line Group Limited; *Int'l*, pg. 1018
WOODLAWN CEMETERY OF CHICAGO, INC.—See Service Corporation International; *U.S. Public*, pg. 1871
ZIMMERMAN- AUER FUNERAL HOME, INC.—See Service Corporation International; *U.S. Public*, pg. 1872

812220 — CEMETERIES AND CREMATORIES

ACKERMAN & CO.; *U.S. Private*, pg. 59
ALLEGHANY MEMORIAL PARK LLC—See Axar Capital Management L.P.; *U.S. Private*, pg. 411
ARBOR MEMORIAL SERVICES INC.—See Fairfax Financial Holdings Limited; *Int'l*, pg. 2606
ARIA CREMATION SERVICES, LLC—See The John P. Brooks Family Corporation; *U.S. Private*, pg. 4059
AUGUSTA MEMORIAL PARK PERPETUAL CARE COMPANY—See Axar Capital Management L.P.; *U.S. Private*, pg. 411
BETH ISRAEL CEMETERY ASSOCIATION OF WOODBRIDGE—See Axar Capital Management L.P.; *U.S. Private*, pg. 411
BIRCHLAWN BURIAL PARK LLC—See Axar Capital Management L.P.; *U.S. Private*, pg. 411
CATHOLIC CEMETERIES ASSOCIATION; *U.S. Private*, pg. 788
CEDAR HILL CEMETERY COMPANY, INC.—See Service Corporation International; *U.S. Public*, pg. 1871
CHAPEL HILL ASSOCIATES, INC.—See Axar Capital Management L.P.; *U.S. Private*, pg. 411
CHINA REDSTONE GROUP, INC.; *Int'l*, pg. 1546
CMS EAST, INC.; *U.S. Private*, pg. 951
COLUMBIA MEMORIAL PARK LLC—See Axar Capital Management L.P.; *U.S. Private*, pg. 411
CORNERSTONE FAMILY SERVICES INC.—See Axar Capital Management L.P.; *U.S. Private*, pg. 411
COVINGTON MEMORIAL GARDENS, INC.—See Axar Capital Management L.P.; *U.S. Private*, pg. 411
CREMATION SOCIETY OF PENNSYLVANIA, INC.—See Service Corporation International; *U.S. Public*, pg. 1870
CREMATION SOCIETY OF WINDSOR & ESSEX COUNTY, INC.—See Service Corporation International; *U.S. Public*, pg. 1869
D2 REALTY SERVICES INC.; *U.S. Private*, pg. 1143
DIGNITY CREMATORIA LIMITED—See Dignity plc; *Int'l*, pg. 2124
FAMILIES FIRST FUNERAL HOME & TRIBUTE CENTRE, INC.—See Service Corporation International; *U.S. Public*, pg. 1869
FOREST LAWN GARDENS, INC.—See Axar Capital Management L.P.; *U.S. Private*, pg. 411
FRIENDS OF MOSDOT GOOR, INC; *U.S. Private*, pg. 1611
F. RUGGIERO & SONS INC.; *U.S. Private*, pg. 1455
FU SHOU YUAN INTERNATIONAL GROUP LIMITED; *Int'l*, pg. 2801
GOLDEN MV HOLDINGS INC.; *Int'l*, pg. 3030
GREENACRES PET CREMATORIUM LIMITED—See CVS Group Plc; *Int'l*, pg. 1890
GREENBRIER PET LOSS SERVICES, LLC—See Matthews International Corporation; *U.S. Public*, pg. 1399
HENRY MEMORIAL PARK LLC—See Axar Capital Management L.P.; *U.S. Private*, pg. 411
HIGHLAND MEMORIAL PARK, INC.—See Axar Capital Management L.P.; *U.S. Private*, pg. 411
INGLEWOOD PARK CEMETERY INC.; *U.S. Private*, pg. 2076
JUNIATA MEMORIAL PARK LLC—See Axar Capital Management L.P.; *U.S. Private*, pg. 411
MEMORY GARDENS MANAGEMENT CORPORATION; *U.S. Private*, pg. 2664
MOUNT AUBURN CEMETERY; *U.S. Private*, pg. 2797
NATIONAL SEPTEMBER 11 MEMORIAL & MUSEUM; *U.S. Private*, pg. 2863
NORTHLAWN MEMORIAL GARDENS—See Axar Capital Management L.P.; *U.S. Private*, pg. 411
OAK HILL CEMETERY LLC—See Axar Capital Management L.P.; *U.S. Private*, pg. 411
PARK LAWN CEMETERY INC.—See Inglewood Park Cemetery Inc.; *U.S. Private*, pg. 2076
THE PET CREMATORIUM LIMITED—See CVS Group Plc; *Int'l*, pg. 1890
THE PET LOSS CENTER - AUSTIN LLC; *U.S. Private*, pg. 4093
REFLECTION POINTE CEMETERY, INC.—See Traditional Service Corporation; *U.S. Private*, pg. 4203
ROCKBRIDGE MEMORIAL GARDENS LLC—See Axar Capital Management L.P.; *U.S. Private*, pg. 412
ROLLING GREEN MEMORIAL PARK LLC—See Axar Capital Management L.P.; *U.S. Private*, pg. 412
ROSE HILL MEMORIAL PARK; *U.S. Private*, pg. 3481
ROSE HILLS COMPANY—See Service Corporation International; *U.S. Public*, pg. 1870
ROSE LAWN CEMETERIES SUBSIDIARY, INCORPORATED—See Axar Capital Management L.P.; *U.S. Private*, pg. 412
ROSELAWN DEVELOPMENT LLC—See Axar Capital Management L.P.; *U.S. Private*, pg. 412
ROSSENDALE PET CREMATORIUM LIMITED—See CVS Group Plc; *Int'l*, pg. 1890
RUSSELL MEMORIAL CEMETERY LLC—See Axar Capital Management L.P.; *U.S. Private*, pg. 412
SHENANDOAH MEMORIAL PARK LLC—See Axar Capital Management L.P.; *U.S. Private*, pg. 412
SIERRA VIEW MEMORIAL PARK—See Axar Capital Management L.P.; *U.S. Private*, pg. 412
SIGNAL LANDMARK—See California Coastal Communities, Inc.; *U.S. Private*, pg. 718
SILVERMERE HAVEN LIMITED—See CVS Group Plc; *Int'l*, pg. 1890
SPRINGHILL MEMORY GARDENS LLC—See Axar Capital Management L.P.; *U.S. Private*, pg. 412
STONEMOR CEMETERY PRODUCTS LLC—See Axar Capital Management L.P.; *U.S. Private*, pg. 412
STONEMOR PARTNERS L.P.—See Axar Capital Management L.P.; *U.S. Private*, pg. 411
STONEMOR PENNSYLVANIA SUBSIDIARY LLC—See Axar Capital Management L.P.; *U.S. Private*, pg. 412
SUNSET MEMORIAL PARK CEMETERY TRUST—See Service Corporation International; *U.S. Public*, pg. 1870
SUNSET MEMORIAL PARK INC.—See Axar Capital Management L.P.; *U.S. Private*, pg. 412
TYCHE SPA—See Matthews International Corporation; *U.S. Public*, pg. 1400
THE VALHALLA CEMETERY COMPANY LLC—See Axar Capital Management L.P.; *U.S. Private*, pg. 412
VALLEY PET CREMATORIUM LIMITED—See CVS Group Plc; *Int'l*, pg. 1890
WHITLEY BROOK CREMATORIUM FOR PETS LIMITED—See CVS Group Plc; *Int'l*, pg. 1890
ZHEJIANG ANXIAN YUAN COMPANY LIMITED—See Anxian Yuan China Holdings Limited; *Int'l*, pg. 486

812310 — COIN-OPERATED LAUNDRIES AND DRYCLEANERS

AUTOMATIC APARTMENT LAUNDRIES, INC.; *U.S. Private*, pg. 399
CENTRAL GEORGIA HEALTH VENTURES, INC.—See Central Georgia Health System Inc.; *U.S. Public*, pg. 821
COMMERCIAL & COIN LAUNDRY EQUIPMENT CO.—See BDT Capital Partners, LLC; *U.S. Private*, pg. 502
CONSOLIDATED SMART SYSTEMS GROUP; *U.S. Private*, pg. 1022
CS LAUNDRY SYSTEM PHILIPPINES CORP.—See BCM Alliance Berhad; *Int'l*, pg. 928
MOVINGPLACE, LLC—See Porch Group, Inc.; *U.S. Public*, pg. 1702
PAC INDUSTRIES, LLC—See EVI Industries, Inc.; *U.S. Public*, pg. 803
SCOTT EQUIPMENT, LLC—See EVI Industries, Inc.; *U.S. Public*, pg. 803
SOUTHWEST FLORIDA FRANCHISES INC.; *U.S. Private*, pg. 3739
UNITED LINEN SERVICES INC.; *U.S. Private*, pg. 4293
WASH MULTIFAMILY LAUNDRY SYSTEMS, LLC—See EQT AB; *Int'l*, pg. 2481

812320 — DRYCLEANING AND LAUNDRY SERVICES (EXCEPT COIN-OPERATED)

ACW MANAGEMENT CORPORATION; *U.S. Private*, pg. 71
AFONWEN LAUNDRY LIMITED; *Int'l*, pg. 189
ALDRICH CLEAN-TECH EQUIPMENT CORP.—See EVI Industries, Inc.; *U.S. Public*, pg. 803
ALEXANDER KARTEN; *U.S. Private*, pg. 163
AMERICAN CLEANERS & LAUNDRY CO.; *U.S. Private*, pg. 227
ANGELICA CORPORATION—See KKR & Co. Inc.; *U.S. Public*, pg. 1239
ARAMARK UNIFORM SERVICES (CANADA) LTD.—See Aramark; *U.S. Public*, pg. 177
ARAMARK UNIFORM SERVICES (ROCHESTER) LLC—See Vestis Corp; *U.S. Public*, pg. 2290
ARAMARK UNIFORM SERVICES (SANTA ANA) LLC—See Vestis Corp; *U.S. Public*, pg. 2290
ARAMARK UNIFORM SERVICES (SYRACUSE) LLC—See Vestis Corp; *U.S. Public*, pg. 2290
A. W. ZENGELER CLEANERS, INC.; *U.S. Private*, pg. 24
BEAUTIFUL RESTAURANT INC.; *U.S. Private*, pg. 508
BEGLEY COMPANY; *U.S. Private*, pg. 514
BERENDSEN LIMITED—See Eurazeo SE; *Int'l*, pg. 2528
BERGMANN'S CLEANING INC.—See Bergmann's Inc.; *U.S. Private*, pg. 531
BERGMANN'S INC.; *U.S. Private*, pg. 531
CLEAN LINEN SERVICES LIMITED; *Int'l*, pg. 1654
DELIAS CLEANERS INC.—See Delphi Management Group, Inc.; *U.S. Private*, pg. 1199
DELPHI MANAGEMENT GROUP, INC.; *U.S. Private*, pg. 1199
DEPENDABLE CLEANERS INC.; *U.S. Private*, pg. 1208

5055

812320 — DRYCLEANING AND LAU...

DEXTER LAUNDRY INC.—See Dexter Apache Holdings, Inc.; *U.S. Private*, pg. 1220
DRYCLEAN USA DEVELOPMENT CORP—See EVI Industries, Inc.; *U.S. Public*, pg. 803
DRYCLEAN USA LICENSE CORP—See EVI Industries, Inc.; *U.S. Public*, pg. 803
DRYVE INC.; *U.S. Private*, pg. 1281
ELIS NORGE AS—See Eurazeo SE; *Int'l*, pg. 2528
EVI INDUSTRIES, INC.; *U.S. Public*, pg. 803
FAULTLESS LAUNDRY COMPANY; *U.S. Private*, pg. 1483
GET INCORPORATED; *U.S. Private*, pg. 1688
GRAND LAUNDRY, INC.—See MGM Resorts International; *U.S. Public*, pg. 1435
GULF HOTEL LAUNDRY SERVICES W.L.L—See Gulf Hotels Group B.S.C.; *Int'l*, pg. 3181
HAKUYOSHA COMPANY LTD.; *Int'l*, pg. 3222
HEALTH SYSTEMS COOPERATIVE LAUNDRIES; *U.S. Private*, pg. 1894
HOLLYWOOD RENTAL SP.Z.O.O.—See Hollywood SA; *Int'l*, pg. 3452
HOLLYWOOD SA; *Int'l*, pg. 3452
HOLLYWOOD TEXTILE SERVICE SP.Z.O.O.—See Hollywood SA; *Int'l*, pg. 3452
HTS AMA SP.Z.O.O.—See Hollywood SA; *Int'l*, pg. 3452
HTS BALTICA SP.Z.O.O.—See Hollywood SA; *Int'l*, pg. 3452
HTS BAXTER SP.Z.O.O.—See Hollywood SA; *Int'l*, pg. 3452
HTS MEDIJ SP.Z.O.O.—See Hollywood SA; *Int'l*, pg. 3452
HTS STARGARD SP.Z.O.O.—See Hollywood SA; *Int'l*, pg. 3452
HTS TARGATZ GMBH—See Hollywood SA; *Int'l*, pg. 3452
IMAGEFIRST HEALTHCARE LAUNDRY SPECIALISTS; *U.S. Private*, pg. 2045
ITU ABSORBTECH, INC.; *U.S. Private*, pg. 2150
LAUNDRY LOCKER INC.—See Mulberrys, LLC; *U.S. Private*, pg. 2811
LAUNDRYLUX INC.; *U.S. Private*, pg. 2398
LAUNDRY SYSTEMS OF TENNESSEE, LLC—See EVI Industries, Inc.; *U.S. Public*, pg. 803
LEVINGERS DRY CLEANERS (PTY) LTD.—See Excellerate Holdings Ltd.; *Int'l*, pg. 2578
MULBERRYS, LLC; *U.S. Private*, pg. 2811
PILGRIM CLEANERS INC.; *U.S. Private*, pg. 3180
PKC INC.—See Loeb Holding Corporation; *U.S. Private*, pg. 2479
POLTEXTIL SP.Z.O.O.—See Hollywood SA; *Int'l*, pg. 3452
PRALMED SP.Z.O.O.—See Hollywood SA; *Int'l*, pg. 3452
PRAL SERWIS WARSZAWA SP.Z.O.O.—See Hollywood SA; *Int'l*, pg. 3452
PRESTIGE CORP.; *U.S. Private*, pg. 3255
PRIDE CLEANERS INC.—See MJV Holdings, LLC; *U.S. Private*, pg. 2753
PURITAN CLEANERS; *U.S. Private*, pg. 3306
REINO LINEN SERVICES INC.—See York Capital Management Global Advisors, LLC; *U.S. Private*, pg. 4590
ROBISON & SMITH, INC.; *U.S. Private*, pg. 3462
SAM MEYERS INC.; *U.S. Private*, pg. 3535
SIR GROUT LLC—See Riverside Partners, LLC; *U.S. Private*, pg. 3446
SWAN SUPER CLEANERS INC.; *U.S. Private*, pg. 3889
TUCHMAN CLEANERS INC.—See U.S. Dry Cleaning Services Corporation; *U.S. Private*, pg. 4270
U.S. DRY CLEANING SERVICES CORPORATION; *U.S. Private*, pg. 4270
U. S. STEEL SERVICES S.R.O.—See United States Steel Corporation; *U.S. Public*, pg. 2237
VESTIS (ROCHESTER), LLC—See Vestis Corp; *U.S. Public*, pg. 2290
VESTIS (SYRACUSE), LLC—See Vestis Corp; *U.S. Public*, pg. 2290
WASCHEREI ELLERICH GMBH—See Clariane SE; *Int'l*, pg. 1643
WHITERIVER LAUNDRY LTD—See Afonwen Laundry Limited; *Int'l*, pg. 189
ZOOTS CORPORATION; *U.S. Private*, pg. 4608

812331 — LINEN SUPPLY

429149 B.C. LTD; *Int'l*, pg. 11
ADMIRAL LINEN SERVICE INC.; *U.S. Private*, pg. 81
ALSCO SERVITEX, INC.—See Alsco Inc.; *U.S. Private*, pg. 202
AMERICAN LINEN SUPPLY CO.—See Alsco Inc.; *U.S. Private*, pg. 202
AMERICAN TEXTILE MAINTENANCE COMPANY; *U.S. Private*, pg. 257
AMERIPRIDE LINEN & UNIFORM SERVICES, INC.—See Aramark; *U.S. Public*, pg. 177
AMERIPRIDE SERVICES INC.—See Aramark; *U.S. Public*, pg. 177
ANGELICA TEXTILE SERVICES, INC.—See KKR & Co Inc.; *U.S. Public*, pg. 1239
A&P COAT, APRON & LINEN SUPPLY; *U.S. Private*, pg. 20
ARAMARK UNIFORM SERVICES JAPAN CORPORATION—See Aramark; *U.S. Public*, pg. 177
ARROW UNIFORM-TAYLOR LLC—See UniFirst Corporation; *U.S. Public*, pg. 2226
ASSOCIATED TEXTILE RENTAL SERVICES—See Vestis Corp; *U.S. Public*, pg. 2290
ATLAS HEALTH CARE LINEN SERVICES CO.; *U.S. Private*, pg. 376
BERENDSEN UK LIMITED—See Eurazeo SE; *Int'l*, pg. 2528
CANADIAN LINEN & UNIFORM SERVICE CO.; *Int'l*, pg. 1284
CHURCHILL LINEN SERVICE INC.—See Alsco Inc.; *U.S. Private*, pg. 202
CLEAN TEXTILE SYSTEMS INC.; *U.S. Private*, pg. 931
CONTINENTAL LINEN SERVICES INC.; *U.S. Private*, pg. 1030
CROWN LINEN SERVICE INCORPORATED; *U.S. Private*, pg. 1111
DEMPSEY UNIFORM & LINEN SUPPLY, INC.; *U.S. Private*, pg. 1204
DOMESTIC LINEN SUPPLY & LAUNDRY COMPANY; *U.S. Private*, pg. 1256
DOMESTIC UNIFORM RENTAL CO.—See Domestic Linen Supply & Laundry Company; *U.S. Private*, pg. 1256
EMERALD TEXTILES, LLC—See Pacific Avenue Capital Partners, LLC; *U.S. Private*, pg. 3065
FALVEY LINEN SUPPLY INC.; *U.S. Private*, pg. 1468
FEDERATED LINEN & UNIFORM SERVICES; *U.S. Private*, pg. 1491
FINELINENS.COM; *U.S. Private*, pg. 1509
G&K SERVICES, LLC—See Cintas Corporation; *U.S. Public*, pg. 496
HOME DYNAMIX LLC—See H.I.G. Capital, LLC; *U.S. Private*, pg. 1832
HOSPITAL LAUNDRY SERVICES, INC.—See Community Health Systems, Inc.; *U.S. Public*, pg. 553
JDRJ INC.—See Cintas Corporation; *U.S. Public*, pg. 496
LINEN KING, LLC—See York Capital Management Global Advisors, LLC; *U.S. Private*, pg. 4590
L&N UNIFORM SUPPLY, LLC—See Vestis Corp; *U.S. Public*, pg. 2290
MACINTOSH LINEN & UNIFORM RENTAL; *U.S. Private*, pg. 2536
MARTIN LINEN SUPPLY COMPANY—See Federated Linen & Uniform Services; *U.S. Private*, pg. 1491
MICKEYS LINEN & TOWEL SUPPLY; *U.S. Private*, pg. 2702
MORGAN LINEN SERVICE INC.; *U.S. Private*, pg. 2784
NIXON UNIFORM SERVICE INC.; *U.S. Private*, pg. 2930
OCEANSIDE INSTITUTIONAL INDUSTRIES; *U.S. Private*, pg. 2990
PALACE LAUNDRY INC.; *U.S. Private*, pg. 3076
PARIS CLEANERS INC.; *U.S. Private*, pg. 3095
SITEX CORPORATION—See Cintas Corporation; *U.S. Public*, pg. 496
SOUTHEAST LINEN ASSOCIATES, INC.; *U.S. Private*, pg. 3726
SUPERIOR LINEN SERVICE INC.; *U.S. Private*, pg. 3878
TARTAN TEXTILE SERVICES, INC.—See Dover Corporation; *U.S. Public*, pg. 683
TEXAS LINEN COMPANY; *U.S. Private*, pg. 3976
TEXTILE SYSTEMS, INC.—See Ascension Health Alliance; *U.S. Private*, pg. 347
UNIFIRST CANADA LTD.—See UniFirst Corporation; *U.S. Public*, pg. 2226
UNIFIRST CORPORATION—See UniFirst Corporation; *U.S. Public*, pg. 2226
U.S. TEXTILES LLC; *U.S. Private*, pg. 4272

812332 — INDUSTRIAL LAUNDERERS

5 STAR HOTEL LAUNDRY, INC; *U.S. Private*, pg. 16
ABSORBTECH, LLC—See Industrial Towel & Uniform; *U.S. Private*, pg. 2068
ALSCO ITALIA SRL—See Alsco Inc.; *U.S. Private*, pg. 202
ANGSTROM TECHNOLOGY LTD.—See ASGARD Partners & Co., LLC; *U.S. Private*, pg. 349
ARAMARK UNIFORM & CAREER APPAREL GROUP, INC.—See Vestis Corp; *U.S. Public*, pg. 2290
ARAMARK UNIFORM & CAREER APPAREL, LLC—See Vestis Corp; *U.S. Public*, pg. 2290
BERENDSEN GMBH—See Eurazeo SE; *Int'l*, pg. 2528
BRENT INDUSTRIES, INC.; *U.S. Private*, pg. 645
CADILLAC UNIFORM & LINEN SUPPLY; *U.S. Private*, pg. 713
CINTAS CANADA LIMITED—See Cintas Corporation; *U.S. Public*, pg. 495
CINTAS CORPORATION NO. 3—See Cintas Corporation; *U.S. Public*, pg. 495
CINTAS NETHERLANDS HOLDINGS B.V.—See Cintas Corporation; *U.S. Public*, pg. 495
CINTAS - R.U.S., L.P.—See Cintas Corporation; *U.S. Public*, pg. 495
CLEAN LINEN SERVICES LIMITED - BANBURY PLANT—See CLEAN Linen Services Limited; *Int'l*, pg. 1654
CLEAN LINEN SERVICES LIMITED - CAMBERLEY PLANT—See CLEAN Linen Services Limited; *Int'l*, pg. 1654
CLEAN LINEN SERVICES LIMITED - READING PLANT—See CLEAN Linen Services Limited; *Int'l*, pg. 1654
COYNE INTERNATIONAL ENTERPRISES CORP.; *U.S. Private*, pg. 1079
COYNE TEXTILE SERVICE INC.—See Coyne International Enterprises Corp.; *U.S. Private*, pg. 1079
CWS-BOCO INTERNATIONAL GMBH—See Franz Haniel & Cie. GmbH; *Int'l*, pg. 2762
ELIS S.A.—See Eurazeo SE; *Int'l*, pg. 2528
GEAR WASH LLC—See Fire-Dex, LLC; *U.S. Private*, pg. 1511
G&K SERVICES, LLC - LAUREL—See Cintas Corporation; *U.S. Public*, pg. 496
HANDCRAFT CLEANERS AND LAUNDERERS INC.—See Puritan Cleaners; *U.S. Private*, pg. 3306
HEILMAN HOLDING COMPANY INC.; *U.S. Private*, pg. 1904
HERITAGE HEALTH CARE SERVICES, INC.; *U.S. Private*, pg. 1923
HOSPITAL LAUNDRY SERVICES; *U.S. Private*, pg. 1987
IMAGE APPAREL FOR BUSINESS INC.; *U.S. Private*, pg. 2044
INDUSTRIAL TOWEL & UNIFORM - NEENAH PLANT—See Industrial Towel & Uniform; *U.S. Private*, pg. 2068
INDUSTRIAL TOWEL & UNIFORM; *U.S. Private*, pg. 2068
IRON CITY INDUSTRIAL CLEANING CORP.; *U.S. Private*, pg. 2139
LIBRA INDUSTRIES, INC.; *U.S. Private*, pg. 2447
PRUDENTIAL OVERALL SUPPLY INC.; *U.S. Private*, pg. 3296
RENTAL UNIFORM SERVICE OF FLORENCE; *U.S. Private*, pg. 3400
SADDORIS COMPANIES, INC.; *U.S. Private*, pg. 3523
TEXTILE CARE SERVICES, INC.; *U.S. Private*, pg. 3978
TEXTILE CARE SERVICES, INC.; *U.S. Private*, pg. 3978
TEXTILIA TVATT & TEXTILSERVICE AB—See Accent Equity Partners AB; *Int'l*, pg. 81
TROPICAL LAUNDRIES—See Goddard Enterprises Limited; *Int'l*, pg. 3019
UNIFIRST HOLDINGS INC—See UniFirst Corporation; *U.S. Public*, pg. 2226
UNITECH SERVICES B.V.—See UniFirst Corporation; *U.S. Public*, pg. 2226
UNITECH SERVICES GMBH—See UniFirst Corporation; *U.S. Public*, pg. 2226
UNITECH SERVICES GROUP, INC.—See UniFirst Corporation; *U.S. Public*, pg. 2226
UNITECH SERVICES GROUP LTD.—See UniFirst Corporation; *U.S. Public*, pg. 2226
UNITECH SERVICES SAS—See UniFirst Corporation; *U.S. Public*, pg. 2226
VICTOR KRAMER CO., INC.—See Compass Group PLC; *Int'l*, pg. 1752
VOGUE LAUNDRY SERVICES LIMITED—See Cathay Pacific Airways Limited; *Int'l*, pg. 1360

812910 — PET CARE (EXCEPT VETERINARY) SERVICES

AMERICAN CRITTER COLLEGE, INC.; *U.S. Private*, pg. 229
ANIMAL HAVEN INC.; *U.S. Private*, pg. 283
ANIMAL HUMANE SOCIETY; *U.S. Private*, pg. 283
AQUARIUM SOFTWARE LIMITED—See Trupanion, Inc.; *U.S. Public*, pg. 2201
ARMITAGE PET CARE LIMITED—See Spectrum Brands Holdings, Inc.; *U.S. Public*, pg. 1915
AUSSIE PET MOBILE, INC.; *U.S. Private*, pg. 395
BANFIELD CHARITABLE TRUST; *U.S. Private*, pg. 465
THE BARKING DOG, LTD.; *U.S. Private*, pg. 3992
BASF ITALIA - NUTRIZIONE ANIMALE—See BASF SE; *Int'l*, pg. 879
BASF NUTRITION ANIMALE—See BASF SE; *Int'l*, pg. 880
BAYSIDE PET RESORT & SPA, INC.; *U.S. Private*, pg. 497
BUTCHER'S PET CARE SP.Z.O.O—See Butcher's Pet Care Ltd.; *Int'l*, pg. 1229
CAERUS CORPORATION; *U.S. Private*, pg. 714
CAMP BOW WOW-BROOMFIELD; *U.S. Private*, pg. 729
CANINE COMPANIONS FOR INDEPENDENCE, INC.; *U.S. Private*, pg. 734
CHARLES RIVER LABORATORIES—See Charles River Laboratories International, Inc.; *U.S. Public*, pg. 480
DANISH CROWN FRANCE S.A.S.—See Danish Crown AmbA; *Int'l*, pg. 1964
DANISH CROWN KOREA LLC—See Danish Crown AmbA; *Int'l*, pg. 1964
DOGTOPIA; *U.S. Private*, pg. 1253
DSSI LLC; *U.S. Private*, pg. 1282
DUO DOGS, INC.; *U.S. Private*, pg. 1291
ELANCO ANIMAL HEALTH, KOREA, LTD.—See Elanco Animal Health Incorporated; *U.S. Public*, pg. 722
ELANCO AUSTRALASIA PTY. LTD.—See Eli Lilly & Company; *U.S. Public*, pg. 731
ELANCO DEUTSCHLAND GMBH—See Eli Lilly & Company; *U.S. Public*, pg. 731
ELANCO US, INC.—See Eli Lilly & Company; *U.S. Public*, pg. 731

N.A.I.C.S. INDEX

FETCH INSURANCE SERVICES, LLC—See Warburg Pincus LLC; *U.S. Private*, pg. 4438
FIRST PET LIFE, INC.; *U.S. Public*, pg. 846
GLOBAL WILDLIFE CONSERVATION; *U.S. Private*, pg. 1719
GO DOG GO INC.—See Pet Stuff Illinois, LLC; *U.S. Private*, pg. 3156
HANKYU HELLO DOG CO., LTD.—See H2O Retailing Corp.; *Int'l*, pg. 3200
HEALTHY PAWS PET INSURANCE LLC—See Aon plc; *Int'l*, pg. 495
HUMANE SOCIETY OF MISSOURI; *U.S. Private*, pg. 2006
INTELLIGENT CONTENT CORP.; *U.S. Private*, pg. 2105
JAPELL PARTNERSHIP SERVICE CO., LTD.—See Arata Corporation; *Int'l*, pg. 536
JOHN PAUL PET, L.L.C.—See John Paul Mitchell Systems; *U.S. Private*, pg. 2223
PEGGY ADAMS ANIMAL RESCUE LEAGUE OF THE PALM BEACHES, INCORPORATED; *U.S. Private*, pg. 3130
PET ASSISTANT HOLDINGS, LLC; *U.S. Private*, pg. 3156
PET DOCTORS OF AMERICA; *U.S. Private*, pg. 3156
PET PARADISE RESORT—See Centripetal Capital Partners, LLC; *U.S. Private*, pg. 830
RADIO SYSTEMS PETSAFE EUROPE LTD.—See Radio Systems Corporation; *U.S. Private*, pg. 3344
SANDY HILL KENNELS, INC.—See General Atlantic Service Company, L.P.; *U.S. Private*, pg. 1663
SOKOLOW-LOGISTYKA SP. Z O.O.—See Danish Crown AmbA; *Int'l*, pg. 1965
SPCA INTERNATIONAL, INC.; *U.S. Private*, pg. 3747
SPECTRUM BRANDS PET LLC—See Spectrum Brands Holdings, Inc.; *U.S. Public*, pg. 1917
SPF-DANMARK A/S—See Danish Crown AmbA; *Int'l*, pg. 1965
TEXAS VET LAB INC.—See Bimeda, Inc.; *U.S. Private*, pg. 560
WHOODLE, LLC—See Red Violet, Inc.; *U.S. Public*, pg. 1770

812921 — PHOTOFINISHING LABORATORIES (EXCEPT ONE-HOUR)

BELCOLOR AG—See Headlam Group plc; *Int'l*, pg. 3301
BURRELL COLOUR INC.—See Jasco Tools Inc.; *U.S. Private*, pg. 2189
CANDID COLOR SYSTEMS, INC.; *U.S. Private*, pg. 733
CEWE COLOR AG & CO. OHG—See CEWE Stiftung & Co. KGaA; *Int'l*, pg. 1425
CEWE COLOR, A.S.—See CEWE Stiftung & Co. KGaA; *Int'l*, pg. 1425
CEWE COLOR BELGIUM S.A.—See CEWE Stiftung & Co. KGaA; *Int'l*, pg. 1425
CEWE COLOR DANMARK A.S.—See CEWE Stiftung & Co. KGaA; *Int'l*, pg. 1425
CEWE COLOR LIMITED—See CEWE Stiftung & Co. KGaA; *Int'l*, pg. 1425
CEWE COLOR MAGYARORSZAG KFT—See CEWE Stiftung & Co. KGaA; *Int'l*, pg. 1425
CEWE COLOR NEDERLAND B.V.—See CEWE Stiftung & Co. KGaA; *Int'l*, pg. 1425
CEWE COLOR S.A.S—See CEWE Stiftung & Co. KGaA; *Int'l*, pg. 1425
CEWE COLOR SP. Z O. O—See CEWE Stiftung & Co. KGaA; *Int'l*, pg. 1425
CEWE STIFTUNG & CO. KGAA; *Int'l*, pg. 1425
DIALAB OY—See Ifolor AG; *Int'l*, pg. 3599
DIGINET GMBH & CO. KG—See CEWE Stiftung & Co. KGaA; *Int'l*, pg. 1425
DIRON WIRTSCHAFTSINFORMATIK GMBH & CO. KG—See CEWE Stiftung & Co. KGaA; *Int'l*, pg. 1425
DISTRICT PHOTO INC.; *U.S. Private*, pg. 1239
DUGGAL COLOR PROJECTS INC.; *U.S. Private*, pg. 1285
FILMET COLOR LABORATORIES INC.; *U.S. Private*, pg. 1506
FOTOCOLOR GMBH—See CEWE Stiftung & Co. KGaA; *Int'l*, pg. 1425
FUJICOLOR CENTRAL EUROPE PHOTOFINISHING GMBH & CO. KG—See FUJIFILM Holdings Corporation; *Int'l*, pg. 2822
FUJIFILM IMAGING GERMANY GMBH & CO. KG—See FUJIFILM Holdings Corporation; *Int'l*, pg. 2822
FUJIFILM IMAGING SYSTEMS GMBH & CO. KG—See FUJIFILM Holdings Corporation; *Int'l*, pg. 2824
IFOLOR AG; *Int'l*, pg. 3599
IFOLOR GMBH—See Ifolor AG; *Int'l*, pg. 3599
IFOLOR OY—See Ifolor AG; *Int'l*, pg. 3599
JAPAN PHOTO HOLDING NORGE AS—See CEWE Stiftung & Co. KGaA; *Int'l*, pg. 1425
LIFETOUCH CANADA INC.—See Apollo Global Management, Inc.; *U.S. Public*, pg. 159
MARCO COLOR LABORATORY, INC.; *U.S. Private*, pg. 2571
MILLERS INC.; *U.S. Private*, pg. 2736
MYSTIC COLOR LAB, INC.—See District Photo Inc.; *U.S. Private*, pg. 1239
PHOTOWORKS, INC.—See Clayton, Dubilier & Rice, LLC; *U.S. Private*, pg. 919
POUNDS PHOTOGRAPHIC LABS, INC.; *U.S. Private*, pg. 3236
P P D, INC.; *U.S. Private*, pg. 3058
QUIK PIX, INC.—See Dalrada Financial Corporation; *U.S. Public*, pg. 621
REKCUT PHOTOGRAPHIC INC.; *U.S. Private*, pg. 3392
SCANDIGITAL INC.; *U.S. Private*, pg. 3561
SHUTTERFLY, INC.—See Apollo Global Management, Inc.; *U.S. Public*, pg. 159
SMUGMUG, INC.; *U.S. Private*, pg. 3699
SNAPFISH LLC—See Apollo Global Management, Inc.; *U.S. Public*, pg. 160
STARFOTO BV—See Ifolor AG; *Int'l*, pg. 3599

812922 — ONE-HOUR PHOTOFINISHING

DUGGAL VISUAL SOLUTIONS, INC.; *U.S. Private*, pg. 1285
XPRESS PRINT (SHANGHAI) CO., LTD.—See A-Smart Holdings Ltd.; *Int'l*, pg. 20

812930 — PARKING LOTS AND GARAGES

ABM PARKING SERVICES, INC.—See ABM Industries, Inc.; *U.S. Public*, pg. 26
ABM PARKING SERVICES, INC.—See ABM Industries, Inc.; *U.S. Public*, pg. 26
ACE PARKING MANAGEMENT INC.; *U.S. Private*, pg. 57
ADR MOBILITY SRL—See Edizione S.r.l.; *Int'l*, pg. 2312
ALCO PARKING CORP.; *U.S. Private*, pg. 154
ALLPRO PARKING, LLC—See Premium Parking Service, LLC; *U.S. Private*, pg. 3252
AMANO PARKING SERVICE LTD.—See Amano Corporation; *Int'l*, pg. 411
AMANO THAI INTERNATIONAL CO., LTD.—See Amano Corporation; *Int'l*, pg. 411
AMERICAN PARKING SYSTEM INC.; *U.S. Private*, pg. 243
AMPCO SYSTEM PARKING—See ABM Industries, Inc.; *U.S. Public*, pg. 26
AMPCO SYSTEM PARKING—See ABM Industries, Inc.; *U.S. Public*, pg. 26
AMPCO SYSTEM PARKING—See ABM Industries, Inc.; *U.S. Public*, pg. 26
AMPCO SYSTEM PARKING—See ABM Industries, Inc.; *U.S. Public*, pg. 26
AMPCO SYSTEM PARKING—See ABM Industries, Inc.; *U.S. Public*, pg. 26
AMPCO SYSTEM PARKING—See ABM Industries, Inc.; *U.S. Public*, pg. 26
APCOA PARKING DEUTSCHLAND GMBH—See Centerbridge Partners, L.P.; *U.S. Private*, pg. 811
APCOA PARKING ESPANA S.A.—See Centerbridge Partners, L.P.; *U.S. Private*, pg. 811
A-PORT S.A.—See Flughafen Zurich AG; *Int'l*, pg. 2713
BAHRAIN CAR PARK COMPANY B.S.C.; *Int'l*, pg. 800
BALTIMORE COUNTY REVENUE AUTHORITIES; *U.S. Private*, pg. 462
BOOMERANG SYSTEMS, INC.; *U.S. Private*, pg. 616
CAMPO GRANDE PARKING LTDA.—See Allos SA; *Int'l*, pg. 359
THE CARLYLE, A ROSEWOOD HOTEL—See Chow Tai Fook Enterprises Limited; *Int'l*, pg. 1585
CENTRO PARKING, INC.—See Central New York Regional Transportation Authority; *U.S. Private*, pg. 823
CITY OF OAKLAND PARKING PARTNERS—See Eldridge Industries LLC; *U.S. Private*, pg. 1351
CITYPARKING INC.; *U.S. Private*, pg. 907
COLONIAL PARKING, INC.—See Forge Company Inc.; *U.S. Private*, pg. 1568
DAIWA HOUSE PARKING CO., LTD.—See Daiwa House Industry Co., Ltd.; *Int'l*, pg. 1945
DAIYOSHI TRUST CO., LTD.—See Daiwa House Industry Co., Ltd.; *Int'l*, pg. 1946
DB BAHNPARK GMBH—See Deutsche Bahn AG; *Int'l*, pg. 2049
DB BARNSDALE AG—See Deutsche Bahn AG; *Int'l*, pg. 2049
DC D.D.; *Int'l*, pg. 1989
DENISON INC.; *U.S. Private*, pg. 1205
DENISON PARKING INC.—See Denison Inc.; *U.S. Private*, pg. 1205
DIAMOND PARKING INC.—See Diamond Parking Services LLC; *U.S. Private*, pg. 1223
DIAMOND PARKING SERVICES LLC; *U.S. Private*, pg. 1223
EDISON PROPERTIES, LLC; *U.S. Private*, pg. 1337
FIRST PARK (PTY) LTD.—See Excellerate Holdings Ltd.; *Int'l*, pg. 2578
FIVE STAR PARKING; *U.S. Private*, pg. 1538
FLY AWAY AIRPORT PARKING SERVICES LLC—See Propark, Inc.; *U.S. Private*, pg. 3284
GARAGE MANAGEMENT CORPORATION CO; *U.S. Private*, pg. 1642
GGMC PARKING, LLC; *U.S. Private*, pg. 1690
HERMANN AUTOMATION GMBH—See Hormann KG Verkaufsgesellschaf; *Int'l*, pg. 3480
IMPERIAL PARKING INDUSTRIES, INC.—See Propark, Inc.; *U.S. Private*, pg. 3284
INDIGO PARK DEUTSCHLAND GMBH—See Fundacion Bancaria Caixa d'Estalvis i Pensions de Barcelona, la Caixa; *Int'l*, pg. 2845
INDIGO PARK SERVICES UK LTD.—See Fundacion Bancaria Caixa d'Estalvis i Pensions de Barcelona, la Caixa; *Int'l*, pg. 2845
INDIGO PARK SLOVAKIA, S.R.O.—See Fundacion Bancaria Caixa d'Estalvis i Pensions de Barcelona, la Caixa; *Int'l*, pg. 2845
INTERNATIONAL PARKING MANAGEMENT, INC.—See LAZ Parking Ltd, LLC; *U.S. Private*, pg. 2402
INTERPARKING HISPANIA, S.A.—See Ageas SA/NV; *Int'l*, pg. 204
INTERPARK LLC; *U.S. Private*, pg. 2122
INTERPARK (SOUTH AFRICA) (PTY) LTD.—See Excellerate Holdings Ltd.; *Int'l*, pg. 2578
IRIDIUM APARCAMIENTOS, S.L.—See ACS, Actividades de Construccion y Servicios, S.A.; *Int'l*, pg. 115
JUNGSEOK ENTERPRISE CO., LTD.—See Hanjin Kal Corp.; *Int'l*, pg. 3252
KARSPACE MANAGEMENT LTD.—See Fundacion Bancaria Caixa d'Estalvis i Pensions de Barcelona, la Caixa; *Int'l*, pg. 2845
KINNEY WEST 83RD ST., INC.—See Eldridge Industries LLC; *U.S. Private*, pg. 1351
LANIER PARKING INC.; *U.S. Private*, pg. 2390
LAZ PARKING LTD, LLC; *U.S. Private*, pg. 2402
MANHATTAN PARKING SYSTEMS GARAGE; *U.S. Private*, pg. 2563
MANHATTAN PARKING SYSTEMS-PARK AVE; *U.S. Private*, pg. 2563
MAZUR PARKPLATZ GMBH—See Flughafen Wien Aktiengesellschaft; *Int'l*, pg. 2712
MCLAURIN PARKING COMPANY INC.; *U.S. Private*, pg. 2640
METEOR PARKING LTD.—See Fundacion Bancaria Caixa d'Estalvis i Pensions de Barcelona, la Caixa; *Int'l*, pg. 2845
METRO PARKING SYSTEMS INC—See Metropolitan Properties Systems; *U.S. Private*, pg. 2689
METROPOLITAN PROPERTIES SYSTEMS; *U.S. Private*, pg. 2689
MHR MANAGEMENT LLC; *U.S. Private*, pg. 2695
MODERN PARKING INC.; *U.S. Private*, pg. 2762
NEW HAVEN CITY PARKING AUTHORITY; *U.S. Private*, pg. 2896
PARK AMERICA INC.; *U.S. Private*, pg. 3095
PARK FAST OF MARYLAND—See Edison Properties, LLC; *U.S. Private*, pg. 1337
PARK-IN COMMERCIAL CENTRE—See Hang Lung Group Limited; *Int'l*, pg. 3245
PARKING COMPANY OF AMERICA, HOTEL DIVISION—See PCA Management; *U.S. Private*, pg. 3119
PARKING COMPANY OF AMERICA, PARKING MANAGEMENT DIVISION—See PCA Management; *U.S. Private*, pg. 3119
PARKING MANAGEMENT, INC.; *U.S. Private*, pg. 3098
PARKING MANAGEMENT ORGANIZATION, LTD.—See Aspirant Group, Inc.; *Int'l*, pg. 631
PARKING SOLUTIONS CO., LTD.—See Daiwa House Industry Co., Ltd.; *Int'l*, pg. 1947
PARKMOBILE USA, INC.—See BCD Holdings N.V.; *Int'l*, pg. 926
PARK 'N FLY, INC.—See Green Courte Partners, LLC; *U.S. Private*, pg. 1772
PARKNOW AUSTRIA GMBH—See Bayerische Motoren Werke Aktiengesellschaft; *Int'l*, pg. 913
PARK ONE INCORPORATED; *U.S. Private*, pg. 3096
PARKWAY CORPORATION; *U.S. Private*, pg. 3099
PAYLESS PARKING, LLC—See Avis Budget Group, Inc.; *U.S. Public*, pg. 249
PCA MANAGEMENT; *U.S. Private*, pg. 3119
THE PHILADELPHIA PARKING AUTHORITY INC.; *U.S. Private*, pg. 4094
PILGRIM PARKING INC.—See Propark, Inc.; *U.S. Private*, pg. 3284
PREFLIGHT LLC—See InterPark LLC; *U.S. Private*, pg. 2122
PREMIUM PARKING SERVICE, LLC; *U.S. Private*, pg. 3252
PRG PARKING CENTURY, LLC—See Green Courte Partners, LLC; *U.S. Private*, pg. 1772
PRG PARKING MANAGEMENT, LLC - ATLANTA—See Green Courte Partners, LLC; *U.S. Private*, pg. 1772
PRG PARKING MANAGEMENT, LLC - DALLAS-CEDAR SPRINGS—See Green Courte Partners, LLC; *U.S. Private*, pg. 1772
PRG PARKING MANAGEMENT, LLC - DALLAS-PLAZA DRIVE—See Green Courte Partners, LLC; *U.S. Private*, pg. 1772
PRG PARKING MANAGEMENT, LLC - DALLAS-VALLEY VIEW—See Green Courte Partners, LLC; *U.S. Private*, pg. 1772
PRG PARKING MANAGEMENT, LLC - ORLANDO—See Green Courte Partners, LLC; *U.S. Private*, pg. 1772

812930 — PARKING LOTS AND GA...

PROMINENT EXCEL SDN. BHD.—See GLOMAC Berhad; *Int'l*, pg. 3008
PROPARK, INC.; *U.S. Private*, pg. 3284
SABA APARCAMIENTOS, S.A.—See Fundacion Bancaria Caixa d'Estalvis i Pensions de Barcelona, la Caixa; *Int'l*, pg. 2845
SAN FRANCISCO PARKING INC.; *U.S. Private*, pg. 3541
SEVEN ONE SEVEN PARKING SERVICES, INC.; *U.S. Private*, pg. 3618
SOVEREIGN SERVICES INC.—See Propark, Inc.; *U.S. Private*, pg. 3284
SS PALM CITY, LLC—See National Storage Affiliates Trust; *U.S. Public*, pg. 1498
STANDARD PARKING CORPORATION IL—See Eldridge Industries LLC; *U.S. Private*, pg. 1351
STANDARD PARKING OF CANADA LTD.—See Eldridge Industries LLC; *U.S. Private*, pg. 1351
ST. LOUIS PARKING COMPANY INC.; *U.S. Private*, pg. 3772
URBIS PARK SAS—See Covivio; *Int'l*, pg. 1821
USA PARKING SYSTEM, INC.—See Eldridge Industries LLC; *U.S. Private*, pg. 1351
USA PARKING SYSTEMS, INC.—See The Frangos Group, LLC; *U.S. Private*, pg. 4030
VALET PARKING SERVICE, LIMITED PARTNERSHIP; *U.S. Private*, pg. 4331

812990 — ALL OTHER PERSONAL SERVICES

2 PLACES AT 1 TIME, INC.—See Accor S.A.; *Int'l*, pg. 92
A2MICILE EUROPE SA; *Int'l*, pg. 30
ACE HANDYMAN SERVICES—See Ace Hardware Corporation; *U.S. Private*, pg. 56
ACTIC GROUP AB; *Int'l*, pg. 118
AEON EAST CHINA (SUZHOU) CO., LTD.—See AEON Co., Ltd.; *Int'l*, pg. 176
AGERO, INC.—See The Cross Country Group, LLC; *U.S. Private*, pg. 4017
AIGUILLE ROCK CLIMBING CENTER, INC—See TOCCA Life Holdings, Inc.; *U.S. Public*, pg. 2161
AIH TOOL REPAIR CENTER—See Bering Straits Native Corporation; *U.S. Private*, pg. 532
AMERICAN CREDIT ALLIANCE INC.; *U.S. Private*, pg. 229
ANANIA & ASSOCIATES INVESTMENT COMPANY LLC; *U.S. Private*, pg. 272
ANNIVERSAIRE INC.—See AOKI Holdings Inc.; *Int'l*, pg. 488
ARISTOCRAT GROUP CORP.; *U.S. Public*, pg. 192
ASTRO COMMUNICATIONS SERVICES, INC.; *U.S. Private*, pg. 362
AUTOLAND, INC.—See Mission Federal Credit Union; *U.S. Private*, pg. 2747
AXA ASSISTANCE USA, INC.—See AXA S.A.; *Int'l*, pg. 754
AXIO RESEARCH, LLC—See New Mountain Capital, LLC; *U.S. Private*, pg. 2900
BABYCENTER, LLC—See Ziff Davis, Inc.; *U.S. Public*, pg. 2404
BAHAMAS CONCIERGE, INC.; *U.S. Private*, pg. 425
BASIC-FIT NV; *Int'l*, pg. 886
BERTELSMANN GLOBAL BUSINESS SERVICES GMBH—See Bertelsmann SE & Co. KGaA; *Int'l*, pg. 990
BEST UPON REQUEST CORPORATE, INC.; *U.S. Private*, pg. 543
BEWLEY'S ORIENTAL CAFES LIMITED—See Campbells/Bewley Group; *Int'l*, pg. 1274
BLACKROCK INVESTMENT MANAGEMENT, LLC—See BlackRock, Inc.; *U.S. Public*, pg. 345
BLUE SKY DATA CORP.—See OTC Markets Group Inc.; *U.S. Public*, pg. 1622
BUILDING SERVICE INDUSTRIAL SUPPLY CO.; *U.S. Private*, pg. 683
CAMBRIDGE CREDIT COUNSELING CORP.; *U.S. Private*, pg. 726
CAPITAL BONDING CORPORATION; *U.S. Private*, pg. 739
CAPITOL CONCIERGE, INC.; *U.S. Private*, pg. 743
CARDIF-ASSURANCES RISQUES DIVERS - ITALY—See BNP Paribas SA; *Int'l*, pg. 1083
CAREMORE MEDICAL ENTERPRISES—See Elevance Health, Inc.; *U.S. Public*, pg. 729
CARREFOUR DRIVE—See Carrefour SA; *Int'l*, pg. 1344
CBL BROOKFIELD SQUARE OP PROPCO, LLC—See CBL & Associates Properties, Inc.; *U.S. Public*, pg. 457
CBL DAKOTA SQUARE MALL OP PROPCO, LLC—See CBL & Associates Properties, Inc.; *U.S. Public*, pg. 457
CBL FAYETTE MALL OP PROPCO, LLC—See CBL & Associates Properties, Inc.; *U.S. Public*, pg. 458
CBL FRONTIER SQUARE PROPCO, LLC—See CBL & Associates Properties, Inc.; *U.S. Public*, pg. 458
CBL HAMILTON PLACE SEARS OP PROPCO, LLC—See CBL & Associates Properties, Inc.; *U.S. Public*, pg. 458
CBL JEFFERSON MALL SELF DEV PROPCO, LLC—See CBL & Associates Properties, Inc.; *U.S. Public*, pg. 458
CBL KIRKWOOD MALL OP PROPCO, LLC—See CBL & Associates Properties, Inc.; *U.S. Public*, pg. 458
CBL LANDING AT ARBOR PLACE OP PROPCO, LLC—See CBL & Associates Properties, Inc.; *U.S. Public*, pg. 458
CBL MID RIVERS MALL OP PROPCO, LLC—See CBL & Associates Properties, Inc.; *U.S. Public*, pg. 458
CBL MONROEVILLE MALL OP PROPCO, LLC—See CBL & Associates Properties, Inc.; *U.S. Public*, pg. 458
CBL NORTHPARK MALL OP PROPCO, LLC—See CBL & Associates Properties, Inc.; *U.S. Public*, pg. 458
CBL POST OAK MALL OP PROPCO, LLC—See CBL & Associates Properties, Inc.; *U.S. Public*, pg. 458
CBL SOUTH COUNTY CENTER OP PROPCO, LLC—See CBL & Associates Properties, Inc.; *U.S. Public*, pg. 458
CBL VALLEY VIEW MALL OP PROPCO, LLC—See CBL & Associates Properties, Inc.; *U.S. Public*, pg. 458
CBL WEST TOWNE CROSSING OP PROPCO, LLC—See CBL & Associates Properties, Inc.; *U.S. Public*, pg. 458
CBL YORK GALLERIA OP PROPCO, LLC—See CBL & Associates Properties, Inc.; *U.S. Public*, pg. 458
CELEBIDDY, INC.; *U.S. Private*, pg. 806
CHECKOUT CHARLIE GMBH—See Bertelsmann SE & Co. KGaA; *Int'l*, pg. 992
CHEMISTRY.COM—See IAC Inc.; *U.S. Public*, pg. 1082
CHICAGO APARTMENT FINDERS INC.; *U.S. Private*, pg. 877
CHS CABIN AND HANDLING SERVICE SUD-WEST GMBH—See Air Berlin PLC & Co. Luftverkehrs KG; *Int'l*, pg. 236
CIBT, INC.—See Kohlberg & Company, LLC; *U.S. Private*, pg. 2337
COBBOSSEECONTEE TELEPHONE CO.—See Telephone & Data Systems, Inc.; *U.S. Public*, pg. 1998
COMPANIONS & HOMEMAKERS INC.; *U.S. Private*, pg. 998
CONSUMER CREDIT COUNSELING SERVICE OF GREATER DALLAS INC.; *U.S. Private*, pg. 1025
CORPORATE CONCIERGE SERVICES, INC.—See Jones Lang LaSalle Incorporated; *U.S. Public*, pg. 1201
CORPORATE PROTECTIVE SECURITY INC.; *U.S. Private*, pg. 1055
CPP CREATING PROFITABLE PARTNERSHIPS GMBH—See CPPGroup Plc; *Int'l*, pg. 1826
CRI CAPITAL CORPORATION—See Sport Haley Holdings, Inc.; *U.S. Private*, pg. 3760
CROSS COUNTRY HOME SERVICES—See The Cross Country Group, LLC; *U.S. Private*, pg. 4017
CYBERDYNE CARE ROBOTICS GMBH—See Cyberdyne Inc.; *Int'l*, pg. 1892
DATELINE UK LTD.; *Int'l*, pg. 1981
DEBTMERICA, LLC; *U.S. Private*, pg. 1186
DEVONSHIRE INDUSTRIES LIMITED; *Int'l*, pg. 2089
DIGITAL CHECK CORP.; *U.S. Private*, pg. 1230
DROISYS INC.; *U.S. Private*, pg. 1279
EASY DATE HOLDINGS LTD; *Int'l*, pg. 2275
EDCO WASTE & RECYCLING SERVICES INC.—See EDCO Disposal Corporation; *U.S. Private*, pg. 1332
ELATE GROUP, INC.; *U.S. Private*, pg. 1350
ENIGHETEN PERSONLIGASSISTANS AB—See Humana AB; *Int'l*, pg. 3530
EN KONKATSU AGENT CO., LTD.—See en-japan inc.; *Int'l*, pg. 2395
ESCRIT INC.; *Int'l*, pg. 2502
EVENTS BY SUPERIOR—See Superior Products Distributors Inc.; *U.S. Private*, pg. 3880
EVOQUA WATER TECHNOLOGIES GMBH—See Xylem Inc.; *U.S. Public*, pg. 2394
FITNESS WORLD A/S—See Leonard Green & Partners, L.P.; *U.S. Private*, pg. 2428
GBS RETIREMENT SERVICES, INC.—See Arthur J. Gallagher & Co.; *U.S. Public*, pg. 205
GESELLSCHAFT FUR KREDITSICHERUNG MBH—See Commerzbank AG; *Int'l*, pg. 1718
GREENPATH INC; *U.S. Private*, pg. 1779
HEIAN CEREMONY SERVICE CO., LTD.; *Int'l*, pg. 3308
HER IMPORTS; *U.S. Public*, pg. 1027
HIREASE, INC.; *U.S. Private*, pg. 1950
HOUSE PARTY, INC.; *U.S. Private*, pg. 1992
HOUSING HELPERS OF COLORADO, LLC; *U.S. Private*, pg. 1992
HRS ERASE INC.; *U.S. Private*, pg. 1998
IBJ INC.; *Int'l*, pg. 3576
IDINE—See TowerBrook Capital Partners, L.P.; *U.S. Private*, pg. 4195
IKK HOLDINGS INC; *Int'l*, pg. 3611
INTERTRAFO OY—See Addtech AB; *Int'l*, pg. 134
IP INDIA FOUNDATION—See International Paper Company; *U.S. Public*, pg. 1155
IRON DATA SOLUTIONS, INC.—See Tyler Technologies, Inc.; *U.S. Public*, pg. 2208
JOHN PAUL SAN FRANCISCO—See Accor S.A.; *Int'l*, pg. 92
JOOLI.COM GMBH—See Elumeo SE; *Int'l*, pg. 2371
KEYSTONE PARTNERS—See Silver Oak Services Partners, LLC; *U.S. Private*, pg. 3661
KIMBERLY-CLARK WORLDWIDE, INC.—See Kimberly-Clark Corporation; *U.S. Public*, pg. 1231
KM WEDDING EVENTS MANAGEMENT, INC.; *U.S. Public*, pg. 1269
LES SERVICES G&K—See Cintas Corporation; *U.S. Public*, pg. 496
LIGHTHOUSE CREDIT FOUNDATION; *U.S. Private*, pg. 2452
LOCIMOBILE, INC.—See MetAlert Inc.; *U.S. Public*, pg. 1427
LOCKHEED MARTIN MANAGEMENT & DATA SYSTEMS—See Lockheed Martin Corporation; *U.S. Public*, pg. 1338
MATCH GROUP, INC.—See IAC Inc.; *U.S. Public*, pg. 1082
MEETIC SA—See IAC Inc.; *U.S. Public*, pg. 1082
MOMENTUM, INC.; *U.S. Private*, pg. 2768
MONEY MANAGEMENT INTERNATIONAL; *U.S. Private*, pg. 2770
MYWEDDING.COM LLC; *U.S. Private*, pg. 2826
NORTHSTAR CONTRACTING GROUP, INC.—See J.F. Lehman & Company, Inc.; *U.S. Private*, pg. 2164
OCCASIONS CATERERS INC.; *U.S. Private*, pg. 2988
PALTALK, INC.; *U.S. Public*, pg. 1635
THE PLUM GROUP, INC.—See Teleo Capital Management, LLC; *U.S. Private*, pg. 3961
POSTAL CENTER INTERNATIONAL; *U.S. Private*, pg. 3234
POULIN VENTURES LLC; *U.S. Private*, pg. 3236
P.S.A. FINANCIAL CENTER, INC.—See PSA Holdings, Inc.; *U.S. Private*, pg. 3297
PT INTERNATIONAL KANSHA KANDOU INDONESIA—See IKK Holdings Inc; *Int'l*, pg. 3611
PUSH INTERACTIVE, LLC—See Logiq, Inc.; *U.S. Public*, pg. 1341
REALHOME.COM INC.; *U.S. Private*, pg. 3368
REAL SOCIAL DYNAMICS, INC.; *U.S. Private*, pg. 3368
RECORDKEEPER RECORDS MANAGEMENT SYSTEMS LTD.—See GRM Information Management Services; *U.S. Private*, pg. 1791
ROSEMONT EXPOSITION SERVICES INC.; *U.S. Private*, pg. 3483
R.O.U CO., LTD.—See AEON Co., Ltd.; *Int'l*, pg. 178
RTL STUDIOS GMBH—See Bertelsmann SE & Co. KGaA; *Int'l*, pg. 996
SDI MEDIA—See Elevation Partners; *U.S. Private*, pg. 1358
SHERATON DETROIT NOVI—See Marriott International, Inc.; *U.S. Public*, pg. 1372
SONOCO BAKER—See Sonoco Products Company; *U.S. Public*, pg. 1908
SPORTSDIRECT.COM FITNESS LIMITED—See Frasers Group plc; *Int'l*, pg. 2765
SPRINGDAY PTY. LTD.—See Madison Dearborn Partners, LLC; *U.S. Private*, pg. 2540
STATISTICS COLLABORATIVE, INC.—See Leonard Green & Partners, L.P.; *U.S. Private*, pg. 2430
SUPERCHECK GMBH—See Allianz SE; *Int'l*, pg. 351
SYNCH-SOLUTIONS; *U.S. Private*, pg. 3902
TANGER BRANSON, LLC—See Tanger Inc.; *U.S. Public*, pg. 1980
TANGER CHARLESTON, LLC—See Tanger Inc.; *U.S. Public*, pg. 1980
TANGER DAYTONA, LLC—See Tanger Inc.; *U.S. Public*, pg. 1980
TANGER FORT WORTH, LLC—See Tanger Inc.; *U.S. Public*, pg. 1980
TANGER JEFFERSONVILLE, LLC—See Tanger Inc.; *U.S. Public*, pg. 1981
TANGER TERRELL, LLC—See Tanger Inc.; *U.S. Public*, pg. 1981
TARA SPA THERAPY, INC.—See Branford Castle, Inc.; *U.S. Private*, pg. 639
TDS METROCOM—See Telephone & Data Systems, Inc.; *U.S. Public*, pg. 1997
THREE RIVERS PACKAGING, INC.—See The Cary Company; *U.S. Private*, pg. 4005
TOWERSTREAM CORP.; *U.S. Public*, pg. 2165
TRIALCARD INCORPORATED—See Odyssey Investment Partners, LLC; *U.S. Private*, pg. 2996
TRIZETTO CORP. - UNION REGIONAL OFFICE—See Cognizant Technology Solutions Corporation; *U.S. Public*, pg. 525
TROOPSDIRECT; *U.S. Private*, pg. 4242
TRS STAFFING SOLUTIONS, INC.—See Fluor Corporation; *U.S. Public*, pg. 860
TRUE.COM; *U.S. Private*, pg. 4248
TUTOR.COM, INC.—See IAC Inc.; *U.S. Public*, pg. 1083
USAA ALLIANCE SERVICES COMPANY—See United Services Automobile Association; *U.S. Private*, pg. 4297
VERIZON WIRELESS MESSAGING SERVICES LTD.—See Verizon Communications Inc.; *U.S. Public*, pg. 2285
VERNON TELEPHONE CO.—See Telephone & Data Systems, Inc.; *U.S. Public*, pg. 1998
VISIONTREE SOFTWARE, INC.—See Intel Corporation; *U.S. Public*, pg. 1138
VOLT ATHLETICS, INC.; *U.S. Private*, pg. 4411
WASHINGTON SQUARE CENTER—See Saul Centers, Inc.; *U.S. Public*, pg. 1842
THE WESTIN SOUTHFIELD DETROIT—See Marriott International, Inc.; *U.S. Public*, pg. 1373
WRAP & SEND SERVICES, LLC; *U.S. Private*, pg. 4572
YARCDATA LLC—See Hewlett Packard Enterprise Company; *U.S. Public*, pg. 1031
ZWEI CO., LTD.—See IBJ Inc.; *Int'l*, pg. 3576

813110 — RELIGIOUS ORGANIZATIONS

N.A.I.C.S. INDEX

813211 — GRANTMAKING FOUNDAT...

THE 410 BRIDGE; *U.S. Private*, pg. 3980
ACCELL DUITSLAND B.V.—See Accell Group N.V.; *Int'l*, pg. 80
ADVENTIST HEALTHCARE; *U.S. Private*, pg. 109
AMERICAN FAMILY ASSOCIATION, INC.; *U.S. Private*, pg. 232
ASSOCIATION OF CHRISTIAN SCHOOLS INTERNATIONAL; *U.S. Private*, pg. 358
AT&T—See AT&T Inc.; *U.S. Public*, pg. 218
BAPTIST MISSIONS INC.; *U.S. Private*, pg. 471
BARNABAS FOUNDATION; *U.S. Private*, pg. 476
BFP GMBH—See Bonduelle SAS; *Int'l*, pg. 1106
BILLY GRAHAM EVANGELISTIC ASSOCIATION; *U.S. Private*, pg. 559
BPI EUROPE B V—See Berry Global Group, Inc; *U.S. Public*, pg. 322
CATHOLIC COMMUNITY FOUNDATION; *U.S. Private*, pg. 788
THE CATHOLIC FOUNDATION FOR THE ROMAN CATHOLIC CHURCH IN NORTHERN COLORADO; *U.S. Private*, pg. 4006
CATHOLIC HEALTHCARE SYSTEM; *U.S. Private*, pg. 792
CHATTANOOGA CHRISTIAN COMMUNITY FOUNDATION; *U.S. Private*, pg. 868
CHOICE MINISTRIES INC.; *U.S. Private*, pg. 888
CHRISTIAN AID MINISTRIES; *U.S. Private*, pg. 890
CHRISTIAN AND MISSIONARY ALLIANCE FOUNDATION, INC.; *U.S. Private*, pg. 890
THE CHRISTIAN BROADCASTING NETWORK INC.; *U.S. Private*, pg. 4009
CHRISTIAN COMMUNITY DEVELOPMENT CORPORATION; *U.S. Private*, pg. 891
CHRIST'S HOUSEHOLD OF FAITH; *U.S. Private*, pg. 890
COOK COMMUNICATIONS MINISTRIES; *U.S. Private*, pg. 1037
CROSS INTERNATIONAL; *U.S. Private*, pg. 1105
DREAM CENTER FOUNDATION, A CALIFORNIA NON-PROFIT CORP.; *U.S. Private*, pg. 1272
FAITH & LEARNING INTERNATIONAL; *U.S. Private*, pg. 1465
FELLOWSHIP FOUNDATION; *U.S. Private*, pg. 1494
FULL GOSPEL BUSINESS MEN'S FELLOWSHIP INTERNATIONAL; *U.S. Private*, pg. 1620
GERMANTOWN LIFE ENRICHMENT CENTER; *U.S. Private*, pg. 1687
GLOBAL MEDIA OUTREACH; *U.S. Private*, pg. 1716
GLOBAL OUTREACH INTERNATIONAL, INC.; *U.S. Private*, pg. 1716
GOOD NEWS PUBLISHERS; *U.S. Private*, pg. 1738
GPT NOMINEES PTY LIMITED—See GPT Group; *Int'l*, pg. 3047
GRACE ALASKA INC.; *U.S. Private*, pg. 1748
HELPING HANDS MINISTRIES, INC.; *U.S. Private*, pg. 1912
INFAITH; *U.S. Private*, pg. 2070
THE INTERCHURCH CENTER; *U.S. Private*, pg. 4057
INTERNATIONAL COOPERATING MINISTRIES; *U.S. Private*, pg. 2116
JACK VAN IMPE MINISTRIES INTERNATIONAL; *U.S. Private*, pg. 2175
KNOX AREA RESCUE MINISTRIES; *U.S. Private*, pg. 2324
LHRET ASCENSION AUSTIN II, LP—See Ventas, Inc.; *U.S. Public*, pg. 2278
LIBERTY MINISTRIES; *U.S. Private*, pg. 2445
LIFE ACTION MINISTRIES; *U.S. Private*, pg. 2448
LUIS PALAU ASSOCIATION; *U.S. Private*, pg. 2512
LUTHERAN SOCIAL SERVICES OF THE SOUTH, INC.; *U.S. Private*, pg. 2517
MEASAT BROADCAST NETWORK SYSTEMS (BVI) LTD—See Astro All Asia Networks plc; *Int'l*, pg. 662
MONKS' BREAD; *U.S. Private*, pg. 2771
MOODY BIBLE INSTITUTE; *U.S. Private*, pg. 2778
MORRIS CERULLO WORLD EVANGELISM; *U.S. Private*, pg. 2786
MORRIS CERULLO WORLD EVANGELISM—See Morris Cerullo World Evangelism; *U.S. Private*, pg. 2787
MORRIS CERULLO WORLD EVANGELISM—See Morris Cerullo World Evangelism; *U.S. Private*, pg. 2787
NATIONAL CHRISTIAN CHARITABLE FOUNDATION, INC.; *U.S. Private*, pg. 2850
NATIONAL RELIGIOUS BROADCASTERS; *U.S. Private*, pg. 2861
NEXT LEVEL CHURCH, INC.; *U.S. Private*, pg. 2920
OPERATION COMPASSION; *U.S. Private*, pg. 3031
PRECEPT MINISTRIES OF REACH OUT, INC.; *U.S. Private*, pg. 3243
PRESENTATION MINISTRIES; *U.S. Private*, pg. 3254
RD MERRILL COMPANY; *U.S. Private*, pg. 3362
RELIANT MISSION, INC.; *U.S. Private*, pg. 3395
THE SISTERS OF THE THIRD ORDER OF ST. FRANCIS; *U.S. Private*, pg. 4118
TCT MINISTRIES, INC.; *U.S. Private*, pg. 3943
THRU THE BIBLE RADIO NETWORK; *U.S. Private*, pg. 4165
TOTUS PRO DEO; *U.S. Private*, pg. 4192
UNITED METHODIST RETIREMENT CENTER; *U.S. Private*, pg. 4294
UPWARD UNLIMITED; *U.S. Private*, pg. 4313
URBAN MINISTRY CENTER; *U.S. Private*, pg. 4314
VISION ATLANTA INC.; *U.S. Private*, pg. 4390
WATERFRONT RESCUE MISSION; *U.S. Private*, pg. 4453
WEGENER REGIO PARTNERS BV—See DPG Media Group NV; *Int'l*, pg. 2189
WORLD HOPE INTERNATIONAL; *U.S. Private*, pg. 4565

813211 — GRANTMAKING FOUNDATIONS

AIDS UNITED; *U.S. Private*, pg. 132
AIR FORCE AID SOCIETY, INC.; *U.S. Private*, pg. 138
ALASKA COMMUNITY FOUNDATION; *U.S. Private*, pg. 150
ALEX'S LEMONADE STAND FOUNDATION FOR CHILDHOOD CANCER; *U.S. Private*, pg. 163
AMERICAN COMMITTEE FOR THE WEIZMANN INSTITUTE OF SCIENCE, INC.; *U.S. Private*, pg. 227
AMERICAN ENDOWMENT FOUNDATION; *U.S. Private*, pg. 231
AMERICAN GIFT FUND; *U.S. Private*, pg. 235
ANNUAL REVIEWS; *U.S. Private*, pg. 285
AYALA FOUNDATION, INC.—See Ayala Corporation; *Int'l*, pg. 774
BALTIMORE COMMUNITY FOUNDATION, INC.; *U.S. Private*, pg. 462
THE BANK OF AMERICA CHARITABLE FOUNDATION, INC.—See Bank of America Corporation; *U.S. Public*, pg. 272
BARCLAYS CAPITAL CHARITABLE TRUST—See Barclays PLC; *Int'l*, pg. 860
THE BEAUMONT FOUNDATION—See Beaumont Health; *U.S. Private*, pg. 508
BERKSHIRE TACONIC COMMUNITY FOUNDATION, INC.; *U.S. Private*, pg. 535
BJ'S CHARITABLE FOUNDATION INC.—See Leonard Green & Partners, L.P.; *U.S. Private*, pg. 2425
BLUE GRASS COMMUNITY FOUNDATION; *U.S. Private*, pg. 589
BOOTS CHARITABLE TRUST—See Walgreens Boots Alliance, Inc.; *U.S. Public*, pg. 2322
BPI FOUNDATION, INC.—See Bank of the Philippine Islands; *Int'l*, pg. 848
BUCKINGHAM FOUNDATION; *U.S. Private*, pg. 678
CATHOLIC COMMUNITY FOUNDATION OF MINNESOTA; *U.S. Private*, pg. 788
CEL EDUCATION FUND; *U.S. Private*, pg. 806
CENTRAL FUND OF ISRAEL; *U.S. Private*, pg. 821
CHESTER COUNTY COMMUNITY FOUNDATION; *U.S. Private*, pg. 875
CHICKASAW FOUNDATION—See The Chickasaw Nation; *U.S. Private*, pg. 4008
CHILDREN'S LEUKEMIA RESEARCH ASSOCIATION, INC.; *U.S. Private*, pg. 885
THE CIGNA GROUP FOUNDATION—See The Cigna Group; *U.S. Public*, pg. 2061
COASTAL BEND COMMUNITY FOUNDATION; *U.S. Private*, pg. 955
COMMUNITY FIRST FOUNDATION; *U.S. Private*, pg. 991
THE COMMUNITY FOUNDATION FOR GREATER NEW HAVEN; *U.S. Private*, pg. 4012
COMMUNITY FOUNDATION FOR MONTEREY COUNTY; *U.S. Private*, pg. 992
COMMUNITY FOUNDATION FOR MUSKEGON COUNTY; *U.S. Private*, pg. 992
COMMUNITY FOUNDATION FOR SOUTHEAST MICHIGAN; *U.S. Private*, pg. 992
COMMUNITY FOUNDATION FOR SOUTHWEST WASHINGTON; *U.S. Private*, pg. 992
COMMUNITY FOUNDATION OF ACADIANA; *U.S. Private*, pg. 992
COMMUNITY FOUNDATION OF GREATER BIRMINGHAM; *U.S. Private*, pg. 992
COMMUNITY FOUNDATION OF GREATER DES MOINES; *U.S. Private*, pg. 992
COMMUNITY FOUNDATION OF GREATER GREENSBORO; *U.S. Private*, pg. 992
COMMUNITY FOUNDATION OF LORAIN COUNTY; *U.S. Private*, pg. 992
COMMUNITY FOUNDATION OF MIDDLE TENNESSEE; *U.S. Private*, pg. 992
COMMUNITY FOUNDATION OF NEW JERSEY; *U.S. Private*, pg. 992
COMMUNITY FOUNDATION OF NORTH LOUISIANA; *U.S. Private*, pg. 992
COMMUNITY FOUNDATION OF SOUTH GEORGIA; *U.S. Private*, pg. 993
COMMUNITY FOUNDATION OF THE GREAT RIVER BEND; *U.S. Private*, pg. 993
COMMUNITY FOUNDATION OF WESTERN NEVADA; *U.S. Private*, pg. 993
COMMUNITY FOUNDATION OF WESTERN PA & EASTERN OH; *U.S. Private*, pg. 993
COMMUNITY FOUNDATION SANTA CRUZ COUNTY; *U.S. Private*, pg. 993
THE COMMUNITY FOUNDATION SERVING RICHMOND & CENTRAL VIRGINIA; *U.S. Private*, pg. 4012
COMMUNITY FOUNDATION SONOMA COUNTY; *U.S. Private*, pg. 993
COMMUNITY INITIATIVES; *U.S. Private*, pg. 995
CONCERN WORLDWIDE LIMITED—See Concern Worldwide; *Int'l*, pg. 1764
DAILY BREAD MINISTRIES; *U.S. Private*, pg. 1145
THE DALLAS FOUNDATION; *U.S. Private*, pg. 4017
DEBARTOLO FAMILY FOUNDATION—See DeBartolo Holdings, LLC; *U.S. Private*, pg. 1186
DEFIANT REQUIEM FOUNDATION; *U.S. Private*, pg. 1191
DENVER FOUNDATION; *U.S. Private*, pg. 1207
DEVELOPMENTAL RESOURCES CORPORATION; *U.S. Private*, pg. 1218
THE DIETRICH FOUNDATION; *U.S. Private*, pg. 4021
EAST TENNESSEE FOUNDATION; *U.S. Private*, pg. 1318
EAST TEXAS COMMUNTIES FOUNDATION, INC.; *U.S. Private*, pg. 1318
ECMC FOUNDATION; *U.S. Private*, pg. 1328
EPILEPSY FOUNDATION OF AMERICA; *U.S. Private*, pg. 1413
ERIE COMMUNITY FOUNDATION; *U.S. Private*, pg. 1420
ESKENAZI HEALTH FOUNDATION; *U.S. Private*, pg. 1426
ESSEX COUNTY COMMUNITY FOUNDATION; *U.S. Private*, pg. 1427
FIDELITY CHARITABLE GIFT FUND; *U.S. Private*, pg. 1502
FIDELITY FOUNDATION; *U.S. Private*, pg. 1503
FLORIDA HOSPITAL FOUNDATION—See Adventist Health System Sunbelt Healthcare Corporation; *U.S. Private*, pg. 109
FORE!KIDS FOUNDATION; *U.S. Private*, pg. 1565
FOSTER CARE TO SUCCESS; *U.S. Private*, pg. 1578
FOUNDATION FOR JEWISH PHILANTHROPIES; *U.S. Private*, pg. 1580
FOUNDATION FOR THE CAROLINAS; *U.S. Private*, pg. 1580
FOUNDATION FOR THE GLOBAL COMPACT; *U.S. Private*, pg. 1580
FREMONT AREA COMMUNITY FOUNDATION; *U.S. Private*, pg. 1608
GAILLARD PERFORMANCE HALL FOUNDATION; *U.S. Private*, pg. 1635
GEORGIA GOAL SCHOLARSHIP PROGRAM, INC.; *U.S. Private*, pg. 1684
GONZMART FAMILY FOUNDATION—See Columbia Restaurant Group; *U.S. Private*, pg. 977
GREATER CEDAR RAPIDS COMMUNITY FOUNDATION; *U.S. Private*, pg. 1769
THE GREATER CINCINNATI FOUNDATION; *U.S. Private*, pg. 4038
GREATER MILWAUKEE FOUNDATION; *U.S. Private*, pg. 1769
GREATER TEXAS FOUNDATION; *U.S. Private*, pg. 1770
GSD EGITIM VAKFI—See GSD Holding A.S.; *Int'l*, pg. 3144
HAMPTON ROADS COMMUNITY FOUNDATION; *U.S. Private*, pg. 1851
HARTFORD FOUNDATION FOR PUBLIC GIVING; *U.S. Private*, pg. 1873
HISPANIC SCHOLARSHIP FUND; *U.S. Private*, pg. 1951
HORATIO ALGER ASSOCIATION OF DISTINGUISHED AMERICANS, INC.; *U.S. Private*, pg. 1980
HORIZONS FOUNDATION; *U.S. Private*, pg. 1983
HURRICANE SANDY NEW JERSEY RELIEF FUND INC.; *U.S. Private*, pg. 2012
IDAHO COMMUNITY FOUNDATION, INC.; *U.S. Private*, pg. 2034
INFAITH COMMUNITY FOUNDATION; *U.S. Private*, pg. 2070
THE JERUSALEM FOUNDATION, INC.; *U.S. Private*, pg. 4059
JEWISHCOLORADO; *U.S. Private*, pg. 2206
JEWISH COMMUNITY FOUNDATION OF GREATER KANSAS CITY; *U.S. Private*, pg. 2205
JEWISH COMMUNITY FOUNDATION OF SAN DIEGO; *U.S. Private*, pg. 2205
JEWISH FUNDERS NETWORK; *U.S. Private*, pg. 2206
JEWISH HEALTHCARE FOUNDATION; *U.S. Private*, pg. 2206
JOHN T. VUCUREVICH FOUNDATION; *U.S. Private*, pg. 2225
KINGSWAY CHARITIES, INC.; *U.S. Private*, pg. 2312
KROCHET KIDS INTL.; *U.S. Private*, pg. 2352
LILIUOKALANI TRUST; *U.S. Private*, pg. 2455
THE LUZERNE FOUNDATION; *U.S. Private*, pg. 4073
MAINE COMMUNITY FOUNDATION; *U.S. Private*, pg. 2552
MCLEOD COOPERATIVE POWER TRUST—See McLeod Cooperative Power Association; *U.S. Private*, pg. 2641
THE MEG & BENNETT GOODMAN FAMILY FOUNDATION; *U.S. Private*, pg. 4077
MIAMI FOUNDATION; *U.S. Private*, pg. 2696
MIDWAYUSA FOUNDATION, INC.; *U.S. Private*, pg. 2719
THE MOODY ENDOWMENT; *U.S. Private*, pg. 4080
MYCHARITY, LTD.—See Blackbaud, Inc.; *U.S. Public*, pg. 341
NANTUCKET COTTAGE HOSPITAL FOUNDATION—See Partners HealthCare System, Inc.; *U.S. Private*, pg. 3102
NATURAL RESOURCE GOVERNANCE INSTITUTE; *U.S. Private*, pg. 2867

813211 — GRANTMAKING FOUNDAT...

NEW ISRAEL FUND; *U.S. Private*, pg. 2897
NEW MEXICO EDUCATIONAL ASSISTANCE FOUNDATION; *U.S. Private*, pg. 2898
NEWTON-WELLESLEY HOSPITAL CHARITABLE FOUNDATION INC.—See Partners HealthCare System, Inc.; *U.S. Private*, pg. 3101
NEW VENTURE FUND; *U.S. Private*, pg. 2907
NEW YORK COMMUNITY TRUST; *U.S. Private*, pg. 2909
NORTHERN NEW YORK COMMUNITY FOUNDATION, INC.; *U.S. Private*, pg. 2953
NORTHERN TRUST MANAGEMENT SERVICES (DEUTSCHLAND) GMBH—See Northern Trust Corporation; *U.S. Public*, pg. 1538
NORTHWESTERN MEMORIAL FOUNDATION—See Northwestern Memorial HealthCare; *U.S. Private*, pg. 2963
OKLAHOMA CITY COMMUNITY FOUNDATION, INC.; *U.S. Private*, pg. 3007
OMAHA COMMUNITY FOUNDATION; *U.S. Private*, pg. 3014
THE OREGON COMMUNITY FOUNDATION; *U.S. Private*, pg. 4089
OUR CHILDREN OUR FUTURE; *U.S. Private*, pg. 3050
PARASOL TAHOE COMMUNITY FOUNDATION; *U.S. Private*, pg. 3093
PARKINSON'S FOUNDATION, INC.; *U.S. Private*, pg. 3098
PAYPAL CHARITABLE GIVING FUND—See PayPal Holdings, Inc.; *U.S. Public*, pg. 1656
PETER E HAAS JR FAMILY FUND; *U.S. Private*, pg. 3158
THE PEW CHARITABLE TRUSTS; *U.S. Private*, pg. 4094
PHILANTHROPIC VENTURES FOUNDATION; *U.S. Private*, pg. 3169
PIKES PEAK COMMUNITY FOUNDATION; *U.S. Private*, pg. 3180
PITTSBURGH FOUNDATION; *U.S. Private*, pg. 3191
PRINCETON AREA COMMUNITY FOUNDATION; *U.S. Private*, pg. 3264
PROTEUS FUND; *U.S. Private*, pg. 3290
THE RAMS CLUB; *U.S. Private*, pg. 4102
RANCHO SANTA FE FOUNDATION; *U.S. Private*, pg. 3352
RESEARCH FOUNDATION OF THE CITY UNIVERSITY OF NEW YORK; *U.S. Private*, pg. 3404
THE RHODE ISLAND FOUNDATION; *U.S. Private*, pg. 4106
RHODE ISLAND PBS FOUNDATION; *U.S. Private*, pg. 3422
ROBERT R. MCCORMICK FOUNDATION; *U.S. Private*, pg. 3458
RODMAN RIDE FOR KIDS; *U.S. Private*, pg. 3470
THE ROSE HILLS FOUNDATION; *U.S. Private*, pg. 4112
SAFA TRUST INC.; *U.S. Private*, pg. 3523
SAN FRANCISCO FOUNDATION; *U.S. Private*, pg. 3540
SAN FRANCISCO PARKS ALLIANCE; *U.S. Private*, pg. 3541
THE SCRNEN FOUNDATION; *U.S. Private*, pg. 4115
SJ MANAGEMENT COMPANY OF SYRACUSE INC.; *U.S. Private*, pg. 3678
SKY HIGH FOR ST. JUDE INC.; *U.S. Private*, pg. 3684
SPECIAL OPERATIONS WARRIOR FOUNDATION, INC.; *U.S. Private*, pg. 3748
STARK COMMUNITY FOUNDATION, INC.; *U.S. Private*, pg. 3787
TCF FOUNDATION—See Huntington Bancshares Incorporated; *U.S. Public*, pg. 1071
THREE RIVERS COMMUNITY FOUNDATION; *U.S. Private*, pg. 4164
THRESHOLD FOUNDATION; *U.S. Private*, pg. 4164
TRIANGLE NORTH HEALTHCARE FOUNDATION, INC.; *U.S. Private*, pg. 4226
UNIDEL FOUNDATION, INC.; *U.S. Private*, pg. 4282
UNITED WAY WORLDWIDE; *U.S. Private*, pg. 4301
U.S. BANCORP FOUNDATION—See U.S. Bancorp; *U.S. Public*, pg. 2212
VETRI FOUNDATION FOR CHILDREN—See Vetri Holdings LLC; *U.S. Private*, pg. 4374
THE WALTON FAMILY FOUNDATION, INC.; *U.S. Private*, pg. 4133
WESTERN COLORADO COMMUNITY FOUNDATION; *U.S. Private*, pg. 4491
THE WINSTON-SALEM FOUNDATION; *U.S. Private*, pg. 4137
WYOMING COMMUNITY FOUNDATION; *U.S. Private*, pg. 4578
XANGO GOODNESS—See XanGo, LLC; *U.S. Private*, pg. 4580

813212 — VOLUNTARY HEALTH ORGANIZATIONS

AARP PUBLICATIONS—See AARP; *U.S. Private*, pg. 33
ACADEMYHEALTH; *U.S. Private*, pg. 46
ALLOSOURCE; *U.S. Private*, pg. 192
AMERICAN ASSOCIATION FOR CANCER RESEARCH; *U.S. Private*, pg. 222
AMERICAN COLLEGE OF CARDIOLOGY; *U.S. Private*, pg. 227
AMERICAN SOCIETY FOR RADIATION ONCOLOGY; *U.S. Private*, pg. 254
AMFAR; *U.S. Private*, pg. 262
APTUS HEALTH, INC.—See KKR & Co. Inc.; *U.S. Public*, pg. 1253
ARTHRITIS FOUNDATION, INC.; *U.S. Private*, pg. 341
AUTISM SOCIETY OF NORTH CAROLINA, INC.; *U.S. Private*, pg. 396
AVANTI HEALTH SYSTEMS; *U.S. Private*, pg. 404
BLUE CROSS BLUE SHIELD OF MICHIGAN FOUNDATION—See Blue Cross Blue Shield of Michigan; *U.S. Private*, pg. 588
THE BOSTON HOME, INC.; *U.S. Private*, pg. 3998
CALIFORNIA TRANSPLANT DONOR NETWORK; *U.S. Private*, pg. 721
CARDIOVASCULAR RESEARCH FOUNDATION; *U.S. Private*, pg. 751
CDC FOUNDATION; *U.S. Private*, pg. 802
CENTRAL OHIO DIABETES ASSOCIATION; *U.S. Private*, pg. 824
CHILDREN'S CANCER RECOVERY FOUNDATION; *U.S. Private*, pg. 883
CHORDOMA FOUNDATION; *U.S. Private*, pg. 888
CHRISTOPHER REEVE FOUNDATION; *U.S. Private*, pg. 892
CLINTON HEALTH ACCESS INITIATIVE, INC.; *U.S. Private*, pg. 944
COORDINATED CARE CORPORATION INDIANA, INC.,—See Centene Corporation; *U.S. Public*, pg. 468
CRITTENDEN HOSPITAL ASSOCIATION; *U.S. Private*, pg. 1102
CROHN'S & COLITIS FOUNDATION OF AMERICA; *U.S. Private*, pg. 1103
THE DEVEREUX FOUNDATION, INC.; *U.S. Private*, pg. 4020
DIABETES RESEARCH & WELLNESS FOUNDATION; *U.S. Private*, pg. 1222
ELIZABETH GLASER PEDIATRIC AIDS FOUNDATION; *U.S. Private*, pg. 1362
EMPATH PARTNERS IN CARE; *U.S. Private*, pg. 1384
ENGINEERING WORLD HEALTH—See Engineers Without Borders-USA, Inc.; *U.S. Private*, pg. 1399
GENESIS CAREGIVERS—See Genesis HealthCare System; *U.S. Private*, pg. 1669
GENESIS HEALTHCARE SYSTEM; *U.S. Private*, pg. 1669
GLOBAL GENES; *U.S. Private*, pg. 1714
HAART INC.; *U.S. Private*, pg. 1837
HAZELDEN BETTY FORD FOUNDATION; *U.S. Private*, pg. 1886
HELEN ROSS MCNABB CENTER, INC.; *U.S. Private*, pg. 1905
HOPEHEALTH; *U.S. Private*, pg. 1979
INTERACT FOR HEALTH; *U.S. Private*, pg. 2107
INTERNATIONAL SOCIETY ON THROMBOSIS AND HAEMOSTASIS, INC.; *U.S. Private*, pg. 2120
THE LEUKEMIA & LYMPHOMA SOCIETY, INC.; *U.S. Private*, pg. 4069
LIGHTHOUSE GUILD INTERNATIONAL; *U.S. Private*, pg. 2453
MARATHON HEALTH, LLC—See General Atlantic Service Company, L.P.; *U.S. Private*, pg. 1663
MASSACHUSETTS BAY HEALTH CARE TRUST FUND; *U.S. Private*, pg. 2603
MELANOMA RESEARCH ALLIANCE; *U.S. Private*, pg. 2661
THE MENDED HEARTS, INC.; *U.S. Private*, pg. 4077
NASHVILLE CARES; *U.S. Private*, pg. 2836
NATIONAL ASSOCIATION OF CHRONIC DISEASE DIRECTORS; *U.S. Private*, pg. 2846
NATIONAL BREAST CANCER FOUNDATION, INC.; *U.S. Private*, pg. 2849
NATIONAL FOUNDATION FOR CANCER RESEARCH; *U.S. Private*, pg. 2854
NEW YORK ORGAN DONOR NETWORK, INC.; *U.S. Private*, pg. 2911
NORTH AMERICAN SPINE SOCIETY; *U.S. Private*, pg. 2941
OTICON SOUTH AFRICA (PTY) LTD.—See Demant A/S; *Int'l*, pg. 2024
PERSONAL CARE PRODUCTS COUNCIL FOUNDATION, INC.; *U.S. Private*, pg. 3155
PETES SAKE CANCER RESPITE FOUNDATION; *U.S. Private*, pg. 3160
PHA LIMITED—See Grainger plc; *Int'l*, pg. 3052
PHYATHAI 2 HOSPITAL CO., LTD.—See Bangkok Dusit Medical Services Public Company Limited; *Int'l*, pg. 834
PRECHECK, INC.—See Cisive Inc.; *U.S. Private*, pg. 901
PRECISIONMED, LLC—See BioIVT, LLC; *U.S. Private*, pg. 562
PROJECT HOPE; *U.S. Private*, pg. 3280
SERVICE ORGANIZATION OF SAN ANTONIO; *U.S. Private*, pg. 3616
SSM HEALTH CARE CORPORATION; *U.S. Private*, pg. 3769
THE STANLEY MEDICAL RESEARCH INSTITUTE; *U.S. Private*, pg. 4120
SUPPLEMENTAL HEALTH CARE SERVICES, INC.; *U.S. Private*, pg. 3881
SWIM ACROSS AMERICA INC.; *U.S. Private*, pg. 3893
TEXAS ORGAN SHARING ALLIANCE; *U.S. Private*, pg. 3976
TOWER CANCER RESEARCH FOUNDATION; *U.S. Private*, pg. 4193
THE ULMAN CANCER FUND FOR YOUNG ADULTS; *U.S. Private*, pg. 4128
UNION HEALTH SERVICE, INC.; *U.S. Private*, pg. 4284
WELLNESS BY CHOICE, LLC—See Centene Corporation; *U.S. Public*, pg. 471
WSCR CORP.—See Dover Corporation; *U.S. Public*, pg. 683

813219 — OTHER GRANTMAKING AND GIVING SERVICES

ACCESS EAST INC; *U.S. Private*, pg. 51
THE AIR FORCE ASSOCIATION; *U.S. Private*, pg. 3983
BALL STATE INNOVATION CORPORATION—See Ball State University; *U.S. Private*, pg. 460
BAPTIST HEALTH SOUTH FLORIDA FOUNDATION—See Baptist Health South Florida, Inc.; *U.S. Private*, pg. 470
BENEFICIAL STATE FOUNDATION; *U.S. Private*, pg. 525
BLACK CONTRACTORS ASSOCIATION OF SAN DIEGO, INC.; *U.S. Private*, pg. 570
BREAKTHROUGH T1D; *U.S. Private*, pg. 643
CARLA & DAVID CRANE FOUNDATION; *U.S. Private*, pg. 763
CHRISTIAN FOUNDATION FOR CHILDREN AND AGING; *U.S. Private*, pg. 891
COMCAST-SPECTACOR FOUNDATION—See Comcast Corporation; *U.S. Public*, pg. 537
COMMONWEALTH CREDIT UNION; *U.S. Private*, pg. 986
THE COMMUNITY FOUNDATION FOR NORTHEAST FLORIDA; *U.S. Private*, pg. 4012
COMMUNITY FOUNDATION OF NORTH TEXAS; *U.S. Private*, pg. 992
CONNECTICUT CHILDREN'S MEDICAL CENTER FOUNDATION, INC.—See Connecticut Children's Medical Center Corporation; *U.S. Private*, pg. 1015
THE COSMETIC EXECUTIVE WOMEN FOUNDATION LTD.—See Cosmetic Executive Women, Inc.; *U.S. Private*, pg. 1062
COUNCIL ON FOUNDATIONS; *U.S. Private*, pg. 1065
EGMONT FONDEN; *Int'l*, pg. 2325
THE FRIENDS OF THE BRIGHAM & WOMEN'S HOSPITAL—See Partners HealthCare System, Inc.; *U.S. Private*, pg. 3102
GIVE2ASIA; *U.S. Private*, pg. 1703
GOOD360; *U.S. Private*, pg. 1738
GREATER KANSAS CITY COMMUNITY FOUNDATION; *U.S. Private*, pg. 1769
GULF COAST COMMUNITY SERVICES ASSOCIATION; *U.S. Private*, pg. 1815
INDIANA ENDOWMENT FUND, INC.; *U.S. Private*, pg. 2062
INTERNATIONAL FINANCE CORPORATION—See The World Bank Group; *U.S. Private*, pg. 4139
INTERNATIONAL MASONRY INSTITUTE; *U.S. Private*, pg. 2118
LEGACY FOUNDATION, INC.; *U.S. Private*, pg. 2416
THE LOS ANGELES CLIPPERS FOUNDATION—See LA Clippers LLC; *U.S. Private*, pg. 2368
MAGIC MOMENTS, INC.; *U.S. Private*, pg. 2546
MEDIA DREAM; *U.S. Private*, pg. 2652
MOISHE HOUSE; *U.S. Private*, pg. 2765
THE PABLOVE FOUNDATION; *U.S. Private*, pg. 4090
PENTAGON FEDERAL CREDIT UNION FOUNDATION—See Pentagon Federal Credit Union; *U.S. Private*, pg. 3140
PERMIAN BASIN AREA FOUNDATION; *U.S. Private*, pg. 3152
PUBLIC HEALTH FOUNDATION ENTERPRISES; *U.S. Private*, pg. 3299
REACH NOW INTERNATIONAL INC.; *U.S. Private*, pg. 3365
THE SPARTANBURG REGIONAL HEALTHCARE SYSTEM FOUNDATION—See Spartanburg Regional Health Services District, Inc.; *U.S. Private*, pg. 3747
ST. VINCENT'S HEALTHCARE FOUNDATION—See Ascension Health Alliance; *U.S. Private*, pg. 348
THE TED ARISON FAMILY FOUNDATION (ISRAEL) A PUBLIC BENEFIT COMPANY LTD.—See Arison Holdings (1998) Ltd.; *Int'l*, pg. 566
UNITED CHARITABLE PROGRAMS; *U.S. Private*, pg. 4288
WORLDWIDE INVENTORY NETWORK; *U.S. Private*, pg. 4569

813311 — HUMAN RIGHTS ORGANIZATIONS

AMERICAN JEWISH COMMITTEE; *U.S. Private*, pg. 239
AMERICAN JEWISH WORLD SERVICE, INC.; *U.S. Private*, pg. 239
AMERICAN RED CROSS; *U.S. Private*, pg. 245
BAYER INTELLECTUAL PROPERTY GMBH—See Bayer Aktiengesellschaft; *Int'l*, pg. 905
CARE-USA; *U.S. Private*, pg. 752
ESSENTIA INSTITUTE OF RURAL HEALTH; *U.S. Private*, pg. 1427
FREEDOM HOUSE, INC.; *U.S. Private*, pg. 1603

N.A.I.C.S. INDEX

813319 — OTHER SOCIAL ADVOCA...

HORRIGAN COLE ENTERPRISES, INC.—See Centerbridge Partners, L.P.; *U.S. Private*, pg. 813
HUMAN RIGHTS DEFENSE; *U.S. Private*, pg. 2006
INTERNATIONAL JUSTICE MISSION; *U.S. Private*, pg. 2118
MERCER HUMAN RESOURCE CONSULTING GMBH—See Marsh & McLennan Companies, Inc.; *U.S. Public*, pg. 1385
PATIENTS & PROVIDERS TO PROTECT ACCESS & CONTAIN HEALTH COSTS; *U.S. Private*, pg. 3109
ROTARY INTERNATIONAL; *U.S. Private*, pg. 3486
SURGICAL EYE EXPEDITIONS INTERNATIONAL; *U.S. Private*, pg. 3884
UNITED COMMUNITY & FAMILY SERVICES INC.; *U.S. Private*, pg. 4289
URGENT ACTION FUND FOR WOMEN'S HUMAN RIGHTS; *U.S. Private*, pg. 4315
WOMEN FOR WOMEN INTERNATIONAL; *U.S. Private*, pg. 4556

813312 — ENVIRONMENT, CONSERVATION AND WILDLIFE ORGANIZATIONS

AF ENERGIJA BALTIC UAB—See AF Gruppen ASA; *Int'l*, pg. 184
AFRICAN WILDLIFE FOUNDATION; *U.S. Private*, pg. 124
ALSTOM ARGENTINA S.A.—See Alstom S.A.; *Int'l*, pg. 379
AMERICAN ANIMAL CONTROL, LLC—See Plunkett's Pest Control, Inc.; *U.S. Private*, pg. 3215
AMERICAN COALITION FOR CLEAN COAL ELECTRICITY; *U.S. Private*, pg. 227
AMERICAN SOCIETY FOR THE PREVENTION OF CRUELTY TO ANIMALS; *U.S. Private*, pg. 254
ANIMAL RESCUE LEAGUE OF BOSTON; *U.S. Private*, pg. 283
ARIZONA HUMANE SOCIETY; *U.S. Private*, pg. 324
BAUER AMBIENTE S.R.L.—See BAUER Aktiengesellschaft; *Int'l*, pg. 892
BEST FRIENDS ANIMAL SOCIETY; *U.S. Private*, pg. 542
BIG CAT RESCUE CORP.; *U.S. Private*, pg. 552
BIOHABITATS, INC.; *U.S. Private*, pg. 562
BUFFALO BAYOU PARTNERSHIP, INC.; *U.S. Private*, pg. 680
CASCADE SIERRA SOLUTIONS; *U.S. Private*, pg. 781
CLEANTECH OPEN; *U.S. Private*, pg. 932
COASTAL CONSERVATION ASSOCIATION; *U.S. Private*, pg. 955
CURIODYSSEY; *U.S. Private*, pg. 1125
DEFENDERS OF WILDLIFE; *U.S. Private*, pg. 1190
DET DANSKE HEDESELSKAB; *Int'l*, pg. 2047
DRONESEED CO.; *U.S. Private*, pg. 1279
ELANCO CANADA LIMITED—See Eli Lilly & Company; *U.S. Public*, pg. 731
ELANCO NEDERLAND B.V.—See Eli Lilly & Company; *U.S. Public*, pg. 731
ELANCO UK AH LIMITED—See Eli Lilly & Company; *U.S. Public*, pg. 731
EMIRATES ENVIRONMENTAL GROUP; *Int'l*, pg. 2381
THE ENERGY FOUNDATION; *U.S. Private*, pg. 4026
ENERGY TRUST OF OREGON, INC.; *U.S. Private*, pg. 1396
FOOD & WATER WATCH; *U.S. Private*, pg. 1560
FOOTHILLS LAND CONSERVANCY; *U.S. Private*, pg. 1562
FORT WORTH ZOOLOGICAL ASSOCIATION INC.; *U.S. Private*, pg. 1575
GASPARILLA ISLAND CONSERVATION & IMPROVEMENT ASSOCIATION, INC.; *U.S. Private*, pg. 1648
GOLDEN GATE NATIONAL PARKS CONSERVANCY; *U.S. Private*, pg. 1732
GREENPEACE, INC.; *U.S. Private*, pg. 1779
HELEN WOODWARD ANIMAL CENTER; *U.S. Private*, pg. 1906
HUMANE SOCIETY CALUMET AREA; *U.S. Private*, pg. 2006
THE HUMANE SOCIETY OF THE UNITED STATES; *U.S. Private*, pg. 4054
INSTITUTO INTERNATIONAL PAPER—See International Paper Company; *U.S. Public*, pg. 1155
IOWA NATURAL HERITAGE FOUNDATION; *U.S. Private*, pg. 2135
JOLSEN MILJOPARK AS—See AF Gruppen ASA; *Int'l*, pg. 184
JORDAN LAKE PRESERVE CORPORATION—See Hilton Grand Vacations Inc.; *U.S. Public*, pg. 1039
KENOSHA COUNTY HUMANE SOCIETY—See Wisconsin Humane Society; *U.S. Private*, pg. 4548
LEAGUE OF CONSERVATION VOTERS, INC.; *U.S. Private*, pg. 2407
LYKES LAND INVESTMENTS, INC.—See Lykes Brothers Inc.; *U.S. Private*, pg. 2519
MASS AUDUBON; *U.S. Private*, pg. 2603
MESSINA WILDLIFE MANAGEMENT; *U.S. Private*, pg. 2679
THE MORTON ARBORETUM; *U.S. Private*, pg. 4080
NATIONAL FOREST FOUNDATION; *U.S. Private*, pg. 2854
NATIONAL WILDLIFE FEDERATION; *U.S. Private*, pg. 2865
NATIONAL WILD TURKEY FEDERATION; *U.S. Private*, pg. 2865
NATURAL SYSTEMS INTERNATIONAL, LLC—See Biohabitats, Inc.; *U.S. Private*, pg. 562
NATUREBRIDGE; *U.S. Private*, pg. 2867
OCEANA, INC.; *U.S. Private*, pg. 2990
OCEAN CONSERVANCY; *U.S. Private*, pg. 2989
OLD DOMINION LAND CONSERVANCY, INC.; *U.S. Private*, pg. 3008
PARK CITIES QUAIL; *U.S. Private*, pg. 3096
PECONIC LAND TRUST, INCORPORATED; *U.S. Private*, pg. 3127
PENOBSCOT RIVER RESTORATION TRUST; *U.S. Private*, pg. 3138
PUERTO RICO CONSERVATION TRUST FUND; *U.S. Private*, pg. 3302
RAINFOREST ALLIANCE; *U.S. Private*, pg. 3348
RESOURCES LEGACY FUND; *U.S. Private*, pg. 3407
ROCKY MOUNTAIN ELK FOUNDATION, INC.; *U.S. Private*, pg. 3468
SANTA BARBARA HUMANE SOCIETY—See Santa Maria Valley Humane Society; *U.S. Private*, pg. 3547
SANTA MARIA VALLEY HUMANE SOCIETY; *U.S. Private*, pg. 3547
SEATTLE AQUARIUM; *U.S. Private*, pg. 3591
SOCIETY FOR THE PROTECTION OF NEW HAMPSHIRE FORESTS; *U.S. Private*, pg. 3703
SOUTHERN NEVADA CONSERVANCY; *U.S. Private*, pg. 3734
THREE RIVERS LAND TRUST, INC.; *U.S. Private*, pg. 4164
TROUT UNLIMITED INC.; *U.S. Private*, pg. 4243
THE TRUSTEES OF RESERVATIONS; *U.S. Private*, pg. 4128
TURTLE SURVIVAL ALLIANCE FOUNDATION; *U.S. Private*, pg. 4262
UNION SPORTSMEN'S ALLIANCE; *U.S. Private*, pg. 4285
UNITED STATES ENVIRONMENTAL PROTECTION AGENCY; *U.S. Private*, pg. 4299
U.S. ENDOWMENT FOR FORESTRY & COMMUNITIES, INC.; *U.S. Private*, pg. 4270
VARMENT GUARD ENVIRONMENTAL SERVICES, INC.—See Plunkett's Pest Control, Inc.; *U.S. Private*, pg. 3215
VIEAU ASSOCIATES INC.—See GZA GeoEnvironmental Inc.; *U.S. Private*, pg. 1822
WASTREN ADVANTAGE, INC.; *U.S. Private*, pg. 4451
THE WESTERN PENNSYLVANIA CONSERVANCY; *U.S. Private*, pg. 4134
WESTERN RESERVE LAND CONSERVANCY; *U.S. Private*, pg. 4496
WILDERNESS SOCIETY; *U.S. Private*, pg. 4519
THE WILDLIFE CENTER OF VIRGINIA; *U.S. Private*, pg. 4136
WISCONSIN HUMANE SOCIETY; *U.S. Private*, pg. 4548

813319 — OTHER SOCIAL ADVOCACY ORGANIZATIONS

944 MEDIA, LLC; *U.S. Private*, pg. 17
ADVOCATE MEDICAL GROUP—See Advocate Health Care Network; *U.S. Private*, pg. 111
AIP FOUNDATION; *Int'l*, pg. 234
ALLIANCE DEFENDING FREEDOM, INC.; *U.S. Private*, pg. 181
AMERICAN SENIORS ASSOCIATION HOLDING GROUP, INC.; *U.S. Public*, pg. 109
BOBBY DODD INSTITUTE; *U.S. Private*, pg. 606
BRIGHTFOCUS FOUNDATION; *U.S. Private*, pg. 652
CAMBA; *U.S. Private*, pg. 725
THE CARNEGIE ENDOWMENT FOR INTERNATIONAL PEACE; *U.S. Private*, pg. 4005
CATALYST CANADA INC.—See Catalyst, Inc.; *U.S. Private*, pg. 787
CATALYST EUROPE AG—See Catalyst, Inc.; *U.S. Private*, pg. 787
CATALYST, INC.; *U.S. Private*, pg. 786
CATALYST INDIA WRC—See Catalyst, Inc.; *U.S. Private*, pg. 787
CATIE'S CLOSET; *U.S. Private*, pg. 792
CATO INSTITUTE; *U.S. Private*, pg. 792
CENTER FOR COMMUNITY CHANGE; *U.S. Private*, pg. 810
CENTROS SOR ISOLINA FERRE INC; *U.S. Private*, pg. 830
CHILDREN INTERNATIONAL; *U.S. Private*, pg. 883
CHILDREN'S LAW CENTER OF CALIFORNIA; *U.S. Private*, pg. 885
CHOICES OF LOUISIANA, INC.—See Webster Equity Partners, LLC; *U.S. Private*, pg. 4466
COMMISSION ON ECONOMIC OPPORTUNITY; *U.S. Private*, pg. 985
COMMUNITY SERVICE COUNCIL; *U.S. Private*, pg. 997
CONNECTIONS COMMUNITY SUPPORT PROGRAMS, INC.; *U.S. Private*, pg. 1016
COUNSELING & SUPPORT SERVICES FOR YOUTH; *U.S. Private*, pg. 1065
CREATIVE CONNECTIONS, INC.—See Centerbridge Partners, L.P.; *U.S. Private*, pg. 813
DETROIT SHOREWAY COMMUNITY DEVELOPMENT ORGANIZATION; *U.S. Private*, pg. 1216
DREYER MEDICAL GROUP, LTD.—See Advocate Health Care Network; *U.S. Private*, pg. 111
EASTERSEALS ARC OF NORTHEAST INDIANA, INC.; *U.S. Private*, pg. 1321
FINANCIAL SERVICES ROUNDTABLE—See Bank Policy Institute; *U.S. Private*, pg. 467
FONDAZIONE CASSA DI RISPARMIO DI TORINO; *Int'l*, pg. 2725
FOUNDATION FOR FOOD & AGRICULTURE RESEARCH; *U.S. Private*, pg. 1580
FRLP, INC.—See Federal Realty Investment Trust; *U.S. Public*, pg. 825
FSG, INC.; *U.S. Private*, pg. 1618
THE GERONTOLOGICAL SOCIETY OF AMERICA; *U.S. Private*, pg. 4032
GLOBAL POVERTY PROJECT, INC.; *U.S. Private*, pg. 1716
GOODWILL INDUSTRIES-MANASOTA, INC.; *U.S. Private*, pg. 1740
GRYYT, LLC; *U.S. Private*, pg. 1800
HEALTHY NEIGHBORHOODS, INC.; *U.S. Private*, pg. 1898
HENRY M. JACKSON FOUNDATION FOR THE ADVANCEMENT OF MILITARY MEDICINE, INC.; *U.S. Private*, pg. 1918
HIGH POINT TREATMENT CENTER; *U.S. Private*, pg. 1936
HITOPS INC.; *U.S. Private*, pg. 1953
HOSPICE OF CLEVELAND COUNTY, INC.; *U.S. Private*, pg. 1985
HOUSTON REGIONAL HIV/AIDS RESOURCE GROUP, INC.; *U.S. Private*, pg. 1994
HUMAN RIGHTS FIRST; *U.S. Private*, pg. 2006
INDIANA SOYBEAN ALLIANCE; *U.S. Private*, pg. 2063
INGALLS DEVELOPMENT FOUNDATION INC.—See University of Chicago; *U.S. Private*, pg. 4308
INNOVATIONS FOR POVERTY ACTION; *U.S. Private*, pg. 2081
INSURANCE INSTITUTE FOR HIGHWAY SAFETY; *U.S. Private*, pg. 2095
INTEGRATED COMMUNITY SOLUTIONS, INC.; *U.S. Private*, pg. 2099
INTERNATIONAL ASSOCIATION OF FIRE FIGHTERS; *U.S. Private*, pg. 2114
LA CASA DE DON PEDRO, INC.; *U.S. Private*, pg. 2368
LIVIN AGAIN LLC.—See Organicell Regenerative Medicine, Inc.; *U.S. Public*, pg. 1615
LUTHERAN SOCIAL SERVICES OF NORTHEAST FLORIDA; *U.S. Private*, pg. 2517
M.A.P. INTERNATIONAL INC.; *U.S. Private*, pg. 2528
MARIAN MEDICAL CENTER—See Catholic Health Initiatives; *U.S. Private*, pg. 789
MATRIX HUMAN SERVICES; *U.S. Private*, pg. 2612
MEMORIAL HERMANN FOUNDATION; *U.S. Private*, pg. 2664
MERCHANT AVIATION LLC—See Aeroports de Paris S.A.; *Int'l*, pg. 181
MERCY GENERAL HEALTH PARTNERS—See Trinity Health Corporation; *U.S. Private*, pg. 4233
MIDDLE EAST INVESTMENT INITIATIVE; *U.S. Private*, pg. 2711
MISSION NEIGHBORHOOD HEALTH CENTER; *U.S. Private*, pg. 2747
MODIVCARE, INC.; *U.S. Public*, pg. 1455
MOZILLA FOUNDATION; *U.S. Private*, pg. 2802
THE NATIONAL ASSOCIATION FOR GUN RIGHTS, INC.; *U.S. Private*, pg. 4081
NATIONAL BUSINESS AVIATION ASSOCIATION, INC.; *U.S. Private*, pg. 2849
NATIONAL CAUCUS & CENTER ON BLACK AGING, INC.; *U.S. Private*, pg. 2850
NATIONAL FISHERIES INSTITUTE INC.; *U.S. Private*, pg. 2854
NATIONAL SAFETY COUNCIL; *U.S. Private*, pg. 2862
NATIVE AMERICAN HERITAGE ASSOCIATION; *U.S. Private*, pg. 2866
NORTHWEST COMMUNITY ACTION PROGRAMS OF WYOMING INC.; *U.S. Private*, pg. 2959
THE ONESTAR FOUNDATION; *U.S. Private*, pg. 4088
OPPORTUNITY FINANCE NETWORK; *U.S. Private*, pg. 3033
ORBIS CLINICAL, LLC—See Webster Equity Partners, LLC; *U.S. Private*, pg. 4467
OSHMAN FAMILY JEWISH COMMUNITY CENTER; *U.S. Private*, pg. 3047
POVERTY SOLUTIONS, INC.; *U.S. Private*, pg. 3236
PROMISE HOUSE, INC.—See Jonathan's Place; *U.S. Private*, pg. 2231
QUINCY COMMUNITY ACTION PROGRAMS, INC.; *U.S. Private*, pg. 3327
REAGAN-UDALL FOUNDATION; *U.S. Private*, pg. 3367
REFINERY TERMINAL FIRE COMPANY; *U.S. Private*, pg. 3384
R STREET INSTITUTE; *U.S. Private*, pg. 3331
SALVADORAN AMERICAN HUMANITARIAN FOUNDATION; *U.S. Private*, pg. 3535
SAN DIEGO VENTURE GROUP—See CONNECT; *U.S. Private*, pg. 1014
SCAN GROUP; *U.S. Private*, pg. 3561

813319 — OTHER SOCIAL ADVOCA...

SEARCH FOR COMMON GROUND; *U.S. Private*, pg. 3586
SEVA FOUNDATION; *U.S. Private*, pg. 3618
SOCIAL SECURITY ADVOCATES FOR THE DISABLED, LLC—See Brown & Brown, Inc.; *U.S. Public*, pg. 402
SOLUTIONS RECOVERY INC.—See AAC Holdings, Inc.; *U.S. Private*, pg. 31
SOUTHEASTERN COMMUNITY & FAMILY SERVICES, INC.; *U.S. Private*, pg. 3727
SOUTHEAST KANSAS COMMUNITY ACTION PROGRAM, INC.; *U.S. Private*, pg. 3725
STOTTECOMPAGNIET APS—See Humana AB; *Int'l*, pg. 3530
ST. VINCENT DE PAUL OF SEATTLE/KING COUNTY; *U.S. Private*, pg. 3773
THIRD SECTOR NEW ENGLAND, INC.; *U.S. Private*, pg. 4145
TOTAL ACTION AGAINST POVERTY; *U.S. Private*, pg. 4190
TRANSITCENTER, INC.; *U.S. Private*, pg. 4208
TRI-CITY COMMUNITY ACTION PROGRAM INC.; *U.S. Private*, pg. 4221
UNITED NEGRO COLLEGE FUND, INC.; *U.S. Private*, pg. 4295
VALLEY IMPROVEMENT ASSOCIATION, INC.; *U.S. Private*, pg. 4334
VITAMIN ANGEL ALLIANCE, INC.; *U.S. Private*, pg. 4405
WAYNE ACTION GROUP FOR ECONOMIC SOLVENCY, INC.; *U.S. Private*, pg. 4459
WORLD AFFAIRS COUNCIL OF PHILADELPHIA; *U.S. Private*, pg. 4564
YOUNG AMERICA'S FOUNDATION; *U.S. Private*, pg. 4592

813410 — CIVIC AND SOCIAL ORGANIZATIONS

60 PLUS ASSOCIATION; *U.S. Private*, pg. 16
AAA ALLIED GROUP, INC—See The American Automobile Association, Inc.; *U.S. Private*, pg. 3985
AARP; *U.S. Private*, pg. 32
AMERICANS FOR PROSPERITY; *U.S. Private*, pg. 259
AMERICA VOTES; *U.S. Private*, pg. 220
ARIZONA BIKE WEEK CHARITIES; *U.S. Private*, pg. 323
ASSOCIATION OF SOCIAL WORK BOARDS; *U.S. Private*, pg. 359
THE AUTO CLUB GROUP; *U.S. Private*, pg. 3990
AVALON CORPUS CHRISTI TRANSITIONAL CENTER, LLC—See Corecivic, Inc.; *U.S. Public*, pg. 577
AVALON TRANSITIONAL CENTER DALLAS, LLC—See Corecivic, Inc.; *U.S. Public*, pg. 577
AVALON TULSA, LLC—See Corecivic, Inc.; *U.S. Public*, pg. 577
BAPTIST HOSPITAL FOUNDATION INC—See Ascension Health Alliance; *U.S. Private*, pg. 347
BIPARTISAN POLICY CENTER; *U.S. Private*, pg. 563
BOB WOODRUFF FOUNDATION; *U.S. Private*, pg. 605
BONNEY LAKE FOOD BANK; *U.S. Private*, pg. 615
BOYS & GIRLS CLUBS OF BOSTON; *U.S. Private*, pg. 629
CALIFORNIANS AGAINST HIGHER HEALTHCARE COSTS; *U.S. Private*, pg. 721
CAROLINA CLUB—See Apollo Global Management, Inc.; *U.S. Public*, pg. 149
CARVER TRANSITIONAL CENTER, LLC—See Corecivic, Inc.; *U.S. Public*, pg. 577
CATHOLIC CHARITIES MAINE; *U.S. Private*, pg. 788
CENTER CLUB, INC.—See BNP Paribas SA; *Int'l*, pg. 1087
THE CHICAGO COUNCIL ON GLOBAL AFFAIRS; *U.S. Private*, pg. 4008
CITIHOPE INTERNATIONAL, INC.; *U.S. Private*, pg. 901
CITIZEN ENGAGEMENT LABORATORY; *U.S. Private*, pg. 902
CITIZENS UNITED; *U.S. Private*, pg. 904
CITY CLUB LA—See Apollo Global Management, Inc.; *U.S. Public*, pg. 149
THE CLEVELAND CLINIC FOUNDATION; *U.S. Private*, pg. 4010
THE CLUB AT MEDITERRA INC; *U.S. Private*, pg. 4010
COMMITTEE FOR A RESPONSIBLE FEDERAL BUDGET; *U.S. Private*, pg. 985
THE COMMUNITY GROUP; *U.S. Private*, pg. 4012
CONCERTED SERVICES, INC.; *U.S. Private*, pg. 1009
CONSERVATIVE REFORM NETWORK; *U.S. Private*, pg. 1019
COSTCO WHOLESALE MEMBERSHIP, INC.—See Costco Wholesale Corporation; *U.S. Public*, pg. 586
CSA FRATERNAL LIFE; *U.S. Private*, pg. 1116
CUBAN CLUB FOUNDATION, INC.; *U.S. Private*, pg. 1119
DALLAS JEWISH COMMUNITY FOUNDATION; *U.S. Private*, pg. 1150
DCC HONG KONG LTD.—See Adamantem Capital Management Pty Limited; *Int'l*, pg. 123
DELTA SIGMA THETA SORORITY, INC.; *U.S. Private*, pg. 1201
DEMOCRACY WORKS INC.; *U.S. Private*, pg. 1204
DRESS FOR SUCCESS WORLDWIDE; *U.S. Private*, pg. 1276
EMERGENCY NURSES ASSOCIATION; *U.S. Private*, pg. 1380
THE EVANGELICAL LUTHERAN GOOD SAMARITAN FOUNDATION—See Sanford Health; *U.S. Private*, pg. 3545
FAIRFIELD GLADE COMMUNITY CLUB; *U.S. Private*, pg. 1463
FLORIDA STATE ELKS ASSOCIATION, INC.; *U.S. Private*, pg. 1550
FORT WORTH TRANSITIONAL CENTER, LLC—See Corecivic, Inc.; *U.S. Public*, pg. 577
THE FREEDOM FORUM INC.; *U.S. Private*, pg. 4030
FUTURES WITHOUT VIOLENCE; *U.S. Private*, pg. 1627
GATEWAY ECONOMIC DEVELOPMENT CORPORATION OF GREATER CLEVELAND; *U.S. Private*, pg. 1650
THE GLOBAL FUND FOR WOMEN, INC.; *U.S. Private*, pg. 4033
GOODWILL INDUSTRIES-SUNCOAST, INC.; *U.S. Private*, pg. 1740
GOVERNMENT ACCOUNTABILITY INSTITUTE; *U.S. Private*, pg. 1746
THE GRAND LODGE OF MARYLAND; *U.S. Private*, pg. 4037
GROWTH ORGANIZATION OF TOPEKA / SHAWNEE COUNTY, INC.; *U.S. Private*, pg. 1796
HADASSAH, THE WOMEN'S ZIONIST ORGANIZATION OF AMERICA, INC.; *U.S. Private*, pg. 1838
HARMONIE CLUB OF THE CITY OF NEW YORK; *U.S. Private*, pg. 1866
HEALTHWISE, INCORPORATED—See KKR & Co. Inc.; *U.S. Public*, pg. 1254
HEART OF COMPASSION DISTRIBUTION, INC.; *U.S. Private*, pg. 1898
HERITAGE SCHOOLS, INC.; *U.S. Private*, pg. 1924
HUI HULIAU; *U.S. Private*, pg. 2004
HUMANCO KFT—See Gedeon Richter Plc.; *Int'l*, pg. 2910
INDEPENDENCE FUND, INC.; *U.S. Private*, pg. 2058
INTERNATIONAL FOUNDATION FOR ELECTION SYSTEMS; *U.S. Private*, pg. 2117
INTERNATIONAL MARCH OF THE LIVING; *U.S. Private*, pg. 2118
INTER TRIBAL COUNCIL OF ARIZONA, INC.; *U.S. Private*, pg. 2106
INTERVAL INTERNATIONAL ARGENTINA S.A.—See Marriott Vacations Worldwide Corporation; *U.S. Public*, pg. 1373
INTERVAL INTERNATIONAL EGYPT LTD.—See Marriott Vacations Worldwide Corporation; *U.S. Public*, pg. 1373
INTERVAL INTERNATIONAL FINLAND OY—See Marriott Vacations Worldwide Corporation; *U.S. Public*, pg. 1373
INTERVAL INTERNATIONAL ITALIA SRL—See Marriott Vacations Worldwide Corporation; *U.S. Public*, pg. 1373
INTERVAL INTERNATIONAL LIMITED—See Marriott Vacations Worldwide Corporation; *U.S. Public*, pg. 1373
INTERVAL INTERNATIONAL SINGAPORE (PTE) LTD.—See Marriott Vacations Worldwide Corporation; *U.S. Public*, pg. 1373
JCC ASSOCIATION; *U.S. Private*, pg. 2194
J.P. MORGAN CHASE COMMUNITY DEVELOPMENT GROUP—See JPMorgan Chase & Co.; *U.S. Public*, pg. 1208
KIND CAMPAIGN; *U.S. Private*, pg. 2306
KOREAN WOMEN'S ASSOCIATION; *U.S. Private*, pg. 2343
LAND TRUST OF SANTA CRUZ COUNTY; *U.S. Private*, pg. 2384
LET FREEDOM RING, INC.; *U.S. Private*, pg. 2433
THE LONGHORN COUNCIL, BOY SCOUTS OF AMERICA; *U.S. Private*, pg. 4072
LUTHERAN COMMUNITY SERVICES NORTHWEST; *U.S. Private*, pg. 2517
LUTHERAN SERVICES FLORIDA INC.; *U.S. Private*, pg. 2517
MAKE-A-WISH FOUNDATION OF GREATER LOS ANGELES; *U.S. Private*, pg. 2556
MARILLAC ST. VINCENT FAMILY SERVICES; *U.S. Private*, pg. 2574
MIF, L.L.C.—See Marriott International, Inc.; *U.S. Public*, pg. 1371
MILITARY WARRIORS SUPPORT FOUNDATION; *U.S. Private*, pg. 2729
MILWAUKEE JEWISH FEDERATION, INC.; *U.S. Private*, pg. 2739
NATIONAL AUDUBON SOCIETY, INC.; *U.S. Private*, pg. 2847
NATIONAL GEOGRAPHIC SOCIETY; *U.S. Private*, pg. 2855
NATIONAL LAW ENFORCEMENT OFFICERS MEMORIAL FUND; *U.S. Private*, pg. 2858
THE NATURE CONSERVANCY; *U.S. Private*, pg. 4082
NAVY-MARINE CORPS RELIEF SOCIETY; *U.S. Private*, pg. 2874
NAVY MUTUAL AID ASSOCIATION; *U.S. Private*, pg. 2873
NORTHEAST KANSAS COMMUNITY ACTION PROGRAM, INC.; *U.S. Private*, pg. 2950
NORTHERN KENTUCKY AREA DEVELOPMENT DISTRICT; *U.S. Private*, pg. 2953
ONE LOVE FOUNDATION; *U.S. Private*, pg. 3020
ORGANIZING FOR ACTION; *U.S. Private*, pg. 3041
PAN AMERICAN DEVELOPMENT FOUNDATION; *U.S. Private*, pg. 3083
THE PENNSYLVANIA COALITION AGAINST DOMESTIC VIOLENCE; *U.S. Private*, pg. 4092
PHI MU FRATERNITY; *U.S. Private*, pg. 3168
PINE BUSH EQUIPMENT CO. INC.; *U.S. Public*, pg. 3182
PIONEER HUMAN SERVICES, INC.; *U.S. Private*, pg. 3187
PITTSBURGH MERCY HEALTH SYSTEM, INC.; *U.S. Private*, pg. 3191
POLISH ROMAN CATHOLIC UNION OF AMERICA; *U.S. Private*, pg. 3224
PROHEALTH PHYSICIANS; *U.S. Private*, pg. 3280
PRO MUJER INC.; *U.S. Private*, pg. 3270
RESTORE ONE; *U.S. Private*, pg. 3410
RHEA LANA'S, INC.; *U.S. Private*, pg. 3421
RIVIERA DUNES MARINA CONDOMINIUM ASSOCIATION, INC.; *U.S. Private*, pg. 3448
ROUND HILL CLUB; *U.S. Private*, pg. 3488
SAMARITANS FEET INTERNATIONAL; *U.S. Private*, pg. 3536
SAN FRANCISCO TRAVEL ASSOCIATION; *U.S. Private*, pg. 3541
SER JOBS FOR PROGRESS INC. OF SAN ANTONIO; *U.S. Private*, pg. 3612
SHEBOYGAN SYMPHONY ORCHESTRA INC.; *U.S. Private*, pg. 3629
SHELTERING PALMS FOUNDATION INC; *U.S. Private*, pg. 3631
SIERRA CLUB; *U.S. Private*, pg. 3646
SINGING BEACH CLUB INC.; *U.S. Private*, pg. 3670
SINGLE STOP USA; *U.S. Private*, pg. 3670
STATE SERVICES ORGANIZATION, INC.; *U.S. Private*, pg. 3792
STROUM JEWISH COMMUNITY CENTER; *U.S. Private*, pg. 3841
SUPPORT OUR TROOPS, INC.; *U.S. Private*, pg. 3882
SURFRIDER FOUNDATION; *U.S. Private*, pg. 3884
S.V.D.P. MANAGEMENT, INC.; *U.S. Private*, pg. 3519
TDS TELECOM—See Telephone & Data Systems, Inc.; *U.S. Public*, pg. 1997
THRIVENT FINANCIAL FOR LUTHERANS FOUNDATION; *U.S. Private*, pg. 4165
TRIBAL LAW AND POLICY INSTITUTE; *U.S. Private*, pg. 4227
TRI-VALLEY OPPORTUNITY COUNCIL, INC.; *U.S. Private*, pg. 4224
TURQUOISE COUNCIL OF AMERICANS & EURASIANS; *U.S. Private*, pg. 4261
THE UNION CLUB OF THE CITY OF NEW YORK; *U.S. Private*, pg. 4129
THE UNION LEAGUE CLUB; *U.S. Private*, pg. 4129
UNITED THROUGH READING; *U.S. Private*, pg. 4301
UNITED WAY OF GREATER MERCER COUNTY, INC.—See United Way of the Virginia Peninsula; *U.S. Private*, pg. 4301
UNITED WAY OF THE VIRGINIA PENINSULA; *U.S. Private*, pg. 4301
UNIVERSITY CLUB OF MILWAUKEE; *U.S. Private*, pg. 4307
URBAN RESOURCE INSTITUTE; *U.S. Private*, pg. 4315
VETERANS INC.; *U.S. Private*, pg. 4374
VETERANS OF FOREIGN WARS OF THE UNITED STATES; *U.S. Private*, pg. 4374
VETERAN TICKETS FOUNDATION; *U.S. Private*, pg. 4373
VIETNAM VETERANS OF AMERICA, INC.; *U.S. Private*, pg. 4381
VIETNAM VETERANS WORKSHOP INC.; *U.S. Private*, pg. 4381
VITAL VOICES GLOBAL PARTNERSHIP; *U.S. Private*, pg. 4405
THE VOLCKER ALLIANCE; *U.S. Private*, pg. 4132
WESTERN AREA COUNCIL—See Dairy Farmers of America, Inc.; *U.S. Private*, pg. 1146
WILLIAM PENN ASSOCIATION; *U.S. Private*, pg. 4524
WOMEN HELPING WOMEN; *U.S. Private*, pg. 4556
WOMENS CAMPAIGN INTERNATIONAL; *U.S. Private*, pg. 4556
WOODLANDS RELIGIOUS COMMUNITY INC.; *U.S. Private*, pg. 4559
THE YALE CLUB OF NEW YORK CITY; *U.S. Private*, pg. 4139
YOUTH DEVELOPMENT, INC.; *U.S. Private*, pg. 4594

813910 — BUSINESS ASSOCIATIONS

A C CENTER, INC.; *U.S. Private*, pg. 18
ADVANCED ENERGY ECONOMY; *U.S. Private*, pg. 89
ADVENTIST HEALTH SYSTEM; *U.S. Private*, pg. 108
ADVENTIST HEALTH SYSTEM SUNBELT HEALTHCARE CORPORATION; *U.S. Private*, pg. 108
ADVENTIST MIDWEST HEALTH—See Adventist Health System Sunbelt Healthcare Corporation; *U.S. Private*, pg. 108
AFP (SHANGHAI) LIMITED—See Sealed Air Corporation; *U.S. Private*, pg. 1852
AGRAVIS RAIFFEISEN AG; *Int'l*, pg. 214
AGROPUR COOPERATIVE; *Int'l*, pg. 220
AIR-CONDITIONING, HEATING, AND REFRIGERATION INSTITUTE; *U.S. Private*, pg. 140

N.A.I.C.S. INDEX

813910 — BUSINESS ASSOCIATIO...

THE ALAMEDA COUNTY FAIR ASSOCIATION; *U.S. Private*, pg. 3983
AMBITECH ENGINEERING COPRORATION—See Zachry Holdings, Inc.; *U.S. Private*, pg. 4596
AMERICAN ARBITRATION ASSOCIATION; *U.S. Private*, pg. 222
AMERICAN ASSOCIATION OF STATE HIGHWAY & TRANSPORTATION OFFICIALS; *U.S. Private*, pg. 223
THE AMERICAN BANKERS ASSOCIATION; *U.S. Private*, pg. 3985
AMERICAN BEVERAGE ASSOCIATION; *U.S. Private*, pg. 224
AMERICAN BUSINESS MEDIA—See Software & Information Industry Association, Inc.; *U.S. Private*, pg. 3705
AMERICAN FARMLAND TRUST; *U.S. Private*, pg. 233
AMERICAN FUEL AND PETROCHEMICAL MANUFACTURERS; *U.S. Private*, pg. 234
AMERICAN INSTITUTE OF STEEL CONSTRUCTION; *U.S. Private*, pg. 238
AMERICAN PUBLIC WORKS ASSOCIATION; *U.S. Private*, pg. 245
AMERICAN SOCIETY FOR TESTING & MATERIALS; *U.S. Private*, pg. 254
AMERICAN SOYBEAN ASSOCIATION; *U.S. Private*, pg. 255
ARKANSAS FARM BUREAU FEDERATION; *U.S. Private*, pg. 325
ARKANSAS FARM BUREAU INVESTMENT—See Arkansas Farm Bureau Federation; *U.S. Private*, pg. 325
ASPLUNDH FAMILY PUBLIC FOUNDATION INC.; *U.S. Private*, pg. 353
THE ASSOCIATED GENERAL CONTRACTORS OF AMERICA; *U.S. Private*, pg. 3989
ASSOCIATION OF NATIONAL ADVERTISERS, INC.; *U.S. Private*, pg. 358
ATHLETES FIRST, LLC—See General Catalyst Partners; *U.S. Private*, pg. 1664
ATHLETES FIRST, LLC—See Mastry Management LLC; *U.S. Private*, pg. 2608
ATLANTICARE HEALTH SYSTEM, INC.—See Geisinger Health System; *U.S. Private*, pg. 1656
BANK ADMINISTRATION INSTITUTE; *U.S. Private*, pg. 466
BARNABAS HEALTH, INC.; *U.S. Private*, pg. 476
BEAUMONT HEALTH; *U.S. Private*, pg. 508
BENSALEM RACING ASSOCIATION, INC.—See International Turf Investment Co., Inc.; *U.S. Private*, pg. 2121
BPI INFORMATION SYSTEMS OF OHIO, INC.; *U.S. Private*, pg. 629
BRITISH POTATO COUNCIL; *Int'l*, pg. 1171
BUSINESS MARKETING ASSOCIATION, INC.—See Association of National Advertisers, Inc.; *U.S. Private*, pg. 358
CALIFORNIA ASSOCIATION OF FOOD BANKS; *U.S. Private*, pg. 717
CALIFORNIA ASSOCIATION OF REALTORS; *U.S. Private*, pg. 717
CALIFORNIA FARM BUREAU FEDERATION; *U.S. Private*, pg. 719
CANADIAN ADVANCED TECHNOLOGY ALLIANCE; *Int'l*, pg. 1282
CANADIAN ASSOCIATION OF INTERNET PROVIDERS—See Canadian Advanced Technology Alliance; *Int'l*, pg. 1282
CARONDELET HEALTH CORPORATION—See Ascension Health Alliance; *U.S. Private*, pg. 347
CATA BIOMETRICS GROUP—See Canadian Advanced Technology Alliance; *Int'l*, pg. 1282
CATHOLIC HEALTH INITIATIVES; *U.S. Private*, pg. 789
CENTRAL BERING SEA FISHERMEN'S ASSOCIATION; *U.S. Private*, pg. 819
CHARLOTTE REGIONAL BUSINESS ALLIANCE; *U.S. Private*, pg. 857
CHRISTIAN CARE COMMUNITIES; *U.S. Private*, pg. 890
COLORADANS FOR RESPONSIBLE ENERGY DEVELOPMENT; *U.S. Private*, pg. 973
COLORADO CATTLEMEN'S AGRICULTURAL LAND TRUST—See Colorado Cattlemen's Association; *U.S. Private*, pg. 973
COMPUTING TECHNOLOGY INDUSTRY ASSOCIATION; *U.S. Private*, pg. 1006
CONFEDERATION NATIONALE DU CREDIT MUTUEL; *Int'l*, pg. 1767
CONNECTICUT CHILDREN'S MEDICAL CENTER CORPORATION, INC.; *U.S. Private*, pg. 1015
CORN REFINERS ASSOCIATION; *U.S. Private*, pg. 1050
CORPORATE SERVICE CENTER, INC.; *U.S. Private*, pg. 1056
CPO COMMERCE, INC.—See Sycamore Partners Management, LP; *U.S. Private*, pg. 3896
CTIA-THE WIRELESS ASSOCIATION; *U.S. Private*, pg. 1118
CTS ELECTRONICS MANUFACTURING SOLUTIONS—See Benchmark Electronics, Inc.; *U.S. Public*, pg. 295
CURAE HEALTH, INC.; *U.S. Private*, pg. 1124
DAMARTEX UK LTD—See Damartex SA; *Int'l*, pg. 1956
DAMART SWISS AG—See Damartex SA; *Int'l*, pg. 1956
DELUXE CORPORATION OMNIBUS PLAN VEBA TRUST; *U.S. Private*, pg. 1202

DENTONS GROUP; *U.S. Private*, pg. 1206
DESTINATION PACKWOOD ASSOCIATION; *U.S. Private*, pg. 1215
DET NORSKE VERITAS-NORTH & CENTRAL AMERICA—See DNV GL Group AS; *Int'l*, pg. 2151
DEUTSCHER SPARKASSEN- UND GIROVERBAND E.V.; *Int'l*, pg. 2085
DLA PIPER GALLASTEGUI Y LOZANO—See DLA Piper Global; *Int'l*, pg. 2140
DLA PIPER GLOBAL; *Int'l*, pg. 2140
DOWNTOWN DAYTON SPECIAL IMPROVEMENT DISTRICT INC.; *U.S. Private*, pg. 1269
EDISON ELECTRIC INSTITUTE; *U.S. Private*, pg. 1336
EGYPTIAN ELECTRIC COOPERATIVE ASSOCIATION—See Touchstone Energy Cooperative, Inc.; *U.S. Private*, pg. 4192
ELECTRONIC INDUSTRIES ALLIANCE INC.; *U.S. Private*, pg. 1355
ENACTUS; *U.S. Private*, pg. 1389
ENTERPRISE FLORIDA, INC.; *U.S. Private*, pg. 1403
ETG INTERNATIONAL LLC; *U.S. Private*, pg. 1431
FEDERAL RESERVE BANK OF RICHMOND; *U.S. Private*, pg. 1491
FEDERATION NATIONALE DES BANQUES POPULAIRES—See Groupe BPCE; *Int'l*, pg. 3094
FEDERATION NATIONALE DES CAISSES D'EPARGNE—See Groupe BPCE; *Int'l*, pg. 3097
FELLESKJOPET AGRI SA; *Int'l*, pg. 2633
FINANCIAL PLANNING ASSOCIATION; *U.S. Private*, pg. 1508
FIRSTHEALTH OF THE CAROLINAS, INC.; *U.S. Private*, pg. 1532
FLORIDA HOME BUILDERS ASSOCIATION, INC.; *U.S. Private*, pg. 1549
FLORIDA HOSPITAL MEDICAL GROUP, INC.—See Adventist Health System Sunbelt Healthcare Corporation; *U.S. Private*, pg. 109
FLORIDA PRESS ASSOCIATION INC.; *U.S. Private*, pg. 1550
FRANCISCAN HEALTH SYSTEM; *U.S. Private*, pg. 1587
FREEDOM PARTNERS; *U.S. Private*, pg. 1604
FUNDACION BANCARIA CAIXA D'ESTALVIS I PENSIONS DE BARCELONA, LA CAIXA; *Int'l*, pg. 2845
GEISINGER HEALTH SYSTEM; *U.S. Private*, pg. 1656
GEORGIA ELECTRIC MEMBERSHIP CORPORATION; *U.S. Private*, pg. 1684
GEORGIA FARM BUREAU FEDERATION; *U.S. Private*, pg. 1684
GLOBAL BUSINESS TRAVEL ASSOCIATION; *U.S. Private*, pg. 1712
GO2 COMMUNICATIONS, INC.—See Gemspring Capital Management, LLC; *U.S. Private*, pg. 1659
THE GOOD SAMARITAN HEALTH SERVICES FOUNDATION OF LEBANON, PENNSYLVANIA—See WellSpan Health; *U.S. Private*, pg. 4477
GOVERNMENT EMPLOYEES HEALTH ASSOCIATION, INC.; *U.S. Private*, pg. 1746
GOWLING WLG INTERNATIONAL LIMITED; *Int'l*, pg. 3045
GREATER NEW YORK HOSPITAL ASSOCIATION; *U.S. Private*, pg. 1770
GREEK NATIONAL TOURIST ORGANIZATION; *Int'l*, pg. 3069
GRINDROD LIMITED; *Int'l*, pg. 3086
HARTFORD HEALTHCARE CORPORATION; *U.S. Private*, pg. 1873
THE HEALTH CARE AUTHORITY OF THE CITY OF ANNISTON; *U.S. Private*, pg. 4043
HEIWA KISEN KAISHA, LTD.—See Idemitsu Kosan Co., Ltd.; *Int'l*, pg. 3590
HIGHMARK HEALTH; *U.S. Private*, pg. 1940
HLB MANN JUDD AUSTRALASIAN ASSOCIATION; *Int'l*, pg. 3430
ILLINOIS LIFE & HEALTH INSURANCE GUARANTY ASSOCIATION; *U.S. Private*, pg. 2042
ILLINOIS TECHNOLOGY ASSOCIATION—See Chicagoland Entrepreneurial Center; *U.S. Private*, pg. 879
INDIANA FARM BUREAU INC.; *U.S. Private*, pg. 2062
THE INSTITUTE OF FINANCIAL OPERATIONS; *U.S. Private*, pg. 4056
INSTITUTE OF REAL ESTATE MANAGEMENT—See National Association of Realtors; *U.S. Private*, pg. 2847
INTER-INDUSTRY CONFERENCE ON AUTO COLLISION REPAIR; *U.S. Private*, pg. 2107
INTERNATIONAL ACCOUNTS PAYABLE PROFESSIONALS—See The Institute of Financial Operations; *U.S. Private*, pg. 4056
INTERNATIONAL ASSOCIATION OF AMUSEMENT PARKS & ATTRACTIONS; *U.S. Private*, pg. 2114
INTERNATIONAL AUTOMOTIVE TECHNICIANS' NETWORK, INC.—See Vista Equity Partners, LLC; *U.S. Private*, pg. 4400
INTERNATIONAL FERTILIZER DEVELOPMENT CENTER; *U.S. Private*, pg. 2116
IOWA FARM BUREAU FEDERATION; *U.S. Private*, pg. 2134
IPC; *U.S. Private*, pg. 2136
J.C. LEWIS PRIMARY HEALTH CARE CENTER INC.; *U.S. Private*, pg. 2160

JONES-ONSLOW ELECTRIC MEMBERSHIP CORPORATION; *U.S. Private*, pg. 2234
KANSAS LIVESTOCK ASSOCIATION; *U.S. Private*, pg. 2261
LAWRENCE COUNTY ECONOMIC DEVELOPMENT CORPORATION; *U.S. Private*, pg. 2401
LIVERPOOL VICTORIA FRIENDLY SOCIETY LIMITED—See Allianz SE; *Int'l*, pg. 353
LOS ANGELES FIREMEN'S RELIEF ASSOCIATION; *U.S. Private*, pg. 2496
LOUISIANA THOROUGHBRED BREEDERS ASSOCIATION; *U.S. Private*, pg. 2500
MAGNET INC.; *U.S. Private*, pg. 2547
MARITIME EXCHANGE FOR THE DELAWARE RIVER AND BAY; *U.S. Private*, pg. 2576
MASSACHUSETTS HOSPITAL ASSOCIATION, INC.; *U.S. Private*, pg. 2604
MATERIAL HANDLING INDUSTRY; *U.S. Private*, pg. 2609
MEJERIFORENINGEN—See Arla Foods amba; *Int'l*, pg. 573
MERCY HEALTH—See Bon Secours Mercy Health, Inc.; *U.S. Private*, pg. 612
METALS SERVICE CENTER INSTITUTE; *U.S. Private*, pg. 2682
METHODIST HEALTHCARE MINISTRIES OF SOUTH TEXAS, INC.; *U.S. Private*, pg. 2683
METROPOLITAN OPERA ASSOCIATION, INC.; *U.S. Private*, pg. 2689
MISSISSIPPI FARM BUREAU CASUALTY INSURANCE COMPANY—See Southern Farm Bureau Casualty Insurance Company; *U.S. Private*, pg. 3731
MISSISSIPPI FARM BUREAU INSURANCE COMPANIES; *U.S. Private*, pg. 2748
MONROE COUNTY BAR ASSOCIATION; *U.S. Private*, pg. 2773
MONTEFIORE MEDICAL CENTER; *U.S. Private*, pg. 2776
MOTION PICTURE ASSOCIATION OF AMERICA, INC.; *U.S. Private*, pg. 2795
MOTOR & EQUIPMENT MANUFACTURERS ASSOCIATION; *U.S. Private*, pg. 2796
MOUNT VERNON NEIGHBORHOOD HEALTH CENTER; *U.S. Private*, pg. 2798
MRA-THE MANAGEMENT ASSOCIATION, INC.; *U.S. Private*, pg. 2805
NATIONAL APARTMENT ASSOCIATION; *U.S. Private*, pg. 2844
THE NATIONAL ASSOCIATION FOR FEMALE EXECUTIVES—See Bonnier AB; *Int'l*, pg. 1109
NATIONAL ASSOCIATION FOR STOCK CAR AUTO RACING, INC.; *U.S. Private*, pg. 2845
NATIONAL ASSOCIATION OF CHARTER SCHOOL AUTHORIZERS; *U.S. Private*, pg. 2846
NATIONAL ASSOCIATION OF COLLEGE STORES, INC.; *U.S. Private*, pg. 2846
NATIONAL ASSOCIATION OF COMMUNITY HEALTH CENTERS; *U.S. Private*, pg. 2846
NATIONAL ASSOCIATION OF HOME BUILDERS; *U.S. Private*, pg. 2847
NATIONAL ASSOCIATION OF REALTORS; *U.S. Private*, pg. 2847
NATIONAL BEER WHOLESALERS ASSOCIATION; *U.S. Private*, pg. 2848
NATIONAL COMMITTEE FOR QUALITY ASSURANCE; *U.S. Private*, pg. 2851
NATIONAL COOPERATIVE BUSINESS ASSOCIATION CLUSA INTERNATIONAL; *U.S. Private*, pg. 2851
NATIONAL COURT APPOINTED SPECIAL ADVOCATE ASSOCIATION; *U.S. Private*, pg. 2852
NATIONAL DEFENSE INDUSTRIAL ASSOCIATION; *U.S. Private*, pg. 2852
NATIONAL ELECTRICAL MANUFACTURERS ASSOCIATION; *U.S. Private*, pg. 2853
NATIONAL FEDERATION OF INDEPENDENT BUSINESS; *U.S. Private*, pg. 2853
NATIONAL FOOTBALL LEAGUE PLAYERS ASSOCIATION; *U.S. Private*, pg. 2854
NATIONAL FOUNDATION FOR CREDIT COUNSELING; *U.S. Private*, pg. 2854
NATIONAL MUSIC PUBLISHERS' ASSOCIATION; *U.S. Private*, pg. 2859
NATIONAL PORK BOARD; *U.S. Private*, pg. 2860
NATIONAL RESTAURANT ASSOCIATION; *U.S. Private*, pg. 2862
NEW JERSEY LIFE & HEALTH INSURANCE GUARANTY ASSOCIATION; *U.S. Private*, pg. 2897
NEWSPAPER ASSOCIATION OF AMERICA; *U.S. Private*, pg. 2917
NEW YORK SHIPPING ASSOCIATION, INC.; *U.S. Private*, pg. 2912
NORTHSHORE UNIVERSITY HEALTHSYSTEM; *U.S. Private*, pg. 2957
NUTRIENTS FOR LIFE FOUNDATION; *U.S. Private*, pg. 2974
OCHSNER SYSTEM PROTECTION COMPANY; *U.S. Private*, pg. 2992
ONE PICA, INC; *U.S. Private*, pg. 3020
THE OPTICAL SOCIETY OF AMERICA, INC.; *U.S. Private*, pg. 4088
PACKAGING MACHINERY MANUFACTURERS INSTI-

813910 — BUSINESS ASSOCIATIO...

TUTE, INC.; *U.S. Private*, pg. 3072
PENN STATE HEALTH; *U.S. Private*, pg. 3134
PENNSYLVANIA PROFESSIONAL LIABILITY JOINT UNDERWRITING ASSOCIATION; *U.S. Private*, pg. 3137
PENNSYLVANIA PROPERTY AND CASUALTY INSURANCE GUARANTY ASSOCIATION; *U.S. Private*, pg. 3137
PEOPLEFORBIKES COALITION LTD; *U.S. Private*, pg. 3141
PETROLEUM EQUIPMENT INSTITUTE; *U.S. Private*, pg. 3162
PLAINS COTTON COOPERATIVE ASSOCIATION; *U.S. Private*, pg. 3195
PORTLAND CEMENT ASSOCIATION; *U.S. Private*, pg. 3232
PREFERRED HOTELS GROUP; *U.S. Private*, pg. 3248
PROFESSIONAL RODEO COWBOYS ASSOCIATION; *U.S. Private*, pg. 3276
PROMAXBDA; *U.S. Private*, pg. 3282
PROPANE EDUCATION & RESEARCH COUNCIL, INC.; *U.S. Private*, pg. 3284
PROVIDENCE HEALTH & SERVICES—See Providence St. Joseph Health; *U.S. Private*, pg. 3294
PROVIDENCE ST. JOSEPH HEALTH; *U.S. Private*, pg. 3294
RISKPRONET INTERNATIONAL INC.; *U.S. Private*, pg. 3441
SAINT FRANCIS HEALTH SYSTEM, INC.; *U.S. Private*, pg. 3529
SANFORD HEALTH; *U.S. Private*, pg. 3545
SAN FRANCISCO MARKET CORPORATION; *U.S. Private*, pg. 3540
SARASOTA COUNTY PUBLIC HOSPITAL DISTRICT; *U.S. Private*, pg. 3549
SCRIPPS HEALTH; *U.S. Private*, pg. 3580
SERC RELIABILITY CORPORATION; *U.S. Private*, pg. 3613
SERVICE CORPS OF RETIRED EXECUTIVES ASSOCIATION; *U.S. Private*, pg. 3615
SINOTRANS SHIPPING LIMITED—See China Merchants Group Limited; *Int'l*, pg. 1523
SISTERS OF MERCY HEALTH SYSTEM; *U.S. Private*, pg. 3676
SOUTH CENTRAL INDIANA RURAL ELECTRIC MEMBERSHIP CORPORATION; *U.S. Private*, pg. 3721
SOUTHERN ASSOCIATION OF COLLEGES & SCHOOLS COMMISSION ON COLLEGES; *U.S. Private*, pg. 3729
SOUTH IOWA MUNICIPAL ELECTRIC COOPERATIVE ASSOCIATION; *U.S. Private*, pg. 3722
SPECIALTY FOOD ASSOCIATION, INC.; *U.S. Private*, pg. 3749
ST. JOSEPH HEALTH SYSTEM—See Providence St. Joseph Health; *U.S. Private*, pg. 3295
SUTTER HEALTH; *U.S. Private*, pg. 3887
SYNTHETIC ORGANIC CHEMICAL MANUFACTURERS ASSOCIATION; *U.S. Private*, pg. 3905
TAYLOR ELECTRIC COOPERATIVE—See Touchstone Energy Cooperative, Inc.; *U.S. Private*, pg. 4192
TELECOMMUNICATIONS INDUSTRY ASSOCIATION; *U.S. Private*, pg. 3960
TENNESSEE HOSPITAL ASSOCIATION; *U.S. Private*, pg. 3968
TEXAS BANKERS ASSOCIATION; *U.S. Private*, pg. 3974
THUNDERBIRD HEALTH CENTER; *U.S. Private*, pg. 4166
TOBACCO MERCHANTS ASSOCIATION OF THE UNITED STATES, INC.; *U.S. Private*, pg. 4180
TODD WADENA ELECTRIC COOPERATIVE; *U.S. Private*, pg. 4181
TONETSU KOSAN CO., LTD.—See Dowa Holdings Co., Ltd.; *Int'l*, pg. 2184
TOWER HEALTH; *U.S. Private*, pg. 4193
TRINITY HEALTH CORPORATION; *U.S. Private*, pg. 4233
UNITED EGG PRODUCERS; *U.S. Private*, pg. 4291
UNITED STATES MEAT EXPORT FEDERATION INC.; *U.S. Private*, pg. 4299
UNITED STATES TELECOM ASSOCIATION; *U.S. Private*, pg. 4300
UNITED TRANSPORTATION UNION INSURANCE ASSOCIATION; *U.S. Private*, pg. 4301
USA POULTRY & EGG EXPORT COUNCIL; *U.S. Private*, pg. 4321
U.S. SOYBEAN EXPORT COUNCI; *U.S. Private*, pg. 4272
VELOSI EUROPE LIMITED—See I Squared Capital Advisors (US) LLC; *U.S. Private*, pg. 2024
VERMONT SKI AREAS ASSOCIATION, INC.; *U.S. Private*, pg. 4367
VISION COUNCIL OF AMERICA; *U.S. Private*, pg. 4390
WABASH VALLEY POWER ASSOCIATION INC.—See Touchstone Energy Cooperative, Inc.; *U.S. Private*, pg. 4192
WASHINGTON COUNTY CHAMBER OF COMMERCE; *U.S. Private*, pg. 4447
WASHINGTON STATE HOSPITAL ASSOCIATION; *U.S. Private*, pg. 4449
WELLSPAN HEALTH; *U.S. Private*, pg. 4476
WESTERN ELECTRICITY COORDINATING COUNCIL; *U.S. Private*, pg. 4492
WESTERN NEW YORK PUBLIC BROADCASTING ASSOCIATION; *U.S. Private*, pg. 4494
WESTERN UNITED STATES AGRICULTURAL TRADE ASSOCIATION; *U.S. Private*, pg. 4498
WHARTON COUNTY ELECTRIC COOPERATIVE, INC.; *U.S. Private*, pg. 4504
WILKINSON COUNTY INDUSTRIAL DEVELOPMENT AUTHORITY; *U.S. Private*, pg. 4521
WINDSOR SHADE TOBACCO COMPANY, INC.; *U.S. Private*, pg. 4539
WINE & SPIRITS WHOLESALERS OF AMERICA, INC.; *U.S. Private*, pg. 4540
WORKERS' COMPENSATION RATING & INSPECTION BUREAU OF MASSACHUSETTS; *U.S. Private*, pg. 4563
WORLDWIDE ERC; *U.S. Private*, pg. 4569
YAZOO VALLEY ELECTRIC POWER ASSOCIATION; *U.S. Private*, pg. 4587

813920 — PROFESSIONAL ORGANIZATIONS

ACADEMY OF GENERAL DENTISTRY; *U.S. Private*, pg. 46
ADVOCATE HEALTH CARE NETWORK; *U.S. Private*, pg. 110
AFTERMARKET AUTO PARTS ALLIANCE, INC.; *U.S. Private*, pg. 124
ALLIANCE FOR BANGLADESH WORKER SAFETY; *U.S. Private*, pg. 182
AMERICAN ACADEMY OF PHYSICAL MEDICINE & REHABILITATION; *U.S. Private*, pg. 221
AMERICAN ARMED FORCES MUTUAL AID ASSOCIATION; *U.S. Private*, pg. 222
AMERICAN ASSOCIATION FOR CLINICAL CHEMISTRY, INC.; *U.S. Private*, pg. 222
AMERICAN ASSOCIATION OF AIRPORT EXECUTIVES; *U.S. Private*, pg. 223
AMERICAN ASSOCIATION OF NURSE ANESTHETISTS; *U.S. Private*, pg. 223
AMERICAN ASSOCIATION OF NURSE PRACTITIONERS; *U.S. Private*, pg. 223
AMERICAN ASSOCIATION OF ORAL AND MAXILLOFACIAL SURGEONS; *U.S. Private*, pg. 223
AMERICAN ASSOCIATION OF ORTHOPAEDIC SURGEONS; *U.S. Private*, pg. 223
THE AMERICAN BOARD OF ANESTHESIOLOGY, INC.; *U.S. Private*, pg. 3986
AMERICAN BOARD OF MEDICAL SPECIALTIES; *U.S. Private*, pg. 224
AMERICAN COLLEGE OF RHEUMATOLOGY, INC.; *U.S. Private*, pg. 227
AMERICAN HEALTH INFORMATION MANAGEMENT ASSOCIATION; *U.S. Private*, pg. 235
AMERICAN HEALTH LAWYERS ASSOCIATION INC.; *U.S. Private*, pg. 235
AMERICAN OCCUPATIONAL THERAPY ASSOCIATION, INC.; *U.S. Private*, pg. 242
AMERICAN OPTOMETRIC ASSOCIATION; *U.S. Private*, pg. 242
AMERICAN PSYCHIATRIC ASSOCIATION; *U.S. Private*, pg. 244
AMERICAN SOCIETY FOR BIOCHEMISTRY AND MOLECULAR BIOLOGY; *U.S. Private*, pg. 253
AMERICAN SOCIETY FOR CLINICAL PATHOLOGY; *U.S. Private*, pg. 253
AMERICAN SOCIETY FOR MICROBIOLOGY; *U.S. Private*, pg. 253
AMERICAN SOCIETY OF ANESTHESIOLOGISTS; *U.S. Private*, pg. 254
AMERICAN SOCIETY OF APPRAISERS; *U.S. Private*, pg. 254
AMERICAN SOCIETY OF PENSION PROFESSIONALS & ACTUARIES, INC.; *U.S. Private*, pg. 254
AMERICAN SPEECH-LANGUAGE-HEARING ASSOCIATION; *U.S. Private*, pg. 255
AO NORTH AMERICA; *U.S. Private*, pg. 289
APPALACHIAN EMERGENCY PHYSICIANS; *U.S. Private*, pg. 295
ARCADIS RUIWITELIJKE OHTWILLELING BV—See ARCADIS N.V.; *Int'l*, pg. 541
ARTEMIS GLOBAL LIFE SCIENCES LIMITED; *Int'l*, pg. 581
ARTHROSCOPY ASSOCIATION OF NORTH AMERICA; *U.S. Private*, pg. 341
ASCENSION HEALTH ALLIANCE; *U.S. Private*, pg. 346
ASSOCIATION FOR COMPUTING MACHINERY; *U.S. Private*, pg. 358
ASSOCIATION FOR MOLECULAR PATHOLOGY; *U.S. Private*, pg. 358
ASSOCIATION FOR TALENT DEVELOPMENT; *U.S. Private*, pg. 358
ASSOCIATION OF THE UNITED STATES ARMY; *U.S. Private*, pg. 359
ATP TOUR, INC.; *U.S. Private*, pg. 381
BAKER TILLY INTERNATIONAL LIMITED; *Int'l*, pg. 805
BAPTIST MEMORIAL HEALTH CARE CORPORATION—See Anderson Regional Health System; *U.S. Private*, pg. 277
BEACON HEALTH SYSTEM, INC.; *U.S. Private*, pg. 504
BIG TEN ACADEMIC ALLIANCE; *U.S. Private*, pg. 554
BROCKTON VISITING NURSE ASSOCIATION; *U.S. Private*, pg. 660
CABRINI HEALTH LIMITED; *Int'l*, pg. 1246
CALIFORNIA DENTAL ASSOCIATION; *U.S. Private*, pg. 719
CALIFORNIA TEACHING FELLOWS FOUNDATION; *U.S. Private*, pg. 721
CAPITAL ASSOCIATED INDUSTRIES, INC.—See Catapult Employers Association, Inc.; *U.S. Private*, pg. 787
CAPITAL INVESTMENTS & VENTURES CORP.; *U.S. Private*, pg. 741
CARE NEW ENGLAND HEALTH SYSTEM, INC.; *U.S. Private*, pg. 751
CATHOLIC HEALTH SYSTEM, INC.; *U.S. Private*, pg. 791
CATHOLIC MEDICAL PARTNERS - ACCOUNTABLE CARE IPA, INC.—See Catholic Health System, Inc.; *U.S. Private*, pg. 791
CATHOLIC MEDICAL PARTNERS - ACCOUNTABLE CARE IPA, INC.—See Mount St. Mary's Hospital of Niagara Falls; *U.S. Private*, pg. 2798
CAZADOR, LLC—See Nana Regional Corporation, Inc.; *U.S. Private*, pg. 2832
CCA GLOBAL PARTNERS, INC. - MANCHESTER—See CCA Global Partners, Inc.; *U.S. Private*, pg. 799
CHIEF EXECUTIVES ORGANIZATION; *U.S. Private*, pg. 881
CHILD DIMENSIONS INSURANCE COMPANY; *U.S. Private*, pg. 882
CITY EMPLOYEES CLUB OF LOS ANGELES; *U.S. Private*, pg. 905
CLEVELAND FOUNDATION; *U.S. Private*, pg. 941
COLLEGE OF AMERICAN PATHOLOGISTS; *U.S. Private*, pg. 968
COMMUNITY FOUNDATION FOR GREATER ATLANTA INC; *U.S. Private*, pg. 992
COMMUNITY PHYSICIANS NETWORK; *U.S. Private*, pg. 996
COMMUNITY SERVICE BUILDING CORPORATION; *U.S. Private*, pg. 997
CONSORTIUM FOR OLDER ADULT WELLNESS; *U.S. Private*, pg. 1023
COOPERATIVE OF AMERICAN PHYSICIANS; *U.S. Private*, pg. 1042
THE COPERNICUS GROUP, INC.—See Arsenal Capital Management LP; *U.S. Private*, pg. 339
CORENET GLOBAL, INC.; *U.S. Private*, pg. 1049
COSMETIC EXECUTIVE WOMEN, INC.; *U.S. Private*, pg. 1062
CPAMERICA, INC.; *U.S. Private*, pg. 1080
CPG SIGNATURE PTE. LTD.—See Downer EDI Limited; *Int'l*, pg. 2185
CREDIT UNION EXECUTIVES SOCIETY, INC.; *U.S. Private*, pg. 1091
CROWE HORWATH INTERNATIONAL; *U.S. Private*, pg. 1109
DELOITTE TOUCHE TOHMATSU LIMITED; *Int'l*, pg. 2014
DRI-THE VOICE OF THE DEFENSE BAR; *U.S. Private*, pg. 1277
DRUG INFORMATION ASSOCIATION; *U.S. Private*, pg. 1279
DUBAI TOURISM & COMMERCE MARKETING; *Int'l*, pg. 2220
ELIA GRID INTERNATIONAL PTE. LTD.—See Elia Group SA; *Int'l*, pg. 2360
ELITE CME INC; *U.S. Private*, pg. 1360
ELKHART GENERAL HOSPITAL, INC.—See Beacon Health System, Inc.; *U.S. Private*, pg. 504
ELLEVATE FINANCIAL LLC—See Ellevate Financial, Inc.; *U.S. Private*, pg. 1363
EMBASSY DENTAL PROFESSIONALS, P.C.—See CPF Dental, LLC; *U.S. Private*, pg. 1080
ENLOE MEDICAL CENTER; *U.S. Private*, pg. 1401
ERNST & YOUNG GLOBAL LIMITED; *Int'l*, pg. 2494
FEDERAL FLOOD CERTIFICATION LLC—See MetLife, Inc.; *U.S. Public*, pg. 1430
GENERAL DYNAMICS CORP. - CONVAIR DIVISION—See General Dynamics Corporation; *U.S. Public*, pg. 914
GOLF COURSE SUPERINTENDENTS ASSOCIATION OF AMERICA; *U.S. Private*, pg. 1736
GRANT THORNTON INTERNATIONAL LIMITED; *Int'l*, pg. 3059
GREAT CIRCLE; *U.S. Private*, pg. 1762
GREENHOUSE SCHOLARS; *U.S. Private*, pg. 1778
GROUPE TERA SA; *Int'l*, pg. 3111
HACKENSACK MERIDIAN HEALTH, INC.; *U.S. Private*, pg. 1838
HARBOR-UCLA MEDICAL FOUNDATION, INC.; *U.S. Private*, pg. 1859
HEALTHCARE ASSOCIATION OF NEW YORK STATE; *U.S. Private*, pg. 1895
HEALTHCARE INFORMATION & MANAGEMENT SYSTEMS SOCIETY; *U.S. Private*, pg. 1895
HEALTHCARE USA OF MISSOURI, LLC—See CVS Health Corporation; *U.S. Public*, pg. 615
HEALTHINSIGHT MANAGEMENT CORPORATION; *U.S. Private*, pg. 1896
HEALTHINSIGHT NEW MEXICO—See HealthInsight Man-

N.A.I.C.S. INDEX

813990 — OTHER SIMILAR ORGAN...

agement Corporation; *U.S. Private,* pg. 1896
HEALTHINSIGHT OF NEVADA—See HealthInsight Management Corporation; *U.S. Private,* pg. 1896
HEALTHINSIGHT OREGON—See HealthInsight Management Corporation; *U.S. Private,* pg. 1896
HEALTHINSIGHT UTAH—See HealthInsight Management Corporation; *U.S. Private,* pg. 1896
HEALTHSOURCE GLOBAL STAFFING, INC.—See AMN Healthcare Services, Inc.; *U.S. Public,* pg. 125
HENDRICK HEALTH SYSTEM; *U.S. Private,* pg. 1914
HENRY FORD HEALTH SYSTEM; *U.S. Private,* pg. 1918
THE HUNGARY INITIATIVES FOUNDATION; *U.S. Private,* pg. 4054
INDEPENDENT COMMUNITY BANKERS OF AMERICA; *U.S. Private,* pg. 2058
INDEPENDENT ELECTRICAL CONTRACTORS, INC.; *U.S. Private,* pg. 2059
INDIANA STATE TEACHERS ASSOCIATION; *U.S. Private,* pg. 2063
INFORMATION SYSTEMS AUDIT & CONTROL ASSOCIATION, INC.; *U.S. Private,* pg. 2073
INSTITUTE OF ELECTRICAL AND ELECTRONICS ENGINEERS, INC.; *U.S. Private,* pg. 2093
INTERNATIONAL ASSOCIATION OF CHIEFS OF POLICE; *U.S. Private,* pg. 2114
THE INTERNATIONAL ASSOCIATION OF FIRE CHIEFS; *U.S. Private,* pg. 4057
INTERNATIONAL CENTER FOR JOURNALISTS; *U.S. Private,* pg. 2115
INTERNATIONAL CENTER FOR NOT-FOR-PROFIT LAW; *U.S. Private,* pg. 2115
INTERNATIONAL SOCIETY FOR PHARMACEUTICAL ENGINEERING INC.; *U.S. Private,* pg. 2120
INTERNATIONAL SOCIETY FOR THE STUDY OF XENOBIOTICS; *U.S. Private,* pg. 2120
JACOBY & MEYERS, P.C.; *U.S. Private,* pg. 2180
THE JOCKEY CLUB; *U.S. Private,* pg. 4059
KAISER PERMANENTE; *U.S. Private,* pg. 2255
LOGISTICS MANAGEMENT INSTITUTE; *U.S. Private,* pg. 2482
LOYOLA UNIVERSITY HEALTH SYSTEM—See Trinity Health Corporation; *U.S. Private,* pg. 4233
LUTHERAN CHURCH MISSOURI SYNOD; *U.S. Private,* pg. 2517
MANAGED HEALTH NETWORK—See Centene Corporation; *U.S. Public,* pg. 470
MARIN HEALTHCARE DISTRICT; *U.S. Private,* pg. 2574
MASSACHUSETTS MEDICAL SOCIETY; *U.S. Private,* pg. 2604
MATERIALS RESEARCH SOCIETY; *U.S. Private,* pg. 2610
THE MAYOR'S FUND TO ADVANCE NEW YORK CITY; *U.S. Private,* pg. 4076
MCLEOD HEALTH; *U.S. Private,* pg. 2641
MEDICAL EMERGENCY PROFESSIONALS; *U.S. Private,* pg. 2655
MEMORIAL HEALTH SERVICES; *U.S. Private,* pg. 2663
MEMORIAL HOSPITAL OF SOUTH BEND, INC.—See Beacon Health System, Inc.; *U.S. Private,* pg. 504
MHM SERVICES, INC.—See Centene Corporation; *U.S. Public,* pg. 469
MHZ NETWORKS; *U.S. Private,* pg. 2695
MIDWEST AORTIC & VASCULAR INSTITUTE, P.C.; *U.S. Private,* pg. 2719
MILLION DOLLAR ROUND TABLE THE PREMIER ASSOCIATION OF FINANCIAL PROFESSIONALS; *U.S. Private,* pg. 2737
MODERN LANGUAGE ASSOCIATION; *U.S. Private,* pg. 2761
MOTORCYCLE SAFETY FOUNDATION, INC.; *U.S. Private,* pg. 2797
MR/DD BOARD, INC.; *U.S. Private,* pg. 2805
NAFSA; *U.S. Private,* pg. 2830
NATIONAL ASSOCIATION FOR COLLEGE ADMISSION COUNSELING; *U.S. Private,* pg. 2845
NATIONAL ASSOCIATION OF INDEPENDENT FEE APPRAISERS, INC.—See American Society of Appraisers; *U.S. Private,* pg. 254
NATIONAL BOARD FOR PROFESSIONAL TEACHING STANDARDS; *U.S. Private,* pg. 2849
NATIONAL COUNCIL OF TEACHERS OF MATHEMATICS; *U.S. Private,* pg. 2852
NATIONAL FIRE PROTECTION ASSOCIATION; *U.S. Private,* pg. 2853
THE NATIONAL GUARD ASSOCIATION OF THE UNITED STATES; *U.S. Private,* pg. 4082
NATIONAL QUALITY FORUM; *U.S. Private,* pg. 2861
NATIONAL SOCIETY OF BLACK ENGINEERS; *U.S. Private,* pg. 2863
NATIONAL URBAN LEAGUE; *U.S. Private,* pg. 2864
NBC TELEVISION AFFILIATES ASSOCIATION; *U.S. Private,* pg. 2874
NEBRASKA METHODIST HEALTH SYSTEM INC.; *U.S. Private,* pg. 2878
THE NEMOURS FOUNDATION; *U.S. Private,* pg. 4082
NEWFOUND AREA NURSING ASSOCIATION—See Lakes Region Visiting Nurse Association; *U.S. Private,* pg. 2376
NEW YORK COUNTY HEALTH SERVICES REVIEW ORGANIZATION; *U.S. Private,* pg. 2909
NEW YORK STATE NURSES ASSOCIATION; *U.S. Private,* pg. 2912
NISSCO RESTAURANT DEALER GROUP, INC.; *U.S. Private,* pg. 2929
NORTH SCOTTSDALE INDEPENDENT—See Independent Newspapers, Inc.; *U.S. Private,* pg. 2060
NORTHWELL HEALTH, INC.; *U.S. Private,* pg. 2958
OLIVER STREET DERMATOLOGY HOLDINGS LLC—See ABRY Partners, LLC; *U.S. Private,* pg. 42
PADI AMERICAS—See Capital Investments & Ventures Corp.; *U.S. Private,* pg. 741
THE PERMANENTE FEDERATION, LLC—See Kaiser Permanente; *U.S. Private,* pg. 2256
PHYSICIAN PARTNERS OF AMERICA, LLC; *U.S. Private,* pg. 3175
PHYSICIANS ENDOSCOPY, LLC—See Kelso & Company, L.P.; *U.S. Private,* pg. 2279
PRAGER METIS INTERNATIONAL LLC; *U.S. Private,* pg. 3241
PRGX BRASIL LTDA.—See PRGX Global, Inc.; *U.S. Private,* pg. 3257
PROFESSIONAL ASSOCIATION FOR CHILDHOOD EDUCATION; *U.S. Private,* pg. 3274
PROFESSIONAL PHOTOGRAPHERS OF AMERICA; *U.S. Private,* pg. 3276
THE PROFESSIONAL PUTTERS ASSOCIATION—See Putt-Putt, LLC; *U.S. Private,* pg. 3308
PROMOTIONAL PRODUCTS ASSOCIATION INTERNATIONAL; *U.S. Private,* pg. 3283
PUBLIC COMPANY ACCOUNTING OVERSIGHT BOARD; *U.S. Private,* pg. 3298
QUALIS HEALTH—See HealthInsight Management Corporation; *U.S. Private,* pg. 1896
RETAIL INDUSTRY LEADERS ASSOCIATION; *U.S. Private,* pg. 3411
SCORE ASSOCIATION; *U.S. Private,* pg. 3575
SESAC PERFORMING RIGHTS, INC.—See Blackstone Inc.; *U.S. Public,* pg. 357
SOCIETY FOR LEUKOCYTE BIOLOGY; *U.S. Private,* pg. 3703
SOCIETY FOR NEUROSCIENCE; *U.S. Private,* pg. 3703
SOCIETY OF BEHAVIORAL MEDICINE; *U.S. Private,* pg. 3704
SOCIETY OF MANUFACTURING ENGINEERS; *U.S. Private,* pg. 3704
SOCIETY OF PHOTO-OPTICAL INSTRUMENTATION ENGINEERS; *U.S. Private,* pg. 3704
SOUTH EAST AREA HEALTH EDUCATION CENTER; *U.S. Private,* pg. 3722
SOUTHERN MOTOR CARRIERS ASSOCIATION, INC.; *U.S. Private,* pg. 3733
SPARROW HEALTH SYSTEM—See University of Michigan; *U.S. Private,* pg. 4309
SPAULDING REHABILITATION NETWORK—See Partners HealthCare System, Inc.; *U.S. Private,* pg. 3101
ST. LUKE'S HEALTH NETWORK, INC.; *U.S. Private,* pg. 3773
ST. PETER'S HEALTH PARTNERS; *U.S. Private,* pg. 3773
SUTTER MEDICAL CENTER FOUNDATION—See Sutter Health; *U.S. Private,* pg. 3887
THEATRE COMMUNICATIONS GROUP, INC.; *U.S. Private,* pg. 4140
TMC HEALTHCARE; *U.S. Private,* pg. 4179
UNITED ELECTRICAL, RADIO & MACHINE WORKERS OF AMERICA; *U.S. Private,* pg. 4291
UNITED SPINAL ASSOCIATION; *U.S. Private,* pg. 4298
UNITED STATES BARTENDER'S GUILD; *U.S. Private,* pg. 4298
UNITE HERE; *U.S. Private,* pg. 4287
UNIVERSITY OF WISCONSIN MEDICAL FOUNDATION; *U.S. Private,* pg. 4310
UPMC PINNACLE—See University of Pittsburgh Medical Center; *U.S. Private,* pg. 4310
US AIRLINE PILOTS ASSOCIATION; *U.S. Private,* pg. 4317
VISITING NURSE CORPORATION OF COLORADO, INC.; *U.S. Private,* pg. 4393
VISITING NURSE & HOSPICE OF VERMONT AND NEW HAMPSHIRE; *U.S. Private,* pg. 4392
VISUAL EFFECTS SOCIETY; *U.S. Private,* pg. 4404
WABASH MEMORIAL HOSPITAL ASSOCIATION; *U.S. Private,* pg. 4423
WAIANAE DISTRICT COMPREHENSIVE HEALTH & HOSPITAL BOARD, INCORPORATED; *U.S. Private,* pg. 4426
WAREHOUSING EDUCATION AND RESEARCH COUNCIL—See Material Handling Industry; *U.S. Private,* pg. 2609
WESTERN INSTITUTIONAL REVIEW BOARD, INC.—See Arsenal Capital Management LP; *U.S. Private,* pg. 339
WILLIAM BEAUMONT HOSPITAL—See Beaumont Health; *U.S. Private,* pg. 508

813930 — LABOR UNIONS AND SIMILAR LABOR ORGANIZATIONS

ARCELORMITTAL STEELTON LLC—See Cleveland-Cliffs, Inc.; *U.S. Public,* pg. 514
ASKLEPIOS KLINIKEN VERWALTUNGS - GESELLSCHAFT MBH - LABOR & COLLECTIVE BARGAINING LAW DIVISION—See Asklepios Kliniken GmbH & Co. KGaA; *Int'l,* pg. 622
THE BAKERY, CONFECTIONERY, TOBACCO WORKERS AND GRAIN MILLERS INTERNATIONAL UNION; *U.S. Private,* pg. 3991
CARBORUNDUM VENTURES INC.—See Compagnie de Saint-Gobain SA; *Int'l,* pg. 1729
CHANGE TO WIN; *U.S. Private,* pg. 848
COMMUNICATIONS WORKERS OF AMERICA; *U.S. Private,* pg. 989
CPWR-THE CENTER FOR CONSTRUCTION RESEARCH AND TRAINING; *U.S. Private,* pg. 1081
EDENRED (INDIA) PVT LTD—See Edenred S.A.; *Int'l,* pg. 2307
EDENRED PORTUGAL LDA—See Edenred S.A.; *Int'l,* pg. 2308
HAWAII CARPENTERS VACATION & HOLIDAY FUND; *U.S. Private,* pg. 1881
IN2VATE, LLC.—See iLearningEngines, Inc.; *U.S. Public,* pg. 1101
INTERNATIONAL ASSOCIATION OF BRIDGE, STRUCTURAL, ORNAMENTAL, AND REINFORCING IRON WORKERS; *U.S. Private,* pg. 2114
INTERNATIONAL BROTHERHOOD OF ELECTRICAL WORKERS; *U.S. Private,* pg. 2114
INTERNATIONAL BROTHERHOOD OF TEAMSTERS; *U.S. Private,* pg. 2114
IUPAT DISTRICT COUNCIL 21; *U.S. Private,* pg. 2150
IUPAT DISTRICT COUNCIL 9; *U.S. Private,* pg. 2150
JOBSOHIO BEVERAGE SYSTEM; *U.S. Private,* pg. 2217
THE LABORERS PACIFIC SOUTHWEST REGIONAL ORGANIZING COALITION; *U.S. Private,* pg. 4067
LAS VEGAS POLICE PROTECTIVE ASSOCIATION CIVILIAN EMPLOYEES, INC.; *U.S. Private,* pg. 2394
LC ENTERPRISES LLC; *U.S. Private,* pg. 2403
NATIONAL RIGHT TO WORK COMMITTEE; *U.S. Private,* pg. 2862
NORTH BAY JOBS WITH JUSTICE; *U.S. Private,* pg. 2942
OFFICE & PROFESSIONAL EMPLOYEES INTERNATIONAL UNION; *U.S. Private,* pg. 3001
SERVICE EMPLOYEES INTERNATIONAL UNION; *U.S. Private,* pg. 3615
UNION BENEFITS TRUST; *U.S. Private,* pg. 4284
UNITED STATES STEEL CORP.—See United States Steel Corporation; *U.S. Public,* pg. 2237
WORKERS UNITED; *U.S. Private,* pg. 4563

813940 — POLITICAL ORGANIZATIONS

CONSERVATIVE PARTY; *Int'l,* pg. 1770
TEA PARTY PATRIOTS, INC.; *U.S. Private,* pg. 3944

813990 — OTHER SIMILAR ORGANIZATIONS (EXCEPT BUSINESS, PROFESSIONAL, LABOR, AND POLITICAL ORGANIZATIONS)

AAA CLUB ALLIANCE INC.—See The American Automobile Association, Inc.; *U.S. Private,* pg. 3985
AGTEGRA COOPERATIVE; *U.S. Private,* pg. 130
THE AMERICAN AUTOMOBILE ASSOCIATION, INC.; *U.S. Private,* pg. 3985
AMERICAN FILM INSTITUTE; *U.S. Private,* pg. 234
AMERICAN PUBLIC MEDIA GROUP; *U.S. Private,* pg. 244
ATLANTA SYMPHONY ORCHESTRA; *U.S. Private,* pg. 371
BELLA VISTA VILLAGE PROPERTY OWNERS ASSOCIATION; *U.S. Private,* pg. 519
BIG TEN CONFERENCE; *U.S. Private,* pg. 554
BOSTON ATHLETIC ASSOCIATION; *U.S. Private,* pg. 621
BOSTON BIOMEDICAL ASSOCIATES LLC—See Factory CRO BV; *Int'l,* pg. 2601
CALLICOTTE RANCH HOA, LLC—See BOK Financial Corporation; *U.S. Public,* pg. 367
CAROLINA MOTOR CLUB, INC.; *U.S. Private,* pg. 768
CONNECT; *U.S. Private,* pg. 1014
COSTCO WHOLESALE EMPLOYEE CLUB—See Costco Wholesale Corporation; *U.S. Public,* pg. 586
CRICKET AUSTRALIA; *Int'l,* pg. 1849
DAIWA COSMOS CONSTRUCTION CO., LTD.—See Daiwa House Industry Co., Ltd.; *Int'l,* pg. 1945
THE ENERGY COOPERATIVE, INC.; *U.S. Private,* pg. 4026
ENGINEERS WITHOUT BORDERS-USA, INC.; *U.S. Private,* pg. 1399
FAMILY FEDERATION FOR WORLD PEACE & UNIFICATION; *U.S. Private,* pg. 1469
FEDERATED CO-OPERATIVES LIMITED; *Int'l,* pg. 2630
FEDERATION INTERNATIONALE DE FOOTBALL ASSOCIATION; *Int'l,* pg. 2631
GOLDEN RAIN FOUNDATION; *U.S. Private,* pg. 1732
HOLSTEIN ASSOCIATION USA, INC.; *U.S. Private,* pg. 1968
HOMER ELECTRIC ASSOCIATION, INC.; *U.S. Private,* pg. 1973
INTERNATIONAL PROCESSING CORP—See ReConserve, Inc.; *U.S. Private,* pg. 3371

813990 — OTHER SIMILAR ORGAN...

KANSAS ELECTRIC POWER COOPERATIVE, INC.; *U.S. Private*, pg. 2260
LANDUS COOPERATIVE; *U.S. Private*, pg. 2387
MAJOR LEAGUE BASEBALL; *U.S. Private*, pg. 2555
MEPT 501, INC.; *U.S. Private*, pg. 2667
MOUNTRAIL-WILLIAMS ELECTRIC COOPERATIVE; *U.S. Private*, pg. 2801
NATIONAL ASSOCIATION OF PROFESSIONAL BASEBALL LEAGUES, INC.; *U.S. Private*, pg. 2847
NATIONAL BASKETBALL ASSOCIATION; *U.S. Private*, pg. 2848
NATIONAL BASKETBALL PLAYERS ASSOCIATION; *U.S. Private*, pg. 2848
NATIONAL CUTTING HORSE ASSOCIATION; *U.S. Private*, pg. 2852
NATIONAL FOOTBALL LEAGUE; *U.S. Private*, pg. 2854
NATIONAL GAS & OIL COOPERATIVE—See The Energy Cooperative, Inc.; *U.S. Private*, pg. 4026
NATIONAL HOCKEY LEAGUE; *U.S. Private*, pg. 2856
NBA CHINA—See National Basketball Association; *U.S. Private*, pg. 2848
NEIGHBORHOOD ASSISTANCE CORPORATION OF AMERICA; *U.S. Private*, pg. 2881
NORTHWEST IOWA SYMPHONY ORCHESTRA; *U.S. Private*, pg. 2961
THE OHIO HIGH SCHOOL ATHLETIC ASSOCIATION; *U.S. Private*, pg. 4088
PAC-12 CONFERENCE; *U.S. Private*, pg. 3063
RICHLAND TOWERS - KANSAS CITY, LLC—See American Tower Corporation; *U.S. Public*, pg. 111
SANDPIPER COVE DIV.—See Purcell Co., Inc.; *U.S. Private*, pg. 3304
TAHOE DONNER ASSOCIATION; *U.S. Private*, pg. 3923
TOUCHSTONE ENERGY COOPERATIVE, INC.; *U.S. Private*, pg. 4192
TRAVEL & EVENT SERVICES, LLC—See Viad Corp.; *U.S. Public*, pg. 2291
UNITED STATES OLYMPIC COMMITTEE; *U.S. Private*, pg. 4299
UNITED STATES POLO ASSOCIATION, INC.; *U.S. Private*, pg. 4299
WASHINGTON ST. TAMMANY ELECTRIC COOPERATIVE INC.; *U.S. Private*, pg. 4449
THE WORLD BANK GROUP; *U.S. Private*, pg. 4139
ZOGSPORTS LLC; *U.S. Private*, pg. 4607

814110 — PRIVATE HOUSEHOLDS

PARTIES THAT COOK LLC; *U.S. Private*, pg. 3101

921110 — EXECUTIVE OFFICES

ABM FACILITY SOLUTIONS GROUP, LLC—See ABM Industries, Inc.; *U.S. Public*, pg. 25
APEX MEDICAL CORPORATION - NORWELL EXECUTIVE OFFICE—See Tenex Capital Management, L.P.; *U.S. Private*, pg. 3966
AUTO CLUB TRUST, FSB - OMAHA (132ND ST.) BRANCH—See The Auto Club Group; *U.S. Private*, pg. 3990
THE AVENAL PROGRESS—See Lee Enterprises, Incorporated; *U.S. Public*, pg. 1300
BAYER (CHINA) LIMITED—See Bayer Aktiengesellschaft; *Int'l*, pg. 901
CIMARRON INC. - EXECUTIVE OFFICE—See Cimarron Inc.; *U.S. Private*, pg. 897
CLEAN WATER SERVICES; *U.S. Private*, pg. 931
DANZER SERVICES, INC.—See Danzer AG; *Int'l*, pg. 1970
DILLARD'S FORT WORTH DIVISION—See Dillard's Inc.; *U.S. Public*, pg. 666
DILLARD'S SAINT LOUIS DIVISION—See Dillard's Inc.; *U.S. Public*, pg. 666
DILLARD'S SOUTHEAST DIVISION—See Dillard's Inc.; *U.S. Public*, pg. 666
FALCON-LEWISVILLE—See Whippoorwill Associates, Inc.; *U.S. Private*, pg. 4507
HELENA PLASTICS—See Helena Laboratories Corporation; *U.S. Private*, pg. 1906
LOUISVILLE WATER CO. INC.; *U.S. Private*, pg. 2500
LYONS BANCORP, INC.; *U.S. Public*, pg. 1350
MOUNT PLEASANT WATERWORKS; *U.S. Private*, pg. 2798
POKAGON BAND OF POTAWATOMI INDIANS; *U.S. Private*, pg. 3222
TUCKER COUNTY COMMISSION; *U.S. Private*, pg. 4256

921120 — LEGISLATIVE BODIES

HEALTH MANAGEMENT ASSOCIATES, LLC—See Community Health Systems, Inc.; *U.S. Public*, pg. 553

921130 — PUBLIC FINANCE ACTIVITIES

AEON HOUSING LOAN SERVICE CO., LTD.—See AEON Co., Ltd.; *Int'l*, pg. 176

AIG CONSUMER FINANCE GROUP, INC.—See American International Group, Inc.; *U.S. Public*, pg. 104
ALBRIDGE SOLUTIONS, INC.—See The Bank of New York Mellon Corporation; *U.S. Public*, pg. 2038
AUSTRALIAN UNITY LIMITED; *Int'l*, pg. 722
AUTODRIVE1; *U.S. Private*, pg. 398
AVIS BUDGET GROUP, INC.; *U.S. Public*, pg. 248
BCS INFORMATION SYSTEMS PRIVATE LIMITED—See HSBC Holdings plc; *Int'l*, pg. 3503
BNKC (CAMBODIA) MFI PLC—See BNK Financial Group Inc.; *Int'l*, pg. 1079
BOWRING MARSH (DUBLIN) LIMITED—See Marsh & McLennan Companies, Inc.; *U.S. Public*, pg. 1374
BRISTOL-MYERS SQUIBB BUSINESS SERVICES LIMITED—See Bristol-Myers Squibb Company; *U.S. Public*, pg. 385
CAMS FINANCIAL INFORMATION SERVICES PRIVATE LIMITED—See Computer Age Management Services Limited; *Int'l*, pg. 1758
CASSA DEPOSITI E PRESTITI S.P.A.; *Int'l*, pg. 1354
CHEX SYSTEMS INC.—See Fidelity National Infor; *U.S. Public*, pg. 832
CLOSE BROTHERS ASSET FINANCE GMBH—See Close Brothers Group plc; *Int'l*, pg. 1661
COMPAGNIE FINANCIERE DES CIMENTS SA—See Heidelberg Materials AG; *Int'l*, pg. 3316
CSL FINANCE PLC—See CSL Limited; *Int'l*, pg. 1865
DEUTSCHE PFANDBRIEFBANK AG - ESCHBORN—See Hypo Real Estate Holding AG; *Int'l*, pg. 3553
DEXIA KOMMUNALBANK DEUTSCHLAND AG—See Helaba Landesbank Hessen-Thuringen; *Int'l*, pg. 3327
ECN CAPITAL CORP.; *Int'l*, pg. 2292
EDELWEISS CUSTODIAL SERVICES LIMITED—See Edelweiss Financial Services Ltd.; *Int'l*, pg. 2306
EPIC BPIFRANCE; *Int'l*, pg. 2460
ESSAR SECURITIES LIMITED; *Int'l*, pg. 2508
FCMB GROUP PLC; *Int'l*, pg. 2627
FEXCO HOLDINGS; *Int'l*, pg. 2649
FIRST AMERICAN LENDERS ADVANTAGE—See First American Financial Corporation; *U.S. Public*, pg. 836
G CAPITAL PUBLIC COMPANY LIMITED; *Int'l*, pg. 2861
GLOBAL PREMIUM FINANCE COMPANY—See Marsh & McLennan Companies, Inc.; *U.S. Public*, pg. 1375
GRACEKENNEDY TRADE FINANCE LIMITED—See GraceKennedy Limited; *Int'l*, pg. 3049
GREAT AMERICAN TITLE AGENCY, INC.; *U.S. Private*, pg. 1762
GRIID INFRASTRUCTURE INC.; *U.S. Public*, pg. 969
HANA CAPITAL CO., LTD.—See Hana Financial Group, Inc.; *Int'l*, pg. 3240
HFC BANK LIMITED—See HSBC Holdings plc; *Int'l*, pg. 3505
HITACHI INTERNATIONAL TREASURY LTD.—See Hitachi, Ltd.; *Int'l*, pg. 3414
HOANG QUAN APPRAISAL CO., LTD.—See Hoang Quan Consulting - Trading - Service Real Estate Corporation; *Int'l*, pg. 3436
HONGKONG INTERNATIONAL TRADE FINANCE (JAPAN) KK—See HSBC Holdings plc; *Int'l*, pg. 3507
HRB RESOURCES LLC—See H&R Block, Inc.; *U.S. Public*, pg. 976
HSBC FORFAITING LTD.—See HSBC Holdings plc; *Int'l*, pg. 3504
HSBC HOLDINGS BV—See HSBC Holdings plc; *Int'l*, pg. 3504
HSBC INVOICE FINANCE UK LTD—See HSBC Holdings plc; *Int'l*, pg. 3504
HYPO PFANDBRIEF BANK INTERNATIONAL S.A.—See Hypo Real Estate Holding AG; *Int'l*, pg. 3553
HYPO PUBLIC FINANCE BANK—See Hypo Real Estate Holding AG; *Int'l*, pg. 3553
INTERMOUNTAIN POWER AGENCY; *U.S. Private*, pg. 2113
MARSH TREASURY SERVICES (DUBLIN) LIMITED—See Marsh & McLennan Companies, Inc.; *U.S. Public*, pg. 1384
MERCHANT BANK OF SRI LANKA & FINANCE PLC—See Bank of Ceylon; *Int'l*, pg. 841
MORGAN STANLEY INTERNATIONAL LTD.—See Morgan Stanley; *U.S. Public*, pg. 1473
MORGAN STANLEY SOUTH AFRICA (PTY) LTD.—See Morgan Stanley; *U.S. Public*, pg. 1473
OEC LTD.—See Cresco, Ltd.; *Int'l*, pg. 1840
PARADIGM TAX GROUP—See The Riverside Company; *U.S. Private*, pg. 4109
PPL ENERGY FUNDING CORPORATION—See PPL Corporation; *U.S. Public*, pg. 1711
STANDARD & POOR'S S.A. DE C.V.—See S&P Global Inc.; *U.S. Public*, pg. 1831
SUNSTAGE CO., LTD.—See BELLUNA CO. LTD.; *Int'l*, pg. 967
TEXAS LOTTERY COMMISSION; *U.S. Private*, pg. 3976
UNITED STATES MINT; *U.S. Private*, pg. 4299
UNITED STUDENT AID FUNDS INC.; *U.S. Private*, pg. 4300
WESBANK—See FirstRand Limited; *Int'l*, pg. 2690

CORPORATE AFFILIATIONS

921140 — EXECUTIVE AND LEGISLATIVE OFFICES, COMBINED

ALIBABA GROUP HOLDING LIMITED - HANGZHOU OFFICE—See Alibaba Group Holding Limited; *Int'l*, pg. 325
BORR DRILLING MANAGEMENT AS—See Borr Drilling Limited; *Int'l*, pg. 1114
DANZER SERVICES EUROPE GMBH—See Danzer AG; *Int'l*, pg. 1969
DKSH MANAGEMENT LTD.—See Diethelm Keller Holding Limited; *Int'l*, pg. 2116
NAVAJO AGRICULTURAL PRODUCTS INDUSTRY INC.; *U.S. Private*, pg. 2872
RIVIERA PARTNERS; *U.S. Private*, pg. 3448
SHARP CORPORATION - TOKYO—See Hon Hai Precision Industry Co., Ltd.; *Int'l*, pg. 3458
SPRINGER SCIENCE+BUSINESS MEDIA B.V.—See BC Partners LLP; *Int'l*, pg. 925

921150 — AMERICAN INDIAN AND ALASKA NATIVE TRIBAL GOVERNMENTS

THE CHICKASAW NATION; *U.S. Private*, pg. 4008
FORT SILL APACHE TRIBE OF OKLAHOMA; *U.S. Private*, pg. 1575
PRAIRIE BAND POTAWATOMI NATION; *U.S. Private*, pg. 3242
SEMINOLE TRIBE OF FLORIDA, INC.; *U.S. Private*, pg. 3604
UNITED SOUTH AND EASTERN TRIBES, INC.; *U.S. Private*, pg. 4297

921190 — OTHER GENERAL GOVERNMENT SUPPORT

1ST AMERICAN SYSTEMS AND SERVICES, LLC; *U.S. Private*, pg. 3
1ST AMERICAN SYSTEMS AND SERVICES—See 1st American Systems And Services, LLC; *U.S. Private*, pg. 3
A. HAROLD & ASSOCIATES, LLC; *U.S. Private*, pg. 23
ARCHIMEDES GLOBAL, INC.; *U.S. Private*, pg. 311
AUSTRALIAN CONSULATE GENERAL—See Australian Trade and Investment Commission; *Int'l*, pg. 722
AXOM TECHNOLOGIES, LLC—See Sagewind Capital LLC; *U.S. Private*, pg. 3527
BEST VALUE TECHNOLOGY, INC. (BVTI); *U.S. Private*, pg. 543
BNA PLUS—See Bloomberg L.P.; *U.S. Private*, pg. 584
THE BOSTON CONSULTING GROUP PTY. LTD. - CANBERRA—See The Boston Consulting Group, Inc.; *U.S. Private*, pg. 3998
BRIGHTON CROMWELL, LLC—See AE Industrial Partners, LP; *U.S. Private*, pg. 112
BRIMTEK, INC.—See Digital Barriers plc; *Int'l*, pg. 2120
CAPSTONE CORPORATION; *U.S. Private*, pg. 746
CARNEY, INC.; *U.S. Private*, pg. 766
CITY OF GLENDALE MUNICIPAL PROPERTY CORP.; *U.S. Private*, pg. 906
CITY OF SCOTTSDALE MUNICIPAL PROPERTY CORPORATION; *U.S. Private*, pg. 906
COMPLETE PROFESSIONAL SERVICES, LLC; *U.S. Private*, pg. 1001
CRITERION SYSTEMS, INC.; *U.S. Private*, pg. 1101
DAVISTRAPP LLC—See FederalConference.com; *U.S. Private*, pg. 1491
DELAN ASSOCIATES, INC.; *U.S. Private*, pg. 1193
EDC CONSULTING LLC; *U.S. Private*, pg. 1332
E-MANAGEMENT; *U.S. Private*, pg. 1302
ESRI AUSTRALIA PTY. LTD.—See Boustead Singapore Limited; *Int'l*, pg. 1120
EWA GOVERNMENT SYSTEMS, INC.—See Sagewind Capital LLC; *U.S. Private*, pg. 3528
FACCHINA GLOBAL SERVICES LLC; *U.S. Private*, pg. 1459
FAST ASSETS SDN. BHD.—See Fast Energy Holdings Berhad; *Int'l*, pg. 2621
FEDSTORE CORPORATION; *U.S. Private*, pg. 1492
GENTECH ASSOCIATES, INC.; *U.S. Private*, pg. 1679
GFF (ILE DE FRANCE)—See Caisse des Depots et Consignations; *Int'l*, pg. 1258
GOVERNMENT CONTRACT SOLUTIONS, INC.; *U.S. Private*, pg. 1746
GOVERNMENT SOURCING SOLUTIONS; *U.S. Private*, pg. 1746
H2 PERFORMANCE CONSULTING; *U.S. Private*, pg. 1836
HIGH PLAINS COMPUTING, INC.; *U.S. Private*, pg. 1936
INFOSYS INTERNATIONAL, INC.; *U.S. Private*, pg. 2074
INTEC LLC; *U.S. Private*, pg. 2097
INTEGRATED SYSTEMS IMPROVEMENT SERVICES, INC.—See KCB Management LLC; *U.S. Private*, pg. 2269
INTEGRITY MANAGEMENT CONSULTING, INC.; *U.S. Private*, pg. 2103

N.A.I.C.S. INDEX

IPKEYS TECHNOLOGIES LLC—See The Chickasaw Nation; *U.S. Private*, pg. 4008
ISR GROUP, INC.; *U.S. Private*, pg. 2146
ITA INTERNATIONAL, LLC; *U.S. Private*, pg. 2148
IZ TECHNOLOGIES, INC.; *U.S. Private*, pg. 2152
LEONARD CONSULTING LLC; *U.S. Private*, pg. 2423
LOGISTICS SUPPORT INC.; *U.S. Private*, pg. 2482
MAXIMUS, INC.; *U.S. Public*, pg. 1402
MIRACORP INC.; *U.S. Private*, pg. 2746
MISSION CRITICAL PARTNERS; *U.S. Private*, pg. 2747
NEWARK LEGAL & COMMUNICATIONS CENTER URBAN RENEWAL CORPORATION—See Port Authority of New York & New Jersey; *U.S. Private*, pg. 3229
NEW YORK POWER AUTHORITY, INC.; *U.S. Private*, pg. 2911
P3S CORPORATION; *U.S. Private*, pg. 3062
PHACIL, INC.—See Sagewind Capital LLC; *U.S. Private*, pg. 3527
PROVIDEO MANAGEMENT, INC.; *U.S. Private*, pg. 3295
R3 STRATEGIC SUPPORT GROUP, INC.; *U.S. Private*, pg. 3340
SAFEBUILT, INC.; *U.S. Private*, pg. 3524
SC3 LLC—See General Dynamics Corporation; *U.S. Public*, pg. 916
SEACORP, LLC; *U.S. Private*, pg. 3584
SERVICES CONSEIL EXPERTISE TERRITOIRE S.A.—See Caisse des Depots et Consignations; *Int'l*, pg. 1258
SOS INTERNATIONAL LTD.—See SOS International LLC; *U.S. Private*, pg. 3716
SPECTRUM COMM. INC.; *U.S. Private*, pg. 3752
VETERAN CORPS OF AMERICA; *U.S. Private*, pg. 4373
VETERANS ENTERPRISE TECHNOLOGY SOLUTIONS, INC.; *U.S. Private*, pg. 4373
VINITECH, INC.; *U.S. Private*, pg. 4385
THE WESTWOOD GROUP, INC.; *U.S. Private*, pg. 4134
YORKTOWN SYSTEMS GROUP, INC.; *U.S. Private*, pg. 4591

922120 — POLICE PROTECTION

MORRISONVILLE FARMERS COOP CO; *U.S. Private*, pg. 2790
RUSS DARROW CHRYSLER & JEEP OF CEDARBURG—See Russ Darrow Group, Inc.; *U.S. Private*, pg. 3505

922130 — LEGAL COUNSEL AND PROSECUTION

ARCHER & GREINER P.C.; *U.S. Private*, pg. 310
ASSOCIATED COUNSEL FOR THE ACCUSED; *U.S. Private*, pg. 355
IMS CONSULTING & EXPERT SERVICES; *U.S. Private*, pg. 2051
LOWENSTEIN SANDLER PC—See Lowenstein Sandler PC; *U.S. Private*, pg. 2505
LOWENSTEIN SANDLER PC—See Lowenstein Sandler PC; *U.S. Private*, pg. 2505
PARAGON LEGAL GROUP, P.C.; *U.S. Private*, pg. 3091
SHIPMAN & GOODWIN; *U.S. Private*, pg. 3637
SLATER GORDON SOLUTIONS LEGAL LIMITED—See Allegro Funds Pty. Ltd.; *Int'l*, pg. 336
SMITH, GAMBRELL & RUSSELL, LLP—See Smith, Gambrell & Russell; *U.S. Private*, pg. 3696

922140 — CORRECTIONAL INSTITUTIONS

AVALON CORRECTIONAL SERVICES, INC.—See Corecivic, Inc.; *U.S. Public*, pg. 577
CORECIVIC, INC.; *U.S. Public*, pg. 577
FULHAM CORRECTIONAL CENTRE—See The GEO Group, Inc.; *U.S. Public*, pg. 2075
THE GEO GROUP AUSTRALIA PTY, LTD.—See The GEO Group, Inc.; *U.S. Public*, pg. 2075
THE GEO GROUP, INC.; *U.S. Public*, pg. 2075
THE GEO GROUP LTD.—See The GEO Group, Inc.; *U.S. Public*, pg. 2075
THE GEO GROUP UK LTD—See The GEO Group, Inc.; *U.S. Public*, pg. 2075
GREAT PLAINS CORRECTIONAL FACILITY—See The GEO Group, Inc.; *U.S. Public*, pg. 2075
JUNEE CORRECTIONAL CENTRE—See The GEO Group, Inc.; *U.S. Public*, pg. 2075
KUTAMA SINTHUMULE CORRECTIONAL CENTRE—See The GEO Group, Inc.; *U.S. Public*, pg. 2075
MARK CORRECTIONAL SYSTEMS—See Kullman Buildings Corp.; *U.S. Private*, pg. 2357
NEBRASKA DEPARTMENT OF CORRECTIONAL SERVICES; *U.S. Private*, pg. 2878
PARKLEA CORRECTIONAL CENTRE—See The GEO Group, Inc.; *U.S. Public*, pg. 2075
PHILADELPHIA PRISON SYSTEM; *U.S. Private*, pg. 3169
SOUTH AFRICA CUSTODIAL MANAGEMENT INC.—See The GEO Group, Inc.; *U.S. Public*, pg. 2075
WEST TEXAS ISF—See Management & Training Corporation; *U.S. Private*, pg. 2560

922160 — FIRE PROTECTION

ABC FIRE EXTINGUISHER CO. INC.—See BlackRock, Inc.; *U.S. Public*, pg. 346
ABCO FIRE PROTECTION, INC.—See Align Capital Partners, LLC; *U.S. Private*, pg. 167
ADVANCED SAFETY SYSTEMS INC.—See Littlejohn & Co., LLC; *U.S. Private*, pg. 2471
AI FIRE, LLC—See TruArc Partners, L.P.; *U.S. Private*, pg. 4244
ANGUS FIRE (S.A.) LIMITED—See Carrier Global Corporation; *U.S. Public*, pg. 440
ASSETCO PLC; *Int'l*, pg. 643
ASSOCIATED FIRE PROTECTION; *U.S. Private*, pg. 355
ATLANTIS FIRE PROTECTION—See Capital Alignment Partners, Inc.; *U.S. Private*, pg. 738
ATLANTIS FIRE PROTECTION—See Lynch Holdings, LLC; *U.S. Private*, pg. 2520
BECO HOLDING COMPANY, INC.—See H.I.G. Capital, LLC; *U.S. Private*, pg. 1827
BLIVEX ENERGY TECHNOLOGY CO., LTD.; *Int'l*, pg. 1064
CATALANA DE SEGURETAT I COMUNICACIONS, S.L.—See Grupo Villar Mir, S.A.U.; *Int'l*, pg. 3138
CERTASITE GRAND RAPIDS LLC—See The Riverside Company; *U.S. Private*, pg. 4108
CHINA YUAN HONG FIRE CONTROL GROUP HOLDINGS LTD; *Int'l*, pg. 1565
CHUBB FRANCE—See Carrier Global Corporation; *U.S. Public*, pg. 441
CHUBB SINGAPORE PRIVATE LIMITED—See Carrier Global Corporation; *U.S. Public*, pg. 441
CIMC OFFSHORE ENGINEERING HOLDINGS CO., LTD.—See China International Marine Containers (Group) Co., Ltd.; *Int'l*, pg. 1511
CIMC SECURITY TECHNOLOGY CO., LTD.—See China International Marine Containers (Group) Co., Ltd.; *Int'l*, pg. 1511
CIMC-TIANDA HOLDINGS COMPANY LIMITED; *Int'l*, pg. 1608
CIMC TRANSPACK TECHNOLOGY CO., LTD.—See China International Marine Containers (Group) Co., Ltd.; *Int'l*, pg. 1511
CJ SUPPRESSION, INC.—See Fortis Fire & Safety, Inc.; *U.S. Private*, pg. 1576
COMERCIAL DE MATERIALES DE INCENDIOS, S.L.—See Grupo Villar Mir, S.A.U.; *Int'l*, pg. 3138
CONCEJO AB; *Int'l*, pg. 1763
CRAYNON FIRE PROTECTION, INC.—See The Riverside Company; *U.S. Private*, pg. 4108
CY-FAIR VOLUNTEER FIRE DEPARTMENT; *U.S. Private*, pg. 1133
DANFOSS SEMCO A/S—See Danfoss A/S; *Int'l*, pg. 1961
DISTRIBUTION INTERNATIONAL, INC.—See TopBuild Corp.; *U.S. Public*, pg. 2163
EAU ET FEU—See Carrier Global Corporation; *U.S. Public*, pg. 441
ENGIE FIRE SERVICES AUSTRALIA PTY LIMITED—See ENGIE SA; *Int'l*, pg. 2431
FB FIRE TECHNOLOGIES LTD.—See Ilustrato Pictures International Inc.; *Int'l*, pg. 3616
FEDERAL FIRE ENGINEERING PTE LTD—See Federal International (2000) Ltd; *Int'l*, pg. 2630
FIREBUS SYSTEMS, INC.—See China Automation Group Limited; *Int'l*, pg. 1483
FIRE-DEX, LLC; *U.S. Private*, pg. 1511
FIRE FIGHTING ENTERPRISES LIMITED—See Halma plc; *Int'l*, pg. 3231
FIRE INSPECTOR COMPANY LIMITED—See Firetrade Engineering PCL; *Int'l*, pg. 2679
FIRE & LIFE SAFETY AMERICA, INC.—See Blue Point Capital Partners, LLC; *U.S. Private*, pg. 590
FIRELINE, INC.; *U.S. Private*, pg. 1512
FIRE PROTECTION ENGINEERING AS—See HitecVision AS; *Int'l*, pg. 3426
FIRE RESCUE SAFETY AUSTRALIA PTY LTD.—See Bunzl plc; *Int'l*, pg. 1218
FIRE SERVICE COLLEGE LIMITED—See Capita plc; *Int'l*, pg. 1309
FIRETRACE USA, LLC—See Halma plc; *Int'l*, pg. 3231
FORTIS FIRE & SAFETY, INC.; *U.S. Private*, pg. 1576
FYRNETICS (HONG KONG) LIMITED—See Carrier Global Corporation; *U.S. Public*, pg. 441
GELTECH SOLUTIONS, INC.; *U.S. Public*, pg. 910
HALL & KAY FIRE ENGINEERING—See Carrier Global Corporation; *U.S. Public*, pg. 441
HARN ENGINEERING SOLUTIONS PUBLIC COMPANY LIMITED; *Int'l*, pg. 3278
HOCHIKI EUROPE (U.K.) LTD.—See Hochiki Corporation; *Int'l*, pg. 3437
HONEYWELL ANALYTICS AG—See Honeywell International Inc.; *U.S. Public*, pg. 1048
HONEYWELL ANALYTICS AG—See Honeywell International Inc.; *U.S. Public*, pg. 1048
HONEYWELL ANALYTICS FRANCE S.A.—See Honeywell International Inc.; *U.S. Public*, pg. 1048
HONEYWELL ANALYTICS LIMITED—See Honeywell International Inc.; *U.S. Public*, pg. 1048
HONEYWELL ANALYTICS—See Honeywell International Inc.; *U.S. Public*, pg. 1048
HONEYWELL LIFE SAFETY—See Honeywell International Inc.; *U.S. Public*, pg. 1048
IMPACT FIRE SERVICES, LLC—See TruArc Partners, L.P.; *U.S. Private*, pg. 4244
INTEGRATED FIRE PROTECTION LLC—See Blue Point Capital Partners, LLC; *U.S. Private*, pg. 590
INTUMESCENT PROTECTIVE COATINGS LIMITED—See Fieldway Group Limited; *Int'l*, pg. 2655
J.W. D'ANGELO CO., INC.—See Core & Main, Inc.; *U.S. Public*, pg. 576
KELLER'S, INC.—See Capital Alignment Partners, Inc.; *U.S. Private*, pg. 738
KELLER'S, INC.—See Lynch Holdings, LLC; *U.S. Private*, pg. 2521
KIDDE AUSTRALIA PTY LTD.—See Carrier Global Corporation; *U.S. Public*, pg. 441
KIDDE-FENWAL, INC.—See Carrier Global Corporation; *U.S. Public*, pg. 441
KIDDE FIRE SAFETY—See Carrier Global Corporation; *U.S. Public*, pg. 440
KNOWSLEY SK LTD.—See Electricite de France S.A.; *Int'l*, pg. 2351
LOTOS STRAZ SP. Z O.O.—See Grupa LOTOS S.A.; *Int'l*, pg. 3117
MARSHAL OFFSHORE & MARINE ENGRG CO., LTD.—See 9R Limited; *Int'l*, pg. 17
MCDONOUGH FIRE SERVICE—See Wm. F. McDonough Plumbing, Inc.; *U.S. Private*, pg. 4552
MEADOWLANDS FIRE PROTECTION CORP.—See EMCOR Group, Inc.; *U.S. Public*, pg. 738
NATIONAL FIRE & SAFETY, INC.—See Highview Capital, LLC; *U.S. Private*, pg. 1942
NATIONAL FIRE SOLUTIONS (QLD) PTY LTD—See Evergreen Capital L.P.; *U.S. Public*, pg. 1439
NATIONAL FIRE SOLUTIONS (WA) PTY LTD—See Evergreen Capital L.P.; *U.S. Public*, pg. 1439
OAK FIRE PROTECTION LIMITED—See Galliford Try Holdings plc; *Int'l*, pg. 2874
PERFORMANCE SYSTEMS INTEGRATION, LLC; *U.S. Private*, pg. 3150
PERIMETER SOLUTIONS LP—See EverArc Holdings Limited; *Int'l*, pg. 2563
PIPER FIRE PROTECTION, INC.—See Fortis Fire & Safety, Inc.; *U.S. Private*, pg. 1576
PRO-AM SAFETY, INC.; *U.S. Private*, pg. 3270
THE PROTECTOSEAL COMPANY; *U.S. Private*, pg. 4101
PYRENE CORPORATION—See Carrier Global Corporation; *U.S. Public*, pg. 441
RAPID FIRE PROTECTION, INC.—See Pye-Barker Fire & Safety, LLC; *U.S. Private*, pg. 3309
RAPID FIRE SAFETY & SECURITY LLC—See Financial Investments Corporation; *U.S. Private*, pg. 1507
RICH FIRE PROTECTION COMPANY, INC.—See APi Group Corporation; *Int'l*, pg. 514
RURAL METRO CORPORATION—See KKR & Co. Inc.; *U.S. Public*, pg. 1252
RURAL/METRO FIRE DEPT., INC.—See KKR & Co. Inc.; *U.S. Public*, pg. 1251
S.A. COMUNALE CO., INC.—See EMCOR Group, Inc.; *U.S. Public*, pg. 737
SAIRE S.R.L.—See Compagnia Finanziaria de Benedetti S.p.A.; *Int'l*, pg. 1722
SAVAL B.V.—See Electricite de France S.A.; *Int'l*, pg. 2352
SAVAL N.V.—See Electricite de France S.A.; *Int'l*, pg. 2352
SCIENS BUILDING SOLUTIONS, LLC—See The Carlyle Group Inc.; *U.S. Public*, pg. 2053
SHENZHEN CIMC INDUSTRY & CITY DEVELOPMENT CO., LTD.—See China International Marine Containers (Group) Co., Ltd.; *Int'l*, pg. 1512
SHUNG CHING BEIJING HUASHENG EMERGENCY EQUIPMENT SYSTEMS CO., LTD.—See CIMC-TianDa Holdings Company Limited; *Int'l*, pg. 1609
SPACE AGE ELECTRONICS, INC.—See DelCam Holdings, LLC; *U.S. Private*, pg. 1196
SPARTAN MOTORS USA, INC.—See AIP, LLC; *U.S. Private*, pg. 135
STANDARD AUTOMATIC FIRE ENTERPRISES INC.—See APi Group Corporation; *Int'l*, pg. 513
SURELAND INDUSTRIAL FIRE SAFETY LIMITED—See Bain Capital, LP; *U.S. Public*, pg. 437
TREASURE VALLEY FIRE PROTECTION, INC.—See Pye-Barker Fire & Safety, LLC; *U.S. Private*, pg. 3309
TRIPLE 'M' FIRE—See BSA Limited; *Int'l*, pg. 1201
UNITED STATES ALLIANCE FIRE PROTECTION, INC.—See APi Group Corporation; *Int'l*, pg. 514
UNITED STATES ALLIANCE FIRE PROTECTION, INC.—See APi Group Corporation; *Int'l*, pg. 514
UNIVERSAL SECURITY INSTRUMENTS, INC.; *U.S. Public*, pg. 2262
VFP FIRE SYSTEMS, INC.—See APi Group Corporation; *Int'l*, pg. 514
VIPOND FIRE PROTECTION, INC.—See APi Group Corporation; *Int'l*, pg. 514
WANYOU FIRE ENGINEERING GROUP COMPANY LIMITED—See CIMC-TianDa Holdings Company Limited; *Int'l*, pg. 1609

922190 — FIRE PROTECTION

922190 — OTHER JUSTICE, PUBLIC ORDER, AND SAFETY ACTIVITIES

ALLIANCE SOLUTIONS GROUP, INC.; U.S. Private, pg. 184
CHURCH & DWIGHT (AUSTRALIA) PTY. LTD.—See Church & Dwight Co., Inc.; U.S. Public, pg. 493
GLOBAL PUBLIC SAFETY, LLC—See Rekor Systems, Inc.; U.S. Public, pg. 1778
HEALTH & SAFETY INSTITUTE INC.—See Waud Capital Partners LLC; U.S. Private, pg. 4457
HUBIFY COMMUNICATIONS PTY LIMITED—See Hubify Limited; Int'l, pg. 3520
NATIONAL SAFETY COMMISSION (NSC); U.S. Private, pg. 2862
NEVADA PF LLC; U.S. Private, pg. 2891
NUKK-FREEMAN & CERRA, P.C.; U.S. Private, pg. 2973
PIONEER ELECTRONICS OF CANADA INC—See EQT AB; Int'l, pg. 2470
PRO SAFETY SERVICES, LLC—See Kelso & Company, L.P.; U.S. Private, pg. 2280

923110 — ADMINISTRATION OF EDUCATION PROGRAMS

ACADEMIES AUSTRALASIA GROUP LIMITED; Int'l, pg. 77
ADVANCED PRACTICE STRATEGIES, INC.—See Bertelsmann SE & Co. KGaA; Int'l, pg. 991
ALDAR EDUCATION - SOLE PROPRIETORSHIP LLC—See ALDAR Properties PJSC; Int'l, pg. 304
ALISRA FOR EDUCATION & INVESTMENT CO. PLC; Int'l, pg. 329
ALSUWAIKET EDUCATION DIVISION—See AlSuwaiket Trading & Contracting Co.; Int'l, pg. 383
AMBASSADOR PROGRAMS, INC.; U.S. Private, pg. 217
APPLETON LEARNING CORPORATION; U.S. Private, pg. 297
ASPEN GROUP, INC.; U.S. Public, pg. 213
CAREER SYSTEMS DEVELOPMENT CORPORATION—See Owl Companies; U.S. Private, pg. 3055
CENTURA COLLEGE; U.S. Private, pg. 830
CHARTER SCHOOLS USA INC.; U.S. Private, pg. 858
CHINA DISTANCE EDUCATION HOLDINGS LIMITED; Int'l, pg. 1498
CHINA EDUCATION RESOURCES INC.; Int'l, pg. 1499
CHINAEDU CORPORATION—See ChinaEdu Holdings Ltd.; Int'l, pg. 1568
CULTURAL EXPERIENCES ABROAD; U.S. Private, pg. 1122
EDSERV SOFTSYSTEMS LIMITED; Int'l, pg. 2315
EDUCATION FIRST; U.S. Private, pg. 1338
EDUCATION TECHNOLOGY PARTNERS; U.S. Private, pg. 1339
EDUCERE, LLC; U.S. Private, pg. 1340
EDVENTURECO PTY LTD—See AWN Holdings Limited; Int'l, pg. 753
EDVISORS NETWORK, INC.; U.S. Private, pg. 1340
ENDRISS GMBH—See Amadeus Fire AG; Int'l, pg. 405
E.ON ACADEMY GMBH—See E.ON SE; Int'l, pg. 2252
FIVEABLE, INC.; U.S. Private, pg. 1538
FROG STREET PRESS, INC.—See Brentwood Associates; U.S. Private, pg. 646
FUN AND FUNCTION LLC; U.S. Private, pg. 1622
FUSION ACADEMY & LEARNING CENTER; U.S. Private, pg. 1625
GALILEO GLOBAL EDUCATION; Int'l, pg. 2873
GLOBAL EDUCATION COMMUNITIES CORP; Int'l, pg. 2995
GOLDFISH SWIM SCHOOL—See Goldfish Swim School Franchising LLC; U.S. Private, pg. 1735
HEALTH EDUCATION SOLUTIONS, INC.—See Nelnet, Inc.; U.S. Public, pg. 1504
HUMAN ACADEMY SHANGHAI CO., LTD.—See Human Holdings Co., Ltd.; Int'l, pg. 3529
THE ILSC EDUCATION GROUP, INC.—See Quad Partners, LLC; U.S. Private, pg. 3314
THE INDEPENDENT INSTITUTE OF EDUCATION (PTY) LTD—See ADvTECH Limited; Int'l, pg. 169
INSEEC EXECUTIVE EDUCATION SASU—See Cinven Limited; Int'l, pg. 1612
INSYGHT; U.S. Private, pg. 2096
IOWA LUTHERAN HOSPITAL MEDICAL EDUCATION FOUNDATION—See UnityPoint Health; U.S. Private, pg. 4303
JK ASSOCIATES, INC.; U.S. Private, pg. 2211
THE LEARNING EXPERIENCE—See Golden Gate Capital Management II, LLC; U.S. Private, pg. 1731
MEDICAL EDUCATION BROADCAST NETWORK; U.S. Private, pg. 2655
MEDICAL TECHNOLOGY MANAGEMENT INSTITUTE, LLC—See The College of Health Care Professions; U.S. Private, pg. 4011
MESA AIRLINES PILOT DEVELOPMENT, INC.—See Mesa Air Group, Inc.; U.S. Public, pg. 1425
METEOR EDUCATION LLC—See Bain Capital, LP; U.S. Private, pg. 431
MOSAICA EDUCATION; U.S. Private, pg. 2792
NATIONAL HERITAGE ACADEMIES, INC.; U.S. Private, pg. 2856
NEW YORK KIDS CLUB; U.S. Private, pg. 2910
OPTION SIX, INC.; U.S. Private, pg. 3035
OWL EDUCATION & TRAINING, INC.—See Owl Companies; U.S. Private, pg. 3055
PHARMCON, INC.—See Moelis Asset Management LP; U.S. Private, pg. 2764
REDHILL EDUCATION LIMITED—See iCollege Limited; Int'l, pg. 3582
SLATE SOLUTIONS, INC.—See Genstar Capital, LLC; U.S. Private, pg. 1679
SMARTWORKS LEARNING CENTRE PTE LTD.—See AEC Education plc; Int'l, pg. 171
SPEAR EDUCATION, LLC—See Avista Capital Partners, L.P.; U.S. Private, pg. 409
SUP SANTE S.A.R.L.—See Gift SAS; Int'l, pg. 2970
SURGENT HOLDING CORP—See Moelis Asset Management LP; U.S. Private, pg. 2764
TEACHERS OF TOMORROW LLC—See Gauge Capital LLC; U.S. Private, pg. 1652
TESTMASTERS EDUCATIONAL SERVICES, INC.; U.S. Private, pg. 3973
UDEMY, INC.; U.S. Public, pg. 2217

923120 — ADMINISTRATION OF PUBLIC HEALTH PROGRAMS

A10 CLINICAL SOLUTIONS, INC.; U.S. Private, pg. 29
AIDS ACTION COMMITTEE OF MA, INC.; U.S. Private, pg. 131
ALBERTA HEALTH SERVICES; Int'l, pg. 297
AQUA ILLINOIS - VERMILION COUNTY DIVISION—See Essential Utilities Inc.; U.S. Public, pg. 795
ARLINGTON TOMORROW FOUNDATION; U.S. Private, pg. 329
CAREFIRST, INC.; U.S. Private, pg. 753
CATHOLIC HEALTH SERVICES OF LONG ISLAND; U.S. Private, pg. 790
THE CHAN SOON-SHIONG FAMILY FOUNDATION; U.S. Private, pg. 4007
DIVERSIFIED SERVICE OPTIONS INC.—See GuideWell Mutual Holding Corporation; U.S. Private, pg. 1813
EXETER HEALTH RESOURCES, INC.—See Beth Israel Lahey Health Inc; U.S. Private, pg. 545
FIRST COAST SERVICE OPTIONS INC.—See GuideWell Mutual Holding Corporation; U.S. Private, pg. 1813
FUNDACION BANMEDICA—See UnitedHealth Group Incorporated; U.S. Public, pg. 2241
FURSTENBERG INSTITUT GMBH—See Asklepios Kliniken GmbH & Co. KGaA; Int'l, pg. 623
GLOBAL BEHAVIORAL SOLUTIONS LLC; U.S. Private, pg. 1712
HEALTHCARE SOLUTIONS MANAGEMENT GROUP, INC.—See Cardinal Health, Inc.; U.S. Public, pg. 434
HEALTH DESIGNS, INC.; U.S. Private, pg. 1893
HEALTHEQUITY, INC.; U.S. Public, pg. 1015
HEALTH FITNESS CORPORATION—See Trustmark Mutual Holding Company; U.S. Private, pg. 4251
HERAEUS MEDICAL COMPONENTS CARIBE—See Heraeus Holding GmbH; Int'l, pg. 3358
HMR PLAN LLC—See Profile Development, LLC; U.S. Private, pg. 3277
HUMANA GOVERNMENT BUSINESS, INC.—See Humana, Inc.; U.S. Public, pg. 1070
INTERNATIONAL CENTER FOR ENVIROMENTAL ARTS; U.S. Private, pg. 2115
INVOCARE AUSTRALIA PTY LIMITED—See TPG Capital, L.P.; U.S. Private, pg. 2174
LEHIGH VALLEY HEALTH NETWORK, INC.; U.S. Private, pg. 2418
MEDIXALL GROUP, INC.—See TBG Holdings Corp.; U.S. Private, pg. 3941
MENTAL HEALTH CARE, INC.; U.S. Private, pg. 2667
NEIGHBORLY CARE NETWORK; U.S. Private, pg. 2881
NOVITAS SOLUTIONS INC.—See GuideWell Mutual Holding Corporation; U.S. Private, pg. 1813
OOO BOEHRINGER INGELHEIM—See C.H. Boehringer Sohn AG & Co. KG; Int'l, pg. 1243
OPELOUSAS GENERAL HEALTH SYSTEM; U.S. Private, pg. 3028
PEACH STATE HEALTH PLAN INC.—See Centene Corporation; U.S. Public, pg. 470
REACH EAP, LLC—See Highmark Health; U.S. Private, pg. 1940
SCENIC AREA DEVELOPMENT AND MANAGEMENT COMPANY—See Huangshan Tourism Development Co., Ltd.; Int'l, pg. 3513
SHAPE UP—See Marlin Equity Partners, LLC; U.S. Private, pg. 2585
SIRTEX MEDICAL LIMITED—See CDH China Management Company Limited; Int'l, pg. 1370
UNISON—See UnitedHealth Group Incorporated; U.S. Public, pg. 2238

CORPORATE AFFILIATIONS

VISION SERVICE PLAN; U.S. Private, pg. 4391
VMS BIOMARKETING; U.S. Private, pg. 4408
WEBMD HEALTH SERVICES GROUP, INC.—See KKR & Co. Inc.; U.S. Public, pg. 1254
WELLTOK, INC.; U.S. Private, pg. 4478

923130 — ADMINISTRATION OF HUMAN RESOURCE PROGRAMS (EXCEPT EDUCATION, PUBLIC HEALTH, AND VETERANS&APOS; AFFAIRS PROGRAMS)

AABAKUS, INC.—See New Mountain Capital, LLC; U.S. Private, pg. 2901
ABSOLUTE TOTAL CARE, INC.—See Centene Corporation; U.S. Public, pg. 467
ACTUARIAL CONSULTANTS, INC.—See CBIZ, Inc.; U.S. Public, pg. 456
ADMINISTRATIVE RESOURCES, INC.; U.S. Private, pg. 80
AGA ASSISTANCE AUSTRALIA PTY LTD.—See Allianz SE; Int'l, pg. 341
AXA ASSISTANCE (BEIJING) CO., LTD.—See AXA S.A.; Int'l, pg. 754
AXA ASSISTANCE CANADA INC.—See AXA S.A.; Int'l, pg. 754
CALIFORNIA PUBLIC EMPLOYEES' RETIREMENT SYSTEM; U.S. Private, pg. 720
COMMUNITY SERVICE, INC.—See BNP Paribas SA; Int'l, pg. 1087
CORPORATE FAMILY NETWORK; U.S. Private, pg. 1055
EAGLE CLAIMS SERVICES, INC.—See CorVel Corporation; U.S. Public, pg. 585
EDENRED BULGARIA AD—See Edenred S.A.; Int'l, pg. 2307
EDENRED CZ S.R.O.—See Edenred S.A.; Int'l, pg. 2307
FIDELITY EMPLOYER SERVICES COMPANY LLC—See FMR LLC; U.S. Private, pg. 1555
FIRST NATION GROUP LLC; U.S. Private, pg. 1521
FRAGROUND FRAPORT GROUND SERVICES GMBH—See Cerberus Capital Management, L.P.; U.S. Private, pg. 840
FUND FOR THE PUBLIC INTEREST, INC.; U.S. Private, pg. 1622
HEALTH PLANS, INC.—See Harvard Pilgrim Health Care, Inc.; U.S. Private, pg. 1875
INTER PARTNER ASSISTANCE CO., LTD.—See AXA S.A.; Int'l, pg. 755
INTER PARTNER ASSISTANCE GREECE—See AXA S.A.; Int'l, pg. 755
INTER PARTNER ASSISTANCE LTD—See AXA S.A.; Int'l, pg. 755
INTER PARTNER ASSISTANCE S.A.—See AXA S.A.; Int'l, pg. 755
LIFE CREATE LIMITED—See Fujitsu Limited; Int'l, pg. 2834
LORD ASIA INTERNATIONAL LTD—See Parker Hannifin Corporation; U.S. Public, pg. 1641
MAESTRO HEALTH, INC.—See Marpai, Inc; U.S. Public, pg. 1370
MARITZ MOTIVATION SOLUTIONS INC.—See Maritz Holdings Inc.; U.S. Private, pg. 2577
MEDOPTIONS, INC.; U.S. Private, pg. 2658
MEMORIAL ENDOSCOPY CENTER—See HCA Healthcare, Inc.; U.S. Public, pg. 1002
MIRACLE FLIGHTS; U.S. Private, pg. 2745
MONDIAL ASSISTANCE TURKEY—See Allianz SE; Int'l, pg. 354
MOOREPAY LIMITED—See Bain Capital, LP; U.S. Private, pg. 442
NEXT GENERATION ENROLLMENT, INC.—See Vista Equity Partners, LLC; U.S. Private, pg. 4399
NGA HUMAN RESOURCES SWEDEN AB—See Alight, Inc.; U.S. Public, pg. 76
NHIC, CORP.—See Veritas Capital Fund Management, LLC; U.S. Public, pg. 4364
NORTHGATEARINSO ARGENTINA SA—See Alight, Inc.; U.S. Public, pg. 77
NORTHGATEARINSO AUSTRALIA PTY LTD—See Alight, Inc.; U.S. Public, pg. 77
NORTHGATEARINSO BELGIUM BV—See Alight, Inc.; U.S. Public, pg. 77
NORTHGATEARINSO BELGIUM PEOPLE SERVICES SA—See Alight, Inc.; U.S. Public, pg. 77
NORTHGATEARINSO CANADA INC.—See Alight, Inc.; U.S. Public, pg. 77
NORTHGATEARINSO DEUTSCHLAND AG—See Alight, Inc.; U.S. Public, pg. 77
NORTHGATEARINSO FINLAND OY—See Alight, Inc.; U.S. Public, pg. 77
NORTHGATEARINSO FRANCE S.A.S.—See Alight, Inc.; U.S. Public, pg. 77
NORTHGATEARINSO ITALIA S.R.L.—See Alight, Inc.; U.S. Public, pg. 77
NORTHGATEARINSO LUXEMBOURG SA—See Alight, Inc.; U.S. Public, pg. 77
NORTHGATEARINSO MADRID SA—See Alight, Inc.; U.S. Public, pg. 77

N.A.I.C.S. INDEX

926110 — ADMINISTRATION OF G...

NORTHGATEARINSO MALAYSIA SDN BHD—See Alight, Inc.; *U.S. Public*, pg. 77
NORTHGATEARINSO MILANO S.R.L.—See Alight, Inc.; *U.S. Public*, pg. 77
NORTHGATEARINSO PHILIPPINES INC.—See Alight, Inc.; *U.S. Public*, pg. 77
NORTHGATEARINSO SINGAPORE PTE LTD—See Alight, Inc.; *U.S. Public*, pg. 77
NORTHGATEARINSO THAILAND (CO.) LTD—See Alight, Inc.; *U.S. Public*, pg. 77
NORTHWEST SENIOR & DISABILITY SERVICES; *U.S. Private*, pg. 2961
OUTCOMES INCORPORATED—See Cardinal Health, Inc.; *U.S. Public*, pg. 434
PARADIGM GROUP, LLC—See New Mountain Capital, LLC; *U.S. Private*, pg. 2901
QUANTUM HEALTH, LLC—See Warburg Pincus LLC; *U.S. Private*, pg. 4439
RADSITE LLC—See RadNet, Inc.; *U.S. Public*, pg. 1761
RISKSENSE, INC.(1)—See Lumen Technologies, Inc.; *U.S. Public*, pg. 1347
ROBIDUS GROEP B.V.—See Aegon N.V.; *Int'l*, pg. 175
ROWLANDS & BARRANCA AGENCY, INC.—See Brown & Brown, Inc.; *U.S. Public*, pg. 402
SHL GROUP LIMITED—See Exponent Private Equity LLP; *Int'l*, pg. 2589
SHL (UK) LIMITED—See Exponent Private Equity LLP; *Int'l*, pg. 2589
THOMSONS ONLINE BENEFITS LTD.—See Marsh & McLennan Companies, Inc.; *U.S. Public*, pg. 1386
TRINET - BRADENTON—See General Atlantic Service Company, L.P.; *U.S. Private*, pg. 1663
ZELLIS UK LIMITED—See Bain Capital, LP; *U.S. Private*, pg. 452

924110 — ADMINISTRATION OF AIR AND WATER RESOURCE AND SOLID WASTE MANAGEMENT PROGRAMS

374WATER, INC.; *U.S. Public*, pg. 3
ABTECH HOLDINGS, INC.; *U.S. Private*, pg. 45
ADI GROUP INC.; *Int'l*, pg. 145
ADI SYSTEMS ASIA PACIFIC LIMITED—See ADI Group Inc.; *Int'l*, pg. 145
ADI SYSTEMS USA INC.—See ADI Group Inc.; *Int'l*, pg. 145
A.I.S. AG; *Int'l*, pg. 24
ALTEAU S.A.—See Caisse des Depots et Consignations; *Int'l*, pg. 1257
A. MORTON THOMAS & ASSOCIATES INC.; *U.S. Private*, pg. 23
AQSEPTENCE GROUP SRL.—See Brookfield Corporation; *Int'l*, pg. 1182
AQUALIA GESTION INTEGRAL DEL AGUA S.A.—See Fomento de Construcciones y Contratas, S.A.; *Int'l*, pg. 2722
.A.S.A. ABFALL SERVICE AG—See Fomento de Construcciones y Contratas, S.A.; *Int'l*, pg. 2722
.A.S.A. ABFALL SERVICE HALBENRAIN GMBH—See Fomento de Construcciones y Contratas, S.A.; *Int'l*, pg. 2722
.A.S.A. AREAL SPOL. S.R.O—See Fomento de Construcciones y Contratas, S.A.; *Int'l*, pg. 2722
AVACON WASSER GMBH—See E.ON SE; *Int'l*, pg. 2251
BEWG (M) SDN BHD—See Beijing Enterprises Water Group Limited; *Int'l*, pg. 950
BIOTECHPROGRESS SCIENTIFIC RESEARCH & PRODUCTION CO. ZAO; *Int'l*, pg. 1043
BLUMETRIC ENVIRONMENTAL INC.; *Int'l*, pg. 1075
BQE WATER INC.; *Int'l*, pg. 1133
CALIFORNIA AMERICAN WATER COMPANY—See American Water Works Company, Inc.; *U.S. Public*, pg. 112
CASELLA RECYCLING, LLC—See Casella Waste Systems, Inc.; *U.S. Public*, pg. 446
CLAYTON COUNTY WATER AUTHORITY; *U.S. Private*, pg. 918
CORE LABORATORIES AUSTRALIA PTY LTD—See Core Laboratories N.V.; *Int'l*, pg. 1798
COUNTY SANITATION DISTRICTS OF LOS ANGELES COUNTY; *U.S. Private*, pg. 1068
DARCO ENGINEERING PTE LTD.—See Darco Water Technologies Limited; *Int'l*, pg. 1972
DARCO INDUSTRIAL WATER SDN. BHD.—See Darco Water Technologies Limited; *Int'l*, pg. 1972
DARCO WATER SYSTEMS SDN. BHD.—See Darco Water Technologies Limited; *Int'l*, pg. 1972
DARCO WATER TECHNOLOGIES LIMITED; *Int'l*, pg. 1972
DATANG ENVIRONMENT INDUSTRY GROUP CO., LTD.—See China Datang Corporation; *Int'l*, pg. 1496
DELAWARE RIVER WATERFRONT CORPORATION; *U.S. Private*, pg. 1195
DELTA INFRA B.V.—See Delta N.V.; *Int'l*, pg. 2019
DELTA INVESTERINGS MAATSCHAPPIJ B.V.—See Delta N.V.; *Int'l*, pg. 2019
DELTA MILIEU GROENCOMPOST B.V.—See Delta N.V.; *Int'l*, pg. 2019
DELTA MILIEU RECYCLING B.V.—See Delta N.V.; *Int'l*, pg. 2019

DELTIUS B.V.—See Delta N.V.; *Int'l*, pg. 2019
DURR SYSTEMS CANADA INC.—See Durr AG; *Int'l*, pg. 2231
ENVIRONMENTAL CLEAN TECHNOLOGIES LIMITED; *Int'l*, pg. 2454
EPCOR WATER SERVICES, INC.—See EPCOR Utilities, Inc.; *Int'l*, pg. 2459
ESN ENERGIESYSTEMENORD GMBH—See E.ON SE; *Int'l*, pg. 2257
EVOQUA WATER TECHNOLOGIES—See Xylem Inc.; *U.S. Public*, pg. 2394
GK INDUSTRIAL REFUSE SYSTEMS—See Bestige Holdings LLC; *U.S. Private*, pg. 544
GRAND STRAND WATER & SEWER AUTHORITY; *U.S. Private*, pg. 1753
GREEN BAY WATER UTILITY; *U.S. Private*, pg. 1771
GREEN COMPLIANCE WATER DIVISION LTD.—See Arjun Infrastructure Partners Limited; *Int'l*, pg. 568
GUADALUPE-BLANCO RIVER AUTHORITY; *U.S. Private*, pg. 1808
GULF COAST WATER AUTHORITY; *U.S. Private*, pg. 1815
HARPETH VALLEY UTILITIES DISTRICT OF DAVIDSON & WILLIAMSON COUNTIES; *U.S. Private*, pg. 1868
IMPROCHEM (PTY) LIMITED—See AECI Limited; *Int'l*, pg. 171
INDAVER NEDERLAND B.V.—See Delta N.V.; *Int'l*, pg. 2019
INTEGRATED WATER SERVICES, INC.—See Sciens Capital Management LLC; *U.S. Private*, pg. 3574
INTERNETPLATFORM ZEELAND B.V.—See Delta N.V.; *Int'l*, pg. 2019
LITRO ENERGIE NEDERLAND B.V.—See Delta N.V.; *Int'l*, pg. 2019
MERCIA WASTE MANAGEMENT LTD.—See Fomento de Construcciones y Contratas, S.A.; *Int'l*, pg. 2723
NORTHUMBRIAN WATER GROUP PLC—See CK Hutchison Holdings Limited; *Int'l*, pg. 1637
NRC NY ENVIRONMENTAL SERVICES, INC.—See Republic Services, Inc.; *U.S. Public*, pg. 1788
OUTWORX GROUP—See Guggenheim Partners, LLC; *U.S. Private*, pg. 1811
PERC WATER CORPORATION—See Consolidated Water Co. Ltd.; *Int'l*, pg. 1771
SEVERN WASTE SERVICES LIMITED—See Fomento de Construcciones y Contratas, S.A.; *Int'l*, pg. 2723
SHANGHAI DARCO ENVIROTECH COMPANY LIMITED—See Darco Water Technologies Limited; *Int'l*, pg. 1972
SIMSMETAL SERVICES PTY LIMITED—See Sims Limited; *U.S. Public*, pg. 1884
STEAG POWER MINERALS GMBH—See Energeticky a Prumyslovy Holding, a.s.; *Int'l*, pg. 2420
STORTPLAATS KOEGORSPOLDER B.V.—See Delta N.V.; *Int'l*, pg. 2019
TDS TELECOM—See Telephone & Data Systems, Inc.; *U.S. Public*, pg. 1997
URBASER, LTD.—See Platinum Equity, LLC; *U.S. Private*, pg. 3209
WASTE MANAGEMENT PACIFIC PTY. LIMITED—See Cleanaway Waste Management Limited; *Int'l*, pg. 1655
WATERKEEPER ALLIANCE INC.; *U.S. Private*, pg. 4453

924120 — ADMINISTRATION OF CONSERVATION PROGRAMS

AFG-UPL II LLC.; *U.S. Private*, pg. 123
CALIFORNIA DEPARTMENT OF CONSERVATION; *U.S. Private*, pg. 719
KEEN TECHNICAL SOLUTIONS LLC; *U.S. Private*, pg. 2272
MINOL USA; *U.S. Private*, pg. 2744
THE TRUST FOR PUBLIC LAND; *U.S. Private*, pg. 4128

925110 — ADMINISTRATION OF HOUSING PROGRAMS

BELLWETHER HOUSING; *U.S. Private*, pg. 520
BROOKFIELD HOMES ONTARIO LTD.—See Brookfield Corporation; *Int'l*, pg. 1187
CARRFOUR SUPPORTIVE HOUSING, INC.; *U.S. Private*, pg. 771
HOUSING AND URBAN DEVELOPMENT CORPORATION LIMITED; *Int'l*, pg. 3491
MANUFACTURED HOUSING PROPERTIES INC.; *U.S. Public*, pg. 1362
MINNEAPOLIS PUBLIC HOUSING AUTHORITY; *U.S. Private*, pg. 2743
NEW HAMPSHIRE HOUSING FINANCE AUTHORITY; *U.S. Private*, pg. 2896
PINELLAS COUNTY HOUSING AUTHORITY; *U.S. Private*, pg. 3183
SCIC HABITAT—See Caisse des Depots et Consignations; *Int'l*, pg. 1258
TAMPA HOUSING AUTHORITY; *U.S. Private*, pg. 3929
TWIN CITY CHRISTIAN HOMES, INC.; *U.S. Private*, pg. 4264
WORKING BUILDINGS, LLC—See Keystone Group, L.P.; *U.S. Private*, pg. 2299

925120 — ADMINISTRATION OF URBAN PLANNING AND COMMUNITY AND RURAL DEVELOPMENT

ALPHAVILLE URBANISMO S.A.—See Blackstone Inc.; *U.S. Public*, pg. 360
ARROW RESOURCES DEVELOPMENT, INC.; *U.S. Private*, pg. 335
BOTSWANA DEVELOPMENT CORPORATION LIMITED; *Int'l*, pg. 1118
CAISSE DES DEPOTS ET CONSIGNATIONS - LOCAL & REGIONAL DEVELOPMENT—See Caisse des Depots et Consignations; *Int'l*, pg. 1257
CARL M. FREEMAN ASSOCIATES, INC.; *U.S. Private*, pg. 762
CARL M. FREEMAN COMMUNITIES, LLC—See Carl M. Freeman Associates, Inc.; *U.S. Private*, pg. 762
CITIC GUOAN GROUP CO., LTD.—See CITIC Group Corporation; *Int'l*, pg. 1620
CMP PLANNING LTD.—See Chugoku Marine Paints, Ltd.; *Int'l*, pg. 1595
COMMUNITY DEVELOPMENT, INC.—See Associations, Inc.; *U.S. Private*, pg. 359
COYOTE SYSTEM SAS; *Int'l*, pg. 1823
CTC PUBLIC BENEFIT CORPORATION—See Concurrent Technologies Corporation; *U.S. Private*, pg. 1011
DENTSU ASIA PTE. LTD.—See Dentsu Group Inc.; *Int'l*, pg. 2036
DISTRITO CASTELLANA NORTE, S.A.—See Banco Bilbao Vizcaya Argentaria, S.A.; *Int'l*, pg. 817
EURAMEX MANAGEMENT GROUP, LLC; *U.S. Private*, pg. 1433
EXPORT CREDIT INSURANCE & GUARANTEE (PTY) LTD—See Botswana Development Corporation Limited; *Int'l*, pg. 1118
MIAMI DOWNTOWN DEVELOPMENT AUTHORITY; *U.S. Private*, pg. 2696
NANA DEVELOPMENT CORPORATION—See Nana Regional Corporation, Inc.; *U.S. Private*, pg. 2832
NORTH CAROLINA RURAL ECONOMIC DEVELOPMENT CENTER, INC.; *U.S. Private*, pg. 2943
OPA CO., LTD—See AEON Co., Ltd.; *Int'l*, pg. 177
PASCO ECONOMIC DEVELOPMENT COUNCIL, INC.; *U.S. Private*, pg. 3104
PINELLAS COUNTY UTILITIES; *U.S. Private*, pg. 3183
RURAL FINANCE CORPORATION OF VICTORIA—See Bendigo & Adelaide Bank Ltd.; *Int'l*, pg. 971
SPORTS & EXHIBITION AUTHORITY OF PITTSBURGH & ALLEGHENY COUNTY; *U.S. Private*, pg. 3760
UNITED NATIONS DEVELOPMENT CORPORATION; *U.S. Private*, pg. 4295
U.S. BANCORP COMMUNITY DEVELOPMENT CORPORATION—See U.S. Bancorp; *U.S. Public*, pg. 2212
WEST BAY RESIDENTIAL SERVICES, INC.; *U.S. Private*, pg. 4483
WORLD NEIGHBORS, INC.—See Feed The Children, Inc.; *U.S. Private*, pg. 1492
WYOMING BUSINESS COUNCIL; *U.S. Private*, pg. 4578

926110 — ADMINISTRATION OF GENERAL ECONOMIC PROGRAMS

AGA KHAN DEVELOPMENT NETWORK; *Int'l*, pg. 198
AGA KHAN FUND FOR ECONOMIC DEVELOPMENT S.A.—See Aga Khan Development Network; *Int'l*, pg. 199
ARTIS-NAPLES; *U.S. Private*, pg. 343
AUSTRALIAN TRADE AND INVESTMENT COMMISSION; *Int'l*, pg. 722
BRAC; *Int'l*, pg. 1133
CENTRAL FLORIDA PARTNERSHIP, INC.; *U.S. Private*, pg. 820
CETCO ENERGY SERVICES COMPANY LLC—See Minerals Technologies, Inc.; *U.S. Public*, pg. 1448
CETCO ENERGY SERVICES DE MEXICO, S.A. DE C.V.—See Minerals Technologies, Inc.; *U.S. Public*, pg. 1448
CETCO ENERGY SERVICES LIMITED—See Minerals Technologies, Inc.; *U.S. Public*, pg. 1448
CETCO ENERGY SERVICES (MALAYSIA) SDN. BHD.—See Minerals Technologies, Inc.; *U.S. Public*, pg. 1448
CETCO OILFIELD SERVICES COMPANY NIGERIA LIMITED—See Minerals Technologies, Inc.; *U.S. Public*, pg. 1448
CETCOPOLAND, CETCO SP. Z.O.O. S.K.A.—See Minerals Technologies, Inc.; *U.S. Public*, pg. 1449
CETCO SP. Z O.O.—See Minerals Technologies, Inc.; *U.S. Public*, pg. 1449
CHILDREN'S SERVICES OF ROXBURY, INC.; *U.S. Private*, pg. 885
CONFEDERATED TRIBES OF WARM SPRINGS; *U.S. Private*, pg. 1012
DIVERSIFIED BUSINESS COMMUNICATIONS UK—See Diversified Communications; *U.S. Private*, pg. 1241
EMPYREAN ENERGY PLC; *Int'l*, pg. 2392

926110 — ADMINISTRATION OF G...

ERICO D.O.O.—See Hisense Co., Ltd.; *Int'l*, pg. 3407
FONDS DE SOLIDARITE DES TRAVAILLEURS DU QUEBEC; *Int'l*, pg. 2725
GORENJE GTI D.O.O.—See Hisense Co., Ltd.; *Int'l*, pg. 3407
GREAT AMERICAN OPPORTUNITIES, INC.—See The Southwestern Company; *U.S. Private*, pg. 4119
GREATER TAMPA CHAMBER OF COMMERCE; *U.S. Private*, pg. 1770
HONG KONG TOURISM BOARD - NEW YORK—See Hong Kong Tourism Board; *Int'l*, pg. 3467
HONG KONG TOURISM BOARD; *Int'l*, pg. 3467
IA ENERGY CORP.; *U.S. Private*, pg. 2027
IDAHO DEPARTMENT OF COMMERCE; *U.S. Private*, pg. 2034
INDOP D.O.O.—See Hisense Co., Ltd.; *Int'l*, pg. 3407
INNOGY SE—See E.ON SE; *Int'l*, pg. 2258
INSTITUTE FOR BUILDING TECHNOLOGY AND SAFETY; *U.S. Private*, pg. 2093
JEEVES INFORMATION SYSTEMS UK LTD—See Battery Ventures, L.P.; *U.S. Private*, pg. 489
KEMIS-TERMOCLEAN D.O.O.—See Hisense Co., Ltd.; *Int'l*, pg. 3407
MARVIN TRAUB ASSOCIATES, INC.; *U.S. Private*, pg. 2598
MARYLAND ECONOMIC DEVELOPMENT CORPORATION; *U.S. Private*, pg. 2600
MISSISSIPPI COUNTY, ARKANSAS, ECONOMIC OPPORTUNITY COMMISSION, INC.; *U.S. Private*, pg. 2748
PARK AVENUE ARMORY; *U.S. Private*, pg. 3095
PIDC - REGIONAL DEVELOPMENT CORPORATION—See Wells Fargo & Company; *U.S. Public*, pg. 2344
PT. CETCO OILFIELD SERVICES INDONESIA—See Minerals Technologies, Inc.; *U.S. Public*, pg. 1449
PUERTO RICO INDUSTRIAL DEVELOPMENT COMPANY; *U.S. Private*, pg. 3302
QUESTAR ENERGY SERVICES, INC.—See Dominion Energy, Inc.; *U.S. Public*, pg. 674
TAMPA BAY PARTNERSHIP FOR REGIONAL ECONOMIC DEVELOPMENT, INC.; *U.S. Private*, pg. 3929
TAMPA DOWNTOWN PARTNERSHIP, INC.; *U.S. Private*, pg. 3929
TAPE; *U.S. Private*, pg. 3932
TBS WORKFORCE PTY LTD.—See Aquirian Limited; *Int'l*, pg. 528

926120 — REGULATION AND ADMINISTRATION OF TRANSPORTATION PROGRAMS

AMERICAN BUREAU OF SHIPPING; *U.S. Private*, pg. 225
ANGLO ARDMORE SHIP MANAGEMENT LIMITED—See Ardmore Shipping Corporation; *Int'l*, pg. 556
ARDMORE SHIPPING (ASIA) PTE LIMITED—See Ardmore Shipping Corporation; *Int'l*, pg. 556
ASSOCIATION OF AMERICAN RAILROADS; *U.S. Private*, pg. 358
CENTRAL NEW YORK REGIONAL TRANSPORTATION AUTHORITY; *U.S. Private*, pg. 823
CONTRACTUM LIMITED—See Verra Mobility Corporation; *U.S. Public*, pg. 2286
COPENHAGEN MALMO PORT; *Int'l*, pg. 1793
CTI TAXI TRUCKS PTY. LTD.—See CTI Logistics Limited; *Int'l*, pg. 1871
D&D TRAFFIC MANAGEMENT PTY LTD.—See AVADA Group Limited; *Int'l*, pg. 734
DELAWARE RIVER PORT AUTHORITY OF PENNSYLVANIA & NEW JERSEY; *U.S. Private*, pg. 1195
THE DRIVERY GMBH—See Hella GmbH & Co. KGaA; *Int'l*, pg. 3332
ENAIRE; *Int'l*, pg. 2396
EPC HUNGARY KFT—See Verra Mobility Corporation; *U.S. Public*, pg. 2286
EURO PARKING COLLECTION, PLC—See Verra Mobility Corporation; *U.S. Public*, pg. 2286
FORE RIVER TRANSPORTATION CORPORATION—See FGV Holdings Bhd; *Int'l*, pg. 2649
INDIANAPOLIS AIRPORT AUTHORITY; *U.S. Private*, pg. 2063
LINEMARK TRAFFIC CONTROL PTY LTD.—See AVADA Group Limited; *Int'l*, pg. 734
MAERSK LOGISTICS & SERVICES PERU S.A.—See A.P. Moller-Maersk A/S; *Int'l*, pg. 27
MISSOURI DEPARTMENT OF TRANSPORTATION; *U.S. Private*, pg. 2749
MVD EXPRESS; *U.S. Private*, pg. 2821
NIAGARA FRONTIER TRANSPORTATION AUTHORITY; *U.S. Private*, pg. 2924
NJ TRANSIT CORPORATION; *U.S. Private*, pg. 2930
ORBIS TRANSPORT SP. Z O.O.—See Accor S.A.; *Int'l*, pg. 92
PENNSYLVANIA TURNPIKE COMMISSION; *U.S. Private*, pg. 3137
PLATEPASS, L.L.C.—See Verra Mobility Corporation; *U.S. Public*, pg. 2286
PLATINUM TRAFFIC SERVICES PTY LTD.—See AVADA Group Limited; *Int'l*, pg. 734
PORT OF OAKLAND; *U.S. Private*, pg. 3230
PORT OF PORTLAND; *U.S. Private*, pg. 3230
REGIONAL TRANSPORTATION AUTHORITY; *U.S. Private*, pg. 3389
ROAD SAFETY CONSULTING N.V.—See DEKRA e.V.; *Int'l*, pg. 2009
SCA - SCHEDULE COORDINATION AUSTRIA GMBH—See Deutsche Lufthansa AG; *Int'l*, pg. 2066
SOUTH CAROLINA DEPARTMENT OF TRANSPORTATION; *U.S. Private*, pg. 3720
VERIFACT TRAFFIC PTY LTD.—See AVADA Group Limited; *Int'l*, pg. 734
VIRGINIA PORT AUTHORITY; *U.S. Private*, pg. 4388

926130 — REGULATION AND ADMINISTRATION OF COMMUNICATIONS, ELECTRIC, GAS, AND OTHER UTILITIES

ABU DHABI WATER & ELECTRICITY AUTHORITY; *Int'l*, pg. 73
ATC MANAGEMENT INC.; *U.S. Private*, pg. 365
AUSTRALIAN ENERGY MARKET OPERATOR LIMITED; *Int'l*, pg. 721
B.C. HYDRO; *Int'l*, pg. 789
BILFINGER INDUSTRIAL SERVICES BETEILIGUNGS GMBH—See Bilfinger SE; *Int'l*, pg. 1027
BONNEVILLE POWER ADMINISTRATION; *U.S. Private*, pg. 615
BRISTOL VIRGINIA UTILITIES; *U.S. Private*, pg. 657
CELLE-UELZEN NETZ GMBH—See E.ON SE; *Int'l*, pg. 2251
CEPS, A.S.; *Int'l*, pg. 1420
CLAY COUNTY RURAL TELEPHONE COOPERATIVE, INC.; *U.S. Private*, pg. 917
COMPANHIA ENERGETICA DE MINAS GERAIS - CEMIG; *Int'l*, pg. 1747
COMPANHIA ENERGETICA DO PIAUI SA—See Equatorial Energia SA; *Int'l*, pg. 2484
THE COMPLIANCE GROUP, INC.—See First Reserve Management, L.P.; *U.S. Private*, pg. 1526
CONNECTICUT MUNICIPAL ELECTRICAL ENERGY COOPERATIVE; *U.S. Private*, pg. 1016
CORN BELT ENERGY CORPORATION; *U.S. Private*, pg. 1050
CYPRUS TELECOMMUNICATIONS AUTHORITY; *Int'l*, pg. 1897
DENTON COUNTY ELECTRIC COOPERATIVE, INC.—See CoServ Utility Holdings, L.P.; *U.S. Private*, pg. 1062
ECHO MANAGED SERVICES LTD.—See Arjun Infrastructure Partners Limited; *Int'l*, pg. 568
ECOLAB SERVICES ARGENTINA S.R.L.—See Ecolab Inc.; *U.S. Public*, pg. 714
EMERALD COAST UTILITIES AUTHORITY; *U.S. Private*, pg. 1379
ENEL COLINA SA—See Enel S.p.A.; *Int'l*, pg. 2412
ENERGIE UND WASSER POTSDAM GMBH—See E.ON SE; *Int'l*, pg. 2257
ENERGIE UND WASSER WAHLSTEDT/BAD SEGEBERG GMBH & CO. KG—See E.ON SE; *Int'l*, pg. 2257
ENERGY PROFESSIONALS, LLC; *U.S. Private*, pg. 1395
ENVIROMISSION LIMITED; *Int'l*, pg. 2454
ESN SICHERHEIT UND ZERTIFIZIERUNG GMBH—See E.ON SE; *Int'l*, pg. 2257
FAST SOLAR SDN. BHD.—See Fast Energy Holdings Berhad; *Int'l*, pg. 2621
FORTUM CHARGE & DRIVE INDIA PRIVATE LIMITED—See Fortum Oyj; *Int'l*, pg. 2740
GRAND HAVEN BOARD OF LIGHT & POWER; *U.S. Private*, pg. 1752
GRAND RIVER DAM AUTHORITY; *U.S. Private*, pg. 1753
GRIDSENSE INC.—See Franklin Electric Co., Inc.; *U.S. Public*, pg. 878
GUAM POWER AUTHORITY; *U.S. Private*, pg. 1808
GUTHRIE COUNTY RURAL ELECTRIC COOPERATIVE ASSOCIATION; *U.S. Private*, pg. 1820
HARRIMAN UTILITY BOARD; *U.S. Private*, pg. 1868
HEAG SUDHESSISCHE ENERGIE AG; *Int'l*, pg. 3302
INNOAGE PEI S.A.M.—See Aliaxis S.A./N.V.; *Int'l*, pg. 324
JUSEV CHARGING NETWORK SDN. BHD.—See Dancomech Holdings Berhad; *Int'l*, pg. 1959
KLINIKEN MILTENBERG-ERLENBACH GMBH—See Fresenius SE & Co. KGaA; *Int'l*, pg. 2779
MANCHASOL 2 CENTRAL TERMOSOLAR DOS, S.L.—See ACS, Actividades de Construccion y Servicios, S.A.; *Int'l*, pg. 115
MARAFIQ COMPANY—See Abdullah Al-Othaim Markets Company; *Int'l*, pg. 59
MCLEOD COOPERATIVE POWER ASSOCIATION; *U.S. Private*, pg. 2641
MICO SERVICES LIMITED—See Carillion plc; *Int'l*, pg. 1330
MOMENTUM TELECOM, INC.—See Court Square Capital Partners, L.P.; *U.S. Private*, pg. 1069
MUNICIPAL ELECTRIC AUTHORITY OF GEORGIA; *U.S. Private*, pg. 2814
NETZ-UND WINDSERVICE (NWS) GMBH—See E.ON SE; *Int'l*, pg. 2256
NEW YORK STATE ELECTRIC & GAS CORPORATION—See Iberdrola, S.A.; *Int'l*, pg. 3571
PENNSYLVANIA POWER COMPANY—See FirstEnergy Corp.; *U.S. Public*, pg. 849
REALGY, LLC; *U.S. Private*, pg. 3368
RIBAGRANDE ENERGIA, S.L.—See ACS, Actividades de Construccion y Servicios, S.A.; *Int'l*, pg. 116
RPC BRAMLAGE FOOD GMBH—See Berry Global Group, Inc; *U.S. Public*, pg. 324
SERVIZIO ELETTRICO NAZIONALE SPA—See Enel S.p.A.; *Int'l*, pg. 2414
SOLSONICA—See EEMS Italia S.p.A; *Int'l*, pg. 2317
SOUTH CAROLINA PUBLIC SERVICE AUTHORITY; *U.S. Private*, pg. 3720
SPIE FLEISCHHAUER GMBH—See Caisse de Depot et Placement du Quebec; *Int'l*, pg. 1255
STADTWERKE DUSSELDORF AG—See EnBW Energie Baden-Wurttemberg AG; *Int'l*, pg. 2400
STADTWERKE FORST GMBH—See ENGIE SA; *Int'l*, pg. 2429
STADTWERKE FORST GMBH—See E.ON SE; *Int'l*, pg. 2257
STADTWERKE SINSHEIM VERSORGUNGS GMBH & CO. KG—See EnBW Energie Baden-Wurttemberg AG; *Int'l*, pg. 2400
ST BRIDES PARTNERS LTD.—See Fandango Holdings Plc; *Int'l*, pg. 2613
SUNDURANCE ENERGY, LLC; *U.S. Private*, pg. 3866

926140 — REGULATION OF AGRICULTURAL MARKETING AND COMMODITIES

ADM AGRO INDUSTRIES INDIA PRIVATE LIMITED—See Archer-Daniels-Midland Company; *U.S. Public*, pg. 181
ADM AUSTRALIA PTY. LIMITED—See Archer-Daniels-Midland Company; *U.S. Public*, pg. 181
ADM CZERNIN, S.A.—See Archer-Daniels-Midland Company; *U.S. Public*, pg. 181
ADM DIRECT POLSKA SP. Z O.O.—See Archer-Daniels-Midland Company; *U.S. Public*, pg. 181
ADM HAMBURG AKTIENGESELLSCHAFT—See Archer-Daniels-Midland Company; *U.S. Public*, pg. 182
AG PRODUCERS CO-OP; *U.S. Private*, pg. 125
AGRI PRODUCTS INC—See The Kroger Co.; *U.S. Public*, pg. 2107
AGROMINO A/S; *Int'l*, pg. 220
AMEROPA NORTH AMERICA, INC.—See Ameropa AG; *Int'l*, pg. 424
ARCHER-DANIELS-MIDLAND PHILIPPINES, INC.—See Archer-Daniels-Midland Company; *U.S. Public*, pg. 184
ARCHER DANIELS MIDLAND SINGAPORE, PTE. LTD.—See Archer-Daniels-Midland Company; *U.S. Public*, pg. 184
ATALANTA NOVA SRL—See Gellert Global Group; *U.S. Private*, pg. 1656
BASSETT & WALKER INTERNATIONAL, INC.; *Int'l*, pg. 888
BECK AG; *U.S. Private*, pg. 510
BENSON HILL HOLDINGS, INC.—See Benson Hills, Inc.; *U.S. Public*, pg. 296
BENSON HILLS, INC.; *U.S. Public*, pg. 296
CALAVO GROWERS, INC.; *U.S. Public*, pg. 422
CERESCO; *Int'l*, pg. 1422
CHS BROADBENT PTY. LTD.—See CHS INC.; *U.S. Public*, pg. 491
COMPANIA INTEGRADORA MERCANTIL AGRICOLA, S.A. DE C.V.—See Empresas ICA S.A.B. de C.V.; *Int'l*, pg. 2390
CONSERV FS INC.; *U.S. Private*, pg. 1019
COOPER LAND COMPANY OF NEW JERSEY, INC.—See Bayer Aktiengesellschaft; *Int'l*, pg. 907
CORTEVA AGRISCIENCE (CAMBODIA) CO., LTD.—See Corteva, Inc.; *U.S. Public*, pg. 581
CORTEVA AGRISCIENCE CANADA COMPANY—See Corteva, Inc.; *U.S. Public*, pg. 581
CORTEVA AGRISCIENCE CROATIA LLC—See Corteva, Inc.; *U.S. Public*, pg. 581
CORTEVA AGRISCIENCE GERMANY GMBH—See Corteva, Inc.; *U.S. Public*, pg. 581
CORTEVA AGRISCIENCE MAROC SARL—See Corteva, Inc.; *U.S. Public*, pg. 581
CORTEVA AGRISCIENCE ROMANIA S.R.L.—See Corteva, Inc.; *U.S. Public*, pg. 581
CORTEVA AGRISCIENCE SRB D.O.O.—See Corteva, Inc.; *U.S. Public*, pg. 581
CORTEVA AGRISCIENCE VIETNAM CO., LTD.—See Corteva, Inc.; *U.S. Public*, pg. 581
DAIRY FARMERS OF AMERICA, INC.; *U.S. Private*, pg. 1145
DESAB S.A.—See Corteva, Inc.; *U.S. Public*, pg. 581
DGO GROBHANDEL GMBH—See AGRAVIS Raiffeisen AG; *Int'l*, pg. 215
EMPRESAS IANSA S.A.—See ED&F Man Holdings Limited; *Int'l*, pg. 2303
ENQUICKFIX LIMITED—See ENL Limited; *Int'l*, pg. 2441
FANE VALLEY CO-OPERATIVE SOCIETY LTD.; *Int'l*, pg. 2613
FARMS.COM LTD.; *Int'l*, pg. 2620

FGL HANDELSGESELLSCHAFT MBH—See AGRAVIS Raiffeisen AG; *Int'l*, pg. 215
FOREST AGRI SERVICES LTD.; *Int'l*, pg. 2732
GENESIS IBRC INDIA LIMITED; *Int'l*, pg. 2921
GHANA COCOA BOARD; *Int'l*, pg. 2958
GRAINCOM GMBH—See AGRAVIS Raiffeisen AG; *Int'l*, pg. 215
GROWMARK, INC.; *U.S. Private*, pg. 1795
HERDADE DE RIO FRIO, S.A.—See CORTICEIRA AMORIM, S.G.P.S., S.A.; *Int'l*, pg. 1807
HOEGEMEYER HYBRIDS, INC.—See Corteva, Inc.; *U.S. Public*, pg. 584
INSPECTORATE AMERICA CORPORATION—See Bureau Veritas S.A.; *Int'l*, pg. 1222
MASHONALAND TOBACCO HOLDINGS (PVT) LTD.—See Pyxus International, Inc.; *U.S. Public*, pg. 1740
PBC LIMITED—See Ghana Cocoa Board; *Int'l*, pg. 2958
PIONEER HI-BRED MAGYARORSZAG KFT—See Corteva, Inc.; *U.S. Public*, pg. 584
PIONEER HI-BRED NORTHERN EUROPE SERVICE DIVISION GMBH—See Corteva, Inc.; *U.S. Public*, pg. 584
PIONEER HI-BRED POLAND SP Z O.O.—See Corteva, Inc.; *U.S. Public*, pg. 584
PIONEER HI-BRED ROMANIA S.R.L.—See Corteva, Inc.; *U.S. Public*, pg. 584
P.T. INDONESIA TRI SEMBILAN—See Pyxus International, Inc.; *U.S. Public*, pg. 1741
RANGEN, INC. - COMMODITIES DIVISION—See Wilbur-Ellis Company; *U.S. Private*, pg. 4518
ROB-SEE-CO; *U.S. Private*, pg. 3456
SEWARD CO-OP GROCERY & DELI; *U.S. Private*, pg. 3619
SOCIETE INDUSTRIELLE DES OLEAGINEUX-SIO—See Archer-Daniels-Midland Company; *U.S. Public*, pg. 185
TOSHOKU LTD.—See Cargill, Inc.; *U.S. Private*, pg. 760

926150 — REGULATION, LICENSING, AND INSPECTION OF MISCELLANEOUS COMMERCIAL SECTORS

ACIRL QUALITY TESTING SERVICES PTY LTD—See ALS Limited; *Int'l*, pg. 377
AFI FLIGHT INSPECTION GMBH—See Advent International Corporation; *U.S. Private*, pg. 98
ALEXIUM INC—See Alexium International Group Limited; *Int'l*, pg. 307
AMERICAN INDUSTRIAL HYGIENE ASSOCIATION; *U.S. Private*, pg. 237
APPLUS+ VELOSI—See I Squared Capital Advisors (US) LLC; *U.S. Private*, pg. 2023
ARCHON TECHNOLOGIES LTD; *Int'l*, pg. 549
AUTOMOBILE INSPECTION SYSTEM INC.—See Aucnet Inc.; *Int'l*, pg. 700
AVALON COPY CENTERS OF AMERICA, INC.—See Surge Private Equity LLC; *U.S. Private*, pg. 3884
BIOTRON LIMITED; *Int'l*, pg. 1043
BLDG.WORKS-USA, INC.; *U.S. Private*, pg. 580
BON JOUR INTERNATIONAL LICENSING DIVISION—See Bon Jour Capital; *U.S. Private*, pg. 612
BRUNEL GMBH—See Brunel International N.V.; *Int'l*, pg. 1199
CHAMPIONS (UK) PLC.; *Int'l*, pg. 1440
COBHAM FLIGHT INSPECTION LIMITED—See Advent International Corporation; *U.S. Private*, pg. 99
COINS PORTUGAL UNIP LDA—See Cotecna Inspection S.A.; *Int'l*, pg. 1816
COLORLIGHT US, INC.—See Colorlight Cloud Tech Ltd.; *Int'l*, pg. 1704
COTECNA - BEIJING—See Cotecna Inspection S.A.; *Int'l*, pg. 1816
COTECNA CERTIFICADORA SERVICES LTDA—See Cotecna Inspection S.A.; *Int'l*, pg. 1816
COTECNA DEL ECUADOR SA—See Cotecna Inspection S.A.; *Int'l*, pg. 1816
COTECNA DEL PARAGUAY S.A.—See Cotecna Inspection S.A.; *Int'l*, pg. 1816
COTECNA DESTINATION INSPECTION LTD—See Cotecna Inspection S.A.; *Int'l*, pg. 1816
COTECNA EL SALVADOR—See Cotecna Inspection S.A.; *Int'l*, pg. 1816
COTECNA GOZETIM AS—See Cotecna Inspection S.A.; *Int'l*, pg. 1816
COTECNA, INC.—See Cotecna Inspection S.A.; *Int'l*, pg. 1816
COTECNA INSPECTION ARGENTINA SA—See Cotecna Inspection S.A.; *Int'l*, pg. 1816
COTECNA INSPECTION BANGLADESH LIMITED—See Cotecna Inspection S.A.; *Int'l*, pg. 1816
COTECNA INSPECTION CONGO SARL—See Cotecna Inspection S.A.; *Int'l*, pg. 1816
COTECNA INSPECTION EGYPT, S.A.E.—See Cotecna Inspection S.A.; *Int'l*, pg. 1816
COTECNA INSPECTION FRANCE SARL—See Cotecna Inspection S.A.; *Int'l*, pg. 1816
COTECNA INSPECTION GMBH—See Cotecna Inspection S.A.; *Int'l*, pg. 1816
COTECNA INSPECTION, INC.—See Cotecna Inspection S.A.; *Int'l*, pg. 1816
COTECNA INSPECTION INDIA PVT. LTD.—See Cotecna Inspection S.A.; *Int'l*, pg. 1816
COTECNA INSPECTION JAPAN LIMITED—See Cotecna Inspection S.A.; *Int'l*, pg. 1816
COTECNA INSPECTION KOREA INC.—See Cotecna Inspection S.A.; *Int'l*, pg. 1816
COTECNA INSPECTION LTD.—See Cotecna Inspection S.A.; *Int'l*, pg. 1816
COTECNA INSPECTION PHILIPPINES, INC.—See Cotecna Inspection S.A.; *Int'l*, pg. 1816
COTECNA INSPECTION S.A.; *Int'l*, pg. 1816
COTECNA INSPECTION SA—See Cotecna Inspection S.A.; *Int'l*, pg. 1816
COTECNA INSPECTION SL—See Cotecna Inspection S.A.; *Int'l*, pg. 1816
COTECNA INSPECTION SOUTH AFRICA PTY. LTD.—See Cotecna Inspection S.A.; *Int'l*, pg. 1816
COTECNA INSPECTION THAILAND—See Cotecna Inspection S.A.; *Int'l*, pg. 1816
COTECNA INSPECTION URUGUAY SA—See Cotecna Inspection S.A.; *Int'l*, pg. 1816
COTECNA INSPECTION (VOSTOK) LLC—See Cotecna Inspection S.A.; *Int'l*, pg. 1816
COTECNA INTERNATIONAL TRADE CONSULTING (SHANGHAI) LTD—See Cotecna Inspection S.A.; *Int'l*, pg. 1816
COTECNA IRAQ—See Cotecna Inspection S.A.; *Int'l*, pg. 1816
COTECNA KAZAKHSTAN LLP—See Cotecna Inspection S.A.; *Int'l*, pg. 1816
COTECNA LATIN AMERICA S.A.—See Cotecna Inspection S.A.; *Int'l*, pg. 1816
COTECNA QUALITY SRL—See Cotecna Inspection S.A.; *Int'l*, pg. 1816
COTECNA S.A. - HONG KONG—See Cotecna Inspection S.A.; *Int'l*, pg. 1816
COTECNA SAUDI ARABIA CO. LTD.—See Cotecna Inspection S.A.; *Int'l*, pg. 1816
COTECNA SENEGAL SARL—See Cotecna Inspection S.A.; *Int'l*, pg. 1816
COTECNA SERVICOS ANGOLA LIMITADA—See Cotecna Inspection S.A.; *Int'l*, pg. 1816
COTECNA SERVICOS LTDA—See Cotecna Inspection S.A.; *Int'l*, pg. 1816
COTECNA SERVICOS LTDA—See Cotecna Inspection S.A.; *Int'l*, pg. 1816
COTECNA SINGAPORE PTE. LTD.—See Cotecna Inspection S.A.; *Int'l*, pg. 1816
COTECNA TRADE SERVICES MALAYSIA SDN BHD—See Cotecna Inspection S.A.; *Int'l*, pg. 1816
COTECNA TRADE SERVICES—See Cotecna Inspection S.A.; *Int'l*, pg. 1816
COTECNA UKRAINE LIMITED—See Cotecna Inspection S.A.; *Int'l*, pg. 1816
COTECNA VIETNAM, CO., LTD.—See Cotecna Inspection S.A.; *Int'l*, pg. 1816
DEKRA CERTIFICATION B.V.—See DEKRA e.V.; *Int'l*, pg. 2007
DEKRA CERTIFICATION HONG KONG LTD.—See DEKRA e.V.; *Int'l*, pg. 2007
DEKRA CERTIFICATION INC.—See DEKRA e.V.; *Int'l*, pg. 2007
DEKRA CERTIFICATION K.K.—See DEKRA e.V.; *Int'l*, pg. 2007
DEKRA CERTIFICATION LTD.—See DEKRA e.V.; *Int'l*, pg. 2007
DEKRA CERTIFICATION (PROPRIETARY) LTD.—See DEKRA e.V.; *Int'l*, pg. 2007
DEKRA CERTIFICATION S.A.S.—See DEKRA e.V.; *Int'l*, pg. 2008
DEKRA CERTIFICATION, S.L.U.—See DEKRA e.V.; *Int'l*, pg. 2008
DEKRA CERTIFICATION—See DEKRA e.V.; *Int'l*, pg. 2007
DEKRA CERTIFICATION SP. Z O.O.—See DEKRA e.V.; *Int'l*, pg. 2008
DEKRA CERTIFICATION S.R.L.—See DEKRA e.V.; *Int'l*, pg. 2008
DEKRA CTI TESTING AND CERTIFICATION LTD.—See DEKRA e.V.; *Int'l*, pg. 2007
DEKRA E.V.; *Int'l*, pg. 2006
DEKRA EXAM GMBH—See DEKRA e.V.; *Int'l*, pg. 2008
DEKRA EXPERTISE S.A.S.—See DEKRA e.V.; *Int'l*, pg. 2008
DEKRA INDUSTRIAL S.R.O.—See DEKRA e.V.; *Int'l*, pg. 2009
DEKRA INSPECTION S.A.—See DEKRA e.V.; *Int'l*, pg. 2009
DEKRA SERTIFIKASYON A.S.—See DEKRA e.V.; *Int'l*, pg. 2009
DEKRA SOLUTIONS B.V.—See DEKRA e.V.; *Int'l*, pg. 2009
DEKRA TESTING AND CERTIFICATION CHINA LTD.—See DEKRA e.V.; *Int'l*, pg. 2009
DEKRA TESTING AND CERTIFICATION GMBH—See DEKRA e.V.; *Int'l*, pg. 2009
DEKRA TESTING & CERTIFICATION SPOL S R.O.—See DEKRA e.V.; *Int'l*, pg. 2009
DEKRA TESTING SERVICES (ZHEJIANG) LTD.—See DEKRA e.V.; *Int'l*, pg. 2009
DEKRA WIT (HANGZHOU) CERTIFICATION CO. LTD.—See DEKRA e.V.; *Int'l*, pg. 2009
ENS INTERNATIONAL PTY. LTD.—See AWN Holdings Limited; *Int'l*, pg. 753
ERIC RYAN CORPORATION—See Renodis, Inc.; *U.S. Private*, pg. 3399
FUGRO TECHNICAL SERVICES (GUANGZHOU) LTD.—See Fugro N.V.; *Int'l*, pg. 2808
GATEWAY SERVICES LIMITED—See Cotecna Inspection S.A.; *Int'l*, pg. 1816
INSPECTORATE INTERNATIONAL LIMITED—See Bureau Veritas S.A.; *Int'l*, pg. 1222
INSPECTORATE SUISSE S.A.—See Bureau Veritas S.A.; *Int'l*, pg. 1222
KURTEC INSPECTION SERVICES SDN BHD—See I Squared Capital Advisors (US) LLC; *U.S. Private*, pg. 2023
MARRIOTT PERU LICENSING COMPANY SAC—See Marriott International, Inc.; *U.S. Public*, pg. 1371
MORAE GLOBAL CORP.; *U.S. Private*, pg. 2781
NYSE REGULATION, INC.—See Intercontinental Exchange, Inc.; *U.S. Public*, pg. 1143
OPUS BILPROVNING AB—See Searchlight Capital Partners, L.P.; *U.S. Private*, pg. 3590
OPUS INSPECTION VICS SINDH (PVT) LTD.—See Searchlight Capital Partners, L.P.; *U.S. Private*, pg. 3590
PHARMA-BIO SERV, INC.; *U.S. Public*, pg. 1684
PHARMA-BIO SERV LTD.—See PHARMA-BIO SERV, INC.; *U.S. Public*, pg. 1684
PHARMA-BIO SERV PR, INC.—See PHARMA-BIO SERV, INC.; *U.S. Public*, pg. 1684
PHARMA-BIO SERV, S.L.—See PHARMA-BIO SERV, INC.; *U.S. Public*, pg. 1684
PREMIUM INSPECTION & TESTING, INC.; *U.S. Private*, pg. 3252
PRICE FOR PROFIT; *U.S. Private*, pg. 3258
RLI CHICAGO REGIONAL OFFICE—See RLI Corp.; *U.S. Public*, pg. 1802
THE STEEL INDEX LIMITED—See S&P Global Inc.; *U.S. Public*, pg. 1832
TECNATOM FRANCE S.A.S.—See Enel S.p.A.; *Int'l*, pg. 2414
THELMA PTY LTD.—See ICSGlobal Limited; *Int'l*, pg. 3586
VELOSI AMERICA LLC—See I Squared Capital Advisors (US) LLC; *U.S. Private*, pg. 2023
VELOSI CERTIFICATION BUREAU LIMITED—See I Squared Capital Advisors (US) LLC; *U.S. Private*, pg. 2024
VELOSI INTERNATIONAL ITALY SRL—See I Squared Capital Advisors (US) LLC; *U.S. Private*, pg. 2024
VIACOM CONSUMER PRODUCTS INC.—See National Amusements, Inc.; *U.S. Private*, pg. 2844
VIANORM B.V.—See DEKRA e.V.; *Int'l*, pg. 2010

927110 — SPACE RESEARCH AND TECHNOLOGY

ASM GERMANY SALES B.V—See ASM INTERNATIONAL N.V.; *Int'l*, pg. 626
BESI KOREA LTD.—See BE Semiconductor Industries N.V.; *Int'l*, pg. 931
COBHAM MICROWAVE FILTER COMPONENTS—See Advent International Corporation; *U.S. Private*, pg. 99
EUROCKOT LAUNCH SERVICES GMBH—See Airbus SE; *Int'l*, pg. 247
FUGRO-GEOS LTD.—See Fugro N.V.; *Int'l*, pg. 2808
FUGRO-GEOS PTE LTD.—See Fugro N.V.; *Int'l*, pg. 2808
FUGRO TECHNICAL SERVICES LTD.—See Fugro N.V.; *Int'l*, pg. 2808
FUGRO WEINHOLD ENGINEERING GMBH—See Fugro N.V.; *Int'l*, pg. 2808
GARVEY SPACECRAFT CORPORATION—See Vector Space Systems; *U.S. Private*, pg. 4353
GLOBAL AEROSPACE, INC.—See Global Aerospace Underwriting Managers Limited; *Int'l*, pg. 2993
GLOBAL AEROSPACE UNDERWRITING MANAGERS LIMITED; *Int'l*, pg. 2993
HONEYWELL AEROSPACE ELECTRONIC SYSTEMS—See Honeywell International Inc.; *U.S. Public*, pg. 1047
IHI AEROSPACE CO., LTD.—See IHI Corporation; *Int'l*, pg. 3604
JET PROPULSION LABORATORY—See California Institute of Technology; *U.S. Private*, pg. 719
KBRWYLE AEROSPACE GROUP—See KBR, Inc.; *U.S. Public*, pg. 1216
KBRWYLE SCIENCE, TECHNOLOGY & ENGINEERING GROUP—See KBR, Inc.; *U.S. Public*, pg. 1216
THE LASALLE NETWORK; *U.S. Private*, pg. 4067
LOCKHEED MARTIN UK AMPTHILL LIMITED—See Lockheed Martin Corporation; *U.S. Public*, pg. 1338
MACDONALD, DETTWILER & ASSOCIATES INC.—See Advent International Corporation; *U.S. Private*, pg. 103
MARYLAND AEROSPACE, INC.—See Redwire Corporation; *U.S. Public*, pg. 1771

927110 — SPACE RESEARCH AND ...

MOMENTUS INC.; *U.S. Public,* pg. 1460
MOOG SPACE & DEFENSE GROUP—See Moog Inc.; *U.S. Public,* pg. 1470
NEW MEXICO SPACEPORT AUTHORITY; *U.S. Private,* pg. 2898
NORTHROP GRUMMAN AEROSPACE SYSTEMS—See Northrop Grumman Corporation; *U.S. Public,* pg. 1539
QINETIQ SPACE NV—See Redwire Corporation; *U.S. Public,* pg. 1771
RMA TRANSPORTATION SERVICES INC.; *U.S. Private,* pg. 3451
SEQUA CORPORATION—See Veritas Capital Fund Management, LLC; *U.S. Private,* pg. 4364
SPACEA SYSTEMS/LORAL, LLC—See Advent International Corporation; *U.S. Private,* pg. 104
SPACEDEV INC.—See Sierra Nevada Corporation; *U.S. Private,* pg. 3647
STARSEM—See Airbus SE; *Int'l,* pg. 246
STRATEGIC FUNDRAISING, INC.; *U.S. Private,* pg. 3835

928110 — NATIONAL SECURITY

3M CANADA COMPANY—See 3M Company; *U.S. Public,* pg. 5
ACCURATE BACKGROUND, INC.—See Boathouse Capital Management, LLC; *U.S. Private,* pg. 603
ANDREWS INTERNATIONAL—See Audax Group, Limited Partnership; *U.S. Private,* pg. 386
ANDURIL INDUSTRIES, INC.; *U.S. Private,* pg. 280
ARES GROUP, INC.; *U.S. Private,* pg. 318
AWE PLC; *Int'l,* pg. 752
BUTLER AMERICA AEROSPACE LLC—See HCL Technologies Ltd.; *Int'l,* pg. 3298
CAE INDIA PRIVATE LIMITED—See CAE Inc.; *Int'l,* pg. 1248
CAE UK PLC—See CAE Inc.; *Int'l,* pg. 1249
CIRCADENCE CORPORATION; *U.S. Private,* pg. 899
CLEARSTAR LOGISTICS, INC.—See ClearStar, Inc.; *U.S. Private,* pg. 938
COVENANT SERVICES WORLDWIDE, LLC; *U.S. Private,* pg. 1072
ELITE RECRUITING GROUP LLC; *U.S. Private,* pg. 1361
GLOBAL ORDNANCE LLC; *U.S. Private,* pg. 1716
GLOBAL STRATEGIES—See Global Strategies, Incorporated; *U.S. Private,* pg. 1718
HOMELAND SECURITY SOLUTIONS, INC. (HSSI); *U.S. Private,* pg. 1973
IDS INTERNATIONAL GOVERNMENT SERVICES LLC; *U.S. Private,* pg. 2038
INVERTIX COMMUNICATIONS MISSION SYSTEM OPERATIONS—See Altamira Technologies Corporation; *U.S. Private,* pg. 204
JMA SOLUTIONS; *U.S. Private,* pg. 2214
KINGFISHER SYSTEMS, INC.; *U.S. Private,* pg. 2311
KRATOS ARABIA, LTD.—See Kratos Defense & Security Solutions, Inc.; *U.S. Public,* pg. 1276
L3 COMMUNICATION APPLIED TECHNOLOGIES/JAYCOR—See L3Harris Technologies, Inc.; *U.S. Public,* pg. 1281
MACAULAY-BROWN, INC.—See Veritas Capital Fund Management, LLC; *U.S. Private,* pg. 4360
MARQUETTE COPPERSMITHING CO., INC.; *U.S. Private,* pg. 2587
MASS CONSULTANTS LIMITED—See Cohort plc; *Int'l,* pg. 1896
MVP HEALTH CARE INC.—See MVP Health Care Inc.; *U.S. Private,* pg. 2822
NCI SERVICES, INC.—See Elliott Management Corporation; *U.S. Private,* pg. 1368
NCI SERVICES, INC.—See Veritas Capital Fund Management, LLC; *U.S. Private,* pg. 4362
NORTHROP GRUMMAN NAVIGATION SYSTEMS—See Northrop Grumman Corporation; *U.S. Public,* pg. 1540
SAGE MANAGEMENT ENTERPRISE, LLC; *U.S. Private,* pg. 3526
SAGE MANAGEMENT—See Sage Management Enterprise, LLC; *U.S. Private,* pg. 3526
SAGE MANAGEMENT—See Sage Management Enterprise, LLC; *U.S. Private,* pg. 3526
SAGE MANAGEMENT—See Sage Management Enterprise, LLC; *U.S. Private,* pg. 3526
SOTERA DEFENSE SOLUTIONS, INC.—See Jacobs Engineering Group, Inc.; *U.S. Public,* pg. 1186

928120 — INTERNATIONAL AFFAIRS

AMERICAN IMMIGRATION LAWYERS ASSOCIATION; *U.S. Private,* pg. 237
BLS INTERNATIONAL SERVICES BELARUS INC.—See BLS International Services Limited; *Int'l,* pg. 1066
BLS INTERNATIONAL SERVICES CANADA INC.—See BLS International Services Limited; *Int'l,* pg. 1066
BLS INTERNATIONAL SERVICES CHINA INC.—See BLS International Services Limited; *Int'l,* pg. 1066
BLS INTERNATIONAL SERVICES DOMINICAN REPUBLIC INC.—See BLS International Services Limited; *Int'l,* pg. 1066
BLS INTERNATIONAL SERVICES EGYPT INC.—See BLS International Services Limited; *Int'l,* pg. 1066
BLS INTERNATIONAL SERVICES GHANA INC.—See BLS International Services Limited; *Int'l,* pg. 1066
BLS INTERNATIONAL SERVICES INDONESIA INC.—See BLS International Services Limited; *Int'l,* pg. 1066
BLS INTERNATIONAL SERVICES JORDAN INC.—See BLS International Services Limited; *Int'l,* pg. 1066
BLS INTERNATIONAL SERVICES KAZAKHSTAN INC.—See BLS International Services Limited; *Int'l,* pg. 1066
BLS INTERNATIONAL SERVICES KUWAIT INC.—See BLS International Services Limited; *Int'l,* pg. 1067
BLS INTERNATIONAL SERVICES LEBANON INC.—See BLS International Services Limited; *Int'l,* pg. 1066
BLS INTERNATIONAL SERVICES LIMITED; *Int'l,* pg. 1066
BLS INTERNATIONAL SERVICES LIMITED—See BLS International Services Limited; *Int'l,* pg. 1066
BLS INTERNATIONAL SERVICES LIMITED—See BLS International Services Limited; *Int'l,* pg. 1066
BLS INTERNATIONAL SERVICES LIMITED—See BLS International Services Limited; *Int'l,* pg. 1066
BLS INTERNATIONAL SERVICES LTD.—See BLS International Services Limited; *Int'l,* pg. 1066
BLS INTERNATIONAL SERVICES MAURITANIA INC.—See BLS International Services Limited; *Int'l,* pg. 1066
BLS INTERNATIONAL SERVICES NIGERIA INC.—See BLS International Services Limited; *Int'l,* pg. 1066
BLS INTERNATIONAL SERVICES NORWAY AS—See BLS International Services Limited; *Int'l,* pg. 1066
BLS INTERNATIONAL SERVICES OMAN INC.—See BLS International Services Limited; *Int'l,* pg. 1066
BLS INTERNATIONAL SERVICES PAKISTAN INC.—See BLS International Services Limited; *Int'l,* pg. 1066
BLS INTERNATIONAL SERVICES PHILIPPINES INC.—See BLS International Services Limited; *Int'l,* pg. 1066
BLS INTERNATIONAL SERVICES QATAR INC.—See BLS International Services Limited; *Int'l,* pg. 1066
BLS INTERNATIONAL SERVICES REPUBLIC OF COTE D'IVOIRE INC.—See BLS International Services Limited; *Int'l,* pg. 1066
BLS INTERNATIONAL SERVICES RUSSIA INC.—See BLS International Services Limited; *Int'l,* pg. 1066
BLS INTERNATIONAL SERVICES SAUDIARABIA INC.—See BLS International Services Limited; *Int'l,* pg. 1066
BLS INTERNATIONAL SERVICES SENEGAL INC.—See BLS International Services Limited; *Int'l,* pg. 1066
BLS INTERNATIONAL SERVICES SINGAPORE PTE LTD—See BLS International Services Limited; *Int'l,* pg. 1066
BLS INTERNATIONAL SERVICES SOUTH AFRICA INC.—See BLS International Services Limited; *Int'l,* pg. 1066
BLS INTERNATIONAL SERVICES TURKEY INC.—See BLS International Services Limited; *Int'l,* pg. 1066
BLS INTERNATIONAL SERVICES UAE INC.—See BLS International Services Limited; *Int'l,* pg. 1066
BLS INTERNATIONAL SERVICES UKRAINE INC.—See BLS International Services Limited; *Int'l,* pg. 1066
BLS INTERNATIONAL SERVICES UNITED KINGDOM INC.—See BLS International Services Limited; *Int'l,* pg. 1067
BLS INTERNATIONAL SERVICES VIETNAM INC.—See BLS International Services Limited; *Int'l,* pg. 1067
BLS INTERNATIONAL (THAILAND) LTD.—See BLS International Services Limited; *Int'l,* pg. 1066
COX & KINGS GLOBAL SERVICES LLC—See Cox & Kings Limited; *Int'l,* pg. 1822
COX & KINGS GMBH—See Cox & Kings Limited; *Int'l,* pg. 1822
GOTHAM DIGITAL SCIENCE, LLC—See Aon plc; *Int'l,* pg. 493
INTERDEAN AUGUSTE DALEIDEN SARL—See EAC Invest AS; *Int'l,* pg. 2261
INTERDEAN BULGARIA EOOD—See EAC Invest AS; *Int'l,* pg. 2261
INTERDEAN B.V.—See EAC Invest AS; *Int'l,* pg. 2261
INTERDEAN CENTRAL ASIA LLC—See EAC Invest AS; *Int'l,* pg. 2261
INTERDEAN EASTERN EUROPE GES.M.B.H—See EAC Invest AS; *Int'l,* pg. 2261
INTERDEAN HUNGARIA NEMZETKOZI KOLTOZTETO KFT—See EAC Invest AS; *Int'l,* pg. 2261
INTERDEAN INTERNATIONALE SPEDITION GES.M.B.H—See EAC Invest AS; *Int'l,* pg. 2262
INTERDEAN INTERNATIONAL RELOCATION SA—See EAC Invest AS; *Int'l,* pg. 2261
INTERDEAN INTERNATIONAL RELOCATION UKRAINE LLC—See EAC Invest AS; *Int'l,* pg. 2262
INTERDEAN INT' MOVERS S.R.L.—See EAC Invest AS; *Int'l,* pg. 2261
INTERDEAN LIMITED—See EAC Invest AS; *Int'l,* pg. 2262
INTERDEAN RELOCATION SERVICES NV—See EAC Invest AS; *Int'l,* pg. 2262
INTERDEAN SA—See EAC Invest AS; *Int'l,* pg. 2262
INTERDEAN, SPOL S.R.O—See EAC Invest AS; *Int'l,* pg. 2262
INTERDEAN SP. Z.O.O—See EAC Invest AS; *Int'l,* pg. 2262
INTERDEAN SRL—See EAC Invest AS; *Int'l,* pg. 2262
INTERNATIONELLA HOTELL- OCH RESTAURANGSKOLAN IHR AB—See AcadeMedia AB; *Int'l,* pg. 76
QUOPRRO GLOBAL SERVICES PVT. LTD.—See Cox & Kings Limited; *Int'l,* pg. 1823
RAPIDVISA INC.—See Boundless Immigration Inc.; *U.S. Private,* pg. 623
SANTA FE BELGRADE—See EAC Invest AS; *Int'l,* pg. 2262
SANTA FE INDIA PRIVATE LIMITED—See EAC Invest AS; *Int'l,* pg. 2262
SANTA FE MOVING AND RELOCATION SERVICES PHILS., INC.—See EAC Invest AS; *Int'l,* pg. 2262
SANTA FE RELOCATION SERVICES JAPAN K.K.—See EAC Invest AS; *Int'l,* pg. 2262
SANTA FE RELOCATION SERVICES KOREA CO. LTD.—See EAC Invest AS; *Int'l,* pg. 2262
SANTA FE RELOCATION SERVICES LLC—See EAC Invest AS; *Int'l,* pg. 2262
SANTA FE RELOCATION SERVICES SDN. BHD.—See EAC Invest AS; *Int'l,* pg. 2262
SANTA FE RELOCATION SERVICES—See EAC Invest AS; *Int'l,* pg. 2262
SANTA FE RELOCATION SERVICES—See EAC Invest AS; *Int'l,* pg. 2262
SANTA FE RELOCATION SERVICES TAIWAN CO., LTD.—See EAC Invest AS; *Int'l,* pg. 2262
WORCESTER COMMUNITY ACTION COUNCIL, INC.; *U.S. Private,* pg. 4562